S0-BMU-796

Hislop's
Art Sales Index

2004
35th annual edition

August 2002 to August 2003

for

Oil Paintings, Works on Paper, Miniatures, Prints, Photographs and Sculpture

Edited by
Duncan Hislop

Published by

ART SALES INDEX LTD
194 THORPE LEA ROAD, EGHAM, SURREY, TW20 8HA, ENGLAND

ISBN 0 903872 78 1

Published, computer composition and typeset by
Art Sales Index Ltd
194 Thorpe Lea Road, Egham, Surrey TW20 8HA, ENGLAND
Tel: ++ 44 (0) 1784 451145 Fax: ++ 44 (0) 1784 451144
Email: info@art-sales-index.com Internet: www.art-sales-index.com

Printed and bound by
Polestar BPC
Exeter,Devon

Contents

Introduction . . . . 7 - 9
French Introduction . . . . .9 - 10
German Introduction . . . . .11 - 12
Million Pound Club . . . . .13 - 16
Auction Season Analysis . . . . .17 - 20
Auction Houses, Sale Dates and Catalogue Titles . . . . . . .21 - 39
Artist Cross Reference names .40 - 43
Auction Sale Listings for Artists by Medium . . . . .47 - 2272

www.art-sales-index.com

INTRODUCTION

The Art Sales Index contains the price and details of Oil Paintings, Watercolours, Drawings, Miniatures, Prints and Sculpture sold at public auction around the world during the twelve month period of the international auction season, from August in one year until August in the following year. The works of 40,000 Old Master, 19th Century, Modern and Contemporary artists are represented. ASI records in the region of 140,000 sale results each season and handles around 3,000 catalogues from 450 different auctioneers. Sale prices are listed in ascending order. For each artist, Oil Paintings are given first, followed by Prints, Sculpture, Miniatures, Works on Paper which includes crayon, drawings, gouache, pastel, pencil, watercolour and mixed media ending with Photographs.

Starting Price

Items for the different media qualify for entry when they exceed a certain "starting" price. Over the years, starting prices have been adjusted to take inflation into account. Currently these are £250/$400/400 Euro for Oil Paintings and Works on Paper. £1000/ $1500/1500 Euro for Miniatures and Sculpture. £2000/$3000/3000 Euro for Prints and Photographs. £5000/$7000/7000 Euro for the categories 'after', 'circle', 'style', 'follower', 'studio' and for Schools of a country.

Sources of information

Over the last thirty five years ASI has gained considerable experience in accurately extracting information from auction catalogues, price lists and other information provided by auctioneers. Each catalogue is processed by at least six trained personnel. However, ASI cannot be held responsible for errors unwittingly made, nor for unknowingly reproducing incorrect information. ASI cannot vouch for the authenticity of pictures recorded. Here we must rely on the reputation and integrity of the auctioneer. The price a picture reaches at auction can be influenced by many factors, condition, subject matter and size are just a few. We recommend that the reader makes a thorough research when buying and selling at auction, consulting reference books and obtaining advice from experienced sources.

"Bought-in" pictures

Pictures offered for sale at auction usually have a "reserve" placed on them by the owner in order that they should not be sold at a price, which he considers to be below their real value.The Auction House may provide estimates as a guide to the potential buyer. If the bidding does not reach the reserve, the pictures are deemed to have been unsold. These lots are known as "bought-in". ASI does not record "bought-in" works. The majority of auctioneers exclude these "bought-in" prices from their price lists. However, there might be occasions when a "bought-in" price is inadvertently included. If any price is of particular importance to a subscriber, then he would be advised to check directly with the auctioneer.

Prices, buyer's premium and exchange rates

ASI does not include the Buyer's Premium. The price recorded is the "hammer" price, which is the value called out at auction and at which the item is "knocked down" to the bidder. Buyer's and seller's premiums can vary between auction houses, in recent years prices over a certain value attract different rates. The following example for Sotheby's is 19.5% on the first £70,000 or $100,000 and 10% on the remainder. Local taxes may also need to be taken into consideration. During the course of the auction season, all entries to the ASI Data Bank are made at the weekly exchange rate applicable to the date of the sale.

Presentation of artists' names

The convention adopted by ASI in the presentation of artists' names is to show the surname first, followed by the forenames, followed by the "de", "de la", "van" and "von" etc. Hence, Sir Anthony van Dyck is listed as "DYCK, Sir Anthony van." Le Corbusier is shown as "CORBUSIER, le". An exception is made where the "de", etc is embedded in the name, for example: Anne Louis Girodet de Roucy Trioson is shown as "GIRODET DE ROUCY TRIOSON, Anne Louis". Where the qualifications "after", "circle", "attrib", "studio" and "style" are used, they are shown after the name. A picture catalogued as "Style of Abraham Calraet" is shown as "CALRAET, Abraham (style)".

Wherever possible, ASI uses the name given by the auctioneer in the sale catalogue. Obvious spelling mistakes are corrected but other changes are kept to a minimum. However, in some instances, and especially with Old Masters, it is necessary to adopt standardisation (there are 15 ways of spelling Bartholomew in European languages!). Also, the presentation of an artist's name is not uniform throughout the world. But there are certain "conventions" which responsible auctioneers follow.

Average Weekly exchange rates to the Pound Sterling over the past five seasons

Country and Currency Code	2002/2003	2001/2002	Auction Season 2000/2001	1999/2000	1998/1999
Australia (A.D)	2.70	2.75	2.72	2.54	2.59
Austria (A.S)	-	22.17	22.44	21.99	20.30
Belgium (B.FR)	-	65.00	65.80	64.46	59.52
Canada (C.D)	2.39	2.28	2.20	2.33	2.47
Czech Republic (C.KR)	47.03	51.28	56.61	57.71	55.92
Denmark (D.KR)	11.21	13.15	12.16	11.90	10.97
Eire (E.P)	-	1.26	1.28	1.25	1.15
Europe (Euro)	1.51	1.6	1.6	-	-
Finland (F.M)	-	9.58	9.69	9.48	8.77
France (F.FR)	-	10.57	10.69	10.49	9.67
Germany (DM)	-	3.15	3.19	3.12	2.88
Greece (G.D)	-	549.11	554.78	545.66	467.90
Hong Kong (HK.D)	12.43	11.34	11.26	12.34	12.69
Hungary (H.F)	370.33	396.52	418.04	-	-
Italy (I.L)	-	3120.28	3158.42	3094.08	2853.77
Mexico (M.P)	16.52	13.56	13.60	15.01	16.00
Netherlands (D.FL)	-	3.55	3.59	3.51	3.25
New Zealand (NZ.D)	3.03	3.32	3.44	3.19	3.09
Norway (N.KR)	11.46	12.49	13.15	13.09	12.56
Poland (P.Z)	6.29	5.98	6.12	6.65	6.08
Singapore (S.D)	2.79	2.62	2.55	2.69	2.77
Slovakia (SL.K)	60.06	-	-	-	-
South Africa (SA.R)	14.07	14.85	11.14	10.14	9.90
Spain (S.P)	-	268.12	271.40	265.85	245.26
Sweden (S.KR)	13.81	14.89	14.41	13.58	13.32
Switzerland (S.FR)	2.23	2.36	2.49	2.53	2.36
Taiwan (T.D)	54.93	50.058	46.07	51.32	52.66
USA (US.D)	1.59	1.45	1.44	1.58	1.6

Note 1: Exchange rates used throughout the year are those applicable to the date of the sale.
Note 2: Sales in Israel, Argentina, Uruguay and Venezuela are recorded in US Dollars.
Note 3: Since 2002, Austria, Belgium, Eire, Finland, France, Germany, Greece, Italy, Netherlands and Spain are recorded in Euros.

These conventions are best illustrated by quoting directly from a Christie's catalogue:

a) a work catalogued with the name(s) or recognised designation of an artist, without qualification, is in our opinion a work by the artist;

b) in other cases, in our opinion, the following expressions, with the following meanings are used:

attributed to probably a work by the artist in whole or in part (ASI use "attrib");
studio of a work by an unknown hand in the studio of the artist which may or may not have been executed under the artist's direction (ASI use "studio");
circle of a work by an (as yet) unidentified but distinct hand, closely associated with the named artist but not necessarily his pupil (ASI use "circle");
style/follower of a work by a painter working in the artist's style, contemporary or nearly contemporary, but not neccessarily his pupil (ASI use "style");
manner of a work executed in the artist's style but of a later date (ASI use "style");
after a copy (of any date) of a known work of the artist (ASI use "after").

Note also the views on signatures as recorded in Sotheby's catalogues:

a) references to signature, inscription, dates refer to the present state of the work;

b) the term "bears a signature" and/or "date" and/or "inscription" means that in our opinion the artist's name and/or date and/or inscription have been added by another hand;

c) the term "signed" and/or "dated" and/or "inscribed" means that in our opinion the signature and/or date and/or inscription are from the hand of the artist.

Medium and dimensions

All pictures listed are oil on canvas unless otherwise stated. Sales in other media follow afterwards. The measurements of pictures are "height by width" and measurements of 3-dimensional pieces are "height by width by depth".

Abbreviations

Abbreviations used in the index include:

attrib = attributed to
b/w = black and white
bears sig = bears signature
C = Century
c. = circa
chk = chalk
chl = charcoal
cm = centimetres
col = colour
d = dated
dr = drawing
est = estimate
exec = executed
exhib = exhibited
f = foundry
fl = flourished
htd = heightened
i = inscribed
in = inches
incl = including
indis = indistinct
init = initials
jnr = junior
lit = literature
mono = monogram
num = number
pat = patina
prov = provenance
/R = illustrated in catalogue
rec = rectangular
rem = remains of
s = signed
sig = signature
snr = senior
st = stamped
W/C = watercolour
? = unknown dates and nationality of artist
= lot number

How to read an entry:

LEEUW, Adrian de (19th C) Belgian

£1389 $2333 €2500 Horse drawn carriage in winter (67x107cm-26x42in) s.d. 5-Mar-2 Koller, Zurich #6483/R est:2500-3500 (S.FR 3500)

LEEUW, Adrian de	artist's name
(19th C) Belgian	artist's dates of birth and death and nationality
£1389 $2333 €2500	hammer price realised in Pounds Sterling, US Dollars and Euro
Horse drawn carriage in winter	title or description of picture
(67x107cm-26x42in)	dimensions, height by width in centimetres & inches
s.d.	signed and dated
5-Mar-2	date of auction
Koller, Zurich	auctioneer's name and place of sale
#6483/R	lot number and reproduced in the sale catalogue
est:2500-3500	low and high estimate in currency of sale
(S.FR 3500)	currency of sale and local price

INTRODUCTION

Le volume d'Art Sales Index (Répertoire des Ventes d'Oeuvres d'Art) donnent le prix et les détails relatifs à des peintures à l'huile, aquarelles, dessins, estampes et sculptures vendus aux enchères dans le monde entier au cours des douze mois écoulés-du mois d'août au mois de juillet de l'année suivante. Nous appelons cette période la "saison de ventes". Dans ces deux volumes figurent quelques 40,000 Maitres anciens, artistes du 19ème siècle, artistes modernes et contemporains. Chaque saison, L'ASI traite plus de 140,000 résultats de ventes et dispose de 3,000 catalogues de vente provenant de 450 commissaires-priseurs différents.Les oeuvres en tous genres peuvent être répertoriées lorsque leur prix initial dépasse un certain seuil. Au fil des ans, les prix initiaux ont été relevés pour tenir compte de l'inflation. Les niveaux de prix pour la saison figurent à la page des sous-titres du chapitre approprié. Les Prix de vente sont répertoriés par ordre croissant. Pour chaque artiste, les peintures à l'huile figurent en première place, suivies des aquarelles, dessins, miniatures et des sculptures. Chacune des techniques est differenciées par sections.

Sources d'Information

Le Répertoire est compilé à partir de catalogues, de listes de prix et autres informations fournies par les commissaires-priseurs. L'ASI recueille les informations avec le plus grand soin. Toutefois, l'ASI ne peut être tenu responsable des erreurs accidentelles ni de la reproduction involontaire d'informations erronnées. L'ASI ne peut pas garantir l'authenticité des tableaux répertoriés. La réputation et l'intégrité du commissaire-priseur en sont le meilleur garant.

Tableaux "rachetés" (ou "Invendus")

Le propriétaire d'un tableau mis aux enchères place généralement une "réserve" sur ce tableau pour éviter qu'il ne soit vendu à un prix qu'il considère inférieur à sa valeur réelle. Si les enchères n'atteignent pas ce niveau, on considère que le tableau n'a pas été vendu. En Angleterre, ces articles sont appelés "Rachetés" (ou Invendus) L'ASI ne répertorie que les ventes réelles: les prix "rachetés" ne sont pas enregistrés. La plupart des commissaires-priseurs principaux ne font pas figurer les prix "rachetés" sur leurs listes de prix. Il peut cependant arriver que des commissaires-priseurs fassent figurer ces prix "rachetés" sur leurs listes. L'ASI n'est pas toujours à même de faire la distinction. Lorsqu'un prix spécifique est d'une importance capitale il est conseillé de procéder à une vérification auprès des commissaires-priseurs eux-mêmes.

Prix, taux de change et commission

Le prix indiqué par l'ASI est, dans tous les cas, le prix "du marteau" celui qui est atteint lors des enchères et auquel l'oeuvre est adjugée à l'enchérisseur. Dans la plupart des pays, l'acheteur doit s'attendre à payer des frais supplémentaires de 5 à 15%. Au Royaume-Uni, ces frais sont appelés "Buyer's Premium" (Commission). Cette commission n'est pas comprise dans le prix indiqué. Les impôts locaux ou nationaux, les commissions ne sont pas non plus ajoutés au prix indiqué. Lorsqu'une "paire" de tableaux a été vendue, le prix s'entend pour la paire, et non pour chacun des tableaux.

Présentation du nom des artistes

L'ASI a convenu de présenter le nom des artistes en faisant figurer d'abord le nom de famille, puis les prénoms, puis les particules "de", "de la", "van", "von", etc. Ainsi, Sir Anthony van Dyck figure sous "DYCK, Sir Anthony van". Le Corbusier figure sous "CORBUSIER, le". Une exception est faite lorsque le "de" etc fait partie intégrante du nom, par exemple: Anne Louis Girodet de Roucy Trioson figure sous "GIROUDET DE ROUCY TRIOSON, Anne Louis". Lorsque les termes "d'apres", "cercle de", "attrib", "atelier de" et "style" sont utilisés, ils viennent après le nom. Un tableau répertorié "Style d'Abraham Calraet" figure sous "CALRAET, Abraham (style)". Dans toute la mesure du possible, l'ASI utilise le nom donné par le commissaire-priseur dans le catalogue de vente. Les fautes trop évidentes sont rectifiées, mais on limite autant que possible les autres modifications. Pourtant, dans certains cas - tout particulièrement avec les maîtres anciens - il convient d'adopter un nom standard (le nom Bartholomew revêt quinze orthographes différentes dans les langues européennes!) De plus, la présentation du nom d'un artiste n'est pas uniforme dans le monde entier. Mais il existe certaines "conventions" que les commissaires-priseurs sérieux suivent généralement. Le plus simple est de citer directement un catalogue de Christie's:

a) Une oeuvre cataloguée avec le(s) nom(s) ou la désignation, reconnue d'un artiste, sans autre qualificatif, est selon nous l'oeuvre de cet artiste.
b) Dans les autres cas, on utilise les expressions suivantes, qui signifient:

attribué à	Selon nous, probablement une oeuvre de l'artiste en totalité ou en partie (l'ASI utilise "attrib")
atelier de	Selon nous, une oeuvre exécutée dans l'atelier de l'artiste, et peut-être supervisée par lui (l'ASI utilise "studio")
cercle de	Selon nous, une oeuvre de la période de l'artiste et témoignant de son influence (l'ASI utilise "circle")
dans le style de	Selon nous, une oeuvre exécutée dans le style de l'artiste, mais pas nécessairement par un élève (l'ASI utilise "style")
a la manière de	Selon nous, une oeuvre exécutée dans le style de l'artiste, mais à une date ultérieure (l'ASI utilise "style")
d'après	Selon nous, une copie (date quelconque) d'une oeuvre de l'artiste (l'ASI utilise "after")

Noter également le point de vue sur la signature tel qu'il figure sur les catalogues de Sotheby's:

a) Les références à la signature, à l'inspection et aux dates visent l'état actuel de l'oeuvre.
b) Le terme porte une "signature" et/ou une "date" et/ou une "inscription" signifie que, selon nous, le nom de l'artiste et/ou la date et/ou l'inscription ont été ajoutés par une autre main.
c) Le terme "signé" et/ou "daté" et/ou "inscrit" signifie que, selon nous, la signature et/ou la date et/ou l'inscription sont de la main de l'artiste.

Types d'oeuvres et dimentions

Chaque artiste à sa section. Il y à la section huile qui figure toujours en première place, puis la section aquarelle, dessin, miniature et aussi la section sculpture. Les dimensions des tableaux s'entendent "hauteur x largeur" et les dimensions des pièces tridimentionnelles s'entendent "hauteur x largeur x profondeur".

Abréviations

Les abréviations utilisées dans le Répertoire sont:

attrib = attribué à
b/w = noir et blanc
bears sig = porte signature
C = siècle
c. = environ
chk = craiel
chl = fusain
cm = centimètres
col = couleur
d = daté
dr = dessin
est = estimation
exec = realiser
exhib = exposer
f = la fonderie
fl = fleuri
htd = rehaussé
i = inscrit
ins = les pouces
incl = inclus
indis = illisible
inits = initiales
jnr = junior
lit = littérature
mono = monogramme
num = numero
pat = patiné
prov = provenance
/R = illustré sur catalogue
rec = rectangulaire
rem = rappeler de
s = signé
sig = signature
snr = senior
st = porte un cachet
W/C = aquarelle
= numero de lot
(?) = nationalité et dates de l'artiste inconnues

Comment lire une entrée

ADNET, Françoise (1924-) French
£674 $1025 €1200 La poupée à la pendule Louis XVI (45x54cm-18x21in) s. 6-Nov-2 Beaussant & Lefevre, Paris #72

ADNET, Françoise	Nom et prénom de l'artiste
(1924-) French	Nationalité de l'artiste: Dates de naissance et décès
£674 $1025 €1200	Prix obtenu en livres, dollars et en Euro
La poupée à la pendule Louis XVI	Titre ou description du tableau
(45x54cm - 18x21in)	Dimensions, hauteur par largeur, en cms et pouces
s.	Signé
6-Nov-2	Date de la vente aux enchères
Beaussant & Lefevre, Paris	Commissaires-priseurs

#72 No de lot du tableau

EINLEITUNG
Die Art Sales Index enthalten Preise und Details über Ölgemälde, Aquarelle, Zeichnungen, Miniaturen, Druckgraphiken und Skulpturen, die auf weltweiten, öffentlichen Auktionen während der 12- monatigen Auktionssaison (von August eines Jahres bis August des nächsten Jahres) verkauft wurden. Werke von etwa 40.000 Künstlern, dazu zählen alte Meister, die Künstler des 19. Jahrhundert sowie moderne und zeitgenössische Künstler, sind in beiden Bänden aufgeführt. Art Sales Index bearbeitet jede Saison etwa 140.000 Verkaufsergebnisse aus über 3,000 Katalogen von 450 verschiedenen Auktionatoren. Verkaufspreise stehen in aufsteigender Reihenfolge. Für jeden Künstler werden zuerst Ölgemälde augeführt, gefolgt von Druckgraphiken, Skulpturen, Miniaturen und Werken auf Papier, die Kreide, Zeichenstift, Gouache, Bleistift, Aquarelle und gemischte Medien enthalten.

PREISGRENZE
Die Kunstobjekte der verschiedenen Medien kommen dann für eine Eintragung in Frage, wenn sie über einer bestimmten Preisgrenze liegen. Um den Inflationsfaktor zu berücksichtigen, hat sich diese Grenze über die Jahre hin verändert. Momentan ist der Limitpreis 400 Euro für Ölgemälde und Aquarelle, 1.500 Euro für Skulpturen und Miniaturen, 7.000 Euro für die Kategorien "Nach, Umkreis, Art, Studio", Schule eines Landes oder Druckgraphiken.

VERÄNDERUNGEN FÜR DIESE JAHRESAUSGABE
In der diesjährigen Ausgabe gab es ein paar Veränderungen. In jeder Saison erhält ASI mehr Kunstkataloge von einer grösseren Anzahl von Auktionshäuser. Um diese erhöhte Anzahl von Eintragungen zu erfassen, haben wir die Dimensionen des Buches vergrössert. Das verbeserte Seitenformat macht Eintragungen leichter lesbar. Art Sales Index führt ein sehr straffes Produktionsprogramm, sodass wir bereits vier Wochen nach Ende der Auktionssaison in Druck gehen können. Aus diesem Grund ist der Art Sales Index zu Beginn der neuen Saison erhältlich. Da manche Auktionshäuser ihre Kataloge und Preislisten nicht rechtzeitig senden oder Nachfragen nicht termingerecht beantwortet können, schliessen wir in der diesjährigen Ausgabe solche Verkäufe von der vorhergehenden Saison mit ein.

BEZUGSQUELLEN FÜR INFORMATIONEN
Unsere vierzigjährige Erfahrung ermöglicht es us, detailierte und exakte Informationen aus Katalogen, Preislisten und anderen Informationsquellen von Autionatoren zu entnehmen. Jeder Katalog wird von mindestens sechs geschulten Mitarbeitern bearbeitet. Allerdings kann Art Sakes Index keine Verantwortung oder Haftung für Fehler oder falsche Information, die unbewusst abgedruckt worden sind, übernehmen. Art Sales Index übernimmt keine Garantie für die Echtheit der aufgeführten Bilder. Wir verlassen uns auf den Ruf und die Integrität des Auktionators. Der Preis, der für ein Bild bei der Auktion erreicht wird, hängt von vielen Faktoren ab. Zustand, Thema und Grösse sind nur ein paar. Wir empfehlen dem Leser vor Kauf und Verkauf durch Auktionen genaue Nachforschungen anzustellen, Nachschlagwerke einzusehen und Rat von erfahrenen Quellen zu beziehen.

UNVERKAUFTE LOSE
Gemälde, die auf Auktionen zum Verkauf angeboten werden, sind vom Besitzter gewöhnlich mit einen 'Niedrigstpreis' eingereicht worden, damit sie nicht zu einem Preis verkauft werden, der zu tief unter dem tatsächlichen Wert liegt. Das Auktionshaus kann eine Schätzung als Richtlinie für den Käufer erstellen. Wird dieser Limitpreis beim Bieten nicht erreicht, so werden diese Lose als nicht verkauft betrachtet und als 'bought-in' beschrieben, die von ASI nicht verzeichnet werden. Obwohl die meisten Auktionshäuser die unverkauften Lose nicht in ihre Preislisten einschliessen, könnte es jedoch vorkommen, dass ein 'bought-in' Preis unabsichtlich aufgeführt worden ist. Müssten Sie über einen gewissen Preis absolute Sicherheit haben, raten wir Ihnen, direkt beim Auktionator nachzufragen.

PREISE, KÄUFERPRÄMIE UND WECHSELKURSE
Die von Art Sales Index aufgeführten Preise enthalten keine Käuferprämie. Der angegebene Preis ist der Zuschlagspreis, also der Preis, der auf der Auktion ausgerufen wird und zu dem der Gegenstand dem Bieter zugeschlagen wird. Käufer- und Verkäuferprämien sind von Auktionshaus zu Auktionshaus verschieden. Sotheby's z.B. berechnet 19.5% für die ersten UK£70,000 oder $100,000 und 10% für den restlichen Betrag. Örtliche Steuern sollten ebenfalls in Erwägung gezogen werden. Während der Auktionssaison werden alle Eintragungen in der Art Sales Index Data Bank mit der wöchentlichen Umtauschrate aufgeführt, die für das Datum des Verkaufs in Frage kommt.

SCHREIBUNG DER NAMEN DER KÜNSTLER
Die Reihenfolge, in der die Namen der Künstler aufgeführt sind, ist so angeordnet, dass der Familienname zuerst, dann Vorname(n) und dahinter "de", "de la", "van" und "von" etc. stehen. Somit findet man Sir Anthony van Dyck als "DYCK, Sir Anthony van". Le Corbusier ist als "CORBUSIER, le" angegeben. Eine Ausnahme wird gemacht, wenn "de" zwischen den Namen steht, z.B. Anne Louis Girodet de Roucy Trioson wird dann als "GIRODET DE ROUCY TRIOSON, Anne Louis" aufgefuehrt. Wenn nähere Bestimmungen angegeben sind, wie "after", "circle", "attrib", "studio", stehen diese nach dem Namen. Ein Gemälde, das als "Style of Abraham Calraet" katalogisiert ist, findet man als "CALRAET, Abraham (style)".

Wo möglich, verwendet Art Sales Index den Namen, der vom Auktionator im Verkaufskatalog angegeben ist. Eindeutige Schreibfehler werden berichtigt. Andere Änderungen sind auf ein Minimum beschränkt. In manchen Fällen, besonders bei alten Meistern, ist es notwendig, eine Vereinheitlichung vorzunehmen (in den europäischen Sprachen gibt es 15 verschiedene Möglichkeiten Bartholomew zu schreiben). Hinzu kommt, dass die Namensschreibung eines Künstlers weltweit nicht universal ist. Es bestehen jedoch gewisse Richtlinien, an die sich viele Auktionatoren halten. Als bestes Beispiel geben wir einige Katalogauszüge von Christie's an:

a) Ein Werk, das mit dem Namen, bzw. den Namen oder mit dem Erkennungszeichen eines Künstlers aufgeführt ist, aber keine nähere Beschreibung hat, ist unserer Meinung nach ein Werk dieses Künstlers.

b) In anderen Fällen werden unserer Meinung nach folgende Ausdrücke mit folgenden Bedeutungen verwendet:

attributed to	Wahrscheinlich ein ganz oder zum Teil vom Künstler ausgeführtes Werk (Art Sales Index verwendet die Bezeichnung "attrib")
studio of	Ein Werk von unbekannter Hand, das im Studio des Künstlers mit oder ohne dessen Aufsicht entstanden ist. (Art Sales Index verwendet die Bezeichnung "studio")
circle of	Ein Werk einer (bisher) unbekannten Hand, welches unter dem Einfluss des Künstlers entstand, aber nicht unbedingt von einem seiner Schüler stammt. (Art Sales Index verwendet die Bezeichnung "circle")
style of *follower of*	Ein Werk eines Malers, der im Stil des Künstlers arbeitet, zeitgenössisch oder fast zeitgenössisch, aber nicht unbedingt sein Schüler war. (Art Sales Index verwendet die Bezeichnung "style")
manner of	Ein Werk ausgeführt im Stil des Künstlers, aber zu einem späteren Zeitpunkt. (Art Sales Index verwendet die Bezeichnung "style")
after	Eine Reproduktion (beliebiges Datum) eines Werkes des Künstlers. (Art Sales Index verwendet die Bezeichnung "after")

Bitte nehmen Sie auch die Anmerkung im Sotheby's Katalog zur Kenntnis:
a) Bemerkungen über die Unterschrift, Inschrift und Daten beziehen sich auf den gegenwärtigen Zustand des Werkes.
b) Die Bezeichnung "bears signature" (trägt Unterschrift) und/oder "date" (Datum) und/oder "inscription" (Inschrift), bedeutet unserer Meinung nach, dass die Unterschrift, und/oder Datum, und/oder Inschrift von anderer Hand hinzugefügt wurde.
c) Die Bezeichnung "signed" (unterschrieben), und/oder "date" (Datum) und/oder "inscribed" (Inschrift) bedeutet unserer Meinung nach, dass die Unterschrift, und/oder Datum, und/oder Inschrift von der Hand des Künstlers sind.

ABKÜRZUNGEN
Zu den in diesem Index verwendeten Abkürzungen gehören:

attrib = zugeschrieben
b/w = schwarz/weiss
bears sig = trägt Unterschrift
C = Jahrhundert
c = circa
chk = Kreide
chl = Kohle
cm = Zentimeter
col = Farbe
d = datiert
dr = Zeichnung
est = Schätzung
exec = ausgeführt
exhib = ausgestellt
f = Giesserei
fl = tätig
htd = gehöht
i = mit Inschrift
in = Zoll
incl = einschliesslich
indis = undeutlich
init = Initiale
jnr = Junior
lit = Literatur
mono = Monogramm
num = Nummer
pat = Patina
prov = Herkunft
/R = illustriert
rec = rechteckig
rem = Überreste
s = unterschrieben
sig = Unterschrift
snr = Senior
st = gestempelt
W/C = Aquarell
? = unbekannte Daten und Nationalität des Künstlers
= Katalog Nummer

Medien und Masse
Falls nicht anders angegeben, fallen die aufgeführten Gemälde in die Kategorie Öl auf Leinwand. Verkäufe in anderen Medien folgen anschliessend. Bildermasse sind in Höhe mal Breite angegeben. Die Masse von dreidimensionalen Werken sind in Höhe mal Breite mal Tiefe dargestellt.

WIE VERSTEHT MAN EINE EINTRAGUNG

LEEUW, Adrian de (19th C) Belgian
£1389 $2333 €2500 Horse drawn carriage in winter (67x107cm - 26x42in) s. 5-Mar-3 Koller, Zuerich #6483/R est: 2500-3500 (S.FR 3500)

LEEUW, Adrian de	Name des Künstlers
(19th C) Belgian	Geburts- und Todesjahr des Künstlers und Nationalität
£1389 $2333 €2500	erzielter Preis in Pounds Sterling, US Dollars and Euro
(67x107cm 26x42in)	Grösse, Höhe mal Breite in Zentimeter und Zoll
s.	unterschrieben
5-Mar-3	Tag der Auktion
Koller, Zurich	Name des Auktionators und Verkaufsort
# 6483	Katalognummer des Bildes
R	Reproduziert im Verkaufskatalog
est. 2500-3500	Niedriger und Hoher Schätzwert
(S.FR 3500)	Währung des Verkaufs Erzielter örtlicher Verkaufspreis

THE £1,000,000 CLUB

for artists whose work has sold for over £1 million during the 2002/2003 season

ARP, Jean (1887-1966) French
£1,712,329 $2,671,233 €2,500,000 Femme. 14-Apr-3 Laurence Calmels, Paris

BACON, Francis (1909-1992) British
£1,392,405 $2,200,000 €2,088,608 Three studies of Henrietta Moraes. 12-Nov-2 Sotheby's, New York

BELLOWS, George (1882-1925) American
£1,870,968 $2,900,000 €2,806,452 Gramercy Park. 5-Dec-2 Christie's, Rockefeller NY

BONNARD, Pierre (1867-1947) French
£3,800,000 $6,232,000 €5,700,000 Matinee au cannet. 4-Feb-3 Sotheby's, London

BOSSCHAERT, Ambrosius (elder) (1573-1621) Flemish
£1,612,903 $2,548,387 €2,500,000 Bouquet de tulipes et roses dans un vase sur entablement. 18-Dec-2 Piasa, Paris

CAILLEBOTTE, Gustave (1848-1894) French
£2,564,103 $4,000,000 €3,846,155 Le pont de l'Europe. 6-Nov-2 Christie's, Rockefeller NY

CALDER, Alexander (1898-1976) American
£1,487,342 $2,350,000 €2,231,013 S-Shaped vine. 13-Nov-2 Christie's, Rockefeller NY

CASSATT, Mary (1844-1926) American
£1,153,846 $1,800,000 €1,730,769 Maternite. 5-Nov-2 Sotheby's, New York

CEZANNE, Paul (1839-1906) French
£9,627,330 $15,500,000 €14,440,995 Portrait de Paul Cezanne. 7-May-3 Christie's, Rockefeller NY
£2,564,103 $4,000,000 €3,846,155 L'estaque vu a travers les arbres. 6-Nov-2 Christie's, Rockefeller NY
£1,153,846 $1,800,000 €1,730,769 Le potager de Pissarro a pontoise. 5-Nov-2 Sotheby's, New York

CHAGALL, Marc (1887-1985) French/Russian
£1,474,359 $2,300,000 €2,211,539 La grande roue. 6-Nov-2 Christie's, Rockefeller NY

CHASE, William Merritt (1849-1916) American
£1,225,806 $1,900,000 €1,838,709 Afternoon in the park. 4-Dec-2 Sotheby's, New York

DALI, Salvador (1904-1989) Spanish
£1,200,000 $1,968,000 €1,800,000 Jeune vierge autosodomisee par les cornes de sa propre chastete. 4-Feb-3 Sotheby's, London

DEGAS, Edgar (1834-1917) French
£5,900,621 $9,500,000 €8,850,932 Danseuse. 6-May-3 Sotheby's, New York
£5,714,286 $9,200,000 €8,571,429 Petite danseuse de quatorze ans. 7-May-3 Christie's, Rockefeller NY
£2,173,913 $3,500,000 €3,260,870 Danseuses pres d'un portant. 6 May-3 Sotheby's, New York
£1,153,846 $1,800,000 €1,730,769 La toilette. 5-Nov-2 Sotheby's, New York

DELVAUX, Paul (1897-1994) Belgian
£1,500,000 $2,505,000 €2,175,000 Le nu et le mannequin. 24-Jun-3 Christie's, London

DEWING, Thomas W (1851-1938) American
£2,000,000 $3,100,000 €3,000,000 Song. 4-Dec-2 Sotheby's, New York

EAKINS, Thomas (1844-1916) American
£2,962,963 $4,800,000 €4,444,445 Cowboys in the Badlands. 22-May-3 Christie's, Rockefeller NY

ERNST, Max (1891-1976) German
£1,410,257 $2,200,000 €2,115,386 Le roi jouant avec le reine. 5-Nov-2 Sotheby's, New York

FEININGER, Lyonel (1871-1956) American/German
£1,290,323 $2,000,000 €1,935,485 Die zeitungsleser - Newspaper readers. 4-Nov-2 Phillips, New York

FONTANA, Lucio (1899-1968) Italian
£1,225,000 $2,045,750 €1,837,500 Concetto Spaziale, La fine de dio. 25-Jun-3 Sotheby's, London

FRANCIS, Sam (1923-1994) American
£1,500,000 $2,400,000 €2,250,000 Big orange. 14-May-3 Christie's, Rockefeller NY

GAUGUIN, Paul (1848-1903) French
£6,800,000 $11,356,001 €10,200,000 Incantation or L'Apparition. 23-Jun-3 Sotheby's, London
£2,692,308 $4,200,000 €4,038,462 Cabane sous les arbres. 6-Nov-2 Christie's, Rockefeller NY
£1,739,130 $2,800,000 €2,608,695 Nature morte a l'estampe japonaise. 7-May-3 Christie's, Rockefeller NY
£1,400,000 $2,338,000 €2,100,000 Village sous la neige. 23-Jun-3 Sotheby's, London

GEROME, Jean Léon (1824-1904) French
£1,000,000 $1,640,000 €1,500,000 Interieur grec, le Gynecce. 3-Jun-3 Sotheby's, London

GIACOMETTI, Alberto (1901-1966) Swiss
£2,236,025 $3,600,000 €3,354,038 Homme qui marche III. 7-May-3 Christie's, Rockefeller NY
£1,217,949 $1,900,000 €1,826,924 Figurine dans une boite entre deux boites qui sont des maisons. 5-Nov-2 Sotheby's, New York
£1,012,658 $1,569,620 €1,600,000 La cage, premier version. 28-Sep-2 Christie's, Paris

GOGH, Vincent van (1853-1890) Dutch
£3,800,000 $6,346,000 €5,510,000 Nature morte, vase avec oeillets. 24-Jun-3 Christie's, London
£3,000,000 $5,010,000 €4,350,000 Une liseuse de romans. 24-Jun-3 Christie's, London

GONZALEZ, Julio (1876-1942) Spanish
£1,987,180 $3,100,000 €2,980,770 Homme gothique. 6-Nov-2 Christie's, Rockefeller NY

GOYA Y LUCIENTES, Francisco Jose de (1746-1828) Spanish
£2,839,506 $4,600,000 €4,259,259 Still life of dead hares. 24-Jan-3 Christie's, Rockefeller NY

GUSTON, Philip (1913-1980) American
£1,075,949 $1,700,000 €1,613,924 Painted in bed. 12-Nov-2 Sotheby's, New York

HALS, Frans (elder) (c.1580-1666) Dutch
£1,604,938 $2,600,000 €2,407,407 Portrait of a gentleman in a black coat and cape holding gloves. 23-Jan-3 Sotheby's, New York

HOCKNEY, David (1937-) British
£1,645,570 $2,600,000 €2,468,355 Portrait of Nick Wilder. 13-Nov-2 Christie's, Rockefeller NY

HODLER, Ferdinand (1853-1918) Swiss
£1,115,880 $1,763,090 €1,673,820 Geneva lake with Mont-Blanc in the early morning. 26-Nov-2 Phillips, Zurich

JAWLENSKY, Alexej von (1864-1941) Russian
£1,923,077 $3,000,000 €2,884,616 Junges madchen mit den grunen Augen. 6-Nov-2 Christie's, Rockefeller NY
£1,383,648 $2,158,491 €2,200,000 Halbakt - Nude half figure. 8-Oct-2 Sotheby's, London

JOHNS, Jasper (1930-) American
£5,696,203 $9,000,000 €8,544,305 O through 9. 13-Nov-2 Christie's, Rockefeller NY
£1,139,241 $1,800,000 €1,708,862 Untitled. 12-Nov-2 Sotheby's, New York

KIRCHNER, Ernst Ludwig (1880-1938) German
£2,000,000 $3,120,000 €3,000,000 Rote akte - Red nudes. 9-Oct-2 Sotheby's, London

KLEIN, Yves (1928-1962) French
£2,937,500 $4,700,000 €4,406,250 Re 2. 14-May-3 Christie's, Rockefeller NY

KLINE, Franz (1910-1962) American
£2,594,937 $4,100,000 €3,892,406 Ninth Street. 12-Nov-2 Sotheby's, New York

KOONING, Willem de (1904-1997) American/Dutch
£7,594,937 $12,000,000 €11,392,406 Orestes. 12-Nov-2 Sotheby's, New York
£2,151,899 $3,400,000 €3,227,849 Woman. 12-Nov-2 Sotheby's, New York
£1,455,696 $2,300,000 €2,183,544 Woman. 12-Nov-2 Sotheby's, New York
£1,265,823 $2,000,000 €1,898,735 Untitled VIII. 12-Nov-2 Sotheby's, New York
£1,062,500 $1,700,000 €1,593,750 Untitled V. 13-May-3 Sotheby's, New York

KOONS, Jeff (1955-) American
£1,185,898 $1,850,000 €1,778,847 Self portrait. 11-Nov-2 Phillips, New York

LANDSEER, Sir Edwin (1802-1873) British
£1,150,000 $1,851,500 €1,725,000 Scene in Chillingham Park, portrait of Lord Ossulston or death of the wild bull. 19-Feb-3 Christie's, London

LEGER, Fernand (1881-1955) French
£3,205,128 $5,000,000 €4,807,692 Les deux acrobates. 6-Nov-2 Christie's, Rockefeller NY
£1,987,180 $3,100,000 €2,980,770 Les femmes a la toilette. 6-Nov-2 Christie's, Rockefeller NY
£1,410,257 $2,185,898 €2,200,000 Marie l'acrobate. 9-Dec-2 Piasa, Paris
£1,282,051 $2,000,000 €1,923,077 Composition les trois soeurs. 5-Nov-2 Sotheby's, New York
£1,128,205 $1,748,718 €1,760,000 Disque rouge. 9-Dec-2 Piasa, Paris

LICHTENSTEIN, Roy (1923-1997) American
£4,113,924 $6,500,000 €6,170,886 Happy tears. 13-Nov-2 Christie's, Rockefeller NY
£2,784,810 $4,400,000 €4,177,215 Step-on can with leg. 12-Nov-2 Sotheby's, New York
£1,202,532 $1,900,000 €1,803,798 Reclining bather. 12-Nov-2 Sotheby's, New York

MACKE, August (1887-1914) German
£2,515,723 $3,924,528 €4,000,000 Zwei frauen vor dem hutladen - Two women in front of a hat shop. 8-Oct-2 Sotheby's, London
£1,132,075 $1,766,038 €1,800,000 Waldspaziergang - Forest walk. 8-Oct-2 Sotheby's, London

MAGRITTE, René (1898-1967) Belgian
£2,361,111 $3,754,167 €3,400,000 L'oiseau de ciel. 5-May-3 Bernaerts, Antwerp
£1,900,000 $3,097,000 €2,850,000 Barricades mysterieuses. 3-Feb-3 Christie's, London
£1,700,000 $2,839,000 €2,550,000 L'Acte de Foi. 23-Jun-3 Sotheby's, London

MANTEGNA, Andrea (1431-1506) Italian
£15,740,740 $25,500,000 €23,611,110 Descent into Limbo. 23-Jan-3 Sotheby's, New York

MARTIN, John (1789-1854) British
£1,500,000 $2,415,000 €2,250,000 Pandemonium. 19-Feb-3 Christie's, London

MATISSE, Henri (1869-1954) French
£2,820,513 $4,400,000 €4,230,770 Nature morte, serviette a carreaux. 5-Nov-2 Sotheby's, New York

MILLAIS, Sir John Everett (1829-1896) British
£1,100,000 $1,826,000 €1,650,000 Sleeping. 11-Jun-3 Christie's, London

MIRO, Joan (1893-1983) Spanish
£2,500,000 $4,175,000 €3,750,000 Personnages et l'etoile. 23-Jun-3 Sotheby's, London
£1,712,329 $2,671,233 €2,500,000 Piege. 14-Apr-3 Laurence Calmels, Paris
£1,600,000 $2,672,000 €2,320,000 Le coq. 24-Jun-3 Christie's, London
£1,250,000 $1,950,000 €1,875,000 L'oiseau boum-boum fait sa priere a la tete pelure d'oignon. 5-Nov-2 Sotheby's, New York

MODIGLIANI, Amedeo (1884-1920) Italian
£4,935,898 $7,700,000 €7,403,847 Giovanotto dai capelli rossi. 5-Nov-2 Sotheby's, New York
£2,435,898 $3,800,000 €3,653,847 Beatrice hastings devant une porte. 6-Nov-2 Christie's, Rockefeller NY

MONDRIAN, Piet (1872-1944) Dutch
£4,472,050 $7,200,000 €6,708,075 Composition in white, blue and yellow: C. 7-May-3 Christie's, Rockefeller NY

MONET, Claude (1840-1926) French
£10,897,437 $17,000,000 €16,346,156 Nympheas. 5-Nov-2 Sotheby's, New York
£1,925,466 $3,100,000 €2,888,199 Bateaux de peche. 6-May-3 Sotheby's, New York
£1,794,872 $2,800,000 €2,692,308 Fleurs dans un pot - roses et brouillard. 5-Nov-2 Sotheby's, New York
£1,500,000 $2,505,000 €2,175,000 Le Dam a Zaandam, le soir. 24-Jun-3 Christie's, London

MORAN, Thomas (1837-1926) American
£1,709,678 $2,650,000 €2,564,517 Green river, Wyoming. 5-Dec-2 Christie's, Rockefeller NY

MUNCH, Edvard (1863-1944) Norwegian
£1,050,000 $1,753,500 €1,575,000 From Asgardstrand. 23-Jun-3 Sotheby's, London

MUNNINGS, Sir Alfred (1878-1959) British
£1,350,000 $2,133,000 €2,025,000 Beryl Riley-Smith on Snowflake. 27-Nov-2 Christie's, London

NEWMAN, Barnett (1905-1970) American
£2,215,190 $3,500,000 €3,322,785 White fire 1. 13-Nov-2 Christie's, Rockefeller NY

PICABIA, Francis (1878-1953) French
£1,095,890 $1,720,548 €1,600,000 Amoureux, apres la pluie. 15-Apr-3 Laurence Calmels, Paris

PICASSO, Pablo (1881-1973) Spanish
£4,000,000 $6,520,000 €6,000,000 Femme dans un fauteuil. 3-Feb-3 Christie's, London
£3,910,257 $6,100,000 €5,865,386 La guenon et son petit. 6-Nov-2 Christie's, Rockefeller NY
£2,550,000 $4,258,500 €3,825,000 Le Baiser. 23-Jun-3 Sotheby's, London
£2,115,385 $3,300,000 €3,173,078 Mere aux enfants a l'orange. 5-Nov-2 Sotheby's, New York
£1,900,000 $3,173,000 €2,850,000 Courses de Taureaux. 23-Jun-3 Sotheby's, London
£1,794,872 $2,800,000 €2,692,308 Le repos - Marie Therese Walter. 6-Nov-2 Christie's, Rockefeller NY
£1,600,000 $2,608,000 €2,400,000 Femme assise dans un fauteuil. 3-Feb-3 Christie's, London
£1,550,000 $2,526,500 €2,325,000 Poireaux. 3-Feb-3 Christie's, London
£1,282,051 $2,000,000 €1,923,077 Le fils de l'artiste en arlequin - Portrait of Paulo. 5-Nov-2 Sotheby's, New York
£1,025,641 $1,600,000 €1,538,462 Femme assise dans un fauteuil tresse - en gris. 5-Nov-2 Sotheby's, New York
£1,000,000 $1,670,000 €1,450,000 L'Arlesienne. 24-Jun-3 Christie's, London

PISSARRO, Camille (1830-1903) French
£3,105,590 $5,000,000 €4,658,385 Route de Rocquencourt. 6-May-3 Sotheby's, New York
£1,602,564 $2,500,000 €2,403,846 La route par la neige, Louveciennes. 6-Nov-2 Christie's, Rockefeller NY

POLLOCK, Jackson (1912-1956) American
£2,937,500 $4,700,000 €4,406,250 Number 17. 13-May-3 Sotheby's, New York

REMBRANDT (1606-1669) Dutch
£6,200,000 $10,354,001 €8,990,000 Self-portrait with shaded eyes. 10-Jul-3 Sotheby's, London

REMINGTON, Frederic (1861-1909) American
£1,096,774 $1,700,000 €1,645,161 Scare in a pack train. 5-Dec-2 Christie's, Rockefeller NY

RENOIR, Pierre Auguste (1841-1919) French
£13,043,479 $21,000,000 €19,565,219 Dans les roses, Madame Leon Clapisson. 6-May-3 Sotheby's, New York
£2,400,000 $3,912,000 €3,600,000 Canotiers a Argenteuil. 3-Feb-3 Christie's, London

REYNOLDS, Sir Joshua (1723-1792) British
£2,400,000 $3,984,000 €3,600,000 Portrait of Mary Wordsworth, Lady Kent, seated in a landscape. 12-Jun-3 Sotheby's, London

RICCIO, Andrea (1470-1532) Italian
£3,000,000 $4,710,000 €4,500,000 Bust of the Virgin and child. 10-Dec-2 Sotheby's, London

RICHTER, Gerhard (1932-) German
£1,875,000 $3,000,000 €2,812,500 Abstract composition. 14-May-3 Christie's, Rockefeller NY
£1,858,974 $2,900,000 €2,788,461 Troisdorf. 11-Nov-2 Phillips, New York
£1,312,500 $2,100,000 €1,968,750 Laacher meadow. 14-May-3 Christie's, Rockefeller NY
£1,300,000 $2,132,000 €1,950,000 Clouds. 6-Feb-3 Sotheby's, London
£1,265,823 $2,000,000 €1,898,735 Blue. 12-Nov-2 Sotheby's, New York
£1,125,000 $1,800,000 €1,687,500 Davos S. 13-May-3 Sotheby's, New York

ROBINSON, Theodore (1852-1896) American
£1,172,840 $1,900,000 €1,759,260 Boats at a landing. 21-May-3 Sotheby's, New York

RODIN, Auguste (1840-1917) French
£1,250,000 $1,950,000 €1,875,000 La grande ombre. 6-Nov-2 Christie's, Rockefeller NY

ROTHKO, Mark (1903-1970) American
£9,125,001 $14,600,000 €13,687,502 White and black on wine. 14-May-3 Christie's, Rockefeller NY
£3,750,000 $6,000,000 €5,625,000 Brown and black in reds. 14-May-3 Christie's, Rockefeller NY

RUSCHA, Edward (1937-) American
£1,012,658 $1,600,000 €1,518,987 Desire. 13-Nov-2 Christie's, Rockefeller NY

RYSSELBERGHE, Theo van (1862-1926) Belgian
£1,538,462 $2,400,000 €2,307,693 Voiliers sur l'escault. 5-Nov-2 Sotheby's, New York

SARGENT, John Singer (1856-1925) British/American
£1,290,323 $2,000,000 €1,935,485 Jacques Barenton. 4-Dec-2 Sotheby's, New York

SCHIELE, Egon (1890-1918) Austrian
£11,300,000 $18,871,000 €16,950,000 Krumau landscape, town and river. 23-Jun-3 Sotheby's, London

SHINN, Everett (1876-1953) American
£2,129,032 $3,300,000 €3,193,548 Footlight flirtation. 4-Dec-2 Sotheby's, New York

SLOAN, John (1871-1951) American
£1,666,667 $2,700,000 €2,500,001 Easter Eve. 21-May-3 Sotheby's, New York
£1,354,839 $2,100,000 €2,032,259 Gray and brass. 4-Dec-2 Sotheby's, New York

STAEL, Nicolas de (1914-1955) French
£1,000,000 $1,670,000 €1,500,000 Ciel. 26-Jun-3 Christie's, London

STELLA, Frank (1936-) American
£2,437,500 $3,900,000 €3,656,250 Bethlehem's hospital. 14-May-3 Christie's, Rockefeller NY

STUBBS, George (1724-1806) British
£1,750,000 $2,922,500 €2,537,500 Dark bay thoroughbred in a landscape. 9-Jul-3 Bonhams, New Bond Street

THIEBAUD, Wayne (1920-) American
£1,772,152 $2,800,000 €2,658,228 Freeways. 12-Nov-2 Sotheby's, New York

TISSOT, James Jacques Joseph (1836-1902) French
£1,400,000 $2,324,000 €2,100,000 La cheminee. 11-Jun-3 Christie's, London
£1,400,000 $2,212,000 €2,100,000 Seaside - also known as July, La Reverie, or Ramsgate Harbour. 27-Nov-2 Christie's, London

TWOMBLY, Cy (1929-) American
£3,227,848 $5,100,000 €4,841,772 Untitled. 12-Nov-2 Sotheby's, New York
£1,666,667 $2,600,000 €2,500,001 Bolsena. 11-Nov-2 Phillips, New York
£1,400,000 $2,338,000 €2,100,000 Bolsena. 26-Jun-3 Christie's, London
£1,093,750 $1,750,000 €1,640,625 Bolsena. 15-May-3 Phillips, New York

WARHOL, Andy (1928-1987) American
£2,848,101 $4,500,000 €4,272,152 Big electric chair. 13-Nov-2 Christie's, Rockefeller NY
£2,812,500 $4,500,000 €4,218,750 Marlon. 14-May-3 Christie's, Rockefeller NY
£2,658,228 $4,200,000 €3,987,342 Lavender Marilyn 1. 12-Nov-2 Sotheby's, New York
£2,564,103 $4,000,000 €3,846,155 Silver Liz. 11-Nov-2 Phillips, New York
£1,518,987 $2,400,000 €2,278,481 Self portrait. 13-Nov-2 Christie's, Rockefeller NY
£1,518,987 $2,400,000 €2,278,481 Self portrait. 12-Nov-2 Sotheby's, New York
£1,343,750 $2,150,000 €2,015,625 Campbell's soup can - pepper pot. 14-May-3 Christie's, Rockefeller NY
£1,250,000 $2,000,000 €1,875,000 Dance diagram. 14-May-3 Christie's, Rockefeller NY
£1,187,500 $1,900,000 €1,781,250 Four foot flowers. 13-May-3 Sotheby's, New York
£1,139,241 $1,800,000 €1,708,862 Two Marilyns. 12-Nov-2 Sotheby's, New York
£1,100,000 $1,804,000 €1,650,000 Six skulls. 5-Feb-3 Christie's, London

WITTEL, Gaspar van (1653-1736) Dutch
£1,800,000 $3,006,000 €2,610,000 Rome, a view of the apse of Saint Peter's Basilica looking east. 10-Jul-3 Sotheby's, London
£1,700,000 $2,839,000 €2,465,000 Naples, a view of the Darsena. 10-Jul-3 Sotheby's, London

WOUWERMAN, Philips (1619-1668) Dutch
£1,000,000 $1,570,000 €1,500,000 Landscape with stag hunt in full cry, fording a stream. 12-Dec-2 Sotheby's, London

These 149 sales account for £363,138,504 - $581,464,203 of the total market turnover

AUCTION SEASON ANALYSIS

These tables have been compiled from sale results recorded by Art Sales Index Ltd for the 2002/2003 auction season
120,701 entries were made for 36,227 artists,
2,418 auction catalogues were received from 424 auction houses,
turnover recorded was £1.45 billion, $2.32 billion.
Total number of entries in this edition - 123,476.

SALES BY NATIONALITY OF ARTIST OR SCULPTOR

Country	Quantity	UK £(m)	US $(m)
Australia/New Zealand	4,444	25.37	39.89
Austria	2,855	28.43	46.18
Belgium	4,791	31.28	50.33
Canada	2,880	13.76	21.97
Flemish	1,171	23.09	36.92
France	18,799	335.73	537.46
Germany	8,648	91.74	146.53
Netherlands	5,411	71.62	115.55
Hungary	1,439	10.72	16.82
Italy	8,326	114.17	182.19
Israel	176	0.84	1.33
Oriental	1,140	16.27	26.07
Others	4,484	21.40	33.86
Poland	414	1.42	2.26
Russia	1,537	27.45	43.52
Scandinavia	9,705	43.31	68.91
South Africa	538	0.89	1.42
South America	1,043	19.46	31.13
Spain/Portugal	4,934	93.23	149.79
Switzerland	2,643	32.39	51.64
United Kingdom	22,061	127.33	203.72
USA	13,262	323.74	513.59

NUMBER OF WORKS SOLD BY MEDIUM IN STERLING PRICE BANDS

	Works on Paper	Oils	Sculpture	Miniatures	Prints
less than 1,000	16,355	27,127	138	5	6
1,000 - 4,999	11,798	28,184	2,993	295	3,119
5,000 - 9,999	2,401	7,704	898	55	1,061
10,000 - 24,999	1,852	6,034	794	20	558
25,000 - 49,999	663	2,375	357	11	163
50,000 - 99,999	299	1,287	213	3	39
100,000 - 249,999	199	884	148	1	18
250,000 - 499,999	54	310	49	-	3
500,000 - 999,999	18	153	24	-	-
Over £1 million	14	122	12	-	3

TOTAL VALUE OF WORKS SOLD BY MEDIUM IN STERLING PRICE BANDS

(figures are in Million Pounds)

	Works on Paper	Oils	Sculpture	Miniatures	Prints
less than 1,000	8.58	14.86	0.12	0.01	-
1,000 - 4,999	25.70	64.53	7.10	0.67	9.24
5,000 - 9,999	16.59	53.60	6.36	0.36	7.12
10,000 - 24,999	28.43	92.65	12.29	0.30	8.29
25,000 - 49,999	22.54	81.27	12.46	0.35	5.35
50,000 - 99,999	20.65	88.19	14.93	0.17	2.69
100,000 - 249,999	30.30	130.44	22.87	0.10	2.88
250,000 - 499,999	17.98	105.84	16.12	-	1.01
500,000 - 999,999	11.67	104.35	15.42	-	-
Over £1 million	29.19	305.10	26.12	-	6.16

Number of Works Sold by Medium in US Dollar Price Bands

	Works on Paper	Oils	Sculpture	Miniatures	Prints
less than 1,000	11,312	17,660	4	-	3
1,000 - 4,999	14,575	31,411	2,413	234	1,971
5,000 - 9,999	3,207	9,271	1,025	92	1,649
10,000 - 24,999	2,533	8,173	1,028	41	911
25,000 - 49,999	1,050	3,532	493	15	294
50,000 - 99,999	508	1,912	290	6	94
100,000 - 249,999	299	1,235	220	2	34
250,000 - 499,999	108	488	93	-	9
500,000 - 999,999	38	251	38	-	2
Over $1 million	23	207	22	-	3

Total Value of Works Sold by Medium in Dollar Price Bands

(figures are in Million Dollars)

	Works on Paper	Oils	Sculpture	Miniatures	Prints
less than 1,000	7.27	11.58	-	-	-
1,000 - 4,999	33.05	75.23	6.99	0.66	7.46
5,000 - 9,999	22.36	65.62	7.20	0.65	11.51
10,000 - 24,999	39.25	126.97	15.98	0.59	13.73
25,000 - 49,999	36.23	122.38	17.12	0.55	10.13
50,000 - 99,999	34.30	132.49	20.20	0.40	6.12
100,000 - 249,999	45.83	188.60	32.75	0.28	5.02
250,000 - 499,999	36.91	169.50	32.21	-	3.05
500,000 - 999,999	26.01	173.31	26.64	-	1.10
Over $1 million	57.37	596.75	53.77	-	9.97

SALES BY COUNTRY

Country	Quantity	Currency (m)	UK £(m)	US $(m)
Argentina US$	32	0.54	0.34	0.54
Australia	3,862	63.44	23.77	37.38
Austria	2,986	21.13	14.04	22.22
Belgium	4,627	19.52	13.16	20.88
Canada	3,689	33.12	14.01	22.35
Czech Republic	311	34.98	0.75	1.19
Denmark	4,301	128.03	11.41	18.02
Eire	1,873	10.23	6.78	10.69
Finland	1,579	8.28	5.54	8.83
France	15,724	189.76	126.32	200.69
Germany	8,261	56.57	37.92	60.29
Hong Kong	513	148.81	11.84	19.06
Hungary	998	3,340.88	9.09	14.20
Israel US$	92	0.95	0.60	0.95
Italy	5,302	50.81	33.50	52.99
Mexico	132	8.11	0.50	0.80
Netherlands	3,819	33.56	22.36	35.30
New Zealand	979	11.38	3.79	5.96
Norway	1,071	61.48	5.38	8.52
Russia	16	0.03	0.02	0.03
Slovak Republic	197	20.05	0.31	0.48
South Africa	708	14.05	1.05	1.67
Spain	2,234	12.38	8.11	12.82
Sweden	4,044	265.61	19.60	31.07
Switzerland	3,412	48.89	21.83	35.02
United Kingdom	29,550	431.25	431.25	690.74
Uruguay US$	148	0.42	0.26	0.42
USA	20,241	997.64	629.38	997.64

Auction house, date, catalogue title and reference code

Please note, the absence of a catalogue indicates that no fine art was sold

Auction house, date, catalogue title and reference code

AB Stockholms Auktionsverk, Stockholm - Sweden
6 Nov 2 Modern Art
4 Dec 2 International Auction
7 May 3 Modern Art
4 Jun 3 Fine Art & Antiques

Alderfer's, Hatfield, PA - USA
18 Sep 2 Fine Art

Allgauer Auktionshaus, Kempten - Germany
11 Jul 2 Paintings & Works of Art - S31
7 Nov 2 Paintings & Fine Art - H32
10 Jan 3 Paintings & Fine Art - W33
10 Apr 3 Paintings & Fine Art - F34

Altermann Galleries, Santa Fe, NM - USA
18 May 2 Collectors Sale - Dallas, TX
20 Jul 2 Works by Tom Lovell
9 Aug 2 Grant MacDonald & Richard Loffler
9 Nov 2 Collectors Sale
23 May 3 Collectors Sale XXIII
27 Jun 3 Nelson Boren and Kim Wiggins collection

Amberes, Antwerp - Belgium
16 Sep 2 Paintings & Fine Art - No.70
14 Oct 2 Paintings & Fine Art - No.71
25 Nov 2 Paintings & Fine Art - No.72
2 Dec 2 Paintings & Fine Art - No.73
16 Dec 2 Paintings & Fine Art - No.74
17 Feb 3 Paintings & Fine Art - No.75
17 Mar 3 Paintings & Fine Art - No.76
28 Apr 3 Paintings & Fine Art - No.77
26 May 3 Paintings & Fine Art - No.78
23 Jun 3 Fine Art - 79

Ambrose, Loughton - UK
31 Oct 2 Fine Art
5 Dec 2 Fine Art
23 Jan 3 Fine Art
27 Mar 3 Fine Art

Amersham Auction Rooms, Amersham - UK
5 Sep 2 Fine Art
3 Oct 2 Fine Art
7 Nov 2 Fine Art
6 Feb 3 Fine Art
3 Apr 3 Fine Art
1 May 3 Fine Art
5 Jun 3 Fine Art

Anaf, Lyon - France
20 Oct 2 Fine Art
1 Dec 2 Paintings & Fine Art
4 Dec 2 Art Deco & Art Nouveau
9 Feb 3 Paintings & Fine Art
30 Mar 3 Paintings & Fine Art
15 Jun 3 Paintings & Fine Art
16 Jun 3 The Collection of Jean Thierry de Valenclos
18 Jun 3 Modern Lithographs

Anders Antik, Landskrona - Sweden
27 Oct 2 Paintings & Works of Art
15 Dec 2 Christmas Auction
18 May 3 International Spring Auction

Anderson & Garland, Newcastle - UK
24 Sep 2 Oil Paintings, Watercolours & Prints - MH135
17 Jun 3 Oil Paintings, Watercolours & Prints

Andrew Hartley, Ilkley - UK
14 Aug 2 Fine Art
9 Oct 2 Fine Art
4 Dec 2 Fine Art
12 Feb 3 Fine Art
9 Apr 3 Fine Art
18 Jun 3 Fine Art

Ansorena, Madrid - Spain
17 Jun 2 Paintings & Fine Art - No.246
7 Oct 2 Paintings & Fine Art - No.248
8 Oct 2 Paintings & Fine Art - No.248
13 Nov 2 Paintings & Fine Art - No.249
18 Dec 2 Paintings & Fine Art - No.250
21 Jan 3 Paintings & Fine Art - No.251
4 Mar 3 Paintings & Fine Art - No.252
8 Apr 3 Paintings & Fine Art - No.253

Anthemion, Cardiff - UK
20 Nov 2 Fine Art - A037
19 Mar 3 Fine Art - A041
16 Apr 3 Sporting Memorabilia - A043
16 Jul 3 Fine Art

Arce Subastas, Barcelona - Spain
5 Feb 2 Fine Art

Arnold, Frankfurt - Germany
5 Sep 2 Paintings & Fine Art
23 Nov 2 Paintings & Fine Art - A147
30 Nov 2 Modern & Contemporary Art
8 Mar 3 Paintings & Fine Art
14 Jun 3 Fine Art

Artcurial Briest, Paris - France
29 Oct 2 Fine Art
30 Oct 2 Fine Art
9 Dec 2 Art Deco & Design - with Poulain & Le Fur
10 Dec 2 Modern Art - with Poulain & Le Fur
11 Dec 2 Modern Art & Gold Sculpture - with Poulain & Le Fur
11 Dec 2 Contemporary Art - with Poulain & Le Fur
14 Dec 2 Old Master Paintings - with Claude Aguttes
26 Feb 3 Modern & Contemporary Art - with Poulain & Le Fur
6 Mar 3 Fine Art - with Poulain & Le Fur
13 Mar 3 Fine Art - with Poulain & Le Fur
29 Apr 3 Modern & Contemporary Art
27 May 3 Lefevre-Utile Collection - with Poulain & Le Fur, Fattori
25 Jun 3 Works Of Art
30 Jun 3 The Perrot-Moore Collection
30 Jun 3 Modern Art
1 Jul 3 Modern Art
2 Jul 3 Modern Art
2 Jul 3 20th Century Decorative Art
2 Jul 3 Prints & Illustrated Books
10 Jul 3 Modern & Contemporary Art

Arte, Seville - Spain
14 Nov 2 Paintings
5 Feb 3 Fine Art

Arthur James, Delray Beach, FL - USA
16 Jul 2 Oil Paintings & Watercolours
1 Oct 2 Fine Art
5 Nov 2 Fine Art
20 Jan 3 Fine Art
18 Feb 3 Fine Art
18 Mar 3 Fine Art
22 Apr 3 Fine Art

Aspire, Cleveland, OH - USA
23 Sep 2 Fine Art
25 Oct 2 Fine Art
23 Jan 3 Fine Art
28 Mar 3 Fine Art
30 May 3 Fine Art & Antiques

Auktion Burkard, Luzern - Switzerland
23 Nov 2 20th Century & Contemporary Art - No.54

Auktionhaus Geble, Radolfzell - Germany
23 Mar 2 Fine Art - No.61
31 Aug 2 Fine Art - No.62
30 Nov 2 Fine Art - No.63
5 Apr 3 Fine Art - No.64

Auktionhaus Georg Rehm, Augsburg - Germany
14 Jun 2 Fine Art - No.171
27 Sep 2 17th-20th Century Oil Paintings - No.174
8 Nov 2 Fine Art - No.175
6 Dec 2 Fine Art - No.176
7 Feb 3 Fine Art - No.177
21 Mar 3 Fine Art - No.178

Auktionhaus Zofingen, Zofingen - Switzerland
29 Nov 2 Fine Art - No.28

Australian Art Auctions, Sydney - Australia
21 Oct 2 Australian & International Paintings
7 Apr 3 International Art - No.118

Babuino, Rome - Italy
24 Jun 2 The Contents of a Noble Flat by the Quirinale

15 Oct 2 Fine Art
12 Nov 2 Modern & Contemporary Art
11 Mar 3 Fine Paintings from a Roman Collection
1 Apr 3 Paintings & Furniture from Private Collections
20 May 3 Old Master Paintings

Barridoff Galleries, Portland, ME - USA
8 Aug 1 Fine Paintings

Bassenge, Berlin - Germany
29 Nov 2 Uncommon Prints - No.80
29 Nov 2 15th-19th Century Art - No.80
30 Nov 2 20th Century Art - No.80
6 Dec 2 Photographs - No.80
6 Dec 2 Decorative Graphics - No.80
30 May 3 Photographs - No.81

Bearnes, Exeter - UK
16 Jul 2 Pictures
17 Sep 2 Fine Art
8 Oct 2 Fine Art
15 Oct 2 Autumn Sale - SE30
4 Mar 3 Spring Sale - SE31
18 Mar 3 Fine Art - EX149
8 Apr 3 Fine Art - EX150
29 Apr 3 Fine Art - EX151
13 May 3 Fine Art - EX152
19 May 3 Evening Sales including BBC Bargain Hunt Live - SF10
3 Jun 3 Fine Art - EX153
24 Jun 3 Works Of Art & Collector's Items - EX154
1 Jul 3 Summer Sale

Beaussant & Lefevre, Paris - France
13 Nov 2 Photographs
15 Nov 2 Old Master Paintings
9 Dec 2 Modern & Contemporary Art
16 Dec 2 Asian Art
18 Dec 2 Paintings & Fine Art
5 Feb 3 Photographs & Books
28 Feb 3 Paintings & Fine Art
25 Apr 3 Paintings & Fine Art
16 May 3 Contents of Languedoc Castle
23 May 3 Paintings & Fine Art
11 Jun 3 Art Nouveau
23 Jun 3 Fine Art

Bergmann, Erlangen - Germany
14 Sep 2 Fine Art
7 Dec 2 Fine Art - No.68

Berlinghof, Heidelberg - Germany
6 Jul 2 Fine Art - No.97
21 Sep 2 Paintings & Fine Art - No.98
30 Nov 2 Fine Art - No.99
10 May 3 Paintings & Fine Art - No.100

Bernaerts, Antwerp - Belgium
23 Sep 2 Fine Art - No.64
21 Oct 2 Romantic & Modern Masters
18 Nov 2 Old Masters - No.67
16 Dec 2 Paintings & Fine Art - No.68
24 Feb 3 Paintings & Fine Art
24 Mar 3 Paintings
5 May 3 Sabena Collection in Bankruptcy
12 May 3 Paintings & Fine Art
23 Jun 3 Art & Antiques

Biddle & Webb, Birmingham - UK
3 May 2 Pictures & Prints - No.3084
2 Aug 2 Fine Art - No.3121
6 Sep 2 Pictures & Prints
6 Dec 2 Paintings - No.3166
10 Jan 3 Fine Art - No.3176
7 Feb 3 Pictures & Prints - No.3190
7 Mar 3 Fine Art - No.3201

Bigwood, Stratford upon Avon - UK
27 Sep 2 Fine Art
20 Dec 2 Fine Art

Binoche, Paris - France
11 Oct 2 Paintings
20 Nov 2 Paintings
23 May 3 Old Master & Modern Paintings

Blache, Grenoble - France
14 Oct 2 Fine Art

Blanchet, Paris - France
31 May 2 Paintings & Furniture
27 Nov 2 Modern & Contemporary Paintings
14 May 3 Modern & Contemporary Art

Blomqvist, Oslo - Norway
27 May 2 Spring Auction - No.2
21 Oct 2 Autumn Auction
2 Dec 2 Paintings & Fine Art - No.5-6
17 Mar 3 Fine Art - No.1
28 Apr 3 Paintings & Fine Art - No.2
2 Jun 3 Summer Auction

Blomqvist Lysaker, Oslo - Norway
26 Aug 2 Paintings & Works of Art
23 Sep 2 Paintings and Works of Art
28 Oct 2 Paintings & Works of Art
25 Nov 2 Paintings & Works of Art
27 Jan 3 Fine Art - No.20
17 Feb 3 Fine Art - No.21

Bolland & Marotz, Bremen - Germany
21 Sep 2 Fine Art - No.115
29 Nov 2 Fine Art - No.116
28 Mar 3 Fine Art - No.117

Bondu, Paris - France
19 Dec 2 Paintings & Fine Arts

Bonhams, Bath - UK
22 Oct 2 Pictures Prints
18 Nov 2 Fine Art - B1226
2 Dec 2 Paintings & Works on Paper - B1228
10 Feb 3 County Sale - 10038
17 Feb 3 Pictures & Prints - 10050
10 Mar 3 County Sale - 10086
7 Apr 3 Paintings & Works on Paper - 10145
9 Jun 3 The Cockpit Sale - 10262
23 Jun 3 Pictures - 10234
21 Jul 3 Paintings & Works On Paper - 10452

Bonhams, Bayswater - UK
23 Sep 2 The Contents of a Belgravia Residence - T0630

Bonhams, Bury St Edmunds - UK
22 Jul 2 The Athenaeum Sale - I349
16 Dec 2 Athenaeum Sale - I356
5 Mar 3 Athenaeum Sale - 10080
25 Jun 3 Athenaeum Sale - 10249

Bonhams, Chester - UK
23 Sep 2 Prints & Paintings - C1788 & C1789
6 Nov 2 Three Day Fine Sale - C1795, C1796, C1797
25 Nov 2 County Sale - C1799 & C1800
4 Feb 3 Oil Paintings & Watercolours - 10033
27 Feb 3 Oil Paintings, Watercolours & Prints - 10070
15 Apr 3 Books, Maps & Pictures - 10161
4 Jun 3 Chester Sale - 10254

Bonhams, Par, Cornwall - UK
3 Oct 2 County Sale
7 Nov 2 Works of Art & Pictures - P488
6 Mar 3 Furniture & Works of Art - 10084
12 Jun 3 Fine Art - No.10268

Bonhams, Edinburgh - UK
22 Aug 2 The Scottish Sale - E3634
12 Sep 2 County Sale
10 Oct 2 County Sale - E3639
17 Oct 2 19th & 20th Century Paintings - 3640
14 Nov 2 County Sale - E3643
5 Dec 2 Fine Paintings - E3647
19 Dec 2 Fine Art - E3649
23 Jan 3 Art & Antiques - 10021
20 Feb 3 County Sale - 10058
28 Mar 3 Contents of 1-4 Charlotte Square - 10229
10 Apr 3 19th & 20th Century Paintings - 10154
17 Apr 3 Art & Antiques - 10172

Bonhams, Ipswich - UK
9 Sep 2 The Contents of Brancaster Hall, Norfolk - IH10
17 Sep 2 County Sale - 1351
30 Sep 2 Athenaeum & East Anglian View Sales - 1352 - Bury St Edmunds
22 Oct 2 County Sale - I353
26 Nov 2 County Sale - I355
14 Jan 3 County Sale - 10008
18 Feb 3 County Sale - 10054

15 Apr 3 County Sale - 10257

Bonhams, Knightsbridge - UK
6 Sep 2 The Goodwood Revival - Goodwood
10 Sep 2 British & Continental Oil Paintings - 28850
17 Sep 2 Modern Pictures & Sculpture - 28855
24 Sep 2 British & Continental Watercolours & Drawings - 28858
8 Oct 2 British & Continental Oil Paintings - 28860
15 Oct 2 Modern Pictures & Sculpture
17 Oct 2 Islamic & Indian Art
22 Oct 2 British & Continental Watercolours & Drawings - 28862
12 Nov 2 British & Continental Oil Paintings - 28863
26 Nov 2 British & Continental Watercolours & Drawings - 28866
28 Nov 2 Sporting & Ornithological Pictures - 29086
3 Dec 2 Modern Paintings - 29072
7 Jan 3 British & Continental Oil Paintings - 10003
14 Jan 3 Modern Pictures & Sculpture - 10011
21 Jan 3 British & Continental Watercolours & Drawings - 10018
12 Feb 3 Oil Paintings incl. Dogs in Art II - 10047
18 Feb 3 Modern Pictures - 10056
25 Feb 3 British & Continental Watercolours & Drawings - 10068
4 Mar 3 Maritime - 10078
11 Mar 3 Oil Paintings incl. Nudes in Art - 10094
18 Mar 3 Vision 21 - 10111
25 Mar 3 British & Continental Watercolours & Drawings - 10121
8 Apr 3 British & Continental Oil Paintings - 10150
15 Apr 3 Modern Paintings - 10166
29 Apr 3 British & Continental Watercolours & Drawings - 10182
1 May 3 Islamic Art - 10185
13 May 3 British & Continental Oil Paintings - 10298
20 May 3 Modern Pictures - 10307
21 May 3 Watercolours & Drawings incl. Flowers in Art - 10306
3 Jun 3 Sporting Art
10 Jun 3 British & Continental Oil Paintings - 10314
17 Jun 3 Modern Pictures - 10316
24 Jun 3 British & Continental Watercolours & Drawings - 10318
8 Jul 3 British & Continental Oil Paintings - 10322
9 Jul 3 Old Master Drawings - 10511
15 Jul 3 Modern Pictures - 10326
22 Jul 3 British & Continental Watercolours & Drawings - 10330

Bonhams, Knowle - UK
31 Jul 2 County Sale - K1466
21 Aug 2 County Sale - K1468
11 Sep 2 County Sale
2 Oct 2 Fine Art
30 Oct 2 County Sale - K1476
13 Nov 2 Fine Art - K1477
27 Nov 2 Paintings incl. Works of Art by Snaffles - K1478
18 Dec 2 County Sale - K1482
14 Jan 3 County Sale - 10009
28 Jan 3 County Sale - 10025
11 Feb 3 Pictures - 10041
18 Feb 3 County Sale - 10055
18 Mar 3 County Sale - 10109
15 Apr 3 Paintings incl. Works of Art by Snaffles - 10164
20 May 3 County Sale
24 Jun 3 Paintings, Furniture & Works of Art - 10426

Bonhams, Leeds - UK
20 Aug 2 County Sale - L1050
17 Sep 2 Works of Art
1 Oct 2 Modern & Contemporary Art - L1053
19 Nov 2 Yorkshire & Victorian Paintings, Drawings, Watercolours & Prints - L1057
4 Feb 3 The Graham Watson Collection - 10034
25 Mar 3 Paintings - 10110
10 Jun 3 Oil Painting, Watercolours & Prints L.S. Lowry - No.10287

Bonhams, New Bond Street, London - UK
15 Aug 2 Marine Pictures - 31350 & 31351
10 Sep 2 The Gerald Godfrey Collection - 31334
24 Sep 2 20th Century British Art & Design - 31342
1 Oct 2 Miniatures & Silhouettes - 31217
29 Oct 2 19th Century & Decorative Sale - 31361
30 Oct 2 Old Master Paintings & Drawings - 31341
5 Nov 2 British & Continental Watercolours & Drawings - 31358
5 Nov 2 Fine Miniatures - 31218
19 Nov 2 19th Century Paintings - 31336
3 Dec 2 20th Century British Art - 31359
4 Dec 2 Prints - 31355
9 Dec 2 Old Master Drawings - 31378
10 Dec 2 Old Master Paintings - 31365
21 Jan 3 The Harrison Line Collection - 10017
22 Jan 3 The Marine Sale - 10019
3 Feb 3 Impressionist & Modern Art - 10031
4 Mar 3 Miniatures & Silhouettes - 10077
11 Mar 3 British & Continental Watercolours & Drawings - 10095
18 Mar 3 19th Century Paintings - 10104
25 Mar 3 20th Century British Art - 10117
31 Mar 3 Prints - 10133
1 Apr 3 The Greek Sale - 10135
9 Apr 3 Old Master Paintings & Drawings - 10167
29 Apr 3 Travel & Topographical Paintings - 10184
22 May 3 Fine Portrait Miniatures - 10168
12 Jun 3 British & Continental Watercolours & Drawings - 10244
12 Jun 3 Japanese Encounters - 10244
17 Jun 3 19th Century Paintings - 10233
24 Jun 3 20th Century British Art - 10243
30 Jun 3 Prints - 10248
1 Jul 3 Portrait Miniatures & Silhouettes - 10245
9 Jul 3 Old Master Paintings - No.10195

Bonhams, Norwich - UK
1 Jul 3 The East Anglian View

Bonhams, Sevenoaks - UK
17 Sep 2 Fine Art
18 Mar 3 Fine Art - 10103
13 May 3 Fine Art - 10236

Bonhams, Oxford - UK
17 Sep 2 Fine Art
8 Oct 2 County Sale incl. Pictures - D1843
12 Nov 2 County Sale - D1846
26 Nov 2 Paintings & Works of Art - D1847
11 Mar 3 Paintings & Works of Art - 10090
13 May 3 County sale - 10288
3 Jun 3 Pictures

Bonhams & Doyles, New York, NY - USA
11 Feb 3 Dogs in Art

Bonhams & James Adam, Dublin - Eire
3 Dec 2 Important Irish Art - No.3065
28 May 3 Important Irish Art - No.3067

Bonhams & Langlois, Jersey - UK
26 Mar 3 Channel Island Sale - 10123

Bonhams, Brooks & Langlois, Jersey - UK
27 Nov 2 Selected Antiques & Works of Art - 70026

Boos Gallery, Bloomfield Hills, MI - USA
18 Sep 2 Fine Paintings & Sculpture - No.234
20 Nov 2 Fine Art
15 Jan 3 Fine Art
3 Apr 3 Fine Art
11 Jun 3 Fine Paintings & Decorative Art - No.238

Bracketts, Tunbridge Wells - UK
14 Feb 3 Fine Art
23 May 3 Fine Art
11 Jul 3 Fine Art

Bretagne Encheres, Saint Malo - France
21 Jun 3 Fine Art - No.42

Brightwells, Leominster - UK
28 Aug 2 Fine Art
25 Sep 2 Fine Art
16 Oct 2 Antiques
4 Nov 2 Fine Art
4 Dec 2 Antiques
8 Jan 3 Fine Art
29 Jan 3 Fine Art
27 Feb 3 Fine art
19 Mar 3 Antiques
10 Apr 3 Fine Art
30 Apr 3 Fine Art
25 Jun 3 Fine Art
23 Jul 3 Fine Art

Bristol Auction Rooms, Bristol - UK
3 Sep 2 Fine Art
1 Oct 2 Fine Art - no. 54
5 Nov 2 Fine Art
10 Dec 2 Fine Art - No.68
28 Jan 3 Fine Art - No.5
4 Mar 3 Antique & Decorative Items
8 Apr 3 Antique & Decorative Items - No.19

13 May 3 Antique & Decorative Items
17 Jun 3 Antique & decorative Items
22 Jul 3 Antique & Decorative Sale - No.39

Brunk, Ashville, NC - USA
20 Jul 2 Fine Art
7 Sep 2 Fine Art
26 Oct 2 Fine Art
4 Jan 3 Fine Art
22 Feb 3 Fine Art
12 Apr 3 Fine Art

Lilla Bukowskis, Stockholm - Sweden
16 Aug 2 Fine Art - No.148
13 Sep 2 Fine Art - No.149
16 Dec 2 Fine Art - No.150
3 Feb 3 Fine Art - No.151
3 Mar 3 Fine Art - No.152
16 Jun 3 Fine Art - No.153

Bukowskis, Stockholm - Sweden
5 Nov 2 Contemporary Art & Design - No.525
3 Dec 2 International Autumn Auction - No.526
28 Apr 3 Modern Art - No.527
26 May 3 International Spring Auction

Bukowskis & Horhammer, Helsinki - Finland
15 Sep 2 Fine Art - 102
6 Oct 2 Fine Art - 103
27 Oct 2 Fine Art - 104
1 Dec 2 International Autumn Auction - No.105
9 Feb 3 Fine Art - No.106
24 Mar 3 Decorative Art - No.107
10 May 3 International Art - No.108
4 Jun 3 Fine Art - No.109

Butterfields, Los Angeles, CA - USA
29 Sep 2 Decorative Art
23 Feb 3 Sunset Auction
30 Mar 3 20th Century Decorative Art incl. Prints - 7385N & 7395K - with Bonhams
13 Apr 3 Sunset Auction - No.7421T - with Bonhams
18 May 3 Sunset Auction - No.7431T - with Bonhams
29 Jun 3 Sunset Estate Auction - With Bonhams

Butterfields, San Francisco, CA - USA
28 Jul 2 Single Owner Masters - No.7345F
14 Oct 2 Prints, Photographs & 20th Century Fine Art
28 Oct 2 European & American & Decorative Art - 7382G
19 Nov 2 Californian & American Paintings - 7390D - San Francisco & Los Angeles
24 Nov 2 The Connoisseurs Sale
16 Feb 3 Paintings - 7403F
16 Mar 3 Paintings - 7407F - with Bonhams
22 Apr 3 Fine Prints & Photographs incl. 20th Century Paintings & Drawings - No.7422K & 7424U - with Bonhams
5 May 3 Edwin C James Jr Estate - 7435G - Brookline MA with Bonhams
14 May 3 European Paintings - with Bonhams
11 Jun 3 Californian & American Paintings & Sculpture - No.7438D - with Bonhams

CRN Auctions, Cambridge, MA - USA
17 Nov 2 American & European Paintings
14 Dec 2 Paintings & Americana
17 May 3 Fine Art

Caddigan, Hanover, MA - USA
4 Apr 2 Fine Art
9 Feb 3 Fine Art
4 Apr 3 Estate Sale

Calmels, Paris - France
15 Nov 2 Modern & Contemporary Art
15 Nov 2 Pol Bury Collection
24 Nov 2 Cavalero Collection
14 Apr 3 Modern Paintings, Sculptures & Old Masters
15 Apr 3 Modern & Contemporary Paintings
12 Jun 3 The Francois Arp Collection

Camard, Paris - France
8 Nov 2 20th Century Decorative Art
26 Nov 2 Sculptures & Modern Art
27 Nov 2 Furniture & Design
3 Feb 3 Art Nouveau & Art Deco
28 Mar 3 Decorative Art
30 Apr 3 Art Nouveau

23 May 3 Modern Art

Campo, Vlaamse Kaai, Antwerp - Belgium
22 Oct 2 Fine Art - No.51
10 Dec 2 Fine Art - No.52
18 Mar 3 Fine Art - No.54
29 Apr 3 Fine Art - No.55
27 May 3 Fine Art

Campo & Campo, Grote Steenweg, Antwerp - Belgium
22 Oct 2 Modern Art - No.49
3 Dec 2 Paintings & Fine Art - No.50
25 Mar 3 Paintings & Fine Art - No.51
29 Apr 3 Paintings & Fine Art - No.52
27 May 3 Paintings & Fine Art - No.53

Canterbury Auction Galleries, Canterbury - UK
13 Aug 2 Fine Art
15 Oct 2 Fine Art

Capes Dunn, Manchester - UK
9 Jul 2 Oil Paintings & Watercolours
1 Oct 2 Oil Paintings & Watercolours
10 Dec 2 Paintings
18 Mar 3 Oil Paintings & Watercolours
3 Jun 3 Oil Paintings & Watercolours
24 Jun 3 Prints
29 Jul 3 Oil Paintings & Watercolours

Castellana, Madrid - Spain
6 Jun 2 Paintings - No.146
12 Jun 2 Paintings - No.148
3 Jul 2 Paintings - No.150
28 Aug 2 Paintings - No.157
26 Sep 2 Paintings - No.161
19 Nov 2 Pictures & Objects - No.170
16 Dec 2 Paintings & Fine Art - No.174
16 Dec 2 Southern School - No.174
18 Dec 2 Special Christmas Auction - No.178
14 Jan 3 Paintings - No.180
11 Feb 3 Paintings - No.184
11 Mar 3 Fine Art - No.188
7 Apr 3 Paintings - No.192

Chambelland & Giafferi, Paris - France
23 Jun 2 Modern & Contemporary Art
3 Feb 3 Fine Art

Charbonneaux, Paris - France
20 Oct 2 Modern & Contemporary Art
16 Dec 2 Modern & Contemporary Art
31 Jan 3 Contemporary Art
28 Mar 3 Paintings & Sculpture
18 May 3 Modern & Contemporary Art
18 Jun 3 Modern & Contemporary Art

Charlton Hall, Columbia, SC - USA
28 Sep 2 Fine Art
14 Dec 2 Fine Art
29 Mar 3 Fine Art
21 Jun 3 Southern Estates At Auction

Chayette & Cheval, Paris - France
20 Mar 2 Drawings & Posters
20 Oct 2 19th & 20th Century Art
24 Nov 2 Jewish Paintings & Atelier Simonka
24 Jan 3 Fine Art

Cheffins, Cambridge - UK
25 Jun 3 Fine Art & Antiques

Cheffins Grain & Comins, Cambridge - UK
18 Sep 2 Fine Art
10 Dec 2 Olive Cook Sale
15 Jan 3 Drawings, Watercolours & Oil Paintings
26 Feb 3 Fine Art
9 Apr 3 Fine Art

Chochon-Barre & Allardi, Paris - France
7 Nov 2 Old Masters, Sculptures, Modern & Contemporary Art
16 Dec 2 Paintings & Fine Art
27 Feb 3 Mouclier, Durenne, Piet, Lambert & Devez
25 Mar 3 Modern & Contemporary Art

Christie's, Amsterdam - Netherlands
3 Sep 2 Pictures, Watercolours & Drawings - 2555
24 Sep 2 Dutch Interior
25 Sep 2 Sculpture - 2560
23 Oct 2 19th Century European Art - 2563

6 Nov 2 Old Master Pictures - 2566
19 Nov 2 20th Century Decorative Art - 2567
3 Dec 2 20th Century Art - Including Belgian Art - 2570
21 Jan 3 Pictures, Watercolours & Drawings - 2575
29 Apr 3 19th Century European Art - 2581
13 May 3 Property from the Gutmann Collection - 2590
14 May 3 Old Master Paintings - 2583
3 Jun 3 Twentieth Century Art including Belgian Art - 2586
1 Jul 3 Picture, Watercolours & Drawings - 2589

Christie's, Hong Kong
27 Oct 2 Southeast Asian Pictures - 2119
6 Jul 3 Southeast Asian & 20th Century Indian Pictures - 2132
6 Jul 3 Fine Modern & Contemporary Chinese Paintings - 2136
6 Jul 3 Fine Classical Chinese Paintings & Calligraphy - 2137
6 Jul 3 20th Century Chinese Art - 2133
7 Jul 3 The Imperial Sale, Fine Chinese Ceramics and Works of Art - 2138

Christie's, London - UK
24 Sep 2 The Africa Sale - 6623
26 Sep 2 The Freycinet Collection - 6694
1 Oct 2 19th Century Furniture & Sculpture - 6626
9 Oct 2 Picasso: Prints, Ceramics & Metal Works - 6683
22 Oct 2 Italian Art
23 Oct 2 Post-War & Contemporary Art - 6710
31 Oct 2 The Best of Scottish Art - Edinburgh
7 Nov 2 20th Century Art - 6635
13 Nov 2 Japanese Art & Design - 6638
14 Nov 2 European Sculpture & Furniture - 6639
21 Nov 2 British Art on Paper - 6643
22 Nov 2 20th Century British Art - 6644
26 Nov 2 British Pictures 1500-1850 & Victorian Pictures - 6649 & 6645
27 Nov 2 Sporting Art - 6650
27 Nov 2 Important British Art - 6666
3 Dec 2 Old Master, Modern & Contemporary Prints - 6655
4 Dec 2 19th Century European Art - 6636
10 Dec 2 Portrait Miniatures
11 Dec 2 Important Old Master Pictures - 6652
22 Jan 3 The Collection of Monsieur et Madame Gerald Bauer - 6700
3 Feb 3 Impressionist & Modern Art - Evening Sale - 6677
3 Feb 3 The Art of Surreal - Evening Sale - 6718
3 Feb 3 German & Austrian Art - 6627
4 Feb 3 Impressionist & Modern Art - Day Sale - 6685
5 Feb 3 Post-War & Contemporary Art - Evening Sale - 6692
6 Feb 3 Impressionist & Modern Works on Paper - 6691
6 Feb 3 Post-War & Contemporary - Day Sale - 6693
19 Feb 3 The Forbes Collection I - 6747
20 Feb 3 The Forbes Collection II - 6747
20 Feb 3 The Forbes Collection III - 6747
10 Mar 3 Art for Life - in support of Cancer Research
9 Apr 3 Important Old Master Paintings - 6708
15 May 3 Irish Art - 6719
20 May 3 Important Daguerrotypes by Joseph Philibert Girault de Prangey - 6762
21 May 3 Historic War & Striking Portrait Photographs - 6717
22 May 3 Sporting Art - 6722
3 Jun 3 Portrait Miniatures - 6720
5 Jun 3 British Art on Paper - 6724
6 Jun 3 20th Century British & Irish Art - 6725
10 Jun 3 British Pictures 1500-1850 - 6730
10 Jun 3 Victorian Pictures - 6726
11 Jun 3 Important British & Irish Art - 6728
12 Jun 3 Boulle To Jansen : An Important Private European Collection - 6749
12 Jun 3 Boulle To Jansen - Maritime Pictures - 6749
18 Jun 3 Japanese Art & Design - 6733
19 Jun 3 19th Century European Art - 6734
24 Jun 3 Impressionist & Modern Art Evening Sale - 6735
24 Jun 3 Alice Teriade Collection - ALICE-6865
25 Jun 3 Impressionist & Modern Art Day Sale - 6736
26 Jun 3 Impressionist & Modern Works on Paper - 6737
26 Jun 3 Post-War & Contemporary Evening Sale - 6738
27 Jun 3 Post-War & Contemporary Day Sale - 6739
2 Jul 3 Old Master, Modern & Contemporary Prints - 6740
8 Jul 3 Old Master Drawings - 6743
9 Jul 3 Old Master Paintings - 6744

Christie's, Los Angeles, CA - USA
20 Nov 2 California, Western & American Art - 1064
18 Jun 3 California, Western & American Paintings, Drawings & Sculpture - 1249

Christie's, Melbourne - Australia
27 Aug 2 Australian & International Paintings - 1032
25 Nov 2 Australian, International & Contemporary Art - 1035
2 Apr 3 The Estate of the Late Frederick D Bladin - 1045
8 Apr 3 Decorative Art - 1037
6 May 3 Australian, International & Contemporary Art - 1038

Christie's, Milan - Italy
26 May 3 Modern & Contemporary Art - 2424

Christie's, Paris - France
28 Sep 2 Decorative Art - 5031
28 Sep 2 A Collection of Sculptures by Alberto Giacometti
8 Oct 2 Drawings & Paintings from a Parisian Apartment
16 Nov 2 Photography
27 Nov 2 Old Master Pictures & 19th Century Art
27 Nov 2 Old Masters & 19th Century Work - 5037
4 Dec 2 Illustrated Books & Modern Manuscripts - 5022
11 Mar 3 The Fould-Springer & Rothschild Collections - 5042
27 Mar 3 19th Century Drawings - 5045
2 Apr 3 Paintings & Graphic Art - 5046
15 May 3 Amateur Collection - 5061
20 May 3 20th Century Decorative Art - 5051
3 Jul 3 POP HIP HOP-The Collection of Jean-Charles de Castelbajac - No.5033

Christie's, Rockefeller, NY - USA
4 Sep 2 The House Sale - 1109
25 Sep 2 Prints & Multiples - 1111
26 Sep 2 Impressionist & Modern Art - Max-1119
26 Sep 2 Post-War & Contemporary Art - Sauron-1120
2 Oct 2 The House Sale
30 Oct 2 19th Century European Art - 1136
30 Oct 2 Fine 19th Century European Art - 1112
5 Nov 2 19th & 20th Century Prints - 1138
6 Nov 2 Impressionist & Modern Art - Evening Sale - 1147
7 Nov 2 Impressionist & Modern Works on Paper - 1148
13 Nov 2 Post-War & Contemporary - Evening Sale - 1150
14 Nov 2 Post-War & Contemporary Art - Morning Sale - 1151
14 Nov 2 Post-War & Contemporary Art - Afternoon Sale - 1180
20 Nov 2 Latin American Art - 1154
26 Nov 2 Roger Prigent's Malmaison - 1182
3 Dec 2 The House Sale - 1161
5 Dec 2 American Paintings, Drawings & Sculpture - 1124
13 Jan 3 American Indian Art - 1142
15 Jan 3 House Sale - 1187
16 Jan 3 Important Furniture & Folk Art - 1189
21 Jan 3 Captains & Kilns - 1191
22 Jan 3 Old Master & 19th Century Drawings - 1192
22 Jan 3 Drawings by J H W Tischbein - 1192
24 Jan 3 Important Old Master Paintings - 1194
27 Jan 3 20th Century Self-Taught & Outsider Art - 1183
5 Feb 3 The House Sale - 1197
12 Feb 3 Photographs - 1199
13 Feb 3 Prints & Multiples - 1200
27 Feb 3 Impressionist & Modern Art - 1202
4 Mar 3 Fine American Paintings, Drawings & Sculpture - 1205
5 Mar 3 The House Sale - 1204
24 Mar 3 Japanese & Korean Art - 1210
25 Mar 3 Important Japanese Prints - 1298
27 Mar 3 Indian & Southeast Asian Art - 1212
1 Apr 3 The House Sale - 1213
3 Apr 3 The Russell B Aitken Collection of Wildlife Art & Sculpture - 1320
22 Apr 3 Photographs - 1221
23 Apr 3 19th Century European Art - 1207 & 1223
24 Apr 3 19th Century Sculpture & Works of Art - 1222
25 Apr 3 Barye Bronzes: An Important Private Collection - 1296
28 Apr 3 Picasso Lithographs: Themes & Variations - 1322
29 Apr 3 19th & 20th Century Prints - 1226
7 May 3 Impressionist & Modern Art - Evening Sale - 1229
8 May 3 Impressionist & Modern Art - Day Sale - 1230
14 May 3 Post-War & Contemporary Art - Evening Sale - 1232
15 May 3 Post-War & Contemporary Art - Morning Sale - 1233
15 May 3 Post-War & Contemporary Art - Afternoon Sale - 1234
22 May 3 American Paintings, Drawings & Sculpture - 1236
28 May 3 Latin American Art - 1237
30 May 3 Important Old Master Paintings - 1239
4 Jun 3 The House Sale - 1241
29 Jul 3 Maritime - 1257

Christie's, Rome - Italy
26 Nov 2 19th Century Art - 2419
4 Dec 2 Old Master Paintings & Drawings - 2416
18 Dec 2 Modern & Contemporary Art - 2415
20 Feb 3 Furniture & Decorative Art from a Roman Villa - 2423

Christie's, South Kensington - UK
29 Aug 2 British & Continental Paintings - 9443
5 Sep 2 British & Victorian Pictures - 9447
5 Sep 2 20th Century British Art - 9448
19 Sep 2 British & Continental Watercolours & Drawings - 9459
19 Sep 2 Old Master Pictures - OMP-9458
2 Oct 2 British Pop Prints - 9550
17 Oct 2 British & Continental Watercolours & Drawings - 9480
24 Oct 2 British & Continental Paintings - 9487
24 Oct 2 20th Century Prints
30 Oct 2 Old Master Pictures - 9420
31 Oct 2 Maritime - 9492
7 Nov 2 British & Victorian Pictures
14 Nov 2 British & Continental Pictures - 9505
14 Nov 2 20th Century Bronzes & Sculpture - 9507
19 Nov 2 Photographs & Optical Instruments - 9509
21 Nov 2 19th Century European Art - 9513
26 Nov 2 Russian Art - 9521
28 Nov 2 Sporting Art & Dogs
4 Dec 2 20th Century British Art - 9527
4 Dec 2 British Works on Paper - 9314
5 Dec 2 Impressionist, Modern & Post-War Art - 9529
13 Dec 2 Old Master Paintings & Drawings - 9535
23 Jan 3 British & Continental Pictures - 9556
11 Feb 3 Art Nouveau - 9563
13 Feb 3 British & Continental Pictures & Works on Paper - 9566
20 Feb 3 Old Master Paintings - 9570
6 Mar 3 British, Victorian & Scottish Paintings - 9579
18 Mar 3 Objects of Vertu & Portrait Miniatures - 9584 & 9585
20 Mar 3 19th Century European Art - 9589
27 Mar 3 20th Century British Art - 9594
27 Mar 3 British Art on Paper - 9595
3 Apr 3 Impressionist, Modern & Post-War Art - 9632
10 Apr 3 Old Master Paintings - 9607
16 Apr 3 Decorative Objects & Pictures - 9610 & 9612
17 Apr 3 20th Century Prints - 9611
2 May 3 Islamic & Indian Works of Art - 9618
13 May 3 Portrait Miniatures - 9626 & 9627
15 May 3 The Irish Sale - 9625
15 May 3 European Sculpture
21 May 3 Maritime - 9631 & 9739
29 May 3 British & Victorian Pictures - 9636
5 Jun 3 At Home - British & Continental Pictures & Works on Paper - 9641
12 Jun 3 Sporting Art & Dogs - 9646
18 Jun 3 19th Century European Art Incl. Oriental Art - 9652
3 Jul 3 British Art on Paper incl. Original Book illustrations - 9661
3 Jul 3 Twentieth Century British Art - 9660
10 Jul 3 Asian Decorative Art - 9666
11 Jul 3 Old Master Pictures - 9665

Christie's, Zurich - Switzerland
28 Nov 2 Swiss Art - 1305

Chrystals Auctions, Isle of Man - UK
28 Jun 2 Fine Art
6 Dec 2 Fine Art

Clarke Gammon, Guildford - UK
10 Sep 2 Oil Paintings, Watercolours, Drawings & Prints
10 Dec 2 Fine Art

Claude Aguttes, Neuilly-sur-Seine - France
7 Oct 2 Modern & Contemporary Art
7 Nov 2 19th & 20th Century Paintings
17 Dec 2 Art Nouveau & Art Deco
19 Dec 2 19th Century & Oriental Art
23 Dec 2 Sporting Art
1 Feb 3 Modern & Contemporary Art
7 Mar 3 Paintings & Fine Art from a Private Collection
25 Mar 3 Art Nouveau & Art Deco
28 Mar 3 19th Century & Modern Art
7 Apr 3 Comics
16 Jun 3 Old Masters
25 Jun 3 Modern & Contemporary Art
27 Jun 3 19th Century Paintings & Drawings
1 Jul 3 Art Nouveau & Art Deco

Claude Boisgirard, Paris - France
20 Oct 2 Modern & Contemporary Art
6 Nov 2 Paintings
20 Nov 2 Art Nouveau & Art Deco
29 Nov 2 Paintings
17 Dec 2 Paintings & Photographs - Nice
3 Mar 3 Paris School
19 Mar 3 Art Nouveau & Art Deco
24 Mar 3 Modern & Contemporary Art
17 Jun 3 School Of Paris
23 Jun 3 Modern & Contemporary Art
26 Jun 3 Oriental Art

Clevedon Salerooms, Bristol - UK
5 Sep 2 Fine Art
21 Nov 2 Fine Art
6 Mar 3 Fine Art
19 Jun 3 Antiques & Fine Art

Cobbs, Peterborough, NH - USA
13 Oct 2 Sporting Auction

Coeur d'Alene, Hayden, ID - USA
26 Jul 3 19th & 20th Sporting Art

Cornette de St.Cyr, Paris - France
28 Sep 2 Modern & Contemporary Art
26 Oct 2 Contemporary Art
2 Dec 2 Paintings & Fine Art
7 Dec 2 Modern & Contemporary Art
20 Jan 3 Avants-Gardes
3 Feb 3 Modern & Contemporary Art
24 Mar 3 Contemporary Art
26 Apr 3 Modern & Contemporary Prints
28 Apr 3 Modern & Contemporary Art
21 May 3 Modern Art
11 Jun 3 Old Masters & 19th Century Works
9 Jul 3 Modern & Contemporary Art & Prints

Coutau Begarie, Paris - France
30 Oct 2 Modern Paintings
29 Nov 2 Fine Art
26 Feb 3 Fine Art
10 Mar 3 Sporting Art
24 Mar 3 Modern & Decorative Art

Couturier, Paris - France
16 Dec 2 Paintings & Prints

Crafoord, Lund - Sweden
16 Nov 2 Fine Art
8 Feb 3 Fine Art

Credit Municipal, Paris - France
14 Nov 2 Paintings & Decorative Art

Cumbria Auction Rooms, Carlisle - UK
14 Sep 2 Contents of Wrayside
25 Nov 2 Antiques & Works of Art

Dales, Durban - South Africa
4 Feb 3 Paintings
4 Mar 3 Paintings

David Dike, Dallas, TX - USA
19 Oct 2 Texan Art

David Duggleby, Scarborough - UK
29 Jul 2 Fine Art
10 Sep 2 The Whitby Picture Sale
10 Feb 3 Fine Art
11 Mar 3 Fine Art
7 Apr 3 Fine Art
2 Jun 3 Fine Art
28 Jul 3 Fine Art

David Lay, Penzance - UK
16 Oct 2 The Mary 'Boots' Redgrave Collection
17 Oct 2 Paintings, Prints & Other Art
13 Feb 3 Fine Art - No.55
10 Jun 3 Auction of Paintings, Prints & Other Art

De Veres Art Auctions, Dublin - Eire
24 Sep 2 Irish Art
15 Apr 3 Irish Art

De Vuyst, Lokeren - Belgium
5 Oct 2 International Art - No.115
7 Dec 2 International Art - No.116
15 Mar 3 Paintings & Fine Art - No.117
17 May 3 Paintings & Graphic Art - No.118

DeFina, Austinburg, OH - USA
8 Sep 2 Fine Art
5 Apr 3 Decorative Art - with Rachel Davis Fine Arts

Deauville, Deauville - France
16 Aug 2 Important Modern Art
23 Aug 2 Sporting Art
10 Nov 2 Paintings & Objets d'Art
14 Dec 2 Paintings about Horses

Dee Atkinson & Harrison, Driffield - UK
26 Jul 2 Oil Paintings, Watercolours & Prints
20 Sep 2 Fine Art
29 Nov 2 Fine Art
7 Feb 3 Fine Art
28 Mar 3 Antiques
23 May 3 Collective Antiques

Della Rocca, Torino - Italy
10 Dec 2 Paintings & Fine Art

Delvaux, Paris - France
19 Dec 2 Paintings & Decorative Art
28 Mar 3 Modern Paintings
23 Jun 3 Old Masters & Paintings

Deutscher-Menzies, Malvern - Australia
28 Aug 2 Australian & International Fine Art - No.17
11 Nov 2 Lowenstein Sharp Collection - No.18
27 Nov 2 Australian & International Art - No.19
4 Mar 3 Sydney Auction - No.20 - Sydney
4 Jun 3 Australian & International Art - No.21

Dickinson, Davy & Markham, Brigg - UK
11 Feb 3 Fine Art

Digard, Paris - France
18 Dec 2 Modern & Contemporary Art
24 Mar 3 20th Century Art

Dorotheum, Graz - Austria
5 Dec 2 Fine Art & Antiques

Dorotheum, Klagenfurt - Austria
20 Nov 2 Fine Art
14 May 3 Paintings & Works of Art

Dorotheum, Linz - Austria
18 Nov 2 Fine Art
14 May 3 Fine Art

Dorotheum, Prague - Czech Republic
12 Oct 2 Pictures
30 Nov 2 Art & Antiques
8 Mar 3 Art & Antiques
24 May 3 Art & Antiques

Dorotheum, Salzburg - Austria
16 Apr 3 Paintings & Fine Art
5 Jun 3 20th Century Art

Dorotheum, Vienna - Austria
1 Oct 2 Old Master Drawings, Prints before 1900 & Watercolours
2 Oct 2 Old Master Paintings - No. 222
3 Oct 2 Sculptures
15 Oct 2 20th Century Art
16 Oct 2 Fine Art - No. 76
29 Oct 2 Oil Paintings & Watercolours
30 Oct 2 Modern Graphics
12 Nov 2 20th Century Art
21 Nov 2 Christmas Fine Art
25 Nov 2 Fine Art
26 Nov 2 Art Nouveau & 20th Century Works of Art
27 Nov 2 Modern & Contemporary Art
28 Nov 2 Oil Paintings & Watercolours
4 Dec 2 International Auction
10 Dec 2 19th Century Art
11 Dec 2 Fine Art
28 Jan 3 20th Century Art
18 Feb 3 Modern Graphics
25 Feb 3 19th Century Art
11 Mar 3 20th Century Art
19 Mar 3 Fine Art - Neustadt
25 Mar 3 Sculpture
27 Mar 3 Old Master Paintings
28 Mar 3 Old Master Drawings & Watercolours
8 Apr 3 Modern Graphic Art
10 Apr 3 19th Century Art
24 Apr 3 20th Century Art
7 May 3 Imperial Court Memorabilia
19 May 3 Furniture & Decorative Art
20 May 3 Classic & Contemporary Art
21 May 3 Art Nouveau
22 May 3 Oil Paintings & Watercolours of 19th Century
4 Jun 3 Modern Graphics
11 Jun 3 Old Masters

Douglas, South Deerfield, MA - USA
26 Jul 2 Paintings
16 Aug 2 Paintings
6 Sep 2 Fine Art
4 Oct 2 Fine Art
24 Jan 3 Paintings
31 Jan 3 Paintings
28 Feb 3 Fine Art
14 Mar 3 Paintings
28 Mar 3 Paintings
11 Apr 3 Paintings
9 May 3 Antiques & Art

Doutrebente, Paris - France
5 Mar 3 Paintings & Fine Art

Doyle, New York, NY - USA
15 Aug 2 Paintings, Fine Art & Furniture
25 Sep 2 Fine Art - No.209251
9 Oct 2 19th & 20th Century Decorative Art
23 Oct 2 Fine Art
29 Oct 2 American Furniture & Decorations
5 Nov 2 20th Century Art & Design
12 Nov 2 Old Master, Modern & Contemporary Prints - No.211121
10 Dec 2 American & European Paintings
8 Jan 3 Fine Art - No.301081
22 Jan 3 Old Master Paintings & Drawings
5 Feb 3 Fine Art incl. Paintings - No.302051
19 Feb 3 Belle Epoque - No.302191
5 Mar 3 Decorative Art incl. Paintings - No.303051
18 Mar 3 Decorative Art incl. Paintings - No.303181
2 Apr 3 Decorative Art incl. Paintings - No.304021
29 Apr 3 Furniture & Decorative Art - No.304291
30 Apr 3 Old Masters, Modern & Contemporary Prints - No.304301
14 May 3 Furniture & Decorative Art - No.305141
21 May 3 Modern & Contemporary Art. American & European Art
4 Jun 3 19th & 20th Century Decorative Art

Dr Fritz Nagel, Leipzig - Germany
27 Sep 2 Fine Art - No.12
5 Apr 3 Fine Art - No.13

Dr Fritz Nagel, Stuttgart - Germany
20 Jun 2 Paintings & Decorative Art - No.384
24 Jun 2 Decorative Art - No.57
19 Sep 2 Fine Art sale - No.385
23 Sep 2 Fine Art Sale - No.58
18 Oct 2 Modern Art - No.23M
8 Nov 2 Asian Art - China - No.24A
9 Nov 2 Asian Art - Japan - No.24A
27 Nov 2 Adolf Holzel & his Circle
5 Dec 2 Paintings & Fine Art - No.386
9 Dec 2 Fine Art - No.59
27 Mar 3 Fine Art - No.387
31 Mar 3 Fine Art - No.60
2 Apr 3 Modern Art - No.24M
30 May 3 Asian Art - No.25A
31 May 3 Asian Art

Dr Lehr, Berlin - Germany
26 Oct 2 20th Century Art - No.15
26 Apr 3 Pictures - No.16

Dreweatt Neate, Newbury - UK
18 Sep 2 Pictures & Works of Art
6 Nov 2 Entire Contents of Yuki's Belgravia Home - 12031
29 Jan 3 Fine Art
20 May 3 Affordable Paintings

Drouot Estimations, Paris - France
15 Nov 2 Old Master Paintings
29 Nov 2 Modern Paintings
25 Apr 3 Art Deco & Art Nouveau

Du Mouchelle, Detroit, MI - USA
16 Aug 2 Fine Art
20 Sep 2 Fine Art

18 Oct 2 Fine Art
15 Nov 2 Fine Art
13 Dec 2 Fine Art
10 Jan 3 Fine Art
14 Feb 3 Fine Art
14 Mar 3 Fine Art
11 Apr 3 Fine Art
16 May 3 Fine Art
13 Jun 3 Fine Art
18 Jul 3 Fine Art

Duke & Son, Dorchester - UK
4 Jul 2 Fine Art
31 Oct 2 Fine Art
13 Mar 3 Paintings & Books
16 Jun 3 Netherhampton House
3 Jul 3 Paintings & Furniture

Dunbar Sloane, Auckland - New Zealand
21 Aug 2 Fine Art
10 Nov 2 Maritime Auction
4 Dec 2 Blockbuster Art
7 May 3 Investment & Affordable Art

Dunbar Sloane, Wellington - New Zealand
4 Sep 2 New Zealand & Foreign Paintings
23 Oct 2 Fine Art

Duran, Madrid - Spain
23 Sep 2 Paintings & Fine Art - No.374
22 Oct 2 Paintings & Fine Art - No.375
19 Nov 2 Paintings & Fine Art - No.376
17 Dec 2 Paintings & Fine Art - No.377
21 Jan 3 Art & Antiques - No.378
18 Feb 3 Paintings & Fine Art - No.379
25 Mar 3 Paintings & Fine Art - No.380

E & Eve, Paris - France
12 Mar 3 Fine Art

ELR Auctions, Sheffield - UK
4 Oct 2 Fine Art
6 Dec 2 Fine Art
2 Mar 3 Paintings
28 Mar 3 Fine Art

Edgar Horn, Eastbourne - UK
12 Feb 3 Fine Art
2 Apr 3 Fine Art
21 May 3 Fine Art
9 Jul 3 Fine Art

Eldred, East Dennis, MA - USA
26 Jul 2 Marine Art
1 Aug 2 Americana
8 Aug 2 Fine & Decorative Art
21 Aug 2 Paul Jacoulet Prints
22 Nov 2 Americana
6 Dec 2 Fine & Decorative Art - WFDA02
15 Mar 3 The Charlotte Collection - FIN03
28 Mar 3 Americana
9 May 3 Fine, Decorative & Asian Art

Eric Pillon, Calais - France
29 Sep 2 Fine Paintings
10 Nov 2 Impressionist & Modern Art
15 Dec 2 Fine Paintings
16 Mar 3 Fine Paintings
18 May 3 Fine Paintings

Etude Bailleul, Bayeux - France
15 Sep 2 Art in Normandy

Ewbank, Woking - UK
3 Oct 2 Fine Art
12 Dec 2 Fine Art
20 Mar 3 Fine Art
3 Jul 3 Fine Art

Falk & Falk, Zurich - Switzerland
29 Nov 1 Books & Fine Art - No.7
29 Nov 2 Books & Graphic Art - No.8

Falkkloos, Malmo - Sweden
27 Nov 2 Fine Art - No.45

Fallon, Copake, NY - USA
12 Oct 2 Americana
1 Jan 3 Fine Art
22 Mar 3 Americana

Farsetti, Prato - Italy
15 Nov 2 Modern & Contemporary Art - No.112
16 Nov 2 Fine Art - No.113
29 Nov 2 Contemporary Art & Photographs - No.114/I
30 Nov 2 Modern Art - No.114/II
28 Mar 3 Modern & Contemporary Art - No.115

Feletin, Provins - France
15 Sep 2 Modern Paintings
6 Oct 2 Fine Art
3 Nov 2 Old & Modern Art
8 Dec 2 Paintings
19 Jan 3 Paintings
9 Mar 3 Paintings
13 Apr 3 Paintings
25 May 3 Modern Art

Fellows & Sons, Birmingham - UK
1 Oct 2 Paintings - No.629
11 Feb 3 Fine Art
18 Mar 3 Antique Sale

Fenner & Co, Tavistock - UK
10 Feb 3 Fine Art
19 May 3 Fine Art

Ferri, Paris - France
15 Nov 2 Works of Michael Herman-Bierge
18 Dec 2 Paintings & Fine Art

Finan Watkins & Co, Mere - UK
5 Oct 2 Fine Art
11 Jan 3 Antiques
5 Apr 3 Paintings & Fine Art
12 Jul 3 Fine Art

Finarte, Milan - Italy
23 Oct 2 19th Century Art - No.1181
29 Oct 2 Fine Art - No.1182
19 Nov 2 Modern & Contemporary Art - No.1184
27 Nov 2 Old Master Paintings - No.1186
2 Dec 2 Old Master Paintings & Furniture from a Piedmontese House - No.1188
2 Dec 2 Paintings from the Zabert Collection - No.1188
4 Dec 2 Modern & Contemporary Art - No.1189
18 Dec 2 19th Century Paintings - No.1193
18 Mar 3 19th Century Paintings - No.1194 - with Semenzato
27 May 3 19th Century Paintings - No.1206

Finarte, Rome - Italy
23 Oct 2 Paintings & Fine Art
21 Nov 2 Modern & Contemporary Art - No.1185
4 Dec 2 Fine Art from the Kolb-Wartenberg Collection - No.1190

Finarte, Venice - Italy
3 May 3 Furniture & Decorative Art
4 May 3 Furniture & Decorative Art
11 May 3 Old Master Paintings - 03VED2
11 May 3 Paintings by Pietro & Alessandro Longhi - 03VED1
11 May 3 Furniture & Decorative Art

Finarte Semenzato, Milan - Italy
26 Mar 3 Modern & Contemporary Art - No.1197
31 Mar 3 Old Master Paintings & Furniture - No.1200
5 Apr 3 Important Old Master Paintings - No.1202
10 Jun 3 Modern & Contemporary Art, Works on Paper & Drawings - No.1207

Finarte Semenzato, Rome - Italy
24 Mar 3 Fine Furniture & Works of Art - No.1195
25 Mar 3 Paintings & Fine Art - No.1196
10 Apr 3 Modern & Contemporary Art - No.1201

Fraysse, Paris - France
16 Oct 2 Prints & Fine Art
13 Nov 2 Paintings & Fine Art
11 Dec 2 Paintings & Fine Art
26 Feb 3 Paintings & Fine Art
24 Mar 3 Paintings & Fine Art
5 Jun 3 Old Masters & Modern Art

Freeman Fine Arts, Philadelphia, PA - USA
12 Sep 2 Prints - No.1148
20 Sep 2 Paintings - No.1150
19 Oct 2 Fine Americana - No.1153
8 Dec 2 PAFA Artists - No.1158
24 Jan 3 Paintings & Prints - No.1163
12 Apr 3 Americana - No.1168
23 May 3 Books & Prints - No.1172

22 Jun 3 Fine American & European Paintings - No.1176

G.E. Sworder & Son, Stansted - UK
10 Sep 2 Fine Art
22 Oct 2 Fine Art & Furniture
3 Dec 2 Fine Art - No.1203
4 Feb 3 Fine Art - No.204
18 Mar 3 Fine Art & Furniture - No.317
29 Apr 3 Fine Art
10 Jun 3 Fine Art
22 Jul 3 Fine Art & Antiques

Galerie Dobiaschofsky, Bern - Switzerland
6 Nov 2 Fine Art - No.95
8 Nov 2 Swiss Art - No.95
7 May 3 Paintings & Works of Art - No.96-I
9 May 3 Swiss Art - No.96-II

Galerie Fischer, Luzern - Switzerland
20 Nov 2 Fine Art - No.382 & 384
4 Jun 3 Paintings & Fine Art - No.385

Galerie Gloggner, Luzern - Switzerland
9 Nov 2 Old & Modern Art
24 May 3 Paintings

Galerie Koller, Geneva - Switzerland
17 Nov 2 Fine Art - G34

Galerie Koller, Zurich - Switzerland
25 Jun 2 Paintings & Works of Art - W193
24 Sep 2 Fine Art - W194
3 Oct 2 Old Master & 19th Century Paintings
4 Dec 2 Modern Art
4 Dec 2 Modern Art - Z12
28 Mar 3 Old Master & 19th Century Art - A124/2
24 Jun 3 Swiss Art - Z14/1
24 Jun 3 Modern Art - Z14/2

Galerie Kornfeld, Bern - Switzerland
20 Jun 3 19th & 20th Century Art - No.230

Galerie Moderne, Brussels - Belgium
27 Aug 2 Paintings & Fine Art
24 Sep 2 Fine Art
22 Oct 2 Fine Art
19 Nov 2 Fine Art - No.211
17 Dec 2 Paintings & Fine Art - No.212
21 Jan 3 Fine Art
18 Feb 3 Paintings & Fine Art
18 Mar 3 Fine Art
15 Apr 3 Paintings & Fine Art
13 May 3 Paintings & Fine Art

Galerie Stuker, Bern - Switzerland
14 Nov 2 Paintings & Fine Art

Galerie de Chartres, Chartres - France
17 Mar 2 Paintings & Prints
20 Oct 2 Fine Art

Galerie du Rhone, Sion - Switzerland
7 Dec 2 Fine Paintings & Prints - No.22

Galleria Y Remates, Montevideo - Uruguay
30 Jul 2 Uruguayan Art - No.10
6 Aug 2 Uruguayan Art - No.11
10 Oct 2 Uruguayan Art - No.12
17 Oct 2 Uruguayan Art - No.13
19 Nov 2 Uruguayan Art - No.14
20 Nov 2 Uruguayan Art - No.15
5 Jan 3 Paintings
2 Mar 3 Fine Paintings - No.18

Gardiner & Houlgate, Corsham - UK
14 Mar 3 Paintings & Prints - No.8001

George Kidner, Lymington - UK
2 Oct 2 Fine Art
8 Jan 3 Fine Art
16 Apr 3 Works of Art & Paintings
9 Jul 3 Fine Art

Germann, Zurich - Switzerland
4 Jun 2 Paintings, Prints & Sculpture - No.2201
25 Nov 2 Paintings, Sculptures, Watercolours & Drawings - No.2202

Gildings, Market Harborough - UK
13 Aug 2 Fine Art
1 Oct 2 Fine Art
7 Jan 3 Oil Paintings, Watercolours & Prints
25 Mar 3 Fine Art
17 Jun 3 Fine Art

Gioffredo, Nice - France
30 Jul 2 Fine Art
6 Nov 2 Fine Paintings
17 Dec 2 Fine Art
8 Apr 3 Fine Art
8 Jul 3 Fine Art

Glerum, Amsterdam - Netherlands
24 Sep 2 Fine Art - No.227
21 Oct 2 19th Century Paintings - No.230
4 Nov 2 Old Masters
25 Nov 2 Modern & Contemporary Art - No.233
14 Apr 3 19th & 20th Century Art - No.240
12 May 3 Old Master Paintings
26 May 3 Modern Art - No.244

Goldings, Grantham - UK
17 Jul 2 Fine Art
17 Sep 2 Fine Art
12 Nov 2 Fine Art
5 Feb 3 Fine Art
30 Apr 3 Fine Art
25 Jun 3 Antique & Modern Collectables

Goodman, Sydney - Australia
10 Dec 1 Pictures
27 Aug 2 Australian & European Pictures
7 Sep 2 Paintings & Works on Paper
18 Nov 2 11th Sydney National Art Auction
23 Mar 3 Collectables
31 Mar 3 The Jack & Isabella Klompe Collection
1 Apr 3 12th Sydney National Art Auction

Gorringes, Bexhill on Sea - UK
17 Sep 2 Pictures & Prints
25 Mar 3 Fine Art
7 May 3 Fine Art

Gorringes, Lewes - UK
3 Sep 2 Fine Art
15 Oct 2 Fine Art
25 Oct 2 Fine Art
29 Oct 2 Fine Art
2 Dec 2 Fine Art
17 Dec 2 Fine Art
28 Jan 3 Fine Art
11 Feb 3 Fine Art
11 Mar 3 Fine Art
29 Apr 3 Fine Art
12 Jun 3 Paintings
22 Jul 3 Fine Art - LJuly03

Goteborgs Auktionsverk, Goteborg - Sweden
30 Nov 2 Paintings & Works of Art

Grant, Worcester - UK
25 Apr 2 Fine Art
24 Oct 2 Fine Art

Greenslade Hunt, Taunton - UK
28 Feb 2 Pictures
27 Jun 2 Fine Art
10 Oct 2 Paintings
31 Oct 2 Paintings
27 Feb 3 Oil Paintings, Watercolours & Prints

Grev Wedels Plass, Oslo - Norway
31 Aug 2 Fine Art
21 Nov 2 Jubilee Auction
21 Nov 2 Edward Munch Auction
17 Dec 2 Christmas Auction - No.6
26 May 3 Paintings & Decorative Art
18 Jun 3 Summer Auction

Grogan & Co, Dedham, MA - USA
27 Oct 2 Paintings & Decorative Art
2 Feb 3 Fine Art - No.91

Gros & Delettrez, Paris - France
5 Dec 2 19th & 20th Century Paintings
16 Dec 2 Oriental Art

Hagelstam, Helsinki - Finland
12 Sep 2 Fine Art - No.89
24 Oct 2 Fine Art - No.90

30 Nov 2 Fine Art - No.91
19 Dec 2 Christmas Auction - No.92
27 Feb 3 Fine Art - No.93
3 Apr 3 Fine Art - No.94
17 May 3 Paintings & Works of Art
5 Jun 3 Summer Auction - No.96

Halls, Shrewsbury - UK
13 Nov 2 Fine Art
30 Apr 3 Fine Art - No.5016
6 Jun 3 Fine Art

Hamilton Osborne King, Dublin - Eire
30 Jul 2 Fine Art - No.7199
19 Nov 2 Fine Art
14 Apr 3 Mourne Park House
7 Jul 3 Fine Art & Furniture

Hampton & Littlewood, Exeter - UK
23 Oct 2 Paintings & Works of Art
29 Jan 3 Fine Art
30 Apr 3 Fine Art

Hamptons, Godalming - UK
24 Jul 2 English & Continental Paintings & Prints
25 Sep 2 Paintings & Prints
23 Oct 2 English & Continental Paintings & Prints
27 Nov 2 English & Continental Paintings & Prints
26 Mar 3 Paintings, Watercolours & Prints

Hans Stahl, Hamburg - Germany
15 Jun 2 Paintings & Works of Art
28 Sep 2 Fine Art
7 Dec 2 Paintings & Fine Art
8 Feb 3 Fine Art
5 Apr 3 Fine Art

Hans Stahl, Toestorf - Germany
17 Aug 2 Paintings & Works of Art
2 Nov 2 Fine Art
10 May 3 Fine Art

Hans Widmer, St Gallen - Switzerland
6 Nov 2 Paintings - No. 223
26 Nov 2 Paintings & Prints - No.222

Hartung & Hartung, Munich - Germany
5 Nov 2 Books & Graphics - No.105
13 May 3 Books & Graphics - No.107

Harvey Clar, Oakland, CA - USA
21 Sep 2 Fine Art
19 Oct 2 Fine Art
16 Nov 2 Fine Art
7 Dec 2 Fine Art
11 Jan 3 Fine Art
8 Mar 3 Fine Art
5 Apr 3 Fine Art
3 May 3 Fine Art
31 May 3 Fine Art
28 Jun 3 Fine Art

Hassfurther, Vienna - Austria
25 Nov 2 Old Master & Modern Art - No.34
27 May 3 Modern Art - No.35

Hauswedell & Nolte, Hamburg - Germany
6 Dec 2 Contemporary Art after 1945 - No.368
7 Dec 2 Modern Art - No.369
12 Jun 3 Old Masters - No.371
14 Jun 3 Modern Art - No.373

Heathcote Ball, Leicester - UK
28 Feb 2 Paintings & Fine Art
3 Oct 2 Fine Art
13 Feb 3 Fine Art

Heffel, Vancouver - Canada
4 Jul 2 Fine Art
24 Aug 2 Fine Art
28 Sep 2 Modern & International Prints
26 Oct 2 European & American Art
14 Nov 2 Fine Art
6 Feb 3 Fine Canadian Art
6 Mar 3 Paintings
3 Apr 3 European Art
1 May 3 Paintings - on-line
15 May 3 Fine Paintings

Henry Adams, Chichester - UK
17 Sep 2 Maritime
29 Oct 2 Fine Art
28 Jan 3 Fine Art
29 Apr 3 Fine Art
18 Jun 3 Fine Art
29 Jul 3 Fine Art

Herbette, Doullens - France
17 Nov 2 Fine Art
14 Dec 2 Fine Art
23 Mar 3 Sylvain Jacqueline Collection - Lyons-la-Foret
6 Apr 3 Sylvain Jacqueline Collection - Lyons-la-Foret

Herr, Cologne - Germany
26 Oct 2 Art Nouveau & Art Deco - No.50

Hindemae, Ullerslev - Denmark
11 Aug 2 Fine Art - No.9
22 Sep 2 Fine Art - No.10
17 Nov 2 Fine Art - No.11
19 Jan 3 Fine Art - No.12
16 Mar 3 Fine Art - No.13
11 May 3 Fine Art - No.14

Hobbs Parker, Ashford - UK
12 Sep 2 Antiques & Fine Art
18 Sep 2 Paintings
12 Jun 3 Antiques & Fine Art

Hodgins, Calgary - Canada
25 Nov 2 Fine Art
23 Mar 3 Paintings & Fine Art
9 Jun 3 Fine Art

Hogben, Folkestone - UK
20 Apr 2 Fine Art
1 Jun 2 Fine Art
20 Jul 2 Fine Art
12 Oct 2 Fine Art
2 Nov 2 Fine Art
1 Feb 3 Fine Art
22 Feb 3 Fine Art
15 Mar 3 Fine Art
5 Apr 3 Fine Art

Holloways, Banbury - UK
17 Sep 2 Fine Art
13 May 3 Fine Art
24 Jun 3 Fine Art
29 Jul 3 Fine Art

Honiton Galleries, Honiton - UK
7 Feb 3 Fine Art
23 May 3 Fine Art

Horta, Brussels - Belgium
16 Sep 2 Paintings & Fine Art
15 Oct 2 Paintings & Fine Art
11 Nov 2 Paintings & Fine Art
9 Dec 2 Paintings & Fine Art
20 Jan 3 Paintings & Fine Art
17 Feb 3 Paintings & Fine Art
17 Mar 3 Paintings & Fine Art
14 Apr 3 Paintings & Fine Art
19 May 3 Paintings & Fine Art
16 Jun 3 Fine Art

Hotel Des Ventes Mosan, Liege - Belgium
16 Oct 2 Fine Art
11 Dec 2 Paintings & Fine Art
19 Mar 3 Antiques & Object d'Art
18 Jun 3 Antiques & Works Of Art

Hotel de Ventes Vanderkindere, Brussels - Belgium
10 Sep 2 Fine Art
15 Oct 2 Fine Art
19 Nov 2 Fine Art
10 Dec 2 Paintings & Fine Art
14 Jan 3 Paintings & Fine Art
18 Feb 3 Paintings & Fine Art
18 Mar 3 Paintings & Fine Art
2 Apr 3 The Baels Collection
13 May 3 Fine Art

Hugo Ruef, Munich - Germany
11 Jul 2 Paintings & Fine Art - No.493
6 Nov 2 Old & Modern Art - No.494
26 Mar 3 Fine Art - No.496

Il Ponte, Milan - Italy
5 Jun 2 Paintings & Works of Art
28 Oct 2 Grassi Collection - No.187
5 Feb 3 Furniture & Fine Art from a Villa in Veneto - No.190

Illustration House, New York, NY - USA
9 Nov 2 Illustration Art Auction
19 Feb 3 Fine Art
20 Feb 3 Porch Auction - No.13
10 May 3 Fine Paintings

International Art Centre, Auckland - New Zealand
7 Nov 2 Fine Art
27 Mar 3 Fine Paintings

Jackson's, Cedar Falls, IA - USA
18 Sep 2 Paintings
23 Nov 2 American & European Fine Art
7 Mar 3 Decorative Art & Americana
14 Jun 3 Important American & European Fine Art & Antiques

Jacobs & Hunt, Petersfield - UK
13 Sep 2 Fine Art

James Adam, Dublin - Eire
4 Sep 2 Fine Art
25 Sep 2 Important Irish Art - 3064
6 Nov 2 Contemporary & Traditional Art - No.4042
27 Nov 2 Furniture & Decorative Art - No.8080
28 Jan 3 Fine Art
12 Mar 3 Fine Period Paintings and Decorative Art - 8081
26 Mar 3 Irish Art - No.3066
8 Apr 3 Contemporary & Traditional Art - No.4043
21 May 3 Furniture, Paintings & Decorative Art - No.3068
10 Jun 3 Contemporary & Modern Art - 4044

James Julia, Fairfield, ME - USA
11 Jan 3 Paintings & Americana
19 Apr 3 Paintings & Americana

James Thompson, Kirby Lonsdale - UK
31 Jul 2 Oil Paintings & Watercolours
18 Sep 2 Oil Paintings & Watercolours
19 Nov 2 Oil Paintings & Watercolours
15 Jan 3 Oil Paintings & Watercolours
19 Mar 3 Paintings & Prints
21 May 3 Oil Paintings & Watercolours
16 Jul 3 19th & 20th Century Watercolours, Oil Paintings & Prints

Jeffery Burchard, St Pertersberg, FL - USA
21 Jul 2 Fine Art
18 Aug 2 Fine Art
22 Sep 2 Paintings
20 Oct 2 Fine Art
17 Nov 2 Fine Art
19 Jan 3 Fine Art
16 Feb 3 Fine Art
15 Mar 3 Fine Art
26 Apr 3 Fine Art
18 May 3 Fine Art
22 Jun 3 Fine Art

Jim Railton, Alnwick - UK
15 Feb 3 Fine Art
12 Apr 3 Fine Art

Joel, Victoria - Australia
19 Aug 2 Fine Art
18 Nov 2 Australian & European Paintings
12 May 3 Paintings & Fine Art

John Bellman, Billingshurst - UK
19 Sep 2 Fine Art
26 Feb 3 Fine Art

John Moran, Pasadena, CA - USA
29 Oct 2 California & American Paintings
18 Feb 3 Important California & American Art
17 Jun 3 California & American Art

John Nicholson, Haslemere - UK
3 Jul 2 Fine Art
14 Jul 2 Contemporary Russian Paintings
25 Sep 2 Prints, Watercolours & Oil Paintings
29 Sep 2 Contemporary Paintings
8 Dec 2 Superb Contemporary Russian Paintings
18 Dec 2 Fine Art
5 Feb 3 Oil Paintings, Watercolours & Prints
19 Mar 3 Fine Art
24 Jul 3 Fine Art

John Ross & Co, Belfast - N.Ireland
12 Jun 2 Irish Paintings
18 Sep 2 Studio Works of Arthur Avia Buchman
2 Oct 2 Irish Paintings
4 Dec 2 Irish Paintings - No.47
5 Mar 3 Irish Art - No.62

John Taylors, Louth - UK
25 Feb 3 Fine Art

Joron-Derem, Paris - France
28 Feb 3 Fine Art
26 May 3 Paintings

Joyner Fine Art, Toronto - Canada
3 Dec 2 Important Canadian Art
3 Jun 3 Canadian Art - with Waddington's

Karl & Faber, Munich - Germany
4 Jun 2 Paintings - No.203

Karlheinz Kaupp, Staufen - Germany
20 Sep 2 Fine Art
6 Dec 2 Paintings & Fine Art

Karrenbauer, Konstanz - Germany
27 Sep 2 Fine Art & Antiques - No.185
22 Nov 2 Fine Art - No.187
28 Mar 3 Fine Art - No.189

Kastern, Hannover - Germany
7 Dec 2 Fine Art - No.102

Kenneth Van Blarcom, South Natick, MA - USA
3 Nov 2 Fine Art
1 Feb 3 Fine Art
3 May 3 Fine Art
31 May 3 Antique Estate Auction

Ketterer, Hamburg - Germany
28 Sep 2 Fine Art - No.271
7 Dec 2 19th & 20th Century Art incl. Maritime - No.276
28 Mar 3 19th & 20th Century Art - No.278

Ketterer, Munich - Germany
6 Dec 2 Classics of the 20th Century & Munich Art - No.277
5 May 3 The Tremmel Collection - From Impressionism to Expressionism - No.282
5 May 3 The Tremmel Collection - Drawings & Prints - No.282
5 May 3 The Tremmel Collection - Old & New Masters Drawings - No.282
5 May 3 The Tremmel Collection - French Graphics - No.282
6 Jun 3 20th Century Classics & School Of Munich - 280

Keys, Aylsham - UK
16 Aug 2 Oil Paintings, Watercolours & Prints
18 Oct 2 Fine Art
13 Dec 2 Fine Paintings & Prints
14 Feb 3 Oil Paintings, Watercolours & Prints
11 Apr 3 Paintings
20 Jun 3 English & Continental Oil & Watercolours

Kieselbach, Budapest - Hungary
11 Sep 2 Paintings
6 Dec 2 Fine Paintings
11 Apr 3 Fine Paintings
16 May 3 Paintings

Kohn, Paris - France
9 Oct 2 Modern & Contemporary Art - No.1
13 Nov 2 Old Masters - No.2
27 Nov 2 Modern Paintings & Sculptures - No.3
16 Dec 2 Fine Art - No.4
28 Dec 2 Fine Art - No.5 - Cannes
26 Feb 3 Old Master Paintings & Fine Art
3 Mar 3 Contemporary Art
2 Apr 3 Old Master Paintings & Furniture
4 Jun 3 Pictures & Furniture

Kunsthallen, Copenhagen - Denmark
4 Sep 2 Old Master Paintings & Works of Art - No.532
18 Sep 2 Fine Art - No.533
18 Sep 2 Contemporary Art - No.533
23 Oct 2 Modern Paintings
13 Nov 2 Paintings & Works of Art - No.535
4 Dec 2 Contemporary Art & Modern Paintings - No.536
26 Feb 3 Knud Langaa-Jensen's Collection - No.537
26 Feb 3 International Art - No.537
29 Apr 3 International Art - No.538

12 Jun 3 Contemporary & Modern Art - 539

Lacy Scott, Bury St Edmunds - UK
21 Sep 2 Fine Art
14 Dec 2 Fine Art
22 Mar 3 Fine Art

Lane, Penzance - UK
26 Sep 2 Fine Art
10 Dec 2 Important Paintings & Prints
27 Mar 3 Fine Paintings
19 Jun 3 Important Sale Of Pictures & Prints

Lawrences, Bletchingley - UK
9 Dec 2 Fine Art
4 Feb 3 Oil Paintings & Watercolours
18 Mar 3 Fine Art
29 Apr 3 Oil Paintings & Watercolours
10 Jun 3 Fine Art
22 Jul 3 Oil Paintings & Watercolours

Lawrences, Crewkerne - UK
30 Sep 2 Fine Art
17 Oct 2 Fine Art
30 Jan 3 Fine Art
15 May 3 Fine Art

Lawson Menzies, Sydney - Australia
29 Oct 2 Australian & International Paintings - 3543
3 Dec 2 Decorative Art - No.3552
3 Feb 3 Fine Art - No.3555
3 Mar 3 Decorative Art & Paintings - No.3564 & 3561
1 Apr 3 Decorative Art, Paintings & Antique Furniture - No.3563
15 Apr 3 Australian & International Art - No.3562
3 Jun 3 Monthly Emporium
22 Jul 3 Fine Australian & International Art - No.3655

Le Mouel, Paris - France
6 Nov 2 Atelier Mayo

Lemoine & Ferrando, Paris - France
27 Nov 2 Fine Art

Lempertz, Cologne - Germany
2 Nov 2 Vintage Photographs - No.825
2 Nov 2 Photographs & Photographic Works - No.826
16 Nov 2 Old Masters Paintings - No.828
3 Dec 2 Contemporary Art - No.830
4 Dec 2 Modern Art - No.831
4 Dec 2 Modern Art
12 Apr 3 Photographs - No.837
17 May 3 Old Master Paintings & Graphics - No.840
28 May 3 Contemporary Art - No.841
29 May 3 Modern Art - No.842

Lesieur & Le Bars, Le Havre - France
27 Oct 2 Fine Art
24 Nov 2 Paintings
23 Feb 3 Fine Art
12 May 3 Fine Art

Levis, Calgary - Canada
1 Dec 2 Fine Paintings
13 Apr 3 Fine Paintings
1 Jun 3 Fine Art

Libert, Castor, Paris - France
14 Nov 2 Ancient & Modern Prints
20 Nov 2 Fine Art
4 Dec 2 Paintings & Fine Art
12 Mar 3 Contemporary Paintings & Prints
14 Mar 3 Fine Art

Lincoln, Orange, NJ - USA
11 Dec 1 Paintings
12 Feb 2 Paintings
15 Apr 3 Fine Art

Livinec, Gaudcheau & Jezequel, Rennes Cedex - France
17 Aug 2 Paintings, Sculpture & Prints
6 Oct 2 Important Paintings & Fine Art
1 Dec 2 Paintings & Fine Art
4 Mar 3 Paintings & Fine Art
22 Mar 3 Paintings - Saint-Malo

Locke & England, Leamington Spa - UK
26 Sep 2 Fine Art - No.902
31 Oct 2 Fine Art - No.1002
28 Nov 2 Fine Art - No.1102
30 Jan 3 Fine Art - No.103
27 Feb 3 Fine Art
1 May 3 Fine Art
5 Jun 3 Fine Art
3 Jul 3 Fine Art

Lombrail & Teucquam, Paris - France
7 Jul 2 19th & 20th Century Modern Art
9 Oct 2 Fine Art
13 Dec 2 Fine Art
15 Dec 2 Sporting Art
2 Mar 3 Paintings & Fine Art
11 May 3 Japanese Art & Paintings
16 May 3 Paintings

Lots Road, London - UK
25 Aug 2 Fine Art
8 Sep 2 Fine Art
15 Sep 2 Fine Art
22 Sep 2 Fine Art
29 Sep 2 Fine Art
6 Oct 2 Fine Art - No. 0813
13 Oct 2 Fine Art
20 Oct 2 Fine Art
3 Nov 2 Fine Art
10 Nov 2 Fine Art
17 Nov 2 Fine Art - No.819
24 Nov 2 Fine Art - No.820
1 Dec 2 Paintings - No.821
15 Dec 2 Fine Art - No.823
5 Jan 3 FIne Art - No.824
12 Jan 3 Fine Art - No.825
2 Feb 3 Fine Art - No.828
9 Feb 3 Fine Art - No.829
2 Mar 3 Fine Art
9 Mar 3 Fine Art - No.833
23 Mar 3 Fine Art - No.835
6 Apr 3 Fine Art - No.837
13 Apr 3 Fine Art
27 Apr 3 Fine Art - No.839
4 May 3 Fine Art - No.840
11 May 3 Fine Art - No.841
18 May 3 Fine Art
25 May 3 Fine Art
1 Jun 3 Fine Art
15 Jun 3 Contemporary Art & Furniture - 846
6 Jul 3 Fine Art
13 Jul 3 Fine Art
27 Jul 3 Fine Art

Loughlin Bowe, Kilkenny - Eire
8 Oct 2 The Old Rectory

Louis C. Morton, Lomas Virreyes - Mexico
24 Jul 2 Fine Art
17 Oct 2 Modern & Contemporary Art - 280
14 Nov 2 Sporting Art
26 Nov 2 Paintings & Sculpture
28 Nov 2 Books & Works of Art
21 Jan 3 Luis Garcia Rodriguez Collection
23 Jan 3 Fine Art
15 May 3 Modern & Contemporary Art - 309
28 May 3 Antiques, Books & Lithographs - 310

Louis Taylor, Stoke on Trent - UK
9 Sep 2 Fine Art
10 Sep 2 Picture Sale
3 Dec 2 Paintings
3 Mar 3 Fine Art
10 Jun 3 Pictures & Paintings

Lyon & Turnbull, Edinburgh - UK
13 Sep 2 Paintings - No.51
6 Dec 2 Fine Paintings - LT057
14 Feb 3 Paintings - No.62
23 May 3 Fine Paintings - LT068
13 Jun 3 Paintings

Maigret, Paris - France
6 Dec 2 Paintings & Decorative Art
11 Dec 2 Prints & Fine Art
27 Mar 3 Drawings

Mallams, Cheltenham - UK
22 Aug 2 Fine Art
19 Sep 2 Fine Art
7 Nov 2 Fine Art

17 Dec 2 Fine Art
24 Apr 3 Fine Art
29 May 3 Fine Art

Mallams, Oxford - UK
31 Jul 2 Pictures
4 Oct 2 Prints & Drawings
30 Oct 2 Fine Art
18 Dec 2 Fine Art
19 Feb 3 Fine Art
30 Apr 3 Fine Art
9 May 3 Fine Art
28 May 3 Fine Art
23 Jul 3 Oil Paintings, Watercolours & Prints

Martel Maides, Guernsey - UK
28 Nov 2 Fine Art including Channel Island Interest - 802004
20 Mar 3 Selected Antiques - No.802005
12 Jun 3 Selected Antiques - No.802006

Martinot & Savignat, Pontoise - France
7 Dec 2 Modern Art

Mathias Roux, Paris - France
13 Nov 2 Fine Art

Maynards, Vancouver - Canada
24 Sep 2 Fine Art
18 Mar 3 International Fine Art

Mealy's, Castlecomer - Eire
15 Oct 2 Fine Art - C1136 - Tigroney House
12 Nov 2 Paintings & Fine Art - A1137
4 Mar 3 Fine Art
20 May 3 Fine Art

Meeting Art, Vercelli - Italy
14 Sep 2 Modern & Contemporary Art - No.501
19 Oct 2 Fine Art - No.502
23 Nov 2 Modern & Contemporary Art - No.505
4 Jan 3 Modern & Contemporary Art - No.509
1 Mar 3 19th & 20th Century Art - No.511
1 May 3 Modern & Contemporary Art - No.514
17 May 3 Fine Art - 515

Mellors & Kirk, Nottingham - UK
11 Apr 2 Fine Art
4 Jul 2 Fine Art
26 Sep 2 Fine Art
13 Feb 3 Fine Art
10 Jun 3 Antiques & Works of Art
26 Jun 3 Fine Art

Mercier & Cie, Lille - France
20 Oct 2 Paintings, Sculpture & Fine Art
15 Dec 2 Fine Art
16 Feb 3 Paintings & Fine Art
23 Feb 3 Modern & Contemporary Art

Mervyn Carey, Cranbrook - UK
16 Oct 2 Fine Art

Michael Zeller, Lindau - Germany
9 Oct 2 Paintings & Fine Art - No. 74
6 Dec 2 Paintings & Fine Art - No.75
7 May 3 Paintings & Fine Art - No.76

Millon & Associes, Paris - France
20 Sep 2 Fine Art Sale - with Palais des Beaux-Arts
22 Nov 2 Modern Paintings
6 Dec 2 Paintings & Works of Art
16 Dec 2 19th & 20th Century Art incl. Art Nouveau
22 Jan 3 19th & 20th Century Photographs
27 Jan 3 Contemporary Paintings
10 Mar 3 Contemporary Paintings
14 Mar 3 Lucien Coutaud
21 Mar 3 Paintings & Fine Art
26 Mar 3 Modern Art
9 Jul 3 19th Century Modern & Contemporary Art

Mitchells, Cockermouth - UK
6 Mar 3 Fine Art

Moore Allen and Innocent, Cirencester - UK
6 Sep 2 Sporting Sale
20 Sep 2 Fine Art
4 Oct 2 Antique Sale
1 Nov 2 Picture Sale
15 Nov 2 Antiques - No.221
13 Dec 2 Fine Art

3 Jan 3 Fine Art - No.301
7 Mar 3 Fine Art - No.305
4 Apr 3 Paintings - No.307
23 May 3 Fine Art - No.310
11 Jul 3 Fine Art

Morphets, Harrogate - UK
5 Sep 2 Fine Art
28 Nov 2 Christmas Sale
13 Mar 3 Fine Art
5 Jun 3 Fine Art

Morris & Whiteside, Hilton Head Island, SC - USA
25 Oct 2 Renaissance Sale

Mu Terem Galeria, Budapest - Hungary
13 Sep 2 Fine Art
9 Dec 2 Fine Art
12 Apr 3 Fine Art

Muizon & Le Coent, Senlis - France
27 Oct 2 Paintings & Fine Art
16 Jan 3 Fine Art
2 Feb 3 Paintings & Furniture
13 Feb 3 Fine Art

Museumsbygningen, Kobenhavn - Denmark
28 Aug 2 Fine Art - No. 22
3 Sep 2 Modern Paintings - No.22
27 Nov 2 Fine Art - No.23
26 Feb 3 Golden Age, Drawings & Prints - No.24
4 Mar 3 Modern Paintings & Works of Art - No.24
21 May 3 Paintings & Decorative Art - No.26
27 May 3 Modern Paintings & Works of Art

Nadeau, Windsor, CT - USA
21 Sep 2 Furniture & Decorative Art
1 Jan 3 Fine Art
22 Mar 3 Fine Art

Naon & Cia, Buenos Aires - Argentina
3 Jul 2 Paintings & Works of Art
15 Nov 2 Fine Art

Neal & Fletcher, Woodbridge - UK
4 Dec 2 Fine Art
24 Jun 3 Antique & Reproduction Furniture, Pictures & Prints

Neal Auction Company, New Orleans, LA - USA
12 Oct 2 Fine Art
7 Dec 2 Paintings & Fine Art
8 Feb 3 Fine Art
5 Apr 3 Paintings & Fine Art
7 Jun 3 Late Spring Estates Auction

Neales, Nottingham - UK
18 Jul 2 Fine Art - AE033
27 Mar 3 Spring Sale
10 Jul 3 Fine Art

Neret-Minet, Paris - France
21 Nov 2 Fine Art
18 Jan 3 Maritime
28 Mar 3 Fine Art - with Remi Ader
18 May 3 Young Contemporary Creation

Neumeister, Munich - Germany
26 Jun 2 Old Master & Modern Paintings - No.316
27 Jun 2 Fine Art - No.140
25 Sep 2 19th Century Art - No.317
26 Sep 2 Fine Art - No.141
23 Oct 2 Fine Art - No.142
14 Nov 2 Modern Art - No.32
4 Dec 2 Fine Art - No.318
5 Dec 2 Fine Art - No.143
5 Feb 3 Fine Art - No.144
19 Mar 3 Paintings & Works of Art - No.319
20 Mar 3 Fine & Decorative Art - No.145
9 Apr 3 Fine Art - No.146
15 May 3 Modern Art - No.33
15 May 3 The Wolters Collection - No.33

New Orleans Auction, Louisiana, LA - USA
20 Jul 2 Paintings & Fine Art - No.204
20 Sep 2 Fine Art
16 Nov 2 Fine Art
24 Jan 3 Paintings & Fine Art
22 Mar 3 Paintings & Fine Art - No.302
17 May 3 Fine Art - No.303

Newport, Newport - UK
11 Sep 2 Art in Wales - Y400

North East Auctions, Portsmouth, NH - USA
3 Nov 1 Paintings
17 Aug 2 Fine Art
2 Nov 2 Fine Art
1 Mar 3 Fine Art

Oger, Dumont, Paris - France
5 Dec 2 Fine Art
7 Feb 3 20th Century Art
5 Mar 3 Fine Art
16 Jun 3 Modern Art & Old Masters

Osenat, Fontainebleau - France
17 Nov 2 The Empire Sale

Outhwaite & Litherland, Liverpool - UK
6 Aug 2 Painting & Works of Art - 0858
4 Dec 2 Fine Art
21 May 3 Fine Art

Palais de Beaux Arts, Brussels - Belgium
1 Oct 2 Paintings & Fine Art
22 Oct 2 Fine Art
12 Nov 2 Belgian Art
26 Nov 2 Belgian Art
17 Dec 2 Paintings & Fine Art
4 Mar 3 Paintings & Fine Art
1 Apr 3 Fine Art
13 May 3 Belgian Art
27 May 3 Fine Art
17 Jun 3 Fine Art

Pandolfini, Florence - Italy
20 Nov 2 Modern & Contemporary Art
16 Dec 2 19th & 20th Century Art
17 Mar 3 Old Master Paintings, Furniture & Decorative Art

Patersons, Paisley - UK
24 Sep 2 Fine Art
1 Apr 3 Fine Art

Paul Kieffer, Pforzheim - Germany
4 Oct 2 Books, Graphics, Old & Modern Art
14 Feb 3 Books & Graphic Art - No.49

Peron, Melun - France
1 Dec 2 Barbizon School
8 Mar 3 Fine Art

Perrin, Versailles - France
15 Dec 2 Abstract & Contemporary Art
2 Feb 3 Old Master & 19th Century Art
27 Apr 3 Abstract & Contemporary Art

Peschetau-Badin Godeau & Leroy, Paris - France
13 Dec 2 Fine Art
26 Mar 3 Paintings & Decorative Art

Peter Francis, Carmarthen - UK
10 Sep 2 Paintings
22 Oct 2 Fine Art
3 Dec 2 Fine Art
28 Jan 3 Pictures & Works of Art
29 Apr 3 Fine Art
10 Jun 3 Fine Art & Antiques

Peter Webb, Newmarket - New Zealand
6 Aug 2 Affordable Art - No.247
17 Sep 2 New Zealand Paintings - No.248
5 Nov 2 Affordable Art - No.249
25 Nov 2 Maritime Sale
10 Dec 2 Fine New Zealand Paintings & Decorative Art - No.250
25 Feb 3 Affordable Art - No.251
8 Apr 3 Fine International Art - No.252
1 Jul 3 Fine Paintings - 254

Peter Wilson, Nantwich - UK
10 Jul 2 Fine Art
25 Sep 2 Fine Art
27 Nov 2 Fine Art
19 Feb 3 Fine Art

Philippe Schuler, Zurich - Switzerland
17 Jun 2 Paintings & Fine Art - No.85
16 Sep 2 Paintings & Fine Art - No.86
9 Dec 2 Paintings & Fine Art - No.87
17 Mar 3 Paintings & Fine Art - No.88

Phillips, New York, NY - USA
25 Oct 2 Photographs
4 Nov 2 Impressionist & Modern Art Part I
5 Nov 2 Impressionist & Modern Art Part II
11 Nov 2 Contemporary Art Part 1
12 Nov 2 Contemporary Art Part II
19 Nov 2 21st & 20th Century Design Art - NY050302
3 Dec 2 American Art - NY030202
11 Dec 2 Pre-War: 19-20th Century Design Art - NY050502
21 Apr 3 Soho Partnership Benefit Auction
24 Apr 3 Photographs
25 Apr 3 The Seagram Collection of Photographs
15 May 3 Contemporary Art - Part I - NY010103
16 May 3 Contemporary Art - Part II - NY010203
11 Jun 3 20-21st Century Design - NY050103
11 Jun 3 20th Century Art & Design

Phillips, Zurich - Switzerland
26 Nov 2 Swiss Art

Piasa, Paris - France
29 Nov 1 19th & 20th Century Art
23 Oct 2 Fine Art
13 Nov 2 Old Master & Modern Prints
22 Nov 2 Fine Art
28 Nov 2 Oriental Art
4 Dec 2 Old Master & 19th Century Drawings
9 Dec 2 Carre Collection - with Artcurial
10 Dec 2 Louis Carre Collection - with Artcurial
10 Dec 2 Carre Collection - with Artcurial
11 Dec 2 Art Nouveau & Art Deco
12 Dec 2 Modern Prints
13 Dec 2 19th & 20th Century Art
18 Dec 2 Old Master Paintings
20 Dec 2 Fine Art
7 Feb 3 19th & 20th Century Drawings
7 Mar 3 Asian Art
26 Mar 3 Fine Drawings
28 Mar 3 Fine Art
31 Mar 3 Fine Drawings & Prints
25 Apr 3 19th & 20 Century Paintings & Sculpture
29 Apr 3 Prints
21 May 3 Fine Art
3 Jun 3 Art Nouveau
6 Jun 3 Asian Art
12 Jun 3 Modern Prints
13 Jun 3 Oriental Art
18 Jun 3 19th Century Paintings
19 Jun 3 Old Drawings & 19th & 20th Century Works of Art
20 Jun 3 19th & 20th Century Old Masters, Paintings & Sculptures
25 Jun 3 Works OF Art & Historical Souvenirs
27 Jun 3 Important Old Masters

Pierre Berge, Paris - France
11 Oct 2 Paintings & Fine Art
8 Nov 2 Paintings & Fine Art
4 Dec 2 Paintings & Fine Art
10 Dec 2 Modern Paintings
13 Dec 2 Old Master Art & Furniture
26 Mar 3 Paintings & Fine Art
31 Mar 3 Art Nouveau & Art Deco
18 Jun 3 Modern & Contemporary Art
25 Jun 3 Old Masters & Works Of Art
30 Jun 3 Modern paintings & Sculptures

Pinneys, Montreal - Canada
10 Dec 2 Canadian & International Art

Pook & Pook, Downingtown, PA - USA
21 Sep 2 Fine Art
23 Nov 2 Fine Art
22 Feb 3 Paintings & Fine Art
17 May 3 Spring Antique Sale

Porro, Milan - Italy
3 Apr 3 Fine Neapolitan Collection - No.1
20 May 3 Contemporary Art - No.2

Provenance, Pittstown, NJ - USA
29 Sep 2 Fine Art

Quittenbaum, Hamburg - Germany
26 Oct 2 Old Master & Modern Art - No.9
5 Apr 3 Old Master Paintings & Graphics - No.34

Quittenbaum, Munich - Germany
16 Nov 2 Art Deco & Art Nouveau - No.31
7 Dec 2 Modern Design - No.32
10 May 3 Art Nouveau & Art Deco - No.35
31 May 3 Modern Design - No.36

Rabourdin & Choppin de Janvry, Paris - France
10 Jul 2 Paintings & Works of Art
27 Sep 2 Fine Art
18 Oct 2 Fine Art
23 Oct 2 Oriental Art
9 Dec 2 Extraordinary Old Master Sculpture
12 Dec 2 Jewish Painters
16 Dec 2 Old Masters & Modern Art
31 Jan 3 Paintings & Fine Art
7 Mar 3 Paintings & Fine Art
12 Mar 3 Jewish Art
24 Mar 3 Orientalist Art
21 Apr 3 19th & 20th Century Art - Deauville
23 Apr 3 Paintings & Sculptures of 19th & 20th Centuries
14 May 3 Paintings & Bronzes
18 May 3 19th & 20th Century Sculptures
6 Jun 3 Archaeology of 20th Century
13 Jun 3 Old Masters

Rachel Davis, Shaker Heights, OH - USA
21 Sep 2 Works on Paper
22 Mar 3 Fine Prints & Works of Art
3 May 3 The Roger Trlak Collection

Rasmussen, Havnen, Copenhagen - Denmark
24 Aug 2 Paintings - No.28
28 Sep 2 Paintings & Greenland Auction
26 Oct 2 Fine Art - No.30
30 Nov 2 Paintings & Fine Art - No.31
25 Jan 3 Paintings & Fine Art - No.32
22 Feb 3 Paintings & Fine Art - No.33
5 Apr 3 Paintings & Fine Art - No.34
24 May 3 Paintings & Works of Art - No.35

Rasmussen, Copenhagen - Denmark
27 Aug 2 International Auction - No.712
1 Oct 2 Modern Art - No. 714
26 Nov 2 Decorative Art - No.716
2 Dec 2 Paintings & Decorative Art - No.716
25 Feb 3 Works of Art - No.718
5 Mar 3 International Auction - No.718
1 Apr 3 Modern Auction - No.720
26 May 3 International Art - No.721
17 Jun 3 Modern Art & Design - No.723

Rasmussen, Vejle - Denmark
5 Aug 2 Fine Art - No.82
23 Sep 2 Paintings & Fine Art - No.83
11 Nov 2 Fine Art - No.84
13 Jan 3 Paintings & Fine Art - No.85
10 Mar 3 Paintings & Fine Art - No.86
5 May 3 Paintings & Fine Art - No.88

Regis & Thiollet, Argenteuil - France
15 Oct 2 Fine Art

Reiner Dannenberg, Berlin - Germany
21 Sep 2 Fine Art - No.87
7 Dec 2 Fine Art - No.88
29 Mar 3 Fine Art - No.89

Reiss & Sohn, Konigstein - Germany
15 Nov 2 Old Masters & Modern Art - No.87
4 Jun 3 Old and Modern Art - No.90

Renaud, Paris - France
10 Dec 2 1850-1950
18 Dec 2 Alain de la Moussaye Collection

Rendalls, Ashburton - UK
25 Apr 3 The Works of Robert O Lenkiewicz

Ribeyre & Baron, Paris - France
10 Oct 2 Fine Art
20 Dec 2 Fine Art
31 Mar 3 Paintings & Decorative Art

Richardson & Smith, Whitby - UK
6 Sep 2 Fine Art
20 Sep 2 Paintings
24 Oct 2 Fine Art
28 Nov 2 Fine Art
12 Dec 2 Fine Art
30 Jan 3 Fine Art
27 Feb 3 Fine Art
24 Apr 3 Paintings
22 May 3 Antique Furniture & Effects
26 Jun 3 Marine Antiques & Paintings
17 Jul 3 Antique Furniture & Effects

Riddetts, Bournemouth - UK
10 Sep 2 Fine Art
19 Nov 2 Fine Art
28 Jan 3 Fine Art
28 May 3 Fine Art
22 Jul 3 Fine Art - No.1357

Rieunier, Paris - France
18 Nov 2 Atelier Andree Simon
2 Dec 2 Paintings & Furniture
24 Mar 3 Atelier Jacques Dalleas
26 Mar 3 Fine Art
20 Jun 3 Old Masters & Paintings

Rieunier, Bailly-Pommery, Mathias, Paris - France
25 Nov 2 Paintings & Fine Art
6 Dec 2 Paintings & Fine Art
18 Dec 2 Fine Art
21 Mar 3 Fine Art

Ritchie, Toronto - Canada
24 Sep 2 Decorative Art & Canadian Art
3 Dec 2 European & American Art - No.679
25 Mar 3 Canadian Art - No.685
10 Jun 3 European & American Art - No.691

Rogers Jones, Clwyd - UK
26 Nov 2 Fine Art
28 Jan 3 Fine Art

Rosebery Fine Art, London - UK
20 Aug 2 Pictures & Prints
17 Sep 2 Pictures, Prints & Miniatures
12 Nov 2 Fine Art
10 Dec 2 Pictures & Works of Art
21 Jan 3 Fine Art
18 Feb 3 Fine Art
18 Mar 3 Fine Art
13 May 3 Fine Art
17 Jun 3 Fine Art

Rossini, Paris - France
13 Dec 2 Paintings & Furniture
17 Dec 2 19th & 20th Century Art
26 Mar 3 Paintings & Works of Art
31 Mar 3 Modern Paintings & Prints
13 Jun 3 Jewellery & Works Of Art
1 Jul 3 19th & 20th Century Prints, Paintings & Sculptures

Rowley, Little Downham Ely - UK
24 Sep 2 Fine Art
15 Nov 2 Fine Art
18 Feb 3 Fine Art
29 Apr 3 Fine Art
24 Jun 3 Fine Art

Ruellan, Vannes - France
19 Dec 2 Modern Art

Rupert Toovey, Washington - UK
15 Aug 2 Fine Art
12 Sep 2 Fine Art
10 Oct 2 Fine Art
7 Nov 2 Fine Art
11 Dec 2 Fine Art
21 Jan 3 Fine Art
19 Feb 3 Fine Art
19 Mar 3 Antiques & Fine Art
23 Apr 3 Antiques & Fine Art
21 May 3 Fine Art
18 Jun 3 Sale Of Antiques, Fine Art & Collectors' Items
16 Jul 3 Fine Art

Russ Antiques, Waterford, CT - USA
1 Jun 2 Fine Art

SOGA, Bratislava - Slovak Republic
26 Mar 2 Paintings - No.31
4 Jun 2 Paintings - No.32
1 Oct 2 Paintings - No.34
3 Dec 2 Paintings - No.35

Saint Hippolyte, Montreal - Canada
26 Jun 2 Paintings
30 Jul 2 Paintings & Works Of Art
10 Sep 2 Paintings & Works of Art
24 Sep 2 Canadian Art
22 Oct 2 Art, Antiques & Collections
12 Dec 2 Fine Art
12 Feb 3 Fine Art
25 Mar 3 Canadian & International Art

Santa Fe Art, Santa Fe, NM - USA
9 Nov 2 Classic Western American Art

Scarborough Perry Fine Arts, Hove - UK
5 Dec 2 Fine Art
23 Jan 3 Fine Art
6 Mar 3 Fine Art
24 Apr 3 Fine Art
12 Jun 3 Fine Art
31 Jul 3 Fine Art

Schloss Ahlden, Ahlden - Germany
20 Sep 2 Fine Art - No.119
29 Nov 2 Antiques & Modern Art - No.120
9 May 3 Paintings & Fine Art - No.121

Schopmann, Hamburg - Germany
5 Dec 2 Fine Art
10 Apr 3 Fine Art

Schrager Galleries, Milwaukee, WI - USA
17 Jun 2 Fine Art - No.161
9 Sep 2 Fine Art - No.162
18 Nov 2 Fine Art - No.163
20 Jan 3 Fine Art - No.164
31 Mar 3 Fine Art - No.165

Segre, Madrid - Spain
17 Sep 2 Fine Paintings & Decorative Art - No.10
28 Oct 2 Pictures - No.11
17 Dec 2 Fine Paintings - No.12
18 Dec 2 Furniture & Fine Art - No.12
11 Feb 3 Paintings - No.13
1 Apr 3 Paintings - No.14
20 May 3 Paintings - No.15
21 May 3 Furniture & Fine Art - No.15

Selkirks, St Louis, MO - USA
14 Sep 2 Paintings & Works Of Art - 02SEPG
10 Nov 2 20th Century Design & Fine Art - 02MODN
7 Dec 2 Fine Art
15 Mar 3 Spring Gallery
17 May 3 20th Century Design
21 Jun 3 Summer Gallery

Semenzato, Venice - Italy
20 Sep 2 Fine Art
21 Sep 2 Fine Art
22 Sep 2 Fine Art
19 Oct 2 Fine Art
19 Oct 2 Fine Art
20 Oct 2 Fine Art
28 Nov 2 Fine Art from San Gregorio`s Abbey - 02VEM1
29 Nov 2 Fine Art from San Gregorio`s Abbey - 02VEM1
19 Dec 2 Carlo de Carlo's Collection (pt I)
19 Dec 2 Carlo de Carlo's Collection (pt II)
19 Feb 3 Fine Old Master Paintings & Furniture - 03VEA1 - Florence
19 Feb 3 Furniture & Decorative Art - 03VEA2
7 Mar 3 Furniture & Decorative Art - with Finarte
9 Mar 3 Decorative Art - with Finarte
9 Mar 3 Important Old Master Paintings - with Finarte

Shannon's, Milford, CT - USA
24 Oct 2 Fine Art
24 Apr 3 Paintings & Decorative Art

Shapes, Edinburgh - UK
7 Sep 2 Fine Art
5 Oct 2 Paintings & Works of Art - No. 74
2 Nov 2 Paintings & Works of Art - No.72
7 Dec 2 Fine Art
1 Feb 3 Fine Art
1 Mar 3 Fine Art
5 Apr 3 Paintings & Works of Art - No. 79
7 Jun 3 Fine Art

Shapiro, Sydney - Australia
3 Sep 2 Fine Art - Australian & European Paintings - No.3
3 Dec 2 Modern & Contemporary Art - No.4
7 Apr 3 Australian & European Paintings - No.5
10 Jun 3 Australian & International Art & Photography - No.6

Shelley, Hendersonville, NC - USA
21 Nov 2 Fine Art

Sigalas, Stuttgart - Germany
28 Jun 2 Fine Art - No.86
20 Sep 2 Fine Art - No.87
29 Nov 2 Fine Art - No.88
21 Feb 3 Paintings & Fine Art - No.89
11 Apr 3 Paintings & Fine Art - No.90

Simpson's, Houston, TX - USA
2 Feb 3 Fine Art
30 Mar 3 Fine Art

Skinner, Bolton, MA - USA
9 Aug 2 Decorative Art - No.2157
13 Dec 2 Holiday Auction - No.2178
16 Jan 3 Discovery Sale - No.2185
20 Feb 3 Discovery Sale - No.2187
20 Mar 3 Discovery Sale - No.2189

Skinner, Boston, MA - USA
10 May 2 American & European Paintings - No.2141
22 Nov 2 American & European Paintings - No.2168
11 Jan 3 American Indian & Ethnographic Art - No.2132
25 Jan 3 Furniture & Decorative Art - No.2183
23 Feb 3 American Furniture & Decorative Art - No.2144
7 Mar 3 American & European Paintings - No.2190
10 May 3 Decorative Art - No.2202
16 May 3 American & International Paintings - No.2194
8 Jun 3 Furniture & Decorative Art - No.2198

Sloan, North Bethesda, MD - USA
20 Sep 2 The Autumn Auction
9 Nov 2 Paintings & Prints - No.945

Sotheby's, Amsterdam - Netherlands
22 Oct 2 19th Century European Paintings - AM0859
5 Nov 2 Old Master Drawings - AM0863
5 Nov 2 Old Master Paintings -Sor Rusche Collection - AM0875
5 Nov 2 Old Master Paintings - AM0862
26 Nov 2 Modern & Contemporary Art - AM0870
3 Dec 2 Dutch Glory, Art & Collectors - AM0858
18 Feb 3 Of Royal & Noble Descent - AM0877
10 Mar 3 Arcade Auction incl. Paintings - AM0878
15 Apr 3 19th Century European Paintings - AM0881
13 May 3 Old Master Paintings - AM0885
28 May 3 International Young Art - IYA2003

Sotheby's, Hong Kong
27 Apr 3 Fine Chinese Ceramics & Works of Art - HK0193
28 Apr 3 Fine Chinese Paintings - HK0194

Sotheby's Olympia, London - UK
5 Sep 2 Furniture, Rugs & Works of Art - W02848
12 Sep 2 Modern British Paintings - W02818
17 Sep 2 19th Century Paintings & Scottish Pictures - 2809
18 Sep 2 The Patrick & Gilly Morley Collection
30 Sep 2 Interior Decorator
8 Oct 2 The Contents of Fulbeck Hall, Lincolnshire
23 Oct 2 Impressionist & Modern Art - 2810
24 Oct 2 Silver, Miniatures & Vertu - 2887
28 Oct 2 19th Century Furniture & Decorative Art
31 Oct 2 Old Master Paintings - WO2971
6 Nov 2 Sporting Sale - W02918
13 Nov 2 Furniture & Decorative Art - W02857
20 Nov 2 The Welsh & Oak Sale - WO2852
21 Nov 2 Russian Works of Art - W02920
27 Nov 2 Modern British Paintings - W02812
3 Dec 2 19th Century & Early British Paintings & Watercolours - W02811
4 Dec 2 Furniture & Decorative Art - W02851
10 Dec 2 Old Master Paintings - W02813
11 Dec 2 Old Master Drawings - W02817
16 Dec 2 The Marine Sale - W02819
29 Jan 3 19th Century Paintings - W03701
3 Feb 3 Contemporary Art - W03700
11 Feb 3 Furniture & Sculpture - W03776
19 Feb 3 Japanese & Chinese Works of Art - W03750
26 Feb 3 Modern British Paintings - W03702

27 Feb 3 Fine Decorative Art & Design from 1870 - W03810
6 Mar 3 Silver, Miniatures & Vertu - W03765
20 Mar 3 Impressionist & Modern Art - W03703
26 Mar 3 19th Century Paintings - W03704
8 Apr 3 Old Master Paintings - W03705
29 Apr 3 Furniture, Bronzes & Rugs - W03779
13 May 3 The John Entwistle Collection - W03875
20 May 3 19th Century Paintings - W03706
3 Jun 3 Modern British Paintings - W03707
5 Jun 3 Furniture & Decorative Art - W03780
18 Jun 3 Marine Sale - W03851
24 Jun 3 Contemporary Art - W03715
25 Jun 3 Silver & Miniatures - W03767
2 Jul 3 The British Sale - W03720
8 Jul 3 Old Master Paintings - W03709
15 Jul 3 Selected English & Continental Furniture, Bronzes, Sculpture & Rugs - W03782
16 Jul 3 19th Century Paintings - WO3710
22 Jul 3 Interior Decorator - W03850

Sotheby's, London - UK

28 Aug 2 Fine Scottish & Colourist Pictures - L02951 - Gleneagles Hotel, Scotland
2 Oct 2 The Greek Sale - L02134
8 Oct 2 Beck Collection - German Expressionist & Modern Art - 2964
9 Oct 2 Beck Collection - German Expressionist & Modern Art - 2964
9 Oct 2 The German Sale - 2953
10 Oct 2 Old Master & Contemporary Prints - L02193
15 Oct 2 Travel Sale: Mediterranean & the Middle East
21 Oct 2 20th Century Italian Art - 2955
22 Oct 2 Contemporary Art - 2104
22 Oct 2 Impressionist & Modern Art - 2007
29 Oct 2 The Christopher Hodsoll Collection - 2404
30 Oct 2 Art of Flanders - L02960
5 Nov 2 European Sculpture & Works of Art - LO2232
15 Nov 2 The Travel Sale Topographical Pictures - L02162
19 Nov 2 Spanish Paintings from 1850 to 1930 - L02131
20 Nov 2 Russian Pictures - L02141
28 Nov 2 The British Sale: Paintings & Watercolours - L02155
28 Nov 2 Important British Pictures - LO2156
2 Dec 2 Victorian Pictures - L02158
4 Dec 2 Modern British & Irish Art - L02157
5 Dec 2 Old Master, Modern & Contemporary Prints - L02195
10 Dec 2 European Sculpture & Works of Art 900-1900 - L02233
12 Dec 2 Old Master Paintings - L02114
16 Dec 2 Charles and Barbara Robertson Collection: an Informed Eye - L02988
4 Feb 3 Impressionist & Modern Art - Evening Sale - L03002
5 Feb 3 Impressionist & Modern Art - Day Sale - L03003
6 Feb 3 Contemporary Art - Evening Sale - L03020
7 Feb 3 Contemporary Art - Day Sale - L03021
19 Mar 3 The British Sale - L03120
20 Mar 3 The James Watt Sale - L03500
25 Mar 3 Old Master & Contemporary Prints - LO3160
9 Apr 3 European Sculpture & Works of Art 900-1900 - L03230
10 Apr 3 Old Master Paintings - L03030
14 Apr 3 Scottish Pictures - L03130 - Hopetoun House, Scotland
30 Apr 3 Art of the Islamic World incl. 20th Century Middle Eastern Paintings - L03220
7 May 3 Natural History, Travel, Atlases & Maps - L03400
16 May 3 The Irish Sale - L03620
21 May 3 Russian Pictures incl. Important Works from Collection of Fedor Chaliapin - L03110
22 May 3 Photographs - L03200
3 Jun 3 19th Century European Art incl. German & Scandinavian Paintings - L03100
4 Jun 3 Modern British Art - L03140
12 Jun 3 Important British Pictures - L03125
12 Jun 3 The British Sale - L03122
23 Jun 3 Impressionist & Modern Art - Evening Sale - L03004
24 Jun 3 Impressionist & Modern Art - l03005
25 Jun 3 Contemporary Art - Evening Sale - L03022
26 Jun 3 Contemporary Art - L03023
1 Jul 3 Old Master, Modern & Contemporary Prints - LO3161
8 Jul 3 European Sculpture & Works Of Art 900-1900 - LO3231
9 Jul 3 Old Master Drawings - L03040
10 Jul 3 Fine Old Master Paintings Part I - L03031
10 Jul 3 Fine Old Master Painting Part II - L03032
21 Jul 3 Wormington Manor, Country House Sale - L03502 - Worcestershire

Sotheby's, Melbourne - Australia

8 Sep 2 The BP Collection of Australian Contemporary Art - AU0665
26 Nov 2 Fine Australian & International Paintings - AU0661
5 May 3 Fine Australian Paintings - AU0670
5 May 3 The Collection of Sir David Davies - AU0670

Sotheby's, Milan - Italy

5 Mar 3 Maria Antonia Gianetti's Collection - MI0210
12 May 3 Books, Prints & Old Master Drawings - MI0211

Sotheby's, Moscow - Russia

25 Jun 3 International Young Art

Sotheby's, New York, NY - USA

22 Oct 2 Photographs - N07851
24 Oct 2 Photographs - N07831
29 Oct 2 Property from the Estates of David M. Daniels & Stevan Beck Baloga - 7833
29 Oct 2 19th Century European Art
5 Nov 2 Impressionist & Modern Art Part 1 Vol I - N07838
5 Nov 2 The Robert C. Guccione Collection - N07838
6 Nov 2 Impressionist & Modern Art Part II - N07839
12 Nov 2 A Private American Collection - N07841
12 Nov 2 Contemporary Art -Evening Sale - N07842
13 Nov 2 Contemporary Art - Morning Sale - N07843
13 Nov 2 Contemporary Art - Afternoon Sale - N07843
19 Nov 2 Latin American Art - N07847
21 Nov 2 19th Century Paintings & Decorative Art - N07848
4 Dec 2 American Paintings, Drawings & Sculptures - 7854
6 Dec 2 20th Century Decorative Works of Art - N07855
16 Jan 3 Important Americana - N07865
18 Jan 3 Fine Art from a Private American Collection - N07866
18 Jan 3 Sinking Spring Farms: the Appell Family Collection - N07867
21 Jan 3 Old Master Drawings - N07870
21 Jan 3 The Pouncey Collection - N07870A
23 Jan 3 Old Master Paintings - N07871
23 Jan 3 Important Old Master Paintings - N07871
12 Feb 3 Impressionist & Modern Art - N07875
5 Mar 3 American Paintings, Drawings & Sculpture - N07876
27 Mar 3 Fine Chinese Works of Art - N07881
23 Apr 3 Photographs - N07885
24 Apr 3 19th Century European Art - N07886
30 Apr 3 A Celebration of the English Country House incl. the Mitchell Collection - N07884
2 May 3 Prints - N07888
6 May 3 Impressionist & Modern Art - Part I - N07890
7 May 3 Impressionist & Modern Art - Part II - N07892
13 May 3 Contemporary Art - Evening Sale - N07898
14 May 3 Contemporary Art - Morning Sale - N07900
14 May 3 Contemporary Art - Afternoon Sale - N07900
21 May 3 American Paintings, Drawings & Sculpture - N07904
21 May 3 American Art from the Collection of Meyer & Vivian Potamkin - N07904
22 May 3 Important Americana - N07905
27 May 3 Latin American Art - N07907
29 May 3 Old Master Paintings - N07909

Sotheby's, Paris - France

18 Nov 2 Oil Paintings & Drawings - PF2015
3 Dec 2 20th Century Decorative Art - PF2014
17 Dec 2 Fine Furniture & Decorative Art - PF2018
15 May 3 The Karl Lagerfeld Collection: 20th Century Decorative Art - PF3019
25 Jun 3 19 Century Paintings
25 Jun 3 Furniture & Fine Art - PF3008

Sotheby's, Sydney - Australia

25 Aug 2 Fine Australian Paintings - AU0660
26 Aug 2 Art from the Kerry Stokes Collection - AU0667
17 Nov 2 The Fairfax Corporate Collection of Australian Paintings - AU0669

Sotheby's, Tel Aviv - Israel

27 Apr 3 International & Israeli Art - TA0029
13 May 3 International Young Art - IYA2003

Sotheby's, Toronto - Canada

18 Nov 2 Important Canadian Art - No.677 - with Ritchie's
27 May 3 Important Canadian Art - No.689 - with Ritchie's

Sotheby's, Zurich - Switzerland
25 Nov 2 Swiss Art - ZH0297
26 May 3 Swiss Art

South Bay Auctions, Long Island, NY - USA
7 Dec 2 Fine Art - No.217

Stadion, Trieste - Italy
5 Dec 2 Decorative Art, Ceramics & Paintings
1 Mar 3 Prints & Jewellery
22 May 3 Paintings & Decorative Art

Stephan Welz & Co, Johannesburg - South Africa
15 Oct 2 Decorative & Fine Art - Cape Town
11 Nov 2 Oil Paintings, Watercolours, Sculpture & Prints - No.210
25 Nov 2 Decorative Art - No.211
1 Apr 3 Decorative & Fine Art - SA0304
12 May 3 Important South African, British & Continental Art - SA0306 - with Sotheby's

Susanin's, Chicago, IL - USA
23 Jun 2 Fine Art - No.132
22 Sep 2 Fine Art - No.145
20 Oct 2 Fine Art - No.149
1 Dec 2 Fine Art - No.156
11 Jan 3 Fine Art - No.160
25 Jan 3 Fine Art - No.162
1 Feb 3 Fine Art - No.163
1 Mar 3 Fine Art - No.167
30 Mar 3 Fine Art - No.170
5 Apr 3 Fine Art - No.171
12 Apr 3 Fine Art - No.172
19 Apr 3 Fine Art - No.173
26 Apr 3 Fine Art - No.173
10 May 3 Fine Art - No.176
24 May 3 Fine Art - No.178
31 May 3 Fine Art - No.179
7 Jun 3 Fine Art - No.180
14 Jun 3 Fine Art - No.181
21 Jun 3 Fine Art - No.182 - online

Swann Galleries, New York, NY - USA
18 Sep 2 100 Fine Works of Art on Paper - No.1942
19 Sep 2 19th & 20th Century Prints & Drawings - No.1942
21 Oct 2 Important 19th & 20th Century Photographs - No. 1947
6 Nov 2 100 Important Old Master Prints - No.1950
7 Nov 2 Old Master Through Contemporary Prints - No.1950
21 Nov 2 Contemporary Art - Part I - No.1953
5 Dec 2 Photographic Literature & Photographs - No.1954
23 Jan 3 Old Master Drawings - No.1957
10 Feb 3 100 Fine Photographs - No.1959
3 Mar 3 100 Fine Works of Art on Paper - No.1962
4 Mar 3 19th & 20th Century Prints & Drawings - No.1962
1 May 3 Old Master Through Contemporary Prints - No.1969
1 May 3 Rembrandt and His Influence: 100 Master Prints - No.1969
15 May 3 Photographic Literature & Photographs - No.1971
5 Jun 3 American Watercolours & Drawings - No.1973

Tajan, Paris - France
31 Jul 2 Modern & Contemporary Paintings & Sculptures - Monaco
4 Oct 2 Modern & Contemporary Paintings & Sculptures
25 Oct 2 Old Masters
5 Nov 2 Naive Art
6 Nov 2 Decorative Art
18 Nov 2 Paintings, Drawings & Sculpture of 19th Century
22 Nov 2 Old Master & Modern Prints
26 Nov 2 20th Century Decorative Art
27 Nov 2 Contemporary Art
28 Nov 2 Old Master Drawings
29 Nov 2 Janette Ostier Collection
2 Dec 2 19th & 20th Century Art
10 Dec 2 Oriental Art
17 Dec 2 Decorative Art - Four Seasons Hotel
18 Dec 2 Old Master Paintings
18 Dec 2 19th & 20th Century Paintings
20 Dec 2 Old Master Paintings
22 Jan 3 Works on Paper
29 Jan 3 Fine Art
19 Feb 3 Fine Art
28 Feb 3 20th Century Decorative Art
24 Mar 3 Fine Drawings
26 Mar 3 19th & 20th Century Art
26 Mar 3 Old Master Paintings
31 Mar 3 Prints
4 Apr 3 Art Naif
30 Apr 3 19th Century Art
19 May 3 20th Century Decorative Art
19 May 3 Sculpture
27 May 3 Contemporary Art - No.90
3 Jun 3 Jewish Art
4 Jun 3 Oriental Art
12 Jun 3 Impressionist & Modern Paintings & Sculptures
18 Jun 3 Old Masters
25 Jun 3 Old Masters
25 Jun 3 20th Century Decorative Art
26 Jun 3 19th & 20th Century Old Masters & Sculptures

Tayler & Fletcher, Bourton on the Water - UK
25 Mar 3 Fine Art

Teitgen, Nancy - France
8 Dec 2 Fine Art

Tennants, Leyburn - UK
21 Nov 2 Fine Art - LS124
7 Mar 3 Sporting Prints
10 Apr 3 Fine Art
17 Jul 3 Summer Sale

Themis, Brussels - Belgium
19 Nov 2 Important Fine Art

Thierry & Lannon, Brest - France
11 Jun 2 Fine Art
14 Oct 2 Paintings & Fine Art
12 Nov 2 Paintings
9 Dec 2 Fine Art
15 Dec 2 Modern Paintings
10 Mar 3 Fine Art
24 Mar 3 Paintings & Fine Art
11 May 3 Modern Paintings
3 Jun 3 Furniture
19 Jul 3 Modern Paintings

Thomas Adams, Dublin - Eire
5 Feb 2 Fine Art - 0195
5 Mar 2 Fine Art - 0196
9 Apr 2 Fine Art
14 May 2 Fine Art - 0198
21 May 2 Traverslea House - 0199
10 Jun 2 Fine Art - 0200
2 Jul 2 Fine Art
27 Aug 2 Fine Art
17 Sep 2 Fine Art
5 Nov 2 Fine Art
3 Dec 2 Fine Art
21 Jan 3 Fine Art
11 Mar 3 Fine Art
8 Apr 3 Fine Art
13 May 3 Paintings
10 Jun 3 Furniture & Fine Art Sale

Thomaston Place, Thomaston, ME - USA
11 Aug 2 Fine Art
30 Aug 2 Fine Art
28 Sep 2 Fine Art
2 Nov 2 Fine Art
30 Nov 2 Fine Art
1 Feb 3 Fine Art
1 Mar 3 Fine Art
26 Apr 3 Fine Art

Thomson Roddick & Medcalfe, Carlisle - UK
24 Oct 2 Fine Art
17 Jul 3 Fine Art - Naworth Castle, Cumbria

Thomson Roddick & Medcalfe, Edinburgh - UK
17 May 3 Oil Paintings, Watercolours & Prints

Thos Mawer, Lincoln - UK
20 Feb 3 Fine Art

Tiffin King & Nicholson, Carlisle - UK
24 Jun 2 Fine Art - No.350

Toomey, Oak Park, IL - USA
8 Dec 2 Decorative Art & American Paintings
2 Mar 3 Fine Art

Treadway Gallery, Cincinnati, OH - USA
8 Sep 2 20th Century Art & Design - John Toomey Gallery

4 May 3 Fine Art

Trembath Welch, Great Dunmow - UK
11 Nov 2 Fine Art
24 Mar 3 Fine Art - No.1031

Uppsala Auktionskammare, Uppsala - Sweden
29 Sep 2 Decorative Art
8 Dec 2 Paintings & Fine Art
2 Mar 3 Decorative Art
25 May 3 Paintings & Fine Art

Van Ham, Cologne - Germany
31 Oct 2 Photographs - No.219
21 Nov 2 Old Masters - No. 220
7 Dec 2 Modern & Contemporary Art - No.221
10 Apr 3 Old Master Paintings & Drawings - No.222
23 May 3 Photographs - No.223
24 May 3 Modern & Contemporary Art - No.224

Venator & Hansten, Cologne - Germany
27 Sep 2 Graphics - No.88
4 Apr 3 Graphic Art & Books - No.89

Vendu Notarishuis, Rotterdam - Netherlands
5 Nov 2 Art & antiques - No.217
18 Feb 3 Antiques
6 May 3 Paintings & Works of Art - No.218

Vendue Huis, Gravenhage - Netherlands
19 Jun 2 Paintings, Prints & Maps - on-line
6 Nov 2 Art & Antiques
7 May 3 Paintings & Antiques

Villa Grisebach, Berlin - Germany
28 Nov 2 Photography - No.103
29 Nov 2 Selected Works - No.104
29 Nov 2 Affordable Art - No.106
30 Nov 2 19th & 20th Century Art - No.105
30 May 3 Fine Paintings - No.108
31 May 3 19th & 20th Century Art - No.109
31 May 3 Third Floor - No.110

Waddingtons, Toronto - Canada
19 Sep 2 Old Master, Victorian, 19th & 20th Century & Contemporary Prints
18 Nov 2 British, European & American Pictures & Sculptures
1 May 3 Canadiana
9 May 3 Photographs
16 Jun 3 Paintings & Watercolours
17 Jun 3 Decorative Art

Walker's, Ottawa - Canada
24 Jul 2 Fine Art & Antiques
26 Mar 3 Fine Paintings & Decorative Art

Watson's, Christchurch - New Zealand
12 Sep 1 Fine Art
21 Nov 1 Fine Art
20 Mar 2 Fine Art
19 Jun 2 Fine Art
13 May 3 Fine Art

Weidler, Nurnberg - Germany
5 Jul 2 Fine Art - No.735
14 Sep 2 Fine Art - 750
27 Sep 2 Fine Art - No.755
21 Nov 2 Fine Art - No.780
6 Dec 2 Fine Art - No.785
6 Feb 3 Fine Art - No.790
25 Apr 3 Works of Art - No.805

Weschler, Washington, DC - USA
14 Sep 2 American & European Fine Art & 20th Century Decorative Art - No.1258
14 Dec 2 American & European Fine Art & 20th Century Decorative Art - No.1261
12 Apr 3 American Furniture & Decorative Fine Art - No.1264

Whyte's, Dublin - Eire
17 Sep 2 Irish Art
19 Nov 2 Important Irish Art
18 Feb 3 Major Irish Art
29 Apr 3 Irish Art

Wiener Kunst Auktionen, Vienna - Austria
23 Sep 2 Paintings
24 Sep 2 Paintings
25 Sep 2 Paintings & design
22 Oct 2 Historical Tobacco Accessories - No. 41
26 Nov 2 Old Masters from 19th & 20th Century - No.42
27 Nov 2 Asian Art & Antiques - No.42
25 Mar 3 Fine Art - No.43
29 Apr 3 Fine Art - No.44
27 May 3 Paintings & Contemporary Art - No.45

William Jenack, Chester, NY - USA
28 Jul 2 Fine Art
12 Jan 3 Important Fine Art
9 Feb 3 Fine Art

Windibank, Dorking - UK
14 Sep 2 Fine Art
5 Apr 3 Fine Art
24 May 3 Fine Art
12 Jul 3 Fine Art

Wingetts, Wrexham - UK
18 Sep 2 Fine Art
30 Oct 2 Fine Art
4 Dec 2 Fine Art
29 Jan 3 Fine Art
5 Mar 3 Fine Art

Winter Associates, Plainville, CT - USA
15 Oct 2 Fine Art
18 Nov 2 Fine Art
17 Mar 3 Fine Art

Winterberg, Heidelberg - Germany
11 Oct 2 Old Master & Modern Art - No.65
11 Apr 3 Decorative Graphics & Art of 15-20th Centuries - No.66

Wintertons, Lichfield - UK
25 Sep 2 Fine Art
27 Nov 2 Fine Art
29 Jan 3 Fine Art
19 Mar 3 Fine Art
22 May 3 Fine Art
23 Jul 3 Fine Art

Woodwards, Cork - Eire
7 Feb 2 General Sale
14 Mar 2 General Sale
29 Mar 2 General Sale
3 Apr 2 General Sale
25 Apr 2 General Sale
3 May 2 General Sale
29 May 2 General Sale
28 Jun 2 General Sale
17 Jul 2 General Sale
29 Jan 3 Fine Art

Woolley & Wallis, Salisbury - UK
9 Oct 2 Oil Paintings & Watercolours
5 Nov 2 Furniture & Works of Art
26 Mar 3 Paintings & Works of Art

Wright, Chicago, IL - USA
19 Nov 2 Modern & Contemporary Art
8 Dec 2 Modernist 20th Century
1 Jun 3 Modern & Contemporary Art

York Town, York, PA - USA
23 Aug 2 Fine Art
8 Nov 2 Fine Art
21 Feb 3 Fine Art
16 May 3 Fine Art

Number of sales covered in this edition - 2418

CROSS REFERENCES

There are many cases where an artist is more widely known by some cognomen instead of his original name. The most obvious examples are Rembrandt and El Greco, whose real names are, respectively, Rembrandt Harmensz van Rijn and Domenikos Theotokopoulos. A list of these 'common names' is given below and appear in this edition.

A

ADAM, Victor Charles Edouard see ADAM, Edouard (jnr)
ALDINI, Casimiro *see* TOMBA, Casimiro
ALKEN, Samuel Henry *see* ALKEN, Henry (jnr)
ALLEGRI, Antonio *see* CORREGGIO
ALSTON, Abbey *see* ALTSON, Abbey
ALVAREZ DE SOTOMAYOR, Fernando *see* SOTOMAYOR Y ZARAGOZA, Fernando
ANDERSSON, Gustaf Albert *see* ALBERT, Gustaf
APPIAN, Jacques Barthelemy *see* APPIAN, Adolphe
ARANDA, Jose Jimenez *see* JIMENEZ Y ARANDA, Jose
ARDEN, Edward *see* TUCKER, Edward
ARTVELT, Andries van *see* EERTVELT, Andries van
ARZADUN, Carmelo de *see* CARMELO DE ARZADUN

B

BACCHIACA, Francesco *see* UBERTINI, Francesco
BACICCIA *see* GAULLI, Giovanni Battista
BADGER, Clarissa W *see* MUNGER, Clarissa
BADURA, Faye Swengel *see* SWENGEL, Faye
BAGNACAVALLO, Bartolomeo (elder) *see* RAMENGHI, Bartolomeo (elder)
BAKSCHEJEFF, Wassily N *see* BAKSHEEV, Vasily
BARBARELLI, Giorgio *see* GIORGIONE
BARBATELLI, Bernardino *see* POCCETTI, Bernardino
BARBIERI, Giovanni Francesco *see* GUERCINO, Giovanni Francesco
BARRAUD-PELLET, Jeanne *see* JANEBE
BASALDELLA, Afro *see* AFRO
BASALDELLA, Mirko *see* MIRKO
BAUMANN, Elisabeth Jerichau *see* JERICHAU-BAUMANN, Elisabeth
BAUMGÄRTNER, Adolf *see* STOILOFF, Constantin
BEATTIE-BROWN, William *see* BROWN, William Beattie
BEDOLI, Girolamo Francesco *see* MAZZOLA, Girolamo Bedoli
BELIN, Jean *see* FONTENAY, Jean Baptiste Belin de
BERG, Franciscus Johannes Gysbertus van den *see* JOHFRA
BERRETTINI, Pietro da *see* CORTONA, Pietro da
BERTOLETTI, Marcelli *see* PASQUAROSA
BEURDEN, Alexander F W E *see* SCHOONHOVEN VAN BEURDEN, Alexander Franciscus van
BEVERLOO, Cornelis Guillaume *see* CORNEILLE
BIANCA, Angelo dell'Oca *see* DALL`OCA BIANCA, Angelo
BILEVELT, Giovanni *see* BILIVERTI, Giovanni
BISSCHOP, Suze *see* ROBERTSON, Suze
BLEULER, Louis *see* BLEULER, Johann Ludwig
BOLOGNE, Jean de *see* GIAMBOLOGNA
BOLTON-JONES, Hugh *see* JONES, Hugh Bolton
BOOGAARD, Willem Johan *see* BOOGAARD, Willem Jacobus
BORCH, Gerard ter *see* TERBORCH, Gerard
BORTOLUZZI, Bianco Pietro *see* BIANCO, Pieretto
BOSSCHAERT, Thomas *see* WILLEBOIRTS, Thomas
BOUVARD, Antoine Joseph *see* BOUVARD, Joseph Antoine
BOUVIER, Agnes Rose *see* NICHOLL, Agnes Rose
BRAUER, Arik *see* BRAUER, Erich
BREANSKI, Alfred de (jnr) *see* BREANSKI, Alfred Fontville de
BREMEN, Meyer von *see* MEYER VON BREMEN, Johann Georg
BRENNERSTEIN-WICHERA, Raimund Ritter von *see* WICHERA, Raimund von
BRINCK, H A *see* BJULF, Soren Christian
BROWN, Hugh Boycott *see* BOYCOTT-BROWN, Hugh
BUONAMICO, Agostino *see* TASSI, Agostino

C

CAFISSA, Nicolo *see* CASISSA, Nicola
CALIARI, Paolo *see* VERONESE, Paolo
CALISTO DA LODI *see* PIAZZA, Calisto
CANAL, Antonio *see* CANALETTO
CANLASSI, Guido *see* CAGNACCI, Guido
CAPPONI, Raffaelo de *see* GARBO, Raffaellino del
CARLOS-REYMOND *see* REYMOND, Carlos
CARMICHAEL, Herbert *see* SCHMALZ, Herbert Gustave
CASENTINO, Jacopo del *see* LANDINI, Jacopo
CATALA, Luis Alvarez *see* ALVAREZ CATALA, Luis
CATE, Ten *see* TEN CATE
CECCO BRAVO *see* MONTELATICI, Francesco
CELIS, Perez *see* PEREZ CELIS
CERANO *see* CRESPI, Giovanni Battista
CERMAK, Jaroslav *see* CZERMAK, Jaroslav
CEULEN, Cornelis Janssens van *see* JONSON, Cornelis
CHANA ORLOFF *see* ORLOFF, Chana
CHANG YU *see* SAN-YU
CHICHKINE, Ivan Ivanovitch *see* SHISHKIN, Ivan Ivanovich
CIGOLI, Ludovico *see* CARDI, Lodovico
CIHLARZ, Wolfgang *see* SALOME
CLARK OF GREENOCK, William *see* CLARK, William
CLARK, Joseph Dixon (snr) *see* CLARK, Dixon
CLAUDE LORRAIN *see* GELLEE, Claude
CLAVEL, Marie Joseph Leon *see* IWILL, Joseph
CLEMENT, Marcel *see* MARCEL-CLEMENT, Amedee Julien
CLEMENT-SERVEAU *see* SERVEAU, Clement
COECKE, Pieter van Aelst *see* AELST, Pieter Coecke van
COLEMAN, Helen Cordelia *see* ANGELL, Helen Cordelia
COLOMBO, Luigi *see* FILLIA
COLYER, Edwaert *see* COLLIER, Evert
CONRAD-KICKERT *see* KICKERT, Conrad
CORDINGLEY, Georges Ricard *see* RICARD-CORDINGLEY, Georges
CORMIER, Joseph Descomps *see* DESCOMPS, Joe
CORNEILLE DE GROUX, Henri Jules Charles *see* GROUX, Henry de
CORTESE, Guglielmo *see* COURTOIS, Guillaume
COSSINGTON-SMITH, Grace *see* SMITH, Grace Cossington
COSTER, Anne Vallayer *see* VALLAYER-COSTER, Anne
COUVER, Jan van *see* KOEKKOEK, Hermanus (jnr)
CRIVELLONE, Angelo Maria *see* CRIVELLI, Angelo Maria

D

D'ALIGNY, Theodore Caruelle *see* CARUELLE D`ALIGNY, Theodore
D'ARPINO *see* CESARI, Giuseppe
D'ERRICO, Antonio *see* TANZIO DA VARALLO, Antonio d`Enrico
DAVIS, Val *see* DAVIS, J Valentine
DAWIDI *see* DJULWARAK, Dawidi
DECAUX, Vicomtesse Iphigenie *see* MILET-MOREAU, Iphigenie
DEFOREST, Roy *see* FOREST, Roy de
DEGRAIN, Antonio Munoz *see* MUNOZ-DEGRAIN, Antoine
DEHAVEN, Franklin *see* HAVEN, Franklin de
DELAROCHE, Hippolyte *see* DELAROCHE, Paul
DESFILLES, Charles *see* BEGO, Charles
DESMET, Leon *see* SMET, Leon de
DJURIC, Miodrag *see* DADO, Miodrag Djuric
DODERHULTARN *see* PETERSSON, Axel
DOMENICO, Ridolfi di *see* GHIRLANDAIO, Ridolfo
DONAU, Erich Josef *see* DOGARTH, Erich Josef
DREYFUSS, Marcel *see* DYF, Marcel
DRULMAN, Marinus Johannes *see* JONGERE, Marinus de
DUBOIS DRAHONET, Alexandre Jean *see* DRAHONET, Alexandre Jean Dubois
DUBOURG, Victoria *see* FANTIN-LATOUR, Victoria
DUMARESQ, Armand *see* ARMAND-DUMARESQ, Edouard Charles

E

EKMAN, Marie Louise *see* BERGENSTRAHLE, Marie Louise de Geer
EMPOLI, Jacopo da *see* CHIMENTI, Jacopo
ERLER, Erich *see* ERLER-SAMADEN, Erich

F

FERNANDI, Francesco *see* IMPERIALI, Francesco
FIKRET MOUALLA *see* MOUALLA, Fikret
FIORI, Mario da *see* NUZZI, Mario
FIRMIN-GIRARD *see* GIRARD, Marie Firmin
FLETCHER, Edward Henry Eugene *see* FLETCHER, Edwin

FLORES, Pancho *see* FLORES, Francisco
FORTESCUE-BRICKDALE, Eleanor *see* BRICKDALE, Eleanor Fortesque
FOURNIER, Gabriel Francisque Alexis *see* GABRIEL-FOURNIER
FRANCK, Pauwels/Pauvels or FRANCESCHI, Paolo *see* FIAMMINGO, Paolo
FRANCOIS, Gustave *see* BARRAUD, Gustave Francois
FRANK-BOGGS *see* BOGGS, Frank Myers
FRANKY BOY *see* SEVEHON, Francky Boy
FRASER, Garden William *see* GARDEN, William Fraser
FRECHOU, Charles *see* FRECHON, Charles
FRERE, Theodore *see* FRERE, Charles Theodore
FRIIS-NYBO, Poul *see* NYBOE, Friis

G

GALGARIO, Fra *see* GHISLANDI, Vittore
GALVAN, Jesus Guerrero *see* GUERRERO GALVAN, Jesus
GARCIA-TELLA, Jose *see* TELLA, Jose Garcia
GASSEL, Lucas van *see* HELMONT, Lucas van Gassel
GEGO *see* GOLDSCHMIDT, Gertrudis
GEISEL, Theodor S *see* SEUSS, Dr
GERSHOV, Solomon Moiseevich *see* GUERTCHOV, Solomon
GHERARDO DI JACOPO STARNINA *see* STARNINA, Gherardo
GHIDONI, Matteo *see* PITOCCHI, Matteo de
GHIRLANDAIO, Michele di Ridolfo del *see* TOSINI, Michele
GINDERTAEL, Emile van *see* MILO, Jean
GONZALEZ DE LA SERNA, Ismael *see* SERNA, Ismael de la
GRAZIA, Leonardo *see* LEONARDO DA PISTOIA
GREVENBROECK, Charles Laurent *see* GREVENBROECK, Orazio
GRONINGEN, Jan Swart van *see* SWART VAN GRONINGEN, Jan
GROSS, Valentine *see* HUGO, Valentine
GUDIN, Herminie *see* GUDIN, Henriette
GUGGENHEIM, Willy *see* VARLIN
GUIARD, Adelaide Labille *see* LABILLE-GUIARD, Madame Adelaide
GUIDI, Giovanni (elder) *see* SCHEGGIA, Giovanni di Ser Giovanni
GUN, Karl Federovich *see* HUNS, Karlis Fridikh

H

HAARLEM, Cornelis Cornelisz van *see* CORNELISZ, Cornelis van Haarlem
HACHT/HAECHT, Tobias van *see* VERHAECHT, Tobias
HAHN, William *see* HAHN, Karl Wilhelm
HALFORD, Constance *see* REA, Constance
HANSEN, Adolf Heinrich Claus *see* HEINRICH-HANSEN, Adolf
HARTUNG, Julius *see* REICHERT, Carl
HASLEHURST, Ernest William *see* HAZELHUST, Ernest William
HAYNES-WILLIAMS, John *see* WILLIAMS, John Haynes
HEGG, Teresa Maria *see* LANDERSET, Theresa Maria de
HENRY, David Reid *see* REID-HENRY, David M
HIEPES, Tomas *see* YEPES, Tomas
HIRSCH-PAULI, Hanna *see* PAULI, Hanna
HOFFMANN, Kurt R *see* SONDERBORG, Kurt R H
HOHENBERG, Josef Wagner *see* WAGNER-HOHENBERG, Josef
HOLLYER, William Perring *see* HOLLYER, W P
HOOD, George Percy Jacomb *see* JACOMB-HOOD, George Percy
HOYNCK VAN PAPENDRECHT, Jan *see* PAPENDRECHT, Jan Hoynck van
HUGUE, Manuel Martinez *see* MANOLO
HUNTLY, Nancy *see* SHEPPARD, Nancy
HYATT, Anna Vaughn *see* HUNTINGTON, Anna Hyatt

I

IMOLA, Innocenzo *see* FRANCUCCI, Innocenzo
INNOCENTI, Battista degli *see* NALDINI, Giovan Battista
ISUPOV, Aleksei Vladimirovich *see* ISSUPOFF, Alessio
IVANOVITCH, Paul *see* JOANOVITCH, Paul

J

JACKSON, Harriett A E *see* BROWNING, Harriett A E
JACOPO di Rossello *see* FRANCHI, Rossello di Jacopo
JAMES, Willy *see* ROCHAT, Willy
JEANNERET, Charles Edouard *see* CORBUSIER, le
JEGOROV, Andrei A *see* YEGOROV, Andrei
JONES, Allan Gwynne *see* GWYNNE-JONES, Allan
JONES, Joseph John *see* JONES, Joe
JUANES, JUAN DE *see* MASIP, Vicente Juan

K

KABEL, Adrian van der *see* CABEL, Adrian van der
KAISERMANN, Francois *see* KEISERMANN, Franz
KALRAET, Abraham van *see* CALRAET, Abraham van
KAVANAUGH, Marion *see* WACHTEL, Marion K
KEILHAU, Bernhard *see* KEIL, Bernhard
KEMPF VON HARTENKAMPF, Gottlieb Theodor *see* HARTENKAMPF, Gottlieb Theodor Kempf von
KERCKHOVEN, Jacob van de *see* CASTELLO, Jacopo da
KEUNINCK, Kerstiaen de (elder) *see* KONINCK, Kerstiaen de (elder)
KEY SATO *see* SATO, Key
KIKOINE, Jacob *see* YANKEL, Jacques
KINNAIRD, Francis Joseph *see* KINNAIRD, Wiggs
KISELEV, Alexandre Alexandrovitch *see* KISSELEOV, Alexandre Alexandrovitch
KLEIN, Frits *see* KLEIN, Friedrich Franz
KLOCKER, David *see* EHRENSTRAHL, David Klocker von
KLOSSOWSKI, Balthasar *see* BALTHUS
KNIGHTON-HAMMOND, Arthur Henry *see* HAMMOND, Arthur Henry Knighton
KOEKKOEK, Hermanus (jnr) *see* COUVER, Jan van
KOLLER, Johann Rudolf *see* KOLLER, Rudolf
KOMAROMI-KATZ, Endre *see* KACZ, Endre Komaromi
KORFF, Alexander Hugo Bakker *see* BAKKER-KORFF, Alexander Hugo
KOUDRIACHOV, Ivan A *see* KUDRIASHEV, Ivan
KOUYOUMOJIAN, Elvire *see* JAN, Elvire
KOWALSKI-WIERUSZ, Alfred von *see* WIERUSZ-KOWALSKI, Alfred von
KRUSEMAN VAN ELTEN, Hendrik Dirk *see* ELTEN, Hendrik Dirk Kruseman van
KABEL, Adrian van der *see* CABEL, Adrian van der
KAISERMANN, Francois *see* KEISERMANN, Franz
KALRAET, Abraham van *see* CALRAET, Abraham van
KAVANAUGH, Marion *see* WACHTEL, Marion K
KEILHAU, Bernhard *see* KEIL, Bernhard
KEMPF VON HARTENKAMPF, Gottlieb Theodor *see* HARTENKAMPF, Gottlieb Theodor Kempf von
KERCKHOVEN, Jacob van de *see* CASTELLO, Jacopo da
KEUNINCK, Kerstiaen de (elder) *see* KONINCK, Kerstiaen de (elder)
KEY SATO *see* SATO, Key
KIKOINE, Jacob *see* YANKEL, Jacques
KINNAIRD, Francis Joseph *see* KINNAIRD, Wiggs
KISELEV, Alexandre Alexandrovitch *see* KISSELEOV, Alexandre Alexandrovitch
KLEIN, Frits *see* KLEIN, Friedrich Franz
KLOCKER, David *see* EHRENSTRAHL, David Klocker von
KLOSSOWSKI, Balthasar *see* BALTHUS
KNIGHTON-HAMMOND, Arthur Henry *see* HAMMOND, Arthur Henry Knighton
KOEKKOEK, Hermanus (jnr) *see* COUVER, Jan van
KOLLER, Johann Rudolf *see* KOLLER, Rudolf
KOMAROMI-KATZ, Endre *see* KACZ, Endre Komaromi
KORFF, Alexander Hugo Bakker *see* BAKKER-KORFF, Alexander Hugo
KOUDRIACHOV, Ivan A *see* KUDRIASHEV, Ivan
KOUYOUMOJIAN, Elvire *see* JAN, Elvire
KOWALSKI-WIERUSZ, Alfred von *see* WIERUSZ-KOWALSKI, Alfred von
KRUSEMAN VAN ELTEN, Hendrik Dirk *see* ELTEN, Hendrik Dirk Kruseman van

L

LAMBERT, Louis Eugene *see* LAMBERT, Eugene
LAMEN, Jasper van der *see* LAANEN, Jasper van der
LAPIRA *see* PIRA, la
LARSEN, Carl Frederick Emanuel *see* LARSEN, Emanuel
LASSALLE, Louis Simon *see* CABAILLOT, Louis Simon
LAVREINCE, Nicolas (younger) *see* LAFRENSEN, Nicolas (younger)
LEAL, Juan de Valdes *see* VALDES LEAL, Juan de
LECLERC, Sebastien Jacques *see* LECLERC DES GOBELINS, Sebastian
LEDUC, Victor Viollet *see* VIOLLET LE DUC, Victor
LEHMANN, Karl Ernest Rodolphe Heinrich Salem *see* LEHMANN, Henri
LEONE, Andrea di *see* LIONE, Andrea di

LESSER-URY *see* URY, Lesser
LEVIA, Alexis *see* KCHO
LEWIS, George Lennard *see* LEWIS, Lennard
LEYTENS, Gysbrecht *see* LYTENS, Gysbrecht
LHUILLIER, Suzanne *see* PERREGAUX, Suzanne
LICHTENFELS, Eduard Peithner Ritter von *see* PEITHNER VON LICHTENFELS, Eduard
LICK, Armand van der *see* VANDERLICK, Armand
LINDEGGER, Albert *see* LINDI
LINSLEY, Walter *see* MEEGAN, Walter
LISSANDRINO, Alessandro *see* MAGNASCO, Alessandro
LLORENS, Jose Navarro *see* NAVARRO LLORENS, Jose
LLOYD, Frederick John *see* STREVENS, John
LLOYD, Tom *see* LLOYD, Thomas James
LODER, Edwin *see* LODER OF BATH, Edwin
LODER, James *see* LODER OF BATH, James
LOUIS, Seraphine *see* SERAPHINE DE SENLIS
LOUTHERBOURG, Philip James de *see* LOUTHERBOURG, Jacques Philippe de II
LOW, Mary Fairchild *see* MACMONNIES, Mary Fairchild
LUCIANI, Sebastiano *see* PIOMBO, Sebastiano del
LUCIENTES, Francisco Jose de *see* GOYA Y LUCIENTES, Francisco Jose de
LUTERO, Giovanni *see* DOSSI, Dosso
LUYCKX VON LEUXENSTEM, Franz *see* LEUX, Franz
LYON, Corneille de *see* CORNEILLE DE LYON

M

MAES, Dirk *see* MAAS, Dirck
MAHOKIAN, Wartan *see* MAKOKIAN, Vartan
MANSION, Andre Leon Larue *see* LARUE, Andre Leon
MARCHAND, Charles *see* KAUFMANN, Karl
MARELLUS, Jacob *see* MARREL, Jacob
MARKEY *see* ROBINSON, Markey
MARKO C *see* CELEBONOVIC, Marko
MARSELIER, Louis *see* MASRELIEZ, Louis
MARSEUS VAN SCHRIECK, Otto *see* SCHRIECK, Otto Marseus van
MARTIN, Benito Quinquela *see* QUINQUELA MARTIN, Benito
MARTIN, Etienne *see* ETIENNE-MARTIN
MARTINELLI, Niccolo *see* TROMETTA, Nicolo
MARTINIERE, Marie-Francoise-Constance la *see* MAYER, Constance
MARTINO DI BATTISTA *see* SAN DANIELE, Pellegrino da
MASTELLETTA *see* DONDUCCI, Giovanni Andrea
MASTER OF HOVINGHAM *see* POUSSIN, Nicolas
MASTER OF THE GRIGGS CRUCIFIXION *see* TOSCANI, Giovanni di Francesco
MATHIEU, Anna Rosina *see* LISIEWSKA, Anna Rosina
MATOS, John *see* CRASH
MAURICE-MARTIN *see* MARTIN, Maurice
MEER, Jan van der (elder) *see* VERMEER OF HAARLEM, Jan (elder)
MEER, Jan van der (younger) *see* VERMEER OF HAARLEM, Jan (younger)
MELDOLLA, Andrea *see* SCHIAVONE, Andrea
MENARD, Rene *see* MENARD, Emile Rene
MERCIE, Antonin *see* MERCIE, Marius Jean Antonin
MET DE BLES, Herri *see* BLES, Herri met de
MEYER, Louis *see* MEYER, Johan Hendrik Louis
MICHEL, Claude *see* CLODION
MILTON, Victor Marais *see* MARAIS-MILTON, Victor
MOMPO, Manuel Hernandez *see* HERNANDEZ MOMPO, Manuel
MORAZZONE, Pier Francesco *see* MAZZUCHELLI, Pietro Francesco
MOREAU, Paul Charles Chocarne *see* CHOCARNE-MOREAU, Paul Charles
MORENO Y CARBONERO, Jose *see* CARBONERO, Jose Moreno
MOSER, Alexander Padina *see* PADINA-MOSER, Alex
MULIER, Eldina Aldegonda Rinsina *see* LIMBURG STIRUM, Eldina Aldegonda Rinsina van
MUNTZ, Laura Adeline *see* LYALL, Laura Adeline
MURILLO, Gerardo *see* ATL, Dr
MURILLO, Gerardo (attrib) *see* ATL, Dr (attrib)
MURRAY-COOKESLEY, Margaret *see* COOKESLEY, Margaret Murray
MUTTONI, Pietro de/PIETRO DELLA VECCHIA *see* VECCHIA, Pietro della

N

NEGRETTI, Jacopo (elder) *see* PALMA, Jacopo (il Vecchio)
NIEDERHAUSERN, Auguste de *see* NIEDERHAUSERN-RODO
NORMAND, Henrietta *see* RAE, Henrietta
NUYSSEN, Abraham Janssens van *see* JANSSENS, Abraham

O

ON KAWARA *see* KAWARA, On
ONFRAY DE BREVILLE, Jacques *see* JOB, Jacques-Marie-Gaston
ORIZONTE *see* BLOEMEN, Jan Frans van

P

PADILLA, Eugenio Lucas *see* LUCAS Y PADILLA, Eugenio
PAOLO *see* MULLER, Paul Jakob
PARMIGIANINO, Michele *see* ROCCA, Michele
PARMIGIANO, il *see* MAZZOLA, Francesco
PASSIGNANO, Domenico *see* CRESTI, Domenico
PATON, Donald A *see* THOMPSON, Edward H
PAUL, Louis Auguste Albert *see* LOUIS-PAUL, Auguste-Albert
PEDRINI, Giovanni/RICCI, Gian Pietro *see* GIANPIETRINO
PEPPER, Kathleen Daly *see* DALY, Kathleen
PEREZ-VILLAGROSA, Mariano Alonso *see* ALONSO-PEREZ, Mariano
PERRIER, Emilio Sanchez *see* SANCHEZ-PERRIER, Emilio
PICCIO, Giovanni *see* CARNOVALI, Giovanni
PIERINO DEL VAGA/VAGA, Pierino del *see* BUONACCORSI, Pietro
PINCAS, Julius *see* PASCIN, Jules
PIPPI, Giulio *see* ROMANO, Giulio
POLIDORO DI LANZANO *see* LANZANI, Polidoro
POLSON, Evelyn *see* PAGE, Evelyn
POPOVITCH, Ljuba *see* LJUBA
PORTA, Alberto *see* ZUSH
PORTE, Roland de la *see* ROLAND DE LA PORTE, Henri Horace
POSSOM, Clifford *see* TJAPALTJARI, Clifford Possum
POUSSIN, Gaspard *see* DUGHET, Gaspard
POZZOSERRATO *see* TOEPUT, Lodewyk
PRASCH, Wenzel Ignaz *see* BRASCH, Wenzel Ignaz
PREISS, Fritz *see* PREISS, Ferdinand
PRIVAT-LIVEMONT *see* LIVEMONT, Privat
PUNI, Ivan *see* POUGNY, Jean

R

RAIBOLINI, Francesco di Marco *see* FRANCIA, Francesco di Marco
REGGIO, Raffaellino da *see* MOTTA, Raffaellino
REINHOUD *see* D'HAESE, Reinhoud
REISTRUP, K Hansen *see* HANSEN-REISTRUP, K
RENE-HIS *see* HIS, Rene Charles Edmond
RENIERI, Niccolo *see* REGNIER, Nicolas
RENWICK, Lionel Hamilton *see* HAMILTON-RENWICK, Lionel
REUTER, Christian *see* REDER, Christian
RIBERA, Pedro *see* RIBERA, Pierre
RICCIARELLI, Daniele *see* VOLTERRA, Daniele da
RIJN, Harmensz van *see* REMBRANDT
ROBINSON, Annie Louisa *see* SWYNNERTON, Annie
RODE, Edmund A *see* ADLER, Edmund
RODRIGUEZ BAEZ, Juan Guillermo *see* GUILLERMO, Juan
ROE, Colin Graeme *see* GRAEME, Colin
ROESLER, Ettore Franz *see* FRANZ, Ettore Roesler
ROHDE, Lennart *see* RODHE, Lennart
RONNER-KNIP, Henriette *see* RONNER, Henriette
ROSA DA TIVOLI *see* ROOS, Philipp Peter
ROSA, Francesco de *see* ROSA, Pacecco di
ROSE, Antonio *see* ROSE, Julius
ROSENBERG, Mary Ann *see* DUFFIELD, Mary Elizabeth
ROSSI, Francesco del *see* SALVIATI, Francesco
ROTHENSTEIN, Albert *see* RUTHERSTON, Albert
ROUX, Antoine (elder) *see* ROUX, Joseph Ange Antoine
ROUX, Mathieu Antoine *see* ROUX, Antoine (younger)

S

SAINT-CYR-GIRIER, Jean Aime *see* GIRIER, Jean-Aime
SALADO, Juan Bayon *see* BAY SALA
SALVI, Giovanni Battista *see* SASSOFERRATO
SANCHEZ BARBUDO, Salvador *see* BARBUDO, Salvador Sanchez
SANSONI, Guglielmo *see* TATO
SANZIO, Raffaello *see* RAPHAEL
SAUVAGE, Charles Gabriel *see* LEMIRE, Charles Gabriel
SCARPETTA, Antonio *see* MARA, Antonio
SCEVOLA, Lucien Guirand de *see* GUIRAND DE SCEVOLA, Lucien

SCHULTZE-BLUHM, Ursula *see* URSULA
SCHULZE, Alfred Otto Wolfgang *see* WOLS, Wolfgang
SCHYNDEL, Bernardus van *see* SCHENDEL, Bernardus van
SEAILLES, Octavie *see* SEAILLES, Charles Paul
SEATON, John Thomas *see* SETON, John Thomas
SECCOMBE, Beatrice Mary *see* LEECH, Beatrice
SEGONZAC, Andre Dunoyer de *see* DUNOYER DE SEGONZAC, Andre
SHEERBOOM, Andreas *see* SCHEERBOOM, Andries
SHILLING, Alexander *see* SCHILLING, Alexander
SIJS, Maurice *see* SYS, Maurice
SIMONS, Pinckney Marcius *see* MARCIUS-SIMONS, Pinky
SMITH, Thomas Noel *see* NOELSMITH, Thomas
SMITH, Victor *see* SPARRE, Victor
SNAFFLES *see* PAYNE, Charles Johnson
SORELLA, Theresa *see* ANSINGH, Theresa
SOSNOWSKY, Alexandre *see* SOSNO, Sacha
SPADARO, Micco *see* GARGIULIO, Domenico
SPAGNOLETTO, lo *see* RIBERA, Jusepe de
SPAGNUOLO, Giuseppe *see* CRESPI, Giuseppe Maria
SPENCE, Benjamin Edward *see* SPENCE, Benjamin Evans
STANFIELD, William Clarkson *see* STANFIELD, Clarkson
STARN, Doug and Mike *see* STARN TWINS
STOLTENBERG-LERCHE, Vincent *see* LERCHE, Vincent Stoltenberg
STRADANUS *see* STRAET, Jan van der
STRAWALDE *see* BOTTCHER, Jurgen
SWAANSWIJK, Lubertus Jacobus *see* LUCEBERT
SWAINE, Monamy *see* SWAINE, Francis

T

TAIT, Bess Norris *see* NORRIS, Bessie
THEOTOKOPOULOS, Domenikos *see* GRECO, El
THERBUSCH, Anna Dorothea *see* LISIEWSKA, Anna Dorothea
THOMPSON, Wordsworth *see* THOMPSON, Alfred Wordsworth
THORNBERY, William A *see* THORNLEY, William
THORNE-WAITE, Robert *see* WAITE, Robert Thorne
THORNEYCROFT, Sir William Hamo *see* THORNYCROFT, Hamo
TJAPALTJARRI, Billy Stockman *see* STOCKMAN, Billy
TOUR-DONAS, Marthe *see* DONAS, Marthe
TRUCHET, Abel *see* ABEL-TRUCHET

U

UTRILLO, Lucie Valore *see* VALORE, Lucie

V

VALENTIN, Jean de *see* BOULOGNE, Valentin de
VALETTE-FALGORES, Jean *see* PENOT, Jean Vallette
VANDAMME, Suzanne *see* DAMME, Suzanne van
VANLOO, Carle *see* LOO, Carle van
VANVITELLI, Gaspare *see* WITTEL, Gaspar van
VASARELY, Jean Pierre *see* YVARAL
VAUTIER, Ben *see* BEN
VEERENDAEL, Nicolaes van *see* VERENDAEL, Nicolas van
VERHAGEN, Jacobus *see* HAGEN, Jakobus van der
VERMEER, Barent *see* MEER, Barend van der
VERNET, Claude Joseph *see* VERNET, Joseph
VERONESE, Bonifazio/PITATI, Bonfazio *see* BONIFAZIO DI PITATI
VILLAAMIL, Jenaro Perez *see* PEREZ DE VILLAAMIL, Genaro
VILLIERS-HUET, Jean Francois Marie *see* HUET, Francois
VIVANT-DENON, Baron Dominique *see* DENON, Vivant Dominique
VOLKERTS, Poppe *see* FOLKERTS, Poppe
VOLL, Frederick Usher de *see* DEVOLL, Frederick Usher
VOROBIEFF, Maria *see* MAREVNA, Marie
VOS, Leon de *see* DEVOS, Leon

W

WAGEMAKER, Adriaan Barend *see* WAGEMAKER, Jaap
WARBURG, Sophie Elisabeth *see* WARB, Nicolaas
WATERFORD, Marchioness of *see* LOUISA, Marchioness of Waterford
WATSON, Dawson *see* DAWSON-WATSON, Dawson
WEBER, Gottlieb Daniel Paul *see* WEBER, Paul
WEEKES, Herbert William *see* WEEKES, William
WEISSENBRUCH, Hendrik Johannes *see* WEISSENBRUCH, Jan Hendrik
WELHAVEN, Astri *see* HEIBERG, Astri Welhaven
WELLS, John Sanderson *see* SANDERSON-WELLS, John
WILL, Frank *see* FRANK WILL
WINKLER, Ralf *see* PENCK, A R
WITJENS, Adrianus Hendrikus *see* WITJENS, Jacques Stephen
WITTE, Peter de *see* CANDID, Peter
WOLSTENHOLME, Charles Dean *see* WOLSTENHOLME, Dean (jnr)

X

XIAO RUSONG *see* HSIAO JU-SUNG
XIONGQUAN, Ding *see* TING, Walasse

Y

YAKOVLEV, Alexander Evgenievich *see* IACOVLEFF, Alexandre
YEFIMENKO, Viktor *see* IEFIMENKO, Viktor

Z

ZAMPIERI, Domenico *see* DOMENICHINO
ZANETTI, Giuseppe Miti *see* MITI-ZANETTI, Giuseppe
ZEIZIG, Johann Eliazar *see* SCHENAU, Johann Eleazar
ZELOTTI, Giovan Battista *see* FARINATI, Giambattista Zelotti
ZENG JINGWEN *see* KINGMAN, Dong
ZHU DA *see* BADA SHANREN
ZHU MING *see* JU MING
ZUKOWSKI, Stanislaw *see* JOUKOVSKI, Stanislav

Index
to
International Auction Sales for the 2002/2003 Season

STARTING PRICES

Oil Paintings & Works on Paper

£250 - $400 - 400 Euro

Miniatures & Sculpture

£1,000 - $1,500 - 1,500 Euro

Prints & Photographs

£2,000 - $3,000 - 3,000 Euro

Regional "schools"

£5,000 - $7,000 - 7,000 Euro

AABYE, Jorgen (1868-1959) Danish
£681 $1076 €1022 Portrait of a girl and her younger brother (97x83cm-38x33in) 2-Dec-2 Rasmussen, Copenhagen #1798/R (D.KR 8000)
£861 $1309 €1292 Interior from my studio (83x61cm-33x24in) mono.d.1912 exhib. 27-Aug-2 Rasmussen, Copenhagen #1907/R (D.KR 10000)

AACHEN, Hans von (circle) (1552-1616) German
£7800 $12246 €11700 Homage to Ceres (127x99cm-50x39in) prov. 10-Dec-2 Sotheby's, Olympia #327/R est:5000-7000

AACHEN, Hans von (style) (1552-1616) German
£6500 $10855 €9425 Madness of Hercules (60x41cm-24x16in) panel arched top. 11-Jul-3 Christie's, Kensington #27/R est:2000-3000

AADNES, Peder Pedersen (1739-1792) Norwegian
£2176 $3481 €3264 Rector Povl Christopher Holbye (72x60cm-28x24in) s.i.verso. 17-Mar-3 Blomqvist, Oslo #316/R est:40000-60000 (N.KR 25000)

AAE, Arvid (1877-1913) Swedish
£790 $1248 €1185 Three women seated on terrace, sunshine (63x78cm-25x31in) s.d.1908. 5-Apr-3 Rasmussen, Havnen #2005/R (D.KR 8500)

AAGAARD, C F (1833-1895) Danish
£276 $419 €414 Hilly landscape with large farm, girl and cattle (28x42cm-11x17in) with sig.verso. 28-Aug-2 Museumsbygningen, Copenhagen #87 (D.KR 3200)
£296 $461 €444 Woodland with house in background (43x62cm-17x24in) i.verso. 23-Sep-2 Rasmussen, Vejle #71/R (D.KR 3500)
£510 $795 €765 Moonlit coastal cliffs (20x21cm-8x8in) s. cardboard. 5-Aug-2 Rasmussen, Vejle #276/R (D.KR 6000)
£525 $841 €788 Winter at Rosenborg Palace (29x22cm-11x9in) s.d.1853. 13-Jan-3 Rasmussen, Vejle #225/R (D.KR 6000)
£559 $888 €839 Woodland with river (34x46cm-13x18in) s. 5-Mar-3 Rasmussen, Copenhagen #1909/R (D.KR 6000)
£603 $977 €874 Wooded landscape (42x61cm-17x24in) s.d.1872. 24-May-3 Rasmussen, Havnen #2225/R (D.KR 6300)
£652 $1036 €978 Angel holding sheaf of corn and flowers (37x26cm-15x10in) s.d.87. 5-Mar-3 Rasmussen, Copenhagen #1849/R (D.KR 7000)
£690 $1055 €1035 Country road with figures outside a house (44x63cm-17x25in) s. 24-Aug-2 Rasmussen, Havnen #2031/R (D.KR 8000)
£931 $1480 €1397 River through wood (44x62cm-17x24in) s.d.1879. 5-Mar-3 Rasmussen, Copenhagen #1904/R (D.KR 10000)

Works on paper
£426 $672 €639 Stags in Dyrehaven (24x32cm-9x13in) s. pen W/C. 2-Dec-2 Rasmussen, Copenhagen #1826/R (D.KR 5000)

AAGAARD, Carl Frederic (1833-1895) Danish
£320 $506 €480 Picnic (54x80cm-21x31in) s.d.1895. 14-Nov-2 Christie's, Kensington #90
£780 $1232 €1170 Landscape with flowering elder (52x77cm-20x30in) s.d.1895. 7-Apr-3 Bonhams, Bath #120/R
£1378 $2095 €2067 Sunshine in the forest (42x59cm-17x23in) 27-Aug-2 Rasmussen, Copenhagen #1854/R est:8000-10000 (D.KR 16000)
£2871 $4651 €4163 View of Venice towards Santa Maria della Salute (42x60cm-17x24in) s. 26-May-3 Rasmussen, Copenhagen #1114/R est:30000-50000 (D.KR 30000)
£9475 $14401 €14213 Landscape from Jaegersborg Dyrehave (110x162cm-43x64in) s.d.1857 exhib. 27-Aug-2 Rasmussen, Copenhagen #1492/R est:50000-75000 (D.KR 110000)

AAGAARD, Martin (1863-1913) Norwegian
£519 $795 €779 Fjord landscape (50x86cm-20x34in) s. 26-Aug-2 Blomqvist, Lysaker #1004/R (N.KR 6000)
£524 $822 €786 Sailing at night (50x71cm-20x28in) s. 25-Nov-2 Blomqvist, Lysaker #1312 (N.KR 6000)
£606 $927 €909 Seascape (50x75cm-20x30in) s. 26-Aug-2 Blomqvist, Lysaker #1005/R (N.KR 7000)
£1102 $1807 €1598 Seascape with vessels (60x80cm-24x31in) s. 2-Jun-3 Blomqvist, Oslo #3/R (N.KR 12000)

AALTO, Ilmari (1891-1934) Finnish
£478 $736 €760 View of Hogland (45x55cm-18x22in) s. 24-Oct-2 Hagelstam, Helsinki #935/R
£575 $943 €880 Still life (55x46cm-22x18in) s.d.30. 9-Feb-3 Bukowskis, Helsinki #190/R
£2025 $3200 €3200 Still life of jug, bowl and fruit (51x41cm-20x16in) s.d.20. 1-Dec-2 Bukowskis, Helsinki #13/R est:2500-2800
£2183 $3515 €3100 Still life of bottle (47x48cm-19x19in) s.d.17 board. 10-May-3 Bukowskis, Helsinki #31/R est:1500-2000

AALTONA, Veikko (1910-1990) Finnish
£264 $407 €420 Flowers (100x65cm-39x26in) s.d.61. 27-Oct-2 Bukowskis, Helsinki #133/R

AALTONEN, Waino (1894-1966) Finnish
£1293 $2055 €1900 Sketch for The Emblem to Olympic Games 1940 (60x70cm-24x28in) s. 24-Mar-3 Bukowskis, Helsinki #16/R est:1200
£1479 $2381 €2100 Landscape from Vatikuru (30x24cm-12x9in) s.i.d.22/IV 1942. 10-May-3 Bukowskis, Helsinki #54/R est:2000-2300
£1761 $2835 €2500 Girl playing the mandolin (56x46cm-22x18in) s.d.1932. 10-May-3 Bukowskis, Helsinki #83/R est:2500-2800
£2113 $3401 €3000 Boathouse in Syvalahti (44x54cm-17x21in) s.d.12 exhib. 10-May-3 Bukowskis, Helsinki #113/R est:3000-3300
£2468 $3900 €3900 Aabo Harbour seen from the home farmyard (32x45cm-13x18in) s. canvas on board exhib. 1-Dec-2 Bukowskis, Helsinki #15/R est:4000-5000

Sculpture
£1338 $2154 €1900 Boy with hawk (32cm-13in) s.d.1941 bronze. 10-May-3 Bukowskis, Helsinki #4/R est:1500-1800
£4577 $7370 €6500 The pale young maiden (61cm-24in) s. bronze. 10-May-3 Bukowskis, Helsinki #9/R est:8000-10000

AALUND, Martin (1967-) Swedish
£561 $875 €842 Stockholm (73x53cm-29x21in) s.d.94 verso oil acrylic latex vinyl panel. 6-Nov-2 AB Stockholms Auktionsverk #852/R (S.KR 8000)

AARON, Joseph (1959-) American
£484 $750 €726 Overlooking main beach (30x41cm-12x16in) s. i.verso board. 29-Oct-2 John Moran, Pasadena #723

AARONS, George (1896-1980) American

Sculpture
£1623 $2500 €2435 Nude (20cm-8in) s.d.1929 brown pat. bronze prov. 24-Oct-2 Shannon's, Milford #34/R est:1500-2500
£1623 $2500 €2435 Cubist figure (33cm-13in) s.d.1960 brown pat. bronze prov. 24-Oct-2 Shannon's, Milford #119/R est:1500-2500
£5380 $8500 €8070 Thomas Jefferson (61cm-24in) s.d.1937 brown pat. bronze prov. 24-Apr-3 Shannon's, Milford #174/R est:3000-5000

AARTMANN, Nicolaas (1713-1793) Dutch

Works on paper
£446 $696 €700 Village scene, November (12x15cm-5x6in) s.d.1756 bears i.mount pen grey ink grey wash black chk prov. 5-Nov-2 Sotheby's, Amsterdam #128/R

AAS, Alf Jorgen (1915-1981) Norwegian
£357 $549 €536 Man seated (46x38cm-18x15in) s. panel painted 1945 exhib. 28-Oct-2 Blomqvist, Lysaker #1360 (N.KR 4200)

AAS, Nils (1933-) Norwegian

Sculpture
£2462 $3791 €3693 Spire (83x56cm-33x22in) bronze. 28-Oct-2 Blomqvist, Lysaker #1361/R est:15000-20000 (N.KR 29000)

ABA-NOVAK, Vilmos (1894-1941) Hungarian
£1258 $1937 €2000 Road workers (48x68cm-19x27in) s. 28-Oct-2 Il Ponte, Milan #196/R
£6436 $10298 €9654 Circus (25x17cm-10x7in) s.d.31 tempera panel. 16-May-3 Kieselbach, Budapest #19/R (H.F 2200000)
£8606 $13339 €12479 Italian village (50x60cm-20x24in) s. tempera panel. 9-Dec-2 Mu Terem Galeria, Budapest #80/R est:2000000 (H.F 3200000)
£8942 $13950 €13413 St Stephan offering saint crown to Holy Virgin (127x72cm-50x28in) tempera board. 11-Apr-3 Kieselbach, Budapest #205/R est:3000000-3200000 (H.F 3200000)
£10063 $15497 €16000 Exhibition (80x100cm-31x39in) s. i.verso mixed media board. 28-Oct-2 Il Ponte, Milan #171/R est:4000
£13446 $20842 €20169 Dawn of woodsmen (54x77cm-21x30in) s. 6-Dec-2 Kieselbach, Budapest #54/R (H.F 5000000)
£16136 $25010 €24204 Landscape in Felsobanya (56x69cm-22x27in) s. 6-Dec-2 Kieselbach, Budapest #146/R (H.F 6000000)
£16767 $26156 €24312 Market (50x60cm-20x24in) s.d.1938 tempera panel. 12-Apr-3 Mu Terem Galeria, Budapest #206/R est:3000000 (H.F 6000000)
£22356 $34875 €33534 Bathers (90x114cm-35x45in) 11-Apr-3 Kieselbach, Budapest #209/R est:8000000 (H.F 8000000)
£25548 $39599 €38322 Italian landscape (56x70cm-22x28in) s. tempera on board. 6-Dec-2 Kieselbach, Budapest #35/R (H.F 9500000)
£25798 $40245 €37407 Artists' group in Igal (86x60cm-34x24in) s. prov. 13-Sep-2 Mu Terem Galeria, Budapest #92/R est:7500000 (H.F 10000000)
£26893 $41683 €40340 By the Sweep (62x99cm-24x39in) s. tempera on board. 6-Dec-2 Kieselbach, Budapest #187/R (H.F 10000000)
£34102 $52858 €51153 Family (111x93cm-44x37in) painted c.1925. 3-Dec-2 SOGA, Bratislava #119/R est:2700000 (SL.K 2160000)

£40339 $62525 €58492 Town in Umbria (55x70cm-22x28in) s. tempera panel exhib.lit. 9-Dec-2 Mu Terem Galeria, Budapest #132/R est:7500000 (H.F 15000000)
£43856 $68416 €65784 Szekeley Village - Zsogod, 1935 (80x100cm-31x39in) s.d.35 tempera. 11-Sep-2 Kieselbach, Budapest #82/R (H.F 17000000)
£48407 $75030 €72611 Ferry crossing over the river Tisza (89x109cm-35x43in) s. tempera on board. 6-Dec-2 Kieselbach, Budapest #157/R (H.F 18000000)
£61478 $95906 €89143 Lady in red hat (93x78cm-37x31in) tempera prov.exhib. 12-Apr-3 Mu Terem Galeria, Budapest #183/R est:7500000 (H.F 22000000)

Works on paper
£447 $697 €671 Felsobanya (12x22cm-5x9in) s. Indian ink. 11-Apr-3 Kieselbach, Budapest #35/R est:65000-160000 (H.F 160000)
£503 $785 €755 Houses in Nagybanya (17x24cm-7x9in) s. Indian ink. 11-Apr-3 Kieselbach, Budapest #50/R est:65000-180000 (H.F 180000)
£503 $785 €755 Figures (22x20cm-9x8in) Indian ink. 11-Apr-3 Kieselbach, Budapest #199/R est:180000 (H.F 180000)
£1006 $1569 €1509 Nude (57x46cm-22x18in) s. mixed media paper. 11-Apr-3 Kieselbach, Budapest #206/R est:180000-360000 (H.F 360000)
£6436 $10298 €9654 Boats (45x58cm-18x23in) s.d.929 mixed media cardboard. 16-May-3 Kieselbach, Budapest #6/R (H.F 2200000)

ABADES, Juan Martinez (1862-1920) Spanish
£3041 $4743 €4500 Coastal view with boats (18x31cm-7x12in) s. board. 25-Mar-3 Durán, Madrid #100/R
£5000 $7850 €7500 Rocky cove (31x52cm-12x20in) s.d.1900. 21-Nov-2 Christie's, Kensington #179/R est:2500-3500
£6079 $9910 €9180 Sailing ships (33x41cm-13x16in) s. board prov.lit. 11-Feb-3 Segre, Madrid #132/R
£6079 $9910 €9180 Fishing boats (33x41cm-13x16in) s. board prov.lit. 11-Feb-3 Segre, Madrid #131/R
£10452 $16514 €16200 View of harbour (30x60cm-12x24in) s. 18-Dec-2 Ansorena, Madrid #170/R est:13200

Works on paper
£448 $708 €650 Boat on the coast (14x19cm-6x7in) s. pencil dr. 1-Apr-3 Segre, Madrid #159/R
£448 $708 €650 Portrait of the artist's mother (19x17cm-7x7in) s.i. pencil dr. 1-Apr-3 Segre, Madrid #154/R
£449 $709 €700 Seascape (28x19cm-11x7in) s.d.1890 r. 19-Nov-2 Durán, Madrid #695/R
£481 $760 €750 Seascape (28x19cm-11x7in) s.d.1890 dr. 19-Nov-2 Durán, Madrid #694/R
£1452 $2294 €2250 Boats (27x43cm-11x17in) s. pastel. 17-Dec-2 Durán, Madrid #147/R

ABAKANOWICZ, Magdalena (1930-) Polish
Sculpture
£2532 $4000 €3798 Anonymous portrait no.45 (66x26x19cm-26x10x7in) mono.d.1990 sand resin cotton mould on wood base prov. 12-Nov-2 Phillips, New York #250/R est:5000-7000
£32812 $52500 €49218 Small figure with polygon (202x96x22cm-80x38x9in) mono.d.1992 resin on burlap steel construction prov. 14-May-3 Sotheby's, New York #347/R est:40000-60000

ABATE, Teonesto de (1898-1981) Italian
£321 $503 €500 Still life of flowers. s.d.960. 10-Dec-2 Della Rocca, Turin #346/R
£353 $554 €550 River landscape (49x69cm-19x27in) s.d.960. 10-Dec-2 Della Rocca, Turin #347/R

ABATTUCI, Pierre (1871-1942) Belgian
£275 $442 €420 Paysage vallonne avant l'orage (65x90cm-26x35in) s. 20-Jan-3 Horta, Bruxelles #329
£490 $789 €750 Fenaison dans un paysage ensoleille (55x70cm-22x28in) s. 20-Jan-3 Horta, Bruxelles #328
£493 $794 €700 Two dogs with red bows (21x26cm-8x10in) s.i. board. 7-May-3 Vendue Huis, Gravenhage #554/R
£552 $872 €800 Apres-midi a l'etang (70x90cm-28x35in) s. 1-Apr-3 Palais de Beaux Arts, Brussels #494
£605 $944 €950 Vue de Lisseweghe (32x41cm-13x16in) s. panel. 11-Nov-2 Horta, Bruxelles #4
£654 $1052 €1000 Matin a l'etang (50x70cm-20x28in) s. 20-Jan-3 Horta, Bruxelles #330
£886 $1382 €1400 Paysage a l'etang (55x70cm-22x28in) s. 15-Oct-2 Vanderkindere, Brussels #91

ABBATI, Giuseppe (attrib) (1836-1868) Italian
£1069 $1647 €1700 The Arno at Casaccia (11x22cm-4x9in) init. board. 28-Oct-2 Il Ponte, Milan #254

ABBATI, Vincenzo (1812-1868) Italian
£2041 $3245 €3000 Peasants with cattle in grotto by monastery entrance (47x35cm-19x14in) s.d.1830. 19-Mar-3 Neumeister, Munich #494/R est:2000

ABBEELE, van den (?) Belgian
£658 $1066 €1000 Grondegem (60x50cm-24x20in) s. 21-Jan-3 Galerie Moderne, Brussels #261

ABBEMA, Louise (1858-1927) French
£1923 $3019 €3000 Autoportrait (41x37cm-16x15in) s. 16-Dec-2 Millon & Associes, Paris #92/R est:2500-2800
£2692 $4227 €4200 Portrait de Mademoiselle Baretta (72x53cm-28x21in) s.i.d.1880 panel exhib. 16-Dec-2 Millon & Associes, Paris #93/R est:2200-2500
£5000 $7850 €7800 Soiree chez Sarah Bernhardt (35x43cm-14x17in) init. panel. 13-Dec-2 Piasa, Paris #1/R
£16774 $26000 €25161 Flora (156x167cm-61x66in) s.d.1913. 30-Oct-2 Christie's, Rockefeller NY #75/R est:30000-40000

Works on paper
£362 $586 €550 Fleurs et marines, projet d'evantail (65x34cm-26x13in) s. gouache W/C. 22-Jan-3 Tajan, Paris #2
£481 $755 €750 Les japonaises, feuille d'eventail (68x20cm-27x8in) s. W/C. 16-Dec-2 Millon & Associes, Paris #94/R

ABBETT, Robert Kennedy (1926-) American
£9494 $15000 €13766 Late autumn bobwhites (51x76cm-20x30in) s. board. 26-Jul-3 Coeur d'Alene, Hayden #89/R est:10000-15000

ABBEY, Alfred (19th C) British
£764 $1200 €1146 Evening after rain Derwent water (51x76cm-20x30in) s.i.verso. 14-Dec-2 Weschler, Washington #595/R est:800-1200

ABBIATI, Julius (19th C) Austrian?
£350 $567 €525 Figures in an Alpine landscape (74x102cm-29x40in) s. 23-Jan-3 Christie's, Kensington #167

ABBOT, Agnes Anne (1897-1992) American
£1125 $1800 €1688 Winter landscape (20x25cm-8x10in) s. board. 11-Jan-3 James Julia, Fairfield #607 est:800-1200

ABBOTT, Berenice (1898-1991) American
Photographs
£1875 $3000 €2813 Penn Station (27x36cm-11x14in) s.num.9/100 silver print executed c.1982. 15-May-3 Swann Galleries, New York #267/R est:2500-3500
£1875 $3000 €2813 James Joyce (36x28cm-14x11in) s.num.67/100 silver print executed c.1982. 15-May-3 Swann Galleries, New York #268/R est:2000-3000
£1899 $3000 €2849 Cedar Street from William Street, Manhattan (24x19cm-9x7in) i.d.1936 verso gelatin silver print lit. 22-Apr-3 Christie's, Rockefeller NY #29/R est:7000-9000
£1899 $3000 €2849 Ferry, West Street, foot of Liberty Street (20x25cm-8x10in) st.verso photograph. 23-Apr-3 Sotheby's, New York #68/R est:3000-5000
£2025 $3200 €3038 Lumberjack, California (45x39cm-18x15in) s.verso gelatin silver print on masonite prov. 24-Apr-3 Phillips, New York #127/R est:3000-5000
£2051 $3200 €3077 Fifth Avenue theatre interior, entrance from 1885 Broadway, Manhattan (24x18cm-9x7in) s. verso silver print. 21-Oct-2 Swann Galleries, New York #60/R est:2000-3000
£2125 $3400 €3081 Canyon, Broadway and Exchange Place (33x10cm-13x4in) s. gelatin silver print exec.c.1960. 17-May-3 Selkirks, St. Louis #460/R est:1000-1500
£2152 $3400 €3228 Warehouse, water and dock streets, Brooklyn (39x49cm-15x19in) s. gelatin silver print prov.lit. 25-Apr-3 Phillips, New York #219/R est:2500-3500
£2273 $3500 €3410 Houses, Fifth Avenue no 4, 6, 8 (51x41cm-20x16in) s. i.verso gelatin silver print board exec.c.1950 prov.lit. 25-Oct-2 Phillips, New York #81/R est:3000-5000
£2400 $3888 €3600 Greyhound bus terminal (39x49cm-15x19in) silver print. 22-May-3 Sotheby's, London #114/R est:1200-1800
£2405 $3800 €3608 Newsstand, 32nd Street and 3rd Avenue, New York (38x49cm-15x19in) s. gelatin silver print on board prov.lit. 25-Apr-3 Phillips, New York #229/R est:2500-3500
£2454 $4000 €3681 Penn Station (48x38cm-19x15in) s. gelatin silver print. 12-Feb-3 Christie's, Rockefeller NY #5/R est:3000-5000

£2848 $4500 €4272 Jefferson Market Court House (24x19cm-9x7in) s.verso gelatin silver print prov. 25-Apr-3 Phillips, New York #83/R est:3000-5000
£2922 $4500 €4383 General view from penthouse at 56 Seventh Avenue (24x19cm-9x7in) st.i.verso vintage gelatin silver print prov.lit. 25-Oct-2 Phillips, New York #84/R est:5000-7000
£3205 $5064 €5000 New York at night (35x27cm-14x11in) s.verso gelatin silver print lit. 16-Nov-2 Christie's, Paris #268/R est:6000-8000
£3374 $5500 €5061 Canyon, Broadway and Exchange Place (59x15cm-23x6in) s.verso gelatin silver print. 12-Feb-3 Christie's, Rockefeller NY #3/R est:5000-7000
£3481 $5500 €5222 Murray Hill Hotel, 112 Park Avenue, Manhattan (24x19cm-9x7in) photograph prov. 23-Apr-3 Sotheby's, New York #73/R est:7000-10000
£3571 $5500 €5357 Henry Street, looking west from Market Street (19x24cm-7x9in) i.d.Nov 29 1935 num.48 verso gelatin silver print prov.lit. 25-Oct-2 Phillips, New York #83/R est:4000-6000
£3742 $5800 €5613 New York at night (36x28cm-14x11in) silver print. 5-Dec-2 Swann Galleries, New York #378/R est:4000-6000
£3797 $6000 €5696 New York at night (50x40cm-20x16in) s. gelatin silver print prov.exhib.lit. 25-Apr-3 Phillips, New York #217/R est:4000-6000
£4114 $6500 €6171 Court of first model Tenement in New York, 72nd street and first avenue (25x20cm-10x8in) studio st.verso photograph. 23-Apr-3 Sotheby's, New York #74/R est:2500-3500
£4294 $7000 €6441 New York at night (49x39cm-19x15in) s. gelatin silver print. 12-Feb-3 Christie's, Rockefeller NY #214/R est:6000-8000
£4545 $7000 €6818 New York at night (34x27cm-13x11in) s. photograph. 24-Oct-2 Sotheby's, New York #111/R est:6000-9000
£4870 $7500 €7305 Vista from West Street (19x24cm-7x9in) i.d.March 23 1938 num.288 verso gelatin silver print prov.lit. 25-Oct-2 Phillips, New York #85/R est:4000-6000
£5063 $8000 €7595 El station 6th and 9th avenue lines downtown side (19x24cm-7x9in) s. photograph. 23-Apr-3 Sotheby's, New York #67/R est:5000-7000
£5380 $8500 €8070 Gunsmith and police department 6 centre market place, Manhatten. st.verso photograph prov. 23-Apr-3 Sotheby's, New York #76/R est:10000-15000
£5380 $8500 €8070 Exchange place (49x13cm-19x5in) s. gelatin silver print. 25-Apr-3 Phillips, New York #226/R
£6962 $11000 €10443 New York, Fifth Avenue at Eighth Street (39x49cm-15x19in) s. gelatin silver print prov.lit. 25-Apr-3 Phillips, New York #221/R est:2500-3500
£8228 $13000 €12342 El second and third avenue lines, Bowery and Division Street, Manhattan (25x19cm-10x7in) photograph prov. 23-Apr-3 Sotheby's, New York #77/R est:10000-15000
£11392 $18000 €17088 Seven images of New York (26x39cm-10x15in) s. 7 gelatin silver print prov.lit. 25-Apr-3 Phillips, New York #222/R est:8000-12000

ABBOTT, John White (1763-1851) British
Works on paper
£540 $859 €810 Soden Mill, Dunsford (26x19cm-10x7in) pen ink. 4-Mar-3 Bearnes, Exeter #346/R
£800 $1272 €1200 Trees in parkland (25x39cm-10x15in) monochrome wash. 27-Feb-3 Bonhams, Chester #384/R
£2200 $3652 €3300 Figure crossing a bridge (16x13cm-6x5in) d.Feb 3 1829 monochrome W/C sold with three by same hand. 12-Jun-3 Bonhams, New Bond Street #634/R est:1500-2000
£3900 $6396 €5850 Near Rydal Hall (23x18cm-9x7in) init.d.July 10 1791 pen ink W/C. 4-Feb-3 Bonhams, Leeds #273 est:2000-3000

ABBOTT, John White (attrib) (1763-1851) British
£11000 $17490 €16500 Bideford on the river Torridge, Devonshire (69x87cm-27x34in) 19-Mar-3 Sotheby's, London #68/R est:4000-6000
Works on paper
£420 $655 €630 Haldon (18x27cm-7x11in) i.d.1803 pen ink monochromatic W/C wash. 18-Sep-2 Dreweatt Neate, Newbury #41/R

ABBOTT, Lemuel Francis (1760-1803) British
£1300 $2171 €1885 Portrait of Mary Raworth of East Norton (74x61cm-29x24in) mono. 24-Jun-3 Neal & Fletcher, Woodbridge #384 est:1000-1500
£56000 $91840 €84000 Portrait of Vice Admiral Viscount Nelson (29x23cm-11x9in) 28-May-3 Mallams, Oxford #366/R est:3000-5000

ABBOTT, Lemuel Francis (attrib) (1760-1803) British
£892 $1400 €1338 Portrait of a Naval Officer (76x63cm-30x25in) 22-Nov-2 Skinner, Boston #29/R est:600-800

ABBOTT, Yarnell (1870-1938) American
£2994 $5000 €4341 Fishing boats in a harbour (46x61cm-18x24in) s. prov. 22-Jun-3 Freeman, Philadelphia #131/R est:3000-5000
£5195 $8000 €7793 Fishing village (71x91cm-28x36in) s. 24-Oct-2 Shannon's, Milford #7/R est:6000-8000

ABBOUD, Chafik (1926-) Lebanese
£1875 $2963 €2700 Bruxelles (73x92cm-29x36in) s.d. s.i.d.verso prov. 27-Apr-3 Perrin, Versailles #9/R est:2000-2500
£5000 $7950 €7500 Portrait (48x36cm-19x14in) s. wood panel. 30-Apr-3 Sotheby's, London #133/R est:5000-7000

ABBRESCIA, Joe (1936-) American
£6962 $11000 €10095 Listen up fellas (61x91cm-24x36in) s. 26-Jul-3 Coeur d'Alene, Hayden #37/R est:9000-15000

ABDULLA, Ian (1947-) Australian
£893 $1402 €1340 Weighing the pondi (56x76cm-22x30in) acrylic paper. 25-Nov-2 Christie's, Melbourne #222/R (A.D 2500)
£2000 $3220 €3000 Untitled - here I am (101x151cm-40x59in) s.d.1999. 6-May-3 Christie's, Melbourne #298a/R est:5000-7000 (A.D 5000)

ABDULLAH, S (20th C) ?
£357 $521 €550 Indonesian landscape with rice fields (71x118cm-28x46in) s. 19-Jun-2 Vendue Huis, Gravenhage #1

ABDULLAH, Suriosubroto (1878-1941) Javanese
£889 $1476 €1289 Javanese landscape with volcano (51x91cm-20x36in) s. 16-Jun-3 Waddingtons, Toronto #339/R est:2500-3500 (C.D 2000)

ABE, Nobuya (1913-1968) Japanese
£368 $600 €552 Song of bones (65x91cm-26x36in) s. i.verso. 16-Feb-3 Butterfields, San Francisco #2254

ABEELE, Remy van den (1918-1995) Belgian
£576 $921 €800 Composition surrealiste (118x100cm-46x39in) s.d.56 panel. 13-May-3 Palais de Beaux Arts, Brussels #323
£692 $1072 €1100 L'epouventail (70x90cm-28x35in) s.d.70. 5-Oct-2 De Vuyst, Lokeren #356/R
£755 $1170 €1200 Annonciation (80x100cm-31x39in) s.d.68. 5-Oct-2 De Vuyst, Lokeren #355
£1370 $2151 €2000 Untitled (40x86cm-16x34in) s.d.61 panel. 15-Apr-3 Laurence Calmels, Paris #4233/R

ABEL-TRUCHET (1857-1918) French
£1300 $2028 €1950 Concert (38x46cm-15x18in) s. 15-Oct-2 Bonhams, Knightsbridge #249/R est:700-1000
£1899 $3000 €3000 Femme nue dans un salon (45x36cm-18x14in) s. cardboard double-sided. 1-Dec-2 Livinec, Gaudcheau & Jezequel, Rennes #94/R
£2878 $4604 €4000 Paris, les quais de Seine (33x46cm-13x18in) s.d. 18-May-3 Eric Pillon, Calais #21/R
£5769 $9058 €9000 Scene de marche en Bretagne (47x37cm-19x15in) s.panel. 15-Dec-2 Thierry & Lannon, Brest #95/R
£6598 $10490 €9500 Heure du dejeuner (54x65cm-21x26in) s. prov. 30-Apr-3 Tajan, Paris #165/R est:6000

ABEL-TRUCHET (attrib) (1857-1918) French
Sculpture
£19355 $30000 €29033 Chantourne (171cm-67in) mono.verso oil panel metal. 29-Oct-2 Sotheby's, New York #57/R est:10000-15000

ABELA, Eduardo (1891-1965) Cuban
£6028 $9766 €8500 La Granja (25x33cm-10x13in) s. panel. 20-May-3 Segre, Madrid #122/R est:8500

ABELLEYRA CABRAL, Antonio (1911-) Argentinian
£479 $748 €700 Landscape (26x38cm-10x15in) s.d.1961 canvas on board. 8-Apr-3 Ansorena, Madrid #41/R

ABELLO PRAT, Joan (1922-) Spanish
£1053 $1705 €1600 Landscape with trees (46x55cm-18x22in) s.d.73. 21-Jan-3 Ansorena, Madrid #70/R
£1258 $1962 €2000 Vase of flowers (46x38cm-18x15in) s. 23-Sep-2 Durán, Madrid #118/R est:1500
£1342 $2161 €2000 Evening (38x46cm-15x18in) s. s.i.verso. 18-Feb-3 Durán, Madrid #193/R
£1656 $2699 €2500 Village (50x61cm-20x24in) s.d.1945 s.d.verso. 11-Feb-3 Segre, Madrid #187/R
£2138 $3336 €3400 Guinardo, Barcelona (60x73cm-24x29in) s.d.1946 s.i.d.verso. 17-Sep-2 Segre, Madrid #122/R
£3974 $6477 €6000 Harvest (65x81cm-26x32in) s.d.1977 lit. 11-Feb-3 Segre, Madrid #191/R

Works on paper
£755 $1177 €1200 Studies of figures (58x27cm-23x11in) s. ink dr pair. 8-Oct-2 Ansorena, Madrid #505

ABELOOS, Victor (1881-1965) Belgian
£316 $494 €500 Fenaison (45x60cm-18x24in) s. 15-Oct-2 Horta, Bruxelles #257
£392 $631 €600 Chaudron fleuri d'immortelles (87x106cm-34x42in) s. 20-Jan-3 Horta, Bruxelles #450
£728 $1135 €1150 Nu assis au bouquet (110x150cm-43x59in) s. 15-Oct-2 Vanderkindere, Brussels #89
£2192 $3419 €3200 Elegante en kimono (100x70cm-39x28in) s.d.1918 oval. 14-Apr-3 Horta, Bruxelles #86/R est:3500-4500

ABELS, Jacobus Theodorus (1803-1866) Dutch
£1019 $1590 €1600 Evening view of town near the water (16x23cm-6x9in) s. panel. 6-Nov-2 Vendue Huis, Gravenhage #371/R est:2000-2500
£6691 $10705 €9300 Moonlit river landscape (33x43cm-13x17in) mono. panel prov. 17-May-3 Lempertz, Koln #1352/R est:4000

ABERCROMBIE, Gertrude (1909-1977) American
£1887 $3000 €2831 Shell (10x13cm-4x5in) s.d. masonite. 2-Mar-3 Toomey, Oak Park #767/R est:2000-3000
£1935 $3000 €2903 Doors (10x13cm-4x5in) s.d. masonite. 8-Dec-2 Toomey, Oak Park #831/R est:2000-3000
£2358 $3750 €3537 White cat (10x13cm-4x5in) s.d. board. 2-Mar-3 Toomey, Oak Park #766/R est:2000-3000
£3459 $5500 €5189 Demolition doors (15x20cm-6x8in) s.i.d. board. 2-Mar-3 Toomey, Oak Park #768/R est:3000-5000
£3871 $6000 €5807 Giraffes (20x15cm-8x6in) s.d. board. 8-Dec-2 Toomey, Oak Park #832/R est:2000-3000

ABERDAM, Alfred (1894-1963) Polish
£347 $552 €500 Les anges (46x38cm-18x15in) s. 29-Apr-3 Artcurial Briest, Paris #220
£535 $829 €850 Quatre musiciens (41x33cm-16x13in) s. 30-Oct-2 Artcurial Briest, Paris #1

ABERG, Gunnar (1869-1894) Swedish
£388 $628 €563 Bird hunt (41x51cm-16x20in) mono. 25-May-3 Uppsala Auktionskammare, Uppsala #136/R (S.KR 5000)

ABERG, Martin (1888-1946) Swedish
£287 $464 €431 View of a town on the west coast of Sweden (45x55cm-18x22in) s.d.1935. 3-Feb-3 Lilla Bukowskis, Stockholm #551 (S.KR 4000)
£301 $487 €452 Sunny meadow, Hallan's Vadero (60x73cm-24x29in) s.d.1937. 3-Feb-3 Lilla Bukowskis, Stockholm #550 (S.KR 4200)

ABERG, Pelle (1909-1964) Swedish
£288 $449 €432 Interior scene with man and cat on sofa (36x45cm-14x18in) s. panel. 13-Sep-2 Lilla Bukowskis, Stockholm #381 (S.KR 4200)
£412 $642 €618 Cordonnerie (55x46cm-22x18in) s. panel. 13-Sep-2 Lilla Bukowskis, Stockholm #204 (S.KR 6000)
£496 $770 €744 Self portrait with girl, cafe interior (34x42cm-13x17in) s. panel. 8-Dec-2 Uppsala Auktionskammare, Uppsala #243/R (S.KR 7000)
£631 $984 €947 Confirmation (60x73cm-24x29in) s. panel. 5-Nov-2 Bukowskis, Stockholm #107/R (S.KR 9000)
£673 $1022 €1010 Girl at table (65x54cm-26x21in) s. panel. 16-Aug-2 Lilla Bukowskis, Stockholm #650 (S.KR 9800)
£1004 $1616 €1506 Southern street scene (40x33cm-16x13in) s. panel. 7-May-3 AB Stockholms Auktionsverk #873/R (S.KR 13000)
£1095 $1751 €1588 Street scene in Paris (46x38cm-18x15in) s. panel. 18-May-3 Anders Antik, Landskrona #59 (S.KR 14000)
£1255 $1983 €1883 Girl wearing black hat (41x33cm-16x13in) s. cardboard. 28-Apr-3 Bukowskis, Stockholm #169/R est:12000-15000 (S.KR 16500)
£1261 $1968 €1892 Girl wearing green hat (42x34cm-17x13in) s. panel. 5-Nov-2 Bukowskis, Stockholm #108/R est:15000-20000 (S.KR 18000)
£1472 $2296 €2208 Woman wearing hat (41x33cm-16x13in) s. panel. 6-Nov-2 AB Stockholms Auktionsverk #592/R est:8000-10000 (S.KR 21000)
£1800 $2825 €2700 Girl at cafe table (73x30cm-29x12in) s. 16-Dec-2 Lilla Bukowskis, Stockholm #715/R est:15000-18000 (S.KR 25500)
£1986 $3078 €2979 Woman wearing hat with green veil against red background (46x38cm-18x15in) s. panel. 8-Dec-2 Uppsala Auktionskammare, Uppsala #242/R est:25000-30000 (S.KR 28000)
£2017 $3268 €2925 Clown with red background (41x33cm-16x13in) s. panel. 25-May-3 Uppsala Auktionskammare, Uppsala #289/R est:15000-18000 (S.KR 26000)
£2205 $3484 €3308 Model with red gloves (33x24cm-13x9in) s. panel exhib. 28-Apr-3 Bukowskis, Stockholm #168/R est:18000-20000 (S.KR 29000)
£2695 $4177 €4043 Two girls at cafe table (46x38cm-18x15in) s. panel. 4-Dec-2 AB Stockholms Auktionsverk #1792/R est:18000-20000 (S.KR 38000)
£3346 $5287 €5019 The waiter at Rosenbad (60x46cm-24x18in) s. 28-Apr-3 Bukowskis, Stockholm #208/R est:25000-30000 (S.KR 44000)
£4479 $7211 €6719 Girl wearing hat (46x38cm-18x15in) s. panel. 7-May-3 AB Stockholms Auktionsverk #898/R est:20000-25000 (S.KR 58000)

ABERG, Ulrike Victoria (attrib) (1824-1892) Finnish
£323 $510 €500 Moonlight (62x85cm-24x33in) 19-Dec-2 Hagelstam, Helsinki #861

ABILDGAARD, Nicolai Abraham (1743-1809) Danish
£7321 $11128 €10982 Alexander the Great and a soldier visiting Diogenes (43x53cm-17x21in) prov. 27-Aug-2 Rasmussen, Copenhagen #1431/R est:80000 (D.KR 85000)

Works on paper
£372 $587 €558 Harmonious genius (19x9cm-7x4in) s. Indian ink. 5-Apr-3 Rasmussen, Havnen #2080 (D.KR 4000)
£495 $798 €743 Endraegtighedens Genius (19x11cm-7x4in) i.verso wash pen Indian ink. 26-Feb-3 Museumsbygningen, Copenhagen #71 (D.KR 5500)

ABLETT, William Albert (1877-1937) French
£310 $518 €450 Autoportrait au livre (81x65cm-32x26in) s. 10-Jul-3 Artcurial Briest, Paris #148

Works on paper
£241 $403 €350 Jeune femme au sofa (30x47cm-12x19in) studio st. col crayon dr. 10-Jul-3 Artcurial Briest, Paris #14

ABONYI, Erno (1888-?) ?
£298 $471 €447 A red room in the palace (42x52cm-17x20in) s,. 2-Dec-2 Rasmussen, Copenhagen #1710/R (D.KR 3500)

ABRAHAMS, Ivor (1935-) British
Works on paper
£254 $399 €381 Arches (70x82cm-28x32in) s. mixed media panel. 16-Dec-2 Lilla Bukowskis, Stockholm #871 (S.KR 3600)

ABRAHAMSSON, Erik (1871-1907) Swedish
£536 $842 €804 Sunset (53x81cm-21x32in) s. 16-Dec-2 Lilla Bukowskis, Stockholm #166 (S.KR 7600)

ABRAMOVIC, Marina (1946-) Yugoslavian
Works on paper
£1603 $2484 €2500 Wall painting (136x68cm-54x27in) s.d.89 gouache. 3-Dec-2 Christie's, Amsterdam #165/R est:1800-2200

ABRAMOVITSCH, Simon Claude (1903-1953) French
£340 $569 €480 Village en Bourgogne (46x55cm-18x22in) s. 17-Jun-3 Claude Boisgirard, Paris #137/R

ABRAMOWICZ, Leo (1889-1978) Russian
£280 $462 €406 Floral still life (43x36cm-17x14in) s. 6-Jul-3 Lots Road, London #347
£385 $608 €600 Self portrait (35x28cm-14x11in) board. 12-Nov-2 Dorotheum, Vienna #180/R
£769 $1215 €1200 French landscape (29x39cm-11x15in) board. 18-Nov-2 Dorotheum, Linz #250/R
£1250 $1987 €1800 Flowers (62x45cm-24x18in) board. 29-Apr-3 Wiener Kunst Auktionen, Vienna #618/R est:1800-3000

ABRAMS, Lionel (1931-1997) South African
£413 $664 €620 Still life with a bowl (91x120cm-36x47in) s. prov. 12-May-3 Stephan Welz, Johannesburg #374 est:1800-2400 (SA.R 4800)
£516 $831 €774 Abstract composition (151x181cm-59x71in) s. 12-May-3 Stephan Welz, Johannesburg #408 est:1800-2400 (SA.R 6000)

ABRANYI, Lajos (1849-1901) Hungarian
£490 $765 €735 Racing horse (55x68cm-22x27in) s.d.1899. 11-Sep-2 Kieselbach, Budapest #204/R (H.F 190000)

ABRATE, Angelo (1900-1985) Italian
£742 $1158 €1113 Mont Rose (46x55cm-18x22in) s. i. stretcher. 6-Nov-2 Dobiaschofsky, Bern #302/R est:1400 (S.FR 1700)
£1603 $2516 €2500 My valley (120x85cm-47x33in) 10-Dec-2 Della Rocca, Turin #278/R

ABRIL, Ben (1923-1995) American
£692 $1100 €1038 Dock scene (18x36cm-7x14in) s. painted c.1970. 4-May-3 Treadway Gallery, Cincinnati #570/R

£932 $1500 €1398 Old church near Gualala Point, northern California (61x76cm-24x30in) s. i.stretcher prov. 18-Feb-3 John Moran, Pasadena #170 est:2000-3000

Works on paper

£1708 $2750 €2562 Heisler Beach, Rockpile, Laguna (20x29cm-8x11in) s. i.verso W/C. 18-Feb-3 John Moran, Pasadena #83 est:1000-2000

ABSOLON, John (1815-1895) British

Works on paper

£300 $489 €435 Leigh from Southend (28x55cm-11x22in) s.i. W/C. 16-Jul-3 Sotheby's, Olympia #34/R
£15000 $23850 €22500 Olivia resting (39x60cm-15x24in) s. W/C bodycol gum arabic. 19-Mar-3 Sotheby's, London #224/R est:8000-12000

ABSOLON, R G (20th C) British?

£250 $388 €375 Thatched cottage at Bramscombe, Devon. s.d.1928 W/C. 20-Jul-2 Hogben, Folkstone #198

ABT, Otto (1903-1982) Swiss

£611 $954 €917 Dahlias (40x28cm-16x11in) s. casein prov. 6-Nov-2 Hans Widmer, St Gallen #13/R (S.FR 1400)
£1972 $3234 €2859 Game (73x70cm-29x28in) s. 4-Jun-3 Fischer, Luzern #126/R est:3500-4500 (S.FR 4200)
£2431 $3865 €3500 Portrait de femme (41x33cm-16x13in) s. 29-Apr-3 Artcurial Briest, Paris #205/R est:1800-2200

Works on paper

£279 $441 €419 In the artist's studio (15x21cm-6x8in) W/C. 29-Nov-2 Zofingen, Switzerland #2765 (S.FR 650)

ABUJA, Francisco (1924-) Spanish

£252 $387 €400 Homage to Pancho Cossio (42x33cm-17x13in) s. board. 22-Oct-2 Durán, Madrid #48/R

ACCARDI, Carla (1924-) Italian

£1032 $1631 €1600 Green orange purple (28x38cm-11x15in) s.d.91 s.i.d.91. 18-Dec-2 Christie's, Rome #56/R
£1081 $1686 €1600 Studies (49x68cm-19x27in) s.d.82 tempera card set of 3. 26-Mar-3 Finarte Semenzato, Milan #71/R
£2089 $3300 €3300 Egyptian purple (30x40cm-12x16in) s.d.91 vinyl. 29-Nov-2 Farsetti, Prato #306/R
£2278 $3554 €3600 Green on red (50x60cm-20x24in) s.d.1999 vinyl. 14-Sep-2 Meeting Art, Vercelli #816/R
£2353 $3765 €3600 Black-white (40x50cm-16x20in) s.d.1997 vinyl. 4-Jan-3 Meeting Art, Vercelli #394
£2500 $3925 €3900 White red black (40x50cm-16x20in) s.d.1997 vinyl. 23-Nov-2 Meeting Art, Vercelli #349/R
£4167 $6625 €6000 Red white (50x70cm-20x28in) s.i.d.2002 verso vinyl. 1-May-3 Meeting Art, Vercelli #475
£4255 $6894 €6000 Untitled (100x100cm-39x39in) painted plastic four frames prov.lit. 26-May-3 Christie's, Milan #186/R est:6000-8000
£4839 $7645 €7500 White and black (80x105cm-31x41in) s.d.89 s.i.d.verso vinyl. 18-Dec-2 Christie's, Rome #86/R
£5063 $8000 €8000 Planet (46x62cm-18x24in) s.d.1960 tempera casein card. 29-Nov-2 Farsetti, Prato #228/R est:8000
£5161 $8155 €8000 Red-blue (80x60cm-31x24in) s. s.i.verso lit. 18-Dec-2 Christie's, Rome #307/R est:12000

Works on paper

£5532 $8962 €7800 N. 546 (100x78cm-39x31in) s.i. enamel sicofoil. 26-May-3 Christie's, Milan #94/R est:6000-7000

ACEVES, Jose (1909-1968) American

£2179 $3400 €3269 Silla Mountain (28x43cm-11x17in) 19-Oct-2 David Dike, Dallas #209/R est:2000-4000
£7692 $12000 €11538 Desert landscape (61x91cm-24x36in) painted c.1934. 19-Oct-2 David Dike, Dallas #283/R est:15000-20000

ACEVES, Tomas (19th C) Spanish

£7000 $10990 €10500 El patio de un palacio moro - courtyard of a Moorish palace (63x43cm-25x17in) s.i. 19-Nov-2 Sotheby's, London #58/R est:6000-8000

ACHARD, Jean Alexis (1807-1884) French

Works on paper

£351 $548 €520 Etude de sous-bois (26x21cm-10x8in) pen ink wash over crayon. 31-Mar-3 Piasa, Paris #55

ACHEFF, William (1947-) American

£1911 $3000 €2867 Silver teapot and lemons (41x30cm-16x12in) s. i.stretcher prov. 19-Nov-2 Butterfields, San Francisco #8075/R est:5000-7000
£2840 $4600 €4118 Perry Mesa with Red Chile (15x20cm-6x8in) 23-May-3 Altermann Galleries, Santa Fe #39
£4969 $8050 €7205 Zia with Chills (18x13cm-7x5in) 23-May-3 Altermann Galleries, Santa Fe #38
£10959 $16000 €16439 Acoma corn (36x25cm-14x10in) 18-May-2 Altermann Galleries, Santa Fe #100/R
£15401 $24950 €22331 Late summer (30x71cm-12x28in) 23-May-3 Altermann Galleries, Santa Fe #40
£22152 $35000 €32120 Blue skies at Hopi (76x56cm-30x22in) s. 26-Jul-3 Coeur d'Alene, Hayden #111/R est:30000-50000

ACHEN, Georg (1860-1912) Danish

£340 $530 €510 Heath landscape (44x75cm-17x30in) init.d.11 exhib. 5-Aug-2 Rasmussen, Vejle #196/R (D.KR 4000)
£426 $672 €639 The ferry at Svejbaek (75x88cm-30x35in) s.d.06 exhib. 2-Dec-2 Rasmussen, Copenhagen #1809/R (D.KR 5000)
£1210 $1925 €1815 Peasant girl in beechwood, sunshine (46x50cm-18x20in) s.d.84 exhib. 5-Mar-3 Rasmussen, Copenhagen #1913/R est:10000 (D.KR 13000)

ACHENBACH, Andreas (1815-1910) German

£1026 $1559 €1600 Southern coast with fishing boat and figures (26x34cm-10x13in) s.d.1837 canvas on canvas lit. 11-Jul-2 Allgauer, Kempten #2407/R
£1592 $2484 €2500 Sailing boat on a stormy sea (50x70cm-20x28in) s. canvas on canvas lit. 7-Nov-2 Allgauer, Kempten #2731/R est:4000
£1795 $2818 €2800 High surf on rocky coast (37x46cm-15x18in) mono.d.57 bears sig.d.1857 panel. 21-Nov-2 Van Ham, Cologne #1440/R est:3000
£3165 $5000 €5000 Beach by city with old tower and wall (80x58cm-31x23in) s.d.76 lit. 29-Nov-2 Schloss Ahlden, Ahlden #1241/R est:4500
£5449 $8554 €8500 Steamer and sailing boat in stormy seas at harbour entrance (105x75cm-41x30in) s.d.79. 21-Nov-2 Van Ham, Cologne #1441/R est:20000
£15190 $24000 €24000 Market place in Hildesheim (42x63cm-17x25in) s.d.74 exhib. 28-Nov-2 Dorotheum, Vienna #72/R est:26000-30000
£17610 $27119 €28000 Return to harbour in rough seas (49x61cm-19x24in) s.d.93 panel. 22-Oct-2 Sotheby's, Amsterdam #76/R est:16000-18000

Works on paper

£324 $518 €450 Fishing boats near coast (16x25cm-6x10in) pencil W/C. 17-May-3 Lempertz, Koln #1267
£540 $863 €750 Harbour scene (18x35cm-7x14in) mono. w/C. 17-May-3 Lempertz, Koln #1268
£641 $936 €1000 Gustorf Mill (18x26cm-7x10in) s.i.d.65 W/C over pencil. 4-Jun-2 Karl & Faber, Munich #50

ACHENBACH, Oswald (1827-1905) German

£1295 $2072 €1800 Woodland study - by Konigsee (22x32cm-9x13in) s.d.12. Sept. 1842 board. 17-May-3 Lempertz, Koln #1354 est:2000
£2949 $4659 €4600 Vesuvius (24x22cm-9x9in) s. 16-Nov-2 Lempertz, Koln #1418/R est:4500
£3750 $6000 €5625 Mountainous village with people (61x46cm-24x18in) mono. 1-Jan-3 Nadeau, Windsor #25/R est:5000-7000
£4317 $6906 €6000 Italian landscape with grotto in evening (100x78cm-39x31in) s.d.1893. 17-May-3 Lempertz, Koln #1353/R est:7000
£14465 $22277 €23000 An evening stroll on the road to Castel Gandolfo, Italy (91x135cm-36x53in) s.d.1875. 23-Oct-2 Christie's, Amsterdam #88/R est:25000-35000
£20886 $32373 €33000 Upper Italian lake landscape lit by evening sun (66x88cm-26x35in) s.d.1848. 25-Sep-2 Neumeister, Munich #532/R est:40000
£26619 $42590 €37000 Campagna landscape with storm clouds (89x134cm-35x53in) s. prov. 17-May-3 Lempertz, Koln #1355/R est:30000
£51948 $77403 €80000 Punch and Judy show on beach in Bay of Naples (100x151cm-39x59in) s. 26-Jun-2 Neumeister, Munich #673/R est:70000

ACHENBACH, Oswald (attrib) (1827-1905) German

£306 $500 €459 Study of a forest interior (29x23cm-11x9in) bears sig. paper laid down. 16-Feb-3 Butterfields, San Francisco #2034
£1667 $2617 €2600 Early morning mountain landscape near Innsbruck (24x38cm-9x15in) bears s.d.29 August 1843 board. 21-Nov-2 Van Ham, Cologne #1443/R est:3000

ACHTEN, Joseph (1822-1867) German

Works on paper

£365 $569 €540 Seated woman (47x39cm-19x15in) s.d.50 chl chk. 28-Mar-3 Dorotheum, Vienna #150/R

ACHTSCHELLINCK, Lucas (1626-1699) Flemish

£6452 $10194 €10000 Paysage de lac anime de bergers et leurs troupeaux (19x28cm-7x11in) copper. 18-Dec-2 Tajan, Paris #12/R

ACHTSCHELLINCK, Lucas (attrib) (1626-1699) Flemish

£709 $1184 €1000 Paysage de la campagne Flamande anime de promeneurs (18x23cm-7x9in) panel. 18-Jun-3 Tajan, Paris #67
£3500 $5495 €5250 Wooded landscape with figures and dogs in a clearing (62x77cm-24x30in) 13-Dec-2 Christie's, Kensington #95/R est:3000-5000

ACKER, Florimond van (1858-1940) Belgian

£387 $624 €550 Beach view with fishing boat and fishermen (30x40cm-12x16in) panel. 12-May-3 Bernaerts, Antwerp #197/R

ACKERMAN, Ilse (20th C) Finnish

£297 $464 €470 Life in the skerries (34x50cm-13x20in) s.d.80 acrylic. 15-Sep-2 Bukowskis, Helsinki #154/R

ACKERMAN, Paul (1908-1981) French

Works on paper

£263 $426 €400 Procession (50x65cm-20x26in) s. mixed media. 27-Jan-3 Millon & Associes, Paris #37

ACKERMANN, Gerald (1876-1960) British

Works on paper

£420 $701 €609 View through an avenue of trees (23x36cm-9x14in) s. W/C. 20-Jun-3 Keys, Aylsham #597
£800 $1256 €1200 Bit of Old Blakeney (23x36cm-9x14in) s. W/C prov. 13-Dec-2 Keys, Aylsham #599/R
£820 $1246 €1230 Cley Mill, North Norfolk (18x25cm-7x10in) s. W/C. 16-Aug-2 Keys, Aylsham #560/R
£920 $1435 €1380 Morston church (17x34cm-7x13in) s. W/C prov. 18-Sep-2 Dreweatt Neate, Newbury #4/R
£2000 $3140 €3000 Sailing boats at Burnham-Overy-Staithe, North Norfolk (23x33cm-9x13in) s. W/C. 13-Dec-2 Keys, Aylsham #598 est:1500-2000

ACKERMANN, Johanna (19/20th C) German

Works on paper

£556 $883 €800 Standing young man (34x19cm-13x7in) s.d.1907 pencil. 5-May-3 Ketterer, Munich #327/R

ACKERMANN, Max (1887-1975) German

£705 $1107 €1100 Untitled (314x240cm-124x94in) s.d.1974 col pastel chk. 22-Nov-2 Karrenbauer, Konstanz #1800/R
£870 $1426 €1200 Composition (37x13cm-15x5in) i.d.10.9.71 tempera col chk acrylic board. 29-May-3 Lempertz, Koln #502/R
£1379 $2179 €2000 Untitled (32x12cm-13x5in) tempera pencil. 2-Apr-3 Dr Fritz Nagel, Stuttgart #9300/R est:2500
£1392 $2158 €2200 Blue IV (42x30cm-17x12in) s.d.1942 col chk. 28-Sep-2 Ketterer, Hamburg #205/R est:2200-2500
£1392 $2200 €2200 Untitled (43x30cm-17x12in) tempera pastel chl prov. 27-Nov-2 Dr Fritz Nagel, Stuttgart #3127/R est:2800
£1456 $2271 €2300 Lakeside hops (33x24cm-13x9in) i.d.17.III.1970 acrylic board. 18-Oct-2 Dr Fritz Nagel, Stuttgart #454/R est:3400
£1456 $2271 €2300 Faunle (33x27cm-13x11in) s.i.d.21.9.68 verso acrylic masonite. 18-Oct-2 Dr Fritz Nagel, Stuttgart #455/R est:3400
£1519 $2400 €2400 Abstract composition (32x23cm-13x9in) s.d.1952 chl graphite prov.exhib. 27-Nov-2 Dr Fritz Nagel, Stuttgart #3157/R est:3100
£1772 $2800 €2800 Studio dance (19x18cm-7x7in) oil tempera chl chk board prov.exhib. 27-Nov-2 Dr Fritz Nagel, Stuttgart #3053/R est:3600
£1899 $3000 €3000 Untitled - head (25x22cm-10x9in) s. oil tempera masonite exhib. 27-Nov-2 Dr Fritz Nagel, Stuttgart #3050/R est:3900
£1899 $3000 €3000 Untitled - wall picture (30x22cm-12x9in) s.d.1939 tempera board prov.exhib. 27-Nov-2 Dr Fritz Nagel, Stuttgart #3108/R est:5400
£1899 $3000 €3000 Untitled - accumulator (24x33cm-9x13in) s.d.26. Sept. 1970 verso acrylic tempera board prov. 27-Nov-2 Dr Fritz Nagel, Stuttgart #3174/R est:4100
£2089 $3300 €3300 Untitled (37x31cm-15x12in) mono.d. s.d.20.Juli 71 verso acrylic board prov.exhib. 27-Nov-2 Dr Fritz Nagel, Stuttgart #3095/R est:4800
£2278 $3600 €3600 Abstract composition (34x24cm-13x9in) s.d.1969 s.i.d.7.IX.69 verso acrylic board on masonite prov.exhib. 27-Nov-2 Dr Fritz Nagel, Stuttgart #3067/R est:3200
£2278 $3600 €3600 Untitled (33x25cm-13x10in) mono.d.69 s.d.69 verso acrylic board. 29-Nov-2 Sigalas, Stuttgart #1147/R est:4000
£2685 $4322 €4000 Mosaic (31x23cm-12x9in) s.d.1944 paper. 21-Feb-3 Sigalas, Stuttgart #847/R est:6000
£2848 $4500 €4500 Beach (19x29cm-7x11in) s.i.d.1935 oil tempera board prov. 27-Nov-2 Dr Fritz Nagel, Stuttgart #3034/R est:6400
£2848 $4500 €4500 Composition 2 (33x24cm-13x9in) s.i.d.1955 oil tempera masonite prov. 27-Nov-2 Dr Fritz Nagel, Stuttgart #3076/R est:5800
£3101 $4900 €4900 Abstract composition (19x27cm-7x11in) mono.d.1940 oil tempera prov.exhib. 27-Nov-2 Dr Fritz Nagel, Stuttgart #3024/R est:4900
£3481 $5500 €5500 Untitled - abstract composition (29x20cm-11x8in) oil tempera sand board prov. 27-Nov-2 Dr Fritz Nagel, Stuttgart #3077/R est:8200
£3481 $5500 €5500 Untitled - composition (48x32cm-19x13in) s.d.9.XII.65 oil tempera board prov.exhib. 27-Nov-2 Dr Fritz Nagel, Stuttgart #3144/R est:8000
£3797 $6000 €6000 Beach - Bodensee (31x44cm-12x17in) s.i.d.1945 verso oil tempera masonite prov. 27-Nov-2 Dr Fritz Nagel, Stuttgart #3060/R est:9500
£3797 $6000 €6000 Untitled - wall picture (30x21cm-12x8in) s. verso oil tempera board prov. 27-Nov-2 Dr Fritz Nagel, Stuttgart #3109/R est:7400
£3797 $6000 €6000 Untitled - abstract (51x38cm-20x15in) oil tempera board prov.exhib. 27-Nov-2 Dr Fritz Nagel, Stuttgart #3182/R est:8800
£4114 $6500 €6500 Aphrodite (39x47cm-15x19in) s.i.d.1937 oil tempera board prov. 27-Nov-2 Dr Fritz Nagel, Stuttgart #3022/R est:7800
£4114 $6500 €6500 Untitled (22x26cm-9x10in) s. verso oil tempera board exhib. 27-Nov-2 Dr Fritz Nagel, Stuttgart #3068/R est:8200
£4167 $6583 €6000 Untitled (32x25cm-13x10in) s.d.1935 verso oil grisaille board. 26-Apr-3 Dr Lehr, Berlin #2/R est:6000
£4747 $7500 €7500 Abstract couple (30x21cm-12x8in) s.d.1942 s.i.d. verso oil tempera prov.exhib. 27-Nov-2 Dr Fritz Nagel, Stuttgart #3054/R est:6200
£4747 $7500 €7500 Garden in Untersee in summer (50x72cm-20x28in) mono. oil tempera board painted 1942. 30-Nov-2 Geble, Radolfzell #640 est:7000
£5000 $8200 €6900 Composition (17x30cm-7x12in) s.i.d.1943/9 verso tempera chk board. 29-May-3 Lempertz, Koln #500/R est:6000
£5063 $8000 €8000 Untitled - diploid (65x50cm-26x20in) s.d.7.VI.67 stretcher oil tempera prov. 27-Nov-2 Dr Fritz Nagel, Stuttgart #3201/R est:9800
£5517 $8717 €8000 Composition (39x55cm-15x22in) s.i.d.1947 verso masonite. 2-Apr-3 Dr Fritz Nagel, Stuttgart #9302/R est:12000
£5696 $9000 €9000 Figures (42x30cm-17x12in) s.i.d.1937 oil tempera board prov. 27-Nov-2 Dr Fritz Nagel, Stuttgart #3003/R est:9800
£6962 $11000 €11000 Untitled - island picture (65x50cm-26x20in) s.d.april 1959 stretcher oil tempera prov. 27-Nov-2 Dr Fritz Nagel, Stuttgart #3152/R est:14000
£7246 $11884 €10000 Untitled (65x50cm-26x20in) s.d.29.VII.1962 stretcher prov. 31-May-3 Villa Grisebach, Berlin #343/R est:14000-18000
£8354 $13200 €13200 Diagonal movement (88x45cm-35x18in) s.d.1951 s.i.d. verso oil tempera prov.lit. 27-Nov-2 Dr Fritz Nagel, Stuttgart #3089/R est:16000
£8354 $13200 €13200 Untitled - composition (65x50cm-26x20in) s.d.8.Juni 1866 stretcher acrylic prov.exhib. 27-Nov-2 Dr Fritz Nagel, Stuttgart #3177/R est:15000
£8861 $14000 €14000 Moon woman (65x49cm-26x19in) s.d.49 s.i.d. verso oil tempera masonite prov. 27-Nov-2 Dr Fritz Nagel, Stuttgart #3105/R est:19000
£9494 $15000 €15000 Untitled - southern realm (65x50cm-26x20in) s.d.13.II.1964 oil tempera prov. 27-Nov-2 Dr Fritz Nagel, Stuttgart #3043/R est:19000
£9494 $15000 €15000 Untitled (100x90cm-39x35in) s.d.17. Mai 1965 stretcher oil tempera prov. 27-Nov-2 Dr Fritz Nagel, Stuttgart #3194/R est:24000
£9655 $15255 €14000 Untitled (42x31cm-17x12in) s.d. verso board prov. 2-Apr-3 Dr Fritz Nagel, Stuttgart #9301/R est:14000
£10127 $16000 €16000 Untitled (172x37cm-68x15in) s.d.3.IV.1966 s.d.3 April 1966 stretcher oil chl prov.exhib. 27-Nov-2 Dr Fritz Nagel, Stuttgart #3011/R est:22000
£10127 $16000 €16000 Untitled (65x50cm-26x20in) s.d.3.5.1959 stretcher prov. 27-Nov-2 Dr Fritz Nagel, Stuttgart #3059/R est:16000
£10127 $16000 €16000 Untitled - soaring composition (83x51cm-33x20in) i. verso oil tempera prov. 27-Nov-2 Dr Fritz Nagel, Stuttgart #3116/R est:22000
£10759 $17000 €17000 Vertical movement (87x52cm-34x20in) s. s.i.d.1952 verso oil tempera prov. 27-Nov-2 Dr Fritz Nagel, Stuttgart #3122/R est:24000
£11392 $18000 €18000 Concrete (66x50cm-26x20in) s.d.1932 s.i.d. verso oil tempera panel prov. 27-Nov-2 Dr Fritz Nagel, Stuttgart #3134/R est:24000
£14493 $23768 €20000 Composition (120x60cm-47x24in) oil tempera hessian. 31-May-3 Villa Grisebach, Berlin #344/R est:25000-30000
£18705 $30676 €26000 Early hour (185x117cm-73x46in) s. s.i.d. verso prov. 6-Jun-3 Ketterer, Munich #100/R est:23000-25000
£18987 $30000 €30000 Picture 1958 (120x100cm-47x39in) s.i.d.1958 oil tempera prov.exhib. 27-Nov-2 Dr Fritz Nagel, Stuttgart #3037/R est:38000

Works on paper

£252 $392 €400 Striding woman (29x23cm-11x9in) mono.d.1919 chl. 23-Sep-2 Dr Fritz Nagel, Stuttgart #9000/R
£252 $392 €400 Man raising leg (26x17cm-10x7in) mono. chl pencil. 23-Sep-2 Dr Fritz Nagel, Stuttgart #9001/R
£252 $392 €400 Group dancing (23x26cm-9x10in) mono. chl pencil. 23-Sep-2 Dr Fritz Nagel, Stuttgart #9002/R

£380 $600 €600 Bodensee beach (13x18cm-5x7in) mono.d.1937 s.i.d. verso graphite chl prov.exhib. 27-Nov-2 Dr Fritz Nagel, Stuttgart #3156/R

£472 $726 €750 In the tram (21x33cm-8x13in) mono.d.1924 graphite. 26-Oct-2 Dr Lehr, Berlin #2/R

£503 $775 €800 Black Forest country road, Freudenstadt (37x23cm-15x9in) mono.d.1920 s.i.d. verso graphite col chk board. 26-Oct-2 Dr Lehr, Berlin #1/R

£548 $855 €800 Reclining nude (12x34cm-5x13in) s.d.1919 chl ochre. 11-Apr-3 Sigalas, Stuttgart #413

£570 $900 €900 Untitled (16x24cm-6x9in) mono.d.1936 chl graphite prov. 27-Nov-2 Dr Fritz Nagel, Stuttgart #3063/R

£601 $950 €950 Abstract composition (25x16cm-10x6in) mono.d.1950 s.d. verso chl oil chk prov.exhib. 27-Nov-2 Dr Fritz Nagel, Stuttgart #3064/R

£601 $950 €950 Contrapuntal game (33x25cm-13x10in) mono.i.d.1930 graphite prov.exhib. 27-Nov-2 Dr Fritz Nagel, Stuttgart #3098/R

£886 $1400 €1400 Untitled (24x11cm-9x4in) s.d.1954 pastel prov. 27-Nov-2 Dr Fritz Nagel, Stuttgart #3139/R

£949 $1500 €1500 Bodensee beach (24x30cm-9x12in) mono.d.1946 chl prov.exhib. 27-Nov-2 Dr Fritz Nagel, Stuttgart #3099/R est:1900

£975 $1540 €1540 Untitled (25x15cm-10x6in) s.d.1949 Indian ink pastel chk prov.exhib. 27-Nov-2 Dr Fritz Nagel, Stuttgart #3071/R est:1800

£1013 $1600 €1600 Untitled - moon woman (38x25cm-15x10in) s.d.1941 chl prov. 27-Nov-2 Dr Fritz Nagel, Stuttgart #3030/R est:2200

£1013 $1600 €1600 Untitled (17x11cm-7x4in) mono.d.1950 pastel. 29-Nov-2 Sigalas, Stuttgart #1148/R est:1900

£1111 $1756 €1600 Lute player with other figures (24x16cm-9x6in) pastel. 26-Apr-3 Dr Lehr, Berlin #1/R est:2400

£1195 $1840 €1900 Rythm in yellow (31x24cm-12x9in) s.d.1958 s.i.d. verso pastel board. 26-Oct-2 Dr Lehr, Berlin #6/R est:2500

£1203 $1876 €1900 Untitled (48x32cm-19x13in) s.d.1974 pastel. 18-Oct-2 Dr Fritz Nagel, Stuttgart #453/R est:3800

£1203 $1900 €1900 Untitled - female nude (45x20cm-18x8in) mono. chl graphite prov.exhib. 27-Nov-2 Dr Fritz Nagel, Stuttgart #3120/R est:1800

£1370 $2137 €2000 Untitled (48x31cm-19x12in) s.d.1974 pastel. 11-Apr-3 Sigalas, Stuttgart #415 est:2900

£1410 $2186 €2200 Composition with dancing figures (33x24cm-13x9in) s.d.1957 pastel. 6-Dec-2 Karlheinz Kaupp, Staufen #2138/R est:3500

£1519 $2400 €2400 Untitled (31x23cm-12x9in) s.d.1974 pastel prov. 27-Nov-2 Dr Fritz Nagel, Stuttgart #3006/R est:2800

£1519 $2400 €2400 Untitled (32x24cm-13x9in) s.d.1974 pastel prov. 27-Nov-2 Dr Fritz Nagel, Stuttgart #3007/R est:3000

£1614 $2550 €2550 Untitled (48x176cm-19x69in) s.d.1973 pastel prov.exhib. 27-Nov-2 Dr Fritz Nagel, Stuttgart #3040/R est:3000

£1623 $2419 €2500 Untitled (48x31cm-19x12in) s.d.1974 pastel. 28-Jun-2 Sigalas, Stuttgart #575/R

£1646 $2600 €2600 Untitled (48x33cm-19x13in) s.d.1973 pastel prov. 27-Nov-2 Dr Fritz Nagel, Stuttgart #3112/R est:3400

£1646 $2600 €2600 Hymn to the sun (31x49cm-12x19in) s.d.1959 pastel prov. 27-Nov-2 Dr Fritz Nagel, Stuttgart #3178/R est:3300

£1646 $2600 €2600 Untitled (49x31cm-19x12in) s.d.1958 pastel prov. 27-Nov-2 Dr Fritz Nagel, Stuttgart #3179/R est:3300

£1646 $2600 €2600 Warning (38x28cm-15x11in) mono.i.d.1923 graphite prov. 27-Nov-2 Dr Fritz Nagel, Stuttgart #3185/R est:3200

£1646 $2600 €2600 Untitled (49x32cm-19x13in) s.d.1974 pastel prov. 27-Nov-2 Dr Fritz Nagel, Stuttgart #3190/R est:3200

£1646 $2600 €2600 Untitled (49x32cm-19x13in) s.d.16.II.74 pastel prov. 27-Nov-2 Dr Fritz Nagel, Stuttgart #3191/R est:3200

£1709 $2700 €2700 Cafe (32x30cm-13x12in) s.d.1923 s.i.d. verso graphite chl prov.exhib.lit. 27-Nov-2 Dr Fritz Nagel, Stuttgart #3049/R est:3100

£1772 $2800 €2800 Untitled (50x32cm-20x13in) s.d.1973 pastel prov. 27-Nov-2 Dr Fritz Nagel, Stuttgart #3057/R est:3600

£1772 $2800 €2800 Untitled - gramophone (28x23cm-11x9in) s.mono.d.1922 graphite col pen prov.exhib. 27-Nov-2 Dr Fritz Nagel, Stuttgart #3121/R est:3800

£1772 $2800 €2800 Weekend by the sea (14x27cm-6x11in) s.i.d.1935 verso pastel graphite. 27-Nov-2 Dr Fritz Nagel, Stuttgart #3129/R est:3200

£1772 $2800 €2800 Happy movement (31x24cm-12x9in) s.d.1959 pastel prov. 27-Nov-2 Dr Fritz Nagel, Stuttgart #3151/R est:3600

£1835 $2900 €2900 Group of girls (29x21cm-11x8in) pastel tempera prov. 27-Nov-2 Dr Fritz Nagel, Stuttgart #3186/R est:2800

£1899 $3000 €3000 Untitled (26x17cm-10x7in) pastel glass prov.exhib. 27-Nov-2 Dr Fritz Nagel, Stuttgart #3018/R est:4000

£1899 $3000 €3000 Untitled - colour island (48x31cm-19x12in) s.d.1958 pastel prov. 27-Nov-2 Dr Fritz Nagel, Stuttgart #3150/R est:3900

£2083 $3292 €3000 Composition with notes (43x31cm-17x12in) s.d.1945 chl chk. 26-Apr-3 Dr Lehr, Berlin #4/R est:4000

£2089 $3300 €3300 To pleasure (31x23cm-12x9in) s.d.1951 pastel. 29-Nov-2 Villa Grisebach, Berlin #500/R est:2500-3000

£2089 $3300 €3300 Untitled (39x23cm-15x9in) s.d.1930 pastel glass prov.exhib. 27-Nov-2 Dr Fritz Nagel, Stuttgart #3016/R est:3800

£2089 $3300 €3300 Untitled (50x32cm-20x13in) s.i.d.20115 pastel prov. 27-Nov-2 Dr Fritz Nagel, Stuttgart #3058/R est:4000

£2089 $3300 €3300 Moving red (48x32cm-19x13in) s.d.1963 pastel prov. 27-Nov-2 Dr Fritz Nagel, Stuttgart #3133/R est:4200

£2089 $3300 €3300 Untitled - abstract composition (16x18cm-6x7in) s.d.1920 pastel prov. 27-Nov-2 Dr Fritz Nagel, Stuttgart #3142/R est:2200

£2278 $3600 €3600 Untitled - woman with tulip (48x19cm-19x7in) s.mono.d.1932 pastel prov. 27-Nov-2 Dr Fritz Nagel, Stuttgart #3017/R est:4200

£2278 $3600 €3600 Untitled - Rome (48x33cm-19x13in) s.d.17.III.1964 pastel prov. 27-Nov-2 Dr Fritz Nagel, Stuttgart #3042/R est:5200

£2278 $3600 €3600 Untitled (50x32cm-20x13in) s.d.1973 pastel prov.exhib. 27-Nov-2 Dr Fritz Nagel, Stuttgart #3084/R est:4400

£2278 $3600 €3600 Untitled (50x35cm-20x14in) s.d.1974 pastel prov. 27-Nov-2 Dr Fritz Nagel, Stuttgart #3162/R est:4000

£2453 $3777 €3900 Early hours (22x13cm-9x5in) s.d.1939 i. verso pastel paper on board. 26-Oct-2 Dr Lehr, Berlin #5/R est:4000

£2532 $4000 €4000 Untitled (50x35cm-20x14in) s.i.d.1964 pastel prov. 27-Nov-2 Dr Fritz Nagel, Stuttgart #3002/R est:4900

£2532 $4000 €4000 Evening at the lake (17x25cm-7x10in) mono.d.1937 s.i.d. verso chl tempera exhib. 27-Nov-2 Dr Fritz Nagel, Stuttgart #3012/R est:5900

£2564 $3974 €4000 Abstract composition (33x24cm-13x9in) mono.d.1930. 6-Dec-2 Karlheinz Kaupp, Staufen #2065/R est:6500

£2754 $4516 €3800 Untitled (24x33cm-9x13in) s.d.72 pastel. 29-May-3 Lempertz, Koln #503/R est:3500-4000

£2759 $4359 €4000 Untitled (47x31cm-19x12in) s.d.1974 pastel. 5-Apr-3 Geble, Radolfzell #673 est:4000

£2848 $4500 €4500 Untitled - abstract composition (41x17cm-16x7in) s.d.1952 pastel prov. 27-Nov-2 Dr Fritz Nagel, Stuttgart #3072/R est:3600

£2885 $4471 €4500 Woman sat in armchair (25x20cm-10x8in) s.d.1928. 6-Dec-2 Karlheinz Kaupp, Staufen #2032/R est:7000

£2911 $4600 €4600 Untitled (50x32cm-20x13in) s.d.1973 pastel. 27-Nov-2 Dr Fritz Nagel, Stuttgart #3029/R est:3900

£3020 $4862 €4500 Bridging continents (31x24cm-12x9in) s.d.1959 pastel. 21-Feb-3 Sigalas, Stuttgart #846/R est:4500

£3165 $5000 €5000 Untitled - abstract composition (50x32cm-20x13in) s.d.1973 pastel prov. 27-Nov-2 Dr Fritz Nagel, Stuttgart #3143/R est:3800

£3241 $5121 €4700 Untitled (31x48cm-12x19in) s.d.1974 pastel prov. 5-Apr-3 Geble, Radolfzell #672/R est:4700

£3654 $5663 €5700 Dancing (25x16cm-10x6in) col chk exec.c.1930 prov. 6-Dec-2 Ketterer, Munich #105/R est:3800-4800

£4038 $6260 €6300 Untitled (35x50cm-14x20in) s.d.1973 pastel. 7-Dec-2 Ketterer, Hamburg #312/R est:6500-7500

£10127 $16000 €16000 Untitled (65x50cm-26x20in) s.d.1962 s.d.19.Juin 62 prov. 27-Nov-2 Dr Fritz Nagel, Stuttgart #3165/R est:16000

ACKERMANN, Otto (1872-1953) German

£345 $548 €500 Runkel an der Lahn (53x60cm-21x24in) s. 8-Mar-3 Arnold, Frankfurt #533/R

ACKERMANN, Peter (1934-) German

£1923 $3038 €3000 Albrechthoflichtspiele (80x100cm-31x39in) s.d.1969. 14-Nov-2 Neumeister, Munich #510/R est:1500-2000

ACKERT, E (19th C) German?

£811 $1250 €1217 Rendered architectural scene of a ruined abbey (43x38cm-17x15in) s. after Carl George Adolf Hassenpflug. 25-Oct-2 Aspire, Cleveland #3/R est:1500-2500

ACLE, Rosa (?) Uruguayan

£962 $1500 €1443 Composicion (50x54cm-20x21in) s. cardboard. 30-Jul-2 Galleria Y Remates, Montevideo #89/R est:2000-2500

ACS, Agostos (1889-1947) Hungarian

£1282 $2013 €2000 Loving couple (80x132cm-31x52in) s. 10-Dec-2 Dorotheum, Vienna #6/R est:2200-2400

ADAM, Albrecht (1786-1862) German

£608 $949 €900 Brown horse called Wolga (39x35cm-15x14in) i. 31-Mar-3 Dr Fritz Nagel, Stuttgart #7096/R

£1127 $1814 €1600 Lioness with cubs (27x40cm-11x16in) s. i. verso board on panel. 7-May-3 Michael Zeller, Lindau #606/R est:400

£6090 $9256 €9500 Paddock with horse and foal (29x39cm-11x15in) s.d.1854 lit. 11-Jul-2 Allgauer, Kempten #2408/R est:9500

£10692 $16679 €17000 White horse in stable (33x28cm-13x11in) mono. pair. 19-Sep-2 Dr Fritz Nagel, Stuttgart #906/R est:15000

£42000 $68880 €63000 Konig Wilhelm I von Wurttemberg hoch zu ross - King William I of Wurttember on horseback (69x60cm-27x24in) s.d.1838 prov. 3-Jun-3 Sotheby's, London #2/R est:8000-12000

£44000 $72160 €66000 Alexander, Herzog von Wurttemberg - Alexander, Duke of Wurttemberg (70x60cm-28x24in) s.d.1830 prov. 3-Jun-3 Sotheby's, London #1/R est:8000-12000

ADAM, Auguste (19th C) German

£1900 $2983 €2850 Cardinal on his terrace (49x28cm-19x11in) s.d.1880. 21-Nov-2 Christie's, Kensington #146/R est:2000-3000

ADAM, Benno (1812-1892) German

£1447 $2257 €2300 Dogs and hounds (43x58cm-17x23in) s.d.1847. 20-Sep-2 Semenzato, Venice #206/R

£2400 $3792 €3600 Bernese mountain dog with it's litter (37x48cm-15x19in) s.d.1862. 28-Nov-2 Christie's, Kensington #324/R est:6000-8000

£2469 $4000 €3704 Landscape (26x37cm-10x15in) s. paper on canvas. 23-Jan-3 Sotheby's, New York #153/R

£4930 $7937 €7000 Cattle in alpine meadow (60x78cm-24x31in) s.d.1840. 7-May-3 Michael Zeller, Lindau #607/R est:7000

ADAM, Edmond Victor Charles (1868-1938) French
£1613 $2548 €2500 Stamboul navigant par vent arriere (62x92cm-24x36in) s.d.1903. 19-Dec-2 Delvaux, Paris #53/R
£2436 $3824 €3800 Paquebot (63x92cm-25x36in) s.d.1909. 15-Dec-2 Mercier & Cie, Lille #368/R

ADAM, Edouard (1847-1929) French
£1500 $2280 €2250 Austriana under reduced sail (61x91cm-24x36in) s.i.d.1881. 15-Aug-2 Bonhams, New Bond Street #349/R est:1500-2000
£1500 $2430 €2250 Swedish barque Wakefield running out of Le Havre (60x91cm-24x36in) 21-May-3 Christie's, Kensington #589/R est:1000-1500
£1600 $2592 €2400 P and O steamer reefed down in heavy seas (62x91cm-24x36in) s.i.d.1877. 21-May-3 Christie's, Kensington #572/R est:1000-1500
£1700 $2754 €2550 British steamer Rex running out of Le Havre (62x91cm-24x36in) 21-May-3 Christie's, Kensington #587/R est:1500-2500
£1800 $2736 €2700 Barque Shon Quilt leaving Le Havre (58x87cm-23x34in) s.i.d.1876. 15-Aug-2 Bonhams, New Bond Street #348/R est:2000-3000
£2147 $3371 €3350 Vapeur (63x92cm-25x36in) s.d.1906. 24-Nov-2 Lesieur & Le Bars, Le Havre #1/R
£2247 $3550 €3550 Trois-mats Dugay Trouin (60x92cm-24x36in) s. 29-Nov-2 Drouot Estimations, Paris #67
£2600 $4082 €3900 Boats off Le Havre (44x65cm-17x26in) s.i.d.1883. 16-Dec-2 Sotheby's, Olympia #73/R est:1000-1500
£4389 $6846 €6584 Barque Ceraster - voyage (60x90cm-24x35in) s.d.1877. 10-Nov-2 Dunbar Sloane, Auckland #20 est:10000-15000 (NZ.D 14000)
£5921 $9000 €8882 Ship, Cape Sable, leaving Le Havre (61x91cm-24x36in) s.d.1880. 17-Aug-2 North East Auctions, Portsmouth #943/R est:10000-15000
£9211 $14000 €13817 US Ship, Charles Dennis, leaving Cap de la Heve, Le Harve (61x91cm-24x36in) prov. 17-Aug-2 North East Auctions, Portsmouth #939/R est:15000-20000

ADAM, Emil (1843-1924) German
£2740 $4274 €4000 Cheeky little dog (48x60cm-19x24in) s.i.d.1960. 10-Apr-3 Dorotheum, Vienna #92/R est:2000-2500

ADAM, Eugen (1817-1880) German
£633 $981 €1000 Gypsy idyll (56x69cm-22x27in) s. 25-Sep-2 Neumeister, Munich #534/R
£845 $1403 €1200 Les marchands ambulants probablement en Amerique du Sud (25x20cm-10x8in) s.d.1847 cardboard. 13-Jun-3 Rabourdin & Choppin de Janvry, Paris #86/R
£2405 $3800 €3800 Resting gypsy (56x69cm-22x27in) s. 28-Nov-2 Dorotheum, Vienna #206/R est:4500-5500
Works on paper
£655 $1022 €983 Turkish tradesmen by coast (22x32cm-9x13in) s.d.1850 W/C. 6-Nov-2 Dobiaschofsky, Bern #303 est:1900 (S.FR 1500)

ADAM, Hans (?) ?
£256 $397 €400 Hope, grief, pain (52x41cm-20x16in) s.d.1947 s.i. verso. 6-Dec-2 Karlheinz Kaupp, Staufen #2117

ADAM, Josef (1883-?) German
£261 $418 €400 Dutch tavern room with dice players (55x45cm-22x18in) s. lit. 10-Jan-3 Allgauer, Kempten #1509/R
£261 $418 €400 Dutch tavern room with figures (56x46cm-22x18in) s. 10-Jan-3 Allgauer, Kempten #1510/R

ADAM, Joseph Denovan (1842-1896) British
£700 $1092 €1050 Ayrshire cattle at Knockdon, Maybole, Aryshire (66x91cm-26x36in) s. i.verso. 17-Oct-2 Bonhams, Edinburgh #265/R
£1800 $2844 €2700 Ayshire bull and other cattle in a landscape (51x76cm-20x30in) init.d.1873. 2-Dec-2 Bonhams, Bath #90/R est:600-800
£2000 $3040 €3000 Cattle on a highland road (51x84cm-20x33in) s. 28-Aug-2 Sotheby's, London #878/R est:1500-2000
£3600 $5688 €5400 Highland cattle being fed by a man from a wheelbarrow in snowy landscape (53x66cm-21x26in) s. 18-Dec-2 John Nicholson, Haslemere #1219/R est:2500-3000
£13800 $22494 €20010 Still life studies with fruit (61x51cm-24x20in) s.d.1859 panel pair. 16-Jul-3 Sotheby's, Olympia #39/R est:8000-12000
Works on paper
£750 $1215 €1125 Within the fold (91x61cm-36x24in) s.d.1883 W/C exhib. 23-May-3 Lyon & Turnbull, Edinburgh #68/R
£4800 $7488 €7200 Highland cattle (165x122cm-65x48in) s.d.1889 chl paper on canvas prov. 14-Apr-3 Sotheby's, London #42/R est:2000-3000

ADAM, Joseph Denovan (jnr) (?-c.1935) British
£350 $536 €525 Stag (34x24cm-13x9in) init. board. 22-Aug-2 Bonhams, Edinburgh #1080
Works on paper
£1450 $2248 €2175 Calves fascinated by a parasol (59x96cm-23x38in) s. W/C over pencil htd stopping out bodycol. 2-Oct-2 Bonhams, Knowle #55/R est:1500-2500

ADAM, Joseph and Joseph Denovan (19th C) British
£2564 $4026 €4000 Springtime on Clydeside (54x79cm-21x31in) s.d.1867. 21-Nov-2 Weidler, Nurnberg #6759/R

ADAM, Julius II (1852-1913) German
£1769 $2812 €2600 Cat wearing red collar lying on blanket (10x16cm-4x6in) s. panel. 19-Mar-3 Neumeister, Munich #497/R est:1200
£6289 $10000 €9434 Playful kittens (24x32cm-9x13in) s.i.d.1886 panel. 7-Mar-3 Skinner, Boston #587/R est:6000-8000

ADAM, Lambert Sigisbert (attrib) (1700-1759) French
Sculpture
£2885 $4471 €4500 Abondance versant ses dons sur la terre (59cm-23in) terracotta lit. 9-Dec-2 Rabourdin & Choppin de Janvry, Paris #32/R

ADAM, Patrick William (1854-1929) British
£900 $1377 €1350 River landscape, summer (47x36cm-19x14in) s.d.1897. 22-Aug-2 Bonhams, Edinburgh #1078
£3200 $4864 €4800 Stella (75x45cm-30x18in) s.i.d.1900. 28-Aug-2 Sotheby's, London #914/R est:2000-3000

ADAM, Patrick William (attrib) (1854-1929) British
Works on paper
£1000 $1560 €1500 Still life of Irises in a Chinese vase (56x33cm-22x13in) indis sig. pastel. 14-Apr-3 Sotheby's, London #95/R est:800-1200

ADAM, Richard Benno (1873-1937) German
£588 $965 €900 Farmer ploughing (26x30cm-10x12in) s.i. verso canvas on board. 5-Feb-3 Neumeister, Munich #667/R

ADAM, Robert (1728-1792) British
Works on paper
£36000 $57240 €54000 Design for finishing the dome room at Register Office, Edinburgh (60x43cm-24x17in) i. pencil folio of seven. 20-Mar-3 Sotheby's, London #264/R est:5000-8000

ADAM, Victor (1801-1866) French
£2866 $4471 €4500 French infantry from the Napoleonic Wars (38x46cm-15x18in) s. 6-Nov-2 Hugo Ruef, Munich #1001/R est:2200
Works on paper
£387 $624 €550 At the blacksmiths (14x21cm-6x8in) s. W/C. 7-May-3 Michael Zeller, Lindau #608/R
£621 $981 €900 Horse circus (30x42cm-12x17in) s. i. verso pencil htd white. 4-Apr-3 Venator & Hansten, Koln #1742
£922 $1540 €1300 La promenade en caleche (20x31cm-8x12in) s. pen brown ink W/C gouache. 19-Jun-3 Piasa, Paris #150/R

ADAM, William (1846-1931) American
£705 $1100 €1058 River landscape. 21-Sep-2 Harvey Clar, Oakland #1531
£1205 $2000 €1747 Flower garden off the veranda, Monterey (61x91cm-24x36in) s. canvasboard prov. 11-Jun-3 Butterfields, San Francisco #4216/R est:3000-5000

ADAM-SALOMON, Antoine Samuel (1818-1881) French
Photographs
£9295 $14686 €14500 Philosophe (27x21cm-11x8in) mono.i. salt print. 16-Nov-2 Christie's, Paris #209/R est:20000-25000

ADAMETZ, Heinrich Emil (1884-1971) German
£570 $883 €900 Self portrait (61x48cm-24x19in) s.d.1955 canvas on panel study verso. 28-Sep-2 Ketterer, Hamburg #311/R
£759 $1177 €1200 Bathers (110x79cm-43x31in) s.d.1966 i. stretcher. 28-Sep-2 Ketterer, Hamburg #312/R

ADAMI, Valerio (1935-) Italian
£3741 $5949 €5500 Interior (50x60cm-20x24in) s.i.d.1960. 1-Mar-3 Meeting Art, Vercelli #642
£4101 $6725 €5700 L'adulterio della moglie negoziante. s.i.d.Janvier 63 verso exhib. 4-Jun-3 Marc Kohn, Paris #65/R est:5000-7000
£4114 $6418 €6500 Study (60x50cm-24x20in) s.i.d.2000. 14-Sep-2 Meeting Art, Vercelli #801/R

£4225	$7014	€6000	Professione pittore (67x42cm-26x17in) s.d.74 i.verso acrylic. 18-Jun-3 Anaf, Lyon #40/R est:4000-5000
£4645	$7339	€7200	Study for easy-going helper (73x60cm-29x24in) s.i.verso painted 1968. 18-Dec-2 Christie's, Rome #306/R est:12000
£5000	$8350	€7250	Contenitore (99x80cm-39x31in) s.i.d.14.2.68 verso prov.exhib. 27-Jun-3 Christie's, London #179/R est:6000-8000
£5449	$8446	€8500	Stuy for satyr (65x81cm-26x32in) s.i.verso acrylic painted 1995. 4-Dec-2 Finarte, Milan #261/R est:9000
£6597	$10490	€9500	Centaure (81x60cm-32x24in) s.i.verso. 1-May-3 Meeting Art, Vercelli #479
£8013	$11699	€12500	Gym (100x81cm-39x32in) s.i.d.68 s.i.d.verso acrylic. 5-Jun-2 Il Ponte, Milan #121 est:12000-15000
£9000	$14760	€13500	Interno Svedese (92x73cm-36x29in) s.i.d.18.11.70 d.8.2.71 verso prov. 6-Feb-3 Christie's, London #656/R est:5000-7000
£17647	$28235	€27000	Public toilets (146x114cm-57x45in) s.i.verso acrylic painted 1996 lit. 4-Jan-3 Meeting Art, Vercelli #529 est:20000

Works on paper

£1100	$1837	€1595	Il metropolitan (36x48cm-14x19in) s.i.d.14.168 pencil prov. 24-Jun-3 Sotheby's, Olympia #104/R est:800-1200
£1519	$2354	€2400	Personnages a l'antique (44x56cm-17x22in) s. W/C ink. 28-Sep-2 Cornette de St.Cyr, Paris #213 est:3000-3500
£2128	$3447	€3000	Sans titre (75x55cm-30x22in) s. s.d.verso W/C gouache. 23-May-3 Binoche, Paris #28 est:2000-3000
£4252	$6760	€6250	Lo stagno (72x54cm-28x21in) s.i.d.84 W/C. 26-Feb-3 Artcurial Briest, Paris #386/R est:4000-4500
£4872	$7649	€7600	Attack (57x78cm-22x31in) s.i.d.71 mixed media prov. 20-Nov-2 Pandolfini, Florence #124/R

ADAMOFF, Helena (1906-) Russian

£800	$1272	€1200	Jardin au ciel jaune (55x38cm-22x15in) s.d.1958 prov. 20-Mar-3 Sotheby's, Olympia #167/R

ADAMS, Ansel (1902-1984) American

Photographs

£1700	$2754	€2550	Valley view from Wawoma Tunnel (16x22cm-6x9in) s. i.verso silver print card exec.c.1960. 22-May-3 Sotheby's, London #135/R est:1500-2000
£1800	$2916	€2700	Mirror Lake (19x24cm-7x9in) s. i.verso silver print card exec.c.1960. 22-May-3 Sotheby's, London #134/R est:1500-2000
£1899	$3000	€2849	Tree stump and mist, Northern Cascades, Washington (39x49cm-15x19in) s.num.74/115 photograph. 23-Apr-3 Sotheby's, New York #9/R est:4000-6000
£1923	$3000	€2885	Half Dome, moon (24x18cm-9x7in) s.i. verso silver. 21-Oct-2 Swann Galleries, New York #69/R est:1400-1800
£2000	$3240	€3000	El Capitan (24x17cm-9x7in) s. i.verso silver print card exec.c.1960. 22-May-3 Sotheby's, London #133/R est:1500-2000
£2000	$3240	€3000	Half dome, Merced river, winter (18x23cm-7x9in) s. i.verso silver print card exec.c.1960. 22-May-3 Sotheby's, London #136/R est:1500-2000
£2057	$3250	€3086	Leaf pattern, Glacier Bay National Monument, Alaska (18x23cm-7x9in) s. photograph prov.exhib.lit. 23-Apr-3 Sotheby's, New York #93/R est:6000-9000
£2147	$3500	€3221	Morning Merced River Canyon, Yosemite National Park (19x24cm-7x9in) s. i.verso gelatin silver print. 12-Feb-3 Christie's, Rockefeller NY #278/R est:4000-6000
£2308	$3600	€3462	Alfred Stieglitz at an American Place (16x21cm-6x8in) s.i.d. verso silver. 21-Oct-2 Swann Galleries, New York #65/R est:2500-3500
£2532	$4000	€3798	White tombstone San Francisco (22x16cm-9x6in) s. photograph prov.lit. 23-Apr-3 Sotheby's, New York #95/R est:8000-12000
£2532	$4000	€3798	Northern California coast redwoods (24x29cm-9x11in) s. photograph prov.lit. 23-Apr-3 Sotheby's, New York #97/R est:3000-5000
£2597	$4000	€3896	Siesta Lake, Yosemite National Park, California (19x24cm-7x9in) s.num.177 photograph. 24-Oct-2 Sotheby's, New York #10/R est:4000-6000
£2597	$4000	€3896	Rushing water, Merced River (21x24cm-8x9in) s.num.13 photograph. 24-Oct-2 Sotheby's, New York #11/R est:4000-6000
£2597	$4000	€3896	Teklanika River, Mount Mckinley National Park, Alaska (23x29cm-9x11in) s.nu.177 photograph. 24-Oct-2 Sotheby's, New York #12/R est:4000-6000
£2690	$4250	€4035	Oak tree - snowstorm (24x20cm-9x8in) s.num11 photograph. 23-Apr-3 Sotheby's, New York #32/R est:4000-6000
£2761	$4500	€4142	River, cliffs, autumn, Yosemite National Park (26x33cm-10x13in) s. s.i.verso gelatin silver print. 12-Feb-3 Christie's, Rockefeller NY #279/R est:4000-6000
£2848	$4500	€4500	Golden Gate before building of bridge (23x28cm-9x11in) i.d.1932 verso silver gelatin lit.exhib. 28-Nov-2 Villa Grisebach, Berlin #1100/R est:3000-4000
£2848	$4500	€4272	Upper Yosemite Falls, spring (25x19cm-10x7in) s.num.13 prov. 23-Apr-3 Sotheby's, New York #6/R est:3000-5000
£2848	$4500	€4272	Arches, North Court, Mission San Xavier del tac, Tucson, Arizona (39x49cm-15x19in) s.num.74/115 photograph. 23-Apr-3 Sotheby's, New York #11/R est:4000-6000
£2945	$4800	€4418	Silverton, Colorado (39x49cm-15x19in) s.num.13/10 gelatin silver print. 12-Feb-3 Christie's, Rockefeller NY #276/R est:5000-7000
£3165	$5000	€4748	Ice on Ellery Lake, Sierra Nevada (33x48cm-13x19in) s.num.34/50 photograph. 23-Apr-3 Sotheby's, New York #19/R est:6000-9000
£3481	$5500	€5222	Moon and half dome (25x20cm-10x8in) s.num.12 photograph. 23-Apr-3 Sotheby's, New York #4/R est:3500-5000
£3481	$5500	€5222	Cemetery statue and oil derricks, Long Beach, California (38x47cm-15x19in) s.num.74/115 photograph. 23-Apr-3 Sotheby's, New York #10/R est:3000-5000
£3797	$6000	€5696	Trees and cliffs of Eagle Park, winter, Yosemite Valley, California (34x49cm-13x19in) s.num.44/50 photograph. 23-Apr-3 Sotheby's, New York #31/R est:5000-7000
£5063	$8000	€7595	Frozen lake and cliff, Sierra Nevada, California (26x34cm-10x13in) s.i.verso photograph. 23-Apr-3 Sotheby's, New York #3/R est:6000-9000
£5063	$8000	€7595	Half dome, blowing snow, Yosemite National Park, California (40x49cm-16x19in) s.num.74/115 photograph. 23-Apr-3 Sotheby's, New York #5/R est:8000-12000
£5195	$8000	€7793	Desert flower (24x32cm-9x13in) s.i. photograph prov. 22-Oct-2 Sotheby's, New York #2/R est:10000-15000
£5519	$8500	€8279	El Capitan - winter (24x19cm-9x7in) s. photograph. 24-Oct-2 Sotheby's, New York #14/R est:3000-5000
£5696	$9000	€8544	Ahwahnee Hotel, Yosemite (47x36cm-19x14in) gelatin silver print mounted on board prov.lit. 24-Apr-3 Phillips, New York #128/R est:8000-12000
£5696	$9000	€8544	Canyon de chelly, Zrizona (39x49cm-15x19in) s. photograph. 23-Apr-3 Sotheby's, New York #18/R est:7000-10000
£5696	$9000	€8544	Moonrise, Hernandez, New Mexico (37x49cm-15x19in) i. photograph prov. 23-Apr-3 Sotheby's, New York #26/R est:10000-15000
£6013	$9500	€9020	White branches, Mono Lake, California (49x39cm-19x15in) s.num.74/115 photograph. 23-Apr-3 Sotheby's, New York #27/R est:6000-9000
£6410	$9936	€10000	Sunrise, Mt McKinley and Wonder Lake, Alaska (38x48cm-15x19in) s. gelatin silver lit. 6-Dec-2 Bassenge, Berlin #4600/R est:15000
£6962	$11000	€10443	Thunderstorm, Yosemite Valley, California (49x38cm-19x15in) s.num.44/50 photograph. 23-Apr-3 Sotheby's, New York #22/R est:6000-9000
£7143	$11000	€10715	Thunderstorm, Yosemite Valley, California (49x38cm-19x15in) s.i.d.1981. 24-Oct-2 Sotheby's, New York #18/R est:8000-12000
£8228	$13000	€12342	Frozen lake and cliffs, Kaweah Gap, Sierra Nevada (22x25cm-9x10in) s.i.d.1932 photograph prov.exhib.lit. 23-Apr-3 Sotheby's, New York #92/R est:10000-15000
£8861	$14000	€13292	Yosemite in snow (23x18cm-9x7in) with sig. s.d.1933 verso gelatin silver print. 22-Apr-3 Butterfields, San Francisco #2411/R est:3000-5000
£9494	$15000	€14241	Icicles, Ahwahnee Hotel, Yosemite National Park (35x27cm-14x11in) s. gelatin silver print prov.lit. 22-Apr-3 Christie's, Rockefeller NY #11/R est:15000-20000
£11039	$17000	€16559	Winter sunrise, Sierra Nevada from Lone Pine, California (38x49cm-15x19in) s.i.d.1944 photograph. 24-Oct-2 Sotheby's, New York #13/R est:15000-25000
£11688	$18000	€17532	Monolith, the face of half dome, Yosemite National Park, CA (48x36cm-19x14in) s. s.i.verso photograph prov.lit. 22-Oct-2 Sotheby's, New York #3/R est:12000-18000
£13924	$22000	€20886	Clearing winter storm (40x49cm-16x19in) s. photograph. 23-Apr-3 Sotheby's, New York #7/R est:20000-30000
£14286	$22000	€21429	Clearing winter storm (40x49cm-16x19in) s.i.d.1977 photograph prov. 24-Oct-2 Sotheby's, New York #8/R est:20000-30000
£15190	$24000	€22785	Oak tree, snowstorm, Yosemite National Park, California (49x39cm-19x15in) s.i.verso photograph. 23-Apr-3 Sotheby's, New York #8/R est:10000-15000
£15190	$24000	€22785	Winter sunrise, Sierra Nevada from Lone Pine (38x49cm-15x19in) s. photograph. 23-Apr-3 Sotheby's, New York #21/R est:15000-25000
£16883	$26000	€25325	Moonrise, Hernandez, New Mexico (38x49cm-15x19in) s.i. photograph. 24-Oct-2 Sotheby's, New York #15/R est:25000-35000
£19481	$30000	€29222	Monolith, face of half dome (20x15cm-8x6in) s. photograph prov.lit. 24-Oct-2 Sotheby's, New York #17/R est:30000-40000

£20253 $32000 €30380 Yosemite Valley (29x21cm-11x8in) photographs 10 from portfolio III prov.lit. 23-Apr-3 Sotheby's, New York #99/R est:15000-20000
£22785 $36000 €34178 Moonrise, Hernandez, New Mexico (39x49cm-15x19in) s. photograph. 23-Apr-3 Sotheby's, New York #12/R est:25000-35000
£23313 $38000 €34970 Moonrise, Hernandez, New Mexico (39x49cm-15x19in) s. i.verso gelatin silver print. 12-Feb-3 Christie's, Rockefeller NY #280/R est:25000-35000
£26623 $41000 €39935 Untitled (24x19cm-9x7in) photograph portfolio. 24-Oct-2 Sotheby's, New York #22/R est:40000-60000
£29747 $47000 €44621 Yosemite Valley (29x21cm-11x8in) photograph portfolio. 23-Apr-3 Sotheby's, New York #17/R est:50000-70000

ADAMS, Ansel and PETERSEN, Rolf (20th C) American
Photographs
£2051 $3200 €3077 Mount Williamson, Sierra Nevada from Manzanar, California (18x22cm-7x9in) i. verso silver. 21-Oct-2 Swann Galleries, New York #67/R est:2500-3500

ADAMS, Anton (1912-) British
£220 $350 €330 English hunt scene (180x251cm-71x99in) s. 7-Mar-3 Jackson's, Cedar Falls #536/R

ADAMS, C J (1857-1931) British
Works on paper
£1100 $1716 €1650 Figures with plough horses and cart returning home (38x53cm-15x21in) s. 17-Sep-2 Gorringes, Bexhill #1295 est:200-300

ADAMS, Charles James (1857-1931) British
£2200 $3498 €3300 On a highland road (66x102cm-26x40in) 6-Mar-3 Christie's, Kensington #155/R est:500-800
£2600 $4134 €3900 Loading the cattle, Isle of Skye (51x76cm-20x30in) 6-Mar-3 Christie's, Kensington #154/R est:700-1000
Works on paper
£380 $589 €570 Rural landscape with a man and his dog resting by s country path (34x24cm-13x9in) s. W/C. 1-Oct-2 Fellows & Sons, Birmingham #178/R
£400 $624 €600 Harvest time (8x12cm-3x5in) W/C. 20-Sep-2 Dee Atkinson & Harrison, Driffield #646
£520 $842 €754 Heather open landscape (37x55cm-15x22in) s. W/C. 24-May-3 Windibank, Dorking #344
£1000 $1550 €1500 Duck pond (31x23cm-12x9in) s. pencil W/C htd white. 26-Sep-2 Mellors & Kirk, Nottingham #632 est:800-1200
£1450 $2291 €2175 Collecting the flock (27x37cm-11x15in) s. W/C. 7-Apr-3 Bonhams, Bath #28/R est:400-600
£1550 $2449 €2248 Landscape with cattle (33x51cm-13x20in) s. W/C. 23-Jul-3 Brightwells, Leominster #908/R est:400-600
£2300 $3703 €3450 Cattle and drover on a country path. Sheep resting beneath trees (25x38cm-10x15in) s. W/C pair. 19-Feb-3 Mallams, Oxford #354/R est:200-300

ADAMS, Charles James (attrib) (1857-1931) British
Works on paper
£950 $1549 €1425 Rural scene with cottage and figures among haystacks (18x28cm-7x11in) s. W/C. 7-Feb-3 Dee Atkinson & Harrison, Driffield #735

ADAMS, Charles Partridge (1858-1942) American
£1553 $2500 €2330 Stream in landscape (25x38cm-10x15in) s. prov. 18-Feb-3 John Moran, Pasadena #171 est:1500-2500
£1763 $2750 €2645 Monterey coastline (23x30cm-9x12in) s. prov.lit. 9-Nov-2 Santa Fe Art, Santa Fe #109/R est:2000-3000
£5590 $9000 €8385 Mt Spris, Colorado, sunset light in June (61x91cm-24x36in) s. i.stretcher prov. 18-Feb-3 John Moran, Pasadena #98 est:15000-20000
£5988 $10000 €8683 Longs Peak and meeker from Fish Creek (25x36cm-10x14in) i.on stretcher. 17-Jun-3 John Moran, Pasadena #7 est:2500-3500
£17081 $27500 €25622 Panoramic Colorado landscape (34x44cm-13x17in) s. prov. 18-Feb-3 John Moran, Pasadena #67 est:20000-30000
Works on paper
£570 $900 €855 Western landscape. Riverbed (13x18cm-5x7in) s. one W/C gouache board one W/C by William Louis Sonntag. 2-Apr-3 Doyle, New York #3/R
£1118 $1800 €1677 Landscape of snow capped mountains, Estes Park, Colorado (13x18cm-5x7in) s. W/C artist board prov. 18-Feb-3 John Moran, Pasadena #4 est:800-1200

ADAMS, Clement (19th C) British?
£450 $698 €675 Highland landscape with cattle beside a loch (46x81cm-18x32in) s. 31-Oct-2 Duke & Son, Dorchester #237/R

ADAMS, Douglas (1853-1920) British
£250 $418 €363 Derwent water (23x36cm-9x14in) s. 20-Jun-3 Keys, Aylsham #698

ADAMS, Frances Mathilde (1784-1863) British
Works on paper
£676 $1054 €1000 Still life of flowers and insects (52x43cm-20x17in) s.d.1823 W/C. 31-Mar-3 Finarte Semenzato, Milan #421

ADAMS, Frank (fl.1910-1935) British
Works on paper
£4348 $7000 €6522 Seated Alice watching rushing White Rabbit (41x25cm-16x10in) s. W/C ink lit. 10-May-3 Illustration House, New York #35/R est:3500-5000

ADAMS, Franklin (20th C) American
£226 $350 €339 Abstraction (71x61cm-28x24in) s.verso acrylic collage. 7-Dec-2 Neal Auction Company, New Orleans #927
£416 $650 €624 Abstraction (91x91cm-36x36in) s.verso polymer tempera masonite. 12-Oct-2 Neal Auction Company, New Orleans #1388

ADAMS, Geoffrey (20th C) British
£650 $1073 €943 North barrier (55x86cm-22x34in) s. s.i.d.1962 verso oil collage on board. 3-Jul-3 Christie's, Kensington #730/R

ADAMS, George Gammond (1821-1898) British
Sculpture
£2000 $3220 €3000 Venus and Cupid (27x27cm-11x11in) i.d.1872 medallion prov. 20-Feb-3 Christie's, London #176/R

ADAMS, Herbert (1858-1945) American
Sculpture
£1210 $1900 €1815 Debutante 1914 (38cm-15in) s.i.d.MCMXIV brown pat bronze. 10-Dec-2 Doyle, New York #97 est:3000-5000

ADAMS, James L (fl.1874-1890) British
Works on paper
£850 $1394 €1275 Oat field - Rievaulx Abbey. On the Yorkshire Moors (29x48cm-11x19in) s.i.d.1878 W/C. 10-Feb-3 David Duggleby, Scarborough #563/R

ADAMS, John Clayton (1840-1906) British
£250 $388 €375 Rural landscape with bridge over river in the foreground (37x48cm-15x19in) s. 29-Oct-2 Henry Adams, Chichester #509
£300 $474 €450 Crafter's cottage (13x22cm-5x9in) s. board. 12-Nov-2 Bonhams, Knightsbridge #148/R
£1000 $1600 €1500 Cattle watering in a river landscape (51x76cm-20x30in) s. 7-Jan-3 Bonhams, Knightsbridge #207/R est:1000-1500
£1800 $2880 €2700 Ewhurst Hill, near Guildford (70x93cm-28x37in) s. 7-Jan-3 Bonhams, Knightsbridge #206/R est:1800-2500
£2000 $3120 €3000 Harvesting, Surrey (41x61cm-16x24in) s.d.1873. 7-Nov-2 Christie's, Kensington #114/R est:2500-3500
£2500 $3975 €3750 Golden autumn (61x91cm-24x36in) s.d.1896. 6-Mar-3 Christie's, Kensington #439/R est:2500-3500
£4800 $7584 €7200 Fall of the blossom (98x106cm-39x42in) s.d.1886. 2-Dec-2 Sotheby's, London #82/R est:4000-6000
£5500 $8580 €8250 Haymaking (56x92cm-22x36in) s.d.1871. 7-Nov-2 Christie's, Kensington #118/R est:3000-5000

ADAMS, Lilian (fl.1892-1911) British
Works on paper
£241 $378 €362 Country road (46x34cm-18x13in) s. pastel. 25-Nov-2 Hodgins, Calgary #388/R (C.D 600)

ADAMS, Norman (1927-) British
£650 $1034 €975 Winter scene - feeding sheep II (90x120cm-35x47in) init.d.90. 18-Mar-3 Bonhams, Knightsbridge #1
£1800 $2808 €2700 Artist in his environment (125x125cm-49x49in) init.d.85. 12-Sep-2 Sotheby's, Olympia #223/R est:2000-3000
Works on paper
£380 $593 €570 All Saints (50x66cm-20x26in) init.i.d.86 pencil W/C. 17-Sep-2 Rosebery Fine Art, London #598

ADAMS, Robert (1917-) British
Photographs
£2658 $4200 €3987 Abandoned citrus trees, vacant lot, Ontario, California (36x47cm-14x19in) s.i.d.1985 num.2/30 verso gelatin silver print prov. 24-Apr-3 Phillips, New York #179/R est:3000-4000
£7595 $12000 €11393 Summer night, Colorado (13x13cm-5x5in) s.i.d.1978/1985 gelatin silver print prov.lit. 22-Apr-3 Christie's, Rockefeller NY #68/R est:12000-15000
£15190 $24000 €22785 Untitled (15x15cm-6x6in) i.verso six gelatin silver print prov. 24-Apr-3 Phillips, New York #171/R est:8000-12000

ADAMS, Wayman (1883-1959) American
£2108 $3500 €3057 Untitled (38x28cm-15x11in) board. 13-Jun-3 Du Mouchelle, Detroit #2106/R est:700-1200

ADAMS, William Patrick (attrib) (?) American?
£1424 $2250 €2136 Women standing on a wooden bridge (53x36cm-21x14in) 15-Nov-2 Du Mouchelle, Detroit #2002/R est:600-1000

ADAMSON, Crawfurd (1953-) British
£500 $780 €750 La Cote Sauvage (110x120cm-43x47in) s.i.d.1988 stretcher. 17-Oct-2 Bonhams, Edinburgh #99/R

ADAMSON, Harry Curieux (1916-) American
£5063 $8000 €7341 Timber line royalty - stone sheep (71x97cm-28x38in) s.d.1986 prov.lit. 26-Jul-3 Coeur d'Alene, Hayden #87/R est:10000-20000
£8228 $13000 €11931 Aleutian throne room - emperor geese (61x91cm-24x36in) s.d.1984 prov.lit. 26-Jul-3 Coeur d'Alene, Hayden #212/R est:10000-20000
£9494 $15000 €13766 Evening Flotilla Canvasbacks (61x91cm-24x36in) s. prov.lit. 26-Jul-3 Coeur d'Alene, Hayden #30/R est:10000-20000
£11392 $18000 €16518 Flurry of blacks (61x91cm-24x36in) s. prov.lit. 26-Jul-3 Coeur d'Alene, Hayden #78/R est:10000-20000

ADAMSON, Robert and HILL, David Octavius (19th C) British
Photographs
£2125 $3400 €3188 Study of a man posing with a bagpipe, probably John Ban MacKenzie (15x10cm-6x4in) salted paper print from calotype negative. 15-May-3 Swann Galleries, New York #231/R est:3500-4500
£3171 $5200 €4757 Reclining figure in kilt (14x19cm-6x7in) i. salted paper print exec.c.1844. 10-Feb-3 Swann Galleries, New York #2/R est:3000-5000
£3800 $6156 €5700 Miss Bell (16x20cm-6x8in) i.verso salt print exec.c.1840 lit. 21-May-3 Christie's, London #16/R est:1000-1500
£5063 $8000 €7595 Master Miller (20x14cm-8x6in) i. calotype prov.lit. 23-Apr-3 Sotheby's, New York #104/R est:3000-5000
£5696 $9000 €8544 Nasmyth tomb. House of Death (20x15cm-8x6in) calotypes two prov.lit. 23-Apr-3 Sotheby's, New York #105/R est:3000-5000

ADAMSON-ERIC, Eric Karl Hugo (1902-1968) Estonian
£2745 $4502 €4200 Young bare chested woman in clearing (81x65cm-32x26in) s.d.38 panel. 29-Mar-3 Dannenberg, Berlin #536/R est:750

ADAN, Louis Émile (1839-1937) French
£1800 $2862 €2700 An amusing story (21x19cm-8x7in) s. 20-Mar-3 Christie's, Kensington #128/R est:2000-3000
£3896 $6000 €5844 Young boy grinding scissors (54x73cm-21x29in) s. 4-Sep-2 Christie's, Rockefeller NY #323/R est:4000-6000
£6500 $10335 €9750 Elegant ladies at rest beside a pond (78x122cm-31x48in) s. 18-Mar-3 Bonhams, New Bond Street #127/R est:4000-6000
Works on paper
£972 $1546 €1400 Heure du the (39x27cm-15x11in) s.d.1895 W/C. 30-Apr-3 Tajan, Paris #136

ADANSON, J Baptiste (18th C) French
Works on paper
£2482 $4145 €3500 Vue de l'ile de Roda sur le Nil au Caire. Vue de Giza au Caire (35x51cm-14x20in) i. pen grey wash pair. 23-Jun-3 Beaussant & Lefèvre, Paris #189/R est:3000-4000
£3800 $5890 €5700 Genette ov civette des environs de Tunis (48x60cm-19x24in) i.d.1788 W/C prov. 30-Sep-2 Sotheby's, Olympia #551/R est:4000-6000

ADDAMIANO, Natale (1943-) Italian
£1351 $2108 €2000 Animal in landscape (95x105cm-37x41in) s.d.1973. 26-Mar-3 Finarte Semenzato, Milan #101/R

ADDAMS, Charles (1912-1988) American
Works on paper
£2885 $4500 €4328 Couple discuss suitor with their daughter (28x25cm-11x10in) s. pen ink wash W/C en grisaille lit. 9-Nov-2 Illustration House, New York #79/R est:3000-5000
£2950 $4750 €4425 Intrepid explorers about to enter a maze (51x36cm-20x14in) s. pen ink wash gouache sold with tearsheet lit. 10-May-3 Illustration House, New York #13/R est:5000-7000
£3416 $5500 €5124 Wednesday and Pugsley open a refreshment stand (38x33cm-15x13in) s. pen ink wash en grisaille exec.c.1950. 10-May-3 Illustration House, New York #12/R est:5000-8000
£3846 $6000 €5769 Dowagers in theatre balcony, comment on departure of great ape (28x25cm-11x10in) s. pen ink wash W/C en grisaille lit. 9-Nov-2 Illustration House, New York #80/R est:4000-6000
£4658 $7500 €6987 Man in library with variety of weapons, visited by his wife (23x30cm-9x12in) s. pen ink wash gouache exec.c.1940. 10-May-3 Illustration House, New York #14/R est:5000-7000
£4658 $7500 €6987 Leonardo painting the Mona Lisa (30x30cm-12x12in) s. pen ink wash en grisaille lit. 10-May-3 Illustration House, New York #15/R est:5000-7000

ADDERTON, Charles William (1866-?) British
Works on paper
£450 $752 €653 Sandy bay (30x45cm-12x18in) s. W/C. 26-Jun-3 Mellors & Kirk, Nottingham #793
£840 $1386 €1218 Beached boats in a creek (29x44cm-11x17in) s.d.09 W/C. 1-Jul-3 Bearnes, Exeter #467/R
£1000 $1650 €1450 Fishermen's cottages (34x51cm-13x20in) s. W/C. 1-Jul-3 Bearnes, Exeter #469/R est:400-600

ADDEY, Joseph Poole (1852-1922) Irish
Works on paper
£372 $603 €525 Man with dog on a country road (25x37cm-10x15in) s.d.1915 W/C. 20-May-3 Mealy's, Castlecomer #1312/R
£513 $795 €800 Rathfarnham Castle Gate, Dublin (39x54cm-15x21in) s.d.1907 W/C. 3-Dec-2 Bonhams & James Adam, Dublin #118/R
£797 $1307 €1100 Figures on a lane way with goats (38x51cm-15x20in) s.d.1892 W/C. 28-May-3 Bonhams & James Adam, Dublin #41/R est:1000-1500

ADELSWARD, Gustav (1843-1895) French
£3057 $4769 €4800 Peniches dans un paysage fluvial (80x140cm-31x55in) s.d.77. 11-Nov-2 Horta, Bruxelles #133/R est:5000-7500

ADEMOLLO, Luigi (1764-1849) Italian
£2979 $4826 €4200 Scene bucolica. Scena romana. Scene biblica. Scena dall'Odissea. Scena dall'illiade (30x38cm-12x15in) s.d.1839 tempera paper five. 22-May-3 Stadion, Trieste #631/R est:2500-3500
Works on paper
£1282 $2013 €2000 Holy scenes. Chinese ink. 16-Dec-2 Pandolfini, Florence #1
£1329 $2060 €2100 Scene from Roman history (49x40cm-19x16in) i. pen brown wash three. 25-Sep-2 Neumeister, Munich #384/R est:800

ADICKES, David (1927-) American
£641 $1000 €962 Painter with a bird (102x76cm-40x30in) sold with a book about the artist prov. 22-Sep-2 Susanin's, Chicago #5142/R est:600-800

ADLEN, Michel (1899-1980) Russian
£286 $454 €420 La maison au bord du chemin (56x64cm-22x25in) s. 26-Feb-3 Artcurial Briest, Paris #170
£544 $865 €800 Paysage avec une chaumiere (30x55cm-12x22in) s. 3-Mar-3 Claude Boisgirard, Paris #24/R

ADLER, Amy (1966-) ?
Photographs
£13750 $22000 €20625 Mike (101x70cm-40x28in) s.i.d.2001 five cibachrome prints prov. 15-May-3 Christie's, Rockefeller NY #406/R est:25000-35000

ADLER, Edmund (1871-1957) German
£1603 $2484 €2500 Let them all come - Young school boy with stick waiting for his enemies (31x20cm-12x8in) s. panel. 4-Dec-2 Neumeister, Munich #662/R est:2800
£1818 $2945 €2636 Two children in doorway (54x42cm-21x17in) s. 26-May-3 Rasmussen, Copenhagen #1130/R est:25000 (D.KR 19000)

£4131 $6776 €5990 For Grandmother's birthday (55x68cm-22x27in) s. prov. 4-Jun-3 Fischer, Luzern #1149/R est:5000-7000 (S.FR 8800)
£5031 $7748 €8000 Yellow canary (56x69cm-22x27in) s. 23-Oct-2 Christie's, Amsterdam #55/R est:10000-15000
£7186 $12000 €10420 Feeding the young (56x69cm-22x27in) s. prov. 22-Jun-3 Freeman, Philadelphia #17/R est:10000-15000
£8228 $13000 €13000 Broken doll (56x69cm-22x27in) s. 28-Nov-2 Dorotheum, Vienna #252/R est:10000-12000
£8861 $14000 €14000 Dolls' breakfast (56x69cm-22x27in) s. 28-Nov-2 Dorotheum, Vienna #251/R est:10000-12000
£9581 $16000 €13892 Big bother (69x56cm-27x22in) s. prov. 22-Jun-3 Freeman, Philadelphia #19/R est:10000-15000
£14063 $22500 €21095 Honey pot (69x56cm-27x22in) s. 14-May-3 Butterfields, San Francisco #1083/R est:15000-20000

ADLER, Jankel (1895-1949) Polish
£2564 $4000 €3846 Seated woman (65x54cm-26x21in) st.sig. prov. 5-Nov-2 Doyle, New York #3/R est:2000-3000
£5128 $7487 €8000 Still life with pears (63x47cm-25x19in) s. oil mixed media board. 4-Jun-2 Karl & Faber, Munich #157/R est:7000-8000
£7692 $11231 €12000 Flowers in jug (56x38cm-22x15in) s. oil mixed media board. 4-Jun-2 Karl & Faber, Munich #156/R est:7000-8000

ADLER, Jules (1865-1952) French
£513 $805 €800 Sur la route (65x81cm-26x32in) s.d.1906. 16-Dec-2 Millon & Associes, Paris #126
£625 $987 €900 Au verger (46x38cm-18x15in) s. 25-Apr-3 Piasa, Paris #40
£692 $1072 €1100 Portrait de jeune homme (40x32cm-16x13in) s. 30-Oct-2 Artcurial Briest, Paris #173
£755 $1170 €1200 Paysan sur la route (55x47cm-22x19in) s. 4-Oct-2 Tajan, Paris #1

Works on paper
£245 $409 €350 Reunion de famille (39x33cm-15x13in) s. dr. 26-Jun-3 Tajan, Paris #127
£280 $467 €400 Le peintre et le visiteur dans l'atelier (38x32cm-15x13in) s. dr. 26-Jun-3 Tajan, Paris #128

ADLER, Leo (1897-) Austrian
£321 $506 €500 Old steam train in workshop (50x68cm-20x27in) s. board. 18-Nov-2 Dorotheum, Linz #251/R
£412 $663 €618 Via Mala (38x59cm-15x23in) s.d.1961 i. verso board. 7-May-3 Dobiaschofsky, Bern #301/R (S.FR 890)

ADLER, Oscar F (19/20th C) ?
£1097 $1700 €1646 Spring apple trees in bloom (61x76cm-24x30in) s. i.verso. 2-Nov-2 North East Auctions, Portsmouth #37/R

ADLERSPARRE, Sophie (1808-1862) Swedish
£2766 $4287 €4149 Still life of flowers (70x53cm-28x21in) s.d.1858. 3-Dec-2 Bukowskis, Stockholm #22/R est:20000-25000 (S.KR 39000)

ADLOFF, Karl (1819-1863) German
£641 $994 €1000 Sledge ride (31x46cm-12x18in) s. prov. 7-Dec-2 Ketterer, Hamburg #96/R

ADNET, Françoise (1924-) French
£319 $517 €450 Le panier suspendu (41x33cm-16x13in) s. 25-May-3 Feletin, Province #122
£469 $750 €680 Nature morte au violin (33x53cm-13x21in) s. 17-May-3 Selkirks, St. Louis #226
£524 $817 €786 Interior with young ballet dancer (60x92cm-24x36in) s.d.1960. 6-Nov-2 Dobiaschofsky, Bern #304/R (S.FR 1200)
£570 $883 €900 Jeune fille au chapeau de paille (35x27cm-14x11in) s. 29-Sep-2 Eric Pillon, Calais #237/R

ADOLFS, Gerard Pieter (1897-1968) Dutch
£972 $1604 €1400 Indonesian landscape at dusk (30x40cm-12x16in) s.d.32 s.i.d.verso. 1-Jul-3 Christie's, Amsterdam #296/R
£1408 $2268 €2000 Kampong scene (29x39cm-11x15in) s.d.34. 7-May-3 Vendue Huis, Gravenhage #234/R est:2000-2500
£2394 $3855 €3400 Old Soerabaia (29x39cm-11x15in) s. 7-May-3 Vendue Huis, Gravenhage #235/R est:2000-2500

ADOLPH, Carl (18th C) Austrian
£3077 $4831 €4800 Caanards et heron pres d'un etang (75x48cm-30x19in) s.d.1760. 15-Dec-2 Mercier & Cie, Lille #338/R
£5000 $8350 €7250 Landscape with a woodcock, partridge, bird of paradise and other birds (90x135cm-35x53in) s.d.1754. 10-Jul-3 Sotheby's, London #192/R est:8000-12000

ADOLPHE, Albert Jean (1865-1940) American
£370 $600 €555 Portrait of said apple (36x23cm-14x9in) s.i.d.April 12 1965 verso board prov. 24-Jan-3 Freeman, Philadelphia #209/R

ADRIAENSSEN, Alexander (1587-1661) Flemish
£1800 $2898 €2700 Bowl of clams with a plate of fish and oyster on a table (44x63cm-17x25in) panel. 20-Feb-3 Christie's, Kensington #218/R est:1200-1800
£7000 $10920 €10500 Roses and an iris in a glass vase, crab and prawns on a pewter platter on partly draped table (44x56cm-17x22in) mono.d.1656 copper prov. 9-Apr-3 Christie's, London #56/R est:8000-12000

ADRIAN, Marc (1930-) Austrian

Works on paper
£321 $497 €500 No think (34x34cm-13x13in) s.i.d.76 mixed media lit. 6-Dec-2 Karlheinz Kaupp, Staufen #2071/R

ADRIAN-NILSSON, Gosta (1884-1965) Swedish
£1710 $2719 €2565 The water-butt (36x50cm-14x20in) s. panel. 3-Mar-3 Lilla Bukowskis, Stockholm #561 est:15000-20000 (S.KR 23000)
£9110 $14212 €13665 Sailor (43x35cm-17x14in) panel. 5-Nov-2 Bukowskis, Stockholm #38/R est:80000-100000 (S.KR 130000)
£28732 $44821 €43098 Yellow and red figure in landscape (41x39cm-16x15in) s. cardboard. 5-Nov-2 Bukowskis, Stockholm #197/R est:200000-250000 (S.KR 410000)
£57915 $93243 €86873 Head of a smoker (140x75cm-55x30in) s.i.d.1923 exhib.lit. 7-May-3 AB Stockholms Auktionsverk #743/R est:800000-1000000 (S.KR 750000)
£73359 $118108 €110039 Lokstallet - The locomotive stable (62x50cm-24x20in) s. panel painted 1915 prov.exhib.lit. 7-May-3 AB Stockholms Auktionsverk #821/R est:1000000-1200000 (S.KR 950000)
£85844 $133917 €128766 Railway crossing (58x74cm-23x29in) s.d.1915 prov.exhib.lit. 5-Nov-2 Bukowskis, Stockholm #192/R est:1000000-1200000 (S.KR 1225000)
£91255 $144183 €136883 Blast furnace (64x54cm-25x21in) init. painted 1915 prov.exhib.lit. 28-Apr-3 Bukowskis, Stockholm #129/R est:700000-800000 (S.KR 1200000)

Works on paper
£309 $513 €448 Geometric compositions (12x14cm-5x6in) s. Indian ink. 16-Jun-3 Lilla Bukowskis, Stockholm #346 (S.KR 4000)
£558 $887 €837 Abstract composition (9x8cm-4x3in) s. Indian ink. 3-Mar-3 Lilla Bukowskis, Stockholm #792 (S.KR 7500)
£760 $1202 €1140 The machine (11x12cm-4x5in) pencil prov. 28-Apr-3 Bukowskis, Stockholm #127/R (S.KR 10000)
£806 $1257 €1209 Figure of adoration (30x22cm-12x9in) s. W/C htd gold painted 1923 prov. 6-Nov-2 AB Stockholms Auktionsverk #722/R (S.KR 11500)
£851 $1319 €1277 Burning vessel (25x33cm-10x13in) mono. pastel prov. 8-Dec-2 Uppsala Auktionskammare, Uppsala #207/R (S.KR 12000)
£892 $1356 €1338 Composition (25x17cm-10x7in) s.d.55 gouache. 16-Aug-2 Lilla Bukowskis, Stockholm #808 (S.KR 13000)
£1081 $1741 €1622 Lit candles (34x24cm-13x9in) s.d.53 W/C exhib. 7-May-3 AB Stockholms Auktionsverk #650/R est:8000-10000 (S.KR 14000)
£1086 $1694 €1629 Game of sticks (25x35cm-10x14in) s.d.54 s.verso gouache W/C. 5-Nov-2 Bukowskis, Stockholm #32/R est:15000-18000 (S.KR 15500)
£1197 $1987 €1736 The Phoenix (50x34cm-20x13in) s. gouache exhib. 16-Jun-3 Lilla Bukowskis, Stockholm #983/R est:20000-25000 (S.KR 15500)
£1398 $2222 €2097 Krigzon II (25x34cm-10x13in) s. s.verso mixed media exhib. 3-Mar-3 Lilla Bukowskis, Stockholm #776 est:15000-18000 (S.KR 18800)
£1472 $2296 €2208 Figure composition (37x19cm-15x7in) s.d.42 gouache. 5-Nov-2 Bukowskis, Stockholm #39/R est:20000-25000 (S.KR 21000)
£1822 $2842 €2733 Potted plant in window (25x16cm-10x6in) s. gouache. 6-Nov-2 AB Stockholms Auktionsverk #723/R est:15000-20000 (S.KR 26000)
£1931 $3108 €2897 From - The three sailors adventure in Paris (16x25cm-6x10in) W/C exhib.lit. 7-May-3 AB Stockholms Auktionsverk #761/R est:35000-40000 (S.KR 25000)
£1977 $3124 €2966 Knight (22x17cm-9x7in) init. gouache. 28-Apr-3 Bukowskis, Stockholm #128/R est:15000-18000 (S.KR 26000)
£2032 $3170 €3048 Diver (33x41cm-13x16in) s.d.37 gouache. 5-Nov-2 Bukowskis, Stockholm #193/R est:20000-25000 (S.KR 29000)
£2242 $3498 €3363 Lillemor von Johnstone (29x22cm-11x9in) s. gouache gold ground prov. 5-Nov-2 Bukowskis, Stockholm #40/R est:20000-25000 (S.KR 32000)
£2383 $3717 €3575 Epilogue (47x33cm-19x13in) s. mixed media exhib. 5-Nov-2 Bukowskis, Stockholm #245/R est:30000-35000 (S.KR 34000)
£3224 $5029 €4836 Vessel at quay (49x64cm-19x25in) s, gouache. 5-Nov-2 Bukowskis, Stockholm #33/R est:25000-30000 (S.KR 46000)

£3270 $5167 €4905 The burning lantern (51x37cm-20x15in) init. mixed media panel. 28-Apr-3 Bukowskis, Stockholm #123/R est:30000-35000 (S.KR 43000)
£3498 $5527 €5247 Composition VI (68x47cm-27x19in) init. collage executed 1921 prov. 28-Apr-3 Bukowskis, Stockholm #190/R est:70000-80000 (S.KR 46000)
£3650 $5767 €5475 Lady with parasol (26x13cm-10x5in) s.i. gouache exhib. 28-Apr-3 Bukowskis, Stockholm #35/R est:25000-30000 (S.KR 48000)

ADRION, Lucien (1889-1953) French
£828 $1308 €1200 Summer's day on the beach (38x46cm-15x18in) s. canvas on board. 2-Apr-3 Dr Fritz Nagel, Stuttgart #9319/R
£1132 $1766 €1800 Landscape by sea (28x38cm-11x15in) s. board lit. 20-Sep-2 Schloss Ahlden, Ahlden #1299/R est:1800
£1392 $2172 €2200 Paris in the summer (19x25cm-7x10in) s. d.1932 verso board lit. 14-Sep-2 Bergmann, Erlangen #765/R est:1400
£1449 $2377 €2000 Villa in Berlin (54x65cm-21x26in) s. 31-May-3 Villa Grisebach, Berlin #123/R est:3000-4000
£1862 $2942 €2700 Champs Elysees (65x81cm-26x32in) s. 4-Apr-3 Tajan, Paris #177/R
£2098 $3503 €3000 Au bord du lac, Bry-sur-Marine (46x55cm-18x22in) s. s.i.verso. 27-Jun-3 Claude Aguttes, Neuilly #71/R est:4000-5000
£2158 $3540 €3000 View on the river Seine, Paris (60x73cm-24x29in) s. 3-Jun-3 Christie's, Amsterdam #38/R est:1000-1500
£2201 $3412 €3500 Paris, la Place de la Concorde (65x81cm-26x32in) s. 30-Oct-2 Artcurial Briest, Paris #288/R est:3500-4500
£2740 $4274 €4000 Washerwomen on riverbank of French city (50x73cm-20x29in) s. 10-Apr-3 Van Ham, Cologne #1303/R est:4000
£3147 $5255 €4500 Au bord du lac (46x55cm-18x22in) s.d.14 juillet 44. 27-Jun-3 Claude Aguttes, Neuilly #70/R est:4000-5000
£5000 $7950 €7500 L'opera (54x73cm-21x29in) 20-Mar-3 Sotheby's, Olympia #24/R est:4000-6000

ADVOCAAT, Gunnvor (1912-1997) Norwegian
Works on paper
£436 $685 €654 Composition (29x36cm-11x14in) s. 25-Nov-2 Blomqvist, Lysaker #1001/R (N.KR 5000)

AELST, Pieter Coecke van (1502-1550) Flemish
£16981 $26491 €27000 Adoration of the Kings (87x55cm-34x22in) panel. 23-Sep-2 Wiener Kunst Auktionen, Vienna #1/R est:18000-35000

AELST, Pieter Coecke van (after) (1502-1550) Flemish
£4516 $7000 €6774 Adoration of the Magi, King Melchior, King Balthazar (83x99cm-33x39in) panel triptych. 2-Oct-2 Christie's, Rockefeller NY #131/R est:8000-12000

AELST, Pieter Coecke van (attrib) (1502-1550) Flemish
£5128 $7949 €8000 Deploration du Christ (74x64cm-29x25in) panel prov. 6-Dec-2 Rieunier, Bailly-Pommery, Mathias, Paris #10/R est:12000

AELST, Pieter Coecke van (circle) (1502-1550) Flemish
£7200 $11160 €10800 Allegory of the transience of earthly beauty (37x29cm-15x11in) panel. 31-Oct-2 Sotheby's, Olympia #28/R est:5000-7000
£11321 $17547 €18000 Mourning after the Deposition (90x57cm-35x22in) board. 7-Oct-2 Ansorena, Madrid #1/R est:16000
£21583 $34532 €30000 Adoration of the Magi. Nativity. Flight into Egypt (89x104cm-35x41in) panel shaped top triptych. 14-May-3 Christie's, Amsterdam #162/R est:15000-25000

AELST, Pieter Coecke van (studio) (1502-1550) Flemish
£20144 $32230 €28000 Biblical scenes (78x58cm-31x23in) panel triptych prov. 17-May-3 Lempertz, Koln #1024/R est:30000-35000

AELST, Willem van (1626-1683) Dutch
£10480 $16349 €15720 Still life of wine glass, grapes and half peeled oranges (49x37cm-19x15in) s. 6-Nov-2 Dobiaschofsky, Bern #305/R est:17000 (S.FR 24000)
£22013 $34119 €35000 Still life with nautilus goblet (70x57cm-28x22in) s. 2-Oct-2 Dorotheum, Vienna #117/R est:35000-45000
£30000 $46800 €45000 Still life of apricots, plums, red and white currants (41x32cm-16x13in) panel prov. 10-Apr-3 Sotheby's, London #55/R est:50000

AELST, Willem van (attrib) (1626-1683) Dutch
£11806 $18653 €17000 Simple meal (53x43cm-21x17in) 23-Apr-3 Rabourdin & Choppin de Janvry, Paris #77/R est:32000

AEMISEGGER-GIEZENDANNER, Anna Barbara (1831-1905) Swiss
£3261 $5054 €4892 Toggenburg farmstead (20x29cm-8x11in) W/C over pencil. 9-Dec-2 Philippe Schuler, Zurich #4000/R est:3000-5000 (S.FR 7500)
£6114 $9598 €9171 Trip up to the mountain pastures (20x27cm-8x11in) tempera paper. 25-Nov-2 Sotheby's, Zurich #38/R est:5000-7000 (S.FR 14000)

AERENS, Robert (1883-1969) Belgian
£1884 $3090 €2600 Scene historique (110x90cm-43x35in) 27-May-3 Campo & Campo, Antwerp #2 est:800 1100

AERSCHOT, Johan van (20th C) Dutch
£955 $1490 €1500 Javanese woman with children (91x78cm-36x31in) s.i.d.21. 6-Nov-2 Vendue Huis, Gravenhage #282/R est:1500-2000

AESCHBACHER, Arthur (1923-) Swiss
Works on paper
£280 $467 €400 Nature morte (48x32cm-19x13in) s. ink W/C. 26-Jun-3 Tajan, Paris #169
£329 $533 €500 Sans titre (29x12cm-11x5in) s.d. collage. 22-Jan-3 Tajan, Paris #257
£464 $756 €700 Composition (32x49cm-13x19in) s.d.1959 collage gouache. 3-Feb-3 Cornette de St.Cyr, Paris #353
£513 $805 €800 Sans titre (49x35cm-19x14in) s. decollage. 16-Dec-2 Charbonneaux, Paris #103/R
£1667 $2633 €2400 Les asperges de la trinite (55x45cm-22x18in) s.d. s.i.d.verso torn poster on canvas. 27-Apr-3 Perrin, Versailles #88/R est:2000-2500
£2431 $3865 €3500 Paysage-zigazcentric, boulle-trou-madame (80x100cm-31x39in) s.i.d.1968 verso decoupage canvas. 29-Apr-3 Artcurial Briest, Paris #359/R est:3000-4000
£2708 $4279 €3900 Composition (87x38cm-34x15in) s.d. torn poster on panel prov. 27-Apr-3 Perrin, Versailles #89/R est:2000-2500

AESCHBACHER, Hans (1906-) Swiss
Sculpture
£1747 $2742 €2621 Figure VII (36cm-14in) aluminium prov. 25-Nov-2 Sotheby's, Zurich #165/R est:4000-6000 (S.FR 4000)
£3004 $4747 €4506 Figure XVI (39cm-15in) mono.i.d.1959 brass prov.lit. 26-Nov-2 Phillips, Zurich #99/R est:7000-9000 (S.FR 7000)
£3712 $5419 €5568 Figure I (89x17x15cm-35x7x6in) mono.d.1966 aluminium sandstone prov.lit. 4-Jun-2 Germann, Zurich #4/R est:7000-9000 (S.FR 8500)

AFFANDI (1907-1990) Indonesian
£23198 $35725 €34797 Boats at the beach (98x132cm-39x52in) init.d.1969 prov. 27-Oct-2 Christie's, Hong Kong #96/R est:180000-280000 (HK.D 280000)
£24027 $37001 €36041 Village scene. init.d.50. 27-Oct-2 Christie's, Hong Kong #98/R est:130000-180000 (HK.D 290000)
£27195 $44872 €39433 Man on horse (100x137cm-39x54in) init.d.1965 prov. 6-Jul-3 Christie's, Hong Kong #68/R est:240000-300000 (HK.D 350000)
£37283 $57415 €55925 Market under a banyan tree (98x125cm-39x49in) init.d.1966 prov. 27-Oct-2 Christie's, Hong Kong #97/R est:240000-340000 (HK.D 450000)
£37283 $57415 €55925 Portrait of a man holding a flute (139x102cm-55x40in) init.d.1969 prov. 27-Oct-2 Christie's, Hong Kong #99/R est:220000-320000 (HK.D 450000)
£49710 $76553 €74565 Train going by a sugar plantation (97x145cm-38x57in) init.d.1985 prov. 27-Oct-2 Christie's, Hong Kong #101/R est:160000-200000 (HK.D 600000)
£50505 $83333 €73232 Two gypsies (109x109cm-43x43in) init.d.51. 6-Jul-3 Christie's, Hong Kong #70/R est:280000-400000 (HK.D 650000)
£62160 $102564 €90132 Offering sadjen (134x80cm-53x31in) init.d.1960 prov. 6-Jul-3 Christie's, Hong Kong #67/R est:240000-350000 (HK.D 800000)
£115990 $178625 €173985 Self portrait (128x101cm-50x40in) init.d.1975 prov. 27-Oct-2 Christie's, Hong Kong #100/R est:200000-250000 (HK.D 1400000)
£124320 $205128 €180264 Self portrait (97x75cm-38x30in) init.d.1960 lit. 6-Jul-3 Christie's, Hong Kong #69/R est:240000-300000 (HK.D 1600000)

AFFELTRANGER, Hans (1919-) Swiss
Works on paper
£371 $583 €557 Untitled (18x18cm-7x7in) mono.i.d.26/12/96 W/C. 23-Nov-2 Burkhard, Luzern #97/R (S.FR 850)

AFFLECK, William (1869-1909) British
Works on paper
£1000 $1560 €1500 Young milkmaid by a river, a thatched river beyond (36x25cm-14x10in) s. W/C htd white. 18-Sep-2 Dreweatt Neate, Newbury #19/R est:1000-1500

AFFORTUNATI, Aldo (1906-) Italian
£545 $856 €850 View of road (46x60cm-18x24in) s. 16-Dec-2 Pandolfini, Florence #107/R
£675 $1100 €1013 Spanish tavern (38x70cm-15x28in) s. i.d.1946 stretcher. 16-Feb-3 Butterfields, San Francisco #2028
£1200 $1884 €1800 Knife-sharpener. Umbrella mender (36x55cm-14x22in) s. two. 21-Nov-2 Christie's, Kensington #138/R est:1500-2000

AFRICANO, Nicholas (1948-) American
Sculpture
£7097 $11000 €10646 Rebecca (71x30x30cm-28x12x12in) painted glass on marble base executed c.1990 prov.exhib. 26-Sep-2 Christie's, Rockefeller NY #822/R est:8000-12000

AFRO (1912-1976) Italian
£3191 $5170 €4500 Composition (32x33cm-13x13in) s.d.45 tempera pastel paper prov. 26-May-3 Christie's, Milan #44/R est:3500-5000
£10256 $16103 €16000 Untitled (11x13cm-4x5in) s.d.1960 paper. 19-Nov-2 Finarte, Milan #261/R
£200000 $334000 €300000 Testa di Ponte (104x146cm-41x57in) s.d.57 prov.exhib.lit. 26-Jun-3 Christie's, London #11/R est:70000-100000
Works on paper
£2361 $3754 €3400 L'etoile filante (74x54cm-29x21in) s.d.1963 mixed media. 29-Apr-3 Campo, Vlaamse Kaai #12/R est:3500-4000
£4430 $7000 €6645 Untitled (47x63cm-19x25in) s.d.64 crayon ink wash. 22-Apr-3 Butterfields, San Francisco #6028/R est:5000-7000
£14557 $22709 €23000 Composition (60x44cm-24x17in) s.d.1947 mixed media paper on canvas. 14-Sep-2 Meeting Art, Vercelli #839/R est:20000
£55319 $89617 €78000 Case aperte (55x70cm-22x28in) s.d.59 mixed media canvas prov.exhib.lit. 26-May-3 Christie's, Milan #252/R est:70000-100000
£191489 $310213 €270000 Pietra Serena (110x200cm-43x79in) s.d.57 mixed media canvas prov.exhib.lit. 26-May-3 Christie's, Milan #251/R est:80000-120000

AFSARY, Cyrus (1940-) American
£3549 $5750 €5146 Apples and flowers (51x41cm-20x16in) 23-May-3 Altermann Galleries, Santa Fe #209
£3767 $5500 €5651 Indian bounty (51x41cm-20x16in) 18-May-2 Altermann Galleries, Santa Fe #76/R
£7051 $11000 €10577 Indian summer (61x76cm-24x30in) 9-Nov-2 Altermann Galleries, Santa Fe #216
£8333 $13000 €12500 Shady arches (76x102cm-30x40in) 9-Nov-2 Altermann Galleries, Santa Fe #231
£10648 $17250 €15440 Taos (61x91cm-24x36in) 23-May-3 Altermann Galleries, Santa Fe #49

AGACHE, Alfred Pierre (1843-1915) French
£6600 $10494 €9900 Head of a girl with rose corsage (48cm-19in circular) s.d.1890. 5-Mar-3 Bonhams, Bury St Edmunds #420/R est:700-1000

AGAM, Yaacov (1928-) Israeli
Sculpture
£1047 $1623 €1571 Untitled (62x62x3cm-24x24x1in) s. prismograph perspex edition 65/90. 3-Dec-2 Shapiro, Sydney #75/R est:3000-5000 (A.D 2900)

AGAR, Eileen (1899-1991) British
£750 $1163 €1125 Little house (36x30cm-14x12in) s. 3-Dec-2 Bonhams, Knightsbridge #364/R
£1300 $2055 €1950 Both ways (56x38cm-22x15in) s. s.i.stretcher. 27-Nov-2 Sotheby's, Olympia #321/R est:1000-1500
£3200 $5056 €4800 Edith Sitwell the sorceress (56x38cm-22x15in) s. col crayon painted c.1962 exhib. 27-Nov-2 Sotheby's, Olympia #188/R est:4000-6000
Works on paper
£342 $550 €513 Surrealist head (58x38cm-23x15in) gouache oil prov. 20-Jan-3 Arthur James, Florida #455
£550 $869 €825 Tenerife (17x23cm-7x9in) s. W/C executed c.1954 exhib. 27-Nov-2 Sotheby's, Olympia #212/R
£550 $902 €825 Ploumanach (20x20cm-8x8in) s. pencil col felt tip pen W/C bodycol executed 1985 prov. 6-Jun-3 Christie's, London #122/R
£800 $1312 €1200 Pollen (60x51cm-24x20in) mixed media. 3-Jun-3 Sotheby's, Olympia #295/R
£850 $1326 €1275 Triumph of the tree trunk (25x34cm-10x13in) s. gouache prov. 25-Mar-3 Bonhams, New Bond Street #102/R
£1000 $1580 €1500 Three faces (23x31cm-9x12in) mixed media prov. 27-Nov-2 Sotheby's, Olympia #322/R est:800-1200
£2400 $3744 €3600 Abstract composition (81x52cm-32x20in) s. mixed media collage. 12-Sep-2 Sotheby's, Olympia #141/R est:2500-3500

AGAR, John Samuel (attrib) (19th C) British
Works on paper
£2100 $3276 €3150 Portrait of an officer, holding a rifle, Waterloo period (48x29cm-19x11in) W/C. 17-Oct-2 Lawrence, Crewkerne #400/R est:600-800

AGARD, Charles (1866-1950) French
£579 $950 €840 La descente sur nesles au printemps (33x46cm-13x18in) s.i.on stretcher exhib. 4-Jun-3 Doyle, New York #1
£1220 $2000 €1769 Panorama de Nesles (46x53cm-18x21in) s. prov.exhib. 4-Jun-3 Doyle, New York #2 est:2000-3000

AGASSE, Jacques Laurent (1767-1849) Swiss
£17073 $28000 €25610 Pointer in a landscape (24x30cm-9x12in) mono. board prov.exhib. 29-May-3 Sotheby's, New York #148/R est:10000-15000
£90000 $142200 €135000 View of the Thames at Westminster looking towards Lambeth (34x51cm-13x20in) s. prov.exhib.lit. 28-Nov-2 Sotheby's, London #9/R est:100000-150000
£112805 $185000 €169208 Chalon family in London (14x20cm-6x8in) i.verso board exhib. 29-May-3 Sotheby's, New York #147/R est:15000-20000
£250000 $395000 €375000 Head of bay horse (54x38cm-21x15in) i. prov. 27-Nov-2 Christie's, London #25/R est:150000-250000

AGASSE, Jacques Laurent (attrib) (1767-1849) Swiss
£742 $1158 €1113 Sheep's head (14x17cm-6x7in) 6-Nov-2 Dobiaschofsky, Bern #306/R est:2200 (S.FR 1700)
£3600 $5760 €5400 Portrait of a young gentleman wearing a top hat and riding coat (76x64cm-30x25in) bears sig. 13-Mar-3 Duke & Son, Dorchester #294/R est:2500-4500
Works on paper
£680 $1082 €1000 Etude de taureau et chien (22x35cm-9x14in) W/C gouache over crayon. 24-Mar-3 Tajan, Paris #117/R

AGAZZI, Rinaldo (1857-1939) Italian
£2264 $3487 €3600 Valley near Bergamo with brioidge and houses (39x59cm-15x23in) s. cardboard. 23-Oct-2 Finarte, Milan #206/R

AGERO, August (19/20th C) Spanish
Works on paper
£769 $1208 €1200 Portrait of Yonal (32x25cm-13x10in) s.i. crayon prov. 22-Nov-2 Millon & Associes, Paris #91/R
£2500 $3925 €3900 Fighter (30x21cm-12x8in) s. gouache exec.c.1910 prov. 22-Nov-2 Millon & Associes, Paris #92/R

AGERSNAP, Hans (1857-1925) Danish
£279 $444 €419 Landscape with farm and church (53x92cm-21x36in) S. 10-Mar-3 Rasmussen, Vejle #244 (D.KR 3000)
£326 $518 €489 Winter landscape (66x97cm-26x38in) s. 10-Mar-3 Rasmussen, Vejle #89 (D.KR 3500)
£557 $870 €836 Winter landscape with children (51x84cm-20x33in) s.d.1915. 11-Nov-2 Rasmussen, Vejle #660/R (D.KR 6500)

AGGHAZY, Gyula (1850-1919) Hungarian
£2064 $3220 €3096 In a sunny field (66x54cm-26x21in) s. 11-Sep-2 Kieselbach, Budapest #62/R (H.F 800000)

AGHAJANIAN, Sophie (20th C) Irish?
Works on paper
£390 $620 €585 Still life, vase of flowers (50x76cm-20x30in) s. W/C. 5-Mar-3 John Ross, Belfast #37
£620 $905 €930 Reflections (56x84cm-22x33in) s. pastel. 12-Jun-2 John Ross, Belfast #163

AGLIETTI, Romeo (19/20th C) Italian
£818 $1259 €1300 Paysage de Kabylie (50x68cm-20x27in) 23-Oct-2 Rabourdin & Choppin de Janvry, Paris #220/R

AGLIO, Agostino (1777-1857) Italian
Works on paper
£320 $515 €464 Boys fishing (49x38cm-19x15in) s.d.1836 W/C. 12-May-3 Joel, Victoria #381 (A.D 800)
£620 $1017 €930 Sheen Bridge, Ireland. Figures near a cottage, Ornee (20x25cm-8x10in) s. one i. bodycol pair. 4-Feb-3 Bonhams, Leeds #250
£850 $1326 €1275 Palm Sunday (67x118cm-26x46in) indis.i.stretcher W/C. 17-Sep-2 Sotheby's, Olympia #228/R

AGNEESENS, Edouard (1842-1885) Belgian
£1195 $1852 €1900 Portrait of a small boy (46x38cm-18x15in) s.d.74. 5-Oct-2 De Vuyst, Lokeren #2/R est:2000-2500
£1761 $2730 €2800 Interior of artist's studio (47x55cm-19x22in) s. panel. 5-Oct-2 De Vuyst, Lokeren #1/R est:2000-2500

AGNEW, Clark (1905-1959) American
£870 $1400 €1305 Elegant young woman playing piano (79x91cm-31x36in) s.d.1927. 20-Feb-3 Illustration House, New York #2/R est:1600-2400

AGOSTINI, Davide de (1952-) Italian
£321 $503 €500 Waiting (70x50cm-28x20in) s. s.i.d.2001 verso. 23-Nov-2 Meeting Art, Vercelli #151

AGOSTINI, Guido (19th C) Italian
£1000 $1570 €1500 Livorno dalla Aruda di Montcrioru. Portofino, Riviera ligure di Levante (26x22cm-10x9in) s.d.1880 board oval pair. 10-Dec-2 Rosebery Fine Art, London #516 est:1200-1800
£1650 $2574 €2475 Firenze vedute del Ponte Girone (22x28cm-9x11in) one s.i.verso two. 8-Oct-2 Bonhams, Knightsbridge #288/R est:1000-1500
£1781 $2778 €2600 Angler on the Tiber (22x27cm-9x11in) s.d.1884 i. verso board oval. 10-Apr-3 Dorotheum, Vienna #160/R est:2500-2700

AGOSTINI, Max Michel (1914-1997) French
£443 $700 €700 Paysage de Provence (41x27cm-16x11in) s. 27-Nov-2 Blanchet, Paris #97/R
£922 $1494 €1300 Marche pecheurs (37x60cm-15x24in) s. s.i.verso. 21-May-3 Cornette de St.Cyr, Paris #100/R
£2436 $3776 €3800 Iris (61x50cm-24x20in) s. prov. 9-Dec-2 Beaussant & Lefèvre, Paris #18/R

AGOSTINI, Renzo (1944-) Italian
£506 $790 €800 Landscape (35x41cm-14x16in) s.d.1944 cardboard. 19-Oct-2 Semenzato, Venice #83/R

AGOSTINI, Tony (1916-1990) Italian
£532 $888 €750 Vase de fleurs (55x47cm-22x19in) s. 23-Jun-3 Claude Boisgirard, Paris #210
£1250 $1975 €1800 Still life (65x81cm-26x32in) s. s.verso prov. 25-Apr-3 Piasa, Paris #42

AGRAMUNT, Jose Frances (1868-1951) Spanish
£566 $883 €900 Rocky landscape (47x66cm-19x26in) s. 8-Oct-2 Ansorena, Madrid #401/R

AGRASOT Y JUAN, Joaquim (1837-1919) Spanish
£2830 $4500 €4245 Mending (25x16cm-10x6in) s. panel. 7-Mar-3 Skinner, Boston #248/R est:4000-6000
£5769 $9115 €9000 Portrait of lady (24x19cm-9x7in) s. 13-Nov-2 Ansorena, Madrid #125/R
£9589 $14959 €14000 Courtship (57x40cm-22x16in) s. 8-Apr-3 Ansorena, Madrid #225/R est:12600

AGRICOLA, Carl Joseph (1779-1852) German
£443 $700 €700 Portrait of bearded man (16x13cm-6x5in) s.d.1818 panel. 26-Nov-2 Wiener Kunst Auktionen, Vienna #125/R

AGRICOLA, Christoph Ludwig (1667-1719) German
Works on paper
£1500 $2355 €2250 Blue tit perched on a pine branch with a fly. Great tit perched on a pine branch (28x20cm-11x8in) gouache two. 11-Dec-2 Sotheby's, Olympia #182/R est:1500-2000

AGRICOLA, Eduard (1800-?) German
Works on paper
£633 $981 €1000 Hilly landscape near Veji (44x57cm-17x22in) i.d.3 May 1841 pencil. 27-Sep-2 Venator & Hansten, Koln #1215

AGRICOLA, Eduard (attrib) (1800-?) German
£3797 $6000 €6000 Wild romantic mountain landscape with viaduct in background (108x148cm-43x58in) 28-Nov-2 Dorotheum, Vienna #223/R est:6000-8000

AGRICOLA, Lidia (1914-1994) Hungarian
£1032 $1610 €1496 Summer on the meadow (55x75cm-22x30in) s. 13-Sep-2 Mu Terem Galeria, Budapest #163/R est:220000 (H.F 400000)

AGRICOLA, Rudolf Alexander (1912-) Russian
Sculpture
£5128 $7949 €8000 Young man standing (133cm-52in) s. verso dark brown pat.bronze Cast.H.Noack Berlin. 4-Dec-2 Lempertz, Koln #546/R est:6000-8000

AGUADO, Count Olympe Clement (1827-1894) French
Photographs
£2564 $4051 €4000 Groupe de personnages sous une poterne (15x12cm-6x5in) albumin print cxec.c.1860. 16-Nov-2 Christie's, Paris #205/R est:5000-7000

AGUELI, Ivan (1869-1917) Swedish
£4681 $7255 €7022 North African town scene (20x29cm-8x11in) canvas on cardboard. 3-Dec-2 Bukowskis, Stockholm #2/R est:50000-60000 (S.KR 66000)
£5319 $8245 €7979 Portrait of lady (46x38cm-18x15in) cardboard. 4-Dec-2 AB Stockholms Auktionsverk #1604/R est:80000-100000 (S.KR 75000)
£12057 $18688 €18086 Landscape (20x25cm-8x10in) panel. 8-Dec-2 Uppsala Auktionskammare, Uppsala #157/R est:150000-200000 (S.KR 170000)
£14352 $23251 €20810 Coastal landscape with bushes and dunes, Spain (17x24cm-7x9in) canvas on board prov.exhib.lit. 26-May-3 Bukowskis, Stockholm #2/R est:100000-125000 (S.KR 185000)
£19395 $31420 €28123 Olive grove (18x24cm-7x9in) exhib. 26-May-3 Bukowskis, Stockholm #1/R est:150000-175000 (S.KR 250000)
£20424 $33496 €29615 Landscape with road (20x24cm-8x9in) i. exhib. 4-Jun-3 AB Stockholms Auktionsverk #2126/R est:150000-200000 (S.KR 260000)
Works on paper
£709 $1099 €1064 North African landscape. Study of woman (14x21cm-6x8in) s. dr double-sided. 8-Dec-2 Uppsala Auktionskammare, Uppsala #159/R (S.KR 10000)

AGUIARI, Tito (1834-1908) Italian
Works on paper
£2027 $3162 €3000 Mussel gatherers on Zara beach (72x125cm-28x49in) s. W/C. 28-Mar-3 Dorotheum, Vienna #231/R est:3600-4000

AGUILA PIMENTEL, A del (19/20th C) Spanish
£581 $917 €900 Ladies with shawls in the garden (60x40cm-24x16in) s.d.1877. 18-Dec-2 Ansorena, Madrid #345/R

AGUILA Y ACOSTA, Adolfo (19/20th C) Spanish
£2302 $3683 €3200 Street in Tangiers (33x44cm-13x17in) s.i.d.1901. 17-May-3 De Vuyst, Lokeren #98/R est:3300-3800

AGUILAR MORE, Ramon (1924-) Spanish
£1730 $2698 €2750 Spanish dance (71x90cm-28x35in) s. 23-Sep-2 Durán, Madrid #128/R

AGUILAR PONCE (20th C) South American?
£499 $789 €749 Untitled (120x170cm-47x67in) s.d.1968. 26-Nov-2 Louis Morton, Mexico #43/R est:11000 (M.P 8000)

AGUILAR, Sergi (1946-) Spanish
£314 $491 €500 Blanc numero 9 (19x72cm-7x28in) s.i.d.1980 chl dr prov. 17-Sep-2 Segre, Madrid #278/R
£1774 $2803 €2750 From a very deep red (104x151cm-41x59in) s.d.1987 acrylic cardboard on board prov.lit. 17-Dec-2 Segre, Madrid #183/R
Sculpture
£2956 $4552 €4700 Exterior (16x60x70cm-6x24x28in) s.d.1985 steel prov.exhib.lit. 28-Oct-2 Segre, Madrid #163/R est:5900

AGUTTE, Georgette (1867-1922) French
£2468 $3875 €3850 Auto-portrait au chapeau (73x60cm-29x24in) 11-Dec-2 Artcurial Briest, Paris #524/R

AGUZZI, Fabio (1953-) Italian
£769 $1208 €1200 Yellow roses (30x35cm-12x14in) s.i.verso. 23-Nov-2 Meeting Art, Vercelli #216/R
£1042 $1656 €1500 Blue shirt (35x45cm-14x18in) s.i.d.1997 verso. 1-May-3 Meeting Art, Vercelli #196

AHDEN, Waldemar (19th C) German?
£419 $616 €650 Spanish bull fight (22x34cm-9x13in) s. 24-Jun-2 Dr Fritz Nagel, Stuttgart #6005/R

AHL, C F (20th C) ?
£287 $448 €431 Seascape with sailing vessel (100x130cm-39x51in) s. 23-Sep-2 Rasmussen, Vejle #108/R (D.KR 3400)

AHL, Henry Hammond (1869-1953) American
£311 $500 €467 Haystack under stormy skies (20x25cm-8x10in) s. board. 18-Feb-3 Arthur James, Florida #38
£559 $900 €839 Off Plum Island-Newbury, Mass (30x38cm-12x15in) s. i.verso board. 18-Feb-3 Arthur James, Florida #35
£807 $1300 €1211 Sailboat near shore (28x33cm-11x13in) s. s.i.verso board. 18-Feb-3 Arthur James, Florida #36

AHLBORN, August (1796-1857) German
£566 $872 €900 Mountain landscape with the Monch (33x44cm-13x17in) s.d.1834. 26-Oct-2 Quittenbaum, Hamburg #1/R
£9353 $14964 €13000 Monastery by Gulf of Naples near Sorrento (46x33cm-18x13in) s.d.1833. 17-May-3 Lempertz, Koln #1358/R est:8000
Works on paper
£380 $589 €600 Gubbio near Perugia (38x49cm-15x19in) i.d.27 Aug 28 pencil. 27-Sep-2 Venator & Hansten, Koln #1217

AHLERS-HESTERMANN, Friedrich (1883-1973) German
£1090 $1689 €1700 Autumnal landscape (46x55cm-18x22in) s.d.1951. 7-Dec-2 Hauswedell & Nolte, Hamburg #507/R est:2500
£2179 $3378 €3400 Gertrud (90x75cm-35x30in) s.d.1905. 7-Dec-2 Hauswedell & Nolte, Hamburg #505/R est:5000

AHLGREN, Lauri (1929-) Finnish
£1392 $2200 €2200 Oranismin uskallus - Composition (97x130cm-38x51in) s.d.1981 exhib. 30-Nov-2 Hagelstam, Helsinki #170/R est:2000

AHLSTEDT, Fredrik (1839-1901) Finnish
£566 $872 €900 Mountain landscape, Kokkoberget (21x29cm-8x11in) exhib. 24-Oct-2 Hagelstam, Helsinki #1022/R
£719 $1179 €1100 Crescent moon (25x17cm-10x7in) s. 9-Feb-3 Bukowskis, Helsinki #192/R
£2394 $3855 €3400 Malakias - old fisherman from Kangasala (64x47cm-25x19in) s.d.1890 exhib. 10-May-3 Bukowskis, Helsinki #107/R est:2500-2800
£3987 $6300 €6300 Forest interior (61x38cm-24x15in) s. 1-Dec-2 Bukowskis, Helsinki #18/R est:6000-7000
£4114 $6500 €6500 Fishermen by the coast (42x58cm-17x23in) s.d.1877. 1-Dec-2 Bukowskis, Helsinki #17/R est:6500-7000
£4430 $7000 €7000 On the look-out (133x96cm-52x38in) s.d.1897. 1-Dec-2 Bukowskis, Helsinki #16/R est:7000-8000
£6056 $9751 €8600 Longing - girl seated in landscape (65x47cm-26x19in) s.d.92. 10-May-3 Bukowskis, Helsinki #74/R est:6000-8000
£15823 $25000 €25000 Autumn day, landscape from Jomala at Aaland (40x63cm-16x25in) s.d.1876 exhib. 30-Nov-2 Hagelstam, Helsinki #95/R est:28000

AHLSTEDT, Nina (1853-1907) Finnish
£7278 $11500 €11500 Day dreams (71x59cm-28x23in) s.d.1896. 30-Nov-2 Hagelstam, Helsinki #102/R est:10000

AHNERT, Elisabeth (1885-1966) German
Works on paper
£252 $387 €400 Village landscape (25x35cm-10x14in) s.d.1926 W/C pen board. 26-Oct-2 Dr Lehr, Berlin #10/R

AHRENBERG, Johan Jakob (1847-1914) Finnish
Works on paper
£400 $632 €620 An Aabo fantasy (35x64cm-14x25in) s.d.1909 W/C. 19-Dec-2 Hagelstam, Helsinki #918

AHRENDTS, Carl Eduard (1822-1898) Dutch
£724 $1172 €1100 Low tide at dusk (22x25cm-9x10in) init. panel. 21-Jan-3 Christie's, Amsterdam #31 est:1200-1600
£1146 $1766 €1800 Heading for sea (12x15cm-5x6in) s. panel. 3-Sep-2 Christie's, Amsterdam #285/R est:2000-3000
£1268 $2041 €1800 River view with fishing boats (15x22cm-6x9in) s. panel. 7-May-3 Vendue Huis, Gravenhage #427 est:2000-2500
£1572 $2421 €2500 La plage a Scheveningue (19x24cm-7x9in) s.i. panel prov. 22-Oct-2 Sotheby's, Amsterdam #35/R est:3000-5000
£1887 $2906 €3000 Figures with a horse and sledge on the ice. Figures in a winter landscape (12x15cm-5x6in) one mono. panel pair. 22-Oct-2 Sotheby's, Amsterdam #6/R est:3000-5000
£1887 $2906 €3000 Travellers in a summer landscape (29x40cm-11x16in) s. panel prov. 22-Oct-2 Sotheby's, Amsterdam #13/R est:3000-5000

AHRENS, Max (1898-1967) German
£929 $1441 €1450 Fair in Molln (33x45cm-13x18in) s.i.d. panel. 7-Dec-2 Hans Stahl, Hamburg #106/R

AHRER, Herbert C (19/20th C) British?
£550 $853 €825 Victory from Gosport, Portsmouth (23x36cm-9x14in) s.d.1916 style of William Wyllie. 3-Dec-2 Peter Francis, Wales #57/R

AHTELA, H (1881-1968) Finnish
£1373 $2251 €2100 Summer clouds (67x78cm-26x31in) s.d.54. 9-Feb-3 Bukowskis, Helsinki #193/R est:1000
£1569 $2573 €2400 Vuokatti in autumn (68x78cm-27x31in) s.d.56. 9-Feb-3 Bukowskis, Helsinki #194/R est:1000

AHTOLA, Taisto (1917-2000) Finnish
£403 $620 €640 Flowers (33x27cm-13x11in) s. 24-Oct-2 Hagelstam, Helsinki #998
£415 $639 €660 Clown (27x21cm-11x8in) s. 27-Oct-2 Bukowskis, Helsinki #138/R
£442 $703 €650 Nice (30x41cm-12x16in) s. 27-Feb-3 Hagelstam, Helsinki #884
£845 $1361 €1200 Summer's day in the country (38x46cm-15x18in) s. 10-May-3 Bukowskis, Helsinki #225/R
£949 $1500 €1500 The puppets performance (65x81cm-26x32in) s.d.1984. 30-Nov-2 Hagelstam, Helsinki #175/R est:1600

AHUATZI, Armando (1950-) Mexican
£631 $959 €915 Bodegon con peces (60x80cm-24x31in) s.d.1994. 24-Jul-2 Louis Morton, Mexico #78/R est:8000-9000 (M.P 9500)

AI XUAN (20th C) Chinese
£14763 $24359 €21406 Girl beside a window (103x103cm-41x41in) s.d.1985. 6-Jul-3 Christie's, Hong Kong #113/R est:200000-250000 (HK.D 190000)

AIGENS, Christian (1870-1940) Danish
£341 $528 €512 Coastal landscape with two women, evening (46x55cm-18x22in) s. 28-Sep-2 Rasmussen, Havnen #2035 (D.KR 4000)
£386 $602 €579 Boy and girl on terrace with view to the sea (71x89cm-28x35in) s. 11-Nov-2 Rasmussen, Vejle #527 (D.KR 4500)

AIGNER, Fritz (1930-) Austrian
£4167 $6583 €6500 To my friend Francesco Goya and his King Carlos IV (100x70cm-39x28in) s.i.d.98. 18-Nov-2 Dorotheum, Linz #254/R est:13000-15000
£5449 $8609 €8500 The at Saint Malo (82x98cm-32x39in) s.i.d.79 board. 18-Nov-2 Dorotheum, Linz #253/R est:17000-20000

AIKEN, John Macdonald (1880-1961) British
£2600 $4056 €3900 Recital, Mrs MacDonnel of Bridgefield at the piano (14x20cm-6x8in) s. i.d.1929 verso board. 10-Apr-3 Bonhams, Edinburgh #153/R est:300-500

AIKMAN, William (1682-1731) British
£7000 $11130 €10500 Portrait of General James Oglethorpe wearing armour (73x61cm-29x24in) painted oval. 19-Mar-3 Sotheby's, London #33/R est:8000-12000

AIKMAN, William (attrib) (1682-1731) British
£1100 $1749 €1650 Portrait of Leonora Marescoe, Lady Frederick (124x100cm-49x39in) 19-Mar-3 Sotheby's, London #26/R est:1200-1800
£1600 $2544 €2400 Portrait of Thomas Frederick, East India merchant (124x99cm-49x39in) 19-Mar-3 Sotheby's, London #25/R est:2000-3000

AILLAUD, Gilles (1928-) French
£5594 $9343 €8000 Singe en cage (99x132cm-39x52in) s.verso. 25-Jun-3 Claude Aguttes, Neuilly #186/R est:3000-3800
£12179 $19122 €19000 Untitled (97x130cm-38x51in) s.d.1982 prov. 15-Dec-2 Perrin, Versailles #111/R est:15000
Works on paper
£962 $1510 €1500 Crocodile. Hippo (50x65cm-20x26in) s.d.79 W/C pair. 21-Nov-2 Finarte, Rome #163

AINI, Philippe (20th C) French
£314 $487 €500 Figure rouge (62x50cm-24x20in) s. paper. 7-Oct-2 Claude Aguttes, Neuilly #151

AISTROP, E (19/20th C) British
£1200 $1992 €1740 Two terriers (20x16cm-8x6in) s. board. 12-Jun-3 Christie's, Kensington #238/R est:1000-1500

AISTROP, Edward (19/20th C) British
£600 $996 €870 Bull terrier (14x15cm-6x6in) indis i. board. 12-Jun-3 Christie's, Kensington #240/R
£1043 $1700 €1565 Head of a Jack Russell (23x23cm-9x9in) board. 11-Feb-3 Bonhams & Doyles, New York #91/R est:800-1200
£1104 $1800 €1656 Head of a terrier (24x23cm-9x9in) s. i.verso board. 11-Feb-3 Bonhams & Doyles, New York #88/R est:800-1200
£1994 $3250 €2991 Three friends (15x46cm-6x18in) board. 11-Feb-3 Bonhams & Doyles, New York #102/R est:1500-2000

AITCHISON, Craigie (1926-) British
£5500 $8524 €8250 Flowers in a glass (26x21cm-10x8in) board. 4-Dec-2 Sotheby's, London #70/R est:1000-1500

AITKEN, Doug (20th C) American
Photographs
£4000 $6680 €5800 Mirror (51x63cm-20x25in) s.num.1/2 verso col coupler plexiglass prov.lit. 26-Jun-3 Sotheby's, London #107/R est:5000-7000
£6329 $10000 €9494 Lit sign, two telephones (51x64cm-20x25in) s.i. verso chromogenic col print prov.lit. 24-Apr-3 Phillips, New York #68/R est:8000-12000
£13924 $22000 €20886 Passenger (99x124cm-39x49in) cibachrome mounted on plexiglas executed 1999 prov.lit. 14-Nov-2 Christie's, Rockefeller NY #467/R est:10000-15000

AITKEN, James (fl.1880-1935) British
£500 $775 €750 Low tide on the Firth of Forth (61x86cm-24x34in) s. i. canvasboard. 26-Sep-2 Lane, Penzance #243
Works on paper
£260 $426 €390 Fishing boats at sea (14x21cm-6x8in) s. W/C. 4-Jun-3 Bonhams, Chester #302
£500 $815 €750 Headland view from a garden (33x48cm-13x19in) s. W/C. 11-Feb-3 Gorringes, Lewes #895/R
£760 $1246 €1140 Coastal scene with moored rowing boats (30x47cm-12x19in) s. W/C. 4-Jun-3 Bonhams, Chester #301
£820 $1345 €1230 Coastal landscape with harvesters (30x47cm-12x19in) s. W/C. 4-Jun-3 Bonhams, Chester #300
£900 $1395 €1350 Manx shore line (36x69cm-14x27in) s. W/C. 6-Dec-2 Chrystals Auctions, Isle of Man #248b
£1450 $2262 €2175 Glaisdale, Yorkshire, village street scene (30x60cm-12x24in) s. W/C. 10-Sep-2 David Duggleby, Scarborough #192/R est:1500-2250
£1600 $2480 €2400 Cottage by a river, Isle of Man (36x61cm-14x24in) s. W/C. 6-Dec-2 Chrystals Auctions, Isle of Man #248a est:800-1200

AITKEN, James A (1846-1897) British
£455 $700 €683 Iona N.B (29x48cm-11x19in) s.i.d.August 1876. 4-Sep-2 Dunbar Sloane, Wellington #95 est:2000-3000 (NZ.D 1500)
£540 $863 €750 Femme dans un jardin en fleurs (27x44cm-11x17in) s.d.1876. 13-May-3 Vanderkindere, Brussels #241
£1700 $2618 €2550 Figures with a horse and cart on a seaside path, Isle of Man (35x53cm-14x21in) s. 5-Sep-2 Christie's, Kensington #211/R est:1200-1800

AITKEN, John Ernest (1881-1957) British
Works on paper
£400 $628 €600 Busy Dutch coastal view with boats and windmills (25x33cm-10x13in) s. W/C. 13-Dec-2 Keys, Aylsham #620/R
£400 $620 €600 Water mill (51x33cm-20x13in) s. W/C. 6-Dec-2 Chrystals Auctions, Isle of Man #254
£400 $656 €600 Horseman on country road, beneath trees (23x34cm-9x13in) s. W/C. 7-Jun-3 Shapes, Edinburgh #351/R
£520 $816 €780 Thames barges (32x49cm-13x19in) s. W/C. 16-Dec-2 Sotheby's, Olympia #149/R
£732 $1120 €1098 Barges Rotterdam (35x49cm-14x19in) s. W/C. 21-Aug-2 Dunbar Sloane, Auckland #73/R est:2000-3000 (NZ.D 2400)
£860 $1367 €1290 Uilswater (34x49cm-13x19in) s. W/C. 27-Feb-3 Bonhams, Chester #323
£880 $1373 €1320 Durham (34x49cm-13x19in) s. W/C over pencil exhib. 17-Oct-2 Lawrence, Crewkerne #435
£949 $1500 €1500 Sailing boats at harbour (33x49cm-13x19in) s. W/C card. 26-Nov-2 Christie's, Rome #82
£1073 $1695 €1610 Dutch harbour scene (36x51cm-14x20in) s. W/C prov. 3-Apr-3 Heffel, Vancouver #2/R est:2800-3800 (C.D 2500)
£1400 $2226 €2100 Amsterdam haven (37x44cm-15x17in) s. W/C. 27-Feb-3 Bonhams, Chester #321/R est:1000-1400
£1500 $2235 €2250 Fishing boats in Gansey Bay (33x48cm-13x19in) s. W/C. 28-Jun-2 Chrystals Auctions, Isle of Man #196c est:1500-1800
£1750 $2608 €2625 Unloading the catch, Castletown, Isle of Man (25x36cm-10x14in) s. W/C. 28-Jun-2 Chrystals Auctions, Isle of Man #160a est:1600-2000
£2200 $3432 €3190 Waiting for the cargo (13x19cm-5x7in) s. W/C bodycol htd white. 27-Mar-3 Neales, Nottingham #926/R est:300-500

AITKEN, Robert Ingersoll (1878-1949) American
Sculpture
£6452 $10000 €9678 Tired Mercury (66cm-26in) s.i.d.1907 brown pat. prov.exhib. 29-Oct-2 Sotheby's, New York #258/R est:8000-12000

AIVASOVSKI, M (19th C) Russian
£3200 $5312 €4800 Nice with elegant figures looking across the bay (15x10cm-6x4in) s.d.1896 s.i.d.verso panel. 12-Jun-3 Scarborough Perry Fine Arts, Hove #468

AIVAZOFFSKI, Ivan (1817-1900) Russian
£7097 $11000 €10646 Sailing ship on rough seas (49x68cm-19x27in) s.d.1898. 2-Oct-2 Christie's, Rockefeller NY #800/R est:5000-7000
£24000 $37680 €36000 View of Feodosia, 26 September 1897 (17x26cm-7x10in) init. s.i.d.1897 verso. 20-Nov-2 Sotheby's, London #28/R est:15000-20000
£31646 $50000 €47469 At sea (24x39cm-9x15in) s.d.1892 s.verso. 24-Apr-3 Sotheby's, New York #112/R est:15000-20000
£41401 $65000 €62102 Oxen cart by a bay (22x25cm-9x10in) s.d.1868 canvas on board prov. 10-Dec-2 Doyle, New York #215/R est:80000-100000
£41935 $65000 €62903 Landscape with windmills (38x59cm-15x23in) s.d.1860. 29-Oct-2 Sotheby's, New York #110/R est:30000-40000
£55794 $86481 €83691 Venice by moonlight (37x50cm-15x20in) s.d.1861 prov. 3-Oct-2 Koller, Zurich #3089/R est:100000-150000 (S.FR 130000)
£75000 $121500 €112500 Coast of the Dardanelles (30x38cm-12x15in) init.d.1860. 21-May-3 Sotheby's, London #67/R est:30000-50000
£80247 $130000 €116358 Ship in high seas (58x79cm-23x31in) s.d.1864. 21-May-3 Doyle, New York #208/R est:15000-25000
£129032 $200000 €193548 Ship at sea (100x154cm-39x61in) s.d.1895. 29-Oct-2 Sotheby's, New York #111/R est:200000-300000
£135484 $210000 €203226 Shipwreck (110x129cm-43x51in) s.d.1871. 30-Oct-2 Christie's, Rockefeller NY #90/R est:150000-200000
£140000 $219800 €210000 Moonlight in the Ayu Dag (60x95cm-24x37in) s. s.d.1898 verso lit. 20-Nov-2 Sotheby's, London #30/R est:50000-70000
£140000 $226800 €210000 Lowering the boat (65x86cm-26x34in) s.d.1878 prov. 21-May-3 Sotheby's, London #68/R est:70000-100000
£160000 $251200 €240000 The allied naval blockade of Crete, 1897 (103x156cm-41x61in) s.d.1897 s.i. verso lit. 20-Nov-2 Sotheby's, London #25/R est:100000-150000
£220000 $345400 €330000 Marine scene (89x139cm-35x55in) s.d.1853 canvas on board lit. 20-Nov-2 Sotheby's, London #31/R est:80000-100000
Works on paper
£800 $1256 €1200 An oasis halt (11x10cm-4x4in) s. pencil htd. gouache. 20-Nov-2 Sotheby's, London #29/R
£1026 $1590 €1600 Three master in bay (30x33cm-12x13in) s. grisaille W/C. 6-Dec-2 Michael Zeller, Lindau #709/R
£1268 $2041 €1800 Three master in bay (30x33cm-12x13in) s. grisaille W/C. 7-May-3 Michael Zeller, Lindau #609/R est:1050
£1410 $2186 €2200 Rowing boat riding the surf (12x19cm-5x7in) s. W/C. 6-Dec-2 Michael Zeller, Lindau #708/R est:1050
£1900 $3173 €2755 View of the Black Sea with sailing ships in harbour (33x44cm-13x17in) s. pen wash. 25-Jun-3 Cheffins, Cambridge #699/R est:200-300
£2800 $4536 €4200 Passage through the cornfields (27x17cm-11x7in) s.d.1860 sepia. 21-May-3 Sotheby's, London #18/R est:2000-3000
£4292 $6652 €6438 Seascape (28x45cm-11x18in) s. W/C gouache paper on board prov. 3-Oct-2 Koller, Zurich #3102/R est:15000-20000 (S.FR 10000)
£12000 $18840 €18000 By the shore in a stormy sea (16x36cm-6x14in) s.d.1891 pencil htd gouache. 20-Nov-2 Sotheby's, London #26/R est:6000-8000

AIVAZOFFSKI, Ivan (attrib) (1817-1900) Russian
£7600 $11856 €11400 Shipping in a bay moonlight (66x100cm-26x39in) bears sig.d.1887 canvas laid down. 17-Sep-2 Sotheby's, Olympia #217/R est:5000-7000
£8500 $13346 €12750 Bathing at sunset in the cove (38x46cm-15x18in) bears sig.d.1847. 20-Nov-2 Sotheby's, London #39/R est:3000-4000
£22831 $35616 €34247 Rowing boat in the sea of coast (18x24cm-7x9in) i.d.1881. 28-Mar-3 Koller, Zurich #3129/R est:10000-16000 (S.FR 50000)

AIVAZOFFSKI, Ivan (circle) (1817-1900) Russian
£20000 $31400 €30000 Bay of Naples by moonlight (89x133cm-35x52in) 21-Nov-2 Christie's, Kensington #134/R est:10000-15000

AIVAZOFFSKI, Ivan (studio) (1817-1900) Russian
£4459 $7000 €6689 Shipwrech (142x99cm-56x39in) prov. 23-Nov-2 Jackson's, Cedar Falls #3/R est:3000-5000

AIZELIN, Eugène (1821-1902) French
Sculpture
£949 $1500 €1500 Nymphe de Diane (58cm-23in) s.i. pat bronze. 29-Nov-2 Drouot Estimations, Paris #131/R
£1014 $1581 €1500 Marguerite (69x21x25cm-27x8x10in) s.st.f.Barbedienne brown pat bronze. 26-Mar-3 Peschetau-Badin Godeau & Leroy, Paris #40/R
£1257 $2061 €1823 Nymphe de Diane (58cm-23in) s. pat.bronze Cast.Barbedienne. 4-Jun-3 AB Stockholms Auktionsverk #2364/R est:15000-18000 (S.KR 16000)
£1557 $2600 €2258 Boy with a dog (69cm-27in) s. bronze. 21-Jun-3 Selkirks, St. Louis #1102 est:2600-3000

£2468 $3875 €3850 Nymphe de Diane (78x32cm-31x13in) pat bronze Cast Barbedienne. 25-Nov-2 Rieunier, Bailly-Pommery, Mathias, Paris #105/R est:4000
£4430 $6867 €7000 Psyche (85cm-33in) s.d.1863 brown pat bronze Cast Barbedienne. 27-Sep-2 Rabourdin & Choppin de Janvry, Paris #112/R est:8000-8500

AIZKORBE, Faustino (1948-) Spanish
Sculpture
£1572 $2421 €2500 Lady (56cm-22in) s. num.3/9 pat bronze. 22-Oct-2 Durán, Madrid #254/R

AIZPIRI, Paul (1919-) French
£1528 $2384 €2292 Nature morte aux fruits (46x55cm-18x22in) s. 6-Nov-2 Dobiaschofsky, Bern #308/R est:6500 (S.FR 3500)
£2000 $3080 €3000 Portrait de jeune garcon (41x33cm-16x13in) s. prov. 23-Oct-2 Sotheby's, Olympia #801/R est:1500-2000
£6790 $9642 €11000 Vase de fleurs (65x54cm-26x21in) s. 16-Mar-3 Eric Pillon, Calais #262/R
£7407 $10519 €12000 Vase de fleurs (73x60cm-29x24in) s. 16-Mar-3 Eric Pillon, Calais #248/R
£8000 $12400 €12000 Le port de St. Tropez vu de la jetee (63x77cm-25x30in) s. i.verso. 5-Dec-2 Christie's, Kensington #130/R est:5000-7000
£8075 $13000 €12113 St. Tropez (73x93cm-29x37in) s. oil W/C on linen prov. 7-May-3 Sotheby's, New York #411/R est:15000-20000
£8176 $13000 €12264 Femme en chapeau jaune (96x79cm-38x31in) s. 27-Feb-3 Christie's, Rockefeller NY #84/R est:15000
£17949 $28179 €28000 Oiseleur (115x89cm-45x35in) s. 10-Dec-2 Artcurial Briest, Paris #505/R est:28000-35000

AJDUKIEWICZ, Sigismund (attrib) (1861-1917) Polish
£1274 $1987 €2000 Mother with child on garden bench (44x49cm-17x19in) s.d.1913. 6-Nov-2 Hugo Ruef, Munich #1002/R

AJMONE, Giuseppe (1923-) Italian
£236 $369 €350 Female nude (50x32cm-20x13in) s. tempera pastel. 26-Mar-3 Finarte Semenzato, Milan #32
£1772 $2765 €2800 Nude in purple and pink (81x65cm-32x26in) s. painted 1989. 14-Sep-2 Meeting Art, Vercelli #940/R
£4255 $6894 €6000 Cespuglio (99x54cm-39x21in) s.d.60 i.verso prov. 26-May-3 Christie's, Milan #161/R est:5000-7000
Works on paper
£486 $773 €700 Nude (70x50cm-28x20in) s. pencil chl. 1-May-3 Meeting Art, Vercelli #502

AJMONE, Lidio (1884-1945) Italian
£680 $1082 €1000 Self-portrait (45x35cm-18x14in) s. board. 1-Mar-3 Meeting Art, Vercelli #26
£2109 $3353 €3100 Landscape (35x45cm-14x18in) s. board. 1-Mar-3 Meeting Art, Vercelli #260

AKAGI, Kojiro (1934-) Japanese
£4214 $6531 €6700 Nue Ludy au dos (54x65cm-21x26in) s. 7-Oct-2 Claude Aguttes, Neuilly #257

AKELEY, Carl Ethan (1864-1926) American
Sculpture
£11613 $18000 €17420 Going and stung, elephants (17cm-7in) i.num.A-8 onr i.num.A-7 brown pat. bronze pair prov. 4-Dec-2 Sotheby's, New York #95/R est:15000-20000

AKEMARR, Abie Loy (20th C) Australian?
£640 $1030 €928 Untitled (122x149cm-48x59in) acrylic painted c.2001. 12-May-3 Joel, Victoria #352 est:1600-2000 (A.D 1600)

AKEN, Josef van (circle) (c.1709-1749) Flemish
£12500 $20750 €18750 Candlelit scene of two gentlemen smoking (89x126cm-35x50in) 12-Jun-3 Sotheby's, London #98/R est:4000-6000

AKEN, Leo van (1856-1904) Belgian
£881 $1374 €1400 Le flutiste (30x26cm-12x10in) panel. 14-Oct-2 Amberes, Antwerp #211

AKERBLOM, Rudolf (1849-1925) Finnish
£443 $700 €700 Fresh breeze (11x27cm-4x11in) s. board. 1-Dec-2 Bukowskis, Helsinki #222/R
£482 $791 €670 Cattle in landscape (22x47cm-9x19in) s. 5-Jun-3 Hagelstam, Helsinki #1000/R
£563 $907 €800 Sunset (47x26cm-19x10in) s. board. 10-May-3 Bukowskis, Helsinki #171/R
£1013 $1600 €1600 The croft, Nagu skerries (23x47cm-9x19in) s. board. 1-Dec-2 Bukowskis, Helsinki #221/R est:1800-2000

AKERS, Vivian Milner (1886-1966) American
£750 $1215 €1125 American landscape (51x61cm-20x24in) s.d.1927. 20-May-3 Sotheby's, Olympia #431/R

AKERSLOOT-BERG, Betzij Rezora (1850-1922) Dutch
£1106 $1748 €1659 Landscape from North Cape (62x98cm-24x39in) s. exhib. 2-Dec-2 Rasmussen, Copenhagen #1409/R est:8000-10000 (D.KR 13000)
£2847 $4669 €4128 Round the coast (86x136cm-34x54in) s. 2-Jun-3 Blomqvist, Oslo #10/R est:25000-35000 (N.KR 31000)

AKERSTROM, Jonas (1759-1795) Swedish
Works on paper
£284 $440 €426 Gustaf Adolf on the Island Ryden (16x23cm-6x9in) Indian ink wash W/C. 3-Dec-2 Bukowskis, Stockholm #537/R (S.KR 4000)

AKERSTROM, Jonas (attrib) (1759-1795) Swedish
£709 $1099 €1064 Adam and Eve in the Garden of Eden (51x45cm-20x18in) 4-Dec-2 AB Stockholms Auktionsverk #1685/R (S.KR 10000)

AKESON, Gerda (1909-1992) Danish
£255 $398 €383 Golden dance (81x64cm-32x25in) s. 5-Aug-2 Rasmussen, Vejle #355/R (D.KR 3000)
£845 $1318 €1268 Dancers (145x128cm-57x50in) 18-Sep-2 Kunsthallen, Copenhagen #144 (D.KR 10000)

AKIN, Louis B (1868-1913) American
£8013 $12500 €12020 Shongopovi (61x36cm-24x14in) s.i.d.1912 prov.lit. 9-Nov-2 Santa Fe Art, Santa Fe #79/R est:6000-8000

AKIN, Malcom (?) French?
£7051 $11071 €11000 Chevaux arabes et leur gardien (40x50cm-16x20in) s. panel. 16-Dec-2 Gros & Delettrez, Paris #187/R est:3000-4000

AKKERINGA, Johannes Evert Hendrik (1861-1942) Dutch
£5282 $8504 €7500 Wooden boat on the beach (14x23cm-6x9in) s. panel. 7-May-3 Vendue Huis, Gravenhage #482/R est:6000-8000
£15094 $23245 €24000 Fisherwoman mending nets, Katwijk (62x82cm-24x32in) s. prov.lit. 22-Oct-2 Sotheby's, Amsterdam #205/R est:20000-25000
Works on paper
£6918 $10654 €11000 Young shell seekers on the beach (28x39cm-11x15in) s. chl W/C htd white. 23-Oct-2 Christie's, Amsterdam #195/R est:8000-12000
£12329 $19356 €18000 In the artist garden, The Hague (38x28cm-15x11in) bears sig W/C executed c.1894. 15-Apr-3 Sotheby's, Amsterdam #100/R est:4000-6000

AKKERMAN, Ben (1920-) Dutch
£3846 $5962 €6000 Untitled (41x41cm-16x16in) s.d.1966 canvas on board prov. 3-Dec-2 Christie's, Amsterdam #351/R est:6000-8000
£3846 $5962 €6000 Untitled - landscape (35x38cm-14x15in) s.d.1965-4-69 canvas on board prov. 3-Dec-2 Christie's, Amsterdam #352/R est:6000-8000

AKKERMAN, Philip (1957-) American
£1200 $1956 €1800 Untitled (30x25cm-12x10in) board. 3-Feb-3 Sotheby's, Olympia #155/R est:300-400
£1583 $2596 €2200 Self portrait (40x35cm-16x14in) s.d.91 board. 3-Jun-3 Christie's, Amsterdam #378/R est:1500-2000
Works on paper
£719 $1180 €1000 Self portrait (39x31cm-15x12in) init.d.89 pencil W/C gouache. 3-Jun-3 Christie's, Amsterdam #379 est:1000-1500
£1100 $1793 €1650 Portrait in black and white (47x30cm-19x12in) gouache. 3-Feb-3 Sotheby's, Olympia #156/R est:300-400

AKKERSDIJK, Jacob (1815-1862) Dutch
£2785 $4400 €4400 Family scene (58x43cm-23x17in) s.d.1838 panel lit. 29-Nov-2 Schloss Ahlden, Ahlden #1160/R est:4200

AKOPIAN, Georges (1912-) Russian
£340 $541 €500 Nature morte aux pichets (46x61cm-18x24in) s. 3-Mar-3 Claude Boisgirard, Paris #25
£612 $973 €900 Paysage de Provence (54x65cm-21x26in) s. 3-Mar-3 Claude Boisgirard, Paris #26
£1020 $1622 €1500 Paysage aux cypres et oliviers (60x72cm-24x28in) s. 3-Mar-3 Claude Boisgirard, Paris #27/R est:1000-1200

AKRITHAKIS, Alexis (1939-) Greek
£3500 $5530 €5250 Untitled (90x119cm-35x47in) 1-Apr-3 Bonhams, New Bond Street #106 est:3500-5000
£12000 $18600 €18000 Travelling (45x63cm-18x25in) s. canvas on board. 2-Oct-2 Sotheby's, London #66/R est:12000-18000

AKUDA, Fanizani (20th C) Zimbabwean
Sculpture
£943 $1462 €1500 Bird and snake (85x25cm-33x10in) s. stone. 7-Oct-2 Claude Aguttes, Neuilly #333

ALANKO, Aarne (1896-1968) Finnish
£266 $415 €420 Pine trees (57x67cm-22x26in) s.d.1948. 12-Sep-2 Hagelstam, Helsinki #913

ALANKO, Uuno (1878-1964) Finnish
£253 $395 €400 Beach flowers (58x46cm-23x18in) s. 12-Sep-2 Hagelstam, Helsinki #940
£288 $472 €400 Landscape (40x65cm-16x26in) s.d.1962. 5-Jun-3 Hagelstam, Helsinki #953
£388 $637 €540 Landscape (73x54cm-29x21in) s.d.1952. 5-Jun-3 Hagelstam, Helsinki #988

ALARCON, Felix (19th C) Spanish
£524 $817 €786 Young woman wearing hat and carrying pan (35x19cm-14x7in) s. panel one of pair. 20-Nov-2 Fischer, Luzern #2000/R (S.FR 1200)
£524 $817 €786 Young woman with umbrella (35x19cm-14x7in) s. panel one of pair. 20-Nov-2 Fischer, Luzern #2001/R (S.FR 1200)

ALARCON, Jose (19th C) Spanish
£1781 $2778 €2600 Model (29x41cm-11x16in) s. 8-Apr-3 Ansorena, Madrid #123/R est:2600

ALARCON-SUAREZ, Jose (19th C) Spanish
£1982 $3250 €2874 After the ball (61x51cm-24x20in) s. 4-Jun-3 Doyle, New York #91 est:2500-3500

ALARION, Aracely (20th C) ?
£460 $754 €667 Sola, study of a girl pouring coffee (65x100cm-26x39in) s. board. 2-Jun-3 David Duggleby, Scarborough #336

ALAUX, Gustave (1887-1965) French
£2531 $3594 €4100 Depart du bien-aime (21x27cm-8x11in) s. panel. 16-Mar-3 Eric Pillon, Calais #201/R

ALAUX, Jean Pierre (1925-) French
£283 $439 €450 Nu feminin (55x38cm-22x15in) s. 3-Nov-2 Feletin, Province #180

ALBA, G (20th C) French
Sculpture
£2000 $3120 €3000 Standing elephant (26x28cm-10x11in) s. green pat bronze. 5-Nov-2 Sotheby's, London #125/R est:2000-3000

ALBACETE, Alfonso (1950-) Spanish
£3145 $4843 €5000 Maria (92x65cm-36x26in) s.d.1981 s.d.verso prov.exhib.lit. 28-Oct-2 Segre, Madrid #160/R est:4800
£12414 $19614 €18000 Painter in his study I (200x122cm-79x48in) s.d.1983 exhib.lit. 1-Apr-3 Segre, Madrid #198/R est:7200

ALBAN, Constant Jozeph (1873-1944) Dutch
Works on paper
£764 $1192 €1200 Demolition near Laurenskerk (68x48cm-27x19in) s.d.22 W/C. 5-Nov-2 Vendu Notarishuis, Rotterdam #22

ALBANI, Francesco (1578-1660) Italian
£5068 $7906 €7500 Madonna and Child (23x29cm-9x11in) canvas on panel oval. 26-Mar-3 Tajan, Paris #13/R
£5793 $9500 €8690 Lot made drunk by his two daughters (44x60cm-17x24in) copper prov. 5-Feb-3 Christie's, Rockefeller NY #282/R est:15000-20000

ALBANI, Francesco (attrib) (1578-1660) Italian
£8904 $13890 €13000 Cupid on fawn before mountain landscape (22x24cm-9x9in) panel prov. 10-Apr-3 Schopman, Hamburg #561 est:2500

ALBANI, Francesco (circle) (1578-1660) Italian
£2416 $3890 €3600 Mythologica scene (62x73cm-24x29in) 24-Feb-3 Bernaerts, Antwerp #140/R
£5405 $8432 €8000 Holy Family with two angels (90x120cm-35x47in) oval. 27-Mar-3 Dorotheum, Vienna #348/R est:6000-8000

ALBANO, Mario (1896-1968) Italian
£476 $757 €700 Old Turin (34x26cm-13x10in) s. s.i.verso cardboard. 1-Mar-3 Meeting Art, Vercelli #12

ALBERMANN, Wilhelm (1835-?) German
Sculpture
£1410 $2214 €2200 Bismarck in uniform (90cm-35in) i. brown pat.bronze. 21-Nov-2 Van Ham, Cologne #1200/R est:600

ALBEROLA, Jean Michel (1953-) French
Works on paper
£1132 $1755 €1800 Acteon fecit (55x38cm-22x15in) i.d.1986 pastel prov. 30-Oct-2 Artcurial Briest, Paris #628/R est:2000-3000

ALBERS, Anton (?) ?
£3433 $5425 €5150 View over Lake Geneva (49x66cm-19x26in) s.d.1829. 28-Nov-2 Christie's, Zurich #6/R est:8000-10000 (S.FR 8000)

ALBERS, Josef (1888-1976) American
£5696 $9000 €9000 Study for Variant (23x30cm-9x12in) mono.i.d.XII.1952 paper. 27-Nov-2 Dorotheum, Vienna #35/R est:9000-14000
£11392 $18000 €17088 Homage to the square green (30x33cm-12x13in) oil graphite on board prov.exhib. 12-Nov-2 Phillips, New York #101/R est:20000-30000
£12903 $20000 €19355 Homage to the square. Receptive (45x45cm-18x18in) mono.d.61 masonite double-sided prov.exhib. 26-Sep-2 Christie's, Rockefeller NY #702/R est:18000-25000
£18750 $30000 €28125 Homage to the square (41x41cm-16x16in) mono.d.65 masonite prov.exhib. 14-May-3 Sotheby's, New York #142/R est:20000-30000
£20312 $32500 €30468 Homage to the square (41x41cm-16x16in) mono.d.64 masonite prov.exhib. 14-May-3 Sotheby's, New York #143/R est:20000-30000
£28000 $45920 €42000 Study for Homage to the Square Soft Southern (61x61cm-24x24in) mono.d.65 s.i.d.1965 verso masonite prov. 6-Feb-3 Christie's, London #693/R est:20000-30000
£31250 $50000 €46875 Homage to the square (81x79cm-32x31in) mono.d.62 s.i.d.verso prov.exhib. 15-May-3 Christie's, Rockefeller NY #107/R est:50000-70000
£34810 $55000 €52215 Variant five greens and blue (40x77cm-16x30in) mono.d.54 s.d.verso masonite prov. 14-Nov-2 Christie's, Rockefeller NY #125/R est:35000-45000
£36392 $57500 €54588 Study for homage to the square (61x61cm-24x24in) mono.d.69 i.verso masonite prov. 13-Nov-2 Sotheby's, New York #298/R est:45000-65000
£42000 $68880 €63000 Homage to the Square (76x76cm-30x30in) mono.d.57-59 masonite prov. 6-Feb-3 Christie's, London #694/R est:25000-35000
£137500 $220000 €206250 Homage to the square - park (122x122cm-48x48in) mono.d.67 i.d.verso masonite prov. 14-May-3 Sotheby's, New York #147/R est:80000-120000
£193750 $310000 €290625 Homaga to the square - assuring (122x122cm-48x48in) mono.d.62 s.i.d.1962 masonite prov.exhib. 14-May-3 Sotheby's, New York #136/R est:80000-120000
Works on paper
£2200 $3586 €3300 K-32 (17x22cm-7x9in) init.d.56 i. pencil prov. 3-Feb-3 Bonhams, New Bond Street #84/R est:1000-1500

ALBERT, Adolphe (19/20th C) French
£427 $700 €619 Golden trees (16x26cm-6x10in) s.i. canvasboard. 5-Jun-3 Swann Galleries, New York #1/R

ALBERT, Ernest (1857-1946) American
£3437 $5500 €4984 Snow at sunset (51x61cm-20x24in) s. 16-May-3 Skinner, Boston #265/R est:6000-8000
£4717 $7500 €7076 In scarlet, green and gold (76x91cm-30x36in) s.d.1938. 4-Mar-3 Christie's, Rockefeller NY #64/R est:10000-15000
£5414 $8500 €8121 Red barn (58x64cm-23x25in) s.d.1920 board exhib. 10-Dec-2 Doyle, New York #86/R est:4000-6000

ALBERT, Ernest (1900-1976) Belgian
£284 $474 €400 Seated nude (101x71cm-40x28in) s. 23-Jun-3 Bernaerts, Antwerp #683
£347 $552 €500 Paysage ensoleille (50x65cm-20x26in) s. cardboard. 29-Apr-3 Campo & Campo, Antwerp #1

£1282 $2013 €2000 Enfants dans le bois (49x61cm-19x24in) s. cardboard exhib. 19-Nov-2 Vanderkindere, Brussels #54 est:1000-1500

ALBERT, Friedrich Wilhelm Ferdinand Theodor (1822-?) German
£880 $1416 €1320 Evening landscape with lake (68x105cm-27x41in) s. 7-May-3 Dobiaschofsky, Bern #307/R (S.FR 1900)

ALBERT, Gustaf (1866-1905) Swedish
£1277 $1979 €1916 Bridge across the Seine (46x38cm-18x15in) s.d.93 exhib. 4-Dec-2 AB Stockholms Auktionsverk #1548/R est:20000-25000 (S.KR 18000)

ALBERT, Jos (1886-1981) Belgian
£348 $543 €550 Coeur brode (24x19cm-9x7in) s. d.1966 verso. 10-Sep-2 Vanderkindere, Brussels #310
£475 $741 €750 Mur rue Langeveld. s.d.1965. 10-Sep-2 Vanderkindere, Brussels #304
£1899 $2962 €3000 Les masques (90x71cm-35x28in) s.d.1959. 10-Sep-2 Vanderkindere, Brussels #379/R est:1000-1500
£2014 $3223 €2800 Still life (55x46cm-22x18in) s.d.1928. 17-May-3 De Vuyst, Lokeren #1/R est:2800-3300
£2014 $3223 €2800 Vase de fleurs, cruche, fruits et coupes sur une table drapee (60x70cm-24x28in) s. 13-May-3 Palais de Beaux Arts, Brussels #28/R est:3600-5000
£3822 $5962 €6000 Composition au panier de fruits et a la gaufre (47x61cm-19x24in) s. 11-Nov-2 Horta, Bruxelles #206 est:3500-4000
Works on paper
£253 $395 €400 Interieur. s.d.1961 W/C ink. 10-Sep-2 Vanderkindere, Brussels #320
£409 $630 €650 L'homme rouge (61x66cm-24x26in) s.d.1915 W/C. 22-Oct-2 Campo, Vlaamse Kaai #3
£475 $741 €750 Interieur (20x26cm-8x10in) s. W/C sold with a pencil dr. 10-Sep-2 Vanderkindere, Brussels #316
£1282 $2013 €2000 Nature morte (57x39cm-22x15in) s. W/C. 10-Dec-2 Campo, Vlaamse Kaai #3/R est:1000-1500

ALBERT-LEFEUVRE, Louis Étienne Marie (19th C) French
Sculpture
£903 $1427 €1400 Muse des bois (36cm-14in) pat bronze onyx base Cast Siot. 19-Dec-2 Bondu, Paris #67/R

ALBERTI, Achille (1860-1943) Italian
Sculpture
£7547 $11698 €12000 Mother (78cm-31in) s. marble lit. 29-Oct-2 Finarte, Milan #360/R est:11000-14000

ALBERTI, Antonio (fl.1420-1442) Italian
£46296 $75000 €69444 Madonna and Child (32x32cm-13x13in) tempera gold ground panel prov.lit. 24-Jan-3 Christie's, Rockefeller NY #26/R est:50000-70000

ALBERTI, Cherubino (1553-1615) Italian
Works on paper
£350 $500 €525 Hercules killing the Hydra (12x15cm-5x6in) pen brown ink wash. 23-Jan-3 Swann Galleries, New York #51/R
£900 $1503 €1305 Study of an arm. Female nude (14x25cm-6x10in) black chk pen ink double-sided prov. 9-Jul-3 Bonhams, Knightsbridge #23/R

ALBERTI, Giovanni (1558-1601) Italian
Works on paper
£316 $500 €500 Une homme barbu tenant un filet. Projet d'architecture (26x17cm-10x7in) i. pen brown ink brown wash prov. 27-Nov-2 Christie's, Paris #33/R

ALBERTI, Giuseppe Vizzotto (1862-1931) Italian
Works on paper
£300 $468 €450 Fisherman in boat before a shrine (51x33cm-20x13in) s.i.d.1898 W/C. 25-Mar-3 Gorringes, Bexhill #1210
£1000 $1620 €1500 View from the lagoon (22x40cm-9x16in) s. pencil W/C. 23-Jan-3 Christie's, Kensington #333/R est:400-600
£1216 $1897 €1800 Fishing boats on the Lagoon, Venice (18x32cm-7x13in) s.d.88 gouache. 28-Mar-3 Dorotheum, Vienna #258/R est:2400-3000

ALBERTIN, Andre Léon (20th C) French
£429 $678 €644 Harbour scene (81x102cm-32x40in) s.d.1938 prov. 3-Apr-3 Heffel, Vancouver #3/R (C.D 1000)

ALBERTINELLI, Mariotto (1474-1515) Italian
£5660 $8830 €9000 Maria with Infant Jesus (92x64cm-36x25in) panel. 23-Sep-2 Wiener Kunst Auktionen, Vienna #3/R est:6500-13000
£16000 $25120 €24000 Madonna and Child with saint John (119x96cm-47x38in) panel. 11-Dec-2 Christie's, London #92/R est:15000-25000
£38956 $61550 €58434 Madonna and Child with Saint John (136x103cm-54x41in) board prov. 15-Nov-2 Naón & Cia, Buenos Aires #75/R

ALBERTINI, Oreste (1887-1953) Italian
£472 $726 €750 Vase of flowers (30x24cm-12x9in) s. cardboard. 23-Oct-2 Finarte, Milan #76
£1088 $1731 €1600 Composition with woman (47x40cm-19x16in) i.verso board. 18-Mar-3 Finarte, Milan #32/R
£9748 $15013 €15500 View of Besano with shepherdess and sheep (60x80cm-24x31in) s. 28-Oct-2 Il Ponte, Milan #287/R est:15000

ALBERTINI, Oreste (attrib) (1887-1953) Italian
£340 $500 €510 Preparing the horse (28x38cm-11x15in) s. board. 23-Jun-2 Susanin's, Chicago #5110/R

ALBERTIS, Sebastiano de (attrib) (1828-1897) Italian
£645 $1019 €1000 Portrait of Emilio Gola (43x32cm-17x13in) i.d.1880 cardboard. 18-Dec-2 Finarte, Milan #127/R

ALBERTO, Pietro (1929-) Italian
£1020 $1622 €1500 Village (50x70cm-20x28in) s.d.1989 acrylic. 1-Mar-3 Meeting Art, Vercelli #615
Works on paper
£316 $494 €500 Wind screaming amongst walls (60x50cm-24x20in) s.d.1994 mixed media cardboard on canvas. 14-Sep-2 Meeting Art, Vercelli #260
£1090 $1711 €1700 Untitled (70x50cm-28x20in) s.i.d.2000 verso mixed media board lit. 23-Nov-2 Meeting Art, Vercelli #288/R

ALBERTS, Willem Jacobus (1912-) Dutch
£348 $543 €550 Field way with trees along a ditch and cows in background (59x48cm-23x19in) s. 21-Oct-2 Glerum, Amsterdam #109
£528 $850 €750 Waterlilies (58x28cm-23x11in) s. 7-May-3 Vendue Huis, Gravenhage #8/R

ALBERTSEN, Andreas Marius Valdemar (1868-1954) Danish
£420 $673 €630 Harbour scene with steamship and vessels by quay, winter (83x118cm-33x46in) s.d.92. 13-Jan-3 Rasmussen, Vejle #75/R (D.KR 4800)

ALBIKER, Karl (1878-1961) German
Works on paper
£338 $527 €500 Standing female nude (35x16cm-14x6in) mono. W/C over pencil. 28-Mar-3 Ketterer, Hamburg #175/R

ALBIN-GUILLOT, Laure (1881-1962) French
Photographs
£3896 $6000 €5844 Nude study (37x30cm-15x12in) s. photograph lit. 24-Oct-2 Sotheby's, New York #158/R est:7000-10000

ALBITZ, Richard (20th C) German
£464 $756 €700 Winter sun over a forest house (90x110cm-35x43in) 28-Jan-3 Dorotheum, Vienna #32/R

ALBOTTO, Francesco (circle) (1722-1758) Italian
£12069 $19069 €17500 Saint Clemente Islant, Venice (49x61cm-19x24in) 5-Apr-3 Finarte Semenzato, Milan #60/R est:12000
£27972 $40000 €41958 Venetian canal scene (89x132cm-35x52in) 22-Jan-3 Doyle, New York #108/R est:18000

ALBOTTO, Francesco (style) (1722-1758) Italian
£12162 $18973 €18000 Venetian capriccio (36x56cm-14x22in) prov. 27-Mar-3 Dorotheum, Vienna #20/R est:8000-10000

ALBOUY, Gerard (1912-1985) French
£276 $441 €400 Maison dans un paysage (54x65cm-21x26in) s. isorel panel. 12-Mar-3 Libert, Castor, Paris #32
£310 $497 €450 Palmiers et maison (35x27cm-14x11in) s. 12-Mar-3 Libert, Castor, Paris #35
£331 $530 €480 Maisons dans un paysage (54x65cm-21x26in) s. isorel panel. 12-Mar-3 Libert, Castor, Paris #33
£331 $530 €480 Bouquet de fleurs (81x65cm-32x26in) s. panel. 12-Mar-3 Libert, Castor, Paris #37
£345 $552 €500 Chemin et deux maisons (73x60cm-29x24in) s. isorel panel. 12-Mar-3 Libert, Castor, Paris #34
£379 $607 €550 Les maisons (33x41cm-13x16in) s. 12-Mar-3 Libert, Castor, Paris #39
£621 $993 €900 Paysage aux palmiers (55x46cm-22x18in) s. 12-Mar-3 Libert, Castor, Paris #27

£621 $993 €900 Le jardin fleuri (46x55cm-18x22in) s. 12-Mar-3 Libert, Castor, Paris #40
£1241 $1986 €1800 Les palmiers (73x60cm-29x24in) s. isorel panel. 12-Mar-3 Libert, Castor, Paris #30/R

ALBRECHT, Gretchen (1943-) New Zealander
£3185 $5000 €4778 Abstract (138x182cm-54x72in) s.d.1977 acrylic. 10-Dec-2 Peter Webb, Auckland #59/R est:10000-15000 (NZ.D 10000)
£5208 $8125 €7812 Lunette, for Fra Angelico (120x240cm-47x94in) s.d.1984 acrylic semi-circular in two sections. 8-Apr-3 Peter Webb, Auckland #70/R est:12000-18000 (NZ.D 15000)
£5623 $8772 €8435 Night Geometries - red (73x110cm-29x43in) s.i.d.1994 acrylic. 17-Sep-2 Peter Webb, Auckland #83/R est:15000-20000 (NZ.D 18500)
£6597 $10292 €9896 Grey cloud, winter sky (129x204cm-51x80in) s.d.1974 acrylic. 8-Apr-3 Peter Webb, Auckland #73/R est:18000-25000 (NZ.D 19000)
Works on paper
£912 $1422 €1368 Current 3 (29x38cm-11x15in) s.i.d.1987 chk pastel on collage. 17-Sep-2 Peter Webb, Auckland #178/R est:2000-3000 (NZ.D 3000)
£919 $1479 €1379 Night geometrics (29x38cm-11x15in) s.d.93 mixed media. 7-May-3 Dunbar Sloane, Auckland #95/R (NZ.D 2600)
£1719 $2681 €2579 Hemisphere (58x75cm-23x30in) s.d.1984 W/C. 8-Apr-3 Peter Webb, Auckland #25/R est:3000-5000 (NZ.D 4950)
£2817 $4648 €4085 Deluge (152x213cm-60x84in) s.d.1988 gouache collage. 1-Jul-3 Peter Webb, Auckland #20/R est:8000-12000 (NZ.D 8000)

ALBRICI, Enrico (1714-1775) Italian
£9434 $14717 €15000 Arrival (20x42cm-8x17in) 22-Sep-2 Semenzato, Venice #130/R est:10000-12500

ALBRIGHT, Adam Emory (1862-1957) American
£3145 $5000 €4718 Children beside the lake (61x76cm-24x30in) s. painted c.1912. 2-Mar-3 Toomey, Oak Park #564/R est:5000-7000

ALBRIZIO, Conrad A (1894-1973) American
£1154 $1800 €1731 Modern pieta (61x76cm-24x30in) masonite prov. 12-Oct-2 Neal Auction Company, New Orleans #651/R est:2000-3000

ALCAIN, Alfredo (1936-) Spanish
£1275 $2053 €1900 Warden's house (60x81cm-24x32in) s.d.62 s.i.d.verso. 18-Feb-3 Durán, Madrid #195/R

ALCALAY, Albert (1917-) American
£287 $450 €431 Wharf (30x117cm-12x46in) s. 22-Nov-2 Skinner, Boston #383/R

ALCALDE, Juan (1918-) Spanish
£1418 $2298 €2000 Calle de ciudad (45x52cm-18x20in) s. prov. 20-May-3 Segre, Madrid #118/R est:1700
£2404 $3774 €3750 Market (80x100cm-31x39in) s. 19-Nov-2 Castellana, Madrid #544/R

ALCAZAR TEJEDOR, Jose (19th C) Spanish
£4194 $6626 €6500 Monk resting (58x100cm-23x39in) s. 17-Dec-2 Durán, Madrid #112/R

ALCIATI, Ambrogio (1878-1929) Italian
£5442 $8653 €8000 Female nude (64x53cm-25x21in) s.i.d.1915. 1-Mar-3 Meeting Art, Vercelli #65

ALCOCK, Edward (fl.1757-1778) British
£3000 $4650 €4500 Portraits of a lady in a white dress, and a gentleman in a red suit (44x30cm-17x12in) s.d.1769 pair prov. 30-Oct-2 Bonhams, New Bond Street #32/R est:2500-3500

ALCORLO BARRERA, Manuel (1935-) Spanish
Works on paper
£385 $608 €600 Seated nude (32x43cm-13x17in) s. W/C dr. 19-Nov-2 Durán, Madrid #691/R

ALCOVER, Manuel (20th C) Spanish
£1379 $2207 €2000 Fishermen (60x73cm-24x29in) s. 11-Mar-3 Castellana, Madrid #50/R

ALDAZ Y SANCHO, Juan (19/20th C) Spanish
£1931 $3070 €2800 Woman amongst flowers (24x19cm-9x7in) s. board. 4-Mar-3 Ansorena, Madrid #183/R

ALDE, Yvette (1911-) French
£638 $1034 €900 Fleurs a la table (64x49cm-25x19in) s. d.1953-56 verso. 26-May-3 Glerum, Amsterdam #82/R

ALDEFELD, Ferdinand (19th C) German
£408 $649 €600 River landscape with ruins and figures (17x22cm-7x9in) s.d.1816 panel. 28-Mar-3 Bolland & Marotz, Bremen #421/R

ALDEGREVER, Heinrich (attrib) (1502-1558) German
£16438 $25644 €24657 Adam and Eve (58x71cm-23x28in) panel. 28-Mar-3 Koller, Zurich #3008/R est:35000-45000 (S.FR 36000)

ALDERSON, D M and E M (20th C) British
Works on paper
£600 $942 €900 Portrait of the hunter Amazon (21x28cm-8x11in) s.d.1932 W/C. 21-Nov-2 Tennants, Leyburn #671
£700 $1099 €1050 Gun dogs on a moor (34x47cm-13x19in) s.d.1965 W/C. 21-Nov-2 Tennants, Leyburn #667/R
£1700 $2669 €2550 Chestnut mare in a stable (35x48cm-14x19in) s.d.1952 W/C. 21-Nov-2 Tennants, Leyburn #669/R est:400-600
£2200 $3454 €3300 Shire horses at work (39x56cm-15x22in) s.d.1974 W/C htd white. 21-Nov-2 Tennants, Leyburn #668/R est:600-800
£2500 $3925 €3750 Bay hunter in a stable (35x47cm-14x19in) s.d.1930 W/C. 21-Nov-2 Tennants, Leyburn #670/R est:400-600

ALDERSON, Dorothy Margaret (1900-1992) British
Works on paper
£420 $664 €630 Snow ploughing in a wintry landscape (15x23cm-6x9in) s.d.90 W/C. 24-Apr-3 Richardson & Smith, Whitby #30
£1800 $2826 €2700 Shire horses and other animals in a farmyard (39x54cm-15x21in) s.d.1976 pencil W/C. 19-Nov-2 Bonhams, Leeds #82a est:1000-1200

ALDERSON, Dorothy Margaret and Elizabeth Mary (20th C) British
£900 $1422 €1350 Trough with cattle and fowl about a farmstead (25x33cm-10x13in) s.d.1986. 24-Apr-3 Richardson & Smith, Whitby #35/R
Works on paper
£250 $410 €375 Portrait of a hunter in landscape setting (25x34cm-10x13in) s.d.1974 W/C. 2-Jun-3 David Duggleby, Scarborough #277
£250 $410 €375 Study of a pony in a stable setting (14x21cm-6x8in) s.d.1977 W/C. 2-Jun-3 David Duggleby, Scarborough #278
£340 $527 €510 Copper King, chestnut foal in a meadow (16x22cm-6x9in) s.i. W/C. 24-Sep-2 Anderson & Garland, Newcastle #250
£360 $590 €540 Farmstead with sheep grazing in the foreground (24x33cm-9x13in) s.d.1976 W/C. 2-Jun-3 David Duggleby, Scarborough #276
£480 $744 €720 Amanda and foal (18x25cm-7x10in) s.i. W/C. 24-Sep-2 Anderson & Garland, Newcastle #251/R
£1700 $2771 €2465 Study of three young calves beside a stone barn (21x25cm-8x10in) s.d.1950 W/C. 17-Jul-3 Tennants, Leyburn #753 est:400-500

ALDIN, Cecil (1870-1935) British
£580 $911 €870 Bulldog (18x10cm-7x4in) s. black chk prov. 10-Dec-2 Rosebery Fine Art, London #703/R
£650 $1034 €975 The Cheshire away from Peckforton Wood (40x71cm-16x28in) s. 7-Mar-3 Tennants, Leyburn #190
£650 $1034 €975 The Belvoir - into the Vale from Clawson Thorns (32x66cm-13x26in) s. 7-Mar-3 Tennants, Leyburn #191
Works on paper
£350 $546 €525 Safe distance (33x27cm-13x11in) s.d.96 pen ink W/C. 10-Oct-2 Greenslade Hunt, Taunton #575/R
£380 $593 €570 Alsation and keeshound (14x26cm-6x10in) pencil chk. 18-Sep-2 Dreweatt Neate, Newbury #73
£400 $632 €600 Huntsman at the gallop (12x17cm-5x7in) s.i. pen ink on ivorine. 7-Apr-3 Bonhams, Bath #41
£440 $678 €660 Dog in an archway (50x39cm-20x15in) s. W/C bodycol over pencil. 22-Oct-2 Bonhams, Knightsbridge #21/R
£480 $758 €720 Overhead bird (19x12cm-7x5in) s.i.verso pen ink. 28-Nov-2 Bonhams, Knightsbridge #34/R
£500 $835 €725 I'll sing you a song (20x17cm-8x7in) s.i.d.1900 pen ink. 24-Jun-3 Bonhams, Knightsbridge #53/R
£550 $875 €825 Huntsman on a grey hunter jumping a fence (27x30cm-11x12in) s. W/C bodycol. 29-Apr-3 Rowley Fine Art, Newmarket #410/R
£650 $1014 €975 Caught in a shower (13x9cm-5x4in) s. pen W/C on ivorine. 25-Mar-3 Bonhams, Knightsbridge #207/R
£700 $1085 €1050 Mischievous puppy (13x18cm-5x7in) s. pencil grey wash ivorine. 4-Dec-2 Christie's, Kensington #165/R
£750 $1223 €1125 Lee-o on a Lee. Lady riding (23x36cm-9x14in) s.i. ink W/C pencil double-sided. 29-Jan-3 Sotheby's, Olympia #188/R
£750 $1223 €1125 As rich as a king (34x25cm-13x10in) s. pastel pencil. 12-Feb-3 Bonhams, Knightsbridge #129/R
£800 $1264 €1200 Touquet (27x38cm-11x15in) s.i. crayon. 26-Nov-2 Bonhams, Knightsbridge #239/R
£1000 $1560 €1500 I've been in Scotland (28x47cm-11x19in) pen ink W/C exhib. 18-Sep-2 Dreweatt Neate, Newbury #72/R est:800-1200

£1100 $1738 €1650 Master of hunt (38x48cm-15x19in) s. i.d.1919 verso pastel black chk linen. 27-Nov-2 Bonhams, Knowle #175 est:800-1200
£1200 $1884 €1800 Sketch of a puppy (12x14cm-5x6in) s.i. black chk black wash htd white prov. 10-Dec-2 Rosebery Fine Art, London #704/R est:500-700
£1400 $2212 €2100 Christmas Eve (20x15cm-8x6in) s. pen ink W/C. 7-Apr-3 Bonhams, Bath #42/R est:1000-1500
£1400 $2324 €2030 Return home (13x18cm-5x7in) s. ink col pencil on ivorine. 12-Jun-3 Christie's, Kensington #22a/R est:1000-1500
£1400 $2338 €2030 Exhausted companions (9x11cm-4x4in) s. W/C ink ivorine. 24-Jun-3 Bonhams, Knightsbridge #52/R est:500-800
£1650 $2607 €2475 Refusal at a hedge (42x28cm-17x11in) s. W/C pen black ink over pencil. 27-Nov-2 Bonhams, Knowle #171 est:1200-1800
£1800 $2844 €2700 Amorous shepherd. Gamboling lambs (20x27cm-8x11in) s. pencil col pencil on ivorine two. 28-Nov-2 Christie's, Kensington #63/R est:2000-3000
£1800 $2880 €2700 Hunt approaches (25x44cm-10x17in) s. pencil col chk. 11-Mar-3 Bonhams, New Bond Street #140/R est:1200-1800
£2000 $3260 €3000 Huntsman and hounds (13x18cm-5x7in) s. pen ink wash dr mica. 14-Feb-3 Keys, Aylsham #510/R est:400-600
£2147 $3500 €3221 Boston terrier (17x19cm-7x7in) s. col chk. 11-Feb-3 Bonhams & Doyles, New York #189/R est:2000-3000
£3200 $5312 €4640 Jim, a bearded collie (66x51cm-26x20in) s.i. col chks. 12-Jun-3 Christie's, Kensington #281/R est:3000-5000
£3400 $5372 €5100 Boxer pup (39x30cm-15x12in) s.d.97 W/C bodycol. 2-Dec-2 Sotheby's, London #74/R est:1500-2000
£3548 $5500 €5322 Sleeping westie. Two terriers (22x34cm-9x13in) s. one black white chk pencil chl two prov. 29-Oct-2 Sotheby's, New York #154/R est:1000-1500
£4000 $6320 €6000 Huntsman (50x69cm-20x27in) s. pastel. 28-Nov-2 Bonhams, Knightsbridge #127/R est:4000-6000
£6500 $10790 €9425 Your Christmas mail (21x27cm-8x11in) s.i. pencil ink col chk. 12-Jun-3 Christie's, Kensington #312/R est:3000-5000

ALDINE, Marc (1917-1956) Italian

£1633 $2596 €2400 Gondolas in Venice (32x41cm-13x16in) s. 18-Mar-3 Finarte, Milan #152/R
£1905 $3029 €2800 View of Venice (32x41cm-13x16in) s. 18-Mar-3 Finarte, Milan #153/R
£3718 $5875 €5800 Venise (35x28cm-14x11in) s. prov. 18-Nov-2 Tajan, Paris #143/R est:4600-6000
£7051 $10929 €11000 Canal in Venice (50x65cm-20x26in) s. 5-Dec-2 Dr Fritz Nagel, Stuttgart #638/R est:6000
£7200 $11232 €10800 Venice (46x61cm-18x24in) s. 17-Sep-2 Sotheby's, Olympia #284/R est:4000-6000
£8500 $13855 €12325 Grand Canal, Venice (38x46cm-15x18in) s. board. 16-Jul-3 Sotheby's, Olympia #256/R est:5000-7000
£9200 $14904 €13800 Venice (38x55cm-15x22in) s. 20-May-3 Sotheby's, Olympia #428/R est:5000-7000
£10191 $16000 €15287 Grand Canal (24x32cm-9x13in) s. 10-Dec-2 Doyle, New York #209/R est:20000-30000
£14194 $22000 €21291 Venetian canal scene (50x65cm-20x26in) s. 30-Oct-2 Christie's, Rockefeller NY #215/R est:10000-15000
£15000 $25050 €22500 Doge's Palace and Bacino di San Marco, Venice (54x81cm-21x32in) s. 18-Jun-3 Christie's, Kensington #140/R est:10000-15000

ALDOR, Janos Laszlo (1895-?) Hungarian

£1923 $3019 €3000 Portrait of young beauty with bare chest (48x39cm-19x15in) s.d.1931 canvas on board. 21-Nov-2 Van Ham, Cologne #1445/R est:3000

ALDRICH, George Ames (1872-1941) American

£1313 $2100 €1970 Early morning, curving dirt road with rising sun (46x61cm-18x24in) s. 11-Jan-3 James Julia, Fairfield #625 est:1000-2000
£4717 $7500 €7076 Evening reflections (71x91cm-28x36in) s.d. 4-May-3 Treadway Gallery, Cincinnati #520/R est:5000-7000

ALDRIDGE, Denis (20th C) British

Works on paper

£420 $655 €630 Hounds cornering a stag (34x49cm-13x19in) s.d.1963 W/C. 10-Oct-2 Greenslade Hunt, Taunton #550/R

ALDRIDGE, Eileen (1916-1990) British

£400 $668 €580 Corner of the studio (46x38cm-18x15in) s. i.verso board. 19-Jun-3 Lane, Penzance #363

ALDRIDGE, F J (1850-1933) British

Works on paper

£498 $768 €747 Of a Dutch harbour scene Scheldt (38x33cm-15x13in) s.i. W/C. 23-Oct-2 Dunbar Sloane, Wellington #1218/R (NZ.D 1600)

ALDRIDGE, Frederick James (1850-1933) British

£320 $499 €480 Leading timber near Woodhall, Lincs (26x47cm-10x19in) s. board. 19-Sep-2 John Bellman, Billingshurst #1359
£850 $1420 €1233 Fishing fleet off Shoreham (35x60cm-14x24in) 26-Jun-3 Mellors & Kirk, Nottingham #914/R
£1450 $2378 €2175 Near Dortrecht Holland, barges on the river (48x74cm-19x29in) s.d.89 s.i.d.1889 verso prov. 5-Feb-3 John Nicholson, Haslemere #1087 est:1000-1500

Works on paper

£260 $395 €390 Schevenigen (25x36cm-10x14in) s. W/C. 16-Aug-2 Keys, Aylsham #596
£260 $413 €390 On the fishing grounds (17x36cm-7x14in) s. W/C. 4-Mar-3 Bonhams, Knightsbridge #253/R
£300 $471 €450 Shipping off Hurst Castle (25x37cm-10x15in) s. W/C stopping out. 16-Dec-2 Sotheby's, Olympia #144/R
£300 $471 €450 Summer in Holland (18x29cm-7x11in) s.i. W/C. 16-Dec-2 Sotheby's, Olympia #148/R
£300 $498 €435 Tug boat and other shipping in harbour (8x18cm-3x7in) s. W/C. 12-Jun-3 Gorringes, Lewes #1665
£300 $474 €435 Venice (39x29cm-15x11in) s.i. W/C oval. 22-Jul-3 Sworder & Son, Bishops Stortford #386/R
£320 $496 €480 Fishing vessels hitting a squall (20x29cm-8x11in) s. W/C bodycol. 24-Sep-2 Bonhams, Knightsbridge #207/R
£400 $624 €600 Bosham harbour (49x74cm-19x29in) s. W/C. 26-Mar-3 Sotheby's, Olympia #132/R
£422 $662 €633 Luggers off Brighton shore (22x34cm-9x13in) s.d.1885 W/C prov. 25-Nov-2 Hodgins, Calgary #162/R (C.D 1050)
£480 $739 €720 Shipping in a harbour (15x21cm-6x8in) s. 23-Oct-2 Hamptons Fine Art, Godalming #70
£500 $785 €750 Shipping entering harbour, storm out to sea (35x54cm-14x21in) s.d.18 W/C. 16-Dec-2 Sotheby's, Olympia #145/R
£500 $785 €750 Shipping in full sail (26x38cm-10x15in) s. W/C. 16-Dec-2 Sotheby's, Olympia #147/R
£500 $790 €750 Sail barges on an estuary (25x36cm-10x14in) s. W/C. 2-Dec-2 Gorringes, Lewes #2633
£520 $868 €754 Venice (26x37cm-10x15in) s. W/C. 25-Jun-3 Cheffins, Cambridge #702/R
£550 $853 €825 Strong breeze in the Channel (47x68cm-19x27in) s.i. W/C. 31-Oct-2 Christie's, Kensington #396/R
£600 $930 €900 On the Thames (27x39cm-11x15in) s. W/C. 25-Sep-2 Hamptons Fine Art, Godalming #300/R
£627 $978 €941 Ships at anchor (27x38cm-11x15in) s. W/C. 7-Nov-2 International Art Centre, Auckland #179/R est:1500-2500 (NZ.D 2000)
£640 $1018 €960 On the Thames (37x55cm-15x22in) s.i. W/C. 27-Feb-3 Bonhams, Chester #409
£680 $1061 €1020 Gusty weather (35x53cm-14x21in) s. W/C. 18-Sep-2 Cheffins Grain & Comins, Cambridge #468/R
£680 $1081 €1020 Sailing into port (35x53cm-14x21in) s.d.1902 W/C. 4-Mar-3 Bearnes, Exeter #341/R
£700 $1043 €1050 Shipping in an estuary (35x53cm-14x21in) s. W/C. 27-Jun-2 Greenslade Hunt, Taunton #699/R
£700 $1134 €1050 Entering harbour (28x52cm-11x20in) s.d.90 W/C. 20-May-3 Sotheby's, Olympia #20/R
£750 $1170 €1125 Shipping in a harbour (25x35cm-10x14in) s.i. W/C htd white. 10-Apr-3 Tennants, Leyburn #819
£800 $1296 €1200 Ostende boats (26x37cm-10x15in) s.i. pencil W/C. 21-May-3 Christie's, Kensington #466/R
£820 $1279 €1230 Fishing boats with town beyond (25x36cm-10x14in) s. W/C. 26-Mar-3 Woolley & Wallis, Salisbury #83/R
£820 $1296 €1189 Shipping at anchor, Venice beyond (36x51cm-14x20in) s. W/C. 22-Jul-3 Gorringes, Lewes #1715/R
£850 $1326 €1275 Moored ships (25x36cm-10x14in) s. W/C. 26-Mar-3 Woolley & Wallis, Salisbury #82/R
£1350 $2052 €2025 Crab boats (20x37cm-8x15in) s.i. W/C. 15-Aug-2 Bonhams, New Bond Street #221/R est:800-1200
£1420 $2343 €2059 Entering port (49x74cm-19x29in) s.i. W/C. 1-Jul-3 Bearnes, Exeter #451/R est:1000-1500
£1450 $2364 €2175 Fishing boats and other vessels heading for port, possibly Dartmouth (50x72cm-20x28in) s. W/C. 29-Jan-3 Hampton & Littlewood, Exeter #370/R est:400-600

ALDRIDGE, John Arthur Malcolm (1905-1984) British

£500 $775 €750 Wagon and Dovecote (42x55cm-17x22in) painted 1947 prov. 6-Oct-2 Lots Road, London #352
£520 $811 €780 Still life with apples and flowers in a jug on a tablecloth (34x44cm-13x17in) s. panel sketch verso double sided. 8-Oct-2 Bonhams, Oxford #164
£750 $1238 €1088 North Essex (36x47cm-14x19in) board prov. 3-Jul-3 Christie's, Kensington #437/R
£950 $1501 €1425 Cornfield with farm buildings in the distance (46x53cm-18x21in) s.d.1955 i.verso board. 18-Dec-2 Mallams, Oxford #658/R
£1400 $2310 €2030 Landscape, May 49 (52x62cm-20x24in) i. board exhib. 1-Jul-3 Bonhams, Norwich #336/R est:1000-1500
£2400 $3936 €3600 Bluegate Hall, Great Bardfield (48x67cm-19x26in) s. s.i.d.Feb 1952 verso board. 3-Jun-3 Sotheby's, Olympia #117/R est:2000-3000

ALDRIDGE, Richard L (fl.1866-1887) British

£3000 $4620 €4500 Bayonne - from the Nive (65x100cm-26x39in) s. i.verso exhib. 3-Sep-2 Shapiro, Sydney #392/R est:10000-15000 (A.D 8400)

ALDWINCKLE, Eric (1909-1980) Canadian/British

£658 $1021 €987 On the ski trail (25x32cm-10x13in) s.d.1942 board. 3-Dec-2 Joyner, Toronto #445 est:400-600 (C.D 1600)

ALDWORTH, Ernest William (1889-1977) British

Works on paper

£800 $1264 €1200 Setting off. In full gallop (37x53cm-15x21in) pencil W/C two. 28-Nov-2 Christie's, Kensington #211/R

ALEANDER, Johan Abraham (1766-1853) Swedish

Works on paper

£709 $1099 €1064 Cottages by the entrance to Stockholm (32x48cm-13x19in) s.d.1800 gouache. 3-Dec-2 Bukowskis, Stockholm #530/R (S.KR 10000)

ALECHINSKY, Pierre (1927-) Belgian

£5786 $8969 €9200 Argument de reserve (45x38cm-18x15in) s.d. i.verso lit. 30-Oct-2 Artcurial Briest, Paris #462a/R est:10000-15000

£7435 $11747 €11153 Pole d'attraction deplace, New York (52x65cm-20x26in) s. i.verso acrylic paper on canvas painted 1979-1985 prov. 1-Apr-3 Rasmussen, Copenhagen #114/R est:100000-125000 (D.KR 80000)

£7692 $11923 €12000 Autant de branches (73x43cm-29x17in) s.i.d.1992 stretcher Indian ink acrylic exhib. 3-Dec-2 Lempertz, Koln #3/R est:10000-12000

£8333 $12917 €13000 Revu et corrige (54x45cm-21x18in) s. s.i.on stretcher acrylic paper on canavs. 3-Dec-2 Christie's, Amsterdam #253/R est:12000-16000

£8467 $13124 €12701 Piece d'eua (50x65cm-20x26in) s. s.d.1976 verso paper on canvas prov. 1-Oct-2 Rasmussen, Copenhagen #92/R est:100000 (D.KR 100000)

£8633 $14158 €12000 Vue de lion (60x75cm-24x30in) s. s.i.d.1996 on stretcher acrylic paper on canvas prov. 3-Jun-3 Christie's, Amsterdam #346/R est:12000-15000

£9220 $14936 €13000 Virage au bleu (38x46cm-15x18in) s. s.i.d.1957 verso prov. 26-May-3 Christie's, Milan #325/R est:8000-10000

£9294 $14684 €13941 Au pied de l'image (66x52cm-26x20in) s. s.d.1978 verso Japan paper on canvas. 1-Apr-3 Rasmussen, Copenhagen #108/R est:100000-125000 (D.KR 100000)

£10897 $17109 €17000 Amovible (61x46cm-24x18in) s.d.1989 lit. 11-Dec-2 Artcurial Briest, Paris #714/R est:20000

£11806 $18653 €17000 Pieces rares (65x52cm-26x20in) s. paper on canvas. 27-Apr-3 Perrin, Versailles #34/R est:15000-18000

£11806 $19479 €17000 Sans titre (82x116cm-32x46in) s. prov.exhib. 1-Jul-3 Artcurial Briest, Paris #498/R est:15000-20000

£14358 $22399 €21537 Tempe et Tempete (100x100cm-39x39in) s.i. verso acrylic paper on canvas painted 1970 prov. 18-Sep-2 Kunsthallen, Copenhagen #18/R est:200000 (D.KR 170000)

£16000 $26720 €23200 Un nombre impair (50x100cm-20x39in) s. s.i.d.1963 verso. 26-Jun-3 Sotheby's, London #236/R est:12000-15000

£16511 $25593 €24767 Novement (96x96cm-38x38in) s.d.1981-82 verso acrylic Indian ink Japan paper on canvas. 1-Oct-2 Rasmussen, Copenhagen #95/R est:200000-250000 (D.KR 195000)

£17308 $27346 €27000 Untitled (63x50cm-25x20in) s. s.i.d.1966 verso. 15-Nov-2 Laurence Calmels, Paris #31/R est:25000

£17736 $27669 €26604 Sortie de bain (95x96cm-37x38in) s. i.verso acrylic paper on canvas painted 1981-82 prov. 18-Sep-2 Kunsthallen, Copenhagen #8/R est:200000 (D.KR 210000)

£17986 $29496 €25000 L'or sans feuille (94x94cm-37x37in) s. s.on stretcher acrylic paper on board prov. 3-Jun-3 Christie's, Amsterdam #345/R est:25000-35000

£19178 $30110 €28000 Sang d'ombre naturel (55x46cm-22x18in) s. i.verso. 15-Apr-3 Laurence Calmels, Paris #4244/R est:8000

£19231 $29808 €30000 La lisiere (81x116cm-32x46in) s. s.d.53 verso prov.exhib. 3-Dec-2 Christie's, Amsterdam #255/R est:20000-30000

£19898 $30843 €29847 Friendship and hostility (100x153cm-39x60in) s. acrylic paper on canvas painted 1966 lit.prov. 1-Oct-2 Rasmussen, Copenhagen #66/R est:350000 (D.KR 235000)

£24223 $38515 €36335 Fantasy animal (101x78cm-40x31in) s. acrylic paper on canvas. 26-Feb-3 Kunsthallen, Copenhagen #64/R est:250000 (D.KR 265000)

£25000 $38500 €37500 Lumiere noire (114x153cm-45x60in) s. s.i.d.1969 verso acrylic paper on canvas prov. 22-Oct-2 Sotheby's, London #364/R est:25000-35000

£25000 $41750 €36250 Feuille epinglee (100x153cm-39x60in) s. s.i.d.1981 verso acrylic paper on canvas prov.exhib. 27-Jun-3 Christie's, London #136/R est:25000-35000

£25180 $41295 €35000 Sans son balais (100x153cm-39x60in) s. s.i.d.1970 verso acrylic paper on canvas prov.exhib. 3-Jun-3 Christie's, Amsterdam #354/R est:40000-60000

£26923 $42269 €42000 Foret originelle (190x99cm-75x39in) s. i.d.1987 verso prov.exhib. 11-Dec-2 Artcurial Briest, Paris #713/R est:40000

£30380 $48000 €48000 Bibemus (100x153cm-39x60in) s. s.i.d.1978 verso acrylic paper on canvas. 26-Nov-2 Sotheby's, Amsterdam #225/R est:50000-70000

£35000 $57400 €52500 Elephantasmagorie (100x154cm-39x61in) s. s.i.d.1967 verso acrylic paper on canvas prov.exhib. 6-Feb-3 Christie's, London #625/R est:25000-35000

£69182 $106541 €110000 De nouvelles dispositions (106x192cm-42x76in) s.d.1962. 22-Oct-2 Campo, Vlaamse Kaai #401/R

Prints

£1923 $2981 €3000 Autour des clintes (59x98cm-23x39in) s.d.1979 num.23/60 aquatint. 3-Dec-2 Christie's, Amsterdam #407 est:2000-3000

Sculpture

£1181 $1948 €1700 Visage et serpent (23x9cm-9x4in) s.num.67/150 gold pat bronze Cast Valsuani. 1-Jul-3 Artcurial Briest, Paris #835/R est:1000-1500

£3401 $5408 €5000 Paire de crypto cylindres. s.num.138/150 gold bronze st.f.Clemente pair. 18-Mar-3 Galerie Moderne, Brussels #636/R est:5000-6000

Works on paper

£855 $1385 €1300 Sans titre (24x14cm-9x6in) s.d. wax crayon pen dr. 22-Jan-3 Tajan, Paris #262/R est:1500-2000

£1182 $1845 €1773 Visage (28x22cm-11x9in) s.d.1988 W/C over etching. 18-Sep-2 Kunsthallen, Copenhagen #52/R est:15000 (D.KR 14000)

£1277 $2068 €1800 Le blanc (45x38cm-18x15in) s.i.d.62 ink prov. 26-May-3 Christie's, Milan #293/R est:2000-2500

£1409 $2269 €2100 Astre (35x29cm-14x11in) s.d.59 ink oil dr. 18-Feb-3 Vanderkindere, Brussels #104

£1887 $2906 €3000 Pays de reves (43x28cm-17x11in) s.d.1972 W/C paper on canvas. 22-Oct-2 Campo & Campo, Antwerp #2/R

£1944 $3072 €2800 Flamenco Wallon (22x17cm-9x7in) s.i.d.1960 Indian ink wash paper on canvas prov. 24-Apr-3 Dorotheum, Vienna #167/R est:2800-3000

£2000 $3340 €2900 Untitled (43x27cm-17x11in) s.d.1971 W/C col crayon paper on canvas. 24-Jun-3 Sotheby's, Olympia #83/R est:2000-3000

£2083 $3292 €3000 Composition (37x23cm-15x9in) s.d.12 avril 1994 W/C. 27-Apr-3 Perrin, Versailles #17/R est:3500-4500

£3048 $4725 €4572 Figure composition (59x98cm-23x39in) s.d.1979 W/C aquatint etching Japan paper. 1-Oct-2 Rasmussen, Copenhagen #94/R est:40000-50000 (D.KR 36000)

£3273 $5073 €4910 Rhizomes (64x96cm-25x38in) s.d.1983 W/C aquatin etching. 4-Dec-2 Kunsthallen, Copenhagen #175/R est:40000 (D.KR 38000)

£4487 $6955 €7000 Niagara Falls (100x60cm-39x24in) s.i.d.1975 W/C aquatint. 3-Dec-2 Christie's, Amsterdam #269/R est:4500-7500

£5667 $9011 €8501 Vents et Marees (44x60cm-17x24in) s.d.I.X.50 Indian ink exhib. 26-Feb-3 Kunsthallen, Copenhagen #19/R est:60000 (D.KR 62000)

£7194 $11799 €10000 Faire mouche (98x66cm-39x26in) s.d.1973 s.i.d.on stretcher W/C gouache paper on canvas. 3-Jun-3 Christie's, Amsterdam #353/R est:12000-16000

£7500 $12000 €10875 Untitled (71x145cm-28x57in) s.d.1965 gouache board prov. 17-May-3 Selkirks, St. Louis #228/R est:6000-8000

£7800 $12012 €11700 Remonter le temps (183x94cm-72x37in) s.i.d.1975 ink prov. 23-Oct-2 Christie's, London #111/R est:10000-15000

£10063 $15597 €16000 L'ombre de Victor Segalen (51x76cm-20x30in) s.d.1982 gouache paper on canvas. 30-Oct-2 Artcurial Briest, Paris #462/R est:15000-18000

£12000 $20040 €17400 La lyonnaise des yeux (183x93cm-72x37in) s.i.d.1976 black ink rice paper prov. 26-Jun-3 Sotheby's, London #242/R est:6000-8000

£13711 $21801 €20567 Blitz-Krieg (36x45cm-14x18in) s.d.III.50 gouache exhib. 26-Feb-3 Kunsthallen, Copenhagen #16/R est:80000 (D.KR 150000)

£17367 $27614 €26051 Promenade familiale (34x37cm-13x15in) s.d.X 49 gouache exhib. 26-Feb-3 Kunsthallen, Copenhagen #4/R est:80000 (D.KR 190000)

£31000 $50840 €46500 Visite d'atelier (100x100cm-39x39in) s.d.1986 s.i.d.1986 stretcher ink acrylic paper on canvas prov. 7-Feb-3 Sotheby's, London #241/R est:18000-25000

ALEGIANI, Francesco (19th C) Italian

£1700 $2635 €2550 Trompe l'oeil of portrait of Beatrice Cenci and other portraits (70x44cm-28x17in) s.i. 31-Oct-2 Sotheby's, Olympia #107/R est:2000-3000

ALENZA Y NIETO, Leonardo (1807-1845) Spanish
£2673 $4170 €4250 Snack (23x27cm-9x11in) 23-Sep-2 Durán, Madrid #136/R
£46154 $72923 €72000 Creating newspapers (38cm-15in circular) s. pair. 14-Nov-2 Arte, Seville #311/R

ALENZA Y NIETO, Leonardo (attrib) (1807-1845) Spanish
£1282 $2026 €2000 Sermon (45x60cm-18x24in) 14-Nov-2 Arte, Seville #232/R

ALERS, Rudolf (attrib) (1812-?) German
£1020 $1622 €1500 Hunters resting in woods by river (74x95cm-29x37in) s.d.1861. 19-Mar-3 Neumeister, Munich #498/R est:1500

ALES, Mikolas (1852-1913) Czechoslovakian
Works on paper
£289 $451 €434 Rest on the Balk (11x7cm-4x3in) mono. Indian ink dr. 12-Oct-2 Dorotheum, Prague #163 (C.KR 14000)
£392 $612 €588 Dragon and princess (11x7cm-4x3in) mono. Indian ink dr. 12-Oct-2 Dorotheum, Prague #289 (C.KR 19000)

ALEXANDER, Charles (attrib) (fl.1868-1894) British
£260 $424 €390 Portrait of a begging terrier (30x23cm-12x9in) s.i.d.97. 28-Jan-3 Gorringes, Lewes #1689

ALEXANDER, Clifford Grear (1870-1954) American
£944 $1500 €1416 Purple mountains (87x122cm-34x48in) s. 7-Mar-3 Skinner, Boston #385/R est:1500-3000

ALEXANDER, Cosmo (1724-1772) British
£620 $1029 €899 Portrait of Mr Bannerman of Fendraught (76x63cm-30x25in) i.d.1741 verso. 13-Jun-3 Lyon & Turnbull, Edinburgh #74
£4800 $7968 €7200 Portrait of Dr William Gordon of Montrose (22x18cm-9x7in) prov.exhib. 12-Jun-3 Sotheby's, London #63/R est:3000-4000

ALEXANDER, David (20th C) British?
£1190 $1893 €1726 Variegated terracotta alpine spine (132x173cm-52x68in) s. acrylic prov. 1-May-3 Heffel, Vancouver #2/R est:2000-2500 (C.D 2750)

ALEXANDER, David T (1947-) Canadian
£904 $1419 €1356 New sky, old land (90x120cm-35x47in) s.i.d.1990 acrylic. 25-Nov-2 Hodgins, Calgary #67/R est:1500-2000 (C.D 2250)
Works on paper
£805 $1280 €1208 Coastal (44x37cm-17x15in) s.d.1988 W/C. 23-Mar-3 Hodgins, Calgary #91/R est:800-1000 (C.D 1900)

ALEXANDER, Dora Block (1888-?) American/Polish
£659 $1100 €956 Landscape (51x61cm-20x24in) s, canvasboard prov. 17-Jun-3 John Moran, Pasadena #94 est:1500-2000

ALEXANDER, Douglas (1871-1945) British
£650 $949 €975 Mountains and landscape, Connemara (51x61cm-20x24in) s. board. 12-Jun-2 John Ross, Belfast #67
£701 $1016 €1100 Lake and mountain landscape with peat stacks (37x52cm-15x20in) s. 29-May-2 Woodwards, Cork #212
£886 $1373 €1400 Western lake and mountain landscape (50x60cm-20x24in) s. board. 25-Sep-2 James Adam, Dublin #102a est:1500-2500
£949 $1472 €1500 Evening near Dhu Lough, Connemara (32x45cm-13x18in) s. canvas on board. 24-Sep-2 De Veres Art Auctions, Dublin #147a est:1500-2000
£1384 $2158 €2200 Landscape with turf stacks (51x61cm-20x24in) s. canvasboard prov. 17-Sep-2 Whyte's, Dublin #123/R est:2500-3500
£1419 $2214 €2100 Sunset sky Bogland, Connemara (50x60cm-20x24in) s. board. 26-Mar-3 James Adam, Dublin #22/R est:2000-4000
£1689 $2635 €2500 Near Ballinahinch, Connemara (52x48cm-20x19in) s. canvasboard. 26-Mar-3 James Adam, Dublin #29/R est:3000-4000
£1849 $2903 €2700 Lake and mountains West of Ireland (51x58cm-20x23in) s. canvasboard. 15-Apr-3 De Veres Art Auctions, Dublin #222/R est:2000-3000
£1892 $2951 €2800 Connemara landscape at Recess (52x48cm-20x19in) s. canvasboard. 26-Mar-3 James Adam, Dublin #28/R est:3000-4000
Works on paper
£278 $458 €400 Kerry coast (26x37cm-10x15in) s. W/C. 7-Jul-3 Hamilton Osborne King, Dublin #211
£380 $589 €600 Lake and mountains landscape (25x36cm-10x14in) s. W/C. 25-Sep-2 James Adam, Dublin #33
£395 $616 €620 Extensive landscape and mountain landscape (24x33cm-9x13in) s. W/C. 6-Nov-2 James Adam, Dublin #27/R
£400 $624 €600 Reflections, Du Lough, Conemara (25x38cm-10x15in) s. W/C. 17-Sep-2 Goldings, Lincolnshire #620
£411 $638 €650 Evening at Oughterard, Co. Galway (23x29cm-9x11in) s. W/C. 25-Sep-2 James Adam, Dublin #2
£420 $651 €630 Lough Finn, Co. Donegal (36x51cm-14x20in) s. W/C. 2-Oct-2 John Ross, Belfast #203/R
£475 $736 €750 Delphi, Connemara (25x30cm-10x12in) s.i.verso W/C. 25-Sep-2 James Adam, Dublin #10
£538 $834 €850 Mount Errigal, Co. Donegal (37x52cm-15x20in) s. W/C prov. 25-Sep-2 James Adam, Dublin #144
£556 $917 €800 Road to Kell, Achill (22x28cm-9x11in) s. W/C. 7-Jul-3 Hamilton Osborne King, Dublin #217
£577 $959 €820 Lakeside landscape (37x52cm-15x20in) s. W/C. 10-Jun-3 James Adam, Dublin #159/R
£604 $972 €900 Cottage besides a loch (38x53cm-15x21in) s. W/C. 18-Feb-3 Whyte's, Dublin #214/R
£633 $981 €1000 River landscape (37x53cm-15x21in) s. W/C prov. 25-Sep-2 James Adam, Dublin #125/R est:1000-1500
£676 $1054 €1000 Bogland scene (22x28cm-9x11in) s. W/C. 26-Mar-3 James Adam, Dublin #17/R est:1000-1200
£676 $1054 €1000 Boglands near Leenane (17x26cm-7x10in) s. W/C. 26-Mar-3 James Adam, Dublin #30a/R est:1000-1500
£705 $1093 €1100 Near Waterville (33x41cm-13x16in) s. W/C. 3-Dec-2 Thomas Adams, Dublin #413
£725 $1188 €1000 Coastal landscape (25x38cm-10x15in) s. W/C. 28-May-3 Bonhams & James Adam, Dublin #175/R est:500-800
£833 $1367 €1150 Glimpse of the lake at Caragh, Co. Kerry. Near Costello, Connemara (22x28cm-9x11in) i.verso W/C pair. 28-May-3 Bonhams & James Adam, Dublin #166/R est:1200-1600
£864 $1227 €1400 West of Ireland bogland study (28x46cm-11x18in) s. W/C. 14-Mar-2 Woodwards, Cork #200
£870 $1426 €1200 An inlet on Lough Corrib (22x28cm-9x11in) s. W/C. 28-May-3 Bonhams & James Adam, Dublin #83/R est:1200-1500
£946 $1476 €1400 Reflection, Dhu Lough, Connemara (27x37cm-11x15in) s. W/C. 26-Mar-3 James Adam, Dublin #81/R est:400-600
£1090 $1711 €1700 Lake and mountains, Connemara (37x53cm-15x21in) s. W/C prov. 19-Nov-2 Whyte's, Dublin #207/R est:1000-1500
£1111 $1767 €1600 Turf stacks, Connemara. Bogpool, Connemara (27x36cm-11x14in) s. W/C pair. 29-Apr-3 Whyte's, Dublin #174/R est:1800-2200
£1232 $2020 €1700 Turf cutters (38x54cm-15x21in) s. W/C. 28-May-3 Bonhams & James Adam, Dublin #77/R est:2000-3000
£1474 $2315 €2300 Brikeen Bridge, Killarney. Connemara Lake (25x36cm-10x14in) s. W/C pair. 19-Nov-2 Whyte's, Dublin #204/R est:1800-2200
£1667 $2617 €2600 Four views including Blarney and Blackrock Castles, County Cork (17x22cm-7x9in) s. W/C four. 19-Nov-2 Whyte's, Dublin #206 est:1500-2000

ALEXANDER, Edwin (1870-1926) British
Works on paper
£1500 $2430 €2250 Poppy seeds and bumble bee (17x10cm-7x4in) mono.d.1900 W/C. 23-May-3 Lyon & Turnbull, Edinburgh #79/R est:400-600

ALEXANDER, Francesca (1837-1917) American
£4062 $6500 €5890 Clorinda Amadei (41x32cm-16x13in) indis.s.i. verso board painted 1863. 16-May-3 Skinner, Boston #15/R est:700-900

ALEXANDER, George (19/20th C) British
£389 $635 €584 Bolton Abbey, Yorkshire (30x46cm-12x18in) s.d.1877. 17-Feb-3 Blomqvist, Lysaker #1005/R (N.KR 4400)

ALEXANDER, Henry (1860-1894) American
£1911 $3000 €2867 Girl at the well (152x91cm-60x36in) s.i. after Felix A Bonnet prov. 19-Nov-2 Butterfields, San Francisco #8173/R est:3000-5000

ALEXANDER, John (fl.1710-1757) British
£3200 $4960 €4800 Portrait of Lord Lewis Gordon, aged 13 (30x25cm-12x10in) i.d.1738 feigned oval. 31-Oct-2 Christie's, London #5/R est:2000-3000
£4200 $6510 €6300 Portrait of Lord Charles Gordon, aged 17 (30x25cm-12x10in) i.d.1738 feigned oval. 31-Oct-2 Christie's, London #4/R est:3000-5000

ALEXANDER, John (1945-) American
Works on paper
£307 $500 €461 Country winter scene (51x71cm-20x28in) s. 2-Feb-3 Simpson's, Houston #178
£633 $1000 €950 Scorpion (20x15cm-8x6in) s. pencil dr. 16-Nov-2 New Orleans Auction, New Orleans #1581/R
£633 $1000 €950 Shrimp (20x15cm-8x6in) s.i. pencil dr. 16-Nov-2 New Orleans Auction, New Orleans #1582/R est:1200-1800

ALEXANDER, John White (1856-1915) American
£844 $1300 €1266 Study for peonies (50x61cm-20x24in) 4-Sep-2 Christie's, Rockefeller NY #366/R est:2000-3000

£45161 $70000 €67742 At the piano - Helen Hopekirk Wison (80x110cm-31x43in) s.d.94 prov.exhib.lit. 4-Dec-2 Sotheby's, New York #23/R est:60000-80000

ALEXANDER, John White (attrib) (1856-1915) American
£3165 $5000 €4748 Floral still life with white roses (25x15cm-10x6in) d.85 prov. 16-Nov-2 New Orleans Auction, New Orleans #1103/R est:5000-8000

ALEXANDER, Lena (fl.1905-1936) British
Works on paper
£900 $1431 €1350 Flowerpiece (51x58cm-20x23in) s. col chk. 6-Mar-3 Christie's, Kensington #214/R

ALEXANDER, William (1767-1816) British
Works on paper
£1000 $1580 €1500 Chinese pagoda (21x17cm-8x7in) pencil grey wash. 15-Nov-2 Sotheby's, London #19/R est:600-800
£2000 $3300 €2900 Portrait of an inferior mandarin of Tourane Bay (37x23cm-15x9in) init. W/C over pencil. 2-Jul-3 Sotheby's, Olympia #181/R est:2000-3000

ALEXANDRINE (1903-) ?
£621 $981 €900 Visiteurs (55x46cm-22x18in) s.d.1963. 4-Apr-3 Tajan, Paris #62

ALEXANDROVNA, Grand Duchess Olga (1882-1960) Russian
£410 $631 €615 Bouquet of summer flowers in vase (37x45cm-15x18in) s. cardboard. 4-Sep-2 Kunsthallen, Copenhagen #13 (D.KR 4800)
£858 $1373 €1287 Spring flowers in woodland (33x24cm-13x9in) s. 13-Jan-3 Rasmussen, Vejle #222/R (D.KR 9800)
£1072 $1672 €1608 Summer landscape (45x66cm-18x26in) s. 11-Nov-2 Rasmussen, Vejle #694/R est:12000-15000 (D.KR 12500)
£1213 $1928 €1820 Still life of cornflowers, daisies and red flowers (60x48cm-24x19in) s. 5-May-3 Rasmussen, Vejle #590/R est:10000 (D.KR 13000)
£1689 $2635 €2534 Still life of objects on table (72x54cm-28x21in) s. 23-Sep-2 Rasmussen, Vejle #140/R est:3000 (D.KR 20000)
Works on paper
£340 $568 €493 Russian winter scene with house in the background (28x36cm-11x14in) s.d.1926 i.verso W/C. 17-Jun-3 Gildings, Market Harborough #455
£406 $625 €609 Still life of flowers, Christmas tree in background (33x31cm-13x12in) s. W/C. 26-Oct-2 Rasmussen, Havnen #2063/R (D.KR 4800)
£936 $1479 €1404 Wooded landscape (27x35cm-11x14in) s.d.1927 W/C. 2-Dec-2 Rasmussen, Copenhagen #1827/R (D.KR 11000)
£1053 $1705 €1527 Troika driving on a cold winter's day (36x55cm-14x22in) s. W/C. 26-May-3 Rasmussen, Copenhagen #1483/R est:5000-10000 (D.KR 11000)
£2400 $3792 €3600 Three flowers on a windowsill. Still life of apples (4x20cm-2x8in) s. W/C two sold with a photograph. 26-Nov-2 Christie's, Kensington #39/R est:500-700

ALEXY, Janko (1894-1970) Czechoslovakian
£2048 $2989 €3072 Woman from Liptov region (47x29cm-19x11in) board. 4-Jun-2 SOGA, Bratislava #57/R est:95000 (SL.K 130000)
Works on paper
£315 $447 €473 Sitting girl in national costume (46x31cm-18x12in) pastel exec.c.1955. 26-Mar-2 SOGA, Bratislava #63/R (SL.K 20000)
£315 $447 €473 In the forest (44x31cm-17x12in) pastel exec.1938. 26-Mar-2 SOGA, Bratislava #64/R (SL.K 20000)
£347 $506 €521 Under Bratislava Castle (30x44cm-12x17in) pastel exec.c.1960. 4-Jun-2 SOGA, Bratislava #58/R est:25000 (SL.K 22000)
£394 $610 €591 River Danube (30x41cm-12x16in) pastel. 1-Oct-2 SOGA, Bratislava #73/R est:25000 (SL.K 25000)
£441 $626 €662 In Sliac woods (51x35cm-20x14in) pastel exec.1942. 26-Mar-2 SOGA, Bratislava #65/R (SL.K 28000)
£630 $895 €945 Landscape (30x45cm-12x18in) pastel exec.1936. 26-Mar-2 SOGA, Bratislava #62/R (SL.K 40000)

ALFANI, Domenico (elder-style) (c.1480-1553) Italian
£13121 $20337 €19682 Adoration of the Kings (170x125cm-67x49in) 3-Dec-2 Bukowskis, Stockholm #421/R est:80000-100000 (S.KR 185000)

ALFANO, Carlo (1932-) Italian
£725 $1188 €1000 Untitled (38x65cm-15x26in) s.d.83 verso acrylic parchment paper collage board prov. 28-May-3 Lempertz, Koln #3
£2319 $3803 €3200 Frammenti di un autoritratto anonimo N 72 (130x130cm-51x51in) s.i.d.74 verso acrylic prov. 28-May-3 Lempertz, Koln #2/R est:3000

ALFELT, Else (1910-1975) Danish
£1772 $2818 €2658 The mountain pass (92x92cm-36x36in) s.d.52 verso plywood. 29-Apr-3 Kunsthallen, Copenhagen #146/R est:25000 (D.KR 19000)
£5302 $8430 €7953 The Dolomites (92x92cm-36x36in) plywood exhib. 26-Feb-3 Kunsthallen, Copenhagen #20/R est:50000 (D.KR 58000)
Works on paper
£718 $1120 €1077 Mountains (31x23cm-12x9in) s.d.43 W/C. 18-Sep-2 Kunsthallen, Copenhagen #92/R (D.KR 8500)
£746 $1187 €1119 March mountains (38x45cm-15x18in) s.d.17 juni 47 W/C prov. 29-Apr-3 Kunsthallen, Copenhagen #21/R (D.KR 8000)
£746 $1187 €1119 March mountains (38x45cm-15x18in) s.d.19 juni 47 W/C exhib.prov. 29-Apr-3 Kunsthallen, Copenhagen #59/R (D.KR 8000)

ALFIAN, Antonio de (16th C) Spanish
£6500 $10075 €9750 Religious scenes with figures (122x79cm-48x31in) i. en grisaille panel double-sided triptych. 30-Oct-2 Bonhams, New Bond Street #113/R est:3000-5000

ALFIERI, Attilio (1904-1992) Italian
£225 $328 €350 Composition (40x55cm-16x22in) s. 4-Jun-2 Karl & Faber, Munich #158/R
£316 $494 €500 Basket (30x30cm-12x12in) s. s.i.verso painted 1979. 14-Sep-2 Meeting Art, Vercelli #380/R
£340 $541 €500 Vase of flowers (75x55cm-30x22in) s. cardboard. 1-Mar-3 Meeting Art, Vercelli #723
£705 $1107 €1100 Still life (40x50cm-16x20in) s. 19-Nov-2 Finarte, Milan #75

ALFONS, Sven (1918-1996) Swedish
£1962 $3061 €2943 Day after day (80x100cm-31x39in) s.d.70 exhib. 5-Nov-2 Bukowskis, Stockholm #136/R est:20000-25000 (S.KR 28000)
£3012 $4849 €4518 The swallows (116x80cm-46x31in) s.d.74 prov.exhib.lit. 7-May-3 AB Stockholms Auktionsverk #795/R est:15000-20000 (S.KR 39000)

ALFORD, John (?) British
£780 $1240 €1170 Off Falmouth (50x75cm-20x30in) s.d.1995 canvasboard. 4-Mar-3 Bristol Auction Rooms #376/R

ALGARDI, Alessandro (circle) (1602-1654) Italian
Sculpture
£11000 $17160 €16500 God the Father holding the Dead Christ in his arms (62cm-24in) white marble giltwood oval prov.lit. 9-Apr-3 Sotheby's, London #64/R est:8000-12000

ALGIE, Jessie (fl.1920's) British
£400 $624 €600 Still life of flowers in a glass vase (51x41cm-20x16in) s. 10-Apr-3 Tennants, Leyburn #1093

ALIBERTI, Dino (1935-) Italian
£340 $541 €500 Hilly landscape (50x40cm-20x16in) s. card on canvas. 1-Mar-3 Meeting Art, Vercelli #141

ALICE, Alex (20th C) French
Works on paper
£297 $469 €430 Troisieme testament (50x36cm-20x14in) s. Chinese ink dr. 7-Apr-3 Claude Aguttes, Neuilly #1/R

ALIN, Henri (1885-1968) French
£306 $477 €459 Summer mountain landscape with small lake (60x73cm-24x29in) s. panel. 6-Nov-2 Dobiaschofsky, Bern #3123/R (S.FR 700)

ALINARI, Fratelli (19th C) Italian
Photographs
£2949 $4659 €4600 Salles des statues et bustes a l'interiuer du Campo Santo (31x42cm-12x17in) st.sig.num.174 salt print exec.c.1853. 16-Nov-2 Christie's, Paris #137/R est:2000-2500

ALINARI, Luca (1943-) Italian
£475 $741 €750 Movements in Lunigiana (40x50cm-16x20in) s. oil mixed media painted 1970. 14-Sep-2 Meeting Art, Vercelli #270/R
£538 $839 €850 Untitled (24x34cm-9x13in) s. acrylic canvas on board painted 1998. 14-Sep-2 Meeting Art, Vercelli #757/R

£563 $935 €800 Le cose parlano (100x70cm-39x28in) exhib. 10-Jun-3 Finarte Semenzato, Milan #303/R est:800-1000
£570 $889 €900 Hills (19x39cm-7x15in) s. oil acrylic canvas on board. 14-Sep-2 Meeting Art, Vercelli #29
£590 $939 €850 Yacht (40x50cm-16x20in) s. painted 1970. 1-May-3 Meeting Art, Vercelli #69
£601 $938 €950 Untitled (19x24cm-7x9in) s. 14-Sep-2 Meeting Art, Vercelli #150
£633 $987 €1000 Untitled (20x45cm-8x18in) oil acrylic. 14-Sep-2 Meeting Art, Vercelli #760/R
£641 $1006 €1000 Rubbish factory (19x29cm-7x11in) s. acrylic fabric on board. 23-Nov-2 Meeting Art, Vercelli #42/R
£646 $1028 €950 Untitled (25x35cm-10x14in) s. canvas on board painted 2001. 1-Mar-3 Meeting Art, Vercelli #552
£654 $1046 €1000 Untitled (30cm-12in circular) s. canvas on board. 4-Jan-3 Meeting Art, Vercelli #205
£850 $1359 €1300 Untitled. oil acrylic canvas on board painted 1996. 4-Jan-3 Meeting Art, Vercelli #65
£884 $1406 €1300 Untitled (39x39cm-15x15in) s. canvas on board. 1-Mar-3 Meeting Art, Vercelli #497
£962 $1510 €1500 Untitled (58x58cm-23x23in) s. canvas on board. 23-Nov-2 Meeting Art, Vercelli #52/R
£972 $1546 €1400 Untitled (39x49cm-15x19in) s. canvas on board. 1-May-3 Meeting Art, Vercelli #296
£1307 $2092 €2000 Landscape (70x70cm-28x28in) s. oil mixed media painted 1983. 4-Jan-3 Meeting Art, Vercelli #711
£1373 $2196 €2100 Landscape (50x70cm-20x28in) s. painted 1988. 4-Jan-3 Meeting Art, Vercelli #223
£1389 $2208 €2000 Cypress (70x70cm-28x28in) s. acrylic painted 1993. 1-May-3 Meeting Art, Vercelli #290
£1699 $2719 €2600 Lambretta on French roads (19x140cm-7x55in) s. i.verso canvas on board. 4-Jan-3 Meeting Art, Vercelli #520
£2083 $3312 €3000 Study (70x70cm-28x28in) s. i.d.1987 verso oil mixed media collage lit. 1-May-3 Meeting Art, Vercelli #440
£2778 $4417 €4000 Everything in the adverbs (100cm-39in circular) i.verso acrylic canvas on board exhib.lit. 1-May-3 Meeting Art, Vercelli #517
£3797 $5924 €6000 Inside the butter man (79cm-31in circular) s. i.verso acrylic canvas on board painted 2000. 14-Sep-2 Meeting Art, Vercelli #840/R est:5000
£4730 $7378 €7000 Too easy - elbow angle (126x126cm-50x50in) acrylic col pencil canvas on board exhib.lit. 28-Mar-3 Farsetti, Prato #233/R
£5072 $8319 €7000 Fra dente e dente (89x89cm-35x35in) acrylic resin canvas on panel lit. 27-May-3 Tajan, Paris #67/R est:7000-9000

Works on paper
£451 $718 €650 Fantastic landscape (18x24cm-7x9in) s. mixed media card on masonite. 1-May-3 Meeting Art, Vercelli #54
£704 $1169 €1000 Untitled (50x70cm-20x28in) s. mixed media. 10-Jun-3 Finarte Semenzato, Milan #263/R
£3548 $5606 €5500 First future (70x100cm-28x39in) s.d.74 s.i.d.verso mixed media on canvas prov.exhib. 18-Dec-2 Christie's, Rome #181/R

ALIOTTI, Claude (1925-1989) French
£497 $800 €746 Boats in a harbour (51x64cm-20x25in) s.d.73. 19-Feb-3 Doyle, New York #23/R

ALIX, Yves (1890-1969) French
£1384 $2145 €2200 Le port d'Antibes (73x116cm-29x46in) s.d.1926. 30-Oct-2 Artcurial Briest, Paris #289 est:1200-1800

ALKEMA, Wobbe (1900-1984) Dutch
£6738 $10915 €9500 Composition no 14 (55x64cm-22x25in) mono.i.d.60 board exhib. 26-May-3 Glerum, Amsterdam #161/R est:3000-5000

ALKEN, Henry (19th C) British
Works on paper
£300 $468 €450 Horseman in winder landscape (18x25cm-7x10in) s. pencil W/C. 11-Apr-3 Keys, Aylsham #231/R
£300 $498 €435 Huntsman on grey with hounds in full cry (23x33cm-9x13in) 10-Jun-3 Peter Francis, Wales #34/R
£650 $1007 €975 Racing on Newmarket Heath (14x21cm-6x8in) s. W/C. 3-Nov-2 Lots Road, London #334

ALKEN, Henry (jnr) (1810-1894) British
£350 $553 €525 Head of a greyhound (21x24cm-8x9in) s. panel. 28-Nov-2 Christie's, Kensington #314/R
£2600 $4108 €3900 Steeple chase, water jump. Hunting in full cry (23x51cm-9x20in) panel pair prov. 28-Nov-2 Sotheby's, London #211 est:2500-4000
£11500 $18630 €17250 Hunt in full cry crossing the path of the York to London coach (33x76cm-13x30in) s. panel prov. 22-May-3 Christie's, London #6/R est:12000-16000
£12000 $19080 €18000 Mail coach. Chaise on the open road (34x28cm-13x11in) s. pair. 19-Mar-3 Sotheby's, London #112/R est:5000-7000

ALKEN, Henry (jnr-attrib) (1810-1894) British
£720 $1123 €1080 Carriage horse joining the hunt (28x43cm-11x17in) panel. 10-Apr-3 Tennants, Leyburn #1033/R

ALKEN, Henry (snr) (1785-1851) British
£848 $1307 €1272 Hunt (19x24cm-7x9in) s. panel. 4-Sep-2 Dunbar Sloane, Wellington #105/R est:3000-5000 (NZ.D 2800)
£2500 $4150 €3625 Huntsman and his groom with saddled bay hunter, meet beyond (23x30cm-9x12in) 12-Jun-3 Christie's, Kensington #67/R est:2500-3500

Works on paper
£400 $664 €580 Over the gate (21x27cm-8x11in) pencil W/C. 12-Jun-3 Christie's, Kensington #7a
£560 $885 €840 Full cry (20x32cm-8x13in) W/C prov. 18-Dec-2 John Nicholson, Haslemere #1058/R
£650 $1053 €975 Arabian horse and groom. Turkish horse (23x33cm-9x13in) s.i. W/C pencil pair. 21-Jan-3 Bonhams, Knightsbridge #19/R
£6500 $10660 €9750 Drawing the cover. Getting away. Hold hard Tom, full cry. The death (26x37cm-10x15in) W/C pencil set of four sold with album of engravings. 3-Jun-3 Bonhams, Knightsbridge #76/R est:7000-10000
£7200 $11376 €10800 High mettled racer (27x37cm-11x15in) W/C over pencil htd bodycol set of six. 28-Nov-2 Sotheby's, London #226/R est:7000-10000

ALKEN, Henry (snr-attrib) (1785-1851) British
Works on paper
£700 $1113 €1050 Huntsmen jumping a fence (25x33cm-10x13in) bears sig. pencil W/C. 29-Apr-3 Rowley Fine Art, Newmarket #412/R

ALKEN, Samuel (18/19th C) British
Works on paper
£800 $1320 €1160 Figures and cattle by Chepstow castle (45x60cm-18x24in) s. pen ink W/C over pencil htd bodycol. 2-Jul-3 Sotheby's, Olympia #201/R

ALKEN, Samuel (jnr) (1784-1825) British
£2300 $3749 €3335 Bull baiting (61x74cm-24x29in) s.d.1806. 21-Jul-3 Bonhams, Bath #75/R est:1800-2200

ALLAN (?) ?
£660 $1049 €990 Windsor Castle. Maple Durham Mill (46x76cm-18x30in) s. i.on stretcher pair. 27-Feb-3 Bonhams, Chester #396

ALLAN, Andrew (fl.1880-1940) British
£370 $577 €555 Arran hills from the Ayrshire coast (33x44cm-13x17in) s. 10-Apr-3 Bonhams, Edinburgh #96

ALLAN, Archibald Russell Watson (1878-1959) British
£250 $408 €375 Cottages by a stream (47x55cm-19x22in) 14-Feb-3 Lyon & Turnbull, Edinburgh #52

ALLAN, David (1744-1796) British
£12000 $19080 €18000 Portrait of two boys (47x58cm-19x23in) painted oval. 19-Mar-3 Sotheby's, London #31/R est:12000-18000
Works on paper
£1800 $2808 €2700 Butcher, charity. Thief, the beggar, father of twenty children (24x18cm-9x7in) s.i. W/C set of five. 14-Apr-3 Sotheby's, London #3a/R est:1200-1800

ALLAN, David (attrib) (1744-1796) British
£2700 $4212 €3915 Portrait of a gentleman (36x28cm-14x11in) 27-Mar-3 Neales, Nottingham #979/R est:3000-5000

ALLAN, Hugh (fl.1880-1898) British
£800 $1232 €1200 Returning home (61x46cm-24x18in) s. 23-Oct-2 Hamptons Fine Art, Godalming #124/R

ALLAN, Robert Weir (1852-1942) British
£820 $1337 €1230 Benares from the east (22x40cm-9x16in) 14-Feb-3 Lyon & Turnbull, Edinburgh #98
£900 $1396 €1350 Harbour entrance. Dutch river scene (35x50cm-14x20in) s. pair. 30-Sep-2 Sotheby's, Olympia #553/R est:1000-1500
£1500 $2370 €2250 Mother and child walking through a cornfield (38x53cm-15x21in) s. 2-Dec-2 Bonhams, Bath #51/R est:1500-2000
£1600 $2640 €2320 Kildonan Burn, Sutherlandshire (36x51cm-14x20in) s. i.on stretcher. 1-Jul-3 Bearnes, Exeter #530/R est:1000-1500
Works on paper
£380 $635 €551 Ilford Bridge, Near Christchurch (34x51cm-13x20in) s. W/C. 17-Jun-3 Rosebery Fine Art, London #636/R
£400 $636 €600 Harvest time (24x35cm-9x14in) s. W/C. 27-Feb-3 Bonhams, Chester #419

£400 $656 €600 Flotilla on the Thames near Tower Bridge (19x36cm-7x14in) s. W/C. 10-Feb-3 Robin Fenner, Tavistock #642
£500 $780 €750 Iford Bridge, Nr Christchurch (34x51cm-13x20in) s. pencil W/C. 17-Oct-2 Christie's, Kensington #158
£1050 $1638 €1575 Crail harbour (28x44cm-11x17in) s.d.1879 W/C. 10-Apr-3 Bonhams, Edinburgh #125 est:600-800

ALLAN, S K (?) British
£580 $957 €841 Watersmeet Gorge, near Lynton, North Devon (41x61cm-16x24in) s. 3-Jul-3 Duke & Son, Dorchester #234

ALLAN, Sir William (1782-1850) British
£4800 $7728 €7200 Stolen child recovered (65x99cm-26x39in) s.d.1840 panel prov. 20-Feb-3 Christie's, London #75/R

ALLAR, Andre Joseph (1845-1926) French
Sculpture
£1484 $2345 €2300 Source (72cm-28in) pat bronze Cast Susse. 19-Dec-2 Bondu, Paris #94/R est:2000

ALLARD, Léon (19/20th C) Belgian
Works on paper
£728 $1187 €1100 Vue du marche (75x91cm-30x36in) s. W/C. 17-Feb-3 Horta, Bruxelles #99

ALLARD-L'OLIVIER, Fernand (1883-1933) Belgian
£318 $497 €500 Port mediterraneen (27x35cm-11x14in) s. panel. 11-Nov-2 Horta, Bruxelles #588
£538 $839 €850 Bacchanale (50x60cm-20x24in) s. 16-Sep-2 Horta, Bruxelles #486
£1218 $1888 €1900 Coucher de soleil. Danseuse a la coiffe de plumes (27x35cm-11x14in) s. panel pair sold with a W/C. 9-Dec-2 Horta, Bruxelles #26 est:1200-1800
£1793 $2869 €2600 Charrette attelee sortant de la mer (81x100cm-32x39in) s.d.1912. 17-Mar-3 Horta, Bruxelles #142/R est:2200-2800
Works on paper
£256 $403 €400 L'Assaut rouge (49x41cm-19x16in) s. chl ink W/C. 10-Dec-2 Vanderkindere, Brussels #93
£340 $541 €500 Vue du village de La Panne (21x30cm-8x12in) s.i.d.1918 chl pastel. 18-Mar-3 Vanderkindere, Brussels #13

ALLBON, Charles Frederick (1856-1926) British
Works on paper
£300 $465 €450 Scheidam, Holland (13x37cm-5x15in) mono.i.d.90 pencil W/C prov. 31-Oct-2 Christie's, Kensington #326/R
£550 $908 €798 Cromer, west cliff (48x34cm-19x13in) s.i. W/C. 1-Jul-3 Bonhams, Norwich #116/R

ALLCOT, John (1888-1973) Australian
£714 $1129 €1071 Towards the heads, Nielsen Park (46x60cm-18x24in) s. board prov. 17-Nov-2 Sotheby's, Paddington #48 est:1800-2800 (A.D 2000)
£717 $1176 €1040 Bathurst sea trials (75x120cm-30x47in) s. board. 3-Jun-3 Lawson Menzies, Sydney #729 (A.D 1800)
£1240 $1972 €1860 Clipper ship 'Sobraon' (39x50cm-15x20in) s. board prov. 5-May-3 Sotheby's, Melbourne #204 est:3000-4000 (A.D 3200)
£1720 $2615 €2580 Swanhilda (47x62cm-19x24in) s.i.d.17 board. 28-Aug-2 Deutscher-Menzies, Melbourne #249/R est:1800-2400 (A.D 4800)
£1720 $2615 €2580 Ben Toirlich (48x58cm-19x23in) s.i. canvas on board. 27-Aug-2 Goodman, Sydney #95 est:2500-3500 (A.D 4800)
£3036 $4705 €4554 Endeavour in Botany Bay (59x74cm-23x29in) s. 29-Oct-2 Lawson Menzies, Sydney #68/R est:8000-9000 (A.D 8500)
£3049 $4817 €4421 HMS Sirius, Sydney Harbour, rounding Bradley's Head (54x69cm-21x27in) s. 22-Jul-3 Lawson Menzies, Sydney #190a/R est:8500-10000 (A.D 7500)
£3817 $6031 €5726 Buckingham (50x63cm-20x25in) s.i. verso canvas on board lit. 2-Apr-3 Christie's, Melbourne #23/R est:2000-4000 (A.D 10000)
Works on paper
£650 $1028 €943 Sailboat off headland (27x26cm-11x10in) s.d.1932 gouache W/C. 22-Jul-3 Lawson Menzies, Sydney #91/R est:2000-3000 (A.D 1600)
£929 $1467 €1394 Thermopylae (30x45cm-12x18in) s. gouache prov. 17-Nov-2 Sotheby's, Paddington #50 est:1200-1800 (A.D 2600)
£1423 $2248 €2063 SS Altcar (33x52cm-13x20in) s.i.d.29 W/C. 22-Jul-3 Lawson Menzies, Sydney #158/R est:4000-5000 (A.D 3500)

ALLEAUME, Ludovic (1859-?) French
£2098 $3503 €3000 Vues de Palestine (18x36cm-7x14in) s.i.d.1891 panel pair. 27-Jun-3 Claude Aguttes, Neuilly #153/R est:2000-3000

ALLEBE, Augustus (1838-1927) Dutch
£10417 $16563 €15000 Fetching water (48x36cm-19x14in) s.d.69 panel prov.lit. 29-Apr-3 Christie's, Amsterdam #170/R est:15000-20000

ALLEGRAIN, Christophe Gabriel (1710-1795) French
Sculpture
£7595 $12000 €11393 Figure of Venus au bain (155cm-61in) marble on green marble plinth. 24-Apr-3 Christie's, Rockefeller NY #265/R est:15000-20000

ALLEGRAIN, Étienne (attrib) (1653-1736) French
£2201 $3412 €3500 Paysages animes (30x44cm-12x17in) pair. 29-Oct-2 Artcurial Briest, Paris #29/R
£3662 $6079 €5200 Paysages (16cm-6in circular) panel pair. 16-Jun-3 Claude Aguttes, Neuilly #7/R est:3000-4000
£3742 $5913 €5800 Paysage de la campagne romaine (70x110cm-28x43in) panel. 20-Dec-2 Tajan, Paris #115/R

ALLEGRAIN, Étienne (circle) (1653-1736) Flemish
£4516 $7000 €6774 Italianate landscape with architectural ruins and figures (79x98cm-31x39in) 2-Oct-2 Christie's, Rockefeller NY #177/R est:10000-15000

ALLEGRETTI, Mario (1945-) Italian?
£446 $687 €700 Moonlit Lagoon with fishing boats (57x68cm-22x27in) s.d.1981. 5-Sep-2 Arnold, Frankfurt #726/R

ALLEGRINI, Francesco (1587-1663) Italian
Works on paper
£443 $700 €665 Nymphs dancing to the music of the satyrs (157x207cm-62x81in) i. black chk pen brown ink brown wash oval prov. 1-Apr-3 Christie's, Rockefeller NY #375/R
£2000 $3340 €2900 Moses and the daughters of Jethro (15x22cm-6x9in) pen ink wash over black chk prov. 9-Jul-3 Bonhams, Knightsbridge #50/R est:2000-3000

ALLEN, Anna Elizabeth (1881-?) American
£531 $850 €770 Florida beach scene (61x86cm-24x34in) s. 18-May-3 Jeffery Burchard, Florida #44/R

ALLEN, Barbra (20th C) British
Works on paper
£280 $434 €420 Armagh City (35x25cm-14x10in) s.d.87 W/C. 4-Dec-2 John Ross, Belfast #80

ALLEN, Charles Curtis (1886-1950) American
£535 $850 €803 Autumn farms (30x40cm-12x16in) i.verso canvasboard prov. 7-Mar-3 Skinner, Boston #442/R
£828 $1300 €1242 Mt. Monadnock (30x40cm-12x16in) s. 22-Nov-2 Skinner, Boston #274/R est:500-600
Works on paper
£255 $400 €383 Farmhouse (36x54cm-14x21in) s. W/C. 22-Nov-2 Skinner, Boston #281/R

ALLEN, Daphne (1899-?) British
Works on paper
£10000 $16600 €15000 Spring. Summer. Autumn, Winter (15x15cm-6x6in) s. i.verso W/C set of four. 12-Jun-3 Sotheby's, London #210/R est:10000-15000

ALLEN, Davida (1951-) Australian
£2713 $4314 €4070 Adolescent girl (110x77cm-43x30in) s.i.d.1993 verso board prov. 5-May-3 Sotheby's, Melbourne #236/R est:3000-5000 (A.D 7000)
£6071 $9532 €9107 With knowledge of my fourth pregnancy (200x166cm-79x65in) s.d.1981 verso prov.exhib. 25-Nov-2 Christie's, Melbourne #52/R est:9000-12000 (A.D 17000)
Works on paper
£366 $578 €531 Couple 1990 (56x76cm-22x30in) s.d.11 Sept 90 pastel pencil. 22-Jul-3 Lawson Menzies, Sydney #213/R est:1200-1800 (A.D 900)

ALLEN, Harry Epworth (1894-1958) British
£290 $452 €435 Ancient gateway to Roche Abbey (16x21cm-6x8in) s. tempera. 25-Mar-3 Bonhams, Leeds #569
£950 $1482 €1425 Strines, Derbyshire (15x19cm-6x7in) s. tempera gouache. 25-Mar-3 Bonhams, Leeds #568
£1600 $2608 €2400 Derbyshire uplands (33x48cm-13x19in) s. tempera. 13-Feb-3 Mellors & Kirk, Nottingham #817/R est:1000-1500
£2600 $4030 €3900 Llanrwst Bridge (35x50cm-14x20in) s. tempera on board. 1-Oct-2 Bonhams, Leeds #277/R est:1500-2500
£2700 $4239 €4050 Village scene, possibly a scene in Ireland (34x40cm-13x16in) s. tempera. 19-Nov-2 Bonhams, Leeds #80/R est:1000-1500
£4000 $6200 €6000 Derbyshire hillside (51x61cm-20x24in) s. tempera linen on board. 1-Oct-2 Bonhams, Leeds #280/R est:3000-4000
£5000 $7950 €7500 Galway landscape (35x50cm-14x20in) s.d.1952 verso egg tempera on board. 5-Mar-3 John Ross, Belfast #162 est:5000-6000
£6700 $10385 €10050 Cows grazing in an extensive wooded landscape (62x76cm-24x30in) s. board. 1-Oct-2 Bonhams, Leeds #276/R est:2500-3500
£7000 $11130 €10500 Evening, Achill (35x50cm-14x20in) s.d.1942 verso egg tempera on board. 5-Mar-3 John Ross, Belfast #153 est:6000-8000
£18500 $28860 €27750 Allotment (72x97cm-28x38in) tempera. 25-Mar-3 Bonhams, Leeds #570/R est:6000-9000
Works on paper
£280 $426 €420 Derbyshire landscape (33x37cm-13x15in) s. pencil W/C. 4-Jul-2 Mellors & Kirk, Nottingham #792/R
£380 $616 €551 Longshore Pool, Derbyshire (23x33cm-9x13in) s. pastel. 1-Aug-3 Dee Atkinson & Harrison, Driffield #647/R
£1300 $2067 €1950 Road near Errigal, Donegal (25x35cm-10x14in) s. pastel. 5-Mar-3 John Ross, Belfast #78 est:1200-1400
£1400 $2170 €2100 Peveril Castle, Castleton, Derbyshire (35x47cm-14x19in) s.i. pencil W/C. 1-Oct-2 Bonhams, Leeds #279/R est:800-1200
£1500 $2385 €2250 Village, West of Ireland (33x48cm-13x19in) s. pastel. 5-Mar-3 John Ross, Belfast #106 est:1600-1800
£1800 $2790 €2700 Stone circle arbor low (56x65cm-22x26in) s. pastel on card exhib. 1-Oct-2 Bonhams, Leeds #278/R est:1500-2000
£3600 $5580 €5400 Derbyshire farmyard with pigs in the foreground (36x51cm-14x20in) s. W/C bodycol. 4-Oct-2 ELR Auctions, Sheffield #255/R est:1000-1400

ALLEN, J W (1803-1852) British
£2031 $3250 €3047 Extensive river landscape with figures and village (102x127cm-40x50in) s.d.1878. 14-May-3 Butterfields, San Francisco #1142/R est:4000-6000

ALLEN, John (?) ?
Works on paper
£450 $716 €675 Harpooning a whale (14x19cm-6x7in) i. pen ink wash after Sieuwart van der Meulen. 29-Apr-3 Bonhams, New Bond Street #206/R

ALLEN, Joseph William (1803-1852) British
£800 $1272 €1200 On the Welsh coast, Bangor (47x61cm-19x24in) 6-Mar-3 Christie's, Kensington #388/R
£1100 $1716 €1650 Gypsy's corner (74x104cm-29x41in) exhib. 7-Nov-2 Christie's, Kensington #81/R est:600-800
£5500 $8525 €8250 View of Dunkeld, on the river Tay, Perthshire (61x91cm-24x36in) s.d.1840. 31-Oct-2 Christie's, London #13/R est:6000-8000
Works on paper
£360 $562 €540 Shepherd and his flock in a rural landscape (18x25cm-7x10in) W/C. 9-Oct-2 Woolley & Wallis, Salisbury #50/R

ALLEN, Junius (1898-1962) American
£1125 $1800 €1688 Lengthening shadows, farmhouse and outbuilding (28x38cm-11x15in) s. 17-Mar-3 Winter Associates, Plainville #120
£2938 $4700 €4407 North Cove Road (58x86cm-23x34in) s.d.1949. 17-Mar-3 Winter Associates, Plainville #121

ALLEN, R (?) British
£320 $493 €480 View of Windsor Castle (20x30cm-8x12in) s. 6-Sep-2 Biddle & Webb, Birmingham #172

ALLEN, Richard (1964-) Australian
£1505 $2288 €2258 Chep and Schweppes (161x120cm-63x47in) s.i.d.verso. 27-Aug-2 Goodman, Sydney #182/R est:2500-4500 (A.D 4200)

ALLEN, Robert C G (20th C) British
Works on paper
£552 $900 €828 Pekinese Jero's Pu Zin (57x38cm-22x15in) indis sig. 11-Feb-3 Bonhams & Doyles, New York #242/R

ALLEN, Thomas (attrib) (1849-1924) American
£4062 $6500 €5890 A rest overlooking the harbour (32x50cm-13x20in) i.verso. 16-May-3 Skinner, Boston #97/R est:700-900

ALLEN, Thomas (fl.1767-1772) British
£4000 $6480 €6000 Airing ship, warships of the fleet lying at anchor offshore (58x78cm-23x31in) 21-May-3 Christie's, Kensington #522/R est:4000-6000

ALLEYN, Edmund (1931-) Canadian
Works on paper
£439 $654 €659 Composition (25x47cm-10x19in) s.d.61 collage oil. 26-Jun-2 Iegor de Saint Hippolyte, Montreal #1 (C.D 1000)

ALLEYNE, Francis (18/19th C) British
£5500 $9130 €8250 Portrait of two brothers (37x29cm-15x11in) oval pair. 12-Jun-3 Sotheby's, London #67/R est:4000-6000

ALLINGHAM, H (1848-1926) British
Works on paper
£3509 $5333 €5264 Farringford, Isle of Wight (37x55cm-15x22in) s. W/C. 19-Aug-2 Joel, Victoria #276/R est:10000-15000 (A.D 10000)

ALLINGHAM, Helen (1848-1926) British
Works on paper
£1050 $1638 €1575 Study of trees. Study of a bush (18x11cm-7x4in) one s. W/C frame as one. 5-Nov-2 Bonhams, New Bond Street #86a est:1000-1500
£2100 $3318 €3150 Bedtime story (8x7cm-3x3in) s. W/C scratching out. 2-Dec-2 Bonhams, Bath #27/R est:800-1200
£3300 $5445 €4785 Side canal, Venice (33x25cm-13x10in) s. W/C. 2-Jul-3 Sotheby's, Olympia #253/R est:2000-3000
£4000 $6640 €6000 Portrait of Alfred, Lord Tennyson (19x16cm-7x6in) s.i.d.1880 W/C. 12-Jun-3 Bonhams, New Bond Street #675/R est:4000-6000
£5200 $8424 €7800 Spring morning (18x22cm-7x9in) s. W/C. 20-May-3 Sotheby's, Olympia #12/R est:4000-6000
£6000 $9420 €9000 Woman at a cottage gate, Moon's Hill, Bedbury Lane, near Freshwater, Isle of Wight (36x27cm-14x11in) s. pencil W/C scratching out. 21-Nov-2 Christie's, London #94/R est:6000-10000
£6500 $10140 €9750 One year old (11x10cm-4x4in) W/C executed c.1877 exhib. 26-Mar-3 Hamptons Fine Art, Godalming #95/R est:2000-3000
£7000 $11480 €10150 Gathering firewood, autumn (32x27cm-13x11in) s. pencil W/C scratching out. 5-Jun-3 Christie's, London #146/R est:7000-10000
£8000 $12960 €12000 Robin's song (17x23cm-7x9in) s.d.77 W/C bodycol prov. 20-May-3 Sotheby's, Olympia #13/R est:7000-10000
£9000 $14850 €13050 Waiting for mother's return (23x20cm-9x8in) s. pencil W/C scratching out. 3-Jul-3 Christie's, Kensington #56/R est:3000-5000
£10500 $17010 €15750 Spring time at lower Denhay, Bridport (31x39cm-12x15in) s. W/C bodycol prov. 20-May-3 Sotheby's, Olympia #14/R est:10000-15000
£12000 $18840 €18000 Apple tree seat (21x27cm-8x11in) s.i. pencil W/C gum arabic with scratching out. 21-Nov-2 Christie's, London #93/R est:12000-18000
£12000 $19320 €18000 Harvest moon (35x27cm-14x11in) s.d.1879 pencil W/C gum arabic scratching out prov.exhib. 20-Feb-3 Christie's, London #54/R est:15000
£12000 $19920 €18000 Sandhills, Witley, view of the artist's house (21x27cm-8x11in) s.d.Sept 1881 W/C prov. 12-Jun-3 Sotheby's, London #278/R est:10000-15000
£15500 $25110 €23250 Feeding fowl (26x21cm-10x8in) s.i. W/C bodycol exhib. 20-May-3 Sotheby's, Olympia #15/R est:10000-15000
£23000 $38180 €34500 Wiltshire cottage (25x33cm-10x13in) s. W/C. 12-Jun-3 Bonhams, New Bond Street #668/R est:12000-18000
£27000 $43740 €40500 Dairy, Farringford (38x31cm-15x12in) s. W/C lit. 20-May-3 Sotheby's, Olympia #16/R est:12000-18000
£38000 $61560 €57000 Whittington, Gloucestershire (34x49cm-13x19in) s. W/C htd bodycol scratching out prov. 20-May-3 Sotheby's, Olympia #17/R est:20000-30000

ALLINSON, Adrian (1890-1959) British
Works on paper
£300 $462 €450 Antecote (28x36cm-11x14in) s.d.25. 3-Sep-2 Gorringes, Lewes #2146

ALLOM, Thomas (1804-1872) British
Works on paper
£260 $411 €390 Devil's Bridge, Switzerland (12x17cm-5x7in) wash. 26-Nov-2 Bonhams, Knightsbridge #92

£600 $936 €900 Greek Church of Baloukli near Constantinople (16x21cm-6x8in) pencil brown wash htd white. 19-Sep-2 Christie's, Kensington #102/R
£900 $1440 €1350 Prospective drawing design for a new church at Torquay, Devon (89x63cm-35x25in) W/C. 11-Mar-3 Bonhams, New Bond Street #27/R
£4200 $6006 €6300 Views of Paris (13x19cm-5x7in) s. pen wash htd white pair prov.lit. 22-Jan-3 Christie's, London #50/R

ALLONGE, Auguste (1833-1898) French
Works on paper
£696 $1100 €1100 Rochers a Fontainebleau (50x34cm-20x13in) s. W/C crayon. 28-Nov-2 Tajan, Paris #136/R
£1139 $1800 €1800 Paysage de bord de mer (49x72cm-19x28in) s.d.1881 W/C htd gouache. 28-Nov-2 Tajan, Paris #141/R

ALLORI, Alessandro (1535-1607) Italian
£9722 $15458 €14000 Saint John the Baptist (157x113cm-62x44in) 3-May-3 Finarte, Venice #155/R est:19000

ALLORI, Alessandro (attrib) (1535-1607) Italian
£22000 $36740 €31900 Portrait of a lady in high necked gown with a ruff and gold brocade trim (67x56cm-26x22in) panel. 9-Jul-3 Christie's, London #93/R est:20000-30000

ALLORI, Alessandro (circle) (1535-1607) Italian
£6000 $9300 €9000 Portrait of gentleman wearing black jacket and white ruff (86x71cm-34x28in) 31-Oct-2 Sotheby's, Olympia #16/R

ALLORI, Cristofano (1577-1621) Italian
£123457 $200000 €185186 Judith holding the head of Holofernes (142x107cm-56x42in) 23-Jan-3 Sotheby's, New York #225/R est:40000

ALLORI, Cristofano (attrib) (1577-1621) Italian
Works on paper
£6289 $10000 €9434 Head of a boy (23x15cm-9x6in) red black chk sold with letter. 5-Mar-3 Doyle, New York #91/R est:1200-1800

ALLORI, Cristofano (studio) (1577-1621) Italian
£5200 $8684 €7540 Tobias and the Angel (41x32cm-16x13in) linen on copper. 9-Jul-3 Bonhams, New Bond Street #160/R est:4000-6000

ALLORI, Cristofano (style) (1577-1621) Italian
£28000 $46760 €40600 Head of a young man in profile, wearing a red hat (49x38cm-19x15in) 8-Jul-3 Sotheby's, Olympia #385/R est:2000-3000

ALLOU, Gilles (attrib) (1670-1751) French
£2703 $4216 €4000 Deux jeunes filles tenant une corbeille de fleurs (94x130cm-37x51in) 26-Mar-3 Tajan, Paris #61/R
£4193 $6626 €6500 Jeune garcon et son chat (76x94cm-30x37in) 20-Dec-2 Tajan, Paris #124/R est:7000
Works on paper
£316 $500 €500 Une mere assise a cote de sa fille. Une etude de bras (26x20cm-10x8in) col chk double- sided sold with 6 drs by other hands prov. 27-Nov-2 Christie's, Paris #150/R

ALLUAUD, Eugène (1866-?) French
£886 $1382 €1400 Le chemin (55x46cm-22x18in) s. 16-Oct-2 Fraysse & Associes, Paris #38

ALMA, Peter (1886-1969) Dutch
£1831 $2948 €2600 Various still life (52x39cm-20x15in) s. 6-May-3 Vendu Notarishuis, Rotterdam #23/R est:1000-1500

ALMA-TADEMA, Anna (1865-1943) British
£4500 $7245 €6750 Flags (81x7cm-32x3in) init. panel prov.exhib.lit. 20-Feb-3 Christie's, London #275/R

ALMA-TADEMA, Lady Laura (1852-1909) British
£3500 $5810 €5250 Stonehenge, Wiltshire (18x26cm-7x10in) s.d.1902 prov. 10-Jun-3 Christie's, London #138/R est:2000-3000
£65000 $102700 €97500 At the doorway (46x23cm-18x9in) s.i. panel. 27-Nov-2 Christie's, London #1/R est:30000-50000

ALMA-TADEMA, Sir Lawrence (1836-1912) British
£1074 $1729 €1600 Joyau (80x65cm-31x26in) panel. 24-Feb-3 Bernaerts, Antwerp #163/R
£5380 $8500 €8070 Tulips, roses and other flowers (50x53cm-20x21in) s. panel prov.lit. 1-Apr-3 Christie's, Rockefeller NY #194/R est:6000-8000
£25000 $39500 €37500 Portrait of Clothilde Enid, daughter of Edward Onslow Ford (39x29cm-15x11in) s.i. panel prov.exhib.lit. 26-Nov-2 Christie's, London #111/R est:30000-50000
£38710 $60000 €58065 Prize for the artists corps (47x24cm-19x9in) s.i.d. panel prov.exhib.lit. 29-Oct-2 Sotheby's, New York #156/R est:60000-80000
£96774 $150000 €145161 Water pets (66x142cm-26x56in) s.i. painted 1874 prov.exhib.lit. 30-Oct-2 Christie's, Rockefeller NY #38/R est:200000-300000
£103226 $160000 €154839 Joseph, overseer of Pharaoh's Granaries (35x46cm-14x18in) s.i. panel painted 1874 prov.exhib.lit. 30-Oct-2 Christie's, Rockefeller NY #40/R est:180000-250000
£130000 $209300 €195000 Harvest festival (32x24cm-13x9in) s.i. panel prov.exhib.lit. 19-Feb-3 Christie's, London #1/R est:80000-120000
£193548 $300000 €290322 Preparation in the Colosseum (153x79cm-60x31in) s.i. painted 1912 prov.exhib.lit. 30-Oct-2 Christie's, Rockefeller NY #41/R est:300000-400000
Works on paper
£1500 $2490 €2250 Head study Lady Alma-Tadema, nee Laura Epps (16x11cm-6x4in) init.d.2.11.86. 12-Jun-3 Bonhams, New Bond Street #677/R est:1000-1500
£10500 $16905 €15750 Untitled. pencil W/C cabinet of works by members of St John's Wood Art Club. 20-Feb-3 Christie's, London #124/R est:15000
£15000 $23550 €22500 Dolce far niente (25x17cm-10x7in) s.i. pencil pen ink W/C prov.exhib.lit. 21-Nov-2 Christie's, London #99/R est:20000-30000

ALMAGRO LOPEZ, Juan (1886-1965) Spanish
£479 $748 €700 Landscape with village (130x100cm-51x39in) s.d.1924. 8-Apr-3 Ansorena, Madrid #39/R

ALMARAZ, Carlos (1941-1989) ?
£1282 $2000 €1923 Laughing and crying jester (18x13cm-7x5in) board prov. 14-Oct-2 Butterfields, San Francisco #2151/R est:3000-5000
Works on paper
£1923 $3000 €2885 Santa Fe IV (76x56cm-30x22in) s.d.88 pastel prov. 14-Oct-2 Butterfields, San Francisco #2152/R est:2500-3500

ALMAVIVA, Marco (1934-) Italian
£577 $912 €900 Untitled (30x40cm-12x16in) s. s.i.d.1982 verso canvas on cardboard. 15-Nov-2 Farsetti, Prato #149/R
£608 $949 €900 Spool (30x39cm-12x15in) s. i.verso canvas on cardboard. 28-Mar-3 Farsetti, Prato #2/R

ALMOND, Darren (1971-) British
Photographs
£5000 $7700 €7500 Dawn and dusk (64x108cm-25x43in) two chromagenic prints executed 1996 prov. 23-Oct-2 Christie's, London #186/R est:7000-10000

ALMOND, William Douglas (1866-1916) British
£340 $530 €510 Cavalier standing before a gateleg table with a jug in his hand (39x19cm-15x7in) s.d.1888. 17-Sep-2 Bonhams, Sevenoaks #214/R

ALMQUIST, Anna (19th C) Swedish
£319 $495 €479 Orebro Palace (28x33cm-11x13in) s.d.1887 panel. 8-Dec-2 Uppsala Auktionskammare, Uppsala #101 (S.KR 4500)

ALMQVIST, Ester (1869-1934) Swedish
£245 $387 €368 The train to Molle (26x40cm-10x16in) s. panel. 16-Nov-2 Crafoord, Lund #12 (S.KR 3500)

ALONSO ALONSO, Francisco (1930-) Spanish
£411 $641 €600 Interior, Menton (84x112cm-33x44in) s. s.i.verso. 8-Apr-3 Ansorena, Madrid #193/R
£440 $687 €700 Tea and apple tart (73x92cm-29x36in) s. s.i.d.1966 verso. 8-Oct-2 Ansorena, Madrid #611/R
£545 $861 €850 Little ladies in gold (50x60cm-20x24in) s. i.verso. 13-Nov-2 Ansorena, Madrid #341/R

ALONSO PALACIOS, Vicente (1955-) Spanish
£287 $448 €425 Celebrations (11x16cm-4x6in) s.i. board. 25-Mar-3 Durán, Madrid #181/R

ALONSO-PEREZ, Mariano (20th C) Spanish
£11613 $18000 €17420 Night on the town (61x43cm-24x17in) s.i. 30-Oct-2 Christie's, Rockefeller NY #185/R est:15000-20000

ALONZI, Robert (1953-) Belgian

£1026 $1610 €1600 La digue (120x90cm-47x35in) s.d.1990 pair. 11-Dec-2 Hotel des Ventes Mosan, Brussels #322 est:1000-1100

ALONZO, Dominique de (19/20th C) French

Sculpture

£1200 $1896 €1800 Female figure (33cm-13in) s. bronze ivory. 14-Nov-2 Christie's, Kensington #278/R est:1200-1500

ALORDA Y PEREZ, Ramon (1848-1899) Spanish

£962 $1519 €1500 Scene in Valencia (33x49cm-13x19in) s. on porcelain. 14-Nov-2 Arte, Seville #363/R

£1154 $1823 €1800 Gypsy (48x32cm-19x13in) s. on porcelain. 14-Nov-2 Arte, Seville #322/R

£1154 $1823 €1800 Man (48x32cm-19x13in) s. on porcelain. 14-Nov-2 Arte, Seville #321/R

ALOTT, Robert (1850-1910) Austrian

£629 $975 €1000 Winter pleasures (21x31cm-8x12in) s. panel. 29-Oct-2 Dorotheum, Vienna #279/R

£1013 $1600 €1600 South Tyrolean city with square and fountain (47x32cm-19x13in) s.d.1908. 29-Nov-2 Sigalas, Stuttgart #1067/R est:1800

£1132 $1755 €1800 Bodighera (42x69cm-17x27in) s.d.1905. 29-Oct-2 Dorotheum, Vienna #71/R est:2500-2900

£2115 $3321 €3300 Busy promenade on southern beach (55x68cm-22x27in) s.d.1895. 21-Nov-2 Van Ham, Cologne #1446/R est:1400

£2213 $3496 €3320 Many figures by a southern coast (42x70cm-17x28in) s. 2-Dec-2 Rasmussen, Copenhagen #1498/R est:15000-20000 (D.KR 26000)

£3226 $5097 €5000 Promeneurs pres d'une villa Italienne en bord de mer (69x42cm-27x17in) s. 17-Dec-2 Rossini, Paris #58/R

£4965 $8043 €7000 Tremosine on Lake Garda (69x107cm-27x42in) s.d.1907 i.verso. 22-May-3 Dorotheum, Vienna #30/R est:7000-8000

£5031 $7849 €8000 Oriental scene (69x43cm-27x17in) s. lit. 20-Sep-2 Schloss Ahlden, Ahlden #1214/R est:7500

£7500 $11850 €11250 Street in Cairo (100x73cm-39x29in) s.d.1884 prov.exhib.lit. 26-Nov-2 Sotheby's, Melbourne #205/R est:6000-8000 (A.D 21000)

ALPER, Nathalie (20th C) American

Works on paper

£600 $972 €870 Horizontal (48x126cm-19x50in) s.d.1977 pencil graphite. 25-May-3 Lots Road, London #332

ALPERIZ, Nicolas (1869-1928) Spanish

£3049 $5000 €4421 Travellers (12x150cm-5x59in) s. 4-Jun-3 Christie's, Rockefeller NY #247/R est:7000-9000

ALPUY, Julio (1919-) Uruguayan

£2625 $4200 €3938 Urban landscape (38x50cm-15x20in) s.d.47 cardboard. 5-Jan-3 Galleria Y Remates, Montevideo #95/R

£10692 $17000 €16038 Eternal heaven (179x127cm-70x50in) s.d.76. 2-Mar-3 Galleria Y Remates, Montevideo #81/R est:22000

Works on paper

£302 $480 €453 Coloured town (12x19cm-5x7in) crayon. 2-Mar-3 Galleria Y Remates, Montevideo #45/R

£321 $510 €482 Urban scene (12x20cm-5x8in) s. ink pencil. 2-Mar-3 Galleria Y Remates, Montevideo #46/R

£388 $620 €582 Paradise (26x34cm-10x13in) s.d.1925 ink W/C. 5-Jan-3 Galleria Y Remates, Montevideo #23/R

£2439 $4000 €3537 Paisaje biologico (60x51cm-24x20in) s.d.1964 mixed media wood relief. 27-May-3 Sotheby's, New York #146

ALSLOOT, Denis van (c.1570-1628) Dutch

£170000 $283900 €246500 Orpheus charming the animals (151x159cm-59x63in) s.d.1610 prov.lit. 10-Jul-3 Sotheby's, London #9/R est:150000-200000

ALT, Duane (1935-) American

£2130 $3450 €3089 Overlooking Portofino (76x102cm-30x40in) 23-May-3 Altermann Galleries, Santa Fe #171

£2740 $4000 €4110 L'apres-midi a Portofino (76x127cm-30x50in) 18-May-2 Altermann Galleries, Santa Fe #261/R

ALT, Franz (1821-1914) Austrian

£4795 $7479 €7000 Karlskirche with figures (43x48cm-17x19in) s. metal. 10-Apr-3 Dorotheum, Vienna #54/R est:7000-9000

Works on paper

£535 $829 €850 Tree study (33x20cm-13x8in) s. pencil. 1-Oct-2 Dorotheum, Vienna #119

£1285 $2005 €1928 Terrace (10x15cm-4x6in) s.d.1858 mixed media. 11-Apr-3 Kieselbach, Budapest #176/R est:380000-460000 (H.F 460000)

£2516 $3899 €4000 Interior of Maria am Gestade (26x18cm-10x7in) s.d.1898 W/C. 1-Oct-2 Dorotheum, Vienna #250/R est:5000-6000

£7051 $11071 €11000 Corso Vitt Emanuele II (32x24cm-13x9in) s.i.d.27 September 1885 W/C. 25-Nov-2 Hassfurther, Vienna #23/R est:10000-12000

ALT, Franz (attrib) (1821-1914) Austrian

£1026 $1590 €1600 Albanian lake with view of Gandolfo Castle in the distance (57x75cm-22x30in) s.i. canvas on canvas. 4-Dec-2 Neumeister, Munich #664/R est:1600

ALT, Jacob (1789-1872) German

£1063 $1679 €1530 Wooded landscape with stream and figures (31x27cm-12x11in) s. bears d. 25-Apr-3 Weidler, Nurnberg #9150/R est:1700

Works on paper

£743 $1159 €1100 Mountain track in Italy (24x31cm-9x12in) s. W/C. 28-Mar-3 Dorotheum, Vienna #175/R

£1384 $2145 €2200 Schwarzbach in Salzkammergut (21x14cm-8x6in) s. W/C over pencil. 1-Oct-2 Dorotheum, Vienna #132/R est:2200-2600

£6803 $10816 €10000 Graben, Vienna (14x21cm-6x8in) s.d.1826 W/C. 19-Mar-3 Neumeister, Munich #345/R est:5000

£10204 $16224 €15000 Old Jagerzeile, Praterstrasse, Vienna (15x23cm-6x9in) s. W/C. 19-Mar-3 Neumeister, Munich #346/R est:5000

ALT, Otmar (1940-) German

£641 $994 €1000 Animal story (32x28cm-13x11in) s.d.71 i.verso. 7-Dec-2 Van Ham, Cologne #3/R

£1014 $1581 €1500 Bird bouquet. Small elephant (15x11cm-6x4in) s.d. s.i.d. verso panel tow. 28-Mar-3 Ketterer, Hamburg #178/R est:1800-2400

£1203 $1900 €1900 Colourful cow (49x40cm-19x16in) acrylic panel. 29-Nov-2 Villa Grisebach, Berlin #504/R est:2000-2500

£1519 $2400 €2400 Story of the buttercup Franz (59x54cm-23x21in) s.d.1967 verso acrylic board. 30-Nov-2 Arnold, Frankfurt #12/R est:600

£1538 $2385 €2400 Little postman (50x40cm-20x16in) s.d.68 s.i. verso. 6-Dec-2 Karlheinz Kaupp, Staufen #2144/R est:1250

£2564 $3974 €4000 Before the rendezvous (40x55cm-16x22in) s. s.i.d.87 stretcher. 3-Dec-2 Lempertz, Koln #7/R est:3500-4000

£2899 $4754 €4000 Fire hen (98x70cm-39x28in) s.d.71 s.i.d.71 stretcher. 31-May-3 Villa Grisebach, Berlin #377/R est:4000-5000

Works on paper

£405 $632 €600 Composition (24x20cm-9x8in) s.i.d. col pen pencil. 28-Mar-3 Ketterer, Hamburg #179/R

ALT, Rudolf von (1812-1905) Austrian

£1317 $2200 €1910 Harvesting the field (26x33cm-10x13in) s. 22-Jun-3 Freeman, Philadelphia #25/R est:4000-6000

£48498 $75172 €72747 Nurnberg, fountain and Church of St Lorenz (48x38cm-19x15in) s.d.1864. 3-Oct-2 Koller, Zurich #3083/R est:50000-70000 (S.FR 113000)

Works on paper

£439 $685 €650 Horse and cart (9x14cm-4x6in) bears i. pencil. 28-Mar-3 Dorotheum, Vienna #108

£655 $1022 €983 Berchtesgaden (13x17cm-5x7in) i. verso W/C over pencil. 6-Nov-2 Dobiaschofsky, Bern #314 est:1200 (S.FR 1500)

£676 $1054 €1000 City palace (10x8cm-4x3in) s. i. verso pencil. 28-Mar-3 Dorotheum, Vienna #127/R

£811 $1265 €1200 Gothic doorway (14x20cm-6x8in) s. pencil. 28-Mar-3 Dorotheum, Vienna #156/R

£946 $1476 €1400 Village square (7x9cm-3x4in) s. W/C sketch. 28-Mar-3 Dorotheum, Vienna #216/R

£1635 $2535 €2600 Budapest (17x49cm-7x19in) s.i. pencil. 1-Oct-2 Dorotheum, Vienna #88/R est:2600-3000

£2162 $3373 €3200 Schonbrunn (19x30cm-7x12in) s. i. verso pencil. 28-Mar-3 Dorotheum, Vienna #101/R est:1700-2000

£4054 $6324 €6000 Interior of Regensburg Cathedral (36x21cm-14x8in) s. W/C sketch. 28-Mar-3 Dorotheum, Vienna #222/R est:12000-15000

£5068 $7905 €7500 Vesta Temple in Rome (35x52cm-14x20in) s. W/C. 28-Mar-3 Dorotheum, Vienna #224/R est:40000-45000

£6329 $10000 €10000 Tree in the Prater, Vienna (24x19cm-9x7in) W/C lit. 26-Nov-2 Wiener Kunst Auktionen, Vienna #31/R est:7000-12000

£6393 $9973 €9590 Portrait of the Csar's Palace Livadio (26x39cm-10x15in) s.i. W/C. 28-Mar-3 Koller, Zurich #3171/R est:15000-25000 (S.FR 14000)

£6757 $10541 €10000 Untersberg near Aigen (25x36cm-10x14in) s. w/C. 25-Mar-3 Wiener Kunst Auktionen, Vienna #111/R est:12000-20000

£10811 $16865 €16000 Lake Garda in a storm (15x23cm-6x9in) s.d.1839 w/C. 25-Mar-3 Wiener Kunst Auktionen, Vienna #112/R est:10000-18000

£10870 $17826 €15000 Teplitz (29x28cm-11x11in) s. W/C. 27-May-3 Wiener Kunst Auktionen, Vienna #18/R est:15000-20000

£13043 $21391 €18000 In the park of Castle Zleb in Blumau (31x46cm-12x18in) s. W/C. 27-May-3 Wiener Kunst Auktionen, Vienna #19/R est:16000-35000

£16000 $24800 €24000 Das Niederosterreichische landhaus (12x18cm-5x7in) s. W/C htd bodycol. 4-Dec-2 Christie's, London #64/R est:7000-10000

£25000 $38750 €37500 Blick vom alten kriegsministerium, auf den Platz Am Hof (14x21cm-6x8in) s.d.1893 W/C htd gouache. 4-Dec-2 Christie's, London #63/R est:7000-10000

£54487 $84455 €85000 View from Upper Belvedere of Vienna (17x24cm-7x9in) s.d.1847 W/C htd white lit. 4-Dec-2 Neumeister, Munich #502/R est:75000

ALT, Rudolf von and PASINI, Alberto (19th C) Austrian/Italian
£17089 $26658 €27000 Landscape with ruins. 15-Oct-2 Babuino, Rome #373/R

ALT, Theodor (1846-1937) Austrian
£769 $1192 €1200 Head portrait of Rudolf Hirth painter from Frenes, about 18 years old (18x13cm-7x5in) canvas on masonite lit. 4-Dec-2 Neumeister, Munich #665/R
£2215 $3434 €3500 Summer idyll on riverbank (38x55cm-15x22in) s.d.97. 25-Sep-2 Neumeister, Munich #535/R est:5000

ALTAMURA, Alessandro (1855-?) Italian
£526 $853 €763 From the park near Versailles (46x39cm-18x15in) indis.sig.i. 26-May-3 Rasmussen, Copenhagen #1312/R (D.KR 5500)
£563 $924 €816 Southern coast with calm sea (9x22cm-4x9in) mono. panel. 4-Jun-3 Fischer, Luzern #2000/R (S.FR 1200)

ALTAMURA, Jean (1852-1878) Greek
£256 $395 €384 Fountain in a park (50x61cm-20x24in) indis.sig. 4-Sep-2 Kunsthallen, Copenhagen #10 (D.KR 3000)
Works on paper
£5500 $8525 €8250 Shipping off the Danish coast (25x39cm-10x15in) s.d.1875 W/C. 2-Oct-2 Sotheby's, London #80/R

ALTDORFER, Albrecht (1480-1538) German
Prints
£4167 $6500 €6251 Crucifixion (15x10cm-6x4in) etching engraving exec.c.1515-17. 6-Nov-2 Swann Galleries, New York #48/R est:2000-3000

ALTEN, Mathias Joseph (1871-1938) German
£304 $475 €456 Impressionist landscape (37x35cm-15x14in) s. board. 13-Apr-3 Butterfields, Los Angeles #7011
£3459 $5500 €5189 House in Grand Rapids (30x48cm-12x19in) s.d. board. 4-May-3 Treadway Gallery, Cincinnati #523/R est:5000-7000

ALTENBOURG, Gerhard (1926-1989) German
Prints
£2917 $4608 €4200 Composition (28x66cm-11x26in) s.mono.i.d.1977 col woodcut board. 26-Apr-3 Dr Lehr, Berlin #20/R est:1800
Works on paper
£6289 $9686 €10000 Sunken, sunken (35x47cm-14x19in) s.mono.i.d.1983 ink W/C lithographic chk tempera. 26-Oct-2 Dr Lehr, Berlin #11/R est:8000

ALTENKIRCH, Otto (1875-1945) German
£1090 $1711 €1700 Portrait of old peasant woman with cow (66x90cm-26x35in) s.d.06. 21-Nov-2 Van Ham, Cologne #1447/R

ALTENKOPF, Joseph (1818-1855) Austrian
£552 $877 €800 Romantic landscape with river and figures (50x63cm-20x25in) s.d.44. 8-Mar-3 Arnold, Frankfurt #534
£1258 $1950 €2000 Landscape with small village and figures (37x45cm-15x18in) s.d.1847. 29-Oct-2 Dorotheum, Vienna #119/R est:2000-2500
£1282 $2013 €2000 Landscape with figures (40x52cm-16x20in) s.d.1850 board. 21-Nov-2 Dorotheum, Vienna #125/R est:2600-3200
£3020 $4862 €4500 Waterfall near bad Gastein, Austria (89x71cm-35x28in) s.d.1846 prov. 18-Feb-3 Sotheby's, Amsterdam #319/R est:6000-8000

ALTHUIS, Willem van (20th C) ?
£641 $994 €1000 Untitled (30x24cm-12x9in) init.d.85 canvas on panel. 3-Dec-2 Christie's, Amsterdam #360/R est:1000-1500

ALTICHIERO da ZEVIO (style) (1330-1385) Italian
£4268 $7000 €6402 Decollation of a Saint (29x24cm-11x9in) gold ground tempera panel arched top. 29-May-3 Sotheby's, New York #79/R est:3000-4000

ALTINK, Jan (1885-1975) Dutch
£4777 $7452 €7500 Gronings landscape (60x80cm-24x31in) d.1948. 6-Nov-2 Vendue Huis, Gravenhage #580/R est:8000-12000
£5282 $8504 €7500 Still life of flowers (49x69cm-19x27in) s.d.48. 7-May-3 Vendue Huis, Gravenhage #558/R est:7500-9000
£6329 $10000 €10000 Landschapte Groningen (64x78cm-25x31in) s. painted c.1930. 26-Nov-2 Sotheby's, Amsterdam #120/R est:18000-25000
£12230 $20058 €17000 Schuur - barn (56x64cm-22x25in) s.d.33 s.i.on stretcher prov. 3-Jun-3 Christie's, Amsterdam #259/R est:15000-20000

ALTMANN, Alexandre (1885-1950) Russian
£1400 $2282 €2100 Paysage (38x55cm-15x22in) s. 3-Feb-3 Bonhams, New Bond Street #10/R est:1000-1500
£1728 $2454 €2800 Jetee de fleurs (55x37cm-22x15in) s. 16-Mar-3 Eric Pillon, Calais #170/R
£1852 $2630 €3000 Vase de fleurs (55x37cm-22x15in) s. 16-Mar-3 Eric Pillon, Calais #169/R
£1887 $2943 €3000 La Seine a Grenelle par temps gris (50x65cm-20x26in) s. 10-Oct-2 Ribeyre & Baron, Paris #61/R est:2000-3000
£2051 $3221 €3200 Dahlias (50x44cm-20x17in) s. 13-Dec-2 Piasa, Paris #37
£2177 $3461 €3200 Bord de ruisseau enneige (81x81cm-32x32in) s. 18-Mar-3 Vanderkindere, Brussels #90 est:1500-2000
£2411 $4027 €3400 Allee de platanes (73x60cm-29x24in) s. 17-Jun-3 Claude Boisgirard, Paris #16 est:1500-2000
£2482 $4145 €3500 Village en hiver (45x61cm-18x24in) s. 17-Jun-3 Claude Boisgirard, Paris #15/R est:3500-4000
£2516 $3899 €4000 Paysage de neige (60x73cm-24x29in) s. 30-Oct-2 Artcurial Briest, Paris #2/R est:3500-4000
£2585 $4110 €3800 Passerelle dans le village (61x50cm-24x20in) s. 24-Mar-3 Coutau Begarie, Paris #251/R
£3205 $5032 €5000 Paysage a l'etang (72x92cm-28x36in) s. 22-Nov-2 Millon & Associes, Paris #79/R
£3481 $5430 €5500 Allee pres de la maison (54x73cm-21x29in) s.i.d.1909. 18-Oct-2 Rabourdin & Choppin de Janvry, Paris #25/R
£3600 $5832 €5400 View of the river Seine (50x65cm-20x26in) s. prov. 21-May-3 Sotheby's, London #92/R est:4000-6000
£4000 $6400 €5800 Chemin sous le neige (60x73cm-24x29in) s. 12-Mar-3 Libert, Castor, Paris #42 est:2000-2500
£4690 $7503 €6800 Paysage de neige (65x81cm-26x32in) s. 12-Mar-3 Rabourdin & Choppin de Janvry, Paris #106/R
£4828 $7724 €7000 Le canal (46x55cm-18x22in) s. 12-Mar-3 Libert, Castor, Paris #41/R est:2500-3000
£5000 $8100 €7500 Summer flowers (54x65cm-21x26in) s. 21-May-3 Sotheby's, London #195/R est:3000-5000
£5082 $8131 €7369 Landscape with avenue (53x78cm-21x31in) s. 18-May-3 Anders Antik, Landskrona #23 est:18000 (S.KR 65000)
£5190 $8200 €8200 Winter landscape (72x91cm-28x36in) s. 1-Dec-2 Bukowskis, Helsinki #226/R est:3000-4000
£5500 $8910 €8250 Trees by the river (54x64cm-21x25in) s. 21-May-3 Sotheby's, London #104/R est:3000-5000
£5800 $9686 €8410 Sunlit walk (90x73cm-35x29in) s. 25-Jun-3 Bonhams, Bury St Edmunds #600 est:500-700
£6000 $10020 €8700 By the river (71x58cm-28x23in) s. sold with a companion. 25-Jun-3 Bonhams, Bury St Edmunds #601 est:600-1000
£7000 $11340 €10500 Still life with yellow and white chrysanthemums (50x44cm-20x17in) s. 21-May-3 Sotheby's, London #197/R est:1500-2000
£7800 $12714 €11700 House by a river in springtime (92x73cm-36x29in) s. 3-Feb-3 Bonhams, New Bond Street #66/R est:3000-5000
£7801 $13028 €11000 Village au bord de riviere (65x54cm-26x21in) s. 17-Jun-3 Claude Boisgirard, Paris #14/R est:5000-6000
£9000 $14580 €13500 Trees by a lake (73x92cm-29x36in) s. 21-May-3 Sotheby's, London #103/R est:3500-4500
£10000 $15700 €15000 House across the river (65x54cm-26x21in) s. 20-Nov-2 Sotheby's, London #83/R est:2000-3000
£12000 $18840 €18000 Winter landscape (101x171cm-40x67in) s. 20-Nov-2 Sotheby's, London #86/R est:4000-6000
£17000 $27540 €25500 River (91x73cm-36x29in) s. 21-May-3 Sotheby's, London #85/R est:3500-4500
£21000 $34020 €31500 Sailing in the sun, South of France (92x65cm-36x26in) s. 21-May-3 Sotheby's, London #93/R est:7000-9000

ALTMANN, Gerard (1877-1940) Dutch
£290 $461 €420 Landscape (50x70cm-20x28in) s. 10-Mar-3 Sotheby's, Amsterdam #197
£526 $853 €800 Still life with zinnias in a copper bowl (50x60cm-20x24in) s. 21-Jan-3 Christie's, Amsterdam #139
£625 $1013 €950 Boats on a river by dusk. Sheep in a meadow (22x26cm-9x10in) s. board on plywood two. 21-Jan-3 Christie's, Amsterdam #212
£828 $1292 €1300 Landscape with goats in the meadow (28x48cm-11x19in) s. 6-Nov-2 Vendue Huis, Gravenhage #38/R
£955 $1490 €1500 Polder landscape with cow (39x59cm-15x23in) s. 5-Nov-2 Vendu Notarishuis, Rotterdam #64/R est:800-1000

ALTMANN, Nathan (1889-1970) Israeli
£27586 $44138 €40000 Portrait de l'oncle de l'artiste (86x74cm-34x29in) s. lit. 12-Mar-3 Rabourdin & Choppin de Janvry, Paris #99/R est:38000

ALTMANN, Roberto (1942-) Cuban
Works on paper
£321 $506 €500 Composition (24x32cm-9x13in) mono.d.1962 gouache. 18-Nov-2 Rieunier, Paris #130

ALTMANN, Sybrand (1822-1890) Dutch
£1083 $1668 €1700 Portrait of Aaltje Korff-Corver (95x76cm-37x30in) s.d.1856 s.verso. 3-Sep-2 Christie's, Amsterdam #130 est:700-900
£1783 $2746 €2800 Portrait of Jan Carel van Wessem (49x39cm-19x15in) panel. 3-Sep-2 Christie's, Amsterdam #131 est:700-900

ALTMUTTER, Placidus-Jacob (1780-1819) Austrian
Works on paper
£2264 $3509 €3600 Clash between Tyroleans and French in 1797 (54x39cm-21x15in) s. col pen. 1-Oct-2 Dorotheum, Vienna #103 est:300-350

ALTOMONTE, Martino (1657-1745) Italian
Works on paper
£1456 $2300 €2300 Head of young bearded saint (22x18cm-9x7in) chk htd white. 29-Nov-2 Bassenge, Berlin #5575/R est:1200
£2986 $4748 €4300 Alexander with the wounded and captured King Poros (12x15cm-5x6in) i. i. verso pen wash prov.lit. 5-May-3 Ketterer, Munich #379/R est:1000-1500

ALTOMONTE, Martino (attrib) (1657-1745) Italian
Works on paper
£597 $932 €950 St Augustin (30x18cm-12x7in) wash pen over pencil. 11-Oct-2 Winterberg, Heidelberg #355

ALTON, Lois (1894-1972) Austrian
£272 $433 €400 Malcesine harbour (50x50cm-20x20in) s. i. verso panel. 20-Mar-3 Neumeister, Munich #2574/R

ALTOON, John (1925-1969) American
Works on paper
£500 $800 €750 Untitled (76x102cm-30x40in) pen ink. 11-Jan-3 Harvey Clar, Oakland #1232

ALTORF, Johan Coenraad (1876-1955) Dutch
Sculpture
£5755 $9439 €8000 Manca bee (20cm-8in) mono.i.d.1911 bronze prov. 3-Jun-3 Christie's, Amsterdam #158/R est:8000-12000
£10072 $16518 €14000 Saint Paul (66cm-26in) mono. wood prov. 3-Jun-3 Christie's, Amsterdam #153/R est:10000-15000

ALTORF, Johan Coenraad and LANOOY, Chris (20th C) Dutch
Sculpture
£3022 $4955 €4200 Monkey (20cm-8in) s.i.d.1915 brown stoneware prov.exhib.lit. 3-Jun-3 Christie's, Amsterdam #157/R est:4000-6000

ALTSON, Abbey (1864-c.1949) British
£2800 $4368 €4200 Model (61x51cm-24x20in) s. 8-Oct-2 Bonhams, Knightsbridge #197/R est:3000-5000
£4580 $7237 €6870 Clarisse (59x49cm-23x19in) s. 2-Apr-3 Christie's, Melbourne #50/R est:7000-12000 (A.D 12000)
£7595 $12000 €11393 Young beauty (102x66cm-40x26in) s. prov. 23-Apr-3 Christie's, Rockefeller NY #119/R est:15000-20000

ALUF, Nic (20th C) ?
Photographs
£9500 $15390 €14250 Sophie Taeuber Arp behind Dada head (15x11cm-6x4in) gelatin silver print exec.c.1920 prov. 21-May-3 Christie's, London #124/R est:3000-5000

ALVAR, Sunol (1935-) Spanish
£597 $932 €950 Bull scene (67x99cm-26x39in) s. s.d.65 verso. 23-Sep-2 Durán, Madrid #268/R
£738 $1189 €1100 Still life with figure (56x46cm-22x18in) s. s.d.1963 verso. 18-Feb-3 Durán, Madrid #58/R
Works on paper
£252 $392 €400 Musicians (62x84cm-24x33in) s. mixed media. 23-Sep-2 Durán, Madrid #602/R

ALVAREZ ALGECIRAS, German (19th C) Spanish
£1419 $2243 €2200 In the inn (25cm-10in circular) s.d.1878 on leather. 18-Dec-2 Ansorena, Madrid #61/R

ALVAREZ AYLLON, E (19/20th C) Spanish
£513 $810 €800 Village (17x32cm-7x13in) s. board. 14-Nov-2 Arte, Seville #351/R

ALVAREZ AYLLON, Emilio (19/20th C) Spanish
£284 $449 €440 Orientalist landscape (19x36cm-7x14in) s. board. 18-Dec-2 Ansorena, Madrid #397
£314 $491 €500 Oriental landscape (19x35cm-7x14in) s. board. 8-Oct-2 Ansorena, Madrid #409/R
£449 $709 €700 Harbour (17x32cm-7x13in) s. board. 19-Nov-2 Durán, Madrid #150/R
£1081 $1686 €1600 Landscapes (33x17cm-13x7in) s. board pair. 25-Mar-3 Durán, Madrid #97/R

ALVAREZ BASSO, Dario (1968-) Venezuelan
£1060 $1727 €1600 Untitled (56x74cm-22x29in) s.d.1990 acrylic mixed media paper prov. 11-Feb-3 Segre, Madrid #229/R
Works on paper
£503 $785 €800 Untitled (51x36cm-20x14in) s.d.1994 s.i.d.verso W/C ink. 17-Sep-2 Segre, Madrid #174/R
£3145 $4843 €5000 Tree (115x146cm-45x57in) s.i.d.1987 verso mixed media. 22-Oct-2 Durán, Madrid #260/R

ALVAREZ BRAVO, Manuel (1902-2002) Mexican
Photographs
£1963 $3200 €2945 Margarita de Bonampak (24x18cm-9x7in) s.i.d.1949/70 verso gelatin silver print. 12-Feb-3 Christie's, Rockefeller NY #70/R est:2000-3000
£2057 $3250 €3086 Muchacha viendo pajaros (17x24cm-7x9in) s. photograph. 23-Apr-3 Sotheby's, New York #128/R est:3000-5000
£2147 $3500 €3221 Retrato de lo Eterno (22x18cm-9x7in) s.verso gelatin silver print. 12-Feb-3 Christie's, Rockefeller NY #68/R est:2500-3500
£2179 $3400 €3269 Ruina de ruinas (22x30cm-9x12in) s. verso silver. 21-Oct-2 Swann Galleries, New York #95/R est:1800-2200
£2195 $3600 €3293 Le tela de la arana, the cobweb (17x23cm-7x9in) s. i.verso platinum print. 10-Feb-3 Swann Galleries, New York #97/R est:4000-6000
£2215 $3500 €3323 Instrumental (20x26cm-8x10in) s. photograph. 23-Apr-3 Sotheby's, New York #127/R est:3000-5000
£2331 $3800 €3497 Dia di Todos Muertos (24x18cm-9x7in) s.i.verso gelatin silver print. 12-Feb-3 Christie's, Rockefeller NY #72/R est:2000-3000
£2405 $3800 €3608 Senor presidente municipal (19x24cm-7x9in) s.i. gelatin silver print prov. 22-Apr-3 Christie's, Rockefeller NY #159/R est:2500-3500
£2597 $4000 €3896 Trabajadores del tropico (17x22cm-7x9in) s.i.d.1950 num.2/5 photograph. 24-Oct-2 Sotheby's, New York #125/R est:3000-5000
£2949 $4600 €4424 Mannequis Riendo (23x28cm-9x11in) i. verso silver. 21-Oct-2 Swann Galleries, New York #93/R est:5000-6000
£3067 $5000 €4601 Senor de Papantla (39x28cm-15x11in) s.i. gelatin silver print. 12-Feb-3 Christie's, Rockefeller NY #71/R est:2500-3500
£3165 $5000 €4748 La buena fama durmiendo (19x24cm-7x9in) s. photograph prov. 23-Apr-3 Sotheby's, New York #126/R est:5000-7000
£3481 $5500 €5222 Ventana a los magueyes - window of Agaves (18x24cm-7x9in) s. gelatine silver print prov.lit. 22-Apr-3 Christie's, Rockefeller NY #18/R est:4000-6000
£4114 $6500 €6171 Dos pares de piernas - two pairs of legs (25x20cm-10x8in) s.i.d.1928-29 gelatin silver print prov.lit. 22-Apr-3 Christie's, Rockefeller NY #158/R est:4000-6000
£4221 $6500 €6332 Pan nuestro (18x22cm-7x9in) s. photograph. 24-Oct-2 Sotheby's, New York #124/R est:4000-6000
£4747 $7500 €7121 La hija de los danzantes - daughter of the dancer (25x18cm-10x7in) s. gelatin silver print prov.lit. 22-Apr-3 Christie's, Rockefeller NY #157/R est:4000-6000
£4908 $8000 €7362 La Buena fama durmiendo (18x24cm-7x9in) s.verso gelatin silver print. 12-Feb-3 Christie's, Rockefeller NY #69/R est:3000-5000
£5195 $8000 €7793 Daydream (24x19cm-9x7in) s.verso gelatin silver print exec.c.1970 prov.lit. 25-Oct-2 Phillips, New York #90/R est:6000-8000
£21472 $35000 €32208 Untitled (23x18cm-9x7in) s.num.25/75 fifteen photographs. 12-Feb-3 Christie's, Rockefeller NY #197/R est:30000-50000

ALVAREZ CATALA, Luis (1836-1901) Spanish
£1552 $2452 €2250 Collector (32cm-13in circular) 7-Apr-3 Castellana, Madrid #87/R
£8000 $12560 €12000 Admirando el cuadro - admiring the painting (30x20cm-12x8in) s.d.1885 panel. 19-Nov-2 Sotheby's, London #54/R est:8000-12000
£38710 $60000 €58065 Difficult decision (44x58cm-17x23in) s.d.1878. 30-Oct-2 Christie's, Rockefeller NY #67/R est:70000-90000
£60000 $100200 €90000 Marriage (67x121cm-26x48in) s. 19-Jun-3 Christie's, London #63/R est:60000-80000

ALVAREZ DE SOTOMAYOR, Maria Rosario (1921-) Spanish
£548 $866 €850 Market in Saint Hildephonsus Square (50x64cm-20x25in) s. board. 17-Dec-2 Durán, Madrid #171/R
£968 $1529 €1500 Feeding little pigs (54x67cm-21x26in) s. 17-Dec-2 Durán, Madrid #169/R

ALVAREZ DIAZ, Emilio (1879-1952) Argentinian
£638 $1027 €950 Flamenco dance (29x32cm-11x13in) s. board. 18-Feb-3 Durán, Madrid #96/R

ALVAREZ, Mabel (1891-1985) American
£932 $1500 €1398 Flowering fruit trees. Figural (12x9cm-5x4in) estate st. board double-sided prov. 18-Feb-3 John Moran, Pasadena #75 est:1000-2000
£7742 $12000 €11613 Family in garden (61x91cm-24x36in) s. masonite prov. 29-Oct-2 John Moran, Pasadena #695 est:15000-30000

ALVAREZ, Xavier (1949-) ?
Sculpture
£1439 $2302 €2000 Entente (69cm-27in) s.num.1/6 brown pat bronze. 18-May-3 Eric Pillon, Calais #284/R

ALVAREZ-SALA, Ventura (1871-?) Spanish
£265 $432 €400 Seascape (10x16cm-4x6in) s. cardboard. 11-Feb-3 Segre, Madrid #18/R

ALVIANI, Getulio (1939-) Italian
Sculpture
£2432 $3795 €3600 Surface (47x41x5cm-19x16x2in) aluminium. 26-Mar-3 Finarte Semenzato, Milan #387/R

ALYN, G Vanoer (18th C) ?
£2027 $3162 €3000 Portrait of lady with dog in palace garden. bears sig.d.1761. 27-Mar-3 Dorotheum, Vienna #327/R est:2000-3000

ALYS, Francis (1959-) Belgian
£26250 $42000 €39375 Untitled (17x20cm-7x8in) enamel on sheet metal diptych painted 1994 prov. 15-May-3 Christie's, Rockefeller NY #340/R est:25000-35000
£26752 $42000 €40128 Untitled. polyptych prov.exhib. 20-Nov-2 Christie's, Rockefeller NY #60/R est:30000-40000
Works on paper
£9146 $15000 €13719 How long since you tasted your mother's cooking (16x32cm-6x13in) i. mixed media board painted c.1990 prov. 28-May-3 Christie's, Rockefeller NY #49/R est:8000-12000

ALZIBAR, Jose de (18th C) Latin American
£875 $1418 €1313 Virgin mourning (62x47cm-24x19in) s.i. 23-Jan-3 Louis Morton, Mexico #130/R est:18000 (M.P 15000)

AMADIO, Vittorio (1934-) Italian
£962 $1519 €1500 Untitled (77x122cm-30x48in) s.d.1997 acrylic paper on canvas. 15-Nov-2 Farsetti, Prato #77/R

AMALFI, Carlo (18th C) Italian
£11392 $18000 €18000 Lady playing music (101x75cm-40x30in) 2-Dec-2 Finarte, Milan #114/R est:13000

AMAN-JEAN, Edmond François (1860-1935) French
£1667 $2617 €2600 Portrait of young woman (41x33cm-16x13in) s.d.78. 21-Nov-2 Van Ham, Cologne #1448/R est:1500

AMAND, Roger (1931-) French
£345 $548 €500 Dome (146x114cm-57x45in) s.d.81. 10-Mar-3 Millon & Associes, Paris #71
£345 $548 €500 Salle d'attente (114x146cm-45x57in) s.d.72. 10-Mar-3 Millon & Associes, Paris #69/R
£345 $548 €500 Miroir brise (114x146cm-45x57in) s.d.74-75. 10-Mar-3 Millon & Associes, Paris #70/R
£414 $658 €600 Colombe du jeudi (89x107cm-35x42in) s. 10-Mar-3 Millon & Associes, Paris #66/R

AMANN, Hermann (1934-) German
Works on paper
£1586 $2649 €2300 Particules (50x65cm-20x26in) s.d.1990 W/C. 10-Jul-3 Artcurial Briest, Paris #344/R est:1500-2000

AMANS, Jacques (1801-1888) American
£3205 $5000 €4808 Portrait of a Louisiana gentleman (91x71cm-36x28in) s. 12-Oct-2 Neal Auction Company, New Orleans #461/R est:8000-12000

AMARAL, Antonio Henrique (1935-) Brazilian
£10191 $16000 €15287 Battlefield 27 (151x151cm-59x59in) s.d.1974 s.i.d.verso. 19-Nov-2 Sotheby's, New York #106/R est:55000

AMAT, Frederic (1953-) Spanish
£530 $864 €800 Untitled (27x21cm-11x8in) s. acrylic paper on board prov. 11-Feb-3 Segre, Madrid #214/R
£2258 $3568 €3500 Untitled (100x200cm-39x79in) s. acrylic wax paper prov. 17-Dec-2 Segre, Madrid #174/R
£3774 $5887 €6000 Pou Mort i Ma (76x104cm-30x41in) s.d.1989 oil wax varnish paper on board exhib.lit. 17-Sep-2 Segre, Madrid #165/R
Works on paper
£1572 $2437 €2500 Machine (72x101cm-28x40in) s. wax pigment paper pulp prov. 30-Oct-2 Artcurial Briest, Paris #629 est:4000-5000
£1974 $3197 €3000 Composition (100x73cm-39x29in) s.d.75-76 mixed media collage. 21-Jan-3 Ansorena, Madrid #304/R est:3000

AMAT, Gabriel (1899-1984) Spanish
£273 $398 €420 Boats (22x31cm-9x12in) s. 17-Jun-2 Ansorena, Madrid #126/R

AMAT, Josep (1901-1991) Spanish
£993 $1609 €1400 Pescadores en en puerto (11x16cm-4x6in) s.d.1913 i.verso panel. 20-May-3 Segre, Madrid #298/R

AMATO, Luigi (20th C) Italian
£348 $543 €522 Seated female nude (100x70cm-39x28in) s. 16-Sep-2 Philippe Schuler, Zurich #6400 (S.FR 800)
£1397 $2180 €2096 Female nude (100x70cm-39x28in) s. 20-Nov-2 Fischer, Luzern #1119/R est:2000-3500 (S.FR 3200)

AMATO, Orazio (1884-1952) Italian
£753 $1175 €1100 Rome from Monte Mario (25x34cm-10x13in) s. board. 10-Apr-3 Finarte Semenzato, Rome #166/R

AMATRUDA, Marilyn (1947-) ?
£702 $1109 €1053 Still life with bust (91x98cm-36x39in) s.d.86. 17-Dec-2 Grev Wedels Plass, Oslo #203/R (N.KR 8000)

AMAURY-DUVAL (1808-1885) French
Works on paper
£833 $1308 €1300 Portrait de femme (48x37cm-19x15in) s. wash dr. 11-Dec-2 Maigret, Paris #140

AMAYA, Armando (1935-) Mexican
Sculpture
£1196 $1866 €1794 Mujer recostada (43x49x33cm-17x19x13in) s.d.1988 bronze. 17-Oct-2 Louis Morton, Mexico #144/R est:23000-25000 (M.P 19000)

AMBERG, Wilhelm (attrib) (1822-1899) German
£1096 $1710 €1600 Peaceful vigil (56x37cm-22x15in) s. prov. 9-Apr-3 Neumeister, Munich #641/R est:250

AMBLER, Christopher Gifford (1886-?) British
Works on paper
£320 $499 €480 Study of a terrier. Humorous sketch (18x17cm-7x7in) s. col chk pen ink sketch double-sided. 9-Oct-2 Woolley & Wallis, Salisbury #134/R
£480 $758 €720 Head of a wirehaired terrier (18x18cm-7x7in) s. col chk. 28-Nov-2 Christie's, Kensington #290/R
£1534 $2500 €2301 Studies of pugs (47x35cm-19x14in) s. pen ink wash. 11-Feb-3 Bonhams & Doyles, New York #59/R est:1200-1800

AMBROGIANI, Pierre (1907-1985) French
£253 $395 €400 Palette (63x51cm-25x20in) s. panel. 20-Oct-2 Chayette & Cheval, Paris #51/R
£449 $704 €700 Acrobates (21x17cm-8x7in) s. cardboard. 10-Dec-2 Renaud, Paris #62
£949 $1481 €1500 Jeune homme a la veste bleue (73x60cm-29x24in) s. 20-Oct-2 Chayette & Cheval, Paris #50
£1013 $1580 €1600 Personnage de theatre (38x46cm-15x18in) 20-Oct-2 Chayette & Cheval, Paris #48
£1019 $1590 €1600 Couple de danseurs (26x35cm-10x14in) s. panel. 10-Nov-2 Eric Pillon, Calais #225/R
£1019 $1590 €1600 Danseurs et musiciens (27x34cm-11x13in) s. panel. 10-Nov-2 Eric Pillon, Calais #222/R
£1216 $1897 €1800 Rivage et barque (50x65cm-20x26in) s. paper on canvas. 31-Mar-3 Rossini, Paris #66/R
£1392 $2158 €2200 Port mediterraneen (45x43cm-18x17in) s. oil paint panel. 29-Sep-2 Eric Pillon, Calais #284/R
£1419 $2243 €2200 Portrait de femme (55x46cm-22x18in) s. 19-Dec-2 Claude Aguttes, Neuilly #229/R
£1456 $2271 €2300 Femme au marche (55x34cm-22x13in) s. 20-Oct-2 Chayette & Cheval, Paris #33
£1678 $2803 €2400 Le gardien de but (81x40cm-32x16in) s. s.i.verso. 26-Jun-3 Tajan, Paris #283 est:2400-3000
£1709 $2666 €2700 Nature morte au compotier (54x80cm-21x31in) s. 20-Oct-2 Chayette & Cheval, Paris #31

£1709	$2666	€2700	Cavaliers et figures (65x46cm-26x18in) s. 20-Oct-2 Chayette & Cheval, Paris #46
£1709	$2666	€2700	Fleurs (79x40cm-31x16in) s. 20-Oct-2 Chayette & Cheval, Paris #49
£1772	$2747	€2800	Paysan dans le Vaucluse (50x25cm-20x10in) s. i.verso. 29-Sep-2 Eric Pillon, Calais #283/R
£1772	$2800	€2800	Bles (27x41cm-11x16in) s. s.i.verso. 27-Nov-2 Blanchet, Paris #89/R
£1799	$2878	€2500	Barque sur la plage (51x65cm-20x26in) s. paper on canvas. 18-May-3 Eric Pillon, Calais #142/R
£1835	$2863	€2900	Fenaison (65x54cm-26x21in) s. 20-Oct-2 Chayette & Cheval, Paris #43/R
£2025	$3159	€3200	Fleurs (73x60cm-29x24in) s. 20-Oct-2 Chayette & Cheval, Paris #41
£2089	$3258	€3300	Fenaison (50x65cm-20x26in) 20-Oct-2 Chayette & Cheval, Paris #44
£2098	$3504	€3000	Paseo dans l'Arene (54x73cm-21x29in) s. s.i.verso panel. 26-Jun-3 Tajan, Paris #282/R est:3000-4000
£2215	$3456	€3500	Scene de corrida (54x73cm-21x29in) s. 20-Oct-2 Chayette & Cheval, Paris #40
£2215	$3456	€3500	Fleurs (73x60cm-29x24in) s. 20-Oct-2 Chayette & Cheval, Paris #34
£2374	$3799	€3300	Paysage de Provence (50x61cm-20x24in) s. 18-May-3 Eric Pillon, Calais #144/R
£2532	$3949	€4000	Fleurs (72x60cm-28x24in) s. 20-Oct-2 Chayette & Cheval, Paris #35/R
£2548	$3975	€4000	Bord de mer (50x65cm-20x26in) s. 10-Nov-2 Eric Pillon, Calais #280/R
£2581	$4077	€4000	Bouquet (65x54cm-26x21in) s. 19-Dec-2 Claude Aguttes, Neuilly #228/R est:4000
£2595	$4048	€4100	Vase blanc (72x60cm-28x24in) s. 20-Oct-2 Chayette & Cheval, Paris #36
£2658	$4147	€4200	Fleurs (81x60cm-32x24in) s. 20-Oct-2 Chayette & Cheval, Paris #28
£2658	$4147	€4200	Remorqueur traversant la ville (54x81cm-21x32in) s. 20-Oct-2 Chayette & Cheval, Paris #30/R
£2658	$4147	€4200	Toreador (100x50cm-39x20in) s. 20-Oct-2 Chayette & Cheval, Paris #45/R
£2878	$4604	€4000	La corrida (46x65cm-18x26in) s. panel. 18-May-3 Eric Pillon, Calais #143/R
£3333	$5167	€5200	Clown (81x65cm-32x26in) s. 4-Dec-2 Pierre Berge, Paris #125/R
£3395	$4821	€5500	Vase de fleurs (73x60cm-29x24in) s. 16-Mar-3 Eric Pillon, Calais #260/R
£3462	$5435	€5400	Maison jaune (60x73cm-24x29in) s.i. 15-Dec-2 Thierry & Lannon, Brest #96/R
£3734	$5825	€5900	Violon rouge (56x74cm-22x29in) s. prov. 20-Oct-2 Chayette & Cheval, Paris #39
£3734	$5825	€5900	Avant la corrida (54x73cm-21x29in) s. d.1963 verso. 20-Oct-2 Chayette & Cheval, Paris #37/R
£3797	$5924	€6000	VUe de Brantes (80x60cm-31x24in) s. 20-Oct-2 Chayette & Cheval, Paris #42
£4304	$6671	€6800	Le model (54x73cm-21x29in) s. panel painted c.1960 prov. 28-Sep-2 Christie's, Paris #42/R est:4000-6000
£4490	$7139	€6600	La corrida (81x60cm-32x24in) s.d.27.3.63 verso panel. 26-Feb-3 Artcurial Briest, Paris #310/R est:5500-6500
£4747	$7405	€7500	Cartouzes (57x73cm-22x29in) 20-Oct-2 Chayette & Cheval, Paris #32/R
£4747	$7405	€7500	Paysage de Provence (60x73cm-24x29in) 20-Oct-2 Chayette & Cheval, Paris #47
£7278	$11354	€11500	Paysage de Provence (81x60cm-32x24in) s. 20-Oct-2 Chayette & Cheval, Paris #27/R

Works on paper

£314	$484	€500	Portrait de Marrakechi (25x19cm-10x7in) s.d.49 crayon W/C. 23-Oct-2 Rabourdin & Choppin de Janvry, Paris #252/R
£362	$586	€550	Nu assis (63x47cm-25x19in) s. ink dr. 22-Jan-3 Tajan, Paris #208
£451	$713	€650	Scene de tauromachie (25x34cm-10x13in) s. wash dr. 25-Apr-3 Piasa, Paris #46
£475	$741	€750	Paysage (36x44cm-14x17in) s. gouache. 20-Oct-2 Chayette & Cheval, Paris #52
£710	$1121	€1100	Baux de Provence (35x55cm-14x22in) s. gouache. 19-Dec-2 Delvaux, Paris #33
£823	$1284	€1300	Figures (32x49cm-13x19in) s. gouache pair. 20-Oct-2 Chayette & Cheval, Paris #54

AMBROGIO, P (19th C) ?

Works on paper

£2200	$3652	€3190	Three masted Spanish barque Palma of Mallorca off Marseilles (42x60cm-17x24in) s.i. pencil pen ink W/C. 12-Jun-3 Christie's, London #553/R est:1000-1500

AMBROSE, John (?) British

£300	$471	€450	Walk by the river (29x39cm-11x15in) s. card. 10-Dec-2 Lane, Penzance #13
£360	$562	€540	Dogana, Venice (38x49cm-15x19in) s. board. 15-Oct-2 Bonhams, Knightsbridge #24/R
£420	$701	€609	Harbour, St Ives (45x51cm-18x20in) s. board. 17-Jun-3 Bonhams, Knightsbridge #5/R
£460	$718	€667	Bells mill bridge, Wordsley (66x91cm-26x36in) s.d.1978. 27-Mar-3 Lane, Penzance #151

AMBROSI, Gustinus (1893-1975) Austrian

£1761	$2730	€2800	Female nude (32cm-13xin) 3-Oct-2 Dorotheum, Vienna #185/R est:1500-1800

Sculpture

£1258	$1950	€2000	Eternal longing (34cm-13in) i.d. verso plaster. 3-Oct-2 Dorotheum, Vienna #174/R est:3800-4400
£1635	$2535	€2600	Orpheus and Eyridike (52cm-20in) s.d.1919 plaster model. 3-Oct-2 Dorotheum, Vienna #180/R est:4500-4800
£1761	$2730	€2800	Two men (16cm-6in) s.d.1911 dark pat.bronze. 3-Oct-2 Dorotheum, Vienna #181/R est:5500-6500
£2885	$4500	€4328	Opus (116cm-46in) i. bronze. 20-Sep-2 Sloan, North Bethesda #285a/R est:1000-1500
£4800	$7488	€7200	Cain's guilt (119cm-47in) s.d.1927 brown green pat bronze lit. 9-Apr-3 Sotheby's, London #211/R est:5000-7000
£11321	$17547	€18000	Eve after the fall of man. s.d.1932 pat.bronze. 3-Oct-2 Dorotheum, Vienna #182/R est:8000-10000

AMEGLIO, Mario (1897-1970) French

£256	$400	€384	Le pont neuf, Paris (33x46cm-13x18in) s. i.d.verso. 9-Oct-2 Doyle, New York #1
£458	$750	€700	Rue commercante (49x59cm-19x23in) s. 7-Feb-3 Oger, Dumont, Paris #46
£480	$749	€720	Venezia, Piazza St Marco et St Giorgio (38x50cm-15x20in) s. i. verso. 6-Nov-2 Dobiaschofsky, Bern #315/R (S.FR 1100)
£637	$994	€1000	Calanques de Piana (24x35cm-9x14in) s. panel. 10-Nov-2 Eric Pillon, Calais #108/R
£897	$1409	€1400	Montmartre sous la neige (46x56cm-18x22in) s. 11-Dec-2 Maigret, Paris #154/R
£900	$1413	€1350	Fishing boats at a Mediterranean town. Fishing vessels in still waters (22x26cm-9x10in) s. board pair. 16-Apr-3 Christie's, Kensington #822/R
£903	$1400	€1355	Busy village street (96x60cm-38x24in) s. 2-Oct-2 Christie's, Rockefeller NY #764/R est:1500-2000
£1081	$1686	€1600	Rues des Martyrs et la Sacre Coeur (73x60cm-29x24in) s. s.i.verso. 25-Mar-3 Chochon-Barre & Allardi, Paris #58/R est:1200-1500
£1127	$1814	€1600	La place du Tertre (46x55cm-18x22in) s. 12-May-3 Lesieur & Le Bars, Le Havre #1/R
£1295	$2072	€1800	Paris, le Rond-Point des Champs-Elysees (59x71cm-23x28in) s. 18-May-3 Eric Pillon, Calais #107/R
£1582	$2468	€2500	Vues de ports mediterraneens (45x55cm-18x22in) panel oval pair. 20-Oct-2 Chayette & Cheval, Paris #73
£1592	$2484	€2500	Montmartre, rue sous la neige (46x55cm-18x22in) s. 10-Nov-2 Eric Pillon, Calais #141/R
£1720	$2683	€2700	Paris, Moulin Rouge (46x55cm-18x22in) s.d.1955. 10-Nov-2 Eric Pillon, Calais #142/R

AMELIN, Albin (1902-1975) Swedish

£610	$969	€915	Farming landscape (44x58cm-17x23in) s.d.27 cardboard. 3-Mar-3 Lilla Bukowskis, Stockholm #148 (S.KR 8200)
£1200	$1884	€1740	Untitled. prov. 15-Dec-2 Anders Antik, Landskrona #1203 est:15000-20000 (S.KR 17000)
£1313	$2179	€1904	Factory workers (91x72cm-36x28in) s.d.50 prov. 16-Jun-3 Lilla Bukowskis, Stockholm #278 est:15000 (S.KR 17000)
£1853	$3076	€2687	Still life of flowers (60x75cm-24x30in) s.d.30 cardboard. 16-Jun-3 Lilla Bukowskis, Stockholm #408 est:25000-30000 (S.KR 24000)
£2032	$3170	€3048	Seated model (130x96cm-51x38in) s.d.40 exhib. 5-Nov-2 Bukowskis, Stockholm #156/R est:20000-25000 (S.KR 29000)
£4247	$6838	€6371	Still life of bird's of Paradise, iris and white amaryllis (100x81cm-39x32in) s.d.41. 7-May-3 AB Stockholms Auktionsverk #755/R est:70000-80000 (S.KR 55000)
£4765	$7434	€7148	Still life of flowers (94x74cm-37x29in) s.d.49 prov. 5-Nov-2 Bukowskis, Stockholm #30/R est:80000-100000 (S.KR 68000)
£4867	$7690	€7301	Still life of flowers (82x65cm-32x26in) s. 28-Apr-3 Bukowskis, Stockholm #163/R est:70000-80000 (S.KR 64000)
£4943	$7810	€7415	Still life of flowers in brown jug (92x72cm-36x28in) s.d.48. 28-Apr-3 Bukowskis, Stockholm #209/R est:80000-100000 (S.KR 65000)
£5019	$7930	€7529	Still life of flowers and jugs (97x130cm-38x51in) s.d.41 prov. 28-Apr-3 Bukowskis, Stockholm #166/R est:80000-100000 (S.KR 66000)
£6307	$9839	€9461	Still life of flowers and statuette (130x95cm-51x37in) s. 5-Nov-2 Bukowskis, Stockholm #158/R est:100000-125000 (S.KR 90000)
£7008	$10932	€10512	Still life of flowers (116x99cm-46x39in) s.d.48. 6-Nov-2 AB Stockholms Auktionsverk #634/R est:125000-150000 (S.KR 100000)
£8059	$12572	€12089	Still life of flowers (100x81cm-39x32in) s.d.45. 5-Nov-2 Bukowskis, Stockholm #158a/R est:100000-125000 (S.KR 115000)

Works on paper

£1544	$2564	€2239	Workers (86x68cm-34x27in) s. gouache. 16-Jun-3 Lilla Bukowskis, Stockholm #409 est:25000-30000 (S.KR 20000)

£1622 $2692 €2352 Three workers (70x100cm-28x39in) s.d.59 gouache. 16-Jun-3 Lilla Bukowskis, Stockholm #407/R est:25000-30000 (S.KR 21000)
£1931 $3108 €2897 Still life of flowers (98x68cm-39x27in) s.d.47 gouache. 7-May-3 AB Stockholms Auktionsverk #682/R est:30000-40000 (S.KR 25000)
£3629 $5843 €5444 Anemones in jug (73x52cm-29x20in) s.d.41 mixed media panel. 7-May-3 AB Stockholms Auktionsverk #846/R est:35000-40000 (S.KR 47000)

AMENNECIER, Mary Antoinette (1888-1960) French
Works on paper
£449 $704 €700 Femmes des iles (29x39cm-11x15in) crayon sanguine chk. 15-Dec-2 Thierry & Lannon, Brest #21

AMER, Ghada (1963-) Egyptian
£5625 $9000 €8438 Untitled 3 - Composition orange (43x42cm-17x17in) s.d.98 acrylic embroidery prov.exhib. 16-May-3 Phillips, New York #102/R est:7000-9000
Works on paper
£833 $1325 €1200 Sans titre, arbre, elephant et etoiles (28x30cm-11x12in) s.d.92 pastel col crayon prov. 29-Apr-3 Artcurial Briest, Paris #471/R
£1923 $3019 €3000 Untitled (26x24cm-10x9in) crayon decoupage prov. 11-Dec-2 Artcurial Briest, Paris #807/R
£4375 $7000 €6563 Untitled no.68 (51x50cm-20x20in) s. i.d.97 on overlap embroidery fixative gel on canvas prov. 14-May-3 Sotheby's, New York #320/R est:8000-12000

AMERICAN SCHOOL
£9868 $15000 €14802 Eagle with sunburst, sky and clouds (41x137cm-16x54in) 17-Aug-2 North East Auctions, Portsmouth #307/R est:8000-12000
Prints
£3026 $4600 €4539 Bird's eye view of Philadelphia (66x89cm-26x35in) hand col lithograph. 17-Aug-2 North East Auctions, Portsmouth #51/R

AMERICAN SCHOOL, 18th/19th C
£7911 $12500 €11867 Triple portrait of children of the Harwood family (104x130cm-41x51in) three part frame. 30-Nov-2 Thomaston Place, Thomaston #75

AMERICAN SCHOOL, 19th C
£3915 $6500 €5677 Figures walking along a country path by a river (30x59cm-12x23in) init. prov. 11-Jun-3 Butterfields, San Francisco #4009/R est:3000-5000
£4037 $6500 €6056 Boy seated in a Windsor chair with a cardinal on his hand (69x56cm-27x22in) prov. 18-Jan-3 Sotheby's, New York #955/R est:2000-3000
£4375 $7000 €6344 The catch, a Hudson River fishing scene (43x61cm-17x24in) 16-May-3 Skinner, Boston #56/R est:4000-6000
£4487 $7000 €6731 Mr and Mrs E Grove Lawrence and family (76x124cm-30x49in) two joined panels. 14-Sep-2 Selkirks, St. Louis #116/R est:12000-16000
£4487 $7000 €6731 Portrait of young sister and brother (91x74cm-36x29in) 21-Sep-2 Nadeau, Windsor #175/R est:6000-9000
£5031 $8000 €7547 Canada Southern railway at Niagara Falls (76x122cm-30x48in) 1-Mar-3 North East Auctions, Portsmouth #766/R
£5500 $9185 €8250 Panning for gold in California (46x61cm-18x24in) board. 18-Jun-3 Christie's, Kensington #177/R est:1500-2000
£5556 $9000 €8056 Capture of Fort Fisher (84x112cm-33x44in) 29-Jul-3 Christie's, Rockefeller NY #160/R est:12000-18000
£6296 $10200 €9129 Home of a senior naval officer along the banks of river (67x104cm-26x41in) painted c.1870 or possibly by British School. 22-May-3 Sotheby's, New York #751
£6918 $11000 €10377 Portrait of a chief, in manner of an upper Missouri river Indian, possibly Mandan (48x38cm-19x15in) 5-Mar-3 Sotheby's, New York #117/R est:12000-18000
£9615 $15000 €14423 Portrait of General Zachary Taylor (76x64cm-30x25in) prov. 20-Sep-2 New Orleans Auction, New Orleans #1220/R est:18000-25000
£9938 $16000 €14907 Wedding portraits of David B Lewis and Susan Bill Lewis (19x25cm-7x10in) two prov. 16-Jan-3 Christie's, Rockefeller NY #405/R est:12000-18000
£9938 $16000 €14907 View of the Capitol (46x61cm-18x24in) i.verso prov. 18-Jan-3 Sotheby's, New York #977/R est:2000-3000
£9938 $16000 €14907 Washington elm, Cambridge, Mass (63x76cm-25x30in) painted c.1840. 18-Jan-3 Sotheby's, New York #830/R est:4000-6000
£11180 $18000 €16770 Tortoiseshell cat playing with caged mouse (32x43cm-13x17in) panel painted c.1850. 18-Jan-3 Sotheby's, New York #913/R est:2000-3000
£28659 $47000 €41556 Two yachting scenes (64x76cm-25x30in) pair. 8-Jun-3 Skinner, Boston #190/R est:600-800
Sculpture
£5280 $8500 €7920 Spread wing eagle (41x20cm-16x8in) carved gilded pine. 16-Jan-3 Christie's, Rockefeller NY #235/R est:3000-5000
£5926 $9600 €8593 Indian weather vane (104x102cm-41x40in) molded copper. 22-May-3 Sotheby's, New York #779
£29630 $48000 €42964 George Washington (100cm-39in) carved walnut exec.c.1876 exhib. 22-May-3 Sotheby's, New York #780
£62963 $102000 €91296 Punch figure (160cm-63in) i. painted pine composition box. 22-May-3 Sotheby's, New York #783
£251852 $408000 €365185 Liberty with shield and eagle (94cm-37in) carved pine. 22-May-3 Sotheby's, New York #784
Works on paper
£5096 $8000 €7644 Two large watermelon slices (30x41cm-12x16in) W/C prov. 23-Nov-2 Pook & Pook, Downington #72/R est:1200-1800
£15854 $26000 €22988 Portrait of James L Arnold aged 7 years (20x15cm-8x6in) i. i.verso W/C. 8-Jun-3 Skinner, Boston #223/R est:1500-2500

AMERICAN SCHOOL, 20th C
£3125 $4750 €4688 Sidewheel steamer, C Vibbard (58x69cm-23x27in) i. paper. 17-Aug-2 North East Auctions, Portsmouth #568/R
Photographs
£2597 $4000 €3896 Frenchman weeping as French flags leave just ahead of German's (39x49cm-15x19in) oversized photograph exhib. 22-Oct-2 Sotheby's, New York #195/R est:3000-5000
£7927 $13000 €11891 Views of America (20x30cm-8x12in) s. silver chromogenic col prints seven portfolio. 10-Feb-3 Swann Galleries, New York #90/R est:10000-15000
£10625 $17000 €15938 American scenes. i. portfolio photograph. 15-May-3 Swann Galleries, New York #141/R est:10000-15000
Prints
£34000 $56100 €49300 Untitled (76x61cm-30x24in) s.i.num.32/200 col screenprint set of eleven portfolio. 2-Jul-3 Christie's, London #341/R est:25000-35000
Sculpture
£5449 $8500 €8174 Untitled, reclining semi nude lady (38x64x30cm-15x25x12in) gilt bronze exec.c.1920. 20-Sep-2 Du Mouchelle, Detroit #35/R est:6000-8000

AMERLING, Friedrich von (1803-1887) Austrian
£2013 $3119 €3200 Man's portrait (54x41cm-21x16in) s.d.848. 29-Oct-2 Dorotheum, Vienna #139/R est:2600-3000
£2436 $3824 €3800 Young lady with red neck scarf (55x45cm-22x18in) s. indis.i.verso. 10-Dec-2 Dorotheum, Vienna #122/R est:3200-4000
£48000 $78720 €72000 In traumen versunken - pensive moment (56x45cm-22x18in) painted c.1835 lit. 3-Jun-3 Sotheby's, London #10/R est:12000-18000
Works on paper
£5072 $8319 €7000 Pope sitting. Love sick girl with song-book. Girl on sofa (24x17cm-9x7in) ink wash ten. 27-May-3 Hassfurther, Vienna #19/R est:8000-10000

AMERLING, Friedrich von (attrib) (1803-1887) Austrian
£2830 $4387 €4500 Girl's portrait (41x33cm-16x13in) 29-Oct-2 Dorotheum, Vienna #172/R est:1800-2000

AMESEDER, Eduard (1856-1938) Austrian
£448 $717 €650 Ships at anchor (65x92cm-26x36in) 11-Mar-3 Dorotheum, Vienna #122/R
£694 $1097 €1000 Camogli harbour, Riviera, Levante (79x18cm-31x7in) s.d.1931 panel. 24-Apr-3 Dorotheum, Vienna #90/R
£764 $1207 €1100 Church in Modling (76x59cm-30x23in) s. 24-Apr-3 Dorotheum, Vienna #52/R

AMICIS, Cristoforo de (1902-1987) Italian
£1736 $2760 €2500 Still life with glass (35x55cm-14x22in) s. s.i.verso. 1-May-3 Meeting Art, Vercelli #581
£3205 $5032 €5000 Grey still life (80x60cm-31x24in) s.d.1943 lit. 23-Nov-2 Meeting Art, Vercelli #446/R
Works on paper
£333 $523 €520 Still life (50x40cm-20x16in) s.d.1980 W/C pencil paper on canvas. 19-Nov-2 Finarte, Milan #58

AMICK, Robert Wesley (1879-1969) American

£1346 $2100 €2019 Plowman in a Western Valley (48x69cm-19x27in) 19-Oct-2 David Dike, Dallas #211/R est:4000-6000
£5161 $8000 €7742 Pioneers (66x120cm-26x47in) s. prov. 4-Dec-2 Sotheby's, New York #150/R est:8000-12000

AMICONI, Bernardo (19th C) Italian

£4600 $7176 €6900 Portrait of a young lady (143x117cm-56x46in) s.d.1874. 10-Sep-2 Bonhams, Knightsbridge #284/R est:5000-7000

AMIET, Cuno (1868-1961) Swiss

£687 $1085 €1031 Fountain of youth (19x14cm-7x6in) i.verso paper. 26-Nov-2 Hans Widmer, St Gallen #1004 est:1600-1800 (S.FR 1600)
£2174 $3370 €3261 Cityscape (22x16cm-9x6in) mono.d.39 panel. 4-Dec-2 Koller, Zurich #145/R est:4000-6000 (S.FR 5000)
£3774 $6113 €6680 Autumn meadow (74x12cm-29x5in) s. 26-May-3 Sotheby's, Zurich #35/R est:120000-150000 (S.FR 8000)
£6481 $10435 €9397 Walkers in the snow (23x28cm-9x11in) mono. board. 9-May-3 Dobiaschofsky, Bern #118/R est:9000 (S.FR 14000)
£6987 $10201 €10481 Still life of flowers (61x50cm-24x20in) mono.d.1960. 4-Jun-2 Germann, Zurich #66/R est:12000-18000 (S.FR 16000)
£7048 $10291 €10572 Self portrait (40x37cm-16x15in) s.d.1937 prov. 17-Jun-2 Philippe Schuler, Zurich #4251/R est:20000-25000 (S.FR 16000)
£11159 $17631 €16739 Roses in a glass vase (55x45cm-22x18in) mono.d.1934 prov. 29-Nov-2 Zofingen, Switzerland #2766/R est:30000 (S.FR 26000)
£11792 $19104 €20873 Portrait of young girl, Susanne (55x46cm-22x18in) mono.d. canvas on board. 26-May-3 Sotheby's, Zurich #122/R est:18000-22000 (S.FR 25000)
£12017 $18987 €18026 Summer garden (35x45cm-14x18in) mono.d.51 panel. 28-Nov-2 Christie's, Zurich #50/R est:25000-30000 (S.FR 28000)
£14847 $21677 €22271 Stormy landscape (32x41cm-13x16in) mono.d.1947 board. 4-Jun-2 Germann, Zurich #72/R est:28000-38000 (S.FR 34000)
£15419 $22511 €23129 Anna Amiet sewing (61x40cm-24x16in) mono.d.1944 prov. 17-Jun-2 Philippe Schuler, Zurich #4252/R est:24000-28000 (S.FR 35000)
£23605 $37296 €35408 Study of a ploughman (54x73cm-21x29in) mono.d.33 s.i.d.33 verso. 26-Nov-2 Phillips, Zurich #22/R est:40000-60000 (S.FR 55000)
£23853 $39835 €34587 Still life with flowers in vase (60x55cm-24x22in) mono.d.15 mono.i. stretcher prov. 20-Jun-3 Kornfeld, Bern #1/R est:60000 (S.FR 52000)
£30837 $45022 €46256 Strawberry girl (81x60cm-32x24in) s.mono.d.1889 prov. 17-Jun-2 Philippe Schuler, Zurich #4250/R est:30000-40000 (S.FR 70000)
£34335 $54249 €51503 View from the studio window in the garden of Oschwand (55x60cm-22x24in) mono.d.25. 26-Nov-2 Phillips, Zurich #70/R est:80000-100000 (S.FR 80000)
£48035 $75415 €72053 Lake Thun (46x61cm-18x24in) mono.d.1932. 25-Nov-2 Sotheby's, Zurich #99/R est:45000-55000 (S.FR 110000)
£52752 $88096 €76490 Popies and cornflowers in field (55x60cm-22x24in) mono.d.29 i. stretcher oil varnish prov. 20-Jun-3 Kornfeld, Bern #3/R est:110000 (S.FR 115000)
£128755 $203433 €193133 Fruit harvest - green apple harvest (55x60cm-22x24in) mono.d.08 prov.exhib.lit. 28-Nov-2 Christie's, Zurich #30/R est:300000-400000 (S.FR 300000)

Works on paper

£330 $482 €495 Girl in garden (33x32cm-13x13in) mono.d.1945 pencil. 17-Jun-2 Philippe Schuler, Zurich #4151 (S.FR 750)
£437 $681 €656 Self portrait (15x10cm-6x4in) mono. pencil. 6-Nov-2 Dobiaschofsky, Bern #1352/R (S.FR 1000)
£498 $831 €722 Kneeling boy (25x20cm-10x8in) mono. chl. 24-Jun-3 Koller, Zurich #45/R (S.FR 1100)
£742 $1158 €1113 Man sleeping in chair (21x11cm-8x4in) mono. mixed media. 6-Nov-2 Dobiaschofsky, Bern #1353/R (S.FR 1700)
£793 $1158 €1190 Girl's portrait (29x20cm-11x8in) mono.d.1946 Indian ink wask. 17-Jun-2 Philippe Schuler, Zurich #4152/R (S.FR 1800)
£860 $1436 €1247 Two kneeling boys (25x27cm-10x11in) mono. chl. 24-Jun-3 Koller, Zurich #46/R (S.FR 1900)
£969 $1415 €1454 Nymphenburg (15x17cm-6x7in) mono.i.d.1888 W/C. 17-Jun-2 Philippe Schuler, Zurich #4150/R (S.FR 2200)
£1502 $2373 €2253 Woman under apple tree (31x22cm-12x9in) mono.d.30 chl. 28-Nov-2 Christie's, Zurich #46/R est:2500-3500 (S.FR 3500)
£1718 $2508 €2577 Woodland stream (30x25cm-12x10in) mono. W/C over pencil chl. 17-Jun-2 Philippe Schuler, Zurich #4153/R est:2500-3000 (S.FR 3900)
£1747 $2742 €2621 Self portrait in front of painting (47x39cm-19x15in) mono. chl. 25-Nov-2 Sotheby's, Zurich #94/R est:4000-6000 (S.FR 4000)
£1852 $2981 €2685 Chateau St-Denis (20x26cm-8x10in) mono. d.39 i.verso W/C over pencil. 9-May-3 Dobiaschofsky, Bern #117/R est:6000 (S.FR 4000)
£2575 $4069 €3863 Winter on the Oschwand (27x34cm-11x13in) mono.d.55 W/C over pencil. 28-Nov-2 Christie's, Zurich #47/R est:2500-3000 (S.FR 6000)
£2736 $4432 €4842 Small snowy landscape (28x18cm-11x7in) mono.d.1921 pencil W/C. 26-May-3 Sotheby's, Zurich #126/R est:4000-6000 (S.FR 5800)
£3004 $4747 €4506 Hornberg from Kalberhoni (21x31cm-8x12in) mono.d.21 i.d.April 1921 verso W/C over pencil. 28-Nov-2 Christie's, Zurich #45/R est:7000-9000 (S.FR 7000)
£3077 $4831 €4800 Jeune bretonne en coiffe (29x22cm-11x9in) init. chl. 15-Dec-2 Thierry & Lannon, Brest #21a
£3620 $6045 €5249 Tree (24x29cm-9x11in) mono. W/C. 24-Jun-3 Koller, Zurich #44/R est:3000-5000 (S.FR 8000)

AMIGONI, Jacopo (1675-1752) Italian

£17000 $26520 €25500 Portrait of William Bateman (100x90cm-39x35in) oval prov. 8-Oct-2 Sotheby's, Olympia #378/R est:10000-15000

AMIGONI, Jacopo (attrib) (1675-1752) Italian

£10345 $16345 €15000 Faune and putti (148x163cm-58x64in) 5-Apr-3 Finarte Semenzato, Milan #122/R est:20000
£130890 $208115 €196335 Diane and Endymion (138x95cm-54x37in) 8-Mar-3 Dorotheum, Prague #34/R est:500000-750000 (C.KR 6000000)

Works on paper

£1049 $1500 €1574 Pan and Syrinx (19x27cm-7x11in) pen brown ink wash over red chk. 23-Jan-3 Swann Galleries, New York #120/R est:1500-2500

AMMAN, Jost (1539-1591) Swiss

Prints

£30000 $46500 €45000 Procession of the Doge in the Piazza San Marco, Venice (108x192cm-43x76in) woodcut on fourteen sheets executed c.1565. 3-Dec-2 Christie's, London #86/R est:30000-50000

AMMANN, Eugen (1882-1978) Swiss

£524 $828 €786 Landscape with three figures by water (119x134cm-47x53in) s. 14-Nov-2 Stuker, Bern #9/R (S.FR 1200)

AMODIO, Giulio (1868-?) Italian

£753 $1175 €1100 Neapolitan fisherman (78x63cm-31x25in) s. 10-Apr-3 Dorotheum, Vienna #167/R
£1489 $2413 €2100 Piccolo interno familiare (47x37cm-19x15in) s. 22-May-3 Stadion, Trieste #329/R est:1500-2000

AMOR, Rick (1948-) Australian

£383 $602 €575 Untitled (54x73cm-21x29in) s.d.Sept 89 acrylic on paper. 15-Apr-3 Lawson Menzies, Sydney #265/R est:1100-1400 (A.D 1000)
£1400 $2254 €2100 Hedges at Baxter (66x46cm-26x18in) s.d.84 s.i.d.verso. 6-May-3 Christie's, Melbourne #205/R est:3000-4000 (A.D 3500)
£1594 $2614 €2391 Cape Schank (35x61cm-14x24in) s.d.85 s.i.d.Jan 85 verso. 4-Jun-3 Deutscher-Menzies, Melbourne #111/R est:5000-7000 (A.D 4000)
£1992 $3267 €2988 Old baths at Elwood (44x72cm-17x28in) d.May 84 verso composition board. 4-Jun-3 Deutscher-Menzies, Melbourne #287a/R est:4000-6000 (A.D 5000)
£5714 $9029 €8571 Boy on the beach 2000 (61x80cm-24x31in) s.d.00 i.d.verso prov. 27-Nov-2 Deutscher-Menzies, Melbourne #12/R est:12000-16000 (A.D 16000)
£6154 $9785 €9231 Pillar (86x86cm-34x34in) s.d.92-00 i.d.May-June 92/Aug 00 verso prov. 4-Mar-3 Deutscher-Menzies, Melbourne #18/R est:14000-18000 (A.D 16000)
£6786 $10585 €10179 Carpark (80x65cm-31x26in) s.d.99 i.d.June/Jul 99 verso. 11-Nov-2 Deutscher-Menzies, Melbourne #1/R est:10000-15000 (A.D 19000)
£10000 $15600 €15000 The city, dusk (96x129cm-38x51in) s.d.93 s.i.d.June July 93 verso. 11-Nov-2 Deutscher-Menzies, Melbourne #32/R est:15000-20000 (A.D 28000)

Works on paper

£345 $514 €518 Mountains (55x74cm-22x29in) s.d.1/9/87 gouache. 27-Aug-2 Christie's, Melbourne #172 est:1000-1500 (A.D 900)
£423 $659 €635 Williamstown (54x74cm-21x29in) s. gouache. 21-Oct-2 Australian Art Auctions, Sydney #167 (A.D 1200)
£876 $1437 €1314 Willsmere, Kew (73x54cm-29x21in) s.i.d.11/3/82 chl. 4-Jun-3 Deutscher-Menzies, Melbourne #288/R (A.D 2200)
£1040 $1674 €1560 Figure on a pier (23x34cm-9x13in) s. gouache. 6-May-3 Christie's, Melbourne #379/R est:2500-3500 (A.D 2600)
£1357 $2144 €2036 Figure in street (36x47cm-14x19in) s.d.91 W/C pencil. 27-Nov-2 Deutscher-Menzies, Melbourne #165/R est:2000-3000 (A.D 3800)

£1692 $2691 €2538 Williamstown (54x74cm-21x29in) s.d.31/10/85 i.verso gouache. 4-Mar-3 Deutscher-Menzies, Melbourne #170/R est:3000-4000 (A.D 4400)

AMOROSI, Antonio (1660-1736) Italian
£3378 $5270 €5000 Boy with basket of cherries (49x39cm-19x15in) prov. 27-Mar-3 Dorotheum, Vienna #367/R est:5000-7000
£4392 $6851 €6500 Boy in landscape (30x32cm-12x13in) 27-Mar-3 Dorotheum, Vienna #1/R est:6000-9000
£19000 $29640 €28500 Boy and girl embracing in a palatial interior. Two children and a monkey (125x92cm-49x36in) pair. 23-Sep-2 Bonhams, Bayswater #403/R est:7000-10000

AMOROSI, Antonio (attrib) (1660-1736) Italian
£300 $467 €450 Portrait of a boy crying (24x19cm-9x7in) 19-Sep-2 Christie's, Kensington #281/R
£39744 $61603 €62000 Bashful boy with his mother and with six more figures (152x192cm-60x76in) canvas on canvas. 4-Dec-2 Neumeister, Munich #576/R est:6000

AMORSOLO, Fernando (1892-1972) Philippino
£3165 $5000 €4748 Spray of orchids (60x49cm-24x19in) s.i. board. 22-Apr-3 Butterfields, San Francisco #6041/R est:6000-8000
£6628 $10207 €9942 Rice field (36x45cm-14x18in) s.d.1952 canvas on board. 27-Oct-2 Christie's, Hong Kong #65/R est:90000-120000 (HK.D 80000)
£8861 $14000 €13292 Lavendera (65x50cm-26x20in) s.d.1956. 22-Apr-3 Butterfields, San Francisco #6042/R est:15000-20000
£13462 $21000 €20193 Washer women beside a river (46x56cm-18x22in) s.i.d.1936 masonite prov. 14-Sep-2 Weschler, Washington #579/R est:15000-25000
£14913 $22966 €22370 Bontoc Igorrotes (60x76cm-24x30in) s.d.1952 board. 27-Oct-2 Christie's, Hong Kong #68/R est:180000-220000 (HK.D 180000)
£16570 $25518 €24855 Ricefield (60x85cm-24x33in) s.d.1954. 27-Oct-2 Christie's, Hong Kong #69/R est:180000-280000 (HK.D 200000)
£18648 $30769 €27040 Winnowing rice (67x93cm-26x37in) s.d.1950. 6-Jul-3 Christie's, Hong Kong #43/R est:260000-300000 (HK.D 240000)
£45568 $70174 €68352 Under the mango tree (59x79cm-23x31in) s.d.1935. 27-Oct-2 Christie's, Hong Kong #67/R est:220000-320000 (HK.D 550000)
Works on paper
£5769 $9000 €8654 Untitled, market scene with horse and carriage (23x31cm-9x12in) s.d.1925 W/C graphite. 14-Oct-2 Butterfields, San Francisco #2128/R est:2000-3000

AMORT, Vilim (1864-?) Czechoslovakian
Sculpture
£1174 $1925 €1702 Seated child holding flaming torch aloft (41cm-16in) i.d.1894 dark pat.bronze. 4-Jun-3 Fischer, Luzern #1361/R est:2500-3000 (S.FR 2500)

AMOS, Anthony (20th C) British
£700 $1127 €1050 Workers in the dock (77x54cm-30x21in) s. paper on board. 14-Jan-3 Bonhams, Knightsbridge #177

AMOS, Arthur C (1892-1955) American
£321 $500 €482 Desert landscape with purple mountains and flowering grass (64x76cm-25x30in) s. 18-Sep-2 Alderfer's, Hatfield #264/R

AMOS, Imre (1907-1945) Hungarian
£2151 $3335 €3119 The good and the bad (35x35cm-14x14in) s.d.1938. 9-Dec-2 Mu Terem Galeria, Budapest #88/R est:600000 (H.F 800000)
£2689 $4168 €3899 On a moonlit yard (28x35cm-11x14in) s. tempera. 9-Dec-2 Mu Terem Galeria, Budapest #101/R est:650000 (H.F 1000000)
£4751 $7411 €7127 Szentendre (60x80cm-24x31in) s. 11-Apr-3 Kieselbach, Budapest #46/R est:1200000-1700000 (H.F 1700000)
Works on paper
£1006 $1569 €1509 Dream with flying clock (31x38cm-12x15in) s. W/C. 11-Apr-3 Kieselbach, Budapest #28/R est:250000-360000 (H.F 360000)
£1614 $2501 €2421 Still life with a lamp and a fluttering curtain in Szentendre (23x28cm-9x11in) s. mixed media. 6-Dec-2 Kieselbach, Budapest #19/R (H.F 600000)
£2151 $3335 €3227 Self portrait on the bank of the Seine with an angel (42x27cm-17x11in) s. W/C. 6-Dec-2 Kieselbach, Budapest #81/R (H.F 800000)
£3074 $4795 €4457 Dark times (58x45cm-23x18in) s.d.1941 ink gouache. 12-Apr-3 Mu Terem Galeria, Budapest #19/R est:480000 (H.F 1100000)

AMPENBERGER, Iris (1916-1981) South African
£442 $699 €663 Two children (54x47cm-21x19in) s. board. 1-Apr-3 Stephan Welz, Johannesburg #210 est:3000-5000 (SA.R 5500)

AMPENBERGER, Stefan (1908-1983) South African
£256 $400 €384 Farm cottages with mountains beyond (30x37cm-12x15in) s. canvas on board. 11-Nov-2 Stephan Welz, Johannesburg #278 (SA.R 4000)
£387 $623 €581 Extensive landscape with a house (37x43cm-15x17in) s. canvas on board. 12-May-3 Stephan Welz, Johannesburg #185 est:5000-7000 (SA.R 4500)
£645 $1038 €968 Taba nchu (37x47cm-15x19in) s. s.i.verso board. 12-May-3 Stephan Welz, Johannesburg #98 est:5000-7000 (SA.R 7500)

AMRHEIN, Wilhelm (1873-1926) Swiss
£1191 $1668 €1787 Swiss mountain wood in winter (65x80cm-26x31in) s.d.17. 29-Nov-1 Falk & Falk, Zurich #674/R est:1800 (S.FR 2800)

AMSDEN, William King (20th C) American
£2187 $3500 €3171 Landscapes (56x74cm-22x29in) s. two. 16-May-3 Skinner, Boston #198/R est:1800-2200

AMSHEWITZ, John Henry (1882-1942) British
£269 $420 €404 Comedy (58x43cm-23x17in) s. prov. 11-Nov-2 Stephan Welz, Johannesburg #477 (SA.R 4200)
£448 $700 €672 Arabesque (35x65cm-14x26in) s. board. 11-Nov-2 Stephan Welz, Johannesburg #478 (SA.R 7000)
£2408 $3876 €3612 Still life with a crystal ball, Chinese figurins and flowers (80x55cm-31x22in) s. board. 12-May-3 Stephan Welz, Johannesburg #574/R est:6000-9000 (SA.R 28000)

AMSTERDAM SCHOOL (17th C) Dutch
£10191 $15898 €16000 Portrait of a Jewish gentleman, wearing a black coat (33x24cm-13x9in) copper. 5-Nov-2 Sotheby's, Amsterdam #231/R est:4000-6000

AMUNDSEN, Hjalmar (20th C) Scandinavian
£793 $1300 €1190 Dying dune, Sag harbor. Fishing (20x25cm-8x10in) s. i.verso board two. 5-Feb-3 Doyle, New York #65/R

AMUNDSEN, Richard (1928-1998) American
Works on paper
£5696 $9000 €8259 Western North American wildlife series (38x64cm-15x25in) s. mixed media set of six. 26-Jul-3 Coeur d'Alene, Hayden #168/R est:10000-15000

AN, Julie (20th C) American
Photographs
£2096 $3500 €3039 Leopard print room (91x76cm-36x30in) s.verso col print. 25-Jun-3 Sotheby's, Moscow #195/R est:800-1000

ANANNY, Terry (1956-) Canadian
£289 $474 €419 Village en hiver (60x75cm-24x30in) s. acrylic. 9-Jun-3 Hodgins, Calgary #16/R (C.D 650)

ANASTASI, Auguste (1820-1889) French
£2177 $3461 €3200 Terrasse de couvent, Italie (39x68cm-15x27in) panel prov. 24-Mar-3 Fraysse & Associes, Paris #45/R
£3205 $4968 €5000 Cottage (39x64cm-15x25in) s.d.1850. 9-Dec-2 Beaussant & Lefèvre, Paris #23/R

ANATOL (1931-) German
£385 $596 €600 Puzzle (51x52cm-20x20in) s.i.d.1991 canvas cardboard on chipboard. 7-Dec-2 Van Ham, Cologne #6/R

ANCELLET, Émile (19/20th C) French
£1871 $2993 €2600 Les marais de Santes, printemps (41x61cm-16x24in) s.d.1900. 15-May-3 Christie's, Paris #318/R est:1500-2000

ANCHER, Anna (1859-1935) Danish
£1026 $1632 €1539 Seascape (16x24cm-6x9in) init.i. 5-May-3 Rasmussen, Vejle #258/R (D.KR 11000)
£3885 $6061 €5828 Interior scene with seated young woman (31x19cm-12x7in) 23-Sep-2 Rasmussen, Vejle #166/R est:20000 (D.KR 46000)
£4729 $7566 €7094 Mother and daughter - study for Missionary meeting (29x35cm-11x14in) 13-Jan-3 Rasmussen, Vejle #1/R est:50000-75000 (D.KR 54000)
£5028 $7994 €7542 Small girl (30x24cm-12x9in) s. 5-Mar-3 Rasmussen, Copenhagen #1519/R est:30000-40000 (D.KR 54000)

£11197 $17020 €16796 Clear moonlit night by Skagen Lighthouse (23x28cm-9x11in) init.d.1904 exhib. 27-Aug-2 Rasmussen, Copenhagen #1468/R est:125000 (D.KR 130000)
£13966 $22207 €20949 Three small sisters (44x61cm-17x24in) s.d.1916 exhib. 5-Mar-3 Rasmussen, Copenhagen #1503/R est:150000-200000 (D.KR 150000)
£21277 $33617 €31916 Three girls making garlands of flowers on bench in garden (52x63cm-20x25in) s.d.1919. 2-Dec-2 Rasmussen, Copenhagen #1118/R est:250000-300000 (D.KR 250000)
£23277 $37011 €34916 Young girls wearing white dressing singing in the morning (40x45cm-16x18in) s. panel. 5-Mar-3 Rasmussen, Copenhagen #1518/R est:300000-350000 (D.KR 250000)
£34043 $53787 €51065 Having dinner in the garden (62x78cm-24x31in) s.d.1917 exhib. 2-Dec-2 Rasmussen, Copenhagen #1110/R est:500000-700000 (D.KR 400000)

Works on paper

£559 $888 €839 Portrait of girl aged three or four (13x18cm-5x7in) s.d.1910 pencil. 5-Mar-3 Rasmussen, Copenhagen #2088/R (D.KR 6000)
£1149 $1815 €1724 Girl reading story book (22x14cm-9x6in) s. pencil chk sold with one by Lundbye and one by Saabye. 2-Dec-2 Rasmussen, Copenhagen #1821/R est:3000 (D.KR 13500)
£1171 $1886 €1757 Children playing Sleeping Beauty (15x20cm-6x8in) s. pencil study. 26-Feb-3 Museumsbygningen, Copenhagen #87 est:1500 (D.KR 13000)
£6982 $11311 €10124 Woman embroidering by window (57x37cm-22x15in) s. pastel. 26-May-3 Bukowskis, Stockholm #273/R est:100000-125000 (S.KR 90000)
£12920 $19638 €19380 Skagen woman with little Helga Ancher on her lap outside white house in sunshine (50x63cm-20x25in) s.d.89 pastel. 27-Aug-2 Rasmussen, Copenhagen #1467/R est:150000 (D.KR 150000)

ANCHER, Helga (1883-1964) Danish

£526 $853 €763 Pink flowers in silver cup (44x38cm-17x15in) init. i.verso panel. 26-May-3 Rasmussen, Copenhagen #1231/R (D.KR 5500)
£1637 $2488 €2456 Summer's day on the beach (30x40cm-12x16in) init.d.47 prov.exhib. 27-Aug-2 Rasmussen, Copenhagen #1483/R est:15000 (D.KR 19000)
£1665 $2564 €2498 Interior scene with the artist's mother Anna Ancher (29x24cm-11x9in) init. panel. 4-Sep-2 Kunsthallen, Copenhagen #149/R est:5000 (D.KR 19500)
£1702 $2689 €2553 Portrait of Jorgen Molt Wengel, 3 years old (41x33cm-16x13in) mono. panel. 2-Dec-2 Rasmussen, Copenhagen #1122/R est:15000 (D.KR 20000)

ANCHER, Michael (1849-1927) Danish

£861 $1309 €1292 Landscape from Fyrrebakken in Skagen (26x39cm-10x15in) init. study. 27-Aug-2 Rasmussen, Copenhagen #1741/R (D.KR 10000)
£1292 $1964 €1938 Portrait of old Christoffer (41x31cm-16x12in) init. 27-Aug-2 Rasmussen, Copenhagen #1480/R est:15000 (D.KR 15000)
£1583 $2517 €2375 Fisherman at the helm (34x26cm-13x10in) init.d.12. 10-Mar-3 Rasmussen, Vejle #65/R est:8000-10000 (D.KR 17000)
£1676 $2665 €2514 The harvester returning home on horseback, evening glow in background (61x44cm-24x17in) sketch. 10-Mar-3 Rasmussen, Vejle #66/R est:18000 (D.KR 18000)
£1699 $2651 €2549 The sheep shearer (25x19cm-10x7in) init. study. 5-Aug-2 Rasmussen, Vejle #19/R est:15000-20000 (D.KR 20000)
£2039 $3181 €3059 Portrait of Engel Saxild (46x40cm-18x16in) init. 5-Aug-2 Rasmussen, Vejle #21/R est:30000 (D.KR 24000)
£2083 $3458 €3020 A meeting (60x40cm-24x16in) init. panel. 12-Jun-3 Kunsthallen, Copenhagen #368/R est:30000 (D.KR 22000)
£2209 $3446 €3314 Portrait of a fishergirl (26x20cm-10x8in) init. 5-Aug-2 Rasmussen, Vejle #22/R est:20000 (D.KR 26000)
£2793 $4441 €4190 Beared fisherman (31x25cm-12x10in) init. 5-Mar-3 Rasmussen, Copenhagen #1508/R est:12000-15000 (D.KR 30000)
£2793 $4441 €4190 Lars Gaihede and two grandchildren (56x38cm-22x15in) s.d.1884. 10-Mar-3 Rasmussen, Vejle #49/R est:30000-40000 (D.KR 30000)
£2907 $4767 €4215 An old house at Skagen (54x41cm-21x16in) s. 4-Jun-3 AB Stockholms Auktionsverk #2464/R est:30000-35000 (S.KR 37000)
£3015 $4582 €4523 Lars Gaihede and his wife by the fireplace - Stifi stirring the pot (55x49cm-22x19in) prov. 27-Aug-2 Rasmussen, Copenhagen #1471/R est:30000-40000 (D.KR 35000)
£3015 $4582 €4523 The fisherman Lars Andersen (51x42cm-20x17in) init.d.24 i.stretcher. 27-Aug-2 Rasmussen, Copenhagen #1478/R est:35000 (D.KR 35000)
£3352 $5330 €5028 Interior scene with man and woman at table (30x41cm-12x16in) init. 10-Mar-3 Rasmussen, Vejle #59/R est:20000-30000 (D.KR 36000)
£4307 $6546 €6461 Skagen fisherman smoking a pipe (37x29cm-15x11in) init.d.09. 27-Aug-2 Rasmussen, Copenhagen #1481/R est:20000-30000 (D.KR 50000)
£4376 $6958 €6564 Interior scene with young lady in rocking chair, Ancher's sitting-room (27x21cm-11x8in) init. 10-Mar-3 Rasmussen, Vejle #50/R est:40000-60000 (D.KR 47000)
£4655 $7402 €6983 Two fishermen looking out to sea (74x58cm-29x23in) init.d.15. 5-Mar-3 Rasmussen, Copenhagen #1522/R est:50000-75000 (D.KR 50000)
£4737 $7201 €7106 Interior scene with two fishermen (74x95cm-29x37in) s. 27-Aug-2 Rasmussen, Copenhagen #1479/R est:60000 (D.KR 55000)
£4766 $7530 €7149 Anna Ancher reading aloud for her mother, Mrs Brondum (22x16cm-9x6in) init. study. 2-Dec-2 Rasmussen, Copenhagen #1432/R est:25000 (D.KR 56000)
£6331 $10067 €9497 Niels and Ane Gaihede in front of their house in Osterby (39x58cm-15x23in) init.d.1890. 5-Mar-3 Rasmussen, Copenhagen #1517/R est:75000-125000 (D.KR 68000)
£6460 $9819 €9690 Two fishermen wearing rainclothes looking out of window (54x48cm-21x19in) init.d.15. 27-Aug-2 Rasmussen, Copenhagen #1477/R est:60000 (D.KR 75000)
£6480 $10368 €9720 Lillian Zahle and her daughter Wanda (40x52cm-16x20in) init.d.10 prov. 13-Jan-3 Rasmussen, Vejle #2/R est:60000 (D.KR 74000)
£7263 $11547 €10895 At the inn - Lars Kruse and four other fishermen trying the snaps (35x42cm-14x17in) s.d.88 exhib. 5-Mar-3 Rasmussen, Copenhagen #1507/R est:50000-60000 (D.KR 78000)
£7449 $11844 €11174 Cinderella - young girl seated by fireplace with cat (106x103cm-42x41in) init. painted 1880-1882. 5-Mar-3 Rasmussen, Copenhagen #1525/R est:80000-120000 (D.KR 80000)
£12104 $19246 €18156 Fishermen pulling in net from boat (90x124cm-35x49in) s.d.1912. 5-Mar-3 Rasmussen, Copenhagen #1512/R est:125000-150000 (D.KR 130000)
£13169 $20544 €19754 Young girl seated in garden (82x69cm-32x27in) init. exhib. 5-Aug-2 Rasmussen, Vejle #16/R est:150000-200000 (D.KR 155000)
£24369 $38990 €36554 Young fishergirl putting stones on net (35x40cm-14x16in) s.indis.d.1885. 17-Mar-3 Blomqvist, Oslo #309/R est:100000-150000 (N.KR 280000)
£34451 $54777 €51677 Mrs Dinesen at Skagen Strand (54x42cm-21x17in) init.d.09. 5-Mar-3 Rasmussen, Copenhagen #1511/R est:300000-400000 (D.KR 370000)
£97872 $154638 €146808 Party in the old drawing room at Brondum's Hotel (80x64cm-31x25in) s.d.10. 2-Dec-2 Rasmussen, Copenhagen #1113/R est:1000000-1200000 (D.KR 1150000)

Works on paper

£372 $592 €558 Fisherwoman (24x16cm-9x6in) init. chl. 5-Mar-3 Rasmussen, Copenhagen #2139 (D.KR 4000)
£1532 $2466 €2298 Portrait of Lars Gaihede (22x16cm-9x6in) s.i.d.Juni 75 pen. 26-Feb-3 Museumsbygningen, Copenhagen #100/R est:3000 (D.KR 17000)

ANCKARSWARD, Michael Gustaf (1792-1878) Swedish

£1013 $1600 €1600 Norwegian farm buildings at a fjord with figures (20x29cm-8x11in) mono. 30-Nov-2 Berlinghof, Heidelberg #272/R est:1800

ANDENMATTEN, Leo (1922-1979) Swiss

£2096 $3270 €3144 Paysage Breton (38x55cm-15x22in) mono.d.54 canvas on board. 8-Nov-2 Dobiaschofsky, Bern #92/R est:4800 (S.FR 4800)

ANDERBOUHR, Paul-Jean (1909-) French

£263 $426 €400 Portrait de femme - Portrait of a woman (73x60cm-29x24in) s.i.verso. 21-Jan-3 Christie's, Amsterdam #424
£701 $1093 €1100 Paris, l'Institut (54x65cm-21x26in) s. 10-Nov-2 Eric Pillon, Calais #112/R
£710 $1121 €1100 Pont des Arts. s. 18-Dec-2 Ferri, Paris #24

ANDEREGG, Nora (1908-) Swiss

£283 $453 €425 St Gallen Rotmonten (46x54cm-18x21in) s.d. masonite. 17-Mar-3 Philippe Schuler, Zurich #8400 (S.FR 600)

ANDERLECHT, Engelbert van (1918-1961) Belgian
Works on paper
£321 $497 €500 Composition (30x26cm-12x10in) st.sig. verso W/C painted 1958. 7-Dec-2 De Vuyst, Lokeren #330/R
£1007 $1612 €1400 Composition (50x70cm-20x28in) s.verso mixed media. 13-May-3 Palais de Beaux Arts, Brussels #321

ANDERMATT, Werner (1916-) Swiss
£704 $1155 €1021 Untitled (84x61cm-33x24in) s. acrylic paper on panel. 4-Jun-3 Fischer, Luzern #2003/R est:1500-1800 (S.FR 1500)

ANDERS, G (19th C) British
£3500 $5530 €5250 Mother nursing her child (93x69cm-37x27in) s.i.d.75. 27-Nov-2 Bonhams, Knowle #216 est:800-1200

ANDERSEN, Adolf (20th C) ?
£300 $474 €450 Sunlit hall interior (40x55cm-16x22in) s. board. 14-Nov-2 Christie's, Kensington #78/R

ANDERSEN, Carl Christian (1849-1906) Danish
£289 $460 €434 Nature morte (87x102cm-34x40in) s. 5-May-3 Rasmussen, Vejle #3/R (D.KR 3100)
£1981 $3011 €2972 Frederiksborg Palace (43x44cm-17x17in) s. 27-Aug-2 Rasmussen, Copenhagen #1836/R est:10000-15000 (D.KR 23000)

ANDERSEN, Cilius (1865-1913) Danish
£1723 $2618 €2585 Packing the horse carriage for Sunday outing (47x72cm-19x28in) s.i.d.1894. 27-Aug-2 Rasmussen, Copenhagen #1861/R est:20000 (D.KR 20000)
£2553 $4034 €3830 Young girl arranging flowers in vase (78x64cm-31x25in) s.d.1895 i.verso. 2-Dec-2 Rasmussen, Copenhagen #1481/R est:30000 (D.KR 30000)

ANDERSEN, Gunnar Aagaard (20th C) Danish
£1645 $2616 €2468 Composition (46x61cm-18x24in) st.sig.d.1951 verso. 26-Feb-3 Kunsthallen, Copenhagen #38/R est:12000 (D.KR 18000)

ANDERSEN, Johannes (fl.1930s) American/Dutch
£1161 $1800 €1742 Indian and burro in pueblo scene (76x102cm-30x40in) s.d.1933. 29-Oct-2 John Moran, Pasadena #704b est:2500-3500

ANDERSEN, Mogens (1916-) Danish
£667 $1114 €967 Still life of glass (33x22cm-13x9in) init. s.d.57 verso. 17-Jun-3 Rasmussen, Copenhagen #51/R (D.KR 7000)
£931 $1480 €1397 Composition (65x55cm-26x22in) s.d.59 verso. 10-Mar-3 Rasmussen, Vejle #639/R (D.KR 10000)
£1292 $2003 €1938 Composition (92x73cm-36x29in) init. i.verso. 4-Dec-2 Kunsthallen, Copenhagen #116a/R est:16000 (D.KR 15000)
£2111 $3294 €3167 Composition (116x89cm-46x35in) init.d.68 exhib. 18-Sep-2 Kunsthallen, Copenhagen #19/R est:30000 (D.KR 25000)
£2540 $3937 €3810 Centaur (126x102cm-50x40in) s.d.60 exhib. 1-Oct-2 Rasmussen, Copenhagen #47/R est:25000-30000 (D.KR 30000)
£3067 $4846 €4601 Composition (120x120cm-47x47in) s. s.d.1963 verso. 1-Apr-3 Rasmussen, Copenhagen #359/R est:20000-25000 (D.KR 33000)
£3532 $5580 €5298 Composition (97x130cm-38x51in) init.d.67 exhib. 1-Apr-3 Rasmussen, Copenhagen #224/R est:30000 (D.KR 38000)
Works on paper
£653 $1038 €980 Nature morte (116x89cm-46x35in) s.d.1954 verso paper cut-out on canvas. 29-Apr-3 Kunsthallen, Copenhagen #34/R (D.KR 7000)

ANDERSEN, Mogens S (1909-2002) Danish
£361 $570 €542 Landscape, grey day, Gelsted (43x60cm-17x24in) s. 17-Nov-2 Hindemae, Ullerslev #7548/R (D.KR 4200)
£473 $761 €710 View with Kerteminde Harbour (50x68cm-20x27in) s. 11-May-3 Hindemae, Ullerslev #352/R (D.KR 5000)
£559 $894 €839 After harvesting, Birkende (43x59cm-17x23in) s.d.1959. 16-Mar-3 Hindemae, Ullerslev #728/R (D.KR 6000)

ANDERSEN, Nils Severin (1897-1972) South African
Works on paper
£413 $664 €620 S.S Nestor blue diamond funnel line (35x53cm-14x21in) s. i.verso W/C. 12-May-3 Stephan Welz, Johannesburg #83 est:1000-1500 (SA.R 4800)

ANDERSEN, Robin Christian (1890-1969) Austrian
£719 $1151 €1000 Still life of fruit (22x31cm-9x12in) s.d.1913 board. 14-May-3 Dorotheum, Linz #370/R
£1727 $2832 €2400 Flowers in vase (50x34cm-20x13in) s. i.verso board. 5-Jun-3 Dorotheum, Salzburg #598/R est:1000-1500
£4747 $7500 €7500 Still life with apples and sweetcorn cobs (82x100cm-32x39in) s. prov. 27-Nov-2 Dorotheum, Vienna #205/R est:6000-9000
£5319 $8617 €7500 Still life of apple, pears and jugs (49x69cm-19x27in) s.d.1913. 20-May-3 Dorotheum, Vienna #122/R est:7000-10000
Works on paper
£504 $826 €700 Still life with blossom buds (42x30cm-17x12in) s. W/C. 5-Jun-3 Dorotheum, Salzburg #772/R

ANDERSEN, Roy H (1930-) American
£1507 $2200 €2261 Apache (18x13cm-7x5in) 18-May-2 Altermann Galleries, Santa Fe #3/R
£3704 $6000 €5371 Hoop dancer (51x41cm-20x16in) 23-May-3 Altermann Galleries, Santa Fe #111
£14722 $23850 €21347 When the stronghearts sing (74x48cm-29x19in) 23-May-3 Altermann Galleries, Santa Fe #109
£17284 $28000 €25062 The pony traders (76x102cm-30x40in) 23-May-3 Altermann Galleries, Santa Fe #110
£17949 $28000 €26924 A wary peace (61x122cm-24x48in) 9-Nov-2 Altermann Galleries, Santa Fe #136
Works on paper
£274 $400 €411 Indian with buffalo hat (18x15cm-7x6in) pencil. 18-May-2 Altermann Galleries, Santa Fe #129/R

ANDERSEN, Wilhelm (1867-1945) Danish
£380 $586 €570 Still life of jug, lemon and glass (55x83cm-22x33in) s. 26-Oct-2 Rasmussen, Havnen #2090 (D.KR 4500)
£511 $807 €767 Dahlias in vase on window ledge (65x84cm-26x33in) s. 2-Dec-2 Rasmussen, Copenhagen #1461/R (D.KR 6000)
£1034 $1571 €1551 Interior scene with Roman bronze bust and vase with white roses (67x57cm-26x22in) s. cardboard exhib. 28-Aug-2 Museumsbygningen, Copenhagen #94/R est:12000 (D.KR 12000)

ANDERSEN-LUNDBY, Anders (1841-1923) Danish
£315 $504 €473 Coastal landscape, vessel at anchor in foreground (27x38cm-11x15in) i.verso. 13-Jan-3 Rasmussen, Vejle #99/R (D.KR 3600)
£665 $1077 €998 Coastal landscape with sailing vessel (34x63cm-13x25in) s. 25-Jan-3 Rasmussen, Havnen #2000/R (D.KR 7500)
£919 $1471 €1379 Figures on jetty (34x52cm-13x20in) s. 13-Jan-3 Rasmussen, Vejle #80/R (D.KR 10500)
£1148 $1860 €1665 Wooded landscape in winter with horse and sleigh (24x34cm-9x13in) s. 26-May-3 Rasmussen, Copenhagen #1450/R est:8000 (D.KR 12000)
£2297 $3721 €3331 Coastal landscape from North Sjaelland looking towards Sweden, winter (42x63cm-17x25in) s.d.1875. 26-May-3 Rasmussen, Copenhagen #1211/R est:25000 (D.KR 24000)
£2539 $4063 €3809 Winter landscape with figures and snow-covered mountains, possibly near Munich (53x76cm-21x30in) s. 13-Jan-3 Rasmussen, Vejle #121/R est:30000 (D.KR 29000)
£6029 $9165 €9044 Winter landscape with figures walking (51x80cm-20x31in) s.d.1880 exhib. 27-Aug-2 Rasmussen, Copenhagen #1420/R est:60000 (D.KR 70000)
£6460 $9819 €9690 Oxen and cart by Himmelsbjergs Islands (81x126cm-32x50in) s.d.1879 exhib. 27-Aug-2 Rasmussen, Copenhagen #1411/R est:80000-100000 (D.KR 75000)
£7660 $12102 €11490 Winter landscape with Munich in background (95x125cm-37x49in) s. 2-Dec-2 Rasmussen, Copenhagen #1182/R est:100000 (D.KR 90000)

ANDERSEN-LUNDBY, Anders (attrib) (1841-1923) Danish
£372 $580 €558 L. from Ermitagen, winter (30x42cm-12x17in) indis.sig. 23-Sep-2 Rasmussen, Vejle #268/R (D.KR 4400)
£1071 $1703 €1607 Seascape with sailing vessels, coast in background (35x63cm-14x25in) s/. 10-Mar-3 Rasmussen, Vejle #460 (D.KR 11500)

ANDERSON, Bobby (?) ?
Works on paper
£650 $1007 €975 Oul Lammas fair, Ballycastle (35x53cm-14x21in) s. W/C. 4-Dec-2 John Ross, Belfast #264a

ANDERSON, Clarence William (1891-1972) American
£1442 $2250 €2163 Buffalo hunt (76x102cm-30x40in) s. prov.lit. 9-Nov-2 Santa Fe Art, Santa Fe #164/R est:3000-5000
£1923 $3000 €2885 Man-o-war (76x58cm-30x23in) s. canvasboard prov. 20-Sep-2 Sloan, North Bethesda #452/R est:3000-5000

ANDERSON, Clayton (1964-) Canadian
£1915 $3026 €2873 Ragged Island (61x91cm-24x36in) s.d.2002 acrylic on board. 14-Nov-2 Heffel, Vancouver #163/R est:3500-4500 (C.D 4750)
£3363 $5381 €5045 Ocean of a thousand rocks (61x79cm-24x31in) s.d.2003 i.verso board. 15-May-3 Heffel, Vancouver #210/R est:3500-4500 (C.D 7500)

£3812 $6099 €5718 Calm morning - Decourcy Island (74x91cm-29x36in) s.d.2003 i.verso acrylic board. 15-May-3 Heffel, Vancouver #207/R est:4000-5000 (C.D 8500)

ANDERSON, G W (fl.1826-1852) British
£480 $730 €720 Great Eastern dragging her anchor (61x91cm-24x36in) indis.sig.d.1868. 15-Aug-2 Bonhams, New Bond Street #309

ANDERSON, Harold (1894-1973) American
£4167 $6500 €6251 Marines raising flag at Iwo Jima (114x86cm-45x34in) s. 9-Nov-2 Illustration House, New York #29/R est:5000-7000

ANDERSON, James Bell (1886-1938) British
£450 $747 €675 Sheep by a river bank (40x51cm-16x20in) s.d.1911. 10-Jun-3 Bonhams, Knightsbridge #111/R

ANDERSON, John MacVicar (1835-1915) British
£3500 $5565 €5250 Columbia market (55x91cm-22x36in) s.i.d.1870. 18-Mar-3 Bonhams, New Bond Street #57/R est:2000-3000
£68000 $108120 €102000 Waterloo Bridge (76x152cm-30x60in) s.d.1866. 19-Mar-3 Sotheby's, London #230/R est:40000-60000
£75000 $124500 €112500 View of Westminster from the River Thames (107x183cm-42x72in) s. 10-Jun-3 Christie's, London #77/R est:50000-80000

ANDERSON, Kjell (1937-) Swedish
Works on paper
£309 $497 €464 The wheel (33x24cm-13x9in) s.d.71 gouache prov. 7-May-3 AB Stockholms Auktionsverk #1054/R (S.KR 4000)

ANDERSON, Lennart (1928-) American
£1451 $2250 €2177 Study for the portrait of Rubens Eshkanian (51x41cm-20x16in) panel prov.exhib. 29-Oct-2 Sotheby's, New York #262/R est:500-700
£1935 $3000 €2903 Causeway, South Harpswell. View of Brunswick, Maine with footbridge (43x51cm-17x20in) two prov.exhib. 29-Oct-2 Sotheby's, New York #261/R est:1000-1500

ANDERSON, Lennart and ROSS, Alvin (20th C) American
£1613 $2500 €2420 Assorted rolls and bread. Lemon and walnuts (33x46cm-13x18in) s. pair. 29-Oct-2 Sotheby's, New York #300/R est:1000-1500

ANDERSON, Oscar (1873-1953) American
£329 $500 €494 Lobster shack (61x76cm-24x30in) s. 15-Aug-2 Doyle, New York #11
£1948 $3000 €2922 Drying sails, Gloucester (76x64cm-30x25in) s. s.i.verso prov. 24-Oct-2 Shannon's, Milford #53/R est:3000-5000

ANDERSON, Percy (1850-1928) British
Works on paper
£320 $506 €464 Portrait of Gladys Beattie Crozier (26x20cm-10x8in) mono. W/C bodycol. 22-Jul-3 Bonhams, Knightsbridge #171/R

ANDERSON, R (?) ?
£2800 $4368 €4200 Figures loading the harvest onto a cart, drawn by two horses (69x102cm-27x40in) s.d.1880. 25-Mar-3 Gildings, Market Harborough #379/R est:2000-2500

ANDERSON, Sophie (1823-1903) British
£7000 $11620 €10150 Maiden holding orange blossom (36x30cm-14x12in) s. 12-Jun-3 Gorringes, Lewes #1637 est:4000-6000
£18000 $29880 €26100 Girl holding a basket and jasmine blossom, with a garland in her hair (53x43cm-21x17in) s. 12-Jun-3 Gorringes, Lewes #1638 est:7000-10000
£32000 $51520 €48000 Guess again (98x75cm-39x30in) s. prov.exhib.lit. 20-Feb-3 Christie's, London #290/R est:30000

ANDERSON, Stanley (1884-1966) British
Works on paper
£1500 $2430 €2250 Road side chat (23x31cm-9x12in) s.i. W/C gouache. 20-May-3 Sotheby's, Olympia #91/R est:1000-2000
£1800 $2916 €2700 Age and youth (21x30cm-8x12in) s.i. W/C. 20-May-3 Sotheby's, Olympia #92/R est:1000-1500

ANDERSON, Victor C (1882-1937) American
£2548 $4000 €3822 Bucket brigade (46x71cm-18x28in) s.d.16 canvas on board prov. 19-Nov-2 Butterfields, San Francisco #8069/R est:3000-5000

ANDERSON, Walter Inglis (1903-1965) American
Works on paper
£2592 $4250 €3758 Ducks in flight (20x28cm-8x11in) W/C. 7-Jun-3 Neal Auction Company, New Orleans #400 est:3000-5000
£4114 $6500 €6171 Mallard ducks (20x28cm-8x11in) W/C. 5-Apr-3 Neal Auction Company, New Orleans #313/R est:4000-6000
£4177 $6600 €6266 Blue jays (20x28cm-8x11in) W/C pencil. 5-Apr-3 Neal Auction Company, New Orleans #314/R est:3000-5000

ANDERSON, Will (fl.1880-1895) British
£500 $790 €750 Figures making their way home from a lakeside hamlet (29x81cm-11x32in) s. 14-Nov-2 Christie's, Kensington #63/R
Works on paper
£280 $451 €420 Labourers at a farm (23x48cm-9x19in) s. W/C. 19-Feb-3 Mallams, Oxford #388/R
£350 $550 €525 Farm near Alton (18x50cm-7x20in) s. W/C. 21-Nov-2 Tennants, Leyburn #621

ANDERSON, William (1757-1837) British
£1200 $1944 €1800 Beach scene with boats and figures (27x37cm-11x15in) s. panel prov. 21-May-3 Christie's, Kensington #538/R est:1500-2000
£1337 $2059 €2006 English hamlet (46x81cm-18x32in) 26-Oct-2 Heffel, Vancouver #1 est:800-1000 (C.D 3250)
£3413 $5530 €4949 Boats in a calm (40x58cm-16x23in) s. prov. 26-May-3 Bukowskis, Stockholm #469/R est:35000-40000 (S.KR 44000)
£4500 $7065 €6750 Shipping in a calm sea (28x34cm-11x13in) s. panel. 16-Dec-2 Sotheby's, Olympia #12/R est:5000-7000
£6800 $10676 €10200 Quayside scenes with Dutch barges (13x19cm-5x7in) init. one d.1801 pair. 16-Dec-2 Sotheby's, Olympia #11/R est:4000-6000
Works on paper
£1852 $3000 €2685 Packet ship in an estuary (22x32cm-9x13in) s.d.1793 W/C prov. 29-Jul-3 Christie's, Rockefeller NY #101/R est:2000-3000
£2823 $4460 €4235 Shipping off a jetty (25x38cm-10x15in) s.d.83 pen ink W/C. 18-Nov-2 Waddingtons, Toronto #169/R est:4000-6000 (C.D 7000)

ANDERSON, William (attrib) (1757-1837) British
£500 $820 €725 Shore scene with figures and sailing barges (11x16cm-4x6in) panel. 9-Jun-3 Bonhams, Bath #107/R
£1700 $2703 €2550 Barges drying their sails on an East Anglian estuary (19x25cm-7x10in) panel. 4-Mar-3 Bonhams, Knightsbridge #286/R est:1000-1500
Works on paper
£1700 $2839 €2465 Thames at London bridge with St. Pauls and monument beyond (29x41cm-11x16in) W/C. 18-Jun-3 Sotheby's, Olympia #15/R est:800-1000

ANDERSSON, Lars (1957-) Swedish
£420 $656 €630 Model (180x131cm-71x52in) init.d.88 prov. 6-Nov-2 AB Stockholms Auktionsverk #891/R (S.KR 6000)

ANDERSSON, Marten (1934-) Swedish
£1004 $1616 €1506 View towards the sea, Nyanforsbergen (50x65cm-20x26in) s.d.1982 panel. 7-May-3 AB Stockholms Auktionsverk #785/R (S.KR 13000)
£1331 $2077 €1997 Landscape with waterfall from Halsingland (60x92cm-24x36in) s.d.1962 prov. 6-Nov-2 AB Stockholms Auktionsverk #604/R est:25000-30000 (S.KR 19000)

ANDERSSON, N (19th C) ?
£943 $1462 €1500 Figures in woodland (28x42cm-11x17in) s.d.887 paper on board. 29-Oct-2 Dorotheum, Vienna #102/R est:1900-2200

ANDERSSON, Nils (1817-1865) Swedish
£850 $1352 €1250 Man with bird cage (45x37cm-18x15in) s.d.1863. 24-Mar-3 Bukowskis, Helsinki #368/R

ANDERSSON, Torsten (1926-) Swedish
£420 $664 €630 Female nude model (66x49cm-26x19in) s.d.44. 16-Nov-2 Crafoord, Lund #19/R (S.KR 6000)
£2703 $4351 €4055 The birch (42x42cm-17x17in) s.d.66 prov. 7-May-3 AB Stockholms Auktionsverk #953/R est:20000-25000 (S.KR 35000)
£2803 $4373 €4205 Sculpture S (64x49cm-25x19in) s. canvas on panel. 5-Nov-2 Bukowskis, Stockholm #468/R est:40000-50000 (S.KR 40000)
£5097 $8205 €7646 Coastal land (36x28cm-14x11in) s.d.54 exhib.prov. 7-May-3 AB Stockholms Auktionsverk #954/R est:20000-25000 (S.KR 66000)
£10512 $16398 €15768 Red sculpture (127x127cm-50x50in) s.d.89 verso prov.exhib.lit. 6-Nov-2 AB Stockholms Auktionsverk #878/R est:150000-200000 (S.KR 150000)

£28571 $46000 €42857 The window I (70x70cm-28x28in) s.d.63 exhib.prov. 7-May-3 AB Stockholms Auktionsverk #955/R est:50000-60000 (S.KR 370000)

ANDERTON, Francis Swithin (1868-1909) British
£2553 $4034 €3830 Young couple at dusk - he's admiring the ring on her finger (90x114cm-35x45in) s. 2-Dec-2 Rasmussen, Copenhagen #1523/R est:30000-35000 (D.KR 30000)

ANDINE, Patrik (1968-) Swedish
£1699 $2735 €2549 Above perinaeum II (87cm-34in circular) s.d.98 panel exhib. 7-May-3 AB Stockholms Auktionsverk #1053/R est:15000-20000 (S.KR 22000)

ANDOE, Joe (1955-) American
£5063 $8000 €7595 Untitled - geese with pink sky (127x152cm-50x60in) s. painted 1990 prov. 13-Nov-2 Sotheby's, New York #126/R est:5000-7000

ANDORFF, Paul (1849-?) German
£2821 $4428 €4400 Sunday in the Berlin Zelten (19x29cm-7x11in) s. canvas on board. 21-Nov-2 Van Ham, Cologne #1449/R est:5800

ANDRADA, Elsa (1920-) Uruguayan
£323 $510 €500 Untitled (80x60cm-31x24in) s.d.97. 18-Dec-2 Castellana, Madrid #12/R
£323 $510 €500 Untitled (81x61cm-32x24in) s. 18-Dec-2 Castellana, Madrid #48/R
£345 $552 €500 Untitled (36x51cm-14x20in) s. 11-Mar-3 Castellana, Madrid #322/R

ANDRADE, Edna Wright (1917-) American
Works on paper
£247 $400 €371 Geometric design (74x74cm-29x29in) s. graphite. 24-Jan-3 Freeman, Philadelphia #100/R

ANDRE, Albert (1869-1954) French
£2516 $3975 €3900 Nature morte, scene de chasse (49x134cm-19x53in) s. 17-Dec-2 Gioffredo, Nice #1/R
£2866 $4471 €4500 Allegorie de la musique (64x50cm-25x20in) s. 10-Nov-2 Eric Pillon, Calais #24/R
£5677 $8969 €8516 Femme cueillant des fruits (51x60cm-20x24in) s. oil sketch verso panel. 14-Nov-2 Stuker, Bern #10/R est:15000-20000 (S.FR 13000)
£6000 $9540 €9000 Le jardin du peintre a Laudun (46x65cm-18x26in) s. prov. 20-Mar-3 Sotheby's, Olympia #35/R est:6500-7500
£7362 $12000 €11043 Vase de roses (33x41cm-13x16in) s. 12-Feb-3 Sotheby's, New York #42/R est:10000-15000
£7362 $12000 €11043 Nature morte (47x56cm-19x22in) s. board. 12-Feb-3 Sotheby's, New York #50/R est:8000-12000
£13605 $21633 €20000 Vue d'un atelier a Montmartre (73x92cm-29x36in) 24-Mar-3 Coutau Begarie, Paris #199/R
£15337 $25000 €23006 Renoir et sa femme, interieur (47x58cm-19x23in) st.sig. painted c.1913-16 prov.exhib.lit. 12-Feb-3 Sotheby's, New York #14/R est:30000-40000
£17730 $29610 €25000 La plage du Grau du Roi (54x65cm-21x26in) s. prov. 20-Jun-3 Piasa, Paris #117/R est:10000-12000
Works on paper
£4557 $7109 €7200 Atelier au bouquet (61x150cm-24x59in) s. peinture a la colle paper on canvas. 20-Oct-2 Chayette & Cheval, Paris #97/R est:12000

ANDRE, Carl (1935-) American
Sculpture
£3800 $6004 €5700 Inside-outside bipair (30x30cm-12x12in) tin prov. 3-Apr-3 Christie's, Kensington #251/R
£9000 $14760 €13500 8 bright magnesium row (1x9x20cm-0x4x8in) magnesium plates eight prov. 6-Feb-3 Christie's, London #695/R est:6000-8000
£12000 $20040 €17400 Scale six (90x90x1cm-35x35x0in) steamrolled steel 6 unit triangle executed 1981 prov.exhib.lit. 27-Jun-3 Christie's, London #228/R est:12000-18000
£12658 $20000 €18987 Copper-zine dipole (5x100x100cm-2x39x39in) cooper east zinc west two units executed 1975 prov.exhib. 14-Nov-2 Christie's, Rockefeller NY #364/R est:18000-22000
£14375 $23000 €21563 Steel-magnesium dipole (5x100x100cm-2x39x39in) steel north magnesium south two units executed 1989 prov. 15-May-3 Christie's, Rockefeller NY #310/R est:15000-20000
£22152 $35000 €33228 68 part steel cut (22x354cm-9x139in) transformer core steel sheet in 68 parts executed 1972 prov.lit. 13-Nov-2 Sotheby's, New York #315/R est:40000-60000
£28000 $45920 €42000 2, 9AL (1x34x137cm-0x13x54in) aluminium eighteen parts prov.exhib. 7-Feb-3 Sotheby's, London #138/R est:20000-30000
£240506 $380000 €360759 100 zinc square (1x200x200cm-0x79x79in) 100 unit zinc square executed 1968 prov.exhib. 13-Nov-2 Christie's, Rockefeller NY #12/R est:350000-450000

ANDRE, Edmond (?-1877) French
£881 $1400 €1322 Connoisseur (46x30cm-18x12in) s. 7-Mar-3 Skinner, Boston #250/R est:1500-2500

ANDREA, Cornelis (1914-) Dutch
£282 $454 €400 Still life of flowers (50x40cm-20x16in) s. 7-May-3 Vendue Huis, Gravenhage #186/R
£355 $574 €500 Vision, Spanish (60x80cm-24x31in) s. d.1994 verso prov.exhib. 26-May-3 Glerum, Amsterdam #267
£541 $845 €850 Gardeners (60x79cm-24x31in) s. i.verso. 5-Nov-2 Vendu Notarishuis, Rotterdam #140/R
£563 $907 €800 Still life of flowers (80x60cm-31x24in) s. 7-May-3 Vendue Huis, Gravenhage #187
£892 $1391 €1400 Tea garden (23x29cm-9x11in) mono. s.verso. 5-Nov-2 Vendu Notarishuis, Rotterdam #132/R

ANDREA, John de (1941-) American
Sculpture
£14241 $22500 €21362 Blond haired woman (163cm-64in) polychromed vinyl. 22-Apr-3 Butterfields, San Francisco #6060/R est:7000-9000

ANDREA, Pat (1942-) Dutch
£3846 $5962 €6000 Wind (100x135cm-39x53in) s.d.1983 s.i.d.on stretcher. 3-Dec-2 Christie's, Amsterdam #291/R est:6000-8000
£4430 $7000 €7000 Le secret III (160x180cm-63x71in) init.d.94. 26-Nov-2 Sotheby's, Amsterdam #260/R est:7000-10000
£6792 $10460 €10800 Untitled (200x200cm-79x79in) s.verso acrylic. 26-Oct-2 Cornette de St.Cyr, Paris #105a/R
Works on paper
£1223 $2006 €1700 Pavlo's problem (67x83cm-26x33in) s.i.d.1972 pencil col pencil gouache collage prov. 3-Jun-3 Christie's, Amsterdam #66/R est:800-1200
£1905 $3029 €2800 Faux plafond (60x70cm-24x28in) s.d.1995 mixed media collage. 24-Mar-3 Claude Boisgirard, Paris #167/R
£2759 $4414 €4000 Chien Andalou (162x188cm-64x74in) s.d.82 pencil. 15-Mar-3 De Vuyst, Lokeren #570/R est:4500-5500

ANDREANI, Arrigo (1889-1951) Italian
£1410 $2059 €2200 Helper (110x87cm-43x34in) s.d.1929. 5-Jun-2 Il Ponte, Milan #253

ANDREAS, Hans (1947-) Austrian
£861 $1403 €1300 Field in Sipan, an island in Yugoslavia (60x70cm-24x28in) s. s.i.d.89 verso. 28-Jan-3 Dorotheum, Vienna #242/R

ANDREASEN, Signe (1853-1919) Danish
£372 $592 €558 Cactus with white flowers - Epiphyllum Hybridum (59x48cm-23x19in) s. 5-Mar-3 Rasmussen, Copenhagen #1844/R (D.KR 4000)
£431 $655 €647 Chrysanthemums (20x23cm-8x9in) mono. 27-Aug-2 Rasmussen, Copenhagen #1884/R (D.KR 5000)

ANDREASSON, Folke (1902-1948) Swedish
£547 $864 €821 Woodland tarn (30x40cm-12x16in) s. 30-Nov-2 Goteborg Auktionsverk, Sweden #503/R (S.KR 7800)
£1217 $1922 €1826 Landscape with red cottage on the west coast (43x38cm-17x15in) init. panel. 28-Apr-3 Bukowskis, Stockholm #99/R est:12000-15000 (S.KR 16000)

ANDREENKO, Mikhail (1895-1982) Russian
£892 $1391 €1400 Interior scene (67x55cm-26x22in) s. panel. 7-Nov-2 Chochon-Barre & Allardi, Paris #68
£922 $1540 €1300 Composition (16x24cm-6x9in) s.d. isorel. 17-Jun-3 Claude Boisgirard, Paris #13

ANDREEV (?) Russian
£1565 $2488 €2300 Sleigh ride. In the carriage (32x53cm-13x21in) s. pair. 24-Mar-3 Bukowskis, Helsinki #369/R est:800

ANDREI, F (19th C) Italian

Sculpture

£11538 $18115 €18000 Woman with child (152cm-60in) i. white marble sold with base. 16-Dec-2 Rabourdin & Choppin de Janvry, Paris #244/R est:23000

ANDREINI, Ferdinando (1843-?) Italian

Sculpture

£5090 $8500 €7381 Bather (76cm-30in) i. white amble with pedestal. 21-Jun-3 Selkirks, St. Louis #1000a/R est:7000-9000

ANDREIS, Alex de (19/20th C) Belgian

£540 $880 €810 Portrait of a musketeer (80x63cm-31x25in) 14-Feb-3 Bracketts, Tunbridge Wells #978/R

£573 $900 €860 Valiant cavalier (81x66cm-32x26in) s. 23-Nov-2 Jackson's, Cedar Falls #6/R

£600 $936 €900 Cavalier (80x65cm-31x26in) s. 26-Mar-3 Sotheby's, Olympia #238/R

£1000 $1580 €1500 Cavalier holding a halberd (81x65cm-32x26in) s. 14-Nov-2 Christie's, Kensington #307/R est:1000-1500

£1090 $1722 €1700 Mousquetaire lisant (81x65cm-32x26in) s.d.1923. 17-Nov-2 Herbette, Doullens #24/R

£1200 $1956 €1740 Portrait of a man (81x65cm-32x26in) s. 16-Jul-3 Sotheby's, Olympia #172/R est:1200-1500

£1806 $2800 €2709 Cavalier holding a sword (84x69cm-33x27in) s. 2-Oct-2 Christie's, Rockefeller NY #779/R est:2000-3000

£4500 $7470 €6750 Arrival of D'Artagnan (81x100cm-32x39in) s. 10-Jun-3 Christie's, London #120/R est:4000-6000

£6627 $11000 €9609 Trader (81x102cm-32x40in) wood panel. 13-Jun-3 Du Mouchelle, Detroit #2030/R est:8000-10000

ANDREO-WOLF, Anne (20th C) French?

Sculpture

£1538 $2415 €2400 Sirene (57cm-22in) num.3/8 bleutee pat bronze Cast Susse. 16-Dec-2 Chochon-Barre & Allardi, Paris #21/R est:2800-3000

ANDREOLI, Andre (?) Italian?

£641 $1000 €962 Via villari (74x64cm-29x25in) s. i.verso prov. 5-Nov-2 Arthur James, Florida #107/R

£833 $1300 €1250 Via S Nazario (71x84cm-28x33in) s. i.verso prov. 5-Nov-2 Arthur James, Florida #108

ANDREOTTI, F (1847-1930) Italian

Works on paper

£411 $637 €617 Venice with view of St Marks Square (23x46cm-9x18in) i. gouache. 24-Sep-2 Koller, Zurich #6590 (S.FR 950)

£411 $637 €617 Venice with the Dogana (43x23cm-17x9in) i. gouache. 24-Sep-2 Koller, Zurich #6592 (S.FR 950)

ANDREOTTI, Federico (1847-1930) Italian

£629 $1000 €944 Distinguished cavalier smoking a pipe (32x26cm-13x10in) s. prov. 5-Mar-3 Christie's, Rockefeller NY #74/R est:2000-3000

£2381 $3786 €3500 Chatting (16x26cm-6x10in) s. board. 18-Mar-3 Finarte, Milan #107/R

ANDRESSCU, Ioan (attrib) (1850-1882) Rumanian

£2055 $3205 €3000 Snowy wood near Barbizon (30x24cm-12x9in) s.d.1881. 10-Apr-3 Van Ham, Cologne #1309/R est:2500

ANDREU, Mariano (1888-1976) Spanish

£11000 $17270 €16500 Bodegon con sombrero de paja - still life with a straw hat (40x108cm-16x43in) s.d.54 board. 19-Nov-2 Sotheby's, London #68/R est:8000-12000

ANDREW, William Charles (?) British?

£800 $1304 €1200 Red ball (34x52cm-13x20in) s. 12-Feb-3 Bonhams, Knightsbridge #120/R

ANDREWS, Ambrose (attrib) (1824-1859) American

£613 $950 €920 Ruins in a mountainous landscape (46x61cm-18x24in) s.indisd.18. 25-Sep-2 Doyle, New York #2/R

ANDREWS, George H (1816-1898) British

Works on paper

£260 $434 €377 Fishing vessels on the Tyne (16x25cm-6x10in) s. pencil wash. 23-Jun-3 Bonhams, Bath #35

£500 $835 €725 Rescue (18x25cm-7x10in) s.d.73 W/C card. 18-Jun-3 Sotheby's, Olympia #30/R

£750 $1223 €1125 Shipping in rough seas (29x47cm-11x19in) s. W/C. 29-Jan-3 Sotheby's, Olympia #114/R est:800-1200

ANDREWS, Henry (19th C) British

£8000 $12720 €12000 Hawking party. Encampment (68x94cm-27x37in) s. pair prov. 18-Mar-3 Bonhams, New Bond Street #31/R est:6000-8000

ANDREWS, Samuel (c.1767-1807) British

Miniatures

£2800 $4368 €4200 Gentleman wearing blue coat with black collar white waistcoat tied cravat (6cm-2xin) init.d.1796 gold frame oval. 5-Nov-2 Bonhams, New Bond Street #77/R est:1800-2200

ANDREWS, Sybil (1898-1992) British

Prints

£2218 $3504 €3327 Wings (32x37cm-13x15in) s.i. num.16/60 col linocut prov.lit. 14-Nov-2 Heffel, Vancouver #5/R est:3000-4000 (C.D 5500)

£2321 $3668 €3482 Timber Jim (21x37cm-8x15in) s.d.1932 col linocut. 27-Nov-2 Deutscher-Menzies, Melbourne #258/R est:5000-8000 (A.D 6500)

£2823 $4460 €4235 Timber Jim (22x37cm-9x15in) s.i. num.59/60 col linocut prov.lit. 14-Nov-2 Heffel, Vancouver #4/R est:5000-7000 (C.D 7000)

£3200 $4992 €4800 Steeplechasing (17x27cm-7x11in) s.i. num.18/50 col linocut. 31-Mar-3 Bonhams, New Bond Street #247/R est:800-1200

£5000 $8350 €7250 Giant cable (31x42cm-12x17in) s.i.d.num.21/50 col linocut. 30-Jun-3 Bonhams, New Bond Street #246/R est:1500-2000

£6000 $9360 €9000 The giant cable (31x43cm-12x17in) s.i. col linocut. 31-Mar-3 Bonhams, New Bond Street #248 est:1200-1800

£6600 $10296 €9900 The timber Jim (22x38cm-9x15in) s.i. num.7/60 col linocut. 31-Mar-3 Bonhams, New Bond Street #249/R est:1500-2000

Works on paper

£850 $1360 €1275 Portrait of a man facing dexter. Portrait of a young man (33x21cm-13x8in) s.d.1931 conte crayon two. 13-Mar-3 Morphets, Harrogate #616

£1888 $2963 €2832 Western red cedar, the passage of time (87x31cm-34x12in) s.i.d.1977 W/C exhib. 25-Nov-2 Hodgins, Calgary #139/R est:3000-3500 (C.D 4700)

ANDREWS, Todd (1947-) American

Sculpture

£959 $1400 €1439 High wind landing (76cm-30in) one of 25 bronze. 18-May-2 Altermann Galleries, Santa Fe #222/R

ANDREWS, Walter (?) British

£278 $450 €417 Mallards in flight (51x107cm-20x42in) s.d.56 i.on stretcher verso. 24-Jan-3 Freeman, Philadelphia #167/R

£380 $631 €570 Pony, two pointers and dead grouse in highland landscape (90x70cm-35x28in) s. 10-Jun-3 Sworder & Son, Bishops Stortford #539/R

ANDREY-PREVOST (1890-1961) French

£340 $530 €510 French street scene (80x98cm-31x39in) indis sig. i.verso. 10-Sep-2 Bonhams, Knightsbridge #2a

ANDRI, Ferdinand (1871-1956) Austrian

£955 $1490 €1500 Horse in landscape (49x63cm-19x25in) s. board. 6-Nov-2 Hugo Ruef, Munich #1006/R

ANDRIC, Branko (1942-) Austrian

£696 $1086 €1100 Net ball (95x140cm-37x55in) acrylic. 15-Oct-2 Dorotheum, Vienna #264/R

ANDRIES, Alex de (19/20th C) Belgian?

£700 $1092 €1050 Portrait of a cavalier (46x38cm-18x15in) s. 8-Apr-3 Bonhams, Knightsbridge #132/R

ANDRIESSE, Erik (1957-1993) Dutch?

£3846 $5962 €6000 Drie schedels - three skulls (160x127cm-63x50in) indis s. acrylic painted 1985 prov. 3-Dec-2 Christie's, Amsterdam #310/R est:7000-9000

£6475 $10619 €9000 Pineapple (254x150cm-100x59in) s.d.2.6.86 gouache. 3-Jun-3 Christie's, Amsterdam #367/R est:7000-9000

Works on paper

£10791 $17698 €15000 Amaryllis (75x100cm-30x39in) s.d.26.186 g, tracing paper polyptych. 3-Jun-3 Christie's, Amsterdam #366/R est:8000-12000

ANDRIESSEN, Alexander (17th C) Dutch

£1321 $2034 €2100 Nature morte au vase de fleurs, becassine et grive (44x29cm-17x11in) bears sig. panel. 25-Oct-2 Tajan, Paris #61 est:2500-3500

ANDRIESSEN, Christiaan (1775-1846) Dutch
Works on paper
£1656 $2583 €2600 Drawing class (18x26cm-7x10in) i.d.12 Sept bears sig.verso pen brown ink W/C black chk prov. 5-Nov-2 Sotheby's, Amsterdam #169/R est:2500-3500
£4331 $6757 €6800 Young couple making music (28x23cm-11x9in) s.d.1800 brush brown ink W/C over black chk. 5-Nov-2 Sotheby's, Amsterdam #170/R est:4000-6000

ANDRIESSEN, Juriaan (1742-1819) Dutch
£1127 $1870 €1600 Farmhouse by river with barge and figures (34x44cm-13x17in) mono. panel. 14-Jun-3 Arnold, Frankfurt #700/R est:2400
Works on paper
£3185 $4968 €5000 Wooded path at Treslong, near Hillegom (25x19cm-10x7in) s.i.d.1789 verso black chk W/C. 5-Nov-2 Sotheby's, Amsterdam #165/R est:3500-4500

ANDRIESSEN, Mari Silvester (1897-?) Dutch
Sculpture
£1583 $2596 €2200 De annunciatie - Annunciation (24cm-9in) mono. bronze conceived 1936 prov.exhib.lit. 3-Jun-3 Christie's, Amsterdam #173/R est:1400-1600

ANDRIEU, Pierre (attrib) (1821-1892) French
£1773 $2961 €2500 L'entree des croises a Constantinople (65x81cm-26x32in) 18-Jun-3 Tajan, Paris #151/R est:3000-4000

ANDRIUOLI, Mimmo (1946-) Italian
£253 $395 €400 This happens (50x50cm-20x20in) s. i.d.1999 verso acrylic. 14-Sep-2 Meeting Art, Vercelli #390/R
£278 $442 €400 Visit (50x40cm-20x16in) s. painted 2002. 1-May-3 Meeting Art, Vercelli #308
£316 $494 €500 Sunday (50x60cm-20x24in) s. i.verso lit. 14-Sep-2 Meeting Art, Vercelli #882/R
£321 $503 €500 Party on the terrace (80x70cm-31x28in) s. s.verso painted 2001. 23-Nov-2 Meeting Art, Vercelli #421/R
£348 $543 €550 Party on the terrace (70x50cm-28x20in) s. s.i.verso painted 2001. 14-Sep-2 Meeting Art, Vercelli #490/R
£523 $837 €800 On the beach (70x100cm-28x39in) s. 4-Jan-3 Meeting Art, Vercelli #214

ANDROUSOW, Vadime (1895-1975) Russian
Sculpture
£5298 $8636 €8000 Femme a la mandoline (58cm-23in) s. num.4/VII terracotta. 3-Feb-3 Camard, Paris #228/R est:10000

ANDROUSOW, Victor (20th C) Russian
Sculpture
£3038 $4800 €4800 Femme a la toilette (52cm-20in) s.d.41 pat terracotta. 26-Nov-2 Tajan, Paris #138/R est:4000-4500

ANDROUTZOS, Nicolas (?) ?
Works on paper
£355 $592 €500 Ruines antiques (45x58cm-18x23in) s. W/C. 23-Jun-3 Beaussant & Lefèvre, Paris #111

ANELAY, Henry (1817-1883) British
£1274 $2000 €1911 No.4 - the Vicar of Wakefield's family determined to go to church genteelly (46x60cm-18x24in) s.i. 10-Dec-2 Peter Webb, Auckland #139/R est:5000-7000 (NZ.D 4000)

ANESI, Paolo (attrib) (1697-1773) Italian
£380 $593 €570 Mediterranean mountainous landscape with a waterfall, fishermen in the foreground (16x24cm-6x9in) 10-Sep-2 Bonhams, Knightsbridge #25/R

ANG KIUKOK (1931-) Philippino
£9114 $14035 €13671 Thinking man series (81x61cm-32x24in) s.d.77 canvas on board prov.lit. 27-Oct-2 Christie's, Hong Kong #72/R est:70000-90000 (HK.D 110000)

ANGAS, George French (1822-1886) British
Works on paper
£100000 $161000 €150000 Native people of Australia (44x32cm-17x13in) W/C gouache set of 12. 6-May-3 Christie's, Melbourne #114/R est:250000-300000 (A.D 250000)

ANGELI, Eduard (1942-) Austrian
Sculpture
£1517 $2428 €2200 In the reeds (180x118x220cm-71x46x87in) s.d.84 pastel. 11-Mar-3 Dorotheum, Vienna #277/R est:3000-5000
Works on paper
£1042 $1646 €1500 Untitled (71x101cm-28x40in) s. mixed media board. 24-Apr-3 Dorotheum, Vienna #270/R est:1800-2600

ANGELI, Filippo (attrib) (1600-1640) Italian
£2435 $3994 €3531 La peche miraculeuse (48x63cm-19x25in) 4-Jun-3 AB Stockholms Auktionsverk #2567/R est:20000-30000 (S.KR 31000)

ANGELI, Franco (1935-1988) Italian
£313 $497 €450 Half dollar (70x70cm-28x28in) s.verso. 1-May-3 Meeting Art, Vercelli #33
£388 $617 €570 Half dollar (70x70cm-28x28in) s.verso. 1-Mar-3 Meeting Art, Vercelli #314
£513 $810 €800 Half dollar (100x130cm-39x51in) enamel painted 1981. 15-Nov-2 Farsetti, Prato #1/R
£578 $919 €850 Turbolence (60x80cm-24x31in) s.d.verso painted 1983. 1-Mar-3 Meeting Art, Vercelli #396
£660 $1049 €950 Oriental (100x60cm-39x24in) s.d.1987 verso enamel. 1-May-3 Meeting Art, Vercelli #216
£680 $1082 €1000 Prints (100x60cm-39x24in) s.i.verso enamel. 1-Mar-3 Meeting Art, Vercelli #426
£897 $1409 €1400 Landscape (100x80cm-39x31in) s. enamel painted 1974. 19-Nov-2 Finarte, Milan #71/R
£915 $1464 €1400 Battle (70x100cm-28x39in) s.i. enamel painted 1987. 4-Jan-3 Meeting Art, Vercelli #386
£922 $1494 €1300 Sabaudia (100x70cm-39x28in) s.i.verso enamel prov. 26-May-3 Christie's, Milan #168/R est:1000-1500
£980 $1569 €1500 Untitled (130x100cm-51x39in) s.i.verso enamel. 4-Jan-3 Meeting Art, Vercelli #86
£1013 $1580 €1600 Puppets (130x100cm-51x39in) s.i. enamel. 14-Sep-2 Meeting Art, Vercelli #941/R
£1154 $1812 €1800 Horizon (80x100cm-31x39in) s.verso enamel painted 1986. 21-Nov-2 Finarte, Rome #307
£1156 $1839 €1700 Sabaudia (80x60cm-31x24in) s.i.verso enamel. 1-Mar-3 Meeting Art, Vercelli #339
£1176 $1882 €1800 Landscape (80x100cm-31x39in) s. enamel. 4-Jan-3 Meeting Art, Vercelli #621
£1215 $1932 €1750 Geometry (80x100cm-31x39in) s.i. enamel. 1-May-3 Meeting Art, Vercelli #203
£1242 $1987 €1900 Obelisk (130x100cm-51x39in) s.i.verso enamel. 4-Jan-3 Meeting Art, Vercelli #85
£1282 $2013 €2000 Half dollar (70x120cm-28x47in) s. acrylic enamel. 19-Nov-2 Finarte, Milan #281/R
£1319 $2098 €1900 G. Cromo (130x100cm-51x39in) s.i.verso enamel painted 1988. 1-May-3 Meeting Art, Vercelli #458
£1351 $2108 €2000 Night scene (130x100cm-51x39in) s.i.verso enamel lit. 26-Mar-3 Finarte Semenzato, Milan #229/R
£1410 $2214 €2200 Red moon (130x100cm-51x39in) s.i.verso painted 1986. 23-Nov-2 Meeting Art, Vercelli #337/R
£1479 $2455 €2100 Adrianopoli (60x100cm-24x39in) s.i.verso enamel acrylic. 10-Jun-3 Finarte Semenzato, Milan #269/R est:1600-2200
£1528 $2429 €2200 Gold yellow (80x100cm-31x39in) s.i.verso enamel painted 1986. 1-May-3 Meeting Art, Vercelli #434
£1565 $2488 €2300 Red car (100x130cm-39x51in) s.i. enamel. 1-Mar-3 Meeting Art, Vercelli #609
£1582 $2468 €2500 Turbolence (130x160cm-51x63in) s.i.verso acrylic painted 1987. 14-Sep-2 Meeting Art, Vercelli #788/R
£1603 $2516 €2500 Fragments (100x60cm-39x24in) s.i.verso painted 1982. 19-Nov-2 Finarte, Milan #67/R
£1923 $2981 €3000 Half dollar (70x120cm-28x47in) s.verso acrylic ennamel painted 1985. 4-Dec-2 Finarte, Milan #568/R
£2365 $3689 €3500 Half dollar (100x130cm-39x51in) s.i.verso enamel tulle prov.lit. 26-Mar-3 Finarte Semenzato, Milan #277/R
£2692 $4227 €4200 Fragment (140x100cm-55x39in) s. enamel. 21-Nov-2 Finarte, Rome #271/R
£2710 $4281 €4200 Fragment (100x130cm-39x51in) s.verso. 18-Dec-2 Christie's, Rome #102
£5161 $8155 €8000 Dying (114x88cm-45x35in) s.i.d.1962 verso acrylic enamel exhib. 18-Dec-2 Christie's, Rome #210/R
£7097 $11213 €11000 Explosion (195x129cm-77x51in) s.i.d.1965 verso. 18-Dec-2 Christie's, Rome #208/R est:15000
Works on paper
£479 $748 €700 Untitled (100x70cm-39x28in) s. graphite tempera collage card. 10-Apr-3 Finarte Semenzato, Rome #115
£613 $968 €950 Sabaudia (100x70cm-39x28in) s.i. enamel on canvas prov. 18-Dec-2 Christie's, Rome #101/R
£769 $1192 €1200 Acrobatics (70x100cm-28x39in) s. mixed media. 4-Dec-2 Finarte, Milan #559/R
£833 $1292 €1300 Fragments (70x100cm-28x39in) s. mixed media. 4-Dec-2 Finarte, Milan #575
£1026 $1610 €1600 Oriental (120x90cm-47x35in) s.i.verso enamel. 23-Nov-2 Meeting Art, Vercelli #86/R

£2278 $3600 €3600 Half dollar (100x150cm-39x59in) enamel. 29-Nov-2 Farsetti, Prato #481/R
£4114 $6500 €6500 Sunset (200x150cm-79x59in) s.verso enamel painted 1976 lit. 29-Nov-2 Farsetti, Prato #430/R est:5700

ANGELI, Giuseppe (1709-1798) Italian
£2516 $3875 €4000 Saint Joseph accompagne de deux anges (49x63cm-19x25in) 25-Oct-2 Tajan, Paris #16/R est:5000-6000

ANGELICO, Fra (1387-1455) Italian
£671141 $1080537 €1000000 Saint Peter and Saint Thomas of Aquino by the Cross (21x12cm-8x5in) board exhib.lit. 19-Feb-3 Semenzato, Venice #25/R

ANGELIS, Vitaliano de (20th C) Italian
Sculpture
£1646 $2567 €2600 Pinocchio (160cm-63in) s.st.f.Marinelli bronze marble base. 20-Oct-2 Semenzato, Venice #799/R est:1800-2000

ANGERER, Max (1877-1955) Swiss
£728 $1187 €1100 Mountain chain (52x68cm-20x27in) s. masonite. 28-Jan-3 Dorotheum, Vienna #99/R
£1076 $1668 €1700 View into mountain valley (52x69cm-20x27in) s. bears i. stretcher. 25-Sep-2 Neumeister, Munich #536/R
£1667 $2617 €2600 Sigmundskron mountain in south Tyrol at evening time (50x65cm-20x26in) s. 21-Nov-2 Dorotheum, Vienna #213/R est:2000-2600
£1724 $2759 €2500 From Pillberg towards Rofan (41x58cm-16x23in) s. i. verso prov. 11-Mar-3 Dorotheum, Vienna #88/R est:2200-3000

ANGERER, Victor (studio) (19/20th C) Austrian?
Prints
£10067 $16207 €15000 Crown Prince Rudolf of Austria. Crown Prince Rudolf and Wilhelm. s.d.1869 prov. set of four. 18-Feb-3 Sotheby's, Amsterdam #1283/R

ANGERMANN, Peter (1940-) German
£2102 $3280 €3153 Park in town (105x150cm-41x59in) s.d.87 prov. 5-Nov-2 Bukowskis, Stockholm #451/R est:30000-35000 (S.KR 30000)

ANGERMAYER, Johann Adalbert (1674-c.1740) German
£4676 $7482 €6500 Hunting still life with a boar's head (32x49cm-13x19in) indis sig.d.1710. 14-May-3 Christie's, Amsterdam #140/R est:4000-6000

ANGIBOULT, Francois (1887-1950) Russian
Works on paper
£556 $884 €800 Vue de village (72x62cm-28x24in) gouache cardboard pseudonym of Baronne Helene D'Oettingen. 29-Apr-3 Artcurial Briest, Paris #71
£1736 $2760 €2500 Ville du midi (102x68cm-40x27in) s.i. gouache cardboard pseudonym of Baronne Helene D'Oettingen. 29-Apr-3 Artcurial Briest, Paris #70 est:1000-1200
£2083 $3313 €3000 Le papillon et la rose (102x68cm-40x27in) s.i. gouache cardboard pseudonym of Baronne Helene D'Oettingen. 29-Apr-3 Artcurial Briest, Paris #69/R est:1000-1500

ANGILLIS, Pieter (1685-1734) Flemish
£2800 $4340 €4200 Interior scene with boar drinking. Interior scene with lady selling a cabbage (16x15cm-6x6in) i. one d.1727 one d.1726 verso panel pair. 31-Oct-2 Sotheby's, Olympia #124/R est:3000-5000
£3500 $5530 €5250 Lady and her maid at a fishmonger, river Thames beyond (43x36cm-17x14in) 26-Nov-2 Christie's, London #15/R est:4000-6000
Works on paper
£338 $527 €500 Conjuration de catilina (36x45cm-14x18in) s.i. pen ink wash gouache. 31-Mar-3 Piasa, Paris #19

ANGILLIS, Pieter (attrib) (1685-1734) Flemish
£629 $981 €1000 Vegetables in peasant kitchen (50x39cm-20x15in) 19-Sep-2 Dr Fritz Nagel, Stuttgart #860

ANGLADA-CAMARASA, Herman (1873-1959) Spanish
£6289 $9686 €10000 Three sailing boats (18x13cm-7x5in) painted c.1889 lit. 22-Oct-2 Durán, Madrid #267/R est:10000
£8176 $13000 €12264 Study for girls of Burriana (54x40cm-21x16in) s. panel prov. 7-Mar-3 Skinner, Boston #609/R est:8000-12000

ANGLADA-PINTO, Luis (1873-1946) Spanish
£850 $1393 €1300 Portrait odf woman from Seville (65x53cm-26x21in) s. 7-Feb-3 Oger, Dumont, Paris #49

ANGLADE, Gaston (1854-1927) French
£348 $543 €550 Coucher de soleil sur la ferme (46x61cm-18x24in) s. 15-Oct-2 Horta, Bruxelles #327
£488 $766 €732 Vallee de la Dordogne (33x40cm-13x16in) s. 12-Dec-2 Iegor de Saint Hippolyte, Montreal #1 (C.D 1200)
£552 $877 €800 Bruyere pourpre en bordure de riviere (46x55cm-18x22in) s. 4-Mar-3 Livinec, Gaudcheau & Jezequel, Rennes #23
£793 $1300 €1150 Lilac hills (38x53cm-15x21in) s. 4-Jun-3 Doyle, New York #3 est:1000-1500
£1500 $2370 €2250 Shepherdess with her flock in an extensive landscape with a river and castle beyond (73x110cm-29x43in) s. 14-Nov-2 Christie's, Kensington #231/R est:1500-2000

ANGLADE, Henri Vincent (1876-1956) French
Works on paper
£1757 $2741 €2600 Lady (137x74cm-54x29in) s.d.1904 pastel. 28-Mar-3 Claude Aguttes, Neuilly #56/R

ANGLES, Joaquin (19/20th C) French
Sculpture
£1538 $2569 €2200 Idylle (95cm-37in) s. brown pat bronze. 25-Jun-3 Artcurial Briest, Paris #44/R est:1500-1800

ANGLO-CHINESE SCHOOL, 19th C
£5000 $7800 €7500 Carnedd Llewelyn in full sail (136x84cm-54x33in) 10-Sep-2 Bonhams, New Bond Street #120/R est:2000-4000
£7000 $10920 €10500 Hongs at Canton (75x42cm-30x17in) 10-Sep-2 Bonhams, New Bond Street #119/R est:5000-8000
£12000 $18720 €18000 Waterfront at Shanghai (77x44cm-30x17in) 10-Sep-2 Bonhams, New Bond Street #114/R est:6000-10000
£13000 $20280 €19500 Hongs at Canton (40cm-16xin) 10-Sep-2 Bonhams, New Bond Street #118/R est:3000-5000
£32000 $49280 €48000 View of the Hongs at Canton with different flags (66x109cm-26x43in) painted c.1850. 25-Oct-2 Gorringes, Lewes #896

ANGLO-DUTCH SCHOOL, 17th C
£24000 $39840 €36000 Portrait of a young gentleman in richly embroidered dress (179x98cm-70x39in) prov.exhib. 10-Jun-3 Christie's, London #5/R est:25000-35000

ANGLO-DUTCH SCHOOL, 18th C
£20000 $33200 €29000 British men-o-war in a stiff breeze (89x201cm-35x79in) 16-Jun-3 Duke & Son, Dorchester #198/R est:8000-15000

ANGLO-FLEMISH SCHOOL, 17th C
£32000 $53120 €46400 Still life of a parrot, fruit in a Chinese porcelain dish and a woven basket (86x147cm-34x58in) 16-Jun-3 Duke & Son, Dorchester #185/R est:5000-10000

ANGLO-FLEMISH SCHOOL, 18th C
£5800 $8990 €8700 Wooded river landscape with huntsmen (15x20cm-6x8in) copper pair. 6-Dec-2 Lyon & Turnbull, Edinburgh #11/R est:4000-6000

ANGLO-FRENCH SCHOOL, 19th C
£20645 $32000 €30968 Elegant figures in landscaped gardens. set of six. 2-Oct-2 Christie's, Rockefeller NY #120/R est:12000-18000

ANGLO-HANOVERIAN SCHOOL, 18th C
£10000 $16600 €15000 Portrait of King George II in state robes (75x60cm-30x24in) 10-Jun-3 Christie's, London #28/R est:10000-15000

ANGLO-INDIAN SCHOOL, 19th C
£1879 $3026 €2800 General Sir Rowland Smyth (76x61cm-30x24in) prov. 18-Feb-3 Whyte's, Dublin #93/R est:2000-3000

ANGO, Robert (18th C) French
Works on paper
£699 $1168 €1000 Villa Sacheti (30x45cm-12x18in) dr. 27-Jun-3 Claude Aguttes, Neuilly #15/R
£926 $1500 €1389 Creation of Adam (24x42cm-9x17in) chk. 21-Jan-3 Sotheby's, New York #90/R
£2027 $3162 €3000 Circoncision (35x27cm-14x11in) i. sanguine exhib.lit. 27-Mar-3 Maigret, Paris #71/R

ANGOLO DEL MORO, Marco (fl.1565-1586) Italian
Works on paper
£2817 $4676 €4000 Madonna with kneeling shepherds (27x23cm-11x9in) pen wash. 12-Jun-3 Hauswedell & Nolte, Hamburg #132/R est:3000

ANGQVIST, Olle (1922-) Swedish
£532 $824 €798 Waves - calm (55x134cm-22x53in) s.d.86 verso panel. 8-Dec-2 Uppsala Auktionskammare, Uppsala #288 (S.KR 7500)
£638 $989 €957 Whirlpool I (135x122cm-53x48in) s.d.86 verso panel. 8-Dec-2 Uppsala Auktionskammare, Uppsala #287/R (S.KR 9000)
Works on paper
£596 $929 €894 Untitled (55x45cm-22x18in) init.d.68 mixed media collage assemblage. 5-Nov-2 Bukowskis, Stockholm #355/R (S.KR 8500)

ANGRAND, Charles (1854-1926) French
£40000 $65600 €60000 Pont de pierre, Rouen (80x124cm-31x49in) s.d.81 prov.exhib.lit. 4-Feb-3 Christie's, London #213/R est:120000
Works on paper
£390 $651 €550 L'arc en ciel (52x67cm-20x26in) st.sig. pastel prov. 20-Jun-3 Piasa, Paris #150
£993 $1658 €1400 Femme a la citerne (49x61cm-19x24in) st.sig. chl prov. 20-Jun-3 Piasa, Paris #134
£1748 $2919 €2500 Meule de foin (40x65cm-16x26in) s. chl. 26-Jun-3 Tajan, Paris #51/R est:3000-4000

ANGU, Giuseppe del (attrib) (18th C) Italian
£3200 $5344 €4640 Sea battle between the Turks and Christians outside Carthage (100x143cm-39x56in) i. 18-Jun-3 Sotheby's, Olympia #11/R est:1000-1500

ANGUIANO, Raul (1915-) Mexican
Works on paper
£936 $1478 €1404 Laura (64x45cm-25x18in) s.d.1990 pastel. 26-Nov-2 Louis Morton, Mexico #81/R (M.P 15000)
£1259 $1965 €1889 Boceto para mural (80x64cm-31x25in) s.d.1955 col crayon. 17-Oct-2 Louis Morton, Mexico #20/R est:25000-30000 (M.P 20000)
£2165 $3463 €3139 Mujer cargando una canasta de frutas (32x24cm-13x9in) W/C. 15-May-3 Louis Morton, Mexico #45/R est:38000-40000 (M.P 35000)
£2519 $3929 €3779 Sin titulo (84x69cm-33x27in) s.d.1958 W/C. 17-Oct-2 Louis Morton, Mexico #128/R est:45000-50000 (M.P 40000)

ANGUISSOLA, Sofonisba (circle) (1527-c.1625) Italian
£11218 $17724 €17500 Portrait of woman holding book in hand (66x55cm-26x22in) panel. 16-Nov-2 Lempertz, Koln #1001/R est:10000
£12346 $20000 €18519 Portrait of a lady in a red dress and jewel embroidered belt (16cm-6in circular) panel. 24-Jan-3 Christie's, Rockefeller NY #82/R est:20000-30000

ANGUS, J Colin (1907-) Australian
£356 $544 €534 South of the Warby Ranges (61x71cm-24x28in) s. i.verso board painted c.1975 prov. 26-Aug-2 Sotheby's, Paddington #613 est:1000-2000 (A.D 1000)

ANGUS, May (fl.1887-1888) British
Works on paper
£1400 $2184 €2100 Cat's cradle (61x41cm-24x16in) s. W/C. 26-Mar-3 Hamptons Fine Art, Godalming #44/R est:1500-1800

ANGUS, Rita (1908-1970) New Zealander
£9375 $14625 €14063 Portrait of Christopher Jones (38x34cm-15x13in) prov. 8-Apr-3 Peter Webb, Auckland #41/R est:30000-40000 (NZ.D 27000)
£13889 $21667 €20834 St Luke's church, Waikanae (39x34cm-15x13in) s. s.i.verso board prov. 8-Apr-3 Peter Webb, Auckland #42/R est:50000-65000 (NZ.D 40000)
Works on paper
£4861 $7583 €7292 Floral still life (18x18cm-7x7in) s. pen brown ink W/C exec.c.1942-45 prov. 8-Apr-3 Peter Webb, Auckland #40/R est:8000-12000 (NZ.D 14000)

ANGYAL, Gejza (1888-1956) Czechoslovakian
£1181 $1677 €1772 Town of Kremnica (82x100cm-32x39in) painted 1948. 26-Mar-2 SOGA, Bratislava #38/R est:75000 (SL.K 75000)

ANHALT DESSAU, Leopold von (1794-1871) German
£2819 $4538 €4200 Dessau seen from Schlob Luisium (18x38cm-7x15in) mono.d.1838. 18-Feb-3 Sotheby's, Amsterdam #488/R est:750-950

ANISFELD, Boris (1878-1973) Russian
£11500 $18630 €17250 Young gypsy girl (89x63cm-35x25in) s. prov. 21-May-3 Sotheby's, London #211/R est:10000-15000
£35000 $54950 €52500 Bacchanal (70x100cm-28x39in) s. exhib. 20-Nov-2 Sotheby's, London #105/R est:40000-60000
£38000 $61560 €57000 Autumn leaves (118x87cm-46x34in) s.d.1925 prov.lit. 21-May-3 Sotheby's, London #198/R est:40000-60000
£40000 $64800 €60000 Rhapsody (193x140cm-76x55in) s.i. exhib. 21-May-3 Sotheby's, London #168/R est:50000-70000
Works on paper
£2400 $3768 €3600 Costume design for a ballet (30x24cm-12x9in) gouache over pencil. 20-Nov-2 Sotheby's, London #162/R est:3000-5000

ANIVITTI, Filippo (1876-1955) Italian
£1467 $2435 €2127 Market of Campo Del Fiori, Rome (25x49cm-10x19in) s. 16-Jun-3 Waddingtons, Toronto #334a/R est:2000-3000 (C.D 3300)
Works on paper
£513 $805 €800 View of Rome (59x44cm-23x17in) s. W/C. 16-Dec-2 Pandolfini, Florence #39
£1202 $1948 €1743 Flower stall at the Spanish Steps, Rome (42x45cm-17x18in) s. W/C. 26-May-3 Bukowskis, Stockholm #261/R est:12000-15000 (S.KR 15500)

ANKARCRONA, Alexis (1825-1901) Swedish
£547 $876 €793 Cattle grazing (40x59cm-16x23in) with sig. 18-May-3 Anders Antik, Landskrona #18 (S.KR 7000)
£625 $1001 €906 Cows in meadow (40x59cm-16x23in) s. 18-May-3 Anders Antik, Landskrona #15 (S.KR 8000)
£849 $1410 €1231 Lake landscape with fishermen (71x107cm-28x42in) s.d.86. 16-Jun-3 Lilla Bukowskis, Stockholm #723 (S.KR 11000)

ANKARCRONA, Gustaf (1869-1933) Swedish
£1348 $2089 €2022 Caravan with camels (46x75cm-18x30in) i.verso. 3-Dec-2 Bukowskis, Stockholm #322/R est:25000-30000 (S.KR 19000)

ANKARCRONA, Henrik (1831-1917) Swedish
£1939 $3142 €2812 Desert landscape with bedouins (43x68cm-17x27in) s.d.1873. 26-May-3 Bukowskis, Stockholm #194/R est:30000-35000 (S.KR 25000)
£5400 $8587 €8100 Desert landscape with caravan of men on camels and horses (78x127cm-31x50in) s.d.74. 5-Mar-3 Rasmussen, Copenhagen #1582/R est:50000-75000 (D.KR 58000)
Works on paper
£2051 $3220 €3200 Ecole suedoise (24x34cm-9x13in) s.i.d.81 W/C gouache. 10-Dec-2 Tajan, Paris #110/R est:3200

ANKARCRONA, Johanna (18/19th C) Swedish
£602 $1000 €873 Landscape with figures (44x63cm-17x25in) s.d.1813. 16-Jun-3 Lilla Bukowskis, Stockholm #727 (S.KR 7800)

ANKER, Albert (1831-1910) Swiss
£1038 $1660 €1557 Weaving room (18x20cm-7x8in) bears d.18.1 canvas on board. 17-Mar-3 Philippe Schuler, Zurich #4500 est:2500-3000 (S.FR 2200)
£6944 $11181 €10069 Portrait of village vicar (64x50cm-25x20in) s. 9-May-3 Dobiaschofsky, Bern #60/R est:7000 (S.FR 15000)
£9390 $15399 €13616 Study for: Primary school on the Kirchenfeldbrucke (23x18cm-9x7in) canvas on board lit.exhib.prov. 4-Jun-3 Fischer, Luzern #1217/R est:20000-28000 (S.FR 20000)
£70755 $114623 €125237 Portrait of Bethli Oser (42x36cm-17x14in) mono.i.d.19 Juli prov.exhib.lit. 26-May-3 Sotheby's, Zurich #16/R est:90000-130000 (S.FR 150000)
£87336 $137118 €131004 Girl with puppet (44x32cm-17x13in) prov.exhib.lit. 25-Nov-2 Sotheby's, Zurich #15/R est:140000-180000 (S.FR 200000)
£94421 $149185 €141632 Portrait of Helen Furi (47x39cm-19x15in) s. prov.exhib.lit. 26-Nov-2 Phillips, Zurich #8/R est:220000-280000 (S.FR 220000)
Works on paper
£305 $500 €442 Grandmother with cup (23x29cm-9x11in) i. Indian ink. 4-Jun-3 Fischer, Luzern #2577/R (S.FR 650)
£306 $477 €459 Interior of a cheese makers in Wimmis (21x14cm-8x6in) st.sig.i. pencil. 6-Nov-2 Dobiaschofsky, Bern #1106 (S.FR 700)
£440 $708 €660 Seated young woman (19x12cm-7x5in) d.17 Dez 97 Indian ink. 7-May-3 Dobiaschofsky, Bern #1094/R (S.FR 950)
£1092 $1703 €1638 Farmer's wife spinning (23x28cm-9x11in) pen ink dr prov. 8-Nov-2 Dobiaschofsky, Bern #41/R est:3500 (S.FR 2500)

£1145 $1672 €1718 Interior with two women sewing. Seated young woman (23x34cm-9x13in) pencil chl double-sided. 17-Jun-2 Philippe Schuler, Zurich #4782/R est:2500-3000 (S.FR 2600)

£1233 $1801 €1850 Girl knitting. Hand studies (31x22cm-12x9in) chl quartered double-sided. 17-Jun-2 Philippe Schuler, Zurich #4783/R est:2800-3400 (S.FR 2800)

£1322 $1930 €1983 Portrait of girl (29cm-11in circular) chk htd white. 17-Jun-2 Philippe Schuler, Zurich #4780/R est:2800-3400 (S.FR 3000)

£2183 $3406 €3275 Card reader (60x93cm-24x37in) chl dr paper on board prov. 8-Nov-2 Dobiaschofsky, Bern #42/R est:6000 (S.FR 5000)

£2790 $4408 €4185 Lausanne cathedral (10x17cm-4x7in) i.d.21.Sept 1880 W/C. 28-Nov-2 Christie's, Zurich #13/R est:6000-8000 (S.FR 6500)

£3004 $4747 €4506 Boy's portrait (30x23cm-12x9in) i. verso chl htd white. 28-Nov-2 Christie's, Zurich #15/R est:7000-9000 (S.FR 7000)

£4525 $7557 €6561 Portrait of man wearing hat (30x23cm-12x9in) s. W/C exhib. 24-Jun-3 Koller, Zurich #10/R est:12000-18000 (S.FR 10000)

£9013 $14240 €13520 Peasant room (28x54cm-11x21in) s. pencil chl. 28-Nov-2 Christie's, Zurich #10/R est:15000-20000 (S.FR 21000)

£9259 $14907 €13426 Girl knitting (29x20cm-11x8in) s. W/C over pencil. 9-May-3 Dobiaschofsky, Bern #67/R est:25000 (S.FR 20000)

£15021 $23734 €22532 Old farmer with pipe (34x24cm-13x9in) s.d.1909 W/C prov.exhib. 26-Nov-2 Phillips, Zurich #9/R est:35000-45000 (S.FR 35000)

£15021 $23734 €22532 Old farmer's wife with glasses reading the bible (34x24cm-13x9in) s.d.1909 W/C. 26-Nov-2 Phillips, Zurich #10/R est:35000-45000 (S.FR 35000)

£15284 $23843 €22926 Farmer with pipe and tobacco pouch (33x23cm-13x9in) s.d.1906 W/C over pencil prov. 8-Nov-2 Dobiaschofsky, Bern #47/R est:42000 (S.FR 35000)

£23148 $37269 €33565 Old farmer at the table (35x25cm-14x10in) s. W/C over pencil. 9-May-3 Dobiaschofsky, Bern #59/R est:38000 (S.FR 50000)

ANKER, Albert (attrib) (1831-1910) Swiss

Works on paper

£349 $545 €524 Seated peasant sharpening implement (34x25cm-13x10in) s. ochre lit. 20-Nov-2 Fischer, Luzern #2580/R (S.FR 800)

ANKER, Herman Wedel (1845-1895) Norwegian

£633 $1025 €950 Girl with red headscarf on country road (40x57cm-16x22in) s. panel. 27-Jan-3 Blomqvist, Lysaker #1007/R (N.KR 7000)

£853 $1331 €1280 Girl with red headscarf on country road (40x57cm-16x22in) s. panel. 23-Sep-2 Blomqvist, Lysaker #1002/R (N.KR 10000)

£2262 $3665 €3393 Landscape from Simoe at Modum (62x86cm-24x34in) s.d.94 i.verso. 26-May-3 Grev Wedels Plass, Oslo #32/R est:30000-50000 (N.KR 25000)

ANNA, Margit (1913-1991) Hungarian

£2555 $3960 €3833 Everything-nothing (60x35cm-24x14in) s. 6-Dec-2 Kieselbach, Budapest #129/R (H.F 950000)

£2689 $4168 €3899 Showman (47x37cm-19x15in) s.d.962. 9-Dec-2 Mu Terem Galeria, Budapest #100/R est:750000 (H.F 1000000)

£13413 $20925 €19449 Dancers (70x50cm-28x20in) s. tempera paper on canvas lit. 12-Apr-3 Mu Terem Galeria, Budapest #121/R est:3500000 (H.F 4800000)

Works on paper

£753 $1167 €1092 Self-portrait (27x19cm-11x7in) s. Indian ink autograph letter verso. 9-Dec-2 Mu Terem Galeria, Budapest #92/R est:120000 (H.F 280000)

ANNALA, Matti (1898-1958) Finnish

£261 $429 €400 Mending the nets (45x55cm-18x22in) s. 9-Feb-3 Bukowskis, Helsinki #196/R

ANNENKOFF, Yuri (1889-1974) Russian

£25000 $40500 €37500 Still life with lilies and painting (93x66cm-37x26in) s. 21-May-3 Sotheby's, London #204/R est:25000-35000

Works on paper

£448 $749 €650 Dans le boudoir (20x25cm-8x10in) mono. Indian ink. 9-Jul-3 Cornette de St.Cyr, Paris #146

£3200 $5184 €4800 Costume designs of outlandish ladies and army officer (33x76cm-13x30in) s.d.1928 W/C pen ink set of three. 21-May-3 Sotheby's, London #152/R est:2000-3000

£28000 $43960 €42000 Portrait of Anna Akhmatove (50x33cm-20x13in) mixed media. 20-Nov-2 Sotheby's, London #131/R est:18000-22000

ANNIGONI, Pietro (1910-1988) Italian

£450 $702 €675 Study of reeds (17x26cm-7x10in) canvas on board. 12-Sep-2 Sotheby's, Olympia #34/R

£700 $1092 €1050 Portrait of Sharmini (23x27cm-9x11in) s.i. 12-Sep-2 Sotheby's, Olympia #18/R

£800 $1248 €1200 Portrait of a man (18x13cm-7x5in) s.i.d.LXI red chk. 12-Sep-2 Sotheby's, Olympia #5/R

£1300 $2028 €1950 Landscape (20x25cm-8x10in) s.i.d.LXX canvas on board. 12-Sep-2 Sotheby's, Olympia #22/R est:1000-1500

£1500 $2340 €2250 Battersea Power Station (18x26cm-7x10in) s. board. 12-Sep-2 Sotheby's, Olympia #3/R est:1500-2000

£2089 $3258 €3300 Landscape in Versilia (20x30cm-8x12in) s. cardboard on canvas. 14-Sep-2 Meeting Art, Vercelli #912/R

£2365 $3689 €3500 Landscape (20x25cm-8x10in) s. cardboard on canvas. 26-Mar-3 Finarte Semenzato, Milan #107/R

£2600 $4056 €3900 Nude bending down (40x51cm-16x20in) s. 12-Sep-2 Sotheby's, Olympia #19/R est:800-1200

£3819 $6073 €5500 Landscape (30x40cm-12x16in) s.i. cardboard on canvas. 1-May-3 Meeting Art, Vercelli #530

£4000 $6240 €6000 Portraitof a lady (55x45cm-22x18in) s.i.d.LII board. 12-Sep-2 Sotheby's, Olympia #30/R est:4000-6000

£14000 $21840 €21000 Juanita (78x66cm-31x26in) s.i.d.LVI s.i.stretcher. 12-Sep-2 Sotheby's, Olympia #40/R est:12000-18000

£16000 $24960 €24000 Christ calming the waves (89x75cm-35x30in) init. s.verso. 12-Sep-2 Sotheby's, Olympia #39/R est:10000-15000

£28000 $43680 €42000 Self portrait (34x31cm-13x12in) s. 12-Sep-2 Sotheby's, Olympia #41/R est:7000-9000

Works on paper

£340 $541 €510 Head of a Martyr (27x12cm-11x5in) s.d.67 red chk. 26-Feb-3 Sotheby's, Olympia #153/R

£350 $546 €525 Female nude study (17x12cm-7x5in) pen ink. 12-Sep-2 Sotheby's, Olympia #16/R

£450 $702 €675 Portrait in profile (13x8cm-5x3in) init. pencil. 12-Sep-2 Sotheby's, Olympia #26/R

£481 $755 €750 Profile (44x31cm-17x12in) s. sanguine. 23-Nov-2 Meeting Art, Vercelli #419/R

£600 $936 €900 Gateway (28x34cm-11x13in) s. pen ink. 12-Sep-2 Sotheby's, Olympia #35/R

£700 $1092 €1050 Three Graces (37x31cm-15x12in) s.i. gouache over W/C wash. 12-Sep-2 Sotheby's, Olympia #14/R

£705 $1107 €1100 Female head (28x30cm-11x12in) s. sanguine. 16-Dec-2 Pandolfini, Florence #350

£816 $1298 €1200 Val TRompia (22x30cm-9x12in) s.i.d.1930 Chinese ink lit. 1-Mar-3 Meeting Art, Vercelli #720

£823 $1284 €1300 Face (30x20cm-12x8in) s. sanguine. 14-Sep-2 Meeting Art, Vercelli #871/R

£962 $1490 €1500 Prophet (27x18cm-11x7in) s. sanguine exhib. 4-Dec-2 Finarte, Milan #199

£1000 $1560 €1500 Toledo (37x54cm-15x21in) s.i.d.LV brown ink. 12-Sep-2 Sotheby's, Olympia #12/R est:1000-1500

£1000 $1560 €1500 Countryside (25x37cm-10x15in) s.i.d.LXI W/C. 12-Sep-2 Sotheby's, Olympia #36/R est:400-600

£1026 $1590 €1600 Renaissance head (55x43cm-22x17in) s. pencil. 4-Dec-2 Finarte, Milan #206/R

£1154 $1823 €1800 Head of old man (28x19cm-11x7in) s. sanguine card. 15-Nov-2 Farsetti, Prato #476/R

£1300 $2171 €1885 Female head study (37x27cm-15x11in) s.d.LXXIV chl pastel. 24-Jun-3 Bonhams, New Bond Street #30/R est:600-800

£1389 $2208 €2000 Landscape (50x75cm-20x30in) s.i.d.1932 Chinese ink W/C. 1-May-3 Meeting Art, Vercelli #258

£1400 $2184 €2100 Mullion (34x48cm-13x19in) s.i.d.LVII ink W/C wash. 12-Sep-2 Sotheby's, Olympia #9/R est:600-800

£1486 $2319 €2200 Face (28x19cm-11x7in) s. sanguine card. 28-Mar-3 Farsetti, Prato #116/R

£1600 $2496 €2400 Landscape with a church spire (30x48cm-12x19in) s.i.d.VI-IV-LIV ink wash. 12-Sep-2 Sotheby's, Olympia #11/R est:1200-1800

£1700 $2652 €2550 View of the Thames (31x48cm-12x19in) s.i.d.XLIX pen ink wash. 12-Sep-2 Sotheby's, Olympia #7/R est:1200-1800

£1800 $2808 €2700 London (33x23cm-13x9in) s.i.d.XLIX pen ink wash. 12-Sep-2 Sotheby's, Olympia #2/R est:2000-3000

£1800 $2808 €2700 Portrait of Susie Robozzo (25x22cm-10x9in) s.i.d.LVI brown ink. 12-Sep-2 Sotheby's, Olympia #25/R est:1000-1500

£2000 $3120 €3000 Reclining nude (36x54cm-14x21in) s.d.LXIX chl col chk. 12-Sep-2 Sotheby's, Olympia #23/R est:1500-2000

£2200 $3432 €3300 Nude on divan (36x54cm-14x21in) s.d.LXIX chl col chk. 12-Sep-2 Sotheby's, Olympia #17/R est:1200-1800

£2200 $3432 €3300 Nude on divan (36x54cm-14x21in) s.d.LXIX red grey chk over wash. 12-Sep-2 Sotheby's, Olympia #20/R est:1200-1800

£2400 $3744 €3600 El escorial (37x53cm-15x21in) s.i.d.LV ink wash. 12-Sep-2 Sotheby's, Olympia #10/R est:2000-3000

£2800 $4368 €4200 Female nude study (27x46cm-11x18in) s. red chk. 12-Sep-2 Sotheby's, Olympia #21/R est:1200-1800

£4200 $6552 €6300 Portrait of Barrie Asherton Chin (57x38cm-22x15in) s.i.d.LXVII mixed media board. 12-Sep-2 Sotheby's, Olympia #31/R est:4000-6000

£4400 $6864 €6600 Nude on couch (36x54cm-14x21in) s.d.LXIX chl col chk. 12-Sep-2 Sotheby's, Olympia #15/R est:2500-3000

£4600 $7176 €6900 Shrewd merchant (44x34cm-17x13in) mixed media. 12-Sep-2 Sotheby's, Olympia #29/R est:3000-5000

£7000 $10920 €10500 Self portrait (15x13cm-6x5in) init.i. pen ink. 12-Sep-2 Sotheby's, Olympia #1/R est:2500-3500

£7000 $10920 €10500 Portrait of a dark haired girl (56x38cm-22x15in) s.d.LXIX mixed media board. 12-Sep-2 Sotheby's, Olympia #28/R est:8000-12000

£7500 $11700 €11250 Portrait of a lady (57x39cm-22x15in) s.d.LXIX mixed media. 12-Sep-2 Sotheby's, Olympia #38/R est:5000-7000

ANONYMOUS (?) ?
£10127 $16000 €15191 Whaling scene with men capturing a sperm whale. 26-Apr-3 Thomaston Place, Thomaston #65
Works on paper
£9324 $15385 €13520 Bamboo and plum blossoms (25x32cm-10x13in) ink col silk hanging scroll exec.12-14th Century. 6-Jul-3 Christie's, Hong Kong #402/R est:150000-200000 (HK.D 120000)
£26316 $40000 €39474 Panoramic view of Nagasaki, Japan (41x198cm-16x78in) W/C. 17-Aug-2 North East Auctions, Portsmouth #1023/R est:40000-60000

ANONYMOUS (13/14th C) ?
Works on paper
£62160 $102564 €90132 Gathering immortals (28x510cm-11x201in) ink col silk handscroll. 7-Jul-3 Christie's, Hong Kong #519/R est:500000-700000 (HK.D 800000)

ANONYMOUS (15th/16th C) ?
Works on paper
£17094 $28205 €24786 Secluded dwelling by the river (150x106cm-59x42in) sealed ink silk hanging scroll. 7-Jul-3 Christie's, Hong Kong #515/R est:100000-150000 (HK.D 220000)

ANONYMOUS (16th/17th C) ?
£19635 $31024 €29453 Portrait of gentleman, possibly Philip II (120x93cm-47x37in) 27-Nov-2 Falkkloos, Malmo #77999/R est:30000 (S.KR 280000)

ANONYMOUS (17th/18th C) ?
Works on paper
£17094 $28205 €24786 Portrait of a Manchu lady (63x48cm-25x19in) ink col silk scroll. 7-Jul-3 Christie's, Hong Kong #513/R est:60000-80000 (HK.D 220000)
£18868 $30000 €28302 Origin of Hachiman Shrine (33x100cm-13x39in) ink col silver gold gold leaf handscrolls pair. 24-Mar-3 Christie's, Rockefeller NY #72/R est:30000-35000

ANONYMOUS (18th C) ?
Works on paper
£17610 $28000 €26415 Crafts, music, sports and scenes of everyday life (719x32cm-283x13in) ink col gold gold leaf handscrolls pair. 24-Mar-3 Christie's, Rockefeller NY #73/R est:20000-30000

ANONYMOUS (19th C) ?
£1677 $2616 €2516 I like this picture (38x48cm-15x19in) plate. 11-Apr-3 Kieselbach, Budapest #204/R est:350000-600000 (H.F 600000)
£8228 $13000 €13000 View of Palermo Bay with mount Pellegrino (90x110cm-35x43in) 28-Nov-2 Dorotheum, Vienna #1/R est:13000-16000
£30263 $46000 €45395 Schooner, Frolic (46x58cm-18x23in) i.d.August 23rd 1855. 17-Aug-2 North East Auctions, Portsmouth #670/R est:15000-25000
£56633 $91746 €82118 Coliseum (48x38cm-19x15in) 25-May-3 Uppsala Auktionskammare, Uppsala #96/R est:8000-10000 (S.KR 730000)
Sculpture
£9177 $14500 €14500 Female figure (127cm-50in) marble. 27-Nov-2 Wiener Kunst Auktionen, Vienna #563/R est:2000-6000
Works on paper
£12342 $19500 €19500 View of St Petersburg across the river Neva (62x92cm-24x36in) gouache. 30-Nov-2 Hagelstam, Helsinki #51/R est:5000

ANONYMOUS (20th C) ?
Photographs
£2160 $3500 €3132 The U.S.S Lafayette, capsized in New York Harbor (72x100cm-28x39in) gelatin silver print prov. 29-Jul-3 Christie's, Rockefeller NY #95/R est:3000-5000

ANORO, Manel (1945-) Spanish
Works on paper
£1039 $1517 €1600 Landscape with figures (47x62cm-19x24in) s. mixed media. 17-Jun-2 Ansorena, Madrid #81/R

ANQUETIN, Louis (1861-1932) French
£621 $993 €900 Scene bachique (30x24cm-12x9in) s. cardboard. 12-Mar-3 E & Eve, Paris #74
£1795 $2818 €2800 Elegante au bois (50x61cm-20x24in) s. 16-Dec-2 Rabourdin & Choppin de Janvry, Paris #50/R
Works on paper
£1042 $1698 €1500 Nu (39x26cm-15x10in) s.d.90 sanguine. 19-Jul-3 Thierry & Lannon, Brest #25/R est:1500-2000
£3816 $6182 €5800 Profil de femme (29x23cm-11x9in) pastel. 22-Jan-3 Tajan, Paris #33/R est:6000-6500

ANSALDO, Giovanni Andrea (1584-1638) Italian
Works on paper
£11486 $17919 €17000 Standing male nude (41x22cm-16x9in) i. chk wash. 27-Mar-3 Christie's, Paris #11/R

ANSCOMBE, Robert (fl.1950s) British
£380 $616 €551 French Design v Gardner; bay with a jockey up (51x61cm-20x24in) s.i. 20-May-3 Dreweatt Neate, Newbury #273/R
£500 $810 €725 Caught Out, a bay in a landscape (51x61cm-20x24in) s.i. 20-May-3 Dreweatt Neate, Newbury #272/R

ANSDELL, Richard (1815-1885) British
£1697 $2750 €2546 Last lesson from a Horn Buck (43x56cm-17x22in) s. board. 23-Jan-3 Aspire, Cleveland #5 est:2750-4500
£3000 $4770 €4500 Sheep and lambs marooned in a torrential stream with shepherds in background (32x59cm-13x23in) s.d.1876. 19-Mar-3 James Thompson, Kirby Lonsdale #100/R
£4908 $8000 €7362 Bloodhound in an interior (31x41cm-12x16in) s.d.1847 canvas on masonite. 11-Feb-3 Bonhams & Doyles, New York #124/R est:8000-12000
£5500 $8580 €8250 Mr Geddes and his dog Glory (46x33cm-18x13in) 14-Apr-3 Sotheby's, London #40/R est:6000-8000
£11039 $17000 €16559 Sick lamb (104x212cm-41x83in) prov. 4-Sep-2 Christie's, Rockefeller NY #377/R est:20000-30000
£14000 $21280 €21000 Waiting for master (49x63cm-19x25in) s.d.1837. 28-Aug-2 Sotheby's, London #822/R est:12000-16000

ANSDELL, Richard (attrib) (1815-1885) British
£2801 $4426 €4202 After the hunt (46x60cm-18x24in) s. 16-Nov-2 Crafoord, Lund #1/R est:10000 (S.KR 40000)

ANSDELL, William (19th C) British
£840 $1394 €1218 Head of a terrier. Head of a gun dog (25x30cm-10x12in) s. pair. 12-Jun-3 Christie's, Kensington #297/R

ANSELL, Montgomery (?) British?
£500 $815 €750 Scottish loch and mountain landscapes (48x74cm-19x29in) s. pair. 14-Feb-3 Keys, Aylsham #668

ANSEN-HOFMANN, E (19/20th C) German
£5189 $8302 €7784 Les marchands d'Esclaves (91x124cm-36x49in) s. prov. 17-Mar-3 Philippe Schuler, Zurich #4602/R est:10000-14000 (S.FR 11000)

ANSINGH, Lizzy (1875-1959) Dutch
£724 $1172 €1100 Girl dressing her doll (27x30cm-11x12in) s.d.1916 panel. 21-Jan-3 Christie's, Amsterdam #243n est:1200-1600
£1572 $2421 €2500 Het avontuur (65x51cm-26x20in) s.d.1924. 23-Oct-2 Christie's, Amsterdam #150/R est:2500-3500
£2740 $4301 €4000 An elegant doll (35x28cm-14x11in) s. canvas on panel. 15-Apr-3 Sotheby's, Amsterdam #99/R est:4000-6000
£2830 $4358 €4500 Roepende (100x130cm-39x51in) s.d.1955 s.i.verso prov.exhib. 23-Oct-2 Christie's, Amsterdam #152/R est:5000-7000
£5031 $7748 €8000 Thought of music (87x81cm-34x32in) init.d.1909 prov. 23-Oct-2 Christie's, Amsterdam #153/R est:9000-12000
£18868 $29057 €30000 Het gele gevaar - le peril jaune. s.d.1906 prov.exhib.lit. 23-Oct-2 Christie's, Amsterdam #151/R est:20000-30000

ANSINGH, Theresa (1883-1968) Dutch
£1042 $1719 €1500 Woolltra (58x70cm-23x28in) s. s.i.verso board. 1-Jul-3 Christie's, Amsterdam #483/R est:1200-1600
£2270 $3677 €3200 Interior with a cat on the arm of a chair (76x64cm-30x25in) board. 26-May-3 Glerum, Amsterdam #81/R est:500-600

ANSON, Mark (19th C) British
£1800 $2790 €2700 Fishing vessels beached on the shore at sunset (105x60cm-41x24in) s. 1-Oct-2 Fellows & Sons, Birmingham #26/R est:500-800

ANTCHER, Isaac (1899-1992) Rumanian
£327 $519 €480 Bouquet de fleurs (62x47cm-24x19in) s. 26-Feb-3 Artcurial Briest, Paris #172

£833 $1308 €1300 House (39x46cm-15x18in) s. 12-Dec-2 Rabourdin & Choppin de Janvry, Paris #69/R

ANTEQUERA ALVAREZ, Jose (1935-) Spanish
£258 $408 €400 Clown (61x73cm-24x29in) s. 18-Dec-2 Ansorena, Madrid #207

ANTES, Horst (1936-) German
£284 $460 €400 You have given me this small landscape (4x5cm-2x2in) d.57 col Indian ink paper on board. 24-May-3 Van Ham, Cologne #8/R
£2372 $3676 €3700 Profile head (30x28cm-12x11in) s.d.76 aquatec oil chk. 3-Dec-2 Lempertz, Koln #12/R est:3600
£2899 $4754 €4000 Untitled (28x22cm-11x9in) s. egg oil tempera col chks. 31-May-3 Villa Grisebach, Berlin #361/R est:4500-5500
£8633 $14158 €12000 Kleiner blauer kopf (33x26cm-13x10in) s.i.d.1975 verso prov. 3-Jun-3 Christie's, Amsterdam #324/R est:12000-16000
£13669 $22417 €19000 Figur (45x35cm-18x14in) s.d.1962 d.on stretcher tempera prov. 3-Jun-3 Christie's, Amsterdam #321/R est:18000-22000
£22785 $35316 €36000 Kneeling blue figure with house (65x74cm-26x29in) s. aquatec pastos chk paper on canvas prov. 28-Sep-2 Ketterer, Hamburg #459/R est:15000-20000

Sculpture
£2244 $3478 €3500 Der kopf (45x46x14cm-18x18x6in) s.num.532 corten steel prov. 3-Dec-2 Christie's, Amsterdam #408/R est:4000-6000
£2564 $3974 €4000 Seated nude female torso (62cm-24in) i. 6-Dec-2 Michael Zeller, Lindau #1816/R est:4000
£3205 $4968 €5000 Figure 1000 (220cm-87in) st.sig. rust pat.steel. 3-Dec-2 Lempertz, Koln #9/R est:4000-5000
£3288 $5129 €4800 Head (45x46x13cm-18x18x5in) s. rust pat.steel. 11-Apr-3 Winterberg, Heidelberg #685/R est:4800

Works on paper
£897 $1391 €1400 Standing figure (60x44cm-24x17in) s.i.d.1970 pencil chk. 6-Dec-2 Hauswedell & Nolte, Hamburg #5/R
£1042 $1646 €1500 Untitled (35x26cm-14x10in) s.d.1965 pencil. 26-Apr-3 Dr Lehr, Berlin #46/R
£1899 $3000 €3000 The story for a king (21x33cm-8x13in) s. W/C col pen chk pen. 30-Nov-2 Villa Grisebach, Berlin #440/R est:3000-4000
£2821 $4372 €4400 Composition (23x17cm-9x7in) s. pencil col pen. 6-Dec-2 Hauswedell & Nolte, Hamburg #4/R est:3000
£2878 $4719 €4000 Briefumschlag (40x30cm-16x12in) s.d.1963 pastel prov. 3-Jun-3 Christie's, Amsterdam #323/R est:4000-6000
£3165 $5000 €5000 Large figure (86x61cm-34x24in) s. i. verso chl board. 30-Nov-2 Villa Grisebach, Berlin #441/R est:5000-6000
£3500 $5845 €5075 Untitled (63x45cm-25x18in) s.d.70 col crayon pencil prov. 27-Jun-3 Christie's, London #237/R est:4000-6000
£3597 $5899 €5000 Komposition (50x39cm-20x15in) s. pencil gouache prov. 3-Jun-3 Christie's, Amsterdam #322/R est:4000-6000
£4710 $7725 €6500 Untitled (66x48cm-26x19in) s.i.d.1962 s. verso gouache Indian ink chk. 28-May-3 Lempertz, Koln #10/R est:8000-10000
£5435 $8913 €7500 Blue t-shirt and 8.8.91 (40x30cm-16x12in) s.i. verso aquatec panel. 31-May-3 Villa Grisebach, Berlin #363/R est:8000-10000
£8333 $12917 €13000 Untitled (96x61cm-38x24in) s. aquatec chl paper on board. 3-Dec-2 Lempertz, Koln #10/R est:15000-17000
£11354 $16576 €17031 Figure with teeth in third mouth (91x64cm-36x25in) s. mixed media board on canvas prov. 4-Jun-2 Germann, Zurich #73/R est:30000-35000 (S.FR 26000)

ANTHONE, Gustave (1897-1925) Belgian
£260 $406 €390 Bridge over a river (24x32cm-9x13in) s. board. 15-Oct-2 Bonhams, Knightsbridge #63

ANTHONISSEN, Hendrick van (1606-?) Dutch
£4459 $6955 €7000 Fishing boats in stormy seas, distant view of a town (33x51cm-13x20in) s.d.33 panel prov.exhib.lit. 5-Nov-2 Sotheby's, Amsterdam #27/R est:8000-12000
£7643 $11924 €12000 Boeier and other sailing vessels in a stiff breeze on the Zuiderzee (23x30cm-9x12in) panel prov.exhib.lit. 5-Nov-2 Sotheby's, Amsterdam #84/R est:15000-20000
£8633 $13813 €12000 Shipping in calm with fishing boat (40x60cm-16x24in) panel. 13-May-3 Sotheby's, Amsterdam #57/R est:10000-15000

ANTHONISSEN, Hendrick van (attrib) (1606-?) Dutch
Works on paper
£600 $924 €900 Sailing ships (20x33cm-8x13in) sepia ink en grisaille. 25-Oct-2 Gorringes, Lewes #891

ANTHONISZ, Aert (circle) (1580-1620) Flemish
£17834 $27822 €28000 Heavily armed Dutch four master and other ships at open sea. Armed merchantman (16x23cm-6x9in) copper pair. 5-Nov-2 Sotheby's, Amsterdam #223/R est:20000-30000

ANTHONNIESSEN, Hendrik Joseph (attrib) (18th C) Flemish?
£7500 $11625 €11250 River landscape with traders and townsfolk by a ferry. Landscape with figures by a ferry shop (39x65cm-15x26in) indis sig. pair. 30-Oct-2 Christie's, Kensington #13/R est:8000-12000

ANTHONY, Carol (1943-) American?
Works on paper
£427 $700 €619 New Mexico, early mountain light (28x28cm-11x11in) s.i. col pastel. 5-Jun-3 Swann Galleries, New York #2/R

ANTHONY, Henry Mark (1817-1886) British
£7500 $11850 €11250 Thinking of the future, an Irish sketch (54x86cm-21x34in) prov.exhib.lit. 26-Nov-2 Christie's, London #122/R est:8000-12000

ANTIQUUS, Johannes (1702-1750) Dutch
Works on paper
£2222 $3600 €3333 Woman at fountain. Shepherd under ruined arch (36x24cm-14x9in) chk pen ink wash. 22-Jan-3 Christie's, Rockefeller NY #95a/R est:6000

ANTOINE, Marguerite (1907-1989) ?
£616 $962 €900 Jeune femme nue allongee (87x101cm-34x40in) s. 14-Apr-3 Horta, Bruxelles #157
£865 $1359 €1350 Yvette (90x116cm-35x46in) s.exhib. 19-Nov-2 Vanderkindere, Brussels #157

ANTOINE, Otto (1865-1951) German
£253 $400 €400 View over Friedrichs bridge to Berlin Stock Exchange (20x27cm-8x11in) s. board. 30-Nov-2 Bassenge, Berlin #6749
£449 $696 €700 Schlosschen Sayn am Rhein (50x61cm-20x24in) s. i. stretcher prov. 7-Dec-2 Ketterer, Hamburg #170/R
£641 $994 €1000 Rhein near Koblenz (60x80cm-24x31in) s. 7-Dec-2 Dannenberg, Berlin #644/R

ANTOLINEZ, Jose (circle) (1635-1675) Spanish
£6000 $10020 €8700 The immaculate conception (143x102cm-56x40in) 9-Jul-3 Bonhams, New Bond Street #14/R est:6000-10000

ANTON, Bill (?) ?
£2949 $4600 €4424 Malapai moon (41x51cm-16x20in) 9-Nov-2 Altermann Galleries, Santa Fe #59
£3762 $6095 €5455 Where time stands still (46x61cm-18x24in) board. 23-May-3 Altermann Galleries, Santa Fe #25

ANTON, Victor (20th C) British
£260 $403 €390 Untitled (27x35cm-11x14in) s. scraper board. 24-Sep-2 Bonhams, New Bond Street #73
£450 $698 €675 Untitled (36x49cm-14x19in) s.i.d. scraper board. 24-Sep-2 Bonhams, New Bond Street #72

ANTONELLO DA MESSINA (15th C) Italian
£220000 $367400 €319000 Madonna and Child with a Franciscan monk. Ecce Homo in a trompe l'oeil (15x11cm-6x4in) gold ground double-sided. 9-Jul-3 Christie's, London #81/R est:200000-300000

ANTONI, Janine (1964-) American
Photographs
£24051 $38000 €36077 Coddle (55x41cm-22x16in) s.d.1999 verso cibachrome mounted plexiglas prov.lit. 14-Nov-2 Christie's, Rockefeller NY #422/R est:30000-40000

Sculpture
£14103 $22000 €21155 Lipstick (39x25x37cm-15x10x15in) six lipstick pigment beeswax chewed lard glass. 11-Nov-2 Phillips, New York #1/R est:20000-30000

ANTONI, Louis Ferdinand (1872-1940) French
£3145 $4843 €5000 Depart du cavalier (92x72cm-36x28in) s.d.90 panel. 23-Oct-2 Rabourdin & Choppin de Janvry, Paris #198/R est:4500-5300
£3846 $6038 €6000 Femmes berberes (170x140cm-67x55in) 16-Dec-2 Gros & Delettrez, Paris #346/R

ANTONISSEN, Henri Joseph (1737-1794) Flemish
£4307 $6546 €6461 Shepherd resting (62x91cm-24x36in) s.d.1790. 27-Aug-2 Rasmussen, Copenhagen #1936/R est:60000-80000 (D.KR 50000)

ANTRAL, Louis Robert (1895-1940) French
Works on paper
£382 $603 €550 Quais de Seine en hiver (29x45cm-11x18in) s.d.1921 W/C. 25-Apr-3 Piasa, Paris #44

£625 $987 €900 Bateaux au prt (26x45cm-10x18in) s. W/C. 25-Apr-3 Piasa, Paris #43/R
£694 $1132 €1000 La place du village (44x30cm-17x12in) s. W/C. 19-Jul-3 Thierry & Lannon, Brest #48

ANTWERP SCHOOL (16th C) Flemish
£5183 $8500 €7775 Adoration of the Magi (89x65cm-35x26in) panel. 29-May-3 Sotheby's, New York #21/R est:10000-15000
£8108 $12649 €12000 Scenes from the life of Saint eronica (82x170cm-32x67in) d.1553 panel. 26-Mar-3 Tajan, Paris #113/R est:20000
£11486 $17919 €17000 Christ bearing the Cross (62x42cm-24x17in) panel painted c.1540. 28-Mar-3 Piasa, Paris #8/R est:6000
£11859 $18381 €18500 Woman holding brass (44x32cm-17x13in) panel. 6-Dec-2 Rieunier, Bailly-Pommery, Mathias, Paris #30/R est:18000

ANTWERP SCHOOL (17th C) Flemish
£5036 $8058 €7000 Architectural capriccio with King David and Bathseba (53x71cm-21x28in) panel. 13-May-3 Sotheby's, Amsterdam #78/R est:8000-12000
£7194 $11511 €10000 Village scene in landscape with shepherd and flock (49x71cm-19x28in) panel. 13-May-3 Sotheby's, Amsterdam #4/R est:6000-8000
£9200 $15088 €13340 Figures by a banquet table laden with food (163x238cm-64x94in) 9-Jun-3 Bonhams, Bath #110/R est:6000-8000
£18000 $28080 €27000 Annunciation (37x44cm-15x17in) silvered copper oval prov. 10-Apr-3 Sotheby's, London #30/R est:8000

ANUSZKIEWICZ, Richard (1930-) American
£645 $1000 €968 Untitled (52x122cm-20x48in) s.d.1975 verso. 26-Sep-2 Christie's, Rockefeller NY #799/R est:7000-9000
£1763 $2750 €2645 Untitled (48x60cm-19x24in) acrylic. 5-Nov-2 Doyle, New York #44/R est:3000-5000
Works on paper
£3750 $6000 €5625 Distinctness of red (91x91cm-36x36in) s.d.1965 verso liquitex on board prov. 14-May-3 Sotheby's, New York #139/R est:6000-8000

ANWAR, Ahmad Zakii (1955-) Malaysian
£5828 $9615 €8451 In absence (122x183cm-48x72in) s. acrylic linen exhib. 6-Jul-3 Christie's, Hong Kong #47/R est:55000-105000 (HK.D 75000)

ANZINGER, Siegfried (1953-) Austrian
£1389 $2208 €2000 Mother with child (60x42cm-24x17in) s.d.82 acrylic. 29-Apr-3 Wiener Kunst Auktionen, Vienna #506/R est:2000-2800
£1418 $2298 €2000 Two figures (42x60cm-17x24in) s.d23.4.82 acrylic paper on board. 20-May-3 Dorotheum, Vienna #280/R est:2000-2600
£3901 $6319 €5500 Untitled - monk (50x60cm-20x24in) s. verso. 20-May-3 Dorotheum, Vienna #290/R est:6000-8000
£5696 $8829 €9000 Smoker (128x78cm-50x31in) s.d.6.76. 24-Sep-2 Wiener Kunst Auktionen, Vienna #283/R est:9000-14000
£7595 $12000 €12000 Circus animals (95x135cm-37x53in) 27-Nov-2 Dorotheum, Vienna #287/R est:12000-15000
Sculpture
£1348 $2183 €1900 Mother and child (27cm-11in) painted terracotta. 20-May-3 Dorotheum, Vienna #282/R est:2200-2600
Works on paper
£437 $638 €656 Green cover (59x41cm-23x16in) s.d.1984 W/C. 4-Jun-2 Germann, Zurich #735 (S.FR 1000)
£532 $862 €750 Untitled (58x41cm-23x16in) s.d.85 mixed media. 20-May-3 Dorotheum, Vienna #279/R
£641 $1013 €1000 Two kisses (57x42cm-22x17in) s.mono.i. mixed media. 12-Nov-2 Dorotheum, Vienna #247/R
£662 $1079 €1000 Untitled (63x45cm-25x18in) s.d.82 mixed media. 28-Jan-3 Dorotheum, Vienna #238/R
£662 $1079 €1000 Creation of the horses (29x41cm-11x16in) s.d.02 pencil W/C. 28-Jan-3 Dorotheum, Vienna #305/R
£759 $1200 €1200 Evening nude (39x49cm-15x19in) s.i.d.3/76 col pen. 27-Nov-2 Dorotheum, Vienna #289/R
£795 $1295 €1200 Christ and the lion (29x40cm-11x16in) s.d.99 pen ink pencil col crayon. 28-Jan-3 Dorotheum, Vienna #303/R
£949 $1472 €1500 Mineralogist (59x41cm-23x16in) s.d.84 i. verso. 24-Sep-2 Wiener Kunst Auktionen, Vienna #281/R
£949 $1500 €1500 Untitled (42x55cm-17x22in) s.d.82 acrylic gouache. 27-Nov-2 Dorotheum, Vienna #324/R
£1250 $1987 €1800 Untitled (44x32cm-17x13in) s.d.79 mixed media. 29-Apr-3 Wiener Kunst Auktionen, Vienna #503/R est:1500-2500
£2128 $3447 €3000 Untitled (69x99cm-27x39in) s.d.80 mixed media. 20-May-3 Dorotheum, Vienna #263/R est:3000-4000
£2431 $3865 €3500 Untitled (90x70cm-35x28in) s. mixed media. 29-Apr-3 Wiener Kunst Auktionen, Vienna #495/R est:3000-4500
£6028 $9766 €8500 Cart and horse (68x88cm-27x35in) s.d.97 verso distemper prov. 20-May-3 Dorotheum, Vienna #103/R est:8000-11000

APARICIO GUERRERO, Carlos (1948-) Spanish
£452 $714 €700 Window (65x50cm-26x20in) s.d.99 s.i.d.verso board. 17-Dec-2 Durán, Madrid #97/R
£481 $760 €750 Old tennis shoes (100x81cm-39x32in) s.d.98. 19-Nov-2 Durán, Madrid #748/R
£481 $760 €750 Aranjuez (100x81cm-39x32in) s.d.99. 19-Nov-2 Durán, Madrid #747
£641 $1013 €1000 Main entrance (80x120cm-31x47in) s.d.99 s.i.d.verso. 19-Nov-2 Durán, Madrid #134/R

APARICIO, Victor (1958-) Spanish
£397 $648 €600 Life sea (73x100cm-29x39in) s.i.d.1991 verso prov. 11-Feb-3 Segre, Madrid #293/R
£452 $714 €700 Formula (73x100cm-29x39in) s. s.i.d.1992 verso prov. 17-Dec-2 Segre, Madrid #165/R

APARIN, Sergei (1961-) Russian
£6114 $9537 €9171 Athos (139x179cm-55x70in) panel. 20-Nov-2 Fischer, Luzern #1195/R est:28000-35000 (S.FR 14000)

APELLANIZ, Jesus (1898-1969) Spanish
£2338 $3413 €3600 Samil beach (46x55cm-18x22in) s. i.verso. 17-Jun-2 Ansorena, Madrid #159/R
£3571 $5214 €5500 Bilbao harbour (46x55cm-18x22in) s. 17-Jun-2 Ansorena, Madrid #161/R

APHEL, Fabio (1957-) Italian
£272 $433 €400 Rocky village (50x50cm-20x20in) s. board. 1-Mar-3 Meeting Art, Vercelli #663
£321 $503 €500 Acrobats (50x50cm-20x20in) s. s.i.verso board. 23-Nov-2 Meeting Art, Vercelli #431
£340 $541 €500 Sand castle (80x100cm-31x39in) s. board. 1-Mar-3 Meeting Art, Vercelli #467

APIN, Mochtar (1923-1994) Indonesian
£1823 $2807 €2735 Still life (38x46cm-15x18in) s. 27-Oct-2 Christie's, Hong Kong #93/R est:18000-28000 (HK.D 22000)

APOL, Armand-Adrien-Marie (1879-1950) Belgian
£284 $474 €400 Vue d'Alost (35x45cm-14x18in) s. 17-Jun-3 Palais de Beaux Arts, Brussels #504
£552 $877 €800 Paysage fluvial (75x90cm-30x35in) s. 4-Mar-3 Palais de Beaux Arts, Brussels #278
£604 $972 €900 Bord de canal anime a Gand (42x50cm-17x20in) s. 18-Feb-3 Vanderkindere, Brussels #47
£1418 $2369 €2000 Low tide (70x81cm-28x32in) s. 23-Jun-3 Bernaerts, Antwerp #34/R est:2000-2500
Works on paper
£379 $603 €550 Les baigneuses (33x40cm-13x16in) s.d.1923 gouache. 4-Mar-3 Palais de Beaux Arts, Brussels #276

APOL, L F H (1850-1936) Dutch
£400 $632 €580 Winter landscape with lone figure and windmill (18x25cm-7x10in) s. 24-Jul-3 John Nicholson, Haslemere #1188

APOL, Louis (1850-1936) Dutch
£955 $1471 €1500 Polder landscape with windmills (16x23cm-6x9in) s. panel. 3-Sep-2 Christie's, Amsterdam #162 est:1000-1500
£3237 $5180 €4500 Winter canal landscape at sunset (60x40cm-24x16in) s. 17-May-3 Lempertz, Koln #1359/R est:5000
£3459 $5327 €5500 Approaching train (17x22cm-7x9in) s. panel. 22-Oct-2 Sotheby's, Amsterdam #109/R est:4000-6000
£4225 $6803 €6000 Coast in winter with figures and boats (31x49cm-12x19in) s. 7-May-3 Vendue Huis, Gravenhage #456/R est:7000-9000
£4930 $7937 €7000 Snowy landscape with church (39x59cm-15x23in) s. 7-May-3 Vendue Huis, Gravenhage #466/R est:7000-9000
£6289 $9686 €10000 View of the outskirts of the Delf in winter (56x80cm-22x31in) s. 23-Oct-2 Christie's, Amsterdam #199/R est:8000-12000
£7639 $12146 €11000 Sunny winter's day (39x50cm-15x20in) s. 29-Apr-3 Christie's, Amsterdam #145/R est:4000-6000
£10274 $16130 €15000 View of Dordrecht in winter (55x70cm-22x28in) s. prov. 15-Apr-3 Sotheby's, Amsterdam #111/R est:6000-8000
£12739 $19873 €20000 Winter scene with farm on edge of forest (39x49cm-15x19in) s. 6-Nov-2 Vendue Huis, Gravenhage #563/R est:25000-30000
£58219 $91404 €85000 Snowy landscape at sunset (112x78cm-44x31in) s. 15-Apr-3 Sotheby's, Amsterdam #213/R est:40000-60000
Works on paper
£414 $658 €600 Polder landscape with windmills in winter (10x16cm-4x6in) s. crayon gouache. 10-Mar-3 Sotheby's, Amsterdam #151/R
£556 $894 €834 Landscape with hay waggon and farmstead (11x17cm-4x7in) s. W/C bodycol. 7-May-3 Dobiaschofsky, Bern #325/R (S.FR 1200)
£602 $969 €903 Evening landscape with river (13x18cm-5x7in) s. W/C bodycol. 7-May-3 Dobiaschofsky, Bern #326/R (S.FR 1300)
£987 $1599 €1500 Canal in winter (12x18cm-5x7in) s. black chk gouache. 21-Jan-3 Christie's, Amsterdam #210/R est:1500-2500
£1736 $2865 €2500 Country road in winter (15x21cm-6x8in) s. W/C boydcol paper on cardboard. 1-Jul-3 Christie's, Amsterdam #94/R est:2000-3000

£1944 $3208 €2800 Forest path in winter (14x18cm-6x7in) s. gouache. 1-Jul-3 Christie's, Amsterdam #166/R est:2000-3000
£1972 $3175 €2800 Forest in winter with horse and wagon (17x10cm-7x4in) s. gouache. 7-May-3 Vendue Huis, Gravenhage #455/R est:3000-5000
£2961 $4796 €4500 Wooded winter landscapes (14x17cm-6x7in) s. W/C bodycol pair. 21-Jan-3 Christie's, Amsterdam #213/R est:2500-3500
£4717 $7264 €7500 Winter landscape with travellers on a path (35x54cm-14x21in) s. W/C htd white. 22-Oct-2 Sotheby's, Amsterdam #96/R est:5000-7000

APOLLONIO DI GIOVANNI (1415-1465) Italian
£535484 $846064 €830000 Allegory of Music (65cm-26in circular) tempera board lit. 19-Dec-2 Semenzato, Venice #24/R est:600000

APOTHELOZ, Jean (1900-1965) Swiss
£262 $409 €393 Village en hiver (59x92cm-23x36in) s.d.62 i. verso panel. 6-Nov-2 Dobiaschofsky, Bern #3136 (S.FR 600)

APPAY, Emile (1876-1935) French
£473 $738 €700 Gare et trains la nuit (38x55cm-15x22in) s. 27-Mar-3 Maigret, Paris #325
£574 $896 €850 Pont sur la Seine a Rouen (38x55cm-15x22in) s. 27-Mar-3 Maigret, Paris #326/R
£628 $980 €930 Vue de La Salute (38x55cm-15x22in) s. 27-Mar-3 Maigret, Paris #324/R

Works on paper
£270 $422 €400 Bateaux a quai a Marseille (37x55cm-15x22in) s. W/C. 27-Mar-3 Maigret, Paris #312
£270 $422 €400 Berges d'Orsay (36x53cm-14x21in) s. W/C. 27-Mar-3 Maigret, Paris #319/R
£405 $632 €600 Port de Marseille (38x57cm-15x22in) s. W/C. 27-Mar-3 Maigret, Paris #316/R
£1014 $1581 €1500 Entree du port a Marseille (38x57cm-15x22in) s. W/C. 27-Mar-3 Maigret, Paris #317/R

APPEL, Andreas (19th C) Norwegian?
Works on paper
£861 $1309 €1292 The sloop Meta in 1832 (40x52cm-16x20in) mono. gouache. 28-Aug-2 Museumsbygningen, Copenhagen #43/R (D.KR 10000)

APPEL, Charles P (1857-1936) American
£550 $864 €825 Twilight landscape (22x27cm-9x11in) s. board. 16-Dec-2 Bonhams, Bury St Edmunds #517/R
£3145 $5000 €4718 Landscape at sunset (76x91cm-30x36in) s. painted c.1900. 2-Mar-3 Toomey, Oak Park #662/R est:5000-7000

APPEL, Karel (1921-) Dutch
£2286 $3544 €3429 Composition (67x50cm-26x20in) paper on canvas. 1-Oct-2 Rasmussen, Copenhagen #100/R est:30000 (D.KR 27000)
£2383 $3717 €3575 Head (23x17cm-9x7in) s. paper on panel. 5-Nov-2 Bukowskis, Stockholm #320/R est:30000-35000 (S.KR 34000)
£2421 $3729 €3850 Composition (40x27cm-16x11in) s.d.1983 acrylic cardboard. 26-Oct-2 Cornette de St.Cyr, Paris #34/R
£2532 $3924 €4000 Tete (60x45cm-24x18in) s.i. num.17/60 panel. 28-Sep-2 Ketterer, Hamburg #575/R est:4000-4500
£2585 $4110 €3800 Head (37x26cm-15x10in) s. acrylic prov. 24-Mar-3 Cornette de St.Cyr, Paris #22/R
£2746 $4559 €3982 Composition (25x83cm-10x33in) s. acrylic paper. 12-Jun-3 Kunsthallen, Copenhagen #36/R est:35000 (D.KR 29000)
£3097 $4800 €4646 Three brothers (58x76cm-23x30in) s.d.69 acrylic crayon on paper prov.lit. 26-Sep-2 Christie's, Rockefeller NY #725/R est:6000-8000
£3237 $5309 €4500 Het Stenen Hooft, Amsterdam (61x81cm-24x32in) s.d.42. 3-Jun-3 Christie's, Amsterdam #22/R est:2000-3000
£3261 $5348 €4500 Untitled (32x50cm-13x20in) s.d.59 oil chk prov. 28-May-3 Lempertz, Koln #12/R est:4000-5000
£3895 $6037 €5843 Two figures (67x83cm-26x33in) s. acrylic paper on canvas sold with photograph painted 1974. 1-Oct-2 Rasmussen, Copenhagen #91/R est:50000 (D.KR 46000)
£4430 $7000 €7000 Untitled (24x29cm-9x11in) s. acrylic paper on canvas. 26-Nov-2 Sotheby's, Amsterdam #231/R est:7000-10000
£5256 $8199 €7884 Untitled (38x50cm-15x20in) s. acrylic prov. 6-Nov-2 AB Stockholms Auktionsverk #957/R est:40000-50000 (S.KR 75000)
£5390 $8355 €8085 Figure composition (89x151cm-35x59in) s. acrylic paper on canvas. 8-Dec-2 Uppsala Auktionskammare, Uppsala #277/R est:80000-100000 (S.KR 76000)
£5396 $8418 €8094 Untitled (38x50cm-15x20in) s. acrylic prov. 6-Nov-2 AB Stockholms Auktionsverk #958/R est:40000-50000 (S.KR 77000)
£5674 $9475 €8000 Sans titre (77x57cm-30x22in) s. s.d.verso acrylic paper on canvas. 23-Jun-3 Claude Boisgirard, Paris #145/R est:9000-10000
£6207 $9931 €9000 Tete rouge (57x37cm-22x15in) s.d.83 acrylic wax crayon paper. 15-Mar-3 De Vuyst, Lokeren #494/R est:9500-11000
£7097 $11213 €11000 Composition (51x61cm-20x24in) s. masonite prov. 18-Dec-2 Christie's, Rome #213/R
£7605 $12015 €11408 L'embrassement (116x73cm-46x29in) s. painted 1986. 28-Apr-3 Bukowskis, Stockholm #332/R est:100000-125000 (S.KR 100000)
£7692 $11923 €12000 Figure (46x38cm-18x15in) s. painted c.1975 prov. 3-Dec-2 Christie's, Amsterdam #274/R est:10000-15000
£8163 $12980 €12000 Two figures (81x65cm-32x26in) s. acrylic. 24-Mar-3 Cornette de St.Cyr, Paris #23/R
£8273 $13237 €11500 Rode caracas (79x57cm-31x22in) s. acrylic on print on paper on canvas lit. 17-May-3 De Vuyst, Lokeren #585/R est:12000-14000
£8369 $12972 €12554 Composition with head (89x76cm-35x30in) s. acrylic paper on canvas. 8-Dec-2 Uppsala Auktionskammare, Uppsala #276/R est:80000-100000 (S.KR 118000)
£9475 $14686 €14213 Figure composition (48x77cm-19x30in) s.d.73 acrylic paper on canvas. 4-Dec-2 Kunsthallen, Copenhagen #145/R est:125000 (D.KR 110000)
£10161 $15749 €15242 Figure composition (112x77cm-44x30in) acrylic paper on canvas prov. 1-Oct-2 Rasmussen, Copenhagen #86/R est:125000-150000 (D.KR 120000)
£10256 $15897 €16000 Fille jaune (24x19cm-9x7in) init. s.d.1959 prov. 3-Dec-2 Christie's, Amsterdam #276/R est:10000-15000
£10692 $16572 €17000 Figure (54x65cm-21x26in) s. 30-Oct-2 Artcurial Briest, Paris #463/R est:12000-15000
£11563 $18038 €17345 Composition (65x54cm-26x21in) s. acrylic prov. 6-Nov-2 AB Stockholms Auktionsverk #959/R est:40000-50000 (S.KR 165000)
£12000 $19680 €18000 Untitled (68x83cm-27x33in) s.d.75 acrylic paper on panel. 6-Feb-3 Christie's, London #623/R est:12000-16000
£12025 $19000 €19000 Personnages (120x160cm-47x63in) s. oil acrylic paper on canvas painted 1986 prov. 26-Nov-2 Sotheby's, Amsterdam #228/R est:19000-25000
£12821 $19872 €20000 Profil jaune fille (51x60cm-20x24in) s. s.i.d.1966 on stretcher. 3-Dec-2 Christie's, Amsterdam #277/R est:11000-16000
£14103 $21859 €22000 Teddy bear - circus series (76x56cm-30x22in) s. acrylic wooden relief painted 1977 prov. 3-Dec-2 Christie's, Amsterdam #273/R est:20000-30000
£14423 $22644 €22500 Heine man (76x58cm-30x23in) s.d.1973 prov. 20-Nov-2 Pandolfini, Florence #129/R
£15484 $24000 €23226 Splintered head (81x65cm-32x26in) s. painted 1966 prov. 26-Sep-2 Christie's, Rockefeller NY #724/R est:20000-25000
£15625 $25000 €23438 Two people (99x65cm-39x26in) s. s.i.d.1971 verso acrylic prov. 14-May-3 Sotheby's, New York #238/R est:30000-40000
£15823 $25000 €23735 Paysage (102x152cm-40x60in) s.d.61 i.verso oil oilstick gouache paper on canvas. 13-Nov-2 Sotheby's, New York #324/R est:25000-35000
£16312 $26426 €23000 Trois tetes (65x81cm-26x32in) s. prov. 26-May-3 Christie's, Milan #347/R est:10000-14000
£16935 $26249 €25403 The conversation - figure composition (122x152cm-48x60in) s. painted 1984. 1-Oct-2 Rasmussen, Copenhagen #98/R est:300000 (D.KR 200000)
£18000 $27720 €27000 Untitled (64x80cm-25x31in) s.d.58 prov.exhib. 22-Oct-2 Sotheby's, London #447/R est:20000-30000
£19444 $32083 €28000 Deux oiseaux (51x73cm-20x29in) s. prov. 1-Jul-3 Artcurial Briest, Paris #517/R est:20000-25000
£20312 $32500 €30468 Cycliste (161x120cm-63x47in) s.d.69 acrylic paper on canvas. 14-May-3 Sotheby's, New York #236/R est:40000-60000
£21000 $32340 €31500 Untitled (80x65cm-31x26in) painted 1959 prov.exhib. 22-Oct-2 Sotheby's, London #441/R est:25000-35000
£23000 $38410 €33350 See me again (99x81cm-39x32in) s. i.stretcher prov. 26-Jun-3 Sotheby's, London #233/R est:15000-20000
£25180 $41295 €35000 Happy birthday (203x203cm-80x80in) s.d.75 acrylic. 3-Jun-3 Christie's, Amsterdam #356/R est:40000-60000
£26000 $43420 €37700 Deux personnages (52x68cm-20x27in) s.d.57 oil pastel paper on canvas prov. 26-Jun-3 Sotheby's, London #241/R est:15000-20000
£38462 $59615 €60000 Bataille - two dragons (97x195cm-38x77in) s.d.59 prov. 3-Dec-2 Christie's, Amsterdam #315/R est:65000-95000
£42000 $68880 €63000 Springtime (91x61cm-36x24in) s.d.55 burlap prov.exhib. 6-Feb-3 Christie's, London #612/R est:30000-50000
£63291 $100000 €94937 I mannetje (79x46cm-31x18in) s. prov.exhib. 24-Apr-3 Shannon's, Milford #124/R est:100000-150000
£70513 $109295 €110000 Personnage dans la tempete (130x195cm-51x77in) s.d.62 prov.exhib.lit. 3-Dec-2 Christie's, Amsterdam #313/R est:65000-95000
£80000 $133600 €120000 Composition (140x110cm-55x43in) s.d.54 burlap prov. 25-Jun-3 Sotheby's, London #30/R est:50000-70000
£80000 $133600 €116000 Critournant (130x195cm-51x77in) s.d.59 i.stretcher prov.exhib. 26-Jun-3 Sotheby's, London #239/R est:60000-80000
£86331 $141583 €120000 Gelukkige dag - happy day (115x146cm-45x57in) s. i.on stretcher painted 1964 prov.exhib. 3-Jun-3 Christie's, Amsterdam #381/R est:70000-90000
£160000 $262400 €240000 Nanny (130x115cm-51x45in) s.d.50 s.d.verso prov.exhib.lit. 6-Feb-3 Sotheby's, London #20/R est:250000

£210000 $350700 €315000 Woman with fish (142x110cm-56x43in) s.d.53 s.stretcher burlap prov.exhib. 25-Jun-3 Sotheby's, London #20/R est:140000-180000

Prints

£13043 $20217 €19565 Circus (61x96cm-24x38in) col woodcut canvas panel 30. 4-Dec-2 Koller, Zurich #305/R est:30000-40000 (S.FR 30000)
£14388 $23597 €20000 Circus (76x56cm-30x22in) s.num.II/XX woodengraving three volumes. 3-Jun-3 Christie's, Amsterdam #473/R est:20000-30000

Sculpture

£1250 $1975 €1800 Dancing girl (48cm-19in) s.num.15/60 multiple paint wood. 28-Apr-3 Cornette de St.Cyr, Paris #324 est:2000-2500
£1266 $1962 €2000 Dancing girl (48cm-19in) s.num.24/60 painted wood. 28-Sep-2 Cornette de St.Cyr, Paris #218/R est:1800-2000
£1723 $2670 €2585 Once I was the sun (64x89cm-25x35in) s.num.1/8 picture of 12 ceramic tiles. 4-Dec-2 Kunsthallen, Copenhagen #231/R est:20000 (D.KR 20000)
£1809 $2804 €2714 Dancing girl (51cm-20in) s.num.7/60 painted wood. 4-Dec-2 Kunsthallen, Copenhagen #211/R est:20000 (D.KR 21000)
£2431 $3840 €3500 Clowncat (87x83x13cm-34x33x5in) s.num.4/25 multiple paint wood. 28-Apr-3 Cornette de St.Cyr, Paris #322/R est:4000-4500
£3717 $5874 €5576 Kyk Leef Speel Met Karel Appel. s.d.77 num.241/300 wood in box sold with seven serigraphs. 1-Apr-3 Rasmussen, Copenhagen #326/R est:35000 (D.KR 40000)
£4487 $7000 €6731 Untitled (97cm-38in) s.num.3/8 wood. 30-Mar-3 Susanin's, Chicago #6055/R est:4000-6000
£7000 $11410 €10500 Close together (78cm-31in) s.1/7 painted wood. 3-Feb-3 Bonhams, New Bond Street #80/R est:6000-8000

Works on paper

£877 $1385 €1316 Figures (48x62cm-19x24in) s.d.53 black gouache. 30-Nov-2 Goteborg Auktionsverk, Sweden #504/R (S.KR 12500)
£897 $1391 €1400 Do not enter (25x34cm-10x13in) s.d.84 gouache photocollage. 3-Dec-2 Christie's, Amsterdam #161/R est:1500-2000
£962 $1490 €1500 Manhattan saving bank (26x34cm-10x13in) s.d.84 gouache on photo collage. 3-Dec-2 Christie's, Amsterdam #163/R est:1500-2000
£1582 $2500 €2500 Face (20x13cm-8x5in) s. gouache ink paper on canvas. 26-Nov-2 Sotheby's, Amsterdam #49a/R est:3500-5000
£2115 $3279 €3300 Untitled (45x56cm-18x22in) s. wax crayon. 7-Dec-2 Van Ham, Cologne #9/R est:6500
£2244 $3478 €3500 Head (21x17cm-8x7in) s. pastel gouache paper on canvas. 3-Dec-2 Christie's, Amsterdam #122/R est:3500-4000
£2778 $4583 €4000 Personnages (27x41cm-11x16in) s. gouache wax pastel. 1-Jul-3 Artcurial Briest, Paris #801/R est:3000-4000
£3500 $5425 €5250 Angry rooster (58x76cm-23x30in) s.d.69 wax crayon gouache lit. 5-Dec-2 Christie's, Kensington #211/R est:3000-4000
£3500 $5425 €5250 Me and my girl (58x76cm-23x30in) s.d.69 col wax crayons. 5-Dec-2 Christie's, Kensington #212/R est:3000-4000
£3597 $5899 €5000 Jeune fille - young girl (48x33cm-19x13in) s.d.57 i.verso chl gouache prov. 3-Jun-3 Christie's, Amsterdam #328/R est:6000-8000
£3871 $6000 €5807 Listening to my bird (58x76cm-23x30in) s.d.69 crayon prov.lit. 26-Sep-2 Christie's, Rockefeller NY #728/R est:6000-8000
£4064 $6341 €6096 Untitled (48x62cm-19x24in) s. mixed media. 5-Nov-2 Bukowskis, Stockholm #321/R est:15000-20000 (S.KR 58000)
£4114 $6500 €6500 Untitled (33x41cm-13x16in) s.d.59 wax crayon. 29-Nov-2 Farsetti, Prato #266/R
£4359 $6844 €6800 Composition (28x55cm-11x22in) s.d.61 gouache. 25-Nov-2 Glerum, Amsterdam #354/R est:3000-5000
£4577 $7370 €6500 Figuration (69x50cm-27x20in) s.d.1953 gouache col chks lit. 9-May-3 Schloss Ahlden, Ahlden #1569/R est:3900
£5063 $8000 €8000 Beest (24x31cm-9x12in) init. felt tip pen executed c.1948. 26-Nov-2 Sotheby's, Amsterdam #215/R est:7000-9000
£5556 $8833 €8000 Teste avec bleu (77x57cm-30x22in) s.d.1960 mixed media collage. 1-May-3 Meeting Art, Vercelli #236
£5703 $9011 €8555 Untitled (78x60cm-31x24in) s. mixed media paper on canvas. 28-Apr-3 Bukowskis, Stockholm #337/R est:50000-70000 (S.KR 75000)
£6475 $10619 €9000 Tete (75x55cm-30x22in) s.d.57 gouache prov. 3-Jun-3 Christie's, Amsterdam #329/R est:6000-8000
£6475 $10619 €9000 Compositie (49x64cm-19x25in) s.d.54 wax crayon gouache prov. 3-Jun-3 Christie's, Amsterdam #330/R est:8000-12000
£6875 $11000 €10313 Untitled (69x104cm-27x41in) s.d.63 acrylic chk col crayon paper collage prov. 14-May-3 Sotheby's, New York #237/R est:15000-20000
£7246 $11884 €10000 C'est un oiseau comme la nuit (76x56cm-30x22in) s.d.59 s.i.d. verso gouache col chks Indian ink brush board prov. 31-May-3 Villa Grisebach, Berlin #360/R est:10000-15000
£7639 $12146 €11000 Looking through the window (91x63cm-36x25in) s.d.1981 pastel. 29-Apr-3 Campo, Vlaamse Kaai #6/R est:11000-15000
£7925 $12204 €12600 Figure (65x50cm-26x20in) s. mixed media exec.1963 prov. 26-Oct-2 Cornette de St.Cyr, Paris #28/R
£13291 $21000 €21000 Three heads (49x63cm-19x25in) s.d.53 gouache chk prov. 26-Nov-2 Sotheby's, Amsterdam #214/R est:9600-12500
£17722 $28000 €28000 Vogels (50x65cm-20x26in) s.d.50 gouache chk prov.exhib. 26-Nov-2 Sotheby's, Amsterdam #211/R est:28000-35000

APPEL, Karl (1866-1937) German

Sculpture

£1528 $2414 €2200 Blue boy (66x47x9cm-26x19x4in) s.num.2/60 multiple paint wood. 28-Apr-3 Cornette de St.Cyr, Paris #321/R est:2500-3000

APPEL, Kevin (1967-) American

£12025 $19000 €18038 4 tier bookshelf (141x152cm-56x60in) s.i.d.2000 verso acrylic canvas on panel prov. 14-Nov-2 Christie's, Rockefeller NY #342/R est:15000-20000

APPELGREN, Emilia (1840-?) Swedish

£264 $409 €420 In the forest (28x33cm-11x13in) s. 6-Oct-2 Bukowskis, Helsinki #146/R

APPELMAN, Barend (1640-1686) Dutch

£2600 $4056 €3900 Italianate landscape with a waterfall and anglers in the foreground (50x38cm-20x15in) s. 9-Apr-3 Bonhams, New Bond Street #39/R est:2000-3000

APPENZELLER, Charles Felix (1892-1964) Swiss

£655 $956 €983 Reclining female nude (45x60cm-18x24in) s.d.1915. 4-Jun-2 Germann, Zurich #737 (S.FR 1500)

APPERLEY, George Owen Wynne (1884-1960) British

Works on paper

£676 $1041 €1075 Study of classical scene (25x35cm-10x14in) s.d.1913 gouache. 28-Oct-2 Segre, Madrid #27/R
£1000 $1560 €1500 Venetian Canal (35x25cm-14x10in) s.d.06 W/C bodycol. 5-Nov-2 Bonhams, New Bond Street #133/R est:700-1000
£1132 $1743 €1800 Lake landscape. s. W/C. 22-Oct-2 Durán, Madrid #118/R
£6410 $10128 €10000 Deposition (61x90cm-24x35in) s.d.1917-18 W/C. 19-Nov-2 Durán, Madrid #244/R
£19000 $30020 €28500 Summer night (62x91cm-24x36in) W/C htd bodycol lit. 2-Dec-2 Sotheby's, London #102/R est:20000-30000

APPERT, G (19th C) French

£3526 $5535 €5500 Scene d'auberge (98x130cm-39x51in) s. 11-Dec-2 Maigret, Paris #143/R est:4000-6000

APPIAN, Adolphe (1818-1898) French

£2092 $3430 €3200 Baie mediterraneenne (24x46cm-9x18in) s.d.57. 9-Feb-3 Anaf, Lyon #24/R
£2115 $3279 €3300 Family resting under the tree on the meadow (38x63cm-15x25in) s. 4-Dec-2 Neumeister, Munich #669/R est:1500

APPIAN, Adolphe (attrib) (1818-1898) French

£519 $805 €779 Landscape with sailing ships by shore (27x47cm-11x19in) bears i.d.1869. 24-Sep-2 Koller, Zurich #6520/R (S.FR 1200)

APPIANI, Andrea (circle) (1754-1817) Italian

Works on paper

£4938 $8000 €7407 Athena and Zeus seated in the clouds (51x70cm-20x28in) red chk. 21-Jan-3 Sotheby's, New York #185/R est:7000

APPLEBEE, Leonard (1914-) British

£250 $413 €363 Still life with pot plant (51x66cm-20x26in) mono.d.53. 3-Jul-3 Christie's, Kensington #418

APPLETON, Jean (1911-) Australian

£351 $533 €527 Boys playing (25x30cm-10x12in) s. board. 19-Aug-2 Joel, Victoria #197 est:1000-1500 (A.D 1000)
£2107 $3308 €3161 Flowers (94x61cm-37x24in) s. board. 15-Apr-3 Lawson Menzies, Sydney #228/R est:6000-8000 (A.D 5500)
£2491 $3811 €3737 Room in spring light (121x91cm-48x36in) s. canvas on board prov. 25-Aug-2 Sotheby's, Paddington #188/R est:7000-9000 (A.D 7000)
£2509 $3814 €3764 Interior with pears and still life (111x85cm-44x33in) s. board. 27-Aug-2 Goodman, Sydney #135/R est:4500-6500 (A.D 7000)
£4215 $6617 €6323 Still life with oranges (75x91cm-30x36in) s. board prov. 15-Apr-3 Lawson Menzies, Sydney #23a/R est:6000-9000 (A.D 11000)

APPLETON, Thomas Gold (1812-1884) American

Works on paper

£380 $589 €600 Portrait of Mrs Graham (72x56cm-28x22in) scratched col brush after Th Gainsborough. 25-Sep-2 Neumeister, Munich #386

APPLEYARD, Frederick (1874-1963) British
£300 $474 €435 Fly fishermen casting (13x20cm-5x8in) s. board. 28-Jul-3 David Duggleby, Scarborough #313
£2903 $4500 €4355 Sunset through the trees (81x60cm-32x24in) prov. 2-Oct-2 Christie's, Rockefeller NY #769/R est:2000-3000

APPLEYARD, Joseph (1908-1960) British
Works on paper
£350 $546 €525 York and London stage coach (35x51cm-14x20in) s. pencil pen ink W/C. 19-Sep-2 Christie's, Kensington #66
£520 $811 €780 Leyburn market (31x40cm-12x16in) s.i.d.Aug 1939 pencil pen ink W/C. 10-Apr-3 Tennants, Leyburn #835
£540 $837 €810 Catterick beagles in the Vale of Mowbray, Yorkshire (38x56cm-15x22in) s. W/C. 1-Oct-2 Gildings, Market Harborough #290/R
£750 $1185 €1125 Catterick beagles in the Vale of Mowbray, Yorkshire (38x56cm-15x22in) s. W/C bodycol. 28-Nov-2 Christie's, Kensington #93/R

APSHOVEN, Thomas van (1622-1664) Flemish
£4403 $6824 €7000 Inn with figures (48x65cm-19x26in) 7-Oct-2 Ansorena, Madrid #26/R
£5696 $9000 €9000 Injured foot (40x29cm-16x11in) s. canvas on panel lit. 29-Nov-2 Schloss Ahlden, Ahlden #1125/R est:12000

ARA, Krishna Hawlaji (1914-1985) Indian
Works on paper
£700 $1092 €1050 Still life of flowers (46x32cm-18x13in) s. gouache. 17-Oct-2 Bonhams, Knightsbridge #557/R
£2000 $3120 €3000 Seated female nude (74x56cm-29x22in) s. gouache. 17-Oct-2 Bonhams, Knightsbridge #556/R est:1500-2500

ARAD, Ron (20th C) American
Sculpture
£9677 $15000 €14516 Tinker chair (30x20x32cm-12x8x13in) painted hammered steel lit. 8-Dec-2 Wright, Chicago #197/R est:15000-20000

ARAGO, Jacques Étienne Victor (1790-1855) French
Works on paper
£1200 $1860 €1800 Afrique scenes (37x29cm-15x11in) s.d.1818 W/C. 26-Sep-2 Christie's, London #31/R est:600-800
£1300 $2015 €1950 Nile Hollande, vue prise aux montagnes bleues. Nile Hollande, Aborigines fishing (46x64cm-18x25in) pencil two. 26-Sep-2 Christie's, London #84/R est:1000-2000
£3000 $4650 €4500 Maison de Rawack (28x39cm-11x15in) three s. three s.d.1818 pencil six. 26-Sep-2 Christie's, London #65/R est:3000-5000
£3200 $4960 €4800 Scenes of Timor (28x40cm-11x16in) s.i. pen ink grey wash set of seven. 26-Sep-2 Christie's, London #58/R est:3000-5000
£3200 $4960 €4800 Nile Holland. Port Jackson. Abinghou (26x35cm-10x14in) s.i. pen ink sold with engraving proofs. 26-Sep-2 Christie's, London #82/R est:3000-5000
£3800 $5890 €5700 Bourbon, 1818. Vue prise a Bourbon. Vue de l'encaissement de la riviere de St. Denis (29x37cm-11x15in) s.i.d.1818 pen ink set of three. 26-Sep-2 Christie's, London #32/R est:1000-1500
£5000 $7750 €7500 Yellow and black bird of New Holland. Green parrot. Cassican fluteur. White backed magpie (28x34cm-11x13in) s.i. pencil W/C. 26-Sep-2 Christie's, London #91/R est:3000-5000
£5500 $8525 €8250 Timor sailing craft. Scenes of Timor (30x39cm-12x15in) s.d.1818 pencil ink dr. set of six with other artists. 26-Sep-2 Christie's, London #53/R est:3500-4500
£6000 $9300 €9000 Scenes of Timor (27x35cm-11x14in) s.d.1818 pencil ink dr. set of nine. 26-Sep-2 Christie's, London #54/R est:3000-4000
£6000 $9300 €9000 Marine life (42x30cm-17x12in) two s. pencil pen W/C six with artists Gaudichaud and A. Prevost. 26-Sep-2 Christie's, London #76/R est:2000-3000
£6000 $9300 €9000 Marine life (37x29cm-15x11in) s.d.1817-1819 wash five. 26-Sep-2 Christie's, London #77/R est:1000-1500
£7500 $11625 €11250 Esquisse d'un caracore appt, au Roi de Guebe (36x48cm-14x19in) one s.d.1818 pen ink W/C set of six with other artist. 26-Sep-2 Christie's, London #69/R est:5000-7000
£10000 $15500 €15000 Nouvelle Hollande (29x38cm-11x15in) s.d.1818 pen ink W/C. 26-Sep-2 Christie's, London #33/R est:3000-5000
£12000 $18600 €18000 Nouvelle Hollande, observatoire et cabanes des naturels de la presqu ile Peron 1818. s.i.d.1818 pencil pen ink. 26-Sep-2 Christie's, London #38/R est:3000-5000
£14000 $21700 €21000 Nouvelle Hollande, Peramele de grand natu de la presqu'ile Peron (29x37cm-11x15in) s.i. pen ink W/C. 26-Sep-2 Christie's, London #40/R est:1500-2500
£14000 $21700 €21000 Reception on Timor 1818 (29x35cm-11x14in) i. W/C exhib. 26-Sep-2 Christie's, London #56/R est:12000-18000
£14000 $21700 €21000 Portraits (29x37cm-11x15in) s. pen ink W/C set of 14. 26-Sep-2 Christie's, London #64/R est:10000-15000
£15000 $23250 €22500 Nouvelle Hollande, Aboriginal artefacts (38x29cm-15x11in) s.d.1818 W/C. 26-Sep-2 Christie's, London #39/R est:2000-3000
£15000 $23250 €22500 Nouvelle Hollande, Terre d'endrach (13x23cm-5x9in) s.i. W/C sold with a W/C by Adrien Aime Taunay. 26-Sep-2 Christie's, London #43/R est:3000-5000
£16000 $24800 €24000 Nouvelle Hollande, Vue d'une partie de la parsqu ile Peron (28x34cm-11x13in) s.i. pencil paper on board. 26-Sep-2 Christie's, London #36/R est:7000-10000
£26000 $40300 €39000 Nouvelle Hollande, Huitrier de la presqu'ile peron (37x28cm-15x11in) s.d.1818 pen ink W/C pair. 26-Sep-2 Christie's, London #41/R est:4000-6000
£28000 $43400 €42000 Tamor de carolins, et femme du meme archipel (29x37cm-11x15in) s.d.1819 W/C pen ink set of six exhib. 26-Sep-2 Christie's, London #71/R est:10000-15000
£35000 $54250 €52500 Nid d'autour trouve a L'Ile d'Irk. Dirck Hartog Island, western Australia (26x34cm-10x13in) s. pencil two. 26-Sep-2 Christie's, London #42/R est:5000-8000

ARAGO, Jacques Etienne Victor and PELLION, J A (19th C) French
Works on paper
£13000 $20150 €19500 Iles malouines (22x30cm-9x12in) pencil set of six. 26-Sep-2 Christie's, London #96/R est:5000-8000

ARAGO, Jacques Etienne Victor and TAUNAY, Adrien Aime (19th C) French
Works on paper
£3500 $5425 €5250 Voyage de l'Uranie, insectes studies (37x28cm-15x11in) s.d.1818 pencil W/C set of four. 26-Sep-2 Christie's, London #67/R est:3000-5000
£24000 $37200 €36000 Views of Rio de Janeiro (28x38cm-11x15in) ten s. one i. pen ink wash set of 11. 26-Sep-2 Christie's, London #28/R est:20000-30000

ARAGONESE SCHOOL (18th C) Spanish
£7693 $12847 €11000 Scene de la Vie d'un saint (202x75cm-80x30in) panel four boards. 25-Jun-3 Tajan, Paris #1/R est:12000-15000

ARAKAWA, Shusaku (1936-) Japanese
Works on paper
£719 $1180 €1000 Untitled (52x72cm-20x28in) s.d.1965 col pencil felt pen prov. 3-Jun-3 Christie's, Amsterdam #107/R est:1000-1500

ARAKI, Nobuyoshi (1940-) Japanese
Photographs
£1875 $3000 €2813 Untitled -Tokyo shijyo series (90x107cm-35x42in) s.verso black white photograph executed 1977 prov.exhib. 16-May-3 Phillips, New York #233/R est:3000-4000
£2500 $3850 €3750 Untitled (35x28cm-14x11in) s.d.1983 verso gelatin silver print. 23-Oct-2 Christie's, London #175/R est:2000-3000
£2500 $4000 €3750 Untitled - bondage series (106x135cm-42x53in) s.verso gelatin silver print mounted on aluminum executed 1997. 16-May-3 Phillips, New York #224/R est:6000-8000
£3125 $4969 €4500 Sans titre (60x50cm-24x20in) s.verso silver print. 29-Apr-3 Artcurial Briest, Paris #473/R est:3800-4200
£22500 $36000 €33750 Untitled - kusama (96x78cm-38x31in) s.verso black white photograph executed 1998 prov.exhib. 16-May-3 Phillips, New York #226/R est:4000-6000

ARALICA, Stojan (1883-?) Yugoslavian
£5236 $8325 €7854 View of Cassis (46x55cm-18x22in) s. 8-Mar-3 Dorotheum, Prague #151/R est:40000-60000 (C.KR 240000)

ARAPOFF (20th C) Russian
£9000 $14580 €13500 View of Saint Basil's cathedral, Moscow (65x74cm-26x29in) s.d.37. 21-May-3 Sotheby's, London #102 est:3000-4000

ARAPOFF, Alexis (1904-1948) Russian
£1400 $2268 €2100 Strolling in a Parisian park (32x16cm-13x6in) s. 21-May-3 Sotheby's, London #105/R est:1500-2000
£1773 $2961 €2500 Nature morte au livre et bouquet de fleurs (65x50cm-26x20in) s.d. 17-Jun-3 Claude Boisgirard, Paris #21/R est:2000-2500

£3191 $5330 €4500 La Seine (54x81cm-21x32in) s. 17-Jun-3 Claude Boisgirard, Paris #20 est:5000-6000
£3819 $6035 €5500 Promeneurs sur une terrasse (50x65cm-20x26in) s. 25-Apr-3 Piasa, Paris #3/R
£6738 $11252 €9500 Promenade au bord de mer (54x65cm-21x26in) s. 17-Jun-3 Claude Boisgirard, Paris #19/R est:5000-6000
£10000 $16200 €15000 Yellow tram (46x65cm-18x26in) s. 21-May-3 Sotheby's, London #112a/R est:2500-3500

ARAPOV, Anatoli Afanasevich (1876-1949) Russian
£4082 $6490 €6000 La villa rouge (60x73cm-24x29in) s.d. 3-Mar-3 Claude Boisgirard, Paris #28/R est:1500-2000

ARATYM, Hubert (1936-2000) German
£1392 $2172 €2200 Untitled (44x40cm-17x16in) s.d.78 triptych style. 15-Oct-2 Dorotheum, Vienna #189/R est:2400-3800
£3819 $6035 €5500 Composition (60x82cm-24x32in) s.d.65. 24-Apr-3 Dorotheum, Vienna #200/R est:3000-4500
Works on paper
£486 $768 €700 Untitled (26x19cm-10x7in) s.d.98 W/C. 24-Apr-3 Dorotheum, Vienna #201/R
£696 $1086 €1100 Untitled (35x41cm-14x16in) s.d.1979 pencil W/C. 15-Oct-2 Dorotheum, Vienna #204/R

ARAUJO Y RUANO, Joaquin (1851-1894) Spanish
£2323 $3670 €3600 Goyan figures (180x80cm-71x31in) one s. pair. 18-Dec-2 Ansorena, Madrid #343/R

ARAVANTINOS, Panos (1886-1930) Greek
£7000 $11060 €10500 Scene from Carmen (77x97cm-30x38in) 1-Apr-3 Bonhams, New Bond Street #109 est:6000-8000

ARBESSER, Josef von (1850-?) Austrian
Works on paper
£338 $527 €500 St Mark's Square in Venice (29x21cm-11x8in) s.d.1901 W/C lit. 28-Mar-3 Karrenbauer, Konstanz #1700/R

ARBO, Peter Nicolai (1831-1892) Norwegian
£853 $1331 €1280 View towards the castle (25x39cm-10x15in) s. panel painted 1890. 23-Sep-2 Blomqvist, Lysaker #1004/R (N.KR 10000)
£1467 $2230 €2201 Cattle grazing (24x32cm-9x13in) init.d.Septr.1888 mahogany panel. 31-Aug-2 Grev Wedels Plass, Oslo #127/R est:15000-20000 (N.KR 17000)
£3903 $6088 €5855 Girl wearing Hardanger costume knitting by water (36x26cm-14x10in) s. panel. 21-Oct-2 Blomqvist, Oslo #308/R est:50000-70000 (N.KR 45000)

ARBORELIUS, Olof (1842-1915) Swedish
£421 $665 €632 Seascape with boat at dusk (32x62cm-13x24in) mono. i.verso. 30-Nov-2 Goteborg Auktionsverk, Sweden #134/R (S.KR 6000)
£676 $1054 €1014 Street scene, evening (81x60cm-32x24in) mono. 23-Sep-2 Rasmussen, Vejle #214/R (D.KR 8000)
£806 $1274 €1209 Farm buildings surrounded by lilac trees, cattle and figures at farmyard (38x60cm-15x24in) mono. i.verso. 27-Nov-2 Falkkloos, Malmo #77820/R (S.KR 11500)
£1702 $2638 €2553 Lake landscape with woman at jetty (80x120cm-31x47in) s/. 8-Dec-2 Uppsala Auktionskammare, Uppsala #132/R est:30000-35000 (S.KR 24000)

ARBUCKLE, George Franklin (1909-2001) Canadian
£356 $583 €534 Hauser's barn, Whitechurch Two, July 67 (50x60cm-20x24in) s. board. 3-Jun-3 Joyner, Toronto #269/R (C.D 800)
£370 $574 €555 Beauport farm, North Shore, Quebec (30x40cm-12x16in) s. board prov. 3-Dec-2 Joyner, Toronto #363 (C.D 900)
£515 $803 €773 Spring, Baie St Paul (30x40cm-12x16in) s. i.verso cardboard. 25-Mar-3 Iegor de Saint Hippolyte, Montreal #3 (C.D 1200)
£620 $973 €930 Baie St. Paul, Quebec (30x41cm-12x16in) i. s.verso canvasboard prov. 24-Jul-2 Walker's, Ottawa #402/R est:1500-1800 (C.D 1500)
£1102 $1752 €1653 Glacier Moraine Lake (30x40cm-12x16in) s.i.d.1979. 23-Mar-3 Hodgins, Calgary #37/R est:1600-2000 (C.D 2600)
£2691 $4305 €4037 Totem pole - Vancouver Island (76x102cm-30x40in) s. prov. 15-May-3 Heffel, Vancouver #129/R est:3000-4000 (C.D 6000)
£3000 $4920 €4500 Fishing hole (75x60cm-30x24in) s. 3-Jun-3 Joyner, Toronto #172/R est:4000-5000 (C.D 6750)

ARBUS, Andre (1903-1969) French
Sculpture
£2158 $3453 €3000 Buste d'Apollon (11x6x6cm-4x2x2in) mono. num.2/8 black pat.bronze lit. 19-May-3 Tajan, Paris #196/R est:3000-3500
£8273 $13237 €11500 Acteon (33x10x10cm-13x4x4in) s. gilded bronze lit. 19-May-3 Tajan, Paris #195/R est:6000-8000

ARBUS, Diane (1923-1971) American
Photographs
£2057 $3250 €3086 Untitled (37x37cm-15x15in) s.i.d.1970-71 num.9/75 gelatin silver print. 22-Apr-3 Butterfields, San Francisco #2414/R est:4000-6000
£2577 $4200 €3866 Four people at a gallery opening, N.Y.C (37x37cm-15x15in) s.i.d,1976 num.20/65 gelatin silver print. 12-Feb-3 Christie's, Rockefeller NY #175/R est:4000-6000
£2727 $4200 €4091 Miss Cora Prat, the counterfeit lady (35x28cm-14x11in) s.st.num.verso gelatin silver print board prov.lit. 25-Oct-2 Phillips, New York #37/R est:6000-8000
£3247 $5000 €4871 Erik Bruhn and Rudolf Nureyev (25x24cm-10x9in) sig. by Nureyev s.i.d.1962 num.verso gelatin silver print prov. 25-Oct-2 Phillips, New York #38/R est:7000-10000
£3247 $5000 €4871 Untitled, 8 (51x41cm-20x16in) s.st.verso gelatin silver print 21 of 75 exec.c.1970-71 prov.lit. 25-Oct-2 Phillips, New York #131/R est:5000-7000
£4114 $6500 €6171 Child crying, N.J (36x37cm-14x15in) s.i.d.1967 num.21/75 gelatin silver print lit. 22-Apr-3 Christie's, Rockefeller NY #73/R est:3000-5000
£5519 $8500 €8279 House on a hill, Hollywood, California (51x41cm-20x16in) s.st.verso gelatin silver print 48 of 75 prov.lit. 25-Oct-2 Phillips, New York #132/R est:5000-7000
£5727 $9220 €8591 Teenage couple on Hudson Street, NYC (37x37cm-15x15in) gelatin silver print prov. 9-May-3 Waddingtons, Toronto #146/R est:15000-18000 (C.D 13000)
£8861 $14000 €13292 Three Puerto Rican women (21x20cm-8x8in) s.d.1963 photograph. 23-Apr-3 Sotheby's, New York #227/R est:15000-20000
£10759 $17000 €16139 Untitled (36x36cm-14x14in) s.i.d.1970-71 num.47/75 gelatin silver print lit. 22-Apr-3 Christie's, Rockefeller NY #126/R est:15000-20000
£39241 $62000 €58862 Family one evening in a nudist camp, PA (39x39cm-15x15in) s.num. photograph two prov. 23-Apr-3 Sotheby's, New York #229/R est:60000-90000

ARBUS, Diane and SELKIRK, Neil (20th C) American
Photographs
£3165 $5000 €4748 Untitled (37x37cm-15x15in) s.i.d.num.3/75 photograph. 23-Apr-3 Sotheby's, New York #233/R est:5000-7000
£5195 $8000 €7793 Xmas tree in a living room, Levittown, N Y (37x37cm-15x15in) s.i.d.1963 num.38/50 photograph. 24-Oct-2 Sotheby's, New York #199/R est:8000-12000
£7051 $11000 €10577 Young Brooklyn family going for a Sunday outing (26x25cm-10x10in) s.i.d.verso gelatin silver print lit. 14-Oct-2 Butterfields, San Francisco #1415/R est:5000-7000
£7792 $12000 €11688 Untitled (37x37cm-15x15in) s.i.d.1970-71 num.13/75 photograph. 24-Oct-2 Sotheby's, New York #200/R est:5000-7000
£29114 $46000 €43671 Identical twins Roselle, N J (38x38cm-15x15in) num.47/50 photograph. 23-Apr-3 Sotheby's, New York #228/R est:25000-35000

ARBUTHNOT, Malcolm (1874-1967) British
£260 $406 €390 Boat on pier (25x34cm-10x13in) s.d.1959 board. 26-Mar-3 Bonhams & Langlois, Jersey #105
£340 $530 €510 Boats under tree (35x25cm-14x10in) s.d.1959 board. 26-Mar-3 Bonhams & Langlois, Jersey #106
Works on paper
£480 $749 €720 Boat near rocks (38x55cm-15x22in) s.d.1959 W/C. 26-Mar-3 Bonhams & Langlois, Jersey #104
£580 $905 €870 Cottage on the railway walk (27x38cm-11x15in) s. W/C. 26-Mar-3 Bonhams & Langlois, Jersey #103

ARCAMBOT, Pierre (1914-) French
£700 $1093 €1100 Metro (15x23cm-6x9in) s. acrylic panel. 5-Nov-2 Tajan, Paris #63/R

ARCE, Marco (1968-) ?
Works on paper
£5096 $8000 €7644 Untitled (13x18cm-5x7in) s.i.d. mixed media set of 40. 19-Nov-2 Sotheby's, New York #138/R est:15000

ARCHAMBAULT, Luc (1954-) Canadian
£210 $342 €315 Cote Joulin (76x76cm-30x30in) 12-Feb-3 Iegor de Saint Hippolyte, Montreal #11 (C.D 520)

ARCHER, Charles (1855-1931) British
Works on paper
£600 $936 €870 Apples and a spray of plums (10x13cm-4x5in) s. W/C. 27-Mar-3 Neales, Nottingham #963/R

ARCHER, James (1823-1904) British
£62000 $99820 €93000 Betrothal of Robert Burns and Highland Mary (91x71cm-36x28in) mono. s.i.verso prov.exhib.lit. 20-Feb-3 Christie's, London #355/R est:60000

ARCHIPENKO, Alexander (1887-1964) American/Russian
£20732 $34000 €30061 Silver head (61x46cm-24x18in) prov.exhib. 1-Jun-3 Wright, Chicago #106/R est:30000-40000
Sculpture
£3822 $6000 €5733 Stylized female figure (66cm-26in) s.i.d.1914 bronze with marble base. 20-Nov-2 Boos Gallery, Michigan #442/R est:4000-6000
£5161 $8000 €7742 Who is she (28cm-11in) s.num.1/8 green brown pat. bronze prov.lit. 26-Sep-2 Christie's, Rockefeller NY #602/R est:15000-20000
£11218 $17388 €17500 Nude female torso (48cm-19in) s.i.d.22 green pat.bronze. 6-Dec-2 Karlheinz Kaupp, Staufen #875/R est:8000
£24845 $40000 €37268 Torso - female figure (64cm-25in) s.num.12/12 blue green pat. bronze conceived 1945 prov.lit. 8-May-3 Christie's, Rockefeller NY #191/R est:50000-70000
£41667 $65000 €62501 Seated black concave - seated figure (77cm-30in) s.i.d.1916 num.7/8 silver plated bronze prov.lit. 7-Nov-2 Christie's, Rockefeller NY #310/R est:80000-120000
£46584 $75000 €69876 Torso in space (51cm-20in) i. polished terracotta conceived 1935 prov.lit. 7-May-3 Sotheby's, New York #308/R est:60000-80000
£48077 $75000 €72116 Torso in space (51cm-20in) i.num.VIII polished terracotta conceived 1935 prov.exhib.lit. 6-Nov-2 Sotheby's, New York #250/R est:60000-80000
£96154 $150000 €144231 Ray (229cm-90in) s.num.2 aluminum cast 1958 prov.exhib.lit. 7-Nov-2 Christie's, Rockefeller NY #303/R est:60000-80000
£128205 $200000 €192308 Torso in space (152cm-60in) s.num.4/6 green brown pat. bronze cast 1967 prov.lit. 7-Nov-2 Christie's, Rockefeller NY #311/R est:250000-350000
£350000 $584500 €507500 Gruppe, feminine solitude (78cm-31in) s. white marble exec.c.1920 prov.exhib.lit. 24-Jun-3 Christie's, London #66/R est:350000-450000
£559006 $900000 €838509 Blue dancer (105cm-41in) s.d.1913 num.1/10 blue pat bronze prov.lit. 6-May-3 Sotheby's, New York #31/R est:700000-900000
£576923 $900000 €865385 Blue dancer (106cm-42in) s.d.13 num.6/8 blue pat. bronze prov.lit. 6-Nov-2 Christie's, Rockefeller NY #30/R est:700000-1000000
Works on paper
£1266 $2000 €1899 Untitled - figurative study in black (58x36cm-23x14in) s. pen ink. 22-Apr-3 Butterfields, San Francisco #6012/R est:3000-5000
£2215 $3500 €3323 Untitled - figurative study in black and grey (58x36cm-23x14in) s. pen pencil. 22-Apr-3 Butterfields, San Francisco #6011/R est:4000-6000
£2532 $4000 €3798 Untitled - figurative study in blue (58x36cm-23x14in) s. col pencil. 22-Apr-3 Butterfields, San Francisco #6006/R est:5000-7000
£3481 $5500 €5222 Untitled - figurative study in blue and orange (58x36cm-23x14in) s. col pencil. 22-Apr-3 Butterfields, San Francisco #6007/R est:5000-7000
£4908 $8000 €7362 Lying figure (36x57cm-14x22in) s.i. gouache pencil. 12-Feb-3 Sotheby's, New York #66/R est:10000-12000
£8750 $14000 €13125 Two nudes (53x38cm-21x15in) s.i. pencil dr. 11-Jan-3 Harvey Clar, Oakland #1445

ARCIMBOLDO, Giuseppe (after) (1527-1593) Italian
£11538 $17885 €18000 Allegory of Seasons (80x60cm-31x24in) 4-Dec-2 Finarte, Rome #914/R est:5000

ARCIMBOLDO, Giuseppe (style) (1527-1593) Italian
£5844 $8708 €9000 Spring (64x59cm-25x23in) 26-Jun-2 Neumeister, Munich #618/R est:3000

ARCULARIO, Francesco (?-1752) Italian
£3205 $4968 €5000 Egyptian port with ancient ruins, pyramid shaped monument and figures (127x175cm-50x69in) canvas on canvas. 4-Dec-2 Neumeister, Munich #578/R est:6000
£3846 $5962 €6000 Landscape with ancient ruins and figures (127x175cm-50x69in) canvas on canvas. 4-Dec-2 Neumeister, Munich #577/R est:7000

ARDEN, Charlotte Leonie (1859-1904) Belgian
£327 $510 €520 Summer landscape with haymakers (17x35cm-7x14in) s. canvas on panel. 23-Sep-2 Bernaerts, Antwerp #31/R
£886 $1382 €1400 Promenade en borde de Meuse (40x60cm-16x24in) s. 15-Oct-2 Vanderkindere, Brussels #48 est:1400-1800

ARDEN, Henri (1858-1917) Belgian
£377 $591 €550 Barques de peche (28x35cm-11x14in) s. panel. 15-Apr-3 Galerie Moderne, Brussels #376/R
£576 $921 €800 Barque de peche au coucher du soleil (25x35cm-10x14in) s. panel. 19-May-3 Horta, Bruxelles #503
£1282 $1987 €2000 Port de peche coucher du soleil (45x75cm-18x30in) s. 9-Dec-2 Horta, Bruxelles #378 est:1500-2000

ARDEN-QUIN, Carmelo (1913-) Uruguayan
£2564 $4026 €4000 Bleu, blanc, noir 5 (35x34cm-14x13in) s.i.d. verso acrylic cardboard. 16-Dec-2 Charbonneaux, Paris #104/R est:4000-4500
£3165 $4937 €5000 Ovix, serie hal (73x60cm-29x24in) s.i.d.72 verso. 20-Oct-2 Charbonneaux, Paris #97/R est:6000-8000
Works on paper
£641 $1006 €1000 Sans titre (24x31cm-9x12in) s.d. collage. 16-Dec-2 Charbonneaux, Paris #105/R
£705 $1107 €1100 Sans titre (33x24cm-13x9in) s.d. collage mixed media. 16-Dec-2 Charbonneaux, Paris #107/R
£774 $1223 €1200 Composition (27x20cm-11x8in) s. gouache collage. 18-Dec-2 Digard, Paris #141
£795 $1295 €1200 Untitled (30x21cm-12x8in) s.d.1962 collage. 3-Feb-3 Cornette de St.Cyr, Paris #357
£993 $1619 €1500 Untitled (28x22cm-11x9in) s.d.1956 collage. 3-Feb-3 Cornette de St.Cyr, Paris #356
£1250 $1975 €1800 Composition (24x31cm-9x12in) s.d. collage cardboard prov. 27-Apr-3 Perrin, Versailles #28/R est:1200-1500

ARDISSONE, Yolande (1872-?) French
£283 $450 €425 Cottages (33x24cm-13x9in) s. 7-Mar-3 Skinner, Boston #515/R
£305 $500 €442 Bateaux (30x30cm-12x12in) s. i.on stretcher. 4-Jun-3 Doyle, New York #6
£427 $700 €619 Base nautique a carnac (33x41cm-13x16in) s. i.on stretcher. 4-Jun-3 Doyle, New York #5
£513 $800 €770 Entree fleurie (33x41cm-13x16in) s. i.stretcher. 9-Oct-2 Doyle, New York #3
£610 $1000 €885 Erquy (74x51cm-29x20in) s. i.on stretcher. 4-Jun-3 Doyle, New York #4 est:2000-3000
£839 $1300 €1259 Reflect a josseliy (46x56cm-18x22in) s. i.stretcher. 25-Sep-2 Doyle, New York #7/R
£897 $1400 €1346 Vineyard (38x79cm-15x31in) s. 9-Oct-2 Doyle, New York #5
£940 $1513 €1400 Amandiers en fleurs. s. 23-Feb-3 Mercier & Cie, Lille #234/R
£955 $1500 €1433 Maison a carnac (18x22cm-7x9in) s. i.on stretcher. 10-Dec-2 Doyle, New York #260/R est:2500-3500
£968 $1500 €1452 Golfe du Morbihan (38x46cm-15x18in) s. i.stretcher. 25-Sep-2 Doyle, New York #6/R est:1500-2000
£988 $1600 €1433 Bouquet of cosmos (91x74cm-36x29in) s. i.stretcher prov. 21-May-3 Doyle, New York #244/R est:3000-4000
£994 $1600 €1491 Bateaux de pesce (74x94cm-29x37in) s. prov. 19-Feb-3 Doyle, New York #55 est:3000-4000
£1006 $1600 €1509 Honfleur (46x56cm-18x22in) s. i.stretcher. 18-Mar-3 Doyle, New York #6/R est:1800-2200
£1069 $1550 €1604 Bateaux de peche (71x91cm-28x36in) 1-Jun-2 Russ Antiques, Waterford #157
£1069 $1700 €1604 Saint Colomban (38x46cm-15x18in) s. i. on stretcher. 5-Mar-3 Doyle, New York #1/R est:1500-2000
£1154 $1800 €1731 Hostelerie de d'or (74x91cm-29x36in) s. i.stretcher. 9-Oct-2 Doyle, New York #4 est:3000-4000
£1180 $1900 €1770 Viaduc d'antheon (66x81cm-26x32in) s. i.stretcher. 19-Feb-3 Doyle, New York #54 est:3000-4000
£1543 $2500 €2237 Fleurs et fruits (74x61cm-29x24in) s. i.stretcher. 21-May-3 Doyle, New York #235/R est:2500-3500
£1592 $2500 €2388 Sauzon (29x36cm-11x14in) s. i.on stretcher. 10-Dec-2 Doyle, New York #258/R est:3000-4000
£1592 $2500 €2388 Ciel Breton (29x36cm-11x14in) s. i.on stretcher. 10-Dec-2 Doyle, New York #259/R est:3000-4000
£2160 $3500 €3132 Printemps (74x91cm-29x36in) s. i.stretcher. 21-May-3 Doyle, New York #234/R est:3000-4000
£2469 $4000 €3580 Sailboats in an inlet (99x99cm-39x39in) s. 21-May-3 Doyle, New York #258/R est:4000-6000

ARDIZZONE, Catherine (?) British
Works on paper
£360 $587 €540 Majorca (30x53cm-12x21in) init. pencil W/C. 28-Jan-3 Henry Adams, Chichester #414

ARDIZZONE, Edward (1900-1979) British
Works on paper
£750 $1208 €1125 Court room scene (30x20cm-12x8in) init. pencil. 14-Jan-3 Bonhams, Knightsbridge #219/R
£1000 $1550 €1500 Lovers by a cattle bridge (25x38cm-10x15in) init. pen black ink grey wash prov.exhib. 4-Dec-2 Christie's, Kensington #212/R est:1000-1500
£1100 $1749 €1650 Bird man (27x38cm-11x15in) init. W/C. 26-Feb-3 Sotheby's, Olympia #139/R est:600-800
£1100 $1804 €1650 Arise Sir Duncan (24x20cm-9x8in) s.i.d.15.1.60 pen ink. 6-Jun-3 Christie's, London #100/R est:600-800
£1200 $1908 €1800 What curious creatures my dear (18x26cm-7x10in) init.i. pen ink wash. 26-Feb-3 Sotheby's, Olympia #138/R est:400-600
£1300 $2015 €1950 Snorkeling in the Riviera (18x26cm-7x10in) init. pen black ink W/C prov.exhib. 4-Dec-2 Christie's, Kensington #208/R est:1200-1800
£1500 $2475 €2175 Gossips (25x30cm-10x12in) init. pencil acetate. 3-Jul-3 Christie's, Kensington #246/R est:600-800
£1700 $2635 €2550 Perplexed model (19x29cm-7x11in) init. pencil w/ prov.exhib. 4-Dec-2 Christie's, Kensington #209/R est:1500-2500
£1800 $2916 €2700 In the studio (15x19cm-6x7in) init. ink W/C exhib. 20-May-3 Sotheby's, Olympia #137/R est:800-1200
£1900 $2983 €2850 Shadowy beach (25x35cm-10x14in) init. i.verso pen ink W/C prov.exhib. 21-Nov-2 Christie's, London #124/R est:2000-3000
£2000 $3100 €3000 Girls at Southend (18x25cm-7x10in) init. W/C. 4-Dec-2 Christie's, Kensington #211/R est:1500-2000
£2600 $4264 €3770 Swimming in Hyde Park (25x33cm-10x13in) init. pencil W/C prov.exhib. 5-Jun-3 Christie's, London #192/R est:1800-2400
£3200 $5248 €4640 At the Haywood galley (29x28cm-11x11in) pen ink W/C prov.exhib. 5-Jun-3 Christie's, London #193/R est:1500-2500
£5500 $8635 €8250 Bar at the Shirland (37x50cm-15x20in) init. pen black ink W/C prov.exhib. 16-Dec-2 Sotheby's, London #86/R est:6000-8000
£5500 $9020 €8250 Saloon bar at the Shirland (27x30cm-11x12in) pen ink W/C prov.exhib. 6-Jun-3 Christie's, London #99/R est:2500-3500

ARDIZZONE, Edward (attrib) (1900-1979) British
Works on paper
£280 $456 €420 North African nude figures on a terrace (48x56cm-19x22in) W/C. 14-Feb-3 Keys, Aylsham #412

ARDON, Mordecai (1896-1992) Israeli
£1517 $2428 €2200 Composition (30x50cm-12x20in) oil sand plaster cardboard. 12-Mar-3 Rabourdin & Choppin de Janvry, Paris #208/R
£21519 $34000 €32279 White leaf (41x27cm-16x11in) s.d.60 s.i.d.on stretcher prov.lit. 27-Apr-3 Sotheby's, Tel Aviv #38/R est:30000-40000
£88608 $140000 €132912 Old stones (114x146cm-45x57in) s.d.1965 prov.lit. 27-Apr-3 Sotheby's, Tel Aviv #24a/R est:150000-200000

ARDOUVIN, Pierre (20th C) French
Works on paper
£510 $811 €750 Ete indien (24x31cm-9x12in) s.i.d.2000 verso W/C prov. 24-Mar-3 Cornette de St.Cyr, Paris #194/R

ARDUINO, Nicola (1887-1974) Italian
£816 $1298 €1200 Venice (50x60cm-20x24in) s.d.1946. 1-Mar-3 Meeting Art, Vercelli #46

ARELLANO, Juan de (1614-1676) Spanish
£35220 $54239 €56000 Bouquet de fleurs retenu par un noeud bleu (47x39cm-19x15in) s. 25-Oct-2 Tajan, Paris #42/R est:10000-12000
£58621 $92621 €85000 Basket of flowers (51x65cm-20x26in) s. 7-Apr-3 Castellana, Madrid #463/R est:85000
£120000 $200400 €174000 Landscape with tulips, irises, narcissi and roses (63x89cm-25x35in) s. exhib.lit. 10-Jul-3 Sotheby's, London #44/R est:80000-120000

ARELLANO, Juan de (attrib) (1614-1676) Spanish
£35862 $57021 €52000 Bouquets de fleurs dans des vases ornes (98x73cm-39x29in) i. pair. 5-Mar-3 Oger, Dumont, Paris #41/R est:50000-60000

ARENAS, Braulio (1913-1987) Chilean
Works on paper
£1918 $3011 €2800 Five love cards of the Portuguese woman (31x22cm-12x9in) s. col crayon. 15-Apr-3 Laurence Calmels, Paris #4123/R

ARENDS, Karl Oskar (1863-1932) German
£577 $894 €900 Bavarian landscape in evening light (61x64cm-24x25in) s. 5-Dec-2 Dr Fritz Nagel, Stuttgart #639/R

ARENTSZ, Arent (1586-1635) Dutch
£9000 $14130 €13500 River landscape with fisherman by a bridge, Slot Muiden beyond (18x16cm-7x6in) mono. panel prov.lit. 12-Dec-2 Sotheby's, London #142/R est:10000-15000
£10811 $16865 €16000 Fishermen on riverbank (48x40cm-19x16in) panel. 27-Mar-3 Dorotheum, Vienna #169/R est:30000-40000

ARENYS, Ricardo (1914-) Spanish
Works on paper
£313 $506 €475 Horse (50x36cm-20x14in) s. dr. 21-Jan-3 Durán, Madrid #62/R

AREVALO, Xavier (20th C) Mexican
Works on paper
£742 $1187 €1076 Mujer (77x56cm-30x22in) s.d.1989 W/C. 15-May-3 Louis Morton, Mexico #159/R est:18000 (M.P 12000)

ARGELES, Rafael Escriche (1894-?) Spanish
£1900 $3173 €2850 Blue hat (81x60cm-32x24in) s. 18-Jun-3 Christie's, Kensington #108/R est:2000-3000

ARGENTIERI, Alfeo (1878-1955) Austrian
£2000 $3100 €3000 Fisherwoman (70x58cm-28x23in) s. 5-Dec-2 Christie's, Kensington #92/R est:2000-3000

ARGIMON, Daniel (1929-1996) Spanish
£489 $793 €690 Personaje (73x60cm-29x24in) s.d.1963 verso oil mixed media. 20-May-3 Segre, Madrid #202/R
Works on paper
£1006 $1570 €1600 Untitled (100x81cm-39x32in) s.d.86 mixed media on canvas. 8-Oct-2 Ansorena, Madrid #639/R

ARGOV, Michael (1920-) Israeli
£2722 $4300 €4083 Seated woman (49x33cm-19x13in) s.d.47 oil paper on board. 27-Apr-3 Sotheby's, Tel Aviv #43/R est:4000-6000
Works on paper
£476 $757 €700 Composition (63x46cm-25x18in) s.d.63 gouache. 26-Feb-3 Artcurial Briest, Paris #327

ARGYRO, Driva (1973-) Greek
Works on paper
£549 $900 €796 Portraits (90x104cm-35x41in) s.d.2001 cement sawdust papier mache acrylic on board. 28-May-3 Sotheby's, Amsterdam #178/R
£563 $900 €816 Portraits (90x104cm-35x41in) s.d.2001 verso cement sawdust papier mache acrylic board. 13-May-3 Sotheby's, Tel Aviv #27/R
£563 $900 €816 Portraits (90x104cm-35x41in) s. s.d.2001 verso cement sawdust papier mache acrylic on board. 13-May-3 Sotheby's, Tel Aviv #28/R

ARGYROS, Oumbertos (1877-1963) Greek
£2000 $3160 €3000 Rocky landscape (42x60cm-17x24in) 1-Apr-3 Bonhams, New Bond Street #33 est:2000-3000
£3000 $4740 €4500 Landscape with ruins (50x70cm-20x28in) 1-Apr-3 Bonhams, New Bond Street #29 est:3000-5000
£4200 $6636 €6300 View of Myconos (49x70cm-19x28in) 1-Apr-3 Bonhams, New Bond Street #34 est:4000-6000
£8000 $12400 €12000 View of Rhodes (50x70cm-20x28in) s. board. 2-Oct-2 Sotheby's, London #37/R
£14000 $21700 €21000 Moment of reflection (62x82cm-24x32in) s. 2-Oct-2 Sotheby's, London #87/R est:6000-8000
£15000 $23250 €22500 Reposing in the boudoir (60x80cm-24x31in) s. 2-Oct-2 Sotheby's, London #89/R est:10000-15000
£18000 $27900 €27000 View of Heidelberg (60x81cm-24x32in) s. 2-Oct-2 Sotheby's, London #38/R est:10000-15000

ARIAS MURRUETA, Gustavo (20th C) Mexican?
Works on paper
£299 $454 €434 Untitled (30x40cm-12x16in) s. mixed media. 24-Jul-2 Louis Morton, Mexico #25/R (M.P 4500)

ARIAS, Francisco (1912-1977) Spanish
£4610 $7468 €6500 Maternidad de la Guerra (95x80cm-37x31in) s. exhib.lit. 20-May-3 Segre, Madrid #130/R est:5800

ARIAS, J (?) Spanish
£1200 $1956 €1740 Women collecting water in a Spanish town (39x8cm-15x3in) s. 21-Jul-3 Bonhams, Bath #93/R est:500-800

ARICHA, Avigdor (20th C) ?
Works on paper
£290 $450 €435 Head of a man (45x33cm-18x13in) pencil prov. 3-Dec-2 Bonhams, Knightsbridge #305

ARICO, Rodolfo (1930-) Italian
£577 $842 €900 Composition (68x73cm-27x29in) s.d.58. 5-Jun-2 Il Ponte, Milan #50

ARIKHA, Avigdor (1929-) Israeli
£7092 $11489 €10000 Noirs (97x130cm-38x51in) s.d.59 exhib. 24-May-3 Van Ham, Cologne #15/R est:14000
Works on paper
£1282 $2000 €1923 Israeli (65x34cm-26x13in) s.d.6.6.66 ink prov. 14-Oct-2 Butterfields, San Francisco #2030/R est:4000-6000

ARINA, Seppo (1922-) Finnish
£302 $496 €420 Woman (57x46cm-22x18in) s.d.1963. 5-Jun-3 Hagelstam, Helsinki #972

ARIOLI, Fioravante (1890-?) Italian
£372 $580 €550 Church entrance (51x42cm-20x17in) s.d.935. 28-Mar-3 Farsetti, Prato #471

ARKHIPOV, Abram (1862-1930) Russian
£120000 $194400 €180000 Russian beauty at her embroidery (114x88cm-45x35in) s. 21-May-3 Sotheby's, London #137/R est:150000-200000

ARKLEY, Howard (1951-1999) Australian
Works on paper
£681 $1035 €1022 Study for Oriental wave study (25x18cm-10x7in) pencil ink synthetic polymer paint. 28-Aug-2 Deutscher-Menzies, Melbourne #141/R (A.D 1900)
£2789 $4573 €4184 Through the peel of the orange (91x56cm-36x22in) s.d.82 synthetic polymer paint prov. 4-Jun-3 Deutscher-Menzies, Melbourne #167/R est:8000-10000 (A.D 7000)
£2789 $4573 €4184 Abstract (169x120cm-67x47in) synthetic polymer paint ink exec.c.1974. 4-Jun-3 Deutscher-Menzies, Melbourne #168/R est:8000-12000 (A.D 7000)
£5000 $7700 €7500 Cottage by a stream (75x56cm-30x22in) synthetic polymer. 8-Sep-2 Sotheby's, Melbourne #3/R est:15000-20000 (A.D 14000)
£7500 $11550 €11250 Purple bird (76x56cm-30x22in) synthetic polymer on paper. 8-Sep-2 Sotheby's, Melbourne #90/R est:12000-18000 (A.D 21000)
£9302 $14791 €13953 Spot the difference (160x200cm-63x79in) s.d.1983 i.verso prov. 5-May-3 Sotheby's, Melbourne #152/R est:25000-35000 (A.D 24000)
£18571 $28600 €27857 Still life petunias (160x120cm-63x47in) s. i.d.1987 synthetic polymer on canvas exhib. 8-Sep-2 Sotheby's, Melbourne #48/R est:60000-80000 (A.D 52000)
£22857 $35200 €34286 Hedge on street corner (175x135cm-69x53in) s.d.88 i.verso synthetic polymer. 8-Sep-2 Sotheby's, Melbourne #10/R est:80000-120000 (A.D 64000)

ARKWRIGHT, Edith (fl.1884) British
£2800 $4368 €4200 Little girl with a labrador, an English toy terrier, a bichon frise and it's puppy (130x86cm-51x34in) mono. 26-Mar-3 Sotheby's, Olympia #150/R est:2000-3000

ARLAUD, Benjamin (fl.1701-1721) Swiss
Miniatures
£2000 $3120 €3000 Louis XV as a child wearing ermine lined blue cloak with fleur-de-lys motif (4cm-2xin) card wood frame oval. 5-Nov-2 Bonhams, New Bond Street #29/R est:2000-3000

ARLAUD, Marc Louis (attrib) (1772-1845) Swiss
£2657 $4438 €3800 Portraits d'Andre Poupart et de sa femmenee Marie Bechet (81x65cm-32x26in) pair. 27-Jun-3 Piasa, Paris #96/R est:4000-6000

ARLINGSSON, Erling (1904-1982) Swedish
£1087 $1717 €1631 Garden scene (40x50cm-16x20in) init. panel. 30-Nov-2 Goteborg Auktionsverk, Sweden #667/R est:15000 (S.KR 15500)
£1217 $1922 €1826 Horses grazing (39x50cm-15x20in) init. i.d.1968 verso cardboard. 28-Apr-3 Bukowskis, Stockholm #112/R est:15000-20000 (S.KR 16000)
£1418 $2199 €2127 In the valley (41x55cm-16x22in) mono. panel. 8-Dec-2 Uppsala Auktionskammare, Uppsala #211/R est:22000-25000 (S.KR 20000)
£1521 $2403 €2282 Autumn by the waterfall (51x56cm-20x22in) init. 28-Apr-3 Bukowskis, Stockholm #111/R est:20000-25000 (S.KR 20000)
£2057 $3188 €3086 Landscape with road (60x77cm-24x30in) s. double-sided. 8-Dec-2 Uppsala Auktionskammare, Uppsala #213/R est:12000-15000 (S.KR 29000)
£2102 $3280 €3153 October in Fryksdalen (55x65cm-22x26in) init. 5-Nov-2 Bukowskis, Stockholm #178b/R est:25000-28000 (S.KR 30000)
£2281 $3605 €3422 Coastal landscape, Skallen, Haverdal (54x67cm-21x26in) init. 28-Apr-3 Bukowskis, Stockholm #199/R est:30000-40000 (S.KR 30000)
£2313 $3608 €3470 Washerwomen (25x30cm-10x12in) init. panel. 5-Nov-2 Bukowskis, Stockholm #27/R est:30000-35000 (S.KR 33000)
£2482 $3848 €3723 Vessel in the skerries (55x61cm-22x24in) mono. 8-Dec-2 Uppsala Auktionskammare, Uppsala #212/R est:15000-18000 (S.KR 35000)
£2803 $4373 €4205 Washerwoman (61x48cm-24x19in) s.d.1940 canvas on panel. 5-Nov-2 Bukowskis, Stockholm #28/R est:20000-25000 (S.KR 40000)
£3861 $6216 €5792 Landscape with blue sea and boats (55x61cm-22x24in) init. 7-May-3 AB Stockholms Auktionsverk #757/R est:25000-30000 (S.KR 50000)

ARMAN, Fernandez (1928-) American/French
£475 $736 €750 Toucher (23x28cm-9x11in) s. acrylic col ink. 28-Sep-2 Cornette de St.Cyr, Paris #231
£1905 $3029 €2800 Allure 5 (41x33cm-16x13in) s.d.1960 prov.lit. 24-Mar-3 Cornette de St.Cyr, Paris #50/R
£2639 $4196 €3800 Sans titre (108x73cm-43x29in) s.i. colere de violoncelle paper. 29-Apr-3 Artcurial Briest, Paris #533/R est:2500-3000
£3043 $4991 €4200 Hammer accumulation (127x96cm-50x38in) s.d.77 Indian ink gouache board prov.exhib. 28-May-3 Lempertz, Koln #14/R est:3500
£5500 $9185 €7975 Cavalyres (109x74cm-43x29in) s.d.71 acrylic board prov. 24-Jun-3 Sotheby's, Olympia #73/R est:4000-6000
£6289 $9748 €10000 Pinceaux (92x60cm-36x24in) s. acrylic collage brushes canvas on panel prov. 30-Oct-2 Artcurial Briest, Paris #572/R est:8000-12000
£8163 $12980 €12000 Tubes (81x60cm-32x24in) s. acrylic tubes. 1-Mar-3 Meeting Art, Vercelli #365 est:10000
£15161 $23955 €23500 Coulees de peintures (100x81cm-39x32in) s. oil tubes painted 1966. 19-Dec-2 Ruellan, Paris #72/R est:15000
£20000 $33400 €29000 Untitled (163x131cm-64x52in) s. acrylic paint tubes exec.c.1987 prov. 26-Jun-3 Sotheby's, London #166/R est:15000-20000
£22581 $35000 €33872 Celebration (201x150cm-79x59in) s.i.verso acrylic painted brushes on canvas painted 1989 prov. 26-Sep-2 Christie's, Rockefeller NY #764/R est:25000-30000
Prints
£2619 $4164 €3850 Music stop no 2 (204x152cm-80x60in) s.num.EA col serigraph lit. 26-Feb-3 Artcurial Briest, Paris #543/R est:3000-4000
Sculpture
£943 $1462 €1500 Inclusion (49x12x3cm-19x5x1in) s.num.J brushes resin. 30-Oct-2 Artcurial Briest, Paris #634 est:1500-2000
£943 $1462 €1500 Sans titre (44x26x9cm-17x10x4in) s.num.34/35 crushed col tubes cardboard plexi box. 30-Oct-2 Artcurial Briest, Paris #636/R est:1500-2000
£949 $1481 €1500 Violon (50x50cm-20x20in) s. num.278/600 serigraph on plexiglas lit. 31-Jul-2 Tajan, Paris #76/R est:1500-2400
£962 $1490 €1500 Double chassis (29x20cm-11x8in) s.i. num.45/140 pol bronze exec.1994 lit. 7-Dec-2 De Vuyst, Lokeren #9/R est:1500-2000
£1042 $1656 €1500 Accumulation (44x26x9cm-17x10x4in) s.num.19/35 col tubes wood plexiglas box. 29-Apr-3 Artcurial Briest, Paris #370/R est:1500-2000
£1100 $1738 €1650 Visage antique decoupe (20cm-8in) s. num.EA1/3 gold pat bronze. 3-Apr-3 Christie's, Kensington #275/R
£1121 $1749 €1682 Cut camera (34x50cm-13x20in) s.num.60/95 dark gold pat.bronze. 5-Nov-2 Bukowskis, Stockholm #388/R est:25000-30000 (S.KR 16000)
£1132 $1755 €1800 Inclusion (23x9x3cm-9x4x1in) s.num.J col crayon. 30-Oct-2 Artcurial Briest, Paris #635/R est:800-1200
£1141 $1802 €1712 Untitled (65x44x4cm-26x17x2in) s.num.34/100 paintbrushes painted infused in plexiglas on socle. 28-Apr-3 Bukowskis, Stockholm #966/R est:15000-20000 (S.KR 15000)
£1146 $1810 €1650 Liberte (70x53x17cm-28x21x7in) num.68/75 collage wood plexiglas lithograph. 28-Apr-3 Cornette de St.Cyr, Paris #331/R est:1200-1500
£1236 $1989 €1854 Accumulation of stamps (47x32x8cm-19x13x3in) s.num.23/100 mixed media wooden box. 7-May-3 AB Stockholms Auktionsverk #1088/R est:15000-18000 (S.KR 16000)
£1250 $2063 €1800 Violon 1 (56x20x7cm-22x8x3in) s.num.75/150 verso cut up bronze. 1-Jul-3 Artcurial Briest, Paris #837/R est:1500-2000
£1274 $2000 €1911 Waiting to exhale (17x13cm-7x5in) s.num.41 cast resin cigars. 19-Nov-2 Wright, Chicago #269/R est:2000-3000

£1319	$2177	€1900	Violon 2 (58x20x10cm-23x8x4in) s.num.75/150 cut up bronze Cast Valsuani. 1-Jul-3 Artcurial Briest, Paris #838/R est:1200-1500
£1351	$2108	€2000	Pile ou face (33x17x4cm-13x7x2in) s.num.18/75 aluminium pat bronze. 25-Mar-3 Chochon-Barre & Allardi, Paris #29/R est:2000-2200
£1367	$2242	€1900	Hello Pablo (30cm-12in) s.num.5/100 bronze st.f.Bocquel conceived 1995. 3-Jun-3 Christie's, Amsterdam #190/R est:1800-2200
£1371	$2180	€2057	Chupa Chup (50cm-20in) s.num.31/50 lollipops in plexiglas. 26-Feb-3 Kunsthallen, Copenhagen #142/R est:20000 (D.KR 15000)
£1410	$2186	€2200	Les pinceaux (21cm-8in) s.num.57/100 bronze st.f.Bocquel cast 1989. 3-Dec-2 Christie's, Amsterdam #73/R est:1800-2200
£1439	$2360	€2000	Bonne Sante (41cm-16in) s.num.7/30 bottle tops in perspex. 3-Jun-3 Christie's, Amsterdam #191/R est:2000-3000
£1463	$2326	€2150	Pile ou face (33x17x4cm-13x7x2in) s.num.3/75 aluminium pat bronze. 26-Feb-3 Artcurial Briest, Paris #544/R est:1500-2000
£1464	$2270	€2196	Chupa Chup (42cm-17in) s.num.18/50 lollipops in plexiglass. 4-Dec-2 Kunsthallen, Copenhagen #157/R est:20000 (D.KR 17000)
£1582	$2500	€2500	Macho (31cm-12in) i.num.2/60 bronze. 26-Nov-2 Sotheby's, Amsterdam #76/R est:3000-4000
£1582	$2468	€2500	Screw accumulation (40x30cm-16x12in) s. screws plexiglas. 14-Sep-2 Meeting Art, Vercelli #723/R
£1583	$2532	€2200	Violon decoupe (58cm-23in) s.num.125/150 bronze. 16-May-3 Lombrail & Teucquam, Paris #60/R
£1749	$2763	€2624	Rites of Spring (37cm-15in) s.num.15/25 green gold pat.bronze. 28-Apr-3 Bukowskis, Stockholm #974/R est:35000-40000 (S.KR 23000)
£1752	$2733	€2628	Ange musicien (60cm-24in) s.num.54/100 polished green pat.bronze incl.round stone socle. 6-Nov-2 AB Stockholms Auktionsverk #733/R est:35000-40000 (S.KR 25000)
£1752	$2733	€2628	Venus aux Cuilleres (53cm-21in) s.num.89/100 polished bronze stainless incl.round stone socle. 6-Nov-2 AB Stockholms Auktionsverk #734/R est:35000-40000 (S.KR 25000)
£1772	$2747	€2800	Accumulation de reveils (42x35x9cm-17x14x4in) s.num.3/100 alarm clocks plexiglas. 28-Sep-2 Cornette de St.Cyr, Paris #227/R est:2800-3000
£1772	$2747	€2800	Accumulation de Chupa Chups (42x35x10cm-17x14x4in) s.num.9/50 lollipops plexiglas. 28-Sep-2 Cornette de St.Cyr, Paris #229/R est:2800-3000
£1773	$2961	€2500	Jetons de casino (30x20x4cm-12x8x2in) s. num.31/75 casino chips in plexiglass. 20-Jun-3 Piasa, Paris #209/R est:2500-3000
£1795	$2836	€2800	Corbeille a papiers (71x51cm-28x20in) paper plexiglas. 15-Nov-2 Laurence Calmels, Paris #22/R
£1918	$3011	€2800	Full-up (10x6x3cm-4x2x1in) sardine tin prov.exhib.lit. 15-Apr-3 Laurence Calmels, Paris #4119/R
£1962	$3041	€3100	Accumulation de Chupa Chups (42x35x9cm-17x14x4in) s.num.24/50 lollipops plexiglas. 28-Sep-2 Cornette de St.Cyr, Paris #228/R est:2800-3000
£1962	$3061	€3100	Artemis et acteon (7x3cm-3x1in) s.num.7/8 col gold brooch. 20-Oct-2 Charbonneaux, Paris #178/R est:3400-3800
£1986	$3217	€2800	Poubelle (60x40x10cm-24x16x4in) screwed up paper plexiglas box. 24-May-3 Van Ham, Cologne #14/R est:2000
£1986	$3316	€2800	Violon (35cm-14in) s. num.38/75 pat bronze. 20-Jun-3 Piasa, Paris #208/R est:2500-3000
£2000	$3340	€2900	Venus au violon (6cm-2in) s.num.6/8 gold brooch case. 9-Jul-3 Cornette de St.Cyr, Paris #208/R est:3000-3500
£2025	$3159	€3200	La famille. s.i. 18 carat gold pendant brooch. 31-Jul-2 Tajan, Paris #78/R est:3500-4000
£2051	$3179	€3200	Waiting to exhale (400x245x40cm-157x96x16in) s.num.48/100 cigars polyester raisin cast 1997. 3-Dec-2 Christie's, Amsterdam #71/R est:1400-1600
£2051	$3179	€3200	Double chassis (29cm-11in) s.d. num.3/140 bronze cast 1994. 3-Dec-2 Christie's, Amsterdam #74/R est:1500-2000
£2148	$3458	€3200	Tranches de trompettes (53x24x25cm-21x9x10in) s. welded bronze Cast Immart. 23-Feb-3 Mercier & Cie, Lille #200/R
£2153	$3338	€3230	Femme au violon (59cm-23in) s.num.17/100 polished green pat.bronze on black marble socle. 4-Dec-2 Kunsthallen, Copenhagen #183/R est:30000 (D.KR 25000)
£2172	$3389	€3258	Statue of Liberty (73cm-29in) s.d.97/100 green pat.bronze. 5-Nov-2 Bukowskis, Stockholm #387/R est:40000-45000 (S.KR 31000)
£2215	$3500	€3323	Slice of Liberty (80x25cm-31x10in) i.num.8/150 green pat. bronze prov. 22-Apr-3 Butterfields, San Francisco #6059/R est:4000-6000
£2237	$3512	€3490	Vingt US dollars (5x5cm-2x2in) st.sig. gold lit. 11-Dec-2 Artcurial Briest, Paris #646/R
£2244	$3478	€3500	Bon sante (40cm-16in) s. bottle tops in perspex executed 1995. 3-Dec-2 Christie's, Amsterdam #72/R est:1500-2000
£2292	$3621	€3300	Venus au montre (35cm-14in) s. multiple bronze edition of 100. 28-Apr-3 Cornette de St.Cyr, Paris #337 est:3500-4000
£2345	$3916	€3400	Colere de violon (6cm-2in) s.num.4/8 gold resin pendant case. 9-Jul-3 Cornette de St.Cyr, Paris #207/R est:3000-3500
£2400	$4008	€3480	Venus aux trombones (48cm-19in) s.num.98/100 green gold pat bronze edition of 100 sold with base. 24-Jun-3 Sotheby's, Olympia #70/R est:2000-3000
£2436	$3824	€3800	Violons (6cm-2in) st.sig. num.3/8 gold. 11-Dec-2 Artcurial Briest, Paris #635/R
£2468	$3875	€3850	Deux violons (6cm-2in) st.sig. num.6/8 gold. 11-Dec-2 Artcurial Briest, Paris #644/R
£2483	$4146	€3600	Inclusion de tulipes (41x30x10cm-16x12x4in) s.num.75/100 flowers resin. 9-Jul-3 Cornette de St.Cyr, Paris #211/R est:3500-4000
£2510	$3965	€3765	Untitled (49cm-19in) s.num.76/100 green pat.bronze on stone socle. 28-Apr-3 Bukowskis, Stockholm #971/R est:40000-50000 (S.KR 33000)
£2564	$4000	€3846	Saxophone (78x25cm-31x10in) s.num.10/10 nickel plate bronze. 14-Oct-2 Butterfields, San Francisco #2097/R est:4000-6000
£2692	$4227	€4200	Trois coulees (6cm-2in) st.sig. gold lit. 11-Dec-2 Artcurial Briest, Paris #626/R
£2692	$4227	€4200	Violon et brosses (7cm-3in) st.sig. num.8/8. 11-Dec-2 Artcurial Briest, Paris #622/R
£2692	$4227	€4200	Circus (7x5cm-3x2in) st.sig. num.6/8 gold. 11-Dec-2 Artcurial Briest, Paris #636/R
£2733	$4263	€4100	A coeur de la musique (43cm-17in) s.num.10/100 polished pat.bronze incl. socle Cast Bocquel. 6-Nov-2 AB Stockholms Auktionsverk #728/R est:20000-25000 (S.KR 39000)
£2733	$4263	€4100	Statue of Liberty (75cm-30in) s.num.125/150 green pat.bronze. 5-Nov-2 Bukowskis, Stockholm #390/R est:45000-50000 (S.KR 39000)
£2756	$4328	€4300	Saxophone (76cm-30in) s.verso num.III/X bronze. 23-Nov-2 Meeting Art, Vercelli #103/R
£2778	$4417	€4000	Saxophoe (76cm-30in) s.verso num.I/X bronze marble base. 1-May-3 Meeting Art, Vercelli #451 est:4000
£2803	$4373	€4205	Tenor saxophones - wall sculpture (94x130cm-37x51in) s.num.18/99 brass. 6-Nov-2 AB Stockholms Auktionsverk #731/R est:25000-30000 (S.KR 40000)
£2890	$4566	€4335	Ophelia (51cm-20in) s.num.I/XXX green pat.bronze on stone socle. 28-Apr-3 Bukowskis, Stockholm #973/R est:35000-40000 (S.KR 38000)
£3043	$4717	€4565	Violons coupe (64cm-25in) s. bronze marble socle. 4-Dec-2 Koller, Zurich #173/R est:7000-11000 (S.FR 7000)
£3077	$4769	€4800	Violin (57x18cm-22x7in) s.num.36/150 pol bronze marble base. 7-Dec-2 De Vuyst, Lokeren #493/R est:5000-6000
£3077	$4831	€4800	Venus au violon (7cm-3in) st.sig. gold. 11-Dec-2 Artcurial Briest, Paris #627/R
£3077	$4831	€4800	Successivement (7cm-3in) st.sig. gold. 11-Dec-2 Artcurial Briest, Paris #633/R
£3103	$5183	€4500	Inclusion de cigares (40x24x7cm-16x9x3in) s.num.26/100 cigars resin. 9-Jul-3 Cornette de St.Cyr, Paris #212/R est:4500-5000
£3145	$4874	€5000	Violin (64x19cm-25x7in) s. num.91/100 polished bronze. 5-Oct-2 De Vuyst, Lokeren #514/R est:5000-6000
£3165	$5000	€5000	Statue de la Liberte (73x25x20cm-29x10x8in) s. num.11/30 bronze exec.1987 prov. 27-Nov-2 Tajan, Paris #71/R
£3167	$5290	€4592	Violon coupe (64cm-25in) bronze marble socle. 24-Jun-3 Koller, Zurich #303/R est:1500-2500 (S.FR 7000)
£3205	$5032	€5000	Violin (61x25x7cm-24x10x3in) s. num.4/150 golden bronze plexiglass. 21-Nov-2 Finarte, Rome #107/R
£3346	$5287	€5019	Ophelia (51cm-20in) s.num.29/100 green pat.bronze on stone socle. 28-Apr-3 Bukowskis, Stockholm #972/R est:35000-40000 (S.KR 44000)
£3500	$5425	€5250	Colourscape (99x99cm-39x39in) s.num.28/75 paint tubes in plexiglas executed 1973. 5-Dec-2 Christie's, Kensington #285/R est:3000-5000
£3548	$5606	€5500	Inclusion de boulons (27x22x4cm-11x9x2in) s.d.63 resin metal prov.lit. 18-Dec-2 Christie's, Rome #130/R
£3673	$5841	€5400	Lyrism masculinum (127cm-50in) s.num.6/8 bronze st.f.Bonvicini. 26-Feb-3 Artcurial Briest, Paris #404a/R est:20000-25000
£3673	$5841	€5400	Parties de nikae (91x69cm-36x27in) s.d.63 i.verso coup de statue polyester black panel lit. 26-Feb-3 Artcurial Briest, Paris #405/R est:3000-4000
£3854	$6013	€5781	Water taps (45x26x13cm-18x10x5in) s. water taps in plexiglas. 5-Nov-2 Bukowskis, Stockholm #368/R est:35000-40000 (S.KR 55000)
£3871	$6000	€5807	Statue of Liberty (80x28x13cm-31x11x5in) s.num.74/150 green pat. bronze executed 1985. 26-Sep-2 Christie's, Rockefeller NY #767/R est:6000-8000
£3957	$6331	€5500	Violin (57x18cm-22x7in) s. num 8/20 brown pat bronze marble base. 17-May-3 De Vuyst, Lokeren #583/R est:5000-6000
£4000	$6520	€6000	Violon decoupe (56cm-22in) s.num.26/100 gold pat. bronze executed c.1994. 3-Feb-3 Sotheby's, Olympia #72/R est:4000-6000
£4167	$6542	€6500	Ferrari accumulation (39x24x5cm-15x9x2in) s. model car prov. 20-Nov-2 Pandolfini, Florence #137/R est:8500

£4200 $6846 €6300 Venus aux trombones (48cm-19in) s.num.XXI/XXX green gold pat. bronze. 3-Feb-3 Sotheby's, Olympia #70/R est:2000-3000
£4247 $6838 €6371 Accumulation of coins (27x28cm-11x11in) s.d.63 plastic metal on wood prov. 7-May-3 AB Stockholms Auktionsverk #1018/R est:8000-10000 (S.KR 55000)
£4500 $7335 €6750 Accumulation de rouages (25x17cm-10x7in) s.d.60 verso watch movements in perspex box lit. 3-Feb-3 Sotheby's, Olympia #88/R est:3000-4000
£4684 $7306 €7400 Violin chair (85cm-33in) i. verso brown black pat.bronze. 18-Oct-2 Dr Fritz Nagel, Stuttgart #459/R est:8200
£6657 $10385 €9986 Tubes Suedois (100x100cm-39x39in) s. one of 75 paint tubes in plexiglas. 5-Nov-2 Bukowskis, Stockholm #369/R est:25000-30000 (S.KR 95000)
£8000 $12320 €12000 Accumulation of matchboxes (90x60x4cm-35x24x2in) s. matchboxes polyester resin in plexiglass executed 1988 prov. 22-Oct-2 Sotheby's, London #349/R est:5000-7000
£8500 $13940 €12750 Venus au violon (93cm-37in) s. violin in plexiglas incl.wood bronze base one of 12 prov. 6-Feb-3 Christie's, London #670/R est:10000-15000
£9000 $13860 €13500 Untitled (91x122cm-36x48in) s.d.NY 82 col pencil polyester resin in plexiglass prov. 22-Oct-2 Sotheby's, London #347/R est:4000-6000
£9000 $13860 €13500 Clic clac (50x70cm-20x28in) s.d.71 camera parts polyester resin in plexiglass prov. 22-Oct-2 Sotheby's, London #350/R est:7000-9000
£9000 $13950 €13500 Violon coupe 2000 (79cm-31in) s. wood gold pat. bronze wire violin and case. 5-Dec-2 Christie's, Kensington #282/R est:10000-15000
£9119 $14135 €14500 Pied de table (70x50x45cm-28x20x18in) s. soldered violin parts bronze. 30-Oct-2 Artcurial Briest, Paris #452/R est:18000-25000
£9310 $15548 €13500 Violon menagere (88x56x29cm-35x22x11in) s. cut up violin cutlery 116 pieces plexiglas box lit. 9-Jul-3 Cornette de St.Cyr, Paris #206/R est:7000-9000
£9574 $15511 €13500 Cube telephone (25x25x25cm-10x10x10in) telephone parts in plexiglass prov. 26-May-3 Christie's, Milan #277/R est:12000-16000
£9615 $14904 €15000 Violon, menagere (88x56x29cm-35x22x11in) s. violin plexiglas cutlry one of 99 exec.1973 lit. 7-Dec-2 Cornette de St.Cyr, Paris #130/R est:15000-20000
£10000 $16700 €14500 Pour ma jolie, guitar (65x44x15cm-26x17x6in) s.num.3/8 verso bronze. 26-Jun-3 Sotheby's, London #164/R est:10000-15000
£10417 $17188 €15000 Inclusion (82x39x5cm-32x15x2in) s.d.70 burnt violin resin. 1-Jul-3 Artcurial Briest, Paris #531/R est:18000-25000
£11538 $18115 €18000 Lion (81x37cm-32x15in) s.d.1963 bronze lit. 21-Nov-2 Finarte, Rome #341/R est:18000-20000
£11635 $17918 €18500 Violon, menagere (89x56x29cm-35x22x11in) s. violin plexiglas one of 99 exec.1973 lit. 26-Oct-2 Cornette de St.Cyr, Paris #60/R est:20000
£12821 $20128 €20000 Violons (121x65x42cm-48x26x17in) s. gilt pat bronze wood prov. 20-Nov-2 Pandolfini, Florence #143/R est:25000
£13194 $20847 €19000 Table basse aux violons enchevetres (50x100x90cm-20x39x35in) s.num.EA 1/2 soldered bronze violins glass prov. 27-Apr-3 Perrin, Versailles #97/R est:15000-20000
£13889 $22083 €20000 Untitled (81x60cm-32x24in) s. clarinet acrylic canvas on board. 1-May-3 Meeting Art, Vercelli #237 est:10000
£13912 $22119 €20450 L'heure musical (63x23x19cm-25x9x7in) gold pat bronze soldered watch faces Cast Bocquel. 26-Feb-3 Artcurial Briest, Paris #404/R est:18000-25000
£14000 $23380 €20300 Violon prisonnier (63x33x31cm-25x13x12in) s.num.2/2 bronze wood. 26-Jun-3 Sotheby's, London #165/R est:10000-15000
£14583 $24063 €21000 Vincent's bike (109x140x20cm-43x55x8in) s. cut up bike brushes acrylic. 1-Jul-3 Artcurial Briest, Paris #831/R est:20000-25000
£15000 $24600 €22500 Venus with violin (88x38x25cm-35x15x10in) s. violin resin series of 12 prov. 7-Feb-3 Sotheby's, London #196/R est:15000-20000
£15190 $24000 €24000 Erato (122cm-48in) s.num.1/8 polished pat.bronze. 1-Dec-2 Bukowskis, Helsinki #370/R est:17000-20000
£16026 $25160 €25000 Super-imposition (151x121cm-59x48in) s. paintbrushes acrylic board lit. 23-Nov-2 Meeting Art, Vercelli #370/R est:25000
£16312 $25284 €24468 Violon sur belon (86x28x13cm-34x11x5in) s. wood concrete pt. 8-Dec-2 Uppsala Auktionskammare, Uppsala #361/R est:150000-200000 (S.KR 230000)
£17361 $28646 €25000 Pyraviole (58x41x28cm-23x16x11in) s. num.4/8 verso soldered bronze Cast Bocquel. 1-Jul-3 Artcurial Briest, Paris #536/R est:20000-25000
£18082 $27846 €28750 Hommage a Yves Klein (66x32x21cm-26x13x8in) s.i. pigment violin resin exec.1992 lit. 26-Oct-2 Cornette de St.Cyr, Paris #59/R est:25000
£18794 $30447 €26500 Poubelle organique (100x50x12cm-39x20x5in) pieces of taps in plexiglass. 23-May-3 Camard, Paris #186/R est:6000-8000
£18987 $30000 €28481 Untitled (254x152x13cm-100x60x5in) acrylic paint brushes on canvas painted 1987 prov. 13-Nov-2 Sotheby's, New York #326/R est:30000-40000
£20567 $34348 €29000 Les Violoncelles et archets (122x113x51cm-48x44x20in) s.num.1/1 wood prov. 20-Jun-3 Piasa, Paris #29/R est:20000-30000
£22152 $34557 €35000 Venus aux pinceaux (142x55x57cm-56x22x22in) s. num.3/8 part painted bronze. 31-Jul-2 Tajan, Paris #60/R est:40000-50000
£23741 $37749 €34900 Sans titre (244x182cm-96x72in) brushes acrylic canvas. 26-Feb-3 Artcurial Briest, Paris #403/R est:25000-35000
£24113 $39064 €34000 Smashed cello (162x132x19cm-64x52x7in) s. smashed cello lit. 23-May-3 Camard, Paris #187/R est:8000-10000
£24558 $39047 €36100 Colere de violoncelle calcine (170x100x13cm-67x39x5in) s. burnt violin prov. 26-Feb-3 Artcurial Briest, Paris #402/R est:30000-35000
£26923 $42269 €42000 La plume est plus forte que l'epee (50x70x10cm-20x28x4in) s.d.1961 ink stands prov.exhib.lit. 11-Dec-2 Artcurial Briest, Paris #734/R est:55000

Works on paper

£411 $638 €650 Accumulation de tampons (30x30cm-12x12in) s. tampons. 28-Sep-2 Cornette de St.Cyr, Paris #235
£561 $875 €842 Paint tubes (74x55cm-29x22in) s. collage paper on canvas. 5-Nov-2 Bukowskis, Stockholm #394/R (S.KR 8000)
£691 $1113 €1030 Accumulation (25x28cm-10x11in) s. ink tampon. 23-Feb-3 Mercier & Cie, Lille #62
£849 $1368 €1274 Sans titre (76x56cm-30x22in) s. mixed media paper on canvas. 7-May-3 AB Stockholms Auktionsverk #1138/R (S.KR 11000)
£900 $1467 €1350 Violscape (32x23cm-13x9in) s.i.d.Jan 83 black marker pen crayon gouache. 3-Feb-3 Sotheby's, Olympia #68/R est:1000-1500
£1831 $2948 €2600 Violins jaunes et bleues (74x54cm-29x21in) s. mixed media paper on canvas. 10-May-3 Bukowskis, Helsinki #287/R est:3000-3500
£2778 $4416 €4000 Cachet (61x50cm-24x20in) s.d.1957 verso printed objects. 29-Apr-3 Artcurial Briest, Paris #532/R est:3000-4000
£3620 $6045 €5249 Chicago Riffle (76x56cm-30x22in) s. gouache. 24-Jun-3 Koller, Zurich #178/R est:8000-18000 (S.FR 8000)
£4615 $7246 €7200 Violons. s. paper relief prov. 20-Nov-2 Pandolfini, Florence #133/R est:9500
£4747 $7500 €7500 UN. (13x107cm-5x42in) thongs assemblage cardboard exec.1982. 27-Nov-2 Tajan, Paris #36/R est:7500-9000
£6329 $9873 €10000 Untitled (81x61cm-32x24in) s. col. tubes painted 2000. 14-Sep-2 Meeting Art, Vercelli #811/R est:10000
£8228 $13000 €13000 Tubes (61x121cm-24x48in) s. paint tubes oil on canvas executed c.1985. 26-Nov-2 Sotheby's, Amsterdam #250/R est:13000-15000
£9000 $15030 €13050 Untitled (107x92cm-42x36in) s. spraypoint pencil paper on canvas prov. 26-Jun-3 Sotheby's, London #168/R est:5000-7000
£10862 $16945 €16293 Dirty painting (146x114cm-57x45in) s. mixed media canvas. 6-Nov-2 AB Stockholms Auktionsverk #960/R est:225000-250000 (S.KR 155000)
£11111 $17667 €16000 Untitled (92x73cm-36x29in) s. tubes canvas on board exec.1997. 1-May-3 Meeting Art, Vercelli #457 est:15000
£11111 $18333 €16000 Arrete prefectoral (99x49cm-39x19in) s.i.d.avril 1961 verso folded paper box prov.exhib.lit. 1-Jul-3 Artcurial Briest, Paris #532/R est:16000-20000
£22000 $36740 €31900 General hardware (80x59cm-31x23in) metal polyester resin plexiglass prov.exhib.lit. 26-Jun-3 Sotheby's, London #146/R est:18000-25000

ARMANDO (1929-) Dutch

£305 $497 €460 Untitled (73x146cm-29x57in) s.d.1992 verso diptych. 11-Feb-3 Segre, Madrid #279/R
£1538 $2385 €2400 Ladder (80x60cm-31x24in) painted 1992. 7-Dec-2 Van Ham, Cologne #10/R est:2800
£2089 $3300 €3300 Kopf (100x90cm-39x35in) s. i.d.15/9/90 on stretcher. 26-Nov-2 Sotheby's, Amsterdam #251/R est:3000-4000
£2158 $3540 €3000 Kopf - head (105x105cm-41x41in) s. i.d.stretcher acrylic. 3-Jun-3 Christie's, Amsterdam #368/R est:3000-5000
£2658 $4200 €4200 Fahne (70x50cm-28x20in) s. i.d.1981 on stretcher. 26-Nov-2 Sotheby's, Amsterdam #279/R est:3500-4500
£4167 $6458 €6500 Schuldige landschaft (60x80cm-24x31in) s.i.d.23.9.87 diptych prov. 3-Dec-2 Christie's, Amsterdam #288/R est:4000-6000
£9494 $15000 €15000 Boulons sur fond noir (120x60cm-47x24in) s.d.7/60 verso screwbolts on black painted wood exhib. 26-Nov-2 Sotheby's, Amsterdam #269/R est:8000-12000
£12950 $21237 €18000 6X zwart (42x34cm-17x13in) s.d.12/62 painted sheet metal nails on board. 3-Jun-3 Christie's, Amsterdam #365/R est:9000-12000

Works on paper

£284 $460 €400 Ast (18x13cm-7x5in) s.d.82 pencil W/C. 26-May-3 Glerum, Amsterdam #258

ARMANIOUS, Hany (1962-) Australian
£613 $962 €920 Untitled - abstract figure (54x36cm-21x14in) s. oil on paper prov. 15-Apr-3 Lawson Menzies, Sydney #72/R est:1000-1500 (A.D 1600)

ARMES, Thomas W (fl.1928-1933) British
£850 $1403 €1233 Picnickers (52x70cm-20x28in) 1-Jul-3 Bonhams, Norwich #263/R

ARMESTO, Alvarez Primitivo (19th C) Spanish
£541 $843 €800 Peasant woman (45x33cm-18x13in) s.d.1920 board. 25-Mar-3 Durán, Madrid #691/R

ARMFIELD (?) British
£1000 $1580 €1500 Terriers chasing a badger in the undergrowth (48x58cm-19x23in) 24-Apr-3 Scarborough Perry Fine Arts, Hove #626

ARMFIELD, Diana (1920-) British
£820 $1312 €1189 Raidi on the path between the aspens (28x21cm-11x8in) init. i.verso board. 13-May-3 Bristol Auction Rooms #478/R
Works on paper
£700 $1113 €1050 Summer flowers (22x15cm-9x6in) init. col chks. 26-Feb-3 Sotheby's, Olympia #314/R

ARMFIELD, Edward (19th C) British
£286 $443 €429 Terriers (29x39cm-11x15in) s. 29-Oct-2 Lawson Menzies, Sydney #91 (A.D 800)
£320 $493 €480 Grey pony, setters and doves outside a stable (40x58cm-16x23in) 22-Oct-2 Bonhams, Bath #155
£350 $553 €525 Terriers ratting (30x39cm-12x15in) s. panel. 28-Nov-2 Christie's, Kensington #300
£450 $700 €675 Fox hunt (76x63cm-30x25in) s. 6-Nov-2 Sotheby's, Olympia #152/R
£550 $913 €798 Terries rabbiting (71x91cm-28x36in) indis sig.d. 12-Jun-3 Christie's, Kensington #232/R
£580 $922 €870 Terries by a foxhole (41x30cm-16x12in) s. 20-Mar-3 Ewbank, Send #379/R
£580 $922 €870 Two spaniels by a hearth (41x30cm-16x12in) s. 20-Mar-3 Ewbank, Send #380
£638 $1034 €900 Terrier ratting in a barn (40x30cm-16x12in) s. pair. 20-May-3 Mealy's, Castlecomer #966/R
£780 $1303 €1131 Terriers ratting (89x69cm-35x27in) s. 8-Jul-3 Bonhams, Knightsbridge #81/R
£783 $1221 €1175 Two hunting dogs and fox (41x31cm-16x12in) s. 16-Sep-2 Philippe Schuler, Zurich #3457 (S.FR 1800)
£800 $1328 €1160 Terriers rabbiting (25x36cm-10x14in) s. 12-Jun-3 Christie's, Kensington #233/R
£850 $1385 €1275 Hunting scenes (15x21cm-6x8in) s. pair. 29-Jan-3 Sotheby's, Olympia #105/R est:800-1200
£900 $1422 €1350 Stable friends (41x61cm-16x24in) s. 28-Nov-2 Christie's, Kensington #131/R
£1000 $1580 €1500 Sharp lookout. Hot breakfast (30x41cm-12x16in) s. pair. 28-Nov-2 Christie's, Kensington #285/R est:400-600
£1050 $1638 €1575 Terriers in a stable. Terriers attacking a hedgehog (31x40cm-12x16in) s. pair. 17-Sep-2 Bonhams, Sevenoaks #226/R est:600-800
£1100 $1716 €1650 Terriers ratting (30x41cm-12x16in) s. pair. 6-Nov-2 Sotheby's, Olympia #158/R est:1200-1800
£1300 $2158 €1885 Terriers ratting. Spaniels at a door (30x41cm-12x16in) s. pair. 12-Jun-3 Christie's, Kensington #245/R est:1200-1800
£1650 $2690 €2475 Three terriers in a barn (63x76cm-25x30in) s. 11-Feb-3 Bonhams, Knowle #83 est:800-1200
£1700 $2822 €2465 Spaniels putting mallards up (71x91cm-28x36in) 12-Jun-3 Christie's, Kensington #285/R est:1500-2000
£2147 $3500 €3221 Terriers ratting. Surrounded (30x41cm-12x16in) s. two painted c.1880. 11-Feb-3 Bonhams & Doyles, New York #97 est:4000-6000

ARMFIELD, Edward (attrib) (19th C) British
£420 $685 €609 In danger (40x30cm-16x12in) bears sig. 16-Jul-3 Sotheby's, Olympia #72/R
£720 $1116 €1080 Terriers ratting in a barn (13x15cm-5x6in) panel. 1-Nov-2 Moore Allen & Innocent, Cirencester #260/R
£780 $1115 €1170 Spaniel and terrier (21x29cm-8x11in) board. 28-Feb-2 Greenslade Hunt, Taunton #434/R

ARMFIELD, George (fl.1840-1875) British
£310 $499 €465 Sailing vessels on a stormy day, off Isle of Wight (18x28cm-7x11in) s.i.verso painted 1866. 9-May-3 Mallams, Oxford #100
£361 $600 €523 Friends (20x30cm-8x12in) s.verso. 11-Jun-3 Boos Gallery, Michigan #542/R
£380 $619 €570 Trouble (18x16cm-7x6in) s. i.verso. 12-Feb-3 Bonhams, Knightsbridge #127/R
£385 $600 €578 Portrait of two setters (30x41cm-12x16in) s. 21-Sep-2 Pook & Pook, Downington #274/R
£450 $684 €675 Terriers ratting in a barn (28x39cm-11x15in) s. 4-Jul-2 Mellors & Kirk, Nottingham #862
£460 $750 €690 Terrier taking a rabbit (14x19cm-6x7in) bers mono. panel. 13-Feb-3 Mellors & Kirk, Nottingham #811
£650 $1060 €975 Noise in the shrubbery (23x30cm-9x12in) s. board. 12-Feb-3 Bonhams, Knightsbridge #133/R
£764 $1177 €1200 Caught at last (28x38cm-11x15in) s. 4-Sep-2 James Adam, Dublin #62/R est:700-1000
£850 $1377 €1275 Spaniels and a pheasant (25x36cm-10x14in) s. 20-May-3 Sotheby's, Olympia #203/R
£1000 $1520 €1500 Farmyard scene with horses and chickens (18x28cm-7x11in) s.d.1861. 14-Aug-2 Andrew Hartley, Ilkley #643/R est:1000-1400
£1300 $2041 €1950 Terriers with a rabbit in a barn (25x35cm-10x14in) s. 21-Nov-2 Tennants, Leyburn #770/R est:800-1200
£1397 $2250 €2096 Hunting dogs. Sleeping dogs. (13x15cm-5x6in) s. board two. 23-Feb-3 Butterfields, Los Angeles #7069 est:500-700
£1500 $2445 €2250 Ambush (46x62cm-18x24in) s. 12-Feb-3 Bonhams, Knightsbridge #125/R est:800-1200
£1500 $2490 €2175 Terrier (19x17cm-7x7in) s. board painted oval. 12-Jun-3 Christie's, Kensington #242/R est:1000-1500
£1534 $2500 €2301 Flirtation (23x30cm-9x12in) board. 11-Feb-3 Bonhams & Doyles, New York #98/R est:1500-2000
£1698 $2649 €2700 Cornered (46x36cm-18x14in) s. 17-Sep-2 Whyte's, Dublin #119/R est:2000-3000
£2300 $3634 €3450 Gun dogs in a wood (72x92cm-28x36in) s.d.1869. 7-Apr-3 Bonhams, Bath #108/R est:2000-3000
£3354 $5500 €4863 Rabbit hunting (50x61cm-20x24in) s. 4-Jun-3 Christie's, Rockefeller NY #235/R est:6000-8000
£3811 $6250 €5526 Two terriers locked out (51x61cm-20x24in) s. 7-Jun-3 Neal Auction Company, New Orleans #254/R est:6000-8000
£4088 $6500 €6132 Terriers rabbiting (70x91cm-28x36in) s. 30-Apr-3 Sotheby's, New York #564/R est:6000-8000

ARMFIELD, George (attrib) (fl.1840-1875) British
£661 $965 €992 Four terriers attacking mouse trap (25x41cm-10x16in) mono. panel. 17-Jun-2 Philippe Schuler, Zurich #4324/R (S.FR 1500)
£680 $1108 €1020 Guardians of the rat hole (39cm-15in circular) bears another sig.d. 30-Jan-3 Lawrence, Crewkerne #712/R
£750 $1170 €1125 Spaniels putting up mallard in a marsh (46x61cm-18x24in) 10-Apr-3 Tennants, Leyburn #1023/R
£769 $1200 €1154 Terrier. 21-Sep-2 Harvey Clar, Oakland #1416
£897 $1400 €1346 Terrier. 21-Sep-2 Harvey Clar, Oakland #1417
£900 $1467 €1350 Gamekeeper's larder (25x31cm-10x12in) 12-Feb-3 Bonhams, Knightsbridge #145/R
£1004 $1587 €1506 Terriers by mousetrap (25x41cm-10x16in) mono. panel. 14-Nov-2 Stuker, Bern #50/R est:3000-3500 (S.FR 2300)

ARMFIELD, Maxwell (1882-1972) British
Works on paper
£800 $1272 €1200 Leaves and toadstools (25x20cm-10x8in) mono.i. ink W/C exhib. 26-Feb-3 Sotheby's, Olympia #142/R

ARMFIELD, Stuart (1916-2000) British
£1000 $1590 €1500 Edge of sleep (56x76cm-22x30in) incised sig. tempera on board prov. 26-Feb-3 Sotheby's, Olympia #311/R est:1000-1500
Works on paper
£250 $388 €375 Dades Gorge, South Morocco (54x73cm-21x29in) s.i. pencil pen brown ink W/C. 4-Dec-2 Christie's, Kensington #237
£850 $1343 €1275 Still life with lilies in a vase (72x47cm-28x19in) s. W/C. 27-Nov-2 Sotheby's, Olympia #76/R

ARMINGTON, Caroline (1875-1939) American/Canadian
£489 $802 €709 Untitled - children with goat (41x51cm-16x20in) canvas on board. 1-Jun-3 Levis, Calgary #1/R est:1500-2000 (C.D 1100)

ARMINGTON, Frank Milton (1876-1941) Canadian
£2453 $3826 €3900 Femme a l arobe rouge dans un jardin (50x61cm-20x24in) s. 9-Oct-2 Marc Kohn, Paris #15/R
£3831 $6052 €5747 Une vieille maison a la clarte (61x51cm-24x20in) s.d.1927 i.verso prov. 18-Nov-2 Sotheby's, Toronto #6/R est:8000-10000 (C.D 9500)

ARMITAGE, Alfred (fl.1889-1905) British
£1950 $3257 €2828 Fish seller Treworveneth Street Newlyn (48x33cm-19x13in) s. 19-Jun-3 Lane, Penzance #390 est:2000-2500
£5800 $8990 €8700 Old Dame's shop, Penzance (157x191cm-62x75in) s. painted c.1892. 26-Sep-2 Lane, Penzance #250/R est:4500-6000

ARMITAGE, Arnold (1899-1991) American
£833 $1300 €1250 Twin boys sliding down banister, Holsum bread ca 1940's (33x71cm-13x28in) s. board gouache acetate sheet. 9-Nov-2 Illustration House, New York #7/R

ARMITAGE, David (1943-) New Zealander
£295 $460 €443 Bed (185x143cm-73x56in) s.d.1973 acrylic dye on canvas exhib. 6-Aug-2 Peter Webb, Auckland #199 est:1000-2000 (NZ.D 1000)

ARMITAGE, Kenneth (1916-) British
Sculpture
£800 $1272 €1200 Head in hands on a stool (28cm-11in) white plastic. 19-Mar-3 John Nicholson, Haslemere #1112
£6500 $10855 €9425 Two seated figures (24cm-9in) init.num.5/6 brown pat bronze. 24-Jun-3 Bonhams, New Bond Street #125/R est:4000-6000
£10000 $15600 €15000 Seated figure with arms raised (35cm-14in) black pat. bronze cast 1957 prov.lit. 25-Mar-3 Bonhams, New Bond Street #127/R est:5000-7000
£12000 $18600 €18000 Pandarus, version II (188cm-74in) dark green pat. prov.exhib.lit. 4-Dec-2 Sotheby's, London #88/R est:12000-18000

ARMLEDER, John M (1948-) Swiss
£4367 $6856 €6551 Untitled (125x125cm-49x49in) s.d.1984 verso varnish perforated pavatex prov.exhib.lit. 25-Nov-2 Germann, Zurich #121/R est:15000-20000 (S.FR 10000)
Works on paper
£700 $1141 €1050 U 40 drop cloth (29x31cm-11x12in) s.d.1992 verso mixed media on linen packed cardboard pizza box. 3-Feb-3 Sotheby's, Olympia #177/R
£897 $1391 €1400 Untitled (41x31cm-16x12in) mono.d.1983 gouache silver gold. 6-Dec-2 Hauswedell & Nolte, Hamburg #29/R

ARMOUR, G D (1864-1949) British
£320 $509 €480 The field master (32x38cm-13x15in) s. 7-Mar-3 Tennants, Leyburn #82

ARMOUR, George Denholm (1864-1949) British
£850 $1411 €1233 Seen in the motor lights, the hunt returning home (34x46cm-13x18in) s.i. board. 12-Jun-3 Christie's, Kensington #21/R
£900 $1494 €1305 Theoty and practice. Poor by honest eh? (20x29cm-8x11in) s. pen ink two prov. 12-Jun-3 Christie's, Kensington #22/R
Works on paper
£250 $398 €375 Circus scene (16x22cm-6x9in) pencil. 25-Feb-3 Bonhams, Knightsbridge #73/R
£300 $477 €450 Fisherman smoking a pipe (14x21cm-6x8in) init. pencil. 25-Feb-3 Bonhams, Knightsbridge #75/R
£320 $499 €480 Theory or practise, or why the engagement was broken off (22x29cm-9x11in) s. pen ink. 10-Oct-2 Greenslade Hunt, Taunton #569/R
£340 $541 €510 On the Shannon fishing from a coll (21x31cm-8x12in) s.i. pencil. 25-Feb-3 Bonhams, Knightsbridge #68/R
£360 $572 €540 Looking over the prize (20x21cm-8x8in) init. pencil. 25-Feb-3 Bonhams, Knightsbridge #79/R
£500 $790 €750 Modern Laocoon, an incident on the field of Waterloo (16x23cm-6x9in) s. pen ink. 28-Nov-2 Christie's, Kensington #311/R
£1200 $1908 €1800 Soldiers camp, Morocco (33x43cm-13x17in) s. W/C. 6-Mar-3 Christie's, Kensington #192/R est:1500-2000

ARMOUR, Mary (1902-2000) British
£500 $775 €750 Bridge, North Glen Sannox (16x23cm-6x9in) s. board. 7-Dec-2 Shapes, Edinburgh #309/R
£1000 $1650 €1450 Near Kilbarchan, Renfrewshire (20x30cm-8x12in) s.d.66 board. 3-Jul-3 Christie's, Kensington #447/R est:1000-1500
£1000 $1650 €1450 Gleniffer Braes, Renfrewshire (20x27cm-8x11in) s. board. 3-Jul-3 Christie's, Kensington #449/R est:1000-1500
£1100 $1782 €1650 Clyde at Wemyss Bay (15x23cm-6x9in) s.d.70 board. 23-May-3 Lyon & Turnbull, Edinburgh #73/R est:400-800
£1500 $2430 €2250 Teallachs from Gruinard (30x50cm-12x20in) s.d.75. 23-May-3 Lyon & Turnbull, Edinburgh #31/R est:1500-2000
£1800 $2736 €2700 Summer on the farm (41x51cm-16x20in) s. 28-Aug-2 Sotheby's, London #1037/R est:2000-3000
£1900 $2964 €2850 Raasay. Landscape (27x41cm-11x16in) s.d.1984 double-sided prov. 17-Sep-2 Sotheby's, Olympia #73/R est:1800-2500
£2800 $4284 €4200 Sunny day at Milngavie, Glasgow (50x60cm-20x24in) s. board prov. 22-Aug-2 Bonhams, Edinburgh #1127/R est:2500-3000
£3000 $4680 €4500 Magnolias (60x45cm-24x18in) s.d.1976. 14-Apr-3 Sotheby's, London #92/R est:2000-3000
£5000 $7750 €7500 Still life with anemones (63x76cm-25x30in) s. 6-Dec-2 Lyon & Turnbull, Edinburgh #108/R est:6000-8000
£5800 $8874 €8700 Arran (24x34cm-9x13in) s.d.72 board. 22-Aug-2 Bonhams, Edinburgh #965/R est:2000-3000
£8000 $12160 €12000 Still life with spirea (76x64cm-30x25in) s.d.71 i.verso. 28-Aug-2 Sotheby's, London #1033/R est:8000-12000
£9000 $13770 €13500 Studio interior (60x50cm-24x20in) s.d.72. 22-Aug-2 Bonhams, Edinburgh #976/R est:7000-9000
£13000 $19890 €19500 Still life of dark Christmas roses (60x60cm-24x24in) s.d.1982 exhib. 22-Aug-2 Bonhams, Edinburgh #1036/R est:10000-15000
Works on paper
£620 $967 €930 Spring at the Duchal, Kilmalcolm (31x36cm-12x14in) s.i.d.1968 pastel. 17-Oct-2 Bonhams, Edinburgh #100

ARMSTRONG, Arthur (1924-1996) Irish
£1528 $2429 €2200 Still life with lamp (36x25cm-14x10in) board prov. 29-Apr-3 Whyte's, Dublin #63/R est:1200-1500
£1600 $2560 €2400 Peninsular shore near Schull Co Cork (61x76cm-24x30in) s. board prov. 15-May-3 Christie's, Kensington #211/R est:1000-1500
£1772 $2747 €2800 Ballyrubbock (60x75cm-24x30in) s.i.verso board. 25-Sep-2 James Adam, Dublin #140/R est:3000-5000
£1923 $3019 €3000 Snow scene in abstract (75x60cm-30x24in) s. board. 19-Nov-2 Hamilton Osborne King, Dublin #453/R est:2000-3000
£1957 $3209 €2700 Sun breaking through (51x61cm-20x24in) s. board. 28-May-3 Bonhams & James Adam, Dublin #48/R est:2000-3000
£3986 $6536 €5500 Ben Bulben (76x61cm-30x24in) s. board. 28-May-3 Bonhams & James Adam, Dublin #76/R est:6000-10000
£5000 $8000 €7500 Studio still life 1 (81x71cm-32x28in) s. board. 16-May-3 Sotheby's, London #124/R est:5000-7000
Works on paper
£411 $638 €650 West of Ireland landscape (25x35cm-10x14in) W/C prov. 25-Sep-2 James Adam, Dublin #9
£2200 $3520 €3300 Studio two (51x38cm-20x15in) s. col chk gouache prov. 16-May-3 Sotheby's, London #139/R est:800-1200

ARMSTRONG, Augustus (fl.1717-1743) British
Works on paper
£3300 $5115 €4950 Portrait of Sir Andrew Fountaine, Warden of the Mint of Narford Hall (28x20cm-11x8in) col chk prov.lit. 30-Sep-2 Bonhams, Ipswich #308 est:1000-1500

ARMSTRONG, Bruce (1957-) Australian
Sculpture
£1056 $1648 €1830 Reciprocate (72cm-28in) painted wood prov. 31-Mar-3 Goodman, Sydney #135 (A.D 2800)

ARMSTRONG, Geoffrey (20th C) South African?
£267 $437 €387 Victoria Island Strait (90x120cm-35x47in) s.i.d.1978 acrylic. 9-Jun-3 Hodgins, Calgary #191/R (C.D 600)
£402 $631 €603 Grey dawn breaking (120x120cm-47x47in) s.i. acrylic. 25-Nov-2 Hodgins, Calgary #155/R (C.D 1000)
£542 $856 €813 Northern solitude (122x152cm-48x60in) d.1976. 1-Dec-2 Levis, Calgary #2/R (C.D 1350)

ARMSTRONG, Ian (1923-) Australian
£690 $1083 €1035 Jacob and Angel (101x91cm-40x36in) s. 15-Apr-3 Lawson Menzies, Sydney #225/R est:2000-3000 (A.D 1800)
£1708 $2614 €2562 Holiday - mentones (81x101cm-32x40in) s.d.58 board prov. 26-Aug-2 Sotheby's, Paddington #672/R est:5000-8000 (A.D 4800)
£1916 $2854 €2874 Mrs Margaret Shaw (152x91cm-60x36in) s.d.91 linen exhib. 27-Aug-2 Christie's, Melbourne #242/R est:6000-8000 (A.D 5000)
Works on paper
£383 $602 €575 Study for the road makers (27x37cm-11x15in) s. gouache. 15-Apr-3 Lawson Menzies, Sydney #153/R est:1200-1500 (A.D 1000)

ARMSTRONG, John (1893-1973) British
£400 $660 €580 Pale day (16x24cm-6x9in) tempera board painted c.1968 prov. 3-Jul-3 Christie's, Kensington #667
£600 $936 €900 Explosion (38x38cm-15x15in) i. board. 12-Sep-2 Sotheby's, Olympia #197/R
Works on paper
£360 $562 €540 Pesticide (25x23cm-10x9in) init. gouache. 12-Sep-2 Sotheby's, Olympia #196/R
£600 $936 €900 Mould - penicillin (32x46cm-13x18in) pastel gouache. 12-Sep-2 Sotheby's, Olympia #190/R
£650 $1014 €975 Paper (30x15cm-12x6in) init. ink gouache. 12-Sep-2 Sotheby's, Olympia #195/R
£900 $1404 €1350 Straight from the tap no.2 (39x29cm-15x11in) W/C exhib. 12-Sep-2 Sotheby's, Olympia #198/R
£1100 $1716 €1650 Metals are chemicals (27x24cm-11x9in) init. W/C gouache exhib. 12-Sep-2 Sotheby's, Olympia #193/R est:1200-1800
£1200 $2004 €1740 Mediterranean townscape (45x63cm-18x25in) init.d.30 gouache card. 24-Jun-3 Bonhams, New Bond Street #60/R est:1000-1500
£1500 $2340 €2250 Cinema (27x19cm-11x7in) init. gouache. 12-Sep-2 Sotheby's, Olympia #194/R est:1000-1500

ARMSTRONG, Robert (1953-) Irish
£1181 $1877 €1700 River at Aughavanagh (91x117cm-36x46in) s.d.1990 verso. 29-Apr-3 Whyte's, Dublin #133/R est:2000-3000
£1806 $2871 €2600 Landscape with cattle and river bed (91x117cm-36x46in) s.d.1991 verso. 29-Apr-3 Whyte's, Dublin #132/R est:2000-3000

ARMSTRONG, Rolf (1881-1960) American
Works on paper
£11180 $18000 €16770 Nude woman seated at lake's edge (107x79cm-42x31in) s. pastel sandboard exec.c.1934 exhib.lit. 10-May-3 Illustration House, New York #110/R est:20000-30000

ARMSTRONG, William (1822-1914) Canadian/Irish
Works on paper
£328 $508 €492 Smalls bush camp (13x18cm-5x7in) indis.i.d.May 14, 61 W/C graphite. 24-Sep-2 Ritchie, Toronto #3062/R (C.D 800)
£645 $1019 €968 Entrance to Nipissing River (20x30cm-8x12in) s.d.1903 W/C. 14-Nov-2 Heffel, Vancouver #224/R est:2000-3000 (C.D 1600)
£1022 $1676 €1533 Indians paddling across Manitouawning Bay (21x31cm-8x12in) s.d.99 W/C. 3-Jun-3 Joyner, Toronto #226/R est:1500-2000 (C.D 2300)

ARMSTRONG, William Weaver (1862-1906) American
£1274 $2000 €1911 Sierra peaks (56x91cm-22x36in) s. 20-Nov-2 Christie's, Los Angeles #9/R est:2500-3500

ARNAL, François (1924-) French
£513 $805 €800 Bombardement 47 (72x60cm-28x24in) s. s.i.d.1965 verso prov. 24-Nov-2 Laurence Calmels, Paris #5/R
£608 $961 €912 Untitled (49x58cm-19x23in) s. 28-Apr-3 Bukowskis, Stockholm #305/R (S.KR 8000)
£706 $1108 €1059 Peinture Matricielle IV (100x130cm-39x51in) s.d.62. 16-Dec-2 Lilla Bukowskis, Stockholm #441 (S.KR 10000)
£759 $1267 €1100 Composition (54x65cm-21x26in) s. 10-Jul-3 Artcurial Briest, Paris #294
£962 $1510 €1500 Untitled (72x93cm-28x37in) s.d.86 prov. 24-Nov-2 Laurence Calmels, Paris #8/R
£1282 $2013 €2000 Serie des choix (73x60cm-29x24in) s.d.87 s.i.d.verso prov. 24-Nov-2 Laurence Calmels, Paris #6/R
£1282 $2013 €2000 Champs essentiels XIII (50x76cm-20x30in) s.d.62 s.i.d.verso. 24-Nov-2 Laurence Calmels, Paris #12/R
£1572 $2437 €2500 La tour de Londres (73x92cm-29x36in) s.d.90 acrylic. 30-Oct-2 Artcurial Briest, Paris #639/R est:2500-3000
£1586 $2649 €2300 La pierre a sang (110x164cm-43x65in) s. s.i.d.2/55 verso exhib. 9-Jul-3 Cornette de St.Cyr, Paris #215 est:2500-3000
£1923 $3019 €3000 Emerveillemnets (130x195cm-51x77in) s.d.85 s.i.d.versoprov. 24-Nov-2 Laurence Calmels, Paris #10/R
£2051 $3200 €3077 Bombardement (102x76cm-40x30in) two s.i.d.1966 i.verso oil spraypaint three. 14-Sep-2 Weschler, Washington #587/R est:2000-3000
£2089 $3300 €3300 Bombardement 1961, repos du guerrier (130x196cm-51x77in) s. s.d.1965 verso. 26-Nov-2 Camard, Paris #144/R est:3800
£2564 $4026 €4000 Emerveillements (73x92cm-29x36in) s.d.85 s.i.d.verso prov. 24-Nov-2 Laurence Calmels, Paris #14/R
£2692 $4227 €4200 Voyeurs I (97x130cm-38x51in) s.d.75 s.i.d.verso prov. 24-Nov-2 Laurence Calmels, Paris #11/R
£2885 $4529 €4500 Bombardement 73 (195x130cm-77x51in) s.i.d.1966 verso acrylic. 11-Dec-2 Artcurial Briest, Paris #730/R
£4167 $6542 €6500 Papillons rouges (60x85cm-24x33in) s.d.50 prov. 24-Nov-2 Laurence Calmels, Paris #13/R
£9615 $15096 €15000 Vie et mort des mers (195x114cm-77x45in) s.d.53 s.i.d.verso prov. 24-Nov-2 Laurence Calmels, Paris #7/R est:8000

ARNALD, George (1763-1841) British
£950 $1548 €1425 On the Dart (35x43cm-14x17in) s.i. indis d. 29-Jan-3 Sotheby's, Olympia #21/R est:800-1200

ARNALD, George (attrib) (1763-1841) British
£450 $693 €675 Drover with cattle crossing a bridge before a ruin (30x43cm-12x17in) s.d.1795. 5-Sep-2 Christie's, Kensington #107/R

ARNAUD, Julia (19th C) French
£1200 $1884 €1800 Geraniums and pelagoniums in a basket (89x116cm-35x46in) s. 21-Nov-2 Christie's, Kensington #85/R est:2000-3000

ARNAUD-DURBECK, Jean Baptiste Francois (1827-?) French
Works on paper
£346 $540 €550 Elegant scene with picnic and musicians in castle grounds (28x31cm-11x12in) W/C prov.lit. 20-Sep-2 Karlheinz Kaupp, Staufen #2138

ARNDTS, Otto (1879-?) German
£283 $442 €450 Flower garden with peacock (48x70cm-19x28in) s. i. verso. 21-Sep-2 Bolland & Marotz, Bremen #581/R

ARNE, Gustav (1925-) Swedish
£245 $387 €368 Bathing huts at Viken (38x45cm-15x18in) s.d.53. 16-Nov-2 Crafoord, Lund #16/R (S.KR 3500)

ARNEGGER, A (19/20th C) Austrian
£1392 $2158 €2200 Winter snow on the Dolomites (70x100cm-28x39in) s. 26-Sep-2 Neumeister, Munich #2684/R est:1200

ARNEGGER, Alois (1879-1967) Austrian
£357 $568 €536 Moonlit alpine winter landscape (60x90cm-24x35in) s. 4-Mar-3 Dales, Durban #14 (SA.R 4500)
£504 $826 €700 Evening sun over snowy mountain village (70x100cm-28x39in) s. 5-Jun-3 Dorotheum, Salzburg #539/R
£609 $956 €950 Twig gatherers in autumn woods (75x100cm-30x39in) s. 21-Nov-2 Dorotheum, Vienna #243/R
£798 $1300 €1157 Alpine sunset (61x91cm-24x36in) 18-Jul-3 Du Mouchelle, Detroit #2071/R est:1200-1500
£807 $1251 €1211 Lake by the forest (38x51cm-15x20in) s. board. 6-Dec-2 Kieselbach, Budapest #42/R (H.F 300000)
£833 $1308 €1300 Landscape with woodland stream (95x140cm-37x55in) s. canvas on plywood. 21-Nov-2 Dorotheum, Vienna #231/R
£897 $1418 €1400 Alpine scene (70x100cm-28x39in) s. 12-Nov-2 Dorotheum, Vienna #110/R
£935 $1496 €1300 Landscape with house by stream and figures (69x100cm-27x39in) s. 14-May-3 Dorotheum, Klagenfurt #1/R
£962 $1519 €1500 Grossglockner (74x100cm-29x39in) s. 12-Nov-2 Dorotheum, Vienna #73/R est:1800-2600
£1019 $1600 €1529 Twilight in the Alps (66x104cm-26x41in) s. prov. 14-Dec-2 Weschler, Washington #631/R est:1000-1500
£1103 $1610 €1655 French coast (90x120cm-35x47in) painted c.1900. 4-Jun-2 SOGA, Bratislava #178/R est:65000 (SL.K 70000)
£1172 $1876 €1700 Winter landscape (70x99cm-28x39in) s. 11-Mar-3 Dorotheum, Vienna #70/R est:1800-2400
£1218 $1912 €1900 Countryside in spring (73x100cm-29x39in) s. 21-Nov-2 Dorotheum, Vienna #230/R est:2200-3000
£1241 $1986 €1800 Alpine scene (73x100cm-29x39in) s. board. 11-Mar-3 Dorotheum, Vienna #86/R est:1500-2200
£1282 $2013 €2000 Alpine glow. s. 21-Nov-2 Dorotheum, Vienna #242/R est:1600-2000
£1329 $2100 €2100 Winter in the Dolomites (70x98cm-28x39in) s. 30-Nov-2 Hagelstam, Helsinki #47/R est:2500
£1538 $2385 €2400 Capri (80x135cm-31x53in) s. 5-Dec-2 Dorotheum, Graz #2/R est:1800
£1795 $2836 €2800 Southern landscape (60x80cm-24x31in) i. 12-Nov-2 Dorotheum, Vienna #104/R est:1000-1600
£1901 $3061 €2700 Meadow in bloom (74x100cm-29x39in) s. 10-May-3 Bukowskis, Helsinki #357/R est:1500-1700
£2484 $4000 €3726 Gravedona, Lake Maggoire, Italy (61x91cm-24x36in) s. 20-Jan-3 Arthur James, Florida #629
£3265 $5192 €4800 Naples (90x124cm-35x49in) s. 19-Mar-3 Neumeister, Munich #500/R est:3800
£3526 $5535 €5500 On the Ligurian coast (90x120cm-35x47in) s. 21-Nov-2 Van Ham, Cologne #1450/R est:4000
£4839 $7500 €7259 Mediterranean coastal village (71x102cm-28x40in) s. 1-Oct-2 Arthur James, Florida #115
£6500 $10855 €9750 Sorrento, the Amalfi coast (68x106cm-27x42in) s. 18-Jun-3 Christie's, Kensington #167/R est:3000-5000

ARNEGGER, Alwin (1883-1916) Austrian
£822 $1282 €1200 Woman gathering kindling wood in autumn wood (74x101cm-29x40in) s. 10-Apr-3 Van Ham, Cologne #1311/R

ARNEGGER, Gottfried (1905-) Austrian
£1282 $2000 €1923 Italian villa with gardens and view of mountains and water (61x81cm-24x32in) s. 18-Sep-2 Alderfer's, Hatfield #240/R est:1500-2500

ARNESEN, Vilhelm (1865-1948) Danish
£340 $538 €510 Seascape with schooner and rowing boat (29x43cm-11x17in) s.d.1920. 27-Nov-2 Museumsbygningen, Copenhagen #76 (D.KR 4000)
£372 $592 €558 Chinese junk (21x28cm-8x11in) s.i.d.18.12.1899. 5-Mar-3 Rasmussen, Copenhagen #1923 (D.KR 4000)
£431 $655 €647 Steam ship off the coast at Aandalsnaes, mountains in background (45x71cm-18x28in) s.i.d.12 juli 1910. 27-Aug-2 Rasmussen, Copenhagen #1913/R (D.KR 5000)
£465 $716 €698 Seascape with sailing boats (37x89cm-15x35in) s.d.1892. 26-Oct-2 Rasmussen, Havnen #3096 (D.KR 5500)
£483 $764 €725 Ship in Copenhagen Harbour (71x47cm-28x19in) s. 5-Apr-3 Rasmussen, Havnen #2103/R (D.KR 5200)
£511 $807 €767 Seascape with vessels off Helsingor (21x38cm-8x15in) s. 2-Dec-2 Rasmussen, Copenhagen #1422/R (D.KR 6000)
£523 $841 €785 Seascape with sailing boat, Gilleleje Harbour (72x102cm-28x40in) s.d.1919. 22-Feb-3 Rasmussen, Havnen #2021/R (D.KR 5800)
£527 $822 €791 Seascape with vessels off Kronborg (48x75cm-19x30in) s. 5-Aug-2 Rasmussen, Vejle #57/R (D.KR 6200)
£549 $856 €824 Three master sailing vessel in the Mediterranean (46x71cm-18x28in) s.d.1894. 22-Sep-2 Hindemae, Ullerslev #7188/R (D.KR 6500)

£567 $913 €851 Georg Stage 1 in Kattegat (52x74cm-20x29in) s.d.1918. 11-May-3 Hindemae, Ullerslev #678/R (D.KR 6000)
£815 $1288 €1223 Seascape with sailing vessel and ferry (67x100cm-26x39in) 13-Nov-2 Kunsthallen, Copenhagen #58/R (D.KR 9500)
£838 $1332 €1257 Seascape with three master and smaller boats (30x34cm-12x13in) s.d.1920. 5-Mar-3 Rasmussen, Copenhagen #2004/R (D.KR 9000)
£851 $1345 €1277 The harbour in Catania (76x111cm-30x44in) s.d.1937. 2-Dec-2 Rasmussen, Copenhagen #1393/R (D.KR 10000)
£1034 $1571 €1551 From Hamburg Harbour (61x92cm-24x36in) s.d.94. 27-Aug-2 Rasmussen, Copenhagen #1770/R est:6000-8000 (D.KR 12000)
£1210 $1925 €1815 Seascape with sailing vessels, steamer and rowing boat (49x71cm-19x28in) s.d.1934. 5-Mar-3 Rasmussen, Copenhagen #2006/R est:10000-12000 (D.KR 13000)
£1257 $1999 €1886 The coast of Sumatra (22x29cm-9x11in) s.d.9.12.99. 5-Mar-3 Rasmussen, Copenhagen #2012/R est:10000 (D.KR 13500)
£1292 $1964 €1938 Three master in high seas (123x110cm-48x43in) s.d.1912. 27-Aug-2 Rasmussen, Copenhagen #1763/R est:15000-20000 (D.KR 15000)
£1627 $2635 €2359 From Helsingor Harbour (48x75cm-19x30in) s.d.1922. 26-May-3 Rasmussen, Copenhagen #1359/R est:8000 (D.KR 17000)
£2871 $4651 €4163 View across Aalborg Harbour (46x70cm-18x28in) s.i.d.88. 26-May-3 Rasmussen, Copenhagen #1136/R est:25000-30000 (D.KR 30000)
£3000 $5010 €4350 Shipping off Kronborg (48x75cm-19x30in) s. 18-Jun-3 Sotheby's, Olympia #102/R est:1000-2000
£4200 $6552 €6300 Lagoon, Venice (65x94cm-26x37in) s.i. 17-Sep-2 Sotheby's, Olympia #281/R est:4000-6000
£4255 $6723 €6383 From Copenhagen Harbour (64x105cm-25x41in) s.d.1889. 2-Dec-2 Rasmussen, Copenhagen #1168/R est:75000 (D.KR 50000)
£9362 $14791 €14043 Gleam of light across the sea (142x205cm-56x81in) s.d.1910. 2-Dec-2 Rasmussen, Copenhagen #1407/R est:100000 (D.KR 110000)

ARNESON, Robert (1930-1992) American
Sculpture
£5128 $8000 €7692 Self portrait (17x13cm-7x5in) s.i.d.1981 glazed ceramic. 14-Oct-2 Butterfields, San Francisco #2096/R est:4000-6000
£5484 $8500 €8226 Black and white mask (5x14x14cm-2x6x6in) sig. d.verso glazed ceramic prov. 8-Dec-2 Wright, Chicago #231/R est:4000-6000
£29677 $46000 €44516 Big head of Jackson Pollock (27x24x32cm-11x9x13in) num.1 bronze prov. 8-Dec-2 Wright, Chicago #198/R est:25000-30000

ARNIM, Elsa von (1888-1980) German
£288 $472 €400 Still life with ceramic jugs and apples (73x59cm-29x23in) s. 4-Jun-3 Reiss & Sohn, Konigstein #128/R

ARNING, Eddie (1898-1992) American
Works on paper
£1852 $3000 €2778 Stretch out on the Marlboro spread (35x81cm-14x32in) crayon oil pastel executed c.1972 prov.exhib. 27-Jan-3 Christie's, Rockefeller NY #98/R est:3500-4500

ARNO, Peter (1904-1968) American
Works on paper
£2329 $3750 €3494 Clerk and customer at liquor store (43x30cm-17x12in) s. brush ink wash. 10-May-3 Illustration House, New York #17/R est:3500-5000
£2640 $4250 €3960 Older woman points out embracing couple to hotel man (46x33cm-18x13in) s. chl wash. 10-May-3 Illustration House, New York #16/R est:3500-5000
£5769 $9000 €8654 Snow shovelor perturbed at faulty cigarette lighter (41x30cm-16x12in) s. pen ink W/C crayon. 9-Nov-2 Illustration House, New York #78/R est:7000-10000

ARNOLD, Christian (1889-1960) German
Works on paper
£451 $713 €650 Corner (55x40cm-22x16in) mono. W/C over pencil. 26-Apr-3 Dr Lehr, Berlin #49/R
£570 $900 €900 Houses in Odenwald (40x55cm-16x22in) mono.d.46 W/C over pencil. 29-Nov-2 Bolland & Marotz, Bremen #487/R
£609 $889 €950 Night watch (56x41cm-22x16in) mono.i.d.26 W/C over pencil. 4-Jun-2 Karl & Faber, Munich #163/R
£633 $981 €1000 Flowers (52x45cm-20x18in) mono. W/C gouache over pencil. 28-Sep-2 Ketterer, Hamburg #166/R
£802 $1170 €1250 Tired girl (57x42cm-22x17in) mono.d.26 W/C over pencil. 4-Jun-2 Karl & Faber, Munich #161/R
£833 $1217 €1300 Invalid lying on bed (57x40cm-22x16in) mono.d.26 W/C over pencil. 4-Jun-2 Karl & Faber, Munich #164/R
£1081 $1686 €1600 Houses in the suburbs (59x41cm-23x16in) mono. W/C. 28-Mar-3 Ketterer, Hamburg #186/R est:1200-1500
£1266 $1962 €2000 Still life with cactus and amaryllis (54x39cm-21x15in) mono. W/C. 28-Sep-2 Ketterer, Hamburg #167/R est:2000-2500

ARNOLD, Edward (1824-1866) American/German
£7000 $11620 €10150 Spanish barque Palma of Mallorca off the entrance to Port Mahon, Minorca (76x102cm-30x40in) s.i.d.1858. 12-Jun-3 Christie's, London #526/R est:2500-4000

ARNOLD, Eldridge (20th C) American
Sculpture
£3481 $5500 €5222 Bird perched on driftwood. s.d.1981 exhib.lit. 3-Apr-3 Christie's, Rockefeller NY #241/R est:3000-5000

ARNOLD, Heinrich (1879-1929) Austrian
£288 $453 €450 Tyrolean alley (75x55cm-30x22in) s.d.27. 21-Nov-2 Dorotheum, Vienna #263/R

ARNOLD, Henry (19/20th C) ?
Sculpture
£3000 $4800 €4500 Figure of a young lady (63cm-25in) s. green pat. bronze st.f.Susse. 15-May-3 Christie's, Kensington #404/R est:3000-4000

ARNOLD, Johann Friedrich (c.1780-1809) German
Works on paper
£698 $1110 €1047 Still life of fruit and insects (72x56cm-28x22in) s. sepia. 5-Mar-3 Rasmussen, Copenhagen #2079/R (D.KR 7500)

ARNOLD, Josef (1891-1967) Austrian
£972 $1546 €1400 Schloss Prosels, Vols am Schlern (31x34cm-12x13in) s. board lit. 29-Apr-3 Wiener Kunst Auktionen, Vienna #572/R
£1282 $2013 €2000 Still life of flowers (70x70cm-28x28in) s.d.1959. 21-Nov-2 Dorotheum, Vienna #253/R est:1100-1300

ARNOLD, Liz (1964-) British
£1500 $2310 €2250 Chicken (107x76cm-42x30in) s.i.d.1995 acrylic on canvas prov. 23-Oct-2 Christie's, London #251/R est:1500-2000

ARNOLD, Phyllis (1938-) British
£260 $403 €390 Poultry telling tales (9x12cm-4x5in) s. acrylic on vellum. 4-Dec-2 John Ross, Belfast #23
£260 $403 €390 Poultry - tug of war (9x12cm-4x5in) s. acrylic on vellum. 4-Dec-2 John Ross, Belfast #24
Works on paper
£350 $543 €525 In the farmyard (10x15cm-4x6in) s. gouache. 2-Oct-2 John Ross, Belfast #21
£350 $543 €525 Feathered company (10x15cm-4x6in) s. gouache. 2-Oct-2 John Ross, Belfast #22

ARNOLDI, Charles (1946-) American
£5380 $8500 €8070 Delta (106x81cm-42x32in) s.d.Aug 22 1990 verso acrylic prov. 13-Nov-2 Sotheby's, New York #124/R est:4000-6000
Prints
£2215 $3500 €3323 Untitled (79x58cm-31x23in) s.d.1989 monotype print. 22-Apr-3 Butterfields, San Francisco #2247/R est:2500-3000

ARNOLDI, Per (1941-) Danish
£259 $396 €389 Composition in blue and yellow (50x40cm-20x16in) s.d.84 verso. 24-Aug-2 Rasmussen, Havnen #2222/R (D.KR 3000)
£280 $445 €420 Landscape, section (40x50cm-16x20in) s.d.01 verso. 29-Apr-3 Kunsthallen, Copenhagen #11 (D.KR 3000)
£280 $445 €420 Composition (65x80cm-26x31in) s. 29-Apr-3 Kunsthallen, Copenhagen #36 (D.KR 3000)
£422 $659 €633 Project 1965 (100x81cm-39x32in) s. prov. 18-Sep-2 Kunsthallen, Copenhagen #88/R (D.KR 5000)
£1330 $2154 €1995 Seven sections with hats and balls - composition. s. 25-Jan-3 Rasmussen, Havnen #2197/R est:20000-30000 (D.KR 15000)
£2534 $3953 €3801 Compositions (30x20cm-12x8in) s.d.93/94 verso eight. 18-Sep-2 Kunsthallen, Copenhagen #241/R est:30000 (D.KR 30000)
£2956 $4611 €4434 Compositions (40x50cm-16x20in) s.d.94 verso four. 18-Sep-2 Kunsthallen, Copenhagen #253/R est:40000 (D.KR 35000)

ARNOULD, Reynold (1919-1980) French
£284 $474 €400 Composition (55x38cm-22x15in) s.d. 23-Jun-3 Delvaux, Paris #57
£426 $711 €600 Composition (81x100cm-32x39in) st.sig. 23-Jun-3 Delvaux, Paris #37
£567 $948 €800 Portrait (77x68cm-30x27in) s. canvas on panel. 23-Jun-3 Delvaux, Paris #45/R
£567 $948 €800 Nature morte a la cruche (73x100cm-29x39in) s.d. 23-Jun-3 Delvaux, Paris #88

£674 $1125 €950 Composition (93x72cm-37x28in) s. acrylic. 23-Jun-3 Delvaux, Paris #87
£851 $1421 €1200 Paysage allegorique (146x114cm-57x45in) s.d.3-VI-41. 23-Jun-3 Delvaux, Paris #31/R
£993 $1658 €1400 Vision de l'amour (114x163cm-45x64in) s.d. 23-Jun-3 Delvaux, Paris #32/R
Works on paper
£340 $569 €480 La danse (47x58cm-19x23in) s. gouache. 23-Jun-3 Delvaux, Paris #63
£532 $888 €750 Homme a son bureau (35x42cm-14x17in) st.sig. gouache. 23-Jun-3 Delvaux, Paris #52/R

ARNOUX, Guy (?-1951) French
Works on paper
£1122 $1785 €1650 Portrait de Jean Michel Frank (73x46cm-29x18in) s.i. Chinese ink ink prov. 19-Mar-3 Claude Boisgirard, Paris #8/R
£1190 $1893 €1750 Portrait de Jean Michel Frank (73x46cm-29x18in) s.i. Chinese ink ink prov. 19-Mar-3 Claude Boisgirard, Paris #9/R

ARNTZENIUS, Alida Margaretha Maria (1872-1954) Dutch
£377 $588 €550 White roses in a pot (50x39cm-20x15in) s. 14-Apr-3 Glerum, Amsterdam #157/R

ARNTZENIUS, Elise Claudine (1902-1982) Dutch
£313 $516 €450 Colourful flowers on a ledge (24x30cm-9x12in) s. 1-Jul-3 Christie's, Amsterdam #260
£417 $688 €600 Rhododendrons in a white vase (50x60cm-20x24in) s.d.50. 1-Jul-3 Christie's, Amsterdam #261
Works on paper
£325 $474 €500 Roses in white vase (45x36cm-18x14in) s. W/C. 19-Jun-2 Vendue Huis, Gravenhage #5/R

ARNTZENIUS, Floris (1864-1925) Dutch
£2603 $4086 €3800 Self portrait (32x21cm-13x8in) s. canvas on panel exhib. 15-Apr-3 Sotheby's, Amsterdam #118/R est:3500-5000
Works on paper
£3165 $5000 €4748 View of a coastal town (28x38cm-11x15in) s. W/C. 17-Nov-2 CRN Auctions, Cambridge #27/R
£3425 $5377 €5000 Moored boat in a canal (25x17cm-10x7in) s. W/C htd white. 15-Apr-3 Sotheby's, Amsterdam #146/R est:5000-7000
£18868 $29057 €30000 View of the Veerkade, The Hague (45x43cm-18x17in) s. W/C prov. 22-Oct-2 Sotheby's, Amsterdam #118/R est:20000-25000
£23973 $37637 €35000 Carriages on Het Lang Voorhout, The Hague (32x51cm-13x20in) s. W/C. 15-Apr-3 Sotheby's, Amsterdam #236/R est:20000-30000

ARNTZENIUS, Floris (attrib) (1864-1925) Dutch
Works on paper
£528 $850 €750 Street scene with many figures (11x18cm-4x7in) W/C. 7-May-3 Vendue Huis, Gravenhage #101/R

ARNTZENIUS, Paul (1883-1965) Dutch
£382 $596 €600 Still life with fruit basket (43x58cm-17x23in) s. d.1955 verso. 6-Nov-2 Vendue Huis, Gravenhage #127/R
£461 $746 €700 In t veld, near Leiden (40x46cm-16x18in) s. exhib. 21-Jan-3 Christie's, Amsterdam #340
£573 $894 €900 Still life with jug (40x30cm-16x12in) s. d.1932 verso exhib. 6-Nov-2 Vendue Huis, Gravenhage #129/R
£764 $1192 €1200 Meadow landscape with village on the horizon (31x48cm-12x19in) s. 6-Nov-2 Vendue Huis, Gravenhage #128/R

ARNZ, Albert (1832-1914) German
£545 $849 €818 Shepherd with his flock alongside a cottage (27x37cm-11x15in) s.d.61. 11-Nov-2 Stephan Welz, Johannesburg #426/R (SA.R 8500)

AROCH, Arieh (1908-1974) Russian
Works on paper
£6329 $10000 €9494 Untitled with profile of figure (27x15cm-11x6in) s. pastel ink pencil executed c.1966. 27-Apr-3 Sotheby's, Tel Aviv #69/R est:9000-12000

ARONS, Jan (1936-) Dutch
£255 $397 €400 Abstract relief (40x30cm-16x12in) s.d.56. 6-Nov-2 Vendue Huis, Gravenhage #146

ARONS, Philipp (1821-1902) German
£480 $749 €720 Gentilhomme lisant (17x13cm-7x5in) s.d.1874 panel. 6-Nov-2 Dobiaschofsky, Bern #321/R (S.FR 1100)

AROSENIUS, Ivar (1878-1909) Swedish
£4478 $7343 €6493 Man in autumn landscape (117x84cm-46x33in) init.d.07. 4-Jun-3 AB Stockholms Auktionsverk #2302/R est:50000-60000 (S.KR 57000)
Works on paper
£278 $461 €403 Olc Kruse as jumping-jack (23x14cm-9x6in) s.d.01 W/C. 16-Jun-3 Lilla Bukowskis, Stockholm #607 (S.KR 3600)
£390 $605 €585 I owe you (11x13cm-4x5in) s. Indian ink. 4-Dec-2 AB Stockholms Auktionsverk #1647/R (S.KR 5500)
£419 $650 €629 The end - road sweepers in light of street lamp (19x15cm-7x6in) mono.d.03 W/C. 29-Sep-2 Uppsala Auktionskammare, Uppsala #59 (S.KR 6000)
£851 $1319 €1277 Old man riding on Pegasus (20x19cm-8x7in) init.d.01 W/C. 4-Dec-2 AB Stockholms Auktionsverk #1757/R (S.KR 12000)
£1021 $1675 €1480 I wonder (13x7cm-5x3in) init.d.08 pencil crayon exhib. 4-Jun-3 AB Stockholms Auktionsverk #2301/R (S.KR 13000)
£1939 $3142 €2812 Illustrations (23x31cm-9x12in) init.d.08 W/C four in one frame. 26-May-3 Bukowskis, Stockholm #29/R est:30000-35000 (S.KR 25000)
£2270 $3518 €3405 Comic figure scenes. init.d.08 W/C four in one frame. 4-Dec-2 AB Stockholms Auktionsverk #1756/R est:40000-50000 (S.KR 32000)

ARP, Carl (1867-1913) German
£1132 $1766 €1800 Sunshine on rocks (83x68cm-33x27in) s.d.1901. 21-Sep-2 Bolland & Marotz, Bremen #448/R est:2500
£1154 $1812 €1800 Landscape with Vesuvius (70x120cm-28x47in) s.i. 22-Nov-2 Karrenbauer, Konstanz #1802/R est:600

ARP, Jean (1887-1966) French
£5449 $7955 €8500 Untitled (37x50cm-15x20in) s. paper prov. 5-Jun-2 Il Ponte, Milan #152 est:10000-12000
£10092 $16853 €14633 White shape on grey and black (52x52cm-20x20in) s. verso board relief prov. 20-Jun-3 Kornfeld, Bern #8/R est:25000 (S.FR 22000)
£20833 $32500 €31250 Tete-levant (42x37cm-17x15in) s. oil cardboard relief executed 1958 prov.lit. 6-Nov-2 Sotheby's, New York #261/R est:25000-35000
£38732 $64296 €55000 Configuration (61x50cm-24x20in) exhib. 12-Jun-3 Laurence Calmels, Paris #64/R est:50000-80000
£84507 $140282 €120000 Two heads (30x40cm-12x16in) s.d.Apr 26 stretcher stitched string exhib. 12-Jun-3 Laurence Calmels, Paris #53/R est:150000-200000
£91549 $151972 €130000 Nose head (39x35cm-15x14in) cut out cardboard relief exhib.lit. 12-Jun-3 Laurence Calmels, Paris #8/R est:200000-300000
£250000 $407500 €375000 Danseuse II (61x50cm-24x20in) string oil painted 1930 prov.exhib.lit. 3-Feb-3 Christie's, London #157/R est:240000
£295775 $490986 €420000 Mouth (30x23cm-12x9in) polychrome painted cut out cardboard exhib.lit. 12-Jun-3 Laurence Calmels, Paris #50/R est:150000-200000
£602740 $946301 €880000 Point virgule (46x28cm-18x11in) panel cardboard exhib.lit. 15-Apr-3 Laurence Calmels, Paris #4246/R est:200000
Sculpture
£1158 $1865 €1737 Le crane qui vole (30x24cm-12x9in) s.num.138/300 polished brass on plexi. 7-May-3 AB Stockholms Auktionsverk #779/R est:20000-25000 (S.KR 15000)
£1548 $2400 €2322 Amega dans l'omega (16x12cm-6x5in) s.i.d.1960 num.4/30 wood relief. 26-Sep-2 Christie's, Rockefeller NY #545/R est:3000-5000
£2215 $3500 €3500 Petit coeur. init. num.1/2 gold. 26-Nov-2 Camard, Paris #87/R
£3859 $6059 €6020 Palette (5x7cm-2x3in) st.sig. gold lit. 11-Dec-2 Artcurial Briest, Paris #564/R
£5828 $9500 €8742 Couronne de serpents (44cm-17in) i.num.4/5 verso polished bronze executed 1960 prov.lit. 12-Feb-3 Sotheby's, New York #78/R est:10000-15000
£6211 $10000 €9317 Composition dans un cercle no.5 (38x38cm-15x15in) i.num.3/5 duraluminum executed 1962 prov.lit. 7-May-3 Sotheby's, New York #353/R est:5000-7000
£6338 $10521 €9000 Shell (12cm-5in) num.4/5 bronze Cast Susse exhib.lit. 12-Jun-3 Laurence Calmels, Paris #42/R est:10000-15000
£7914 $12978 €11000 Relief concrete R (31x22cm-12x9in) s.i. aluminium relief prov. 6-Jun-3 Ketterer, Munich #144/R est:13000-15000
£9155 $15197 €13000 As the result of a paper toy (14cm-6in) num.4/5 bronze Cast Susse exhib.lit. 12-Jun-3 Laurence Calmels, Paris #47/R est:20000-30000
£10563 $17535 €15000 Torso, profile (11cm-4in) num.0/10 bronze Cast Clementi exhib.lit. 12-Jun-3 Laurence Calmels, Paris #74/R est:15000-20000

£11268 $18704 €16000 Born of a spring (23cm-9in) s.num.4/5 chased silver exhib.lit. 12-Jun-3 Laurence Calmels, Paris #71/R est:15000-20000

£12676 $21042 €18000 Alarming configuration (12cm-5in) num.6/10 bronze Cast Susse exhib.lit. 12-Jun-3 Laurence Calmels, Paris #68/R est:15000-20000

£14085 $23380 €20000 Shell hat (28cm-11in) num.2/5 bronze st.f.Georges Rudier exhib.lit. 12-Jun-3 Laurence Calmels, Paris #32/R est:30000-40000

£14085 $23380 €20000 Heads or tails (32cm-13in) laminated welded bronze exhib.lit. 12-Jun-3 Laurence Calmels, Paris #65/R est:25000-35000

£15000 $25050 €21750 Nombril dans un cercle (39cm-15in) s. marble executed 1962 prov.exhib.lit. 24-Jun-3 Sotheby's, London #162/R est:18000-25000

£15493 $25718 €22000 Crystal (7cm-3in) num.1/5 bronze Cast Georges Rudier exhib.lit. 12-Jun-3 Laurence Calmels, Paris #29/R est:10000-15000

£17606 $29225 €25000 Lingam (16cm-6in) num.1/5 bronze Cast George Rudier exhib.lit. 12-Jun-3 Laurence Calmels, Paris #43/R est:20000-30000

£17606 $29225 €25000 Flower's sigh (14cm-6in) num.4/5 bronze Cast Clementi exhib.lit. 12-Jun-3 Laurence Calmels, Paris #67/R est:30000-40000

£17606 $29225 €25000 Doll, cut out no 32 (30x19cm-12x7in) s.num.2/5 verso bronze relief on duralumin exhib.lit. 12-Jun-3 Laurence Calmels, Paris #75/R est:10000-15000

£18519 $30000 €26853 Shell and head (20x20x15cm-8x8x6in) polished bronze blk marble base 3/5 exhib.lit. 21-May-3 Doyle, New York #35/R est:20000-30000

£22535 $37408 €32000 Concrete relief O, known as head surrounded by animalcules (44x31cm-17x12in) s.num.2/5 verso duralumin relief exhib.lit. 12-Jun-3 Laurence Calmels, Paris #57/R est:20000-30000

£23944 $39746 €34000 Cloud bowl (15cm-6in) rose marble lit. 12-Jun-3 Laurence Calmels, Paris #46/R est:30000-40000

£23944 $39746 €34000 Cut out nice 26, also called nice (50x50cm-20x20in) s.d.num.3/5 verso bronze on duralumin lit. 12-Jun-3 Laurence Calmels, Paris #69/R est:20000-30000

£24648 $40915 €35000 Crystal shell (27cm-11in) num.4/5 bronze Cast Georges Rudier exhib.lit. 12-Jun-3 Laurence Calmels, Paris #28/R est:40000-50000

£24648 $40915 €35000 Relief as the result of torn papers (25x44cm-10x17in) painted plaster exhib.lit. 12-Jun-3 Laurence Calmels, Paris #41/R est:15000-20000

£24648 $40915 €35000 Constellation (40x35cm-16x14in) aluminium relief exhib.lit. 12-Jun-3 Laurence Calmels, Paris #55/R est:40000-60000

£25000 $41000 €37500 Configuration (50x48cm-20x19in) painted wood relief prov.lit. 5-Feb-3 Sotheby's, London #202/R est:40000

£28169 $46761 €40000 Amphora, constellation (31x21cm-12x8in) wood relief lit. 12-Jun-3 Laurence Calmels, Paris #56/R est:30000-40000

£29577 $49099 €42000 Threshold with plant crenellations (72cm-28in) num.5/5 laminated welded bronze exhib.lit. 12-Jun-3 Laurence Calmels, Paris #62/R est:40000-50000

£31690 $52606 €45000 Heart of a monument (13cm-5in) white marble lit. 12-Jun-3 Laurence Calmels, Paris #16/R est:40000-50000

£31690 $52606 €45000 Figure-flower-fall (27x21cm-11x8in) waxed lime-wood exhib.lit. 12-Jun-3 Laurence Calmels, Paris #70/R est:40000-50000

£35714 $57500 €53571 Tete florale (47cm-19in) i.num.3/5 polished bronze i.f.Susse Fres cast 1960 prov.lit. 7-May-3 Sotheby's, New York #314/R est:60000-80000

£36620 $60789 €52000 Torso-vase (76cm-30in) mono.num.I/V bronze Cast Georges Rudier exhib.lit. 12-Jun-3 Laurence Calmels, Paris #63/R est:60000-80000

£38462 $60000 €57693 Configuration (63x57cm-25x22in) s.i.d.1953 verso oil wood relief. 7-Nov-2 Christie's, Rockefeller NY #355/R est:30000-40000

£42254 $70141 €60000 Concrete sculpture, Mirr (15cm-6in) num.2/5 bronze Cast George Rudier exhib.lit. 12-Jun-3 Laurence Calmels, Paris #17/R est:25000-30000

£42254 $70141 €60000 Yawning shell (15cm-6in) white marble exhib.lit. 12-Jun-3 Laurence Calmels, Paris #30/R est:40000-50000

£45775 $75986 €65000 Configuration (24x29cm-9x11in) painted wood relief exhib.lit. 12-Jun-3 Laurence Calmels, Paris #26/R est:60000-80000

£45775 $75986 €65000 Torso and navel (32x24cm-13x9in) polychrome painted wood relief exhib.lit. 12-Jun-3 Laurence Calmels, Paris #54/R est:120000-150000

£49296 $81831 €70000 Gnome form (39cm-15in) num.0/5 bronze Cast Susse exhib.lit. 12-Jun-3 Laurence Calmels, Paris #20/R est:70000-90000

£49296 $81831 €70000 Shadow figure (71cm-28in) mono.num.I/III bronze Cast Georges Rudier exhib.lit. 12-Jun-3 Laurence Calmels, Paris #33/R est:80000-120000

£56338 $93521 €80000 Small leaning Egyptian figure (26cm-10in) bronze 1 from edition of 5 Cast Georges Rudier exhib.lit. 12-Jun-3 Laurence Calmels, Paris #14/R est:30000-40000

£56338 $93521 €80000 Evocation of a form, human, lunar, spectral (37cm-15in) mono.num.I/III bronze Cast Georges Rudier exhib.lit. 12-Jun-3 Laurence Calmels, Paris #45/R est:50000-60000

£63380 $105211 €90000 Straightening up (30cm-12in) white Carrara marble lit. 12-Jun-3 Laurence Calmels, Paris #19/R est:50000-70000

£70423 $116901 €100000 Gnome, also called Kaspar (46cm-18in) num.5/5 bronze Cast Susse exhib.lit. 12-Jun-3 Laurence Calmels, Paris #15/R est:80000-100000

£70423 $116901 €100000 Bud figure (80cm-31in) mono.num.0 bronze Cast Georges Rudier exhib.lit. 12-Jun-3 Laurence Calmels, Paris #18/R est:100000-120000

£70423 $116901 €100000 Thales of Miletus (106cm-42in) mono.num.4/5 bronze st.f.Susse exhib.lit. 12-Jun-3 Laurence Calmels, Paris #31/R est:120000-150000

£70513 $110000 €105770 Apparat d'une danse (178cm-70in) brown pat. bronze conceived c.1961 prov.lit. 6-Nov-2 Sotheby's, New York #294/R est:100000-150000

£73944 $122746 €105000 Beautiful person (88cm-35in) white marble exec.c.1963. 12-Jun-3 Laurence Calmels, Paris #66/R est:80000-120000

£76923 $120000 €115385 Torse-gerbe (76cm-30in) init.num.V/V brown pat. bronze conceived 1958 prov.lit. 7-Nov-2 Christie's, Rockefeller NY #316a/R est:140000-180000

£77465 $128592 €110000 Small Venus of Meudon (49cm-19in) mono.num.o/V bronze Cast Georges Rudier exhib.lit. 12-Jun-3 Laurence Calmels, Paris #61/R est:60000-80000

£84507 $140282 €120000 Leaf on crystal (62cm-24in) mono.num.0/5 bronze st.f.Susse exhib.lit. 12-Jun-3 Laurence Calmels, Paris #21/R est:60000-80000

£84507 $140282 €120000 Mask (32x32cm-13x13in) polished wood relief exhib.lit. 12-Jun-3 Laurence Calmels, Paris #49/R est:80000-100000

£105634 $175352 €150000 Dress with eye and naval, dressing (31x23cm-12x9in) s.d.1927 polychrome painted cardboard relief prov.exhib.lit. 12-Jun-3 Laurence Calmels, Paris #27/R est:200000-300000

£119718 $198732 €170000 Bottles-Navel (56x35cm-22x14in) i.verso polychrome painted wood relief exhib.lit. 12-Jun-3 Laurence Calmels, Paris #25/R est:200000-250000

£161972 $268873 €230000 Paolo e Francesca, variant 1 (17x19cm-7x7in) polished wood relief exhib.lit. 12-Jun-3 Laurence Calmels, Paris #24/R est:100000-150000

£167702 $270000 €251553 Torse chevalier (86cm-34in) init.num.I/V brown pat. bronze cast 1959 prov.lit. 7-May-3 Sotheby's, New York #311/R est:100000-150000

£232394 $385775 €330000 Idol (106cm-42in) num.3/3 bronze Cast Georges Rudier exhib.lit. 12-Jun-3 Laurence Calmels, Paris #44/R est:150000-200000

£232394 $385775 €330000 Head with red nose (36x27cm-14x11in) painted wood relief on cardboard lit. 12-Jun-3 Laurence Calmels, Paris #52/R est:250000-350000

£845070 $1402817 €1200000 Big head, small torso (66x57cm-26x22in) s.verso painted wood relief exhib.lit. 12-Jun-3 Laurence Calmels, Paris #9/R est:400000-500000

£1712329 $2671233 €2500000 Femme (136x100cm-54x39in) painted wood relief exec.1927 exhib.lit. 14-Apr-3 Laurence Calmels, Paris #4016/R est:600000-800000

Works on paper

£2778 $4583 €4000 Composition (23x22cm-9x9in) s. collage cardboard prov. 1-Jul-3 Artcurial Briest, Paris #787/R est:5000-7000

£2790 $4408 €4185 Bushes and leaves (34x25cm-13x10in) s. W/C pencil prov. 28-Nov-2 Christie's, Zurich #102/R est:5000-7000 (S.FR 6500)

£3333 $5167 €5200 Le sidege de l'air (21x16cm-8x6in) s. verso collage W/C. 7-Dec-2 Hauswedell & Nolte, Hamburg #509/R est:6000

£3475 $5595 €5213 Sans titre (37x26cm-15x10in) pencil prov. 7-May-3 AB Stockholms Auktionsverk #1150/R est:40000-50000 (S.K 45000)

£4225 $7014 €6000 Composition (58x41cm-23x16in) s. chl wash exec.c.1960-61. 12-Jun-3 Laurence Calmels, Paris #59/R est:10000-15000

£4225 $7014 €6000 Crucifixion (59x44cm-23x17in) s. chl stump cut out exec.c.1950-53. 12-Jun-3 Laurence Calmels, Paris #76/R est:5000-10000

£5208 $8229 €7500 Untitled (25x22cm-10x9in) s. col paper collage. 26-Apr-3 Dr Lehr, Berlin #50/R est:4000

£5521 $9000 €8282 Collage no.3 (69x29cm-27x11in) col glass prov.exhib. 12-Feb-3 Sotheby's, New York #97/R est:12000-18000

£8025 $13000 €11636 Composition (30x23cm-12x9in) s. i.verso ink col chk pencil W/C laid paper prov.exhib. 21-May-3 Doyle, New York #6/R est:3000-5000

£9155 $15197 €13000 Torso (44x26cm-17x10in) s. chl stump exec.c.1960. 12-Jun-3 Laurence Calmels, Paris #58/R est:10000-15000

£17606 $29225 €25000 Doll bearing Schwitters (60x16cm-24x6in) collage gouache part of collage by Kurt Schwitters exhib. 12-Jun-3 Laurence Calmels, Paris #40/R est:40000-60000

£21127 $35070 €30000 The hand (27x22cm-11x9in) s. torn etchings collage. 12-Jun-3 Laurence Calmels, Paris #1/R est:8000-12000

£22535 $37408 €32000 Midday bird (39x39cm-15x15in) collage pencil gouache exhib. 12-Jun-3 Laurence Calmels, Paris #60/R est:20000-30000

£26761 $44423 €38000 Constellation (27x12cm-11x5in) cut out paper collage exhib. 12-Jun-3 Laurence Calmels, Paris #2/R est:15000-20000
£28169 $46761 €40000 Torn papers (16x12cm-6x5in) torn paper collage. 12-Jun-3 Laurence Calmels, Paris #3/R est:15000-20000
£28169 $46761 €40000 Spring collage (13x10cm-5x4in) s.d. torn paper gouache collage. 12-Jun-3 Laurence Calmels, Paris #73/R est:10000-15000
£29577 $49099 €42000 Geometrical collage (32x23cm-13x9in) collage exhib. 12-Jun-3 Laurence Calmels, Paris #4/R est:50000-70000
£35211 $58451 €50000 Watch (31x24cm-12x9in) collage ink wash lit. 12-Jun-3 Laurence Calmels, Paris #23/R est:70000-90000
£35211 $58451 €50000 Navel and winged navel (38x33cm-15x13in) torn paper collage gouache exhib.lit. 12-Jun-3 Laurence Calmels, Paris #48/R est:50000-60000
£91549 $151972 €130000 Collage (35x39cm-14x15in) paper cut out collage exhib. 12-Jun-3 Laurence Calmels, Paris #5/R est:100000-120000
£273292 $440000 €409938 Tete objet a traire (38x36cm-15x14in) s. fabric painted cardboard collage prov.exhib.lit. 6-May-3 Sotheby's, New York #36/R est:250000

ARP, Jean and Sophie Taeuber (20th C) French
Sculpture
£154930 $257183 €220000 Chalice (29cm-11in) polychrome painted wood lit. 12-Jun-3 Laurence Calmels, Paris #35/R est:100000-150000

ARPA, Jose (1860-1952) Spanish
£307 $500 €461 Sunset landscape with villa (18x23cm-7x9in) s. board. 16-Feb-3 Jeffery Burchard, Florida #56

ARPAD, Romek (1883-1960) Hungarian
£897 $1400 €1301 Still life with tea set (71x61cm-28x24in) s. 13-Apr-3 Butterfields, Los Angeles #7039

ARPS, Bernardus (1865-1938) Dutch
£300 $486 €450 Bullrushes in a vase, an amaryllis and books on a side table (45x35cm-18x14in) s. board. 23-Jan-3 Christie's, Kensington #184

ARQUER BUIGAS, Cayetano de (1932-) Spanish
£774 $1223 €1200 Girls (60x73cm-24x29in) s.d.69 s.d.verso. 18-Dec-2 Ansorena, Madrid #355/R

ARRANZ BRAVO, Eduard (1941-) Spanish
Works on paper
£346 $540 €550 Blue still life (69x69cm-27x27in) s.d.1980 gouache wax. 17-Sep-2 Segre, Madrid #279/R
£724 $1144 €1050 Untitled (48x32cm-19x13in) s. pastel prov. 1-Apr-3 Segre, Madrid #242/R

ARREDONDO Y CALMACHE, Ricardo (1850-1911) Spanish
£8784 $13703 €13000 Toledo walls (21x45cm-8x18in) board. 25-Mar-3 Durán, Madrid #200/R est:13000
£11486 $17919 €17000 Patio, Toledo (48x71cm-19x28in) s. 25-Mar-3 Durán, Madrid #202/R est:16000

ARRIAGA, Esteban (1922-) Spanish
£440 $687 €700 Beach (60x81cm-24x32in) s. 8-Oct-2 Ansorena, Madrid #406/R

ARRIBAS, Jose Antonio (1943-) Spanish
£490 $764 €725 Composition with portrait (90x122cm-35x48in) s.i.d.85. 25-Mar-3 Durán, Madrid #122/R

ARRIETA, Jose Agustin (1802-1879) Mexican
£1534 $2500 €2301 Portrait of Augustin Iturbide, first President of Mexico (79x102cm-31x40in) 2-Feb-3 Simpson's, Houston #387
£30488 $50000 €45732 Naturaleza muerta con papaya y limon (46x62cm-18x24in) s. painted c.1870 prov.exhib. 28-May-3 Christie's, Rockefeller NY #3/R est:60000-80000
£30488 $50000 €45732 Naturaleza muerta con cesto y verduras (46x62cm-18x24in) s. painted c.1870 prov.exhib. 28-May-3 Christie's, Rockefeller NY #4/R est:60000-80000
£91463 $150000 €132621 La familia Mexicana, la pensativa (93x113cm-37x44in) s.d.1851 prov.exhib.lit. 27-May-3 Sotheby's, New York #33

ARROYO Y LORENZO, Manuel (1854-1902) Spanish
£1104 $1612 €1700 Washerwoman (31x17cm-12x7in) s. board. 17-Jun-2 Ansorena, Madrid #147/R

ARROYO, Edouard (1937-) Spanish
£7095 $11068 €10500 Parmi les peintres (80x100cm-31x39in) s.i.d.1969 verso. 26-Mar-3 Finarte Semenzato, Milan #252/R
£17000 $27880 €25500 Maison de la culture du cote de valdepenas II (196x145cm-77x57in) s.d.68 prov. 7-Feb-3 Sotheby's, London #214/R est:10000-15000
£31000 $50840 €46500 Heureux qui comme ulysse a fait un long voyage II (220x180cm-87x71in) s.d.78 s.i.d.1978 verso acrylic prov.exhib. 7-Feb-3 Sotheby's, London #233/R est:12000-15000
£75000 $125250 €108750 A la Tate Gallery Jose Maria blanco white est surveille par un envoye (200x230cm-79x91in) s.d.1979 s.i.d.1979 verso prov.exhib.lit. 26-Jun-3 Sotheby's, London #210/R est:12000-15000

Sculpture
£1384 $2131 €2200 Composition (67cm-26in) s. bronze. 22-Oct-2 Campo, Vlaamse Kaai #403

Works on paper
£1181 $1948 €1700 Jean-Charles de Castelbajac en ramoneur (104x68cm-41x27in) s.i.d.1982 verso lead pencil wax crayon. 3-Jul-3 Christie's, Paris #47/R est:1000-1500
£1761 $2747 €2800 Brelan (33x27cm-13x11in) s.d.1983 W/C. 8-Oct-2 Christie's, Paris #153
£1763 $2768 €2750 Fausto (32x39cm-13x15in) s.d.1988 mixed media. 16-Dec-2 Castellana, Madrid #804/R
£1897 $3034 €2750 Fausto (31x37cm-12x15in) s.d.1978 mixed media. 11-Mar-3 Castellana, Madrid #21/R
£2152 $3508 €3250 Flamenco dancer (30x37cm-12x15in) s. mixed media exec.1989. 11-Feb-3 Castellana, Madrid #15/R
£4500 $7335 €6750 Ramoneur XVIII (102x73cm-40x29in) s.i.d.1979 crayon prov. 3-Feb-3 Sotheby's, Olympia #112/R est:2000-3000
£4591 $7116 €7300 Acteur (72x53cm-28x21in) s. mixed media paper on canvas. 30-Oct-2 Artcurial Briest, Paris #460/R est:5000-6000
£4710 $7725 €6500 Waldorf Astoria (100x87cm-39x34in) s.d.1987 collage bodycol over white chk. 31-May-3 Villa Grisebach, Berlin #350/R est:4000-6000
£5000 $8150 €7500 Ramoneur XVI (102x73cm-40x29in) s.i.d.1979 pencil prov. 3-Feb-3 Sotheby's, Olympia #111/R est:2000-3000
£5660 $8830 €9000 Alamein (62x49cm-24x19in) s.d.1969 gouache paper on canvas. 17-Sep-2 Segre, Madrid #163/R est:4000
£13000 $21190 €19500 Ramoneur (97x78cm-38x31in) s.i.d.79 verso pencil collage on board prov. 3-Feb-3 Sotheby's, Olympia #164/R est:3000-4000
£19500 $32565 €28275 Parmi les peintres (102x81cm-40x32in) sand paper collage on board prov. 24-Jun-3 Sotheby's, Olympia #55/R est:4000-6000

ARRUE Y VALLE, Jose (1885-1977) Spanish
Works on paper
£5161 $8155 €8000 Basque party (41x61cm-16x24in) s. gouache. 17-Dec-2 Durán, Madrid #215/R

ARRUE Y VALLE, Jose (attrib) (1885-1977) Spanish
Works on paper
£710 $1121 €1100 Basque celebration (69x93cm-27x37in) W/C. 18-Dec-2 Ansorena, Madrid #246/R

ARRUMBIDE, A L (20th C) Spanish
Miniatures
£1419 $2243 €2200 Odalisk (6x11cm-2x4in) s.i.d. 1948 after Mariano Fortuny. 18-Dec-2 Segre, Madrid #601/R

ARRUTI Y POLA, Eugenio (1845-1889) Spanish
£743 $1159 €1100 Paths by marshes (38x55cm-15x22in) s.i. 26-Mar-3 Rieunier, Paris #16/R

ARRYCKS, Lydie (20th C) ?
Works on paper
£506 $785 €800 Angoisse metaphysique (178x145cm-70x57in) s. pastel chk. 28-Sep-2 Cornette de St.Cyr, Paris #240/R

ARSENIUS, John (1818-1903) Swedish
£754 $1177 €1131 Portrait of horse (60x74cm-24x29in) s. 13-Sep-2 Lilla Bukowskis, Stockholm #424 (S.KR 11000)
£853 $1382 €1237 Horsemen parade at Ladugards field (18x32cm-7x13in) s. prov.lit. 26-May-3 Bukowskis, Stockholm #100/R (S.KR 11000)
£2250 $3645 €3263 Landscape with horses (32x21cm-13x8in) s. one d.85 two in one frame. 26-May-3 Bukowskis, Stockholm #101/R est:15000-20000 (S.KR 29000)
£4255 $6596 €6383 Cavalry captain Carl August Tamm at Fogelsta (65x89cm-26x35in) s.indis.d.187. 3-Dec-2 Bukowskis, Stockholm #301/R est:60000-80000 (S.KR 60000)

ARSON, Alphonse Alexandre (1822-c.1880) French
Sculpture
£1100 $1793 €1595 Frog riding on a coursing hare (11cm-4in) s. bronze lit. 21-Jul-3 Sotheby's, London #20/R est:500-700

ARSTE, Karl (1899-1942) German
£314 $491 €500 Summer landscape with house near Worpswede (51x76cm-20x30in) s.d.32 panel. 21-Sep-2 Bolland & Marotz, Bremen #328/R

ART, Berthe (1857-1934) Belgian
Works on paper
£250 $398 €375 Still life of flowers, oranges and songbirds (80x52cm-31x20in) s. pastel. 27-Feb-3 Greenslade Hunt, Taunton #1272
£567 $948 €800 Chrysanthemes jaunes et genets (84x45cm-33x18in) s. pastel exhib. 17-Jun-3 Palais de Beaux Arts, Brussels #505

ART, Raymond (1919-) Belgian
£256 $403 €400 Composition abstraite (40x62cm-16x24in) s. paper. 11-Dec-2 Hotel des Ventes Mosan, Brussels #327
£506 $790 €800 L'aube (97x129cm-38x51in) s.d.76 i.d.verso. 16-Oct-2 Hotel des Ventes Mosan, Brussels #270
£696 $1086 €1100 La notte (80x119cm-31x47in) s. s.i.verso. 16-Oct-2 Hotel des Ventes Mosan, Brussels #277

ART-LANGUAGE (fl.1968) British
£2381 $3786 €3500 Study for hostages (128x89cm-50x35in) s.d.1991 acrylic prov. 24-Mar-3 Cornette de St.Cyr, Paris #120/R

ARTAN, Louis (1837-1890) Belgian
£288 $453 €450 Marine (28x56cm-11x22in) s. 19-Nov-2 Vanderkindere, Brussels #6
£359 $579 €550 Barques de peche echouees (21x39cm-8x15in) s. 20-Jan-3 Horta, Bruxelles #335
£545 $845 €850 Barques de peche en mer du Nord (77x115cm-30x45in) s. 9-Dec-2 Horta, Bruxelles #73
£641 $1006 €1000 Marine (30x60cm-12x24in) s.d.1882. 19-Nov-2 Vanderkindere, Brussels #144
£710 $1121 €1100 Peniche sur le canal (59x38cm-23x15in) s.i. 17-Dec-2 Palais de Beaux Arts, Brussels #453
£1154 $1788 €1800 Barques de peche au coucher du soleil (37x65cm-15x26in) s. 9-Dec-2 Horta, Bruxelles #72 est:1800-2200
£1195 $1852 €1900 Bourrasque (38x60cm-15x24in) s. 1-Oct-2 Palais de Beaux Arts, Brussels #427 est:1250-1700
£1200 $1992 €1200 Marine (32x60cm-13x24in) s. 16-Jun-3 Horta, Bruxelles #374
£1583 $2532 €2200 Bord de mer anime (25x40cm-10x16in) s. canvas on panel. 13-May-3 Vanderkindere, Brussels #178 est:1200-1600
£1646 $2567 €2600 Bateaux de peche en Mer du Nord (65x100cm-26x39in) s. 10-Sep-2 Vanderkindere, Brussels #305 est:1000-1500

ARTAN, Louis (attrib) (1837-1890) Belgian
£710 $1121 €1100 Marin (25x50cm-10x20in) canvas laid down. 17-Dec-2 Palais de Beaux Arts, Brussels #454

ARTEAGA Y ALFARO, Matias (1630-1703) Spanish
£5806 $9174 €9000 Marriage of the Virgin (55x66cm-22x26in) 18-Dec-2 Ansorena, Madrid #99/R est:9000

ARTEMOFF, Georges (1892-1965) Russian
£811 $1265 €1200 Jeune femme nue assise (60x48cm-24x19in) s. panel. 26-Mar-3 Millon & Associes, Paris #103
£1351 $2108 €2000 Tete d'africain (45x33cm-18x13in) s. cardboard. 26-Mar-3 Millon & Associes, Paris #102/R
Sculpture
£16667 $26167 €26000 Combat avec le tigre (80x200cm-31x79in) s. pat wood relief. 11-Dec-2 Piasa, Paris #25/R est:12000
Works on paper
£816 $1298 €1200 Nu a la guitare (63x48cm-25x19in) s. grattage. 3-Mar-3 Claude Boisgirard, Paris #29

ARTENS, Peter von (1937-) Colombian
£15244 $25000 €22104 Limones y sandias (102x107cm-40x42in) s. exhib. 27-May-3 Sotheby's, New York #70
£20701 $32500 €31052 Still life with paper (95x106cm-37x42in) s. s.verso painted c.1998 prov. 19-Nov-2 Sotheby's, New York #153/R est:30000

ARTER, Charles John (1860-1923) American
£1139 $1800 €1709 Goose girl (53x38cm-21x15in) s. 17-Nov-2 CRN Auctions, Cambridge #13/R
£2163 $3375 €3245 Japanese beauty (38x53cm-15x21in) s. 28-Mar-3 Aspire, Cleveland #29/R est:500-700
£2848 $4500 €4272 Peasant girl with geese (53x38cm-21x15in) s. 24-Apr-3 Shannon's, Milford #195/R est:3000-5000
£3247 $5000 €4871 Flowers and a wine glass on a tabletop (46x56cm-18x22in) s.d.84. 24-Oct-2 Shannon's, Milford #75/R est:4000-6000

ARTHUR, William (19th C) New Zealander
Works on paper
£637 $1000 €956 New Zealand butterfly (22x14cm-9x6in) s. i.d.1880 verso w/. 10-Dec-2 Peter Webb, Auckland #24/R est:1500-2000 (NZ.D 2000)

ARTIOLI, Bruno (1943-) Italian
£314 $502 €480 Seascape (40x50cm-16x20in) s. ss.i.verso oil sand board lit. 4-Jan-3 Meeting Art, Vercelli #706
£340 $541 €500 Back home (70x80cm-28x31in) s. oil mixed media. 1-Mar-3 Meeting Art, Vercelli #460
£347 $552 €500 Beached boat (35x50cm-14x20in) s. s.verso oil sand board painted 2000. 1-May-3 Meeting Art, Vercelli #100
£347 $552 €500 Beached boat (40x40cm-16x16in) s. oil sand board. 1-May-3 Meeting Art, Vercelli #285
£359 $575 €550 Parasol on the beach (60x60cm-24x24in) s. s.verso oil sand board lit. 4-Jan-3 Meeting Art, Vercelli #726
£374 $595 €550 Beach (30x50cm-12x20in) s. s.v oil sand board. 1-Mar-3 Meeting Art, Vercelli #665
£392 $627 €600 Boat and parasol (50x70cm-20x28in) s. s.verso oil sand painted 2000. 4-Jan-3 Meeting Art, Vercelli #67
£425 $680 €650 Loneliness (50x60cm-20x24in) s. s.verso oil sand board. 4-Jan-3 Meeting Art, Vercelli #79
£490 $784 €750 Huts and parasols (50x80cm-20x31in) s. oil sand painted 2000. 4-Jan-3 Meeting Art, Vercelli #202
£510 $811 €750 Dunes (50x70cm-20x28in) s. oil sand board. 1-Mar-3 Meeting Art, Vercelli #468
£625 $994 €900 Beach (50x70cm-20x28in) s. oil sand board lit. 1-May-3 Meeting Art, Vercelli #496
£1156 $1839 €1700 Beached boat (100x120cm-39x47in) s. s.verso oil sand board. 1-Mar-3 Meeting Art, Vercelli #500

ARTS, Alexis (1940-) Canadian
£383 $624 €575 Fishing at midnight, Holland (53x99cm-21x39in) s. i. verso. 12-Feb-3 Iegor de Saint Hippolyte, Montreal #12 (C.D 950)
£387 $604 €581 Marina, Lachine Que, en plein air (46x61cm-18x24in) s. 30-Jul-2 Iegor de Saint Hippolyte, Montreal #6 (C.D 960)
£453 $702 €680 On his way to the barn (40x70cm-16x28in) s. 3-Dec-2 Joyner, Toronto #420 est:800-1200 (C.D 1100)
£484 $755 €726 Campus McGill, rue Sherbrooke, Mtl, Qc (71x106cm-28x42in) s. 30-Jul-2 Iegor de Saint Hippolyte, Montreal #7 (C.D 1200)

ARTS, Dorus (1901-1961) Dutch
£1057 $1659 €1586 Unloading the fishing boat at low tide (51x71cm-20x28in) s. 10-Dec-2 Pinneys, Montreal #60 est:2200-2800 (C.D 2600)
£1210 $1911 €1815 Skaters on a frozen pond (51x77cm-20x30in) s. 18-Nov-2 Waddingtons, Toronto #200/R est:3000-3500 (C.D 3000)

ARTSCHWAGER, Richard (1923-) American
£18000 $30060 €26100 Left pinch (63x89cm-25x35in) s.i.d.80 verso acrylic cellotex mirror formica prov. 26-Jun-3 Sotheby's, London #134/R est:10000-15000
Works on paper
£3000 $5010 €4350 Untitled (47x63cm-19x25in) s.d.87 chl prov. 26-Jun-3 Sotheby's, London #266/R est:3000-4000

ARTUS, Charles (1897-1978) French
Sculpture
£1361 $2163 €2000 Ours (11x19cm-4x7in) s. plaster prov. 23-Mar-3 Herbette, Doullens #141/R
£1419 $2214 €2100 Merle (11x15cm-4x6in) medaille pat bronze. 25-Mar-3 Chochon-Barre & Allardi, Paris #30/R est:1500-1800
£1429 $2271 €2100 Panthere (11x17cm-4x7in) s.d.1907 plaster prov. 23-Mar-3 Herbette, Doullens #140/R
£1701 $2704 €2500 Antilope (22cm-9in) s. plaster prov. 23-Mar-3 Herbette, Doullens #144/R
£2109 $3353 €3100 Coq (33x22cm-13x9in) s. plaster prov. 23-Mar-3 Herbette, Doullens #139/R
£2721 $4327 €4000 Levrier (21x31cm-8x12in) s.st.f.Valsuani black pat bronze. 23-Mar-3 Herbette, Doullens #134/R
£2721 $4327 €4000 Brocard (16x32cm-6x13in) s. plaster prov. 23-Mar-3 Herbette, Doullens #145/R
£2789 $4435 €4100 Caniche royal (18x18cm-7x7in) s. plaster prov. 23-Mar-3 Herbette, Doullens #147/R
£3061 $4867 €4500 Pigeon boulant (32x13cm-13x5in) s.st.f.Valsuani black pat bronze. 23-Mar-3 Herbette, Doullens #135/R
£3401 $5408 €5000 Truie (28x50cm-11x20in) s. plaster prov. 23-Mar-3 Herbette, Doullens #137/R
£3741 $5949 €5500 Chien couche (9x34cm-4x13in) s.st.f.Valsuani brown pat bronze prov. 23-Mar-3 Herbette, Doullens #136/R
£10408 $16549 €15300 Corbeau freux (35x32cm-14x13in) s.st.f.Valsuani black pat bronze. 23-Mar-3 Herbette, Doullens #133/R
£10544 $16765 €15500 Poule sultane (42x44cm-17x17in) s.st.f.Valsuani black pat bronze. 23-Mar-3 Herbette, Doullens #132/R

£17007 $27041 €25000 Ibis rouges (50x67cm-20x26in) s.st.f.Rudier brown pat bronze prov. 23-Mar-3 Herbette, Doullens #131/R

ARTZ, Constant (1870-1951) Dutch
£601 $938 €950 Rising storm above a lake (53x82cm-21x32in) 21-Oct-2 Glerum, Amsterdam #10/R
£701 $1093 €1100 Duck family (17x22cm-7x9in) s. panel. 5-Nov-2 Vendu Notarishuis, Rotterdam #235/R
£892 $1373 €1400 Ducks along the waterside (18x24cm-7x9in) s. plywood. 3-Sep-2 Christie's, Amsterdam #242/R
£952 $1514 €1400 Canards a la riviere (18x23cm-7x9in) s. panel. 19-Mar-3 Hotel des Ventes Mosan, Brussels #303
£1056 $1701 €1500 Duck family at the edge of the water (40x60cm-16x24in) s. 7-May-3 Vendue Huis, Gravenhage #430/R est:2000-3000
£1103 $1754 €1600 Duck with ducklings on the riverside (24x18cm-9x7in) s. panel. 10-Mar-3 Sotheby's, Amsterdam #105/R est:1500-2000
£1210 $1864 €1900 Ducks and ducklings on a sunlit meadow (40x50cm-16x20in) s. plywood. 3-Sep-2 Christie's, Amsterdam #193/R est:1000-1500
£1250 $2063 €1800 Duck and ducklings on a riverbank (18x24cm-7x9in) s. plywood pair. 1-Jul-3 Christie's, Amsterdam #569/R est:1200-1600
£1266 $1975 €2000 Ducks on the water (24x17cm-9x7in) s. 21-Oct-2 Glerum, Amsterdam #39/R est:1500-2500
£1316 $2132 €2000 Ducks with ducklings on the waterside (18x24cm-7x9in) s. plywood. 21-Jan-3 Christie's, Amsterdam #265 est:1000-1500
£1549 $2494 €2200 Ducks on the waters' edge (39x80cm-15x31in) s. 6-May-3 Vendu Notarishuis, Rotterdam #54 est:1500-2000
£1781 $2778 €2600 Duck family at the bank of a ditch (18x24cm-7x9in) s. panel. 14-Apr-3 Glerum, Amsterdam #74/R est:2000-2500
£1831 $2948 €2600 Ducks at the edge of the water (39x49cm-15x19in) s. panel. 7-May-3 Vendue Huis, Gravenhage #555/R est:2800-3200
£1944 $3208 €2800 Ducks by the waterside (18x24cm-7x9in) s. plywood. 1-Jul-3 Christie's, Amsterdam #563/R est:2000-3000
£3947 $6395 €6000 Ducks by a river (40x50cm-16x20in) s. prov. 21-Jan-3 Christie's, Amsterdam #147/R est:3000-5000
£7000 $10920 €10500 Duck and her young on the river bank (58x98cm-23x39in) s. 26-Mar-3 Sotheby's, Olympia #261/R est:5000-7000

Works on paper
£889 $1476 €1289 Mother duck and her young on a river bank (34x53cm-13x21in) s. W/C. 16-Jun-3 Waddingtons, Toronto #219/R est:2000-3000 (C.D 2000)
£1250 $2025 €1900 Ducks and ducklings on a river bank (35x51cm-14x20in) s. ink W/C htd white. 21-Jan-3 Christie's, Amsterdam #200/R est:2000-3000
£1447 $2345 €2200 Under the willow (53x74cm-21x29in) s. W/C htd white. 21-Jan-3 Christie's, Amsterdam #192/R est:1500-2000
£1800 $2916 €2700 Landscape with ducks (37x52cm-15x20in) s. W/C. 20-May-3 Sotheby's, Olympia #419/R est:1200-1500
£2500 $4050 €3750 Ducks on a riverbank (33x50cm-13x20in) s. W/C two. 20-May-3 Sotheby's, Olympia #420/R est:3000-5000

ARTZ, David Adolf Constant (1837-1890) Dutch
£407 $643 €611 Farm at Katwijk, Beinnen (38x27cm-15x11in) s. 30-Nov-2 Goteborg Auktionsverk, Sweden #175/R (S.KR 5800)
£828 $1292 €1300 Market stall (49x39cm-19x15in) s. board. 6-Nov-2 Vendue Huis, Gravenhage #17/R
£1887 $2906 €3000 Little girl resting in the woods (24x30cm-9x12in) s. panel. 22-Oct-2 Sotheby's, Amsterdam #54/R est:3000-5000
£4110 $6452 €6000 Awaiting father's return on Scheveningen beach (26x17cm-10x7in) s. panel. 15-Apr-3 Sotheby's, Amsterdam #96/R est:5000-7000
£14500 $22475 €21750 Piggy back (46x30cm-18x12in) s. prov. 5-Dec-2 Bonhams, Edinburgh #19/R est:8000-12000

Works on paper
£1400 $2184 €2100 Shepherd girl (34x51cm-13x20in) s.d.1875-8 W/C. 5-Nov-2 Bonhams, New Bond Street #1/R est:800-1200
£3145 $4843 €5000 Preparing lunch (52x35cm-20x14in) s. pencil W/C gouache htd white exhib.lit. 23-Oct-2 Christie's, Amsterdam #215/R est:4000-6000
£5137 $8065 €7500 Children playing on the beach (41x33cm-16x13in) s. W/C. 15-Apr-3 Sotheby's, Amsterdam #125/R est:4000-6000
£7000 $11480 €10500 Fisherman and his family (58x63cm-23x25in) s. pencil W/C htd white. 5-Jun-3 Christie's, Kensington #842/R est:1000-1500

ARUS, Joseph Raoul (1848-1921) French
£183 $287 €275 Paysage (11x14cm-4x6in) s. s.i. verso panel. 12-Dec-2 Iegor de Saint Hippolyte, Montreal #4 (C.D 450)

ARVIN, Irmgard (20th C) American
£696 $1100 €1044 Hydrangeas in glass bowl (51x61cm-20x24in) s. board. 22-Apr-3 Arthur James, Florida #175

ARY, Henry (1802-1859) American
£27273 $42000 €40910 View of Mt Merino from Hudson, New York (61x91cm-24x36in) s.d.1851 prov.exhib. 24-Oct-2 Shannon's, Milford #105/R est:30000-50000

ASCENZI, Ettore (19th C) Italian
Works on paper
£343 $536 €497 Music lesson (55x37cm-22x15in) s.i. W/C prov. 26-Mar-3 Walker's, Ottawa #32/R est:1200-1600 (C.D 800)
£533 $885 €773 Jester and monk entertaining cavaliers in a courtyard (56x75cm-22x30in) s.d.1882 W/C. 16-Jun-3 Waddingtons, Toronto #327/R est:2000-2500 (C.D 1200)
£880 $1443 €1320 Flower sellers Trevi Fountain Rome (52x36cm-20x14in) s. W/C. 7-Feb-3 Honiton Galleries, Honiton #304/R

ASCH, Pieter Jansz van (1603-1678) Dutch
£1884 $2750 €2826 Continental pastoral landscape (48x56cm-19x22in) oak panel. 3-Nov-1 North East Auctions, Portsmouth #1197
£5033 $8104 €7500 Southern landscape with drovers and travellers on a path, town beyond (41x52cm-16x20in) mono. panel. 18-Feb-3 Sotheby's, Amsterdam #222/R est:6000-8000

ASCH, Pieter Jansz van (attrib) (1603-1678) Dutch
£1321 $2047 €2100 Rider on horseback with his falconer and his dogs on a country road (27x35cm-11x14in) panel. 4-Nov-2 Glerum, Amsterdam #29/R est:1800-2200

ASCHENBACH, Ernst (1872-1954) Norwegian
£301 $490 €452 Winter landscape (30x44cm-12x17in) s. 17-Feb-3 Blomqvist, Lysaker #1007/R (N.KR 3400)
£323 $507 €485 Winter landscape with house (34x56cm-13x22in) s. 25-Nov-2 Blomqvist, Lysaker #1008/R (N.KR 3700)
£357 $549 €536 Lofoten (72x100cm-28x39in) s. 28-Oct-2 Blomqvist, Lysaker #1001 (N.KR 4200)
£362 $586 €543 Winter landscape (30x45cm-12x18in) s. 27-Jan-3 Blomqvist, Lysaker #1012/R (N.KR 4000)
£450 $689 €675 Mountain landscape (66x107cm-26x42in) s. 26-Aug-2 Blomqvist, Lysaker #1015 (N.KR 5200)
£779 $1192 €1169 Capercaillie on pine trunk (100x73cm-39x29in) s. 26-Aug-2 Blomqvist, Lysaker #1014/R (N.KR 9000)

ASCHENBERGK, A (19th C) ?
£1006 $1560 €1600 Idyllic landscape with figures (64x95cm-25x37in) s. 29-Oct-2 Dorotheum, Vienna #281/R est:1800-2000

ASCHENBRENNER, Lennart (1943-) Swedish
£456 $711 €684 9-81 (81x100cm-32x39in) s.d.81 prov. 5-Nov-2 Bukowskis, Stockholm #398/R (S.KR 6500)
£841 $1312 €1262 J-I-9 (114x147cm-45x58in) s.d.89. 5-Nov-2 Bukowskis, Stockholm #399/R (S.KR 12000)
£1158 $1865 €1737 The glove has been thrown (180x100cm-71x39in) s.d.81. 7-May-3 AB Stockholms Auktionsverk #972/R est:10000-12000 (S.KR 15000)

ASCHENBROICH, Heinrich (1839-1909) German
£1218 $1888 €1900 After the bath (30x22cm-12x9in) s. panel. 5-Dec-2 Schopman, Hamburg #514 est:1800

ASCHMANN, Johann Jakob (1747-1809) Swiss
Works on paper
£1111 $1789 €1611 View of the Schnabelberg towards Horgen (35x56cm-14x22in) i. ink brush dr prov. 9-May-3 Dobiaschofsky, Bern #23/R (S.FR 2400)
£1343 $2162 €1947 View over Lake Lauerzer to Schwanau castle (34x49cm-13x19in) i. brush ink dr prov. 9-May-3 Dobiaschofsky, Bern #25/R est:2800 (S.FR 2900)
£1747 $2725 €2621 View of Mels towards Sargans in the district of St Gallen (31x53cm-12x21in) i. W/C prov. 8-Nov-2 Dobiaschofsky, Bern #19/R est:5000 (S.FR 4000)

ASCIONE, Aniello (attrib) (fl.1680-1708) Italian
£14744 $23147 €23000 Still life with putti and parrot (124x150cm-49x59in) 16-Dec-2 Rabourdin & Choppin de Janvry, Paris #170/R est:25000-30000
£16084 $26860 €23000 Nature morte aux raisins, figues, peches et oiseau (96x128cm-38x50in) 25-Jun-3 Pierre Berge, Paris #25/R est:15000-20000

ASCO, Franco (1903-1980) Italian
Sculpture
£1154 $1788 €1800 Force (70cm-28in) s. plaster. 5-Dec-2 Stadion, Trieste #762/R

ASEN, Karl Theodor (1875-1927) German
£1282 $2013 €2000 Painter and model in studio (82x66cm-32x26in) s.d.1911. 21-Nov-2 Van Ham, Cologne #1452/R est:1800

ASH, Thomas Morris (fl.1882-1891) British
£350 $571 €525 Sheep and cattle at a mountain beck (51x73cm-20x29in) s. canvas on board. 13-Feb-3 Christie's, Kensington #77
£450 $702 €675 Near Capel Curig, North Wales (20x40cm-8x16in) s. i.verso. 11-Sep-2 Bonhams, Newport #226/R

ASHBURNER, William F (fl.1900-1932) British
Works on paper
£1600 $2592 €2400 Gathering bluebells (36x26cm-14x10in) s. W/C. 20-May-3 Sotheby's, Olympia #219/R est:800-1200

ASHBURNHAM, George Percy (1815-1886) British
Works on paper
£650 $1086 €943 Church interiors (42x32cm-17x13in) W/C pair. 24-Jun-3 Bonhams, Knightsbridge #48/R

ASHER, Louis (1804-1878) German
£1456 $2256 €2300 Girl in Blankensee costume looking out of window (37x29cm-15x11in) s. panel. 28-Sep-2 Hans Stahl, Hamburg #132/R est:2500

ASHFORD, William (1746-1824) British
£14000 $22400 €21000 View of Loch Lene (53x74cm-21x29in) 15-May-3 Christie's, London #14/R est:7000-10000
Works on paper
£8108 $12649 €12000 Scalp in the County of Wicklow (38x50cm-15x20in) W/C sold with an engraving by Thomas Milton. 26-Mar-3 James Adam, Dublin #10/R est:8000-10000

ASHKIN, Michael (1955-) American
Sculpture
£1677 $2600 €2516 No.33 (122x640cm-48x252in) s.d.1996 num.33 envirotex oil dirt acrylic N-scale models wood. 26-Sep-2 Christie's, Rockefeller NY #868/R est:4000-6000

ASHLEY, Clifford Warren (1881-1947) American
£427 $700 €641 Covered bridge (51x74cm-20x29in) s. 5-Feb-3 Doyle, New York #63/R

ASHOONA, Kaka (1928-) North American
Sculpture
£1348 $2103 €2248 Transforming shaman (37x25x17cm-15x10x7in) green stone carving. 13-Apr-3 Levis, Calgary #56/R est:4500-5500 (C.D 3100)
£2935 $4578 €4894 Mother and twins (48x41x30cm-19x16x12in) green stone carving. 13-Apr-3 Levis, Calgary #55/R est:9000-12000 (C.D 6750)

ASHTON, James (1860-1935) Australian
£344 $543 €516 Fishing off Port Adelaide, Spencer Gulf (44x59cm-17x23in) s. 1-Apr-3 Lawson Menzies, Sydney #489 (A.D 900)
Works on paper
£279 $457 €405 Untitled, seascape (17x38cm-7x15in) s. W/C. 3-Jun-3 Lawson Menzies, Sydney #765 (A.D 700)

ASHTON, Julian Howard (1877-1964) Australian
£788 $1198 €1182 Blue mountains (52x69cm-20x27in) s.d.1930. 28-Aug-2 Deutscher-Menzies, Melbourne #314/R (A.D 2200)

ASHTON, Julian Richard (1913-) Australian
£313 $489 €470 Picking up the pilot, Orient line, passenger liner (38x38cm-15x15in) s.d.1935 panel. 10-Nov-2 Dunbar Sloane, Auckland #7 est:1000-2000 (NZ.D 1000)

ASHTON, Julian Rossi (1851-1942) British
£2143 $3386 €3215 Effect of fog (33x12cm-13x5in) s.d.95 board. 18-Nov-2 Goodman, Sydney #116 est:3500-5000 (A.D 6000)
£3929 $6207 €5894 New South Wales landscape (26x48cm-10x19in) s.d.1889 W/C gouache prov. 17-Nov-2 Sotheby's, Paddington #78/R est:1000-1500 (A.D 11000)
£25000 $39250 €37500 Chess game (70x90cm-28x35in) s.d.1878 prov. 25-Nov-2 Christie's, Melbourne #32/R est:40000-60000 (A.D 70000)
Works on paper
£1538 $2446 €2307 Singleton's Mill, Hawkesbury river (24x34cm-9x13in) s.i.d.98 W/C prov. 4-Mar-3 Deutscher-Menzies, Melbourne #241/R est:3500-4000 (A.D 4000)
£1964 $3103 €2946 Portrait of a girl (44x30cm-17x12in) s.d.93 W/C. 27-Nov-2 Deutscher-Menzies, Melbourne #103/R est:7000-9000 (A.D 5500)
£2481 $3920 €3722 Ball dress (34x23cm-13x9in) s.d.1889 i.verso W/C exhib. 2-Apr-3 Christie's, Melbourne #64/R est:2000-3000 (A.D 6500)

ASHTON, Luigi (19th C) British?
£4800 $7536 €7200 Church and convent near Palanza, Lake Maggiore (72x92cm-28x36in) s.d.1869 panel. 19-Nov-2 Bonhams, New Bond Street #105/R est:3000-5000

ASHTON, Sir John William (1881-1963) Australian/British
£269 $409 €404 Approaching storm (25x28cm-10x11in) s. board. 27-Aug-2 Goodman, Sydney #224 (A.D 750)
£464 $734 €696 Parramatta River (31x40cm-12x16in) s. canvas on board. 17-Nov-2 Sotheby's, Paddington #23/R est:1500-3000 (A.D 1300)
£610 $994 €915 Shipping in a harbour (29x39cm-11x15in) s. board. 11-Feb-3 Bonhams, Knowle #80
£890 $1361 €1335 Sydney (46x61cm-18x24in) s.i.d.1930 prov. 25-Aug-2 Sotheby's, Paddington #157 est:2500-4500 (A.D 2500)
£929 $1458 €1394 New growth, after the bushfire (35x43cm-14x17in) s. canvasboard prov. 25-Nov-2 Christie's, Melbourne #354/R est:3000-5000 (A.D 2600)
£960 $1546 €1392 Notre Dame, Paris (22x28cm-9x11in) s. board. 12-May-3 Joel, Victoria #337 est:1000-2000 (A.D 2400)
£1087 $1772 €1631 Boat sheds (26x36cm-10x14in) s. canvasboard. 3-Feb-3 Lawson Menzies, Sydney #412 est:3000-4000 (A.D 3000)
£1250 $1938 €1875 Harbour scene (26x36cm-10x14in) s. canvasboard. 29-Oct-2 Lawson Menzies, Sydney #65/R est:4000-5000 (A.D 3500)
£1717 $2713 €2576 Afternoon light, Paris (35x43cm-14x17in) s. i.verso canvas on board. 2-Apr-3 Christie's, Melbourne #40 est:3000-5000 (A.D 4500)
£1792 $2724 €2688 Mosman Bay looking towards Cremorne Point (28x38cm-11x15in) s. 27-Aug-2 Goodman, Sydney #23/R est:2000-4000 (A.D 5000)
£1900 $3059 €2755 Moonrise (32x43cm-13x17in) s. board. 12-May-3 Joel, Victoria #306 est:3000-4000 (A.D 4750)
£2132 $3390 €3198 Warriewood vista (47x64cm-19x25in) s. 5-May-3 Sotheby's, Melbourne #269/R est:2000-4000 (A.D 5500)
£2299 $3425 €3449 South of France (49x64cm-19x25in) s.i. 27-Aug-2 Christie's, Melbourne #192/R est:5000-7000 (A.D 6000)
£4070 $6471 €6105 View on Sydney Harbour (50x60cm-20x24in) s.d.1930. 5-May-3 Sotheby's, Melbourne #273/R est:8000-10000 (A.D 10500)
£5694 $8712 €8541 Ponte Santa Trinita, Florence (41x57cm-16x22in) s.d.13 prov. 26-Aug-2 Sotheby's, Paddington #563/R est:15000-20000 (A.D 16000)

ASHTON, William (18th C) British
Works on paper
£304 $475 €456 Sand storm in desert (21x33cm-8x13in) s.d.1902 mono.i.verso W/C. 9-Nov-2 Sloan, North Bethesda #534/R

ASHTON, William (1809-1858) British
Works on paper
£310 $484 €465 Horseman with dog on a moorland track, sheep and windmill beyond (26x33cm-10x13in) s. W/C. 10-Sep-2 David Duggleby, Scarborough #113

ASINS RODRIGUEZ, Elena (1940-) Spanish
Works on paper
£1277 $1992 €2030 Inverted dolmen (24x48cm-9x19in) s.i.d.1996 verso collage on wood diptych. 17-Sep-2 Segre, Madrid #169/R

ASKENAZY, Maurice (1888-1961) American
£1398 $2250 €2097 Floral still life (61x51cm-24x20in) s. 18-Feb-3 John Moran, Pasadena #95a est:2000-3000

ASKEVOLD, Anders Monsen (1834-1900) Norwegian
£732 $1200 €1061 Capioller Mountain (38x48cm-15x19in) s. oil on paper. 30-May-3 Aspire, Cleveland #30/R est:1500-3000
£1233 $1923 €1800 Waterfall in Norwegian highlands (34x49cm-13x19in) s. 10-Apr-3 Van Ham, Cologne #1312/R est:2200
£2183 $3406 €3275 Norwegian mountains with homebound cows (44x67cm-17x26in) s.i.d.1880 prov.lit. 9-Nov-2 Galerie Gloggner, Luzern #14/R est:2800-3500 (S.FR 5000)
£2611 $4178 €3917 At the outfarm (37x57cm-15x22in) s.d.1886 panel. 17-Mar-3 Blomqvist, Oslo #343/R est:30000-40000 (N.KR 30000)

£2692 $4173 €4200 Norwegian fjord landscape (40x66cm-16x26in) s.d.1892 canvas on canvas lit. 7-Dec-2 Bergmann, Erlangen #767/R est:2500
£3133 $5013 €4700 Calm day on the fjord (46x64cm-18x25in) s.d.1872. 17-Mar-3 Blomqvist, Oslo #311/R est:30000-40000 (N.KR 36000)
£3633 $5740 €5450 Figures and cattle by the ferry (72x116cm-28x46in) s.i. 2-Dec-2 Blomqvist, Oslo #306/R est:50000-70000 (N.KR 42000)
£3857 $6325 €5593 Fjord landscape on the west coast of Norway (40x68cm-16x27in) s.d.1892. 2-Jun-3 Blomqvist, Oslo #84/R est:50000-70000 (N.KR 42000)
£4526 $7241 €6789 Milkmaid and cows in thicket (56x41cm-22x16in) s.i.d.1884. 17-Mar-3 Blomqvist, Oslo #355/R est:50000-60000 (N.KR 52000)
£4671 $7381 €7007 Figures and boats on fjord in summer (56x90cm-22x35in) s.d.1891. 2-Dec-2 Blomqvist, Oslo #354/R est:50000-70000 (N.KR 54000)
£4758 $7517 €7137 Landscape from Sognefjord (46x70cm-18x28in) s.d.1887 i.stretcher. 2-Dec-2 Blomqvist, Oslo #361/R est:60000-80000 (N.KR 55000)
£4867 $7690 €7301 Returning from the mountains - herders and cattle (60x46cm-24x18in) s.d.1883. 28-Apr-3 Blomqvist, Oslo #308/R est:70000-90000 (N.KR 55000)
£5048 $8077 €7572 Landscape from Lofthus in Hardanger (45x70cm-18x28in) s.d.1887. 17-Mar-3 Blomqvist, Oslo #334/R est:50000-70000 (N.KR 58000)
£5536 $8747 €8304 Steam boat arriving (56x90cm-22x35in) s.d.1891. 2-Dec-2 Blomqvist, Oslo #320/R est:50000-70000 (N.KR 64000)
£7372 $11500 €11058 Steamer on the fjord (53x83cm-21x33in) s.d.1890. 21-Oct-2 Blomqvist, Oslo #330/R est:80000-100000 (N.KR 85000)
£8850 $13982 €13275 Fjord landscape, west coast of Norway with figures and boats (56x90cm-22x35in) s.d.1893 indis.i.stretcher. 28-Apr-3 Blomqvist, Oslo #319/R est:80000-100000 (N.KR 100000)
£10444 $16710 €15666 Vestland's fjord with activity at water's edge (58x82cm-23x32in) s.d.1870. 17-Mar-3 Blomqvist, Oslo #341/R est:120000-150000 (N.KR 120000)

ASLUND, Acke (1881-1958) Swedish
£2411 $3738 €3617 Horses playing in garden (67x88cm-26x35in) s.i.d.1933. 8-Dec-2 Uppsala Auktionskammare, Uppsala #187/R est:10000-12000 (S.KR 34000)

ASLUND, Kjell (1948-) Swedish
£1236 $1989 €1854 Water lilies (89x68cm-35x27in) s.d.1996. 7-May-3 AB Stockholms Auktionsverk #961/R est:10000-12000 (S.KR 16000)

ASMUSSEN, Anton (1857-1904) German
Works on paper
£634 $1002 €920 Moonlight on the Ostsee (24x36cm-9x14in) s. i. verso pastel. 5-Apr-3 Hans Stahl, Hamburg #147/R

ASOLA, Bernardino and Giovanni da (16th C) Italian
£27586 $43862 €40000 Bishop with saints (122x142cm-48x56in) board. 9-Mar-3 Semenzato, Venice #40/R

ASOMA, Tudashi (20th C) Japanese
£741 $1200 €1112 Angled umbrellas (132x127cm-52x50in) s.d.67 prov. 24-Jan-3 Freeman, Philadelphia #229/R est:1000-1500
£2535 $4082 €3600 Paysage A (88x116cm-35x46in) s. exhib. 7-May-3 Vendue Huis, Gravenhage #145/R est:1500-2000

ASPA, Rosario (19th C) British
Works on paper
£280 $468 €406 View of Ely Cathedral (11x21cm-4x8in) s.i.d.1880 W/C. 24-Jun-3 Rowley Fine Art, Newmarket #379/R

ASPDEN, David (1935-) Australian
£1362 $2070 €2043 Wooster street (100x76cm-39x30in) s.i.d.80 verso prov. 28-Aug-2 Deutscher-Menzies, Melbourne #360/R est:3400-4000 (A.D 3800)
£1433 $2236 €2483 Burning chat (171x147cm-67x58in) s.i.verso prov. 31-Mar-3 Goodman, Sydney #54/R (A.D 3800)
£4800 $7728 €7200 Untitled I (244x167cm-96x66in) s.i.d.69 verso acrylic lit. 6-May-3 Christie's, Melbourne #74/R est:12000-18000 (A.D 12000)
Works on paper
£308 $489 €462 Abstract (71x53cm-28x21in) gouache. 4-Mar-3 Deutscher-Menzies, Melbourne #267/R (A.D 800)
£854 $1307 €1281 Abstract (107x79cm-42x31in) mono. synthetic polymer paint painted c.1987 prov. 26-Aug-2 Sotheby's, Paddington #688 est:600-800 (A.D 2400)

ASPELL, Peter (1918-) Canadian
£342 $544 €513 Death of Sardanapolis (28x33cm-11x13in) s.d.1989 i.verso matt board. 6-Mar-3 Heffel, Vancouver #4/R (C.D 800)
£404 $646 €606 Red aristocrat (22x30cm-9x12in) s.d.1987 i.verso board prov. 15-May-3 Heffel, Vancouver #147 est:800-1200 (C.D 900)
£426 $681 €639 Pond magic VIII (30x23cm-12x9in) s.d.1987 i.verso board prov. 15-May-3 Heffel, Vancouver #75 est:800-1200 (C.D 950)
£427 $679 €641 Untitled (89x109cm-35x43in) s.d.1980. 6-Mar-3 Heffel, Vancouver #5/R (C.D 1000)
£427 $679 €641 Fire over the land (30x23cm-12x9in) s.d.1987 i.verso matt board. 6-Mar-3 Heffel, Vancouver #2/R (C.D 1000)
£470 $747 €705 Ancient landscape, Ozymandius (36x25cm-14x10in) s.d.1988 matt board. 6-Mar-3 Heffel, Vancouver #1/R (C.D 1100)
£1230 $1906 €1845 Untitled (140x208cm-55x82in) s. 24-Sep-2 Maynards, Vancouver #396 est:3000-5000 (C.D 3000)

ASPEREN, Piet Hein van (1895-1969) Dutch
£382 $589 €600 Horse-drawn cart on a quay (49x69cm-19x27in) s. 3-Sep-2 Christie's, Amsterdam #221

ASPERTINI, Amico (attrib) (1474-1552) Italian
Prints
£2500 $3900 €3750 Expulsion of Adam and Eve from Paradise (23x32cm-9x13in) engraving executed c.1545. 25-Mar-3 Sotheby's, London #1/R est:3000-5000

ASPEVIG, Clyde (1951-) American
£4669 $7750 €6770 Spring thaw (46x71cm-18x28in) s. 14-Jun-3 Jackson's, Cedar Falls #12/R est:7500-10000
£5195 $8000 €7793 Mt. Lindsey (51x61cm-20x24in) 25-Oct-2 Morris & Whiteside, Hilton Head Island #146 est:9000-12000
£17405 $27500 €25237 Across the greasewood flats (91x137cm-36x54in) s. 26-Jul-3 Coeur d'Alene, Hayden #192/R est:25000-35000
£31646 $50000 €45887 Lake o'Hara, B.C (102x127cm-40x50in) s. prov. 26-Jul-3 Coeur d'Alene, Hayden #164/R est:30000-50000

ASPINWALL, Reginald (1858-1921) British
£360 $562 €540 Passing shower, Morecambe Bay (24x35cm-9x14in) i.verso panel. 6-Nov-2 Bonhams, Chester #348
£400 $624 €600 Morecambe Bay with fishing boats (25x35cm-10x14in) s. board. 18-Sep-2 James Thompson, Kirby Lonsdale #70
£760 $1208 €1140 Farmstead (29x39cm-11x15in) s. 19-Mar-3 James Thompson, Kirby Lonsdale #48
Works on paper
£320 $509 €480 Upland landscape with shepherd driving a flock of sheep (23x33cm-9x13in) s.d.1888 W/C. 18-Mar-3 Capes Dunn, Manchester #453
£750 $1193 €1125 Welsh moorland (29x45cm-11x18in) s. 19-Mar-3 James Thompson, Kirby Lonsdale #47

ASSCHE, G van (?) Belgian?
£1277 $2068 €1800 Bergere devant une ferme (57x75cm-22x30in) 26-May-3 Amberes, Antwerp #86

ASSCHE, Henri van (1774-1841) Belgian
£1268 $2041 €1800 Village view with cows on a path (32x40cm-13x16in) s. panel. 12-May-3 Bernaerts, Antwerp #37 est:1500-1750
£1500 $2445 €2250 Extensive wooded river landscape with figures and animals on a track (38x51cm-15x20in) 14-Feb-3 Keys, Aylsham #704/R

ASSCHER, Sofy (20th C) ?
£1800 $2790 €2700 Toasting the chef (175x230cm-69x91in) s. after Francis Brunery. 3-Nov-2 Lots Road, London #335 est:800-1200

ASSE, Genevieve (1923-) French
£2279 $3623 €3350 Inspiration Norvegienne (40x40cm-16x16in) s. s.i.d.69 verso. 26-Feb-3 Artcurial Briest, Paris #441/R est:2000-3000
£2639 $4196 €3800 Composition (5x51cm-2x20in) s. paper prov.exhib. 29-Apr-3 Artcurial Briest, Paris #551/R est:2500-3000
£3673 $5841 €5400 Espace (88x105cm-35x41in) s. s.i.d.59 verso. 26-Feb-3 Artcurial Briest, Paris #440/R est:4000-5000
Works on paper
£918 $1450 €1377 Untitled (76x54cm-30x21in) s. gouache on canvas. 15-Nov-2 Naón & Cia, Buenos Aires #88/R

ASSELBERGS, Alphonse (1839-1916) Belgian
£759 $1185 €1200 Winter landscape with trees near a wall (22x37cm-9x15in) s. panel. 21-Oct-2 Bernaerts, Antwerp #617/R
£2420 $3776 €3800 Travaux a la scierie (70x100cm-28x39in) s. 11-Nov-2 Horta, Bruxelles #207 est:3500-5000

ASSELBERGS, Jan (1937-) Dutch
Works on paper
£461 $746 €700 Anneke (62x46cm-24x18in) s.d.65 brown chk prov. 21-Jan-3 Christie's, Amsterdam #466/R

ASSELIN, Maurice (1882-1947) French
£764 $1215 €1100 Le port de Saint-Tropez (31x47cm-12x19in) s.i.d.26 paper on isorel panel. 29-Apr-3 Artcurial Briest, Paris #178
£849 $1316 €1350 Jeune femme lisant (60x73cm-24x29in) s. 30-Oct-2 Artcurial Briest, Paris #290
Works on paper
£260 $403 €390 The Siene, Paris (26x36cm-10x14in) s.d.1911 W/C. 3-Dec-2 Bonhams, Knightsbridge #202/R
£694 $1132 €1000 Maternite (60x46cm-24x18in) s.d.23 chl pastel. 19-Jul-3 Thierry & Lannon, Brest #247

ASSELYN, Jan (1610-1652) Dutch
£380 $593 €570 Military figure on horseback and others by a well (43x46cm-17x18in) i.verso. 18-Oct-2 Keys, Aylsham #591
£10811 $16865 €16000 View of Tomb of Caecilia Metella near Rome (38x31cm-15x12in) 27-Mar-3 Dorotheum, Vienna #133/R est:18000-24000

ASSELYN, Jan (attrib) (1610-1652) Dutch
£3185 $4904 €5000 Italianate landscape with muleteers crossing a river (65x56cm-26x22in) 3-Sep-2 Christie's, Amsterdam #48/R est:5000-7000
£9459 $14757 €14000 Southern coastal landscape with fishermen (57x84cm-22x33in) 27-Mar-3 Dorotheum, Vienna #375/R est:15000-20000
£10811 $16865 €16000 Assault in front of castle ruins (71x94cm-28x37in) 27-Mar-3 Dorotheum, Vienna #313/R est:3000-5000
Works on paper
£325 $500 €488 Landscape with drovers (31x24cm-12x9in) i. graphite wash. 23-Oct-2 Doyle, New York #10

ASSERETO, Giovacchino (1600-1649) Italian
£650000 $1085500 €942500 Salome presenting the head of John the Baptist to Herod (112x142cm-44x56in) prov. 9-Jul-3 Christie's, London #98/R est:80000-120000

ASSETTO, Franco (1911-) Italian
Works on paper
£462 $729 €720 Anatomic flowers (52x38cm-20x15in) mixed media exec.1950. 12-Nov-2 Babuino, Rome #289/R

ASSIER DE LATOUR, Edmond (19th C) French
£1148 $1860 €1665 Hunting scene with dogs barking (80x119cm-31x47in) s.d.1901. 26-May-3 Rasmussen, Copenhagen #1475/R est:15000 (D.KR 12000)

ASSMUS, Robert (1837-?) German
£966 $1526 €1400 Mountain lake with figures (92x159cm-36x63in) i. 5-Apr-3 Dr Fritz Nagel, Leipzig #3904/R

ASSTEYN, Bartholomeus (1607-?) Dutch
Works on paper
£2405 $3728 €3800 Tulip and spider (30x20cm-12x8in) mono.i. gouache. 25-Sep-2 Neumeister, Munich #352/R est:1300

AST, Balthasar van der (1590-1656) Dutch
£41401 $64586 €65000 Still life of carnation and rosemary in a wan-li vase (28x21cm-11x8in) s. panel prov. 5-Nov-2 Sotheby's, Amsterdam #260/R est:70000-90000
Works on paper
£3400 $5678 €4930 Tulip 'Merveille Brueghel' and spider (31x20cm-12x8in) mono.i. W/C gouache. 9-Jul-3 Sotheby's, London #110/R est:4000-6000

ASTI, Angelo (1847-1903) French
£1220 $2000 €1769 Auburn haired beauty (36x23cm-14x9in) s. 4-Jun-3 Doyle, New York #7 est:1000-1500
£1937 $3100 €2809 Portrait of a young woman reading (46x32cm-18x13in) s. panel. 16-May-3 Skinner, Boston #24/R est:1500-2500
£5063 $8000 €7595 Nue a la libellule (56x81cm-22x32in) s.d.85 prov. 23-Apr-3 Christie's, Rockefeller NY #107/R est:10000-15000

ASTLEY, Charles E (19/20th C) Australian
£1300 $2067 €1950 Swagman on a bush road (96x61cm-38x24in) s. indis i.d. 29-Apr-3 Bonhams, New Bond Street #4/R est:1000-1500

ASTLEY, Francis (18/19th C) British
£1400 $2198 €2100 Portrait of Thomas Phillips (74x62cm-29x24in) i. 10-Dec-2 Bristol Auction Rooms #930/R est:400-600

ASTLEY, John (attrib) (1730-1787) British
£1500 $2460 €2250 Portrait of a girl with a ribbon in her hair (41x36cm-16x14in) 29-May-3 Christie's, Kensington #37/R est:500-800

ASTOIN, Marie (1924-) French
£828 $1308 €1200 Estuaire (50x65cm-20x26in) s. 4-Apr-3 Tajan, Paris #204
£828 $1308 €1200 Vallons en Provence (54x65cm-21x26in) s. 4-Apr-3 Tajan, Paris #203
£833 $1308 €1300 Matin en Provence (33x41cm-13x16in) s. 15-Dec-2 Eric Pillon, Calais #196/R
£1042 $1698 €1500 Le ramendage des filets sur le port (54x73cm-21x29in) s. 19-Jul-3 Thierry & Lannon, Brest #185/R est:1500-1800

ASTON, Charles Reginald (1832-1908) British
Works on paper
£280 $437 €420 Cliffs at Babbcombe (45x29cm-18x11in) s. W/C htd white. 18-Sep-2 Dreweatt Neate, Newbury #70

ASTON, Evelin Winifred (fl.1924-1975) British
£500 $791 €750 Treport, France (55x45cm-22x18in) s. 27-Nov-2 Sotheby's, Olympia #282/R
£700 $1105 €1050 Tea in the kitchen (54x47cm-21x19in) s. board. 27-Nov-2 Sotheby's, Olympia #281/R

ASTORRI, E (?) ?
Sculpture
£3205 $5032 €5000 Petit joueur de billes (167x69x73cm-66x27x29in) s. brown pat bronze. 22-Nov-2 Millon & Associes, Paris #150/R

ASTROM, Werner (1885-1979) Finnish
£1111 $1822 €1700 Waiting for the artist (94x80cm-37x31in) s.d.1924. 9-Feb-3 Bukowskis, Helsinki #394/R est:1500
Works on paper
£314 $487 €500 Nude model (59x76cm-23x30in) s.d.62 W/C. 6-Oct-2 Bukowskis, Helsinki #329/R

ASTRUP, Nikolai (1880-1928) Norwegian
Prints
£3097 $4894 €4646 Ploughing at night (18x26cm-7x10in) s. col woodcut lit. 28-Apr-3 Blomqvist, Oslo #335/R (N.KR 35000)
£38009 $61575 €57014 Mountain landscape with meadow buttercups and houses at night (37x46cm-15x18in) s. woodcut hand col. 26-May-3 Grev Wedels Plass, Oslo #73/R est:500000 (N.KR 420000)

ASTUDIN, Nicolai (1848-1925) German
£1026 $1610 €1600 Burg Gutenfels am Rhein (67x87cm-26x34in) s. 21-Nov-2 Van Ham, Cologne #1453/R

ATALAYA, Enrique (1851-1914) Spanish
£545 $861 €850 Path by statue (11x7cm-4x3in) s. cardboard. 13-Nov-2 Ansorena, Madrid #266/R
£1266 $1975 €2000 Personnages au village. Le matador (20x13cm-8x5in) s. panel pair. 15-Oct-2 Regis & Thiollet, Argentuil #186
£1510 $2431 €2250 Chez les orfevres (21x15cm-8x6in) s. board. 18-Feb-3 Durán, Madrid #237/R
£2244 $3522 €3500 Untitled (61x45cm-24x18in) s. board. 16-Dec-2 Castellana, Madrid #56/R
Works on paper
£316 $491 €500 Rue Saint Victor (11x7cm-4x3in) s. gouache. 29-Sep-2 Eric Pillon, Calais #116/R
£316 $491 €500 Rue Clovis (10x7cm-4x3in) s. gouache. 29-Sep-2 Eric Pillon, Calais #117/R
£316 $491 €500 Rue des Bernardin (11x7cm-4x3in) s. gouache. 29-Sep-2 Eric Pillon, Calais #118/R
£316 $491 €500 Rue des Marronniers (11x7cm-4x3in) s. gouache. 29-Sep-2 Eric Pillon, Calais #119/R
£316 $491 €500 Le parc (11x7cm-4x3in) s. gouache. 29-Sep-2 Eric Pillon, Calais #120/R
£316 $491 €500 La Rue de Nevers (11x7cm-4x3in) s. gouache. 29-Sep-2 Eric Pillon, Calais #121/R

ATAMIAN, Charles Garabed (1872-1947) Turkish
Works on paper
£300 $468 €450 Sur la plage (23x30cm-9x12in) s. W/C. 17-Oct-2 David Lay, Penzance #1187/R

ATGET, Eugène (1857-1927) French
Photographs
£1829 $3000 €2744 Interieur d'un ascleur (19x22cm-7x9in) i.num.332 verso albumen print exec.c.1910. 10-Feb-3 Swann Galleries, New York #30/R est:4000-5000
£3481 $5500 €5222 Rue de Lava Maria (22x18cm-9x7in) i.num.6477 arrowroot print. 23-Apr-3 Sotheby's, New York #164/R est:6000-9000
£3750 $6000 €5625 Boutique de L'epoque, Empire (21x16cm-8x6in) i.d.1902 verso photograph. 15-May-3 Swann Galleries, New York #199/R est:5000-7500
£8228 $13000 €12342 Kiosque a fleurs (23x18cm-9x7in) i.num.123 photograph. 23-Apr-3 Sotheby's, New York #163/R est:6000-9000
£9091 $14000 €13637 Boutique, 16 Rue Dupetit-Thouars (22x18cm-9x7in) i.num.238 verso albumen print exec.c.1910 prov.lit. 25-Oct-2 Phillips, New York #2/R est:10000-15000

ATHERTON, John (1900-1952) American
Works on paper
£976 $1600 €1415 Rocky landscape (46x41cm-18x16in) s. gouache on scratchboard prov. 1-Jun-3 Wright, Chicago #267/R est:2500-3500

ATILA (1931-1987) French
£443 $687 €700 Deux mages (146x114cm-57x45in) s.d. i.d.verso. 28-Sep-2 Cornette de St.Cyr, Paris #244
£1006 $1560 €1600 Quand un soldat (162x130cm-64x51in) s.d.70. 5-Oct-2 De Vuyst, Lokeren #16/R est:1000-1500

ATILA, Ede Kardy (1931-1987) French
£705 $1107 €1100 Regard qui traine (195x195cm-77x77in) s.d.74 s.i.d.verso prov. 24-Nov-2 Laurence Calmels, Paris #24/R
£769 $1208 €1200 Untitled (89x116cm-35x46in) s.d.62 prov. 24-Nov-2 Laurence Calmels, Paris #23/R
£962 $1510 €1500 Homme engin (130x195cm-51x77in) s.d.79 s.i.d.verso prov. 24-Nov-2 Laurence Calmels, Paris #19/R
£962 $1510 €1500 Gilet de sauvetage (130x195cm-51x77in) s.d.75 s.i.d.verso prov. 24-Nov-2 Laurence Calmels, Paris #18/R
£962 $1510 €1500 Flipper (130x130cm-51x51in) s.d.81 s.i.d.verso prov.exhib. 24-Nov-2 Laurence Calmels, Paris #17/R
£1154 $1812 €1800 Archer d'arc-en-ciel (162x130cm-64x51in) s.d.1984 prov. 24-Nov-2 Laurence Calmels, Paris #20/R
£1154 $1812 €1800 Allumette volante (162x130cm-64x51in) s.d.1964 s.i.verso prov. 24-Nov-2 Laurence Calmels, Paris #21/R
£1154 $1812 €1800 Yeux pour antennes (116x89cm-46x35in) s.d.74 s.i.d.versoprov. 24-Nov-2 Laurence Calmels, Paris #25/R
Works on paper
£769 $1208 €1200 Untitled (90x62cm-35x24in) s.d.1980 waterpaint mixed media prov. 24-Nov-2 Laurence Calmels, Paris #16/R
£769 $1208 €1200 Untitled (92x61cm-36x24in) s.d.76 waterpaint mixed media prov. 24-Nov-2 Laurence Calmels, Paris #15/R

ATKINS, Anna (1799-1871) ?
Photographs
£3247 $5000 €4871 Adiantum cuneatum (26x20cm-10x8in) i. cyanotype photograph prov.lit. 24-Oct-2 Sotheby's, New York #42/R est:6000-9000

ATKINS, Caven (1907-) Canadian
Works on paper
£601 $937 €902 Landscape (36x53cm-14x21in) s.d.40 W/C. 25-Mar-3 Ritchie, Toronto #169/R est:250-350 (C.D 1400)

ATKINS, Edward A (19th C) British
£280 $442 €420 Blackberry gatherers (28x38cm-11x15in) s.d.1869 b,. 2-Dec-2 Gorringes, Lewes #2820
£600 $990 €870 Highgate archway viaduct. Millfield lane, Highgate (62x75cm-24x30in) s. d.1877 d.1894-1899 board pair. 2-Jul-3 Sotheby's, Olympia #326/R

ATKINS, Samuel (fl.1787-1808) British
Works on paper
£1500 $2369 €2250 Dismasted warship in a storm (22x25cm-9x10in) s. W/C over pencil prov. 28-Nov-2 Sotheby's, London #231/R est:1500-2000
£1500 $2430 €2250 Gentle breeze in the Channel (39x53cm-15x21in) pen black ink W/C. 21-May-3 Christie's, Kensington #367/R est:1500-2000
£1586 $2522 €2300 Trois mats et embarcations de la Cie des Indes (22x32cm-9x13in) i. W/C pen oval pair. 4-Mar-3 Livinec, Gaudcheau & Jezequel, Rennes #414
£2600 $4134 €3900 Shipping on a stormy sea (34x48cm-13x19in) s. pen ink W/C over pencil. 19-Mar-3 Sotheby's, London #183/R est:1500-2000
£4000 $6480 €6000 32 gun British frigate preparing to sail. On-coming merchantman narrowly missing a Dutch hoy (22x32cm-9x13in) s. pen ink W/C oval pair prov. 22-Jan-3 Bonhams, New Bond Street #306/R est:4000-6000

ATKINS, William Edward (1842-1910) British
£2600 $4238 €3900 HMS Victory and HMS Duke of Wellington in Portsmouth harbour (32x66cm-13x26in) sold with two watercolours. 14-Feb-3 Lyon & Turnbull, Edinburgh #151
Works on paper
£300 $468 €450 Two masted frigate off a coast (48x38cm-19x15in) s.d.02 W/C. 18-Oct-2 Keys, Aylsham #657
£300 $465 €450 Approaching the turn mark (19x28cm-7x11in) s. pencil W/C. 31-Oct-2 Christie's, Kensington #402/R
£550 $853 €825 H.M training brig Martin entering the harbour at Portsmouth. H.M training brig Martin running out (23x15cm-9x6in) s. pen ink W/C htd white pair. 31-Oct-2 Christie's, Kensington #323/R

ATKINSON, George (19/20th C) British
£430 $671 €645 Still life with poppies and a Chinese figure (53x66cm-21x26in) s. 7-Nov-2 Mallams, Cheltenham #319

ATKINSON, George Mounsey Wheatley (1806-1884) British
£7643 $11083 €12000 City of New York on the Daunt Rock (50x76cm-20x30in) 29-May-2 Woodwards, Cork #214
£25478 $36943 €40000 Visit of Queen Victoria to Cork Harbour (44x65cm-17x26in) s.d. 29-May-2 Woodwards, Cork #213

ATKINSON, George Mounsey Wheatley (circle) (1806-1884) British
£23000 $36800 €34500 View of Cork Harbour (76x129cm-30x51in) prov. 16-May-3 Sotheby's, London #16/R est:3000-5000

ATKINSON, John (1863-1924) British
Works on paper
£250 $395 €375 On the grouse moor (18x30cm-7x12in) s.i. pencil W/C. 28-Nov-2 Christie's, Kensington #34
£340 $530 €510 North Yorkshire moorland landscape (24x32cm-9x13in) s. W/C. 10-Sep-2 David Duggleby, Scarborough #184
£400 $648 €600 Harvesting (27x38cm-11x15in) s. pencil W/C htd white scratching out. 23-Jan-3 Christie's, Kensington #315
£400 $668 €580 Autumn - a lumberman and two horses in a clearing (29x42cm-11x17in) s. W/C. 17-Jun-3 Anderson & Garland, Newcastle #313
£560 $874 €840 Two figures in a village lane (20x30cm-8x12in) s. W/C. 10-Sep-2 David Duggleby, Scarborough #69/R
£680 $1102 €1020 Haymaking (14x22cm-6x9in) s. W/C scratching out. 20-May-3 Sotheby's, Olympia #26/R
£700 $1085 €1050 Village street scene with mother and child (26x36cm-10x14in) s. W/C. 24-Sep-2 Anderson & Garland, Newcastle #376/R
£700 $1106 €1050 Mr W Thompson's otter hounds on the Esk (33x49cm-13x19in) s.i. verso W/C htd white. 28-Nov-2 Christie's, Kensington #305/R
£700 $1085 €1050 Plough team with extensive landscape (23x33cm-9x13in) s. W/C. 31-Oct-2 Duke & Son, Dorchester #120/R
£1050 $1659 €1575 Yorkshire farmyard (38x56cm-15x22in) s. W/C. 13-Nov-2 Halls, Shrewsbury #342/R est:800-1200
£1700 $2839 €2465 Landscapes, foxhunting scenes (20x13cm-8x5in) W/C sketchbooks. 17-Jun-3 Anderson & Garland, Newcastle #314 est:600-900
£1800 $2808 €2700 Gleaners (36x53cm-14x21in) s.d.07. 9-Oct-2 Andrew Hartley, Ilkley #662/R est:2500-3500
£2500 $4175 €3625 Whitby Sands, morning (22x29cm-9x11in) s. i.verso W/C prov.lit. 17-Jun-3 Anderson & Garland, Newcastle #312/R est:2800-4600
£3400 $5372 €5100 Loading the cart (51x61cm-20x24in) s. W/C. 24-Apr-3 Richardson & Smith, Whitby #241 est:3000-4000

ATKINSON, John Gunson (fl.1849-1885) British
£320 $496 €480 Pool on the Llugwy (30x50cm-12x20in) s. 29-Oct-2 Henry Adams, Chichester #557
£720 $1123 €1080 Near Capel Curig Old road to Dolywydellin, North Wales. Near Dolgelly, North Wales (30x51cm-12x20in) s. s.i.verso pair. 11-Sep-2 Bonhams, Newport #233/R

ATKINSON, Maud Tindal (fl.1906-1937) British
Works on paper
£5500 $8635 €8250 Sir Galahad (72x53cm-28x21in) s. pencil W/C htd gold scratching out. 21-Nov-2 Christie's, London #83/R est:3000-5000

ATKINSON, William Edwin (1862-1926) Canadian
£300 $469 €435 Evening mist (21x26cm-8x10in) s.d.1922 panel. 26-Mar-3 Walker's, Ottawa #207/R (C.D 700)
£432 $670 €648 Riverside cottage (21x26cm-8x10in) s.d.98 canvas on board. 3-Dec-2 Joyner, Toronto #437 est:600-800 (C.D 1050)

£803 $1261 €1205 Strolling along the lane (30x45cm-12x18in) s.d.1894. 25-Nov-2 Hodgins, Calgary #31/R est:2200-2500 (C.D 2000)

Works on paper

£267 $437 €401 Walking home (24x38cm-9x15in) s.d.1914 W/C. 3-Jun-3 Joyner, Toronto #605 (C.D 600)

ATKYNS, Lee (1913-1987) American

£552 $850 €828 Grand Canyon (61x76cm-24x30in) s.d.1954 board. 8-Sep-2 Treadway Gallery, Cincinnati #594/R

ATL, Dr (1875-1964) Mexican

Works on paper

£989 $1583 €1434 Nabui dormida (20x31cm-8x12in) s.d.1922 chl. 15-May-3 Louis Morton, Mexico #147 est:18000-20000 (M.P 16000)
£1889 $2947 €2834 Mujer (26x39cm-10x15in) s. chl. 17-Oct-2 Louis Morton, Mexico #35/R est:32000-36000 (M.P 30000)
£3774 $6000 €5661 The Katunes (21x25cm-8x10in) six i.verso W/C stencils ten album exec.c.1945. 29-Apr-3 Christie's, Rockefeller NY #422/R est:3500-4500
£7317 $12000 €10976 Arbol tropical (47x61cm-19x24in) atl colours board exec.c.1955 prov. 28-May-3 Christie's, Rockefeller NY #99/R est:15000-18000

ATLAN, Jean (1913-1960) French

£5855 $9251 €8783 Composition (61x50cm-24x20in) s.d.XXXXV veneer prov.exhib.lit. 1-Apr-3 Rasmussen, Copenhagen #134/R est:50000 (D.KR 63000)
£12925 $20551 €19000 Untitled (102x72cm-40x28in) s.d.1957 oil stump cardboard lit. 24-Mar-3 Cornette de St.Cyr, Paris #5/R est:30000
£13000 $20020 €19500 Pierres Brulees (81x65cm-32x26in) s. s.i.verso masonite prov.exhib.lit. 22-Oct-2 Sotheby's, London #431/R est:15000-20000
£20000 $32800 €30000 Hejaz (60x92cm-24x36in) s.d.58 i.verso prov.lit. 6-Feb-3 Christie's, London #618/R est:20000-30000
£27564 $43276 €43000 Untitled (50x73cm-20x29in) s. painted 1958 prov.lit. 15-Dec-2 Perrin, Versailles #71/R est:45000
£29000 $47560 €43500 Untitled (54x81cm-21x32in) s. prov.lit. 7-Feb-3 Sotheby's, London #224/R est:30000-40000
£31646 $50000 €50000 Untitled (100x65cm-39x26in) s. painted 1955 prov.lit. 27-Nov-2 Tajan, Paris #8/R est:55000-70000
£33571 $53379 €49350 Sans titre (116x730cm-46x287in) s.d.56 prov.exhib.lit. 26-Feb-3 Artcurial Briest, Paris #442/R est:30000-40000
£35000 $58450 €50750 Untitled (116x73cm-46x29in) s. painted 1957 prov.exhib.lit. 27-Jun-3 Christie's, London #117/R est:40000-60000
£49306 $77903 €71000 Mukden (130x81cm-51x32in) s.d. s.i.d.verso prov.exhib.lit. 27-Apr-3 Perrin, Versailles #33/R est:70000-80000
£54000 $90180 €78300 Diptyque vertical (54x81cm-21x32in) s.d.59 stretcher burlap two parts prov.exhib.lit. 26-Jun-3 Sotheby's, London #183/R est:30000-40000
£59615 $93596 €93000 Sarragosse II (116x73cm-46x29in) s.d.1958 prov.exhib.lit. 15-Dec-2 Perrin, Versailles #60/R est:70000
£75862 $119862 €110000 Livre des Rois I (130x81cm-51x32in) s.d.58 s.i.d.on stretcher prov.exhib.lit. 2-Apr-3 Christie's, Paris #19/R est:90000

Works on paper

£1111 $1766 €1600 Sans titre (26x20cm-10x8in) s.i.d.Mai 1957 crayons felt tip collage prov.lit. 29-Apr-3 Artcurial Briest, Paris #553/R est:2000-3000
£3042 $4806 €4563 Composition I (27x22cm-11x9in) s. mixed media. 28-Apr-3 Bukowskis, Stockholm #306/R est:40000-60000 (S.KR 40000)
£3491 $5656 €5062 Composition (28x23cm-11x9in) s. gouache. 25-May-3 Uppsala Auktionskammare, Uppsala #312/R est:50000-60000 (S.KR 45000)
£4348 $6739 €6522 Composition (45x53cm-18x21in) s. pastel exec.c.1957 prov. 7-Dec-2 Galerie du Rhone, Sion #512/R est:9000-12000 (S.FR 10000)
£4500 $7335 €6750 Untitled (45x53cm-18x21in) s.d.59 gouache W/C. 3-Feb-3 Sotheby's, Olympia #75/R est:4000-6000
£4861 $7729 €7000 Sans titre (28x37cm-11x15in) s.d.52 pastel lit. 29-Apr-3 Artcurial Briest, Paris #552a/R est:5000-6000
£6389 $10094 €9200 Sans titre (31x23cm-12x9in) s.d. pastel prov.lit. 27-Apr-3 Perrin, Versailles #52/R est:5000-6000
£7586 $11986 €11000 Untitled (25x32cm-10x13in) s. pastel prov. 2-Apr-3 Christie's, Paris #32/R est:6000

ATLEE, Emilie Des (1915-) American

£329 $500 €494 Between showers (38x81cm-15x32in) s. i.verso. 18-Aug-2 Jeffery Burchard, Florida #108/R

ATRA, Kaarlo (20th C) Finnish

£288 $472 €400 Street in Torneaa (33x46cm-13x18in) s.d.1926. 4-Jun-3 Bukowskis, Helsinki #244/R

ATSCHKO (20th C) ?

Sculpture

£1603 $2340 €2500 Composition (50x40cm-20x16in) s.d.59 bronze. 5-Jun-2 Il Ponte, Milan #155 est:2000-2500

ATTAR, Suad (1942-) Iraqi

£8500 $13515 €12750 Tender moment (181x152cm-71x60in) s.d.99 exhib. 30-Apr-3 Sotheby's, London #156/R est:8000-12000

Works on paper

£2500 $3975 €3750 Girl with dove (64x84cm-25x33in) s.d.1992 mixed media. 30-Apr-3 Sotheby's, London #158/R est:3000-5000

ATTARDI, Ugo (1923-) Italian

£962 $1510 €1500 Lovers in Rome (32x45cm-13x18in) s. paper on canvas. 23-Nov-2 Meeting Art, Vercelli #176/R
£1389 $2208 €2000 Roman evening (30x40cm-12x16in) s. 1-May-3 Meeting Art, Vercelli #529
£1528 $2429 €2200 Nude (40x30cm-16x12in) s. 1-May-3 Meeting Art, Vercelli #358
£1807 $2891 €2620 Sll. with wine, fish and flowers (30x40cm-12x16in) s. board. 11-Mar-3 Babuino, Rome #370/R
£1923 $3019 €3000 Along the Tiber (30x40cm-12x16in) s. 21-Nov-2 Finarte, Rome #232
£2436 $3824 €3800 The Tiber turning (50x70cm-20x28in) s.d.979. 21-Nov-2 Finarte, Rome #217/R
£2452 $3874 €3800 Landscape (65x95cm-26x37in) s.d.40 prov. 18-Dec-2 Christie's, Rome #76/R
£3117 $4988 €4520 Vicky (30x39cm-12x15in) s. board. 11-Mar-3 Babuino, Rome #249/R
£3226 $5097 €5000 Melba (115x95cm-45x37in) s.d.972 s.i.d.verso prov.exhib. 18-Dec-2 Christie's, Rome #162/R
£3404 $5515 €4800 Nudo di donna (50x70cm-20x28in) s. 26-May-3 Christie's, Milan #128/R est:3000-4000

ATTERSEE, Christian Ludwig (1940-) Austrian

£1377 $2258 €1900 A glass horse (62x44cm-24x17in) s.i.d.88 acrylic col chk board. 28-May-3 Lempertz, Koln #16/R est:1800
£2025 $3200 €3200 Washing the tongue stone (44x31cm-17x12in) s.i.d.74 acrylic varnish casein W/C Indian ink board. 27-Nov-2 Dorotheum, Vienna #318/R est:3200-4500
£2848 $4500 €4500 Resting (62x43cm-24x17in) s.i.d.91 acrylic varnish casein col chk pen pencil chl board. 27-Nov-2 Dorotheum, Vienna #319/R est:4000-5500
£2848 $4500 €4500 Night door (84x60cm-33x24in) s.i.d.87 s.i.d. verso acrylic varnish casein chk board prov. 27-Nov-2 Dorotheum, Vienna #322/R est:4500-6000
£10759 $17000 €17000 Rascalwith lemon (105x80cm-41x31in) s.i.d.77 acrylic varnish col chk chl exhib. 27-Nov-2 Dorotheum, Vienna #284/R est:16000-24000

Works on paper

£414 $662 €600 Sekt boat (30x21cm-12x8in) s.i.d.86 pencil gouache. 11-Mar-3 Dorotheum, Vienna #259/R
£1026 $1621 €1600 Two magical forks (44x31cm-17x12in) s.i.d.72 casein pencil chl board. 12-Nov-2 Dorotheum, Vienna #240/R est:2300-4500
£1517 $2428 €2200 Cat weather (42x60cm-17x24in) s.i. mixed media. 11-Mar-3 Dorotheum, Vienna #230/R est:1800-2200
£1517 $2428 €2200 Jewellery soup (42x60cm-17x24in) s.i. mixed media. 11-Mar-3 Dorotheum, Vienna #232/R est:1800-2200
£1655 $2648 €2400 Flesh light (42x60cm-17x24in) s.i. mixed media. 11-Mar-3 Dorotheum, Vienna #231/R est:1800-2200
£3165 $4905 €5000 Cats (46x44cm-18x17in) mono.i.d.1969 verso mixed media board lit. 24-Sep-2 Wiener Kunst Auktionen, Vienna #241/R est:5000-7500

ATTERSEE, Christian Ludwig (attrib) (1940-) Austrian

Works on paper

£696 $1086 €1100 Geometric composition (70x30cm-28x12in) s.d.83 mixed media collage wood relief lit. 14-Sep-2 Bergmann, Erlangen #771/R

ATTWELL, Mabel Lucie (1879-1964) British

Works on paper

£290 $464 €435 Cartoon of a little girl upset at having all her hair off (23x18cm-9x7in) s. W/C. 10-Jan-3 Biddle & Webb, Birmingham #165
£1200 $1908 €1800 An you know what men are (30x25cm-12x10in) s. pencil W/C. 4-May-3 Lots Road, London #345/R est:400-600
£1300 $2067 €1950 Bride, God bless her, the bridegroom, God bless him (26x23cm-10x9in) s. pencil W/C. 4-May-3 Lots Road, London #346/R est:300-500

ATTWELL, Mabel Lucie (attrib) (1879-1964) British
Works on paper
£320 $458 €480 Wig wam (35x27cm-14x11in) pencil W/C. 28-Feb-2 Greenslade Hunt, Taunton #402/R

ATTWOOD, Thomas Reginald (1865-1926) New Zealander
£281 $446 €422 Lake Manapouri (49x65cm-19x26in) s. 25-Feb-3 Peter Webb, Auckland #39 (NZ.D 800)
£424 $683 €636 Lake scene with boat (49x90cm-19x35in) s. 7-May-3 Dunbar Sloane, Auckland #101 (NZ.D 1200)
£608 $948 €912 Near Tiahape (75x49cm-30x19in) s.i. 17-Sep-2 Peter Webb, Auckland #154/R est:1200-2200 (NZ.D 2000)
Works on paper
£339 $529 €509 Coastal landscape (44x90cm-17x35in) s. 6-Aug-2 Peter Webb, Auckland #105/R est:1000-2000 (NZ.D 1150)

ATWOOD, Clare (1866-1962) British
£1200 $1932 €1800 Market day (76x60cm-30x24in) s. 18-Feb-3 Bonhams, Knightsbridge #29/R est:1200-1800

ATWOOD, Robert (1892-?) American
£234 $375 €339 Mountain landscape, spring (40x50cm-16x20in) s. board. 16-May-3 Skinner, Boston #225/R

ATYEO, Sam (1911-1990) Australian
Works on paper
£374 $569 €561 Abstract (39x27cm-15x11in) s. W/C. 28-Aug-2 Deutscher-Menzies, Melbourne #429/R (A.D 1045)
£518 $849 €777 Hot Saturday afternoon Toorak Road (47x60cm-19x24in) s. W/C exec.c.1933-39. 4-Jun-3 Deutscher-Menzies, Melbourne #367/R (A.D 1300)

AUBANEL, Jean Philippe (1953-) French
£338 $527 €500 Untitled (80x120cm-31x47in) acrylic paper on canvas. 30-Mar-3 Anaf, Lyon #317

AUBERJONOIS, René (1872-1957) Swiss
£522 $809 €783 Three jockeys on horses (20x18cm-8x7in) mono.i. pencil. 9-Dec-2 Philippe Schuler, Zurich #3510 (S.FR 1200)
£7075 $11462 €12524 Petit tetras (48x44cm-19x17in) s. lit. 26-May-3 Sotheby's, Zurich #81/R est:15000-20000 (S.FR 15000)
Works on paper
£292 $461 €438 Mother and child (31x26cm-12x10in) mono. pencil prov. 26-Nov-2 Hans Widmer, St Gallen #1025 (S.FR 680)
£343 $542 €515 Young lady sitting at her dressing table (36x24cm-14x9in) s. i.verso pencil paper on board exhib. 26-Nov-2 Hans Widmer, St Gallen #1022 (S.FR 800)
£408 $644 €612 Trainer with predator (33x24cm-13x9in) mono.d.1930 pencil prov. 26-Nov-2 Hans Widmer, St Gallen #1021 (S.FR 950)
£429 $678 €644 Grape harvest I - vine-grower by horse and wagon with transport barrel (20x14cm-8x6in) mono. pencil. 26-Nov-2 Hans Widmer, St Gallen #1024 (S.FR 1000)
£472 $746 €708 Grape harvest II - vine-grower at opening of transport barrel (16x13cm-6x5in) mono. pencil prov. 26-Nov-2 Hans Widmer, St Gallen #1023 (S.FR 1100)
£880 $1416 €1320 Reclining girl (24x35cm-9x14in) s.d.1936 pencil prov. 7-May-3 Dobiaschofsky, Bern #1410/R (S.FR 1900)
£961 $1499 €1442 Last round (23x18cm-9x7in) mono.i.d.98 pencil. 6-Nov-2 Dobiaschofsky, Bern #1361/R est:2200 (S.FR 2200)

AUBERT, Jean Ernest (1824-1906) French
£2927 $4800 €4244 Le concert mysterieux (68x45cm-27x18in) s.d.1888. 4-Jun-3 Christie's, Rockefeller NY #225/R est:4000-6000

AUBERTIN, Bernard (1934-) French
£380 $589 €600 La lumiere de la matiere-couleur (22x12cm-9x5in) s.i.d.verso. 28-Sep-2 Cornette de St.Cyr, Paris #245/R
£380 $589 €600 La lumiere de la matiere-couleur (22x12cm-9x5in) s.i.d.verso. 28-Sep-2 Cornette de St.Cyr, Paris #246/R
£1761 $2730 €2800 Clous (100x100cm-39x39in) s.i.d.1960/1976 verso clous acrylic panel. 30-Oct-2 Artcurial Briest, Paris #459/R est:2500-3000
£2756 $4328 €4300 Monochrome rouge (150x75cm-59x30in) s.i.d.1974 prov. 15-Dec-2 Perrin, Versailles #135/R
£3712 $5828 €5568 Monchrome grillage rouge (102x52cm-40x20in) s.i.d.1987 verso acrylic over metal mesh on panel prov. 23-Nov-2 Burkhard, Luzern #48/R est:8000-10000 (S.FR 8500)
Works on paper
£440 $687 €700 Tableau de feu (44x44cm-17x17in) mixed media matches cardboard exec.c.1960. 11-Oct-2 Binoche, Paris #151
£440 $687 €700 Tableau de feu (64x49cm-25x19in) mixed media matches cardboard. 11-Oct-2 Binoche, Paris #152
£577 $906 €900 Semema (100x700cm-39x276in) s.i.d. red gouache brulure. 16-Dec-2 Charbonneaux, Paris #113
£1081 $1686 €1600 Dessin de feu (70x100cm-28x39in) matches collage exec.1974. 26-Mar-3 Finarte Semenzato, Milan #98/R

AUBERY, Jean (1880-?) French
£1419 $2243 €2200 Paysage provencal (46x55cm-18x22in) s. 19-Dec-2 Claude Aguttes, Neuilly #227/R
£3000 $4620 €4500 Route de village en ete (54x65cm-21x26in) s. prov. 23-Oct-2 Sotheby's, Olympia #620/R est:800-1200

AUBINIERE, L (?) ?
£1200 $1908 €1800 Sailing at dawn (38x51cm-15x20in) s. 4-Mar-3 Bonhams, Knightsbridge #306c/R est:600-800

AUBINIERE, W L (?) ?
Works on paper
£764 $1200 €1146 San Francisco Harbour (25x33cm-10x13in) s.d.1888 grisaille board. 22-Nov-2 Eldred, East Dennis #621/R

AUBLET, Albert (1851-1938) French
£801 $1258 €1250 Tunis (46x35cm-18x14in) s.i.d.1902. 10-Dec-2 Tajan, Paris #111/R
£1923 $3019 €3000 Tunisiennes conversant (32x23cm-13x9in) s.i.d.1923 cardboard. 16-Dec-2 Gros & Delettrez, Paris #154/R est:3000-3500

AUBREY, Christopher (19th C) New Zealander
Works on paper
£2456 $3832 €3684 View from Marsden Hill, New Plymouth (22x38cm-9x15in) s.d.1896 W/C. 27-Mar-3 International Art Centre, Auckland #88/R est:7000-12000 (NZ.D 7000)
£6897 $10759 €10346 Upper Hutt railway station circa 1890 (34x55cm-13x22in) s W/C. 7-Nov-2 International Art Centre, Auckland #72/R est:30000-40000 (NZ.D 22000)
£8150 $12715 €12225 Diamond lake, Pigeon Island, Lake Wanaka (42x66cm-17x26in) s.d.1886 W/C. 7-Nov-2 International Art Centre, Auckland #101/R est:15000-25000 (NZ.D 26000)
£8150 $12715 €12225 Lake Manapouri (37x65cm-15x26in) s.d.1888 W/C. 7-Nov-2 International Art Centre, Auckland #102/R est:15000-25000 (NZ.D 26000)
£9646 $14952 €14469 Clifdene Station on the Waiau River, Southland (37x62cm-15x24in) s.d.1881 W/C prov. 4-Dec-2 Dunbar Sloane, Auckland #59/R est:20000-30000 (NZ.D 30000)
£12539 $19561 €18809 Wellington City with old Government buildings (44x75cm-17x30in) s.d.1888 W/C. 7-Nov-2 International Art Centre, Auckland #71/R est:35000-45000 (NZ.D 40000)

AUBRY, Étienne (attrib) (1745-1781) French
Works on paper
£709 $1184 €1000 Le retour de fils indigne (37x50cm-15x20in) brown ink wash black crayon. 19-Jun-3 Piasa, Paris #146/R

AUBRY, Louis François (1767-1851) French
Miniatures
£1282 $2026 €2000 Napoleon en buste (9x7cm-4x3in) s. oval. 17-Nov-2 Osenat, Fontainebleau #239

AUBURTIN, Jean François (1866-1930) French
£2113 $3401 €3000 Belle-Ile, la cote sauvage (36x52cm-14x20in) s. 11-May-3 Thierry & Lannon, Brest #131/R est:2500-3000
Works on paper
£833 $1308 €1300 Domois (32x50cm-13x20in) mono.i. gouache. 15-Dec-2 Thierry & Lannon, Brest #70
£833 $1308 €1300 Rochers pres de Donnant (32x50cm-13x20in) mono. gouache. 15-Dec-2 Thierry & Lannon, Brest #76
£897 $1409 €1400 Soleil couchant (32x50cm-13x20in) mono. gouache. 15-Dec-2 Thierry & Lannon, Brest #71
£897 $1409 €1400 Etude pour voilier rouge (31x50cm-12x20in) mono. gouache. 15-Dec-2 Thierry & Lannon, Brest #77
£962 $1510 €1500 Cote sauvage (32x50cm-13x20in) mono. gouache. 15-Dec-2 Thierry & Lannon, Brest #74
£1197 $1927 €1700 Paysage de Bretagne au voilier (27x73cm-11x29in) mono. gouache. 11-May-3 Thierry & Lannon, Brest #110 est:1200-1500
£1218 $1912 €1900 Soleil rose a Donnant (32x50cm-13x20in) i.verso gouache. 15-Dec-2 Thierry & Lannon, Brest #75
£1282 $2013 €2000 Plage des Grands Sables (32x50cm-13x20in) mono. gouache. 15-Dec-2 Thierry & Lannon, Brest #72

£1303 $2098 €1850 Envolee d'oiseaux sur une plage de Belle-lle (39x75cm-15x30in) mono. gouache. 11-May-3 Thierry & Lannon, Brest #109/R est:1200-1500
£1444 $2324 €2050 Trois sinagots dans le Golfe du Morbihan (27x73cm-11x29in) mono. gouache. 11-May-3 Thierry & Lannon, Brest #111/R est:1200-1500
£1474 $2315 €2300 Effet de lumiere a Donnant (31x50cm-12x20in) mono. gouache. 15-Dec-2 Thierry & Lannon, Brest #73

AUDEGEM, Clothilde van den (?) Belgian?
£290 $475 €400 Fleurs (34x26cm-13x10in) s. 27-May-3 Campo, Vlaamse Kaai #232

AUDENAERT, August (1842-1953) Belgian
£1233 $1936 €1800 Les poivrots (104x80cm-41x31in) s. canvas laid down. 15-Apr-3 Galerie Moderne, Brussels #375 est:1500-2000

AUDETTE, Yvonne (1930-) Australian
£1724 $2707 €2586 Moving symbols no.1 (122x155cm-48x61in) init. board. 15-Apr-3 Lawson Menzies, Sydney #231/R est:5000-8000 (A.D 4500)
£3295 $5238 €4943 Bathers No 2 (117x152cm-46x60in) s.d.2001 s.i.d.2001 verso board prov. 5-May-3 Sotheby's, Melbourne #210/R est:5000-8000 (A.D 8500)
£3571 $5643 €5357 Balancing (86x101cm-34x40in) init.d.78 i.d.verso. 26-Nov-2 Sotheby's, Melbourne #41/R est:15000-20000 (A.D 10000)
£6071 $9471 €9107 At the World's Fair (121x85cm-48x33in) init.d.66 s.i.d.66 verso board. 11-Nov-2 Deutscher-Menzies, Melbourne #30/R est:15000-20000 (A.D 17000)
£6406 $9801 €9609 Cantata No.29 (91x76cm-36x30in) s.d.1978 i.d.verso. 25-Aug-2 Sotheby's, Paddington #59/R est:12000-18000 (A.D 18000)

AUDOUIN, Louis (1883-1968) French
£1399 $2336 €2000 Sale, Bab Mrisa, porte du Mellah (40x50cm-16x20in) s.i. panel exhib. 27-Jun-3 Claude Aguttes, Neuilly #145/R est:1500-2000

AUDUBON, J J (1785-1851) American/French
Prints
£6507 $9500 €9761 Summer or wood duck. handcol aquatint. 3-Nov-1 North East Auctions, Portsmouth #746/R est:5000-7000

AUDUBON, John James (1785-1851) American/French
Prints
£2303 $3500 €3455 Elephant folio of moose. hand col lithograph. 30-Aug-2 Thomaston Place, Thomaston #91
£3526 $5500 €5289 White crowned pigeon (58x69cm-23x27in) num.36 executed c.1833. 30-Mar-3 Simpson's, Houston #450
£4605 $7000 €6908 Golden Eagle (94x64cm-37x25in) handcol aquatint prov. 17-Aug-2 North East Auctions, Portsmouth #43/R est:7000-10000
£14474 $22000 €21711 Ivory billed woodpecker. num.14 handcol aquatint. 17-Aug-2 North East Auctions, Portsmouth #41/R est:7000-10000
£17105 $26000 €25658 Brown pelican (99x64cm-39x25in) handcol aquatint. 17-Aug-2 North East Auctions, Portsmouth #38/R

AUDUBON, John James (after) (1785-1851) American/French
Prints
£4114 $6500 €6171 Belted kingfisher (62x54cm-24x21in) hand col engraving. 22-Apr-3 Butterfields, San Francisco #2002/R est:6000-8000
£4114 $6500 €6171 Great Cinerous Owl (99x67cm-39x26in) hand col engraving. 22-Apr-3 Butterfields, San Francisco #2006/R est:6000-8000
£4630 $7500 €6714 American black bear (55x68cm-22x27in) col lithograph. 23-May-3 Freeman, Philadelphia #491/R est:2500-4000
£7453 $12000 €11180 REd shouldered hawk (97x65cm-38x26in) hand col aquatint engraving by R Havell. 16-Jan-3 Sotheby's, New York #51/R est:12000-15000
£8176 $13000 €12264 American robin (99x66cm-39x26in) hand col engraving aquatint. 29-Apr-3 Doyle, New York #53/R est:6000-8000
£16770 $27000 €25155 Purple heron (56x87cm-22x34in) hand col aquatint engraving by R Havell. 16-Jan-3 Sotheby's, New York #59/R est:20000-30000
£20186 $32500 €30279 Blue crane or heron. Scarlet ibis (62x94cm-24x37in) hand col aquatint engraving two. 16-Jan-3 Sotheby's, New York #62/R est:25000-30000
£24845 $40000 €37268 Ivory billed woodpecker (97x65cm-38x26in) hand col aquatint engraving by R Havell. 16-Jan-3 Sotheby's, New York #54/R est:40000-60000
£29503 $47500 €44255 Mallard duck (59x91cm-23x36in) hand col aquatint engraving by R Havell. 16-Jan-3 Sotheby's, New York #57/R est:40000-60000
£34161 $55000 €51242 Carolina parrot (84x60cm-33x24in) hand col engraving aquatint by R Havell. 16-Jan-3 Sotheby's, New York #50/R est:40000-60000
£34161 $55000 €51242 Brown pelican (97x65cm-38x26in) hand col aquatint engraving by R Havell. 16-Jan-3 Sotheby's, New York #58/R est:50000-70000
£35714 $57500 €53571 Roseate spoonbill (56x90cm-22x35in) hand col aquatint engraving by R Havell. 16-Jan-3 Sotheby's, New York #63/R est:40000-60000
£35714 $57500 €53571 Common American swan (65x97cm-26x38in) hand col etching engraving aquatint by R Havell. 16-Jan-3 Sotheby's, New York #65/R est:50000-60000

AUDY, Jonny (19th C) French
Works on paper
£300 $489 €435 Bay racing horse with jockey up (38x61cm-15x24in) s.d.69 W/C. 16-Jul-3 Sotheby's, Olympia #29/R
£449 $696 €700 Chevaux sautant l'obstacle (13x20cm-5x8in) W/C. 4-Dec-2 Libert, Castor, Paris #33
£513 $795 €800 Cavalier et chevaux (14x26cm-6x10in) s. W/C. 4-Dec-2 Piasa, Paris #123
£1603 $2452 €2500 Course, saut de haies (70x131cm-28x52in) s. W/C. 23-Aug-2 Deauville, France #93/R

AUER, Grigor (1882-1967) Finnish
£340 $541 €500 Carelian (60x47cm-24x19in) s.d.1946. 27-Feb-3 Hagelstam, Helsinki #906
£354 $562 €520 Landscape (40x50cm-16x20in) s.d.1929. 27-Feb-3 Hagelstam, Helsinki #810
£418 $652 €660 By the bonfire (58x83cm-23x33in) s. 12-Sep-2 Hagelstam, Helsinki #914/R
£444 $729 €680 Spring (46x61cm-18x24in) s.d.1939. 9-Feb-3 Bukowskis, Helsinki #197/R
£845 $1361 €1200 By the blazing fire (58x85cm-23x33in) s. 10-May-3 Bukowskis, Helsinki #41/R
£1223 $1957 €1700 Beach in winter, Barosund (41x61cm-16x24in) s.d.1919 board. 17-May-3 Hagelstam, Helsinki #130/R est:1000

AUER, Robert (1873-1952) Austrian
£3789 $5873 €5684 Nude in the bathroom (214x113cm-84x44in) painted 1909. 3-Dec-2 SOGA, Bratislava #144/R est:70000 (SL.K 240000)

AUERBACH, Arnold (1898-1978) British
Works on paper
£1400 $2184 €2100 Golden angel (49x38cm-19x15in) s. W/C. 18-Sep-2 Cheffins Grain & Comins, Cambridge #480/R est:300-400

AUERBACH, Frank (1931-) British/German
£42000 $70140 €60900 J.Y.M seated (39x38cm-15x15in) painted 1991 prov. 27-Jun-3 Christie's, London #189/R est:30000-40000
£45000 $75150 €65250 Head of Gerda Boehm (71x61cm-28x24in) board prov. 26-Jun-3 Sotheby's, London #229/R est:35000-45000
£60000 $92400 €90000 Julia (81x81cm-32x32in) acrylic on board prov.exhib.lit. 23-Oct-2 Christie's, London #102/R est:60000-80000
£240000 $400800 €360000 Primrose Hill Summer (122x122cm-48x48in) i.d.1968 verso panel prov.exhib.lit. 26-Jun-3 Christie's, London #18/R est:180000-220000
£350000 $584500 €525000 Looking towards Mornington Crescent Station - Night (127x127cm-50x50in) i.d.1972-3 verso board prov.exhib.lit. 25-Jun-3 Sotheby's, London #44/R est:180000-250000

Works on paper
£950 $1511 €1425 Study for the studios (21x25cm-8x10in) ink chl gouache pencil. 18-Mar-3 Bonhams, Knightsbridge #4

AUFDENBLATTEN, Emil (?-1959) Swiss
£696 $1085 €1044 Mountain village in Wallis area (60x50cm-24x20in) s. board. 16-Sep-2 Philippe Schuler, Zurich #3351/R (S.FR 1600)
£696 $1085 €1044 Summer alpine landscape in Wallis area (49x60cm-19x24in) s. board. 16-Sep-2 Philippe Schuler, Zurich #3352 (S.FR 1600)
£1703 $2657 €2555 View of the Matterhorn from Blatten (40x55cm-16x22in) s. 8-Nov-2 Dobiaschofsky, Bern #102/R est:3800 (S.FR 3900)

AUGE, Philippe (1935-) French
£344 $550 €516 Composition I (55x46cm-22x18in) s. 16-Mar-3 Butterfields, San Francisco #1088
£545 $850 €818 Still life with pears and cherries (48x48cm-19x19in) s. 30-Mar-3 Susanin's, Chicago #6073/R
£823 $1300 €1235 Cherries on small table (41x33cm-16x13in) s. 22-Apr-3 Arthur James, Florida #431

AUGIZEAU, Maurice (1945-) French
£570 $889 €900 Les Sables d'Olonne (44x75cm-17x30in) s. 10-Sep-2 Vanderkindere, Brussels #401

AUGUR, David (19th C) American
Works on paper
£2564 $4000 €3846 Columns surmounted by a building, the sun and a US frigate (25x20cm-10x8in) i.d.1855 W/C ink prov. 21-Sep-2 Pook & Pook, Downington #137/R est:4000-5000
£3205 $5000 €4808 Diamond surrounded by the sun, moon, heart and trees (18x25cm-7x10in) i. W/C ink prov. 21-Sep-2 Pook & Pook, Downington #138/R est:5000-6000

AUGUST, Johann (19th C) Austrian
£1127 $1814 €1600 St Martin am Montblanc (39x63cm-15x25in) s. i. verso. 7-May-3 Michael Zeller, Lindau #615/R est:1200

AUGUSTIN, Edgar (1936-) German?
Sculpture
£1474 $2285 €2300 Girl's head (30x34x13cm-12x13x5in) si. verso. 7-Dec-2 Ketterer, Hamburg #393/R est:2500-2600
Works on paper
£256 $397 €400 Reclining nude (14x18cm-6x7in) s.d.1965 pencil. 6-Dec-2 Hauswedell & Nolte, Hamburg #32/R
£1410 $2186 €2200 Seated couple (96x57cm-38x22in) s.d.1988 pastel chk prov. 7-Dec-2 Ketterer, Hamburg #394/R est:2300-2400

AUGUSTIN, Jean Baptiste Jacques (1759-1832) French
Miniatures
£3800 $6346 €5510 Lady in a white veil (6cm-2xin) s. gilt metal mount oval exec.c.1805. 25-Jun-3 Sotheby's, Olympia #22/R est:4000-6000
£4800 $7872 €6960 Self portrait of the artist, wearing moss green coat (6x5cm-2x2in) enamel on copper rectangular. 3-Jun-3 Christie's, London #43/R est:800-1200

AUGUSTIN, Jean Baptiste Jacques (attrib) (1759-1832) French
Miniatures
£2482 $4021 €3500 La reine Marie Antoinette (6cm-2in circular) mivory gilded brass prov. 21-May-3 Piasa, Paris #279/R est:2500-3000

AUGUSTINER, Werner (1922-1986) Austrian
£1026 $1590 €1600 Red light scene (76x54cm-30x21in) s.d.69. 5-Dec-2 Dorotheum, Graz #4/R est:1100
£1410 $2186 €2200 Red light scene (135x155cm-53x61in) 5-Dec-2 Dorotheum, Graz #3/R est:2200

AUGUSTSON, Goran (1936-) Finnish
£327 $536 €500 Birds and the sea (50x60cm-20x24in) s.d.98 acrylic. 9-Feb-3 Bukowskis, Helsinki #198/R
£329 $513 €520 Cloudy (61x70cm-24x28in) s.d.96 acrylic. 15-Sep-2 Bukowskis, Helsinki #160/R
£563 $907 €800 Chinese narrative (50x60cm-20x24in) s.d.98 acrylic. 10-May-3 Bukowskis, Helsinki #218/R
£845 $1361 €1200 Dreaming composition (67x87cm-26x34in) s.d.95 acrylic. 10-May-3 Bukowskis, Helsinki #212/R
£903 $1427 €1400 Composition - Con amina (80x100cm-31x39in) s.d.1993. 19-Dec-2 Hagelstam, Helsinki #924/R
Works on paper
£288 $472 €400 Shapes (42x53cm-17x21in) s.d.82 gouache. 4-Jun-3 Bukowskis, Helsinki #249/R
£291 $454 €460 The rain fugue (90x70cm-35x28in) s.d.92 gouache. 15-Sep-2 Bukowskis, Helsinki #161/R
£582 $908 €920 From the dairy (73x81cm-29x32in) s. gouache. 12-Sep-2 Hagelstam, Helsinki #1022
£759 $1200 €1200 Composition (114x134cm-45x53in) s.d.87 gouache. 1-Dec-2 Bukowskis, Helsinki #303/R

AUJAME, Jean (1905-1965) French
£764 $1215 €1100 Paysage a la riviere (60x73cm-24x29in) s.d.58. 29-Apr-3 Artcurial Briest, Paris #280
£2083 $3292 €3000 Fenetre ouverte sur le verger (81x60cm-32x24in) s. 25-Apr-3 Piasa, Paris #47/R

AULIE, Reidar (1904-1977) Norwegian
£392 $612 €588 Sketch from a town (16x23cm-6x9in) s. panel. 23-Sep-2 Blomqvist, Lysaker #1006/R (N.KR 4600)
£436 $685 €654 Dormitory town (45x54cm-18x21in) s. panel. 25-Nov-2 Blomqvist, Lysaker #1012/R (N.KR 5000)
£518 $865 €751 Factories (63x100cm-25x39in) s. s.d.Januar 1975 verso. 18-Jun-3 Grev Wedels Plass, Oslo #153 (N.KR 6000)
£877 $1386 €1316 Sunflowers (90x75cm-35x30in) s.d.47 s.i.verso exhib. 17-Dec-2 Grev Wedels Plass, Oslo #206/R (N.KR 10000)
£1357 $2199 €2036 Man, trees and houses (57x70cm-22x28in) s. 26-May-3 Grev Wedels Plass, Oslo #23/R est:15000-20000 (N.KR 15000)
£1443 $2222 €2165 Tivoli (54x65cm-21x26in) s. painted 1960. 28-Oct-2 Blomqvist, Lysaker #1002/R est:20000-22000 (N.KR 17000)
£1644 $2597 €2466 Camping (30x41cm-12x16in) s. s.i.stretcher panel. 2-Dec-2 Blomqvist, Oslo #424/R est:18000-22000 (N.KR 19000)
£1821 $2841 €2732 Man with horse and cartfull of coal (45x70cm-18x28in) s.d.34 s.i.d. verso panel. 21-Oct-2 Blomqvist, Oslo #364/R est:20000-25000 (N.KR 21000)
£2611 $4178 €3917 Special edition (46x55cm-18x22in) s.d.51 i.verso panel exhib. 17-Mar-3 Blomqvist, Oslo #430/R est:30000-40000 (N.KR 30000)
£2715 $4398 €4073 From a ship-yard (53x96cm-21x38in) s. exhib. 26-May-3 Grev Wedels Plass, Oslo #24/R est:30000-40000 (N.KR 30000)
£5204 $8118 €7806 Starry night (110x159cm-43x63in) s.d.39. 21-Oct-2 Blomqvist, Oslo #379/R est:70000-90000 (N.KR 60000)

AULT, George C (1891-1948) American
£25806 $40000 €38709 Summer landscape (41x76cm-16x30in) s. exhib. 4-Dec-2 Sotheby's, New York #89/R est:60000-80000
£116129 $180000 €174194 Daylight at Russell's corner (46x71cm-18x28in) s.d.44 prov.exhib.lit. 5-Dec-2 Christie's, Rockefeller NY #139/R est:200000-300000

AULT, George C (attrib) (1891-1948) American
£5696 $9000 €8544 Urban transportation (61x51cm-24x20in) prov. 24-Apr-3 Shannon's, Milford #85/R est:15000-25000

AUMOND, Eugene (?) ?
£1574 $2534 €2361 In the bistro (58x73cm-23x29in) s. 7-May-3 Dobiaschofsky, Bern #330/R est:4500 (S.FR 3400)

AUMONIER, James (1832-1911) British
£323 $510 €485 Driving home the flock (36x52cm-14x20in) s.indis.d.1883. 18-Nov-2 Waddingtons, Toronto #93/R (C.D 800)
Works on paper
£440 $691 €660 Labourers return (48x74cm-19x29in) s. pencil W/C. 16-Apr-3 Christie's, Kensington #1091
£650 $1066 €975 Lady seated beside Brighton chain pier (18x25cm-7x10in) s.i.d.1896 pencil W/C. 5-Jun-3 Christie's, Kensington #844
£1100 $1837 €1595 Kingston- on-Thames (38x69cm-15x27in) s.d.1882 pencil W/C htd white. 26-Jun-3 Mellors & Kirk, Nottingham #825/R est:700-1000

AUMONT, Louis (1805-1879) Danish
£2584 $4186 €3747 Portraits of young couple (29x22cm-11x9in) s. pair. 26-May-3 Rasmussen, Copenhagen #1250/R est:30000-35000 (D.KR 27000)
£5106 $8068 €7659 Portrait of the brothers Theodor and Thorvald Damborg as children (65x55cm-26x22in) s. i.stretcher. 2-Dec-2 Rasmussen, Copenhagen #1145/R est:60000-80000 (D.KR 60000)

AURELI, Giuseppe (1858-1929) Italian
£280 $437 €420 Cardinal thoughts (36x51cm-14x20in) s.i. 7-Nov-2 Mallams, Cheltenham #329

AURILI, R (19th C) Italian
Sculpture
£6897 $11034 €10000 Nu assis sur un banc en train de mettre un bandage au pied. marble. 17-Mar-3 Amberes, Antwerp #424/R

AURILI, Richard (1854-?) Italian?
Sculpture
£1795 $2818 €2800 Homme et sirene (64cm-25in) s. marble executed with Goldscheider. 11-Dec-2 Maigret, Paris #224/R est:1700-2500

AUSLEGER, Rudolf (1897-1974) German
£2609 $4278 €3600 Still life (59x73cm-23x29in) s.d.32 board double-sided. 31-May-3 Villa Grisebach, Berlin #210/R est:4500-5500
Works on paper
£403 $636 €580 Bornholm smoking kiln (64x53cm-25x21in) s.d.1934 gouache. 26-Apr-3 Dr Lehr, Berlin #52/R

AUSTEN, Alexander (fl.1891-1909) British
£365 $569 €529 Three gentlemen in an interior (28x38cm-11x15in) s. prov. 26-Mar-3 Walker's, Ottawa #82/R (C.D 850)
£500 $775 €750 Flower girl. Fruit seller (30x20cm-12x8in) s. two. 31-Oct-2 Duke & Son, Dorchester #306a/R
£500 $800 €750 Figures in a tavern interior (26x36cm-10x14in) s. sold with a companion. 7-Jan-3 Bonhams, Knightsbridge #235/R
£565 $892 €848 Tuning the violin (46x30cm-18x12in) s. 18-Nov-2 Waddingtons, Toronto #116/R (C.D 1400)

AUSTIN, Charles Percy (1883-1948) American
£2083 $3250 €3125 Indians on horseback. 21-Sep-2 Harvey Clar, Oakland #1484

AUSTIN, E (?) British
£850 $1309 €1275 Boat house (76x127cm-30x50in) s. 5-Sep-2 Christie's, Kensington #157/R

AUSTIN, Robert Sargent (1895-1973) British
Works on paper
£340 $568 €493 White stars and lace (21x17cm-8x7in) s. i.verso W/C. 25-Jun-3 Bonhams, Bury St Edmunds #520

AUSTIN, Robert Sargent (attrib) (1895-1973) British
Works on paper
£300 $489 €450 Country church at night fall (9x12cm-4x5in) init. pencil W/C htd white. 13-Feb-3 Mellors & Kirk, Nottingham #788

AUSTIN, T (19th C) British
£2000 $3100 €3000 Leaving home (61x91cm-24x36in) s.d.1853. 3-Dec-2 Sotheby's, Olympia #149/R est:2000-3000

AUSTIN, W H (?) British?
Works on paper
£250 $360 €375 Apples and grapes (25x30cm-10x12in) W/C. 25-Apr-2 Grant, Worcester #308

AUSTIN, William Frederick (19th C) British
Works on paper
£320 $528 €464 Old silk mill, Derby (25x41cm-10x16in) s.d.1901 W/C. 3-Jul-3 Ewbank, Send #323/R
£520 $868 €754 Panoramic view of Norwich (38x79cm-15x31in) s. W/C. 20-Jun-3 Keys, Aylsham #618

AUSTRIAN SCHOOL, 16th C
£12950 $20719 €18000 Allegory of the glorification of King Maximilian II (88x128cm-35x50in) canvas on panel. 17-May-3 Lempertz, Koln #1101/R est:6000

AUSTRIAN SCHOOL, 18th C
£4268 $7000 €6402 Expulsion of Heliodorus from the temple (112x84cm-44x33in) 29-May-3 Sotheby's, New York #8/R est:8000-12000
£6323 $9990 €9800 Saint Nicolas Day (40x54cm-16x21in) exhib. 18-Dec-2 Beaussant & Lefèvre, Paris #34/R

AUSTRIAN SCHOOL, 19th C
£5033 $8104 €7500 Still life with flowers (97x72cm-38x28in) 18-Feb-3 Sotheby's, Amsterdam #320/R est:6000-8000
£8000 $13360 €12000 Young lovers (140x86cm-55x34in) 18-Jun-3 Christie's, Kensington #93/R est:8000-12000
Sculpture
£2742 $4250 €4113 Figure of a Bishop (57cm-22in) silvered gilt wood. 29-Oct-2 Sotheby's, New York #255/R est:2500-3500

AUSTRIAN, Ben (1870-1921) American
£4491 $7500 €6512 Chicks in a straw hat (30x41cm-12x16in) s.d.1920. 22-Jun-3 Freeman, Philadelphia #90/R est:3000-5000
£6748 $11000 €10122 Chicks in a straw basket with blanket (30x36cm-12x14in) s.d.1919. 16-Feb-3 Jeffery Burchard, Florida #16

AUTARD, Georges (1951-) French
Works on paper
£253 $392 €400 Tableau noir (102x130cm-40x51in) mixed media prov. 28-Sep-2 Cornette de St.Cyr, Paris #247

AUTERE, Hannes (1888-1967) Finnish
Sculpture
£1268 $2041 €1800 The boat being shipwrecked (23x34cm-9x13in) s.d.22 wood relief lit. 10-May-3 Bukowskis, Helsinki #12/R est:2000-2500
£1268 $2041 €1800 Madonna (35cm-14in) s.d.22 wood. 10-May-3 Bukowskis, Helsinki #23/R est:700-1000
£1582 $2500 €2500 In the sauna (24x28cm-9x11in) s.d.55 wood relief exhib. 1-Dec-2 Bukowskis, Helsinki #1/R est:2500-2800

AUTISSIER, Louis Marie (1772-1830) French
Miniatures
£6500 $10660 €9425 Pregnant lady seated in a wooden chair (19x12cm-7x5in) s.d. black painted wood frame rec. 3-Jun-3 Christie's, London #240/R est:4000-6000

AUTREAU, Jacques (1657-1745) French
£2564 $4026 €4000 Portraits (15x36cm-6x14in) three in one frame. 15-Dec-2 Mercier & Cie, Lille #302/R

AUTY, Charles (fl.1881-1919) British
Works on paper
£580 $864 €870 Manx cottage near Dalby (30x46cm-12x18in) s.d.1896 W/C. 28-Jun-2 Chrystals Auctions, Isle of Man #157

AUVRAY, Charles (?) ?
Sculpture
£1258 $1962 €2000 Group of smiths (57cm-22in) s. bronze. 23-Sep-2 Bernaerts, Antwerp #165 est:2500-3000

AUVRAY, Felix (1800-1833) French
£3049 $5000 €4574 L'avenement de pepin le bref au trone (54x65cm-21x26in) indis sig.d.1829 prov.lit. 29-May-3 Sotheby's, New York #143/R est:5000-7000

AUVRAY, Louis (1810-1890) French
Works on paper
£256 $405 €400 Sainte Trinite church in Paris (16x26cm-6x10in) mono.d.19 juin 1872 pen over pencil W/C prov. 16-Nov-2 Lempertz, Koln #1291/R

AUZOU, Pauline (1775-1835) French
Works on paper
£473 $738 €700 Portrait de peintre (55x45cm-22x18in) pierre noire prov. 31-Mar-3 Piasa, Paris #56
£506 $800 €800 Etude de deux femmes drapees (33x26cm-13x10in) col chk. 27-Nov-2 Christie's, Paris #175
£567 $948 €800 Portrait d'un peintre (55x45cm-22x18in) pierre noire prov. 19-Jun-3 Piasa, Paris #140
£676 $1054 €1000 Portrait d'hhomme en buste (30x23cm-12x9in) W/C over crayon oval. 27-Mar-3 Maigret, Paris #30/R
£1216 $1897 €1800 Buste d'homme (40x38cm-16x15in) chl chk. 26-Mar-3 Piasa, Paris #90

AUZOU, Pauline (attrib) (1775-1835) French
£676 $1054 €1000 Portrait de femme en buste (46x38cm-18x15in) 28-Mar-3 Piasa, Paris #54

AVALLONE, Mario (1899-?) Italian
£641 $1006 €1000 View of village (66x54cm-26x21in) s. board. 10-Dec-2 Della Rocca, Turin #340

AVALLONE, Pasquale (?) ?
£393 $625 €590 Grimavera (23x30cm-9x12in) s. painted c.1940. 4-May-3 Treadway Gallery, Cincinnati #491/R

AVANZI, Vittorio (1850-1910) Italian
£2250 $3645 €3263 Music time, Capri (104x82cm-41x32in) s.i. 26-May-3 Bukowskis, Stockholm #260/R est:20000-25000 (S.KR 29000)

AVATI, James (1912-) American
£1282 $2000 €1923 Woman standing at robotic spy, wary man with gun nearby (76x61cm-30x24in) s. masonite. 9-Nov-2 Illustration House, New York #152/R est:2500-3500

AVEDON, Richard (1923-) American
Photographs
£2761 $4500 €4142 Dorian Leigh, coat by Dior, Avenue Montaigne, Paris (45x35cm-18x14in) s.num.13/75 gelatin silver print. 12-Feb-3 Christie's, Rockefeller NY #259/R est:4000-6000
£4430 $7000 €6645 Igor Stravinsky, composer, New York City (25x61cm-10x24in) s.verso three gelatin silver print on mounted canvas prov.lit. 24-Apr-3 Phillips, New York #41/R est:10000-15000
£4747 $7500 €7121 Bellboym Eden Rock Hotel, Taormina, Sicily (12x18cm-5x7in) s.d.1947 gelatin silver print prov.lit. 24-Apr-3 Phillips, New York #174/R est:9000-12000

£6494 $10000 €9741 Natassja Kinski and the serpent (71x109cm-28x43in) s. num.85/200 photograph. 24-Oct-2 Sotheby's, New York #229/R est:10000-15000
£7362 $12000 €11043 Nastassja Kinski and the serpent, Los Angeles, California, June 14 (81x125cm-32x49in) s.num.80/200 gelatin silver print. 12-Feb-3 Christie's, Rockefeller NY #45/R est:9000-12000
£10000 $16200 €15000 Andy Warhol and members of the factory (20x25cm-8x10in) s.verso silver print 12 from edition of 15 triptych lit. 22-May-3 Sotheby's, London #142/R est:10000-15000
£10127 $16000 €15191 Dovima with elephants, evening dress by Dior, cirque d'Hiver, Paris (25x19cm-10x7in) s.num.15/100 photograph. 23-Apr-3 Sotheby's, New York #241/R est:10000-15000
£12987 $20000 €19481 Andy Warhol and members of the factory (20x76cm-8x30in) s.i.verso gelatin silver print 1 of 50 3 in one mount prov.lit. 25-Oct-2 Phillips, New York #39/R est:24000-28000
£14724 $24000 €22086 Lewis Alcindor, a basketball player (49x39cm-19x15in) s.num.5/8 s.i. verso gelatin silver print. 12-Feb-3 Christie's, Rockefeller NY #37/R est:18000-22000
£20779 $32000 €31169 Noto, Sicily (36x28cm-14x11in) s.i.d.7.14.47 num.8/13 verso gelatin silver print prov.lit. 25-Oct-2 Phillips, New York #29/R est:14000-18000
£89610 $138000 €134415 Family, work in progress. gelatin silver prints on paper 31 prov.lit. 25-Oct-2 Phillips, New York #46/R est:70000-100000

AVELEN, Johannes van den (17th C) Dutch
Prints
£20000 $32200 €30000 Garden views (53x32cm-21x13in) hand col engravings 4 double-page 39 folio. 7-May-3 Sotheby's, London #18/R est:20000-30000

AVENALI, Marcello (1912-1981) Italian
£833 $1308 €1300 Garden (57x77cm-22x30in) s. board. 21-Nov-2 Finarte, Rome #346/R

AVENDANO, Serafin de (1838-1916) Spanish
£1026 $1621 €1600 Landscape (25x15cm-10x6in) s. board. 19-Nov-2 Durán, Madrid #122/R

AVENNEVILLE, Chantel (20th C) French
£250 $395 €375 Portrait of a young boy (38x45cm-15x18in) s. 27-Nov-2 Sotheby's, Olympia #125/R

AVERCAMP, Hendrick (1585-1634) Dutch
Works on paper
£5096 $7949 €8000 Standing man watching a skating boy (13x7cm-5x3in) pen brown ink W/C prov.lit. 5-Nov-2 Sotheby's, Amsterdam #45/R est:5000-7000

AVERIN, Alexandre (1952-) Russian
£250 $388 €375 Before the dance lesson (27x22cm-11x9in) s. 8-Dec-2 John Nicholson, Haslemere #175/R
£250 $388 €375 Boy in a sailor hat (33x22cm-13x9in) s. 29-Sep-2 John Nicholson, Haslemere #185/R
£260 $403 €390 Evening on the Offing, Cannes (35x24cm-14x9in) s. 8-Dec-2 John Nicholson, Haslemere #176
£300 $465 €450 Small ships (22x33cm-9x13in) s. 8-Dec-2 John Nicholson, Haslemere #7
£300 $465 €450 In the fields of poppies (33x24cm-13x9in) s. 8-Dec-2 John Nicholson, Haslemere #177/R
£350 $543 €525 Ballerina with friends (35x27cm-14x11in) s. 8-Dec-2 John Nicholson, Haslemere #174/R
£350 $543 €525 Walking with my dog (41x33cm-16x13in) s. 8-Dec-2 John Nicholson, Haslemere #200
£377 $581 €600 By the lake (38x27cm-15x11in) s. 22-Oct-2 Durán, Madrid #687/R
£425 $659 €638 Near the delphinium bush (46x38cm-18x15in) s. 8-Dec-2 John Nicholson, Haslemere #193
£475 $736 €713 Kate with toy ships (33x24cm-13x9in) s. 29-Sep-2 John Nicholson, Haslemere #81/R
£490 $760 €735 Walk along the beach (33x22cm-13x9in) s. 8-Dec-2 John Nicholson, Haslemere #39/R
£500 $775 €750 Sunset in Antibes (38x55cm-15x22in) s. 29-Sep-2 John Nicholson, Haslemere #56
£500 $775 €750 Near the bush of blooming roses (46x38cm-18x15in) s. 29-Sep-2 John Nicholson, Haslemere #123/R
£525 $814 €788 Summer day (46x33cm-18x13in) s. 8-Dec-2 John Nicholson, Haslemere #42/R
£575 $891 €863 Near the bush of blooming roses (55x46cm-22x18in) s. 8-Dec-2 John Nicholson, Haslemere #41/R
£592 $959 €900 Girls on the beach (38x46cm-15x18in) s. 21-Jan-3 Durán, Madrid #721/R
£600 $930 €900 Pony ride (33x46cm-13x18in) s. 8-Dec-2 John Nicholson, Haslemere #40/R
£724 $1172 €1100 Beach (40x50cm-16x20in) s. exhib. 21-Jan-3 Durán, Madrid #719/R
£743 $1159 €1100 Stroll (55x38cm-22x15in) s. 25-Mar-3 Durán, Madrid #729/R
£755 $1177 €1200 Seashore (43x54cm-17x21in) s. 23-Sep-2 Durán, Madrid #698/R
£800 $1240 €1200 Near the fountain in the Luxemburg Garden (38x55cm-15x22in) s. 8-Dec-2 John Nicholson, Haslemere #37/R
£800 $1240 €1200 Thoughtful moments (46x61cm-18x24in) s. 29-Sep-2 John Nicholson, Haslemere #83/R
£850 $1318 €1275 Girls playing on the beach (38x55cm-15x22in) s. 29-Sep-2 John Nicholson, Haslemere #80/R
£855 $1386 €1300 Women by the sea (54x65cm-21x26in) s. 21-Jan-3 Durán, Madrid #720/R
£1100 $1705 €1650 Young girls on the beach (46x55cm-18x22in) s. 8-Dec-2 John Nicholson, Haslemere #38/R

AVERY, Frances (1910-) American
£854 $1400 €1238 Fireworks display (25x35cm-10x14in) s.i.d. canvasboard. 5-Jun-3 Swann Galleries, New York #3/R

AVERY, Kenneth Newell (1882-1949) American
£745 $1200 €1118 Pasadena hills (71x61cm-28x24in) s. i.verso. 18-Feb-3 John Moran, Pasadena #26

AVERY, Milton (1885-1965) American
£3205 $5000 €4808 Blue fish (14x22cm-6x9in) s.d. press board. 18-Sep-2 Swann Galleries, New York #74/R est:6000-9000
£7051 $11000 €10577 Blue portrait (41x30cm-16x12in) s.d.1949 canvasboard prov. 5-Nov-2 Arthur James, Florida #61
£18868 $30000 €28302 Avery in green beret (51x41cm-20x16in) s.d.1962 i.verso oil pencil canvasboard prov. 5-Mar-3 Sotheby's, New York #101/R est:30000-40000
£24691 $40000 €37037 Child in a red rocker (46x76cm-18x30in) s. board painted c.1940 prov. 21-May-3 Sotheby's, New York #134/R est:80000-120000
£35959 $52500 €53939 Man with three fish (61x91cm-24x36in) s. 3-Nov-1 North East Auctions, Portsmouth #751/R est:45000-65000
£56197 $79800 €84296 Woman with scarf (61x46cm-24x18in) board. 8-Aug-1 Barridorf, Portland #45/R est:60000-90000
£58642 $95000 €87963 Yellow tulips (51x41cm-20x16in) s.d.1949 prov.exhib. 21-May-3 Sotheby's, New York #11/R est:80000-120000
£64516 $100000 €96774 Nude on a yellow blanket (38x56cm-15x22in) s.d.1946 board. 5-Dec-2 Christie's, Rockefeller NY #128/R est:120000-180000
£70968 $110000 €106452 Young girl (75x46cm-30x18in) s. s.i.d.1931 verso canvas on board. 5-Dec-2 Christie's, Rockefeller NY #204/R est:50000-70000
£77419 $120000 €116129 Nude on a red stool (76x63cm-30x25in) s. s.i.d.1940 verso. 5-Dec-2 Christie's, Rockefeller NY #134/R est:100000-150000
£86420 $140000 €129630 Fish (71x91cm-28x36in) s.d.1948 prov.exhib. 21-May-3 Sotheby's, New York #133/R est:125000-175000
£90323 $140000 €135485 Aquarium (66x107cm-26x42in) s.d.1948 s.i.d.verso exhib. 5-Dec-2 Christie's, Rockefeller NY #122/R est:150000-250000
£135802 $220000 €203703 Mandolin with flowers (71x91cm-28x36in) s.d.1948 s.i.d.verso prov.exhib. 22-May-3 Christie's, Rockefeller NY #76/R est:80000-120000
£246914 $400000 €370371 Trees and shrubs (117x96cm-46x38in) s.d.1953 i.verso. 21-May-3 Sotheby's, New York #126/R est:200000-300000
£277419 $430000 €416129 Rough sea (86x112cm-34x44in) s.d.1946 s.i.d.verso. 5-Dec-2 Christie's, Rockefeller NY #129/R est:200000-300000
£401235 $650000 €601853 Bathers by river (71x91cm-28x36in) s.d.1943 s.i.d.verso prov.exhib. 22-May-3 Christie's, Rockefeller NY #75/R est:300000-500000

Prints
£1707 $2800 €2475 Study of a girl (40x25cm-16x10in) s.d. col monotype exhib. 5-Jun-3 Swann Galleries, New York #7/R est:5000-8000
£2761 $4500 €4142 Umbrella by the sea (12x18cm-5x7in) s. drypoint one of 100 exec.1948. 13-Feb-3 Christie's, Rockefeller NY #7/R

Works on paper
£1341 $2200 €1944 Seated nude, the thinker (27x20cm-11x8in) s.d. pen ink exhib. 5-Jun-3 Swann Galleries, New York #8/R est:3000-5000
£1585 $2600 €2298 Landscape study (43x35cm-17x14in) s. pen ink. 5-Jun-3 Swann Galleries, New York #4/R est:2000-3000
£4268 $7000 €6189 Reclining nude (17x28cm-7x11in) s. pen ink. 5-Jun-3 Swann Galleries, New York #6/R est:5000-8000
£15432 $25000 €23148 Hill and meadow (57x77cm-22x30in) sd.1943 i.verso W/C prov. 21-May-3 Sotheby's, New York #118/R est:25000-35000
£15432 $25000 €23148 Trees on hillside (46x60cm-18x24in) s.d.1954 i.verso W/C crayon gouache prov.exhib. 21-May-3 Sotheby's, New York #132/R est:15000-25000
£16129 $25000 €24194 Little harbour (46x30cm-18x12in) s.i.verso W/C gouache prov.exhib. 4-Dec-2 Sotheby's, New York #73/R est:20000-30000
£19355 $30000 €29033 Poor fish (57x79cm-22x31in) s.d.1948 W/C. 5-Dec-2 Christie's, Rockefeller NY #205/R est:40000-60000
£26235 $42500 €39353 Trees (46x60cm-18x24in) s.d.1956 W/C gouache pencil. 21-May-3 Sotheby's, New York #131/R est:20000-30000

£37037 $60000 €55556 Rock sitter (57x79cm-22x31in) s.d.1945 W/C prov. 21-May-3 Sotheby's, New York #117/R est:60000-80000
£61290 $95000 €91935 Moon path (66x51cm-26x20in) s.d.1957 W/C prov. 5-Dec-2 Christie's, Rockefeller NY #193/R est:40000-60000

AVI, Kenan (1951-) Israeli
Sculpture
£1111 $1767 €1600 Suffer. s.num.13/100 bronze exec.c.1979-1982. 29-Apr-3 Campo & Campo, Antwerp #2/R

AVIA, Amalia (1930-) Spanish
£1773 $2872 €2500 Bar la Rubia (40x50cm-16x20in) s. s.i.d.1980 verso panel. 20-May-3 Segre, Madrid #164/R est:2500
£4138 $6538 €6000 Patio with flowers (49x61cm-19x24in) s.d.1964 board. 1-Apr-3 Segre, Madrid #166/R

AVIAT, Jules Charles (1844-?) French
£1418 $2369 €2000 Elegante a l'eventail (117x81cm-46x32in) s.d.1894. 18-Jun-3 Piasa, Paris #2 est:1000-1500
£8000 $12720 €12000 Elegantes a l'arrivee des pecheurs dans la baie Arcachon (63x105cm-25x41in) s. 20-Mar-3 Christie's, Kensington #141/R est:8000-12000

AVLICHOS, Georgios (1842-1900) Greek
£2700 $4266 €4050 Portrait of a young man (24x19cm-9x7in) 1-Apr-3 Bonhams, New Bond Street #13 est:1500-2000

AVNER, Herve (1954-) French?
£1410 $2214 €2200 Bretonnes sur les rochers (50x65cm-20x26in) s. oil pastel. 15-Dec-2 Thierry & Lannon, Brest #222
£1410 $2214 €2200 Regards sur la mer (50x65cm-20x26in) s. oil pastel. 15-Dec-2 Thierry & Lannon, Brest #221/R
Works on paper
£775 $1247 €1100 Le Bois d'Amour (30x40cm-12x16in) pastel. 11-May-3 Thierry & Lannon, Brest #240c

AVONDO, Vittorio (attrib) (1836-1910) Italian
£943 $1453 €1500 Beach in Fiumicino (18x39cm-7x15in) i.d.1866. 28-Oct-2 Il Ponte, Milan #258/R

AVRAMIDIS, Joannis (1922-) Austrian
Sculpture
£1282 $1987 €2000 Three figures (40x25x5cm-16x10x2in) s.i. 6-Dec-2 Hauswedell & Nolte, Hamburg #33/R est:1600
£6962 $11000 €11000 Head 2 (30cm-12in) s.i. black pat.bronze. 30-Nov-2 Villa Grisebach, Berlin #357/R est:6000-7000
£51282 $79487 €80000 Large half torso (169cm-67in) brown pat.bronze exhib. 3-Dec-2 Lempertz, Koln #22/R est:60000-70000
£64189 $100135 €95000 Figures (170x85x50cm-67x33x20in) s. num.1/3 pat.bronze exhib.lit. 25-Mar-3 Wiener Kunst Auktionen, Vienna #7/R est:80000-120000

AXELSON, Axel (1854-1892) Swedish
£426 $672 €639 Church interior with figures, Lambertus church (31x20cm-12x8in) s.i.d.1878. 2-Dec-2 Rasmussen, Copenhagen #1600/R (D.KR 5000)

AXELSON, Victor (1883-1953) Swedish
£456 $711 €684 French town scene (56x46cm-22x18in) s. panel prov. 6-Nov-2 AB Stockholms Auktionsverk #673/R (S.KR 6500)
£618 $995 €927 Landscape (46x55cm-18x22in) s.d.27 panel exhib. 7-May-3 AB Stockholms Auktionsverk #736/R (S.KR 8000)
£736 $1148 €1104 View of Stockholm (65x54cm-26x21in) s.d.41 panel. 6-Nov-2 AB Stockholms Auktionsverk #654/R (S.KR 10500)
£927 $1492 €1391 Hazy sunshine over Slussen (53x45cm-21x18in) s.d.1931 panel exhib.lit. 7-May-3 AB Stockholms Auktionsverk #735/R (S.KR 12000)

AXENTOWICZ, Theodor (1859-1938) Polish
Works on paper
£1471 $2412 €2250 Young woman standing by tree (94x69cm-37x27in) s. pastel. 29-Mar-3 Dannenberg, Berlin #540/R est:800
£2553 $4264 €3600 Benediction du pain (83x68cm-33x27in) s. W/C exec.c.1900. 17-Jun-3 Claude Boisgirard, Paris #22/R est:3200-3500
£3378 $5270 €5000 Polish girl on cold winter's day (98x68cm-39x27in) s. pastel. 28-Mar-3 Dorotheum, Vienna #269/R est:5000-6000

AXILETE, Alexis (?-1931) French
£949 $1481 €1500 Jeunes filles sumbolistes (73x100cm-29x39in) s. 15-Oct-2 Regis & Thiollet, Argentuil #187

AYCOCK, Alice (1946-) American
Works on paper
£287 $450 €431 How to catch and manufacture ghosts (84x107cm-33x42in) s.i.d.1980 pencil vellum. 21-Nov-2 Swann Galleries, New York #7/R

AYER, Mary Lewis (1878-?) American
£267 $425 €401 Portrait of a seated woman (87x71cm-34x28in) s. 7-Mar-3 Skinner, Boston #581/R

AYERS, Duffy (20th C) British
£300 $468 €450 Portrait of Daphne Charlton (43x35cm-17x14in) i.verso. 15-Oct-2 Bonhams, Knightsbridge #17/R

AYLING, Albert W (?-1905) British
Works on paper
£700 $1098 €1050 Approach to Betws-Y-Coed (59x89cm-23x35in) s. W/C. 20-Nov-2 Sotheby's, Olympia #39/R

AYLING, George (1887-1960) British
£2000 $3140 €3000 London Bridge (60x72cm-24x28in) s. board. 16-Dec-2 Sotheby's, Olympia #171/R est:2000-3000

AYLWARD, James de Vine (fl.1895-1917) British
£550 $880 €825 Comrades (22x29cm-9x11in) s, panel. 11-Mar-3 Bonhams, Knightsbridge #38/R
£838 $1400 €1215 Latest news (20x13cm-8x5in) s. indis d. board. 29-Jun-3 Butterfields, Los Angeles #7030/R est:2000-3000

AYLWARD, William James (1875-1956) American
£2640 $4250 €3960 Men on rigging of ship (41x61cm-16x24in) s. oil en grisaille painted c.1905. 10-May-3 Illustration House, New York #43/R est:2500-3500

AYMOND, Philippe (20th C) French?
Works on paper
£310 $490 €450 Apocalypse mania (50x38cm-20x15in) col ink. 7-Apr-3 Claude Aguttes, Neuilly #5/R

AYO, Robert Aillaud (1926-) French
£306 $500 €459 Le bain de pieds (65x81cm-26x32in) s.d.66. 16-Feb-3 Butterfields, San Francisco #2123

AYON, L (19th C) ?
£1156 $1839 €1700 Madrid (23x50cm-9x20in) s.i. 19-Mar-3 Neumeister, Munich #502/R est:1000
£1497 $2380 €2200 Madrid (35x61cm-14x24in) s.i. 19-Mar-3 Neumeister, Munich #501/R est:1500

AYOTTE, Leo (1909-1976) Canadian
£387 $604 €581 Nature morte aux pommes de terre (20x25cm-8x10in) s. cardboard. 30-Jul-2 Iegor de Saint Hippolyte, Montreal #10 (C.D 960)
£514 $792 €771 Paysage (20x15cm-8x6in) s.d.75 cardboard. 22-Oct-2 Iegor de Saint Hippolyte, Montreal #1 (C.D 1250)
£702 $1046 €1053 Paysage a la maison (40x51cm-16x20in) s.d.67. 26-Jun-2 Iegor de Saint Hippolyte, Montreal #2 (C.D 1600)
£1355 $2114 €2033 Rue de village (40x50cm-16x20in) s.d. panel. 30-Jul-2 Iegor de Saint Hippolyte, Montreal #9 (C.D 3360)

AYRES, Donald (20th C) British
£250 $390 €375 Extensive landscape with figures, horse and cart, cattle and oasthouse (89x140cm-35x55in) s.d.69. 16-Oct-2 Mervyn Carey, Tenterden #133
£300 $468 €450 Hunting at Postbridge (30x40cm-12x16in) s. sold with print of the same. 10-Oct-2 Greenslade Hunt, Taunton #598
£1000 $1560 €1500 Captain R E Wallace in Badgeworthy (52x102cm-20x40in) s. i.verso. 10-Oct-2 Greenslade Hunt, Taunton #597/R est:800-1200

AYRES, George P and HESLER, Alexander (19th C) American
Photographs
£2057 $3250 €3086 Abraham Lincoln (68x53cm-27x21in) d.1897 oversized platinum print. 22-Apr-3 Butterfields, San Francisco #2397/R est:3000-4000

AYRES, Gillian (1930-) British
£750 $1223 €1088 Untitled - abstract (52x76cm-20x30in) s.d.73 acrylic on paper prov. 15-Jul-3 Bonhams, Knightsbridge #126/R

£1400 $2282 €2030 Untitled (89x60cm-35x24in) init. oil paper on board. 15-Jul-3 Bonhams, Knightsbridge #128/R est:600-800
£1900 $2945 €2850 Abstract composition (43x155cm-17x61in) s. board. 26-Sep-2 Lane, Penzance #170/R est:2000-3000

AYRTON, Michael (1921-1975) British
Sculpture
£1200 $1848 €1800 Alberti (30cm-12in) brown pat bronze sold with wooden base. 5-Sep-2 Christie's, Kensington #602/R est:800-1200
£1442 $2250 €2163 Head of a man (41x18x20cm-16x7x8in) bronze sold with a W/C by the same hand. 14-Oct-2 Butterfields, San Francisco #2019/R est:3000-5000
£1600 $2560 €2400 Sea figure (45cm-18in) brown pat bronze exec.1974. 15-May-3 Lawrence, Crewkerne #1005/R est:1000-1500
£1900 $3173 €2755 Afternoon (9cm-4in) num.2/12 brown pat bronze prov. 24-Jun-3 Bonhams, New Bond Street #122/R est:800-1200
£3500 $5425 €5250 Invader (38cm-15in) s.num.4/12 dark brown pat. bronze. 4-Dec-2 Christie's, Kensington #508/R est:3000-5000
£4000 $6560 €6000 Icarus fallen (41cm-16in) dark brown pat. bronze conceived 1960 lit. 6-Jun-3 Christie's, London #58/R est:3000-5000
Works on paper
£340 $537 €510 Fighting colossus, with crouching figures over heavenly forms (33x48cm-13x19in) s. pencil W/C. 12-Nov-2 Goldings, Lincolnshire #169
£448 $700 €672 Bull man (55x40cm-22x16in) s.d.19.8.63 mixed media collage. 11-Nov-2 Stephan Welz, Johannesburg #442 (SA.R 7000)
£820 $1320 €1230 Paros (23x30cm-9x12in) pencil grey wash prov. 19-Feb-3 Mallams, Oxford #380/R

AYRTON, Millicent E (?) British
£600 $942 €900 Glass table - vase of poppies, roses and daises (57x49cm-22x19in) canvasboard. 10-Dec-2 Lane, Penzance #297

AZEMA, Louis (1876-1963) French
£617 $877 €1000 Lavandieres (44x57cm-17x22in) s. 16-Mar-3 Eric Pillon, Calais #236/R

AZI, Asad (1955-) Israeli?
Works on paper
£1139 $1800 €1709 Jewish bride (105x61cm-41x24in) s.d.90 verso mixed media on canvas prov. 27-Apr-3 Sotheby's, Tel Aviv #94/R est:2000-3000

AZIZ, Abdul (1928-2002) Javanese
£3885 $6410 €5633 Nude with flowers (35x29cm-14x11in) s. 6-Jul-3 Christie's, Hong Kong #61/R est:14000-18000 (HK.D 50000)

AZPIROZ, Manuel de (1903-1953) Spanish
£662 $1079 €1000 Oriental landscape (92x73cm-36x29in) s. 11-Feb-3 Segre, Madrid #248/R

AZZAWI, Dia (1939-) Iraqi
Works on paper
£1800 $2862 €2700 Drawings consecrated to love (24x24cm-9x9in) s.d.74 pen ink W/C over pencil two in one frame. 30-Apr-3 Sotheby's, London #160/R est:2000-3000
£1800 $2862 €2700 Untitled. Man with bird (35x32cm-14x13in) s.d.1973 one s.d.72 pen ink W/C pencil pair. 30-Apr-3 Sotheby's, London #162/R est:2000-3000
£2500 $3975 €3750 Youssef Al Khal (69x49cm-27x19in) s.d.87 gouache pen ink over pencil. 30-Apr-3 Sotheby's, London #159/R est:3000-5000

AZZI, Giovanni Battista (attrib) (c.1781-1857) Italian
£1667 $2583 €2600 Hagar with Ismael in the wilderness (50x67cm-20x26in) panel. 4-Dec-2 Neumeister, Munich #580/R est:2000

AZZINARI, Franco (1949-) Italian
£380 $592 €600 Peach tree in bloom (30x20cm-12x8in) s.d.1985. 14-Sep-2 Meeting Art, Vercelli #869/R
£621 $993 €950 Cherry trees in bloom (40x25cm-16x10in) s.d.1996. 4-Jan-3 Meeting Art, Vercelli #75

BAADE, Knud Andreassen (1808-1879) Norwegian
£829 $1301 €1244 Mountain study (13x35cm-5x14in) s. panel. 25-Nov-2 Blomqvist, Lysaker #1016 (N.KR 9500)
£1837 $3012 €2664 Seascape with sailing vessel in moonlight (75x85cm-30x33in) s.d.1879. 2-Jun-3 Blomqvist, Oslo #91/R est:30000-35000 (N.KR 20000)
£3503 $5604 €5255 Summer's day in a Norwegian fjord (77x120cm-30x47in) 13-Jan-3 Rasmussen, Vejle #91/R est:40000 (D.KR 40000)
Works on paper
£341 $532 €512 Old hut, Lyngdal (12x24cm-5x9in) s. W/C pencil. 23-Sep-2 Blomqvist, Lysaker #1008 (N.KR 4000)
£752 $1226 €1128 Kaarevig (42x57cm-17x22in) s.d.1855 pencil wash. 17-Feb-3 Blomqvist, Lysaker #1010 (N.KR 8500)

BAADSGAARD, Alfrida (1839-1912) Danish
£574 $930 €832 Thistles with brown background (27x22cm-11x9in) s.indis.d.1890. 26-May-3 Rasmussen, Copenhagen #1235/R (D.KR 6000)

BAAGOE, Carl (1829-1902) Danish
£520 $837 €780 Seascape with sailing vessels off the coast of Hornbaek (32x51cm-13x20in) s.i.d.Aug.87. 11-May-3 Hindemae, Ullerslev #665/R (D.KR 5500)
£617 $994 €926 Seascape with sailing ship off the coast of Hornbaek (32x51cm-13x20in) s.i.d.aug.87. 19-Jan-3 Hindemae, Ullerslev #7445/R (D.KR 7000)
£698 $1110 €1047 Seascape with sailing vessels and steamer off Kronborg (40x64cm-16x25in) s.d.76. 10-Mar-3 Rasmussen, Vejle #455/R (D.KR 7500)
£701 $1100 €1052 Ships at high sea (23x33cm-9x13in) s. canvas on board. 23-Nov-2 Jackson's, Cedar Falls #13/R
£721 $1160 €1082 Sailing vessels off Hveen (32x47cm-13x19in) s.d.1865. 22-Feb-3 Rasmussen, Havnen #2361/R (D.KR 8000)
£885 $1406 €1328 Sailing vessels at sea, cloudy day (24x34cm-9x13in) s.d.83. 5-Mar-3 Rasmussen, Copenhagen #1996/R (D.KR 9500)
£1244 $2015 €1804 Seascape with sailing ship off Kronborg (41x64cm-16x25in) s. 24-May-3 Rasmussen, Havnen #2005/R est:12000-15000 (D.KR 13000)
£1617 $2555 €2426 Seascape with view towards Hven from Humlebaek (53x69cm-21x27in) s.d.84. 2-Dec-2 Rasmussen, Copenhagen #1384/R est:20000 (D.KR 19000)
£1872 $2958 €2808 Off Helsingor Harbour (27x39cm-11x15in) s.d.1858. 2-Dec-2 Rasmussen, Copenhagen #1395/R est:20000 (D.KR 22000)
£2390 $3681 €3800 Tall ships and a steamer on open sea (61x94cm-24x37in) s.d.1882. 23-Oct-2 Christie's, Amsterdam #84/R est:2000-3000
£3002 $4683 €4503 Coastal landscape with sailing vessels, Copenhagen in background (39x61cm-15x24in) s.d.1869. 11-Nov-2 Rasmussen, Vejle #607/R est:15000 (D.KR 35000)
£3166 $5034 €4749 Calm day at Oresund towards Hven (40x62cm-16x24in) s.d.1876. 5-Mar-3 Rasmussen, Copenhagen #1563/R est:25000 (D.KR 34000)
£3172 $5043 €4758 Seascape with vessels at Sundet (69x104cm-27x41in) s.d.1891. 29-Apr-3 Kunsthallen, Copenhagen #521/R est:35000 (D.KR 34000)
£3280 $5314 €4920 Seascape off Kronborg (36x57cm-14x22in) s.d.1861. 25-Jan-3 Rasmussen, Havnen #2248/R est:8000-10000 (D.KR 37000)

BAAR-PLOMMER, Anna (1836-1890) Austrian
£577 $906 €900 Tyrolean mountain landscape (13x18cm-5x7in) s. board. 10-Dec-2 Dorotheum, Vienna #190

BABBAGE, Frank (19/20th C) British
£750 $1245 €1088 Rebecca, a bay hunter with Billy, in a stable (30x35cm-12x14in) s.d.1894 panel. 12-Jun-3 Christie's, Kensington #56/R
£3400 $5644 €4930 Beardcote Blaze, prize-winning shire horse (51x68cm-20x27in) s.d.1901. 12-Jun-3 Christie's, Kensington #83/R est:2000-3000

BABBAGE, Herbert Ivan (1875-1916) New Zealander
£700 $1169 €1015 Beached St, Ives fishing boat preparing to sail (23x27cm-9x11in) s.d.1911 canvasboard. 19-Jun-3 Lane, Penzance #15

BABBERGER, Auguste (1885-1936) German
Works on paper
£516 $847 €748 Salve Regina angels (28x36cm-11x14in) s.i.d.1934 pastel. 4-Jun-3 Fischer, Luzern #2582/R (S.FR 1100)

BABER, J (?) ?
£3200 $4992 €4800 Busy skating scene with crowds of figures on a frozen lake (45x56cm-18x22in) indis.sig. 13-Sep-2 Lyon & Turnbull, Edinburgh #125/R est:800-1200

BABOULENE, Eugène (1905-1994) French
£550 $864 €825 Interior scene with flowers in vases on a chest of drawers (41x33cm-16x13in) s. prov. 10-Dec-2 Rosebery Fine Art, London #650/R
£881 $1365 €1400 Vue de Paris (22x27cm-9x11in) s. s.i.d.1954 verso panel. 30-Oct-2 Artcurial Briest, Paris #350
£993 $1658 €1400 Bouquet printanier (33x22cm-13x9in) s. s.i.verso. 23-Jun-3 Claude Boisgirard, Paris #190

£1266 $1962 €2000 Le moulin a huile (33x41cm-13x16in) s. s.i.d.1958 verso prov. 28-Sep-2 Christie's, Paris #40/R est:2500-3000
£1418 $2369 €2000 Dejeuner (38x46cm-15x18in) s. s.i.d.verso. 23-Jun-3 Claude Boisgirard, Paris #191/R est:2200-2500
£2979 $4974 €4200 Vue de provins (60x91cm-24x36in) s.i.d.verso. 23-Jun-3 Delvaux, Paris #144/R est:4500-6000
£3143 $4966 €4715 Portrait of Moya Dyring (35x27cm-14x11in) s.i.d.1954 prov. 26-Nov-2 Sotheby's, Melbourne #148/R est:9000-12000 (A.D 8800)

BABOULET, François (1915-) French
£310 $471 €465 Fraises et cerises (22x27cm-9x11in) s. 29-Aug-2 Christie's, Kensington #41

BABUREN, Dirck van (circle) (17th C) Dutch
£5000 $7800 €7500 Denial of Saint Peter (57x85cm-22x33in) panel. 10-Apr-3 Christie's, Kensington #261/R est:6000-8000
£9434 $14717 €15000 Resurrection of Saint Lazarus (140x187cm-55x74in) 20-Sep-2 Millon & Associes, Paris #658/R est:10000-15000

BACARISAS, Gustavo (19/20th C) Spanish
£3462 $5469 €5400 Landscape (52x70cm-20x28in) s. 13-Nov-2 Ansorena, Madrid #180/R

BACCANI, Attilio (19th C) Italian
£1700 $2720 €2550 Portrait of a young boy standing in a doorway (72x49cm-28x19in) s.d.1876. 11-Mar-3 Bonhams, Knightsbridge #247/R est:2000-3000
£2323 $3670 €3600 Fruit seller (53x35cm-21x14in) s.dd.1891 board. 18-Dec-2 Finarte, Milan #112/R

BACCARINI, Lino (1893-1973) Italian
£680 $1082 €1000 Landscape with houses (50x65cm-20x26in) s. 18-Mar-3 Finarte, Milan #157/R
£692 $1065 €1100 Dancer (63x42cm-25x17in) s.d.1920 board. 28-Oct-2 Il Ponte, Milan #322

BACCI, Baccio Maria (1888-1974) Italian
£2581 $4077 €4000 Forte dei Marmi (21x42cm-8x17in) board painted 1913 lit. 18-Dec-2 Christie's, Rome #146/R
£5484 $8665 €8500 Pisa bell tower (50x35cm-20x14in) init.d. cardboard painted 1913 prov.lit. 18-Dec-2 Christie's, Rome #148/R
£6090 $9622 €9500 Summer celebrations (86x104cm-34x41in) s.d.29. 15-Nov-2 Farsetti, Prato #493/R
£10135 $15811 €15000 On the train (73x53cm-29x21in) init. cardboard on board painted 1922. 28-Mar-3 Farsetti, Prato #757/R est:11000

BACCI, Edmondo (1913-) Italian
£2179 $3400 €3269 Avvenimento no 229 (110x87cm-43x34in) s.i. i.verso prov. 14-Sep-2 Weschler, Washington #588/R est:1500-2500

BACH, Elvira (1951-) German
£2365 $3689 €3500 Untitled (100x80cm-39x31in) s.d.1986 verso acrylic. 28-Mar-3 Ketterer, Hamburg #191/R est:3500-4500
£3986 $6536 €5500 Embrace, hold tight, or (100x80cm-39x31in) s.i.d.85 verso acrylic. 31-May-3 Villa Grisebach, Berlin #393/R est:3500-4500
£6522 $10696 €9000 Untitled - I am not good, I am not cross (160x130cm-63x51in) s.d.1983 verso dispersion col. 28-May-3 Lempertz, Koln #17/R est:8000-10000

Works on paper
£949 $1500 €1500 Snake woman (88x62cm-35x24in) s.d.1982 verso gouache. 29-Nov-2 Villa Grisebach, Berlin #515/R est:2000-3000
£978 $1604 €1350 Woman with snake (42x30cm-17x12in) s.d.84 Indian ink brush W/C dispersion col chks. 31-May-3 Villa Grisebach, Berlin #734/R est:1200-1400

BACH, Florence Julia (1887-1978) American
Works on paper
£818 $1300 €1227 Portrait of my mother (102x71cm-40x28in) s.d.1916 i.verso pastel on canvas. 7-Mar-3 Skinner, Boston #309/R est:1800-2200

BACH, Guido (1828-1905) German
£700 $1113 €1050 Sphinx at Giza (49x49cm-19x19in) s.i.d.1876. 29-Apr-3 Bonhams, New Bond Street #114/R
Works on paper
£500 $830 €725 Portrait of grieving lady with figure of man behind (53x39cm-21x15in) W/C. 12-Jun-3 Hobbs Parker, Ashford #483/R

BACH, J R (19/20th C) British?
£650 $988 €975 Italian beauties (81x33cm-32x13in) one s. pair. 9-Jul-2 Capes Dunn, Manchester #780/R

BACHARACH, Herman Ilfeld (1899-1976) American
Works on paper
£621 $1000 €932 Elfin figure smoking pipe outside toadstool house (33x25cm-13x10in) s. W/C. 20-Feb-3 Illustration House, New York #7 est:1200-1800

BACHE, Otto (1839-1927) Danish
£325 $527 €488 Horses in coastal meadow (32x35cm-13x14in) s. i.verso panel study. 21-May-3 Museumsbygningen, Copenhagen #69 (D.KR 3400)
£450 $725 €675 Head of horse with harness (40x46cm-16x18in) init. study. 26-Feb-3 Museumsbygningen, Copenhagen #48/R (D.KR 5000)
£517 $786 €776 Bull (30x40cm-12x16in) s.on stretcher study painted c.1864. 27-Aug-2 Rasmussen, Copenhagen #1897/R (D.KR 6000)
£862 $1319 €1293 At end of day riding to hounds, Frijsenborg (26x42cm-10x17in) s. sketch. 24-Aug-2 Rasmussen, Havnen #2256/R (D.KR 10000)
£1397 $2221 €2096 Gundogs in action (46x37cm-18x15in) init.d.94. 5-Mar-3 Rasmussen, Copenhagen #1590/R est:15000 (D.KR 15000)
£19966 $31147 €29949 Dogs not admitted - park scene with dogs by gate (130x184cm-51x72in) s.d.1870. 5-Aug-2 Rasmussen, Vejle #118/R est:150000-200000 (D.KR 235000)
£86124 $139522 €124880 Figures in Kobmager Street, Round Tower in background (78x54cm-31x21in) s.d.1893. 26-May-3 Rasmussen, Copenhagen #1133/R est:800000 (D.KR 900000)

Works on paper
£943 $1472 €1415 Horses outside Lindenborg Inn (28x39cm-11x15in) c. chl on white painted background. 11-Nov-2 Rasmussen, Vejle #461/R (D.KR 11000)

BACHELIER, Charles Claude (fl.1834-1852) French
Prints
£6500 $10530 €9750 Panorama of the city of St. Peterburg (40x23cm-16x9in) col lithograph after Josef Bernardazzi. 21-May-3 Sotheby's, London #5/R est:3000-5000

BACHELIER, Jean Jacques (studio) (1724-1806) French
£3103 $4966 €4500 Cheval et loup (88x115cm-35x45in) prov. 11-Mar-3 Christie's, Paris #246/R

BACHELIN, Auguste (1830-1890) Swiss
£873 $1362 €1310 Bank of Neuenburg lake near Marin (28x55cm-11x22in) mono. 8-Nov-2 Dobiaschofsky, Bern #13/R (S.FR 2000)

BACHELIN, Auguste (attrib) (1830-1890) Swiss
£568 $886 €852 Resting at the top (26x53cm-10x21in) mono. board on panel. 6-Nov-2 Dobiaschofsky, Bern #323/R (S.FR 1300)

BACHEM, Bele (1916-) German
£481 $702 €750 Grandfather with child (20x18cm-8x7in) mixed media. 4-Jun-2 Karl & Faber, Munich #169
Works on paper
£513 $749 €800 Girl with flowers (29x23cm-11x9in) s. mixed media. 4-Jun-2 Karl & Faber, Munich #165/R
£962 $1404 €1500 Two girls walking (17x22cm-7x9in) s.d.1941 mixed media. 4-Jun-2 Karl & Faber, Munich #166/R est:1200
£962 $1404 €1500 Girl with dog in music room (23x17cm-9x7in) s.d.1944 mixed media. 4-Jun-2 Karl & Faber, Munich #168/R est:1200
£1154 $1788 €1800 Girl with butterfly metamorphosis (103x39cm-41x15in) s. pastel. 5-Dec-2 Schopman, Hamburg #552 est:2000
£1603 $2340 €2500 Circus scene with dancers (27x28cm-11x11in) s.d.1943 mixed media. 4-Jun-2 Karl & Faber, Munich #167/R est:1800

BACHER, Hugo (19th C) American
£938 $1500 €1407 Interior scene (66x91cm-26x36in) 17-May-3 Pook & Pook, Downington #273/R est:800-1200

BACHER, Otto Henry (1856-1909) American
Works on paper
£391 $610 €587 Untitled (30x41cm-12x16in) pastel. 28-Mar-3 Aspire, Cleveland #75/R

BACHIS, Lidia (1969-) Italian
Works on paper
£392 $627 €600 Lola at sunset (75x50cm-30x20in) s.i.d.2001 mixed media on canvas. 4-Jan-3 Meeting Art, Vercelli #95

BACHLIN, J J (18th C) Swiss?
Works on paper
£2318 $3592 €3477 Brugg (31x52cm-12x20in) s.d. W/C pen. 3-Oct-2 Koller, Zurich #3219 est:5000-7000 (S.FR 5400)

BACHMANN, Adolphe (19/20th C) Swiss
£258 $408 €400 Bouquet de roses (35x27cm-14x11in) s. panel. 19-Dec-2 Delvaux, Paris #54
£629 $975 €1000 Woodland lake - upper Bavaria (40x52cm-16x20in) s.i.d.1909 verso canvas on board. 29-Oct-2 Dorotheum, Vienna #179/R
£2397 $3764 €3500 Vue de Venise (46x61cm-18x24in) s. 21-Apr-3 Rabourdin & Choppin de Janvry, Paris #65/R est:3500-4000

BACHMANN, Alfred (1863-1954) German
£292 $455 €438 Landscape from Skagen with thatched houses (36x60cm-14x24in) s.d.1902. 11-Nov-2 Rasmussen, Vejle #528 (D.KR 3400)
£2885 $4529 €4500 Vue de la Corne d'Or (26x40cm-10x16in) s. panel. 16-Dec-2 Gros & Delettrez, Paris #475 est:4500-5000

BACHMANN, Edwin (1900-1960) Swiss
£870 $1348 €1305 Walensee seen from Niederurnen (90x115cm-35x45in) s.d.1941 i. verso. 9-Dec-2 Philippe Schuler, Zurich #3802 (S.FR 2000)
£1073 $1695 €1610 Walensee with Alvier chain of mountains (60x80cm-24x31in) s. 26-Nov-2 Hans Widmer, St Gallen #1027/R est:1800-3200 (S.FR 2500)

BACHMANN, Gustav (20th C) Danish
£409 $645 €614 Two girls from Fano chatting by the kitchen door (66x51cm-26x20in) s.i. 2-Dec-2 Rasmussen, Copenhagen #1606 (D.KR 4800)

BACHMANN, Hans (1852-1917) Swiss
£365 $576 €548 Farewell walk (69x50cm-27x20in) 29-Nov-2 Zofingen, Switzerland #2780 (S.FR 850)
£415 $647 €623 Armour (21x15cm-8x6in) mono. board prov.lit. 9-Nov-2 Galerie Gloggner, Luzern #17 (S.FR 950)
£515 $814 €773 Old part of the village of Brienz with church (32x24cm-13x9in) board lit. 29-Nov-2 Zofingen, Switzerland #2779 (S.FR 1200)
£1659 $2622 €2489 Going to a christening in the Bernese Oberland in winter (46x41cm-18x16in) board. 14-Nov-2 Stuker, Bern #56/R est:4400-4800 (S.FR 3800)
£3009 $4845 €4514 Afternoon nap (33x24cm-13x9in) s. 7-May-3 Dobiaschofsky, Bern #331/R est:6500 (S.FR 6500)
£10480 $16349 €15720 Farm workers near the haystacks (65x100cm-26x39in) s.i. exhib. 8-Nov-2 Dobiaschofsky, Bern #60/R est:27000 (S.FR 24000)
£13100 $20568 €19650 Journey to the christening (107x151cm-42x59in) s. 25-Nov-2 Sotheby's, Zurich #122/R est:7000-9000 (S.FR 30000)

BACHMANN, Karl (1874-1924) Hungarian
£1135 $1771 €1703 Still life with writing materials on table (15x21cm-6x8in) s. panel. 20-Nov-2 Fischer, Luzern #1173/R est:2500-3500 (S.FR 2600)

BACHMANN, Max (1862-1921) American
Sculpture
£3185 $5000 €4778 Bust of an American Indian (58cm-23in) s.d.1902 brown pat bronze. 19-Nov-2 Butterfields, San Francisco #8122/R est:4000-6000

BACHMANN, Otto (1915-1996) Swiss
£395 $624 €593 Travellers at the warehouse fire (29x35cm-11x14in) board. 26-Nov-2 Hans Widmer, St Gallen #1028 (S.FR 920)
£610 $1000 €885 Harlequin and madchen in white (91x61cm-36x24in) s.d.1958 masonite. 4-Jun-3 Doyle, New York #8 est:1000-1500
£742 $1158 €1113 Fortune-tellers (33x26cm-13x10in) mono.d.39 s.verso canvas on board. 8-Nov-2 Dobiaschofsky, Bern #226/R (S.FR 1700)
£759 $1200 €1139 Woman adorned with roses (58x30cm-23x12in) s.d.1958 masonite. 2-Apr-3 Doyle, New York #9/R
£1659 $2605 €2489 Convalescent (100x81cm-39x32in) s.d.1955. 25-Nov-2 Sotheby's, Zurich #144/R est:2500-4500 (S.FR 3800)
Works on paper
£665 $1051 €998 Young girl (40x32cm-16x13in) s.d.1946 pencil dr. 29-Nov-2 Zofingen, Switzerland #2781 est:800 (S.FR 1550)

BACHMANN, Rudolf (1877-1933) Austrian
£912 $1423 €1450 Medieval city in the snow (100x73cm-39x29in) s. 9-Oct-2 Michael Zeller, Lindau #621/R

BACHRACH-BAREE, Emmanuel (1863-1943) Austrian
£253 $392 €400 Smoking break - officer smoking by fortress (35x45cm-14x18in) s. 26-Sep-2 Neumeister, Munich #2688
£519 $774 €800 Two men on horseback speaking to shepherdess (16x21cm-6x8in) s.i. verso panel. 26-Jun-2 Neumeister, Munich #676/R

BACHTIGER, Augustin Meinrad (1888-1971) Swiss
£343 $542 €515 Gossau with view of Andreas church (40x45cm-16x18in) s.d.43 board double-sided. 26-Nov-2 Hans Widmer, St Gallen #1029 (S.FR 800)

BACK, Admiral Sir George (1796-1878) British
Works on paper
£3000 $4770 €4500 Lower view of the Ramparts from Hareskin River (12x19cm-5x7in) s.i.d.June 20 1826 W/C set of three. 29-Apr-3 Bonhams, New Bond Street #178/R est:800-1200

BACK, Yngve (1904-1990) Finnish
£329 $513 €520 Midsummer Night (36x48cm-14x19in) s.d.38. 15-Sep-2 Bukowskis, Helsinki #171/R
£392 $643 €600 Archipelago (65x81cm-26x32in) s.d.85. 9-Feb-3 Bukowskis, Helsinki #205/R
£423 $680 €600 Mid summer (99x119cm-39x47in) s. 10-May-3 Bukowskis, Helsinki #263/R
£612 $1003 €850 Selling in the market (59x89cm-23x35in) s.d.85. 4-Jun-3 Bukowskis, Helsinki #264/R

BACKER, Jacob Adriaensz (1608-1651) Dutch
£4317 $6906 €6000 Salome with the head of St John the Baptist (97x116cm-38x46in) prov. 17-May-3 Lempertz, Koln #1001/R est:8000

BACKER, Jacob de (1560-c.1590) Flemish
£15723 $24371 €25000 Saint Peter's liberation (72x105cm-28x41in) board. 7-Oct-2 Ansorena, Madrid #6/R est:23000
£16352 $25346 €26000 The Last Judgement (223x266cm-88x105in) 2-Oct-2 Dorotheum, Vienna #115/R est:30000-35000

BACKER, Jacob de (attrib) (1560-c.1590) Flemish
£15000 $23550 €22500 Allegory of Music (105x80cm-41x31in) panel. 11-Dec-2 Christie's, London #25/R est:25000

BACKER, Jacob de (circle) (1560-c.1590) Flemish
£9000 $14040 €13500 Virgin and Child wiith Saint Catherine (116x86cm-46x34in) panel prov. 9-Apr-3 Christie's, London #15/R est:10000-15000

BACKHOUSE, John Philamon (1845-1905) New Zealander
£878 $1369 €1317 Whares and Wakanui (15x22cm-6x9in) s. board. 7-Nov-2 International Art Centre, Auckland #96/R est:2500-3500 (NZ.D 2800)
£1333 $2080 €2000 Auckland Harbour (11x16cm-4x6in) st.sig. verso board. 27-Mar-3 International Art Centre, Auckland #91/R est:3500-4500 (NZ.D 3800)
£1411 $2201 €2117 Pink and white terraces of Rotomahana (6x11cm-2x4in) s. board pair. 7-Nov-2 International Art Centre, Auckland #97/R est:2000-3000 (NZ.D 4500)

BACKMANSSON, Hugo (1860-1953) Finnish
£310 $503 €450 View across Algiers (24x29cm-9x11in) s.d.1914. 25-May-3 Uppsala Auktionskammare, Uppsala #141/R (S.KR 4000)
£329 $513 €520 Tangier (55x46cm-22x18in) s. 12-Sep-2 Hagelstam, Helsinki #873
£346 $533 €550 From the south (40x30cm-16x12in) s.i. 27-Oct-2 Bukowskis, Helsinki #143/R
£353 $579 €540 Beach in Tangier (27x35cm-11x14in) s.i. 9-Feb-3 Bukowskis, Helsinki #203/R
£361 $573 €530 African woman (33x25cm-13x10in) s.d.1920. 27-Feb-3 Hagelstam, Helsinki #915/R
£410 $673 €570 Tangier (35x27cm-14x11in) s. 5-Jun-3 Hagelstam, Helsinki #954/R
£414 $654 €600 Tangier (33x41cm-13x16in) s. 3-Apr-3 Hagelstam, Helsinki #1040
£440 $678 €700 Tangier (30x54cm-12x21in) s.d.1919. 27-Oct-2 Bukowskis, Helsinki #146/R
£475 $779 €660 Tangier (42x50cm-17x20in) s. 5-Jun-3 Hagelstam, Helsinki #886
£504 $826 €700 Alley (39x56cm-15x22in) s.d.1927. 4-Jun-3 Bukowskis, Helsinki #255/R
£523 $858 €800 Red croft (31x48cm-12x19in) s.i.d.1949. 9-Feb-3 Bukowskis, Helsinki #202/R
£949 $1500 €1500 Windy day, Tangier (41x33cm-16x13in) s.i. 1-Dec-2 Bukowskis, Helsinki #20/R est:1200-1400
£968 $1529 €1500 Farm (50x35cm-20x14in) s. 19-Dec-2 Hagelstam, Helsinki #843/R est:750
£2065 $3262 €3200 Horse (38x45cm-15x18in) s.d.1931. 19-Dec-2 Hagelstam, Helsinki #823/R est:650

Works on paper

£417 $684 €580 Bedouin (25x17cm-10x7in) s.d.1898 W/C. 5-Jun-3 Hagelstam, Helsinki #982
£437 $703 €620 Coastal landscape (36x49cm-14x19in) s.i.d.1908 gouache. 10-May-3 Bukowskis, Helsinki #52/R
£755 $1239 €1050 Southern harbour (35x50cm-14x20in) s.d.1927 W/C. 4-Jun-3 Bukowskis, Helsinki #252/R
£1139 $1800 €1800 Tangier (33x45cm-13x18in) s.d.1906 mixed media. 30-Nov-2 Hagelstam, Helsinki #78/R est:1000
£1268 $2041 €1800 View from Tangier (18x26cm-7x10in) s.i.d.1909 gouache. 10-May-3 Bukowskis, Helsinki #168/R est:600-800

BACKSTROM, Barbro (1939-1990) Swedish

Sculpture

£1749 $2763 €2624 Wall movement (20cm-8in) s.d.1970 num.1/5 gold pat.bronze sold with wood socle. 28-Apr-3 Bukowskis, Stockholm #900/R est:15000-18000 (S.KR 23000)
£4205 $6559 €6308 Three figures (20x24cm-8x9in) metal netting in wooden box. 5-Nov-2 Bukowskis, Stockholm #403/R est:60000-80000 (S.KR 60000)
£7605 $12015 €11408 Three bodies (40x75cm-16x30in) s.d.87-8 net sculpture. 28-Apr-3 Bukowskis, Stockholm #902/R est:125000-150000 (S.KR 100000)

BACKUS, Albert (1906-1996) American

£9938 $16000 €14907 Wind over the glades (76x91cm-30x36in) s. i.verso. 18-Feb-3 Arthur James, Florida #72

BACKVIS, François (1857-1926) Belgian

£331 $540 €500 Moutons dans la bergerie (46x56cm-18x22in) s. 17-Feb-3 Horta, Bruxelles #72
£385 $604 €600 Moutons au pre (38x52cm-15x20in) s. 19-Nov-2 Vanderkindere, Brussels #76
£538 $839 €850 Bouquet de roses (33x46cm-13x18in) s. 15-Oct-2 Vanderkindere, Brussels #61
£1410 $2186 €2200 Resting on the field (60x90cm-24x35in) s. 7-Dec-2 De Vuyst, Lokeren #14/R est:2200-2800
£4173 $6676 €5800 Wolves (101x170cm-40x67in) s.d.1886. 17-May-3 De Vuyst, Lokeren #540/R est:5000-7000

BACON, Francis (1909-1992) British

£500000 $820000 €750000 Study for a portrait (25x20cm-10x8in) s. i.d.1979 verso prov.exhib. 5-Feb-3 Christie's, London #3/R est:400000-500000
£1392405 $2200000 €2088608 Three studies of Henrietta Moraes (36x31cm-14x12in) s. i.d.1966 verso triptych prov.exhib. 12-Nov-2 Sotheby's, New York #48/R est:1800000-2200000

Prints

£1923 $3019 €3000 Oedipus and the Sphinx (128x89cm-50x35in) s.i. col lithograph after Ingres prov. 15-Dec-2 Perrin, Versailles #29/R
£1964 $3084 €2946 Untitled (47x36cm-19x14in) s.num.17/20 etching aquatint prov. 25-Nov-2 Christie's, Melbourne #384 est:2500-3500 (A.D 5500)
£2083 $3437 €3000 Homme ecrivant (101x71cm-40x28in) s.num.75/150 col lithograph exec.c.1980. 2-Jul-3 Artcurial Briest, Paris #88/R est:3500-4500
£2100 $3465 €3045 Inspired by the Oresteia of Aeschylus (40x95cm-16x37in) s.num.59/150 col lithograph triptych. 2-Jul-3 Christie's, London #50/R est:1500-2500
£2340 $3791 €3300 Metropolitan Museum of Art (114x86cm-45x34in) s. num.156/170 col lithograph lit. 24-May-3 Van Ham, Cologne #24/R est:3300
£2516 $4000 €3774 Etude de corps humain (46x33cm-18x13in) s.num.72/150 col lithograph. 4-Mar-3 Swann Galleries, New York #134/R est:2500-3500
£2553 $4136 €3600 Untitled (49x36cm-19x14in) s. offset lithograph. 20-May-3 Dorotheum, Vienna #226/R est:2000-2400
£2569 $4240 €3700 Autoportrait (51x93cm-20x37in) s.num.60 col lithograph triptych. 2-Jul-3 Artcurial Briest, Paris #87/R est:3000-4000
£2600 $4082 €3900 Oedipus and the sphinx after Ingres (128x89cm-50x35in) s.num.41/150 col lithograph. 17-Apr-3 Christie's, Kensington #5/R est:1200-1800
£2838 $4456 €4257 Man at washbasin (51x39cm-20x15in) s. col etching aquatint. 25-Nov-2 Germann, Zurich #213/R est:4500-5500 (S.FR 6500)
£3013 $4701 €4520 Second version of Triptych 1944 - small version (62x46cm-24x18in) s.num.54/60 col lithographs three. 5-Nov-2 Bukowskis, Stockholm #501/R est:30000-40000 (S.KR 43000)
£3125 $5156 €4500 Inspire de Oreste de Eschyle (47x101cm-19x40in) s.num.58/150 col lithograph triptych. 2-Jul-3 Artcurial Briest, Paris #85/R est:4500-5500
£3439 $5400 €5159 Self portrait (34x89cm-13x35in) s.i. col lithograph triptych. 21-Nov-2 Swann Galleries, New York #9/R est:5000-8000
£3500 $5775 €5075 Study for a portrait of Pope Innocent X (95x69cm-37x27in) s.num.30/60 col lithograph. 2-Jul-3 Christie's, London #49/R est:3500-4500
£4000 $6200 €6000 Three studies for self portrait (47x103cm-19x41in) s.i. col lithograph three on one sheet. 3-Dec-2 Christie's, London #88/R est:2500-3500
£4000 $6200 €6000 Seated figure (101x71cm-40x28in) s.i. aquatint. 4-Dec-2 Bonhams, New Bond Street #240/R est:2000-3000
£4054 $6324 €6000 Study from human body (163x121cm-64x48in) st.sig. eau forte aquatint drypoint. 26-Mar-3 Finarte Semenzato, Milan #11/R
£4861 $8021 €7000 Metropilitan Museum of Art (122x94cm-48x37in) s.num.41/170 col lithograph. 2-Jul-3 Artcurial Briest, Paris #88a/R est:5000-6000
£5031 $8000 €7547 Metropolitan triptych (62x110cm-24x43in) s.num.45/99 three col aquatint on one sheet. 3-Mar-3 Swann Galleries, New York #98/R est:8000-12000
£5208 $8229 €7500 Repons, hommage a Berlioz (71x168cm-28x66in) s.num.7/60 col lithograph triptych. 26-Apr-3 Cornette de St.Cyr, Paris #107/R est:7000-8000
£5674 $9191 €8000 Estudio para el Retarto del Papa Inocencio X (116x77cm-46x30in) s. lithograph Arches paper. 20-May-3 Segre, Madrid #211/R est:8000
£6000 $9300 €9000 Study for portrait pf Pope Innocent X (116x77cm-46x30in) s.i. col lithograph. 3-Dec-2 Christie's, London #89/R est:4000-5000
£6500 $10725 €9425 Triptychon (86x61cm-34x24in) s.num.108/180 col lithograph triptych. 1-Jul-3 Sotheby's, London #166/R est:7000-8000

BACON, Henry (1839-1912) American

£335 $550 €503 French maid (46x33cm-18x13in) s. indis d. 5-Feb-3 Doyle, New York #64/R
£12500 $20000 €18750 On the lookout (72x49cm-28x19in) s.d.1880. 14-May-3 Butterfields, San Francisco #1132/R est:20000-30000

Works on paper

£545 $850 €818 Caravan crossing a valley (36x51cm-14x20in) s.d.1903 W/C. 9-Nov-2 Sloan, North Bethesda #545/R

BACON, Irving R (1875-1962) American

£513 $800 €770 Continental village landscape with figure and cows (41x33cm-16x13in) s.i. 18-Sep-2 Boos Gallery, Michigan #295/R

BACON, Peggy (1895-1987) American

£1210 $1900 €1815 Friend of foe? (25x36cm-10x14in) s.i.d.1967 masonite. 14-Dec-2 Weschler, Washington #729/R est:1000-1500

Works on paper

£396 $650 €574 Salvador Dali (36x23cm-14x9in) s.i. chl prov.exhib. 1-Jun-3 Wright, Chicago #183/R

BADAROCCO, Giovanni Raffaelo (1648-1726) Italian

Works on paper

£1149 $1792 €1700 Saint Claire (29x20cm-11x8in) i. pen ink wash over crayon. 31-Mar-3 Piasa, Paris #18/R

BADCOCK, Douglas (20th C) New Zealander

£244 $373 €366 Skippers Canyon (47x59cm-19x23in) s.d.65 board. 21-Aug-2 Dunbar Sloane, Auckland #505 (NZ.D 800)
£360 $529 €540 Winter evening central Otago (69x87cm-27x34in) s. board prov. 19-Jun-2 Watson's, Christchurch #34/R est:600-1000 (NZ.D 1100)
£439 $684 €659 Bleached town, Central Otago (40x50cm-16x20in) s.d.1963 board. 27-Mar-3 International Art Centre, Auckland #214 (NZ.D 1250)
£785 $1114 €1178 Arrowtown, Central Otago (67x87cm-26x34in) s. board prov. 21-Nov-1 Watson's, Christchurch #48/R est:2000-3000 (NZ.D 2700)

BADCOCK, John (?) New Zealander?

Works on paper

£289 $462 €419 Custom House, Timaru (54x72cm-21x28in) s.d.86 W/C. 13-May-3 Watson's, Christchurch #4/R (NZ.D 800)

BADEL, Jules-Louis (1840-1869) Swiss

£480 $749 €720 Still life with summer flowers in stone vase (81x66cm-32x26in) s. canvas on pavatex. 20-Nov-2 Fischer, Luzern #2008/R (S.FR 1100)

£1101 $1608 €1652 Wooded landscape with mother and child (65x47cm-26x19in) 17-Jun-2 Philippe Schuler, Zurich #4254/R est:2500-3000 (S.FR 2500)

BADEN, Hans Jurriaens van (attrib) (1604-1663) Dutch
£1800 $2826 €2700 Church interior with elegant gentleman conversing and dogs playing (49x65cm-19x26in) indis sig.d.1649 panel. 10-Dec-2 Bonhams, New Bond Street #13/R est:2000-3000

BADEN, J P (19th C) British?
£1000 $1570 €1500 Children and cattle at a pool (46x66cm-18x26in) indis sig. 16-Dec-2 Bonhams, Bury St Edmunds #542 est:600-800

BADENS, Francesco (1571-1618) Flemish
£60000 $100200 €87000 Venus and Adonis (127x175cm-50x69in) prov. 10-Jul-3 Sotheby's, London #15/R est:60000-80000

BADER, Anne (19th C) ?
£300 $475 €450 Still life of roses (46x38cm-18x15in) s. canvas on canvas. 29-Nov-2 Zofingen, Switzerland #2394 (S.FR 700)

BADGER, Samuel Finley Morse (1873-1919) American
£2039 $3100 €3059 Ship, Chancelor (25x41cm-10x16in) s.d.01. 17-Aug-2 North East Auctions, Portsmouth #968/R est:1500-2500
£4605 $7000 €6908 American three masted schooner, E I Morrison (56x91cm-22x36in) s.d.99. 17-Aug-2 North East Auctions, Portsmouth #984/R
£34539 $52500 €51809 Seven masted schooner, Thomas W Lawson (64x104cm-25x41in) s.d.06 lit. 17-Aug-2 North East Auctions, Portsmouth #789/R est:20000-30000

BADILE, Antonio (1516-1560) Italian
Works on paper
£1747 $2725 €2621 Adoration of the Shepherds (15x26cm-6x10in) wash Indian ink htd white prov. 20-Nov-2 Fischer, Luzern #2405/R est:5000-7000 (S.FR 4000)

BADIN, Jules (19/20th C) French
£2208 $3356 €3400 Three girls singing and playing music (81x100cm-32x39in) s.d.1884. 6-Jul-2 Berlinghof, Heidelberg #190/R est:1800

BADIOLA, Txomin (1957-) Spanish
£1161 $1835 €1800 Yoes, who's afraid of art? (61x86cm-24x34in) s.i.d.1989 acrylic mixed media paper prov.exhib.lit. 17-Dec-2 Segre, Madrid #207/R

BADMIN, Stanley Roy (1906-1989) British
Works on paper
£400 $648 €600 Plough, near Bures, Essex (11x20cm-4x8in) s.i. pen ink htd white. 20-May-3 Sotheby's, Olympia #104/R
£1100 $1716 €1650 Long Melford Mill (18x23cm-7x9in) s.i. W/C prov. 18-Sep-2 Cheffins Grain & Comins, Cambridge #459/R est:1200-1800
£1100 $1782 €1650 Oak before ash (14x22cm-6x9in) s.i.d.May 20 79 W/C gouache exhib. 20-May-3 Sotheby's, Olympia #98/R est:800-1200
£1500 $2430 €2250 Spring evening, West Burton, Sussex (17x24cm-7x9in) s.i. ink W/C exhib. 20-May-3 Sotheby's, Olympia #100/R est:1000-2000
£1600 $2496 €2400 Village life (19x15cm-7x6in) W/C over pencil. 5-Nov-2 Bonhams, New Bond Street #168/R est:800-1200
£1700 $2754 €2550 Elder tree (17x20cm-7x8in) s.i. W/C prov. 20-May-3 Sotheby's, Olympia #99/R est:600-800
£1900 $3078 €2850 Stopham Bridge, Sussex (20x12cm-8x5in) s.i. ink W/C gouache. 20-May-3 Sotheby's, Olympia #103/R est:800-1200
£2400 $3888 €3600 Flooded valley near Stopham (15x26cm-6x10in) s. pencil W/C gouache. 20-May-3 Sotheby's, Olympia #94/R est:1000-2000
£2600 $4212 €3900 Ash and blackthorne on the South Down's Way (17x26cm-7x10in) s.d.April 1976 W/C gouache exhib. 20-May-3 Sotheby's, Olympia #95/R est:1500-2500
£2600 $4212 €3900 Watersplash Lane, Burpham (19x17cm-7x7in) s.i. ink W/C exhib. 20-May-3 Sotheby's, Olympia #102/R est:1000-2000
£3000 $4860 €4500 View across the Adur valley (26x42cm-10x17in) s.i. pencil W/C. 20-May-3 Sotheby's, Olympia #97/R est:3000-5000
£3400 $5508 €5100 East Dean (18x29cm-7x11in) s.i.d.Oct 74 ink W/C. 20-May-3 Sotheby's, Olympia #93/R est:1500-2500
£4200 $6720 €6300 Whitestone pond, Hampstead (17x33cm-7x13in) s. W/C pen ink over pencil exhib. 15-May-3 Lawrence, Crewkerne #890/R est:2500-3500

BADT, Kurt (1890-?) German
£485 $707 €728 Landscape with trees and lake (70x82cm-28x32in) s.d.1922. 17-Jun-2 Philippe Schuler, Zurich #7317 (S.FR 1100)

BADUR, Frank (1944-) Swedish?
£965 $1554 €1448 Composition (50x50cm-20x20in) s.verso. 7-May-3 AB Stockholms Auktionsverk #958/R (S.KR 12500)
£2052 $3222 €3078 From lover East Side I (40x60cm-16x24in) s.d.1990 verso acrylic. 23-Nov-2 Burkhard, Luzern #160/R est:4000-4500 (S.FR 4700)

BAECHLER, Donald (1956-) American
£7595 $12000 €11393 Thistle (117x91cm-46x36in) init.d.2001 acrylic collage paper prov. 13-Nov-2 Sotheby's, New York #587/R est:8000-12000
£7911 $12500 €11867 Cone (117x91cm-46x36in) init.d.2001 acrylic fabric on paper prov. 12-Nov-2 Phillips, New York #139/R est:5000-7000
£11250 $18000 €16875 Zagreb picture (244x173cm-96x68in) s.i.d.1982-83 acrylic prov.exhib. 15-May-3 Christie's, Rockefeller NY #397a/R est:18000-22000
£16250 $26000 €24375 Thistle - poultry concentrate (128x103cm-50x41in) init.i.d.98 verso oil mixed media collage prov. 14-May-3 Sotheby's, New York #448/R est:30000-40000
£26389 $43542 €38000 Hours and jewels (216x215cm-85x85in) init.i.d.10/86 verso acrylic collage tissue canvas prov.lit. 3-Jul-3 Christie's, Paris #32/R est:30000-40000

Works on paper
£629 $975 €1000 Sans titre (27x21cm-11x8in) s. ink dr. 30-Oct-2 Artcurial Briest, Paris #640
£735 $1168 €1080 Sans titre (27x21cm-11x8in) mono.d.89 ink dr. 26-Feb-3 Artcurial Briest, Paris #351
£735 $1168 €1080 Sans titre (27x21cm-11x8in) mono.d.89 ink dr. 26-Feb-3 Artcurial Briest, Paris #352
£1928 $3200 €2892 Crown study (35x27cm-14x11in) s.d.99 gouache prov. 11-Jun-3 Phillips, New York #362/R est:1000-2000
£3000 $4740 €4500 Dead dog (89x90cm-35x35in) pencil tempera collage exec.1983 prov. 3-Apr-3 Christie's, Kensington #239/R
£3364 $5247 €5046 Still life of fruit (67x52cm-26x20in) init.d.90 W/C mixed media prov. 5-Nov-2 Bukowskis, Stockholm #452/R est:50000-60000 (S.KR 48000)
£4015 $6465 €6023 Flower (58x34cm-23x13in) init.d.92 collage gouache prov. 7-May-3 AB Stockholms Auktionsverk #959/R est:50000-60000 (S.KR 52000)
£4345 $6778 €6518 Red abstract with standing figure (115x90cm-45x35in) init.d.95 gouache collage prov. 6-Nov-2 AB Stockholms Auktionsverk #847/R est:60000-80000 (S.KR 62000)
£21875 $35000 €32813 Ahmad's flower no.8 (194x101cm-76x40in) i.d.94 gouache printed paper collage on paper prov. 15-May-3 Christie's, Rockefeller NY #397/R est:18000-22000

BAELLIEUR, Cornelis de (attrib) (17th C) Flemish
£3497 $5839 €5000 L'annonciation (46x33cm-18x13in) htd gold panel. 27-Jun-3 Piasa, Paris #37/R est:6000-8000

BAELLIEUR, Cornelis de (elder-attrib) (1607-1671) Flemish
£8500 $13175 €12750 Jephthah's daughter (50x64cm-20x25in) copper prov. 30-Oct-2 Christie's, Kensington #4/R est:5000-8000

BAEN, Jan de (1633-1702) Dutch
£4000 $6200 €6000 Portrait of a gentleman in a garden, in an embroidered jacket and red gown (126x95cm-50x37in) s.d.1676. 30-Oct-2 Christie's, Kensington #42/R est:4000-6000
£22293 $34777 €35000 Portrait of a young boy seated full length with a sheep on a rock (102x79cm-40x31in) prov. 6-Nov-2 Christie's, Amsterdam #63/R est:15000-25000

BAER, Carola (1857-1940) Austrian
£414 $646 €650 Meadow landscape (27x33cm-11x13in) s. board. 6-Nov-2 Hugo Ruef, Munich #1017

BAER, Fritz (1850-1919) German
£304 $474 €450 On the Amper (26x33cm-10x13in) s. i. verso board. 26-Mar-3 Hugo Ruef, Munich #66
£1079 $1727 €1500 Schleissheim avenue (58x64cm-23x25in) s. i. stretcher. 15-May-3 Neumeister, Munich #210/R est:1500-1800
£2785 $4316 €4400 Summer meadow with poppies (65x86cm-26x34in) s. 25-Sep-2 Neumeister, Munich #537/R est:4000

BAER, Jo (1929-) American
£5380 $8500 €8070 Untitled - from the Korean series (183x183cm-72x72in) s.d.1968/69 verso prov. 22-Apr-3 Butterfields, San Francisco #6070/R est:10000-15000

BAERDEMAEKER, Felix de (1836-1878) Belgian
£417 $658 €650 City in the Ardennes (50x77cm-20x30in) s.d.1871 panel. 18-Nov-2 Bernaerts, Antwerp #313/R

BAERENTZEN, Emilius (1799-1868) Danish
£596 $941 €894 Self portrait of the artist sitting at table with book and pipe (88x73cm-35x29in) 2-Dec-2 Rasmussen, Copenhagen #1693/R (D.KR 7000)
£1210 $1925 €1815 Portrait of Mrs Wraaby (27x21cm-11x8in) 5-Mar-3 Rasmussen, Copenhagen #1713/R est:5000 (D.KR 13000)

BAERTLING, Olle (1911-1981) Swedish
£1622 $2611 €2433 Itrecar - composition (65x85cm-26x33in) s.i.d.1948. 7-May-3 AB Stockholms Auktionsverk #791/R est:25000-30000 (S.KR 21000)
£2085 $3357 €3128 Interior scene with Lisa, the artist's wife (92x73cm-36x29in) s.d.1944 panel. 7-May-3 AB Stockholms Auktionsverk #769/R est:30000-35000 (S.KR 27000)
£2102 $3280 €3153 Red blue (101x72cm-40x28in) s. d.1949 verso. 6-Nov-2 AB Stockholms Auktionsverk #565/R est:25000-30000 (S.KR 30000)
£2593 $4045 €3890 Kseha - Lucerne (43x81cm-17x32in) s. s.d.1949 verso. 5-Nov-2 Bukowskis, Stockholm #277/R est:40000-50000 (S.KR 37000)
£4064 $6341 €6096 Composition (60x92cm-24x36in) s.d.1952 verso prov.exhib. 6-Nov-2 AB Stockholms Auktionsverk #551/R est:30000-40000 (S.KR 58000)
£4765 $7434 €7148 Tso (92x60cm-36x24in) s.d.1966 verso. 5-Nov-2 Bukowskis, Stockholm #280a/R est:60000-80000 (S.KR 68000)
£5380 $8500 €8500 Tsi (92x60cm-36x24in) s.d.1966 verso exhib. 1-Dec-2 Bukowskis, Helsinki #374/R est:8000-10000
£8409 $13118 €12614 Wach (130x81cm-51x32in) s.d.1955 verso. 5-Nov-2 Bukowskis, Stockholm #280/R est:100000-125000 (S.KR 120000)
£11212 $17491 €16818 Composition - Kortar (81x130cm-32x51in) s.d.1960 verso prov. 5-Nov-2 Bukowskis, Stockholm #279/R est:175000-200000 (S.KR 160000)
£13688 $21627 €20532 Iras (130x81cm-51x32in) s.d.1959 verso prov.exhib. 28-Apr-3 Bukowskis, Stockholm #278/R est:200000-250000 (S.KR 180000)
£19691 $31703 €29537 Yoyaka - composition (180x92cm-71x36in) s.d.1970 verso prov. 7-May-3 AB Stockholms Auktionsverk #943/R est:200000-225000 (S.KR 255000)
£21023 $32796 €31535 Ogria (92x180cm-36x71in) s.d.1960 verso. 6-Nov-2 AB Stockholms Auktionsverk #613/R est:300000-325000 (S.KR 300000)
£28897 $45658 €43346 Ogriam (180x92cm-71x36in) s.d.1960 verso. 28-Apr-3 Bukowskis, Stockholm #277a/R est:400000-450000 (S.KR 380000)

BAERWALDT, Jo (19/20th C) Belgian
£385 $596 €600 Dreve d'hetres au chateau de Van Praet a Schoten (80x120cm-31x47in) s. 3-Dec-2 Campo & Campo, Antwerp #4

BAES, Émile (1879-1954) Belgian
£479 $748 €700 Nu drape (46x56cm-18x22in) s. 14-Apr-3 Horta, Bruxelles #27
£552 $872 €800 Modele dans l'atelier (100x80cm-39x31in) s. 1-Apr-3 Palais de Beaux Arts, Brussels #504
£680 $1082 €1000 Nu regardant la mer en Afrique du Nord (46x55cm-18x22in) s. 18-Mar-3 Vanderkindere, Brussels #75
£823 $1284 €1300 Nature morte aux fleurs et aux pommes (92x72cm-36x28in) s. panel. 10-Sep-2 Vanderkindere, Brussels #343
£1307 $2105 €2000 Nu assis au perroquet (61x50cm-24x20in) s. 14-Jan-3 Vanderkindere, Brussels #451/R est:2500-3500
£1361 $2163 €2000 Nu assis devant la tenture (60x50cm-24x20in) s. 18-Mar-3 Vanderkindere, Brussels #5/R est:2000-3000
£1596 $2473 €2394 Femme nue (146x114cm-57x45in) s. 3-Dec-2 Bukowskis, Stockholm #332/R est:25000-30000 (S.KR 22500)
£1745 $2809 €2600 Nu au clair obscur (134x80cm-53x31in) s. 18-Feb-3 Vanderkindere, Brussels #140/R
£1899 $2962 €3000 Nu au paravent japonais (122x86cm-48x34in) s. 15-Oct-2 Horta, Bruxelles #88
£2353 $3859 €3600 Nu se coiffant (100x80cm-39x31in) s. 7-Feb-3 Oger, Dumont, Paris #50/R
£2381 $3786 €3500 La jeune tisserande (45x55cm-18x22in) s. panel. 24-Mar-3 Rabourdin & Choppin de Janvry, Paris #102/R est:3500-4000
£2590 $4144 €3600 Spanish woman (150x50cm-59x20in) s. 17-May-3 De Vuyst, Lokeren #12/R est:3500-4500
£3205 $5032 €5000 Nu devant le miroir (130x90cm-51x35in) s. 19-Nov-2 Vanderkindere, Brussels #30/R est:2500-3750
£5696 $8886 €9000 Nu assis dans un fauteuil (150x90cm-59x35in) s. 15-Oct-2 Vanderkindere, Brussels #60/R est:2500-3500

BAES, Firmin (1874-1945) Belgian
£570 $889 €900 Bord de Meuse (25x42cm-10x17in) s.i.d.aout 1899 panel. 15-Oct-2 Vanderkindere, Brussels #53
£641 $1006 €1000 Paysage (36x51cm-14x20in) s.i.d.1900 canvas on cardboard. 19-Nov-2 Vanderkindere, Brussels #48
£6500 $10790 €6500 Paysage (90x120cm-35x47in) s.d.1902. 16-Jun-3 Horta, Bruxelles #163 est:6500-7500

Works on paper
£374 $595 €550 Massif d'Hortensias (42x54cm-17x21in) s. pastel. 18-Mar-3 Galerie Moderne, Brussels #539/R
£605 $944 €950 La ferme blanche a Faulx (42x75cm-17x30in) s.i.d.1943 verso pastel canvas on cardboard. 11-Nov-2 Horta, Bruxelles #17
£801 $1258 €1250 Temps gris (43x55cm-17x22in) s. pastel. 19-Nov-2 Vanderkindere, Brussels #539
£884 $1406 €1300 Torse de femme (65x54cm-26x21in) s. s.i.verso pastel. 18-Mar-3 Galerie Moderne, Brussels #638/R
£1224 $1947 €1800 Portrait de Gitane (63x50cm-25x20in) s.d.1911 pastel. 18-Mar-3 Galerie Moderne, Brussels #547/R est:3000-4000
£1438 $2315 €2200 Les pommes rouges (49x59cm-19x23in) s. s.i.verso pastel. 20-Jan-3 Horta, Bruxelles #398 est:2000-3000
£1503 $2420 €2300 La tricoteuse (58x70cm-23x28in) s. pastel. 14-Jan-3 Vanderkindere, Brussels #160/R est:2000-3000
£1644 $2564 €2400 Temps d'orage (59x80cm-23x31in) s. s.i.verso pastel. 14-Apr-3 Horta, Bruxelles #26 est:2000-3000
£1911 $2981 €3000 Laboureur (60x48cm-24x19in) s. chl dr. 11-Nov-2 Horta, Bruxelles #16 est:1200-1800
£2194 $3466 €3400 Les clivias (60x75cm-24x30in) s. pastel. 17-Dec-2 Palais de Beaux Arts, Brussels #455/R est:3300-4500

BAES, Lionel (1839-1913) Belgian
£392 $631 €600 Le garcon de cafe (27x46cm-11x18in) s. panel. 20-Jan-3 Horta, Bruxelles #9
£419 $700 €608 Portrait of a working man (41x25cm-16x10in) s. board. 28-Jun-3 Harvey Clar, Oakland #1160

BAES, Rachel (1912-1983) Belgian
£660 $1049 €950 Les initees (116x89cm-46x35in) s. d.1973 verso. 29-Apr-3 Campo & Campo, Antwerp #3/R
£828 $1316 €1200 Le divan jaune (44x60cm-17x24in) s. 4-Mar-3 Palais de Beaux Arts, Brussels #280
£903 $1435 €1300 Bataille des eperons d'or (100x80cm-39x31in) s.d.1957 verso panel. 29-Apr-3 Campo, Vlaamse Kaai #8
£943 $1462 €1500 L'annonciation (80x65cm-31x26in) s. s.i.d.1966. 5-Oct-2 De Vuyst, Lokeren #18/R est:1400-1800
£1034 $1645 €1500 La visite (65x54cm-26x21in) s. 4-Mar-3 Palais de Beaux Arts, Brussels #281 est:750-1000
£1223 $1957 €1700 Oracles (100x80cm-39x31in) s. s.i.d.1957 verso. 17-May-3 De Vuyst, Lokeren #14/R est:1200-1600
£2069 $3310 €3000 Nymphes de la Seine (130x162cm-51x64in) s.d.54 s.i.d.1954 verso. 15-Mar-3 De Vuyst, Lokeren #14/R est:2200-2600

BAETS, Marc (18th C) Flemish
£2400 $4008 €3480 River landscape. Village landscape (18x21cm-7x8in) panel pair. 9-Jul-3 Bonhams, New Bond Street #131/R est:2000-3000
£4392 $6851 €6500 Village on river with figures and boats (20x28cm-8x11in) panel prov. 27-Mar-3 Dorotheum, Vienna #373/R est:5000-7500
£6000 $9420 €9000 Rhenish river landscape with figures resting on a track (23x29cm-9x11in) panel. 10-Dec-2 Bonhams, New Bond Street #153/R est:3000-4000

BAEZA, Manuel (1915-1986) Spanish
£586 $932 €850 Vase of flowers (50x61cm-20x24in) s. 4-Mar-3 Ansorena, Madrid #4/R
£710 $1121 €1100 Still life with lemon (46x38cm-18x15in) s. 17-Dec-2 Durán, Madrid #183/R
£962 $1519 €1500 Circus scene (41x33cm-16x13in) s. 13-Nov-2 Ansorena, Madrid #285/R

BAGARIA, Luis (1882-1940) Spanish
Works on paper
£303 $482 €440 Figures (31x48cm-12x19in) s. ink dr. 4-Mar-3 Ansorena, Madrid #381/R
£419 $663 €650 Comic (49x45cm-19x18in) s.d.1928 ink dr. 18-Dec-2 Ansorena, Madrid #974/R

BAGEL, Moses (1908-1995) French
£1042 $1656 €1500 Composition (31x25cm-12x10in) st.sig. paper painted c.1805. 29-Apr-3 Artcurial Briest, Paris #223/R est:1000-1200

Works on paper
£486 $773 €700 Composition (18x16cm-7x6in) st.sig. st.i.verso gouache cardboard exec.c.1930. 29-Apr-3 Artcurial Briest, Paris #222/R
£521 $828 €750 Composition a la fleche (23x15cm-9x6in) st.sig. W/C ink exec.c.1930. 29-Apr-3 Artcurial Briest, Paris #224
£556 $884 €800 Composition, noir (31x24cm-12x9in) st.sig. W/C exec.c.1930. 29-Apr-3 Artcurial Briest, Paris #226
£816 $1298 €1200 Personnage (25x20cm-10x8in) s.i.d.1928 W/C ink paper on cardboard prov. 26-Feb-3 Artcurial Briest, Paris #173/R

BAGELAAR, Ernst Wilhelm Jan (1775-1837) Flemish
Works on paper
£268 $439 €410 Public execution (10x13cm-4x5in) i. W/C pen. 29-Mar-3 Dannenberg, Berlin #541/R

BAGER, Henrik (20th C) Swedish

£430 $688 €624 Girl on beach (56x66cm-22x26in) mono.d.87. 18-May-3 Anders Antik, Landskrona #19 (S.KR 5500)

BAGER, Johann Daniel (1734-1815) German

£6090 $9622 €9500 Still life of fruit with grapes and melon (51x71cm-20x28in) s.d.1780. 15-Nov-2 Reiss & Sohn, Konigstein #2/R est:12000

BAGETTI, Giuseppe Pietro (1764-1831) Italian

Works on paper

£8500 $13345 €12750 Monastery of Montserrat, near Barcelona (51x80cm-20x31in) W/C prov. 11-Dec-2 Sotheby's, Olympia #253/R est:3000-4000

BAGETTI, Tomaso (attrib) (?) Italian

Works on paper

£1772 $2800 €2658 Battle of the Centaurs and Lapiths (545x856cm-215x337in) pen brown ink W/C bodycol. 1-Apr-3 Christie's, Rockefeller NY #376/R est:3000-5000

BAGG, Henry Howard (1852-1928) American

£253 $400 €380 River landscape (30x46cm-12x18in) s. 1-Dec-2 Susanin's, Chicago #5038/R

BAGGE, Eva (1871-1964) Swedish

£355 $590 €515 In the beech wood (23x20cm-9x8in) s.d.38 panel prov. 16-Jun-3 Lilla Bukowskis, Stockholm #975 (S.KR 4600)

£603 $934 €905 Six years old - portrait of boy (40x31cm-16x12in) s. 4-Dec-2 AB Stockholms Auktionsverk #1770/R (S.KR 8500)

£864 $1417 €1253 Boy making music (65x53cm-26x21in) s.d.45. 4-Jun-3 AB Stockholms Auktionsverk #2153/R (S.KR 11000)

£957 $1484 €1436 Interior scene with flowers in window (43x49cm-17x19in) s.d.1943 canvas on panel prov. 3-Dec-2 Bukowskis, Stockholm #27/R est:8000-10000 (S.KR 13500)

£957 $1484 €1436 Interior scene with open window towards summer verdue (38x47cm-15x19in) s.d.36 panel prov. 3-Dec-2 Bukowskis, Stockholm #28/R est:8000-10000 (S.KR 13500)

£1319 $2137 €1913 Clay pot and fruit in pewter dish (33x41cm-13x16in) s. prov. 26-May-3 Bukowskis, Stockholm #140/R est:10000-12000 (S.KR 17000)

£1707 $2765 €2475 Still life of oranges (56x40cm-22x16in) s.d.62. 26-May-3 Bukowskis, Stockholm #138/R est:25000-30000 (S.KR 22000)

Works on paper

£278 $461 €403 Morning glow (19x24cm-7x9in) s/ W/C gouache prov. 16-Jun-3 Lilla Bukowskis, Stockholm #970 (S.KR 3600)

£293 $487 €425 Oland towards to sea (24x33cm-9x13in) s. W/C gouache prov. 16-Jun-3 Lilla Bukowskis, Stockholm #973 (S.KR 3800)

£371 $615 €538 Arild (19x24cm-7x9in) s. W/C gouache prov. 16-Jun-3 Lilla Bukowskis, Stockholm #967 (S.KR 4800)

£2172 $3519 €3149 Girl from Brittany (23x17cm-9x7in) s. W/C prov.lit. 26-May-3 Bukowskis, Stockholm #64/R est:8000-10000 (S.KR 28000)

BAGGE, Halvor (20th C) Scandinavian

£931 $1480 €1397 Two Italian small boys (30x27cm-12x11in) s.i.d.1929. 5-Mar-3 Rasmussen, Copenhagen #1925/R (D.KR 10000)

BAGGE, Magnus-Thulstrupp (1825-1894) Norwegian

£2269 $3562 €3404 Primeval forest with hunter (45x68cm-18x27in) s.d.1858 lit. 21-Nov-2 Grev Wedels Plass, Oslo #5/R est:30000-40000 (N.KR 26000)

BAGGESEN, Mie (19th C) Danish?

£2412 $3666 €3618 Flowers in glass vase and oranges on ledge (36x46cm-14x18in) i.stretcher after Prof.Jensen. 27-Aug-2 Rasmussen, Copenhagen #1403/R est:30000-40000 (D.KR 28000)

BAGIOLI, Alessandro (1879-1965) Italian

£321 $503 €500 Farms (26x40cm-10x16in) s. s.i.d.1929 verso board. 16-Dec-2 Pandolfini, Florence #135/R

£1026 $1610 €1600 Poor meal (62x118cm-24x46in) s. 16-Dec-2 Pandolfini, Florence #113/R est:1300

BAGLEY, Laurence (20th C) British

£650 $988 €975 Liner Pendennis Castle (61x91cm-24x36in) s. 15-Aug-2 Bonhams, New Bond Street #370a

BAGLIONE, Cavaliere Giovanni (circle) (1571-1644) Italian

£35484 $56065 €55000 Judith and Olophernes (212x157cm-83x62in) 18-Dec-2 Beaussant & Lefèvre, Paris #21/R est:10000

BAGSHAWE, Joseph Richard (1870-1909) British

£250 $395 €375 North East coast seascape (33x51cm-13x20in) board prov. 24-Apr-3 Richardson & Smith, Whitby #55

£1050 $1659 €1575 Coble and figures rowing, steamship and other vessels (23x33cm-9x13in) s.d. panel. 28-Nov-2 Richardson & Smith, Whitby #610

£1050 $1743 €1575 Fishing boats in a storm (58x89cm-23x35in) s. 10-Jun-3 Bonhams, Leeds #200/R est:1000-1200

£6500 $10270 €9750 Staithes Coble with fishermen hauling the catch (61x76cm-24x30in) prov. 24-Apr-3 Richardson & Smith, Whitby #110 est:5000-7000

Works on paper

£420 $655 €630 Woodland scene with gate (24x34cm-9x13in) s.d.May 1 08 W/C. 10-Sep-2 David Duggleby, Scarborough #268

£720 $1138 €1080 Fishing boats at Scarborough (23x36cm-9x14in) s. W/C. 24-Apr-3 Richardson & Smith, Whitby #148

£1073 $1695 €1610 Fishing scene (27x37cm-11x15in) s. W/C. 3-Apr-3 Heffel, Vancouver #6/R est:300-400 (C.D 2500)

£2500 $3950 €3750 Northern European coastal scene with vessels and figures on the shore (33x48cm-13x19in) W/C prov. 24-Apr-3 Richardson & Smith, Whitby #120/R est:2500-3000

£4200 $6636 €6300 Helpmates (30x46cm-12x18in) W/C prov. 24-Apr-3 Richardson & Smith, Whitby #200 est:3000-4000

BAHIEU, Jules G (19th C) Belgian

£314 $490 €471 Fishing boats at sea (21x41cm-8x16in) s. panel. 20-Nov-2 Fischer, Luzern #2010/R (S.FR 720)

£750 $1200 €1088 Produce market (65x40cm-26x16in) s. 16-May-3 Skinner, Boston #27/R

£1058 $1661 €1650 Poules (36x18cm-14x7in) s. panel pair. 15-Dec-2 Eric Pillon, Calais #52/R

BAHNER, Hermann (1867-1933) German

£545 $845 €850 Cattle in Hessen landscape (44x67cm-17x26in) s. 7-Dec-2 Ketterer, Hamburg #146/R

BAHNER, Margrethe (19th C) Danish?

£1005 $1628 €1457 Still life of flowers in basket (40x50cm-16x20in) s.d.1880. 24-May-3 Rasmussen, Havnen #2006/R (D.KR 10500)

BAI XUESHI (1915-) Chinese

Works on paper

£870 $1426 €1200 Mountain landscape (67x46cm-26x18in) s.d.1987 seals Indian ink col hanging scroll. 30-May-3 Dr Fritz Nagel, Stuttgart #1209/R

BAIER, Jean (1932-) ?

£300 $475 €450 Composition in grey, white and black (38x38cm-15x15in) s.d.1958 verso. 29-Nov-2 Zofingen, Switzerland #2782 (S.FR 700)

£386 $610 €579 Composition with red (20x40cm-8x16in) s.i. verso painted 1958. 29-Nov-2 Zofingen, Switzerland #2783 (S.FR 900)

BAIGENT, Richard (19th C) British

£550 $913 €798 Winchester from the South (25x36cm-10x14in) panel. 16-Jun-3 Duke & Son, Dorchester #206

BAIITSU, Yamamoto (1783-1856) Japanese

Works on paper

£5660 $9000 €8490 Pine, bamboo and plum (124x42cm-49x17in) s. ink silk hanging scrolls triptych prov. 24-Mar-3 Christie's, Rockefeller NY #44/R est:5000-7000

BAIKOFF, Feodor (1825-1879) Russian

£11000 $17820 €16500 Travelers on the Caucasian Plain (42x77cm-17x30in) s.d.1878. 21-May-3 Sotheby's, London #20/R est:7000-9000

BAIL, Antoine Jean (1830-1918) French

£1441 $2248 €2162 Scene de famille (38x57cm-15x22in) s. 6-Nov-2 Dobiaschofsky, Bern #325/R est:6000 (S.FR 3300)

BAIL, Joseph (1862-1921) French

£1736 $2760 €2500 Huitres et bouquets (50x61cm-20x24in) s.d.1880. 30-Apr-3 Tajan, Paris #72/R

£1899 $3000 €2849 Vase of poppies. s. 16-Nov-2 Harvey Clar, Oakland #1381

£2000 $3240 €3000 Mother and kittens in a pot (24x29cm-9x11in) s. 20-May-3 Sotheby's, Olympia #391/R est:2000-3000

£2800 $4368 €4200 Kitchen boy cleaning a pot (21x25cm-8x10in) s. 8-Oct-2 Bonhams, Knightsbridge #82/R est:1500-2000

£3000 $4890 €4350 Sewing by the window (38x46cm-15x18in) s. 16-Jul-3 Sotheby's, Olympia #204/R est:2000-3000
£4483 $7128 €6500 Tete de dentelliere (73x60cm-29x24in) s. 8-Mar-3 Peron, Melun #19
£5500 $9020 €8250 Polishing the copper (65x54cm-26x21in) s. 3-Jun-3 Sotheby's, London #155/R est:6000-8000
£15000 $25050 €22500 Dejeuner a l'hospice de Beaune (88x116cm-35x46in) s. prov. 19-Jun-3 Christie's, London #52/R est:15000-20000
£20570 $32500 €30855 Lettre de son pere (93x74cm-37x29in) s. 24-Apr-3 Sotheby's, New York #37/R est:10000-15000

BAIL, Louis le (1866-1929) French
£493 $794 €700 Paysage de printemps (49x46cm-19x18in) s. 11-May-3 Thierry & Lannon, Brest #372

BAILEY, Albert E (fl.1890-1904) British
£250 $410 €375 Swans by a punt on still waters (30x46cm-12x18in) s. 5-Jun-3 Christie's, Kensington #766
£1500 $2385 €2250 Lily pool (70x91cm-28x36in) s. 6-Mar-3 Christie's, Kensington #434/R est:1500-2000

BAILEY, Beezy (1962-) South African
£523 $826 €785 Lenin's on sale again (70x55cm-28x22in) s.d.02 i.verso. 1-Apr-3 Stephan Welz, Johannesburg #514 est:7000-10000 (SA.R 6500)

BAILEY, David (1938-) British
Photographs
£5500 $8910 €8250 David Bailey's box of pin-ups (37x31cm-15x12in) halftone prints set of 36 folio. 22-May-3 Sotheby's, London #187/R est:1200-1800

BAILEY, Frederick Victor (20th C) British
£500 $810 €750 Still life with grapes and jug (30x40cm-12x16in) s. board. 20-May-3 Bonhams, Knightsbridge #125/R
£600 $972 €900 Still life with lemons and oranges (24x34cm-9x13in) s. board. 20-May-3 Bonhams, Knightsbridge #128/R

BAILEY, Henrietta Davidson (1874-1950) American
Prints
£1707 $2800 €2475 Lone pine (51x30cm-20x12in) s.i. col woodblock. 7-Jun-3 Neal Auction Company, New Orleans #373 est:1500-2500
Works on paper
£962 $1500 €1443 Mummy (23x30cm-9x12in) s. pencil dr sold with a photo. 12-Oct-2 Neal Auction Company, New Orleans #1361/R est:1500-2500

BAILEY, Henry (1848-1933) British
£2564 $4000 €3846 Dawn and noon (107x81cm-42x32in) s. pair. 12-Apr-3 Weschler, Washington #513/R est:5000-7000

BAILEY, Nancy (20th C) British
£320 $522 €480 Mousehole harbour (51x76cm-20x30in) s. 13-Feb-3 David Lay, Penzance #251
£400 $664 €580 Ferry crossing, Malpas (41x56cm-16x22in) s. i.verso. 10-Jun-3 David Lay, Penzance #245
£500 $830 €725 Mousehole harbour, with figures in boats (45x90cm-18x35in) s.i.verso. 12-Jun-3 Bonhams, Cornwall #581/R

BAILEY, William (1930-) American
Works on paper
£1146 $1800 €1719 Seated female nude (26x16cm-10x6in) s. brush ink wash exec.c.1955 sold with three drs. 21-Nov-2 Swann Galleries, New York #12/R est:2000-3000

BAILEY, Winifred (1886-1979) British
£320 $502 €480 Beach scene with children playing and woman hanging out washing (18x20cm-7x8in) board. 16-Apr-3 George Kidner, Lymington #103/R

BAILIE, Samuel (1879-1926) British
Works on paper
£380 $592 €600 Jeux de flechettes (31x44cm-12x17in) s.d.1911 chl htd gouache dr. 15-Oct-2 Vanderkindere, Brussels #70

BAILLIE, Charles Cameron (fl.1925-1931) British
£2000 $3180 €3000 Illicit still (144x94cm-57x37in) s. board. 6-Mar-3 Christie's, Kensington #251/R est:2000-3000

BAILLIE, William (1905-) British
£1600 $2432 €2400 Dying flower heads (86x112cm-34x44in) s. exhib. 28-Aug-2 Sotheby's, London #1043/R est:1500-2000

BAILLY, Alice (1872-1938) Swiss
Works on paper
£858 $1356 €1287 Wedding party (14x14cm-6x6in) s. mixed media. 28-Nov-2 Christie's, Zurich #72/R (S.FR 2000)
£4717 $7642 €8349 La foret enchantee (110x113cm-43x44in) pencil chl oil prov. 26-May-3 Sotheby's, Zurich #98/R est:10000-15000 (S.FR 10000)

BAILLY, C Durieux (?) Belgian?
£314 $487 €500 Trompe l'oeil (59x50cm-23x20in) s. 1-Oct-2 Palais de Beaux Arts, Brussels #453

BAILLY, Louis (1905-) Belgian
Works on paper
£280 $437 €420 Esmeralda and Quasimodo (27x21cm-11x8in) s.d.12 W/C. 9-Apr-3 Cheffins Grain & Comins, Cambridge #591/R

BAILY, Edward Hodges (1788-1867) British
Sculpture
£4255 $6596 €6383 Fisherboy (65cm-26in) s.d.1852 marble. 3-Dec-2 Bukowskis, Stockholm #231/R est:50000-70000 (S.KR 60000)

BAIN, Donald (1904-1979) British
£520 $822 €780 Still life of mixed roses (44x39cm-17x15in) s. 19-Dec-2 Bonhams, Edinburgh #345
£1250 $1938 €1875 Backwater (25x30cm-10x12in) s. board. 7-Dec-2 Shapes, Edinburgh #328 est:800-1200
£2600 $4030 €3900 Riviera (31x24cm-12x9in) s. board. 7-Dec-2 Shapes, Edinburgh #329 est:800-1200
£2700 $4185 €4050 Chapelle (56x47cm-22x19in) s.d.1947. 2-Nov-2 Shapes, Edinburgh #302/R est:600-800

BAIN, Jean (19th C) French
£655 $1022 €983 Winter village in evening (77x113cm-30x44in) s. 6-Nov-2 Dobiaschofsky, Bern #326/R est:1900 (S.FR 1500)

BAINBRIDGE, Arthur (19/20th C) British
Works on paper
£750 $1170 €1125 View of Ashby de la Launde (37x54cm-15x21in) s.d.1895 W/C. 8-Oct-2 Sotheby's, Olympia #398/R

BAINES, Henry (1823-1894) British
£1300 $2145 €1885 High bridge, Kings Lynn (37x31cm-15x12in) pair. 1-Jul-3 Bonhams, Norwich #233 est:800-1200

BAINES, Thomas (1820-1875) British
£10000 $15500 €15000 Attacking in the Amatolas (46x63cm-18x25in) bears sig. 24-Sep-2 Christie's, London #214/R est:10000-15000
Works on paper
£4000 $6200 €6000 Wildebeest, Quagga and ostriches on the salt pan (28x39cm-11x15in) s.i.d.April 14 1863 W/C. 24-Sep-2 Christie's, London #215/R est:4000-6000

BAINES, Thomas (attrib) (1820-1875) British
£2800 $4340 €4200 East Indiaman in Table Bay (30x41cm-12x16in) 24-Sep-2 Christie's, London #216/R est:3000-5000

BAIRD, Annie (1932-1999) New Zealander
Works on paper
£307 $435 €461 Dunedin (76x58cm-30x23in) s.d.1993 W/C. 20-Mar-2 Watson's, Christchurch #47/R est:900-1600 (NZ.D 1000)

BAIRD, John (1843-1894) Australian
Sculpture
£4615 $7200 €6923 Bust of Kerosene Shale son (48cm-19in) on square plinth. 8-Apr-3 Christie's, Melbourne #283/R est:6000-8000 (A.D 12000)

BAIRD, Nathaniel Hughes (1865-c.1930) British
£300 $462 €450 Portrait of a terrier, Rory (41x30cm-16x12in) mono. 3-Sep-2 Gorringes, Lewes #2302
Works on paper
£680 $1074 €1020 Taking horse to water (22x36cm-9x14in) mono. W/C. 2-Dec-2 Bonhams, Bath #26/R
£900 $1404 €1350 Man goeth forth (28x33cm-11x13in) mono. W/Cover pencil. 10-Oct-2 Rupert Toovey, Partridge Green #1450/R

£1333 $2187 €1933 Draught horse pulling a sailing barge along a canal (28x38cm-11x15in) mono. W/C. 9-Jun-3 Hodgins, Calgary #91/R est:1000-1500 (C.D 3000)
£1689 $2770 €2449 Heavy horses and carts alongside a canal (44x48cm-17x19in) mono. W/C. 9-Jun-3 Hodgins, Calgary #92/R est:1500-2000 (C.D 3800)

BAIRD, William Baptiste (1847-1917) American
£377 $600 €566 Alpine landscape (56x81cm-22x32in) s. painted c.1880. 2-Mar-3 Toomey, Oak Park #706/R
£759 $1200 €1200 Silhouette sur un port (24x32cm-9x13in) s. 2-Dec-2 Tajan, Paris #17
£769 $1200 €1154 Woodland landscape with stag (33x46cm-13x18in) s. 1-Aug-2 Eldred, East Dennis #937c
£791 $1266 €1100 Coq et poules picorant (16x22cm-6x9in) mono. cardboard. 19-May-3 Horta, Bruxelles #435
£1258 $2000 €1887 Pastoral landscape (56x81cm-22x32in) s. painted c.1880. 2-Mar-3 Toomey, Oak Park #599/R est:2000-3000
£1698 $2750 €2462 Barnyard activity (53x79cm-21x31in) s.i. canvas on board. 21-May-3 Doyle, New York #76/R est:5000-7000
£1800 $3006 €2610 Vera Cruz, Mexico (24x33cm-9x13in) s. 18-Jun-3 Sotheby's, Olympia #34/R est:1000-1500

BAISCH, Hermann (1846-1894) German
£423 $701 €600 Dutch landscape with cows at a trough (38x54cm-15x21in) s. 14-Jun-3 Arnold, Frankfurt #701/R
£474 $734 €711 From the forest (26x35cm-10x14in) cardboard painted c.1890. 3-Dec-2 SOGA, Bratislava #185/R (SL.K 30000)

BAISCH, Hermann (attrib) (1846-1894) German
£645 $948 €1000 Extensive wooded landscape (43x73cm-17x29in) canvas on board. 20-Jun-2 Dr Fritz Nagel, Stuttgart #748/R

BAITELLO, Giorgio (20th C) Italian?
£1899 $2962 €3000 Mercato (20x27cm-8x11in) s.d.1926 board. 18-Oct-2 Dr Fritz Nagel, Stuttgart #462/R est:4200

BAITLER, Zoma (1908-1994) Uruguayan
£333 $520 €500 Spring (24x29cm-9x11in) s. 10-Oct-2 Galleria Y Remates, Montevideo #99/R
£385 $600 €578 La consergerie (44x32cm-17x13in) s. 30-Jul-2 Galleria Y Remates, Montevideo #38/R
£406 $650 €609 Square (27x39cm-11x15in) s. 5-Jan-3 Galleria Y Remates, Montevideo #68/R
£438 $700 €657 Stroll (41x51cm-16x20in) s. 5-Jan-3 Galleria Y Remates, Montevideo #67/R
£440 $700 €660 Cook (60x50cm-24x20in) s. 2-Mar-3 Galleria Y Remates, Montevideo #16/R
£513 $800 €770 En el bosque (60x50cm-24x20in) 30-Jul-2 Galleria Y Remates, Montevideo #39/R
£531 $850 €797 The Seine (49x60cm-19x24in) s. 5-Jan-3 Galleria Y Remates, Montevideo #61/R
£538 $860 €807 Wood (50x60cm-20x24in) s. 5-Jan-3 Galleria Y Remates, Montevideo #64/R
£566 $900 €849 Landscape in Israel (49x55cm-19x22in) s. 2-Mar-3 Galleria Y Remates, Montevideo #15/R
£575 $920 €863 Paris (36x48cm-14x19in) s.i.d.1949. 5-Jan-3 Galleria Y Remates, Montevideo #65
£577 $900 €866 Sacre coeur (60x50cm-24x20in) s. 30-Jul-2 Galleria Y Remates, Montevideo #109/R
£881 $1400 €1322 Fishing boats (39x41cm-15x16in) s. s.i.verso. 2-Mar-3 Galleria Y Remates, Montevideo #14/R
£938 $1500 €1407 Landscape (59x68cm-23x27in) s. d.1941 verso. 5-Jan-3 Galleria Y Remates, Montevideo #59/R
£1000 $1600 €1500 Brooklyn bridge (51x61cm-20x24in) s. 5-Jan-3 Galleria Y Remates, Montevideo #60/R
£1115 $1750 €1673 Rodo Park (50x61cm-20x24in) s. 20-Nov-2 Galleria Y Remates, Montevideo #40/R
£1115 $1750 €1673 Bridge over the Miguelete (50x75cm-20x30in) s. 20-Nov-2 Galleria Y Remates, Montevideo #41/R
£1195 $1900 €1793 River (81x81cm-32x32in) s. 2-Mar-3 Galleria Y Remates, Montevideo #12/R
£1250 $2000 €1875 Interior (85x65cm-33x26in) s.d.74. 5-Jan-3 Galleria Y Remates, Montevideo #58/R
£2063 $3300 €3095 Prado (90x102cm-35x40in) s.d.43. 5-Jan-3 Galleria Y Remates, Montevideo #55/R
£4487 $7000 €6731 Melancolia de la tarde (110x195cm-43x77in) s. s.i.d.febrero 1940 verso burlap prov. 30-Jul-2 Galleria Y Remates, Montevideo #115/R est:9000-12000

BAIXERAS Y VERDAGUER, Dionisio (1862-1943) Spanish
£5310 $8390 €7700 Fishermen with Barcelona harbour in background (48x84cm-19x33in) s. 1-Apr-3 Segre, Madrid #131/R
£15094 $23547 €24000 Preparing the fishing lines (71x116cm-28x46in) s.d.1895. 17-Sep-2 Segre, Madrid #114/R est:20000

BAIZE, Wayne (1943-) American
Works on paper
£1096 $1600 €1644 Big Bend cow country (33x66cm-13x26in) col pencil. 18-May-2 Altermann Galleries, Santa Fe #151/R

BAJ, Enrico (1924-2003) Italian
£962 $1510 €1500 Untitled (48x60cm-19x24in) s. acrylic collage cardboard. 23-Nov-2 Meeting Art, Vercelli #282/R
£2032 $3170 €3048 Figure (52x42cm-20x17in) s. acrylic. 6-Nov-2 AB Stockholms Auktionsverk #954/R est:8000-10000 (S.KR 29000)
£3767 $5877 €5500 Soldier (45x55cm-18x22in) s. oil collage polymer painted 1985. 10-Apr-3 Finarte Semenzato, Rome #202/R est:6500
£3797 $5924 €6000 Small crowd (50x60cm-20x24in) s. acrylic collage painted 1989. 14-Sep-2 Meeting Art, Vercelli #817/R
£3846 $6038 €6000 Mr Medina (44x31cm-17x12in) s. acrylic collage painted 1974 lit. 19-Nov-2 Finarte, Milan #128/R est:4600
£4861 $7729 €7000 Le plus beau du quartier (49x70cm-19x28in) s. s.i.d.1954 verso cardboard. 1-May-3 Meeting Art, Vercelli #215
£8654 $13413 €13500 Mountain (73x92cm-29x36in) s. oil mixed media wallpaper painted 1958 prov.lit. 4-Dec-2 Finarte, Milan #297/R est:12000
£10000 $16400 €15000 Lady (80x60cm-31x24in) s. oil plastic passementerie wood pearls objects fabric on boa. 6-Feb-3 Christie's, London #645/R est:10000-15000
£16000 $25280 €24000 Femme en turquoise (146x114cm-57x45in) s. acrylic collage fabric rope wood metal painted 1969 prov.lit. 3-Apr-3 Christie's, Kensington #247/R est:20000
Sculpture
£1181 $1877 €1700 Personnage decore (30x34x6cm-12x13x2in) s.num.8/20 various objects resin. 29-Apr-3 Artcurial Briest, Paris #368/R est:1000-1500
£1560 $2528 €2200 Generle (53cm-21in) s. num.21/30 perspex with medals. 22-May-3 Stadion, Trieste #221/R est:1400-1800
Works on paper
£307 $500 €461 Untitled (69x79cm-27x31in) s.verso mixed media collage. 1-Feb-3 Susanin's, Chicago #5004
£317 $500 €500 Horatius Nelson (80x70cm-31x28in) s.i.verso shells collage. 2-Dec-2 Tajan, Paris #232
£402 $639 €603 Composition (47x35cm-19x14in) s.i. crayon Indian ink. 26-Feb-3 Kunsthallen, Copenhagen #43 (D.KR 4400)
£1410 $2186 €2200 Teucro (83x41cm-33x16in) s. polymer wood fabric. 4-Dec-2 Finarte, Milan #534/R
£2639 $4354 €3800 Horatius Nelson Duke of Bronte (79x70cm-31x28in) s.i.verso mixed media panel. 1-Jul-3 Artcurial Briest, Paris #836/R est:1000-1200
£2738 $4325 €4107 Man in profile (30x24cm-12x9in) s. mixed media collage. 28-Apr-3 Bukowskis, Stockholm #316/R est:25000-30000 (S.KR 36000)
£7358 $11479 €11037 Untitled (86x67cm-34x26in) s. mixed media collage. 5-Nov-2 Bukowskis, Stockholm #325/R est:100000-125000 (S.KR 105000)
£10500 $17535 €15225 Untitled (65x50cm-26x20in) s. mixed media fabric exec.c.1960 prov. 26-Jun-3 Sotheby's, London #205/R est:4000-6000
£14184 $22979 €20000 Vito Da Corato (92x73cm-36x29in) s. i.d.1966 collage braiding oil badges wood cloth prov.exhib.lit. 26-May-3 Christie's, Milan #362/R est:12000-16000
£15058 $24243 €22587 Female figure (140x118cm-55x46in) s.verso mixed media collage prov. 7-May-3 AB Stockholms Auktionsverk #1115/R est:150000-200000 (S.KR 195000)
£16000 $24640 €24000 Il Re e la Regina (113x127cm-44x50in) i.on stretcher cotton fabric passementerie medals collage. 23-Oct-2 Christie's, London #117/R est:15000-20000
£25000 $38500 €37500 Generale (120x100cm-47x39in) s. fabric embroidery objects collage panel prov.lit. 22-Oct-2 Christie's, London #42/R est:25000-35000
£35000 $54600 €52500 Decore au merite du progres (130x97cm-51x38in) s.i. stretcher mixed media pebbles oil on canvas painted 1959. 21-Oct-2 Sotheby's, London #51/R est:25000-30000
£45890 $72048 €67000 Portrait (73x60cm-29x24in) s. i.verso mixed media on canvas prov.exhib.lit. 15-Apr-3 Laurence Calmels, Paris #4125/R est:15000

BAJ, Enrico and KOSTABI, Mark (20th C) Italian/American
Works on paper
£231 $358 €360 Untitled (46x31cm-18x12in) s.d.1992 pencil. 4-Dec-2 Finarte, Milan #224

BAKALOWICZ, Ladislaus (1833-1904) Polish
£950 $1548 €1425 Cardinal Richelieu (26x16cm-10x6in) s. panel. 29-Jan-3 Sotheby's, Olympia #261/R est:600-800
£3000 $4680 €4500 Spring. Winter (32x15cm-13x6in) s. panel pair. 17-Sep-2 Sotheby's, Olympia #256/R est:3000-4000

£3165	$5000	€5000	Sortie de Rome de Charles V (65x92cm-26x36in) s.i.d. 29-Nov-2 Drouot Estimations, Paris #53 est:7000
£9494	$15000	€15000	Moscow burning (66x91cm-26x36in) s.i. 1-Dec-2 Bukowskis, Helsinki #227/R est:6000-8000

Works on paper

£1300	$2119	€1950	Reclining nude (34x63cm-13x25in) s. col chk. 29-Jan-3 Sotheby's, Olympia #349/R est:600-800

BAKELS, Reinier Sybrand (1873-1956) Dutch

£599	$964	€850	Town canal by evening light (36x51cm-14x20in) 7-May-3 Vendue Huis, Gravenhage #485/R
£845	$1361	€1200	Delft harbour (64x55cm-25x22in) s. 7-May-3 Vendue Huis, Gravenhage #495/R
£845	$1361	€1200	Dredger (35x68cm-14x27in) s. 7-May-3 Vendue Huis, Gravenhage #511
£915	$1474	€1300	City view of Enkhuizen (61x78cm-24x31in) 7-May-3 Vendue Huis, Gravenhage #502/R
£915	$1474	€1300	Polder landscape with moored boats in foreground (38x59cm-15x23in) s.d.17. 7-May-3 Vendue Huis, Gravenhage #503/R
£986	$1587	€1400	Fishing boats on the land (42x63cm-17x25in) 7-May-3 Vendue Huis, Gravenhage #489/R
£1127	$1814	€1600	Mill, Texel (68x84cm-27x33in) 7-May-3 Vendue Huis, Gravenhage #488 est:900-1200
£1127	$1814	€1600	View of Maassluis (62x42cm-24x17in) s.d.25 verso. 7-May-3 Vendue Huis, Gravenhage #510 est:1000-1500
£1408	$2268	€2000	View of city of Amsterdam (38x57cm-15x22in) s. 7-May-3 Vendue Huis, Gravenhage #508/R est:1500-2000
£1408	$2268	€2000	View of port of Maassluis (47x55cm-19x22in) 7-May-3 Vendue Huis, Gravenhage #512 est:1000-1500
£2254	$3628	€3200	View of town of Amersfoort in winter (84x68cm-33x27in) s. lit. 7-May-3 Vendue Huis, Gravenhage #496/R est:2000-2500
£2676	$4308	€3800	Harbour mouth of Veere (41x60cm-16x24in) s. d.1915 verso exhib.lit. 7-May-3 Vendue Huis, Gravenhage #493/R est:2500-3500

BAKER OF LEAMINGTON, Thomas (1809-1869) British

£2000	$3100	€3000	Distant view of Coventry (20cm-8in circular) panel. 31-Oct-2 Locke & England, Leamington Spa #181 est:1800-2500
£12143	$19186	€18215	On the road to Warwick (32x48cm-13x19in) s.d.1860 prov. 26-Nov-2 Sotheby's, Melbourne #181/R est:20000-30000 (A.D 34000)
£13571	$21443	€20357	Leamington Spa and Warwick Castle in the distance (30x46cm-12x18in) s.d.1840 prov. 26-Nov-2 Sotheby's, Melbourne #180/R est:20000-30000 (A.D 38000)

BAKER, Alan Douglas (1914-1987) Australian

£286	$451	€429	Country scene Southern Highlands (27x33cm-11x13in) s.d.40 board. 18-Nov-2 Goodman, Sydney #51 (A.D 800)
£464	$734	€696	Still life of red flowers (13x29cm-5x11in) s. board. 18-Nov-2 Goodman, Sydney #192 (A.D 1300)
£536	$846	€804	Hickson St The Rocks (29x37cm-11x15in) s. board. 18-Nov-2 Goodman, Sydney #182 (A.D 1500)
£554	$875	€831	Still life of white blossom (18x42cm-7x17in) s. board. 18-Nov-2 Goodman, Sydney #7 (A.D 1550)
£632	$960	€948	Helianthus (39x49cm-15x19in) s. board. 19-Aug-2 Joel, Victoria #273 est:1500-2000 (A.D 1800)
£643	$1016	€965	Calendula (25x42cm-10x17in) s. board. 18-Nov-2 Goodman, Sydney #69 (A.D 1800)
£763	$1206	€1145	Untitled, still life (25x30cm-10x12in) s. board. 7-Apr-3 Shapiro, Sydney #446 (A.D 2000)
£802	$1267	€1203	Untitled, still life (20x25cm-8x10in) s. board prov. 7-Apr-3 Shapiro, Sydney #445/R (A.D 2100)
£986	$1498	€1479	Wattle (26x35cm-10x14in) s. board. 27-Aug-2 Goodman, Sydney #177 est:2400-3500 (A.D 2750)
£1000	$1580	€1500	Petunias white (29x37cm-11x15in) s. board. 18-Nov-2 Goodman, Sydney #71 est:2500-3500 (A.D 2800)
£1226	$1925	€1839	Apricot nectar roses (55x44cm-22x17in) s. 15-Apr-3 Lawson Menzies, Sydney #57/R est:3500-5500 (A.D 3200)
£1318	$2095	€1977	Cascade petunias (44x37cm-17x15in) s. board. 5-May-3 Sotheby's, Melbourne #288/R est:3000-5000 (A.D 3400)
£1322	$2035	€1983	Apricot blossom (25x45cm-10x18in) s. board prov. 3-Sep-2 Shapiro, Sydney #373 est:3000-5000 (A.D 3700)
£1429	$2214	€2144	Helianthus (39x49cm-15x19in) s. board. 29-Oct-2 Lawson Menzies, Sydney #24/R est:5000-6000 (A.D 4000)
£1429	$2214	€2144	Cecil Brunner roses (26x35cm-10x14in) s. board. 29-Oct-2 Lawson Menzies, Sydney #39/R est:4000-5000 (A.D 4000)
£1792	$2724	€2688	Peach blossom (66x91cm-26x36in) s. composition board exhib. 28-Aug-2 Deutscher-Menzies, Melbourne #246/R est:5500-7500 (A.D 5000)
£1792	$2724	€2688	Hadley roses (39x59cm-15x23in) s. board. 27-Aug-2 Goodman, Sydney #43/R est:4000-6000 (A.D 5000)
£1916	$3008	€2874	River scene (44x58cm-17x23in) s. board. 15-Apr-3 Lawson Menzies, Sydney #53/R est:1000-2000 (A.D 5000)
£3036	$4705	€4554	Perennial phlox (70x75cm-28x30in) s. board. 29-Oct-2 Lawson Menzies, Sydney #66/R est:9000-12000 (A.D 8500)

BAKER, Alfred (19th C) British

Works on paper

£360	$583	€540	Figures fishing on the banks of Loch Awe with Kilchurn Castle beyond (49x75cm-19x30in) s. W/C. 23-May-3 Honiton Galleries, Honiton #634

BAKER, Arthur (19th C) British

£500	$825	€725	Landscape with a farm, cattle, sheep and horse by a pond (30x46cm-12x18in) s. 3-Jul-3 Ewbank, Send #310

BAKER, Christina Asquith (1868-1960) Australian

£2789	$4573	€4184	Shrine of Remembrance, Melbourne (76x63cm-30x25in) s. lit. 4-Jun-3 Deutscher-Menzies, Melbourne #308/R est:3000-5000 (A.D 7000)

BAKER, Dennis (1951-) Australian

Works on paper

£394	$599	€591	Lady of Emerald City (75x54cm-30x21in) s. W/C chl pastel. 27-Aug-2 Goodman, Sydney #55 (A.D 1100)
£893	$1411	€1340	Pink watermelon (80x100cm-31x39in) s. pastel. 18-Nov-2 Goodman, Sydney #67/R (A.D 2500)

BAKER, Elisha Taylor (1827-1890) American

£938	$1500	€1407	Ships in a harbour sunset (15x30cm-6x12in) s.d. paper on board. 15-Mar-3 Selkirks, St. Louis #336 est:600-800
£2922	$4500	€4383	Harbour scene at dusk (76x64cm-30x25in) s. board prov. 24-Oct-2 Shannon's, Milford #202/R est:5000-7000
£3247	$5000	€4871	Sunset and dawn (51x30cm-20x12in) s. pair prov. 24-Oct-2 Shannon's, Milford #206/R est:6000-8000
£3289	$5000	€4934	Herreshoff steam launch, Henrietta, off Atlantic Highlands, New Jersey (46x81cm-18x32in) s. 17-Aug-2 North East Auctions, Portsmouth #1071/R est:8000-12000
£5592	$8500	€8388	Seawanhaka Corinthian yacht club tender (30x56cm-12x22in) s. 17-Aug-2 North East Auctions, Portsmouth #1008/R est:8000-12000
£14194	$22000	€21291	Centennial pilot boat no.7 (56x91cm-22x36in) mono. 5-Dec-2 Christie's, Rockefeller NY #24/R est:20000-30000

BAKER, George A (1821-1880) American

£1923	$3000	€2885	Portrait of a young lady holding a rose (69x56cm-27x22in) 20-Sep-2 Du Mouchelle, Detroit #2001/R est:1500-2000
£2083	$3250	€3125	Portrait of a young lady (69x56cm-27x22in) 20-Sep-2 Du Mouchelle, Detroit #2002/R est:1500-2000

BAKER, George Herbert (1878-1943) American

Works on paper

£267	$425	€401	Along the Whitewater River (13x18cm-5x7in) s. pastel exec.c.1924. 2-Mar-3 Toomey, Oak Park #552/R

BAKER, Gladys M (1889-?) British

£480	$758	€720	The critic (62x52cm-24x20in) s. 4-Apr-3 Moore Allen & Innocent, Cirencester #655/R

BAKER, Jan (1939-) Norwegian

£1821	$2841	€2732	Man on horseback and bird (65x87cm-26x34in) s.d.1990. 21-Oct-2 Blomqvist, Oslo #426/R est:20000-25000 (N.KR 21000)
£2163	$3417	€3245	Man fishing and swallows in flight (74x100cm-29x39in) s.d.90. 2-Dec-2 Blomqvist, Oslo #480/R est:30000-40000 (N.KR 25000)

BAKER, K Siegfried (1922-) German

£253	$392	€400	Canal in Dutch city (50x60cm-20x24in) s. panel. 27-Sep-2 Auktionhaus Georg Rehm, Augsburg #8007/R
£350	$546	€550	Romantic landscape with figures by lake (30x40cm-12x16in) s. panel exhib. 8-Nov-2 Auktionhaus Georg Rehm, Augsburg #8008

BAKER, Kenneth (20th C) South African

£258	$402	€387	District six (55x46cm-22x18in) s. board. 15-Oct-2 Stephan Welz, Johannesburg #212 est:1200-1500 (SA.R 4200)
£399	$623	€599	Two Malay women (64x48cm-25x19in) s. canvas on board. 15-Oct-2 Stephan Welz, Johannesburg #504 est:2500-4000 (SA.R 6500)

BAKER, Roger (1928-) American

£903	$1400	€1355	Girl in the blue room (48x56cm-19x22in) s.i.d.1952 board. 29-Oct-2 Sotheby's, New York #263/R est:500-700
£1774	$2750	€2661	Hammock (30x40cm-12x16in) s. 29-Oct-2 Sotheby's, New York #264/R est:300-400

Works on paper

£451 $700 €677 Portraits of Mario Amaya and John Cranko (21x31cm-8x12in) s.d.1957 pencil two. 29-Oct-2 Sotheby's, New York #267/R

£580 $900 €870 Portraits of Guy Laroche and Michael Thomas (27x21cm-11x8in) s.i.d.1956 panel two exhib. 29-Oct-2 Sotheby's, New York #266/R est:500-700

BAKER, Samuel Henry (1824-1909) British

£340 $564 €493 Mountain landscape (51x76cm-20x30in) s. 12-Jun-3 Gorringes, Lewes #1669

£1150 $1817 €1725 Summer time (61x92cm-24x36in) s. i.verso. 18-Dec-2 John Nicholson, Haslemere #1274/R est:1000-1500

Works on paper

£260 $434 €377 Woodland river scene (39x62cm-15x24in) s. W/C. 9-Jul-3 George Kidner, Lymington #139/R

£300 $471 €450 Upland landscape (38x62cm-15x24in) s. W/C. 25-Nov-2 Bonhams, Chester #880

£480 $744 €720 Lake at Bredon, Worcestershire (39x31cm-15x12in) s. W/C. 3-Dec-2 Sotheby's, Olympia #118/R

£700 $1141 €1050 Pont Mallwyd, near Dinas Mowddwy (57x98cm-22x39in) W/C exhib. 29-Jan-3 Sotheby's, Olympia #60/R

BAKER, W (19th C) British

£1986 $3177 €2880 Maori salutation, Wanganui River, New Zealand (67x44cm-26x17in) s.i. 13-May-3 Watson's, Christchurch #81/R est:10000-20000 (NZ.D 5500)

BAKER, William (19th C) British

Works on paper

£300 $477 €450 Loch Awe, Kilchurn Castle (52x77cm-20x30in) s. W/C. 25-Feb-3 Bonhams, Knightsbridge #28/R

£380 $635 €551 Sailing barges on the Dutch coast (49x68cm-19x27in) s.d.1919 w/. 17-Jun-3 Anderson & Garland, Newcastle #243

BAKER, William George (1864-1929) New Zealander

£421 $665 €632 Cosmos Parks, Lake Wakatipe, New Zealand (41x61cm-16x24in) s. 27-Nov-2 Falkkloos, Malmo #78006/R (S.KR 6000)

£687 $1002 €1031 Steamship and sailboats (59x84cm-23x33in) s. 12-Sep-1 Watson's, Christchurch #40 est:3000-5000 (NZ.D 2300)

£2070 $3250 €3105 Settler's home, Taihape (90x136cm-35x54in) s.i. 10-Dec-2 Peter Webb, Auckland #57/R est:7000-10000 (NZ.D 6500)

Works on paper

£470 $734 €705 Milford Sound (36x52cm-14x20in) s. W/C. 7-Nov-2 International Art Centre, Auckland #128/R est:1000-2000 (NZ.D 1500)

BAKER-CLACK, Arthur (1877-1955) Australian

£1254 $1906 €1881 French hillside village (26x35cm-10x14in) s. wood panel. 28-Aug-2 Deutscher-Menzies, Melbourne #303/R est:4000-5000 (A.D 3500)

£1714 $2657 €2571 Spanish courtyard (36x45cm-14x18in) s. board. 29-Oct-2 Lawson Menzies, Sydney #10/R est:5500-7500 (A.D 4800)

BAKHUYZEN, Alexandre H (1826-1878) Dutch

£1310 $2083 €1900 Figures on a country road (29x44cm-11x17in) s.d.1859 panel. 10-Mar-3 Sotheby's, Amsterdam #109 est:1500-2000

BAKHUYZEN, Gerardina Jacoba van de Sande (1826-1895) Dutch

£1154 $1788 €1800 Still life of fruit (25x30cm-10x12in) s. 5-Dec-2 Dr Fritz Nagel, Stuttgart #640/R est:1500

£3205 $5032 €5000 Flowers in vase on window ledge (66x56cm-26x22in) s. 23-Nov-2 Arnold, Frankfurt #687/R est:10000

£9028 $14354 €13000 Rhodondenrons and primulas on a ledge (15x22cm-6x9in) s. panel. 29-Apr-3 Christie's, Amsterdam #5/R est:7000-9000

£13836 $21308 €22000 Peaches, grapes and pumpkin in a sunny corner of a vegetable garden (51x73cm-20x29in) s.d.1860. 23-Oct-2 Christie's, Amsterdam #128/R est:15000-20000

£18868 $29057 €30000 Wild roses (20x28cm-8x11in) s.d.1868 panel. 23-Oct-2 Christie's, Amsterdam #139/R est:12000-16000

BAKHUYZEN, Hendrick van de Sande (1795-1860) Dutch

£12579 $19371 €20000 Daily activities along a river in a hilly landscape (55x70cm-22x28in) s.d.1830 panel prov.exhib. 23-Oct-2 Christie's, Amsterdam #129/R est:20000-30000

£100694 $160104 €145000 Sorting the catch on the beach of Scheveningen (72x97cm-28x38in) s. panel. 29-Apr-3 Christie's, Amsterdam #192/R est:20000-30000

Works on paper

£700 $1092 €1050 Cattle and sheep grazing in a landscape (32x43cm-13x17in) s.d.1846 W/C. 9-Apr-3 Cheffins Grain & Comins, Cambridge #563/R

BAKHUYZEN, Hendrick van de Sande (attrib) (1795-1860) Dutch

Works on paper

£224 $350 €336 Landscape with travellers (30x38cm-12x15in) chk dr. 28-Mar-3 Aspire, Cleveland #21/R

BAKHUYZEN, Julius Jacobus van de Sande (1835-1925) Dutch

£458 $737 €650 Woman near barn in the forest (38x43cm-15x17in) s.d.1905. 6-May-3 Vendu Notarishuis, Rotterdam #42/R

£1090 $1711 €1700 In the country (15x20cm-6x8in) s. panel. 21-Nov-2 Van Ham, Cologne #1455/R est:1600

£1146 $1789 €1800 Maannacht te Ruurlo (31x42cm-12x17in) s. 6-Nov-2 Vendue Huis, Gravenhage #543 est:1500-2000

£5346 $8233 €8500 De melkbocht - milking time (46x38cm-18x15in) s. canvas on panel prov. 23-Oct-2 Christie's, Amsterdam #198/R est:5000-7000

£5660 $8717 €9000 Herdsmen with cattle on a country road, Drenthe (75x103cm-30x41in) s. painted c.1885. 22-Oct-2 Sotheby's, Amsterdam #104/R est:8000-12000

£9028 $14354 €13000 Guiding the cattle along a path on a sunny afternoon (66x105cm-26x41in) s. prov. 29-Apr-3 Christie's, Amsterdam #131/R est:10000-15000

BAKHUYZEN, Ludolf (1631-1708) Dutch

£4196 $7007 €6000 Navires Hollandais sur une mer agitee (48x65cm-19x26in) 25-Jun-3 Tajan, Paris #34/R est:6000-8000

£19512 $32000 €29268 Shipping in a storm off a rocky coast (77x110cm-30x43in) indis sig. 29-May-3 Sotheby's, New York #2/R est:20000-30000

£70000 $109900 €105000 Dutch and English men of war with a galley and other shipping (68x94cm-27x37in) s.d.1701 prov.lit. 12-Dec-2 Sotheby's, London #30/R est:30000-40000

Works on paper

£75540 $120863 €105000 Man-of-War together with other boats and fishermen hauling catch (32x41cm-13x16in) s. pen oil panel. 13-May-3 Sotheby's, Amsterdam #38/R est:20000-30000

BAKHUYZEN, Ludolf (attrib) (1631-1708) Dutch

£1772 $2747 €2800 Two master on stormy sea (38x58cm-15x23in) 28-Sep-2 Hans Stahl, Hamburg #213/R est:3000

£6329 $10000 €10000 Coastal landscape with boats (49x57cm-19x22in) s. canvas on canvas. 29-Nov-2 Bolland & Marotz, Bremen #648/R est:2500

BAKHUYZEN, Ludolf (style) (1631-1708) Dutch

£9434 $14623 €15000 Ships in heavy seas (40x53cm-16x21in) i. 2-Oct-2 Dorotheum, Vienna #91/R est:15000-20000

BAKKER, Johannes (jnr) (1913-) Dutch

£482 $767 €700 Winter landscape with windmills along a waterway (28x34cm-11x13in) s. panel. 10-Mar-3 Sotheby's, Amsterdam #286

BAKOS, Jozef G (1891-1977) American

£6250 $9750 €9375 Monarch of the canyon (61x76cm-24x30in) s. i.verso prov.lit. 9-Nov-2 Santa Fe Art, Santa Fe #205/R est:8000-12000

BAKSHEEV, Vasily (1862-1958) Russian

£10443 $16500 €15665 At the Dacha (101x74cm-40x29in) s.d.89. 24-Apr-3 Sotheby's, New York #120/R est:18000-25000

BAKST, Andre (20th C) ?

Works on paper

£431 $680 €620 Projet de decor de theatre (31x51cm-12x20in) s.i.d.janvier 1939 Indian ink gouache. 25-Apr-3 Drouot Estimations, Paris #2

BAKST, Léon (1866-1924) Russian

Prints

£6500 $10530 €9750 Costume design fot Madame Trouhanova in la peri (48x34cm-19x13in) s.i.d.1911 num.54/100 col lithograph. 21-May-3 Sotheby's, London #163/R est:6000-8000

Works on paper

£1154 $1800 €1731 Costume design for a Foreigner in Oedipus at Colonna (30x23cm-12x9in) s.i. gouache. 18-Sep-2 Swann Galleries, New York #25/R est:2000-3000

£1800 $2916 €2700 Female nude (44x30cm-17x12in) s.d.1915 pencil. 21-May-3 Sotheby's, London #157/R est:1800-2500

£1900 $3097 €2850 Costume design for Le Priseur in la Pisanelle ou la mort parfumee (30x20cm-12x8in) s.i. pencil gouache. 3-Feb-3 Bonhams, New Bond Street #42/R est:800-1200

£2000 $3260 €3000 Costume design for 2 serviteurs in Phaedre (27x17cm-11x7in) s.i. pencil gouache. 3-Feb-3 Bonhams, New Bond Street #41/R est:1000-2000

£2600 $4238 €3900 Costume design for the Princesses Bathilde and Mathilde in la nuit Ensorcelee ballet (33x24cm-13x9in) pencil gouache prov. 3-Feb-3 Bonhams, New Bond Street #43/R est:800-1200

£9000 $14130 €13500 Costume design for The Queen's guard in Judith (29x22cm-11x9in) s.d.22 gouache gold silver paint over pencil prov.lit. 20-Nov-2 Sotheby's, London #151/R est:10000-15000

£15000 $23550 €22500 Costume design for an Egyptian slave of Menelas in Helene de Sparte (27x20cm-11x8in) s.d.1912 W/C htd gold silver paint over pencil exhib.prov. 20-Nov-2 Sotheby's, London #152/R est:15000-20000

BAKSTEEN, Dirk (1886-1971) Dutch

£828 $1324 €1200 Fermette (19x21cm-7x8in) panel. 17-Mar-3 Amberes, Antwerp #180

£1761 $2712 €2800 Ferme en campine (45x55cm-18x22in) s. 22-Oct-2 Campo, Vlaamse Kaai #404/R

£5517 $8828 €8000 Kempish village (60x75cm-24x30in) s.d.1954 exhib. 15-Mar-3 De Vuyst, Lokeren #554/R est:8000-10000

BALA, Iwan (1956-) British

Works on paper

£300 $468 €450 Language (30x27cm-12x11in) s.d.86 chl wash. 11-Sep-2 Bonhams, Newport #302

£550 $863 €825 Horizon, Wales. Janus at cross roads (18x23cm-7x9in) s.d.01 pen ink pastel pair. 20-Nov-2 Sotheby's, Olympia #95/R

BALACA Y CANSECO, Eduardo (1840-1914) Spanish

£579 $921 €840 Portrait of gentleman with medals (127x95cm-50x37in) s.d.1881. 4-Mar-3 Ansorena, Madrid #323/R

BALAKCHINE, Evgueni (1961-) Russian

£275 $426 €413 Still life with lilacs in a wattle basket (54x65cm-21x26in) s. 29-Sep-2 John Nicholson, Haslemere #61

£338 $527 €500 Vase of flowers (45x50cm-18x20in) s. 25-Mar-3 Durán, Madrid #731/R

BALANDE, Gaston (1880-1971) French

£321 $503 €500 Cote de l'Esterel (27x40cm-11x16in) s. panel. 24-Nov-2 Lesieur & Le Bars, Le Havre #3

£408 $649 €600 Coine de ferme (27x35cm-11x14in) s. panel. 26-Feb-3 Artcurial Briest, Paris #156

£816 $1298 €1200 Le port de la Rochelle (26x34cm-10x13in) s. panel. 26-Feb-3 Artcurial Briest, Paris #155

£833 $1358 €1200 Le vieux chateau pres de la riviere (58x72cm-23x28in) s. 19-Jul-3 Thierry & Lannon, Brest #301

£987 $1540 €1550 Chateau fort dominant la riviere a Castelnau (27x35cm-11x14in) s.d. 10-Nov-2 Eric Pillon, Calais #10/R

£1258 $1950 €2000 Le cirque (54x65cm-21x26in) s. exhib. 4-Oct-2 Tajan, Paris #13 est:1800-2400

£1354 $2139 €2031 Mykonos (54x76cm-21x30in) s.i.d.1939. 14-Nov-2 Stuker, Bern #57/R est:3500-4500 (S.FR 3100)

£1441 $2277 €2162 Acropolis, Athens (53x73cm-21x29in) s.i.d.1949. 14-Nov-2 Stuker, Bern #58/R est:3500-4500 (S.FR 3300)

£1523 $2483 €2300 Retour de peche (50x61cm-20x24in) s.d.08. 2-Feb-3 Muizon & Le Coent, Paris #47

£2431 $3840 €3500 Vers le pont de Valentre, Cahors (54x65cm-21x26in) s. prov. 25-Apr-3 Piasa, Paris #51/R est:3000

£2500 $4075 €3600 La Seine a Mantes la jolie (50x65cm-20x26in) s. 19-Jul-3 Thierry & Lannon, Brest #100 est:3500-4000

£3169 $5261 €4500 Voiles rouges (54x73cm-21x29in) s. 11-Jun-3 Beaussant & Lefèvre, Paris #2/R est:2000-3000

£18987 $30000 €30000 Patineurs (124x140cm-49x55in) s.d.1929. 27-Nov-2 Marc Kohn, Paris #10/R est:10000-15000

Works on paper

£266 $420 €420 Fonderie (27x31cm-11x12in) s.d.56 gouache. 27-Nov-2 Blanchet, Paris #67

BALCAR, Jiri (1929-1968) Czechoslovakian

£1816 $2942 €2633 Still life with kerosene lamp (80x105cm-31x41in) s.d.57. 24-May-3 Dorotheum, Prague #135/R est:80000-120000 (C.KR 80000)

£2270 $3678 €3292 Six o'clock in the afternoon (83x58cm-33x23in) s.d.57. 24-May-3 Dorotheum, Prague #134/R est:100000-150000 (C.KR 100000)

BALDASSINI, Guglielmo (1885-1952) Italian

£440 $678 €700 Marine (24x37cm-9x15in) s. cardboard. 23-Oct-2 Finarte, Milan #121

BALDERO, Giorgio (19th C) Italian

£1049 $1700 €1574 Cavaliers in a tavern at a game of chess (46x58cm-18x23in) s. 24-Jan-3 New Orleans Auction, New Orleans #1383/R est:1800-2500

BALDESSARI, John (1931-) American

Photographs

£8544 $13500 €12816 Blue hope (18x124cm-7x49in) s.i.d.85 black white photograph with gouache prov. 12-Nov-2 Phillips, New York #116/R est:12000-18000

£26250 $42000 €39375 Helicopter over tract house with red sky (244x183cm-96x72in) two gelatin silver print oil tint vinyl paint diptych exec.1990. 15-May-3 Christie's, Rockefeller NY #313/R est:35000-45000

£32911 $52000 €49367 Brutus killer Caesar (272x249cm-107x98in) gelatin silver prints mounted on board triptych. 14-Nov-2 Christie's, Rockefeller NY #437/R est:60000-80000

Works on paper

£5063 $8000 €7595 Study for blasted allegories return (40x101cm-16x40in) s.d.78 pastel oil stick photographs vinyl on board. 22-Apr-3 Butterfields, San Francisco #6075/R est:10000-15000

BALDESSARI, Roberto Iras (1894-1965) Italian

£503 $785 €800 Fishermen on Sorrento beach (50x60cm-20x24in) s. 21-Sep-2 Bolland & Marotz, Bremen #584/R

£3022 $4835 €4200 Vue de Venise (60x50cm-24x20in) s. 17-May-3 De Vuyst, Lokeren #17/R est:4500-5500

£8387 $13252 €13000 Study of rivver (47x30cm-19x12in) s.i. gouache tempera exec.c.1919. 18-Dec-2 Christie's, Rome #147/R

Works on paper

£2595 $4100 €4100 Female nude (20x16cm-8x6in) s.d.1916 pencil dr. 30-Nov-2 Farsetti, Prato #680/R

BALDESSARI, Roberto Iras (attrib) (1894-1965) Italian

£600 $978 €900 Sicilian village scene (40x30cm-16x12in) mono. 13-Feb-3 Christie's, Kensington #174

BALDESSIN, George (1939-1978) Australian

Prints

£1577 $2397 €2366 Personnage with striped dress (50x50cm-20x20in) s.d.1967 num.5/25 et. aquatint lit. 28-Aug-2 Deutscher-Menzies, Melbourne #280/R est:4000-6000 (A.D 4400)

£1786 $2804 €2679 Personage and emblems (101x50cm-40x20in) s.i.num. col etching aquatint edition 10. 25-Nov-2 Christie's, Melbourne #255/R est:4000-6000 (A.D 5000)

Sculpture

£1792 $2724 €2688 Figure in enclosure (43cm-17in) bronze prov.exhib. 28-Aug-2 Deutscher-Menzies, Melbourne #203/R est:4000-5000 (A.D 5000)

£2115 $3363 €3173 Figure in enclosure (43cm-17in) bronze prov.exhib. 4-Mar-3 Deutscher-Menzies, Melbourne #190/R est:4000-5000 (A.D 5500)

£2642 $4175 €3831 Me and M.E (30x27x22cm-12x11x9in) bronze executed c.1964 prov.exhib. 22-Jul-3 Lawson Menzies, Sydney #140/R est:7000-9000 (A.D 6500)

£2679 $4152 €4019 Untitled (30cm-12in) bronze exec.c.1965. 29-Oct-2 Lawson Menzies, Sydney #3/R est:10000-15000 (A.D 7500)

BALDINI, Pietro Paolo (17th C) Italian

Works on paper

£3000 $5010 €4350 Madonna and child in glory appearing to two kneeling female saints (34x24cm-13x9in) bears i. pen brown ink htd white over blk chk. 9-Jul-3 Sotheby's, London #47/R est:2000-2500

BALDOCK, Charles E (fl.1890-1905) British

£620 $1035 €899 Portrait of the Suffolk Punch (43x58cm-17x23in) s. 20-Jun-3 Keys, Aylsham #677/R

BALDOCK, James Walsham (c.1822-1898) British

£600 $948 €900 Ploughing team (30x45cm-12x18in) s.d.1889. 7-Apr-3 David Duggleby, Scarborough #392/R

BALDOCK, Stan (1921-) British

£400 $620 €600 Portrait of Sir Edward Heath (91x71cm-36x28in) s. s.i.d.26/10/94 verso. 3-Dec-2 Bonhams, Knightsbridge #346

BALDOU, Mademoiselle (18th C) French
Works on paper
£390 $632 €550 Portrait presume de Louis XVII (17x14cm-7x6in) s.d.1791 pencil htd chk. 21-May-3 Piasa, Paris #349

BALDREY, Samuel Henry (fl.1897-1899) British
Works on paper
£320 $502 €480 Quiet corner of Salhouse Broad, Norfolk (43x76cm-17x30in) s.d.1886 W/C. 13-Dec-2 Keys, Aylsham #570

BALDUCCIO, Giovanni (c.1300-1360) Italian
Sculpture
£134340 $209570 €213600 Nativity scene (30x39x15cm-12x15x6in) marble. 21-Sep-2 Semenzato, Venice #128/R

BALDUNG GRIEN, Hans (circle) (1484-1545) German
£9500 $14725 €14250 The Flight into Egypt (105x66cm-41x26in) panel. 31-Oct-2 Sotheby's, Olympia #24/R est:5000-7000

BALDUNG GRIEN, Hans (studio) (1484-1545) German
£6452 $9484 €10000 Kneeling angel holding sticks (26x32cm-10x13in) i.d.1529 i. verso panel. 20-Jun-2 Dr Fritz Nagel, Stuttgart #701/R est:18000

BALDUS, Edouard Denis (1813-1882) French
Photographs
£2564 $4051 €4000 Maison Carree a Nimes de la Mission Heliographique (28x36cm-11x14in) salt print lit. 16-Nov-2 Christie's, Paris #39/R est:4000-6000

BALDWIN, Betty (1889-1981) Canadian
£302 $493 €453 Mountain Hill, Quebec (25x30cm-10x12in) s. 12-Feb-3 Iegor de Saint Hippolyte, Montreal #14 (C.D 750)
£324 $516 €470 Magna of winter, Quebec from Levis (41x51cm-16x20in) s.d.1950 i.verso panel. 1-May-3 Heffel, Vancouver #5/R (C.D 750)

BALDWIN, George C (c.1818-1879) American
£10063 $16000 €15095 Portrait of a child with a whip (76x64cm-30x25in) 1-Mar-3 North East Auctions, Portsmouth #484/R est:5000-8000

BALDWIN, Samuel (fl.1843-1858) British
£535 $829 €803 Rest by the Way. Toy seller (25x20cm-10x8in) s.d.1868 verso two prov. 3-Dec-2 Ritchie, Toronto #3024/R est:700-1000 (C.D 1300)

BALDWIN, Samuel (attrib) (fl.1843-1858) British
£350 $500 €525 An autumn evening (25x39cm-10x15in) board. 28-Feb-2 Greenslade Hunt, Taunton #423

BALDWYN, Charles H C (fl.1887-1912) British
Works on paper
£6500 $10790 €9425 Turkeys and chickens in courtyard (61x94cm-24x37in) s.d. pencil W/C. 12-Jun-3 Christie's, Kensington #135/R est:1000-1500

BALE, Alice Marian Ellen (1875-1955) Australian
£351 $533 €527 Castlemaine Street (19x29cm-7x11in) i. i.verso. 19-Aug-2 Joel, Victoria #282 est:1000-1500 (A.D 1000)
£786 $1241 €1179 Camellias (39x29cm-15x11in) prov.exhib. 18-Nov-2 Joel, Victoria #153/R est:1200-1500 (A.D 2200)
£1075 $1634 €1613 Portrait of Clara (49x38cm-19x15in) canvasboard prov. 28-Aug-2 Deutscher-Menzies, Melbourne #237/R est:3500-5000 (A.D 3000)

BALE, C T (fl.1866-1875) British
£500 $780 €750 Still life of fruit in vase (33x43cm-13x17in) s. 10-Sep-2 Louis Taylor, Stoke on Trent #1118

BALE, Charles Thomas (fl.1866-1875) British
£300 $474 €450 Young puppeteers (16x20cm-6x8in) mono.d.1868. 14-Nov-2 Christie's, Kensington #1/R
£352 $550 €528 Still life of fruit and butterfly (29x39cm-11x15in) mono.d.1871. 11-Nov-2 Stephan Welz, Johannesburg #30 (SA.R 5500)
£550 $847 €825 Plums, grapes and peaches (20x30cm-8x12in) s. 5-Sep-2 Christie's, Kensington #350/R
£600 $1002 €870 Still life with a comport of fruit, ewer and wine glass (60x50cm-24x20in) s. 9-Jul-3 Edgar Horn, Eastbourne #309/R
£660 $1102 €957 Peaches, other fruit and stoneware jar on a ledge (20x31cm-8x12in) mono. 24-Jun-3 Bonhams, Knowle #77
£780 $1201 €1170 Oranges, cherries, grapes and ginger jar (36x46cm-14x18in) s. 5-Sep-2 Christie's, Kensington #348/R
£800 $1248 €1200 Still life of mixed fruit in a bowl and beerstein on an oak sideboard (48x74cm-19x29in) s. 18-Oct-2 Keys, Aylsham #692/R
£800 $1272 €1200 Grapes and plums on a stone ledge (24x29cm-9x11in) s. 6-Mar-3 Christie's, Kensington #630/R
£840 $1310 €1260 Grapes, apples and other fruit on a draped table (61x50cm-24x20in) mono.d.1871. 7-Nov-2 Christie's, Kensington #251
£850 $1394 €1275 Fruit, a gourd, and stoneware tankard on a wooden ledge (46x36cm-18x14in) s. 29-May-3 Christie's, Kensington #315/R
£860 $1350 €1290 Fruit in a glass dish and on a stone ledge with a shawl and wine glasses (61x50cm-24x20in) s.d.1893. 15-Apr-3 Bonhams, Knowle #123
£900 $1404 €1350 Apples, grapes a pear and a blue jug on a table (35x46cm-14x18in) s. 7-Nov-2 Christie's, Kensington #250/R
£950 $1501 €1425 Pair of still lives of dead game, fruit, pottery (35x45cm-14x18in) s. pair. 12-Nov-2 Bonhams, Knightsbridge #150/R
£1000 $1560 €1500 Grapes, peaches, redcurrants and butterfly on a mossy bank (36x46cm-14x18in) mono.d.1871. 7-Nov-2 Christie's, Kensington #245/R est:1500-2000
£1000 $1590 €1500 Grapes, pears an apple, jug and game on a shelf (35x46cm-14x18in) mono. 6-Mar-3 Christie's, Kensington #631/R est:800-1200
£1050 $1712 €1523 Still life of fruit, pumpkin and an ewer (45x35cm-18x14in) mono. pair. 21-Jul-3 Bonhams, Bath #99/R est:500-700
£1300 $2028 €1950 Still life with oranges and jug. Still life with bird and apples (36x46cm-14x18in) s. pair. 17-Sep-2 Sotheby's, Olympia #171/R est:1000-1500
£1300 $2132 €1950 Fruit, a gourd, and stoneware tankard on a ledge (61x51cm-24x20in) mono.d.1872 prov.exhib. 29-May-3 Christie's, Kensington #311/R est:1500-2000
£1741 $2750 €2612 Still life with fruit and flowers. s.d.75. 26-Apr-3 Thomaston Place, Thomaston #40
£2000 $3080 €3000 Fruit, grouse and vase on a table. Fruit and ginger jar on a table (46x36cm-18x14in) s. pair. 5-Sep-2 Christie's, Kensington #336/R est:2000-3000
£3659 $6000 €5489 Various fruit on a silver tray, with a jar on a draped ledge (71x91cm-28x36in) s.d.1885. 5-Feb-3 Christie's, Rockefeller NY #193/R est:6000-8000

BALE, Charles Thomas (attrib) (fl.1866-1875) British
£320 $512 €464 Still life of flowers, grapes and fruit on a shelf (47x59cm-19x23in) 19-May-3 Bearnes, Exeter #173
£340 $537 €493 Still life of a jug and fruit on a ledge (36x46cm-14x18in) 22-Jul-3 Gorringes, Lewes #1718
£7800 $12324 €11700 Summer flowers (51x41cm-20x16in) board. 13-Nov-2 Halls, Shrewsbury #410 est:300-500

BALEN, Hendrik van (circle) (1575-1632) Flemish
£6000 $9360 €9000 Feast of Archelous (53x73cm-21x29in) panel. 10-Apr-3 Christie's, Kensington #2/R est:8000-12000

BALESTRA, Antonio (attrib) (1666-1740) Italian
£15000 $25050 €21750 Joseph interepreting dreams (97x127cm-38x50in) prov. 8-Jul-3 Sotheby's, Olympia #453/R est:8000-12000

BALESTRA, Antonio (circle) (1666-1740) Italian
£4487 $6955 €7000 Salomon worshipping the idols (200x146cm-79x57in) 4-Dec-2 Christie's, Rome #478/R

BALESTRIERI, Lionello (1872-1958) Italian
£1013 $1600 €1600 Lady in interior (35x43cm-14x17in) s. 26-Nov-2 Christie's, Rome #32

BALFOUR, J Lawson (1870-1966) Australian
Works on paper
£840 $1327 €1260 Woman in a pink dress holding a parasol (37x14cm-15x6in) s. W/C gouache. 2-Apr-3 Christie's, Melbourne #14/R est:2000-3000 (A.D 2200)

BALFOUR-BROWNE, Vincent (1880-1963) British
Works on paper
£600 $972 €900 Pheasant in undergrowth (15x20cm-6x8in) s.d.1955 W/C. 21-Jan-3 Bonhams, Knightsbridge #274/R

BALINK, Hendricus (1882-1963) American
Works on paper
£2115 $3300 €3173 Takequala of Taos (36x25cm-14x10in) crayon. 9-Nov-2 Altermann Galleries, Santa Fe #110

BALINT, Arpad (1870-?) Hungarian
£300 $468 €450 Portrait of a ram (80x61cm-31x24in) s. 17-Sep-2 Rosebery Fine Art, London #582
£7547 $12000 €11321 Young girls dancing in a summer meadow (96x202cm-38x80in) s. 5-Mar-3 Christie's, Rockefeller NY #67/R est:4000-6000

BALINT, Endre (1914-1986) Hungarian
£2017 $3126 €3026 Wooden tale (90x23cm-35x9in) s. board. 6-Dec-2 Kieselbach, Budapest #130/R (H.F 750000)
£2017 $3126 €2925 Glass (30x30cm-12x12in) s.d.73 s.i.d.1973 verso prov.exhib. 9-Dec-2 Mu Terem Galeria, Budapest #93/R est:440000 (H.F 750000)
£9681 $15006 €14037 The bird of beauty has flown up (18x61cm-7x24in) s. s.d.1961 verso panel exhib.lit. 9-Dec-2 Mu Terem Galeria, Budapest #108/R est:2500000 (H.F 3600000)

Works on paper
£1022 $1584 €1482 Potato picture (32x45cm-13x18in) mixed media prov.exhib. 9-Dec-2 Mu Terem Galeria, Budapest #91/R est:300000 (H.F 380000)
£1397 $2180 €2026 Bird (61x27cm-24x11in) W/C exhib.lit. 12-Apr-3 Mu Terem Galeria, Budapest #107/R est:400000 (H.F 500000)
£1419 $2213 €2058 Man with the head of a cat (29x17cm-11x7in) s.d.956 mixed media. 13-Sep-2 Mu Terem Galeria, Budapest #104/R est:300000 (H.F 550000)
£1806 $2817 €2619 Three generations without head (63x48cm-25x19in) pastel prov. 13-Sep-2 Mu Terem Galeria, Budapest #101/R est:550000 (H.F 700000)
£1806 $2817 €2619 Self-portrait (50x40cm-20x16in) s.d.1935 pencil silver paint W/C exhib.lit. 13-Sep-2 Mu Terem Galeria, Budapest #108/R est:320000 (H.F 700000)

BALKE, Peder (1804-1887) Norwegian
£2269 $3562 €3404 Sailing boat in moonlight (8x12cm-3x5in) s. panel. 21-Nov-2 Grev Wedels Plass, Oslo #94/R est:20000-30000 (N.KR 26000)

BALKENHOL, Stephan (1957-) German
£1290 $2000 €1935 Blackboard drawing - man and lizard (186x130cm-73x51in) s.d.1994 acrylic oilstick on panel prov.exhib. 26-Sep-2 Christie's, Rockefeller NY #872/R est:5000-7000
£5000 $8000 €7500 Blackboard drawing zebra and elephant (185x129cm-73x51in) s.d.1994 acrylic oilstick on wood pair. 16-May-3 Phillips, New York #118/R est:8000-12000

Sculpture
£6000 $10020 €8700 Giraffe und man (59x43x20cm-23x17x8in) init.num.20/25 bronze st.f.Schmake executed 2000 prov. 27-Jun-3 Christie's, London #279/R est:6000-8000
£6159 $10101 €8500 Little rider (47x55x14cm-19x22x6in) col concrete metal scole exhib. 28-May-3 Lempertz, Koln #20/R est:8000-10000
£18354 $29000 €27531 Man on black swan (167x40x38cm-66x16x15in) executed 1999 prov. 14-Nov-2 Christie's, Rockefeller NY #319/R est:30000-40000
£20000 $33400 €29000 Stehender akt (158x24x20cm-62x9x8in) painted wood executed 1994 prov. 27-Jun-3 Christie's, London #247/R est:20000-30000
£20000 $33400 €29000 Kleiner mann mit schwarzer hose (150x21x25cm-59x8x10in) painted cedar wood executed c.1997-99 prov. 27-Jun-3 Christie's, London #278/R est:20000-30000
£29487 $45705 €46000 Relief of man's head (145x169x13cm-57x67x5in) col wood prov.exhib. 3-Dec-2 Lempertz, Koln #26/R est:45000-50000
£38000 $62320 €57000 Drei Frauen (157x24x24cm-62x9x9in) painted wood in three parts prov. 6-Feb-3 Christie's, London #729/R est:40000-60000
£46795 $73000 €70193 Head of a man (380x140x140cm-150x55x55in) wawa wood paint executed 1992 prov.exhib.lit. 11-Nov-2 Phillips, New York #45/R est:80000-120000
£53797 $85000 €80696 Untitled (160x34x24cm-63x13x9in) Wawa wood paint exec.1997 prov. 13-Nov-2 Sotheby's, New York #512/R est:80000-120000

Works on paper
£306 $487 €450 Study of sculpture (21x14cm-8x6in) s.d.verso crayon prov. 24-Mar-3 Cornette de St.Cyr, Paris #116/R
£612 $973 €900 Taittinger (21x14cm-8x6in) s.d.verso col crayon ink prov. 24-Mar-3 Cornette de St.Cyr, Paris #117/R

BALL, Alan (1962-) British
£1000 $1630 €1500 Structural damage (157x194cm-62x76in) acrylic painted 1994. 3-Feb-3 Sotheby's, Olympia #29/R est:1000-1500

BALL, Martin (1952-) New Zealander
£526 $837 €789 Untitled - from the garden series (100x75cm-39x30in) s.d.1990. 25-Feb-3 Peter Webb, Auckland #44/R est:2000-3000 (NZ.D 1500)

BALL, Sydney (1933-) Australian
£3200 $5152 €4800 Shiraz cross (170x124cm-67x49in) s.i.on stretcher prov.exhib. 6-May-3 Christie's, Melbourne #72/R est:8000-12000 (A.D 8000)

BALL, Wilfred Williams (1853-1917) British
Works on paper
£260 $424 €390 Near days lock (13x23cm-5x9in) s.d.91 W/C. 14-Feb-3 Keys, Aylsham #467
£400 $624 €600 Still day on the lagoon, Venice (19x11cm-7x4in) s.i.d.87 W/C. 9-Oct-2 Woolley & Wallis, Salisbury #90/R
£400 $632 €600 Near Amsterdam (14x24cm-6x9in) s. W/C. 26-Nov-2 Bonhams, Knightsbridge #78/R
£420 $659 €630 Bridge near he public gardens, Venice (18x28cm-7x11in) s.d.1909 W/C. 16-Dec-2 Bonhams, Bury St Edmunds #389/R
£480 $739 €720 Sailing barges on the Norfolk Broads (17x27cm-7x11in) s.d.97 W/C. 22-Oct-2 Sworder & Son, Bishops Stortford #680/R
£650 $1073 €943 Red House Farm, Surrey (16x25cm-6x10in) s.i.d.99 pencil W/C two. 3-Jul-3 Christie's, Kensington #57
£720 $1109 €1080 Landscape with windmill (15x25cm-6x10in) s.d.98 W/C. 22-Oct-2 Sworder & Son, Bishops Stortford #693/R
£900 $1503 €1305 River landscape with figures in punt near windmill (36x40cm-14x16in) s.d.1903 W/C. 12-Jul-3 Windibank, Dorking #355
£1000 $1540 €1500 Summer evening, St Ives (23x38cm-9x15in) s.d.1899 W/C. 3-Sep-2 Gorringes, Lewes #2167/R est:600-800
£1500 $2355 €2250 St Ives town and harbour (24x38cm-9x15in) s.d.1899 W/C. 10-Dec-2 Lane, Penzance #326 est:1500-2000

BALLA, Bela (1882-1965) Hungarian
£516 $805 €748 After rain (34x42cm-13x17in) s. cardboard. 13-Sep-2 Mu Terem Galeria, Budapest #41/R est:180000 (H.F 200000)
£619 $966 €898 Flower still life (59x47cm-23x19in) s. cardboard. 13-Sep-2 Mu Terem Galeria, Budapest #159/R est:220000 (H.F 240000)
£753 $1167 €1092 Discussion by Lake Bodi in Felsobanya (58x69cm-23x27in) 9-Dec-2 Mu Terem Galeria, Budapest #61/R est:240000 (H.F 280000)
£861 $1334 €1248 Autumn on the edge of the woods (50x40cm-20x16in) s. card. 9-Dec-2 Mu Terem Galeria, Budapest #67/R est:240000 (H.F 320000)
£950 $1482 €1378 Meadow in bright sunshine (51x64cm-20x25in) s. 12-Apr-3 Mu Terem Galeria, Budapest #34/R est:280000 (H.F 340000)
£1062 $1657 €1540 Poppy land (49x59cm-19x23in) s.verso board. 12-Apr-3 Mu Terem Galeria, Budapest #97/R est:180000 (H.F 380000)
£1076 $1667 €1560 In the harbour (39x49cm-15x19in) card. 9-Dec-2 Mu Terem Galeria, Budapest #54/R est:200000 (H.F 400000)
£2794 $4359 €4051 Small village in the sunshine (90x101cm-35x40in) s. 12-Apr-3 Mu Terem Galeria, Budapest #40/R est:750000 (H.F 1000000)
£2958 $4585 €4437 In the park (54x65cm-21x26in) cardboard. 6-Dec-2 Kieselbach, Budapest #144/R (H.F 1100000)

BALLA, Giacomo (1871-1958) Italian
£3288 $5129 €4800 Pattern for lamp shade (13x32cm-5x13in) tempera paper. 10-Apr-3 Finarte Semenzato, Rome #289/R
£7447 $12064 €10500 Motivo per ceramica (22x22cm-9x9in) s. tempera pencil paper. 26-May-3 Christie's, Milan #213/R est:5000-7000
£210000 $327600 €315000 Dinamismo d' automobile (49x77cm-19x30in) s. s.i.verso enamel on paper painted 1913 prov.exhib.lit. 21-Oct-2 Sotheby's, London #4/R est:220000-280000

Works on paper
£5484 $8665 €8500 Future sea (56x23cm-22x9in) s.d.1919 gouache card. 18-Dec-2 Christie's, Rome #145/R

BALLA, Luce (1904-1994) Italian
£943 $1453 €1500 Chores in town (56x28cm-22x11in) s.i.d.1947 verso. 28-Oct-2 Il Ponte, Milan #187
£1258 $1937 €2000 First lights (54x29cm-21x11in) s. i.d.1945 verso. 28-Oct-2 Il Ponte, Milan #189

BALLABENE, Rudolf Raimund (1890-1968) Austrian
£1013 $1580 €1600 Flowers (69x88cm-27x35in) mono.d.50. 15-Oct-2 Dorotheum, Vienna #103/R
£1655 $2648 €2400 Still life with flowers in blue jug and bowl of lemons (52x42cm-20x17in) mono. 11-Mar-3 Dorotheum, Vienna #80/R est:1200-1700

BALLAGH, Robert (1943-) Irish
£7500 $12375 €10875 Lady in red looking at Patrick Scott painting (182x122cm-72x48in) s. acrylic. 6-Jul-3 Lots Road, London #355 est:7000-10000

BALLAINE, Jerrold (1934-) American
£252 $400 €378 Couple (39x33cm-15x13in) s. painted c.1970. 4-May-3 Treadway Gallery, Cincinnati #620/R

BALLANTINE, Mary (fl.1920-1939) British
£2516 $4000 €3774 Still life with flowers (61x91cm-24x36in) s.d.1944. 30-Apr-3 Sotheby's, New York #567/R est:4000-6000

BALLANTYNE, Robert Michael (1825-1894) British
Works on paper
£361 $567 €542 Canadian Indian (49x32cm-19x13in) s. W/C. 25-Nov-2 Hodgins, Calgary #381/R (C.D 900)

BALLARD, Brian (1943-) Irish
£400 $636 €600 Hanker, Finland (15x20cm-6x8in) s.d.87 board. 5-Mar-3 John Ross, Belfast #19
£580 $922 €870 Rocky shore (11x21cm-4x8in) s.d.78 board. 5-Mar-3 John Ross, Belfast #84
£1000 $1460 €1600 Lough and trees (36x26cm-14x10in) s.d.91. 14-May-2 Thomas Adams, Dublin #398
£1026 $1610 €1600 Still life with mantle clock and daisies (20x25cm-8x10in) s.d.2002. 19-Nov-2 Whyte's, Dublin #190 est:1500-2000
£1050 $1628 €1575 Still life (25x35cm-10x14in) s.d.92 board. 4-Dec-2 John Ross, Belfast #18 est:600-700
£1250 $1825 €2000 Female nude (77x62cm-30x24in) s.d.87. 14-May-2 Thomas Adams, Dublin #1a
£1342 $2161 €2000 Still life with reflections (36x25cm-14x10in) s.d.1992 board. 18-Feb-3 Whyte's, Dublin #178/R est:2500-3500
£1500 $2190 €2250 Poppies and clock (30x36cm-12x14in) s.d.2002. 12-Jun-2 John Ross, Belfast #152 est:1000-1200
£1768 $2511 €2900 Blue bottle (28x38cm-11x15in) s. board prov. 5-Mar-2 Thomas Adams, Dublin #353
£1800 $2862 €2700 Evening (40x50cm-16x20in) s.d.89 board. 5-Mar-3 John Ross, Belfast #70 est:1500-1800
£1806 $2871 €2600 On the Lagan (25x36cm-10x14in) s.d.1988 board prov. 29-Apr-3 Whyte's, Dublin #209/R est:1800-2200
£1899 $2943 €3000 Blue jug and poppies (10x14cm-4x6in) s.d.2001. 24-Sep-2 De Veres Art Auctions, Dublin #173/R est:2500-3500
£1923 $3019 €3000 Still life with iris and lilies in jug (51x41cm-20x16in) s.d.1993. 19-Nov-2 Whyte's, Dublin #189/R est:3000-4000
£2000 $2920 €3200 Still life, blue jugs, tankard, books on a table (41x50cm-16x20in) s.d.91. 14-May-2 Thomas Adams, Dublin #402
£2051 $3221 €3200 Five bottles and orchids (25x36cm-10x14in) s.d.2000 i.verso. 19-Nov-2 Whyte's, Dublin #187/R est:3000-4000
£2100 $3255 €3150 Nude study, girl holding her knees (25x36cm-10x14in) s.d.89 board. 2-Oct-2 John Ross, Belfast #247 est:1000-1500
£2148 $3458 €3200 Still life, inisfree (41x51cm-16x20in) s.d.1995 i.verso. 18-Feb-3 Whyte's, Dublin #176/R est:3000-4000
£2215 $3434 €3500 Woman at the window (59x36cm-23x14in) s.d.89 board. 24-Sep-2 De Veres Art Auctions, Dublin #10/R est:4000-5000
£2250 $3285 €3600 Mountains Connemara (66x102cm-26x40in) s. card. 14-May-2 Thomas Adams, Dublin #412
£2516 $3925 €4000 Jug and bowl, Cill Rialaig (41x51cm-16x20in) s.d.1996 i.verso canvasboard. 17-Sep-2 Whyte's, Dublin #173/R est:3000-4000
£2516 $3925 €4000 Two jugs and brushes (36x25cm-14x10in) s.d.1987 i.verso board prov. 17-Sep-2 Whyte's, Dublin #176/R est:3000-4000
£2600 $3796 €3900 Fruit and blue bottle (36x46cm-14x18in) s.d.1986 board. 12-Jun-2 John Ross, Belfast #46 est:800-1000
£2685 $4322 €4000 Orchids and fruit (46x61cm-18x24in) s.d.1988 s.i.verso. 18-Feb-3 Whyte's, Dublin #136/R est:4000-6000
£2740 $4301 €4000 Still life with bust (60x74cm-24x29in) s.d.89. 15-Apr-3 De Veres Art Auctions, Dublin #143/R est:4000-6000
£2821 $4428 €4400 Lemon, flowers and apricots (61x46cm-24x18in) s.d.2001 i.verso canvas on board. 19-Nov-2 Whyte's, Dublin #119/R
£2877 $4516 €4200 Poppies and fruit (36x25cm-14x10in) s. board. 15-Apr-3 De Veres Art Auctions, Dublin #202/R est:3000-4000
£3000 $4890 €4500 Irises (44x57cm-17x22in) s. 2-Feb-3 Lots Road, London #346/R est:2000-3500
£3200 $4960 €4800 Sunflowers and daisies (51x86cm-20x34in) s. 2-Oct-2 John Ross, Belfast #29 est:3300-3600
£3522 $5494 €5600 Still life with clock (46x61cm-18x24in) s.d.2001. 17-Sep-2 Whyte's, Dublin #159/R est:5000-6000
£3562 $5592 €5200 Model in shadow (41x51cm-16x20in) s.d.1985 board. 15-Apr-3 De Veres Art Auctions, Dublin #104/R est:3000-4000
£3800 $5548 €5700 Blue vase and poppies (61x76cm-24x30in) s. 12-Jun-2 John Ross, Belfast #171 est:2750-3250
£3900 $6201 €5850 Clandeboye nude II (50x76cm-20x30in) s.d.84 board. 5-Mar-3 John Ross, Belfast #141 est:2500-3000

BALLAVOINE, Jules Frederic (1855-1901) French
£1595 $2600 €2393 Finette (35x27cm-14x11in) s.i. 11-Feb-3 Bonhams & Doyles, New York #190/R est:2500-3500
£1720 $2700 €2580 Elegant lady (35x27cm-14x11in) s. panel. 22-Nov-2 Skinner, Boston #43/R est:3000-5000
£1832 $2895 €2748 Untitled, reclining nude (34x47cm-13x19in) s. 7-Apr-3 Shapiro, Sydney #532/R est:5000-7000 (A.D 4800)
£2347 $3850 €3403 Elegant woman fishing from rowing boat by shore (33x25cm-13x10in) s. 4-Jun-3 Fischer, Luzern #1082/R est:5000-6000 (S.FR 5000)
£5128 $8051 €8000 Portraits de jeunes femmes. s. panel pair. 15-Dec-2 Mercier & Cie, Lille #358/R est:4200

BALLE, Mogens (1921-1988) Danish
£392 $623 €588 Composition (24x33cm-9x13in) init. 29-Apr-3 Kunsthallen, Copenhagen #38 (D.KR 4200)
£422 $659 €633 Figure composition (36x52cm-14x20in) s. paper. 18-Sep-2 Kunsthallen, Copenhagen #147/R (D.KR 5000)
£466 $742 €699 Composition (38x46cm-15x18in) s.d.1961 exhib. 29-Apr-3 Kunsthallen, Copenhagen #4/R (D.KR 5000)
£476 $742 €714 Composition (24x33cm-9x13in) init. 5-Aug-2 Rasmussen, Vejle #348/R (D.KR 5600)
£499 $799 €749 Composition (22x23cm-9x9in) init. 13-Jan-3 Rasmussen, Vejle #292/R (D.KR 5700)
£689 $1047 €1034 Well known creature - abstract composition (46x55cm-18x22in) init. i.d.1968 verso. 3-Sep-2 Museumsbygningen, Copenhagen #481/R (D.KR 8000)
£718 $1120 €1077 Composition (56x49cm-22x19in) init. 18-Sep-2 Kunsthallen, Copenhagen #66/R (D.KR 8500)
£775 $1202 €1163 Composition (44x50cm-17x20in) s. 4-Dec-2 Kunsthallen, Copenhagen #75a/R (D.KR 9000)
£1056 $1647 €1584 Composition (46x55cm-18x22in) init. 18-Sep-2 Kunsthallen, Copenhagen #49/R est:7000 (D.KR 12500)
£1072 $1758 €1608 Children (65x40cm-26x16in) init. painted c.1955. 27-May-3 Museumsbygningen, Copenhagen #475/R (D.KR 11000)
£1105 $1723 €1658 Composition (38x46cm-15x18in) init. 5-Aug-2 Rasmussen, Vejle #341/R est:10000-15000 (D.KR 13000)
£1115 $1739 €1673 Composition (50x61cm-20x24in) init. 11-Nov-2 Rasmussen, Vejle #120/R est:6000-8000 (D.KR 13000)
£1170 $1918 €1755 Children (65x40cm-26x16in) init. painted c.1955. 27-May-3 Museumsbygningen, Copenhagen #473/R est:8000-10000 (D.KR 12000)
£1249 $1898 €1874 Abstract composition in red, black and blue (38x46cm-15x18in) init. 3-Sep-2 Museumsbygningen, Copenhagen #573/R est:6000 (D.KR 14500)
£1859 $2937 €2789 Diptychon (35x83cm-14x33in) init.d.59 triptych in one frame. 1-Apr-3 Rasmussen, Copenhagen #125/R est:15000-20000 (D.KR 20000)
£2097 $3502 €3041 Public garden (81x100cm-32x39in) s.d.66 prov. 17-Jun-3 Rasmussen, Copenhagen #4/R est:25000-30000 (D.KR 22000)
£2328 $3701 €3492 Composition (43x67cm-17x26in) mono. 10-Mar-3 Rasmussen, Vejle #771/R est:20000 (D.KR 25000)
£3205 $4968 €5000 Red figure (67x29cm-26x11in) s. board prov. 3-Dec-2 Christie's, Amsterdam #318/R est:1900-4500

BALLERINI, Augusto (1857-1897) Italian
£17834 $28000 €26751 View of Iguazu Falls (92x300cm-36x118in) s.i.d.93 prov. 19-Nov-2 Sotheby's, New York #68/R est:20000

BALLESIO, Francesco (1860-1923) Italian
£1218 $1924 €1900 Allegory (60x24cm-24x9in) s.i.d.1886. 14-Nov-2 Arte, Seville #313/R
£1282 $2026 €2000 Odalisk (60x24cm-24x9in) s.d.1886. 14-Nov-2 Arte, Seville #312/R
£3145 $4843 €5000 Interior with figures (47x31cm-19x12in) s.d.1885. 23-Oct-2 Finarte, Milan #32/R

BALLESTER, Rosalie (1949-) French
Works on paper
£504 $806 €700 Rebus de la lune blanche (92x73cm-36x29in) s. mixed media. 18-May-3 Neret-Minet, Paris #226
£540 $863 €750 Trois fois l'infini (100x100cm-39x39in) s. mixed media canvas. 18-May-3 Neret-Minet, Paris #83

BALLINGALL, Alexander (fl.1880-1910) British
Works on paper
£700 $1085 €1050 On the Thames (48x73cm-19x29in) s.i.d.1907 W/C. 6-Dec-2 Lyon & Turnbull, Edinburgh #2
£1200 $1908 €1800 Unloading the catch, Largo, Fife (48x72cm-19x28in) s.d.1907 pencil W/C prov. 6-Mar-3 Christie's, Kensington #141/R est:1000-1500

BALLINGALL, John (19th C) British
£700 $1113 €1050 Boys fishing on a rocky promontory (15x20cm-6x8in) panel. 20-Mar-3 Ewbank, Send #404

BALLIQUANT, A (19th C) French
£1013 $1580 €1600 La bergerie (51x92cm-20x36in) s. 20-Oct-2 Galerie de Chartres, Chartres #101 est:1500-2000

BALLUE, Pierre Ernest (1855-1928) French
£1026 $1600 €1539 Paysage avec Ruisseau (38x55cm-15x22in) s. 20-Sep-2 Sloan, North Bethesda #384/R est:2000-3000
£1709 $2649 €2700 En barque sur la riviere (47x66cm-19x26in) s. 29-Sep-2 Eric Pillon, Calais #48/R

£1962 $3100 €3100 Pecheur pres de la riviere, printemps (38x56cm-15x22in) s. 1-Dec-2 Peron, Melun #75

BALLUF, Ernst (1921-) Austrian
Works on paper
£504 $806 €700 San Giorgio - Venice (27x36cm-11x14in) s. W/C. 14-May-3 Dorotheum, Linz #432/R
£903 $1426 €1300 Calm landscape (28x43cm-11x17in) s.d.79 mixed media. 24-Apr-3 Dorotheum, Vienna #213/R

BALMELLI, Attilio (1887-1971) Italian
£394 $634 €571 Sunny wooded landscape (46x62cm-18x24in) s.d.1946 board. 7-May-3 Dobiaschofsky, Bern #3099 (S.FR 850)

BALMER, Barbara (1929-) British
£720 $1123 €1080 Summer landscape (91x106cm-36x42in) s. board. 28-Mar-3 Bonhams, Edinburgh #179

BALMER, Paul Friedrich Wilhelm (1865-1922) Swiss
£258 $407 €387 Cascades near Sorrent (33x23cm-13x9in) s.d.1904 board. 29-Nov-2 Zofingen, Switzerland #2786 (S.FR 600)
£783 $1213 €1175 Boy with hoop (100x80cm-39x31in) s.d.1908. 9-Dec-2 Philippe Schuler, Zurich #3803/R (S.FR 1800)

BALMER, Wilhelm (1837-1907) Swiss
£393 $613 €590 Still life with wine bottles and books (17x22cm-7x9in) mono.d.1895 board. 6-Nov-2 Dobiaschofsky, Bern #329/R (S.FR 900)

BALMFORD, Hurst (1871-1950) British
£440 $704 €660 Watch house, Polperro (56x41cm-22x16in) s. 14-Mar-3 Gardiner & Houlgate, Bath #178/R
£1450 $2320 €2175 Fishing boats in the village harbour (43x53cm-17x21in) s. board. 14-Mar-3 Gardiner & Houlgate, Bath #179/R est:100-150
£2500 $4075 €3750 St Ives harbour (38x48cm-15x19in) s. board. 13-Feb-3 David Lay, Penzance #44/R est:2500-3000

BALOGH, Bela (19/20th C) ?
£329 $510 €494 Still life with fruit, flowers and tankard (61x91cm-24x36in) s. 3-Dec-2 Ritchie, Toronto #3095/R (C.D 800)
£370 $574 €555 Still life with fruit, flowers and ewer (61x80cm-24x31in) s. 3-Dec-2 Ritchie, Toronto #3096/R est:1000-1500 (C.D 900)

BALOGH, Endre Kompoczy (1911-1977) Hungarian
£479 $800 €695 French garden party scene with figures and toy dogs (76x61cm-30x24in) s. 22-Jun-3 Jeffery Burchard, Florida #38/R

BALOGH, Rudolf (20th C) ?
Photographs
£5844 $9000 €8766 Factory stillstand (44x32cm-17x13in) i.verso photograph prov. 22-Oct-2 Sotheby's, New York #118/R est:2500-3500

BALS, Wim (1973-) Belgian
£252 $387 €400 You can't beat the feeling (30x24cm-12x9in) s. panel. 22-Oct-2 Campo, Vlaamse Kaai #15
£314 $484 €500 Nature morte au figues (24x30cm-9x12in) panel. 22-Oct-2 Campo, Vlaamse Kaai #13
£377 $581 €600 Nature morte a la cruche et aux prunes (30x40cm-12x16in) s. prov.lit. 22-Oct-2 Campo, Vlaamse Kaai #14
£435 $713 €600 Nature morte aux raisins (24x30cm-9x12in) s. panel. 27-May-3 Campo, Vlaamse Kaai #8
£440 $678 €700 Lamp (24x18cm-9x7in) s.d.1999 panel. 22-Oct-2 Campo & Campo, Antwerp #7

BALSAMO, Vincenzo (1935-) Italian
£680 $1082 €1000 Miscellaneous (45x30cm-18x12in) s.d.2001 verso paper on canvas. 1-Mar-3 Meeting Art, Vercelli #337
£962 $1510 €1500 Landscape (41x51cm-16x20in) s. board. 23-Nov-2 Meeting Art, Vercelli #173/R
£962 $1510 €1500 Untitled (60x40cm-24x16in) s.d.1998 cardboard on canvas. 23-Nov-2 Meeting Art, Vercelli #278/R
£1042 $1656 €1500 Hot sun (50x40cm-20x16in) s.d.1984 verso. 1-May-3 Meeting Art, Vercelli #188
£1266 $1975 €2000 Composition (60x60cm-24x24in) s. painted 1992. 14-Sep-2 Meeting Art, Vercelli #824/R
£1282 $2013 €2000 Untitled (60x50cm-24x20in) s.d.1997 verso. 23-Nov-2 Meeting Art, Vercelli #32/R
£1282 $2013 €2000 Untitled (60x60cm-24x24in) s.d.1991. 23-Nov-2 Meeting Art, Vercelli #96/R
£1923 $3019 €3000 Untitled (100x100cm-39x39in) s. painted 1990. 23-Nov-2 Meeting Art, Vercelli #329/R

BALSGAARD, Carl Vilhelm (1812-1893) Danish
£701 $1121 €1052 Still life of fruit and glass of wine (17x25cm-7x10in) s.d.1854. 13-Jan-3 Rasmussen, Vejle #43/R (D.KR 8000)

BALSHAW, Fred (fl.1896-1905) British
Works on paper
£260 $406 €390 Landscape with female figure walking along a road, cottages beyond (25x36cm-10x14in) s. W/C. 18-Sep-2 Dreweatt Neate, Newbury #92

BALSON, Ralph (1890-1964) Australian
£1786 $2821 €2679 Still life (48x60cm-19x24in) s.indis d. 26-Nov-2 Sotheby's, Melbourne #21/R est:15000-20000 (A.D 5000)
£3226 $4903 €4839 Untitled, non objective painting (100x71cm-39x28in) s.d.57 i.verso card prov. 28-Aug-2 Deutscher-Menzies, Melbourne #194/R est:12000-18000 (A.D 9000)
£13523 $20690 €20285 Constructive painting (54x69cm-21x27in) s.d.48 board prov. 25-Aug-2 Sotheby's, Paddington #60/R est:40000-50000 (A.D 38000)
Works on paper
£2001 $3042 €3002 Abstract (46x59cm-18x23in) s.d.51 pastel prov. 28-Aug-2 Deutscher-Menzies, Melbourne #172/R est:5500-7500 (A.D 5585)

BALTEN, Pieter (attrib) (1525-1598) Flemish
£1923 $2981 €3000 Egg seller (17x13cm-7x5in) i.verso copper. 6-Dec-2 Rieunier, Bailly-Pommery, Mathias, Paris #8/R
£2390 $3704 €3800 Peasant woman with tankard (31x24cm-12x9in) panel prov. 2-Oct-2 Dorotheum, Vienna #373/R est:3800-5000
£2465 $4092 €3500 Arbaletrier (17x17cm-7x7in) panel. 11-Jun-3 Cornette de St.Cyr, Paris #11 est:4000-5000

BALTERMANTS, Dmitri (1912-1990) Russian
Photographs
£2215 $3500 €3323 Attack! (34x51cm-13x20in) gelatin silver print prov.lit. 22-Apr-3 Christie's, Rockefeller NY #39/R est:4000-6000
£7500 $12000 €11250 Grief (50x59cm-20x23in) i. silver print exhib. 15-May-3 Swann Galleries, New York #280/R est:15000-25000

BALTHUS (1908-2001) French
£124224 $200000 €186336 Etude pour 'partie des cartes' (44x63cm-17x25in) init.d.1947 board prov.lit. 7-May-3 Christie's, Rockefeller NY #20/R est:300000-500000
£224359 $350000 €336539 Frederique au chandail rouge (49x44cm-19x17in) panel painted 1955 prov.exhib.lit. 5-Nov-2 Sotheby's, New York #46/R est:400000-600000
Works on paper
£10000 $15800 €15000 Costume design for Despina (25x16cm-10x6in) init.i.d.1950 pencil W/C prov. 3-Apr-3 Christie's, Kensington #199/R est:15000
£12000 $18600 €18000 Basket of fruit (36x47cm-14x19in) s.i.d.1965 pencil W/C prov.exhib.lit. 5-Dec-2 Christie's, Kensington #197/R est:12000-18000
£23148 $37269 €34722 Etude de jeune femme (38x27cm-15x11in) mono.i.d.1970 pencil exhib.lit. 7-May-3 Dobiaschofsky, Bern #333/R est:65000 (S.FR 50000)
£25000 $41750 €36250 Etude pour nu devant la cheminee (30x19cm-12x7in) mono. pencil executed 1954 prov.exhib.lit. 24-Jun-3 Sotheby's, London #227/R est:25000-35000
£55000 $90200 €82500 Etude pour jeune femme endormie, portrait de Jeanette (30x30cm-12x12in) s.i.d.1943 chl pencil chk prov.exhib.lit. 5-Feb-3 Sotheby's, London #133/R est:60000

BALTZ, Lewis (1945-) American
Photographs
£2532 $4000 €3798 Morgan Hill (15x22cm-6x9in) s.i.d.1973 verso gelatin silver print prov. 25-Apr-3 Phillips, New York #59/R est:4000-6000
£3038 $4800 €4557 Palo Alto (15x22cm-6x9in) s.i.d.1973 verso gelatin silver print prov. 25-Apr-3 Phillips, New York #178/R est:3000-5000

BALUNIN, Mikhail Abramovich (1875-c.1939) Russian
Works on paper
£1338 $2154 €1900 Summer evening dance (33x50cm-13x20in) s. W/C. 10-May-3 Bukowskis, Helsinki #394/R est:1700-2000
£3200 $5024 €4800 Village scenes (24x30cm-9x12in) s. W/C gouache pair. 20-Nov-2 Sotheby's, London #124/R est:1500-2000

BALWE, Arnold (1898-1983) German
£1456 $2256 €2300 Dutch landscape (23x36cm-9x14in) mono.d.1926 s.i.d. verso. 28-Sep-2 Ketterer, Hamburg #117/R est:2000-2200

£4459 $6955 €7000 Jetty on Chiemsee in winter (65x108cm-26x43in) s.i. verso. 6-Nov-2 Hugo Ruef, Munich #1020/R est:4500
£5435 $8913 €7500 Friesian farmstead (70x100cm-28x39in) s. s.i.d.1938 verso prov. 29-May-3 Lempertz, Koln #506/R est:7000
£11268 $18141 €16000 Garden poppies (85x49cm-33x19in) s. s.i. verso lit. 9-May-3 Schloss Ahlden, Ahlden #1535/R est:18500
£12975 $20500 €20500 House in summer (65x100cm-26x39in) s. s.i. verso. 30-Nov-2 Villa Grisebach, Berlin #335/R est:500-7000
£13462 $21269 €21000 Country garden (77x99cm-30x39in) s. s. stretcher. 14-Nov-2 Neumeister, Munich #517/R est:15000-20000
£20863 $33381 €29000 Larkspur (100x81cm-39x32in) s. s.i. verso. 15-May-3 Neumeister, Munich #211/R est:12000-15000

BALZE, Raymond (1818-1909) French
£559 $888 €839 Landscape from Liguria la Spezzia (24x32cm-9x13in) panel. 5-Mar-3 Rasmussen, Copenhagen #1798/R (D.KR 6000)
£1266 $2000 €2000 Source (70x71cm-28x28in) s.d.1890. 29-Nov-2 Coutau Begarie, Paris #5
£3038 $4800 €4800 Portrait presume de Jeanne d'Aragone (83x70cm-33x28in) 29-Nov-2 Coutau Begarie, Paris #32/R

BAMA, James E (1926-) American
£1258 $2000 €1887 Portrait of a cowboy (9x10cm-4x4in) s.d.80 oil pencil board. 5-Mar-3 Sotheby's, New York #145/R est:800-1200
£4259 $6900 €6176 Still life, feed bags (30x41cm-12x16in) board. 23-May-3 Altermann Galleries, Santa Fe #132
Works on paper
£8974 $14000 €13461 Faith sings good (48x33cm-19x13in) W/C. 9-Nov-2 Altermann Galleries, Santa Fe #86

BAMBER, Bessie (fl.1900-1910) British
£1300 $2119 €1950 Kitten (9x14cm-4x6in) init. oil on ivorine. 29-Jan-3 Sotheby's, Olympia #211/R est:400-600
£1800 $2916 €2700 Kittens (19x31cm-7x12in) init.d.14 oil on ivorine. 20-May-3 Sotheby's, Olympia #256/R est:2000-3000
£2000 $3100 €3000 Four kittens (56x30cm-22x12in) init. panel. 3-Dec-2 Sotheby's, Olympia #88/R est:2000-3000
£2100 $3465 €3045 Study of eight kittens (36x112cm-14x44in) mono.d.1909 panel. 3-Jul-3 Duke & Son, Dorchester #205/R est:800-1500
Works on paper
£600 $930 €900 Portrait of a grey long haired cat (36x24cm-14x9in) init. W/C. 24-Sep-2 Anderson & Garland, Newcastle #324/R

BAMBERGER, Fritz (1814-1873) German
£1552 $2514 €2250 Coastal landscape (28x43cm-11x17in) s. prov. 25-May-3 Uppsala Auktionskammare, Uppsala #52/R est:15000-20000 (S.KR 20000)
£1572 $2453 €2500 Spanish landscape with aqueduct and palm trees (28x39cm-11x15in) panel. 11-Oct-2 Winterberg, Heidelberg #483/R est:3400
£2885 $4471 €4500 Southern coast landscape (36x50cm-14x20in) s.i. 5-Dec-2 Dr Fritz Nagel, Stuttgart #641/R est:5500
£3885 $6216 €5400 Starnberger See with Roseninsel and Zugspitze (25x47cm-10x19in) s. prov. 17-May-3 Lempertz, Koln #1361/R est:5000
Works on paper
£360 $590 €500 Old Spanish herder sitting by wall (30x23cm-12x9in) s.i. 23 Marzo 1850 W/C over pencil htd bodycol. 4-Jun-3 Reiss & Sohn, Konigstein #215
£1582 $2468 €2500 Aschaffenburg (12x63cm-5x25in) s. W/C htd white lit.prov. 14-Sep-2 Bergmann, Erlangen #725/R est:3500

BAMBINI, Nicolo (1651-1736) Italian
£16000 $26720 €23200 Ariadne and Theseus (94x127cm-37x50in) 11-Jul-3 Christie's, Kensington #245/R est:6000-8000

BAMBURY, Stephen (1951-) New Zealander
£1849 $3050 €2681 Eternal persistence (20x20cm-8x8in) s.i.d.2000 verso resin graphite two aluminium panel. 1-Jul-3 Peter Webb, Auckland #10/R est:3000-4000 (NZ.D 5250)
Works on paper
£1667 $2600 €2501 Elaborated from two fundamental principles (38x38cm-15x15in) s.d.1988-89 verso mixed media aluminium. 27-Mar-3 International Art Centre, Auckland #33/R est:4000-7000 (NZ.D 4750)
£1673 $2760 €2426 Of certain magnetic (17x17cm-7x7in) i. s.i.d.1993 verso chemical actions 23 carat gold two brass pane. 1-Jul-3 Peter Webb, Auckland #9/R est:3000-4000 (NZ.D 4750)

BAMFYLDE, Coplestone Warre (1719-1791) British
£6500 $10335 €9750 Still life of an artist's palette wreathed with roses (43x63cm-17x25in) s. 19-Mar-3 Sotheby's, London #101/R est:4000-6000
Works on paper
£1050 $1617 €1575 Sidmouth from Peak Field (24x46cm-9x18in) i.verso pencil grey washes ink dr. 23-Oct-2 Hampton & Littlewood, Exeter #403/R est:1000-1200

BAMFYLDE, Coplestone Warre (attrib) (1719-1791) British
Works on paper
£304 $475 €456 View of the English countryside (24x36cm-9x14in) W/C. 14-Sep-2 Weschler, Washington #594/R

BAN, Bela (1909-1972) Hungarian
Works on paper
£419 $654 €608 Woman seated (33x26cm-13x10in) s.d.945 ink exhib.lit. 12-Apr-3 Mu Terem Galeria, Budapest #104/R est:100000 (H.F 150000)

BANCHIERI, Giuseppe (1927-) Italian
£506 $790 €800 Still life with mirror (20x30cm-8x12in) s.d.1986 board. 14-Sep-2 Meeting Art, Vercelli #771/R

BANCROFT, Elias (?-1924) British
£290 $441 €435 Landscape with sheep grazing on a cliff top (23x33cm-9x13in) s.i.d.1879. 16-Aug-2 Keys, Aylsham #765
Works on paper
£650 $1086 €943 Country house at Chiddingstone, Kent (54x75cm-21x30in) s. W/C. 24-Jun-3 Bonhams, Knightsbridge #66/R
£2500 $3975 €3750 Brethrens kitchen, Leycester Hospital, Warwick (55x77cm-22x30in) s.d.1880 i.d.verso W/C bodycol. 19-Mar-3 Sotheby's, London #232/R est:2000-3000

BANCROFT, Milton Herbert (1867-1947) American
£833 $1300 €1250 Huntress (102x69cm-40x27in) s.i.d.1910 after Kenyon Cox. 9-Oct-2 Doyle, New York #6

BANCROFT, Milton Herbert (attrib) (1867-1947) American
£692 $1100 €1038 Portrait of a woman seated in a landscape (178x86cm-70x34in) indis.sig. oval. 29-Apr-3 Doyle, New York #7

BAND, Max (1900-1974) Israeli?
£285 $447 €428 Young boy reading (34x25cm-13x10in) s. 10-Dec-2 Pinneys, Montreal #71 (C.D 700)
£389 $650 €564 Still life of strawberries (20x25cm-8x10in) canvasboard. 17-Jun-3 John Moran, Pasadena #9
£524 $817 €786 Cello player (91x74cm-36x29in) s. 20-Nov-2 Fischer, Luzern #2012/R (S.FR 1200)
£641 $1006 €1000 Paris roofs (54x80cm-21x31in) s. 12-Dec-2 Rabourdin & Choppin de Janvry, Paris #62/R
£813 $1276 €1220 Venice view (46x58cm-18x23in) s. 10-Dec-2 Pinneys, Montreal #68 est:1400-1800 (C.D 2000)
£1282 $2013 €2000 PO. of lady (92x65cm-36x26in) s. 12-Dec-2 Rabourdin & Choppin de Janvry, Paris #54/R
£1379 $2207 €2000 Student (34x25cm-13x10in) s. 12-Mar-3 Rabourdin & Choppin de Janvry, Paris #76/R

BANDAU, Joachim (1936-) German
Works on paper
£742 $1166 €1113 Untitled (43x31cm-17x12in) s.d.1997W/C prov. 23-Nov-2 Burkhard, Luzern #76/R (S.FR 1700)

BANDEIRA, Antonio (1922-1967) Brazilian
£18000 $27900 €27000 Soleil et arbres noirs (41x46cm-16x18in) s.d.55 s.i.d.1955 verso acrylic. 5-Dec-2 Christie's, Kensington #201/R est:6000-8000
£48611 $80208 €70000 L'arbre s'bleu (100x81cm-39x32in) s.d.56 s.i.d.1956 verso. 1-Jul-3 Artcurial Briest, Paris #511/R est:30000-40000

BANDELLI, Enrico (1941-) Italian
£385 $604 €600 Up and down for Settignano (110x110cm-43x43in) s. s.i.verso painted 1997. 23-Nov-2 Meeting Art, Vercelli #159/R
£588 $941 €900 No time to dream (100x200cm-39x79in) s. s.i.verso painted 2000. 4-Jan-3 Meeting Art, Vercelli #99
£729 $1159 €1050 Villani's froth (100x200cm-39x79in) s. s.i.verso. 1-May-3 Meeting Art, Vercelli #327

BANDI, Hans (1896-1973) Swiss?
£349 $552 €524 Horses (69x99cm-27x39in) s.d.1954. 14-Nov-2 Stuker, Bern #59/R (S.FR 800)

BANDO, Toshio (1890-1973) Japanese
£1006 $1560 €1600 L'oiseau mort (16x22cm-6x9in) s. 30-Oct-2 Artcurial Briest, Paris #291 est:500-600

£1179 $1839 €1769 Kneeling Japanese woman carrying out washing ritual (45x38cm-18x15in) s. 20-Nov-2 Fischer, Luzern #1130/R est:3000-3500 (S.FR 2700)
£1935 $3058 €3000 Red fish (22x27cm-9x11in) s. 19-Dec-2 Claude Aguttes, Neuilly #188/R
£2069 $3455 €3000 Chiots (22x27cm-9x11in) s. 10-Jul-3 Artcurial Briest, Paris #149/R est:3000-3500
£2778 $4389 €4000 Girl in red dress (32x24cm-13x9in) s. 25-Apr-3 Piasa, Paris #56/R est:4000
£6069 $9650 €8800 Grenade, poire et noix (22x27cm-9x11in) s. 5-Mar-3 Doutrebente, Paris #50/R est:1200-1500

BANFORD, David (20th C) American
£320 $500 €464 Snowcapped peaks and mountains (46x36cm-18x14in) s. board. 13-Apr-3 Butterfields, Los Angeles #7020

BANG, Christian (1868-?) Danish
£723 $1143 €1085 Wooded landscape with animals by water (90x121cm-35x48in) mono. 30-Nov-2 Rasmussen, Havnen #2221 (D.KR 8500)

BANG, L (19/20th C) Danish
£1115 $1750 €1673 Landscape with fishermen (94x160cm-37x63in) s. 20-Nov-2 Boos Gallery, Michigan #500/R est:3000-5000

BANGALA, England (c.1925-) Australian
Works on paper
£2321 $3575 €3482 Modj - rainbow serpent (183x86cm-72x34in) s.verso ochre pigments on bark. 8-Sep-2 Sotheby's, Melbourne #50/R est:7000-10000 (A.D 6500)

BANKOFF, Lou (20th C) American
£256 $400 €384 Floral still life (30x41cm-12x16in) s. board. 29-Mar-3 Charlton Hall, Columbia #353/R
£417 $650 €626 Ben-ami (25x20cm-10x8in) s. 29-Mar-3 Charlton Hall, Columbia #151/R
£833 $1300 €1250 Spring in the park (20x25cm-8x10in) s. board. 29-Mar-3 Charlton Hall, Columbia #131/R est:100-150

BANKS, Robert (1911-) British
£900 $1467 €1305 Venetian Canal scene (53x74cm-21x29in) 21-Jul-3 Sotheby's, London #621

BANKS, Thomas J (1828-1896) British
£550 $913 €825 Highland river landscape (23x42cm-9x17in) mono.d.78 board. 10-Jun-3 Bonhams, Knightsbridge #263/R

BANNATYNE, John James (1835-1911) British
£1700 $2601 €2550 On the moorehead of Glenfalloch (50x75cm-20x30in) s. 22-Aug-2 Bonhams, Edinburgh #1163 est:400-600
£2300 $3519 €3450 Arran from Torrisdale, Kintyre (51x76cm-20x30in) s. 22-Aug-2 Bonhams, Edinburgh #1162/R est:400-600
Works on paper
£347 $575 €503 Eilean Donan, Loch Duich (37x66cm-15x26in) s.i. W/C. 16-Jun-3 Waddingtons, Toronto #196/R (C.D 780)
£427 $670 €641 Sailboats at sunset off the coast (34x52cm-13x20in) s. W/C. 10-Dec-2 Pinneys, Montreal #81 (C.D 1050)
£1200 $1860 €1800 Cattle resting in a mountainous landscape (28x47cm-11x19in) s. pencil W/C. 31-Oct-2 Christie's, London #74/R est:1000-1500

BANNER, Alfred (fl.1878-1914) British
£300 $468 €450 Sheep in a landscape (20x30cm-8x12in) s.d.1882 board. 26-Mar-3 Woolley & Wallis, Salisbury #196/R

BANNER, Delmar (1896-?) British
£450 $707 €675 Lakeland fells (51x63cm-20x25in) s.d.1948 board. 21-Nov-2 Tennants, Leyburn #833

BANNER, Fiona (1966-) British
Works on paper
£2600 $4342 €3770 Helicopter (100x130cm-39x51in) s.i.d.1997 pencil prov. 24-Jun-3 Sotheby's, Olympia #14/R est:2500-3500

BANNISTER, Edward M (1833-1901) American
£5929 $9250 €8894 Cows in a landscape (25x30cm-10x12in) init. 20-Sep-2 Sloan, North Bethesda #472/R est:2000-4000
£12739 $20000 €19109 Country landscape with man fishing at a pond (46x66cm-18x26in) s. 23-Nov-2 Pook & Pook, Downington #376/R est:7000-9000

BANTING, John (1902-1970) British
£290 $441 €435 Abstract symbols (23x23cm-9x9in) s.d.1921 gouache. 16-Aug-2 Keys, Aylsham #874
£300 $483 €450 Leaves (40x25cm-16x10in) 18-Feb-3 Bonhams, Knightsbridge #46
£800 $1248 €1200 Surreal still life (52x77cm-20x30in) s.d.1964 acrylic on board. 27-Mar-3 Christie's, Kensington #639/R
£1277 $2068 €1800 Composition aux fleurs (30x41cm-12x16in) s.d.verso. 23-May-3 Binoche, Paris #23/R est:2500-3000
£2600 $4056 €3900 Spring (55x40cm-22x16in) s.d.1930 board. 6-Nov-2 Dreweatt Neate, Newbury #12/R est:3000-5000
£3500 $5460 €5250 Portrait (55x40cm-22x16in) board. 6-Nov-2 Dreweatt Neate, Newbury #13/R est:3000-5000

BANTING, Sir Frederick Grant (1891-1941) Canadian
£2468 $3849 €3579 Dundas Harbour (20x27cm-8x11in) s.i.d.Aug 3 1927 panel prov.exhib. 26-Mar-3 Walker's, Ottawa #239/R est:4000-5000 (C.D 5750)
£2468 $3849 €3579 Lake in autumn (27x34cm-11x13in) panel prov. 26-Mar-3 Walker's, Ottawa #240/R est:4000-5000 (C.D 5750)
£2468 $3849 €3579 Forest pool, spring day (27x34cm-11x13in) panel prov. 26-Mar-3 Walker's, Ottawa #241/R est:4000-5000 (C.D 5750)
£2621 $4141 €3932 Slaterdyke (16x23cm-6x9in) s.i.d.1925 panel prov.exhib. 14-Nov-2 Heffel, Vancouver #149/R est:4200-4600 (C.D 6500)
£2667 $4373 €4001 Farm in summer. Lake scene (22x27cm-9x11in) i.d.1939 panel two prov. 27-May-3 Sotheby's, Toronto #59/R est:4000-6000 (C.D 6000)
£2889 $4738 €4334 Winter road (26x36cm-10x14in) panel. 27-May-3 Sotheby's, Toronto #175/R est:4000-6000 (C.D 6500)
£4222 $6924 €6333 Village in snow (26x36cm-10x14in) estate st.d.Oct 3 1979 verso panel prov. 27-May-3 Sotheby's, Toronto #20/R est:6000-8000 (C.D 9500)
£4292 $6695 €6223 Beaver dam (53x66cm-21x26in) exhib. 26-Mar-3 Walker's, Ottawa #269/R est:15000-20000 (C.D 10000)
£6867 $10712 €9957 Quebec lake (53x66cm-21x26in) prov. 26-Mar-3 Walker's, Ottawa #262/R est:14000-18000 (C.D 16000)
£8584 $13391 €12447 Haymaking, Quebec (61x75cm-24x30in) panel prov. 26-Mar-3 Walker's, Ottawa #268/R est:15000-20000 (C.D 20000)
£15880 $24773 €23026 St. Tite Caps, Quebec (53x66cm-21x26in) prov.exhib. 26-Mar-3 Walker's, Ottawa #238/R est:30000-35000 (C.D 37000)

BAR, Bonaventure de (attrib) (1700-1729) French
£10135 $15811 €15000 Scene galante dans un parc (23x29cm-9x11in) copper. 26-Mar-3 Tajan, Paris #73/R

BARABAS, Miklos (1810-1898) Hungarian
£1345 $2084 €2018 Portrait of a Hungarian nobleman (74x59cm-29x23in) s. 6-Dec-2 Kieselbach, Budapest #181/R (H.F 500000)
£1548 $2415 €2322 Portrait of a man (26x21cm-10x8in) s.d.1841. 11-Sep-2 Kieselbach, Budapest #160/R (H.F 600000)
£6449 $10061 €9674 Little boy with coloured ball (105x81cm-41x32in) 11-Sep-2 Kieselbach, Budapest #63/R (H.F 2500000)

BARABINO, Angelo (1883-1950) Italian
£3401 $5408 €5000 Scrivia rocks (32x42cm-13x17in) s. board. 18-Mar-3 Finarte, Milan #20/R

BARAGANA, Casimiro (1925-) Spanish
£658 $1066 €1000 Landscape with trees (37x46cm-15x18in) s. d.1975 verso board. 21-Jan-3 Ansorena, Madrid #270/R

BARANOFF-ROSSINE, Vladimir (1888-1942) Russian
£48000 $75360 €72000 Red roofs (35x42cm-14x17in) painted c.1910 lit. 20-Nov-2 Sotheby's, London #148/R est:40000-60000
£95000 $149150 €142500 Adam and Eve (47x65cm-19x26in) lit. 20-Nov-2 Sotheby's, London #147/R est:80000-120000
Works on paper
£271 $428 €420 Composition (20x26cm-8x10in) st.mono. pencil ink wash. 17-Dec-2 Rossini, Paris #15

BARATTA, Carlo Alberto (1754-1815) Italian
Works on paper
£411 $650 €650 Etudes pour un plafond et un mur (39x28cm-15x11in) graphite gouache prov. 27-Nov-2 Christie's, Paris #90/R

BARATTA, Carlo Alberto (attrib) (1754-1815) Italian
Works on paper
£1258 $1950 €2000 Crowning Mary (30x20cm-12x8in) wash pen. 1-Oct-2 Dorotheum, Vienna #1/R est:1600-1800

BARATTI, Filippo (19/20th C) Italian
£125000 $198750 €187500 Waterloo Place (96x126cm-38x50in) s.d.1886. 18-Mar-3 Bonhams, New Bond Street #82/R est:100000-150000

BARBA, Juan (1915-1982) Spanish
£329 $533 €500 Gypsies (42x55cm-17x22in) s. board. 21-Jan-3 Ansorena, Madrid #258/R

BARBA, Mercedes (1923-) Spanish
£897 $1418 €1400 Donkey ride (35x24cm-14x9in) s. s.i.verso. 13-Nov-2 Ansorena, Madrid #249/R

BARBAGLIA, Giuseppe (1841-1910) Italian
£645 $1019 €1000 Girl with hat (25x17cm-10x7in) init. 18-Dec-2 Finarte, Milan #62/R

BARBARINI, Emil (1855-1930) Austrian
£1899 $3000 €3000 Mountain landscape with farmhouses and figures (55x68cm-22x27in) mono. 28-Nov-2 Dorotheum, Vienna #249/R est:4500-5500
£2041 $3245 €3000 Hallstadt Lake with view of the Dachstein (27x40cm-11x16in) s.d.1875 paper on board. 25-Feb-3 Dorotheum, Vienna #182/R est:4500-5000
£2532 $4000 €4000 Village street in the evening (53x42cm-21x17in) s.i.verso. 28-Nov-2 Dorotheum, Vienna #39/R est:4200-4800
£7200 $11232 €10800 Marche a Anvers. Marche aux fleurs, Bruxelles (21x32cm-8x13in) s.i.verso panel pair. 8-Oct-2 Bonhams, Knightsbridge #240/R est:2000-3000

BARBARINI, Franz (1804-1873) Austrian
£786 $1226 €1179 Donau landscape near Durnstein, Wachau in evening (15x23cm-6x9in) s. board. 6-Nov-2 Dobiaschofsky, Bern #332/R est:3000 (S.FR 1800)
£1603 $2436 €2500 Romantic landscape with oxen cart and figures in front of house on hillside (37x50cm-15x20in) s. lit. 11-Jul-2 Allgauer, Kempten #2419/R
£1644 $2564 €2400 Tree studies (17x24cm-7x9in) s. board two. 10-Apr-3 Van Ham, Cologne #1317/R est:2500
£3425 $5377 €5000 Hay harvest near Hallein near Salzburg (73x99cm-29x39in) mono.d.865. 16-Apr-3 Dorotheum, Salzburg #80/R est:7000-9000

BARBARINI, Franz (attrib) (1804-1873) Austrian
£1781 $2778 €2600 Landscape with figures, small village in distance (56x71cm-22x28in) 10-Apr-3 Dorotheum, Vienna #90/R est:2600-2800

BARBARINI, Gustav (1840-1909) Austrian
£648 $1044 €972 Mountain landscape with chalet and figures (54x64cm-21x25in) bears sig.d.80. 7-May-3 Dobiaschofsky, Bern #334/R (S.FR 1400)
£962 $1490 €1500 Romantic village landscape with cattle and figures (73x100cm-29x39in) s. canvas on canvas lit. 7-Dec-2 Bergmann, Erlangen #772/R
£1266 $1962 €2000 Upper Inn valley with figures and animals (65x102cm-26x40in) mono. 27-Sep-2 Weidler, Nurnberg #8700/R
£3767 $5914 €5500 Lower Inn valley (70x105cm-28x41in) mono. i. verso. 16-Apr-3 Dorotheum, Salzburg #87/R est:5000-7000

BARBARINI, Gustav (attrib) (1840-1909) Austrian
£1164 $1828 €1700 On the way home (55x68cm-22x27in) bears mono.d.870. 16-Apr-3 Dorotheum, Salzburg #99/R est:1500-1800

BARBARO, Giovanni (?) Italian?
Works on paper
£520 $811 €780 Still life with stoneware flagon and fruit (29x73cm-11x29in) s. W/C. 26-Mar-3 Woolley & Wallis, Salisbury #111/R

BARBARO, Giovanni (attrib) (?) Italian?
£300 $456 €450 Vase of summer flowers by fruit bowls on a table (56x90cm-22x35in) s. canvas on board. 29-Aug-2 Christie's, Kensington #17
Works on paper
£280 $448 €420 Still life of apples, grapes and pineapples (56x28cm-22x11in) s. W/C. 10-Jan-3 Biddle & Webb, Birmingham #239

BARBARO, Saverio (1924-) Italian
£372 $580 €550 Seascape in Rab (38x46cm-15x18in) s.d.1959. 28-Mar-3 Farsetti, Prato #55

BARBASAN, Mariano (1864-1924) Spanish
£1342 $2161 €2000 Carnival (22cm-9in circular) s. 18-Feb-3 Durán, Madrid #165/R
£1494 $2300 €2241 Market scene (10x18cm-4x7in) s. i.verso panel. 27-Oct-2 Grogan, Boston #53 est:2000-4000
£4200 $6678 €6300 Young girls in the street. Young boys in the street (18x29cm-7x11in) mono. panel pair. 20-Mar-3 Christie's, Kensington #85/R est:4000-6000
£4795 $7479 €7000 Landscape with goats (19x16cm-7x6in) s. 8-Apr-3 Ansorena, Madrid #219/R
£18000 $28260 €27000 Paisaje montanoso - mountain landscape (145x212cm-57x83in) 19-Nov-2 Sotheby's, London #77/R est:10000-15000
£18000 $27900 €27000 Card player's refreshments (23x38cm-9x15in) s.d.1895 panel. 4-Dec-2 Christie's, London #5/R est:15000-20000
Works on paper
£586 $932 €850 Venice (54x18cm-21x7in) s. W/C. 4-Mar-3 Ansorena, Madrid #665
£1517 $2412 €2200 Italian landscape (53x18cm-21x7in) s. W/C. 4-Mar-3 Ansorena, Madrid #666/R

BARBATA, Laura Anderson (1958-) American
Sculpture
£14013 $22000 €21020 Group of six totems. wood stone metal exec.c.1990 prov.lit. set of 6. 19-Nov-2 Sotheby's, New York #46/R est:22000

BARBEAU, Marcel (1925-) Canadian
£489 $802 €709 Reflets printaniers no.4 (48x64cm-19x25in) acrylic on paper. 1-Jun-3 Levis, Calgary #3/R est:2000-2500 (C.D 1100)
Works on paper
£203 $319 €305 Untitled (16x15cm-6x6in) s.d.51 W/C. 12-Dec-2 Iegor de Saint Hippolyte, Montreal #5 (C.D 500)

BARBEDIENNE FOUNDRY (19/20th C) French
Sculpture
£897 $1400 €1346 Nude fallen warrior offering the olive branch of peace (38cm-15in) s. prov. 20-Sep-2 New Orleans Auction, New Orleans #618/R est:1200-1800

BARBEDIENNE, Ferdinand (1810-1892) French
Sculpture
£7042 $11338 €10000 Seated Goddess (217cm-85in) s. bronze incl.walnut pedestal. 10-May-3 Bukowskis, Helsinki #331/R est:10000-12000

BARBELLA, Constantino (1852-1925) Italian
Sculpture
£1635 $2518 €2600 Woman from Scanno (24cm-9in) s. terracotta. 23-Oct-2 Finarte, Milan #112/R
£2848 $4500 €4500 Love song (47cm-19in) s. pat bronze. 26-Nov-2 Christie's, Rome #224/R

BARBER, Alfred R (fl.1879-1893) British
£6071 $9593 €9107 Family of rabbits (46x61cm-18x24in) s. prov. 26-Nov-2 Sotheby's, Melbourne #209/R est:12000-18000 (A.D 17000)

BARBER, Charles Burton (1845-1894) British
£850 $1326 €1275 Portrait of the artist's father (102x74cm-40x29in) s. 11-Apr-3 Keys, Aylsham #662
£1481 $2296 €2222 Pets (28x36cm-11x14in) s.d.92 millboard. 3-Dec-2 Ritchie, Toronto #2027/R est:3000-5000 (C.D 3600)

BARBER, Charles Vincent (1784-1854) British
Works on paper
£400 $636 €600 View of Cardinganshire (53x79cm-21x31in) indis.i. W/C. 18-Mar-3 Capes Dunn, Manchester #459

BARBER, John (1898-1965) American
£1806 $2854 €2800 Vue de Calvaire a Etretat (38x61cm-15x24in) s.d.1925. 19-Dec-2 Claude Aguttes, Neuilly #162/R
£1935 $3058 €3000 View of Etretat (38x61cm-15x24in) s.d.1895. 19-Dec-2 Claude Aguttes, Neuilly #163/R

BARBER, Joseph Moseley (fl.1858-1889) British
£400 $624 €600 Cottage interior, with mother at a table, child by the open door (36x46cm-14x18in) s.d.1872. 6-Nov-2 Bonhams, Chester #518
£1100 $1793 €1650 Cottage interior with woman and child by a doorway (14x18cm-6x7in) s.d.1872. 12-Feb-3 Andrew Hartley, Ilkley #931/R est:1200-1500

BARBER, Lucius (?-1767) British
Miniatures
£1550 $2511 €2325 Lady in a decollete white dress (5cm-2xin) enamel gilt metal frame. 22-May-3 Bonhams, New Bond Street #24/R est:1000-1500

BARBER, Sam (1943-) American
£409 $650 €614 Iris (24x29cm-9x11in) s. board. 7-Mar-3 Skinner, Boston #392/R
£409 $650 €614 Path to the beach (25x30cm-10x12in) s. board. 7-Mar-3 Skinner, Boston #472/R
£574 $900 €861 Autumn landscape (61x77cm-24x30in) s. board exhib. 22-Nov-2 Skinner, Boston #284/R est:1000-1500
£3065 $4750 €4598 Iris primrose and water lilies (122x102cm-48x40in) s.d.1985 board exhib. 1-Oct-2 Arthur James, Florida #27

BARBER, Thomas (1768-1843) British
£1600 $2496 €2400 Portrait of Catherine Elizabeth Burnside (76x63cm-30x25in) prov. 8-Oct-2 Sotheby's, Olympia #385/R est:2000-3000
£3000 $4680 €4500 Portrait of Colonel John Elliott (77x64cm-30x25in) prov. 8-Oct-2 Sotheby's, Olympia #384/R est:2000-3000

BARBER, Thomas Stanley (fl.1891-1899) British
£260 $406 €390 River Conway, North Wales (20x40cm-8x16in) s. 11-Sep-2 Bonhams, Newport #227/R
£1000 $1430 €1500 Figures in a country landscape (30x61cm-12x24in) s. pair. 28-Feb-2 Greenslade Hunt, Taunton #438/R est:500-800
£1400 $2198 €2100 Welsh river and mountain landscape with figures fishing (43x81cm-17x32in) 13-Dec-2 Keys, Aylsham #675/R est:1000-1250

BARBERA, Enrico (1947-) Italian
£897 $1391 €1400 Summer (120x150cm-47x59in) s.i.d.1984 verso. 4-Dec-2 Finarte, Milan #538/R

BARBERIS, Eugène de (1851-?) French
£2387 $3772 €3700 Cavalier dans un village (55x73cm-22x29in) s. 19-Dec-2 Claude Aguttes, Neuilly #204/R

BARBETA, Joan (1911-1990) Spanish
£297 $469 €460 Carmen (72x57cm-28x22in) s.i.d.1940 verso. 18-Dec-2 Ansorena, Madrid #328/R

BARBIER, Andre (1883-1970) French
£327 $507 €520 Bord de mer en Normandie (46x37cm-18x15in) s. 4-Oct-2 Tajan, Paris #15
£2346 $3331 €3800 Regate sur la riviere (46x61cm-18x24in) s. 16-Mar-3 Eric Pillon, Calais #129/R

BARBIER, Antoine (1859-?) French
£449 $704 €700 Ships in Istanbul harbour (89x70cm-35x28in) s. 10-Dec-2 Dorotheum, Vienna #131/R

BARBIER, Georges (1882-1932) French
Works on paper
£380 $600 €600 Danseuse (26x22cm-10x9in) s.i.d.1926 W/C gouache. 26-Nov-2 Camard, Paris #55
£461 $747 €650 Femme au loup (25x18cm-10x7in) s.d.1922 gouache. 23-May-3 Camard, Paris #38
£461 $747 €650 Gentilhomme (25x18cm-10x7in) s.d.1923 gouache. 23-May-3 Camard, Paris #39
£1509 $2400 €2264 Danseuse des ballets Russes (26x20cm-10x8in) s.d.1918 W/C gouache over pencil. 3-Mar-3 Swann Galleries, New York #35/R est:2500-3500

BARBIER, Jean Jacques le (1738-1826) French
£962 $1519 €1500 Enfants jouant avec un satyre (27x21cm-11x8in) i. panel exhib. 15-Nov-2 Beaussant & Lefèvre, Paris #77
£145270 $226622 €215000 Magnanimite de Lycurgue (131x171cm-52x67in) s.dd.1791 exhib.lit. 26-Mar-3 Rossini, Paris #118/R est:45700-60900

BARBIERE, Domenico del (c.1506-1565) Italian
Prints
£3800 $5928 €5700 Amphiaraus (33x23cm-13x9in) etching. 25-Mar-3 Sotheby's, London #2/R est:1500-2000

BARBIERI, Eugenio (1927-) Italian
£385 $604 €600 Stone pickers at river (63x80cm-25x31in) s.d.53 masonite. 16-Dec-2 Pandolfini, Florence #265

BARBIERI, Giovanni Battista (attrib) (c.1580-?) Italian
Works on paper
£949 $1500 €1500 Putto assis (23x13cm-9x5in) col chk. 27-Nov-2 Christie's, Paris #68/R est:800-1200

BARBIERI, Giuseppe (1746-1806) Italian
Works on paper
£2025 $3200 €3200 Interieur d'une temple avec des tombeaux (43x57cm-17x22in) i. black chk pen brown ink brown wash. 27-Nov-2 Christie's, Paris #102/R est:1500-2000

BARBIERI, Paolo Antonio (attrib) (1603-1649) Italian
£3354 $5500 €5031 Birds in a landscape (100x129cm-39x51in) 29-May-3 Sotheby's, New York #94/R est:6000-8000

BARBIERS, Pieter (elder-attrib) (1717-1780) Dutch
Works on paper
£1500 $2325 €2250 Country house with farmers harvesting in the foreground (54x67cm-21x26in) gouache. 9-Dec-2 Bonhams, New Bond Street #55/R est:1600-2000

BARBIERS, Pieter Bartolomeusz III (1772-1837) Dutch
Works on paper
£1958 $2800 €2937 Landscape with a watering place for cattle and two resting figures (61x78cm-24x31in) s. W/C. 23-Jan-3 Swann Galleries, New York #227/R est:2000-3000

BARBIERS, Pieter Bartolomeusz III (attrib) (1772-1837) Dutch
Works on paper
£1146 $1789 €1800 Peasant family at their farm amongst woods (31x39cm-12x15in) pen black ink W/C. 5-Nov-2 Sotheby's, Amsterdam #158/R est:2000-3000

BARBLAN, Oscar (1909-1987) Swiss
£472 $755 €708 Female (50x34cm-20x13in) s. board. 17-Mar-3 Philippe Schuler, Zurich #8405 (S.FR 1000)
£800 $1248 €1200 Cherry trees in a landscape (51x73cm-20x29in) s.indis d. 15-Oct-2 Bonhams, Knightsbridge #239/R
£800 $1288 €1200 Barcelona (67x53cm-26x21in) s.i.d.35 board. 18-Feb-3 Bonhams, Knightsbridge #22/R

BARBUDO, Salvador Sanchez (1858-1917) Spanish
£938 $1425 €1407 Retrato de magistrado (69x42cm-27x17in) s. 3-Jul-2 Naón & Cia, Buenos Aires #37/R est:1500-1800
£4932 $7693 €7200 Turkey in the field (39x79cm-15x31in) s.i. board. 8-Apr-3 Ansorena, Madrid #218/R est:7200
£23734 $37500 €35601 La coronacion (44x72cm-17x28in) s.d.89. 24-Apr-3 Sotheby's, New York #121/R est:30000-40000

BARCELO, Miguel (1957-) Spanish
£24306 $38646 €35000 Menjan-se la cua (105x75cm-41x30in) s. acrylic pencil prov.lit. 29-Apr-3 Artcurial Briest, Paris #450/R est:30000-40000
£26000 $43420 €37700 Steak frites (52x58cm-20x23in) s.i.d.1984 verso oil mixed media collage prov. 26-Jun-3 Sotheby's, London #265/R est:18000-25000
£28000 $46760 €40600 Dibi (29x29cm-11x11in) s.i.d.92 oil sand string resin prov.exhib.lit. 27-Jun-3 Christie's, London #246/R est:25000-35000
£28387 $44852 €44000 Skull and bones (75x55cm-30x22in) s.d.93 oil pencil fabric paper prov.exhib. 17-Dec-2 Segre, Madrid #179/R est:30000
£120000 $184800 €180000 Huitres III (200x200cm-79x79in) s.d.1989 oil mixed media on canvas prov. 23-Oct-2 Christie's, London #142/R est:120000-160000
£170000 $283900 €246500 Cala marcal no.1 (200x300cm-79x118in) s.i.d.1984 oil mixed media prov. 27-Jun-3 Christie's, London #266/R est:120000-160000
£220000 $367400 €330000 Constelacio no. 6 (201x201cm-79x79in) s.i.d.89 verso oil sand resin prov.exhib. 26-Jun-3 Christie's, London #35/R est:220000-280000
Works on paper
£1772 $2800 €2658 Salomon (32x23cm-13x9in) chl executed 1985 prov. 12-Nov-2 Phillips, New York #245/R est:4000-6000
£53459 $82862 €85000 Caquis Pourris (65x81cm-26x32in) mixed media on canvas painted 1997. 7-Oct-2 Ansorena, Madrid #80/R
£84615 $133692 €132000 Three totems and four skulls (163x197cm-64x78in) s.i.d.2000 verso masonite on canvas. 13-Nov-2 Ansorena, Madrid #45/R est:132000
£100000 $164000 €150000 Galerie Louvre (245x212cm-96x83in) synthetic resin staples newspaper cardboard prov. 6-Feb-3 Christie's, London #636/R est:60000-80000
£140000 $233800 €210000 Cuina Mallorquina (200x300cm-79x118in) s.i.d.85 verso mixed media canvas. 26-Jun-3 Christie's, London #38/R est:150000-200000

£225000 $375750 €337500 Le Noyau Noir (230x285cm-91x112in) s.i.d.111.89 verso mixed media canvas prov.exhib. 25-Jun-3 Sotheby's, London #37/R est:250000-350000
£470000 $770800 €705000 Tres equis (67x102cm-26x40in) s.i.d.90 verso mixed media on canvas prov.lit. 6-Feb-3 Sotheby's, London #28/R est:300000
£580000 $893200 €870000 Veronica (163x131cm-64x52in) s. s.i.d.IX.90 verso pigment glue seaweed saw scratches on canvas. 22-Oct-2 Sotheby's, London #332/R est:300000-600000

BARCHUS, Eliza R (1857-1959) American
£478 $750 €717 Mt Hood (25x30cm-10x12in) s. artist board. 23-Nov-2 Jackson's, Cedar Falls #62/R
£764 $1200 €1146 Mt Rainier (61x41cm-24x16in) s. 23-Nov-2 Jackson's, Cedar Falls #61/R
£1048 $1750 €1520 Portland (41x61cm-16x24in) s. i.verso. 17-Jun-3 John Moran, Pasadena #167 est:2000-3000
£1299 $2000 €1949 View of Mount Hood (91x56cm-36x22in) s. i.verso. 27-Oct-2 Grogan, Boston #77 est:600-900
£1592 $2500 €2388 View of Mt Hood with a lake in the foreground (41x61cm-16x24in) s. 19-Nov-2 Butterfields, San Francisco #8165/R est:2500-3000
£3165 $5000 €4589 Three sisters (48x71cm-19x28in) s. 26-Jul-3 Coeur d'Alene, Hayden #240/R est:3000-5000

BARCIK, Andrej (1928-) Czechoslovakian
Works on paper
£788 $1150 €1182 Symbolic motif (62x81cm-24x32in) mixed media board. 4-Jun-2 SOGA, Bratislava #290/R est:35000 (SL.K 50000)
£1449 $2058 €2174 Still life with grinder (47x58cm-19x23in) mixed media exec.1957. 26-Mar-2 SOGA, Bratislava #267/R est:32000 (SL.K 92000)

BARCLAY, Edgar (1842-1913) British
£340 $530 €510 Figure resting by his cart with his cat (49x38cm-19x15in) s. 17-Sep-2 Bonhams, Ipswich #411

BARCLAY, John Maclaren (attrib) (1811-1886) British
Works on paper
£253 $400 €380 Portrait of a gentleman (38x33cm-15x13in) s.i. pastel. 5-Apr-3 Neal Auction Company, New Orleans #512/R

BARCLAY, John Rankin (1884-1962) British
Works on paper
£270 $421 €405 St Ives Harbour (24x30cm-9x12in) s. W/C. 15-Oct-2 Bearnes, Exeter #387/R
£540 $886 €783 Dinon (30x24cm-12x9in) s.d.1913 gouache linen. 7-Jun-3 Shapes, Edinburgh #422

BARCLAY, McClelland (1891-1943) American
£1859 $2900 €2789 Striding woman wearing fashionable green suit (86x46cm-34x18in) s. 9-Nov-2 Illustration House, New York #113/R est:4000-7000
£1859 $2900 €2789 Smiling woman in orange at cocktail bar (86x46cm-34x18in) s. 9-Nov-2 Illustration House, New York #114/R est:4000-6000
£3846 $6000 €5769 Untitled, figures on a beach (61x53cm-24x21in) painted c.1920. 18-Oct-2 Du Mouchelle, Detroit #60/R est:5000-7000

BARCSAY, Jeno (1900-1998) Hungarian
£2375 $3705 €3444 Head of a woman (55x49cm-22x19in) s. 12-Apr-3 Mu Terem Galeria, Budapest #149/R est:650000 (H.F 850000)
£2958 $4585 €4437 Woman sitting (111x90cm-44x35in) s. 6-Dec-2 Kieselbach, Budapest #155/R (H.F 1100000)
£5160 $8049 €7482 Composition (24x25cm-9x10in) s. cardboard exhib. 13-Sep-2 Mu Terem Galeria, Budapest #110/R est:750000 (H.F 2000000)
£7266 $11334 €10899 Small plan of freso (34x20cm-13x8in) s. 11-Apr-3 Kieselbach, Budapest #153/R est:2500000-2600000 (H.F 2600000)
£8606 $13339 €12479 Row of houses in a small town (24x45cm-9x18in) s. lit. 9-Dec-2 Mu Terem Galeria, Budapest #95/R est:950000 (H.F 3200000)
£43028 $66694 €62391 Easel in front of the window (51x27cm-20x11in) s. exhib.lit. 9-Dec-2 Mu Terem Galeria, Budapest #35/R est:2800000 (H.F 16000000)
Works on paper
£753 $1167 €1092 Artist colony in Szentendre (30x44cm-12x17in) s. W/C. 9-Dec-2 Mu Terem Galeria, Budapest #19/R est:190000 (H.F 280000)
£1290 $2012 €1871 Woman's face (49x37cm-19x15in) s. W/C. 13-Sep-2 Mu Terem Galeria, Budapest #105/R est:380000 (H.F 500000)

BARD, James (1815-1897) American
£13014 $19000 €19521 Paddle towboat, Victoria (76x127cm-30x50in) s.i. lit. 3-Nov-1 North East Auctions, Portsmouth #67/R est:10000-15000
£15753 $23000 €23630 Martha Washington (76x127cm-30x50in) s.d.1864 lit. 3-Nov-1 North East Auctions, Portsmouth #66/R est:10000-15000
£16438 $24000 €24657 Sidewheel towboat, Mary J Finn (71x122cm-28x48in) s.d.1876 lit. 3-Nov-1 North East Auctions, Portsmouth #65/R est:6000-9000
£21918 $32000 €32877 Paddle towboat, Osego (89x132cm-35x52in) lit. 3-Nov-1 North East Auctions, Portsmouth #62/R est:25000-35000
£21918 $32000 €32877 Sidewheel steamboat, Belle (74x122cm-29x48in) s. prov.lit. 3-Nov-1 North East Auctions, Portsmouth #68/R est:15000-25000
£22866 $37500 €34299 Sidewheeler, Creole (79x127cm-31x50in) s.i.d.1852 prov. 8-Feb-3 Neal Auction Company, New Orleans #338/R est:30000-50000
£28767 $42000 €43151 Paddle wheel towboat, John Birbeck (74x130cm-29x51in) s.d.1860 lit. 3-Nov-1 North East Auctions, Portsmouth #70/R est:10000-15000
£51370 $75000 €77055 US Mail paddle steamer, George Law (81x132cm-32x52in) s.d.1853 prov. 3-Nov-1 North East Auctions, Portsmouth #61/R est:30000-50000
£55921 $85000 €83882 Sidewheeler, Milton Marton (76x127cm-30x50in) s.d.1868 sold with documents and photos prov.lit. 17-Aug-2 North East Auctions, Portsmouth #874/R est:80000-120000
Works on paper
£23602 $38000 €35403 Steamboat Henry Smith (18x29cm-7x11in) s. W/C prov.lit. 16-Jan-3 Christie's, Rockefeller NY #412/R est:40000-60000

BARD, James and John (19th C) American
£44521 $65000 €66782 Steamboat, Wilson G Hunt (74x124cm-29x49in) s.d.1849 lit. 3-Nov-1 North East Auctions, Portsmouth #69/R est:15000-25000

BARDASANO BAOS, Jose (1910-1979) Spanish
£742 $1187 €1076 Soldado (31x27cm-12x11in) s. 15-May-3 Louis Morton, Mexico #14/R (M.P 12000)
£742 $1187 €1076 Boedgon con pescados (19x27cm-7x11in) s. 15-May-3 Louis Morton, Mexico #154/R (M.P 12000)
£866 $1385 €1256 Locomotoro (15x17cm-6x7in) s. 15-May-3 Louis Morton, Mexico #165/R est:12000-18000 (M.P 14000)
£881 $1356 €1400 Soldier on horseback (27x22cm-11x9in) s. board. 22-Oct-2 Durán, Madrid #123/R
£1419 $2243 €2200 Woman (61x50cm-24x20in) s. 18-Dec-2 Ansorena, Madrid #150/R
£2834 $4421 €4251 Paisaje con rio (56x45cm-22x18in) s. 17-Oct-2 Louis Morton, Mexico #55/R est:50000-55000 (M.P 45000)
Works on paper
£495 $792 €718 Retrato de una dama (23x18cm-9x7in) s. pastel. 15-May-3 Louis Morton, Mexico #5 (M.P 8000)

BARDELLINI, Pietro (1728-1806) Italian
£4528 $6974 €7200 Vierge a l'enfant et seraphins (17x14cm-7x6in) copper oval. 25-Oct-2 Tajan, Paris #26/R est:4000-6000
£5063 $8000 €8000 Paris' judgement (75x101cm-30x40in) 2-Dec-2 Finarte, Milan #137/R est:12000

BARDENFLETH, P (19th C) German
£338 $527 €507 Classic interior (51x43cm-20x17in) s.d.1820 prov. 23-Sep-2 Rasmussen, Vejle #233/R (D.KR 4000)

BARDI, Luigi (19/20th C) Italian
£1800 $2736 €2700 Grape pickers. i.verso after Bartolome Esteban Murillo. 29-Aug-2 Christie's, Kensington #108/R est:1500-2000

BARDOLET, Coll (1912-) Spanish
Works on paper
£483 $768 €700 Figures (26x48cm-10x19in) s. W/C gouache. 4-Mar-3 Ansorena, Madrid #683/R

BARDONE, Guy (1927-) French
£397 $624 €620 Deux chemins (46x33cm-18x13in) s. s.i.d.57 verso. 22-Nov-2 Millon & Associes, Paris #81
£1216 $1897 €1800 Bouteille et champignons (46x61cm-18x24in) s. s.i.d.1963 verso. 30-Mar-3 Anaf, Lyon #8/R
£1216 $1897 €1800 Montagne, l'hiver (81x65cm-32x26in) s. s.i.verso. 30-Mar-3 Anaf, Lyon #7
£1485 $2346 €2228 Zinnias et poires (92x73cm-36x29in) s. 17-Nov-2 Koller, Geneva #1331 (S.FR 3400)
£1931 $3225 €2800 Les impatientes (81x100cm-32x39in) s. 10-Jul-3 Artcurial Briest, Paris #257/R est:3000-4000

BARDOU, Emmanuel (1744-1818) Swiss
Sculpture
£8562 $13356 €12500 Frederick the Great on horseback (33cm-13in) gilded bronze. 10-Apr-3 Van Ham, Cologne #1100/R est:20000

BARDUCCI, N (19th C) Italian?
£3226 $5000 €4839 Giant's stairway (44x37cm-17x15in) s.d.78 prov. 29-Oct-2 Sotheby's, New York #23/R est:7000-10000

BARDWELL, George W (20th C) American
£382 $600 €573 Gloucester Harbor (30x41cm-12x16in) s. 22-Nov-2 Skinner, Boston #355/R

BARDWELL, Thomas (1704-1767) British
£4747 $7405 €7500 Portrait of Admiral Vernon Old Grog holding a telescope (198x127cm-78x50in) prov. 15-Oct-2 Mealy's, Castlecomer #166/R est:2500-3500
£35000 $58100 €52500 Portrait of the broke and the Bowes families (98x111cm-39x44in) i. 12-Jun-3 Sotheby's, London #6/R est:40000-60000

BAREAU, Georges (1866-1931) French
Sculpture
£1800 $2934 €2610 Figure of a labourer (68cm-27in) s. dark brown pat. bronze i.f.F Barbedienne. 15-Jul-3 Sotheby's, Olympia #101/R est:2000-3000
£2535 $4082 €3600 Victoria (60cm-24in) s. dark brown pat.bronze Cast.F.Barbedienne. 9-May-3 Schloss Ahlden, Ahlden #2052/R est:3900
£3459 $5396 €5500 Vulcanos (95cm-37in) s. brown pat.bronze Cast.Barbedienne, Paris. 20-Sep-2 Schloss Ahlden, Ahlden #1658/R est:5800

BAREIS, Alfred (1899-1969) Austrian
Works on paper
£405 $632 €600 Backyard with water pump (55x55cm-22x22in) s.d.1922 W/C. 28-Mar-3 Dorotheum, Vienna #316/R

BARELO, Francisco de (17th C) Italian?
£1585 $2600 €2298 Virgin and Child enthroned with donors (22x16cm-9x6in) indis.sig.d.1644 copper. 4-Jun-3 Christie's, Rockefeller NY #193/R est:5000-7000

BARENGER, James (jnr) (1780-1831) British
£1200 $1956 €1800 Hunter by a stable (20x25cm-8x10in) s.d.1824. 29-Jan-3 Sotheby's, Olympia #98/R est:800-1200
£1624 $2500 €2436 Kill (71x91cm-28x36in) 4-Sep-2 Christie's, Rockefeller NY #373/R est:5000-7000

BARETTA, Michele (1916-1987) Italian
£1020 $1622 €1500 Sacca di Scardovari (30x40cm-12x16in) s.d.1982 board. 1-Mar-3 Meeting Art, Vercelli #478
£1282 $2013 €2000 Girl with sunflowers (50x70cm-20x28in) s. masonite. 10-Dec-2 Della Rocca, Turin #338/R
£1410 $2214 €2200 Girl with flowers (70x50cm-28x20in) s.d.70 masonite. 10-Dec-2 Della Rocca, Turin #343/R
£1582 $2468 €2500 Anglers (60x80cm-24x31in) s.d.1965 board. 14-Sep-2 Meeting Art, Vercelli #934/R
£6250 $9938 €9000 Elsa, the cat and myself (80x60cm-31x24in) s.d.1978 s.d.verso board exhib.lit. 1-May-3 Meeting Art, Vercelli #577 est:4000
Works on paper
£694 $1104 €1000 Maternity (50x70cm-20x28in) s. mixed media card. 1-May-3 Meeting Art, Vercelli #270

BARETTE, Francois (1899-1979) French
Works on paper
£259 $405 €410 Le cochon (23x31cm-9x12in) studio st. chl. 15-Sep-2 Etude Bailleul, Bayeux #4/R
£259 $405 €410 Couple de danseurs (21x16cm-8x6in) studio st. gouache. 15-Sep-2 Etude Bailleul, Bayeux #26
£304 $474 €480 Ballet en fete (32x50cm-13x20in) s. gouache. 15-Sep-2 Etude Bailleul, Bayeux #30/R
£304 $474 €480 Denseuses orientales (65x50cm-26x20in) s. gouache. 15-Sep-2 Etude Bailleul, Bayeux #36/R
£316 $494 €500 La pause pendant la repetition (33x50cm-13x20in) studio st. gouache. 15-Sep-2 Etude Bailleul, Bayeux #37/R
£335 $523 €530 Centaures dansant autour de couple endormi (50x37cm-20x15in) s. gouache. 15-Sep-2 Etude Bailleul, Bayeux #28/R

BARFUSS, Ina (1949-) German
£2319 $3803 €3200 Untitled (207x150cm-81x59in) s.d.84 resin. 28-May-3 Lempertz, Koln #21/R est:3000
Works on paper
£262 $383 €393 Untitled (37x46cm-15x18in) s.d.1985 gouache. 4-Jun-2 Germann, Zurich #743/R (S.FR 600)
£349 $510 €524 Untitled (85x65cm-33x26in) s.d.1994 gouache. 4-Jun-2 Germann, Zurich #746/R (S.FR 800)

BARGATZKI, A (19th C) ?
£699 $1090 €1049 Autumn wood with angler by stream (68x98cm-27x39in) 20-Nov-2 Fischer, Luzern #2017/R est:1800-2200 (S.FR 1600)

BARGHEER, Eduard (1901-1979) German
£281 $450 €407 Sailing vessel in a winter harbour (41x51cm-16x20in) s. 16-May-3 Skinner, Boston #336/R
£1489 $2413 €2100 Fishermen with nets (40x54cm-16x21in) s.d. tempera pencil. 24-May-3 Van Ham, Cologne #29/R est:2500
£2051 $3179 €3200 Coastal scene, houses by sea (48x63cm-19x25in) s. bears d. oil tempera over pencil. 4-Dec-2 Lempertz, Koln #556/R est:3000
£4808 $7452 €7500 Ischia - S. Angelo d'Ischia (30x39cm-12x15in) s.d.64. 4-Dec-2 Lempertz, Koln #553/R est:6000-8000
£6218 $9638 €9700 Garden at night (41x55cm-16x22in) s.d.52-53 i.d. verso exhib. 4-Dec-2 Lempertz, Koln #552/R est:7000-8000
£10127 $16000 €16000 Ships in harbour (60x74cm-24x29in) s. prov. 30-Nov-2 Villa Grisebach, Berlin #331/R est:1000-12000
Works on paper
£440 $678 €700 Marrakech (21x30cm-8x12in) s.d.1961 i. verso W/C. 26-Oct-2 Dr Lehr, Berlin #32/R
£609 $962 €950 Houses by the sea II (48x60cm-19x24in) s.d.1940 i. verso W/C over pencil. 15-Nov-2 Reiss & Sohn, Konigstein #417/R
£633 $1000 €1000 Forio (25x20cm-10x8in) s.d.1973 i. verso W/C. 30-Nov-2 Arnold, Frankfurt #27/R
£641 $994 €1000 Head study III (28x22cm-11x9in) s.d.48 W/C over pencil. 4-Dec-2 Lempertz, Koln #555/R
£870 $1426 €1200 Bright morning (22x31cm-9x12in) s.d.65 i. verso W/C prov. 29-May-3 Lempertz, Koln #511/R
£870 $1426 €1200 Castle by the Inn (29x40cm-11x16in) s.d.73 W/C over pencil. 31-May-3 Villa Grisebach, Berlin #745/R
£962 $1490 €1500 Blue town (30x43cm-12x17in) s.d.72 W/C. 7-Dec-2 Van Ham, Cologne #23/R est:2500
£1014 $1664 €1400 Untitled - seaside town (43x60cm-17x24in) s.d.53 W/C over pencil. 29-May-3 Lempertz, Koln #509/R
£1042 $1646 €1500 Untitled (22x31cm-9x12in) s.d.1965 W/C. 26-Apr-3 Dr Lehr, Berlin #54/R est:2000
£1139 $1800 €1800 Southern Italian town (30x42cm-12x17in) s.d.70 W/C. 29-Nov-2 Sigalas, Stuttgart #1154/R est:1950
£1218 $1888 €1900 Southern houses (40x56cm-16x22in) s.d.1968 W/C. 7-Dec-2 Hauswedell & Nolte, Hamburg #512 est:2400
£1282 $1987 €2000 Landscape with blue houses - seaside ruins (32x43cm-13x17in) W/C over pencil prov. 4-Dec-2 Lempertz, Koln #559/R est:1800
£1282 $1987 €2000 Procession (41x60cm-16x24in) s.d.1949 W/C. 7-Dec-2 Hauswedell & Nolte, Hamburg #511/R est:2000
£1418 $2298 €2000 Houses in Ischia (18x32cm-7x13in) s.d.62 W/C. 20-May-3 Dorotheum, Vienna #186/R est:2200-2500
£1544 $2485 €2300 Fishermen (30x44cm-12x17in) s.d.1958 W/C. 21-Feb-3 Sigalas, Stuttgart #855/R est:2800
£1731 $2683 €2700 Seaside houses (21x28cm-8x11in) s.d.49 W/C over pencil. 4-Dec-2 Lempertz, Koln #557/R est:2000
£1761 $2923 €2500 Houses on Ischia (19x27cm-7x11in) s. pencil W/C. 14-Jun-3 Hauswedell & Nolte, Hamburg #1009/R est:3000
£2101 $3446 €2900 Pink yellow composition (44x62cm-17x24in) s.d.55 W/C over pencil. 31-May-3 Villa Grisebach, Berlin #744/R est:2500-3000
£2174 $3565 €3000 Fishermen on beach (43x55cm-17x22in) s.d.54 W/C over pencil. 29-May-3 Lempertz, Koln #510/R est:2500
£2319 $3803 €3200 Composition (29x46cm-11x18in) s.d.55 W/C over pencil semi transparent paper. 31-May-3 Villa Grisebach, Berlin #743/R est:2000-2500
£2899 $4754 €4000 Cityscape (44x62cm-17x24in) s.d.57 W/C bodycol. 31-May-3 Villa Grisebach, Berlin #297/R est:3000-4000
£3077 $4769 €4800 Southern houses among palm trees (30x43cm-12x17in) s.d.51 W/C over pencil prov. 4-Dec-2 Lempertz, Koln #558/R est:3200
£3288 $5129 €4800 Mediterranean city (31x43cm-12x17in) s.i.d. verso W/C. 11-Apr-3 Winterberg, Heidelberg #702/R est:3200
£3986 $6536 €5500 Forio d'Ischia (42x60cm-17x24in) s.d. W/C over pencil. 31-May-3 Villa Grisebach, Berlin #296/R est:6000-8000
£10692 $16679 €17000 Sudliches dorf - Southern village, hoses in the rain (31x48cm-12x19in) s.d.50 W/C prov. 9-Oct-2 Sotheby's, London #226/R est:6000-9000

BARGONI, Gian Carlo (1936-) Italian
£224 $348 €350 Red contrasts (50x70cm-20x28in) s.i.d.62 verso. 5-Dec-2 Stadion, Trieste #763
£284 $460 €400 Sviluppo giallo verde su ritmi neri (65x70cm-26x28in) s.i.d.1963 prov. 26-May-3 Christie's, Milan #302

BARGUE, Charles (1826-1883) French
Works on paper
£437 $700 €634 Artist sketching (12x16cm-5x6in) studio st. W/C graphite two. 16-May-3 Skinner, Boston #18/R

BARILE, Xavier J (1891-1981) American
£299 $475 €449 Evening bather (30x23cm-12x9in) board painted c.1951. 2-Mar-3 Toomey, Oak Park #738/R

BARILLI, Aristide (20th C) Italian?
£567 $919 €800 Paesaggio collinare (35x43cm-14x17in) s.d.1963 faesite. 22-May-3 Stadion, Trieste #265

BARILLOT, Léon (1844-1929) French
Works on paper
£705 $1107 €1100 Lapins (12x21cm-5x8in) s. W/C. 13-Dec-2 Piasa, Paris #43

BARISON, Giuseppe (1853-1930) Italian
£2979 $4826 €4200 Una visita (40x27cm-16x11in) s.d.1877 i.d.verso panel. 22-May-3 Stadion, Trieste #389/R est:3500-4500
£3846 $5962 €6000 Thought (40x50cm-16x20in) s. 5-Dec-2 Stadion, Trieste #820/R
Works on paper
£769 $1192 €1200 Portrait of young woman with hat (30x22cm-12x9in) s. W/C. 5-Dec-2 Stadion, Trieste #870

BARJOLA, Juan (1919-) Spanish
£12710 $20081 €19700 Montmartre (68x81cm-27x32in) s. 18-Dec-2 Ansorena, Madrid #171/R est:12700

BARKER OF BATH (19th C) British
£800 $1280 €1200 Cattle watering at a wooded pool (28x42cm-11x17in) board. 11-Mar-3 Bonhams, Knightsbridge #327/R

BARKER OF BATH, John Joseph (fl.1835-1866) British
£420 $647 €630 Shepherd and sheep on a country lane (46x66cm-18x26in) s. 22-Oct-2 Bonhams, Bath #231
£500 $780 €750 Cattle watering in a woodland river. Landscape scene with cattle (74x62cm-29x24in) s. verso bears sig.H S Tuke double-sided. 17-Oct-2 Lawrence, Crewkerne #455
£800 $1304 €1200 Plough team at rest under a tree (54x74cm-21x29in) s. 17-Feb-3 Bonhams, Bath #60/R
£3000 $4800 €4500 Malvern (59x105cm-23x41in) s. 15-May-3 Lawrence, Crewkerne #966/R est:3000-4000

BARKER OF BATH, Joseph (19th C) British
£860 $1402 €1290 Wooded landscape with logging team (76x127cm-30x50in) s. 17-Feb-3 Bonhams, Bath #50

BARKER OF BATH, Thomas (1769-1847) British
£1200 $1896 €1800 Figures resting beneath a lone tree (21x26cm-8x10in) panel. 2-Dec-2 Bonhams, Bath #80/R est:1200-1800
£1700 $2652 €2550 Village boy (76x61cm-30x24in) init.d.1841. 7-Nov-2 Christie's, Kensington #224 est:1000-1500
£2000 $3180 €3000 Travelers in a rocky landscape with a river and mountains beyond (61x104cm-24x41in) 19-Mar-3 Sotheby's, London #81 est:2000-3000
£2800 $4396 €4200 Rocky wooded landscape with a haycart on a country track (92x117cm-36x46in) 10-Dec-2 Bonhams, New Bond Street #118/R est:3000-5000
£6200 $10292 €9300 Portrait of Princess Caraboo of Javasu, wearing a green cloak (61x48cm-24x19in) prov.lit. 10-Jun-3 Christie's, London #45/R est:4000-6000

BARKER OF BATH, Thomas (attrib) (1769-1847) British
£260 $400 €390 Shepherd, sheep and dog by an open stile (26x22cm-10x9in) panel. 22-Oct-2 Bonhams, Bath #207
£300 $468 €450 Figures before a lakeside village (46x66cm-18x26in) 7-Nov-2 Christie's, Kensington #79/R
£704 $1126 €1021 Harvesters (68x55cm-27x22in) bears sig. 18-May-3 Anders Antik, Landskrona #145 (S.KR 9000)

BARKER, Cicely Mary (1895-?) British
Works on paper
£270 $419 €405 Young boy seated on a couch leaning over and talking to a fairy on his window. init. prov. 3-Oct-2 Ewbank, Send #490
£290 $450 €435 Madonna and Child (20x13cm-8x5in) init. W/C prov. 3-Oct-2 Ewbank, Send #486
£500 $775 €750 Portrait of a young girl wearing a cap (38x23cm-15x9in) init.d.January 1 1920 pastel. 3-Oct-2 Ewbank, Send #487
£1600 $2480 €2400 Cecilie, figures walking in a garden with summer flowers (48x25cm-19x10in) i.verso prov. 3-Oct-2 Ewbank, Send #489 est:500-800
£2400 $3720 €3600 Fairy music (28x23cm-11x9in) i.verso W/C prov. 3-Oct-2 Ewbank, Send #485/R est:600-800

BARKER, Clive (1940-) British
Sculpture
£2400 $3936 €3600 Leg vase (34cm-13in) st.sig.i.num.4/6 aluminium. 3-Jun-3 Sotheby's, Olympia #310/R est:800-1200
Works on paper
£387 $600 €581 Nix (28x20cm-11x8in) ink magic marker painted c.1990 prov. 8-Dec-2 Toomey, Oak Park #761/R
£850 $1394 €1275 Still life (47x37cm-19x15in) s. pencil W/C. 3-Jun-3 Sotheby's, Olympia #167/R

BARKER, David (1941-) New Zealander
£940 $1467 €1410 Waikato River (51x76cm-20x30in) s.d.1984 acrylic on board. 7-Nov-2 International Art Centre, Auckland #18/R est:4000-6000 (NZ.D 3000)
£1307 $2105 €1961 Lagoon with reflections (70x76cm-28x30in) s.d.82 acrylic board. 7-May-3 Dunbar Sloane, Auckland #7/R est:3800-5000 (NZ.D 3700)

BARKER, George H (1908-) American
£287 $450 €431 Autumn landscape (51x66cm-20x26in) s. 23-Nov-2 Jackson's, Cedar Falls #78/R

BARKER, J (19th C) British
£1220 $2000 €1830 Gravel diggers (86x112cm-34x44in) indis sig. 5-Feb-3 Doyle, New York #14/R est:2000-4000

BARKER, John (19th C) British
£780 $1209 €1170 Left in charge - scene with dog and sheep, Glen Novis (52x41cm-20x16in) s. s.i.verso. 4-Dec-2 AB Stockholms Auktionsverk #1864/R (S.KR 11000)
£1300 $2028 €1950 Left in charge, scene in Ben Nevis (52x41cm-20x16in) s. s.i.verso. 14-Apr-3 Sotheby's, London #41/R est:1000-1500

BARKER, John Joseph (fl.1835-1866) British
£5000 $7900 €7250 Figures and timber cart on country lanes (76x127cm-30x50in) s. pair. 22-Jul-3 Gorringes, Lewes #1667/R est:5000-8000

BARKER, Joseph (fl.1843-1848) British
£500 $820 €750 Wooded landscape with figures on a path (56x43cm-22x17in) s. 4-Feb-3 Sworder & Son, Bishops Stortford #108/R

BARKER, Kit (1916-1988) British
£400 $632 €600 Vezelay, Burgundy (61x102cm-24x40in) s.i.d.73 verso prov. 27-Nov-2 Sotheby's, Olympia #277/R

BARKER, Marion (fl.1883-1909) British
£560 $913 €840 Red cap (17x12cm-7x5in) mono.d.1908 canvasboard. 30-Jan-3 Lawrence, Crewkerne #738/R

BARKER, W (?) ?
£300 $468 €450 Valley landscape, with cattle watering (50x75cm-20x30in) s.d.1902. 10-Sep-2 David Duggleby, Scarborough #292

BARKER, William Dean (19th C) British
£321 $508 €482 Cambrian homestead (51x76cm-20x30in) d.1874. 1-Dec-2 Levis, Calgary #207/R (C.D 800)

BARKER, Wright (1864-1941) British
£980 $1597 €1421 Guardsman, a foxhound (18x23cm-7x9in) s.i. panel. 21-Jul-3 Bonhams, Bath #76/R
£1500 $2445 €2175 Hunter Peacock within extensive landscape (53x71cm-21x28in) s.i.d.1929. 17-Jul-3 Tennants, Leyburn #876/R est:1500-2000
£2200 $3652 €3190 Terrier at a rabbit hole (56x76cm-22x30in) s.d.1911. 12-Jun-3 Christie's, Kensington #269/R est:1500-2000
£2695 $4177 €4043 Sceptre (72x91cm-28x36in) s. painted c.1913. 3-Dec-2 Bukowskis, Stockholm #334/R est:50000-70000 (S.KR 38000)
£3800 $5966 €5700 Prudence, polo pony tethered by a tree (52x68cm-20x27in) s.i. 16-Dec-2 Bonhams, Bury St Edmunds #505/R est:2000-3000
£4000 $6240 €6000 Beechnut II (71x91cm-28x36in) s.i.d.1913. 6-Nov-2 Sotheby's, Olympia #86/R est:1500-2500
£4000 $6240 €6000 Morning mists (75x94cm-30x37in) s. 14-Apr-3 Sotheby's, London #37/R est:4000-6000
£4200 $6552 €6300 Bay and chestnut hunter with a terrier (61x91cm-24x36in) s. 6-Nov-2 Sotheby's, Olympia #87/R est:1500-2500

£5400 $8802 €7830 Highland cattle in a Scottish glen (76x102cm-30x40in) s. 17-Jul-3 Tennants, Leyburn #886/R est:3500-5500
£13000 $21580 €19500 Three clumber spaniels resting in a woodland landscape (89x69cm-35x27in) s. 10-Jun-3 Bonhams, Leeds #168/R est:3000-5000
£48889 $81156 €70889 Yellow Russian retrievers (135x178cm-53x70in) s. prov. 10-Jun-3 Ritchie, Toronto #78/R est:28000-32000 (C.D 110000)
£60000 $91200 €90000 Awaiting the guns (121x183cm-48x72in) s. i.verso prov.exhib. 28-Aug-2 Sotheby's, London #1050/R est:40000-60000

Works on paper

£1491 $2400 €2237 Recumbent fox terrier in landscape, hunters in distance (41x61cm-16x24in) s. 22-Feb-3 Brunk, Ashville #795/R

BARLACH, Ernst (1870-1938) German

Prints

£3623 $5942 €5000 Racing Barbar (29x40cm-11x16in) s.i. lithograph. 29-May-3 Lempertz, Koln #519/R est:5000

Sculpture

£2465 $4092 €3500 Christ mask I (15x10x6cm-6x4x2in) s. bronze. 14-Jun-3 Hauswedell & Nolte, Hamburg #1019/R est:4000
£4114 $6377 €6500 Tilla Durieux III (18x12x14cm-7x5x6in) s. verso black pat.bronze Cast.Noack Berlin marble socle. 28-Sep-2 Ketterer, Hamburg #71/R est:8000-9000
£7051 $10929 €11000 Monks reading II (4x14x10cm-2x6x4in) s. bronze Cast.H.Noack Berlin exhib.lit. 4-Dec-2 Lempertz, Koln #564/R est:13000
£7051 $10929 €11000 Couple kissing I (18x16x8cm-7x6x3in) bronze. 7-Dec-2 Hauswedell & Nolte, Hamburg #520/R est:12500
£7246 $11884 €10000 Portrait of Tilla Durieux III (18cm-7in) plaster prov.exhib. 29-May-3 Lempertz, Koln #514/R est:8000-9000
£7692 $11923 €12000 Blind man (53x10x6cm-21x4x2in) bronze. 7-Dec-2 Hauswedell & Nolte, Hamburg #522/R est:12500
£8451 $14028 €12000 Kissing couple III (17x12x7cm-7x5x3in) s. bronze. 14-Jun-3 Hauswedell & Nolte, Hamburg #1018/R est:12500
£8805 $13736 €14000 Freezing old woman (23cm-9in) i. bronze st.f.H Noack prov.exhib.lit. 9-Oct-2 Sotheby's, London #189/R est:20000-30000
£9155 $15197 €13000 Monk reading I (15x13x7cm-6x5x3in) bronze. 14-Jun-3 Hauswedell & Nolte, Hamburg #1016/R est:15000
£9507 $15782 €13500 Monk reading II (14x12x8cm-6x5x3in) bronze. 14-Jun-3 Hauswedell & Nolte, Hamburg #1017/R est:14000
£10897 $16891 €17000 Monks reading II (14x12x8cm-6x5x3in) bronze. 7-Dec-2 Hauswedell & Nolte, Hamburg #519/R est:12500
£14103 $21859 €22000 Man reading book (46cm-18in) stucco. 7-Dec-2 Hauswedell & Nolte, Hamburg #523/R est:20000
£18116 $29710 €25000 Lonely figure (59cm-23in) s. brown pat.bronze prov. 30-May-3 Villa Grisebach, Berlin #41/R est:20000-25000
£40881 $63774 €65000 Russische bettlerin II - Russian beggar woman II (43cm-17in) i. bronze st.f.H Noack prov.lit. 9-Oct-2 Sotheby's, London #190/R est:45000-65000
£64103 $99359 €100000 Man singing (49cm-19in) s.st.f.Noack bronze exec.1928 exhib.lit. 4-Dec-2 Lempertz, Koln #21/R est:100000-120000
£169014 $280563 €240000 Man counting gold (41x36x36cm-16x14x14in) wood. 14-Jun-3 Hauswedell & Nolte, Hamburg #1013/R est:400000

Works on paper

£503 $785 €800 Standing woman (14x10cm-6x4in) s.i. pen ink pencil paper on mount prov. 9-Oct-2 Sotheby's, London #163/R
£1667 $2650 €2400 Seated couple (18x25cm-7x10in) s. chl paper on board. 5-May-3 Ketterer, Munich #811/R est:2000-3000
£1667 $2650 €2400 Two male figures (23x25cm-9x10in) i. chl. 5-May-3 Ketterer, Munich #814/R est:1200-1400
£1736 $2760 €2500 Woodcutters in wood (21x32cm-8x13in) s. chl. 5-May-3 Ketterer, Munich #808/R est:5000-6000
£2642 $4121 €4200 Crucified (24x30cm-9x12in) s. pencil lit. 20-Sep-2 Schloss Ahlden, Ahlden #1317/R est:4200
£3077 $4769 €4800 Two male figures resting (22x27cm-9x11in) i.d.14.Juni 1911 pen. 7-Dec-2 Hauswedell & Nolte, Hamburg #524/R est:6000
£4430 $7000 €7000 Thoughtful figure (35x25cm-14x10in) chl prov. 30-Nov-2 Villa Grisebach, Berlin #200/R est:6000-8000
£7692 $11923 €12000 Spendthrift (51x36cm-20x14in) s.d.27.4.21 chl. 7-Dec-2 Hauswedell & Nolte, Hamburg #525/R est:12000

BARLACH, Ernst (attrib) (1870-1938) German

Sculpture

£2656 $4250 €3851 Figure leaning to the side with arms extended (41cm-16in) black stone rec. pedestal base. 17-May-3 Selkirks, St. Louis #230/R est:5000-6000

BARLAG, Philip (1840-1913) Norwegian

£302 $505 €438 High mountains (25x36cm-10x14in) s. i.stretcher. 18-Jun-3 Grev Wedels Plass, Oslo #155 (N.KR 3500)
£312 $477 €468 By the fjord (24x32cm-9x13in) s. panel. 26-Aug-2 Blomqvist, Lysaker #1022/R (N.KR 3600)
£531 $865 €797 Mountain landscape with cheese farm (33x50cm-13x20in) s,. 17-Feb-3 Blomqvist, Lysaker #1013/R (N.KR 6000)
£584 $952 €876 Winter in the woods (28x20cm-11x8in) s. panel. 17-Feb-3 Blomqvist, Lysaker #1014/R (N.KR 6600)
£849 $1307 €1274 Millhouse and waterfall (45x38cm-18x15in) s.stretcher. 28-Oct-2 Blomqvist, Lysaker #1003/R (N.KR 10000)
£2182 $3425 €3273 Woman seated on woodland path (66x53cm-26x21in) s.d.74. 21-Nov-2 Grev Wedels Plass, Oslo #89/R est:30000-40000 (N.KR 25000)
£2500 $4100 €3750 Vestlandsfjord - fjord on the west coast (93x138cm-37x54in) s.d.1872. 3-Jun-3 Sotheby's, London #265/R est:3000-5000

BARLAND, Adam (fl.1843-1875) British

£550 $891 €798 Extensive landscape, with figures and sheep in foreground (30x55cm-12x22in) s. 29-Jul-3 Henry Adams, Chichester #604
£600 $972 €870 Extensive landscape, with cattle and figures by a river (30x55cm-12x22in) s. 29-Jul-3 Henry Adams, Chichester #605
£1150 $1794 €1725 Figures by a rushing stream (45x80cm-18x31in) Loch and highlands beyond. 25-Mar-3 Gildings, Market Harborough #423/R est:1000-1500
£1350 $2200 €2025 Landscape with lake (81x107cm-32x42in) 14-Feb-3 Du Mouchelle, Detroit #2012/R est:3000-4000

BARLAND, Adam (attrib) (fl.1843-1875) British

£448 $712 €672 Old mill in Monmouthshire (77x52cm-30x20in) 5-May-3 Rasmussen, Vejle #639/R (D.KR 4800)

BARLIER, Andre (?) French

£385 $600 €578 Cottage (3x4cm-1x2in) s. panel. 9-Nov-2 Sloan, North Bethesda #573/R

BARLOW, Francis (1626-1704) British

Works on paper

£2200 $3454 €3300 Pheasant in a wooded landscape, with deer beyond (14x18cm-6x7in) init.d.1684 pencil pen ink wash prov. 21-Nov-2 Christie's, London #1/R est:2500-3500

BARLOW, Gordon (?) British

£450 $702 €675 Springtime, blue bell woods, Nesfield (48x58cm-19x23in) s.i.verso. 9-Oct-2 Andrew Hartley, Ilkley #762

BARLOW, Gordon Clifford (?) British

£250 $390 €375 Upper Wharfedale (48x61cm-19x24in) s. 11-Apr-3 Keys, Aylsham #729
£280 $437 €420 Threshfield (51x61cm-20x24in) s. board. 25-Mar-3 Bonhams, Leeds #587
£600 $942 €900 Carnoustie open (51x61cm-20x24in) s. i.on stretcher. 21-Nov-2 Tennants, Leyburn #860/R

BARLOW, John Noble (1861-1924) American/British

£286 $451 €429 In the forest (39x29cm-15x11in) s. canvas on board. 18-Nov-2 Joel, Victoria #380 (A.D 800)
£4430 $7000 €6645 Along the coast (91x152cm-36x60in) s.d.1893 prov. 24-Apr-3 Shannon's, Milford #180/R est:4000-6000

BARLOW, Myron (1873-1937) American

£4518 $7500 €6551 Apple market (102x102cm-40x40in) s. 11-Jun-3 Boos Gallery, Michigan #469/R est:8000-12000

BARNABE, Duilio (1914-1961) Italian

£4828 $8062 €7000 Femmes en conversation (149x206cm-59x81in) s.d.1953. 10-Jul-3 Artcurial Briest, Paris #268/R est:7000-8000
£6973 $11087 €10250 Deux nonnes (14x146cm-6x57in) s. painted c.1958. 26-Feb-3 Artcurial Briest, Paris #311/R est:5000-7000

Works on paper

£476 $757 €700 Nature morte a la theiere (34x64cm-13x25in) s. gouache chl. 26-Feb-3 Artcurial Briest, Paris #312

BARNADAS, Ramon (1909-1981) Spanish

£692 $1079 €1100 April fair (60x73cm-24x29in) s. 8-Oct-2 Ansorena, Madrid #441/R

BARNARD, Edward Herbert (1855-1909) American

£625 $1000 €906 Logging in New Hampshire (46x70cm-18x28in) s. 16-May-3 Skinner, Boston #209/R
£1097 $1700 €1646 River landscape (61x91cm-24x36in) s. prov. 29-Oct-2 John Moran, Pasadena #620a est:2000-3000
£1707 $2800 €2561 Impressionistic landscape (36x51cm-14x20in) s. 8-Feb-3 Neal Auction Company, New Orleans #389/R est:3000-5000
£2038 $3200 €3057 Locust trees, Chatham (36x46cm-14x18in) s. 14-Dec-2 CRN Auctions, Cambridge #34/R
£2244 $3500 €3366 Trees by the water. painted c.1906. 21-Sep-2 Harvey Clar, Oakland #1465

BARNARD, George N (1819-1922) American
Photographs
£10443 $16500 €15665 Views of Sherman's campaign (25x36cm-10x14in) albumen print set of 10. 23-Apr-3 Sotheby's, New York #50/R est:8000-12000

BARNARD, Timothy (20th C) American
Sculpture
£1719 $2750 €2579 Untitled. s. bronze cement base. 11-Jan-3 Harvey Clar, Oakland #1208

BARNBAL, W H (?) ?
£600 $948 €900 Man in cricket whites and a young lady resting in a punt (34x70cm-13x28in) s. board. 18-Dec-2 John Nicholson, Haslemere #1182/R

BARNEKOW, Brita (1868-1936) Danish
£298 $471 €447 Interior, possibly from bank manager Barnekow's home (34x29cm-13x11in) init.d.1885 verso. 2-Dec-2 Rasmussen, Copenhagen #1648 (D.KR 3500)
£2412 $3666 €3618 Great Grandmother's wedding dress (84x55cm-33x22in) sold with lithograph of same subject. 27-Aug-2 Rasmussen, Copenhagen #1451/R est:25000 (D.KR 28000)

BARNES, Archibald George (1887-1934) British
£5000 $7900 €7500 Portrait of a lady, seated (102x76cm-40x30in) s. 27-Nov-2 Sotheby's, Olympia #68/R est:2000-3000

BARNES, E C (19th C) British
£1000 $1660 €1500 Roasting chestnuts (46x35cm-18x14in) mono. 10-Jun-3 Bonhams, Knightsbridge #92/R est:700-900

BARNES, Edward Charles (fl.1856-1882) British
£1056 $1700 €1584 Woman with parrot (36x30cm-14x12in) s. 19-Feb-3 Doyle, New York #38 est:2000-3000
£2900 $4582 €4350 Conversation at the smithy (51x61cm-20x24in) s. 27-Nov-2 Bonhams, Knowle #235 est:2000-3000
£3500 $5530 €5250 Feeding the ducks (61x51cm-24x20in) s. 13-Nov-2 Halls, Shrewsbury #380/R est:3000-4000

BARNES, Frank (19/20th C) ?
£530 $817 €795 TSS Maori off Sinclair Head, Wellington NZ (49x74cm-19x29in) s.i.d.1915 board. 4-Sep-2 Dunbar Sloane, Wellington #76/R est:1000-2000 (NZ.D 1750)

BARNES, Matthew (1880-1951) American
£2229 $3500 €3344 Flats (52x63cm-20x25in) s. s.verso painted c.1920 prov.exhib. 19-Nov-2 Butterfields, San Francisco #8334/R est:3000-5000

BARNES, Robert (1840-1895) British
Works on paper
£2100 $3297 €3150 Wash day (44x57cm-17x22in) W/C. 16-Dec-2 Bonhams, Bury St Edmunds #399/R est:2000-3000
£6500 $10205 €9750 Overseeing the chores (44x58cm-17x23in) mono.d.1876 pencil W/C htd white. 16-Apr-3 Christie's, Kensington #1032/R est:3000-5000

BARNES, Robert M (1947-) American
£722 $1119 €1083 South coast aspect (75x101cm-30x40in) s.verso prov. 3-Dec-2 Shapiro, Sydney #64 est:2000-4000 (A.D 2000)

BARNES, Samuel John (1847-1901) British
£320 $522 €480 Highland landscape with stags paused on rough track (45x60cm-18x24in) s. board. 29-Jan-3 Dreweatt Neate, Newbury #136
£850 $1386 €1275 Highland river landscape with sheep grazing beyond (76x127cm-30x50in) s.d.98/99. 29-Jan-3 Dreweatt Neate, Newbury #135

BARNES, W M (?) ?
£789 $1200 €1184 Clipper ship, Daniel Barnes (66x91cm-26x36in) s. 17-Aug-2 North East Auctions, Portsmouth #1170/R

BARNES, Wilfred M (1892-1955) Canadian
£311 $510 €467 Lumiere D'Ete (24x33cm-9x13in) panel prov. 3-Jun-3 Joyner, Toronto #480 (C.D 700)

BARNET, Will (1911-) American
Works on paper
£2561 $4200 €3713 Mother and child (29x24cm-11x9in) s.i. pencil imitation vellum. 5-Jun-3 Swann Galleries, New York #9/R est:800-1200

BARNETT, Isa (1924-2001) American
Works on paper
£248 $400 €372 Two policemen with corpse at bottom of staircase (20x20cm-8x8in) pen ink wash. 20-Feb-3 Illustration House, New York #8/R
£769 $1200 €1154 Woman and escorts about to enter western saloon (28x71cm-11x28in) s. gouache. 9-Nov-2 Illustration House, New York #172/R

BARNETT, James D (fl.1855-1891) British
£723 $1200 €1048 On the Rhine (23x51cm-9x20in) s. board. 11-Jun-3 Boos Gallery, Michigan #517/R est:800-1200

BARNETT, Rita Wolpe (20th C) American
£613 $950 €920 Three sisters (61x76cm-24x30in) s.d.51. 8-Dec-2 Freeman, Philadelphia #115/R

BARNETT, Thomas P (1870-1929) American
£1769 $2600 €2654 Missouri clay industries (76x102cm-30x40in) s.d.27. 23-Jun-2 Susanin's, Chicago #5124/R est:900-1100

BARNEY, Frank A (1862-?) American
£503 $800 €755 Wooded landscape with brook and man fishing (30x41cm-12x16in) s. 22-Mar-3 Nadeau, Windsor #204
£599 $1000 €869 Sailboats off panoramic coastal landscape (56x71cm-22x28in) s. 17-Jun-3 John Moran, Pasadena #185 est:1000-2000
£599 $1000 €869 Autumn river landscape (51x76cm-20x30in) s. board prov. 17-Jun-3 John Moran, Pasadena #186 est:1000-2000

BARNEY, Matthew (1967-) American
Photographs
£2585 $4110 €3800 Untitled (39x58cm-15x23in) s. num.9/40 photoengraving exec.2002. 24-Mar-3 Cornette de St.Cyr, Paris #100/R
£6329 $10000 €9494 Cremaster 2 the royal cell of baby Fay (71x51cm-28x20in) s.d.98 verso laminated c-print self lubricating acrylic frame. 12-Nov-2 Phillips, New York #184/R est:10000-15000
£6944 $11458 €10000 Cremaster 3, plumb line (61x51cm-24x20in) s.d.01 verso col photo prov. 1-Jul-3 Artcurial Briest, Paris #546/R est:10000-15000
£65000 $108550 €97500 Cremaster 2 - The Metamorphosis (137x109cm-54x43in) 4/6 C-print self-lubricating frame exc.1999 prov.exhib.lit. 26-Jun-3 Christie's, London #43/R est:50000-70000
£101266 $160000 €151899 Cremaster 2. Drone ensemble (107x259cm-42x102in) s.d.99 cibachrome prints acrylic prov.exhib.lit. 14-Nov-2 Christie's, Rockefeller NY #468/R est:100000-150000
£126582 $200000 €189873 Cremaster 4. Isle of Man (42x38cm-17x15in) s.num.1/3 verso cibachrome prints five two prov.lit. 13-Nov-2 Christie's, Rockefeller NY #2/R est:150000-200000

Works on paper
£13125 $21000 €19688 Cremaster 4 - the man in black (41x34cm-16x13in) d.99 verso graphite petroleum jelly beeswax on billboard magazine. 15-May-3 Phillips, New York #1/R est:20000-30000

BARNEY, Tina (1945-) American?
Photographs
£1948 $3000 €2922 Conversation (122x152cm-48x60in) s.d.1987 num.7/10 verso col chromogenic print prov.lit. 25-Oct-2 Phillips, New York #168/R est:4000-6000

BARNFATHER, Michael D (20th C) British?
£320 $496 €480 Farm in winter (37x46cm-15x18in) s. 25-Sep-2 Hamptons Fine Art, Godalming #393/R

BARNOIN, Henri Alphonse (1882-1935) French
£1081 $1686 €1600 Voiliers au mouillage (57x71cm-22x28in) s. gouache. 28-Mar-3 Claude Aguttes, Neuilly #148
£1408 $2268 €2000 Chaumiere sur la riviere en Bretagne (38x46cm-15x18in) s. panel. 11-May-3 Thierry & Lannon, Brest #324/R est:1800-2200
£1631 $2643 €2300 Lavandiere - Canal des Alpilles (60x73cm-24x29in) s. i.verso. 26-May-3 Joron-Derem, Paris #69/R est:2000-3000
£1634 $2631 €2500 Bateaux de peche par calme plat (50x73cm-20x29in) s. 18-Jan-3 Neret-Minet, Paris #180/R
£2113 $3401 €3000 Retour de peche, la cotriade (50x72cm-20x28in) s.d.1920. 11-May-3 Thierry & Lannon, Brest #134/R est:2500-3000

£2468 $3875 €3850 Thoniers a maree basse (38x46cm-15x18in) s. 15-Dec-2 Thierry & Lannon, Brest #99
£2581 $4000 €3872 Market day in Normandy (46x55cm-18x22in) s. 2-Oct-2 Christie's, Rockefeller NY #772/R est:5000-7000
£3000 $4650 €4500 Yachts in a calm at the harbour mouth (46x55cm-18x22in) s. 31-Oct-2 Christie's, Kensington #466/R est:3000-5000
£4196 $7007 €6000 Port de Bretagne (73x61cm-29x24in) s. 27-Jun-3 Claude Aguttes, Neuilly #45/R est:4500-6000
£4966 $7896 €7300 Les bouquinistes a Paris aupres de pont-neuf (46x55cm-18x22in) s. 2-Mar-3 Lombrail & Teucquam, Paris #165/R
£6000 $9480 €9300 Marche du Fadriet (49x60cm-19x24in) s. i.verso. 18-Dec-2 Digard, Paris #136/R
£6090 $9561 €9500 Thoniers sous voiles (46x55cm-18x22in) s. 15-Dec-2 Thierry & Lannon, Brest #103
£6859 $10769 €10700 Place du marche en Bretagne (46x55cm-18x22in) s. 15-Dec-2 Eric Pillon, Calais #123/R
£7042 $11338 €10000 Scene de marche a Questembert (54x65cm-21x26in) s. 11-May-3 Thierry & Lannon, Brest #1356/R est:9000-12000
£8333 $13083 €13000 Marche sur la place (60x73cm-24x29in) s. s.i.verso. 15-Dec-2 Thierry & Lannon, Brest #100
£10897 $17109 €17000 Marche aux etoffes (65x81cm-26x32in) s. 15-Dec-2 Thierry & Lannon, Brest #102
£17308 $27173 €27000 Marche aux etoffes a Concarneau (59x71cm-23x28in) s. 15-Dec-2 Thierry & Lannon, Brest #101 est:12000

Works on paper
£1923 $3019 €3000 Retour de peche (55x46cm-22x18in) s.pastel. 15-Dec-2 Eric Pillon, Calais #129/R
£2260 $3526 €3300 Street scene in Quimper - Brittany (54x65cm-21x26in) s.d.1922 pastel. 10-Apr-3 Van Ham, Cologne #1318/R est:2500

BARNS-GRAHAM, Wilhelmina (1912-) British
£1300 $2028 €1950 Black boat, Porthmeor (10x10cm-4x4in) s.d.1990 i.verso acrylic card. 16-Oct-2 David Lay, Penzance #327/R est:300-400
£2000 $3120 €3000 Painting in relief (15x10cm-6x4in) s.d.1983 s.i.verso paper acrylic card. 16-Oct-2 David Lay, Penzance #328/R est:400-500

Works on paper
£950 $1568 €1378 St. Andrews Bay (13x18cm-5x7in) s.d.1981 pencil W/C pen ink. 3-Jul-3 Christie's, Kensington #650/R
£1400 $2184 €2100 Untitled (10x13cm-4x5in) s.d.1982 mixed media. 16-Oct-2 David Lay, Penzance #329 est:300-400

BARNSLEY, James MacDonald (1861-1929) Canadian
£658 $1021 €987 Sailing by a lighthouse (31x75cm-12x30in) s.d.1888. 3-Dec-2 Joyner, Toronto #232/R est:2000-2500 (C.D 1600)
£658 $1021 €987 Tending to her chores (26x36cm-10x14in) s. canvas on board. 3-Dec-2 Joyner, Toronto #436 est:1500-1800 (C.D 1600)
£1829 $2872 €2744 View of a country road at sunset (37x44cm-15x17in) s.d.89. 10-Dec-2 Pinneys, Montreal #153 est:2500-3500 (C.D 4500)

BAROCCI, Federico (1526-1612) Italian

Works on paper
£7432 $11595 €11000 Head of the Virgin (39x24cm-15x9in) chk prov.lit. 27-Mar-3 Christie's, Paris #57/R est:12000
£50676 $79054 €75000 Saint Francis recevant les stigmates (26x17cm-10x7in) chk prov. 27-Mar-3 Christie's, Paris #5/R est:50000

BAROCCI, Federico (after) (1526-1612) Italian

Works on paper
£890 $1389 €1300 Anatomical studies (27x20cm-11x8in) i. pen. 11-Apr-3 Winterberg, Heidelberg #113/R

BAROCCI, Federico (attrib) (1526-1612) Italian
£12057 $18809 €19050 Madonna (260x210cm-102x83in) 15-Oct-2 Babuino, Rome #151/R est:12000

Works on paper
£1689 $2635 €2500 Head of saint looking up (31x23cm-12x9in) crayon pastel stump prov. 26-Mar-3 Piasa, Paris #1/R

BAROCCI, Federico (style) (1526-1612) Italian
£35000 $54250 €52500 Portrait of gentleman, said to be Guidobaldo della Rovere (47x36cm-19x14in) 31-Oct-2 Sotheby's, Olympia #20/R est:2000-3000

BAROJA, Ricardo (1871-1953) Spanish
£6383 $10340 €9000 El Retiro (65x45cm-26x18in) panel. 20-May-3 Segre, Madrid #107/R est:2400

BARON, Henri Charles Antoine (1816-1885) French
£1391 $2157 €2087 Femme lisant (46x38cm-18x15in) prov.exhib. 7-Dec-2 Galerie du Rhone, Sion #504/R est:2500-3500 (S.FR 3200)
£2016 $3185 €3024 Osteria San Georgio (65x46cm-26x18in) s. canvas on masonite. 18-Nov-2 Waddingtons, Toronto #243/R est:5000-7000 (C.D 5000)
£2532 $4000 €3798 At the fountain (53x43cm-21x17in) s. 5-Apr-3 Neal Auction Company, New Orleans #149/R est:3000-5000

Works on paper
£600 $942 €900 Wedding reception (28x61cm-11x24in) W/C prov. 10-Dec-2 Capes Dunn, Manchester #778

BARON, Karol (1939-) Czechoslovakian

Works on paper
£315 $460 €473 Brikeles (84x59cm-33x23in) pastel exec.c.1975. 4-Jun-2 SOGA, Bratislava #259/R est:11000 (SL.K 20000)
£583 $828 €875 Still life I (58x62cm-23x24in) pastel exec.1972. 26-Mar-2 SOGA, Bratislava #262/R (SL.K 37000)

BARON, Theodor (1840-1899) Belgian
£253 $395 €400 Riviere en Ardennes (39x27cm-15x11in) s. panel. 10-Sep-2 Vanderkindere, Brussels #295
£538 $839 €850 Bergere dans un paysage (39x59cm-15x23in) s.d.1870 panel. 15-Oct-2 Horta, Bruxelles #45
£986 $1568 €1450 Paysage lacustre (41x76cm-16x30in) s. 18-Mar-3 Vanderkindere, Brussels #62

BARON-RENOUARD (1918-) French
£1189 $1985 €1700 Composition (100x100cm-39x39in) s. 25-Jun-3 Claude Aguttes, Neuilly #197/R est:1600-1800

BARR, David (1939-) American
£1037 $1700 €1504 Relief construction (41x46cm-16x18in) s.d.1968 lacquered wood prov. 1-Jun-3 Wright, Chicago #284/R est:2000-3000
£1220 $2000 €1769 Relief construction No.17 (51x51cm-20x20in) s.i.d.1963 verso lacquered wood. 1-Jun-3 Wright, Chicago #280/R est:2000-3000
£1524 $2500 €2210 Relief construction no.35 (53x61cm-21x24in) s.i.d.1968 verso lacquered wood. 1-Jun-3 Wright, Chicago #279/R est:2000-3000
£2744 $4500 €3979 Structurist relief no.23 (36x43cm-14x17in) s.i.d.1960 lacquered wood prov. 1-Jun-3 Wright, Chicago #281/R est:2000-3000

BARR, Robert Allen (1890-1959) Canadian
£301 $476 €452 Samovar figurine and daffodils (76x64cm-30x25in) d.1946. 1-Dec-2 Levis, Calgary #3/R (C.D 750)
£328 $508 €492 Silver symphony (77x64cm-30x25in) s.d.1946 exhib. 24-Sep-2 Ritchie, Toronto #3186b (C.D 800)

BARR, William (1867-1933) American
£621 $1000 €932 Coastal (30x41cm-12x16in) s. indis.d.1919 verso prov. 18-Feb-3 John Moran, Pasadena #95d
£710 $1100 €1065 Flowering dunes (30x41cm-12x16in) s. 29-Oct-2 John Moran, Pasadena #726
£1056 $1700 €1584 House and oaks in landscape (30x41cm-12x16in) s. prov. 18-Feb-3 John Moran, Pasadena #95c est:2000-3000

BARRA, Didier (1590-1650) French
£18310 $30394 €26000 Le festin de Balthazar dans un palais Romain (62x98cm-24x39in) prov.lit. 13-Jun-3 Rossini, Paris #82/R est:15000-20000

BARRABBINO, Simone (1585-?) Italian

Works on paper
£2025 $3200 €3200 La presentation au temple (40x25cm-16x10in) i. black chk pen brown ink brown wash prov. 27-Nov-2 Christie's, Paris #52/R est:2000-3000

BARRACHINA, Francisco (1940-) Spanish
£1132 $1766 €1800 Portrait of girl (46x33cm-18x13in) s.d.1991. 8-Oct-2 Ansorena, Madrid #268/R

BARRACLOUGH, James P (?-1942) British
£420 $655 €630 Portrait of a young lady in a blue dress (92x79cm-36x31in) s.d.1922. 10-Apr-3 Tennants, Leyburn #944
£750 $1223 €1088 Portrait of a gentleman wearing Masonic robes (128x102cm-50x40in) s.i.d.1938. 17-Jul-3 Tennants, Leyburn #803

BARRADAS, Rafael (1890-1929) Uruguayan

Works on paper
£629 $1000 €944 Guillermo C de Pro Calderon (29x18cm-11x7in) s.i. ink dr prov. 2-Mar-3 Galleria Y Remates, Montevideo #51/R
£1006 $1600 €1509 Beggar (28x18cm-11x7in) s.i. ink dr. 2-Mar-3 Galleria Y Remates, Montevideo #52/R
£1384 $2200 €2076 Andres Etchebarne Bidart and Guillermo C de Pro (35x28cm-14x11in) s.i. chl pastel. 2-Mar-3 Galleria Y Remates, Montevideo #53/R
£1793 $2833 €2600 Portrait of peasant woman (35x26cm-14x10in) s. W/C wax crayon. 1-Apr-3 Segre, Madrid #395/R
£2345 $3705 €3400 In the bar (35x26cm-14x10in) s. W/C wax crayon. 1-Apr-3 Segre, Madrid #394/R

£3205 $5000 €4808 Male figure (23x13cm-9x5in) s. col crayon lit. 10-Oct-2 Galleria Y Remates, Montevideo #65/R

BARRAGAN, Jose Luis (1956-) Spanish
£308 $486 €480 Sail (73x100cm-29x39in) 14-Nov-2 Arte, Seville #446/R

BARRAGE, Fadi (1940-1988) Lebanese
£1800 $2862 €2700 Torso and head (28x38cm-11x15in) s.d.76 board. 30-Apr-3 Sotheby's, London #130/R est:2000-3000
£2500 $3975 €3750 Window (49x60cm-19x24in) s. acrylic. 30-Apr-3 Sotheby's, London #131/R est:2500-3500

BARRALET, John James (1747-1815) British
Works on paper
£1800 $2844 €2700 Portrait of an Irish gentleman sitting on a turf (48x37cm-19x15in) s. pen ink W/C over pencil. 28-Nov-2 Sotheby's, London #220/R est:2000-3000

BARRATT OF STOCKBRIDGE, Thomas (fl.1852-1893) British
£7500 $11850 €11250 James Goater on Sultan (63x86cm-25x34in) mono.i.d.1856 prov.lit. 27-Nov-2 Christie's, London #46/R

BARRATT, Walter (19/20th C) Australian
£538 $845 €807 Stamford clipper under full sail with steamer in background (42x66cm-17x26in) s.indis.i.d.1923. 25-Nov-2 Peter Webb, Auckland #31/R (NZ.D 1700)

BARRAU, Ferdinando (?) ?
£392 $643 €600 Boy with hat (31x25cm-12x10in) cardboard. 5-Feb-3 Arte, Seville #761/R

BARRAU, Laureano (1864-1957) Spanish
£1419 $2243 €2200 Study of village (13x22cm-5x9in) s. canvas on cardboard. 17-Dec-2 Segre, Madrid #55/R
£7947 $12954 €12000 By the sea (195x105cm-77x41in) s. 11-Feb-3 Castellana, Madrid #32/R est:14000
£10345 $16448 €15000 Washerwomen (40x56cm-16x22in) s. 4-Mar-3 Ansorena, Madrid #158/R

BARRAUD, Aime (1902-1954) Swiss
£391 $607 €587 Village outskirts (46x55cm-18x22in) s. 9-Dec-2 Philippe Schuler, Zurich #3804 (S.FR 900)
£1408 $2310 €2042 Red berries in glass vase (46x33cm-18x13in) s. 4-Jun-3 Fischer, Luzern #1252/R est:3000-4000 (S.FR 3000)

BARRAUD, Charles Decimus (1822-1897) New Zealander/British
£2424 $3733 €3636 Waiau River (44x75cm-17x30in) s. W/C. 4-Sep-2 Dunbar Sloane, Wellington #31/R est:8000-15000 (NZ.D 8000)
£70175 $109474 €105263 View of Wellington (42x65cm-17x26in) s.d.1851. 27-Mar-3 International Art Centre, Auckland #83/R est:150000-250000 (NZ.D 200000)
Works on paper
£470 $734 €705 Shag Rock (16x31cm-6x12in) s.d.1870 W/C. 7-Nov-2 International Art Centre, Auckland #98/R est:2000-3000 (NZ.D 1500)
£940 $1467 €1410 Remarkables and Lake Wakatipu (24x36cm-9x14in) W/C. 7-Nov-2 International Art Centre, Auckland #83/R est:2500-3500 (NZ.D 3000)

BARRAUD, Francis Philip (1824-1901) British
Works on paper
£400 $624 €600 Notre Dome, Poitiers (11x17cm-4x7in) s.i. pencil W/C. 17-Oct-2 Christie's, Kensington #134/R

BARRAUD, François (1899-1934) Swiss
£1033 $1694 €1498 Female nude wearing sunhat sitting on bench (65x54cm-26x21in) s. 4-Jun-3 Fischer, Luzern #1239/R est:2000-3000 (S.FR 2200)
£1586 $2363 €2379 Less casses dents (18x33cm-7x13in) s.d.1932 i. verso. 25-Jun-2 Koller, Zurich #6640/R est:5000-7000 (S.FR 3600)
£9906 $16047 €17534 La petite vierge - St Nitouche (20x16cm-8x6in) s.d. s.i. stretcher prov. 26-May-3 Sotheby's, Zurich #77/R est:5000-7000 (S.FR 21000)

BARRAUD, Gustave François (1883-1968) Swiss
£262 $414 €393 Pommier (60x60cm-24x24in) s. 17-Nov-2 Koller, Geneva #1329 (S.FR 600)
£328 $517 €492 Villeneuve (48x59cm-19x23in) s.d.1918. 17-Nov-2 Koller, Geneva #1342 (S.FR 750)
£926 $1491 €1343 Lumieres du matin (73x54cm-29x21in) s. i.verso. 9-May-3 Dobiaschofsky, Bern #197/R (S.FR 2000)
£1116 $1763 €1674 Female nude sitting, viewed from the back (30x22cm-12x9in) s. 29-Nov-2 Zofingen, Switzerland #2789/R est:1500 (S.FR 2600)
£1174 $1925 €1702 Demasquee (73x99cm-29x39in) s. 4-Jun-3 Fischer, Luzern #1263/R est:2500-3500 (S.FR 2500)
Works on paper
£913 $1415 €1370 Nu de dos (62x45cm-24x18in) s. init.d.37 verso pastel cardboard. 7-Dec-2 Galerie du Rhone, Sion #353/R est:1500-2000 (S.FR 2100)

BARRAUD, Henry and William (19th C) British
£60000 $94800 €90000 Last resource (112x142cm-44x56in) s.d.1836 prov.exhib. 27-Nov-2 Christie's, London #67/R est:70000-100000

BARRAUD, Maurice (1889-1954) Swiss
£961 $1499 €1442 Lac de Lugano (23x34cm-9x13in) s. 8-Nov-2 Dobiaschofsky, Bern #166/R (S.FR 2200)
£1389 $2236 €2014 Florence in summer (50x65cm-20x26in) 9-May-3 Dobiaschofsky, Bern #201/R est:4500 (S.FR 3000)
£2402 $3771 €3603 Francisca (43x39cm-17x15in) s. prov. 25-Nov-2 Germann, Zurich #10/R est:8000-10000 (S.FR 5500)
£2441 $4004 €3539 Seated female nude with arms crossed above head (51x33cm-20x13in) s. 4-Jun-3 Fischer, Luzern #1240/R est:4500-6000 (S.FR 5200)
£2620 $4087 €3930 La Colonne St Marc (48x45cm-19x18in) s. 20-Nov-2 Fischer, Luzern #1273/R est:6000-8000 (S.FR 6000)
£3286 $5390 €4765 Sidi-Bou-Said (36x45cm-14x18in) s. prov. 4-Jun-3 Fischer, Luzern #1241/R est:6000-8000 (S.FR 7000)
£3394 $5667 €4921 Female nude (62x47cm-24x19in) board. 24-Jun-3 Koller, Zurich #54/R est:4000-7000 (S.FR 7500)
£3774 $6113 €6680 Colonne St Mark (48x45cm-19x18in) s. 26-May-3 Sotheby's, Zurich #87/R est:8000-12000 (S.FR 8000)
£3863 $6103 €5795 Nu au jardin (78x66cm-31x26in) s. pavatex prov. 26-Nov-2 Phillips, Zurich #56/R est:5000-7000 (S.FR 9000)
£4367 $6900 €6551 Still life - figures et raisins (42x45cm-17x18in) s. i. verso. 14-Nov-2 Stuker, Bern #62/R est:12000-15000 (S.FR 10000)
£4398 $7081 €6377 Maisons a Cassis (49x61cm-19x24in) s.d.38 prov. 9-May-3 Dobiaschofsky, Bern #200/R (S.FR 9500)
£6114 $9537 €9171 Contrejour - seated female nude (78x58cm-31x23in) s. s.i. stretcher. 6-Nov-2 Hans Widmer, St Gallen #50/R est:12000-20000 (S.FR 14000)
£6438 $10172 €9657 Femme au siphon bleu (61x50cm-24x20in) s.d.1919. 26-Nov-2 Phillips, Zurich #32/R (S.FR 15000)
£6438 $10172 €9657 Lady guitar player (62x77cm-24x30in) s. 26-Nov-2 Phillips, Zurich #67/R est:15000-20000 (S.FR 15000)
£10550 $17619 €15298 Tightrope walker (85x106cm-33x42in) s.d.51 i. verso board. 20-Jun-3 Kornfeld, Bern #10/R est:25000 (S.FR 23000)
Works on paper
£278 $447 €417 Woman's head (45x33cm-18x13in) s. chl. 7-May-3 Dobiaschofsky, Bern #1416/R (S.FR 600)
£328 $514 €492 Jeune femme assise (30x23cm-12x9in) s. pencil. 25-Nov-2 Germann, Zurich #683 (S.FR 750)
£349 $510 €524 Jeune femme assise (30x23cm-12x9in) s. pencil. 4-Jun-2 Germann, Zurich #747 (S.FR 800)
£349 $545 €524 Woman looking in window (41x36cm-16x14in) s. col pen. 6-Nov-2 Dobiaschofsky, Bern #1368 (S.FR 800)
£437 $638 €656 Lacycliste (31x46cm-12x18in) s. pencil. 4-Jun-2 Germann, Zurich #748 (S.FR 1000)
£463 $745 €695 Young woman in blue coat before fence (25x27cm-10x11in) s. W/C over pencil. 7-May-3 Dobiaschofsky, Bern #1423/R (S.FR 1000)
£573 $853 €860 Bull fight in arena (24x39cm-9x15in) s. Indian ink pencil. 25-Jun-2 Koller, Zurich #6642/R (S.FR 1300)
£655 $1028 €983 Leda and the swan (24x29cm-9x11in) W/C Indian ink. 25-Nov-2 Germann, Zurich #9/R est:1000-1300 (S.FR 1500)
£1389 $2236 €2014 Jeune fille assisse (43x31cm-17x12in) s. mixed media. 9-May-3 Dobiaschofsky, Bern #205/R est:5000 (S.FR 3000)
£1659 $2622 €2489 Nu assis (64x47cm-25x19in) s. W/C. 17-Nov-2 Koller, Geneva #1309 (S.FR 3800)
£2315 $3727 €3357 La Sulamite (75x56cm-30x22in) s. i.verso mixed media panel. 9-May-3 Dobiaschofsky, Bern #206/R est:4500 (S.FR 5000)

BARRAUD, William (1810-1850) British
£2800 $4424 €4200 Dark bay hunter before a lake view (63x76cm-25x30in) s.d.1845. 27-Nov-2 Bonhams, Knowle #225 est:2000-3000
£7000 $10990 €10500 Faithful companion (76x63cm-30x25in) s. 19-Nov-2 Bonhams, New Bond Street #75/R est:4000-6000

BARRE, Jean Auguste (1811-1896) French
Sculpture
£1056 $1754 €1500 Rachel (48cm-19in) s.d.1847 plaster. 16-Jun-3 Oger, Dumont, Paris #104/R est:300-400

BARRÉ, Martin (1924-1993) French
£7292 $12031 €10500 Composition (81x64cm-32x25in) s.d.56. 1-Jul-3 Artcurial Briest, Paris #549/R est:8000-12000

BARREDA, Ernesto (1927-) Chilean
£962 $1500 €1443 Celda (100x81cm-39x32in) s.i.verso. 5-Nov-2 Doyle, New York #4/R est:3000-4000

BARREIRA, Vicente (20th C) Spanish
£428 $693 €650 Andalucian woman with shawl (71x45cm-28x18in) s. 21-Jan-3 Ansorena, Madrid #262/R

BARREIRO, Jose Maria (1940-) Spanish
£921 $1492 €1400 Concert (64x50cm-25x20in) s. cardboard. 21-Jan-3 Durán, Madrid #125/R
Works on paper
£710 $1121 €1100 Painter (22x31cm-9x12in) s.d.91 mixed media cardboard. 17-Dec-2 Durán, Madrid #90/R

BARREL (?) American?
£1677 $2700 €2516 Vast snow scene with 2 cabins nestled in tree-lined background (89x89cm-35x35in) s. 21-Feb-3 York Town, York #1283a

BARRENSCHEEN, Herman (1882-1953) Swiss
£469 $770 €680 Self portrait (31x26cm-12x10in) s. d.1926 verso panel. 4-Jun-3 Fischer, Luzern #2007/R (S.FR 1000)

BARRERA, Antonio (1889-?) Italian
£481 $755 €750 Minaret (50x39cm-20x15in) s.d.28 exhib. 16-Dec-2 Pandolfini, Florence #91

BARRERA, Nicolas (1919-) Ukranian
£568 $886 €852 Camargue landscape (46x55cm-18x22in) s. 6-Nov-2 Dobiaschofsky, Bern #334 (S.FR 1300)

BARRET, George (18/19th C) British
£11538 $17885 €18000 View of Dargle called Dahool, Co Wicklow (100x125cm-39x49in) prov. 3-Dec-2 Bonhams & James Adam, Dublin #26/R
Works on paper
£190 $300 €300 Blackrock Castle, Cork Harbour (15x23cm-6x9in) W/C. 27-Nov-2 James Adam, Dublin #117/R

BARRET, George (attrib) (18/19th C) British
Works on paper
£260 $411 €390 Figures in an arcadian river landscape (17x27cm-7x11in) W/C. 27-Nov-2 Bonhams, Knowle #170
£750 $1245 €1088 New Bottle bridge, near Dalkeith (36x43cm-14x17in) W/C pen ink. 16-Jun-3 Duke & Son, Dorchester #133

BARRET, George (snr) (1728-1784) British
£13000 $20280 €19500 Extensive wooded landscape (99x102cm-39x40in) 14-Apr-3 Hamilton Osborne King, Dublin #1504/R est:15000-20000
£14000 $22120 €21000 View of the Thames from Richmond Hill (74x107cm-29x42in) 28-Nov-2 Sotheby's, London #105/R est:8000-12000
£22000 $35200 €33000 Mars and foals, cattle and sheep in parkland (61x76cm-24x30in) prov. 15-May-3 Christie's, London #5/R est:20000-30000
£30000 $48000 €45000 View of Dolbadarn Castle, Llanberis (64x77cm-25x30in) prov. 15-May-3 Christie's, London #4/R est:30000-50000
£46000 $73140 €69000 River landscape with fishermen in the foreground (46x70cm-18x28in) prov. 19-Mar-3 Sotheby's, London #67/R est:6000-8000
£50000 $79000 €75000 Landscape with rustics and cattle by a house in the foreground (59x90cm-23x35in) s. 28-Nov-2 Sotheby's, London #107/R est:6000-8000
£160000 $256000 €240000 Wooded mountainous river landscape with anglers (100x137cm-39x54in) prov.exhib. 15-May-3 Christie's, London #2/R est:100000-150000
£320000 $512000 €480000 Mountainous wooded river landscape with waterfall (96x126cm-38x50in) prov. 15-May-3 Christie's, London #3/R est:100000-150000
Works on paper
£380 $616 €570 View of Mt Etna (16x22cm-6x9in) W/C. 21-Jan-3 Bonhams, Knightsbridge #271/R

BARRET, George (snr-attrib) (1728-1784) British
£6800 $10744 €10200 Wooded landscape with figures by a lake, and a distant town (86x108cm-34x43in) 28-Nov-2 Sotheby's, London #121/R est:3000-5000

BARRET, J (18/19th C) British
£11500 $18285 €17250 Flying childers (100x125cm-39x49in) s.i. 19-Mar-3 Sotheby's, London #104/R est:10000-15000

BARRETT, F Gould (fl.1923-1927) British
Works on paper
£420 $655 €630 Semur le marche (21x28cm-8x11in) s.i.d.1923 W/C. 9-Oct-2 Woolley & Wallis, Salisbury #30/R

BARRETT, Jerry (1824-1906) British
£1379 $2124 €2069 Coastal landscape, Italy with three figures in foreground (34x93cm-13x37in) s.d.1885. 27-Oct-2 Anders Antik, Landskrona #179/R est:20000-25000 (S.KR 20000)

BARRETT, Margaret (1939-) British
£1300 $2132 €1950 Neck and neck (50x76cm-20x30in) s. 3-Jun-3 Bonhams, Knightsbridge #64/R est:1500-2000

BARRETT, Max (1937-1997) British
Sculpture
£1400 $2324 €2030 Standing nude (66cm-26in) s. yew wood. 10-Jun-3 David Lay, Penzance #472/R est:1000-1400

BARRETT, Oliver Glen (1903-1970) American
£503 $800 €755 Mystical burn of the desert (58x53cm-23x21in) board. 28-Feb-3 Douglas, South Deerfield #11

BARRETT, R Granger (20th C) British
Works on paper
£202 $319 €303 In full sail, the ocean racers of the 1860's (12x57cm-5x22in) s. i.verso W/C gouache prov. 18-Nov-2 Waddingtons, Toronto #6/R (C.D 500)

BARRIAS, Louis Ernest (1841-1905) French
Sculpture
£962 $1510 €1500 Printemps (39x24x22cm-15x9x9in) num.7127 biscuit. 15-Dec-2 Mercier & Cie, Lille #277/R
£2611 $4074 €4100 Nature uncovering herself in front of Science (24cm-9in) s. st.f.Susse brown pat bronze lit. 8-Nov-2 Camard, Paris #125/R
£3642 $5937 €5500 Allegorie de la musique (33cm-13in) s. gold pat bronze Cast Thiebaut Freres two groups. 16-Feb-3 Mercier & Cie, Lille #193/R est:4800-5300
£3800 $5928 €5700 Allegorical figure of music (76cm-30in) s.st.f.Thiebaut green brown pat bronze lit. 5-Nov-2 Sotheby's, London #159/R est:4000-5000
£6452 $10000 €9678 First Funeral (51cm-20in) s. brown pat bronze st.f.Thiebaut Freres prov.exhib.lit. 29-Oct-2 Sotheby's, New York #213/R est:6000-8000
£9527 $14862 €14100 Le nature se devoilant devant la science (73x26x17cm-29x10x7in) s.st.f.Susse col pat bronze. 31-Mar-3 Pierre Berge, Paris #175/R est:12000-15000
£10638 $17234 €15000 Nature covering herself before knowledge (62cm-24in) i. gilded silvered brass Cast.Susse Freres, Paris. 21-May-3 Dorotheum, Vienna #244/R est:15000-18000
£11613 $18000 €17420 Nature revealing herself before science (58cm-23in) st.sig. parcel gilt silver patinated bronze. 6-Dec-2 Sotheby's, New York #151/R est:20000-30000

BARRIBAL, William (fl.1919-1938) British
Works on paper
£1300 $2158 €1950 Mirror (44x32cm-17x13in) s. W/C bodycol. 12-Jun-3 Bonhams, New Bond Street #692/R est:1000-1500

BARRIBAL, William (attrib) (fl.1919-1938) British
£360 $562 €522 Glamorous lady in a hat (49x39cm-19x15in) 27-Mar-3 Lane, Penzance #131

BARRIE, Mardi (1931-) British
£320 $509 €480 Summer bay (46x57cm-18x22in) s. board prov. 6-Mar-3 Christie's, Kensington #349
£450 $716 €675 Rain swept, Castle Fields (68x94cm-27x37in) s. board prov. 6-Mar-3 Christie's, Kensington #248

BARRINGER, Gwendoline (1883-1960) Australian
Works on paper
£421 $640 €632 Coastal haystacks (38x37cm-15x15in) s. W/C. 19-Aug-2 Joel, Victoria #241 est:2000-3000 (A.D 1200)

BARRINGTON, Arthur (?) ?
Works on paper
£650 $1086 €943 Washer women at a river bank (35x52cm-14x20in) s. W/C. 17-Jun-3 Anderson & Garland, Newcastle #320/R

BARRIO, Evaristo (19th C) Spanish
£1415 $2208 €2250 Circus scene (24x36cm-9x14in) s.d.1888 board. 23-Sep-2 Durán, Madrid #168/R

BARRIVIERA, Lino Bianchi (1906-1985) Italian
£3082 $4808 €4500 Circus (81x117cm-32x46in) s.d.1962 i.verso. 10-Apr-3 Finarte Semenzato, Rome #261

BARRON Y CARRILLO, Manuel (1814-1884) Spanish
£6090 $9622 €9500 Washerwomen at river (67x94cm-26x37in) s. 14-Nov-2 Arte, Seville #288/R
£12903 $20387 €20000 Landscape with cattle (54x109cm-21x43in) lit. 18-Dec-2 Ansorena, Madrid #80/R est:20000
£38994 $60440 €62000 View of the Guadalquivir (92x125cm-36x49in) s.i.d.1854. 7-Oct-2 Ansorena, Madrid #54/R est:42000

BARRON, Howard (1900-1991) British
£421 $640 €632 Storm over the Liverpool, NSW (48x64cm-19x25in) s. 19-Aug-2 Joel, Victoria #219 est:1500-2000 (A.D 1200)
£561 $853 €842 Valley view, McPherson Rangers, Murrwillumba, NSW (41x59cm-16x23in) s.d.32 board. 19-Aug-2 Joel, Victoria #152 est:1500-2500 (A.D 1600)
£561 $853 €842 In the shade of the Old Rivergum (49x64cm-19x25in) s.d.38. 19-Aug-2 Joel, Victoria #238 est:1000-2000 (A.D 1600)

BARRON, Manuel (19th C) ?
£12338 $18013 €19000 Seascape (45x84cm-18x33in) s.d.1847. 12-Jun-2 Castellana, Madrid #92/R est:18000

BARROW, Edith Isabel (?-1930) British
£1150 $1875 €1725 Fishing harbour (36x51cm-14x20in) s. 13-Feb-3 David Lay, Penzance #93 est:1000-1500
Works on paper
£260 $411 €377 Still life of lilies in a glass vase (71x45cm-28x18in) s. W/C. 22-Jul-3 Bonhams, Knightsbridge #211/R
£420 $685 €630 Glass of cut roses (42x28cm-17x11in) s.d.1888 W/C pencil. 30-Jan-3 Lawrence, Crewkerne #643/R

BARROW, Julian (1939-) British
£250 $390 €375 Expansive view of a country house (46x61cm-18x24in) s.d.1974. 27-Mar-3 Christie's, Kensington #457
£280 $440 €420 Badami market (28x23cm-11x9in) s. prov. 10-Dec-2 Clarke Gammon, Guildford #7
£300 $471 €450 Strand Road, Calcutta (20x28cm-8x11in) s. prov. 10-Dec-2 Clarke Gammon, Guildford #5
£380 $597 €570 Bhubaneswar tank (23x30cm-9x12in) s. prov. 10-Dec-2 Clarke Gammon, Guildford #6
£600 $942 €900 Washing in the Jumanu, Agra (25x33cm-10x13in) s. prov. 10-Dec-2 Clarke Gammon, Guildford #2/R
£800 $1264 €1200 Swan walk, London (41x51cm-16x20in) s. 14-Nov-2 Christie's, Kensington #65/R
£850 $1335 €1275 Balaji Ghat, Varansai (23x33cm-9x13in) s. prov. 10-Dec-2 Clarke Gammon, Guildford #8

BARRUETA, A (19/20th C) Spanish
£1224 $1947 €1800 Nature morte au moulin a cafe et a la coupe de fruits (65x92cm-26x36in) s. 24-Mar-3 Coutau Begarie, Paris #246/R

BARRUOL, Isabelle (20th C) French
Works on paper
£619 $990 €860 Sans titre (80x80cm-31x31in) s. mixed media canvas. 18-May-3 Neret-Minet, Paris #58

BARRY (?) ?
£1000 $1600 €1500 Portrait of William Lister (51x61cm-20x24in) 15-Mar-3 Hogben, Folkstone #189 est:180-280

BARRY, Anne Meredith (1932-) Canadian
£267 $437 €401 Striped sail (62x67cm-24x26in) s.d.70 board. 3-Jun-3 Joyner, Toronto #595 (C.D 600)
£2111 $3462 €3061 Sunrise at night, Anchorage (90x120cm-35x47in) s.i.d.1996. 9-Jun-3 Hodgins, Calgary #130/R est:200-3500 (C.D 4750)

BARRY, Edith Cleaves (1883-1969) American
£4870 $7500 €7305 Fashion show (41x51cm-16x20in) s. prov. 24-Oct-2 Shannon's, Milford #208/R est:5000-7000

BARRY, François Pierre Bernard (1813-1905) French
£1058 $1661 €1650 Barque et voilier pres de la Normandie (24x32cm-9x13in) s. painted 1841. 13-Dec-2 Rossini, Paris #175

BARRY, Robert (1936-) American
£2600 $4004 €3900 Untitled - gray (107x107cm-42x42in) painted 1989 prov.exhib. 23-Oct-2 Christie's, London #164/R est:4000-6000

BARRY, William (19th C) British
£1600 $2624 €2400 View of Balmoral and the Dee looking west (127x101cm-50x40in) indis sig.d.1876-77. 5-Jun-3 Christie's, Kensington #730/R est:500-800

BARSUMIAN, Lisa (20th C) American
£602 $946 €903 Mountain Ash (55x50cm-22x20in) s.i. 25-Nov-2 Hodgins, Calgary #265/R (C.D 1500)

BART, Andreas (19th C) ?
£2210 $3426 €3315 Winter countryside (90x160cm-35x63in) painted c.1880. 3-Dec-2 SOGA, Bratislava #184/R est:98000 (SL.K 140000)

BARTA, Ladislas (1902-) Hungarian
£816 $1298 €1200 La Grue no 4 (66x80cm-26x31in) s. 3-Mar-3 Claude Boisgirard, Paris #31/R
£865 $1341 €1350 Interior with a young woman (81x61cm-32x24in) s. 7-Dec-2 De Vuyst, Lokeren #19/R
£2041 $3245 €3000 Femme au renard (73x60cm-29x24in) s. 3-Mar-3 Claude Boisgirard, Paris #30 est:4000-5000

BARTELS, Hans von (1856-1913) German
£256 $397 €400 Landscape (33x47cm-13x19in) s.i.d. 7-Dec-2 Ketterer, Hamburg #142/R
£297 $470 €446 Landscape from Regenstein (35x52cm-14x20in) s.i.d.78 panel. 5-Apr-3 Rasmussen, Havnen #2182/R (D.KR 3200)
£1233 $1923 €1800 Rotterdam harbour (72x101cm-28x40in) s.d.11. 10-Apr-3 Schopman, Hamburg #698 est:980
£1384 $2131 €2200 Moored fishing vessels in the Laguna, Venice (34x35cm-13x14in) s.i. exhib. 23-Oct-2 Christie's, Amsterdam #181/R est:2500-3500
£1447 $2257 €2300 Fishing boats in evening light (80x103cm-31x41in) s.i.d.96. 21-Sep-2 Bolland & Marotz, Bremen #450/R est:2500
£1572 $2421 €2500 Child in the dunes, Brittany (33x46cm-13x18in) s. canvas on board exhib. 23-Oct-2 Christie's, Amsterdam #176/R est:3000-5000
£1736 $2865 €2500 Seascape at dusk (80x104cm-31x41in) s.i.d.96. 1-Jul-3 Christie's, Amsterdam #151/R est:3000-5000
£2201 $3390 €3500 Fisherman from Voledam (47x34cm-19x13in) s.d.12 canvas on board exhib. 23-Oct-2 Christie's, Amsterdam #174/R est:2500-3500
£2516 $3925 €4000 Peasant girl in meadow (48x34cm-19x13in) s. bears i.d.95 lit. 20-Sep-2 Schloss Ahlden, Ahlden #1303/R est:3800
£3019 $4649 €4800 On daddy's lap - fisherman from Urk (47x33cm-19x13in) s.i.d.08 canvas on board exhib. 23-Oct-2 Christie's, Amsterdam #170/R est:2000-3000
£4088 $6296 €6500 Fishing fleet in a stiff breeze on the Zuiderzee (105x73cm-41x29in) s. exhib. 23-Oct-2 Christie's, Amsterdam #172/R est:4000-6000
£5000 $7950 €7500 Monastero di Madonna del Sasso, Locarno (181x140cm-71x55in) s.d.84. 20-Mar-3 Christie's, Kensington #56/R est:5000-7000
Works on paper
£487 $726 €750 Mother with baby by fire (46x32cm-18x13in) i. brush over pencils. gouache over pencil. 26-Jun-2 Neumeister, Munich #567/R
£506 $785 €800 Cemetery of San Miniato near Florence (32x46cm-13x18in) s.i.d.94. 25-Sep-2 Neumeister, Munich #387/R
£1258 $1937 €2000 Breezy day, Scheveningen (30x21cm-12x8in) s.i.d.94 pencil W/C htd white exhib. 23-Oct-2 Christie's, Amsterdam #169/R est:1200-1600
£1384 $2131 €2200 Marche au poisson (32x45cm-13x18in) s.i.d.1905 pencil W/C gouache. 23-Oct-2 Christie's, Amsterdam #182/R est:2500-3500
£2642 $4068 €4200 Quiet moment, fishing lighting his pipe (29x31cm-11x12in) s.i.d.10 pencil gouache exhib. 23-Oct-2 Christie's, Amsterdam #173/R est:2500-3500

BARTELS, Hermann (1928-) German
£1538 $2385 €2400 Four coloured stripes (102x85cm-40x33in) s.i. verso oil synthetic resin panel exhib. 7-Dec-2 Ketterer, Hamburg #55/R est:2200-2400

BARTELS, Karl (20th C) ?
£566 $872 €900 Sunlit beach, Bornholm. Coastal study (22x32cm-9x13in) init.i.d.10.9.92 cardboard two. 23-Oct-2 Christie's, Amsterdam #175/R
£671 $1047 €980 Sunny winter's day (39x54cm-15x21in) s. 11-Apr-3 Winterberg, Heidelberg #720

BARTELS, Minna (?) German
£252 $392 €400 Poppies and basket on meadow floor (61x48cm-24x19in) s. 9-Oct-2 Michael Zeller, Lindau #623/R

BARTFAY, Julius (1888-1979) Czechoslovakian
Sculpture
£1358 $2105 €2037 Svatopluk (54cm-21in) bronze exec.c.1935. 3-Dec-2 SOGA, Bratislava #43/R est:49000 (SL.K 86000)

BARTH, A (20th C) German
£723 $1114 €1150 Castle interior scene (40x32cm-16x13in) s. 26-Oct-2 Quittenbaum, Hamburg #2/R

BARTH, Amade (1899-1926) Swiss
£676 $1041 €1014 Nature morte (48x57cm-19x22in) s. masonite exhib. 23-Oct-2 Kunsthallen, Copenhagen #394/R (D.KR 8000)
£1141 $1802 €1712 Still life of mackerels (33x46cm-13x18in) st.sig. exhib. 28-Apr-3 Bukowskis, Stockholm #56/R est:30000-35000 (S.KR 15000)

BARTH, Anna (20th C) German
£759 $1177 €1200 Elegant couple eating oysters (34x25cm-13x10in) i.d.1871 after Mieris panel. 26-Sep-2 Neumeister, Munich #2690/R

BARTH, Carl (1896-1976) German
£565 $882 €848 House with chair (60x80cm-24x31in) s. s.i.d.1932 verso tempera. 16-Sep-2 Philippe Schuler, Zurich #3508/R (S.FR 1300)

BARTH, Carl Wilhelm (1847-1919) Norwegian
£1928 $3163 €2796 Fishing village from Southern Norway (25x37cm-10x15in) s. i.stretcher. 2-Jun-3 Blomqvist, Oslo #37/R est:15000-18000 (N.KR 21000)

BARTH, Larry (1957-) American
Sculpture
£5380 $8500 €8070 Pheasant hen and a meadow lark. s.d.1981 wood sand grass sold with another. 3-Apr-3 Christie's, Rockefeller NY #243/R est:6000-9000

BARTH, Otto (1876-1916) Austrian
Works on paper
£1216 $1897 €1800 Winter's night (27x31cm-11x12in) s. gouache. 28-Mar-3 Dorotheum, Vienna #308/R est:800-1000

BARTH, Paul Basilius (1881-1955) Swiss
£386 $610 €579 Town under cloudy skies (49x59cm-19x23in) s.d.32 board. 26-Nov-2 Hans Widmer, St Gallen #1035/R (S.FR 900)
£401 $642 €602 At the window - Normandy (54x46cm-21x18in) s.d. board. 17-Mar-3 Philippe Schuler, Zurich #8406 (S.FR 850)
£515 $814 €773 Interior with female nude (46x37cm-18x15in) s.d.54 board. 29-Nov-2 Zofingen, Switzerland #2792 (S.FR 1200)
£655 $1035 €983 Self portrait (17x22cm-7x9in) s.d.1942 verso board. 14-Nov-2 Stuker, Bern #63 est:1800-2400 (S.FR 1500)
£687 $1085 €1031 Olive grove (38x45cm-15x18in) s.d.37. 29-Nov-2 Zofingen, Switzerland #2793 est:2500 (S.FR 1600)
£699 $1090 €1049 Bodensee in the rain (38x46cm-15x18in) s.d.51 board. 6-Nov-2 Dobiaschofsky, Bern #335/R est:2000 (S.FR 1600)
£1288 $2034 €1932 Woman with red shawl (45x42cm-18x17in) s.d.23 masonite. 28-Nov-2 Christie's, Zurich #61/R est:3000-4000 (S.FR 3000)
£1310 $2057 €1965 Laissez passer - sea coast (65x81cm-26x32in) s. 25-Nov-2 Sotheby's, Zurich #51/R est:3000-5000 (S.FR 3000)
£3433 $5425 €5150 Riesmuhle (54x64cm-21x25in) s.d.53. 28-Nov-2 Christie's, Zurich #69/R est:3500-4500 (S.FR 8000)

BARTH, Theodor (1875-1949) Swiss
£437 $681 €656 Deaconess (30x25cm-12x10in) s. i. stretcher. 6-Nov-2 Dobiaschofsky, Bern #336/R (S.FR 1000)

BARTH, Uta (1958-) American
Photographs
£2658 $4200 €3987 Ground no.45 (70x86cm-28x34in) s.d.1994 num,4/5 col coupler print lit. 22-Apr-3 Christie's, Rockefeller NY #106/R est:2500-3500

BARTH, Wolf (1926-) Swiss
£2402 $3747 €3603 Enluminure (110x75cm-43x30in) s.verso egg tempera. 8-Nov-2 Dobiaschofsky, Bern #284/R est:4200 (S.FR 5500)

BARTHALOT, Dordonne (20th C) French
£300 $486 €450 Reclining demi draped nude (46x61cm-18x24in) s. 20-May-3 Bonhams, Knightsbridge #88

BARTHELEMY, Camille (1890-1961) Belgian
£2051 $3221 €3200 Vue de ville (95x45cm-37x18in) s. 10-Dec-2 Campo, Vlaamse Kaai #14 est:800-1200
£5137 $8014 €7500 Ruelle sous la neige a Diest (57x44cm-22x17in) s.d.22. 14-Apr-3 Horta, Bruxelles #132/R est:8000-12000
£7500 $12450 €7500 Canal a Bruges au coucher du soleil (64x80cm-25x31in) s.d.25. 16-Jun-3 Horta, Bruxelles #66/R est:4000-6000
£9500 $15770 €9500 Vue du village de Sainte-Cecile (80x100cm-31x39in) s.d.29. 16-Jun-3 Horta, Bruxelles #9500/R est:7000-9000

BARTHELEMY, Catherine (20th C) French
£2098 $3503 €3000 Henri Texier quarter (116x89cm-46x35in) s. 25-Jun-3 Claude Aguttes, Neuilly #193 est:3200-3500

BARTHELEMY, Gerard (1927-) French?
£409 $634 €650 La Lieutenance a Honfleur (46x55cm-18x22in) s. 6-Oct-2 Feletin, Province #121

BARTHELEMY, L (19/20th C) French
Sculpture
£1401 $2186 €2200 Danseuse aux cymbales (27cm-11in) ivory pat bronze marble base. 6-Nov-2 Tajan, Paris #11/R

BARTHOLDI, Frederic Auguste (1834-1904) French
Sculpture
£949 $1500 €1500 Lion de Belfort (16x27cm-6x11in) s. brown pat bronze marble socle Cast Thiebaut and Gavignot. 27-Nov-2 Lemoine & Ferrando, Paris #171/R est:1500-1800
£1000 $1590 €1500 Figure of an artist (35cm-14in) s.i. silver pat bronze. 29-Apr-3 Sotheby's, Olympia #165/R est:700-1000
£4000 $6240 €6000 Seven Swabians (28x41cm-11x16in) s.i.d.Aug 1855 brown pat bronze green marble plinth lit. 9-Apr-3 Sotheby's, London #140/R est:4000-6000
Works on paper
£567 $948 €800 Projet de statue a l'effigie de Champollion (32x23cm-13x9in) s. pen brown ink. 19-Jun-3 Piasa, Paris #143

BARTHOLOME, Albert (1848-1928) French
Sculpture
£6250 $9938 €9000 Jeune femme alanguie (52x46cm-20x18in) s. brown pat bronze lit. 30-Apr-3 Tajan, Paris #144/R est:12000

BARTHOLOME, Léon (19/20th C) Belgian
£493 $794 €700 Les roches au fer a cheval a Pempoel a Bretagne (55x76cm-22x30in) s. canvas on panel. 12-May-3 Bernaerts, Antwerp #29/R

BARTHOLOMEW, F W and WILLIAMSON, W A (19th C) British
£540 $837 €810 Boats in choppy sea (76x127cm-30x50in) s.d.1880. 6-Dec-2 Chrystals Auctions, Isle of Man #214

BARTHOLOMEW, Valentine (1799-1879) British
Works on paper
£380 $593 €570 Portrait of two young ladies in a landscape (51x41cm-20x16in) s.d.1851. 9-Oct-2 Andrew Hartley, Ilkley #618
£1000 $1650 €1450 Still life of morning glory and berries (25x33cm-10x13in) s. W/C over pencil htd bodycol gum arabic. 2-Jul-3 Sotheby's, Olympia #305/R est:1200-1800
£1950 $3062 €2925 Still life of flowers in a vase (30x33cm-12x13in) s.d.1845 W/C pair. 16-Dec-2 Bonhams, Bury St Edmunds #442 est:1800-2200
£3500 $5810 €5250 Still life with roses in a vase. Still life with blossoms in a vase (41x32cm-16x13in) s. W/C over pencil bodycol scratching out. 12-Jun-3 Sotheby's, London #146/R est:3000-5000

BARTL, Felix (1910-) German
£1027 $1603 €1500 Village in winter with figures and animals (80x91cm-31x36in) s.d.1938 lit. 10-Apr-3 Allgauer, Kempten #2702/R est:1900

BARTL, Jozsef (1932-) Hungarian
£774 $1207 €1122 Dotted heart shape (60x55cm-24x22in) s.d.79. 13-Sep-2 Mu Terem Galeria, Budapest #125/R est:200000 (H.F 300000)

BARTLETT, Charles William (1860-?) British
Works on paper
£400 $668 €580 Leaving for the day (78x59cm-31x23in) s. W/C. 24-Jun-3 Bonhams, Knightsbridge #79
£1100 $1793 €1595 Evening in Brittany (61x75cm-24x30in) s.d.1908 col chk W/C. 16-Jul-3 Sotheby's, Olympia #103/R est:600-800

BARTLETT, Dana (1878-1957) American
£1613 $2500 €2420 Verdugo Canyon (30x41cm-12x16in) s. i.verso board. 21-Jul-2 Jeffery Burchard, Florida #32/R
£1863 $3000 €2795 Eucalyptus landscape (36x25cm-14x10in) s. board prov. 18-Feb-3 John Moran, Pasadena #6 est:1000-2000
£6587 $11000 €9551 Landscape - Laguna Canyon (66x76cm-26x30in) s. board prov. 17-Jun-3 John Moran, Pasadena #75 est:10000-15000
£12903 $20000 €19355 Laguna coast (51x61cm-20x24in) i.stretcher prov. 29-Oct-2 John Moran, Pasadena #654a est:8000-12000

BARTLETT, Geoffrey Roy (1952-) Australian
Sculpture
£4598 $6851 €6897 Study for Yallourn, maquette for Expo 1988, Brisbane (112x77x42cm-44x30x17in) bronze brass prov.exhib. 27-Aug-2 Christie's, Melbourne #69/R est:12000-15000 (A.D 12000)

BARTLETT, Gray (1885-1951) American
£312 $500 €468 Country landscape with a winding steam (36x46cm-14x18in) s. 16-Mar-3 Butterfields, San Francisco #1043

BARTLETT, Jennifer (1941-) American
Works on paper
£1187 $1900 €1781 Untitled (23x23cm-9x9in) s.d.00 gouache prov. 16-May-3 Phillips, New York #220/R est:2500-3500
£2025 $3200 €3038 Untitled (23x23cm-9x9in) s.d.00 gouache prov. 12-Nov-2 Phillips, New York #244/R est:2500-3500

BARTLETT, Morton (1909-1992) American
Photographs
£2469 $4000 €3704 Untitled. Ballerina (9x10cm-4x4in) vintage gelatin silver photograph two prov.exhib. 27-Jan-3 Christie's, Rockefeller NY #82/R est:2000-3000
Sculpture
£20988 $34000 €31482 Untitled - doll (60x23x13cm-24x9x5in) painted plaster fabric hair executed c.1950 prov.lit. 27-Jan-3 Christie's, Rockefeller NY #84/R est:20000-30000

BARTLETT, Paul Wayland (1881-1925) American
Sculpture
£5600 $8736 €8400 Bear cub from The Bohemian Bear Tamer (24x25cm-9x10in) s. brown pat bronze lit. 9-Apr-3 Sotheby's, London #175/R est:4000-6000

BARTLETT, William H (1858-1932) British
£4500 $7111 €6750 Landing the catch (41x61cm-16x24in) s.d.1902. 2-Dec-2 Sotheby's, London #38/R est:5000-7000
£15200 $24776 €22040 Fishing off the coast of Ireland (59x92cm-23x36in) s.d.1881. 16-Jul-3 Sotheby's, Olympia #98/R est:6000-9000
Works on paper
£720 $1145 €1080 April harvest; fishing boat and figures collecting seaweed (25x36cm-10x14in) s. W/C. 6-Mar-3 Scarborough Perry Fine Arts, Hove #546/R

BARTLETT, William Henry (attrib) (1809-1854) British
£726 $1132 €1089 Fort Chambly (23x35cm-9x14in) panel. 30-Jul-2 Iegor de Saint Hippolyte, Montreal #11 (C.D 1800)

BARTLEY, Edwin (attrib) (?) British
Works on paper
£977 $1554 €1466 Untitled - Zealand landscape (44x74cm-17x29in) W/C. 3-Mar-3 Lawson Menzies, Sydney #450 est:500-700 (A.D 2600)

BARTOLENA, Cesare (attrib) (1830-1903) Italian
£8333 $13083 €13000 General Lamorna wounded during the Krimean battle (126x211cm-50x83in) 16-Dec-2 Pandolfini, Florence #85/R est:15000

BARTOLENA, Giovanni (1866-1942) Italian
£3165 $4937 €5000 Black cow (24x29cm 9x11in) s. board exhib.lit. 19-Oct-2 Semenzato, Venice #333/R est:5000-7000
£3797 $6000 €6000 Landscape (12x31cm-5x12in) s. board prov. 26-Nov-2 Christie's, Rome #186/R est:8000
£4088 $6296 €6500 Horse in Campolecciano (16x20cm-6x8in) s.d.916 board. 23-Oct-2 Finarte, Milan #136/R
£5102 $8112 €7500 Landscape with animals and figure (35x47cm-14x19in) s. board prov. 18-Mar-3 Finarte, Milan #98/R

BARTOLI, Amerigo (1890-1971) Italian
£513 $805 €800 Profile of young woman (37x25cm-15x10in) s.d.1940 board. 21-Nov-2 Finarte, Rome #201

BARTOLI, Jacques (1920-) French
£870 $1400 €1305 Jockeys (41x33cm-16x13in) s. i.verso paper on canvas prov. 19-Feb-3 Doyle, New York #17a

BARTOLINI, Frederico (19/20th C) Italian
Works on paper
£671 $1100 €973 Young Italian maidens (46x28cm-18x11in) one s. one s.d.71 W/C two. 4-Jun-3 Doyle, New York #87/R est:1500-2500

BARTOLINI, Luciano (1948-1994) Italian
£705 $1093 €1100 Light breaths (30x20cm-12x8in) s.i.d.1991-92 acrylic gold leaf diptych. 4-Dec-2 Finarte, Milan #562/R
£769 $1192 €1200 Light breath (30x20cm-12x8in) s.i.d.1992 verso acrylic enamel paper diptych. 4-Dec-2 Finarte, Milan #576
£3077 $4769 €4800 Ghost tales (38x50cm-15x20in) tempera paper set of 16. 4-Dec-2 Finarte, Milan #565/R est:4000
Works on paper
£481 $745 €750 Breath (40x41cm-16x16in) s.d.1990 verso mosaic. 4-Dec-2 Finarte, Milan #532
£769 $1192 €1200 Kleenex (42x48cm-17x19in) s.d.1974 verso Kleenex. 4-Dec-2 Finarte, Milan #561
£1410 $2186 €2200 Egybtian acrobatics (73x92cm-29x36in) mixed media collage exhib.lit. 4-Dec-2 Finarte, Milan #560/R
£1603 $2484 €2500 Comparing them you could notice they were exactly the same (99cm-39in circular) mixed media collage exec.1979 exhib.lit. 4-Dec-2 Finarte, Milan #529/R

BARTOLINI, Luigi (1892-1963) Italian
£353 $554 €550 Roofs (18x14cm-7x6in) s. board. 21-Nov-2 Finarte, Rome #331
£479 $748 €700 Lovers (18x13cm-7x5in) s. cardboard on canvas. 10-Apr-3 Finarte Semenzato, Rome #190/R
£959 $1496 €1400 Painter on terrace (20x25cm-8x10in) s. board painted 1939. 10-Apr-3 Finarte Semenzato, Rome #138/R
Works on paper
£780 $1264 €1100 Ritratto di giovanetta (32x24cm-13x9in) s.d.1927 pencil ink gouache. 26-May-3 Christie's, Milan #53
£1282 $2013 €2000 Landscape with house (37x48cm-15x19in) s. chl card on masonite. 19-Nov-2 Finarte, Milan #150/R

BARTOLINI, Ubaldo (1944-) Italian
£1076 $1700 €1700 Autumn path (80x60cm-31x24in) s.i.d.77 verso. 29-Nov-2 Farsetti, Prato #72/R
£1538 $2385 €2400 Landscape (50x70cm-20x28in) s. painted 1987 lit. 4-Dec-2 Finarte, Milan #570/R

BARTOLO DI FREDI (c.1330-1410) Italian
£200000 $334000 €290000 Saint John the Baptist. Saint John the Evangelist (170x52cm-67x20in) gold ground panel shaped top pair prov.lit. 9-Jul-3 Christie's, London #77/R est:300000-500000

BARTOLO, Andrea di (attrib) (fl.1389-1428) Italian
£22831 $35616 €34247 John the Evangelist (37x22cm-15x9in) panel. 28-Mar-3 Koller, Zurich #3001/R est:20000-30000 (S.FR 50000)
£22831 $35616 €34247 Matthew the Evangelist with angel (37x23cm-15x9in) panel prov. 28-Mar-3 Koller, Zurich #3002/R est:20000-30000 (S.FR 50000)

BARTOLO, Taddeo di (1363-1422) Italian
£107595 $170000 €170000 Holy bishop and knight (112x34cm-44x13in) tempera gold board prov.lit. 29-Nov-2 Semenzato, Venice #535/R est:140000-160000

BARTOLOMMEO, Fra (1472-1517) Italian
Works on paper
£2516 $3925 €4000 La mise au tombeau (28x41cm-11x16in) wash prov. 14-Oct-2 Amberes, Antwerp #153

BARTOLOMMEO, Fra (attrib) (1472-1517) Italian
£6897 $10621 €10346 Madonna and Child in classical landscape (93cm-37in circular) 27-Oct-2 Anders Antik, Landskrona #117/R est:60000-80000 (S.KR 100000)

BARTOLOMMEO, Fra (style) (1472-1517) Italian
£17000 $26690 €25500 Annunciation (85x65cm-33x26in) canvas on panel. 10-Dec-2 Sotheby's, Olympia #301/R est:6000-8000
£32168 $53720 €46000 Annonciation (73x58cm-29x23in) panel. 27-Jun-3 Piasa, Paris #1/R est:12000

BARTOLONI, Lillo (1946-) Italian
£386 $618 €560 Camel (80x70cm-31x28in) s.d.1988. 11-Mar-3 Babuino, Rome #291/R

BARTOLOZZI, Francesco (1727-1815) Italian
Works on paper
£1000 $1570 €1500 Holy Family with the Infant St. John (28x21cm-11x8in) red chk wash. 11-Dec-2 Sotheby's, Olympia #247/R est:1200-1500
£2600 $4342 €3770 Vision of Saint Francis (21x32cm-8x13in) i. red chk wash after Guercino. 8-Jul-3 Christie's, London #60/R est:1500-2500

BARTOLOZZI, Francesco (attrib) (1727-1815) Italian
Works on paper
£850 $1394 €1275 Portrait of a young girl (13x12cm-5x5in) red chk prov. 5-Jun-3 Christie's, Kensington #854/R
£1300 $2041 €1950 Venus and Adonis (26x36cm-10x14in) pen ink over black chk after Guercino. 11-Dec-2 Sotheby's, Olympia #240/R est:1200-1800

BARTOLOZZI, Rafael Lozano (1943-) Spanish
Works on paper
£724 $1144 €1050 Untitled 2 (48x32cm-19x13in) s.d.1982 W/C prov. 1-Apr-3 Segre, Madrid #244/R
£724 $1144 €1050 Untitled 3 (48x32cm-19x13in) s.d.1982 gouache prov. 1-Apr-3 Segre, Madrid #239/R
£724 $1144 €1050 Untitled 1 (48x32cm-19x13in) s.d.1982 W/C gouacheprov. 1-Apr-3 Segre, Madrid #238/R

BARTOLUZZI, Millo (19th C) Italian
Works on paper
£1600 $2624 €2400 Overlooking St. Mark's Square, Santa Maria della Salute in the distance (25x44cm-10x17in) s. pencil W/C bodycol. 5-Jun-3 Christie's, Kensington #868 est:300-500

BARTON, Del Katherine (20th C) Australian
Works on paper
£264 $412 €458 School boy (75x56cm-30x22in) s.d.2000 pencil pastel prov. 31-Mar-3 Goodman, Sydney #39 (A.D 700)

BARTON, Donald Blagge (1903-1990) American
£813 $1300 €1220 Winter farm scene (48x69cm-19x27in) s. 11-Jan-3 James Julia, Fairfield #515 est:1400-1800

BARTON, Mary (1861-1949) British
£285 $441 €450 Still life study of a vase of tulips (50x39cm-20x15in) s. 25-Sep-2 James Adam, Dublin #129
£1384 $2158 €2200 Spanish idyll (41x50cm-16x20in) s. board prov. 17-Sep-2 Whyte's, Dublin #65/R est:1500-2000
Works on paper
£620 $1011 €930 Landscape with river and cattle (41x71cm-16x28in) s. W/C. 12-Feb-3 Edgar Horn, Eastbourne #305
£769 $1208 €1200 Wet day on Lough Eske, County Donegal (34x53cm-13x21in) s. i.verso W/C exhib.lit. 19-Nov-2 Whyte's, Dublin #61/R

BARTON, Nixie (1948-) Canadian
£805 $1280 €1208 Lemon and tulips (60x60cm-24x24in) s.d.1997 acrylic. 23-Mar-3 Hodgins, Calgary #8/R est:1000-1500 (C.D 1900)
Works on paper
£196 $305 €326 Checkerboard tulips (50x35cm-20x14in) s.i.d.1990 mixed media board prov. 13-Apr-3 Levis, Calgary #303/R (C.D 450)

BARTON, Ralph (1891-1931) American
Works on paper
£5280 $8500 €7920 Monk surrounded by dragonfly and God with incense burner (43x28cm-17x11in) s.i. gouache ink exec.c.1915. 10-May-3 Illustration House, New York #10/R est:5000-7500

BARTON, Rose Maynard (1856-1929) British
Works on paper
£3400 $5270 €5100 Study of child with ducks, little teaser (43x56cm-17x22in) i.verso pastel. 6-Dec-2 Biddle & Webb, Birmingham #150
£6200 $10044 €9300 In Kensington gore (34x24cm-13x9in) s.d.90 W/C gouache prov. 20-May-3 Sotheby's, Olympia #29/R est:3000-5000
£6522 $10696 €9000 Changing of the guard, Dublin Castle (28x18cm-11x7in) s. W/C. 28-May-3 Bonhams & James Adam, Dublin #36/R est:10000-15000
£15000 $24000 €22500 Quadriga, Hyde Park Corner (50x35cm-20x14in) s.d.1921 W/C. 16-May-3 Sotheby's, London #28/R est:12000-16000
£15217 $24957 €21000 Grosvenor Street in the nineties (52x71cm-20x28in) s.d.1893 W/C. 28-May-3 Bonhams & James Adam, Dublin #35/R est:12000-18000

BARTONIEK, Anna (1896-?) Hungarian
£3354 $5232 €5031 Self portrait with shingled hair (70x60cm-28x24in) s. 11-Sep-2 Kieselbach, Budapest #106/R (H.F 1300000)

BARTSCH, Carl-Frederick (1829-1908) Danish
£326 $508 €489 Landscape with sheep by cromlech (16x36cm-6x14in) s. 11-Nov-2 Rasmussen, Vejle #677/R (D.KR 3800)
£335 $543 €486 From Dyrehaven (26x33cm-10x13in) s. 24-May-3 Rasmussen, Havnen #2010 (D.KR 3500)
£383 $605 €575 Landscape with cattle (25x33cm-10x13in) s. 2-Dec-2 Rasmussen, Copenhagen #1336/R (D.KR 4500)
£419 $666 €629 Landscape from Kullen (28x39cm-11x15in) s. 10-Mar-3 Rasmussen, Vejle #316/R (D.KR 4500)
£745 $1184 €1118 Horses by farm (29x39cm-11x15in) s. 5-Mar-3 Rasmussen, Copenhagen #1827/R (D.KR 8000)

BARTSCH, Reinhard (1925-1990) German
£392 $643 €600 Paris Notre Dame (70x80cm-28x31in) s.d.77 s.i. verso. 29-Mar-3 Dannenberg, Berlin #544/R

BARTSCH, Wilhelm (1871-1953) German
£327 $510 €520 Winter in Worpswede (36x43cm-14x17in) s. board. 21-Sep-2 Bolland & Marotz, Bremen #331/R
£952 $1514 €1400 Fishing boat on beach (38x58cm-15x23in) mono. canvas on panel. 28-Mar-3 Bolland & Marotz, Bremen #309/R

BARTZ, Rupprecht (17th C) German
Works on paper
£2986 $4748 €4300 Artist in studio (10x15cm-4x6in) s.i.d.1636 pen wash. 5-May-3 Ketterer, Munich #220/R est:400-600

BARUCCI, Pietro (1845-1917) Italian
£2000 $3120 €3000 Young harvester (110x53cm-43x21in) s.i. 8-Apr-3 Bonhams, Knightsbridge #166/R est:2000-3000
£3800 $6194 €5700 Ruins outside Rome (85x56cm-33x22in) s.i. 29-Jan-3 Sotheby's, Olympia #318/R est:3000-4000
£3963 $6500 €5746 View of Palazzo Donn'Anna along the coast of Posillipo, Bay of Naples (61x109cm-24x43in) s. 4-Jun-3 Christie's, Rockefeller NY #230/R est:5000-7000
£5743 $8959 €8500 Shepherd with flock in Roman Campagna (71x151cm-28x59in) s.i. 27-Mar-3 Dr Fritz Nagel, Stuttgart #790/R est:3000
£6329 $10000 €9494 Tilling the fields (60x117cm-24x46in) s.i. 23-Apr-3 Christie's, Rockefeller NY #76/R est:15000-20000
£6329 $10000 €9494 Harvest time (60x117cm-24x46in) s. 23-Apr-3 Christie's, Rockefeller NY #77/R est:15000-20000
Works on paper
£1221 $1930 €1832 Untitled, country dance (44x73cm-17x29in) s. paper on cotton exec.c.1910 prov. 7-Apr-3 Shapiro, Sydney #491/R est:3000-5000 (A.D 3200)

BARUCHELLO, Gianfranco (1924-) Italian
£566 $872 €900 Norsicov (20x20cm-8x8in) s.i.d.1979 verso paint. 26-Oct-2 Cornette de St.Cyr, Paris #144/R

£566 $872 €900 Start saying your prayers (20x20cm-8x8in) s.i.d.1979 verso. 26-Oct-2 Cornette de St.Cyr, Paris #145/R
£769 $1208 €1200 Untitled (20x20cm-8x8in) s.d.1977 s.d.verso enamel on tin. 21-Nov-2 Finarte, Rome #28

Works on paper
£769 $1208 €1200 Soon it will be winter. Today hs been very tiring (22x15cm-9x6in) s.d.1976 mixed media card pair. 21-Nov-2 Finarte, Rome #36

BARWIG, Franz (1868-1931) Austrian
Sculpture
£3165 $5000 €5000 Heron (25cm-10in) i. pat.bronze. 26-Nov-2 Dorotheum, Vienna #324/R est:5000-6000
£4255 $6894 €6000 Eva (37cm-15in) i. pat.bronze. 21-May-3 Dorotheum, Vienna #246/R est:6000-8000

BARY-DOUSSIN, J von (1874-?) ?
Sculpture
£3481 $5396 €5500 Shepherd and his flock (68cm-27in) s. bronze. 25-Sep-2 Christie's, Amsterdam #575/R est:1500-2000

BARYE (?) French
Sculpture
£2941 $4824 €4500 Lion marchant (23x39x10cm-9x15x4in) s. brown pat bronze marble socle Cast Barbedienne. 7-Feb-3 Oger, Dumont, Paris #142/R

BARYE, A-L (1796-1875) French
Sculpture
£1655 $2632 €2400 Jaguar devorant un lievre (11x27cm-4x11in) green pat bronze Cast F Barbedienne. 10-Mar-3 Coutau Begarie, Paris #238/R
£5195 $7584 €8000 Singe monte sur un gnou (23x25cm-9x10in) s. bronze. 11-Jun-2 Thierry & Lannon, Brest #96/R est:600-800

BARYE, Alfred (1839-1882) French
Sculpture
£1439 $2360 €2000 Elephant (26cm-10in) s. gold pat bronze. 3-Jun-3 Piasa, Paris #24/R est:800-1000
£1603 $2500 €2405 Lion and Lioness (23cm-9in) st.sig. bronze pair. 8-Aug-2 Eldred, East Dennis #811/R est:1000-2000
£1800 $2808 €2700 Arab huntsman on horseback (73x51cm-29x20in) s. pat. brown. 15-Oct-2 Sotheby's, London #153/R est:1800-2500
£2200 $3432 €3300 Dog with a pheasant and rabbit (23x20cm-9x8in) s. brown pat bronze. 5-Nov-2 Sotheby's, London #90/R est:2000-3000

BARYE, Alfred (after) (1839-1882) French
Sculpture
£2848 $4415 €4500 Peasant girl (80cm-31in) i. bronze. 25-Sep-2 Christie's, Amsterdam #571/R est:5000-7000

BARYE, Antoine-Louis (1796-1875) French
Sculpture
£696 $1100 €1044 Tortue - turtle (11cm-4in) bronze lit. 3-Apr-3 Christie's, Rockefeller NY #343/R est:600-800
£949 $1500 €1424 Lapin, oreilles dressees - rabbit, ears erect (8cm-3in) bronze lit. 3-Apr-3 Christie's, Rockefeller NY #331/R est:1000-1500
£949 $1500 €1424 Faisan tete tournee a gauche - pheasant, head turned to left (11cm-4in) i. bronze lit. 3-Apr-3 Christie's, Rockefeller NY #334/R est:1200-1800
£949 $1500 €1424 Cigogne posee sur une tortue - stork standing on a turtle (7cm-3in) bronze lit. 3-Apr-3 Christie's, Rockefeller NY #341/R est:1000-1500
£949 $1500 €1424 Recumbent doe (6cm-2in) s. red brown pat bronze lit. 25-Apr-3 Christie's, Rockefeller NY #62/R est:1500-2500
£949 $1500 €1424 Doe resting (9cm-4in) s. brown pat bronze lit. 25-Apr-3 Christie's, Rockefeller NY #68/R est:2000-3000
£1000 $1590 €1500 Petit cerf effraye (76x9cm-30x4in) s. green brown pat bronze black marble base lit. 29-Apr-3 Sotheby's, Olympia #121/R est:1200-1800
£1013 $1600 €1520 Pointer (9cm-4in) s.num.11 brown pat bronze sold with marble plinth lit. 25-Apr-3 Christie's, Rockefeller NY #39/R est:2000-3000
£1013 $1600 €1520 Recumbent doe (7cm-3in) s. red brown pat bronze lit. 25-Apr-3 Christie's, Rockefeller NY #64/R est:1500-2500
£1013 $1600 €1520 Golden pheasant of China (11cm-4in) s.st.num.4658 brown pat bronze sold with marble plinth lit. 25-Apr-3 Christie's, Rockefeller NY #83/R est:2500-3500
£1013 $1600 €1520 Pheasant (11cm-4in) s. red brown pat bronze lit. 25-Apr-3 Christie's, Rockefeller NY #85/R est:2000-3000
£1013 $1600 €1520 Java deer (13cm-5in) s.st.d.1838 lacquered silver lit. 25-Apr-3 Christie's, Rockefeller NY #109/R est:2500-3500
£1020 $1622 €1500 Levrette attrapant un lievre (20x31cm-8x12in) s. bronze. 23-Mar-3 Herbette, Doullens #149/R
£1076 $1700 €1614 Lievre effraye - frightened hare (4cm-2in) i. bronze lit. 3-Apr-3 Christie's, Rockefeller NY #332/R est:700-1000
£1076 $1700 €1614 Lava deer (13cm-5in) s.indis.d.1838 red brown pat bronze sold with marble plinth lit. 25-Apr-3 Christie's, Rockefeller NY #108/R est:2000-3000
£1090 $1700 €1635 Standing lion (28x46cm-11x18in) s. bronze. 22-Sep-2 Susanin's, Chicago #5046/R est:2000-4000
£1139 $1800 €1800 Tigre marchant (21cm-8in) s. green pat bronze. 29-Nov-2 Drouot Estimations, Paris #134
£1139 $1800 €1709 Lievre assis - seated hare (8cm-3in) i. bronze lit. 3-Apr-3 Christie's, Rockefeller NY #333/R est:800-1200
£1139 $1800 €1709 Ours assis - reclining bear (10cm-4in) i. bronze marble base lit. 3-Apr-3 Christie's, Rockefeller NY #338/R est:2000-3000
£1139 $1800 €1709 Lion crushing a snake (13cm-5in) s.st.f.F.Barbedienne brown pat bronze sold with marble plinth lit. 25-Apr-3 Christie's, Rockefeller NY #18/R est:2500-3500
£1139 $1800 €1709 Ratel stealing eggs from a nest (10cm-4in) s. brown pat bronze lit. 25-Apr-3 Christie's, Rockefeller NY #38/R est:3000-5000
£1139 $1800 €1709 Stag with head raised (11cm-4in) s. brown pat bronze lit. 25-Apr-3 Christie's, Rockefeller NY #113/R est:1500-2500
£1151 $1842 €1600 Lapin, oreilles dressees (6x7x4cm-2x3x2in) brown pat bronze. 18-May-3 Rabourdin & Choppin de Janvry, Paris #25/R est:1600-1800
£1203 $1900 €1805 Kevel (10cm-4in) i. bronze lit. 3-Apr-3 Christie's, Rockefeller NY #335/R est:1200-1800
£1203 $1900 €1805 Deer (16cm-6in) s. brown pat bronze sold with marble plinth lit. 25-Apr-3 Christie's, Rockefeller NY #57/R est:3000-5000
£1203 $1900 €1805 Walking panther (14x10cm-6x4in) s. st.verso green brown pat bronze bas-relief lit. 25-Apr-3 Christie's, Rockefeller NY #106/R est:800-1200
£1203 $1900 €1805 Seated cat (9cm-4in) s. lacquered silver sold with marble plinth lit. 25-Apr-3 Christie's, Rockefeller NY #153/R est:1200-1800
£1250 $1963 €1950 Basset a l'arret (15x30cm-6x12in) s. brown pat bronze Cast Barbedienne. 10-Dec-2 Renaud, Paris #106/R
£1266 $2000 €1899 Hercules and the Erymanthian boar (13cm-5in) s. red brown pat bronze sold with marble plinth lit. 25-Apr-3 Christie's, Rockefeller NY #73/R est:1000-1500
£1266 $2000 €1899 Rabbit, ears erect (6cm-2in) s.i.num.43 rust brown pat bronze lit. 25-Apr-3 Christie's, Rockefeller NY #90/R est:1000-1500
£1266 $2000 €1899 Gazelle of Ethiopia (8cm-3in) s.i.d.1837 brown pat bronze lit. 25-Apr-3 Christie's, Rockefeller NY #110/R est:2000-3000
£1342 $2161 €2000 Faisan blesse (21x10x12cm-8x4x5in) black green pat bronze. 23-Feb-3 Lesieur & Le Bars, Le Havre #5/R
£1392 $2200 €2088 Kite carrying off a hare (15cm-6in) s. brown pat bronze lit. 25-Apr-3 Christie's, Rockefeller NY #80/R est:2500-3500
£1392 $2200 €2088 Seated hare (8cm-3in) s. rust brown pat bronze lit. 25-Apr-3 Christie's, Rockefeller NY #92/R est:1200-1800
£1392 $2200 €2088 Rabbit, ears down (5cm-2in) s. col pat bronze lit. 25-Apr-3 Christie's, Rockefeller NY #94/R est:1000-1500
£1400 $2226 €2100 Daine couchee (5x10cm-2x4in) s. green brown pat bronze. 29-Apr-3 Sotheby's, Olympia #131/R est:900-1200
£1468 $2452 €2100 Basset assis (14x25cm-6x10in) s. brown pat bronze Cast F.Barbedienne. 30-Jun-3 Pierre Berge, Paris #20/R est:1300-1500
£1474 $2285 €2300 Tigre terrassant une biche (29x46x18cm-11x18x7in) s. brown pat bronze lit. 7-Dec-2 Martinot & Savignat, Pontoise #73/R
£1500 $2340 €2250 Elephant of Cochinchina (14x20cm-6x8in) s. green brown pat bronze lit. 5-Nov-2 Sotheby's, London #126/R est:1500-2000
£1500 $2340 €2250 Stork on a tortoise (8cm-3in) s.st.f.F Barbedienne brown pat bronze. 9-Apr-3 Sotheby's, London #157/R est:1500-2000
£1519 $2400 €2279 Ratel stealing eggs from a nest (10cm-4in) s. red brown pat bronze sold with marble plinth lit. 25-Apr-3 Christie's, Rockefeller NY #37/R est:3000-5000
£1519 $2400 €2279 Spaniel with a duck (16cm-6in) s. brown pat bronze lit. 25-Apr-3 Christie's, Rockefeller NY #42/R est:3000-5000
£1519 $2400 €2279 English basset no 2 (10cm-4in) s. brown pat bronze lit. 25-Apr-3 Christie's, Rockefeller NY #43/R est:2500-3500
£1519 $2400 €2279 Pheasant (12cm-5in) s.num.7154/2807 brown pat bronze sold with marble plinth prov.lit. 25-Apr-3 Christie's, Rockefeller NY #86/R est:2000-3000
£1519 $2400 €2279 Seated hare (9cm-4in) s. red brown pat bronze lit. 25-Apr-3 Christie's, Rockefeller NY #88/R est:1200-1800
£1519 $2400 €2279 Stag, head raised (12cm-5in) s.i. brown pat bronze sold with marble plinth lit. 25-Apr-3 Christie's, Rockefeller NY #112/R est:2500-3500
£1519 $2400 €2279 Goat or ram grazing (6cm-2in) s.num.194 brown pat bronze lit. 25-Apr-3 Christie's, Rockefeller NY #122/R est:1500-2500
£1538 $2569 €2200 Lionne marchant (11x22cm-4x9in) s. brown pat bronze Cast Barbedienne. 30-Jun-3 Pierre Berge, Paris #21/R est:1200-1500
£1582 $2500 €2373 Kevel (8cm-3in) s. red brown pat bronze sold with marble plinth lit. 25-Apr-3 Christie's, Rockefeller NY #116/R est:2000-3000
£1582 $2500 €2373 Frightened ibex (7cm-3in) brown pat bronze lit. 25-Apr-3 Christie's, Rockefeller NY #121/R est:1000-1500

£1600	$2544	€2400	Lievre effraye (4cm-2in) s.num.43 green brown pat bronze st.f.F.Barbedienne. 29-Apr-3 Sotheby's, Olympia #137/R est:1000-1500
£1613	$2548	€2500	Tigre qui marche (14x25x7cm-6x10x3in) s. black pat bronze Cast Barbedienne lit. 18-Dec-2 Ferri, Paris #29/R
£1646	$2600	€2469	Axis deer (17cm-7in) s. red brown pat bronze sold with marble plinth lit. 25-Apr-3 Christie's, Rockefeller NY #58/R est:3000-5000
£1646	$2600	€2469	Eagle carrying off a snake (13cm-5in) s. col pat bronze lit. 25-Apr-3 Christie's, Rockefeller NY #76/R est:3000-5000
£1646	$2600	€2469	Rabbit, ears down (3cm-1in) brown pat bronze sold with marble plinth lit. 25-Apr-3 Christie's, Rockefeller NY #95/R est:1000-1500
£1701	$2704	€2500	Lion et proie (41x48cm-16x19in) s. pat bronze. 23-Mar-3 Herbette, Doullens #152/R
£1772	$2800	€2658	Seated basset, short coat (13cm-5in) s.num.1559 col pat bronze lit. 25-Apr-3 Christie's, Rockefeller NY #44/R est:2500-3500
£1772	$2800	€2658	Jaguar devouring an agouti (7cm-3in) s. red brown pat bronze prov.exhib.lit. 25-Apr-3 Christie's, Rockefeller NY #129/R est:4000-6000
£1772	$2800	€2658	Seated cat (9cm-4in) s. brown pat bronze sold with marble plinth prov.lit. 25-Apr-3 Christie's, Rockefeller NY #155/R est:1200-1800
£1800	$2808	€2700	Pheasant (11x13cm-4x5in) s.num.22385 brown green pat bronze st.f.F Barbedienne. 9-Apr-3 Sotheby's, London #172/R est:2000-3000
£1899	$3000	€2849	Cavalier arabe tuant ub lion - Arab rider killing a lion (39cm-15in) i. bronze lit. 3-Apr-3 Christie's, Rockefeller NY #330/R est:10000-15000
£1899	$3000	€2849	Eagle carrying off a snake (14cm-6in) s. red brown pat bronze lit. 25-Apr-3 Christie's, Rockefeller NY #75/R est:3000-5000
£1899	$3000	€2849	Rabbit, ears down (4cm-2in) s. black lacquer brown pat bronze lit. 25-Apr-3 Christie's, Rockefeller NY #89/R est:800-1200
£1899	$3000	€2849	Kevel (10cm-4in) s. brown pat bronze lit. 25-Apr-3 Christie's, Rockefeller NY #118/R est:1500-2500
£1899	$3000	€2849	Family of ibex (6cm-2in) s.i.num.652 brown pat bronze lit. 25-Apr-3 Christie's, Rockefeller NY #123/R est:2000-3000
£1899	$3000	€2849	Panther attacking a civet cat (11cm-4in) s.st. rust brown pat bronze lit. 25-Apr-3 Christie's, Rockefeller NY #133/R est:5000-8000
£1899	$3000	€2849	Sleeping jaguar (9cm-4in) s.i. col pat bronze lit. 25-Apr-3 Christie's, Rockefeller NY #135/R est:5000-8000
£2000	$3120	€3000	Reclining panther (7x19cm-3x7in) s. brown pat bronze. 9-Apr-3 Sotheby's, London #183/R est:1800-2000
£2000	$3180	€3000	Lion au serpent (13x17cm-5x7in) s.st.f.F.Barbedienne brown pat bronze lit. 29-Apr-3 Sotheby's, Olympia #117/R est:2500-3000
£2025	$3200	€3038	Thesee combattant ie centaure bienor - Theseus slaying the centaur bienor (34cm-13in) i. bronze lit. 3-Apr-3 Christie's, Rockefeller NY #329/R est:8000-12000
£2025	$3200	€3038	Standing basset, head turned to left (16cm-6in) s.i.num.13 and 037 brown pat bronze lit. 25-Apr-3 Christie's, Rockefeller NY #48/R est:4000-6000
£2025	$3200	€3038	Rabbit, ears down (3cm-1in) s.num.18 brown pat bronze lit. 25-Apr-3 Christie's, Rockefeller NY #91/R est:1500-2500
£2025	$3200	€3038	Rabbit, ears erect (4cm-2in) s. brown pat bronze lit. 25-Apr-3 Christie's, Rockefeller NY #96/R est:1000-1500
£2025	$3200	€3038	Recumbent panther (7cm-3in) s.num.0 18 red brown pat bronze lit. 25-Apr-3 Christie's, Rockefeller NY #128/R est:5000-8000
£2025	$3200	€3038	Jaguar devouring a hare (13cm-5in) s. brown pat bronze lit. 25-Apr-3 Christie's, Rockefeller NY #134/R est:3000-5000
£2200	$3432	€3300	Spaniel fetching a goose (14x21cm-6x8in) s. brown pat bronze lit. 9-Apr-3 Sotheby's, London #122/R est:2000-3000
£2215	$3500	€3323	Lionne du Senegal - lioness of Senegal (20cm-8in) i. bronze lit. 3-Apr-3 Christie's, Rockefeller NY #318/R est:2500-3500
£2215	$3500	€3323	Cerf, la jambe gauche levee - stag, left foreleg raised (18cm-7in) i. bronze lit. 3-Apr-3 Christie's, Rockefeller NY #336/R est:2500-3500
£2215	$3500	€3323	Elephant du Senegal - elephant of Senegal (13cm-5in) i. bronze lit. 3-Apr-3 Christie's, Rockefeller NY #344/R est:2500-3500
£2215	$3500	€3323	Arab riding a dromedary (23cm-9in) s. brown pat bronze lit. 25-Apr-3 Christie's, Rockefeller NY #8/R est:4000-6000
£2215	$3500	€3323	Standing basset, head turned to right (17cm-7in) s. brown pat bronze sold with marble plinth. 25-Apr-3 Christie's, Rockefeller NY #47/R est:4000-6000
£2215	$3500	€3323	Listening stag (19cm-7in) s. brown pat bronze lit. 25-Apr-3 Christie's, Rockefeller NY #67/R est:3000-5000
£2215	$3500	€3323	Kevel (11cm-4in) s.num.637 red brown pat bronze prov.exhib.lit. 25-Apr-3 Christie's, Rockefeller NY #117/R est:3000-5000
£2405	$3800	€3608	Tortoise (2cm-1in) s. brown pat bronze lit. 25-Apr-3 Christie's, Rockefeller NY #4/R est:500-800
£2405	$3800	€3608	Lion crushing a snake no 3 (13cm-5in) s.i. red brown pat bronze. 25-Apr-3 Christie's, Rockefeller NY #19/R est:5000-8000
£2405	$3800	€3608	Spaniel pointing a rabbit (11cm-4in) s.num.1838 brown pat bronze lit. 25-Apr-3 Christie's, Rockefeller NY #41/R est:2500-3500
£2405	$3800	€3608	Deer (16cm-6in) s. brown pat bronze sold with marble plinth lit. 25-Apr-3 Christie's, Rockefeller NY #56/R est:3000-5000
£2405	$3800	€3608	Gazelle of Ethiopia (8cm-3in) s.i.d.1837 brown pat bronze sold with marble plinth lit. 25-Apr-3 Christie's, Rockefeller NY #111/R est:2500-3500
£2452	$3874	€3800	Lion tenant un guib (11x27x11cm-4x11x4in) s. pat bronze lit. 19-Dec-2 Delvaux, Paris #56/R est:2500
£2500	$3900	€3750	Lion and serpent (13x16cm-5x6in) s. green brown pat bronze. 9-Apr-3 Sotheby's, London #155/R est:2500-3500
£2532	$4000	€3798	Tigre devorant un gavial - tiger devouring a gavial (11cm-4in) i. bronze marble base lit. 3-Apr-3 Christie's, Rockefeller NY #321/R est:3000-5000
£2532	$4000	€3798	Lion holding a guib (11cm-4in) s.i.num.9 brown pat bronze prov.exhib.lit. 25-Apr-3 Christie's, Rockefeller NY #21/R est:6000-8000
£2532	$4000	€3798	Stag rubbing his antlers against a tree (23cm-9in) s. brown pat bronze sold with marble plinth lit. 25-Apr-3 Christie's, Rockefeller NY #70/R est:5000-8000
£2532	$4000	€3798	Hercules and the Erymanthian boar (14cm-6in) s. red brown pat bronze sold with marble plinth lit. 25-Apr-3 Christie's, Rockefeller NY #72/R est:1200-1800
£2532	$4000	€3798	Standing ibex (13cm-5in) brown pat bronze. 25-Apr-3 Christie's, Rockefeller NY #120/R est:1500-2500
£2532	$4000	€3798	Walking tiger (10cm-4in) s. red brown pat bronze lit. 25-Apr-3 Christie's, Rockefeller NY #131/R est:4000-6000
£2532	$4000	€3798	Seated cat (9cm-4in) s. col pat bronze lit. 25-Apr-3 Christie's, Rockefeller NY #152/R est:1200-1800
£2532	$4000	€3798	Seated cat (9cm-4in) s.st. col pat bronze lit. 25-Apr-3 Christie's, Rockefeller NY #154/R est:1200-1800
£2607	$4250	€3780	Untitled (25x38x18cm-10x15x7in) bronze. 18-Jul-3 Du Mouchelle, Detroit #2065/R est:4500-5500
£2658	$4200	€3987	Tortoise (3cm-1in) s.num.6051 green brown pat bronze sold with marble plinth lit. 25-Apr-3 Christie's, Rockefeller NY #3/R est:1000-1500
£2658	$4200	€3987	Seated lion (20cm-8in) s.num.15 brown pat bronze lit. 25-Apr-3 Christie's, Rockefeller NY #16/R est:3000-5000
£2658	$4200	€3987	Recumbent fawn (4cm-2in) s. brown pat bronze lit. 25-Apr-3 Christie's, Rockefeller NY #59/R est:1500-2500
£2700	$4293	€4050	Cheval Turc (11x12cm-4x5in) s.st.f.F.Barbedienne brown pat bronze. 29-Apr-3 Sotheby's, Olympia #126/R est:3000-5000
£2800	$4368	€4200	Greyhound retrieving a hare (21x32cm-8x13in) s. green brown pat bronze lit. 5-Nov-2 Sotheby's, London #88/R est:3000-5000
£2800	$4452	€4200	Cheval demi-sang (14x17cm-6x7in) s. brown pat bronze lit. 29-Apr-3 Sotheby's, Olympia #116/R est:3000-3500
£2848	$4500	€4272	Jaguar qui marche no.1 - Walking jaguar no.1 (13cm-5in) i. bronze marble base. 3-Apr-3 Christie's, Rockefeller NY #319/R est:2000-3000
£2848	$4500	€4272	Lion devorant un sanglier - lion devouring a boar (17cm-7in) i. bronze lit. 3-Apr-3 Christie's, Rockefeller NY #323/R est:4000-6000
£2848	$4500	€4272	Lion devouring a doe (14cm-6in) s.num.2 black pat bronze lit. 25-Apr-3 Christie's, Rockefeller NY #23/R est:7000-10000
£2848	$4500	€4272	Parrot perched on a branch (20cm-8in) s. red brown pat bronze lit. 25-Apr-3 Christie's, Rockefeller NY #82/R est:4000-6000
£2887	$4793	€4100	Crocodile (20cm-8in) st.f.Barbedienne bronze prov. 16-Jun-3 Oger, Dumont, Paris #101/R est:1000
£2953	$4754	€4400	Aigle aux ailes deployees (34x24x25cm-13x9x10in) black brown pat bronze Cast Barbedienne. 23-Feb-3 Lesieur & Le Bars, Le Havre #6/R
£2993	$4759	€4400	Tigre marchant (22x42cm-9x17in) s. green pat bronze Cast Barbedienne. 23-Mar-3 Herbette, Doullens #148/R
£3000	$4620	€4500	Lion crushing a serpent (34x46cm-13x18in) s. green black bronze. 5-Sep-2 Sotheby's, Olympia #126/R est:3000-4000
£3000	$4770	€4500	Lapin oreilles couchees (4x7cm-2x3in) s. silver lit. 29-Apr-3 Sotheby's, Olympia #134/R est:3000-3500
£3038	$4709	€4800	Taureau debout (19x28cm-7x11in) s. brown pat bronze exec.c.1887 Cast Barbedienne. 27-Sep-2 Rabourdin & Choppin de Janvry, Paris #99/R est:5000-5500
£3038	$4800	€4557	Ours monte sur un arbre, mangeant un hibou - bear in a tree, devouring an owl (19cm-7in) i. bronze lit. 3-Apr-3 Christie's, Rockefeller NY #339/R est:3000-5000
£3038	$4800	€4557	Seated lion no 4 (18cm-7in) s. rust brown pat bronze sold with marble plinth prov.lit. 25-Apr-3 Christie's, Rockefeller NY #17/R est:5000-8000
£3038	$4800	€4557	Lion holding a guib (11cm-4in) s.num.23 brown pat bronze sold with marble plinth lit. 25-Apr-3 Christie's, Rockefeller NY #22/R est:6000-8000

£3038 $4800 €4557 Stag of France, leg raised (20cm-8in) s. brown pat bronze sold with marble plinth lit. 25-Apr-3 Christie's, Rockefeller NY #69/R est:3000-5000
£3038 $4800 €4557 Stag attacked by a tiger (6cm-2in) num.35 red brown pat bronze lit. 25-Apr-3 Christie's, Rockefeller NY #140/R est:1200-1800
£3165 $5000 €4748 Taureau attaque par un tigre - bull attacked by a tiger (22cm-9in) i. bronze lit. 3-Apr-3 Christie's, Rockefeller NY #320/R est:5000-7000
£3165 $5000 €4748 Ours debout no.2 - standing bear no.2 (25cm-10in) i. bronze lit. 3-Apr-3 Christie's, Rockefeller NY #337/R est:3000-5000
£3165 $5000 €4748 Stork standing on a tortoise (8cm-3in) num.707 red brown pat bronze prov.exhib.lit. 25-Apr-3 Christie's, Rockefeller NY #1/R est:2500-3000
£3165 $5000 €4748 Panther holding a gazelle (8cm-3in) s. brown pat bronze lit. 25-Apr-3 Christie's, Rockefeller NY #127/R est:4000-6000
£3165 $5000 €4748 Seated cat (9cm-4in) s. brown pat bronze lit. 25-Apr-3 Christie's, Rockefeller NY #156/R est:1200-1800
£3205 $5064 €5000 Elephant du Senegal (14x19x6cm-6x7x2in) s.st.f.F.Barbedienne brown pat bronze lit. 18-Nov-2 Tajan, Paris #72/R est:4600-6000
£3290 $5199 €5100 Jaguar qui marche (11x22x7cm-4x9x3in) s.st.f.Barbedienne brown pat bronze lit. 18-Dec-2 Ferri, Paris #28/R
£3354 $5199 €5300 Cheval surpris par un lion (38cm-15in) s. green brown pat bronze. 27-Sep-2 Rabourdin & Choppin de Janvry, Paris #98/R est:5000-5200
£3481 $5500 €5222 Guerrier tartare arretant son cheval - tartan warrior checking his horse (34cm-13in) i. bronze lit. 3-Apr-3 Christie's, Rockefeller NY #327/R est:12000-18000
£3481 $5500 €5222 Seated lion no 2 (21cm-8in) s.num.48 brown pat bronze marble plinth lit. 25-Apr-3 Christie's, Rockefeller NY #15/R est:5000-8000
£3481 $5500 €5222 Lion devouring a boar (17cm-7in) s. red brown pat bronze lit. 25-Apr-3 Christie's, Rockefeller NY #24/R est:5000-8000
£3481 $5500 €5222 Python swallowing a doe (8cm-3in) s.i. brown pat bronze lit. 25-Apr-3 Christie's, Rockefeller NY #159/R est:6000-8000
£3500 $5565 €5250 Basset Anglais numero 2 (10x14cm-4x6in) s.st.f.F.Barbedienne green pat bronze lit. 29-Apr-3 Sotheby's, Olympia #118 est:3000-3500
£3526 $5571 €5500 Le lion qui marche (39x10x23cm-15x4x9in) s.st.f.F.Barbedienne black pat bronze lit. 18-Nov-2 Tajan, Paris #63/R est:4600-6000
£3797 $6000 €5696 Tiger qui marche - waking tiger (21cm-8in) i. bronze lit. 3-Apr-3 Christie's, Rockefeller NY #324/R est:3000-5000
£3797 $6000 €5696 Lion qui marche - walking lion (23cm-9in) i. bronze lit. 3-Apr-3 Christie's, Rockefeller NY #325/R est:3000-5000
£3797 $6000 €5696 Le general Bonaparte - General Bonapart (36cm-14in) i. bronze lit. 3-Apr-3 Christie's, Rockefeller NY #328/R est:12000-18000
£3797 $6000 €5696 Tortoise (2cm-1in) s. brown pat bronze lit. 25-Apr-3 Christie's, Rockefeller NY #5/R est:500-800
£3797 $6000 €5696 Arab riding a dromedary (28cm-11in) s. col pat bronze marble plinth lit. 25-Apr-3 Christie's, Rockefeller NY #9/R est:4000-6000
£3797 $6000 €5696 Seated basset, long coat (13cm-5in) s.num.111 brown pat bronze lit. 25-Apr-3 Christie's, Rockefeller NY #45/R est:3000-5000
£3797 $6000 €5696 Standing bull (19cm-7in) s. brown pat bronze sold with marble plinth lit. 25-Apr-3 Christie's, Rockefeller NY #149/R est:4000-6000
£3800 $6042 €5700 Panthere de Tunis (9x20cm-4x8in) s.st.f.F.Barbedienne green brown pat bronze. 29-Apr-3 Sotheby's, Olympia #129/R est:1200-1800
£4000 $6240 €6000 Eagle and heron (31x31cm-12x12in) s.num.43 green brown pat bronze st.f.F.Barbedienne lit. 5-Nov-2 Sotheby's, London #105/R est:4000-5000
£4000 $6240 €6000 Charles VII victorious (30x23cm-12x9in) s. green brown pat bronze. 9-Apr-3 Sotheby's, London #182/R est:4000-6000
£4114 $6500 €6171 Crocodile (20cm-8in) bronze lit. 3-Apr-3 Christie's, Rockefeller NY #342/R est:1500-2000
£4114 $6500 €6171 Rearing bull (21cm-8in) s.num.95 col pat bronze lit. 25-Apr-3 Christie's, Rockefeller NY #147/R est:5000-8000
£4430 $6911 €7000 Famille de cerfs (22x25x13cm-9x10x5in) s. col pat bronze Cast Barbedienne. 20-Oct-2 Mercier & Cie, Lille #123/R est:7000-7500
£4430 $7000 €6645 Lion assis, no.2 - seated lion no.2 (21cm-8in) i. bronze lit. 3-Apr-3 Christie's, Rockefeller NY #345/R est:3000-5000
£4430 $7000 €6645 Panther of India (14cm-6in) s. col pat bronze sold with marble plinth prov.lit. 25-Apr-3 Christie's, Rockefeller NY #125/R est:4000-6000
£4430 $7000 €6645 Jaguar devouring a crocodile (8cm-3in) s. rust brown pat bronze sold with marble plinth prov.lit. 25-Apr-3 Christie's, Rockefeller NY #143/R est:5000-8000
£4500 $7155 €6750 Cheval percheron (20x16cm-8x6in) s. green pat bronze lit. 29-Apr-3 Sotheby's, Olympia #119/R est:3000-5000
£4557 $7063 €7200 Thesee et le Centaure Bienor (34x38x10cm-13x15x4in) green brown pat bronze exec.c.1890 Cast Barbedienne. 27-Sep-2 Rabourdin & Choppin de Janvry, Paris #106/R est:7500-7800
£4616 $7293 €7200 Taureau debout (19x29x10cm-7x11x4in) s.st.f.F.Barbedienne brown pat bronze lit. 18-Nov-2 Tajan, Paris #62/R est:6000-9000
£4747 $7500 €7121 Lioness of Senegal (20cm-8in) s. brown pat bronze lit. 25-Apr-3 Christie's, Rockefeller NY #124/R est:5000-8000
£4800 $7488 €7200 Elephant d'aise (14x16cm-6x6in) s.i. green pat bronze. 9-Apr-3 Sotheby's, London #153/R est:3000-5000
£4800 $8016 €6960 Asian elephant (14x16cm-6x6in) s. dk brown pat bronze. 8-Jul-3 Sotheby's, London #191/R est:3500-4500
£5063 $8000 €7595 Tiger devouring a gavial (11cm-4in) s.indis.d.1836 num.1069 col pat bronze sold with plinth prov.lit. 25-Apr-3 Christie's, Rockefeller NY #142/R est:5000-8000
£5380 $8500 €8070 Walking lion (23cm-9in) s. brown pat bronze lit. 25-Apr-3 Christie's, Rockefeller NY #11/R est:4000-6000
£5380 $8500 €8070 Two dogs pointing pheasants (12cm-5in) s. brown pat bronze sold with marble plinth lit. 25-Apr-3 Christie's, Rockefeller NY #40/R est:4000-6000
£5380 $8500 €8070 Stag, doe and fawn (22cm-9in) s.num.2204 and 1989 brown pat bronze lit. 25-Apr-3 Christie's, Rockefeller NY #66/R est:5000-8000
£5449 $8609 €8500 Thesee combattant le minotaure (45x16x29cm-18x6x11in) s. brown pat bronze lit. 18-Nov-2 Tajan, Paris #67/R est:6000-7500
£5500 $9185 €7975 Pair of perfume burners (10cm-4in) st.sig. green brown pat bronze two. 8-Jul-3 Sotheby's, London #183/R est:3000-5000
£5696 $9000 €8544 Vulture, enclosed in its wings (13cm-5in) s. brown pat bronze sold with marble plinth lit. 25-Apr-3 Christie's, Rockefeller NY #77/R est:2500-3500
£5696 $9000 €8544 Pheasant (11cm-4in) s.num.645 modele red brown pat bronze prov.exhib.lit. 25-Apr-3 Christie's, Rockefeller NY #84/R est:3000-5000
£5696 $9000 €8544 Wolf holding a stag by the throat (22cm-9in) s. brown pat bronze sold with marble plinth lit. 25-Apr-3 Christie's, Rockefeller NY #101/R est:10000-15000
£5897 $9259 €9200 Cheval surpris par un lion (38x37x15cm-15x15x6in) green blacl pat bronze. 24-Nov-2 Lesieur & Le Bars, Le Havre #5/R
£6000 $9420 €9000 Cavalier arabe tuant un sanglier - Arab warrior killing a wild boar (29x32cm-11x13in) s. brown pat. bronze lit. 10-Dec-2 Sotheby's, London #169/R est:7000-9000
£6000 $9360 €9000 Crocodile (3x19cm-1x7in) s. green brown pat bronze lit. 5-Nov-2 Sotheby's, London #106/R est:3000-4000
£6000 $9540 €9000 Braque (9x17cm-4x7in) s.num.16 brown pat bronze lit. 29-Apr-3 Sotheby's, Olympia #115/R est:4000-6000
£6013 $9500 €9020 Stag, doe and fawn (22cm-9in) s.num.20 brown pat bronze lit. 25-Apr-3 Christie's, Rockefeller NY #65/R est:5000-8000
£6013 $9500 €9020 Stag brought down by two greyhounds (34cm-13in) s.i.num.08 brown pat bronze lit. 25-Apr-3 Christie's, Rockefeller NY #99/R est:15000-25000
£6013 $9500 €9020 Bull brought down by a bear (14cm-6in) s. col pat bronze lit. 25-Apr-3 Christie's, Rockefeller NY #146/R est:5000-8000
£6090 $9439 €9500 Cavalier tartare (34x32x14cm-13x13x6in) s.st.f.Barbedienne silver pat bronze. 4-Dec-2 Anaf, Lyon #22/R est:10000
£6129 $9684 €9500 Singe monte sur gnou (23x25cm-9x10in) s. brown pat bronze. 19-Dec-2 Bondu, Paris #87/R est:8000
£6250 $9938 €9000 Taureau terrassant un ours (15x28cm-6x11in) brown pat bronze. 30-Apr-3 Tajan, Paris #19/R
£6329 $10000 €9494 Walking tiger (21x100cm-8x39in) s. brown pat bronze lit. 25-Apr-3 Christie's, Rockefeller NY #10/R est:4000-6000
£6362 $10306 €9225 Lapit and centaur (77cm-30in) s. green pat.bronze Cast Barbedienne. 26-May-3 Bukowskis, Stockholm #312/R est:20000-25000 (S.KR 82000)
£6410 $10128 €10000 Guerrier tartare arretant son cheval (37cm-15in) s. green pat bronze red marble base. 18-Nov-2 Tajan, Paris #66/R est:3800-4000
£6962 $11000 €10443 Guerrier tartare arretant son cheval, tartan warrior checking his horse (37cm-15in) i. bronze prov.lit. 3-Apr-3 Christie's, Rockefeller NY #326/R est:18000-22000
£6962 $11000 €10443 Elephant of Senegal (14cm-6in) s. brown pat bronze sold with marble plinth lit. 25-Apr-3 Christie's, Rockefeller NY #6/R est:6000-8000
£6962 $11000 €10443 Walking lion (23cm-9in) s. red brown pat bronze lit. 25-Apr-3 Christie's, Rockefeller NY #12/R est:5000-8000
£6962 $11000 €10443 Arab rider killing a boar (29cm-11in) s. brown pat bronze lit. 25-Apr-3 Christie's, Rockefeller NY #25/R est:10000-15000
£6962 $11000 €10443 Standing basset, head turned to right (17cm-7in) s.num.031 col pat bronze lit. 25-Apr-3 Christie's, Rockefeller NY #46/R est:4000-6000

£6962 $11000 €10443 Stad, doe and two fawns (18cm-7in) s.num.8 red brown pat bronze lit. 25-Apr-3 Christie's, Rockefeller NY #55/R est:4000-6000
£6962 $11000 €10443 Chimera (12cm-5in) s. col pat bronze lit. 25-Apr-3 Christie's, Rockefeller NY #74/R est:1500-3500
£6962 $11000 €10443 Kite or Eagle carrying off a hare (18cm-7in) s.i. brown pat bronze. 25-Apr-3 Christie's, Rockefeller NY #81/R est:3000-5000
£6962 $11000 €10443 Standing jaguar (13cm-5in) s.st.d.1840 brown pat bronze lit. 25-Apr-3 Christie's, Rockefeller NY #132/R est:5000-8000
£7500 $12525 €10875 Seated basset hound (13x26cm-5x10in) s. num.2 dk brown pat bronze. 8-Jul-3 Sotheby's, London #190/R est:4000-6000
£7595 $12000 €11393 Elephant of Asia (14cm-6in) s. brown pat bronze sold with marble plinth prov.lit. 25-Apr-3 Christie's, Rockefeller NY #7/R est:5000-8000
£7595 $12000 €11393 Tiger attacking an antelope (33cm-13in) s. brown pat bronze lit. 25-Apr-3 Christie's, Rockefeller NY #138/R est:8000-12000
£7595 $12000 €11393 Python crushing a gazelle (16cm-6in) s.i. col pat bronze lit. 25-Apr-3 Christie's, Rockefeller NY #158/R est:8000-12000
£7800 $12168 €11700 Turkish horse (13x12cm-5x5in) s.num.43 green brown pat bronze st.f.F Barbedienne. 9-Apr-3 Sotheby's, London #151/R est:6000-8000
£8228 $12835 €13000 Elephant terrassant un tigre (23x35x19cm-9x14x7in) green pat bronze. 18-Oct-2 Rabourdin & Choppin de Janvry, Paris #57
£8228 $13000 €12342 Ours fuyant des chiens - bear fleeing from dogs (31cm-12in) bronze lit. 3-Apr-3 Christie's, Rockefeller NY #340/R est:8000-12000
£8228 $13000 €12342 Turkish horse no 3, left foreleg raised (18cm-7in) s. black brown pat bronze lit. 25-Apr-3 Christie's, Rockefeller NY #31/R est:10000-15000
£8228 $13000 €12342 Charles VII victorious (30cm-12in) s. brown pat bronze marble plinth prov.lit. 25-Apr-3 Christie's, Rockefeller NY #53/R est:8000-12000
£8633 $13813 €12000 Thesee combattant le centaure Bienor (56cm-22in) s.st.f.F.Barbedienne green brown pat bronze. 18-May-3 Rabourdin & Choppin de Janvry, Paris #38/R est:12000-14000
£8861 $14000 €13292 Half-blood horse, head raised (14cm-6in) s.num.702 brown model pat bronze prov.exhib.lit. 25-Apr-3 Christie's, Rockefeller NY #33/R est:5000-8000
£8861 $14000 €13292 Bear brought down by hounds (26cm-10in) s. col pat bronze lit. 25-Apr-3 Christie's, Rockefeller NY #35/R est:12000-18000
£8861 $14000 €13292 Tom, Algerian greyhound (19cm-7in) s. col pat bronze sold with marble plinth lit. 25-Apr-3 Christie's, Rockefeller NY #49/R est:5000-8000
£8861 $14000 €13292 Tiger attacking an antelope (33cm-13in) s. red brown pat bronze sold with wooden plinth lit. 25-Apr-3 Christie's, Rockefeller NY #139/R est:8000-12000
£9000 $15030 €13050 Reclining bear (17x21cm-7x8in) s. dk brown green pat bronze incl veined red marble base prov. 8-Jul-3 Sotheby's, London #181/R est:8000-12000
£9934 $16192 €15000 La paix (50cm-20in) s. brown pat bronze. 16-Feb-3 Mercier & Cie, Lille #181/R est:12000-15000
£10000 $15700 €15000 Theseus and the minatour (45cm-18in) s.i. brown pat. bronze lit. 10-Dec-2 Sotheby's, London #171/R est:10000-15000
£10127 $16000 €15191 Reclining bear (14cm-6in) s.num.160/271/2050 col pat bronze lit. 25-Apr-3 Christie's, Rockefeller NY #36/R est:5000-8000
£10127 $16000 €15191 Ape riding a gnu (23cm-9in) s. red brown pat bronze lit. 25-Apr-3 Christie's, Rockefeller NY #87/R est:10000-15000
£10759 $17000 €16139 Eagle with spread wings and open beak (24cm-9in) s. brown pat bronze lit. 25-Apr-3 Christie's, Rockefeller NY #79/R est:7000-10000
£10759 $17000 €16139 Panther seizing a stag (32cm-13in) s.num.171 black brown pat bronze lit. 25-Apr-3 Christie's, Rockefeller NY #137/R est:8000-12000
£10759 $17000 €16139 Standing bull (17cm-7in) s.st.num.9 brown pat bronze lit. 25-Apr-3 Christie's, Rockefeller NY #148/R est:7000-10000
£10759 $17000 €16139 Ocelot carrying off a heron (18cm-7in) s.num.590 modele brown pat bronze prov.exhib.lit. 25-Apr-3 Christie's, Rockefeller NY #157/R est:15000-25000
£11392 $18000 €17088 Two young lions (15cm-6in) s.num.2 brown pat bronze lit. 25-Apr-3 Christie's, Rockefeller NY #13/R est:10000-15000
£11392 $18000 €17088 Mule (22cm-9in) s.num.606 red brown model pat bronze prov.exhib.lit. 25-Apr-3 Christie's, Rockefeller NY #34/R est:4000-6000
£11392 $18000 €17088 Duke of Orleans (36cm-14in) s.i. brown pat bronze sold with marble plinth lit. 25-Apr-3 Christie's, Rockefeller NY #98/R est:7000-10000
£12025 $19000 €18038 Eagle holding a heron (32cm-13in) s. brown pat bronze sold with marble plinth lit. 25-Apr-3 Christie's, Rockefeller NY #78/R est:8000-12000
£12658 $20000 €18987 Lion crushing a snake no 1 (26cm-10in) s.d.18 avril 1866 brown pat bronze exhib.lit. 25-Apr-3 Christie's, Rockefeller NY #20/R est:8000-12000
£12658 $20000 €18987 Equestrienne in 1830 costume (37cm-15in) s.i. brown pat bronze sold with marble plinth lit. 25-Apr-3 Christie's, Rockefeller NY #97/R est:7000-10000
£13699 $21507 €20000 Thesee et le centaure Bienor (75x38x33cm-30x15x13in) st. green pat bronze exec.c.1880 Cast Barbedienne. 21-Apr-3 Rabourdin & Choppin de Janvry, Paris #49/R est:22000-25000
£15823 $25000 €23735 Panther seizing a stag (37cm-15in) s. col pat bronze lit. 25-Apr-3 Christie's, Rockefeller NY #136/R est:8000-12000
£16456 $26000 €24684 Two Arab riders killing a lion (37cm-15in) s.num.4 brown pat bronze sold with marble plinth lit. 25-Apr-3 Christie's, Rockefeller NY #26/R est:25000-35000
£17722 $28000 €26583 Gaston de Foix (33cm-13in) s.i. brown pat bronze sold with marble plinth prov.exhib.lit. 25-Apr-3 Christie's, Rockefeller NY #52/R est:6000-8000
£17722 $28000 €26583 Stag, doe and two fawns (18cm-7in) s.num.718 modele brown pat bronze prov.exhib.lit. 25-Apr-3 Christie's, Rockefeller NY #54/R est:10000-15000
£18987 $30000 €28481 Horse surprised by a tiger (24cm-9in) s. red brown pat bronze lit. 25-Apr-3 Christie's, Rockefeller NY #27/R est:10000-15000
£18987 $30000 €28481 Turkish horse no 3, left foreleg raised (18cm-7in) s. col pat bronze prov.exhib.lit. 25-Apr-3 Christie's, Rockefeller NY #32/R est:10000-15000
£18987 $30000 €28481 Gaston de Foix (34cm-13in) s. brown pat bronze lit. 25-Apr-3 Christie's, Rockefeller NY #51/R est:5000-8000
£19500 $30420 €29250 Turkish horse (13x13cm-5x5in) s. plaster wax ebonised wood perspex vitrine prov.exhib.lit. 5-Nov-2 Sotheby's, London #109/R est:25000-35000
£24051 $38000 €36077 Tiger devouring a gavial (19cm-7in) s.st.num.6 brown pat bronze lit. 25-Apr-3 Christie's, Rockefeller NY #141/R est:10000-15000
£26000 $43420 €37700 Cheval Turc No.2 (32x30cm-13x12in) ls. num.42 dark green pat bronze incl green marble socle. 8-Jul-3 Sotheby's, London #186/R est:15000-25000
£28481 $45000 €42722 Horse attacked by a lion (40cm-16in) s. red brown pat bronze sold with marble plinth lit. 25-Apr-3 Christie's, Rockefeller NY #28/R est:15000-25000
£30380 $48000 €45570 Stag stripping his antlers, with doe and fawn (26cm-10in) s. modele red brown pat bronze prov.exhib.lit. 25-Apr-3 Christie's, Rockefeller NY #71/R est:12000-18000
£30380 $48000 €45570 Theseus slaying the centaur Bienor (34cm-13in) s.st. red brown pat bronze sold with wooden plinth lit. 25-Apr-3 Christie's, Rockefeller NY #144/R est:8000-12000
£31000 $48360 €46500 Three seated goddesses (33cm-13in) s. green brown pat bronze lit. 5-Nov-2 Sotheby's, London #138/R est:30000-50000
£31646 $50000 €47469 Seated lion no 1 (36cm-14in) s. brown pat bronze lit. 25-Apr-3 Christie's, Rockefeller NY #14/R est:12000-18000
£31646 $50000 €47469 Bull attacked by a tiger (22cm-9in) s.st.num.673 col pat bronze sold with wood plinth prov.exhib.lit. 25-Apr-3 Christie's, Rockefeller NY #145/R est:8000-12000
£37975 $60000 €56963 Elk hunt (53cm-21in) s. red brown pat bronze prov.exhib.lit. 25-Apr-3 Christie's, Rockefeller NY #100/R est:100000-150000
£41139 $65000 €61709 Tartar warrior checking his horse (37cm-15in) s. silvered bronze sold with wooden plinth lit. 25-Apr-3 Christie's, Rockefeller NY #30/R est:20000-30000
£53797 $85000 €80696 Tartare warrior checking his horse (33cm-13in) s. red brown modele pat bronze prov.exhib.lit. 25-Apr-3 Christie's, Rockefeller NY #29/R est:20000-30000
£53797 $85000 €80696 Python crushing a crocodile (17cm-7in) s.num.618 modele col pat bronze prov.exhib.lit. 25-Apr-3 Christie's, Rockefeller NY #160/R est:15000-25000
£101266 $160000 €151899 Theseus slaying the minotaur (45cm-18in) s.num.2371 col pat bronze sold with marble plinth lit. 25-Apr-3 Christie's, Rockefeller NY #151/R est:20000-30000
£151899 $240000 €227849 Theseus slaying the minotaur (45cm-18in) s.num.580 modele brown pat bronze prov.exhib.lit. 25-Apr-3 Christie's, Rockefeller NY #150/R est:40000-60000
£196203 $310000 €294305 Roger carrying off Angelica on the hippogriff (51cm-20in) s. col pat bronze sold with wooden plinth prov.exhib.lit. 25-Apr-3 Christie's, Rockefeller NY #50/R est:60000-80000

Works on paper

£705 $1093 €1100 Etude de lionne (13x18cm-5x7in) studio st. graphite dr. 9-Dec-2 Beaussant & Lefèvre, Paris #24/R

£6410 $10128 €10000 Taureau (17x27cm-7x11in) s. W/C prov.exhib.lit. 18-Nov-2 Sotheby's, Paris #52/R est:4000

BARYE, Antoine-Louis (after) (1796-1875) French
Sculpture
£6643 $11094 €9500 Basset debout (17x30cm-7x12in) bears sig.num.3 brown pat bronze. 30-Jun-3 Pierre Berge, Paris #19/R est:350-400
£10897 $17218 €17000 Ours attaque par trois dogues (26x32cm-10x13in) s.num.7385 brown pat bronze. 14-Nov-2 Credit Municipal, Paris #78/R est:3000-3500

BARZAGHI, Francesco (1839-1892) Italian
Sculpture
£5579 $8815 €8369 Girl with small dog (103cm-41in) s.i.d.1872 marble. 29-Nov-2 Zofingen, Switzerland #2246/R est:6500 (S.FR 13000)
£7296 $11528 €10944 Small fisherman (103cm-41in) s.i.d.1872 marble. 29-Nov-2 Zofingen, Switzerland #2245/R est:6500 (S.FR 17000)

BARZAGHI-CATTANEO, Antonio (1837-1922) Swiss
£1200 $2004 €1800 Discreet glance (41x32cm-16x13in) mono. s.d.1876 verso. 18-Jun-3 Christie's, Kensington #143/R est:1500-2000

BARZAGLI, Massimo (1960-) Italian
£272 $433 €400 Flowers (45x55cm-18x22in) s.d.1994 paper. 1-Mar-3 Meeting Art, Vercelli #456
£385 $604 €600 Composition (60x60cm-24x24in) s.d.1999 verso. 23-Nov-2 Meeting Art, Vercelli #12
£641 $1006 €1000 Line on blue ground (99x69cm-39x27in) s.d.92 verso paper on canvas. 20-Nov-2 Pandolfini, Florence #154/R

BARZANTI, Licinio (1857-1944) Italian
£1491 $2400 €2237 Pink, red and yellow roses spilling from a basket (64x79cm-25x31in) s. 19-Feb-3 Doyle, New York #17 est:1500-2500
£6600 $10758 €9900 Vase of flowers (100x70cm-39x28in) s.i. 29-Jan-3 Sotheby's, Olympia #344/R est:4000-6000

BASAGLIA, Vittorio (1936-) Italian
£633 $987 €1000 Cactus (70x150cm-28x59in) s.d.1957. 19-Oct-2 Semenzato, Venice #89/R

BASCH, Andor (1885-?) Hungarian
£727 $1133 €1054 Still life with bananas (35x44cm-14x17in) s. board. 12-Apr-3 Mu Terem Galeria, Budapest #177/R est:220000 (H.F 260000)
£968 $1501 €1404 Studio (29x39cm-11x15in) s.d.1923 papercard. 9-Dec-2 Mu Terem Galeria, Budapest #191/R est:150000 (H.F 360000)
£2048 $3276 €3072 Landscape in south France (54x65cm-21x26in) board. 16-May-3 Kieselbach, Budapest #56/R (H.F 700000)
£2958 $4585 €4437 Landscape in Provence with a still life (100x81cm-39x32in) s. panel. 6-Dec-2 Kieselbach, Budapest #20/R (H.F 1100000)
£4841 $7503 €7262 Studio still life in Southern France (88x68cm-35x27in) s. panel. 6-Dec-2 Kieselbach, Budapest #82/R (H.F 1800000)

BASCH, Edith (1895-?) Hungarian
£490 $765 €735 Girl in red dress (83x65cm-33x26in) 11-Sep-2 Kieselbach, Budapest #154/R (H.F 190000)
£1174 $1831 €1761 Man in black shirt with oranges (99x75cm-39x30in) 11-Apr-3 Kieselbach, Budapest #198/R est:350000-420000 (H.F 420000)

BASCH, Julius Gyula (1851-1928) Hungarian
£6690 $10771 €9500 Kaiser Franz Joseph I and Kaiserin Elisabeth von Osterreich (76x60cm-30x24in) two. 7-May-3 Dorotheum, Vienna #128/R est:12000-16000

BASCHET, Francois (20th C) French
Sculpture
£2119 $3454 €3200 L'oiseau balancel (60cm-24in) s. metal inox aluminium. 1-Feb-3 Claude Aguttes, Neuilly #192/R est:3660-3960

BASCHINDJAGHIAN, Gevork Zacharovich (1857-1925) Russian
£7746 $12472 €11000 Strolling in moonlight (107x53cm-42x21in) s. 10-May-3 Bukowskis, Helsinki #383/R est:6000-8000

BASCOULES, Jean Desire (1886-1976) French
£3103 $4966 €4500 Place du Gouvernement, Alger (47x61cm-19x24in) s. 12-Mar-3 E & Eve, Paris #86/R est:2500-3000

BASE, Rachel (?) ?
£310 $490 €450 Bouquet de roses. s. cardboard. 2-Apr-3 Vanderkindere, Brussels #539

BASELEER, Richard (1867-1951) Belgian
£2536 $4159 €3500 Sur l'Escaut. s. 27-May-3 Campo & Campo, Antwerp #15/R est:4000-6000

BASELITZ, Georg (1938-) German
£35000 $57400 €52500 Anna (132x97cm-52x38in) s.i.d.92 d.verso prov.exhib. 6-Feb-3 Sotheby's, London #13/R est:80000
£72785 $115000 €109178 Das motive von (146x114cm-57x45in) init.d.88 s.i.d.verso prov.exhib. 13-Nov-2 Sotheby's, New York #527/R
£125000 $200000 €187500 Hirtenkopf (249x200cm-98x79in) init.d.86 prov. 14-May-3 Christie's, Rockefeller NY #43/R est:250000-350000
£153846 $240000 €230769 Birke (199x140cm-78x55in) s.d.70 i.d.verso prov.exhib.lit. 11-Nov-2 Phillips, New York #25/R est:275000-375000
£160000 $267200 €240000 Ciao America III (250x200cm-98x79in) s.i.d.19.IX.88 verso prov.exhib. 26-Jun-3 Christie's, London #129/R est:120000-180000
£180000 $295200 €270000 Die poetishe kugel (111x171cm-44x67in) painted 1964 prov.exhib.lit. 5-Feb-3 Christie's, London #19/R est:200000-300000
£190000 $317300 €285000 Graue Hunde, drei streifen (163x130cm-64x51in) s.d.68 s.i.d.66-68 verso s.d.67 stretcher prov.exhib.lit. 25-Jun-3 Sotheby's, London #19/R est:180000-250000

Works on paper
£5660 $8774 €9000 Kohle (75x53cm-30x21in) s.d.27.1.84 chl prov. 30-Oct-2 Artcurial Briest, Paris #480/R est:5000-7000
£7595 $12000 €12000 Untitled - dog (43x33cm-17x13in) mono. Indian ink. 27-Nov-2 Dorotheum, Vienna #60/R est:10000-15000
£15484 $24000 €23226 Sachsische landschaft - Saxon landscape (48x63cm-19x25in) s. brush India ink W/C executed 1964 prov.exhib. 26-Sep-2 Christie's, Rockefeller NY #774/R est:12000-18000
£17266 $27626 €24000 A cow - two strips (37x29cm-15x11in) mono.d. s.i.d.1966 verso W/C Indian ink brush oil chk prov. 15-May-3 Neumeister, Munich #386/R est:20000-22000
£25157 $39245 €40000 Hirte - shepherd (52x42cm-20x17in) s. i.d.66 verso pencil chl gouache prov.exhib. 9-Oct-2 Sotheby's, London #227/R est:30000-40000

BASETER, Caroline A (19th C) British?
£2244 $3500 €3366 Tabletop still life with books and white rose (38x56cm-15x22in) s. 20-Sep-2 Sloan, North Bethesda #397/R est:2500-3500

BASILE, Matteo (1974-) Italian
£1277 $2068 €1800 Gorgeous (81x106cm-32x42in) s.i.d.2001 verso plotter painting photographic card on aluminium. 20-May-3 Porro, Milan #3/R est:2200-2400

Works on paper
£1923 $2981 €3000 31.12.99 (113x91cm-44x36in) s.i.d.1999-2000 verso plotter painting. 4-Dec-2 Finarte, Milan #456/R est:3200
£2568 $4005 €3800 Untitled (120x120cm-47x47in) plotter painting exec.2000. 26-Mar-3 Finarte Semenzato, Milan #140/R

BASILICO, Gabriele (1944-) Italian
Photographs
£3000 $4620 €4500 Roma 2000, colosseo (90x100cm-35x39in) gelatin silver print executed 2000 prov.lit. 22-Oct-2 Christie's, London #59/R est:3000-4000

BASILIDES, Barna (1903-1967) Hungarian
£2286 $3543 €3429 Hilly landscape (56x71cm-22x28in) s. 6-Dec-2 Kieselbach, Budapest #60/R (H.F 850000)
£5916 $9170 €8874 Winter in Budapest (80x100cm-31x39in) s. 6-Dec-2 Kieselbach, Budapest #37/R (H.F 2200000)

BASKERVILLE, Charles (1896-1994) American
£258 $400 €387 Bride for the pasha (89x74cm-35x29in) s. 7-Dec-2 Neal Auction Company, New Orleans #934
£288 $450 €432 After the rain, Umbria (14x16cm-6x6in) s. s.i.d.1952 verso masonite. 12-Apr-3 Weschler, Washington #563/R

BASKIN, Leonard (1922-2000) American
Sculpture
£1037 $1700 €1504 Dutch artist (18x28x25cm-7x11x10in) s.num.9/15 bronze prov. 1-Jun-3 Wright, Chicago #252/R est:2500-3500
£1051 $1640 €1577 Man with birds (76cm-30in) s.d.1974 brown pat.bronze prov. 5-Nov-2 Bukowskis, Stockholm #240/R est:15000-20000 (S.KR 15000)
£11728 $19000 €17592 Owl (51cm-20in) brown pat. bronze cast 1960 prov.exhib.lit. 21-May-3 Sotheby's, New York #30/R est:10000-15000
£21341 $35000 €30944 Apotheosis (160x183x86cm-63x72x34in) carved oak prov. 1-Jun-3 Wright, Chicago #250/R est:25000-35000

Works on paper
£258 $400 €387 Disco Medusa (18x28cm-7x11in) s.d.1981 pen ink W/C prov. 2-Nov-2 North East Auctions, Portsmouth #112

£318 $500 €477 Head of a man (43x56cm-17x22in) s.d.1956 pen ink exhib. 14-Dec-2 Weschler, Washington #721/R
£350 $550 €525 Portrait of a man (25x18cm-10x7in) s.d.55 pen ink. 14-Dec-2 Weschler, Washington #720/R
£579 $950 €840 Standing man (54x37cm-21x15in) s.d. pen ink wash. 5-Jun-3 Swann Galleries, New York #14/R
£915 $1500 €1327 Eagle headed Zeus (100x66cm-39x26in) s.d. pen ink wash. 5-Jun-3 Swann Galleries, New York #12/R est:1000-1500
£915 $1500 €1327 Standing male nude (90x46cm-35x18in) s.i. brush ink pencil exhib. 5-Jun-3 Swann Galleries, New York #13/R est:2000-3000
£915 $1500 €1327 Erithrean Sibyl (78x48cm-31x19in) s.i.d. pen ink. 5-Jun-3 Swann Galleries, New York #15/R est:800-1200
£1098 $1800 €1592 Self portrait (58x38cm-23x15in) s.d. pen ink W/C. 5-Jun-3 Swann Galleries, New York #11/R

BASOLI, Antonio (1774-1848) Italian

Works on paper

£1600 $2672 €2320 View of a fantastic Piazza (38x49cm-15x19in) s.i.d.1846 pen ink W/C black chk. 9-Jul-3 Bonhams, Knightsbridge #4/R est:1000-1500

BASQUIAT, Jean Michel (1960-1988) American

£7911 $12500 €11867 Vehement alley cats (51x44cm-20x17in) oilstick on paper painted c.1982 prov. 12-Nov-2 Phillips, New York #243/R est:6000-8000
£21875 $35000 €32813 Untitled (56x76cm-22x30in) col oil crayon painted 1985 prov.exhib. 14-May-3 Sotheby's, New York #398/R est:25000-35000
£22152 $35000 €33228 Untitled (76x57cm-30x22in) s.d.83 verso col oilstick masking tape gouache paper collage prov. 14-Nov-2 Christie's, Rockefeller NY #395/R est:20000-30000
£37500 $60000 €56250 Rammelzee/toxic video (28x40cm-11x16in) oil marker one VHS paper set of six executed 1983 prov. 16-May-3 Phillips, New York #138/R est:50000-70000
£49057 $75547 €78000 Untitled (214x214cm-84x84in) acrylic xerox prov.lit. 26-Oct-2 Cornette de St.Cyr, Paris #77/R est:90000
£50633 $80000 €75950 Untitled (76x101cm-30x40in) s.verso acrylic col ink col crayon chl graphite gouache board. 14-Nov-2 Christie's, Rockefeller NY #390/R est:70000-90000
£58000 $89320 €87000 Robotman and woman (56x76cm-22x30in) s.verso oilstick felt tip pen pencil painted c.1982 exhib.lit. 22-Oct-2 Sotheby's, London #390/R est:40000-60000
£85443 $135000 €128165 Untitled (76x56cm-30x22in) s.d.82 verso oil col crayon paper prov. 13-Nov-2 Sotheby's, New York #558/R est:150000-200000
£132911 $210000 €199367 Untitled (89x79cm-35x31in) s. i.d.1981 verso oil oilstick col trasfer prov. 12-Nov-2 Sotheby's, New York #66/R est:150000-200000
£160000 $246400 €240000 Pedestrian 2 (153x137cm-60x54in) s. i.d.1984 verso acrylic oilstick prov.exhib.lit. 22-Oct-2 Sotheby's, London #391/R est:120000-150000
£187500 $300000 €281250 Skin flint (218x179cm-86x70in) s. i.d.84 verso acrylic oilstick col transfer collage on canvas. 14-May-3 Sotheby's, New York #400/R est:300000-400000
£212500 $340000 €318750 Santo 1 (91x91cm-36x36in) s.i.d.82 verso oil acrylic col crayon paper on canvas prov.lit. 14-May-3 Christie's, Rockefeller NY #48/R est:250000-350000
£250000 $400000 €375000 Busted atlas 2 (152x152cm-60x60in) s. s.i.verso acrylic canvas on wood prov.exhib.lit. 13-May-3 Sotheby's, New York #40/R est:400000-600000
£300000 $462000 €450000 Pharynx (218x172cm-86x68in) s. i.d.1985 verso acrylic oilstick xerox collage on canvas prov. 22-Oct-2 Sotheby's, London #394/R est:300000-400000
£310000 $517700 €465000 Untitled - Crown (185x253cm-73x100in) s. acrylic oilstick xerox collage paper on linen exc.88 prov.lit. 25-Jun-3 Sotheby's, London #40/R est:150000-200000
£400000 $640000 €600000 Untitled (104x179cm-41x70in) s.on stretcher acrylic oilstick on burlap painted 1980 prov.exhib. 14-May-3 Sotheby's, New York #326/R est:250000-350000
£401899 $635000 €602849 Untitled (198x129cm-78x51in) acrylic painted 1981 prov.lit. 13-Nov-2 Christie's, Rockefeller NY #75/R est:400000-600000
£420000 $646800 €630000 Made in Japan I (154x98cm-61x39in) s. i.d.82 verso acrylic oilstick paper collage on canvas prov. 22-Oct-2 Sotheby's, London #397/R est:200000-300000
£443038 $700000 €664557 Stroll (183x183cm-72x72in) s. i.d.82 verso acrylic oilstick canvas on tied wood supports. 13-Nov-2 Christie's, Rockefeller NY #33/R est:500000-700000
£569620 $900000 €854430 In this case (197x189cm-78x74in) s. i.d.1983 verso acrylic oilstick prov.lit. 12-Nov-2 Sotheby's, New York #26/R est:1000000-1500000
£576923 $900000 €865385 Dos cabezas II (213x213cm-84x84in) acrylic oil stick on canvas prov.exhib.lit. 11-Nov-2 Phillips, New York #33/R est:1000000-1500000
£750000 $1200000 €1125000 Pater (213x183cm-84x72in) s.i.d.1982 verso acrylic oil col oilstick prov.exhib.lit. 14-May-3 Christie's, Rockefeller NY #27/R est:1500000-2000000
£961539 $1500000 €1442309 Untitled (183x244cm-72x96in) s.d.1982 acrylic oilstick on plywood diptych prov.exhib.lit. 11-Nov-2 Phillips, New York #30/R est:1500000-2500000

Works on paper

£5903 $9385 €8500 Portrait of Shannon Dawson (35x28cm-14x11in) ink prov.exhib.lit. 29-Apr-3 Artcurial Briest, Paris #478/R est:8000-10000
£9062 $14500 €13593 Untitled (15x20cm-6x8in) i.verso black marker blue ballpoint pen executed c.1981 prov. 16-May-3 Phillips, New York #149/R est:8000-12000
£12179 $19122 €19000 Soothsayer (48x35cm-19x14in) s.d.83 wax crayon. 11-Dec-2 Artcurial Briest, Paris #742/R est:25000
£12821 $20128 €20000 Untitled (76x56cm-30x22in) pastel exec.1983 prov. 11-Dec-2 Artcurial Briest, Paris #745/R est:25000
£16456 $26000 €24684 Skull (18x18cm-7x7in) crayon col pencil prov. 13-Nov-2 Sotheby's, New York #600/R est:20000-30000
£18987 $30000 €28481 Untitled (72x103cm-28x41in) s.d.87 col crayons graphite prov. 14-Nov-2 Christie's, Rockefeller NY #391/R est:40000-60000
£19000 $29260 €28500 Untitled (35x27cm-14x11in) s.verso col pencil executed 1981 prov.exhib. 22-Oct-2 Sotheby's, London #389/R est:15000-20000
£23077 $36231 €36000 Trick black soap (48x35cm-19x14in) s.d.83 wax crayon. 11-Dec-2 Artcurial Briest, Paris #741/R est:40000
£25316 $40000 €37974 Skeleton (76x56cm-30x22in) s.d.85 pencil crayon prov. 13-Nov-2 Sotheby's, New York #562/R est:35000-45000
£26000 $43420 €37700 Muscles of right orbit (57x76cm-22x30in) s.i.d.1985 MAR 28 wax crayon prov. 26-Jun-3 Sotheby's, London #263/R est:18000-25000
£26282 $41263 €41000 Untitled (76x56cm-30x22in) s.verso wax crayon prov.exhib.lit. 15-Dec-2 Perrin, Versailles #151/R est:55000
£28481 $45000 €42722 Untitled (107x91cm-42x36in) wax crayon on mylar executed c.1983 prov. 14-Nov-2 Christie's, Rockefeller NY #399/R est:50000-70000
£28481 $45000 €42722 Untitled (107x91cm-42x36in) wax crayon on mylar executed c.1983 prov. 14-Nov-2 Christie's, Rockefeller NY #400/R est:50000-70000
£31646 $50000 €47469 Untitled (134x101cm-53x40in) s. wax crayon on mylar executed c.1983 prov. 14-Nov-2 Christie's, Rockefeller NY #398/R est:60000-80000
£34014 $54082 €50000 Squelette (76x56cm-30x22in) s.d.1985 col crayon pastel graphite prov. 24-Mar-3 Cornette de St.Cyr, Paris #83/R est:70000
£43038 $68000 €64557 Untitled (134x101cm-53x40in) wax crayon on mylar executed c.1983 prov. 14-Nov-2 Christie's, Rockefeller NY #397/R est:60000-80000
£50566 $77872 €80400 Untitled (100x70cm-39x28in) wax crayon exhib.lit. 26-Oct-2 Cornette de St.Cyr, Paris #81/R est:70000

BASQUIAT, Jean Michel and WARHOL, Andy (20th C) American

£21875 $35000 €32813 Amorosi - painted with Francesco Clemente (128x180cm-50x71in) s.d.1984 overlap oilstick acrylic silkscreen prov. 14-May-3 Sotheby's, New York #422/R est:40000-60000

BASSANO, Francesco (15/16th C) Italian

£17000 $26690 €25500 Flight into Egypt (42x92cm-17x36in) prov. 12-Dec-2 Sotheby's, London #112/R est:8000-12000

BASSANO, Jacobo (school) (1515-1592) Italian

£3396 $5230 €5400 Announcing Jesus to the shepherds (104x147cm-41x58in) 23-Oct-2 Finarte, Rome #433/R

BASSANO, Jacobo (studio) (1515-1592) Italian

£5000 $7800 €7500 Baptism of Saint Ludmilla (186x133cm-73x52in) prov. 19-Sep-2 Christie's, Kensington #275/R est:2000-4000
£8228 $13000 €13000 Abraham leaves for Canaan (74x96cm-29x38in) 2-Dec-2 Finarte, Milan #111/R est:15000
£13000 $20410 €19500 Mountainous winter landscape with peasants gathering firewood (75x107cm-30x42in) 12-Dec-2 Sotheby's, London #118/R est:10000-15000
£32000 $53440 €46400 Annunciation to the shepherds (128x119cm-50x47in) prov.lit. 9-Jul-3 Christie's, London #105/R est:20000-30000

BASSANO, Jacobo (style) (1515-1592) Italian

£5532 $8574 €8298 At the barrel makers workshop (89x133cm-35x52in) bears sig. 3-Dec-2 Bukowskis, Stockholm #429/R est:50000-60000 (S.KR 78000)

£12000 $20040 €17400 Street market with townsfolk dressed for carnival (136x183cm-54x72in) 11-Jul-3 Christie's, Kensington #189/R est:8000-12000

BASSANO, Leandro (1557-1622) Italian
£3793 $6031 €5500 Portrait of Bernardino Morando (25x21cm-10x8in) i.verso board. 9-Mar-3 Semenzato, Venice #34/R
£6500 $10205 €9750 Entombment (19x25cm-7x10in) copper prov. 10-Dec-2 Bonhams, New Bond Street #260/R est:4000-6000
£11000 $17160 €16500 Queen of Sheba before King Solomon (53x41cm-21x16in) copper prov. 10-Apr-3 Sotheby's, London #23/R est:12000
£19231 $29808 €30000 Deluge (182x266cm-72x105in) indis.sig. 9-Dec-2 Thierry & Lannon, Brest #224/R est:30000
£43972 $71234 €62000 Ecce Homo (109x90cm-43x35in) lit. 20-May-3 Babuino, Rome #30/R

BASSANO, Leandro (attrib) (1557-1622) Italian
Works on paper
£2703 $4216 €4000 Young man (13x10cm-5x4in) i. crayon sanguine. 26-Mar-3 Piasa, Paris #2/R

BASSANO, Leandro (circle) (1557-1622) Italian
£6000 $9420 €9000 Saint Francis receiving the Stigmata (51x47cm-20x19in) 10-Dec-2 Sotheby's, Olympia #308/R est:6000-8000

BASSEN, Bartholomeus van (1590-1652) Dutch
£10191 $15898 €16000 Interior of an imaginary classical church with elegant couple (38x50cm-15x20in) bears sig.d.1639 panel prov. 5-Nov-2 Sotheby's, Amsterdam #42/R est:10000-15000
£36943 $57631 €58000 Church interior with elegant company conversing in the aisle (48x69cm-19x27in) indis.sig.d.1640 panel exhib. 6-Nov-2 Christie's, Amsterdam #77/R est:30000-58000

BASSEN, Bartholomeus van (attrib) (1590-1652) Dutch
£851 $1345 €1277 Church interior with monk asking elegant couple for money (91x143cm-36x56in) 2-Dec-2 Rasmussen, Copenhagen #1634/R (D.KR 10000)
£1284 $2003 €1900 Christ et la femme adultere (34x47cm-13x19in) panel. 28-Mar-3 Piasa, Paris #31/R

BASSETT, Reveau Mott (1897-1981) American
£2130 $3450 €3089 Two ducks (41x51cm-16x20in) 23-May-3 Altermann Galleries, Santa Fe #212
£6164 $9000 €9246 Ducks landscape (61x76cm-24x30in) 18-May-2 Altermann Galleries, Santa Fe #225/R

BASSETTI, Marcantonio (1588-1630) Italian
£148148 $240000 €222222 Dead Christ supported by the Virgin and Mary Magdalen (38x29cm-15x11in) oil on slate. 24-Jan-3 Christie's, Rockefeller NY #83/R est:80000-120000

BASSFORD, Wallace (1900-) American
£385 $600 €578 Palm Beach interlude (9x8cm-4x3in) s. s.i.verso. 9-Nov-2 Sloan, North Bethesda #620/R
£449 $700 €674 Roses and anemonies (49x41cm-19x16in) s. s.i.verso. 9-Nov-2 Sloan, North Bethesda #620a/R
£528 $850 €792 Summer swim (99x69cm-39x27in) s. prov. 19-Feb-3 Doyle, New York #28

BASSINGTHWAITE, Paul (1963-) British
£280 $445 €420 Midday (45x36cm-18x14in) s.verso. 26-Feb-3 Sotheby's, Olympia #320/R
£360 $583 €540 Path to mountain (51x41cm-20x16in) s.verso. 20-May-3 Bonhams, Knightsbridge #118/R

BASSINGTON, A (20th C) British?
£400 $632 €600 At the start (44x49cm-17x19in) s.d.99 pencil W/C. 28-Nov-2 Christie's, Kensington #198/R

BASSMAN, Lillian (1947-) American?
Photographs
£2500 $4050 €3750 Fashion study, Evelyn Tripp, for Harper's Baxaar (35x28cm-14x11in) s.verso silver print. 22-May-3 Sotheby's, London #169/R est:2000-3000

BASSO, Ferdinando del (1887-1973) Italian
£897 $1409 €1400 Italien market scene (14x22cm-6x9in) paper on board. 10-Dec-2 Dorotheum, Vienna #10/R

BASTEDA, L (19/20th C) ?
Works on paper
£1500 $2490 €2175 Spanish general cargo steamers Adela Roca and J Jover Serra (38x74cm-15x29in) s.i.d.1903 W/C bodycol pair. 12-Jun-3 Christie's, London #531/R est:1000-1500

BASTERT, Nicolaas (1854-1939) Dutch
£545 $849 €818 Exterior of a barn with green doors (31x43cm-12x17in) s. 11-Nov-2 Stephan Welz, Johannesburg #428 (SA.R 8500)
£637 $994 €1000 View of Breukelen on the River Vecht (26x36cm-10x14in) s. board. 6-Nov-2 Vendue Huis, Gravenhage #554
£1842 $2984 €2800 View from Nieuwersluis on Weerestein (42x58cm-17x23in) s. 21-Jan-3 Christie's, Amsterdam #332/R est:2000-3000
£3503 $5395 €5500 Gezigt op Loenen aan de Vecht (40x60cm-16x24in) s. s.stretcher. 3-Sep-2 Christie's, Amsterdam #168/R est:2500-3500
£4167 $6625 €6000 Country idyll (36x58cm-14x23in) s. prov. 29-Apr-3 Christie's, Amsterdam #147/R est:4000-6000
£4403 $6780 €7000 Zomerdag Aan de Vecht (63x100cm-25x39in) s. prov. 22-Oct-2 Sotheby's, Amsterdam #110/R est:8000-12000

BASTET, Jean Tancrede Celestin (1858-1942) French
Works on paper
£252 $392 €400 Pommiers en fleurs (34x24cm-13x9in) W/C. 14-Oct-2 Blache, Grenoble #19

BASTIAAN, A (?) ?
£380 $592 €600 Sous bois (53x73cm-21x29in) 16-Sep-2 Amberes, Antwerp #175

BASTIANI, Lazzaro (1425-1512) Italian
£4200 $6510 €6300 Pentecost (84x126cm-33x50in) panel. 31-Oct-2 Sotheby's, Olympia #6/R
£7595 $12000 €12000 Praying in the olive grove (36x26cm-14x10in) board. 29-Nov-2 Semenzato, Venice #615/R est:5000-6000

BASTIANUTTO, Riccardo (?) Italian
£238 $379 €350 Wood at dusk (80x60cm-31x24in) s. 1-Mar-3 Stadion, Trieste #192

BASTIEN LEPAGE, Jules (attrib) (1848-1884) French
£1560 $2418 €2340 Woman at well (54x74cm-21x29in) 3-Dec-2 Bukowskis, Stockholm #330/R est:25000-30000 (S.KR 22000)

BASTIEN, Alfred (1873-1955) Belgian
£285 $444 €450 Vue des dunes (38x55cm-15x22in) s. 15-Oct-2 Horta, Bruxelles #239
£308 $477 €480 Sous-bois au Rouge-Cloitre (38x56cm-15x22in) s. panel. 9-Dec-2 Horta, Bruxelles #443
£336 $540 €500 Vase de fleurs (30x22cm-12x9in) s. panel. 18-Feb-3 Vanderkindere, Brussels #144
£380 $592 €600 La source de l'empereur (72x112cm-28x44in) s. 15-Oct-2 Vanderkindere, Brussels #76
£387 $624 €550 Still life with Delft ewer, oranges, garlic and melon (60x50cm-24x20in) s. 12-May-3 Bernaerts, Antwerp #602/R
£409 $634 €650 Bord d'etang en automne (38x56cm-15x22in) s. 1-Oct-2 Palais de Beaux Arts, Brussels #430
£432 $691 €600 Chasseur en Afrique (54x30cm-21x12in) s.i.d.1906 panel. 19-May-3 Horta, Bruxelles #31
£476 $757 €700 Etang du rouge cloitre (36x48cm-14x19in) s. panel. 19-Mar-3 Hotel des Ventes Mosan, Brussels #233
£506 $790 €800 Paysage anime en Algerie (36x55cm-14x22in) s. panel. 15-Oct-2 Vanderkindere, Brussels #46
£538 $834 €850 Etang arbore (48x60cm-19x24in) s. panel. 24-Sep-2 Galerie Moderne, Brussels #797
£548 $855 €800 Vase fleuri de roses (42x34cm-17x13in) s. panel. 14-Apr-3 Horta, Bruxelles #324
£552 $877 €800 Nature morte au homard (54x64cm-21x25in) s. 4-Mar-3 Palais de Beaux Arts, Brussels #282
£612 $978 €850 Cruche, poissons et fruits sur une table (37x55cm-15x22in) s. panel. 13-May-3 Palais de Beaux Arts, Brussels #212
£633 $987 €1000 Still life with flowers and fruit (54x68cm-21x27in) s. 21-Oct-2 Bernaerts, Antwerp #109/R est:1000-1250
£637 $994 €1000 Marche Orientaliste (22x34cm-9x13in) s. panel. 11-Nov-2 Horta, Bruxelles #704
£662 $1079 €1000 Vaches au pre (38x55cm-15x22in) s. panel. 17-Feb-3 Horta, Bruxelles #24
£764 $1192 €1200 Le bain au clair de lune (45x65cm-18x26in) s. i.verso canvas on panel. 11-Nov-2 Horta, Bruxelles #703
£1154 $1812 €1800 Forest walk (81x102cm-32x40in) s.d.1937. 19-Nov-2 Hamilton Osborne King, Dublin #421/R est:1000-1500
£1503 $2420 €2300 Etang au rouge-cloitre (70x90cm-28x35in) s. 14-Jan-3 Vanderkindere, Brussels #29 est:2000-3000
£1509 $2325 €2400 Nature morte de fleurs (80x100cm-31x39in) s. 22-Oct-2 Campo, Vlaamse Kaai #407/R
Works on paper
£323 $510 €500 Sous-bois enneige. s. gouache. 17-Dec-2 Galerie Moderne, Brussels #872
£452 $714 €700 Vue de port. s. mixed media. 17-Dec-2 Galerie Moderne, Brussels #909/R

£769 $1207 €1200 Cavalier arabe (48x59cm-19x23in) s.i.d.18 pastel gouache W/C. 10-Dec-2 Tajan, Paris #112 est:2000

BASTIN, Ernest (c.1870-?) Belgian
Sculpture
£1218 $1912 €1900 Cheval de trait (53cm-21in) s.st.f. Usines Vojave brown pat bronze marble socle. 10-Dec-2 Vanderkindere, Brussels #151/R est:625-875

BASTIN, Henri (1896-1979) Australian
£307 $457 €461 Dance (50x60cm-20x24in) s.d.1971 enamel on board. 27-Aug-2 Christie's, Melbourne #276 (A.D 800)
£320 $515 €480 Sunrise (48x74cm-19x29in) s.d.1968 acrylic paper on board. 6-May-3 Christie's, Melbourne #254 (A.D 800)
£789 $1199 €1184 Little wonder waterfall (44x59cm-17x23in) s.d.1975 enamel board. 28-Aug-2 Deutscher-Menzies, Melbourne #257/R (A.D 2200)
Works on paper
£351 $533 €527 Native ware (35x47cm-14x19in) s.d.1964 mixed media. 19-Aug-2 Joel, Victoria #269 est:1000-1500 (A.D 1000)
£383 $571 €575 Gum trees (35x53cm-14x21in) s.d.1964 gouache W/C. 27-Aug-2 Christie's, Melbourne #173a est:500-800 (A.D 1000)
£430 $654 €645 Central Australian landscape (35x46cm-14x18in) s.d.1959 W/C. 28-Aug-2 Deutscher-Menzies, Melbourne #127/R (A.D 1200)

BATAILLE, Willem (1867-1933) Belgian
£321 $503 €500 Lever du soleil dans les dunes (30x40cm-12x16in) s. panel. 19-Nov-2 Vanderkindere, Brussels #64
£414 $654 €600 Fermette fleurie (45x55cm-18x22in) s. 2-Apr-3 Vanderkindere, Brussels #534

BATCHELDER, Stephen (1849-1932) British
Works on paper
£260 $434 €377 Wherries on the Norfolk Broads approaching storm (25x41cm-10x16in) s. W/C. 20-Jun-3 Keys, Aylsham #579/R
£260 $434 €377 Reedham (30x48cm-12x19in) s.d.1920 W/C. 20-Jun-3 Keys, Aylsham #580
£270 $421 €405 Sailing barges (13x26cm-5x10in) s. W/C. 17-Sep-2 Bonhams, Sevenoaks #237
£300 $489 €450 Wroxham Broad (28x53cm-11x21in) s.i. 14-Feb-3 Keys, Aylsham #600
£300 $501 €435 Acle bridge (28x58cm-11x23in) s.d.29.6.26 W/C. 20-Jun-3 Keys, Aylsham #585
£300 $495 €435 Beautiful Belaugh, Broadland (32x59cm-13x23in) s. i.verso W/C. 1-Jul-3 Bonhams, Norwich #117/R
£325 $504 €488 Windmill in winter landscape (23x15cm-9x6in) s. W/C. 24-Sep-2 Rowley Fine Art, Newmarket #321/R
£440 $726 €638 Old drainage mill, near Stalham (19x13cm-7x5in) s. W/C. 1-Jul-3 Bonhams, Norwich #61
£450 $734 €675 Braodland landscape with cattle on bank in foreground (15x23cm-6x9in) s. W/C. 14-Feb-3 Keys, Aylsham #594/R
£550 $864 €825 Yacht and wherry on the Norfolk Broads (13x8cm-5x3in) s. W/C pair oval. 13-Dec-2 Keys, Aylsham #583
£580 $957 €841 Yachts on the Broads, Reedham ferry (20x31cm-8x12in) s. W/C. 1-Jul-3 Bonhams, Norwich #98
£600 $978 €900 Drover with cattle and child in lane (15x23cm-6x9in) s. W/C. 14-Feb-3 Keys, Aylsham #590/R
£600 $1002 €870 Fishing fleet in Lowestoft harbour (15x23cm-6x9in) s. W/C. 20-Jun-3 Keys, Aylsham #575/R
£600 $990 €870 On the Broads (20x16cm-8x6in) s.d.1885 W/C pair. 1-Jul-3 Bonhams, Norwich #102
£620 $973 €930 Buckenham Ferry, River Yare. South Walsham Broad (10x15cm-4x6in) mono.i. W/C pair. 13-Dec-2 Keys, Aylsham #582
£650 $1014 €975 Near Reedham, Norfolk (28x43cm-11x17in) s.d.1890 W/C. 18-Oct-2 Keys, Aylsham #611/R
£650 $1007 €975 Single masted sailing boat moored beside Reeds (13x25cm-5x10in) s. W/C. 24-Sep-2 Rowley Fine Art, Newmarket #318/R
£680 $1108 €1020 Wherry passing Irstead Church and a sailing boat at the entrance to Salhouse (13x25cm-5x10in) s. W/C pair. 14-Feb-3 Keys, Aylsham #592/R
£720 $1116 €1080 Martham Church from Heigham Sands (12x25cm-5x10in) s. W/C bodycol. 30-Sep-2 Bonhams, Ipswich #356/R
£720 $1174 €1080 Wherries and yachts near St Bennets Abbey (33x48cm-13x19in) s.d.1884 W/C. 14-Feb-3 Keys, Aylsham #601/R
£750 $1223 €1125 Worn out cider ovens reach, River Bure, Yarmouth (28x61cm-11x24in) s. W/C. 14-Feb-3 Keys, Aylsham #598/R
£750 $1223 €1125 Wherry on the Norfolk Broads (20x43cm-8x17in) s. W/C. 14-Feb-3 Keys, Aylsham #602/R
£850 $1386 €1275 Distant scene, Yarmouth (13x25cm-5x10in) s. W/C. 14-Feb-3 Keys, Aylsham #589/R
£900 $1467 €1350 Rain and shine, Irstead Church from Barton Broad (23x33cm-9x13in) s. W/C. 14-Feb-3 Keys, Aylsham #591/R
£900 $1404 €1350 Horning ferry (15x28cm-6x11in) s.i. W/C. 11-Apr-3 Keys, Aylsham #580/R
£950 $1473 €1425 River Yare (26x20cm-10x8in) s. W/C htd white sold with a companion. 30-Sep-2 Bonhams, Ipswich #316/R
£1000 $1670 €1450 Figures on a white hulled yacht on the Norfolk Broads (28x41cm-11x16in) s. W/C. 20-Jun-3 Keys, Aylsham #578/R est:1000-1200
£1150 $1794 €1725 From back of GER Station. Town river scene and old wherries, Nort River (27x58cm-11x23in) s.i. W/C two. 5-Nov-2 Bristol Auction Rooms #937/R est:1200-1500
£1150 $1921 €1668 Mill at Pennygate, grapes mill (36x28cm-14x11in) s. W/C prov. 20-Jun-3 Keys, Aylsham #583/R est:1200-1600
£1750 $2713 €2625 Yachts and wherry on Oulton Broad (23x34cm-9x13in) s. i.verso W/C. 30-Sep-2 Bonhams, Ipswich #350/R est:1000-1500
£1750 $2853 €2625 White hulled yachts on the Norfolk Broads on a summers day (28x43cm-11x17in) s. W/C. 14-Feb-3 Keys, Aylsham #599/R est:1200-1500
£2000 $3260 €3000 Eel set near Wroxham Broad, river Bure (30x53cm-12x21in) s. W/C. 14-Feb-3 Keys, Aylsham #597/R est:900-1200
£2600 $4238 €3900 Wherries on the Norfolk Broads passing Irstead Church (38x61cm-15x24in) s.d.1908 W/C. 14-Feb-3 Keys, Aylsham #603/R est:1500-2000

BATCHELOR, Roland (1889-1990) British
Works on paper
£360 $565 €540 London docks (23x30cm-9x12in) s.d.51 W/C. 16-Dec-2 Bonhams, Bury St Edmunds #415
£360 $565 €540 Boats by the River Deben at Bawdsey (12x17cm-5x7in) s.i. ink W/C. 16-Dec-2 Bonhams, Bury St Edmunds #417/R
£400 $652 €600 Normandy, a bustling town square (20x18cm-8x7in) s.i. W/C pen ink. 11-Feb-3 Fellows & Sons, Birmingham #84/R
£420 $659 €630 Boulogne (16x17cm-6x7in) s.i. W/C. 15-Apr-3 Bonhams, Knightsbridge #61/R
£720 $1188 €1044 Springtime in Paris (21x23cm-8x9in) s. W/C. 1-Jul-3 Bearnes, Exeter #415/R

BATE, Rutledge (1891-?) American
£344 $550 €499 Woman painting on the shore (25x30cm-10x12in) s. 17-May-3 CRN Auctions, Cambridge #29

BATELLI, Chiti (1932-) Italian
£507 $791 €750 Landscape (50x70cm-20x28in) s.d.89 s.d.verso. 28-Mar-3 Farsetti, Prato #474

BATEMAN, Arthur (1883-1970) British
£320 $502 €480 Landscape with farm buildings (51x61cm-20x24in) s.d.49. 21-Nov-2 Tennants, Leyburn #831
£480 $754 €720 Richmond, Yorkshire (53x74cm-21x29in) s. 21-Nov-2 Tennants, Leyburn #830

BATEMAN, Henry Mayo (1887-1970) British
Works on paper
£600 $930 €900 Demonstrator at the ice rink slips (36x24cm-14x9in) s.i. pencil pen black ink prov. 4-Dec-2 Christie's, Kensington #175/R
£650 $1007 €975 Local snooker champion shows Olympic games form (31x25cm-12x10in) s.i. pencil pen black ink prov. 4-Dec-2 Christie's, Kensington #179/R
£700 $1148 €1050 General (10x11cm-4x4in) s.d.18 sold with a drawing by William Heath Robinson. 6-Jun-3 Christie's, London #102/R
£850 $1377 €1275 Diamonds, a game of bridge (24x23cm-9x9in) s. pen wash. 21-Jan-3 Bonhams, Knightsbridge #60/R
£900 $1395 €1350 The Smythe-Robinsons of Tidlington take their meals in a cool shady spot (37x22cm-15x9in) s.i.d.1913 pencil pen black ink grey wash prov. 4-Dec-2 Christie's, Kensington #173/R
£1100 $1760 €1650 Plumber (28x20cm-11x8in) pen ink prov. 11-Mar-3 Bonhams, New Bond Street #143/R est:1000-1500
£1300 $2015 €1950 Footballer tries chess (30x22cm-12x9in) s.i. pencil pen black ink prov. 4-Dec-2 Christie's, Kensington #177/R est:800-1200
£1600 $2480 €2400 Private view (36x25cm-14x10in) s.i.d.1914 pencil pen black ink prov. 4-Dec-2 Christie's, Kensington #174/R est:1000-1500

BATEMAN, James (1815-1849) British
£320 $502 €480 Leda and the swan (34x39cm-13x15in) s. panel. 10-Dec-2 Rosebery Fine Art, London #525
£11500 $17940 €17250 Temptation, a terrier and a sleeping mastiff outside a barn (71x91cm-28x36in) s.indis.d.18. 10-Apr-3 Tennants, Leyburn #1025/R est:7000-9000

BATEMAN, James (1893-1959) British
£1250 $1938 €1875 End of day, farmer watering his horses in a stream (18x25cm-7x10in) panel. 18-Jul-2 Neales, Nottingham #700 est:400-800

BATEMAN, Piers (1947-) Australian
£281 $427 €422 Panton Hills (62x76cm-24x30in) s.d.68 board. 19-Aug-2 Joel, Victoria #305 (A.D 800)

BATEMAN, Robert (1930-) Canadian
£1200 $1944 €1800 Mute swan (21x25cm-8x10in) s.d.1985 board. 20-May-3 Sotheby's, Olympia #63/R est:400-600
£4032 $6371 €6048 Mouse country (43x78cm-17x31in) s. masonite prov. 18-Nov-2 Sotheby's, Toronto #131/R est:10000-15000 (C.D 10000)
Works on paper
£900 $1458 €1350 Bison head. Lion (25x34cm-10x13in) s. pen ink two prov. 20-May-3 Sotheby's, Olympia #65/R

BATES, David (c.1841-1921) British
£1100 $1749 €1650 Return from the village (21x31cm-8x12in) s. s.i.verso. 5-Mar-3 Bonhams, Bury St Edmunds #395 est:600-900
£1150 $1783 €1725 Stream near Bromsgrove (20x15cm-8x6in) s. i. verso board. 2-Oct-2 Bonhams, Knowle #60 est:700-1000
£1200 $1896 €1800 On the Llugwy near Capel Curig (35x52cm-14x20in) s.d.1903 s.i.d.verso. 2-Dec-2 Bonhams, Bath #119/R est:1500-2000
£1442 $2250 €2163 Moel Slabod, North Wales. 21-Sep-2 Harvey Clar, Oakland #1406
£1451 $2250 €2177 Landscape with woman and child (48x74cm-19x29in) s.d.1877. 7-Dec-2 Neal Auction Company, New Orleans #287/R est:2500-3500
£1500 $2475 €2175 Path through the woods, Capel Curig (58x43cm-23x17in) s.i.verso. 3-Jul-3 Duke & Son, Dorchester #239 est:600-1200
£1600 $2528 €2400 By the brook, Mathon (49x75cm-19x30in) s.d.1887 i.d.verso. 2-Apr-3 Edgar Horn, Eastbourne #300/R est:1000-1500
£1700 $2652 €2550 Tom's mill, Betws-y-Coed (46x36cm-18x14in) s.d.1895. 8-Oct-2 Bonhams, Knightsbridge #67/R est:500-700
£1800 $3006 €2610 Windy day (40x61cm-16x24in) s.d.1873. 17-Jun-3 Bonhams, New Bond Street #83/R est:2000-3000
£2000 $3140 €3000 Near Bettws-y-Coed (59x90cm-23x35in) s.d.1891. 20-Nov-2 Anthemion, Cardiff #582 est:2000-2500
£2483 $3823 €3725 Northern landscape with farm and woman holding basket, summer (41x61cm-16x24in) s.d.1909 i.verso. 27-Oct-2 Anders Antik, Landskrona #177/R est:10000-12000 (S.KR 36000)
£2585 $4110 €3800 English river landscape with children (31x46cm-12x18in) s.d.1888. 25-Feb-3 Dorotheum, Vienna #206/R est:1800-2000
£2600 $4030 €3900 Pool near Malvern (36x61cm-14x24in) s.d.1882 s.i.d.verso. 3-Dec-2 Sotheby's, Olympia #114/R est:2000-3000
£3200 $4864 €4800 Near Capel Curig (24x34cm-9x13in) s.d.1898 s.i.d.verso artist's board. 4-Jul-2 Mellors & Kirk, Nottingham #827 est:1000-1500
£3500 $5460 €5250 Hay sledge, North Wales (34x45cm-13x18in) s.d.1900 i.verso. 11-Sep-2 Bonhams, Newport #242/R est:3500-4500
£3500 $5530 €5250 Byways in Shakespeare's country (29x43cm-11x17in) s.d.1902 s.d. verso. 27-Nov-2 Peter Wilson, Nantwich #66/R est:2000-2500
£5000 $8150 €7500 Mother and child gathering wood by forest stream (44x34cm-17x13in) s.d.1881. 11-Feb-3 Fellows & Sons, Birmingham #14/R est:2000-2800
£5200 $8216 €7800 Near the Speech House, Forest of Dean (76x61cm-30x24in) s.d.1887 s.i.d.verso. 27-Nov-2 Bonhams, Knowle #212 est:2000-3000
£6329 $10000 €9494 Snowy egret (91x61cm-36x24in) s.i.d.87 overlap prov. 13-Nov-2 Sotheby's, New York #609/R est:12000-18000
Works on paper
£300 $474 €450 River scene with cattle and farm (25x36cm-10x14in) s.i.d.1904 W/C. 2-Apr-3 Edgar Horn, Eastbourne #285/R
£420 $651 €630 Mountain road, Betws-y-Coed (25x34cm-10x13in) s. W/C. 1-Oct-2 Fellows & Sons, Birmingham #144/R
£450 $707 €675 In the Welsh Hills (24x35cm-9x14in) s. W/C prov. 20-Nov-2 Sotheby's, Olympia #44/R
£480 $778 €696 Faggot gatherers by a stream (35x50cm-14x20in) s.d.1904 W/C. 29-Jul-3 Henry Adams, Chichester #467/R
£550 $902 €825 Figures on a wooded track (53x36cm-21x14in) s.d.1908 pencil W/C. 5-Jun-3 Christie's, Kensington #939
£600 $1002 €870 Driving sheep (36x52cm-14x20in) s.d.1908 pencil W/C htd white. 26-Jun-3 Mellors & Kirk, Nottingham #834/R
£2000 $3260 €3000 Welsh cottage near Talgarth. Path through the wood (36x26cm-14x10in) s. pencil W/C htd white pair. 13-Feb-3 Mellors & Kirk, Nottingham #778/R est:1200-1600

BATES, David (attrib) (c.1841-1921) British
£447 $711 €671 Summer landscape (41x52cm-16x20in) with sig. 5-Mar-3 Rasmussen, Copenhagen #1625 (D.KR 4800)

BATES, George William (1930-) Canadian
£238 $390 €357 Chrysanthemums (61x46cm-24x18in) s. i.verso. 6-Feb-3 Heffel, Vancouver #002/R (C.D 600)
£238 $390 €357 Lynn Creek (61x76cm-24x30in) s. i.verso. 6-Feb-3 Heffel, Vancouver #003/R (C.D 600)
£258 $423 €387 Neck and neck (51x76cm-20x30in) s. i.verso. 6-Feb-3 Heffel, Vancouver #004/R (C.D 650)

BATES, Maxwell (1906-1980) Canadian
£2621 $4141 €3932 Spring landscape (51x61cm-20x24in) s.d.1973 i.verso board. 14-Nov-2 Heffel, Vancouver #66/R est:3000-4000 (C.D 6500)
£2754 $4379 €4131 Field with distant trees (60x75cm-24x30in) s.i.d.1978. 23-Mar-3 Hodgins, Calgary #103/R est:4500-5500 (C.D 6500)
£3139 $5022 €4709 Old woman (75x60cm-30x24in) s.d.1969 prov.lit. 15-May-3 Heffel, Vancouver #87/R est:5000-7000 (C.D 7000)
£3778 $6196 €5478 Gloucester Road, London (60x75cm-24x30in) s.i. board exhib. 9-Jun-3 Hodgins, Calgary #337/R est:4000-5000 (C.D 8500)
Works on paper
£217 $339 €363 Untitled - We thought she had brought the burgermeister (37x29cm-15x11in) ink. 13-Apr-3 Levis, Calgary #405/R (C.D 500)
£467 $765 €677 Tropical morning (43x51cm-17x20in) W/C ink. 1-Jun-3 Levis, Calgary #5/R est:1250-1500 (C.D 1050)
£489 $802 €709 Untitled - owl (51x43cm-20x17in) W/C ink. 1-Jun-3 Levis, Calgary #4/R est:1250-1500 (C.D 1100)
£2130 $3408 €3195 Night of the nepenthe (51x36cm-20x14in) s.d.1967 W/C prov.exhib.lit. 15-May-3 Heffel, Vancouver #84/R est:3000-4000 (C.D 4750)

BATES, Robert (1943-) British
Works on paper
£400 $640 €600 Grotto on the Maharees (10x15cm-4x6in) s.d.2002 pen black ink W/C htd white. 15-May-3 Christie's, Kensington #195/R
£420 $672 €630 Winter's afternoon, Castlegregory (10x23cm-4x9in) s.d.2001 pen black ink W/C bodycol. 15-May-3 Christie's, Kensington #194/R
£450 $720 €675 Summer in my part of the county (19x38cm-7x15in) s.d.1999 pen black ink W/C prov. 15-May-3 Christie's, Kensington #196/R
£620 $967 €930 Returning to the valley of Vision (10x16cm-4x6in) s.d.1999 pencil pen ink W/C. 27-Mar-3 Christie's, Kensington #327/R

BATES, W E (1812-?) British
£1800 $3006 €2610 Pulling in the nets (31x56cm-12x22in) s.d.59. 25-Jun-3 Bonhams, Bury St Edmunds #575/R est:2000-3000

BATH, William (fl.1840-1851) British
£1500 $2355 €2250 Extensive river landscape with cattle watering in foreground (94x124cm-37x49in) s.indis d. 13-Dec-2 Keys, Aylsham #686/R est:1500-2000

BATHA, Gerard (1937-) South African
Works on paper
£387 $623 €581 Extensive landscape with houses in the distance (49x67cm-19x26in) s. W/C. 12-May-3 Stephan Welz, Johannesburg #184 est:5000-7000 (SA.R 4500)

BATONI, Pompeo (1708-1787) Italian
£110000 $182600 €165000 Portrait of Edward Augustus, Duke of York (135x99cm-53x39in) s.i. 12-Jun-3 Sotheby's, London #12/R est:80000-120000
£185185 $300000 €277778 Portrait of Henry Hutchinson O'Hara (74x61cm-29x24in) prov.lit. 23-Jan-3 Sotheby's, New York #74/R est:150000-200000

BATONI, Pompeo (attrib) (1708-1787) Italian
£7931 $12610 €11500 Venice triumphing (36x56cm-14x22in) lit. 9-Mar-3 Semenzato, Venice #24/R
£10000 $15700 €15000 Portrait of a Cardinal, holding a letter (97x71cm-38x28in) 12-Dec-2 Sotheby's, London #197/R est:8000-12000
Miniatures
£15000 $23400 €22500 Prince James Francis Edward Stuart, the Old Pretender, wearing grey coat (7cm-3xin) gilt frame oval prov. 5-Nov-2 Bonhams, New Bond Street #30/R est:5000-7000
Works on paper
£380 $600 €600 Quatre etudes de jambes (25x34cm-10x13in) i. red chk. 27-Nov-2 Christie's, Paris #110/R
£1081 $1686 €1600 Hercules (31x26cm-12x10in) pierre noire chk. 27-Mar-3 Maigret, Paris #159/R
£1216 $1897 €1800 Etude de tete (32x27cm-13x11in) pierre noire htd white. 27-Mar-3 Maigret, Paris #160/R

BATSON, Frank (fl.1890-1926) British
£360 $562 €540 Netting fish on a river (32x56cm-13x22in) 26-Mar-3 Hamptons Fine Art, Godalming #193

BATT, Arthur (1846-1911) British
£440 $682 €660 Kitten among wild flowers (10x9cm-4x4in) s.d.94 board. 24-Sep-2 Anderson & Garland, Newcastle #514
£780 $1217 €1170 Calf in a stable (20x30cm-8x12in) s.d.1885. 9-Oct-2 Woolley & Wallis, Salisbury #236/R
£870 $1357 €1305 Spaniel and terrier in a barn (34x41cm-13x16in) s.d.1889. 10-Apr-3 Tennants, Leyburn #1026/R

£1227 $2000 €1841 Terrier on a branch (15x23cm-6x9in) s.d.1908 board. 11-Feb-3 Bonhams & Doyles, New York #197/R est:2500-3500
£1300 $2041 €1950 Study of a donkey and foal (12x14cm-5x6in) s.d.1887. 25-Nov-2 Cumbria Auction Rooms, UK #333/R est:400-600
£1688 $2565 €2532 Caballos y perro (64x92cm-25x36in) s.d.1877. 3-Jul-2 Naón & Cia, Buenos Aires #15/R est:2000-2500
£2000 $3280 €3000 Mid-day rest, donkeys and foal resting at a crossroads (62x107cm-24x42in) s.d.1884. 3-Jun-3 Bonhams, Oxford #62/R est:2000-3000
£3681 $6000 €5522 Travelling companion (25x35cm-10x14in) s.d.89. 11-Feb-3 Bonhams & Doyles, New York #161/R est:6000-8000

BATTAGLIA, Alessandro (1870-1940) Italian
£2115 $3087 €3173 Children playing and women working in village (46x76cm-18x30in) s.i.d.1925. 17-Jun-2 Philippe Schuler, Zurich #4366/R est:2000-2500 (S.FR 4800)

BATTAGLIA, Carlo (1933-) Italian
£473 $786 €686 Chirone (80x200cm-31x79in) s.d.1975 verso. 12-Jun-3 Kunsthallen, Copenhagen #65 (D.KR 5000)
£473 $786 €686 Occaso (80x200cm-31x79in) s.d.1976 verso. 12-Jun-3 Kunsthallen, Copenhagen #66 (D.KR 5000)

BATTAGLIA, Xante (1943-) Italian
£261 $418 €400 Post-ancient face (70x50cm-28x20in) s. painted 1995. 4-Jan-3 Meeting Art, Vercelli #583
£321 $503 €500 Raped face (80x100cm-31x39in) s. s.i.verso oil acrylic plastic. 23-Nov-2 Meeting Art, Vercelli #284/R
£327 $523 €500 Ancient-cosmic face (80x100cm-31x39in) s.i.verso oil acrylic plastic stone. 4-Jan-3 Meeting Art, Vercelli #58
£353 $554 €550 Ancient figure (80x60cm-31x24in) s.d.2002 mixed media on canvas plastic. 23-Nov-2 Meeting Art, Vercelli #454/R
£481 $755 €750 Metaphysical Calabria (50x60cm-20x24in) s. s.i.verso. 23-Nov-2 Meeting Art, Vercelli #16a

Works on paper
£261 $418 €400 Raped painting (40x50cm-16x20in) s. mixed media on canvas. 4-Jan-3 Meeting Art, Vercelli #332
£313 $497 €450 Ancient figure (100x80cm-39x31in) s.d.1992 verso mixed media plastic on canvas. 1-May-3 Meeting Art, Vercelli #18
£316 $494 €500 Raped face (90x90cm-35x35in) s. mixed media plastic on canvas exec.2002. 14-Sep-2 Meeting Art, Vercelli #900/R
£327 $523 €500 Present, ancient present (100x70cm-39x28in) s. s.i.verso mixed media on canvas. 4-Jan-3 Meeting Art, Vercelli #369
£654 $1046 €1000 Face-painting (160x100cm-63x39in) s. mixed media stone plastic on canvas. 4-Jan-3 Meeting Art, Vercelli #72

BATTAILLE, Irene (1913-) Belgian
£292 $464 €420 Voiliers (28x40cm-11x16in) s. cardboard. 29-Apr-3 Campo & Campo, Antwerp #420
£377 $589 €600 Barques de peche dans le port (58x63cm-23x25in) board. 14-Oct-2 Amberes, Antwerp #127
£486 $773 €700 Village en Espagne (70x90cm-28x35in) s. 29-Apr-3 Campo & Campo, Antwerp #8/R
£521 $828 €750 Au jardin (90x100cm-35x39in) s.d.1961. 29-Apr-3 Campo & Campo, Antwerp #9/R
£1528 $2429 €2200 Petit port (50x58cm-20x23in) s. 29-Apr-3 Campo, Vlaamse Kaai #14/R est:550-650

Works on paper
£347 $552 €500 Serre (29x40cm-11x16in) s. W/C. 29-Apr-3 Campo, Vlaamse Kaai #16

BATTARBEE, Rex E (1893-1969) Australian

Works on paper
£605 $956 €908 Ghost Gum, Macdonnell Range, near Alice Springs. Egoota, tribesman (41x51cm-16x20in) s. s.i.verso one d.1957 W/C pair. 18-Nov-2 Waddingtons, Toronto #22/R (C.D 1500)

BATTEM, Gerard van (1636-1684) Dutch
£850 $1369 €1275 Rest on the Flight into Egypt (12x9cm-5x4in) s. copper. 20-Feb-3 Christie's, Kensington #226/R

BATTERSBY, Martin (1914-1982) British
£720 $1123 €1080 Still life with cowboy boots and violin (62x56cm-24x22in) s.d.80 board. 15-Oct-2 Bonhams, Knightsbridge #198/R
£750 $1178 €1125 Noticeboard (61x76cm-24x30in) s.d.67. 15-Apr-3 Bonhams, Knightsbridge #216/R

BATTHYANY, Gyula (1887-1959) Hungarian
£5030 $7847 €7545 Boy with a hat (102x70cm-40x28in) s.d.1937 board. 11-Apr-3 Kieselbach, Budapest #142/R est:1800000 (H.F 1800000)
£9029 $14086 €13544 Young woman in Oriental town (100x70cm-39x28in) s. 11-Sep-2 Kieselbach, Budapest #155/R (H.F 3500000)
£13413 $20925 €19449 Dance (74x60cm-29x24in) s. 12-Apr-3 Mu Terem Galeria, Budapest #151/R est:3000000 (H.F 4800000)
£25548 $39599 €37045 Night scene (92x69cm-36x27in) s. prov.exhib. 9-Dec-2 Mu Terem Galeria, Budapest #217/R est:5500000 (H.F 9500000)

BATTISS, Walter (1906-1982) South African
£688 $1107 €1032 Extensive landscape (25x40cm-10x16in) s. s.i.verso board. 12-May-3 Stephan Welz, Johannesburg #152 est:6000-8000 (SA.R 8000)
£1118 $1800 €1677 Extensive landscape with flowering aloes (26x34cm-10x13in) s. canvas on board. 12-May-3 Stephan Welz, Johannesburg #588/R est:9000-12000 (SA.R 13000)
£1229 $1916 €1844 Two figures embracing. Three figures (39x49cm-15x19in) s. cut out hardboard double-sided. 15-Oct-2 Stephan Welz, Johannesburg #454/R est:9000-12000 (SA.R 20000)
£2150 $3461 €3225 Woman standing near water (26x30cm-10x12in) s. board. 12-May-3 Stephan Welz, Johannesburg #522/R est:15000-18000 (SA.R 25000)
£2562 $3997 €3843 Abstract forms in grey (42x55cm-17x22in) s. board. 11-Nov-2 Stephan Welz, Johannesburg #536/R est:25000-35000 (SA.R 40000)
£2572 $4064 €3858 African family (49x59cm-19x23in) s. 1-Apr-3 Stephan Welz, Johannesburg #461/R est:30000-50000 (SA.R 32000)
£3439 $5537 €5159 Still life with fruit and bottles (33x44cm-13x17in) s. canvas on board. 12-May-3 Stephan Welz, Johannesburg #572/R est:25000-35000 (SA.R 40000)

Works on paper
£224 $350 €336 Tonga Island, Pacific (35x49cm-14x19in) s.i. pen ink prov. 11-Nov-2 Stephan Welz, Johannesburg #276 (SA.R 3500)
£320 $500 €480 Blue and white flowers (25x20cm-10x8in) s. W/C. 11-Nov-2 Stephan Welz, Johannesburg #521 (SA.R 5000)
£344 $554 €516 Extensive landscape with a tree (19x25cm-7x10in) s. W/C. 12-May-3 Stephan Welz, Johannesburg #148 est:3000-5000 (SA.R 4000)
£352 $550 €528 Matala (30x50cm-12x20in) s.i.d.14.6.72 W/C. 11-Nov-2 Stephan Welz, Johannesburg #277 (SA.R 5500)
£384 $600 €576 I saw this dance (33x49cm-13x19in) s.i.d.1982 pen ink. 11-Nov-2 Stephan Welz, Johannesburg #484 (SA.R 6000)
£416 $650 €624 Ua Huka, Marquesas (23x46cm-9x18in) s.i. W/C over pencil. 11-Nov-2 Stephan Welz, Johannesburg #483 (SA.R 6500)
£553 $862 €830 Composition of people and animals (47x66cm-19x26in) s.d.1970 W/C. 15-Oct-2 Stephan Welz, Johannesburg #455 est:3000-5000 (SA.R 9000)
£641 $999 €962 Figural composition in an interior (34x49cm-13x19in) s.d.1982 pen ink. 11-Nov-2 Stephan Welz, Johannesburg #584 (SA.R 10000)
£705 $1099 €1058 Gathering of figures near four huts (25x34cm-10x13in) s.d.1941 W/C. 11-Nov-2 Stephan Welz, Johannesburg #572/R (SA.R 11000)
£2408 $3876 €3612 Fool Island bank note (20x30cm-8x12in) one s. W/C collage pair. 12-May-3 Stephan Welz, Johannesburg #582/R est:12000-18000 (SA.R 28000)

BATTISTA, Giovanni (1858-1925) Italian
£500 $780 €725 Fishermen in the bay of Naples (22x38cm-9x15in) s. panel. 27-Mar-3 Lane, Penzance #76

Works on paper
£316 $491 €500 Capri - Blue Grotto (31x51cm-12x20in) s. gouache. 25-Sep-2 Neumeister, Munich #389/R
£375 $600 €563 View along the Amalfi coast (74x48cm-29x19in) s. gouache. 12-Jan-3 William Jenack, New York #212
£503 $780 €800 Bay of Naples (18x30cm-7x12in) s. W/C. 1-Oct-2 Dorotheum, Vienna #204/R
£541 $843 €800 Faraglioni, Capri (17x30cm-7x12in) s. W/C paper on board. 28-Mar-3 Dorotheum, Vienna #259/R
£680 $1088 €1020 River lined with houses and mountains beyond (36x53cm-14x21in) s. W/C. 8-Jan-3 Brightwells, Leominster #1047/R
£1014 $1581 €1500 Amalfi (28x43cm-11x17in) s. W/C. 28-Mar-3 Dorotheum, Vienna #256/R est:1200-1400
£1050 $1628 €1575 Neapolitan coastal scene, fishermen drawing in the catch (41x69cm-16x27in) s. gouache. 31-Oct-2 Greenslade Hunt, Taunton #581/R est:300-500

BATTY, Edward (19th C) British
£1300 $2028 €1950 Gundog waiting (31x41cm-12x16in) s. indis d. 6-Nov-2 Sotheby's, Olympia #154/R est:1200-1800

BATTYANY, Gyula (1888-1959) Hungarian
£20169 $31263 €30254 Evening lights in the port (80x100cm-31x39in) 6-Dec-2 Kieselbach, Budapest #77/R (H.F 7500000)

BAUCH, Jan (1898-1995) Czechoslovakian
£2478 $3866 €3717 King Saul (100x56cm-39x22in) s.d.1967. 12-Oct-2 Dorotheum, Prague #146/R est:100000-150000 (C.KR 120000)
£4086 $6620 €6129 Landscape with river (62x85cm-24x33in) s.d.42. 24-May-3 Dorotheum, Prague #131/R est:120000-200000 (C.KR 180000)
Works on paper
£347 $537 €521 Reclining nude (22x32cm-9x13in) pastel exec.c.1960. 1-Oct-2 SOGA, Bratislava #223/R est:28000 (SL.K 22000)

BAUCHANT, Andre (1873-1958) French
£927 $1511 €1400 Bouquet de fleurs au vase (26x34cm-10x13in) s.d.1955. 1-Feb-3 Claude Aguttes, Neuilly #212
£1241 $2073 €1800 Deux fillettes en bleu dans la montagne (26x34cm-10x13in) s.d.1929 canvas on panel. 10-Jul-3 Artcurial Briest, Paris #150 est:1800-2500
£1702 $2843 €2400 Paysage au grand vase de tulipes (13x16cm-5x6in) s. canvas on panel. 18-Jun-3 Pierre Berge, Paris #158/R est:1500-2000
£2421 $3776 €3800 Portrait d'homme (24x20cm-9x8in) s.d.1923 cardboard prov. 5-Nov-2 Tajan, Paris #16/R
£2548 $3975 €4000 Cinq oiseaux sur les branches (25x20cm-10x8in) s.d.1931. 5-Nov-2 Tajan, Paris #19/R
£2621 $4141 €3800 Couple dans la campagne (30x38cm-12x15in) s.d.1925 paper on canvas prov.exhib. 4-Apr-3 Tajan, Paris #49/R
£3205 $4968 €5000 Ulysse abandonnant Circe (66x81cm-26x32in) i.verso painted c.1925 prov. 4-Dec-2 Pierre Berge, Paris #128/R
£3449 $5449 €5000 Promenade dans la foret (35x46cm-14x18in) s.d.1930 prov. 4-Apr-3 Tajan, Paris #51/R
£3548 $5500 €5322 Vase de roses sur un muret (56x46cm-22x18in) s.d.26. 26-Sep-2 Christie's, Rockefeller NY #556/R est:7000-9000
£4000 $6160 €6000 La riviere et les rochers (38x55cm-15x22in) s.d.1938 prov. 22-Oct-2 Sotheby's, London #159/R est:6000-8000
£4483 $7083 €6500 Chevaliers de l'Apocalypse (71x93cm-28x37in) s.d.1943 prov. 2-Apr-3 Christie's, Paris #3/R est:9000
£4514 $7132 €6500 Femmes aux oeillets (61x45cm-24x18in) s.d.1948 cardboard exhib. 25-Apr-3 Piasa, Paris #4/R
£4803 $7013 €7205 Plaisirs champetres (50x65cm-20x26in) s.d.1954 s.i. verso. 4-Jun-2 Germann, Zurich #9/R est:10000-12000 (S.FR 11000)
£7500 $11550 €11250 Chameau dans le desert (48x65cm-19x26in) s.d.1941 panel prov. 22-Oct-2 Sotheby's, London #158/R est:12000-15000
£7500 $11550 €11250 Paysage enchante (73x104cm-29x41in) s.d.1929 prov. 22-Oct-2 Sotheby's, London #160/R est:15000-20000
£9000 $13860 €13500 Scene de village (56x72cm-22x28in) s.d.1942 board prov. 22-Oct-2 Sotheby's, London #153/R est:18000-25000
£21380 $33780 €31000 Foire champetre, Tourangelle (65x81cm-26x32in) s.d.1944. 4-Apr-3 Tajan, Paris #94/R est:22000
£34000 $52360 €51000 Grande composition aux fleurs (89x116cm-35x46in) s.d.1930 prov. 22-Oct-2 Sotheby's, London #146/R est:30000-40000

BAUCK, Jeanna Maria Charlotta (1840-1926) Swedish
£1723 $2618 €2585 Sunset over village on the outskirts of birchwood (76x116cm-30x46in) s.d.1878. 27-Aug-2 Rasmussen, Copenhagen #1676/R est:20000 (D.KR 20000)

BAUD-BOVY, Auguste (1848-1899) Swiss
£1135 $1771 €1703 Au lever du soleil (54x43cm-21x17in) s.i. 20-Nov-2 Fischer, Luzern #1256/R est:2500-3000 (S.FR 2600)
£1310 $2044 €1965 Lake landscape with fishermen hauling in nets (46x66cm-18x26in) s. 20-Nov-2 Fischer, Luzern #1254/R est:3000-4000 (S.FR 3000)
£6987 $11039 €10481 Chevres (129x94cm-51x37in) s. 17-Nov-2 Koller, Geneva #1234/R est:25000 (S.FR 16000)

BAUDE, François-Charles (1880-1953) French
£2069 $3290 €3000 La mort de Werther (76x102cm-30x40in) s. exhib. 5-Mar-3 Doutrebente, Paris #51/R est:2000-3000

BAUDESSON, Nicolas (1611-1680) French
£5031 $7799 €8000 Flowers in glass vase (40x32cm-16x13in) 2-Oct-2 Dorotheum, Vienna #291/R est:8000-10000
£10000 $15700 €15000 Still life of flowers in a stone vase on a ledge (72x58cm-28x23in) 12-Dec-2 Sotheby's, London #212/R est:10000-15000

BAUDESSON, Nicolas (attrib) (1611-1680) French
£1290 $2039 €2000 Jetee de fleurs (43x27cm-17x11in) 20-Dec-2 Tajan, Paris #111
£5000 $7750 €7500 Still life of lilies and other flowers in glass vase (52x67cm-20x26in) 31-Oct-2 Sotheby's, Olympia #147/R est:5000-7000

BAUDET, Jean (1914-) French
£311 $510 €451 Market scene (50x60cm-20x24in) s. 9-Jun-3 Hodgins, Calgary #29/R (C.D 700)

BAUDIT, Amedee (1825-1890) French
£845 $1386 €1225 Hut by water (30x46cm-12x18in) s.d.1884 prov. 4-Jun-3 Fischer, Luzern #1230/R est:2000-2500 (S.FR 1800)
£1582 $2500 €2500 Pecheurs sur les etangs de Lacanau (30x65cm-12x26in) s. s.i.d.1886 verso. 29-Nov-2 Drouot Estimations, Paris #69

BAUDIT, Louis (1870-1960) Swiss
£440 $687 €700 Fishing boats on Lake Geneva (35x90cm-14x35in) s.d.1927. 20-Sep-2 Sigalas, Stuttgart #994/R
£830 $1311 €1245 Voilier sur le lac (35x24cm-14x9in) s.d.1932 mono.i.d.verso. 17-Nov-2 Koller, Geneva #1220/R (S.FR 1900)
£2390 $3728 €3800 Fleurs dans un vase japonais (65x40cm-26x16in) s. 9-Oct-2 Lombrail & Teucquam, Paris #17/R
£2445 $3815 €3668 Sailing boat on Lake Geneva (35x91cm-14x36in) s.d.1927. 20-Nov-2 Fischer, Luzern #2018/R est:1400-1600 (S.FR 5600)
Works on paper
£304 $472 €456 Fishermen hanging out nets on seashore (42x35cm-17x14in) s.i.d.1932 pencil wash htd chk. 9-Dec-2 Philippe Schuler, Zurich #3512 (S.FR 700)

BAUDOUIN, Anne (20th C) French
£1748 $2920 €2500 Peniche sur reve (54x65cm-21x26in) s. 25-Jun-3 Claude Aguttes, Neuilly #295 est:2850-3000

BAUDREXEL, Eduard (1890-?) German
£414 $646 €650 Portrait of a young boy (100x84cm-39x33in) s.d.1919 lit. 7-Nov-2 Allgauer, Kempten #2742/R

BAUDRY, Paul (1828-1886) French
£9524 $15143 €14000 Jane Essler (59x35cm-23x14in) s.i. panel prov.exhib. 24-Mar-3 Fraysse & Associes, Paris #46/R est:1500
Works on paper
£294 $482 €450 Scene de massacre (23x25cm-9x10in) i. pen ink wash. 7-Feb-3 Piasa, Paris #72
£507 $791 €750 Nu feminin de dos (35x23cm-14x9in) i. graphite. 26-Mar-3 Rieunier, Paris #30/R
£3226 $5000 €4839 Portrait of Raphael Suares (46x32cm-18x13in) s.d.1875 pencil. 29-Oct-2 Sotheby's, New York #64/R est:1500-2000

BAUDUIN, Raphael (1870-1943) Belgian
£696 $1086 €1100 Composition au panier de fleurs et de fruits (102x107cm-40x42in) s.d.1898. 16-Sep-2 Horta, Bruxelles #388

BAUER, Bettina (20th C) Austrian
£2270 $3677 €3200 Composition (101x60cm-40x24in) s. 22-May-3 Stadion, Trieste #341/R est:3000-4000

BAUER, Carl Franz (1879-1954) Austrian
£600 $930 €900 Dark bay horse in stable (42x50cm-17x20in) s.i. board. 29-Oct-2 Henry Adams, Chichester #592/R
Works on paper
£513 $810 €800 Before the battle (34x46cm-13x18in) s.i. mixed media paper on board. 12-Nov-2 Dorotheum, Vienna #10/R
£563 $907 €800 Marscha - last racehorse of Kaiser Franz Joseph I (19x14cm-7x6in) s. W/C. 7-May-3 Dorotheum, Vienna #98/R
£676 $1054 €1000 Steeple chase (34x48cm-13x19in) s.d.1937 W/C. 28-Mar-3 Dorotheum, Vienna #313/R
£823 $1284 €1300 Austria Preis 1948 (22x36cm-9x14in) s.i. W/C Indian ink chk board. 15-Oct-2 Dorotheum, Vienna #114/R
£828 $1324 €1200 The favourite (31x47cm-12x19in) s. mixed media paper on board. 11-Mar-3 Dorotheum, Vienna #31/R
£897 $1434 €1300 Hunting party (29x44cm-11x17in) s. mixed media oil board. 11-Mar-3 Dorotheum, Vienna #30/R

BAUER, Emil (1891-1960) Swiss
£262 $409 €393 Davos in winter (34x44cm-13x17in) s.d.1918. 20-Nov-2 Fischer, Luzern #2019/R (S.FR 600)

BAUER, Frank (1964-) German
£2244 $3478 €3500 Cynthia in the bathtub (100x150cm-39x59in) s.i.d.97 verso. 7-Dec-2 Van Ham, Cologne #17/R est:3800
£2695 $4366 €3800 Reclining female nude (100x150cm-39x59in) s. verso prov. 24-May-3 Van Ham, Cologne #38/R est:3800

BAUER, Hans (1883-?) German
£423 $680 €600 Early spring landscape (50x69cm-20x27in) s i. verso board. 7-May-3 Michael Zeller, Lindau #618/R

BAUER, J (18/19th C) ?
£667 $1107 €967 Duet (63x79cm-25x31in) s. 16-Jun-3 Waddingtons, Toronto #359/R est:1500-2500 (C.D 1500)

BAUER, Johann Balthazar (1811-1883) German
£897 $1391 €1400 Romantic grazing landscape with cows, sheep, goat and farming couple (39x57cm-15x22in) s. canvas on chipboard lit. 7-Dec-2 Bergmann, Erlangen #773/R

BAUER, John (1882-1918) Swedish
Sculpture
£1489 $2309 €2234 Humpe (11cm-4in) init. dark pat.bronze on stone socle st.f.Bergman lit. 3-Dec-2 Bukowskis, Stockholm #64/R est:15000-20000 (S.KR 21000)
Works on paper
£310 $503 €450 On the horseback. Drawings (18x21cm-7x8in) W/C Indian ink double-sided. 26-May-3 Bukowskis, Stockholm #30/R (S.KR 4000)
£353 $554 €530 Giant in deep thought (22x15cm-9x6in) s. pencil. 16-Dec-2 Lilla Bukowskis, Stockholm #527 (S.KR 5000)
£579 $961 €840 Christmas goat (38x30cm-15x12in) s.d.1909 W/C. 16-Jun-3 Lilla Bukowskis, Stockholm #465 (S.KR 7500)
£2553 $3957 €3830 The gate in the mountains - Trollet Dunseklump (24x25cm-9x10in) s. W/C. 3-Dec-2 Bukowskis, Stockholm #56/R est:20000-25000 (S.KR 36000)
£5532 $8574 €8298 Two girls by the water (15x15cm-6x6in) d.19 mars 1911 gouache Indian ink htd white. 4-Dec-2 AB Stockholms Auktionsverk #1660/R est:40000-45000 (S.KR 78000)

BAUER, Karl (1905-1993) Austrian
Works on paper
£1154 $1823 €1800 Worthersee (42x57cm-17x22in) mixed media. 12-Nov-2 Dorotheum, Vienna #137/R est:1200-1600

BAUER, Marius Alexander Jacques (1867-1932) Dutch
Works on paper
£304 $474 €480 Donkey riders (15x8cm-6x3in) mono. sepia prov. sold with two booklets about artist. 21-Oct-2 Glerum, Amsterdam #53
£3165 $4937 €5000 Eastern market (75x63cm-30x25in) s. W/C prov. 21-Oct-2 Glerum, Amsterdam #5/R est:2500-3000
£3774 $5811 €6000 Citadel te Cairo (59x68cm-23x27in) s. pencil col chk W/C htd white executed 1917 prov. 23-Oct-2 Christie's, Amsterdam #142/R est:3500-5000

BAUER, Nicolaas (1767-1820) Dutch
£3077 $4862 €4800 Storm off the coast (34x45cm-13x18in) s. panel. 16-Nov-2 Lempertz, Koln #1005/R est:2000
£4317 $6906 €6000 Shipping offshore in a gale (53x76cm-21x30in) s. panel. 14-May-3 Christie's, Amsterdam #157/R est:4000-6000

BAUER, Rudolf (1889-1967) Polish
£12500 $19250 €18750 Lines (77x116cm-30x46in) s.i. s.verso board painted 1922 prov.exhib. 22-Oct-2 Sotheby's, London #182/R est:14000-18000
Works on paper
£328 $511 €492 Lily (26x20cm-10x8in) s. W/C ink bodycol. 6-Nov-2 Dobiaschofsky, Bern #1380 (S.FR 750)
£699 $1090 €1049 In the bordello (46x35cm-18x14in) s. W/C Indian ink bodycol. 6-Nov-2 Dobiaschofsky, Bern #1381/R (S.FR 1600)

BAUER, William (1923-) German
£419 $700 €608 Garden party (69x79cm-27x31in) s. 21-Jun-3 Selkirks, St. Louis #1031

BAUER-STUMPF, Johanna (1873-1964) Dutch
£764 $1192 €1200 Still life with three vases with flowers (46x56cm-18x22in) s. board. 6-Nov-2 Vendue Huis, Gravenhage #97/R
£1517 $2412 €2200 Flower still life (27x37cm-11x15in) s. panel. 10-Mar-3 Sotheby's, Amsterdam #302/R est:800-1200

BAUERLE, Carl Wilhelm Friedrich (1831-1912) German
£480 $744 €720 Young girl holding basket of bread (49x55cm-19x22in) s. 2-Oct-2 Bonhams, Knowle #98
£4000 $6360 €6000 Young botanist (62x51cm-24x20in) s. 20-Mar-3 Christie's, Kensington #170/R est:4000-6000

BAUERNFEIND, Gustav (1848-1904) Austrian
£280000 $467600 €420000 Entrance to the Temple Mount in Jerusalem (102x70cm-40x28in) s.i. panel prov. 19-Jun-3 Christie's, London #19/R est:250000-350000

BAUERREISS, Ida Maria (20th C) German
£714 $1043 €1100 Southern Spanish city (47x67cm-19x26in) s.d. board. 14-Jun-2 Auktionhaus Georg Rehm, Augsburg #8005/R
£714 $1043 €1100 Street in southern village (47x67cm-19x26in) s. board. 14-Jun-2 Auktionhaus Georg Rehm, Augsburg #8006/R
£764 $1192 €1200 Southern houses with palms (68x47cm-27x19in) s. board. 8-Nov-2 Auktionhaus Georg Rehm, Augsburg #8012/R

BAUES, N de (fl.c.1600) Flemish
£7000 $10920 €10500 Adoration of the Magi (175x130cm-69x51in) s. 10-Apr-3 Sotheby's, London #35/R est:8000-12000

BAUFFE, Victor (1849-1921) Dutch
£253 $395 €400 Roses in a glass vase (37x29cm-15x11in) s. 21-Oct-2 Glerum, Amsterdam #89/R
£414 $646 €650 Heather landscape with figure near farm (26x34cm-10x13in) s. 6-Nov-2 Vendue Huis, Gravenhage #552/R
£428 $693 €650 Ditch in a polder landscape (30x40cm-12x16in) s. canvas on board. 21-Jan-3 Christie's, Amsterdam #180
£552 $872 €800 Riverside farmstead (33x49cm-13x19in) s. canvas on panel. 5-Apr-3 Hans Stahl, Hamburg #27/R
Works on paper
£329 $513 €480 Fisherman in a boat on a polder canal with windmill (24x36cm-9x14in) s. W/C. 14-Apr-3 Glerum, Amsterdam #65/R

BAUGNIES, René de (1869-1962) Belgian
£256 $403 €400 Moulin a eau sous la neige (46x59cm-18x23in) s. panel. 10-Dec-2 Vanderkindere, Brussels #56

BAUGNIET, Charles (1814-1886) Flemish
£18841 $30899 €26000 La visite a la nourrice (73x90cm-29x35in) s. panel. 27-May-3 Campo, Vlaamse Kaai #10/R est:25000-30000
£31250 $50000 €46875 Garland of flowers (80x107cm-31x42in) s. panel. 14-May-3 Butterfields, San Francisco #1068/R est:10000-150000

BAUGNIET, Marcel Louis (1896-1995) Belgian
£449 $704 €700 Composition geometrique (64x80cm-25x31in) s. 11-Dec-2 Hotel des Ventes Mosan, Brussels #319
£2483 $3972 €3600 Deux croix (35x48cm-14x19in) s.d.1929 paper. 15-Mar-3 De Vuyst, Lokeren #543/R est:4000-5000
£2821 $4372 €4400 Composition (38x32cm-15x13in) s.d.1926 oil collage paper. 7-Dec-2 De Vuyst, Lokeren #553/R est:3800-4400
Works on paper
£288 $460 €400 Geometrie (29x43cm-11x17in) s.d.1976 mixed media cardboard. 13-May-3 Vanderkindere, Brussels #104
£372 $580 €550 Joueur de tennis (28x21cm-11x8in) s.d.1929 W/C. 26-Mar-3 Millon & Associes, Paris #60
£432 $691 €600 Paysage metaphysique (27x36cm-11x14in) s.d.1976 mixed media paper on canvas. 13-May-3 Vanderkindere, Brussels #99
£513 $795 €800 Trapeze bleujaune (22x17cm-9x7in) s.d.1936 gouache pencil. 3-Dec-2 Christie's, Amsterdam #39/R
£516 $815 €800 Promethee (36x52cm-14x20in) s.d.1917 W/C exhib. 17-Dec-2 Palais de Beaux Arts, Brussels #458
£545 $845 €850 La cadran solaire (23x23cm-9x9in) s.i.d.1930 gouache. 3-Dec-2 Christie's, Amsterdam #41/R
£601 $950 €950 Composition (36x48cm-14x19in) s.d.1927 gouache. 26-Nov-2 Palais de Beaux Arts, Brussels #233
£791 $1266 €1100 Autoportrait (35x26cm-14x10in) s.d.1970 mixed media collage paper on canvas. 13-May-3 Vanderkindere, Brussels #106
£833 $1292 €1300 Two circles, 1 retangle, 1 triangle (35x26cm-14x10in) s.d.1930 gouache pencil. 3-Dec-2 Christie's, Amsterdam #40/R est:800-1200
£881 $1365 €1400 Virgule rouge (40x31cm-16x12in) s.i.d.1990 gouache. 5-Oct-2 De Vuyst, Lokeren #21/R
£1310 $2097 €1900 Composition (32x47cm-13x19in) s.d.1975 collage. 15-Mar-3 De Vuyst, Lokeren #18/R est:2000-2600
£1871 $2993 €2600 Construction (51x35cm-20x14in) s.i.d.1930 W/C pencil. 17-May-3 De Vuyst, Lokeren #20/R est:2400-2800

BAUHAUS (20th C) European
Prints
£44872 $69551 €70000 Folder (50x41cm-20x16in) s. 2 etchings 3 col lithographs 2 woodcuts. 7-Dec-2 Hauswedell & Nolte, Hamburg #534/R

BAUKNECHT, Philipp (1884-1933) German
£6987 $10900 €10481 Larch in snowy mountain landscape (59x61cm-23x24in) s. 6-Nov-2 Hans Widmer, St Gallen #14/R est:10000-20000 (S.FR 16000)

BAUM, E J (?) ?
£559 $888 €839 Southern scene with three boys playing cards (53x42cm-21x17in) s. 10-Mar-3 Rasmussen, Vejle #512/R (D.KR 6000)

BAUM, Karl (20th C) German
£828 $1316 €1200 Estate of Fritz Boehle, Sachsenhausen mountain (53x68cm-21x27in) s.d.1911 board. 8-Mar-3 Arnold, Frankfurt #544/R

BAUM, Otto (1900-1977) German

Sculpture

£	$	€	Details
£1655	$2615	€2400	Eva (36cm-14in) s.i. verso dark pat.wood. 2-Apr-3 Dr Fritz Nagel, Stuttgart #9306/R est:2500
£6289	$9811	€10000	Shepherd and dog (146cm-57in) wood executed c.1935 prov. 9-Oct-2 Sotheby's, London #241/R est:4500-6500
£10692	$16679	€17000	Kranich - crane (105cm-41in) wood on stone base executed c.1936 prov. 9-Oct-2 Sotheby's, London #242/R est:6000-9000

BAUM, Paul (1859-1932) German

£	$	€	Details
£769	$1208	€1200	Castle ruins on rocky hillside (31x21cm-12x8in) s. board. 21-Nov-2 Van Ham, Cologne #1462/R
£9434	$14717	€15000	Summer landscape near Knokke (37x50cm-15x20in) 9-Oct-2 Michael Zeller, Lindau #625/R est:2500
£16000	$26240	€24000	Autumn landscape with mill (58x75cm-23x30in) s.d.1894 prov.exhib.lit. 4-Feb-3 Christie's, London #238/R est:30000
£43836	$68822	€64000	Spring landscape (62x79cm-24x31in) s.d.1904. 15-Apr-3 Sotheby's, Amsterdam #93/R est:15000-20000

BAUM, Paul (attrib) (1859-1932) German

£	$	€	Details
£1392	$2158	€2200	Couple meeting on treelined road (38x64cm-15x25in) 28-Sep-2 Hans Stahl, Hamburg #100/R est:1700

BAUM, Walter Emerson (1884-1956) American

£	$	€	Details
£1218	$1900	€1827	Mood in winter (30x41cm-12x16in) s. board. 18-Sep-2 Alderfer's, Hatfield #361/R est:2000-3000
£1250	$2000	€1875	Landscape, paradise Valley, Poconos (46x61cm-18x24in) s. 17-May-3 Pook & Pook, Downington #203/R est:5000-10000
£1497	$2500	€2171	Pennsylvania Hills. Landscape (30x40cm-12x16in) s. double-sided. 22-Jun-3 Freeman, Philadelphia #167/R est:2500-4000
£1923	$3000	€2885	Bucks County scene, landscape with farm house (61x76cm-24x30in) s.i.d.1944. 21-Sep-2 Pook & Pook, Downington #275/R est:12000-18000
£2070	$3250	€3105	Street scene (51x61cm-20x24in) s. i.verso canvasboard. 10-Dec-2 Doyle, New York #80/R est:2500-3500
£2201	$3500	€3302	Late winter. Country village in winter (30x41cm-12x16in) i.verso sold with W/C two. 5-Mar-3 Doyle, New York #3/R est:1000-1500
£2244	$3500	€3366	Winter landscape, Little Lehigh (61x71cm-24x28in) s. i.verso board. 11-Aug-2 Thomaston Place, Thomaston #30
£2258	$3500	€3387	Winter landscape (36x43cm-14x17in) s. board. 8-Dec-2 Freeman, Philadelphia #133/R est:3000-5000
£2532	$4000	€3798	Creek, Allentown (30x36cm-12x14in) s.i. s.verso board prov. 17-Nov-2 Jeffery Burchard, Florida #84/R
£3125	$5000	€4688	Sellersville meadows (58x76cm-23x30in) s.i. i.verso. 17-May-3 Pook & Pook, Downington #204/R est:7000-12000
£3205	$5000	€4808	Bucks County, landscape with country road and houses (41x51cm-16x20in) s.d.5/8/46 masonite. 18-Sep-2 Alderfer's, Hatfield #351/R est:5000-7000
£3226	$5000	€4839	Roadside houses (71x91cm-28x36in) s. board. 8-Dec-2 Freeman, Philadelphia #177/R est:6000-10000
£3438	$5500	€5157	Village Leidytown, spring (76x91cm-30x36in) s.verso. 17-May-3 Pook & Pook, Downington #165/R est:15000-25000
£3871	$6000	€5807	Autumn (41x51cm-16x20in) s. s.i.verso board. 8-Dec-2 Freeman, Philadelphia #167/R est:5000-8000
£3871	$6000	€5807	Spring (91x76cm-36x30in) s. i.d.1934 verso. 8-Dec-2 Freeman, Philadelphia #181/R est:6000-8000
£4063	$6500	€6095	Indian town church, Cherryville, Pa (38x51cm-15x20in) s. 17-May-3 Pook & Pook, Downington #166/R est:5000-10000
£4459	$7000	€6689	Landscape with house among trees (99x74cm-39x29in) s. s.d.1949 verso. 23-Nov-2 Pook & Pook, Downington #210/R est:5000-6000
£5660	$9000	€8490	Village in winter (77x102cm-30x40in) s. executed 1925 prov. 4-Mar-3 Christie's, Rockefeller NY #59/R est:12000-18000
£5696	$9000	€8544	Allentown (46x61cm-18x24in) s. canvasboard. 26-Apr-3 Jeffery Burchard, Florida #44
£6090	$9500	€9135	Winter landscape (41x51cm-16x20in) s. canvasboard. 9-Nov-2 Sloan, North Bethesda #621/R
£7186	$12000	€10420	April, spring day (76x91cm-30x36in) s. s.i.d.1925 verso prov. 22-Jun-3 Freeman, Philadelphia #168/R est:10000-15000
£10759	$17000	€16139	Road to Sellersville (51x61cm-20x24in) s. s.i.verso canvasboard. 26-Apr-3 Jeffery Burchard, Florida #45
£11613	$18000	€17420	Autumn creek, Bucks county. Center Bridge (63x76cm-25x30in) s. board double-sided. 8-Dec-2 Freeman, Philadelphia #179/R est:20000-30000
£16026	$25000	€24039	Montgomeryville, Pa (76x91cm-30x36in) s.i.d.1925. 21-Sep-2 Pook & Pook, Downington #276/R est:25000-30000
£22581	$35000	€33872	River town (102x127cm-40x50in) s.i.verso prov.lit. 4-Dec-2 Sotheby's, New York #45/R est:35000-50000

Works on paper

£	$	€	Details
£696	$1100	€1044	Winter landscape with stream (46x28cm-18x11in) s. W/C gouache prov. 17-Nov-2 Jeffery Burchard, Florida #84a/R
£791	$1250	€1187	Summer landscape with stream. Winter landscape with stream (43x25cm-17x10in) pastel double-sided prov. 17-Nov-2 Jeffery Burchard, Florida #84b/R
£2419	$3750	€3629	Landscape (38x48cm-15x19in) init.d.20 gouache board. 29-Oct-2 John Moran, Pasadena #655 est:2000-3500

BAUMANN, F (?) ?

£	$	€	Details
£357	$568	€536	Moonlit view of cottage alongside stream (48x80cm-19x31in) s. 4-Mar-3 Dales, Durban #16 (SA.R 4500)

BAUMANN, Fred (1947-) Swiss

£	$	€	Details
£463	$745	€671	Emmental in spring (90x122cm-35x48in) mono.d.77 panel. 7-May-3 Dobiaschofsky, Bern #341/R (S.FR 1000)

BAUMANN, Gustave (1881-1971) American

Prints

£	$	€	Details
£1923	$3000	€2885	Superstition mountains (20x20cm-8x8in) s.d.49 num.50/125 woodblock print prov.lit. 9-Nov-2 Santa Fe Art, Santa Fe #100/R est:4000-6000
£2179	$3400	€3269	Sycamore (28x25cm-11x10in) s.i.num.65/100 col woodcut exec.c.1920. 7-Nov-2 Swann Galleries, New York #535/R est:3000-5000
£2516	$4000	€3774	Pine and Aspen (33x32cm-13x13in) s.i.num.40 col woodcut executed c.1920. 1-May-3 Swann Galleries, New York #396/R est:4000-6000
£2690	$4250	€4035	Redwood (31x31cm-12x12in) s.i.num.30/125 hand col woodcut. 22-Apr-3 Butterfields, San Francisco #2011/R est:3000-5000
£2704	$4300	€4056	Summer breezes (28x25cm-11x10in) s.i. col woodcut. 7-Mar-3 Jackson's, Cedar Falls #630/R est:3500-4500
£2767	$4400	€4151	April (33x33cm-13x13in) s.i.num.62/120 col woodcut executed c.1936. 1-May-3 Swann Galleries, New York #397/R est:4000-6000
£2813	$4500	€4220	Talpa chapel (36x33cm-14x13in) s. col woodcut. 17-Mar-3 Winter Associates, Plainville #100
£3205	$5000	€4808	Church, Ranchos de Taos (25x28cm-10x11in) i.num17/100 woodblock print prov.lit. 9-Nov-2 Santa Fe Art, Santa Fe #103/R est:6000-8000
£3425	$5000	€5138	Palo verde and ocotea (25x30cm-10x12in) s. col woodcut. 3-Nov-1 North East Auctions, Portsmouth #289/R est:2000-3000
£3718	$5800	€5577	Cedar, Grand Canyon after rain (33x33cm-13x13in) s.i. col woodcut. 18-Sep-2 Swann Galleries, New York #47/R est:3000-5000
£3896	$6000	€5844	April (33x36cm-13x14in) s.i.num.24 of 120 col woodblock. 8-Sep-2 Treadway Gallery, Cincinnati #388/R est:4500-6500
£4487	$7000	€6731	Palo verde and ocotea (23x28cm-9x11in) s.i. num.36/125 woodblock print prov.lit. 9-Nov-2 Santa Fe Art, Santa Fe #102/R est:6000-7000
£5063	$8000	€7595	Bright angel trail (25x29cm-10x11in) s.i.num.28/125 col woodcut. 22-Apr-3 Butterfields, San Francisco #2010/R est:6000-8000
£5195	$8000	€7793	Singing woods (33x33cm-13x13in) s.i.num.61 of 120 col woodblock. 8-Sep-2 Treadway Gallery, Cincinnati #386/R est:4500-6500
£5769	$9000	€8654	Cottonwood Tassels (33x33cm-13x13in) s.i. num.59/125 woodblock print prov.lit. 9-Nov-2 Santa Fe Art, Santa Fe #101/R est:6000-7000
£11538	$18000	€17307	Fifth Avenue (34x28cm-13x11in) s.i.d.1917 col woodcut. 7-Nov-2 Swann Galleries, New York #534/R est:12000-18000

BAUMANN, Karl Herman (1911-1984) American

£	$	€	Details
£700	$1100	€1050	Church nocturne (38x48cm-15x19in) s. canvasboard lit. 19-Nov-2 Butterfields, San Francisco #8333/R
£1274	$2000	€1911	Backyard in spring (67x55cm-26x22in) s.d. i.verso panel. 19-Nov-2 Butterfields, San Francisco #8332/R est:3000-5000
£1433	$2250	€2150	Through the window (76x61cm-30x24in) s.d.46 i.verso. 19-Nov-2 Butterfields, San Francisco #8331/R est:3000-5000

BAUMBERGER, Otto (1889-1961) Swiss

£	$	€	Details
£441	$643	€662	Interiorwith still life (34x27cm-13x11in) mono.d.1919. 17-Jun-2 Philippe Schuler, Zurich #4256 (S.FR 1000)
£3712	$5790	€5568	Piano player and diners in restaurant (55x65cm-22x26in) mono.d.40. 6-Nov-2 Hans Widmer, St Gallen #129/R est:6500-11000 (S.FR 8500)

BAUMEISTER, Willi (1889-1955) German

£	$	€	Details
£4717	$7358	€7500	Pinter and model (49x38cm-19x15in) s. i.verso oil on card painted 1913 prov.lit. 9-Oct-2 Sotheby's, London #389/R est:9000-12000
£5346	$8340	€8500	Female nude dedicated to Camille Corot (51x31cm-20x12in) s.i.d.1910 i.verso board prov.exhib.lit. 9-Oct-2 Sotheby's, London #379/R est:12000-18000
£11034	$17434	€16000	Two girls (57x48cm-22x19in) mono.i. board prov. 2-Apr-3 Dr Fritz Nagel, Stuttgart #9309/R est:18000
£12579	$19371	€20000	In the bath - two female nudes (58x40cm-23x16in) mono. board on panel. 26-Oct-2 Dr Lehr, Berlin #39/R est:24000

£22759 $35959 €33000 Pale wall of figures (24x37cm-9x15in) s.d.1947 board on masonite prov. 2-Apr-3 Dr Fritz Nagel, Stuttgart #9312/R est:20000
£26415 $41208 €42000 Eidos erdfarben - Eidos earth-colours (42x32cm-17x13in) s. oil pencil on masonite prov.lit. 9-Oct-2 Sotheby's, London #357/R est:60000-90000
£30769 $47692 €48000 Blaue Mauer (29x38cm-11x15in) s.i.d.1952 oil synthetic resin card prov.exhib.lit. 4-Dec-2 Lempertz, Koln #29/R est:40000-50000
£44025 $68679 €70000 Jacques callot gewidmet VI - Dedicated to Jacques Callot VI (40x80cm-16x31in) s.d.41 s.on stretcher prov.exhib.lit. 8-Oct-2 Sotheby's, London #34/R est:100000-150000
£47468 $75000 €75000 Summer festival - white on yellow (54x64cm-21x25in) s.d.12.47 i. verso oil resin spray masonite prov.exhib.lit. 27-Nov-2 Dr Fritz Nagel, Stuttgart #3044/R est:95000
£49275 $80812 €68000 Tschun-li (45x34cm-18x13in) s.d.1949 board prov. 30-May-3 Villa Grisebach, Berlin #64/R est:60000-80000
£50314 $78491 €80000 Afrikanischer stil - African style (44x53cm-17x21in) s.d.42 i.d.verso oil pencil on board prov.exhib.lit. 9-Oct-2 Sotheby's, London #356/R est:45000-65000
£69182 $107925 €110000 Steingarten - Stone garden (65x54cm-26x21in) s.d.42 prov.exhib.lit. 8-Oct-2 Sotheby's, London #30/R est:90000-130000
£157233 $245283 €250000 Eidos VII (100x82cm-39x32in) s. oil sand on canvas painted 1939 prov.exhib.lit. 8-Oct-2 Sotheby's, London #32/R est:300000-400000
£250000 $417500 €375000 Faust-Studie (100x130cm-39x51in) s.i.d.1953 verso board prov.lit. 26-Jun-3 Christie's, London #46/R est:220000-260000

Prints

£1899 $3000 €3000 Untitled (43x34cm-17x13in) mono.i. lithograph. 27-Nov-2 Dr Fritz Nagel, Stuttgart #3036/R est:2900
£2089 $3300 €3300 Untitled (52x35cm-20x14in) s. lithograph. 27-Nov-2 Dr Fritz Nagel, Stuttgart #3035/R est:2900
£2174 $3565 €3000 Two epochs (36x46cm-14x18in) s. lithograph W/C gouache. 29-May-3 Lempertz, Koln #528/R est:2000
£5862 $9262 €8500 Montaru (59x69cm-23x27in) s.d.53 i.5/90 col serigraph. 2-Apr-3 Dr Fritz Nagel, Stuttgart #9311/R est:8500

Works on paper

£1620 $2608 €2300 Figural composition (31x16cm-12x6in) s. pencil chl. 7-May-3 Michael Zeller, Lindau #1069/R est:2000
£2516 $3925 €4000 Dialogue from saul (18x22cm-7x9in) s. pencil chl excuted 1943 prov.lit. 9-Oct-2 Sotheby's, London #334/R est:5000-7000
£3145 $4906 €5000 African games on a light brown background (16x28cm-6x11in) s. pencil chl executed 1942-43 prov.lit. 9-Oct-2 Sotheby's, London #333/R est:5000-7000
£4717 $7358 €7500 Ball player (30x19cm-12x7in) s.d.35 pencil on card prov.lit. 9-Oct-2 Sotheby's, London #336/R est:9000-12000
£5346 $8340 €8500 Group of figures from Esther (31x48cm-12x19in) s.d.44 chl pastel pencil prov.lit. 9-Oct-2 Sotheby's, London #337/R est:12000-18000
£7051 $10929 €11000 Relief with figures VIII (29x48cm-11x19in) s.i.d. chl col oil chk. 7-Dec-2 Hauswedell & Nolte, Hamburg #535/R est:7500
£9295 $14407 €14500 Ball player (45x35cm-18x14in) s.d.1932 pencil chl. 4-Dec-2 Lempertz, Koln #566/R est:14000-16000
£13208 $20604 €21000 Felsige eidos erdfarben - Rocky eidos earth colours (46x35cm-18x14in) s.d.41 gouache sand pencil prov.lit. 9-Oct-2 Sotheby's, London #365/R est:30000-40000

BAUMER, Eduard (1892-1977) German

Works on paper

£11348 $18383 €16000 Mountains behind the Laboratorio, Tropea (54x72cm-21x28in) s.mono.d.13.X.69 mixed media. 20-May-3 Dorotheum, Vienna #188/R est:1600-2400

BAUMGARTNER, A (19/20th C) European

£260 $387 €400 Hungarian horse market (15x31cm-6x12in) s. panel. 27-Jun-2 Neumeister, Munich #2689
£304 $474 €480 Catch of fish (80x58cm-31x23in) s. 12-Sep-2 Hagelstam, Helsinki #915
£900 $1368 €1350 Venetian fisherfolk at the lagoon (76x52cm-30x20in) s. 29-Aug-2 Christie's, Kensington #252/R

BAUMGARTNER, Fritz (1929-) German

£1528 $2429 €2200 Green woman 5 (100x80cm-39x31in) s. s.i.d.1972 verso lit. 1-May-3 Meeting Art, Vercelli #508

BAUMGARTNER, H (1868-1927) German

£962 $1500 €1443 Mountainous landscape with family picnicking by a stream (69x97cm-27x38in) s. 21-Sep-2 Pook & Pook, Downington #401/R est:2000-2500

BAUMGARTNER, J Jay (1865-1946) American

£692 $1100 €1038 Secret stream (51x38cm-20x15in) s.d.June 1899. 8-Mar-3 Harvey Clar, Oakland #1195

BAUMGARTNER, Johann Wolfgang (1712-1761) German

£19500 $30615 €29250 Apotheosis of Saint Louis (80x60cm-31x24in) 10-Dec-2 Bonhams, New Bond Street #308/R est:8000-12000

Works on paper

£629 $981 €1000 Death of Absalom (11x11cm-4x4in) pen brush htd bodycol. 11-Oct-2 Winterberg, Heidelberg #357/R
£4054 $6324 €6000 Martyre des Jesuites (38x27cm-15x11in) s. chk pen ink wash. 27-Mar-3 Christie's, Paris #146/R

BAUMGARTNER, Thomas (1892-1962) German

£4870 $7256 €7500 Couple in traditional costume of Chiemsee (77x61cm-30x24in) s.d.1920 i. verso i. stretcher. 26-Jun-2 Neumeister, Munich #678/R est:3000

BAUMGRAS, Peter (1827-1904) American

£5031 $8000 €7547 Still life of cauliflowers, strawberries and turnips (36x46cm-14x18in) s.d.1890 prov.lit. 5-Mar-3 Sotheby's, New York #12/R est:7000-10000

BAUR, Karl-Albert von (1855-1907) German

£441 $643 €662 Weissenburg in Breisgau (41x51cm-16x20in) s. 17-Jun-2 Philippe Schuler, Zurich #7318 (S.FR 1000)

BAURE, Albert (?-1930) French

£6250 $10125 €9500 Competitors (74x93cm-29x37in) s. 21-Jan-3 Durán, Madrid #153/R

BAURIEDL, Otto (1879-1956) German

£1712 $2671 €2500 On the edge of the Alps (74x95cm-29x37in) s. 10-Apr-3 Van Ham, Cologne #1320/R est:2500

BAWDEN, Edward (1903-1989) British

Prints

£3600 $5724 €5400 Lindsell Church (61x155cm-24x61in) s.d.1960 num.32/40 screen print. 29-Apr-3 Gorringes, Lewes #2147
£4800 $7488 €7200 Brighton Pier (53x11cm-21x4in) s.i. num.13/50 col linocut. 31-Mar-3 Bonhams, New Bond Street #256/R est:1000-1500
£5000 $8350 €7250 Brighton Pier (53x114cm-21x45in) s.i.d.num.17/40 col linocut. 30-Jun-3 Bonhams, New Bond Street #251/R est:3000-5000

Works on paper

£950 $1530 €1425 The bridge (37x55cm-15x22in) s.d.1963 pen ink. 14-Jan-3 Bonhams, Knightsbridge #218/R
£1300 $2093 €1950 Caerhays Castle, Cornwall - entrance to the stable yard (49x64cm-19x25in) s. W/C prov. 15-Jan-3 Cheffins Grain & Comins, Cambridge #408/R
£1500 $2325 €2250 Beach at Ballyguin (45x57cm-18x22in) s.d.1965 W/C. 3-Dec-2 Bonhams, Knightsbridge #402/R est:2000-3000
£1550 $2558 €2248 Millhouse in a landscape (30x40cm-12x16in) s. W/C over pencil. 1-Jul-3 Bonhams, Norwich #134/R est:600-900
£1800 $2952 €2700 Oleander (64x47cm-25x19in) s.i.d.1988 pencil W/C. 4-Feb-3 Sworder & Son, Bishops Stortford #131/R est:750-1000
£2550 $4182 €3825 Wooden church and buildings (42x55cm-17x22in) s.d.1959 washes scratching out htd red white gouache. 2-Jun-3 David Duggleby, Scarborough #271/R est:1000-1500
£2700 $4428 €4050 Mill (44x55cm-17x22in) s.d.1948 pencil W/C bodycol prov.exhib. 6-Jun-3 Christie's, London #144/R est:3000-5000
£4000 $6440 €6000 Village church on the edge of parkland (49x64cm-19x25in) s. W/C. 15-Jan-3 Cheffins Grain & Comins, Cambridge #407/R
£4800 $7920 €6960 Muchish Mountain (46x58cm-18x23in) s.d.1962 pen black ink W/C bodycol prov. 3-Jul-3 Christie's, Kensington #302/R est:1200-1800

BAXENDALE, John (20th C) British

Works on paper

£300 $468 €450 Three long-tailed tits on branches with catkins and fir cones (26x39cm-10x15in) s.d.1972 W/C gouache. 26-Mar-3 Woolley & Wallis, Salisbury #47/R

BAXTER, Brian (20th C) New Zealander?

£588 $864 €882 Sea, sand, snow, kaikoura (45x90cm-18x35in) s.d.77 board prov. 19-Jun-2 Watson's, Christchurch #57/R est:250-750 (NZ.D 1800)

BAXTER, Charles (1809-1879) British
£2000 $3180 €3000 Lady with casket (61x51cm-24x20in) 6-Mar-3 Christie's, Kensington #551/R est:1500-2000
£2000 $3280 €3000 Lost in thought (56x46cm-22x18in) s.d.1851 i.verso painted oval. 29-May-3 Christie's, Kensington #287/R est:3000-5000
£4333 $7193 €6283 Portrait of a young girl carrying a basket of grapes (93x71cm-37x28in) prov. 16-Jun-3 Waddingtons, Toronto #170/R est:7000-9000 (C.D 9750)

BAXTER, Charles (attrib) (1809-1879) British
£350 $571 €525 Moment's reflection (30x26cm-12x10in) board. 13-Feb-3 Christie's, Kensington #114/R

BAXTER, David A (?) British?
Works on paper
£260 $406 €390 Harvesting scene (36x51cm-14x20in) s. W/C. 2-Aug-2 Biddle & Webb, Birmingham #61

BAXTER, Evelyn (1925-) Australian
£632 $960 €948 Mixed roses (54x65cm-21x26in) s. 19-Aug-2 Joel, Victoria #213 est:2000-3000 (A.D 1800)
£1053 $1600 €1580 Magnolias (62x64cm-24x25in) s. 19-Aug-2 Joel, Victoria #169 est:1500-2500 (A.D 3000)

BAXTER, Glen (1944-) British
Works on paper
£625 $1031 €900 Attending to Uncle Norman's. (58x80cm-23x31in) s.d.1987 ink wax crayon prov. 3-Jul-3 Christie's, Paris #28/R

BAYENS, Hans (1924-) Dutch
Sculpture
£1583 $2596 €2200 Begijntjes (34cm-13in) bronze. 3-Jun-3 Christie's, Amsterdam #400/R est:1800-2200

BAYER, Franz (1932-) Yugoslavian
£641 $1013 €1000 History of soldiers (60x86cm-24x34in) s.d.1983 masonite. 12-Nov-2 Dorotheum, Vienna #230/R

BAYER, Herbert (1900-1985) German
£5580 $9151 €7700 Cosmic (127x106cm-50x42in) s.i.d.1958/47 s.i.d. verso acrylic prov. 29-May-3 Lempertz, Koln #531/R est:8000
Photographs
£1948 $3000 €2922 Hands act (34x25cm-13x10in) s.d.1932 num.16/40 photograph. 24-Oct-2 Sotheby's, New York #167/R est:3000-5000
£2922 $4500 €4383 Lonely metropolitan (34x27cm-13x11in) s.d.1932 num.16/40 photograph. 24-Oct-2 Sotheby's, New York #166/R est:5000-7000
Works on paper
£285 $441 €450 Poster sketch (65x48cm-26x19in) s.d.1962 pastel chk col chk paper collage. 28-Sep-2 Ketterer, Hamburg #488/R
£405 $632 €600 The rocks that missed Ulysses (40x37cm-16x15in) s.i.d.1954 Indian ink col chk. 28-Mar-3 Ketterer, Hamburg #201/R
£1592 $2500 €2388 Untitled (14x14cm-6x6in) s.d. triac prov. 19-Nov-2 Wright, Chicago #155/R est:3000-5000

BAYERLEIN, Fritz (1872-1955) German
£385 $585 €600 Parkland (87x67cm-34x26in) s. 11-Jul-2 Hugo Ruef, Munich #579

BAYERN, Clara V (20th C) German?
£321 $487 €500 Yellow roses in vase (70x65cm-28x26in) s.d.1925. 11-Jul-2 Hugo Ruef, Munich #580/R

BAYES, Gilbert (1872-1953) British
Sculpture
£950 $1501 €1425 Equestrian group, showing a first world war soldier leading three horses (26x26cm-10x10in) s.bronze marble base. 13-Nov-2 Sotheby's, Olympia #125/R est:1000-1500
£4400 $6864 €6600 Bacchante (73cm-29in) s. brown pat bronze ebonised wood socle exhib.lit. 5-Nov-2 Sotheby's, London #148/R est:3000-5000

BAYES, Walter (attrib) (1869-1956) British
£680 $1074 €986 Terrace (23x23cm-9x9in) board. 22-Jul-3 Gorringes, Lewes #1553

BAYEU Y SUBIAS, Francisco (style) (1734-1795) Spanish
£14740 $23879 €21373 Baile de Seguidillas entre Quatro. Entrada y la fiesta, Plaza de Toros (63x52cm-25x20in) pair. 26-May-3 Bukowskis, Stockholm #460/R est:80000-100000 (S.KR 190000)

BAYHA, Edwin F (19/20th C) American
Works on paper
£870 $1400 €1305 Heads of beautiful young women comprise a question mark (64x36cm-25x14in) estate st. pencil gouache. 10-May-3 Illustration House, New York #155/R

BAYLISS, Edwin Butler (1874-?) British
£410 $636 €615 Travellers on country track (71x91cm-28x36in) s. 2-Oct-2 Bonhams, Knowle #93

BAYLOR, Edna Ellis (1882-?) American
£478 $750 €717 Still life with spring blossoms (30x25cm-12x10in) s. canvasboard. 22-Nov-2 Skinner, Boston #162/R

BAYLY, Clifford (1927-) British
£500 $785 €750 Alignment six, horns of consecration, Knossos, Crete (120x120cm-47x47in) s.d.82 board. 15-Apr-3 Bonhams, Knightsbridge #148/R

BAYNES, Frederick Thomas (1824-1874) British
Works on paper
£300 $462 €450 Still life of primroses in a terracotta jug (18x13cm-7x5in) s. W/C oval. 23-Oct-2 Hamptons Fine Art, Godalming #86/R

BAYNES, Keith (1887-1977) British
Works on paper
£450 $711 €653 Circus Act (49x35cm-19x14in) s. gouache board. 22-Jul-3 Sotheby's, Olympia #263/R

BAYROS, Franz von (1866-1924) Austrian
Works on paper
£468 $748 €650 Two women playing erotic games in library (30x29cm-12x11in) s.pseudonym wash pen over pencil board. 13-May-3 Hartung & Hartung, Munich #2565/R
£791 $1266 €1100 Erotic scene (30x28cm-12x11in) s. wash pen board. 13-May-3 Hartung & Hartung, Munich #2564/R
£935 $1496 €1300 Two women playing love games (30x29cm-12x11in) s. wash pen over pencil board. 13-May-3 Hartung & Hartung, Munich #2563/R
£1301 $2030 €1900 Female artist (30x29cm-12x11in) s.i. wash Indian ink pen brush. 11-Apr-3 Winterberg, Heidelberg #629/R est:1850

BAYSER-GRATRY, Margueritte de (20th C) French
Sculpture
£1806 $2854 €2800 Gazelle (34x23x7cm-13x9x3in) s. brown pat.bronze Cast.C.Valsuani. 17-Dec-2 Claude Aguttes, Neuilly #42/R est:1500-2300

BAZAINE, Jean (1904-1995) French
£1218 $1912 €1900 Port de peche (27x21cm-11x8in) s.d.45 chl prov. 10-Dec-2 Piasa, Paris #363
£2516 $3899 €4000 Verre et fleurs (35x27cm-14x11in) s.d.41 prov. 30-Oct-2 Artcurial Briest, Paris #641/R est:3800-4200
£3712 $5790 €5568 Printemps noir (27x22cm-11x9in) s.d.62 i. verso. 6-Nov-2 Dobiaschofsky, Bern #339/R est:7500 (S.FR 8500)
£6000 $9240 €9000 Premier Mars (14x24cm-6x9in) s. s.i.d.1963 verso prov.exhib.lit. 22-Oct-2 Sotheby's, London #429/R est:6000-8000
£19858 $32170 €28000 Naissance du jour (163x115cm-64x45in) s.d.71 exhib.lit. 24-May-3 Van Ham, Cologne #41/R est:10000
£21154 $32788 €33000 Menageres au petit jour (100x73cm-39x29in) s.d.45 s.i.d.verso. 9-Dec-2 Piasa, Paris #41/R est:12000-15000
Works on paper
£321 $503 €500 Composition (21x26cm-8x10in) s.d.64 crayon dr. 10-Dec-2 Piasa, Paris #123
£449 $704 €700 Arbres (21x17cm-8x7in) s.d.45 chl prov. 10-Dec-2 Piasa, Paris #358
£513 $805 €800 Composition (21x31cm-8x12in) s.d.45 chl dr. 10-Dec-2 Piasa, Paris #119
£577 $906 €900 Paysage (21x30cm-8x12in) s.d.45 ink chl prov. 10-Dec-2 Piasa, Paris #362
£641 $1006 €1000 Composition abstraite (27x21cm-11x8in) s.d.45 Chinese ink dr. 10-Dec-2 Piasa, Paris #117
£641 $1006 €1000 Paysage de Bretagne (17x21cm-7x8in) s.d.45 Chinese ink chl dr. 10-Dec-2 Piasa, Paris #118
£705 $1107 €1100 Grand arbre (17x21cm-7x8in) s.d.45 Chinese ink dr. 10-Dec-2 Piasa, Paris #120
£705 $1107 €1100 Anse de Kerleven (17x21cm-7x8in) s.d.45 ink chl prov. 10-Dec-2 Piasa, Paris #359

£759 $1185 €1200 Espace marin (9x24cm-4x9in) s.d.1971 W/C pastel. 20-Oct-2 Claude Boisgirard, Paris #42
£769 $1208 €1200 Port de Dieppe (21x30cm-8x12in) s.i.d.45 prov. 10-Dec-2 Piasa, Paris #361
£851 $1421 €1200 Composition abstraite (8x24cm-3x9in) s.d.53 gouache W/C prov. 20-Jun-3 Piasa, Paris #190
£1064 $1777 €1500 Composition abstraite (8x24cm-3x9in) s.d.54 W/C. 20-Jun-3 Piasa, Paris #189 est:1200-1800
£1282 $2013 €2000 Kerleven (13x21cm-5x8in) s.d.45 ink chl prov. 10-Dec-2 Piasa, Paris #364
£1392 $2200 €2200 Composition (10x24cm-4x9in) s.d.54 gouache. 27-Nov-2 Blanchet, Paris #129/R
£1410 $2214 €2200 Trees (20x16cm-8x6in) s.d.45 chl prov. 10-Dec-2 Piasa, Paris #365
£1923 $3019 €3000 Chiffons de travail (24x33cm-9x13in) s.d.92 W/C crayon. 10-Dec-2 Piasa, Paris #126/R
£2244 $3522 €3500 Arbres et maisons (21x30cm-8x12in) s.d.45 W/C prov.exhib. 10-Dec-2 Piasa, Paris #345
£2564 $4026 €4000 Marelle (74x52cm-29x20in) init. s.i.d.1947 verso W/C gouache. 10-Dec-2 Piasa, Paris #128/R
£3205 $5032 €5000 Figure de nuit (16x28cm-6x11in) s.d.46 W/C exhib.lit. 10-Dec-2 Piasa, Paris #122
£3526 $5535 €5500 Port de pehe (29x23cm-11x9in) s.d.46 chl prov. 10-Dec-2 Piasa, Paris #360
£4167 $6542 €6500 Mer (24x30cm-9x12in) s.d.46 W/C prr. 10-Dec-2 Piasa, Paris #355 est:3000
£4487 $7045 €7000 Maison et rocher (22x30cm-9x12in) s.d.46 W/C wax crayon prov.exhib. 10-Dec-2 Piasa, Paris #353 est:3000
£5128 $8051 €8000 Composition (38x46cm-15x18in) s.d.44 W/C prov. 10-Dec-2 Piasa, Paris #341 est:4000
£5769 $9058 €9000 Arbres du soir (34x51cm-13x20in) s.d.44 W/C prov. 10-Dec-2 Piasa, Paris #343 est:4000
£5769 $9058 €9000 Paysage au crepuscule (40x32cm-16x13in) s.d.45 W/C prov.exhib.lit. 10-Dec-2 Piasa, Paris #346/R est:4000
£6090 $9561 €9500 Oiseaux de nuit (39x39cm-15x15in) s.i.d.94 Chinese ink wash collage. 10-Dec-2 Piasa, Paris #127/R est:3000
£6329 $9873 €10000 Bain (34x58cm-13x23in) s.d.1941 W/C gouache prov.exhib. 20-Oct-2 Claude Boisgirard, Paris #41/R est:10000-12000
£6410 $10064 €10000 Torse en plein air (56x37cm-22x15in) s.d.45 W/C prov.exhib. 10-Dec-2 Piasa, Paris #344/R est:4000
£6410 $10064 €10000 Port au soleil levant (27x39cm-11x15in) s.d.46 W/C prov.exhib. 10-Dec-2 Piasa, Paris #349 est:3500
£6410 $10064 €10000 Comediens (26x20cm-10x8in) s.d.47 W/C gouache pastel prov.exhib. 10-Dec-2 Piasa, Paris #356/R est:3000
£6410 $10064 €10000 Printemps (23x31cm-9x12in) s.d.47 W/C prov.exhib. 10-Dec-2 Piasa, Paris #357 est:3000
£7051 $11071 €11000 Voile dans les rochers (26x31cm-10x12in) s.d.46 W/C prov.exhib. 10-Dec-2 Piasa, Paris #351 est:3000
£7692 $12077 €12000 Untitled (49x69cm-19x27in) s.d.88 W/C. 10-Dec-2 Piasa, Paris #124/R est:3000
£8333 $13083 €13000 Atelier (27x34cm-11x13in) s.d.46 W/C. 10-Dec-2 Piasa, Paris #121 est:3000
£8974 $14090 €14000 Bateaux (40x30cm-16x12in) s.d.46 W/C prov.exhib.lit. 10-Dec-2 Piasa, Paris #354/R est:4500
£9615 $15096 €15000 Saint-Guenole (24x31cm-9x12in) s.d.46 W/C prov.exhib. 10-Dec-2 Piasa, Paris #350 est:3000
£9615 $15096 €15000 Arbres et maisons le soir (32x42cm-13x17in) s.d.45 W/C prov.exhib. 10-Dec-2 Piasa, Paris #348/R est:5000
£10256 $16103 €16000 Maisons a Saint-Guenole (22x30cm-9x12in) s.d.46 W/C prov. 10-Dec-2 Piasa, Paris #352/R est:3500
£11538 $17885 €18000 Untitled (46x51cm-18x20in) s.d.46 W/C gouache. 9-Dec-2 Piasa, Paris #40/R est:6000-8000
£12821 $20128 €20000 Arbres et maisons (41x50cm-16x20in) s.d.45 W/C prov.exhib. 10-Dec-2 Piasa, Paris #347/R est:7000
£14744 $23147 €23000 Figure sur fond d'arbres (50x40cm-20x16in) s.d.45 W/C prov.exhib. 10-Dec-2 Piasa, Paris #342/R est:7000

BAZE, Paul (1901-1985) French
£446 $696 €700 Femme et son chien (65x50cm-26x20in) s. 7-Nov-2 Chochon-Barre & Allardi, Paris #75

BAZIOTES, William (1912-1963) American
£11250 $18000 €16875 Star figure (62x51cm-24x20in) s. s.i.d.1948 verso prov.exhib. 14-May-3 Sotheby's, New York #106/R est:25000-35000

Works on paper
£976 $1600 €1415 Untitled, glyphic studies (22x27cm-9x11in) st.sig. pencil exec.c.1945. 5-Jun-3 Swann Galleries, New York #16/R est:2000-3000

BAZOVSKY, Milos Alexander (1899-1968) Czechoslovakian
£253 $392 €380 Village (8x22cm-3x9in) tempera paper painted c.1952. 3-Dec-2 SOGA, Bratislava #56/R (SL.K 16000)
£599 $874 €899 Liptov region (32x47cm-13x19in) tempera board painted c.1940. 4-Jun-2 SOGA, Bratislava #65/R est:45000 (SL.K 38000)
£866 $1343 €1299 Cradle (32x49cm-13x19in) tempera board. 1-Oct-2 SOGA, Bratislava #70/R est:55000 (SL.K 55000)
£929 $1440 €1394 Little church (28x41cm-11x16in) tempera painted c.1946-48. 1-Oct-2 SOGA, Bratislava #69/R est:59000 (SL.K 59000)
£1260 $1953 €1890 Barn (24x36cm-9x14in) board. 1-Oct-2 SOGA, Bratislava #68/R est:80000 (SL.K 80000)
£2048 $2908 €3072 Dawn (38x24cm-15x9in) board painted 1949. 26-Mar-2 SOGA, Bratislava #55/R est:120000 (SL.K 130000)
£2447 $3793 €3671 Village (25x39cm-10x15in) veneer painted c.1952. 3-Dec-2 SOGA, Bratislava #55/R est:150000 (SL.K 155000)
£3071 $4361 €4607 Friends (36x21cm-14x8in) painted c.1955. 26-Mar-2 SOGA, Bratislava #54/R est:190000 (SL.K 195000)
£3560 $5197 €5340 Dove cot (29x42cm-11x17in) board painted c.1953-57. 4-Jun-2 SOGA, Bratislava #63/R est:195000 (SL.K 226000)
£4253 $6209 €6380 Still life II (38x37cm-15x15in) canvas on board painted c.1953-57. 4-Jun-2 SOGA, Bratislava #62/R est:220000 (SL.K 270000)

Works on paper
£284 $414 €426 Autumn (24x37cm-9x15in) brown chl exec.c.1937. 4-Jun-2 SOGA, Bratislava #66/R est:18000 (SL.K 18000)
£441 $626 €662 Woman with scarf on her head (28x41cm-11x16in) red chk exec.c.1932. 26-Mar-2 SOGA, Bratislava #59/R (SL.K 28000)
£630 $895 €945 Hay-loft (24x33cm-9x13in) gouache exec.c.1940. 26-Mar-2 SOGA, Bratislava #58/R (SL.K 40000)
£756 $1074 €1134 Shepherd (28x40cm-11x16in) Gouache W/C exec.c.1935. 26-Mar-2 SOGA, Bratislava #57/R (SL.K 48000)

BAZZANI, Giuseppe (1690-1769) Italian
£16456 $26000 €26000 Alexander in Apelle's studio (50x36cm-20x14in) paper. 27-Nov-2 Finarte, Milan #94/R est:15000-18000
£49655 $78455 €72000 Saint Maragret's ecstasy (273x170cm-107x67in) en grisaille. 5-Apr-3 Finarte Semenzato, Milan #104/R est:60000

BAZZANTI, Pietro (19/20th C) Italian

Sculpture
£3600 $5616 €5400 Girl mending a fishing net (76cm-30in) indis.sig. white marble. 9-Apr-3 Sotheby's, London #90/R est:3000-5000

BAZZARO, Ernesto (1859-1937) Italian

Sculpture
£1203 $1900 €1900 Flight to Egypt (50cm-20in) s. pat bronze. 26-Nov-2 Christie's, Rome #1/R

BAZZARO, Leonardo (1853-1937) Italian
£1625 $2470 €2438 Venecia (50x35cm-20x14in) s. board. 3-Jul-2 Naón & Cia, Buenos Aires #29/R est:2500-3500
£2691 $4197 €4037 Lavadaiae (31x45cm-12x18in) s. panel. 11-Nov-2 Stephan Welz, Johannesburg #438/R est:25000-40000 (SA.R 42000)
£3871 $6116 €6000 Reading in the garden (50x35cm-20x14in) s. board. 18-Dec-2 Finarte, Milan #55/R est:8000
£4082 $6490 €6000 Boat in Chioggia (239x60cm-94x24in) s. board. 18-Mar-3 Finarte, Milan #24/R

BAZZARO, Leonardo (attrib) (1853-1937) Italian
£1379 $2193 €2000 Venice (50x40cm-20x16in) s. 5-Mar-3 Sotheby's, Milan #51/R

BAZZICALUVA, Ercole (17th C) Italian

Works on paper
£19000 $31730 €27550 Extensive river landscape with falconer on a horse. Extensive river landscape with hunter shooting (23x35cm-9x14in) pen brown ink pair. 8-Jul-3 Christie's, London #31/R est:15000-20000

BAZZICALUVA, Ercole (attrib) (17th C) Italian

Works on paper
£8784 $13703 €13000 Chasse au faucon. Chasse a l'affut (22x34cm-9x13in) pen dr pair. 27-Mar-3 Maigret, Paris #63/R est:5000-7000

BAZZINO (19th C) Italian

Sculpture
£2188 $3500 €3173 Boy and girl with grapes (58cm-23in) s. marble. 17-May-3 CRN Auctions, Cambridge #65

BEACH, Ernest G (1865-c.1934) British

Works on paper
£600 $978 €870 Heavy horses ploughing (23x33cm-9x13in) s. W/C. 17-Jul-3 Thomson, Roddick & Medcalf, Carlisle #50/R

BEACH, Thomas (1738-1806) British
£732 $1200 €1061 Portrait of a gentleman, in a red coat (76x63cm-30x25in) painted oval. 4-Jun-3 Christie's, Rockefeller NY #168/R
£760 $1170 €1140 Portrait of a gentleman, in a black jacket (76x63cm-30x25in) s.d.1787. 5-Sep-2 Christie's, Kensington #55/R
£828 $1275 €1300 Half length portrait of R I H Coxe (73x61cm-29x24in) s.d.1772 oval. 4-Sep-2 James Adam, Dublin #79/R est:1000-1500
£950 $1549 €1425 Head and shoulders portrait of a gentleman, T Eyre, wearing white cravat (61x73cm-24x29in) s.i.d.1776 oval. 11-Feb-3 Fellows & Sons, Birmingham #43/R

£1039 $1600 €1559 Portrait of a gentleman, thought to be Edmund Burke (50x39cm-20x15in) 4-Sep-2 Christie's, Rockefeller NY #226/R est:800-1200
£1083 $1668 €1700 Half length portrait of Thomas Eyre (73x61cm-29x24in) s.d.1776 oval. 4-Sep-2 James Adam, Dublin #77/R est:1000-1500

BEADLE, James Princep (1863-1947) British
£9500 $15009 €14250 Sounds of guns, the forced march, arrival of the 62nd field battery at Modder river (63x127cm-25x50in) s. exhib. 2-Dec-2 Sotheby's, London #70/R est:7000-9000

BEADLE, Paul John (1917-1992) New Zealander/British
Sculpture
£1884 $2940 €2826 Table sculpture depicting nine arts and crafts (25x25cm-10x10in) mono. bronze. 17-Sep-2 Peter Webb, Auckland #75/R est:4000-6000 (NZ.D 6200)

BEADLE, Peter (20th C) New Zealander
£262 $371 €393 Cromwell Gorge (54x70cm-21x28in) s. board prov. 21-Nov-1 Watson's, Christchurch #31/R (NZ.D 900)
£328 $481 €492 On the moonlight trail (49x60cm-19x24in) s. board prov. 19-Jun-2 Watson's, Christchurch #24/R est:800-1200 (NZ.D 1000)
£353 $569 €530 Mitre Peak and Milford Sound (44x74cm-17x29in) s. s.d.1972 verso board. 7-May-3 Dunbar Sloane, Auckland #98 (NZ.D 1000)
£465 $660 €698 Breakaway herd (68x90cm-27x35in) s. board prov. 21-Nov-1 Watson's, Christchurch #5/R (NZ.D 1600)
£465 $660 €698 Skippers Canyon, Shotover River (70x100cm-28x39in) s. board prov. 21-Nov-1 Watson's, Christchurch #9/R (NZ.D 1600)
£930 $1321 €1395 Gold coach and escort (59x88cm-23x35in) s. board prov. 21-Nov-1 Watson's, Christchurch #50/R est:1800-3000 (NZ.D 3200)

BEAL, Gifford (1879-1956) American
£577 $900 €866 Central Park hack (25x33cm-10x13in) s. panel prov. 21-Sep-2 Pook & Pook, Downington #20/R
£2078 $3200 €3117 By the pier (30x38cm-12x15in) s. board. 4-Sep-2 Christie's, Rockefeller NY #344/R est:3000-5000
£2656 $4250 €3984 Rural street scene (46x56cm-18x22in) s. board. 11-Jan-3 James Julia, Fairfield #169 est:3000-5000
£9434 $15000 €14151 Fifth Avenue bus (71x91cm-28x36in) s. prov.exhib. 5-Mar-3 Sotheby's, New York #92/R est:12000-18000
£16456 $26000 €24684 Snowstorm, Columbus Avenue (30x41cm-12x16in) s. oil gouache panel prov. 24-Apr-3 Shannon's, Milford #96/R est:25000-35000
£24359 $38000 €36539 Summer day, Rockport (64x81cm-25x32in) s.i. prov. 21-Sep-2 Pook & Pook, Downington #191/R est:10000-15000
Works on paper
£519 $800 €779 Dark sky, Cape Ann (34x50cm-13x20in) s. W/C gouache prov. 4-Sep-2 Christie's, Rockefeller NY #342/R
£574 $900 €861 Catskills from Kingston (33x48cm-13x19in) s. W/C. 22-Nov-2 Skinner, Boston #220/R est:800-1200
£864 $1400 €1253 Rocks, Stagefort Park (38x51cm-15x20in) gouache board prov. 21-May-3 Doyle, New York #114/R

BEAL, Reynolds (1867-1951) American
£4870 $7500 €7305 New York Harbour (30x41cm-12x16in) s. board prov. 24-Oct-2 Shannon's, Milford #93/R est:7000-9000
£9740 $15000 €14610 View of the bay (46x61cm-18x24in) s.d.1909 prov. 24-Oct-2 Shannon's, Milford #87/R est:15000-20000
£17742 $27500 €26613 Lefever lock (74x91cm-29x36in) s.d.1920 prov. 4-Dec-2 Sotheby's, New York #48/R est:25000-35000
£18868 $30000 €28302 Ferry to Rondout, New York (74x91cm-29x36in) s.d.1914 lit. 5-Mar-3 Sotheby's, New York #90/R est:30000-50000
Works on paper
£305 $500 €442 Ringling Bros, circus wagon (11x17cm-4x7in) s. chl. 5-Jun-3 Swann Galleries, New York #18/R
£350 $550 €525 Saco river bridge (20x29cm-8x11in) s.d.1963 W/C gouache graphite. 22-Nov-2 Skinner, Boston #295/R
£545 $850 €818 Cape Haiti (21x30cm-8x12in) s.i.d.1923 crayon pencil dr. 9-Nov-2 Sloan, North Bethesda #548/R
£1111 $1800 €1611 Fishermen, Northwest channel. Marina (18x25cm-7x10in) one s.d.1941 W/C gouache over pencil htd white pair. 21-May-3 Doyle, New York #113/R est:1500-2500
£1146 $1800 €1719 Whale Key Light, Berry Island (25x35cm-10x14in) s.d.1941 W/C. 22-Nov-2 Skinner, Boston #368/R est:700-900
£1585 $2600 €2298 Sells floto side show (28x35cm-11x14in) s.i.d. col pastel. 5-Jun-3 Swann Galleries, New York #17/R est:1800-2200

BEALE, Charles (1660-1714) British
£4000 $6520 €5800 Portraits of two children, head and shoulders (43x35cm-17x14in) pair oval. 21-Jul-3 Sotheby's, London #132/R est:2000-3000

BEALE, Mary (attrib) (1632-1697) British
£1500 $2340 €2250 Portrait of Mr Justice Selden (76x63cm-30x25in) 26-Mar-3 Woolley & Wallis, Salisbury #278/R est:1500-2500
£2600 $4056 €3900 Nell Gwyn (60x74cm-24x29in) 14-Sep-2 Cumbria Auction Rooms, UK #59/R est:1000-1500

BEALE, Sarah Sophia (20th C) British
£1266 $1975 €2000 Interior with figures (51x70cm-20x28in) s. panel. 21-Oct-2 Bernaerts, Antwerp #83/R est:1500-2000

BEALE, Shell (19/20th C) British?
Works on paper
£600 $948 €900 Gentlemen driving out (61x96cm-24x38in) s. pencil bodycol. 28-Nov-2 Christie's, Kensington #67/R

BEALES, L F (19th C) American
£329 $500 €494 Narragansett Bay at sunset (38x64cm-15x25in) s. i.verso. 17-Aug-2 North East Auctions, Portsmouth #971

BEALING, Nicola (1963-) British?
Works on paper
£280 $434 €420 Choir boys romping with a whale (30x46cm-12x18in) init. W/C. 26-Sep-2 Lane, Penzance #104

BEALS, Willis H (1859-?) American
£239 $375 €359 Pond and cottages (38x23cm-15x9in) s.d.1886. 23-Nov-2 Jackson's, Cedar Falls #301/R

BEAMAN, Waldo Gamaliel (1852-1937) American
£382 $600 €573 Late autumn in the Rocky Mountains (30x40cm-12x16in) s.d.92 panel. 22-Nov-2 Skinner, Boston #73/R

BEAMENT, Thomas Harold (1898-1984) Canadian
£206 $319 €309 Covered bridge (30x40cm-12x16in) s. panel prov. 3-Dec-2 Joyner, Toronto #357/R (C.D 500)
£311 $510 €467 Hunter (50x65cm-20x26in) s. 3-Jun-3 Joyner, Toronto #544 (C.D 700)
£329 $507 €494 Hunter's cabin (23x27cm-9x11in) s.i.d.1929 verso panel. 22-Oct-2 Iegor de Saint Hippolyte, Montreal #4 (C.D 800)
£370 $570 €555 Wood sleigh (23x27cm-9x11in) s.d.1929 panel. 22-Oct-2 Iegor de Saint Hippolyte, Montreal #3 (C.D 900)
£472 $736 €708 Fall cottage (30x33cm-12x13in) s. 25-Mar-3 Ritchie, Toronto #99y/R est:700-900 (C.D 1100)

BEAMISH, I A (19th C) British?
Works on paper
£320 $499 €480 Still life with grapes, hazelnuts and pear on a mossy bank (23x33cm-9x13in) s.d.1884 pencil W/C htd white. 19-Sep-2 Christie's, Kensington #157

BEAN, Ainslie H (fl.1870-1886) British
Works on paper
£450 $702 €675 View of Venice (29x62cm-11x24in) s.d.1885 W/C. 17-Sep-2 Sotheby's, Olympia #187/R

BEANLAND, Frank (1936-) British
£350 $581 €525 White, lemon and turquoise (135x135cm-53x53in) s. i.d.1976 verso. 10-Jun-3 Bonhams, Leeds #110
£2000 $3280 €3000 Untitled. oil wood three fold double-sided screen two. 3-Jun-3 Sotheby's, Olympia #302/R est:2000-3000

BEAR, George Telfer (1874-1973) British
£580 $945 €841 Still life of roses with an orange (46x31cm-18x12in) board. 21-Jul-3 Bonhams, Bath #37/R

BEAR, Jessie Drew (1877-1962) American
£272 $425 €408 Tropical fish, Antibes (30x41cm-12x16in) s.i.d.1952. 20-Sep-2 Freeman, Philadelphia #82/R

BEARD, William Holbrook (1824-1900) American
£1257 $2100 €1823 Mississippi genre scene (41x66cm-16x26in) i.verso. 22-Jun-3 Freeman, Philadelphia #87/R est:1000-1500
£1603 $2500 €2405 Land and riverscape (51x41cm-20x16in) d.1879. 20-Sep-2 Du Mouchelle, Detroit #2155/R est:2000-3000

BEARDEN, Ed (1919-1980) American
Works on paper
£929 $1450 €1394 Landscape (30x48cm-12x19in) W/C executed c.1944. 19-Oct-2 David Dike, Dallas #167/R

BEARDEN, Romare (1914-1988) American
Prints
£1840 $3000 €2760 Morning (55x71cm-22x28in) s.i. col lithograph exec.1979. 13-Feb-3 Christie's, Rockefeller NY #227/R
£2179 $3400 €3269 Bopping at Birdland, walking bass (86x61cm-34x24in) s.num.36/175 col lithograph. 19-Sep-2 Swann Galleries, New York #141/R est:2000-3000
£2848 $4500 €4272 Family (50x66cm-20x26in) s.num.6/25 col aquatint. 22-Apr-3 Butterfields, San Francisco #2250/R est:2500-3500
£3396 $5400 €5094 Quilting time (46x59cm-18x23in) s.num.129/175 col lithograph. 3-Mar-3 Swann Galleries, New York #96/R est:3000-5000
£11321 $18000 €16982 Prevalence of ritual (102x82cm-40x32in) s.i.num.2/100 sequentially col screenprint set of five. 29-Apr-3 Christie's, Rockefeller NY #596/R est:8000-10000
Works on paper
£2675 $4200 €4013 Landscape with reclining figure (52x67cm-20x26in) s. W/C. 21-Nov-2 Swann Galleries, New York #18/R est:4000-6000
£7097 $11000 €10646 Blue bird (24x17cm-9x7in) s. printed paper collage on board executed c.1968. 26-Sep-2 Christie's, Rockefeller NY #769/R est:7000-9000

BEARDSLEY, Aubrey (1872-1898) British
Works on paper
£2000 $3100 €3000 Female centaur (8x6cm-3x2in) pen black ink. 4-Dec-2 Christie's, Kensington #144/R est:1200-1800

BEARE, George (attrib) (18th C) British
£1050 $1712 €1523 Portrait of Thomas Goldney Esq (74x61cm-29x24in) i. 21-Jul-3 Bonhams, Bath #50/R est:1000-1500

BEARNE, Edward H (19th C) British
Works on paper
£320 $528 €464 Dogana Venice (20x33cm-8x13in) s.d.1892 W/C bodycol. 3-Jul-3 Duke & Son, Dorchester #66

BEARY, C R (19th C) ?
£3518 $5629 €5101 Caravan (105x190cm-41x75in) s.d.1875. 18-May-3 Anders Antik, Landskrona #39 est:50000 (S.KR 45000)

BEATON, Sir Cecil (1904-1980) British
£1500 $2310 €2250 Scene from My Fair Lady (76x56cm-30x22in) s. board. 5-Sep-2 Christie's, Kensington #531/R est:800-1200
Works on paper
£450 $702 €675 Stage design (29x36cm-11x14in) pen ink W/C. 26-Mar-3 Hamptons Fine Art, Godalming #78
£650 $1014 €975 Two negro ladies from Martinique (45x37cm-18x15in) brush ink w, executed 1937 exhib. 27-Mar-3 Christie's, Kensington #252
£650 $1073 €943 On road block near Sickering (44x29cm-17x11in) i.d.1940 pencil grey wash pen black ink prov. 3-Jul-3 Christie's, Kensington #240/R
£900 $1423 €1350 Costume designs (34x26cm-13x10in) s. pencil gouache W/C fabric samples attached pair. 27-Nov-2 Sotheby's, Olympia #8/R est:1000-1500
£1600 $2528 €2400 Importance of being Ernest (60x47cm-24x19in) s. ink W/C pair. 27-Nov-2 Sotheby's, Olympia #7/R est:1500-2000

BEATSON, Charles (19/20th C) British
£500 $785 €750 White quill (74x51cm-29x20in) s. 16-Apr-3 Christie's, Kensington #535/R

BEATTIE, Basil (1935-) British
£1900 $3097 €2850 Odds and evens (213x196cm-84x77in) oil wax on cotton duck painted 1996 prov. 3-Feb-3 Sotheby's, Olympia #20/R est:1500-2000
£4500 $6930 €6750 Witness V (213x183cm-84x72in) s.i.d.1992 on stretcher oil wax on cotton duck canvas. 23-Oct-2 Christie's, London #228/R est:2000-3000

BEATTIE, Edwin Robert (1845-1917) British
Works on paper
£700 $1134 €1050 Old churchyard, St. Nicholas Liverpool (26x36cm-10x14in) s. W/C. 21-Jan-3 Bonhams, New Bond Street #152/R

BEATTIE, Robert (19/20th C) Irish?
£400 $620 €600 Flowers sellers at the foot of Nelsons Column, Dublin (51x61cm-20x24in) s. 2-Oct-2 John Ross, Belfast #220
£500 $775 €750 First market day, Market Street, Portadown (51x61cm-20x24in) s. 2-Oct-2 John Ross, Belfast #12
Works on paper
£280 $409 €420 Basin Harbour, Newry (28x38cm-11x15in) s. W/C. 12-Jun-2 John Ross, Belfast #264

BEATTY, Frank T (1899-?) American
£438 $700 €657 Pigeon harbour cove (30x41cm-12x16in) s. masonite. 15-Mar-3 Eldred, East Dennis #124/R

BEATTY, John William (1869-1941) Canadian
£913 $1424 €1523 Untitled - on the canal, Holland (18x23cm-7x9in) s.i.d.1912 oil paper board. 13-Apr-3 Levis, Calgary #3/R est:2800-3200 (C.D 2100)
£1235 $1914 €1853 In the stable (21x26cm-8x10in) s. panel prov. 3-Dec-2 Joyner, Toronto #178/R est:3500-4500 (C.D 3000)
£1411 $2230 €2117 Field at harvest (26x35cm-10x14in) s. panel sold with a book prov. 18-Nov-2 Sotheby's, Toronto #85/R est:3000-4000 (C.D 3500)
£1613 $2548 €2420 Cattle by the river (20x25cm-8x10in) s.d.1921 panel prov. 14-Nov-2 Heffel, Vancouver #226/R est:3500-4500 (C.D 4000)
£1689 $2770 €2534 Hills, Canoe Lake, Algonquin Park (21x26cm-8x10in) s. panel prov. 3-Jun-3 Joyner, Toronto #9/R est:3000-5000 (C.D 3800)
£1803 $2812 €2614 Autumn landscape with barn, Ontario (23x29cm-9x11in) s. canvasboard prov. 26-Mar-3 Walker's, Ottawa #204/R est:4000-5000 (C.D 4200)
£1889 $3098 €2834 Along shore, Granby (25x34cm-10x13in) s.d.28 panel prov.exhib. 27-May-3 Sotheby's, Toronto #221/R est:2000-3000 (C.D 4250)
£1956 $3207 €2934 Near Port Hope (21x26cm-8x10in) s. board prov. 3-Jun-3 Joyner, Toronto #112/R est:3000-5000 (C.D 4400)
£2111 $3462 €3167 Country road (26x34cm-10x13in) s. panel. 3-Jun-3 Joyner, Toronto #223/R est:3000-4000 (C.D 4750)
£2133 $3499 €3200 Rapid, Northern Ontario (31x36cm-12x14in) s. 3-Jun-3 Joyner, Toronto #235/R est:5000-7000 (C.D 4800)
£2222 $3644 €3333 Autumn, Algonquin Park (28x37cm-11x15in) s. panel prov. 27-May-3 Sotheby's, Toronto #204/R est:3000-5000 (C.D 5000)
£2466 $3946 €3699 Country house (23x27cm-9x11in) s.verso board prov. 15-May-3 Heffel, Vancouver #15/R est:2500-3500 (C.D 5500)
£3086 $4784 €4629 Harbour Katwyke (35x60cm-14x24in) exhib.lit. 3-Dec-2 Joyner, Toronto #264/R est:8000-10000 (C.D 7500)

BEATY, Charles (?) ?
£260 $395 €390 Broaland landscape with wherries and other boats (20x36cm-8x14in) s.d.1888. 16-Aug-2 Keys, Aylsham #745
£300 $456 €450 Fishing boats at jetty, Yarmouth (20x36cm-8x14in) s.d.1885. 16-Aug-2 Keys, Aylsham #854

BEAU, Alcide le (1872-1943) French
£1127 $1814 €1600 Paysage aux collines bleues (44x53cm-17x21in) s. panel. 11-May-3 Thierry & Lannon, Brest #192 est:1000-1200
£2465 $3968 €3500 La cale de Rosbras a travers les arbres (41x33cm-16x13in) s. 11-May-3 Thierry & Lannon, Brest #193/R est:3800-4400
£5000 $7850 €7800 Symphony (65x81cm-26x32in) s. 15-Dec-2 Thierry & Lannon, Brest #148
£6250 $10188 €9000 Bord de mer a l'arbre japonisant (64x54cm-25x21in) s. 19-Jul-3 Thierry & Lannon, Brest #140 est:8000-10000
Works on paper
£290 $461 €420 La lecture (27x41cm-11x16in) s. W/C. 10-Mar-3 Thierry & Lannon, Brest #66
£308 $483 €480 Paysage (28x35cm-11x14in) s. W/C. 15-Dec-2 Thierry & Lannon, Brest #59
£417 $633 €650 Paysage (24x32cm-9x13in) s. exec.c.1910 W/C. 16-Aug-2 Deauville, France #57
£528 $850 €750 Paysage vallonee aux grands arbres (24x33cm-9x13in) s. chl. col.crayons. 11-May-3 Thierry & Lannon, Brest #66
£634 $1020 €900 Paysage de neige (24x31cm-9x12in) s. W/C. 11-May-3 Thierry & Lannon, Brest #91
£634 $1020 €900 Paysage provencal (24x32cm-9x13in) s. W/C. 11-May-3 Thierry & Lannon, Brest #317

BEAU, Henri (1863-1949) Canadian
£1067 $1749 €1601 Meules de foin (21x27cm-8x11in) s. canvas on board painted c.1895. 3-Jun-3 Joyner, Toronto #90/R est:2500-3500 (C.D 2400)
Works on paper
£193 $302 €290 Study of a woman in profile (15x15cm-6x6in) init. graphite. 25-Mar-3 Ritchie, Toronto #149/R (C.D 450)

BEAUBRUN, Charles (attrib) (1604-1692) French
£1800 $2826 €2700 Portrait of a lady in a red dress (63x47cm-25x19in) panel painted oval prov. 10-Dec-2 Bonhams, New Bond Street #63/R est:1000-1500

£1900 $3059 €2850 Portrait of a lady with pearl drop earrings and necklace (35x27cm-14x11in) panel. 20-Feb-3 Christie's, Kensington #327/R est:1000-1500

BEAUBRUN, Charles and Henri (17th C) French
£2128 $3553 €3000 Portrait presume de la Marquise de Sevigne (34x26cm-13x10in) 18-Jun-3 Tajan, Paris #113/R est:3000-4000

BEAUCE, Jean (1818-1875) French
£304 $474 €480 Tentes sur la plage (38x51cm-15x20in) s. 20-Oct-2 Chayette & Cheval, Paris #121
£1422 $2361 €2062 Pensive soldier (46x36cm-18x14in) s.d.1847. 16-Jun-3 Waddingtons, Toronto #274/R est:1000-1500 (C.D 3200)
£17073 $28000 €24756 French expeditionary force in Mexico (65x97cm-26x38in) s.d.1869. 27-May-3 Sotheby's, New York #142

BEAUCLERK, Lady Diana (1734-1808) British
Works on paper
£320 $499 €480 Bacchus and wood nymphs reveling in a woodland landscape (35x27cm-14x11in) pencil W/C. 27-Mar-3 Christie's, Kensington #39

BEAUDIN, Andre (1895-1979) French
£771 $1203 €1157 La rue de la nuit (47x27cm-19x11in) s.d.55. 5-Nov-2 Bukowskis, Stockholm #296/R (S.KR 11000)
£1923 $3038 €3000 Liseron (100x65cm-39x26in) s.d.76 prov.exhib. 15-Nov-2 Laurence Calmels, Paris #10a/R
£2532 $3949 €4000 La porte vitree (33x55cm-13x22in) s.d.1948. 20-Oct-2 Claude Boisgirard, Paris #37/R est:4000-5000
£4487 $6955 €7000 Danae (81x101cm-32x40in) s.d.1947 prov.exhib. 7-Dec-2 Cornette de St.Cyr, Paris #74/R est:8000
£4800 $7632 €7200 Femme endormie (81x65cm-32x26in) s. prov. 20-Mar-3 Sotheby's, Olympia #207/R est:4000-6000
£7500 $12525 €10875 Portrait (41x33cm-16x13in) s.d.1929 prov. 24-Jun-3 Christie's, London #10/R est:1500-2000
Sculpture
£9816 $16000 €14724 L'eveil (48cm-19in) init.i.num.2/6 gold pat, bronze. 12-Feb-3 Sotheby's, New York #82/R est:10000-15000
Works on paper
£545 $855 €850 Calligraphe (28x23cm-11x9in) s.d.1959 W/C. 13-Dec-2 Piasa, Paris #46
£576 $921 €800 Allegorie au nu (29x22cm-11x9in) s.d. gouache W/C. 18-May-3 Charbonneaux, Paris #122
£3769 $5992 €5540 Vaches et pigeon paon (72x90cm-28x35in) s. chl dr exhib. 26-Feb-3 Artcurial Briest, Paris #60/R est:5000-7000

BEAUDOIN, Mario (1962-) Canadian
£400 $656 €580 St. Francois, Ile D'Orlean (55x70cm-22x28in) s.i. acrylic board. 9-Jun-3 Hodgins, Calgary #273/R (C.D 900)
£602 $946 €903 Glissade (60x90cm-24x35in) s.i. acrylic. 25-Nov-2 Hodgins, Calgary #145/R (C.D 1500)

BEAUDUIN, Jean (1851-1916) Belgian
£921 $1492 €1400 Vue de Sannois, effet de soleil (19x24cm-7x9in) s.i.d.93 s.i.verso. 21-Jan-3 Christie's, Amsterdam #95/R est:700-900
£1079 $1727 €1500 Jeune femme reveuse (55x38cm-22x15in) s.d.96. 13-May-3 Palais de Beaux Arts, Brussels #214 est:1500-2000
£9500 $15865 €14250 Summer's day (65x54cm-26x21in) s.d.1890. 18-Jun-3 Christie's, Kensington #104/R est:5000-7000

BEAUFAUX, Polydore (1829-?) Belgian
£1013 $1580 €1600 Portrait of a woman (50x40cm-20x16in) s.d.1877. 21-Oct-2 Bernaerts, Antwerp #147/R est:900-1100

BEAUFORT, C (19th C) British
£1800 $2844 €2700 Returning from the day's shoot (46x56cm-18x22in) after Antoine Charles Horace Vernet. 28-Nov-2 Christie's, Kensington #75/R est:2000-3000

BEAUFORT, Jean (20th C) ?
£348 $550 €522 Venetian canal (51x91cm-20x36in) painted c.1940. 15-Nov-2 Du Mouchelle, Detroit #2270/R

BEAUFORT, Reverend William Louis (1771-1849) Irish
Works on paper
£4500 $7200 €6750 Augustinian Abbey. Slane Abbey (23x25cm-9x10in) s.i.d.1810 pencil ink W/C two. 15-May-3 Christie's, London #32/R

BEAUFRERE, Adolphe (1876-1960) French
£634 $1020 €900 Paysage meridional synthetique (21x25cm-8x10in) board. 11-May-3 Thierry & Lannon, Brest #325/R
£1493 $2434 €2150 Bretonne devant la Laita, la voile rouge (13x14cm-5x6in) studio st. panel on canvas. 19-Jul-3 Thierry & Lannon, Brest #102b/R est:2000-2500
£1761 $2835 €2500 La chaumiere au toit violet (16x20cm-6x8in) s. st.sig.verso paper on canvas. 11-May-3 Thierry & Lannon, Brest #328 est:2500-2800
£2042 $3288 €2900 La jeune Algerienne (27x24cm-11x9in) s. paper on panel. 11-May-3 Thierry & Lannon, Brest #326/R est:3000-3500
£2113 $3401 €3000 Paysage breton anime (27x24cm-11x9in) st. paper. 11-May-3 Thierry & Lannon, Brest #140 est:3000-3500
£2115 $3321 €3300 Paysage du Pouldu (21x24cm-8x9in) s.i. s.verso. 15-Dec-2 Thierry & Lannon, Brest #108
£2465 $3968 €3500 Paysage breton synthetique (20x16cm-8x6in) s. paper on canvas. 11-May-3 Thierry & Lannon, Brest #139/R est:2500-3000
£3194 $5207 €4600 Paysage des bords de l'Aven (25x27cm-10x11in) studio st. paper on canvas. 19-Jul-3 Thierry & Lannon, Brest #102 est:2800-3000
£3380 $5442 €4800 Le pecheur et sa barque en bord de mer (34x26cm-13x10in) s. paper on canvas. 11-May-3 Thierry & Lannon, Brest #141/R est:4000-5000
£3590 $5636 €5600 Paysage algerien aux grands arbres (46x36cm-18x14in) cardboard. 15-Dec-2 Thierry & Lannon, Brest #109/R
£3819 $6226 €5500 Gardien de vaches aux environs de pont-Aven (39x31cm-15x12in) s. isorel. 19-Jul-3 Thierry & Lannon, Brest #102c est:6000-7000
£4085 $6576 €5800 Paysage au champ vert (22x30cm-9x12in) st. 11-May-3 Thierry & Lannon, Brest #138/R est:2800-3000
£4648 $7483 €6600 Paysage a la montagne mauve (25x28cm-10x11in) st. board. 11-May-3 Thierry & Lannon, Brest #142 est:4500-5000
£6452 $10194 €10000 Champ jaune (23x17cm-9x7in) st.sig. paper on canvas prov. 18-Dec-2 Tajan, Paris #16/R est:15000
£9507 $15306 €13500 La baignade sur l'Aven (46x56cm-18x22in) 11-May-3 Thierry & Lannon, Brest #137/R est:8000-9000
Prints
£1666 $2616 €2600 Bouquet dans un vase japonais (18x14cm-7x6in) s.mono.i. etching. 22-Nov-2 Tajan, Paris #70/R est:2400-2800
£1795 $2818 €2800 Femmes au tub (33x21cm-13x8in) mono.i. etching panel. 22-Nov-2 Tajan, Paris #58/R est:2600-3000
Works on paper
£243 $386 €350 Personnage dans un sous bois (18x14cm-7x6in) st.mono. chl Indian ink wash dr. 29-Apr-3 Artcurial Briest, Paris #16
£282 $454 €400 Maison pres de l'allee arboree (12x18cm-5x7in) st. pen col.crayons. 11-May-3 Thierry & Lannon, Brest #50
£282 $454 €400 Paysage aux quatres arbres (27x20cm-11x8in) s. chl. 11-May-3 Thierry & Lannon, Brest #287
£308 $483 €480 Pecheurs et barque (22x17cm-9x7in) s. W/C. 15-Dec-2 Thierry & Lannon, Brest #318
£317 $510 €450 Village provencal (20x26cm-8x10in) st. chl. 11-May-3 Thierry & Lannon, Brest #51
£486 $792 €700 L'oasis. studio st. wash double-sided. 19-Jul-3 Thierry & Lannon, Brest #49
£903 $1472 €1300 Paysage a la mare et a la vache (18x18cm-7x7in) s.d.35 W/C gouache. 19-Jul-3 Thierry & Lannon, Brest #83/R
£972 $1585 €1400 Paysage au chemin jaune (12x12cm-5x5in) studio st. mixed media. 19-Jul-3 Thierry & Lannon, Brest #49a
£980 $1558 €1440 Bretonne sur la falaise (18x16cm-7x6in) st.mono. W/C pencil. 26-Feb-3 Artcurial Briest, Paris #23
£1338 $2154 €1900 Jeus d'enfants au Parc Montsouris a Paris (16x21cm-6x8in) s.d.1907 W/C pen. 11-May-3 Thierry & Lannon, Brest #81 est:1200-1500
£2535 $4082 €3600 La chapelle St Leger sur le Belon (24x21cm-9x8in) st. mixed media. 11-May-3 Thierry & Lannon, Brest #327/R est:2500-2800

BEAUGUREAU, W (19th C) French
£920 $1500 €1380 Battle scene (30x38cm-12x15in) s. panel. 2-Feb-3 Grogan, Boston #29 est:800-1200

BEAULIEU, Elisabeth Chales de (1861-1946) German
£647 $1036 €900 Window view (61x50cm-24x20in) s. 15-May-3 Neumeister, Munich #218/R

BEAULIEU, Henri de (1819-1884) French
£11465 $18000 €17198 Allegory (207x107cm-81x42in) s.i. prov. 21-Nov-2 Sotheby's, New York #187/R est:20000-30000

BEAULIEU, Paul Vanier (1910-1995) Canadian
£248 $400 €372 Snow scene (48x58cm-19x23in) 9-May-3 Douglas, South Deerfield #1
£965 $1438 €1448 Les yeux noirs (55x45cm-22x18in) s.d.45 isorel. 26-Jun-2 Iegor de Saint Hippolyte, Montreal #3 (C.D 2200)
£1906 $3049 €2859 Maison abstraite (72x91cm-28x36in) s.d.1969. 15-May-3 Heffel, Vancouver #74/R est:6000-8000 (C.D 4250)
£2222 $3644 €3333 Dans la cuisine (14x17cm-6x7in) s. prov. 3-Jun-3 Joyner, Toronto #193/R est:1500-2000 (C.D 5000)
£2222 $3644 €3333 Canadian goose (89x116cm-35x46in) s.d.56 prov. 27-May-3 Sotheby's, Toronto #27/R est:5000-7000 (C.D 5000)

£2466 $3946 €3699 Still life (56x71cm-22x28in) s.d.1982. 15-May-3 Heffel, Vancouver #72/R est:6000-8000 (C.D 5500)
£2469 $3802 €3704 Hiver dans les Laurentides (61x122cm-24x48in) s.d.74. 22-Oct-2 Iegor de Saint Hippolyte, Montreal #10 (C.D 6000)
£3226 $5097 €4839 Nature morte (38x46cm-15x18in) s.d.50 prov. 18-Nov-2 Sotheby's, Toronto #115/R est:5000-7000 (C.D 8000)
£6855 $10831 €10283 Nature morte aux pichets (74x100cm-29x39in) s.d.53 s.i.d.verso. 18-Nov-2 Sotheby's, Toronto #29/R est:12000-15000 (C.D 17000)

Works on paper

£203 $319 €305 Nature morte (14x27cm-6x11in) s. W/C. 10-Dec-2 Pinneys, Montreal #133 (C.D 500)
£407 $638 €611 Soleil couchant (32x50cm-13x20in) s.d.60 ink gouache pastel. 12-Dec-2 Iegor de Saint Hippolyte, Montreal #6 (C.D 1000)
£429 $670 €644 Floating village (20x30cm-8x12in) s.d.70 mixed media. 25-Mar-3 Iegor de Saint Hippolyte, Montreal #7 (C.D 1000)
£524 $854 €786 Seated man (31x24cm-12x9in) s. ink W/C. 12-Feb-3 Iegor de Saint Hippolyte, Montreal #17 (C.D 1300)
£1121 $1794 €1682 Still life with fruit (38x56cm-15x22in) s.d.1965 W/C. 15-May-3 Heffel, Vancouver #73/R est:3000-4000 (C.D 2500)
£1317 $2028 €1976 Coq (63x48cm-25x19in) s.d.69 W/C ink. 22-Oct-2 Iegor de Saint Hippolyte, Montreal #11 (C.D 3200)

BEAUMONT, Annie (19th C) British

£700 $1092 €1015 Preparing to sail - fishing boats in harbour (34x46cm-13x18in) s. canvasboard. 27-Mar-3 Lane, Penzance #177

BEAUMONT, Arthur Edwaine (1890-1978) American

Works on paper

£2950 $4750 €4425 Home Base-Port Au prince-Haiti (19x25cm-7x10in) s.i. W/C prov. 18-Feb-3 John Moran, Pasadena #82 est:2000-3000

BEAUMONT, Arthur J (1877-1956) American

£680 $1061 €1020 St Ives Harbour (36x46cm-14x18in) s.d.1906 board. 17-Oct-2 David Lay, Penzance #1013
£2315 $3750 €3473 At the harbor (66x81cm-26x32in) s. indis.d.28 s.verso. 24-Jan-3 Freeman, Philadelphia #203/R est:600-1000

BEAUMONT, Claudio Francesco (attrib) (1694-1766) Italian

£18987 $30000 €30000 Scipione's charity (123x178cm-48x70in) 2-Dec-2 Finarte, Milan #154/R est:40000

BEAUMONT, George Howland (1753-1827) British

£445 $695 €650 Castle ruins by the sea (17x14cm-7x6in) s.i.d. verso panel. 11-Apr-3 Winterberg, Heidelberg #207

BEAUMONT, John Thomas Barber (1774-1841) British

Miniatures

£1100 $1782 €1650 Gentleman wearing blue coat (8cm-3xin) init. gold frame seed pearls plaitec hair. 22-May-3 Bonhams, New Bond Street #98/R est:500-700
£1800 $2952 €2610 Gentleman in a black coat, knotted cravat (7cm-3xin) init. gilt metal frame prov. 3-Jun-3 Christie's, London #229/R est:800-1200
£2000 $3140 €3000 Young girl holding fruit in the folds of her white dress (7cm-3xin) init. silver gilt frame oval. 10-Dec-2 Christie's, London #166/R est:2000-3000

BEAUQUESNE, Wilfrid Constant (1847-1913) French

£545 $828 €850 Nun nursing and protecting a wounded soldier (46x32cm-18x13in) s. lit. 11-Jul-2 Allgauer, Kempten #2424/R
£705 $1100 €1058 Two horsemen (23x33cm-9x13in) s.d.1883 board. 5-Nov-2 Arthur James, Florida #362
£786 $1226 €1179 Street battle (33x24cm-13x9in) s. 6-Nov-2 Dobiaschofsky, Bern #340/R est:1800 (S.FR 1800)
£1146 $1789 €1800 Sonnerie d'appel, militaire (50x67cm-20x26in) s.d.1897. 11-Nov-2 Horta, Bruxelles #659 est:1500-2000
£3265 $5192 €4800 Batterie soutenue (50x70cm-20x28in) s.d.1896. 26-Feb-3 Coutau Begarie, Paris #151/R est:3500

BEAUREGARD, Charles G (c.1856-d.1919) Canadian

£2675 $4200 €4013 Cows watering by a stream (55x96cm-22x38in) s. 14-Dec-2 Weschler, Washington #660/R est:2000-3000

BEAUREGARD, Daniel (?) American

£385 $600 €578 Impressionist market scene with figures (18x13cm-7x5in) s. panel. 18-Sep-2 Alderfer's, Hatfield #282

BEAUVAIS, Armand (1840-1911) French

£298 $486 €450 Eglise dans un village de l'Oise (30x19cm-12x7in) indis.sig. panel. 2-Feb-3 Muizon & Le Coent, Paris #32

BEAUVAIS, Arnold (1886-?) British

£300 $477 €450 Cap Pillar at Wivenhoe, Essex (41x51cm-16x20in) s.d.50 board. 30-Apr-3 Halls, Shrewsbury #275/R

BEAUVAIS, Lubin de (19/20th C) French

Works on paper

£1020 $1622 €1500 Elegantes a la Belle Epoque (26x21cm-10x8in) s. W/C. 21-Mar-3 Rieunier, Bailly-Pommery, Mathias, Paris #88

BEAUVAIS, Walter (1942-) British

£250 $390 €375 Beach scene (19x25cm-7x10in) s. board. 15-Sep-2 Lots Road, London #358
£250 $400 €363 Bathers (28x28cm-11x11in) s. board. 18-May-3 Lots Road, London #346
£260 $413 €390 Beach scene (34x44cm-13x17in) board. 23-Mar-3 Lots Road, London #353/R
£300 $489 €450 Beach scene (44x59cm-17x23in) s. 2-Feb-3 Lots Road, London #353a/R
£300 $486 €435 Beach scene (40x50cm-16x20in) s. board. 3-Aug-3 Lots Road, London #364
£320 $512 €480 Beach scene (39x49cm-15x19in) s. board. 12-Jan-3 Lots Road, London #346/R
£320 $502 €480 Boating scene, France (55x85cm-22x33in) s. panel. 15-Dec-2 Lots Road, London #340a
£350 $546 €525 Yachts in sail (61x46cm-24x18in) s. panel. 13-Oct-2 Lots Road, London #354
£550 $853 €825 Bathers and yachters (31x84cm-12x33in) s. panel. 6-Oct-2 Lots Road, London #360a
£550 $880 €825 Beach scene (24x34cm-9x13in) s. panel. 5-Jan-3 Lots Road, London #354
£600 $990 €870 At the seaside (51x76cm-20x30in) s. 3-Jul-3 Christie's, Kensington #455

BEAUVALET (fl.1832-1845) French

Works on paper

£14865 $23189 €22000 Vases, coupes, bas-reliefs, armes et objet (52x40cm-20x16in) s. W/C gouache dr album. 27-Mar-3 Christie's, Paris #166/R est:10000-15000

BEAUVALLET, Pierre Nicolas and BRALLE, Jean Marie Nicolas (18th C) French

Works on paper

£612 $972 €900 Fontaine du Gros Caillou (44x26cm-17x10in) W/C pen ink over crayon prov. 24-Mar-3 Tajan, Paris #73

BEAUVERIE, Charles Joseph (1839-1924) French

£1322 $1969 €1983 Woman by spring in garden (61x46cm-24x18in) s.d.1883. 25-Jun-2 Koller, Zurich #6517/R est:3000-4000 (S.FR 3000)

BEAUVOIR, H de (20th C) French

£769 $1208 €1200 Le marche aux herbes (73x92cm-29x36in) s. i.d.38 verso. 16-Dec-2 Gros & Delettrez, Paris #43/R

BEAVIS, Richard (1824-1896) British

£450 $716 €675 Clearing timber, Brittany (30x51cm-12x20in) s. i.verso. 6-Mar-3 Christie's, Kensington #470
£3309 $5295 €4600 Landing the catch (86x125cm-34x49in) s.d.1872. 17-May-3 Lempertz, Koln #1364/R est:3000

BEBB, Minnie Rosa (1857-?) British

£780 $1271 €1170 Tabby kitten seated on a book (34x30cm-13x12in) s.d.1895. 29-Jan-3 Hampton & Littlewood, Exeter #406/R

BEBIE, Henry (1824-1888) American

£1173 $1900 €1760 Lady in fine white gown with guitar (69x56cm-27x22in) s. 24-Jan-3 New Orleans Auction, New Orleans #1368/R est:1000-1500
£2115 $3300 €3173 Portrait of a young girl (137x112cm-54x44in) 9-Nov-2 Sloan, North Bethesda #607/R est:4000-6000

BECCAFUMI, Domenico (attrib) (1486-1551) Italian

£1375 $2200 €2063 Madonna and Child (13x11cm-5x4in) panel prov. 14-May-3 Doyle, New York #49/R est:2000-3000
£14744 $22853 €23000 Tete de. portant un voile (22x16cm-9x6in) paper. 4-Dec-2 Piasa, Paris #1/R est:15000

BECCARIA, Angelo (1820-1897) Italian

£2041 $3245 €3000 Shipwreck (32x44cm-13x17in) init. cardboard. 1-Mar-3 Meeting Art, Vercelli #262

BECH, Poul Anker (1942-) Danish

£270 $422 €405 Evening picture with figures (57x77cm-22x30in) s. 18-Sep-2 Kunsthallen, Copenhagen #202 (D.KR 3200)

£402 $639 €603 View from an aeroplane (27x33cm-11x13in) s. 26-Feb-3 Kunsthallen, Copenhagen #35 (D.KR 4400)
£686 $1070 €1029 Composition (40x93cm-16x37in) init. panel prov. 11-Nov-2 Rasmussen, Vejle #72/R (D.KR 8000)
£815 $1271 €1223 Coming back from holiday (87x103cm-34x41in) s. panel prov. 11-Nov-2 Rasmussen, Vejle #77/R (D.KR 9500)
£1034 $1602 €1551 Composition (82x100cm-32x39in) s. 4-Dec-2 Kunsthallen, Copenhagen #91/R est:15000 (D.KR 12000)
£1335 $2229 €1936 Clouds above the barrow (62x54cm-24x21in) s. s.d.1992 verso. 17-Jun-3 Rasmussen, Copenhagen #59/R est:12000-15000 (D.KR 14000)
£1525 $2547 €2211 The last battle (50x62cm-20x24in) s. s.d.1990, 19 verso. 17-Jun-3 Rasmussen, Copenhagen #55/R est:12000-15000 (D.KR 16000)
£1766 $2790 €2649 Winter dream (54x62cm-21x24in) s. prov. 1-Apr-3 Rasmussen, Copenhagen #353/R est:15000 (D.KR 19000)

Works on paper
£306 $477 €459 Interior scene with figure (43x35cm-17x14in) s.d.90 W/C. 5-Aug-2 Rasmussen, Vejle #302/R (D.KR 3600)
£420 $667 €630 Clearing among trees (28x45cm-11x18in) s. W/C. 29-Apr-3 Kunsthallen, Copenhagen #12 (D.KR 4500)

BECHER, Arthur E (1877-1941) German
£1801 $2900 €2702 Musician serenading sultan and harem (66x46cm-26x18in) s. painted c.1910. 10-May-3 Illustration House, New York #95/R est:2000-3000
£2564 $4000 €3846 Knight speaking to maiden in castle's tower (91x64cm-36x25in) s. 9-Nov-2 Illustration House, New York #63/R est:3500-5000

BECHER, Bernd and Hilla (20th C) German
Photographs
£2258 $3500 €3387 Winding tower, Wales (30x41cm-12x16in) gelatin silver print. 26-Sep-2 Christie's, Rockefeller NY #812/R est:4000-6000
£5063 $8000 €7595 Three ansiohtn eines wuppertaler schwebebahn bahnhofs (70x40cm-28x16in) s. three gelatin silver prints on board executed 1972. 14-Nov-2 Christie's, Rockefeller NY #404/R est:10000-15000
£6329 $10000 €9494 Gas plant (51x41cm-20x16in) init.d.69 gelatin silver print in 2 parts prov. 13-Nov-2 Sotheby's, New York #514/R est:8000-12000
£6646 $10500 €9969 Cooling towers (22x30cm-9x12in) s.d.72 2 gelatin silver print on board prov. 25-Apr-3 Phillips, New York #195/R est:10000-15000
£11000 $18040 €16500 Wasserturme - water towers (40x31cm-16x12in) i. silver gelatin prints two prov. 6-Feb-3 Christie's, London #719/R est:15000-20000
£12000 $19680 €18000 Hochofen - blast furnaces (24x18cm-9x7in) s.d.1971 gelatine silver print on board six prov. 6-Feb-3 Christie's, London #718/R est:10000-15000
£13924 $22000 €20886 Water towers (29x24cm-11x9in) s.d.72 2 gelatin silver print prov. 25-Apr-3 Phillips, New York #196/R est:18000-22000
£18987 $30000 €28481 Kohlesilos (40x30cm-16x12in) s. num.1-4 four gelatin silver prints executed 1971 prov. 14-Nov-2 Christie's, Rockefeller NY #403/R est:40000-60000
£22785 $36000 €34178 Gas holders (30x24cm-12x9in) s.d.72 2 gelatin silver print prov. 25-Apr-3 Phillips, New York #197/R est:18000-22000
£22785 $36000 €34178 Water towers (30x24cm-12x9in) s.d.72 2 gelatin silver print prov. 25-Apr-3 Phillips, New York #198/R est:18000-22000
£23000 $35420 €34500 Winding towers Great Britain (39x30cm-15x12in) s.i.verso nine gelatin silver prints executed 1983 prov. 23-Oct-2 Christie's, London #198/R est:20000-30000
£24051 $38000 €36077 Water cooling plant (29x24cm-11x9in) s.d.72 2 gelatin silver print prov. 25-Apr-3 Phillips, New York #199 est:18000-22000
£34810 $55000 €52215 Water towers - New York rooftops (171x137cm-67x54in) s.i.num.1-9 nine gelatin silver prints executed 1978-79 prov. 14-Nov-2 Christie's, Rockefeller NY #401/R est:70000-90000
£47468 $75000 €71202 Blast furnace, heads (173x239cm-68x94in) s.i. num.1-5 verso fifteen gelatin silver prints on board. 14-Nov-2 Christie's, Rockefeller NY #402/R est:60000-80000
£51250 $82000 €76875 Water towers (58x50cm-23x20in) s.i.d.1972-95 black white photograph set of eight. 15-May-3 Phillips, New York #14/R est:40000-60000

BECHI, Luigi (1830-1919) Italian
£3291 $5200 €5200 On the beach (12x35cm-5x14in) s. 26-Nov-2 Christie's, Rome #143/R est:2500
£30063 $47500 €45095 New baby (100x83cm-39x33in) s. 24-Apr-3 Sotheby's, New York #135/R est:40000-60000

BECHTEL, John Howard (20th C) Canadian?
£233 $383 €338 By the sea (81x122cm-32x48in) board. 1-Jun-3 Levis, Calgary #9/R (C.D 525)

BECHTOLD, Erwin (1925-) German
£387 $612 €600 Untitled (40x35cm-16x14in) s.verso oil pencil canvas on board prov.exhib. 17-Dec-2 Segre, Madrid #209/R

BECK, Billy de (1890-1942) American
Works on paper
£1242 $2000 €1863 Barney and Sunshine do their utmost to avoid arriving Captain Jawge (10x43cm-4x17in) init. pen ink. 10-May-3 Illustration House, New York #33/R est:1000-1500

BECK, Gustav Kurt (1902-) Austrian
£500 $770 €750 Italian landscape (55x86cm-22x34in) s. 3-Sep-2 Shapiro, Sydney #399/R est:700-900 (A.D 1400)

BECK, I F (19th C) Scandinavian
£2800 $4424 €4200 Chattering lory sitting on a branch of an orange tree (40x28cm-16x11in) s.d.1844 panel. 15-Nov-2 Sotheby's, London #10/R est:3000-5000

BECK, Jacob Samuel (attrib) (1715-1778) German
£1097 $1733 €1700 Still life with copper (18x27cm-7x11in) panel. 20-Dec-2 Tajan, Paris #100/R
£5732 $8943 €9000 Still life of peaches and an apricot on a pewter plate (59x68cm-23x27in) 5-Nov-2 Sotheby's, Amsterdam #321/R est:10000-15000

BECK, Johann Heinrich (1788-1875) German
£962 $1462 €1500 Romantic wooded landscapes (28x37cm-11x15in) s.i.d.1843 board two. 17-Aug-2 Hans Stahl, Toestorf #65/R est:1200

BECK, Lucy Boyd (1916-) Australian
£1057 $1670 €1533 Joy of life (57x39cm-22x15in) s. col glaze on ceramic tile. 22-Jul-3 Lawson Menzies, Sydney #94/R est:2000-2500 (A.D 2600)

BECK, Sidney (1936-) South African
£448 $700 €672 Woman in disgrace (50x60cm-20x24in) s. board. 11-Nov-2 Stephan Welz, Johannesburg #574/R (SA.R 7000)

BECK, Wilhelm (19th C) German
£1373 $2251 €2100 Prussian-French battle (98x155cm-39x61in) tempera paper. 5-Feb-3 Il Ponte, Milan #371
£1961 $3216 €3000 Prussian-French battle (100x213cm-39x84in) tempera paper. 5-Feb-3 Il Ponte, Milan #404

BECK, William Francis ver (1858-1933) American
Works on paper
£2484 $4000 €3726 Airplane with bears (56x38cm-22x15in) s. W/C ink. 10-May-3 Illustration House, New York #26/R est:1500-2500

BECKENKAMP, Kaspar Benedikt (1747-1828) German
£769 $1215 €1200 Portrait of Clemens Wenzeslaus von Sachsen (39x34cm-15x13in) 16-Nov-2 Lempertz, Koln #1007/R

BECKER, Adolf von (1831-1909) Finnish
£570 $889 €900 Dog (9x17cm-4x7in) s. 12-Sep-2 Hagelstam, Helsinki #905
£719 $1180 €1000 Meditation (46x38cm-18x15in) s.d.1899 exhib. 4-Jun-3 Bukowskis, Helsinki #257/R
£1709 $2700 €2700 The actor (76x51cm-30x20in) s. 1-Dec-2 Bukowskis, Helsinki #23/R est:3000-4000
£2342 $3700 €3700 Boats at anchor (28x35cm-11x14in) s. board. 1-Dec-2 Bukowskis, Helsinki #22/R est:5000-6000

BECKER, August (1822-1887) German
£366 $578 €530 Landscape with cave entrance (34x25cm-13x10in) s.d.1885 panel. 5-Apr-3 Quittenbaum, Hamburg #5/R

BECKER, Carl Georg (20th C) German
£685 $1068 €1000 Bottles and colours (75x100cm-30x39in) s.d.68 panel. 10-Apr-3 Schopman, Hamburg #669

BECKER, Carl Ludwig Friedrich (1820-1900) German
£1224 $1947 €1800 Fleeing the storm (47x60cm-19x24in) s.d.1849. 19-Mar-3 Neumeister, Munich #509/R est:2000

BECKER, Carl Ludwig Friedrich (attrib) (1820-1900) German
£2055 $3205 €3000 Court scene (63x75cm-25x30in) 10-Apr-3 Dorotheum, Vienna #80/R est:3400-3800

BECKER, Charles Hunter (19/20th C) American
£683 $1100 €1025 Irene, with parasol (66x76cm-26x30in) s.d.1922 exhib. 18-Feb-3 John Moran, Pasadena #165

BECKER, Claus (1903-1983) German
£649 $948 €1000 Summer landscape in Holstein (59x79cm-23x31in) s. panel. 15-Jun-2 Hans Stahl, Hamburg #160/R
£912 $1414 €1450 Farmstead in the snow (52x65cm-20x26in) s.d.45 panel. 2-Nov-2 Hans Stahl, Toestorf #95/R

BECKER, Curt Georg (1904-1972) German
£506 $800 €800 Italian woman (101x80cm-40x31in) mono.d.1959 i. verso. 30-Nov-2 Arnold, Frankfurt #31/R
Works on paper
£253 $400 €400 Study of a nude man with female head (46x29cm-18x11in) s.d.50 red ochre dr. 30-Nov-2 Geble, Radolfzell #710
£353 $536 €550 Reclining female nude (15x27cm-6x11in) s.d.30 W/C. 31-Aug-2 Geble, Radolfzell #677/R
£1139 $1800 €1800 Female nude standing (80x58cm-31x23in) s.d.65 W/C mixed media. 30-Nov-2 Geble, Radolfzell #709 est:1250

BECKER, Edmund (fl.1770-1800) British
Works on paper
£600 $942 €900 Montgomery (23x33cm-9x13in) i. pencil wash sold with another by same hand. 16-Dec-2 Bonhams, Bury St Edmunds #425

BECKER, Ernst August (fl.1840-1854) German
£650 $1066 €975 Page (46x36cm-18x14in) i.stretcher exhib. 29-May-3 Christie's, Kensington #248/R
£1154 $1788 €1800 Half-length portrait of Carl Heinrich Theodor Staudinger in uniform (85x73cm-33x29in) mono. i.d.1837 verso. 4-Dec-2 Neumeister, Munich #671/R est:2000

BECKER, Frederick W (1888-1974) American
£559 $900 €839 Sycamores in a landscape (23x18cm-9x7in) s. paper laid down. 18-Feb-3 John Moran, Pasadena #4a
£659 $1100 €956 Portrait of Indian braves (64x51cm-25x20in) s. 17-Jun-3 John Moran, Pasadena #106a est:1000-2000
£705 $1100 €1058 Late October Taos, New Mexico (30x23cm-12x9in) canvasboard. 19-Oct-2 David Dike, Dallas #91/R
£1032 $1600 €1548 Sycamores in landscape (58x46cm-23x18in) s. board prov. 29-Oct-2 John Moran, Pasadena #706 est:1000-1500
£1210 $1900 €1815 Taos canyon, New Mexico. Big Bend, Texas (23x30cm-9x12in) one s.i.verso panel one s. board pair prov. 19-Nov-2 Butterfields, San Francisco #8093/R est:2000-3000
£2070 $3250 €3105 Lone tree on the Carmel coast. Crashing waves (30x41cm-12x16in) one s. canvas on board one board on board pair prov. 19-Nov-2 Butterfields, San Francisco #8286/R est:2000-3000
£3846 $6000 €5769 Young Indian woman (81x71cm-32x28in) 19-Oct-2 David Dike, Dallas #215/R est:8000-10000

BECKER, Frederick W (attrib) (1888-1974) American
£538 $850 €780 Old mill (69x89cm-27x35in) 5-Apr-3 DeFina, Austinburg #1288

BECKER, Fridolin (1830-1895) Dutch
£1096 $1710 €1600 Italian girl with an apple in her hand on the terrace (40x27cm-16x11in) s. panel. 14-Apr-3 Glerum, Amsterdam #103/R est:600-800

BECKER, Harry (1865-1928) British
Works on paper
£300 $495 €435 Chickens (13x20cm-5x8in) pencil prov. 1-Jul-3 Bonhams, Norwich #123
£380 $597 €570 Scything (17x25cm-7x10in) pencil. 16-Dec-2 Bonhams, Bury St Edmunds #424/R

BECKER, Hermann (1817-1885) German
£698 $1110 €1047 Family portrait of father, mother and daughter (37x30cm-15x12in) s.i.d.1852. 5-Mar-3 Rasmussen, Copenhagen #1792/R (D.KR 7500)

BECKER, Walter (20th C) French
£503 $785 €800 Female nude sunbathing on boat (54x73cm-21x29in) s.d.1950 lit. 20-Sep-2 Karlheinz Kaupp, Staufen #2023/R
£1154 $1823 €1800 Nausikaa discovering Odysseus (90x106cm-35x42in) mono.i.d.1978. 14-Nov-2 Neumeister, Munich #739/R est:1800-2000

BECKET, Maria A (?-1904) American
£503 $800 €755 Path through an autumn wood (51x61cm-20x24in) s. 7-Mar-3 Skinner, Boston #453/R

BECKETT, Clarice (1887-1935) Australian
£2491 $3811 €3737 Beach (24x34cm-9x13in) s. pulpboard. 25-Aug-2 Sotheby's, Paddington #115/R est:5000-7000 (A.D 7000)
£2847 $4356 €4271 Across the bay (22x29cm-9x11in) s. pulpboard prov.exhib. 25-Aug-2 Sotheby's, Paddington #175/R est:12000-18000 (A.D 8000)
£4215 $6280 €6323 Beaumaris seascape (22x35cm-9x14in) card. 27-Aug-2 Christie's, Melbourne #173/R est:7000-10000 (A.D 11000)
£5769 $9173 €8654 Setting sun, Beaumaris (30x25cm-12x10in) s. board prov. 4-Mar-3 Deutscher-Menzies, Melbourne #111/R est:14000-18000 (A.D 15000)
£6130 $9625 €9195 Misty day (30x40cm-12x16in) s. board painted c.1931 prov. 15-Apr-3 Lawson Menzies, Sydney #22/R est:15000-20000 (A.D 16000)
£8000 $12880 €12000 Farewell summer (54x44cm-21x17in) s. prov.exhib. 6-May-3 Christie's, Melbourne #92/R est:20000-30000 (A.D 20000)
£11923 $18957 €17885 Red roofs (30x51cm-12x20in) s. i.verso canvas on board painted c.1932 prov. 4-Mar-3 Deutscher-Menzies, Melbourne #37/R est:32000-38000 (A.D 31000)

BECKING, Horst (1937-) German
Works on paper
£544 $865 €800 Composition. s. mixed media. 18-Mar-3 Galerie Moderne, Brussels #198
£816 $1298 €1200 Composition. s. mixed media. 18-Mar-3 Galerie Moderne, Brussels #200

BECKMANN, Johann (1809-1882) German
£2564 $4000 €3846 Landscape with hunters loading deer in a canoe (71x104cm-28x41in) s. prov. 14-Sep-2 Selkirks, St. Louis #726/R est:5000-6000

BECKMANN, Max (1884-1950) German
£335484 $520000 €503226 Rote tulpen und feuerlilien - red tulips and tiger lily (78x75cm-31x30in) s.d.35 prov.exhib.lit. 4-Nov-2 Phillips, New York #21/R est:500000-700000
£529032 $820000 €793548 Stilleben mit negerplastik - still life with African sculpture (55x45cm-22x18in) s.d.1924 prov.exhib.lit. 4-Nov-2 Phillips, New York #19/R est:850000-1200000
£579710 $950725 €800000 Landscape near Saint-Cyr-sur-Mer (72x105cm-28x41in) s.i.d.31 prov.exhib.lit. 30-May-3 Villa Grisebach, Berlin #53/R est:900000-1200000
Prints
£1923 $2981 €3000 King and demagogue (38x25cm-15x10in) s. lithograph. 7-Dec-2 Hauswedell & Nolte, Hamburg #547/R est:2000
£1923 $2981 €3000 Dancing couple (17x10cm-7x4in) s. panel. 7-Dec-2 Hauswedell & Nolte, Hamburg #549/R est:2800
£2025 $3200 €3200 Girl with cat (12x16cm-5x6in) s.i. drypoint prov. 30-Nov-2 Villa Grisebach, Berlin #144/R est:2500-3500
£2051 $3200 €3077 Bildnis Nalia mit aufgestutzen Armen und Glas (21x16cm-8x6in) s. drypoint. 7-Nov-2 Swann Galleries, New York #544/R est:3500-5000
£2138 $3400 €3207 Die Seiltanzer (26x25cm-10x10in) s. drypoint one of 125. 2-May-3 Sotheby's, New York #78/R est:3000-4000
£2174 $3565 €3000 Carousel (29x26cm-11x10in) s. drypoint. 31-May-3 Villa Grisebach, Berlin #223/R est:3500-4500
£2174 $3565 €3000 Admiral Cafe (26x30cm-10x12in) s. lithograph. 29-May-3 Lempertz, Koln #534/R est:4000
£2215 $3500 €3500 The Negro (29x26cm-11x10in) s.i.d. drypoint prov. 30-Nov-2 Villa Grisebach, Berlin #147/R est:3500-4500
£2319 $3803 €3200 Snake woman (29x25cm-11x10in) s. drypoint. 31-May-3 Villa Grisebach, Berlin #219/R est:3500-4500
£2658 $4200 €4200 Negro dance (25x25cm-10x10in) s.i.d. drypoint prov. 30-Nov-2 Villa Grisebach, Berlin #149/R est:3000-4000
£3077 $4800 €4616 Niggertanz (26x26cm-10x10in) s. drypoint edition of 75. 7-Nov-2 Swann Galleries, New York #541/R est:4000-6000
£3237 $5309 €4500 Memorial service for King Laudamus (19x15cm-7x6in) s.i.d. drypoint. 6-Jun-3 Ketterer, Munich #38/R est:5000-7000
£3597 $5899 €5000 Toilette (22x15cm-9x6in) s. woodcut. 4-Jun-3 Reiss & Sohn, Konigstein #335/R est:2000
£3797 $6000 €6000 Carousel (29x26cm-11x10in) s.i.d. drypoint prov. 30-Nov-2 Villa Grisebach, Berlin #146/R est:4500-5500
£3797 $6000 €6000 Christmas 1919 (18x24cm-7x9in) s. drypoint prov. 30-Nov-2 Villa Grisebach, Berlin #151/R est:6000-7000

£3797 $6000 €6000 Nudes dancing (47x37cm-19x15in) s. lithograph. 30-Nov-2 Villa Grisebach, Berlin #246/R est:4000-5000
£3873 $6430 €5500 Storm striking (18x26cm-7x10in) s.d. drypoint etching. 14-Jun-3 Hauswedell & Nolte, Hamburg #1033/R est:4500
£3873 $6430 €5500 Behind the scenes (21x31cm-8x12in) s. drypoint etching. 14-Jun-3 Hauswedell & Nolte, Hamburg #1034/R est:5000
£4085 $6780 €5800 In the tram (29x44cm-11x17in) s. drypoint etching. 14-Jun-3 Hauswedell & Nolte, Hamburg #1037/R est:6000
£4114 $6500 €6500 The large man (31x21cm-12x8in) s.i.d. drypoint prov. 30-Nov-2 Villa Grisebach, Berlin #148/R est:3000-4000
£4348 $7130 €6000 The night (45x35cm-18x14in) s.i.d. lithograph. 31-May-3 Villa Grisebach, Berlin #220/R est:3000-4000
£4348 $7130 €6000 Caller (34x26cm-13x10in) s. drypoint. 31-May-3 Villa Grisebach, Berlin #221/R est:7000-9000
£4487 $6955 €7000 Here is spirit (34x26cm-13x10in) s.i. bears d.1922 etching. 4-Dec-2 Lempertz, Koln #570/R est:7000
£5786 $9026 €9200 Der jahrmarkt (54x38cm-21x15in) s. drypoint. 9-Oct-2 Sotheby's, London #434/R est:7500-9500
£5986 $9937 €8500 Man reading I - self portrait (21x15cm-8x6in) lithograph. 14-Jun-3 Hauswedell & Nolte, Hamburg #1041/R est:5000
£6250 $9938 €9000 Toilette (22x15cm-9x6in) s. 5-May-3 Ketterer, Munich #815/R est:2500-3500
£6338 $10521 €9000 Queen Bar II (30x24cm-12x9in) s.i. drypoint etching. 14-Jun-3 Hauswedell & Nolte, Hamburg #1038/R est:7500
£6338 $10521 €9000 Woman with candle (30x15cm-12x6in) s. woodcut. 14-Jun-3 Hauswedell & Nolte, Hamburg #1043/R est:12000
£8451 $14028 €12000 The big man (31x21cm-12x8in) s.i.d. drypoint etching. 14-Jun-3 Hauswedell & Nolte, Hamburg #1035/R est:12000
£9494 $15000 €15000 Self-portrait in car (50x66cm-20x26in) s. lithograph exec.1923 one of 50 prov. 29-Nov-2 Villa Grisebach, Berlin #52/R est:20000-25000
£11392 $18000 €18000 Woman at night (25x32cm-10x13in) s. drypoint prov. 30-Nov-2 Villa Grisebach, Berlin #145/R est:15000-17000
£19231 $29808 €30000 Fair scenes (56x41cm-22x16in) s. etching ten. 4-Dec-2 Lempertz, Koln #571/R est:35000-40000
£20126 $31396 €32000 Jahrmarkt (56x42cm-22x17in) s.st.num.XXXIV drypoint deluxe portfolio. 9-Oct-2 Sotheby's, London #431/R est:40000-47000
£25000 $39750 €36000 Self portrait (25x19cm-10x7in) s. num.4/40 lithograph. 5-May-3 Ketterer, Munich #817/R est:6000-8000
£64220 $107248 €93119 Self portrait with bowler hat (32x25cm-13x10in) s.i. drypoint. 20-Jun-3 Kornfeld, Bern #12/R est:150000 (S.FR 140000)
£98624 $164702 €143005 Eden Bar group portrait (49x50cm-19x20in) s.i. woodcut. 20-Jun-3 Kornfeld, Bern #14/R est:225000 (S.FR 215000)
£163522 $255094 €260000 Studie zu malepartus - Study for malepartus (67x46cm-26x18in) s.i. lithograph crayon executed 1919 prov. 8-Oct-2 Sotheby's, London #19/R est:160000-220000
£223270 $348302 €355000 Die Holle (90x67cm-35x26in) s.i.d.1918 num.1/75 lithograph portfolio. 9-Oct-2 Sotheby's, London #432/R est:225000-325000

Works on paper

£2532 $4000 €4000 Two heads (30x22cm-12x9in) s.i. i. verso pencil. 30-Nov-2 Villa Grisebach, Berlin #143/R est:4000-5000
£3774 $5887 €6000 Man with top hat and cigar (26x20cm-10x8in) s.d.1901 pen ink prov. 9-Oct-2 Sotheby's, London #162/R est:4500-6500
£3841 $6299 €5300 Kneeling female nude (15x13cm-6x5in) s.d.08 chl. 29-May-3 Lempertz, Koln #533/R est:3500
£19231 $29808 €30000 Portrait of Paul Cassirer (23x24cm-9x9in) s.i.d. pencil. 7-Dec-2 Hauswedell & Nolte, Hamburg #537/R est:30000
£28000 $45920 €42000 Nudist cafe (27x37cm-11x15in) s. s.i.d.1944 verso pen ink prov.exhib.lit. 6-Feb-3 Christie's, London #464/R est:45000
£141304 $231739 €195000 Still life with lamp (61x48cm-24x19in) s.d.36 prov.exhib. 30-May-3 Villa Grisebach, Berlin #52/R est:70000-90000
£260000 $434200 €377000 Margarethe Wichert, daughter of Professor Wichert (75x45cm-30x18in) s.d.30 pastel prov.exhib. 24-Jun-3 Christie's, London #32/R est:120000-180000

BECKMANN, Wilhelm Christiaan Constant (19/20th C) German

£256 $397 €400 Expressionist view of garden summer-house with swimming pool (67x65cm-26x26in) mono. masonite. 7-Dec-2 Dannenberg, Berlin #649/R

BECKMANN, Wilhelm Robert August (1852-1942) German

£475 $741 €750 Interior (54x42cm-21x17in) s. 15-Oct-2 Dorotheum, Vienna #13/R

BECKWITH, James Carroll (1852-1917) American

£2987 $4750 €4481 Finding of the lyre (6x8cm-2x3in) s. board painted c.1890. 4-May-3 Treadway Gallery, Cincinnati #528/R est:4000-6000
£3064 $4750 €4596 Portrait of Tito (64x51cm-25x20in) s.i.d.1878 prov. 29-Oct-2 Sotheby's, New York #161/R est:2000-3000

Works on paper

£5414 $8500 €8121 Seated woman (33x25cm-13x10in) s.d.05 pastel over graphite. 10-Dec-2 Doyle, New York #54/R est:8000-12000

BECON, Yves (20th C) French

£268 $432 €400 Le Dourduff en Bretagne (54x65cm-21x26in) s. 23-Feb-3 Lesieur & Le Bars, Le Havre #7

BECQUER, Joaquin (19th C) Spanish

£3546 $5745 €5000 Romantic landscape with figures at the foot of a mountain (47x35cm-19x14in) s.d.1854. 20-May-3 Segre, Madrid #85/R est:5800

BECQUEREL, Andre-Vincent (19/20th C) French

Sculpture

£949 $1481 €1500 Couple de vieux (39cm-15in) pat bronze ivory marble base. 16-Sep-2 Horta, Bruxelles #58
£1206 $1953 €1700 Panthere a l'affut (20x64cm-8x25in) s.d.1931 brown pat. bronze st.f.Susse Freres. 23-May-3 Camard, Paris #4/R est:1200-2200
£1519 $2400 €2279 Head of a panther (22cm-9in) i.verso bronze on marble plinth. 3-Apr-3 Christie's, Rockefeller NY #309/R est:1000-1500
£2848 $4443 €4500 Golden wedding (25cm-10in) s. col bronze ivory marble stand lit. 21-Oct-2 Bernaerts, Antwerp #679/R est:5000-5500
£4747 $7405 €7500 Golden wedding (38cm-15in) s. col bronze ivory marble stand lit. 21-Oct-2 Bernaerts, Antwerp #678/R est:9000-10000

BEDA, Giulio (attrib) (1879-1954) Italian

£1361 $2163 €2000 Pre-alpine landscape in early autumn (130x173cm-51x68in) s. 19-Mar-3 Neumeister, Munich #510/R est:2000

BEDARD, Georges Noel (1924-) French

£315 $488 €500 Couteau, grenade et verre (33x46cm-13x18in) s.d.1952. 4-Oct-2 Tajan, Paris #19

BEDARD, Pierre (1960-) Canadian

£244 $401 €354 Le neige en abundance (45x60cm-18x24in) s.i. board. 9-Jun-3 Hodgins, Calgary #14/R (C.D 550)

BEDARRIDE, Fred (1915-1984) French

£282 $468 €400 Kafka et sa fiancee, I (83x62cm-33x24in) prov.exhib. 18-Jun-3 Anaf, Lyon #41/R

BEDAT, Celine (20th C) French

Works on paper

£302 $483 €420 Emeraude (60x60cm-24x24in) s. mixed media canvas. 18-May-3 Neret-Minet, Paris #170/R

BEDEL, Marie Augustin Maurice (19/20th C) French

Works on paper

£372 $580 €550 Biches et cerf (27x38cm-11x15in) s. W/C. 27-Mar-3 Maigret, Paris #221/R
£2414 $3838 €3500 La venerie a Chantilly a la fin du XIXeme siecle. s.d.1897 W/C fan shape. 10-Mar-3 Coutau Begarie, Paris #188/R est:2000-2500

BEDFORD, Celia (1904-1959) British

£600 $948 €900 Lady in a tea shop (64x76cm-25x30in) s. prov. 27-Nov-2 Sotheby's, Olympia #249/R

BEDFORD, John Bates (1823-?) British

Works on paper

£360 $562 €540 Horsemans Farm, near Haywards Heath, Sussex (25x36cm-10x14in) mono.d.1865. 15-Oct-2 Gorringes, Lewes #2195

BEDFORD, Paddy (20th C) Australian

Works on paper

£4693 $7274 €7040 Waloorrji, big wind dreaming (135x122cm-53x48in) i.verso natural pigments binder linen prov. 3-Dec-2 Shapiro, Sydney #163/R est:7000-9000 (A.D 13000)

BEDIA, Jose (1959-) Cuban

£5488 $9000 €7958 Aquellas extranas confluencial (119x239cm-47x94in) s.d.01 oilstick acrylic prov. 27-May-3 Sotheby's, New York #119
£11585 $19000 €17378 Candela (147x347cm-58x137in) i. painted c.1990 prov.exhib. 28-May-3 Christie's, Rockefeller NY #51/R est:18000-22000
£16561 $26000 €24842 Up to when? (240x420cm-94x165in) s.i.d.95 acrylic prov.lit. 19-Nov-2 Sotheby's, New York #47/R est:45000

Works on paper

£1220 $2000 €1830 Kunanfinda (97x130cm-38x51in) s.i.d.96 ink photo collage prov. 28-May-3 Christie's, Rockefeller NY #159/R est:4000-6000
£7317 $12000 €10976 Lugar donde escoger (119x239cm-47x94in) s.i.d.01 ink crayon prov. 28-May-3 Christie's, Rockefeller NY #149/R est:15000-20000

£8917 $14000 €13376 Isla del Perro, Isla Sola - Dog Island, Lonely Island (119x239cm-47x94in) s.d.94 ink prov. 20-Nov-2 Christie's, Rockefeller NY #57/R est:16000-18000

BEDINI, Paolo (1844-1924) Italian
£3800 $6156 €5700 Cellist (50x36cm-20x14in) s. 20-May-3 Sotheby's, Olympia #368/R est:1500-2000
£5500 $8965 €8250 Game of he loves me (27x32cm-11x13in) s. 12-Feb-3 Bonhams, Knightsbridge #66/R est:2500-3500
Works on paper
£800 $1248 €1200 Cavalier (22x15cm-9x6in) s. W/C htd white. 26-Mar-3 Sotheby's, Olympia #237/R

BEDYS, Jan (1814-1899) Dutch
£8176 $12755 €13000 Extensive landscape with river meadows (70x119cm-28x47in) s. 19-Sep-2 Dr Fritz Nagel, Stuttgart #907/R est:2500

BEECHAM, Tom (1926-2000) American
£2690 $4250 €3901 Whitetails at dawn (61x91cm-24x36in) s. 26-Jul-3 Coeur d'Alene, Hayden #20/R est:5000-7500

BEECHER, William Ward (20th C) American
£531 $850 €770 Floral still life in an architectural niche (51x41cm-20x16in) s.d.51. 16-May-3 Skinner, Boston #161/R

BEECHEY, Captain Richard Brydges (1808-1895) British
£27000 $41040 €40500 Irish Brigantine Sligo and other vessels in rough weather below lighthouse (92x138cm-36x54in) s.d.1874. 15-Aug-2 Bonhams, New Bond Street #410/R est:30000-40000
Works on paper
£1000 $1580 €1500 View of a town in Canada (34x48cm-13x19in) s.i.d.1844 pen black ink W/C. 15-Nov-2 Sotheby's, London #64/R est:600-800

BEECHEY, Sir William (1753-1839) British
£2500 $3900 €3750 Portrait of a lady in a green dress (76x63cm-30x25in) 7-Nov-2 Christie's, Kensington #51/R est:3000-5000
£7800 $12948 €11700 Portrait of the artist (45x32cm-18x13in) 12-Jun-3 Sotheby's, London #72/R est:4000-6000
£17284 $28000 €25926 Portrait of Mrs Hatfield (240x147cm-94x58in) prov.exhib.lit. 23-Jan-3 Sotheby's, New York #255/R est:10000
£47000 $74260 €70500 Portrait of Richard Thompson seated holding gun, retriever at his feet (240x148cm-94x58in) prov.exhib.lit. 26-Nov-2 Christie's, London #27/R est:20000-30000
£85000 $135150 €127500 Portrait of Matthew Boulton (125x99cm-49x39in) prov.lit. 20-Mar-3 Sotheby's, London #34/R est:40000-60000
£132000 $209880 €198000 Portrait of James Watt (124x99cm-49x39in) prov.exhib.lit. 20-Mar-3 Sotheby's, London #43/R est:40000-60000
Works on paper
£537 $864 €800 Miss O'Neill as Isabella in the fatal marriage (19x15cm-7x6in) s. i.verso W/C. 18-Feb-3 Whyte's, Dublin #101/R

BEECHEY, Sir William (attrib) (1753-1839) British
£2250 $3555 €3375 Lt Mark Kent RN wearing uniform (60x50cm-24x20in) prov. 2-Dec-2 Bonhams, Bath #69/R est:1500-2500
£2710 $4200 €4065 Portrait of a gentleman, holding a walking stick (76x63cm-30x25in) prov. 2-Oct-2 Christie's, Rockefeller NY #122/R est:3000-5000

BEECHEY, Sir William (circle) (1753-1839) British
£5000 $8000 €7500 Vaughan boys (64x76cm-25x30in) 11-Mar-3 Gorringes, Lewes #2547/R est:1000-1500

BEECROFT, Vanesa (1969-) American
Photographs
£3472 $5729 €5000 VB21 016 ali (100x70cm-39x28in) col photo prov.lit. 1-Jul-3 Artcurial Briest, Paris #875/R est:4000-6000
£4430 $7000 €6645 VB43.038.ALI (63x88cm-25x35in) digital cibachrome print exec.2000 one of 6 prov. 13-Nov-2 Sotheby's, New York #498/R est:8000-10000
£5063 $8000 €7595 VB02 performance (102x104cm-40x41in) vibracolour print exec.1994 one of 3 prov. 13-Nov-2 Sotheby's, New York #438/R est:8000-12000
£5938 $9500 €8907 VB 11 performance - Galerie Analix, Geneva (161x105cm-63x41in) vibracolor print executed 1995 prov. 14-May-3 Sotheby's, New York #387/R est:8000-12000
£6000 $9240 €9000 Navy seals (102x135cm-40x53in) digital col print executed 1999 prov. 22-Oct-2 Christie's, London #57/R est:6000-8000
£6250 $10000 €9375 VB 26 1997, Galleria Lia Rumma, Naples (101x152cm-40x60in) vibracolor print executed 1997 prov. 14-May-3 Sotheby's, New York #389/R est:8000-12000
£8228 $13000 €12342 VB38, US Navy, Museum of Contemporary Art, San Diego (127x157cm-50x62in) digital print on c-type paper executed 2000 prov. 12-Nov-2 Phillips, New York #162/R est:15000-20000
£10000 $15400 €15000 VB 43.029 te. VB 43.069 te. VB 43.074 te (101x114cm-40x45in) digital print on c-type paper on foam in three parts prov. 22-Oct-2 Sotheby's, London #313/R est:20000-30000
£10759 $17000 €16139 VB43.037.ali (63x89cm-25x35in) digital print c-type paper executed 2000 prov.exhib. 14-Nov-2 Christie's, Rockefeller NY #474/R est:10000-15000
£13924 $22000 €20886 VB 43.038 ALI 2000 (132x190cm-52x75in) digital print on c-type paper executed 2000. 12-Nov-2 Phillips, New York #159/R est:20000-30000
Works on paper
£1582 $2500 €2373 Untitled - green legs I (58x46cm-23x18in) W/C graphite executed 1998 prov. 12-Nov-2 Phillips, New York #208/R est:2500-3500

BEEK, Bernardus Antonie van (1875-1941) Dutch
£514 $801 €750 Three calves in a meadow (26x33cm-10x13in) s. board. 14-Apr-3 Glerum, Amsterdam #134/R

BEEK, Jurrien (1879-1965) Dutch
£1019 $1590 €1600 Fishing boats on the beach (78x98cm-31x39in) s. 6-Nov-2 Vendue Huis, Gravenhage #54/R est:1700-2000
£1034 $1644 €1500 Harbour scene (80x100cm-31x39in) s. 10-Mar-3 Sotheby's, Amsterdam #201/R est:1500-2000
£1408 $2268 €2000 Riviera, Cote d'Azur, Cannes (58x78cm-23x31in) s. 7-May-3 Vendue Huis, Gravenhage #6/R est:1000-1200

BEEK, Samuel van (1878-1957) Dutch
£1338 $2087 €2100 Parrot (75x45cm-30x18in) s. 6-Nov-2 Vendue Huis, Gravenhage #6/R est:2000-3000

BEELAERTS, Maria Johanna Jacoba Gerardina (1848-1915) Dutch
£556 $917 €800 Cherries and a pumpkin (25x38cm-10x15in) s. 1-Jul-3 Christie's, Amsterdam #108

BEELDEMAKER, Adriaen Cornelisz (c.1625-1709) Dutch
£1000 $1550 €1500 Portrait of a gentleman, his hand pointing to a book on a table (88x72cm-35x28in) s.d.1660. 30-Oct-2 Bonhams, New Bond Street #109/R est:1200-1800
£1026 $1590 €1600 Landscape with dogs hunting boar (45x58cm-18x23in) 5-Dec-2 Dr Fritz Nagel, Stuttgart #590/R est:3000
£3500 $5460 €5250 Lurcher and spaniel in a rocky landscape. Spaniels in a rocky landscape (46x61cm-18x24in) one s.d.1693 pair. 9-Apr-3 Bonhams, New Bond Street #18/R est:4000-6000

BEELDEMAKER, Adriaen Cornelisz (attrib) (c.1625-1709) Dutch
£1081 $1686 €1600 Hunter with spaniels in mountainous landscape (36x49cm-14x19in) panel. 27-Mar-3 Dorotheum, Vienna #319/R

BEELER, Joe Neil (1931-) American
£1442 $2250 €2163 North on Santa Fe (23x30cm-9x12in) s. prov. 9-Nov-2 Santa Fe Art, Santa Fe #15/R est:2000-3000
Sculpture
£1796 $3000 €2604 Crossing the river (41cm-16in) green pat. bronze walnut base. 21-Jun-3 Selkirks, St. Louis #202/R est:4000-6000
£3165 $5000 €4589 Charlie dye (30cm-12in) bronze sold with Frank Polk roping a calf. 26-Jul-3 Coeur d'Alene, Hayden #236/R est:4000-8000
£11538 $18000 €17307 Chief goes to Washington (48cm-19in) bronze. 9-Nov-2 Altermann Galleries, Santa Fe #128
Works on paper
£962 $1500 €1443 Amigos (33x25cm-13x10in) s. i.verso W/C gouache prov. 9-Nov-2 Santa Fe Art, Santa Fe #130/R est:1000-2000
£1763 $2750 €2645 Illustrated letter to Dean Krakel.1965 (28x20cm-11x8in) i. W/C ink gouache prov. 9-Nov-2 Santa Fe Art, Santa Fe #12/R est:800-1200

BEELT, Cornelis (fl.1660-1702) Dutch
£6000 $9660 €9000 Horse fair, said to be Valkenburg, with figures in wagons and horseback (67x103cm-26x41in) 20-Feb-3 Christie's, Kensington #256/R est:4000-6000

BEELT, Cornelis (attrib) (fl.1660-1702) Dutch
£3957 $6331 €5500 Coastal landscape with elegant company by a fish stall on a beach (103x153cm-41x60in) 14-May-3 Christie's, Amsterdam #136/R est:6000-8000
£5755 $9209 €8000 Beach scene with fishermen unloading catch (64x99cm-25x39in) panel. 13-May-3 Sotheby's, Amsterdam #52/R est:8000-12000

BEEN, Daniel (1885-1976) Dutch
£414 $646 €650 Plan-C, Rotterdam in the winter (57x74cm-22x29in) s. 5-Nov-2 Vendu Notarishuis, Rotterdam #149
£486 $802 €700 Blue irises on a ledge (60x81cm-24x32in) s. 1-Jul-3 Christie's, Amsterdam #268

BEER, Dick (1893-1938) Swedish
£425 $684 €638 Harbour town (32x40cm-13x16in) s.d.1924 panel. 7-May-3 AB Stockholms Auktionsverk #877/R (S.KR 5500)
£2242 $3498 €3363 Street scene, Marrakech (91x73cm-36x29in) s.d.1915. 6-Nov-2 AB Stockholms Auktionsverk #608/R est:18000-20000 (S.KR 32000)

BEER, Jan de (studio) (1475-1542) Flemish
£6294 $10511 €9000 La nativite (32x24cm-13x9in) panel. 25-Jun-3 Tajan, Paris #16/R est:7000-9000

BEER, Jan de (style) (1475-1542) Flemish
£6000 $10020 €8700 Adoration of the Magi (70x54cm-28x21in) oak panel shaped top prov. 10-Jul-3 Sotheby's, London #106/R est:10000-15000

BEER, John (fl.1895-1915) British
Works on paper
£243 $380 €365 Finis (17x24cm-7x9in) s.i. W/C. 11-Nov-2 Stephan Welz, Johannesburg #406 (SA.R 3800)
£280 $442 €420 Schooling a mare (23x36cm-9x14in) s.i. W/C bodycol. 28-Nov-2 Bonhams, Knightsbridge #74/R
£280 $437 €420 Arriving at the race in a horse and carriage (23x33cm-9x13in) s. bodycol. 25-Mar-3 Bonhams, Knightsbridge #88
£280 $448 €406 Mare and foal in a stable (34x52cm-13x20in) s.d.94 W/C. 13-May-3 Bristol Auction Rooms #489/R
£320 $499 €480 Paddock, possibly at Epsom (24x45cm-9x18in) s.i.d.1902 W/C htd bodycol. 25-Mar-3 Bonhams, Knightsbridge #6/R
£380 $600 €570 Brief rest for a gentleman, thought to be Edward VII (30x23cm-12x9in) s. W/C htd white. 28-Nov-2 Bonhams, Knightsbridge #76
£400 $624 €600 Shooting party sets off (26x37cm-10x15in) s.i. W/C bodycol. 25-Mar-3 Bonhams, Knightsbridge #7/R
£400 $624 €600 Flushing them out on a rough shoot (26x36cm-10x14in) s. bodycol. 25-Mar-3 Bonhams, Knightsbridge #8/R
£420 $664 €630 Fence, Warwick (13x17cm-5x7in) s.i. bodycol. 28-Nov-2 Bonhams, Knightsbridge #73/R
£600 $948 €900 Steeplechasers (23x34cm-9x13in) s. W/C bodycol. 28-Nov-2 Bonhams, Knightsbridge #68/R
£600 $966 €900 Racehorse Diamond Jubilee in four victories (47x61cm-19x24in) W/C htd white executed c.1900. 18-Feb-3 Rowley Fine Art, Newmarket #322/R
£609 $949 €914 In training. Victory. Yearling (17x24cm-7x9in) s.i. two d.95 W/C three. 11-Nov-2 Stephan Welz, Johannesburg #407/R (SA.R 9500)
£720 $1123 €1080 The Royal Stakes (25x34cm-10x13in) s.i.d.1906 W/C. 6-Nov-2 Sotheby's, Olympia #83/R
£946 $1476 €1400 The Finish, for the Gold Cup, Ascot 1907 (25x35cm-10x14in) s.i. W/C. 28-Mar-3 Dorotheum, Vienna #237/R
£1400 $2324 €2030 Diamond Jubilee winning the 2000 guineas, Newmarket, Epson derby, St.Leger, Stakes (47x61cm-19x24in) s.i. W/C bodycol. 12-Jun-3 Christie's, Kensington #112a/R est:1000-1500

BEER, Willem S de (1941-) South African
£350 $553 €525 Stag by a stream (50x76cm-20x30in) s. 28-Nov-2 Bonhams, Knightsbridge #84
£350 $553 €525 Stag in landscape (50x76cm-20x30in) s. 28-Nov-2 Bonhams, Knightsbridge #85
£1100 $1826 €1595 Bright morning - red fox in the snow (51x76cm-20x30in) s. 12-Jun-3 Christie's, Kensington #34/R est:1000-1500

BEER, William Andrew Edward (1862-1954) British
£720 $1123 €1080 Portraits of prize racing pigeons, Mendip Pride and Lone Star (29x40cm-11x16in) pair. 8-Apr-3 Bristol Auction Rooms #577/R

BEERBOHM, Sir Max (1872-1956) British
Works on paper
£1400 $2310 €2030 Mr Boyd Morrison and Mr Gordon Craig (20x25cm-8x10in) i.d.1926 pen black ink col crayon prov.exhib.lit. 3-Jul-3 Christie's, Kensington #242/R est:800-1200
£1700 $2703 €2550 Frontispiece for Wooded landscaper's pamphlet (29x32cm-11x13in) s.i. i.verso pencil lit. 26-Feb-3 Sotheby's, Olympia #49/R est:800-1200
£2400 $3816 €3600 If the age limit is raised to forty five (16x17cm-6x7in) i. pencil executed c.1917 lit. 26-Feb-3 Sotheby's, Olympia #51/R est:1000-1500
£2800 $4452 €4200 Self caricature (26x16cm-10x6in) pen ink lit. 26 Fcb-3 Sotheby's, Olympia #46/R est:1000-1500
£3200 $4960 €4800 Count Boni de Castellani (31x27cm-12x11in) s.i.d.1912 pencil wash. 3-Dec-2 Bonhams, New Bond Street #37/R est:2000-3000
£3400 $5406 €5100 Mr. Carson Q.C (31x13cm-12x5in) s.i. ink gouache exhib.lit. 26-Feb-3 Sotheby's, Olympia #50/R est:2000-3000
£3800 $5890 €5700 Sudden appearance of Mr Beerbohm in the New English Art Club (40x32cm-16x13in) i. pencil wash. 3-Dec-2 Bonhams, New Bond Street #35/R est:4000-6000
£4500 $7380 €6525 King! god bless him! (31x19cm-12x7in) i. pen ink W/C crayon exhib.lit. 5-Jun-3 Christie's, London #187/R est:3000-5000
£4800 $7440 €7200 Sudden and belated recognition of Mr Will Rothenstein as the Messiah (31x19cm-12x7in) s.i.d.Febuary 1906 pen ink W/C exhib. 3-Dec-2 Bonhams, New Bond Street #36/R est:2500-3500
£5500 $8524 €8250 Significant form (32x21cm-13x8in) s.i. pencil W/C exhib.lit. 4-Dec-2 Sotheby's, London #21/R est:3000-5000

BEERE, Gerald Butler (20th C) New Zealander
Works on paper
£1608 $2492 €2412 Ruanakia; Militia armed forces camp, possibly on shores of Lake Taupo (32x49cm-13x19in) s.i. W/C. 4-Dec-2 Dunbar Sloane, Auckland #18/R est:5000-10000 (NZ.D 5000)

BEERMAN, John (1958-) American
£2885 $4500 €4328 Winter twilight, seaside (41x66cm-16x26in) s.d.97 linen. 5-Nov-2 Doyle, New York #59/R est:3000-5000

BEERNAERT, Euphrosine (1831-1901) Flemish
£1184 $1918 €1800 Cows in a wooded meadow (60x95cm-24x37in) s.d.1860. 21-Jan-3 Christie's, Amsterdam #24/R est:2000-3000

BEERNAERTS, A (20th C) Belgian
£884 $1406 €1300 Nude (101x78cm-40x31in) s. 24-Mar-3 Bernaerts, Antwerp #828 est:1500-2000

BEERS, Jan van (1852-1927) Belgian
£552 $883 €800 Small boy with dog in a rowing boat (24x33cm-9x13in) s. 15-Mar-3 De Vuyst, Lokeren #321
£795 $1295 €1200 Aan mijnen vriend Felix (55x46cm-22x18in) 17-Feb-3 Amberes, Antwerp #238
£900 $1449 €1350 Portrait of a lady reading (21x15cm-8x6in) s. panel. 15-Jan-3 Cheffins Grain & Comins, Cambridge #429/R
£1181 $1948 €1700 Une belle dans un foret (32x24cm-13x9in) s. panel. 1-Jul-3 Christie's, Amsterdam #37/R est:1500-2000
£1241 $1974 €1800 Elegante a la rose (33x23cm-13x9in) s.d.1881 panel. 4-Mar-3 Palais de Beaux Arts, Brussels #403/R est:1600-2000
£2600 $4056 €3900 Lady with a basket of flowers (33x24cm-13x9in) s.i.d.1881 panel. 26-Mar-3 Sotheby's, Olympia #253/R est:2000-3000
£4054 $6324 €6000 Le bal masquee (33x23cm-13x9in) s. panel. 25-Mar-3 Campo & Campo, Antwerp #214/R est:6500-7500

BEERS, Julie Hart (1835-1913) American
£1000 $1600 €1450 Looking up the stream (31x26cm-12x10in) s.d.74 i.verso board. 16-May-3 Skinner, Boston #58/R est:2500-3500

BEERSTRATEN, Anthonie (circle) (17th C) Dutch
£10072 $16115 €14000 Winter landscape with figures on a frozen waterway in a village (59x83cm-23x33in) 14-May-3 Christie's, Amsterdam #131/R est:2500-3500

BEERSTRATEN, Jan Abrahamsz (attrib) (1622-1666) Dutch
£1935 $3000 €2903 Landscape with classical ruins (46x64cm-18x25in) panel. 7-Dec-2 Neal Auction Company, New Orleans #114/R est:4000-6000
£6608 $9648 €9912 Seascape (48x65cm-19x26in) prov. 17-Jun-2 Philippe Schuler, Zurich #4326/R est:15000-20000 (S.FR 15000)

BEERSTRATEN, Jan Abrahamsz (style) (1622-1666) Dutch
£8000 $12480 €12000 Mediterranean harbour scene with a Dutch man-o-war (75x109cm-30x43in) prov. 8-Apr-3 Sotheby's, Olympia #165/R est:8000-12000

BEERSTRATEN, Johannes (17th C) Dutch
£8000 $13360 €11600 Capriccio harbour scene with figures before a church (87x122cm-34x48in) s.i.d.1665 prov. 8-Jul-3 Sotheby's, Olympia #406/R est:4000-6000

BEERT, Osias I (c.1570-1624) Flemish
£32000 $49920 €48000 Tulips, roses, irises and other flowers in a glass vase on ledge with butterflies (33x22cm-13x9in) panel. 9-Apr-3 Christie's, London #11/R est:20000-30000

BEERT, Osias I (studio) (c.1570-1624) Flemish
£10500 $16275 €15750 Still life of fruit and walnuts, wine glasses, bread and knife (51x66cm-20x26in) i.verso panel. 31-Oct-2 Sotheby's, Olympia #42/R est:7000-10000

BEERT, Osias I (style) (c.1570-1624) Flemish
£8000 $12480 €12000 Grapes and mulberries on pewter platters, pears,cherries and strawberries in wanli kraak bowls (59x70cm-23x28in) init.d.1614 panel. 10-Apr-3 Christie's, Kensington #6/R est:4000-6000

BEESON, Charles Richard (1909-) British
£400 $628 €600 Stow fair (51x77cm-20x30in) s.d.45. 21-Nov-2 Tennants, Leyburn #859

BEEST, Albertus van (1820-1860) Dutch
Works on paper
£1975 $3200 €2864 Heavy seas off a lighthouse (34x57cm-13x22in) s. W/C paper on board. 29-Jul-3 Christie's, Rockefeller NY #113/R est:2000-3000

BEEST, Sybrand van (1610-1674) Dutch
£2548 $3975 €4000 Kitchen interior with a maid plucking a duck and a little boy eating porridge (30x25cm-12x10in) bears sig prov.exhib.lit. 5-Nov-2 Sotheby's, Amsterdam #3/R est:5000-7000
£3822 $5962 €6000 Kitchen interior with a maid cleaning turnips (34x40cm-13x16in) indis sig.d.1665 panel prov.exhib.lit. 5-Nov-2 Sotheby's, Amsterdam #6/R est:7000-9000

BEEST, Sybrand van (attrib) (1610-1674) Dutch
£1616 $2521 €2424 Woman with dog in kitchen (41x48cm-16x19in) i.d.1658 masonite. 6-Nov-2 Dobiaschofsky, Bern #342/R est:4500 (S.FR 3700)

BEEVER, Emanuel Samson van (1876-1912) Dutch
£1000 $1520 €1500 Final touch (46x24cm-18x9in) s.d.98 s.i.verso. 29-Aug-2 Christie's, Kensington #239/R est:1200-1800

BEFANI, Achille Formis (1832-1906) Italian
£4082 $6490 €6000 Peasant girl with goat (67x34cm-26x13in) s. 18-Mar-3 Finarte, Milan #93/R
£8805 $13560 €14000 Lake with boats (39x68cm-15x27in) s. 23-Oct-2 Finarte, Milan #116/R est:13000-15000

BEFANIO, Gennaro (1866-?) French
£377 $600 €566 Mrs Florence Cabell (81x65cm-32x26in) s.d.1905 i.verso. 7-Mar-3 Skinner, Boston #570/R

BEGA, Cornelis Pietersz (1620-1664) Dutch
Prints
£1900 $2964 €2850 Mother seated in an inn (39x26cm-15x10in) etching. 25-Mar-3 Sotheby's, London #3/R est:1800-2200
Works on paper
£2095 $3268 €3100 Woaman standing by chair (27x16cm-11x6in) chk prov. 27-Mar-3 Christie's, Paris #141/R

BEGARAT, Eugène (1943-) French
£451 $640 €730 Promenade sur sentier fleuri (60x49cm-24x19in) s. 17-Mar-2 Galerie de Chartres, Chartres #135
£621 $987 €900 La plage (46x55cm-18x22in) s. 9-Mar-3 Feletin, Province #208

BEGAS, Karl-Joseph (1794-1854) German
£19231 $30192 €30000 Portrait of Jakob Salomon Bartholdy (72x59cm-28x23in) s.d.1824 lit. 21-Nov-2 Van Ham, Cologne #1464/R est:10000

BEGEYN, Abraham (1637-1697) Dutch
£4545 $7000 €6818 Italianate landscape with cattle in a stream by ruins (52x62cm-20x24in) s.d.1664 prov. 4-Sep-2 Christie's, Rockefeller NY #241/R est:5000-7000
£7547 $11698 €12000 Southern landscape with shepherds and flock (72x65cm-28x26in) 2-Oct-2 Dorotheum, Vienna #185/R est:12000-16000
£10219 $15840 €15329 In front of an inn in Italy (62x53cm-24x21in) s. 6-Dec-2 Kieselbach, Budapest #118/R (H.F 3800000)
£73701 $119395 €106866 Mediterranean harbour scene with European and Oriental traders (170x265cm-67x104in) s.d.1660. 26-May-3 Bukowskis, Stockholm #402/R est:1000000-1200000 (S.KR 950000)

BEHAM, Hans Sebald (1500-1550) German
Prints
£2051 $3200 €3077 Women's bath house (29cm-11in circular) woodcut exec.c.1525. 6-Nov-2 Swann Galleries, New York #50/R est:1500-2500

BEHAM, Hans Sebald (attrib) (1500-1550) German
Works on paper
£10191 $15898 €16000 Naked warrior on a rearing charger (11x11cm-4x4in) mono.d.1549 pen brown ink. 5-Nov-2 Sotheby's, Amsterdam #4/R est:1500-2000

BEHAN, John (1938-) Irish
Sculpture
£1635 $2551 €2600 James Joyce (41x14x8cm-16x6x3in) sif bronze. 17-Sep-2 Whyte's, Dublin #102/R est:2000-3000
£2877 $4516 €4200 Icarus (43x56cm-17x22in) bronze prov.exhib. 15-Apr-3 De Veres Art Auctions, Dublin #269 est:1800-2200
£3101 $4807 €4900 Sons of Ulster (46x22x23cm-18x9x9in) bronze. 24-Sep-2 De Veres Art Auctions, Dublin #139/R est:2000-3000
£3205 $5032 €5000 Flight of birds (51cm-20in) bronze with marble plinth. 19-Nov-2 Whyte's, Dublin #182/R est:2000-3000

BEHM, Karl (1858-1905) German
£3526 $5500 €5289 Fisherman's tale (72x56cm-28x22in) d.1889. 20-Sep-2 Sloan, North Bethesda #440a/R est:6000-8000

BEHM, Vilhelm (1859-1934) Swedish
£480 $730 €720 Autumn landscape (48x62cm-19x24in) s. 16-Aug-2 Lilla Bukowskis, Stockholm #622 (S.KR 7000)
£695 $1154 €1008 Lake landscape in evening glow (70x110cm-28x43in) s.d.1887. 16-Jun-3 Lilla Bukowskis, Stockholm #499 (S.KR 9000)
£1135 $1759 €1703 Spring landscape with the artist under parasol (54x72cm-21x28in) s.i.d.89. 4-Dec-2 AB Stockholms Auktionsverk #1556/R est:14000-16000 (S.KR 16000)

BEHN, Andreas von (1650-1713) Swedish
£1915 $2968 €2873 Portrait of Anna Juliana Horn of Kanckas (52x46cm-20x18in) d.1687 oval. 4-Dec-2 AB Stockholms Auktionsverk #1688/R est:25000-30000 (S.KR 27000)

BEHR, Carel Jacobus (1812-1895) Dutch
£563 $907 €800 View of Delft (25x39cm-10x15in) s. panel. 7-May-3 Vendue Huis, Gravenhage #369/R

BEHRENDSEN, August (1819-1886) German
£300 $475 €450 Obersee in Bavarian Alps (25x34cm-10x13in) s.i.verso painted 1882. 29-Nov-2 Zofingen, Switzerland #2319 (S.FR 700)

BEHRENS, Howard (20th C) American
£3442 $5300 €5163 Willows by Giverny lily pond (61x51cm-24x20in) 25-Oct-2 Morris & Whiteside, Hilton Head Island #55 est:5500-6000

BEHRENS, Walter (1911-) Spanish
£379 $607 €550 Blue morning (71x47cm-28x19in) s. egg tempera panel. 11-Mar-3 Dorotheum, Vienna #159/R

BEHRENS-HANGELER, Herbert (1898-1981) German
£3043 $4991 €4200 Dream (65x81cm-26x32in) mono. mono.i. stretcher exhib. 31-May-3 Villa Grisebach, Berlin #208/R est:5000-7000
£3481 $5500 €5500 In summer (60x80cm-24x31in) mono. i.d.1937 stretcher. 30-Nov-2 Villa Grisebach, Berlin #269/R est:6000-8000

BEHRMANN, Adolf (1876-1942) Russian
£1502 $2464 €2178 Still life with Asian items (73x60cm-29x24in) s. 4-Jun-3 Fischer, Luzern #2010/R est:1000-1200 (S.FR 3200)

BEHZAD, Hossein (20th C) Iranian
Works on paper
£12821 $20128 €20000 Untitled (67x41cm-26x16in) one s. gouache pair. 16-Dec-2 Gros & Delettrez, Paris #46/R est:15000-20000

BEHZAD, Hossein (attrib) (20th C) Iranian
£2113 $3507 €3000 La rencontre du calife omeyyade Hicham ibn Abd al-Malik avec la caravane (44x30cm-17x12in) two sheets. 13-Jun-3 Piasa, Paris #317/R est:3000-4000
£2113 $3507 €3000 Portraits de deux siamoises (40x23cm-16x9in) i.verso sold with text. 13-Jun-3 Piasa, Paris #318/R est:3000-4000
£2817 $4676 €4000 Salen, messager de Dieu (43x30cm-17x12in) i.verso. 13-Jun-3 Piasa, Paris #316/R est:4000-6000
£2958 $4910 €4200 Histoire des sept dormants (31x20cm-12x8in) sold with pages of text. 13-Jun-3 Piasa, Paris #315/R est:4000-6000

BEICH, Joachim Franz (1665-1748) German
£949 $1472 €1500 Arcadian landscape (42x53cm-17x21in) 27-Sep-2 Karrenbauer, Konstanz #1603/R est:1500

BEINASCHI, Giovan Battista (attrib) (1636-1688) Italian
£8065 $12742 €12500 Saint Teresa of Avila (84x69cm-33x27in) 18-Dec-2 Piasa, Paris #4/R est:3000

BEINKE, Fritz (1842-1907) German
£918 $1422 €1450 The king is coming! (32x24cm-13x9in) s. 28-Sep-2 Hans Stahl, Hamburg #51/R
£1161 $1707 €1800 Shepherd letting sheep out of barn (33x26cm-13x10in) s. panel. 20-Jun-2 Dr Fritz Nagel, Stuttgart #749/R est:2900
£1161 $1707 €1800 Small girl feeding geese and sheep (33x26cm-13x10in) s. panel. 20-Jun-2 Dr Fritz Nagel, Stuttgart #750/R
£1401 $2186 €2200 Boyish prank at the village school (40x31cm-16x12in) s. lit. 7-Nov-2 Allgauer, Kempten #2749/R est:2200
£1549 $2494 €2200 Young girl feeding ducks in field (24x32cm-9x13in) s. panel. 10-May-3 Hans Stahl, Toestorf #29/R est:2500

BEISCHLAGER, Emil (1897-1978) Austrian
£348 $543 €550 Cyclamen and lemons (40x35cm-16x14in) s.d.1929. 15-Oct-2 Dorotheum, Vienna #87/R
£414 $662 €600 Flowers (45x33cm-18x13in) s.d.1967 tempera. 11-Mar-3 Dorotheum, Vienna #150/R
£609 $962 €950 Summer in the mountains (58x72cm-23x28in) s.d. 12-Nov-2 Dorotheum, Vienna #130/R
£633 $987 €1000 Still life with fish (49x78cm-19x31in) s.d.1931. 15-Oct-2 Dorotheum, Vienna #85/R
£795 $1295 €1200 Village on the water (46x49cm-18x19in) s.d.1967 tempera. 28-Jan-3 Dorotheum, Vienna #149/R
£1325 $2159 €2000 Turnitz in the snow (60x55cm-24x22in) 28-Jan-3 Dorotheum, Vienna #153/R est:2200-3200

BEITHAN, Emil (1878-?) Belgian
£773 $1221 €1160 Petunias in pot on a table with watch-chain and pill box (38x38cm-15x15in) s. 29-Nov-2 Zofingen, Switzerland #2395 (S.FR 1800)

BEJAR, Feliciano (20th C) Spanish
£446 $700 €669 Great trees (69x53cm-27x21in) s. 28-Jul-2 William Jenack, New York #291
Sculpture
£1008 $1572 €1512 Magiscopio (97x39cm-38x15in) s.d.1977 metal glass. 17-Oct-2 Louis Morton, Mexico #11 est:15000-20000 (M.P 16000)

BEJAR, Juan (1946-) Spanish
£2075 $3217 €3300 Untitled (92x72cm-36x28in) board. 7-Oct-2 Ansorena, Madrid #90/R est:3300

BEJAR, Pablo Antonio (1869-1921) Spanish
Works on paper
£2400 $3744 €3600 Portrait of a lady in a white satin dress (220x129cm-87x51in) s.d.1915 pastel. 17-Sep-2 Sotheby's, Olympia #276/R est:2000-3000

BEJARANO, Manuel C (1827-1891) Spanish
£1154 $1823 €1800 Portrait of Antonio Canovas del Castillo (60cm-24xin) s.i.d.1871. 14-Nov-2 Arte, Seville #306/R

BEKAERT, Piet (1939-2000) Belgian
£1667 $2583 €2600 Terrace (100x100cm-39x39in) s.d.92. 7-Dec-2 De Vuyst, Lokeren #496/R est:2800-3500
£1731 $2683 €2700 Terrace (100x80cm-39x31in) s.d.1991. 7-Dec-2 De Vuyst, Lokeren #570/R est:2500-3000
£1887 $2925 €3000 White roses (120x120cm-47x47in) s.d.1986. 5-Oct-2 De Vuyst, Lokeren #585/R est:3500-4000
£3899 $6005 €6200 Horses in Camargue (150x500cm-59x197in) s.d.1986. 22-Oct-2 Campo & Campo, Antwerp #11/R

BEKAY, Khalid El (1966-) Moroccan
Works on paper
£1915 $3102 €2700 Contemplacion (100x204cm-39x80in) s.d.2002 collage panel. 20-May-3 Porro, Milan #18/R est:3600-3800

BEKE, Daniel van (1669-1728) Dutch
£3142 $5153 €4556 Putti and cupids by fountain (100x140cm-39x55in) s.d.1707. 4-Jun-3 AB Stockholms Auktionsverk #2538/R est:40000-50000 (S.KR 40000)

BEKEL, Josef (attrib) (1806-1865) Czechoslovakian
Works on paper
£413 $644 €620 Portrait of a young man in a chair (26x18cm-10x7in) W/C. 12-Oct-2 Dorotheum, Prague #288/R (C.KR 20000)

BELANGER, Louis (1736-1816) French
Works on paper
£702 $1137 €1053 Romantic landscape with waterfall (46x66cm-18x26in) s. gouache. 3-Feb-3 Lilla Bukowskis, Stockholm #419 (S.KR 9800)
£3846 $6038 €6000 Promenade de bebe (45x65cm-18x26in) s.d.1780 pen ink wash W/C prov. 13-Dec-2 Pierre Berge, Paris #18/R est:8000

BELANGER, Louis (attrib) (1736-1816) French
Works on paper
£567 $919 €800 Bergere et troupeau pres d'un ermitage (16x22cm-6x9in) gouache. 21-May-3 Piasa, Paris #350

BELANGER, Louis Joseph Octave (1886-1972) Canadian
£242 $394 €363 Neige Ste Adele (41x56cm-16x22in) s. 12-Feb-3 Iegor de Saint Hippolyte, Montreal #21 (C.D 600)

BELANYI, Viktor (1877-1955) Hungarian
£1800 $2952 €2700 Vase of flowers (48x31cm-19x12in) s. board. 3-Jun-3 Sotheby's, London #112/R est:2000-3000

BELAVARY, Bela (19th C) Hungarian
£258 $393 €387 From a pink rococo drawing room (31x36cm-12x14in) s. panel. 27-Aug-2 Rasmussen, Copenhagen #1909 (D.KR 3000)

BELAY, Pierre de (1890-1947) French
£845 $1361 €1200 Nu de dos (19x24cm-7x9in) s.d.1926 board. 11-May-3 Thierry & Lannon, Brest #329 est:2000-2500
£1285 $2094 €1850 Nu allonge sur le dos (22x27cm-9x11in) s.d.1927 cardboard. 19-Jul-3 Thierry & Lannon, Brest #304 est:800-1000
£1319 $2151 €1900 Jeune marin a Concarneau (16x38cm-6x15in) s.d.1923 cardboard. 19-Jul-3 Thierry & Lannon, Brest #305 est:2000-2500
£2083 $3396 €3000 Helene au bas noir (41x33cm-16x13in) s.d.41. 19-Jul-3 Thierry & Lannon, Brest #105 est:2800-3200
£2449 $3894 €3600 Scene de Fete Foraine (50x61cm-20x24in) s. paper on canvas. 26-Feb-3 Artcurial Briest, Paris #258/R est:3000-3500
£3521 $5669 €5000 La cueillette des pommes (50x61cm-20x24in) s.d.24 board. 11-May-3 Thierry & Lannon, Brest #143/R est:5000-6000
£4966 $7747 €7350 Le retour de la peche, Concarneau le port (50x61cm-20x24in) s.d. s.i.verso. 31-Mar-3 Rossini, Paris #75/R
£5282 $8504 €7500 Le petit pot rouge (55x65cm-22x26in) s.i.d.24 s.verso board. 11-May-3 Thierry & Lannon, Brest #145/R est:7500-8000
£6338 $10204 €9000 Le port de Dinan (38x46cm-15x18in) s. 11-May-3 Thierry & Lannon, Brest #146/R est:6000-8000
£6897 $10966 €10000 Le retour de la peche (50x61cm-20x24in) s. i.verso painted c.1940. 4-Mar-3 Livinec, Gaudcheau & Jezequel, Rennes #77/R
£6897 $10966 €10000 Le marche aux poissons (81x100cm-32x39in) s.d.28 panel. 4-Mar-3 Livinec, Gaudcheau & Jezequel, Rennes #79/R
£8333 $13083 €13000 Trois marins sur le port de Douarnenez (50x61cm-20x24in) s. 15-Dec-2 Thierry & Lannon, Brest #106 est:12000
£11458 $18677 €16500 Marins a Treboul (46x54cm-18x21in) s. 19-Jul-3 Thierry & Lannon, Brest #104 est:10000-12000
Works on paper
£313 $509 €450 Marin de dos a Concarneau (32x23cm-13x9in) s.i.d.1926 chl. 19-Jul-3 Thierry & Lannon, Brest #28
£333 $543 €480 Scene de marche a Honfleur (25x32cm-10x13in) s.i.d.1923 crayon. 19-Jul-3 Thierry & Lannon, Brest #27
£347 $566 €500 Le vieux sonneur (32x26cm-13x10in) s.d.18 ink wash. 19-Jul-3 Thierry & Lannon, Brest #29
£347 $566 €500 Rue de Chartres (37x27cm-15x11in) s.d.1941 W/C. 19-Jul-3 Thierry & Lannon, Brest #50
£408 $658 €580 Femme de Pont l'Abbe (32x21cm-13x8in) s.i.d.1926 chl. 11-May-3 Thierry & Lannon, Brest #288
£443 $687 €700 Concarneau, le retour des pecheurs (15x20cm-6x8in) s.d.1935 W/C on engraving. 29-Sep-2 Eric Pillon, Calais #188/R

£513 $805 €800 Eglise et rue St Nicolas a Bruxelles (46x38cm-18x15in) s.d.45 gouache. 16-Dec-2 Chochon-Barre & Allardi, Paris #22
£528 $850 €750 Marin a Audierne (31x22cm-12x9in) s.d.1928 chl. 11-May-3 Thierry & Lannon, Brest #52
£537 $864 €800 Bretonne en coiffe. Nu assis (23x32cm-9x13in) s.d.1945 W/C double-sided. 23-Feb-3 Lesieur & Le Bars, Le Havre #9
£563 $907 €800 Marin de dos a Audierne. s.i.d.1930 chl. 11-May-3 Thierry & Lannon, Brest #54
£563 $907 €800 Etude de Bretonnes. Nu de face (34x25cm-13x10in) s.d.1845 wash double-sided. 11-May-3 Thierry & Lannon, Brest #289
£629 $1051 €900 La baraque de foire (38x46cm-15x18in) s. graphite dr. 25-Jun-3 Claude Aguttes, Neuilly #209/R
£654 $1052 €1000 Dans la loge de l'opera (31x24cm-12x9in) s. gouache. 20-Jan-3 Horta, Bruxelles #468
£974 $1530 €1520 Nu (47x36cm-19x14in) s.d.26 chl crayon. 15-Dec-2 Thierry & Lannon, Brest #25
£1655 $2632 €2400 Bouquet de fleurs au vase bleu (26x36cm-10x14in) s.d.1944 pastel d'epoque treilliste. 4-Mar-3 Livinec, Gaudcheau & Jezequel, Rennes #76/R
£1677 $2650 €2650 Helene a la lecture (27x33cm-11x13in) s.d.1946 gouache. 1-Dec-2 Livinec, Gaudcheau & Jezequel, Rennes #91b/R
£1899 $2962 €3000 Petit cafe en province (36x43cm-14x17in) s.d.1928 gouache. 20-Oct-2 Chayette & Cheval, Paris #4/R
£2098 $3504 €3000 Sonneur dans un village Breton (32x25cm-13x10in) s. gouache prov. 26-Jun-3 Tajan, Paris #44/R est:3000-3500
£2500 $4075 €3600 Le Tombereau (39x50cm-15x20in) s. gouache. 19-Jul-3 Thierry & Lannon, Brest #84/R est:4000-5000

BELCASTRO, Alfredo (1893-1961) Italian
£558 $882 €837 Mountain landscape (47x57cm-19x22in) s.indis.i. panel. 29-Nov-2 Zofingen, Switzerland #2396 (S.FR 1300)

BELCHER, George (1875-1947) British
Works on paper
£270 $435 €405 Grocer and farmer's man (33x23cm-13x9in) s. pencil. 9-May-3 Mallams, Oxford #72

BELDA MORALES, Jose (19th C) Spanish
£304 $481 €475 Seascape (18x24cm-7x9in) s. 14-Nov-2 Arte, Seville #390/R

BELDER, Joseph de (1871-1927) Belgian
£353 $554 €550 Nature morte aux pensees (50x70cm-20x28in) s. 10-Dec-2 Campo, Vlaamse Kaai #119
£2878 $4604 €4000 Still life with flowers (74x57cm-29x22in) s. 17-May-3 De Vuyst, Lokeren #99/R est:2200-2600

BELGIAN SCHOOL, 16th C
£27673 $43170 €44000 Adam and Eve (137x100cm-54x39in) panel. 23-Sep-2 Wiener Kunst Auktionen, Vienna #5/R est:11000-22000

BELGIAN SCHOOL, 17th C
£6962 $11000 €11000 Nature morte au vase fleuri (118x98cm-46x39in) pair. 2-Dec-2 Amberes, Antwerp #1338

BELGIAN SCHOOL, 19th C
£4795 $7479 €7193 Still life with rose, fruit and bird's nest (40x32cm-16x13in) 28-Mar-3 Koller, Zurich #3133/R est:4000-7000 (S.FR 10500)

BELGRANO, Jose Denis (1844-1917) Spanish
£5674 $9191 €8000 Conversation in the park (47x30cm-19x12in) s. 22-May-3 Dorotheum, Vienna #127/R est:9000-11000
£6483 $10308 €9400 Stroll (40x26cm-16x10in) s. board. 4-Mar-3 Ansorena, Madrid #155/R

BELIMBAU, Adolfo (1845-1938) Italian
£13000 $21710 €19500 Love birds (81x61cm-32x24in) s. 18-Jun-3 Christie's, Kensington #147/R est:8000-10000

BELINE, George (1887-1971) American/Russian
£449 $700 €674 Harbour scene with fishing shacks and fishing boats (23x30cm-9x12in) s. panel exhib. 1-Aug-2 Eldred, East Dennis #1074/R

BELINFANTE, Willy (1922-) Dutch
£321 $503 €500 Fashion show (60x50cm-24x20in) s.d.73. 25-Nov-2 Glerum, Amsterdam #221/R

BELIYE, Alexander (1874-1934) British
£2817 $4535 €4000 Village road, Koreiz, Krim (45x35cm-18x14in) s. board. 10-May-3 Bukowskis, Helsinki #403/R est:2000-2200

BELKIN, Arnold (1930-1992) Mexican/Canada
£3092 $4947 €4483 Marat asesinato no. 10 (178x140cm-70x55in) s.d.1971. 15-May-3 Louis Morton, Mexico #49/R est:55000-60000 (M.P 50000)
Works on paper
£247 $396 €358 Untitled (25x37cm-10x15in) s.d.1981 col crayons grafitti. 15-May-3 Louis Morton, Mexico #170 (M.P 4000)

BELKNAP, Zedekiah (1781-1858) American
£3822 $6000 €5733 Portrait of a man (69x56cm-27x22in) panel. 22-Nov-2 Eldred, East Dennis #852/R est:3000-5000
£4430 $7000 €6645 Portrait of Frank H Pierce, nephew of 14th President Franklin Pierce (76x58cm-30x23in) panel prov. 17-Nov-2 CRN Auctions, Cambridge #20/R

BELL, A D (20th C) British
Works on paper
£900 $1395 €1350 Hunting scenes (24x16cm-9x6in) s. W/C htd white set of four. 1-Oct-2 Fellows & Sons, Birmingham #208/R

BELL, A David (20th C) American
Works on paper
£479 $800 €695 Tall sail ship in moderate seas off a coast (25x36cm-10x14in) s. W/C gouache two prov. 17-Jun-3 John Moran, Pasadena #89a

BELL, Ada (fl.1880-1907) British
£320 $493 €480 Mixed summer flowers in a glass vase (20x15cm-8x6in) s. panel. 24-Oct-2 Christie's, Kensington #120

BELL, Arthur George (1849-1916) British
Works on paper
£300 $471 €450 Wet day, Sandwich, Kent (35x53cm-14x21in) s. W/C. 21-Nov-2 Clevedon Sale Rooms #229

BELL, Caroline M (?-1940) American
£387 $600 €581 Long Island barn (43x48cm-17x19in) s.verso artist board. 7-Dec-2 South Bay, Long Island #174/R
£549 $850 €824 Motif no 1, Rockport. 7-Dec-2 South Bay, Long Island #168/R
£581 $900 €872 Silence of winter. Autumnal landscape (28x33cm-11x13in) artist board double-sided. 7-Dec-2 South Bay, Long Island #169/R
£774 $1200 €1161 Barn in vegetable field (41x51cm-16x20in) masonite board. 7-Dec-2 South Bay, Long Island #166/R

BELL, Charles (1935-1995) American
£30380 $48000 €45570 Clown and monkey (127x158cm-50x62in) s. painted 1972 prov.lit. 14-Nov-2 Christie's, Rockefeller NY #169/R est:50000-70000
£63291 $100000 €94937 Gum ball no.8 (122x122cm-48x48in) s. painted 1975 lit. 14-Nov-2 Christie's, Rockefeller NY #168/R est:100000-150000
£118750 $190000 €178125 Finis coronat opus (137x188cm-54x74in) s. painted 1995 prov.lit. 15-May-3 Christie's, Rockefeller NY #164/R est:150000-200000

BELL, Clara Louise (1886-?) American
Works on paper
£906 $1450 €1359 Evening in the parlour (30x46cm-12x18in) s. pastel gouache. 11-Jan-3 James Julia, Fairfield #337d est:2000-3000

BELL, Darrell (1959-) Canadian
£281 $441 €422 Riot of weeds (75x60cm-30x24in) s.i.d.1993. 25-Nov-2 Hodgins, Calgary #134/R (C.D 700)
Works on paper
£201 $315 €302 Tree reflections (75x40cm-30x16in) s.d.1997 W/C. 25-Nov-2 Hodgins, Calgary #259/R (C.D 500)

BELL, David C (1950-) British
Works on paper
£400 $668 €580 Arctic Viking hull (31x51cm-12x20in) s. W/C. 18-Jun-3 Sotheby's, Olympia #128/R

BELL, Florence (1832-1915) British
£5500 $8690 €8250 Elaine with the armour of Launcelot (44x22cm-17x9in) i.d.1870 panel feigned arched top after Arthur Hughes. 26-Nov-2 Christie's, London #110/R est:2000-3000

BELL, George Henry Frederick (1878-1966) Australian
£677 $1111 €982 Portrait of Betty in a blue blouse (46x30cm-18x12in) i.verso painted c.1940. 4-Jun-3 Deutscher-Menzies, Melbourne #304/R (A.D 1700)

£717 $1090 €1076 View of the bay (44x59cm-17x23in) s. 27-Aug-2 Goodman, Sydney #209 (A.D 2000)
£860 $1308 €1290 Still life (51x38cm-20x15in) s.d.53. 28-Aug-2 Deutscher-Menzies, Melbourne #372/R (A.D 2400)
£5694 $8712 €8541 Floral still life (60x49cm-24x19in) s. painted 1947 prov. 26-Aug-2 Sotheby's, Paddington #564/R est:20000-25000 (A.D 16000)
Works on paper
£239 $392 €347 Argentine (35x31cm-14x12in) s. conte. 4-Jun-3 Deutscher-Menzies, Melbourne #408/R (A.D 600)

BELL, James Torrington (1898-1970) British
£300 $489 €450 Harvest time (45x61cm-18x24in) 14-Feb-3 Lyon & Turnbull, Edinburgh #121

BELL, John Christopher (fl.1846-1869) British
£4430 $7000 €6645 Five ptarmigans on a rock ledge (57x78cm-22x31in) s.d.1864 prov. 3-Apr-3 Christie's, Rockefeller NY #217/R est:15000-25000

BELL, Leland (1922-1991) American
£696 $1100 €1044 Portrait of Ulla Green (76x71cm-30x28in) s. i. on stretcher. 2-Apr-3 Doyle, New York #12/R
£949 $1500 €1424 Self portrait (66x28cm-26x11in) s. i.verso canvas on masonite painted 1953. 2-Apr-3 Doyle, New York #11/R est:400-600
Works on paper
£411 $650 €617 Two Swedes (38x23cm-15x9in) s.d.55 i.d.55 verso W/C gouache. 2-Apr-3 Doyle, New York #10/R

BELL, Lilian Russell (fl.1899-1933) British
Works on paper
£950 $1482 €1425 Figures in a village street, possibly Robin Hood's Bay (63x40cm-25x16in) s. W/C. 10-Apr-3 Tennants, Leyburn #836

BELL, Quentin (1910-) British
£800 $1264 €1200 Path to the green (56x96cm-22x38in) s.d.1946 prov. 27-Nov-2 Sotheby's, Olympia #91/R

BELL, Robert Anning (1863-1933) British
Works on paper
£300 $467 €450 Satyr and nymph (26x37cm-10x15in) pencil W/C htd bodycol prov. 19-Sep-2 Christie's, Kensington #5/R

BELL, Stuart H (1823-1896) British
£900 $1386 €1350 South pier lighthouse, Sunderland (51x61cm-20x24in) s.d.1884. 3-Sep-2 Gorringes, Lewes #2291

BELL, Thomas Currie (fl.1892-1925) British
£750 $1170 €1125 Dutch harbour scene (25x35cm-10x14in) s.d.1912. 13-Sep-2 Lyon & Turnbull, Edinburgh #24/R

BELL, Trevor (1930-) British
£1100 $1705 €1650 Little up-side-down lady (91x61cm-36x24in) s. i.d.61 on stretcher prov. 4-Dec-2 Christie's, Kensington #602/R est:800-1200
£3200 $5088 €4800 Fishing boats (66x167cm-26x66in) s.d.9.57. 18-Mar-3 Bonhams, Knightsbridge #18 est:1500-2000

BELL, V (?) ?
£300 $456 €450 Still life with fruit and vessels (38x46cm-15x18in) s. board. 14-Aug-2 Andrew Hartley, Ilkley #654

BELL, Vanessa (1879-1961) British
£5500 $8580 €8250 Charleston from the pond (46x36cm-18x14in) s. exhib. 27-Mar-3 Christie's, Kensington #477/R est:6000-8000
£11000 $17050 €16500 Roses (41x34cm-16x13in) s.d.1933 prov.exhib. 4-Dec-2 Sotheby's, London #19/R est:8000-12000
£16000 $24800 €24000 Decorative panel with flowers and goldfish (48x137cm-19x54in) board lit. 4-Dec-2 Sotheby's, London #14/R est:10000-15000
£27000 $44280 €39150 Pinks (40x38cm-16x15in) painted c.1935 prov. 4-Jun-3 Sotheby's, London #44/R est:8000-12000
Works on paper
£550 $858 €825 Lady playing a lyre (27x20cm-11x8in) bears estate st. pencil after Corot prov. 17-Sep-2 Bonhams, Knightsbridge #226/R
£1900 $3021 €2850 Still life with vase (47x32cm-19x13in) init.d.1917 W/C. 26-Feb-3 Sotheby's, Olympia #172/R est:800-1200

BELL, Werner (1888-?) Austrian
£2026 $3323 €3100 Portrait of Henriette Weissmann (66x38cm-26x15in) s.d.1888. 29-Mar-3 Dannenberg, Berlin #546/R est:200

BELL-SMITH, Frederick Marlett (1846-1923) Canadian/British
£407 $638 €611 Little Nell and her grandfather. Mr Bumble, the Beadle leaving (15x15cm-6x6in) s. one i.verso board pair. 10-Dec-2 Pinneys, Montreal #165 (C.D 1000)
£645 $1019 €968 Dinner time, Hope, BC (15x15cm-6x6in) s.i.d.1919 board prov. 14-Nov-2 Heffel, Vancouver #169/R est:1200-1500 (C.D 1600)
£739 $1153 €1233 Untitled - Fraser Canyon (25x40cm-10x16in) s. canvasboard prov. 13-Apr-3 Levis, Calgary #4a/R est:2500-3500 (C.D 1700)
£978 $1604 €1467 Fraser Valley (15x15cm-6x6in) s. board. 3-Jun-3 Joyner, Toronto #276/R est:1000-1200 (C.D 2200)
£1196 $1865 €1994 In the Rockies (48x34cm-19x13in) s. canvasboard prov. 13-Apr-3 Levis, Calgary #4/R est:3500-4500 (C.D 2750)
£1556 $2551 €2334 Marine scene. Street in Coventry (37x63cm-15x25in) s.d.1908 one oil one W/C pair. 27-May-3 Sotheby's, Toronto #38/R est:4000-6000 (C.D 3500)
£1570 $2511 €2355 Parliament buildings (36x25cm-14x10in) s. s.i.verso canvas on board. 15-May-3 Heffel, Vancouver #173/R est:4000-4500 (C.D 3500)
£1613 $2548 €2420 Rocky mountains lake (33x53cm-13x21in) s.d.87 prov. 18-Nov-2 Sotheby's, Toronto #183/R est:4000-6000 (C.D 4000)
£1749 $2711 €2624 Flight of little Nell and her grandfather from the old curiosity shop (24x29cm-9x11in) s. canvas on board. 3-Dec-2 Joyner, Toronto #211/R est:2500-3500 (C.D 4250)
£1778 $2916 €2667 Sailboats off rocky shore (62x90cm-24x35in) s. indis d.92 prov. 27-May-3 Sotheby's, Toronto #39/R est:3000-5000 (C.D 4000)
£1889 $3098 €2739 Confluence of the bow and spray (30x48cm-12x19in) 1-Jun-3 Levis, Calgary #10/R est:5000-6000 (C.D 4250)
£2218 $3504 €3327 Chancellor, Valley of the Ottertail (41x51cm-16x20in) s.i. s.verso prov. 14-Nov-2 Heffel, Vancouver #160/R est:4000-6000 (C.D 5500)
£2444 $4009 €3666 Street scene with trolley car (24x16cm-9x6in) s. board. 3-Jun-3 Joyner, Toronto #288/R est:2000-3000 (C.D 5500)
£2444 $4009 €3544 Sunlit peaks (75x51cm-30x20in) s. 9-Jun-3 Hodgins, Calgary #401/R est:7000-9000 (C.D 5500)
£2667 $4373 €4001 Day in the park, London (19x26cm-7x10in) s. board. 3-Jun-3 Joyner, Toronto #4/R est:3000-4000 (C.D 6000)
£4025 $6400 €6038 On the Thames (45x64cm-18x25in) s. 23-Mar-3 Hodgins, Calgary #40/R est:5000-7000 (C.D 9500)
Works on paper
£193 $301 €280 Lake Louise, Alberta (9x15cm-4x6in) s. W/C. 26-Mar-3 Walker's, Ottawa #471 (C.D 450)
£222 $350 €333 Coast of Maine (28x41cm-11x16in) s.i.verso W/C prov. 14-Nov-2 Heffel, Vancouver #164 (C.D 550)
£242 $382 €363 Sailboats off the coast (22x47cm-9x19in) s. W/C prov. 14-Nov-2 Heffel, Vancouver #266 (C.D 600)
£244 $401 €354 Bon Echo Bay (23x10cm-9x4in) W/C. 1-Jun-3 Levis, Calgary #12/R (C.D 550)
£267 $437 €401 Surf on a rocky shoreline (14x22cm-6x9in) s. W/C. 3-Jun-3 Joyner, Toronto #538 (C.D 600)
£309 $478 €464 Gathering kelp, Bay of Fundy (16x29cm-6x11in) s.d.20th Feb 1889 i.verso W/C. 3-Dec-2 Joyner, Toronto #352 (C.D 750)
£536 $837 €777 Summer pleasures (25x55cm-10x22in) s. W/C. 26-Mar-3 Walker's, Ottawa #250/R est:1500-2000 (C.D 1250)
£723 $1135 €1085 Clam diggers, low tide (21x46cm-8x18in) s. W/C. 25-Nov-2 Hodgins, Calgary #355/R (C.D 1800)
£773 $1205 €1121 Grand pre and the Basin of Minas (33x53cm-13x21in) s.i. W/C. 26-Mar-3 Walker's, Ottawa #251/R est:1500-2000 (C.D 1800)
£823 $1276 €1235 Drying stand in a river canyon (25x39cm-10x15in) s. W/C. 3-Dec-2 Joyner, Toronto #88/R est:2000-2500 (C.D 2000)
£889 $1458 €1334 On the Thames (26x36cm-10x14in) s. W/C. 3-Jun-3 Joyner, Toronto #190/R est:2000-3000 (C.D 2000)
£889 $1458 €1334 Cattle grazing by a village stream (31x47cm-12x19in) s.d.1910 W/C. 3-Jun-3 Joyner, Toronto #417/R est:2500-3500 (C.D 2000)
£889 $1458 €1289 Untitled - railway through the Rockies (36x48cm-14x19in) W/C. 1-Jun-3 Levis, Calgary #11/R est:2500-3000 (C.D 2000)
£897 $1435 €1346 Glacier cascade in Selkirks (25x33cm-10x13in) s.d.1913 i.verso W/C. 15-May-3 Heffel, Vancouver #3/R est:1800-2200 (C.D 2000)
£907 $1433 €1361 Twilight, low tide on the Thames (37x36cm-15x14in) s. s.verso W/C executed c.1918 prov. 14-Nov-2 Heffel, Vancouver #252/R est:3000-4000 (C.D 2250)
£984 $1525 €1476 On Westminster Bridge (30x23cm-12x9in) s. i.verso W/C prov. 24-Sep-2 Ritchie, Toronto #3084/R est:2500-3000 (C.D 2400)
£1044 $1639 €1566 Mt Biddle, near Banff (23x32cm-9x13in) s. W/C executed c.1913. 25-Nov-2 Hodgins, Calgary #109/R est:2500-3000 (C.D 2600)
£1067 $1749 €1601 Fraser canyon with train trestle (32x23cm-13x9in) s. W/C. 3-Jun-3 Joyner, Toronto #65/R est:1500-2000 (C.D 2400)
£1121 $1794 €1682 Staple Inn, Holborn (27x37cm-11x15in) s.i.d.1908 W/C on board prov. 15-May-3 Heffel, Vancouver #162/R est:3000-4000 (C.D 2500)
£1121 $1794 €1682 Selling flowers (19x31cm-7x12in) s. W/C prov. 15-May-3 Heffel, Vancouver #198/R est:3000-4000 (C.D 2500)
£1129 $1784 €1694 Rocky Mountain Camp, Lake O'Hara (24x35cm-9x14in) s. W/C. 14-Nov-2 Heffel, Vancouver #27/R est:3000-3500 (C.D 2800)
£1200 $1968 €1740 Street scene near Westminster (22x26cm-9x10in) s. W/C prov. 9-Jun-3 Hodgins, Calgary #32/R est:3000-3500 (C.D 2700)

£1210 $1911 €1815 Parting day (29x62cm-11x24in) s. i.v, W/C executed c.1905 exhib. 14-Nov-2 Heffel, Vancouver #267/R est:2500-3000 (C.D 3000)
£1317 $2041 €1976 Mountain peak through the pines (46x30cm-18x12in) s. W/C. 3-Dec-2 Joyner, Toronto #27/R est:3000-4000 (C.D 3200)
£1511 $2478 €2267 Parisian street scene at dusk (19x26cm-7x10in) s. W/C. 3-Jun-3 Joyner, Toronto #256/R est:2000-3000 (C.D 3400)
£1867 $3061 €2801 Rapids in the Rockies (30x45cm-12x18in) s. W/C prov.lit. 3-Jun-3 Joyner, Toronto #14/R est:3000-4000 (C.D 4200)
£2218 $3504 €3327 Field workers, Holland (30x46cm-12x18in) s.d.1902 W/C prov. 14-Nov-2 Heffel, Vancouver #23/R est:4000-5000 (C.D 5500)
£3708 $5895 €5562 Mt. Sir Donald, Selkirks (66x44cm-26x17in) s. W/C prov. 23-Mar-3 Hodgins, Calgary #36/R est:3000-5000 (C.D 8750)

BELLA, Gabriele (attrib) (18th C) Italian
£3041 $4743 €4500 Scene from Venetian street life (35x58cm-14x23in) one of pair prov. 27-Mar-3 Dorotheum, Vienna #58/R est:2000-3500
£3041 $4743 €4500 Venetian capriccio (35x58cm-14x23in) one of pair prov. 27-Mar-3 Dorotheum, Vienna #59/R est:2000-3500

BELLA, Stefano Della (1610-1664) Italian
Prints
£2767 $4400 €4151 La mort sur un champ de bataille (22x29cm-9x11in) etching. 1-May-3 Swann Galleries, New York #138/R est:6000-9000
Works on paper
£1056 $1701 €1500 Donna a cavallo con bambino (8x7cm-3x3in) i. pen brown ink blk pencil other sketch attrib Marucelli two. 12-May-3 Sotheby's, Milan #17/R est:1500-1800
£30864 $50000 €46296 Fanciful ewer (36x26cm-14x10in) i. chk pen ink wash prov. 22-Jan-3 Christie's, Rockefeller NY #35/R est:35000

BELLA, Stefano Della (attrib) (1610-1664) Italian
Works on paper
£295 $475 €443 Fisherman at stream's edge holding a pole and fish (15x18cm-6x7in) i. pen ink. 22-Feb-3 Brunk, Ashville #161/R
£950 $1492 €1425 Travellers. Fisherman (14x19cm-6x7in) pen ink over black chk pair. 11-Dec-2 Sotheby's, Olympia #22/R

BELLA, Vincenzo la (1872-1954) Italian
£696 $1100 €1100 Inn (41x44cm-16x17in) s. panel. 26-Nov-2 Christie's, Rome #232
£1474 $2285 €2300 Venetian carnival (50x70cm-20x28in) s.i. cardboard. 5-Dec-2 Stadion, Trieste #746/R

BELLAARD, Henk (1896-?) Dutch
£845 $1361 €1200 Ship-building yard (44x59cm-17x23in) s. 7-May-3 Vendue Huis, Gravenhage #7/R

BELLAGIO (19th C) Italian
£2357 $3865 €3418 Street in southern town (57x34cm-22x13in) s.d.1874. 4-Jun-3 AB Stockholms Auktionsverk #2419/R est:15000-20000 (S.KR 30000)

BELLAMY, John Haley (attrib) (1836-1914) American
Sculpture
£8075 $13000 €12113 Spread wing eagle (11x24cm-4x9in) carved painted gilded. 16-Jan-3 Christie's, Rockefeller NY #264/R est:8000-12000

BELLANDI, Ernesto (1842-?) Italian
Works on paper
£308 $483 €480 On the swing (22x32cm-9x13in) s.i. pencil W/C. 16-Dec-2 Pandolfini, Florence #4

BELLANDI, Giorgio (1930-) Italian
£1015 $1482 €1585 Untitled (146x140cm-57x55in) s.d.64. 5-Jun-2 Il Ponte, Milan #26
£1603 $2340 €2500 Untitled (240x340cm-94x134in) s.d.64. 5-Jun-2 Il Ponte, Milan #37
£1603 $2340 €2500 House of. (240x240cm-94x94in) s.i.d.1964. 5-Jun-2 Il Ponte, Milan #49

BELLANGE, Hippolyte (1800-1866) French
£4808 $7548 €7500 Depart du bac (18x24cm-7x9in) s. panel. 16-Dec-2 Rabourdin & Choppin de Janvry, Paris #197/R est:8000
Works on paper
£340 $530 €510 Old musician with young lad and dog (16x13cm-6x5in) s.d.1831 W/C pencil. 17-Oct-2 Lawrence, Crewkerne #397/R
£380 $616 €570 Veteran and young child (14x16cm-6x6in) s. pencil W/C. 23-Jan-3 Christie's, Kensington #354

BELLANGE, Jacques (c.1575-1616) Italian
Prints
£5500 $9075 €7975 Diana and the hunter (47x21cm-19x8in) etching. 1-Jul-3 Sotheby's, London #2/R est:6000-7000
£19000 $31350 €27550 Death of Portia (24x19cm-9x7in) etching. 1-Jul-3 Sotheby's, London #1/R est:8000-12000

BELLANGER, Auguste (?) French
£1126 $1835 €1700 Aperitif (46x61cm-18x24in) s. 3-Feb-3 Chambelland & Giafferi, Paris #337 est:450

BELLANGER, René-Charles (1895-1964) French
£903 $1427 €1400 Nice (54x65cm-21x26in) s. cardboard on panel lit. 18-Dec-2 Digard, Paris #150

BELLANY, John (1942-) British
£900 $1431 €1350 Figures by the sea (61x51cm-24x20in) s. 26-Feb-3 Sotheby's, Olympia #393/R est:1000-1500
£1100 $1804 €1650 Fishing boat (51x76cm-20x30in) s. 3-Jun-3 Sotheby's, Olympia #259/R est:1000-1500
£1200 $1968 €1800 Portrait of a woman with a headscarf (75x61cm-30x24in) s. 3-Jun-3 Sotheby's, Olympia #258/R est:800-1200
£1200 $1980 €1740 Scottish landscape (61x91cm-24x36in) s. s.verso board. 3-Jul-3 Christie's, Kensington #725/R est:1000-1500
£1400 $2226 €2100 Veronica in hours (61x76cm-24x30in) s. 26-Feb-3 Sotheby's, Olympia #388/R est:1000-1500
£1500 $2340 €2250 Tommy Tucker (57x40cm-22x16in) s. i.verso. 12-Sep-2 Sotheby's, Olympia #149/R est:800-1200
£1500 $2325 €2250 Portrait of a lady with crow (76x61cm-30x24in) s. 4-Dec-2 Christie's, Kensington #526/R est:2000-3000
£1500 $2369 €2250 Portrait of a woman (61x51cm-24x20in) s. 27-Nov-2 Sotheby's, Olympia #219/R est:1200-1800
£1500 $2340 €2250 Female portrait (51x41cm-20x16in) s. 27-Mar-3 Christie's, Kensington #549/R est:1000-1500
£1500 $2460 €2250 Woman of the north (76x60cm-30x24in) i.verso. 3-Jun-3 Sotheby's, Olympia #257/R est:1200-1800
£1800 $2790 €2700 Portrait of a woman with fish (61x51cm-24x20in) s. 4-Dec-2 Christie's, Kensington #523/R est:2000-3000
£1800 $2862 €2700 Portrait of a lady (76x51cm-30x20in) s. 6-Mar-3 Christie's, Kensington #269/R est:2000-3000
£1800 $2808 €2700 Beached boats at Aldburgh (91x91cm-36x36in) s. 26-Mar-3 Hamptons Fine Art, Godalming #214/R est:2000-3000
£1900 $2945 €2850 Figure composition. Abstract figures (159x116cm-63x46in) s.verso two. 4-Dec-2 Christie's, Kensington #530/R est:1000-1500
£1900 $3001 €2850 Ancient mariner (61x51cm-24x20in) s. i.verso. 27-Nov-2 Sotheby's, Olympia #218/R est:1000-1500
£2000 $3180 €3000 Self portrait (91x61cm-36x24in) s. prov. 6-Mar-3 Christie's, Kensington #266/R est:2000-3000
£2200 $3388 €3300 In the harbour (51x61cm-20x24in) s. prov. 5-Sep-2 Christie's, Kensington #682/R est:800-1200
£2200 $3432 €3300 Portraitof a woman (76x61cm-30x24in) s. 12-Sep-2 Sotheby's, Olympia #147/R est:1200-1800
£2200 $3410 €3300 Still life with flowers in a vase (91x91cm-36x36in) s. 4-Dec-2 Christie's, Kensington #586/R est:2000-3000
£2200 $3498 €3300 Portrait of a girl with seagull (61x51cm-24x20in) s. 26-Feb-3 Sotheby's, Olympia #394/R est:1000-1500
£2200 $3608 €3300 Crail harbour (76x101cm-30x40in) s. i.d.95 stretcher. 3-Jun-3 Sotheby's, Olympia #215/R est:2500-3000
£2400 $3792 €3600 Self portrait (75x55cm-30x22in) s. s.i.d.1984 verso board. 27-Nov-2 Sotheby's, Olympia #315/R est:1500-2000
£2400 $3744 €3600 Double portrait (122x91cm-48x36in) s. 27-Mar-3 Christie's, Kensington #547/R est:2500-3500
£2400 $3744 €3600 Accordionist (121x90cm-48x35in) s. 10-Apr-3 Bonhams, Edinburgh #33/R est:3000-5000
£2400 $3936 €3600 Trawler in dry dock (61x76cm-24x30in) s. 3-Jun-3 Sotheby's, Olympia #233/R est:1200-1800
£2500 $3975 €3750 Man and wife (91x91cm-36x36in) s. 26-Feb-3 Sotheby's, Olympia #401/R est:2500-3500
£2800 $4312 €4200 Woman of the North Sea (76x55cm-30x24in) s. 5-Sep-2 Christie's, Kensington #641/R est:1700-2000
£2800 $4452 €4200 Portrait of a lady in a landscape (101x76cm-40x30in) s. 6-Mar-3 Christie's, Kensington #268/R est:2500-3500
£2800 $4620 €4060 Bass rock fable (76x61cm-30x24in) s.i. 3-Jul-3 Christie's, Kensington #569/R est:1500-2000
£3000 $4770 €4500 Crail harbour (91x122cm-36x48in) s. 6-Mar-3 Christie's, Kensington #271/R est:3000-5000
£3000 $4680 €4500 Birds of paradise (152x122cm-60x48in) 14-Apr-3 Sotheby's, London #193/R est:3000-5000
£3000 $4920 €4500 Self portrait with nude (122x91cm-48x36in) s. i.d.94 verso. 3-Jun-3 Sotheby's, Olympia #261/R est:3000-5000
£3200 $4960 €4800 Salome (151x120cm-59x47in) i. s.i.verso. 5-Dec-2 Bonhams, Edinburgh #34/R est:4000-6000
£3400 $5304 €5100 Spirit of the sea (91x91cm-36x36in) s. s.i.d.95 stretcher. 12-Sep-2 Sotheby's, Olympia #151/R est:1500-2000
£3400 $5610 €4930 Still life with teapots and sangria jug (91x122cm-36x48in) s. i.verso. 3-Jul-3 Christie's, Kensington #639/R est:1500-2000
£3500 $5565 €5250 Woman with lap dog (123x93cm-48x37in) s. s.i.d.1969 verso board. 6-Mar-3 Christie's, Kensington #273/R est:3000-5000
£3800 $6042 €5700 Artemis (91x91cm-36x36in) s. 26-Feb-3 Sotheby's, Olympia #398/R est:3000-5000
£4000 $6240 €6000 Queen of the night (213x171cm-84x67in) i.stretcher. 17-Oct-2 Bonhams, Edinburgh #93 est:4000-6000

£4000	$6320	€6000	Flowers in a blue vase (91x91cm-36x36in) s. 27-Nov-2 Sotheby's, Olympia #221/R est:2500-3500
£4000	$6240	€6000	Still life of jugs, flowers and vases (123x91cm-48x36in) s. 26-Mar-3 Hamptons Fine Art, Godalming #194/R est:2500-3500
£4000	$6600	€5800	Strathmore harbour (91x122cm-36x48in) s. 3-Jul-3 Christie's, Kensington #697/R est:3000-5000
£4200	$6552	€6300	Crail Harbour (91x122cm-36x48in) s. 26-Mar-3 Hamptons Fine Art, Godalming #206/R est:3500-4500
£4400	$6864	€6600	Red tulips (91x91cm-36x36in) s/ i.d.94 verso. 12-Sep-2 Sotheby's, Olympia #150/R est:2000-3000
£4600	$7084	€6900	Harbour (91x122cm-36x48in) s. 23-Oct-2 Hamptons Fine Art, Godalming #138/R est:3500-4500
£4800	$7872	€7200	Harbour scene (91x121cm-36x48in) s. s.d.93 stretcher. 3-Jun-3 Sotheby's, Olympia #288/R est:4000-6000
£5000	$7800	€7500	Sarah's table (173x173cm-68x68in) s.verso. 17-Oct-2 Bonhams, Edinburgh #55/R est:6000-8000
£5000	$7900	€7500	Fish monger (98x74cm-39x29in) s. paper painted c.1965 prov. 27-Nov-2 Sotheby's, Olympia #189/R est:6000-8000
£5200	$8112	€7800	Harbour Macduff (91x122cm-36x48in) s. i.d.96 verso. 12-Sep-2 Sotheby's, Olympia #140/R est:3000-5000
£5200	$8216	€7800	Eymouth harbour (91x122cm-36x48in) s. 27-Nov-2 Hamptons Fine Art, Godalming #400/R est:3500-4500
£5500	$8525	€8250	Still life with bird of paradise flowers (122x91cm-48x36in) s. 31-Oct-2 Christie's, London #205/R est:6000-8000
£5500	$8745	€8250	Crail (91x91cm-36x36in) s. s.i.d.94 verso. 26-Feb-3 Sotheby's, Olympia #400/R est:2500-3500
£6000	$9360	€9000	Three Graces (217x203cm-85x80in) s. 17-Oct-2 Bonhams, Edinburgh #104/R est:6000-8000
£6500	$9945	€9750	Fisher in the snow (249x188cm-98x74in) 22-Aug-2 Bonhams, Edinburgh #1097/R est:7000-10000
£7500	$11475	€11250	St. Monance (152x173cm-60x68in) s. s.verso. 22-Aug-2 Bonhams, Edinburgh #1094/R est:5000-7000
£7500	$11625	€11250	Voyage (185x180cm-73x71in) 5-Dec-2 Bonhams, Edinburgh #49/R est:8000-12000
£8000	$12400	€12000	Labyrinth (172x171cm-68x67in) s.i.verso. 5-Dec-2 Bonhams, Edinburgh #48/R est:8000-12000
£8000	$12480	€12000	St. Monans (122x152cm-48x60in) s. i.d.84 verso. 14-Apr-3 Sotheby's, London #188/R est:6000-8000
£10000	$15300	€15000	Persecuted (186x186cm-73x73in) i. board. 22-Aug-2 Bonhams, Edinburgh #1092/R est:10000-15000

Works on paper

£280	$442	€420	Figure and reindeer in a landscape (60x85cm-24x33in) s. black ink wash. 27-Nov-2 Hamptons Fine Art, Godalming #117
£350	$546	€525	Still life with flowers in a vase (37x28cm-15x11in) s. pencil W/C. 27-Mar-3 Christie's, Kensington #640/R
£380	$600	€570	Portrait (60x41cm-24x16in) s. black ink wash. 27-Nov-2 Hamptons Fine Art, Godalming #119
£380	$600	€570	Portrait of a gypsy girl, a landscape beyond (61x43cm-24x17in) s. black ink wash. 27-Nov-2 Hamptons Fine Art, Godalming #120
£500	$770	€750	Boats at the quay (37x55cm-15x22in) s. W/C. 5-Sep-2 Christie's, Kensington #670
£500	$825	€725	Ace of clubs, two of hearts (38x28cm-15x11in) s. chl W/C prov. 3-Jul-3 Christie's, Kensington #571/R
£550	$858	€825	Portrait of a girl with plaits (37x28cm-15x11in) s. pencil W/C. 27-Mar-3 Christie's, Kensington #548
£550	$908	€798	Bird portrait (74x54cm-29x21in) s. pencil W/C. 3-Jul-3 Christie's, Kensington #608
£600	$936	€900	Fish gutter (75x65cm-30x26in) s. pencil. 10-Apr-3 Bonhams, Edinburgh #1
£700	$1078	€1050	Fishing harbour (37x55cm-15x22in) s. W/C. 5-Sep-2 Christie's, Kensington #688/R
£700	$1092	€1050	Clairvoyant (58x37cm-23x15in) s. W/C. 26-Mar-3 Hamptons Fine Art, Godalming #98
£700	$1148	€1050	Owl (36x27cm-14x11in) s. pencil W/C. 3-Jun-3 Sotheby's, Olympia #234/R
£700	$1148	€1050	Fishwife (37x28cm-15x11in) s. pencil W/C. 3-Jun-3 Sotheby's, Olympia #236/R
£700	$1155	€1015	Puffin portrait with caged fish (75x55cm-30x22in) s.d.1981 pencil W/C. 3-Jul-3 Christie's, Kensington #572/R
£780	$1209	€1170	Still life with beautiful birds (76x56cm-30x22in) s. mixed media. 6-Dec-2 Lyon & Turnbull, Edinburgh #85/R
£800	$1248	€1200	Silver Crest, in harbour (37x56cm-15x22in) s. pencil W/C. 10-Apr-3 Bonhams, Edinburgh #22
£800	$1248	€1200	Librarian (57x36cm-22x14in) s.i. W/C. 26-Mar-3 Hamptons Fine Art, Godalming #99
£900	$1404	€1350	Fishing boats in a harbour (56x74cm-22x29in) s. pencil W/C. 27-Mar-3 Christie's, Kensington #594/R
£900	$1404	€1350	Milky way, mother and child (37x28cm-15x11in) s. W/C. 10-Apr-3 Bonhams, Edinburgh #8/R
£900	$1476	€1350	Portrait of a woman (55x37cm-22x15in) s. pencil W/C. 3-Jun-3 Sotheby's, Olympia #235/R
£900	$1485	€1305	Self portrait (74x54cm-29x21in) s.d.1981 chl W/C. 3-Jul-3 Christie's, Kensington #570/R
£1000	$1560	€1500	Fishing boats in a harbour (55x75cm-22x30in) s. pencil W/C. 27-Mar-3 Christie's, Kensington #598/R est:1000-1500
£1600	$2544	€2400	Crail harbour (56x75cm-22x30in) s. s.verso pencil W/C. 6-Mar-3 Christie's, Kensington #270/R est:1000-1500
£1800	$2790	€2700	Milky way in dry dock (56x75cm-22x30in) s. W/C. 5-Dec-2 Bonhams, Edinburgh #111 est:1500-2500
£1800	$2808	€2700	Whither goest thou (76x57cm-30x22in) s.i. pencil W/C. 10-Apr-3 Bonhams, Edinburgh #11 est:2000-3000
£1900	$2964	€2850	Sisters (76x56cm-30x22in) s. W/C. 26-Mar-3 Hamptons Fine Art, Godalming #97 est:800-1000
£2200	$3432	€3300	Fancy hat (55x63cm-22x25in) s. pencil W/C exhib. 17-Sep-2 Sotheby's, Olympia #78/R est:1200-1800
£2200	$3630	€3190	Fishing boats in a harbour (38x57cm-15x22in) s. W/C bodycol. 3-Jul-3 Christie's, Kensington #695/R est:800-1200
£2400	$3744	€3600	Still life of flowers (75x57cm-30x22in) s. W/C. 17-Oct-2 Bonhams, Edinburgh #112 est:2000-3000

BELLE, Alexis Simon (1674-1734) French

£11348	$18950	€16000	Portrait de Louis, Duc d'Orleans (130x96cm-51x38in) exhib.lit. 23-Jun-3 Beaussant & Lefèvre, Paris #275/R est:20000-30000
£17021	$28426	€24000	Portrait de Auguste-Marie-Jeanne de Baben-Baden, Duchesse d'Orleans (146x113cm-57x44in) exhib.lit. 23-Jun-3 Beaussant & Lefèvre, Paris #274/R est:30000-40000

BELLE, Alexis Simon (attrib) (1674-1734) French

£4800	$7584	€7200	Portrait of Captain Hercules Baker (127x102cm-50x40in) prov. 26-Nov-2 Christie's, London #11/R est:4000-6000
£10322	$16309	€16000	Portrait presume de Louis XV (116x89cm-46x35in) prov. 20-Dec-2 Tajan, Paris #138/R est:10000

BELLE, Alexis Simon (circle) (1674-1734) French

£5379	$8553	€7800	Portrait d'homme en armure (83x66cm-33x26in) 4-Mar-3 Livinec, Gaudcheau & Jezequel, Rennes #32/R

BELLE, Anne Marie (c.1663-1718) French

Miniatures

£1900	$2964	€2850	Prince James Francis Edward Stuart, the Old Pretender (4cm-2xin) vellum silver gilt frame oval. 5-Nov-2 Bonhams, New Bond Street #31/R est:600-800

BELLE, Charles Ernest de (1873-1939) Canadian/Hungarian

Works on paper

£260	$395	€390	Winter (20x25cm-8x10in) pastel. 4-Jul-2 Heffel, Vancouver #7 (C.D 600)
£261	$410	€392	Kneeling woman in a white gown (29x24cm-11x9in) init. pastel. 25-Nov-2 Hodgins, Calgary #129/R (C.D 650)
£282	$446	€423	Reflections (27x22cm-11x9in) s.i. pastel prov. 14-Nov-2 Heffel, Vancouver #232 (C.D 700)
£348	$543	€580	Untitled - fallen snow (22x14cm-9x6in) init. pastel prov. 13-Apr-3 Levis, Calgary #25/R (C.D 800)

BELLE, Karel van (1884-1959) Belgian

£484	$765	€750	Le marchand de fleurs (107x203cm-42x80in) s. 17-Dec-2 Palais de Beaux Arts, Brussels #629
£540	$863	€750	Femme au levrier se promenant dans les dunes. s.d.1952. 13-May-3 Palais de Beaux Arts, Brussels #320a/R
£556	$878	€800	Portrait de dame au bouquet de fleurs (72x57cm-28x22in) 28-Apr-3 Amberes, Antwerp #320
£570	$918	€850	Chez la marchande de fleurs (60x70cm-24x28in) s.d.1924. 18-Feb-3 Vanderkindere, Brussels #6
£694	$1146	€1000	La belle (42x29cm-17x11in) s. panel. 1-Jul-3 Christie's, Amsterdam #171
£748	$1190	€1100	Nature morte (75x98cm-30x39in) s.d.1930. 18-Mar-3 Galerie Moderne, Brussels #568/R
£1127	$1814	€1600	The letter (97x156cm-38x61in) s.d.1942. 12-May-3 Bernaerts, Antwerp #685/R est:1500-2000

BELLE, Marcel (1871-1948) French

£380	$600	€600	Foret de rambouillet (27x35cm-11x14in) s. panel exhib. 27-Nov-2 Blanchet, Paris #14/R

BELLEFLEUR, Léon (1910-) Canadian

£1070	$1658	€1605	Manege (37x26cm-15x10in) s.d.62 prov. 3-Dec-2 Joyner, Toronto #187/R est:1500-2000 (C.D 2600)
£1210	$1911	€1815	Untitled abstract (42x61cm-17x24in) s.d.70 canvas on board prov.lit. 18-Nov-2 Sotheby's, Toronto #179/R est:5000-7000 (C.D 3000)
£1228	$1830	€1842	Dans les dunes (51x61cm-20x24in) s. s.i.verso. 26-Jun-2 Iegor de Saint Hippolyte, Montreal #4 (C.D 2800)
£1557	$2430	€2336	Le bas du fleuve (38x46cm-15x18in) s.d.84. 10-Sep-2 Iegor de Saint Hippolyte, Montreal #6 (C.D 3800)
£1564	$2424	€2346	Les lunatiques (45x37cm-18x15in) s.d.65. 3-Dec-2 Joyner, Toronto #213/R est:2500-3500 (C.D 3800)
£1855	$2931	€2783	Le faisan effarouche (71x53cm-28x21in) s. s.d.65 verso prov. 18-Nov-2 Sotheby's, Toronto #175/R est:5000-7000 (C.D 4600)
£2823	$4460	€4235	Abstract composition (117x89cm-46x35in) s.d.65 prov. 18-Nov-2 Sotheby's, Toronto #64/R est:8000-10000 (C.D 7000)
£2889	$4738	€4334	Chateaux du couchant (101x81cm-40x32in) s.d.75 s.i.d.verso prov. 27-May-3 Sotheby's, Toronto #182/R est:7000-9000 (C.D 6500)
£3111	$5102	€4667	Tour de guet (89x117cm-35x46in) s.d.78 s.i.d.verso prov. 27-May-3 Sotheby's, Toronto #183/R est:6000-8000 (C.D 7000)

Works on paper
£921 $1372 €1382 Stratosphere (54x40cm-21x16in) s.i.d.93 mixed media. 26-Jun-2 Iegor de Saint Hippolyte, Montreal #5 (C.D 2100)

BELLEGAMBE, Jean (attrib) (1470-1534) French
£2564 $4051 €4000 Vierge allaitant l'enfant (39x28cm-15x11in) panel. 12-Nov-2 Palais de Beaux Arts, Brussels #445/R est:5000-7000

BELLEGARDE, Claude (1927-) French
£464 $756 €700 Matrice (46x38cm-18x15in) s. paint aluminium prov. 31-Jan-3 Charbonneaux, Paris #56
£650 $1034 €975 Pasion I (73x115cm-29x45in) s. 18-Mar-3 Bonhams, Knightsbridge #19
£795 $1295 €1200 Typogravure de l'astronaute (53x67cm-21x26in) s.d. s.i.d.verso paint aluminium. 31-Jan-3 Charbonneaux, Paris #57/R
£861 $1403 €1300 Typogravure du cosmonaute (53x73cm-21x29in) s.d. s.i.d.verso paint aluminium. 31-Jan-3 Charbonneaux, Paris #58/R
£1300 $2119 €1950 Transfiguration (130x107cm-51x42in) s.i.d.60 verso. 3-Feb-3 Sotheby's, Olympia #198/R est:1200-1600

BELLEGHEM, Jos van (1894-) Belgian
£284 $474 €400 Shrimp fishermen. 23-Jun-3 Bernaerts, Antwerp #190

BELLEI, Gaetano (1857-1922) Italian
£7000 $10990 €10500 Study of a lady in a pink brimmed hat (58x48cm-23x19in) s. 19-Nov-2 Bonhams, New Bond Street #84/R est:7000-10000
£9434 $14528 €15000 Kids on the door (60x55cm-24x22in) s. lit. 23-Oct-2 Finarte, Milan #41/R est:15000-18000
£16456 $26000 €24684 Love letter (71x52cm-28x20in) s. 23-Apr-3 Christie's, Rockefeller NY #113/R est:12000-16000

BELLEL, A (?) ?
£1491 $2400 €2237 Woman holding basket of flowers (81x64cm-32x25in) s. 22-Feb-3 Brunk, Ashville #358/R

BELLEL, Jean-Joseph (1816-1898) French
£567 $948 €800 Traversee du desert (22x32cm-9x13in) 23-Jun-3 Beaussant & Lefèvre, Paris #147
£1064 $1777 €1500 Paysages d'Afrique du Nord (16x34cm-6x13in) one mono. cardboard pair. 23-Jun-3 Beaussant & Lefèvre, Paris #150 est:200-300
£2128 $3553 €3000 Paysage Algerien (6x39cm-2x15in) 23-Jun-3 Beaussant & Lefèvre, Paris #149 est:100-150

BELLEMAIN, A (20th C) French
£573 $836 €860 Still life with carnations (55x46cm-22x18in) s.d.1929. 17-Jun-2 Philippe Schuler, Zurich #7319 (S.FR 1300)
£573 $836 €860 Still life with roses (55x46cm-22x18in) s.d.1929. 17-Jun-2 Philippe Schuler, Zurich #7320/R (S.FR 1300)

BELLENGE, Michel Bruno (attrib) (1726-1793) French
£3311 $5165 €4900 Guirlandes de fleurs (63x72cm-25x28in) pair oval. 28-Mar-3 Piasa, Paris #64/R

BELLERIVE, Marcel (1934-) Canadian
Works on paper
£206 $317 €309 Untitled (55x65cm-22x26in) s.d.66 mixed media. 22-Oct-2 Iegor de Saint Hippolyte, Montreal #12 (C.D 500)

BELLEROCHE, Albert de (1864-1944) French
£685 $1068 €1000 Timidite (65x49cm-26x19in) s. 14-Apr-3 Horta, Bruxelles #171
£1800 $2844 €2700 Artist's wife (81x65cm-32x26in) 3-Apr-3 Christie's, Kensington #55/R

BELLERUCHE, A (19/20th C) French
£420 $652 €630 Nude study (65x49cm-26x19in) s. 3-Dec-2 Sotheby's, Olympia #210/R

BELLET, Auguste Émile (?-1911) French
£1687 $2750 €2531 Lady in a bonnet with a pink ribbon (65x55cm-26x22in) s.i. 16-Feb-3 Butterfields, San Francisco #2042 est:1000-1500
£2200 $3586 €3300 Portrait of a lady in a bonnet and red dress (69x85cm-27x33in) s. board. 12-Feb-3 Bonhams, Knightsbridge #314/R est:2000-3000

BELLET, Pierre (19/20th C) French
£1064 $1723 €1500 Desnudo feminino (59x39cm-23x15in) s. 20-May-3 Segre, Madrid #45/R est:1500

BELLETESTE, Jean Antoine (c.1731-c.1811) French
Sculpture
£10563 $17535 €15000 Quatre saisons (18cm-7in) ivory socle four executed with his studio. 16-Jun-3 Anaf, Lyon #50/R est:15000-20000

BELLETTE, Jean Mary (1909-1991) Australian
£573 $872 €860 Still life (33x30cm-13x12in) s.d.34 canvasboard. 28-Aug-2 Deutscher-Menzies, Melbourne #386/R (A.D 1600)
£1550 $2465 €2325 Allegorical landscape (31x38cm-12x15in) paper on board exhib. 5-May-3 Sotheby's, Melbourne #259/R est:4000-6000 (A.D 4000)
£1916 $3008 €2874 Nude (39x49cm-15x19in) s.d.56 board. 15-Apr-3 Lawson Menzies, Sydney #152/R est:6000-9000 (A.D 5000)
£2071 $3273 €3107 Pyrmont girl (65x51cm-26x20in) init. i.verso. 17-Nov-2 Sotheby's, Paddington #21/R est:5000-8000 (A.D 5800)
Works on paper
£536 $846 €804 Sydney foreshore (37x44cm-15x17in) s. pastel. 18-Nov-2 Goodman, Sydney #186 (A.D 1500)
£1600 $2576 €2400 Hill End (40x45cm-16x18in) s.i. ink W/C gouache on card. 6-May-3 Christie's, Melbourne #223/R est:1200-1800 (A.D 4000)

BELLEVOIS, Jacob Adriaensz (1621-1675) Dutch
£13669 $21871 €19000 Zeeland fleet on the Merwede, Dordrecht in the distance (94x107cm-37x42in) s. panel. 14-May-3 Christie's, Amsterdam #185/R est:12000-16000

BELLI, Benito (19th C) ?
£270 $422 €430 Soldier (23x17cm-9x7in) s.d.1887 board. 17-Sep-2 Segre, Madrid #74/R

BELLI, Enrico (fl.1880-1884) British/Italian
£469 $750 €704 Dispute at cards (64x76cm-25x30in) s. 12-Jan-3 William Jenack, New York #261

BELLI, Luigi (1848-?) Italian
Works on paper
£662 $1059 €920 Progetto per la decorazione d'un interno d'une cattedrale gotica (85x53cm-33x21in) s.d.1873 W/C. 17-May-3 Meeting Art, Vercelli #198/R

BELLIAS, Richard (1921-1974) French
£250 $403 €375 Still life with pewter jug (38x55cm-15x22in) s. 14-Jan-3 Bonhams, Knightsbridge #184/R

BELLINGEN, Jan van (c.1770-1828) Flemish
£1923 $2981 €3000 Summer landscape with shepherd and figure on a mule (40x53cm-16x21in) s. panel. 4-Dec-2 Neumeister, Munich #672/R est:3000

BELLINGHAM-SMITH, Elinor (1906-) British
£1500 $2400 €2250 River (141x183cm-56x72in) init. 15-May-3 Lawrence, Crewkerne #1009/R est:1500-2500

BELLINI, Bellino (1741-1799) Italian
£1046 $1715 €1600 Portrait of a lady. Portrait of a gentleman (78x58cm-31x23in) mono.i.d.1785 pair. 5-Feb-3 Neumeister, Munich #658/R est:1000

BELLINI, Emmanuel (1904-1989) French
Works on paper
£283 $439 €450 Caleche devant le palais de Monaco (36x54cm-14x21in) s.d.62 W/C. 3-Nov-2 Feletin, Province #214

BELLINI, Enzo (1932-) Italian
£340 $541 €500 Girl and magpie (90x90cm-35x35in) s. 1-Mar-3 Meeting Art, Vercelli #532

BELLINI, Filippo (attrib) (1550-1604) Italian
Works on paper
£1200 $2004 €1740 Standing female saint with two putti (26x12cm-10x5in) red chk squared transfer prov. 9-Jul-3 Bonhams, Knightsbridge #42/R est:800-1200

BELLINI, Gentile (1429-1507) Italian
£150000 $250500 €217500 Portrait of Doge Agostino Barbarigo, bust length, behind a marble parapet (66x52cm-26x20in) indis.s. panel prov.exhib.lit. 10-Jul-3 Sotheby's, London #33/R est:150000-200000

BELLINI, Giovanni (1430-1516) Italian
£308642 $500000 €462963 Two crucified thieves (79x29cm-31x11in) tempera on panel prov.lit. 24-Jan-3 Christie's, Rockefeller NY #76/R est:500000-700000

BELLINI, Giovanni (circle) (1430-1516) Italian
£4861 $7729 €7000 Madonna and Child (41x53cm-16x21in) board. 4-May-3 Finarte, Venice #554/R est:7000

BELLINI, Giovanni (style) (1430-1516) Italian
£5200 $8684 €7540 The Madonna and Child (35x28cm-14x11in) panel prov. 8-Jul-3 Sotheby's, Olympia #315/R est:4000-6000

BELLINI, Jacopo (school) (1400-1470) Italian
£9615 $15192 €15000 Body of Christ being held by his mother and Peter (83x66cm-33x26in) panel. 16-Nov-2 Lempertz, Koln #1007a/R est:15000

BELLINI, Jacopo (style) (1400-1470) Italian
£12000 $18600 €18000 The Nativity (26x45cm-10x18in) tempera gold ground panel prov.lit. 31-Oct-2 Sotheby's, Olympia #3/R est:6000-8000

BELLIS, Antonio de (?-1656) Italian
£31034 $49034 €45000 Martyrdom of Saint Bartholomew (122x97cm-48x38in) prov.lit. 5-Apr-3 Finarte Semenzato, Milan #88/R est:70000
£49383 $80000 €74075 Christ and the woman of Samaria at the well (228x174cm-90x69in) prov. 24-Jan-3 Christie's, Rockefeller NY #150/R est:60000-80000

BELLIS, Hubert (1831-1902) Belgian
£288 $463 €440 Composition florale (32x46cm-13x18in) s. canvas on panel. 20-Jan-3 Horta, Bruxelles #309
£380 $592 €600 Nature morte aux crevettes (26x39cm-10x15in) s. panel. 16-Oct-2 Hotel des Ventes Mosan, Brussels #150
£411 $642 €650 Nature morte aux huitres et aux crevettes (21x32cm-8x13in) s. panel. 15-Oct-2 Horta, Bruxelles #5
£513 $805 €800 Still life with game (52x64cm-20x25in) s. 16-Dec-2 Bernaerts, Antwerp #326
£651 $1015 €950 Nature morte aux pommes et aux oranges (35x50cm-14x20in) s. 14-Apr-3 Horta, Bruxelles #342
£1046 $1684 €1600 Pots de fleurs (71x58cm-28x23in) s. 14-Jan-3 Vanderkindere, Brussels #468 est:1250-1750
£1319 $2177 €1900 Strawberries and pink roses on a ledge (23x35cm-9x14in) s. panel. 1-Jul-3 Christie's, Amsterdam #146/R est:1200-1600
£1529 $2385 €2400 Still life with flowers and fruit (44x62cm-17x24in) s. 6-Nov-2 Vendue Huis, Gravenhage #533/R est:2000-3000
£2270 $3790 €3200 Nature morte aux raisins et pommes (54x82cm-21x32in) s. 17-Jun-3 Palais de Beaux Arts, Brussels #509/R est:2500-3500
£2800 $4452 €4200 Vase de fleurs (80x56cm-31x22in) s. 18-Mar-3 Bonhams, New Bond Street #20/R est:2000-3000

BELLMAN, J J (?) British?
£1050 $1638 €1575 Huntsmen and hounds on a path (35x26cm-14x10in) s. board. 9-Oct-2 Woolley & Wallis, Salisbury #316/R est:400-600

BELLMER, Hans (1902-1975) French/Polish
Photographs
£15190 $24000 €22785 La poupee (12x8cm-5x3in) gelatin silver prints 10 bound in a volume prov.lit. 22-Apr-3 Christie's, Rockefeller NY #165/R est:18000-22000
£31646 $50000 €47469 Les jeux de la poupee (14x14cm-6x6in) hand col gelatin silver prints set of 15 prov.lit. 22-Apr-3 Christie's, Rockefeller NY #166/R est:25000-35000
Sculpture
£40000 $65600 €60000 Toupie (54cm-21in) st.sig. num.0/8 painted bronze prov.lit. 5-Feb-3 Sotheby's, London #197/R est:28000
Works on paper
£786 $1211 €1250 Fille Phallus (19x23cm-7x9in) s.d.1963 W/C Indian ink. 26-Oct-2 Dr Lehr, Berlin #43/R
£1812 $2971 €2500 Untitled (19x13cm-7x5in) s. pencil. 31-May-3 Villa Grisebach, Berlin #508/R est:2500-3000
£13878 $21789 €21650 Untitled (46x31cm-18x12in) graphite dr htd white gouache. 11-Dec-2 Artcurial Briest, Paris #522/R est:15000

BELLOC, Jean Baptiste (?-c.1914) French
Sculpture
£1090 $1711 €1700 Combattant arabe (41cm-16in) s.st.f.Jollet gilt pat bronze. 10-Dec-2 Tajan, Paris #203/R est:2300

BELLOMONTE, Carlo (1958-) Italian
Sculpture
£980 $1569 €1500 Loneliness (35cm-14in) s.d.1978 bronze lit. 4-Jan-3 Meeting Art, Vercelli #441

BELLON, Michel (1927-1986) French
Works on paper
£348 $543 €550 Le miroir aux oiseaux (44x35cm-17x14in) s. W/C. 20-Oct-2 Charbonneaux, Paris #45 est:600

BELLONI, Giorgio (1861-1944) Italian
£2452 $3874 €3800 Seascape (26x37cm-10x15in) s. board. 18-Dec-2 Finarte, Milan #106
£7692 $11231 €12000 Diva (130x101cm-51x40in) s. 5-Jun-2 Il Ponte, Milan #267

BELLONI, Serge (1925-) Italian
£1474 $2285 €2300 Vignes (72x93cm-28x37in) s. 4-Dec-2 Pierre Berge, Paris #127

BELLOTTO, Bernardo (1720-1780) Italian
£128545 $200531 €192818 Details of Venice (33x44cm-13x17in) 11-Apr-3 Kieselbach, Budapest #189/R est:46000000 (H.F 46000000)
£543210 $880000 €814815 Market square at Pirna (47x79cm-19x31in) prov.exhib.lit. 24-Jan-3 Christie's, Rockefeller NY #163/R est:500000-800000
Prints
£2800 $4368 €4200 La place du vieux marchen et l'eglise de la Sainte croix a dresde (54x84cm-21x33in) etching. 25-Mar-3 Sotheby's, London #6/R est:2200-2500

BELLOTTO, Bernardo (studio) (1720-1780) Italian
£57746 $92972 €82000 Dresden (97x168cm-38x66in) i. 10-May-3 Hans Stahl, Toestorf #86/R est:80000

BELLOWS, Albert F (1829-1883) American
Works on paper
£329 $500 €494 Church, Kent (20x30cm-8x12in) s.i. W/C gouache. 18-Aug-2 Jeffery Burchard, Florida #32/R
£1198 $2000 €1737 Country landscape with figures on a pathway (32x50cm-13x20in) s. W/C paper on paper board. 22-Jun-3 Freeman, Philadelphia #92/R est:1200-1800

BELLOWS, George (1882-1925) American
£41935 $65000 €62903 Nude girl with fruit - seated semi nude (110x102cm-43x40in) s. painted 1919 prov.exhib.lit. 4-Dec-2 Sotheby's, New York #56/R est:60000-80000
£1870968 $2900000 €2806452 Gramercy Park (86x112cm-34x44in) s. prov.exhib.lit. 5-Dec-2 Christie's, Rockefeller NY #94/R est:2000000-3000000
Prints
£2358 $3750 €3537 Business men's bath (30x43cm-12x17in) s.i. lithograph edition of 43. 2-May-3 Sotheby's, New York #5/R est:3000-5000
£2516 $4000 €3774 Artists judging works of art (37x48cm-15x19in) s.i.num.14 lithograph. 2-May-3 Sotheby's, New York #59/R est:4000-6000
£2532 $4000 €3798 Benediction in Georgia (41x51cm-16x20in) s.i.num.77 lithograph. 24-Apr-3 Shannon's, Milford #94/R est:4000-6000
£5346 $8500 €8019 Dance in the madhouse (46x62cm-18x24in) s.i. lithograph. 2-May-3 Sotheby's, New York #3 est:6000-8000
£9434 $15000 €14151 Pool player (13x25cm-5x10in) s.i. lithograph edition of 40. 2-May-3 Sotheby's, New York #4/R est:8000-12000
£18868 $30000 €28302 Dempsey and Firpo (46x57cm-18x22in) s.i. lithograph edition of 103 prov. 2-May-3 Sotheby's, New York #60/R est:40000-60000
Works on paper
£2259 $3750 €3276 Jean (25x10cm-10x4in) pencil. 13-Jun-3 Du Mouchelle, Detroit #2075/R est:700-1200

BELLUCCI, Antonio (1654-1726) Italian
£9057 $14128 €14400 Adoration of the Magi (110x210cm-43x83in) 22-Sep-2 Semenzato, Venice #282/R est:19000-25000
£41000 $63960 €61500 Allegory of Vanity (164x156cm-65x61in) prov. 10-Apr-3 Sotheby's, London #87/R est:25000
Works on paper
£2222 $3600 €3333 Diana and Endymion (27x18cm-11x7in) chk pen ink prov. 22-Jan-3 Christie's, Rockefeller NY #52/R est:3000

BELLUCCI, Antonio (attrib) (1654-1726) Italian
£11486 $17919 €17000 Susannah and the elders (163x154cm-64x61in) prov. 27-Mar-3 Dorotheum, Vienna #18/R est:10000-15000

BELLVER, Fernando (1954-) Spanish
Works on paper
£530 $864 €800 Tea, love (68x68cm-27x27in) s.d.1982 gouache ink wax crayon. 11-Feb-3 Segre, Madrid #260/R
£645 $1019 €1000 Minipimer (55x75cm-22x30in) s.d.1982 W/C gouache col wax crayon. 17-Dec-2 Segre, Madrid #204/R

BELLYNCK, Hubert Émile (1859-?) French
£972 $1546 €1400 Panier de peches et cuivre (50x60cm-20x24in) s. 30-Apr-3 Tajan, Paris #76

BELMONDO, Paul (1898-1982) French?
Sculpture
£1295 $2072 €1800 Tete de jeune fille (30cm-12in) s.d. pat.terracotta prov. 19-May-3 Tajan, Paris #148/R est:1800-2000
£1899 $2943 €3000 Offrande (12x22cm-5x9in) s. brown red pat bronze bas relief exec.c.1940 Cast E. Godard. 29-Sep-2 Eric Pillon, Calais #153/R
£3237 $5180 €4500 Femme accroupiee a sa toilette, genou gauche plie (42cm-17in) s. pat.terracotta prov. 19-May-3 Tajan, Paris #150/R est:2500-3000
£5036 $8057 €7000 La ville d'Alger recevant les fruits du travail (50x73cm-20x29in) black gilt pat.bronze lit. 19-May-3 Tajan, Paris #217/R est:7000-9000
£7914 $12663 €11000 Tete de jeune femme (32cm-13in) s. green pat.bronze prov. 19-May-3 Tajan, Paris #154/R est:6000-8000
Works on paper
£245 $409 €350 Nu, modele lisant (27x22cm-11x9in) s. pencil dr. 26-Jun-3 Tajan, Paris #108
£245 $409 €350 Nu, modele assis (27x22cm-11x9in) s. pencil dr. 26-Jun-3 Tajan, Paris #109
£759 $1206 €1100 Nu marchant (63x47cm-25x19in) s.i. sanguine. 7-Mar-3 Rabourdin & Choppin de Janvry, Paris #37

BELMONTE, Leo (?) French?
£2532 $4000 €4000 The young artist (173x121cm-68x48in) s.d.1889. 1-Dec-2 Bukowskis, Helsinki #232/R est:5000-6000

BELONOG, Anatoli (1946-) Russian
£316 $499 €474 Coastal landscape with mother and child (70x80cm-28x31in) s. 30-Nov-2 Goteborg Auktionsverk, Sweden #510/R (S.KR 4500)
£318 $497 €500 Children with rowing boat at the lakeside (60x80cm-24x31in) s. i.d.2001 verso. 7-Nov-2 Allgauer, Kempten #2751/R
£350 $546 €550 Children bathing at the lakeside (60x80cm-24x31in) s. i.d.2001 verso lit. 7-Nov-2 Allgauer, Kempten #2750/R
£414 $646 €650 Children picking flowers at the lakeside (80x60cm-31x24in) s.d.2000 i.verso. 7-Nov-2 Allgauer, Kempten #2752/R
£453 $689 €680 July (64x91cm-25x36in) s,. 16-Aug-2 Lilla Bukowskis, Stockholm #752 (S.KR 6600)

BELSKY, Vladimir (1949-) Russian
£250 $388 €375 Corner of the spring garden (27x35cm-11x14in) s. 29-Sep-2 John Nicholson, Haslemere #22
£250 $388 €375 Still life with crimea roses (46x33cm-18x13in) s. 29-Sep-2 John Nicholson, Haslemere #63
£283 $436 €450 Garden in spring (41x33cm-16x13in) s. 22-Oct-2 Durán, Madrid #691/R
£300 $465 €450 Seaside of Spain (27x41cm-11x16in) s. board. 29-Sep-2 John Nicholson, Haslemere #100/R
£346 $533 €550 Venice at dusk (33x48cm-13x19in) s. 22-Oct-2 Durán, Madrid #692/R
£387 $612 €600 Terrace by the sea (61x46cm-24x18in) s. 17-Dec-2 Durán, Madrid #661/R
£400 $620 €600 Evening walk at sea (35x50cm-14x20in) s. 29-Sep-2 John Nicholson, Haslemere #102/R
£400 $620 €600 Early morning (38x55cm-15x22in) s. 29-Sep-2 John Nicholson, Haslemere #103/R
£450 $698 €675 Beginning of summer (40x50cm-16x20in) s. 29-Sep-2 John Nicholson, Haslemere #101/R
£484 $765 €750 Rose bush (38x46cm-15x18in) s. 17-Dec-2 Durán, Madrid #660/R
£600 $930 €900 Still life with lilac (50x61cm-20x24in) s. 8-Dec-2 John Nicholson, Haslemere #69/R
£625 $969 €938 South port (33x46cm-13x18in) s. 8-Dec-2 John Nicholson, Haslemere #71/R

BELTON, Liam (20th C) Irish?
£1745 $2809 €2600 Images with mortar and pestle (61x86cm-24x34in) s. i.d.1992 verso prov. 18-Feb-3 Whyte's, Dublin #181/R est:3000-4000

BELTRAME, Alfredo (1901-1996) Austrian?
£486 $773 €700 Landscape with figures (50x70cm-20x28in) s.d.1970. 1-May-3 Meeting Art, Vercelli #493

BELTRAN BOFILL, Juan (1934-) Spanish
£2961 $4796 €4500 Ginger hair (61x46cm-24x18in) s. s.i.d.1991 verso. 21-Jan-3 Durán, Madrid #689/R

BELTRAN MESSA, Enric (1940-) Spanish
£409 $638 €650 Portrait of Beato Escriva de Balaguer (55x46cm-22x18in) s. 8-Oct-2 Ansorena, Madrid #296/R

BELTRAN-MASSES, Frederico (1885-1949) Spanish
£1419 $2243 €2200 Coq (41x45cm-16x18in) s. 19-Dec-2 Claude Aguttes, Neuilly #179/R
£4397 $6816 €6596 L'oeuillet rouge (107x98cm-42x39in) s. exhib. 4-Dec-2 AB Stockholms Auktionsverk #1885/R est:60000-80000 (S.KR 62000)
£5000 $8150 €7250 Deillettes rouges (107x99cm-42x39in) s. exhib. 16-Jul-3 Sotheby's, Olympia #268/R est:5000-7000
Works on paper
£609 $962 €950 Lady with dog (48x31cm-19x12in) s.d.1937 pastel. 19-Nov-2 Durán, Madrid #86/R

BELVEDERE, Andrea (1642-1732) Italian
£38000 $59660 €57000 Peonies, poppies, iris, tulip and other flowers in landscape (98x173cm-39x68in) prov. 11-Dec-2 Christie's, London #100/R est:25000-35000

BELVEDERE, Andrea (circle) (1642-1732) Italian
£17834 $27822 €28000 Tulips,roses,narcissi,other flowers. Tulips, narcissi, cornflowers, roses (37x27cm-15x11in) slate octagonal pair. 6-Nov-2 Christie's, Amsterdam #83/R est:7000-10000

BEM, Elizaveta Merkurevna (1843-1914) Russian
£2000 $3160 €3000 View of Tsarskoe Selo Palace (14x22cm-6x9in) s.d.95 pencil W/C on cardboard. 26-Nov-2 Christie's, Kensington #20/R est:600-800
Works on paper
£1100 $1782 €1650 Winter. Spring (9x13cm-4x5in) s.i. W/C pair. 21-May-3 Sotheby's, London #99/R est:1000-1500

BEMELMANS, Ludwig (1898-1963) American
£2623 $4250 €3803 Seated by a pond, Ville d'Avray (81x61cm-32x24in) s. i.verso. 21-May-3 Doyle, New York #148/R est:6000-8000
£5484 $8500 €8226 Portrait in yellow (56x46cm-22x18in) s.d. sold with book. 8-Dec-2 Toomey, Oak Park #752/R est:10000-15000
£5732 $9000 €8598 Ville de avery - Pepito's return from market (61x81cm-24x32in) s. prov. 10-Dec-2 Doyle, New York #159/R est:8000-12000
£7246 $11884 €10000 Now I lay me down to sleep (46x67cm-18x26in) s. canvas on panel prov. 27-May-3 Wiener Kunst Auktionen, Vienna #104/R est:10000-20000
Works on paper
£500 $795 €750 Design for Hansi (44x36cm-17x14in) s.i. W/C col chk. 29-Apr-3 Bonhams, New Bond Street #204/R
£679 $1100 €985 Quiet please (38x46cm-15x18in) init. pen ink tracing paper. 21-May-3 Doyle, New York #154/R
£1299 $2000 €1949 Jardin des plates, Paris (33x38cm-13x15in) s.d.38 W/C graphite prov. 24-Oct-2 Shannon's, Milford #226/R est:2000-3000
£1543 $2500 €2237 People in automobiles, four. Portrait of Ernst Lubistch (13x15cm-5x6in) four s. one init. pen ink wash five. 21-May-3 Doyle, New York #153/R est:2000-3000
£3704 $6000 €5371 No fruit, no flowers, not a rose (46x61cm-18x24in) s.i. pen ink W/C. 21-May-3 Doyle, New York #147/R est:6000-8000
£5714 $9029 €8571 Chasse au renaud (55x75cm-22x30in) s.i. W/C prov. 18-Nov-2 Goodman, Sydney #235/R (A.D 16000)

BEMMEL, Christoph von (1707-1783) German
Works on paper
£481 $745 €750 Winter landscape (17x22cm-7x9in) s. gouache. 6-Dec-2 Maigret, Paris #40

BEMMEL, Christoph von (attrib) (1707-1783) German
£1400 $2282 €2100 Wooed landscape with riders in the foreground (55x70cm-22x28in) 12-Feb-3 Bonhams, Knightsbridge #35/R est:800-1200

BEMMEL, Georg Christoph Gottlieb von I (attrib) (1738-1794) German
Works on paper
£313 $497 €450 Southern river landscape with figures (18x20cm-7x8in) gouache. 5-May-3 Ketterer, Munich #277/R

BEMMEL, Wilhelm von (1630-1708) Dutch
Works on paper
£282 $468 €400 Mountain stream (24x33cm-9x13in) pencil brush wash. 12-Jun-3 Hauswedell & Nolte, Hamburg #39/R

BEMMEL, Wilhelm von (attrib) (1630-1708) Dutch
£3830 $5936 €5745 Italianate landscape with figures (96x155cm-38x61in) bears sig. 3-Dec-2 Bukowskis, Stockholm #491/R est:30000-40000 (S.KR 54000)
Works on paper
£300 $462 €450 Boats and shipping in harbour (20x28cm-8x11in) gouache. 25-Oct-2 Gorringes, Lewes #885

BEMPORAD, Franco (1926-) Italian
£962 $1404 €1500 Structure (70x50cm-28x20in) s.i.d.79 verso acrylic. 5-Jun-2 Il Ponte, Milan #36/R

BEN (1935-) Swiss
£458 $737 €700 Je suis handicape (23x30cm-9x12in) s.d.1993 acrylic cardboard. 20-Jan-3 Cornette de St.Cyr, Paris #53
£600 $930 €900 Si Ben est le fils de Ben (50x61cm-20x24in) s. 3-Dec-2 Bonhams, Knightsbridge #58/R
£633 $981 €1000 Deux lignes droites (38x65cm-15x26in) s.d. acrylic palisade. 28-Sep-2 Cornette de St.Cyr, Paris #252 est:1000-1200
£1509 $2325 €2400 Encore un portrait fait avec n'importe quoi (35x25cm-14x10in) s.i.d.1996 verso acrylic brush paint tray. 26-Oct-2 Cornette de St.Cyr, Paris #43/R
£1572 $2437 €2500 Ecriture (35x45cm-14x18in) s. s.d.1976 verso acrylic black white photo cardboard. 30-Oct-2 Artcurial Briest, Paris #454 est:3000-4000
£1739 $2696 €2609 Mon dieu donnez nous notre art (50x60cm-20x24in) i. verso acrylic material collage painted panel. 4-Dec-2 Koller, Zurich #206/R est:3500-5000 (S.FR 4000)
£2222 $3534 €3200 Si la vie est art pourquoi faire de l'art (60x73cm-24x29in) s.d.92 s.i.verso acrylic. 29-Apr-3 Artcurial Briest, Paris #364/R est:3000-4000
£2609 $4043 €3914 J'ai peur de me tromper (55x46cm-22x18in) s. prov. 4-Dec-2 Koller, Zurich #207/R est:6000-8000 (S.FR 6000)
£2621 $4377 €3800 J'attend la baisse (35x41cm-14x16in) s. oil wood plastic goose. 9-Jul-3 Cornette de St.Cyr, Paris #224/R est:3500-4000
£2862 $4407 €4550 Une astuce de plus, tout en art est une astuce de plus (30x30cm-12x12in) s. acrylic panel. 26-Oct-2 Cornette de St.Cyr, Paris #44/R est:3000
£3673 $5841 €5400 Qu'es aquo (100x100cm-39x39in) s.i.d.85 verso acrylic. 26-Feb-3 Artcurial Briest, Paris #407/R est:5000-6000
£5440 $8378 €8650 En art, c'est le courage qui compte (50x65cm-20x26in) s.i.d.1987 acrylic panel. 26-Oct-2 Cornette de St.Cyr, Paris #45/R est:5000
£6803 $10816 €10000 Io dubito - I doubt (114x146cm-45x57in) s. i.verso painted 1971. 24-Mar-3 Cornette de St.Cyr, Paris #44/R
Sculpture
£2051 $3179 €3200 Propositions pour une toile de peintre (32x26x6cm-13x10x2in) s.i.d.1967 box with canvas and 19 photos. 3-Dec-2 Lempertz, Koln #489/R est:3000
£2192 $3441 €3200 Boite mystere 61 (10x6x7cm-4x2x3in) wood paper. 15-Apr-3 Laurence Calmels, Paris #4120/R
Works on paper
£316 $491 €500 Ce disque 45 tours passe en 78 tours est une creation musicale (40x30cm-16x12in) s.d. vinyl paper. 28-Sep-2 Cornette de St.Cyr, Paris #251
£805 $1297 €1200 A vendre, 500 Fr (38x32cm-15x13in) gouache collage exhib. 23-Feb-3 Mercier & Cie, Lille #159/R
£818 $1267 €1300 La joconde (33x27cm-13x11in) i. offset felt collage. 30-Oct-2 Artcurial Briest, Paris #574
£1410 $2186 €2200 Art goes up in smoke (66x45cm-26x18in) s.i.d.1985 collage of cigarette butts. 3-Dec-2 Lempertz, Koln #488/R est:2500
£1586 $2649 €2300 L'oiseau oisif du club mediterranee (50x62cm-20x24in) s.d. mixed media panel. 9-Jul-3 Cornette de St.Cyr, Paris #222/R est:2500-3000
£2621 $4377 €3800 L'oiseau ethnologue qui aime (64x100cm-25x39in) s.d. mixed media panel. 9-Jul-3 Cornette de St.Cyr, Paris #221/R est:4000-4500
£2690 $4492 €3900 Allez, un peu de courage (50x61cm-20x24in) s.d. paint wood mange disque. 9-Jul-3 Cornette de St.Cyr, Paris #219/R est:1800-2000

BEN ALI R'BATI (1861-1939) Moroccan
Works on paper
£2158 $3540 €3000 Osta Hasan au milieu de ses barils (35x24cm-14x9in) s. W/C. 4-Jun-3 Tajan, Paris #193/R est:3000-5000
£3597 $5900 €5000 The, danseuse et musiciens (31x46cm-12x18in) s. W/C. 4-Jun-3 Tajan, Paris #189/R est:6000-8000
£3597 $5900 €5000 Travaux agricoles hors des murs (37x52cm-15x20in) s. W/C. 4-Jun-3 Tajan, Paris #192/R est:5000-7000
£3957 $6489 €5500 Scene animee autour de la villa blanche (27x42cm-11x17in) s. W/C. 4-Jun-3 Tajan, Paris #194/R est:3000-5000
£4317 $7079 €6000 Le couscous servi aux invites (31x46cm-12x18in) s. W/C. 4-Jun-3 Tajan, Paris #188/R est:7000-10000
£4317 $7079 €6000 Le bateau royal a Tanger (35x49cm-14x19in) s. W/C. 4-Jun-3 Tajan, Paris #190/R est:6000-8000
£4317 $7079 €6000 Halte de la caravane aux abords de la ville (37x52cm-15x20in) s. W/C. 4-Jun-3 Tajan, Paris #191/R est:5000-7000
£4317 $7079 €6000 Scene de marche au pied des remparts (36x43cm-14x17in) s. W/C. 4-Jun-3 Tajan, Paris #195/R est:6000-8000
£6410 $10064 €10000 Cortege royal (47x63cm-19x25in) s. W/C lit. 16-Dec-2 Gros & Delettrez, Paris #38/R est:15000-20000
£25900 $42476 €36000 Cortege du sultan rendant a la mosquee (38x53cm-15x21in) s. W/C. 4-Jun-3 Tajan, Paris #187/R est:13000-16000

BEN BELLA, M (1946-) ?
£1879 $3026 €2800 Composition bleue et rose (197x132cm-78x52in) s. 23-Feb-3 Mercier & Cie, Lille #103

BEN SHALOM, Itzik (1945-) Israeli
Sculpture
£1069 $1689 €1550 Composition (55cm-22in) s.d. num.29/50 bronze marble socle. 5-Apr-3 Hans Stahl, Hamburg #495/R est:1700

BENAGLIA, Enrico (1938-) Italian
£582 $908 €850 Green door (45x35cm-18x14in) s. 10-Apr-3 Finarte Semenzato, Rome #306
£641 $1006 €1000 Frightened ship (40x30cm-16x12in) s. s.i.d.verso. 21-Nov-2 Finarte, Rome #230
£1090 $1711 €1700 Mozart's toy (60x50cm-24x20in) s. s.i.d.1992 verso. 21-Nov-2 Finarte, Rome #62

BENANTEUR, Abdallah (1931-) ?
£993 $1619 €1500 Sans titre (89x116cm-35x46in) 1-Feb-3 Claude Aguttes, Neuilly #348/R

BENARD, Auguste Sebastien (attrib) (1810-?) French
Works on paper
£385 $596 €600 Chevaux atteles (14x20cm-6x8in) s. W/C. 4-Dec-2 Piasa, Paris #127

BENARROUCHE, Yoel (20th C) Israeli
£321 $503 €500 Rabbin (82x60cm-32x24in) s. 12-Dec-2 Rabourdin & Choppin de Janvry, Paris #162
£385 $604 €600 Barmitzva (65x81cm-26x32in) 12-Dec-2 Rabourdin & Choppin de Janvry, Paris #161

BENATI, Davide (1949-) Italian
£2465 $4092 €3500 Suoni, silenzio (140x210cm-55x83in) s.i.d.1992 verso oil papier-mache W/C. 10-Jun-3 Finarte Semenzato, Milan #298/R est:140-210
Works on paper
£851 $1379 €1200 Lotus Solus (70x100cm-28x39in) s.i.d.1982 verso W/C tempera collage paper on canvas. 26-May-3 Christie's, Milan #76

BENCZUR, Gyula Julius de (1844-1920) Hungarian
£6454 $10004 €9358 Portrait of a young man (54x43cm-21x17in) s. prov. 9-Dec-2 Mu Terem Galeria, Budapest #148/R est:1900000 (H.F 2400000)

BENDA, Wladyslav T (1873-1948) American
Works on paper
£1731 $2700 €2597 Beautiful woman standing in front of lunette (46x58cm-18x23in) s. chl pencil. 9-Nov-2 Illustration House, New York #61/R est:3000-4000

BENDALL, Mildred (1891-1977) British/French
£360 $587 €522 Still life of alstroemerias (51x41cm-20x16in) s. 15-Jul-3 Bonhams, Knightsbridge #100
£1400 $2324 €2030 Vase of nasturtiums (61x51cm-24x20in) s. 10-Jun-3 David Lay, Penzance #8 est:900-1200

BENDEMANN, Eduard Julius Friedrich (1811-1889) German
£570 $900 €900 Jacob and Rahel (25x34cm-10x13in) paper on board. 29-Nov-2 Bassenge, Berlin #5833/R

BENDER, Ferdinand (19th C) ?
£679 $1100 €1019 Portrait of a gentleman, believed to be Carl Maria Faber (109x81cm-43x32in) s.d.1857 oval. 24-Jan-3 Freeman, Philadelphia #222/R est:1500-2000

BENDER, Sarah E de Wolfe (1852-1935) American
£821 $1272 €1232 Epicurean (32x22cm-13x9in) painted c.1890. 3-Dec-2 SOGA, Bratislava #152/R (SL.K 52000)
£958 $1600 €1389 Still life with roses. s. artist board. 28-Jun-3 Harvey Clar, Oakland #1205

BENDINI, Vasco (1922-) Italian
£641 $936 €1000 Proteus (92x73cm-36x29in) s.i.d.1964. 5-Jun-2 Il Ponte, Milan #23
£1765 $2824 €2700 Untitled (140x160cm-55x63in) s.d.1976 verso lit. 4-Jan-3 Meeting Art, Vercelli #600

BENDIXEN, Herman (1919-1977) Norwegian
£297 $458 €446 Landscape from Reine in Lofoten (35x46cm-14x18in) s. panel. 28-Oct-2 Blomqvist, Lysaker #1004 (N.KR 3500)

BENDIXEN, Siegfried Detlev (1786-1864) German
Works on paper
£300 $492 €450 Lady and gentleman in Continental interiors (43x32cm-17x13in) s.d.1844 W/C pair. 3-Jun-3 Bonhams, Oxford #17

BENDLEIN, Christian (attrib) (18th C) German?
£513 $810 €800 River landscape with figure (27x38cm-11x15in) 15-Nov-2 Reiss & Sohn, Konigstein #4

BENDRE, Narayan Shridhar (1910-1992) Indian
£9800 $15288 €14700 Boats on the Brahmaputra (96x101cm-38x40in) s. 17-Oct-2 Bonhams, Knightsbridge #575/R est:10000-12000
£18648 $30769 €27040 Untitled (90x100cm-35x39in) s.d. 6-Jul-3 Christie's, Hong Kong #74/R est:120000-180000 (HK.D 240000)

BENDTSEN, Folmer (1907-1993) Swedish
£254 $394 €381 Village street, Bornholm (42x47cm-17x19in) s.d.35 prov. 1-Oct-2 Rasmussen, Copenhagen #288 (D.KR 3000)
£337 $546 €506 Harbour scene, from Sydhavnen (46x54cm-18x21in) s.d.51. 25-Jan-3 Rasmussen, Havnen #2143 (D.KR 3800)
£353 $558 €530 From Alexandravej (46x55cm-18x22in) s. 1-Apr-3 Rasmussen, Copenhagen #617 (D.KR 3800)
£372 $587 €558 Suburb (66x82cm-26x32in) s.d.46. 1-Apr-3 Rasmussen, Copenhagen #502 (D.KR 4000)
£380 $593 €570 Gardeners by greenhouses (94x123cm-37x48in) s.d.43. 22-Sep-2 Hindemae, Ullerslev #7633/R (D.KR 4500)
£466 $722 €699 From Listed, Bornholm (85x100cm-33x39in) s.d.36. 1-Oct-2 Rasmussen, Copenhagen #335/R (D.KR 5500)
£467 $729 €701 Town scene, winter (46x56cm-18x22in) s.d.60. 5-Aug-2 Rasmussen, Vejle #311/R (D.KR 5500)
£569 $911 €854 Tanker off an industrial harbour (60x73cm-24x29in) s.d.65. 13-Jan-3 Rasmussen, Vejle #287 (D.KR 6500)
£604 $954 €906 Town scene near Alexandravej (55x46cm-22x18in) s.d.55. 1-Apr-3 Rasmussen, Copenhagen #581/R (D.KR 6500)
£635 $984 €953 Winter landscape with wall (65x100cm-26x39in) s.d.62. 1-Oct-2 Rasmussen, Copenhagen #323/R (D.KR 7500)
£914 $1453 €1371 Street scene with figure, Norrebro (86x101cm-34x40in) s.d.50. 26-Feb-3 Kunsthallen, Copenhagen #277/R (D.KR 10000)
£1001 $1672 €1451 Alexandravej (70x100cm-28x39in) s.d.66. 17-Jun-3 Rasmussen, Copenhagen #141 (D.KR 10500)
£1101 $1706 €1652 Winter at Norrebro with children playing (70x100cm-28x39in) s.d.68. 1-Oct-2 Rasmussen, Copenhagen #327/R est:15000 (D.KR 13000)
£1141 $1757 €1712 Evening, Norrebro (85x100cm-33x39in) s.d.33. 23-Oct-2 Kunsthallen, Copenhagen #429/R est:8000 (D.KR 13500)
£1191 $1883 €1787 Street scene with couple talking, summer evening (67x80cm-26x31in) s.d.55 prov. 27-Nov-2 Museumsbygningen, Copenhagen #548/R est:10000-15000 (D.KR 14000)
£1192 $1990 €1728 Figures walking on Alexandravej, winter (73x92cm-29x36in) s/. 17-Jun-3 Rasmussen, Copenhagen #63/R est:15000-20000 (D.KR 12500)
£1277 $2017 €1916 Winter's day with figures in Southern harbour (73x93cm-29x37in) s.d.70. 30-Nov-2 Rasmussen, Havnen #2202/R est:8000-12000 (D.KR 15000)
£1352 $2083 €2028 Winter's day, Sydhavnen (60x81cm-24x32in) s. 23-Oct-2 Kunsthallen, Copenhagen #102/R est:10000 (D.KR 16000)
£1397 $2166 €2096 Two men chatting by the timber place by Alexandravej (60x81cm-24x32in) s.d.1965. 1-Oct-2 Rasmussen, Copenhagen #266/R est:8000-10000 (D.KR 16500)
£2323 $3671 €3485 Throwing snowball, Alexandravej (85x135cm-33x53in) s.d.57 exhib. 1-Apr-3 Rasmussen, Copenhagen #71/R est:40000 (D.KR 25000)

BENE, Geza (1900-1960) Hungarian
£2064 $3220 €3096 Boat on the shore (39x42cm-15x17in) tempera. 11-Sep-2 Kieselbach, Budapest #115/R (H.F 800000)
£3912 $6103 €5672 Still life with tulips (40x30cm-16x12in) s. paper on board. 12-Apr-3 Mu Terem Galeria, Budapest #161/R est:650000 (H.F 1400000)
Works on paper
£894 $1395 €1296 Riverside (21x28cm-8x11in) s.d.951 W/C. 12-Apr-3 Mu Terem Galeria, Budapest #17/R est:150000 (H.F 320000)
£1006 $1569 €1459 Reapers (48x56cm-19x22in) s.d.928 W/C. 12-Apr-3 Mu Terem Galeria, Budapest #217/R est:280000 (H.F 360000)

BENEDETTI, Edgardo de (1900-?) Italian
£710 $1121 €1100 Rural landscape with lake (60x80cm-24x31in) s. 18-Dec-2 Finarte, Milan #244

BENEDETTI, M de (?) Italian
£9615 $15192 €15000 Les quatre saisons (300x90cm-118x35in) three s.i. set of four prov. 18-Nov-2 Tajan, Paris #180/R est:15000-18000

BENEDIT, Luis F (1937-) Argentinian
Sculpture
£4878 $8000 €7073 Environment for a fish (109x72x15cm-43x28x6in) s.i.d.68 mixed media plexiglas prov. 27-May-3 Sotheby's, New York #66

BENEDITO-VIVES, Manuel (1875-1963) Spanish
£2194 $3466 €3400 Listening in (78x61cm-31x24in) s. 17-Dec-2 Segre, Madrid #82/R
£4025 $6279 €6400 Peasants eating (66x48cm-26x19in) s. prov. 17-Sep-2 Segre, Madrid #104a/R

BENEFIAL, Marco (1684-1764) Italian
Works on paper
£439 $685 €650 Servant (26x28cm-10x11in) pierre noire. 27-Mar-3 Maigret, Paris #166/R

BENEFIAL, Marco (attrib) (1684-1764) Italian
£5769 $8942 €9000 Saint Joseph (49x39cm-19x15in) 4-Dec-2 Christie's, Rome #445/R est:15000

BENELLI, Gino (19/20th C) Italian
£480 $759 €720 Monk and watchman drinking in wine cellar (35x51cm-14x20in) 14-Nov-2 Stuker, Bern #70/R (S.FR 1100)
£1250 $2012 €1875 Monk and watchman drinking in wine cellar (34x51cm-13x20in) s. 7-May-3 Dobiaschofsky, Bern #346/R est:2900 (S.FR 2700)

BENES, Vlastimil (1919-1981) Czechoslovakian
£3526 $5571 €5500 Elysium (101x85cm-40x33in) s.i.d.66 s.i. verso board. 12-Nov-2 Dorotheum, Vienna #201/R est:1800-2500
£3526 $5571 €5500 Avenue (96x130cm-38x51in) s.d.67 i. stretcher. 12-Nov-2 Dorotheum, Vienna #200/R est:2200-2800

BENESCH, Gustav (19th C) ?
Works on paper
£252 $390 €400 Freihaus with food market (24x32cm-9x13in) s. W/C. 1-Oct-2 Dorotheum, Vienna #283/R

BENESCH, Josef Ferdinand (1875-1954) Austrian
£1069 $1657 €1700 Deer in forest clearing (69x106cm-27x42in) s. 29-Oct-2 Dorotheum, Vienna #50/R est:2000-2300

BENET, Rafael (1889-1979) Spanish
Works on paper
£379 $603 €550 Reclining female nude (20x26cm-8x10in) s.d.1927 pencil dr. 4-Mar-3 Ansorena, Madrid #404/R

BENETIK, Rudi (1960-) Austrian
Works on paper
£417 $654 €650 Sun, ants and lots of manure (31x41cm-12x16in) s.d.1986 wax chk. 20-Nov-2 Dorotheum, Klagenfurt #79
£577 $906 €900 Pax (64x49cm-25x19in) s.d.81 mixed media board. 20-Nov-2 Dorotheum, Klagenfurt #34/R

BENEZIT, Emanuel Charles Louis (1887-1975) French
£256 $397 €400 Garndes baigneuses (70x57cm-28x22in) s. 9-Dec-2 Beaussant & Lefèvre, Paris #26
£263 $400 €395 Trees in bloom (46x38cm-18x15in) s.d.17 s.i.d.verso. 15-Aug-2 Doyle, New York #14

BENGALA, Engund (20th C) Australian
Sculpture
£1106 $1748 €1917 Hollow log coffin (216cm-85in) wood. 1-Apr-3 Goodman, Sydney #9 est:2000-3000 (A.D 2900)

BENGER, Berenger (1868-1935) British
Works on paper
£300 $471 €450 Mountain valley, Norway (59x48cm-23x19in) indis sig. pencil W/C. 16-Apr-3 Christie's, Kensington #1035

BENGSTON, Billy Al (1934-) American
£1840 $3000 €2760 Nakookoo draculas (206x196cm-81x77in) acrylic canvas on panel prov. 16-Feb-3 Butterfields, San Francisco #2130 est:4000-6000
Works on paper
£516 $825 €748 KA'AO (74x157cm-29x62in) W/C collage shadowbox prov. 17-May-3 Selkirks, St. Louis #290/R

BENGTS, Oskar (1885-1966) Finnish
£290 $458 €420 Landscape (56x66cm-22x26in) s. 3-Apr-3 Hagelstam, Helsinki #1059

BENGTSSON, Dick (1936-1989) Swedish
£27330 $42635 €40995 Kolingen and Bobban (77x141cm-30x56in) panel prov.exhib.lit. 5-Nov-2 Bukowskis, Stockholm #354/R est:500000-600000 (S.KR 390000)

BENJAMIN, Herman (?) ?
£559 $872 €811 Scene at the market place (50x58cm-20x23in) s. 12-Apr-3 Mu Terem Galeria, Budapest #128/R est:180000 (H.F 200000)

BENJAMIN, Jason (20th C) Australian
£4065 $6423 €5894 Surrender (122x122cm-48x48in) s. i.d.2000 verso. 22-Jul-3 Lawson Menzies, Sydney #18/R est:7000-8000 (A.D 10000)
£8527 $13558 €12791 Love can hear this (122x182cm-48x72in) s.d.01 i.verso prov. 5-May-3 Sotheby's, Melbourne #101/R est:12000-18000 (A.D 22000)

BENK, Johannes (1844-1914) Austrian
Sculpture
£9810 $15500 €15500 Woman with Cupid (102cm-40in) s. marble. 27-Nov-2 Wiener Kunst Auktionen, Vienna #562/R est:3000-7000

BENKA, Martin (1888-1971) Czechoslovakian
£1386 $2148 €2079 Slovak man (48x38cm-19x15in) board. 1-Oct-2 SOGA, Bratislava #46/R est:110000 (SL.K 88000)
£2048 $2908 €3072 Near Liptivsky Hradok (14x32cm-6x13in) canvas on board double-sided painted c.1935. 26-Mar-2 SOGA, Bratislava #48/R est:90000 (SL.K 130000)
£2126 $3296 €3189 Betka Figurova from Bosaca village (60x38cm-24x15in) 1-Oct-2 SOGA, Bratislava #44/R est:135000 (SL.K 135000)
£2914 $4516 €4371 Jan Rados from Bosaca village (60x38cm-24x15in) 1-Oct-2 SOGA, Bratislava #43/R est:135000 (SL.K 185000)
£4989 $7733 €7484 Moravian room (66x87cm-26x34in) painted c.1914-16. 3-Dec-2 SOGA, Bratislava #41/R est:395000 (SL.K 316000)
£5828 $8508 €8742 Spisske Podhradie (48x64cm-19x25in) 4-Jun-2 SOGA, Bratislava #55/R est:320000 (SL.K 370000)
£8663 $12648 €12995 At the foot of Choc Hill (61x71cm-24x28in) painted c.1921. 4-Jun-2 SOGA, Bratislava #54/R est:450000 (SL.K 550000)
£9867 $15294 €14801 On the way to the mountains (45x67cm-18x26in) painted c.1937. 3-Dec-2 SOGA, Bratislava #40/R est:450000 (SL.K 625000)
£17562 $24938 €26343 Amused by her beauty (113x100cm-44x39in) painted 1942. 26-Mar-2 SOGA, Bratislava #47/R est:890000 (SL.K 1115000)
Works on paper
£284 $403 €426 Wood-cutter (24x31cm-9x12in) blue ink exec.c.1940. 26-Mar-2 SOGA, Bratislava #49/R (SL.K 18000)
£837 $1297 €1256 Zdikov (19x26cm-7x10in) pen Indian ink brush W/C dr exec.1958. 3-Dec-2 SOGA, Bratislava #42/R (SL.K 53000)

BENKHARD (20th C) ?
£2200 $3388 €3300 Female nude (140x115cm-55x45in) s.d.1932. 24-Oct-2 Christie's, Kensington #183/R est:1200-1800

BENLLIURE Y GIL, Jose (1855-1937) Spanish
£13101 $20700 €19652 Figures in the street (13x20cm-5x8in) s. board. 15-Nov-2 Naón & Cia, Buenos Aires #106/R
£22000 $36740 €33000 Outside the blacksmiths (21x32cm-8x13in) s. panel. 19-Jun-3 Christie's, London #61/R est:12000-16000
£22000 $36740 €31900 Travelling circus (14x21cm-6x8in) s. panel. 17-Jun-3 Bonhams, New Bond Street #105/R est:10000-15000
£44000 $71720 €66000 Musician's apprentice (38x54cm-15x21in) s. panel. 29-Jan-3 Sotheby's, Olympia #320/R est:25000-40000

BENLLIURE Y GIL, Juan Antonio (19th C) Spanish
£878 $1370 €1300 Nude (71x80cm-28x31in) s. 25-Mar-3 Durán, Madrid #161/R
£1284 $2003 €1900 Woman from Valencia (101x70cm-40x28in) s. 25-Mar-3 Durán, Madrid #162/R

BENLLIURE Y GIL, Mariano (1862-1947) Spanish
Sculpture
£5519 $8058 €8500 Jose Ribera (48cm-19in) s.i. exec.1886 bronze. 12-Jun-2 Castellana, Madrid #70/R
Works on paper
£1557 $2460 €2336 Bullfight (49x21cm-19x8in) s. W/C. 15-Nov-2 Naón & Cia, Buenos Aires #117/R

BENLLIURE Y ORTIZ, Jose (1884-1916) Spanish
£60000 $94200 €90000 Virgen de los desamparados, Valencia - Virgin of the Desamparados, Valencia (99x170cm-39x67in) indis sig. prov. 19-Nov-2 Sotheby's, London #30/R est:50000-70000

BENLLIURE, Blas (1852-1936) Spanish
£323 $510 €500 Fruit (30x40cm-12x16in) s.i.d.1927. 17-Dec-2 Durán, Madrid #38/R
£903 $1427 €1400 Fruit (27x64cm-11x25in) s.d.1921. 17-Dec-2 Durán, Madrid #82/R

BENN (1905-1989) Polish
£567 $948 €800 Vase de mimosas (73x54cm-29x21in) s. prov.lit. 17-Jun-3 Claude Boisgirard, Paris #28/R
£586 $938 €850 Maison rouge (46x55cm-18x22in) s. 12-Mar-3 Rabourdin & Choppin de Janvry, Paris #63

BENN, Ben (1884-1983) American
£518 $850 €751 Woman in pink suit (61x38cm-24x15in) s. 5-Jun-3 Swann Galleries, New York #19/R
£602 $1000 €873 Still life with lemons (25x30cm-10x12in) s.d.56 masonite. 11-Jun-3 Phillips, New York #547
£637 $1000 €956 Fishing boats in heavy sea (29x34cm-11x13in) s. canvasboard prov.exhib. 14-Dec-2 Weschler, Washington #738/R est:700-900
£1341 $2200 €1944 Baseball in Central Park (76x36cm-30x14in) s.d. 5-Jun-3 Swann Galleries, New York #20/R est:3000-5000
£8025 $13000 €12038 Staten Island landscape (41x51cm-16x20in) s.d.18 s.d.verso prov.exhib.lit. 21-May-3 Sotheby's, New York #78/R est:7000-10000
Works on paper
£609 $950 €914 Floral still life. Female nude (29x38cm-11x15in) s. W/C double-sided. 19-Sep-2 Swann Galleries, New York #152/R

BENN, Benejou (1905-1989) Polish
£321 $503 €500 Vase de muguet (35x28cm-14x11in) s.d.1958. 12-Dec-2 Rabourdin & Choppin de Janvry, Paris #24

BENNEDSEN, Jens Christian (1893-1967) Danish
£282 $443 €409 Winter landscape. 15-Dec-2 Anders Antik, Landskrona #374 (S.KR 4000)
£544 $865 €800 Brook in winter (95x135cm-37x53in) s. 27-Feb-3 Hagelstam, Helsinki #1006
£600 $912 €900 Depths of winter (95x134cm-37x53in) s. 29-Aug-2 Christie's, Kensington #40

BENNEKENSTEIN, Hermann (19th C) German
£588 $965 €900 Nemi See in the evening (16x23cm-6x9in) mono.d.57 i. verso paper on board. 29-Mar-3 Dannenberg, Berlin #547/R

BENNER, Emmanuel Michel (1873-1965) French
£2639 $4169 €3800 Lecon (84x130cm-33x51in) s.d.1907. 25-Apr-3 Piasa, Paris #70/R

BENNER, Gerrit (1897-1981) Dutch
£14388 $23597 €20000 Landschaps compositie met rood (80x100cm-31x39in) s. painted c.1959 exhib. 3-Jun-3 Christie's, Amsterdam #313/R est:20000-25000
£28481 $45000 €45000 Fries landschap (80x100cm-31x39in) s.verso prov. 26-Nov-2 Sotheby's, Amsterdam #212/R est:30000-40000
£28846 $44712 €45000 Zeiltjes - sailing boats (60x75cm-24x30in) s. verso executed 1979 prov.exhib. 3-Dec-2 Christie's, Amsterdam #250/R est:25000-35000

Works on paper

£705 $1093 €1100 Landscape (37x56cm-15x22in) s. W/C. 3-Dec-2 Christie's, Amsterdam #167/R est:1800-2800
£1282 $1987 €2000 Working farmer (65x50cm-26x20in) s. gouache W/C. 3-Dec-2 Christie's, Amsterdam #245/R est:3000-5000
£2308 $3623 €3600 Boer near a church (75x100cm-30x39in) s. gouache. 25-Nov-2 Glerum, Amsterdam #183/R est:1800-2200
£3205 $4968 €5000 Man and bird (63x48cm-25x19in) s. gouache prov. 3-Dec-2 Christie's, Amsterdam #246/R est:5000-7000
£3481 $5500 €5500 Landschap (36x54cm-14x21in) s. gouache. 26-Nov-2 Sotheby's, Amsterdam #222/R est:6000-8000
£5036 $8259 €7000 Landscape (50x64cm-20x25in) gouache executed c.1972 prov. 3-Jun-3 Christie's, Amsterdam #352/R est:7000-9000
£5128 $7949 €8000 Horse riders (48x63cm-19x25in) s. gouache prov. 3-Dec-2 Christie's, Amsterdam #248/R est:8000-12000
£7051 $10929 €11000 Het huis - the house (50x65cm-20x26in) s. gouache pastel executed c.1946-47 prov.exhib. 3-Dec-2 Christie's, Amsterdam #242/R est:6000-8000
£8861 $14000 €14000 Ruiters (50x65cm-20x26in) s. gouache executed c.1973. 26-Nov-2 Sotheby's, Amsterdam #227/R est:12000-15000

BENNER, Henri (1776-c.1818) French

Miniatures

£3800 $6346 €5510 Grand Duchess Maria Pavlovna. card gilt metal mount oval exec.c.1815. 25-Jun-3 Sotheby's, Olympia #39/R est:1200-1800
£4000 $6680 €5800 Grand Duchess Anna Pavlovna, Queen of the Netherlands (14cm-6xin) card gilt metal mount oval exec.c.1815. 25-Jun-3 Sotheby's, Olympia #38/R est:1200-1800
£4500 $7515 €6525 Alexander I Pavlovich (13cm-5xin) s.d.1815 card gilt metal mount oval. 25-Jun-3 Sotheby's, Olympia #40/R est:2500-3500

BENNET, Baron Karl Stefan (1800-1878) Swedish

£3797 $6000 €5696 Landscape with castle and village in the distance (64x96cm-25x38in) s. prov. 24-Apr-3 Sotheby's, New York #168/R est:7000-9000

BENNETT, Alfred (19th C) British

£1500 $2490 €2175 On the Ouse, near Lewes (41x61cm-16x24in) s.d.90. 12-Jun-3 Gorringes, Lewes #1704 est:1500-2000

BENNETT, Andrew (20th C) Australian

£300 $465 €450 Schooner, Westward, passing Eddystone Light (59x90cm-23x35in) s. i.verso. 1-Oct-2 Bristol Auction Rooms #485

BENNETT, F M (1874-1953) British

£320 $512 €480 Mother and child standing before a half timbered house (28x33cm-11x13in) s. 10-Jan-3 Biddle & Webb, Birmingham #67

BENNETT, Frank Moss (1874-1953) British

£300 $468 €435 Haddon Hall, Deryshire (10x14cm-4x6in) init. board prov. 27-Mar-3 Neales, Nottingham #994
£500 $835 €725 Interior scene with hunt members improvising a game of skittles with candles and oranges (38x50cm-15x20in) s.d.1930. 17-Jun-3 Anderson & Garland, Newcastle #431/R
£550 $897 €798 Target practice (36x51cm-14x20in) s. 16-Jul-3 Sotheby's, Olympia #100/R
£700 $1162 €1015 Blacksmith's cottage, Ashton, Devon (36x25cm-14x10in) s. board. 12-Jun-3 Gorringes, Lewes #1599
£1000 $1590 €1500 Half timbered country house with sleeping dog and chickens (34x24cm-13x9in) s. canvas on panel. 27-Feb-3 Bonhams, Chester #474 est:1000-1400
£1200 $1848 €1800 Winning hand (37x48cm-15x19in) s.d.1931 paper on board prov. 5-Sep-2 Christie's, Kensington #297/R est:1200-1800
£2000 $3340 €2900 Coachman (35x25cm-14x10in) s. 8-Jul-3 Bonhams, Knightsbridge #95/R est:2000-3000
£4000 $6320 €6000 One more for luck (42x32cm-17x13in) s.d.1931 i.stretcher prov. 26-Nov-2 Christie's, London #158/R est:4000-6000
£4573 $7500 €6860 Chessmates (25x35cm-10x14in) s.d.1916 prov. 5-Feb-3 Christie's, Rockefeller NY #179/R est:3000-5000
£5200 $8112 €7800 Preparing for the hunt (41x2cm-16x1in) s.d.1931. 6-Nov-2 Sotheby's, Olympia #92/R est:3000-4000
£6250 $9625 €9375 Untitled - uninvited guests (36x51cm-14x20in) s.d.1922. 3-Sep-2 Shapiro, Sydney #432/R est:18000-24000 (A.D 17500)
£6800 $10880 €10200 Relaxation after a day in the fields (39x51cm-15x20in) s.d.1925. 13-Mar-3 Morphets, Harrogate #586/R est:4000-5000
£7000 $11410 €10500 Huntsmen and hounds in a courtyard (39x55cm-15x22in) s. canvasboard. 29-Jan-3 Sotheby's, Olympia #225/R est:6000-8000
£8500 $13515 €12750 Tomorrows order (25x35cm-10x14in) s.d.1950 prov. 18-Mar-3 Bonhams, New Bond Street #111/R est:3000-5000

Works on paper

£1000 $1520 €1500 Anglers fishing from a river bank (41x48cm-16x19in) s.i. 16-Aug-2 Keys, Aylsham #612

BENNETT, Godwin (1888-?) British

£280 $437 €420 Quite haven, North Wales (51x61cm-20x24in) s. 6-Nov-2 Bonhams, Chester #521
£280 $465 €420 West Country harbour (44x72cm-17x28in) s. board. 15-Jun-3 Lots Road, London #370
£350 $557 €525 Sussex watermill (26x35cm-10x14in) s. canvasboard. 6-Mar-3 Christie's, Kensington #491/R
£500 $785 €750 St. Ives, Cornwall (50x60cm-20x24in) s. 15-Apr-3 Bonhams, Knightsbridge #134/R

BENNETT, Joseph Hastings (1889-1969) American

£475 $750 €713 Ladies harvesting the field. s. 16-Nov-2 Harvey Clar, Oakland #1395

BENNETT, Portia Mary (1898-1989) Australian

Works on paper

£286 $451 €429 Boat on lake (15x20cm-6x8in) s. W/C. 18-Nov-2 Goodman, Sydney #20 (A.D 800)
£393 $621 €590 White rowing boat (37x45cm-15x18in) s. W/C. 18-Nov-2 Goodman, Sydney #117 (A.D 1100)

BENNETT, William (1811-1871) British

Works on paper

£260 $426 €390 Across the common (23x33cm-9x13in) s. pencil W/C. 4-Feb-3 Bonhams, Leeds #226
£419 $663 €650 Landscape (37x54cm-15x21in) s. W/C card. 18-Dec-2 Finarte, Milan #97

BENNETT, William James (1787-1844) American

Prints

£10559 $17000 €15839 City of Washington from beyond the Navy yard (50x67cm-20x26in) hand col engraving executed c.1833 after painting by George Cooke. 16-Jan-3 Sotheby's, New York #6/R est:5000-7000

BENNETT, William Rubery (1893-1987) Australian

£357 $564 €536 Afternoon on Hawkesbury River (13x17cm-5x7in) s. board. 18-Nov-2 Goodman, Sydney #112 (A.D 1000)
£561 $853 €842 Nolan like landscape (15x20cm-6x8in) s. i.verso board. 19-Aug-2 Joel, Victoria #185 est:1500-2000 (A.D 1600)
£615 $960 €923 Figures on a beach (15x20cm-6x8in) s. 8-Apr-3 Christie's, Melbourne #272/R est:2000-3000 (A.D 1600)
£880 $1417 €1276 Campfire (25x34cm-10x13in) s. canvasboard. 12-May-3 Joel, Victoria #329 est:2000-2500 (A.D 2200)
£1341 $2105 €2012 Boiling the billy (23x28cm-9x11in) s. board. 15-Apr-3 Lawson Menzies, Sydney #62/R est:2500-3500 (A.D 3500)
£1357 $2104 €2036 Looking into Burragorang valley (39x46cm-15x18in) i.verso canvasboard painted c.1940-41 prov. 29-Oct-2 Lawson Menzies, Sydney #9/R est:6000-8000 (A.D 3800)
£1550 $2465 €2325 Sylvan glade, Burragorang valley (24x29cm-9x11in) s. s.i.d.1966 verso canvasboard. 5-May-3 Sotheby's, Melbourne #272/R est:3000-5000 (A.D 4000)
£1649 $2506 €2474 Robertson, afternoon (25x43cm-10x17in) s. painted c.1948 prov. 28-Aug-2 Deutscher-Menzies, Melbourne #251/R est:5000-7000 (A.D 4600)
£1673 $2744 €2510 Morning sunshine, Burragorang valley (38x45cm-15x18in) s. i.verso. 4-Jun-3 Deutscher-Menzies, Melbourne #333/R est:4000-6000 (A.D 4200)
£1829 $2891 €2652 Landscape, Victoria (49x60cm-19x24in) s. board. 22-Jul-3 Lawson Menzies, Sydney #75/R est:5000-8000 (A.D 4500)
£1964 $3045 €2946 Bush road (25x30cm-10x12in) s. i.verso canvas on board prov. 29-Oct-2 Lawson Menzies, Sydney #132 est:2800-3500 (A.D 5500)
£1992 $3267 €2988 Cloud shadows, Burragorang Valley (38x46cm-15x18in) s. painted c.1968. 4-Jun-3 Deutscher-Menzies, Melbourne #69/R est:5000-7000 (A.D 5000)
£2115 $3363 €3173 Prelude to a storm, Robertson (38x45cm-15x18in) s. i.verso. 4-Mar-3 Deutscher-Menzies, Melbourne #135/R est:5000-7000 (A.D 5500)
£3053 $4824 €4580 Valley view, Burragorang (24x29cm-9x11in) s. i.verso board. 2-Apr-3 Christie's, Melbourne #32/R est:3000-5000 (A.D 8000)
£3101 $4930 €4652 Hawkesbury River from Richmond lookout (37x44cm-15x17in) s. i.verso. 5-May-3 Sotheby's, Melbourne #314/R est:5000-8000 (A.D 8000)
£3984 $6534 €5976 By-way, Kangaroo valley (51x61cm-20x24in) s. i.verso. 4-Jun-3 Deutscher-Menzies, Melbourne #161/R est:7000-10000 (A.D 10000)

BENNETTER, Johan Jacob (1822-1904) Norwegian
£2719 $4241 €4079 Moonlit seascape with sailing vessels (41x61cm-16x24in) s.d.1874. 5-Aug-2 Rasmussen, Vejle #41/R est:12000-15000 (D.KR 32000)

BENNEWITZ VON LOFEN, Karl (elder) (1826-1895) German
£1200 $1992 €1800 Dutch interior with a lady and her daughter preparing vegetables (43x57cm-17x22in) s.d.1885. 10-Jun-3 Bonhams, Leeds #149/R est:1200-1500
£1408 $2338 €2000 Autumn woods with pond and deer (84x112cm-33x44in) s. canvas on canvas. 14-Jun-3 Arnold, Frankfurt #798/R est:4000

BENNEWITZ, O (19/20th C) German
£1224 $1947 €1800 Taufers in Tyrol (73x100cm-29x39in) s. i.d.1898 verso. 19-Mar-3 Neumeister, Munich #511/R est:1200

BENNINGER, John J (20th C) American
£267 $425 €401 Last retreat for Mr Smythe (56x66cm-22x26in) s. board painted c.1937. 2-Mar-3 Toomey, Oak Park #749/R
£267 $425 €401 Spring plowing from 35,000 feet (25x30cm-10x12in) s. board painted c.1947. 2-Mar-3 Toomey, Oak Park #797/R
£440 $700 €660 Through the valley (51x66cm-20x26in) s. board painted c.1947. 2-Mar-3 Toomey, Oak Park #753/R
£472 $750 €708 Aestheter (51x66cm-20x26in) s. board painted c.1955. 2-Mar-3 Toomey, Oak Park #748/R
£692 $1100 €1038 Horror of war (23x38cm-9x15in) s. board painted c.1942. 2-Mar-3 Toomey, Oak Park #752/R
Works on paper
£440 $700 €660 Nude study (19x16cm-7x6in) s.d. i.verso pastel chl. 4-May-3 Treadway Gallery, Cincinnati #587/R

BENOIS, Albert (19/20th C) Russian
Works on paper
£335 $530 €520 The fairway (16x26cm-6x10in) s.d.1922 W/C. 19-Dec-2 Hagelstam, Helsinki #904

BENOIS, Albert Nikolaievitch (1852-1936) Russian
Works on paper
£1056 $1701 €1500 The meeting (30x40cm-12x16in) s.d.1919 W/C. 10-May-3 Bukowskis, Helsinki #390/R est:2500-2700

BENOIS, Alexander (1870-1960) Russian
Works on paper
£922 $1540 €1300 Un salon (29x40cm-11x16in) s. W/C. 23-Jun-3 Beaussant & Lefèvre, Paris #305/R
£1006 $1600 €1509 Les cordeliers, stage set (30x48cm-12x19in) s.i. W/C. 8-Mar-3 Harvey Clar, Oakland #1319
£1100 $1726 €1650 Costume design for The Juggler in Act II of Raymonde (24x18cm-9x7in) init.d.1946 pencil pen W/C htd gold double-sided prov. 20-Nov-2 Sotheby's, London #161/R est:1000-1500
£1138 $1900 €1650 Costumn design (30x22cm-12x9in) s. indis d. W/C ink. 22-Jun-3 Freeman, Philadelphia #65/R est:500-800
£1200 $1896 €1800 Three costume designs (24x16cm-9x6in) s.i.d.1953 pencil W/C htd gold paint set of three. 26-Nov-2 Christie's, Kensington #40/R est:1200-1800
£1600 $2608 €2400 Costume design for the nutcracker suiter by Tchaikovsky (37x26cm-15x10in) s.d.1937 Indian ink W/C. 3-Feb-3 Bonhams, New Bond Street #44/R est:300-500
£1677 $2800 €2432 View outside the gates (25x33cm-10x13in) s.d.1940 i.verso W/C gouache paperboard. 22-Jun-3 Freeman, Philadelphia #66/R est:1000-1500
£1800 $2826 €2700 Church of San Lorenzo, Milan (25x32cm-10x13in) s. pen ink W/C over pencil. 20-Nov-2 Sotheby's, London #176/R est:600-800
£1923 $2923 €3000 La bourgeoisie locale au theatre (28x40cm-11x16in) s.d.1916 verso gouache. 10-Jul-2 Rabourdin & Choppin de Janvry, Paris #28/R est:3000-3200
£2395 $4000 €3473 Landscape (31x48cm-12x19in) i.d.1939 W/C. 22-Jun-3 Freeman, Philadelphia #67/R est:500-800
£2400 $3816 €3600 Sunlit courtyard (45x59cm-18x23in) s.d.1931 W/C. 4-Mar-3 Bearnes, Exeter #403/R est:800-1200
£2600 $4082 €3900 Stage design for Amphion (28x38cm-11x15in) mono.d.8.11.1931 pencil Indian ink exhib.prov. 20-Nov-2 Sotheby's, London #173/R est:2000-3000
£3800 $6194 €5700 Decor design for le Pavillon d'Armide (25x34cm-10x13in) s. indis i. pencil Indian ink W/C prov. 3-Feb-3 Bonhams, New Bond Street #47/R est:1000-1500
£4000 $6480 €6000 Moored boats (27x37cm-11x15in) s.d.1934 W/C over pencil. 21-May-3 Sotheby's, London #79/R est:4000-6000
£4192 $7000 €6078 Castle (32x45cm-13x18in) s.d.1945 i.verso W/C over ink. 22-Jun-3 Freeman, Philadelphia #55/R est:1000-1500
£4600 $7498 €6900 Salon de Madame de Maintenon, Fontainbleu (55x43cm-22x17in) s.i.d.1935 W/C over pencil exhib. 3-Feb-3 Bonhams, New Bond Street #46/R est:1200-1800
£5500 $8634 €8250 Stage design for Les noces de Psyche (47x63cm-19x25in) s.i.d.1927 pencil pen W/C gouache htd gold silver. 20-Nov-2 Sotheby's, London #154/R est:6000-8000
£5500 $8965 €8250 Costume design for la Foule des spectateurs in Petrouchka, 1948 (26x46cm-10x18in) s. pen ink W/C prov. 3-Feb-3 Bonhams, New Bond Street #48/R est:2500-3500
£6000 $9420 €9000 Stage set design for Sadko (48x64cm-19x25in) bears sig.d.1930 s.i.verso W/C gouache over pencil card. 20-Nov-2 Sotheby's, London #172/R est:4000-6000
£6000 $9720 €9000 Landscapes (25x38cm-10x15in) s.i.d.1933 W/C ink over pencil pair. 21-May-3 Sotheby's, London #95/R est:5000-7000
£6500 $10206 €9750 Stage design for the Nutcracker (28x47cm-11x19in) s.d.15.VI 1954 W/C htd gouache. 20-Nov-2 Sotheby's, London #153/R est:3000-5000
£7000 $10990 €10500 View of Peterhof (24x30cm-9x12in) s.d.1892-1918 gouache. 20-Nov-2 Sotheby's, London #175/R est:3000-5000
£13000 $21060 €19500 Costume design for Petroushka (30x21cm-12x8in) s.d.1936 W/C pen over pencil set of six. 21-May-3 Sotheby's, London #145/R est:6000-8000
£24000 $37680 €36000 View of the Monument to Nicholas I and St Isaac's Cathedral, St Petersburg (43x59cm-17x23in) s. i.d.1922 verso gouache over pencil. 20-Nov-2 Sotheby's, London #104/R est:8000-12000

BENOIS, Leon (19th C) French
£1986 $3078 €2979 Nature morte aux peches, groseilles et cerises (38x55cm-15x22in) s. 4-Dec-2 AB Stockholms Auktionsverk #1871/R est:25000-30000 (S.KR 28000)

BENOIS, Nicola (1901-1988) Russian
Works on paper
£3704 $6000 €5371 Decor design for Gioconda (51x66cm-20x26in) s. i.verso gouache W/C India ink prov. 21-May-3 Doyle, New York #27/R est:600-900

BENOIT, Jacqueline (1928-) French?
£759 $1199 €1100 Maison au bord de l'eau (37x45cm-15x18in) s.d.1967. 4-Apr-3 Tajan, Paris #43/R
£1401 $2186 €2200 Rencontre (64x81cm-25x32in) s.d.1966. 5-Nov-2 Tajan, Paris #44

BENOIT, L (?) ?
£1745 $2809 €2600 Panier de fleurs (60x81cm-24x32in) s. 23-Feb-3 Lesieur & Le Bars, Le Havre #10/R

BENOIT, Léon (?) French
£4000 $6680 €6000 Summer flowers in a basket on a table (60x81cm-24x32in) s. 18-Jun-3 Christie's, Kensington #34/R est:3000-4000

BENOIT-LEVY, Jules (1866-c.1925) French
£253 $400 €400 Chouan (42x33cm-17x13in) s.d.1893. 27-Nov-2 Lemoine & Ferrando, Paris #75
£1218 $1912 €1900 Repas du cardinal (61x50cm-24x20in) s. prov. 21-Nov-2 Neret-Minet, Paris #27

BENOIT-LISON, Francois (20th C) French
£1623 $2645 €2450 Mascarade (130x97cm-51x38in) s.verso. 1-Feb-3 Claude Aguttes, Neuilly #334/R est:2500-2600

BENOUVILLE, Francois Léon (1821-1859) French
Works on paper
£449 $696 €700 Portrait de jeune femme (37x29cm-15x11in) s. crayon stump. 4-Dec-2 Piasa, Paris #140

BENOUVILLE, Francois Léon and CHAPU, Michel Antoine (19th C) French
Works on paper
£1226 $1900 €1839 Head study. Study of a man (29x22cm-11x9in) pencil two prov. 29-Oct-2 Sotheby's, New York #11/R est:600-800

BENOUVILLE, Jean-Achille (1815-1891) French
Works on paper
£759 $1200 €1200 Une etude d'arbre (50x32cm-20x13in) col chk. 27-Nov-2 Christie's, Paris #251/R

BENQUET, A (?) French?
£3082 $4839 €4500 Facteurs dans la grande lande (25x32cm-10x13in) s.i. on metal. 15-Apr-3 Laurence Calmels, Paris #4108/R
£3767 $5914 €5500 Dans les landes un concert dans la foret (44x34cm-17x13in) i. 15-Apr-3 Laurence Calmels, Paris #4110/R est:800
£3767 $5914 €5500 Groupe d'enfants, place Gambetta (30x37cm-12x15in) s. cardboard exhib. 15-Apr-3 Laurence Calmels, Paris #4109/R

BENRATH, Frederic (1930-) French
£1277 $2132 €1800 Composition (73x60cm-29x24in) s. 23-Jun-3 Claude Boisgirard, Paris #158/R est:1200-1500

BENRIMO, Thomas (1887-1958) American
£14423 $22500 €21635 Goat song (89x109cm-35x43in) s. masonite panel prov.lit. 9-Nov-2 Santa Fe Art, Santa Fe #121/R est:15000-25000

BENSA, Alexander von (1820-1902) Austrian
£1905 $3029 €2800 Rider at river bank (26x39cm-10x15in) s. i.verso panel. 25-Feb-3 Dorotheum, Vienna #28/R est:2800-3500
£2778 $4417 €4000 Cavallerie attack (22x36cm-9x14in) s. panel. 29-Apr-3 Wiener Kunst Auktionen, Vienna #547/R est:4000-6000

BENSELL, George F (1837-1879) American
£16129 $25000 €24194 Closing in (76x91cm-30x36in) s. board painted c.1855 prov.exhib. 5-Dec-2 Christie's, Rockefeller NY #162/R est:20000-30000

BENSING, Frank C (1893-1983) American
£2215 $3500 €3323 Catch of the day (56x74cm-22x29in) s.d.1948. 24-Apr-3 Shannon's, Milford #201/R est:3500-4500

BENSLEY, Mick (20th C) British
Works on paper
£300 $489 €450 Three Lowesoft drifters at sea (23x36cm-9x14in) s. W/C. 14-Feb-3 Keys, Aylsham #547
£350 $585 €508 Fishing boats off the North Norfolk coast in olden times (23x38cm-9x15in) s.d.1992 W/C. 20-Jun-3 Keys, Aylsham #786/R

BENSO, Giulio (1601-1668) Italian
Works on paper
£3380 $5611 €4800 Two male nudes (23x12cm-9x5in) wash pen over graphite. 12-Jun-3 Hauswedell & Nolte, Hamburg #41/R est:4000

BENSO, Giulio (attrib) (1601-1668) Italian
Works on paper
£676 $1054 €1000 Ermite a son pupitre (21x18cm-8x7in) pen wash. 27-Mar-3 Maigret, Paris #40/R

BENSON, Ambrosius (?-1550) Flemish
£30769 $48615 €48000 Madonna and Child (66x47cm-26x19in) board. 14-Nov-2 Arte, Seville #156/R

BENSON, Ambrosius (attrib) (?-1550) Flemish
£8333 $12917 €13000 Portrait of young woman (61x50cm-24x20in) panel. 5-Dec-2 Dr Fritz Nagel, Stuttgart #591/R est:5800

BENSON, Eugene (1839-1908) American
£245 $400 €368 Landscape with ocean view (13x33cm-5x13in) i.verso panel. 2-Feb-3 Grogan, Boston #50

BENSON, Frank W (1862-1951) American
£33440 $52500 €50160 Dublin woods (51x45cm-20x18in) s.d.31. 22-Nov-2 Skinner, Boston #272/R est:25000-35000
£58642 $95000 €87963 Mount Monadnock (41x51cm-16x20in) s. painted c.1890 prov.exhib. 21-May-3 Sotheby's, New York #169/R est:60000-80000
£141935 $220000 €212903 Shadow (72x89cm-28x35in) s.d.30 canvas on masonite prov.exhib. 5-Dec-2 Christie's, Rockefeller NY #150/R est:250000-350000
£387097 $600000 €580646 Eleanor holding a shell (77x641cm-30x252in) s.d.1902 prov.exhib.lit. 5-Dec-2 Christie's, Rockefeller NY #70/R est:700000-1000000

Prints
£2893 $4600 €4340 Moonlight (17x22cm-7x9in) s.num.26/50 etching drypoint. 4-Mar-3 Swann Galleries, New York #146/R est:1000-1500

Works on paper
£19863 $29000 €29795 Perching grouse (41x36cm-16x14in) s.d.35 W/C en grisaille prov.exhib. 3-Nov-1 North East Auctions, Portsmouth #744/R est:12000-18000
£34591 $55000 €51887 Chickadees and snow (48x36cm-19x14in) s. W/C chl exhib. 1-Mar-3 North East Auctions, Portsmouth #705/R est:7000-12000
£98765 $160000 €148148 White canoe (52x63cm-20x25in) s.d.27 W/C pencil prov. 21-May-3 Sotheby's, New York #168/R est:50000-70000

BENSON, Frank W (attrib) (1862-1951) American
£4717 $7311 €7500 Four young woman by the sea (128x137cm-50x54in) s.d.1909. 2-Nov-2 Hans Stahl, Toestorf #41/R est:3000

BENSON, Thomas (19th C) British?
£500 $815 €750 Bloodhound in an extensive landscape (64x76cm-25x30in) s.d.1879. 12-Feb-3 Bonhams, Knightsbridge #140/R

BENSON, Tressa Emerson (1896-?) American
£1899 $3000 €2849 Path from the village (61x91cm-24x36in) s. 24-Apr-3 Shannon's, Milford #210/R est:4000-6000

BENSON, W (?) British?
£675 $1100 €1013 Otterhounds closing in (38x61cm-15x24in) s. two. 11-Feb-3 Bonhams & Doyles, New York #120 est:1200-1800

BENT, Jan van der (attrib) (1650-1690) Dutch
£1474 $2388 €2137 Landscape with herders and cattle (72x92cm-28x36in) 26-May-3 Bukowskis, Stockholm #434/R est:25000-30000 (S.KR 19000)

BENTABOLE, Louis (?-1880) French
£1603 $2516 €2500 Fire in small harbour town in Normandy (27x40cm-11x16in) s. 21-Nov-2 Van Ham, Cologne #1472/R est:2500

BENTELE, Fidelis (1830-1901) German
£680 $1082 €1000 Death of St Joseph of Nazareth in the presence of Christ and Mary (155x88cm-61x35in) s.d.1874. 20-Mar-3 Neumeister, Munich #2589/R

BENTIVOGLIO, Cesare (1868-1952) Italian
£652 $1070 €900 Alberi sul fiume (44x20cm-17x8in) mono. 27-May-3 Finarte, Milan #14/R
£1159 $1901 €1600 Marina al tramonto (31x47cm-12x19in) mono. board. 27-May-3 Finarte, Milan #16/R est:700-800

BENTLEY, Alfred (1879-1923) British
£330 $538 €495 Marlaix, Brittany (40x30cm-16x12in) s. s.i.verso. 17-Feb-3 Bonhams, Bath #88

BENTLEY, Augustus (?) British?
£1300 $2028 €1950 Market outside Antwerp Cathedral (112x86cm-44x34in) s. 8-Oct-2 Bonhams, Knightsbridge #246/R est:600-800

BENTLEY, Charles (1806-1854) British
Works on paper
£450 $734 €653 Conversation on the beach (22x35cm-9x14in) s. W/C. 16-Jul-3 Sotheby's, Olympia #30/R
£550 $908 €798 Figures kneeling at an altar (49x70cm-19x28in) s.d.1851 W/C over pencil htd bodycol. 2-Jul-3 Sotheby's, Olympia #279/R
£613 $1000 €920 Shipwreck on a rocky coast with sailors on the shore (31x45cm-12x18in) pencil W/C bodycol. 16-Feb-3 Butterfields, San Francisco #2044
£700 $1155 €1015 Couple in courtly dress on a terrace (29x21cm-11x8in) s. W/C over pencil htd bodycol gum arabic. 2-Jul-3 Sotheby's, Olympia #179/R
£1000 $1620 €1500 Bringing in the derelict (36x56cm-14x22in) init. pencil W/C bodycol. 21-May-3 Christie's, Kensington #419/R est:700-900
£1900 $3001 €2850 Shipping off the coast (33x50cm-13x20in) s. W/C over pencil htd bodycol scratching out. 28-Nov-2 Sotheby's, London #233/R est:1500-2000
£3000 $4830 €4500 Coast of Normandy (33x47cm-13x19in) s. W/C. 15-Jan-3 Cheffins Grain & Comins, Cambridge #362/R
£4400 $6996 €6600 Shipping off Scarborough (32x46cm-13x18in) s. W/C over pencil htd bodycol. 19-Mar-3 Sotheby's, London #154/R est:4000-6000

BENTLEY, Charles (attrib) (1806-1854) British
Works on paper
£280 $437 €420 Coastal scene with figures, huts and upturned boat (21x65cm-8x26in) W/C bodycol. 6-Nov-2 Bonhams, Chester #390

BENTLEY, Claude (1915-1990) American
£323 $475 €485 Palmyra (132x117cm-52x46in) s.d.61. 23-Jun-2 Susanin's, Chicago #5037/R
£531 $850 €797 Walk on the hillside (127x154cm-50x61in) s.d.88 i.verso. 16-Mar-3 Butterfields, San Francisco #1092

BENTLEY, John W (1880-1951) American
£600 $942 €900 Fale hut of Chief Tugaga Safune village, Savaii Island. Snow patched stream (20x25cm-8x10in) s. i.verso canvas on board two. 16-Apr-3 Christie's, Kensington #926/R
£779 $1200 €1169 Decker church. s.i. painted c.1920. 8-Sep-2 Treadway Gallery, Cincinnati #611/R
£1100 $1705 €1650 Trees in autumn (61x76cm-24x30in) s. 5-Dec-2 Christie's, Kensington #72/R est:600-800
£1282 $2000 €1923 Autumn (30x38cm-12x15in) s.d.1914. 22-Sep-2 Susanin's, Chicago #5108/R est:2000-3000

BENTON, Fletcher (1931-) American
Sculpture
£1227 $2000 €1841 Balanced, unbalanced F (52cm-20in) i. stainless steel prov. 16-Feb-3 Butterfields, San Francisco #2129 est:3000-5000
£1442 $2250 €2163 Folded circle (29x51cm-11x20in) gilt pat bronze. 14-Oct-2 Butterfields, San Francisco #2099/R est:3000-5000

BENTON, Thomas Hart (1889-1975) American
£25806 $40000 €38709 Landscape with deer (13x16cm-5x6in) s.d.56 panel prov. 4-Dec-2 Sotheby's, New York #57/R est:20000-30000
£40719 $68000 €59043 Figure organisation (41x51cm-16x20in) s.i. prov. 18-Jun-3 Christie's, Los Angeles #92/R est:40000-60000
£45161 $70000 €67742 Still life (60x44cm-24x17in) s. tempera on board painted c.1935 prov. 4-Dec-2 Sotheby's, New York #66/R est:75000-100000
£51613 $80000 €77420 Lost penny (67x48cm-26x19in) s.d.1941 oil tempera on board prov. 5-Dec-2 Christie's, Rockefeller NY #114/R est:60000-80000
£70968 $110000 €106452 Train in the desert (34x49cm-13x19in) s. canvasboard painted c.1926-28 prov.exhib.lit. 4-Dec-2 Sotheby's, New York #58/R est:60000-80000
£77419 $120000 €116129 Study for instruments of power (35x57cm-14x22in) s. masonite prov. 5-Dec-2 Christie's, Rockefeller NY #113/R est:150000-250000
£129032 $200000 €193548 City (84x63cm-33x25in) s.d.20 prov.exhib.lit. 3-Dec-2 Phillips, New York #65/R est:150000-250000
£203704 $330000 €305556 Shooting the rapids (51x61cm-20x24in) s.d.73 prov. 22-May-3 Christie's, Rockefeller NY #80/R est:200000-300000
Prints
£2044 $3250 €3066 Country politics (122x142cm-48x56in) s.d.1973 lithograph one of 250. 30-Apr-3 Doyle, New York #154/R est:3000-4000
£2057 $3250 €2983 New England farm (23x36cm-9x14in) s. lithograph. 26-Jul-3 Coeur d'Alene, Hayden #57/R est:1500-2500
£2949 $4600 €4424 Race (26x34cm-10x13in) s. lithograph edition of 250. 7-Nov-2 Swann Galleries, New York #548/R est:4000-6000
£3846 $6000 €5769 Huck Finn (41x53cm-16x21in) s. lithograph edition of 100. 10-Nov-2 Selkirks, St. Louis #733/R est:6000-9000
Works on paper
£1829 $3000 €2652 Swamp (24x21cm-9x8in) init. pencil exec.c.1941. 5-Jun-3 Swann Galleries, New York #21/R est:3000-5000
£2848 $4500 €4130 Water tower. Ozark man (15x10cm-6x4in) one s. one s.d.1924 pencil ink pen pair. 26-Jul-3 Coeur d'Alene, Hayden #241/R est:3000-5000
£3171 $5200 €4598 Landscape with a train and a car (20x34cm-8x13in) s. pen black ink gray wash exhib. 5-Jun-3 Swann Galleries, New York #22/R est:7000-10000
£5031 $8000 €7547 Cotton pickers (22x29cm-9x11in) s. W/C ink pencil. 4-Mar-3 Christie's, Rockefeller NY #77/R est:6000-8000
£7547 $12000 €11321 Plug cut and blackstone (33x51cm-13x20in) s.i. W/C pencil executed c.1930 prov. 5-Mar-3 Sotheby's, New York #99/R est:12000-18000
£7742 $12000 €11613 Oklahoma farms (23x36cm-9x14in) ink wash exec.c.1940. 8-Dec-2 Toomey, Oak Park #822/R est:8000-12000
£9494 $15000 €14241 Missouri depot (26x37cm-10x15in) s. ink graphite W/C prov. 3-Apr-3 Christie's, Rockefeller NY #163/R est:12000-18000
£17610 $28000 €26415 Utah Desert (27x42cm-11x17in) s.d.52 gouache en grisaille pencil prov. 4-Mar-3 Christie's, Rockefeller NY #97/R est:12000-18000
£24516 $38000 €36774 Buffalo River (54x36cm-21x14in) s.d.68 W/C pencil paper on board prov. 5-Dec-2 Christie's, Rockefeller NY #141/R est:25000-35000
£40123 $65000 €60185 Oil well (75x50cm-30x20in) s. W/C pencil gouache. 22-May-3 Christie's, Rockefeller NY #81/R est:30000-50000

BENTZEN, Axel (1893-1952) Danish
£270 $417 €405 Interior from the artist's studio (90x120cm-35x47in) init. 26-Oct-2 Rasmussen, Havnen #2144 (D.KR 3200)
£306 $496 €444 Portrait of woman (70x54cm-28x21in) init. 24-May-3 Rasmussen, Havnen #4035 (D.KR 3200)
£320 $509 €480 Portrait of man (100x74cm-39x29in) init.d.17. 26-Feb-3 Kunsthallen, Copenhagen #231 (D.KR 3500)
£339 $525 €509 Daffodils and primula in window (65x55cm 26x22in) init. 1-Oct-2 Rasmussen, Copenhagen #313 (D.KR 4000)
£373 $593 €560 Interior scene with red flower (110x92cm-43x36in) s.verso exhib. 29-Apr-3 Kunsthallen, Copenhagen #215 (D.KR 4000)
£381 $637 €552 Street scene (69x69cm-27x27in) init.d.22. 17-Jun-3 Rasmussen, Copenhagen #150/R (D.KR 4000)
£443 $718 €665 Landscape from Allinge (64x53cm-25x21in) init. 25-Jan-3 Rasmussen, Havnen #2231 (D.KR 5000)
£465 $734 €698 Man seated by window (90x75cm-35x30in) init.d.42 verso. 1-Apr-3 Rasmussen, Copenhagen #548/R (D.KR 5000)
£466 $742 €699 From the artist's studio (70x80cm-28x31in) init. 29-Apr-3 Kunsthallen, Copenhagen #214 (D.KR 5000)
£468 $726 €702 Flowers on window ledge (81x61cm-32x24in) init. 28-Sep-2 Rasmussen, Havnen #2169 (D.KR 5500)
£485 $771 €728 Sitting-room interior with flowers on table (112x90cm-44x35in) init. exhib. 5-May-3 Rasmussen, Vejle #2/R (D.KR 5200)
£620 $1035 €899 Sunshine coming through window (130x100cm-51x39in) init. init.d.50 verso. 17-Jun-3 Rasmussen, Copenhagen #148/R (D.KR 6500)
£745 $1192 €1118 Blue interior with nude woman (76x96cm-30x38in) mono. 16-Mar-3 Hindemae, Ullerslev #732/R (D.KR 8000)
£746 $1187 €1119 View through a window (92x68cm-36x27in) init. 29-Apr-3 Kunsthallen, Copenhagen #246/R (D.KR 8000)
£1162 $1836 €1743 Still life of flowers (115x100cm-45x39in) 1-Apr-3 Rasmussen, Copenhagen #590/R (D.KR 12500)

BENTZEN, N P A (1812-1876) Danish
£541 $870 €812 Portraits of Peter Chr Hansen and his wife Kirstine (36x29cm-14x11in) s.d.1846 pair. 26-Feb-3 Museumsbygningen, Copenhagen #55 (D.KR 6000)

BENTZEN, Reimer (20th C) Scandinavian?
£326 $518 €489 From the south of Greenland (59x79cm-23x31in) init.d.1927. 10-Mar-3 Rasmussen, Vejle #471 (D.KR 3500)

BENTZEN-BILKVIST, Johannes (1865-1934) Danish
£287 $465 €416 Landscape from Odsherred (71x99cm-28x39in) s.d.1899. 24-May-3 Rasmussen, Havnen #2066 (D.KR 3000)

BENVENUTI, Benvenuto (1881-1959) Italian
£903 $1427 €1400 Wall with cypress (16x19cm-6x7in) s.verso cardboard. 18-Dec-2 Finarte, Milan #231

BENVENUTI, E (19/20th C) Italian
Works on paper
£303 $467 €455 Venetian canal scene (73x43cm-29x17in) s. W/C. 4-Sep-2 Dunbar Sloane, Wellington #90 est:500-1000 (NZ.D 1000)

BENVENUTI, Eugenio (19/20th C) Italian
Works on paper
£370 $574 €555 Gondola on the canal (40x25cm-16x10in) s. W/C htd gouache. 3-Dec-2 Ritchie, Toronto #3082/R est:1200-1600 (C.D 900)
£2000 $3340 €3000 By the edge of the lagoon, Venice. Harbour on a Venetian island (37x67cm-15x26in) s. W/C pair. 18-Jun-3 Christie's, Kensington #141/R est:1500-2000

BENVENUTI, Pietro (1769-1844) Italian
Works on paper
£450 $752 €653 Holy Family (26x20cm-10x8in) i. pen ink black chk squared for transfer. 9-Jul-3 Bonhams, Knightsbridge #56/R

BENVENUTI, Pietro (attrib) (1769-1844) Italian
£24000 $39120 €34800 Portrait of George Rowley of Priory Hill and his sisters, Mary and Charlotte (223x178cm-88x70in) prov. 21-Jul-3 Sotheby's, London #174/R est:8000-12000

BENWELL, Joseph Austin (fl.1865-1886) British
£7000 $10920 €10500 Caravan of camels crossing the desert, mountains beyond (112x85cm-44x33in) s. 15-Oct-2 Sotheby's, London #233/R est:7000-10000

Works on paper
£2800 $4368 €4200 Arabs praying in the desert with a caravan of camels beyond (38x50cm-15x20in) s. W/C over pencil htd bodycol. 15-Oct-2 Sotheby's, London #256/R est:3000-4000
£2800 $4452 €4200 Head of the caravan, mount Sinai (32x22cm-13x9in) s.d.1882 W/C bodycol exhib. 29-Apr-3 Bonhams, New Bond Street #99/R est:3000-4000

BENWELL, Joseph Austin (attrib) (fl.1865-1886) British
Works on paper
£380 $619 €570 Arab camp near an oasis (27x35cm-11x14in) W/C. 29-Jan-3 Hampton & Littlewood, Exeter #357/R

BENZ, J (19th C) German
£396 $591 €594 Still life of fruit with grapes and peaches in basket (41x45cm-16x18in) s. 25-Jun-2 Koller, Zurich #6465 (S.FR 900)
£419 $624 €629 Still life of flowers in basket (41x46cm-16x18in) 25-Jun-2 Koller, Zurich #6466 (S.FR 950)
£705 $1050 €1058 Still life of fruit including melon, grapes and peaches (49x65cm-19x26in) s.d.63. 25-Jun-2 Koller, Zurich #6467 (S.FR 1600)

BENZ, J Albert (1846-1926) Swiss
£1410 $2186 €2200 Still life of pumpkin, grapes, raspberries, plums and basket (49x64cm-19x25in) s.d.1863. 4-Dec-2 Neumeister, Munich #673/R est:2200

BENZ, Severin (1834-1898) German
£244 $400 €366 Bountiful harvest (56x66cm-22x26in) s. 9-Feb-3 William Jenack, New York #438
£250 $400 €375 Panoramic landscape with cottage and sailboat (43x66cm-17x26in) s. 12-Jan-3 William Jenack, New York #208

BENZONI, Giovanni Maria (1809-1873) Italian
Sculpture
£14610 $22500 €21915 Diana the huntress (135cm-53in) i. marble with plinth. 28-Oct-2 Butterfields, San Francisco #3185/R est:25000-35000

BEOTHY, Étienne (1897-1961) Hungarian
Sculpture
£4167 $6583 €6000 Suzanne (47cm-19in) s.num.3/6 brown pat bronze Cast Blanchet prov.lit. 27-Apr-3 Perrin, Versailles #101/R est:3000-4000
£10060 $15694 €15090 The man (38cm-15in) bronze. 11-Apr-3 Kieselbach, Budapest #40/R est:2800000-3600000 (H.F 3600000)
Works on paper
£709 $1184 €1000 L'escadrille monte (58x43cm-23x17in) s.i.d. ink. 23-Jun-3 Claude Boisgirard, Paris #121/R

BERALDO, Franco (1944-) Italian
£327 $523 €500 Landscape (20x30cm-8x12in) s. s.i.verso. 4-Jan-3 Meeting Art, Vercelli #551
£327 $523 €500 Landscape (20x30cm-8x12in) s. 4-Jan-3 Meeting Art, Vercelli #648
£475 $741 €750 Still life (40x50cm-16x20in) s. s.verso. 14-Sep-2 Meeting Art, Vercelli #872/R
£490 $784 €750 Landscape (30x40cm-12x16in) s. paper on canvas. 4-Jan-3 Meeting Art, Vercelli #689
£521 $828 €750 Landscape (30x40cm-12x16in) s. painted 1995. 1-May-3 Meeting Art, Vercelli #70
£523 $837 €800 Landscape (30x40cm-12x16in) s. painted 1996. 4-Jan-3 Meeting Art, Vercelli #155
£694 $1104 €1000 Landscape (50x70cm-20x28in) s. s.verso. 1-May-3 Meeting Art, Vercelli #498
£980 $1569 €1500 Landscape (60x80cm-24x31in) s. 4-Jan-3 Meeting Art, Vercelli #218
£980 $1569 €1500 Landscape (50x70cm-20x28in) s. 4-Jan-3 Meeting Art, Vercelli #499
£1020 $1622 €1500 Venice (50x70cm-20x28in) s. 1-Mar-3 Meeting Art, Vercelli #768
£1026 $1610 €1600 Window (80x60cm-31x24in) s. 23-Nov-2 Meeting Art, Vercelli #457/R
Works on paper
£320 $508 €470 Landscape (16x16cm-6x6in) s.verso mosaic. 1-Mar-3 Meeting Art, Vercelli #436
£601 $938 €950 Still life (30x40cm-12x16in) s. fresco on canvas. 14-Sep-2 Meeting Art, Vercelli #853/R
£705 $1107 €1100 Landscape (60x50cm-24x20in) s. fresco on canvas. 23-Nov-2 Meeting Art, Vercelli #188/R

BERANGER, Emmanuel (19th C) French
£3000 $4860 €4500 Quick repair (41x31cm-16x12in) s.d.1857 panel. 20-May-3 Sotheby's, Olympia #369/R est:1000-1500

BERANGER, Jean Baptiste Antoine Émile (1814-1883) French
£3822 $6000 €5733 Young parents (50x61cm-20x24in) s.d.1878. 21-Nov-2 Sotheby's, New York #175/R est:8000-12000

BERANN, Heinrich (1915-) Austrian
£1282 $2013 €2000 Celestial harp (96x81cm-38x32in) board. 21-Nov-2 Dorotheum, Vienna #310/R est:2000-3000

BERARD, August (19th C) French?
Works on paper
£3800 $5890 €5700 Bresil, Vue prise du Mouillage de L'Uranie. pres le fort de Vilegagnon a Rio de Janeiro (29x37cm-11x15in) i. pencil exhib. 26-Sep-2 Christie's, London #30/R est:2000-3000

BERARD, Christian (1902-1949) French
Works on paper
£270 $422 €400 Projet de decor avec personnage fabuleux (43x26cm-17x10in) st.verso wash. 31-Mar-3 Pierre Berge, Paris #6
£338 $527 €500 La ballerine (33x49cm-13x19in) st.verso gouache. 31-Mar-3 Pierre Berge, Paris #8/R
£355 $592 €500 Nu d'homme (42x32cm-17x13in) studio st. ink wash. 23-Jun-3 Claude Boisgirard, Paris #77/R
£405 $632 €600 Deux borreaux (23x30cm-9x12in) st.verso gouache pair. 31-Mar-3 Pierre Berge, Paris #2/R
£574 $896 €850 Le bourreau (23x30cm-9x12in) st. gouache. 31-Mar-3 Pierre Berge, Paris #1
£601 $950 €902 Deux tetes (30x15cm-12x6in) s. gouache ink paper on card prov. 2-Apr-3 Doyle, New York #73/R
£638 $1066 €900 Pour la machine infernale (26x37cm-10x15in) studio st. gouache exec.c.1934. 23-Jun-3 Claude Boisgirard, Paris #80
£1132 $1755 €1800 Ruth et Lia regardent le chemin des aubes. L'archange et le jardinier (24x19cm-9x7in) s. gouache ink W/C double-sided exec.c.1943. 30-Oct-2 Artcurial Briest, Paris #235 est:300-400
£1757 $2741 €2600 Deux hommes nus (19x22cm-7x9in) st. W/C. 31-Mar-3 Pierre Berge, Paris #17/R est:2200-2300
£6383 $10340 €9000 Figures d'anges sur des nuages. gouache cut out seven in three frames. 20-May-3 Christie's, Paris #57/R est:9000-12000

BERAUD, Jean (1849-1936) French
£6500 $10530 €9750 Artist in his studio (16x9cm-6x4in) s.d.76 board. 20-May-3 Sotheby's, Olympia #410/R est:5000-7000
£148387 $230000 €222581 La Madeleine (25x33cm-10x13in) s. panel prov.exhib.lit. 29-Oct-2 Sotheby's, New York #94/R est:200000-300000
£225806 $350000 €338709 L'accident - port Saint Denis (31x45cm-12x18in) s. panel prov. 30-Oct-2 Christie's, Rockefeller NY #71/R est:300000-400000
Works on paper
£1887 $2906 €3000 Loge (21x27cm-8x11in) s. pen dr. 27-Oct-2 Muizon & Le Coent, Paris #46
£19497 $30025 €31000 Le train de banlieue (34x48cm-13x19in) s. W/C gouache prov. 22-Oct-2 Sotheby's, Amsterdam #89/R est:7000-9000

BERAUD, Louis (20th C) French
£379 $622 €580 Jeune fille aux colombes (65x54cm-26x21in) s. 7-Feb-3 Oger, Dumont, Paris #54

BERBERIAN, Ovanes (20th C) American
£839 $1300 €1259 Evening glow (46x61cm-18x24in) s. prov. 29-Oct-2 John Moran, Pasadena #742

BERCHEM, Nicolaes (1620-1683) Dutch
£40000 $66800 €58000 Extensive wooded landscape with the meeting of Granida and Daifilo (130x176cm-51x69in) prov.lit. 9-Jul-3 Christie's, London #35/R est:30000-50000
£185185 $300000 €277778 Battle between Alexander and Porus (111x153cm-44x60in) s. prov.exhib.lit. 23-Jan-3 Sotheby's, New York #38/R est:250000-350000
Works on paper
£2800 $4676 €4060 Young shepherd and shepherdess in a landscape (22x18cm-9x7in) i. black white chk wash. 8-Jul-3 Christie's, London #105/R est:2000-3000

BERCHEM, Nicolaes (attrib) (1620-1683) Dutch
£1227 $2000 €1841 Italianate landscape with mother and boy, dog and sheep (46x56cm-18x22in) s.d.1656 panel. 16-Feb-3 Jeffery Burchard, Florida #51
£1290 $1897 €2000 Southern landscape with herders and animals (37x49cm-15x19in) s. panel. 20-Jun-2 Dr Fritz Nagel, Stuttgart #702 est:3000

£2270 $3518 €3405 River landscape with herders and cattle (34x44cm-13x17in) panel. 3-Dec-2 Bukowskis, Stockholm #446/R est:40000-50000 (S.KR 32000)

BERCHERE, Narcisse (1819-1891) French
£2013 $3099 €3200 Marche arabe (24x19cm-9x7in) s. panel. 23-Oct-2 Rabourdin & Choppin de Janvry, Paris #133/R
£5782 $9194 €8500 Vieux pont en Egypte (22x38cm-9x15in) s. 24-Mar-3 Rabourdin & Choppin de Janvry, Paris #134/R est:9000-10000
Works on paper
£946 $1476 €1400 Untitled (20x28cm-8x11in) s. W/C. 27-Mar-3 Maigret, Paris #207

BERCHMANS, Émile (1867-1947) Belgian
£759 $1200 €1200 Promenade autour de lac (32x50cm-13x20in) mono. 26-Nov-2 Palais de Beaux Arts, Brussels #41
Works on paper
£285 $444 €450 Nu allonge (31x44cm-12x17in) s. chl white pencil. 16-Oct-2 Hotel des Ventes Mosan, Brussels #172

BERCHMANS, Jules (1883-1951) Belgian
Works on paper
£274 $427 €400 Chateau en ete (57x74cm-22x29in) s. mixed media. 14-Apr-3 Horta, Bruxelles #504
£331 $540 €500 Vue de la Panne (42x57cm-17x22in) pastel. 17-Feb-3 Horta, Bruxelles #423
£342 $534 €500 Ville orientale (43x57cm-17x22in) s. mixed media. 14-Apr-3 Horta, Bruxelles #503

BERCKHEYDE, Gerrit Adriaensz (1638-1698) Dutch
£50955 $79490 €80000 View of Haarlem with St Bavo's Cathedral (66x92cm-26x36in) s. lit. 6-Nov-2 Christie's, Amsterdam #78/R est:25000-35000

BERCKHEYDE, Gerrit Adriaensz (attrib) (1638-1698) Dutch
£8333 $13083 €13000 St Kunibert in Cologne (65x81cm-26x32in) bears sig. prov.lit.exhib. 21-Nov-2 Van Ham, Cologne #1309/R est:16000
£24204 $37758 €38000 Dam, Amsterdam with the Town Hall and the Waag (91x112cm-36x44in) 6-Nov-2 Christie's, Amsterdam #74/R est:25000-35000

BERDANIER, Paul F (1879-1961) American
£574 $900 €861 Clouds (23x30cm-9x12in) s. canvasboard. 22-Nov-2 Skinner, Boston #243/R

BERDIA, Norberto (1900-1983) Uruguayan
£600 $930 €900 Tiger (61x46cm-24x18in) s. board. 25-Sep-2 Hamptons Fine Art, Godalming #415/R

BERDOT, Jean Georges (1614-?) French
£13986 $23357 €20000 Haltes militaires devant de vastes paysages panoramiques (13x17cm-5x7in) copper pair. 25-Jun-3 Tajan, Paris #49/R est:22000-25000

BERDYSZAK, Jan (1934-) American?
£793 $1300 €1150 Concentrative areas active, mystic passive (89x89cm-35x35in) acrylic canvas on wood diptych prov.exhib. 1-Jun-3 Wright, Chicago #340/R est:2500-3500

BERENTZ, Christian (circle) (1658-1722) German
£9500 $14820 €14250 Still life with basket of fruit and peaches on a plate (5x668cm-2x263in) 9-Oct-2 Woolley & Wallis, Salisbury #350/R est:8000-12000

BERENY, Robert (1887-1953) Hungarian
£1677 $2616 €2516 Lying girl (65x80cm-26x31in) s. 11-Sep-2 Kieselbach, Budapest #132/R (H.F 650000)
£6449 $10061 €9674 Girl in white dress in the garden (65x80cm-26x31in) s. 11-Sep-2 Kieselbach, Budapest #65/R (H.F 2500000)
£7739 $12073 €11222 Scratchers (49x69cm-19x27in) s. cardboard. 13-Sep-2 Mu Terem Galeria, Budapest #31/R est:850000 (H.F 3000000)
£14791 $22926 €22187 Ball players (50x61cm-20x24in) s.verso oil on cardboard. 6-Dec-2 Kieselbach, Budapest #195/R (H.F 5500000)
£40339 $62525 €60509 Red dressed woman in a green room (88x67cm-35x26in) s. 6-Dec-2 Kieselbach, Budapest #176/R (H.F 15000000)
£61478 $95906 €92217 Sunlit courtyard of villa (88x66cm-35x26in) s. 11-Apr-3 Kieselbach, Budapest #131/R est:8000000-22000000 (H.F 22000000)

BERESFORD, Cecilia Melanie (fl.1865-1885) British
Works on paper
£1100 $1715 €1650 Frutta de Campagna (49x32cm-19x13in) s.d.1875 pencil W/C htd white. 19-Sep-2 Christie's, Kensington #14/R est:700-1000

BERESFORD, Frank Ernest (1881-1967) British
£450 $707 €675 Dash of colour (23x18cm-9x7in) s.d.29 panel. 19-Nov-2 Bonhams, Leeds #142
£460 $731 €690 Corner house, Kyoto, Japan (36x25cm-14x10in) s.d.09 s.i.verso panel. 29 Apr-3 Bonhams, New Bond Street #32

BERESKINE, Paraskewe von (20th C) German
£1282 $1987 €2000 Peasant women on track (41x51cm-16x20in) mono. prov. 4-Dec-2 Lempertz, Koln #572/R est:2500

BERETTA, Emilio Maria (1907-) Swiss
£371 $586 €557 Tessin river landscape (50x65cm-20x26in) s.d.46. 14-Nov-2 Stuker, Bern #71 (S.FR 850)

BERETTA, Petrus Augustus (1805-1866) Dutch
£1400 $2184 €2100 Skaters on a frozen river in a town (35x49cm-14x19in) s. panel. 9-Oct-2 Woolley & Wallis, Salisbury #268/R est:1000-1500
£2917 $4638 €4200 Winterfun on a frozen canal by the Oosterpoort, Delft (53x49cm-21x19in) s. panel. 29-Apr-3 Christie's, Amsterdam #18/R est:4000-6000

BEREUTER, Joachim (1946-) German
£414 $654 €600 Still life (50x60cm-20x24in) s. panel. 5-Apr-3 Hans Stahl, Hamburg #114

BERG, A (?) ?
£1027 $1603 €1500 Southern mountain landscape with lake (47x66cm-19x26in) s. 9-Apr-3 Neumeister, Munich #645/R est:600

BERG, Adolf Julius (1820-1873) Swedish
£430 $688 €624 Moonlit landscape with sailing boat (25x29cm-10x11in) s. panel. 18-May-3 Anders Antik, Landskrona #83 (S.KR 5500)

BERG, Adrian (1929-) British
£300 $489 €435 View over Hyde Park (23x77cm-9x30in) s.d.13.11.70 s.d.verso. 15-Jul-3 Bonhams, Knightsbridge #174
£700 $1092 €1050 Regent's Park, autumn (94x94cm-37x37in) s.i.d.86 verso prov. 27-Mar-3 Christie's, Kensington #620/R

BERG, Albert (1825-1884) German
Works on paper
£563 $935 €800 West side of the Acropolis (28x52cm-11x20in) i.d.74 mono.i. verso pencil W/C htd bodycol. 12-Jun-3 Hauswedell & Nolte, Hamburg #332/R

BERG, Anna Carolina van den (1873-1942) Dutch
£414 $658 €600 Flower still life with roses (35x26cm-14x10in) s. canvas on panel. 10-Mar-3 Sotheby's, Amsterdam #301

BERG, Bente (1931-) ?
£406 $650 €609 Farm and landscape (18x20cm-7x8in) board. 10-Jan-3 Du Mouchelle, Detroit #2105/R

BERG, Christian (1893-1976) Swedish
Sculpture
£2803 $4373 €4205 Marine shape (29cm-11in) init. polished bronze incl.stone socle st.f.Pettersson lit. 6-Nov-2 AB Stockholms Auktionsverk #615/R est:20000-25000 (S.KR 40000)
£4905 $7652 €7358 Torso-45 III (30cm-12in) init.num.3 polished bronze sold with granite socle lit. 5-Nov-2 Bukowskis, Stockholm #150/R est:65000-75000 (S.KR 70000)
£9110 $14212 €13665 Park sculpture (41cm-16in) init.num.2 polished bronze on marble socle prov.lit. 5-Nov-2 Bukowskis, Stockholm #154/R est:150000-200000 (S.KR 130000)
£11563 $18038 €17345 Church sculpture I (45cm-18in) init.d.29 num.1 silvered bronze sold with socle lit. 5-Nov-2 Bukowskis, Stockholm #74/R est:175000-200000 (S.KR 165000)

BERG, Else (1877-1942) Dutch
£2244 $3478 €3500 Portrait of a farmer (68x58cm-27x23in) s. painted c.1929. 3-Dec-2 Christie's, Amsterdam #13/R est:2500-3500

BERG, Freek van den (1918-2000) Dutch
£1218 $1912 €1900 Ruijter quay (80x95cm-31x37in) s. 25-Nov-2 Glerum, Amsterdam #100 est:1000-1500

£2128 $3447 €3000 Reclining nude woman (40x50cm-16x20in) s. 26-May-3 Glerum, Amsterdam #59/R est:3000-4000

BERG, George Louis (1870-1941) American
£1006 $1600 €1509 Autumn view of a mountain through birches (69x91cm-27x36in) s. 1-Mar-3 North East Auctions, Portsmouth #696/R est:1200-2200

BERG, Gunnar (1864-1894) Norwegian
£1134 $1781 €1701 Boats in harbour (32x41cm-13x16in) 25-Nov-2 Blomqvist, Lysaker #1018/R est:15000-18000 (N.KR 13000)
£3742 $5988 €5613 Beach boats, Nordland (32x45cm-13x18in) s.d.1881 canvas on panel. 17-Mar-3 Blomqvist, Oslo #325/R est:30000-35000 (N.KR 43000)
£6092 $9748 €9138 From Solvaer Harbour (23x32cm-9x13in) s.d.88 paper on panel. 17-Mar-3 Blomqvist, Oslo #302/R est:25000-30000 (N.KR 70000)

BERG, Gunnar (attrib) (1864-1894) Norwegian
£2479 $4066 €3595 Fishing village up north (30x50cm-12x20in) panel. 2-Jun-3 Blomqvist, Oslo #36/R est:20000-25000 (N.KR 27000)

BERG, Hans J F (1813-1874) Norwegian
Works on paper
£262 $411 €393 Fishing boats by shore (23x33cm-9x13in) W/C. 25-Nov-2 Blomqvist, Lysaker #1019/R (N.KR 3000)
£271 $439 €407 Farm by river, Lie Namsund (35x48cm-14x19in) s. W/C. 27-Jan-3 Blomqvist, Lysaker #1022/R (N.KR 3000)

BERG, Hendrik Andries van den (1821-1880) Dutch
£584 $853 €900 Herder with cows in summer landscape (17x21cm-7x8in) s. panel exhib.lit. 14-Jun-2 Auktionhaus Georg Rehm, Augsburg #8007/R

BERG, Jacobus Everardus van den (1802-1861) Dutch
£949 $1500 €1424 Untitled (30x43cm-12x17in) s. panel. 1-Dec-2 Susanin's, Chicago #5063/R

BERG, Jos van den (1905-1978) Dutch
£382 $596 €600 Roses in a vase (38x48cm-15x19in) s. 6-Nov-2 Vendue Huis, Gravenhage #189/R

BERG, Louis de (19th C) ?
£2051 $3200 €3077 Coastal town scene with fishermen. Boats off a jetty (41x65cm-16x26in) s. pair. 14-Sep-2 Weschler, Washington #574/R est:1200-1800

BERG, S van den (19/20th C) Dutch
£1892 $2952 €2838 Southern European town scene (32x37cm-13x15in) s. panel sketch verso. 5-Nov-2 Bukowskis, Stockholm #11/R est:15000-20000 (S.KR 27000)

BERG, Siep van den (1913-) Dutch
£1899 $3000 €3000 Bollenvelden te Haarlem (39x31cm-15x12in) mono.d.1.5.49 board. 26-Nov-2 Sotheby's, Amsterdam #15/R est:2000-3000

BERG, Simon van den (1812-1891) Dutch
£828 $1275 €1300 Cattle in a meadow (26x34cm-10x13in) s. panel. 3-Sep-2 Christie's, Amsterdam #100/R est:700-900

BERG, Svante (1885-1946) Swedish
£296 $465 €429 Nude study. prov. 15-Dec-2 Anders Antik, Landskrona #16 (S.KR 4200)
£469 $751 €680 Still life of flowers (81x65cm-32x26in) s.d.41. 18-May-3 Anders Antik, Landskrona #90 (S.KR 6000)
£771 $1219 €1157 Still life of fruit (54x65cm-21x26in) s.d.41 prov. 27-Nov-2 Falkkloos, Malmo #77657/R (S.KR 11000)
£911 $1421 €1367 Landscape, San Gimignano (36x32cm-14x13in) s. d.1926 verso cardboard prov. 5-Nov-2 Bukowskis, Stockholm #5/R est:8000-10000 (S.KR 13000)
£1699 $2735 €2549 Still life of gladiolus, lupines and iris (100x71cm-39x28in) s. panel. 7-May-3 AB Stockholms Auktionsverk #731/R est:20000-25000 (S.KR 22000)
£2665 $4210 €3998 Women sunbathing (100x130cm-39x51in) s. prov.lit. 27-Nov-2 Falkkloos, Malmo #77651/R est:30000 (S.KR 38000)

BERG, Werner (1904-1981) Austrian
£5797 $9507 €8000 Councillor Viktor Matejka (56x36cm-22x14in) s. i.d.55 verso prov. 27-May-3 Wiener Kunst Auktionen, Vienna #88/R est:10000-20000

BERG, Willem van den (1886-1970) Dutch
£318 $490 €500 Elderly an older woman (16x10cm-6x4in) s. panel. 3-Sep-2 Christie's, Amsterdam #279
£609 $950 €914 Limburg (36x28cm-14x11in) s. board. 30-Mar-3 Susanin's, Chicago #6086/R
£987 $1599 €1500 Shells (40x50cm-16x20in) s.d.1964 s.i.verso board. 21-Jan-3 Christie's, Amsterdam #360/R est:1500-2000
£1795 $2800 €2693 Two fishermen (71x71cm-28x28in) s. 30-Mar-3 Susanin's, Chicago #6085/R est:3000-4000
£2105 $3411 €3200 Peasants returning home (46x46cm-18x18in) s.d.1956 board. 21-Jan-3 Christie's, Amsterdam #456/R est:2000-3000
£4610 $7468 €6500 Children in the snow (30x40cm-12x16in) s. board. 26-May-3 Glerum, Amsterdam #57/R est:1400-1800
£10000 $16000 €15000 Fishmongers (85x100cm-33x39in) s.d.1960 prov. 14-May-3 Butterfields, San Francisco #1064/R est:4000-6000
Works on paper
£481 $750 €722 Untitled (23x30cm-9x12in) s.i.d.65 pen ink. 30-Mar-3 Susanin's, Chicago #6088/R

BERGAIGNE, Hans (17th C) Dutch
£12739 $19873 €20000 Extensive river landscape with soldiers resting by a tree (12x17cm-5x7in) s. copper prov. 6-Nov-2 Christie's, Amsterdam #53/R est:15000-20000

BERGALLO, Ricardo (20th C) South American?
£314 $500 €471 Still life (76x88cm-30x35in) s.d.64. 2-Mar-3 Galleria Y Remates, Montevideo #100/R

BERGAMESE SCHOOL (17th C) Italian
£10127 $16000 €16000 Still life with rugs and musical instruments (75x120cm-30x47in) 27-Nov-2 Finarte, Milan #46

BERGAMINI (?) Italian
£9353 $14964 €13000 Les enfants espiegles (49x80cm-19x31in) s.i. 14-May-3 Rabourdin & Choppin de Janvry, Paris #21/R est:13000-15000

BERGAMINI, Francesco (1815-1883) Italian
£2000 $3260 €3000 Opportune moment (51x68cm-20x27in) s.i. 13-Feb-3 Christie's, Kensington #184/R est:1500-2500
£4790 $8000 €6946 Interior classroom scene (51x84cm-20x33in) s. 21-Jun-3 Selkirks, St. Louis #1042/R est:14000-16000
£9375 $15000 €14063 Young schoolmaster (51x82cm-20x32in) s.i. 14-May-3 Butterfields, San Francisco #1049/R est:12000-18000
£11872 $18521 €17808 Hurrah, the teacher is asleep (49x80cm-19x31in) s.i. 28-Mar-3 Koller, Zurich #3116/R est:25000-35000 (S.FR 26000)

BERGE, Edward (1876-1924) American
Sculpture
£2848 $4500 €4272 Boy with geese (25cm-10in) s. brown green pat. bronze. 26-Apr-3 Jeffery Burchard, Florida #50a
£3750 $6000 €5625 Young boy playing pan flute with frogs at his feet (46cm-18in) s.st.f.Roman Bronze Works bronze water fountain. 15-Mar-3 Jeffery Burchard, Florida #94a/R
£6563 $10500 €9845 Poppy (58cm-23in) s.st.f.American Art Foundry green pat bronze. 15-Mar-3 Jeffery Burchard, Florida #94/R

BERGEN, Ary (1886-1950) German
£616 $962 €900 Alsterlauf, Hamburg (75x58cm-30x23in) s.d.33. 10-Apr-3 Schopman, Hamburg #671

BERGEN, Carl von (1853-1933) German
£1973 $3137 €2900 Outdoor meal (80x60cm-31x24in) s. 28-Mar-3 Bolland & Marotz, Bremen #424/R est:2700
£2109 $3353 €3100 Outdoor music in the evening (87x68cm-34x27in) s.i.d.1918. 28-Mar-3 Bolland & Marotz, Bremen #424a est:3500

BERGEN, Claus (1885-1964) German
£705 $1093 €1100 Viking long ship (39x69cm-15x27in) s. board. 6-Dec-2 Michael Zeller, Lindau #717/R
£1259 $2001 €1850 Sailing ship at sea (70x101cm-28x40in) s. 20-Mar-3 Neumeister, Munich #2590/R est:1500
Works on paper
£609 $956 €950 Naval battle (44x58cm-17x23in) s. W/C gouache. 21-Nov-2 Van Ham, Cologne #1473

BERGEN, Dirck van (1645-1690) Dutch
£7000 $10920 €10500 Farmyard scene (37x47cm-15x19in) s. 10-Apr-3 Sotheby's, London #60/R est:7000

BERGEN, Dirck van (attrib) (1645-1690) Dutch
£943 $1453 €1500 Un jeune patre se reposant avec son troupeau (22x28cm-9x11in) panel. 25-Oct-2 Tajan, Paris #74/R est:1500-2000
£992 $1568 €1488 Untitled (21x25cm-8x10in) panel. 7-Apr-3 Shapiro, Sydney #522/R est:2500-3500 (A.D 2600)
£1396 $2262 €2024 Landscape with cattle (75x98cm-30x39in) 26-May-3 Bukowskis, Stockholm #438/R est:25000-30000 (S.KR 18000)
£2402 $3747 €3603 Peasants with cattle by ford (69x83cm-27x33in) 20-Nov-2 Fischer, Luzern #1047/R est:4000-6000 (S.FR 5500)

BERGENSTRAHLE, Marie Louise de Geer (1944-) Swedish
£347 $559 €521 Untitled (99x62cm-39x24in) s.d.1967 verso. 7-May-3 AB Stockholms Auktionsverk #1038/R (S.KR 4500)
£2102 $3280 €3153 Three ladies in Paris (46x55cm-18x22in) s.d.1973 prov. 5-Nov-2 Bukowskis, Stockholm #413/R est:15000-18000 (S.KR 30000)
£8494 $13676 €12741 Babies and Olle Baertling's paintings (56x150cm-22x59in) s.d.1979. 7-May-3 AB Stockholms Auktionsverk #1041/R est:125000-150000 (S.KR 110000)
Sculpture
£2008 $3232 €3012 Untitled (25x25x25cm-10x10x10in) s.d.1967 object. 7-May-3 AB Stockholms Auktionsverk #1040/R est:18000-20000 (S.KR 26000)
Works on paper
£561 $875 €842 Examination by the doctor (35x50cm-14x20in) s.d.1973 gouache. 5-Nov-2 Bukowskis, Stockholm #414/R (S.KR 8000)

BERGER, Einar (1893-1960) Norwegian
£297 $466 €446 Cormorants and midnight sun (52x40cm-20x16in) s. panel. 25-Nov-2 Blomqvist, Lysaker #1020 (N.KR 3400)
£354 $538 €531 Fishing vessel in midnight sun (46x55cm-18x22in) s. panel. 31-Aug-2 Grev Wedels Plass, Oslo #43/R (N.KR 4100)
£398 $649 €597 Shipwreck (46x55cm-18x22in) s. panel. 17-Feb-3 Blomqvist, Lysaker #1015/R (N.KR 4500)
£408 $649 €600 Lofoten coast in winter (93x100cm-37x39in) s.d.41. 28-Mar-3 Bolland & Marotz, Bremen #542/R
£482 $762 €723 Fishing boats in harbour (34x50cm-13x20in) s. 17-Dec-2 Grev Wedels Plass, Oslo #135/R (N.KR 5500)

BERGER, Georges (c.1908-1976) French
£255 $397 €400 Paris, Montmartre (55x46cm-22x18in) s. 10-Nov-2 Eric Pillon, Calais #268/R
Works on paper
£270 $422 €400 Quais et bouquinistes (45x60cm-18x24in) s.d.54 pastel. 28-Mar-3 Neret-Minet, Paris #15/R
£270 $422 €400 Quais en automne (43x35cm-17x14in) s.d.55 pastel. 28-Mar-3 Neret-Minet, Paris #13

BERGER, Hans (1882-1977) Swiss
£1373 $2170 €2060 A l'ombre des chenes (34x45cm-13x18in) s.d.54 s.i. stretcher. 28-Nov-2 Christie's, Zurich #63/R est:3000-5000 (S.FR 3200)
£1803 $2848 €2705 Des toits (59x70cm-23x28in) s. s.i. stretcher. 28-Nov-2 Christie's, Zurich #64/R est:3500-4500 (S.FR 4200)
£3863 $6103 €5795 Ciel de Mars (82x70cm-32x28in) s.d.45 s.i. stretcher prov.exhib. 28-Nov-2 Christie's, Zurich #65/R est:4000-6000 (S.FR 9000)
Works on paper
£231 $373 €347 Rooftop (25x33cm-10x13in) s. W/C. 7-May-3 Dobiaschofsky, Bern #350 (S.FR 500)
£360 $576 €500 Zugspitze and Eibsee (28x37cm-11x15in) s. w/C. 13-May-3 Hartung & Hartung, Munich #2568/R
£3493 $5485 €5240 Self portrait (54x74cm-21x29in) fresco. 25-Nov-2 Sotheby's, Zurich #127/R est:8000-12000 (S.FR 8000)

BERGER, Joseph (1798-1870) French
£1603 $2484 €2500 PO. de medecin (73x60cm-29x24in) 5-Dec-2 Gros & Delettrez, Paris #80

BERGER, R (?) German
£600 $924 €900 Portrait of a lady (132x93cm-52x37in) s.d.1904. 8-Sep-2 Lots Road, London #345

BERGER, Robert le (1905-) French
£633 $987 €1000 Hotel des deux lions (46x39cm-18x15in) s. i. verso canvas on panel. 15-Oct-2 Dorotheum, Vienna #133/R
£660 $1075 €950 La Seine au Vert Galant (50x61cm-20x24in) s. 19-Jul-3 Thierry & Lannon, Brest #359

BERGERET, Denis Pierre (1846-1910) French
£353 $546 €550 Nature morte aux huitres (50x61cm-20x24in) s. 8-Dec-2 Feletin, Province #40/R

BERGERET, Pierre-Nolasque (1782-1863) French
Works on paper
£481 $745 €750 Capriccio (28x21cm-11x8in) s.i. pen ink. 4-Dec-2 Piasa, Paris #139

BERGES, Werner (1941-) German
Works on paper
£580 $951 €800 A little Spanish (56x75cm-22x30in) s.i.d.89 W/C Indian ink. 31-May-3 Villa Grisebach, Berlin #753/R
£652 $1070 €900 Quite obsequious (56x75cm-22x30in) s.i.d.89 W/C. 31-May-3 Villa Grisebach, Berlin #754/R

BERGFELD, O (19/20th C) ?
£1069 $1657 €1700 Winter village (71x120cm-28x47in) s. 29-Oct-2 Dorotheum, Vienna #245/R est:2200-2600

BERGH, Edvard (1828-1880) Swedish
£305 $473 €458 Woodland path in sunshine (29x25cm-11x10in) s. panel. 8-Dec-2 Uppsala Auktionskammare, Uppsala #112 (S.KR 4300)
£311 $488 €467 Waterfall, Nasforssen (46x59cm-18x23in) s.d.60. 16-Dec-2 Lilla Bukowskis, Stockholm #878 (S.KR 4400)
£496 $770 €744 Landscape with rapids (53x77cm-21x30in) s. 8-Dec-2 Uppsala Auktionskammare, Uppsala #51/R (S.KR 7000)
£645 $1019 €968 Green wooded landscape with herder and cattle on road (85x117cm-33x46in) s. 27-Nov-2 Falkkloos, Malmo #77811/R (S.KR 9200)
£1571 $2577 €2278 Lake landscape with fishermen in punt (64x84cm-25x33in) s.d.1864. 4-Jun-3 AB Stockholms Auktionsverk #2345/R est:25000-30000 (S.KR 20000)
£2560 $4147 €3712 Landscape with figures by waterfall (61x48cm-24x19in) init. 26-May-3 Bukowskis, Stockholm #152/R est:25000-30000 (S.KR 33000)
£3546 $5496 €5319 Pastoral landscape with cattle by waterway (85x118cm-33x46in) s.d.1873 prov. 3-Dec-2 Bukowskis, Stockholm #371/R est:40000-50000 (S.KR 50000)

BERGH, H J van den (19/20th C) Dutch
£433 $645 €665 Meadow with cows (50x70cm-20x28in) s. 28-Jun-2 Sigalas, Stuttgart #775

BERGH, Mathys van den (1617-1687) Dutch
Works on paper
£385 $550 €578 Expulsion of Hagar and Ishmael (18x29cm-7x11in) s.d.1666 black chk. 23-Jan-3 Swann Galleries, New York #196/R

BERGH, Rickard (1858-1919) Swedish
£1885 $3092 €2733 Landscape with Klockar farm, Tyreso (87x123cm-34x48in) exhib. 4-Jun-3 AB Stockholms Auktionsverk #2154/R est:10000-12000 (S.KR 24000)

BERGHE, Christoffel van den (1617-1642) German
£179012 $290000 €268518 Tulips, roses and other flowers in a gilt mounted porcelain vase on a ledge (30x21cm-12x8in) copper prov. 23-Jan-3 Sotheby's, New York #39/R est:250000-350000

BERGHE, F van den (20th C) Belgian
Works on paper
£1538 $2385 €2400 Table fleurie devant une fenetre (110x101cm-43x40in) s. pastel cardboard. 9-Dec-2 Horta, Bruxelles #237 est:3000-3700

BERGHE, Frits van den (1883-1939) Belgian
£5396 $8633 €7500 Homme barbu (46x35cm-18x14in) s. 13-May-3 Palais de Beaux Arts, Brussels #162/R est:7500-12500
£15823 $24684 €25000 Adam en Eva (66x44cm-26x17in) s. painted 1930 prov. lit. 21-Oct-2 Bernaerts, Antwerp #670/R est:25000-30000
Works on paper
£31447 $49057 €50000 La naissance (54x45cm-21x18in) W/C exhib. 14-Oct-2 Amberes, Antwerp #213/R
£47170 $73113 €75000 Clowns (59x45cm-23x18in) s. W/C gouache exec.1925 exhib.lit. 5-Oct-2 De Vuyst, Lokeren #466/R

BERGLAND, Don (20th C) Canadian
£382 $599 €573 Northern landscape (40x50cm-16x20in) s.i.d.1986 acrylic. 25-Nov-2 Hodgins, Calgary #370/R (C.D 950)
£522 $820 €783 Hagenborg Farm (50x60cm-20x24in) s.i.d.1981 acrylic prov. 25-Nov-2 Hodgins, Calgary #133/R (C.D 1300)
£667 $1093 €967 Churchyard (50x60cm-20x24in) s.i.d.1984. 9-Jun-3 Hodgins, Calgary #6/R est:1200-1500 (C.D 1500)
£803 $1261 €1205 Atnarko (75x100cm-30x39in) s.i.d.1981 acrylic prov. 25-Nov-2 Hodgins, Calgary #275/R est:1500-1800 (C.D 2000)

£847 $1347 €1271 Chrome Island (55x70cm-22x28in) s. acrylic prov. 23-Mar-3 Hodgins, Calgary #6/R est:1200-1500 (C.D 2000)

BERGLER, Joseph (younger) (1753-1829) Austrian
£270 $427 €405 Head of a philosopher (15x12cm-6x5in) s. panel. 12-Nov-2 Bonhams, Knightsbridge #34/R
Works on paper
£420 $600 €630 Seated philosopher and two youths (20x16cm-8x6in) s. pen ink. 23-Jan-3 Swann Galleries, New York #354/R

BERGMAN (?) ?
Sculpture
£1300 $2080 €1950 Figure (23cm-9in) cold painted bronze white marble base. 15-May-3 Christie's, Kensington #347/R est:1000-1500

BERGMAN, Anna-Eva (1909-1987) Swedish/French
£1042 $1656 €1500 Cap artique (46x64cm-18x25in) s.d.1978 acrylic silver leaf panel. 29-Apr-3 Artcurial Briest, Paris #554/R est:1500-2000
Works on paper
£1044 $1671 €1566 Untitled (34x24cm-13x9in) init.d.1961 i.verso mixed media panel. 17-Mar-3 Blomqvist, Oslo #404/R (N.KR 12000)
£1044 $1671 €1566 Haut (35x25cm-14x10in) init.d.1961 i.verso mixed media panel. 17-Mar-3 Blomqvist, Oslo #405/R (N.KR 12000)
£1393 $2228 €2090 Montagne d'argent (64x49cm-25x19in) init.d.1958 i.verso mixed media paper on canvas. 17-Mar-3 Blomqvist, Oslo #403/R est:20000-25000 (N.KR 16000)

BERGMAN, Franz (19/20th C) Austrian
Sculpture
£1154 $1812 €1800 Nubian warrior on camel (23cm-9in) i. bronze bronze wooden socle. 11-Dec-2 Dorotheum, Vienna #151/R est:1000-1400
£1300 $2119 €1950 Snipe (24cm-9in) st. cold painted bronze. 11-Feb-3 Sotheby's, Olympia #321/R est:800-1200
£1534 $2500 €2301 Nude with detachable robe (28cm-11in) bronze. 14-Feb-3 Du Mouchelle, Detroit #2002/R est:3000-3500
£1900 $3097 €2850 Woodcock (23cm-9in) st. cold painted bronze. 11-Feb-3 Sotheby's, Olympia #320/R est:800-1200
£3000 $4620 €4500 Lute player in a tent (39cm-15in) cold painted bronze exec.c.1900. 28-Oct-2 Sotheby's, Olympia #18/R est:3000-4000
£3000 $4620 €4500 Arab taking tea in a tent (37cm-15in) cold painted bronze. 28-Oct-2 Sotheby's, Olympia #19/R est:3000-4000
£3600 $5724 €5400 Figure of a dancer (42cm-17in) s. cold painted metamorphic. 27-Feb-3 Sotheby's, Olympia #72/R est:3000-3500

BERGMAN, Karl (1891-1965) Swedish
£294 $455 €441 Pine tree in sunshine on rock in the skerries (60x83cm-24x33in) s. 29-Sep-2 Uppsala Auktionskammare, Uppsala #202 (S.KR 4200)

BERGMAN, Oskar (1879-1963) Swedish
£282 $443 €423 Visby town wall (35x53cm-14x21in) s.d.1925. 16-Dec-2 Lilla Bukowskis, Stockholm #877 (S.KR 4000)
£347 $577 €503 Birches in Halsingland (37x51cm-15x20in) s.d.1935 canvas on panel. 16-Jun-3 Lilla Bukowskis, Stockholm #1009 (S.KR 4500)
£446 $678 €669 Seagull skerry (43x68cm-17x27in) s.d.1931. 16-Aug-2 Lilla Bukowskis, Stockholm #539 (S.KR 6500)
£993 $1539 €1490 Twilight, Torup (56x40cm-22x16in) s.i.d.1932 panel. 3-Dec-2 Bukowskis, Stockholm #294/R est:20000-25000 (S.KR 14000)
£1631 $2528 €2447 Winter in the skerries (32x46cm-13x18in) s. panel. 3-Dec-2 Bukowskis, Stockholm #80/R est:15000-20000 (S.KR 23000)
£1911 $3000 €2867 Forest interior (66x51cm-26x20in) s.d.1905. 22-Nov-2 Skinner, Boston #218/R est:3000-5000
£12025 $19480 €17436 Landscape from Balderup, Arild (87x133cm-34x52in) s.d.1920 lit. 26-May-3 Bukowskis, Stockholm #168/R est:175000-200000 (S.KR 155000)

Works on paper
£319 $495 €479 Winter in Falun (25x36cm-10x14in) s.d.1945 W/C. 8-Dec-2 Uppsala Auktionskammare, Uppsala #191/R (S.KR 4500)
£390 $605 €585 Winter hill (17x12cm-7x5in) s. W/C prov. 3-Dec-2 Bukowskis, Stockholm #81/R (S.KR 5500)
£426 $660 €639 Spring in Provence (14x10cm-6x4in) s. W/C prov. 3-Dec-2 Bukowskis, Stockholm #125/R (S.KR 6000)
£426 $660 €639 Spring in the skerries (14x10cm-6x4in) s. W/C prov. 3-Dec-2 Bukowskis, Stockholm #126/R (S.KR 6000)
£444 $719 €666 Oak grove with spring flowers (33x39cm-13x15in) s. W/C. 3-Feb-3 Lilla Bukowskis, Stockholm #700 (S.KR 6200)
£446 $709 €669 Winter landscape (27x36cm-11x14in) s. W/C. 3-Mar-3 Lilla Bukowskis, Stockholm #240 (S.KR 6000)
£446 $709 €669 The red house (34x50cm-13x20in) s.i.d.1926. 3-Mar-3 Lilla Bukowskis, Stockholm #320 (S.KR 6000)
£496 $770 €744 Star lit night (21x29cm-8x11in) s.d.1917 W/C. 3-Dec-2 Bukowskis, Stockholm #122/R (S.KR 7000)
£508 $813 €737 Spring landscape (17x25cm-7x10in) s. i.verso W/C. 18-May-3 Anders Antik, Landskrona #62 (S.KR 6500)
£525 $872 €761 Pine trees by mountain (35x50cm-14x20in) s.d.Maj 1939 W/C. 16-Jun-3 Lilla Bukowskis, Stockholm #1012 (S.KR 6800)
£550 $902 €798 Spring landscape with silver birches by water (5x4cm-2x2in) s. W/C. 4-Jun-3 AB Stockholms Auktionsverk #2170/R (S.KR 7000)
£595 $946 €893 Autumn evening (36x52cm-14x20in) s.d.1928 W/C. 3-Mar-3 Lilla Bukowskis, Stockholm #321 (S.KR 8000)
£603 $934 €905 River running through spring landscape with silver birches (11x8cm-4x3in) s. W/C. 4-Dec-2 AB Stockholms Auktionsverk #1639/R (S.KR 8500)
£628 $1031 €911 Spring landscape from Herrokna, Stjernhov (25x36cm-10x14in) s.d.April 1943 W/C. 4-Jun-3 AB Stockholms Auktionsverk #2268/R (S.KR 8000)
£638 $989 €957 Early spring (42x59cm-17x23in) s.d.1931 W/C. 3-Dec-2 Bukowskis, Stockholm #17/R (S.KR 9000)
£638 $989 €957 Sunset on the beach (22x28cm-9x11in) s.d.1953 W/C. 4-Dec-2 AB Stockholms Auktionsverk #1641/R (S.KR 9000)
£674 $1044 €1011 Spring landscape with silver birches (13x9cm-5x4in) s. W/C. 4-Dec-2 AB Stockholms Auktionsverk #1638/R (S.KR 9500)
£707 $1159 €1025 Part of the town wall, Visby (27x37cm-11x15in) s.d.1952 W/C. 4-Jun-3 AB Stockholms Auktionsverk #2269/R (S.KR 9000)
£851 $1319 €1277 Twilight over Stockholm (14x10cm-6x4in) s. W/C prov. 3-Dec-2 Bukowskis, Stockholm #12/R (S.KR 12000)
£851 $1319 €1277 Summer landscape (39x55cm-15x22in) s.d.1954 W/C. 4-Dec-2 AB Stockholms Auktionsverk #1636/R (S.KR 12000)
£922 $1429 €1383 Archipelago at dusk (35x51cm-14x20in) s.d.1914 W/C. 4-Dec-2 AB Stockholms Auktionsverk #1646/R (S.KR 13000)
£931 $1508 €1350 Clump of silver birches in winter (17x24cm-7x9in) s. gouache. 25-May-3 Uppsala Auktionskammare, Uppsala #205/R (S.KR 12000)
£931 $1508 €1350 December day by Vaksala (25x36cm-10x14in) s.d.1942 gouache. 25-May-3 Uppsala Auktionskammare, Uppsala #206 (S.KR 12000)
£943 $1546 €1367 Summer landscape from Ro, Uppland (25x35cm-10x14in) s.d.Juli 1938 W/C. 4-Jun-3 AB Stockholms Auktionsverk #2274/R (S.KR 12000)
£1021 $1675 €1480 Summer landscape with mill, Karsjo, Halsingland (24x35cm-9x14in) s.i.d.1935 W/C. 4-Jun-3 AB Stockholms Auktionsverk #2265/R (S.KR 13000)
£1042 $1731 €1511 Summer in the skerries (36x54cm-14x21in) s.d.1941 W/C. 16-Jun-3 Lilla Bukowskis, Stockholm #534 (S.KR 13500)
£1064 $1649 €1596 Shopping in the market square, Grasse, France (22x28cm-9x11in) s.i.d.1950 W/C. 4-Dec-2 AB Stockholms Auktionsverk #1637/R est:6000-8000 (S.KR 15000)
£1086 $1760 €1575 Spring landscape with silver birches and wood anemones (32x23cm-13x9in) s/ gouache. 25-May-3 Uppsala Auktionskammare, Uppsala #204/R (S.KR 14000)
£1086 $1760 €1575 Clump of silver birches in spring (35x50cm-14x20in) s.d.1934 gouache. 25-May-3 Uppsala Auktionskammare, Uppsala #208/R (S.KR 14000)
£1099 $1704 €1649 Spring landscape with silver birches, wood anemones and church (17x12cm-7x5in) W/C. 3-Dec-2 Bukowskis, Stockholm #124/R est:12000-15000 (S.KR 15500)
£1164 $1885 €1688 Clump of silver birches (26x19cm-10x7in) s. W/C. 25-May-3 Uppsala Auktionskammare, Uppsala #202/R est:10000-12000 (S.KR 15000)
£1178 $1932 €1708 Coastal landscape with silver birches in spring (18x12cm-7x5in) s. W/C. 4-Jun-3 AB Stockholms Auktionsverk #2169/R est:8000-10000 (S.KR 15000)
£1301 $2069 €1952 The Golden Peace (35x49cm-14x19in) s.d.1944 W/C. 3-Mar-3 Lilla Bukowskis, Stockholm #900 est:12000-15000 (S.KR 17500)
£1396 $2262 €2024 From Ostergotland, Leonardbergs farm (36x50cm-14x20in) s.d.maj 1952 W/C exhib. 26-May-3 Bukowskis, Stockholm #19/R est:20000-22000 (S.KR 18000)
£1414 $2319 €2050 Silver birches in spring (25x20cm-10x8in) s. W/C. 4-Jun-3 AB Stockholms Auktionsverk #2267/R est:15000-18000 (S.KR 18000)
£1552 $2514 €2250 Still life with teddy bear (38x55cm-15x22in) s.d.April 1944 W/C prov. 26-May-3 Bukowskis, Stockholm #123/R est:20000-22000 (S.KR 20000)
£1629 $2639 €2362 Trees in blossom (19x13cm-7x5in) s.d.1942 verso W/C. 26-May-3 Bukowskis, Stockholm #17/R est:8000-10000 (S.KR 21000)
£1773 $2748 €2660 Spring landscape with silver birches (35x25cm-14x10in) s. W/C. 3-Dec-2 Bukowskis, Stockholm #15/R est:20000-25000 (S.KR 25000)
£1844 $2858 €2766 Winter at Saltsjobaden (37x55cm-15x22in) s.d.Mars 1949. 3-Dec-2 Bukowskis, Stockholm #79/R est:20000-25000 (S.KR 26000)

£2017 $3268 €2925 Olive trees against blue sky (26x37cm-10x15in) s.d.1950 W/C. 26-May-3 Bukowskis, Stockholm #16/R est:15000-18000 (S.KR 26000)
£2172 $3519 €3149 Visby town wall (36x54cm-14x21in) s.i.d.1952 W/C. 26-May-3 Bukowskis, Stockholm #18/R est:20000-22000 (S.KR 28000)
£2278 $3736 €3303 Spring landscape with flowers (35x51cm-14x20in) s.i.d.april 1940 W/C. 4-Jun-3 AB Stockholms Auktionsverk #2275/R est:12000-15000 (S.KR 29000)
£2638 $4273 €3825 May evening at Lannersta (38x46cm-15x18in) s.d.1945 W/C. 26-May-3 Bukowskis, Stockholm #15/R est:20000-25000 (S.KR 34000)
£2695 $4177 €4043 Birch grove in autumn (51x37cm-20x15in) s.d.1934 W/C. 3-Dec-2 Bukowskis, Stockholm #127/R est:30000-35000 (S.KR 38000)

BERGMAN, Oskar (attrib) (1879-1963) Swedish
Works on paper
£386 $641 €560 Garden in autumn (30x45cm-12x18in) s.d.1943 W/C. 16-Jun-3 Lilla Bukowskis, Stockholm #1011 (S.KR 5000)

BERGMANN, Julius Hugo (1861-1940) German
£440 $687 €700 Woman with animals by water in evening (75x92cm-30x36in) s. lit. 20-Sep-2 Karlheinz Kaupp, Staufen #1925

BERGMANN, Max (1884-1955) German
£510 $795 €800 Cows in water (40x60cm-16x24in) s. board. 6-Nov-2 Hugo Ruef, Munich #1022/R
£510 $795 €800 Bull's head (60x80cm-24x31in) s. lit. 8-Nov-2 Auktionhaus Georg Rehm, Augsburg #8020/R
£597 $932 €950 Ceasar, the dog (34x50cm-13x20in) s.d.1909. 11-Oct-2 Winterberg, Heidelberg #871/R
£833 $1292 €1300 Peasant ploughing (68x99cm-27x39in) s. prov. 7-Dec-2 Ketterer, Hamburg #155/R
£1086 $1760 €1575 Man with horses (55x74cm-22x29in) s.d.12. 26-May-3 Bukowskis, Stockholm #242/R (S.KR 14000)
£1772 $2765 €2800 Cows in river (70x95cm-28x37in) s. 18-Oct-2 Dr Fritz Nagel, Stuttgart #463/R est:2500
£1887 $2943 €3000 Peasants returning home on ox cart (70x100cm-28x39in) s. 9-Oct-2 Michael Zeller, Lindau #628/R est:3000

BERGMANN, P (19th C) German
£255 $400 €383 Abraham casting out Hagar and Ishmael (61x51cm-24x20in) s. canvas on board. 23-Nov-2 Jackson's, Cedar Falls #223/R

BERGMANS, Jacques (20th C) Belgian?
£256 $397 €400 Town alley with houses in Gent (50x60cm-20x24in) s.d.1946 s.i.d.1946 verso exhib. 7-Dec-2 De Vuyst, Lokeren #23

BERGNER, Audrey (20th C) Israeli
£714 $1114 €1071 Ayers Rock (100x283cm-39x111in) s.d.88 s.i.verso polyptych. 11-Nov-2 Deutscher-Menzies, Melbourne #158/R (A.D 2000)

BERGNER, Yosl (1920-) Israeli
£3165 $5000 €4748 White angel (82x81cm-32x32in) s.d.1961. 27-Apr-3 Sotheby's, Tel Aviv #53/R est:5000-7000

BERGOLLI, Aldo (1916-1972) Italian
£1731 $2717 €2700 Village in calabria (100x70cm-39x28in) s. painted 1957. 19-Nov-2 Finarte, Milan #80/R

BERGSLIEN, Knud Larsen (1827-1908) Norwegian
£28708 $46507 €41627 Hunters on the way down from the mountains (71x60cm-28x24in) s.d.1868. 26-May-3 Rasmussen, Copenhagen #1212/R est:300000 (D.KR 300000)

BERGSLIEN, Knud Larsen (attrib) (1827-1908) Norwegian
£426 $647 €639 In the light of the candle (29x36cm-11x14in) panel. 16-Aug-2 Lilla Bukowskis, Stockholm #492 (S.KR 6200)

BERGSLIEN, Nils (1853-1928) Norwegian
£19081 $29766 €28622 At church - old man and young woman with two children seated (47x38cm-19x15in) s.d.1882 lit. 21-Oct-2 Blomqvist, Oslo #332/R est:170000-200000 (N.KR 220000)
Works on paper
£2002 $3203 €3003 Timbermenn (28x24cm-11x9in) s. W/C gouache lit. 17-Mar-3 Blomqvist, Oslo #401/R est:18000-22000 (N.KR 23000)

BERGSTAD, Terje (1938-) Norwegian
Works on paper
£865 $1367 €1298 Church facade (55x41cm-22x16in) init. mixed media. 2-Dec-2 Blomqvist, Oslo #484/R (N.KR 10000)

BERGSTROM, Alfred (1869-1930) Swedish
£358 $580 €537 View from South Station Road, Stockholm (53x36cm-21x14in) s. panel exhib. 3-Feb-3 Lilla Bukowskis, Stockholm #878 (S.KR 5000)
£659 $1068 €956 Sunset in Corcarneau's Harbour (26x33cm-10x13in) s.d.94 canvas on panel. 26-May-3 Bukowskis, Stockholm #42/R (S.KR 8500)
£1939 $3142 €2812 Terpsichore (101x101cm-40x40in) 26-May-3 Bukowskis, Stockholm #39/R est:40000-50000 (S.KR 25000)
£7092 $10993 €10638 Early day in spring (100x140cm-39x55in) s. exhib. 3-Dec-2 Bukowskis, Stockholm #33/R est:60000-80000 (S.KR 100000)

BERGSTROM, August (1839-1917) Swedish
£1092 $1757 €1550 Summer evening (65x95cm-26x37in) s.d.91. 10-May-3 Bukowskis, Helsinki #365/R est:1200-1500

BERGSTROM, Endis (1866-1950) Swedish
£297 $486 €431 The child. d.1898. 8-Feb-3 Crafoord, Lund #67 (S.KR 4200)

BERILLE, Francis (20th C) French
£276 $439 €400 Les Becasses (41x32cm-16x13in) s.d.1993. 10-Mar-3 Coutau Begarie, Paris #205
Works on paper
£448 $713 €650 Limicoles rares (32x25cm-13x10in) s. W/C. 10-Mar-3 Coutau Begarie, Paris #213/R
£586 $932 €850 Canards plongeurs (29x22cm-11x9in) s.d.1975 W/C gouache. 10-Mar-3 Coutau Begarie, Paris #224/R
£759 $1206 €1100 Sangliers (59x79cm-23x31in) gouache wash. 10-Mar-3 Coutau Begarie, Paris #212

BERJONNEAU, Jehan (1890-1972) French
£405 $632 €600 La marne (33x41cm-13x16in) s.i. 25-Mar-3 Chochon-Barre & Allardi, Paris #63
£3165 $5000 €5000 Marche a Kairouan (81x100cm-32x39in) s. 1-Dec-2 Anaf, Lyon #24/R

BERKA, Johann (attrib) (1758-1815) Czechoslovakian
£443 $700 €665 Three Cavaliers in 17th century costume conversing with a lady (56x74cm-22x29in) s. 18-Nov-2 Schrager Galleries, Milwaukee #1100

BERKE, Ernest (1921-) American
Sculpture
£1582 $2500 €2294 January, the tough month (46cm-18in) bronze prov. 26-Jul-3 Coeur d'Alene, Hayden #235/R est:5000-8000
£2096 $3500 €3039 Crazy Horse (46cm-18in) bronze. 21-Jun-3 Selkirks, St. Louis #203/R est:5000-7000

BERKE, Hubert (1908-1979) German
£580 $951 €800 Untitled (49x62cm-19x24in) s.d.52 tempera. 28-May-3 Lempertz, Koln #31/R
£1154 $1788 €1800 Autumnal (72x49cm-28x19in) s.i.d.1950 masonite. 3-Dec-2 Lempertz, Koln #33/R est:2000
£1923 $2981 €3000 Untitled (150x120cm-59x47in) s.d.1959 s.i.d. verso. 3-Dec-2 Lempertz, Koln #34/R est:4000-5000
Works on paper
£385 $596 €600 Spring (31x24cm-12x9in) s.i.d.1978 W/C Indian ink. 3-Dec-2 Lempertz, Koln #37/R
£475 $736 €750 Sketch for book cover (32x62cm-13x24in) s.i. mixed media wax chk W/C bodycol. 27-Sep-2 Venator & Hansten, Koln #1689
£496 $804 €700 Mutations (62x48cm-24x19in) s.i.d.1970 mixed media. 24-May-3 Van Ham, Cologne #46/R
£580 $951 €800 Boy's death (48x30cm-19x12in) s.i. W/C ochre. 28-May-3 Lempertz, Koln #30/R
£580 $951 €800 Skripta 2 (48x62cm-19x24in) s.i.d.57 Indian ink ink chk. 28-May-3 Lempertz, Koln #32/R
£993 $1609 €1400 Sylt (82x48cm-32x19in) s.i.d.60 W/C Indian ink. 24-May-3 Van Ham, Cologne #45/R
£1026 $1590 €1600 Metamorphosis (47x61cm-19x24in) s.d.1947 gouache Indian ink. 3-Dec-2 Lempertz, Koln #35/R

BERKES, Antal (1874-1938) Hungarian
£252 $392 €400 Winter in Budapest (40x50cm-16x20in) s. 21-Sep-2 Bolland & Marotz, Bremen #451/R
£315 $488 €473 Vaci street (28x39cm-11x15in) painted c.1935. 1-Oct-2 SOGA, Bratislava #124/R est:25000 (SL.K 20000)
£323 $511 €485 Summer's day with figures on main road (42x51cm-17x20in) s. 2-Dec-2 Rasmussen, Copenhagen #1537 (D.KR 3800)
£382 $589 €600 Evening activities on a city square (40x50cm-16x20in) s. 3-Sep-2 Christie's, Amsterdam #189

£468 $740 €702 Parisian street scene (36x40cm-14x16in) s. 2-Dec-2 Rasmussen, Copenhagen #1512 (D.KR 5500)
£556 $889 €850 Street scene with many figures (40x50cm-16x20in) s. lit. 10-Jan-3 Allgauer, Kempten #1527/R
£700 $1099 €1050 Carriages and figures on a Parisian street (74x100cm-29x39in) s. 16-Apr-3 Christie's, Kensington #867/R
£1103 $1709 €1655 View at Szechenyi Spa in Budapest (98x111cm-39x44in) painted c.1935. 1-Oct-2 SOGA, Bratislava #123/R est:59000 (SL.K 70000)
£1174 $1831 €1702 Boulevard in the evening (50x70cm-20x28in) s. 12-Apr-3 Mu Terem Galeria, Budapest #215/R est:250000 (H.F 420000)
£1677 $2616 €2516 Paris, 1911 (73x108cm-29x43in) s.d.1911. 11-Sep-2 Kieselbach, Budapest #138/R (H.F 650000)
£1748 $2709 €2535 Busy boulevard (60x79cm-24x31in) s. 9-Dec-2 Mu Terem Galeria, Budapest #202/R est:400000 (H.F 650000)
£1816 $2834 €2633 Pedestrians on a Sunday (75x100cm-30x39in) s. 12-Apr-3 Mu Terem Galeria, Budapest #65/R est:480000 (H.F 650000)
£2580 $4024 €3741 Commotion in a big city (76x101cm-30x40in) s.d.1915. 13-Sep-2 Mu Terem Galeria, Budapest #23/R est:400000 (H.F 1000000)
£3200 $5024 €4800 Paris street at night (80x100cm-31x39in) s.d.1920 board. 16-Apr-3 Christie's, Kensington #859/R est:800-1200
£4303 $6669 €6239 Clothild palaces (60x80cm-24x31in) s. 9-Dec-2 Mu Terem Galeria, Budapest #197/R est:450000 (H.F 1600000)

BERKEY, John (1932-) American
£1118 $1800 €1677 Horsedrawn sports car in futuristic fantastic cityscape (58x36cm-23x14in) s. acrylic. 20-Feb-3 Illustration House, New York #12 est:2000-3000

BERKOWSKI, Clara (1857-?) German
£1024 $1628 €1536 Portrait of small boy (101x60cm-40x24in) s. 5-Mar-3 Rasmussen, Copenhagen #1791/R (D.KR 11000)

BERLAND, Ruben (1955-) Cuban
£12739 $20000 €19109 Cold day by the mountain waterfall (122x122cm-48x48in) s. s.i.verso acrylic painted 2000 prov. 20-Nov-2 Christie's, Rockefeller NY #145/R

BERLANDINA, Jane (1898-?) American
£391 $625 €567 Abstraction (56x86cm-22x34in) s.d. 17-May-3 Selkirks, St. Louis #292

BERLEWI, Henrik (20th C) Polish
£1783 $2782 €2800 Chardons (55x45cm-22x18in) s.d.1948. 6-Nov-2 Claude Boisgirard, Paris #4 est:800-1000
£2635 $4111 €3900 Mandolin (65x92cm-26x36in) s.d.1952 prov.exhib. 26-Mar-3 Millon & Associes, Paris #133/R

BERLIN, Joseph (19th C) Belgian
£1465 $2285 €2300 La coiffure de la future mariee (58x46cm-23x18in) s. panel. 11-Nov-2 Horta, Bruxelles #147 est:2500-3500

BERLIN, Sven Paul (1911-2000) British
£450 $702 €675 Yellow boat at Inch Mary (30x41cm-12x16in) s.d.1965 board. 17-Oct-2 David Lay, Penzance #1394
Works on paper
£350 $571 €525 Plucking a cock (33x20cm-13x8in) s.i.d.1954. 13-Feb-3 David Lay, Penzance #157
£350 $578 €508 Lovers (30x20cm-12x8in) s.d.96 pencil on board. 3-Jul-3 Christie's, Kensington #702
£780 $1303 €1131 King - Saul for black granite the dark monarch (56x39cm-22x15in) s.d.1957 ink dr. 19-Jun-3 Lane, Penzance #181

BERLINGERI, Cesare (1948-) Italian
£523 $837 €800 Untitled (30x35cm-12x14in) s.d.1983. 4-Jan-3 Meeting Art, Vercelli #603
£641 $1006 €1000 Yellow invasion (40x50cm-16x20in) s.i.d.1999 verso acrylic mixed media. 23-Nov-2 Meeting Art, Vercelli #33/R
£654 $1046 €1000 Untitled (40x30cm-16x12in) s.d.1983. 4-Jan-3 Meeting Art, Vercelli #609
£1392 $2172 €2200 Yellow room (60x50cm-24x20in) s.i.d.1999 verso acrylic mixed media. 14-Sep-2 Meeting Art, Vercelli #799/R
£1536 $2458 €2350 Holy (33x50cm-13x20in) s.i.d.1990 verso. 4-Jan-3 Meeting Art, Vercelli #377
£1709 $2700 €2700 Folding (70x66cm-28x26in) s.i.d.1992 verso oil pigment. 29-Nov-2 Farsetti, Prato #218/R
£1765 $2824 €2700 Folding (41x39cm-16x15in) s.i.verso. 4-Jan-3 Meeting Art, Vercelli #593
£1891 $2969 €2950 Folding (28x60cm-11x24in) s.i.d.1991 verso. 23-Nov-2 Meeting Art, Vercelli #84/R
£2500 $3925 €3900 Untitled (30x47cm-12x19in) s.i.d.1991 verso. 23-Nov-2 Meeting Art, Vercelli #331/R
Works on paper
£1597 $2540 €2300 Overseas (60x54cm-24x21in) s.i.d.1999 mixed media on canvas. 1-May-3 Meeting Art, Vercelli #192

BERLOT, Jean Baptiste (1775-?) French
£3704 $6000 €5556 Classical garden landscape with figures (33x42cm-13x17in) s.i.d.1810. 23-Jan-3 Sotheby's, New York #221/R est:8000

BERMAN, Eugene (1899-1972) American/Russian
£864 $1400 €1253 Set designs for Amahl and the night visitors. Bluebeard's castle (38x28cm-15x11in) s.i.d.1952 s.i.verso blk red ink wash board two on one prov. 21-May-3 Doyle, New York #22/R est:1200-1600
£3395 $5500 €4923 Pisan Canto (89x114cm-35x45in) mono.d.1971 mono.i.d.71 verso. 21-May-3 Doyle, New York #31/R est:7000-9000
£3871 $6000 €5807 Zebeulon (101x81cm-40x32in) init.d. s.i.d.1949. 26-Sep-2 Christie's, Rockefeller NY #547/R est:8000-12000
£9259 $15000 €13426 Pyramids (127x91cm-50x36in) mono.d.1949 mono.i.d.1949 verso prov.exhib. 21-May-3 Doyle, New York #25/R est:8000-12000
Works on paper
£671 $1100 €973 Theatrical study (29x22cm-11x9in) s.d. pen ink wash W/C. 5-Jun-3 Swann Galleries, New York #24/R
£793 $1300 €1150 Rigoletto act II (25x26cm-10x10in) s.i.d. W/C pen ink. 5-Jun-3 Swann Galleries, New York #23/R
£854 $1400 €1238 Don Juan. Make-up for Don Basilio, Barber of Seville (35x27cm-14x11in) init.i. one d.1952 one d.1954 gouache ink drs pair. 5-Jun-3 Swann Galleries, New York #26/R

BERMAN, Leonid (1898-1976) Russian
£645 $1000 €968 Du vent sur la plage (61x91cm-24x36in) s.d.48 s.i.d.verso. 25-Sep-2 Doyle, New York #9/R
£1887 $3000 €2831 Comacchio (86x127cm-34x50in) init.d.54 init.i.d.54 verso prov.exhib. 5-Mar-3 Doyle, New York #5/R est:2500-3500

BERMAN, Wallace (1926-1976) American
Works on paper
£3797 $6000 €5696 Untitled (61x66cm-24x26in) s. collage on board positive image verifax prov. 13-Nov-2 Sotheby's, New York #290/R est:5000-7000

BERMOND, Romain (20th C) French
Works on paper
£576 $921 €800 Tout le monde est content (40x40cm-16x16in) s. mixed media wood. 18-May-3 Neret-Minet, Paris #68/R
£590 $944 €820 La grande queue leu-leu (49x55cm-19x22in) s. mixed media wood. 18-May-3 Neret-Minet, Paris #167/R
£2302 $3683 €3200 Poder (145x114cm-57x45in) s. mixed media canvas. 18-May-3 Neret-Minet, Paris #109/R est:2750-3120

BERMUDEZ, Cundo (1914-) Cuban
Works on paper
£15854 $26000 €23781 Mujer peinando a su amante (25x19cm-10x7in) gouache ink painted c.1945 prov. 28-May-3 Christie's, Rockefeller NY #26/R est:12000-16000

BERMUDO MATEOS, Jose (19th C) Spanish
£779 $1138 €1200 Washerwomen (34x27cm-13x11in) s. cardboard. 17-Jun-2 Ansorena, Madrid #148/R

BERMYN, Philippe (1905-1972) French
Works on paper
£503 $810 €750 Projet de fontaine (54x96cm-21x38in) s. W/C. 23-Feb-3 Mercier & Cie, Lille #33a

BERNAERTS, Nicasius (1620-1678) Flemish
£2703 $4216 €4000 Nature morte aux gibiers et poissons (77x95cm-30x37in) 28-Mar-3 Piasa, Paris #43/R

BERNALDO, Allan T (1900-1988) Australian
Works on paper
£351 $533 €527 Red roses in a blue vase (45x37cm-18x15in) s. W/C. 19-Aug-2 Joel, Victoria #174 est:800-1200 (A.D 1000)
£378 $620 €567 Still life of roses (61x51cm-24x20in) s. W/C card. 4-Jun-3 Deutscher-Menzies, Melbourne #328/R (A.D 950)
£491 $747 €737 Stage coach, early days (51x72cm-20x28in) s.d.83 W/C. 19-Aug-2 Joel, Victoria #253 est:1500-2500 (A.D 1400)
£571 $903 €857 Rest for man and beast (36x52cm-14x20in) s. W/C. 18-Nov-2 Joel, Victoria #359 est:1500-2500 (A.D 1600)
£596 $907 €894 Mixed bunch (59x54cm-23x21in) s. W/C. 19-Aug-2 Joel, Victoria #233 est:1600-2000 (A.D 1700)
£1149 $1713 €1724 Autumn roses (39x49cm-15x19in) s. W/C lit. 27-Aug-2 Christie's, Melbourne #203/R est:3000-5000 (A.D 3000)

£1609 $2398 €2414 Timber dray (54x86cm-21x34in) s. W/C. 27-Aug-2 Christie's, Melbourne #219/R est:3000-5000 (A.D 4200)
£2682 $4211 €4023 Aboriginal stockman (40x48cm-16x19in) s. W/C executed c.1968. 15-Apr-3 Lawson Menzies, Sydney #34/R est:7800-9800 (A.D 7000)

BERNARD, Bruce (1928-2000) British
Photographs
£15500 $23870 €23250 Lucian Freud posing as Henry Moore. Lucian Freud standing with portrait of Leigh Bowery (39x50cm-15x20in) s.i.d.1996 bromide prints col coupler prints set of four. 23-Oct-2 Christie's, London #104/R est:5000-7000

BERNARD, Charles Pierre (19/20th C) French
£1656 $2600 €2484 Three mischievous kittens (54x64cm-21x25in) s. canvasboard prov. 14-Dec-2 Weschler, Washington #606/R est:1000-1500

BERNARD, Émile (1868-1941) French
£1103 $1766 €1600 Portrait de femme (76x64cm-30x25in) s. 12-Mar-3 Libert, Castor, Paris #50 est:2000-2500
£1418 $2199 €2127 Walking to the church in Tonnerre (83x61cm-33x24in) s. cardboard. 3-Dec-2 Bukowskis, Stockholm #329/R est:25000-30000 (S.KR 20000)
£1707 $2765 €2475 Maison aux Gallinaces (106x75cm-42x30in) s. panel painted c.1915-1919. 26-May-3 Bukowskis, Stockholm #246/R est:20000-25000 (S.KR 22000)
£1757 $2741 €2600 Portrait d'Armene Ohanian (50x54cm-20x21in) s.d.1914. 28-Mar-3 Delvaux, Paris #28
£1899 $3000 €3000 Elegante a la fourrure (106x71cm-42x28in) s.d.1907. 2-Dec-2 Tajan, Paris #30
£2014 $3283 €2900 Promenade dans le parc (92x73cm-36x29in) s. 19-Jul-3 Thierry & Lannon, Brest #305a est:4000-6000
£2922 $4266 €4500 Jeune femme de profil. 11-Jun-2 Thierry & Lannon, Brest #108b
£4167 $6875 €6000 Arbres et taillis dans la cour de la pension Gloannec (46x33cm-18x13in) i. 1-Jul-3 Rossini, Paris #67/R
£6069 $9710 €8800 Les trois Graces (106x79cm-42x31in) s.d.1912. 12-Mar-3 Libert, Castor, Paris #47/R est:4000-5000
£6294 $10510 €9000 Le petit dejeuner (57x70cm-22x28in) s. panel. 27-Jun-3 Claude Aguttes, Neuilly #82/R est:6000-8000
£7241 $11586 €10500 Nature morte aux oranges sur une table (46x55cm-18x22in) s. 12-Mar-3 Libert, Castor, Paris #49/R est:3000-4000
£12162 $18973 €18000 Deux femmes arabes au bord du Nil (61x50cm-24x20in) s.d.1893 prov.lit. 26-Mar-3 Tajan, Paris #25/R
£12500 $19875 €18000 Le Gripaut a Tonnerre (67x94cm-26x37in) s.d.1918 lit. 29-Apr-3 Campo & Campo, Antwerp #12/R est:14500-16500
£14000 $23380 €20300 Nature morte aux oranges (46x55cm-18x22in) s. 24-Jun-3 Sotheby's, London #204/R est:10000-12000
£38462 $60000 €57693 Trois femmes au bord de fleuve (62x45cm-24x18in) s.d.1895 prov.lit. 6-Nov-2 Sotheby's, New York #149/R est:70000-90000
£230000 $384100 €333500 Scene de cabaret - Julie la Rousse (56x73cm-22x29in) s.d.1887 board prov.lit. 24-Jun-3 Sotheby's, London #120/R est:60000-80000
Prints
£2500 $4125 €3600 Exposition de 16 toiles peintes par Van Gogh (40x29cm-16x11in) col wood engraving. 2-Jul-3 Artcurial Briest, Paris #1/R est:1000-1500
Works on paper
£279 $453 €419 Window in roof (34x26cm-13x10in) s. Indian ink W/C. 3-Feb-3 Lilla Bukowskis, Stockholm #966 (S.KR 3900)
£345 $552 €500 L'arbre (35x30cm-14x12in) s. W/C. 12-Mar-3 Libert, Castor, Paris #48
£377 $589 €600 Deux femmes de dos (20x13cm-8x5in) mono.d.1884 Chinese ink chl htd W/C. 11-Oct-2 Binoche, Paris #116
£432 $614 €700 Forteresse medievale italienne (34x48cm-13x19in) studio st.verso sepia ink wash. 16-Mar-3 Eric Pillon, Calais #83/R
£448 $717 €650 Rue de Pont Aven (27x37cm-11x15in) s. ink wash. 12-Mar-3 Libert, Castor, Paris #46
£489 $817 €700 Portrait de Bretonne. Etudes (20x17cm-8x7in) bears st.sig. pencil dr double-sided. 26-Jun-3 Tajan, Paris #39/R
£500 $795 €750 Deux nus (36x28cm-14x11in) s. brush ink wash over pencil. 20-Mar-3 Sotheby's, Olympia #182/R
£690 $1103 €1000 Rome (41x30cm-16x12in) s.i. wash. 12-Mar-3 Libert, Castor, Paris #51
£737 $1157 €1150 Nu accroupi (30x22cm-12x9in) sanguine. 15-Dec-2 Thierry & Lannon, Brest #292
£8592 $14262 €12200 Couple de paysans. Etude de paysans (31x20cm-12x8in) init. W/C double-sided. 11-Jun-3 Beaussant & Lefèvre, Paris #4/R est:500-600

BERNARD, François (1814-?) French
£4355 $6750 €6533 Portrait of Mathilde Ramos (104x79cm-41x31in) s.d.1860 prov. 7-Dec-2 Neal Auction Company, New Orleans #448/R est:7000-9000

BERNARD, Jan (1765-1833) Dutch
£692 $1079 €1100 Herders with animals at ford (15x12cm-6x5in) panel. 19-Sep-2 Dr Fritz Nagel, Stuttgart #862/R

BERNARD, Jean Baptiste (18th C) ?
£4500 $7065 €6750 Gentleman courting a lady in an idyllic river landscape. Wise man addressing a shepherdess (28x26cm-11x10in) oval pair. 10-Dec-2 Bonhams, New Bond Street #290/R est:5000-7000

BERNARD, Jean Francois Armand Felix (1829-1894) French
£807 $1259 €1211 Hilly landscape (117x95cm-46x37in) s. 5-Aug-2 Rasmussen, Vejle #133/R (D.KR 9500)

BERNARD, Joseph (1864-1933) French
£4267 $6912 €6187 Admiring the ring (52x26cm-20x10in) s. panel. 26-May-3 Bukowskis, Stockholm #248/R est:20000-25000 (S.KR 55000)
Sculpture
£7692 $11923 €12000 Three Graces (35cm-14in) s. brown pat.bronze Cast.A.A.Hebrard. 5-Dec-2 Dr Fritz Nagel, Stuttgart #786/R est:2000

BERNARD, Jules (19th C) French
£1731 $2683 €2700 In summer (53x26cm-21x10in) s. panel lit. 7-Dec-2 Kastern, Hannover #23/R est:1300
Works on paper
£446 $696 €700 Nu allonge (15x20cm-6x8in) s. W/C. 10-Nov-2 Eric Pillon, Calais #15/R

BERNARD, Louis Michel (1885-1962) French
£1439 $2360 €2000 La priere dans le desert (45x58cm-18x23in) s. panel. 4-Jun-3 Tajan, Paris #241/R est:2000-3000

BERNARD, M (19th C) German
£938 $1500 €1407 Alpine Genre scene (79x64cm-31x25in) 16-May-3 Du Mouchelle, Detroit #1007/R

BERNARD, Margaret (fl.1883-1924) British
Works on paper
£540 $859 €810 Going to school (31x50cm-12x20in) s.d.99 W/C. 4-Mar-3 Bearnes, Exeter #333/R

BERNARD, Pierre (1704-1777) French
Works on paper
£1456 $2300 €2300 Portrait de femme en cape bleue (64x53cm-25x21in) pastel lit. 2-Dec-2 Rieunier, Paris #46/R

BERNARD, Renee (20th C) French
Works on paper
£769 $1207 €1200 Maternite marocaine (48x36cm-19x14in) s.i. gouache. 10-Dec-2 Tajan, Paris #114/R

BERNARD, Samuel (1615-1687) French
Miniatures
£2222 $3511 €3200 Portrait de Louis XIV en armure (4x3cm-2x1in) oval prov.exhib. 25-Apr-3 Beaussant & Lefèvre, Paris #1/R est:4500

BERNARD, Victor (1817-?) French
Sculpture
£1392 $2172 €2200 Buste de Carpeaux (47cm-19in) s.i.d.1875 green pat bronze Cast Barbedienne. 16-Sep-2 Horta, Bruxelles #56
£9000 $14040 €13500 Bust of Jean Baptiste Carpeaux (47cm-19in) s.i. green pat bronze. 9-Apr-3 Sotheby's, London #101/R est:10000-15000

BERNARDI, Domenico de (1892-1963) Italian
£4808 $7548 €7500 View of Bertinoro (102x120cm-40x47in) s.d.1936 exhib. 16-Dec-2 Pandolfini, Florence #276/R est:1400
Works on paper
£244 $356 €380 Sea at Pegli (13x18cm-5x7in) s.d.1942 W/C. 5-Jun-2 Il Ponte, Milan #4

BERNARDI, Joseph (1826-1907) German
£273 $425 €410 Mountain lakeside village (39x56cm-15x22in) s. 14-Sep-2 Weschler, Washington #582/R
£472 $731 €750 Muhlsturzhorn in the Bavarian mountains (55x45cm-22x18in) s. 29-Oct-2 Dorotheum, Vienna #284/R

BERNARDINO DA ASOLA (attrib) (16th C) Italian
£6731 $10433 €10500 Madonna and Child (120x141cm-47x56in) 4-Dec-2 Christie's, Rome #431/R est:8000-12000

BERNASCONI, Ugo (1874-1960) Argentinian
£1361 $2163 €2000 Vase of flowers (45x53cm-18x21in) init. 18-Mar-3 Finarte, Milan #223/R

BERNATH, Aurel (1895-1982) Hungarian
Works on paper
£645 $1000 €935 Fishermen (32x43cm-13x17in) s.d.1932 mixed media. 9-Dec-2 Mu Terem Galeria, Budapest #17/R est:220000 (H.F 240000)
£671 $1046 €1007 Bathing couple, 1936 (30x38cm-12x15in) s.d.1936 W/C. 11-Sep-2 Kieselbach, Budapest #207/R (H.F 260000)
£3218 $5149 €4827 Peasants (27x37cm-11x15in) s. Indian ink gouache gold paint. 16-May-3 Kieselbach, Budapest #32/R (H.F 1100000)
£6436 $10298 €9654 Table still life with bunch of flowers (57x74cm-22x29in) s. pastel. 16-May-3 Kieselbach, Budapest #54/R (H.F 2200000)
£13457 $21531 €20186 Marili before blue background, birthday (73x60cm-29x24in) s. pastel. 16-May-3 Kieselbach, Budapest #26/R (H.F 4600000)

BERNATZIK, Wilhelm (1853-1906) Austrian
£641 $1006 €1000 Salzkammergut lake (57x80cm-22x31in) s. 10-Dec-2 Dorotheum, Vienna #248/R
£7971 $13072 €11000 Country house (38x55cm-15x22in) s. 27-May-3 Hassfurther, Vienna #20/R est:8000-10000

BERNDTSON, Gunnar Fredrik (1854-1895) Finnish
£57595 $91000 €91000 Meeting by the shore - man by tree, woman in canoe (24x19cm-9x7in) s. panel lit. 30-Nov-2 Hagelstam, Helsinki #117/R est:90000
£69620 $110000 €110000 On the look-out (26x13cm-10x5in) s. panel exhib.lit. 1-Dec-2 Bukowskis, Helsinki #25/R est:30000-35000

BERNE-BELLECOUR, Étienne Prosper (1838-1910) French
£755 $1200 €1133 French sailor (36x25cm-14x10in) s. panel painted c.1880. 4-May-3 Treadway Gallery, Cincinnati #169/R
£9500 $14725 €14250 Soldiers resting (100x66cm-39x26in) s.d.1883. 4-Dec-2 Christie's, London #80/R est:12000-18000

BERNE-BELLECOUR, Jean Jacques (1874-?) French
£932 $1500 €1398 French sailor on the shore eating rations (36x25cm-14x10in) s. wood panel. 19-Jan-3 Jeffery Burchard, Florida #93a/R

BERNER, Bernd (1930-) German
£1594 $2614 €2200 Flat space 438 (80x75cm-31x30in) s.i.d.1976 verso prov.exhib. 28-May-3 Lempertz, Koln #33/R est:3000
£2308 $3577 €3600 Surface picture (140x125cm-55x49in) s. s.i.d.XII.63 verso. 6-Dec-2 Hauswedell & Nolte, Hamburg #41/R est:3500

BERNERS, Lord Gerald (1883-1950) British
£300 $474 €450 Florentine loggia (25x40cm-10x16in) s. board. 7-Apr-3 Bonhams, Bath #64

BERNHARD, Franz (1934-) German
Sculpture
£1667 $2583 €2600 Untitled (18x50x23cm-7x20x9in) s.i. num.2/5 brown green pat.bronze. 3-Dec-2 Lempertz, Koln #38/R est:2000

BERNHARD, Fritz (1895-1966) Swiss
£322 $509 €483 Tower in Mendrision (58x42cm-23x17in) s.i.d.21 verso. 29-Nov-2 Zofingen, Switzerland #2798 (S.FR 750)

BERNHARD, Ruth (1905-) American
Photographs
£1923 $3000 €2885 Classic torso (23x18cm-9x7in) s.num.26/75 gelatin silver print sold with a book. 10-Nov-2 Selkirks, St. Louis #643/R est:2500-3500
£1948 $3000 €2922 Two forms (34x27cm-13x11in) s.i.d.1963 photograph. 24-Oct-2 Sotheby's, New York #4/R est:3000-5000
£2273 $3500 €3410 Draped torso (34x22cm-13x9in) s.i.d.1962 photograph. 24-Oct-2 Sotheby's, New York #1/R est:3000-5000
£2273 $3500 €3410 Classic torso with hands (35x27cm-14x11in) s.i.d.1952 photograph. 24-Oct-2 Sotheby's, New York #3/R est:4000-6000
£6962 $11000 €10443 In the box - horizontal (20x35cm-8x14in) s.i.d.1962 photograph. 23-Apr-3 Sotheby's, New York #1/R est:8000-12000
£9202 $15000 €13803 In the box - horizontal (26x47cm-10x19in) s. s.d.1987 verso gelatin silver print. 12-Feb-3 Christie's, Rockefeller NY #46/R est:8000-12000

BERNHARDT, Sarah (1844-1923) French
£283 $450 €425 Lion and lioness (51x76cm-20x30in) s. 7-Mar-3 Jackson's, Cedar Falls #853/R

BERNI, Antonio (1905-1981) Argentinian
£2632 $4263 €4000 Portrait of woman (51x38cm-20x15in) s. cardboard. 21-Jan-3 Ansorena, Madrid #149/R
£11329 $17900 €16994 Boy (82x62cm-32x24in) s. 15-Nov-2 Naón & Cia, Buenos Aires #25/R
£63694 $100000 €95541 Bald toreador (100x79cm-39x31in) s.d.28 board on panel prov.exhib.lit. 20-Nov-2 Christie's, Rockefeller NY #10/R est:100000-200000

BERNIER, Camille (1823-1903) French
£1469 $2452 €2100 Chemin dans un sous-bois (40x30cm-16x12in) s.d.1858. 25-Jun-3 Artcurial Briest, Paris #533/R est:800-1200
£4207 $6689 €6100 Landes pres de Bannalec (95x149cm-37x59in) s.d.61 prov. 4-Mar-3 Livinec, Gaudcheau & Jezequel, Rennes #74/R

BERNIER, Georges (1862-1918) Belgian
£2516 $3874 €4000 Troupeau de vaches en bord de riviere (98x176cm-39x69in) s. 22-Oct-2 Galerie Moderne, Brussels #133/R

BERNIER, Pascal (1960-) ?
Sculpture
£3000 $4620 €4500 Accident de chasse (84x40x62cm-33x16x24in) taxidermied monkey bandages executed 1994-98 prov. 22-Oct-2 Sotheby's, London #478/R est:3000-4000

BERNIK, Janez (1933-) Yugoslavian
£611 $960 €917 Untitled (43x52cm-17x20in) s. s.d.1976 stretcher acrylic lit. 23-Nov-2 Burkhard, Luzern #174/R (S.FR 1400)

BERNINGER, John E (20th C) American
£513 $800 €770 Autumn landscape (30x36cm-12x14in) s. board. 18-Sep-2 Alderfer's, Hatfield #376/R
£962 $1500 €1443 Winter landscape with river (41x51cm-16x20in) s. board. 18-Sep-2 Alderfer's, Hatfield #375/R est:1200-1500
£2358 $3750 €3537 River through wooded rocky landscape (41x51cm-16x20in) s.d.1930 board. 18-Mar-3 Arthur James, Florida #278
£3459 $5500 €5189 Two houses near railroad yards in the valley (64x76cm-25x30in) s.d.1930. 18-Mar-3 Arthur James, Florida #102
£5769 $9000 €8654 Winter landscape with river and snow covered farm buildings (64x76cm-25x30in) s. 18-Sep-2 Alderfer's, Hatfield #356/R est:6000-8000

BERNINGHAUS, J Charles (1905-1988) American
£705 $1100 €1058 Lower river (30x41cm-12x16in) 19-Oct-2 David Dike, Dallas #280/R
£1843 $2875 €2765 New Mexico landscape (56x41cm-22x16in) s. canvas on board prov. 9-Nov-2 Santa Fe Art, Santa Fe #235/R est:4000-5000
£4969 $8050 €7205 Houses with trees and flowers (76x61cm-30x24in) 23-May-3 Altermann Galleries, Santa Fe #157

BERNINGHAUS, O E (1874-1952) American
£36859 $57500 €55289 Home from the hunt (51x41cm-20x16in) s. panel prov.lit. 9-Nov-2 Santa Fe Art, Santa Fe #159/R est:75000-100000
Works on paper
£32051 $50000 €48077 Winter in Potosi (41x51cm-16x20in) s.d.1920 gouache on board. 9-Nov-2 Santa Fe Art, Santa Fe #35/R est:70000-90000

BERNINGHAUS, Oscar E (1874-1952) American
£4969 $8050 €7205 Some traveling ranchers (28x36cm-11x14in) 23-May-3 Altermann Galleries, Santa Fe #88
£9554 $15000 €14331 Out west (19x30cm-7x12in) s. board. 19-Nov-2 Butterfields, San Francisco #8088/R est:20000-30000
£32258 $50000 €48387 Travelling through the mountains (41x51cm-16x20in) s. prov. 4-Dec-2 Sotheby's, New York #145/R est:50000-70000
£92466 $135000 €138699 Taos Indians and the Sangre de Cristos (51x41cm-20x16in) board. 18-May-2 Altermann Galleries, Santa Fe #37/R
£103226 $160000 €154839 Overland mail (89x102cm-35x40in) s.d.46 prov. 5-Dec-2 Christie's, Rockefeller NY #177/R est:200000-300000
Works on paper
£1603 $2500 €2405 Indian brave on a horse (25x18cm-10x7in) pen ink. 9-Nov-2 Altermann Galleries, Santa Fe #95
£4140 $6500 €6210 Apache. Apache teepee (18x25cm-7x10in) bears init.i.d.1927 ink W/C pastel pair prov. 19-Nov-2 Butterfields, San Francisco #8094/R est:4000-6000
£15569 $26000 €22575 Indian in war bonnet (53x38cm-21x15in) s.i.verso W/C gouache. 18-Jun-3 Christie's, Los Angeles #87/R est:25000-35000

BERNINI, Giovanni Lorenzo (1598-1680) Italian
Works on paper
£60000 $100200 €87000 Young boy with long hair (22x17cm-9x7in) i. verso black red white chk prov. 8-Jul-3 Christie's, London #38/R est:40000-60000

BERNINI, Giovanni Lorenzo (after) (1598-1680) Italian
Sculpture
£13924 $22000 €20886 Group of Apollo and Daphne (101cm-40in) i. marble. 24-Apr-3 Christie's, Rockefeller NY #293/R est:25000-35000

BERNOUD, Eugene (19/20th C) French
Sculpture
£1800 $2808 €2700 Elephant calling (21x17cm-8x7in) s. brown green pat bronze ivory. 5-Nov-2 Sotheby's, London #127/R est:2000-3000

BERNSTEIN, Schlomo (19/20th C) ?
£345 $552 €500 La Seine a Paris (24x33cm-9x13in) s. cardboard on canvas. 12-Mar-3 Rabourdin & Choppin de Janvry, Paris #181

BERNSTEIN, Theresa F (1890-?) American
£617 $1000 €926 Vase of flowers (107x86cm-42x34in) s. tempera on paper. 24-Jan-3 Freeman, Philadelphia #93/R est:700-1000
£1161 $1800 €1742 Robinson's yard (43x53cm-17x21in) s. 8-Dec-2 Freeman, Philadelphia #131/R est:1200-1800
£1847 $2900 €2771 Gloucester cottage (23x31cm-9x12in) s. board prov. 22-Nov-2 Skinner, Boston #376/R est:2000-3000
£1887 $3000 €2831 Beach scene (29x35cm-11x14in) s. i.verso board. 7-Mar-3 Skinner, Boston #488/R est:2000-2500
£1946 $3250 €2822 Still life with fruit basket (41x56cm-16x22in) s. panel. 22-Jun-3 Freeman, Philadelphia #122/R est:1500-2500
£6169 $9500 €9254 Gloucester Harbour (41x51cm-16x20in) s. prov. 24-Oct-2 Shannon's, Milford #138/R est:9000-12000
Works on paper
£481 $750 €722 Central Park, Strawberry fields (33x41cm-13x16in) s. mixed media. 18-Sep-2 Alderfer's, Hatfield #348/R
£579 $950 €840 Performers backstage (48x31cm-19x12in) s.d. col pastel. 5-Jun-3 Swann Galleries, New York #28/R

BERNTSEN, Frans (1903-) Dutch
£1783 $2782 €2800 View of Schelde canal in Amsterdam. s.d.1929. 6-Nov-2 Vendue Huis, Gravenhage #584/R est:2000-3000

BERNY D'OUVILLE, Claude Charles Antoine (1775-1842) French
Miniatures
£1100 $1716 €1650 Lady wearing black dress with white lace neckline, belt with silver buckle (8cm-3xin) s.d.1825 wood frame gilt mount rec. 5-Nov-2 Bonhams, New Bond Street #135/R est:800-1000

BERONNEAU, Andre (1905-) French
£310 $493 €465 French harbour (26x34cm-10x13in) s. panel. 18-Mar-3 Bonhams, Sevenoaks #214
£399 $650 €599 Canal scene (25x20cm-10x8in) board. 14-Feb-3 Du Mouchelle, Detroit #2018/R
£742 $1173 €1113 Two sailing ships in calm seas (46x65cm-18x26in) s. i.d.1931 stretcher. 14-Nov-2 Stuker, Bern #84 est:800-1000 (S.FR 1700)
£830 $1311 €1245 Saint Tropez harbour (46x65cm-18x26in) s. i.d.1931 stretcher. 14-Nov-2 Stuker, Bern #83 est:800-1000 (S.FR 1900)
£1972 $3175 €2800 Barques au mouillage devant la Ville Close (46x55cm-18x22in) s. 11-May-3 Thierry & Lannon, Brest #331 est:2000-2500

BEROUD, Louis (1852-1910) French
£25316 $40000 €37974 Place de la Republique (76x60cm-30x24in) s.d.1881. 24-Apr-3 Sotheby's, New York #4/R est:50000-70000
£65000 $108550 €97500 Symphonie en rouge et or (114x146cm-45x57in) s.d.1895 prov.exhib. 19-Jun-3 Christie's, London #42/R est:30000-40000

BERQUES, Yosz (?) Israeli
£1321 $2074 €1982 Tea party (13x20cm-5x8in) s. board prov. 10-Dec-2 Pinneys, Montreal #72 est:200-300 (C.D 3250)

BERRAN, Robert (20th C) American
£994 $1600 €1491 Bear cub tries to pilfer fisherman's catch (58x71cm-23x28in) s. 19-Feb-3 Illustration House, New York #234/R est:2000-3000
£1180 $1900 €1770 Fisherman confronts swarm of bees as bears investigate hive (56x71cm-22x28in) s. 19-Feb-3 Illustration House, New York #233/R est:2000-3000
Works on paper
£621 $1000 €932 Policeman father and little leaguer on bicyle (51x46cm-20x18in) s. gouache. 19-Feb-3 Illustration House, New York #209/R est:1500-2000

BERRE, Jean Baptiste (1777-1838) Belgian
£946 $1476 €1400 Cows and sheep grazing (24x35cm-9x14in) s.d.1829 panel. 26-Mar-3 Hugo Ruef, Munich #11/R est:1200

BERRE, Jean Baptiste (attrib) (1777-1838) Belgian
£1129 $1784 €1750 Pastoral scene (31x41cm-12x16in) 20-Dec-2 Tajan, Paris #162 est:3000

BERRES, Joseph von (1821-1912) Austrian
£1301 $2043 €1900 Battle scene near Koniggratz (53x79cm-21x31in) s. 16-Apr-3 Dorotheum, Salzburg #100/R est:3000-4500
£2420 $3752 €3630 Gallopp (51x105cm-20x41in) s. board. 6-Dec-2 Kieselbach, Budapest #170/R (H.F 900000)
£2550 $4106 €3800 Italianate landscapes (27x55cm-11x22in) s. panel pair. 18-Feb-3 Sotheby's, Amsterdam #295/R est:1200-1800

BERRIE, John Archibald Alexander (1887-1962) British
£300 $465 €450 Daffodils in a vase (51x41cm-20x16in) 31-Oct-2 Duke & Son, Dorchester #230

BERRIO, Gaspar Miguel de (attrib) (1700-1786) Bolivian
£3049 $5000 €4574 Virgen Immaculada (159x109cm-63x43in) painted c.1750-1760 prov. 28-May-3 Christie's, Rockefeller NY #61/R est:10000-15000

BERROCAL, Miguel (1933-) Spanish
£319 $533 €450 Composition (30x41cm-12x16in) s.d. paint material. 23-Jun-3 Delvaux, Paris #149
Sculpture
£949 $1500 €1500 Toreador (28x22x20cm-11x9x8in) s. num.303/2000 gilt tin exec.1972. 27-Nov-2 Tajan, Paris #57/R
£1035 $1635 €1500 Maria de la O (17x11x7cm-7x4x3in) s. num.48/200 gold pat bronze. 4-Apr-3 Tajan, Paris #285
£1069 $1657 €1700 Maja - opus 162 (9x21cm-4x8in) s.num.574/1000 pol bronze exec.1977-1978 lit. sold with inst book. 5-Oct-2 De Vuyst, Lokeren #26/R est:1700-2000
£1108 $1728 €1750 Paloma Jet (26cm-10in) s. pat bronze. 16-Sep-2 Horta, Bruxelles #37
£1266 $1975 €2000 Bust of Richelieu (19cm-7in) s. gilt pat bronze. 15-Oct-2 Horta, Bruxelles #169
£1348 $2183 €1900 Hoplite (18x14x14cm-7x6x6in) brass dark pat.bronze. 24-May-3 Van Ham, Cologne #49/R est:3800
£1392 $2200 €2200 Cheval (38x34x18cm-15x13x7in) s. bronze. 26-Nov-2 Palais de Beaux Arts, Brussels #236/R est:2500-3750
£1429 $2271 €2100 Romeo et Juliette. s. exec.c.1966-67 bronze. 18-Mar-3 Vanderkindere, Brussels #160/R est:1600-2400
£1439 $2302 €2000 Cheval cabre (40cm-16in) s.num.533/2.000 natural pat bronze. 19-May-3 Horta, Bruxelles #42 est:1500-2000
£1522 $2496 €2100 Goliath (25cm-10in) s.i. brass. 31-May-3 Quittenbaum, Munich #201/R est:1100
£1538 $2385 €2400 Caballo cassinaide, opus 170 (38x39cm-15x15in) s.num.757/2000 dark brown pat bronze exec.1978-1979 lit. 7-Dec-2 De Vuyst, Lokeren #24/R est:2800-3300
£1586 $2522 €2300 Romeo and Juliette (24x21x9cm-9x8x4in) s. num.2164 tin. 7-Mar-3 Claude Aguttes, Neuilly #13/R
£1899 $3000 €2849 Richelieu. s.num.518/2000 brass puzzle sculpture. 16-Nov-2 Harvey Clar, Oakland #1454
Works on paper
£319 $533 €450 Composition (38x47cm-15x19in) s. W/C ink material. 23-Jun-3 Delvaux, Paris #153
£355 $592 €500 Composition (37x45cm-15x18in) s. W/C ink material. 23-Jun-3 Delvaux, Paris #152

BERROETA, Pierre de (1914-) French
Works on paper
£540 $863 €750 Composition a fond bleu (48x63cm-19x25in) s.d. gouache W/C. 18-May-3 Eric Pillon, Calais #170/R
£576 $921 €800 Composition a fond orange (48x63cm-19x25in) s.d. gouache W/C. 18-May-3 Eric Pillon, Calais #169/R

BERRUECO, Luis (18th C) Mexican
£9756 $16000 €14146 Angel Jehudial (76x37cm-30x15in) s. 27-May-3 Sotheby's, New York #127

BERRUGUETE, Pedro (circle) (c.1450-1504) Spanish
£7500 $11700 €11250 Saint Jerome and Saint George (144x71cm-57x28in) panel. 8-Apr-3 Sotheby's, Olympia #112/R est:4000-6000

BERRY, Arthur (1925-1994) British
Works on paper
£250 $390 €375 Burslem girl (76x53cm-30x21in) s.d.71 pastel. 25-Mar-3 Bonhams, Leeds #557

BERRY, Patrick Vincent (1843-1914) American
£353 $550 €530 Pastoral scene (43x69cm-17x27in) s. 30-Mar-3 Susanin's, Chicago #6029/R

BERRY, Peter Robert (1912-1988) Swiss
£515 $814 €773 Two jockeys on the St Moritz lake (28x22cm-11x9in) s.d.1956 verso. 29-Nov-2 Zofingen, Switzerland #2799 est:2801 (S.FR 1200)

BERRY, Ruth Linnell (1909-) American
£239 $375 €359 Distant mountains (25x35cm-10x14in) canvasboard. 22-Nov-2 Skinner, Boston #285/R
£302 $475 €453 Still life with pink zinnias (43x55cm-17x22in) s. prov. 22-Nov-2 Skinner, Boston #163/R

BERRY, W (19th C) British?
£1700 $2771 €2550 Faggot gatherer in winter (75x134cm-30x53in) s.d.1865. 29-Jan-3 Sotheby's, Olympia #86/R est:1800-2500

BERSERIK, Herman (1921-) Dutch
£2014 $3304 €2800 Trimmers op de Velhorst (31x35cm-12x14in) s.d.1985 acrylic canvas on board. 3-Jun-3 Christie's, Amsterdam #62/R est:1500-2000

BERSIER, Jean Eugene (1895-1978) French
£500 $810 €750 Still life with fish and lemon (33x41cm-13x16in) s. board. 20-May-3 Bonhams, Knightsbridge #111/R

BERT, Émile (1814-1847) Belgian
£845 $1361 €1200 Hilly landscape with soldiers near a pond (76x115cm-30x45in) s. 12-May-3 Bernaerts, Antwerp #26/R

BERTA, Maria Cristina della (1969-) Italian
£993 $1609 €1400 Viaggio no 1 (100x120cm-39x47in) s.i.d.2002 verso. 20-May-3 Porro, Milan #12/R est:2000-2200

BERTALAN, Albert (1899-?) Hungarian
£795 $1295 €1200 Enfants dans le parc (82x65cm-32x26in) s. cardboard. 1-Feb-3 Claude Aguttes, Neuilly #300/R

BERTAUX, Léon (after) (1827-?) French
Sculpture
£2658 $4120 €4200 Untitled (30x23cm-12x9in) bronze relief. 25-Sep-2 Christie's, Amsterdam #573/R est:800-1200

BERTELLI, Luca (16th C) Italian
Prints
£25949 $41000 €41000 Allegory of Death (37x26cm-15x10in) etching after Titian. 29-Nov-2 Bassenge, Berlin #5202/R est:8000

BERTELLI, Renato Guiseppe (1900-1974) Italian
Sculpture
£20833 $34375 €30000 Profilo continuo, testa di Mussolini (32cm-13in) s.d.MCMXXXV num.2/10 green pat bronze prov.exhib. 2-Jul-3 Artcurial Briest, Paris #668/R est:12000-15000

BERTELSEN, Albert (1921-) Danish
£257 $401 €386 Light, Faroe Islands (40x50cm-16x20in) s.d.1985 oil pastel. 11-Nov-2 Rasmussen, Vejle #2374/R (D.KR 3000)
£442 $689 €663 Stampesvej - street scene from Vejle with figures (68x84cm-27x33in) mono.d.52 exhib. 5-Aug-2 Rasmussen, Vejle #309/R (D.KR 5200)
£593 $919 €890 Rust (100x81cm-39x32in) mono. st.sig.d.1985 verso. 1-Oct-2 Rasmussen, Copenhagen #223/R (D.KR 7000)
£1955 $3109 €2933 House in Paris (50x60cm-20x24in) s.d.1977. 10-Mar-3 Rasmussen, Vejle #658/R est:15000-18000 (D.KR 21000)
£2048 $3257 €3072 Light on mountain road (65x80cm-26x31in) s.d.75. 10-Mar-3 Rasmussen, Vejle #659/R est:12000-15000 (D.KR 22000)
£2916 $4549 €4374 Mountain farmer (65x70cm-26x28in) s. s.d.1975 verso. 11-Nov-2 Rasmussen, Vejle #86/R est:10000-15000 (D.KR 34000)
£2974 $4699 €4461 Old things (40x100cm-16x39in) mono. s.d.1973 verso. 1-Apr-3 Rasmussen, Copenhagen #305/R est:10000 (D.KR 32000)
£2980 $4737 €4470 Figures by church (56x64cm-22x25in) s.d.1975 verso. 10-Mar-3 Rasmussen, Vejle #656/R est:20000-25000 (D.KR 32000)
£3002 $4683 €4503 Norwegian coastal cliffs, vessel in foreground (90x110cm-35x43in) s.d.74 s.d.1974 verso. 11-Nov-2 Rasmussen, Vejle #83/R est:20000-30000 (D.KR 35000)
£4749 $7550 €7124 Bonfire evening (50x120cm-20x47in) s.d.1975. 10-Mar-3 Rasmussen, Vejle #657/R est:40000 (D.KR 51000)
£5250 $8137 €7875 Still life of objects (79x126cm-31x50in) s.d.1971 verso. 1-Oct-2 Rasmussen, Copenhagen #145/R est:25000-30000 (D.KR 62000)

BERTELSMANN, Walter (1877-1963) Dutch
£288 $447 €450 Fields and pastures on cloudy day (36x57cm-14x22in) s.d.1906 lit. 6-Dec-2 Karlheinz Kaupp, Staufen #2074/R
£881 $1374 €1400 Flooded countryside, Juli 1925 (50x70cm-20x28in) s. s.i. verso board. 21-Sep-2 Bolland & Marotz, Bremen #338/R
£1392 $2200 €2200 Weser estuary under high summer clouds (50x68cm-20x27in) s.d.24 board. 29-Nov-2 Bolland & Marotz, Bremen #491/R est:830

BERTEMES, Fernand (1964-) Luxembourger
£962 $1510 €1500 Personnages (70x100cm-28x39in) s.d.9-89 paper on canvas. 19-Nov-2 Vanderkindere, Brussels #88 est:400-600

BERTHAULT, Josephine (19/20th C) French
£651 $1015 €950 Travaux de couture dans un interieur. s. 14-Apr-3 Horta, Bruxelles #178

BERTHELEMY, Jean Simon (circle) (1743-1811) French
£4573 $7500 €6860 Jupiter and Antiope (36x38cm-14x15in) 29-May-3 Sotheby's, New York #133/R est:5000-7000

BERTHELSEN, Christian (1839-1909) Danish
£317 $503 €476 Landscape with lake (29x40cm-11x16in) s. 10-Mar-3 Rasmussen, Vejle #296 (D.KR 3400)
£323 $504 €485 Edge of wood with man and wheelbarrow (66x53cm-26x21in) init. 5-Aug-2 Rasmussen, Vejle #188/R (D.KR 3800)
£335 $533 €503 Wooded landscape with thatched house, girl and sheep (26x34cm-10x13in) s.d.1871. 10-Mar-3 Rasmussen, Vejle #211 (D.KR 3600)
£420 $664 €630 Cottage by waterway (46x66cm-18x26in) s. 16-Nov-2 Crafoord, Lund #53/R (S.KR 6000)
£633 $988 €950 Woodland glade with small lake and stags (79x111cm-31x44in) s. 23-Sep-2 Rasmussen, Vejle #95/R (D.KR 7500)
£785 $1271 €1138 Wooded landscape with figures (66x91cm-26x36in) s. 24-May-3 Rasmussen, Havnen #2190/R (D.KR 8200)
£930 $1451 €1395 Coastal landscape from Svendborgsund with schooner and other boats (68x96cm-27x38in) mono. 11-Aug-2 Hindemae, Ullerslev #7403/R (D.KR 11000)

BERTHELSEN, Johann (1883-1969) American
£764 $1200 €1146 St Paul's Chapel (8x6cm-3x2in) s. canvasboard. 19-Nov-2 Wright, Chicago #101/R est:1000-1500
£1258 $2000 €1887 Central Park in winter (30x41cm-12x16in) s. canvasboard. 18-Mar-3 Doyle, New York #10/R est:2000-3000
£1389 $2250 €2014 United Nations (30x23cm-12x9in) s. canvasboard. 21-May-3 Doyle, New York #164/R est:3000-4000
£1415 $2250 €2123 United Nations, rush hour (15x20cm-6x8in) s. canvasboard. 18-Mar-3 Doyle, New York #11/R
£1424 $2250 €2136 Grant's tomb and St. Paul's church (20x15cm-8x6in) s. board prov. 24-Apr-3 Shannon's, Milford #231/R est:1500-2500
£1572 $2500 €2358 Times Square at night (23x30cm-9x12in) s. i.verso canvasboard. 18-Mar-3 Doyle, New York #9/R est:800-1200
£1781 $2600 €2672 Winter, New York (56x76cm-22x30in) 3-Nov-1 North East Auctions, Portsmouth #268/R est:1000-1500
£1887 $3000 €2831 Washington Square, nocturne (15x20cm-6x8in) s. s.i.verso canvasboard. 18-Mar-3 Doyle, New York #12/R
£2273 $3500 €3410 Brooklyn Bridge in winter (23x30cm-9x12in) s. canvasboard prov. 24-Oct-2 Shannon's, Milford #3/R est:3000-5000
£2315 $3750 €3357 Washington Square. Columbus Circle. United Nations seen from Welfare Island (15x20cm-6x8in) s. canvasboard three. 21-May-3 Doyle, New York #162/R est:2500-3500
£2389 $3750 €3584 Fifth Avenue - winter (41x30cm-16x12in) s. canvasboard. 10-Dec-2 Doyle, New York #136/R est:4000-6000
£2500 $4025 €3750 Figure scene in New York (28x38cm-11x15in) s. 19-Feb-3 Mallams, Oxford #429/R est:2000-3000
£2778 $4500 €4028 Washington Square Park. Central Park. Looking east from the United Nations (13x18cm-5x7in) s. canvasboard three. 21-May-3 Doyle, New York #163/R est:2500-3500
£2800 $4508 €4200 St Paul's Chapel, New York (23x18cm-9x7in) s. board pair. 19-Feb-3 Mallams, Oxford #428/R est:2000-3000
£2922 $4500 €4383 St Paul's Church, New York (30x23cm-12x9in) canvasboard prov. 24-Oct-2 Shannon's, Milford #95/R est:4000-6000
£3045 $4750 €4568 Times Square. 21-Sep-2 Harvey Clar, Oakland #1471

£3085 $4750 €4628 Skyline from the East River (18x30cm-7x12in) s. canvasboard prov. 24-Oct-2 Shannon's, Milford #1/R est:5000-7000
£3086 $5000 €4475 Gramercy Park (41x51cm-16x20in) s. i.verso canvasboard. 21-May-3 Doyle, New York #160/R est:5000-7000
£3165 $5000 €4748 United Nations (46x61cm-18x24in) s. s.i.verso prov. 24-Apr-3 Shannon's, Milford #140/R est:4000-6000
£3481 $5500 €5222 Union Square (41x51cm-16x20in) s. 24-Apr-3 Shannon's, Milford #138/R est:5000-7000
£3846 $6000 €5769 Snowy day, New York (51x41cm-20x16in) s. canvasboard. 12-Apr-3 Weschler, Washington #571/R est:6000-8000
£3896 $6000 €5844 Little church around the corner (46x36cm-18x14in) s. i.stretcher. 24-Oct-2 Shannon's, Milford #94/R est:6000-8000
£4012 $6500 €5817 Fifth Avenue. Trinity Church (30x23cm-12x9in) s. two. 21-May-3 Doyle, New York #161/R est:5000-7000
£4114 $6500 €6171 Washington Square and arch (41x30cm-16x12in) s.i.verso canvasboard prov. 24-Apr-3 Shannon's, Milford #11/R est:4000-6000
£4114 $6500 €6171 Brooklyn Bridge (41x30cm-16x12in) s.i.d.1947 verso canvasboard prov. 24-Apr-3 Shannon's, Milford #12/R est:4000-6000
£6169 $9500 €9254 Trinity Church. Fifth Ave (20x15cm-8x6in) s. canvasboard pair prov. 24-Oct-2 Shannon's, Milford #219/R est:5000-7000
£8642 $14000 €12531 Fifth Avenue (61x51cm-24x20in) s. 21-May-3 Doyle, New York #159/R est:3000-5000

BERTHOLLE, Jean (1909-1996) French
£1156 $1839 €1700 Le bon samaritain III (27x34cm-11x13in) s.d. paper on panel prov. 26-Feb-3 Artcurial Briest, Paris #548 est:600-800

BERTHOME-SAINT-ANDRE (1905-1977) French
£317 $500 €500 Portrait d'officier de marine (80x50cm-31x20in) s. 2-Dec-2 Tajan, Paris #140
£1135 $1895 €1600 La sieste (46x65cm-18x26in) s. 20-Jun-3 Piasa, Paris #160/R est:2000-3000
£1135 $1895 €1600 Paysage (60x73cm-24x29in) s. 20-Jun-3 Piasa, Paris #162/R est:2000-3000
£1135 $1895 €1600 Le jupon noir (61x50cm-24x20in) s. 20-Jun-3 Piasa, Paris #165/R est:2000-3000
£1206 $2013 €1700 Le jupon blanc (72x60cm-28x24in) s. 20-Jun-3 Piasa, Paris #164/R est:2000-3000
£1631 $2724 €2300 Apres-midi (73x90cm-29x35in) s. 20-Jun-3 Piasa, Paris #161/R est:2000-3000
£1844 $3079 €2600 Le chemin de sable (73x92cm-29x36in) s. 20-Jun-3 Piasa, Paris #163/R est:2000-3000

BERTHOME-SAINT-ANDRE, Louis (1905-1977) French
£355 $574 €500 Portrait de Madame Betty Mayet (100x81cm-39x32in) s. 26-May-3 Joron-Derem, Paris #37
£392 $612 €620 Modele (65x47cm-26x19in) s. s.verso. 20-Oct-2 Chayette & Cheval, Paris #99b
£513 $795 €800 Jeune fille se coiffant (65x52cm-26x20in) s.d.1935. 7-Dec-2 Martinot & Savignat, Pontoise #40
£1033 $1694 €1498 Jeune filles aux pivoines (60x48cm-24x19in) s. 4-Jun-3 Fischer, Luzern #1094/R est:220-2500 (S.FR 2200)
£2119 $3454 €3200 Promenade dans le parc (73x93cm-29x37in) s. 31-Jan-3 Rabourdin & Choppin de Janvry, Paris #54/R
£2649 $4318 €4000 Jeune femme pensive (60x74cm-24x29in) s.d.44. 31-Jan-3 Rabourdin & Choppin de Janvry, Paris #139/R
Works on paper
£324 $518 €450 Falbalas (35x27cm-14x11in) s.d.1950 Indian ink W/C. 16-May-3 Lombrail & Teucquam, Paris #246

BERTHON, George Theodore (1806-1892) Canadian
£2667 $4373 €4001 Portrait of a young lady (63x46cm-25x18in) s.d.1845 board prov. 27-May-3 Sotheby's, Toronto #157/R est:5000-7000 (C.D 6000)
£3333 $5467 €5000 Portrait of two children (55x45cm-22x18in) board on canavs prov. 27-May-3 Sotheby's, Toronto #158/R est:8000-10000 (C.D 7500)

BERTHON, Nicolas (1831-1888) French
£897 $1409 €1400 Ijsselmeer harbour (45x65cm-18x26in) s. 21-Nov-2 Dorotheum, Vienna #140/R est:2000-2600

BERTHON, Paul (1872-1909) French
Works on paper
£1923 $2981 €3000 Femme (27x21cm-11x8in) s.d.1898 gouache. 3-Dec-2 Sotheby's, Paris #2/R

BERTHOT, Jake (1939-) American
£465 $734 €698 Crossways (51x51cm-20x20in) s.d.75 verso exhib.prov. 1-Apr-3 Rasmussen, Copenhagen #304/R (D.KR 5000)

BERTHOUD, Alfred-Henri (1848-1906) Swiss
£472 $731 €750 Mountain landscape (17x34cm-7x13in) s. panel. 29-Oct-2 Dorotheum, Vienna #95/R

BERTHOUD, Auguste Henri (1829-1887) Swiss
£1080 $1771 €1566 Lac de choux (61x114cm-24x45in) s. 4-Jun-3 Fischer, Luzern #1080/R est:2300-2500 (S.FR 2300)

BERTHOUD, Léon (1822-1892) Swiss
£1310 $2044 €1965 Cows in shallow water in part of the lake's edge (22x37cm-9x15in) s.d.1897 masonite. 8-Nov-2 Dobiaschofsky, Bern #5/R est:2400 (S.FR 3000)
£2628 $4074 €4100 Scene de guerre dans un village indien (58x100cm-23x39in) s.d.1867. 5-Dec-2 Gros & Delettrez, Paris #42/R est:3000-3500

BERTHOUD, Paul François (1870-?) French
Sculpture
£3247 $5000 €4871 Art noveau figural vase (33cm-13in) s.i. dark brown pat. bronze. 27-Oct-2 Grogan, Boston #120 est:2000-3000

BERTI, Renato (20th C) Italian
£480 $749 €720 Falling at the fence (32x41cm-13x16in) s. panel prov. 17-Sep-2 Rosebery Fine Art, London #609/R

BERTI, Vinicio (1921-1991) Italian
£321 $503 €500 Meeting (60x80cm-24x31in) acrylic. 16-Dec-2 Pandolfini, Florence #372
£481 $755 €750 Great antagonist H-H1-H5 (80x60cm-31x24in) s.d.1972 s.i.d.verso. 20-Nov-2 Pandolfini, Florence #97/R
£705 $1107 €1100 Antagonism (80x60cm-31x24in) s.d.1970-71 acrylic. 16-Dec-2 Pandolfini, Florence #379/R
Works on paper
£609 $962 €950 Positive constructions (50x70cm-20x28in) s.d.1972 waterpaint on canvas. 15-Nov-2 Farsetti, Prato #44
£929 $1469 €1450 Look high (120x80cm-47x31in) s.i.d.1990-91 waterpaint on canvas. 15-Nov-2 Farsetti, Prato #238/R
£962 $1519 €1500 Ban 9H (80x120cm-31x47in) s.d.1986 waterpaint on canvas. 15-Nov-2 Farsetti, Prato #346/R
£1026 $1621 €1600 Meeting in time (60x80cm-24x31in) s.d.1962 waterpaint on canvas. 15-Nov-2 Farsetti, Prato #279/R

BERTIN, Émile (1878-1957) French
Works on paper
£566 $900 €849 Celestine (47x47cm-19x19in) s.i. W/C gouache over pencil. 27-Feb-3 Christie's, Rockefeller NY #69

BERTIN, François Édouard (1797-1871) French
Works on paper
£1560 $2606 €2200 Paysage rocheux. Personnages dans un paysage (22x29cm-9x11in) st.sig. pen brown ink brown wash black crayon pair. 19-Jun-3 Piasa, Paris #154 est:1500-1800

BERTIN, Jean-Victor (1775-1842) French
£3481 $5500 €5500 Abreuvoir pres d'une ferme (16x22cm-6x9in) 2-Dec-2 Rieunier, Paris #48/R
£3846 $6038 €6000 Bouquet d'arbres (61x52cm-24x20in) s.d.1807. 16-Dec-2 Rabourdin & Choppin de Janvry, Paris #176/R
£6081 $9486 €9000 Paysage classique a la riviere (33x40cm-13x16in) s. 28-Mar-3 Piasa, Paris #49/R
£10000 $16700 €14500 Arcadian landscape at sunset, figures dancing near a tomb, temple beyond (68x84cm-27x33in) i. 9-Jul-3 Bonhams, New Bond Street #122/R est:10000-15000
£30000 $47100 €45000 Classical landscape with Marius fleeing Rome (81x114cm-32x45in) s.d.1826 exhib.lit. 12-Dec-2 Sotheby's, London #57/R est:30000-40000
£30380 $48000 €48000 Vue de Tivoli (95x120cm-37x47in) i. 27-Nov-2 Christie's, Paris #40/R est:30000-50000
£60927 $99311 €92000 Cavaliers sur un pont dans un paysage (75x109cm-30x43in) s.d.1812. 17-Feb-3 Horta, Bruxelles #203/R
£62252 $101470 €94000 Conversation dans un paysage anime (75x109cm-30x43in) s.d.1812. 17-Feb-3 Horta, Bruxelles #204/R est:22000

BERTIN, Jean-Victor (attrib) (1775-1842) French
£817 $1259 €1300 Vue d'une citadelle (38x46cm-15x18in) 25-Oct-2 Tajan, Paris #138/R est:900-1200

BERTIN, Nicolas (1668-1736) French
£2564 $3974 €4000 Joseph et la femme de Putiphar (61x50cm-24x20in) 6-Dec-2 Rieunier, Bailly-Pommery, Mathias, Paris #27/R est:5000

BERTIN, Nicolas (attrib) (1668-1736) French
Works on paper
£743 $1159 €1100 Jugement de Paris (22x17cm-9x7in) sanguine. 27-Mar-3 Maigret, Paris #5

BERTIN, Roger (1915-) French
£1859 $2881 €2900 Paris, toits et Tour Eiffel (64x93cm-25x37in) s. 6-Dec-2 Rieunier, Bailly-Pommery, Mathias, Paris #92/R

BERTINI, Gianni (1922-) Italian
£284 $474 €400 Plastique dans typhon (45x26cm-18x10in) s. 18-Jun-3 Pierre Berge, Paris #109
£310 $518 €450 Le fil d'Ariane (73x54cm-29x21in) s.d.55 paper on canvas. 10-Jul-3 Artcurial Briest, Paris #330
£641 $1006 €1000 Selene at night (65x50cm-26x20in) s.d.1959 oil mixed media cardboard on canvas. 23-Nov-2 Meeting Art, Vercelli #265/R
£641 $1006 €1000 Esculapius' plac (48x69cm-19x27in) s.d.1962 oil mixed media paper on canvas. 23-Nov-2 Meeting Art, Vercelli #280/R
£705 $1107 €1100 Rentree de heros (61x38cm-24x15in) s. s.i.d.verso prov. 16-Dec-2 Charbonneaux, Paris #224
£1282 $2013 €2000 Untitled (54x65cm-21x26in) s. s.i.d.53 verso prov. 24-Nov-2 Laurence Calmels, Paris #27/R
£1410 $2214 €2200 Untitled (62x50cm-24x20in) s. 24-Nov-2 Laurence Calmels, Paris #28/R
£1667 $2633 €2600 Composition (50x31cm-20x12in) s. 15-Nov-2 Farsetti, Prato #283/R
£1795 $2818 €2800 Desespoir (92x73cm-36x29in) s. s.i.d.1961 verso prov. 24-Nov-2 Laurence Calmels, Paris #26/R
£2244 $3522 €3500 Stationnement (100x81cm-39x32in) s. s.i.d.1958 verso prov. 24-Nov-2 Laurence Calmels, Paris #29/R
£2384 $3886 €3600 Composition (111x94cm-44x37in) s.d.1958. 3-Feb-3 Cornette de St.Cyr, Paris #365/R
£2436 $3824 €3800 Autoroute (61x50cm-24x20in) s.d.1966 paint over photograph prov. 24-Nov-2 Laurence Calmels, Paris #30/R
£2619 $4164 €3850 Artemis chasseresse au mazarin (162x129cm-64x51in) s.i.d.1990 oil acrylic. 26-Feb-3 Artcurial Briest, Paris #409/R est:3500-4000
£3205 $5032 €5000 Good morning (140x70cm-55x28in) s. s.i.d.1950 verso tempera board prov.lit. 20-Nov-2 Pandolfini, Florence #95/R est:6000

Works on paper
£282 $446 €440 Composition (50x33cm-20x13in) s. felt-tip pen. 15-Nov-2 Farsetti, Prato #265
£316 $494 €500 Untitled (30x20cm-12x8in) s.d.1956 mixed media paper on board. 14-Sep-2 Meeting Art, Vercelli #95
£481 $755 €750 Composition (40x33cm-16x13in) s.d.1957 mixed media. 23-Nov-2 Meeting Art, Vercelli #277/R
£587 $975 €851 Composition (64x48cm-25x19in) s. gouache. 12-Jun-3 Kunsthallen, Copenhagen #7 (D.KR 6200)
£625 $987 €900 Cyclope se dechaine (73x54cm-29x21in) s.d. s.i.d.verso mixed media serigraph canvas. 27-Apr-3 Perrin, Versailles #77/R
£729 $1152 €1050 La petite Amalthee (45x38cm-18x15in) s.d.verso mixed media canvas. 28-Apr-3 Cornette de St.Cyr, Paris #346/R
£2089 $3300 €3300 Pandora's box (80x59cm-31x23in) s.d.57 mixed media paper on canvas. 29-Nov-2 Farsetti, Prato #420/R

BERTINI, Giuseppe (1825-1898) Italian
£448 $713 €650 Study of head (20x16cm-8x6in) i.verso cardboard oval. 7-Mar-3 Semenzato, Venice #151/R

BERTINI, L (?) Italian
£962 $1510 €1500 Men drinking in tavern with girl (55x68cm-22x27in) 23-Nov-2 Arnold, Frankfurt #689/R est:1000

BERTLE, Hans (1879-?) German?
£288 $453 €450 Portrait of young woman wearing black shawl (80x70cm-31x28in) s. 23-Nov-2 Arnold, Frankfurt #690/R
£317 $504 €460 Summer in the mountains (55x45cm-22x18in) s. panel. 8-Mar-3 Arnold, Frankfurt #547

BERTOIA, Harry (1915-1978) American
Sculpture
£1013 $1600 €1520 Untitled (66cm-26in) wire on aluminium base. 1-Dec-2 Susanin's, Chicago #5033/R
£1506 $2500 €2259 Spray (75cm-30in) wire chromed steel base exec.c.1970. 11-Jun-3 Phillips, New York #503/R est:1500-2000
£2097 $3250 €3146 Untitled (9x61cm-4x2x0in) brass silver bronze over steel prov. 8-Dec-2 Wright, Chicago #164/R est:2000-3000
£2097 $3250 €3146 Untitled (7x5x5cm-3x2x2in) multi construction prov. 8-Dec-2 Wright, Chicago #167/R est:3000-5000
£2278 $3600 €3417 Steel figureal. stainless steel sheaf wire. 3-Apr-3 Boos Gallery, Michigan #120/R est:2500-3500
£2500 $4075 €3750 Tree (78cm-31in) stainless steel executed c.1960 prov. 3-Feb-3 Sotheby's, Olympia #60/R est:2500-3500
£3548 $5500 €5322 Untitled (11x8x3cm-4x3x1in) brass silver bronze over steel prov. 8-Dec-2 Wright, Chicago #163/R est:3000-4000
£3871 $6000 €5807 Untitled - plant forms (12x10x5cm-5x4x2in) bronze brass silver prov.exhib. 8-Dec-2 Wright, Chicago #165/R est:7000-9000
£4518 $7500 €6777 Untitled (27x10x10cm-11x4x4in) wire plaster exec.c.1960 prov. 11-Jun-3 Phillips, New York #139/R est:4000-6000
£5769 $9000 €8654 Sonambient (105cm-41in) aluminium prov. 5-Nov-2 Doyle, New York #62/R est:10000-15000
£6129 $9500 €9194 Untitled (20cm-8in) metal rods. 7-Dec-2 South Bay, Long Island #68/R
£7419 $11500 €11129 Untitled (91cm-36in) painted metal rods sold with LP record. 7-Dec-2 South Bay, Long Island #67/R
£9375 $15000 €14063 Bush no.1 (26x29x29cm-10x11x11in) grey blue brown pat. bronze executed 1963 prov.exhib. 14-May-3 Sotheby's, New York #117/R est:8000-12000
£9554 $15000 €14331 Sounding sculpture (39x15x7cm-15x6x3in) berylium copper stainless steel brass. 19-Nov-2 Phillips, New York #123/R est:12000-16000
£9677 $15000 €14516 Untitled - spray (37x18cm-15x7in) stainless steel prov. 8-Dec-2 Wright, Chicago #161/R est:5000-7000
£10323 $16000 €15485 Untitled (180x47x22cm-71x19x9in) steel nickel melt coated brass executed c.1950. 26-Sep-2 Christie's, Rockefeller NY #801/R est:12000-18000
£11613 $18000 €17420 Untitled (36x7x7cm-14x3x3in) bronze coated wire prov.exhib. 8-Dec-2 Wright, Chicago #162/R est:10000-15000
£15060 $25000 €22590 Sounding sculpture (39cm-15in) beryllium copper bronze exec.c.1960 prov. 11-Jun-3 Phillips, New York #147/R est:10000-15000
£16026 $25000 €24039 Sound sculpture (89x74cm-35x29in) berylliam copper bronze exec.c.1970 sold with a book prov. 14-Oct-2 Butterfields, San Francisco #2080/R est:10000-20000
£18065 $28000 €27098 Untitled - sounding sculpture (11x6x6cm-4x2x2in) beryllium copper silver brass prov. 8-Dec-2 Wright, Chicago #166/R est:10000-15000
£19277 $32000 €28916 Sounding sculpture (115cm-45in) beryllium copper bronze exec.c.1960. 11-Jun-3 Phillips, New York #130/R est:25000-30000
£22581 $35000 €33872 Sculpture for sonambient (203x46x46cm-80x18x18in) beryllium copper rods brass tops silvered brass base prov. 26-Sep-2 Christie's, Rockefeller NY #803/R est:30000-40000
£24000 $40080 €34800 Sound sculpture (150x35x17cm-59x14x7in) beryllium copper rods exec.c.1970 prov.exhib. 26-Jun-3 Sotheby's, London #155/R est:12000-15000
£28025 $44000 €42038 Untitled (127x127x29cm-50x50x11in) wall sculpture welded steel cut nails prov. 19-Nov-2 Phillips, New York #124/R est:40000-60000
£32258 $50000 €48387 Untitled - sonambient (43x7x7cm-17x3x3in) beryllium copper bronze prov. 8-Dec-2 Wright, Chicago #168/R est:20000-30000
£55484 $86000 €83226 U. (38x17x9cm-15x7x4in) ebony silver stainless steel prov. 8-Dec-2 Wright, Chicago #185/R est:40000-50000

BERTOLETTI, Nino (1890-1971) Italian
£1233 $1923 €1800 Portrait of Pasquarosa (45x30cm-18x12in) lit. 10-Apr-3 Finarte Semenzato, Rome #189/R

BERTOLINI, Angel Marcos (20th C) Italian?
£288 $450 €432 Desnudo (61x81cm-24x32in) s. i.verso board. 10-Nov-2 Selkirks, St. Louis #599

BERTOLOTTI, Cesare (1855-1932) Italian
£8844 $14061 €13000 Landscape in Lombardy (59x109cm-23x43in) s. canvas on masonite. 18-Mar-3 Finarte, Milan #13/R

BERTON-MAIRE, Marie (19/20th C) French
£566 $872 €900 Cour mauresque a Alger (45x38cm-18x15in) s. i.verso. 23-Oct-2 Rabourdin & Choppin de Janvry, Paris #241/R

BERTONI, A (19th C) Italian
£433 $671 €650 Landscape (40x82cm-16x32in) s. 24-Sep-2 Koller, Zurich #6588 (S.FR 1000)

BERTOS, Francesco (fl.1693-1734) Italian
Sculpture
£31481 $51000 €47222 Bacchus. Ceres (35cm-14in) bronze two lit. 23-Jan-3 Sotheby's, New York #194/R est:15000

BERTOUNESQUE, Andre (1937-) Canadian
£242 $377 €363 Promeneuses sur le rivage (15x45cm-6x18in) s. isorel. 30-Jul-2 Iegor de Saint Hippolyte, Montreal #24 (C.D 600)
£261 $410 €392 Plein soleil (40x50cm-16x20in) s.i. board. 25-Nov-2 Hodgins, Calgary #263/R (C.D 650)
£267 $437 €387 Un racourci (60x50cm-24x20in) s.i. board. 9-Jun-3 Hodgins, Calgary #169/R (C.D 600)

BERTRAM, Abel (1871-1954) French
£404 $650 €606 Figures on a beach (18x28cm-7x11in) st.sig. canvas on panel. 19-Feb-3 Doyle, New York #80
£709 $1107 €1050 La Jetee a Gravelines (19x26cm-7x10in) s. panel. 25-Mar-3 Chochon-Barre & Allardi, Paris #65/R
£864 $1227 €1400 Modele assis (47x38cm-19x15in) s. 17-Mar-2 Galerie de Chartres, Chartres #136

£1056 $1701 €1500 Paysage a l'etang et aux deux vaches (50x65cm-20x26in) s. 11-May-3 Thierry & Lannon, Brest #332 est:1500-2000

BERTRAM, Paul (fl.1900s) British
Works on paper
£295 $466 €460 Landscape (25x33cm-10x13in) s. W/C. 12-Nov-2 Mealy's, Castlecomer #1107

BERTRAND, Eugène (19/20th C) French
£3268 $5261 €5000 Interieur anime (50x67cm-20x26in) s.d.1897. 14-Jan-3 Vanderkindere, Brussels #212/R est:4500-6000

BERTRAND, Gaston (1910-1994) Belgian
£1111 $1767 €1600 Caserne a Odile, France (33x41cm-13x16in) s. painted c.1945. 29-Apr-3 Campo & Campo, Antwerp #15/R est:750-1250
£3924 $6122 €6200 Variation Medicis (46x55cm-18x22in) s.d.1975 s.i.d.verso. 15-Oct-2 Horta, Bruxelles #111
£4167 $6625 €6000 Femme en rouge (35x22cm-14x9in) mono.d.1986 panel lit. 29-Apr-3 Campo & Campo, Antwerp #14/R est:5000-5500
£5755 $9439 €8000 Pour un jardin de dieu (82x65cm-32x26in) s.d.53-57 s.i.d.verso. 3-Jun-3 Christie's, Amsterdam #316/R est:8000-12000
£6329 $10000 €10000 L'homme a la toge (81x65cm-32x26in) s.d.1961-1969 lit. 26-Nov-2 Palais de Beaux Arts, Brussels #237/R est:10000-12000
Works on paper
£272 $425 €408 Monti (27x37cm-11x15in) s.d.53 i.verso W/C. 9-Nov-2 Sloan, North Bethesda #531/R

BERTRAND, Huguette Aimee (1922-) French
£405 $632 €600 Composition (35x27cm-14x11in) s.d.1952 verso. 28-Mar-3 Charbonneaux, Paris #27
£449 $704 €700 Matam (89x116cm-35x46in) s. s.i.d.verso. 16-Dec-2 Charbonneaux, Paris #211
£676 $1054 €1000 Abdul (100x81cm-39x32in) s. s.i.d.1956 verso. 28-Mar-3 Charbonneaux, Paris #29/R
£743 $1159 €1100 Composition 62 (100x73cm-39x29in) s. s.i.d.1954 verso. 28-Mar-3 Charbonneaux, Paris #28/R

BERTRAND, Paulin Andre (1852-1940) French
£2436 $3824 €3800 View of Rue du Montmartre, Paris in autumn (46x66cm-18x26in) s. 21-Nov-2 Van Ham, Cologne #1476/R est:4000

BERTRAND, Pierre-Philippe (1884-1975) French
£417 $650 €626 Fleurs des champs (61x51cm-24x20in) s. s.i.stretcher. 5-Nov-2 Arthur James, Florida #163
£493 $794 €700 Paysage a la riviere et au pont (38x46cm-15x18in) s. 11-May-3 Thierry & Lannon, Brest #333

BERTUCHI NIETO, Mariano (1885-1955) Spanish
£538 $850 €807 Landscape with North African figures (46x56cm-18x22in) s. 3-Apr-3 Boos Gallery, Michigan #289/R
£5128 $8103 €8000 Market in Morocco (48x67cm-19x26in) s. 14-Nov-2 Arte, Seville #388/R

BERTZEK (?) ?
£1178 $1932 €1708 Young woman wearing Renaissance clothes (33x22cm-13x9in) s. panel. 4-Jun-3 AB Stockholms Auktionsverk #2410/R est:25000-30000 (S.KR 15000)

BERUETE, Aureliano de (1845-1911) Spanish
£12000 $18840 €18000 Vista del Tajo - view if the Tajo River (15x27cm-6x11in) s. i.d.Abril 1912 verso board prov.exhib. 19-Nov-2 Sotheby's, London #23/R est:12000-18000
£35000 $54950 €52500 El Guadarrama en otono desde el plantio - view of the Guadarrama in autumn from the planto (39x54cm-15x21in) s. painted c.1910 prov.exhib. 19-Nov-2 Sotheby's, London #2/R est:40000-60000

BERVOETS, Freddy (1941-) Belgian
£348 $550 €550 Soir de fete (40x50cm-16x20in) s. masonite. 2-Dec-2 Tajan, Paris #115
£440 $682 €700 Face-lift (75x110cm-30x43in) mono. acrylic paper on canvas painted c.1987. 5-Oct-2 De Vuyst, Lokeren #35/R
£503 $775 €800 Composition (60x85cm-24x33in) mono. paper. 22-Oct-2 Campo, Vlaamse Kaai #410
£8633 $13813 €12000 Warrior (230x200cm-91x79in) s. painted 1967. 17-May-3 De Vuyst, Lokeren #490/R est:12000-14000
Works on paper
£446 $696 €700 Robot (62x48cm-24x19in) s.d.61 gouache. 5-Nov-2 Vendu Notarishuis, Rotterdam #118/R
£566 $872 €900 Prisoner (64x96cm-25x38in) s.d.1984 mixed media. 22-Oct-2 Campo & Campo, Antwerp #15
£694 $1104 €1000 Composition (78x106cm-31x42in) s. mixed media. 29-Apr-3 Campo, Vlaamse Kaai #21
£903 $1435 €1300 Composition (111x73cm-44x29in) d.1969 verso gouache. 29-Apr-3 Campo, Vlaamse Kaai #20
£1887 $2906 €3000 Composition (98x138cm-39x54in) s. mixed media. 22-Oct-2 Campo, Vlaamse Kaai #409/R

BERVOETS, Leo (1892-1978) Belgian
Works on paper
£690 $1097 €1000 Soiree dansante (50x71cm-20x28in) s. W/C. 4-Mar-3 Palais de Beaux Arts, Brussels #284 est:300-375

BERWICK, G (20th C) British?
£650 $1034 €975 Valley farmstead (71x91cm-28x36in) s. 6-Mar-3 Christie's, Kensington #159/R

BESCHEY, Balthasar (1708-1776) Flemish
£5743 $8959 €8500 Tribute to Ceres, the Goddess of Agriculture (46x61cm-18x24in) copper prov. 27-Mar-3 Dorotheum, Vienna #140 est:8000-12000
£7742 $12232 €12000 Madonna and Child with Saints (151x80cm-59x31in) s.d.1746. 17-Dec-2 Segre, Madrid #66/R est:13000

BESCHEY, Balthasar (attrib) (1708-1776) Flemish
£2000 $3340 €2900 Wooded landscape with the Holy Family with the infant Saint John the Baptist (43x56cm-17x22in) panel. 11-Jul-3 Christie's, Kensington #54/R est:3000-5000
£2128 $3553 €3000 Bacchus (43x33cm-17x13in) panel. 18-Jun-3 Tajan, Paris #60/R est:3000-4000
£2532 $4000 €4000 Virgin (47x39cm-19x15in) panel. 29-Nov-2 Coutau Begarie, Paris #88
£5128 $8051 €8000 Ascension of Maria (70x86cm-28x34in) copper. 21-Nov-2 Van Ham, Cologne #1310/R est:15000

BESCHEY, Jan Frans (1717-1799) Flemish?
£854 $1400 €1238 Portrait of a gentleman, in a red velvet jacket (16x63cm-6x25in) s.d.1752. 4-Jun-3 Christie's, Rockefeller NY #163/R

BESCHEY, Karel (1706-1776) Flemish
£15000 $23550 €22500 Elegant company conversing on a wooded country road with travellers (20x37cm-8x15in) panel. 10-Dec-2 Bonhams, New Bond Street #281/R est:8000-12000

BESCO, Donald (1941-) Canadian
£341 $539 €512 Winter on the banks of the Grand River (41x74cm-16x29in) hardboard. 1-Dec-2 Levis, Calgary #6/R (C.D 850)
£726 $1147 €1089 Fogo Island, Newfoundland (46x61cm-18x24in) s.i.verso board. 14-Nov-2 Heffel, Vancouver #171/R est:1200-1500 (C.D 1800)
£762 $1220 €1143 Winter day, Galt, Ontario (61x41cm-24x16in) s. i.verso board. 15-May-3 Heffel, Vancouver #200/R est:1000-1200 (C.D 1700)
£905 $1403 €1358 Old flatiron (60x90cm-24x35in) s. 3-Dec-2 Joyner, Toronto #236/R est:2000-3000 (C.D 2200)
£978 $1604 €1467 Cloudburst, Front St. (57x100cm-22x39in) s. board. 3-Jun-3 Joyner, Toronto #285/R est:2500-3000 (C.D 2200)

BESFI, G (19th C) Italian
Sculpture
£1761 $2835 €2500 Bust of a young woman (76cm-30in) s. col marble. 12-May-3 Bernaerts, Antwerp #77/R est:1250-1500

BESHAW, F (19th C) British
£3600 $5688 €5400 Flying Dutchman, winner of the Derby (46x71cm-18x28in) indis sig. s.i.verso. 28-Nov-2 Bonhams, Knightsbridge #61/R est:800-1200

BESKOW, Bo (1906-1989) Swedish
£284 $440 €426 Linda - portrait of young girl wearing green blouse (68x55cm-27x22in) s. 8-Dec-2 Uppsala Auktionskammare, Uppsala #219/R (S.KR 4000)

BESLER, Basilius (17th C) German?
Prints
£2201 $3500 €3302 Sunflower (85x74cm-33x29in) col engraving copper plate. 30-Apr-3 Sotheby's, New York #443/R est:4000-6000
£2830 $4500 €4245 Lily and centaurium (85x75cm-33x30in) col engraving copper plate. 30-Apr-3 Sotheby's, New York #447/R est:4000-6000

BESNARD, Albert (1849-1934) French
£900 $1422 €1350 Contemplation (62x50cm-24x20in) s. 14-Nov-2 Christie's, Kensington #131
£1517 $2534 €2200 Jeune femme au voile blanc (62x47cm-24x19in) s.d.1895. 10-Jul-3 Artcurial Briest, Paris #122/R est:1200-1500

Works on paper
£31690 $52606 €45000 La terre, l'eau, le fue, l'air (46x188cm-18x74in) s.i.d. gouache chl paper on canvas four. 11-Jun-3 Beaussant & Lefèvre, Paris #5/R est:40000-45000

BESNARD, Jean Baptiste (18th C) French
£2027 $3162 €3000 Petits denicheurs d'oiseaux (34x42cm-13x17in) 26-Mar-3 Tajan, Paris #58/R
£5263 $8632 €7631 Le diseur de bonnes aventures (110x134cm-43x53in) 4-Jun-3 AB Stockholms Auktionsverk #2555/R est:50000-70000 (S.KR 67000)

BESNARD, Jean Baptiste (attrib) (18th C) French
£1268 $2104 €1800 Parents entoures de leurs enfants en train de joueur dans un interieur (33x24cm-13x9in) 16-Jun-3 Claude Aguttes, Neuilly #24/R est:2000-3000

BESNARD-FORTIN, Jeanne (?) French
Works on paper
£278 $453 €400 Jeux d'enfants sur la plage (18x11cm-7x4in) studio st. W/C. 19-Jul-3 Thierry & Lannon, Brest #254

BESNARD-GIRAUDIAS, Helene (1906-) French
£1923 $3019 €3000 Jardin des Oudaias (45x54cm-18x21in) s. s.i.d.1968 verso. 10-Dec-2 Tajan, Paris #115/R est:4000

BESNES E IRIGOYEN, Juan Manuel (1788-1865) Uruguayan?
Works on paper
£5688 $9100 €8532 Pages, glasses and feathers (57x86cm-22x34in) i. mixed media cardboard. 5-Jan-3 Galleria Y Remates, Montevideo #35/R

BESPARTO, Francesco Pablo (20th C) ?
£380 $585 €570 River landscape (71x90cm-28x35in) s. 22-Oct-2 Bonhams, Bath #12

BESS, Georges (20th C) French?
Works on paper
£276 $436 €400 Lama blac (50x36cm-20x14in) s. col ink. 7-Apr-3 Claude Aguttes, Neuilly #7

BESSA, Pancrace (1772-1846) French
Works on paper
£494 $701 €800 Etude de Reine Marguerite (35x25cm-14x10in) s.verso pen ink wash over crayon. 17-Mar-2 Galerie de Chartres, Chartres #29
£617 $877 €1000 Etude de gueules de loup (42x32cm-17x13in) s.verso gouache over crayon. 17-Mar-2 Galerie de Chartres, Chartres #30
£926 $1500 €1389 Study of spray snapdragons (45x31cm-18x12in) s.verso W/C. 21-Jan-3 Sotheby's, New York #106/R
£926 $1500 €1389 Study of peaches on branch (44x32cm-17x13in) s.verso W/C over pencil. 21-Jan-3 Sotheby's, New York #105/R
£1064 $1777 €1500 Marguerites (21x14cm-8x6in) mono. W/C black crayon. 19-Jun-3 Piasa, Paris #184/R est:1500-2000
£1173 $1665 €1900 Etude de tulipe (30x18cm-12x7in) s. W/C gouache over crayon. 17-Mar-2 Galerie de Chartres, Chartres #28/R
£1420 $2016 €2300 Etude de tulipes et leurs petales (37x25cm-15x10in) s.verso W/C over crayon. 17-Mar-2 Galerie de Chartres, Chartres #27
£3237 $5309 €4500 Jete de fleurs (30x21cm-12x8in) s.d.1827 W/C. 5-Jun-3 Fraysse & Associes, Paris #5/R est:4500-6000

BESSE, Raymond (1899-1969) French
£315 $447 €510 Place Saint-Andre des Arts (53x65cm-21x26in) s. 17-Mar-2 Galerie de Chartres, Chartres #137
£458 $737 €650 Venise (60x72cm-24x28in) s. 11-May-3 Thierry & Lannon, Brest #334

BESSERVE, René (1883-1959) French
£1689 $2635 €2500 Odalisque (116x125cm-46x49in) s. 26-Mar-3 Millon & Associes, Paris #89/R

BESSET, Cyrille (1864-1902) French
£372 $603 €558 Autumn landscape with figure (38x47cm-15x19in) s.d.94. 25-Jan-3 Rasmussen, Havnen #2035 (D.KR 4200)

BESSI, Prof Guiseppi (1857-1922) Italian
Sculpture
£1700 $2771 €2550 Bust of Beatrice (52cm-20in) s.i. tinted alabaster. 11-Feb-3 Sotheby's, Olympia #318/R est:1800-2500

BESSONOF, Boris (20th C) Russian
£12000 $18840 €18000 The Queen's Temple at Versailles (65x81cm-26x32in) s. 20-Nov-2 Sotheby's, London #61/R est:2500-3500

BESSOUD, Bernard (1947-) French
Sculpture
£4113 $6664 €5800 Chimpanze (47x53x27cm-19x21x11in) s. num.1/8 pat bronze. 25-May-3 Feletin, Province #70

BEST PONTONES, Fernando (1889-1957) Mexican
£1067 $1750 €1547 Lago de Chapala (28x38cm-11x15in) s. masonite. 28-May-3 Louis Morton, Mexico #87/R est:16000-18000 (M.P 18000)
£12195 $20000 €17683 Iztaccihuatl (65x101cm-26x40in) s.d.1919 prov.exhib. 27-May-3 Sotheby's, New York #46

BEST, Arthur W (1859-1935) American
£683 $1100 €1025 Small cabin above wooded lake (46x53cm-18x21in) indis.sig. prov. 18-Feb-3 John Moran, Pasadena #99b
£1592 $2500 €2388 Multnomah Falls, Oregon (91x56cm-36x22in) s.d.88 prov. 19-Nov-2 Butterfields, San Francisco #8168/R est:3000-5000
Works on paper
£446 $700 €669 Indian encampment with two teepees and camp fires in foreground (23x23cm-9x9in) s. W/C. 19-Apr-3 James Julia, Fairfield #288/R

BEST, Hans (1874-1942) German
£380 $589 €600 Village mayor (61x50cm-24x20in) s. board. 25-Sep-2 Neumeister, Munich #539/R
£573 $894 €900 Portrait of hunter (30x22cm-12x9in) s. board. 6-Nov-2 Hugo Ruef, Munich #1023/R

BEST, Mary Ellen (1809-?) British
Works on paper
£600 $954 €900 Portrait of Frederic Stansfield Herries (15x14cm-6x6in) s. i.verso W/C over pencil htd bodycol. 19-Mar-3 Sotheby's, London #123/R

BESTA, Willibald (1886-1949) Polish
£391 $614 €610 Still life with crockery and tulips (60x75cm-24x30in) s. 21-Nov-2 Van Ham, Cologne #1477

BESTER, Willie (1956-) South African
£989 $1592 €1484 Rewind fast forward (60x30cm-24x12in) s.d.98 oi. board found objects. 12-May-3 Stephan Welz, Johannesburg #553 est:7000-10000 (SA.R 11500)
£1118 $1800 €1677 Fish heads (60x30cm-24x12in) s.d.99 oil board with objects. 12-May-3 Stephan Welz, Johannesburg #87 est:5000-7000 (SA.R 13000)

BESWICK, S (19/20th C) British?
Works on paper
£250 $390 €375 Children by cottages in a village lane (50x74cm-20x29in) s.d.1911 W/C htd white. 17-Sep-2 Rosebery Fine Art, London #596/R

BETHELL, Worden Charles (1899-1951) American
£573 $900 €860 Desert landscape (51x61cm-20x24in) s. 23-Nov-2 Jackson's, Cedar Falls #70/R
£955 $1500 €1433 California mountain landscape (51x61cm-20x24in) s. 23-Nov-2 Jackson's, Cedar Falls #69/R est:500-700

BETHKE, Hermann (1825-1895) German
£5806 $9000 €8709 Afternoon lesson (77x62cm-30x24in) s.d.1887. 30-Oct-2 Christie's, Rockefeller NY #155/R est:10000-15000
£6013 $9500 €9500 Grandfather returns home (70x53cm-28x21in) s. lit. 29-Nov-2 Schloss Ahlden, Ahlden #1191/R est:9500

BETHMONT, Charles Henri (19th C) French
£1761 $2730 €2800 On the Marne (38x59cm-15x23in) s.d.1881. 29-Oct-2 Dorotheum, Vienna #258/R est:3800-4200

BETIGNY, Ernest (1873-1960) Belgian
£301 $470 €440 Portrait de Marcel Tricot (40x50cm-16x20in) s. 14-Apr-3 Horta, Bruxelles #6
£449 $696 €700 L'atelier de l'artiste (40x50cm-16x20in) s. 9-Dec-2 Horta, Bruxelles #258
£586 $938 €850 Composition au chaudron, aux pommes et au chou rouge (70x80cm-28x31in) s. 17-Mar-3 Horta, Bruxelles #7

BETREMIEUX, Laurent (1959-) French?
Works on paper
£321 $497 €500 Soirees d'hiver (140x140cm-55x55in) s.d.1968 mixed media paper on canvas. 9-Dec-2 Beaussant & Lefèvre, Paris #12

BETTATI, Giovanni (c.1700-1777) Italian
Works on paper
£1000 $1570 €1500 Design for a cup and cover with alternates (43x27cm-17x11in) pen ink wash over black chk framing lines. 11-Dec-2 Sotheby's, Olympia #215/R est:1200-1500
£1300 $2041 €1950 Design for a mirror frame with putti. Andirons (37x27cm-15x11in) pen ink wash black chk three exhib. 11-Dec-2 Sotheby's, Olympia #212/R est:1000-1500

BETTENCOURT, Pierre (1917-) French
Sculpture
£1173 $1853 €1700 Lunettes optiques (153x66cm-60x26in) mono. i.verso relief. 4-Apr-3 Tajan, Paris #265
£5063 $8000 €8000 Stele du temple (250x170cm-98x67in) s.i.d.1982 verso relief. 27-Nov-2 Tajan, Paris #86/R est:9000-15000
Works on paper
£1899 $3000 €3000 Irrumateur nostalgique (122x105cm-48x41in) mixed media panel exec.1981. 2-Dec-2 Tajan, Paris #236/R
£4710 $7725 €6500 Nuits de Babylone (122x159cm-48x63in) mono.i.verso mixed media panel. 27-May-3 Tajan, Paris #52/R est:5000-6000
£6338 $10521 €9000 Sans titre (34x26cm-13x10in) butterfly wings collage. 11-Jun-3 Beaussant & Lefèvre, Paris #207/R est:1800-2200

BETTERA, Bartolomeo (1639-?) Italian
£45732 $75000 €68598 Still life of musical instrument and books all resting on a table (98x127cm-39x50in) prov. 29-May-3 Sotheby's, New York #52/R est:60000-80000

BETTERA, Bartolomeo (attrib) (1639-?) Italian
£48000 $74880 €72000 Still life of musical instruments with lutes, violins, guitar, harp and other objects (114x146cm-45x57in) prov. 10-Apr-3 Sotheby's, London #75/R est:20000

BETTERA, Bartolomeo (circle) (1639-?) Italian
£11556 $19182 €16756 Still life with musical instruments (71x97cm-28x38in) bears sig. 10-Jun-3 Ritchie, Toronto #168/R est:5000-7000 (C.D 26000)

BETTERA, Bartolomeo (studio) (1639-?) Italian
£12000 $18840 €18000 Lutes, guitar, a celestial globe on a marble table draped with Turkish rug (104x145cm-41x57in) 10-Dec-2 Bonhams, New Bond Street #30/R est:12000-15000

BETTS, Anna Whelan (19/20th C) American
£516 $800 €774 Seated lady with parasol (51x18cm-20x7in) s.i. board. 8-Dec-2 Freeman, Philadelphia #114/R

BETTS, Ethel Franklin (19/20th C) American
£2329 $3750 €3494 Japanese children and visitors (46x33cm-18x13in) s. oil en grisaille. 10-May-3 Illustration House, New York #40/R est:4000-7000

BETTS, Grace (1883-1978) American
Works on paper
£545 $850 €818 Grand Canyon. gouache. 21-Sep-2 Harvey Clar, Oakland #1483

BETTS, Harold H (1881-?) American
£269 $425 €404 Boats in the harbour. s. 16-Nov-2 Harvey Clar, Oakland #1268

BETTS, Virginia Battaile (20th C) American
£2700 $4293 €4050 Still life of flowers in a vase (120x90cm-47x35in) s. 18-Mar-3 Sworder & Son, Bishops Stortford #412a/R est:1200-1500

BETYNA, Paul (1887-1967) German
£408 $649 €600 Fehrbelliner See (54x66cm-21x26in) s. 28-Mar-3 Bolland & Marotz, Bremen #543/R

BETZ, Andor (?) German
£272 $433 €400 Evening pleasures (70x100cm-28x39in) s.i. i. verso panel. 20-Mar-3 Neumeister, Munich #2592/R

BEUCKER, Pascal de (1861-1945) ?
£1700 $2720 €2550 Still life of roses in an Oriental vase and daisies in an Oriental bowl (60x40cm-24x16in) s.d.1909. 8-Jan-3 George Kidner, Lymington #198/R est:800-1200
£6329 $9873 €10000 Still life with roses and Canton vase (30x40cm-12x16in) s. 21-Oct-2 Bernaerts, Antwerp #107/R est:1000-1500

BEUL, Armand de (1874-?) Belgian
£449 $704 €700 Paysage aux moutons (36x55cm-14x22in) s.d.1912. 10-Dec-2 Vanderkindere, Brussels #163
£2174 $3565 €3000 Galanterie (50x80cm-20x31in) s. 27-May-3 Campo, Vlaamse Kaai #47/R est:4000-5000

BEUL, Frans de (1849-1919) Belgian
£270 $422 €400 Vaches a l'abreuvoir (87x70cm-34x28in) s. 25-Mar-3 Campo & Campo, Antwerp #40
£377 $589 €600 Kempisch landschap te Genk (39x54cm-15x21in) s. 23-Sep-2 Bernaerts, Antwerp #663
£601 $938 €950 Sheep in the dunes (17x24cm-7x9in) s. panel. 21-Oct-2 Bernaerts, Antwerp #737
£949 $1500 €1424 Young shepherdess (71x56cm-28x22in) s. 2-Apr-3 Doyle, New York #29/R est:2000-3000
£1139 $1777 €1800 Saddled horses and chickens (17x24cm-7x9in) s. panel. 21-Oct-2 Bernaerts, Antwerp #132/R est:1500-1800
£1795 $2818 €2800 Peasant woman with cows (64x90cm-25x35in) s. 21-Nov-2 Van Ham, Cologne #1478/R est:2000

BEUL, Henri de (1845-1900) Belgian
£240 $400 €348 Interior scene with an ironing woman (30x20cm-12x8in) s.d.1861 board prov. 21-Jun-3 Selkirks, St. Louis #1024/R
£1139 $1777 €1800 Berger et son troupeau (62x43cm-24x17in) s.d.1898. 10-Sep-2 Vanderkindere, Brussels #299 est:1700-2000
£2014 $3223 €2800 Coq et poules picorant (21x29cm-8x11in) s.d.1863 panel. 13-May-3 Palais de Beaux Arts, Brussels #234/R est:2900-3500
£3038 $4739 €4800 Sweet shepherdess (79x60cm-31x24in) s.d.1874. 21-Oct-2 Bernaerts, Antwerp #79/R est:4500-5000
£3100 $4898 €4650 Shepherdess (65x83cm-26x33in) s. panel prov. 2-Dec-2 Bonhams, Bath #106/R est:4000-6000

BEULAS, José (1921-) Spanish
£2830 $4358 €4500 REd earth (46x65cm-18x26in) s. s.i.verso. 22-Oct-2 Durán, Madrid #197/R est:4500
£3548 $5606 €5500 Burnt lines (92x73cm-36x29in) s.d.89. 18-Dec-2 Ansorena, Madrid #177/R
£6452 $10194 €10000 View of Toledo (73x92cm-29x36in) s. 17-Dec-2 Durán, Madrid #220/R est:5000
Works on paper
£535 $823 €850 Landscape (32x45cm-13x18in) s.d.51 W/C double-sided. 22-Oct-2 Durán, Madrid #119/R

BEURDEN, Alfons van (jnr) (1878-1962) Belgian
£390 $651 €550 Antwerp harbour (49x59cm-19x23in) s. 23-Jun-3 Bernaerts, Antwerp #33/R
£417 $658 €650 Lissewege in de sneeuw (65x75cm-26x30in) s. 18-Nov-2 Bernaerts, Antwerp #325/R
£709 $1184 €1000 Woodview with woman near a lake (90x114cm-35x45in) s. 23-Jun-3 Bernaerts, Antwerp #178/R
£1111 $1767 €1600 Grand place animee a Anvers (55x65cm-22x26in) s. 29-Apr-3 Campo & Campo, Antwerp #3103/R est:1000-1500
£1389 $2208 €2000 Voiliers dans le port (91x115cm-36x45in) s. 29-Apr-3 Campo & Campo, Antwerp #302/R est:2200-2600
Sculpture
£3129 $4976 €4600 Bacchanal (75x35cm-30x14in) s. carved marble. 24-Mar-3 Bernaerts, Antwerp #153/R est:3750-4500
£6026 $9521 €9400 La jeunesse de Diane (42cm-17in) s.verso st.f.Cie des Bronzes bronze ivory incl base. 18-Nov-2 Bernaerts, Antwerp #343/R est:6000-8000

BEURDEN, Alphonse van (snr) (1854-1938) Belgian
£278 $442 €400 Chevaux dans la prairie (40x50cm-16x20in) s. 29-Apr-3 Campo, Vlaamse Kaai #308
£390 $651 €550 Etude d'un nu (52x41cm-20x16in) panel. 23-Jun-3 Amberes, Antwerp #133

BEURMANN, Emil (1862-1951) Swiss
£472 $746 €708 Half-length portrait of an elegant lady in a low-cut dress and stole (49x39cm-19x15in) s. 29-Nov-2 Zofingen, Switzerland #2801 (S.FR 1100)
Works on paper
£279 $441 €419 Southern Lower Alps landscape with house on river bank (33x23cm-13x9in) s. W/C. 26-Nov-2 Hans Widmer, St Gallen #1042 (S.FR 650)

£308 $450 €462 Woman from Hasliberg wearing hat (35x23cm-14x9in) s. i. verso W/C. 17-Jun-2 Philippe Schuler, Zurich #4155 (S.FR 700)

BEUTNER, Johannes (1890-1960) German

Works on paper

£516 $794 €820 Sachsen suburb (44x34cm-17x13in) mono.d.1948 W/C board. 26-Oct-2 Dr Lehr, Berlin #48/R

BEUYS, Joseph (1921-1986) German

Prints

£2183 $3188 €3275 Deer (55x75cm-22x30in) s. col lithograph lit. 4-Jun-2 Germann, Zurich #222/R est:5500-6500 (S.FR 5000)

Sculpture

£1026 $1590 €1600 From: artist's post (32x23x1cm-13x9x0in) plastic margarine white chocolate prov. 3-Dec-2 Lempertz, Koln #42/R
£1548 $2400 €2322 Capri battery (13x13x13cm-5x5x5in) s.num.49/50 artificial lemon light bulb and socket. 25-Sep-2 Christie's, Rockefeller NY #249/R est:2000-2500
£1834 $2879 €2751 Object (41x31x3cm-16x12x1in) s.i. window wiper prov. 25-Nov-2 Germann, Zurich #35/R est:4000-6000 (S.FR 4200)
£1923 $2981 €3000 Capri battery (18x18x18cm-7x7x7in) s.i. bulb lemon. 3-Dec-2 Lempertz, Koln #55/R est:2400
£5128 $7949 €8000 Boxes (63x31x18cm-25x12x7in) s.i. verso num.52/200 zinc iron pyrites gauze. 3-Dec-2 Lempertz, Koln #43/R est:10000
£6159 $10101 €8500 La zappa (75x35x7cm-30x14x3in) s.i. num.5/35 iron wood. 28-May-3 Lempertz, Koln #41/R est:6500-7000
£7051 $10929 €11000 Enterprise 18.11.72, 18:5:16 hours (41x30x15cm-16x12x6in) i. num.24/24 zinc box photograph camera felt. 3-Dec-2 Lempertz, Koln #45/R est:15000-18000
£12000 $19680 €18000 Ziege Deine Wunde - Show your wounds (107x79x5cm-42x31x2in) photographic negative black film between glass plates prov.lit. 6-Feb-3 Christie's, London #704/R est:8000-12000

Works on paper

£418 $661 €627 Guten einkauf (28x16cm-11x6in) s. paper bag. 28-Apr-3 Bukowskis, Stockholm #1025/R (S.KR 5500)
£528 $814 €840 Untitled (10x15cm-4x6in) s. card prov. 26-Oct-2 Cornette de St.Cyr, Paris #99/R
£629 $969 €1000 Enterprize (10x15cm-4x6in) s. card exec.1978 prov. 26-Oct-2 Cornette de St.Cyr, Paris #98/R
£927 $1511 €1400 Untitled (30x21cm-12x8in) graphite exec.1969 prov.exhib. 3-Feb-3 Cornette de St.Cyr, Paris #367/R
£1042 $1656 €1500 Sans titre (18x12cm-7x5in) s.d.68 collage felt. 29-Apr-3 Artcurial Briest, Paris #479/R est:1500-2000
£1282 $1987 €2000 Haupstrom (29x21cm-11x8in) s. i.d.1977 verso handwritten tex. 3-Dec-2 Christie's, Amsterdam #157/R est:1500-2000
£1282 $1987 €2000 Untitled (53x38cm-21x15in) s.d.1970 gouache on newspaper prov. 3-Dec-2 Christie's, Amsterdam #158/R est:1000-1500
£1361 $2163 €2000 Jambe d'Orwell. fabric label exec.1984 exhib.lit. 24-Mar-3 Cornette de St.Cyr, Paris #111/R
£1923 $2981 €3000 DDR house with oven (42x13cm-17x5in) s. pencil. 3-Dec-2 Lempertz, Koln #41/R est:4000-5000
£2319 $3803 €3200 Untitled (30x21cm-12x8in) s. verso pencil. 28-May-3 Lempertz, Koln #35/R est:4000
£2532 $4000 €4000 Appeal to the alternative (72x100cm-28x39in) s.i. mixed media newspaper on board prov. 27-Nov-2 Dorotheum, Vienna #89/R est:4000-6000
£2532 $4000 €4000 Appeal to the alternative (72x100cm-28x39in) s.i. mixed media newspaper on board prov. 27-Nov-2 Dorotheum, Vienna #90/R est:4000-6000
£3009 $4845 €4514 Untitled (53x39cm-21x15in) s.d.1962 Indian ink pencil. 7-May-3 Dobiaschofsky, Bern #1432/R est:4000 (S.FR 6500)
£3243 $5059 €4800 Food for thought (88x19cm-35x7in) s.d.1975 typed text. 26-Mar-3 Finarte Semenzato, Milan #159/R
£5362 $8794 €7400 Cutting the umbilical chord (9x13cm-4x5in) s.i. verso collage pencil newspaper lit. 28-May-3 Lempertz, Koln #36/R est:4000
£8974 $13910 €14000 Untitled (21x29cm-8x11in) pencil. 3-Dec-2 Lempertz, Koln #40/R est:18000-22000
£21519 $34000 €34000 Suit (170x60cm-67x24in) st.sig. wool prov.lit. 27-Nov-2 Tajan, Paris #81/R est:35000-40000

BEVAN, Irvine (fl.1908-1915) British

Works on paper

£961 $1499 €1442 Sir Richard Strachan's action, 3 November 1805 (31x48cm-12x19in) s. i.mount W/C over pencil pair. 11-Nov-2 Stephan Welz, Johannesburg #412/R est:20000-30000 (SA.R 15000)

BEVAN, Robert (1865-1925) British

£2000 $3120 €3000 Windmill and haystacks, Poland (21x26cm-8x10in) canvasboard painted c.1901 prov.exhib. 27-Mar-3 Christie's, Kensington #495/R est:3000-5000

Works on paper

£105000 $172200 €157500 Horse mart, Barbican (28x40cm-11x16in) pencil squared for transfer executed c.1920 prov.exhib. 6-Jun-3 Christie's, London #154/R est:15000-20000

BEVAN, Tony (1951-) British

Works on paper

£15000 $25050 €21750 Head and neck (134x121cm-53x48in) s. pigment acrylic canvas prov. 26-Jun-3 Sotheby's, London #124/R est:15000-20000

BEVERLEY, William Roxby (1811-1889) British

Works on paper

£260 $434 €377 Dutch fishing boats (15x27cm-6x11in) init. W/C over pencil. 24-Jun-3 Bonhams, Knightsbridge #137
£360 $590 €540 Strand, Scarborough (25x35cm-10x14in) W/C htd white. 4-Feb-3 Bonhams, Leeds #248
£500 $790 €725 Windswept landscape (16x27cm-6x11in) one s. W/C bodycol pair. 22-Jul-3 Bonhams, Knightsbridge #217/R
£720 $1109 €1080 Cornstooks near Arundel (23x46cm-9x18in) W/C. 22-Oct-2 Bonhams, Knightsbridge #193/R
£1111 $1800 €1611 On the Medway (16x31cm-6x12in) s. W/C gouache prov. 29-Jul-3 Christie's, Rockefeller NY #110/R est:2500-3500
£3500 $5740 €5075 Hungerford Bridge, London (24x34cm-9x13in) pencil W/C htd white scratching out prov. 5-Jun-3 Christie's, London #113/R est:2500-3500
£10000 $14300 €15000 Scarborough from the strand (9x34cm-4x13in) s. pencil W/C bodycol gum scratching out prov.exhib.lit. 22-Jan-3 Christie's, London #58/R est:6000

BEVERLEY, William Roxby (attrib) (1811-1889) British

Works on paper

£420 $676 €630 Wherries on a Suffolk River (14x30cm-6x12in) W/C. 15-Jan-3 Cheffins Grain & Comins, Cambridge #353/R

BEVORT, Jan (?) Dutch?

£387 $624 €550 Katwijkse fishing boats (69x99cm-27x39in) s. 6-May-3 Vendu Notarishuis, Rotterdam #120/R

BEWER, Clemens (1820-1884) German

£7092 $11489 €10000 Laurel-wreath (127x169cm-50x67in) s. 22-May-3 Dorotheum, Vienna #75/R est:12000-15000

BEWICK, Pauline (1935-) Irish

£962 $1490 €1500 Sean the giant (80x111cm-31x44in) s.i.d.1974 pen ink W/C. 3-Dec-2 Bonhams & James Adam, Dublin #137/R est:1500-2500

Works on paper

£382 $596 €600 Her room (25x36cm-10x14in) s.d.1963 pen ink. 6-Nov-2 James Adam, Dublin #75/R
£458 $760 €650 John Moley on the stage doing this veras imitation of things (28x44cm-11x17in) ink. 10-Jun-3 James Adam, Dublin #113/R
£959 $1505 €1400 Circus monkey (69x56cm-27x22in) s. W/C prov. 15-Apr-3 De Veres Art Auctions, Dublin #204/R est:1400-1800
£2089 $3237 €3300 Floating over town (61x80cm-24x31in) s.d.1976 pen ink W/C. 25-Sep-2 James Adam, Dublin #31/R est:3000-4000
£2264 $3532 €3600 Pat growing things (58x77cm-23x30in) s.d.1979 W/C pen ink exhib. 17-Sep-2 Whyte's, Dublin #165/R est:2000-3000
£2405 $3728 €3800 Woman and her dog (78x57cm-31x22in) s. pen ink W/C. 25-Sep-2 James Adam, Dublin #70/R est:3000-4000
£8054 $12966 €12000 Woman and bull, Rossbeigh (80x58cm-31x23in) s.d.1979 W/C pen ink prov. lit. 18-Feb-3 Whyte's, Dublin #65/R est:8000-10000

BEYER, Carl (1826-1903) German

£1088 $1731 €1600 Painting trousers in the studio of the theatre scenery painter (24x29cm-9x11in) s.d.1860 board. 19-Mar-3 Neumeister, Munich #515/R est:2000

BEYER, Eugène (1817-1893) German

£3846 $5962 €6000 Christians against Muslims (122x171cm-48x67in) s.d.1849. 4-Dec-2 Finarte, Rome #757/R

BEYER, Jan de (1703-1780) Swiss

Works on paper

£4630 $7500 €6945 View of the house and gardens at Ockenburgh (16x22cm-6x9in) s.i.d.1754 W/C over chk exhib. 21-Jan-3 Sotheby's, New York #135/R est:4000

BEYER, Otto (1885-1962) German
£886 $1400 €1400 Fishermen on beach (50x80cm-20x31in) s.d.54. 30-Nov-2 Bassenge, Berlin #6141/R
£2013 $3200 €3020 Port (50x51cm-20x20in) s. 27-Feb-3 Christie's, Rockefeller NY #89/R
£3548 $5606 €5500 Expressionist landscape (62x80cm-24x31in) s. 18-Dec-2 Castellana, Madrid #56/R

BEYER, Tom (1907-1981) German
£323 $474 €500 Cuxhaven harbour (70x80cm-28x31in) s. 24-Jun-2 Dr Fritz Nagel, Stuttgart #5957/R

BEYEREN, Abraham van (1620-1690) Dutch
£12950 $20719 €18000 Still life with partridge, turkey, orange, goblet, mortar, knife (64x59cm-25x23in) mono.d.1664. 13-May-3 Sotheby's, Amsterdam #44/R est:30000-50000
£53957 $86331 €75000 Gapes and other fruits in a wan-li kraak porcelain bowl, with plucked chicken (101x87cm-40x34in) init. prov. 14-May-3 Christie's, Amsterdam #192/R est:50000-70000
£60000 $94200 €90000 Lbster with grapes and peach in porcelain bowl (62x78cm-24x31in) init. 11-Dec-2 Christie's, London #59/R est:60000-80000

BEYLE, Pierre Marie (1838-1902) French
£1655 $2648 €2400 Alentours de new York (30x43cm-12x17in) s.i.d.1885. 12-Mar-3 Libert, Castor, Paris #52 est:1200-1500
£4054 $6324 €6000 Young women on beach (66x50cm-26x20in) s. 27-Mar-3 Dr Fritz Nagel, Stuttgart #792/R est:1500
£5247 $8500 €7608 Fleur des Greves (99x71cm-39x28in) s.i. 21-May-3 Doyle, New York #219/R est:8000-12000

BEYSCHLAG, Robert (1838-1903) German
£3165 $4905 €5000 Holy Family resting on the road to Egypt (86x132cm-34x52in) s.i. 25-Sep-2 Neumeister, Munich #540/R est:8000
Works on paper
£342 $534 €500 Girl with cat (24x17cm-9x7in) s. pencil dr lit. 10-Apr-3 Allgauer, Kempten #2590

BEZARD, Jean Louis (1799-?) French
Works on paper
£355 $592 €500 Henri de Bourbon au tombeau de fleurete (21x16cm-8x6in) s. W/C gouache black crayon. 18-Jun-3 Piasa, Paris #5

BEZOMBES, Roger (1913-1994) French
£570 $883 €900 Le parc de Versailles (52x36cm-20x14in) s. panel. 29-Sep-2 Eric Pillon, Calais #236/R
£897 $1400 €1346 Bouquet Louis XIV (61x57cm-24x22in) s. s.i.verso panel. 5-Nov-2 Doyle, New York #58/R
£2051 $3179 €3200 Moulin Rouge (75x35cm-30x14in) s. panel prov.exhib. 5-Dec-2 Gros & Delettrez, Paris #115/R
£11538 $17885 €18000 Chaste Suzanne (114x146cm-45x57in) s. s.i.verso painted 1945 prov.exhib. 4-Dec-2 Pierre Berge, Paris #126/R est:22000
£16026 $25160 €25000 Le roi de la nuit (183x65cm-72x26in) s. panel prov.exhib.lit. 16-Dec-2 Gros & Delettrez, Paris #48/R est:22000-30000
£21277 $35532 €30000 Hommage a Gaugin (205x144cm-81x57in) s. 18-Jun-3 Pierre Berge, Paris #171/R est:15000-20000
Works on paper
£285 $444 €450 La fuite en Egypte (23x18cm-9x7in) s. gouache sold with a monotype. 20-Oct-2 Charbonneaux, Paris #47 est:450-500
£2830 $4358 €4500 Dignitaire au cafe. Figures devant une echoppe de dinanderie (23x18cm-9x7in) s. gouache W/C pair. 23-Oct-2 Rabourdin & Choppin de Janvry, Paris #245/R

BEZOR, Annette Thea (1950-) Australian
£2151 $3269 €3227 Decorum II (139x202cm-55x80in) s.i.verso prov. 28-Aug-2 Deutscher-Menzies, Melbourne #154/R est:7000-9000 (A.D 6000)

BEZZI, Bartolomeo (1851-1925) Italian
£4403 $6780 €7000 Lady (40x29cm-16x11in) s. 23-Oct-2 Finarte, Milan #177/R

BEZZI, Giovanni Francesco (attrib) (?-1571) Italian
£17419 $27523 €27000 Holy Family (18x14cm-7x6in) panel. 18-Dec-2 Tajan, Paris #1/R est:18000
Works on paper
£2168 $3620 €3100 Venus et amour. Elements architecturaux (23x12cm-9x5in) i. pen brown ink wash double-sided. 27-Jun-3 Claude Aguttes, Neuilly #14/R est:2500-3000

BEZZOLA, Mario (1881-1968) Italian
Works on paper
£748 $1190 €1100 Trees in bloom in Mondello (35x55cm-14x22in) s.d.1947 pastel card. 18-Mar-3 Finarte, Milan #192/R

BHATTACHARJEE, Bikash (1940-) Indian
£7382 $12179 €10704 She with a newspaper (102x106cm-40x42in) s.d.81 indis.i.verso. 6-Jul-3 Christie's, Hong Kong #101/R est:65000-85000 (HK.D 95000)

BHENGU, Gerard (1910-1990) South African
Works on paper
£3611 $5814 €5417 Bird chaser (21x32cm-8x13in) s. W/C. 12-May-3 Stephan Welz, Johannesburg #544/R est:20000-30000 (SA.R 42000)

BIAI FOGLEIN, Istvan (1905-1974) Hungarian
£1006 $1569 €1459 On the harness racing (80x60cm-31x24in) s. 12-Apr-3 Mu Terem Galeria, Budapest #63/R est:300000 (H.F 360000)
£1479 $2293 €2145 The show (95x113cm-37x44in) s. prov.exhib. 9-Dec-2 Mu Terem Galeria, Budapest #206/R est:480000 (H.F 550000)
£1956 $3052 €2836 Scene in the coffee house (37x44cm-15x17in) s. panel. 12-Apr-3 Mu Terem Galeria, Budapest #64/R est:350000 (H.F 700000)
Works on paper
£538 $834 €780 Acrobats (43x29cm-17x11in) s. W/C. 9-Dec-2 Mu Terem Galeria, Budapest #15/R est:140000 (H.F 200000)
£559 $872 €839 Street (37x26cm-15x10in) s. W/C. 11-Apr-3 Kieselbach, Budapest #170/R est:60000-200000 (H.F 200000)

BIALETTI, Felice (1864-1958) Italian
Sculpture
£1258 $1937 €2000 Dominating thought (75cm-30in) bronze lit. 23-Oct-2 Finarte, Milan #111/R
£6000 $10020 €8700 Deep in thought (76x49cm-30x19in) s. dk green pat bronze. 8-Jul-3 Sotheby's, London #228/R est:6000-8000
£8500 $13345 €12750 Esausta (37x49x41cm-15x19x16in) s. brown pat. bronze lit. 10-Dec-2 Sotheby's, London #160/R est:3000-5000

BIANCHI, Alberto (1882-1969) Italian
£680 $1082 €1000 Nap (80x60cm-31x24in) s. 1-Mar-3 Meeting Art, Vercelli #197
Works on paper
£452 $714 €700 Racket (65x41cm-26x16in) s. pastel card. 18-Dec-2 Finarte, Milan #154/R

BIANCHI, Domenico (1955-) Italian
£850 $1318 €1275 Untitled (200x125cm-79x49in) init.d.84 verso oil wax wood on canvas. 5-Dec-2 Christie's, Kensington #248/R
Works on paper
£3846 $5962 €6000 Untitled (80x60cm-31x24in) wax card. 4-Dec-2 Finarte, Milan #491/R
£4487 $7045 €7000 Untitled (80x60cm-31x24in) s.d.99 wax. 21-Nov-2 Finarte, Rome #277/R

BIANCHI, Gerardo (1845-1922) Italian
£7823 $12439 €11500 Maternity (65x50cm-26x20in) s. 18-Mar-3 Finarte, Milan #170/R

BIANCHI, L (19/20th C) ?
£566 $877 €900 Still life with antiquities (26x21cm-10x8in) s. panel. 29-Oct-2 Dorotheum, Vienna #35/R

BIANCHI, Luigi (1828-1914) Italian
£320 $508 €470 Donnalucata, beach (30x50cm-12x20in) s.d.1973 cardboard on canvas. 1-Mar-3 Meeting Art, Vercelli #671
£1677 $2650 €2600 Portrait of Sigismondo Nappi (58x43cm-23x17in) board. 18-Dec-2 Finarte, Milan #100/R
£2308 $3577 €3600 Back from the mountains (101x62cm-40x24in) s. 4-Dec-2 Finarte, Rome #775/R est:5000

BIANCHI, Mose (1840-1904) Italian
£3165 $5000 €5000 Lady in profile (49x35cm-19x14in) init. cardboard. 26-Nov-2 Christie's, Rome #151/R est:6000
£6452 $10194 €10000 Pastoral scene (30x25cm-12x10in) s. painted c.1895 prov.lit. 18-Dec-2 Finarte, Milan #56/R est:9000
Works on paper
£1224 $1947 €1800 Seated farmer. Young woman (32x24cm-13x9in) pencil double-sided prov. 18-Mar-3 Finarte, Milan #177/R
£2564 $4026 €4000 Cart in the rain (25x35cm-10x14in) s. W/C. 10-Dec-2 Della Rocca, Turin #385/R est:1500

BIANCHI, Mose (attrib) (1840-1904) Italian
£1509 $2325 €2400 Two women (24x18cm-9x7in) init. board. 23-Oct-2 Finarte, Milan #180

BIANCHI, Pietro (1694-1740) Italian
Works on paper
£67901 $110000 €101852 Diana and actaeon. Rape of Europa (30x48cm-12x19in) gouache pair octagonal shaped prov. 23-Jan-3 Sotheby's, New York #76/R est:60000-80000

BIANCHI, Vincentius (?) Italian?
£500 $800 €750 Untitled (9x7cm-4x3in) i.verso copper after Guido Reni. 7-Jan-3 Bonhams, Knightsbridge #77/R

BIANCHINI, Arthur (1869-1955) Swedish
£323 $510 €485 Coastal landscape from Sandhamn (54x76cm-21x30in) s,. 27-Nov-2 Falkkloos, Malmo #77622/R (S.KR 4600)
£1348 $2089 €2022 View in Stockholm (48x62cm-19x24in) s. 3-Dec-2 Bukowskis, Stockholm #339/R est:20000-25000 (S.KR 19000)
£2560 $4147 €3712 Flying the flags in the harbour, Sandhamn (106x73cm-42x29in) s. 26-May-3 Bukowskis, Stockholm #93/R est:25000-30000 (S.KR 33000)

BIANCHINI, C (1860-1905) French
£250 $390 €375 Naked putto (50x23cm-20x9in) s. after a Renaissance artist. 22-Sep-2 Lots Road, London #355

BIANCO, Baccio del (attrib) (1604-1656) Italian
£780 $1303 €1100 Marchand ambulant (13x20cm-5x8in) panel. 18-Jun-3 Tajan, Paris #12

BIANCO, Pieretto (1875-1937) Italian
£962 $1490 €1500 Portrait of Livio Boni, cello player (47x53cm-19x21in) s.i.d.15 cardboard. 4-Dec-2 Finarte, Rome #787/R
£2075 $3196 €3300 Canal in Venice (46x32cm-18x13in) s. 23-Oct-2 Finarte, Milan #148/R
Works on paper
£461 $747 €650 Canala a Venezia (28x18cm-11x7in) s. W/C. 22-May-3 Stadion, Trieste #375/R

BIANCO, Remo (1922-1990) Italian
Sculpture
£1307 $2092 €2000 Print art (25x25cm-10x10in) papier mache exec.1950. 4-Jan-3 Meeting Art, Vercelli #398
Works on paper
£321 $503 €500 TD (21x18cm-8x7in) mixed media gold leaf board. 23-Nov-2 Meeting Art, Vercelli #50
£5128 $8051 €8000 Print (120x100cm-47x39in) s.d.1958 mixed media gold leaf. 23-Nov-2 Meeting Art, Vercelli #87/R

BIARD, François Auguste (1799-1882) French
£774 $1223 €1200 Jeune mere et ses enfants (40x32cm-16x13in) 20-Dec-2 Tajan, Paris #167
£1474 $2315 €2300 Attaque de la diligence (66x101cm-26x40in) s. 13-Dec-2 Piasa, Paris #49

BIASI DA TEULADA, Giuseppe (1885-1945) Italian
£423 $656 €635 Les animaux et les pierres se partagent ma nuit (116x81cm-46x32in) s.d.62 s.i.d.62 stretcher. 1-Oct-2 Rasmussen, Copenhagen #252/R (D.KR 5000)

BIASI, Guido (1933-1984) Italian
£411 $641 €600 Voyage (60x50cm-24x20in) s.d.1976 verso. 10-Apr-3 Finarte Semenzato, Rome #305
Works on paper
£1014 $1581 €1500 Mnemotheque (60x72cm-24x28in) s.d.1971 pencil acrylic. 26-Mar-3 Finarte Semenzato, Milan #103/R

BIBBY, Max (?) British?
£1400 $2170 €2100 Off Greenwich, barges on the Thames (48x61cm-19x24in) s. board. 26-Sep-2 Lane, Penzance #353 est:1500-1800

BIBEL, Leon (1913-1995) American
£4878 $8000 €7073 Flagbearers (76x76cm-30x30in) prov. 1-Jun-3 Wright, Chicago #211/R est:9000-12000
£4878 $8000 €7073 Dead end (76x91cm-30x36in) prov. 1-Jun-3 Wright, Chicago #212/R est:9000-12000
Works on paper
£732 $1200 €1061 Women in the fields (31x24cm-12x9in) estate st.verso brush pen ink card stock. 5-Jun-3 Swann Galleries, New York #32/R
£976 $1600 €1415 Unemployed (30x25cm-12x10in) brush ink prov. 1-Jun-3 Wright, Chicago #209/R est:1500-2000
£976 $1600 €1415 Injured at work (25x30cm-10x12in) brush ink prov. 1-Jun-3 Wright, Chicago #210/R est:1500-2000
£1220 $2000 €1769 Machine cog (32x23cm-13x9in) estate st.verso brush pen ink card stock. 5-Jun-3 Swann Galleries, New York #30/R est:1500-2500

BIBERSTEIN, Michael (1948-) Swiss
£3000 $4890 €4500 Untitled (70x118cm-28x46in) canvas on board in two parts painted 1987 prov.exhib. 3-Feb-3 Sotheby's, Olympia #110/R est:1000-1500

BIBIENA, Giuseppe Galli (1696-1756) Italian
Works on paper
£4013 $6500 €6020 Agony in the garden (45x33cm-18x13in) i. pen ink wash prov. 22-Jan-3 Christie's, Rockefeller NY #43/R

BIBIENA, Giuseppe Galli (attrib) (1696-1756) Italian
Works on paper
£1633 $2596 €2400 Interior of palace (37x34cm-15x13in) pen ik wash. 24-Mar-3 Tajan, Paris #19/R

BICAT, Andre (1909-1996) French
£300 $465 €450 Bowl of fruit with striped wallpaper (46x61cm-18x24in) s. board. 3-Dec-2 Bonhams, Knightsbridge #136/R
£300 $477 €450 Night thoughts in the city (46x61cm-18x24in) s. 18-Mar-3 Bonhams, Knightsbridge #25
£400 $620 €600 Confrontation (55x46cm-22x18in) s. board. 3-Dec-2 Bonhams, Knightsbridge #137/R
£420 $680 €630 Summer treporti (70x86cm-28x34in) s. 20-May-3 Bonhams, Knightsbridge #7/R
£500 $795 €750 Landscape woman (51x61cm-20x24in) s.d.65. 18-Mar-3 Bonhams, Knightsbridge #24
£1000 $1590 €1500 Band (81x117cm-32x46in) s. 18-Mar-3 Bonhams, Knightsbridge #23 est:1000-1500
£1200 $1860 €1800 Chords (76x102cm-30x40in) s. 3-Dec-2 Bonhams, Knightsbridge #127/R est:1000-1500
Works on paper
£300 $486 €450 Pines near Pisa (40x61cm-16x24in) s. 20-May-3 Bonhams, Knightsbridge #1/R

BICCHI, Silvio (1874-1948) Italian
£769 $1208 €1200 Sailing boat (16x25cm-6x10in) s.i.d.906 verso cardboard. 16-Dec-2 Pandolfini, Florence #128/R
Works on paper
£709 $1149 €1000 Ritratto di pianista. Nel bosco (55x46cm-22x18in) s.d.1927 mixed media two. 22-May-3 Stadion, Trieste #257/R
£833 $1317 €1300 Portrait of Mussolini (49x33cm-19x13in) pastel exec.1921. 15-Nov-2 Farsetti, Prato #451/R

BICCI DI LORENZO (1373-1452) Italian
£65000 $108550 €94250 Miracle of Saint Nicholas of Bari (31x27cm-12x11in) tempera panel prov.lit. 9-Jul-3 Christie's, London #75/R est:70000-100000

BICCI, Lorenzo di (c.1350-1427) Italian
£123457 $200000 €185186 Madonna and Child enthroned (82x48cm-32x19in) i. tempera on panel arched top. 24-Jan-3 Christie's, Rockefeller NY #23/R est:100000-150000

BICKEL, Karl (1886-1982) Swiss
£437 $681 €656 Golgatha (49x60cm-19x24in) mono. s.i.verso masonite. 8-Nov-2 Dobiaschofsky, Bern #236/R (S.FR 1000)

BICKERSTAFF, George (1893-1954) American
£260 $380 €390 University road, Belfast (51x36cm-20x14in) s. board. 12-Jun-2 John Ross, Belfast #120
£404 $650 €606 Landscape, flower fields (61x76cm-24x30in) s. prov. 18-Feb-3 John Moran, Pasadena #164
£419 $700 €608 Mountain landscape (64x76cm-25x30in) s. 17-Jun-3 John Moran, Pasadena #189
£484 $750 €726 Autumn landscape with stream (61x76cm-24x30in) s. painted c.1925. 8-Dec-2 Toomey, Oak Park #739/R

BICKNELL, Albion Harris (1837-1915) American
£440 $700 €660 Near saugus centre, Massachusetts (43x18cm-17x7in) mono.i. verso panel. 22-Mar-3 New Orleans Auction, New Orleans #1137/R
£1529 $2400 €2294 In the shallow, scen with geese and punt (38x53cm-15x21in) s. panel. 22-Nov-2 Skinner, Boston #72/R est:2000-3000

BICKNELL, Evelyn M (1857-1936) American
£352 $550 €528 Spring landscape with tree on a grassy hill (20x28cm-8x11in) s. board. 28-Mar-3 Eldred, East Dennis #679/R

BICKNELL, Frank Alfred (1866-1943) American
£764 $1200 €1146 Marshland clouds (30x41cm-12x16in) s. board. 23-Nov-2 Jackson's, Cedar Falls #59/R

BICTBICHIELS, J (19th C) ?
£1300 $2119 €1950 Girl in a barn washing a copper pan at a barrel (40x32cm-16x13in) panel. 29-Jan-3 Dreweatt Neate, Newbury #141/R est:1000-1500

BIDA, Alexandre (1823-1895) French
Works on paper
£270 $422 €400 Portrait d'homme (28x22cm-11x9in) s.d.1854 chl oval. 28-Mar-3 Delvaux, Paris #9/R
£284 $443 €420 Deux femmes turques (29x24cm-11x9in) s. crayon htd chk. 31-Mar-3 Piasa, Paris #66
£323 $504 €510 Le Sacre de Charles VII (24x18cm-9x7in) s. pencil. 15-Sep-2 Feletin, Province #103

BIDAULD, Jean Joseph Xavier (1758-1846) French
£4938 $8000 €7407 View of a waterfall (25x39cm-10x15in) i.d.1787 paper on canvas. 23-Jan-3 Sotheby's, New York #109/R est:10000-15000
£11111 $18000 €16667 Francois I at the fountain of Vaucluse (61x50cm-24x20in) prov. 23-Jan-3 Sotheby's, New York #219/R est:20000

BIDAULD, Jean Joseph Xavier (attrib) (1758-1846) French
£3000 $4650 €4500 Italianate landscape with village and mountains beyond (35x48cm-14x19in) 31-Oct-2 Sotheby's, Olympia #189/R est:3000-4000
£15248 $25465 €21500 Paysage montagneux (32x40cm-13x16in) bears apocryphe Corot sig. paper. 23-Jun-3 Beaussant & Lefèvre, Paris #280/R est:6000-8000

BIDDLE, George (1885-1973) American
£968 $1500 €1452 Nude in a landscape (36x25cm-14x10in) s.i.d.1919 i.d.July 14 1919 verso panel. 8-Dec-2 Freeman, Philadelphia #142/R est:1500-2500

BIDDLE, Laurence (1888-?) British
£350 $553 €525 Still life of flowers in an Oriental bowl on a ledge (30x43cm-12x17in) s.indis.d. panel. 27-Nov-2 Hamptons Fine Art, Godalming #346
£400 $644 €600 Vase of pansies, cornflowers and violets (44x66cm-17x26in) s.d.33. 14-Jan-3 Bonhams, Knightsbridge #20/R
£400 $648 €600 Still life with pansies (35x53cm-14x21in) s.d.31 panel. 20-May-3 Sotheby's, Olympia #244/R
£590 $909 €885 Spring flowers (18x29cm-7x11in) s.d.33 board. 5-Sep-2 Christie's, Kensington #341/R
£600 $942 €900 Pansies and primulas (31x37cm-12x15in) s.d.27 board lit. 16-Apr-3 Christie's, Kensington #889/R
£1450 $2233 €2175 Still life of mixed flowers in a vase (30x41cm-12x16in) s. panel. 23-Oct-2 Hamptons Fine Art, Godalming #177/R est:600-800
£1800 $2790 €2700 Still life of pansies and other flowers in a Chinese porcelain bowl (33x51cm-13x20in) s.d.1948. 4-Dec-2 Neal & Fletcher, Woodbridge #263 est:2000-3000
£2100 $3276 €3150 Flowerpiece (34x52cm-13x20in) s.d.49 panel prov. 10-Apr-3 Bonhams, Edinburgh #54/R est:1000-1500

BIDDULPH, Sir M (1823-1904) British
Works on paper
£355 $592 €500 Citadelle de Corfou (12x22cm-5x9in) d.4 mai 1860 pencil W/C. 23-Jun-3 Beaussant & Lefèvre, Paris #109

BIDLO, Mike (1955-) American
£5000 $8200 €7500 Not Picasso, head of a woman (81x64cm-32x25in) s.verso prov. 7-Feb-3 Sotheby's, London #190/R est:5000-7000
£25000 $40000 €37500 Not Pollock (91x153cm-36x60in) s.d.84 verso oil enamel prov. 15-May-3 Christie's, Rockefeller NY #366/R est:18000-22000

BIE, Erasme de (1629-1675) Flemish
£30000 $47100 €45000 Antwerp, procession on the Meir with elegant townsfolk (85x117cm-33x46in) s. prov. 12-Dec-2 Sotheby's, London #10/R est:30000-40000

BIEDERMAN, Charles (1906-) American
£2896 $4750 €4199 Untitled - Portrait of man with red shirt (41x36cm-16x14in) s.d.1933-7 oil on linen prov. 1-Jun-3 Wright, Chicago #150/R est:5000-7000
£7317 $12000 €10610 Untitled (46x38cm-18x15in) s.d.1935 oil on linen prov. 1-Jun-3 Wright, Chicago #144/R est:15000-20000
£8537 $14000 €12379 Untitled (71x91cm-28x36in) s.d.1935 oil on linen prov. 1-Jun-3 Wright, Chicago #146/R est:9000-12000
£9146 $15000 €13262 Untitled (81x64cm-32x25in) s.d.1935 oil on linen prov. 1-Jun-3 Wright, Chicago #147/R est:15000-20000
£9756 $16000 €14146 No.39 (74x91cm-29x36in) s.d.1935 i.verso oil on linen prov. 1-Jun-3 Wright, Chicago #142/R est:20000-30000
£9756 $16000 €14146 No.32 (71x91cm-28x36in) s.d.1935 oil on linen. 1-Jun-3 Wright, Chicago #143/R est:20000-30000
£14024 $23000 €20335 Untitled (61x51cm-24x20in) s.i.d.1936 oil on linen prov. 1-Jun-3 Wright, Chicago #135/R est:15000-20000
£14634 $24000 €21219 Untitled (91x71cm-36x28in) s.d.1935 oil on linen prov. 1-Jun-3 Wright, Chicago #145/R est:20000-25000
Works on paper
£915 $1500 €1327 Untitled - two figures (20x18cm-8x7in) s.d.1933 pencil ink wash prov. 1-Jun-3 Wright, Chicago #148/R est:2000-3000
£2439 $4000 €3537 Untitled (48x38cm-19x15in) s.d.1939 mixed media collage gouache prov. 1-Jun-3 Wright, Chicago #140/R est:5000-7000
£3049 $5000 €4421 Untitled (56x41cm-22x16in) s.i.d.37 ink. 1-Jun-3 Wright, Chicago #138/R est:6000-8000
£3659 $6000 €5306 Untitled (48x38cm-19x15in) s.d.1935 ink col pencil. 1-Jun-3 Wright, Chicago #141/R est:7000-9000
£5183 $8500 €7515 Untitled (43x33cm-17x13in) s.d.1937 gouache prov. 1-Jun-3 Wright, Chicago #134/R est:5000-7000

BIEDERMANN, Johann Jakob (1763-1830) Swiss
£13100 $20568 €19650 Mollis (33x44cm-13x17in) mono. 25-Nov-2 Sotheby's, Zurich #11/R est:30000-40000 (S.FR 30000)
£28384 $44563 €42576 Lucern with Pilatus (33x44cm-13x17in) mono. 25-Nov-2 Sotheby's, Zurich #4/R est:40000-60000 (S.FR 65000)

BIEGAS, Boleslas (1877-1954) Polish
£1689 $2635 €2500 Cathedrale fantastique (48x57cm-19x22in) panel. 26-Mar-3 Millon & Associes, Paris #153/R
£5161 $8155 €8000 Regards dans le lointain (52x32cm-20x13in) s. cardboard prov. 18-Dec-2 Tajan, Paris #38/R est:12000
Sculpture
£2207 $3686 €3200 Le satyre du bois de Boulogne (48cm-19in) s.num. black pat bronze. 10-Jul-3 Artcurial Briest, Paris #249/R est:3000-3500
£10764 $17760 €15500 L'effroi (175x35x40cm-69x14x16in) s.i.d.1910 green pat bronze st.f.Alexis Rudier. 1-Jul-3 Claude Aguttes, Neuilly #186/R est:4500-6000

BIEGEL, Peter (1913-1988) British
£500 $780 €750 Matador standing at the Snailwell stud, Newmarket (51x61cm-20x24in) s.d.61. 26-Mar-3 Sotheby's, Olympia #146/R
£620 $967 €930 Sketch of Anglo (32x34cm-13x13in) s.i.d.2.5.68 board. 6-Nov-2 Sotheby's, Olympia #101/R est:500-700
£950 $1549 €1425 Bulbarrow, Dorset (39x49cm-15x19in) s. board prov. 30-Jan-3 Lawrence, Crewkerne #747/R
£2800 $4340 €4200 Huntsman and hounds in an extensive landscape (51x41cm-20x16in) s. 31-Oct-2 Duke & Son, Dorchester #321/R est:1500-3000
£3200 $4960 €4800 Heythrop - Shallowford, Exmoor with Captain R E Wallace (41x51cm-16x20in) s. prov. 31-Oct-2 Duke & Son, Dorchester #323/R est:3000-4000
£5200 $8060 €7800 Reaching for it - the open ditch (51x61cm-20x24in) s. i.verso. 31-Oct-2 Duke & Son, Dorchester #322/R est:2500-4500
£6000 $9300 €9000 Hunter chasers (41x51cm-16x20in) s. prov. 31-Oct-2 Duke & Son, Dorchester #320/R est:1500-2500
£8000 $12480 €12000 Grand National, jumping Becher's first time round (49x74cm-19x29in) s.d.62 prov. 17-Oct-2 Lawrence, Crewkerne #1589/R est:3000-5000
Works on paper
£250 $400 €375 Pleader: Gillingham and Shaftsbury Show (22x26cm-9x10in) s.i.d.76 W/C pencil. 15-May-3 Lawrence, Crewkerne #939
£700 $1078 €1050 Huntsman on horse with hounds in foreground. s. mixed media. 6-Sep-2 Moore Allen & Innocent, Cirencester #886
£950 $1530 €1425 Not the hunted fox (26x38cm-10x15in) s. i.verso W/C prov. 15-Jan-3 Cheffins Grain & Comins, Cambridge #400/R

BIELCHOWSKI, Karl August (1826-1883) German
£1389 $2236 €2014 Two fisherwomen dancing (101x81cm-40x32in) s.d.1872. 7-May-3 Dobiaschofsky, Bern #356/R est:5500 (S.FR 3000)

BIELEN, Stanley (20th C) American
£262 $425 €393 White and pink (25x23cm-10x9in) s. prov. 24-Jan-3 Freeman, Philadelphia #177/R

BIELER, André Charles (1896-1989) Canadian

£658 $1021 €987 La forge, Ste famille, Ile d'Orlean (30x40cm-12x16in) s. painted 1977 prov. 3-Dec-2 Joyner, Toronto #259/R est:3000-4000 (C.D 1600)
£1067 $1749 €1601 Auction at Glenora (26x34cm-10x13in) s. acrylic panel prov.exhib. 3-Jun-3 Joyner, Toronto #401/R est:800-1200 (C.D 2400)
£1152 $1786 €1728 Japanese fishing village (30x40cm-12x16in) s. board prov. 3-Dec-2 Joyner, Toronto #303/R est:1200-1500 (C.D 2800)
£1222 $2005 €1833 Matin d'ete (36x51cm-14x20in) s.i.d.1969 masonite prov. 27-May-3 Sotheby's, Toronto #131/R est:2500-4000 (C.D 2750)
£1906 $3049 €2859 St. Urbain (51x61cm-20x24in) s. i.d.1979 verso prov. 15-May-3 Heffel, Vancouver #67/R est:4500-5500 (C.D 4250)
£2469 $3827 €3704 Madame Girard Misere (50x40cm-20x16in) s.d.32 prov.exhib. 3-Dec-2 Joyner, Toronto #133/R est:6000-8000 (C.D 6000)

Works on paper

£311 $510 €467 Outside the stable (22x29cm-9x11in) s. indis d. mixed media. 3-Jun-3 Joyner, Toronto #571 (C.D 700)

BIELER, Ernest (1863-1948) Swiss

£3167 $5290 €4592 La mere de Laurent (52x64cm-20x25in) s. prov. 24-Jun-3 Koller, Zurich #20/R est:7000-10000 (S.FR 7000)
£6335 $10579 €9186 Autumn landscape (84x134cm-33x53in) tempera panel prov. 24-Jun-3 Koller, Zurich #33/R est:8000-12000 (S.FR 14000)
£8145 $13602 €11810 Le retour de la procession (85x110cm-33x43in) s. tempera board lit. 24-Jun-3 Koller, Zurich #23/R est:16000-24000 (S.FR 18000)
£20000 $31000 €30000 Chevres dans un sous-bois, Saviese (57x92cm-22x36in) s. painted c.1898 lit. 7-Dec-2 Galerie du Rhone, Sion #464/R est:40000-60000 (S.FR 46000)
£29167 $45208 €43751 Jeune saviesanne (34x28cm-13x11in) s.d.1918 tempera prov. 7-Dec-2 Galerie du Rhone, Sion #464a/R est:80000-120000 (S.FR 67100)

Works on paper

£655 $1035 €983 Cheval au charbon (29x19cm-11x7in) chl gouache. 17-Nov-2 Koller, Geneva #1303 (S.FR 1500)
£943 $1528 €1670 Deux nus assis sure la margelle d'un puits (43x47cm-17x19in) s. pencil prov. 26-May-3 Sotheby's, Zurich #52/R est:2000-4000 (S.FR 2000)
£1415 $2292 €2505 Etude pour les heures (65x46cm-26x18in) s.i. pastel. 26-May-3 Sotheby's, Zurich #53/R est:3000-5000 (S.FR 3000)
£1415 $2292 €2505 Etude pour les heures (62x50cm-24x20in) s.i. pastel. 26-May-3 Sotheby's, Zurich #55/R est:3000-5000 (S.FR 3000)
£1659 $2589 €2489 View of Sion (24x34cm-9x13in) mono.i. chl dr. 8-Nov-2 Dobiaschofsky, Bern #64/R est:2200 (S.FR 3800)
£1887 $3057 €3339 Rose tricotant (36x25cm-14x10in) s. st.sig.i. verso pencil. 26-May-3 Sotheby's, Zurich #37/R est:4000-5000 (S.FR 4000)
£2043 $3167 €3065 Bacchant (49x39cm-19x15in) s. pierre noire pencil W/C prov.lit. 7-Dec-2 Galerie du Rhone, Sion #465/R est:3000-4000 (S.FR 4700)
£2969 $4662 €4454 Chateau Morestel a Grone (64x39cm-25x15in) s.i. gouache pastel. 25-Nov-2 Sotheby's, Zurich #88/R est:5000-7000 (S.FR 6800)
£3275 $5142 €4913 Saint Saphorin (50x62cm-20x24in) st.sig. prov. 25-Nov-2 Sotheby's, Zurich #104/R est:6000-8000 (S.FR 7500)
£3538 $5731 €6263 Crepuscule a Saint Saphorin (48x63cm-19x25in) st.sig. pastel. 26-May-3 Sotheby's, Zurich #58/R est:6000-8000 (S.FR 7500)
£3774 $6113 €6680 Crepuscule - la foret (32x49cm-13x19in) mono. pastel. 26-May-3 Sotheby's, Zurich #59/R est:3000-5000 (S.FR 8000)
£4405 $6432 €6608 Vignobles au Lac Leman (42x60cm-17x24in) s.i. pastel chk chl prov. 17-Jun-2 Philippe Schuler, Zurich #4156/R est:12000-15000 (S.FR 10000)
£4481 $7259 €7932 Valaisanne (35x22cm-14x9in) s. pencil Indian ink W/C. 26-May-3 Sotheby's, Zurich #38/R est:10000-12000 (S.FR 9500)
£6438 $10172 €9657 Arbre (65x50cm-26x20in) s. gouache over pencil prov. 28-Nov-2 Christie's, Zurich #18/R est:15000-20000 (S.FR 15000)
£6438 $10172 €9657 Paysage de Saviese (99x67cm-39x26in) s. gouache over pencil prov. 28-Nov-2 Christie's, Zurich #23/R est:12000-15000 (S.FR 15000)
£9607 $15083 €14411 Crepuscule en montagne (29x50cm-11x20in) st.sig. pastel. 25-Nov-2 Sotheby's, Zurich #101/R est:1500-2000 (S.FR 22000)
£16309 $25768 €24464 Deux femmes (39x66cm-15x26in) s. W/C over pencil prov. 28-Nov-2 Christie's, Zurich #20/R est:18000-22000 (S.FR 38000)

BIELFIELD, Henry (1802-?) British

£800 $1256 €1200 Meeting of day and light (36x41cm-14x16in) s.i.verso. 16-Apr-3 Christie's, Kensington #507/R

BIELING, Hermann Friedrich (1887-1964) Dutch

£446 $696 €700 Church in Najac (59x39cm-23x15in) s. 5-Nov-2 Vendu Notarishuis, Rotterdam #240
£789 $1279 €1200 Garden (40x50cm-16x20in) s.d.33. 21-Jan-3 Christie's, Amsterdam #361/R est:1200-1600
£789 $1279 €1200 Blossoming tree (45x53cm-18x21in) s. 21-Jan-3 Christie's, Amsterdam #390 est:1200-1600
£828 $1292 €1300 Rocky coast of Brittany (42x81cm-17x32in) s.d.51. 5-Nov-2 Vendu Notarishuis, Rotterdam #54/R
£828 $1292 €1300 Street in Marrakech (71x56cm-28x22in) s. d.35 verso. 5-Nov-2 Vendu Notarishuis, Rotterdam #56/R
£892 $1373 €1400 Hilligersberg (24x31cm-9x12in) s.d.36 s.i.d.verso canvas on panel. 3-Sep-2 Christie's, Amsterdam #407/R
£1042 $1719 €1500 Nasturtium and poppies (44x65cm-17x26in) s.d.43. 1-Jul-3 Christie's, Amsterdam #340/R est:1800-2200
£1053 $1705 €1600 Farmyard with a blossoming tree (55x46cm-22x18in) s.d.50. 21-Jan-3 Christie's, Amsterdam #388/R est:1500-2000
£1529 $2385 €2400 Still life with cacti (59x44cm-23x17in) s. 5-Nov-2 Vendu Notarishuis, Rotterdam #9 est:1000-1500
£1645 $2664 €2500 Still life with apples (48x78cm-19x31in) s. 21-Jan-3 Christie's, Amsterdam #472/R est:2500-3500
£1667 $2750 €2400 Cactuses (50x60cm-20x24in) s. 1-Jul-3 Christie's, Amsterdam #342/R est:1500-2000
£2113 $3401 €3000 Still life of cacti (81x51cm-32x20in) s. 6-May-3 Vendu Notarishuis, Rotterdam #203/R est:1500-2000
£2930 $4571 €4600 House with studio (34x41cm-13x16in) init. exhib. 6-Nov-2 Vendue Huis, Gravenhage #655/R est:3500-4000

BIEN, Julius (1826-1909) American/German

Prints

£2174 $3500 €3261 Blue crane, or heron (49x73cm-19x29in) hand col chromolithograph after John James Audubon. 16-Jan-3 Christie's, Rockefeller NY #18/R est:1500-2500

BIENAIME, Luigi (1795-1878) Italian

Sculpture

£30000 $47100 €45000 Dancing Bacchante (149cm-59in) s.d.1846 white marble prov. 10-Dec-2 Sotheby's, London #177/R est:10000-15000

BIENNOURY, Victor (1823-1893) French

Works on paper

£516 $800 €774 Woman at a window (43x24cm-17x9in) pencil chk pencil prov. 29-Oct-2 Sotheby's, New York #15/R est:500-700
£1032 $1600 €1548 Study of a nude with drapery (41x19cm-16x7in) s.indis i. pencil. 29-Oct-2 Sotheby's, New York #12/R est:600-800

BIER, Wolfgang (1943-) German

Works on paper

£253 $392 €400 Indian skulls (80x90cm-31x35in) s.d.1978/79 bears i. biro leather board. 28-Sep-2 Ketterer, Hamburg #555/R

BIERGE, Roland (1922-) French

£256 $405 €400 Paysage a Longueil Anel (60x92cm-24x36in) s.d.1953. 15-Nov-2 Ferri, Paris #78
£256 $405 €400 Nu couche (75x162cm-30x64in) s. lit. 15-Nov-2 Ferri, Paris #89/R
£256 $405 €400 Instruments de la passion (60x112cm-24x44in) s. exhib. 15-Nov-2 Ferri, Paris #84
£256 $405 €400 Bouquet de marguerites (50x50cm-20x20in) s.d.1971. 15-Nov-2 Ferri, Paris #131
£256 $405 €400 Hommage a Leonard de Vinci (92x73cm-36x29in) s.d.1968. 15-Nov-2 Ferri, Paris #139
£256 $405 €400 Untitled (50x61cm-20x24in) s.d.1977. 15-Nov-2 Ferri, Paris #182
£256 $405 €400 Untitled (81x65cm-32x26in) s.d.1977. 15-Nov-2 Ferri, Paris #174
£256 $405 €400 Untitled (23x31cm-9x12in) s.d.1977 paper. 15-Nov-2 Ferri, Paris #208
£256 $405 €400 Untitled (31x26cm-12x10in) s.d.1977 paper. 15-Nov-2 Ferri, Paris #221
£256 $405 €400 Untitled (26x31cm-10x12in) s.d.1977 paper. 15-Nov-2 Ferri, Paris #231
£256 $405 €400 Untitled (31x40cm-12x16in) s.d.1983. 15-Nov-2 Ferri, Paris #257
£256 $405 €400 Polychromie (42x30cm-17x12in) s.d.1980 paper. 15-Nov-2 Ferri, Paris #256
£269 $425 €420 Untitled (65x54cm-26x21in) s.d.1975. 15-Nov-2 Ferri, Paris #180
£276 $436 €430 Arbres (44x44cm-17x17in) s. panel. 15-Nov-2 Ferri, Paris #93
£276 $436 €430 Polychromie (24x24cm-9x9in) s.d.1982 paper. 15-Nov-2 Ferri, Paris #284
£288 $456 €450 Dormeuse (61x50cm-24x20in) s.verso after Vermeer. 15-Nov-2 Ferri, Paris #82
£288 $456 €450 Deposition de Croix (86x69cm-34x27in) s.d.1970 canvas on board after Fra Bartolomeo. 15-Nov-2 Ferri, Paris #143
£288 $456 €450 Madiran 2 (65x81cm-26x32in) s.d.1977. 15-Nov-2 Ferri, Paris #213
£288 $456 €450 Montjouvain (26x31cm-10x12in) s.d.1978 paper. 15-Nov-2 Ferri, Paris #225
£288 $456 €450 Buech (31x26cm-12x10in) s.i.d.1977 paper on panel. 15-Nov-2 Ferri, Paris #233

£288 $456 €450 Untitled (50x50cm-20x20in) s.d.1976. 15-Nov-2 Ferri, Paris #245
£288 $456 €450 Fugue (36x34cm-14x13in) s.d.1990 paper on panel. 15-Nov-2 Ferri, Paris #303
£288 $456 €450 Untitled (81x100cm-32x39in) s.d.1990. 15-Nov-2 Ferri, Paris #301
£295 $466 €460 Nature morte (32x27cm-13x11in) s.d.1974 paper on panel. 15-Nov-2 Ferri, Paris #224/R
£308 $486 €480 Maisons a Odelveldstraadt (60x73cm-24x29in) s.d.1967. 15-Nov-2 Ferri, Paris #110
£321 $506 €500 Quais (130x180cm-51x71in) s. 15-Nov-2 Ferri, Paris #72
£321 $506 €500 Quai (22x33cm-9x13in) s. panel exhib. 15-Nov-2 Ferri, Paris #75
£321 $506 €500 Paysage a Balsieges (60x81cm-24x32in) s. 15-Nov-2 Ferri, Paris #98
£321 $506 €500 Grands arbres (80x65cm-31x26in) s.d.1959. 15-Nov-2 Ferri, Paris #94
£321 $506 €500 Composition (54x81cm-21x32in) s.d.1968. 15-Nov-2 Ferri, Paris #137
£321 $506 €500 Pochade (26x45cm-10x18in) s.d.1969 afterTitian. 15-Nov-2 Ferri, Paris #141
£321 $506 €500 Attitude de mademoiselle Vinteuil (32x24cm-13x9in) s.d.1967. 15-Nov-2 Ferri, Paris #1150
£321 $506 €500 Composition (60x73cm-24x29in) s.d.1973. 15-Nov-2 Ferri, Paris #173
£321 $506 €500 Untitled (50x61cm-20x24in) s.d.1978. 15-Nov-2 Ferri, Paris #243
£321 $506 €500 Untitled (31x31cm-12x12in) s.d.1990 paper. 15-Nov-2 Ferri, Paris #169
£321 $506 €500 Hommage a Louis David (45x30cm-18x12in) s.d.1989 paper on canvas. 15-Nov-2 Ferri, Paris #289
£353 $557 €550 Untitled (50x61cm-20x24in) s.d.1976. 15-Nov-2 Ferri, Paris #176
£353 $557 €550 Untitled (73x100cm-29x39in) s.d.1990. 15-Nov-2 Ferri, Paris #283
£353 $557 €550 Divertissement 6 (46x38cm-18x15in) s.d.1980 paper on panel oval. 15-Nov-2 Ferri, Paris #286
£353 $557 €550 Untitled (130x97cm-51x38in) s.d.1991. 15-Nov-2 Ferri, Paris #298
£385 $608 €600 Chevre (79x91cm-31x36in) s. 15-Nov-2 Ferri, Paris #80
£385 $608 €600 Pirovac (51x56cm-20x22in) s. 15-Nov-2 Ferri, Paris #100
£385 $608 €600 Terrasse sur la mer (120x195cm-47x77in) s.d.1967. 15-Nov-2 Ferri, Paris #152
£385 $608 €600 Elegante au chapeau jaune (33x32cm-13x13in) s.d.1970. 15-Nov-2 Ferri, Paris #148
£385 $608 €600 Rhytmes, quantites, valeurs (147x82cm-58x32in) s.d.1973. 15-Nov-2 Ferri, Paris #159
£385 $608 €600 Untitled (73x92cm-29x36in) s.d.1991. 15-Nov-2 Ferri, Paris #279
£385 $608 €600 Lagune II (120x120cm-47x47in) s.d.1988. 15-Nov-2 Ferri, Paris #302
£385 $608 €600 Untitled (146x114cm-57x45in) s.d.1975. 15-Nov-2 Ferri, Paris #296
£417 $658 €650 Marianne (27x22cm-11x9in) s. canvas on board. 15-Nov-2 Ferri, Paris #62
£417 $658 €650 Fruits a la boite de the (55x46cm-22x18in) s. 15-Nov-2 Ferri, Paris #121/R
£436 $689 €680 Zoulou sur le sentier de guerre (146x97cm-57x38in) s.d.1987. 15-Nov-2 Ferri, Paris #277
£449 $709 €700 Maison dans les arbres, l'hiver (41x33cm-16x13in) s.d.1945 masonite. 15-Nov-2 Ferri, Paris #57/R
£449 $709 €700 Portrait a la robe brodee (100x65cm-39x26in) s.d.1948 lit. 15-Nov-2 Ferri, Paris #70/R
£449 $709 €700 Paysage provencal (40x80cm-16x31in) s. 15-Nov-2 Ferri, Paris #77/R
£449 $709 €700 Nu (100x100cm-39x39in) s.d.1960 exhib. 15-Nov-2 Ferri, Paris #87/R
£449 $709 €700 Butterflies (115x82cm-45x32in) s.d.1976. 15-Nov-2 Ferri, Paris #175
£483 $806 €700 Vooruistreven (39x31cm-15x12in) s.i.d.6 juillet 83 s.verso panel oval. 10-Jul-3 Artcurial Briest, Paris #328
£513 $810 €800 Couseuses (67x60cm-26x24in) s.d.1949 paper on board lit. 15-Nov-2 Ferri, Paris #69/R
£513 $810 €800 Michel (31x26cm-12x10in) s. canvas on board. 15-Nov-2 Ferri, Paris #63
£513 $810 €800 Table (118x122cm-46x48in) exhib. 15-Nov-2 Ferri, Paris #88
£513 $810 €800 Charge de fruits (46x55cm-18x22in) s.d.1964. 15-Nov-2 Ferri, Paris #103
£538 $839 €850 Pichets et fruits (48x65cm-19x26in) s. 20-Oct-2 Chayette & Cheval, Paris #84/R
£545 $861 €850 Bouquet d'anemones (55x46cm-22x18in) s.d.1973. 15-Nov-2 Ferri, Paris #136
£545 $861 €850 Savane (30x46cm-12x18in) s.d.1989 paper on panel. 15-Nov-2 Ferri, Paris #262/R
£551 $871 €860 Ataon, Venise V (200x185cm-79x73in) d.1985. 15-Nov-2 Ferri, Paris #291
£577 $912 €900 Paysage a Saint-Bonnet (130x195cm-51x77in) s. exhib. 15-Nov-2 Ferri, Paris #79/R
£577 $912 €900 Paysage au soleil jaune (16x27cm-6x11in) s.d.50. 15-Nov-2 Ferri, Paris #76
£641 $1013 €1000 Arbres au Plessis-Brion (58x56cm-23x22in) s.d.1960. 15-Nov-2 Ferri, Paris #99/R
£641 $1013 €1000 Composition en rouge et or (73x100cm-29x39in) s.d.1967. 15-Nov-2 Ferri, Paris #151
£641 $1013 €1000 Composition (162x130cm-64x51in) s. 15-Nov-2 Ferri, Paris #247
£705 $1114 €1100 Portrait d'Evelyne Eyffel (132x81cm-52x32in) exhib.lit. 15-Nov-2 Ferri, Paris #119/R
£705 $1114 €1100 Montjouvain (146x114cm-57x45in) s.d.1979. 15-Nov-2 Ferri, Paris #240/R
£769 $1215 €1200 Midi a quatorze heures (162x130cm-64x51in) s.dd.1983. 15-Nov-2 Ferri, Paris #268
£801 $1266 €1250 Apres la battue au renard (81x65cm-32x26in) s. lit. 15-Nov-2 Ferri, Paris #101/R
£833 $1317 €1300 Nature morte (80x80cm-31x31in) s.d.1970 exhib. 15-Nov-2 Ferri, Paris #135
£962 $1519 €1500 Nature morte aux deux as (100x100cm-39x39in) s. d.1963 verso exhib. 15-Nov-2 Ferri, Paris #122/R
£962 $1519 €1500 Dans la foulee (162x97cm-64x38in) s.d.1982. 15-Nov-2 Ferri, Paris #261
£962 $1519 €1500 Fugue (100x100cm-39x39in) s.d.1991. 15-Nov-2 Ferri, Paris #295/R
£1282 $2026 €2000 September (148x130cm-58x51in) s.d.1973 exhib. 15-Nov-2 Ferri, Paris #161/R
£1282 $2026 €2000 Aux Basques (120x120cm-47x47in) s.d.1988. 15-Nov-2 Ferri, Paris #304/R
£1346 $2127 €2100 Cote d'Azur (114x162cm-45x64in) s. exhib. 15-Nov-2 Ferri, Paris #127/R
£1346 $2127 €2100 Allee aux oliviers (114x146cm-45x57in) s.d.62 exhib. 15-Nov-2 Ferri, Paris #142/R
£1603 $2532 €2500 Ninive (140x140cm-55x55in) s.d.1976 exhib. 15-Nov-2 Ferri, Paris #246/R
£1795 $2836 €2800 Battle (195x130cm-77x51in) s.d.1971. 15-Nov-2 Ferri, Paris #156/R

Works on paper

£256 $405 €400 Arrigan (66x51cm-26x20in) s.d.1983-84 W/C. 15-Nov-2 Ferri, Paris #23
£269 $425 €420 Nu assis (43x45cm-17x18in) s.d.1957 gouache. 15-Nov-2 Ferri, Paris #11
£897 $1418 €1400 Modele endormi (32x50cm-13x20in) s. chl. 15-Nov-2 Ferri, Paris #9/R

BIERK, David (20th C) Canadian

£1070 $1658 €1605 Cloud study I (46x66cm-18x26in) s.i.d.14 April 1988 prov. 3-Dec-2 Joyner, Toronto #313/R est:3000-5000 (C.D 2600)
£3293 $5500 €4775 Vermont summer 1990 (127x239cm-50x94in) 29-Jun-3 Butterfields, Los Angeles #7073/R est:400-600

Works on paper

£773 $1205 €1160 Landscape (34x35cm-13x14in) init. mixed media on board. 25-Mar-3 Ritchie, Toronto #167/R est:1500-2000 (C.D 1800)

BIERMANN, Aenne (1898-1933) German

Photographs

£2516 $3899 €4000 Tension (24x18cm-9x7in) i. verso silver gelatine. 31-Oct-2 Van Ham, Cologne #43/R est:3200

BIERSTADT, Albert (1830-1902) American/German

£6289 $10000 €9434 Standing cowboy with horse (36x46cm-14x18in) init. paper on board prov. 4-Mar-3 Christie's, Rockefeller NY #30/R est:10000-15000
£8805 $14000 €13208 Landscape with cows (34x49cm-13x19in) oil paper on canvas prov. 5-Mar-3 Sotheby's, New York #31/R est:10000-20000
£11321 $18000 €16982 Landscape with trees and lake (32x34cm-13x13in) mono. oil on paper prov. 5-Mar-3 Sotheby's, New York #118/R est:12000-18000
£16026 $25000 €24039 Mount Rosalie, Mount Evans, Colorado (20x28cm-8x11in) s. oil paper on canvas prov.lit. 9-Nov-2 Santa Fe Art, Santa Fe #89/R est:30000-40000
£24193 $37500 €36290 Landscape study, Yosemite, California (30x48cm-12x19in) s. paper on canvas prov. 4-Dec-2 Sotheby's, New York #115/R est:25000-35000
£50633 $80000 €73418 Headwaters of the Green River, wind river mountains, Wyoming (30x46cm-12x18in) s. oil paper on canvas. 26-Jul-3 Coeur d'Alene, Hayden #96/R est:30000-50000
£51613 $80000 €77420 Three sisters (36x48cm-14x19in) bears sig oil paper on canvas. 5-Dec-2 Christie's, Rockefeller NY #161/R est:70000-100000
£77419 $120000 €116129 Niagara Falls (36x48cm-14x19in) s. oil on paper prov.exhib. 5-Dec-2 Christie's, Rockefeller NY #4/R est:150000-250000
£77419 $120000 €116129 Wasatch Mountains (77x112cm-30x44in) s. prov.exhib. 5-Dec-2 Christie's, Rockefeller NY #154/R est:100000-150000
£83871 $130000 €125807 Mountain scene (56x76cm-22x30in) mono. painted c.1870 prov.exhib.lit. 3-Dec-2 Phillips, New York #17/R est:140000-180000
£253086 $410000 €379629 Ten views (35x48cm-14x19in) paper on board prov. 21-May-3 Sotheby's, New York #200/R est:400000-600000
£277778 $450000 €416667 Yosemite (52x77cm-20x30in) mono. prov. 21-May-3 Sotheby's, New York #217/R est:300000-500000

£467742 $725000 €701613 Sunset in California, Yosemite (72x56cm-28x22in) mono. prov.exhib.lit. 4-Dec-2 Sotheby's, New York #140/R est:500000-700000
£774194 $1200000 €1161291 Golden light of California (97x153cm-38x60in) s. prov.exhib. 5-Dec-2 Christie's, Rockefeller NY #159/R est:1000000-1500000
Works on paper
£4839 $7500 €7259 Coastal scene with sailboats (8x18cm-3x7in) init. W/C exec.c.1865 prov. 8-Dec-2 Toomey, Oak Park #688/R est:9000-12000

BIERSTADT, Albert (attrib) (1830-1902) American/German
£833 $1300 €1250 Landscape with waterfall and figures (15x13cm-6x5in) s.d.1859 panel. 1-Aug-2 Eldred, East Dennis #793/R

BIERUMA-OOSTING, Jeanne (1898-1995) Dutch
£2128 $3447 €3000 Luxembourg Gardens (49x59cm-19x23in) s.verso painted 1939. 26-May-3 Glerum, Amsterdam #46/R est:1500-2000

BIES, Martinus Johannes (1894-1975) Dutch
£724 $1172 €1100 Four seasons (23x23cm-9x9in) s. board set of four. 21-Jan-3 Christie's, Amsterdam #264 est:1000-1500

BIESE, Helmi (1867-1933) Finnish
£1379 $2124 €2069 Winter landscape with deep tracks in the snow (95x72cm-37x28in) s. 27-Oct-2 Anders Antik, Landskrona #316/R est:15000-20000 (S.KR 20000)
£2025 $3200 €3200 View across water (30x60cm-12x24in) s. 1-Dec-2 Bukowskis, Helsinki #27/R est:2000-2500

BIESEBROECK, Jules van (1873-1965) Belgian
£461 $770 €650 La truie (50x60cm-20x24in) s.d.54 panel. 23-Jun-3 Bernaerts, Antwerp #413/R
£769 $1208 €1200 Porteuse d'eau dans l'Atlas (50x65cm-20x26in) s. 16-Dec-2 Gros & Delettrez, Paris #395
£8993 $14749 €12500 Battage du grain en Afrique du nord (80x100cm-31x39in) s. panel lit. 4-Jun-3 Tajan, Paris #312/R est:10000-15000

BIEVRE, Marie de (1865-?) Belgian
£411 $642 €650 La cassette fleurie (56x43cm-22x17in) s. 15-Oct-2 Vanderkindere, Brussels #107
£4063 $6500 €6095 Still life with flowers in an urn on a ledge (109x99cm-43x39in) s. 14-May-3 Butterfields, San Francisco #1069/R est:10000-15000

BIG, Ymer (20th C) French
£345 $548 €500 Bateaux devant la chaumiere (50x70cm-20x28in) s. 10-Mar-3 Thierry & Lannon, Brest #158/R

BIGELOW, Daniel Folger (1823-1910) American
£299 $475 €449 Figure in a wooded landscape. s. board painted c.1900. 4-May-3 Treadway Gallery, Cincinnati #506/R
£548 $850 €822 Expansive landscape (30x46cm-12x18in) s. painted c.1880. 8-Dec-2 Toomey, Oak Park #635/R
£1205 $2000 €1747 Country road by a river with covered bridge. Summer countryside (16x24cm-6x9in) s. pair prov. 11-Jun-3 Butterfields, San Francisco #4016/R est:3000-5000

BIGGI, Felice Fortunato (17th C) Italian
£10692 $16572 €17000 Still lives of flowers and vegetables (65x95cm-26x37in) pair. 29-Oct-2 Finarte, Milan #461/R est:10000-12000

BIGGS, Robert (20th C) American
£346 $550 €519 Still life (51x61cm-20x24in) s.d. 2-Mar-3 Toomey, Oak Park #777/R

BIGGS, Walter (1886-1968) American
£2019 $3250 €3029 Couple walking in snowy landscape (86x66cm-34x26in) s. oil en grisaille. 10-May-3 Illustration House, New York #90/R est:3000-5000
£3727 $6000 €5591 Couple pausing on bridge above canal (94x81cm-37x32in) s.d.36 sold with partial tearsheet. 10-May-3 Illustration House, New York #89/R est:7000-10000
£5128 $8000 €7692 Group of elderly people (71x122cm-28x48in) 9-Nov-2 Illustration House, New York #158/R est:8000-12000

BIGNAMI, Vespasiano (1841-1929) Italian
Works on paper
£949 $1500 €1424 Young girl playing with a small dog (23x30cm-9x12in) mono. W/C. 26-Apr-3 Jeffery Burchard, Florida #58

BIGOT, Georges (1860-1927) French
£769 $1208 €1200 Le long du quai (19x24cm-7x9in) s. panel. 10-Dec-2 Campo, Vlaamse Kaai #37
Works on paper
£705 $1107 €1100 Les canards (36x50cm-14x20in) s. ink wash. 11-Dec-2 Maigret, Paris #157

BIGOT, Raymond (1872-1953) French
Works on paper
£282 $454 €400 La chouette (32x50cm-13x20in) s.i.d.1952 gouache Indian ink. 12-May-3 Lesieur & Le Bars, Le Havre #6
£282 $454 €400 Hulotte (21x26cm-8x10in) s. gouache W/C. 12-May-3 Lesieur & Le Bars, Le Havre #11/R

BIGOT, Trophime (attrib) (fl.1620-1635) French
£4131 $6444 €6197 Peter Denies Christ (103x124cm-41x49in) canvas on canvas. 12-Oct-2 Dorotheum, Prague #10/R est:400000-600000 (C.KR 200000)

BIHAN, le (19th C) ?
£8013 $12500 €12020 Sinking of CSS Alabama by USS Kearsage off Cherbourg Peninsula (41x61cm-16x24in) s. 12-Oct-2 Neal Auction Company, New Orleans #463/R est:10000-15000

BIHARI, Sandor (1856-1906) Hungarian
£727 $1133 €1054 Street leading to the homestead (32x48cm-13x19in) s. papercard. 12-Apr-3 Mu Terem Galeria, Budapest #44/R est:180000 (H.F 260000)

BILAS, Peter (1952-) British
£688 $1107 €1032 Fleet in Table Bay (68x103cm-27x41in) s.d.87. 12-May-3 Stephan Welz, Johannesburg #467/R est:8000-12000 (SA.R 8000)

BILBAO Y MARTINEZ, Gonzalo (1860-1938) Spanish
£705 $1114 €1100 Portrait of lady (52x36cm-20x14in) s. 14-Nov-2 Arte, Seville #383/R
£3548 $5500 €5322 Seamstresses by a window (70x50cm-28x20in) s. 3-Dec-2 Christie's, Rockefeller NY #623/R est:7000-9000
Works on paper
£1282 $2026 €2000 Smoking the pipe (76x46cm-30x18in) s.i. W/C. 13-Nov-2 Ansorena, Madrid #193/R

BILCOQ, Marie Marc Antoine (1755-1838) French
£949 $1481 €1500 Interieur de cuisine (20x24cm-8x9in) panel. 20-Oct-2 Mercier & Cie, Lille #285 est:1800-2250

BILCOQ, Marie Marc Antoine (attrib) (1755-1838) French
£1293 $2055 €1900 L'heureuse famille (25x21cm-10x8in) panel. 2-Mar-3 Lombrail & Teucquam, Paris #151/R

BILDERS, Johannes Wernardus (1811-1890) Dutch
£416 $650 €624 River landscape (31x46cm-12x18in) s. 11-Nov-2 Stephan Welz, Johannesburg #16 (SA.R 6500)
£753 $1175 €1100 Forest landscape with three figures near a river and a house (11x15cm-4x6in) s. panel. 14-Apr-3 Glerum, Amsterdam #143/R
£1210 $1888 €1900 Heather near Wolfheze (66x104cm-26x41in) prov. 6-Nov-2 Vendue Huis, Gravenhage #443/R est:2000-3000
£1408 $2310 €2042 Two figures on woodland path (29x47cm-11x19in) s. panel. 4-Jun-3 Fischer, Luzern #1065/R est:3000-4500 (S.FR 3000)
£2113 $3401 €3000 Hilly landscape with flock of sheep (52x47cm-20x19in) s. panel. 6-May-3 Vendu Notarishuis, Rotterdam #30/R est:4000-6000
£4088 $6296 €6500 Wolfheze - cowherds and cattle near a fen at dusk (32x47cm-13x19in) s. panel. 23-Oct-2 Christie's, Amsterdam #223/R est:5000-7000

BILDERS, Johannes Wernardus (attrib) (1811-1890) Dutch
£1224 $1947 €1800 Paysage anime (56x71cm-22x28in) 18-Mar-3 Vanderkindere, Brussels #117 est:1000-1500

BILDERS-BOSSE, Maria Philippina (1837-1900) Dutch
£552 $877 €800 Boerenerf (45x39cm-18x15in) s. panel prov. 10-Mar-3 Sotheby's, Amsterdam #147/R

BILEK, Alois (1887-1960) French
£330 $522 €495 Krkonose mountains viewed from Vysoke nad Jizerou (50x59cm-20x23in) s. paper-board. 30-Nov-2 Dorotheum, Prague #105 (C.KR 16000)
£454 $717 €681 Still life with apples and knife (32x40cm-13x16in) s. plywood. 30-Nov-2 Dorotheum, Prague #81/R (C.KR 22000)

£2682 $4238 €4023 Spring (160x130cm-63x51in) s. 30-Nov-2 Dorotheum, Prague #76/R est:120000-180000 (C.KR 130000)

BILEK, Frantisek (1872-1941) Czechoslovakian
Sculpture
£4540 $7355 €6810 Awe (52cm-20in) mono.i.d.1921 pat.wood. 24-May-3 Dorotheum, Prague #248/R est:80000-120000 (C.KR 200000)
Works on paper
£289 $456 €434 He's gone (32x26cm-13x10in) mono.i. ink white pencil dr. 30-Nov-2 Dorotheum, Prague #132/R (C.KR 14000)

BILINSKA, Anna (c.1857-1893) Polish
Works on paper
£1911 $2981 €3000 Jeune fille aux cheveux blonds (45x36cm-18x14in) s.d.1892 pastel. 6-Nov-2 Claude Boisgirard, Paris #7 est:2500-3000

BILIVERTI, Giovanni (school) (1576-1666) Italian
£18239 $28088 €29000 Joseph and wife (226x305cm-89x120in) 23-Oct-2 Finarte, Rome #512/R est:28000-32000

BILKO, Franz (1894-1968) Austrian
£295 $465 €443 Christ at the well (55x68cm-22x27in) s.i. i.verso painted 1933-34. 27-Nov-2 Falkkloos, Malmo #78319/R (S.KR 4200)

BILL, J C (19th C) British?
£3445 $5237 €5168 Gundogs in landscapes (42x62cm-17x24in) one s.d.1858 pair. 27-Aug-2 Rasmussen, Copenhagen #1778/R est:40000 (D.KR 40000)

BILL, Max (1908-1994) Swiss
£6329 $9810 €10000 Untitled - radiation (41x41cm-16x16in) s.d.1972-75 s.i. verso prov.exhib.lit. 28-Sep-2 Ketterer, Hamburg #487/R est:12000-15000
£12446 $19665 €18669 1,3,5, light and dark (40x40cm-16x16in) s.i.d.1970 verso acrylic prov. 26-Nov-2 Phillips, Zurich #100/R est:12000-18000 (S.FR 29000)
Sculpture
£1493 $2494 €2165 Twins as quarter ball (20x40x30cm-8x16x12in) s. wood. 24-Jun-3 Koller, Zurich #310/R est:3000-4000 (S.FR 3300)
£4367 $6856 €6551 Pyramid with curved side (18cm-7in) granite prov. 25-Nov-2 Sotheby's, Zurich #154/R est:10000-15000 (S.FR 10000)
£15000 $25050 €21750 Halbe kugel um zwei achsen (36cm-14in) polished black granite executed c.1965-66 lit. 27-Jun-3 Christie's, London #143/R est:10000-15000

BILLE, Carl (1815-1898) Danish
£258 $407 €387 Seascape with sailing ship (20x30cm-8x12in) s. 13-Nov-2 Kunsthallen, Copenhagen #60 (D.KR 3000)
£284 $472 €412 Seascape with vessel in high seas (22x28cm-9x11in) s. panel. 12-Jun-3 Kunsthallen, Copenhagen #363/R (D.KR 3000)
£345 $545 €500 Ships in stormy seas (13x18cm-5x7in) s. Indian ink wash. 5-Apr-3 Hans Stahl, Hamburg #150
£388 $589 €582 Moonlit seascape with rowing boat (24x34cm-9x13in) s/. 28-Aug-2 Museumsbygningen, Copenhagen #95 (D.KR 4500)
£431 $655 €647 Seascape with vessels off rocky coast in high seas (27x40cm-11x16in) s. 27-Aug-2 Rasmussen, Copenhagen #1756/R (D.KR 5000)
£480 $749 €720 Coastal landscape with vessel in moonlight (43x67cm-17x26in) s.d.1873. 13-Sep-2 Lilla Bukowskis, Stockholm #606 (S.KR 7000)
£553 $874 €830 Moonlit night in Venice (20x33cm-8x13in) 2-Dec-2 Rasmussen, Copenhagen #1486/R (D.KR 6500)
£635 $990 €953 Coastal landscape from Humlebaek with boats and figures at moonlight (32x48cm-13x19in) s/. 11-Nov-2 Rasmussen, Vejle #626/R (D.KR 7400)
£643 $1003 €965 Seascape with fishing boat and sailing ship (32x21cm-13x8in) s. 11-Nov-2 Rasmussen, Vejle #609/R (D.KR 7500)
£646 $982 €969 Full moon over the sea (34x50cm-13x20in) s.d.85. 27-Aug-2 Rasmussen, Copenhagen #1719/R (D.KR 7500)
£691 $1120 €1037 Seascape with sailing vessels off Norwegian rocky coast (32x41cm-13x16in) s.d.1858. 25-Jan-3 Rasmussen, Havnen #2094 (D.KR 7800)
£700 $1112 €1050 Coastal landscape with figures and sailing boats on calm waters, moonlight (27x37cm-11x15in) s. 5-May-3 Rasmussen, Vejle #281/R (D.KR 7500)
£785 $1271 €1138 Seascape with steamer and sailing vessel (19x35cm-7x14in) s. 24-May-3 Rasmussen, Havnen #2071/R (D.KR 8200)
£851 $1345 €1277 Seascape with Danish schooner (32x39cm-13x15in) s. 27-Nov-2 Museumsbygningen, Copenhagen #60/R (D.KR 10000)
£900 $1431 €1350 Transatlantic paddle steamer in a heavy swell (64x130cm-25x51in) s.d.1873. 4-Mar-3 Bonhams, Knightsbridge #281/R
£938 $1501 €1360 Fishing boats in moonlight (43x60cm-17x24in) s.d.1873. 18-May-3 Anders Antik, Landskrona #85 (S.KR 12000)
£1119 $1780 €1679 Seascape with steamer and sailing ship in high seas (71x110cm-28x43in) s.d.1874. 5-May-3 Rasmussen, Vejle #266/R est:15000 (D.KR 12000)
£1191 $1883 €1787 Seascape with French schooner in fresh breeze (35x57cm-14x22in) s.d.1886. 27-Nov-2 Museumsbygningen, Copenhagen #59/R est:6000-8000 (D.KR 14000)
£1274 $1988 €1911 Seascape with sailing vessels and figures in rowing boat (28x39cm-11x15in) s.d.1866. 5-Aug-2 Rasmussen, Vejle #39/R est:15000 (D.KR 15000)
£1728 $2834 €2506 Seascape with sailing vessels (44x67cm-17x26in) s.d.1877. 4-Jun-3 AB Stockholms Auktionsverk #2428/R est:15000-20000 (S.KR 22000)
£1850 $3090 €2683 Danish frigate off a headland (45x67cm-18x26in) s.d.1873. 18-Jun-3 Sotheby's, Olympia #62/R est:2000-3000
£1862 $2961 €2793 Three master and steamship at sea, sunset (110x168cm-43x66in) 5-Mar-3 Rasmussen, Copenhagen #1998/R est:25000 (D.KR 20000)
£3481 $5500 €5222 Danish frigate (84x71cm-33x28in) s. 1-Dec-2 Susanin's, Chicago #5022/R

BILLE, Carl (attrib) (1815-1898) Danish
£335 $540 €503 Sailing vessel in moonlight (26x42cm-10x17in) 19-Jan-3 Hindemae, Ullerslev #7450/R (D.KR 3800)

BILLE, Edmond (1878-1959) Swiss
£3302 $5283 €4953 Church in Wallis mountain village (53x76cm-21x30in) s.d. 17-Mar-3 Philippe Schuler, Zurich #4502/R est:2000-3000 (S.FR 7000)
£6522 $10109 €9783 Nature morte aux coings et a la maison rouge (54x43cm-21x17in) s. prov. 7-Dec-2 Galerie du Rhone, Sion #467/R est:15000-20000 (S.FR 15000)
£6840 $10943 €10260 Paysannes et soldat (70x115cm-28x45in) s.d. 17-Mar-3 Philippe Schuler, Zurich #4501/R est:8000-12000 (S.FR 14500)
£7391 $11457 €11087 L'Illgraben vu de la Noble Contree (36x63cm-14x25in) s.d.17 eternit. 7-Dec-2 Galerie du Rhone, Sion #470/R est:20000-25000 (S.FR 17000)
Works on paper
£1130 $1752 €1695 Vache a l'etable (35x49cm-14x19in) mixed media. 7-Dec-2 Galerie du Rhone, Sion #468/R est:5000-7000 (S.FR 2600)
£2028 $3245 €3042 View from fields over farmsteads, snowy mountain chain beyond (29x48cm-11x19in) s.d.17 gouache. 17-Mar-3 Philippe Schuler, Zurich #4287/R est:1500-2000 (S.FR 4300)

BILLE, Ejler (1910-) Danish
Works on paper
£411 $654 €617 Surrealistic composition (23x30cm-9x12in) Indian ink executed c.1934. 26-Feb-3 Kunsthallen, Copenhagen #40 (D.KR 4500)
£1378 $2136 €2067 Composition (22x32cm-9x13in) s.d.42 crayon. 4-Dec-2 Kunsthallen, Copenhagen #12/R est:15000 (D.KR 16000)

BILLE, S (19th C) Danish
£384 $603 €576 Ship off Copenhagen (73x112cm-29x44in) s. 25-Nov-2 Blomqvist, Lysaker #1022 (N.KR 4400)

BILLE, Vilhelm (1864-1908) Danish
£306 $496 €444 Seascape with the frigate Jylland in moonlight (47x43cm-19x17in) s. 24-May-3 Rasmussen, Havnen #2168 (D.KR 3200)
£405 $632 €608 Seascape with sailing vessel (43x60cm-17x24in) mono. 22-Sep-2 Hindemae, Ullerslev #7189/R (D.KR 4800)
£440 $677 €660 Seascape with sailing vessels off coast with lighthouse (60x95cm-24x37in) s. 26-Oct-2 Rasmussen, Havnen #3109 (D.KR 5200)

BILLE, Willy (1889-1944) Danish
£238 $362 €357 Three ships off the coast (100x110cm-39x43in) painted c.1930. 4-Jul-2 Heffel, Vancouver #2 (C.D 550)

BILLET, Pierre (1837-1922) French
£2000 $3140 €3000 La bergere (66x48cm-26x19in) s.d.1890. 19-Nov-2 Bonhams, New Bond Street #162/R est:2000-3000

BILLETTO, Alfredo (20th C) Italian?
£590 $974 €850 Composition no 3 (50x50cm-20x20in) s.i.d.68 verso oil collage prov.exhib. 1-Jul-3 Christie's, Amsterdam #397

BILLGREN, Ernst (1957-) Swedish

£3089 $4973 €4634 Seated model (81x49cm-32x19in) init. oil tempera panel. 7-May-3 AB Stockholms Auktionsverk #1043/R est:25000-30000 (S.KR 40000)
£9110 $14212 €13665 Care (72x105cm-28x41in) init. s.d.90 verso panel prov.lit. 6-Nov-2 AB Stockholms Auktionsverk #850/R est:80000-100000 (S.KR 130000)
£16988 $27351 €25482 Seals in the bathroom (149x171cm-59x67in) mono. oil and mosaic panel prov.exhib.lit. 7-May-3 AB Stockholms Auktionsverk #1031/R est:200000-300000 (S.KR 220000)
£21724 $33889 €32586 Yellow sitting room (162x130cm-64x51in) mono. panel mosaic painted 1994 prov.exhib.lit. 6-Nov-2 AB Stockholms Auktionsverk #848/R est:300000-350000 (S.KR 310000)

Sculpture

£1544 $2486 €2316 Plaits (26cm-10in) mono.num.1/7 pat.bronze prov.exhib.lit. 7-May-3 AB Stockholms Auktionsverk #982/R est:20000-25000 (S.KR 20000)
£2433 $3845 €3650 Half bird (18x17x21cm-7x7x8in) s. mosaic sculpture prov. 28-Apr-3 Bukowskis, Stockholm #942/R est:15000-18000 (S.KR 32000)
£2523 $3936 €3785 Head of a bear (22x22x20cm-9x9x8in) init.num.8/10 mixed media mosaic. 5-Nov-2 Bukowskis, Stockholm #418/R est:50000-60000 (S.KR 36000)
£3118 $4926 €4677 Duck play (53cm-21in) s.num.5/6 glass. 28-Apr-3 Bukowskis, Stockholm #940a/R est:30000-35000 (S.KR 41000)
£5606 $8746 €8409 Ducks swimming (17cm-7in) mono. bronze two exhib.lit. 6-Nov-2 AB Stockholms Auktionsverk #849/R est:80000-100000 (S.KR 80000)
£6236 $9852 €9354 Orre faar ring - one large and one small bird on grass (60cm-24in) s. mosaic mixed media exhib.lit. 28-Apr-3 Bukowskis, Stockholm #943/R est:70000-80000 (S.KR 82000)
£22425 $34982 €33638 Style of life (120x139x61cm-47x55x24in) s. mosaic sculpture mixed media lit. 5-Nov-2 Bukowskis, Stockholm #454/R est:400000-500000 (S.KR 320000)

Works on paper

£2523 $3936 €3785 Bird (62cm-24in circular) init. s.d.89 verso mixed media panel. 5-Nov-2 Bukowskis, Stockholm #417/R est:60000-70000 (S.KR 36000)
£2738 $4325 €4107 Roe-deer with calf (65x80cm-26x31in) init. mixed media panel shaped top executed 1990-91. 28-Apr-3 Bukowskis, Stockholm #940/R est:40000-50000 (S.KR 36000)
£3498 $5527 €5247 The crow (83x110cm-33x43in) init. s.d.84 verso mixed media panel lit. 28-Apr-3 Bukowskis, Stockholm #1003/R est:10000-15000 (S.KR 46000)
£3650 $5767 €5475 Black and white landscape (64x111cm-25x44in) init. mixed media panel shaped prov. 28-Apr-3 Bukowskis, Stockholm #939/R est:40000-50000 (S.KR 48000)

BILLGREN, Helene (1952-) Swedish

Works on paper

£420 $656 €630 Collection (42x35cm-17x14in) s.verso chl executed 1992 exhib. 6-Nov-2 AB Stockholms Auktionsverk #876/R (S.KR 6000)

BILLGREN, Ola (1940-2001) Swedish

£860 $1376 €1247 Study (37x24cm-15x9in) s.d.63 dr. 18-May-3 Anders Antik, Landskrona #46 (S.KR 11000)
£2662 $4205 €3993 Garment XIX Botticelli (96x96cm-38x38in) s.d.91 verso. 28-Apr-3 Bukowskis, Stockholm #1023/R est:50000-70000 (S.KR 35000)
£4639 $7329 €6959 Revelation (47x68cm-19x27in) s.d.93 verso. 28-Apr-3 Bukowskis, Stockholm #885/R est:60000-80000 (S.KR 61000)
£6657 $10385 €9986 Painting (150x125cm-59x49in) s.d.82 verso. 5-Nov-2 Bukowskis, Stockholm #412/R est:140000-150000 (S.KR 95000)
£11913 $18584 €17870 Escalier d'Honneur (79x98cm-31x39in) s.d.94. 6-Nov-2 AB Stockholms Auktionsverk #868/R est:125000-150000 (S.KR 170000)
£14015 $21864 €21023 Town wall, Camona (126x147cm-50x58in) s.d.91 verso panel exhib. 6-Nov-2 AB Stockholms Auktionsverk #803/R est:250000-300000 (S.KR 200000)
£21293 $33643 €31940 The dancer (185x147cm-73x58in) s.d.90 s. prov.exhib.lit. 28-Apr-3 Bukowskis, Stockholm #913/R est:200000-250000 (S.KR 280000)
£28732 $44821 €43098 Baroque altar (167x200cm-66x79in) s.d.1996 verso prov.exhib.lit. 5-Nov-2 Bukowskis, Stockholm #402/R est:350000-400000 (S.KR 410000)
£30888 $49730 €46332 Interior scene with bed (171x202cm-67x80in) s.d.94 verso exhib. 7-May-3 AB Stockholms Auktionsverk #985/R est:400000-500000 (S.KR 400000)
£31535 $49194 €47303 The moon (166x252cm-65x99in) 15 pieces prov.lit. 5-Nov-2 Bukowskis, Stockholm #448/R est:500000-600000 (S.KR 450000)
£50456 $78711 €75684 Cafe (53x59cm-21x23in) s.d.66 lit. 5-Nov-2 Bukowskis, Stockholm #386/R est:800000-1000000 (S.KR 720000)

Works on paper

£596 $929 €894 Spanish landscape (18x36cm-7x14in) s.d.74 W/C. 5-Nov-2 Bukowskis, Stockholm #356/R (S.KR 8500)
£664 $1102 €963 Woman at a cafe (19x21cm-7x8in) s.d.64 pencil dr. 16-Jun-3 Lilla Bukowskis, Stockholm #301 (S.KR 8600)
£701 $1093 €1052 Interior scene with woman (33x42cm-13x17in) s.d.62 wash. 5-Nov-2 Bukowskis, Stockholm #357/R (S.KR 10000)
£1051 $1640 €1577 Interior (36x44cm-14x17in) s.d.67 Indian ink wash. 6-Nov-2 AB Stockholms Auktionsverk #869/R est:10000-12000 (S.KR 15000)
£6027 $9402 €9041 The Queen (65x49cm-26x19in) s.d.77 W/C. 5-Nov-2 Bukowskis, Stockholm #361/R est:40000-50000 (S.KR 86000)
£7008 $10932 €10512 The bathroom (21x9cm-8x4in) s.d.69 W/C. 6-Nov-2 AB Stockholms Auktionsverk #870/R est:60000-80000 (S.KR 100000)

BILLING, Frederick W (1835-1914) American

£932 $1500 €1398 Rockaway Beach (23x30cm-9x12in) i.d.July 4 1876 board. 15-Jan-3 Boos Gallery, Michigan #672/R est:2000-3000
£5414 $8500 €8121 Grand Canyon of the Yellowstone (71x61cm-28x24in) init. prov.exhib. 19-Nov-2 Butterfields, San Francisco #8079/R est:2000-4000

BILLING, Teodor (1817-1892) Swedish

£438 $687 €657 Orbyhus Palace, Uppland (37x49cm-15x19in) s. 16-Dec-2 Lilla Bukowskis, Stockholm #868/R (S.KR 6200)
£504 $817 €731 Environs de lac du Quatre Cantons en Suisse (49x65cm-19x26in) s.i.d.1859. 25-May-3 Uppsala Auktionskammare, Uppsala #84/R (S.KR 6500)
£1050 $1660 €1575 Landscape, possibly from Nacka (100x145cm-39x57in) s. prov. 16-Nov-2 Crafoord, Lund #13/R est:10000 (S.KR 15000)
£1203 $1900 €1900 Swans by the bridge (68x100cm-27x39in) s.d.71. 1-Dec-2 Bukowskis, Helsinki #233/R est:1800-2000
£2025 $3200 €3200 Lake in the forest (56x90cm-22x35in) s. 1-Dec-2 Bukowskis, Helsinki #234/R est:1800-2000

BILLINGHURST, Alfred John (1880-1963) British

£400 $644 €580 Full-length nude portrait of a young girl (18x14cm-7x6in) s. 7-May-3 Gorringes, Bexhill #913

Works on paper

£300 $468 €450 Lady seated on a rock (33x49cm-13x19in) s. pencil W/C. 27-Mar-3 Christie's, Kensington #288
£320 $496 €480 Punting near Richmond Bridge (23x29cm-9x11in) s. W/C bodycol. 4-Dec-2 Christie's, Kensington #260
£2100 $3360 €3150 Road near St Julien, Ypres 1917 (34x51cm-13x20in) s.i.d. W/C. 11-Mar-3 Bonhams, New Bond Street #114/R est:1000-1500

BILLMEIER, Richard (1921-) Canadian

£244 $383 €366 Abstraction (77x122cm-30x48in) s. 12-Dec-2 Iegor de Saint Hippolyte, Montreal #6b (C.D 600)

BILLNEY, Voitler (19th C) ?

£2402 $3747 €3603 Arab woman collecting water (33x40cm-13x16in) s. 6-Nov-2 Dobiaschofsky, Bern #350/R est:5500 (S.FR 5500)

BILLOIN, Charles (1813-1869) Belgian

£476 $757 €700 Portrait of girl (40x35cm-16x14in) s.d.1855. 24-Mar-3 Bernaerts, Antwerp #255/R

BILLOTTE, René (1846-1915) French

Works on paper

£885 $1406 €1328 Horse and cart on road at night (52x71cm-20x28in) s. pastel. 5-Mar-3 Rasmussen, Copenhagen #1911/R (D.KR 9500)

BILQUIN, Jean (1938-) Belgian

£1007 $1612 €1400 Composition with two figures (172x141cm-68x56in) s. s.d.87 verso. 17-May-3 De Vuyst, Lokeren #35/R est:1200-1500
£1727 $2763 €2400 Composition (200x248cm-79x98in) s. 17-May-3 De Vuyst, Lokeren #34/R est:1600-1800

Works on paper

£759 $1214 €1100 Composition (128x98cm-50x39in) s.i.d.90 mixed media collage paper on panel. 15-Mar-3 De Vuyst, Lokeren #26

BILS, Claude (1884-1968) French
£314 $500 €471 Street scene (64x46cm-25x18in) s.indis.i. paper on canvas. 18-Mar-3 Doyle, New York #28/R

BILTIUS, Cornelis (17th C) Dutch
£4026 $6482 €6000 Trompe l'oeil with a hunting still life of birds and a flacon in a niche (55x47cm-22x19in) 18-Feb-3 Sotheby's, Amsterdam #949/R est:2000-3000

BILU, Asher (1936-) Australian
£880 $1417 €1276 Column (245x183cm-96x72in) s.d.78 acrylic on board. 12-May-3 Joel, Victoria #363a est:1000-2000 (A.D 2200)
Works on paper
£1100 $1771 €1595 Red abstract (245x183cm-96x72in) mixed media. 12-May-3 Joel, Victoria #248a est:2000-3000 (A.D 2750)

BIMBI, Bartolomeo (1648-1725) Italian
£28000 $43680 €42000 Tulips, roses and other flowers with butterflies in a sculpted vase on a ledge (73x58cm-29x23in) mono.d.1696. 9-Apr-3 Christie's, London #96/R est:12000-18000

BIMBI, Bartolomeo (attrib) (1648-1725) Italian
£45000 $75150 €65250 Still life of fruits and figs in an open landscape (89x117cm-35x46in) 10-Jul-3 Sotheby's, London #46/R est:30000-40000

BIMMERMANN, Caesar (1821-1890) German
£5769 $9058 €9000 Approaching storm over idyllic river landscape (92x129cm-36x51in) s. 21-Nov-2 Van Ham, Cologne #1479/R est:10000

BINARD, Henri (1862-1939) Belgian
Works on paper
£578 $919 €850 Symbolic landscape with kneeling nude and swans (37x45cm-15x18in) s. pastel paper on canvas. 24-Mar-3 Bernaerts, Antwerp #163/R

BINDER, Alois (19th C) German
£352 $567 €500 Monk with full glass (20x16cm-8x6in) s. panel. 7-May-3 Michael Zeller, Lindau #628
£400 $624 €600 Beer drinker (33x25cm-13x10in) s. 11-Apr-3 Keys, Aylsham #629/R

BINDER, Erwin (20th C) American
Sculpture
£1139 $1800 €1709 Transcendence of man (94cm-37in) s.d.1976 num.2/10 bronze. 5-Apr-3 DeFina, Austinburg #1374 est:3000-5000

BINDER, Jacob (19/20th C) German
£609 $943 €914 Alpine meadow (22x22cm-9x9in) s. board. 9-Dec-2 Philippe Schuler, Zurich #4019 (S.FR 1400)

BINDER, Tony (1868-1944) British
£272 $433 €400 Plonlein in Rothenburg ob der Tauber (41x33cm-16x13in) s.d.1925 i. verso. 28-Mar-3 Bolland & Marotz, Bremen #426/R

BINDER, Tony (attrib) (1868-1944) British
£258 $407 €387 Girl in low-cut dress with bunch of flowers in front of a mirror (61x50cm-24x20in) i.verso. 29-Nov-2 Zofingen, Switzerland #2399 (S.FR 600)

BINDESBOLL, Thorvald (1846-1908) Danish
Works on paper
£254 $394 €381 Sketch for cushion cover (30x31cm-12x12in) mono.d.74 W/C Indian ink pencil. 1-Oct-2 Rasmussen, Copenhagen #393/R (D.KR 3000)
£271 $420 €407 Ornament from Isis Temple, Pompei (21x21cm-8x8in) s.d.12 feb 1869 Indian ink W/C. 1-Oct-2 Rasmussen, Copenhagen #396/R (D.KR 3200)
£271 $420 €407 Composition with dolphins, red in middle (27x32cm-11x13in) s.d.Dec 1875 W/C Indian ink gouache. 1-Oct-2 Rasmussen, Copenhagen #405/R (D.KR 3200)

BINDING, Wellesley (20th C) New Zealander
£702 $1095 €1053 Vivian girls reunion (32x149cm-13x59in) s. acrylic board. 27-Mar-3 International Art Centre, Auckland #22/R (NZ.D 2000)
£702 $1095 €1053 Surprised at the motel (32x149cm-13x59in) s. acrylic board. 27-Mar-3 International Art Centre, Auckland #23/R (NZ.D 2000)

BINDLEY, Frank (fl.1872-1887) British
£650 $1001 €975 Low tide (61x51cm-24x20in) s. 5-Sep-2 Christie's, Kensington #292/R

BINDON, Francis (c.1700-1765) British
£1258 $1962 €2000 Swift's man (81x62cm-32x24in) i.verso. 17-Sep-2 Whyte's, Dublin #199/R est:2000-4000

BINET, Adolphe Gustave (1854-1897) French
£950 $1482 €1425 Livestock around the well (49x65cm-19x26in) s. 26-Mar-3 Sotheby's, Olympia #272/R

BINET, George (1865-1949) French
£503 $810 €750 Cheval a l'ecurie (13x22cm-5x9in) s. 23-Feb-3 Lesieur & Le Bars, Le Havre #13
£897 $1364 €1400 Elegante au jardin (22x13cm-9x5in) s. panel. 16-Aug-2 Deauville, France #102/R
£993 $1559 €1450 Village fortifie en Haute Provence (26x33cm-10x13in) s. 21-Apr-3 Rabourdin & Choppin de Janvry, Paris #72/R
£1544 $2485 €2300 Bouquet de roses (60x73cm-24x29in) s. 23-Feb-3 Lesieur & Le Bars, Le Havre #12/R
£5986 $9637 €8500 Marche a Caudebec (33x45cm-13x18in) s. 12-May-3 Lesieur & Le Bars, Le Havre #12/R
£16139 $25177 €25500 Terrasse dominant Le Havre (98x146cm-39x57in) s.d.1934. 20-Oct-2 Claude Boisgirard, Paris #17/R est:9000-10000

BING, Ilse (1899-1998) German
Photographs
£2273 $3500 €3410 Couple, Place de la Concorde with Eiffel Tower (18x28cm-7x11in) s.d.1933 i.verso photograph prov. 22-Oct-2 Sotheby's, New York #89/R est:4000-6000
£3797 $6000 €5696 Chair and tree on the Champs Elysees, Paris (28x22cm-11x9in) s.d.1931 gelatin silver print prov.lit. 22-Apr-3 Christie's, Rockefeller NY #154/R est:10000-15000

BINGER, Charles (20th C) American
£1923 $3000 €2885 Man and girl in sinking Titanic (58x48cm-23x19in) s. board. 9-Nov-2 Illustration House, New York #153/R est:3000-4000

BINGHAM, George Caleb (1811-1879) American
£2516 $4000 €3774 Colonel Caleb Smith (72x61cm-28x24in) painted 1837 prov.lit. 5-Mar-3 Sotheby's, New York #34/R est:8000-12000

BINGHAM, James (1917-1971) American
£280 $434 €420 Travelling people (51x66cm-20x26in) s. board. 2-Oct-2 John Ross, Belfast #263
£280 $434 €420 Returning with the milk pales (50x76cm-20x30in) s. board. 4-Dec-2 John Ross, Belfast #125
£350 $557 €525 Stroll with mother (76x50cm-30x20in) s. board. 5-Mar-3 John Ross, Belfast #41
£400 $584 €600 Birthday party (41x51cm-16x20in) s. board. 12-Jun-2 John Ross, Belfast #292
£420 $613 €630 Clown (48x38cm-19x15in) s. board. 12-Jun-2 John Ross, Belfast #230
£450 $657 €675 Clown (48x38cm-19x15in) s. board. 12-Jun-2 John Ross, Belfast #306
£460 $713 €690 Twilight, Donegal (66x56cm-26x22in) s. board. 2-Oct-2 John Ross, Belfast #68
£520 $759 €780 Thatcher at work (38x48cm-15x19in) s. board. 12-Jun-2 John Ross, Belfast #17
£522 $815 €820 Cottage by the roadside with figures (45x68cm-18x27in) s. board. 6-Nov-2 James Adam, Dublin #140/R
£550 $803 €825 In deep thought (51x69cm-20x27in) s. board. 12-Jun-2 John Ross, Belfast #114
£650 $949 €975 Returing home (51x91cm-20x36in) s. board. 12-Jun-2 John Ross, Belfast #162
Works on paper
£774 $1200 €1161 Joe sweats it out (33x48cm-13x19in) s. W/C board exec.c.1945. 8-Dec-2 Toomey, Oak Park #759/R

BINGLEY, Herbert Harding (fl.1927-1933) British
Works on paper
£250 $400 €375 Fishing boats returning to Whitby Harbour (23x38cm-9x15in) s. W/C. 11-Mar-3 David Duggleby, Scarborough #44/R

BINGLEY, James George (1841-1920) British
Works on paper
£600 $990 €870 Cottage at Plaistow, West Sussex (30x27cm-12x11in) init. pencil W/C htd white. 3-Jul-3 Christie's, Kensington #60/R
£820 $1345 €1230 Itchenor, West Sussex. Near Porlock, Somersetshire (25x35cm-10x14in) init. W/C pair. 4-Jun-3 Bonhams, Chester #400a

BINJE, Franz (1835-1900) Belgian
£483 $772 €700 Homme a la chaumiere (50x36cm-20x14in) s. 17-Mar-3 Horta, Bruxelles #54
£949 $1481 €1500 Mill at Knokke (40x70cm-16x28in) s. 21-Oct-2 Bernaerts, Antwerp #504/R est:1000-1400

BINKS, Reuben Ward (fl.1924-1948) British
Works on paper
£330 $515 €495 Portrait of greyhound (25x36cm-10x14in) s. 10-Sep-2 Louis Taylor, Stoke on Trent #1158a
£420 $664 €630 Black labrador with a pheasant (23x28cm-9x11in) s. W/C bodycol oval. 28-Nov-2 Christie's, Kensington #365
£859 $1400 €1289 Sunny boy (37x29cm-15x11in) s.i.d.1926 gouache on linen. 11-Feb-3 Bonhams & Doyles, New York #208/R est:600-800
£1400 $2324 €2030 Po Pan, a Pekinese (29x24cm-11x9in) s.i. W/C bodycol. 12-Jun-3 Christie's, Kensington #314/R est:1500-2000
£2454 $4000 €3681 Puck of Hartlebury, a Pekinese (34x44cm-13x17in) s.i. W/C prov. 11-Feb-3 Bonhams & Doyles, New York #232/R est:2500-3500

BINNEY, Don (1940-) New Zealander
£877 $1368 €1316 Landscape. s.d.1997 board. 27-Mar-3 International Art Centre, Auckland #163/R (NZ.D 2500)
£1520 $2371 €2280 Untitled (58x70cm-23x28in) s.d.1984 acrylic on paper. 17-Sep-2 Peter Webb, Auckland #142/R est:4500-6500 (NZ.D 5000)
£17241 $26897 €25862 Te henga (75x63cm-30x25in) s.d.1973. 7-Nov-2 International Art Centre, Auckland #34/R est:50000-70000 (NZ.D 55000)
Works on paper
£637 $1000 €956 Te Henga (31x38cm-12x15in) s.d.28 January 1966 crayon dr. 10-Dec-2 Peter Webb, Auckland #17/R est:2000-3000 (NZ.D 2000)
£732 $1150 €1098 Karekare (35x42cm-14x17in) s.d.September 1982 wax crayon. 10-Dec-2 Peter Webb, Auckland #16/R est:2500-3500 (NZ.D 2300)
£1881 $2934 €2822 Remuera jug IV (56x76cm-22x30in) s.d.1995 mixed media. 7-Nov-2 International Art Centre, Auckland #39/R est:6000-10000 (NZ.D 6000)
£3521 $5810 €5105 Remuera jug V (58x41cm-23x16in) s.d.1995 mixed media prov. 1-Jul-3 Peter Webb, Auckland #19/R est:4000-6000 (NZ.D 10000)

BINOIT, Peter (circle) (17th C) German
£15000 $25050 €21750 Iris, forget-me-not, lilies of the valley and other flowers in a roemer on wooden ledge (48x33cm-19x13in) init.d.1616 panel. 9-Jul-3 Christie's, London #57/R est:15000-20000

BINYON, Edward (1830-1876) British
£2400 $3720 €3600 Mediterranean xebecs off the coast of Capri (25x38cm-10x15in) one s. one s.i.d.1873 pair. 31-Oct-2 Christie's, Kensington #465/R est:2000-3000
Works on paper
£280 $434 €420 On the Mediterranean coast, possibly Cannes (20x51cm-8x20in) s.d.1862 W/C touches white. 25-Sep-2 Hamptons Fine Art, Godalming #287
£400 $660 €580 View of Monaco (20x48cm-8x19in) s.d.1862 W/C bodycol. 3-Jul-3 Duke & Son, Dorchester #145/R

BINZER, Carl von (1824-1904) German
£7034 $11255 €10200 Portraits d'Emmanuel de Riverileux et son epouse (100x81cm-39x32in) s.d.1866 pair. 14-Mar-3 Libert, Castor, Paris #40/R

BINZER, William (fl.1865) German/Australian
£305 $466 €458 White terraces, Rotomahana (43x58cm-17x23in) s. board. 21-Aug-2 Dunbar Sloane, Auckland #117 est:1000-2000 (NZ.D 1000)

BION, Cyril W (1889-1976) British
£550 $853 €825 Cottages and landscape near Ballymoney (51x61cm-20x24in) mono. 2-Oct-2 John Ross, Belfast #146
£550 $880 €825 Seascape (51x61cm-20x24in) init. 15-May-3 Christie's, Kensington #214/R

BION, Gottlieb (1804-1876) Swiss
£1206 $2013 €1700 Scene d'interieur (33x26cm-13x10in) s.d.1855 panel. 18-Jun-3 Hotel des Ventes Mosan, Brussels #177 est:1820-1960

BIONDA, Mario (1913-1985) Italian
£769 $1208 €1200 Hilly landscape (35x45cm-14x18in) 19-Nov-2 Finarte, Milan #157
£1538 $2385 €2400 Savudrija 2 (90x130cm-35x51in) s.d.60. 4-Dec-2 Finarte, Milan #330/R
£2436 $3824 €3800 Between sunrise and dusk (80x61cm-31x24in) s.d.56 exhib. 19-Nov-2 Finarte, Milan #132/R

BIONDETTI, Andrea (1851-1946) Italian
Works on paper
£1290 $2039 €2000 Sighs bridge. View of the Grand Canal. Palaace in Venice (30x19cm-12x7in) s. W/C set of 3. 18-Dec-2 Finarte, Milan #249

BIOTTEL, John (20th C) Irish?
£490 $765 €770 Still life with pear on desk (24x26cm-9x10in) s. board. 6-Nov-2 James Adam, Dublin #69/R

BIOULES, Vincent (1938-) French?
£1458 $2319 €2100 La nuit de Juillet (130x195cm-51x77in) s. s.i.d.verso. 29-Apr-3 Artcurial Briest, Paris #595/R est:2700-3000
£2639 $4196 €3800 La ponche, le reve II (200x300cm-79x118in) s. i.d.verso prov.exhib. 29-Apr-3 Artcurial Briest, Paris #596/R est:2700-3000

BIRCH, David (20th C) British
£800 $1312 €1200 Norwich (45x61cm-18x24in) s. canvas on board. 3-Jun-3 Sotheby's, Olympia #96/R
£980 $1529 €1470 Extensive view of the South Wales coast (62x126cm-24x50in) s. 11-Sep-2 Bonhams, Newport #419

BIRCH, Larson (?) British?
£360 $558 €540 Dunnywater (33x33cm-13x13in) s. board. 4-Dec-2 John Ross, Belfast #156

BIRCH, Lionel (1858-1930) British
£320 $502 €480 St. Catherine's Hill, Winchester (61x91cm-24x36in) 15-Apr-3 Bonhams, Knightsbridge #117

BIRCH, Samuel John Lamorna (1869-1955) British
£420 $672 €630 Stormy landscape (20x25cm-8x10in) s. chl. 11-Mar-3 Gorringes, Lewes #2453
£680 $1081 €1020 Landscape above Lamorna Cove, Cornwall (28x38cm-11x15in) i.verso board. 5-Mar-3 Bonhams, Bury St Edmunds #398/R
£1000 $1570 €1500 Fisherman in a landscape (28x38cm-11x15in) s.d.1954 board. 15-Apr-3 Bonhams, Knightsbridge #135/R est:800-1200
£2000 $3300 €2900 Maharange head, New Zealand (50x75cm-20x30in) s.d.1936. 1-Jul-3 Bearnes, Exeter #542/R est:2000-3000
£2800 $4564 €4200 Early spring, with farm set amongst trees. Sunrise over fir trees (15x22cm-6x9in) s.d.1892 panel pair. 29-Jan-3 Hampton & Littlewood, Exeter #419/R est:800-1200
£3000 $4560 €4500 River Deveron - the bridge at Rothiemay (24x37cm-9x15in) s.d.98 board. 28-Aug-2 Sotheby's, London #869/R est:3000-4000
£3000 $4680 €4500 Crossing the stream (51x62cm-20x24in) s. 25-Mar-3 Bonhams, New Bond Street #9/R est:3000-5000
£3548 $5500 €5322 Sunlit forest stream (36x43cm-14x17in) s.i. panel prov. 7-Dec-2 Neal Auction Company, New Orleans #289/R est:5000-7000
£3800 $6042 €5700 Bridge at Rothiemay, Abedeenshire (33x40cm-13x16in) s.i.verso board. 6-Mar-3 Christie's, Kensington #199/R est:3000-5000
£3800 $6346 €5510 Washing boat on the seine at Paris (23x33cm-9x13in) s.d.1896. 20-Jun-3 Keys, Aylsham #661/R est:3000-5000
£4400 $6996 €6600 Road beside the Seine (38x30cm-15x12in) s.d.1896. 29-Apr-3 Gorringes, Lewes #2156
£7097 $11000 €10646 River landscape with a sluice (46x61cm-18x24in) s. prov. 7-Dec-2 Neal Auction Company, New Orleans #288/R
Works on paper
£250 $390 €375 Cottages at St Levan near St Buryan (18x23cm-7x9in) s. i.verso W/C pencil. 17-Oct-2 David Lay, Penzance #1424
£270 $427 €392 Near Paris plage (23x33cm-9x13in) s. W/C. 23-Jul-3 Mallams, Oxford #207/R
£280 $442 €406 On the canal near Macclesfield (23x27cm-9x11in) init. W/C. 22-Jul-3 Bonhams, Knightsbridge #218/R
£330 $538 €495 Landscape (18x23cm-7x9in) s. W/C. 13-Feb-3 David Lay, Penzance #369
£350 $546 €525 Loch Lomond (12x25cm-5x10in) s.i.d.1946 W/C. 18-Sep-2 Dreweatt Neate, Newbury #28/R
£360 $562 €540 Figure on a track (18x24cm-7x9in) s.d.1906 W/C. 15-Oct-2 Bearnes, Exeter #356/R
£380 $597 €570 Woodland scene (24x35cm-9x14in) s. pencil W/C htd white. 19-Nov-2 Bonhams, Leeds #22
£380 $619 €570 Rock pool (13x18cm-5x7in) s.d.1902 W/C. 13-Feb-3 David Lay, Penzance #469
£400 $620 €600 Wet Sunday evening, Plymouth (43x61cm-17x24in) s.i.d.Dec.15th 1918 W/C. 26-Sep-2 Lane, Penzance #193
£400 $652 €600 Mousehole harbour (15x23cm-6x9in) s.d.1940. 13-Feb-3 David Lay, Penzance #468
£420 $655 €609 Fir trees in a landscape (25x35cm-10x14in) s. W/C. 27-Mar-3 Lane, Penzance #70/R
£424 $674 €636 River landscape (28x43cm-11x17in) s. W/C. 18-Mar-3 Maynards, Vancouver #50/R (C.D 1000)
£425 $672 €638 The Tweed at Berwick (13x20cm-5x8in) s.i. pencil col wash. 18-Dec-2 Mallams, Oxford #562/R

£500 $780 €750 Dawn (22x28cm-9x11in) s. s.i. indis d.Feb 1911 W/C. 6-Nov-2 Bonhams, Chester #515/R
£500 $780 €750 Moray, Scotland (21x28cm-8x11in) s.i.d.1944 pencil W/C. 27-Mar-3 Christie's, Kensington #318/R
£520 $811 €780 Roman encampment Land's End (23x28cm-9x11in) s. W/C. 17-Oct-2 David Lay, Penzance #1401
£550 $869 €825 Sheep in a river landscape (26x38cm-10x15in) s.d.1890 W/C. 26-Nov-2 Bonhams, Knightsbridge #18/R
£550 $897 €825 Mountain stream (13x18cm-5x7in) s. W/C pen ink. 28-Jan-3 Gorringes, Lewes #1628
£550 $886 €825 River in summer (24x35cm-9x14in) s. W/C. 18-Feb-3 Bonhams, Knightsbridge #188/R
£600 $984 €900 River scene (24x34cm-9x13in) s. pencil W/C gouache black ink. 3-Jun-3 Sotheby's, Olympia #12/R
£600 $990 €870 View of Trewooef (17x23cm-7x9in) s. pencil W/C. 3-Jul-3 Christie's, Kensington #295/R
£650 $1040 €975 Study at Boisy la Reine, near Paris (25x18cm-10x7in) s.d.1896 W/C. 11-Mar-3 Gorringes, Lewes #2454
£700 $1092 €1050 Extensive open landscape with cottages beyond (34x49cm-13x19in) s. pencil W/C. 18-Sep-2 Dreweatt Neate, Newbury #77/R
£700 $1120 €1050 Open landscape with cattle watering (23x33cm-9x13in) s.d.1897 W/C. 11-Mar-3 Gorringes, Lewes #2455
£800 $1240 €1200 St. Ives Harbour (24x34cm-9x13in) s. W/C. 3-Dec-2 Bonhams, Knightsbridge #201/R
£800 $1320 €1160 Chickens in the farmyard (23x28cm-9x11in) s.d.1910 pencil W/C bodycol. 3-Jul-3 Christie's, Kensington #292/R
£900 $1413 €1350 Anglers in a sunlit lake inlet (34x49cm-13x19in) s. W/C over pencil bodycol. 15-Apr-3 Bonhams, Knowle #79
£950 $1501 €1425 Mill house beside a river (23x34cm-9x13in) s.d.1891 W/C. 26-Nov-2 Bonhams, Knightsbridge #17/R
£1000 $1550 €1500 Evensong - Lalant from Hayle (30x41cm-12x16in) s. W/C prov. 31-Oct-2 Duke & Son, Dorchester #128/R est:600-1000
£1100 $1749 €1650 Frosty morning, Vale of East Okement, Okehampton (25x35cm-10x14in) s. W/C. 29-Apr-3 Bonhams, Knightsbridge #19/R est:1200-1800
£1450 $2277 €2175 Evensong -Lelant from Hayle. s. W/C prov. 10-Dec-2 Lane, Penzance #59/R est:1450-1750
£1600 $2480 €2400 Pohutakawas at Whangerei, New Zealand, lake and wooded landscape (94x132cm-37x52in) s.d.1937 W/C. 26-Sep-2 Lane, Penzance #377/R est:1500-1750
£1650 $2756 €2393 Cornish quay in summer (28x38cm-11x15in) s. W/C pencil. 25-Jun-3 Brightwells, Leominster #982/R est:600-1000
£1900 $3173 €2755 Wind gust, lane near Monte Roda (28x33cm-11x13in) s.i. W/C. 20-Jun-3 Keys, Aylsham #506/R est:1200-1600

BIRCH, Thomas (1779-1851) American
£4421 $7250 €6632 Portrait of a girl with her dog, probably the artist's daughter (76x64cm-30x25in) s. 8-Feb-3 Neal Auction Company, New Orleans #549/R est:5000-7000
£6790 $11000 €9846 Sailing off the coast (51x76cm-20x30in) s.d.1830 prov. 29-Jul-3 Christie's, Rockefeller NY #154/R est:10000-15000
£9259 $15000 €13889 Falconer's shipwreck (102x152cm-40x60in) s.d.1828 prov.lit. 21-May-3 Sotheby's, New York #209/R est:20000-40000
£11111 $18000 €16111 Treacherous Cove (79x91cm-31x36in) s. indis d. prov. 29-Jul-3 Christie's, Rockefeller NY #153/R est:15000-25000
£54839 $85000 €82259 Philadelphia harbour (51x77cm-20x30in) prov. 4-Dec-2 Sotheby's, New York #136/R est:30000-50000

BIRCH, Thomas (attrib) (1779-1851) American
£14474 $22000 €21711 American ship at sea (30x114cm-12x45in) panel above trumeau mirror. 17-Aug-2 North East Auctions, Portsmouth #682/R

BIRCHALL, William Minshall (1884-1941) British
Works on paper
£270 $451 €392 Eventide near Greenwich (13x18cm-5x7in) s.i.d.1930 W/C. 18-Jun-3 Sotheby's, Olympia #117/R
£290 $455 €435 Ship portrait of the steam and sail ship SS Fengtien (17x26cm-7x10in) s.i.d.1934 pencil W/C bodycol. 10-Dec-2 Rosebery Fine Art, London #702/R
£300 $456 €450 Passing the Lizard (21x31cm-8x12in) s.i.d.1917 W/C htd white. 15-Aug-2 Bonhams, New Bond Street #274/R
£340 $541 €510 Old Father Thames, N Woolwich (18x16cm-7x6in) s.d.1929 W/C. 29-Apr-3 Henry Adams, Chichester #230
£400 $624 €580 Viceroy of India - a liner (13x19cm-5x7in) s.d.1936 W/C. 27-Mar-3 Lane, Penzance #181
£450 $684 €675 Somewhere in the North Sea (27x44cm-11x17in) s.i.d.1916 W/C bodycol. 15-Aug-2 Bonhams, New Bond Street #277
£500 $760 €750 Britain's might (21x31cm-8x12in) s.i.d.1917 W/C bodycol. 15-Aug-2 Bonhams, New Bond Street #276/R
£500 $775 €750 Below Gravesend, war and pleasure (29x48cm-11x19in) s.i.d.1913 W/C. 24-Sep-2 Anderson & Garland, Newcastle #329/R
£500 $795 €750 Tower Bridge, London (18x16cm-7x6in) s.d.1929. 29-Apr-3 Henry Adams, Chichester #229
£520 $790 €780 Before the breeze (25x35cm-10x14in) s.i. W/C htd white. 15-Aug-2 Bonhams, New Bond Street #239/R
£600 $972 €900 US clipper Rainbow (22x28cm-9x11in) s.i. pencil W/C. 21-May-3 Christie's, Kensington #470/R
£700 $1064 €1050 North sea weather (25x36cm-10x14in) s.i.d.1924 W/C htd white. 15-Aug-2 Bonhams, New Bond Street #278/R
£750 $1208 €1125 Off the Fastnet, guarding an oil tanker (21x31cm-8x12in) s.d.1917 W/C. 15-Jan-3 Cheffins Grain & Comins, Cambridge #380/R
£850 $1377 €1275 P and O liner Morea leaving Tilbury (36x52cm-14x20in) s.i.d.1928 pencil pen ink W/C. 21-May-3 Christie's, Kensington #486/R
£920 $1481 €1380 Sailing Day, Tilbury (23x33cm-9x13in) s. W/C. 9-May-3 Mallams, Oxford #48/R
£1000 $1520 €1500 Leaving Portsmouth. Leaving for Blighty. Passing fighters. Cross Channel (14x25cm-6x10in) s.i.d.1918 W/C over pencil four. 15-Aug-2 Bonhams, New Bond Street #273/R est:1000-1500

BIRCHER, Alfred Thompson (?) British?
£6329 $10000 €9494 Sailboat along rocky coast (36x58cm-14x23in) s. panel. 26-Apr-3 Thomaston Place, Thomaston #60

BIRCK, Alphonse (1859-?) French
£2949 $4659 €4600 Tunisienne en costume traditionnel (55x47cm-22x19in) s. panel. 14-Nov-2 Credit Municipal, Paris #50 est:900-1200

BIRD, Cyril Kenneth (1887-1965) British
Works on paper
£1100 $1760 €1650 War's humanising invoice - shelter trench (38x27cm-15x11in) s.i. pen ink. 11-Mar-3 Bonhams, New Bond Street #142/R est:600-900

BIRD, Edward (attrib) (1772-1819) British
£900 $1404 €1350 The chairmender (46x61cm-18x24in) panel. 15-Oct-2 Gorringes, Lewes #2318/R
£5000 $7950 €7500 Family portrait (58x45cm-23x18in) panel. 19-Mar-3 Sotheby's, London #102/R est:6000-8000

BIRD, Harrington (1846-1936) British
£1400 $2282 €2100 Signorina with jockey up, 1900 (38x49cm-15x19in) s.d.1900 prov. 11-Feb-3 Bonhams, Knowle #66 est:1500-2000

BIRD, Samuel C (19th C) British
£5000 $8300 €7500 Thames from London Bridge, looking towards St. Paul's (121x183cm-48x72in) s.d.1890. 12-Jun-3 Sotheby's, London #232/R est:6000-8000

BIRDSALL, Amos (attrib) (1865-1938) American
£427 $700 €641 Crashing surf (76x91cm-30x36in) 9-Feb-3 William Jenack, New York #215

BIRGER, Hugo (1854-1887) Swedish
£61273 $100487 €88846 Evening idyll - the artist's wife Mathilda in Villerville (55x72cm-22x28in) s.d.86. 4-Jun-3 AB Stockholms Auktionsverk #2181/R est:400000-500000 (S.KR 780000)

BIRGER-ERICSON, Birger (1904-1994) Swedish
£297 $473 €446 Utopian (50x61cm-20x24in) s. panel. 3-Mar-3 Lilla Bukowskis, Stockholm #700 (S.KR 4000)
£456 $721 €684 Young mannequin (61x50cm-24x20in) s. cardboard. 28-Apr-3 Bukowskis, Stockholm #292/R (S.KR 6000)
£645 $1044 €968 The angler (122x51cm-48x20in) s. panel. 3-Feb-3 Lilla Bukowskis, Stockholm #631 (S.KR 9000)
£760 $1202 €1140 Rescued (34x46cm-13x18in) s.d.30 panel. 28-Apr-3 Bukowskis, Stockholm #292a/R (S.KR 10000)
£931 $1509 €1397 Landscape from Vaxholm (60x74cm-24x29in) s. panel. 3-Feb-3 Lilla Bukowskis, Stockholm #202 (S.KR 13000)
£989 $1562 €1484 In the saloon (48x64cm-19x25in) s. panel. 28-Apr-3 Bukowskis, Stockholm #290/R (S.KR 13000)
£1255 $1983 €1883 Garden idyll (46x55cm-18x22in) s. panel. 28-Apr-3 Bukowskis, Stockholm #286/R est:8000-10000 (S.KR 16500)
£1407 $2223 €2111 Show-window, NK (44x49cm-17x19in) s. panel. 28-Apr-3 Bukowskis, Stockholm #284/R est:15000-18000 (S.KR 18500)
£1825 $2884 €2738 Street scene from Visby (46x54cm-18x21in) s.d.43 panel. 28-Apr-3 Bukowskis, Stockholm #285/R est:8000-10000 (S.KR 24000)
£2593 $4045 €3890 Fantasy landscape (17x21cm-7x8in) s.i. cardboard. 5-Nov-2 Bukowskis, Stockholm #162a/R est:20000-25000 (S.KR 37000)

BIRKEMOSE, Jens (1943-) Danish
£345 $528 €518 Composition in red (61x47cm-24x19in) s.d.82 verso. 24-Aug-2 Rasmussen, Havnen #2290/R (D.KR 4000)
£442 $689 €663 Portrait (65x45cm-26x18in) s.d.62. 5-Aug-2 Rasmussen, Vejle #345/R (D.KR 5200)
£931 $1444 €1397 Abstract composition (75x60cm-30x24in) init.d.82 s.d.82 verso. 1-Oct-2 Rasmussen, Copenhagen #170/R (D.KR 11000)

£1493 $2373 €2240 Hamlet's black box (73x60cm-29x24in) s.d.1996 verso. 29-Apr-3 Kunsthallen, Copenhagen #112/R est:20000 (D.KR 16000)
£1525 $2547 €2211 Composition (181x131cm-71x52in) s.d.91-92 verso. 17-Jun-3 Rasmussen, Copenhagen #135 est:20000 (D.KR 16000)
£1673 $2643 €2510 Composition (130x90cm-51x35in) s.verso. 1-Apr-3 Rasmussen, Copenhagen #310/R est:20000-25000 (D.KR 18000)
£1801 $2810 €2702 Figures in an energy filled landscape (140x122cm-55x48in) init. s.d.83 verso masonite. 11-Nov-2 Rasmussen, Vejle #106/R est:20000-25000 (D.KR 21000)
£1943 $3030 €2915 Composition (80x60cm-31x24in) init. painted 1999. 18-Sep-2 Kunsthallen, Copenhagen #233/R est:20000 (D.KR 23000)
£2002 $3343 €2903 Composition (100x82cm-39x32in) init. s.i.d.1989-1990 verso. 17-Jun-3 Rasmussen, Copenhagen #12/R est:10000-12000 (D.KR 21000)
£2371 $3675 €3557 Composition (135x89cm-53x35in) s.d.93 verso. 1-Oct-2 Rasmussen, Copenhagen #175/R est:20000-25000 (D.KR 28000)
£2416 $3818 €3624 Composition (140x100cm-55x39in) init. init.d.1986 verso. 1-Apr-3 Rasmussen, Copenhagen #215/R est:25000 (D.KR 26000)
£2607 $4145 €3911 Composition (80x100cm-31x39in) mono. d.1998-2002 verso. 10-Mar-3 Rasmussen, Vejle #676/R est:30000 (D.KR 28000)
£3346 $5286 €5019 C. (140x110cm-55x43in) s.i.d.1986 verso. 1-Apr-3 Rasmussen, Copenhagen #203/R est:20000-25000 (D.KR 36000)

BIRKHAMMER, Axel (1874-1936) Danish
£350 $532 €525 Cattle grazing in a meadow before a farmstead (36x53cm-14x21in) s. i.verso. 29-Aug-2 Christie's, Kensington #223/R
£414 $650 €621 Hillside (44x65cm-17x26in) s. 22-Nov-2 Skinner, Boston #303/R
£438 $701 €657 Lake by wood (71x108cm-28x43in) s. 13-Jan-3 Rasmussen, Vejle #134/R (D.KR 5000)

BIRKHOLM, Jens (1869-1915) Danish
£353 $568 €530 Landscape from Svanninge, Faaborg (31x56cm-12x22in) mono. 19-Jan-3 Hindemae, Ullerslev #7287 (D.KR 4000)
£479 $776 €719 Coastal landscape with cliff (47x57cm-19x22in) init.d.08. 25-Jan-3 Rasmussen, Havnen #2132/R (D.KR 5400)

BIRKLE, Albert (1900-1986) Austrian/German
£641 $1006 €1000 Street scene (51x46cm-20x18in) s. chl dr. 21-Nov-2 Dorotheum, Vienna #452/R
£7372 $11426 €11500 Portrait of Else Starosta (64x57cm-25x22in) s.i.d.1927 cardboard prov. 6-Dec-2 Ketterer, Munich #77/R est:13000-14000
£83333 $129167 €130000 Portrait of Maler Kath (61x42cm-24x17in) s. s.i.verso painted 1924 prov.exhib.lit. 6-Dec-2 Ketterer, Munich #75/R est:50000-70000

Works on paper
£517 $828 €750 King Saul (75x52cm-30x20in) s.i. mixed media. 11-Mar-3 Dorotheum, Vienna #169/R
£556 $878 €800 Public Prosecutor Steiner (48x39cm-19x15in) s.i.d.1940 chl. 26-Apr-3 Dr Lehr, Berlin #76/R
£1026 $1621 €1600 Concentration camp (38x55cm-15x22in) s.d.1945 chk bodycol. 15-Nov-2 Reiss & Sohn, Konigstein #423/R est:1500
£2179 $3378 €3400 Insanity (47x62cm-19x24in) s. i.verso chl exec.c.1925 prov. 6-Dec-2 Ketterer, Munich #70/R est:2500-3000
£5797 $9507 €8000 Street scene (64x91cm-25x36in) s. i.d.1920 verso. 31-May-3 Villa Grisebach, Berlin #229/R est:8000-10000

BIRKMYER, James B (fl.1880-1898) British
£260 $426 €377 Chudleigh Glen, forest scene with children and stream (56x76cm-22x30in) s. 3-Jun-3 Capes Dunn, Manchester #149

BIRKS, Geoffrey W (1929-1993) British
Works on paper
£1050 $1638 €1575 Scolding for scoundrels (25x26cm-10x10in) s. pencil pen ink W/C. 25-Mar-3 Bonhams, Leeds #555/R est:500-700
£1200 $1872 €1800 Northern landscape (26x35cm-10x14in) s. W/C. 25-Mar-3 Bonhams, Leeds #556 est:500-700

BIRLEY, Sir Oswald (1880-1952) British
£450 $702 €675 Portrait of Rt Hon William (132x106cm-52x42in) s.d.1927. 12-Sep-2 Sotheby's, Olympia #77/R
£1500 $2369 €2250 Extensive landscape (64x76cm-25x30in) s.d.1920. 27-Nov-2 Sotheby's, Olympia #126/R est:1500-2000
Works on paper
£250 $389 €375 Shipping off Spithead (15x30cm-6x12in) init.i.d.Aug 12 pencil W/C htd white. 19-Sep-2 Christie's, Kensington #165

BIRLEY, Sir Oswald (attrib) (1880-1952) British
£2000 $3120 €3000 Nude in an artist's studio (60x50cm-24x20in) bears sig. 17-Oct-2 Lawrence, Crewkerne #516/R est:2000-3000

BIRMANN, Peter (1758-1844) Swiss
Works on paper
£480 $749 €720 Staubbach in the Lauterbrunnen valley (69x52cm-27x20in) i. sepia Indian ink over pencil. 6-Nov-2 Dobiaschofsky, Bern #1242/R (S.FR 1100)
£3718 $5874 €5800 Large waterfall near Tivoli (86x66cm-34x26in) s. gouache. 16-Nov-2 Lempertz, Koln #1203/R est:6000
£4317 $6906 €6000 Entry to the Villa Maecenas (46x67cm-18x26in) s.i.d.1786 exhib. 17-May-3 Lempertz, Koln #1205/R est:6500

BIRMANN, Peter (attrib) (1758-1844) Swiss
£529 $772 €794 Ruins by monastery courtyard (38x30cm-15x12in) 17-Jun-2 Philippe Schuler, Zurich #7405 (S.FR 1200)

BIRNIE, Johan (1866-1958) Dutch
£493 $794 €700 Bulb-field (30x41cm-12x16in) s. 6-May-3 Vendu Notarishuis, Rotterdam #207/R

BIRNIE, William (1929-) British
£320 $499 €480 Oban fishing boat (14x14cm-6x6in) s. board. 17-Oct-2 Bonhams, Edinburgh #91

BIRNSTENGEL, Richard (1881-1968) German
£283 $436 €450 Woodland hut at dusk (70x100cm-28x39in) s.d.1905 i. verso. 23-Oct-2 Neumeister, Munich #613

BIROLLI, Renato (1906-1959) Italian
£3846 $6038 €6000 Fishing tools (50x70cm-20x28in) s.d.1949 tempera oil paper. 23-Nov-2 Meeting Art, Vercelli #98/R
£7639 $12146 €11000 Nude (48x66cm-19x26in) s.d.1947 paper on canvas. 1-May-3 Meeting Art, Vercelli #346 est:10000
£10127 $15797 €16000 Black veil (50x65cm-20x26in) s.d.1941. 14-Sep-2 Meeting Art, Vercelli #980/R est:15000
£11392 $18000 €18000 Venetian lagoon (50x60cm-20x24in) s.d.946 s.i.d.verso. 30-Nov-2 Farsetti, Prato #661/R est:19000
£14839 $23445 €23000 Scales (55x80cm-22x31in) s.d.1951 prov.exhib.lit. 18-Dec-2 Christie's, Rome #284/R est:30000
£28369 $45957 €40000 Espansione n. 2 (99x80cm-39x31in) s.i.d.1957 verso prov.exhib.lit. 26-May-3 Christie's, Milan #266/R est:40000-60000
£50000 $77000 €75000 Incendio nelle cinque terre (115x145cm-45x57in) s.d.1957 s.i.d.verso prov.exhib.lit. 22-Oct-2 Christie's, London #22/R est:50000-70000

Works on paper
£481 $755 €750 History (28x22cm-11x9in) s.d.40 ink W/C. 19-Nov-2 Finarte, Milan #3
£962 $1490 €1500 Big yellow house (23x34cm-9x13in) s. W/C paper on canvas exec.1932. 4-Dec-2 Finarte, Milan #245/R est:1800
£1905 $3029 €2800 Composition with animal (24x32cm-9x13in) s.i.d.1947 pastel. 1-Mar-3 Meeting Art, Vercelli #682

BIRON, H (19th C) Swedish
£1923 $3000 €2885 Table top still life of flowers (99x79cm-39x31in) s. 12-Apr-3 Weschler, Washington #544/R est:1000-1500

BIRREN, Joseph P (1864-1933) American
£4717 $7500 €7076 At day's end (24x20cm-9x8in) s. painted c.1910. 4-May-3 Treadway Gallery, Cincinnati #527/R est:4500-6500

BIRREN, Joseph Pierre (1865-1933) American
£318 $500 €477 Oceanfront overlook (15x23cm-6x9in) s. canvasboard. 23-Nov-2 Jackson's, Cedar Falls #345/R

BIRSTINGER, Leopold (1903-1983) Austrian
£8696 $14261 €12000 In the artist's garden (47x61cm-19x24in) mono. prov. 27-May-3 Wiener Kunst Auktionen, Vienna #98/R est:7000-12000

BIRTLES, Harry (fl.1880-1905) British
Works on paper
£340 $537 €510 Cattle grazing on Salisbury Meadows in the shade of a tree (8x21cm-3x8in) s. W/C. 2-Apr-3 Edgar Horn, Eastbourne #269/R
£900 $1458 €1350 Shepherds driving sheep on a path in the hills (22x32cm-9x13in) s.d.1884 W/C. 20-May-3 Sotheby's, Olympia #191/R

BIRTWHISTLE, Cecil H (1910-1990) British
£300 $465 €450 View from the Hermitage, Richmond, Surrey (92x71cm-36x28in) s. 3-Dec-2 Bonhams, Knightsbridge #91/R

BIRZA, Rob (1962-) ?
£4487 $6955 €7000 Olifje and Jerome (200x160cm-79x63in) s.i.d.1989 on stretcher acrylic. 3-Dec-2 Christie's, Amsterdam #380/R est:8000-12000
Works on paper
£769 $1192 €1200 Abstract composition (24x37cm-9x15in) s.d.87 chl gouache. 3-Dec-2 Christie's, Amsterdam #378/R est:1200-1600
£769 $1192 €1200 Abstract red (29x20cm-11x8in) s.d.87 wax crayon gouache. 3-Dec-2 Christie's, Amsterdam #379/R est:1200-1600

BISCHOF, Anton (1877-?) German
Works on paper
£582 $908 €850 Annual fair with carousel (33x29cm-13x11in) s. W/C ink dr. 10-Apr-3 Allgauer, Kempten #2592/R
£616 $962 €900 Evening churchgoers in winter (31x26cm-12x10in) s. W/C gouache lit. 10-Apr-3 Allgauer, Kempten #2591/R

BISCHOFF, Elmer Nelson (1916-1991) American
Works on paper
£5063 $8000 €7595 Untitled - seated woman with braid (36x43cm-14x17in) i.d.1968 chl ink wash. 22-Apr-3 Butterfields, San Francisco #6048/R est:10000-12000

BISCHOFF, Franz A (1864-1929) American
£2038 $3200 €3057 Spring landscape. Turkeys. Winding stream (17x25cm-7x10in) s. three prov. 20-Nov-2 Christie's, Los Angeles #14/R est:3000-5000
£2108 $3500 €3057 Coast at sunset (33x46cm-13x18in) s. board prov. 11-Jun-3 Butterfields, San Francisco #4246/R est:4000-6000
£2410 $4000 €3495 Wooded California landscape (43x36cm-17x14in) s. oil paper on masonite. 11-Jun-3 Boos Gallery, Michigan #344/R est:8000-12000
£3057 $4800 €4586 Cove, Southern California (33x48cm-13x19in) s. board prov. 20-Nov-2 Christie's, Los Angeles #10/R est:5000-7000
£3822 $6000 €5733 Grand Tetons (33x48cm-13x19in) s. board prov. 20-Nov-2 Christie's, Los Angeles #93/R est:7000-9000
£4217 $7000 €6115 California landscape (30x41cm-12x16in) s. prov. 11-Jun-3 Butterfields, San Francisco #4245/R est:6000-8000
£6211 $10000 €9317 Utah, barns in red rock landscape (33x48cm-13x19in) s. board prov. 18-Feb-3 John Moran, Pasadena #115 est:15000-20000
£6211 $10000 €9317 Ocean scene (33x48cm-13x19in) s. board prov. 18-Feb-3 John Moran, Pasadena #151 est:6000-9000
£6410 $10000 €9615 Western mountainous landscape (38x53cm-15x21in) s. board. 18-Sep-2 Boos Gallery, Michigan #289/R est:15000-20000
£7097 $11000 €10646 Orange hills (33x48cm-13x19in) s. board prov. 29-Oct-2 John Moran, Pasadena #617 est:8000-12000
£8696 $14000 €13044 California coastline with cypress trees (33x48cm-13x19in) s. board. 15-Jan-3 Boos Gallery, Michigan #662/R est:20000-30000
£9317 $15000 €13976 Barn in atmospheric landscape (23x46cm-9x18in) s. prov. 18-Feb-3 John Moran, Pasadena #15 est:8000-10000
£9375 $15000 €14063 Carmel Coast (66x81cm-26x32in) s. s.d.1921 verso. 11-Jan-3 James Julia, Fairfield #194 est:5000-7000
£10180 $17000 €14761 Rocky coastal (33x48cm-13x19in) s. board prov. 17-Jun-3 John Moran, Pasadena #28 est:10000-15000
£10559 $17000 €15839 Santa Rosa Island, St, Pedro Harbour, California (38x51cm-15x20in) s. artist board. 15-Jan-3 Boos Gallery, Michigan #661/R est:20000-30000
£12258 $19000 €18387 Picking flowers (30x41cm-12x16in) s. canvasboard prov. 29-Oct-2 John Moran, Pasadena #620 est:10000-15000
£25641 $40000 €38462 Mountain river landscape with fisherman (46x56cm-18x22in) s. 18-Sep-2 Boos Gallery, Michigan #298/R est:40000-60000
£28846 $45000 €43269 California rocky coastal landscape (51x102cm-20x40in) s. 18-Sep-2 Boos Gallery, Michigan #297/R est:60000-80000
£41401 $65000 €62102 Utah barnyards (91x76cm-36x30in) s. i.verso prov.exhib. 19-Nov-2 Butterfields, San Francisco #8267/R est:35000-50000
£55901 $90000 €83852 Sand dunes and rocky coast (61x79cm-24x31in) s. s.i.verso prov. 18-Feb-3 John Moran, Pasadena #44 est:35000-55000
Works on paper
£4969 $8000 €7454 Still life, grapes on vine (7x20cm-3x8in) s. W/C prov. 18-Feb-3 John Moran, Pasadena #83b est:3000-5000
£5096 $8000 €7644 Roses (21x26cm-8x10in) s. W/C gouache prov. 20-Nov-2 Christie's, Los Angeles #47/R est:10000-15000

BISCHOFF, J C (18/19th C) ?
£2394 $3855 €3400 Classical landscape with figures (26x43cm-10x17in) s.d.1813. 10-May-3 Berlinghof, Heidelberg #197/R est:1500

BISCHOFFSHAUSEN, Hans (1927-1987) Austrian
£2703 $4216 €4000 Espace dilate (55x46cm-22x18in) s.i.d.1963 verso. 28-Mar-3 Charbonneaux, Paris #37/R est:1000
Works on paper
£486 $768 €700 Blind (31x24cm-12x9in) s.mono.i.d.76 pencil gouache. 24-Apr-3 Dorotheum, Vienna #225/R
£1899 $3000 €3000 Untitled (50x65cm-20x26in) s.d.VIII.59 silk paper sand graphite board exhib. 27-Nov-2 Dorotheum, Vienna #232/R est:2400-3200

BISEO, Cesare (1843-1909) Italian
£2532 $4000 €4000 Oriental party (53x28cm-21x11in) s. 26-Nov-2 Christie's, Rome #107 est:4000-4500

BISGYER, Barbara (1933-) American
Sculpture
£1806 $2800 €2709 Female figures (69x51cm-27x20in) s. brown pat bronze black plinth exec.c.1970. 8-Dec-2 Toomey, Oak Park #849/R est:1500-2500

BISHOP, Alfred (19th C) British
£620 $967 €930 Grey horse in stable (63x76cm-25x30in) s.d.1890. 9-Oct-2 Woolley & Wallis, Salisbury #320/R
£8000 $12640 €12000 Groom with two hunters and champion greyhound at the gates to Bygrave House (71x91cm-28x36in) s.d.1870. 13-Nov-2 Halls, Shrewsbury #414/R est:4000-5000

BISHOP, Henry (1868-1939) British
£650 $1060 €975 Saw mill (56x44cm-22x17in) s.i. 29-Jan-3 Sotheby's, Olympia #241/R

BISHOP, Isabel (1902-1988) American
Works on paper
£267 $425 €401 Yawn (5x8cm-2x3in) init. pen ink prov. 3-May-3 Rachel Davis, Shaker Heights #170/R
£283 $450 €425 Putting on jacket number 2 (15x8cm-6x3in) s. pen ink prov. 3-May-3 Rachel Davis, Shaker Heights #168/R
£457 $750 €663 Man at a store counter. Figure at a counter (19x10cm-7x4in) s. pen ink double-sided. 5-Jun-3 Swann Galleries, New York #39/R

BISHOP, James (1927-) American
£4000 $6680 €5800 Untitled (55x55cm-22x22in) oil wash paper prov. 24-Jun-3 Sotheby's, Olympia #109/R est:1500-2000

BISHOP, Richard (1887-1975) American
£3323 $5250 €4818 Springer spaniel (41x30cm-16x12in) s.d.1938 board. 26-Jul-3 Coeur d'Alene, Hayden #190/R est:4000-6000
£4114 $6500 €6171 Two American egrets flying through a wooded swamp (30x40cm-12x16in) s.d.51 board. 3-Apr-3 Christie's, Rockefeller NY #189/R est:1500-2500

BISHOP, W Follen (1856-1936) British
Works on paper
£600 $954 €900 Cattle and doves in the street at Porlock weir (52x35cm-20x14in) s. W/C. 4-Mar-3 Bearnes, Exeter #373/R
£3000 $4740 €4500 Figures in woodland with a hunt approaching (58x99cm-23x39in) s. W/C. 2-Dec-2 Gorringes, Lewes #2839/R est:3000-5000

BISI, Luigi (1814-1886) Italian
£3357 $5606 €4800 Procession dans une eglise (80x65cm-31x26in) s. 25-Jun-3 Pierre Berge, Paris #23/R est:3800-4500

BISKINIS, Dimitrios (1891-1947) Greek
£4000 $6320 €6000 Young girl sitting on a chair (72x45cm-28x18in) 1-Apr-3 Bonhams, New Bond Street #45 est:4000-6000

BISMOUTH, Maurice (1885-1965) French
£372 $580 €550 Oriental a la priere (24x16cm-9x6in) s.i. cardboard. 25-Mar-3 Chochon-Barre & Allardi, Paris #67
£612 $973 €900 Portrait de femme tatouee (40x30cm-16x12in) s. panel. 24-Mar-3 Rabourdin & Choppin de Janvry, Paris #98
£962 $1510 €1500 Rabbin (41x33cm-16x13in) s. panel. 12-Dec-2 Rabourdin & Choppin de Janvry, Paris #130/R
£5449 $8554 €8500 Ghriba de Djerba (80x125cm-31x49in) s. 14-Dec-2 Artcurial Briest, Paris #68/R

BISON, Giuseppe Bernardino (1762-1844) Italian
£15603 $24184 €23405 Venetian landscape with riders (49x69cm-19x27in) panel prov. 4-Dec-2 AB Stockholms Auktionsverk #1958/R est:80000-100000 (S.KR 220000)
£49645 $76950 €74468 Elegant figures in palace interior (49x69cm-19x27in) panel prov. 4-Dec-2 AB Stockholms Auktionsverk #1957/R est:300000-400000 (S.KR 700000)
Works on paper
£385 $550 €578 Study of a standing young male in classical robe (21x14cm-8x6in) pen ink wash. 23-Jan-3 Swann Galleries, New York #165/R
£500 $785 €750 Ceiling design (26x37cm-10x15in) pen ink wash over black chk prov. 11-Dec-2 Sotheby's, Olympia #263/R
£743 $1159 €1100 Building with two statues in the garden (29x21cm-11x8in) chk pen ink wash. 27-Mar-3 Christie's, Paris #208/R

£900 $1413 €1350 Breaded figure seated in front of a large barrel. Sketch of a woman (12x14cm-5x6in) s. pen ink wash over black chk double-sided. 11-Dec-2 Sotheby's, Olympia #244/R
£1200 $1884 €1800 Trinity (54x43cm-21x17in) pen ink wash htd white. 11-Dec-2 Sotheby's, Olympia #246/R est:1200-1500
£1216 $1897 €1800 Sea god (19x27cm-7x11in) s. graphite pen ink wash prov. 27-Mar-3 Christie's, Paris #67/R
£2800 $4676 €4060 Jupiter and Juno. Another study for Jupiter (16x24cm-6x9in) s.i. pen brown ink wash blk chk double-sided. 9-Jul-3 Sotheby's, London #66/R est:1200-1500
£3800 $6346 €5510 Three figures in a rocky, mountainous landsape with a full moon (21x29cm-8x11in) bears i. verso pen brown ink wash blk chk. 9-Jul-3 Sotheby's, London #67/R est:1000-1500
£4392 $6851 €6500 Herminie chez les bergers (20x32cm-8x13in) s. graphite pen ink wash. 27-Mar-3 Christie's, Paris #44/R
£4500 $7515 €6525 Vestal Virgin reclining near a holy fire in a tomb (44x30cm-17x12in) bodycol. 8-Jul-3 Christie's, London #56/R est:4000-6000

BISON, Giuseppe Bernardino (attrib) (1762-1844) Italian
£346 $537 €519 Campagna (21x30cm-8x12in) i. verso pen. 24-Sep-2 Koller, Zurich #6450 (S.FR 800)
£3145 $4874 €5000 Landscapes (34x46cm-13x18in) two prov. 2-Oct-2 Dorotheum, Vienna #302/R est:7000-9000
£5986 $9937 €8500 Capriccio veneziano (41x68cm-16x27in) tempera. 11-Jun-3 Dorotheum, Vienna #36/R est:6000-9000
Works on paper
£878 $1370 €1300 Etudes de voussures (14x19cm-6x7in) s. pen Chinese ink wash. 27-Mar-3 Maigret, Paris #2
£1484 $2345 €2300 Soldats dans une grange. Alchimiste (17cm-7in circular) gouache pair. 18-Dec-2 Piasa, Paris #99/R
£1572 $2437 €2500 Fantasy landscape (50x71cm-20x28in) gouache paper on panel. 2-Oct-2 Dorotheum, Vienna #304/R est:2500-3000

BISON, Giuseppe Bernardino (style) (1762-1844) Italian
£13000 $20280 €19500 Venice, view of the Grand Canal with a regatta (49x81cm-19x32in) 8-Apr-3 Sotheby's, Olympia #262/R est:7000-9000

BISSCHOP, Christoffel (1828-1904) Dutch
£5634 $9070 €8000 Elegant lady in front of mirror (34x26cm-13x10in) s. panel. 7-May-3 Vendue Huis, Gravenhage #367/R est:3000-4000

BISSCHOP, Christoffel (attrib) (1828-1904) Dutch
£700 $1148 €1050 Quiet contemplation (41x32cm-16x13in) board. 5-Jun-3 Christie's, Kensington #620/R

BISSCHOP, Jan de (1628-1671) Dutch
Works on paper
£1783 $2782 €2800 Studies of the Apollo Belvedere and one of Gaul and his wife (9x22cm-4x9in) pen brown ink wash exhib.lit. 5-Nov-2 Sotheby's, Amsterdam #88/R est:3000-4000
£2400 $4008 €3480 Four studies after classical sculptures (9x22cm-4x9in) pen brn ink wash. 9-Jul-3 Sotheby's, London #2/R est:1000-1500
£2420 $3776 €3800 Two figure studies, after the Antique (9x14cm-4x6in) s. red chk brown wash. 5-Nov-2 Sotheby's, Amsterdam #89/R est:1800-2200

BISSCHOP, Jan de (attrib) (1628-1671) Dutch
Works on paper
£443 $700 €700 Une femme assise pres d'un putto tirant une fleche (8x15cm-3x6in) i. pen brown ink brown wash prov. 27-Nov-2 Christie's, Paris #9a
£1266 $2000 €2000 Extensive landscape with Roman ruins (13x22cm-5x9in) pen wash. 29-Nov-2 Bassenge, Berlin #5049/R est:2400

BISSCHOPS, Charles (1894-1975) Belgian
£385 $596 €600 Cavalier au soleil couchant (66x101cm-26x40in) s. 9-Dec-2 Horta, Bruxelles #275
£446 $696 €700 Jeune Orientale au chapeau de paille (46x38cm-18x15in) s. 11-Nov-2 Horta, Bruxelles #566
£615 $954 €960 Vues de Baeza et de la Puerta del Sol a Tolede (27x35cm-11x14in) s. panel pair. 9-Dec-2 Horta, Bruxelles #274
Works on paper
£2448 $4087 €3500 Medersa Sahrij a Fez. Minaret a Meknes (100x75cm-39x30in) s. Indian ink dr pair. 27-Jun-3 Claude Aguttes, Neuilly #144/R est:2000-3000

BISSCHOPS, Joseph (1901-1978) Belgian
£321 $497 €500 Souk au Maroc (45x58cm-18x23in) s. panel. 9-Dec-2 Horta, Bruxelles #446

BISSEN, Rudolf (1846-1911) Danish
£466 $740 €699 Beech wood with couple resting by brook (101x82cm-40x32in) s.d.93. 5-Mar-3 Rasmussen, Copenhagen #1894/R (D.KR 5000)
£1769 $2812 €2600 River landscape with meadow (72x102cm-28x40in) s.d.06 exhib. 25-Feb-3 Dorotheum, Vienna #194/R est:2200-2600

BISSEN, Vilhelm Christian Gottlieb (1836-1913) Danish
Sculpture
£1106 $1748 €1659 Mercury as a boy (134cm-53in) s.d.1886 brown pat.plaster incl.white wood base exhib.lit. 27-Nov-2 Museumsbygningen, Copenhagen #212/R est:5000 (D.KR 13000)

BISSI, Cirno Sergio (1902-1987) Italian
£284 $443 €420 Masked ball (17x29cm-7x11in) s. board. 28-Mar-3 Farsetti, Prato #432
£372 $580 €550 Dancers (60x50cm-24x20in) s.d.70. 28-Mar-3 Farsetti, Prato #458
£385 $608 €600 Dancers (80x60cm-31x24in) s. 15-Nov-2 Farsetti, Prato #409
£513 $805 €800 View of Florence Duomo (50x30cm-20x12in) s. 16-Dec-2 Pandolfini, Florence #254/R
£897 $1409 €1400 Carnival ball (39x53cm-15x21in) s. paper. 16-Dec-2 Pandolfini, Florence #262/R
£1250 $2000 €1875 Dancers (70x50cm-28x20in) s. 14-May-3 Butterfields, San Francisco #1185/R est:3000-5000
Works on paper
£641 $1006 €1000 Carnival party (43x59cm-17x23in) s.d.54 mixed media. 16-Dec-2 Pandolfini, Florence #261/R

BISSIER, Jules (1893-1965) German
£8696 $14261 €12000 7.1.57 (19x22cm-7x9in) s.d.7.1.57 egg oil tempera linen prov.exhib. 31-May-3 Villa Grisebach, Berlin #322/R est:12000-15000
£9615 $14904 €15000 Monti 60-26 (19x23cm-7x9in) s.i.d.1960 egg oil tempera gold foil prov. 6-Dec-2 Ketterer, Munich #158/R est:14000-16000
£10897 $16891 €17000 A-6 Juni 65 (22x25cm-9x10in) s.i.d.1965 egg oil tempera prov.exhib. 6-Dec-2 Ketterer, Munich #159/R est:14000-16000
Works on paper
£1389 $2194 €2000 Untitled (49x58cm-19x23in) s.d.18.11.1955 Indian ink. 26-Apr-3 Dr Lehr, Berlin #79/R est:3000
£2244 $3478 €3500 Composition (35x44cm-14x17in) s.d.8.II.55 Indian ink brush. 6-Dec-2 Hauswedell & Nolte, Hamburg #53/R est:3500
£7424 $11655 €11136 Untitled (17x23cm-7x9in) s.d.1960 W/C prov. 25-Nov-2 Germann, Zurich #46/R est:18000-22000 (S.FR 17000)

BISSIERE, Roger (1884-1964) French
£1560 $2528 €2200 Nature morte aux fruits (30x61cm-12x24in) s. panel. 26-May-3 Joron-Derem, Paris #18 est:1000-1500
£2790 $4352 €4046 Vase de fleurs (75x41cm-30x16in) s. panel prov. 26-Mar-3 Walker's, Ottawa #29/R est:6000-8000 (C.D 6500)
£2903 $4587 €4500 Rouge et noir (41x33cm-16x13in) s.d.52 oil mixed media prov. 18-Dec-2 Christie's, Rome #171/R
£4000 $6360 €6000 Nu couche sur linge blanc (35x64cm-14x25in) s. board prov. 20-Mar-3 Sotheby's, Olympia #160/R est:3500-5500
£14000 $23380 €20300 Composition (32x72cm-13x28in) s.d.54 prov.exhib. 27-Jun-3 Christie's, London #138/R est:9000-12000
£23188 $38029 €32000 Composition 87 (65x54cm-26x21in) s.d.52 oil tempera prov.exhib. 29-May-3 Lempertz, Koln #548/R est:15000
Works on paper
£1282 $2013 €2000 Composition (38x33cm-15x13in) s. chl exec.1950. 20-Nov-2 Binoche, Paris #31

BISSILL, George (1896-1973) British
£500 $820 €750 Miners (57x66cm-22x26in) 3-Jun-3 Sotheby's, Olympia #95/R
£1500 $2369 €2250 Harlequins (44x37cm-17x15in) s. 27-Nov-2 Sotheby's, Olympia #94/R est:1500-2000

BISSOLO, Pier Francesco (c.1470-1554) Italian
£62000 $96720 €93000 Madonna and Child with Saint John (40x51cm-16x20in) panel prov. 10-Apr-3 Sotheby's, London #24/R est:30000-50000

BISSOLO, Pier Francesco (style) (c.1470-1554) Italian
£5600 $8680 €8400 Madonna and Child enthroned, landscape beyond (54x42cm-21x17in) bears sig.d.1517 panel. 31-Oct-2 Sotheby's, Olympia #4/R est:2000-3000

BISSON, C H (18th C) American
£962 $1500 €1395 Portrait of Mrs Thomas Willing (64x76cm-25x30in) s.d.1737. 30-Mar-3 Simpson's, Houston #488

BISSON, E Privat (?) French?
£417 $658 €600 Nature morte aux fruits et aux fleurs (104x158cm-41x62in) s. 23-Apr-3 Rabourdin & Choppin de Janvry, Paris #16/R

BISSON, Edouard (1856-?) French
£600 $978 €900 Goddesses dancing on Mount Olympus (41x51cm-16x20in) s.d.1902. 13-Feb-3 Christie's, Kensington #186/R
£1972 $3273 €2800 Le printemps (100x61cm-39x24in) s. 11-Jun-3 Beaussant & Lefèvre, Paris #6/R est:1500
£6962 $11000 €11000 Girl with flowers and angels in background (159x127cm-63x50in) s.d.1909. 26-Nov-2 Wiener Kunst Auktionen, Vienna #77/R est:2000-4000

BISSON, Jacques (attrib) (?-1737) French
£450 $693 €675 Portrait of a gentleman, in a black coat (74x61cm-29x24in) s.d.1729. 5-Sep-2 Christie's, Kensington #27/R

BISTES, Alexandre (20th C) French?
£3019 $4679 €4800 Pivoines (81x60cm-32x24in) s. 7-Oct-2 Claude Aguttes, Neuilly #315/R est:5350

BISTOLFI, Leonardo (1859-1933) Italian
Sculpture
£1216 $1897 €1800 Portrait of Giuseppe Zanardelli (56x51x10cm-22x20x4in) init. plaster releuf. 31-Mar-3 Finarte Semenzato, Milan #43/R
£1392 $2172 €2200 Allegorical group (62cm-24in) mono. black pat.bronze Cast.Fonderia Punagalli Torino E Amerio. 18-Oct-2 Dr Fritz Nagel, Stuttgart #469/R est:3500
£1905 $3029 €2800 Victory (61cm-24in) init.i. pat bronze. 1-Mar-3 Stadion, Trieste #509

BISTTRAM, Emil (1895-1976) American
£2439 $4000 €3537 Untitled (150x135cm-59x53in) s.i.d.1962-64 oil on linen. 1-Jun-3 Wright, Chicago #272/R est:1000-2000
Works on paper
£1154 $1800 €1731 Last supper (20x20cm-8x8in) W/C. 9-Nov-2 Altermann Galleries, Santa Fe #7
£4487 $7000 €6731 Two Hopi Kachinas, corn dancers (56x43cm-22x17in) s.d.66 W/C graphite prov.lit. 9-Nov-2 Santa Fe Art, Santa Fe #115/R est:10000-15000

BITAY, Arpad (1900-1935) Hungarian
£950 $1482 €1378 Picnic (100x121cm-39x48in) s. 12-Apr-3 Mu Terem Galeria, Budapest #96/R est:250000 (H.F 340000)

BITRAN, Albert (1929-) French
£561 $875 €842 Composition sous la lampe (120x60cm-47x24in) s.d.60 exhib. 5-Nov-2 Bukowskis, Stockholm #303/R (S.KR 8000)
£617 $963 €926 Untitled composition (65x50cm-26x20in) s.d.75. 11-Nov-2 Rasmussen, Vejle #80/R (D.KR 7200)
£863 $1416 €1200 Terres de silence (89x116cm-35x46in) s. i.d.65/66 verso prov. 3-Jun-3 Christie's, Amsterdam #92/R est:1200-1600
£933 $1483 €1400 Atelier (81x65cm-32x26in) s.d.59 exhib. 29-Apr-3 Kunsthallen, Copenhagen #179/R (D.KR 10000)
£1497 $2380 €2200 Composition (38x46cm-15x18in) s.d.58 canvas on canvas prov. 26-Feb-3 Artcurial Briest, Paris #549 est:1000-1200
£3205 $5032 €5000 Composition ocre (56x55cm-22x22in) s. painted 1979. 10-Dec-2 Piasa, Paris #157 est:800
Works on paper
£310 $481 €465 Composition (56x41cm-22x16in) s.d.65 gouache collage. 4-Dec-2 Kunsthallen, Copenhagen #72 (D.KR 3600)
£326 $519 €489 Composition (52x39cm-20x15in) s.d.58 gouache. 29-Apr-3 Kunsthallen, Copenhagen #57 (D.KR 3500)

BITRON, Albert (20th C) French
£422 $650 €633 Debut un nature morte (130x94cm-51x37in) s.i.d.1964. 8-Sep-2 Treadway Gallery, Cincinnati #733/R

BITTAR, Antoine (1957-) Canadian
£403 $637 €605 Maltese merchants (30x41cm-12x16in) s.i.d.2001 board. 14-Nov-2 Heffel, Vancouver #139/R est:1200-1500 (C.D 1000)
£429 $670 €622 Bruine, Quebec (15x20cm-6x8in) s.i. panel prov. 26-Mar-3 Walker's, Ottawa #227/R est:1000-1500 (C.D 1000)
£578 $948 €867 Behind the parliaments, Ottawa (30x40cm-12x16in) s. 3-Jun-3 Joyner, Toronto #463 est:1500-2000 (C.D 1300)
£807 $1291 €1211 Shadows, Sutton, QC (51x61cm-20x24in) s. s.i.d.2002 verso. 15-May-3 Heffel, Vancouver #226/R est:2000-2500 (C.D 1800)
£978 $1604 €1467 Country ride, Southern France (19x25cm-7x10in) s. board. 3-Jun-3 Joyner, Toronto #339/R est:1000-1500 (C.D 2200)
£1411 $2230 €2117 Street in Gloucester (41x51cm-16x20in) s.i.d.2001. 14-Nov-2 Heffel, Vancouver #137/R est:1300-1600 (C.D 3500)
£1481 $2296 €2222 Quebec rooftops (30x40cm-12x16in) s. board prov. 3-Dec-2 Joyner, Toronto #286/R est:2000-2500 (C.D 3600)

BITTAR, Pierre (1934-) French
£701 $1100 €1052 Little Traverse Bay coastal landscape (46x43cm-18x17in) s. 20-Nov-2 Boos Gallery, Michigan #478/R est:1500-2000
£1911 $3000 €2867 Little Traverse Bay (28x36cm-11x14in) s. 20-Nov-2 Boos Gallery, Michigan #477/R est:1500-2000

BITTER, Ary (1883-1960) French
Sculpture
£1149 $1792 €1700 Jeune fille au faon (27x72x22cm-11x28x9in) s.st.f.LNJL brown green pat bronze. 26-Mar-3 Millon & Associes, Paris #163
£1358 $2200 €2037 Satyr and two fauns (23x91cm-9x36in) st.f.Suisse Freres art deco bronze. 25-Jan-3 Skinner, Boston #2183/R est:3000-5000
£3642 $5937 €5500 Jeune fille enlevant un faon a la biche (44x74cm-17x29in) s.st.f.Susse green pat bronze. 17-Feb-3 Horta, Bruxelles #91
£4000 $6240 €6000 Antelope bookends (21x16cm-8x6in) st.f.Susse brown pat bronze wood pair. 9-Apr-3 Sotheby's, London #160/R est:4000-6000

BITTER, Theo (1916-1994) Dutch
£346 $550 €519 On the bench, a Green Bay Packers player (100x100cm-39x39in) s.d.72. 7-Mar-3 Skinner, Boston #600/R
£1549 $2494 €2200 Bouquet of flowers in a bucket (59x49cm-23x19in) s.d.38. 7-May-3 Vendue Huis, Gravenhage #188/R est:2200-2600

BIVA, Henri (1848-1928) French
£1439 $2302 €2000 Bord de riviere (38x46cm-15x18in) s. panel. 15-May-3 Christie's, Paris #122/R est:2000-3000
£1807 $3000 €2620 Wooded landscape (56x74cm-22x29in) s. 11-Jun-3 Boos Gallery, Michigan #570/R est:6000-8000
£3593 $6000 €5210 Woodland interior with brook (32x26cm-13x10in) s. 22-Jun-3 Freeman, Philadelphia #30/R est:5000-8000
£8500 $13855 €12325 Etang en ile de France (54x65cm-21x26in) s. 16-Jul-3 Sotheby's, Olympia #233a/R est:2500-3500
Works on paper
£696 $1100 €1100 Arbres au bord de l'etang (54x45cm-21x18in) s. W/C. 1-Dec-2 Peron, Melun #56

BIVEL, Fernand Achille Lucien (1888-1950) French
£1139 $1800 €1800 Au bord de lac (55x46cm-22x18in) s. 1-Dec-2 Livinec, Gaudcheau & Jezequel, Rennes #92/R
£2778 $4416 €4000 Repos dans un parc (50x61cm-20x24in) s. 29-Apr-3 Artcurial Briest, Paris #202/R est:4500-5000
£17949 $28359 €28000 Pique-nique sur la plage en Bretagne (200x139cm-79x55in) s. 18-Nov-2 Tajan, Paris #207/R est:6000-9000
Works on paper
£748 $1190 €1100 Couple sur les hauteurs de Tunis (16x21cm-6x8in) s.d.1918 W/C. 24-Mar-3 Rabourdin & Choppin de Janvry, Paris #267/R

BJELOCVETOV, Andrej (1923-1997) Czechoslovakian
£372 $580 €558 Portrait of a girl (54x46cm-21x18in) s.d.56. 12-Oct-2 Dorotheum, Prague #86/R (C.KR 18000)

BJERG, Johannes C (1886-1955) Danish
Sculpture
£6979 $11026 €10469 Woman with snake (198cm-78in) plaster exhib.prov. 27-Nov-2 Museumsbygningen, Copenhagen #561/R est:5000 (D.KR 82000)

BJERKE-PETERSEN, Vilhelm (1909-1957) Danish
£284 $440 €426 Landscape by the sea, Sardal (19x24cm-7x9in) mono.d.53 panel. 8-Dec-2 Uppsala Auktionskammare, Uppsala #245 (S.KR 4000)
£366 $581 €549 Composition (50x61cm-20x24in) grisaille masonite. 26-Feb-3 Kunsthallen, Copenhagen #78 (D.KR 4000)
£413 $641 €620 Surrealistic composition (46x38cm-18x15in) s.d.45 masonite. 4-Dec-2 Kunsthallen, Copenhagen #48 (D.KR 4800)
£422 $659 €633 Cliffs, South Koster (27x35cm-11x14in) init.d.52. 18-Sep-2 Kunsthallen, Copenhagen #89/R (D.KR 5000)
£423 $656 €635 Surrealistic landscape with trees and hands (54x65cm-21x26in) init.d.46 masonite. 1-Oct-2 Rasmussen, Copenhagen #179/R (D.KR 5000)
£480 $749 €720 Fantasy landscape (46x55cm-18x22in) s.d.44 panel. 13-Sep-2 Lilla Bukowskis, Stockholm #48 (S.KR 7000)
£541 $897 €784 Sunset (65x55cm-26x22in) s. panel. 16-Jun-3 Lilla Bukowskis, Stockholm #41 (S.KR 7000)
£593 $919 €890 Floating object (37x49cm-15x19in) init.d.49 panel. 1-Oct-2 Rasmussen, Copenhagen #22/R (D.KR 7000)
£772 $1243 €1158 Composition (33x41cm-13x16in) init.d.48. 7-May-3 AB Stockholms Auktionsverk #1126/R (S.KR 10000)
£1004 $1616 €1506 Untitled (31x40cm-12x16in) init.d.51. 7-May-3 AB Stockholms Auktionsverk #1128/R (S.KR 13000)
£1859 $2937 €2789 Surrealistic landscape (80x100cm-31x39in) s.d.46 masonite. 1-Apr-3 Rasmussen, Copenhagen #238/R est:20000 (D.KR 20000)
£2085 $3357 €3128 Composition (63x73cm-25x29in) s.d.47 panel. 7-May-3 AB Stockholms Auktionsverk #1127/R est:15000-18000 (S.KR 27000)
£2326 $3605 €3489 Composition (70x96cm-28x38in) 4-Dec-2 Kunsthallen, Copenhagen #50/R est:30000 (D.KR 27000)

Works on paper
£875 $1382 €1313 Three blue shapes (47x59cm-19x23in) init.d.32 chk pencil. 28-Apr-3 Bukowskis, Stockholm #324/R (S.KR 11500)

BJERKLIE, John (20th C) American
£2500 $4000 €3625 Yellow and black (185x157cm-73x62in) painted canvas wood mixed media. 17-May-3 Selkirks, St. Louis #294/R est:500-700

BJERRE, Kristen (1869-1943) Danish
£850 $1325 €1275 Interior from Lomberg Church near Lemvig (34x43cm-13x17in) s.d.1890. 5-Aug-2 Rasmussen, Vejle #95/R (D.KR 10000)
£3823 $5964 €5735 Church interior with figures, Ferring Church (66x76cm-26x30in) s.d.1910 prov. 5-Aug-2 Rasmussen, Vejle #93/R est:20000-30000 (D.KR 45000)

BJERRE, Niels (1864-1942) Danish
£263 $420 €395 Landscape with church and houses (44x74cm-17x29in) init.d.1922. 13-Jan-3 Rasmussen, Vejle #197 (D.KR 3000)
£448 $686 €672 Landscape (45x74cm-18x29in) init.d.1919. 24-Aug-2 Rasmussen, Havnen #2172 (D.KR 5200)

BJORCK, Oscar (1860-1929) Swedish
£260 $400 €390 Profile of a girl (43x36cm-17x14in) 8-Sep-2 DeFina, Austinburg #414
£412 $626 €618 Summer landscape with arbour (44x63cm-17x25in) s. cardboard prov. 16-Aug-2 Lilla Bukowskis, Stockholm #196 (S.KR 6000)
£780 $1209 €1170 Siesta at the harbour (30x46cm-12x18in) s. cardboard prov. 3-Dec-2 Bukowskis, Stockholm #197/R (S.KR 11000)
£1164 $1885 €1688 Fisherman from Skagen (39x32cm-15x13in) s. 26-May-3 Bukowskis, Stockholm #7/R est:20000-25000 (S.KR 15000)
£3404 $5379 €5106 View of the sea with jetty (43x65cm-17x26in) s. 2-Dec-2 Rasmussen, Copenhagen #1388/R est:35000 (D.KR 40000)

BJORK, Jakob (1726-1793) Swedish
£1474 $2388 €2137 Marquis Louis d'Havringcourt (64x51cm-25x20in) i.verso. 26-May-3 Bukowskis, Stockholm #359/R est:25000-30000 (S.KR 19000)

BJORK, Jakob (attrib) (1726-1793) Swedish
£413 $628 €620 Portrait of young man wearing olive coloured coat (50x43cm-20x17in) 28-Aug-2 Museumsbygningen, Copenhagen #16/R (D.KR 4800)

BJORKLUND, Rickard (1897-1974) Swedish
£276 $425 €414 Spring (60x85cm-24x33in) s.d.1930. 27-Oct-2 Anders Antik, Landskrona #10/R (S.KR 4000)

BJORKLUND-RASMUSSEN, Poul (1909-1984) Danish
£366 $581 €549 Tove Fredskilde (100x81cm-39x32in) init.d.57 exhib. 26-Feb-3 Kunsthallen, Copenhagen #239 (D.KR 4000)

BJORN, Christian Aleth (1859-1945) Danish
£699 $1132 €1014 Canal with many vessels (36x56cm-14x22in) s.d.1890. 24-May-3 Rasmussen, Havnen #2099/R (D.KR 7300)

BJULF, Soren Christian (1890-1958) Danish
£309 $497 €464 The fisherwomen at Gammel Strand (56x47cm-22x19in) s. 19-Jan-3 Hindemae, Ullerslev #7480/R (D.KR 3500)
£315 $498 €473 Fisherwomen at Gammel Strand (70x88cm-28x35in) s. 30-Nov-2 Rasmussen, Havnen #2257/R (D.KR 3700)
£506 $800 €800 Fish market in Copenhagen (47x39cm-19x15in) mono. 29-Nov-2 Schloss Ahlden, Ahlden #1295/R
£580 $922 €870 Fisherwoman selling fish (49x40cm-19x16in) s. 3-Mar-3 Lilla Bukowskis, Stockholm #386 (S.KR 7800)
£600 $912 €900 Fish sellers before the Copenhagen Stock Exchange, Christianbord Castle (71x101cm-28x40in) s. 29-Aug-2 Christie's, Kensington #221/R
£689 $1116 €999 Fisherwomen at Gammel Strand (75x90cm-30x35in) s. 24-May-3 Rasmussen, Havnen #2193 (D.KR 7200)
£935 $1458 €1403 The fishwives at Gammel Strand (75x95cm-30x37in) s. 5-Aug-2 Rasmussen, Vejle #280/R (D.KR 11000)
£1000 $1630 €1500 Continental market scene (67x93cm-26x37in) s. 12-Feb-3 Bonhams, Knightsbridge #234/R est:1000-1500
£1108 $1795 €1662 Vegetable market with figures, postman and policeman (100x83cm-39x33in) s. 25-Jan-3 Rasmussen, Havnen #2044/R est:8000-10000 (D.KR 12500)

BJULF, Soren Christian (attrib) (1890-1958) Danish
£279 $444 €419 Washerwomen at Gammel Strand (65x55cm-26x22in) s. 10-Mar-3 Rasmussen, Vejle #451 (D.KR 3000)
£292 $455 €438 Fisherwomen at Gammel Strand (78x95cm-31x37in) s. 11-Nov-2 Rasmussen, Vejle #478/R (D.KR 3400)
£298 $474 €447 Village street with figures, Roskilde Cathedral in background (57x67cm-22x26in) s. 10-Mar-3 Rasmussen, Vejle #243 (D.KR 3200)
£306 $496 €444 Fisherwomen at Gammel Strand (55x66cm-22x26in) s. 24-May-3 Rasmussen, Havnen #2043/R (D.KR 3200)
£338 $527 €507 Ladies shopping from the fishwives at Gammel Strand (65x54cm-26x21in) s. 11-Aug-2 Hindemae, Ullerslev #7304/R (D.KR 4000)
£342 $551 €513 Fishermen and fisherwomen at Gammel Strand (59x85cm-23x33in) s.d.21. 22-Feb-3 Rasmussen, Havnen #2060/R (D.KR 3800)
£372 $592 €558 Fishwives at Gammel Strand (64x54cm-25x21in) s. 10-Mar-3 Rasmussen, Vejle #448 (D.KR 4000)
£372 $596 €558 Gentleman buying fish in winter (46x40cm-18x16in) s. 16-Mar-3 Hindemae, Ullerslev #350/R (D.KR 4000)
£391 $619 €587 Fisherwomen, postman and police at Gammel Strand (70x92cm-28x36in) s. 30-Nov-2 Rasmussen, Havnen #2220 (D.KR 4600)
£400 $632 €600 Fisherwomen at Gammel Strand (95x75cm-37x30in) 30-Nov-2 Rasmussen, Havnen #2246 (D.KR 4700)
£442 $689 €663 The fishwives at Gammel Strand (66x57cm-26x22in) s. 5-Aug-2 Rasmussen, Vejle #278/R (D.KR 5200)
£450 $725 €675 From Gammel Strand with fisherwomen and postman (70x100cm-28x39in) s. 22-Feb-3 Rasmussen, Havnen #2048/R (D.KR 5000)
£465 $734 €698 Fisherwomen and figures at Gammel Strand (48x42cm-19x17in) s. 5-Apr-3 Rasmussen, Havnen #2047 (D.KR 5000)
£468 $754 €702 Flower sellers and policeman at Hojbro Plads (54x47cm-21x19in) s. 22-Feb-3 Rasmussen, Havnen #2202 (D.KR 5200)
£497 $776 €746 Fisherwomen at Gammel Strand (71x95cm-28x37in) s. 11-Nov-2 Rasmussen, Vejle #477 (D.KR 5800)
£497 $776 €746 The flower sellers (68x58cm-27x23in) s. 11-Nov-2 Rasmussen, Vejle #479 (D.KR 5800)
£517 $791 €776 Winter's day at Gammel Strand with fisherwomen (76x95cm-30x37in) s. 24-Aug-2 Rasmussen, Havnen #2066/R (D.KR 6000)
£523 $841 €785 From the flower market at Hojbro Plads (57x49cm-22x19in) s,. 22-Feb-3 Rasmussen, Havnen #2270 (D.KR 5800)
£549 $846 €824 Fisherwomen at Gammel Strand (75x90cm-30x35in) s. 26-Oct-2 Rasmussen, Havnen #2128/R (D.KR 6500)
£576 $934 €864 Fisherwomen and postman at Gammel Strand (80x100cm-31x39in) s. 25-Jan-3 Rasmussen, Havnen #2005/R (D.KR 6500)
£603 $923 €905 Fisherwomen and other figures at Gammel Strand (84x96cm-33x38in) d. 24-Aug-2 Rasmussen, Havnen #2019/R (D.KR 7000)
£681 $1056 €1022 From Hojbro Plads (95x80cm-37x31in) s. 28-Sep-2 Rasmussen, Havnen #2029/R (D.KR 8000)
£761 $1172 €1142 The fisherwomen at Gammel Strand (75x96cm-30x38in) s. 26-Oct-2 Rasmussen, Havnen #2000/R (D.KR 9000)

BJURSTROM, Tor (1888-1966) Swedish
£618 $1025 €896 Still life of flowers, dish and glass (50x63cm-20x25in) s. canvas on panel. 16-Jun-3 Lilla Bukowskis, Stockholm #50/R (S.KR 8000)
£1135 $1759 €1703 Landscape with buildings (73x92cm-29x36in) s. panel. 8-Dec-2 Uppsala Auktionskammare, Uppsala #210/R est:20000-25000 (S.KR 16000)
£1141 $1802 €1712 Kaleidoscope in oval (60x73cm-24x29in) s. painted 1958. 28-Apr-3 Bukowskis, Stockholm #118/R est:20000-25000 (S.KR 15000)
£1313 $2114 €1970 Green landscape with figure on path (60x73cm-24x29in) s. panel. 7-May-3 AB Stockholms Auktionsverk #840/R est:15000-20000 (S.KR 17000)
£1473 $2327 €2210 Still life of objects on table (53x68cm-21x27in) s. 30-Nov-2 Goteborg Auktionsverk, Sweden #516/R est:20000 (S.KR 21000)
£1673 $2643 €2510 Composition (92x73cm-36x29in) s. painted 1962. 28-Apr-3 Bukowskis, Stockholm #120/R est:35000-40000 (S.KR 22000)
£1825 $2884 €2738 Landscape with houses (46x65cm-18x26in) s. d.1944 verso panel. 28-Apr-3 Bukowskis, Stockholm #94/R est:20000-25000 (S.KR 24000)
£1977 $3124 €2966 Composition with green circle (64x88cm-25x35in) st.sig. painted c.1920. 28-Apr-3 Bukowskis, Stockholm #119/R est:30000-35000 (S.KR 26000)
£2102 $3280 €3153 Landscape from the south of France (72x62cm-28x24in) s. painted c.1925. 5-Nov-2 Bukowskis, Stockholm #15/R est:25000-30000 (S.KR 30000)
£2104 $3324 €3156 Coastal landscape with figures on pier (53x64cm-21x25in) s. panel. 30-Nov-2 Goteborg Auktionsverk, Sweden #515/R est:25000 (S.KR 30000)
£2433 $3845 €3650 Gothenburg's Harbour (59x74cm-23x29in) s. painted 1940s. 28-Apr-3 Bukowskis, Stockholm #93/R est:40000-45000 (S.KR 32000)
£2703 $4351 €4055 Woman (133x94cm-52x37in) s. 7-May-3 AB Stockholms Auktionsverk #670/R est:40000-50000 (S.KR 35000)

£3802 $6008 €5703 Town scene with Swedish flags (64x88cm-25x35in) st.sig. painted c.1920 exhib.lit. 28-Apr-3 Bukowskis, Stockholm #110/R est:50000-60000 (S.KR 50000)

BLAAS, E von (1843-1932) Austrian

£316 $480 €474 Portrait of a girl (29x21cm-11x8in) s. 19-Aug-2 Joel, Victoria #153 (A.D 900)

BLAAS, Eugen von (1843-1932) Austrian

£550 $852 €825 Portrait of a woman (45x30cm-18x12in) s.d.1900. 3-Dec-2 Sotheby's, Olympia #215/R
£1600 $2672 €2400 Young Spanish beauty (27x21cm-11x8in) s.d.1886 panel. 18-Jun-3 Christie's, Kensington #109/R est:1500-2000
£2553 $4136 €3600 Venetian on the balcony (33x26cm-13x10in) s.d.1870 panel. 22-May-3 Dorotheum, Vienna #78/R est:4000-5000
£4000 $6240 €6000 Portrait of a boy (42x35cm-17x14in) s.d.1884. 26-Mar-3 Sotheby's, Olympia #183/R est:4000-6000
£5479 $8548 €8219 Portrait of Venetian woman (20x16cm-8x6in) s. panel study verso. 28-Mar-3 Koller, Zurich #3108/R est:14000-18000 (S.FR 12000)
£5806 $9000 €8709 Elegant lady (33x24cm-13x9in) s. panel prov.exhib. 30-Oct-2 Christie's, Rockefeller NY #170/R est:10000-15000
£6962 $11000 €10443 Young beauty with a flowered shawl (25x20cm-10x8in) s. prov. 1-Apr-3 Christie's, Rockefeller NY #191/R est:7000-9000
£7097 $11000 €10646 Head of a young boy (27x22cm-11x9in) s. panel. 30-Oct-2 Christie's, Rockefeller NY #161/R est:7000-9000
£12258 $19000 €18387 Young beauty (27x21cm-11x8in) s. panel. 30-Oct-2 Christie's, Rockefeller NY #160/R est:7000-9000
£50633 $80000 €75950 Introduction (77x103cm-30x41in) s. prov. 24-Apr-3 Sotheby's, New York #74/R est:70000-90000
£51613 $80000 €77420 Musette (126x74cm-50x29in) s.d.1900 panel prov. 30-Oct-2 Christie's, Rockefeller NY #30/R est:60000-90000
£70968 $110000 €106452 Farewell (95x41cm-37x16in) panel. 30-Oct-2 Christie's, Rockefeller NY #31/R est:60000-80000
£75949 $120000 €113924 Daydreaming (140x74cm-55x29in) s. prov.lit. 24-Apr-3 Sotheby's, New York #11/R est:120000-180000
£90000 $139500 €135000 Confidences (84x52cm-33x20in) s.d.1885 panel. 4-Dec-2 Christie's, London #103/R est:100000-150000
£135484 $210000 €203226 Secrets (76x98cm-30x39in) s.d.1884 prov. 30-Oct-2 Christie's, Rockefeller NY #29/R est:100000-150000
£148387 $230000 €222581 Mussel gatherers (109x183cm-43x72in) s. prov. 30-Oct-2 Christie's, Rockefeller NY #33/R est:250000-350000
£154839 $240000 €232259 New suitor (91x110cm-36x43in) s.d.1906 prov. 30-Oct-2 Christie's, Rockefeller NY #32/R est:100000-150000
£225806 $350000 €338709 Gossiping at the well (89x109cm-35x43in) s.d.1907 prov. 30-Oct-2 Christie's, Rockefeller NY #28/R est:120000-160000

Works on paper

£1582 $2500 €2500 Girl wearing shawl round shoulders (38x28cm-15x11in) s.d.94 W/C. 26-Nov-2 Wiener Kunst Auktionen, Vienna #42/R est:2500-5000

BLAAS, Julius von (1845-1922) Austrian

£1290 $2012 €1935 Racing horse, 1910 (57x74cm-22x29in) s.d.1910. 11-Sep-2 Kieselbach, Budapest #29/R (H.F 500000)
£1400 $2184 €2100 Turul (60x73cm-24x29in) s.d.1898. 26-Mar-3 Sotheby's, Olympia #202/R est:400-800

Works on paper

£845 $1361 €1200 Kaiser Franz Joseph I von Osterreich (29x23cm-11x9in) s. pencil htd white oval. 7-May-3 Dorotheum, Vienna #116/R

BLAAS, Karl von (1815-1894) Austrian

£1027 $1603 €1500 Portrait of Antonie Freifrau von Doblhoff (71x57cm-28x22in) s.i.d.1875 verso two. 10-Apr-3 Dorotheum, Vienna #149/R est:1600-1800
£1560 $2528 €2200 Girl with blond locks (45x35cm-18x14in) s.d.1842. 22-May-3 Dorotheum, Vienna #76/R est:2400-2800
£1935 $2845 €3000 Portrait of young girl (24x19cm-9x7in) s. panel. 20-Jun-2 Dr Fritz Nagel, Stuttgart #754/R est:2000

BLAAS, Karl von (attrib) (1815-1894) Austrian

£1258 $1950 €2000 Troubadour heading towards castle (25x36cm-10x14in) 2-Oct-2 Dorotheum, Vienna #388/R est:2500-3500

BLACHE, Christian (1838-1920) Danish

£255 $403 €383 Seascape from Copenhagen Harbour (19x30cm-7x12in) s. 30-Nov-2 Rasmussen, Havnen #2223 (D.KR 3000)
£287 $465 €416 Seascape with sailing vessels near the coast (40x63cm-16x25in) s. 26-May-3 Rasmussen, Copenhagen #1373/R (D.KR 3000)
£374 $592 €561 Seascape with sailing vessels (22x34cm-9x13in) s.d.87. 30-Nov-2 Rasmussen, Havnen #2211/R (D.KR 4400)
£423 $651 €635 Coastal landscape with vessels at Oresund (28x38cm-11x15in) s.d.1919. 26-Oct-2 Rasmussen, Havnen #3037 (D.KR 5000)
£443 $699 €665 Ringkjoping - study of waves (33x52cm-13x20in) s.i.d.83. 27-Nov-2 Museumsbygningen, Copenhagen #72 (D.KR 5200)
£474 $720 €711 Paddlesteamer at sea, grey day (36x53cm-14x21in) s.d.1863. 27-Aug-2 Rasmussen, Copenhagen #1749/R (D.KR 5500)
£495 $798 €743 Seascape with many vessels (39x63cm-15x25in) s.d.1910. 22-Feb-3 Rasmussen, Havnen #2206/R (D.KR 5500)
£511 $807 €767 Seascape with Norwegian vessel (41x53cm-16x21in) s. 30-Nov-2 Rasmussen, Havnen #2014/R (D.KR 6000)
£574 $930 €832 Coastal landscape with rowing boat at sea (39x63cm-15x25in) s.i.d.87. 26-May-3 Rasmussen, Copenhagen #1366/R (D.KR 6000)
£646 $982 €969 Seascape with sailing vessels and steamship (36x62cm-14x24in) s.i.d.1912. 27-Aug-2 Rasmussen, Copenhagen #1729/R (D.KR 7500)
£653 $1038 €980 Ship-wreck in the breakers (80x51cm-31x20in) s.d.1876. 5-May-3 Rasmussen, Vejle #263/R (D.KR 7000)
£653 $1038 €980 Vessels in a Norwegian fjord (47x69cm-19x27in) s. d.1872 verso. 5-May-3 Rasmussen, Vejle #267/R (D.KR 7000)
£766 $1210 €1149 The frigate Jylland in open seas (74x68cm-29x27in) s.d.89. 2-Dec-2 Rasmussen, Copenhagen #1428/R (D.KR 9000)
£788 $1261 €1182 Coastal landscape with man fishing from jetty (29x44cm-11x17in) 13-Jan-3 Rasmussen, Vejle #81/R (D.KR 9000)
£931 $1480 €1397 Fishermen by their boats at water's edge (39x59cm-15x23in) s.d.13/9-1916. 5-Mar-3 Rasmussen, Copenhagen #1981/R (D.KR 10000)
£943 $1472 €1415 View of Copenhagen Harbour (31x54cm-12x21in) s.d.1911. 11-Nov-2 Rasmussen, Vejle #606/R (D.KR 11000)
£1140 $1779 €1710 Coastal landscape from Tannis Bay (83x126cm-33x50in) s.d.1906 exhib. 23-Sep-2 Rasmussen, Vejle #124/R est:15000 (D.KR 13500)
£1210 $1925 €1815 Norwegian three master and Danish sailing vessels in a calm (40x53cm-16x21in) s. 5-Mar-3 Rasmussen, Copenhagen #1965/R est:12000 (D.KR 13000)
£1277 $2017 €1916 Cloudy day in Sundet off Snekkersten (40x63cm-16x25in) s.i.d.1908. 2-Dec-2 Rasmussen, Copenhagen #1361/R est:15000-20000 (D.KR 15000)
£1483 $2403 €2150 Coastal landscape north of Helsingor (62x85cm-24x33in) s.d.88. 26-May-3 Rasmussen, Copenhagen #1367/R est:15000 (D.KR 15500)
£1689 $2635 €2534 Seascape with sailing ship (95x64cm-37x25in) s.d.1910. 23-Sep-2 Rasmussen, Vejle #119/R est:20000 (D.KR 20000)
£1694 $2659 €2456 Copenhagen's inlet. 15-Dec-2 Anders Antik, Landskrona #204 est:15000-20000 (S.KR 24000)
£3259 $5182 €4889 The lifeboat being taken to the shipwreck, Jylland (70x105cm-28x41in) s.d.1871 exhib. 5-Mar-3 Rasmussen, Copenhagen #1564/R est:40000-50000 (D.KR 35000)

Works on paper

£254 $391 €381 Entrance to the fishing village Raa (41x33cm-16x13in) s.d.1885 pencil W/C. 26-Oct-2 Rasmussen, Havnen #3104 (D.KR 3000)

BLACK, Andrew (1850-1916) British

£620 $967 €930 Banff shore (30x45cm-12x18in) s. 17-Oct-2 Bonhams, Edinburgh #218
£766 $1210 €1149 Preparing for the fishing, Tarbert (36x56cm-14x22in) s.d.1875. 18-Nov-2 Waddingtons, Toronto #177/R (C.D 1900)

BLACK, Calvin and Ruby (20th C) American?

£1852 $3000 €2778 Helen G. Lola Spider girl. Mrs Helen Rose Keck. In God we trust. Possum Trot portrait. s.i. panel set of five different sizes. 27-Jan-3 Christie's, Rockefeller NY #1/R est:4000-6000
£1975 $3200 €2963 Hand caved dolls. Crying room. Ideiot box, possum trot sings (10x37cm-4x15in) panel set of three different sizes prov. 27-Jan-3 Christie's, Rockefeller NY #2/R est:1000-1500

Sculpture

£4321 $7000 €6482 Possum Trot figures with spider (68x30cm-27x12in) wood metal paint fabric executed c.1952-1972 prov. 27-Jan-3 Christie's, Rockefeller NY #3/R est:10000-15000
£6790 $11000 €10185 Untitled - Possum Trot figure (114x38x13cm-45x15x5in) carved wood paint fabric executed c.1952-1972. 27-Jan-3 Christie's, Rockefeller NY #5/R est:12000-18000

BLACK, Dorrit (1891-1951) Australian

£9964 $15246 €14946 Nude with cigarette (46x38cm-18x15in) s. painted c.1930 canvas on board prov.exhib. 26-Aug-2 Sotheby's, Paddington #508/R est:30000-40000 (A.D 28000)

Prints

£2143 $3386 €3215 Toucans (23x23cm-9x9in) s.i. col linocut. 27-Nov-2 Deutscher-Menzies, Melbourne #276/R est:4000-6000 (A.D 6000)
£3226 $4903 €4839 Argentina (19x15cm-7x6in) init.i. col linocut exec.c.1929 lit. 28-Aug-2 Deutscher-Menzies, Melbourne #268/R est:8000-10000 (A.D 9000)

Works on paper
£786 $1234 €1179 Studies for, study with two figures (17x14cm-7x6in) one pencil one gouache pair prov.lit. 25-Nov-2 Christie's, Melbourne #290/R (A.D 2200)
£1226 $1925 €1839 Trees (39x30cm-15x12in) s. W/C. 15-Apr-3 Lawson Menzies, Sydney #248/R est:3500-4500 (A.D 3200)
£2143 $3321 €3215 Still life (25x21cm-10x8in) s. W/C. 29-Oct-2 Lawson Menzies, Sydney #20/R est:5000-7000 (A.D 6000)

BLACK, Laverne Nelson (1887-1938) American
£2885 $4500 €4328 Burros and Adobes (18x36cm-7x14in) s. oil on paperboard prov.lit. 9-Nov-2 Santa Fe Art, Santa Fe #43/R est:5000-7000
£34839 $54000 €52259 Native Americans on horseback (56x51cm-22x20in) s. 7-Dec-2 Selkirks, St. Louis #255/R est:20000-25000
Sculpture
£4488 $7000 €6732 Untitled (41x43x18cm-16x17x7in) i. bronze prov.lit. 9-Nov-2 Santa Fe Art, Santa Fe #178/R est:10000-15000

BLACK, Olive Parker (1868-1948) American
£892 $1400 €1338 Bend in the stream (48x61cm-19x24in) s. 10-Dec-2 Doyle, New York #61/R est:2500-3500
£2760 $4250 €4140 Brook in spring (41x61cm-16x24in) s. 24-Oct-2 Shannon's, Milford #27/R est:4000-6000
£3025 $4750 €4538 Meandering stream (51x76cm-20x30in) s. 19-Nov-2 Butterfields, San Francisco #8040/R est:4000-6000
£3947 $6395 €6000 Sunlit landscape with pond (51x61cm-20x24in) s. 21-Jan-3 Christie's, Amsterdam #98/R est:1200-1600
£4114 $6500 €6171 Reflection of a soring day (51x61cm-20x24in) s. prov. 24-Apr-3 Shannon's, Milford #59/R est:5000-7000
£7595 $12000 €11393 Summer afternoon (36x51cm-14x20in) s. 24-Apr-3 Shannon's, Milford #25/R est:3000-5000

BLACK, Richard (20th C) American
£745 $1200 €1118 Young girl in field of daisies serenaded by bird (46x38cm-18x15in) s. 19-Feb-3 Illustration House, New York #211/R est:1600-2400

BLACKADDER, Elizabeth (1931-) British
£900 $1431 €1350 Two figures in a room (30x41cm-12x16in) s.d.1966 board. 6-Mar-3 Christie's, Kensington #237/R
£1200 $1860 €1800 Seated figure II (25x30cm-10x12in) s.d.1972 exhib. 31-Oct-2 Christie's, London #199/R est:1500-2500
£2000 $3120 €3000 White tower, Mykonos (71x91cm-28x36in) s.d.1965 prov.exhib. 14-Apr-3 Sotheby's, London #175/R est:2000-3000
£2800 $4368 €4200 Still life with heart (41x41cm-16x16in) s.d.1977 s.i.verso. 17-Oct-2 Bonhams, Edinburgh #35 est:800-1200
£4800 $7344 €7200 Red carnations and Portuguese cloth (63x76cm-25x30in) s.d.1967 s.i.on stretcher. 22-Aug-2 Bonhams, Edinburgh #971/R est:6000-8000
Works on paper
£520 $811 €780 Still life with animals and birds (15x18cm-6x7in) sd.1983 s.i.verso W/C. 17-Oct-2 Bonhams, Edinburgh #89
£900 $1404 €1350 In the park (44x45cm-17x18in) s. W/C. 17-Oct-2 Bonhams, Edinburgh #84
£950 $1482 €1425 Tuscan landscape (46x75cm-18x30in) s. W/C. 17-Oct-2 Bonhams, Edinburgh #70
£1100 $1749 €1650 Passion flowers (19x14cm-7x6in) s.d.1978 pencil W/C. 6-Mar-3 Christie's, Kensington #235/R est:500-800
£1100 $1826 €1595 Study of a lily (10x13cm-4x5in) s.d.1979 W/C. 10-Jun-3 David Lay, Penzance #99/R
£1300 $2067 €1950 Mexican plate (24x35cm-9x14in) s.d.1970 bodycol prov. 6-Mar-3 Christie's, Kensington #236/R est:800-1200
£1400 $2170 €2100 Island and pink cloud (46x58cm-18x23in) s.d.1970 W/C bodycol prov. 31-Oct-2 Christie's, London #204/R est:1500-2500
£1500 $2385 €2250 Cathedral, Cuidad (40x49cm-16x19in) s.d.1970 pencil W/C. 6-Mar-3 Christie's, Kensington #239/R est:2000-3000
£1500 $2340 €2250 Erigera, Portugal (57x100cm-22x39in) s. W/C prov. 14-Apr-3 Sotheby's, London #178/R est:1500-2000
£1800 $2772 €2700 Abstract with carpet design (105x70cm-41x28in) s.d.1972 W/C. 5-Sep-2 Christie's, Kensington #747/R est:2000-3000
£1800 $2790 €2700 Cats and flowers (14x18cm-6x7in) s.d.1980 pencil W/C. 5-Dec-2 Bonhams, Edinburgh #145 est:1500-2000
£1900 $3021 €2850 Still life, green and grey (56x71cm-22x28in) s. W/C bodycol prov.exhib. 6-Mar-3 Christie's, Kensington #241/R est:1500-2000
£2200 $3410 €3300 Coca asleep (20x29cm-8x11in) s.d.1981 pencil crayon W/C prov. 31-Oct-2 Christie's, London #195/R est:2500-3500
£2200 $3498 €3300 Still life with Japanese box (61x91cm-24x36in) s.d.1981 pencil W/C bodycol exhib. 6-Mar-3 Christie's, Kensington #240/R est:2000-3000
£3000 $4680 €4500 Abyssinian cat (32x47cm-13x19in) s.d.1973 pastel pencil. 17-Oct-2 Bonhams, Edinburgh #6/R est:1000-1500
£3800 $5890 €5700 Hellebore Orientalis (53x66cm-21x26in) s.d.1982 pencil W/C prov. 31-Oct-2 Christie's, London #201/R est:4000-6000
£5500 $8525 €8250 Shirley poppies in a striped blue jug (46x43cm-18x17in) s.d.1981 s.i.verso pencil W/C prov. 31-Oct-2 Christie's, London #202/R est:4000-6000
£6000 $9300 €9000 Gold boxes and flute (63x150cm-25x59in) s.d.1981 s.i.verso pencil W/C gold paint prov. 31-Oct-2 Christie's, London #194/R est:5000-8000
£8500 $13175 €12750 Two irises (78x58cm-31x23in) s.d.1989 pencil W/C exhib. 31-Oct-2 Christie's, London #200/R est:6000-8000
£18000 $27900 €27000 Cats and gladioli (57x76cm-22x30in) s.d.1989 pencil W/C exhib. 31-Oct-2 Christie's, London #193/R est:7000-10000

BLACKBURN, Arthur (19/20th C) British
£480 $749 €720 Autumn's golden glow (20x25cm-8x10in) s. i.verso. 9-Oct-2 Andrew Hartley, Ilkley #775/R

BLACKBURN, Jemima (1823-1909) British
Works on paper
£700 $1113 €1050 Ruins at Eleusis, Greece (23x31cm-9x12in) init.i.d.April 1884 W/C sold with another by same hand. 29-Apr-3 Bonhams, New Bond Street #137/R

BLACKBURN, Joseph (1700-?) American
£30645 $47500 €45968 Portrait of Mrs Samuel Gardiner, nee Elizabeth Clarke (91x71cm-36x28in) 2-Nov-2 North East Auctions, Portsmouth #632/R est:25000-40000

BLACKBURN, Mavis (1923-) British
£500 $775 €750 At the seaside (52x87cm-20x34in) s. 25-Sep-2 Peter Wilson, Nantwich #54/R

BLACKBURN, Morris (1902-1979) American
£839 $1300 €1259 Abstract still life with bottle (46x56cm-18x22in) s.d.46. 8-Dec-2 Freeman, Philadelphia #126/R

BLACKHAM, Dorothy Isobel (1896-1975) Irish
£1507 $2366 €2200 Spring landscape near Glenasmole (50x34cm-20x13in) i.verso board. 15-Apr-3 De Veres Art Auctions, Dublin #192/R est:1000-2000
Works on paper
£390 $613 €570 Sorting the fish, Portugal (22x33cm-9x13in) gouache. 15-Apr-3 De Veres Art Auctions, Dublin #124/R

BLACKHAM, Warren (19th C) British
Works on paper
£470 $766 €705 Birmingham horse fair (53x79cm-21x31in) s.d.1884 W/C over pencil. 28-Jan-3 Bonhams, Knowle #297

BLACKLOCK, William Kay (1872-?) British
£750 $1223 €1125 Artist's daughter (20x18cm-8x7in) init.d.1911. 13-Feb-3 David Lay, Penzance #131/R
£800 $1304 €1200 Quiet read (11x9cm-4x4in) s. 12-Feb-3 Andrew Hartley, Ilkley #845/R
£2300 $3588 €3450 Fishing boats, Polperro (30x36cm-12x14in) init. s.i.verso board. 17-Oct-2 David Lay, Penzance #1434/R est:1000-1500
£8000 $13360 €11600 Landing the catch (24x34cm-9x13in) s.d.1913. 18-Jun-3 Sotheby's, Olympia #89/R est:2000-3000
£17000 $26860 €25500 Sewing by the river (33x41cm-13x16in) s. canvas on board. 26-Nov-2 Christie's, London #160/R est:10000-15000
Works on paper
£250 $390 €375 Springtime, clifftop (23x23cm-9x9in) s. W/C. 17-Oct-2 David Lay, Penzance #1433
£550 $913 €825 Interior scene with a woman washing clothes. Cottage interior with woman beside a window (29x23cm-11x9in) s. W/C htd white pair. 10-Jun-3 Bonhams, Leeds #71
£560 $874 €840 Wooded river landscape with angler in distance (18x25cm-7x10in) s. W/C. 11-Apr-3 Keys, Aylsham #437/R
£1000 $1590 €1500 Lakeside with figures and boats (20x28cm-8x11in) s. W/C. 3-Mar-3 Louis Taylor, Stoke on Trent #849
£1000 $1600 €1500 On the Riva degli Schiavoni, Venice (24x32cm-9x13in) s.i.d.1901 W/C. 11-Mar-3 Bonhams, New Bond Street #97/R est:1000-1500
£1150 $1748 €1725 Harbour mouth, Polperro, Cornwall (25x38cm-10x15in) s.d.1923 i.verso W/C. 14-Aug-2 Andrew Hartley, Ilkley #560/R est:1200-1500
£1300 $2080 €1950 Campanile from the steps of Santa Maria della Salute, Venice (23x26cm-9x10in) s.i.d.1901 W/C. 11-Mar-3 Bonhams, New Bond Street #98/R est:800-1200
£1700 $2652 €2550 Mending the nets (23x30cm-9x12in) s. W/C. 5-Nov-2 Bonhams, New Bond Street #165/R est:1200-1800

£2100 $3507 €3045 Harbour mouth, Polperro, Cornwall (27x38cm-11x15in) s. W/C. 17-Jun-3 Anderson & Garland, Newcastle #319/R est:1500-2500

BLACKMAN, Charles (1928-) Australian

£2321 $3668 €3482 Barry Humphries (49x35cm-19x14in) s. conte executed c.1963-54. 27-Nov-2 Deutscher-Menzies, Melbourne #138/R est:4000-6000 (A.D 6500)

£2429 $3837 €3644 Lychees, nature morte (73x96cm-29x38in) s. i.verso paper on board prov. 26-Nov-2 Sotheby's, Melbourne #78 est:8000-12000 (A.D 6800)

£2857 $4514 €4286 Flowers in a garden (41x56cm-16x22in) s. board prov. 17-Nov-2 Sotheby's, Paddington #3/R est:6000-10000 (A.D 8000)

£3065 $4567 €4598 Woman at window (49x74cm-19x29in) paper on board. 27-Aug-2 Christie's, Melbourne #312/R est:8000-12000 (A.D 8000)

£3559 $5445 €5339 Girl on a swing (121x91cm-48x36in) oil chl on board prov. 26-Aug-2 Sotheby's, Paddington #604/R est:10000-15000 (A.D 10000)

£3659 $5780 €5306 Horse in moonlight (48x73cm-19x29in) s. board. 22-Jul-3 Lawson Menzies, Sydney #126/R est:13000-15000 (A.D 9000)

£3846 $6115 €5769 Lovers embracing (71x48cm-28x19in) s. canvas on board. 4-Mar-3 Deutscher-Menzies, Melbourne #82/R est:12000-18000 (A.D 10000)

£4023 $5994 €6035 Playing cards within glove (35x27cm-14x11in) s. canvas on board. 27-Aug-2 Christie's, Melbourne #191/R est:6000-10000 (A.D 10500)

£4070 $6471 €6105 Dark bridge, evening (56x75cm-22x30in) s.d.51 i.verso glass on board prov. 5-May-3 Sotheby's, Melbourne #27/R est:16000 (A.D 10500)

£4400 $7084 €6600 Still life with flowers (62x75cm-24x30in) prov. 6-May-3 Christie's, Melbourne #144/R est:15000-20000 (A.D 11000)

£4598 $6851 €6897 Auguste (30x23cm-12x9in) s. board painted c.1957. 27-Aug-2 Christie's, Melbourne #88/R est:12000-18000 (A.D 12000)

£5338 $8167 €8007 Girl with cat (121x91cm-48x36in) oil chl on board prov. 26-Aug-2 Sotheby's, Paddington #527/R est:12000-18000 (A.D 15000)

£5357 $8464 €8036 Salome 1991 (145x95cm-57x37in) s. pastel. 27-Nov-2 Deutscher-Menzies, Melbourne #90/R est:16000-20000 (A.D 15000)

£5376 $8172 €8064 Girl dreaming (40x35cm-16x14in) s. painted c.1963. 28-Aug-2 Deutscher-Menzies, Melbourne #100/R est:16000-20000 (A.D 15000)

£5600 $9016 €8400 Two figures and a car (53x72cm-21x28in) s. acrylic on paper. 6-May-3 Christie's, Melbourne #85/R est:15000-20000 (A.D 14000)

£5600 $9016 €8400 Faces beneath the flowers (48x74cm-19x29in) s.d.1968 canvas paper on board. 6-May-3 Christie's, Melbourne #120/R est:12000-18000 (A.D 14000)

£6000 $9660 €9000 Young girl (41x51cm-16x20in) with sig.d.62 prov. 6-May-3 Christie's, Melbourne #135/R est:15000-20000 (A.D 15000)

£7473 $11434 €11210 Family friend (122x101cm-48x40in) s. painted c.1974 prov. 26-Aug-2 Sotheby's, Paddington #521/R est:20000-30000 (A.D 21000)

£8541 $13068 €12812 Mother and child (122x101cm-48x40in) s. painted c.1974 prov. 26-Aug-2 Sotheby's, Paddington #522/R est:22000-28000 (A.D 24000)

£8571 $13371 €12857 Girl with stripes (58x96cm-23x38in) s.d.61. 11-Nov-2 Deutscher-Menzies, Melbourne #3/R est:25000-35000 (A.D 24000)

£8602 $13075 €12903 They brought her ribbons and great clusters of flowers (48x66cm-19x26in) s. composition board painted c.1980 prov. 28-Aug-2 Deutscher-Menzies, Melbourne #18/R est:18000-24000 (A.D 24000)

£9253 $14157 €13880 Still life and nude (122x101cm-48x40in) s. painted c.1974 prov. 26-Aug-2 Sotheby's, Paddington #511/R est:20000-30000 (A.D 26000)

£9375 $14625 €14063 Schoolgirl (92x67cm-36x26in) s.d.1955 board prov. 8-Apr-3 Peter Webb, Auckland #106/R est:25000-40000 (NZ.D 27000)

£9562 $15681 €14343 Three children on a mountain (100x135cm-39x53in) s.d.7th Feb 55 oil enamel paper board. 4-Jun-3 Deutscher-Menzies, Melbourne #76/R est:26000-32000 (A.D 24000)

£10000 $15800 €15000 Vase of flowers in a blue interior (100x150cm-39x59in) s. 27-Nov-2 Deutscher-Menzies, Melbourne #58/R est:30000-40000 (A.D 28000)

£11429 $17829 €17144 Double image (61x74cm-24x29in) s. 11-Nov-2 Deutscher-Menzies, Melbourne #80/R est:25000-35000 (A.D 32000)

£11744 $17968 €17616 Children playing (48x74cm-19x29in) s. prov. 25-Aug-2 Sotheby's, Paddington #56/R est:28000-35000 (A.D 33000)

£11923 $18957 €17885 Girl with flowers (137x91cm-54x36in) s. d.1961 verso prov. 4-Mar-3 Deutscher-Menzies, Melbourne #105/R est:40000-60000 (A.D 31000)

£12100 $18512 €18150 Dreaming with flowers (122x120cm-48x47in) oil chl on board prov. 26-Aug-2 Sotheby's, Paddington #515/R est:18000-25000 (A.D 34000)

£12308 $19569 €18462 Alice at the keyhole (68x51cm-27x20in) s. 4-Mar-3 Deutscher-Menzies, Melbourne #59/R est:40000-60000 (A.D 32000)

£14235 $21779 €21353 Girl combing hair (47x61cm-19x24in) s. board prov. 25-Aug-2 Sotheby's, Paddington #48/R est:40000-60000 (A.D 40000)

£14337 $21792 €21506 Ghost flower (104x76cm-41x30in) s. i.verso composition board prov. 28-Aug-2 Deutscher-Menzies, Melbourne #10/R est:45000-65000 (A.D 40000)

£14343 $23522 €21515 Evening table (122x183cm-48x72in) s. paper prov.exhib. 4-Jun-3 Deutscher-Menzies, Melbourne #93/R est:40000-50000 (A.D 36000)

£15000 $23400 €22500 It is cheaper to ride on the roofs of taxis than inside them (137x168cm-54x66in) s.d.73 lit. 11-Nov-2 Deutscher-Menzies, Melbourne #70/R est:35000-45000 (A.D 42000)

£15200 $24472 €22800 Poet under tree (120x180cm-47x71in) s. painted c.1989 prov. 6-May-3 Christie's, Melbourne #49/R est:40000-50000 (A.D 38000)

£15302 $23413 €22953 Breakfast nook (122x101cm-48x40in) s. oil chl on board prov. 26-Aug-2 Sotheby's, Paddington #510/R est:20000-30000 (A.D 43000)

£15658 $23957 €23487 Girl seated (122x101cm-48x40in) s. painted c.1974 prov. 26-Aug-2 Sotheby's, Paddington #502/R est:55000-65000 (A.D 44000)

£16000 $25760 €24000 Kiss (74x48cm-29x19in) s. oil canvaspaper on board prov. 6-May-3 Christie's, Melbourne #104/R est:30000-40000 (A.D 40000)

£16154 $25685 €24231 Picnic (62x75cm-24x30in) s.d.1954 composition board. 4-Mar-3 Deutscher-Menzies, Melbourne #61/R est:50000-70000 (A.D 42000)

£16487 $25061 €24731 Market flowers (117x179cm-46x70in) s. paper on canvas prov.exhib. 28-Aug-2 Deutscher-Menzies, Melbourne #107/R est:55000-75000 (A.D 46000)

£16733 $27442 €25100 Portrait of Georges Morca (90x78cm-35x31in) s. paper board painted c.1956 prov. 4-Jun-3 Deutscher-Menzies, Melbourne #26/R est:40000-50000 (A.D 42000)

£17442 $27733 €26163 Spring hill (62x75cm-24x30in) s. board. 5-May-3 Sotheby's, Melbourne #173/R est:35000-45000 (A.D 45000)

£18462 $29354 €27693 Night flight (90x221cm-35x87in) s. i.verso diptych prov. 4-Mar-3 Deutscher-Menzies, Melbourne #83/R est:55000-75000 (A.D 48000)

£19286 $30279 €28929 Girl with flowers (62x75cm-24x30in) s.d.1957 board. 25-Nov-2 Christie's, Melbourne #62/R est:35000-45000 (A.D 54000)

£22358 $35325 €32419 Barbara and her flowers 1956. s. enamel on litho paper on board prov. 22-Jul-3 Lawson Menzies, Sydney #21/R est:65000-75000 (A.D 55000)

£29885 $44529 €44828 Two schoolgirls (74x62cm-29x24in) enamel on compressed card painted c.1956 prov. 27-Aug-2 Christie's, Melbourne #8/R est:50000-70000 (A.D 78000)

£30357 $47964 €45536 Interior with flowers and table (122x102cm-48x40in) s. i.on stretcher. 27-Nov-2 Deutscher-Menzies, Melbourne #24/R est:55000-75000 (A.D 85000)

£30651 $45671 €45977 Christabel and her image (195x133cm-77x52in) oil chl painted c.1966 exhib.lit. 27-Aug-2 Christie's, Melbourne #62/R est:60000-80000 (A.D 80000)

£30651 $45671 €45977 Two figures (122x91cm-48x36in) s. board painted c.1960 prov. 27-Aug-2 Christie's, Melbourne #71/R est:50000-70000 (A.D 80000)

£31008 $49302 €46512 Woman with gladioli (120x100cm-47x39in) s. i.d.1964 verso prov.lit. 5-May-3 Sotheby's, Melbourne #13/R est:80000 (A.D 80000)

£40000 $64400 €60000 Schoolgirl (73x61cm-29x24in) s. board painted 1953 prov. 6-May-3 Christie's, Melbourne #43/R est:100000-150000 (A.D 100000)

£40230 $59943 €60345 Woman and flowers (91x121cm-36x48in) s.d.59 board. 27-Aug-2 Christie's, Melbourne #32/R est:80000-120000 (A.D 105000)

£53846 $85615 €80769 Boats at Williamstown (95x129cm-37x51in) s. composition board prov. 4-Mar-3 Deutscher-Menzies, Melbourne #40/R est:140000-180000 (A.D 140000)

£96429 $149464 €144644 Suddenly everything happened (109x121cm-43x48in) s.d.1956 tempera oil enamel composition board prov.exhib. 29-Oct-2 Lawson Menzies, Sydney #47/R est:160000-300000 (A.D 270000)

Works on paper

£268 $420 €402 Dancing figure (30x25cm-12x10in) s. prov. 25-Nov-2 Christie's, Melbourne #207 (A.D 750)
£286 $449 €429 Paris (30x25cm-12x10in) s.i. ink prov. 25-Nov-2 Christie's, Melbourne #287 (A.D 800)
£357 $557 €536 Into the darkness (25x40cm-10x16in) init.i.d.24.10.85 pastel. 11-Nov-2 Deutscher-Menzies, Melbourne #175/R (A.D 1000)
£393 $609 €590 Alice (27x30cm-11x12in) s. chl. 29-Oct-2 Lawson Menzies, Sydney #365 (A.D 1100)
£393 $617 €590 Whisper (25x33cm-10x13in) s. ink prov. 25-Nov-2 Christie's, Melbourne #320 (A.D 1100)
£429 $673 €644 Couple (25x33cm-10x13in) s. ink prov. 25-Nov-2 Christie's, Melbourne #282 (A.D 1200)
£458 $723 €794 Asian figures (52x72cm-20x28in) s.d.73 ink dr. 1-Apr-3 Goodman, Sydney #96 (A.D 1200)
£538 $817 €807 Star trails (19x24cm-7x9in) s.i. ink pastel. 27-Aug-2 Goodman, Sydney #6 (A.D 1500)
£560 $902 €840 Figure and house on stilts (32x41cm-13x16in) s. ink. 6-May-3 Christie's, Melbourne #212 est:2000-3000 (A.D 1400)
£563 $879 €845 Cat dreaming (16x21cm-6x8in) s.d.78 W/C. 21-Oct-2 Australian Art Auctions, Sydney #144 (A.D 1600)
£643 $1015 €965 Cat (19x24cm-7x9in) init.i.d.31.12.85 W/C pen ink. 27-Nov-2 Deutscher-Menzies, Melbourne #172/R est:2000-3000 (A.D 1800)
£714 $1129 €1071 Study for a rose tree (71x51cm-28x20in) s.d.70 pastel. 18-Nov-2 Joel, Victoria #267 est:5000-8000 (A.D 2000)
£920 $1370 €1380 Reclining figure (20x24cm-8x9in) s.d.54 chl. 27-Aug-2 Christie's, Melbourne #277 est:1500-2000 (A.D 2400)
£1154 $1834 €1731 Weeping woman with flowers (35x35cm-14x14in) init. chl. 4-Mar-3 Deutscher-Menzies, Melbourne #216/R est:1200-1600 (A.D 3000)
£1200 $1932 €1740 Vase of flowers (50x37cm-20x15in) s. W/C. 12-May-3 Joel, Victoria #260a est:3000-3500 (A.D 3000)
£1429 $2257 €2144 Bouquet (58x44cm-23x17in) s.d.14.1.86 ink W/C prov. 26-Nov-2 Sotheby's, Melbourne #92 est:5000-7500 (A.D 4000)
£1609 $2526 €2414 Darkness is banished (75x56cm-30x22in) s. ink wash. 15-Apr-3 Lawson Menzies, Sydney #148/R est:3800-5000 (A.D 4200)
£1615 $2568 €2423 Schoolgirls (22x30cm-9x12in) s. chl pen ink exec.c.1953 exhib. 4-Mar-3 Deutscher-Menzies, Melbourne #12/R est:4500-6000 (A.D 4200)
£1649 $2506 €2474 Girls (23x36cm-9x14in) s.d.1955 pencil ink prov. 28-Aug-2 Deutscher-Menzies, Melbourne #323/R est:3500-5500 (A.D 4600)
£1793 $2940 €2690 Barbara sleeping (26x33cm-10x13in) s. i.verso chl. 4-Jun-3 Deutscher-Menzies, Melbourne #372/R est:3000-5000 (A.D 4500)
£1916 $2854 €2874 Beach figures (53x71cm-21x28in) s.d.1967 chl ink. 27-Aug-2 Christie's, Melbourne #210 est:5000-8000 (A.D 5000)
£1938 $3081 €2907 Airport (38x31cm-15x12in) s.i.d.75 ink W/C. 5-May-3 Sotheby's, Melbourne #339/R est:5000-8000 (A.D 5000)
£1964 $3104 €2946 Portrait of Sylvia Delprat (119x96cm-47x38in) s. s.i.d.73 verso pastel. 27-Nov-2 Deutscher-Menzies, Melbourne #128/R est:6500-8000 (A.D 5500)
£2107 $3140 €3161 Artist with reclining nude and cat (30x47cm-12x19in) s.d.83 W/C ink. 27-Aug-2 Christie's, Melbourne #161 est:4500-6000 (A.D 5500)
£2293 $3645 €3440 Grand Hotel (46x60cm-18x24in) s.d.7.7.90 W/C. 4-Mar-3 Deutscher-Menzies, Melbourne #155/R est:7000-9000 (A.D 5960)
£2330 $3541 €3495 Actor's breakfast (75x55cm-30x22in) s.i. synthetic polymer paint. 28-Aug-2 Deutscher-Menzies, Melbourne #177/R est:8000-12000 (A.D 6500)
£2679 $4179 €4019 Black cat at the window (54x74cm-21x29in) s.d.61 chl. 11-Nov-2 Deutscher-Menzies, Melbourne #4/R est:8000-12000 (A.D 7500)
£2692 $4281 €4038 Double image (76x56cm-30x22in) s. chl exec.c.1962. 4-Mar-3 Deutscher-Menzies, Melbourne #58/R est:9000-12000 (A.D 7000)
£2857 $4514 €4286 Florentines (48x35cm-19x14in) s.d.62 conte prov. 27-Nov-2 Deutscher-Menzies, Melbourne #72/R est:7000-9000 (A.D 8000)
£3036 $4705 €4554 Daisy Bates (73x102cm-29x40in) s. chl. 29-Oct-2 Lawson Menzies, Sydney #48/R est:9000-12000 (A.D 8500)
£3461 $5504 €5192 Alice in Wonderland (97x132cm-38x52in) s. felt tip pen. 4-Mar-3 Deutscher-Menzies, Melbourne #107/R est:10000-15000 (A.D 9000)
£3488 $5547 €5232 Discussion (47x34cm-19x13in) s.d.1962 chl prov. 5-May-3 Sotheby's, Melbourne #355/R est:6000-9000 (A.D 9000)
£4065 $6423 €5894 Schoolgirl 1968 (72x52cm-28x20in) s. chl exhib. 22-Jul-3 Lawson Menzies, Sydney #11/R est:11000-15000 (A.D 10000)
£4215 $6617 €6323 Schoolgirl's dream (31x94cm-12x37in) s. ink wash. 15-Apr-3 Lawson Menzies, Sydney #8/R est:11000-14000 (A.D 11000)
£4400 $7084 €6600 Two girls (67x47cm-26x19in) s. ink W/C. 6-May-3 Christie's, Melbourne #118/R est:8000-10000 (A.D 11000)
£4615 $7338 €6923 Haystacks in the moonlight (96x128cm-38x50in) s.d.55 enamel paper composition board prov.lit. 4-Mar-3 Deutscher-Menzies, Melbourne #125/R est:14000-18000 (A.D 12000)
£4781 $7841 €7172 Yellow reverie (119x86cm-47x34in) s. W/C synthetic polymer paint exec.c.1967. 4-Jun-3 Deutscher-Menzies, Melbourne #121/R est:8000-12000 (A.D 12000)
£5577 $8867 €8366 Two schoolgirls (25x35cm-10x14in) s. init.d.53-54 verso gouache. 4-Mar-3 Deutscher-Menzies, Melbourne #57/R est:9000-12000 (A.D 14500)
£5814 $9244 €8721 Moon watcher (106x80cm-42x31in) s. i.verso chl pastel prov.exhib. 5-May-3 Sotheby's, Melbourne #41/R est:30000 (A.D 15000)
£7200 $11592 €10800 Titania and bottom (75x61cm-30x24in) s. W/C executed c.1970. 6-May-3 Christie's, Melbourne #139/R est:14000-18000 (A.D 18000)
£7308 $11619 €10962 Shadowed figure (104x75cm-41x30in) s. chl pastel exhib. 4-Mar-3 Deutscher-Menzies, Melbourne #13/R est:10000-15000 (A.D 19000)
£7857 $12257 €11786 Schoolgirls (76x103cm-30x41in) s. chl. 11-Nov-2 Deutscher-Menzies, Melbourne #2/R est:8000-12000 (A.D 22000)
£17241 $25690 €25862 Girls (147x142cm-58x56in) s.d.62 chl ink paper on board. 27-Aug-2 Christie's, Melbourne #5/R est:25000-35000 (A.D 45000)
£17921 $27240 €26882 Tea ceremony (151x181cm-59x71in) s. chl exhib.lit. 28-Aug-2 Deutscher-Menzies, Melbourne #70/R est:28000-35000 (A.D 50000)

BLACKMAN, W (19/20th C) American

£950 $1473 €1425 Maid by an archway holding a jug (53x43cm-21x17in) s. 6-Dec-2 Chrystals Auctions, Isle of Man #169

BLACKMAN, Walter (1847-1928) American

£2313 $3700 €3470 Portrait of an Italian girl with red scarf. s. exhib. 1-Jan-3 Nadeau, Windsor #19/R est:2500-4000
£2778 $4500 €4028 Venetian flower girls (56x97cm-22x38in) s. 21-May-3 Doyle, New York #99/R est:5000-7000
£4006 $6250 €6009 European scene with a girl poling (53x97cm-21x38in) s. 28-Mar-3 Eldred, East Dennis #685/R est:3000-4000

BLACKMORE, Arthur Edwards (1854-1921) British/American

£484 $750 €726 Landscape (43x58cm-17x23in) 4-Oct-2 Douglas, South Deerfield #1

BLACKMORE, Thomas (18th C) British?

£724 $1100 €1086 Net fishing schooner coming into port (64x74cm-25x29in) s. 17-Aug-2 North East Auctions, Portsmouth #421/R

BLACKSHAW, Basil (1932-) British

£2600 $4134 €3900 Buildings, Culcavey (17x23cm-7x9in) s. board. 5-Mar-3 John Ross, Belfast #94 est:1000-1500
£3800 $5548 €5700 Frances (61x51cm-24x20in) s.d.55. 12-Jun-2 John Ross, Belfast #124 est:4000-5000
£5380 $8339 €8500 Valley, Dromara (38x61cm-15x24in) s. prov. 24-Sep-2 De Veres Art Auctions, Dublin #24 est:9000-12000
£16000 $25600 €24000 Portrait of a girl (91x71cm-36x28in) oil col pastel. 16-May-3 Sotheby's, London #143/R est:12000-15000

Works on paper

£280 $434 €420 Merry Christmas (12x10cm-5x4in) s. pen ink dr. 4-Dec-2 John Ross, Belfast #89a
£2000 $2920 €3000 Field (36x48cm-14x19in) mixed media. 12-Jun-2 John Ross, Belfast #47 est:2000-2500
£2000 $3180 €3000 Pond and landscape (15x20cm-6x8in) s. mixed media. 5-Mar-3 John Ross, Belfast #58 est:2200-2500

BLACKWOOD, David L (1941-) Canadian

£2575 $4017 €3863 Cod trap fisherman with lone cod (51x41cm-20x16in) s.d.1995 tempera on masonite. 25-Mar-3 Ritchie, Toronto #117/R est:3000-4000 (C.D 6000)

Prints

£1667 $2734 €2501 Resettlement (41x93cm-16x37in) s.i.d.1982 num.41/50 col etching prov. 27-May-3 Sotheby's, Toronto #122a/R est:3000-3500 (C.D 3750)
£1707 $2697 €2561 Ledgy rocks, for Ismael Tiller (91x61cm-36x24in) d.1990 col etching. 1-Dec-2 Levis, Calgary #7/R est:4500-5500 (C.D 4250)
£1822 $2897 €2733 Wesleyville, night oassage Bennetts High Island (49x79cm-19x31in) s.i.d.1981 col etching aquatint. 23-Mar-3 Hodgins, Calgary #80/R est:2000-2500 (C.D 4300)
£1889 $3098 €2834 Brian and Martin Winsor sleeping (82x50cm-32x20in) s.i.d.1985 num.2/50 col etching prov. 27-May-3 Sotheby's, Toronto #121/R est:3000-4000 (C.D 4250)
£1992 $3167 €2988 Hauling job Sturges house (32x79cm-13x31in) s.i.d.1979 col etching aquatint. 23-Mar-3 Hodgins, Calgary #43/R est:2000-2500 (C.D 4700)
£2904 $4473 €4356 Fire in Indian Bay (51x81cm-20x32in) etching. 28-Sep-2 Heffel, Vancouver #8 (C.D 7000)

£6048 $9556 €9072 Fire down on the Labrador (81x50cm-32x20in) s.i.d.1980 num.22/50 col etching aquatint. 18-Nov-2 Sotheby's, Toronto #57/R est:15000-20000 (C.D 15000)

Works on paper

£433 $688 €628 Black rock light (18x34cm-7x13in) s.i.d.2000 Indian ink. 1-May-3 Heffel, Vancouver #8/R (C.D 1000)
£1190 $1952 €1785 Uncle Cluney's kite over Wesleyville (38x91cm-15x36in) s.d.1989 i.verso pencil prov. 6-Feb-3 Heffel, Vancouver #007/R est:3500-4500 (C.D 3000)
£1512 $2389 €2268 Aunt Rene Sturge (42x44cm-17x17in) s.d.1973 pencil. 14-Nov-2 Heffel, Vancouver #188/R est:2000-3000 (C.D 3750)

BLADEL, Fritz (20th C) German

£278 $434 €440 Farmstead in the mountains (67x78cm-26x31in) s. 14-Sep-2 Weidler, Nurnberg #7068

BLADH, Johan (1893-1976) Swedish

£461 $715 €692 Cottage interior with open fire and woman knitting (61x50cm-24x20in) s.d.59. 8-Dec-2 Uppsala Auktionskammare, Uppsala #228 (S.KR 6500)

BLAILE, Alfred Henri (1878-1967) Swiss

£417 $671 €626 Le Pont Maire - Ile St Louis (46x38cm-18x15in) s.i.d.1901 i. verso. 7-May-3 Dobiaschofsky, Bern #3126 (S.FR 900)

BLAIN, Christophe (20th C) French?

Works on paper

£828 $1308 €1200 Donjon-Potron Minet (41x29cm-16x11in) s. Chinese ink. 7-Apr-3 Claude Aguttes, Neuilly #9/R

BLAIR, Andrew (fl.1847-1885) British

Works on paper

£300 $468 €450 Wreck (42x60cm-17x24in) s.d.1889 W/C. 28-Mar-3 Bonhams, Edinburgh #158

BLAIR, Charles Henry (19th C) British

£683 $1100 €1025 Kittens with strawberries (25x36cm-10x14in) s. 19-Jan-3 Jeffery Burchard, Florida #4/R

Works on paper

£500 $785 €750 Caught in the act (48x61cm-19x24in) s.d.92 black white chk. 21-Nov-2 Tennants, Leyburn #691/R

BLAIR, John (1850-1934) British

Works on paper

£280 $437 €420 Crail (18x26cm-7x10in) s.i. W/C. 13-Sep-2 Lyon & Turnbull, Edinburgh #65/R
£480 $797 €696 Newark Castle, St. Monans (34x50cm-13x20in) s.i. W/C. 13-Jun-3 Lyon & Turnbull, Edinburgh #69

BLAIR, Philippa (1945-) New Zealander

£259 $396 €389 Soft ladder (46x280cm-18x110in) s. acrylic. 21-Aug-2 Dunbar Sloane, Auckland #569 (NZ.D 850)
£1433 $2250 €2150 Hellow yellow (300x75cm-118x30in) s.d.1976 acrylic exhib. 10-Dec-2 Peter Webb, Auckland #114/R est:2000-3000 (NZ.D 4500)

BLAIR, Streeter (1888-1966) American

£1210 $1900 €1815 Fall pasture (67x137cm-26x54in) s.i.d.62 prov. 19-Nov-2 Butterfields, San Francisco #8340/R est:3000-5000

BLAIRAT, Marcel (1849-?) French

Works on paper

£331 $540 €500 Lavandieres a l'Oued (18x24cm-7x9in) s. W/C. 31-Jan-3 Rabourdin & Choppin de Janvry, Paris #145/R

BLAIS, Jean Charles (1956-) French

£1572 $2437 €2500 Personnage (102x74cm-40x29in) oil silk paper collage prov. 30-Oct-2 Artcurial Briest, Paris #581 est:2500-3000
£1973 $3137 €2900 Sans titre (60x58cm-24x23in) s.d.1990 verso paint torn poster prov. 26-Feb-3 Artcurial Briest, Paris #389/R est:2000-2500
£9615 $15096 €15000 Untitled (165x310cm-65x122in) s.d.84 verso paint on poster exhib. 11-Dec-2 Artcurial Briest, Paris #743/R est:20000
£10417 $17188 €15000 Marin aux 2 coeurs (272x280cm-107x110in) oil gouache pieces of poster canvas exhib.lit. 3-Jul-3 Christie's, Paris #78/R est:15000-20000

Sculpture

£1474 $2315 €2300 Untitled (32x35x20cm-13x14x8in) s.d.1981 paint on bucket. 15-Dec-2 Perrin, Versailles #154/R

Works on paper

£417 $688 €600 Portrait de Jean-Charles de Castelbajac (24x32cm-9x13in) s.i. pastel gouache lit. 3-Jul-3 Christie's, Paris #114/R
£426 $711 €600 Dans le noir (34x34cm-13x13in) s. paint chk pencil torn poster prov. 18-Jun-3 Charbonneaux, Paris #65
£881 $1365 €1400 Deux foix nuit (40x29cm-16x11in) i.d.II II 83 col wax pastel gouache prov. 30-Oct-2 Artcurial Briest, Paris #583
£942 $1545 €1300 Untitled (34x26cm-13x10in) s. W/C pastel chk. 28-May-3 Lempertz, Koln #51/R
£942 $1545 €1300 Untitled (37x26cm-15x10in) s. col chk W/C. 28-May-3 Lempertz, Koln #52/R
£1100 $1793 €1650 Untitled (124x28cm-49x11in) s.d.1994 gouache prov.exhib. 3-Feb-3 Sotheby's, Olympia #169/R est:500-700
£1293 $2055 €1900 Bonsoir (37x26cm-15x10in) s.i.d.1982 pastel chl prov. 24-Mar-3 Cornette de St.Cyr, Paris #133/R
£1384 $2145 €2200 Sans titre (50x65cm-20x26in) s. lacquer glycerophtalique. 30-Oct-2 Artcurial Briest, Paris #471/R est:2500-3000
£1793 $2995 €2600 Sans titre (100x70cm-39x28in) s. paint collage exec.c.1988. 10-Jul-3 Artcurial Briest, Paris #342/R est:3000-4000
£1887 $2925 €3000 Sans titre (60x61cm-24x24in) s.d.84 gouache prov. 30-Oct-2 Artcurial Briest, Paris #579 est:3000-4000
£2041 $3245 €3000 Untitled (75x75cm-30x30in) s.d.1988 gouache collage. 24-Mar-3 Cornette de St.Cyr, Paris #132/R
£2979 $4974 €4200 Tete d'homme de dos (78x115cm-31x45in) W/C gouache prov. 20-Jun-3 Piasa, Paris #228/R est:3000-4000
£3191 $5330 €4500 Tete d'homme de dos, bande marron (79x134cm-31x53in) W/C gouache prov. 20-Jun-3 Piasa, Paris #227/R est:5000-6000
£3194 $5047 €4600 Au charbon (61x47cm-24x19in) s.i.d.verso gouache epingles prov. 28-Apr-3 Cornette de St.Cyr, Paris #349/R est:5000-6000
£3333 $5267 €4800 Sans titre (62x77cm-24x30in) s.d.19.10.84 ink gouache pastel prov. 27-Apr-3 Perrin, Versailles #143/R est:4500-5000
£3459 $5362 €5500 Dans le vent (75x61cm-30x24in) s. mixed media collage prov. 30-Oct-2 Artcurial Briest, Paris #580/R est:3000-4000
£3910 $6139 €6100 Untitled (225x119cm-89x47in) s.d.1990 mixed media prov. 15-Dec-2 Perrin, Versailles #147/R
£4747 $7500 €7500 Running blue man (129x100cm-51x39in) gouache prov. 27-Nov-2 Tajan, Paris #98/R
£8333 $13750 €12000 Untitled (32x63cm-13x25in) s. s.d.84 verso pastel lit. 3-Jul-3 Christie's, Paris #75/R est:3500-4500

BLAKE, Benjamin (?-1830) British

£280 $437 €420 Still life of game (31x26cm-12x10in) 8-Oct-2 Bonhams, Knightsbridge #50/R
£280 $437 €420 Still life of game (31x26cm-12x10in) 8-Oct-2 Bonhams, Knightsbridge #49/R
£400 $632 €600 Larder study (18x23cm-7x9in) card. 6-Apr-3 Lots Road, London #340/R

BLAKE, Benjamin (attrib) (?-1830) British

£320 $499 €480 Sportsman's larder (19x14cm-7x6in) 17-Oct-2 Lawrence, Crewkerne #1581/R
£480 $782 €720 Game larder (20x15cm-8x6in) 13-Feb-3 Christie's, Kensington #30
£1200 $1896 €1800 Game in a larder. Day's bag (29x34cm-11x13in) one on canvas one on board pair. 28-Nov-2 Christie's, Kensington #47/R est:1000-1500
£1200 $1992 €1740 Game and a barrel of oysters in a larder. Game and a basket of eggs in a larder (30x25cm-12x10in) pair. 12-Jun-3 Christie's, Kensington #130a/R est:1500-2000
£1900 $2964 €2850 Game larders (15x20cm-6x8in) canvas on board pair. 10-Apr-3 Tennants, Leyburn #1082/R est:800-1200

BLAKE, Buckeye (1946-) American

Sculpture

£1090 $1700 €1635 Kid Russell and Monte (48x48x30cm-19x19x12in) i. bronze prov. 9-Nov-2 Santa Fe Art, Santa Fe #56/R est:3000-4000

Works on paper

£629 $1000 €944 Their tails were all matted and their backs were all raw (46x38cm-18x15in) s.d.93 gouache pencil W/C on board prov. 4-Mar-3 Christie's, Rockefeller NY #89/R est:1500-2500

BLAKE, Leo (1887-1976) American

£318 $500 €477 New England fall landscape with covered bridge and carriage (23x30cm-9x12in) s. canvasboard. 23-Nov-2 Jackson's, Cedar Falls #95/R
£377 $600 €566 Sunlight through the friendly old tree (41x46cm-16x18in) s. i.verso canvasboard. 7-Mar-3 Skinner, Boston #419/R
£510 $800 €765 Sunny Berkshire birches (46x36cm-18x14in) s. artist's board. 23-Nov-2 Jackson's, Cedar Falls #115/R

BLAKE, Leonard (19th C) British
£13830 $21436 €20745 Young girl picking summer flowers (68x46cm-27x18in) s.d.1881. 8-Dec-2 Uppsala Auktionskammare, Uppsala #81/R est:20000-25000 (S.KR 195000)

BLAKE, Peter (1932-2001) British
£4000 $6600 €5800 Marilyn Monroe silver (76x46cm-30x18in) s.i.d.1989-90 silver paint photo collage on board. 3-Jul-3 Christie's, Kensington #589/R est:1200-1800
£7500 $12525 €10875 Marilyn Monroe, red and green (60x42cm-24x17in) s.i.d.1990 verso enamel paint postcard collage panel prov. 26-Jun-3 Sotheby's, London #223/R est:3000-5000
£52000 $81640 €78000 Doktor K. Tortur (61x25cm-24x10in) acrylic collage board painted 1965 prov.exhib. 22-Nov-2 Christie's, London #109/R est:20000-30000

Works on paper
£320 $499 €480 Head of a woman (15x10cm-6x4in) pencil executed c.1956 prov. 15-Oct-2 Bonhams, Knightsbridge #83
£650 $1021 €975 Nude, back view (37x27cm-15x11in) s.d.1955 pencil prov. 15-Apr-3 Bonhams, Knightsbridge #110

BLAKE, Thomas C (20th C) British
£241 $400 €349 Highland sunset (41x51cm-16x20in) s. 14-Jun-3 Jackson's, Cedar Falls #23/R
£247 $383 €371 Morning in the highlands (61x91cm-24x36in) s.i.on stretcher. 3-Dec-2 Ritchie, Toronto #3110/R (C.D 600)
£480 $750 €720 Highland sunset (51x66cm-20x26in) s.i. i.verso. 14-Sep-2 Weschler, Washington #589/R
£491 $800 €737 Misty river valley landscape (71x97cm-28x38in) s. 16-Feb-3 Jeffery Burchard, Florida #67a

BLAKE, William (1757-1827) British
Prints
£10897 $17000 €16346 Illustrations for the Book of Job (38x28cm-15x11in) engravings set of 20. 7-Nov-2 Swann Galleries, New York #397/R est:7000-10000

Works on paper
£9790 $14000 €14685 Fate (15x22cm-6x9in) i. pencil. 23-Jan-3 Swann Galleries, New York #395/R est:6000-9000
£12000 $18960 €18000 Cumea (17x12cm-7x5in) i. pen ink W/C over pencil. 28-Nov-2 Sotheby's, London #236/R est:10000-15000
£22000 $34760 €33000 Judgement of Solomon (13x17cm-5x7in) pen ink W/C htd bodycol over pencil prov. 28-Nov-2 Sotheby's, London #235/R est:15000-20000

BLAKELEY, John Harold (1887-?) British
Works on paper
£540 $842 €810 Beached fishing boats at Staithes (23x34cm-9x13in) s. W/C sold with a companion. 10-Sep-2 David Duggleby, Scarborough #119/R

BLAKELOCK, Ralph Albert (1847-1919) American
£566 $900 €849 Forest interior, sunset (36x28cm-14x11in) s. canvas on masonite. 29-Apr-3 Doyle, New York #8/R
£928 $1550 €1346 Woodlands (25x33cm-10x13in) s. panel. 21-Jun-3 Selkirks, St. Louis #152/R est:3000-4000
£1603 $2484 €2500 Sous-bois (26x39cm-10x15in) s. 5-Dec-2 Gros & Delettrez, Paris #41/R
£1677 $2700 €2516 Landscape with autumn sunset (10x18cm-4x7in) s.i. panel. 22-Feb-3 Pook & Pook, Downington #304/R est:2500-3500
£1708 $2750 €2562 Two figures in tonal wooded landscape (23x30cm-9x12in) s. wood panel. 18-Feb-3 John Moran, Pasadena #101 est:3000-4000
£1911 $3000 €2867 Autumnal landscape (13x18cm-5x7in) s. panel. 23-Nov-2 Pook & Pook, Downington #359/R est:3000-3500
£2070 $3250 €3105 Rose (33x28cm-13x11in) init. 10-Dec-2 Doyle, New York #35/R est:4000-6000
£5689 $9500 €8249 Landscape moonlight (71x76cm-28x30in) s. board prov. 17-Jun-3 John Moran, Pasadena #59 est:10000-15000
£6173 $10000 €8951 Mist in the valley (36x61cm-14x24in) 21-May-3 Doyle, New York #83/R est:5000-7000
£7643 $12000 €11465 Rip van Winkle (99x53cm-39x21in) s. prov. 10-Dec-2 Doyle, New York #34/R est:10000-15000
£16774 $26000 €25161 Sunset over mountains (51x30cm-20x12in) s. prov. 5-Dec-2 Christie's, Rockefeller NY #11/R est:30000-50000
£33951 $55000 €50927 Moonlight on the Columbia River (56x91cm-22x36in) s. painted c.1885 prov.exhib.lit. 21-May-3 Sotheby's, New York #50/R est:60000-80000
£40123 $65000 €60185 Indian camp (42x62cm-17x24in) s. painted c.1871 prov.exhib.lit. 21-May-3 Sotheby's, New York #49/R est:80000-120000

BLAKELOCK, Ralph Albert (attrib) (1847-1919) American
£299 $500 €434 Sunlit landscape (30x36cm-12x14in) 21-Jun-3 Selkirks, St. Louis #151/R
£335 $550 €503 Autumnal landscape (10x15cm-4x6in) s.verso panel. 9-Feb-3 William Jenack, New York #353
£503 $800 €755 Indian camp at dusk (18x23cm-7x9in) s. panel. 7-Mar-3 Jackson's, Cedar Falls #639/R
£518 $850 €777 Moonlit landscape (18x25cm-7x10in) panel. 9-Feb-3 William Jenack, New York #334
£1146 $1800 €1719 Impressionist landscape (51x61cm-20x24in) 14-Dec-2 Charlton Hall, Columbia #501/R est:2000-3000

BLAKENEY, Baz (1959-) Australian
Works on paper
£698 $1109 €1047 Art man versus the conceptualists (120x122cm-47x48in) s. synthetic polymer board exhib. exec.2001. 5-May-3 Sotheby's, Melbourne #338/R (A.D 1800)

BLAKESLEE, Frederic (20th C) American
£2795 $4500 €4193 German airfield strafed by the Allies (71x51cm-28x20in) 10-May-3 Illustration House, New York #169/R est:5000-8000

BLAMEY, Norman (1914-) British
£340 $534 €510 Anglican priest (89x33cm-35x13in) board. 14-Dec-2 Lacy Scott, Bury St.Edmunds #458/R
£3500 $5460 €5250 Cellar window (114x165cm-45x65in) board. 27-Mar-3 Christie's, Kensington #570/R est:1000-1500

Works on paper
£260 $408 €390 Female nude (46x22cm-18x9in) pen ink. 14-Dec-2 Lacy Scott, Bury St.Edmunds #457/R

BLAMPIED, Edmund (1886-1966) British
£260 $424 €390 Gathering seaweed (19x27cm-7x11in) 14-Feb-3 Lyon & Turnbull, Edinburgh #117
£387 $600 €581 Jersey Harbour (23x33cm-9x13in) s. W/C sold with two prints. 7-Dec-2 Selkirks, St. Louis #120/R
£700 $1092 €1050 Figures under a parasol (19x28cm-7x11in) s. board. 26-Mar-3 Bonhams & Langlois, Jersey #112
£13000 $20410 €19500 Fording the stream (58x79cm-23x31in) s. exhib. 22-Nov-2 Christie's, London #21/R est:8000-12000

Works on paper
£850 $1343 €1275 Vraic harvesters (20x28cm-8x11in) s. pencil dr. 27-Nov-2 Bonhams, Brooks & Langlois, Jersey #97/R
£1026 $1600 €1539 River barges on the Seine (25x38cm-10x15in) s. W/C. 9-Nov-2 Sloan, North Bethesda #584/R est:1500-2000
£1419 $2200 €2129 Une rencontre (28x25cm-11x10in) s.d.1934 sanguine exhib. 7-Dec-2 Selkirks, St. Louis #117 est:1200-1800
£2300 $3634 €3450 Jersey vraicing (18x28cm-7x11in) s.i.verso pastel. 27-Nov-2 Bonhams, Brooks & Langlois, Jersey #101/R est:1000-1500

BLANC, Horace le (1580-1637) French
£9091 $15182 €13000 Procession de la Vierge vers le Chateau St Ange (138x179cm-54x70in) prov. 25-Jun-3 Sotheby's, Paris #2/R est:10000-15000

BLANC, Joel (20th C) French?
Sculpture
£1063 $1680 €1680 Trotteur (20x26cm-8x10in) s.num.4/8 brown pat bronze Cast Landowski. 27-Nov-2 Lemoine & Ferrando, Paris #174/R est:1700-2000

BLANC, Louis-Ammy (1810-1885) German
£14493 $23768 €20000 Allegoria della musica e della poesia (77x96cm-30x38in) 27-May-3 Finarte, Milan #90/R est:20000-25000

BLANC-FONTAINE, Henri (1819-1897) French
£327 $510 €520 Le lac d'Annecy (36x51cm-14x20in) 14-Oct-2 Blache, Grenoble #22

BLANCH, Lucille (1895-1981) American
£488 $800 €708 Irresistible movement (91x56cm-36x22in) s. prov. 1-Jun-3 Wright, Chicago #275/R

BLANCH, Xavier (1918-1999) Spanish
Works on paper
£448 $713 €650 Breakfast (63x48cm-25x19in) s. wax crayon. 4-Mar-3 Ansorena, Madrid #382/R

BLANCHARD, Antoine (1910-1988) French
£566 $900 €849 Place de L'opera, Paris (53x69cm-21x27in) s. 7-Mar-3 Jackson's, Cedar Falls #535/R est:1500-2000

£643 $1009 €965 Street scene in Paris (13x18cm-5x7in) s. 25-Nov-2 Hodgins, Calgary #59/R (C.D 1600)
£2000 $3140 €3000 Le Moulin Rouge (46x55cm-18x22in) s. s.i.verso. 19-Nov-2 Bonhams, New Bond Street #179/R est:4000-6000
£2036 $3400 €2952 Paris - Place de la Victoire (32x45cm-13x18in) s. 24-Jun-3 Koller, Zurich #103/R est:3000-4500 (S.FR 4500)
£2183 $3450 €3275 Champs Elysees with Arc de Triomphe (46x55cm-18x22in) s. 14-Nov-2 Stuker, Bern #98/R est:6000-7000 (S.FR 5000)
£2278 $3600 €3417 Notre Dame de Paris (51x61cm-20x24in) s. s.i.verso. 16-Nov-2 New Orleans Auction, New Orleans #326/R est:4000-7000
£2303 $3500 €3455 Parisian street scene with figures (46x61cm-18x24in) s. 18-Aug-2 Jeffery Burchard, Florida #98/R
£3049 $5000 €4421 Haussmann Boulevard, Paris (46x53cm-18x21in) s. oil on linen. 30-May-3 Aspire, Cleveland #45/R est:5000-8000
£3750 $6000 €5625 Paris street scene under snowfall (33x46cm-13x18in) s. 14-May-3 Butterfields, San Francisco #1184/R est:3000-5000
£3800 $5966 €5700 Boulevard by the Seine, Notre Dame beyond (51x61cm-20x24in) s. 21-Nov-2 Christie's, Kensington #3/R est:3000-5000
£3800 $6042 €5700 La Madeleine sous la neige (46x56cm-18x22in) s. 18-Mar-3 Bonhams, New Bond Street #132/R est:3000-5000
£3819 $5958 €5729 Place de la Republique, Paris (32x44cm-13x17in) s. 8-Apr-3 Peter Webb, Auckland #122/R est:12000-15000 (NZ.D 11000)
£3819 $5958 €5729 Cafe de la Piax, Paris (32x44cm-13x17in) s. 8-Apr-3 Peter Webb, Auckland #123/R est:12000-15000 (NZ.D 11000)
£3819 $5958 €5729 Place de la Republique, Paris (32x44cm-13x17in) s. 8-Apr-3 Peter Webb, Auckland #124/R est:12000-15000 (NZ.D 11000)
£4000 $6280 €6000 Porte St. Denis (33x46cm-13x18in) s. s.i.verso. 19-Nov-2 Bonhams, New Bond Street #180/R est:3000-5000
£4140 $6500 €6210 L'opera (13x18cm-5x7in) s. 10-Dec-2 Doyle, New York #246/R est:5000-7000
£4140 $6500 €6210 Parisian street scene (13x18cm-5x7in) s. 10-Dec-2 Doyle, New York #247/R est:5000-7000
£4200 $6552 €6300 Le Madeleine (33x46cm-13x18in) s. 26-Mar-3 Woolley & Wallis, Salisbury #242/R est:3000-5000
£4500 $7515 €6750 Quai de Gesvres, place du chatelet, Paris (33x46cm-13x18in) s. i.verso painted 1900. 18-Jun-3 Christie's, Kensington #12/R est:5000-7000
£4800 $7488 €7200 Le Champs Elysee (33x46cm-13x18in) s. 26-Mar-3 Woolley & Wallis, Salisbury #243/R est:3000-5000
£5000 $7750 €7500 Porte St Denis, Paris (33x46cm-13x18in) s. i. verso prov. 2-Oct-2 Bonhams, Knowle #69/R est:2500-3500
£5161 $8000 €7742 L'Arc de Triomphe, Paris (36x46cm-14x18in) s. 30-Oct-2 Christie's, Rockefeller NY #222/R est:10000-15000
£5161 $8000 €7742 Place de la Madeline, Paris (46x55cm-18x22in) s. 30-Oct-2 Christie's, Rockefeller NY #223/R est:10000-15000
£5161 $8000 €7742 Winter along the Seine, Paris (33x46cm-13x18in) s. 30-Oct-2 Christie's, Rockefeller NY #224/R est:10000-15000
£5200 $8060 €7800 Porte St Martin - grands boulevards sous la neige, Paris (33x46cm-13x18in) s. i. verso. 2-Oct-2 Bonhams, Knowle #81/R est:2000-3000
£5500 $8965 €8250 Les varietes (61x91cm-24x36in) s. s.i.verso. 3-Feb-3 Bonhams, New Bond Street #100/R est:6000-8000
£5500 $8910 €8250 Arc de Triomphe (46x55cm-18x22in) s. 20-May-3 Sotheby's, Olympia #435/R est:3000-4000
£5800 $8990 €8700 Place de Louvre (33x46cm-13x18in) s. 3-Dec-2 Sotheby's, Olympia #306/R est:2500-3500
£6000 $9300 €9000 Rue en Paris (32x46cm-13x18in) s. 3-Dec-2 Sotheby's, Olympia #307/R est:2500-3500
£6000 $9780 €9000 Quai des Gesvres, le Theatre du chatel, Paris 1900 (33x46cm-13x18in) s. s.i.verso. 3-Feb-3 Bonhams, New Bond Street #97/R est:3000-5000
£6452 $10000 €9678 Pedestrians on a busy Parisian street (33x46cm-13x18in) s. 30-Oct-2 Christie's, Rockefeller NY #227/R est:10000-15000
£7000 $11410 €10500 Place du Luxembourg, le Pantheon, Paris 1900 (33x46cm-13x18in) s. s.i.verso. 3-Feb-3 Bonhams, New Bond Street #98/R est:3000-5000
£7500 $11775 €11250 Boulevard de la Madeleine (46x55cm-18x22in) s. s.i.verso. 19-Nov-2 Bonhams, New Bond Street #177/R est:4000-6000
£7500 $11775 €11250 Sous la neige, Paris (61x92cm-24x36in) s. s.i.verso. 19-Nov-2 Bonhams, New Bond Street #182/R est:6000-8000
£7500 $12225 €11250 Le Madeleine (60x91cm-24x36in) s. s.i.verso. 3-Feb-3 Bonhams, New Bond Street #99/R est:6000-8000
£7500 $12225 €11250 Le louvre, Passerelle des arts (61x91cm-24x36in) s. s.i.verso. 3-Feb-3 Bonhams, New Bond Street #101/R est:6000-8000
£7600 $11780 €11400 Busy Parisian street scene in winter (46x54cm-18x21in) s. s.i.verso prov. 2-Oct-2 Bonhams, Knowle #79/R est:3000-5000
£19000 $31730 €28500 Place de la Madelaine. Une marche aux fleurs (60x91cm-24x36in) s. pair. 18-Jun-3 Christie's, Kensington #11/R est:7000-10000

BLANCHARD, Antoine (attrib) (1910-1988) French

£1210 $1911 €1815 Parisian street scenes (51x61cm-20x24in) bears sig. pair. 18-Nov-2 Waddingtons, Toronto #234/R est:2500-3500 (C.D 3000)
£2278 $3600 €3417 Madeleine (30x43cm-12x17in) s. 16-Nov-2 New Orleans Auction, New Orleans #327/R est:4000-7000

BLANCHARD, Antoine (jnr) (1930-) French

£3065 $4750 €4598 Moulin rouge (61x76cm-24x30in) s. painted c.1950. 8-Dec-2 Toomey, Oak Park #753/R est:6000-8000

BLANCHARD, F L (20th C) British

Works on paper

£260 $421 €390 Recorder leaving West India dock (37x46cm-15x18in) s. ink htd white. 21-Jan-3 Bonhams, New Bond Street #163/R
£400 $648 €600 An unnamed Harrison line ship at sea (38x47cm-15x19in) s. W/C. 21-Jan-3 Bonhams, New Bond Street #162/R

BLANCHARD, Maria (1881-1932) Spanish

£12950 $20719 €18000 Portrait de fillette (27x22cm-11x9in) 14-May-3 Blanchet, Paris #111/R est:10000-12000
£41921 $65397 €62882 Portrait of a girl (97x70cm-38x28in) s. pastel paper on canvas. 6-Nov-2 Dobiaschofsky, Bern #355/R est:22000 (S.FR 96000)
£105590 $170000 €158385 Nu aux enfants (81x130cm-32x51in) s. painted 1924 prov.exhib.lit. 7-May-3 Sotheby's, New York #198/R est:180000-220000

Works on paper

£3493 $5450 €5240 Children at breakfast (60x73cm-24x29in) pastel paper on canvas. 6-Nov-2 Dobiaschofsky, Bern #354/R est:15000 (S.FR 8000)

BLANCHARD, Remy (1958-1993) French

£1139 $1766 €1800 Vue d'Holywood/LA la nuit (173x185cm-68x73in) s.i.d. i.verso acrylic. 28-Sep-2 Cornette de St.Cyr, Paris #257/R est:2000-3000

BLANCHE, Jacques Émile (1861-1942) French

£600 $948 €900 Portrait of a girl, head and shoulders (54x46cm-21x18in) s.i.d.81 i.verso. 14-Nov-2 Christie's, Kensington #51/R
£755 $1177 €1200 Woman's portrait (38x55cm-15x22in) mono.d.02 lit. 20-Sep-2 Schloss Ahlden, Ahlden #1207/R
£897 $1391 €1400 Beach scene (48x50cm-19x20in) s. panel. 7-Dec-2 Van Ham, Cologne #52/R
£2258 $3568 €3500 View of Paris (27x35cm-11x14in) mono. s.i.d.1938 verso panel prov. 18-Dec-2 Ferri, Paris #33/R
£3165 $5000 €5000 Reines marguerites (38x46cm-15x18in) s. s.verso cardboard. 27-Nov-2 Blanchet, Paris #39/R
£3200 $5120 €4800 Portrait of Marshall Foch (161x115cm-63x45in) s.d.1920. 11-Mar-3 Bonhams, Knightsbridge #319/R est:2000-3000
£3700 $5883 €5550 Marble arch (17x50cm-7x20in) s.i.d.October 1908 verso board. 26-Feb-3 Sotheby's, Olympia #38/R est:3000-4000
£5036 $8058 €7000 Vase de fleurs devant la fenetre ouvrant sur le parc (65x81cm-26x32in) init.d. 18-May-3 Eric Pillon, Calais #57/R
£7000 $11130 €10500 Grey Bay at Dieppe (38x55cm-15x22in) init.i. exhib. 26-Feb-3 Sotheby's, Olympia #39/R est:3000-4000
£47436 $74474 €74000 Peinture de chevalet (40x32cm-16x13in) s.d.83. 10-Dec-2 Renaud, Paris #31/R est:15000

BLANCHET, Alexandre (1882-1961) Swiss

£858 $1356 €1287 Paysage - Haute Savoie (50x61cm-20x24in) mono.d.21 prov.exhib. 28-Nov-2 Christie's, Zurich #54/R (S.FR 2000)
£1288 $2034 €1932 Paysage montagnard (54x65cm-21x26in) s.d.39. 26-Nov-2 Hans Widmer, St Gallen #1044/R est:800-2000 (S.FR 3000)

BLANCHET, Louis Gabriel (1705-1772) French

£8805 $13560 €14000 Le repas (64x55cm-25x22in) s.d.1751 oval. 25-Oct-2 Tajan, Paris #132/R est:9000-10000

Works on paper

£420 $701 €609 Ripa Grande, Rome (24x40cm-9x16in) i. black white chk. 9-Jul-3 Bonhams, Knightsbridge #8/R

BLANCHET, Thomas (1614-1689) French

£10500 $16485 €15750 Architectural capriccio with figures, balcony and courtyard (65x82cm-26x32in) 12-Dec-2 Sotheby's, London #198/R est:10000-15000
£17610 $27119 €28000 View of the Forum with market scene (100x73cm-39x29in) exhib.lit. 23-Oct-2 Finarte, Rome #526/R est:23000-26000

BLANCO MERINO, Rafael (19th C) Spanish

£724 $1172 €1100 Garden with fountain (114x43cm-45x17in) s. 21-Jan-3 Ansorena, Madrid #228/R

BLANCO NINO, Ignacio (1900-) Spanish

£302 $486 €450 Christ embracing Saint Bernard (111x78cm-44x31in) s. s.i.verso. 18-Feb-3 Durán, Madrid #626/R

BLANCO, Antonio (1927-1999) Philippino

£10878 $17949 €15773 Portrait of Ni Rani (25x20cm-10x8in) s.i. 6-Jul-3 Christie's, Hong Kong #5/R est:65000-85000 (HK.D 140000)
£12428 $19138 €18642 Still life (32x41cm-13x16in) s. 27-Oct-2 Christie's, Hong Kong #33/R est:130000-160000 (HK.D 150000)

Works on paper

£3480 $5359 €5220 Portrait of a girl (30cm-12in circular) s. pencil gouache oil on paper prov. 27-Oct-2 Christie's, Hong Kong #16/R est:18000-28000 (HK.D 42000)

BLANCO, J M (?) ?
£600 $936 €900 Matador (44x29cm-17x11in) s. board. 10-Sep-2 Bonhams, Knightsbridge #204/R

BLAND, E (19/20th C) British
£350 $553 €525 Fishing vessels by the cliffs at dawn (41x61cm-16x24in) s.d.1902. 14-Nov-2 Christie's, Kensington #11/R

BLAND, Emily Beatrice (1864-1951) British
£450 $752 €653 Spring flowers (37x49cm-15x19in) s. board prov. 8-Jul-3 Bonhams, Knightsbridge #195/R
£950 $1482 €1425 Still life of mixed flowers in vases (56x47cm-22x19in) s. 26-Mar-3 Hamptons Fine Art, Godalming #155

BLAND, John F (1856-1899) British
£280 $456 €420 Evening coastal scene with shipwreck beneath cliffs (50x75cm-20x30in) s.d.1882. 29-Jan-3 Hampton & Littlewood, Exeter #395/R

BLANDIN, Armand (1804-?) Swiss
£780 $1303 €1100 La halte en foret (41x33cm-16x13in) s.d.1833. 20-Jun-3 Piasa, Paris #38/R

BLANES VIALE, Pedro (1879-1926) Uruguayan
£1935 $3058 €3000 Girl (55x21cm-22x8in) s.d.99. 18-Dec-2 Ansorena, Madrid #363/R
£9146 $15000 €13719 Cerro de Arequita (65x81cm-26x32in) s. painted c.1917 prov. 28-May-3 Christie's, Rockefeller NY #74/R est:25000-35000
£12739 $20000 €19109 Terrace (115x90cm-45x35in) s. painted c.1920 prov. 20-Nov-2 Christie's, Rockefeller NY #67/R est:30000-40000
£37580 $59000 €56370 Sun and shadow (131x115cm-52x45in) s.i.d.1924 prov.lit. 19-Nov-2 Sotheby's, New York #27/R est:70000

BLANES, Juan Manuel (1830-1901) Uruguayan
£469 $750 €704 Venice at night (48x33cm-19x13in) s. cardboard. 5-Jan-3 Galleria Y Remates, Montevideo #40
£2885 $4500 €4328 Garibaldi soldier (28x17cm-11x7in) prov. 10-Oct-2 Galleria Y Remates, Montevideo #67/R

BLANES, Nicanor (?) ?
£1090 $1700 €1635 Puente de Venecia (25x15cm-10x6in) s. board. 30-Jul-2 Galleria Y Remates, Montevideo #43/R est:1500-2000

BLANK, Franz J (1932-) Austrian
£1528 $2384 €2292 Max and Moritz (100x120cm-39x47in) s.d.5/2001 acrylic. 20-Nov-2 Fischer, Luzern #1194/R est:2500-3500 (S.FR 3500)
£1747 $2725 €2621 Mickey Mouse (120x120cm-47x47in) s.d.7/2000 acrylic. 20-Nov-2 Fischer, Luzern #1193/R est:3000-4000 (S.FR 4000)

BLANT, Julien le (1851-?) French
Works on paper
£550 $869 €825 Portrait of Abdelkader bin El Hadj in French military uniform (36x20cm-14x8in) s.i. chl W/C. 5-Apr-3 Finan Watkins & Co, Mere #200/R
£580 $916 €870 Portrait of a trumpeter of French 11th Artillery Regiment (33x18cm-13x7in) s.d.1917 chl W/C. 5-Apr-3 Finan Watkins & Co, Mere #201/R

BLARCOM, Mary van (20th C) American?
£427 $700 €619 Pine pattern (30x25cm-12x10in) s. s.i.verso masonite painted c.1940. 5-Jun-3 Swann Galleries, New York #42/R

BLARENBERGHE, Henri Desire van (attrib) (1734-1812) French
Works on paper
£3205 $5032 €5000 Idyllic river landscape with washerwomen on shore (19x24cm-7x9in) gouache. 21-Nov-2 Van Ham, Cologne #1312/R est:3000

BLARENBERGHE, Henri Joseph van (1741-1826) French
Miniatures
£13000 $20410 €19500 L'arrivee, horsemen dismounting before town ramparts crowded with onlookers offering wine (5x7cm-2x3in) rectangular. 10-Dec-2 Christie's, London #65/R est:6000-8000

BLARENBERGHE, Louis Nicolas van (1716-1794) French
Miniatures
£8000 $12560 €12000 Landscape scenes with figures (3x7cm-1x3in) parchment silver gilt prov.lit. 10-Dec-2 Christie's, London #63/R est:6000-8000
Works on paper
£820 $1279 €1230 Les saltimbanques au village (10x14cm-4x6in) gouache oval. 10-Sep-2 Iegor de Saint Hippolyte, Montreal #7/R (C.D 2000)
£3611 $5706 €5200 Fete de village (17x13cm-7x5in) s.d.1770 ivory prov.lit. 25-Apr-3 Beaussant & Lefèvre, Paris #23/R

BLARENBERGHE, Louis Nicolas van (attrib) (1716-1794) French
Works on paper
£828 $1292 €1300 Views of military encampments (17x22cm-7x9in) gouache vellum on card pair. 5-Nov-2 Sotheby's, Amsterdam #120/R

BLAS, M de (?) ?
£256 $405 €400 Composition (80x64cm-31x25in) s. acrylic. 19-Nov-2 Durán, Madrid #674/R

BLASCHKE, Franz Josef (1916-1984) German?
£321 $503 €500 View over the Rhine of Cologne cathedral and Kaiser Wilhelm bridge (30x44cm-12x17in) s. board. 21-Nov-2 Van Ham, Cologne #1481
£481 $745 €750 Figure in a fountain (61x86cm-24x34in) s. acrylic gouache. 7-Dec-2 Van Ham, Cologne #55

BLASCHNIK, Arthur (1823-?) German
£285 $441 €450 Sybil temple in Tivoli (28x22cm-11x9in) s.i. W/C over pencil htd white. 25-Sep-2 Neumeister, Munich #391/R

BLASCO FERRER, Eleuterio (1907-) Spanish
£345 $545 €500 Village (60x73cm-24x29in) s. 1-Apr-3 Segre, Madrid #348/R
Works on paper
£283 $442 €450 Head of man wearing hat (63x48cm-25x19in) s. chl dr. 8-Oct-2 Ansorena, Madrid #485

BLASHFIELD, Edwin Howland (1848-1936) American
£2244 $3500 €3366 Untitled (66x99cm-26x39in) 18-Oct-2 Du Mouchelle, Detroit #2012/R est:4000-6000

BLASHKO, Abe (1920-) American
Works on paper
£854 $1400 €1238 Preview. Study of two men (49x37cm-19x15in) s.d. pencil double-sided sold with a lithograph. 5-Jun-3 Swann Galleries, New York #48/R
£976 $1600 €1415 Sideshow attraction. Study of a seated man (37x58cm-15x23in) s.i.d. pencil double-sided sold with a lithograph. 5-Jun-3 Swann Galleries, New York #49/R est:3000-5000
£1159 $1900 €1681 Skidrow cafe. Study of a city (39x37cm-15x15in) s.i.d. conte crayon double-sided. 5-Jun-3 Swann Galleries, New York #46/R est:3000-5000
£1463 $2400 €2121 Side street (29x37cm-11x15in) s.i.d. pencil. 5-Jun-3 Swann Galleries, New York #43/R est:4000-6000
£3537 $5800 €5129 Pillars. Study of a man writing at a desk (51x32cm-20x13in) s.d. i.verso pencil double-sided sold with a lithograph. 5-Jun-3 Swann Galleries, New York #50/R est:5000-8000

BLASK, Kujahn (1902-1970) German
£931 $1444 €1397 Turquoise blue composition (90x70cm-35x28in) s.d.1948 verso prov. 1-Oct-2 Rasmussen, Copenhagen #171 (D.KR 11000)

BLAT, Ismael (1901-1987) Spanish
£851 $1379 €1200 Venditrice di mele (72x60cm-28x24in) s. 22-May-3 Stadion, Trieste #303/R
£1613 $2548 €2500 Woman (82x66cm-32x26in) s. 17-Dec-2 Durán, Madrid #67/R

BLATAS, Arbit (1908-) American/Lithuanian
£417 $650 €626 View of the Seine (76x117cm-30x46in) s. 10-Nov-2 Selkirks, St. Louis #741/R
£679 $1100 €985 Outdoor cafe (81x66cm-32x26in) s. 21-May-3 Doyle, New York #224/R
£818 $1267 €1300 Rue de village dans le midi (45x55cm-18x22in) s. 30-Oct-2 Artcurial Briest, Paris #3 est:1500-2000
£2013 $3200 €3020 Parisian scene (66x80cm-26x31in) s. 27-Feb-3 Christie's, Rockefeller NY #63/R est:5000
£5975 $9500 €8963 Vase de fleurs (91x72cm-36x28in) s. prov. 27-Feb-3 Christie's, Rockefeller NY #94/R
Sculpture
£1098 $1800 €1592 Jacques Lipchitz (102x36x41cm-40x14x16in) bronze prov. 1-Jun-3 Wright, Chicago #255/R est:2500-3500

BLATTER, Bruno (19th C) German
£629 $981 €1000 Playing cards (60x80cm-24x31in) 23-Sep-2 Dr Fritz Nagel, Stuttgart #6965/R
£676 $1088 €960 Two men playing chess (80x60cm-31x24in) 7-May-3 Michael Zeller, Lindau #629
£1292 $1964 €1938 Interior scene with men playing chess (71x86cm-28x34in) s. 27-Aug-2 Rasmussen, Copenhagen #1550/R est:10000-12000 (D.KR 15000)

BLAU, Tina (1845-1916) Austrian
£10135 $15811 €15000 Windmill in Dordrecht (24x33cm-9x13in) i. verso panel. 25-Mar-3 Wiener Kunst Auktionen, Vienna #139/R est:10000-20000
£16136 $25010 €24204 By the river Tisza at Szolnok (35x62cm-14x24in) s. board. 6-Dec-2 Kieselbach, Budapest #16/R (H.F 6000000)
£28369 $45957 €40000 Avenue of poplars in Lower Austria (60x80cm-24x31in) s. 22-May-3 Dorotheum, Vienna #47/R est:45000-55000
£44872 $70449 €70000 Spring in the Prater (65x100cm-26x39in) s.d.97 exhib. 25-Nov-2 Hassfurther, Vienna #26/R est:50000-60000

BLAUVELT, Charles F (1824-1900) American
£25157 $40000 €37736 Warming up (91x127cm-36x50in) s.d.1857. 5-Mar-3 Sotheby's, New York #53/R est:7000-10000

BLAUVELT, Charles F (attrib) (1824-1900) American
£769 $1200 €1154 Coachman having a dream (30x25cm-12x10in) s. 28-Mar-3 Eldred, East Dennis #566/R

BLAYNEY, Robert (20th C) British?
£260 $406 €390 Street scene (22x30cm-9x12in) panel exhib. 9-Oct-2 Woolley & Wallis, Salisbury #284/R

BLAZEBY, J (19th C) British
£1500 $2340 €2250 Two year old Shorthorn bullock (49x65cm-19x26in) s.d.1854. 7-Nov-2 Christie's, Kensington #181/R est:2000-3000

BLAZEY, Lawrence E (1902-1999) American
Works on paper
£244 $400 €354 Rail road tower. s.d.41 W/C. 30-May-3 Aspire, Cleveland #102/R

BLAZICEK, Oldrich (1887-1953) Hungarian
£578 $913 €867 Old Krenek (38x18cm-15x7in) s. i. verso cardboard. 30-Nov-2 Dorotheum, Prague #50/R (C.KR 28000)
£979 $1517 €1469 Winter in Prague (39x50cm-15x20in) cardboard painted c.1930. 3-Dec-2 SOGA, Bratislava #226/R est:45000 (SL.K 62000)
£1249 $2023 €1874 Evening ofEpiphany (50x40cm-20x16in) board. 24-May-3 Dorotheum, Prague #74/R est:40000-60000 (C.KR 55000)
£2891 $4511 €4337 Landscape with village (85x100cm-33x39in) s.d.934. 12-Oct-2 Dorotheum, Prague #41/R est:100000-150000 (C.KR 140000)
£10216 $16549 €15324 Dalmatian motif (100x115cm-39x45in) s.d.1912. 24-May-3 Dorotheum, Prague #82/R est:150000-230000 (C.KR 450000)

BLECHEN, Karl (1798-1840) German
£8000 $13120 €12000 Felsental des anio bei Tivoli - rocky valley near Tivoli (37x32cm-15x13in) oil paper on board. 3-Jun-3 Sotheby's, London #14/R est:10000-15000
£16456 $26000 €26000 Self portrait (23x18cm-9x7in) i. verso. 29-Nov-2 Bassenge, Berlin #5837/R est:9000

BLECKMANN, Wilhelm Christiaan Constant (1853-1942) Dutch
£304 $474 €480 View of a field with village in background (23x55cm-9x22in) s. 21-Oct-2 Glerum, Amsterdam #59
£573 $883 €900 Tending to the bulb fields (25x38cm-10x15in) s. board. 3-Sep-2 Christie's, Amsterdam #271
£5828 $9615 €8451 Figure under palmtrees (35x25cm-14x10in) s. panel prov.exhib.lit. 6-Jul-3 Christie's, Hong Kong #21/R est:45000-65000 (HK.D 75000)

BLECKNER, Ross (1949-) American
£6013 $9500 €9020 Blue star (46x46cm-18x18in) s.i.d.2001 linen prov. 13-Nov-2 Sotheby's, New York #576/R est:10000-15000
£7595 $12000 €11393 Colour cells (76x76cm-30x30in) s.i.d.1997 verso linen. 13-Nov-2 Sotheby's, New York #580/R est:12000-18000
£12000 $20040 €17400 Untitled (91x91cm-36x36in) s.d.2001 verso prov. 26-Jun-3 Sotheby's, London #292/R est:12000-15000
£12658 $20000 €18987 Untitled (122x152cm-48x60in) init.d.90 prov.exhib. 14-Nov-2 Christie's, Rockefeller NY #378/R est:25000-35000
£22500 $36000 €33750 Brother, brother (122x101cm-48x40in) s.i.d.1985 oil on linen prov. 15-May-3 Christie's, Rockefeller NY #380/R est:18000-22000
£25000 $40000 €37500 Companion (213x152cm-84x60in) s.i.d.1987 prov. 15-May-3 Christie's, Rockefeller NY #381/R est:40000-60000
£31250 $50000 €46875 Middle brothers (214x244cm-84x96in) s. i.d.1997 verso prov. 14-May-3 Sotheby's, New York #375/R est:50000-70000
£34810 $55000 €52215 From unknown quantities of light (274x263cm-108x104in) executed 1988 prov. 12-Nov-2 Phillips, New York #141/R est:70000-90000
£36250 $58000 €54375 Blue star (270x270cm-106x106in) s.d.2001 oil on linen prov. 16-May-3 Phillips, New York #139/R est:60000-80000
£37500 $60000 €56250 New radical (213x266cm-84x105in) i.verso oil on linen painted 2000 prov. 16-May-3 Phillips, New York #117/R est:60000-80000
£37975 $60000 €56963 Blue net (152x152cm-60x60in) s.i.d.2000 oil on linen prov. 12-Nov-2 Phillips, New York #145/R est:20000-30000
£47468 $75000 €71202 Unknown quanties of light - part V (274x366cm-108x144in) painted 1988 prov.exhib. 14-Nov-2 Christie's, Rockefeller NY #376/R est:40000-60000
£50000 $80000 €75000 Middle brothers (214x183cm-84x72in) s.i.d.1997 verso prov. 15-May-3 Christie's, Rockefeller NY #379/R est:50000-70000
Works on paper
£1852 $3000 €2685 Untitled (41x30cm-16x12in) s.d.9/95 verso W/C encaustic. 21-May-3 Doyle, New York #54/R est:3000-5000

BLEEKER, Maria Anna (1885-1918) Dutch
£599 $964 €850 Greyhound and hunting hound (33x44cm-13x17in) s.d.1887 panel. 7-May-3 Vendue Huis, Gravenhage #356/R

BLEIJS, Johannes Coenraad (1868-1952) Dutch
£701 $1093 €1100 Still life of flowers (119x78cm-47x31in) s.d.1913. 6-Nov-2 Vendue Huis, Gravenhage #66/R

BLEIKER, Heinrich (attrib) (1884-1975) Swiss
Works on paper
£300 $446 €450 Alpine procession at Churfirsten (22x32cm-9x13in) s.d.1965 goauche panel. 25-Jun-2 Koller, Zurich #6629 (S.FR 680)

BLEILE-LECHLEITNER, J (19th C) Austrian
£1509 $2340 €2400 Still life with azaleas and pansies (72x55cm-28x22in) s. 29-Oct-2 Dorotheum, Vienna #86/R est:2800-3200

BLEINBERGER, Stephen (20th C) American
Works on paper
£245 $400 €368 Navigating the North Sound (56x71cm-22x28in) s. 2-Feb-3 Simpson's, Houston #155

BLEK (1951-) French
Works on paper
£1266 $1962 €2000 Danseurs (148x200cm-58x79in) s.d. pochoir collage palisade. 28-Sep-2 Cornette de St.Cyr, Paris #258/R est:500-700

BLEKEN, Hakon (1929-) Norwegian
£1623 $2564 €2435 Figure in landscape (80x65cm-31x26in) s.d.82. 17-Dec-2 Grev Wedels Plass, Oslo #211/R est:20000-30000 (N.KR 18500)
Works on paper
£366 $575 €549 Composition (49x65cm-19x26in) s. chl. 25-Nov-2 Blomqvist, Lysaker #1025 (N.KR 4200)
£436 $685 €654 Composition (49x64cm-19x25in) d. chl W/C. 25-Nov-2 Blomqvist, Lysaker #1024 (N.KR 5000)
£954 $1488 €1431 Drama (48x64cm-19x25in) s.d.71 i.verso chl. 21-Oct-2 Blomqvist, Oslo #459/R (N.KR 11000)

BLEKER, Dirck (1622-1672) Dutch
£4200 $6510 €6300 An allegorical scene with Moses and Aaron and a pope (37x46cm-15x18in) panel. 30-Oct-2 Christie's, Kensington #44/R est:4000-6000

BLENNER, Carle J (1864-1952) American
£774 $1200 €1161 Floral still life (74x51cm-29x20in) s. painted c.1890. 8-Dec-2 Toomey, Oak Park #744/R
£5063 $8000 €7595 Floral still life (69x114cm-27x45in) s. 24-Apr-3 Shannon's, Milford #171/R est:8000-12000

BLES, David Joseph (1821-1899) Dutch
£2055 $3226 €3000 Elegant lady and her dog by a fire place (18x12cm-7x5in) s. panel. 15-Apr-3 Sotheby's, Amsterdam #68/R est:3000-5000
£15000 $23550 €22500 Trio on a hot day at the Dutch country seat, Batavia (52x73cm-20x29in) s. s.i.d. September 1874 verso panel. 19-Nov-2 Bonhams, New Bond Street #18/R est:15000-20000

BLES, David Joseph (attrib) (1821-1899) Dutch

Works on paper

£3600 $5580 €5400 Bless the split milk (25x20cm-10x8in) mono. pencil W/C htd white. 26-Sep-2 Mellors & Kirk, Nottingham #658/R est:3000-4000

BLES, Joseph (1825-1875) Dutch

£1083 $1689 €1700 Buitenlust (51x61cm-20x24in) s. 6-Nov-2 Vendue Huis, Gravenhage #384/R est:4000-5000
£1517 $2428 €2200 Town festival in the Netherlands (8x11cm-3x4in) s. panel. 15-Mar-3 De Vuyst, Lokeren #27/R est:1000-1500
£3145 $4843 €5000 By the waterside (19x26cm-7x10in) one s. one indis sig. panel pair. 23-Oct-2 Christie's, Amsterdam #10/R est:5000-7000

BLEULER, Johann Heinrich (1758-1823) Swiss

Works on paper

£897 $1391 €1400 Rheinfall near Schaffhausen (48x71cm-19x28in) s.d.1819 gouache. 5-Dec-2 Dr Fritz Nagel, Stuttgart #562/R

BLEULER, Johann Heinrich (attrib) (1758-1823) Swiss

Works on paper

£1261 $1954 €1892 La Vallee de Chamonix (32x47cm-13x19in) gouache prov. 7-Dec-2 Galerie du Rhone, Sion #446/R est:3500-4500 (S.FR 2900)

BLEULER, Johann Heinrich (younger) (1787-1857) Swiss

Works on paper

£1596 $2618 €2314 Landscape (43x60cm-17x24in) s.d.1837 gouache. 4-Jun-3 Fischer, Luzern #2702/R est:1500-2000 (S.FR 3400)

BLEULER, Johann Heinrich (younger-attrib) (1787-1857) Swiss

Works on paper

£522 $809 €783 La Vallee de Chamonix vue de Col des Montets (26x37cm-10x15in) gouache. 7-Dec-2 Galerie du Rhone, Sion #447/R (S.FR 1200)

BLEULER, Johann Heinrich (younger-circle) (1787-1857) Swiss

Works on paper

£1435 $2224 €2153 Maison au bord de la riviere (27x38cm-11x15in) gouache prov. 7-Dec-2 Galerie du Rhone, Sion #448/R est:4000-5000 (S.FR 3300)

BLEULER, Johann Ludwig (1792-1850) Swiss

Works on paper

£1027 $1603 €1500 Vue de Scheveningen, vers le ains de Mer (39x56cm-15x22in) s. gouache. 10-Apr-3 Van Ham, Cologne #1334/R est:1800
£1392 $2158 €2200 Constance (35x47cm-14x19in) s.i. col gouache. 27-Sep-2 Karrenbauer, Konstanz #1604/R est:1400
£2227 $3519 €3341 View of Meiringen in Hasle valley (46x67cm-18x26in) gouache. 14-Nov-2 Stuker, Bern #9070 est:6000-7000 (S.FR 5100)
£2271 $3542 €3407 Vue de la ruine de Haldenstein (32x48cm-13x19in) s.i. gouache over etching. 20-Nov-2 Fischer, Luzern #2728/R est:2500-3500 (S.FR 5200)
£2838 $4456 €4257 Vue du Dodi au Canton de Glarus (32x48cm-13x19in) i. gouache. 25-Nov-2 Sotheby's, Zurich #3/R est:3000-5000 (S.FR 6500)
£4225 $6930 €6126 La Chute du Rhin pres de Schafhause (50x74cm-20x29in) s.i. gouache. 4-Jun-3 Fischer, Luzern #2704/R est:9000-11000 (S.FR 9000)
£5677 $8913 €8516 Vue de Fluelen au Lac des Quatre Cantons (49x71cm-19x28in) bears i. gouache. 25-Nov-2 Sotheby's, Zurich #2/R est:6000-8000 (S.FR 13000)

BLEYENBERG, Karel (1913-) Dutch

Works on paper

£775 $1247 €1100 Workhouse in Slenaken (38x52cm-15x20in) s.i. gouache exhib. 7-May-3 Vendue Huis, Gravenhage #203/R

BLEYL, Fritz (1880-1966) German

Works on paper

£886 $1400 €1400 Kneeling figure (26x33cm-10x13in) pencil. 30-Nov-2 Bassenge, Berlin #6142/R

BLIECK, Maurice (1876-1922) Belgian

£641 $1006 €1000 Vue du port d'Ostende anime (61x41cm-24x16in) s. 19-Nov-2 Vanderkindere, Brussels #116
£784 $1263 €1200 Cargos a quai (42x60cm-17x24in) s. 20-Jan-3 Horta, Bruxelles #403
£897 $1409 €1400 Quai enneige (55x65cm-22x26in) s. 19-Nov-2 Vanderkindere, Brussels #28

Works on paper

£1233 $1923 €1800 Vue nocturne de Paris (60x55cm-24x22in) s. mixed media. 14-Apr-3 Horta, Bruxelles #85 est:1800-2200

BLIGH, Jabez (fl.1880-1891) British

Works on paper

£280 $454 €406 Study of mushrooms (20x35cm-8x14in) W/C htd white. 20-May-3 Dreweatt Neate, Newbury #191/R

BLIND, Rudolph (1846-1889) British

£1191 $1883 €1787 Cupid and Psyche (81x60cm-32x24in) s. 2-Dec-2 Rasmussen, Copenhagen #1728/R est:15000 (D.KR 14000)

BLINKS, Thomas (1860-1912) British

£3800 $5776 €5700 Pointer in a landscape (64x85cm-25x33in) s. prov. 28-Aug-2 Sotheby's, London #816/R est:4000-6000
£10000 $16200 €15000 On the point (64x85cm-25x33in) st.sig. prov. 22-May-3 Christie's, London #14 est:6000-8000
£48611 $70000 €72917 Pointers on the scent (95x66cm-37x26in) st.sig. prov. 15-Jan-3 Christie's, Rockefeller NY #176/R est:70000
£104167 $150000 €156251 Setters on the scent (49x74cm-19x29in) s. prov. 15-Jan-3 Christie's, Rockefeller NY #175/R est:70000

Works on paper

£1039 $1548 €1600 Hounds crossing a stream (38x53cm-15x21in) s. W/C. 28-Jun-2 Woodwards, Cork #207
£3067 $5000 €4601 Sporting dogs (36x26cm-14x10in) s. col chk pair. 11-Feb-3 Bonhams & Doyles, New York #218/R est:3000-5000

BLISS, Douglas Percy (1900-1984) British

£1650 $2607 €2475 Snowball fight (50x60cm-20x24in) 7-Apr-3 Bonhams, Bath #66/R est:800-1200

Works on paper

£550 $875 €825 Conversation at Arles, Gauguin and Van Gogh (25x28cm-10x11in) s.i. pencil W/C gouache prov. 26-Feb-3 Sotheby's, Olympia #141/R

BLISS, Robert R (1925-1981) American

£531 $850 €770 Brimmer Street (56x91cm-22x36in) s. masonite prov. 16-May-3 Skinner, Boston #318/R
£534 $850 €801 Clam diggers (76x122cm-30x48in) s.d.1962 i.verso. 7-Mar-3 Jackson's, Cedar Falls #751/R

BLOAS, Paul (20th C) French?

Works on paper

£1346 $2113 €2100 Manteau de papier (80x58cm-31x23in) s.i. mixed media. 15-Dec-2 Thierry & Lannon, Brest #225

BLOC, Andre (1896-1966) French

£646 $1028 €950 Ressac (100x81cm-39x32in) s.i.d.1961 oil collage. 26-Feb-3 Artcurial Briest, Paris #550
£759 $1185 €1200 Coniugation (130x88cm-51x35in) s.i.d.1960 verso polymer. 19-Oct-2 Semenzato, Venice #110/R

Sculpture

£1161 $1835 €1800 Untitled (41x12x20cm-16x5x8in) brass exec.c.1960. 18-Dec-2 Christie's, Rome #96
£1355 $2141 €2100 Flamme (80cm-31in) s. tin lacquer. 18-Dec-2 Digard, Paris #162/R
£3846 $6038 €6000 Trophee (44x31cm-17x12in) s. iron copper tin prov.exhib. 24-Nov-2 Laurence Calmels, Paris #292/R est:5000

BLOCH, Albert (1882-1961) American

£70000 $114800 €105000 Night in the valley (66x77cm-26x30in) mono. painted 1915-17 prov.lit. 4-Feb-3 Christie's, London #266/R est:100000

BLOCH, Carl (1834-1890) Danish

£342 $526 €513 Italian woman sleeping (46x37cm-18x15in) s. 4-Sep-2 Kunsthallen, Copenhagen #175 (D.KR 4000)
£512 $814 €768 Portrait of Caroline Mathilde Stromback (22x18cm-9x7in) indis.sig. panel. 5-Mar-3 Rasmussen, Copenhagen #1678/R (D.KR 5500)
£631 $1015 €947 Fisherman seated at table with bottles and glass (26x19cm-10x7in) s.d.1880 panel oval. 26-Feb-3 Museumsbygningen, Copenhagen #14/R (D.KR 7000)
£1281 $1973 €1922 Interior scene with seated women (120x87cm-47x34in) s. 4-Sep-2 Kunsthallen, Copenhagen #90/R est:18000 (D.KR 15000)

BLOCH, Carl (attrib) (1834-1890) Danish
£298 $471 €447 Christ bringing the robber to Paradise (67x41cm-26x16in) prov. 2-Dec-2 Rasmussen, Copenhagen #1774/R (D.KR 3500)

BLOCH, Marcel (1884-?) French
£1529 $2385 €2400 Elegantes, Place de l'Opera (27x22cm-11x9in) s. 10-Nov-2 Eric Pillon, Calais #128/R

BLOCH, Marjorie (1956-) Irish
£450 $698 €675 Autumn sky (20x25cm-8x10in) mono.d.01 board. 2-Oct-2 John Ross, Belfast #140
£450 $698 €675 Cote d'Azur (30x40cm-12x16in) mono.d.01 board. 4-Dec-2 John Ross, Belfast #26
£550 $853 €825 Room in Spain (35x45cm-14x18in) mono.d.02 verso board. 4-Dec-2 John Ross, Belfast #63
£1000 $1550 €1500 Evening, Mandalay (89x89cm-35x35in) mono.d.02. 2-Oct-2 John Ross, Belfast #118 est:1200-1400

BLOCH, Paul (1869-?) Danish
£576 $934 €864 Interior scene with two women (37x33cm-15x13in) s. panel. 25-Jan-3 Rasmussen, Havnen #2246/R (D.KR 6500)

BLOCKSIDGE, T (19th C) British
£700 $1001 €1050 Earl Strafford on his way to execution (100x127cm-39x50in) s.d.1871 si.d.verso. 11-Apr-2 Mellors & Kirk, Nottingham #557

BLOEMAERT, Abraham (1564-1651) Dutch
£4487 $6955 €7000 Last supper for Christ (39x29cm-15x11in) s.indis.d. lit. 4-Dec-2 Neumeister, Munich #583/R est:4000
£35971 $57554 €50000 Adoration of the shepherds (51x38cm-20x15in) s. panel prov.lit. 14-May-3 Christie's, Amsterdam #170/R est:50000-70000
Works on paper
£1592 $2484 €2500 Anchorite in meditation (13x9cm-5x4in) pen brown ink wash over black chk prov. 5-Nov-2 Sotheby's, Amsterdam #38/R est:4000-6000
£2229 $3478 €3500 Studies of a seated woman (15x17cm-6x7in) black chk prov. 5-Nov-2 Sotheby's, Amsterdam #18/R est:4000-6000
£3395 $5500 €5093 Head of woman (15x12cm-6x5in) chk htd white. 21-Jan-3 Sotheby's, New York #148/R
£3503 $5465 €5500 Christ preaching on the Sea of Galilee (28x32cm-11x13in) s.d.1649 pen brown ink wash htd white black chk prov. 5-Nov-2 Sotheby's, Amsterdam #10/R est:6000-8000
£3800 $6346 €5510 Study of a seated figure (28x19cm-11x7in) red chk htd white. 9-Jul-3 Sotheby's, London #92/R est:2500-3500
£4459 $6955 €7000 Roman charity (22x17cm-9x7in) black chk brown wash htd white prov.lit. 5-Nov-2 Sotheby's, Amsterdam #6/R est:8000-12000
£4938 $8000 €7407 Virgin, half length (17x25cm-7x10in) chk pen ink prov. 22-Jan-3 Christie's, Rockefeller NY #88/R est:10000
£5096 $7949 €8000 Two women and shepherd on the way to market (10x15cm-4x6in) s. pen brown ink wash over black chk prov.exhib. 5-Nov-2 Sotheby's, Amsterdam #9/R est:10000-15000
£8000 $13360 €11600 Studies of a boy, and a leg (21x14cm-8x6in) red chk htd white prov. 8-Jul-3 Christie's, London #95/R est:3000-5000
£10764 $17007 €15500 Tetes (21x15cm-8x6in) i. sanguine htd white 3 in one frame prov. 25-Apr-3 Beaussant & Lefèvre, Paris #4/R est:6000

BLOEMAERT, Adriaen (attrib) (1610-1666) Dutch
Works on paper
£355 $592 €500 Paysans a l'entree d'un village (15x19cm-6x7in) bears sig. pen W/C wash. 20-Jun-3 Rieunier, Paris #6/R

BLOEMAERT, Hendrick (1601-1672) Dutch
£3185 $4968 €5000 Portrait of a gentleman, aged 47 (108x78cm-43x31in) s.i.d.1650 panel prov.exhib.lit. 5-Nov-2 Sotheby's, Amsterdam #95/R est:6000-8000
£5000 $7850 €7500 Portrait of a lady in a black dress with white embroidered collar and cuffs (70x59cm-28x23in) s.d.1647 panel. 10-Dec-2 Bonhams, New Bond Street #64/R est:6000-8000
£35000 $54600 €52500 Meeting of Pope Leo the great and Attila (191x315cm-75x124in) s.d.1643. 9-Apr-3 Christie's, London #58/R est:15000-20000
Works on paper
£850 $1335 €1275 Girl reading a book (12x10cm-5x4in) i.verso black chk ink wash htd white sold painting. 13-Dec-2 Christie's, Kensington #302/R

BLOEMEN, Jan Frans van (1662-1749) Flemish
£11538 $17538 €18000 Herding idyll (73x99cm-29x39in) 17-Aug-2 Hans Stahl, Toestorf #132/R est:13000
£13605 $21633 €20000 Bergers dans un paysage italianisant (49x65cm-19x26in) 21-Mar-3 Rieunier, Bailly-Pommery, Mathias, Paris #59/R
£17568 $27405 €26000 Forest landscape with two women before monument (78x58cm-31x23in) 27-Mar-3 Dorotheum, Vienna #26/R est:25000-35000
£48000 $75360 €72000 Extensive river landscape with peasants (123x174cm-48x69in) prov.lit. 11-Dec-2 Christie's, London #109/R est:50000-80000

BLOEMEN, Jan Frans van (attrib) (1662-1749) Flemish
£2097 $3250 €3146 Classical landscape (30x41cm-12x16in) copper pair. 2-Nov-2 North East Auctions, Portsmouth #116/R
£9756 $16000 €14634 Classical landscape with shepherds (135x98cm-53x39in) prov. 29-May-3 Sotheby's, New York #92/R est:10000-15000
Works on paper
£338 $527 €500 Grotte dans un paysage (19x26cm-7x10in) wash over crayon. 31-Mar-3 Piasa, Paris #47

BLOEMEN, Jan Frans van (circle) (1662-1749) Flemish
£6000 $10020 €8700 Classical landscape with figures resting beside a river (55x69cm-22x27in) 8-Jul-3 Sotheby's, Olympia #425/R est:3000-4000
£8000 $12400 €12000 Mountainous river landscape with fishermen and other figures (76x99cm-30x39in) with sig. 30-Oct-2 Christie's, Kensington #108/R est:6000-8000

BLOEMEN, Jan Frans van (studio) (1662-1749) Flemish
£6000 $9360 €9000 Classical landscape with figures resting by stream (48x38cm-19x15in) prov. 10-Apr-3 Sotheby's, London #69/R est:8000

BLOEMEN, Jan Frans van (style) (1662-1749) Flemish
£7792 $12000 €11688 Arcadian landscapes (48x36cm-19x14in) canvas on board pair. 23-Oct-2 Doyle, New York #99/R est:3000-5000

BLOEMEN, Pieter van (1657-1720) Flemish
£1800 $2826 €2700 Cavalry soldiers beside an inn at a field camp (29x32cm-11x13in) mono. 10-Dec-2 Bonhams, New Bond Street #203/R est:2000-3000
£1899 $2943 €3000 Cavalry battle (26x36cm-10x14in) mono. panel lit. 27-Sep-2 Karrenbauer, Konstanz #1605/R est:3000
£3077 $4769 €4800 Shepherd by bridge (40x58cm-16x23in) init. 4-Dec-2 Christie's, Rome #301/R
£3521 $5775 €5105 Busy barn (55x75cm-22x30in) bears mono. 4-Jun-3 Fischer, Luzern #1013/R est:8000-10000 (S.FR 7500)
£9000 $14130 €13500 Peasant and his family with their livestock in a courtyard. Travellers and their livestock (57x79cm-22x31in) pair. 10-Dec-2 Bonhams, New Bond Street #219/R est:10000-15000
£22152 $35000 €35000 Landscapes with shepherds (67x82cm-26x32in) pair. 2-Dec-2 Finarte, Milan #155/R est:45000

BLOEMEN, Pieter van (attrib) (1657-1720) Flemish
£850 $1318 €1275 Gypsy encampment (44x54cm-17x21in) 6-Dec-2 Lyon & Turnbull, Edinburgh #13/R
£2000 $3120 €3000 Landscape with soldiers making camp beside a road (43x54cm-17x21in) init. 8-Apr-3 Sotheby's, Olympia #174/R est:1500-2000
£5500 $9185 €7975 Military encampment with figures cooking in the foreground (48x56cm-19x22in) init.d.1702. 11-Jul-3 Christie's, Kensington #113/R est:2000-3000

BLOEMERS, Arnoldus (c.1786-1844) Dutch
£1899 $2962 €3000 Still life with grapes and a white rose on a marble plinth (20x20cm-8x8in) mono. 21-Oct-2 Glerum, Amsterdam #188/R est:3000-5000
£4573 $7500 €6631 Fruit and acorn on a wooden ledge (35x32cm-14x13in) mono. 4-Jun-3 Christie's, Rockefeller NY #256/R est:6000-8000
£16774 $26000 €25161 Still life with assorted flowers (49x40cm-19x16in) init. prov. 29-Oct-2 Sotheby's, New York #38/R est:30000-40000
£27465 $45592 €39000 Still life with flowers, fruit and vegetables (65x54cm-26x21in) mono. canvas on canvas. 14-Jun-3 Arnold, Frankfurt #707/R est:9000

BLOHM, Roy (1922-1995) Norwegian
£1448 $2346 €2172 A secret (81x100cm-32x39in) s. s.i.verso panel exhib. 26-May-3 Grev Wedels Plass, Oslo #68/R est:20000-30000 (N.KR 16000)

BLOIS, François B de (1829-1913) Canadian
£3045 $4750 €4568 Village of Clermount at sunrise (64x109cm-25x43in) s. 12-Oct-2 Neal Auction Company, New Orleans #146/R est:5000-7000

BLOKLAND, Mathilde van (1851-1917) Belgian?
£471 $772 €650 Nature morte aux huitres et aux moules (45x67cm-18x26in) s. 27-May-3 Campo & Campo, Antwerp #233

BLOM, Gerhard (1866-1930) Danish

£559 $888 €839 Silver birches on the shore, frosty evening (80x102cm-31x40in) s.d.1917. 5-Mar-3 Rasmussen, Copenhagen #2055/R (D.KR 6000)

BLOM, Jan (1622-1685) Dutch

£11000 $17270 €16500 Courtyard of an Italianate villa with hunting party, and coach and four (68x63cm-27x25in) bears sig.d.1654. 12-Dec-2 Sotheby's, London #168/R est:8000-12000

BLOM, Willem Adriaan (1927-) South African

£295 $460 €443 Fruit on a table (50x75cm-20x30in) s.d.63 board. 15-Oct-2 Stephan Welz, Johannesburg #207 est:1500-2000 (SA.R 4800)
£305 $483 €458 Fruit on a table (47x58cm-19x23in) s.d.59 board. 1-Apr-3 Stephan Welz, Johannesburg #498 est:3000-5000 (SA.R 3800)
£344 $554 €516 Still life with fruit and a table (49x74cm-19x29in) s.d.63 board. 12-May-3 Stephan Welz, Johannesburg #378 est:2000-4000 (SA.R 4000)

BLOMFIELD, Charles (1848-1926) New Zealander

£242 $373 €363 Northland coastal landscape (24x33cm-9x13in) s. canvas on board. 4-Sep-2 Dunbar Sloane, Wellington #113/R (NZ.D 800)
£421 $669 €632 Kauri tree (29x24cm-11x9in) indis sig. board. 25-Feb-3 Peter Webb, Auckland #82 est:1500-2500 (NZ.D 1200)
£424 $653 €636 Rata and Nikau, Kaipara Coast (21x28cm-8x11in) s.d.1912 board. 4-Sep-2 Dunbar Sloane, Wellington #114 est:600-1200 (NZ.D 1400)
£573 $900 €860 Kauri tree (28x24cm-11x9in) s. board. 10-Dec-2 Peter Webb, Auckland #93/R est:2500-3000 (NZ.D 1800)
£789 $1232 €1184 Lake Te Anau (20x32cm-8x13in) s.d.1891. 27-Mar-3 International Art Centre, Auckland #143/R (NZ.D 2250)
£807 $1259 €1211 Near Greymouth (29x39cm-11x15in) board. 27-Mar-3 International Art Centre, Auckland #74/R (NZ.D 2300)
£1216 $1897 €1824 Halt on the road, with riverbed and mountains, Otago (30x40cm-12x16in) s.d.1881. 17-Sep-2 Peter Webb, Auckland #152/R est:6000-8000 (NZ.D 4000)
£1232 $2033 €1786 Buller Gorge (59x48cm-23x19in) s.d.1901 board. 1-Jul-3 Peter Webb, Auckland #77/R est:4000-6000 (NZ.D 3500)
£1368 $2134 €2052 Views of the Rangitikei Tokorangi. Silverwater (29x39cm-11x15in) s.d.1889 board pair. 17-Sep-2 Peter Webb, Auckland #153/R est:6000-8000 (NZ.D 4500)
£1378 $2219 €2067 Lion Rock, Piha, with two horseriders on beach (17x29cm-7x11in) s. 7-May-3 Dunbar Sloane, Auckland #33/R est:4500-6500 (NZ.D 3900)
£1404 $2189 €2106 Ngapuke Rapids Wanganui River (34x52cm-13x20in) s. 27-Mar-3 International Art Centre, Auckland #116/R est:5000-7000 (NZ.D 4000)
£1754 $2737 €2631 Champagne Geyser (46x30cm-18x12in) s.d.1908 board. 27-Mar-3 International Art Centre, Auckland #102/R est:7000-10000 (NZ.D 5000)
£1899 $2981 €2849 Shipwrecked (43x66cm-17x26in) prov. 25-Nov-2 Peter Webb, Auckland #11/R est:9000-13000 (NZ.D 6000)
£2105 $3284 €3158 Roadless north (75x51cm-30x20in) s.i. on stretcher. 27-Mar-3 International Art Centre, Auckland #112/R est:10000-15000 (NZ.D 6000)
£2158 $3366 €3237 Hohono Peaks, West Coast road (40x30cm-16x12in) s. board. 27-Mar-3 International Art Centre, Auckland #115/R est:7000-10000 (NZ.D 6150)
£2465 $4067 €3574 Piha Beach and Lion Rock (21x36cm-8x14in) s. board. 1-Jul-3 Peter Webb, Auckland #98/R est:4000-5000 (NZ.D 7000)
£2821 $4401 €4232 Green Stone River, Lake Wakatipu (45x65cm-18x26in) s. 7-Nov-2 International Art Centre, Auckland #135/R est:10000-16000 (NZ.D 9000)
£3158 $4926 €4737 View from the bottom of the White Terraces, Rotomahana (39x60cm-15x24in) s.d.1906. 27-Mar-3 International Art Centre, Auckland #103/R est:12000-18000 (NZ.D 9000)
£3762 $5868 €5643 White terraces, Rotomahana (40x60cm-16x24in) s.d.1907. 7-Nov-2 International Art Centre, Auckland #78/R est:12000-18000 (NZ.D 12000)
£6944 $10833 €10416 Piha (45x91cm-18x36in) s.d.1904. 8-Apr-3 Peter Webb, Auckland #79/R est:12000-18000 (NZ.D 20000)
£12539 $19561 €18809 Tourists visiting the pink terraces of Rotomahana (71x102cm-28x40in) s.d.1905. 7-Nov-2 International Art Centre, Auckland #74/R est:35000-50000 (NZ.D 40000)

BLOMFIELD, Charles (attrib) (1848-1926) New Zealander

£244 $373 €366 Lake Terraces (34x43cm-13x17in) 21-Aug-2 Dunbar Sloane, Auckland #100 (NZ.D 800)

BLOMMAERT, Maximilian (attrib) (17/18th C) Flemish

£4610 $7699 €6500 Cascade dans un paysage anime de paysans et de promeneurs (116x158cm-46x62in) 18-Jun-3 Tajan, Paris #74/R est:8000-10000

BLOMME, Alphonse-Joseph (1889-1979) Belgian

£252 $387 €400 Portrait of farmer (70x62cm-28x24in) s. panel. 22-Oct-2 Campo & Campo, Antwerp #16
£297 $469 €460 Vue de village (70x79cm-28x31in) s. panel. 17-Dec-2 Palais de Beaux Arts, Brussels #461
£303 $486 €440 Harbour (45x60cm-18x24in) s. panel. 15-Mar-3 De Vuyst, Lokeren #28
£353 $546 €550 Snowy landscape (59x69cm-23x27in) s. panel. 7-Dec-2 De Vuyst, Lokeren #30
£795 $1295 €1200 Portrait de famille avec enfants a la mer du Nord (133x141cm-52x56in) s.d.1921. 17-Feb-3 Horta, Bruxelles #118
£797 $1307 €1100 Vue a Venise (31x33cm-12x13in) s. 27-May-3 Campo & Campo, Antwerp #32
£1325 $2159 €2000 Portrait de famille sur fond de paysage (133x141cm-52x56in) s.d.1921. 17-Feb-3 Horta, Bruxelles #119
£1987 $3238 €3000 Mer (132x390cm-52x154in) s. 17-Feb-3 Horta, Bruxelles #115/R
£2119 $3454 €3200 Attente (132x140cm-52x55in) s.i.d.1921. 17-Feb-3 Horta, Bruxelles #116/R
£2384 $3886 €3600 Aube (132x140cm-52x55in) s. 17-Feb-3 Horta, Bruxelles #117/R est:3500

BLOMMENDAEL, Reyer Jacobsz van (?-1675) Dutch

£30405 $47432 €45000 Messenger with crown of Saul before David (227x226cm-89x89in) bears sig. lit. 27-Mar-3 Dorotheum, Vienna #302/R est:25000-35000

BLOMMER, Edla (1817-1908) Finnish

£1076 $1678 €1700 The young man (28x21cm-11x8in) s.verso. 15-Sep-2 Bukowskis, Helsinki #164/R est:300

BLOMMER, Nils Jakob Olsson (1816-1853) Swedish

£2412 $3666 €3618 Small girl giving milk to young goat (39x29cm-15x11in) s. panel. 27-Aug-2 Rasmussen, Copenhagen #1904/R est:30000-40000 (D.KR 28000)
£4085 $6699 €5923 Young girl by balustrade (37x30cm-15x12in) s.d.1845. 4-Jun-3 AB Stockholms Auktionsverk #2277/R est:20000-25000 (S.KR 52000)

BLOMMERS (?) Dutch

Works on paper

£9000 $14220 €13050 Shore scene with numerous figures and sailing vessels (36x48cm-14x19in) s. W/C. 23-Jul-3 Brightwells, Leominster #924 est:200-400

BLOMMERS, Bernardus Johannes (1845-1914) Dutch

£1447 $2345 €2200 Digging in the dunes (21x27cm-8x11in) s. panel. 21-Jan-3 Christie's, Amsterdam #214/R est:3000-5000
£1842 $2984 €2800 Shellfisher going home (19x26cm-7x10in) s. panel. 21-Jan-3 Christie's, Amsterdam #227/R est:2000-3000
£5696 $9000 €8544 Family meal (39x48cm-15x19in) s. 23-Apr-3 Christie's, Rockefeller NY #140y/R est:12000-16000
£6289 $9686 €10000 Peaceful Monet (13x9cm-5x4in) s. panel prov. 22-Oct-2 Sotheby's, Amsterdam #189/R est:10000-15000
£6690 $10771 €9500 Mother and child (40x32cm-16x13in) s. panel. 7-May-3 Vendue Huis, Gravenhage #443/R est:10000-12000
£12766 $20681 €18000 Housework in the courtyard of a farmhouse (43x34cm-17x13in) s. 22-May-3 Dorotheum, Vienna #53/R est:6500-7500
£13000 $20410 €19500 Children at the beach (77x54cm-30x21in) s. 19-Nov-2 Sotheby's, London #168/R est:15000-20000
£31000 $48670 €46500 Shell fisherman (36x51cm-14x20in) s. 19-Nov-2 Sotheby's, London #169/R est:20000-30000
£76389 $121458 €110000 Playing in the surf (47x62cm-19x24in) s. 29-Apr-3 Christie's, Amsterdam #126/R est:30000-50000

Works on paper

£2166 $3400 €3249 Bij de Wieg (10x8cm-4x3in) s. W/C prov. 10-Dec-2 Doyle, New York #189/R est:3000-4000
£5346 $8233 €8500 Happy mother (23x28cm-9x11in) s. W/C. 22-Oct-2 Sotheby's, Amsterdam #95/R est:7000-8000

BLOMMERS, Bernardus Johannes (attrib) (1845-1914) Dutch

£4063 $6500 €6095 Mother and her children by a window (41x51cm-16x20in) s. 14-May-3 Butterfields, San Francisco #1060/R est:3000-5000

BLOMMESTEIN, Louise Alice (1882-1965) Dutch
£1274 $1987 €2000 Nude standing in the middle of white lilies (159x79cm-63x31in) s.d.1907. 6-Nov-2 Vendue Huis, Gravenhage #660/R est:600-800

BLOMSTEDT, Juhana (1937-) Finnish
£1620 $2608 €2300 Dondo (100x81cm-39x32in) s.d.87 verso. 10-May-3 Bukowskis, Helsinki #247/R est:1800-2000

BLOMSTEDT, Vaino (1871-1947) Finnish
£1079 $1770 €1500 From Aaland, Saltvik (75x59cm-30x23in) s. 5-Jun-3 Hagelstam, Helsinki #944/R est:2000
£1835 $2900 €2900 Elk among silver birches on shore (51x120cm-20x47in) s.d.37. 1-Dec-2 Bukowskis, Helsinki #30/R est:2000-2500
£1887 $2906 €3000 Winter (40x59cm-16x23in) s. 24-Oct-2 Hagelstam, Helsinki #1032 est:2000
£1899 $3000 €3000 Children playing at water's edge (80x116cm-31x46in) s,. 1-Dec-2 Bukowskis, Helsinki #29/R est:2000-2500
£2911 $4600 €4600 Sunday in summer in the park (90x83cm-35x33in) s. 1-Dec-2 Bukowskis, Helsinki #28/R est:4500-5000
£8228 $13000 €13000 Beach idyll (59x91cm-23x36in) s.d.1927. 30-Nov-2 Hagelstam, Helsinki #136/R est:8000
Works on paper
£1223 $1957 €1700 Fagervik, church boats (43x58cm-17x23in) s.d.1928 mixed media board. 17-May-3 Hagelstam, Helsinki #137/R est:2000

BLOND, Maurice (1899-1974) French
£500 $810 €725 Circus (46x33cm-18x13in) s. board. 23-May-3 Dee Atkinson & Harrison, Driffield #653/R

BLONDAL, Gunnlaugur (1893-1962) Icelandic
Works on paper
£651 $1028 €977 Houses in village, Iceland (61x46cm-24x18in) gouache chk. 1-Apr-3 Rasmussen, Copenhagen #591/R (D.KR 7000)

BLONDEL, Andre (?) French?
£340 $541 €500 Nature morte et l'arbre (25x21cm-10x8in) studio st. cardboard double-sided painted c.1936 prov. 26-Feb-3 Artcurial Briest, Paris #182
£408 $649 €600 La plage (32x20cm-13x8in) paper prov. 26-Feb-3 Artcurial Briest, Paris #179
£490 $779 €720 La pose (28x22cm-11x9in) studio st. oil gouache prov. 26-Feb-3 Artcurial Briest, Paris #175
£1122 $1785 €1650 Portrait du peintre Simone Julienne (70x50cm-28x20in) s. painted c.1948 prov.exhib. 26-Feb-3 Artcurial Briest, Paris #174 est:1500-1800
£1463 $2326 €2150 Nature morte au portrait (60x50cm-24x20in) s.d.45 prov. 26-Feb-3 Artcurial Briest, Paris #180/R est:1800-2000
£1887 $2925 €3000 Le pose (41x33cm-16x13in) s. painted c.1948 prov.lit. 30-Oct-2 Artcurial Briest, Paris #5 est:1000-1200
Works on paper
£408 $649 €600 Promenade au jardin (21x25cm-8x10in) s. gouache oil prov. 26-Feb-3 Artcurial Briest, Paris #176

BLONDEL, Émile (1893-1970) French
£769 $1192 €1200 Bouquet de fleurs (55x46cm-22x18in) s.d.1961. 5-Dec-2 Gros & Delettrez, Paris #25
£828 $1308 €1200 Bouquet devant la plage (46x55cm-18x22in) s.d.1957. 4-Apr-3 Tajan, Paris #30
£900 $1476 €1350 Strolling on a summer's day (32x23cm-13x9in) s. panel. 5-Jun-3 Christie's, Kensington #705/R
£2759 $4358 €4000 Lapin Agile (46x65cm-18x26in) s. 4-Apr-3 Tajan, Paris #109
£2759 $4358 €4000 Bouquinistes (46x54cm-18x21in) s.d.1951. 4-Apr-3 Tajan, Paris #105/R

BLONDEL, Merry Joseph (1781-1853) French
£1282 $1987 €2000 Allegory of Music (25cm-10in circular) paper on cardboard. 6-Dec-2 Rieunier, Bailly-Pommery, Mathias, Paris #49/R
Works on paper
£420 $600 €630 Study for a wall or ceiling decoration with attributes of the arts (32x26cm-13x10in) pen ink wash. 23-Jan-3 Swann Galleries, New York #299/R

BLONDIN, Charles (?) French
£548 $866 €850 Moulin Rouge (27x34cm-11x13in) s. 17-Dec-2 Durán, Madrid #134/R

BLOOD, Brian (20th C) American
£964 $1600 €1398 Monterey Harbour (23x30cm-9x12in) init. i.verso canvasboard. 11-Jun-3 Butterfields, San Francisco #4339/R est:2000-3000

BLOOD, Gerry (20th C) British
£300 $489 €435 On the Gower (69x89cm-27x35in) s. 16-Jul-3 Anthemion, Cardiff #941
£600 $936 €900 Port Einon, Gower Peninsular (70x89cm-28x35in) s. 11-Sep-2 Bonhams, Newport #414

BLOOMER, H (?) ?
£962 $1500 €1443 Russian river (36x51cm-14x20in) s. 21-Sep-2 Harvey Clar, Oakland #1397

BLOOMER, Hiram R (1845-1910) American
£994 $1600 €1491 Pond landscape (20x38cm-8x15in) s. prov. 18-Feb-3 John Moran, Pasadena #52a est:1200-1800
£2329 $3750 €3494 Landscape (25x46cm-10x18in) s. d.1904 verso board prov. 18-Feb-3 John Moran, Pasadena #40c est:2500-3000

BLOOMFIELD, Harry (1870-?) British
Works on paper
£719 $1180 €1000 Ballerine de dos (56x44cm-22x17in) s.d. pastel. 5-Jun-3 Fraysse & Associes, Paris #19

BLOOMFIELD, John (1950-) Australian
£429 $669 €644 Lighthouse, Vaucluse (76x76cm-30x30in) s. s.i.verso. 11-Nov-2 Deutscher-Menzies, Melbourne #153/R (A.D 1200)

BLOOT, Pieter de (1602-1658) Dutch
£5732 $8943 €9000 Utrecht, the mariakerk with travellers, pilgrims and beggars outside the city wall (34x47cm-13x19in) mono.d.16 panel prov.exhib.lit. 5-Nov-2 Sotheby's, Amsterdam #15/R est:10000-15000
£6000 $9420 €9000 Dune landscape with bandits ambushing travellers in wagons (36x53cm-14x21in) s.d.1636 panel prov. 13-Dec-2 Christie's, Kensington #46/R est:6000-8000

BLOOT, Pieter de (attrib) (1602-1658) Dutch
£900 $1395 €1350 Peasants brawling outside a tavern (31x49cm-12x19in) panel. 30-Oct-2 Bonhams, New Bond Street #120/R
£2500 $4175 €3625 Peasants eating mussels and drinking in a tavern (44x36cm-17x14in) panel. 11-Jul-3 Christie's, Kensington #73/R est:3000-5000
£5282 $8768 €7500 Patineurs sur une riviere gelee pres d'un moulin (38x51cm-15x20in) panel oval. 16-Jun-3 Claude Aguttes, Neuilly #22/R est:7000-8000

BLOPPOEL, Antoon van (1879-1971) Dutch
£300 $477 €450 Meadow (60x49cm-24x19in) s. 9-Mar-3 Lots Road, London #355/R

BLOS, Carl (1860-1941) German
£2405 $3800 €3800 Portrait of a girl in national costume next to peonies (90x100cm-35x39in) s. 28-Nov-2 Dorotheum, Vienna #225/R est:4500-4800

BLOSSFELDT, Karl (1865-1932) German
Photographs
£10127 $16000 €16000 Equisetum Hiemale (13x18cm-5x7in) i. verso silver gelatin lit.exhib. 28-Nov-2 Villa Grisebach, Berlin #1109/R est:15000-25000
£22152 $35000 €35000 Ascepias Syriaca (30x24cm-12x9in) i. verso silver gelatin lit.exhib. 28-Nov-2 Villa Grisebach, Berlin #1110/R est:25000-45000
£26000 $42120 €39000 Rhamnus Purshiana, Buchthorn, Kreuzdorngewachs Junger Spross (29x24cm-11x9in) init.i. gelatin silver print exec.c.1920 prov.lit. 21-May-3 Christie's, London #119/R est:30000-35000

BLOSSOM, Christopher (1956-) American
£7792 $12000 €11688 Downeaster A.G Ropes departing New York (46x61cm-18x24in) 25-Oct-2 Morris & Whiteside, Hilton Head Island #104 est:12000-15000

BLOSSOM, David (1927-1995) American
Works on paper
£897 $1400 €1346 Couple in evening dress, Ford Galaxie 500 waiting at curb (36x66cm-14x26in) gouache board executed c.1961. 9-Nov-2 Illustration House, New York #125/R

BLOT, Jacques Émile (1885-1960) French
£253 $395 €400 Portrait du tenor Koubistky (52x32cm-20x13in) s.d. 18-Oct-2 Rabourdin & Choppin de Janvry, Paris #12

BLOUET, Abel (1795-1853) French
Works on paper
£709 $1184 €1000 Projet de restauration du temple d'Aphaia a Egine (13x18cm-5x7in) pencil W/C. 23-Jun-3 Beaussant & Lefèvre, Paris #67

BLOW, Sandra (1925-) British
£750 $1163 €1125 Untitled (91x68cm-36x27in) 3-Dec-2 Bonhams, Knightsbridge #293/R
£2200 $3388 €3300 Patines of bright (122x142cm-48x56in) s.d.98 overlap acrylic exhib. 5-Sep-2 Christie's, Kensington #755/R est:2500-3500
Works on paper
£340 $541 €510 Untitled (10x10cm-4x4in) s.d.2002 W/C. 18-Mar-3 Bonhams, Knightsbridge #32
£350 $578 €508 Abstract (9x9cm-4x4in) s.d.02 felt tip pen W/C. 3-Jul-3 Christie's, Kensington #742
£800 $1248 €1200 Untitled abstract (66x66cm-26x26in) s.d.88 s.d.verso collage. 25-Mar-3 Bonhams, New Bond Street #123/R
£1000 $1560 €1500 Untitled abstract (66x66cm-26x26in) s.d.88 s.i.verso collage. 25-Mar-3 Bonhams, New Bond Street #124/R est:800-1200
£7300 $11315 €10950 Collage (127x101cm-50x40in) chl oil paper on canvas exhib. 4-Dec-2 Christie's, Kensington #621/R est:3000-5000

BLUEMNER, Oscar (1867-1938) American
£245161 $380000 €367742 In low key (60x85cm-24x33in) s. panel prov.exhib.lit. 5-Dec-2 Christie's, Rockefeller NY #201/R est:250000-350000
£258065 $400000 €387098 Triad brilliant, Passaic river hills (57x75cm-22x30in) s. panel prov.exhib. 5-Dec-2 Christie's, Rockefeller NY #142/R est:500000-700000
Works on paper
£244 $400 €354 Canal Newark (13x20cm-5x8in) mono.i.d.Nov 5 13 crayon. 1-Jun-3 Wright, Chicago #199/R
£488 $800 €708 View at Soho-Bloomfield (12x15cm-5x6in) init.i.d.17 pencil black crayon. 5-Jun-3 Swann Galleries, New York #52/R
£2287 $3750 €3316 Oaks pond and two drawing of Bloomfield Lock (13x15cm-5x6in) s.i.d.1922 chl. 1-Jun-3 Wright, Chicago #200/R est:2500-3500
£3313 $5500 €4804 Red barn (8x10cm-3x4in) d.1920 verso gouache prov. 11-Jun-3 Boos Gallery, Michigan #349/R est:6000-8000
£7742 $12000 €11613 Untitled - red barn (13x17cm-5x7in) i.verso gouache paper on board prov. 4-Dec-2 Sotheby's, New York #74/R est:15000-25000
£135802 $220000 €203703 Silver moon (34x25cm-13x10in) mono.d.1927 s.i.d.verso W/C gouache paper on board prov.exhib.lit. 21-May-3 Sotheby's, New York #1/R est:60000-80000

BLUHM, Norman (1920-) American
£667 $1107 €967 Clotho II (76x170cm-30x67in) i.d.1971 acrylic on paper. 10-Jun-3 Ritchie, Toronto #100/R est:1800-2200 (C.D 1500)
£903 $1435 €1300 Fresco no 19 (126x106cm-50x42in) s.d.87 verso acrylic paper on canvas prov. 29-Apr-3 Artcurial Briest, Paris #555 est:700-900
Works on paper
£750 $1223 €1125 Abstract composition (61x50cm-24x20in) s.d.62 W/C. 3-Feb-3 Bonhams, New Bond Street #83/R

BLUHM, Oscar (19/20th C) German
Works on paper
£1200 $1908 €1800 Elegant society (42x31cm-17x12in) s. gouache. 20-Mar-3 Christie's, Kensington #114/R est:1500-2000

BLUM, Jerome S (1884-1956) American
£4268 $7000 €6189 Still life with eggplant (51x66cm-20x26in) s.d.1920 exhib. 1-Jun-3 Wright, Chicago #194/R est:9000-12000

BLUM, Karl (1888-?) German
£314 $491 €500 Evening on the old Rhine (90x80cm-35x31in) s. s.i. verso. 11-Oct-2 Winterberg, Heidelberg #878/R

BLUM, Ludwig (1891-1975) Israeli
£2600 $4004 €3900 Ronda (45x37cm-18x15in) s.i.d.1922 prov. 23-Oct-2 Sotheby's, Olympia #626/R est:2500-3500

BLUM, Maurice (1832-1909) French
£742 $1158 €1113 Interior with girl cleaning (21x13cm-8x5in) s. masonite. 6-Nov-2 Dobiaschofsky, Bern #358/R est:3500 (S.FR 1700)

BLUM, Robert Frederick (1857-1903) American
Works on paper
£629 $1000 €944 Portrait of J f Huffington, or Washington (25x20cm-10x8in) s.indis.i.d. pencil dr. 2-Mar-3 Toomey, Oak Park #604/R
£1951 $3200 €2829 Four leaf clover (12x23cm-5x9in) s.i.d. brush ink gouache card stock. 5-Jun-3 Swann Galleries, New York #53/R est:1000-1500

BLUM, Thierry (20th C) French
Sculpture
£1419 $2214 €2100 Direct du gauche (47x54x84cm-19x21x33in) s.d.2002 num.2/8 brown pat bronze. 26-Mar-3 Millon & Associes, Paris #177/R

BLUME, Bernhard Johannes (1937-) German
£1090 $1689 €1700 Nature (60x40cm-24x16in) s.d.68 s.d. stretcher acrylic. 3-Dec-2 Lempertz, Koln #59/R est:1800

BLUME-SIEBERT, Ludwig (1853-1929) German
£2055 $3205 €3000 Visiting grandfather (26x20cm-10x8in) s. panel. 10-Apr-3 Dorotheum, Vienna #22/R est:2600-2800

BLUMENFELD, Erwin (20th C) ?
Photographs
£4545 $7000 €6818 Untitled, Paris (34x27cm-13x11in) st.i.verso solarized gelatin silver print prov.lit. 25-Oct-2 Phillips, New York #93/R est:6000-9000

BLUMENSCHEIN, Ernest L (1874-1960) American
£2987 $4750 €4481 New Mexico afternoon (15x18cm-6x7in) s.d.1912 panel prov. 5-Mar-3 Sotheby's, New York #136/R est:8000-12000
£15287 $24000 €22931 Taos landscape. Three windmills (46x56cm-18x22in) s. i.verso board double-sided. 10-Dec-2 Doyle, New York #130/R est:14000-18000
£16667 $26000 €25001 Starving man and wolf in desolate landscape (76x48cm-30x19in) s. lit. 9-Nov-2 Illustration House, New York #163/R est:18000-24000

BLUMENTHAL, Hermann (1905-1942) German
Sculpture
£1549 $2572 €2200 Three boys (59x33x2cm-23x13x1in) bronze relief. 14-Jun-3 Hauswedell & Nolte, Hamburg #1045/R est:1800

BLUNCK, Ditlev Conrad (1798-1853) Danish
£426 $672 €639 Portrait of boy (32x29cm-13x11in) 2-Dec-2 Rasmussen, Copenhagen #1275/R (D.KR 5000)
£466 $740 €699 Portrait of the author Christian Winther (48x38cm-19x15in) s.i.d.1830. 5-Mar-3 Rasmussen, Copenhagen #1677/R (D.KR 5000)

BLUNCK-HEIKENDORF, Heinrich (1891-1963) German
£1923 $2981 €3000 Autumn landscape (58x68cm-23x27in) s.d.27 i. verso. 5-Dec-2 Schopman, Hamburg #611 est:3600

BLUNDELL, Alfred Richard (1883-1968) British
£440 $682 €660 Bowl of wild flowers (50x61cm-20x24in) s.d.52 board. 30-Sep-2 Bonhams, Ipswich #366

BLUNT, J H (19th C) British?
£340 $530 €510 Bull Point Lighthouse and Torris Peak (28x48cm-11x19in) s. 17-Sep-2 Bonhams, Oxford #34

BLUVERTIGO, Andy (1971-) Italian
£2411 $3906 €3400 Occasioni (90x90cm-35x35in) s. acrylic. 20-May-3 Porro, Milan #1/R est:3500-3700

BLYHOOFT, Jacques Zacharias (17th C) Dutch
Works on paper
£1000 $1670 €1450 Mountainous landscape with peasants on a track in the foreground (17x15cm-7x6in) s.d.1679 pen brown ink wash prov.exhib. 9-Jul-3 Sotheby's, London #98/R est:1400-1800

BLYK, Frans Jacobus van den (1806-1876) Dutch
£692 $1079 €1100 Figures on frozen river (41x54cm-16x21in) s. 9-Oct-2 Michael Zeller, Lindau #632/R
£4545 $6773 €7000 Seascape (61x83cm-24x33in) s.d.1873. 26-Jun-2 Neumeister, Munich #687/R est:2800

BLYTH, Robert Henderson (1919-1970) British

£700 $1092 €1050 Potted plant (75x62cm-30x24in) s. 10-Apr-3 Bonhams, Edinburgh #20

£3600 $5616 €5400 Catalonian shadows (76x63cm-30x25in) s. exhib. 17-Oct-2 Bonhams, Edinburgh #54/R est:800-1200

£7000 $11340 €10500 Paris window (76x60cm-30x24in) s. board exhib. 23-May-3 Lyon & Turnbull, Edinburgh #30/R est:2000-3000

Works on paper

£450 $702 €675 Drying nets (21x23cm-8x9in) s. ink W/C. 10-Apr-3 Bonhams, Edinburgh #27

BLYTHE, David Gilmour (1815-1865) American

£17610 $28000 €26415 Family prayers. Sequel (46x56cm-18x22in) s. pair prov.exhib.lit. 4-Mar-3 Christie's, Rockefeller NY #9/R est:15000-20000

BO, Giacinto (1832-1912) Italian

£1837 $2920 €2700 Source of the Po (54x92cm-21x36in) s. cardboard. 1-Mar-3 Meeting Art, Vercelli #99

£2721 $4327 €4000 From the cliffs (65x124cm-26x49in) s. 1-Mar-3 Meeting Art, Vercelli #232

BOAK, Robert Creswell (1875-?) Irish

Works on paper

£380 $589 €570 Rocks on the County Antrim coast (63x99cm-25x39in) s. W/C. 4-Dec-2 John Ross, Belfast #22

BOBAK, Bruno (1923-) Canadian

£413 $649 €620 Near Millville, Quebec (30x41cm-12x16in) s.i. s.verso. 24-Jul-2 Walker's, Ottawa #253/R est:500-700 (C.D 1000)

£578 $948 €867 Alders and blackbirds (55x75cm-22x30in) s. 3-Jun-3 Joyner, Toronto #395/R est:2000-3000 (C.D 1300)

£667 $1093 €1001 Springtime (30x40cm-12x16in) s. prov. 3-Jun-3 Joyner, Toronto #359/R est:800-1200 (C.D 1500)

£723 $1135 €1085 Northern Port (41x61cm-16x24in) s.i. s.verso. 24-Jul-2 Walker's, Ottawa #405/R est:1800-2400 (C.D 1750)

£868 $1362 €1302 Late summer evening (76x102cm-30x40in) i. s.verso. 24-Jul-2 Walker's, Ottawa #411/R est:3000-3500 (C.D 2100)

BOBAK, Molly Lamb (1922-) Canadian

£448 $717 €672 Art school still life (61x50cm-24x20in) s.d.1955 board. 15-May-3 Heffel, Vancouver #43 est:1200-1600 (C.D 1000)

£482 $761 €723 Anemones (28x18cm-11x7in) canvasboard. 1-Dec-2 Levis, Calgary #10/R (C.D 1200)

£741 $1148 €1112 Horse show (17x27cm-7x11in) s. s.d.1988 verso canvasboard. 3-Dec-2 Joyner, Toronto #120/R est:1200-1500 (C.D 1800)

£957 $1492 €1595 Late poppies (20x13cm-8x5in) s. canvasboard prov. 13-Apr-3 Levis, Calgary #8/R est:1500-2000 (C.D 2200)

£1076 $1722 €1614 Saint John (30x41cm-12x16in) s.i.verso board. 15-May-3 Heffel, Vancouver #160/R est:2500-3000 (C.D 2400)

£2444 $4009 €3666 Rue de Seine, Paris (60x50cm-24x20in) s.d.52 board. 3-Jun-3 Joyner, Toronto #136/R est:6000-8000 (C.D 5500)

Works on paper

£267 $437 €387 Untitled - pansies (18x13cm-7x5in) W/C. 1-Jun-3 Levis, Calgary #18 (C.D 600)

£578 $948 €838 Anemones (50x40cm-20x16in) s. W/C. 9-Jun-3 Hodgins, Calgary #22/R est:1200-1500 (C.D 1300)

£667 $1093 €1001 Still life (46x37cm-18x15in) s. W/C. 3-Jun-3 Joyner, Toronto #396/R est:1500-2000 (C.D 1500)

BOBELDIJK, F (1876-1964) Dutch

£3901 $6319 €5500 Le marche a Amsterdam (67x93cm-26x37in) 26-May-3 Amberes, Antwerp #19

BOBELDIJK, Felicien (1876-1964) Dutch

£255 $397 €400 Souvenirs d'un Cotillon (74x99cm-29x39in) s. prov.exhib. 6-Nov-2 Vendue Huis, Gravenhage #581/R

BOBERG, Anna (1864-1935) Swedish

£1844 $2858 €2766 Blue mountains, Lofoten (65x100cm-26x39in) s. exhib. 3-Dec-2 Bukowskis, Stockholm #95/R est:30000-40000 (S.KR 26000)

BOBERG, Jorgen (1940-) Swedish

£296 $461 €444 Mountain landscape early morning (38x30cm-15x12in) masonite. 18-Sep-2 Kunsthallen, Copenhagen #90 (D.KR 3500)

Works on paper

£1524 $2362 €2286 Surrealistic animal compositions. Indian ink Indian ink six sold with box prov. 1-Oct-2 Rasmussen, Copenhagen #211/R est:20000 (D.KR 18000)

BOBLETER, Franz Xaver (attrib) (1808-1869) Austrian

£314 $491 €500 Maria (62x47cm-24x19in) i. verso. 23-Sep-2 Dr Fritz Nagel, Stuttgart #6915/R

BOCARIC, Spiro (1878-1941) Austrian

£1956 $3052 €2934 By the well (110x85cm-43x33in) s. 11-Apr-3 Kieselbach, Budapest #128/R est:700000 (H.F 700000)

£2313 $3678 €3400 Farming girl from Serbia (53x43cm-21x17in) 25-Feb-3 Dorotheum, Vienna #217/R est:1800-2000

BOCCACCINO, Boccaccio (style) (c.1467-c.1524) Italian

£5033 $8104 €7500 Madonna and Child (34x26cm-13x10in) panel prov.lit. 18-Feb-3 Sotheby's, Amsterdam #191/R est:2000-3000

BOCCALARO, Domenico (attrib) (fl.1490-1510) Italian

Sculpture

£12000 $18840 €18000 Figure of St. Sebastian (116cm-46in) lit. 10-Dec-2 Sotheby's, London #48/R est:8000-12000

BOCCHINO, Vincent (19/20th C) Italian

£6377 $10458 €8800 Le retour du marche (65x47cm-26x19in) s.d.1911. 27-May-3 Artcurial Briest, Paris #96/R est:6000-7000

BOCCIA, Edward E (1921-) American

£385 $600 €578 Self portrait with pink beret (124x104cm-49x41in) s.d.1956 exhib. 10-Nov-2 Selkirks, St. Louis #744/R

BOCCIONI, Umberto (1882-1916) Italian

Prints

£1923 $3019 €3000 Mother sowing (14x11cm-6x4in) s. eau forte aquatint exec.1910 lit. 21-Nov-2 Finarte, Rome #79/R

BOCH, Anna (1848-1933) Belgian

£449 $704 €700 Paysage au bord de l'eau (15x20cm-6x8in) s. panel. 11-Dec-2 Hotel des Ventes Mosan, Brussels #287

£3642 $5937 €5500 Vue de village en fin d'ete (44x54cm-17x21in) s. panel. 17-Feb-3 Horta, Bruxelles #143/R

£4828 $7724 €7000 Promenade en Bretagne (55x51cm-22x20in) s. painted c.1910. 15-Mar-3 De Vuyst, Lokeren #437/R est:7400-8600

£9434 $14623 €15000 Interior (70x60cm-28x24in) s.d.06 exhib. 5-Oct-2 De Vuyst, Lokeren #548/R est:13000-15000

Works on paper

£755 $1162 €1200 Femme assise (20x14cm-8x6in) s.d.1907. 22-Oct-2 Campo, Vlaamse Kaai #415

£922 $1540 €1300 Vue animee (45x38cm-18x15in) s. pastel. 18-Jun-3 Hotel des Ventes Mosan, Brussels #199

BOCHMANN, Gregor von (elder) (1850-1930) German

£823 $1275 €1300 Animals and figures in barn (44x65cm-17x26in) s. canvas on panel. 25-Sep-2 Neumeister, Munich #541/R

£1154 $1812 €1800 Peasant crossing bridge with horse drawn cart (57x81cm-22x32in) s. 20-Nov-2 Dorotheum, Klagenfurt #2/R est:1800

£1295 $2072 €1800 Fishing boats on beach (8x13cm-3x5in) s. one oil one W/C paper two. 17-May-3 Lempertz, Koln #1270 est:1500

£1507 $2351 €2200 Loading ships on Dutch coast (33x44cm-13x17in) s. 10-Apr-3 Van Ham, Cologne #1337/R est:3500

£1795 $2818 €2800 Peasants with horse and cart by village (30x47cm-12x19in) s.d.1879 panel. 21-Nov-2 Van Ham, Cologne #1483/R est:3000

Works on paper

£377 $588 €550 On the mudflats at low tide (9x14cm-4x6in) s.d.08 W/C board. 10-Apr-3 Van Ham, Cologne #1336/R

£504 $806 €700 Summer landscape (8x13cm-3x5in) s.d.97 gouache. 17-May-3 Lempertz, Koln #1271

BOCHMANN, Johann (20th C) German?

£725 $1058 €1088 Autumn wood with lake (60x100cm-24x39in) painted c.1920. 4-Jun-2 SOGA, Bratislava #173/R est:30000 (SL.K 46000)

BOCION, François (1828-1890) Swiss

£1528 $2384 €2292 Boots on Lake Geneva (22x36cm-9x14in) s. W/C over pencil. 8-Nov-2 Dobiaschofsky, Bern #16/R est:4200 (S.FR 3500)

£2153 $3423 €3100 Lac en Suisse (27x36cm-11x14in) s. panel. 30-Apr-3 Tajan, Paris #59/R

£2830 $4585 €5010 Scene de plage a Bordighera (27x41cm-11x16in) paper on board prov. 26-May-3 Sotheby's, Zurich #23/R est:7000-9000 (S.FR 6000)

£4405 $6432 €6608 Lake Geneva near Vevey (42x28cm-17x11in) mono.d.1885 prov. 17-Jun-2 Philippe Schuler, Zurich #4257/R est:12000-15000 (S.FR 10000)

£13194 $21771 €19000 Promeneuse assise pre d'un lac (28x36cm-11x14in) s.d. 1-Jul-3 Rossini, Paris #68/R

£40773 $64421 €61160 Pecheur sur le Denantou (43x70cm-17x28in) s.d.1883 prov.lit. 28-Nov-2 Christie's, Zurich #17/R est:70000-80000 (S.FR 95000)

Works on paper
£873 $1362 €1310 Chateau au clair de lune (19x25cm-7x10in) W/C gouache prov.lit. 8-Nov-2 Dobiaschofsky, Bern #18/R (S.FR 2000)
£1019 $1640 €1529 Study for rider (32x36cm-13x14in) pencil htd. 7-May-3 Dobiaschofsky, Bern #111/R (S.FR 2200)

BOCK, Adolf (1890-1968) Finnish
£1473 $2327 €2210 Three master vessel (50x40cm-20x16in) s.d.1958. 27-Nov-2 Falkkloos, Malmo #77808/R est:30000 (S.KR 21000)
£2109 $3353 €3100 Southern harbour (40x50cm-16x20in) s.d.1936. 24-Mar-3 Bukowskis, Helsinki #38/R est:2000
£3309 $5295 €4600 Morning in the harbour (61x80cm-24x31in) s.d.1927. 17-May-3 Hagelstam, Helsinki #79/R est:4500
Works on paper
£324 $531 €450 Sailing vessel (20x19cm-8x7in) s.d.1950 W/C. 4-Jun-3 Bukowskis, Helsinki #260/R
£331 $543 €460 Stormy seas (21x28cm-8x11in) s.d.1951 gouache. 4-Jun-3 Bukowskis, Helsinki #259/R
£538 $839 €850 Town scene, Helsingborg (60x50cm-24x20in) s.d.1951 gouache. 12-Sep-2 Hagelstam, Helsinki #837
£633 $987 €1000 Seascape with vessel at night (29x23cm-11x9in) s.i.d.24.II.29 gouache. 15-Sep-2 Bukowskis, Helsinki #169/R
£2911 $4600 €4600 Mayflower - ship's portrait (30x40cm-12x16in) s.d.1951 gouache. 1-Dec-2 Bukowskis, Helsinki #31/R est:2500-2800
£3165 $5065 €4400 Southern harbour, Helsingfors (20x27cm-8x11in) s.d.1923 gouache. 17-May-3 Hagelstam, Helsinki #78/R est:2000

BOCK, Adolf Georg Friedrich (1854-1917) German
£685 $1068 €1000 Trouble brewing (40x29cm-16x11in) s. panel. 10-Apr-3 Van Ham, Cologne #1339/R

BOCK, Hansl (1893-1973) German
£423 $680 €600 Sunny morning (45x57cm-18x22in) s. board. 7-May-3 Michael Zeller, Lindau #644/R

BOCK, Ludwig (1886-1955) German
£764 $1192 €1200 Still life of flowers (76x59cm-30x23in) s. 6-Nov-2 Hugo Ruef, Munich #1029/R

BOCK, Ludwig Maria (1905-1983) German
£705 $1107 €1100 Still life of flowers (66x49cm-26x19in) mono.d.25 chipboard. 21-Nov-2 Dorotheum, Vienna #302/R

BOCK, Theophile Emile Achille de (1851-1904) Dutch
£525 $745 €850 Paysage anime (33x60cm-13x24in) s. canvas on panel. 17-Mar-2 Galerie de Chartres, Chartres #105
£750 $1170 €1125 Water mill (22x32cm-9x13in) s. panel sold with a farm scene by W Muller. 26-Mar-3 Sotheby's, Olympia #198/R
£1136 $1784 €1704 Figure on a forest path (48x28cm-19x11in) s. canvas on board prov. 24-Jul-2 Walker's, Ottawa #3/R est:3000-5000 (C.D 2750)
£1139 $1777 €1800 Trees on the fen (23x31cm-9x12in) s. panel. 21-Oct-2 Glerum, Amsterdam #32/R est:700-1000
£1181 $1877 €1700 Castle Doorwerth seen from the grounds (29x38cm-11x15in) s. canvas on panel. 29-Apr-3 Christie's, Amsterdam #116/R est:1200-1600
£2397 $3764 €3500 Figure crossing a bridge in a wooded landscape (56x46cm-22x18in) s. 15-Apr-3 Sotheby's, Amsterdam #134/R est:3500-5000
£7534 $11829 €11000 Dune landscape (112x202cm-44x80in) s. 15-Apr-3 Sotheby's, Amsterdam #254/R est:8000-12000

BOCK, Thomas (1790-1857) Australian
Works on paper
£1550 $2465 €2325 Portrait of a lady (24x19cm-9x7in) crayon pencil oval prov. 5-May-3 Sotheby's, Melbourne #203/R est:3000-4000 (A.D 4000)
£1744 $2773 €2616 Portrait of a young man (24x19cm-9x7in) W/C oval prov. 5-May-3 Sotheby's, Melbourne #202/R est:2000-3000 (A.D 4500)

BOCKLIN, Arnold (attrib) (1827-1901) Swiss
£439 $685 €659 Pastoral landscape with wanderers (22x29cm-9x11in) 13-Sep-2 Lilla Bukowskis, Stockholm #85 (S.KR 6400)
£680 $1082 €1000 Rocky landscape with hermit (19x13cm-7x5in) oil study paper on board. 19-Mar-3 Neumeister, Munich #516/R est:1300

BOCKLIN, Carlo (1870-?) Swiss
£10870 $17826 €15000 Morning mist (103x150cm-41x59in) mono.d.1899 tempera panel exhib.lit. 31-May-3 Villa Grisebach, Berlin #108/R est:3000-4000

BOCQUET, Louis Rene (18th C) French
Works on paper
£507 $791 €750 Etude de costumes de l'opera (24x17cm-9x7in) i. pen W/C. 27-Mar-3 Maigret, Paris #97/R

BOCQUET, Paul (1868-1947) French
£566 $877 €900 Echappee sur villers-allerand (33x41cm-13x16in) s.d.1937. 30-Oct-2 Artcurial Briest, Paris #175

BOCZEWSKA, Maria (1940-) ?
£811 $1346 €1176 Cherries (90x100cm-35x39in) s. 16-Jun-3 Lilla Bukowskis, Stockholm #532 (S.KR 10500)

BODARD, Pierre (1881-?) French
£567 $919 €800 Etude preparatoire du groupe central (73x60cm-29x24in) st. 23-May-3 Binoche, Paris #42
£27660 $44809 €39000 Les arums (194x130cm-76x51in) s. 23-May-3 Binoche, Paris #34/R est:15000-20000
Works on paper
£284 $460 €400 Etude des deux personnages du premier plan (43x62cm-17x24in) st. black crayon col crayon. 23-May-3 Binoche, Paris #44
£284 $460 €400 Etude du nu allonge au premier plan (29x44cm-11x17in) st. black crayon sanguine. 23-May-3 Binoche, Paris #47
£319 $517 €450 Etude de nus pour le groupe central (44x29cm-17x11in) st. black crayon. 23-May-3 Binoche, Paris #41
£567 $919 €800 Etude preparatoire, composition generale (53x36cm-21x14in) st. black crayon Indian ink. 23-May-3 Binoche, Paris #45/R
£1135 $1838 €1600 Mise au carreau (61x49cm-24x19in) st. black crayon Indian ink. 23-May-3 Binoche, Paris #37/R est:200-300

BODAREWSKI, Nikolai (1850-1921) Russian
Works on paper
£648 $1044 €940 Bajan begins his story (48x33cm-19x13in) s.i. bears d.1909 W/C over pencil. 7-May-3 Dobiaschofsky, Bern #359/R (S.FR 1400)

BODDINGTON, Edwin H (1836-1905) British
£400 $624 €580 Quiet evening on the Thames (8x13cm-3x5in) s. indis d. 27-Mar-3 Neales, Nottingham #1012
£420 $659 €630 Anglers on a riverbank on a summer's day (30x61cm-12x24in) init. 16-Apr-3 Christie's, Kensington #625/R
£450 $729 €675 Calm evening on the Trent (31x61cm-12x24in) init. 20-May-3 Sotheby's, Olympia #178/R
£700 $1141 €1050 Extensive landscape with drover, cattle and sheep on a country track (58x89cm-23x35in) s.d.1869. 12-Feb-3 Bonhams, Knightsbridge #218/R
£800 $1312 €1200 Figures by a loch. Anglers on a lake (25x46cm-10x18in) s.d.1867 pair. 29-May-3 Christie's, Kensington #90/R
£1150 $1794 €1725 Pond near Crawley, Sussex (19x39cm-7x15in) s. one i.stretcher one indis.i. pair. 15-Oct-2 Bearnes, Exeter #414/R est:800-1200
£3500 $5705 €5250 Autumn evening Molesford on Thames. Old ruin on Thames (30x60cm-12x24in) s.i.d.verso pair. 29-Jan-3 Sotheby's, Olympia #85/R est:2000-3000

BODDINGTON, Edwin H (attrib) (1836-1905) British
£2866 $4500 €4299 Travelers along a roadside stream with distant windmill (102x137cm-40x54in) 23-Nov-2 Jackson's, Cedar Falls #12/R est:5000-7500

BODDINGTON, Edwin H and SHAYER, William (19th C) British
£3000 $4920 €4500 Evening at the ford (61x91cm-24x36in) s. 29-May-3 Christie's, Kensington #116 est:2500-3500

BODDINGTON, Henry John (1811-1865) British
£4000 $6200 €6000 Figures in conversation before a cottage, Norfolk (30x41cm-12x16in) 30-Sep-2 Bonhams, Ipswich #468/R est:2500-3500
£6000 $9420 €9000 Cattle watering in a river landscape (48x84cm-19x33in) bears sig.d.1853 prov. 19-Nov-2 Bonhams, New Bond Street #54/R est:6000-8000

BODDINGTON, Henry John (attrib) (1811-1865) British
£633 $1000 €1000 River landscape with angler sitting on a tree-trunk (45x81cm-18x32in) 30-Nov-2 Geble, Radolfzell #656
£1370 $2137 €2000 Stone bridge over river (45x81cm-18x32in) 10-Apr-3 Dorotheum, Vienna #46/R est:3000-4000
£4600 $7084 €6900 Windsor Castle from the Thames (71x91cm-28x36in) prov. 5-Sep-2 Christie's, Kensington #118/R est:3000-5000

BODDY, William James (c.1831-1911) British
Works on paper
£380 $616 €551 Barges at their moorings, River Ouse, York (18x25cm-7x10in) s. 23-May-3 Dee Atkinson & Harrison, Driffield #679/R
£550 $875 €825 At Hastings (18x34cm-7x13in) s.i.d.1892 W/C. 25-Feb-3 Bonhams, Knightsbridge #183/R
£760 $1186 €1140 Scarborough, herring fleet outside the harbour (23x45cm-9x18in) s.i.d.1898 W/C. 10-Sep-2 David Duggleby, Scarborough #106

BODE, Adolf (1904-1970) German

£411 $650 €650 Boats on the beach (80x95cm-31x37in) s. 30-Nov-2 Arnold, Frankfurt #46/R

BODE, Leopold (1831-1906) German

£1582 $2500 €2500 Morning walk (82x52cm-32x20in) s. lit. 29-Nov-2 Schloss Ahlden, Ahlden #1213/R est:2800

BODE, Wilhelm (1830-1893) German

£2911 $4513 €4600 River valley in pre-alps (55x72cm-22x28in) s. 25-Sep-2 Neumeister, Munich #542/R est:4000

BODECKER, Erich (1904-1971) German

Sculpture

£2179 $3378 €3400 Milkmaid with cow (66cm-26in) mono. concrete wood tin lit. 3-Dec-2 Lempertz, Koln #60/R est:3800-4000

£2754 $4516 €3800 Black Eve. mono. col cement. 28-May-3 Lempertz, Koln #55/R est:3800

BODELSON, Dan (1949-) American

£3846 $6000 €5769 Breaking camp (61x91cm-24x36in) 9-Nov-2 Altermann Galleries, Santa Fe #39

BODEMAN, Willem (1806-1880) Dutch

£4255 $6894 €6000 Home coming of herdsman with flock (51x44cm-20x17in) mono. panel. 22-May-3 Dorotheum, Vienna #57/R est:6000-8000

BODEN, Samuel Standige (1826-1896) British

Works on paper

£600 $936 €900 Norwich from the river (25x37cm-10x15in) s.d.75 W/C. 18-Sep-2 Dreweatt Neate, Newbury #67/R

BODENHAUSEN, Cuno von (1852-?) German

£406 $650 €609 Portrait of a lady in orange (60x44cm-24x17in) s.i. 16-Mar-3 Butterfields, San Francisco #1015

BODENMULLER, Alphons (1847-1886) German

£3663 $5677 €5495 Small girl with black cat (97x67cm-38x26in) painted c.1865. 3-Dec-2 SOGA, Bratislava #153/R est:290000 (SL.K 232000)

BODIFEE, Paul (1866-1938) Dutch

£446 $696 €700 View of village with small bridge over a ditch (58x88cm-23x35in) s. 6-Nov-2 Vendue Huis, Gravenhage #555

£461 $746 €700 Flowering church garden (46x62cm-18x24in) s.d.1914. 21-Jan-3 Christie's, Amsterdam #258

£479 $748 €700 Polder landscape (26x38cm-10x15in) s. canvas on panel. 14-Apr-3 Glerum, Amsterdam #133

£694 $1146 €1000 Birch trees by a stream in summer (42x29cm-17x11in) s. cardboard sold with another by the same hand. 1-Jul-3 Christie's, Amsterdam #178

£845 $1361 €1200 Farm with blossom trees (31x40cm-12x16in) s. 7-May-3 Vendue Huis, Gravenhage #11/R

BODILLY, Frank (1860-1926) British

£1450 $2277 €2175 Pause from work, two girls one mending a net the other knitting (52x34cm-20x13in) mono. 10-Dec-2 Lane, Penzance #359 est:1500-2000

BODIN, Heinrich (1907-1957) Swiss

Works on paper

£261 $407 €392 Parisian street scene (45x57cm-18x22in) s. W/C. 16-Sep-2 Philippe Schuler, Zurich #3174 (S.FR 600)

BODINE, A Aubrey (1897-1969) American

Photographs

£2308 $3600 €3462 Pennsylvania train yard, Baltimore (41x35cm-16x14in) s. verso ferrotype silver. 21-Oct-2 Swann Galleries, New York #84/R est:2000-3000

BODINI, Floriano (1933-) Italian

Sculpture

£3077 $4831 €4800 Pope (39x37x14cm-15x15x6in) s.d.80 bronze. 20-Nov-2 Pandolfini, Florence #147/R

BODINIER, Guillaume (1795-1872) French

Works on paper

£1689 $2635 €2500 Femme vue de dos (27x24cm-11x9in) mono.i.d.1829 W/C gouache over crayon. 31-Mar-3 Piasa, Paris #67

BODLEY, Josselin (1893-1974) British

£550 $875 €825 Vendome (46x38cm-18x15in) s.i.d.1934. 26-Feb-3 Sotheby's, Olympia #258/R

BODMER, Paul (1886-1983) Swiss

£1135 $1658 €1703 Dolderwald (130x73cm-51x29in) s. prov. 4-Jun-2 Germann, Zurich #100/R est:2000-3000 (S.FR 2600)

£1315 $2156 €1907 Three girls singing (114x82cm-45x32in) s. board. 4-Jun-3 Fischer, Luzern #1249/R est:2800-3000 (S.FR 2800)

Works on paper

£705 $1029 €1058 Girl (72x46cm-28x18in) chl. 17-Jun-2 Philippe Schuler, Zurich #4157/R (S.FR 1600)

BODOM, Erik (1829-1879) Norwegian

£300 $475 €450 Northern Norwegian coastal scene with stone hut (68x74cm-27x29in) 13-Nov-2 Kunsthallen, Copenhagen #3 (D.KR 3500)

BODTKER, Maria (1865-1937) Norwegian

£785 $1233 €1178 Still life of roses (52x65cm-20x26in) s. 25-Nov-2 Blomqvist, Lysaker #1030/R (N.KR 9000)

£939 $1464 €1409 Still life of roses (52x65cm-20x26in) s. 23-Sep-2 Blomqvist, Lysaker #1016 (N.KR 11000)

BOE, Frants Didrik (1820-1891) Norwegian

£1770 $2796 €2655 Roses and forget-me-nots (25x37cm-10x15in) s.d.1885 lit. 28-Apr-3 Blomqvist, Oslo #304/R est:22000-26000 (N.KR 20000)

£1828 $2924 €2742 Pansy and rose (15x20cm-6x8in) s.d.1 Novbr.1871 panel lit. 17-Mar-3 Blomqvist, Oslo #305/R est:18000-22000 (N.KR 21000)

£1837 $3012 €2664 Still life of apples (23x26cm-9x10in) s.d.1859. 2-Jun-3 Blomqvist, Oslo #212/R est:25000-30000 (N.KR 20000)

£3009 $4754 €4514 Wild flowers in glass on stone ledge (38x32cm-15x13in) s.d.1880 i.stretcher lit. 28-Apr-3 Blomqvist, Oslo #307/R est:40000-50000 (N.KR 34000)

£3122 $5120 €4527 Strawberries on stone (22x27cm-9x11in) s.i.d.1856 lit. 2-Jun-3 Blomqvist, Oslo #166a/R est:35000-45000 (N.KR 34000)

£5222 $8355 €7833 Landscape from Hestemann Island (47x70cm-19x28in) s.i.d.1882 i.verso canvas on panel. 17-Mar-3 Blomqvist, Oslo #361/R est:70000-90000 (N.KR 60000)

£6092 $9748 €9138 Rose and ring (22x27cm-9x11in) s.i.d.1854 prov.exhib.lit. 17-Mar-3 Blomqvist, Oslo #315/R est:80000-100000 (N.KR 70000)

£6428 $10542 €9321 Shell and carnations (22x27cm-9x11in) s.i.d.1853 prov.exhib.lit. 2-Jun-3 Blomqvist, Oslo #166/R est:40000-50000 (N.KR 70000)

£11678 $18452 €17517 The thrush and the last rowanberries (46x56cm-18x22in) s.d.1865 exhib.lit. 2-Dec-2 Blomqvist, Oslo #341/R est:90000-110000 (N.KR 135000)

BOE, Frants Didrik (attrib) (1820-1891) Norwegian

£766 $1240 €1149 Still life of herrings, pike and onions on table (42x57cm-17x22in) init.d.1840. 21-May-3 Museumsbygningen, Copenhagen #40/R (D.KR 8000)

BOECK, Felix de (1898-1995) Belgian

£419 $663 €650 Composition (16x10cm-6x4in) s.verso panel. 17-Dec-2 Palais de Beaux Arts, Brussels #475

£496 $829 €700 Composition rouge (17x17cm-7x7in) s.d.verso panel. 17-Jun-3 Palais de Beaux Arts, Brussels #526

£1722 $2807 €2600 Maternite (61x45cm-24x18in) s.d.1954. 17-Feb-3 Horta, Bruxelles #121

£2517 $4102 €3800 Drogenbos, lumiere du soir (73x52cm-29x20in) s.d.1976 verso. 17-Feb-3 Horta, Bruxelles #120

£4422 $7031 €6500 Drogenbos, reeks nachtlichten (80x60cm-31x24in) s. s.i.d.verso panel. 18-Mar-3 Galerie Moderne, Brussels #574/R est:4000-6000

£5862 $9379 €8500 Baby's head (63x71cm-25x28in) s.d.1927 board on panel. 15-Mar-3 De Vuyst, Lokeren #460/R est:8500-10000

Works on paper

£828 $1324 €1200 Head of a hippopotamus (26x31cm-10x12in) s.d.1930 pencil dr. 15-Mar-3 De Vuyst, Lokeren #75

BOECK, Johann Friedrich (1811-c.1871) German

£1923 $2981 €3000 Moonlit mountains (78x60cm-31x24in) s. 5-Dec-2 Schopman, Hamburg #517 est:2400

BOECKEL, Louis van (1857-1944) Belgian

Sculpture

£3099 $4989 €4400 Raptor with prey (60x85cm-24x33in) s. cast iron. 12-May-3 Bernaerts, Antwerp #672/R est:5000-6000

BOECKHORST, Jan (1605-1668) German
£45517 $72372 €66000 Scipio's moderation (158x203cm-62x80in) prov.lit. 4-Mar-3 Ansorena, Madrid #52/R

BOECKHORST, Jan (attrib) (1605-1668) German
£959 $1496 €1400 Head of woman (49x37cm-19x15in) panel. 10-Apr-3 Van Ham, Cologne #1159/R

BOECKL, Herbert (1894-1966) Austrian
£37975 $60000 €60000 Still life with hyacinth, mussel and fruit (60x78cm-24x31in) s.d.1932 prov. 27-Nov-2 Dorotheum, Vienna #161/R est:65000-80000
£44928 $73681 €62000 Woman at garden gate (49x39cm-19x15in) lit. 27-May-3 Hassfurther, Vienna #21/R est:30000-40000
£57971 $95072 €80000 Landscape in the storm with quarry and Scots pine (85x70cm-33x28in) lit. 27-May-3 Hassfurther, Vienna #22/R est:50000-60000

Works on paper
£2899 $4754 €4000 Bathers (43x60cm-17x24in) ink. 27-May-3 Wiener Kunst Auktionen, Vienna #80/R est:4000-8000
£3481 $5500 €5500 Child's portrait (53x37cm-21x15in) s.d.1930 chl. 26-Nov-2 Wiener Kunst Auktionen, Vienna #121/R est:2000-4000
£7971 $13072 €11000 Girl (49x36cm-19x14in) d.1919 chl lit. 27-May-3 Wiener Kunst Auktionen, Vienna #75/R est:7000-12000
£7971 $13072 €11000 St Kathrein landscape (43x59cm-17x23in) s.d.50 W/C. 27-May-3 Wiener Kunst Auktionen, Vienna #77/R est:6000-12000
£9420 $15449 €13000 Donawitz (38x51cm-15x20in) i. 27-May-3 Wiener Kunst Auktionen, Vienna #78/R est:10000-18000

BOEHLE, Fritz (1873-1916) German
£1901 $3061 €2700 St Francis with white deer in wood (66x98cm-26x39in) s.d.1907 board. 10-May-3 Hans Stahl, Toestorf #1/R est:2500
£2374 $3894 €3300 Returning home (75x98cm-30x39in) masonite. 4-Jun-3 Reiss & Sohn, Konigstein #2/R est:5000
£3597 $5899 €5000 Dutch river landscape (123x188cm-48x74in) s.d.1900. 4-Jun-3 Reiss & Sohn, Konigstein #3/R est:8000
£5036 $8259 €7000 St Hieronymous in his cell (83x112cm-33x44in) s.d.1903. 4-Jun-3 Reiss & Sohn, Konigstein #4/R est:8000
£5396 $8849 €7500 Portrait of Berthe Boehle (48x39cm-19x15in) i. verso board. 4-Jun-3 Reiss & Sohn, Konigstein #1/R est:5000

BOEHM, Adolph (1844-?) German
£800 $1232 €1200 Venetian canal scene. Priest crossing a Venetian bridge (38x23cm-15x9in) panel pair. 24-Oct-2 Christie's, Kensington #148/R

BOEHM, Aino von (?) Finnish?
£528 $814 €840 Still life of flowers in vase (47x31cm-19x12in) s. 24-Oct-2 Hagelstam, Helsinki #874/R

BOEHM, E (19th C) ?
£411 $642 €650 Peasant woman by spring outside farmstead (48x38cm-19x15in) 14-Sep-2 Weidler, Nurnberg #6525/R

BOEHM, Eduard (1830-1890) German/Austrian
£250 $398 €375 Setters in an alpine landscape (74x61cm-29x24in) 27-Feb-3 Richardson & Smith, Whitby #424
£472 $731 €750 Mountain landscape with angler (42x58cm-17x23in) s. 29-Oct-2 Dorotheum, Vienna #30/R
£494 $780 €741 Alpine landscape with wanderer on path (69x54cm-27x21in) s. 2-Dec-2 Rasmussen, Copenhagen #1591/R (D.KR 5800)
£588 $965 €900 Traveller by foamy mountain stream (55x69cm-22x27in) s. i.verso. 5-Feb-3 Neumeister, Munich #678/R
£641 $1000 €962 Partie aus Baicin (38x58cm-15x23in) s. 20-Sep-2 New Orleans Auction, New Orleans #490/R est:900-1200
£753 $1175 €1100 Traveller and rider at a memorial with distant romantic alpine landscape (69x93cm-27x37in) s. lit. 10-Apr-3 Allgauer, Kempten #2736/R
£759 $1177 €1200 Mountain valley (68x105cm-27x41in) s. 25-Sep-2 Neumeister, Munich #543/R
£800 $1304 €1200 Partie aus Untersteier bai Ehrenhausen. Gevirgspartie aus Tirol (55x69cm-22x27in) s. pair. 13-Feb-3 Christie's, Kensington #153/R
£833 $1292 €1300 Steiermark scene at sunset (74x100cm-29x39in) s. i. verso. 5-Dec-2 Neumeister, Munich #2767/R
£977 $1387 €1466 In the forest (92x47cm-36x19in) painted c.1870. 26-Mar-2 SOGA, Bratislava #178/R est:38000 (SL.K 62000)
£1346 $2087 €2100 Mountain lake with figures (69x105cm-27x41in) s. 4-Dec-2 Neumeister, Munich #680/R est:1600
£1410 $2186 €2200 Mountain stream in valley with traveller on a path (68x55cm-27x22in) 4-Dec-2 Neumeister, Munich #681/R est:1400
£1918 $2992 €2800 Steiermark at sunset (74x100cm-29x39in) s. i. verso. 10-Apr-3 Dorotheum, Vienna #221/R est:2800-3200
£1918 $2992 €2800 Tyrol (62x46cm-24x18in) s.d.1891. 10-Apr-3 Dorotheum, Vienna #256/R est:2400-2600
£2051 $3221 €3200 River landscape with woods and resting figures, mountains in background (68x105cm-27x41in) s. 21-Nov-2 Dorotheum, Vienna #136/R est:3000-4500
£4717 $7264 €7500 Partie aus baiern. Partie aus Steiermark (72x96cm-28x38in) s. pair. 23-Oct-2 Christie's, Amsterdam #54/R est:6000-8000

BOEHM, Eduard (attrib) (1830-1890) German/Austrian
£732 $1200 €1061 Headed home (51x81cm-20x32in) bears sig. 4-Jun-3 Doyle, New York #10 est:1000-1500

BOEHM, L (?) ?
£317 $495 €476 Mountain landscape with river and mother and child on path (70x100cm-28x39in) s,. 11-Nov-2 Rasmussen, Vejle #2086 (D.KR 3700)

BOEHM, R (19th C) ?
£488 $800 €708 Flirtation (36x46cm-14x18in) s.d.84. 4-Jun-3 Doyle, New York #11

BOEHM, Sir Joseph Edgar (1834-1890) British
Sculpture
£2372 $3700 €3558 Huntsman and horse (15cm-6in) brown pat. bronze. 20-Sep-2 Sloan, North Bethesda #289/R est:3000-5000
£3200 $4864 €4800 Highland athlete (64cm-25in) s.i. brown pat. bronze. 28-Aug-2 Sotheby's, London #852/R est:2000-3000

BOEHM, Tuomas von (1916-2000) Finnish
£576 $921 €800 Man at table (40x26cm-16x10in) s. canvas on board. 17-May-3 Hagelstam, Helsinki #171/R
£1583 $2532 €2200 Still life (27x45cm-11x18in) s.d.1953 board. 17-May-3 Hagelstam, Helsinki #172/R est:1000

BOEHM-HENNES, Leonie (20th C) German?
Sculpture
£2465 $3968 €3500 Dancer (32cm-13in) i. verso wood ivory style of Agathon Leonard. 10-May-3 Quittenbaum, Munich #694/R est:3800

BOEHME, Karl Theodor (1866-1939) German
£252 $392 €400 Vulcano in evening light (42x53cm-17x21in) s.i.d.1904 canvas on board. 19-Sep-2 Dr Fritz Nagel, Stuttgart #909/R
£1090 $1711 €1700 After the storm (112x150cm-44x59in) 10-Dec-2 Dorotheum, Vienna #112/R est:3200-3600
£2715 $4399 €3937 Breakers and rocky coast (101x132cm-40x52in) s.i.d.1897. 26-May-3 Bukowskis, Stockholm #239b/R est:35000-40000 (S.KR 35000)

BOEHME, Karl Theodor (attrib) (1866-1939) German
£258 $393 €387 Northern fjord landscape with mountains (55x68cm-22x27in) s.d.33. 27-Aug-2 Rasmussen, Copenhagen #1841/R (D.KR 3000)

BOEHME, Max (1965-) Austrian
Works on paper
£207 $331 €300 Untitled (65x48cm-26x19in) s.d.95 mixed media silver. 11-Mar-3 Dorotheum, Vienna #265/R
£517 $828 €750 Untitled (64x45cm-25x18in) s.i.d.90 mixed media cloth on canvas. 11-Mar-3 Dorotheum, Vienna #264/R

BOEL, John Henry (19/20th C) British
£144 $222 €216 View of a lake (36x25cm-14x10in) 26-Oct-2 Heffel, Vancouver #3 (C.D 350)
£270 $451 €392 Mountain stream in a Scottish landscape (48x72cm-19x28in) s.d.1907. 19-Jun-3 Lane, Penzance #327
£310 $490 €465 Mountain lake landscape (51x76cm-20x30in) s.d.1912. 27-Nov-2 Bonhams, Knowle #243
£450 $734 €675 On the river Tweed, near Peebles. Loch Muick, near Ballater (51x76cm-20x30in) mono. one d.1919 one d.1920 pair. 13-Feb-3 Christie's, Kensington #80/R
£600 $912 €900 Summer river landscape with figure on a path by cottages (48x74cm-19x29in) s.d.1898. 16-Aug-2 Keys, Aylsham #617/R
£1000 $1590 €1500 Figures on a sunlit lane, Tintern Abbey beyond (61x91cm-24x36in) 6-Mar-3 Christie's, Kensington #418/R est:700-1000

BOEL, Pieter (attrib) (1622-1674) Flemish
£769 $1192 €1200 Resting by watermill (31x37cm-12x15in) mono. 5-Dec-2 Schopman, Hamburg #518

BOELEMA DE STOMME, Maerten (17th C) Dutch
£32374 $51799 €45000 Silver tazza, an upturned roemer, partly peeled lemon, knife and hazelnuts on draped table (44x34cm-17x13in) bears sig panel prov. 14-May-3 Christie's, Amsterdam #182/R est:15000-20000

BOELTZIG, Reinhold (attrib) (1863-?) German

Sculpture

£1000	$1630	€1500	Kneeling woman with a dish of fruit (36cm-14in) s. tinted alabaster. 11-Feb-3 Sotheby's, Olympia #346/R est:600-900

BOER, Hessel de (1921-) Dutch

£347	$573	€500	Dutch landscape (47x65cm-19x26in) s. board. 1-Jul-3 Christie's, Amsterdam #272/R
£637	$994	€1000	Still life with fruit bowl (67x82cm-26x32in) s.d.46. 6-Nov-2 Vendue Huis, Gravenhage #177/R
£851	$1379	€1200	Still life with a table with dish, jar, vase and jug (48x47cm-19x19in) s. 26-May-3 Glerum, Amsterdam #150
£1401	$2186	€2200	Winter square 1813 in The Hague (59x72cm-23x28in) s. 6-Nov-2 Vendue Huis, Gravenhage #242/R est:1500-2000

BOER, Otto de (1797-1856) Dutch

£1026	$1610	€1600	Adoration of the Shepherds (68x53cm-27x21in) s.d.1830. 21-Nov-2 Van Ham, Cologne #1488/R est:1000

BOEREWAARD, Door (1893-1972) Belgian

£278	$442	€400	Marine (60x70cm-24x28in) s. 29-Apr-3 Campo, Vlaamse Kaai #25
£377	$585	€600	Still life of flowers (100x70cm-39x28in) s. 5-Oct-2 De Vuyst, Lokeren #40
£382	$607	€550	Canal au printemps (80x100cm-31x39in) s. 29-Apr-3 Campo, Vlaamse Kaai #24
£436	$702	€650	Marina with boats (70x100cm-28x39in) s. 24-Feb-3 Bernaerts, Antwerp #764/R
£503	$775	€800	Le long du canal (44x63cm-17x25in) s. 22-Oct-2 Campo, Vlaamse Kaai #416

BOERS, Sebastian Theodorus Voorn (1828-1893) Dutch

£541	$845	€850	Still life with flowers and fruit (43x34cm-17x13in) s. 6-Nov-2 Vendue Huis, Gravenhage #464
£2740	$4301	€4000	Flowers still life and butterfly on a stone ledge (22x31cm-9x12in) s. panel prov. 15-Apr-3 Sotheby's, Amsterdam #26/R est:4000-6000

BOESEN, A V (1812-1857) Danish

£1676	$2665	€2514	Landscape from Italy, possibly Capri (22x31cm-9x12in) init. panel. 10-Mar-3 Rasmussen, Vejle #202/R est:12000 (D.KR 18000)

BOESEN, Johannes (1847-1916) Danish

£603	$916	€905	Road through woods (65x97cm-26x38in) mono.d.1892 exhib. 27-Aug-2 Rasmussen, Copenhagen #1824/R (D.KR 7000)
£681	$1076	€1022	Spring morning on the outskirts of Vejle fjord (36x59cm-14x23in) s. exhib. 2-Dec-2 Rasmussen, Copenhagen #1287/R (D.KR 8000)
£766	$1240	€1111	Coastal landscape with Kronborg in background (22x34cm-9x13in) init.d.24/1/67. 26-May-3 Rasmussen, Copenhagen #1372/R (D.KR 8000)

BOETS, Johan Hans (attrib) (17th C) Dutch?

£2432	$3795	€3600	Vertumnus and Pomona (38x28cm-15x11in) panel. 26-Mar-3 Tajan, Paris #133 est:3000

BOETTCHER, Manfred (1933-2001) German

£535	$823	€850	Still life with coffee cup (28x45cm-11x18in) s. panel. 26-Oct-2 Dr Lehr, Berlin #57/R
£1006	$1550	€1600	Berlin street scene (38x50cm-15x20in) s. panel. 26-Oct-2 Dr Lehr, Berlin #56/R

BOETTI, Alighiero e (1940-1994) Italian

Works on paper

£2192	$3419	€3200	Untitled (41x30cm-16x12in) s. mixed media collage paper on canvas. 10-Apr-3 Finarte Semenzato, Rome #100/R
£4422	$7031	€6500	Untitled (95x69cm-37x27in) s. graphite collage col crayon paper on canvas. 24-Mar-3 Cornette de St.Cyr, Paris #106/R
£6884	$11290	€9500	Faccine (80x67cm-31x26in) col.crayons. 27-May-3 Tajan, Paris #50/R est:18500-20000
£7000	$10780	€10500	Oggetto e soggetto - object and subject (72x102cm-28x40in) s.d.1980 verso blue ballpoint pen prov. 23-Oct-2 Christie's, London #168/R est:7000-9000
£7692	$12077	€12000	Andrea Pazienza's exhibition (100x70cm-39x28in) s. mixed media card on canvas exec.1991. 21-Nov-2 Finarte, Rome #169/R est:8000-10000
£9000	$15030	€13050	Ordine e disordine - order and disorder (79x59cm-31x23in) ballpoint pen on card executed c.1981-82 prov. 27-Jun-3 Christie's, London #158/R est:10000-15000
£9500	$15580	€14250	Una, due, tre, cento parole al vento (87x25cm-34x10in) i. s.i.overlap embroidered tapestry. 7-Feb-3 Sotheby's, London #201/R est:5000-7000
£10127	$16000	€15191	Pack (70x101cm-28x40in) i. ballpoint pen executed 1982 prov. 13-Nov-2 Sotheby's, New York #319/R est:20000-25000
£10625	$17000	€15938	Aerei - airplane (23x48cm-9x19in) s.d.1983 verso ball point pen paper on canvas three sheets prov. 14-May-3 Sotheby's, New York #377/R est:15000-20000
£10884	$17306	€16000	Ononimo (70x100cm 28x39in) i. pen. 1-Mar-3 Meeting Art, Vercelli #363 est:15000
£14000	$22960	€21000	Ononimo - Homonymous (70x100cm-28x39in) s.i.d.1974 verso blue ballpoint pen card prov. 6-Feb-3 Christie's, London #653/R est:8000-12000
£18000	$30060	€26100	Nomo auto (101x71cm-40x28in) s. verso ball point pen paper on canvas parts exec.c.1979 prov. 26-Jun-3 Sotheby's, London #218/R est:15000-25000
£20000	$32800	€30000	Untitled - nero su bianco e bianco su nero (118x108cm-46x43in) s.verso embroidery prov. 6-Feb-3 Christie's, London #639/R est:25000-35000
£20000	$32800	€30000	Verita nuda e cruda - The naked truth (100x70cm-39x28in) s.verso ball-point pen panel four prov. 6-Feb-3 Christie's, London #650/R est:35000-45000
£25000	$38500	€37500	Il silenzio e oro - silence is golden (113x99cm-44x39in) embroidery executed 1988 prov. 23-Oct-2 Christie's, London #172/R est:25000-35000
£25000	$41750	€36250	Mille novecento ottantotto - nineteen eighty eight (110x110cm-43x43in) s. indis i. embroidery executed 1988 prov.exhib. 27-Jun-3 Christie's, London #160/R est:25000-35000
£25000	$41750	€36250	Sragionando in lungo e in largo - babbling away about this and that (100x280cm-39x110in) s.i. verso ballpoint pen paper on canvas executed 1983 prov.exhib. 27-Jun-3 Christie's, London #165/R est:30000-40000
£26000	$43420	€37700	Oggi trentunesimo giorno del settimo mese dell'anno (109x110cm-43x43in) s.i.d.31 overlap embroidered tapestry. 26-Jun-3 Sotheby's, London #143/R est:25000-35000
£26250	$42000	€39375	Mille novecento ottantotto variente ive - one thousand, nine hundred eighty eight (100x107cm-39x42in) i.on overlap embroidered tapestry executed 1988 prov.exhib. 16-May-3 Phillips, New York #184/R est:40000-60000
£28000	$45920	€42000	Oggi diciannovesimo quarto mese anno uno nove otto nove (107x115cm-42x45in) i. s.d.19-4-89 verso embroidered tapestry prov. 7-Feb-3 Sotheby's, London #146/R est:25000-35000
£31410	$45859	€49000	July seventh (108x110cm-43x43in) s. embroidery exec.1988. 5-Jun-2 Il Ponte, Milan #161/R est:40000-50000
£34810	$55000	€52215	Untitled (105x110cm-41x43in) s.i.d.3.12.1988 embroidery prov. 14-Nov-2 Christie's, Rockefeller NY #385/R est:40000-60000
£40000	$61600	€60000	Alternandosi e dividendosi (111x112cm-44x44in) s. overlap executed 1989 prov. 22-Oct-2 Christie's, London #46/R est:25000-35000
£43038	$68000	€64557	Andar a capo (100x210cm-39x83in) s.i.d.1980 col ink three sheets prov. 14-Nov-2 Christie's, Rockefeller NY #384/R est:45000-55000
£80000	$133600	€116000	Opera postale - postal work. stamps envelopes spraypaint on canvas various sizes prov. 27-Jun-3 Christie's, London #162/R est:30000-40000
£88608	$140000	€132912	Untitled (197x208cm-78x82in) embroidery on stretcher executed 1983. 13-Nov-2 Sotheby's, New York #317/R est:80000-120000
£100000	$156000	€150000	Cinquemilacentocinque (202x212cm-80x83in) i. embroidered tapestry executed 1983 prov. 21-Oct-2 Sotheby's, London #36/R est:55000-65000
£120000	$196800	€180000	Tutto (93x138cm-37x54in) s.i.d.1988 embroidery prov.exhib. 5-Feb-3 Christie's, London #22/R est:130000-160000
£260000	$405600	€390000	Tutto (231x211cm-91x83in) s.d.1988-89 on overlap embroidered tapestry prov.exhib. 21-Oct-2 Sotheby's, London #32/R est:250000-300000
£280000	$431200	€420000	Tempo in tempo col tempo (125x222cm-49x87in) s.i.d.1983 on overlap embroidered tapestry executed 1983 prov. 22-Oct-2 Christie's, London #49/R est:250000-300000

BOETTINGER, Hugo (1880-1934) Czechoslovakian

£908	$1471	€1362	Before a storm (50x40cm-20x16in) s. board. 24-May-3 Dorotheum, Prague #75/R est:40000-60000 (C.KR 40000)

BOETTO, Giulio (1894-1967) Italian

£5442	$8653	€8000	Concert in the grass (71x117cm-28x46in) s. board. 1-Mar-3 Meeting Art, Vercelli #71

BOEUFF, Pierre le (19/20th C) French
£450 $684 €675 Bustling Continental marketplace (41x60cm-16x24in) s. 29-Aug-2 Christie's, Kensington #165/R
£620 $980 €930 Bustling Continental market place (46x36cm-18x14in) s. 14-Nov-2 Christie's, Kensington #111/R
£700 $1064 €1050 Lisieux, Normandy (58x74cm-23x29in) s. i.verso. 29-Aug-2 Christie's, Kensington #265/R
£988 $1600 €1433 St. Maclou, Rouen. Falaise, Normandy (51x69cm-20x27in) s. two. 21-May-3 Doyle, New York #230/R est:3000-5000

BOEVER, Jean François de (1872-1949) Belgian
Works on paper
£597 $926 €950 L'agonie d'un monde (53x36cm-21x14in) s. gouache black chk lit. 5-Oct-2 De Vuyst, Lokeren #76/R

BOEZINGER, Franz (1906-1974) Swiss
£304 $472 €456 Cherry tree in blossom (66x48cm-26x19in) mono. masonite. 9-Dec-2 Philippe Schuler, Zurich #8705 (S.FR 700)

BOFILL BOSCH, Fidel (1934-) Spanish
£270 $422 €400 Santorini (24x33cm-9x13in) s. s.i.verso board. 25-Mar-3 Durán, Madrid #40/R
£287 $448 €425 Landscape in Musser (24x33cm-9x13in) s. s.i.verso canvas on cardboard. 25-Mar-3 Durán, Madrid #39/R

BOFILL, A (19/20th C) Spanish
Sculpture
£10000 $16300 €15000 Semi clad female holding a lantern (38cm-15in) s. gilt bronze glass col enamel. 11-Feb-3 Christie's, Kensington #254/R est:6000-7000

BOGAERT, Andre (1920-1986) Belgian
£1250 $1987 €1800 La lumiere de l'ete (70x60cm-28x24in) s. panel. 29-Apr-3 Campo & Campo, Antwerp #16/R est:1250-1750
£1250 $1987 €1800 Tour Eiffel (100x100cm-39x39in) s.verso panel. 29-Apr-3 Campo & Campo, Antwerp #17/R
Works on paper
£396 $633 €550 Composition (152x123cm-60x48in) s.verso collage panel. 17-May-3 De Vuyst, Lokeren #38

BOGAERT, Bram (1921-) Dutch
£1261 $1968 €1892 Geelpuntzwart (39x43cm-15x17in) s.d.oct 1966 verso panel. 5-Nov-2 Bukowskis, Stockholm #362/R est:20000-25000 (S.KR 18000)
£1923 $2981 €3000 Blauwpuntingeel (51x52cm-20x20in) s. s.i.verso painted plaster relief exhib. 3-Dec-2 Christie's, Amsterdam #279/R est:3500-4500
Works on paper
£646 $1001 €969 Composition in yellow and blue (63x50cm-25x20in) s.d.91 gouache. 4-Dec-2 Kunsthallen, Copenhagen #244/R (D.KR 7500)
£709 $1099 €1064 Circles in purple and white (64x99cm-25x39in) s.d.69 gouache. 8-Dec-2 Uppsala Auktionskammare, Uppsala #273/R (S.KR 10000)
£755 $1170 €1200 Composition (98x68cm-39x27in) s.d.66 gouache. 5-Oct-2 De Vuyst, Lokeren #43/R
£755 $1170 €1200 Composition (66x99cm-26x39in) s.d.65 gouache. 5-Oct-2 De Vuyst, Lokeren #44/R
£881 $1365 €1400 Composition (62x48cm-24x19in) s.d.91 polymer. 5-Oct-2 De Vuyst, Lokeren #45/R
£1295 $2124 €1800 Blue (73x88cm-29x35in) s.d.65 gouache. 3-Jun-3 Christie's, Amsterdam #138/R est:1200-1600
£1667 $2650 €2400 Composition (47x63cm-19x25in) s.d.1962 gouache. 29-Apr-3 Campo, Vlaamse Kaai #27/R est:2600-3000
£2878 $4604 €4000 Composition (62x76cm-24x30in) s.d.94 gouache. 13-May-3 Palais de Beaux Arts, Brussels #29/R est:1750-2500
£3793 $6069 €5500 Round blue and black (102x123cm-40x48in) s.d.67 s.i.d.1967 verso polymer exhib. 15-Mar-3 De Vuyst, Lokeren #483/R est:5500-7000

BOGAERT, Gaston (1918-) Belgian
£316 $500 €500 Escaliers (38x46cm-15x18in) s. panel. 26-Nov-2 Palais de Beaux Arts, Brussels #44
£321 $497 €500 Ciel de pluie (46x55cm-18x22in) s. s.i.verso panel. 7-Dec-2 De Vuyst, Lokeren #33
£411 $650 €650 Antennes (46x55cm-18x22in) s. panel. 26-Nov-2 Palais de Beaux Arts, Brussels #281
£504 $806 €700 Voyage au long cours (61x50cm-24x20in) s. s.i.d.1983 verso panel. 17-May-3 De Vuyst, Lokeren #39
£556 $883 €800 La maison muree (30x40cm-12x16in) s. 29-Apr-3 Campo, Vlaamse Kaai #26
£570 $900 €900 La ville souterraine (82x77cm-32x30in) s. panel. 26-Nov-2 Palais de Beaux Arts, Brussels #46
£759 $1200 €1200 Fortin (54x65cm-21x26in) s. panel. 26-Nov-2 Palais de Beaux Arts, Brussels #283
£823 $1300 €1300 Ciel bleu d'hiver (54x65cm-21x26in) s. panel. 26-Nov-2 Palais de Beaux Arts, Brussels #45/R
£886 $1400 €1400 L'ouverture (60x50cm-24x20in) s. panel. 26-Nov-2 Palais de Beaux Arts, Brussels #282
£955 $1490 €1500 Le phare du bout du monde (53x64cm-21x25in) s. panel. 11-Nov-2 Horta, Bruxelles #582 est:1000-1500
£1079 $1727 €1500 Autoportrait (61x50cm-24x20in) s. panel. 13-May-3 Palais de Beaux Arts, Brussels #216 est:1000-1500

BOGAERT, Hendrik (17th C) Dutch
£2885 $4471 €4500 Two couples in a tavern with violinist (32x47cm-13x19in) s. panel lit. 4-Dec-2 Neumeister, Munich #584/R est:4000

BOGAERT, Ludo (1936-) Canadian
Works on paper
£261 $410 €392 Still occupied - magpies with hornets nest (58x44cm-23x17in) s.i.d.1973 W/C. 25-Nov-2 Hodgins, Calgary #268/R (C.D 650)

BOGAERT, Mattehus van den (1670-1736) Dutch
Works on paper
£1905 $3028 €2800 Trompe l'oeil aux cartes (327x25cm-129x10in) s. pen ink W/C pair. 24-Mar-3 Tajan, Paris #18

BOGAERTS, Henri (1841-1902) Dutch
£367 $569 €580 Image of Admiral Michiel de Ruyter (91x111cm-36x44in) s. 24-Sep-2 Glerum, Amsterdam #449/R

BOGAERTS, Jan (1878-1962) Dutch
£764 $1200 €1146 Study of a bull (61x80cm-24x31in) mono.d.1923. 14-Dec-2 Weschler, Washington #623/R est:1000-1500
£1146 $1766 €1800 Park in spring (41x51cm-16x20in) s.indisd.1907. 3-Sep-2 Christie's, Amsterdam #236/R est:2000-3000
£1783 $2746 €2800 Autumn idyl (60x50cm-24x20in) s.d.1914. 3-Sep-2 Christie's, Amsterdam #231/R est:3000-4000
£2740 $4301 €4000 Still life with strawberries (30x51cm-12x20in) s.d.1920. 15-Apr-3 Sotheby's, Amsterdam #98/R est:5000-7000
£4140 $6376 €6500 Pink carnations on a marble ledge (40x60cm-16x24in) s.d.1910. 3-Sep-2 Christie's, Amsterdam #274/R est:4000-6000
£4795 $7479 €7000 Cornflowers (54x34cm-21x13in) s.d.1921. 14-Apr-3 Glerum, Amsterdam #169/R est:6000-8000
£5346 $8233 €8500 Still life with pink roses, fan and a box on a marble ledge (39x50cm-15x20in) s.d.1916. 23-Oct-2 Christie's, Amsterdam #192/R est:8000-12000
£5556 $8833 €8000 Still life with apples on a white Delft gadrooned charger (50x55cm-20x22in) s.d.1937. 29-Apr-3 Christie's, Amsterdam #163/R est:7000-9000
£13836 $21308 €22000 Still life with a flowering azalea and fruit in creamware dish (60x71cm-24x28in) s.d.1912. 23-Oct-2 Christie's, Amsterdam #191/R est:15000-20000

BOGART, Françoise (20th C) French
£2436 $3776 €3800 Geelle (55x68cm-22x27in) s.d.77 s.i.d.verso painted plaster relief. 3-Dec-2 Christie's, Amsterdam #294/R est:2500-3500
Works on paper
£4088 $6336 €6500 Green red (41x73cm-16x29in) s.d.63 s.i.d.1963 verso polymer. 5-Oct-2 De Vuyst, Lokeren #583/R est:8000-9000

BOGDANI, Jakob (1660-1724) Hungarian
£8805 $13648 €14000 Flowers (56x76cm-22x30in) mono. 7-Oct-2 Ansorena, Madrid #41/R est:9000
£70000 $109900 €105000 Muscovy, tufted duck, and other birds beside a stream (72x124cm-28x49in) s. prov. 12-Dec-2 Sotheby's, London #44/R est:80000-120000

BOGDANI, Jakob (after) (1660-1724) Hungarian
£5000 $7950 €7500 Cockerel, hens, pigeons and a guinea pig in a wooded landscape (122x97cm-48x38in) 30-Apr-3 Halls, Shrewsbury #316 est:5000-7000

BOGDANI, Jakob (attrib) (1660-1724) Hungarian
£19000 $29640 €28500 Shelldrake and other ducks around a rock pool in a wooded landscape (101x115cm-40x45in) 9-Apr-3 Bonhams, New Bond Street #107/R est:10000-15000

BOGDANI, Jakob (style) (1660-1724) Hungarian
£5500 $8635 €8250 Still life with a magpie and red squirrel in a landscape setting (56x99cm-22x39in) bears sig. 10-Dec-2 Sotheby's, Olympia #378a/R est:3000-5000

BOGDANOFF-BJELSKI, Nikolai (1868-1945) Russian
£3800 $6004 €5700 Portrait of a girl (69x50cm-27x20in) s.d.1925 board. 26-Nov-2 Christie's, Kensington #44/R est:3000-4000
£6536 $10719 €10000 Two children and sledge in melting snows by wood (77x67cm-30x26in) s. 8-Feb-3 Hans Stahl, Hamburg #71/R est:9000
£6608 $9846 €9912 Four boys by fire (71x86cm-28x34in) s.cyrillic. 25-Jun-2 Koller, Zurich #6522/R est:15000-20000 (S.FR 15000)
£10000 $15700 €15000 The first lesson (78x66cm-31x26in) s. 20-Nov-2 Sotheby's, London #120/R est:12000-15000
£10563 $17007 €15000 Spring games (78x68cm-31x27in) s. 10-May-3 Bukowskis, Helsinki #388/R est:20000-22000
£14000 $22120 €21000 Children in a winter landscape (70x89cm-28x35in) s. d.1927 verso. 26-Nov-2 Christie's, Kensington #24/R est:15000-20000
£15000 $23550 €22500 Boys around campfire (70x88cm-28x35in) s. 20-Nov-2 Sotheby's, London #123/R est:20000-30000
£23000 $36110 €34500 Riding through the forest (79x69cm-31x27in) s. 20-Nov-2 Sotheby's, London #125/R est:25000-35000
£30000 $48600 €45000 Meandering woodland river (88x70cm-35x28in) s. 21-May-3 Sotheby's, London #126/R est:15000-20000

BOGDANOVE, Abraham J (1888-1946) American
£2866 $4500 €4299 Late fall on the Maine coast (51x61cm-20x24in) s. board. 19-Apr-3 James Julia, Fairfield #202/R est:3000-5000

BOGDANOVIC, Bogomir (20th C) Russian?
Works on paper
£2244 $3500 €3366 Winter Central Park (99x66cm-39x26in) W/C. 9-Nov-2 Altermann Galleries, Santa Fe #225

BOGELUND-JENSEN, Thor (1890-1959) Danish
Works on paper
£466 $722 €699 Motor racing - Glostrup near Copenhagen (83x58cm-33x23in) s.d.1922 gouache sketch. 1-Oct-2 Rasmussen, Copenhagen #388/R (D.KR 5500)

BOGER, Frederik (1820-1880) German
£510 $795 €800 Mountain lake with figures (33x26cm-13x10in) s. lit. 7-Nov-2 Allgauer, Kempten #2765/R

BOGERT, George H (1864-1944) American
£705 $1100 €1058 Venetian canal scene (71x99cm-28x39in) s. 18-Sep-2 Alderfer's, Hatfield #242/R
£741 $1200 €1112 Isle of Wight (51x69cm-20x27in) 24-Jan-3 Freeman, Philadelphia #148/R est:1000-1500
£1290 $2000 €1935 Venice (51x76cm-20x30in) s. 8-Dec-2 Toomey, Oak Park #620/R est:2500-3500
£1748 $2500 €2622 Seaside cottage at dusk (56x89cm-22x35in) s. 11-Dec-1 Lincoln, Orange #475/R

BOGGS, Frank Myers (1855-1926) French/American
£884 $1406 €1300 Place de la Concorde (60x70cm-24x28in) s. 18-Mar-3 Galerie Moderne, Brussels #172
£1667 $2750 €2400 Voilier a quai, maree basse (24x30cm-9x12in) s. 1-Jul-3 Rossini, Paris #71/R
£3379 $5373 €4900 Paris, temps gris, animations sur le Parvis de Notre-Dame (76x102cm-30x40in) s.i.d.24 jan 1907. 5-Mar-3 Doutrebente, Paris #53/R est:4000-5000
£3797 $6000 €5696 At the docks (53x81cm-21x32in) s. 24-Apr-3 Shannon's, Milford #109/R est:8000-12000
£3822 $5962 €6000 Entree du port (50x65cm-20x26in) s. 8-Nov-2 Pierre Berge, Paris #9/R
£3822 $5962 €6000 Vue de Rouen (50x65cm-20x26in) s. 8-Nov-2 Pierre Berge, Paris #11/R
£4800 $7824 €7200 Bassin d'Honfleur (38x56cm-15x22in) s.d.84 s.i.verso. 3-Feb-3 Bonhams, New Bond Street #30/R est:4000-6000
£5732 $8943 €9000 Vue de Paris, Notre-Dame (50x65cm-20x26in) s.d.22. 8-Nov-2 Pierre Berge, Paris #10/R
£6013 $9500 €9020 Harbour, Venice (69x30cm-27x12in) s. prov. 5-Apr-3 Neal Auction Company, New Orleans #222/R est:12000-18000
£6918 $11000 €10377 Along the canal (73x92cm-29x36in) s. 4-Mar-3 Christie's, Rockefeller NY #45/R est:6000-8000
£8333 $13167 €13000 La Seine a Paris et le Pont-Neuf (65x81cm-26x32in) s.i. 15-Nov-2 Laurence Calmels, Paris #5a/R
Works on paper
£272 $425 €408 Canal de l'Oucy (16x20cm-6x8in) s.i.d.1905 W/C over pencil. 19-Sep-2 Swann Galleries, New York #162/R
£321 $503 €500 A Paris (39x23cm-15x9in) s.i.d.1903 W/C chl. 13-Dec-2 Piasa, Paris #126
£449 $704 €700 Place de Bruges (32x40cm-13x16in) s.i. W/C chl. 13-Dec-2 Piasa, Paris #127
£449 $696 €700 Moulin en Hollande (17x23cm-7x9in) s. W/C. 5-Dec-2 Gros & Delettrez, Paris #49
£481 $755 €750 La cathedrale de Lisieux (45x38cm-18x15in) s.i. W/C dr. 11-Dec-2 Maigret, Paris #148/R
£517 $822 €750 La Cathedrale de Soissons (25x40cm-10x16in) s.i.d. W/C. 5-Mar-3 Doutrebente, Paris #24/R
£573 $894 €900 Ruelle de Rouen (34x23cm-13x9in) s.d.1904 W/C over chl. 8-Nov-2 Pierre Berge, Paris #12
£651 $1022 €950 Lisieux (45x37cm-18x15in) s. W/C. 21-Apr-3 Rabourdin & Choppin de Janvry, Paris #40/R
£692 $1072 €1100 Paris (37x44cm-15x17in) s.i. W/C. 4-Oct-2 Tajan, Paris #29
£774 $1223 €1200 Interior of church (37x45cm-15x18in) s.i. W/C over crayon. 19-Dec-2 Claude Aguttes, Neuilly #5/R
£855 $1385 €1300 Severac-le-Chateau (27x40cm-11x16in) s.i. W/C chl. 22-Jan-3 Tajan, Paris #35 est:1200-1500
£1056 $1754 €1500 Paris, Notre Dame au quai de la Tournelle (31x39cm-12x15in) s.i. chl W/C. 11-Jun-3 Beaussant & Lefèvre, Paris #51/R est:1500-1800
£1090 $1689 €1700 Mantes (29x42cm-11x17in) s.i.d.1902 W/C. 6-Dec-2 Rieunier, Bailly-Pommery, Mathias, Paris #74/R
£1090 $1711 €1700 Place de la Concorde (25x40cm-10x16in) s.i. W/C. 16-Dec-2 Rabourdin & Choppin de Janvry, Paris #102/R
£1293 $2055 €1900 Paris, la Seine et l'Ile de la Cite (24x33cm-9x13in) s.i. W/C pencil. 26-Feb-3 Artcurial Briest, Paris #15 est:1000-1200
£1314 $2063 €2050 Paris, Place de la Concorde (46x55cm-18x22in) s. W/C. 11-Dec-2 Maigret, Paris #149/R est:2000-3000
£1401 $2186 €2200 Place des Vosges (26x40cm-10x16in) s. chl W/C. 7-Nov-2 Chochon-Barre & Allardi, Paris #148/R
£1565 $2488 €2300 Paris, peniches a quai (24x33cm-9x13in) s.i. W/C pencil. 26-Feb-3 Artcurial Briest, Paris #16 est:1000-1200
£1592 $2484 €2500 Notre-Dame et l'Institut (25x38cm-10x15in) s.d.1904 W/C. 7-Nov-2 Chochon-Barre & Allardi, Paris #149
£1613 $2548 €2500 La Seine a Paris (36x47cm-14x19in) s.i. W/C over crayon. 19-Dec-2 Claude Aguttes, Neuilly #4/R
£2113 $3507 €3000 Paris, la Seine a l'Institut (42x51cm-17x20in) s.i. W/C. 11-Jun-3 Beaussant & Lefèvre, Paris #49/R est:1500-2000
£3061 $4867 €4500 Le garde dans la cour des lions (53x33cm-21x13in) s.i. W/C. 24-Mar-3 Rabourdin & Choppin de Janvry, Paris #154/R est:1500-1800
£4304 $6671 €6800 Paris, La Place Blanche (53x80cm-21x31in) s. W/C. 29-Sep-2 Eric Pillon, Calais #204/R

BOGH, Carl Henrik (1827-1893) Danish
£272 $424 €408 Light hazy morning by water's edge (42x59cm-17x23in) s. 5-Aug-2 Rasmussen, Vejle #203/R (D.KR 3200)
£323 $511 €485 Landscape with lake (45x63cm-18x25in) bears sig. 30-Nov-2 Rasmussen, Havnen #2242 (D.KR 3800)
£511 $792 €767 Landscape with stag (122x89cm-48x35in) s. 28-Sep-2 Rasmussen, Havnen #2172 (D.KR 6000)
£521 $829 €782 Bull and cat in farmyard, Dybeck Manor in Skaane (38x59cm-15x23in) s.i.d.1867. 10-Mar-3 Rasmussen, Vejle #133/R (D.KR 5600)
£544 $848 €816 Young woman cleaning copper kettle in yard (41x27cm-16x11in) s. 5-Aug-2 Rasmussen, Vejle #240/R (D.KR 6400)
£788 $1261 €1182 Children and puppies in front of house (30x41cm-12x16in) s. 13-Jan-3 Rasmussen, Vejle #146/R (D.KR 9000)
£1119 $1780 €1679 Two sows in front of pigsty (43x33cm-17x13in) s.d.1864. 5-May-3 Rasmussen, Vejle #608/R est:10000 (D.KR 12000)
£1583 $2517 €2375 Young man arriving with flowers and vegetables for his chosen one (22x38cm-9x15in) s. 5-Mar-3 Rasmussen, Copenhagen #1501/R est:20000 (D.KR 17000)
£2703 $4216 €4055 Norwegian landscape from Dovre with shepherd boy, sheep and cattle (144x123cm-57x48in) s.d.1885 exhib. 23-Sep-2 Rasmussen, Vejle #194/R est:30000 (D.KR 32000)

BOGHOSIAN, Varujan (1926-) American
Sculpture
£2070 $3250 €3105 48 (72x11cm-28x4in) mixed media wood prov. 19-Nov-2 Wright, Chicago #243/R est:2000-3000
£2160 $3500 €3132 Achilles heel (41x28x3cm-16x11x1in) s.i.d.1974 verso wood prov. 21-May-3 Doyle, New York #19/R est:2000-4000

BOGLE, John (c.1746-1803) British
Miniatures
£1600 $2624 €2320 Lady in white dress with pleated collar (4cm-2xin) init.d.1786 gilt metal frame. 3-Jun-3 Christie's, London #207/R est:1200-1500
£2200 $3432 €3300 Young girl wearing low cut white dress with frilled trim and pink ribbon bow (6cm-2xin) s.d.1800 gold frame plaited hair set in red leather case oval. 5-Nov-2 Bonhams, New Bond Street #62/R est:800-1200

BOGLIARDI, Oreste (1900-1968) Italian

£1538 $2415 €2400 Composition (47x32cm-19x13in) s. tempera paper prov.lit. 20-Nov-2 Pandolfini, Florence #88

BOGMAN, Hermanus Adrianus Charles (jnr) (1890-1965) Dutch

£282 $454 €400 Cows in the meadow with mills on the horizon (21x14cm-8x6in) init. panel. 7-May-3 Vendue Huis, Gravenhage #587/R

£307 $500 €461 Harbour view (18x23cm-7x9in) board. 31-Jan-3 Douglas, South Deerfield #8

£669 $1077 €950 Winter landscape with horse and wagon near haystack (19x33cm-7x13in) s. panel. 7-May-3 Vendue Huis, Gravenhage #25

£789 $1279 €1200 Roses in an earthenware vase (60x50cm-24x20in) s. 21-Jan-3 Christie's, Amsterdam #262/R est:900-1200

BOGMAN, Hermanus Charles Christiaan (1861-1921) Dutch

£506 $790 €800 Two horses in a field (14x22cm-6x9in) s. panel. 21-Oct-2 Glerum, Amsterdam #154/R

£592 $959 €900 Two cows by a fence (46x61cm-18x24in) s. 21-Jan-3 Christie's, Amsterdam #215

£724 $1172 €1100 Harvesters at work (40x60cm-16x24in) s. 21-Jan-3 Christie's, Amsterdam #218 est:800-1200

£1241 $1974 €1800 Peasant with his cattle on a country road (48x75cm-19x30in) s. 10-Mar-3 Sotheby's, Amsterdam #250/R est:1000-1500

BOGO, Christian (1882-1945) Danish

£363 $573 €545 Moored boat in a sunlit harbour (47x62cm-19x24in) s. 18-Nov-2 Waddingtons, Toronto #187/R (C.D 900)

£373 $600 €560 Seascape, four masted ship and small sailing vessels (71x99cm-28x39in) 22-Feb-3 Brunk, Ashville #854/R

£467 $729 €701 Seascape with sailing vessels (70x100cm-28x39in) s. 5-Aug-2 Rasmussen, Vejle #63/R (D.KR 5500)

£500 $800 €750 Square rigger under sail, a stream ship on the horizon (67x98cm-26x39in) s. 8-Jan-3 George Kidner, Lymington #195/R

£600 $936 €900 Shipping off Copenhagen harbour (71x100cm-28x39in) s. 17-Sep-2 Sotheby's, Olympia #215/R

£700 $1134 €1050 Danish windjammer running past Kronborg Castle. Danish barque at sea (69x98cm-27x39in) s. pair. 21-May-3 Christie's, Kensington #694/R

£1099 $1704 €1649 Finnish training ship off Kronborg Palace (92x138cm-36x54in) s.d.43. 4-Dec-2 AB Stockholms Auktionsverk #1905/R est:18000-20000 (S.KR 15500)

£1300 $2028 €1950 Norwegian shipping (70x102cm-28x40in) s. 17-Sep-2 Sotheby's, Olympia #214/R est:500-700

£1700 $2839 €2465 Tall ship with sailing boats (70x100cm-28x39in) s. 18-Jun-3 Sotheby's, Olympia #103/R est:1000-1500

BOGOLIUBOV, Alexei Petrovich (1824-1896) Russian

£20000 $32400 €30000 Launching the ship (25x32cm-10x13in) s.d.1887 panel. 21-May-3 Sotheby's, London #66/R est:4000-6000

Works on paper

£1700 $2686 €2550 Ten seascape studies (3x6cm-1x2in) one s. one indis sig. ink paper on cardboard framed as one. 26-Nov-2 Christie's, Kensington #9/R est:1400-1800

BOGOMAZOV, Alexander (1880-1930) Russian

£52174 $85565 €72000 Abstract landscape (61x65cm-24x26in) prov.exhib. 29-May-3 Lempertz, Koln #550/R est:40000-50000

BOGUET, Didier (1755-1839) French

Works on paper

£7692 $12077 €12000 Vue de san Vito, pres de Subiaco (78x131cm-31x52in) s.d.1823 gouache stump prov.exhib. 21-Nov-2 Neret-Minet, Paris #74/R est:4000-6000

BOHACEK, Karel (1886-1928) Czechoslovakian

Works on paper

£619 $978 €929 Burning witches (59x82cm-23x32in) s. mixed media. 30-Nov-2 Dorotheum, Prague #154/R (C.KR 30000)

BOHATSCH, Erwin (1951-) Austrian

£475 $741 €750 Untitled (57x39cm-22x15in) s.d.88 acrylic. 15-Oct-2 Dorotheum, Vienna #220/R

£1633 $2596 €2400 Dreiklang (158x143cm-62x56in) i.d.9.84 s.verso prov. 26-Feb-3 Artcurial Briest, Paris #363/R est:1500-2000

£9420 $15449 €13000 Travesty (190x190cm-75x75in) s.i.d.82 verso prov. 27-May-3 Wiener Kunst Auktionen, Vienna #217/R est:15000-18000

BOHEMEN, Kees van (1928-1986) Dutch

£1899 $3000 €3000 Untitled (106x168cm-42x66in) painted c.1960 prov. 26-Nov-2 Sotheby's, Amsterdam #61/R est:3000-4000

£2483 $3972 €3600 Figure (98x67cm-39x26in) s.d.79 acrylic paper. 15-Mar-3 De Vuyst, Lokeren #493/R est:4000-5000

£4167 $6458 €6500 Untitled (101x101cm-40x40in) s.d.67. 3-Dec-2 Christie's, Amsterdam #289/R est:5000-7000

Works on paper

£1439 $2360 €2000 Cows in a landscape (74x99cm-29x39in) s.d.85 pastel. 3-Jun-3 Christie's, Amsterdam #54/R est:2000-3000

BOHLER, Hans (1884-1961) Austrian

£742 $1158 €1113 Mountain landscape (79x91cm-31x36in) i. verso. 6-Nov-2 Dobiaschofsky, Bern #361/R est:1800 (S.FR 1700)

£7971 $13072 €11000 Still life of flowers (58x74cm-23x29in) i.verso. 27-May-3 Wiener Kunst Auktionen, Vienna #52/R est:10000-20000

Works on paper

£1519 $2400 €2400 Woman wearing hat (47x31cm-19x12in) s.d.18.VII.05 gouache. 27-Nov-2 Dorotheum, Vienna #121/R est:1800-2600

BOHM, A (18/19th C) ?

£4038 $6340 €6300 Druid festival (87x112cm-34x44in) s. 21-Nov-2 Van Ham, Cologne #1484/R est:2200

BOHM, Alfred (1830-1895) German

£4255 $6894 €6000 Inner courtyard with musician (80x55cm-31x22in) s.d.78. 22-May-3 Dorotheum, Vienna #92/R est:7000-9000

BOHM, Alfred (1850-1885) German

£503 $785 €800 Farmstead in northern German river landscape (64x92cm-25x36in) s. 21-Sep-2 Dannenberg, Berlin #546/R

BOHM, C Curry (1894-1972) American

£1572 $2500 €2358 Mountain landscape (12x16cm-5x6in) s. board painted c.1940. 4-May-3 Treadway Gallery, Cincinnati #546/R est:3000-4000

BOHM, Gustav (attrib) (1885-?) Austrian

£1100 $1793 €1650 Summer's day (53x43cm-21x17in) bears sigd.1917 board. 29-Jan-3 Sotheby's, Olympia #348/R est:800-1200

BOHM, Max (1868-1923) American

£535 $829 €850 Retour des champs au crepuscule (45x81cm-18x32in) s.d.1899 prov. 30-Oct-2 Artcurial Briest, Paris #127

£745 $1200 €1118 Church interior with seated girl, standing girl and organ player (91x28cm-36x11in) s.d.1890. 19-Jan-3 Jeffery Burchard, Florida #82/R

BOHM, Pal (1839-1905) Hungarian

£1238 $1932 €1857 Hussar riding (61x49cm-24x19in) s. 11-Sep-2 Kieselbach, Budapest #86/R (H.F 480000)

£2244 $3522 €3500 Still life of fruit (34x53cm-13x21in) s. two. 21-Nov-2 Van Ham, Cologne #1487/R est:2800

£2655 $4141 €3850 Bivouac (29x50cm-11x20in) s. panel. 12-Apr-3 Mu Terem Galeria, Budapest #47/R est:700000 (H.F 950000)

£3191 $5170 €4500 Still life with apples and pears (34x53cm-13x21in) s. 22-May-3 Dorotheum, Vienna #87/R est:3800-4200

£4200 $6552 €6300 Preparing the meal (49x100cm-19x39in) s. 17-Sep-2 Sotheby's, Olympia #275/R est:3000-4000

£5063 $7848 €8000 Fishing family eating midday meal on riverbank (67x120cm-26x47in) s.i. 25-Sep-2 Neumeister, Munich #544/R est:7500

£12855 $20053 €19283 Making dinner (67x120cm-26x47in) s. 11-Apr-3 Kieselbach, Budapest #45/R est:250000-4600000 (H.F 4600000)

BOHM, Pal (attrib) (1839-1905) Hungarian

£1299 $1935 €2000 Still life of fruit - plums, damsons, grapes (47x38cm-19x15in) i. 26-Jun-2 Neumeister, Munich #692/R

BOHMER, Heinrich (1852-1930) German

£390 $569 €600 Forest clearing (98x151cm-39x59in) lit. 14-Jun-2 Auktionhaus Georg Rehm, Augsburg #8021

£629 $969 €1000 Autumnal park landscape (80x120cm-31x47in) s. 23-Oct-2 Neumeister, Munich #614/R

£680 $1082 €1000 Birch wood - Vogelsberg (80x110cm-31x43in) s. s. verso. 28-Mar-3 Bolland & Marotz, Bremen #427/R

£897 $1391 €1400 Autumnal wood with deer (100x81cm-39x32in) s. 6-Dec-2 Michael Zeller, Lindau #721/R

£2244 $3478 €3500 Deer by woodland stream (42x62cm-17x24in) s. s.i. verso prov. 7-Dec-2 Ketterer, Hamburg #148/R est:1000-1200

BOHMER-FEST, Ferdinand (20th C) German

£327 $523 €500 Winter day at the Rhein with romantic church (46x68cm-18x27in) s. lit. 10-Jan-3 Allgauer, Kempten #1550/R

BOHMER-FEST, Heinrich (20th C) German

£288 $453 €450 Boats in harbour of small Dutch town (95x130cm-37x51in) s. 21-Nov-2 Van Ham, Cologne #1485

BOHN, Heinrich (19th C) German
£617 $919 €950 Figures in woodland (61x49cm-24x19in) s.d.1866. 26-Jun-2 Neumeister, Munich #693
BOHNSTEDT, Ludwig Franz Karl (1822-1885) Russian
£12000 $19440 €18000 Mountain landscape (76x125cm-30x49in) s. 21-May-3 Sotheby's, London #61a/R est:12000-18000
BOHRMANN, Karl (1928-) German
£652 $1070 €900 Untitled (55x59cm-22x23in) s. acrylic col chks. 31-May-3 Villa Grisebach, Berlin #763/R
£1026 $1590 €1600 Untitled - reclining nude (34x45cm-13x18in) acrylic chk cotton prov. 3-Dec-2 Lempertz, Koln #64/R est:1200
Works on paper
£504 $806 €700 Untitled (29x23cm-11x9in) s. mixed media. 15-May-3 Neumeister, Munich #687/R
£759 $1177 €1200 Head (32x28cm-13x11in) s. pencil col pen gouache dispersion letraset. 28-Sep-2 Ketterer, Hamburg #424/R
£1266 $1962 €2000 Greek battle (50x65cm-20x26in) s.d.1962 col pen pencil W/C board. 28-Sep-2 Ketterer, Hamburg #423/R est:1400-1600
BOHROD, Aaron (1907-1992) American
£833 $1300 €1250 Cotton pickers (20x15cm-8x6in) s. board prov. 10-Nov-2 Selkirks, St. Louis #745
£1039 $1600 €1559 Nightfall (15x23cm-6x9in) s. painted c.1940. 8-Sep-2 Treadway Gallery, Cincinnati #659/R est:2000-3000
£1667 $2600 €2501 The glass (30x61cm-12x24in) s. 22-Sep-2 Susanin's, Chicago #5086/R est:3000-4000
£2358 $3750 €3537 Southern scene with figures (20x15cm-8x6in) s. masonite painted c.1940. 2-Mar-3 Toomey, Oak Park #642/R est:2000-3000
£3057 $4800 €4586 Fingers (22x28cm-9x11in) s. tempera ink on board exhib. 14-Dec-2 Weschler, Washington #730/R est:1500-2500
£3548 $5500 €5322 Tile wall (23x23cm-9x9in) s. panel painted c.1975. 8-Dec-2 Toomey, Oak Park #830/R est:4500-6500
Works on paper
£292 $450 €438 Dancer (28x140cm-11x55in) s. W/C gouache exec.c.1940. 8-Sep-2 Treadway Gallery, Cincinnati #662/R
BOIJE, Fredrik (18/19th C) Swedish?
£669 $1064 €1004 Mother and child (33x26cm-13x10in) s.d.1812 verso. 3-Mar-3 Lilla Bukowskis, Stockholm #285 (S.KR 9000)
BOIJER-POIJARVI, Wille (1899-1975) Finnish
£258 $408 €400 Lake landscape (38x46cm-15x18in) s.d.1948. 19-Dec-2 Hagelstam, Helsinki #812
BOILAUGES, Fernand (1891-?) French
£637 $993 €1000 Restaurant du Faisant Dore (35x60cm-14x24in) s. panel. 5-Nov-2 Tajan, Paris #29/R
BOILEAU, Alexandre (?-1900) French
£5479 $8603 €8000 Chateau (38x65cm-15x26in) s. cardboard. 15-Apr-3 Laurence Calmels, Paris #4098/R est:1200
BOILLE, Luigi (1926-) Italian
£1164 $1816 €1700 Untitled (115x89cm-45x35in) s.d.64. 10-Apr-3 Finarte Semenzato, Rome #234/R
BOILLY, Jules (1796-1874) French
Works on paper
£348 $543 €550 Portrait d'homme (22x16cm-9x6in) s. chl htd white. 18-Oct-2 Raboudin & Choppin de Janvry, Paris #119
£400 $624 €600 Portrait of a man (26x18cm-10x7in) s.d.1829 chk. 17-Oct-2 Christie's, Kensington #141
BOILLY, Jules (attrib) (1796-1874) French
Works on paper
£709 $1184 €1000 Portrait d'homme (33x26cm-13x10in) pastel. 18-Jun-3 Piasa, Paris #7
BOILLY, Louis Léopold (1761-1845) French
£3497 $5840 €5000 Portrait de jeune fille a la robe rouge (22x16cm-9x6in) 25-Jun-3 Tajan, Paris #76/R est:6000-8000
£3537 $5624 €5200 Portrait de Jean Baptiste Montagne de la Roque (22x16cm-9x6in) 24-Mar-3 Fraysse & Associes, Paris #40/R est:2200
£4336 $7241 €6200 Portrait de femme a la robe bleue. Portrait d'homme (22x16cm-9x6in) pair. 25-Jun-3 Sotheby's, Paris #73/R est:4000-5000
£4676 $7669 €6500 Portrait de gentilhomme en buste (21x15cm-8x6in) 5-Jun-3 Fraysse & Associes, Paris #15/R est:6000-8000
£18868 $29434 €30000 L'innocent - le panier fleuri (61x51cm-24x20in) prov.exhib.lit. 10-Oct-2 Ribeyre & Baron, Paris #29/R est:60000-80000
Works on paper
£28571 $45429 €42000 Accident pres de la Porte Saint-Denis (36x51cm-14x20in) i. pen Chinese ink crayon wash htd gouache prov. 24-Mar-3 Tajan, Paris #62/R est:15000
BOILLY, Louis Leopold (attrib) (1761-1845) French
£289 $479 €419 Boy folding a letter (47x38cm-19x15in) bears sig.d.1819. 16-Jun-3 Waddingtons, Toronto #269/R (C.D 650)
Works on paper
£374 $595 €550 Reprimande maternelle (13x17cm-5x7in) pen ink wash. 26-Feb-3 Coutau Begarie, Paris #173/R
BOISFREMONT, Charles Boulanger de (1773-1838) French
Works on paper
£979 $1400 €1469 La lecon (31x21cm-12x8in) pen ink pencil htd white. 23-Jan-3 Swann Galleries, New York #287/R est:1000-1500
BOISGONTIER, Henri (19/20th C) French
£629 $1025 €950 Bord d'etang (38x55cm-15x22in) s. 2-Feb-3 Muizon & Le Coent, Paris #31
BOISROND, François (1959-) French
£419 $663 €650 Lit (31x23cm-12x9in) mono. acrylic. 18-Dec-2 Digard, Paris #85
£1192 $1943 €1800 En piste (80x80cm-31x31in) s.d.1996 verso. 1-Feb-3 Claude Aguttes, Neuilly #196/R est:1800-2000
£1573 $2438 €2500 La terrasse (195x130cm-77x51in) mono. s.i.d.verso. 4-Oct-2 Tajan, Paris #30 est:2500-3000
£1603 $2484 €2500 Comme chez soi (74x60cm-29x24in) mono.d.1996 s.d.verso acrylic. 7-Dec-2 Cornette de St.Cyr, Paris #126/R
£2013 $3119 €3200 La grue travailleuse (99x99cm-39x39in) mono. s.i.verso acrylic prov. 30-Oct-2 Artcurial Briest, Paris #473/R est:2500-3000
£2516 $3899 €4000 Les vacances (162x130cm-64x51in) mono.d. s.i.verso acrylic prov. 30-Oct-2 Artcurial Briest, Paris #474/R est:4000-6000
£2619 $4164 €3850 La vie est belle (201x157cm-79x62in) init.d.90 s.i.d.90 verso acrylic prov. 26-Feb-3 Artcurial Briest, Paris #391/R est:3500-4000
Works on paper
£330 $482 €495 Untitled composition (66x50cm-26x20in) gouache. 17-Jun-2 Philippe Schuler, Zurich #4010 (S.FR 750)
£330 $482 €495 Untitled composition (65x50cm-26x20in) gouache. 17-Jun-2 Philippe Schuler, Zurich #4011 (S.FR 750)
£661 $965 €992 Untitled composition (65x50cm-26x20in) gouache. 17-Jun-2 Philippe Schuler, Zurich #4009/R (S.FR 1500)
BOISSEAU, Émile Andre (1842-1923) French
Sculpture
£15484 $24000 €23226 Le crepuscule (63cm-25in) s. marble. 29-Oct-2 Sotheby's, New York #106/R est:25000-35000
BOISSELIER, Antoine (1790-1857) French
£19753 $32000 €29630 View of temple at Paestum (29x41cm-11x16in) i.verso paper on canvas. 23-Jan-3 Sotheby's, New York #232/R est:30000
BOISSEREE, Frederick (fl.1876-1877) British
Works on paper
£620 $986 €930 Welsh river landscape with angler on a bank (13x22cm-5x9in) s. W/C pair. 27-Feb-3 Bonhams, Chester #313
BOISSEVAIN, William (1927-) Australian
£1286 $2031 €1929 Native boys (90x121cm-35x48in) s.d.80 i.verso board. 26-Nov-2 Sotheby's, Melbourne #108/R est:3000-5000 (A.D 3600)
£1301 $2055 €1886 Emus (79x104cm-31x41in) s. board. 22-Jul-3 Lawson Menzies, Sydney #123/R est:2500-4500 (A.D 3200)
£1456 $2286 €2184 Untitled - distant view (90x120cm-35x47in) s.d.87 acrylic on board prov. 15-Apr-3 Lawson Menzies, Sydney #253/R est:2500-3500 (A.D 3800)
£1607 $2523 €2411 Heron (90x120cm-35x47in) s.d.80 board. 25-Nov-2 Christie's, Melbourne #202/R est:4000-6000 (A.D 4500)
£2129 $3364 €3194 Landscape (91x121cm-36x48in) s.d.77 board prov. 27-Nov-2 Deutscher-Menzies, Melbourne #184/R est:2000-4000 (A.D 5960)
£3257 $4852 €4886 Poppies (89x105cm-35x41in) s.d.87 board prov. 27-Aug-2 Christie's, Melbourne #174/R est:4000-6000 (A.D 8500)
Works on paper
£301 $478 €452 Reclining nude (59x75cm-23x30in) s. mixed media. 3-Mar-3 Lawson Menzies, Sydney #417 (A.D 800)
£498 $782 €747 Untitled - gum trees (90x67cm-35x26in) s.d.86 W/C ink prov. 15-Apr-3 Lawson Menzies, Sydney #252/R est:1500-2000 (A.D 1300)

BOISSIEU, Jean Jacques de (1736-1810) French
Works on paper
£570 $900 €900 Paysage montagneux (18x25cm-7x10in) i.verso pen brown ink W/C. 27-Nov-2 Christie's, Paris #196/R
£1200 $2004 €1740 Three figures playing cards, with other figure studies (12x19cm-5x7in) black lead ink wash prov. 8-Jul-3 Christie's, London #78/R est:1200-1800
£1899 $2943 €3000 River landscape with mill and figures (22x37cm-9x15in) mono.d.1791 W/C. 25-Sep-2 Neumeister, Munich #354/R est:1000
£5128 $7949 €8000 Paysans du Charolais (31x47cm-12x19in) mono.d.1791 sepia ink wash. 4-Dec-2 Libert, Castor, Paris #21/R

BOISSIEU, Jean Jacques de (attrib) (1736-1810) French
£577 $906 €900 Turkish man smoking opium (38x31cm-15x12in) 19-Nov-2 Castellana, Madrid #45/R
Works on paper
£513 $795 €800 Southern landscape with figures (14x22cm-6x9in) i. brush. 6-Dec-2 Bassenge, Berlin #7796
£897 $1434 €1300 Etude de personnages, joueurs de cartes (12x19cm-5x7in) pen brown ink grey wash prov. 12-Mar-3 E & Eve, Paris #23/R

BOISSON, Alfred (?) French
£344 $550 €499 Montpellier (26x38cm-10x15in) s.i. board double-sided. 16-May-3 Skinner, Boston #338/R
£937 $1500 €1359 On the coast (43x61cm-17x24in) s. 16-May-3 Skinner, Boston #332/R est:1000-1500

BOIT, Edward Darley (1840-c.1915) American
£7742 $12000 €11613 Ships on a beach (32x46cm-13x18in) s.d.81. 3-Dec-2 Phillips, New York #47/R est:15000-20000
Works on paper
£323 $500 €485 View of Spoleto, Italy (30x43cm-12x17in) s.i.d.26 May 1909 W/C. 2-Nov-2 North East Auctions, Portsmouth #75/R
£452 $700 €678 Village on a hillside, Perugia (28x36cm-11x14in) s.i.d.09 W/C. 2-Nov-2 North East Auctions, Portsmouth #73/R

BOITARD, François (c.1670-c.1715) French
Works on paper
£285 $444 €450 Trouville les Regates (31x47cm-12x19in) s.i.d.38 W/C. 15 Sep-2 Etude Bailleul, Bayeux #117/R
£380 $592 €600 La Seine, pres de Honfleur (30x45cm-12x18in) s.i. W/C. 15-Sep-2 Etude Bailleul, Bayeux #116/R
£601 $938 €950 Ouistreham le port (22x34cm-9x13in) s.i.d.36. 15-Sep-2 Etude Bailleul, Bayeux #118/R

BOITIER, Thierry (20th C) French?
Works on paper
£360 $576 €500 Au hasard du temps (40x40cm-16x16in) s. mixed media canvas. 18-May-3 Neret-Minet, Paris #34
£691 $1105 €960 Peut-etre ici (100x100cm-39x39in) s. mixed media canvas. 18-May-3 Neret-Minet, Paris #107

BOIVIN, Émile (1846-1920) French
£448 $717 €650 Village dans les montagnes (36x25cm-14x10in) s. 12-Mar-3 E & Eve, Paris #95
£2449 $3894 €3600 L'arrivee de la caravane (33x46cm-13x18in) s. 24-Mar-3 Rabourdin & Choppin de Janvry, Paris #197/R est:3450-3800

BOIX-VIVES, Anselme (1899-1969) French
Works on paper
£1274 $1987 €2000 Rencontre d'amoureux (47x67cm-19x26in) s.d.1968 gouache oil felt-tip pen panel lit. 5-Nov-2 Tajan, Paris #62/R
£1887 $2925 €3000 Sans titre, serie des Papes (65x50cm-26x20in) s. gouache. 30-Oct-2 Artcurial Briest, Paris #643/R est:3000-4000

BOIZOT, Simon Louis (after) (1743-1809) French
Sculpture
£9790 $16350 €14000 L'enlevement de Proserpine et d'Orithye (49x57cm-19x22in) brown pat bronze pair lit. 25-Jun-3 Sotheby's, Paris #23/R est:18000-25000
£14103 $21859 €22000 Portrait de Louis XVI de France (36x22x14cm-14x9x6in) terracotta lit. 9-Dec-2 Rabourdin & Choppin de Janvry, Paris #51/R est:4500

BOJESEN, Claus (1948-) Danish
£338 $527 €507 The large Bastian (130x97cm-51x38in) s.d.1990 verso. 18-Sep-2 Kunsthallen, Copenhagen #200 (D.KR 4000)

BOK, Hannes Vajn (1914-1964) American
£3846 $6000 €5769 Man with sword and fire breathing dragon (64x46cm-25x18in) s.d.1944. 9-Nov-2 Illustration House, New York #60/R est:7000-9000

BOKATSAMBIS, Vikentios (1856-1932) Greek
Works on paper
£2600 $4056 €3900 Portrait of a lady (53x38cm-21x15in) s. W/C over pencil htd bodycol. 15-Oct-2 Sotheby's, London #60/R est:2000-3000
£6000 $9300 €9000 Portrait of girl (43x32cm-17x13in) s. W/C gouache. 2-Oct-2 Sotheby's, London #85/R est:4000-6000

BOKELMANN, Christian Ludwig (1844-1894) German
£4225 $6803 €6000 North German farmstead (54x63cm-21x25in) s.d.86. 10-May-3 Hans Stahl, Toestorf #65/R est:1400

BOKKENHEUSER, Borge (1910-1976) Danish
£259 $396 €389 Landscape (65x80cm-26x31in) s. 24-Aug-2 Rasmussen, Havnen #2161 (D.KR 3000)

BOKLIN, Per Erik (1913-1999) Swedish
Works on paper
£425 $684 €638 Composition (12x18cm-5x7in) s.d.57 gouache pencil. 7-May-3 AB Stockholms Auktionsverk #918/R (S.KR 5500)

BOKLUND, Johan-Kristofer (1817-1880) Swedish
£314 $515 €455 Back yard with monks (32x25cm-13x10in) s.d.1856. 4-Jun-3 AB Stockholms Auktionsverk #2198/R (S.KR 4000)
£2346 $3753 €3402 Bartering (135x98cm-53x39in) s.d.1855 i.verso exhib.lit. 18-May-3 Anders Antik, Landskrona #31 est:25000 (S.KR 30000)
£3404 $5277 €5106 The farewell (77x92cm-30x36in) s.d.1844 exhib. 3-Dec-2 Bukowskis, Stockholm #174/R est:25000-30000 (S.KR 48000)

BOKLUND, Johan-Kristofer (attrib) (1817-1880) Swedish
£759 $1200 €1200 Garden with peacock and child feeding birds (65x48cm-26x19in) 30-Nov-2 Hagelstam, Helsinki #40/R

BOKS, Evert Jan (1838-1914) Dutch
£4000 $6280 €6000 Le coq de la vieille tante (72x56cm-28x22in) s.d.1882 panel. 19-Nov-2 Bonhams, New Bond Street #12/R est:4000-6000
£6849 $10753 €10000 Un duo (44x61cm-17x24in) s.d.1889 panel. 15-Apr-3 Sotheby's, Amsterdam #78/R est:4000-6000
£20886 $32582 €33000 In the library (78x108cm-31x43in) s.d.1904. 21-Oct-2 Bernaerts, Antwerp #89/R est:10000-15000

BOKS, Martinus (1849-1895) Dutch
£318 $490 €500 Dune landscape (18x32cm-7x13in) s. panel. 3-Sep-2 Christie's, Amsterdam #164

BOL, Ferdinand (1616-1680) Dutch
£12230 $19568 €17000 Elijah fed by angel (135x153cm-53x60in) 13-May-3 Sotheby's, Amsterdam #68/R est:15000-20000
£38849 $62158 €54000 Young woman wearing pearls (121x91cm-48x36in) s.d.1648 prov.lit. 17-May-3 Lempertz, Koln #1005/R est:60000-80000
Prints
£5775 $9586 €8200 Holy Family in a room (18x21cm-7x8in) etching. 12-Jun-3 Hauswedell & Nolte, Hamburg #44/R est:8000
Works on paper
£3395 $5500 €5093 Standing man in Oriental dress (16x12cm-6x5in) pen ink wash prov.lit. 21-Jan-3 Sotheby's, New York #139/R est:8000
£4514 $7177 €6500 Lady as shepherdess (20x13cm-8x5in) brush ink chl wash prov.lit. 5-May-3 Ketterer, Munich #439/R est:8000-10000
£17834 $27822 €28000 Messenger of God appearing to Joshua (18x26cm-7x10in) pen brown ink wash prov.lit. 5-Nov-2 Sotheby's, Amsterdam #56/R est:30000-40000

BOL, Hans (1534-1593) Dutch
Works on paper
£48387 $76452 €75000 Jacquerie (8x11cm-3x4in) s.d.1590 W/C gouache. 17-Dec-2 Galerie Moderne, Brussels #679/R est:80000

BOLAND, C H D (1850-?) Belgian
£1241 $1986 €1800 Vue portuaire (52x49cm-20x19in) 17-Mar-3 Amberes, Antwerp #188

BOLAND, Charles H D (1850-?) Belgian
£321 $503 €500 Vache et chien a l'etable (35x45cm-14x18in) s. 19-Nov-2 Vanderkindere, Brussels #146
£513 $795 €800 Le moulin de la galette (90x52cm-35x20in) s.verso. 3-Dec-2 Campo & Campo, Antwerp #15

£556 $883 €800 Chien de chasse et sa proie (83x70cm-33x28in) s. 29-Apr-3 Campo, Vlaamse Kaai #29
£612 $973 €900 Automne au bois - chien de chasse (44x65cm-17x26in) s. i. verso. 24-Mar-3 Bernaerts, Antwerp #70/R
£1519 $2354 €2400 En visite (44x66cm-17x26in) s. 24-Sep-2 Galerie Moderne, Brussels #855/R
£1887 $2943 €3000 Le jour de l'an (42x63cm-17x25in) 14-Oct-2 Amberes, Antwerp #130/R
£4167 $6458 €6500 Every man in his humour (87x61cm-34x24in) s.verso. 3-Dec-2 Campo & Campo, Antwerp #16/R est:4500-5500

Works on paper

£285 $444 €450 Un gourmet - bulldog (22x14cm-9x6in) W/C. 16-Sep-2 Amberes, Antwerp #179

BOLAY, Veronica (20th C) Irish?

Works on paper

£972 $1546 €1400 Tree (61x48cm-24x19in) s. pastel. 29-Apr-3 Whyte's, Dublin #28/R est:1500-2000

BOLDEN, Hawkins (20th C) American

Sculpture

£926 $1500 €1389 Untitled (203x29cm-80x11in) metal paint wood fabric prov. 27-Jan-3 Christie's, Rockefeller NY #97/R est:2000-3000

BOLDINI (?) Italian

Works on paper

£1064 $1777 €1500 Portrait de jeune garcon (29x23cm-11x9in) s.i.d.28 juin 1884 pen brown ink. 19-Jun-3 Piasa, Paris #212a/R est:1500

BOLDINI, Giovanni (1842-1931) Italian

£4783 $7413 €7175 Washerwomen on rivershore and girl with water jug (42x26cm-17x10in) s. panel prov. 9-Dec-2 Philippe Schuler, Zurich #3882/R est:15000-20000 (S.FR 11000)
£7595 $12000 €11393 Allegri conversari (16x30cm-6x12in) panel prov.exhib.lit. 24-Apr-3 Sotheby's, New York #139/R est:15000-20000
£9420 $15449 €13000 Guardiano di maili (19x44cm-7x17in) s. panel lit. 27-May-3 Finarte, Milan #131/R est:10000-12000
£42949 $67429 €67000 Jeune fille au chignon (31x40cm-12x16in) panel prov.lit. 10-Dec-2 Artcurial Briest, Paris #464/R est:45000-60000
£63226 $99897 €98000 Lady in sitting room (23x14cm-9x6in) s. board painted 1874 prov.lit. 18-Dec-2 Finarte, Milan #93/R est:85000

Works on paper

£962 $1490 €1500 Portrait de. de profil (17x11cm-7x4in) crayon. 4-Dec-2 Piasa, Paris #195/R
£1795 $2818 €2800 Study of female head (11x15cm-4x6in) s. crayon dr. 13-Dec-2 Piasa, Paris #45/R
£2013 $3099 €3200 Caricature (24x13cm-9x5in) indis.sig. W/C. 28-Oct-2 Il Ponte, Milan #225/R
£16312 $27241 €23000 Portrait de femme (26x31cm-10x12in) s.d.1909 chl. 19-Jun-3 Piasa, Paris #216/R est:5000-6000
£48387 $76452 €75000 Portrait presume de Madame Lucie Gerard (54x46cm-21x18in) s. pastel prov.lit. 18-Dec-2 Tajan, Paris #6/R est:100000

BOLDINI, Giovanni (attrib) (1842-1931) Italian

£1069 $1647 €1700 Peasant woman (25x17cm-10x7in) s. board. 28-Oct-2 Il Ponte, Milan #275/R

BOLDISZAR, Istvan (1897-1984) Hungarian

£1084 $1690 €1572 Garden of the summer house (70x90cm-28x35in) s. 13-Sep-2 Mu Terem Galeria, Budapest #183/R est:350000 (H.F 420000)
£1806 $2817 €2709 Nagybanya with Kereszthegy in the background (76x101cm-30x40in) s. 11-Sep-2 Kieselbach, Budapest #11/R (H.F 700000)

BOLDUC, Blanche (1906-) Canadian

£285 $447 €428 La ferme en ete (30x40cm-12x16in) init. board. 10-Dec-2 Pinneys, Montreal #193 (C.D 700)
£565 $892 €848 Interior (32x51cm-13x20in) s. board prov. 14-Nov-2 Heffel, Vancouver #18/R est:1800-2250 (C.D 1400)

BOLDUC, David (1945-) Canadian

£576 $893 €864 Colares 8 (54x45cm-21x18in) s.i.d.84 canvasboard prov. 3-Dec-2 Joyner, Toronto #76/R est:1500-1800 (C.D 1400)
£800 $1312 €1160 Untitled - red notations (104x74cm-41x29in) oil on paper. 1-Jun-3 Levis, Calgary #19/R est:2250-2500 (C.D 1800)
£803 $1269 €1205 Alsace (193x99cm-76x39in) d.1978 acrylic collage. 1-Dec-2 Levis, Calgary #302/R (C.D 2000)
£1606 $2538 €2409 Log (244x198cm-96x78in) d.1979 acrylic. 1-Dec-2 Levis, Calgary #301/R (C.D 4000)
£1778 $2916 €2667 Come up (171x137cm-67x54in) s.i.d.1980 verso acrylic prov. 27-May-3 Sotheby's, Toronto #28/R est:4000-6000 (C.D 4000)
£1864 $2964 €2796 Red (90x75cm-35x30in) s.i.d.1995 acrylic. 23-Mar-3 Hodgins, Calgary #61/R est:2000-3000 (C.D 4400)

BOLDUC, Yvonne (1905-) Canadian

£247 $380 €371 Scierie en hiver (37x67cm-15x26in) s. panel. 22-Oct-2 Iegor de Saint Hippolyte, Montreal #13 (C.D 600)
£325 $511 €488 Traineau dans le village (28x36cm-11x14in) s. 12-Dec-2 Iegor de Saint Hippolyte, Montreal #7 (C.D 800)
£615 $959 €923 Scene de village (21x27cm-8x11in) s. isorel. 10-Sep-2 Iegor de Saint Hippolyte, Montreal #7b (C.D 1500)

BOLINGER, Franz Josef (1903-) American

£481 $750 €722 Palm trees (61x41cm-24x16in) s. 20-Sep-2 Freeman, Philadelphia #93/R

BOLINK, Meryn (1967-) Dutch

Sculpture

£2848 $4500 €4500 Hand (36x17x9cm-14x7x4in) mixed media executed 1994 prov.exhib.lit. 26-Nov-2 Sotheby's, Amsterdam #308/R est:5000-6000

BOLIVIAN SCHOOL, 19th C

£7643 $12000 €11465 Saint Isidro (106x82cm-42x32in) i. 19-Nov-2 Sotheby's, New York #64/R est:20000

BOLLE, Martin (1912-1968) Belgian

£288 $460 €400 Verre fleuri de roses (60x50cm-24x20in) s. panel. 19-May-3 Horta, Bruxelles #28
£414 $658 €600 Clown (50x40cm-20x16in) panel. 4-Mar-3 Palais de Beaux Arts, Brussels #287
£514 $801 €750 Le clown au nez rouge (60x50cm-24x20in) s.d.54. 14-Apr-3 Horta, Bruxelles #498
£609 $956 €950 Elegante devant le miroir. Portrait de jeune fille au chapeau (60x50cm-24x20in) s. one d.1961 one d.1964 panel pair. 19-Nov-2 Vanderkindere, Brussels #81
£651 $1015 €950 Le clown (60x50cm-24x20in) s.d.47. 14-Apr-3 Horta, Bruxelles #497
£701 $1093 €1100 Le modele posant pour le peintre (80x100cm-31x39in) s. 11-Nov-2 Horta, Bruxelles #569
£1151 $1842 €1600 Les ballerines (60x50cm-24x20in) s. 19-May-3 Horta, Bruxelles #27 est:800-1200
£1154 $1812 €1800 Clown (60x50cm-24x20in) s. one d.1961 one d.1976 one d.1966 panel three. 19-Nov-2 Vanderkindere, Brussels #74 est:375-625

BOLLENDONK, Walter (1897-1977) American

£256 $400 €384 Seascape with crashing surf (41x51cm-16x20in) s. masonite. 18-Sep-2 Alderfer's, Hatfield #295/R

BOLLHAGEN, Franz (1881-1971) Swiss

£392 $627 €600 Woman reading by Hopfensee (62x97cm-24x38in) s. 10-Jan-3 Allgauer, Kempten #1552/R
£458 $732 €700 View over Teger Lake (60x80cm-24x31in) s. lit. 10-Jan-3 Allgauer, Kempten #1551/R

BOLLIER, Andre (?) French

£897 $1434 €1300 Paysage du port (54x65cm-21x26in) s. 12-Mar-3 E & Eve, Paris #105

BOLLIGER, Rodolphe (19th C) Swiss

£558 $882 €837 Quarry with trees and bushes (32x41cm-13x16in) s.d.12 i.verso. 26-Nov-2 Hans Widmer, St Gallen #1051/R (S.FR 1300)
£1223 $1907 €1835 Mon portrait (38x31cm-15x12in) s. i.d. verso panel. 6-Nov-2 Hans Widmer, St Gallen #121/R est:1400-2800 (S.FR 2800)

BOLLING, Svein (1948-) Norwegian

£537 $821 €806 Light and shadow (60x73cm-24x29in) s. painted 1972. 26-Aug-2 Blomqvist, Lysaker #1040/R (N.KR 6200)
£648 $1082 €940 Man and dog running (24x33cm-9x13in) s. exhib. 18-Jun-3 Grev Wedels Plass, Oslo #156/R (N.KR 7500)

Works on paper

£4337 $6765 €6506 Bollinger - dark (117x97cm-46x38in) s. pastel executed 2000 exhib. 21-Oct-2 Blomqvist, Oslo #446/R est:55000-65000 (N.KR 50000)

BOLLONGIER, Hans (1600-1644) Dutch

£11000 $17270 €16500 Street scene with quack surrounded by peasants (30x25cm-12x10in) panel painted c.1630. 12-Dec-2 Sotheby's, London #151/R est:8000-12000

BOLOGNESE SCHOOL (16th C) Italian

£6081 $9487 €9000 Annunciation (43x26cm-17x10in) mono. panel painted c.1550. 26-Mar-3 Tajan, Paris #1/R

Works on paper

£47297 $73784 €70000 Grotesque head (20x25cm-8x10in) i. brush ink wash prov. 27-Mar-3 Christie's, Paris #51/R est:5000

BOLOGNESE SCHOOL (17th C) Italian
£2703 $4216 €4000 Landscape capriccio with ruins and playing putti (75x62cm-30x24in) prov. 27-Mar-3 Dorotheum, Vienna #342/R est:2800-3500
£4268 $7000 €6402 Mystic marriage of Saint Catherine (24x19cm-9x7in) copper. 29-May-3 Sotheby's, New York #95/R est:4000-6000
£6604 $10236 €10500 Lady with vase (93x77cm-37x30in) 29-Oct-2 Finarte, Milan #482 est:5000-6000
£7547 $11698 €12000 Portrait of gentleman (21x14cm-8x6in) board. 29-Oct-2 Finarte, Milan #452/R
£9797 $15284 €14500 Transverberation de Sainte Therese (36x27cm-14x11in) copper. 28-Mar-3 Piasa, Paris #1/R
£22886 $37075 €33185 Interior from a butcher shop (132x182cm-52x72in) 26-May-3 Bukowskis, Stockholm #384/R est:80000-100000 (S.KR 295000)

BOLOGNESE SCHOOL (18th C) Italian
£5517 $8772 €8000 Mary Magdalene (93x154cm-37x61in) 5-Mar-3 Sotheby's, Milan #217/R
£9000 $15030 €13050 Diana and Endymion (170x122cm-67x48in) prov. 8-Jul-3 Sotheby's, Olympia #443/R est:6000-8000
£69182 $107233 €110000 Hercules battling the Hydra (172x172cm-68x68in) octagonal. 2-Oct-2 Dorotheum, Vienna #268/R est:15000-25000
Works on paper
£6892 $10751 €10200 Holy Family with Saint John (99x79cm-39x31in) pastel oval. 31-Mar-3 Finarte Semenzato, Milan #504/R

BOLOGNESE SCHOOL (18th C) Italian
£9146 $15000 €13719 Venus and Donis (145x193cm-57x76in) 29-May-3 Sotheby's, New York #27/R est:8000-12000

BOLONACHI, Constantin (1837-1907) Greek
£32000 $50560 €48000 Morning catch (21x45cm-8x18in) 1-Apr-3 Bonhams, New Bond Street #20 est:25000-35000
£50000 $77500 €75000 Boats at sea (43x67cm-17x26in) s. prov. 2-Oct-2 Sotheby's, London #18/R est:50000-70000
£60000 $94800 €90000 Before dusk (67x60cm-26x24in) 1-Apr-3 Bonhams, New Bond Street #26 est:45000-65000
£85000 $131750 €127500 Hauling in the catch (69x135cm-27x53in) s.d.71 prov. 2-Oct-2 Sotheby's, London #12/R est:70000-90000
£130000 $201500 €195000 Crossing (54x104cm-21x41in) s. 2-Oct-2 Sotheby's, London #36/R est:100000-150000
£140000 $217000 €210000 Fishing in calm waters (63x117cm-25x46in) s. prov. 2-Oct-2 Sotheby's, London #32/R est:100000-150000

BOLONACHI, Constantin (attrib) (1837-1907) Greek
£26282 $40737 €41000 Holiday house (60x100cm-24x39in) s. 5-Dec-2 Stadion, Trieste #685/R est:22000

BOLOTOWSKY, Ilya (1907-1981) American/Russian
£1603 $2500 €2405 Miniature yellow rhomb (35x20cm-14x8in) init.d.73 s.i.d.verso acrylic panel prov. 5-Nov-2 Doyle, New York #33/R est:1500-2000
£5488 $9000 €7958 Black, blue and red horizontal (102x183cm-40x72in) s.d.1967 verso oil on linen prov. 1-Jun-3 Wright, Chicago #294/R est:3000-5000
£11585 $19000 €16798 Untitled (107x107cm-42x42in) s.d.1969 oil on linen prov. 1-Jun-3 Wright, Chicago #293/R est:6000-8000
Sculpture
£4807 $7500 €7211 Untitled, rhomboid column. s. acrylic wood sold with a sketch prov. 14-Oct-2 Butterfields, San Francisco #2100/R est:6000-10000
Works on paper
£2070 $3250 €3105 Mural study (18x27cm-7x11in) ink board two panels prov. 19-Nov-2 Wright, Chicago #152/R est:800-1000

BOLT, N P (1886-1965) Danish
Works on paper
£657 $1051 €986 Interior scene with young girl by mirror (72x72cm-28x28in) s. pastel. 13-Jan-3 Rasmussen, Vejle #7/R (D.KR 7500)

BOLT, Ronald William (1938-) Canadian
£400 $656 €580 Wave study no.5 (30x30cm-12x12in) s.i.d.1977. 9-Jun-3 Hodgins, Calgary #174/R (C.D 900)

BOLTANSKI, Christian (1944-) French
£1351 $2108 €2000 Desespere (22x23cm-9x9in) tempera collage mixed media card. 26-Mar-3 Finarte Semenzato, Milan #172/R
£1622 $2530 €2400 Grand pere et petit Christian (30x23cm-12x9in) tempera collage mixed media card. 26-Mar-3 Finarte Semenzato, Milan #173/R
Photographs
£12658 $20000 €18987 Monument (105x198cm-41x78in) 26 red photographs light bulbs electrical wire prov. 12-Nov-2 Phillips, New York #105/R est:20000-30000
£25000 $38500 €37500 Monument (210x238cm-83x94in) thirty antracit photos fifty three red photo electric wire prov. 23-Oct-2 Christie's, London #173/R est:25000-35000
Sculpture
£1250 $2063 €1800 Composition (16x23cm-6x9in) wood sugar wire netting. 1-Jul-3 Artcurial Briest, Paris #815/R est:2000-2500
£3819 $6302 €5500 La sacoche (40x60cm-16x24in) i. clay wire netting iron box. 1-Jul-3 Artcurial Briest, Paris #553/R est:4000-6000
£5769 $8942 €9000 Untitled (40x64x12cm-16x25x5in) tempera glass metal wood. 6-Dec-2 Hauswedell & Nolte, Hamburg #57/R est:9000
£11250 $18000 €16875 Le Lycee chase no.16 (130x63x30cm-51x25x12in) gelatin silver print electric lamp ten tin boxes executed 1987. 15-May-3 Christie's, Rockefeller NY #357/R est:20000-30000
£16000 $26720 €23200 Reliquaire (179x90x35cm-70x35x14in) wire mesh steel cotton sheet transparency electric light. 27-Jun-3 Christie's, London #256/R est:10000-15000
£23734 $37500 €35601 Lessons of darkness. oxidized copper wire tin candles in 13 parts exec.1987 prov. 13-Nov-2 Sotheby's, New York #470/R est:25000-35000
Works on paper
£1111 $1833 €1600 J'ai appris la conversation (17x13cm-7x5in) bears sig.i.verso felt tip collage photo exec.c.1972-73. 1-Jul-3 Artcurial Briest, Paris #816/R est:1800-2200
£10000 $16400 €15000 Monument (208x61cm-82x24in) black white photos col photos light bulbs electrical wire prov. 7-Feb-3 Sotheby's, London #285/R est:8000-12000

BOLTON, Alice (fl.1874-1879) British
£500 $765 €750 Portrait of a young girl in a white dress (109x74cm-43x29in) s. 22-Aug-2 Mallams, Cheltenham #248

BOLTON, Hale William (1885-1920) American
£1923 $3000 €2885 Texas landscape (51x66cm-20x26in) painted c.1918. 19-Oct-2 David Dike, Dallas #96/R est:3000-6000
£1923 $3000 €2885 Autumn landscape (41x51cm-16x20in) 19-Oct-2 David Dike, Dallas #116/R est:3000-6000

BOLTON, Tim Scott (1947-) British
£260 $406 €390 Salisbury Cathedral (52x40cm-20x16in) s.d.1988 board. 26-Mar-3 Woolley & Wallis, Salisbury #140/R

BOLZE, Carl (1832-1913) Austrian
£2025 $3139 €3200 Alpine landscape with farmstead by river (25x46cm-10x18in) s.d.879 lit. 25-Sep-2 Neumeister, Munich #545/R est:2500

BOMAR, Bill (1919-1991) American
Works on paper
£769 $1200 €1154 Tres piedras (25x33cm-10x13in) mixed media exhib. 19-Oct-2 David Dike, Dallas #154/R

BOMBERG, David (1890-1957) British
£750 $1170 €1125 Four Bedouins (34x47cm-13x19in) i.verso oil on paper. 27-Mar-3 Christie's, Kensington #262/R
£5500 $8689 €8250 Portrait of Dinora (51x41cm-20x16in) painted c.1928/29. 27-Nov-2 Sotheby's, Olympia #86/R est:3000-5000
£9000 $15030 €13050 Flowers, evening (89x60cm-35x24in) 24-Jun-3 Bonhams, New Bond Street #62/R est:10000-15000
£18000 $29520 €26100 Two figures (57x50cm-22x20in) board painted 1932 prov. 4-Jun-3 Sotheby's, London #67/R est:12000-18000
Works on paper
£450 $702 €675 Arabs, Palestine (32x23cm-13x9in) chl white chk executed 1923 prov. 27-Mar-3 Christie's, Kensington #260/R
£700 $1092 €1050 Sappers under hill (20x26cm-8x10in) black ink W/C over pencil prov. 15-Oct-2 Bonhams, Knightsbridge #41/R
£1600 $2496 €2400 Two figures (26x20cm-10x8in) s.d.19 pen ink wash. 15-Oct-2 Bonhams, Knightsbridge #38/R est:1200-1800
£1916 $2854 €2874 Figure in doorway (26x19cm-10x7in) s.d.19 ink prov.exhib. 27-Aug-2 Christie's, Melbourne #354/R est:4000-6000 (A.D 5000)
£2300 $3657 €3450 Conspirators, top of the stairs (46x33cm-18x13in) s. chl. 26-Feb-3 Sotheby's, Olympia #187/R est:2500-3500

BOMBLED, Karel Frederik (1822-1902) Dutch
£3500 $5670 €5250 Grand Steeple-Chase de Paris. Prix du Jockey-Club (20x53cm-8x21in) s.i.d.1877 pair. 22-May-3 Christie's, London #62/R est:1500-2000

BOMBLED, Louis Charles (1862-1927) French

£443 $687 €700 Les chiens (11x20cm-4x8in) s. panel. 29-Sep-2 Eric Pillon, Calais #40/R

£860 $1342 €1290 Grand steeplechase de Paris, Auteuil. Prix du Jockey Club (19x51cm-7x20in) s.i. panel pair. 15-Oct-2 Stephan Welz, Johannesburg #389 est:7000-10000 (SA.R 14000)

£1552 $2483 €2250 Chantilly (16x22cm-6x9in) s.i. board. 11-Mar-3 Castellana, Madrid #55/R

£1552 $2483 €2250 Robert (16x22cm-6x9in) s.i. board. 11-Mar-3 Castellana, Madrid #54/R

BOMBOIS, Camille (1883-1970) French

£621 $1000 €932 Scene de rue (33x41cm-13x16in) s. 7-May-3 Sotheby's, New York #227/R est:10000-15000

£1154 $1800 €1731 River scene (33x41cm-13x16in) s. 10-Nov-2 Selkirks, St. Louis #571 est:3000-4000

£1266 $2000 €1899 Untitled - Le pont Baules (19x27cm-7x11in) s. 22-Apr-3 Butterfields, San Francisco #6020/R est:3000-5000

£2230 $3500 €3345 Sous-bois d'automne (27x35cm-11x14in) s. 22-Nov-2 Skinner, Boston #321/R est:7000-9000

£2759 $4358 €4000 Paysage (14x22cm-6x9in) s. 4-Apr-3 Tajan, Paris #68/R

£3416 $5500 €5124 Les deux moulins de Pen-nement (24x33cm-9x13in) s. 7-May-3 Sotheby's, New York #229/R est:10000-15000

£3988 $6500 €5982 Les pecheurs (25x36cm-10x14in) s. painted c.1950 prov. 12-Feb-3 Sotheby's, New York #121/R est:8000-12000

£4000 $6320 €5800 Still life (22x27cm-9x11in) s. 4-Apr-3 Tajan, Paris #7/R

£4200 $6468 €6300 Bord de riviere (16x24cm-6x9in) s. painted c.1928 prov. 22-Oct-2 Sotheby's, London #162/R est:4000-6000

£6135 $10000 €9203 Pecheur au bord de la riviere (20x28cm-8x11in) s. painted c.1945. 12-Feb-3 Sotheby's, New York #54/R est:10000-15000

£6211 $10000 €9317 Le leveur de poids (46x55cm-18x22in) s. prov. 7-May-3 Sotheby's, New York #225/R est:10000-15000

£6369 $9936 €10000 Chevaux dans la clairiere (39x49cm-15x19in) s. panel exhib. 5-Nov-2 Tajan, Paris #36/R est:10000-12000

£7000 $11130 €10500 Etang aux nenuphars (54x65cm-21x26in) s. 20-Mar-3 Sotheby's, Olympia #172/R est:8000-12000

£8176 $13000 €12264 Parc des Buttes Chaumont (50x64cm-20x25in) s. prov. 27-Feb-3 Christie's, Rockefeller NY #125/R est:10000

£12000 $18480 €18000 Coucher de soleil (38x46cm-15x18in) s. prov. 22-Oct-2 Sotheby's, London #157/R est:15000-20000

£12821 $20128 €20000 Paysage anime (16x22cm-6x9in) s. 10-Dec-2 Piasa, Paris #457/R est:2000

£17628 $27500 €26442 Villeneuve sur yonne, sens porte (81x60cm-32x24in) s.i.verso prov. 6-Nov-2 Sotheby's, New York #335/R est:25000-35000

BOMHALS, Suzanne (1912-) Belgian

£506 $800 €800 Chevauchee (75x95cm-30x37in) s. 26-Nov-2 Palais de Beaux Arts, Brussels #285/R

BOMMEL, Elias Pieter van (1819-1890) Dutch

£2201 $3434 €3500 Market square in Hungary (52x84cm-20x33in) panel. 23-Sep-2 Wiener Kunst Auktionen, Vienna #69/R est:4000-9000

£2308 $3508 €3600 Winter's day in Haarlem (15x23cm-6x9in) bears sig. panel. 17-Aug-2 Hans Stahl, Toestorf #36 est:3500

£2609 $4070 €3914 Coastal landscape with sailing ships and figures (28x39cm-11x15in) s.d.1871 panel. 16-Sep-2 Philippe Schuler, Zurich #3459/R est:4000-5000 (S.FR 6000)

£2740 $4301 €4000 Dutch river view (29x39cm-11x15in) s.d.1871 panel. 15-Apr-3 Sotheby's, Amsterdam #53/R est:4000-6000

£2830 $4387 €4500 Cornmill from the area of (33x46cm-13x18in) s.d.1879. 29-Oct-2 Dorotheum, Vienna #183/R est:3400-3800

£2848 $4500 €4500 Dutch ships by moonlight (31x52cm-12x20in) s.i.d.1881 panel. 28-Nov-2 Dorotheum, Vienna #169/R est:3600-4000

£5443 $8600 €8600 House on river mouth (39x49cm-15x19in) s. lit. 29-Nov-2 Schloss Ahlden, Ahlden #1355/R est:4500

£6250 $9938 €9000 Winteransicht und kirche zu Haarlem (15x23cm-6x9in) s. s.i.d.1874 panel. 29-Apr-3 Christie's, Amsterdam #87/R est:7000-9000

£7801 $12638 €11000 Picture of Dordrecht (27x40cm-11x16in) s. 22-May-3 Dorotheum, Vienna #52/R est:14000-16000

£10417 $16563 €15000 Busy market on a sunny day (25x32cm-10x13in) s. panel. 29-Apr-3 Christie's, Amsterdam #14/R est:12000-16000

£16000 $26720 €24000 Skaters on a frozen canal (50x76cm-20x30in) s. 18-Jun-3 Christie's, Kensington #55/R est:10000-15000

£18868 $29057 €30000 Busy market day on Het Kerkplein in Zaltbommel (30x42cm-12x17in) s.d.1852 panel prov. 22-Oct-2 Sotheby's, Amsterdam #147/R est:30000-50000

£47945 $75274 €70000 View of the Singel near the Brouwersgracht, Amsterdam (65x101cm-26x40in) s. 15-Apr-3 Sotheby's, Amsterdam #171/R est:70000-90000

£53459 $82327 €85000 Townsfolk on a quay, Middelburg (93x126cm-37x50in) s.d.52. 22-Oct-2 Sotheby's, Amsterdam #142/R est:55000-65000

BOMMELS, Peter (1951-) German

£2564 $3974 €4000 Arrival of the triumvirate (212x180cm-83x71in) s.i.d.81 verso dispersion cotton. 3-Dec-2 Lempertz, Koln #61/R est:4000-5000

BOMPARD, Maurice (1857-1936) French

£428 $684 €620 Rose blanche dans un vase (35x24cm-14x9in) s. 12-Mar-3 Libert, Castor, Paris #53

£2000 $3160 €3000 Lavandeuses (74x61cm-29x24in) s. 3-Apr-3 Christie's, Kensington #30/R

£2250 $3645 €3263 Desert landscape with nomads resting (60x97cm-24x38in) s. 26-May-3 Bukowskis, Stockholm #251/R est:40000-50000 (S.KR 29000)

£2308 $3600 €3462 Grand Canal at sunset (50x72cm-20x28in) s. 14-Sep-2 Weschler, Washington #583/R est:2000-3000

£3000 $4710 €4500 Vase of peacock feathers, swords and a pistol, other objects (146x97cm-57x38in) s. 21-Nov-2 Christie's, Kensington #81/R est:2500-3500

£3191 $4947 €4787 Desert landscape with nomads (60x97cm-24x38in) s. 3-Dec-2 Bukowskis, Stockholm #324/R est:40000-50000 (S.KR 45000)

£3673 $5841 €5400 Vue de Venise (73x60cm-29x24in) s. 26-Feb-3 Artcurial Briest, Paris #132/R est:5000-6000

£4200 $6678 €6300 Entrance to the Grand Canal, Venice (98x131cm-39x52in) s. 20-Mar-3 Christie's, Kensington #43/R est:4000-6000

BOMPIANI, Augusto (1851-1930) Italian

Works on paper

£680 $1082 €1000 Youth (56x40cm-22x16in) s. mixed media card. 1-Mar-3 Meeting Art, Vercelli #194

£1014 $1581 €1500 Young Italian woman (62x49cm-24x19in) s. W/C. 28-Mar-3 Dorotheum, Vienna #232/R est:1600-1800

BOMPIANI, Valentino (1898-1992) Italian

£1026 $1610 €1600 Interior with figure (30x50cm-12x20in) cardboard painted 1966 prov. 21-Nov-2 Finarte, Rome #197/R

BON, Angelo Del (1898-1952) Italian

£645 $1019 €1000 Marine at dawn (38x46cm-15x18in) s.prov. 18-Dec-2 Christie's, Rome #35

£1154 $1788 €1800 Still life (67x47cm-26x19in) s. painted 1947. 4-Dec-2 Finarte, Milan #279/R

£1218 $1888 €1900 Flowers in crystal vase (46x33cm-18x13in) painted 1949 lit. 4-Dec-2 Finarte, Milan #327/R

£1284 $2003 €1900 Mountainous landscape (40x30cm-16x12in) s. 26-Mar-3 Finarte Semenzato, Milan #362/R

£1667 $2583 €2600 Wood (60x70cm-24x28in) s. 4-Dec-2 Finarte, Milan #274/R

£1795 $2782 €2800 Snow in Castiglione (37x46cm-15x18in) s. painted 1937. 4-Dec-2 Finarte, Milan #286/R

£1923 $3019 €3000 Seated nude (79x65cm-31x26in) s. painted 1938 prov.exhib.lit. 19-Nov-2 Finarte, Milan #93/R

£1923 $3019 €3000 Boy with little vase (90x70cm-35x28in) s. painted 1926 exhib.lit. 19-Nov-2 Finarte, Milan #269/R

£2308 $3623 €3600 Monza, bridge on the Lambro (50x60cm-20x24in) s. painted 1936 lit. 19-Nov-2 Finarte, Milan #50/R

£2308 $3623 €3600 Snow on the hill (54x65cm-21x26in) s. painted 1949 exhib.lit. 19-Nov-2 Finarte, Milan #119/R

£2821 $4428 €4400 Orta lake (65x54cm-26x21in) s. painted 1949 exhib.lit. 19-Nov-2 Finarte, Milan #109/R

BONALUMI, Agostino (1935-) Italian

£2244 $3276 €3500 Composition (30x30cm-12x12in) s. 5-Jun-2 Il Ponte, Milan #118/R

£5063 $7899 €8000 Red (100x100cm-39x39in) s. painted 2000. 14-Sep-2 Meeting Art, Vercelli #828/R

£5442 $8653 €8000 Blue (50x90cm-20x35in) s.d.1981. 1-Mar-3 Meeting Art, Vercelli #352

£6536 $10458 €10000 Red (60x70cm-24x28in) s.d.1983. 4-Jan-3 Meeting Art, Vercelli #615

£7051 $11071 €11000 Yellow (114x146cm-45x57in) s. d.1997 verso lit. 23-Nov-2 Meeting Art, Vercelli #366/R est:10000

£7986 $12698 €11500 Yellow (100x100cm-39x39in) s.d.1978 verso. 1-May-3 Meeting Art, Vercelli #467 est:7000

£10507 $17232 €14500 Untitled (99x110cm-39x43in) s.d.65 verso prov. 28-May-3 Lempertz, Koln #59/R est:6000-7000

£11348 $18383 €16000 Bianco (97x130cm-38x51in) s.verso bent canvas. 26-May-3 Christie's, Milan #246/R est:16000-20000

£13514 $21081 €20000 Composition (100x100cm-39x39in) s.i.d.1971 verso. 26-Mar-3 Finarte Semenzato, Milan #291/R

£15000 $23250 €22500 Sin titulo (151x250cm-59x98in) s.d.68 on stretcher on two canvases. 5-Dec-2 Christie's, Kensington #202/R est:4000-6000

£24000 $37440 €36000 Bianco (151x121cm-59x48in) s.d.67 verso tempera shaped canvas prov. 21-Oct-2 Sotheby's, London #25/R est:20000-25000

Works on paper

£652 $1070 €900 Untitled (49x72cm-19x28in) s. pencil paper collage board. 28-May-3 Lempertz, Koln #60/R

£1026 $1590 €1600 Plan (50x39cm-20x15in) s.d.83 W/C relief. 4-Dec-2 Finarte, Milan #223/R

£2568 $4005 €3800 Final surface (51x73cm-20x29in) s.i. 26-Mar-3 Finarte Semenzato, Milan #238/R

£5677 $8288 €8516 Untitled (100x120cm-39x47in) s.d.1959 verso. 4-Jun-2 Germann, Zurich #20/R est:14000-16000 (S.FR 13000)

BONAMICI, Louis (1878-1966) Italian
£2000 $3100 €3000 Sunlit courtyard (46x38cm-18x15in) s. 5-Dec-2 Christie's, Kensington #89/R est:2000-3000

BONANOMI, Cesar (19th C) Italian
£2152 $3357 €3400 Ombres et lumierres (81x100cm-32x39in) s.i.d.1913 stretcher exhib. 15-Oct-2 Dorotheum, Vienna #21/R est:4400-5800
£2532 $3949 €4000 Les heures chaudes (81x100cm-32x39in) s.i. stretcher. 15-Oct-2 Dorotheum, Vienna #20/R est:4400-5800

BONAS, Jordi (1937-) French
£915 $1474 €1300 L'orchestre (60x80cm-24x31in) s. 11-May-3 Thierry & Lannon, Brest #241

BONATTI, V (20th C) Italian
£327 $536 €500 Portrait of woman (50x37cm-20x15in) s.i.d.1913 verso. 5-Feb-3 Il Ponte, Milan #592

BONAVIA, Carlo (fl.1740-1756) Italian
£12414 $19614 €18000 Saint Vito's tomb (56x50cm-22x20in) 3-Apr-3 Porro, Milan #30/R est:25000
£26207 $41407 €38000 View of Tivoli with bathers (42x57cm-17x22in) copper. 3-Apr-3 Porro, Milan #34/R est:40000
£46207 $73007 €67000 View of Baia with castle. View of Bacoli Marina (43x87cm-17x34in) pair prov.lit. 3-Apr-3 Porro, Milan #39/R est:90000

BONAVIA, Carlo (attrib) (18th C) Italian
£6081 $9487 €9000 Landscape by the sea with fishermen (50x75cm-20x30in) 26-Mar-3 Tajan, Paris #9/R est:8000
£10000 $15700 €15000 Rocky river landscape with washerwomen and a fisherman near a waterfall (100x76cm-39x30in) 10-Dec-2 Bonhams, New Bond Street #78/R est:10000-15000

BONAZZA, Antonio (18th C) Italian
Sculpture
£15823 $25000 €25000 Virgin (165cm-65in) marble. 28-Nov-2 Semenzato, Venice #6/R est:28000
£22152 $35000 €35000 Saint Anthony (163cm-64in) stone. 28-Nov-2 Semenzato, Venice #7/R est:20000
£31646 $50000 €50000 Saint Joseph with Child (154cm-61in) stone. 28-Nov-2 Semenzato, Venice #8/R est:28000

BOND, Henry (?) British?
Photographs
£3600 $6012 €5220 Untitled (121x160cm-48x63in) s.d.1996 verso C type print aluminium lit. 24-Jun-3 Sotheby's, Olympia #40/R est:3000-4000

BOND, Herbert (19/20th C) British
£440 $686 €638 Sunny day on a river (11x17cm-4x7in) s.i.verso. 27-Mar-3 Neales, Nottingham #1005
£700 $1162 €1050 Sunny day on the river (28x44cm-11x17in) s. s.i.verso. 10-Jun-3 Bonhams, Knightsbridge #240/R

BOND, John (1945-) British
Works on paper
£520 $858 €754 Two figures sitting on a breakwater (32x36cm-13x14in) s.d.1986 W/C. 1-Jul-3 Bonhams, Norwich #182

BOND, Richard Sebastian (1808-1886) British
£280 $445 €420 Driver and cattle by a ford (51x91cm-20x36in) s. 27-Feb-3 Bonhams, Chester #465
£406 $650 €609 Mountain landscape with river rapids. s. 1-Jan-3 Nadeau, Windsor #31/R
£600 $960 €900 Gipsy camp, Preath Mawr (74x120cm-29x47in) s.d.1875 s.i.verso. 15-May-3 Lawrence, Crewkerne #984

BOND, Simon (1947-) British
Works on paper
£500 $780 €750 Illustrations for a hundred and one uses of a dead cat (21x15cm-8x6in) s. pen ink pair lit. 27-Mar-3 Christie's, Kensington #233
£550 $858 €825 Illustrations for a hundred and one uses of a dead cat (15x21cm-6x8in) s. pen ink pair lit. 27-Mar-3 Christie's, Kensington #231
£550 $858 €825 Illustrations for a hundred and one uses of a dead cat (15x21cm-6x8in) s. pen ink pair lit. 27-Mar-3 Christie's, Kensington #232

BOND, Terence James (1946-) British
Works on paper
£300 $465 €450 Robin on a pine tree branch in winter (33x26cm-13x10in) s. W/C. 31-Oct-2 Ambrose, Loughton #78/R
£500 $775 €750 Study of a kestrel in a tree (68x46cm-27x18in) s. W/C. 31-Oct-2 Ambrose, Loughton #80/R
£1000 $1560 €1500 Long eared owl (99x75cm-39x30in) s. s.d.september 1994 gouache panel. 6-Nov-2 Sotheby's, Olympia #143/R est:600-800

BOND, W H (fl.1896-1907) British
£400 $616 €600 Sailing boat high-and-dry with horse and carts (12x17cm-5x7in) s. panel. 3-Sep-2 Bristol Auction Rooms #526

BOND, William Joseph J C (1833-1926) British
£380 $623 €570 Shore scene with figures and horse (19x26cm-7x10in) s. panel. 4-Jun-3 Bonhams, Chester #297
£450 $734 €653 Coastal scene with figures and fishing boats at low tide (12x15cm-5x6in) s. panel. 17-Jul-3 Tennants, Leyburn #816
£460 $718 €690 Shore scene with fishing boats and figures, possibly the Wirral coast (11x18cm-4x7in) panel. 6-Nov-2 Bonhams, Chester #355
£480 $715 €720 Peel Castle (13x15cm-5x6in) s. panel. 28-Jun-2 Chrystals Auctions, Isle of Man #196g
£960 $1498 €1440 Caernarvon Harbour. In the Dee Valley (18x22cm-7x9in) s. s.i.verso canvasboard pair. 6-Nov-2 Bonhams, Chester #354
£1350 $2214 €2025 Moored fishing boats (22x17cm-9x7in) s.d.99 board. 4-Jun-3 Bonhams, Chester #296 est:700-1000
£2013 $3200 €3020 Harbour views with masted vessels (20x19cm-8x7in) s.d.81 canvas on panel pair. 7-Mar-3 Skinner, Boston #338/R est:2000-4000
£2100 $3444 €3150 Fishing boat and figures on the shore (24x19cm-9x7in) s. board. 4-Jun-3 Bonhams, Chester #295/R est:100-1500
Works on paper
£360 $562 €540 Old mill (18x22cm-7x9in) s.d.88 W/C. 6-Nov-2 Bonhams, Chester #341

BONDE, Peter (1958-) Danish
£743 $1175 €1115 Attempting colour bearing (92x73cm-36x29in) s.d.261089 prov. 1-Apr-3 Rasmussen, Copenhagen #312/R (D.KR 8000)
£777 $1235 €1166 Composition (100x80cm-39x31in) s.d.1995 verso. 26-Feb-3 Kunsthallen, Copenhagen #179/R (D.KR 8500)
£847 $1312 €1271 U.T. - brown and black composition (100x80cm-39x31in) s.d.100691 verso prov. 1-Oct-2 Rasmussen, Copenhagen #157/R (D.KR 10000)
£847 $1312 €1271 Ilona meeting the doubt behind the inspiration (93x73cm-37x29in) s.d.17.05.83 verso. 1-Oct-2 Rasmussen, Copenhagen #191/R (D.KR 10000)
£947 $1469 €1421 House-trained signs (101x81cm-40x32in) s.d.26.06.83. 4-Dec-2 Kunsthallen, Copenhagen #197/R (D.KR 11000)
£3125 $4875 €4688 He was checking out - she was checking in (240x200cm-94x79in) s/d/1996 verso. 18-Sep-2 Kunsthallen, Copenhagen #129/R est:30000 (D.KR 37000)

BONDT, D de (17th C) Dutch
£1250 $1975 €1875 Continental harbour scene with rocky island (50x75cm-20x30in) 7-Apr-3 Bonhams, Bath #87/R est:1000-1500

BONDT, Daniel de (17th C) Dutch
£6200 $10354 €8990 Mediterranean coastal inlet with crab catchers and other figures in the foreground (52x77cm-20x30in) s. 11-Jul-3 Christie's, Kensington #101/R est:4000-6000

BONDUEL, Léon (19th C) French
Sculpture
£1763 $2750 €2645 L'alerte (56x84x30cm-22x33x12in) s.d.1889 pat bronze. 12-Oct-2 Neal Auction Company, New Orleans #552/R est:2000-3000

BONE, Andrew (20th C) British
£750 $1215 €1125 Chura bull elephant (33x48cm-13x19in) s. 23-Jan-3 Christie's, Kensington #71/R

BONE, Charles Richard (1809-c.1880) British
Works on paper
£900 $1422 €1350 Adoration of the Magi (47x21cm-19x8in) s.d.1829 W/C oval top. 27-Nov-2 Bonhams, Brooks & Langlois, Jersey #75/R

BONE, Freda C (20th C) Irish?
Works on paper
£280 $448 €420 Culdall Bay, Co Donegal (16x23cm-6x9in) s.i.d.1928 pencil W/C prov. 15-May-3 Christie's, Kensington #206/R

BONE, Henry (1755-1834) British

£4200 $6510 €6300 Sophonisba Regina (20x16cm-8x6in) s.d.1808 enamel after Titan with a Cavalier after Velasquez two. 6-Dec-2 Lyon & Turnbull, Edinburgh #22/R est:2000-3000
£64000 $101760 €96000 Portrait of James Watt (20x17cm-8x7in) enamel on porcelain after Sir William Beechey. 20-Mar-3 Sotheby's, London #134/R est:4000-6000

Miniatures

£1700 $2805 €2465 Mrs John Halkett (7cm-3xin) s.d.June 1807 enamel gilt metal frame brooch oval. 1-Jul-3 Bonhams, New Bond Street #93/R est:700-900
£2200 $3564 €3300 Young genleman wearing grey coat (6cm-2xin) init. i.verso gold frame. 22-May-3 Bonhams, New Bond Street #81/R est:800-1200
£3100 $5053 €4650 Marquess of Thomand (13x10cm-5x4in) i.d.1808 oval. 29-Jan-3 Brightwells, Leominster #860/R est:1700-2300
£3500 $5495 €5250 John Williams Hope (9cm-4xin) s.i. enamel on copper prov.exhib.lit. 10-Dec-2 Christie's, London #37/R est:3000-5000
£4000 $6240 €6000 George IV when Prince Reagent wearing Field Marshal's red uniform (6cm-2xin) s.i.d.1816 enamel on gold papier- mache frame oval. 5-Nov-2 Bonhams, New Bond Street #162/R est:1000-1500
£7000 $10990 €10500 Charles Grey wearing a blue coat (9cm-4xin) s. enamel on copper. 10-Dec-2 Christie's, London #38/R est:2000-3000
£30000 $46800 €45000 Thomas Howard 4th Duke of Norfolk wearing dark blue velvet coat (21cm-8xin) s.i. enamel ebonised wood tudor style frame rec. 5-Nov-2 Bonhams, New Bond Street #117/R est:10000-15000
£36000 $58320 €54000 Sofonisba Regina (20cm-8xin) s.d.1808 prov.e. 22-May-3 Bonhams, New Bond Street #126/R est:10000-15000
£38000 $59280 €57000 Horatio 1st Vicount Nelson wearing Vice-Admiral's undress uniform (12cm-5xin) s.d.1812 enamel ormolu mount oval. 5-Nov-2 Bonhams, New Bond Street #116/R est:15000-20000
£38000 $61560 €57000 Gentleman wearing black double slashed to reveal white (21cm-8xin) s. prov.exhib. 22-May-3 Bonhams, New Bond Street #127/R est:10000-15000

BONE, Henry Pierce (1779-1855) British

£2564 $4000 €3846 Depicting Isaac Newton (20x18cm-8x7in) d.1847 verso. 8-Aug-2 Eldred, East Dennis #701/R est:5500-6500

Miniatures

£2200 $3608 €3190 Princess Augusta Sophia (4cm-2xin) s.i.d.1840 enamel on gold prov. 3-Jun-3 Christie's, London #41/R est:1800-2200
£8000 $12560 €12000 Henry Bone, the artist father (12cm-5xin) enamel on copper oval. 10-Dec-2 Christie's, London #39/R est:3000-5000

BONE, Phyllis Mary (1896-1972) British

Sculpture

£800 $1312 €1200 Grizly bear (21x35cm-8x14in) s.d.1929 bronze. 5-Jun-3 Sotheby's, Olympia #110/R

BONE, Sir Muirhead (1876-1953) British

Prints

£2200 $3674 €3190 Spanish Good Friday (32x20cm-13x8in) s.i. drypoint. 30-Jun-3 Bonhams, New Bond Street #256/R est:2200-2800
£3270 $5200 €4905 Manhattan excavation (31x26cm-12x10in) s. drypoint. 1-May-3 Swann Galleries, New York #401/R est:4000-6000

Works on paper

£300 $489 €450 Industrial street scene with horse and cart (24x30cm-9x12in) s. ink wash. 11-Feb-3 Fellows & Sons, Birmingham #126/R
£300 $474 €450 Dreaming spires of Oxford (6x14cm-2x6in) s. pencil W/C wash. 7-Apr-3 Bonhams, Bath #43
£331 $550 €480 Untitled (13x20cm-5x8in) W/C. 13-Jun-3 Du Mouchelle, Detroit #2098/R
£358 $588 €537 Tower of the Vela Granada (10x13cm-4x5in) s. pen ink. 4-Jun-3 Deutscher-Menzies, Melbourne #420/R (A.D 900)
£450 $743 €653 Coinbra, Portugal (20x28cm-8x11in) s.i. chl W/C. 3-Jul-3 Christie's, Kensington #299/R
£475 $750 €750 Egyptian rooms in the British Museum (14x22cm-6x9in) s. pencil. 30-Nov-2 Bassenge, Berlin #6145/R
£500 $810 €750 Beaulieu, Hampshire (16x25cm-6x10in) s. pencil. 21-May-3 Bonhams, Knightsbridge #31/R
£500 $825 €725 Lifeboat day, Sheringham (18x21cm-7x8in) s.i.d.1936 W/C prov.exhib. 1-Jul-3 Bonhams, Norwich #128/R
£663 $1100 €961 Constantinople (20x28cm-8x11in) brushed ink. 13-Jun-3 Du Mouchelle, Detroit #2099/R
£800 $1320 €1160 Slipway, Cromer (27x43cm-11x17in) s.indis.d. pencil W/C bodycol htd white. 3-Jul-3 Christie's, Kensington #296/R
£820 $1255 €1230 Spanish Africa (12x21cm-5x8in) s.i.d.May 31 col pencil. 22-Aug-2 Bonhams, Edinburgh #1082/R
£840 $1378 €1260 Children playing on Cromer Beach (23x34cm-9x13in) s.i.d.1937 pen ink W/C htd white. 4-Feb-3 Bonhams, Leeds #293
£900 $1404 €1350 Bay at St. Vincent (27x37cm-11x15in) s. W/C pencil. 14-Apr-3 Sotheby's, London #151/R
£904 $1500 €1311 St Giles fair (28x20cm-11x8in) W/C. 13-Jun-3 Du Mouchelle, Detroit #2096/R est:500-900

BONE, Stephen (1904-1958) British

£260 $406 €390 Man seated by a grand piano (58x48cm-23x19in) s. 18-Oct-2 Keys, Aylsham #859
£300 $480 €450 Calm spring evening, Weymouth (24x34cm-9x13in) s. s.i.verso panel. 15-May-3 Lawrence, Crewkerne #1004

BONE, William Drummond (1907-1979) British

£260 $406 €390 Harvest landscape in the Cotswolds (61x76cm-24x30in) s.d.76 board. 13-Sep-2 Lyon & Turnbull, Edinburgh #35/R
£270 $448 €392 Storm clouds (60x90cm-24x35in) s. board. 13-Jun-3 Lyon & Turnbull, Edinburgh #78
£2000 $3040 €3000 On the river (71x91cm-28x36in) s. board. 28-Aug-2 Sotheby's, London #1031/R est:2000-3000

BONECHI, Lorenzo (1955-) Italian

Works on paper

£1918 $2992 €2800 Conversation (56x76cm-22x30in) s. gouache exec.1990. 10-Apr-3 Finarte Semenzato, Rome #228

BONECHI, Matteo (1672-1754) Italian

£1689 $2635 €2500 Birth of the Virgin (27x20cm-11x8in) paper. 27-Mar-3 Christie's, Paris #34/R

BONET, Paul (1889-1971) French

Works on paper

£641 $994 €1000 Vie de lenine (25x32cm-10x13in) crayon gouache prov. 4-Dec-2 Christie's, Paris #28/R

BONEVARDI, Marcelo (1929-1994) Argentinian

£1063 $1680 €1595 Pillar (87x28cm-34x11in) i.verso. 15-Nov-2 Naón & Cia, Buenos Aires #16/R

Works on paper

£321 $500 €482 Weather vane (51x36cm-20x14in) s.i.d.77 chl col chk. 5-Nov-2 Doyle, New York #6/R

BONFANTI, Arturo (1905-1978) Italian

£1410 $2186 €2200 Untitled (18x20cm-7x8in) s.i.d.1971 verso. 4-Dec-2 Finarte, Milan #578/R
£3056 $4858 €4400 P.d.A. (35x41cm-14x16in) s.i.d.1972 verso acrylic board. 1-May-3 Meeting Art, Vercelli #197

Works on paper

£481 $745 €750 Chinese vase (21x12cm-8x5in) s. W/C. 4-Dec-2 Finarte, Milan #232/R

BONFANTI, Gino (1900-) Italian

£354 $562 €520 Naviglio in Milan (50x70cm-20x28in) s. 1-Mar-3 Stadion, Trieste #472

BONFANTINI, Sergio (1910-1989) Italian

£327 $523 €500 Belltower, Frace (70x45cm-28x18in) s. oil tempera pencil paper on board. 4-Jan-3 Meeting Art, Vercelli #122
£1282 $2013 €2000 Yellow cube (70x45cm-28x18in) s.i.d.1969 verso. 23-Nov-2 Meeting Art, Vercelli #475/R

BONFIELD, George R (1802-1898) American

£288 $450 €432 Seascape with sailboats and fishermen by the shore (41x61cm-16x24in) s. 21-Sep-2 Pook & Pook, Downington #288/R

BONFILS, Gaston (1855-1946) French

£513 $800 €770 Portrait of a lady, with a poppy in her hair (56x48cm-22x19in) s. 12-Oct-2 Neal Auction Company, New Orleans #342
£611 $954 €917 Musicians and women drinking in interior (66x81cm-26x32in) s. 6-Nov-2 Dobiaschofsky, Bern #362/R (S.FR 1400)

BONFILS, Louise (1856-1933) Danish

£255 $398 €383 Harbour scene (55x41cm-22x16in) s. 5-Aug-2 Rasmussen, Vejle #2181 (D.KR 3000)
£255 $403 €383 Fishing boat on beach by Hornbaek Harbour (29x49cm-11x19in) s.d.1910. 30-Nov-2 Rasmussen, Havnen #2140 (D.KR 3000)

BONGERS, Ryan (20th C) Dutch

£552 $877 €800 Untitled (60x30cm-24x12in) s. 10-Mar-3 Sotheby's, Amsterdam #340
£586 $932 €850 Female nude (40x55cm-16x22in) s. 10-Mar-3 Sotheby's, Amsterdam #341 est:300-500

BONHEUR, Auguste (1824-1884) French
£4545 $7136 €6818 Cattle in the Pyrenees (56x89cm-22x35in) i. s.verso. 24-Jul-2 Walker's, Ottawa #42/R est:9000-12000 (C.D 11000)
£6962 $11000 €10443 Landscape with cattle (100x140cm-39x55in) indis sig. prov. 24-Apr-3 Sotheby's, New York #103/R est:15000-20000

BONHEUR, Ferdinand (19th C) French
£545 $845 €850 Cavalier oriental (21x41cm-8x16in) s. 9-Dec-2 Beaussant & Lefèvre, Paris #13/R
£980 $1578 €1500 Marines (22x41cm-9x16in) s. panel pair. 18-Jan-3 Neret-Minet, Paris #153

BONHEUR, I (1827-1901) French
Sculpture
£1667 $2600 €2501 Racehorse and jockey (30x28cm-12x11in) s. 8-Nov-2 York Town, York #262a

BONHEUR, Isidore (1827-1901) French
Sculpture
£968 $1529 €1500 Bull (18x18cm-7x7in) s. bronze marble base lit. 18-Dec-2 Segre, Madrid #820/R
£1528 $2384 €2292 Bull about to charge (50cm-20in) i. bronze wood onyx socle. 20-Nov-2 Fischer, Luzern #1401/R est:1800-2500 (S.FR 3500)
£2000 $3120 €3000 Standing stag (39x27cm-15x11in) s.st.f.Peyrol brown pat bronze. 5-Nov-2 Sotheby's, London #108/R est:2000-3000
£2911 $4542 €4600 Muletier espagnol (35x32cm-14x13in) s.st.f.Peyrol brown pat bronze. 15-Oct-2 Horta, Bruxelles #187/R
£3706 $6189 €5300 Jument et son poulain (19x32cm-7x13in) s. brown pat bronze. 30-Jun-3 Pierre Berge, Paris #24/R est:700-800
£4610 $7468 €6500 Jockey a cheval - Derby (37cm-15in) s.i. base lustrous pat bronze. 23-May-3 Camard, Paris #7/R est:4500-6000
£4610 $7468 €6500 Pur sang (39cm-15in) s.base brown green pat bronze st.f.Estray. 23-May-3 Camard, Paris #11/R est:4500-6000
£4800 $7488 €7200 Pacing bull (34x53cm-13x21in) s.st.f.Peyrol brown pat bronze lit. 5-Nov-2 Sotheby's, London #122/R est:5000-8000
£7000 $10920 €10500 Hunting dog (31x61cm-12x24in) s.st.f.Peyrol brown pat bronze exhib. 5-Nov-2 Sotheby's, London #91/R est:6000-8000
£7194 $11511 €10000 L'accolade (72x97cm-28x38in) s. brown pat bronze. 18-May-3 Eric Pillon, Calais #26/R
£11000 $17160 €16500 Mounted jockey (34x26cm-13x10in) s.st.f.Peyrol brown pat bronze lit. 5-Nov-2 Sotheby's, London #104/R est:10000-15000
£14000 $21980 €21000 Musketeer (105x71cm-41x28in) s. dark brown pat. 10-Dec-2 Sotheby's, London #161/R est:15000-20000
£16312 $26426 €23000 Pur sang, encolure relevee (69x85cm-27x33in) s. base pat bronze st.f.Estray. 23-May-3 Camard, Paris #14/R est:8000-10000
£22013 $35000 €33020 Two polo players (36x57cm-14x22in) s. brown pat bronze. 30-Apr-3 Sotheby's, New York #559/R est:15000-25000
£78000 $121680 €117000 Mounted jockey (94x71cm-37x28in) s. brown pat bronze st.Peyrol lit. 9-Apr-3 Sotheby's, London #126/R est:30000-50000

BONHEUR, Juliette Peyrol (1830-1891) French
£1550 $2573 €2248 Sheep with lambs grazing (30x38cm-12x15in) s. 10-Jun-3 Louis Taylor, Stoke on Trent #919
£4167 $6542 €6500 Canards et poussins (32x41cm-13x16in) s.d.1859. 13-Dec-2 Piasa, Paris #186/R

BONHEUR, Rosa (1822-1899) French
£694 $1104 €1000 Agneau (16x20cm-6x8in) st.sig. paper on canvas. 30-Apr-3 Tajan, Paris #79
£940 $1513 €1400 Paysage au rocher (26x37cm-10x15in) s. 23-Feb-3 Lesieur & Le Bars, Le Havre #14/R
£943 $1462 €1500 Moutons dans un pre (21x30cm-8x12in) s. paper on canvas. 30-Oct-2 Artcurial Briest, Paris #161 est:1200-1500
£962 $1510 €1500 Bords de riviere (20x24cm-8x9in) st.sig. paper on cardboard. 16-Dec-2 Millon & Associes, Paris #146/R est:1500-2000
£1000 $1640 €1500 Vaches sous l'arbre (26x35cm-10x14in) s. panel. 5-Jun-3 Christie's, Kensington #777/R est:1000-1500
£1266 $2000 €2000 Berger landais (33x20cm-13x8in) st.sig. paper on canvas. 29-Nov-2 Drouot Estimations, Paris #45
£1620 $2609 €2430 Two rams grazing (22x39cm-9x15in) s. 7-May-3 Dobiaschofsky, Bern #363/R est:4500 (S.FR 3500)
£1887 $2925 €3000 Etude de tetes d'animaux (32x40cm-13x16in) st.sig. paper on canvase. 30-Oct-2 Artcurial Briest, Paris #160/R est:2700-3000
£3089 $5127 €4479 Seaweed gatherers on beach, Brittany (51x77cm-20x30in) s.d.1877. 16-Jun-3 Lilla Bukowskis, Stockholm #28 est:20000-25000 (S.KR 40000)
£4756 $7800 €6896 Taureaux dans un pre (40x69cm-16x27in) s. i.verso prov. 4-Jun-3 Christie's, Rockefeller NY #248/R est:7000-9000
£4861 $7729 €7000 Tigres couches (30x38cm-12x15in) s. prov. 30-Apr-3 Tajan, Paris #78/R
£11321 $18000 €16982 Two horses in a stable (63x98cm-25x39in) s. prov.lit. 30-Apr-3 Sotheby's, New York #557/R est:20000-30000
£22436 $35224 €35000 Trois jeunes pantheres couchees (50x60cm-20x24in) st.sig. lit. 10-Dec-2 Renaud, Paris #38/R est:45000
Sculpture
£1200 $1824 €1800 Un mouton broutant (14x21cm-6x8in) s. brown pat. bronze. 28-Aug-2 Sotheby's, London #855/R est:1200-1800
£1400 $2184 €2100 Walking bull (17x27cm-7x11in) s.i.indis.st.f. brown pat bronze. 9-Apr-3 Sotheby's, London #185/R est:1500-2000
£1772 $2800 €2658 Standing bull (15cm-6in) i. bronze on marble base. 3-Apr-3 Christie's, Rockefeller NY #315/R est:1000-1500
£2209 $3490 €3314 Taureau Beuglant, the bellowing bull (13x23cm-5x9in) bronze. 1-Dec-2 Levis, Calgary #208/R (C.D 5500)
Works on paper
£705 $1100 €1058 Study for the horse fair (31x37cm-12x15in) chl over pencil dr double-sided. 9-Nov-2 Sloan, North Bethesda #530/R
£1100 $1837 €1650 Three goats (20x25cm-8x10in) s. pencil W/C. 18-Jun-3 Christie's, Kensington #23/R est:1200-1800
£1379 $2207 €2000 Belier (23x17cm-9x7in) studio st. W/C prov. 12-Mar-3 E & Eve, Paris #56 est:2000-2300

BONHOMME, Léon (1870-1924) French
£1605 $2279 €2600 Nature morte aux pommes (38x55cm-15x22in) s. 16-Mar-3 Eric Pillon, Calais #130/R
Works on paper
£382 $607 €550 Scene de maison close (26x18cm-10x7in) s.d.1920 W/C chl. 29-Apr-3 Artcurial Briest, Paris #61

BONI, Giacomo Antonio (attrib) (1688-1766) Italian
Works on paper
£1351 $2108 €2000 Study for ceiling (37x51cm-15x20in) chk pen ink wash. 27-Mar-3 Christie's, Paris #20/R

BONIFACIO, Alfonso Gomez (1934-) Spanish
£1282 $2013 €2000 Untitled (60x60cm-24x24in) s.d.1968 prov. 16-Dec-2 Castellana, Madrid #409/R
£2893 $4455 €4600 Landscape (81x110cm-32x43in) s.i.d.1992 verso prov. 28-Oct-2 Segre, Madrid #149/R est:4000

BONIFAZIO DI PITATI (studio) (1487-1553) Italian
£6329 $10000 €10000 Adoration of the Magi (133x210cm-52x83in) prov. 27-Nov-2 Finarte, Milan #51/R

BONIN, Maurice (1911-) French
£1465 $2286 €2300 Paris, Pont-Neuf (60x73cm-24x29in) s. s.i.d.1985 verso. 5-Nov-2 Tajan, Paris #108/R

BONINGTON, Richard Parkes (1802-1828) British
£385 $600 €578 Cottage near Halifax, Yorkshire (30x23cm-12x9in) s.verso cardboard. 18-Sep-2 Jackson's, Cedar Falls #754/R
Works on paper
£500 $825 €725 Study of three man in renaissance dress (8x7cm-3x3in) pencil pen blk ink border. 2-Jul-3 Sotheby's, Olympia #283/R
£1300 $2028 €1950 Beached fishing boats on Whitby Sands. s. W/C. 20-Sep-2 Richardson & Smith, Whitby #188 est:750-850
£3179 $5181 €4800 Sailing boat on river (6x14cm-2x6in) s. W/C pen. 3-Feb-3 Chambelland & Giafferi, Paris #330/R
£5800 $9222 €8700 Study of old houses (21x19cm-8x7in) pencil htd white prov. 19-Mar-3 Sotheby's, London #173/R est:3000-4000

BONINGTON, Richard Parkes (attrib) (1802-1828) British
£1690 $2721 €2400 Harbour in morning (25x30cm-10x12in) 7-May-3 Michael Zeller, Lindau #647/R est:1200
£1900 $3002 €2755 Beach scene with fishing boats (20x25cm-8x10in) panel. 22-Jul-3 Gorringes, Lewes #1592/R est:2000-3000
£2013 $3099 €3200 Fiances (45x61cm-18x24in) s. 28-Oct-2 Il Ponte, Milan #222/R
£2658 $4253 €3854 Coastal landscape with vessel and figures on beach (30x60cm-12x24in) 18-May-3 Anders Antik, Landskrona #104 est:10000 (S.KR 34000)
Works on paper
£673 $1043 €1050 Sailing boat off English coast (16x24cm-6x9in) W/C board prov. 7-Dec-2 Ketterer, Hamburg #8/R
£4800 $7584 €7200 Santa Marie Della Salute and Piazzetta, Venice (15x24cm-6x9in) W/C over pencil htd bodycol. 28-Nov-2 Sotheby's, London #267/R est:2000-3000

BONITO, Giuseppe (1705-1789) Italian
£17834 $27822 €28000 Woman holding a spindle, together with two boys (74x63cm-29x25in) canvas on board. 5-Nov-2 Sotheby's, Amsterdam #327/R est:10000-15000

BONIVENTO, Eugenio (1880-1956) Italian
£545 $845 €850 Saint Giorgio Island (23x30cm-9x12in) s. board. 4-Dec-2 Finarte, Rome #780
£1088 $1731 €1600 View of Chioggia (24x20cm-9x8in) s. board. 1-Mar-3 Meeting Art, Vercelli #249
£1170 $1896 €1650 Tragetto S Barnaba. S Giorgio, Venezia (12x16cm-5x6in) s. i.verso panel pair. 22-May-3 Stadion, Trieste #330/R est:700-1000

Works on paper
£500 $810 €750 Rialto Bridge, Venice (27x45cm-11x18in) s. W/C. 21-May-3 Bonhams, Knightsbridge #83/R

BONNAR, James King (1885-1961) American
£828 $1300 €1242 Winter landscape with stream, snow covered banks and man with wagon (41x51cm-16x20in) s. s.d.1950 verso board. 19-Apr-3 James Julia, Fairfield #262/R
£1000 $1600 €1450 Seaside cottage (45x54cm-18x21in) s. canvasboard. 16-May-3 Skinner, Boston #274/R est:1500-2000
Works on paper
£519 $800 €779 Summer at Gloucester (36x53cm-14x21in) s. W/C. 27-Oct-2 Grogan, Boston #107

BONNAR, William (1800-1853) British
£2700 $4185 €4050 Mask (36x46cm-14x18in) s.d.1836 exhib. 5-Dec-2 Bonhams, Edinburgh #127/R est:1200-1500

BONNARD, Pierre (1867-1947) French
£27338 $43741 €38000 Vue de coursive et de cheminee de bateau (21x27cm-8x11in) s. panel painted c.1926. 16-May-3 Lombrail & Teucquam, Paris #125/R
£97872 $163447 €138000 La promenade au bord de la riviere (26x46cm-10x18in) s. exhib.lit. 20-Jun-3 Piasa, Paris #14/R est:60000-80000
£102564 $160000 €153846 Enfants et Chevreaux (130x46cm-51x18in) st.sig. painted c.1899 prov.lit. 6-Nov-2 Sotheby's, New York #148/R est:180000-220000
£141026 $220000 €211539 Sous-bois - esquisse (70x78cm-28x31in) st.sig. painted c.1923 prov.lit. 6-Nov-2 Sotheby's, New York #153/R est:20000-300000
£180000 $300600 €270000 Femme blonde lisant (36x46cm-14x18in) s. panel painted c.1905 prov. 23-Jun-3 Sotheby's, London #15/R est:160000-200000
£223776 $373706 €320000 Femme assis dans l'atelier (48x63cm-19x25in) st.sig. paper on canvas painted c.1909 prov.exhib.lit. 30-Jun-3 Pierre Berge, Paris #39/R est:320000-350000
£230000 $377200 €345000 La Seine a Vernon (35x76cm-14x30in) s. painted c.1923 prov.lit. 4-Feb-3 Christie's, London #298/R est:160000
£278481 $434430 €440000 Fenetre ouverte (50x65cm-20x26in) s. tempera paper on canvas prov.exhib.lit. 20-Oct-2 Claude Boisgirard, Paris #26/R
£310559 $500000 €465839 Trois ages (45x34cm-18x13in) s.d.1893 prov.exhib.lit. 6-May-3 Sotheby's, New York #14/R est:600000-800000
£420000 $701400 €609000 Baigneurs a la fin du jour (48x69cm-19x27in) s. prov.exhib.lit. 24-Jun-3 Christie's, London #26/R est:100000-150000
£3800000 $6232000 €5700000 Matinee au cannet (88x113cm-35x44in) s. painted 1932 prov.exhib.lit. 4-Feb-3 Sotheby's, London #16/R est:3000000
Prints
£1923 $3019 €3000 Le marchand des quatre saisons (41x53cm-16x21in) col lithograph vellum. 11-Dec-2 Maigret, Paris #8 est:2600-2800
£1944 $3092 €2800 Femme au parapluie (22x12cm-9x5in) mono. col lithograph. 5-May-3 Ketterer, Munich #2/R est:400-600
£2215 $3500 €3500 Les raisins (33x25cm-13x10in) s.num.34/80 lithograph exhib. 1-Dec-2 Bukowskis, Helsinki #376/R est:2500-3000
£2324 $3858 €3300 Les boulevards (27x33cm-11x13in) s. col lithograph. 12-Jun-3 Piasa, Paris #25
£2372 $3724 €3700 Coin de rue (41x53cm-16x21in) col lithograph vellum. 11-Dec-2 Maigret, Paris #5 est:2000-2400
£2390 $3800 €3585 Cover for the second Album d'estampes originales (58x86cm-23x34in) col lithograph edition of 100. 29-Apr-3 Christie's, Rockefeller NY #401/R est:3000-4000
£2639 $4196 €3800 Le canotage (27x47cm-11x19in) col lithograph. 5-May-3 Ketterer, Munich #7/R est:2500-3500
£2949 $4629 €4600 Place le soir (41x53cm-16x21in) col lithograph vellum. 11-Dec-2 Maigret, Paris #9 est:3000-3200
£2986 $4748 €4300 L'Arc de Triomphe (31x46cm-12x18in) s. col lithograph. 5-May-3 Ketterer, Munich #12/R est:2500-3500
£3013 $4730 €4700 Avenue du bois (31x46cm-12x18in) col lithograph. 11-Dec-2 Maigret, Paris #4/R est:3000-3400
£3333 $5300 €4800 Avenue du bois (31x46cm-12x18in) s. col lithograph. 5-May-3 Ketterer, Munich #5/R est:2500-3500
£3592 $5962 €5100 Place le soir (27x43cm-11x17in) col lithograph. 12-Jun-3 Piasa, Paris #24/R
£4615 $7246 €7200 Rue vue d'en haut (53x41cm-21x16in) mono.num.49 col lithograph. 11-Dec-2 Maigret, Paris #15 est:1800-2000
£5208 $8281 €7500 Coin de rue (11x14cm-4x6in) s. col lithograph. 5-May-3 Ketterer, Munich #10/R est:6500-7500
£5769 $9058 €9000 Rue le soir sous la pluie (41x53cm-16x21in) s.num.87 col lithograph vellum. 11-Dec-2 Maigret, Paris #11/R est:4500-5000
£5903 $9385 €8500 Rue, le soir, sous la pluie (25x35cm-10x14in) s.i. col lithograph. 5-May-3 Ketterer, Munich #9/R est:7000-9000
£6218 $9762 €9700 Boulevard (41x53cm-16x21in) s.num.5 col lithograph vellum. 11-Dec-2 Maigret, Paris #10/R est:4600-5000
£6923 $10869 €10800 Maison dans la cour (53x42cm-21x17in) s.num.46 col lithograph. 11-Dec-2 Maigret, Paris #7/R est:3000-3200
£6944 $11042 €10000 L'enfant a la lampe (33x46cm-13x18in) col lithograph. 5-May-3 Ketterer, Munich #8/R est:6500-7500
Sculpture
£1459 $2306 €2189 Chien assis (14cm-6in) mono. num.9/12 pat bronze. 29-Nov-2 Zofingen, Switzerland #2247/R est:4000 (S.FR 3400)
Works on paper
£329 $533 €500 La grotte (10x15cm-4x6in) st.init. black crayon dr. 22-Jan-3 Tajan, Paris #97
£942 $1461 €1500 Marthe a sa toilette (20x14cm-8x6in) st.mono. ink pen. 4-Oct-2 Tajan, Paris #31 est:1500-2000
£1069 $1700 €1604 Etude pour dingo (12x11cm-5x4in) mono. pencil prov.exhib. 27-Feb-3 Christie's, Rockefeller NY #19/R
£1181 $1865 €1700 Bateau a quai (13x15cm-5x6in) crayon dr. 25-Apr-3 Piasa, Paris #76/R est:2500
£1346 $2046 €2100 Portrait de jeune fille (31x22cm-12x9in) st.init. graphite W/C dr exhib. 16-Aug-2 Deauville, France #37/R
£1410 $2144 €2200 Nu aux bras leves (31x23cm-12x9in) st.init. chl dr exhib. 16-Aug-2 Deauville, France #38/R
£1597 $2524 €2300 Jeune femme au bouquet (17x11cm-7x4in) chl dr. 25-Apr-3 Piasa, Paris #78/R est:1000
£1847 $2882 €2900 Promenade ombragee (10x16cm-4x6in) st.init. graphite dr. 10-Nov-2 Eric Pillon, Calais #23/R
£2051 $3118 €3200 Femme de dos et homme au chapeau assis (22x12cm-9x5in) graphite dr prov. 16-Aug-2 Deauville, France #39/R
£2553 $4136 €3600 Jeune femme et son chien (30x18cm-12x7in) s. graphite. 21-May-3 Cornette de St.Cyr, Paris #11/R est:4000-6000
£3846 $6038 €6000 Petit canal de la Sciagne (13x17cm-5x7in) init. graphite dr exec.c.1930. 10-Dec-2 Piasa, Paris #262/R
£4487 $6955 €7000 Nu au tub (15x12cm-6x5in) mono. crayon dr. 9-Dec-2 Piasa, Paris #2/R est:8000-10000
£5128 $8051 €8000 Paysage (24x31cm-9x12in) Chinese ink dr. 10-Dec-2 Piasa, Paris #260/R
£8108 $13054 €12162 La Chambre d'enfant (16x11cm-6x4in) ink executed c.1897 exhib.prov. 26-Feb-3 Museumsbygningen, Copenhagen #43/R est:50000-75000 (D.KR 90000)
£134615 $211346 €210000 Port de peceehe (32x50cm-13x20in) s. gouache prov. 10-Dec-2 Piasa, Paris #205/R est:100000-150000
£137821 $213622 €215000 Vase de fleurs (62x38cm-24x15in) s. gouache exhib.lit. 9-Dec-2 Piasa, Paris #11/R est:100000-130000
£180000 $300600 €261000 Port de peche (32x60cm-13x24in) s. gouache exec.c.1942 prov. 24-Jun-3 Christie's, London #64/R est:180000-250000

BONNAT, Léon (1833-1922) French
£1319 $2085 €1900 Etude de cheval (32x21cm-13x8in) init. panel. 25-Apr-3 Piasa, Paris #74/R est:900
£27419 $42500 €41129 Meditation (146x103cm-57x41in) s.d.1884 prov. 29-Oct-2 Sotheby's, New York #16/R est:50000-70000
Works on paper
£270 $422 €400 Veille (16x10cm-6x4in) mono. pen ink over crayon. 31-Mar-3 Piasa, Paris #68
£412 $650 €650 Oedipe et Antigone (27x18cm-11x7in) s.i. chl sanguine wash. 28-Nov-2 Tajan, Paris #186
£4516 $7000 €6774 Study for the assumption of the Virgin, Church of St. Andre, Bayonne (57x49cm-22x19in) pencil W/C prov. 29-Oct-2 Sotheby's, New York #75/R est:2000-3000
£16774 $26000 €25161 Study for la lutte de Jacob (53x37cm-21x15in) s.d.1876 pencil black chk. 29-Oct-2 Sotheby's, New York #70/R est:6000-8000

BONNAUD, Paul (20th C) French
£634 $1020 €900 Porteuses d'eau en Kabylie (73x54cm-29x21in) s. 12-May-3 Lesieur & Le Bars, Le Havre #13/R

BONNEFOIT, Alain (1939-) French
£1000 $1600 €1500 Paris (64x53cm-25x21in) s. 11-Jan-3 Harvey Clar, Oakland #1203
£1224 $1947 €1800 Nu de profil (70x50cm-28x20in) s.d.98 oil gouache ink paper on canvas. 26-Feb-3 Artcurial Briest, Paris #333 est:800-1000
£1364 $2073 €2100 Sortilege (78x110cm-31x43in) s.d.1998 paper on canvas. 7-Jul-2 Lombrail & Teucquam, Paris #74/R
Works on paper
£252 $390 €400 Nude (40x29cm-16x11in) s.d.96 W/C pen dr. 5-Oct-2 De Vuyst, Lokeren #46/R
£275 $442 €420 Barbara (50x35cm-20x14in) s. W/C. 19-Jan-3 Feletin, Province #133
£312 $506 €440 Louise (25x38cm-10x15in) s. W/C. 25-May-3 Feletin, Province #119
£494 $701 €800 Nu assis (39x24cm-15x9in) s. mixed media cardboard. 16-Mar-3 Eric Pillon, Calais #229/R
£634 $1020 €900 Nu assis (99x64cm-39x25in) s.d.87 Sumi ink paper on canvas. 12-May-3 Lesieur & Le Bars, Le Havre #14/R
£1224 $1947 €1800 Nu assis (70x50cm-28x20in) s.d.96 gouache pastel ink paper on canvas. 26-Feb-3 Artcurial Briest, Paris #332 est:800-1000

BONNEFOY, Henri-Arthur (1839-1917) French
£10377 $16085 €16500 Still life of fruit and vegetables (81x100cm-32x39in) s.d.1857. 29-Oct-2 Finarte, Milan #397/R est:4000-6000

BONNEN, Kaspar (1968-) Danish
£446 $705 €669 Composition (75x75cm-30x30in) s.d.1999 stretcher. 1-Apr-3 Rasmussen, Copenhagen #248 (D.KR 4800)

£477 $796 €692 Composition (75x75cm-30x30in) s.d.1999 stretcher. 17-Jun-3 Rasmussen, Copenhagen #157 (D.KR 5000)

BONNEN, Peter (1945-) Danish
Sculpture
£1766 $2790 €2649 Untitled (45x50x50cm-18x20x20in) s.d.c.1970 pat iron in two parts. 1-Apr-3 Rasmussen, Copenhagen #171/R est:25000 (D.KR 19000)
£2230 $3524 €3345 Untitled (92x23x10cm-36x9x4in) one s. pat iron in two parts executed c.1979. 1-Apr-3 Rasmussen, Copenhagen #174/R est:30000-40000 (D.KR 24000)

BONNET, Anne (1908-1960) Belgian
£496 $829 €700 Nature morte (27x41cm-11x16in) s.d. canvas on panel. 18-Jun-3 Pierre Berge, Paris #157
£759 $1214 €1100 Composition (24x41cm-9x16in) s.d.49. 15-Mar-3 De Vuyst, Lokeren #31
£1887 $2925 €3000 Voiles (46x38cm-18x15in) s.d.54 s.i.d.1954 panel. 5-Oct-2 De Vuyst, Lokeren #482/R est:3500-4500
Works on paper
£411 $642 €650 L'oiseau (25x25cm-10x10in) s. gouache. 16-Oct-2 Hotel des Ventes Mosan, Brussels #311
£538 $839 €850 Composition abstraite (29x23cm-11x9in) s. gouache. 16-Oct-2 Hotel des Ventes Mosan, Brussels #301
£570 $889 €900 Composition aux rectangles (33x25cm-13x10in) s. gouache. 16-Oct-2 Hotel des Ventes Mosan, Brussels #303
£1139 $1777 €1800 Nature morte au broc (33x61cm-13x24in) s. gouache. 16-Oct-2 Hotel des Ventes Mosan, Brussels #289 est:1500-1800

BONNET, François (1811-1894) French
£321 $500 €482 Mountain landscape (15x25cm-6x10in) s. board. 18-Sep-2 Boos Gallery, Michigan #168/R
£1218 $1900 €1827 Landscape with houses (38x33cm-15x13in) s. board. 18-Sep-2 Boos Gallery, Michigan #169/R est:1200-1800
£1218 $1900 €1827 Villa Borghese (30x25cm-12x10in) 18-Sep-2 Boos Gallery, Michigan #174/R est:1000-1500
£2323 $3670 €3600 Maisons a Rome (38x1cm-15x0in) paper on cardboard. 18-Dec-2 Renaud, Paris #60
£2517 $4204 €3600 Le portique d'octavie a Rome (32x27cm-13x11in) paper on canvas. 25-Jun-3 Sotheby's, Paris #85/R est:2000-3000

BONNET, Jordi (20th C) Canadian
Sculpture
£858 $1339 €1287 Icarus (37x89cm-15x35in) s. polished aluminum. 25-Mar-3 Ritchie, Toronto #185/R est:500-700 (C.D 2000)

BONNET, Rudolf (1895-1978) Dutch
Works on paper
£458 $737 €650 Balinese lad (22x22cm-9x9in) init.i.d.47 chl dr. 7-May-3 Vendue Huis, Gravenhage #236
£4971 $7655 €7457 Portrait of J Tjanteng (56x51cm-22x20in) s.i.d.73 chl. 27-Oct-2 Christie's, Hong Kong #7/R est:40000-50000 (HK.D 60000)
£5439 $8974 €7887 Seated man (40x30cm-16x12in) s.i.d.48 pastel. 6-Jul-3 Christie's, Hong Kong #13/R est:70000-100000 (HK.D 70000)
£14913 $22966 €22370 Landscape with gunung agung at dusk (68x82cm-27x32in) s.i.d.1951 W/C bodycol paper on board lit. 27-Oct-2 Christie's, Hong Kong #15/R est:95000-125000 (HK.D 180000)
£108780 $179487 €157731 Two women and their wares (112x68cm-44x27in) s.i.d.1975 pastel chl lit. 6-Jul-3 Christie's, Hong Kong #8/R est:220000-300000 (HK.D 1400000)
£108780 $179487 €157731 Study of the mural work in Makasar (152x76cm-60x30in) s.i.d.Jun 46 chl lit. 6-Jul-3 Christie's, Hong Kong #9/R est:220000-300000 (HK.D 1400000)

BONNEVIE, Mai Bente (20th C) Scandinavian
£255 $392 €383 Future memory (76x56cm-30x22in) s. acrylic panel painted 1989. 28-Oct-2 Blomqvist, Lysaker #1011/R (N.KR 3000)

BONNEVILLE, François (1650-1715) French
£645 $1019 €1000 Paysage d'orage (32x42cm-13x17in) metal. 20-Dec-2 Tajan, Paris #109

BONNEY, Richard (?) British
£380 $593 €570 Hauling in (56x76cm-22x30in) s. board. 17-Oct-2 David Lay, Penzance #1117

BONNIER, Olle (1925-) Swedish
£541 $870 €812 Frost (41x33cm-16x13in) s.d.59. 7-May-3 AB Stockholms Auktionsverk #924/R (S.KR 7000)
£1369 $2163 €2054 Spanish glow (32x90cm-13x35in) s.d.20/2-58 tempera paper on panel. 28-Apr-3 Bukowskis, Stockholm #248/R est:25000-30000 (S.KR 18000)
£1390 $2238 €2085 Composition (55x61cm-22x24in) S.D.72 T. PA. 7-May-3 AB Stockholms Auktionsverk #919/R est:18000-20000 (S.KR 18000)
£6178 $9946 €9267 Composition - 1956 (51x150cm-20x59in) s.d.56 oil sand prov. 7-May-3 AB Stockholms Auktionsverk #948/R est:50000-60000 (S.KR 80000)
£8494 $13676 €12741 1950s theme (45x44cm-18x17in) init.d.50 i.verso tempera paper lit. 7-May-3 AB Stockholms Auktionsverk #937/R est:90000-100000 (S.KR 110000)
£24710 $39784 €37065 Canary intermezzo (84x137cm-33x54in) init.d.49 s.i.d.1950 verso. 7-May-3 AB Stockholms Auktionsverk #928/R est:300000-400000 (S.KR 320000)
Works on paper
£418 $661 €627 Composition (6x14cm-2x6in) init.d.47 Indian ink. 28-Apr-3 Bukowskis, Stockholm #246b/R (S.KR 5500)
£618 $1025 €896 Catalina (73x94cm-29x37in) s.d.58 mixed media. 16-Jun-3 Lilla Bukowskis, Stockholm #524 (S.KR 8000)
£849 $1368 €1274 Cosmic composition (105x75cm-41x30in) s. pastel. 7-May-3 AB Stockholms Auktionsverk #923/R (S.KR 11000)
£913 $1442 €1370 Untitled (31x43cm-12x17in) s.i.d.52 mixed media. 28-Apr-3 Bukowskis, Stockholm #249/R (S.KR 12000)

BONNY, John (fl.1870-1892) British
Works on paper
£280 $437 €420 Figures on a path beside a ford (25x36cm-10x14in) s. pencil W/C htd white. 27-Mar-3 Christie's, Kensington #38

BONO, Primitif (fl.1920-1940) Italian
£2381 $3786 €3500 Le jour s'eveille, Oran (73x92cm-29x36in) s. i.verso. 24-Mar-3 Rabourdin & Choppin de Janvry, Paris #120/R est:3500-3800

BONOMI, Giovanni (19th C) Italian
£1667 $2650 €2400 Shepherd with flock near Milan (50x63cm-20x25in) s. i. verso. 29-Apr-3 Wiener Kunst Auktionen, Vienna #548/R est:2000-4000

BONONI, Carlo (circle) (1569-1632) Italian
£6000 $9420 €9000 Angles kneeling near a book and a carinal's hat (156x126cm-61x50in) fragment. 13-Dec-2 Christie's, Kensington #228/R est:8000-12000

BONQUART, Adolphe (1864-1915) French
£5128 $8051 €8000 Paquebot (87x145cm-34x57in) s. 24-Nov-2 Lesieur & Le Bars, Le Havre #10/R

BONSDORFF, Margaretha von (?) ?
£348 $543 €550 Town scene (114x180cm-45x71in) s. 12-Sep-2 Hagelstam, Helsinki #841

BONTJES VAN BEEK, Olga (1896-1995) German
£472 $736 €750 Winter evening on the heath (30x40cm-12x16in) mono. s. verso panel. 21-Sep-2 Bolland & Marotz, Bremen #340/R
£786 $1226 €1250 Still life with artichokes and lemons (50x60cm-20x24in) s. s.d.1983 verso verso panel. 21-Sep-2 Bolland & Marotz, Bremen #339/R

BONVICINO, Alessandro (1498-1554) Italian
£8805 $13648 €14000 Christ at the pillory (67x45cm-26x18in) prov. 2-Oct-2 Dorotheum, Vienna #24/R est:14000-20000

BONVIN, François (1817-1887) French
£1736 $2760 €2500 Nature morte, bottle of port and glasses on a ledge (12x10cm-5x4in) s.d.68 panel. 29-Apr-3 Christie's, Amsterdam #110/R est:3000-5000
£10127 $15797 €16000 La vieille servante (46x33cm-18x13in) s.d.1884 prov.lit. 15-Oct-2 Regis & Thiollet, Argentuil #188
Works on paper
£878 $1370 €1300 Forgeron assis (42x31cm-17x12in) s.d.1857. 27-Mar-3 Christie's, Paris #211/R
£7092 $11844 €10000 L'orpheline convoquee par la Mere superieure (38x83cm-15x33in) s.d.1869 W/C gouache pen brown ink black crayon. 19-Jun-3 Piasa, Paris #202/R est:8000-10000
£13287 $22189 €19000 Le musicien (31x24cm-12x9in) s.d.1853 chl. 25-Jun-3 Sotheby's, Paris #96/R est:5000-8000

BONVIN, François (after) (1817-1887) French
£7800 $12402 €11310 Still life depicting teapot, teacup and fruit (33x41cm-13x16in) bears sig.d.1861. 22-Mar-3 Lacy Scott, Bury St.Edmunds #478 est:700-900

BONZAGNI, Aroldo (1887-1918) Italian
Works on paper
£1479 $2455 €2100 Abdicazione (25x25cm-10x10in) s. W/C Indian ink. 10-Jun-3 Finarte Semenzato, Milan #202/R est:1800-2200

BONZANIGO, Giuseppe Maria (1725-1820) Italian
Sculpture
£87241 $140458 €129990 Portrait of the youthful Jerome Bonaparte (55x42cm-22x17in) carved wood. 18-Feb-3 Sotheby's, Amsterdam #280/R est:12000-18000

BOOGAARD, Willem Jacobus (1842-1887) Dutch
Works on paper
£1181 $1948 €1700 Admiring the horses (27x36cm-11x14in) s.d.1872 W/C. 1-Jul-3 Christie's, Amsterdam #555 est:800-1200

BOOGERS, Ad (20th C) ?
£377 $581 €600 Mass (183x157cm-72x62in) s.d.1985 verso. 22-Oct-2 Campo & Campo, Antwerp #18

BOOK, Alarik (1860-1936) Finnish
£277 $429 €440 Evening light (73x60cm-29x24in) s.d.1899. 6-Oct-2 Bukowskis, Helsinki #151/R

BOOK, Max Mikael (1953-) Swedish
£1051 $1640 €1577 Drottningholm (40x58cm-16x23in) s.d.2000 verso panel. 6-Nov-2 AB Stockholms Auktionsverk #889/R est:10000-12000 (S.KR 15000)
£1390 $2238 €2085 Untitled (78x96cm-31x38in) s. d.1983 verso. 7-May-3 AB Stockholms Auktionsverk #999/R est:12000-15000 (S.KR 18000)
£1622 $2611 €2433 Av South (100x115cm-39x45in) s.d.1988 verso. 7-May-3 AB Stockholms Auktionsverk #1011/R est:25000-30000 (S.KR 21000)
£1931 $3108 €2897 Hotel Bakelit II (215x153cm-85x60in) s.d.1982 verso exhib. 7-May-3 AB Stockholms Auktionsverk #1064/R est:30000-40000 (S.KR 25000)
£3398 $5470 €5097 Motor (140x230cm-55x91in) s.d.90-91 verso. 7-May-3 AB Stockholms Auktionsverk #1063/R est:50000-60000 (S.KR 44000)
Works on paper
£463 $746 €695 Gedod (24x36cm-9x14in) s.d.90/91 verso mixed media panel. 7-May-3 AB Stockholms Auktionsverk #1051/R (S.KR 6000)
£618 $995 €927 Panorama (23x40cm-9x16in) s.verso mixed media panel. 7-May-3 AB Stockholms Auktionsverk #1050/R (S.KR 8000)
£701 $1093 €1052 KE PA (24x36cm-9x14in) s.d.1990 mixed media panel. 6-Nov-2 AB Stockholms Auktionsverk #913/R (S.KR 10000)
£841 $1312 €1262 Capsize (60x83cm-24x33in) s.d.1992/94 verso mixed media panel. 6-Nov-2 AB Stockholms Auktionsverk #798/R (S.KR 12000)
£2803 $4373 €4205 The cultivators (80x120cm-31x47in) s.d.1990 verso mixed media canvas prov. 6-Nov-2 AB Stockholms Auktionsverk #902/R est:40000-50000 (S.KR 40000)

BOOM, Charles (1858-1939) Belgian
£362 $594 €500 La fille du peintre et son chien (64x44cm-25x17in) s. c.1910. 27-May-3 Campo, Vlaamse Kaai #25
£2300 $3496 €3450 Lace maker (20x16cm-8x6in) s.d.1903 panel. 29-Aug-2 Christie's, Kensington #144/R est:1500-2000

BOON, Willem (1902-) Dutch
£486 $802 €700 Fruit seller (75x55cm-30x22in) s.d.1933. 1-Jul-3 Christie's, Amsterdam #269/R

BOONEN, Arnold (1669-1729) Dutch
£20980 $35036 €30000 Jeune fille avec son petit chien. Jeune garcon tenant un perroquet (48x40cm-19x16in) s. one d.1732 panel pair oval painted with J.Gollevens. 25-Jun-3 Tajan, Paris #30/R est:14000-18000
£75000 $117000 €112500 Candle-lit interior with young man seated at table holding roemer (41x34cm-16x13in) s. prov. 10-Apr-3 Sotheby's, London #44/R est:30000

BOONSTRA, Klaas (1905-) Dutch
Works on paper
£590 $974 €850 Composition (55x53cm-22x21in) s.d.49 pastel. 1-Jul-3 Christie's, Amsterdam #421

BOONZAIER, Gregoire (1909-) South African
£891 $1389 €1337 Still life with a green teapot, mug and two tomatoes (24x29cm-9x11in) s.d.1930 board. 15-Oct-2 Stephan Welz, Johannesburg #468/R est:12000 18000 (SA.R 14500)
£921 $1437 €1382 White roses in a blue vase (40x30cm-16x12in) s.d.1963. 15-Oct-2 Stephan Welz, Johannesburg #467/R est:8000-12000 (SA.R 15000)
£1106 $1725 €1659 Pondokkies, toilet en blou bakkie, crossroads, kaap (29x44cm-11x17in) s.d.1982 s.i.verso board. 15-Oct-2 Stephan Welz, Johannesburg #464 est:5000-8000 (SA.R 18000)
£1720 $2769 €2580 Cottage Newlands (27x38cm-11x15in) s.d.1922 indis i.verso board. 12-May-3 Stephan Welz, Johannesburg #460/R est:25000-35000 (SA.R 20000)
£1892 $3046 €2838 Still life of blossoms in a blue vase (34x24cm-13x9in) s.d.1969. 12-May-3 Stephan Welz, Johannesburg #563/R est:10000-15000 (SA.R 22000)
£2050 $3198 €3075 Street scene with trees and houses (32x39cm-13x15in) s.d.1934. 11-Nov-2 Stephan Welz, Johannesburg #539/R est:20000-30000 (SA.R 32000)
£3439 $5537 €5159 Still life of spring flowers (40x37cm-16x15in) s.d.1934. 12-May-3 Stephan Welz, Johannesburg #566/R est:18000-24000 (SA.R 40000)
£3869 $6230 €5804 Still life of fruit and a vase (40x50cm-16x20in) s.d.1956. 12-May-3 Stephan Welz, Johannesburg #573/R est:20000-30000 (SA.R 45000)
£4421 $6986 €6632 Cape Town Harbour (75x62cm-30x24in) s.d.1949. 1-Apr-3 Stephan Welz, Johannesburg #468/R est:60000-90000 (SA.R 55000)
Works on paper
£257 $406 €386 Pine trees (37x27cm-15x11in) s.d.1980 W/C. 1-Apr-3 Stephan Welz, Johannesburg #207 est:3000-5000 (SA.R 3200)
£258 $415 €387 Bearded man (45x32cm-18x13in) s.d.1971 i.v chl prov. 12-May-3 Stephan Welz, Johannesburg #356 est:1800-2400 (SA.R 3000)
£362 $572 €543 Venetian canal (30x44cm-12x17in) s.d.1973 W/C. 1-Apr-3 Stephan Welz, Johannesburg #464 est:5000-8000 (SA.R 4500)
£384 $600 €576 Woodcutters (36x47cm-14x19in) s.d.1976 W/C over pencil. 11-Nov-2 Stephan Welz, Johannesburg #587 (SA.R 6000)
£430 $671 €645 Cape cottages (23x26cm-9x10in) s.d.1952 W/C. 15-Oct-2 Stephan Welz, Johannesburg #465 est:5000-8000 (SA.R 7000)
£482 $762 €723 Old house with veranda, district six, Cape town (27x37cm-11x15in) s.d.1970 i.verso W/C. 1-Apr-3 Stephan Welz, Johannesburg #466 est:6000-9000 (SA.R 6000)
£522 $814 €783 Shacks (30x50cm-12x20in) s.d.1982 chk pastel. 15-Oct-2 Stephan Welz, Johannesburg #463 est:4000-6000 (SA.R 8500)
£523 $826 €785 Figures in the street, district six (35x42cm-14x17in) s.d.1957 W/C htd white. 1-Apr-3 Stephan Welz, Johannesburg #467 est:7000-10000 (SA.R 6500)
£553 $862 €830 Fishing village (23x29cm-9x11in) s.d.1945 chk pastel. 15-Oct-2 Stephan Welz, Johannesburg #462 est:3000-5000 (SA.R 9000)
£676 $1054 €1014 Fishermen's cottages near Cape Aghulas (36x52cm-14x20in) s.d.1956 s.i.verso W/C htd white. 15-Oct-2 Stephan Welz, Johannesburg #466 est:6000-9000 (SA.R 11000)
£1032 $1661 €1548 View of a tree. Het nie reg gekom nie (37x55cm-15x22in) s.i.d.1976 chl pastel ink wash W/C double-sided. 12-May-3 Stephan Welz, Johannesburg #579/R est:12000-18000 (SA.R 12000)
£1290 $2077 €1935 Moon flowers (53x38cm-21x15in) s.d.1975 brush ink pastel htd. 12-May-3 Stephan Welz, Johannesburg #559/R est:10000-15000 (SA.R 15000)

BOOSTROM, Harry (1917-1996) Swedish
£701 $1093 €1052 Untitled (22x27cm-9x11in) s. prov. 5-Nov-2 Bukowskis, Stockholm #257/R (S.KR 10000)

BOOSTROM, Harry (attrib) (1917-1996) Swedish
Works on paper
£1004 $1616 €1506 Background for discussion (61x132cm-24x52in) gouache. 7-May-3 AB Stockholms Auktionsverk #929/R (S.KR 13000)

BOOT, Henri F (1877-1963) Dutch
£255 $397 €400 Interior with woman seated (31x26cm-12x10in) s. 5-Nov-2 Vendu Notarishuis, Rotterdam #66

BOOTH, E C (19th C) British
Works on paper
£360 $562 €540 Robin Hoods Bay, Yorkshire (33x52cm-13x20in) s.i.d.1891 W/C. 10-Sep-2 David Duggleby, Scarborough #93/R

BOOTH, Edward C (1821-1883) British
Works on paper
£320 $534 €464 Fish sellers (23x33cm-9x13in) s.i.d.1893 W/C. 26-Jun-3 Richardson & Smith, Whitby #575
£320 $525 €464 Whitby Sands, low tide with children collecting shellfish (32x48cm-13x19in) s.i. W/C. 5-Jun-3 Morphets, Harrogate #396
£380 $623 €570 Summer harvest fields (21x16cm-8x6in) s.d.1881 W/C pair. 10-Feb-3 David Duggleby, Scarborough #562/R
£420 $668 €630 On the sands (34x49cm-13x19in) s.d.1841 W/C. 25-Feb-3 Bonhams, Knightsbridge #184/R
£620 $1035 €899 Cullercoats. Sandsend (33x51cm-13x20in) s.d.1891 W/C pair. 17-Jun-3 Gildings, Market Harborough #442/R

BOOTH, Eunice Ellenetta (1852-1942) American
Works on paper
£528 $850 €792 Coastal landscape (25x36cm-10x14in) s. W/C gouache prov. 18-Feb-3 John Moran, Pasadena #86

BOOTH, Franklin (1874-1948) American
Works on paper
£828 $1300 €1242 Wood nymphs deep in the forest (25x20cm-10x8in) s. pen ink sold with W/C by Henry Bispham and W Cresson. 10-Dec-2 Doyle, New York #156/R est:2500-3500
£932 $1500 €1398 Hiker on redwood trail, house and sea in distance (36x25cm-14x10in) s. W/C chl board exhib. 10-May-3 Illustration House, New York #60/R est:1500-2500

BOOTH, James W (1867-1953) British
£300 $468 €450 Haymaking (26x36cm-10x14in) board. 25-Mar-3 Bonhams, Leeds #616
£560 $885 €840 Scalby Beck (36x52cm-14x20in) s. 7-Apr-3 David Duggleby, Scarborough #396
£960 $1517 €1440 Horses and cart on a North Yorkshire beach (22x30cm-9x12in) s. board. 7-Apr-3 David Duggleby, Scarborough #395/R
Works on paper
£380 $623 €570 Ramsdale Mill, Robin Hoods Bay (35x23cm-14x9in) s. W/C. 2-Jun-3 David Duggleby, Scarborough #247
£660 $1043 €990 Still life of roses in a vase (46x29cm-18x11in) s. W/C. 7-Apr-3 David Duggleby, Scarborough #341/R
£740 $1169 €1073 Horse grazing (25x35cm-10x14in) s. W/C. 28-Jul-3 David Duggleby, Scarborough #241/R
£1020 $1591 €1530 Heavy horses ploughing (26x36cm-10x14in) s. W/C. 10-Sep-2 David Duggleby, Scarborough #104/R est:500-800

BOOTH, Kate E (fl.1850-1870) British
Works on paper
£260 $411 €390 Unloading the catch in Whitby harbour (34x26cm-13x10in) s.i.d.1897 W/C. 7-Apr-3 David Duggleby, Scarborough #344
£320 $506 €480 Unloading fish at Whitby (33x25cm-13x10in) s.d. W/C. 24-Apr-3 Richardson & Smith, Whitby #239/R

BOOTH, Peter (1940-) Australian
£5357 $8893 €9128 Untitled - man with a gun (41x66cm-16x26in) s.verso prov. 10-Jun-3 Shapiro, Sydney #91/R est:12000-16000 (A.D 13500)
£10714 $16714 €16071 Volcano II (71x122cm-28x48in) exhib. 11-Nov-2 Deutscher-Menzies, Melbourne #65/R est:18000-24000 (A.D 30000)
£10769 $17123 €16154 Painting (111x182cm-44x72in) s.i.d.1983 verso prov. 4-Mar-3 Deutscher-Menzies, Melbourne #24/R est:30000-40000 (A.D 28000)
£14286 $22286 €21429 Painting, road (61x132cm-24x52in) 11-Nov-2 Deutscher-Menzies, Melbourne #31/R est:20000-25000 (A.D 40000)
Works on paper
£304 $463 €456 Dream, men and fences (7x9cm-3x4in) ink gouache. 28-Aug-2 Deutscher-Menzies, Melbourne #393 (A.D 850)
£609 $926 €914 Untitled, comet (18x26cm-7x10in) s.verso pastel prov. 28-Aug-2 Deutscher-Menzies, Melbourne #356/R (A.D 1700)
£824 $1253 €1236 Untitled, two men (16x25cm-6x10in) pastel prov. 28-Aug-2 Deutscher-Menzies, Melbourne #357/R (A.D 2300)
£996 $1633 €1494 Seascape (26x37cm-10x15in) pastel prov. 4-Jun-3 Deutscher-Menzies, Melbourne #287/R (A.D 2500)
£1036 $1699 €1554 Fragmented landscape (55x74cm-22x29in) s.verso W/C ink. 4-Jun-3 Deutscher-Menzies, Melbourne #130/R est:2000-3000 (A.D 2600)
£1275 $2091 €1913 Drawing, man in flames (35x49cm-14x19in) chl pastel prov. 4-Jun-3 Deutscher-Menzies, Melbourne #170/R est:2500-3500 (A.D 3200)
£1833 $3005 €2750 Dream (56x75cm-22x30in) s.i.d.1978 verso pastel. 4-Jun-3 Deutscher-Menzies, Melbourne #171/R est:4500-6500 (A.D 4600)
£1923 $3057 €2885 Guardians (56x75cm-22x30in) i. pastel prov. 4-Mar-3 Deutscher-Menzies, Melbourne #189/R est:4500-6500 (A.D 5000)
£2151 $3269 €3227 Painting (72x52cm-28x20in) s.d.1972 verso synthetic polymer paint card. 28-Aug-2 Deutscher-Menzies, Melbourne #57/R est:4000-6000 (A.D 6000)
£2678 $4205 €4017 For Anno (56x50cm-22x20in) s.i.verso synthetic polymer paint painted c.1976 prov. 25-Nov-2 Christie's, Melbourne #50/R est:7000-10000 (A.D 7500)

BOOTH, Raymond C (1929-) British
£260 $411 €390 Spring glade (21x12cm-8x5in) s.d.1963 board. 27-Nov-2 Bonhams, Knowle #232
£2903 $4500 €4355 Magnolea soulangeana (22x34cm-9x13in) s.d.1954 oil on paper prov. 29-Oct-2 Sotheby's, New York #289/R est:2000-3000

BOOTH, S Lawson (?-1928) British
£5380 $8500 €8070 Valley of Jehosephat, South Wall of Jerusalem (60x91cm-24x36in) s. painted 1915. 27-Apr-3 Sotheby's, Tel Aviv #1/R est:8000-12000

BOOTH, W Hunton (19/20th C) British
Works on paper
£800 $1232 €1200 Shipwreck off Bamburgh (64x97cm-25x38in) s.d.1905 W/C. 24-Oct-2 Thomson, Roddick & Medcalf, Carlisle #324

BOOTY, Frederick William (1840-1924) British
Works on paper
£370 $592 €555 Robin Hoods Bay with ship in distress (8x17cm-3x7in) d.1904 W/C. 11-Mar-3 David Duggleby, Scarborough #28
£370 $614 €555 Possibly the entrance to Whitby Harbour (12x19cm-5x7in) s. W/C. 10-Jun-3 Bonhams, Leeds #95
£400 $624 €600 Beached fishing boats, with figures and a horse (26x36cm-10x14in) s. W/C. 10-Apr-3 Tennants, Leyburn #820
£520 $868 €754 Sandsend, near Whitby (26x36cm-10x14in) s.d.1914 W/C. 9-Jul-3 Edgar Horn, Eastbourne #287/R
£600 $948 €900 River Derwent and Old Malton Priory (44x72cm-17x28in) s. W/C. 7-Apr-3 David Duggleby, Scarborough #319/R
£620 $980 €930 Whitby Abbey and lighthouses from the South in stormy seas (48x72cm-19x28in) s.d.1903 W/C. 7-Apr-3 David Duggleby, Scarborough #312/R
£660 $1056 €990 Robin Hoods Bay. North Yorkshire village scene (24x34cm-9x13in) s. W/C pair. 11-Mar-3 David Duggleby, Scarborough #137
£1750 $2835 €2538 Market Place, Hull (58x97cm-23x38in) s.d.1907 W/C. 23-May-3 Dee Atkinson & Harrison, Driffield #695/R est:600-800
£1800 $2844 €2700 Vessels off Scarborough (84x64cm-33x25in) s.d.1902 W/C. 24-Apr-3 Richardson & Smith, Whitby #130/R est:1500-2000
£3000 $4920 €4500 Paddle steamer and fishing boats outside Scarborough harbour (86x66cm-34x26in) s.s.1902 W/C on canvas. 2-Jun-3 David Duggleby, Scarborough #298/R est:3000-4000
£6600 $10428 €9900 Trinity Church, Hull market day (51x71cm-20x28in) s.d.1906 W/C. 29-Nov-2 Dee Atkinson & Harrison, Driffield #877/R est:4000-6000

BOR, Pal (1889-1982) Hungarian
£1677 $2616 €2432 Moszkva square (74x61cm-29x24in) s.d.72. 12-Apr-3 Mu Terem Galeria, Budapest #192/R est:380000 (H.F 600000)
£2689 $4168 €3899 Still life with glass (58x33cm-23x13in) s.d.1929 canvas card exhib. 9-Dec-2 Mu Terem Galeria, Budapest #10/R est:440000 (H.F 1000000)
Works on paper
£568 $885 €824 Positano (25x35cm-10x14in) s.d.1927 W/C. 13-Sep-2 Mu Terem Galeria, Budapest #8/R est:140000 (H.F 220000)

BOR, Paul (?-1669) Dutch
£25478 $39745 €40000 Three daughters of Cecrops finding Erichthonius (138x99cm-54x39in) bears sig.d.1639 prov.lit. 5-Nov-2 Sotheby's, Amsterdam #271/R est:40000-60000

BORBEREKI, Zoltan (1907-1992) Hungarian?
£34960 $54189 €52440 Blue dressed girl from Rome (165x100cm-65x39in) s. tempera on board. 6-Dec-2 Kieselbach, Budapest #165/R (H.F 13000000)

BORDES, Leonard (1898-1969) French

£411 $645 €600 Place de village animee en Normandie (50x61cm-20x24in) s. cardboard. 21-Apr-3 Rabourdin & Choppin de Janvry, Paris #43/R

BORDUAS, Paul Emile (1905-1960) Canadian

£17778 $29156 €26667 Fete papoue (47x55cm-19x22in) s.d.48 prov. 27-May-3 Sotheby's, Toronto #53/R est:20000-30000 (C.D 40000)
£18667 $30613 €28001 Untitled composition with green (90x72cm-35x28in) s.verso painted c.1959 prov.lit. 3-Jun-3 Joyner, Toronto #70/R est:50000-70000 (C.D 42000)
£19556 $32071 €29334 Quand mes reves partent en guerre (30x20cm-12x8in) s.d.47 prov.lit. 3-Jun-3 Joyner, Toronto #41/R est:35000-45000 (C.D 44000)
£28889 $47378 €43334 Bombardement (60x72cm-24x28in) s.d.58 prov. 27-May-3 Sotheby's, Toronto #190/R est:70000-90000 (C.D 65000)
£66667 $109333 €100001 Petales et pieux (50x61cm-20x24in) s.d.57 prov. 27-May-3 Sotheby's, Toronto #54/R est:75000-100000 (C.D 150000)

Works on paper

£203 $317 €305 Modeles nues (51x61cm-20x24in) s. chl. 30-Jul-2 Iegor de Saint Hippolyte, Montreal #27 (C.D 505)
£242 $377 €363 Jeune femme assise (42x27cm-17x11in) chl. 30-Jul-2 Iegor de Saint Hippolyte, Montreal #26 (C.D 600)
£1815 $2958 €2723 Untitled (23x27cm-9x11in) s.d.51 ink prov. 12-Feb-3 Iegor de Saint Hippolyte, Montreal #24/R (C.D 4500)
£3049 $4787 €4574 Le chant du guerrier (28x21cm-11x8in) s.d.54 ink exhib.prov. 12-Dec-2 Iegor de Saint Hippolyte, Montreal #9 (C.D 7500)
£5040 $7964 €7560 Untitled (58x45cm-23x18in) s.d.54 W/C prov. 18-Nov-2 Sotheby's, Toronto #173/R est:8000-10000 (C.D 12500)

BOREIN, Edward (1872-1945) American

Prints

£1887 $3000 €2831 Bucking horse (15x10cm-6x4in) s. etching. 8-Mar-3 Harvey Clar, Oakland #1304
£1899 $3000 €2754 Umatilla horse dance (13x23cm-5x9in) s. etching prov.lit. 26-Jul-3 Coeur d'Alene, Hayden #5/R est:2000-3000
£2201 $3500 €3302 Overland mail (13x25cm-5x10in) s. etching. 8-Mar-3 Harvey Clar, Oakland #1302
£2532 $4000 €3671 Navajos (23x30cm-9x12in) s. etching prov.lit. 26-Jul-3 Coeur d'Alene, Hayden #6/R est:2000-3000
£3797 $6000 €5506 Blackfoot Chief No.2 (20x28cm-8x11in) s. etching prov. 26-Jul-3 Coeur d'Alene, Hayden #4/R est:2000-3000

Works on paper

£258 $400 €387 Will Rogers plays polo (13x20cm-5x8in) i.d.1925 pen ink. 7-Dec-2 Neal Auction Company, New Orleans #437
£276 $430 €414 Hoses and mule (18x33cm-7x13in) ink graphite prov.lit. 9-Nov-2 Santa Fe Art, Santa Fe #167/R
£449 $700 €674 Indian on pony (20x33cm-8x13in) ink prov.lit. 9-Nov-2 Santa Fe Art, Santa Fe #166/R
£452 $700 €678 Cowboy on horseback (15x25cm-6x10in) india ink prov. 29-Oct-2 John Moran, Pasadena #812
£1419 $2200 €2129 Round up (15x29cm-6x11in) s. pencil. 3-Dec-2 Christie's, Rockefeller NY #580/R est:1000-1500
£3045 $4750 €4568 Horse and rider (13x13cm-5x5in) s. W/C prov.lit. 9-Nov-2 Santa Fe Art, Santa Fe #176/R est:8000-10000
£3797 $6000 €5506 Cowboy on a horse (15x15cm-6x6in) s. W/C prov. 26-Jul-3 Coeur d'Alene, Hayden #24/R est:4000-7000
£3797 $6000 €5506 Roping a steer. Four figures. Cowboy and Indian sketches (18x25cm-7x10in) one s. pen ink mixed media set of three prov. 26-Jul-3 Coeur d'Alene, Hayden #183/R est:5000-10000
£4455 $6950 €6683 Three wandering longhorns (28x51cm-11x20in) ink board prov.lit. 9-Nov-2 Santa Fe Art, Santa Fe #194/R est:20000-30000
£4487 $7000 €6731 Cowboy on horse (13x18cm-5x7in) s. W/C gouache prov.lit. 9-Nov-2 Santa Fe Art, Santa Fe #31/R est:12000-18000
£4968 $7750 €7452 Navajos in the desert (23x38cm-9x15in) s. W/C prov.lit. 9-Nov-2 Santa Fe Art, Santa Fe #193/R est:10000-12000
£8333 $13000 €12500 Two caballeros (23x28cm-9x11in) W/C prov.lit. 9-Nov-2 Santa Fe Art, Santa Fe #83/R est:22500-32500
£12025 $19000 €17436 Buckaroo (18x18cm-7x7in) s. W/C prov. 26-Jul-3 Coeur d'Alene, Hayden #166/R est:8000-12000
£63291 $100000 €91772 Rounding up a stray (36x43cm-14x17in) s.d.1922 W/C prov.exhib. 26-Jul-3 Coeur d'Alene, Hayden #203/R est:50000-75000

BOREL, Jeannie (1928-) German

£330 $528 €495 Interior (100x100cm-39x39in) s.d. 17-Mar-3 Philippe Schuler, Zurich #8411 (S.FR 700)

BOREN, James (1921-1990) American

£1299 $2000 €1949 Texas Longhorn (23x30cm-9x12in) s.d.1968. 8-Sep-2 Treadway Gallery, Cincinnati #596/R est:2500-3500
£3185 $5000 €4778 Bad day for traveling (61x91cm-24x36in) s.i.d.1972 prov. 19-Nov-2 Butterfields, San Francisco #8111/R est:7000-9000
£4614 $7475 €6690 Taos pueblo (28x43cm-11x17in) 23-May-3 Altermann Galleries, Santa Fe #13
£5769 $9000 €8654 South of Laredo (71x102cm-28x40in) 9-Nov-2 Altermann Galleries, Santa Fe #162
£6507 $9500 €9761 Waiting for the last train (71x102cm-28x40in) 18-May-2 Altermann Galleries, Santa Fe #140/R
£7099 $11500 €10294 January evening (61x91cm-24x36in) 23-May-3 Altermann Galleries, Santa Fe #9
£9554 $15000 €14331 When the morning sun is welcome (30x48cm-12x19in) s.i.d.1978 prov. 19-Nov-2 Butterfields, San Francisco #8110/R est:10000-12000

Works on paper

£1667 $2600 €2501 Acoma (38x56cm-15x22in) W/C. 9-Nov-2 Altermann Galleries, Santa Fe #161
£1849 $2700 €2774 Old Abilene (51x74cm-20x29in) W/C. 18-May-2 Altermann Galleries, Santa Fe #141/R
£1986 $2900 €2979 Old timers (53x74cm-21x29in) W/C. 18-May-2 Altermann Galleries, Santa Fe #139/R
£2885 $4500 €4328 By Arizona moonlight (56x76cm-22x30in) gouache. 9-Nov-2 Altermann Galleries, Santa Fe #159
£3185 $5000 €4778 Cowboy saddling his horse (42x58cm-17x23in) mono.d.1978 gouache prov. 19-Nov-2 Butterfields, San Francisco #8112/R est:4000-6000
£3205 $5000 €4808 Late winter sunset (36x43cm-14x17in) W/C. 9-Nov-2 Altermann Galleries, Santa Fe #158
£3425 $5000 €5138 On the outskirts of Kayenta (76x56cm-30x22in) W/C. 18-May-2 Altermann Galleries, Santa Fe #70/R
£6689 $10435 €10034 Heading for summer pasture (76x109cm-30x43in) gouache. 9-Nov-2 Altermann Galleries, Santa Fe #160

BOREN, Nelson (1952-) American

Works on paper

£2216 $3700 €3213 Saddle up (41x43cm-16x17in) W/C. 27-Jun-3 Altermann Galleries, Santa Fe #11
£2597 $4000 €3896 Spare (94x53cm-37x21in) W/C. 25-Oct-2 Morris & Whiteside, Hilton Head Island #47 est:4500-5000
£3054 $5100 €4428 Saddle headrest (43x114cm-17x45in) W/C. 27-Jun-3 Altermann Galleries, Santa Fe #10
£4132 $6900 €5991 Old boots new bike (66x104cm-26x41in) W/C. 27-Jun-3 Altermann Galleries, Santa Fe #7
£4491 $7500 €6512 Sunshine flowers (71x114cm-28x45in) W/C. 27-Jun-3 Altermann Galleries, Santa Fe #12
£8219 $12000 €12329 Old Arizona boots (147x94cm-58x37in) W/C. 18-May-2 Altermann Galleries, Santa Fe #170/R
£8642 $14000 €12531 Fix in the saddle (112x150cm-44x59in) W/C. 23-May-3 Altermann Galleries, Santa Fe #51
£8982 $15000 €13024 Day dreaming (127x155cm-50x61in) W/C. 27-Jun-3 Altermann Galleries, Santa Fe #3

BORENSTEIN, Samuel (1908-1969) Canadian

£732 $1149 €1098 House in la Barre a Plouffe (30x41cm-12x16in) s.d.Jan 3 1964 i.verso board prov. 10-Dec-2 Pinneys, Montreal #142 (C.D 1800)
£2218 $3504 €3327 Still life (46x41cm-18x16in) s.d.August 22/62 prov. 18-Nov-2 Sotheby's, Toronto #113/R est:4000-6000 (C.D 5500)
£4234 $6690 €6351 Sainte Lucie, the Laurentians (61x91cm-24x36in) s.d.April 9 1967 masonite prov.lit. 18-Nov-2 Sotheby's, Toronto #161/R est:8000-10000 (C.D 10500)

BORES, Francisco (1898-1972) Spanish

£2778 $4583 €4000 Composition (25x34cm-10x13in) s.d.64 paper prov. 2-Jul-3 Artcurial Briest, Paris #708/R est:4000-5000
£3546 $5922 €5000 Nature morte (22x27cm-9x11in) s.d.43 panel prov. 20-Jun-3 Piasa, Paris #197/R est:5000-7000
£4625 $7215 €6938 Still life (34x42cm-13x17in) s.d.45. 6-Nov-2 AB Stockholms Auktionsverk #939/R est:30000-35000 (S.KR 66000)
£4897 $7786 €7100 Houses (24x29cm-9x11in) s.d.31. 4-Mar-3 Ansorena, Madrid #223/R
£5762 $9104 €8643 Paysage de Hadsten (33x41cm-13x16in) s.d.50. 1-Apr-3 Rasmussen, Copenhagen #78/R est:60000-80000 (D.KR 62000)
£5860 $9141 €9200 Citron et peche (33x22cm-13x9in) s.d.43 panel. 7-Nov-2 Claude Aguttes, Neuilly #17/R est:4500
£6376 $10265 €9500 Table et verres (46x38cm-18x15in) s.d.30 lit. 18-Feb-3 Durán, Madrid #233/R
£7000 $11130 €10500 Nature morte (38x46cm-15x18in) s.d.41. 20-Mar-3 Sotheby's, Olympia #69/R est:4000-6000
£8996 $14934 €13044 Nature morte au vase (46x55cm-18x22in) s.d.50 exhib. 12-Jun-3 Kunsthallen, Copenhagen #3/R est:50000 (D.KR 95000)
£9830 $15630 €14450 Nature morte aux fleurs (46x55cm-18x22in) s.d.48 prov. 26-Feb-3 Artcurial Briest, Paris #304/R est:5300-6800
£10345 $16552 €15000 Still life in blue (21x33cm-8x13in) s.d.42 board. 11-Mar-3 Castellana, Madrid #354/R est:13000
£11000 $18370 €15950 Le pianiste (38x46cm-15x18in) s.d.29 prov. 24-Jun-3 Christie's, London #9/R est:2500-3500
£11538 $18115 €18000 Ombre et soleil (46x55cm-18x22in) s.d.61 prov.exhib.lit. 10-Dec-2 Piasa, Paris #227/R est:7000
£14396 $22170 €22890 Panier de raisins (46x54cm-18x21in) s.d.1968 i.verso prov.lit. 28-Oct-2 Segre, Madrid #125/R est:22890
£14423 $22788 €22500 Still life (65x54cm-26x21in) s.d.65 lit. 19-Nov-2 Durán, Madrid #249/R
£14780 $23057 €22170 Nature morte aux bananas (65x81cm-26x32in) s.d.49. 18-Sep-2 Kunsthallen, Copenhagen #12/R est:100000 (D.KR 175000)

£15723 $24528 €25000 Panier de noix (50x61cm-20x24in) s.d.1946 i.verso. 17-Sep-2 Segre, Madrid #157/R est:23000
£16447 $26645 €25000 Green apples. s.d.49. 21-Jan-3 Ansorena, Madrid #301/R est:22800
£16470 $25693 €24705 Nature morte au couteau (53x65cm-21x26in) s.d.49. 18-Sep-2 Kunsthallen, Copenhagen #25/R est:75000 (D.KR 195000)
£17949 $28179 €28000 Nature morte au couteau (54x65cm-21x26in) s.d.59 prov.exhib.lit. 10-Dec-2 Piasa, Paris #226/R est:6000
£18701 $27304 €28800 Composition in green (60x73cm-24x29in) s.d.49 prov. 17-Jun-2 Ansorena, Madrid #116/R est:28000
£24359 $38244 €38000 Danseuse assise (100x81cm-39x32in) s.d.33 lit. 10-Dec-2 Piasa, Paris #224/R est:16000
£25641 $40256 €40000 Composition en bleu (81x100cm-32x39in) s.d.62 prov.lit. 10-Dec-2 Piasa, Paris #225/R est:15000

Works on paper
£943 $1462 €1500 Le poisson (29x38cm-11x15in) s.d.69 gouache. 30-Oct-2 Artcurial Briest, Paris #339 est:1800-2000
£1064 $1777 €1500 Nature morte aux oranges (20x32cm-8x13in) s.d.62 gouache. 18-Jun-3 Pierre Berge, Paris #160/R est:1500-2000
£1887 $2906 €3000 Figures and electric cables (23x18cm-9x7in) s.d.1929 W/C. 28-Oct-2 Segre, Madrid #107/R est:3000
£4200 $6636 €6300 Bather (37x27cm-15x11in) s.d.48 gouache. 3-Apr-3 Christie's, Kensington #175/R
£4255 $7106 €6000 Le modele assoupi (24x31cm-9x12in) s.d.42 W/C gouache prov. 20-Jun-3 Piasa, Paris #196/R est:4000-6000

BOREUX, Rene (?) Belgian
£380 $589 €600 Vallee de la Meuse (30x40cm-12x16in) s. panel. 24-Sep-2 Galerie Moderne, Brussels #959

BORG, Axel (1847-1916) Swedish
£1361 $2205 €2042 Elk in landscape (46x65cm-18x26in) s. 3-Feb-3 Lilla Bukowskis, Stockholm #89 est:8000-10000 (S.KR 19000)
£3299 $5411 €4784 Winter landscape with elks in evening light (92x131cm-36x52in) s. 4-Jun-3 AB Stockholms Auktionsverk #2326/R est:20000-25000 (S.KR 42000)

BORG, Carl Oscar (1879-1947) American/Swedish
£3205 $5000 €4808 Horsemen on the Mesa (18x23cm-7x9in) s. oil paper on board prov.lit. 9-Nov-2 Santa Fe Art, Santa Fe #67/R est:10000-15000
£3293 $5500 €4775 Santa Barbara coastal (51x71cm-20x28in) s. 17-Jun-3 John Moran, Pasadena #34 est:6000-8000
£14151 $22500 €21227 California oaks (76x102cm-30x40in) s.i. s.verso painted 1935 prov.lit. 5-Mar-3 Sotheby's, New York #111/R est:25000-35000
£25137 $41225 €36449 Indians - Oraibi, Arizona (63x76cm-25x30in) s. prov.lit. 4-Jun-3 AB Stockholms Auktionsverk #2223/R est:250000-300000 (S.KR 320000)
£38217 $60000 €57326 Red rock wall (76x86cm-30x34in) s. prov. 20-Nov-2 Christie's, Los Angeles #61/R est:50000-70000

Works on paper
£274 $428 €411 Cowboy riding (10x16cm-4x6in) s.d.43 Indian ink W/C. 13-Sep-2 Lilla Bukowskis, Stockholm #273 (S.KR 4000)
£561 $886 €842 Autumn day near Vanern (20x25cm-8x10in) s. gouache. 30-Nov-2 Goteborg Auktionsverk, Sweden #207/R (S.KR 8000)
£608 $949 €900 Landscapes (29x39cm-11x15in) s.i. W/C pair. 27-Mar-3 Maigret, Paris #211
£903 $1500 €1309 Spring day in the forum (76x61cm-30x24in) s. pencil W/C prov.exhib. 11-Jun-3 Butterfields, San Francisco #4209/R est:3000-5000
£1014 $1581 €1500 Paysage de Californie (44x69cm-17x27in) s. w. 27-Mar-3 Maigret, Paris #212
£1282 $2000 €1923 Wagon camp (23x38cm-9x15in) W/C. 9-Nov-2 Altermann Galleries, Santa Fe #19
£1667 $2600 €2501 Shepherd at sunset (33x25cm-13x10in) W/C. 9-Nov-2 Altermann Galleries, Santa Fe #18
£1923 $3000 €2885 Mission by the river (20x30cm-8x12in) s. W/C prov.lit. 9-Nov-2 Santa Fe Art, Santa Fe #138/R est:3000-5000
£3012 $5000 €4367 The movie (13x18cm-5x7in) s. pencil gouache. 11-Jun-3 Butterfields, San Francisco #4305/R est:3000-5000
£3614 $6000 €5240 Indian across the plain (30x41cm-12x16in) s. pencil gouache prov. 11-Jun-3 Butterfields, San Francisco #4322/R est:7000-10000

BORGEAUD, Georges (1913-1997) Swiss
£939 $1540 €1362 Le vieux quartier (22x27cm-9x11in) s. i.d.17.II.1968 verso. 4-Jun-3 Fischer, Luzern #1254/R est:2200-2500 (S.FR 2000)
£1019 $1640 €1478 Church going (63x48cm-25x19in) s.d.1962 paper. 9-May-3 Dobiaschofsky, Bern #102/R (S.FR 2200)
£1304 $2022 €1956 La cerise (22x24cm-9x9in) s. init.d.1979 verso. 7-Dec-2 Galerie du Rhone, Sion #254/R est:1500-2000 (S.FR 3000)
£1921 $3036 €2882 Les coings (35x46cm-14x18in) s.d.971 i. verso. 14-Nov-2 Stuker, Bern #103/R est:3000-4000 (S.FR 4400)

BORGEAUD, Marius (1861-1924) Swiss
£23585 $38208 €41745 Repas sur table blanche (65x81cm-26x32in) s. prov.exhib.lit. 26-May-3 Sotheby's, Zurich #65/R est:50000-70000 (S.FR 50000)

BORGELLA, Frederic (19th C) French
£1479 $2381 €2100 Snake dance (44x52cm-17x20in) s.d.92 panel lit. 9-May-3 Schloss Ahlden, Ahlden #1501/R est:2200

BORGELLI, G (19/20th C) ?
£1115 $1750 €1673 Continental flower stand with figures (89x53cm-35x21in) s. 20-Nov-2 Boos Gallery, Michigan #540/R

BORGEN, Hans Fredrik (1852-1907) Norwegian
£1990 $3144 €2985 Coastal scene with brig (34x63cm-13x25in) s.d.1881. 2-Dec-2 Blomqvist, Oslo #318/R est:25000-30000 (N.KR 23000)
£2176 $3481 €3264 Landscape with waterfall and sawmill (85x132cm-33x52in) s.d.1879. 17-Mar-3 Blomqvist, Oslo #312/R est:25000-30000 (N.KR 25000)

BORGES, Phil (1950-) American
Photographs
£2057 $3250 €3086 Yama, 8Lhasa, Tibet (41x41cm-16x16in) with sig.d.1994/96 versonum.35/40 toned gelatin silver print. 22-Apr-3 Butterfields, San Francisco #2418/R est:4000-6000

BORGESE, Leonardo (1904-1986) Italian
Works on paper
£238 $379 €350 Sword fighter (35x24cm-14x9in) s.d.1928 mixed media. 24-Mar-3 Finarte Semenzato, Rome #281/R
£578 $919 €850 Masks (35x24cm-14x9in) s.d.1938 mixed media. 24-Mar-3 Finarte Semenzato, Rome #280/R

BORGHESE, Franz (1941-) Italian
£1090 $1711 €1700 Figures (40x50cm-16x20in) s. s.verso. 19-Nov-2 Finarte, Milan #61
£1154 $1812 €1800 Couple in landscape (40x50cm-16x20in) s. s.i.verso. 19-Nov-2 Finarte, Milan #56
£1242 $1987 €1900 Flying missile (50x40cm-20x16in) s. 4-Jan-3 Meeting Art, Vercelli #730
£1282 $2013 €2000 Guardian angel (50x50cm-20x20in) s. s.i.verso acrylic. 23-Nov-2 Meeting Art, Vercelli #168/R
£1806 $2854 €2800 Portrait (100x89cm-39x35in) s. s.i. prov. 18-Dec-2 Christie's, Rome #79/R
£1923 $2981 €3000 Chess players (49x54cm-19x21in) s. painted 1982. 4-Dec-2 Finarte, Milan #331 est:2600
£2025 $3159 €3200 Winter (70x60cm-28x24in) s. acrylic. 14-Sep-2 Meeting Art, Vercelli #931/R
£2292 $3644 €3300 Arrest (70x70cm-28x28in) s.d.1974. 1-May-3 Meeting Art, Vercelli #597

Works on paper
£359 $575 €550 Architect (34x30cm-13x12in) s. Chinese ink W/C. 4-Jan-3 Meeting Art, Vercelli #446
£415 $660 €610 Fighters (50x35cm-20x14in) s. Chinese ink W/C. 1-Mar-3 Meeting Art, Vercelli #540
£417 $654 €650 Doctor (35x25cm-14x10in) s. Chinese ink W/C. 23-Nov-2 Meeting Art, Vercelli #385/R
£483 $768 €710 Doctor and lady (50x35cm-20x14in) s. gouache card. 1-Mar-3 Meeting Art, Vercelli #687
£1081 $1686 €1600 Souvenir tree (40x50cm-16x20in) s. mixed media on canvas. 26-Mar-3 Finarte Semenzato, Milan #118/R

BORGHI, Enrica (1966-) Italian
Sculpture
£1603 $2484 €2500 Untitled (55x36x23cm-22x14x9in) s.d.1998 polymer. 4-Dec-2 Finarte, Milan #463/R

BORGHIGIANI, Faustina (18th C) Italian
£621 $993 €900 Virgin (29x19cm-11x7in) s. slate oval. 17-Mar-3 Pandolfini, Florence #491/R

BORGIANNI, Guido (1915-) American
£449 $704 €700 View of Florence (70x50cm-28x20in) s. d.1976 verso. 16-Dec-2 Pandolfini, Florence #339
£513 $810 €800 View of Florence (64x78cm-25x31in) s. 15-Nov-2 Farsetti, Prato #422/R

BORGIOTTI, Mario (1906-1977) Italian
£452 $714 €700 Urban landscape with bridge (35x46cm-14x18in) s.d.35 board. 18-Dec-2 Finarte, Milan #33

BORGO, Lewis J (1876-?) American
£478 $750 €717 Point lookout, Long Island, New York (50x64cm-20x25in) s. i.d.1941 verso panel. 22-Nov-2 Skinner, Boston #337/R

BORGOGNA, Juan de (?-1533) Spanish
£25926 $42000 €38889 Adoration of the shepherds (57x87cm-22x34in) panel transferred to masonite prov.exhib. 24-Jan-3 Christie's, Rockefeller NY #30/R est:30000-50000

BORGOGNONI, Romeo (1875-1944) Italian
£839 $1325 €1300 Old bridge in Pavia (23x23cm-9x9in) s. board. 18-Dec-2 Finarte, Milan #141/R

BORGONOVO, Giovanni (1881-1975) Italian
£1361 $2163 €2000 Countryside (54x66cm-21x26in) s. board. 1-Mar-3 Meeting Art, Vercelli #82

BORIONE, Bernard Louis (1865-?) French
£3200 $5216 €4640 Court musicians (65x81cm-26x32in) s.i. 16-Jul-3 Sotheby's, Olympia #201/R est:2000-3000
£4200 $6846 €6300 Good read (33x25cm-13x10in) s.i. panel. 29-Jan-3 Sotheby's, Olympia #300/R est:2000-3000
£5696 $9000 €8544 Cardinal and two gentlemen (64x81cm-25x32in) 15-Nov-2 Du Mouchelle, Detroit #2004/R est:5000-8000

Works on paper
£252 $390 €400 Collation du cardinal (41x33cm-16x13in) s.i.d.1912 W/C. 6-Oct-2 Livinec, Gaudcheau & Jezequel, Rennes #20
£318 $500 €477 Interior scene with red frocked Cardinal seated with gentleman beside him (30x20cm-12x8in) s.d.1898 W/C. 19-Apr-3 James Julia, Fairfield #250/R

BORIS, Rosa (20th C) American
£323 $500 €485 Portrait of a woman (51x61cm-20x24in) painted c.1950. 8-Dec-2 Toomey, Oak Park #827/R

BORISOV, Aleksandr Alekseevich (1866-1934) Russian
£2000 $3160 €3000 Snowy landscape (40x60cm-16x24in) s.d.1911 canvas on board. 26-Nov-2 Christie's, Kensington #21/R est:2000-3000

BORISOV, Sergei (1975-) Russian
£349 $545 €524 In the garden (59x49cm-23x19in) s. i.d.1996 verso. 6-Nov-2 Dobiaschofsky, Bern #3191 (S.FR 800)

BORISSOVA, Nadeschda (1977-) Russian
£463 $745 €671 Samoskworetschje (57x70cm-22x28in) s. i.d.1995 verso. 7-May-3 Dobiaschofsky, Bern #365/R (S.FR 1000)

BORJE, Gideon (1891-1969) Swedish
£423 $665 €635 Haverdal, Halland (65x80cm-26x31in) s. 16-Dec-2 Lilla Bukowskis, Stockholm #122 (S.KR 6000)
£575 $896 €863 Landscape from La Gaude (51x60cm-20x24in) s. painted 1928. 6-Nov-2 AB Stockholms Auktionsverk #688/R (S.KR 8200)
£701 $1093 €1052 Kraangede rapids (60x73cm-24x29in) s. panel prov.exhib.lit. 6-Nov-2 AB Stockholms Auktionsverk #651/R (S.KR 10000)
£771 $1203 €1157 View of Riddarsholmen, Stockholm (63x47cm-25x19in) s. painted 1935. 6-Nov-2 AB Stockholms Auktionsverk #663/R (S.KR 11000)
£5323 $8411 €7985 View from Sodermalarstrand across the old town (37x45cm-15x18in) s.d.1919 panel. 28-Apr-3 Bukowskis, Stockholm #5/R est:25000-30000 (S.KR 70000)

BORLASE, Nancy (1914-) New Zealander
£500 $815 €725 Suburban scene (55x45cm-22x18in) init. board. 15-Jul-3 Bonhams, Knightsbridge #143/R

BORLE, Louis (?) Belgian?
£291 $454 €460 Effets de lumiere dans une clairiere (116x80cm-46x31in) s. 16-Sep-2 Horta, Bruxelles #303
£380 $592 €600 Moissonneur (63x101cm-25x40in) s. 16-Sep-2 Horta, Bruxelles #304

BORMAN, Johannes (17th C) Dutch
£20000 $33400 €29000 Peaches on a salver, fruit and wine glass with casket of grapes on draped ledge (76x64cm-30x25in) s. 9-Jul-3 Bonhams, New Bond Street #8/R est:15000-20000

BORMAN, Johannes (attrib) (17th C) Dutch
£5674 $8794 €8511 Still life of grapes and peaches on dish (29x37cm-11x15in) panel. 3-Dec-2 Bukowskis, Stockholm #455/R est:100000-125000 (S.KR 80000)

BORNFRIEND, Jacob (1904-1976) British
£320 $525 €480 Untitled (101x80cm-40x31in) s. 3-Jun-3 Sotheby's, Olympia #285/R
£650 $1066 €975 Still life with a jug, apples and flowers (33x55cm-13x22in) s. board. 3-Jun-3 Sotheby's, Olympia #280/R
£650 $1066 €975 Still life on a table (63x54cm-25x21in) i.verso board prov. 3-Jun-3 Sotheby's, Olympia #284/R
£650 $1034 €975 Two white tables (130x79cm-51x31in) s. 29-Apr-3 Gorringes, Lewes #2245
£1400 $2226 €2100 Still life of fruit on a table (51x102cm 20x40in) s. 29-Apr-3 Gorringes, Lewes #2244

BORNSTEIN, Eli (20th C) American

Sculpture
£1585 $2600 €2298 Structurist relief no.31-11 (64x64x10cm-25x25x4in) s.i.d.1963 verso enamel on plexiglas aluminum prov. 1-Jun-3 Wright, Chicago #282/R est:2000-3000
£1768 $2900 €2564 Structurist relief (69x61x15cm-27x24x6in) s.d.1960 verso lacquered wood prov. 1-Jun-3 Wright, Chicago #283/R est:2000-3000
£3354 $5500 €4863 Structurist relief no.1 (76x53x13cm-30x21x5in) s.i.d.1966 verso lacquered wood prov. 1-Jun-3 Wright, Chicago #286/R est:2000-3000
£6707 $11000 €9725 Structurist relief no.1-1 (99x69x18cm-39x27x7in) oil on wood prov.exhib. 1-Jun-3 Wright, Chicago #285/R est:4000-5000

BOROFSKY, Jonathan (1942-) American

Sculpture
£2803 $4373 €4205 Standing man at 28 16952 (235x62cm-93x24in) s.num.4/9 white varnished polyester foam. 6-Nov-2 AB Stockholms Auktionsverk #790/R est:50000-70000 (S.KR 40000)
£3083 $4810 €4625 Man 2783734 (277x90cm-109x35in) s. contoured aluminium. 6-Nov-2 AB Stockholms Auktionsverk #866/R est:40000-50000 (S.KR 44000)
£11875 $19000 €17813 Man with a briefcase, cut out (226x98cm-89x39in) s. aluminum cut out executed 1979 prov.exhib.lit. 14-May-3 Sotheby's, New York #429/R est:15000-20000

Works on paper
£1088 $1731 €1600 Untitled (30x23cm-12x9in) s.verso ink exec.1978-79 prov. 24-Mar-3 Cornette de St.Cyr, Paris #118/R

BOROMISZA, Tibor (1880-1960) Hungarian
£774 $1207 €1122 On the river bank (31x38cm-12x15in) s. tempera paper. 13-Sep-2 Mu Terem Galeria, Budapest #156/R est:120000 (H.F 300000)
£18825 $29178 €27296 Haymarket I (60x80cm-24x31in) s.i.d.912 verso exhib. 9-Dec-2 Mu Terem Galeria, Budapest #70/R est:3000000 (H.F 7000000)

BORONDA, Lester David (1886-1951) American
£516 $800 €774 Early California Senorita (81x61cm-32x24in) s.d.40 board. 7-Dec-2 Harvey Clar, Oakland #1177

BOROUGHS, J (?) ?
£1400 $2324 €2030 Pheasant shoot (61x89cm-24x35in) s. 12-Jun-3 Christie's, Kensington #126/R est:1000-1500
£1635 $2600 €2453 Summer day (64x94cm-25x37in) s. prov. 5-Mar-3 Doyle, New York #7/R est:2000-3000

BOROWER, Djawid (20th C) ?
£411 $650 €650 Picture of an Austrian Schilling (210x160cm-83x63in) s.d.1997/98 verso. 30-Nov-2 Arnold, Frankfurt #53/R
£506 $800 €800 Picture of an Austrian Schilling (160x120cm-63x47in) s.d.1997/98 verso. 30-Nov-2 Arnold, Frankfurt #54/R

BORRA, Pompeo (1898-1973) Italian
£724 $1144 €1130 Horse rider (32x23cm-13x9in) painted 1968. 12-Nov-2 Babuino, Rome #347/R
£737 $1076 €1150 Star evolutions (58x44cm-23x17in) s. 5-Jun-2 Il Ponte, Milan #1
£1149 $1792 €1700 Landscape (80x60cm-31x24in) s. 28-Mar-3 Farsetti, Prato #269/R
£2740 $4274 €4000 Beached boats (40x50cm-16x20in) s. 10-Apr-3 Finarte Semenzato, Rome #172/R

BORRACK, John Leo (1933-) Australian

Works on paper
£214 $327 €321 May evening, Briagolong (65x99cm-26x39in) s.d.76 W/C prov. 26-Aug-2 Sotheby's, Paddington #794 (A.D 600)
£214 $338 €321 Edge of the lake (36x52cm-14x20in) s.d.79 W/C. 27-Nov-2 Deutscher-Menzies, Melbourne #257/R (A.D 600)
£464 $724 €696 Flood plaine, Jardine river (72x99cm-28x39in) s.d.90 gouache prov. 11-Nov-2 Deutscher-Menzies, Melbourne #177/R (A.D 1300)

BORRAS Y ABELLA, Vicente (1867-1945) Spanish
£780 $1217 €1170 Portrait of a man (36x26cm-14x10in) s. panel. 26-Mar-3 Sotheby's, Olympia #196/R

BORRAS, Jorge (1952-) French
Sculpture
£1154 $1812 €1800 Frileuse (22x19cm-9x7in) s. num.2/8 bronze. 15-Dec-2 Lombrail & Teucquam, Paris #23/R
£1268 $2041 €1800 Papillon (21cm-8in) s.num.4/8 green pat bronze Cast Candide. 11-May-3 Lombrail & Teucquam, Paris #217/R

BORRAS, Vicente (19th C) Spanish
£18345 $29353 €25500 Les saltimbanques sur la route traversant le hameau (90x131cm-35x52in) s. 16-May-3 Lombrail & Teucquam, Paris #102/R

BORREGAARD, Eduard (1902-1978) Danish
£296 $459 €444 Still life of jug and fruit (98x69cm-39x27in) s.d.1930 panel. 1-Oct-2 Rasmussen, Copenhagen #312 (D.KR 3500)

BORRELL, Juli (1877-1957) Spanish
£275 $450 €420 Strolling (14x10cm-6x4in) board. 5-Feb-3 Arte, Seville #764/R

BORRILLY, Jean-Baptiste (fl.1790-1796) French
£2200 $3410 €3300 River landscape with shepherd and shepherdess resting (27x36cm-11x14in) s. panel. 30-Oct-2 Bonhams, New Bond Street #148/R est:1000-1500

BORRONI, Giovanni Angelo (attrib) (1684-1772) Italian
Works on paper
£405 $632 €600 Madonna and Child (11x8cm-4x3in) sanguine pen wash oval. 27-Mar-3 Maigret, Paris #79

BORROW, William H (fl.1863-1893) British
£820 $1279 €1230 Hauling in the nets (46x81cm-18x32in) s. 26-Mar-3 Woolley & Wallis, Salisbury #199/R
Works on paper
£308 $487 €462 Harbour scene with sailing boats (19x32cm-7x13in) s. W/C. 16-Nov-2 Crafoord, Lund #60/R (S.KR 4400)

BORSA, Roberto (1880-1965) Italian
£376 $616 €545 Landscape with tower (20x59cm-8x23in) s. 4-Jun-3 Fischer, Luzern #2017/R (S.FR 800)

BORSATO, Giuseppe (c.1770-1849) Italian
£4403 $6824 €7000 Interior of St Mark's basilica, Venice (25x18cm-10x7in) s.d.1842 verso panel. 2-Oct-2 Dorotheum, Vienna #11/R est:4500-5500

BORSCHKE, Karl (1886-1941) Austrian
£347 $538 €521 Female nude in front of mirror (60x45cm-24x18in) painted c.1920. 3-Dec-2 SOGA, Bratislava #193/R (SL.K 22000)
£347 $538 €521 Female nude (60x45cm-24x18in) painted c.1920. 3-Dec-2 SOGA, Bratislava #194 (SL.K 22000)

BORSELEN, Helena Maria van (1867-1947) Dutch
£347 $573 €500 Peonies in a tin jug (51x40cm-20x16in) s.d.1913. 1-Jul-3 Christie's, Amsterdam #172

BORSELEN, Jan Willem van (1825-1892) Dutch
£10417 $16563 €15000 Polder landscape near Gouda (45x72cm-18x28in) bears sig painted c.1867. 29-Apr-3 Christie's, Amsterdam #191/R est:15000-20000
£20382 $31796 €32000 Pasture landscape with peasants and horses and wagon (44x69cm-17x27in) s. prov. 6-Nov-2 Vendue Huis, Gravenhage #440/R est:25000-35000
Works on paper
£2051 $3221 €3200 Children playing by Dutch canal (23x36cm-9x14in) s. W/C. 21-Nov-2 Van Ham, Cologne #1490/R est:3500
£2397 $3740 €3500 Children playing by Dutch canal (23x36cm-9x14in) s. W/C. 10-Apr-3 Van Ham, Cologne #1341/R est:3500

BORSOS, Jozsef (1821-1883) Hungarian
£21928 $34208 €31796 Painter's dream (55x44cm-22x17in) s.d.851 panel prov.exhib.lit. 13-Sep-2 Mu Terem Galeria, Budapest #56/R est:2000000 (H.F 8500000)

BORSOS, Miklos (1906-1991) Hungarian
Sculpture
£1614 $2501 €2421 Bird (12cm-5in) s. white marble. 6-Dec-2 Kieselbach, Budapest #126/R (H.F 600000)

BORSSELER, Pieter (attrib) (17th C) Dutch
£1014 $1581 €1500 Portrait of lady in black headpiece and black dress with bright collar (76x63cm-30x25in) prov. 27-Mar-3 Dorotheum, Vienna #394/R est:1000-2000

BORSSOM, Anthonie van (1630-1677) Dutch
Works on paper
£3503 $5465 €5500 Two ducks and three ducklings. Ducks and chickens (15x13cm-6x5in) pen brown ink double-sided prov.exhib.lit. 5-Nov-2 Sotheby's, Amsterdam #57/R est:5000-7000

BORSSOM, Anthonie van (attrib) (1630-1677) Dutch
Works on paper
£993 $1658 €1400 Marine (10x13cm-4x5in) pen brown ink brown wash. 19-Jun-3 Piasa, Paris #52

BORSTEL, R A (fl.1891-1917) Australian/British
£401 $650 €602 The Chillicothe (35x46cm-14x18in) s.d.1920 canvas on board. 21-Jan-3 Christie's, Rockefeller NY #362/R

BORSTEL, Reginald Arthur (1875-1922) Australian
£2368 $3600 €3552 Barque, Conswa Castle (46x61cm-18x24in) s.d.97 board. 17-Aug-2 North East Auctions, Portsmouth #928/R est:4000-6000

BORTNYIK, Sandor (1893-1976) Hungarian
£826 $1288 €1239 Flower piece, 1942 (58x42cm-23x17in) s.d.1942. 11-Sep-2 Kieselbach, Budapest #169/R (H.F 320000)
£43856 $68416 €65784 Geometrical composition, 1923 (62x62cm-24x24in) s. 11-Sep-2 Kieselbach, Budapest #94/R (H.F 17000000)

BORTOLLUZZI, Patrice (1950-) French?
Works on paper
£425 $667 €620 Yacht dans le Bassin du Commerce au Havre (38x58cm-15x23in) s. gouache. 21-Apr-3 Rabourdin & Choppin de Janvry, Paris #37/R
£596 $936 €870 Le paquebot la Normandie, vu du pont de la Champagne (38x58cm-15x23in) s. gouache. 21-Apr-3 Rabourdin & Choppin de Janvry, Paris #35/R

BORTOLUZZI, Camillo (1868-1933) Italian
£6987 $10900 €10481 Gondolas on Grand Canal in summer (63x95cm-25x37in) s. 6-Nov-2 Dobiaschofsky, Bern #364/R est:18000 (S.FR 16000)

BOS, Gerard van den (1825-1898) Dutch
£545 $850 €818 Mother and daughter (38x43cm-15x17in) s. 30-Mar-3 Susanin's, Chicago #6023/R

BOS, Harry (20th C) ?
£260 $379 €400 Rotterdam harbour (60x100cm-24x39in) s. 19-Jun-2 Vendue Huis, Gravenhage #58

BOS, Henk (1901-) Dutch
£288 $450 €432 Still life (43x41cm-17x16in) s. 20-Oct-2 Susanin's, Chicago #5048/R
£897 $1400 €1346 Still life with cups and eggs (61x51cm-24x20in) s. 30-Mar-3 Susanin's, Chicago #6094/R
£1282 $2000 €1923 Still life of apples, cheese, bread, pewter coffee urn and green bottle (89x79cm-35x31in) s. 12-Apr-3 Brunk, Ashville #744/R est:1500-3000
£1899 $3000 €3000 Stilleven met bloemen (81x70cm-32x28in) s. s.verso. 26-Nov-2 Sotheby's, Amsterdam #24/R est:3000-4000

BOS, Jan (1926-) Dutch
£1370 $2137 €2000 Escaped bird (50x39cm-20x15in) s.d.1846 panel lit. 14-Apr-3 Glerum, Amsterdam #39/R est:2000-3000

BOS, Willem (1906-1977) Dutch
£321 $508 €482 Ships in Rotterdam harbour (61x91cm-24x36in) 1-Dec-2 Levis, Calgary #209/R (C.D 800)
Works on paper
£390 $569 €600 Sea port (49x69cm-19x27in) s. chl W/C. 19-Jun-2 Vendue Huis, Gravenhage #60

BOSANQUET, J Claude (19th C) British?
Works on paper
£1146 $1662 €1800 Ballintemple Village (23x40cm-9x16in) W/C. 29-May-2 Woodwards, Cork #211

BOSANQUET, John E (attrib) (fl.1854-1861) Irish
Works on paper
£1208 $1945 €1800 Dripsey Castle, Co Cork (61x80cm-24x31in) W/C. 18-Feb-3 Whyte's, Dublin #94/R est:1800-2200

BOSBOOM, D (19th C) Dutch
£2745 $4502 €4200 Square with figures (65x85cm-26x33in) s. 9-Feb-3 Anaf, Lyon #29/R

BOSBOOM, Johannes (1817-1891) Dutch
£559 $906 €850 Consistorie kamer (35x28cm-14x11in) s. paper on panel prov.exhib. 21-Jan-3 Christie's, Amsterdam #230/R
£1439 $2302 €2000 Church interior (14x10cm-6x4in) s. panel. 17-May-3 Lempertz, Koln #1367/R est:1500
£5556 $8833 €8000 Sunlit church interior (16x12cm-6x5in) s. indis d. panel. 29-Apr-3 Christie's, Amsterdam #129/R est:4000-6000
£5822 $9082 €8500 Church interior with figures (35x24cm-14x9in) s. 14-Apr-3 Glerum, Amsterdam #70/R est:3000-4000
£9434 $14528 €15000 Church interior with figures (29x23cm-11x9in) s. panel. 23-Oct-2 Christie's, Amsterdam #216/R est:10000-15000
£21384 $32931 €34000 Interior of the Saint Jacob church, Antwerp (85x65cm-33x26in) s. prov.exhib. 22-Oct-2 Sotheby's, Amsterdam #218/R est:30000-50000

Works on paper
£828 $1292 €1300 Church square with figures in the foreground (27x18cm-11x7in) s. W/C. 6-Nov-2 Vendue Huis, Gravenhage #408/R
£1842 $2984 €2800 Kerk te Alkmaar (12x8cm-5x3in) s. W/C htd white prov. 21-Jan-3 Christie's, Amsterdam #229/R est:1000-1500
£3158 $5116 €4800 Schaapskooi, Zuid-Laren (28x54cm-11x21in) s. pw. W/C exhib. 21-Jan-3 Christie's, Amsterdam #234/R est:1500-2000
£3425 $5377 €5000 Interior of the Portuguese Synagogue, Amsterdam (38x30cm-15x12in) W/C prov. 15-Apr-3 Sotheby's, Amsterdam #128/R est:5000-7000
£13889 $22083 €20000 Service in the church of Hattem (42x32cm-17x13in) s. pen ink wash W/C htd white prov.exhib.lit. 29-Apr-3 Christie's, Amsterdam #133/R est:30000-50000

BOSCH, Hieronymus (after) (1450-1516) Dutch
Prints
£45570 $72000 €72000 Christ carrying the cross (33x41cm-13x16in) copperplate. 29-Nov-2 Bassenge, Berlin #5204/R est:30000

BOSCH, Hieronymus (circle) (1450-1516) Dutch
Works on paper
£148148 $240000 €222222 Hell scene with monsters and figures (26x20cm-10x8in) pen ink. 21-Jan-3 Sotheby's, New York #20/R est:40000

BOSCH, Hieronymus (studio) (1450-1516) Dutch
£150000 $250500 €217500 Last judgement (84x95cm-33x37in) with sig. panel prov.exhib.lit. 9-Jul-3 Christie's, London #25/R est:80000-120000

BOSCH, Hieronymus (style) (1450-1516) Dutch
£7742 $11381 €12000 Temptation of St Anthony (60x73cm-24x29in) 20-Jun-2 Dr Fritz Nagel, Stuttgart #703/R est:20000

BOSCHETTI, Benedetto (19th C) Italian
Sculpture
£1800 $3006 €2610 Marcus Aurelius (43cm-17in) dk brown pat bronze incl blk mottled red marble base. 8-Jul-3 Sotheby's, London #171/R est:2000-3000
£2000 $3340 €2900 Sophocles (67cm-26in) s.i. dk brown pat bronze incl red blk veined marble socle. 8-Jul-3 Sotheby's, London #172/R est:2000-3000
£7595 $12000 €11393 Figure of the Augustus prima porta (103cm-41in) i. bronze on columnar pedestal. 24-Apr-3 Christie's, Rockefeller NY #214/R est:10000-15000

BOSCHI, A (19th C) Italian
£2000 $3140 €3000 Cobbler. Seamstress (31x23cm-12x9in) s. pair. 19-Nov-2 Bonhams, New Bond Street #83/R est:1000-1500

BOSCHI, Achille (1852-1930) Italian
£800 $1304 €1200 Mediterranean waif standing in the shade (74x56cm-29x22in) s. 13-Feb-3 Christie's, Kensington #177/R

BOSCHI, Fabrizio (1570-1642) Italian
Works on paper
£633 $1000 €1000 Le Christ chez Simon le Pharisien (24x40cm-9x16in) red chk red wash. 27-Nov-2 Christie's, Paris #50/R

BOSCO, Nathalie (20th C) ?
Works on paper
£446 $714 €620 En diagonale (65x50cm-26x20in) s. mixed media canvas. 18-May-3 Neret-Minet, Paris #116

BOSCO, Pierre (1909-) French
£360 $576 €500 Chevaux (50x61cm-20x24in) s. d.verso. 14-May-3 Blanchet, Paris #148

BOSCOLI, Andrea (1560-1607) Italian
Works on paper
£1000 $1550 €1500 Christ fallen on the road to Cavalry (16x11cm-6x4in) pen ink wash lit. 9-Dec-2 Bonhams, New Bond Street #94/R est:1000-1500
£6944 $11042 €10000 Donkey miracle - Scene from the life of St Anthony of Padua (23x16cm-9x6in) i. pen wash paper on board prov. 5-May-3 Ketterer, Munich #340/R est:8000-10000
£8000 $13360 €11600 Male nude seen from behind (38x47cm-15x19in) blk chk red chk pen brown ink wash htd white. 9-Jul-3 Sotheby's, London #18/R est:3000-4000
£17097 $27013 €26500 Illustrations for the 'Gerusalemme Liberata' by Tasso (24x17cm-9x7in) pen ink wash over sanguine prov. 18-Dec-2 Beaussant & Lefèvre, Paris #17/R est:5000

BOSCOVITS, Fritz (younger) (1871-1965) Swiss
£326 $509 €489 Winter landscape with view of Zollikon and Zurichsee (32x27cm-13x11in) s.d.1920 board. 16-Sep-2 Philippe Schuler, Zurich #3356 (S.FR 750)

BOSELLI, Felice (attrib) (1650-1732) Italian
£851 $1421 €1200 Nature morte de gibier, becasse, canard sauvage et grive (44x59cm-17x23in) 18-Jun-3 Tajan, Paris #17
£5172 $8224 €7500 Still life with chickens (81x38cm-32x15in) 5-Mar-3 Sotheby's, Milan #198/R est:7000

BOSELLI, Felice (circle) (1650-1732) Italian
£21475 $34574 €32000 Still life of fish and mushrooms. Still life of hare on a ledge (79x91cm-31x36in) canvas on board pair. 18-Feb-3 Sotheby's, Amsterdam #928/R est:4000-6000

BOSHIER, Derek (1937-) British
£350 $543 €525 Boy (102x107cm-40x42in) s.d.2000 exhib. 4-Dec-2 Christie's, Kensington #611/R
£350 $543 €525 Flag (91x96cm-36x38in) s.d.2000 exhib. 4-Dec-2 Christie's, Kensington #612/R
£420 $693 €609 Viewer (169x152cm-67x60in) shaped. 3-Jul-3 Christie's, Kensington #708
£550 $853 €825 Tabloid (157x66cm-62x26in) s.d.2000 exhib. 4-Dec-2 Christie's, Kensington #610/R

BOSHOFF, Adriaan (1935-) South African
£545 $849 €818 Extensive landscape with trees and mountains in the distance (31x46cm-12x18in) s. board. 11-Nov-2 Stephan Welz, Johannesburg #557 (SA.R 8500)
£563 $889 €845 Batsman (22x17cm-9x7in) s. canvas on board. 1-Apr-3 Stephan Welz, Johannesburg #504 est:4000-6000 (SA.R 7000)
£723 $1143 €1085 Two women at a washline (21x33cm-8x13in) s. canvas on board. 1-Apr-3 Stephan Welz, Johannesburg #505 est:5000-8000 (SA.R 9000)
£1345 $2099 €2018 Figures on a mountainous road (45x35cm-18x14in) s. canvas on board. 11-Nov-2 Stephan Welz, Johannesburg #555/R est:10000-15000 (SA.R 21000)
£1376 $2215 €2064 Forest scene (59x38cm-23x15in) s. canavs on board. 12-May-3 Stephan Welz, Johannesburg #575/R est:7000-10000 (SA.R 16000)

£3439 $5537 €5159 Two women resting under a tree (50x79cm-20x31in) s. canvas on board. 12-May-3 Stephan Welz, Johannesburg #525/R est:18000-24000 (SA.R 40000)

BOSHOFF, Aggy (20th C) British?
£750 $1163 €1125 Garden patio (200x200cm-79x79in) s.d.97. 4-Dec-2 Christie's, Kensington #471/R

BOSIERS, René (1875-1927) Belgian
£360 $562 €540 Seated female nude (90x48cm-35x19in) s. canvas on board. 8-Apr-3 Bonhams, Knightsbridge #303
£1013 $1580 €1600 Natiepaarden (90x105cm-35x41in) s. exhib. 21-Oct-2 Bernaerts, Antwerp #668 est:600-750
£1203 $1876 €1900 Yachts at sea (117x82cm-46x32in) s. 21-Oct-2 Bernaerts, Antwerp #12/R est:2000-3000
Works on paper
£2278 $3554 €3600 Op de mosselkaai (90x124cm-35x49in) s. pastel. 21-Oct-2 Bernaerts, Antwerp #14/R est:1500-2000

BOSIO, François Joseph (studio) (1769-1845) French
Sculpture
£9615 $14904 €15000 Portrait de la reine Hortense (66x40x21cm-26x16x8in) pat bronze exec.1810. 9-Dec-2 Rabourdin & Choppin de Janvry, Paris #120/R

BOSIO, Jean François (attrib) (1764-1827) French
Works on paper
£980 $1608 €1500 Dejeuner frais. Glaces (23x30cm-9x12in) i. pen ink wash two. 7-Feb-3 Piasa, Paris #34

BOSKE, Joachim (20th C) ?
Works on paper
£380 $589 €600 Lighthouse keeper's daughter (26x36cm-10x14in) s.d.74 mixed media. 24-Sep-2 De Veres Art Auctions, Dublin #15

BOSKERCK, R W van (1855-1932) American
£1923 $3000 €2885 Landscape. 21-Sep-2 Nadeau, Windsor #107/R est:2500-4000

BOSKERCK, Robert Ward van (1855-1932) American
£290 $475 €435 Autumn, Woodstock, VT (41x61cm-16x24in) s. 9-Feb-3 William Jenack, New York #96
£1100 $1694 €1650 Village lane (36x51cm-14x20in) s.i.d.1895. 24-Oct-2 Christie's, Kensington #221/R est:1000-1500
£1138 $1798 €1650 Cattle by the mill stream (39x60cm-15x24in) s. 22-Jul-3 Lawson Menzies, Sydney #287/R est:3000-5000 (A.D 2800)
£1600 $2496 €2400 River landscape (61x81cm-24x32in) s. 17-Sep-2 Sotheby's, Olympia #291/R est:1200-1800
£4777 $7500 €7166 River landscape. Boat along the river (64x51cm-25x20in) s. two. 10-Dec-2 Doyle, New York #14/R est:3000-5000

BOSLEY, Frederick Andrew (1881-1942) American
£510 $800 €765 Portrait of a young man (53x43cm-21x17in) prov. 22-Nov-2 Skinner, Boston #109/R

BOSMA, Wim (1902-) Dutch
Works on paper
£287 $441 €450 Boats in a harbour (35x43cm-14x17in) s.verso gouache W/C. 3-Sep-2 Christie's, Amsterdam #378
£552 $877 €800 Harbour scene (34x44cm-13x17in) s. W/C. 10-Mar-3 Sotheby's, Amsterdam #203/R

BOSMAN, Louis (19/20th C) ?
£316 $500 €474 Barnyard scene (51x61cm-20x24in) s.d.1916. 30-Nov-2 Thomaston Place, Thomaston #162

BOSQUE GARCIA, Sergio (1943-) Spanish
Works on paper
£2830 $4415 €4500 Thinking about the fight (167x110cm-66x43in) s.d.93 mixed media. 23-Sep-2 Durán, Madrid #205/R

BOSS, Eduard (1873-1958) Swiss
£262 $409 €393 Still life (50x59cm-20x23in) s. 6-Nov-2 Dobiaschofsky, Bern #365/R (S.FR 600)
£529 $788 €794 Winter landscape with farmstead (65x54cm-26x21in) s.d.07. 25-Jun-2 Koller, Zurich #6578 (S.FR 1200)
£648 $1044 €940 Still life with apples (30x40cm-12x16in) s.d.18. 9-May-3 Dobiaschofsky, Bern #140/R (S.FR 1400)
£730 $1153 €1095 Still life of apples (39x52cm-15x20in) s.d.20 board. 28-Nov-2 Christie's, Zurich #60/R (S.FR 1700)

BOSS, Prosper (?) ?
£621 $981 €900 Les enfants de choeur. s. three in one frame. 1-Apr-3 Palais de Beaux Arts, Brussels #509

BOSSCHAERT, Ambrosius (attrib) (17th C) Flemish
£5435 $8913 €7500 Nature morte aux fleurs (95x135cm-37x53in) s. 27-May-3 Campo, Vlaamse Kaai #28/R est:8000-10000

BOSSCHAERT, Ambrosius (elder) (1573-1621) Flemish
£1612903 $2548387 €2500000 Bouquet de tulipes et roses dans un vase sur entablement (23x17cm-9x7in) copper. 18-Dec-2 Piasa, Paris #26/R est:800000-1000000

BOSSCHAERT, Ambrosius (younger-circle) (1609-1645) Dutch
£23171 $38000 €34757 Tulips, peonies and other flowers in glass vase with seashells on a ledge (53x35cm-21x14in) panel. 30-May-3 Christie's, Rockefeller NY #2/R est:12000-18000

BOSSCHAERT, Jean Baptiste (1667-1746) Flemish
£10072 $16115 €14000 Garland with flowers and other flowers tied with ribbon (54x80cm-21x31in) 13-May-3 Sotheby's, Amsterdam #85/R est:15000-20000
£15000 $25050 €21750 Still life of various flowers, stone urn and ledge with a young woman (138x103cm-54x41in) 10-Jul-3 Sotheby's, London #195/R est:15000-20000

BOSSCHAERT, Johannes (17th C) Dutch
£123457 $200000 €185186 Still life of flowers in a vase resting on a ledge with a lizard and insects (37x25cm-15x10in) bears mono.d.1687. 23-Jan-3 Sotheby's, New York #38a/R est:30000-40000

BOSSCHE, Balthasar van den (attrib) (1681-1715) Flemish
£986 $1637 €1400 Painter's studio (48x38cm-19x15in) 11-Jun-3 Dorotheum, Vienna #300/R
£3774 $5849 €6000 Tax Collector (52x61cm-20x24in) 2-Oct-2 Dorotheum, Vienna #429/R est:6000-8000
£7051 $11141 €11000 Atelier du peintre. Atelier du sculpteur (49x62cm-19x24in) pair. 15-Nov-2 Beaussant & Lefèvre, Paris #34/R est:10000-12000

BOSSCHE, Dominique van den (?-1906) Belgian
Sculpture
£4200 $6552 €6300 Bacchante entertaining Pan (101cm-40in) s. brown pat bronze lit. 9-Apr-3 Sotheby's, London #201/R est:4000-6000

BOSSCHE, Guy van den (20th C) Belgian
£347 $552 €500 Composition (92x65cm-36x26in) s.d.1990. 29-Apr-3 Campo, Vlaamse Kaai #315

BOSSCHE, Hubert van den (1874-1957) Belgian
£822 $1282 €1200 Vase fleuri (66x81cm-26x32in) s. panel oval. 14-Apr-3 Horta, Bruxelles #57

BOSSE, Louise (1878-1929) Austrian
Works on paper
£321 $506 €500 Garden (14x14cm-6x6in) s. collage. 12-Nov-2 Dorotheum, Vienna #9

BOSSER, Jacques (1946-) French
Works on paper
£1042 $1656 €1500 Veega (120x163cm-47x64in) s.d.98 i.verso mixed media panel. 29-Apr-3 Artcurial Briest, Paris #597/R est:1500-2000

BOSSHARD, Rodolphe-Theophile (1889-1960) Swiss
£1659 $2589 €2489 Female nude standing (28x20cm-11x8in) s.d.17 board. 8-Nov-2 Dobiaschofsky, Bern #122/R est:4500 (S.FR 3800)
£3265 $5192 €4800 Paysage de Provence (50x65cm-20x26in) s. 26-Feb-3 Artcurial Briest, Paris #293 est:600-800
£5652 $8761 €8478 Le chateau (5x46cm-2x18in) mono.d.1947. 9-Dec-2 Philippe Schuler, Zurich #3805/R est:14000-18000 (S.FR 13000)
£5660 $9170 €10019 Le pont romain Promontogno (55x46cm-22x18in) s.d.1942 i.d. verso. 26-May-3 Sotheby's, Zurich #110/R est:8000-14000 (S.FR 12000)
£7194 $11799 €10000 Reclining female nude (38x55cm-15x22in) s. i. verso. 6-Jun-3 Ketterer, Munich #48/R est:5000-6000
£9955 $16624 €14435 La mort du cygne (100x81cm-39x32in) s. i.d. verso. 24-Jun-3 Koller, Zurich #34/R est:25000-45000 (S.FR 22000)

£10730 $16953 €16095 Paysage de Lavaux avec lac et bateau, vu depuis Chexbres (37x45cm-15x18in) s.i.d.32 paper on board exhib.lit. 26-Nov-2 Phillips, Zurich #60/R est:25000-30000 (S.FR 25000)
£13514 $21081 €20000 Baigneuse couche sur le cote (50x73cm-20x29in) s. 31-Mar-3 Rossini, Paris #79/R
£13889 $22361 €20139 Jeune fille nue (188x110cm-74x43in) s. 9-May-3 Dobiaschofsky, Bern #169/R est:34000 (S.FR 30000)

Works on paper
£522 $809 €783 Le moulin, Syracuse (31x22cm-12x9in) s.i.d.48 pencil. 7-Dec-2 Galerie du Rhone, Sion #357/R (S.FR 1200)

BOSSHARDT, Caspar (1823-1887) Swiss
£3896 $6039 €5844 Deer hunter (92x102cm-36x40in) s.d.1857. 24-Sep-2 Koller, Zurich #6628/R est:6000-9000 (S.FR 9000)

BOSSI, Domenico (1765-1853) Italian
Miniatures
£1300 $2002 €1950 Lady in a dress with patterned trim and shawl (8cm-3in circular) s.i.d.18 gilt metal frame. 24-Oct-2 Sotheby's, Olympia #93/R est:1200-1800
£1400 $2338 €2030 Alexander I Pavlovich (4cm-2xin) s. gilt metal mount oval exec.c.1805. 25-Jun-3 Sotheby's, Olympia #42/R est:1200-1800
£3200 $4928 €4800 Gentleman in a blue coat (6cm-2in circular) s.d.1796 gilt metal frame. 24-Oct-2 Sotheby's, Olympia #92/R est:1500-2000

BOSSO, Francesco (1864-1933) Italian
£510 $811 €750 Lake bank (29x21cm-11x8in) s. cardboard. 1-Mar-3 Meeting Art, Vercelli #185
£2839 $4485 €4400 Flowers (36x26cm-14x10in) s. board pair. 18-Dec-2 Finarte, Milan #202/R est:3500

BOSSOLI, Carlo (1815-1884) Italian
Works on paper
£2200 $3432 €3300 Figures in a hilly landscape near a town, Turkey (24x41cm-9x16in) s. gouache. 15-Oct-2 Sotheby's, London #74/R est:2500-3500
£2200 $3498 €3300 Stags and hinds in a mountainous landscape a bay beyond (28x43cm-11x17in) s. gouache. 4-Mar-3 Bearnes, Exeter #329/R est:400-600
£2288 $3752 €3500 Lochranza (27x45cm-11x18in) s.i. gouache paper on board. 29-Mar-3 Dannenberg, Berlin #550/R est:3000
£2600 $4056 €3900 Abergeldie Castle, Dee Side (34x54cm-13x21in) s.d.1856 i.on mount W/C. 14-Apr-3 Sotheby's, London #7/R est:2500-3500
£3200 $4992 €4800 Choill Hills looking on Balmoral (35x56cm-14x22in) s.d.1856 i.on mount W/C. 14-Apr-3 Sotheby's, London #8/R est:2000-3000
£3800 $5928 €5700 Birkhall Ballater (35x55cm-14x22in) s.d.1856 i.verso W/C. 14-Apr-3 Sotheby's, London #9/R est:1500-2000
£4200 $6552 €6300 At Ballater Water (34x54cm-13x21in) s.d.1856 i.on mount W/C. 14-Apr-3 Sotheby's, London #6/R est:3000-5000
£6608 $9648 €9912 Escorial Palace in Madrid province (26x46cm-10x18in) s. W/C gouache. 17-Jun-2 Philippe Schuler, Zurich #4788/R est:3000-4000 (S.FR 15000)
£83333 $135000 €125000 Views of Constantinople (38x59cm-15x23in) s.d.1846 gouache pair. 23-Jan-3 Sotheby's, New York #95/R est:150000-200000

BOSSOLI, F (19th C) Italian
£1378 $2095 €2067 Procession in a Gothic church (60x45cm-24x18in) s. 27-Aug-2 Rasmussen, Copenhagen #1598/R est:12000-15000 (D.KR 16000)

BOSSUET, François Antoine (1798-1889) Belgian
£504 $806 €700 Ruelle animee (21x13cm-8x5in) s. 13-May-3 Vanderkindere, Brussels #11
£4676 $7482 €6500 Vue sur l'Hopital Saint Jean a Bruges (28x36cm-11x14in) s.d.73 panel. 13-May-3 Palais de Beaux Arts, Brussels #32/R est:4000-6000
£9000 $14760 €13500 Le Grand Canal, Venise (50x71cm-20x28in) s.d.78. 3-Jun-3 Sotheby's, London #181/R est:8000-12000

BOSTICK, William Allison (1913-) American
£361 $600 €523 Opera house finale (61x76cm-24x30in) s.d.1966 acrylic masonite prov. 11-Jun-3 Boos Gallery, Michigan #347/R

BOSTIK, Vaclav (1913-) Czechoslovakian
Works on paper
£315 $488 €473 Geometry (25x23cm-10x9in) pastel exec.c.1980. 1-Oct-2 SOGA, Bratislava #228/R est:20000 (SL.K 20000)

BOSTON, Frederick James (1855-1932) American
£377 $600 €566 Wind clouds (20x25cm-8x10in) s. i.verso canvasboard. 22-Mar-3 New Orleans Auction, New Orleans #1144/R
£422 $700 €612 Untitled (43x61cm-17x24in) 13-Jun-3 Du Mouchelle, Detroit #2220/R

BOSTON, Joseph H (1860-1954) American
£774 $1200 €1161 Woman on a sofa (41x30cm-16x12in) s. panel painted c.1910 prov. 8-Dec-2 Toomey, Oak Park #698/R
£1198 $2000 €1737 Sunset on the river (63x76cm-25x30in) s. 22-Jun-3 Freeman, Philadelphia #89/R est:800-1200

BOSTON, Paul (1952-) Australian
£1538 $2446 €2307 Chopping blocks (152x122cm-60x48in) s.verso oil moulded relief prov. 4-Mar-3 Deutscher-Menzies, Melbourne #188/R est:5000-8000 (A.D 4000)
£1643 $2595 €2465 Groupling (122x168cm-48x66in) s.i.d.1999 board prov. 27-Nov-2 Deutscher-Menzies, Melbourne #6/R est:6000-8000 (A.D 4600)
£1786 $2785 €2679 Painting no 5 (86x127cm-34x50in) s.i.d.1994 verso linen. 11-Nov-2 Deutscher-Menzies, Melbourne #62/R est:4000-6000 (A.D 5000)
£2071 $3273 €3107 Untitled (137x91cm-54x36in) prov. 26-Nov-2 Sotheby's, Melbourne #83/R est:6000-8000 (A.D 5800)
£7143 $11000 €10715 Painting No.5 (228x152cm-90x60in) s.d.1990 i.verso oil on linen exhib. 8-Sep-2 Sotheby's, Melbourne #18/R est:4000-6000 (A.D 20000)

Works on paper
£571 $903 €857 Untitled (76x56cm-30x22in) pastel prov. 27-Nov-2 Deutscher-Menzies, Melbourne #112/R est:2000-3000 (A.D 1600)
£1000 $1590 €1500 Piled up story stack (112x74cm-44x29in) pastel prov. 4-Mar-3 Deutscher-Menzies, Melbourne #226/R est:2000-3000 (A.D 2600)
£1000 $1590 €1500 Letters and figures (107x74cm-42x29in) W/C ink wash prov. 4-Mar-3 Deutscher-Menzies, Melbourne #227/R est:3000-4500 (A.D 2600)
£1500 $2310 €2250 Pastel no.2 (49x65cm-19x26in) s.d.1988 verso gouache chl pastel. 8-Sep-2 Sotheby's, Melbourne #32/R est:2000-3000 (A.D 4200)

BOTELLO, Angel (1913-1986) Spanish
£2390 $3800 €3585 Surreal landscape (64x61cm-25x24in) s.i. painted c.1950. 5-May-3 Butterfields, San Francisco #98/R est:6000-8000
£2516 $4000 €3774 Two women in profile (38x38cm-15x15in) s. painted c.1950. 5-May-3 Butterfields, San Francisco #97/R est:8000-12000
£3459 $5500 €5189 Portrait of a lady (36x30cm-14x12in) s. painted c.1950. 5-May-3 Butterfields, San Francisco #96/R est:6000-8000
£7643 $12000 €11465 Girls with flowers (61x46cm-24x18in) s. panel painted c.1980 prov. 19-Nov-2 Sotheby's, New York #155/R est:20000
£7692 $12000 €11538 Figures on a beach (60x49cm-24x19in) s. board after Gaugin. 5-Nov-2 Doyle, New York #1/R est:1500-2000
£10828 $17000 €16242 Girls bowling (61x91cm-24x36in) s. panel painted c.1980 prov. 19-Nov-2 Sotheby's, New York #156/R est:25000

BOTERO, Fernando (1932-) Colombian
£31847 $50000 €47771 Still life with coffee pot (71x77cm-28x30in) s.d.62 prov. 20-Nov-2 Christie's, Rockefeller NY #128/R
£33537 $55000 €50306 Santa Teresita del Nino Jesus (60x62cm-24x24in) s.d.66 prov. 28-May-3 Christie's, Rockefeller NY #119/R est:70000-90000
£39634 $65000 €59451 Poodle (93x84cm-37x33in) s.d.67 prov. 28-May-3 Christie's, Rockefeller NY #124/R est:70000-90000
£41159 $67500 €59681 Tres monjas (36x126cm-14x50in) s.d.61 prov. 27-May-3 Sotheby's, New York #103
£121019 $190000 €181529 Archangel (152x130cm-60x51in) s.d.88 prov. 20-Nov-2 Christie's, Rockefeller NY #41/R est:220000-260000
£121951 $200000 €176829 Still life (107x150cm-42x59in) s.d.83 s.verso prov.lit. 27-May-3 Sotheby's, New York #15
£127389 $200000 €191084 Still life with photograph (103x135cm-41x53in) s.d.82 prov. 20-Nov-2 Christie's, Rockefeller NY #43/R est:200000-205000
£365854 $600000 €530488 Antes del paseo (200x272cm-79x107in) s. prov.exhib.lit. 27-May-3 Sotheby's, New York #17

Prints
£2903 $4587 €4500 Dance (41x28cm-16x11in) s. num.1/3 lithograph prov. 18-Dec-2 Ansorena, Madrid #447/R

Sculpture
£24390 $40000 €36585 Cabeza de hombre (31cm-12in) s.num.2/6 sf.f.verso brown pat bronze exec.1987 one of 6 prov.lit. 28-May-3 Christie's, Rockefeller NY #121/R est:50000-70000
£30488 $50000 €44208 Culebra (33x170x72cm-13x67x28in) s.num.4/6 gold pat bronze prov.exhib.lit. 27-May-3 Sotheby's, New York #14

£89172 $140000 €133758 Seated woman (42x38x38cm-17x15x15in) st.sig. num.EA2/2 brown pat bronze prov. 19-Nov-2 Sotheby's, New York #44/R est:200000
£95541 $150000 €143312 Cat (53x31cm-21x12in) s. num.1/6 brown pat bronze exec.2000 prov.exhib. 20-Nov-2 Christie's, Rockefeller NY #40/R est:150000-200000
£101911 $160000 €152867 Maternity (47x23cm-19x9in) s.st.f. num.5/6 brown pat bronze exec.1995 lit. 20-Nov-2 Christie's, Rockefeller NY #16/R est:120000-140000

Works on paper
£2346 $3331 €3800 Portrait de picador (27x29cm-11x11in) s. felt-tip pen dr. 16-Mar-3 Eric Pillon, Calais #247/R
£6000 $9480 €9000 Man with doves (30x21cm-12x8in) s.d.52 pen brush ink. 3-Apr-3 Christie's, Kensington #146a/R
£8537 $14000 €12379 Flores (69x64cm-27x25in) s. ink wash pastel chl board exec.c.1957 prov. 27-May-3 Sotheby's, New York #95
£15385 $25692 €22308 Picator (42x33cm-17x13in) s.d.85 pencil prov. 24-Jun-3 Koller, Zurich #163/R est:30000-40000 (S.FR 34000)
£21341 $35000 €30944 Society woman (44x36cm-17x14in) s.d.80 graphite chk paper on board prov.exhib. 27-May-3 Sotheby's, New York #118
£29000 $47560 €43500 Man drawing a still life (35x43cm-14x17in) s.d.76 pencil htd gouache prov. 6-Feb-3 Christie's, London #486/R est:20000
£82803 $130000 €124205 Woman in red (157x109cm-62x43in) s.d.80 W/C pastel prov.lit. 19-Nov-2 Sotheby's, New York #38/R est:100000

BOTH, Andries (1608-1650) Dutch
£7194 $11511 €10000 Steadfast philospher (82x60cm-32x24in) i. 13-May-3 Sotheby's, Amsterdam #32/R est:10000-15000

BOTH, Andries (attrib) (1608-1650) Dutch
Works on paper
£2302 $3683 €3200 Un pecheur tenant une epuisette et un seau (154x191cm-61x75in) i. pen brown ink. 15-May-3 Christie's, Paris #196/R est:1500-2000

BOTH, Jan (1618-1652) Dutch
£4113 $6376 €6170 Italian landscape with figures (54x64cm-21x25in) mono. 3-Dec-2 Bukowskis, Stockholm #448/R est:60000-80000 (S.KR 58000)

BOTH, Jan (attrib) (1618-1652) Dutch
Works on paper
£1543 $2500 €2315 View of the Tiber Valley (20x29cm-8x11in) pen ink wash htd white. 21-Jan-3 Sotheby's, New York #3144/R

BOTHAMS, Walter (c.1850-1914) British
Works on paper
£380 $597 €570 Sheep in a field (13x25cm-5x10in) s. W/C bodycol. 21-Nov-2 Tennants, Leyburn #618
£400 $624 €600 Salisbury Cathedral (27x47cm-11x19in) s. pencil W/C htd white. 27-Mar-3 Christie's, Kensington #139

BOTKE, Cornelius (1887-1954) American
£1433 $2250 €2150 Desert landscape (41x51cm-16x20in) s. canvasboard prov. 19-Nov-2 Butterfields, San Francisco #8315/R est:3000-5000
£1708 $2750 €2562 Grand Canyon (51x61cm-20x24in) s. i.verso wood panel. 18-Feb-3 John Moran, Pasadena #114c est:3000-4000
£1958 $3250 €2839 Gardens at Chateau de Saint-Cloud in autumn. Garden fountain (30x37cm-12x15in) one s.i. canvas on board pair. 11-Jun-3 Butterfields, San Francisco #4203/R est:3000-5000
£3548 $5500 €5322 Carmel Valley, 1926 (30x41cm-12x16in) s. i.indis.d. verso board. 29-Oct-2 John Moran, Pasadena #662 est:5000-7000

BOTKE, Jessie Arms (1883-1971) American
£4819 $8000 €6988 Flamingos and lotus (25x20cm-10x8in) s. oil gilt board prov. 11-Jun-3 Butterfields, San Francisco #4298/R est:10000-15000
£5988 $10000 €8683 Blue Macaw (33x23cm-13x9in) i.verso oil gold leaf canvasboard exhib.prov. 17-Jun-3 John Moran, Pasadena #25 est:12000-18000
£10897 $17000 €16346 Study for The Oaks Hotel mural, Ojai (28x99cm-11x39in) s. i.verso oil goldleaf masonite prov.exhib. 14-Sep-2 Weschler, Washington #613/R est:15000-25000
£11613 $18000 €17420 Cockatoos in foliage (20x25cm-8x10in) s. board. 29-Oct-2 John Moran, Pasadena #614 est:10000-15000
£12422 $20000 €18633 Hawaii no 1, cockatoos in lush Hawaiian foliage (23x30cm-9x12in) oil gold leaf board prov. 18-Feb-3 John Moran, Pasadena #16/R est:15000-20000

Works on paper
£1592 $2500 €2388 Mallard drake (37x52cm-15x20in) s. i.verso W/C prov. 19-Nov-2 Butterfields, San Francisco #8326/R est:3000-5000

BOTKIN, Henry Albert (1896-1983) American
Works on paper
£1280 $2100 €1856 Volta (61x84cm-24x33in) s. s.i.d.1965 verso mixed media collage prov. 1-Jun-3 Wright, Chicago #270/R est:2000-3000

BOTO, Martha (1925-) Argentinian
£786 $1234 €1179 La Cruz (100x65cm-39x26in) s.d.1954 s.i.d. verso. 25-Nov-2 Germann, Zurich #38/R est:2000-3000 (S.FR 1800)

BOTT, Francis (1904-1998) German
£641 $994 €1000 Composition (11x15cm-4x6in) s. paper. 7-Dec-2 Van Ham, Cologne #67/R
£865 $1341 €1350 Composition (21x27cm-8x11in) 7-Dec-2 Ketterer, Hamburg #382/R
£1150 $1817 €1725 Burwood (64x81cm-25x32in) s.d.1959. 2-Dec-2 Gorringes, Lewes #2591/R est:1000-1500
£1293 $2055 €1900 Composition (34x48cm-13x19in) s. acrylic painted 1957. 24-Mar-3 Claude Boisgirard, Paris #153/R
£1357 $2267 €1968 Composition with leopard (30x38cm-12x15in) s.i. tempera W/C oil chk. 24-Jun-3 Koller, Zurich #172/R est:1500-2500 (S.FR 3000)
£1810 $3023 €2625 Composition (69x45cm-27x18in) s.d.61. 24-Jun-3 Koller, Zurich #174/R est:4400-6000 (S.FR 4000)
£1965 $3085 €2948 Untitled (59x72cm-23x28in) s.d.1962 lit. 25-Nov-2 Germann, Zurich #103/R est:5000-7000 (S.FR 4500)
£3077 $4769 €4800 Composition (54x84cm-21x33in) s.d.58 board on plywood. 7-Dec-2 Van Ham, Cologne #65/R est:6000

Works on paper
£541 $843 €800 Abstract (50x65cm-20x26in) s.d.58 mixed media. 28-Mar-3 Karrenbauer, Konstanz #1706
£769 $1192 €1200 Untitled (22x30cm-9x12in) s. gouache. 7-Dec-2 Ketterer, Hamburg #383/R

BOTT, Nicholas J (1941-) Canadian
£1244 $2041 €1804 October snow (75x100cm-30x39in) s.i.d.1955-56. 9-Jun-3 Hodgins, Calgary #56/R est:3000-4000 (C.D 2800)

BOTTANI, Giuseppe (1717-1784) Italian
Works on paper
£360 $601 €522 Male nude (20x27cm-8x11in) i. black white chk. 9-Jul-3 Bonhams, Knightsbridge #34/R

BOTTCHER, Jurgen (1931-) German
£1389 $2194 €2000 Swimming (42x58cm-17x23in) s.i.d.4.V.1981 Indian ink feltpen biro. 26-Apr-3 Dr Lehr, Berlin #481/R est:1800
£2536 $4159 €3500 Untitled (50x71cm-20x28in) s.d.29.1.1989 W/C collage. 28-May-3 Lempertz, Koln #418/R est:6000

Works on paper
£3472 $5486 €5000 Composition (36x55cm-14x22in) s.d.4.XI.1987 pen rose petals cardboard. 26-Apr-3 Dr Lehr, Berlin #480/R est:2400

BOTTELEY, H (?) British?
Works on paper
£260 $403 €390 Study of fish. s. W/C three in one frame. 26-Sep-2 Lane, Penzance #324

BOTTERO, Daniel (1950-) Argentinian
Works on paper
£10191 $16000 €15287 Untitled (133x137cm-52x54in) s.d.2002 mixed media on canvas prov. 20-Nov-2 Christie's, Rockefeller NY #140/R est:10000-15000

BOTTGER, Herbert (1898-1954) German
£3333 $5167 €5200 Winter evening (40x50cm-16x20in) mono. 4-Dec-2 Lempertz, Koln #577/R est:3000
£5641 $8744 €8800 Still life of flowers (45x40cm-18x16in) mono.d.43 exhib. 7-Dec-2 Van Ham, Cologne #62/R est:10000

BOTTICELLI, Sandro (1440-1510) Italian
£80000 $133600 €116000 Madonna and Child with the young Saint John the Baptist and Archangel Gabriel (86cm-34in circular) panel. 9-Jul-3 Christie's, London #74/R est:50000-80000
£154321 $250000 €231482 Christ on the Cross adored by Saints Monica and other Saint (76x91cm-30x36in) panel and possibly by studio prov.exhib.lit. 24-Jan-3 Christie's, Rockefeller NY #75/R est:250000-350000

BOTTICELLI, Sandro (studio) (1440-1510) Italian
£37000 $61790 €53650 Christ and woman of Samaria at the well (79x166cm-31x65in) panel prov. 10-Jul-3 Sotheby's, London #154/R est:20000-30000

BOTTIGLIERI, Gennaro (19th C) Italian
£306 $487 €450 Still life (26x40cm-10x16in) s. board on cardboard. 1-Mar-3 Meeting Art, Vercelli #33

BOTTING, Roy (20th C) British
£519 $804 €820 Orange divan (21x38cm-8x15in) s. i.d.1950 verso board. 24-Sep-2 De Veres Art Auctions, Dublin #123

BOTTINI, Georges (1873-1907) French
£897 $1391 €1400 Auto-portrait (40x32cm-16x13in) painted c.1895 prov.exhib.lit. 9-Dec-2 Beaussant & Lefèvre, Paris #21

BOTTINI, S (19th C) Italian
£2400 $3912 €3600 Blowing bubbles (49x37cm-19x15in) s. 13-Feb-3 Christie's, Kensington #199/R est:1200-1800

BOTTMAN, A (after) (19th C) Latvian
£48000 $77760 €72000 View of the west Dvina River, riga from iron bridge with cathedral St. Peter's church (66x117cm-26x46in) 21-May-3 Sotheby's, London #142/R est:25000-35000

BOTTOM, Robert (1944-) British
£260 $403 €390 Still life (36x30cm-14x12in) s. board. 2-Oct-2 John Ross, Belfast #279

BOTTOMLEY, Albert Ernest (1873-1950) British
£500 $775 €750 Horseguard's parade, London (35x46cm-14x18in) s.d.1927. 4-Dec-2 Christie's, Kensington #435/R
£500 $815 €750 Showery weather, April (46x61cm-18x24in) s.d.1921 i.verso. 13-Feb-3 David Lay, Penzance #226

BOTTOMLEY, Edwin (1865-1929) British
Works on paper
£400 $652 €600 Hay cart (28x43cm-11x17in) s. W/C. 13-Feb-3 David Lay, Penzance #81
£500 $810 €750 Horse and cart on a rural track (24x45cm-9x18in) s.d.1914 W/C. 21-May-3 Bonhams, Knightsbridge #85/R

BOTTON, Jean Isy de (1898-1978) French
£710 $1100 €1065 Les iris bleus (61x46cm-24x18in) s.i. verso prov. 1-Oct-2 Arthur James, Florida #440
£774 $1200 €1161 Paris carousel sur la butte Montmartre (53x71cm-21x28in) s.i.d.1939. 1-Oct-2 Arthur James, Florida #441

BOUBAT, Edouard (1923-) French
Photographs
£2454 $4000 €3681 Lella, Bretagne (34x25cm-13x10in) s. i.d.1948 verso gelatin silver print. 12-Feb-3 Christie's, Rockefeller NY #113/R est:2500-3500

BOUCART, Gaston H (1878-1962) French
£903 $1453 €1355 Fishermen returning home (50x65cm-20x26in) s. 7-May-3 Dobiaschofsky, Bern #3138 est:900 (S.FR 1950)
£2025 $3200 €3200 Canal a Venise (22x27cm-9x11in) s. panel. 1-Dec-2 Peron, Melun #83

BOUCHARD, Edith Marie (1924-) Canadian
£484 $765 €726 Vieil interieur (33x41cm-13x16in) s. canvas on board prov. 14-Nov-2 Heffel, Vancouver #17/R est:1500-2000 (C.D 1200)

BOUCHARD, Lorne Holland (1913-1978) Canadian
£215 $335 €323 Eskimo summer camp, Pangnirtug (20x25cm-8x10in) s. s.i.d.verso panel. 25-Mar-3 Iegor de Saint Hippolyte, Montreal #13 (C.D 500)
£215 $335 €312 Lake near St. Urbain, Quebec (25x35cm-10x14in) s.i.d.1946 oil on aluminum. 26-Mar-3 Walker's, Ottawa #439/R (C.D 500)
£279 $435 €405 Morning mist, Perce Quebec (30x41cm-12x16in) s.i.d.1954 canvasboard prov. 26-Mar-3 Walker's, Ottawa #256/R (C.D 650)
£285 $447 €428 October woods (30x41cm-12x16in) s. s.i.d.1961 verso board. 10-Dec-2 Pinneys, Montreal #13 (C.D 700)
£489 $802 €734 March - lake of two mountains (35x60cm-14x24in) s. board. 3-Jun-3 Joyner, Toronto #367/R est:800-1200 (C.D 1100)

BOUCHARD, Louis Henri (1875-1960) French
Sculpture
£3500 $5460 €5250 Little shepherdess (33x31cm-13x12in) s.d.1912 brown pat bronze st.f.Siot. 9-Apr-3 Sotheby's, London #190/R est:3500-4500
£4500 $7065 €6750 Le greffeur - man grafting a vine (35cm-14in) s. brown pat. bronze. 10-Dec-2 Sotheby's, London #150/R est:3000-5000
£5800 $9106 €8700 En vendange - harvesting grapes (31cm-12in) s.d.1911 brown pat. bronze. 10-Dec-2 Sotheby's, London #149/R est:3000-5000

BOUCHARD, Marie Cecile (1920-) Canadian
£244 $383 €366 Scene d'interieur en Charlevoix (30x40cm-12x16in) 12-Dec-2 Iegor de Saint Hippolyte, Montreal #11 (C.D 600)
£407 $638 €611 Hiver en Charlevoix (41x41cm-16x16in) s. board. 12-Dec-2 Iegor de Saint Hippolyte, Montreal #10 (C.D 1000)
£806 $1274 €1209 Interior, charlevoix, Quebec (42x55cm-17x22in) s. board painted c.1940 prov. 14-Nov-2 Heffel, Vancouver #16/R est:1500-2000 (C.D 2000)

BOUCHARD, Paul (1853-1937) French
£3600 $5832 €5400 In the harem (32x46cm-13x18in) s. 20-May-3 Sotheby's, Olympia #362/R est:3000-5000
£11613 $18000 €17420 Old Moscow (50x61cm-20x24in) s. prov. 3-Dec-2 Christie's, Rockefeller NY #653/R est:6000-8000

BOUCHARD, Paul (after) (1853-1937) French
£8500 $13346 €12750 Red Square under snow (38x56cm-15x22in) bears sig.d.1894. 20-Nov-2 Sotheby's, London #44/R est:3500-4500

BOUCHARD, Simone Mary (1912-1945) Canadian
£1008 $1593 €1512 Still life on table (30x49cm-12x19in) s.i.verso board prov. 14-Nov-2 Heffel, Vancouver #12/R est:1200-1600 (C.D 2500)

BOUCHARDON, Edme (1698-1762) French
Works on paper
£1689 $2635 €2500 Mythological scenes. sanguine set of 4. 26-Mar-3 Piasa, Paris #41/R
£1772 $2800 €2800 Le vendeur de moulins (24x18cm-9x7in) red chk. 27-Nov-2 Christie's, Paris #158/R est:3000-5000
£2200 $3454 €3300 Study of hands (31x34cm-12x13in) red chk. 11-Dec-2 Sotheby's, Olympia #154/R est:1500-2000
£3103 $4966 €4500 Contre-epreuves pour les bas-reliefs de la fontaine de la rue de Grenelle (53x41cm-21x16in) sanguine four in one frame prov. 12-Mar-3 E & Eve, Paris #21/R est:3000-4000

BOUCHARDON, Edme (attrib) (1698-1762) French
Works on paper
£297 $425 €446 Christ lying beside his open tomb. Mechanical studies (21x37cm-8x15in) red chk double-sided. 23-Jan-3 Swann Galleries, New York #248/R

BOUCHAUD, Jean (1891-1977) French
Works on paper
£1655 $2648 €2400 Rue de Laghouat (24x33cm-9x13in) s.i. pencil W/C gouache. 12-Mar-3 E & Eve, Paris #100/R est:2500-3000

BOUCHE, Georges (1874-1941) French
£926 $1491 €1343 Garden (46x38cm-18x15in) s. 7-May-3 Dobiaschofsky, Bern #368/R (S.FR 2000)

BOUCHE, Louis (1896-1969) American
£531 $850 €797 Queens landscape, man and his dog walking (28x48cm-11x19in) s.d.1945. 17-Mar-3 Winter Associates, Plainville #150
£1280 $2100 €1856 Playthings (91x76cm-36x30in) s. prov. 1-Jun-3 Wright, Chicago #238/R est:1000-1500

BOUCHENE, Dimitri (1893-1993) French
£1800 $2916 €2700 Flowers in blue and white (73x92cm-29x36in) s. 21-May-3 Sotheby's, London #106/R est:2000-3000
£4500 $7066 €6750 View from the balcony (76x101cm-30x40in) s. 20-Nov-2 Sotheby's, London #143/R est:5000-7000
Works on paper
£4000 $6280 €6000 Yachting in San Tropez (48x62cm-19x24in) s. pastel. 20-Nov-2 Sotheby's, London #146/R est:2000-3000

BOUCHER, A (?) ?
Sculpture
£2600 $4134 €3900 Au but, three figures (34cm-13in) s.num.A622 bronze red marble base st.f.Siot lit. 29-Apr-3 Sotheby's, Olympia #156/R est:1800-2200

BOUCHER, Alcide (19/20th C) French
Works on paper
£12000 $19320 €18000 Studies of the iris (32x22cm-13x9in) s.i.d. W/C 74 folio. 7-May-3 Sotheby's, London #25/R est:12000-18000

BOUCHER, Alfred (1850-1934) French
Sculpture
£1090 $1711 €1700 Buste de jeune femme (87x65cm-34x26in) white marble. 22-Nov-2 Piasa, Paris #36/R
£2207 $3531 €3200 Trois athletes (32x41x21cm-13x16x8in) s.st.f.Siot brown pat bronze marble base. 14-Mar-3 Libert, Castor, Paris #67/R
£2658 $4120 €4200 Au but (32x41cm-13x16in) s. black brown pat bronze Cast Siot. 29-Sep-2 Eric Pillon, Calais #129/R
£2766 $4481 €3900 Le Terrassier (68cm-27in) s. pat bronze Cast Barbedienne. 26-May-3 Joron-Derem, Paris #151/R est:4000-5000
£95000 $148200 €142500 Morning glory (104cm-41in) s. white marble lit. 9-Apr-3 Sotheby's, London #93/R est:100000-150000

BOUCHER, François (1703-1770) French
£216049 $350000 €324074 Earth (81x71cm-32x28in) s. oval prov. 23-Jan-3 Sotheby's, New York #93/R est:300000-500000
£302469 $490000 €453704 Venus and cupid (93x163cm-37x64in) s. shaped canvas prov.exhib.lit. 24-Jan-3 Christie's, Rockefeller NY #104/R est:600000-800000
£493827 $800000 €740741 Le joueur de flagelet (55x44cm-22x17in) s.d.1766 oval. 23-Jan-3 Sotheby's, New York #90/R est:800000-1200000
Works on paper
£2365 $3689 €3500 Chaumiere et bergere (21x16cm-8x6in) i. crayon prov. 26-Mar-3 Piasa, Paris #43/R
£3000 $5010 €4350 Apostle preaching, with figures in the background (34x48cm-13x19in) black white chk prov. 8-Jul-3 Christie's, London #74/R est:4000-6000
£3243 $5059 €4800 Groupe de putti volant (20x16cm-8x6in) i. chk prov. 27-Mar-3 Christie's, Paris #95/R
£4321 $7000 €6482 Young shepherdess (33x20cm-13x8in) chk prov. 21-Jan-3 Sotheby's, New York #113/R est:10000
£4430 $7000 €7000 Une jeune mere avec deux enfants dans un paysage (23x18cm-9x7in) red chk pen brown ink prov. 27-Nov-2 Christie's, Paris #161/R est:7000-10000
£4430 $7000 €7000 Un putto allonge sur un nuage (20x23cm-8x9in) col chk prov. 27-Nov-2 Christie's, Paris #162/R est:6000-8000
£5442 $8653 €8000 Repos pendant la Fuite en Egypte (21x24cm-8x9in) pen ink wash over pierre noire. 24-Mar-3 Fraysse & Associes, Paris #35/R est:4500
£5532 $9238 €7800 Jeune homme au lavoir avec un chien (34x22cm-13x9in) black crayon white chk prov. 19-Jun-3 Piasa, Paris #97/R est:8000-10000
£6013 $9500 €9500 Une jeune fille, un bebe dans ses bras, deux enfants jouant a cote (27x18cm-11x7in) col chk. 27-Nov-2 Christie's, Paris #160/R est:10000-15000
£7095 $11068 €10500 Putti in landscape (23x22cm-9x9in) i. chk. 27-Mar-3 Christie's, Paris #94/R est:12000
£8163 $12980 €12000 Academie d'homme (33x23cm-13x9in) i. sanguine htd white prov. 21-Mar-3 Millon & Associes, Paris #22/R
£8165 $12982 €12000 Psyche et l'Amour sur des nuages (20x31cm-8x12in) pen ink wash sanguine over crayon lit. 24-Mar-3 Tajan, Paris #34/R
£14967 $23798 €22000 Renaud et Armide (20x31cm-8x12in) pen ink wash sanguine over crayon. 24-Mar-3 Tajan, Paris #33/R est:15000
£18000 $30060 €26100 Male nude seated in profile (31x43cm-12x17in) i. red chk prov.lit. 8-Jul-3 Christie's, London #72/R est:20000-30000
£26282 $40737 €41000 Deux femmes de profil (27x31cm-11x12in) crayon htd pastel prov.lit. 4-Dec-2 Piasa, Paris #66/R est:30000
£32653 $51919 €48000 Zephyr et Flore (32x24cm-13x9in) crayon pastel htd chk W/C. 24-Mar-3 Tajan, Paris #35/R
£37037 $60000 €55556 Young shepherdess presenting flower to shepherd (25x32cm-10x13in) chk prov.lit. 22-Jan-3 Christie's, Rockefeller NY #66/R est:20000
£37415 $59490 €55000 Chinoise jouant avec un chat (25x17cm-10x7in) sanguine htd chk prov.exhib.lit. 24-Mar-3 Tajan, Paris #32/R est:30000
£38462 $59615 €60000 Nativity (29x37cm-11x15in) pen ink wash chk prov.exhib.lit. 4-Dec-2 Piasa, Paris #65/R est:40000
£48000 $80160 €69600 Portrait of a young girl (26x21cm-10x8in) s. black red white chk prov. 8-Jul-3 Christie's, London #71/R est:25000-35000

BOUCHER, François (after) (18th C) French
£7338 $11741 €10200 Elegant shepherdess scene (100x150cm-39x59in) 17-May-3 Lempertz, Koln #1008/R est:12000

BOUCHER, François (attrib) (18th C) French
Works on paper
£962 $1510 €1500 Tete de jeune garcon (14x11cm-6x4in) pierre noire sanguine chk. 14-Dec-2 Artcurial Briest, Paris #3/R
£1090 $1689 €1700 Deux amours (17x11cm-7x4in) sanguine. 4-Dec-2 Piasa, Paris #61/R
£1700 $2839 €2465 Two putti, one holding an arrow and apple, other one holding a quiver and two doves (16x12cm-6x5in) black red chk prov.lit. 8-Jul-3 Christie's, London #73/R est:2000-4000
£2405 $3752 €3800 Peste (29x35cm-11x14in) pen ink prov. 18-Oct-2 Rabourdin & Choppin de Janvry, Paris #96/R
£2838 $4427 €4200 Deux jeunes filles en buste (22x21cm-9x8in) chk. 27-Mar-3 Christie's, Paris #96/R

BOUCHER, François (circle) (18th C) French
£7643 $11924 €12000 Hebes, Goddess of Beauty (68x103cm-27x41in) 6-Nov-2 Hugo Ruef, Munich #970/R est:1500

BOUCHER, François (studio) (18th C) French
Works on paper
£962 $1510 €1500 Venus et dex amours (23x32cm-9x13in) pierre noire sanguine pastel stump. 13-Dec-2 Rossini, Paris #136

BOUCHER, Gaston (19th C) French
£280 $450 €420 Still life with fruit on a brass charger (38x56cm-15x22in) s. 19-Feb-3 Doyle, New York #60

BOUCHET, Auguste (?-1937) French
£4430 $6911 €7000 Vue de vales, en Ardeche (38x70cm-15x28in) s.d.1871 exhib. 16-Oct-2 Fraysse & Associes, Paris #36/R est:5000-7000

BOUCHET, Robert (20th C) French
£949 $1500 €1500 Femme nue dans l'atelier (73x100cm-29x39in) s.d.27. 27-Nov-2 Lemoine & Ferrando, Paris #80 est:1000-1200

BOUCHEZ, Charles (1811-?) French
£3082 $4839 €4500 Father's return (21x27cm-8x11in) s.d.1848 panel. 15-Apr-3 Sotheby's, Amsterdam #77/R est:5000-7000

BOUCHOR, Joseph Felix (1853-1937) French
£719 $1151 €1000 Les bateaux de la Marina Grande-Capri (38x46cm-15x18in) s. 13-May-3 Palais de Beaux Arts, Brussels #336

BOUCHOT, Claire (?-1938) French
Works on paper
£800 $1336 €1160 River landscape in France with figures and goats in the foreground (38x50cm-15x20in) s.d.1797 gouache. 17-Jun-3 Anderson & Garland, Newcastle #289/R

BOUDA, Cyril (1901-1984) Czechoslovakian
Works on paper
£499 $809 €724 Fruit seller (21x17cm-8x7in) s.d.1941 ink W/C. 24-May-3 Dorotheum, Prague #178/R est:20000-30000 (C.KR 22000)

BOUDET, Pierre (1925-) French
£308 $459 €462 Italian street (40x33cm-16x13in) s. pavatex. 25-Jun-2 Koller, Zurich #6662 (S.FR 700)
£321 $497 €500 Chaloupe au qaui (30x40cm-12x16in) 5-Dec-2 Gros & Delettrez, Paris #48
£403 $624 €640 Plage de Deauville (22x27cm-9x11in) s. panel. 7-Oct-2 Claude Aguttes, Neuilly #308
£441 $656 €662 Oasis (46x31cm-18x12in) s. pavatex. 25-Jun-2 Koller, Zurich #6663/R (S.FR 1000)
£446 $696 €700 Palmeraie (46x31cm-18x12in) s. panel. 10-Nov-2 Eric Pillon, Calais #110/R
£478 $745 €750 Vue de Taormine (49x32cm-19x13in) s.i.d.1967 panel. 10-Nov-2 Eric Pillon, Calais #109/R
£529 $788 €794 Street cafe (49x32cm-19x13in) s.i.d.Sept 67 pavatex. 25-Jun-2 Koller, Zurich #6664 (S.FR 1200)
£570 $889 €900 Coin de Versailles (55x55cm-22x22in) s. panel. 20-Oct-2 Chayette & Cheval, Paris #99
£617 $919 €926 Street scene (60x60cm-24x24in) s.i.d.Juni 59 pavatex. 25-Jun-2 Koller, Zurich #6665 (S.FR 1400)
£661 $985 €992 Pont de la Concorde, Paris (79x98cm-31x39in) s.d.77 pavatex. 25-Jun-2 Koller, Zurich #6671/R (S.FR 1500)
£705 $1050 €1058 Pont Neuf, Paris (45x60cm-18x24in) s.i.d.mars 64 pavatex. 25-Jun-2 Koller, Zurich #6666/R est:1600-2200 (S.FR 1600)
£969 $1444 €1454 Tourists in Spanish street (81x100cm-32x39in) bears i. pavatex. 25-Jun-2 Koller, Zurich #6667/R est:2000-3000 (S.FR 2200)
£1076 $1668 €1700 Vue de Honfleur (60x73cm-24x29in) s. 29-Sep-2 Eric Pillon, Calais #245/R
£1083 $1689 €1700 Paris, la Concorde et la Chambre des Deputes (80x99cm-31x39in) s. panel. 10-Nov-2 Eric Pillon, Calais #102/R
£1241 $1974 €1800 Venise, quai St Martin et la Salute (40x50cm-16x20in) 9-Mar-3 Feletin, Province #211

£1389 $2209 €2000 Venise, la salute vue du quai des esclavons (46x61cm-18x24in) s.i. d.Juill.74 verso isorel panel. 29-Apr-3 Artcurial Briest, Paris #314/R est:1400-1600
£1447 $2242 €2300 Honfleur, la Lieutenance (50x60cm-20x24in) s. 6-Oct-2 Feletin, Province #113b/R
£1736 $2760 €2500 La vieille ville, place animee (81x100cm-32x39in) s. isorel panel. 29-Apr-3 Artcurial Briest, Paris #312/R est:2002-2500

BOUDEWYNS, Adriaen Frans (1644-1711) Flemish
£7692 $12077 €12000 Idyllic southern landscape with figures resting (45x60cm-18x24in) panel. 21-Nov-2 Van Ham, Cologne #1314/R est:11000

BOUDEWYNS, Adriaen Frans (attrib) (1644-1711) Flemish
£2051 $3179 €3200 View of Paris with market alon the Seine (30x43cm-12x17in) 4-Dec-2 Christie's, Rome #373

Works on paper
£550 $864 €825 Italianate river landscape with travellers and distant village (23x36cm-9x14in) ink red chk wash. 11-Dec-2 Sotheby's, Olympia #106/R

BOUDEWYNS, Adriaen Frans and BOUT, Pieter (attrib) (17/18th C) Flemish
£1300 $2093 €1950 Wooded landscape with shepherds and other figures with a flock of sheep on a track (34x45cm-13x18in) 20-Feb-3 Christie's, Kensington #52/R est:500-800

BOUDEWYNS, Frans (attrib) (18th C) Flemish

Works on paper
£469 $770 €680 Landscape with water (31x40cm-12x16in) s. bears d. ochre. 4-Jun-3 Fischer, Luzern #2405/R (S.FR 1000)

BOUDIN, Eugène (1824-1898) French
£5449 $8282 €8500 Paturage au bord de la Touque (21x32cm-8x13in) s. panel prov.lit. 16-Aug-2 Deauville, France #71/R est:10500
£6410 $10064 €10000 Forge du quai vallee a Trouville (21x27cm-8x11in) s. panel prov.exhib.lit. 11-Dec-2 Fraysse & Associes, Paris #11 est:6000
£7000 $11130 €10500 La forge du quai vallee a Trouville (22x27cm-9x11in) s. panel painted c.1885-89 prov.exhib.lit. 20-Mar-3 Sotheby's, Olympia #41/R est:8000-10000
£8027 $12763 €11800 Paturage Normand (18x27cm-7x11in) s.d.92 panel lit. 26-Feb-3 Artcurial Briest, Paris #105/R est:4000-5000
£11000 $18040 €16500 Etude de ciel (20x27cm-8x11in) st.init. paper prov.lit. 5-Feb-3 Sotheby's, London #214/R est:12000
£11571 $18282 €17357 Trouville (30x36cm-12x14in) s.i.d.92. 27-Nov-2 Falkkloos, Malmo #77618/R est:10000 (S.KR 165000)
£12950 $20719 €18000 Vaches au bord de la Touques (42x55cm-17x22in) s. lit. 14-May-3 Blanchet, Paris #68/R est:20000-25000
£14557 $22709 €23000 Maree base a Honfleur (16x27cm-6x11in) s.d.60 panel prov.lit. 16-Oct-2 Fraysse & Associes, Paris #39/R est:10000-12000
£15484 $24000 €23226 Benodet, Un Pardon (35x46cm-14x18in) s.d.1872 panel prov.exhib.lit. 26-Sep-2 Christie's, Rockefeller NY #527/R est:18000-22000
£18000 $27720 €27000 Maree basse a berck (15x27cm-6x11in) s. oil paper on panel painted c.1875-78 prov.lit. 22-Oct-2 Sotheby's, London #106/R est:20000-30000
£18590 $29186 €29000 Bretagne, soleil couchant (41x65cm-16x26in) s. prov.exhib.lit. 10-Dec-2 Pierre Berge, Paris #6/R est:40000
£19231 $30385 €30000 Vaches au bord de la mer (54x73cm-21x29in) s. painted c.1885-2890 prov.exhib.lit. 18-Nov-2 Tajan, Paris #130/R est:30000-32000
£19231 $30192 €30000 Boeufs dans un prairie (41x55cm-16x22in) s. painted c.1880-85 prov.exhib.lit. 11-Dec-2 Fraysse & Associes, Paris #10/R est:25000
£22360 $36000 €33540 Hopital Camfrout, le rivage (22x46cm-9x18in) s. oil paper on canvas prov.lit. 8-May-3 Christie's, Rockefeller NY #157/R est:25000-35000
£26282 $41263 €41000 Pardon a Benodet (36x46cm-14x18in) s.d.1872 panel lit. 15-Dec-2 Eric Pillon, Calais #117/R
£26573 $44378 €38000 Maree basse a Berck (17x28cm-7x11in) s. paper on panel prov.lit. 30-Jun-3 Artcurial Briest, Paris #44/R est:40000-60000
£28000 $45920 €42000 Maree basse a Honfleur (20x27cm-8x11in) init.d.60 panel prov.lit. 5-Feb-3 Sotheby's, London #103/R est:25000
£30769 $46769 €48000 Plage de Plougastel (36x57cm-14x22in) s.d.1870 prov.exhib.lit. 16-Aug-2 Deauville, France #80/R est:60000
£32051 $50000 €48077 Maree basse, Rivage (26x21cm-10x8in) s. panel painted c.1888-95 prov. 7-Nov-2 Christie's, Rockefeller NY #218/R est:40000-60000
£35000 $58450 €50750 Berck, pecheuses assises sur la greve (15x26cm-6x10in) s.i. paper on panel painted 1875 prov.lit. 24-Jun-3 Sotheby's, London #104/R est:20000-30000
£35276 $57500 €52914 Fecamp, le bassin (41x32cm-16x13in) s.i.d.83 board prov.exhib.lit. 12-Feb-3 Sotheby's, New York #11/R est:40000-60000
£38000 $63460 €55100 Chanal a Trouville maree basse (27x21cm-11x8in) s. panel painted 1883. 24-Jun-3 Sotheby's, London #109/R est:38000-45000
£38462 $60000 €57693 Le Havre, le bassin du commerce (41x32cm-16x13in) s.i.d.94 panel prov. 6-Nov-2 Sotheby's, New York #102/R est:60000-80000
£40123 $65000 €58178 Etretat, La Falaise d'Amont (46x66cm-18x26in) s.d.88 prov.exhib.lit. 21-May-3 Doyle, New York #196/R est:75000-85000
£45000 $75150 €65250 Les laveuses d'Etretat (39x54cm-15x21in) s.d.90 prov.exhib.lit. 25-Jun-3 Christie's, London #112/R est:40000-50000
£49032 $77471 €76000 Bassin de DEauville (26x35cm-10x14in) s. panel prov. 18-Dec-2 Ferri, Paris #31/R est:80000
£49383 $80000 €71605 Berck, Scene de Plage, Maree Basse (46x76cm-18x30in) s.d.77 prov.exhib.lit. 21-May-3 Doyle, New York #203/R est:90000-120000
£58000 $95120 €87000 Marche a TRouville (37x46cm-15x18in) s.d.78 board prov.lit. 4-Feb-3 Christie's, London #212/R est:70000
£59615 $93596 €93000 Maree basse, pecheurs (52x22cm-20x9in) s.d.91 lit. 16-Dec-2 Rabourdin & Choppin de Janvry, Paris #61/R est:85000-90000
£65000 $106600 €97500 Berck, pecheuses sur la plage (15x22cm-6x9in) s.i.d.76 panel prov.lit. 4-Feb-3 Sotheby's, London #11/R est:70000
£68000 $111520 €102000 Passe de Trouville (45x65cm-18x26in) s. painted c.1878-82 prov.lit. 4-Feb-3 Christie's, London #202/R est:90000
£68000 $113560 €98600 Honfleur le port (20x27cm-8x11in) s. board painted c.1858-62 prov.lit. 24-Jun-3 Sotheby's, London #108/R est:30000-40000
£70513 $110000 €105770 Saint Valery sur somme, Peniches sur le canal (50x74cm-20x29in) s.i.d.91 prov.lit. 6-Nov-2 Sotheby's, New York #121/R est:80000-120000
£70513 $110000 €105770 Caudebec-en-Caux, Bateaux sur la Seine (51x74cm-20x29in) s.d.89 prov.exhib.lit. 7-Nov-2 Christie's, Rockefeller NY #213/R est:80000-120000
£71429 $115000 €107144 Trouville. les jetees maree basse (33x41cm-13x16in) s.d.96 panel prov.lit. 7-May-3 Sotheby's, New York #122/R est:150000-200000
£75000 $123000 €112500 Berck, groupe de peceheuses assises sur la greve (19x31cm-7x12in) s.i.d.75 paper on panel prov.lit. 4-Feb-3 Sotheby's, London #8/R est:80000
£75000 $123000 €112500 Le Havre, avant-port (27x35cm-11x14in) s.i.d.89 panel prov.exhib.lit. 4-Feb-3 Christie's, London #210/R est:55000
£76923 $120000 €115385 Dieppe, voiliers a l'ancre (41x32cm-16x13in) s.i.d.96 panel prov.lit. 7-Nov-2 Christie's, Rockefeller NY #201/R est:70000-90000
£80000 $133600 €116000 L'ecluse a Saint Valery sur somme (49x61cm-19x24in) s.d.91 prov.exhib.lit. 25-Jun-3 Christie's, London #107/R est:100000-150000
£100000 $163000 €150000 Bordeaux, bateaux sur la Garonne (40x66cm-16x26in) s.d.74 prov. 3-Feb-3 Bonhams, New Bond Street #6/R est:60000-80000
£102564 $161026 €160000 Rivage au Portrieux a maree basse (51x73cm-20x29in) s.i.d.73 prov.lit. 10-Dec-2 Artcurial Briest, Paris #466/R est:120000-150000
£136646 $220000 €204969 Fecamp, le bassin (41x56cm-16x22in) s.i.d.92 prov.lit. 8-May-3 Christie's, Rockefeller NY #148/R est:140000-180000
£180000 $300600 €261000 Sur la plage de Trouville (21x34cm-8x13in) s.d.6 panel painted 1867 prov.exhib.lit. 24-Jun-3 Christie's, London #48/R est:150000-250000
£220000 $360800 €330000 Rotterdam, la Meuse (78x111cm-31x44in) s.i.d.80 prov.exhib.lit. 4-Feb-3 Sotheby's, London #14/R est:350000
£580000 $951200 €870000 Scene de plage a Trouville (19x36cm-7x14in) s.d.74 panel prov.exhib.lit. 4-Feb-3 Sotheby's, London #1/R est:400000
£900000 $1467000 €1350000 Scene de plage (35x57cm-14x22in) s.d.65 panel prov.exhib.lit. 3-Feb-3 Christie's, London #56/R est:1500000

Works on paper
£1014 $1581 €1500 Trois voiliers et une barque (12x17cm-5x7in) crayon. 26-Mar-3 Piasa, Paris #101
£2308 $3646 €3600 Silhouette aux abords d'un phare pres du rivage (14x21cm-6x8in) st.mono. pastel lit. 18-Nov-2 Tajan, Paris #141/R est:3000-4600
£3700 $5883 €5550 Phare environs d'Honfleur (13x21cm-5x8in) st.init. pastel. 20-Mar-3 Sotheby's, Olympia #10/R est:4000-6000
£3700 $6142 €5365 Two dogs (13x18cm-5x7in) init. pastel. 12-Jun-3 Gorringes, Lewes #1741 est:3000-5000
£5031 $7849 €8000 Phare au bout de la digue (8x12cm-3x5in) mono. pastel. 11-Oct-2 Binoche, Paris #120/R
£5208 $8281 €7500 Moulin en Hollande (15x21cm-6x8in) s. W/C. 29-Apr-3 Artcurial Briest, Paris #22/R est:7500-8000
£7000 $11480 €10500 Phare a Honfleur (15x22cm-6x9in) pastel exec.1872 prov. 5-Feb-3 Sotheby's, London #212/R
£7947 $12954 €12000 Ferme, St Simeon. Bretonnes d'une eglise. Voilier de peche. one s. pencil W/C four in one frame. 2-Feb-3 Muizon & Le Coent, Paris #40
£10191 $15898 €16000 Environs d'Honfleur (14x21cm-6x8in) s. pastel lit. 7-Nov-2 Chochon-Barre & Allardi, Paris #77/R

£13000 $21710 €19500 Rivage aux environs de Trouville. Maree basse (21x28cm-8x11in) s.st.init. pastel exec c.1865. 26-Jun-3 Christie's, London #351/R est:8000-12000

BOUDIN, Eugène (attrib) (1824-1898) French
Works on paper
£321 $500 €482 Three boats (30x41cm-12x16in) init. W/C pencil. 12-Oct-2 Neal Auction Company, New Orleans #343

BOUDNIK, Vladimir (1924-1968) Czechoslovakian
Works on paper
£318 $515 €477 Structural print (12x26cm-5x10in) s.d.1965 mixed media. 24-May-3 Dorotheum, Prague #203/R est:10000-15000 (C.KR 14000)

BOUDON, Gerard (?) French?
Sculpture
£1544 $2485 €2300 Grand canard (44cm-17in) st.f.Royaume brown green pat bronze. 23-Feb-3 Mercier & Cie, Lille #183/R

BOUDRY, A (?) Belgian
£1161 $1835 €1800 Retour a la ferme (88x130cm-35x51in) s. 17-Dec-2 Galerie Moderne, Brussels #646

BOUDRY, Alois (1851-1938) Belgian
£270 $422 €400 Homme a pipe (25x21cm-10x8in) s. 25-Mar-3 Campo & Campo, Antwerp #20
£305 $500 €458 Un moment de repos apres le menage (50x44cm-20x17in) s. prov. 5-Feb-3 Christie's, Rockefeller NY #192/R
£435 $713 €600 Belle femme (61x48cm-24x19in) s. 27-May-3 Campo & Campo, Antwerp #36
£578 $919 €850 Portrait de femme (40x32cm-16x13in) s.d.1885 panel. 18-Mar-3 Galerie Moderne, Brussels #541/R
£641 $1006 €1000 La conversation pres de l'atre (50x60cm-20x24in) s. 10-Dec-2 Campo, Vlaamse Kaai #48
£1026 $1610 €1600 Jeune fille dans la cuisine (19x25cm-7x10in) s. 10-Dec-2 Campo, Vlaamse Kaai #47 est:1000-1300
£1027 $1603 €1500 Yolande a la caissette de citrons (109x93cm-43x37in) s.d.1925. 14-Apr-3 Horta, Bruxelles #152 est:2000-3000

BOUDRY, Pol (1914-1976) Belgian
£570 $889 €900 Still life with flowers (35x32cm-14x13in) s. 21-Oct-2 Bernaerts, Antwerp #713/R

BOUFFLERS, Stanislas Jean de (1738-1815) French
Works on paper
£20000 $33400 €29000 Voltaire seated at a desk wearing a cap (22x19cm-9x7in) pen ink wash rubbed red chk prov.lit. 8-Jul-3 Christie's, London #75/R est:10000-15000

BOUG D'ORSCHWILLIER, Hippolyte (1810-1868) French
Works on paper
£603 $1007 €850 Aga sur le Bosphore (10x17cm-4x7in) s. W/C pencil. 23-Jun-3 Beaussant & Lefèvre, Paris #71

BOUGH (1822-1878) British
£320 $493 €480 Washing day, Brig O'Turk (13x18cm-5x7in) s. i.verso. 24-Oct-2 Thomson, Roddick & Medcalf, Carlisle #307/R

BOUGH, Sam (1822-1878) British
£177 $280 €280 ON the Kelvin, Scotland (46x61cm-18x24in) i.stretcher. 27-Nov-2 James Adam, Dublin #99
£900 $1431 €1350 Vossevangen, Norway (25x35cm-10x14in) s.d.1858 i.verso panel prov. 6-Mar-3 Christie's, Kensington #37/R
£1000 $1540 €1500 On the moors, figures and animals (56x76cm-22x30in) s. board. 24-Oct-2 Thomson, Roddick & Medcalf, Carlisle #308/R
£1474 $2315 €2300 Low tide (23x38cm-9x15in) s.d.1866. 21-Nov-2 Van Ham, Cologne #1493/R est:2200
£1500 $2445 €2250 Aberdeen (14x10cm-6x4in) s.d.1856. 12-Feb-3 Andrew Hartley, Ilkley #855 est:400-600
£3433 $5356 €4978 Weir, Lancaster (56x82cm-22x32in) s. 26-Mar-3 Walker's, Ottawa #73/R est:10000-12000 (C.D 8000)
£3459 $5500 €5189 Arrival of the mail (22x31cm-9x12in) s.d.1862 i.verso board. 7-Mar-3 Skinner, Boston #218/R est:3000-5000
£7400 $11248 €11100 Dalston Hall, Cumberland (28x41cm-11x16in) s. i.verso board. 28-Aug-2 Sotheby's, London #804/R est:5000-7000
£11000 $17160 €16500 Inchcolm and the Priory (60x90cm-24x35in) s.d.1857 prov. 28-Mar-3 Bonhams, Edinburgh #133/R est:8000-12000
£16000 $25440 €24000 Highland cattle crossing the Echaeg, Argyllshire (66x107cm-26x42in) s.i.d.1855 prov. 6-Mar-3 Christie's, Kensington #36/R est:10000-15000

Works on paper
£300 $486 €450 Castle Kennely Earl of Stair (27x32cm-11x13in) s.verso W/C. 23-May-3 Honiton Galleries, Honiton #677
£360 $562 €540 Windy day (32x43cm-13x17in) s.d.1842 W/C. 6-Nov-2 Bonhams, Chester #334
£800 $1312 €1200 Meadow brook, Pencaitland (28x44cm-11x17in) s.d.1861 i.verso W/C htd white. 5-Jun-3 Christie's, Kensington #921/R
£1000 $1570 €1500 The lock - evening, landscape with horse, figures and sailing boats (63x47cm-25x19in) s. W/C. 25-Nov-2 Cumbria Auction Rooms, UK #313 est:800-1200
£1000 $1640 €1500 Figures on a highland track (45x76cm-18x30in) s.d.1864 pencil W/C prov. 5-Jun-3 Christie's, Kensington #915/R est:1000-1500
£1150 $1909 €1668 On a rainy day (13x23cm-5x9in) s.i.d.1858 W/C. 13-Jun-3 Lyon & Turnbull, Edinburgh #138 est:500-800
£1900 $2888 €2850 Beauly Abbey (36x50cm-14x20in) s.i.d.1873 W/C. 28-Aug-2 Sotheby's, London #867/R est:1500-2000

BOUGHTON, George Henry (1833-1905) American/British
£576 $893 €864 Fading light (24x46cm-9x18in) bears sig prov. 3-Dec-2 Ritchie, Toronto #3039/R est:800-1000 (C.D 1400)
£881 $1400 €1322 Gathering mussels (15x28cm-6x11in) s. panel sold with two letters. 5-Mar-3 Doyle, New York #8/R est:2000-3000
£3200 $4992 €4800 Andrew Marvell visiting his friend John Milton (69x166cm-27x65in) s. 10-Sep-2 Bonhams, Knightsbridge #234/R est:3000-5000
£4403 $7000 €6605 Summer (76x51cm-30x20in) s. canvas over panel. 4-Mar-3 Christie's, Rockefeller NY #42/R est:7000-9000
£11688 $18000 €17532 Storyteller, Redwood, New York (76x112cm-30x44in) init. painted c.1853/58 prov. 24-Oct-2 Shannon's, Milford #37/R est:12000-18000

Works on paper
£335 $550 €486 Landscape with farmhouse (17x25cm-7x10in) init. gouache board. 5-Jun-3 Swann Galleries, New York #54/R
£1234 $1900 €1851 Portrait of a woman in white (24x20cm-9x8in) init. W/C gouache prov. 4-Sep-2 Christie's, Rockefeller NY #347/R est:1000-1500

BOUGHTON, H (fl.1827-1872) British
£500 $770 €750 Portrait of Sir Francis Wood (76x63cm-30x25in) 5-Sep-2 Christie's, Kensington #58/R

BOUGUEREAU, William Adolphe (1825-1905) French
£17722 $28000 €26583 Study of a young girl's head (46x38cm-18x15in) prov. 23-Apr-3 Christie's, Rockefeller NY #121/R est:18000-25000
£113924 $180000 €170886 Le sommeil (62x51cm-24x20in) s. painted 1864 prov.exhib.lit. 23-Apr-3 Christie's, Rockefeller NY #9/R est:200000-300000
£202532 $320000 €303798 Tete de fillette - tete avec mains (46x37cm-18x15in) s.d.1890 canvas on masonite prov. 24-Apr-3 Sotheby's, New York #58/R est:200000-300000
£290323 $450000 €435485 L'amour a l epine (126x80cm-50x31in) s.d.1894 prov.lit. 29-Oct-2 Sotheby's, New York #40/R est:300000-400000
£329114 $520000 €493671 La reverence (133x72cm-52x28in) s.d.1898 prov.exhib.lit. 24-Apr-3 Sotheby's, New York #62/R est:550000-750000
£419355 $650000 €629033 Les agneaux (182x92cm-72x36in) s.d.1897. 29-Oct-2 Sotheby's, New York #42/R est:700000-1000000

BOUHUIJS, Jacob (1902-1983) Dutch
£674 $1091 €950 Trinacria (45x67cm-18x26in) s.d.49 exhib. 26-May-3 Glerum, Amsterdam #140/R
£922 $1494 €1300 Tug (25x27cm-10x11in) s.d.49. 26-May-3 Glerum, Amsterdam #139/R
£1560 $2528 €2200 Musical harlequins (90x120cm-35x47in) s. 26-May-3 Glerum, Amsterdam #151/R est:2000-3000
£2128 $3447 €3000 Horse market (70x80cm-28x31in) s. 26-May-3 Glerum, Amsterdam #141/R est:1200-1600

BOUILLE, Etienne (1858-1933) French
£769 $1192 €1200 Port de Plouemanac (33x46cm-13x18in) s. 5-Dec-2 Gros & Delettrez, Paris #64
£1282 $1987 €2000 Ramasseurs de goemon (46x65cm-18x26in) s. 5-Dec-2 Gros & Delettrez, Paris #63/R

BOUILLION, Michel de (17th C) Flemish
£1000 $1560 €1500 Angel appearing to the Holy Family (95x75cm-37x30in) s. 19-Sep-2 Christie's, Kensington #182/R est:1500-2000
£7190 $11791 €11000 Nature morte aux fruits, a la miche et aux etains. Nature morte aux fleurs et aux fruits (35x53cm-14x21in) pair prov. 9-Feb-3 Anaf, Lyon #30/R est:13000

BOUISSET, Firmin (after) (19th C) French
£11739 $19252 €16200 Le petit ecolier (119x89cm-47x35in) painted c.1900. 27-May-3 Artcurial Briest, Paris #68/R est:3000-4000

BOUKERCHE, Emile (1918-1979) French?
£3061 $4867 €4500 Jeune femme et son fiance (82x65cm-32x26in) s. 24-Mar-3 Rabourdin & Choppin de Janvry, Paris #213/R est:5000-5500

BOUKERCHE, Miloud (?-1979) Algerian
£513 $805 €800 Elegante sur la terrasse, Algerie (80x52cm-31x20in) s. 16-Dec-2 Gros & Delettrez, Paris #362

BOULANGE, L J B (1812-1878) French
£390 $604 €585 Girl and hens in courtyard (37x39cm-15x15in) s. board. 24-Sep-2 Koller, Zurich #6506 (S.FR 900)

BOULANGE, Louis Jean Baptiste (1812-1878) French
£1282 $2013 €2000 Lavandieres (38x54cm-15x21in) s. 13-Dec-2 Piasa, Paris #55/R

BOULANGE, Louis Jean Baptiste (attrib) (1812-1878) French
£387 $615 €581 French harbour town (16x27cm-6x11in) bears init. panel. 3-Mar-3 Lilla Bukowskis, Stockholm #501 (S.KR 5200)

BOULANGER, Graciela Rodo (1935-) Bolivian
£4037 $6500 €6056 Enfant et chat (61x51cm-24x20in) s.d.1971 i.verso. 18-Feb-3 Arthur James, Florida #124

BOULANGER, Gustave Clarence Rodolphe (1824-1888) French
£11613 $18000 €17420 Arab horseman (54x82cm-21x32in) s.d.1865. 30-Oct-2 Christie's, Rockefeller NY #98/R est:12000-16000
£75949 $120000 €113924 Le harem du palais (84x114cm-33x45in) s.d.1877 prov. 24-Apr-3 Sotheby's, New York #46/R est:200000-300000

BOULANGER, Hyppolite (?) Belgian?
£1266 $1962 €2000 Bord de Meuse anime (40x60cm-16x24in) s. 24-Sep-2 Galerie Moderne, Brussels #916/R est:1000-1500

BOULANGER, Yvette (1932-) Canadian?
£215 $335 €323 Effet d'automne dans l'eau River Rouge (30x41cm-12x16in) s.d.80 s.i.d.verso masonite prov. 25-Mar-3 Ritchie, Toronto #113 (C.D 500)

BOULARD, Auguste (1825-1897) French
£481 $750 €760 Scene pastorale (45x60cm-18x24in) s. 15-Sep-2 Feletin, Province #86
£2115 $3321 €3300 Portrait d'enfant (40x32cm-16x13in) mono. 13-Dec-2 Peschetau-Badin Godeau & Leroy, Paris #67

BOULAYE, Paul A la (19th C) Belgian
£629 $981 €1000 Portrait of a young woman (73x59cm-29x23in) s. 23-Sep-2 Bernaerts, Antwerp #227
£1164 $1816 €1700 Elegante a la gerbe de roses (117x89cm-46x35in) s.d.1897 canvas on panel. 14-Apr-3 Horta, Bruxelles #173 est:2000-2500
£2405 $3800 €3800 Young woman feeding chick in a garden (71x58cm-28x23in) s. 27-Nov-2 James Adam, Dublin #91/R est:4000-6000

BOULCH, Jean Pierre le (1940-2001) French
£556 $878 €800 Nus (130x162cm-51x64in) s.d. acrylic. 28-Apr-3 Cornette de St.Cyr, Paris #449

BOULENGER, Hippolyte (1837-1874) Belgian
£654 $1052 €1000 Canal borde de peupliers (40x30cm-16x12in) indis.sig. 20-Jan-3 Horta, Bruxelles #10
Works on paper
£1026 $1610 €1600 Paysage (11x29cm-4x11in) studio st.d.juillet 1881 verso W/C. 10-Dec-2 Vanderkindere, Brussels #94 est:250-400

BOULEZ, Jules (1889-1960) Belgian
£791 $1266 €1100 Still life with flowers (72x61cm-28x24in) s. 17-May-3 De Vuyst, Lokeren #49

BOULIER, Lucien (1882-1963) French
£256 $405 €400 La petite danseuse (38x46cm-15x18in) s. panel. 14-Nov-2 Credit Municipal, Paris #58
£294 $482 €450 Baigneuse (53x43cm-21x17in) s. cardboard. 7-Feb-3 Oger, Dumont, Paris #58
£532 $862 €750 Modele pensif (55x44cm-22x17in) s. 26-May-3 Joron-Derem, Paris #48/R

BOULLOGNE, Bon de (elder) (1649-1717) French
£13462 $20865 €21000 Flore et Zephyr (80x64cm-31x25in) 4-Dec-2 Libert, Castor, Paris #47/R est:15000

BOULLOGNE, Bon de (elder-attrib) (1649-1717) French
£7595 $12000 €12000 Samson et Dalila (36x57cm-14x22in) prov. 27-Nov-2 Christie's, Paris #34/R est:12000-18000

BOULLOGNE, Louis de (18th C) French
£94406 $157657 €135000 Le feu ou Venus demandant a Vulcain des armes pour Enee (152x172cm-60x68in) s.d.1723 prov. 25-Jun-3 Sotheby's, Paris #17/R est:60000-80000

BOULLOGNE, Louis de (younger) (1654-1733) French
£8392 $14014 €12000 Personnages dans un paysage avec forteresse (150x138cm-59x54in) s.d.1724 prov. 25-Jun-3 Sotheby's, Paris #18/R est:15000-20000
£13000 $21710 €18850 Arcadian landscape with figures dancing (107x119cm-42x47in) s. prov. 10-Jul-3 Sotheby's, London #206/R est:8000-12000
Works on paper
£4500 $7515 €6525 Seated nude, seen from behind (42x53cm-17x21in) s.d.1707 black white chk. 8-Jul-3 Christie's, London #63/R est:5000-8000

BOULLOGNE, Louis de (younger-attrib) (1654-1733) French
£5449 $8609 €8500 Triomphe d'Amphitrite (74x106cm-29x42in) 15-Nov-2 Beaussant & Lefèvre, Paris #50/R

BOULT, Augustus S (fl.1815-1853) British
£1582 $2500 €2373 Newbury coach drawn by four grey mares (56x71cm-22x28in) i. prov. 3-Apr-3 Christie's, Rockefeller NY #185/R est:6000-8000

BOULT, Francis Cecil (fl.1877-1895) British
£807 $1300 €1211 Fox hunting scene of a man jumping with two hounds (23x33cm-9x13in) s.d.1888 board. 22-Feb-3 Pook & Pook, Downington #58/R
£807 $1300 €1211 Fox hunting scene of a man jumping with two hounds (23x33cm-9x13in) s.d.1888 board. 22-Feb-3 Pook & Pook, Downington #59/R

BOULTBEE, John (1745-1812) British
£10000 $16200 €15000 Mambrino, grey stallion in a wooded landscape (58x76cm-23x30in) s. prov. 22-May-3 Christie's, London #54/R est:5000-8000

BOUMAN, Hans (1951-) ?
Works on paper
£816 $1298 €1200 Face (130x89cm-51x35in) s.d.1990 verso mixed media collage. 24-Mar-3 Claude Boisgirard, Paris #172/R

BOUMEESTER, Christine (1904-1971) Dutch
£647 $1036 €900 Abstract (33x55cm-13x22in) s.d.51 s.i.verso. 17-May-3 De Vuyst, Lokeren #50/R
£705 $1107 €1100 Untitled (94x68cm-37x27in) s.d.56 s.i.d.verso prov.exhib. 24-Nov-2 Laurence Calmels, Paris #46/R
£769 $1208 €1200 Composition (54x65cm-21x26in) s.d.60 prov.exhib. 24-Nov-2 Laurence Calmels, Paris #57/R
£833 $1308 €1300 Untitled (54x65cm-21x26in) s.d.62 prov.exhib. 24-Nov-2 Laurence Calmels, Paris #45/R
£833 $1308 €1300 Untitled (38x46cm-15x18in) s.d.57. 24-Nov-2 Laurence Calmels, Paris #47/R
£833 $1308 €1300 Untitled (46x55cm-18x22in) s.d.59 prov.exhib. 24-Nov-2 Laurence Calmels, Paris #54/R
£962 $1510 €1500 Untitled (46x55cm-18x22in) s.d.60 prov.exhib. 24-Nov-2 Laurence Calmels, Paris #50/R
£962 $1510 €1500 Untitled (50x65cm-20x26in) s.d.60 prov.exhib. 24-Nov-2 Laurence Calmels, Paris #51/R
£962 $1510 €1500 Untitled (50x65cm-20x26in) s.d.62 prov.exhib. 24-Nov-2 Laurence Calmels, Paris #56/R
£962 $1510 €1500 Formes disparaissent quand elles regardent l'oeil (46x55cm-18x22in) s. s.i.verso masonite. 24-Nov-2 Laurence Calmels, Paris #55/R
£1154 $1812 €1800 Untitled (54x65cm-21x26in) s.d.58 prov.exhib. 24-Nov-2 Laurence Calmels, Paris #44/R
£1154 $1812 €1800 Untitled (73x92cm-29x36in) s.d.57 s.i.d.verso prov.exhib. 24-Nov-2 Laurence Calmels, Paris #48/R
£1154 $1812 €1800 Untitled (46x61cm-18x24in) s.d.60 prov.exhib. 24-Nov-2 Laurence Calmels, Paris #52/R
£1282 $2013 €2000 Untitled (33x55cm-13x22in) s.d.57 prov. 24-Nov-2 Laurence Calmels, Paris #49/R
£1603 $2516 €2500 Cimes sauvages (73x92cm-29x36in) s.d.1967 s.i.d.verso prov.exhib.lit. 24-Nov-2 Laurence Calmels, Paris #53/R
£1701 $2704 €2500 Untitled (54x65cm-21x26in) s.d.1958 prov.exhib. 24-Mar-3 Claude Boisgirard, Paris #160/R
£1987 $3120 €3100 Untitled (92x73cm-36x29in) s.d.58 prov.exhib. 24-Nov-2 Laurence Calmels, Paris #43/R
£3046 $4966 €4600 Composition (157x251cm-62x99in) s.d.1964. 3-Feb-3 Cornette de St.Cyr, Paris #373/R

Works on paper
£449 $704 €700 Untitled (47x62cm-19x24in) s. crayon dr prov.exhib. 24-Nov-2 Laurence Calmels, Paris #33/R
£449 $704 €700 Untitled (48x62cm-19x24in) s.d.60 crayon dr prov.exhib. 24-Nov-2 Laurence Calmels, Paris #39/R
£513 $805 €800 Untitled (45x61cm-18x24in) s.d.59 crayon dr prov.exhib. 24-Nov-2 Laurence Calmels, Paris #36/R
£577 $906 €900 Untitled (47x62cm-19x24in) s.d.58 crayon dr prov.exhib. 24-Nov-2 Laurence Calmels, Paris #38/R
£641 $1006 €1000 Untitled (13x22cm-5x9in) s.d.43 W/C 2 in one frame prov.exhib. 24-Nov-2 Laurence Calmels, Paris #40/R
£705 $1107 €1100 Untitled (47x62cm-19x24in) s.d.53 col crayon pastel dr prov.exhib. 24-Nov-2 Laurence Calmels, Paris #34/R
£769 $1208 €1200 Untitled (74x81cm-29x32in) s. col crayon chl. 24-Nov-2 Laurence Calmels, Paris #35/R
£769 $1208 €1200 Untitled (54x42cm-21x17in) s. W/C prov.exhib. 24-Nov-2 Laurence Calmels, Paris #41/R
£833 $1308 €1300 Untitled (31x37cm-12x15in) s.d.53 W/C. 24-Nov-2 Laurence Calmels, Paris #42/R
£1154 $1812 €1800 Untitled (23x44cm-9x17in) s.d.39 pastel prov.exhib. 24-Nov-2 Laurence Calmels, Paris #37/R

BOUMEESTER, Cornelis (1652-1733) Dutch
£3741 $5986 €5200 Seastorm off coast (28x37cm-11x15in) s. grisaille panel. 17-May-3 Lempertz, Koln #1009/R est:4000
Works on paper
£6369 $9936 €10000 Beach at Scheveningen with fishermen unloading their vessels (59x83cm-23x33in) s. ink oil wash prov.exhib.lit. 5-Nov-2 Sotheby's, Amsterdam #26/R est:10000-15000

BOUNOURE, Micheline (1924-1981) ?
Works on paper
£2740 $4301 €4000 Axolotl a Mante (39x26cm-15x10in) collage. 15-Apr-3 Laurence Calmels, Paris #4126/R

BOUQUET, André (1897-1971) French
£382 $596 €600 Vast (37x54cm-15x21in) s. painted 1979. 5-Nov-2 Tajan, Paris #54/R

BOUQUET, Michel (1807-1890) French
£1370 $2137 €2000 Fishing boats on calm waters with volcano in background (39x70cm-15x28in) s. 14-Apr-3 Glerum, Amsterdam #27/R est:1800-2500

BOUQUILLON, Albert (1908-1997) ?
Sculpture
£1090 $1711 €1700 Selene (48x57cm-19x22in) plaster. 15-Dec-2 Mercier & Cie, Lille #273/R

BOURAINE, M (20th C) French
Sculpture
£4430 $7000 €7000 Amazon armed with spear and shield (32x81cm-13x32in) i. pat.bronze. 26-Nov-2 Dorotheum, Vienna #323/R est:5000-6000

BOURAINE, Marcel (20th C) French
Sculpture
£949 $1481 €1500 Art deco group of a kneeling woman depicting summer (35cm-14in) s. pat bronze. 21-Oct-2 Bernaerts, Antwerp #562/R est:1000-1500
£1410 $2186 €2200 Danseuse nue Art-Deco (39cm-15in) s. silver bronze lit. 3-Dec-2 Campo & Campo, Antwerp #24/R est:1000-2000
£2500 $3950 €3750 Ballerina (29cm-11in) s. silvered bronze ivory. 14-Nov-2 Christie's, Kensington #295/R est:3000-4000
£2600 $4160 €3900 Fan dancer (39cm-15in) cold pat. bronze. 15-May-3 Christie's, Kensington #403/R est:1400-1600
£5000 $8000 €7500 Diana with fawns (73cm-29in) s. cold pat. bronze. 15-May-3 Christie's, Kensington #431/R est:5000-7000

BOURBON, Philippe de and BRAGANCE (19th C) French
Works on paper
£1020 $1622 €1500 Cavaliers devant les remparts de Fes (29x34cm-11x13in) s.i.d.1897 W/C. 24-Mar-3 Rabourdin & Choppin de Janvry, Paris #136/R est:1600-1800

BOURBOULON, Alfred (20th C) French
Works on paper
£426 $711 €600 Soldat grec (19x16cm-7x6in) s.d.1931 W/C gouache prov. 23-Jun-3 Beaussant & Lefèvre, Paris #77/R

BOURCART, Émile (1827-1900) French
£1962 $3100 €3100 Apres la fenaison (34x46cm-13x18in) s. panel. 1-Dec-2 Peron, Melun #65
£2115 $3321 €3300 La sortie de l'ecole en Orient. s.d.1892 panel. 16-Dec-2 Millon & Associes, Paris #131/R est:2500-3000

BOURCE, Henri Jacques (1826-1899) Belgian
£759 $1185 €1200 Jeune elegante de profil (57x44cm-22x17in) s. 15-Oct-2 Horta, Bruxelles #94

BOURDELLE, Émile Antoine (1861-1929) French
Sculpture
£1310 $2044 €1965 Small woman's head (19cm-7in) bronze. 20-Nov-2 Fischer, Luzern #1423/R est:3000-4000 (S.FR 3000)
£1548 $2400 €2322 Tete de femme (22cm-9in) s. dark brown pat. bronze prov. 26-Sep-2 Christie's, Rockefeller NY #524/R est:3000-5000
£1975 $2805 €3200 Rieuse (19cm-7in) s. brown pat bronze. 16-Mar-3 Eric Pillon, Calais #85/R
£2778 $4416 €4000 Buste du compositeur Vincent d'Indy (32cm-13in) mono.st.f.Alexis Rudier black pat bronze lit. 29-Apr-3 Artcurial Briest, Paris #151/R est:3000-5000
£3145 $5000 €4718 Headless figure pouring from a jug (36cm-14in) mono. num.V st.f.Valsuani brown pat bronze. 18-Mar-3 Arthur James, Florida #103
£4807 $7500 €7211 Maine du Guerrier (35x19cm-14x7in) s.i.indis.num.VII brown pat bronze st.f.Valsuani. 14-Oct-2 Butterfields, San Francisco #2003/R est:6000-10000
£5000 $7700 €7500 Madame Roussel au chapeau (46cm-18in) mono.num.II bronze edition of 6 st.f.Valsuani prov.lit. 23-Oct-2 Sotheby's, Olympia #665/R est:6000-8000
£5000 $7950 €7500 Ruth la Glaneuse (52cm-20in) s.num. bronze st.f.Susse. 20-Mar-3 Sotheby's, Olympia #53/R est:6000-8000
£6800 $11084 €10200 Le belier retif (53cm-21in) s.i.d.1909 bronze prov. 3-Feb-3 Bonhams, New Bond Street #39/R est:5000-7000
£17419 $27000 €26129 Adam (66cm-26in) s.d.89 brown pat. bronze st.f.Susse prov.exhib.lit. 29-Oct-2 Sotheby's, New York #233/R est:20000-30000
£19000 $31730 €27550 Beethoven aux grands cheveux, grand masque, dit 2eme etude (47cm-19in) init.i.d.1889 num. green pat. bronze st.f.Valsuani lit. 25-Jun-3 Christie's, London #117/R est:18000-24000
£19355 $30000 €29033 Small Herakles the archer (37x44cm-15x17in) s.d.1909 green pat. bronze prov.exhib.lit. 29-Oct-2 Sotheby's, New York #232/R est:25000-35000
£74534 $120000 €111801 Grand guerrier de Montauban avec jambe (210cm-83in) i.num.4 brown pat. bronze cast 1988 lit. 8-May-3 Christie's, Rockefeller NY #171/R est:150000-200000
Works on paper
£2838 $4427 €4200 Etudes (30x19cm-12x7in) W/C pen ink crayon set of 10. 26-Mar-3 Piasa, Paris #131/R

BOURDIL, Andre (1911-1982) French
Works on paper
£959 $1505 €1400 Portrait d'Aube (43x33cm-17x13in) s.i.d.1955 graphite. 15-Apr-3 Laurence Calmels, Paris #4129/R
£3082 $4839 €4500 Viol (38x60cm-15x24in) s. s.i.d.1941 verso cardboard prov.lit. 15-Apr-3 Laurence Calmels, Paris #4128/R

BOURDIN, Guy (1928-1991) French?
Photographs
£4514 $7448 €6500 Untitled (51x76cm-20x30in) cibachrome. 3-Jul-3 Christie's, Paris #101/R est:800-1200

BOURDON, Sébastien (1616-1671) French
£5769 $9058 €9000 Faille de paysans sur la route du marche (35x48cm-14x19in) 14-Dec-2 Artcurial Briest, Paris #47/R est:12000

BOURDON, Sebastien (attrib) (1616-1671) French
£2518 $4129 €3500 Portrait de gentilhomme en pourpoint rose en buste (7x6cm-3x2in) copper oval. 5-Jun-3 Fraysse & Associes, Paris #6/R est:800-1200
£5031 $7748 €8000 Portrait de la Reine Christine de Suede (106x87cm-42x34in) 25-Oct-2 Tajan, Paris #5/R est:3000-4000

BOURET, Eutrope (1833-1906) French
Sculpture
£1006 $1570 €1600 Figaro (29cm-11in) s. bronze ivory. 23-Sep-2 Durán, Madrid #282/R

BOURGAIN, Gustave (?-1921) French
Works on paper
£350 $550 €525 Armee d'Egypte guide (48x28cm-19x11in) s.d.1909 W/C prov. 14-Dec-2 Weschler, Washington #605/R

BOURGEAT, Jean Francois (20th C) French
£610 $1000 €885 Vue de Coillure (46x56cm-18x22in) s.i. 4-Jun-3 Doyle, New York #13 est:1500-2500
£881 $1400 €1322 La Cote a Douarnenez (46x56cm-18x22in) s. s.i.verso. 18-Mar-3 Doyle, New York #14/R
£881 $1400 €1322 Bord de Seine, pres de Moret (38x46cm-15x18in) s. s.i.verso. 18-Mar-3 Doyle, New York #15/R
£1220 $2000 €1769 Bord du Loing a moret (61x74cm-24x29in) s. i.verso. 4-Jun-3 Doyle, New York #14 est:2000-3000
£1538 $2400 €2307 Champs fleurie (74x91cm-29x36in) s. 9-Oct-2 Doyle, New York #14 est:2200-2800

BOURGEOIS DE MERCEY, Frederic (1805-1860) French
£24000 $37440 €36000 View of Edinburgh from Carlton Hill (84x130cm-33x51in) s. lit. 14-Apr-3 Sotheby's, London #5/R est:25000-35000

BOURGEOIS du CASTELET, Constant (1767-1836) French
Works on paper
£769 $1100 €1154 View of Italianate gardens with cypress tress (42x28cm-17x11in) s.d.1786 brush ink wash. 23-Jan-3 Swann Galleries, New York #281/R est:800-1200
£816 $1298 €1200 Chateau de Vincennes (24x32cm-9x13in) s. wash over crayon. 24-Mar-3 Tajan, Paris #72/R
£1543 $2500 €2315 Pope borne in procession through the Basilica of Santa Maria Maggiore, Rome (17x24cm-7x9in) pen ink wash. 21-Jan-3 Sotheby's, New York #202/R
£2160 $3500 €3240 Trajan's column. Pantheon (24x17cm-9x7in) pen ink wash pair. 21-Jan-3 Sotheby's, New York #204/R est:6000

BOURGEOIS, Charles Arthur (1838-1886) French
Sculpture
£1900 $3154 €1900 Le charmeur de serpents (57cm-22in) s. pat bronze. 16-Jun-3 Horta, Bruxelles #498 est:1500-2000
£2800 $4368 €4200 Snake charmer (56cm-22in) s. brown pat bronze lit. 5-Nov-2 Sotheby's, London #151/R est:3000-5000

BOURGEOIS, Eugène (1855-1909) French
£320 $534 €464 Farmhand returning home on a summer's day (34x24cm-13x9in) s.d.85. 17-Jun-3 Rosebery Fine Art, London #511/R

BOURGEOIS, Louise (1911-) American/French
Prints
£12000 $19680 €18000 Topiary - the art of improving nature (98x70cm-39x28in) s.d.1988 num.23/28 copperplate etchings nine in portfolio prov. 6-Feb-3 Christie's, London #705/R est:12000-16000
Sculpture
£6329 $10000 €9494 Give or take - how do you feel this morning (12x23x15cm-5x9x6in) i.d.90 num.VI AP brown gold pat. bronze prov. 13-Nov-2 Sotheby's, New York #328/R est:10000-15000
£9375 $15000 €14063 Give or take III (6x24x36cm-2x9x14in) init.d.93 num.24/25 brown gold pat. bronze st.f. prov. 14-May-3 Sotheby's, New York #174/R est:12000-18000
£12000 $18480 €18000 Give or take II (7x23x24cm-3x9x9in) s.d.91 num.21/30 bronze prov. 22-Oct-2 Sotheby's, London #474/R est:6000-8000
£19231 $30192 €30000 Untitled (25x12x7cm-10x5x3in) init. marble prov. 11-Dec-2 Artcurial Briest, Paris #751/R est:40000
£21875 $35000 €32813 Untitled - house 2 (24x12x7cm-9x5x3in) init. marble exec.1994 prov. 15-May-3 Christie's, Rockefeller NY #185/R est:35000-45000
Works on paper
£11000 $18370 €15950 Untitled (50x32cm-20x13in) ink pencil double-sided exec.c.1950 prov. 26-Jun-3 Sotheby's, London #136/R est:12000-15000
£12658 $20000 €18987 Untitled (33x21cm-13x8in) s. ink double-sided executed 1947 prov.exhib. 12-Nov-2 Phillips, New York #129/R est:20000-30000

BOURGEOIS, Sir Peter Francis (1756-1811) British
Works on paper
£620 $967 €930 River scene with cattle (18x28cm-7x11in) ink sepia wash dr. 15-Oct-2 Canterbury Auctions, UK #206/R

BOURKE, Brian (1936-) Irish
£1541 $2404 €2250 Sweeney in a tree (61x46cm-24x18in) s. 8-Apr-3 Thomas Adams, Dublin #397
£2162 $3373 €3200 Dublin landscape (95x62cm-37x24in) s. i.verso board. 26-Mar-3 James Adam, Dublin #136/R est:3000-4000
Sculpture
£1419 $2214 €2100 Head of a woman (71cm-28in) carved painted wood. 26-Mar 3 James Adam, Dublin #36/R est:800-1200
Works on paper
£429 $610 €700 Portrait of BM (76x56cm-30x22in) s.d. pastel pencil. 3-Apr-2 Woodwards, Cork #174
£446 $696 €700 Seated figure (76x52cm-30x20in) s.i.d.1966 mixed media. 6-Nov-2 James Adam, Dublin #77/R
£705 $1107 €1100 Self portrait (74x50cm-29x20in) s. gouache over crayon. 19-Nov-2 Hamilton Osborne King, Dublin #539/R
£833 $1308 €1300 Interior (81x56cm-32x22in) s.i.d.1966 mixed media prov. 19-Nov-2 Whyte's, Dublin #171/R
£1319 $2098 €1900 Portrait of C W (71x53cm-28x21in) s.i.d.September 1986 W/C pastel conte. 29-Apr-3 Whyte's, Dublin #56/R est:2000-3000
£1519 $2354 €2400 Landscape (71x51cm-28x20in) s.d.1962 mixed media. 24-Sep-2 De Veres Art Auctions, Dublin #176/R est:2500-3500
£1745 $2809 €2600 Figure in a landscape (66x48cm-26x19in) s.d.1970 pastel pencil gouache. 18-Feb-3 Whyte's, Dublin #184/R est:1800-2200
£1806 $2871 €2600 Landscape with ruins, County Kilkenny (75x56cm-30x22in) s.i.d.1975 mixed media on board prov. 29-Apr-3 Whyte's, Dublin #47/R est:2000-3000
£2055 $3226 €3000 Autumn landscape (70x51cm-28x20in) s.i. mixed media. 15-Apr-3 De Veres Art Auctions, Dublin #203/R est:2000-3000

BOURKE-WHITE, Margaret (1904-1971) American
Photographs
£1875 $3000 €2813 Niagara Hudson (24x31cm-9x12in) i. silver print. 15-May-3 Swann Galleries, New York #291/R est:2000-3000
£1899 $3000 €2849 Goodyear blimp (23x32cm-9x13in) s.verso gelatin silver print executed c.1936. 22-Apr-3 Christie's, Rockefeller NY #35/R est:2500-3500
£2147 $3500 €3221 Helicopter view of Liberty (34x26cm-13x10in) s.i.d.1951 gelatin silver print. 12-Feb-3 Christie's, Rockefeller NY #213/R est:4000-6000
£2215 $3500 €3323 United States airship Akron (44x58cm-17x23in) s. photograph. 23-Apr-3 Sotheby's, New York #78/R est:4000-6000
£2308 $3600 €3462 Boy meets girl - praying mantises (33x25cm-13x10in) s.i. verso silver. 21-Oct-2 Swann Galleries, New York #85/R est:4000-5000
£2532 $4000 €3798 Grosvenor Crescent, London (18x25cm-7x10in) i.verso gelatin silver print prov. 24-Apr-3 Phillips, New York #111/R est:5000-7000
£2532 $4000 €3798 Terminal Tower Christmas card (17x6cm-7x2in) warm toned. 23-Apr-3 Sotheby's, New York #62/R est:5000-7000
£2760 $4250 €4140 Pan American Airways clipper flying boat (34x24cm-13x9in) photograph lit. 24-Oct-2 Sotheby's, New York #104/R est:4000-6000
£3117 $4800 €4676 Tower Bridge during the blackout, London (34x26cm-13x10in) i.verso gelatin silver print prov.lit. 25-Oct-2 Phillips, New York #89/R est:6000-8000
£3165 $5000 €4748 Face of Liberty, New York (47x36cm-19x14in) s. oversized photograph. 23-Apr-3 Sotheby's, New York #65/R est:3500-5000
£3165 $5000 €4748 Railroad car (31x48cm-12x19in) d.1939 oversized warm toned. 23-Apr-3 Sotheby's, New York #66/R est:3000-5000
£4114 $6500 €6171 Untitled (25x33cm-10x13in) s. gelatin silver print mounted on board prov. 24-Apr-3 Phillips, New York #110/R est:8000-12000
£4545 $7000 €6818 Hudson River Bridge (33x23cm-13x9in) s.i. warm toned photograph prov. 22-Oct-2 Sotheby's, New York #67/R est:7000-10000
£6962 $11000 €10443 No.9 Niagara Falls power co (33x23cm-13x9in) i.verso gelatin silver print prov. 25-Apr-3 Phillips, New York #81/R est:8000-12000
£9091 $14000 €13637 Organ pipes (53x36cm-21x14in) s. gelatin silver print board exec.c.1931 prov. 25-Oct-2 Phillips, New York #16/R est:12000-18000
£13291 $21000 €19937 Industrial mural studies (34x24cm-13x9in) s. photographs set of six. 23-Apr-3 Sotheby's, New York #72/R est:8000-12000
£16456 $26000 €24684 Chrysler building announcement (14x10cm-6x4in) warm toned. 23-Apr-3 Sotheby's, New York #61/R est:20000-30000
£19481 $30000 €29222 Contour plowing, Walsh Colorado (25x20cm-10x8in) i.verso gelatin silver print prov.lit. 25-Oct-2 Phillips, New York #112/R est:4000-6000

BOURLARD, Antoine Joseph (1826-1899) Belgian
£629 $969 €1000 Marine (70x148cm-28x58in) mono. 22-Oct-2 Galerie Moderne, Brussels #1657
£4487 $7045 €7000 Escapee du charbonnage de l'agrappe a Frameries (160x190cm-63x75in) mono. 19-Nov-2 Servarts Themis, Bruxelles #136

BOURNE, Bob (1931-) British
£260 $406 €390 Studio interior with easel (46x56cm-18x22in) s.i.d.1987 verso board. 16-Oct-2 David Lay, Penzance #234/R
£350 $546 €525 Cricketing incident (46x51cm-18x20in) s.verso board. 16-Oct-2 David Lay, Penzance #236/R
£350 $546 €525 Cornish coast (71x86cm-28x34in) 16-Oct-2 David Lay, Penzance #237/R
£600 $942 €900 Cape Cornwall (101x121cm-40x48in) s.d.85. 15-Apr-3 Bonhams, Knightsbridge #204/R

BOURNE, Evelyn Bodfish (1892-?) American
£542 $850 €813 Provincetown (35x40cm-14x16in) s.verso board. 22-Nov-2 Skinner, Boston #370/R

BOURNE, James (1773-1854) British
Works on paper
£300 $486 €450 Figures on a path in a classical landscape (19x23cm-7x9in) W/C. 21-Jan-3 Bonhams, Knightsbridge #265/R
£310 $508 €465 Northfleet, Kent (24x36cm-9x14in) i. pen ink brown wash. 4-Feb-3 Bonhams, Leeds #277

BOURNE, Samuel (c.1840-1920) British
£490 $769 €735 Mill stream near Tarbert, Loch Fyne (51x75cm-20x30in) 17-Apr-3 Bonhams, Edinburgh #367

BOUROTTE, Auguste (1853-?) Belgian
£637 $994 €1000 Elegante de profil (36x27cm-14x11in) s.d.1903 panel. 11-Nov-2 Horta, Bruxelles #522

BOURQUE, Patricia (1945-) Canadian
£200 $328 €300 Rest time (22x30cm-9x12in) s. tempera on board. 3-Jun-3 Joyner, Toronto #601 (C.D 450)

BOURRET, Michelle (20th C) French
£280 $445 €420 The cat Fout-Chou (24x33cm-9x13in) mono.d.1954. 5-May-3 Rasmussen, Vejle #50/R (D.KR 3000)

BOURSON, Amedee (1833-1905) Belgian
£921 $1372 €1382 Couple et enfant. s.d.1867 oval set of three. 26-Jun-2 Iegor de Saint Hippolyte, Montreal #10/R (C.D 2100)

BOURSSE, Esaias (1631-1672) Dutch
£21154 $32788 €33000 Old woman at spinning wheel (46x51cm-18x20in) bears sig. prov. 5-Dec-2 Dr Fritz Nagel, Stuttgart #592/R est:4000
£31000 $48360 €46500 Interior with old woman at spinning wheel (46x51cm-18x20in) s.d.1667 prov.lit. 10-Apr-3 Sotheby's, London #42/R est:22000

BOUSCHARAIN, Claude (1922-) South African
£307 $479 €461 Pause (92x89cm-36x35in) s.d.8 Dec 1981 i.verso. 15-Oct-2 Stephan Welz, Johannesburg #499 est:5000-8000 (SA.R 5000)

BOUSQUET, Charles (1856-1946) French
£36709 $58000 €55064 Harvester's lunch (103x121cm-41x48in) s.d.88 prov. 23-Apr-3 Christie's, Rockefeller NY #44/R est:30000-40000

BOUSSAC, Louise (?) French
Works on paper
£845 $1403 €1200 Panier de fleurs (50x68cm-20x27in) s. W/C. 13-Jun-3 Rabourdin & Choppin de Janvry, Paris #97

BOUT, Pieter (1658-1719) Flemish
£5068 $7905 €7500 River landscape with figures (37x27cm-15x11in) mono.d.99 prov. 27-Mar-3 Dorotheum, Vienna #135/R est:6000-9000
£6500 $10140 €9750 River landscape with a fortified town (28x36cm-11x14in) panel. 10-Apr-3 Christie's, Kensington #113/R est:5000-7000

BOUT, Pieter (attrib) (1658-1719) Flemish
£1351 $2108 €2000 Shepherdess and flock in wooded landscape (58x48cm-23x19in) panel. 27-Mar-3 Dorotheum, Vienna #304/R est:2000-3000

BOUT, Pieter and BOUDEWYNS, Adriaen Frans (17/18th C) Flemish
£10897 $17218 €17000 Southern harbour with figures (67x81cm-26x32in) 16-Nov-2 Lempertz, Koln #1009/R est:18000

BOUT, Pieter and BOUDEWYNS, Adriaen Frans (style) (17/18th C) Flemish
£6500 $10855 €9425 Italianate landscape with figures and mules in the foreground (91x130cm-36x51in) 8-Jul-3 Sotheby's, Olympia #415/R est:5000-7000

BOUTELLE (19th C) American
£1923 $3000 €2885 Landscape with waterfall and fishermen (30x23cm-12x9in) s.d.1871 board. 18-Sep-2 Alderfer's, Hatfield #323/R est:2000-3000

BOUTEN, Armand (20th C) ?
Works on paper
£818 $1259 €1300 Loving couple (23x29cm-9x11in) s. W/C bodycol over pencil. 26-Oct-2 Dr Lehr, Berlin #61/R

BOUTER, Cornelis (1888-1966) Dutch
£753 $1175 €1100 Calves near a puddle (49x69cm-19x27in) s. 14-Apr-3 Glerum, Amsterdam #116/R
£845 $1361 €1200 Shepherd and flock near a sheep pen (58x99cm-23x39in) s. 6-May-3 Vendu Notarishuis, Rotterdam #94
£889 $1476 €1289 Feeding time (27x30cm-11x12in) s. 16-Jun-3 Waddingtons, Toronto #244/R est:2500-3500 (C.D 2000)
£890 $1389 €1300 Stable interior with horses and farm-hand (60x100cm-24x39in) bears sig. 14-Apr-3 Glerum, Amsterdam #147/R
£1070 $1658 €1605 Preparing dinner (30x25cm-12x10in) s. 3-Dec-2 Ritchie, Toronto #3062a/R est:2500-3500 (C.D 2600)
£1118 $1755 €1677 Peeling onions (32x41cm-13x16in) s. 10-Dec-2 Pinneys, Montreal #46 est:2500-3500 (C.D 2750)
£1210 $1888 €1900 Polder landscape with peasant and cows (39x89cm-15x35in) s. 5-Nov-2 Vendu Notarishuis, Rotterdam #47/R est:1000-1500
£1235 $1914 €1853 Kitchen interior with mother and three children (51x61cm-20x24in) s. 3-Dec-2 Ritchie, Toronto #3062c/R est:4000-6000 (C.D 3000)
£1709 $2666 €2700 View of a canal in a Dutch city (38x59cm-15x23in) s. 21-Oct-2 Glerum, Amsterdam #51/R est:2200-2800
£1728 $2800 €2592 Domestic interior (74x48cm-29x19in) s. 23-Jan-3 Aspire, Cleveland #16 est:3000-5000
£1749 $2711 €2624 Mending time (30x26cm-12x10in) s. 3-Dec-2 Ritchie, Toronto #3026b/R est:2500-3500 (C.D 4250)
£1951 $3063 €2927 Mere et enfants (51x61cm-20x24in) s. 12-Dec-2 Iegor de Saint Hippolyte, Montreal #13 (C.D 4800)
£2361 $3682 €3423 Feeding baby (51x61cm-20x24in) s. 26-Mar-3 Walker's, Ottawa #11/R est:5000-6000 (C.D 5500)
£2933 $4869 €4253 Happy days (56x66cm-22x26in) s. prov. 16-Jun-3 Waddingtons, Toronto #249/R est:5000-7000 (C.D 6600)
£4000 $6280 €6000 An early supper (40x50cm-16x20in) s. 19-Nov-2 Sotheby's, London #166/R est:3000-5000

BOUTER, Pieter (1887-1968) Dutch
£563 $907 €800 Landscape with flock of sheep (59x79cm-23x31in) s. 6-May-3 Vendu Notarishuis, Rotterdam #3/R
£845 $1361 €1200 Milking time (59x99cm-23x39in) s. 7-May-3 Vendue Huis, Gravenhage #3/R

BOUTET DE MONVEL, Bernard (1884-1949) French
£4762 $7571 €7000 Portrait de Mademoiselle de Cosse-Brissac (47x38cm-19x15in) s. painted c.1944. 28-Feb-3 Tajan, Paris #12/R est:6000-7000
£19122 $29831 €28683 Arabian market scene (63x68cm-25x27in) s. 7-Nov-2 International Art Centre, Auckland #165/R est:10000-20000 (NZ.D 61000)
Works on paper
£311 $441 €500 Souvenir d'une guerisson inesperee (43x26cm-17x10in) s.i. pen Indian ink. 20-Mar-2 Chayette & Cheval, Paris #91

BOUTIGNY, Paul Émile (1854-1929) French
£1026 $1590 €1600 Summer meadows (30x39cm-12x15in) s. panel lit. 6-Dec-2 Karlheinz Kaupp, Staufen #2134/R est:1900

BOUTIN, Christophe (1957-) French
£486 $768 €700 Sans titre (200x200cm-79x79in) s.d.verso acrylic. 28-Apr-3 Cornette de St.Cyr, Paris #355
£486 $768 €700 Sans titre (162x130cm-64x51in) s.d.verso. 28-Apr-3 Cornette de St.Cyr, Paris #356

BOUTON, Charles Marie (attrib) (1781-1853) French
£1258 $1937 €2000 Procession a l'interieur d'un cloitre (33x24cm-13x9in) 25-Oct-2 Tajan, Paris #164/R est:1800-2000

BOUTS, Dirk (circle) (c.1415-1475) Dutch
£11250 $18000 €16875 Crucifixion with the Virgin, Mary Magdalene and John the Apostle (59x47cm-23x19in) panel. 14-May-3 Butterfields, San Francisco #1018/R est:20000-30000

BOUTS, Dirk (style) (c.1415-1475) Dutch
£6051 $9439 €9500 The Virgin and Child, a landscape beyond (38x33cm-15x13in) panel. 6-Nov-2 Christie's, Amsterdam #14/R est:3500-5000

BOUTTATS, Frederik (17th C) Flemish
£8741 $14598 €12500 Orphee charmant les animaux (26x45cm-10x18in) panel. 27-Jun-3 Piasa, Paris #43/R est:5000-6000

BOUTTATS, Jacob (attrib) (17th C) Flemish
£5674 $8794 €8511 Paradise (28x39cm-11x15in) panel. 4-Dec-2 AB Stockholms Auktionsverk #2019/R est:100000-150000 (S.KR 80000)

BOUTWOOD, Charles Edward (fl.1881-1887) British
Works on paper
£550 $852 €825 Cabbage girl (60x35cm-24x14in) s. W/C. 3-Dec-2 Sotheby's, Olympia #93/R

BOUVAL, Maurice (1863-1920) French
Sculpture
£1000 $1600 €1500 Figural jardiniere (33cm-13in) s. gilt bronze pewter. 15-May-3 Christie's, Kensington #348/R est:800-1200

BOUVARD (19/20th C) French
£5000 $7850 €7500 Canal a Venise (46x55cm-18x22in) s. 19-Nov-2 Sotheby's, London #101/R est:2000-3000
£7000 $10990 €10500 Gondoles sur un canal a Venice (50x65cm-20x26in) s. 19-Nov-2 Sotheby's, London #103/R est:2000-3000
£10000 $16000 €15000 Extensive Venetian riverscape showing a panoramic view of Grand Canal (51x64cm-20x25in) s. 10-Jan-3 Biddle & Webb, Birmingham #300 est:500-800
£16000 $25120 €24000 Pres de l'eglise Santa Maria della Salute, Venice (60x91cm-24x36in) s. 19-Nov-2 Sotheby's, London #102/R est:3000-5000

BOUVARD, Antoine (1870-1956) French
£5677 $8970 €8800 Canal a Venise (38x55cm-15x22in) s. 19-Dec-2 Claude Aguttes, Neuilly #32/R
£5741 $8152 €9300 Canal (40x50cm-16x20in) s. 16-Mar-3 Eric Pillon, Calais #74/R
£5806 $9174 €9000 Canal a Venise (38x55cm-15x22in) s. 19-Dec-2 Claude Aguttes, Neuilly #31/R
£5893 $9075 €8840 Untitled - Venice Canal (27x35cm-11x14in) s. 3-Sep-2 Shapiro, Sydney #382 est:12000-15000 (A.D 16500)
£6222 $10329 €9022 Grand Canal, Venice (24x33cm-9x13in) s. 16-Jun-3 Waddingtons, Toronto #282/R est:12000-15000 (C.D 14000)
£7432 $11595 €11000 View of Venice (54x81cm-21x32in) s. 28-Mar-3 Claude Aguttes, Neuilly #48/R est:12000
£8000 $12400 €12000 Venetian canal (50x65cm-20x26in) s. 3-Dec-2 Sotheby's, Olympia #308/R est:8000-12000
£8200 $12710 €12300 Santa Maria della salute (50x65cm-20x26in) s. 3-Dec-2 Sotheby's, Olympia #304/R est:8000-12000
£8333 $13250 €12000 View of the laguna of Venice with Santa Maria della Salute in the distance (38x55cm-15x22in) s. 29-Apr-3 Christie's, Amsterdam #113/R est:8000-12000
£8889 $14756 €12889 Sunlight and shadow (65x50cm-26x20in) s. i.on stretcher verso prov. 10-Jun-3 Ritchie, Toronto #118/R est:20000-25000 (C.D 20000)
£9000 $14130 €13500 Gondola on a Venetian canal (24x33cm-9x13in) s. 21-Nov-2 Christie's, Kensington #172/R est:3000-4000
£9000 $14130 €13500 Grand canal, Venice (24x34cm-9x13in) with sig. 21-Nov-2 Christie's, Kensington #173/R est:3000-4000
£10000 $15600 €15000 St Georges, Venice (37x54cm-15x21in) s. prov. 17-Oct-2 Lawrence, Crewkerne #486/R est:7000-10000
£10443 $16500 €16500 Grand canal a Venise, le Campanile. Gondoles a Venise (24x33cm-9x13in) s. pair. 1-Dec-2 Peron, Melun #29
£11200 $17472 €16800 Venetian canal scene (50x66cm-20x26in) s. 17-Sep-2 Sotheby's, Olympia #283/R est:5000-7000
£13548 $21406 €21000 Venise (50x65cm-20x26in) s. 19-Dec-2 Claude Aguttes, Neuilly #33/R est:20000
£14000 $22120 €21000 Venice Grand Canal with sailing ship (48x63cm-19x25in) s. 27-Nov-2 Bonhams, Brooks & Langlois, Jersey #81/R est:10000-15000
£14200 $23288 €21300 Canal in Venice, gondolier at sunset (48x64cm-19x25in) i. 3-Jun-3 Bonhams, Oxford #70/R est:5000-7000
£15000 $24450 €22500 Gondolas and figures before the Piazetta, Venice (48x63cm-19x25in) s. 29-Jan-3 Hampton & Littlewood, Exeter #420/R est:15000-20000
£15385 $24154 €24000 Vue de Venise (33x46cm-13x18in) s. pair. 19-Nov-2 Galerie Moderne, Brussels #233/R est:5000-7000
£17610 $27119 €28000 Venetian canal scene with a gondola (50x65cm-20x26in) s. 23-Oct-2 Christie's, Amsterdam #86/R est:8000-12000
£24000 $37680 €36000 Evening glow, Venice, moored boats on a Venetian canal (53x79cm-21x31in) s. pair. 19-Nov-2 Bonhams, New Bond Street #181/R est:12000-18000
£25000 $39250 €37500 Venetian canal (60x81cm-24x32in) 21-Nov-2 Christie's, Kensington #170/R est:15000-20000

BOUVARD, Auguste (20th C) French
£3024 $4778 €4536 Evening, Venice (24x33cm-9x13in) s. 18-Nov-2 Waddingtons, Toronto #248/R est:10000-15000 (C.D 7500)

BOUVARD, Colette (19th C) French
£900 $1422 €1350 Bell tower - Venetian canal scene (55x38cm-22x15in) s. 7-Apr-3 Bonhams, Bath #53/R

BOUVARD, Noël (1912-1975) French
£2100 $3318 €3150 View in Venice (26x34cm-10x13in) s. 2-Dec-2 Bonhams, Bath #47/R est:1000-1500
£4000 $6280 €6000 Venetian canal (46x61cm-18x24in) s. 21-Nov-2 Christie's, Kensington #171/R est:4000-5000
£4000 $6360 €6000 Venetian canal (49x64cm-19x25in) s. 20-Mar-3 Christie's, Kensington #44/R est:4000-6000
£4500 $7065 €6750 Canal, Venice (52x63cm-20x25in) s. 21-Nov-2 Christie's, Kensington #168/R est:5000-7000
£4500 $7515 €6525 Venetian backwater (49x64cm-19x25in) s. 17-Jun-3 Bonhams, New Bond Street #117/R est:3000-5000
£4800 $7632 €7200 Venetian canal (63x97cm-25x38in) s. 18-Mar-3 Bonhams, New Bond Street #135/R est:5000-8000

BOUVARD, W (20th C) ?
£1550 $2511 €2248 View from an elevated position of Green Park, London (49x59cm-19x23in) s.d.1939. 21-May-3 Rupert Toovey, Partridge Green #18/R est:300-500

BOUVET, Francis (1929-1979) French?
£4110 $6452 €6000 Untitled (73x92cm-29x36in) s.d.1947 verso. 15-Apr-3 Laurence Calmels, Paris #4127/R

BOUVIER DE CACHARD, Regis de (1929-) French
£260 $421 €390 Venice station (70x90cm-28x35in) s.d,58. 20-May-3 Bonhams, Knightsbridge #105

BOUVIER, Arthur (1837-1921) Belgian
£522 $809 €783 La baie d'Alger (60x100cm-24x39in) s.d.16 panel. 9-Dec-2 Philippe Schuler, Zurich #8625 (S.FR 1200)

BOUVIER, Auguste (19th C) French
Works on paper
£400 $624 €600 Haberdashers stall (60x77cm-24x30in) s. W/C. 11-Nov-2 Trembath Welch, Great Dunmow #401

BOUVIER, Augustus Jules (c.1827-1881) British
£5000 $8050 €7500 Knight's enchantment (60x67cm-24x26in) prov. 20-Feb-3 Christie's, London #233/R
Works on paper
£2200 $3542 €3300 Anticipation (32x15cm-13x6in) s.d.1877 pencil W/C scratching out prov.exhib. 20-Feb-3 Christie's, London #107/R

BOUVIER, F A (20th C) French
£250 $395 €375 Les champes elysee (60x55cm-24x22in) s.i. 14-Nov-2 Christie's, Kensington #260

BOUVIER, Joseph Laurent Daniel (attrib) (1841-1901) French
£388 $589 €582 Young girl with Cupid and garland of flowers (25x17cm-10x7in) s. panel. 27-Aug-2 Rasmussen, Copenhagen #1612/R (D.KR 4500)

BOUVIER, Jules (1800-1867) British
Works on paper
£900 $1413 €1350 Spanish girls at a market (54x39cm-21x15in) s. W/C. 16-Apr-3 Christie's, Kensington #677/R
£1400 $2296 €2100 Rebekah (75x61cm-30x24in) s. pencil W/C htd white. 5-Jun-3 Christie's, Kensington #845/R est:1500-2000

BOUVIER, Paul (1857-1940) Swiss
Works on paper
£301 $484 €452 Neustadt old town (35x27cm-14x11in) s. W/C over pencil. 7-May-3 Dobiaschofsky, Bern #3139 (S.FR 650)

BOUVIOLLE, Maurice (1893-1971) French
£3718 $5838 €5800 Jour de marche a Ghardaia (50x65cm-20x26in) s. 10-Dec-2 Tajan, Paris #117/R est:7000
£9353 $15338 €13000 Touggourt (60x81cm-24x32in) s.i.d.1927. 4-Jun-3 Tajan, Paris #238/R est:13000-15000

BOUVY, Firmin (attrib) (1822-1891) German
£3459 $5396 €5500 Marguerite en voyage dans les environs de Seville (51x112cm-20x44in) 14-Oct-2 Amberes, Antwerp #135/R

BOUY, Gaston (1866-?) French
Works on paper
£548 $866 €850 Elegante assise sur accoudoir (46x29cm-18x11in) s. pastel. 18-Dec-2 Rieunier, Bailly-Pommery, Mathias, Paris #32
£641 $1006 €1000 Sacrifice (54x44cm-21x17in) s.d.93 pastel exhib. 16-Dec-2 Millon & Associes, Paris #38

BOUYS, André (1656-1740) French
£9790 $16350 €14000 La collation aux peches (59x73cm-23x29in) exhib.lit. 25-Jun-3 Sotheby's, Paris #31/R est:15000-20000
£17284 $28000 €25926 Still life with silver and biscuits on dish (63x74cm-25x29in) prov. 23-Jan-3 Sotheby's, New York #254/R est:35000

BOUYSSOU, Jacques (1926-1997) French
£443 $687 €700 Le port (19x27cm-7x11in) s. panel. 29-Sep-2 Eric Pillon, Calais #220/R
£443 $687 €700 Paris, L'Arc de Triomphe du Carrousel (22x26cm-9x10in) s. panel. 29-Sep-2 Eric Pillon, Calais #250/R
£465 $754 €674 Les ramasseurs de coques (55x66cm-22x26in) s. d.1969 verso prov. 25-May-3 Uppsala Auktionskammare, Uppsala #325 (S.KR 6000)
£687 $1100 €996 Douarnenez le quai (74x92cm-29x36in) s. 16-May-3 Skinner, Boston #337/R
£833 $1292 €1300 Place St Andre des Arts, Paris (61x71cm-24x28in) s. i. verso. 5-Dec-2 Neumeister, Munich #2768/R
£931 $1508 €1350 Les pecheurs de crevettes (65x81cm-26x32in) s. 25-May-3 Uppsala Auktionskammare, Uppsala #318/R (S.KR 12000)
£937 $1500 €1359 Amsterdam, le Pont Levis (81x100cm-32x39in) s. i.verso. 16-May-3 Skinner, Boston #335/R est:1000-1500
£968 $1500 €1452 Les voiles (64x81cm-25x32in) s. s.i.d.3.12.1984 verso. 16-Jul-2 Arthur James, Florida #407
£1250 $1975 €1800 Au bon coin (54x65cm-21x26in) s. 25-Apr-3 Piasa, Paris #58
£1380 $2180 €2000 Ciel en Normandie (60x72cm-24x28in) s. i.d.1969 verso. 4-Apr-3 Tajan, Paris #172
£1384 $2145 €2200 La lieutenance a Honfleur (46x55cm-18x22in) s.d.verso. 4-Oct-2 Tajan, Paris #32 est:1000-1200
£1401 $2186 €2200 Honfleur, entree du port (46x55cm-18x22in) s. 10-Nov-2 Eric Pillon, Calais #111/R
£1739 $2800 €2609 Honfleur le vieux bassin (66x53cm-26x21in) s. i.verso. 19-Feb-3 Doyle, New York #53/R est:3000-5000
Works on paper
£411 $645 €600 Plage a Deauville (20x26cm-8x10in) s.d.65 W/C. 21-Apr-3 Rabourdin & Choppin de Janvry, Paris #101

BOUZAID, Mal (20th C) New Zealander?
£883 $1422 €1325 Ships on the Hard, Bayswater (101x136cm-40x54in) s.d.91. 7-May-3 Dunbar Sloane, Auckland #28/R (NZ.D 2500)

BOUZIANIS, Georgios (1885-1959) Greek
£2000 $3160 €3000 Lesendes maedchen (29x22cm-11x9in) painted c.1929. 1-Apr-3 Bonhams, New Bond Street #40 est:2000-3000
£36000 $56880 €54000 Sitzende frau (72x50cm-28x20in) painted c.1928. 1-Apr-3 Bonhams, New Bond Street #64 est:35000-45000
£100000 $155000 €150000 Girl with pink dress and black hat (130x80cm-51x31in) s. prov.lit. 2-Oct-2 Sotheby's, London #54/R est:100000-150000

BOVIN, Karl (1907-1985) Danish
£642 $989 €963 Seascape (26x36cm-10x14in) s.d.67 masonite. 23-Oct-2 Kunsthallen, Copenhagen #3 (D.KR 7600)
£1828 $2907 €2742 Summer landscape, Odsherred (50x65cm-20x26in) s.i.d.Okt.42 exhib. 26-Feb-3 Kunsthallen, Copenhagen #269/R est:18000 (D.KR 20000)
£2285 $3633 €3428 Seascape (45x53cm-18x21in) s. 26-Feb-3 Kunsthallen, Copenhagen #235/R est:8000 (D.KR 25000)
£2787 $4348 €4181 Arabian walls (30x40cm-12x16in) s.i.d.1964 exhib. 18-Sep-2 Kunsthallen, Copenhagen #30/R est:10000 (D.KR 33000)
Works on paper
£298 $471 €447 View across Sejero Bay (44x59cm-17x23in) s.i.d.43 prov. 27-Nov-2 Museumsbygningen, Copenhagen #723 (D.KR 3500)

BOWDEN, Beulah Beatrice (1875-?) American
£1519 $2400 €2279 Expressionist landscape with smokestack in distance (79x91cm-31x36in) s. 24-Apr-3 Shannon's, Milford #199/R est:2000-3000

BOWDOIN, Harriette (?-1947) American
£2097 $3250 €3146 Floral still life in oriental vase (76x64cm-30x25in) s. canvas on masonite. 29-Oct-2 John Moran, Pasadena #650a est:2000-3000

BOWEN, Augusta M (fl.1898-1925) British
£280 $440 €420 Still life study of green onyx figure surmounted clock and other artefacts on a table (48x74cm-19x29in) s. 13-Dec-2 Keys, Aylsham #321/R

BOWEN, Denis (1921-) British
£5500 $9020 €7975 Nochturnal image (74x73cm-29x29in) s.i.d.58 verso masonite prov.lit. 4-Jun-3 Sotheby's, London #38/R est:2000-3000

BOWEN, Greta (1880-1981) Irish
£350 $511 €525 Marching bandsmen (30x46cm-12x18in) s. board. 12-Jun-2 John Ross, Belfast #73
£400 $636 €600 Village scene (33x38cm-13x15in) s. board. 5-Mar-3 John Ross, Belfast #79
£600 $930 €900 Village square (40x61cm-16x24in) s. board. 4-Dec-2 John Ross, Belfast #223
£1400 $2170 €2100 Children feeding swans (30x41cm-12x16in) s. board. 2-Oct-2 John Ross, Belfast #144 est:1500-1600
Works on paper
£300 $465 €450 Memory of the Dublin church (43x30cm-17x12in) mixed media. 2-Oct-2 John Ross, Belfast #94

BOWEN, J T (19th C) American
Prints
£2237 $3400 €3356 View of Fairmount Waterworks with Schuylkill in the distance (38x53cm-15x21in) hand col lithograph. 17-Aug-2 North East Auctions, Portsmouth #49/R
£3421 $5200 €5132 View of Fairmount and the Waterworks with bridge (38x56cm-15x22in) hand col lithograph. 17-Aug-2 North East Auctions, Portsmouth #50/R

BOWEN, John T (1801-1856) American
Prints
£4747 $7500 €7121 Femal jaguar (55x71cm-22x28in) hand col lithograph after John James Audubon prov. 3-Apr-3 Christie's, Rockefeller NY #276/R est:3000-4000

BOWEN, Owen (1873-1967) British
£250 $390 €375 Cattle in a river landscape (25x36cm-10x14in) s. board. 20-Sep-2 Richardson & Smith, Whitby #148
£250 $415 €375 Entrance to Harwood dale (48x64cm-19x25in) s. 10-Jun-3 Bonhams, Leeds #201
£250 $413 €363 Still life with flowers (63x76cm-25x30in) s. 3-Jul-3 Christie's, Kensington #493
£260 $406 €390 River landscape with cottage in the foreground (15x28cm-6x11in) s. 9-Apr-3 Andrew Hartley, Ilkley #989
£270 $440 €405 Extensive summer landscape (24x30cm-9x12in) s. 12-Feb-3 Andrew Hartley, Ilkley #955
£280 $440 €420 Vase of chrysanthemums (44x30cm-17x12in) s. board. 15-Apr-3 Bonhams, Knightsbridge #165
£280 $468 €406 Cattle grazing in a field, dwellings beyond (23x30cm-9x12in) 26-Jun-3 Richardson & Smith, Whitby #546
£280 $456 €406 Still life of roses in a vase (36x25cm-14x10in) s. board. 17-Jul-3 Richardson & Smith, Whitby #485
£290 $455 €435 Collingham Bridge (44x56cm-17x22in) s. canvas on hardboard prov. 19-Nov-2 Bonhams, Leeds #134
£290 $481 €435 Flowers in a jug beside a window (64x49cm-25x19in) s. 10-Jun-3 Bonhams, Leeds #205
£320 $499 €480 Still life of a vase of summer flowers (61x51cm-24x20in) s. 10-Apr-3 Tennants, Leyburn #1091
£330 $515 €495 Still life, vase of flowers (43x48cm-17x19in) s. 9-Oct-2 Andrew Hartley, Ilkley #773
£340 $544 €510 Rocks at low tide, near Whitby (24x34cm-9x13in) s. board. 11-Mar-3 David Duggleby, Scarborough #213
£340 $568 €493 Extensive landscape view in summer with figures gathering corn (42x52cm-17x20in) s. 17-Jun-3 Anderson & Garland, Newcastle #438
£360 $558 €540 Moorland scene with sheep grazing (38x48cm-15x19in) s.d.1931 board. 4-Dec-2 Andrew Hartley, Ilkley #1244
£360 $562 €540 Still life of flowers in a blue and green vase (44x54cm-17x21in) s. 25-Mar-3 Bonhams, Leeds #609
£380 $593 €570 Dutch moonlit river scene (28x43cm-11x17in) s. 9-Apr-3 Andrew Hartley, Ilkley #988/R
£400 $628 €600 Artist garden at Collingham (35x25cm-14x10in) s. prov. 19-Nov-2 Bonhams, Leeds #135
£400 $664 €600 View of the wharfe (44x59cm-17x23in) s. 10-Jun-3 Bonhams, Leeds #202
£410 $685 €595 Gatherer (25x36cm-10x14in) s. panel. 9-Jul-3 Edgar Horn, Eastbourne #321
£450 $702 €675 Low tide, Mevagissey Harbour (50x66cm-20x26in) s. 25-Mar-3 Bonhams, Leeds #605/R
£450 $747 €675 Hill Top farm, Appletreewick (41x52cm-16x20in) s. 10-Jun-3 Bonhams, Leeds #203
£450 $747 €675 Still life of summer flowers (63x76cm-25x30in) s. 10-Jun-3 Bonhams, Leeds #204
£450 $752 €653 Still life with flowers (58x51cm-23x20in) s. 18-Jun-3 Andrew Hartley, Ilkley #1194
£450 $734 €653 Windmill beside a canal, sheep and ducks in the foreground (28x38cm-11x15in) s. 17-Jul-3 Tennants, Leyburn #861/R

£470 $733 €705 Robin Hoods Bay (40x30cm-16x12in) s. canvasboard. 25-Mar-3 Bonhams, Leeds #602
£480 $754 €720 Chrysanthemums and nasturtiums (30x35cm-12x14in) s. canvasboard prov. 19-Nov-2 Bonhams, Leeds #136
£483 $764 €725 Old mill in Wharfedale, Yorkshire (51x61cm-20x24in) s. 18-Nov-2 Waddingtons, Toronto #113/R (C.D 1200)
£500 $785 €750 Still life of daffodils and other flowers in a blue vase (61x51cm-24x20in) s. 19-Nov-2 Bonhams, Leeds #133
£500 $815 €750 Cattle watering by a pool at dusk (27x37cm-11x15in) s. 11-Feb-3 Bonhams, Knowle #75
£500 $780 €750 Still life of flowers in a bowl on a table (41x51cm-16x20in) s. 10-Apr-3 Tennants, Leyburn #1092
£500 $815 €725 Yorkshire farmstead with figures beside a stone wall (30x50cm-12x20in) s. 17-Jul-3 Tennants, Leyburn #859
£540 $848 €810 View of Richmond (30x40cm-12x16in) s. canvasboard. 19-Nov-2 Bonhams, Leeds #130
£650 $1014 €975 Glen House Daffodils (58x48cm-23x19in) s. 9-Oct-2 Andrew Hartley, Ilkley #761
£700 $1141 €1015 Watermill beside a river with trees nearby (28x38cm-11x15in) s. 17-Jul-3 Tennants, Leyburn #860
£920 $1444 €1380 Moorland scene with figures, North Yorkshire Moors (40x50cm-16x20in) s. canvasboard. 19-Nov-2 Bonhams, Leeds #137/R
£975 $1511 €1463 Appletreewick (33x43cm-13x17in) s.i. board. 4-Dec-2 Andrew Hartley, Ilkley #1243/R
£1050 $1638 €1575 Milking time (36x46cm-14x18in) s.d.1910. 25-Mar-3 Bonhams, Leeds #608/R est:900-1000
£1140 $1824 €1710 Still life of summer flowers (48x58cm-19x23in) s. exhib. 11-Mar-3 David Duggleby, Scarborough #202 est:1000-1500
£1300 $2041 €1950 Still life of spring flowers in a blue and white jug. Still life of roses (60x50cm-24x20in) s. pair. 19-Nov-2 Bonhams, Leeds #132/R est:800-1200
£1300 $2119 €1885 Evening hour, Solway Firth (43x53cm-17x21in) s. 17-Jul-3 Tennants, Leyburn #862/R est:700-900
£1400 $2184 €2100 Landscape with river and bridge (51x58cm-20x23in) s. 16-Oct-2 Brightwells, Leominster #1172/R est:1500-2000
£3100 $4867 €4650 Fylingthorpe, North Yorkshire Moors (51x61cm-20x24in) s.d.26 i.on stretcher. 19-Nov-2 Bonhams, Leeds #131/R est:1000-1500

Works on paper
£400 $652 €580 Farmer and two shire horse ploughing a field (25x31cm-10x12in) pencil W/C. 17-Jul-3 Tennants, Leyburn #749
£470 $766 €682 Robin Hood's Bay (36x51cm-14x20in) s. W/C. 17-Jul-3 Richardson & Smith, Whitby #538
£1000 $1550 €1500 Dales snowscene with figure (25x36cm-10x14in) s.d.35 i.verso. 4-Dec-2 Andrew Hartley, Ilkley #1127/R est:500-700
£2600 $4056 €3900 View upstream to the bridge from Whitby harbour (24x45cm-9x18in) s.d.1910 W/C. 10-Sep-2 David Duggleby, Scarborough #117/R est:2000-3000

BOWER, Alexander (1875-1952) American
£321 $500 €482 Rocky Maine coast (36x46cm-14x18in) s. 12-Oct-2 Neal Auction Company, New Orleans #1327
£325 $520 €488 Maine coastal scene (36x46cm-14x18in) s. 11-Jan-3 James Julia, Fairfield #463
£452 $700 €678 California landscape with hills under a yellow sunset (64x76cm-25x30in) s. 2-Nov-2 Thomaston Place, Thomaston #39

BOWER, Edward (attrib) (17th C) British
£14000 $22120 €21000 Portrait of Sir Thomas Lawley, 1st Bt standing by table (211x146cm-83x57in) i.d.1630 prov. 26-Nov-2 Christie's, London #5/R est:20000-30000

BOWERS, Stephen J (fl.1874-1891) British
Works on paper
£222 $369 €322 Figures on the Thames near Windsor Castle (37x52cm-15x20in) s. W/C. 16-Jun-3 Waddingtons, Toronto #37/R (C.D 500)
£222 $369 €322 River scene with punters (24x46cm-9x18in) s. W/C. 16-Jun-3 Waddingtons, Toronto #74/R (C.D 500)
£340 $541 €510 At the cottage gate (30x44cm-12x17in) s. W/C. 4-Mar-3 Bearnes, Exeter #388
£520 $806 €780 River Waveney at Beccles (24x51cm-9x20in) s. W/C. 30-Sep-2 Bonhams, Ipswich #297/R

BOWES, David (1957-) American
Works on paper
£850 $1352 €1250 Fata Morgana (25x19cm-10x7in) d.1987 verso collage. 3-Mar-3 Marc Kohn, Paris #40/R

BOWEY, Olwyn (1936-) British
£450 $725 €675 In the greenhouse (52x39cm-20x15in) s.d.94 board. 14-Jan-3 Bonhams, Knightsbridge #3/R
Works on paper
£700 $1113 €1050 Garden (68x88cm-27x35in) s. gouache. 26-Feb-3 Sotheby's, Olympia #348/R

BOWKETT, Jane Maria (1837-1891) British
£1288 $2009 €1868 Anticipation. Lingering hope (61x36cm-24x14in) mono. pair. 26-Mar-3 Walker's, Ottawa #81/R est:4000-5000 (C.D 3000)

BOWKETT, Jane Maria (attrib) (1837-1891) British
£1900 $2964 €2850 Making cherry pie (46x36cm-18x14in) 7-Nov-2 Christie's, Kensington #206/R est:1500-2000

BOWLER, T W (?-1869) British
£375 $578 €563 Rouen, France, riverboats moored beside a bridge with street market (49x38cm-19x15in) s.i.d. 5-Sep-2 Morphets, Harrogate #350/R

BOWLER, Thomas W (1812-1869) British
Works on paper
£512 $799 €768 Two Malay women (22x15cm-9x6in) s.d.June 18th 1853 pencil htd white lit. 11-Nov-2 Stephan Welz, Johannesburg #482/R (SA.R 8000)
£4607 $7187 €6911 Keiskama evening (26x50cm-10x20in) s.i.d.1864 W/C htd white prov.lit. 15-Oct-2 Stephan Welz, Johannesburg #416/R est:8000-120000 (SA.R 75000)

BOWLING, C D (19/20th C) British
Works on paper
£900 $1396 €1350 Sporting scenes (34x24cm-13x9in) s. W/C pair. 3-Dec-2 Sotheby's, Olympia #201/R est:1000-1500

BOWLING, Charles T (1891-1986) American
£2564 $4000 €3846 Fairway (30x38cm-12x15in) board. 19-Oct-2 David Dike, Dallas #256/R est:4000-6000
£5449 $8500 €8174 Evening clouds (51x61cm-20x24in) 19-Oct-2 David Dike, Dallas #242/R est:9000-12000

BOWNESS, William (1809-1867) British
£340 $551 €510 Mrs Thexton of Ashton House, Beetham (80x66cm-31x26in) s.d.1849. 21-May-3 James Thompson, Kirby Lonsdale #209/R
£900 $1458 €1350 Young girl (127x102cm-50x40in) s.d.1845 verso. 21-May-3 James Thompson, Kirby Lonsdale #257
£1000 $1620 €1500 Miss Jeanette Frances Thexton age 7 years (126x101cm-50x40in) 21-May-3 James Thompson, Kirby Lonsdale #208

BOWRING, Joseph (c.1760-1817) British
Miniatures
£1200 $1908 €1800 Gentleman wearing a brown coat with white collar, seascape beyond (7cm-3xin) mono. blue glass gold mounted plaited hair border lit. 4-Mar-3 Bonhams, New Bond Street #130/R est:1200-1800

BOWYER, Jason Richard (1957-) British
£850 $1343 €1275 Studio interior (137x101cm-54x40in) prov. 27-Nov-2 Sotheby's, Olympia #305/R

BOWYER, Robert (1758-1834) British
Miniatures
£1100 $1716 €1650 Hon John Monckton (4cm-2in circular) executed c.1780 oval with seven other miniatures eight. 8-Oct-2 Sotheby's, Olympia #443/R est:800-1200

BOWYER, William (1926-) British
£350 $546 €525 Stone breakers at Mount Abu (51x38cm-20x15in) s.d.89 board prov. 27-Mar-3 Christie's, Kensington #513
£360 $583 €540 Storm over the river (17x32cm-7x13in) s. indis d. board exhib. 20-May-3 Bonhams, Knightsbridge #76/R
£550 $858 €825 Richmond (20x61cm-8x24in) s. canvas on board. 27-Mar-3 Christie's, Kensington #504/R
£650 $1014 €975 View from Walberswick (40x49cm-16x19in) s. board. 27-Mar-3 Christie's, Kensington #508/R
£650 $1014 €975 River Blythe (30x30cm-12x12in) s. board sold with river landscape by same hand. 27-Mar-3 Christie's, Kensington #517
£800 $1248 €1200 Sea wall (46x61cm-18x24in) s. board prov. 27-Mar-3 Christie's, Kensington #511/R
£1000 $1550 €1500 Evening tide (127x101cm-50x40in) s.d.82. 3-Dec-2 Bonhams, Knightsbridge #96/R est:1500-2500
£1000 $1650 €1450 Slipway, Walberswick (53x53cm-21x21in) s.d.88 board. 3-Jul-3 Christie's, Kensington #683/R est:1000-1500
£1200 $1968 €1800 On the beach at Aldeborough (90x70cm-35x28in) s. 3-Jun-3 Sotheby's, Olympia #195/R est:800-1200
£1300 $2028 €1950 Silver sea, Walberswick (71x91cm-28x36in) s.d.88. 27-Mar-3 Christie's, Kensington #518/R est:700-900

£2600 $4056 €3900 Overgrown garden, Walberswick, Suffolk (90x90cm-35x35in) 27-Mar-3 Christie's, Kensington #512/R est:1200-1800
Works on paper
£550 $919 €798 River walk (35x54cm-14x21in) s.d.84 W/C. 17-Jun-3 Bonhams, Knightsbridge #2/R

BOXER, Stanley (1926-) American
£1282 $2000 €1923 Cacophonous bellow of snows (206x206cm-81x81in) 30-Mar-3 Susanin's, Chicago #6120/R est:2000-4000

BOXLER, Anny (1914-2001) Swiss
£1459 $2306 €2189 Loving God goes through the woods (60x73cm-24x29in) s.d.1969 i.verso lit. 26-Nov-2 Hans Widmer, St Gallen #1446/R est:2200-3800 (S.FR 3400)

BOYADJEVA, Liuba (1923-) Bulgarian
Sculpture
£1923 $3019 €3000 Untitled (47x42cm-19x17in) s. brown pat bronze. 24-Nov-2 Laurence Calmels, Paris #300/R

BOYCE, George Price (1826-1897) British
Works on paper
£900 $1395 €1350 Thatched cottage in a wooded landscape (27x45cm-11x18in) s. W/C. 24-Sep-2 Bonhams, Knightsbridge #178/R
£1300 $2028 €1950 Cleeve Abbey, West Somerset (20x28cm-8x11in) s.d.1874 W/C prov. 17-Oct-2 Lawrence, Crewkerne #406/R est:600-800
£5500 $9020 €7975 At Bywell, Northumberland (29x44cm-11x17in) s.d.1881-82 pencil W/C prov.exhib. 5-Jun-3 Christie's, London #113a/R est:3500-4500

BOYCE, W T N (1857-1911) British
Works on paper
£300 $462 €450 Sea scape with boats (30x56cm-12x22in) s. 6-Sep-2 Biddle & Webb, Birmingham #89

BOYCE, William Thomas Nicholas (1857-1911) British
Works on paper
£280 $437 €420 Tug, steamer and sailing vessels leaving a port (33x51cm-13x20in) s.d.1899 W/C over pencil. 10-Apr-3 Tennants, Leyburn #825
£280 $454 €420 Fishing lugger at dusk (47x35cm-19x14in) s.d.1906 W/C. 21-May-3 Christie's, Kensington #467/R
£300 $468 €450 Fishing boats and other vessels off Tynemouth (24x53cm-9x21in) s.d.1902 W/C bodycol. 10-Apr-3 Tennants, Leyburn #824
£340 $527 €510 North Shields harbour at sunset (32x51cm-13x20in) s.d.1900 W/C. 24-Sep-2 Anderson & Garland, Newcastle #330
£360 $558 €540 St Mary's Island and lighthouse (24x50cm-9x20in) s.d.1901 W/C. 24-Sep-2 Anderson & Garland, Newcastle #332
£400 $640 €600 Sail and steam ships in a rough sea (36x53cm-14x21in) s.d.1904 W/C. 11-Mar-3 Gorringes, Lewes #2342
£450 $747 €675 Homecoming (25x53cm-10x21in) s.d.1898 W/C. 10-Jun-3 Sworder & Son, Bishops Stortford #517/R
£650 $1086 €943 Shipping off the North East Coast (33x51cm-13x20in) s.d.1899 W/C. 17-Jun-3 Anderson & Garland, Newcastle #246

BOYCOTT-BROWN, Hugh (1909-1990) British
£280 $434 €420 Aldeburgh beach (17x23cm-7x9in) i.d.April 14th 1990 verso board. 30-Sep-2 Bonhams, Ipswich #373/R
£280 $462 €406 Towards Thorpeness, Aldeburgh (18x23cm-7x9in) init. i.d.1975 verso board. 1-Jul-3 Bonhams, Norwich #277
£300 $465 €450 Dedham Church, Suffolk (26x31cm-10x12in) s. i.verso board. 30-Sep-2 Bonhams, Ipswich #401
£350 $578 €508 Aldeburgh lifeboat (18x23cm-7x9in) init. i.d.1975 verso board. 1-Jul-3 Bonhams, Norwich #276
£400 $632 €600 Windy day, Honfleur (19x25cm-7x10in) init. board. 27-Nov-2 Sotheby's, Olympia #90/R
£400 $652 €600 Palace of Westminster from the Thames at sunset (41x48cm-16x19in) s.d.55. 14-Feb-3 Keys, Aylsham #540/R
£460 $731 €690 Pool of London (29x39cm-11x15in) s.d.53 board. 29-Apr-3 Sworder & Son, Bishops Stortford #393/R
£480 $744 €720 Anstruther, Fife, Scotland (46x61cm-18x24in) s. i.verso. 30-Sep-2 Bonhams, Ipswich #416
£600 $936 €900 On the Thames (36x51cm-14x20in) s. board. 12-Sep-2 Sotheby's, Olympia #124/R
£650 $1073 €943 Boats at Chelsea (30x38cm-12x15in) s.d.73 board. 1-Jul-3 Bonhams, Norwich #289
£1000 $1550 €1500 Yachts and motorboat with wooden jetty, butlers hard on the Hamble (38x48cm-15x19in) s. board. 4-Dec-2 Neal & Fletcher, Woodbridge #243 est:1000-1500
£1200 $1908 €1800 Burlesdon Hants (30x39cm-12x15in) s. board. 26-Feb-3 Sotheby's, Olympia #228/R est:1200-1800
£2000 $3040 €3000 Setting sail under calm waters (60x75cm-24x30in) s. 15-Aug-2 Bonhams, New Bond Street #367/R est:2000-3000

BOYD, Alexander Stuart (1854-1930) British
£360 $558 €540 Palma (23x32cm-9x13in) s.i.d.1916. 3-Dec-2 Bonhams, Knightsbridge #315
Works on paper
£360 $569 €540 Sunday morning in Ibiza (35x25cm-14x10in) s.i.d.April 1910 W/C over pencil. 7-Apr-3 Bonhams, Bath #44/R

BOYD, Alice (fl.1874-1919) British
£4000 $6440 €6000 Saint Columba's farewell to the white horse (35x49cm-14x19in) init.indis.d. board prov.exhib. 20-Feb-3 Christie's, London #89/R

BOYD, Arthur Merric (snr) (1862-1940) Australian
£1769 $2813 €2654 Off St Kilda (10x14cm-4x6in) s.i. canvas on board. 4-Mar-3 Deutscher-Menzies, Melbourne #237/R est:2000-3000 (A.D 4600)

BOYD, Arthur Merric Bloomfield (1920-1999) Australian
£1143 $1806 €1715 Resurrection (50x62cm-20x24in) s. ink executed c.1975. 26-Nov-2 Sotheby's, Melbourne #74 est:3000-5000 (A.D 3200)
£2817 $4394 €4226 On the Shoalhaven (30x23cm-12x9in) s. board. 21-Oct-2 Australian Art Auctions, Sydney #137/R (A.D 8000)
£3393 $5259 €5090 Old boat, Rye, Victoria (33x43cm-13x17in) s. glazed ceramic tile. 29-Oct-2 Lawson Menzies, Sydney #51/R est:9000-15000 (A.D 9500)
£3984 $6534 €5976 Murrumbeena (61x73cm-24x29in) s.d.40 canvas on board. 4-Jun-3 Deutscher-Menzies, Melbourne #82/R est:9000-12000 (A.D 10000)
£4264 $6779 €6396 Shoalhaven landscape (22x15cm-9x6in) s. board prov.exhib. 5-May-3 Sotheby's, Melbourne #9/R est:15000 (A.D 11000)
£4286 $6686 €6429 Swan on Shoalhaven (38x30cm-15x12in) s. board. 11-Nov-2 Deutscher-Menzies, Melbourne #109/R est:14000-18000 (A.D 12000)
£4389 $6935 €6364 Ram at the river (30x23cm-12x9in) s. board. 7-Apr-3 Australian Art Auctions, Sydney #134 (A.D 11500)
£4400 $7084 €6600 Bundanoon (30x22cm-12x9in) s. board. 6-May-3 Christie's, Melbourne #134/R est:9000-12000 (A.D 11000)
£4561 $6933 €6842 Pink landscape and black swan (29x20cm-11x8in) s. board. 19-Aug-2 Joel, Victoria #155/R est:8000-10000 (A.D 13000)
£4651 $7395 €6977 Shoalhaven landscape (22x15cm-9x6in) s. board prov.exhib. 5-May-3 Sotheby's, Melbourne #35/R est:15000 (A.D 12000)
£5039 $8012 €7559 Shoalhaven landscape (22x15cm-9x6in) s. board prov.exhib. 5-May-3 Sotheby's, Melbourne #47/R est:15000 (A.D 13000)
£5039 $8012 €7559 Shoalhaven River (30x23cm-12x9in) s.i. board prov. 5-May-3 Sotheby's, Melbourne #144/R est:12000-14000 (A.D 13000)
£5577 $8867 €8366 Shoalhaven (30x21cm-12x8in) s. board exhib. 4-Mar-3 Deutscher-Menzies, Melbourne #9/R est:14000-18000 (A.D 14500)
£5914 $8989 €8871 Shoalhaven riverbank I (37x29cm-15x11in) s. board. 27-Aug-2 Goodman, Sydney #126/R est:14000-18000 (A.D 16500)
£5961 $9478 €8942 Shoalhaven and black swan (30x21cm-12x8in) s. board exhib. 4-Mar-3 Deutscher-Menzies, Melbourne #8/R est:14000-18000 (A.D 15500)
£6000 $9660 €9000 Shoalhaven River (37x30cm-15x12in) s. board. 6-May-3 Christie's, Melbourne #115/R est:10000-15000 (A.D 15000)
£6375 $10454 €9563 Lovers in a copse (48x63cm-19x25in) composition board prov. 4-Jun-3 Deutscher-Menzies, Melbourne #50/R est:18000-24000 (A.D 16000)
£6773 $11107 €10160 Dromana road (30x33cm-12x13in) s.d.39 canvas on composition board. 4-Jun-3 Deutscher-Menzies, Melbourne #81/R est:12000-15000 (A.D 17000)
£6977 $11093 €10466 Waterfall with figure and birds (37x30cm-15x12in) s. board. 5-May-3 Sotheby's, Melbourne #104/R est:18000-28000 (A.D 18000)
£7143 $11214 €10715 Beach scene (53x70cm-21x28in) s.indis.d.39 canvas on board. 25-Nov-2 Christie's, Melbourne #80/R est:20000-30000 (A.D 20000)
£7143 $11286 €10715 Sheep grazing (55x64cm-22x25in) s. s.i.d.1938 verso board exhib. 27-Nov-2 Deutscher-Menzies, Melbourne #54/R est:25000-30000 (A.D 20000)
£7968 $13068 €11952 Nebuchadnezzar eating a fish (76x61cm-30x24in) s. i.verso prov. 4-Jun-3 Deutscher-Menzies, Melbourne #84/R est:25000-35000 (A.D 20000)
£8400 $13524 €12600 Black swan and sandy river bank (37x29cm-15x11in) s. board. 6-May-3 Christie's, Melbourne #83/R est:10000-15000 (A.D 21000)
£8571 $13371 €12857 Shoalhaven riverbank (105x85cm-41x33in) s. 11-Nov-2 Deutscher-Menzies, Melbourne #21/R est:30000-40000 (A.D 24000)
£8846 $14065 €13269 Wildflower country (61x91cm-24x36in) s. 4-Mar-3 Deutscher-Menzies, Melbourne #81/R est:24000-32000 (A.D 23000)

£9163 $15028 €13745 Wimmera landscape (22x30cm-9x12in) s. composition board painted c.1975 prov. 4-Jun-3 Deutscher-Menzies, Melbourne #8/R est:18000-24000 (A.D 23000)
£10078 $16023 €15117 Lovers (75x47cm-30x19in) s. canvas on board. 5-May-3 Sotheby's, Melbourne #174/R est:35000-50000 (A.D 26000)
£10753 $16344 €16130 Cockatoos and lake at Wimmera (19x25cm-7x10in) s. copper prov. 28-Aug-2 Deutscher-Menzies, Melbourne #15/R est:10000-15000 (A.D 30000)
£10764 $16792 €16146 White Nebuchadnezzar, blind, and white dog on a starry night (20x24cm-8x9in) s. painted c.1972 prov. 8-Apr-3 Peter Webb, Auckland #107/R est:14000-18000 (NZ.D 31000)
£12100 $18512 €18150 Lovers on the beach (50x63cm-20x25in) s. prov. 25-Aug-2 Sotheby's, Paddington #29/R est:30000-40000 (A.D 34000)
£12143 $18943 €18215 Beast and river reflection (152x122cm-60x48in) s. 11-Nov-2 Deutscher-Menzies, Melbourne #76/R est:30000-40000 (A.D 34000)
£12186 $18523 €18279 Australian scapegoat (19x24cm-7x9in) s. copper prov.exhib. 28-Aug-2 Deutscher-Menzies, Melbourne #60/R est:10000-15000 (A.D 34000)
£17204 $26151 €25806 Bush landscape with dam (91x100cm-36x39in) s. painted c.1972 prov. 28-Aug-2 Deutscher-Menzies, Melbourne #59/R est:30000-40000 (A.D 48000)
£21352 $32669 €32028 Shoalhaven (120x90cm-47x35in) s. board. 25-Aug-2 Sotheby's, Paddington #9/R est:60000-80000 (A.D 60000)
£21505 $32688 €32258 Hunting party (109x228cm-43x90in) s. 28-Aug-2 Deutscher-Menzies, Melbourne #128/R est:60000-80000 (A.D 60000)
£23077 $36692 €34616 Bull in summer landscape, Wimmera (91x121cm-36x48in) s. composition board. 4-Mar-3 Deutscher-Menzies, Melbourne #52/R est:50000-70000 (A.D 60000)
£23256 $36977 €34884 Shoalhaven riverbank with burning book (153x122cm-60x48in) s. painted 1989 prov.exhib.lit. 5-May-3 Sotheby's, Melbourne #44/R est:60000-90000 (A.D 60000)
£25090 $38136 €37635 Shoalhaven river with figure and boat (59x44cm-23x17in) s. canvas on board. 28-Aug-2 Deutscher-Menzies, Melbourne #3/R est:50000-60000 (A.D 70000)
£26000 $41860 €39000 Shoalhaven River (121x90cm-48x35in) s.i. board prov. 6-May-3 Christie's, Melbourne #15/R est:65000-85000 (A.D 65000)
£26163 $41599 €39245 Wimmera landscape (60x91cm-24x36in) s. board prov. 5-May-3 Sotheby's, Melbourne #123/R est:35000-55000 (A.D 67500)
£27132 $43140 €40698 Shoalhaven riverbank with figures at cave (153x122cm-60x48in) s. painted 1989 prov.exhib.lit. 5-May-3 Sotheby's, Melbourne #49/R est:70000-90000 (A.D 70000)
£27888 $45737 €41832 Waterfall, Shoalhaven (153x122cm-60x48in) s. prov.exhib. 4-Jun-3 Deutscher-Menzies, Melbourne #48/R est:75000-95000 (A.D 70000)
£28455 $44959 €41260 Shoalhaven with two cockatoos flying through the trees (90x105cm-35x41in) s. painted c.1994 prov. 22-Jul-3 Lawson Menzies, Sydney #31/R est:65000-85000 (A.D 70000)
£28571 $44286 €42857 Jinker on a Sandbank, Shoalhaven (160x183cm-63x72in) painted c.1986. 29-Oct-2 Lawson Menzies, Sydney #42/R est:80000-90000 (A.D 80000)
£28846 $45865 €43269 Moonrise and windmill (91x122cm-36x48in) s. composition board prov. 4-Mar-3 Deutscher-Menzies, Melbourne #78/R est:60000-80000 (A.D 75000)
£28846 $45865 €43269 Shoalhaven river and bride drinking (122x91cm-48x36in) s. prov. 4-Mar-3 Deutscher-Menzies, Melbourne #85/R est:65000-85000 (A.D 75000)
£30000 $47400 €45000 Across the Shoalhaven river (120x90cm-47x35in) s. prov. 17-Nov-2 Sotheby's, Paddington #4/R est:60000-80000 (A.D 84000)
£30876 $50637 €46314 Wimmera landscape with windmill (91x122cm-36x48in) s. enamel composition board. 4-Jun-3 Deutscher-Menzies, Melbourne #45/R est:45000-55000 (A.D 77500)
£34884 $55465 €52326 Harkaway, view from The Grange (63x77cm-25x30in) s. painted 1948 prov.exhib. 5-May-3 Sotheby's, Melbourne #169/R est:50000-70000 (A.D 90000)
£35587 $54448 €53381 Midday, clay bank, Shoalhaven (91x122cm-36x48in) s. painted c.1981 prov. 26-Aug-2 Sotheby's, Paddington #505/R est:80000-120000 (A.D 100000)
£35587 $54448 €53381 Wheatfield, Berwick (54x65cm-21x26in) s. i.verso painted 1948 prov.exhib. 26-Aug-2 Sotheby's, Paddington #517/R est:100000-120000 (A.D 100000)
£35714 $56071 €53571 Wimmera (60x83cm-24x33in) s. board painted c.1959 prov. 25-Nov-2 Christie's, Melbourne #111/R est:100000-150000 (A.D 100000)
£40698 $64709 €61047 Shoalhaven riverbank (153x122cm-60x48in) painted 1989 prov.exhib.lit. 5-May-3 Sotheby's, Melbourne #42/R est:70000-90000 (A.D 105000)
£40925 $62616 €61388 Australian scapegoat series, Venus with digger's hat and black swan (152x366cm-60x144in) s. on three panel prov.exhib. 25-Aug-2 Sotheby's, Paddington #69/R est:120000-160000 (A.D 115000)
£48043 $73505 €72065 Eaglehawk landscape (61x79cm-24x31in) s. i.verso tempera on board painted 1956 prov.exhib. 26-Aug-2 Sotheby's, Paddington #514/R est:150000-250000 (A.D 135000)
£50000 $80500 €75000 Nude standing in a stream with dog and tent (115x138cm-45x54in) s. oil tempera on board painted 1961 prov. 6-May-3 Christie's, Melbourne #51/R est:140000-180000 (A.D 125000)
£50388 $80116 €75582 Shoalhaven riverbank with rose (153x122cm-60x48in) s. painted 1989 prov.exhib.lit. 5-May-3 Sotheby's, Melbourne #15/R est:80000-100000 (A.D 130000)
£52326 $83198 €78489 Lovers with blue bird (160x183cm-63x72in) s. board painted 1962 prov.exhib.lit. 5-May-3 Sotheby's, Melbourne #28/R est:150000-200000 (A.D 135000)
£54264 $86279 €81396 Shoalhaven riverbank with black swan and cockatoo (153x122cm-60x48in) s. painted 1989 prov.exhib.lit. 5-May-3 Sotheby's, Melbourne #32/R est:60000-90000 (A.D 140000)
£60714 $95321 €91071 Seated Nebuchadnezzar and crying lion (172x180cm-68x71in) s. prov.exhib.lit. 25-Nov-2 Christie's, Melbourne #55/R est:12000-150000 (A.D 170000)
£78571 $124143 €117857 Wimmera landscape (91x121cm-36x48in) s. tempera board painted c.1950 prov. 17-Nov-2 Sotheby's, Paddington #11/R est:200000-300000 (A.D 220000)
£131673 $201459 €197510 Bridge in a cave with rainbow (90x121cm-35x48in) s. oil tempera on board prov.exhib. 25-Aug-2 Sotheby's, Paddington #44/R est:400000-600000 (A.D 370000)
£224806 $357442 €337209 Hunter (132x104cm-52x41in) s. oil tempera board painted 1959 prov.exhib.lit. 5-May-3 Sotheby's, Melbourne #20/R est:400000-600000 (A.D 580000)

Prints

£2166 $3357 €3249 Australian scapegoat (62x90cm-24x35in) s. collograph edition 12/20 triptych prov. 3-Dec-2 Shapiro, Sydney #124 est:7000-9000 (A.D 6000)

Sculpture

£4643 $7243 €6965 Dancers (47x32x32cm-19x13x13in) s.num. bronze edition of 9. 11-Nov-2 Deutscher-Menzies, Melbourne #98/R est:14000-18000 (A.D 13000)
£4643 $7243 €6965 Woman on the phone (27x32x27cm-11x13x11in) s. bronze edition 9. 11-Nov-2 Deutscher-Menzies, Melbourne #108/R est:10000-15000 (A.D 13000)
£6071 $9471 €9107 Schoolboy riding a goat (76x34x39cm-30x13x15in) s.num.A.P.2 bronze edition of 9. 11-Nov-2 Deutscher-Menzies, Melbourne #26/R est:18000-24000 (A.D 17000)
£6429 $10029 €9644 Woman protecting her children (80x50x27cm-31x20x11in) s.num. bronze edition of 9. 11-Nov-2 Deutscher-Menzies, Melbourne #75/R est:15000-20000 (A.D 18000)

Works on paper

£500 $820 €750 Embrace (24x34cm-9x13in) s. ink. 3-Jun-3 Sotheby's, Olympia #268/R
£896 $1362 €1344 Distorted figure (31x36cm-12x14in) s. texta. 27-Aug-2 Goodman, Sydney #183/R (A.D 2500)
£928 $1467 €1392 Figures and beast (25x28cm-10x11in) s. pastel executed c.1942. 27-Nov-2 Deutscher-Menzies, Melbourne #173/R est:3000-5000 (A.D 2600)
£1000 $1580 €1500 John Perceval with his dog (35x43cm-14x17in) s. pencil. 27-Nov-2 Deutscher-Menzies, Melbourne #174/R est:3200-4000 (A.D 2800)
£1250 $1962 €1875 Nudes with prostrate beast and rams (50x63cm-20x25in) s. ink. 25-Nov-2 Christie's, Melbourne #358 est:4000-6000 (A.D 3500)
£1400 $2254 €2100 Allegorical studies (19x20cm-7x8in) s. Indian ink four framed as one. 14-Jan-3 Bonhams, Knightsbridge #121/R est:1000-1500
£1400 $2254 €2100 Figure and fire (49x63cm-19x25in) s.d.1969 W/C. 6-May-3 Christie's, Melbourne #221 est:3000-4000 (A.D 3500)
£1434 $2352 €2151 Tosca (63x51cm-25x20in) s.i. pen ink prov. 4-Jun-3 Deutscher-Menzies, Melbourne #340/R est:2500-3500 (A.D 3600)
£1520 $2447 €2280 Fallen figure (50x62cm-20x24in) s.d.1967 W/C. 6-May-3 Christie's, Melbourne #344/R est:3000-4000 (A.D 3800)
£1607 $2491 €2411 Elektra (62x49cm-24x19in) s. mixed media. 29-Oct-2 Lawson Menzies, Sydney #142/R est:5000-7000 (A.D 4500)
£1680 $2705 €2520 Figure with flowers (50x62cm-20x24in) s.d.1967 W/C. 6-May-3 Christie's, Melbourne #359/R est:3000-4000 (A.D 4200)
£1920 $3091 €2880 Ram with figure (49x62cm-19x24in) s.d.1967 W/C. 6-May-3 Christie's, Melbourne #263 est:3000-4000 (A.D 4800)

£3448 $5138 €5172 St. Francis with the wolf I (48x62cm-19x24in) s. pastel prov. 27-Aug-2 Christie's, Melbourne #95/R est:10000-14000 (A.D 9000)
£5000 $7950 €7500 Pulpit rock with figure, fire and cockatoo (73x54cm-29x21in) s. pastel over col lithograph. 4-Mar-3 Deutscher-Menzies, Melbourne #154/R est:7000-10000 (A.D 13000)
£6400 $10304 €9600 Yellow Nebuchadnezzar and white lion (47x63cm-19x25in) s. i.verso pastel executed c.1966 prov. 6-May-3 Christie's, Melbourne #106/R est:15000-20000 (A.D 16000)
£9964 $15246 €14946 Harvest (46x61cm-18x24in) s. twelve painted glazed titles prov. 26-Aug-2 Sotheby's, Paddington #561/R est:20000-25000 (A.D 28000)

BOYD, David (1924-) Australian

£563 $879 €845 Fruit child (20x19cm-8x7in) s. board. 21-Oct-2 Australian Art Auctions, Sydney #89 (A.D 1600)
£611 $965 €917 Angel (15x14cm-6x6in) s. board. 1-Apr-3 Lawson Menzies, Sydney #431 (A.D 1600)
£702 $1067 €1053 Morning sun (24x19cm-9x7in) s.d.2001 board. 19-Aug-2 Joel, Victoria #215 est:2000-3000 (A.D 2000)
£704 $1099 €1056 Dance (32x29cm-13x11in) s. board. 21-Oct-2 Australian Art Auctions, Sydney #84 (A.D 2000)
£753 $1144 €1130 Girl in garden (21x14cm-8x6in) s. board. 27-Aug-2 Goodman, Sydney #7 (A.D 2100)
£840 $1327 €1260 Collecting fruit (20x19cm-8x7in) s. board. 7-Apr-3 Australian Art Auctions, Sydney #97 (A.D 2200)
£954 $1507 €1653 Beautiful story (19x19cm-7x7in) s. board. 1-Apr-3 Goodman, Sydney #25 (A.D 2500)
£1053 $1600 €1580 Trumpet player (44x39cm-17x15in) s.d.1977 board. 19-Aug-2 Joel, Victoria #243 est:3000-4000 (A.D 3000)
£1143 $1771 €1715 Under the wattle tree (29x37cm-11x15in) s. board. 29-Oct-2 Lawson Menzies, Sydney #103/R est:2000-3500 (A.D 3200)
£1145 $1809 €1983 Children (24x29cm-9x11in) s. 1-Apr-3 Goodman, Sydney #28 est:3000-4000 (A.D 3000)
£1147 $1743 €1721 Children playing (34x40cm-13x16in) s. 27-Aug-2 Goodman, Sydney #20 est:2500-3500 (A.D 3200)
£1147 $1743 €1721 Children and sunshine (30x37cm-12x15in) s. board. 27-Aug-2 Goodman, Sydney #56 est:3500-5000 (A.D 3200)
£1278 $2032 €1917 Children at a lake (22x27cm-9x11in) s. board. 3-Mar-3 Lawson Menzies, Sydney #304 est:2500-3500 (A.D 3400)
£1281 $1960 €1922 Child wading (34x40cm-13x16in) s. prov. 25-Aug-2 Sotheby's, Paddington #240 est:1500-2500 (A.D 3600)
£1298 $2050 €1947 Springs bounty (31x39cm-12x15in) s. board. 7-Apr-3 Australian Art Auctions, Sydney #80c (A.D 3400)
£1316 $2092 €1974 Three children by a lake (22x27cm-9x11in) s. board. 3-Mar-3 Lawson Menzies, Sydney #301 est:2500-3500 (A.D 3500)
£1357 $2144 €2036 Chasing cockatoos (29x36cm-11x14in) s. board. 18-Nov-2 Goodman, Sydney #5 est:4000-6000 (A.D 3800)
£1429 $2243 €2144 Europa hurling her wings over a waterfall (30x25cm-12x10in) s.d.1995 board prov. 25-Nov-2 Christie's, Melbourne #381/R est:3500-5000 (A.D 4000)
£1500 $2370 €2250 Nude (29x24cm-11x9in) s. panel. 26-Nov-2 Sotheby's, Melbourne #65/R est:3000-5000 (A.D 4200)
£1595 $2425 €2393 Chasing cockatoos (29x37cm-11x15in) s. board. 27-Aug-2 Goodman, Sydney #1/R est:4500-6500 (A.D 4450)
£1613 $2452 €2420 Children and cockatoos playing in springtime (37x29cm-15x11in) s. board. 27-Aug-2 Goodman, Sydney #99 est:4500-6500 (A.D 4500)
£1637 $2505 €2456 Nudes in the garden (29x40cm-11x16in) s. board prov. 25-Aug-2 Sotheby's, Paddington #147/R est:3500-5500 (A.D 4600)
£1673 $2744 €2510 Red towel (29x37cm-11x15in) s. composition board. 4-Jun-3 Deutscher-Menzies, Melbourne #298/R est:2500-3500 (A.D 4200)
£1720 $2615 €2580 Children in a pond (45x61cm-18x24in) s. composition board. 28-Aug-2 Deutscher-Menzies, Melbourne #308/R est:4000-6000 (A.D 4800)
£1792 $2724 €2688 Picking flowers (30x37cm-12x15in) s. board. 27-Aug-2 Goodman, Sydney #25 est:4500-6500 (A.D 5000)
£1813 $2865 €2720 Music of life (45x38cm-18x15in) s. board. 7-Apr-3 Australian Art Auctions, Sydney #131 (A.D 4750)
£1829 $2891 €2652 Clown and the river swimmer (26x34cm-10x13in) s.d.1992. 22-Jul-3 Lawson Menzies, Sydney #96/R est:4500-5500 (A.D 4500)
£1957 $2995 €2936 At the beach (34x39cm-13x15in) s. board. 25-Aug-2 Sotheby's, Paddington #182/R est:4000-6000 (A.D 5500)
£2000 $3220 €2900 Children playing with blossom (31x26cm-12x10in) s. board. 12-May-3 Joel, Victoria #238/R est:5000-8000 (A.D 5000)
£2091 $3430 €3137 Early morning dip in a mountain stream (34x45cm-13x18in) s. prov. 4-Jun-3 Deutscher-Menzies, Melbourne #295/R est:3000-5000 (A.D 5250)
£2151 $3269 €3227 Children under blossom (50x55cm-20x22in) s. 28-Aug-2 Deutscher-Menzies, Melbourne #307/R est:4000-6000 (A.D 6000)
£2151 $3269 €3227 Goddess of fruit (44x45cm-17x18in) s.d.1972. 27-Aug-2 Goodman, Sydney #45/R est:3000-4000 (A.D 6000)
£2191 $3593 €3287 Walk in the bush (24x32cm-9x13in) s.d.1969 composition board prov. 4-Jun-3 Deutscher-Menzies, Melbourne #297/R est:3000-4500 (A.D 5500)
£2326 $3698 €3489 Children at the seaside (29x39cm-11x15in) s. board. 5-May-3 Sotheby's, Melbourne #312/R est:1000-2000 (A.D 6000)
£2330 $3541 €3495 Cooling off (55x66cm-22x26in) s. 28-Aug-2 Deutscher-Menzies, Melbourne #309/R est:4000-6000 (A.D 6500)
£2390 $3920 €3585 Good morning Mr Boyd, with apologies to Courbet (32x24cm-13x9in) s.d.69 composition board prov. 4-Jun-3 Deutscher-Menzies, Melbourne #296/R est:3000-4000 (A.D 6000)
£2411 $3809 €3617 Sunflowers on the edge of the bush (50x76cm-20x30in) s. i.verso board. 27-Nov-2 Deutscher-Menzies, Melbourne #187/R est:5000-7000 (A.D 6750)
£2679 $4152 €4019 Out of reach (59x74cm-23x29in) s. board. 29-Oct-2 Lawson Menzies, Sydney #26/R est:5000-8000 (A.D 7500)
£2679 $4232 €4019 Children and butterflies (46x55cm-18x22in) s.d.1973. 27-Nov-2 Deutscher-Menzies, Melbourne #176/R est:7000-9000 (A.D 7500)
£2679 $4232 €4019 Girl with apples (50x65cm-20x26in) s.d.1971. 27-Nov-2 Deutscher-Menzies, Melbourne #177/R est:7000-9000 (A.D 7500)
£2682 $4211 €4023 Nude in landscape (44x49cm-17x19in) s. 15-Apr-3 Lawson Menzies, Sydney #254/R est:3300-4500 (A.D 7000)
£2688 $4086 €4032 Reading under the wattle (61x71cm-24x28in) s.d.1981. 28-Aug-2 Deutscher-Menzies, Melbourne #254/R est:6000-8000 (A.D 7500)
£2759 $4110 €4139 In the trees (28x39cm-11x15in) s.d.1972 canvas on board. 27-Aug-2 Christie's, Melbourne #244/R est:4000-6000 (A.D 7200)
£2857 $4429 €4286 Where the river begins (60x75cm-24x30in) s. canvasboard. 29-Oct-2 Lawson Menzies, Sydney #69/R est:4000-6000 (A.D 8000)
£2874 $4511 €4311 Ben Boyd with crucifix (54x64cm-21x25in) s.d.1972 board. 15-Apr-3 Lawson Menzies, Sydney #15/R est:6000-9000 (A.D 7500)
£2884 $4586 €4326 Children (45x50cm-18x20in) s. 4-Mar-3 Deutscher-Menzies, Melbourne #206/R est:5500-7500 (A.D 7500)
£2946 $4655 €4419 Is it gold (100x960cm-39x378in) s. prov. 26-Nov-2 Sotheby's, Melbourne #128 est:6000-8000 (A.D 8250)
£3000 $4830 €4350 Picking apples in the sunshine (44x58cm-17x23in) s. 12-May-3 Joel, Victoria #280 est:6000-8000 (A.D 7500)
£3025 $4628 €4538 Child with sunflower (64x53cm-25x21in) s.d.1974 prov. 25-Aug-2 Sotheby's, Paddington #113/R est:5000-8000 (A.D 8500)
£3065 $4567 €4598 Angel of the orchard (48x63cm-19x25in) s.d.1972. 27-Aug-2 Christie's, Melbourne #155 est:4000-6000 (A.D 8000)
£3065 $4567 €4598 Lot's daughters (118x179cm-46x70in) i. board. 27-Aug-2 Christie's, Melbourne #229/R est:8000-15000 (A.D 8000)
£3101 $4930 €4652 Children playing by the lake (39x44cm-15x17in) s. 5-May-3 Sotheby's, Melbourne #296/R est:5000-8000 (A.D 8000)
£3101 $4930 €4652 Children playing by sea (43x43cm-17x17in) s. 5-May-3 Sotheby's, Melbourne #324 est:4000-6000 (A.D 8000)
£3200 $5152 €4640 Children with sunflowers (54x64cm-21x25in) s. board. 12-May-3 Joel, Victoria #233/R est:8000-10000 (A.D 8000)
£3203 $4900 €4805 Chasing fire-flies in the moonlight, South of France (53x64cm-21x25in) s.d.1973 i.verso. 25-Aug-2 Sotheby's, Paddington #143/R est:8000-12000 (A.D 9000)
£3269 $5198 €4904 Children (50x61cm-20x24in) s. prov. 4-Mar-3 Deutscher-Menzies, Melbourne #203/R est:4000-6000 (A.D 8500)
£3295 $5238 €4943 Children playing under blossom tree (44x59cm-17x23in) s. 5-May-3 Sotheby's, Melbourne #218 est:4000-6000 (A.D 8500)
£3400 $5474 €5100 Orchard at sunset (43x48cm-17x19in) s. board. 6-May-3 Christie's, Melbourne #346 est:5000-6000 (A.D 8500)
£3750 $5962 €5625 Children (50x76cm-20x30in) s. composition board. 4-Mar-3 Deutscher-Menzies, Melbourne #207/R est:5500-7500 (A.D 9750)
£3929 $6207 €5894 Watched by beauty and beast, his honour perceives that wig has no reflection (90x100cm-35x39in) s. board. 18-Nov-2 Goodman, Sydney #146 est:6000-9000 (A.D 11000)
£4215 $6617 €6323 Children in the orchard (49x58cm-19x23in) s. 15-Apr-3 Lawson Menzies, Sydney #169/R est:6000-8000 (A.D 11000)
£4264 $6779 €6396 Children in the orchard (50x60cm-20x24in) s.d.1972 canvasboard. 5-May-3 Sotheby's, Melbourne #335/R est:5000-7000 (A.D 11000)
£4286 $6771 €6429 Day in the country (95x105cm-37x41in) s.d.1980 board. 18-Nov-2 Joel, Victoria #156/R est:14000-16000 (A.D 12000)
£4406 $6918 €6609 Children by the creek with swooping cockatoo (48x68cm-19x27in) s. 15-Apr-3 Lawson Menzies, Sydney #168/R est:6500-9000 (A.D 11500)
£4472 $7065 €6484 Picnic in the hills (50x75cm-20x30in) s. board. 22-Jul-3 Lawson Menzies, Sydney #97/R est:10000-12000 (A.D 11000)
£4845 $7703 €7268 Children by a waterfall (90x75cm-35x30in) s. 5-May-3 Sotheby's, Melbourne #301/R est:6000-8000 (A.D 12500)
£5081 $8029 €7367 Europa and the fairies (52x63cm-20x25in) s.d.1973. 22-Jul-3 Lawson Menzies, Sydney #4/R est:8000-10000 (A.D 12500)
£5364 $8421 €8046 Children in the garden (64x80cm-25x31in) s.d.1973. 15-Apr-3 Lawson Menzies, Sydney #16/R est:5500-7000 (A.D 14000)
£5894 $9313 €8546 Peach blossom tree (75x90cm-30x35in) s. 22-Jul-3 Lawson Menzies, Sydney #118/R est:10000-12000 (A.D 14500)
£5911 $9398 €8867 Four children playing (90x90cm-35x35in) s. 5-May-3 Sotheby's, Melbourne #358/R est:6000-8000 (A.D 15250)
£6322 $9925 €9483 Children by a waterfall (90x74cm-35x29in) s. 15-Apr-3 Lawson Menzies, Sydney #171/R est:8500-10000 (A.D 16500)
£6584 $10073 €9876 Painter on the beach (88x100cm-35x39in) s. board painted 1969 prov. 26-Aug-2 Sotheby's, Paddington #694/R est:12000-18000 (A.D 18500)

£9350 $14772 €13558 Nude (120x90cm-47x35in) s.i.d.1968 stumato oil on board prov. 22-Jul-3 Lawson Menzies, Sydney #27/R est:20000-25000 (A.D 23000)

Works on paper

£357 $550 €536 Young angel musician, be mine (20x17cm-8x7in) s. mixed media. 7-Sep-2 Goodman, Sydney #145 (A.D 1000)
£571 $903 €857 Unusual kind of horn (15x14cm-6x6in) s.d.97 mixed media. 18-Nov-2 Joel, Victoria #198 est:2000-2500 (A.D 1600)
£992 $1567 €1719 Mastering the cello (25x38cm-10x15in) s.d.99 W/C texta mixed media. 1-Apr-3 Goodman, Sydney #68 est:2500-3500 (A.D 2600)

BOYD, Diamuid (20th C) Irish

£549 $912 €780 Dun Laoghaire Harbour (38x46cm-15x18in) s. 10-Jun-3 James Adam, Dublin #240/R

BOYD, Emma Minnie (1856-1936) Australian

Works on paper

£1423 $2248 €2063 Bathing box, morning peninsula (10x13cm-4x5in) s. W/C. 22-Jul-3 Lawson Menzies, Sydney #166/R est:400-500 (A.D 3500)

BOYD, Guy (1923-1988) Australian

Sculpture

£1609 $2398 €2414 Plaque (34cm-13in) s.num.5/9 bronze. 27-Aug-2 Christie's, Melbourne #158/R est:3500-4500 (A.D 4200)
£2299 $3425 €3449 Standing woman (43cm-17in) s.num.10/12 bronze. 27-Aug-2 Christie's, Melbourne #211/R est:4500-5500 (A.D 6000)
£2678 $4232 €4017 Dancing girl (97cm-38in) s.num.10/12 bronze. 18-Nov-2 Joel, Victoria #390 est:8000-10000 (A.D 7500)
£4332 $6715 €6498 Dancing woman (93cm-37in) s.st.f.V F Vitorio Fernando green pat bronze prov. 3-Dec-2 Shapiro, Sydney #73/R est:10000-15000 (A.D 12000)
£6071 $9471 €9107 Dancer (85x95x25cm-33x37x10in) s.d.1987 num.6/12 bronze. 11-Nov-2 Deutscher-Menzies, Melbourne #67/R est:12000-15000 (A.D 17000)
£6429 $10029 €9644 Girl looking over shoulder (125x46x30cm-49x18x12in) s.d.1987 num.5/12 bronze. 11-Nov-2 Deutscher-Menzies, Melbourne #74/R est:14000-18000 (A.D 18000)

BOYD, Jamie (1948-) Australian

£692 $1101 €1038 Hillside (66x30cm-26x12in) s. composition board. 4-Mar-3 Deutscher-Menzies, Melbourne #205/R (A.D 1800)
£704 $1099 €1056 Docklands (65x76cm-26x30in) s. 21-Oct-2 Australian Art Auctions, Sydney #168 (A.D 2000)
£717 $1176 €1040 Shoalhaven (51x39cm-20x15in) s. board. 3-Jun-3 Lawson Menzies, Sydney #819 (A.D 1800)
£956 $1568 €1434 Wimmera landscape (58x90cm-23x35in) s. composition board. 4-Jun-3 Deutscher-Menzies, Melbourne #334/R (A.D 2400)
£1298 $1973 €1947 Shoalhaven Theatre (263x178cm-104x70in) s. 19-Aug-2 Joel, Victoria #267 est:2000-2500 (A.D 3700)

BOYD, John (1957-) British

£3500 $5740 €5250 Gramarye of the sign (75x109cm-30x43in) s. board prov.exhib. 6-Jun-3 Christie's, London #208/R est:4000-6000

BOYD, John G (1940-) British

£300 $498 €435 Summer's day (60x75cm-24x30in) s. 13-Jun-3 Lyon & Turnbull, Edinburgh #2
£1800 $2808 €2700 Jacob herding cattle (101x150cm-40x59in) s. 27-Mar-3 Christie's, Kensington #562/R est:1500-2000

BOYD, Theodore Penleigh (1890-1923) Australian

£842 $1280 €1263 Farm (16x24cm-6x9in) s.d.1913 board. 19-Aug-2 Joel, Victoria #160 est:2000-3000 (A.D 2400)
£2151 $3269 €3227 Near Healesville (46x56cm-18x22in) s. 28-Aug-2 Deutscher-Menzies, Melbourne #124/R est:7000-9000 (A.D 6000)
£3559 $5445 €5339 Across the plains (51x76cm-20x30in) painted c.1910 prov. 26-Aug-2 Sotheby's, Paddington #551/R est:15000-20000 (A.D 10000)
£6130 $9625 €9195 Grose Valley from Govett's Leap (68x78cm-27x31in) painted c.1922 prov. 15-Apr-3 Lawson Menzies, Sydney #47/R est:10000-15000 (A.D 16000)
£12403 $19721 €18605 Harbour headland (42x51cm-17x20in) s.d.22 board prov. 5-May-3 Sotheby's, Melbourne #171/R est:15000-20000 (A.D 32000)
£12920 $20414 €19380 Sydney Harbour (23x64cm-9x25in) i.d.22 i.verso canvas on board prov. 2-Apr-3 Christie's, Melbourne #49/R est:20000-30000 (A.D 33850)

Works on paper

£1100 $1771 €1595 Mornington, Victoria (25x35cm-10x14in) s. W/C. 12-May-3 Joel, Victoria #226/R est:2000-3000 (A.D 2750)

BOYD, William Merric (1888-1959) Australian

Works on paper

£269 $408 €404 White gum (25x24cm-10x9in) s.i. pencil col pencil. 28-Aug-2 Deutscher-Menzies, Melbourne #383/R (A.D 750)

BOYDELL, Creswick (fl.1889-1916) British

Works on paper

£340 $541 €510 First tinge of autumn on the Avon (14x19cm-6x7in) s. W/C. 30-Apr-3 Hampton & Littlewood, Exeter #447/R

BOYE, Maurice (1936-) Swiss

£570 $900 €900 River landscape in summer with figures (77x61cm-30x24in) s. 29-Nov-2 Sigalas, Stuttgart #1074/R

BOYER, Trevor (1948-) British

Works on paper

£350 $553 €525 Ptarmigan in snow (21x26cm-8x10in) s. W/C bodycol. 28-Nov-2 Christie's, Kensington #37/R

BOYHAN, William Matthew (1916-1996) American

£343 $500 €515 At rest (56x69cm-22x27in) s. 10-May-2 Skinner, Boston #128/R

BOYLE, Alicia (1908-1997) Irish

£300 $465 €450 Workman (46x36cm-18x14in) mono. canvasboard. 2-Oct-2 John Ross, Belfast #242
£1000 $1570 €1500 Pilgrims at Templecrone (76x50cm-30x20in) s.d.49 prov. 15-Apr-3 Bonhams, Knightsbridge #10/R est:400-600

Works on paper

£400 $640 €600 Island shore, August (37x48cm-15x19in) s.d.50 pencil W/C. 15-May-3 Christie's, Kensington #224/R

BOYLE, Charles Wellington (1860-1925) American

£2057 $3250 €3086 Acadian Homes Weeks Island, Louisiana (36x23cm-14x9in) s. s.i.d.1906 verso prov. 5-Apr-3 Neal Auction Company, New Orleans #260/R est:5000-7500
£4272 $6750 €6408 Rice girls (51x76cm-20x30in) s.d.1893 prov. 5-Apr-3 Neal Auction Company, New Orleans #346/R est:7500-10000

BOYLE, George A (fl.1884-1899) British

£250 $403 €375 Marine scene (41x66cm-16x26in) s. 14-Jan-3 Bonhams, Ipswich #375
£260 $432 €390 River landscape (22x27cm-9x11in) s. panel. 10-Jun-3 Bonhams, Knightsbridge #262/R
£330 $521 €495 Fishing vessels off a jetty (23x33cm-9x13in) init. board. 18-Dec-2 Mallams, Oxford #651
£338 $527 €507 Evening landscape with trees and watercourse (51x77cm-20x30in) s. 23-Sep-2 Rasmussen, Vejle #277/R (D.KR 4000)
£340 $517 €510 Impressionist landscape with cattle grazing beneath trees (23x33cm-9x13in) init. 16-Aug-2 Keys, Aylsham #766
£420 $647 €630 Cattle and trees beside a pond (25x33cm-10x13in) s. board. 3-Sep-2 Gorringes, Lewes #2125
£600 $960 €900 Fisherman in a harbour (25x35cm-10x14in) s. board. 7-Jan-3 Bonhams, Knightsbridge #236/R

BOYLE, John J (1852-1917) American

£1478 $2291 €2350 Ramasseurs de Varech (36x43cm-14x17in) s. 6-Oct-2 Livinec, Gaudcheau & Jezequel, Rennes #46/R

BOYLEY, Errol (1918-) South African

£192 $300 €288 Seascape (34x44cm-13x17in) s. canvas on board. 11-Nov-2 Stephan Welz, Johannesburg #206 (SA.R 3000)
£222 $363 €333 Portrait of a lady holding a bouquet of roses, Mrs Doris Troskie (90x70cm-35x28in) s. canvas on board. 4-Feb-3 Dales, Durban #8 (SA.R 3000)
£369 $575 €554 Seascape (40x50cm-16x20in) s. board. 15-Oct-2 Stephan Welz, Johannesburg #197 est:2000-3000 (SA.R 6000)
£399 $623 €599 Boats in harbour (66x75cm-26x30in) s. board. 15-Oct-2 Stephan Welz, Johannesburg #490 est:3000-5000 (SA.R 6500)
£443 $727 €665 Seascape (74x90cm-29x35in) s. board. 4-Feb-3 Dales, Durban #7 (SA.R 6000)
£723 $1143 €1085 After the storm (60x90cm-24x35in) s. board. 1-Apr-3 Stephan Welz, Johannesburg #213 est:2500-4000 (SA.R 9000)
£903 $1454 €1355 Shipyard, Hout Bay (54x75cm-21x30in) s. canavs on board. 12-May-3 Stephan Welz, Johannesburg #82 est:4000-6000 (SA.R 10500)
£1247 $2007 €1871 Extensive landscape with cattle grazing (49x75cm-19x30in) s. board. 12-May-3 Stephan Welz, Johannesburg #138 est:3000-5000 (SA.R 14500)

BOYS, George (1930-) South African

£361 $581 €542 Cosmos in the rain (119x96cm-47x38in) s. board. 12-May-3 Stephan Welz, Johannesburg #173 est:1800-2400 (SA.R 4200)
£430 $692 €645 Cosnos in the rain (98x99cm-39x39in) s. board. 12-May-3 Stephan Welz, Johannesburg #364 est:2000-3000 (SA.R 5000)
£430 $692 €645 Abstract (96x119cm-38x47in) acrylic on board. 12-May-3 Stephan Welz, Johannesburg #410 est:2000-3000 (SA.R 5000)

Works on paper

£352 $550 €528 Fighting cock (47x68cm-19x27in) s.d.96 mixed media. 11-Nov-2 Stephan Welz, Johannesburg #164 (SA.R 5500)

BOYS, T S (1803-1874) British

Works on paper

£1700 $2635 €2550 Rouen (42x30cm-17x12in) i. 4-Dec-2 Outhwaite & Litherland, Liverpool #286/R

BOYS, Thomas Shotter (1803-1874) British

Works on paper

£1400 $2240 €2100 Pont du Change, Lyons (18x21cm-7x8in) i.verso W/C two. 11-Mar-3 Bonhams, New Bond Street #11 est:1000-1500
£4000 $6560 €6000 Rozell Bay, Jersey (33x74cm-13x29in) s.i.d.1855 exhib. pencil W/C. 4-Feb-3 Bonhams, Leeds #314 est:6000-8000
£5000 $7150 €7500 Windmill with cattle and drover beneath (6x11cm-2x4in) s.d.1831 pencil W/C bodycol scratching out prov.lit. 22-Jan-3 Christie's, London #52/R est:6000
£6000 $9480 €9000 L'islet in Bouley Bay looking towards the Tour de Rozel, Jersey (16x28cm-6x11in) s.i. W/C over pencil htd bodycol prov.exhib.lit. 28-Nov-2 Sotheby's, London #259/R est:7000-10000
£8500 $12155 €12750 West Porch, Ratisbon cathedral (25x18cm-10x7in) pencil W/C prov.exhib.lit. 22-Jan-3 Christie's, London #54/R est:8000
£9000 $12870 €13500 Figures walking on path through cornfield (6x15cm-2x6in) s.d.1834 pencil W/C scratching out prov.exhib.lit. 22-Jan-3 Christie's, London #53/R est:8000
£26000 $37180 €39000 Breakwaters on Normandy beach (11x19cm-4x7in) pencil W/C gum bodycol scratching out prov.exhib.lit. 22-Jan-3 Christie's, London #51/R est:10000
£65000 $107900 €97500 Near the Tuilleries Garden, Paris (35x24cm-14x9in) s. W/C over pencil, htd bodycol scratching out prov.exhib.lit. 12-Jun-3 Sotheby's, London #25/R est:40000-60000

BOZATLI, Sinasi (1962-) Turkish

£2500 $3950 €3600 Chains (80x100cm-31x39in) s.d.97 acrylic. 24-Apr-3 Dorotheum, Vienna #277/R est:4000-4400

BOZE, Honore (1830-1908) British

£1013 $1479 €1520 Oasis with arabs and horses (56x42cm-22x17in) s. 17-Jun-2 Philippe Schuler, Zurich #4328 (S.FR 2300)

BOZE, Joseph (1744-1826) French

Works on paper

£3597 $5899 €5000 Portrait de gentilhomme a vue ovale (72x58cm-28x23in) s.d.1773 pastel. 5-Jun-3 Fraysse & Associes, Paris #10 est:3500-4500

BOZNANSKA, Olga (1865-1945) Polish

£19000 $31160 €28500 Portrait of Rosa and vase of roses (51x43cm-20x17in) s.i. cardboard prov.exhib. 3-Jun-3 Sotheby's, London #111/R est:3000-5000

BOZZATO, Attilio (19th C) Italian

£1633 $2596 €2400 View of Venice (91x71cm-36x28in) s. 18-Mar-3 Finarte, Milan #150/R

BOZZOLINI, Silvano (1911-) Italian

£310 $518 €450 Harmonies en gris no 3 (70x70cm-28x28in) s.i.d.verso. 9-Jul-3 Cornette de St.Cyr, Paris #236
£513 $810 €800 Squares (80x80cm-31x31in) s. s.i.d.1984 verso. 18-Nov-2 Rieunier, Paris #132
£1724 $2879 €2500 Composition (38x55cm-15x22in) s.d.58. 10-Jul-3 Artcurial Briest, Paris #301 est:700-800
£1899 $3000 €3000 Composition (55x46cm-22x18in) s.d.1956. 27-Nov-2 Blanchet, Paris #142/R
£2564 $4051 €4000 Contrastes dans l'espace (116x146cm-46x57in) s.d.1951 i.d. verso. 14-Nov-2 Neumeister, Munich #748/R est:4000-5000

Works on paper

£276 $461 €400 Composition (24x24cm-9x9in) s.d.22/01/87 collage. 9-Jul-3 Cornette de St.Cyr, Paris #235

BRAAKENSIEK, Johann Henri (1891-1941) Dutch

£780 $1264 €1100 Sunflowers (123x70cm-48x28in) init.d.1918 verso. 26-May-3 Glerum, Amsterdam #149

BRAAQ (1951-1997) British

£300 $474 €450 Girl with mandolin (61x51cm-24x20in) s. 28-Nov-2 Morphets, Harrogate #559/R
£340 $544 €510 Portrait of a mother and daughter (18x13cm-7x5in) s. board oval. 13-Mar-3 Morphets, Harrogate #592
£600 $960 €900 Portrait of a ballet dancer (20x15cm-8x6in) s.d.78 board. 13-Mar-3 Morphets, Harrogate #593/R
£800 $1256 €1200 Red sky (44x69cm-17x27in) s.d.75 panel. 19-Nov-2 Bonhams, Leeds #148/R
£1000 $1580 €1500 Winter industrial landscape, with a figure walking his dog (25x40cm-10x16in) s. 28-Nov-2 Morphets, Harrogate #556/R est:1000-1500
£1200 $1920 €1800 Portrait of a young boy and a walking man (14x10cm-6x4in) s. board. 13-Mar-3 Morphets, Harrogate #598/R est:400-500
£1200 $1968 €1740 Winter estuary Landscape with figures (29x39cm-11x15in) s. board. 5-Jun-3 Morphets, Harrogate #372/R est:800-1000
£1200 $1968 €1740 Cricket match with spectators and dogs on the field (30x39cm-12x15in) s. board. 5-Jun-3 Morphets, Harrogate #374/R est:1400-1700
£1400 $2296 €2030 Industrial city landscape with open land and figures (9x41cm-4x16in) s. board. 5-Jun-3 Morphets, Harrogate #373/R est:1400-1700
£1450 $2291 €2175 Parkland with lake and town beyond (29x38cm-11x15in) s. board. 28-Nov-2 Morphets, Harrogate #557/R est:800-1200
£1600 $2560 €2400 Winter street scene with figures and row of terrace houses (21x27cm-8x11in) s.d.78 board. 13-Mar-3 Morphets, Harrogate #597/R est:900-1100
£1700 $2720 €2550 Winter estuary landscape with figures (30x45cm-12x18in) s. board. 13-Mar-3 Morphets, Harrogate #594/R est:900-1100
£1800 $2952 €2610 Street scene with figures gathered outside John Taylor bric-a-brac shop (9x24cm-4x9in) s. board. 5-Jun-3 Morphets, Harrogate #375/R est:400-600
£2100 $3234 €3150 What have you done with a dog Albert (40x51cm-16x20in) s. board. 5-Sep-2 Morphets, Harrogate #359/R est:1750-2250
£3200 $5120 €4800 Tennis match men's doubles (42x61cm-17x24in) s. board. 13-Mar-3 Morphets, Harrogate #595/R est:2750-3250
£3200 $5120 €4800 Day at the seaside, Punch and Judy show (46x61cm-18x24in) s. board. 13-Mar-3 Morphets, Harrogate #596/R est:2000-2500
£5000 $7900 €7500 BKid, street scene with boy chalking graffiti (61x51cm-24x20in) s.d.75. 28-Nov-2 Morphets, Harrogate #558/R est:2500-3000

Works on paper

£750 $1200 €1125 Portrait of a young girl with a hoop (21x14cm-8x6in) s. pastel. 13-Mar-3 Morphets, Harrogate #600/R
£850 $1394 €1233 Going to work, figures walking towards the town with industrial skyline (19x30cm-7x12in) s. pastel. 5-Jun-3 Morphets, Harrogate #376/R
£900 $1440 €1350 Solitary figure walking quickly past a church steeple (24x16cm-9x6in) s. pastel. 13-Mar-3 Morphets, Harrogate #602/R
£1150 $1817 €1725 On the beach, figures walking on the beach (20x28cm-8x11in) s. pastel. 28-Nov-2 Morphets, Harrogate #582 est:450-500
£1150 $1840 €1725 Ancoates cotton mill, Manchester workers gathering at the mill gates (20x30cm-8x12in) s. pastel. 13-Mar-3 Morphets, Harrogate #601/R est:600-800

BRABAZON, Hercules Brabazon (1821-1906) British

£300 $468 €450 View of St Jean (15x20cm-6x8in) init. col chk. 19-Sep-2 John Bellman, Billingshurst #1432

Works on paper

£260 $411 €390 Study of an arch (13x18cm-5x7in) init. chl W/C. 26-Nov-2 Bonhams, Knightsbridge #124
£300 $486 €450 Sketch of Venice (10x17cm-4x7in) init. pencil crayon. 21-Jan-3 Bonhams, Knightsbridge #280/R
£340 $541 €510 Seville (20x25cm-8x10in) init. pencil wash. 29-Apr-3 Gorringes, Lewes #2028
£350 $546 €525 Nice (13x21cm-5x8in) init.i. pencil W/C. 15-Oct-2 Bearnes, Exeter #353/R
£360 $569 €522 View of a castle by a lake (17x22cm-7x9in) wash. 22-Jul-3 Bonhams, Knightsbridge #201/R
£440 $686 €660 Lake Como (17x27cm-7x11in) init. W/C prov. 17-Oct-2 Lawrence, Crewkerne #429/R
£480 $758 €720 Samaden (26x16cm-10x6in) init. pencil W/C. 2-Dec-2 Bonhams, Bath #22/R
£500 $775 €750 Middle Eastern street scene (25x33cm-10x13in) mono. W/C bodycol. 31-Oct-2 Duke & Son, Dorchester #114/R
£500 $825 €725 Tuscan Castle (11x14cm-4x6in) init. i.verso W/C. 2-Jul-3 Sotheby's, Olympia #261/R
£500 $825 €725 Gorge on the road to Bokhara, Turkestan (19x14cm-7x6in) init. i.verso W/C. 2-Jul-3 Sotheby's, Olympia #268/R
£520 $827 €780 Eastern bazaar (14x18cm-6x7in) init. W/C. 25-Feb-3 Bonhams, Knightsbridge #20/R
£600 $990 €870 Seascape (13x19cm-5x7in) init. i.verso W/C. 2-Jul-3 Sotheby's, Olympia #262/R

£650 $1073 €943 Cernobio, Lake Lugano (11x15cm-4x6in) init. i.verso W/C. 2-Jul-3 Sotheby's, Olympia #260/R
£680 $1122 €986 Mosque of Sidi (17x24cm-7x9in) init. W/C pencil. 2-Jul-3 Sotheby's, Olympia #267/R
£700 $1092 €1050 Odysseus and the sea maidens (24x23cm-9x9in) W/C. 9-Oct-2 Woolley & Wallis, Salisbury #178/R
£700 $1099 €1050 Villa Arson, Nice (17x24cm-7x9in) init.i. col chks. 16-Dec-2 Bonhams, Bury St Edmunds #407/R
£700 $1155 €1015 Doge's Palace, Venice (10x14cm-4x6in) init. pencil W/C htd white. 3-Jul-3 Christie's, Kensington #146/R
£700 $1155 €1015 Blarney Castle (11x14cm-4x6in) init. i.verso W/C pencil. 2-Jul-3 Sotheby's, Olympia #264/R
£750 $1193 €1125 Berne (17x24cm-7x9in) init.i. crayon. 25-Feb-3 Bonhams, Knightsbridge #19/R
£750 $1223 €1088 Embarkation of the Queen of Sheba (17x36cm-7x14in) init. W/C scratching out after Claude Lorrain. 21-Jul-3 Bonhams, Bath #9/R
£800 $1256 €1200 Tunis bazaar (22x28cm-9x11in) init.i. pencil W/C htd white. 16-Apr-3 Christie's, Kensington #1008/R
£900 $1476 €1305 Lakeland landscape (22x30cm-9x12in) W/C htd white. 5-Jun-3 Christie's, London #172/R
£920 $1370 €1380 Italian scene (20x26cm-8x10in) init. W/C gouache. 27-Aug-2 Christie's, Melbourne #263/R est:2000-3000 (A.D 2400)
£1000 $1640 €1450 Gate in Kairouan (30x23cm-12x9in) s.i. pencil W/C bodycol htd white. 5-Jun-3 Christie's, London #176/R est:1200-1800
£1100 $1716 €1650 Tunis, Tunisia (15x23cm-6x9in) init.i. W/C htd white. 5-Nov-2 Bonhams, New Bond Street #134/R est:1000-1500
£1250 $2063 €1813 Algeria (10x13cm-4x5in) init. i.verso W/C. 2-Jul-3 Sotheby's, Olympia #271/R est:800-1200
£1400 $2310 €2030 Cairo (26x19cm-10x7in) s. s. over pencil htd bodycol gum arabic prov. 2-Jul-3 Sotheby's, Olympia #257/R est:1500-2000
£1400 $2310 €2030 Near Constantinople (11x14cm-4x6in) init. i.verso W/C pencil. 2-Jul-3 Sotheby's, Olympia #269/R est:800-1200
£1400 $2310 €2030 Morocco (11x14cm-4x6in) init. i.verso W/C. 2-Jul-3 Sotheby's, Olympia #270/R est:800-1200
£1450 $2378 €2175 Palaces on the Grand Canal, Venice (22x32cm-9x13in) init. W/C htd white. 4-Feb-3 Bonhams, Leeds #269 est:800-1200
£1450 $2393 €2103 Mists on the lagoon, Venice (14x19cm-6x7in) init. i.verso W/C. 2-Jul-3 Sotheby's, Olympia #266/R est:1000-1500
£1550 $2449 €2325 Middle eastern market place with bazzar (21x24cm-8x9in) s. W/C bodycol. 26-Nov-2 Bonhams, Oxford #9 est:300-500
£1700 $2652 €2550 Italianate coastal villa (20x25cm-8x10in) init. W/C bodycol. 5-Nov-2 Bonhams, New Bond Street #131/R est:1000-1500
£1700 $2788 €2465 Street scene, Tunisia (29x22cm-11x9in) s. i.verso pencil W/C htd bodycol. 5-Jun-3 Christie's, London #175/R est:1500-2000
£2000 $3240 €3000 Guidecca Canal, Venice (15x21cm-6x8in) init. W/C gouache prov. 20-May-3 Sotheby's, Olympia #7/R est:1000-2000
£2000 $3280 €2900 Mosque, Kairouan (31x23cm-12x9in) init. i.verso pencil W/C. 5-Jun-3 Christie's, London #174/R est:1800-2500
£2200 $3608 €3300 Piazzetta, Venice (18x20cm-7x8in) init. pencil W/C bodycol. 5-Jun-3 Christie's, Kensington #866/R est:1500-2000
£2200 $3608 €3190 Roman theatre, Arles, Provence (21x29cm-8x11in) s.i. pencil W/C bodycol htd white. 5-Jun-3 Christie's, London #171/R est:1800-2500
£2400 $3744 €3600 Grand canal, Venice (27x26cm-11x10in) init.i. W/C htd white. 5-Nov-2 Bonhams, New Bond Street #132/R est:2000-3000
£2600 $4264 €3770 View of Jaffa, Palestine (19x28cm-7x11in) s.i. pencil W/C bodycol htd white. 5-Jun-3 Christie's, London #173/R est:2000-3000
£4200 $6888 €6090 Santa Maria della Salute, Venice (21x28cm-8x11in) init. i.verso pencil W/C htd bodycol. 5-Jun-3 Christie's, London #169/R est:2500-3500

BRABAZON, Hercules Brabazon (attrib) (1821-1906) British
Works on paper
£1700 $2652 €2550 Continental coastal scene (13x16cm-5x6in) pencil W/C. 9-Oct-2 Woolley & Wallis, Salisbury #156/R est:200-300

BRABY, Newton (?) ?
£280 $434 €420 Portrait of a Dutch girl (29x20cm-11x8in) s.d.1905. 3-Nov-2 Lots Road, London #337
£513 $800 €770 Kept bird (53x64cm-21x25in) s. 9-Oct-2 Doyle, New York #15

BRACCI, Pietro (1700-1773) Italian
Works on paper
£16049 $26000 €24074 Design for the tomb of pope Clement XI (42x26cm-17x10in) s.i.d.1743 chk pen ink wash. 22-Jan-3 Christie's, Rockefeller NY #44/R est:35000

BRACCI, Pietro (attrib) (1700-1773) Italian
Sculpture
£150000 $235500 €225000 Bust of Pope Benedict XIII (76cm-30in) marble socle prov.lit. 10-Dec-2 Sotheby's, London #129/R est:180000-250000

BRACEGIRDLE, Larry (1949-) Canadian
£283 $441 €471 Millie's kitchen (51x41cm-20x16in) s.d.1995 prov. 13-Apr-3 Levis, Calgary #410/R (C.D 650)

BRACH, Malvina (19/20th C) French
Sculpture
£1226 $1900 €1839 Bather (71cm-28in) s. bronze. 1-Oct-2 Arthur James, Florida #118

BRACHO Y MURILLO, Jose Maria (19th C) Spanish
£8609 $14033 €13000 Basket of flowers (81x61cm-32x24in) s. 11-Feb-3 Segre, Madrid #67/R

BRACHT, Eugen (1842-1921) Swiss
£1090 $1689 €1700 Oriental landscape (24x31cm-9x12in) s. lit. 7-Dec-2 Bergmann, Erlangen #778/R est:1500
£1203 $1876 €1900 Heidestudie (56x85cm-22x33in) s. 21-Oct-2 Bernaerts, Antwerp #503/R est:700-870
£2390 $3728 €3800 Woodland path (94x112cm-37x44in) s. i. stretcher. 11-Oct-2 Winterberg, Heidelberg #488/R est:5600
£2785 $4316 €4400 Chateau des quatre tours (44x80cm-17x31in) s.i. canvas on board. 25-Sep-2 Neumeister, Munich #546/R est:5000
£2949 $4571 €4600 Matterhorn seen from Riffelsee with August snow - May 1898 (40x25cm-16x10in) s. i. verso board prov. 7-Dec-2 Ketterer, Hamburg #149/R est:2800-3000
£3481 $5396 €5500 Old fortress on hilltop (47x60cm-19x24in) s.d.1860. 25-Sep-2 Neumeister, Munich #547/R est:3500
£3500 $5740 €5250 Heide auf dem hohen venn bei Malmedy - near Malmedy (49x89cm-19x35in) s. panel. 3-Jun-3 Sotheby's, London #13/R est:4000-6000
£3526 $5571 €5500 Waves breaking off coastal town (42x61cm-17x24in) s.d.1874. 15-Nov-2 Reiss & Sohn, Konigstein #8/R est:6500
£5346 $8340 €8500 Niederburg near Manderscheid (104x119cm-41x47in) s.d.1911. 19-Sep-2 Dr Fritz Nagel, Stuttgart #910/R est:5000

BRACHT, Eugen (attrib) (1842-1921) Swiss
£575 $943 €880 Hilly landscape (46x57cm-18x22in) d.16.Sept.12 board. 8-Feb-3 Hans Stahl, Hamburg #11

BRACK, Cecil John (1920-1999) Australian
£8462 $13454 €12693 Nude on bed (69x50cm-27x20in) s.d.1973 conte prov.exhib.lit. 4-Mar-3 Deutscher-Menzies, Melbourne #11/R est:20000-30000 (A.D 22000)
£53640 $84215 €80460 Green nude. s.d.71 exhib. 15-Apr-3 Lawson Menzies, Sydney #31/R est:140000-180000 (A.D 140000)
£59761 $98008 €86653 Staircase (61x46cm-24x18in) s.d.52 exhib.lit. 4-Jun-3 Deutscher-Menzies, Melbourne #30/R est:150000-180000 (A.D 150000)
£62724 $95340 €94086 Three seagulls (43x91cm-17x36in) s.d.55 prov.exhib.lit. 28-Aug-2 Deutscher-Menzies, Melbourne #24/R est:130000-160000 (A.D 175000)
£78854 $119858 €118281 The club (106x152cm-42x60in) s.d.1989 i.d.1989 verso exhib.lit. 28-Aug-2 Deutscher-Menzies, Melbourne #31/R est:200000-250000 (A.D 220000)
£179283 $294024 €259960 Beginning (183x152cm-72x60in) s.d.1984 prov.exhib.lit. 4-Jun-3 Deutscher-Menzies, Melbourne #34/R est:500000-600000 (A.D 450000)

Works on paper
£2107 $3308 €3161 Untitled - nursery (47x18cm-19x7in) s.d.62 W/C ink. 15-Apr-3 Lawson Menzies, Sydney #124/R est:7000-10000 (A.D 5500)
£2143 $3364 €3215 Study for the first fleet (39x30cm-15x12in) s.d.87 pencil. 25-Nov-2 Christie's, Melbourne #27/R est:10000-15000 (A.D 6000)
£2206 $3376 €3309 Study for the bacon cutter's shop No.1 (32x41cm-13x16in) s.d.55 ink prov.exhib. 25-Aug-2 Sotheby's, Paddington #106/R est:7000-9000 (A.D 6200)
£2299 $3425 €3449 Untitled sketch. s.d.62 W/C ink prov. 27-Aug-2 Christie's, Melbourne #359/R est:7000-10000 (A.D 6000)
£3831 $5709 €5747 Untitled sketch (47x20cm-19x8in) s.d.62 W/C ink prov. 27-Aug-2 Christie's, Melbourne #32a/R est:10000-15000 (A.D 10000)
£4981 $7820 €7472 Nude (63x34cm-25x13in) s.d.65 pencil. 15-Apr-3 Lawson Menzies, Sydney #123/R est:15000-20000 (A.D 13000)
£11200 $18032 €16800 Standing nude with screen (76x56cm-30x22in) s.d.81 conte prov.exhib.lit. 6-May-3 Christie's, Melbourne #82/R est:30000-40000 (A.D 28000)
£12749 $20908 €18486 Two girls on the lines (65x47cm-26x19in) s.d.1977 W/C pen ink prov.exhib.lit. 4-Jun-3 Deutscher-Menzies, Melbourne #11/R est:28000-35000 (A.D 32000)
£14337 $21792 €21506 Nude with chair and carpet (49x64cm-19x25in) s.d.70 pastel exhib.lit. 28-Aug-2 Deutscher-Menzies, Melbourne #68/R est:40000-50000 (A.D 40000)

£25896 $42470 €37549 Conference (43x62cm-17x24in) s.d.56 W/C pen ink prov.exhib.lit. 4-Jun-3 Deutscher-Menzies, Melbourne #23/R est:55000-75000 (A.D 65000)

BRACK, Juditha (18/19th C) German?
Works on paper
£599 $994 €850 Still life of flowers (84x63cm-33x25in) s.d.1918 W/C. 14-Jun-3 Arnold, Frankfurt #711/R

BRACKELEN, Fred (attrib) (1802-1857) Belgian
£264 $394 €396 Tavern (21x25cm-8x10in) metal. 25-Jun-2 Koller, Zurich #6482 (S.FR 600)

BRACKEN, John (17th C) British
£620 $967 €930 Portrait of Elizabeth Lady Chaworth (91x75cm-36x30in) 11-Nov-2 Trembath Welch, Great Dunmow #457/R

BRACKEN, Julia (1871-1942) American
Sculpture
£5901 $9500 €8852 Apache fire hole (25x25x13cm-10x10x5in) s.d.1928 bronze prov. 18-Feb-3 John Moran, Pasadena #111b est:10000-15000

BRACKLE, Jakob (1897-1987) German
£897 $1417 €1300 Meadow (13x24cm-5x9in) s.d.42 i. verso board. 5-Apr-3 Geble, Radolfzell #689/R
£1013 $1580 €1600 Winter landscape (9x13cm-4x5in) s.d.1978 masonite. 18-Oct-2 Dr Fritz Nagel, Stuttgart #460/R est:1500
£1216 $1897 €1800 Women working in field (14x24cm-6x9in) s. bears d.6 board prov. 27-Mar-3 Dr Fritz Nagel, Stuttgart #794/R est:2200
£1572 $2453 €2500 Snowy countryside (43x21cm-17x8in) s.d.43 board. 20-Sep-2 Sigalas, Stuttgart #1074 est:2500
£1582 $2500 €2500 Field landscape with plough (10x20cm-4x8in) s.d.38 board. 29-Nov-2 Sigalas, Stuttgart #1163/R est:2500
£1582 $2500 €2500 Snow-covered lane with bare trees on edge of the path (16x15cm-6x6in) s.d.41 panel. 29-Nov-2 Sigalas, Stuttgart #1165/R est:2500
£1689 $2635 €2500 Village on winter morning (34x41cm-13x16in) s.d.37 prov. 27-Mar-3 Dr Fritz Nagel, Stuttgart #796/R est:3500

BRACKMAN, David (19th C) British
Works on paper
£1600 $2432 €2400 Henrietta crossing Atlantic 1864, to race at Cowes (44x68cm-17x27in) s. gouache. 15-Aug-2 Bonhams, New Bond Street #294/R est:1500-2500

BRACKMAN, Robert (1898-1980) American
£3151 $4600 €4727 Autumn mood, table top still life (61x76cm-24x30in) s. 3-Nov-1 North East Auctions, Portsmouth #252/R
Works on paper
£915 $1500 €1327 Self portrait (35x25cm-14x10in) init. chl col pastel. 5-Jun-3 Swann Galleries, New York #55/R est:1000-1500

BRACONNIER, Frederic (1901-1985) French
£316 $494 €500 Le pont Saint Lambert a Vresse (50x60cm-20x24in) s. 16-Oct-2 Hotel des Ventes Mosan, Brussels #169

BRACONY, Armand Étienne (1825-1894) French
£2482 $4145 €3500 Vue de la Tour de Nesle. Vue de la Conciergerie (28x36cm-11x14in) one s.d.1847 pair. 18-Jun-3 Tajan, Paris #128/R est:4000-6000

BRACONY, Leopold (19/20th C) American
Sculpture
£987 $1500 €1481 Goddess playing lyre with winged cherub at her knee (84cm-33in) s. alabaster exhib. 18-Aug-2 Jeffery Burchard, Florida #90a/R

BRACQUEMOND, Émile Louis (20th C) French
Sculpture
£1282 $2013 €2000 Panther (44cm-17in) bronze marble socle. 23-Nov-2 Arnold, Frankfurt #357/R

BRACQUEMOND, Félix (1833-1914) French
Works on paper
£1161 $1800 €1742 Pheasants feeding (20x33cm-8x13in) s. W/C ink. 7-Dec-2 Neal Auction Company, New Orleans #82/R est:2500-4000

BRACY, Arthur E (?) American
£625 $1000 €938 Double masted schooner on high seas (61x91cm-24x36in) 16-May-3 Du Mouchelle, Detroit #2170/R

BRADBURY, Arthur Royce (1892-1977) British
£280 $448 €420 Figures in a fishing boat (27x38cm-11x15in) s. panel double-sided. 15-May-3 Lawrence, Crewkerne #885/R
£300 $471 €450 Portrait of a lady in a striped scarf, in a landscape (61x50cm-24x20in) s.d.1941. 16-Apr-3 Christie's, Kensington #563/R
Works on paper
£320 $512 €480 Quiet waters (51x37cm-20x15in) s. s.i.verso W/C pencil htd scratching out paper on card. 15-May-3 Lawrence, Crewkerne #876/R
£850 $1360 €1275 Blue summer dress (28x38cm-11x15in) s.d.25 W/C pencil double-sided. 15-May-3 Lawrence, Crewkerne #882/R

BRADBURY, E Louise (fl.1899-1926) British
Works on paper
£1000 $1620 €1500 Game of hoops (32x24cm-13x9in) s. W/C. 21-Jan-3 Bonhams, Knightsbridge #272/R est:400-600

BRADBURY, Gideon Elden (1833-1904) American
£1677 $2600 €2516 On the Saco River. White Mountains (13x10cm-5x4in) s.d.verso board two. 2-Nov-2 North East Auctions, Portsmouth #51/R

BRADDAN, Paul (19th C) British
Works on paper
£250 $408 €375 Old Library, Union Street (50x74cm-20x29in) i. W/C over pencil. 28-Jan-3 Bonhams, Knowle #307

BRADDON, Paul (1864-1938) British
Works on paper
£282 $446 €423 Market day (76x49cm-30x19in) bears another sig. W/C. 18-Nov-2 Waddingtons, Toronto #58/R (C.D 700)

BRADER, Ferdinand A (1833-?) American
Works on paper
£2236 $3600 €3354 Hilly landscape with farmhouse, barn, outbuildings and animals (79x122cm-31x48in) i. pencil exec.1880. 22-Feb-3 Pook & Pook, Downington #90/R est:4000-6000

BRADFORD, William (1827-1892) American
£4167 $6500 €6251 Seascape with distant sailboat (15x36cm-6x14in) s. board. 28-Mar-3 Eldred, East Dennis #695/R est:3000-4000
£6329 $10000 €9494 View of Half Dome, Yosemite (33x36cm-13x14in) s. board exhib. 24-Apr-3 Shannon's, Milford #137/R est:12000-18000
£27420 $42500 €41130 Return of the whales (51x76cm-20x30in) s. 4-Dec-2 Sotheby's, New York #107/R est:40000-60000
£27778 $45000 €41667 Wilbur's Point, Sconticut Neck, Fairhaven, Massachusetts (33x48cm-13x19in) s. board prov. 22-May-3 Christie's, Rockefeller NY #2/R est:25000-35000
£29940 $50000 €43413 Panther among icebergs (25x41cm-10x16in) s.i.d.81. 18-Jun-3 Christie's, Los Angeles #22/R est:25000-35000
£33951 $55000 €50927 Ship and icebergs (23x36cm-9x14in) s.d.74 board. 22-May-3 Christie's, Rockefeller NY #14/R est:30000-50000
£55556 $90000 €83334 In the Arctic (23x36cm-9x14in) s.d.78 board prov. 21-May-3 Sotheby's, New York #208/R est:30000-50000

BRADLEY, Basil (1842-1904) British
£400 $624 €600 Sheep near Cookham, Berkshire (13x22cm-5x9in) s. i.verso panel. 7-Nov-2 Christie's, Kensington #115
Works on paper
£750 $1185 €1125 Luncheon, Paris (36x48cm-14x19in) s.d.1874 i.verso W/C. 24-Apr-3 Richardson & Smith, Whitby #189
£1000 $1630 €1500 An afternoon walk (38x60cm-15x24in) s.d.1881 W/C. 12-Feb-3 Bonhams, Knightsbridge #163/R est:1000-1500
£1500 $2340 €2250 Partridge shooting (39x56cm-15x22in) s. W/C. 10-Oct-2 Greenslade Hunt, Taunton #570/R est:1200-1600

BRADLEY, Basil and TRAPPES, Francis M (19th C) British
£3700 $5846 €5550 Cover side (51x91cm-20x36in) mono. s.i.d.1875 verso. 28-Nov-2 Christie's, Kensington #80/R est:2000-3000

BRADLEY, Cuthbert (1861-1943) British
£833 $1200 €1250 Design for trade sign (23x22cm-9x9in) i. board. 15-Jan-3 Christie's, Rockefeller NY #152/R

Works on paper
£260 $413 €390 Tom Isaac finishing a hunt on foot (15x25cm-6x10in) s. W/C bodycol. 30-Apr-3 Goldings, Lincolnshire #149/R
£280 $456 €420 Midland counties spaniel field trails, Milton Park, Oct 23 1930 (17x28cm-7x11in) s.i. W/C pen ink htd white. 11-Feb-3 Bonhams, Knowle #111

BRADLEY, E J (19th C) British
£2724 $4277 €4250 Flying Dutchman (46x61cm-18x24in) s.d.1889. 19-Nov-2 Castellana, Madrid #28/R est:3500

BRADLEY, Edward (fl.1824-1867) British
Works on paper
£550 $847 €825 Brighton beach (36x49cm-14x19in) bears another sig. W/C. 22-Oct-2 Bonhams, Knightsbridge #32/R

BRADLEY, Helen (1900-1979) British
£9500 $14820 €14250 On the morning after the Royal visit to Manchester (40x51cm-16x20in) mono.i. canvasboard. 25-Mar-3 Bonhams, New Bond Street #76/R est:10000-15000
£26000 $40560 €39000 Oh! the pot market's arrived (41x51cm-16x20in) mono. canvasboard prov. 25-Mar-3 Bonhams, New Bond Street #75/R est:25000-30000
£45000 $70200 €67500 Cricket match (40x51cm-16x20in) s. canvasboard. 25-Mar-3 Bonhams, New Bond Street #77/R est:25000-35000
Works on paper
£2800 $4368 €4200 Midsummer in Alexandra park (31x32cm-12x13in) mono.i. W/C gouache prov. 25-Mar-3 Bonhams, New Bond Street #79/R est:3000-5000
£3600 $5616 €5400 Mother and children by a lakeside (37x55cm-15x22in) s. indis d. W/C. 6-Nov-2 Bonhams, Chester #358 est:700-1000
£26000 $42120 €37700 The knockerup man, town scene at early morning with figures (15x22cm-6x9in) s. W/C. 29-Jul-3 Capes Dunn, Manchester #12/R

BRADLEY, Martin (1931-) British
£400 $660 €580 Angry bird protecting its egg (62x76cm-24x30in) mono.d.55 s.i.d.verso. 3-Jul-3 Christie's, Kensington #724
£420 $651 €630 Les comdattants idiots (35x93cm-14x37in) mono.d.55 board prov. 4-Dec-2 Christie's, Kensington #528
£450 $698 €675 Angry bird at night (71x76cm-28x30in) mono.d.55. 4-Dec-2 Christie's, Kensington #597/R
£647 $1023 €1010 Composition (70x70cm-28x28in) painted 1972. 12-Nov-2 Babuino, Rome #231/R
£654 $1033 €1020 Still life with 2 (100x62cm-39x24in) acrylic paper on canvas painted 1972. 12-Nov-2 Babuino, Rome #136/R
£1147 $1813 €1790 Interior (100x100cm-39x39in) painted 1965. 12-Nov-2 Babuino, Rome #360/R
£1449 $2289 €2260 From Deane II (76x100cm-30x39in) painted 1965. 12-Nov-2 Babuino, Rome #229/R
£1600 $2480 €2400 Les combattants (41x91cm-16x36in) mono.d.55 board. 4-Dec-2 Christie's, Kensington #596/R est:600-800
Works on paper
£280 $434 €420 Soldier (51x38cm-20x15in) mono.i.d.55 brush black ink bodycol prov. 4-Dec-2 Christie's, Kensington #360/R
£400 $660 €580 Wall (115x89cm-45x35in) mono.i.d.58 gouache brush ink. 3-Jul-3 Christie's, Kensington #716

BRADLEY, Robert (1813-?) British
Works on paper
£400 $572 €600 Nottingham Castle from the river Leen (20x31cm-8x12in) s.d.1863 pencil W/C. 11-Apr-2 Mellors & Kirk, Nottingham #536

BRADSHAW, Constance (?-1961) British
Works on paper
£380 $619 €570 High summer (41x48cm-16x19in) W/C. 14-Feb-3 Keys, Aylsham #503/R

BRADSHAW, Elizabeth E (?) Irish?
£2436 $3849 €3800 Portrait study of young boy seated with long haired terrier on his lap (76x63cm-30x25in) indis.sig.d.56. 12-Nov-2 Mealy's, Castlecomer #1312 est:1500-2000

BRADSHAW, Eva Theresa (1871-1938) Canadian
£287 $445 €431 Evening on the lane (38x91cm-15x36in) s. 24-Sep-2 Ritchie, Toronto #3124/R (C.D 700)
£304 $475 €456 Still life of mixed flowers (57x47cm-22x19in) s. 20-Sep-2 Sloan, North Bethesda #453/R
£391 $606 €587 Spring bouquet in a glass vase (52x45cm-20x18in) s. 3-Dec-2 Joyner, Toronto #492 (C.D 950)
£884 $1387 €1326 Floral still life (40x50cm-16x20in) s. 25-Nov-2 Hodgins, Calgary #40/R est:2500-3000 (C.D 2200)
£1867 $3061 €2801 White dress (77x62cm-30x24in) s. 3-Jun-3 Joyner, Toronto #375/R est:4000-5000 (C.D 4200)

BRADSHAW, George Fagan (1887-1960) British
£580 $945 €870 Sunlit waves (41x51cm-16x20in) s. board. 13-Feb-3 David Lay, Penzance #182

BRADSHAW, Glenn Raymond (1922-) American
Works on paper
£287 $450 €431 Gilded surf (97x185cm-38x73in) s. casein. 19-Apr-3 Susanin's, Chicago #5030

BRADY, Charles (1926-1997) Irish/American
£2466 $3871 €3600 Tree in August (70x59cm-28x23in) s. i.d.1965 verso. 15-Apr-3 De Veres Art Auctions, Dublin #267 est:4000-6000
£2595 $4022 €4100 July evening - Waterford (36x41cm-14x16in) s. s.i.d.1962 verso prov. 24-Sep-2 De Veres Art Auctions, Dublin #25 est:4000-6000
£2740 $4301 €4000 Artist's canvas (51x41cm-20x16in) 15-Apr-3 De Veres Art Auctions, Dublin #237 est:3000-4000
£2821 $4372 €4400 Mouth organ (22x29cm-9x11in) s. card prov. 3-Dec-2 Bonhams & James Adam, Dublin #103/R est:4000-5000
£2949 $4629 €4600 Clothes peg (21x36cm-8x14in) s. 19-Nov-2 Whyte's, Dublin #185/R est:4000-5000
£3165 $4905 €5000 Palette of a Tuscan painter (21x36cm-8x14in) s. 24-Sep-2 De Veres Art Auctions, Dublin #66b/R est:5000-7000
£3288 $5162 €4800 Folded envelope (26x36cm-10x14in) s. oil on paper prov. 15-Apr-3 De Veres Art Auctions, Dublin #156/R est:4000-6000
£3333 $5467 €4600 Napkin (41x32cm-16x13in) s.d.1979 panel prov. 28-May-3 Bonhams & James Adam, Dublin #116/R est:4000-6000
£3846 $6038 €6000 Pear (25x28cm-10x11in) s. 19-Nov-2 Hamilton Osborne King, Dublin #537/R est:4000-6000
£4214 $6574 €6700 Haycock (46x56cm-18x22in) s. i.d.1975 prov.exhib. 17-Sep-2 Whyte's, Dublin #37/R est:8000-10000
£4430 $6867 €7000 Brown envelope (26x31cm-10x12in) s. prov. 24-Sep-2 De Veres Art Auctions, Dublin #66a/R est:5000-7000
£4500 $6975 €6750 Pencil (43x33cm-17x13in) s. 2-Oct-2 John Ross, Belfast #164 est:3500-4000
£4805 $7304 €7400 Sugar bag (36x30cm-14x12in) s. 2-Jul-2 Thomas Adams, Dublin #429
£5128 $8051 €8000 Envelope (46x36cm-18x14in) s.d.1970 prov. 19-Nov-2 Whyte's, Dublin #20/R est:5000-7000

BRAEKELEER, Adrien de (1818-1904) Belgian
£500 $835 €725 Domestic contentment (21x26cm-8x10in) s.d.1886 panel. 26-Jun-3 Mellors & Kirk, Nottingham #862
£1575 $2458 €2300 La lecture (52x40cm-20x16in) s. panel. 14-Apr-3 Horta, Bruxelles #151 est:1500-2000
£8904 $13979 €13000 Busy tavern scene (50x63cm-20x25in) s. panel. 15-Apr-3 Sotheby's, Amsterdam #64/R est:10000-15000
£10274 $16130 €15000 Farm yard with a vegetable seller (79x61cm-31x24in) s.d.1842 panel. 15-Apr-3 Sotheby's, Amsterdam #33/R est:5000-7000

BRAEKELEER, F de (19th C) Belgian
£2051 $3221 €3200 Preparation du repas (31x26cm-12x10in) panel exhib. 25-Nov-2 Amberes, Antwerp #152/R
£3819 $6035 €5500 Dans l'atelier de l'artiste (100x122cm-39x48in) 28-Apr-3 Amberes, Antwerp #268

BRAEKELEER, Ferdinand de (19th C) Belgian
£321 $503 €500 Scene de marche (15x20cm-6x8in) panel. 16-Dec-2 Amberes, Antwerp #254
£823 $1284 €1300 Preparation du repas a l'exterieur de l'auberge (34x27cm-13x11in) s. panel. 16-Sep-2 Horta, Bruxelles #414
£2200 $3652 €2200 Scene d'interieur animee (32x40cm-13x16in) s. panel. 16-Jun-3 Horta, Bruxelles #115 est:2200-2800
£6115 $9784 €8500 Barn interior with peasants drinking, smoking and making music (44x59cm-17x23in) s.d.1843 panel. 13-May-3 Sotheby's, Amsterdam #67/R est:6000-8000
£7692 $12077 €12000 L'ecole du village (34x43cm-13x17in) s. panel. 10-Dec-2 Campo, Vlaamse Kaai #124 est:15000-20000
£7692 $12077 €12000 Interieur de ferme, la chute (37x45cm-15x18in) s. wood. 10-Dec-2 Campo, Vlaamse Kaai #124a/R est:20000-24000
£10000 $16600 €10000 Jeune marchande de fruits romaine (100x72cm-39x28in) s. 16-Jun-3 Horta, Bruxelles #114/R est:10000-15000
£14500 $24070 €14500 La chute (38x47cm-15x19in) s.d.1871 s.verso panel. 16-Jun-3 Horta, Bruxelles #116/R est:10000-12000
£48276 $77241 €70000 Het halfvastenverhaal in de school (82x108cm-32x43in) panel. 17-Mar-3 Amberes, Antwerp #197
£66524 $103112 €99786 Unruly schoolboy (72x60cm-28x24in) s.d.1847 panel prov. 3-Oct-2 Koller, Zurich #3092/R est:30000-50000 (S.FR 155000)

BRAEKELEER, Ferdinand de (elder) (1792-1883) Belgian
£886 $1382 €1400 Country fair (39x47cm-15x19in) s.d.1826. 21-Oct-2 Bernaerts, Antwerp #80/R

£5096 $7949 €8000 Fish saleswoman (33x40cm-13x16in) s.i.d.1873 panel. 6-Nov-2 Vendue Huis, Gravenhage #393/R est:9000-12000
£5449 $8554 €8500 Le benedicite (47x39cm-19x15in) s. d.1872 verso panel. 19-Nov-2 Vanderkindere, Brussels #434/R est:5000-7500
£13100 $20699 €19650 La marchande de beur (57x44cm-22x17in) s.i.d.1858 i. verso panel. 14-Nov-2 Stuker, Bern #108/R est:15000-20000 (S.FR 30000)

Works on paper
£705 $1093 €1100 Jeu de dames (27x35cm-11x14in) s. W/C pencil. 3-Dec-2 Campo & Campo, Antwerp #58/R

BRAEKELEER, Ferdinand de (younger) (1828-1857) Belgian
£942 $1545 €1300 Grotte de Neptune (63x73cm-25x29in) s. 27-May-3 Campo & Campo, Antwerp #66

BRAEKELEER, Henri de (1840-1888) Belgian
£582 $914 €850 Le mouline a eau (25x20cm-10x8in) mono. panel. 15-Apr-3 Galerie Moderne, Brussels #349

BRAGAGLIA, Anton Giulio (1889-1963) Italian
Photographs
£4200 $6804 €6300 Julius Evola (23x17cm-9x7in) s. i.verso gelatin silver print prov. 21-May-3 Christie's, London #128/R est:1000-1500

BRAGAGLIA, Arturo (1893-1962) ?
Photographs
£3200 $5184 €4800 Double portrait of Lulu Gould (20x27cm-8x11in) i. silver print exec.c.1929. 22-May-3 Sotheby's, London #75/R est:3000-5000

BRAGG, Charles (1931-) American
£254 $425 €368 Bird handler (61x76cm-24x30in) s. 29-Jun-3 Butterfields, Los Angeles #7002/R

BRAINSFATHER, Bruce (?) British?
Works on paper
£650 $988 €975 Nao, that's not the landmine (33x25cm-13x10in) W/C. 4-Jul-2 Duke & Son, Dorchester #136

BRAITH, Anton (1836-1905) German
£1892 $2951 €2800 Two calves (17x22cm-7x9in) s.d.1898 panel. 26-Mar-3 Hugo Ruef, Munich #70/R est:900
£3205 $5000 €4808 Untitled, cattle (48x66cm-19x26in) 18-Oct-2 Du Mouchelle, Detroit #2079/R
£3662 $6079 €5200 Six goats playing and church procession in background (26x36cm-10x14in) s.i.d.1898 panel. 14-Jun-3 Arnold, Frankfurt #712/R est:9000
£9032 $13277 €14000 Lake Garda (60x50cm-24x20in) s.i.d.1903. 20-Jun-2 Dr Fritz Nagel, Stuttgart #755/R est:15000
£10759 $16677 €17000 Rain shower - sheep getting wet (52x97cm-20x38in) s.d.1873 lit. 25-Sep-2 Neumeister, Munich #548/R est:25000

BRAITH, Anton (attrib) (1836-1905) German
£545 $855 €850 Cows by alpine farmstead (35x45cm-14x18in) i. W/C chl board. 21-Nov-2 Van Ham, Cologne #1494

BRAITHWAITE, Joanna (1962-) New Zealander?
£298 $465 €447 Horse play (20x30cm-8x12in) s. 27-Mar-3 International Art Centre, Auckland #203 (NZ.D 850)
£421 $657 €632 Sleepwalker (70x65cm-28x26in) s.verso. 27-Mar-3 International Art Centre, Auckland #52/R (NZ.D 1200)
£746 $1089 €1119 Something fishy (131x135cm-52x53in) 12-Sep-1 Watson's, Christchurch #177/R (NZ.D 2500)

BRAKEL, Simon van (?) ?
£2069 $3290 €3000 Sailing vessels at sea (80x100cm-31x39in) panel. 10-Mar-3 Sotheby's, Amsterdam #99a est:2000-3000

BRAKEN, Peter van den (1896-1979) Dutch
£260 $379 €400 Sea view (63x68cm-25x27in) s. lit. 19-Jun-2 Vendue Huis, Gravenhage #65

BRAKENBURGH, Richard (1650-1702) Dutch
£4140 $6459 €6500 Family gathered around a table having breakfast in an interior (26x21cm-10x8in) s. panel prov. 5-Nov-2 Sotheby's, Amsterdam #203/R est:5000-7000

BRAKENBURGH, Richard (attrib) (1650-1702) Dutch
£621 $1005 €900 Life of the people (26x19cm-10x7in) panel prov. 25-May-3 Uppsala Auktionskammare, Uppsala #36/R (S.KR 8000)

BRAMANTINO (15/16th C) Italian
£120690 $191897 €175000 Holy Family (70x54cm-28x21in) board lit. 9-Mar-3 Semenzato, Venice #52/R est:160000

BRAMBATI, Luigi (1925-) Italian
£578 $919 €850 Harvest (50x60cm-20x24in) s. 1-Mar-3 Meeting Art, Vercelli #689
£801 $1258 €1250 River angler (80x45cm-31x18in) s. s.i.verso. 23-Nov-2 Meeting Art, Vercelli #136

BRAMER, Josef (1948-) Austrian
£1042 $1646 €1500 Doll (17x13cm-7x5in) mono.d.74 panel. 24-Apr-3 Dorotheum, Vienna #215/R est:900-1300

BRAMER, Leonard (1596-1674) Dutch
£16892 $26351 €25000 Deposition (106x85cm-42x33in) 25-Mar-3 Finarte Semenzato, Rome #121/R est:28000
Works on paper
£510 $795 €800 Finding of Moses (18x16cm-7x6in) i.verso pen black ink grey wash prov. 5-Nov-2 Sotheby's, Amsterdam #32/R
£3165 $4937 €5000 Deux etudes de plafonds (16x22cm-6x9in) pen Chinese ink wash pair. 18-Oct-2 Rabourdin & Choppin de Janvry, Paris #72

BRAMER, Leonard (attrib) (1596-1674) Dutch
£2432 $3795 €3600 Saint-Paul prechant a Lystrie (32x43cm-13x17in) panel. 28-Mar-3 Neret-Minet, Paris #31/R

BRAMHALL, H (?) American
£17419 $27000 €26129 Entering Camden Harbor (46x76cm-18x30in) s. 2-Nov-2 North East Auctions, Portsmouth #728/R est:12000-15000

BRAMLEY, Frank (1857-1915) British
£4200 $6594 €6300 Red and white flowers (38x33cm-15x13in) s.i.verso board painted c.1905. 22-Nov-2 Christie's, London #41/R est:4000-6000

BRAMLEY, R (?) American?
£700 $1134 €1050 American clipper Seawitch riding the ocean swell (61x91cm-24x36in) s. 21-May-3 Christie's, Kensington #695/R

BRANAY, L (20th C) ?
£2400 $3888 €3600 Allegory of plenty (110x150cm-43x59in) s. 23-Jan-3 Christie's, Kensington #94/R est:1500-2500

BRANCACCIO, Carlo (1861-1920) Italian
£4000 $6680 €5800 Place Clichy, Paris (38x46cm-15x18in) s.i. 17-Jun-3 Bonhams, New Bond Street #108/R est:4000-6000
£6100 $9882 €9150 Vicolo Napoli (32x20cm-13x8in) s.i. 20-May-3 Sotheby's, Olympia #427/R est:3000-4000
£17742 $27500 €26613 Impressions of Toledo (30x54cm-12x21in) s.i. 29-Oct-2 Sotheby's, New York #93/R est:30000-40000

BRANCACCIO, Carlo (attrib) (1861-1920) Italian
£900 $1494 €1350 Rocky beach with boats in the distance (49x73cm-19x29in) bears sig.i. 10-Jun-3 Bonhams, Knightsbridge #278/R
£1300 $2028 €1950 Cote de Provence (65x81cm-26x32in) s.i. 26-Mar-3 Sotheby's, Olympia #278/R est:1500-2000
£1519 $2400 €2400 Boats in Posillipo (27x39cm-11x15in) board. 26-Nov-2 Christie's, Rome #17/R
£11000 $17270 €16500 Washerwomen by the banks of a river (191x100cm-75x39in) bears sig. 19-Nov-2 Sotheby's, London #196/R est:10000-15000

BRANCACCIO, Giovanni (1903-1975) Italian
£323 $510 €500 Villa (45x60cm-18x24in) s. board. 18-Dec-2 Finarte, Milan #167/R
£5256 $8147 €8200 Street in Naples with horse drinking and couple in conversation (32x20cm-13x8in) s.i. 4-Dec-2 Neumeister, Munich #683/R est:7000

BRANCUSI, Constantin (1876-1957) Rumanian
Photographs
£2273 $3500 €3410 Study of the sculpture Leda (24x30cm-9x12in) photograph prov. 24-Oct-2 Sotheby's, New York #182/R est:5000-8000
£3247 $5000 €4871 Sculpture, The Kiss in Montparnasse Cemetery (22x17cm-9x7in) photograph executed c.1920 prov. 24-Oct-2 Sotheby's, New York #178/R est:7000-9000
£5000 $8100 €7500 Self portrait in studio (23x17cm-9x7in) s.verso gelatin silver print exec.c.1921 prov. 21-May-3 Christie's, London #132/R est:800-1200
£6494 $10000 €9741 Self portrait in his studio (11x9cm-4x4in) photograph executed c.1921 prov. 24-Oct-2 Sotheby's, New York #181/R est:2500-3500

£7143 $11000 €10715 Sleeping child and the newborn II (29x39cm-11x15in) mono. photograph executed c.1923 prov.lit. 22-Oct-2 Sotheby's, New York #32/R est:10000-15000
£8442 $13000 €12663 Vue d'atelier, eve et platon (45x32cm-18x13in) gelatin silver print board exec.c.1920 prov. 25-Oct-2 Phillips, New York #14/R est:10000-15000
£9740 $15000 €14610 Study of Brancusi's studio with Mlle Pogany II (23x17cm-9x7in) photograph prov. 24-Oct-2 Sotheby's, New York #176/R est:7000-9000
£9740 $15000 €14610 Sleeping muse (17x23cm-7x9in) photograph prov. 22-Oct-2 Sotheby's, New York #30/R est:7000-10000

Sculpture

£85000 $139400 €127500 Etude pour lapriere (9cm-4in) s.st.f.Valsuani brown pat bronze prov. 4-Feb-3 Christie's, London #268/R est:120000

BRAND, Christian Hilfgott (1695-1756) Austrian

£7547 $11698 €12000 Extensive forested landscape with figures (67x79cm-26x31in) s. 2-Oct-2 Dorotheum, Vienna #205/R est:12000-16000
£8176 $12673 €13000 Sylvan landscape with woodcutters (61x52cm-24x20in) s.d.1753 prov.lit. 2-Oct-2 Dorotheum, Vienna #210/R est:10000-15000

BRAND, Christian Hilfgott (attrib) (1695-1756) Austrian

£1419 $2200 €2129 River landscape with peasants in boats (29x46cm-11x18in) 2-Oct-2 Christie's, Rockefeller NY #113/R est:2000-3000

BRAND, Johann Christian (1722-1795) Austrian

£16352 $25346 €26000 View of Schloss Leiben in lower Austria (77x110cm-30x43in) s.d.1794 prov.lit. 2-Oct-2 Dorotheum, Vienna #206/R est:18000-25000
£16352 $25346 €26000 St Joseph's Hermitage near Wurnsdorf in lower Austria (76x110cm-30x43in) s.d.1793 prov. 2-Oct-2 Dorotheum, Vienna #207/R est:18000-25000

Works on paper

£356 $556 €520 Sailing boat off the coast on stormy day (20x20cm-8x8in) wash pencil. 11-Apr-3 Winterberg, Heidelberg #216
£743 $1159 €1100 On the way home (15x19cm-6x7in) s. verso W/C brush Indian ink. 28-Mar-3 Dorotheum, Vienna #81/R

BRAND, Johann Christian (attrib) (1722-1795) Austrian

£2532 $3924 €4000 River landscape with wooden bridge and figures (25x34cm-10x13in) panel. 25-Sep-2 Neumeister, Munich #469/R est:3500

BRANDANI, Enrico (1914-) Italian

£655 $1048 €950 Tobias (60x42cm-24x17in) s. panel. 15-Mar-3 De Vuyst, Lokeren #35
£897 $1434 €1300 Hommage a la folie (60x43cm-24x17in) s. panel. 15-Mar-3 De Vuyst, Lokeren #34/R
£900 $1476 €1350 Le the des Veuves au clair de lune (56x41cm-22x16in) s. board. 29-May-3 Mallams, Cheltenham #371/R

BRANDEIS, Antonietta (1849-1920) Bohemian

£1563 $2500 €2345 View of the Giudecca, Venice with gondola on the lagoon (12x22cm-5x9in) mono. panel. 14-May-3 Butterfields, San Francisco #1058/R est:3000-5000
£2500 $4100 €3750 Casa d'Oro, Venice (21x12cm-8x5in) s. panel. 3-Jun-3 Sotheby's, London #128/R est:3000-5000
£2800 $4396 €4200 Ricci staircase, Doge's Palace, Venice (24x15cm-9x6in) s. board. 19-Nov-2 Bonhams, New Bond Street #102/R est:2500-3500
£3121 $4837 €4682 Barca da Pesca, Venezia (24x15cm-9x6in) s. panel. 3-Dec-2 Bukowskis, Stockholm #178/R est:25000-30000 (S.KR 44000)
£3400 $5338 €5100 Piazza St. Maria Novella (15x25cm-6x10in) s. panel. 19-Nov-2 Bonhams, New Bond Street #104/R est:3000-5000
£4566 $7123 €6849 Chiesa San Tovaso, Venice (15x25cm-6x10in) s. panel. 28-Mar-3 Koller, Zurich #3160/R est:10000-15000 (S.FR 10000)
£5150 $7983 €7725 Ponte Vecchio, Florence (14x25cm-6x10in) s. panel prov. 3-Oct-2 Koller, Zurich #3078/R est:12000-15000 (S.FR 12000)
£5380 $8500 €8070 Venice (23x14cm-9x6in) s. panel prov. 24-Apr-3 Sotheby's, New York #130/R est:6000-8000
£5500 $9020 €8250 Doge's Palace (35x23cm-14x9in) panel. 3-Jun-3 Sotheby's, London #127/R est:4000-6000
£6000 $9300 €9000 Piazza San Marco with a view of the Basillica and the Campanile, Venice (23x34cm-9x13in) s. 4-Dec-2 Christie's, London #112/R est:6000-8000
£6200 $9734 €9300 La porta del Palazzo, Venezia (14x25cm-6x10in) s. panel prov. 19-Nov-2 Sotheby's, London #114/R est:4000-6000
£7000 $10850 €10500 Ponte dei tre archi, Cannaregio. View of Florence (16x23cm-6x9in) s. board pair prov. 4-Dec-2 Christie's, London #111/R est:8000-12000
£7200 $11448 €10800 On the Grand Canal, Venice (15x24cm-6x9in) init. panel prov. 18-Mar-3 Bonhams, New Bond Street #72/R est:4000-6000
£7500 $11925 €11250 Santa Maria della salute and the entrance to the Grand Canal, Venice (14x22cm-6x9in) s. panel prov. 18-Mar-3 Bonhams, New Bond Street #73/R est:3000-5000
£7500 $12300 €11250 View of the Basilica of San Marco (17x23cm-7x9in) s. board. 3-Jun-3 Sotheby's, London #121/R est:4000-6000
£7500 $12300 €11250 Grand Canal and Santa Maria Della Salute (12x21cm-5x8in) init. panel. 3-Jun-3 Sotheby's, London #125/R est:4000-6000
£8000 $13120 €12000 View of the Rialto Bridge, Venice (16x22cm-6x9in) s. board. 3-Jun-3 Sotheby's, London #120/R est:4000-6000
£8000 $13120 €12000 Santa Maria della Salute (21x13cm-8x5in) init, panel. 3 Jun-3 Sotheby's, London #122/R est:4000-6000
£8500 $13940 €12750 View of the Ponte Vecchio, Florence (16x23cm-6x9in) s. board. 3-Jun-3 Sotheby's, London #129/R est:4000-6000
£8750 $14000 €13125 Courtyard at the Doge's Palace, Venice (23x32cm-9x13in) mono. panel. 14-May-3 Butterfields, San Francisco #1045/R est:7000-9000
£9000 $14760 €13500 Santa Maria Della Salute (16x23cm-6x9in) s. board. 3-Jun-3 Sotheby's, London #126/R est:5000-7000
£10000 $15700 €15000 Entrance to the Doge's Palace, Venice. Bridge of Sighs, Venice (24x15cm-9x6in) s. board pair. 21-Nov-2 Tennants, Leyburn #767/R est:4000-6000
£10000 $16400 €15000 Doge's Palace, San Giorgio Maggiore beyond (16x23cm-6x9in) s. panel prov. 3-Jun-3 Sotheby's, London #124/R est:4000-6000
£10000 $16700 €14500 Gondola before a Venetian Palazzo (24x15cm-9x6in) s. indis.i.verso board sold with a companion. 25-Jun-3 Bonhams, Bury St Edmunds #581 est:4000-6000
£10625 $17000 €15938 View of the Piazzetta San Marco, Venice (33x23cm-13x9in) mono. panel. 14-May-3 Butterfields, San Francisco #1046/R est:10000-15000
£15000 $24600 €22500 View of the Doge's Palace, Santa Maria Della Salute beyond (16x23cm-6x9in) s. board. 3-Jun-3 Sotheby's, London #130/R est:4000-6000
£17000 $26690 €25500 Venetian canal scenes (34x25cm-13x10in) init, board pair. 19-Nov-2 Bonhams, New Bond Street #98/R est:10000-15000
£17000 $27880 €25500 Santa Maria della Salute (51x36cm-20x14in) s. 3-Jun-3 Sotheby's, London #123/R est:12000-18000

Works on paper

£698 $1110 €1047 Venice (17x24cm-7x9in) s.d.1896 w/C. 8-Mar-3 Dorotheum, Prague #227/R est:20000-30000 (C.KR 32000)

BRANDELER, Agnes van der (1918-) Dutch

£293 $457 €460 Interior (48x63cm-19x25in) s.d.49. 5-Nov-2 Vendu Notarishuis, Rotterdam #126/R

BRANDELIUS, Gustaf (1833-1884) Swedish

£851 $1319 €1277 Horse race (25x35cm-10x14in) s. 3-Dec-2 Bukowskis, Stockholm #288/R (S.KR 12000)
£851 $1319 €1277 Milkmaid with cow at waterway (25x34cm-10x13in) s.d.81. 4-Dec-2 AB Stockholms Auktionsverk #1790/R (S.KR 12000)
£886 $1400 €1400 Sunday picnic (60x49cm-24x19in) s.d.1865. 1-Dec-2 Bukowskis, Helsinki #236/R
£1152 $1832 €1728 Country girl on road (47x78cm-19x31in) s.d.1878. 3-Mar-3 Lilla Bukowskis, Stockholm #560 est:15000-20000 (S.KR 15500)
£1170 $1814 €1755 Farmer ploughing with oxen (72x135cm-28x53in) s.d.1860. 4-Dec-2 AB Stockholms Auktionsverk #1761/R est:20000-30000 (S.KR 16500)

BRANDENBERG, Johann (attrib) (1661-1729) Swiss

£566 $906 €849 Mary (32x25cm-13x10in) copper. 17-Mar-3 Philippe Schuler, Zurich #4503 est:1500-2000 (S.FR 1200)

BRANDENBURG, Wilhelm (1824-1901) German

£1538 $2431 €2400 River landscape with herders (48x68cm-19x27in) s. 16-Nov-2 Lempertz, Koln #1430/R est:2500
£2564 $4026 €4000 Waterfall on Schwarzach (49x45cm-19x18in) s. 21-Nov-2 Van Ham, Cologne #1495/R est:2500

BRANDENSTEIN, M van (19th C) German

£738 $1188 €1100 Portrait of Olga, Queen of Wurttemberg (64x51cm-25x20in) s.d.18 canvas on board oval. 18-Feb-3 Sotheby's, Amsterdam #1175/R

BRANDER, Fredrik (attrib) (1705-1779) Swedish

£1135 $1759 €1703 Baroness Maria Charlotta Klinckowstrom (71x56cm-28x22in) prov.lit. 3-Dec-2 Bukowskis, Stockholm #404/R est:20000-30000 (S.KR 16000)

BRANDES, Hans Heinrich Jurgen (1803-1868) German

£1603 $2532 €2500 Hunting still life (91x62cm-36x24in) s. 16-Nov-2 Lempertz, Koln #1431/R est:2700

BRANDES, Matthias (1950-) German
£1549 $2572 €2200 Partenza (90x100cm-35x39in) s.i.d.2002 verso. 10-Jun-3 Finarte Semenzato, Milan #353/R est:2000-2400

BRANDES, Peter (1944-) Danish
£2540 $3937 €3810 Composition (157x114cm-62x45in) s.d.1982 paper on canvas. 1-Oct-2 Rasmussen, Copenhagen #243/R est:30000 (D.KR 30000)
£2564 $3974 €4000 Birds nest (210x160cm-83x63in) s.d.1989 acrylic sand. 7-Dec-2 Van Ham, Cologne #71/R est:1500
Works on paper
£1058 $1641 €1587 Composition (62x88cm-24x35in) s.d.80 mixed media sold with catalogue lit. 1-Oct-2 Rasmussen, Copenhagen #255/R est:12000 (D.KR 12500)

BRANDI, Domenico (1683-1736) Italian
£8500 $13175 €12750 Landscape with shepherd playing his pipe and dairymaid with flock (51x74cm-20x29in) s. 31-Oct-2 Sotheby's, Olympia #140/R est:4000-6000

BRANDI, Domenico (attrib) (1683-1736) Italian
£2414 $3814 €3500 Shepherd with donkey, cow and sheep (56x73cm-22x29in) 5-Apr-3 Finarte Semenzato, Milan #76/R est:5000

BRANDIS, August (1862-1947) German
£314 $491 €500 Steps in country park (90x73cm-35x29in) s. 20-Sep-2 Sigalas, Stuttgart #1000/R

BRANDISH-HOLTE, Augustus (19th C) British
£400 $632 €600 Mountainous river landscape with distant cottage (39x59cm-15x23in) 28-Nov-2 Locke & England, Leamington Spa #172/R

BRANDL, Herbert (1959-) Austrian
£9929 $16085 €14000 Untitled (250x220cm-98x87in) prov. 20-May-3 Dorotheum, Vienna #106/R est:12000-16000
Works on paper
£633 $981 €1000 Untitled (50x50cm-20x20in) s.i.d.1992 verso W/C. 24-Sep-2 Wiener Kunst Auktionen, Vienna #285/R
£833 $1325 €1200 Untitled (48x50cm-19x20in) s. verso W/C. 29-Apr-3 Wiener Kunst Auktionen, Vienna #467/R
£2703 $4216 €4000 Untitled (285x152cm-112x60in) s.d.89 mixed media paper canvas exhib. 25-Mar-3 Wiener Kunst Auktionen, Vienna #48/R est:4000-7000

BRANDL, Peter (1668-1739) Bohemian
£2027 $3162 €3000 Portrait of bearded man (71x57cm-28x22in) 28-Mar-3 Delvaux, Paris #127/R est:4000

BRANDL, Peter (attrib) (1668-1739) Bohemian
£833 $1317 €1200 Saint praying (65x48cm-26x19in) 23-Apr-3 Rabourdin & Choppin de Janvry, Paris #69/R
£2065 $3222 €3098 Portrait of old man (36x29cm-14x11in) canvas on canvas. 12-Oct-2 Dorotheum, Prague #8/R est:100000-150000 (C.KR 100000)
£3169 $5261 €4500 Apostles Peter and Paul (54x43cm-21x17in) panel pair. 11-Jun-3 Dorotheum, Vienna #391/R est:3000-5000

BRANDNER, Karl (1898-?) American
£427 $700 €619 Trees (43x53cm-17x21in) s. board. 7-Jun-3 Susanin's, Chicago #5008/R
£427 $700 €619 Mountain landscape (61x69cm-24x27in) s. board. 7-Jun-3 Susanin's, Chicago #5007/R
£579 $950 €840 Michigan barn (38x43cm-15x17in) s. sold with another oil on board two. 31-May-3 Susanin's, Chicago #5027/R

BRANDON, Jacques Émile Edouard (1831-1897) French
£5063 $8000 €7595 La lecon de Talmud (9x15cm-4x6in) s.d.1869 panel. 24-Apr-3 Sotheby's, New York #122/R est:8000-12000
£5696 $9000 €9000 Die Talmudstunde (9x14cm-4x6in) s.d.1859 panel. 28-Nov-2 Dorotheum, Vienna #80/R est:10000-12000

BRANDRETH, Courtenay (?) ?
£2215 $3500 €3323 Red headed ducks in flight (76x91cm-30x36in) s.d.1924 prov. 3-Apr-3 Christie's, Rockefeller NY #193/R est:5000-7000

BRANDRIFF, George Kennedy (1890-1936) American
£3416 $5500 €5124 Seascape (19x24cm-7x9in) s. board prov. 18-Feb-3 John Moran, Pasadena #77a est:8000-12000
£4140 $6500 €6210 Trebour, France (28x36cm-11x14in) canvasboard prov. 19-Nov-2 Butterfields, San Francisco #8228/R est:6000-8000
£5484 $8500 €8226 Land patterns (64x74cm-25x29in) s. i.verso canvas on masonite prov. 29-Oct-2 John Moran, Pasadena #719 est:8000-12000

BRANDS, Eugène (1913-2002) Dutch
£269 $423 €420 Eye of the artist (20x22cm-8x9in) s.i. paper painted 57. 25-Nov-2 Glerum, Amsterdam #323/R
£833 $1375 €1200 Japanese garden (22x31cm-9x12in) s.d.6.1958 paper prov. 1-Jul-3 Christie's, Amsterdam #459/R
£845 $1318 €1268 Woman in portrait (28x23cm-11x9in) s.d.56 paper on canvas. 18-Sep-2 Kunsthallen, Copenhagen #1/R (D.KR 10000)
£929 $1449 €1394 Blauwe schaal (29x29cm-11x11in) s.d.53 s.i.verso. 18-Sep-2 Kunsthallen, Copenhagen #36/R (D.KR 11000)
£1026 $1610 €1600 Garden (30x36cm-12x14in) init. paper exec. c.1972. 25-Nov-2 Glerum, Amsterdam #214/R est:1400-1600
£1218 $1912 €1900 Night (55x50cm-22x20in) s.i.d.62 verso. 25-Nov-2 Glerum, Amsterdam #211/R est:2000-4000
£1266 $2000 €2000 De wereld van het kind (50x55cm-20x22in) s.d.1961 i.d.verso oil paper on board. 26-Nov-2 Sotheby's, Amsterdam #229/R est:2000-4000
£1795 $2782 €2800 Woman in a garden (31x31cm-12x12in) s.d.3.56 oil on paper. 3-Dec-2 Christie's, Amsterdam #89/R est:2600-3000
£1923 $2981 €3000 Besneeuwd landschap (18x44cm-7x17in) s.d.4.57 oil paper on board prov. 3-Dec-2 Christie's, Amsterdam #82/R est:2000-3000
£2564 $3974 €4000 Farmer and his chickens (30x32cm-12x13in) s.d.5.56 oil paper on board. 3-Dec-2 Christie's, Amsterdam #143/R est:4000-6000
£2692 $4173 €4200 De schilder en de kosmos (36x35cm-14x14in) s.d.4.56 oil paper on board prov. 3-Dec-2 Christie's, Amsterdam #87/R est:3000-5000
£2692 $4173 €4200 Mijmerend kind (42x50cm-17x20in) s.d.2.1960 i.verso oil paper on panel prov. 3-Dec-2 Christie's, Amsterdam #88/R est:4000-6000
£2885 $4471 €4500 Exotische vogel - exotic bird (40x49cm-16x19in) s.d.1953 oil on paper. 3-Dec-2 Christie's, Amsterdam #142/R est:4500-6000
£3846 $5962 €6000 Summer landscape (65x75cm-26x30in) s. i.d.1968 on stretcher prov. 3-Dec-2 Christie's, Amsterdam #90/R est:5000-7000
£4317 $7079 €6000 Het rode huis - red house (44x36cm-17x14in) s.d.4.51 oil gouache prov. 3-Jun-3 Christie's, Amsterdam #304/R est:4000-6000
£4827 $7675 €7000 Parisian inspiration (41x43cm-16x17in) s.d.95 oil on paper. 10-Mar-3 Sotheby's, Amsterdam #348 est:4000-6000
£6410 $9936 €10000 Love, base of the universe (125x100cm-49x39in) s. i.d.1988 on stretcher. 3-Dec-2 Christie's, Amsterdam #92/R est:7000-9000
£6410 $9936 €10000 Ochtend nevel (135x120cm-53x47in) s.verso i.d.1974 stretcher exhib.lit. 3-Dec-2 Christie's, Amsterdam #249/R est:9000-12000
£20144 $33036 €28000 De tang - pincers (65x110cm-26x43in) s.d.8.51 s.i.d.verso lit. 3-Jun-3 Christie's, Amsterdam #343/R est:28000-35000
Works on paper
£486 $802 €700 Peinture au fond ocre d'or (25x27cm-10x11in) s.i.verso gouache. 1-Jul-3 Christie's, Amsterdam #457/R
£526 $853 €800 Magic center (23x30cm-9x12in) init. s.i.d.1992 verso gouache. 21-Jan-3 Christie's, Amsterdam #519
£540 $885 €750 April snow (31x39cm-12x15in) init. gouache executed 1997. 3-Jun-3 Christie's, Amsterdam #87/R
£545 $855 €850 Portrait (39x32cm-15x13in) s.d.65 gouache. 25-Nov-2 Glerum, Amsterdam #337/R
£592 $959 €900 Untitled (30x32cm-12x13in) s. gouache. 21-Jan-3 Christie's, Amsterdam #506
£592 $959 €900 Rood venster (28x19cm-11x7in) s.i.d.1995 verso gouache cardboard. 21-Jan-3 Christie's, Amsterdam #523
£592 $959 €900 La nuit (26x26cm-10x10in) s.i.d.1991 gouache. 21-Jan-3 Christie's, Amsterdam #525
£658 $1066 €1000 Black edge (21x26cm-8x10in) s.i.d.1992 verso gouache. 21-Jan-3 Christie's, Amsterdam #524 est:1200-1600
£791 $1298 €1100 Summer time (40x53cm-16x21in) s. i.d.97 verso gouache. 3-Jun-3 Christie's, Amsterdam #81/R est:1500-2000
£855 $1386 €1300 Composition aux noir, rouge et bleu (16x24cm-6x9in) s.i.d.1994 verso gouache. 21-Jan-3 Christie's, Amsterdam #520/R est:1200-1600
£855 $1386 €1300 Landscape at sunset II (29x34cm-11x13in) init. s.i.d.1990 verso gouache. 21-Jan-3 Christie's, Amsterdam #522 est:1000-1500
£863 $1416 €1200 Landschap met accolade-teken (41x37cm-16x15in) s.d.67 s.i.d.verso gouache. 3-Jun-3 Christie's, Amsterdam #84/R est:2000-3000
£897 $1391 €1400 Garden (37x49cm-15x19in) init. d.9.VII.80 verso gouache prov. 3-Dec-2 Christie's, Amsterdam #99/R est:1600-2000
£1026 $1590 €1600 Life and universe, a mystery (42x42cm-17x17in) init. gouache executed 1989. 3-Dec-2 Christie's, Amsterdam #94/R est:1500-2000
£1026 $1590 €1600 Composition (33x30cm-13x12in) s.d.65 gouache. 3-Dec-2 Christie's, Amsterdam #126/R est:1500-2000
£1118 $1812 €1700 White triagle (21x30cm-8x12in) init. s.i.d.1991 verso gouache. 21-Jan-3 Christie's, Amsterdam #521/R est:1200-1600
£1151 $1888 €1600 Composition au fond noir (27x31cm-11x12in) s. i.d.1996 verso gouache. 3-Jun-3 Christie's, Amsterdam #77/R est:1200-1600
£1154 $1788 €1800 Landscape with red cube (39x30cm-15x12in) s.d.66 s.i.d.verso gouache prov. 3-Dec-2 Christie's, Amsterdam #91/R est:2000-3000

£1154 $1788 €1800 Fond d'or (24x52cm-9x20in) init. gouache. 3-Dec-2 Christie's, Amsterdam #128/R est:1500-2000
£1218 $1888 €1900 Een landschap, evening fall II (28x30cm-11x12in) s. s.i.3 Januari 1973-6 gouache. 3-Dec-2 Christie's, Amsterdam #98/R est:1800-2000
£1223 $2006 €1700 Triangle in secret (37x48cm-15x19in) s. i.d.Juli 1993 gouache. 3-Jun-3 Christie's, Amsterdam #79/R est:1600-1800
£1266 $2000 €2000 Untitled (50x40cm-20x16in) init. gouache. 26-Nov-2 Sotheby's, Amsterdam #43/R est:2000-3000
£1282 $1987 €2000 Universal table (58x73cm-23x29in) init. gouache. 3-Dec-2 Christie's, Amsterdam #95/R est:2200-2600
£1282 $1987 €2000 Een Zomerdag (30x37cm-12x15in) init. s.i.d.1988 verso gouache. 3-Dec-2 Christie's, Amsterdam #97/R est:1400-1600
£1410 $2186 €2200 Life before mankind (34x39cm-13x15in) gouache executed 1986. 3-Dec-2 Christie's, Amsterdam #96/R est:1500-2000
£1410 $2186 €2200 Composition (41x48cm-16x19in) gouache prov. 3-Dec-2 Christie's, Amsterdam #148/R est:1500-2000
£1603 $2484 €2500 Composition (40x43cm-16x17in) s.d.64 gouache. 3-Dec-2 Christie's, Amsterdam #130/R est:1800-2200
£1631 $2643 €2300 Woman with hood for perming (55x41cm-22x16in) s.d.1961 s.i.d.1961 verso gouache. 26-May-3 Glerum, Amsterdam #287/R est:2500-3000
£1667 $2583 €2600 Landscape with church (32x28cm-13x11in) s.d.1955 W/C gouache. 3-Dec-2 Christie's, Amsterdam #81/R est:2800-3200
£1795 $2782 €2800 Cornfield II (43x50cm-17x20in) s. s.i.d.9 Maart 1973 gouache prov. 3-Dec-2 Christie's, Amsterdam #93/R est:2400-2800
£1899 $3000 €3000 Dalende zon (40x33cm-16x13in) s.d.65 s.i.d.verso W/C. 26-Nov-2 Sotheby's, Amsterdam #50/R est:1800-2500
£1899 $3000 €3000 Practical joke (48x39cm-19x15in) s.d.62 s.i.d.verso gouache collage prov. 26-Nov-2 Sotheby's, Amsterdam #236/R est:3000-4000
£2158 $3540 €3000 Flowering landscape II (49x56cm-19x22in) s.d.64 gouache. 3-Jun-3 Christie's, Amsterdam #57/R est:3000-5000
£2215 $3500 €3500 Untitled (57x52cm-22x20in) s.d.64 s.d.verso gouache. 26-Nov-2 Sotheby's, Amsterdam #235/R est:3200-4500
£2244 $3478 €3500 De wandeling (43x50cm-17x20in) s.d.9.57 brush ink gouache oil paper on panel. 3-Dec-2 Christie's, Amsterdam #86/R est:3600-4200
£2302 $3776 €3200 Lichtmatroos (23x26cm-9x10in) s.d.1.54 s.i.d.verso gouache prov. 3-Jun-3 Christie's, Amsterdam #56/R est:2000-3000
£2405 $3800 €3800 Untitled (63x98cm-25x39in) s.d.70 gouache. 26-Nov-2 Sotheby's, Amsterdam #41/R est:2700-4000

BRANDT, Bill (1904-1983) German

Photographs

£1800 $2916 €2700 Rainswept roofs, London (19x26cm-7x10in) s. silver print edition 5/25 lit. 22-May-3 Sotheby's, London #152/R est:2000-3000
£1840 $3000 €2760 Young housewife, Bethnal Green (34x29cm-13x11in) s. gelatin silver print. 12-Feb-3 Christie's, Rockefeller NY #57/R est:3000-5000
£2025 $3200 €3038 Maillol, pomone aux bras tombants (22x19cm-9x7in) gelatin silver print. 22-Apr-3 Christie's, Rockefeller NY #163/R est:5000-7000
£2147 $3500 €3221 Francis Bacon, Primrose Hill, London (23x20cm-9x8in) i.d.1963 gelatin silver print. 12-Feb-3 Christie's, Rockefeller NY #87/R est:2000-3000
£2147 $3500 €3221 Campden Hill (34x29cm-13x11in) s. gelatin silver print. 12-Feb-3 Christie's, Rockefeller NY #222/R est:4000-6000
£2200 $3564 €3300 Rene Magritte (34x28cm-13x11in) s. silver print prov.lit. 22-May-3 Sotheby's, London #155/R est:1000-1500
£2203 $3546 €3305 Northumbrian miner at an evening meal (33x28cm-13x11in) s. laid down silver print. 9-May-3 Waddingtons, Toronto #159/R est:1800-2000 (C.D 5000)
£2405 $3800 €3608 Georges Braque (19x23cm-7x9in) gelatin silver print prov.lit. 24-Apr-3 Phillips, New York #141/R est:2000-3000
£2597 $4000 €3896 St. John's Wood (23x20cm-9x8in) photograph. 24-Oct-2 Sotheby's, New York #160/R est:3000-5000
£2785 $4400 €4400 London, East End (33x29cm-13x11in) s. silver gelatin board lit.exhib. 28-Nov-2 Villa Grisebach, Berlin #1118/R est:1500-2000
£2821 $4400 €4232 Female nude (20x18cm-8x7in) i. silver. 21-Oct-2 Swann Galleries, New York #88/R est:6000-9000
£2922 $4500 €4383 Grand Union Canal, Paddington (33x29cm-13x11in) s. gelatin silver print exec.c.1938 prov.lit. 25-Oct-2 Phillips, New York #99/R est:4000-6000
£3571 $5500 €5357 Nude no.62 (34x29cm-13x11in) s.i. photograph. 24-Oct-2 Sotheby's, New York #161/R est:3000-5000
£3571 $5500 €5357 Untitled - nude, arms and legs intertwined (61x52cm-24x20in) oversized print prov.exhib.lit. 22-Oct-2 Sotheby's, New York #99/R est:7000-10000
£3800 $6156 €5700 Campden Hill, nude (34x28cm-13x11in) s. silver print prov.lit. 22-May-3 Sotheby's, London #160/R est:400-600
£4747 $7500 €7121 Untitled (23x20cm-9x8in) i.verso gelatin silver print prov. 24-Apr-3 Phillips, New York #162/R est:6000-8000
£5500 $8910 €8250 Young housewife, Bethnal Green (25x20cm-10x8in) i.verso gelatin silver print prov. 21-May-3 Christie's, London #155/R est:1500-2000
£6962 $11000 €10443 Untitled - London, nude, breast and arm (23x20cm-9x8in) photograph. 23-Apr-3 Sotheby's, New York #178/R est:7000-10000
£7792 $12000 €11688 Untitled - nude, stomach with arm and breasts (61x52cm-24x20in) oversized photograph prov.exhib.lit. 22-Oct-2 Sotheby's, New York #100/R est:7000-10000
£8000 $12960 €12000 Campden Hill, nude (24x20cm-9x8in) st.verso silver print exec.c.1960 prov.lit. 22-May-3 Sotheby's, London #145/R est:800-1200
£10127 $16000 €15191 East Sussex Coast (25x20cm-10x8in) st.verso num.91 gelatin silver print prov.lit. 24-Apr-3 Phillips, New York #37/R est:10000-15000
£11656 $19000 €17484 Nude, London (34x29cm-13x11in) s. gelatin silver print. 12-Feb-3 Christie's, Rockefeller NY #221/R est:9000-12000

BRANDT, Carl (1852-1930) Swedish

£297 $473 €446 Evening sunshine on the pine trees (90x123cm-35x48in) s. 2-Mar-3 Uppsala Auktionskammare, Uppsala #76 (S.KR 4000)
£412 $626 €618 Coastal landscape at sunset (70x130cm-28x51in) s.d.1907. 16-Aug-2 Lilla Bukowskis, Stockholm #743 (S.KR 6000)
£526 $831 €789 Sunny winter landscape (60x95cm-24x37in) s. 30-Nov-2 Goteborg Auktionsverk, Sweden #138/R (S.KR 7500)
£720 $1123 €1080 Mountain landscape (103x99cm-41x39in) s.d.1907. 13-Sep-2 Lilla Bukowskis, Stockholm #380 (S.KR 10500)
£892 $1356 €1338 Winter landscape with red cottage in sunshine (59x93cm-23x37in) s. 16-Aug-2 Lilla Bukowskis, Stockholm #742 (S.KR 13000)
£1158 $1923 €1679 Winter landscape (70x89cm-28x35in) s/. 16-Jun-3 Lilla Bukowskis, Stockholm #813 est:10000-12000 (S.KR 15000)
£1408 $2268 €2000 Evening light (66x92cm-26x36in) s.d.1913. 10-May-3 Bukowskis, Helsinki #358/R est:1000-1200
£1489 $2309 €2234 Winter landscape with cottage in the distance (90x126cm-35x50in) s,. 3-Dec-2 Bukowskis, Stockholm #257/R est:20000-25000 (S.KR 21000)

Works on paper

£335 $532 €503 Moonlit landscape (106x70cm-42x28in) s.d.99 pastel. 2-Mar-3 Uppsala Auktionskammare, Uppsala #295 (S.KR 4500)

BRANDT, Charles (18/19th C) ?

£280 $456 €420 Portrait of a gentleman (52x40cm-20x16in) s.d.1811. 12-Feb-3 Bonhams, Knightsbridge #16

BRANDT, Edgar (1880-1960) French

Sculpture

£3448 $5483 €5000 Antilopes (17x16x8cm-7x6x3in) s. wrought iron book ends pair. 5-Mar-3 Doutrebente, Paris #138/R est:900-1300
£31646 $50000 €50000 Cobra dresse (127x30x30cm-50x12x12in) gilt pat bronze marble cast iron lit. 26-Nov-2 Tajan, Paris #26/R est:50000-70000

BRANDT, Fritz (1853-1905) Canadian/German

£566 $883 €900 Street near Chiogia near Venice (60x40cm-24x16in) s. prov. 19-Sep-2 Dr Fritz Nagel, Stuttgart #911/R

BRANDT, I H (1850-1926) Danish

£254 $391 €381 Coastal landscape with cliffs, Bornholm (32x47cm-13x19in) s.d.1890. 26-Oct-2 Rasmussen, Havnen #2169/R (D.KR 3000)
£255 $398 €383 Waves (28x42cm-11x17in) s.d.1898. 5-Aug-2 Rasmussen, Vejle #244 (D.KR 3000)
£302 $462 €453 Breakers (27x42cm-11x17in) s.d.1918. 24-Aug-2 Rasmussen, Havnen #2009 (D.KR 3500)
£438 $701 €657 Coastal landscape with cliffs, Bornholm (32x46cm-13x18in) s.d.1890. 13-Jan-3 Rasmussen, Vejle #83/R (D.KR 5000)
£442 $689 €663 Interior scene with girl reading (71x49cm-28x19in) s.d.1890. 5-Aug-2 Rasmussen, Vejle #11/R (D.KR 5200)
£515 $803 €773 Coastal landscape with the lion heads at Bornholm (45x65cm-18x26in) s.d.1887. 11-Nov-2 Rasmussen, Vejle #625 (D.KR 6000)
£592 $911 €888 Coastal landscape with cliffs, Bornholm (45x68cm-18x27in) s.d.1897. 26-Oct-2 Rasmussen, Havnen #2183/R (D.KR 7000)
£603 $916 €905 Breakers against the shore (62x96cm-24x38in) s.d.1917. 27-Aug-2 Rasmussen, Copenhagen #1748/R (D.KR 7000)
£724 $1122 €1086 Breakers (75x112cm-30x44in) s.d.1921. 28-Sep-2 Rasmussen, Havnen #2027 (D.KR 8500)
£766 $1240 €1111 Landscape with Dyndalebaekken near Gudhjem (32x38cm-13x15in) init.d.1879. 26-May-3 Rasmussen, Copenhagen #1306/R (D.KR 8000)
£851 $1345 €1277 Breakers by coastal cliffs, Bornholm (62x96cm-24x38in) s.d.1913. 2-Dec-2 Rasmussen, Copenhagen #1398/R (D.KR 10000)

BRANDT, Johannes Herman (1850-1926) Danish

£769 $1169 €1200 View of Alp peak near Garmish-Partenkirchen (63x49cm-25x19in) s.d.1913 lit. 11-Jul-2 Allgauer, Kempten #2449/R

BRANDT, Josef von (1841-1915) Polish
£22000 $34100 €33000 Lone hunter (47x82cm-19x32in) s. painted 1881. 4-Dec-2 Christie's, London #81/R est:15000-20000
£48000 $76320 €72000 Cavalry assault (76x128cm-30x50in) s.i. 18-Mar-3 Bonhams, New Bond Street #22/R est:20000-30000
£55000 $87450 €82500 Cavalry skirmish on the outskirts of a town (76x128cm-30x50in) s.i. 18-Mar-3 Bonhams, New Bond Street #21/R est:10000-15000
£90323 $140000 €135485 Caravan (76x132cm-30x52in) s.i.d.1881. 29-Oct-2 Sotheby's, New York #113/R est:50000-70000

BRANDT, Josef von (circle) (1841-1915) Polish
£11565 $18388 €17000 Cossack fighters on horseback in winter landscape (132x88cm-52x35in) i. 19-Mar-3 Neumeister, Munich #519/R est:12000

BRANDT, Muriel (1909-1981) Irish
£1761 $2747 €2800 Sinead, Bean de Valera (37x30cm-15x12in) s. i.verso board prov. 17-Sep-2 Whyte's, Dublin #100/R est:2000-3000
Works on paper
£310 $514 €440 Portrait of a young boy (53x39cm-21x15in) s. W/C. 10-Jun-3 James Adam, Dublin #76/R

BRANDT, Otto (1828-1892) German
£291 $454 €460 Vue nocturne d'un moulin (15x20cm-6x8in) s. cardboard. 16-Oct-2 Hotel des Ventes Mosan, Brussels #152

BRANDT, Ruth (1936-1989) Irish
£943 $1472 €1500 Still life with mackerel and shell fish (51x38cm-20x15in) 17-Sep-2 Whyte's, Dublin #105/R est:1500-2000

BRANDTNER, Fritz (1896-1969) Canadian
Works on paper
£215 $335 €323 New Brunswick coast (28x38cm-11x15in) s.i.d.68 gouache. 25-Mar-3 Ritchie, Toronto #119/R (C.D 500)
£238 $390 €357 Abstract composition (27x35cm-11x14in) s. ink W/C. 6-Feb-3 Heffel, Vancouver #008/R (C.D 600)
£325 $511 €488 Couple assis (25x20cm-10x8in) s. ink wash. 12-Dec-2 Iegor de Saint Hippolyte, Montreal #15 (C.D 800)
£437 $716 €656 Gaspe No.25 (14x20cm-6x8in) s. gouache mixed media. 6-Feb-3 Heffel, Vancouver #009/R (C.D 1100)
£558 $870 €837 Artist's tent, Georgian Bay (48x61cm-19x24in) s. mixed media cardboard. 25-Mar-3 Iegor de Saint Hippolyte, Montreal #16 (C.D 1300)
£578 $948 €867 Laurentian mountain railway (31x37cm-12x15in) s.d.43 W/C ink. 3-Jun-3 Joyner, Toronto #567 est:700-900 (C.D 1300)
£645 $1019 €968 Abstract composition (15x20cm-6x8in) s. col ink paper on board prov. 14-Nov-2 Heffel, Vancouver #3/R est:1400-1800 (C.D 1600)
£913 $1424 €1523 Moonlight, Alma (44x54cm-17x21in) s.i.d.1968 W/C prov. 13-Apr-3 Levis, Calgary #9/R est:2000-2500 (C.D 2100)
£1000 $1640 €1500 Abstract design - landscape (27x35cm-11x14in) s.d.39 s.i.d.verso ink gouache on board prov. 27-May-3 Sotheby's, Toronto #171/R est:3000-5000 (C.D 2250)
£1030 $1607 €1545 Georgian Bay (42x55cm-17x22in) s.i.d.1946 W/C prov. 25-Mar-3 Ritchie, Toronto #118/R est:1200-1500 (C.D 2400)

BRANE, Jerry (20th C) American
£258 $400 €387 Vessel, rock nude (180x165cm-71x65in) acrylic crayon fabric collage. 7-Dec-2 Harvey Clar, Oakland #1226
£323 $500 €485 Feminie landscape I (168x305cm-66x120in) 7-Dec-2 Harvey Clar, Oakland #1228

BRANEGAN, John F (1843-1909) British/Irish
£600 $948 €900 Bait diggers and Whitby Harbour (30x46cm-12x18in) board. 24-Apr-3 Richardson & Smith, Whitby #155/R
Works on paper
£260 $406 €390 Fishing boats and figures on the beach (15x24cm-6x9in) W/C. 10-Sep-2 David Duggleby, Scarborough #233
£290 $452 €435 Sunderland, fishing boats becalmed (25x46cm-10x18in) s.i. W/C. 10-Sep-2 David Duggleby, Scarborough #105
£350 $550 €525 Yarmouth fisher folk and boats on the beach (25x45cm-10x18in) s.i. W/C. 10-Dec-2 Lane, Penzance #83
£360 $569 €540 Evening off Whitby (25x46cm-10x18in) s. W/C. 24-Apr-3 Richardson & Smith, Whitby #129/R
£380 $593 €570 Beach, Whitby (17x36cm-7x14in) s.i. W/C. 10-Sep-2 David Duggleby, Scarborough #70/R
£400 $624 €600 Staithes, steam tug and fishing boats (26x47cm-10x19in) s.i. W/C. 10-Sep-2 David Duggleby, Scarborough #130
£440 $695 €660 Misty morning, Whitby (25x46cm-10x18in) s.i. W/C. 24-Apr-3 Richardson & Smith, Whitby #131
£450 $702 €675 Moonlight, Whitby (38x51cm-15x20in) s.i. W/C. 18-Oct-2 Keys, Aylsham #535
£460 $718 €690 Fishing boats beached at Upgang, near Whitby (15x24cm-6x9in) s. W/C. 10-Sep-2 David Duggleby, Scarborough #232
£460 $727 €690 Off Whitby (18x33cm-7x13in) s.i. W/C. 24-Apr-3 Richardson & Smith, Whitby #108/R
£560 $874 €840 Misty sunrise, Whitby (26x47cm-10x19in) s. W/C. 10-Sep-2 David Duggleby, Scarborough #62/R
£580 $905 €870 Sunset off Whitby (41x55cm-16x22in) s.i. W/C. 10-Sep-2 David Duggleby, Scarborough #68
£580 $916 €870 Whitby (23x48cm-9x19in) i. W/C. 24-Apr-3 Richardson & Smith, Whitby #170/R
£600 $936 €900 Sandsend, near Whitby (25x48cm-10x19in) s.i. W/C. 10-Sep-2 David Duggleby, Scarborough #71
£620 $967 €930 Moonrise on the Medway (35x53cm-14x21in) s.i. W/C. 10-Sep-2 David Duggleby, Scarborough #199/R
£620 $967 €930 Morning on the Thames (35x53cm-14x21in) s.i. W/C. 10-Sep-2 David Duggleby, Scarborough #200
£620 $1035 €899 Grimsby (23x43cm-9x17in) s.i.d. W/C. 26-Jun-3 Richardson & Smith, Whitby #543
£640 $1024 €960 Moon rise on the Medway (36x53cm-14x21in) s.i. W/C. 11-Mar-3 David Duggleby, Scarborough #100/R
£650 $1014 €975 Grimsby (23x46cm-9x18in) s.i. W/C. 20-Sep-2 Richardson & Smith, Whitby #147
£660 $1049 €990 Fishing boats off coast, North Shields (35x51cm-14x20in) s.i. W/C. 27-Feb-3 Bonhams, Chester #430
£660 $1056 €990 Belfast Lough - becalmed shipping off the coast (23x53cm-9x21in) s.i. W/C. 11-Mar-3 David Duggleby, Scarborough #45/R
£700 $1141 €1050 Misty morning, Whitby. Evening off Whitby (25x43cm-10x17in) s.indis.d. W/C pair. 14-Feb-3 Keys, Aylsham #482
£780 $1232 €1170 Grimsby (20x46cm-8x18in) i. W/C. 24-Apr-3 Richardson & Smith, Whitby #173

BRANEHAN, J F (19th C) ?
Works on paper
£521 $850 €782 Maritime scenes (25x46cm-10x18in) pair W/C. 2-Feb-3 Grogan, Boston #34

BRANGWYN, Sir Frank (1867-1956) British
£2800 $4340 €4200 Second marriage (45x55cm-18x22in) i. board. 24-Sep-2 Bonhams, New Bond Street #54/R est:600-800
£7500 $12300 €11250 Canal, Venice (57x75cm-22x30in) mono. card on canvas prov.lit. 3-Jun-3 Sotheby's, Olympia #38/R est:5000-7000
£9000 $14130 €13500 Flood time (56x41cm-22x16in) s.d.88. 22-Nov-2 Christie's, London #22/R est:6000-8000
£37975 $60000 €56963 Buccaneers (206x231cm-81x91in) s. prov.exhib.lit. 24-Apr-3 Sotheby's, New York #90/R est:30000-50000
£160000 $252800 €240000 Fowey Harbour, Cornwall (93x81cm-37x32in) s.d.1887 prov.exhib.lit. 27-Nov-2 Christie's, London #27/R est:160000-220000
Works on paper
£252 $387 €400 Les halles de Malines (21x42cm-8x17in) s. W/C. 22-Oct-2 Campo, Vlaamse Kaai #34
£320 $509 €480 Study of Christ (81x102cm-32x40in) dr. 29-Apr-3 Gorringes, Lewes #2269
£350 $546 €525 Bridge with cottage beyond. W/C. 19-Sep-2 John Bellman, Billingshurst #1351
£350 $546 €525 Windmill. pastel W/C. 19-Sep-2 John Bellman, Billingshurst #1353
£400 $624 €600 Cahors, night time of Toulouse. W/C. 19-Sep-2 John Bellman, Billingshurst #1352
£420 $647 €630 Monk and scholars (51x41cm-20x16in) pencil. 3-Sep-2 Gorringes, Lewes #2264
£460 $736 €690 Study of quarrymen (53x76cm-21x30in) mono. chl. 13-Mar-3 Duke & Son, Dorchester #105/R
£560 $868 €840 Spoils of piracy (25x37cm-10x15in) init. W/C over pencil htd gouache. 2-Oct-2 Bonhams, Knowle #36
£700 $1085 €1050 Street scene (20x24cm-8x9in) mono. pencil W/C. 24-Sep-2 Bonhams, New Bond Street #23/R
£700 $1085 €1050 Female nude with arm raised (28x12cm-11x5in) mono. col chk. 4-Dec-2 Christie's, Kensington #215
£850 $1318 €1275 Old oak trees, Sussex (53x71cm-21x28in) mono. chl W/C wash. 24-Sep-2 Bonhams, New Bond Street #24
£850 $1386 €1275 Lazy bones (29x42cm-11x17in) init. pencil sanguine. 29-Jan-3 Dreweatt Neate, Newbury #59/R
£1800 $2952 €2700 Market day, Furnes, Belgium (54x70cm-21x28in) init.d.1908 W/C bodycol. 4-Feb-3 Bonhams, Leeds #294 est:1200-1800
£2000 $3160 €3000 Venetian canal at night (69x53cm-27x21in) mono. pencil W/C. 27-Nov-2 Sotheby's, Olympia #97/R est:1000-1500
£2000 $3260 €3000 Figures in boats with bridge and town beyond (41x56cm-16x22in) s.d.1936. 28-Jan-3 Gorringes, Lewes #1794 est:800-1200

BRANGWYN, Sir Frank (attrib) (1867-1956) British
Works on paper
£350 $574 €508 Venice (9x13cm-4x5in) mono. W/C. 1-Jun-3 Lots Road, London #337

BRANSCOMBE, Charles (fl.1803-1819) British
£1200 $1872 €1800 Three hunters and a groom (82x116cm-32x46in) s.i.d.1809. 6-Nov-2 Sotheby's, Olympia #39/R est:800-1200

BRANSOM, Paul (1885-1979) American
Works on paper
£253 $400 €380 Indian pony raid (30x59cm-12x23in) s. chl pastel prov. 3-Apr-3 Christie's, Rockefeller NY #133/R
£2174 $3500 €3261 Muskrats escaping albino beaver (46x30cm-18x12in) s. chl W/C lit. 10-May-3 Illustration House, New York #58/R est:1800-2400

BRANWHITE, Charles (1817-1880) British
£580 $945 €870 View in Leigh Woods, Bristol (57x42cm-22x17in) s. i.verso panel. 30-Jan-3 Lawrence, Crewkerne #720/R
£3600 $5724 €5400 Lumber wagon passing an old mill in the snow (69x105cm-27x41in) s.d.1853. 4-Mar-3 Bristol Auction Rooms #323/R est:2500-3500
Works on paper
£550 $863 €825 River landscape in South Wales (45x76cm-18x30in) s.d.1869 W/C. 20-Nov-2 Sotheby's, Olympia #25/R
£600 $972 €900 Chain ferry (39x69cm-15x27in) s.d.1867 W/C bodycol. 21-May-3 Bonhams, Knightsbridge #21/R
£780 $1232 €1131 Trap set in a dam on an upland stream (39x61cm-15x24in) s. W/C htd white. 22-Jul-3 Bristol Auction Rooms #346/R

BRANWHITE, Charles Brooke (1851-1929) British
£559 $900 €839 Winter landscape at dusk (51x76cm-20x30in) s. 19-Feb-3 Doyle, New York #42
£1000 $1590 €1500 Waterwill in winter (39x32cm-15x13in) init.d.52 panel. 4-Mar-3 Bearnes, Exeter #472/R est:1000-1500
£1100 $1760 €1650 In Bracelet Bay near the Mumbles. Pennard Castle, Gower, South Wales (25x36cm-10x14in) mono.i. pair. 14-Mar-3 Gardiner & Houlgate, Bath #224/R est:1000-1500
Works on paper
£320 $499 €480 Extensive moorland scene with shepherd and flock (33x66cm-13x26in) s. W/C. 9-Apr-3 Andrew Hartley, Ilkley #899
£500 $790 €750 Figures and sheep on Exmoor (56x92cm-22x36in) s. W/C bodycol. 2-Dec-2 Bonhams, Bath #17

BRAQUAVAL, Louis (1856-1919) French
£1500 $2445 €2250 Place de l'Hotel de Ville, Paris (50x61cm-20x24in) s. 13-Feb-3 Christie's, Kensington #228/R est:1500-2000
£1875 $2850 €2813 Marche au Boulogne (38x46cm-15x18in) s. board. 3-Jul-2 Naón & Cia, Buenos Aires #54/R est:2500-3500

BRAQUE, Georges (1882-1963) French
£32051 $50000 €48077 Falaise et bateaux (23x30cm-9x12in) s.d.30 prov.lit. 7-Nov-2 Christie's, Rockefeller NY #297/R est:40000-60000
£48077 $75000 €72116 Compotier et mandoline (46x55cm-18x22in) s. oil paper on canvas painted c.1942 prov. 6-Nov-2 Sotheby's, New York #200/R est:50000-70000
£60000 $100200 €87000 Theiere au bec pointu et pommes (19x33cm-7x13in) s. prov.lit. 24-Jun-3 Christie's, London #17/R est:14000-18000
£64103 $100000 €96155 Pichet, pommes, raisins et verre (31x65cm-12x26in) s. oil sand painted c.1924. 7-Nov-2 Christie's, Rockefeller NY #305/R est:90000-120000
£68323 $110000 €102485 Nature morte a la de trefle (29x31cm-11x12in) s. oil sand on canvas prov.exhib.lit. 8-May-3 Christie's, Rockefeller NY #181/R est:120000-160000
£144231 $225000 €216347 Les arums (120x41cm-47x16in) s. oil sand painted 1941 prov.exhib.lit. 7-Nov-2 Christie's, Rockefeller NY #349/R est:200000-300000
£256410 $400000 €384615 Balustre et crane (45x55cm-18x22in) s.d.38 s.verso prov.exhib.lit. 6-Nov-2 Christie's, Rockefeller NY #53/R est:500000-700000
£282051 $440000 €423077 Nature morte a la pipe (46x55cm-18x22in) s. s.verso oil sand painted 1919 prov.exhib.lit. 5-Nov-2 Sotheby's, New York #28/R est:450000-550000
Prints
£1887 $3000 €2831 Le signe (30x19cm-12x7in) s.num.9/30 grey metallic gold lithograph. 29-Apr-3 Christie's, Rockefeller NY #449/R est:1000-1500
£1923 $3000 €2885 Tete Grecque (53x34cm-21x13in) s.num.12/197 col lithograph. 7-Nov-2 Swann Galleries, New York #554/R est:4000-6000
£1923 $2981 €3000 Untitled (29x24cm-11x9in) s. num.33/50 col eau forte. 4-Dec-2 Finarte, Milan #23/R est:4000
£1923 $2981 €3000 Les etoiles (32x38cm-13x15in) s. col lithograph. 7-Dec-2 Hauswedell & Nolte, Hamburg #562/R est:3500
£2025 $3139 €3200 From 'Cinq posies en hommage a Georges Braque (20x56cm-8x22in) s. num.49/75 col lithograph. 28-Sep-2 Ketterer, Hamburg #292/R est:3000-4000
£2051 $3241 €3200 Theogonie (37x30cm-15x12in) s. eau forte lit. 15-Nov-2 Farsetti, Prato #341/R
£2051 $3179 €3200 Qui ne se grime pas (56x43cm-22x17in) s.d.1923 aquatint drypoint lit. 4-Dec-2 Pierre Berge, Paris #2/R
£2051 $3179 €3200 Large blue bird (55x112cm-22x44in) s.num.89/95 col lithograph. 7-Dec-2 Van Ham, Cologne #73/R est:6000
£2100 $3297 €3150 Oiseau des forets (72x53cm-28x21in) s.num.33/75 col lithograph. 17-Apr-3 Christie's, Kensington #199/R est:2500-3000
£2174 $3370 €3261 Pommes et feuilles (30x45cm-12x18in) s. lithograph. 4-Dec-2 Koller, Zurich #318/R est:5000-7000 (S.FR 5000)
£2192 $3419 €3200 Personnage sur fond rose (39x25cm-15x10in) s.i. col lithograph. 11-Apr-3 Winterberg, Heidelberg #762/R est:2750
£2200 $3388 €3300 Dans le Ciel (24x32cm-9x13in) s.i. col lithograph. 24-Oct-2 Christie's, Kensington #188/R est:2000-2500
£2244 $3478 €3500 Untitled (26x33cm-10x13in) col etching. 4-Dec-2 Lempertz, Koln #580/R est:3600
£2308 $3577 €3600 Grand oiseau bleu (37x104cm-15x41in) s. num.31/95 lithograph. 4-Dec-2 Pierre Berge, Paris #1/R
£2436 $3800 €3654 Si je mourais la-bas (33x58cm-13x23in) s.i. col wood engraving. 18-Sep-2 Swann Galleries, New York #92/R est:3000-5000
£2453 $3826 €3680 Char noir - Char V (24x30cm-9x12in) s.num.28/75 col etching aquatint lit. 5-Nov-2 Bukowskis, Stockholm #502/R est:40000-50000 (S.KR 35000)
£2516 $4000 €3774 Oiseau de passage (59x41cm-23x16in) s.num.28/75 col aquatint. 2-May-3 Sotheby's, New York #87/R est:4000-6000
£2564 $4000 €3846 Thalassa I (11x27cm-4x11in) s.num.20/60 col etching aquatint. 7-Nov-2 Swann Galleries, New York #552/R est:4000-6000
£2564 $3974 €4000 Pommes et feuilles (30x45cm-12x18in) s. col lithograph. 4-Dec-2 Lempertz, Koln #579/R est:3800
£2580 $4153 €3870 Oiseaux en vol (71x58cm-28x23in) s.num.51/75 lithograph. 12-May-3 Stephan Welz, Johannesburg #426/R est:30000-40000 (SA.R 30000)
£2837 $4596 €4000 Athene (57x38cm-22x15in) s. num.47/75 col lithograph lit. 23-May-3 Camard, Paris #109/R est:4500-5500
£3000 $4950 €4350 Oiseau traversant un nuage (41x69cm-16x27in) s.i. col lithograph. 2-Jul-3 Christie's, London #54/R est:3000-5000
£3038 $4800 €4800 Le char II - le char (49x65cm-19x26in) s. col lithograph. 30-Nov-2 Villa Grisebach, Berlin #389/R est:4000-5000
£3041 $4743 €4500 Si je mourais la-bas (26x24cm-10x9in) s. col xilograph lit. 26-Mar-3 Finarte Semenzato, Milan #29/R
£3145 $5000 €4718 Si je mourais la bas (73x47cm-29x19in) s.i. col wood engraving. 2-May-3 Sotheby's, New York #88/R est:6000-8000
£3194 $5046 €4791 L'atelier (42x52cm-17x20in) s.num.74/75 col lithograph. 28-Apr-3 Bukowskis, Stockholm #349/R est:35000-40000 (S.KR 42000)
£3205 $4968 €5000 Magic quotidienne (33x50cm-13x20in) s.num.36/70 aquatint exec.1959. 6-Dec-2 Ketterer, Munich #146/R est:5000-7000
£3333 $5467 €4600 Oiseau bleu (30x37cm-12x15in) s. col etching. 29-May-3 Lempertz, Koln #552/R est:4500
£3590 $5600 €5385 L'oiseau de feu (36x34cm-14x13in) s.num.58/78 col etching. 7-Nov-2 Swann Galleries, New York #551/R est:6000-9000
£3600 $5616 €5400 From, L'ordre des oiseaux (39x49cm-15x19in) s.num.25/30 etching aquatint. 25-Mar-3 Sotheby's, London #66/R est:2000-3000
£3774 $6000 €5661 Etude de nu (27x20cm-11x8in) etching. 2-May-3 Sotheby's, New York #80/R est:4000-6000
£3819 $6302 €5500 Feuillage en couleurs (66x51cm-26x20in) s.num.21/60 col etching aquatint. 2-Jul-3 Artcurial Briest, Paris #12/R est:5000-6000
£3871 $6000 €5807 L'oiseau de feu (64x58cm-25x23in) s.num.67/75 col etching. 25-Sep-2 Christie's, Rockefeller NY #43/R est:5000-7000
£4000 $6200 €6000 Equinox (52x77cm-20x30in) s.num.27/75 col lithograph. 3-Dec-2 Christie's, London #95/R est:3500-4500
£4088 $6500 €6132 Le char (49x65cm-19x26in) s.num.62/75 col lithograph. 29-Apr-3 Christie's, Rockefeller NY #448/R est:5000-7000
£4088 $6500 €6132 Oiseau verni (22x32cm-9x13in) s.num.41/75 varnish lithograph. 29-Apr-3 Christie's, Rockefeller NY #450/R est:3500-4500
£4403 $7000 €6605 Au couchant (48x65cm-19x26in) s.num.36/75 col lithograph. 29-Apr-3 Christie's, Rockefeller NY #455/R est:7000-9000
£4783 $7413 €7175 Oiseau sur fond carmin (32x43cm-13x17in) s. etching. 4-Dec-2 Koller, Zurich #316/R est:11000-15000 (S.FR 11000)
£4808 $7452 €7500 From: the order of the birds (33x47cm-13x19in) col etching. 4-Dec-2 Lempertz, Koln #581/R est:8000
£4930 $8183 €7000 Oiseau noir sur fond vert (42x31cm-17x12in) s.i. col woodcut. 14-Jun-3 Hauswedell & Nolte, Hamburg #1054/R est:6000
£5346 $8500 €8019 Etude de nu (28x20cm-11x8in) s.num.16/30 etching. 29-Apr-3 Christie's, Rockefeller NY #447/R est:7000-9000
£5660 $9000 €8490 L'oiseau de fue (40x38cm-16x15in) s.num.12/50 col etching. 29-Apr-3 Christie's, Rockefeller NY #454/R est:4500-6500
£5975 $9500 €8963 Paris, nature morte sur une table (20x28cm-8x11in) etching. 2-May-3 Sotheby's, New York #81/R est:4000-6000
£6329 $10000 €10000 Theiere et citrons (50x65cm-20x26in) s.i. col lithograph. 30-Nov-2 Villa Grisebach, Berlin #388/R est:10000-12000
£6410 $9936 €10000 Vol de nuit - oiseau XII (38x68cm-15x27in) s. col lithograph. 4-Dec-2 Lempertz, Koln #578/R est:12000-14000
£6918 $11000 €10377 Oiseau traversant un nuage (41x69cm-16x27in) s.num.19/75 col lithograph. 29-Apr-3 Christie's, Rockefeller NY #452/R est:7000-9000
£7547 $12000 €11321 Vol de nuit (39x69cm-15x27in) s.num.12/75 col lithograph. 29-Apr-3 Christie's, Rockefeller NY #453/R est:15000-20000
£9375 $14812 €13500 Les amaryllis (76x56cm-30x22in) s.num.68/75 etching. 26-Apr-3 Cornette de St.Cyr, Paris #17/R est:12000-15000
£11950 $19000 €17925 Bass (45x33cm-18x13in) etching. 2-May-3 Sotheby's, New York #82/R est:8000-12000
£13208 $21000 €19812 Composition, nature morte (34x22cm-13x9in) s.num.49/50 etching. 2-May-3 Sotheby's, New York #83/R est:18000-24000

£16352 $26000 €24528 Bass (46x33cm-18x13in) s.i. etching drypoint. 3-Mar-3 Swann Galleries, New York #37/R est:25000-35000

Sculpture
£4231 $6642 €6600 Alphee (8cm-3in) st.sig. gold lit. 11-Dec-2 Artcurial Briest, Paris #618/R

Works on paper
£6757 $10541 €10000 Coupe aux citrons (30x47cm-12x19in) s. ink dr prov. 26-Mar-3 Tajan, Paris #32/R
£17986 $28777 €25000 Nu allonge et drape (13x20cm-5x8in) init. W/C. 18-May-3 Eric Pillon, Calais #65/R
£18000 $29520 €27000 Nature morte au pichet et fruits (47x54cm-19x21in) s. pastel card prov. 6-Feb-3 Christie's, London #449/R est:30000

BRAQUE, Georges (after) (1882-1963) French
Prints
£4747 $7500 €7500 Hommage a J S Bach (44x59cm-17x23in) s. col etching. 27-Nov-2 Dorotheum, Vienna #225/R est:6500-7000

BRASCASSAT, Jacques Raymond (attrib) (1804-1867) French
£1321 $2113 €1982 Woman with children, goats and dog in meadow (98x130cm-39x51in) 17-Mar-3 Philippe Schuler, Zurich #8622 est:2500-3500 (S.FR 2800)

BRASCH, August (19th C) German
£4747 $7405 €7500 Marchande et son ane allant au marche (75x60cm-30x24in) s.i.d.1853. 16-Sep-2 Horta, Bruxelles #89/R

BRASCH, Hans (1882-1973) German
Works on paper
£823 $1300 €1300 Girl with cat (65x50cm-26x20in) s.d.1926 W/C lit. 29-Nov-2 Schloss Ahlden, Ahlden #1423/R

BRASCH, Sven (1886-1970) Danish
Works on paper
£696 $1162 €1009 Oriental scene (35x28cm-14x11in) s. Indian ink W/C pencil. 17-Jun-3 Rasmussen, Copenhagen #185/R (D.KR 7300)

BRASCH, Wenzel Ignaz (?-1761) Czechoslovakian
£1474 $2285 €2300 Deer hunt (37x51cm-15x20in) indis.s. 4-Dec-2 Neumeister, Munich #631/R est:1500

BRASCH, Wenzel Ignaz (attrib) (?-1761) Czechoslovakian
£1401 $2158 €2200 Wolf with dead game. Deer (9x14cm-4x6in) copper two. 5-Sep-2 Arnold, Frankfurt #837 est:4000

BRASEN, Hans (1849-1930) Danish
£606 $964 €909 Town view with church and harbour (48x69cm-19x27in) with sig.d.1872 verso. 5-May-3 Rasmussen, Vejle #378/R (D.KR 6500)
£1723 $2739 €2585 Country girl chasing geese off lake (19x26cm-7x10in) mono. panel. 5-Mar-3 Rasmussen, Copenhagen #1598/R est:15000 (D.KR 18500)
£3259 $5182 €4889 Sorup near Esrom Lake, summer evening (86x114cm-34x45in) s. exhib. 10-Mar-3 Rasmussen, Vejle #106/R est:30000 (D.KR 35000)
£3636 $5891 €5272 Old farm with couple, Reerso (80x106cm-31x42in) s.d.1904. 26-May-3 Rasmussen, Copenhagen #1166/R est:30000 (D.KR 38000)

BRASILIER, Andre (1929-) French
£3600 $5544 €5400 Le Manoire de la Touche en Anjou (54x65cm-21x26in) s. 23-Oct-2 Sotheby's, Olympia #629/R est:4000-6000
£5660 $9000 €8490 Paysage au champ de ble (81x65cm-32x26in) s.d.1953 prov.exhib.lit. 27-Feb-3 Christie's, Rockefeller NY #109/R est:7000
£6748 $11000 €10122 Femme assise (81x54cm-32x21in) s. 12-Feb-3 Sotheby's, New York #127/R est:10000-15000
£7278 $11500 €11500 Courses a Maison Lafitte (73x100cm-29x39in) s. s.i.verso exhib. 2-Dec-2 Tajan, Paris #57/R
£10968 $17329 €17000 Cavaliers sur la plage (73x100cm-29x39in) s. i.d.1991 verso. 19-Dec-2 Delvaux, Paris #48/R est:10000
£16774 $26000 €25161 Chantal a la corbeille des fruits (73x92cm-29x36in) s. s.i.d.1965 verso prov.exhib. 26-Sep-2 Christie's, Rockefeller NY #620/R est:10000-15000

BRASS, Hans (1885-1959) German
Works on paper
£443 $700 €700 Locomotive (42x27cm-17x11in) s.d.51 pen. 30-Nov-2 Bassenge, Berlin #6152/R

BRASSAI (1899-1984) Hungarian/French
£630 $977 €945 Bathing (24x29cm-9x11in) tempera board painted c.1940. 1-Oct-2 SOGA, Bratislava #127/R est:38000 (SL.K 40000)

Photographs
£1948 $3000 €2922 Conchita with sailors, place d'Italie, Paris (21x30cm-8x12in) s.i.d.1932 num.8/40 photograph. 24-Oct-2 Sotheby's, New York #148/R est:3000-5000
£2400 $3888 €3600 Large scale object, shoelaces (23x17cm-9x7in) i gelatin silver print exec.c.1930 exhib. 21-May-3 Christie's, London #140/R est:3000-5000
£2658 $4200 €3987 Port de Marseille (23x18cm-9x7in) gelatin silver print prov.lit. 24-Apr-3 Phillips, New York #140/R est:4000-6000
£2885 $4558 €4500 La rue Seguier (24x18cm-9x7in) st.verso gelatin silver print exec.c.1933 prov. 16-Nov-2 Christie's, Paris #280/R est:5000-7000
£3291 $5200 €4937 Nude (23x17cm-9x7in) gelatin silver print executed c.1931-33 prov.lit. 24-Apr-3 Phillips, New York #99a est:6000-8000
£3797 $6000 €5696 Bebe a la creme eclipse (27x20cm-11x8in) gelatin silver print prov.lit. 22-Apr-3 Christie's, Rockefeller NY #83/R est:7000-9000
£3846 $6000 €5769 Couple d'amoreux dans un cafe (29x24cm-11x9in) s.verso gelatin silver print. 14-Oct-2 Butterfields, San Francisco #1432/R est:3000-5000
£4200 $6804 €6300 Large scale object, cette statue negre, une pair de cisaux (24x18cm-9x7in) i.verso gelatin silver print exec.c.1932 lit. 21-May-3 Christie's, London #141/R est:2000-4000
£4870 $7500 €7305 Le rendez vous, Deuxieme tableaux (15x20cm-6x8in) s.i. photograph prov.lit. 22-Oct-2 Sotheby's, New York #83/R est:7000-10000
£5938 $9500 €8907 Cage of wild beasts (24x18cm-9x7in) with sig. silver print. 15-May-3 Swann Galleries, New York #294/R est:5000-7500
£10256 $16205 €16000 Colonne Morris (29x22cm-11x9in) st.sig. i.verso gelatin silver print exec.c.1933 prov. 16-Nov-2 Christie's, Paris #275/R est:12000-15000

Works on paper
£2885 $4558 €4500 L'Eglise de Saint-Germain-des-Pres, Paris (23x18cm-9x7in) st.sig. i.verso gelatin silver print exec.c.1955 prov.lit. 16-Nov-2 Christie's, Paris #277/R est:5000-7000

BRASSAUW, Melchior (1709-1757) Flemish
£1401 $2186 €2200 Hurdy girdy player. Old woman singing (10x9cm-4x4in) panel pair prov.exhib.lit. 5-Nov-2 Sotheby's, Amsterdam #112/R est:2000-3000

BRASSEUR, Georges (1880-1950) Belgian
£1700 $2822 €1700 Discussion dans la ruelle (96x75cm-38x30in) s.d.1922. 16-Jun-3 Horta, Bruxelles #441 est:2000-3000

BRASSEUR, Henri (1918-1981) Belgian
£570 $889 €900 Heureux, les coeurs purs (80x80cm-31x31in) s. d.1949 verso panel. 16-Sep-2 Horta, Bruxelles #488

BRATBY, John (1928-1992) British
£285 $476 €413 Portrait of John Wain (43x43cm-17x17in) 12-Jul-3 Windibank, Dorking #256
£290 $484 €421 Portrait of Nigel Brockes (41x36cm-16x14in) s. 12-Jul-3 Windibank, Dorking #257
£300 $501 €435 Scene from a window (127x102cm-50x40in) i. s.verso. 12-Jul-3 Windibank, Dorking #335
£350 $585 €508 Portrait of Sir Robert Mark (41x35cm-16x14in) s. 12-Jul-3 Windibank, Dorking #258
£400 $644 €600 Portrait of Ken Dodd (56x41cm-22x16in) s. 9-May-3 Mallams, Oxford #81
£520 $811 €780 Tuscan hills (38x48cm-15x19in) init. 18-Sep-2 Cheffins Grain & Comins, Cambridge #542/R
£600 $942 €900 Sea III (46x36cm-18x14in) s. i.verso. 13-Dec-2 Keys, Aylsham #387/R
£850 $1403 €1233 Young girl lying on a bed (57x40cm-22x16in) s. board. 3-Jul-3 Christie's, Kensington #576/R
£850 $1352 €1233 Portrait of Ray Moores (157x92cm-62x36in) s. 26-Feb-3 John Bellman, Billingshurst #1739/R
£900 $1449 €1350 Sunflowers (122x61cm-48x24in) s. 14-Jan-3 Bonhams, Knightsbridge #60/R
£950 $1530 €1425 Baker and grocer's wagon (51x61cm-20x24in) studio st. 14-Jan-3 Bonhams, Knightsbridge #187
£1050 $1659 €1575 Patty twice in Hemingway suite (121x91cm-48x36in) s.i. 4-Apr-3 Moore Allen & Innocent, Cirencester #609/R est:600-750
£1200 $1872 €1800 Age (121x91cm-48x36in) s.d.Oct 60. 15-Oct-2 Bonhams, Knightsbridge #269/R est:1500-2000
£1200 $1908 €1800 Decadence in Constantinople (121x91cm-48x36in) s. 26-Feb-3 Sotheby's, Olympia #395/R est:700-900
£1200 $1980 €1740 Carnival character outside Bauer Grunwald (122x91cm-48x36in) s. 3-Jul-3 Christie's, Kensington #575/R est:1500-2000
£1300 $2145 €1885 Self portrait (55x39cm-22x15in) s. 3-Jul-3 Christie's, Kensington #573/R est:600-800

£1400 $2212 €2100 Rabbit (39x54cm-15x21in) s. 27-Nov-2 Sotheby's, Olympia #192/R est:1200-1800
£1400 $2310 €2030 Double portrait of Patty (122x96cm-48x38in) s. 3-Jul-3 Christie's, Kensington #574/R est:1500-2000
£1485 $2480 €2153 Moscow scene in winter (21x91cm-8x36in) s. 12-Jul-3 Windibank, Dorking #252 est:300-500
£1500 $2385 €2250 Gorilla (61x51cm-24x20in) s. 26-Feb-3 Sotheby's, Olympia #379/R est:1500-2000
£1850 $3016 €2775 Sunflower and boat (40x35cm-16x14in) s. 28-Jan-3 Henry Adams, Chichester #464/R est:700-1000
£2000 $3100 €3000 Red sail (122x91cm-48x36in) s. exhib. 4-Dec-2 Christie's, Kensington #578/R est:2000-3000
£2000 $3100 €3000 Brighton marina (122x91cm-48x36in) s.i.d.1983 exhib. 4-Dec-2 Christie's, Kensington #581/R est:2000-3000
£2300 $3772 €3450 Gumboots (91x61cm-36x24in) s. prov. 3-Jun-3 Sotheby's, Olympia #238/R est:1000-1500
£2400 $3816 €3600 Dolly birds and the rialto bridge, one in Franch lam, one in Gauze (121x91cm-48x36in) s. 26-Feb-3 Sotheby's, Olympia #396/R est:600-800
£2400 $3744 €3600 Self portrait (121x60cm-48x24in) board exhib. 27-Mar-3 Christie's, Kensington #544/R est:1000-1500
£2600 $4342 €3770 Sarah dressing (116x80cm-46x31in) canvas on board. 24-Jun-3 Bonhams, New Bond Street #85/R est:1500-2500
£2800 $4592 €4200 Large room in small house by a railway line, Kings Langley (91x122cm-36x48in) s. board prov. 3-Jun-3 Sotheby's, Olympia #237/R est:2500-3500
£3000 $4680 €4500 Jason the artist's son (124x91cm-49x36in) 26-Mar-3 Hamptons Fine Art, Godalming #170/R est:2000-3000
£3200 $4992 €4800 Flowers (132x81cm-52x32in) s. 9-Oct-2 Woolley & Wallis, Salisbury #229/R est:1000-1500
£3200 $5280 €4640 Dickie Platt Stimulus III (54x44cm-21x17in) s. s.i.on overlap. 3-Jul-3 Christie's, Kensington #709/R est:600-800
£3400 $5678 €4930 Sunflowers (68x50cm-27x20in) s. 24-Jun-3 Bonhams, New Bond Street #83/R est:1500-1800
£3800 $5890 €5700 Grass to the gate at Birling Gap (119x86cm-47x34in) s. prov. 4-Dec-2 Sotheby's, London #72/R est:4000-6000
£4000 $6280 €6000 Melons (70x90cm-28x35in) s.d.8' 61. 16-Dec-2 Sotheby's, London #92/R est:4000-6000
£4200 $6468 €6300 Royal red roses in a glass mug (122x89cm-48x35in) s. i.d.Oct 1968 stretcher. 5-Sep-2 Christie's, Kensington #702/R est:2500-3500
£4200 $6552 €6300 Sunflowers in greenhouse (126x76cm-50x30in) s. 27-Mar-3 Christie's, Kensington #636/R est:3000-5000
£4700 $7332 €7050 Dark blue canal and five mooring past, Venice (120x90cm-47x35in) s. exhib. 18-Sep-2 Cheffins Grain & Comins, Cambridge #541/R est:3000-5000
£8000 $12640 €12000 Alice in Wonderland by herself (122x183cm-48x72in) prov. 27-Nov-2 Sotheby's, Olympia #190/R est:8000-12000
£11500 $19205 €16675 Kitchen sink (63x45cm-25x18in) s. board. 24-Jun-3 Bonhams, New Bond Street #82/R est:1000-1500

Works on paper

£260 $403 €390 Aphrodite belly dancer (37x54cm-15x21in) s.i.d.19 Jan 1991 W/C crayon pencil. 1-Oct-2 Fellows & Sons, Birmingham #199/R
£280 $468 €406 Penshurst (54x37cm-21x15in) s.i. pencil W/C pastel. 17-Jun-3 Bonhams, Knightsbridge #139
£300 $477 €450 Aphrodite belly dancer (54x36cm-21x14in) s.d.91 W/C pastel. 29-Apr-3 Henry Adams, Chichester #218
£300 $489 €435 Black plastic cat suit and wide belt (50x40cm-20x16in) s.i.d.24 February 1990 mixed media. 17-Jul-3 Tennants, Leyburn #780
£460 $768 €667 Hotel flowers, Positano (55x41cm-22x16in) s.i.d.December 1989 pencil wax crayon. 17-Jun-3 Bonhams, Knightsbridge #127
£850 $1403 €1233 Study of a crouching boy (27x22cm-11x9in) s.d.1957 pencil. 3-Jul-3 Christie's, Kensington #579/R
£1500 $2505 €2175 Lilies (40x50cm-16x20in) s.d.6.71 W/C. 17-Jun-3 Bonhams, Knightsbridge #4/R est:700-1000

BRATE, Fanny (1861-1940) Swedish

£311 $488 €467 Island in Roslagen (24x40cm-9x16in) s. 16-Dec-2 Lilla Bukowskis, Stockholm #873 (S.KR 4400)

BRAUER, Erich (1929-) Austrian

£6028 $9766 €8500 Round water source (34x40cm-13x16in) s.i.d.Juli 1974 panel. 20-May-3 Dorotheum, Vienna #217/R est:10000-13000
£6475 $10360 €9000 On the cliff (44x17cm-17x7in) s. board. 15-May-3 Neumeister, Munich #410/R est:6000-8000
£6962 $11000 €11000 Kite with many tails (36x28cm-14x11in) s. i. verso tempera panel lit.prov. 29-Nov-2 Schloss Ahlden, Ahlden #1439/R est:7500
£6962 $11000 €11000 Colourful bird (28x38cm-11x15in) s. i. verso prov.lit. 29-Nov-2 Schloss Ahlden, Ahlden #1440/R est:7500
£9220 $14936 €13000 Shepherd (17x28cm-7x11in) s. tempera oil panel prov. 20-May-3 Dorotheum, Vienna #214/R est:7000-10000
£10759 $17000 €17000 Olive tree (53x62cm-21x24in) s. tempera panel lit. 29-Nov-2 Schloss Ahlden, Ahlden #1427/R est:16000
£15190 $24000 €24000 Fish 1962 (65x80cm-26x31in) s. tempera panel lit. 29-Nov-2 Schloss Ahlden, Ahlden #1438/R est:16000

Sculpture

£1034 $1655 €1500 Light and shade (43cm-17in) s. num.82/100 bronze. 11-Mar-3 Dorotheum, Vienna #188/R est:3000-4000

Works on paper

£625 $994 €900 Personnage dans la tempete (18x23cm-7x9in) s. W/C pastel. 29-Apr-3 Artcurial Briest, Paris #135
£2128 $3447 €3000 Figure with animals (27x21cm-11x8in) s. W/C gouache board prov. three. 20-May-3 Dorotheum, Vienna #213/R est:4000-6000
£6962 $11000 €11000 Concrete snake (110x135cm-43x53in) s. W/C board panel. 27-Nov-2 Dorotheum, Vienna #264/R est:12000-16000

BRAUER, Karl (1794-1866) German

£750 $1230 €1125 Portrait of a lady in a green dress and lace bonnet (22x19cm-9x7in) s.d.1840. 5-Jun-3 Christie's, Kensington #595/R est:800-1200

BRAUMULLER, Philipp (20th C) German?

£1731 $2717 €2700 Avenue in Puttbus on Rugen (50x72cm-20x28in) s. board. 21-Nov-2 Van Ham, Cologne #1498/R est:2800

BRAUN, Henri (19th C) French

£1300 $2158 €1885 Saddled dark brown hunter in a stable. Bay hunter in a stable (29x39cm-11x15in) s. board pair. 12-Jun-3 Christie's, Kensington #59/R est:1200-1800

BRAUN, Ludwig (1836-1916) German

£823 $1275 €1300 Soldier at Mars La Tour during Franco-German war (72x59cm-28x23in) 25-Sep-2 Neumeister, Munich #549/R
£2821 $4428 €4400 Battle near Konigsgraz (36x58cm-14x23in) bears sig. panel. 21-Nov-2 Van Ham, Cologne #1499/R est:5000
£4487 $7090 €7000 Red Cross tending wounded soldier in 1870/71 war (115x104cm-45x41in) s. 16-Nov-2 Lempertz, Koln #1432/R est:8000

BRAUN, Mathias Bernhard (1684-1738) Bohemian

Sculpture

£5031 $7799 €8000 Johannes von Nepomuk. painted gilded wood exhib. 3-Oct-2 Dorotheum, Vienna #61/R est:4800-5000

BRAUN, Maurice (1877-1941) American

£2707 $4250 €4061 Summer hillside (41x30cm-16x12in) s. 19-Nov-2 Butterfields, San Francisco #8275/R est:4000-6000
£4870 $7500 €7305 Snow along the river (64x76cm-25x30in) prov. 24-Oct-2 Shannon's, Milford #21/R est:8000-12000
£6369 $10000 €9554 Dahlias (61x51cm-24x20in) s. prov. 19-Nov-2 Butterfields, San Francisco #8258/R est:7000-10000
£7547 $12000 €11321 Rolling hills (40x50cm-16x20in) s. prov. 7-Mar-3 Skinner, Boston #361/R est:8000-12000
£7784 $13000 €11287 Summer California landscape (15x23cm-6x9in) s. board prov. 17-Jun-3 John Moran, Pasadena #14 est:10000-15000
£10241 $17000 €14849 Farm near Julian (46x61cm-18x24in) s. 11-Jun-3 Butterfields, San Francisco #4242/R est:15000-20000
£10843 $18000 €15722 Summertime (36x46cm-14x18in) s. prov. 11-Jun-3 Butterfields, San Francisco #4237/R est:15000-20000
£11321 $18000 €16982 Evening light, California landscape (40x51cm-16x20in) s. prov. 7-Mar-3 Skinner, Boston #357/R est:10000-15000
£14103 $22000 €21155 Eucalyptus and mountains. 21-Sep-2 Harvey Clar, Oakland #1501
£16467 $27500 €23877 California summer landscape (36x46cm-14x18in) s. 17-Jun-3 John Moran, Pasadena #37 est:25000-35000
£24845 $40000 €37268 Glimpse of the Pacific from Point Loma (46x61cm-18x24in) s. i.verso canvas on canvas prov. 18-Feb-3 John Moran, Pasadena #20 est:20000-30000
£25150 $42000 €36468 Fisherman's Cove (41x51cm-16x20in) s. i.on stretcher. 18-Jun-3 Christie's, Los Angeles #7/R est:20000-30000
£35928 $60000 €52096 Landscape, morning in the hills (51x76cm-20x30in) s. prov. 17-Jun-3 John Moran, Pasadena #146 est:25000-35000

BRAUN, Reinhold (1821-1884) German

£1667 $2583 €2600 At the village well with boy, white horse, foal and figures (22x29cm-9x11in) s.d.1878 panel. 4-Dec-2 Neumeister, Munich #684/R est:2800

BRAUND, Dorothy Mary (1926-) Australian

£2321 $3668 €3482 Perpendicular with curves (91x61cm-36x24in) s.d.92 board. 27-Nov-2 Deutscher-Menzies, Melbourne #133a/R est:5000-7000 (A.D 6500)
£2692 $4281 €4038 Fred and Thelma (90x120cm-35x47in) s.d.99 i.verso composition board. 4-Mar-3 Deutscher-Menzies, Melbourne #122/R est:9000-12000 (A.D 7000)

Works on paper

£645 $981 €968 Musicians (36x50cm-14x20in) s.d.85 W/C. 28-Aug-2 Deutscher-Menzies, Melbourne #378/R (A.D 1800)
£702 $1067 €1053 Greek Island (40x53cm-16x21in) W/C. 19-Aug-2 Joel, Victoria #336 est:2000-3000 (A.D 2000)

£1538 $2446 €2307 Dancing lesson (39x48cm-15x19in) s.d.79 pencil W/C bodycol. 4-Mar-3 Deutscher-Menzies, Melbourne #195/R est:2500-3500 (A.D 4000)

BRAUNER, Victor (1903-1966) French/Rumanian

£12766 $20681 €18000 Septaries (81x65cm-32x26in) s.d.VII prov.exhib. 23-May-3 Binoche, Paris #61 est:25000-30000
£40000 $66800 €58000 Terre lumiere (60x73cm-24x29in) s.d.1963 prov. 24-Jun-3 Sotheby's, London #171/R est:20000-30000
£41096 $64521 €60000 Invitation au vol (73x60cm-29x24in) mono.d.1958 lit. 15-Apr-3 Laurence Calmels, Paris #4130/R est:40000
£47945 $75274 €70000 Portrait de Marcelle Ferry (65x54cm-26x21in) s.i.d.1934 lit. 15-Apr-3 Laurence Calmels, Paris #4132/R est:60000
£50000 $83500 €72500 Additivitee spatiale (50x65cm-20x26in) s.d.1956 i.verso encaustic pen ink paper on board prov. 25-Jun-3 Christie's, London #215/R est:50000-70000
£50000 $83500 €72500 Horizon interieur (80x100cm-31x39in) s.d.1961 s.d.verso prov.exhib. 25-Jun-3 Christie's, London #218/R est:30000-40000
£55000 $89650 €82500 Cosmogonie d'un visage (65x54cm-26x21in) s.i.d.1961 prov.exhib. 3-Feb-3 Christie's, London #185/R est:70000
£121118 $195000 €181677 Arbre de la volupte (100x81cm-39x32in) s.d.61 prov. 8-May-3 Christie's, Rockefeller NY #217/R est:200000-300000
£123288 $192329 €180000 Portrait d'Andre Breton (61x50cm-24x20in) s.d.1934 exhib.lit. 14-Apr-3 Laurence Calmels, Paris #4012/R est:50000
£136986 $215068 €200000 Legerement chaude (13x17cm-5x7in) s.i.d.1937 panel. 15-Apr-3 Laurence Calmels, Paris #4247/R est:30000
£178082 $279589 €260000 Nous sommes trahis (97x130cm-38x51in) s.i.d.1934 exhib.lit. 15-Apr-3 Laurence Calmels, Paris #4249/R est:80000
£180000 $295200 €270000 Personnages sur la plage (105x155cm-41x61in) s.d.1955 prov.exhib. 4-Feb-3 Sotheby's, London #49/R est:250000
£479452 $747945 €700000 Etrange cas de Monsieur K (82x100cm-32x39in) s.d.1933 s.i.verso exhib.lit. 14-Apr-3 Laurence Calmels, Paris #4075/R est:150000

Works on paper

£1667 $2583 €2600 Figure (27x21cm-11x8in) s.i.d.1961 Chinese ink. 4-Dec-2 Finarte, Milan #215/R est:3000
£1835 $2845 €2900 Small man (25x11cm-10x4in) mono.d.20.VII.1949 chk prov.exhib.lit. 28-Sep-2 Ketterer, Hamburg #244/R est:3000-3500
£9000 $15030 €13500 Le jardin (65x50cm-26x20in) s.i.d.13 mai 1945 wash crayon pen ink prov. 26-Jun-3 Christie's, London #445/R est:10000-15000
£10959 $17205 €16000 Untitled (65x50cm-26x20in) d.1963 ink. 15-Apr-3 Laurence Calmels, Paris #4131/R est:20000
£12000 $19560 €18000 Composition (22x40cm-9x16in) W/C gouache pen ink exec.c.1936 prov. 3-Feb-3 Christie's, London #153/R
£178082 $279589 €260000 Lion double (60x81cm-24x32in) s.d.46 wax paint cardboard exhib.lit. 15-Apr-3 Laurence Calmels, Paris #4248/R est:120000

BRAUNTUCH, Troy (1954-) American

£1875 $3000 €2813 Untitled (152x152cm-60x60in) s.d.84 on overlap prov.exhib. 14-May-3 Sotheby's, New York #433/R est:3500-4500

Works on paper

£1392 $2200 €2088 Untitled (57x57cm-22x22in) pastel exec.1981 prov. 13-Nov-2 Sotheby's, New York #596/R
£2656 $4250 €3984 Untitled (244x274cm-96x108in) s.d.84 verso chl cotton board in three parts prov. 14-May-3 Sotheby's, New York #430/R est:6000-8000

BRAVO, Claudio (1936-) Chilean

£3871 $6116 €6000 Still life with bouquet (46x55cm-18x22in) s.d.1956. 19-Dec-2 Claude Aguttes, Neuilly #167/R
£7692 $12154 €12000 Model (117x90cm-46x35in) s.d.MCMLXII lit. 19-Nov-2 Durán, Madrid #247/R
£50955 $80000 €76433 In the studio (131x100cm-52x39in) s.d.MCMLXXIV prov. 20-Nov-2 Christie's, Rockefeller NY #31/R est:180000-220000
£828025 $1300000 €1242038 Packet (150x200cm-59x79in) s.d.MCMLXVII prov.lit. 19-Nov-2 Sotheby's, New York #20/R est:1100000

Works on paper

£2564 $4000 €3846 Obladi-oblado (55x44cm-22x17in) s.d.MCMLXX col chk pencil prov.exhib. 5-Nov-2 Doyle, New York #19/R est:2500-3500
£3723 $6032 €5250 Retrato de Lucia Pagueguy Metzer (72x55cm-28x22in) s.d.1961 col pencil gouache. 20-May-3 Segre, Madrid #163/R est:7000
£24204 $38000 €36306 Guitar player (116x97cm-46x38in) s.i.d.MCMLXXIV chl pencil prov. 20-Nov-2 Christie's, Rockefeller NY #30/R est:80000-120000
£24390 $40000 €35366 Los brincos (32x63cm-13x25in) s.d.MCMLXX chl sanguine board prov. 27-May-3 Sotheby's, New York #105
£262195 $430000 €380183 Mystic package (75x110cm-30x43in) s.d.MCMLXVII chk conte crayon ink prov.exhib. 27-May-3 Sotheby's, New York #11

BRAY, Carl G (1917-) American

£1763 $2750 €2645 Desert sunset on mountains (61x76cm-24x30in) s. masonite panel prov. 9-Nov-2 Santa Fe Art, Santa Fe #64/R est:6000-8000

BRAY, Jan de (1627-1697) Dutch

£3500 $5845 €5075 Portrait of a lady, bust-length, in black dress with white lawn collar (58x49cm-23x19in) mono. panel. 9-Jul-3 Bonhams, New Bond Street #71/R est:2000-3000

BRAY, Jan de (attrib) (1627-1697) Dutch

£390 $605 €585 Sampling - interior with man and woman (32x36cm-13x14in) 8-Dec-2 Uppsala Auktionskammare, Uppsala #18 (S.KR 5500)
£6282 $9926 €9800 Portrait de femme a la robe rose (110x86cm-43x34in) indis.s. prov.lit. 15-Nov-2 Beaussant & Lefèvre, Paris #29/R est:4000-5000

Works on paper

£764 $1192 €1200 Study of a milkmaid (36x23cm-14x9in) black white chk. 5-Nov-2 Sotheby's, Amsterdam #207/R

BRAYER, Yves (1907-1990) French

£1655 $2615 €2400 Chateau de Val en Auverge (64x48cm-25x19in) s. W/C Chinese ink. 4-Apr-3 Tajan, Paris #197
£2800 $4340 €4200 Fishing boat and lighthouses (50x65cm-20x26in) s. 3-Dec-2 Sotheby's, Olympia #318/R est:2500-3500
£3576 $5829 €5400 Mas du Sauvage a l'automne (38x55cm-15x22in) s. 17-Feb-3 Horta, Bruxelles #206/R
£3987 $6180 €6300 Femme torero (83x54cm-33x21in) s. s.i.verso lit. 28-Sep-2 Cornette de St.Cyr, Paris #147/R est:2700-3000
£4114 $6500 €6500 Alpilles pres des Baux de Provence (28x35cm-11x14in) s. 2-Dec-2 Tajan, Paris #113/R
£4324 $6746 €6400 Paysage de Mougins (38x46cm-15x18in) s. painted c.1969. 25-Mar-3 Chochon-Barre & Allardi, Paris #69/R est:6500-7000
£4892 $7827 €6800 Marseille, barque pres du rivage (50x65cm-20x26in) s. 18-May-3 Eric Pillon, Calais #125/R
£5127 $7997 €8100 Mas en Provence (46x55cm-18x22in) s. i. verso. 20-Oct-2 Claude Boisgirard, Paris #82/R est:6000-7000
£5696 $8886 €9000 Le palaisde la Berbie a Albie (73x60cm-29x24in) s.i.d.1943 prov. 31-Jul-2 Tajan, Paris #47/R est:10000-12000
£7554 $12086 €10500 Le mas du Sauvage a l'automne (38x55cm-15x22in) s. 18-May-3 Eric Pillon, Calais #117/R
£9615 $15096 €15000 Barroux (59x80cm-23x31in) s.d.1960. 13-Dec-2 Piasa, Paris #28/R est:12000
£9615 $15096 €15000 Vue de Sienne (97x130cm-38x51in) s. 15-Dec-2 Eric Pillon, Calais #206/R
£9655 $15255 €14000 Mas aux Alpilles (73x92cm-29x36in) s. 4-Apr-3 Tajan, Paris #195/R est:15000
£10288 $16460 €14300 Printemps en Provence (50x65cm-20x26in) s. 18-May-3 Eric Pillon, Calais #114/R
£11888 $19853 €17000 Espagnole a la robe rouge (100x81cm-39x32in) s. i.verso. 26-Jun-3 Tajan, Paris #288/R est:15000-18000
£15617 $22177 €25300 Baux de Provence (130x162cm-51x64in) s. i.d.1960 verso. 16-Mar-3 Eric Pillon, Calais #202/R

Works on paper

£353 $554 €550 Aux armees (25x19cm-10x7in) s.i.d.1932 Chinese ink dr. 15-Dec-2 Eric Pillon, Calais #227/R
£397 $648 €600 Pont-Neuf. s. W/C. 3-Feb-3 Cornette de St.Cyr, Paris #277
£759 $1200 €1200 Fete medievale (67x53cm-26x21in) s. crayon ink wash W/C gouache. 29-Nov-2 Drouot Estimations, Paris #97
£1192 $1943 €1800 Cabane du peintre, Camargue (23x31cm-9x12in) s. W/C prov. 3-Feb-3 Cornette de St.Cyr, Paris #278/R
£1389 $2194 €2000 Enfants jouant (22x30cm-9x12in) s. wash dr. 25-Apr-3 Piasa, Paris #59
£1582 $2468 €2500 Paysage des Baux de Provence (39x52cm-15x20in) s. W/C prov. 20-Oct-2 Anaf, Lyon #76/R
£1731 $2717 €2700 Bord de Mediterranee (39x52cm-15x20in) s. W/C. 21-Nov-2 Neret-Minet, Paris #24/R
£1759 $2832 €2639 Rider on beach (39x43cm-15x17in) s. W/C over pencil. 7-May-3 Dobiaschofsky, Bern #375/R est:4500 (S.FR 3800)
£1958 $3270 €2800 Chevaux et herons en Camargue (48x65cm-19x26in) s. W/C. 26-Jun-3 Tajan, Paris #152/R est:2800-3500
£2089 $3258 €3300 Saintes Maries de la mer (30x25cm-12x10in) s.d.1938 gouache. 20-Oct-2 Charbonneaux, Paris #48/R est:1200-1500
£2130 $3429 €3195 Le tournant du moulin a Longchamp (38x51cm-15x20in) s. i. verso W/C over pencil. 7-May-3 Dobiaschofsky, Bern #374/R est:5000 (S.FR 4600)
£2244 $3522 €3500 Petite eglise pres des oliviers (40x53cm-16x21in) s. W/C. 15-Dec-2 Eric Pillon, Calais #204/R
£2365 $3689 €3500 Reception chez le sultan (49x37cm-19x15in) s. W/C gouache. 28-Mar-3 Claude Aguttes, Neuilly #199/R
£2436 $3824 €3800 Cavaliers en Camargue (48x63cm-19x25in) s. W/C gouache. 15-Dec-2 Eric Pillon, Calais #202/R
£2763 $4476 €4200 Les Baux de Provence (40x50cm-16x20in) s.i.d.1946 W/C. 22-Jan-3 Tajan, Paris #100 est:3000-4600
£2878 $4604 €4000 Chevaux en camargue en hiver (46x61cm-18x24in) s. W/C. 18-May-3 Eric Pillon, Calais #111/R
£2911 $4513 €4600 Les gardiens en Camargue (50x64cm-20x25in) s. W/C prov. 28-Sep-2 Christie's, Paris #23/R est:3000-4000
£2968 $4689 €4600 Baux (48x64cm-19x25in) s. W/C. 20-Dec-2 Ribeyre & Baron, Paris #49/R

BRAZ, Osip Emmanuelovich (1873-1936) Russian

£1911 $2981 €3000 Femme de profil (65x54cm-26x21in) s. 6-Nov-2 Claude Boisgirard, Paris #10/R est:3000-4000

BRAZDA, Oskar (1888-?) Czechoslovakian
£600 $978 €870 Garden in summer (80x92cm-31x36in) s.d.1936. 16-Jul-3 Sotheby's, Olympia #260/R

BREA, Ludovico (attrib) (c.1450-1522) French
£17000 $26520 €25500 Madonna and Child with goldfinch (48x34cm-19x13in) tempera panel. 10-Apr-3 Sotheby's, London #17/R est:8000

BREAKER, Charles (?) British?
Works on paper
£400 $624 €600 Boats at Sennan (38x48cm-15x19in) s. W/C. 17-Oct-2 David Lay, Penzance #1082/R

BREAKSPEARE, William A (1856-1914) British
£472 $726 €750 Portrait of girl (39x34cm-15x13in) s. 28-Oct-2 Il Ponte, Milan #310
£641 $994 €1000 Historical scene - three men in tavern (25x20cm-10x8in) s. panel prov. 7-Dec-2 Ketterer, Hamburg #16/R
£3500 $5530 €5250 Newly married (61x46cm-24x18in) s. 26-Nov-2 Christie's, London #103/R est:4000-6000
£3600 $5688 €5400 Artist in studio painting his model as Salome (46x36cm-18x14in) s. 2-Dec-2 Gorringes, Lewes #2729/R est:3000-4000

BREALEY, William Ramsden (1889-?) British
£260 $434 €377 Winston Churchill (75x50cm-30x20in) s. 23-Jun-3 Bonhams, Bath #124

BREANSKI, A de (19th C) British
£800 $1312 €1200 Thames backwater (28x36cm-11x14in) s. panel. 3-Jun-3 Bonhams, Oxford #65
£1053 $1600 €1580 Scottish loch scene (28x48cm-11x19in) mono.d. 19-Aug-2 Joel, Victoria #239/R est:4000-6000 (A.D 3000)

BREANSKI, Alfred Fontville de (1877-1957) British
£400 $624 €600 Bridge at Henley-on-Thames (41x56cm-16x22in) s. 26-Mar-3 Hamptons Fine Art, Godalming #256/R
£667 $1107 €967 On the marshes, evening (46x61cm-18x24in) s. 16-Jun-3 Waddingtons, Toronto #134/R est:2000-2500 (C.D 1500)
£711 $1180 €1031 Burnham Beeches, the pond's pool (30x51cm-12x20in) s. i. indis verso. 16-Jun-3 Waddingtons, Toronto #135/R est:2000-3000 (C.D 1600)
£800 $1272 €1200 Mill stream (46x61cm-18x24in) s. board prov. 6-Mar-3 Christie's, Kensington #488/R
£800 $1328 €1160 Yorkshire coast, Robin Hood's Bay (47x61cm-19x24in) s. i.verso prov. 16-Jun-3 Waddingtons, Toronto #136/R est:2000-3000 (C.D 1800)
£900 $1503 €1305 Serpent's Lake, Gap of Dunloe, Killarney (20x51cm-8x20in) s. s.i.verso. 25-Jun-3 Bonhams, Bury St Edmunds #571/R
£1000 $1520 €1500 Tavy Cleave Dartmoor (49x75cm-19x30in) s. s.i.verso. 4-Jul-2 Mellors & Kirk, Nottingham #836/R est:400-600
£1000 $1560 €1500 On the Llugwy River, North Wales (30x41cm-12x16in) s. i.verso. 9-Oct-2 Woolley & Wallis, Salisbury #298/R est:1000-1500
£1000 $1640 €1500 Highland landscape with cattle watering (38x58cm-15x23in) 4-Feb-3 Lawrences, Bletchingley #1557/R est:1000-1500
£1000 $1600 €1500 Llyn Ddinas, North Wales (50x76cm-20x30in) s. 13-May-3 Bonhams, Knightsbridge #271/R est:1000-1500
£1200 $1908 €1800 Ramblers and delphiniums (61x51cm-24x20in) s. 6-Mar-3 Christie's, Kensington #639/R est:800-1200
£1282 $2026 €2000 Morning mist, Scotland (49x76cm-19x30in) s. 12-Nov-2 Mealy's, Castlecomer #1043
£1300 $2028 €1950 Kilchurn Castle, Loch Awe (51x76cm-20x30in) s. s.i.verso. 17-Sep-2 Sotheby's, Olympia #35/R est:1500-2000
£1400 $2198 €2100 On the river Lyd, Dartmoor (40x61cm-16x24in) s. s.i. verso. 21-Nov-2 Tennants, Leyburn #802/R est:1000-1500
£1600 $2512 €2400 Highland loch (31x51cm-12x20in) s. 21-Nov-2 Tennants, Leyburn #807/R est:800-1200
£1600 $2544 €2400 October morning, Ashridge forest (41x60cm-16x24in) s. canvasboard prov. 6-Mar-3 Christie's, Kensington #489/R est:800-1200
£1600 $2544 €2400 River from Clifton Downs (18x25cm-7x10in) s. panel pair. 3-Mar-3 Louis Taylor, Stoke on Trent #835
£1683 $2659 €2525 In the West Highlands near Ballachuheck (51x74cm-20x29in) s. 27-Nov-2 Falkkloos, Malmo #77800/R est:25000 (S.KR 24000)
£1824 $2900 €2736 Evening light, Loch Fyne (41x56cm-16x22in) s.i. painted c.1880. 2-Mar-3 Toomey, Oak Park #595/R est:2000-3000
£1893 $2934 €2840 Moonrise at Innisfallen, Killarney (61x93cm-24x37in) s. s.i.verso. 3-Dec-2 Ritchie, Toronto #3049/R est:4000-6000 (C.D 4600)
£1900 $2926 €2850 Sunrise. Evening, Burnham Birches (51x30cm-20x12in) s. i.verso pair. 5-Sep-2 Christie's, Kensington #167/R est:1800-2200
£1900 $3097 €2755 Farm in the Scottish highlands (61x92cm-24x36in) with sig. 16-Jul-3 Sotheby's, Olympia #91/R est:2000-3000
£2000 $3160 €3000 River view at sunset (48x66cm-19x26in) s. 17-Dec-2 Gorringes, Lewes #1449
£2000 $3120 €3000 Highland cattle watering (76x61cm-30x24in) s. 26-Mar-3 Woolley & Wallis, Salisbury #256/R est:2000-3000
£2000 $3340 €2900 Llyn Dinas, Snowdonia, North Wales (49x75cm-19x30in) s. 25-Jun-3 Cheffins, Cambridge #781/R est:2000-3000
£2031 $3250 €3047 Evening valley, below Loch Tay (51x76cm-20x30in) s. s.i.verso. 14-May-3 Butterfields, San Francisco #1143/R est:4000-6000
£2200 $3586 €3300 Evening near Dolgelly, North Wales (41x61cm-16x24in) s. s.i.verso. 29-Jan-3 Sotheby's, Olympia #92/R est:1000-1500
£2400 $3816 €3600 Ogwen Vale, North Wales (51x76cm-20x30in) s. i.verso. 6-Mar-3 Christie's, Kensington #487/R est:1200-1800
£2600 $4056 €3900 Dawn, Loch Achray (46x61cm-18x24in) s. i.verso. 14-Apr-3 Sotheby's, London #30/R est:2000-3000
£2800 $4452 €4200 Evening, Derwentwater (51x76cm-20x30in) s. i.verso. 6 Mar-3 Christie's, Kensington #486/R est:2000-3000
£3000 $4740 €4500 Home in county Galway (51x76cm-20x30in) s. 2-Dec-2 Sotheby's, London #85/R est:3000-5000
£3026 $4901 €4388 Great Marlow reach (47x74cm-19x29in) s. d.1904 verso prov. 26-May-3 Bukowskis, Stockholm #236/R est:25000-30000 (S.KR 39000)
£3062 $4961 €4440 Landscapes with cattle watering at sunset, Wales (51x76cm-20x30in) s. indis.i.verso pair. 26-May-3 Rasmussen, Copenhagen #1316/R est:30000-40000 (D.KR 32000)
£3064 $4841 €4596 Autumn evening (21x31cm-8x12in) 30-Nov-2 Rasmussen, Havnen #2272 est:10000-15000 (D.KR 36000)
£3064 $4841 €4596 Loch Garry (21x31cm-8x12in) s. 30-Nov-2 Rasmussen, Havnen #2273 est:10000-15000 (D.KR 36000)
£3503 $5500 €5255 Lyn Ogwen, north Wales (61x91cm-24x36in) s. s.i.verso prov. 23-Nov-2 Jackson's, Cedar Falls #9/R est:5000-7500
£3800 $5928 €5510 In the pass of Killierankle, North Britain with a fisherman on the banks of the river (50x75cm-20x30in) s. i.verso. 28-Mar-3 ELR Auctions, Sheffield #222/R est:2500-3000
£4000 $6640 €5800 Ben Vare and Loch Leven (61x91cm-24x36in) s. s.i.verso prov. 16-Jun-3 Waddingtons, Toronto #166/R est:6000-8000 (C.D 9000)
£4430 $7000 €6645 Autumn morning in Glen Finlas, NB (61x91cm-24x36in) s.i.verso. 24-Apr-3 Shannon's, Milford #107/R est:5000-7000
£4500 $7335 €6750 Early morning Derwentwater (41x61cm-16x24in) s. s.i.verso. 29-Jan-3 Sotheby's, Olympia #91/R est:2000-3000
£4800 $7872 €7200 Evening, the Lledr Valley, North Wales (51x76cm-20x30in) s. s.i.verso. 29-May-3 Christie's, Kensington #104/R est:3000-5000
£5200 $7904 €7800 Summer morning in the gap of Dunloe, Killarney (51x76cm-20x30in) s. s.i.verso. 28-Aug-2 Sotheby's, London #929/R est:4000-6000
£7500 $11925 €11250 Fishing below Loch Coruisk, Invernesshire (51x76cm-20x30in) s. s.i.verso prov. 6-Mar-3 Christie's, Kensington #65/R est:3000-5000
£14000 $21700 €21000 Hills of Callander Loch and mountains landscape with herdsman and highland cattle (48x74cm-19x29in) s. prov. 3-Oct-2 Ewbank, Send #495/R est:5000-8000

Works on paper
£550 $919 €798 Snowdon from Pen-Y-Gwryd, North Wales (34x53cm-13x21in) s. W/C. 25-Jun-3 Cheffins, Cambridge #695
£850 $1318 €1275 Hartslock Wood Goring on Thames (27x37cm-11x15in) s. pencil W/C. 26-Sep-2 Mellors & Kirk, Nottingham #631
£1900 $2964 €2850 Fishing in the Highlands (41x61cm-16x24in) s. 14-Apr-3 Sotheby's, London #26/R est:1500-2000

BREANSKI, Alfred Fontville de (attrib) (1877-1957) British
£2038 $3200 €3057 Highlands loch with cattle (51x76cm-20x30in) 23-Nov-2 Jackson's, Cedar Falls #11/R est:1000-1500

BREANSKI, Alfred de (snr) (1852-1928) British
£1000 $1590 €1500 Droving cattle in a water meadow in a wooded river landscape (51x69cm-20x27in) s. 18-Mar-3 Rosebery Fine Art, London #800/R est:1000-1500
£1300 $2119 €1950 River scene (30x49cm-12x19in) s.d.1875 sold with another attrib to same hand cottage by stream. 29-Jan-3 Sotheby's, Olympia #90/R est:1000-2000
£1550 $2527 €2248 Shepperton Lock (31x41cm-12x16in) s. s.i.verso. 17-Jul-3 Tennants, Leyburn #839/R est:800-1200
£1656 $2600 €2484 Mountainous landscape (64x74cm-25x29in) 13-Dec-2 Du Mouchelle, Detroit #1035/R est:4000-6000
£1900 $3021 €2850 Borrowdale at evening (60x90cm-24x35in) s. 29-Apr-3 Rowley Fine Art, Newmarket #453/R est:800-1200
£2200 $3432 €3300 Cookham Reach (41x61cm-16x24in) s.i.verso. 7-Nov-2 Christie's, Kensington #149/R est:2500-3500
£2200 $3674 €3190 River landscape at sunset with drover and cattle (48x64cm-19x25in) s. 20-Jun-3 Keys, Aylsham #723/R est:1500-2000
£2400 $3936 €3600 Sheep in a highland landscape, evening (31x51cm-12x20in) s.d.1870. 29-May-3 Christie's, Kensington #105/R est:1800-2200
£2500 $3850 €3750 Loch Katrine, sailing boats on the loch at sunset (30x51cm-12x20in) s. 5-Sep-2 Morphets, Harrogate #355/R est:2000-2500
£3500 $5425 €5250 Trossachs (40x60cm-16x24in) s. 5-Dec-2 Bonhams, Edinburgh #39/R est:4000-6000
£3500 $5425 €5250 Eagle Rock, Glencoe (40x60cm-16x24in) s. 5-Dec-2 Bonhams, Edinburgh #40/R est:4000-6000
£3800 $6004 €5700 In the backwaters at Hurley (41x64cm-16x25in) s.d.1880. 12-Nov-2 Bonhams, Knightsbridge #215b/R est:4000-6000

£6000 $9540 €9000 Dee at Bakkater, early morning (61x91cm-24x36in) s. 6-Mar-3 Christie's, Kensington #67/R est:10000-15000
£6000 $9540 €9000 Windsor Castle from the two-path (61x91cm-24x36in) s. 18-Mar-3 Bonhams, New Bond Street #93/R est:6000-8000
£8000 $12720 €12000 Autumn evening- the Foyers, Invernesshire (61x92cm-24x36in) s. s.i.verso. 6-Mar-3 Christie's, Kensington #68/R est:10000-15000
£8750 $14000 €13125 King of Burnham, Beeches (61x91cm-24x36in) s. 15-Mar-3 Selkirks, St. Louis #90/R est:15000-20000
£9000 $13950 €13500 Scotch firs of Arrochar (62x92cm-24x36in) s. s.i.verso. 31-Oct-2 Christie's, London #71/R est:10000-15000
£9000 $14040 €13500 Bealach-Nam-Bo, Loch Katrine (30x40cm-12x16in) s.i. 14-Apr-3 Sotheby's, London #28/R est:6000-8000
£9310 $15081 €13500 Loch Catherine - Scottish highland landscape with cattle (50x76cm-20x30in) 25-May-3 Uppsala Auktionskammare, Uppsala #87/R est:100000-125000 (S.KR 120000)
£9400 $14852 €14100 Golden evening - Brander Pass to Loch Awe (60x90cm-24x35in) s. s.i.verso. 7-Apr-3 Bonhams, Bath #101/R est:4000-6000
£10500 $17535 €15225 Inver-nish - NB (31x45cm-12x18in) s. s.i.verso. 17-Jun-3 Bonhams, New Bond Street #39/R est:6000-8000
£11039 $17000 €16559 Still evening - Innersnaid (61x91cm-24x36in) s. s.i.verso prov. 24-Oct-2 Shannon's, Milford #132/R est:12000-18000
£13000 $20670 €19500 Summer in the Highlands (51x76cm-20x30in) s. s.i.verso. 18-Mar-3 Bonhams, New Bond Street #98/R est:8000-12000
£13374 $20597 €20061 Rosy June evening, Loch Katrine (61x91cm-24x36in) 26-Oct-2 Heffel, Vancouver #11 est:15000-20000 (C.D 32500)
£14000 $21980 €21000 Falls of Inversnaid (50x91cm-20x36in) s. 19-Nov-2 Bonhams, New Bond Street #135/R est:15000-20000
£14194 $22000 €21291 Crafnant, North Wales (61x92cm-24x36in) s. s.i.verso prov. 29-Oct-2 Sotheby's, New York #149/R est:25000-35000
£14500 $22476 €21750 Brander Pass NB (51x76cm-20x30in) s. s.i.verso. 3-Dec-2 Sotheby's, Olympia #155/R est:12000-18000
£15000 $23850 €22500 Morning - a Selkirk Valley (51x76cm-20x30in) s.verso. 18-Mar-3 Bonhams, New Bond Street #99/R est:8000-12000
£16000 $24480 €24000 Heart of Perthshire (43x58cm-17x23in) s. s.i.verso. 22-Aug-2 Bonhams, Edinburgh #955/R est:8000-12000
£16000 $24960 €24000 Evening near Arrochar, NB (61x92cm-24x36in) s. s.i.verso. 10-Apr-3 Tennants, Leyburn #988/R est:5000-7000
£18000 $27900 €27000 Loch Katrine (60x91cm-24x36in) s. s.i.verso. 5-Dec-2 Bonhams, Edinburgh #64/R est:10000-15000
£19000 $29640 €28500 Banks of the Luss (76x127cm-30x50in) s. prov. 14-Apr-3 Sotheby's, London #17/R est:15000-20000
£20000 $30400 €30000 Valleys of the Tay (39x60cm-15x24in) s. s.i.verso. 4-Jul-2 Mellors & Kirk, Nottingham #825/R est:10000-15000
£20000 $31000 €30000 Valley of Ben-An (76x127cm-30x50in) s. 5-Dec-2 Bonhams, Edinburgh #122/R est:20000-30000
£20000 $31200 €30000 Midsummer's Eve, the Lochay NB (51x76cm-20x30in) s. 26-Mar-3 Hamptons Fine Art, Godalming #262/R est:12000-18000
£21000 $31920 €31500 Stronachlacher, the birth place of Rob Roy (76x127cm-30x50in) s. s.i.verso prov. 28-Aug-2 Sotheby's, London #918/R est:20000-30000
£25000 $39500 €37500 Ben Nevis at sunrise (76x127cm-30x50in) s. s.i.verso. 2-Dec-2 Sotheby's, London #88/R est:25000-35000
£26000 $40820 €39000 Summer evening Lake Windermere (56x112cm-22x44in) s. i.verso. 19-Nov-2 Bonhams, New Bond Street #126/R est:7000-10000
£26000 $41340 €39000 July evening, Loch Lomond (55x100cm-22x39in) s. s.i.verso. 6-Mar-3 Christie's, Kensington #66/R est:15000-25000
£31000 $47120 €46500 From the Bramber Pass (61x91cm-24x36in) s. prov. 28-Aug-2 Sotheby's, London #894/R est:25000-35000
£38000 $61940 €57000 Moors of Arrochar. loch Ness N B (59x38cm-23x15in) one s. one s. i.verso pair. 11-Feb-3 Fellows & Sons, Birmingham #39/R est:10000-15000

BREANSKI, Arthur de (20th C) British
£380 $600 €600 River landscape at sunset (31x45cm-12x18in) 30-Nov-2 Berlinghof, Heidelberg #296/R
£1400 $2282 €2030 Sunrise on the Thames. Staines on the Thames (50x75cm-20x30in) s. pair. 21-Jul-3 Bonhams, Bath #64/R est:800-1200

BREANSKI, Gustave de (c.1856-1898) British
£280 $468 €406 Fishing boats off Dover (38x53cm-15x21in) s. 20-Jun-3 Keys, Aylsham #741
£320 $499 €480 Sunny day, Bosham, Sussex (41x51cm-16x20in) s. s.i.verso. 10-Apr-3 Tennants, Leyburn #953
£320 $499 €480 Coastal scene at low tide with fishing boat and figures (29x44cm-11x17in) s. 8-Apr-3 Bonhams, Knightsbridge #282
£380 $608 €570 Fishing off a coastline (76x63cm-30x25in) s. 7-Jan-3 Bonhams, Knightsbridge #61/R
£450 $711 €675 Fishing boat entering harbour with white cliffs (51x69cm-20x27in) s. 18-Dec-2 John Nicholson, Haslemere #1257
£550 $897 €825 Coastal view with fishermen and boat in foreground (25x33cm-10x13in) s. 14-Feb-3 Keys, Aylsham #740/R
£556 $923 €806 Bosham Harbour (41x61cm-16x24in) s. 16-Jun-3 Lilla Bukowskis, Stockholm #210/R (S.KR 7200)
£600 $1002 €870 Fishing boat coming ashore (60x90cm-24x35in) s. 19-Jun-3 Lane, Penzance #458
£695 $1154 €1008 Vessel by jetty (41x61cm-16x24in) s. 16-Jun-3 Lilla Bukowskis, Stockholm #211/R (S.KR 9000)
£700 $1134 €1050 Fishing fleet heading out to sea (30x51cm-12x20in) s.d.1879-80. 21-May-3 Christie's, Kensington #620/R
£748 $1190 €1100 Sailing boat at harbour (61x91cm-24x36in) s. 1-Mar-3 Stadion, Trieste #475
£750 $1230 €1125 Fishing boats and figures in a rowing boat (20x25cm-8x10in) s. 5-Feb-3 John Nicholson, Haslemere #1065
£780 $1232 €1170 Fishing smack off a south coast port (34x44cm-13x17in) s. 2-Dec-2 Bonhams, Bath #121
£1000 $1620 €1500 Running into harbour (63x76cm-25x30in) s. 21-May-3 Christie's, Kensington #617/R est:1200-1800
£1319 $2137 €1913 Fishing boats on stormy seas (62x91cm-24x36in) s.d.1864. 25-May-3 Uppsala Auktionskammare, Uppsala #80/R est:15000-20000 (S.KR 17000)
£1633 $2596 €2400 Seascape (51x76cm-20x30in) s. 19-Mar-3 Neumeister, Munich #520/R est:1800
£1750 $2853 €2625 Tug and fishing boat off a pierhead in rolling seas (59x90cm-23x35in) s. 30-Jan-3 Lawrence, Crewkerne #721/R est:800-1200
£2050 $3116 €3075 Fishing smack running into Newhaven. Fishing vessels becalmed (61x91cm-24x36in) s. pair. 29-Aug-2 Christie's, Kensington #103 est:1000-1500
£2500 $4050 €3750 Off the French coast (61x91cm-24x36in) s. 21-May-3 Christie's, Kensington #627/R est:2500-3500
£3000 $4650 €4500 Running out of harbour (61x91cm-24x36in) s. 31-Oct-2 Christie's, Kensington #510/R est:2000-3000

BREANSKI, Gustave de (attrib) (c.1856-1898) British
£805 $1280 €1208 Calais harbour (51x76cm-20x30in) init.i. 18-Mar-3 Maynards, Vancouver #14/R (C.D 1900)

BREANT, Jean (18th C) French
£283 $438 €425 Rowing boat on lake in evening (22x16cm-9x6in) s. board. 9-Dec-2 Philippe Schuler, Zurich #8626 (S.FR 650)

BREARD, Henri Georges (19/20th C) French
£1800 $2844 €2700 Connoisseur (74x60cm-29x24in) s. 14-Nov-2 Christie's, Kensington #250/R est:2000-3000

BREBNER, W (?) ?
£1411 $2201 €2117 Brig off the coast (40x64cm-16x25in) s. 10-Nov-2 Dunbar Sloane, Auckland #3 est:2000-4000 (NZ.D 4500)

BRECHALL, Martin (1783-1830) American
Works on paper
£828 $1300 €1242 Central square cartouche surrounded by hearts, vines and form vases (33x41cm-13x16in) s.d.1813 W/C. 23-Nov-2 Pook & Pook, Downington #417/R

BRECHER, Samuel (1897-1982) American
£781 $1250 €1172 Pemaquid lighthouse (51x66cm-20x26in) s. 11-Jan-3 James Julia, Fairfield #561 est:1000-1500

BRECHT, George (1926-) American
Works on paper
£2365 $3689 €3500 Untitled (30x14cm-12x6in) s.verso assemblage polymer exhib. 26-Mar-3 Finarte Semenzato, Milan #154/R

BRECKENRIDGE, Hugh Henry (1870-1937) American
£5556 $9000 €8334 Abstaction no.55 (21x23cm-8x9in) canvas on board painted c.1917-35 prov.exhib. 21-May-3 Sotheby's, New York #87/R est:8000-12000
£12346 $20000 €18519 Study for Italian fruit dish 1 (25x27cm-10x11in) s. board painted c.1931 prov.exhib.lit. 21-May-3 Sotheby's, New York #9/R est:10000-15000
£14198 $23000 €21297 Sky drama (32x25cm-13x10in) s. i.verso board painted c.1917 prov.exhib. 21-May-3 Sotheby's, New York #8/R est:10000-15000
£25806 $40000 €38709 Window bouquet (64x79cm-25x31in) s. prov. 5-Dec-2 Christie's, Rockefeller NY #195/R est:50000-70000

BRECKER, Arno (20th C) French
Sculpture
£1064 $1723 €1500 Buste d'homme (13x14x14cm-5x6x6in) s.d.1962 plaster. 26-May-3 Joron-Derem, Paris #139/R est:1000-1200

BREDA, Carl Fredrik von (1759-1818) Swedish
£1939 $3142 €2812 Louise Ramsay (73x62cm-29x24in) 26-May-3 Bukowskis, Stockholm #360/R est:30000-35000 (S.KR 25000)

BREDAEL, Alexandre van (1663-1720) Flemish
£2837 $4397 €4256 Kermes by antique ruins (68x86cm-27x34in) 4-Dec-2 AB Stockholms Auktionsverk #1963/R est:50000-70000 (S.KR 40000)

BREDAEL, Jan Frans van (circle) (18th C) Flemish
£12000 $20040 €17400 Figures and carts on a track near a hamlet (48x61cm-19x24in) panel. 9-Jul-3 Bonhams, New Bond Street #59/R est:7000-10000

BREDAEL, Jan Frans van (elder) (1686-1750) Flemish
£125000 $195000 €187500 River landscape with boats and coach party. River landscape with boats and riders (38x47cm-15x19in) s.d.1745 copper pair. 10-Apr-3 Sotheby's, London #7/R est:60000-80000

BREDAEL, Jan Peter van (younger) (1683-1735) Flemish
£5263 $8526 €8000 Battle scene (50x62cm-20x24in) 21-Jan-3 Ansorena, Madrid #89/R
£5660 $8774 €9000 Battle scene (50x62cm-20x24in) 7-Oct-2 Ansorena, Madrid #45/R
£10638 $16489 €15957 Battle between Turks and Europeans (30x37cm-12x15in) s.indis.d. copper. 8-Dec-2 Uppsala Auktionskammare, Uppsala #35/R est:150000-200000 (S.KR 150000)

BREDAEL, Joris van (1661-c.1706) Flemish
£20270 $31622 €30000 Merry-go-round in inner courtyard of Hofburg in Vienna (169x221cm-67x87in) s.d.1697 i. verso prov.lit. 27-Mar-3 Dorotheum, Vienna #292/R est:30000-50000

BREDAEL, Joseph van (1688-1739) Flemish
£8784 $13703 €13000 Flemish village on river with travellers at rest (26x32cm-10x13in) prov. 27-Mar-3 Dorotheum, Vienna #215/R est:10000-15000
£9434 $14623 €15000 Peasant feast. copper. 2-Oct-2 Dorotheum, Vienna #99/R est:15000-20000
£13000 $21710 €18850 Extensive mountain landscape with travelers on a bridge in a village (35x63cm-14x25in) panel prov. 11-Jul-3 Christie's, Kensington #1/R est:8000-12000
£18000 $28080 €27000 Crowded village landscape with wagons on a path and ferries crossing a river (42x60cm-17x24in) 9-Apr-3 Christie's, London #10/R est:8000-12000
£30000 $50100 €43500 Extensive wooded landscape with travellers on a path (28x38cm-11x15in) marouflaged panel prov.lit. 10-Jul-3 Sotheby's, London #117/R est:30000-40000

BREDAEL, Peeter van (1629-1719) Flemish
£4396 $7342 €6200 Scene de marche dans des ruines antiques (35x51cm-14x20in) s. 18-Jun-3 Tajan, Paris #70/R est:8000-10000
£6122 $9735 €9000 Halte des vachers. Traite des chevres (85x115cm-33x45in) s. pair. 21-Mar-3 Millon & Associes, Paris #12/R

BREDAEL, Peeter van (attrib) (1629-1719) Flemish
£3000 $4680 €4500 Gang of footpads at work on a woodland path (25x36cm-10x14in) panel. 17-Oct-2 David Lay, Penzance #1462/R est:3000-4000
£5743 $8959 €8500 River landscape with mill (14x17cm-6x7in) copper. 26-Mar-3 Tajan, Paris #144/R

BREDAL, Niels-Anders (1841-1888) Danish
£1053 $1705 €1527 The town gate at Ravello (44x33cm-17x13in) s.d.1858 i.stretcher. 26-May-3 Rasmussen, Copenhagen #1553/R (D.KR 11000)
£1617 $2555 €2426 From Tivoli with vegetable stall and woman with waterjug (39x29cm-15x11in) s.d.1873. 2-Dec-2 Rasmussen, Copenhagen #1539/R est:20000 (D.KR 19000)

Works on paper
£468 $740 €702 Temple for Venus and Rome (29x41cm-11x16in) s.i. pencil W/C. 2-Dec-2 Rasmussen, Copenhagen #1839/R (D.KR 5500)

BREDDO, Gastone (1915-1991) Italian
£680 $1082 €1000 Village and eggs (70x50cm-28x20in) s. 1-Mar-3 Meeting Art, Vercelli #461

BREDIN, R Sloan (1881-1933) American
£46584 $75000 €69876 Peonies and Jean (36x30cm-14x12in) s. s.i.verso. 19-Jan-3 Jeffery Burchard, Florida #20/R

BREDOW, Adolf (1875-?) German
£1603 $2484 €2500 Church on winter's evening (89x110cm-35x43in) s. lit. 6-Dec-2 Karlheinz Kaupp, Staufen #2150/R est:2500

BREDOW, Albert (1828-1899) Russian
£800 $1256 €1200 Monks burying treasure beside a monastery (91x137cm-36x54in) s. 13-Dec-2 Keys, Aylsham #687

BREDSDORFF, Axel (1883-1947) Danish
£360 $562 €540 The trio about to play (80x106cm-31x42in) s. 11-Nov-2 Rasmussen, Vejle #533/R (D.KR 4200)
£443 $718 €665 Interior scene with girls sitting on bed (137x182cm-54x72in) s.d.1908. 25-Jan-3 Rasmussen, Havnen #2095 (D.KR 5000)

BREDSDORFF, J U (1845-1928) Danish
£515 $803 €773 Road to church near Vinding, grey day (57x92cm-22x36in) init. exhib. 11-Nov-2 Rasmussen, Vejle #645/R (D.KR 6000)

BREDSDORFF, Majsa (1887-1964) Danish
£255 $403 €383 Christmas tree with colourful decorations (45x38cm-18x15in) mono. s.d.1942 verso. 2-Dec-2 Rasmussen, Copenhagen #1768/R (D.KR 3000)

BREDT, Ferdinand Max (1860-1921) German
£3117 $4551 €4800 Full-length portrait of Tunisian bride in interior of mosque (74x49cm-29x19in) s. board. 15-Jun-2 Hans Stahl, Hamburg #18/R est:2500

BREE, Anthony de (1856-1921) British
£260 $432 €390 Candidates for the fair (28x38cm-11x15in) 10-Jun-3 Bonhams, Knightsbridge #12a
£650 $1027 €975 Bay hunter in a landscape (51x63cm-20x25in) s. 28-Nov-2 Christie's, Kensington #170/R
£700 $1106 €1050 Liver chestnut hunter in a stable yard (51x63cm-20x25in) s. 28-Nov-2 Christie's, Kensington #171/R

BREE, Mathieu Ignace van (1773-1839) Flemish
£849 $1358 €1274 Mother with sick child before crucifix (58x69cm-23x27in) s. panel prov. 17-Mar-3 Philippe Schuler, Zurich #4604 (S.FR 1800)

BREE, Mathieu Ignace van (attrib) (1773-1839) Flemish
Works on paper
£800 $1256 €1200 Two studies of draped male figures (58x29cm-23x11in) black chk he. two prov. 11-Dec-2 Sotheby's, Olympia #238/R

BREE, Philippe Jacques van (1786-1871) Flemish
£1923 $2981 €3000 Jeune femme Italienne (69x49cm-27x19in) mono. panel. 3-Dec-2 Campo & Campo, Antwerp #292/R est:3500-4500

BREEDAM, Camiel van (1936-) Belgian
£633 $987 €1000 Fetes (81x81cm-32x32in) d.1962 oil collage panel. 16-Sep-2 Horta, Bruxelles #305

BREEN, Adam van (17th C) Dutch
£128205 $202564 €200000 Winter landscape with skaters (34x62cm-13x24in) panel prov.lit. 16-Nov-2 Lempertz, Koln #1010/R est:10000

BREEN, Adam van (attrib) (17th C) Dutch
£14744 $23295 €23000 Skaters on lake (33x51cm-13x20in) panel. 13-Nov-2 Marc Kohn, Paris #22/R est:24000-27000

BREEN, Irene (?) American?
£288 $450 €432 Portrait of Helen Leonadd, one of the Flora-Dora gils (114x84cm-45x33in) 28-Mar-3 Douglas, South Deerfield #1

BREENBERG, Bartholomaus (1599-1659) Dutch
£116129 $183484 €180000 Landscape with ruins and figures by fountain (45x67cm-18x26in) mono panel prov. 18-Dec-2 Tajan, Paris #15/R est:60000-75000

Works on paper
£1486 $2319 €2200 Rocky landscape with villa on cliff (23cm-9in circular) i. chk wash lit. 27-Mar-3 Christie's, Paris #143/R
£2548 $3975 €4000 Roman architectural capriccio (9x15cm-4x6in) pen grey ink wash over black chk prov. 5-Nov-2 Sotheby's, Amsterdam #86/R est:5000-6000

BREETVELD, Dolf (1892-1975) Dutch
£1026 $1610 €1600 Abstract composition with blue and green (100x130cm-39x51in) s. i.verso. 25-Nov-2 Glerum, Amsterdam #213/R est:1000-1500
£1090 $1711 €1700 Abstract composition (130x100cm-51x39in) s. i.verso. 25-Nov-2 Glerum, Amsterdam #208/R est:1200-1600
£1560 $2528 €2200 A23 (100x120cm-39x47in) s. i.verso exhib. 26-May-3 Glerum, Amsterdam #272/R est:1000-1500

£1631 $2643 €2300 B73 (100x130cm-39x51in) s.i.verso prov.lit. 26-May-3 Glerum, Amsterdam #265/R est:800-1200

Sculpture

£1410 $2214 €2200 Standing (102cm-40in) s. wood. 25-Nov-2 Glerum, Amsterdam #325/R est:550-750

Works on paper

£340 $551 €480 Composition (50x65cm-20x26in) s. gouache chk. 26-May-3 Glerum, Amsterdam #326/R

£417 $654 €650 Abstract composition with black, grey and red (41x54cm-16x21in) s. chk. 25-Nov-2 Glerum, Amsterdam #243/R

BREHAL, France (20th C) French

Works on paper

£387 $612 €600 Odyssee de l'espece (50x30cm-20x12in) s. collage cardboard. 18-Dec-2 Digard, Paris #235

BREINLINGER, Hans (1888-1963) Swiss

£690 $1090 €1000 Man with bottle in hand (75x50cm-30x20in) s.d.47 egg tempera board. 5-Apr-3 Geble, Radolfzell #691

£1154 $1685 €1800 Farmstead (76x94cm-30x37in) s.d.26. 4-Jun-2 Karl & Faber, Munich #187/R est:2000

£1351 $2108 €2000 Garden flowers (62x47cm-24x19in) s.d.1920 board. 28-Mar-3 Karrenbauer, Konstanz #1708/R est:1800

£4103 $5990 €6400 Portrait of Theodor Daubler (76x93cm-30x37in) s.d.26. 4-Jun-2 Karl & Faber, Munich #188/R est:3000

Works on paper

£338 $527 €500 Peasant with cows (46x46cm-18x18in) s.d.48 mixed media. 28-Mar-3 Karrenbauer, Konstanz #1715

£346 $540 €550 Allgau landscape (70x56cm-28x22in) s.d.1946 mixed media board. 9-Oct-2 Michael Zeller, Lindau #1004/R

£372 $580 €550 Nun praying (68x48cm-27x19in) mono. mixed media board lit. 28-Mar-3 Karrenbauer, Konstanz #1709

BREITBACH, Carl (1833-1904) German

£4808 $7452 €7500 Cobblers workshop (63x82cm-25x32in) s.i.d.1889. 6-Dec-2 Michael Zeller, Lindau #725/R est:5000

Works on paper

£321 $497 €500 Old peasant couple walking on the edge of a village (41x56cm-16x22in) s.indis.i.d.96 W/C bodycol over pencil. 4-Dec-2 Neumeister, Munich #505/R

BREITENBACH, Josef (1896-1984) ?

Photographs

£2273 $3500 €3410 Nude - from the series this beautiful landscape (35x28cm-14x11in) s. prov. 22-Oct-2 Sotheby's, New York #103/R est:3000-5000

£5844 $9000 €8766 Nude - from the series this beautiful landscape (27x35cm-11x14in) s. photograph prov. 22-Oct-2 Sotheby's, New York #104/R est:3000-5000

BREITENSTEIN, Carl August (1864-1921) Dutch

£949 $1481 €1500 Beach scene with figures (29x49cm-11x19in) s. 21-Oct-2 Glerum, Amsterdam #226 est:1500-2000

BREITER, Herbert (1927-) German

£1667 $2633 €2400 Landscape with dark trees and yellow fields (29x37cm-11x15in) mono.d.75 panel prov. 24-Apr-3 Dorotheum, Vienna #212/R est:2400-3200

Works on paper

£380 $592 €600 In the south (29x63cm-11x25in) s.d.1957 chk W/C. 15-Oct-2 Dorotheum, Vienna #139/R

BREITMAYER, M Vern (1889-1966) American

£1899 $3000 €2754 Brook (41x30cm-16x12in) s.d.1920 i.verso board exhib. 26-Apr-3 Jeffery Burchard, Florida #30

BREITNER, Georg Hendrik (1857-1923) Dutch

£256 $374 €400 People in street (31x25cm-12x10in) panel. 4-Jun-2 Karl & Faber, Munich #52/R

£650 $1001 €975 Figures in a workshop (17x20cm-7x8in) init. panel. 24-Oct-2 Christie's, Kensington #200

£18056 $28708 €26000 Op vekenning (26x36cm-10x14in) s. panel prov.exhib. 29-Apr-3 Christie's, Amsterdam #169/R est:12000-16000

£20833 $33125 €30000 Bouwput raadhuisstraat, Amsterdam (80x100cm-31x39in) s. s.i.on stretcher prov.lit. 29-Apr-3 Christie's, Amsterdam #178/R est:40000-60000

£23611 $37542 €34000 Zittend naakt met lichtblauwe doek (89x59cm-35x23in) cardboard prov.exhib.lit. 29-Apr-3 Christie's, Amsterdam #172/R est:20000-30000

£34591 $53270 €55000 Slecht weer, waspitten on a bridge in Amsterdam (60x101cm-24x40in) s. prov.exhib. 23-Oct-2 Christie's, Amsterdam #160/R est:40000-60000

Works on paper

£548 $860 €800 Seated girl. Horse and figure (24x20cm-9x8in) s. pencil dr. double-sided. 15-Apr-3 Sotheby's, Amsterdam #225/R

£890 $1398 €1300 Study of a male nude (42x57cm-17x22in) s. black chk prov.exhib. 15-Apr-3 Sotheby's, Amsterdam #227/R est:1000-1500

£3611 $5742 €5200 Study for a portrait of Mrs Bouwmeester (57x38cm-22x15in) s.i. chl black chk prov.exhib.lit. 29-Apr-3 Christie's, Amsterdam #179/R est:2500-3500

£3699 $5807 €5400 Three girls (52x35cm-20x14in) init. black chk executed c.1905 exhib. 15-Apr-3 Sotheby's, Amsterdam #221/R est:6000-8000

£19444 $30917 €28000 Portrait of the African fighter Adolf Boutar. Three waspitten walking down a street (55x40cm-22x16in) s. black chk W/C htd white double-sided prov.exhib.lit. 29-Apr-3 Christie's, Amsterdam #180/R est:6000-8000

BREKELENKAM, Quiryn Gerritsz van (1620-1668) Dutch

£1800 $3006 €2610 Study of a hermit kneeling before an open book and skulls (49x39cm-19x15in) s. panel. 8-Jul-3 Sotheby's, Olympia #380/R est:1000-2000

£2548 $3975 €4000 Man scaling fish on a table, with a basket and his fishing rod (20x18cm-8x7in) panel prov.exhib.lit. 5-Nov-2 Sotheby's, Amsterdam #4/R est:5000-7000

£6000 $9360 €9000 Old woman seated by a fire in a cottage interior (29x23cm-11x9in) panel exhib. 14-Apr-3 Hamilton Osborne King, Dublin #1470/R est:6000-10000

£6115 $9784 €8500 Hermit seated by an altar in a grotto (48x37cm-19x15in) init.indis d.1663 panel. 14-May-3 Christie's, Amsterdam #184/R est:10000-15000

£9000 $14040 €13500 An interior with a family eating (47x63cm-19x25in) s.d.1661 panel. 9-Apr-3 Christie's, London #37/R est:10000-15000

£46296 $75000 €69444 Woman making lace with a small child beside her (48x34cm-19x13in) s.d.1664 panel prov.exhib.lit. 23-Jan-3 Sotheby's, New York #12/R est:80000-120000

BREKER, Arno (1900-1991) German

Sculpture

£949 $1481 €1500 Amorous girl (29cm-11in) s.i. num.43/300 green pat.bronze Cast.Venturi Arte. 18-Oct-2 Dr Fritz Nagel, Stuttgart #42a/R est:950

£1135 $1838 €1600 Dali (21x13x15cm-8x5x6in) i. bronze marble socle. 24-May-3 Van Ham, Cologne #69/R

£1233 $1923 €1800 Classical nude (58cm-23in) i. bronze Cast.Venturi Arte. 10-Apr-3 Van Ham, Cologne #1101/R est:1250

£2436 $3776 €3800 Seated nude (44cm-17in) mono.d.24 verso clay prov. 4-Dec-2 Lempertz, Koln #583/R est:4500

BREKER, Arno (attrib) (1900-1991) German

Sculpture

£1070 $1658 €1605 Eagle (25cm-10in) mono. black pat. cast bronze yellow variegated marble base. 3-Dec-2 Ritchie, Toronto #3137/R est:2500-3000 (C.D 2600)

BRELING, Heinrich (1849-1914) German

£1258 $1962 €2000 Figures going home from field work (74x97cm-29x38in) s. 11-Oct-2 Winterberg, Heidelberg #490/R est:2400

BRELING, Heinrich (attrib) (1849-1914) German

£1026 $1590 €1600 Old seller sitting at his desk in his counting-house (45x37cm-18x15in) 4-Dec-2 Neumeister, Munich #685/R est:1500

BREM, Rolf (1926-) Swiss

Sculpture

£1092 $1703 €1638 Betty (39cm-15in) s.num.3/5 pat bronze prov. 9-Nov-2 Galerie Gloggner, Luzern #20/R est:3000-3500 (S.FR 2500)

£1572 $2452 €2358 Young woman standing in cape and boots (32cm-13in) s.num.15/15 pat bronze Cast F.Amici. 8-Nov-2 Dobiaschofsky, Bern #234/R est:2800 (S.FR 3600)

£2271 $3542 €3407 Greek war (40x76cm-16x30in) s.num.3/5 pat bronze prov. 9-Nov-2 Galerie Gloggner, Luzern #19/R est:3000-3500 (S.FR 5200)

BREMAN, Co (1865-1938) Dutch
£3205 $4968 €5000 Salland, Zomermorgen (44x70cm-17x28in) s.d.1935 s.i.on stretcher prov. 3-Dec-2 Christie's, Amsterdam #10/R est:6000-8000
£12821 $20128 €20000 Midday in Blaricum (26x54cm-10x21in) s.indis.d. i.verso. 25-Nov-2 Glerum, Amsterdam #74/R est:8000-12000

BREMOND, Jean François (1807-1868) French
£3773 $5811 €6000 Le Baron Nicolas Selliere tenant La Revue des Deux Mondes (100x81cm-39x32in) s. 25-Oct-2 Tajan, Paris #6/R est:6000-7500

BREN, Jeffrey (1944-) Australian
Works on paper
£498 $782 €747 Still life with bottle (56x76cm-22x30in) s. W/C. 15-Apr-3 Lawson Menzies, Sydney #256/R est:1500-2000 (A.D 1300)

BRENAN, James Butler (1825-1889) Irish
£610 $860 €1000 Portrait of a lady (91x69cm-36x27in) s. 7-Feb-2 Woodwards, Cork #264
£680 $1081 €1020 Portrait of a gentleman (35x30cm-14x12in) s.d.1871 sold with a companion. 5-Mar-3 Bonhams, Bury St Edmunds #415
£688 $1129 €950 Portrait of a lady (34x28cm-13x11in) s.d.1834. 28-May-3 Bonhams & James Adam, Dublin #19/R
£21739 $35652 €30000 Cottage interior with figures (68x90cm-27x35in) mono. 28-May-3 Bonhams & James Adam, Dublin #24/R est:18000-22000

BRENDEKILDE, Hans Andersen (1857-1942) Danish
£1537 $2367 €2306 Summer's day near Grevelejren (40x59cm-16x23in) s. 4-Sep-2 Kunsthallen, Copenhagen #139/R est:20000 (D.KR 18000)
£1627 $2635 €2441 Stone-mason and his wife having breakfast, talking to road worker (37x45cm-15x18in) init. 21-May-3 Museumsbygningen, Copenhagen #61 est:12000-15000 (D.KR 17000)
£1914 $3100 €2775 Autumn (90x116cm-35x46in) prov. 26-May-3 Rasmussen, Copenhagen #1460/R est:15000-20000 (D.KR 20000)
£2793 $4441 €4190 Small girl outside a house in Hjembaek (52x67cm-20x26in) s.d.1916 exhib. 5-Mar-3 Rasmussen, Copenhagen #1596/R est:40000-50000 (D.KR 30000)
£3059 $4771 €4589 Winter's day in the village (94x125cm-37x49in) s.d.1892. 5-Aug-2 Rasmussen, Vejle #222 est:40000 (D.KR 36000)
£3352 $5330 €5028 Hen and chicks with old woman (48x52cm-19x20in) s. 5-Mar-3 Rasmussen, Copenhagen #1502/R est:30000-40000 (D.KR 36000)
£3876 $5891 €5814 Outside the farmhouse - small girls feeding chickens (25x32cm-10x13in) s. 27-Aug-2 Rasmussen, Copenhagen #1461/R est:25000 (D.KR 45000)
£4655 $7402 €6983 Feeding the pig (48x65cm-19x26in) s. 5-Mar-3 Rasmussen, Copenhagen #1589/R est:50000-60000 (D.KR 50000)
£5098 $7952 €7647 Village street with chickens in foreground and two women by house (64x70cm-25x28in) s. 5-Aug-2 Rasmussen, Vejle #115/R est:60000-80000 (D.KR 60000)
£5957 $9413 €8936 A sad mother - chicken with flock of ducklings (49x59cm-19x23in) s.d.1913 exhib. 2-Dec-2 Rasmussen, Copenhagen #1323/R est:70000 (D.KR 70000)
£11639 $18506 €17459 Old Line's birthday (77x102cm-30x40in) s.d.1915 exhib. 5-Mar-3 Rasmussen, Copenhagen #1604/R est:125000-150000 (D.KR 125000)
£14925 $24478 €21641 Would you like to taste my apples? (57x87cm-22x34in) s. 4-Jun-3 AB Stockholms Auktionsverk #2407/R est:250000-300000 (S.KR 190000)
£16000 $24960 €24000 Wood in spring (102x126cm-40x50in) s.d.93. 26-Mar-3 Sotheby's, Olympia #260/R est:10000-15000
£27933 $44413 €41900 From a village in Fyn - gentleman telling curious villagers about his adventures (144x222cm-57x87in) s.d.1900 exhib. 5-Mar-3 Rasmussen, Copenhagen #1605/R est:300000 (D.KR 300000)
£28708 $46507 €41627 The first wood anemones, family on outing in spring wood (105x127cm-41x50in) s.d.93. 26-May-3 Rasmussen, Copenhagen #1108/R est:300000-400000 (D.KR 300000)

BRENDEKILDE, Hans Andersen (attrib) (1857-1942) Danish
£380 $593 €570 Heath landscape with Jens the road worker (25x30cm-10x12in) init. 11-Aug-2 Hindemae, Ullerslev #7402/R (D.KR 4500)
£422 $659 €633 From beside a country road (66x63cm-26x25in) init. 23-Sep-2 Rasmussen, Vejle #41 (D.KR 5000)
£540 $859 €810 Landscape with country road (66x63cm-26x25in) init. 10-Mar-3 Rasmussen, Vejle #230/R (D.KR 5800)
£635 $990 €953 Farmhouse with town in background (20x39cm-8x15in) init. 11-Nov-2 Rasmussen, Vejle #646/R (D.KR 7400)
£851 $1345 €1277 Roman landscape with monastery (40x51cm-16x20in) s.i.d.22. 30-Nov-2 Rasmussen, Havnen #2253/R (D.KR 10000)

BRENDEKILDE, Jorgen (1920-1993) Danish
£364 $578 €546 View of a village (15x23cm-6x9in) s. 5-May-3 Rasmussen, Vejle #682/R (D.KR 3900)

BRENDEL, Albert Heinrich (1827-1895) German
Works on paper
£253 $392 €400 Terrace on Capri. mono.i.d.72 W/C gouache. 27-Sep-2 Venator & Hansten, Koln #1229/R

BRENDEL, Albert Heinrich (attrib) (1827-1895) German
£532 $824 €798 Hare (23x29cm-9x11in) 4-Dec-2 AB Stockholms Auktionsverk #1919/R (S.KR 7500)

BRENDEMOE, Markus (1961-) Norwegian
£436 $685 €654 Composition (124x180cm-49x71in) s. verso. 25-Nov-2 Blomqvist, Lysaker #1029/R (N.KR 5000)

BRENDERS, Carl (1937-) Belgian
Works on paper
£10127 $16000 €14684 Disturbed daydreams (71x56cm-28x22in) s. gouache prov. 26-Jul-3 Coeur d'Alene, Hayden #132/R est:15000-25000
£12025 $19000 €17436 Late snow - Great Blue Heron (91x53cm-36x21in) s. gouache prov. 26-Jul-3 Coeur d'Alene, Hayden #173/R est:15000-25000

BRENDSTRUP, Thorald (1812-1883) Danish
£426 $672 €639 Mountain landscape (12x23cm-5x9in) with sig.verso. 2-Dec-2 Rasmussen, Copenhagen #1535/R (D.KR 5000)
£653 $1038 €980 Evening glow at Maribo Lake, horseman and dog on shore (21x18cm-8x7in) init. panel. 5-May-3 Rasmussen, Vejle #356/R (D.KR 7000)
£1098 $1713 €1647 View across Maribo Lake with town in background (102x133cm-40x52in) init.d.46 exhib. 23-Sep-2 Rasmussen, Vejle #73/R est:15000-20000 (D.KR 13000)
£1155 $1803 €1733 Canal scene from Frederiksvaerk with figures on path (49x65cm-19x26in) init.d.73 sold with dr of same subject. 5-Aug-2 Rasmussen, Vejle #184/R est:20000 (D.KR 13600)
£1206 $1833 €1809 Watermill (29x38cm-11x15in) init. 27-Aug-2 Rasmussen, Copenhagen #1891/R est:15000 (D.KR 14000)

BRENET, Albert (1903-) French
£1500 $2505 €2175 Baie du Robert, Martinique (48x72cm-19x28in) s.i.d.1929 board. 18-Jun-3 Sotheby's, Olympia #104/R est:800-1200
Works on paper
£353 $554 €550 Goelette (30x20cm-12x8in) s. gouache. 15-Dec-2 Thierry & Lannon, Brest #82
£458 $737 €650 Taureau de Salers (35x44cm-14x17in) s. gouache. 11-May-3 Thierry & Lannon, Brest #311
£493 $794 €700 Attelage de boeufs (33x48cm-13x19in) s. gouache. 11-May-3 Thierry & Lannon, Brest #117
£704 $1134 €1000 Les dindons (52x72cm-20x28in) s. gouache. 11-May-3 Thierry & Lannon, Brest #112/R est:1000-1200
£775 $1247 €1100 Etude d'oies (45x67cm-18x26in) chl. pastel. 11-May-3 Thierry & Lannon, Brest #118/R
£986 $1587 €1400 Theatre No, etude d'acteurs (52x55cm-20x22in) s.d.1953 gouache. 11-May-3 Thierry & Lannon, Brest #114/R
£1021 $1644 €1450 Mosquee en Tunisie (52x72cm-20x28in) s. gouache. 11-May-3 Thierry & Lannon, Brest #119
£1056 $1701 €1500 Loge d'acteurs theatre No (52x72cm-20x28in) s. st. gouache. 11-May-3 Thierry & Lannon, Brest #115/R est:1500-2000
£2324 $3742 €3300 Le cargo PLM14 (49x78cm-19x31in) s. gouache. 11-May-3 Thierry & Lannon, Brest #308 est:2000-2500
£2465 $3968 €3500 Etude de chevaux et joueurs de polo (51x72cm-20x28in) s. gouache. 11-May-3 Thierry & Lannon, Brest #310/R est:1500-2000
£2516 $3874 €4000 Trois mats sous voiles par temps calme (67x141cm-26x56in) s. gouache. 27-Oct-2 Lesieur & Le Bars, Le Havre #145/R

BRENNAN, Alfred (1853-1921) American
Works on paper
£366 $600 €531 Henri Gervex (43x29cm-17x11in) s.d. pen ink chl. 5-Jun-3 Swann Galleries, New York #56/R

BRENNAN, Angela (1960-) Australian
£1964 $3104 €2946 Untitled 2000 (152x107cm-60x42in) s.d.2000 s.d.verso prov. 27-Nov-2 Deutscher-Menzies, Melbourne #8/R est:7000-10000 (A.D 5500)

BRENNAN, Michael George (1840-1871) British
Works on paper
£250 $405 €375 Charity and war! (17x8cm-7x3in) init.d.1861 pen ink. 21-Jan-3 Bonhams, Knightsbridge #241/R

BRENNEIS, Jo (1910-1994) German
£1282 $1987 €2000 Untitled (42x61cm-17x24in) s.d.53 cardboard. 7-Dec-2 Van Ham, Cologne #75/R est:1900

BRENNER, Carl Christian (1838-1888) American
£3846 $6000 €5769 Winter woodland scene at sunset (76x63cm-30x25in) s.d.1885 prov. 12-Apr-3 Weschler, Washington #564/R est:3000-5000

BRENNIR, Carl (1850-1920) British
£500 $795 €750 Summer's day in Kent (41x61cm-16x24in) indis i. 6-Mar-3 Christie's, Kensington #444/R
£800 $1272 €1200 Rest on the way home (36x53cm-14x21in) s.d.1903. 6-Mar-3 Christie's, Kensington #445/R
£1200 $1956 €1800 Hambledon Common, Surrey (41x61cm-16x24in) sold with a companion. 14-Feb-3 Lyon & Turnbull, Edinburgh #149
£1400 $2184 €2100 Landscsape with figures horse driven cart on country road (51x76cm-20x30in) s.d.1903. 10-Sep-2 Bonhams, Knightsbridge #281/R est:1500-2000

BRENTEL, Friedrich (1580-1651) German
Works on paper
£2675 $4173 €4200 Raising of Lazarus (8x12cm-3x5in) s.d.1647 gouache htd gold vellum on panel. 5-Nov-2 Sotheby's, Amsterdam #1/R est:2000-3000
£10000 $16700 €14500 Venus and Adonis (7x10cm-3x4in) s. gouache paper on panel. 9-Jul-3 Bonhams, New Bond Street #9/R est:5000-7000
£37037 $60000 €55556 Age of bronze (14x22cm-6x9in) s.i.d.1628 gouache on vellum on panel. 23-Jan-3 Sotheby's, New York #1/R est:30000-40000

BRERETON, James Joseph (1954-) British
£850 $1292 €1275 Finola in full sail (61x92cm-24x36in) s. s.i.verso. 15-Aug-2 Bonhams, New Bond Street #376
£1550 $2356 €2325 Blowing hard (101x127cm-40x50in) s. 15-Aug-2 Bonhams, New Bond Street #377/R est:1200-1800
£2222 $3600 €3222 St. Mark and Joseph B Thomas at sea (59x90cm-23x35in) s.i. s.verso. 29-Jul-3 Christie's, Rockefeller NY #182/R est:2000-3000

BRESCIANI, Antonio (1902-1998) Italian
£949 $1500 €1500 Young woman (30x26cm-12x10in) s. panel. 26-Nov-2 Christie's, Rome #267
£1266 $2000 €2000 Chatting (24x30cm-9x12in) canvas on cardboard. 26-Nov-2 Christie's, Rome #265/R

BRESCIANINO, Andrea del (1485-1525) Italian
£17610 $27296 €28000 Madonna with child (67x51cm-26x20in) panel. 2-Oct-2 Dorotheum, Vienna #58/R est:25000-28000

BRESDIN, Rodolphe (1825-1885) French
Prints
£2200 $3432 €3300 La fuite en Egypt (13x10cm-5x4in) s. lithograph with pen ink. 10-Oct-2 Sotheby's, London #16/R est:3000-4000
£2800 $4368 €4200 Le ruisseau sous bois (29x42cm-11x17in) etching. 10-Oct-2 Sotheby's, London #12/R est:4000-5000
£2800 $4368 €4200 La comedie de la mort (33x25cm-13x10in) lithograph. 10-Oct-2 Sotheby's, London #15/R est:4000-5000
£4088 $6500 €6132 La comedie de la mort (22x15cm-9x6in) lithograph. 3-Mar-3 Swann Galleries, New York #3/R est:8000-12000
£4200 $6552 €6300 La sainte famille aux cerfs (42x29cm-17x11in) lithograph executed c.1871. 10-Oct-2 Sotheby's, London #17/R est:4000-6000
£8451 $14028 €12000 Le bon samaritain (56x44cm-22x17in) lithograph. 12-Jun-3 Piasa, Paris #31/R
£10000 $15600 €15000 Le bon Samaritain (63x49cm-25x19in) lithograph. 10-Oct-2 Sotheby's, London #13/R est:8000-10000

BRESGEN, August (20th C) German
£278 $439 €400 Southern landscape, Scicily (71x99cm-28x39in) s.d.24 paper on canvas. 24-Apr-3 Dorotheum, Vienna #48/R

BRESLAU, Marie-Louise-Catharine (1856-1928) Swiss
Works on paper
£3500 $5530 €5250 Nue allongee (60x75cm-24x30in) s.d.1910 pencil chk pastel. 3-Apr-3 Christie's, Kensington #27/R

BRESSLER, Emile (1886-1966) Swiss
£1397 $2208 €2096 Chemin a la campagne (50x61cm-20x24in) s. 17-Nov-2 Koller, Geneva #1315 (S.FR 3200)
£2642 $4094 €4200 Ferme animee en hiver (81x100cm-32x39in) s.d.56. 30-Oct-2 Coutau Begarie, Paris #102/R est:1000-1200
£2790 $4408 €4185 Summer landscape (54x65cm-21x26in) s.d.1919 prov. 29-Nov-2 Zofingen, Switzerland #2810/R est:3500 (S.FR 6500)

BRESSLERN-ROTH, Norbertine (1891-1978) Austrian
£1655 $2648 €2400 Georg J L Ritter von Bresslern u Sterman (33x37cm-13x15in) s.i.d.1918 panel prov. 11-Mar-3 Dorotheum, Vienna #5/R est:2600-3800
£1793 $2869 €2600 Portrait of Georg R v Bresslern (9x7cm-4x3in) s.i.d.22.2.1924 tempera ivory prov. 11-Mar-3 Dorotheum, Vienna #9/R est:1400-2000
£2207 $3531 €3200 Norbertine and Georg Ritter von Bresslern und Sterman (12cm-5in circular) s.i. tempera. 11-Mar-3 Dorotheum, Vienna #92/R est:1900-2600
£19214 $29974 €28821 Flamingos (100x80cm-39x31in) s.d.22 i. verso. 6-Nov-2 Dobiaschofsky, Bern #372/R est:16000 (S.FR 44000)

BRESSY, Richard (1906-) Belgian
£350 $546 €550 Pont a bascule (50x40cm-20x16in) s.d. 11-Nov-2 Horta, Bruxelles #471

BREST, Germain-Fabius (1823-1900) French
£3000 $4860 €4500 Crossing the bridge (32x50cm-13x20in) s. 20-May-3 Sotheby's, Olympia #351/R est:3000-5000
£6410 $10064 €10000 Village de pecheurs sur les bords du Bosphore (13x28cm-5x11in) s. panel. 16-Dec-2 Gros & Delettrez, Paris #258/R est:12000-18000
£16000 $24960 €24000 Bazaar Constantinople (34x49cm-13x19in) s. 15-Oct-2 Sotheby's, London #83/R est:10000-15000
£20000 $31600 €31000 Marche a Istanbul (22x16cm-9x6in) s. panel. 19-Dec-2 Claude Aguttes, Neuilly #121/R est:8000
£31081 $48486 €46000 Scene de rue animee a Istanbul (34x49cm-13x19in) s. 28-Mar-3 Claude Aguttes, Neuilly #186/R est:40000-60000
£35256 $55353 €55000 Marchand de limonade au bazar de Constantinople (86x68cm-34x27in) s. 16-Dec-2 Gros & Delettrez, Paris #278/R est:55000-60000

BRETLAND, Thomas (1802-1874) British
£3000 $4950 €4350 The Baron, a dapple grey hunter, with Tom Thumb, a black pony (74x92cm-29x36in) s.d.1847. 2-Jul-3 Sotheby's, Olympia #148/R est:3000-5000

BRETON, Andre (1896-1966) French
£2397 $3764 €3500 Rebus (11x14cm-4x6in) i. lit. 15-Apr-3 Laurence Calmels, Paris #4140/R
Sculpture
£1712 $2688 €2500 Minuit juste (84x10x10cm-33x4x4in) wood metal. 15-Apr-3 Laurence Calmels, Paris #4135/R
£2740 $4301 €4000 Grande tortue et cacique. stone exhib.lit. two. 15-Apr-3 Laurence Calmels, Paris #4238/R
Works on paper
£685 $1075 €1000 Untitled (14x14cm-6x6in) crayon. 15-Apr-3 Laurence Calmels, Paris #4172/R
£753 $1183 €1100 Deux portraits (13x21cm-5x8in) crayon. 15-Apr-3 Laurence Calmels, Paris #4165/R
£822 $1290 €1200 Esquisses (10x15cm-4x6in) crayon carrd. 15-Apr-3 Laurence Calmels, Paris #4168/R
£890 $1398 €1300 Visage de profil (22x11cm-9x4in) col crayon. 15-Apr-3 Laurence Calmels, Paris #4184/R
£1233 $1936 €1800 Un/. (15x12cm-6x5in) ball-point pen. 15-Apr-3 Laurence Calmels, Paris #4169/R
£1233 $1936 €1800 Frottage de medaille religieuse (11x15cm-4x6in) crayon. 15-Apr-3 Laurence Calmels, Paris #4186/R
£1370 $2151 €2000 Untitled (13x10cm-5x4in) crayon exec.c.1959. 15-Apr-3 Laurence Calmels, Paris #4136/R
£1370 $2151 €2000 Portrait caricatural (12x22cm-5x9in) crayon double-sided. 15-Apr-3 Laurence Calmels, Paris #4164/R
£1507 $2366 €2200 Femme (25x17cm-10x7in) crayon. 15-Apr-3 Laurence Calmels, Paris #4163/R
£1712 $2688 €2500 Untitled. engraving on potato set of 4. 15-Apr-3 Laurence Calmels, Paris #4133/R
£1712 $2688 €2500 Frottage de medaille religieuse (11x14cm-4x6in) crayon. 15-Apr-3 Laurence Calmels, Paris #4188
£1918 $3011 €2800 Portrait de Gerard Legrand (8x22cm-3x9in) decalcomania. 15-Apr-3 Laurence Calmels, Paris #4338/R
£2055 $3226 €3000 Nus feminins (13x10cm-5x4in) ink felt-tip pen. 15-Apr-3 Laurence Calmels, Paris #4170/R
£2192 $3441 €3200 Visages feminins (11x14cm-4x6in) crayon ink. 15-Apr-3 Laurence Calmels, Paris #4162/R
£2192 $3441 €3200 Untitled (11x10cm-4x4in) crayon ball-point pen. 15-Apr-3 Laurence Calmels, Paris #4167/R
£2192 $3441 €3200 Untitled (6x6cm-2x2in) ink crayon. 15-Apr-3 Laurence Calmels, Paris #4173/R
£2397 $3764 €3500 Portrait d'homme (21x13cm-8x5in) crayon. 15-Apr-3 Laurence Calmels, Paris #4150/R
£2397 $3764 €3500 Oiseau (9x15cm-4x6in) i. crayon lit. 15-Apr-3 Laurence Calmels, Paris #4148/R
£2397 $3764 €3500 Poisson (8x9cm-3x4in) crayon ink card. 15-Apr-3 Laurence Calmels, Paris #4166/R
£2397 $3764 €3500 Portrait (11x14cm-4x6in) crayon. 15-Apr-3 Laurence Calmels, Paris #4171/R

£2397 $3764 €3500 Ou est Carthage? (13x10cm-5x4in) i. collage lit. 15-Apr-3 Laurence Calmels, Paris #4242/R
£2740 $4301 €4000 Untitled (15x11cm-6x4in) crayon lit. 15-Apr-3 Laurence Calmels, Paris #4152/R
£2740 $4301 €4000 Breton (5x12cm-2x5in) i. crayon lit. 15-Apr-3 Laurence Calmels, Paris #4161/R
£2877 $4516 €4200 Untitled (10x14cm-4x6in) crayon lit. 15-Apr-3 Laurence Calmels, Paris #4141/R
£3082 $4839 €4500 Petit bagnard pour Elisa. Untitled (7x8cm-3x3in) s.i.d.1957 one felt-tip pen three engraving on potato lit. 15-Apr-3 Laurence Calmels, Paris #4134/R
£3082 $4839 €4500 Untitled (14x11cm-6x4in) ink lit. 15-Apr-3 Laurence Calmels, Paris #4153/R
£3082 $4839 €4500 Personnage fantastique (5x4cm-2x2in) ink crayon. 15-Apr-3 Laurence Calmels, Paris #4190/R
£3082 $4839 €4500 Untitled (7x13cm-3x5in) s. ink. 15-Apr-3 Laurence Calmels, Paris #4189/R
£3082 $4839 €4500 Untitled (10x12cm-4x5in) crayon. 15-Apr-3 Laurence Calmels, Paris #4185/R
£3082 $4839 €4500 Portrait de Jean Jacques Lebel (11x7cm-4x3in) decalcomania. 15-Apr-3 Laurence Calmels, Paris #4337/R
£3425 $5377 €5000 Untitled (10x14cm-4x6in) ink lit. 15-Apr-3 Laurence Calmels, Paris #4158/R
£3767 $5914 €5500 Untitled (22x16cm-9x6in) mono.d.58 collage. 15-Apr-3 Laurence Calmels, Paris #4243/R
£4110 $6452 €6000 Untitled (11x9cm-4x4in) ink wax lit. 15-Apr-3 Laurence Calmels, Paris #4139/R
£4110 $6452 €6000 Untitled (27x20cm-11x8in) s.d.1949 verso frottage crayon lit. 15-Apr-3 Laurence Calmels, Paris #4143/R
£4110 $6452 €6000 Untitled (11x14cm-4x6in) d.1954 ink lit. 15-Apr-3 Laurence Calmels, Paris #4155/R
£4110 $6452 €6000 Untitled (11x14cm-4x6in) mono.i.d.1945 ink lit. 15-Apr-3 Laurence Calmels, Paris #4160/R
£4110 $6452 €6000 Auto-portrait (20x14cm-8x6in) crayon cardboard lit. 15-Apr-3 Laurence Calmels, Paris #4182/R
£4110 $6452 €6000 Untitled (21x10cm-8x4in) ink lit. 15-Apr-3 Laurence Calmels, Paris #4180/R
£4110 $6452 €6000 Grand jeu (13x10cm-5x4in) ink crayon lit. 15-Apr-3 Laurence Calmels, Paris #4241/R
£4452 $6990 €6500 Untitled (12x10cm-5x4in) crayon card lit. 15-Apr-3 Laurence Calmels, Paris #4149/R
£4452 $6990 €6500 Serpent (9x10cm-4x4in) i.d.1945 crayon lit. 15-Apr-3 Laurence Calmels, Paris #4187/R
£5137 $8065 €7500 Grand jeu (13x12cm-5x5in) ink crayon card lit. 15-Apr-3 Laurence Calmels, Paris #4146/R
£5137 $8065 €7500 Untitled (14x11cm-6x4in) col crayon lit. 15-Apr-3 Laurence Calmels, Paris #4154/R
£5137 $8065 €7500 Untitled (10x13cm-4x5in) crayon. 15-Apr-3 Laurence Calmels, Paris #4174/R
£5342 $8388 €7800 Untitled (23x15cm-9x6in) gouache cardboard lit. 15-Apr-3 Laurence Calmels, Paris #4240/R
£5479 $8603 €8000 Portrait de Joyce Mansour. decalcomania set of 3. 15-Apr-3 Laurence Calmels, Paris #4336/R
£6507 $10216 €9500 Portrait de Baudelaire (18x11cm-7x4in) s.i.d.1960 Chinese ink lit. 15-Apr-3 Laurence Calmels, Paris #4181/R
£6849 $10753 €10000 Untitled (15x14cm-6x6in) i. ink wax lit. 15-Apr-3 Laurence Calmels, Paris #4142/R est:2000
£6849 $10753 €10000 Portrait de Charles Fourier (10x7cm-4x3in) mono.d.1961 crayon cardboard lit. 15-Apr-3 Laurence Calmels, Paris #4151/R est:1500
£7534 $11829 €11000 Untitled (13x8cm-5x3in) ink lit. 15-Apr-3 Laurence Calmels, Paris #4138/R est:2000
£8219 $12904 €12000 Petit shinx pourElisa (13x11cm-5x4in) i. wax ink lit. 15-Apr-3 Laurence Calmels, Paris #4147/R est:2000
£8219 $12904 €12000 Untitled (12x15cm-5x6in) mono.verso decalcomania lit. 15-Apr-3 Laurence Calmels, Paris #4159/R
£8904 $13979 €13000 Untitled (25x18cm-10x7in) Chinese ink lit. 15-Apr-3 Laurence Calmels, Paris #4179/R est:2800
£8904 $13979 €13000 Auto-portrait (14x10cm-6x4in) crayon lit. 15-Apr-3 Laurence Calmels, Paris #4183/R
£10274 $16130 €15000 Untitled (27x20cm-11x8in) s.d.1949 frottage crayon lit. 15-Apr-3 Laurence Calmels, Paris #4144/R est:2500
£10274 $16130 €15000 Untitled (15x10cm-6x4in) s.d.1945 ink lit. 15-Apr-3 Laurence Calmels, Paris #4175/R
£10274 $16130 €15000 Untitled (14x9cm-6x4in) ink lit. 15-Apr-3 Laurence Calmels, Paris #4177/R
£10959 $17096 €16000 Cadavre exquis (33x25cm-13x10in) i.verso col crayon dr. 14-Apr-3 Laurence Calmels, Paris #4014/R est:20000
£11644 $18281 €17000 Untitled (22x18cm-9x7in) ink wax lit. 15-Apr-3 Laurence Calmels, Paris #4156/R
£12329 $19356 €18000 Untitled (17x12cm-7x5in) ink wax lit. 15-Apr-3 Laurence Calmels, Paris #4178/R
£13699 $21507 €20000 Portrait d'Apollinaire (27x21cm-11x8in) frottage crayon exec.1949 lit. 15-Apr-3 Laurence Calmels, Paris #4145/R
£13699 $21507 €20000 Vieille lanterne (23x12cm-9x5in) i.verso wax col crayon lit. 15-Apr-3 Laurence Calmels, Paris #4157/R
£17808 $27781 €26000 Rose pour Elisa (28x21cm-11x8in) s.i.d.1945 ink exhib.lit. 14-Apr-3 Laurence Calmels, Paris #4041/R est:10000
£20548 $32055 €30000 Ventriloque (18x13cm-7x5in) wax lit. 14-Apr-3 Laurence Calmels, Paris #4038/R est:1800
£21918 $34411 €32000 Pour Elisa (30x23cm-12x9in) i. gouache W/C. 15-Apr-3 Laurence Calmels, Paris #4137/R est:10000
£23973 $37397 €35000 Famille du condylure (18x21cm-7x8in) mono.i. ink wax lit. 14-Apr-3 Laurence Calmels, Paris #4052/R est:5000
£24658 $38712 €36000 Dessin (23x30cm-9x12in) i.verso ink col crayon exec.with Jacques Herold. 15-Apr-3 Laurence Calmels, Paris #4260/R est:15000
£27397 $42740 €40000 Untitled (20x27cm-8x11in) s. gouache lit. 14-Apr-3 Laurence Calmels, Paris #4039/R est:2000
£27397 $43014 €40000 Dessin (23x30cm-9x12in) ink col crayon exec.with other artists exhib. 15-Apr-3 Laurence Calmels, Paris #4259/R est:15000
£27397 $43014 €40000 Dessin (30x23cm-12x9in) ink collage col crayon exec.with other artists exhib. 15-Apr-3 Laurence Calmels, Paris #4261/R est:15000
£36986 $57699 €54000 Untitled (23x15cm-9x6in) s.i.d.1947 gouache cardboard lit. 14-Apr-3 Laurence Calmels, Paris #4053/R est:8000
£39726 $61973 €58000 Poeme-objet (20x12cm-8x5in) s.i.d.1953 bugs fabric pen shells gouache pins exhib.lit. 14-Apr-3 Laurence Calmels, Paris #4006/R est:60000
£89041 $138904 €130000 Temps de chien (19x25cm-7x10in) s.i. collage exhib.lit. 14-Apr-3 Laurence Calmels, Paris #4018/R est:25000

BRETON, Andre (attrib) (1896-1966) French
Works on paper
£4110 $6452 €6000 Sade en prison (16x24cm-6x9in) i. ink. 15-Apr-3 Laurence Calmels, Paris #4176/R

BRETON, Andre and Elisa (20th C) French
Sculpture
£1712 $2688 €2500 Bouquet (18x16x4cm-7x6x2in) s.d.1959 cl glass cardboard. 15-Apr-3 Laurence Calmels, Paris #4239/R

BRETON, Andre and HUGO, Valentine (20th C) French
Works on paper
£15000 $24600 €22500 Cadavre exquis (32x25cm-13x10in) i.d.1931-32 col chk painted with T.Tzara P.Eluard prov.lit. 5-Feb-3 Sotheby's, London #194/R est:20000
£17808 $27959 €26000 Cadvre exquis (32x25cm-13x10in) i.verso col crayon exec.with Nusch and Paul Eluard. 15-Apr-3 Laurence Calmels, Paris #4252/R

BRETON, Andre and KAHN, Simone (20th C) French
Works on paper
£12329 $19356 €18000 Cadavre exquis (20x15cm-8x6in) i.verso col crayon paper on cardboard exec.with Max Morise lit. 15-Apr-3 Laurence Calmels, Paris #4250/R est:15000

BRETON, Andre and MEGRET, Frederic (20th C) French
Works on paper
£7534 $11829 €11000 Cadavre exquis (25x16cm-10x6in) i.verso gouache exec.1929 with Suzanne Muzard and Georges Sadoul. 15-Apr-3 Laurence Calmels, Paris #4253/R est:18000

BRETON, Andre and MORISE, Max (20th C) French
Works on paper
£41096 $64521 €60000 Cadavre exquis (31x20cm-12x8in) i.verso ink col crayon exec.with Man Ray and Yves Tanguy. 15-Apr-3 Laurence Calmels, Paris #4251/R est:18000

BRETON, Elisa (1906-2000) French
Sculpture
£3425 $5377 €5000 Untitled (36x42x31cm-14x17x12in) taxidermied budgies box. 15-Apr-3 Laurence Calmels, Paris #4191/R
£8904 $13979 €13000 Untitled (26x35x5cm-10x14x2in) s.d.1970 verso bird box exhib. 15-Apr-3 Laurence Calmels, Paris #4193/R
£10959 $17205 €16000 Ne quittez pas (30x25x4cm-12x10x2in) s.i.verso bag mirror collage box exhib. 15-Apr-3 Laurence Calmels, Paris #4194/R
Works on paper
£8219 $12904 €12000 Oiseau-lire (37x19cm-15x7in) s.i.verso pen collage wood exhib. 15-Apr-3 Laurence Calmels, Paris #4192/R

BRETON, Jules Adolphe (1827-1906) French
£2514 $3997 €3771 Young man with torch and rosary (35x26cm-14x10in) s. 5-Mar-3 Rasmussen, Copenhagen #2026/R est:25000 (D.KR 27000)
£5161 $8000 €7742 Mise en tas des oeillettes (24x35cm-9x14in) s. panel prov. 29-Oct-2 Sotheby's, New York #135/R est:10000-15000
£12903 $20000 €19355 La fontaine, Douarnenez (38x30cm-15x12in) s. prov. 30-Oct-2 Christie's, Rockefeller NY #140/R est:10000-15000

£16456 $26000 €24684 Virginie assise dans la jardin de Montgeron (31x42cm-12x17in) s.d.18 Mai 1883. 24-Apr-3 Sotheby's, New York #7/R est:30000-40000
£135484 $210000 €203226 Summer (75x63cm-30x25in) s.d.1891 prov.exhib.lit. 29-Oct-2 Sotheby's, New York #136/R est:40000-60000
Works on paper
£839 $1200 €1259 Femme avec une vache et moutons (23x25cm-9x10in) s.d.1858 brush ink W/C. 23-Jan-3 Swann Galleries, New York #308/R est:1500-2500

BRETON, Louis le (1909-1957) French
Works on paper
£1266 $2000 €2000 Un navire a trois mats dans une tempete (26x30cm-10x12in) s.i. pen W/C gouache. 27-Nov-2 Christie's, Paris #277/R est:2000-3000

BRETT, Donald (19/20th C) ?
£318 $500 €477 Portrait of the ship Lightning (48x76cm-19x30in) s. 23-Nov-2 Pook & Pook, Downington #366/R

BRETT, Dorothy (1883-1977) British/American
Works on paper
£380 $627 €551 Reclining nude (16x16cm-6x6in) s.d.1918 crayon W/C. 3-Jul-3 Christie's, Kensington #402

BRETT, Harold M (1880-1955) American
£1250 $2000 €1813 Barnstable Road (76x87cm-30x34in) s.i. 16-May-3 Skinner, Boston #284/R est:2500-3500
£1312 $2100 €1902 Chatham, Cape Cod, old fishing shanty (63x76cm-25x30in) s. 16-May-3 Skinner, Boston #278/R est:800-1200

BRETT, John (1831-1902) British
£500 $785 €750 Coastal at Penzance Cornwall (55x89cm-22x35in) s.d.1894. 10-Dec-2 Lane, Penzance #274
£2700 $4401 €4050 Extensive coastal view with figures on beach beyond sand dunes (56x86cm-22x34in) s. 14-Feb-3 Keys, Aylsham #686/R est:500-800
£3846 $6000 €5769 Rocky coastline with lighthouse and ships (51x76cm-20x30in) s. 12-Apr-3 Weschler, Washington #507/R est:6000-8000
£125000 $201250 €187500 Pearly summer (108x209cm-43x82in) s.d.1892 s.i.verso prov.exhib.lit. 19-Feb-3 Christie's, London #22/R est:180000-250000
£250000 $395000 €375000 River Dart (46x61cm-18x24in) s. prov.exhib. 28-Nov-2 Sotheby's, London #23/R est:60000-90000

BRETT, John (20th C) British
£1000 $1520 €1500 Sussex coastal landscape, off Newhaven at sunset (120x80cm-47x31in) s. board. 17-Sep-2 Henry Adams, Chichester #160/R est:500-800

BRETT, Molly (fl.1934) British
Works on paper
£1150 $1817 €1668 Four seasons (20x15cm-8x6in) s. W/C set of four. 22-Jul-3 Bonhams, Knightsbridge #17/R est:500-800

BRETT, W P (attrib) (?) American
£641 $1000 €962 Philadelphia waterworks with fisherman, waterfalls and dam (64x86cm-25x34in) 8-Nov-2 York Town, York #585

BRETTE, Pierre (1905-1961) French
Works on paper
£321 $503 €500 Matin (14x18cm-6x7in) s.i. W/C. 15-Dec-2 Thierry & Lannon, Brest #322

BRETTINGHAM, Walter D (1924-) British
£250 $408 €375 Kola inlet - phantom fleet - Opus 18 (69x86cm-27x34in) s.d.66. 14-Feb-3 Keys, Aylsham #302
£390 $612 €585 Convoy eight - the arrival, ships moving up Kola inlet (69x86cm-27x34in) s.d.61. 13-Dec-2 Keys, Aylsham #433/R
£440 $691 €660 Convoy five - N.E. Russia (66x86cm-26x34in) s.d.62. 13-Dec-2 Keys, Aylsham #434
£460 $722 €690 Convoy seven - wireless office (66x86cm-26x34in) s.d.62. 13-Dec-2 Keys, Aylsham #435/R
£520 $848 €780 Unloading at Polyarnoe, N Russia (74x94cm-29x37in) s.d.96. 14-Feb-3 Keys, Aylsham #303/R

BRETZ, Julius (1870-1953) German
£748 $1190 €1100 Windmill by canal (49x62cm-19x24in) s. 28-Mar-3 Bolland & Marotz, Bremen #429/R

BREUER, Henri Joseph (1860-1932) American
£2994 $5000 €4341 Royal arch, half dome, Yosemite (91x107cm-36x42in) s. i.on stretcher prov. 18-Jun-3 Christie's, Los Angeles #53/R est:5000-7000
£3892 $6500 €5643 Landscape, storm and rain (91x107cm-36x42in) s. exhib. 17-Jun-3 John Moran, Pasadena #105 est:8000-12000
£5689 $9500 €8249 Snowy mountain (91x107cm-36x42in) s. 18-Jun-3 Christie's, Los Angeles #55/R est:5000-7000

BREUER, Peter (1856-1930) German
Sculpture
£1101 $1695 €1750 Flyer (50cm-20in) i. pat.bronze lit. 26-Oct-2 Auktionhaus Herr, Cologne #140/R est:1450

BREUGELMANS, Auguste (19/20th C) Belgian
£861 $1403 €1300 Verger au printemps (37x52cm-15x20in) s. 17-Feb-3 Horta, Bruxelles #45

BREUIL, Georges (1904-1997) French
Works on paper
£1434 $2223 €2280 Composition (50x60cm-20x24in) s. mixed media paper on canvas exec.1969. 7-Oct-2 Claude Aguttes, Neuilly #143
£4780 $7409 €7600 Envolee de violons (100x81cm-39x32in) s. mixed media on canvas exec.1980. 7-Oct-2 Claude Aguttes, Neuilly #249/R est:8400

BREUILPONT, Marquis de (1763-1836) French
£755 $1177 €1200 Choc de cavalerie entre francais et turcs. Scene de batailles avec Turcs (35x53cm-14x21in) mono.d.1801 pen wash Indian ink pair. 10-Oct-2 Ribeyre & Baron, Paris #7
Works on paper
£377 $589 €600 Scenes de batailles (29x47cm-11x19in) ink wash htd gouache pair. 10-Oct-2 Ribeyre & Baron, Paris #11
£535 $834 €850 La mort d'un philosophe antique (37x52cm-15x20in) mono.d.1790 pen ink wash htd gouache. 10-Oct-2 Ribeyre & Baron, Paris #10/R
£692 $1079 €1100 Scene de peste (36x52cm-14x20in) mono. ink htd gouache. 10-Oct-2 Ribeyre & Baron, Paris #12
£1006 $1570 €1600 La forge de Paimpont (41x56cm-16x22in) ink wash. 10-Oct-2 Ribeyre & Baron, Paris #13 est:800-850

BREUL, Hugo (1854-1910) American
£534 $850 €801 Confidential friend (76x63cm-30x25in) s.d.1897. 20-Mar-3 Skinner, Bolton #711/R

BREVARD, Lee (20th C) ?
Works on paper
£283 $442 €450 Defile de maillots (45x64cm-18x25in) s.d.74 gouache W/C crayon. 8-Oct-2 Christie's, Paris #155

BREWER, Adrian (1891-1956) American
£2372 $3700 €3558 Bluebonnets after shower (41x36cm-16x14in) canvasboard painted c.1926. 19-Oct-2 David Dike, Dallas #117/R est:5000-7000

BREWER, Henry Charles (1866-1950) British
Works on paper
£1000 $1580 €1500 Continental street scene (34x25cm-13x10in) s.d.1907 W/C. 26-Nov-2 Bonhams, Knightsbridge #201/R
£1400 $2170 €2100 Palace of Westminster (55x78cm-22x31in) s. W/C prov. 6-Dec-2 Lyon & Turnbull, Edinburgh #1/R est:1500-2000

BREWER, Jane (20th C) American
£337 $525 €506 Still life (76x61cm-30x24in) s.d.52 tempera on masonite. 20-Sep-2 Sloan, North Bethesda #449/R
£513 $800 €770 Cubist still life with hat, bucket and chair (76x56cm-30x22in) s.d.52 canvasboard. 20-Sep-2 Sloan, North Bethesda #448/R

BREWER, Nicholas Richard (1857-1949) American
£478 $750 €717 In the hills of Arkansas (30x41cm-12x16in) s. s.i.verso wood panel. 23-Nov-2 Jackson's, Cedar Falls #81/R
£566 $900 €849 In the Croton country (41x51cm-16x20in) s. i.verso panel painted c.1900. 2-Mar-3 Toomey, Oak Park #603/R
£755 $1200 €1133 Where the Pacific breaks (36x51cm-14x20in) s. i.verso board painted c.1920. 2-Mar-3 Toomey, Oak Park #626/R
£968 $1500 €1452 Tonalist landscape (30x41cm-12x16in) s. board painted c.1900. 8-Dec-2 Toomey, Oak Park #637/R est:1000-2000

BREWSTER, Anna Richards (1870-1952) American
£272 $425 €408 Old Boston, Lincolnshire (13x18cm-5x7in) 20-Oct-2 Susanin's, Chicago #5086/R

£581 $900 €872 Bay of Nauplia, Greece (13x41cm-5x16in) s. i.verso canvasboard. 25-Sep-2 Doyle, New York #11/R
£764 $1200 €1146 Tunisia, Carthage (46x61cm-18x24in) s. 22-Nov-2 Skinner, Boston #311/R est:1200-1800
£2065 $3200 €3098 Scene of a bedroom interior (30x38cm-12x15in) s. 2-Nov-2 North East Auctions, Portsmouth #19/R

BREWTNALL, Edward Frederick (1846-1902) British
Works on paper
£1000 $1570 €1500 Frog prince (78x47cm-31x19in) s.d.1880 W/C scratching out. 21-Nov-2 Tennants, Leyburn #694/R est:1000-1500
£2000 $3300 €2900 Cornish beach (33x49cm-13x19in) s. pencil W/C bodycol htd white. 3-Jul-3 Christie's, Kensington #144 est:1500-2000

BREYDEL, Frans (1679-1750) Flemish
£4730 $7378 €7000 Wooded landscape with castle and travellers (31x22cm-12x9in) panel prov. 27-Mar-3 Dorotheum, Vienna #132/R est:7000-10000

BREYDEL, Karel (1678-1733) Flemish
£1548 $2276 €2400 Battlescene (23x29cm-9x11in) panel. 20-Jun-2 Dr Fritz Nagel, Stuttgart #704 est:4700
£1633 $2596 €2400 Choc de cavalerie (37x49cm-15x19in) s. 21-Mar-3 Rieunier, Bailly-Pommery, Mathias, Paris #61/R
£2400 $3912 €3480 Cavalry engagement (18x25cm-7x10in) panel. 21-Jul-3 Sotheby's, London #144/R est:3000-5000
£2436 $3824 €3800 Combats de cavalerie (13x19cm-5x7in) panel pair. 13-Dec-2 Rossini, Paris #157/R
£2516 $3899 €4000 Cavalry engagement (25x33cm-10x13in) panel. 2-Oct-2 Dorotheum, Vienna #439/R est:4000-6000
£2817 $4676 €4000 Cavalry battle (19x27cm-7x11in) panel prov. 11-Jun-3 Dorotheum, Vienna #289/R est:3000-5000

BREYDEL, Karel (attrib) (1678-1733) Flemish
£2400 $3912 €3480 Cavalry melee (18x25cm-7x10in) panel. 21-Jul-3 Sotheby's, London #145/R est:3000-5000
£3165 $5065 €4400 Choc de cavalerie (51x86cm-20x34in) panel. 13-May-3 Vanderkindere, Brussels #16 est:2500-4000

BREYFOGLE, John Winstanley (1874-?) American
£3165 $5000 €4748 Dancer (61x51cm-24x20in) prov. 24-Apr-3 Shannon's, Milford #28/R est:5000-7000

BREYS, Piet van der (20th C) Belgian
£655 $1042 €950 Landscape with house (70x80cm-28x31in) s.d.75. 4-Mar-3 Ansorena, Madrid #246/R

BRIANCHON, Maurice (1899-1979) French
£3727 $6000 €5591 Les marguerites (81x65cm-32x26in) s. prov. 7-May-3 Sotheby's, New York #408/R est:10000-15000
£4114 $6377 €6500 Elegants sur la plage (46x33cm-18x13in) s. 27-Sep-2 Rabourdin & Choppin de Janvry, Paris #74/R est:4200-4500
£4828 $8062 €7000 Jongleur (39x46cm-15x18in) s. cardboard painted c.1933 prov.exhib. 10-Jul-3 Artcurial Briest, Paris #151/R est:6000-7000
£6000 $9540 €9000 La place ensoleilee (60x92cm-24x36in) s. prov. 20-Mar-3 Sotheby's, Olympia #145/R est:8000-12000
£9202 $15000 €13803 La plage (92x64cm-36x25in) s. painted c.1950-60 prov. 12-Feb-3 Sotheby's, New York #107/R est:10000-15000
£10760 $17000 €17000 Cabines de bain (65x92cm-26x36in) s. 2-Dec-2 Tajan, Paris #105/R
£18611 $29406 €26800 Nice, plage du Lido (73x92cm-29x36in) s.d.1934-35. 23-Apr-3 Rabourdin & Choppin de Janvry, Paris #29/R est:30000

BRIANTE, Ezelino (1901-1970) Italian
£319 $517 €450 Costiera meridionale (20x25cm-8x10in) s. panel. 22-May-3 Stadion, Trieste #226/R
£355 $574 €500 Porticciolo meridionale (20x20cm-8x8in) s. board. 22-May-3 Stadion, Trieste #339/R
£369 $575 €554 Mediterranean terrace (38x49cm-15x19in) s. canvas on board. 15-Oct-2 Stephan Welz, Johannesburg #404 est:7000-10000 (SA.R 6000)
£415 $647 €623 Napoli del mare (15x31cm-6x12in) s. i. verso board. 6-Nov-2 Dobiaschofsky, Bern #373 (S.FR 950)
£452 $714 €700 View of Rome (22x35cm-9x14in) s. cardboard. 18-Dec-2 Finarte, Milan #77
£459 $715 €689 Ligurian coast (28x39cm-11x15in) s. i. verso panel. 6-Nov-2 Dobiaschofsky, Bern #3201 (S.FR 1050)
£553 $862 €830 Sunlit courtyard (49x68cm-19x27in) s. canvas on board. 15-Oct-2 Stephan Welz, Johannesburg #405/R est:10000-15000 (SA.R 9000)
£645 $1019 €1000 Rocks (30x40cm-12x16in) indis.sig.d. cardboard. 18-Dec-2 Finarte, Milan #37
£1843 $2875 €2765 Dappled street (68x49cm-27x19in) s. canvas on board. 15-Oct-2 Stephan Welz, Johannesburg #406/R est:10000-15000 (SA.R 30000)

BRICHER, A T (1837-1908) American
Works on paper
£822 $1250 €1233 Riverside copse of trees (23x51cm-9x20in) s. W/C. 30-Aug-2 Thomaston Place, Thomaston #93

BRICHER, Alfred Thompson (1837-1908) American
£14839 $23000 €22259 Quiet bay, Grand Manan (25x36cm-10x14in) s. prov. 2-Nov-2 North East Auctions, Portsmouth #27/R est:18000-24000
£18519 $30000 €27779 Sunrise on the coast (46x36cm-18x14in) mono. i.on stretcher. 21-May-3 Sotheby's, New York #198/R est:15000-25000
£20253 $32000 €30380 Near Nahant, Mass (28x56cm-11x22in) s. prov. 24-Apr-3 Shannon's, Milford #19/R est:25000-35000
£23377 $36000 €35066 Ships off a rocky coast (61x51cm-24x20in) s. 24-Oct-2 Shannon's, Milford #135/R est:25000-35000
£31690 $45000 €47535 Grand Mana (51x71cm-20x28in) 8-Aug-1 Barridorf, Portland #105/R est:40000-60000
£33951 $55000 €50927 Quiet cove (38x84cm-15x33in) mono. painted c.1890 prov. 21-May-3 Sotheby's, New York #196/R est:30000-50000
£36620 $52000 €54930 Fishing off Grand Manan (107x81cm-42x32in) 8-Aug-1 Barridorf, Portland #289/R est:40000-60000
£87097 $135000 €130646 Hunter in the meadows of old Newburyport (56x112cm-22x44in) mono. painted c.1873 prov.exhib.lit. 3-Dec-2 Phillips, New York #16/R est:125000-175000
£90323 $140000 €135485 Sunset (46x96cm-18x38in) mono. 5-Dec-2 Christie's, Rockefeller NY #14/R est:100000-150000
£103226 $160000 €154839 Low tide at Swallow Tail Cove (64x133cm-25x52in) mono. painted c.1890-1900 prov.exhib.lit. 3-Dec-2 Phillips, New York #24/R est:125000-175000
Works on paper
£938 $1500 €1360 Shoreline (13x48cm-5x19in) s. W/C. 17-May-3 CRN Auctions, Cambridge #16
£1205 $2000 €1747 Coastal landscape (18x38cm-7x15in) s. W/C. 11-Jun-3 Boos Gallery, Michigan #588/R est:1500-2500
£1384 $2200 €2076 Rowboats for hire (37x52cm-15x20in) init. W/C gouache. 4-Mar-3 Christie's, Rockefeller NY #22/R est:6000-8000
£1623 $2500 €2435 Stage rocks at Half Moon Beach (28x43cm-11x17in) s. i.verso graphite. 27-Oct-2 Grogan, Boston #71 est:2000-3000
£3065 $4750 €4598 Point Judith, Res Narragansett (25x53cm-10x21in) s. W/C prov. 29-Oct-2 John Moran, Pasadena #638 est:2000-3000
£3165 $5000 €4748 Boats along the dock (51x36cm-20x14in) s. W/C prov. 24-Apr-3 Shannon's, Milford #72/R est:6000-8000
£3896 $6000 €5844 Rocks, shore and sea (25x51cm-10x20in) s. W/C prov. 24-Oct-2 Shannon's, Milford #140/R est:4000-6000
£4717 $7500 €7076 Sailboats in an inlet (25x53cm-10x21in) init. W/C gouache. 4-Mar-3 Christie's, Rockefeller NY #21/R est:5000-7000
£8125 $13000 €12188 New England spring landscape (46x61cm-18x24in) s. W/C gouache prov. 11-Jan-3 James Julia, Fairfield #49 est:7000-9000
£9259 $15000 €13889 Little bass rock, Narragansett Pier (38x67cm-15x26in) mono.i. W/C gouache. 21-May-3 Sotheby's, New York #180/R est:15000-25000
£12658 $20000 €18987 Sailboats near the coast, Long Island (53x38cm-21x15in) s.d.1891 W/C. 24-Apr-3 Shannon's, Milford #160/R est:20000-30000

BRICHER, Alfred Thompson (attrib) (1837-1908) American
Works on paper
£355 $550 €533 Along the banks of the river (23x74cm-9x29in) bears sig pastel. 29-Oct-2 Doyle, New York #47

BRICKDALE, Eleanor Fortesque (1871-1945) British
Works on paper
£650 $1040 €975 Nude and pierrot (16x13cm-6x5in) init. pencil W/C. 8-Jan-3 George Kidner, Lymington #156/R

BRIDDELL, Don (1944-) American
Sculpture
£4114 $6500 €6171 Two mallards. s.d.1981 sold with a lithograph by the same hand. 3-Apr-3 Christie's, Rockefeller NY #245/R est:5000-8000

BRIDELL, Frederick Lee (1831-1863) British
£3750 $6000 €5625 Fiume latte lecco (30x23cm-12x9in) d.1861 board. 14-Mar-3 Du Mouchelle, Detroit #2014/R est:10000-15000

BRIDGE, Elizabeth (1912-1996) British
£2147 $3500 €3221 Fan-fan, Pekinese (41x51cm-16x20in) s. prov. 11-Feb-3 Bonhams & Doyles, New York #246 est:1000-1500

BRIDGEHOUSE, Robert (fl.1844-1846) British
£700 $1113 €1050 Sunset over the loch (61x91cm-24x36in) s.d.1873. 6-Mar-3 Christie's, Kensington #75/R

BRIDGENS, Richard (1785-1846) British
Works on paper
£1200 $1908 €1800 Design for the staircase hall, Aston House (38x26cm-15x10in) i. pen ink over pencil pair. 20-Mar-3 Sotheby's, London #349/R est:400-600
£2500 $3975 €3750 Great library, Aston Hall (32x20cm-13x8in) i. pen ink over pencil two. 20-Mar-3 Sotheby's, London #353/R est:600-800
£3000 $4770 €4500 Designs for Aston Hall (31x50cm-12x20in) one i. pen ink W/C over pencil set of 12. 20-Mar-3 Sotheby's, London #358 est:100-200
£3200 $5088 €4800 Furniture in the saloon, Aston Hall (24x33cm-9x13in) i. pen ink W/C over pencil set of three. 20-Mar-3 Sotheby's, London #351/R est:600-800
£3600 $5724 €5400 Furniture designs for the hall, Aston House (26x38cm-10x15in) one s. i. pen ink over pencil W/C set of five. 20-Mar-3 Sotheby's, London #350/R est:500-700
£4000 $6360 €6000 Furniture for Lady Holte's boudoir, Aston Hall (24x20cm-9x8in) i.d.June 8 1822 pen ink W/C over pencil set of three lit. 20-Mar-3 Sotheby's, London #356 est:600-800
£5000 $7950 €7500 Chimney pieces and fireplaces, Aston Hall (21x28cm-8x11in) i.d.1819-29 pen ink over pencil set of 11. 20-Mar-3 Sotheby's, London #362/R est:2000-3000
£5100 $8109 €7650 Designs for Lady Holte's bedroom, Aston Hall (25x39cm-10x15in) i.d.1824 pen ink W/C over pencil set of five. 20-Mar-3 Sotheby's, London #355/R est:600-800
£5600 $8904 €8400 Furniture for various room, Aston Hall (33x25cm-13x10in) i.d.1820-36 pen ink W/C set of ten. 20-Mar-3 Sotheby's, London #357 est:400-600
£10000 $15900 €15000 Furniture for the great library, Aston House. four s. i. pen ink W/C pencil set of nine. 20-Mar-3 Sotheby's, London #354/R est:1500-2000

BRIDGENS, Richard (attrib) (1785-1846) British
Works on paper
£1000 $1590 €1500 Designs for a garden seat, Aston Hall (24x36cm-9x14in) i.d.1819 pen ink over pencil two. 20-Mar-3 Sotheby's, London #359/R est:100-150

BRIDGES, Fidelia (1834-1923) American
£1097 $1700 €1646 Songbirds in a woodland marsh (41x30cm-16x12in) s.d.1879. 2-Nov-2 North East Auctions, Portsmouth #4/R
£2097 $3250 €3146 River landscape with birch trees (38x56cm-15x22in) s.d.1865 sold with a W/C of St. Martins church by same hand. 2-Nov-2 North East Auctions, Portsmouth #20
£2323 $3600 €3485 Queen Anne's lace. Bird in a cherry tree. Garden with pergola (23x36cm-9x14in) s. panel set of three. 2-Nov-2 North East Auctions, Portsmouth #12/R
£7097 $11000 €10646 Fields of Quen Anne's lace in an extensive landscape (23x41cm-9x16in) panel. 2-Nov-2 North East Auctions, Portsmouth #13/R
Works on paper
£1161 $1800 €1742 Seaside goldenrod (33x23cm-13x9in) s.d.1886 W/C. 2-Nov-2 North East Auctions, Portsmouth #5/R
£1226 $1900 €1839 Sumac in extensive landscape (25x36cm-10x14in) s.d.1876 W/C sold with 2 photographs. 2-Nov-2 North East Auctions, Portsmouth #1/R
£1548 $2400 €2322 Beach plums (25x49cm-10x19in) W/C gouache prov.exhib. 8-Dec-2 Freeman, Philadelphia #105/R est:3000-5000
£3226 $5000 €4839 Seaside flowers and grasses (23x43cm-9x17in) s. W/C. 2-Nov-2 North East Auctions, Portsmouth #3/R
£3896 $6000 €5844 Apple blossoms and sparrows in the rain (48x76cm-19x30in) s.d.1905 W/C prov. 24-Oct-2 Shannon's, Milford #158/R est:7000-9000
£5806 $9000 €8709 Studies of wildflowers, iris, ferns and trees (36x25cm-14x10in) W/C set of seven. 2-Nov-2 North East Auctions, Portsmouth #17/R
£6024 $10000 €8735 Garden in bloom (49x77cm-19x30in) s.d.1879 W/C gouache prov. 11-Jun-3 Butterfields, San Francisco #4026/R est:8000-12000
£8065 $12500 €12098 Birds on branches (13x10cm-5x4in) s. W/C on card sold with photos and W/C. 2-Nov-2 North East Auctions, Portsmouth #2/R

BRIDGMAN, Frederick Arthur (1847-1928) American
£443 $700 €700 Ricin en fleur dans le sud algerien (24x33cm-9x13in) s.i. canvas on cardboard. 28-Nov-2 Piasa, Paris #9
£450 $720 €675 Portrait of a ray (51x40cm-20x16in) s.i.d.July 1891. 7-Jan-3 Bonhams, Knightsbridge #79
£1553 $2500 €2330 Continental cityscape with figures (43x53cm-17x21in) s.i.d.1917. 15-Jan-3 Boos Gallery, Michigan #670/R est:5000-7000
£2344 $3750 €3399 Portrait of a child (109x68cm-43x27in) s.i.d.1910. 16-May-3 Skinner, Boston #142/R est:7000-9000
£3333 $5433 €4800 Procession devant l'Eglise de Quimperle (48x58cm-19x23in) s.d.1871. 19-Jul-3 Thierry & Lannon, Brest #106 est:4000-5000
£3718 $5838 €5800 Conversation devant un portail (46x38cm-18x15in) s.d.1923. 10-Dec-2 Tajan, Paris #133/R est:9000
£5449 $8555 €8500 Jeune femme a la gazelle dans un patio (40x50cm-16x20in) s. 10-Dec-2 Tajan, Paris #132/R est:10000
£5696 $9000 €8544 Nude reclining (33x51cm-13x20in) s.d.9 Feb 80 prov. 24-Apr-3 Shannon's, Milford #77/R est:3000-5000
£9000 $14130 €13500 Young prodigy, Algiers (22x27cm-9x11in) s.d.1873 indis sig.i.verso panel. 19-Nov-2 Bonhams, New Bond Street #92/R est:10000-15000
£10127 $16000 €15191 Les basses pyrenees (69x103cm-27x41in) s.d.1872. 23-Apr-3 Christie's, Rockefeller NY #78/R est:20000-30000
£10135 $15811 €15000 Oriental garden (81x66cm-32x26in) mono. 28-Mar-3 Claude Aguttes, Neuilly #214/R est:16000
£18354 $29000 €27531 Bather (100x61cm-39x24in) s. 24-Apr-3 Sotheby's, New York #48/R est:25000-35000
£19580 $32699 €28000 La belle Orientale (42x28cm-17x11in) s.d.1882. 27-Jun-3 Claude Aguttes, Neuilly #138/R est:30000-40000
£36709 $58000 €55064 An eastern veranda (63x93cm-25x37in) s. prov. 24-Apr-3 Sotheby's, New York #42/R est:80000-120000
£51613 $80000 €77420 Harem boats (100x150cm-39x59in) s. 29-Oct-2 Sotheby's, New York #47/R est:100000-150000

BRIDGMAN, George Brandt (1864-1943) Canadian
Works on paper
£262 $425 €393 Coach in winter (18x25cm-7x10in) s.d.94 W/C. 24-Jan-3 Freeman, Philadelphia #118/R

BRIDLE, Kathleen (20th C) British
Works on paper
£380 $619 €570 Knockinny, Co Fermanagh (28x43cm-11x17in) s.d.1940. 28-Jan-3 Gorringes, Lewes #1638

BRIEDE, Johan (1885-1980) Dutch
£1439 $2360 €2000 Evening sun over a Dutch landscape (40x60cm-16x24in) s.d.1942. 3-Jun-3 Christie's, Amsterdam #18/R est:2500-3500

BRIERLY, Sir Oswald Walter (1817-1894) British
£8500 $12920 €12750 Trading schooner overhauling a first rate off Garrison Point, Sheerness (81x122cm-32x48in) prov. 15-Aug-2 Bonhams, New Bond Street #395/R est:10000-15000
Works on paper
£250 $405 €375 Frigate, Admiralty cutters and other shipping at Spithead (15x30cm-6x12in) init.i.d.Augt.12 pencil W/C. 21-May-3 Christie's, Kensington #460/R
£900 $1395 €1350 Cutters racing inshore on a blustery day (14x23cm-6x9in) s. pencil W/C htd white. 31-Oct-2 Christie's, Kensington #321/R
£1000 $1590 €1500 Tongatabu Island woman, Bay of Islander Tonga (24x17cm-9x7in) s. i.verso W/C. 29-Apr-3 Bonhams, New Bond Street #22/R est:1200-1800
£1800 $2862 €2700 Schooner in heavy seas (16x24cm-6x9in) s.d.1849 W/C. 4-Mar-3 Bearnes, Exeter #340/R est:300-500

BRIERS, C de (17th C) ?
£6983 $11103 €10475 Still life of fruit. Still life of of fruit and game (31x43cm-12x17in) s. pair. 5-Mar-3 Rasmussen, Copenhagen #1632/R est:40000 (D.KR 75000)

BRIET, Arthur (1867-1939) Dutch
£382 $596 €600 Interior with grandfather and children (26x33cm-10x13in) s. board. 8-Nov-2 Auktionhaus Georg Rehm, Augsburg #8027/R
£458 $737 €650 Little man by fire place (19x22cm-7x9in) s. prov. 7-May-3 Vendue Huis, Gravenhage #4
£1447 $2345 €2200 Farm kitchen (32x41cm-13x16in) s. 21-Jan-3 Christie's, Amsterdam #182/R est:2200-2800
£2740 $4301 €4000 Afternoon nap (101x77cm-40x30in) s. 15-Apr-3 Sotheby's, Amsterdam #130/R est:3500-4500
Works on paper
£417 $688 €600 Napels, girls at work (10x7cm-4x3in) s.i. pencil W/C. 1-Jul-3 Christie's, Amsterdam #169/R

BRIGANTI, N (19th C) American/Italian
£344 $550 €516 Landscape of a stream through the woods (61x91cm-24x36in) s. 17-May-3 Pook & Pook, Downington #200f

BRIGANTI, Nicholas P (1895-1989) American
£286 $475 €415 Almalfi coast, Capri (41x61cm-16x24in) s. 14-Jun-3 Jackson's, Cedar Falls #39/R
£1250 $2000 €1875 Market scene (61x91cm-24x36in) s. 14-May-3 Butterfields, San Francisco #1181/R est:3000-5000
£1807 $3000 €2620 Amusing the baby (74x102cm-29x40in) s. 11-Jun-3 Boos Gallery, Michigan #535/R est:5000-7000

BRIGAUDIOT, Jean Pierre (1942-) French
£385 $604 €600 Tableau magnetique (53x53cm-21x21in) s.d.69 verso magnets paint metal. 24-Nov-2 Laurence Calmels, Paris #58/R

BRIGDEN, Frederick Henry (1871-1956) Canadian
£300 $469 €450 River landscape (27x34cm-11x13in) canvasboard. 25-Mar-3 Ritchie, Toronto #65/R (C.D 700)
£329 $510 €494 Forest clearing (22x29cm-9x11in) s. canvasboard. 3-Dec-2 Joyner, Toronto #438 (C.D 800)
£365 $569 €548 Laurentian landscape (27x35cm-11x14in) s. canvasboard prov. 25-Mar-3 Ritchie, Toronto #64/R (C.D 850)
£667 $1093 €1001 Summer, Don Valley (60x75cm-24x30in) s. 3-Jun-3 Joyner, Toronto #13/R est:2500-3500 (C.D 1500)
£751 $1172 €1127 River landscape (52x65cm-20x26in) s. masonite. 25-Mar-3 Ritchie, Toronto #72/R est:1800-2400 (C.D 1750)
£913 $1424 €1523 Across the fields, Hockley Valley (41x51cm-16x20in) s. s.i.d.1953 verso canvasboard. 13-Apr-3 Levis, Calgary #10/R est:2800-3200 (C.D 2100)

Works on paper
£247 $383 €371 Georgian Bay (18x24cm-7x9in) s. W/C prov. 3-Dec-2 Joyner, Toronto #416 (C.D 600)
£533 $875 €773 Summer valley (24x34cm-9x13in) s. W/C. 9-Jun-3 Hodgins, Calgary #152/R est:1400-1800 (C.D 1200)
£533 $875 €773 Untitled - homestead in the valley (28x38cm-11x15in) W/C. 1-Jun-3 Levis, Calgary #20/R est:1600-1800 (C.D 1200)
£1124 $1765 €1686 Snowy road (43x33cm-17x13in) s. W/C. 25-Nov-2 Hodgins, Calgary #357/R est:3000-3250 (C.D 2800)

BRIGDEN, John (?) Australian
Works on paper
£358 $545 €537 Ballet dancer and mask (74x55cm-29x22in) s. pastel. 27-Aug-2 Goodman, Sydney #220 (A.D 1000)

BRIGGS, Henry Perronet (1792-1844) British
£19000 $30590 €28500 Scene from 'The adventures of Ferdinand Count Fathom' (62x76cm-24x30in) s.i. panel prov.exhib. 20-Feb-3 Christie's, London #59/R est:25000
£28000 $46480 €42000 Portrait of Arthur Wellesley, 1st Duke of Wellington (109x85cm-43x33in) prov.lit. 12-Jun-3 Sotheby's, London #76/R est:10000-15000

BRIGHT, Alfred (19/20th C) British
Works on paper
£420 $697 €609 Polly, a bay horse in a stable (37x48cm-15x19in) pencil W/C. 12-Jun-3 Christie's, Kensington #69/R

BRIGHT, B (19/20th C) British
£360 $562 €540 Portrait of Helen Bruen of Oak Park, Carlow (125x95cm-49x37in) s. 17-Sep-2 Sotheby's, Olympia #199/R

BRIGHT, H (1814-1873) British
£450 $711 €653 Woman and child crossing bridge (23x28cm-9x11in) s. 24-Jul-3 John Nicholson, Haslemere #1169

BRIGHT, Harry (fl.1867-1892) British
£440 $704 €660 Blue tits nesting (28x23cm-11x9in) s.d.1887. 14-Mar-3 Gardiner & Houlgate, Bath #66/R
£700 $1120 €1050 Two bullfinches and wren perched on a snowy branch (23x30cm-9x12in) s.d.1887. 14-Mar-3 Gardiner & Houlgate, Bath #67/R
Works on paper
£280 $437 €420 Peregrine falcon on a rock (51x33cm-20x13in) s. W/C. 9-Oct-2 Woolley & Wallis, Salisbury #155/R
£360 $558 €540 Study of a buzzard perched on a lofty rock (30x42cm-12x17in) s.d.1882 W/C htd white. 1-Oct-2 Fellows & Sons, Birmingham #205/R
£750 $1185 €1125 Sparrow hawk (51x33cm-20x13in) s.d.1868 W/C bodycol. 28-Nov-2 Christie's, Kensington #38/R
£880 $1338 €1320 La Roche, winner of the Oaks and Manchester Summer Cup 1900 (23x30cm-9x12in) s. W/C. 16-Aug-2 Keys, Aylsham #300/R

BRIGHT, Harry (attrib) (fl.1867-1892) British
Works on paper
£460 $727 €690 Grouse shooting (22x29cm-9x11in) s.d.1887 W/C. 4-Apr-3 Moore Allen & Innocent, Cirencester #367/R

BRIGHT, Henry (1814-1873) British
£250 $393 €375 Figure, horse and cart in Norfolk wooded landscape (20x28cm-8x11in) 13-Dec-2 Keys, Aylsham #739
£340 $568 €493 Norfolk landscape with sheep grazing in foreground (28x43cm-11x17in) s. 20-Jun-3 Keys, Aylsham #649
£2100 $3297 €3150 Welsh landscape with old croft and watermill (56x102cm-22x40in) s.d.1857. 13-Dec-2 Keys, Aylsham #674 est:2750-3500
£2800 $4368 €4200 Windmill at Scratby, Norfolk (36x61cm-14x24in) panel. 17-Oct-2 David Lay, Penzance #1471/R est:3000-5000
£3300 $5445 €4785 Dedham Village, winter (25x35cm-10x14in) 1-Jul-3 Bonhams, Norwich #226/R est:2000-3000
£3800 $6042 €5700 Sailing barges near a windmill on the Norfolk Broads (25x45cm-10x18in) 19-Mar-3 Sotheby's, London #74 est:2000-3000
£3800 $6270 €5510 Evening (62x86cm-24x34in) s.d.1857 exhib. 1-Jul-3 Bonhams, Norwich #203/R est:3000-4000
Works on paper
£360 $594 €522 Farm buildings (23x33cm-9x13in) s.i. pencil dr. 1-Jul-3 Bonhams, Norwich #70/R
£680 $1061 €1020 Beach scene with fisherfolk and boats (28x43cm-11x17in) s. W/C. 2-Aug-2 Biddle & Webb, Birmingham #395
£750 $1238 €1088 Winter landscape with windmill (19x29cm-7x11in) init. pastel. 2-Jul-3 Sotheby's, Olympia #226/R

BRIGHT, Henry (attrib) (1814-1873) British
£595 $940 €893 Wooded landscape with bridge and figures (25x29cm-10x11in) 16-Nov-2 Crafoord, Lund #51/R (S.KR 8500)

BRIGHT, Henry and DODD, Charles Tattershall (19th C) British
£1200 $1884 €1800 Old bridge and ancient palace on the Medway at Maidstone (30x46cm-12x18in) i. board. 16-Apr-3 Christie's, Kensington #650/R est:1000-1500

BRIGHTWELL, Leonard R (20th C) British
Works on paper
£600 $924 €900 Battle of the mice and frogs, homer (36x49cm-14x19in) s.d.48 W/C. 23-Oct-2 Hamptons Fine Art, Godalming #64/R

BRIGMAN, Anne (1869-1950) American
Photographs
£1948 $3000 €2922 Heart of the storm (24x20cm-9x8in) s. photograph. 24-Oct-2 Sotheby's, New York #76/R est:3000-5000
£1948 $3000 €2922 Woman by the surf (18x24cm-7x9in) s.d.1910 platinum print prov. 22-Oct-2 Sotheby's, New York #129/R est:4000-6000
£4114 $6500 €6171 Soul of the blasted pine (19x24cm-7x9in) s.d.1907 verso photograph prov.lit. 23-Apr-3 Sotheby's, New York #114/R est:4000-6000

BRIGNOLI, Luigi (1881-1952) Italian
£437 $681 €656 Portrait of Hanneli Gerber (124x90cm-49x35in) s.d.1935. 6-Nov-2 Dobiaschofsky, Bern #376/R (S.FR 1000)
£699 $1090 €1049 Summer landscape near Langnau (45x60cm-18x24in) s.d.1935. 6-Nov-2 Dobiaschofsky, Bern #374/R est:2600 (S.FR 1600)
£699 $1090 €1049 View through window of houses in Langnau (55x45cm-22x18in) s.d.1937 i. verso masonite. 6-Nov-2 Dobiaschofsky, Bern #375/R est:2400 (S.FR 1600)

BRIGNONI, Sergio (1903-2002) Swiss
£741 $1193 €1074 Formes dans l'espace (44x46cm-17x18in) s. panel. 9-May-3 Dobiaschofsky, Bern #237/R (S.FR 1600)
£1019 $1640 €1478 Untitled (35x60cm-14x24in) s.d.91. 9-May-3 Dobiaschofsky, Bern #238/R (S.FR 2200)
£1204 $1938 €1746 Formes et couleurs (34x52cm-13x20in) s.d.88 acrylic board. 9-May-3 Dobiaschofsky, Bern #233/R est:3200 (S.FR 2600)
£1204 $1938 €1746 Composition au nu (49x61cm-19x24in) s.d.79 i.verso. 9-May-3 Dobiaschofsky, Bern #236/R est:3000 (S.FR 2600)
£1204 $1938 €1746 Formes et couleurs (38x39cm-15x15in) s.indis.d. acrylic board. 9-May-3 Dobiaschofsky, Bern #241/R est:3000 (S.FR 2600)
£1296 $2087 €1879 Feminin (90x58cm-35x23in) s.d.1990. 9-May-3 Dobiaschofsky, Bern #234/R est:3000 (S.FR 2800)
£1528 $2460 €2216 Interpenetration (41x57cm-16x22in) s. acrylic board. 9-May-3 Dobiaschofsky, Bern #228/R est:3200 (S.FR 3300)
£1616 $2521 €2424 Metamorphose (39x59cm-15x23in) s.d.89 acrylic pavatex. 20-Nov-2 Fischer, Luzern #1300/R est:4000-5000 (S.FR 3700)
£2083 $3354 €3020 Masculin, feminin (60x73cm-24x29in) s.d.90 acrylic board. 9-May-3 Dobiaschofsky, Bern #235/R est:4800 (S.FR 4500)
£3704 $5963 €5371 Composition avec femme (79x99cm-31x39in) s.d.98. 9-May-3 Dobiaschofsky, Bern #230/R est:9500 (S.FR 8000)

£4367 $6856 €6551 Collioure (53x28cm-21x11in) s.d.1932 canvas on board. 25-Nov-2 Sotheby's, Zurich #111/R est:10000-15000 (S.FR 10000)
£5240 $8227 €7860 Landscape with house (50x64cm-20x25in) s.d.1946. 25-Nov-2 Sotheby's, Zurich #139/R est:12000-16000 (S.FR 12000)
£25463 $40995 €36921 Eva (130x97cm-51x38in) s.d.1945. 9-May-3 Dobiaschofsky, Bern #226/R est:30000 (S.FR 55000)

Works on paper

£1135 $1771 €1703 Figures (17x25cm-7x10in) s.d.72 mixed media. 8-Nov-2 Dobiaschofsky, Bern #259/R est:1600 (S.FR 2600)
£1296 $2087 €1879 Figures (36x45cm-14x18in) s.d.80 W/C bodycol. ink. 9-May-3 Dobiaschofsky, Bern #231/R est:3000 (S.FR 2800)
£1459 $2306 €2189 Figures (30x41cm-12x16in) s.d.1990 gouache. 29-Nov-2 Zofingen, Switzerland #2811/R est:4000 (S.FR 3400)
£2096 $3291 €3144 Concert (23x40cm-9x16in) s.d.1955 W/C. 25-Nov-2 Germann, Zurich #1/R est:3000-3500 (S.FR 4800)

BRIGOT, Ernest Paul (1836-?) French

£1250 $1975 €1800 Paysage sous-bois (65x81cm-26x32in) bears sig. 23-Apr-3 Rabourdin & Choppin de Janvry, Paris #2/R

BRIGOT, Ernest Paul (attrib) (1836-?) French

£1571 $2577 €2278 Paysage a la cascade (66x89cm-26x35in) bears sig - G Courbet d.58. 4-Jun-3 AB Stockholms Auktionsverk #2449/R est:25000-30000 (S.KR 20000)

BRIL, Mattheus (younger) (c.1550-1584) Flemish

£6338 $10521 €9000 Coastal landscape with travellers and boats (19x21cm-7x8in) copper. 11-Jun-3 Dorotheum, Vienna #112/R est:9000-12000

BRIL, Mattheus (younger-attrib) (c.1550-1584) Flemish

£7534 $11753 €11000 Saint Anthony's temptations (27cm-11in circular) copper. 8-Apr-3 Ansorena, Madrid #75/R est:11000

BRIL, Paul (1554-1626) Flemish

£75000 $125250 €108750 Italianate landscape with a hawking party approaching a villa (72x102cm-28x40in) prov. 10-Jul-3 Sotheby's, London #10/R est:80000-120000
£140000 $219800 €210000 Cadmus and the dragon (13x10cm-5x4in) copper oval prov.lit. 12-Dec-2 Sotheby's, London #2/R est:20000-30000

BRIL, Paul (attrib) (1554-1626) Flemish

£5346 $8286 €8500 St Hieronymus in landscape (34x27cm-13x11in) copper prov. 2-Oct-2 Dorotheum, Vienna #358/R est:2200-3000
£10063 $15597 €16000 Forested river landscape with figures (33x43cm-13x17in) panel. 2-Oct-2 Dorotheum, Vienna #129/R est:13000-15000

BRIL, Paul (circle) (1554-1626) Flemish

£5595 $9343 €8000 Paysage fluvial avec des pecheurs remontant leur filet (21x26cm-8x10in) copper oval. 25-Jun-3 Tajan, Paris #24/R est:6000-8000
£6000 $10020 €8700 Saint Jerome in a landscape (73x55cm-29x22in) 8-Jul-3 Sotheby's, Olympia #350/R est:6000-8000
£11500 $19205 €16675 Wooded landscape with herdsmen tending goats, town in the distance (15x22cm-6x9in) copper prov. 10-Jul-3 Sotheby's, London #101/R est:6000-8000

BRIL, Paul (style) (1554-1626) Flemish

£9500 $14820 €14250 River landscape with traveller crossing bridge (39x68cm-15x27in) panel. 10-Apr-3 Sotheby's, London #8/R est:8000

BRILL, George Reiter (1867-1918) American

Works on paper

£1098 $1800 €1592 Orange seller (61x46cm-24x18in) s. W/C paper on board. 4-Jun-3 Doyle, New York #17 est:1000-1500

BRILL, Reginald C (1902-1974) British

£1000 $1550 €1500 Italian hill town (46x61cm-18x24in) s. board. 4-Dec-2 Christie's, Kensington #570/R est:1000-1500

BRILLAUD, Francois Eugène (?-1920) French

£2244 $3522 €3500 Baigneuses (135x201cm-53x79in) s.d.1913. 15-Dec-2 Eric Pillon, Calais #65/R

BRILLOUIN, Louis Georges (1817-1893) French

£800 $1280 €1200 Off duty (25x19cm-10x7in) s. 13-May-3 Bonhams, Knightsbridge #87/R
£812 $1300 €1177 In the studio (27x22cm-11x9in) s. panel. 16-May-3 Skinner, Boston #9/R est:1000-1500

BRINA, Francesco (16th C) Italian

£18519 $30000 €27779 Holy Family with the young Saint John the Baptist and Saint Elizabeth (71x61cm-28x24in) panel. 23-Jan-3 Sotheby's, New York #42/R est:30000-40000

BRINA, Francesco (circle) (16th C) Italian

£6400 $9984 €9600 Holy Family with Saint John (67x49cm-26x19in) panel. 10-Apr-3 Sotheby's, London #27/R

BRINCKMANN, Enrique (1938-) Spanish

£1774 $2803 €2750 Heliodora (54x65cm-21x26in) s. s.d.1983 verso board. 17-Dec-2 Durán, Madrid #102/R

BRINDEAU DE JARNY, Louis Edouard (1867-1943) French

£253 $400 €400 Route du Sapin a Rotheneuf (35x27cm-14x11in) s.i. panel. 1-Dec-2 Livinec, Gaudcheau & Jezequel, Rennes #72b

BRINDESI, Jean (19th C) ?

Works on paper

£10256 $16103 €16000 La traversee du Bosphore (27x37cm-11x15in) s. W/C gouache. 16-Dec-2 Gros & Delettrez, Paris #235/R est:10000-15000

BRINDISI, Remo (1918-1996) Italian

£633 $987 €1000 Maternity (40x30cm-16x12in) s. s.verso lit. 14-Sep-2 Meeting Art, Vercelli #480/R
£641 $994 €1000 Figure (40x30cm-16x12in) s. painted 1971. 4-Dec-2 Finarte, Milan #337
£676 $1054 €1000 Figure (71x49cm-28x19in) s. tempera card. 26-Mar-3 Finarte Semenzato, Milan #63
£705 $1107 €1100 Last Supper (30x40cm-12x16in) s. s.verso. 23-Nov-2 Meeting Art, Vercelli #172/R
£755 $1170 €1200 Pastorale (80x60cm-31x24in) s. s.i.d.verso. 30-Oct-2 Artcurial Briest, Paris #403
£833 $1308 €1300 Venice (40x30cm-16x12in) s. s.i.d.1971 verso. 23-Nov-2 Meeting Art, Vercelli #147/R
£833 $1308 €1300 Venice (40x30cm-16x12in) s. s.verso. 23-Nov-2 Meeting Art, Vercelli #186/R
£886 $1382 €1400 Pastoral scene (50x40cm-20x16in) s. painted 1994. 14-Sep-2 Meeting Art, Vercelli #928/R
£1054 $1677 €1550 Venice (30x40cm-12x16in) s. painted 1990. 1-Mar-3 Meeting Art, Vercelli #724
£1088 $1731 €1600 Venice (50x40cm-20x16in) s. s.verso. 1-Mar-3 Meeting Art, Vercelli #471
£1111 $1767 €1600 Man occupying the whole field (70x100cm-28x39in) s.i. s.i.d.1986 verso tempera chl paper on canvas. 1-May-3 Meeting Art, Vercelli #97
£1139 $1777 €1800 Venice (70x100cm-28x39in) s. tempera paper on canvas. 14-Sep-2 Meeting Art, Vercelli #937/R
£1176 $1882 €1800 Venice (50x40cm-20x16in) s. 4-Jan-3 Meeting Art, Vercelli #507
£1215 $1932 €1750 Pastoral (50x40cm-20x16in) s. 1-May-3 Meeting Art, Vercelli #309
£1486 $2319 €2200 Venice (70x60cm-28x24in) s. 26-Mar-3 Finarte Semenzato, Milan #393/R
£1503 $2405 €2300 Untitled (70x50cm-28x20in) s. painted 1975. 4-Jan-3 Meeting Art, Vercelli #515
£1667 $2617 €2600 Venice (50x70cm-20x28in) s. 21-Nov-2 Finarte, Rome #240/R
£1667 $2650 €2400 Lovers (70x50cm-28x20in) s. painted 1970. 1-May-3 Meeting Art, Vercelli #312
£1844 $2987 €2600 Madre d figlio (60x30cm-24x12in) s. prov.exhib. 26-May-3 Christie's, Milan #305 est:2000-2500
£1935 $3058 €3000 Shotting (80x70cm-31x28in) s. s.verso. 18-Dec-2 Christie's, Rome #82/R
£2308 $3623 €3600 La Salute (80x70cm-31x28in) s. 23-Nov-2 Meeting Art, Vercelli #417/R

Works on paper

£256 $403 €400 Winners (40x30cm-16x12in) s. wax crayon cardboard on canvas. 23-Nov-2 Meeting Art, Vercelli #46

BRINDLEY, Charles A (fl.1888-1898) British

Works on paper

£900 $1422 €1305 Brief respite on a crisp, autumnal day (72x53cm-28x21in) s.d.1904 W/C. 22-Jul-3 Bonhams, Knightsbridge #99/R

BRINICARDI, F (19th C) ?

£324 $522 €486 Italian mountain village with women and washing basket (72x100cm-28x39in) s. 22-Feb-3 Rasmussen, Havnen #2053 (D.KR 3600)

BRIONES, Fernando (1905-) Spanish

£755 $1177 €1200 Woman with white flower (17x17cm-7x7in) s. board. 23-Sep-2 Durán, Madrid #51/R

BRIOSCHI, Antonio (1855-1920) Italian
£1408 $2310 €2042 Houses on the Po (70x102cm-28x40in) s. panel. 4-Jun-3 Fischer, Luzern #1071/R est:3000-4000 (S.FR 3000)

BRIOSCHI, Othmar (1854-1912) Austrian
£980 $1558 €1421 Italian hillside village (56x90cm-22x35in) s.i.d.1898. 26-Feb-3 John Bellman, Billingshurst #1822/R
£1859 $2937 €2900 On the coast of Capri (42x67cm-17x26in) s. 16-Nov-2 Lempertz, Koln #1434/R est:1600
£3200 $5248 €4800 Picking olives above an Italian village (58x90cm-23x35in) s.i.d.1890. 5-Jun-3 Christie's, Kensington #706/R est:2000-3000

BRISCOE, Arthur (1873-1943) British
£18000 $29160 €27000 Bowsprit (66x102cm-26x40in) s.d.28 exhib. 21-May-3 Christie's, Kensington #683/R est:10000-15000
Works on paper
£300 $486 €450 Salcombe Bay (34x52cm-13x20in) s.d.34 pencil W/C exhib. 21-May-3 Christie's, Kensington #439/R
£310 $474 €465 Laid up (35x23cm-14x9in) s.i.d.33 W/C pen ink. 21-Aug-2 Bonhams, Knowle #242
£480 $778 €720 Topsail cutter in calm waters (32x23cm-13x9in) s. W/C. 22-Jan-3 Bonhams, New Bond Street #335/R
£1300 $2106 €1950 Topsail schooner under reduced sail offshore (23x32cm-9x13in) s. W/C. 22-Jan-3 Bonhams, New Bond Street #333/R est:800-1200

BRISCOE, Franklin D (1844-1903) American
£633 $1000 €950 Calm foggy morning on the harbour (13x23cm-5x9in) s. 26-Apr-3 Jeffery Burchard, Florida #18
£1806 $2600 €2709 Fishing at sunrise. Bringing in the catch (16x31cm-6x12in) s. board pair. 15-Jan-3 Christie's, Rockefeller NY #132/R
£2436 $3800 €3654 Fishermen on a calm sea at sunrise (24x36cm-9x14in) s. panel. 14-Sep-2 Weschler, Washington #602/R est:1500-2500
£2821 $4400 €4232 Fishermen pulling in nets at sunset (32x39cm-13x15in) s. panel. 14-Sep-2 Weschler, Washington #603/R est:2000-4000

BRISEDOU, Silvestre Alexis (19th C) French
Miniatures
£1266 $1962 €2000 Ladies (17x13cm-7x5in) s.d.1835 pair. 26-Sep-2 Castellana, Madrid #232/R

BRISGAND, Gustave (?-1950) French
Works on paper
£705 $1029 €1058 Woman's portrait (48cm-19in circular) s. pastel chk. 17-Jun-2 Philippe Schuler, Zurich #4012/R (S.FR 1600)

BRISLISNI, Prof B (19/20th C) Italian
Sculpture
£2885 $4500 €4328 Allegorical female (86cm-34in) executed c.1900. 11-Apr-3 Du Mouchelle, Detroit #2047/R est:1500-2000

BRISPOT, Henri (1846-1928) French
£1935 $3000 €2903 Toast (49x61cm-19x24in) s. 2-Oct-2 Christie's, Rockefeller NY #781/R est:2000-3000

BRISS, Sami (1930-) French
£1346 $2113 €2100 Cafetiere noire (46x33cm-18x13in) s.panel. 12-Dec-2 Rabourdin & Choppin de Janvry, Paris #170/R

BRISSET, Émile (1860-1904) French
£881 $1374 €1400 Canon (80x65cm-31x26in) s.d.1900. 23-Sep-2 Bernaerts, Antwerp #638/R

BRISSON, Maurice (attrib) (1915-) French
£438 $700 €657 Paris street scene (61x91cm-24x36in) s. 11-Jan-3 James Julia, Fairfield #631

BRISSON, Pierre Marie (1955-) French
£1923 $3019 €3000 La chambre (89x116cm-35x46in) s. i.d.verso acrylic mixed media. 16-Dec-2 Charbonneaux, Paris #228/R est:3000-3500
Works on paper
£1987 $3238 €3000 Roue tourne (150x155cm-59x61in) s. i.verso mixed media on canvas exec.1996 prov. 3-Feb-3 Cornette de St.Cyr, Paris #377/R

BRISSOT DE WARVILLE, Felix-Saturnin (1818-1892) French
£1203 $1900 €1900 Pecheur en barque (16x25cm-6x10in) s. panel. 1-Dec-2 Peron, Melun #7
£1268 $2104 €1800 Chasseur et son chien traversant une riviere (41x33cm-16x13in) s. 13-Jun-3 Rabourdin & Choppin de Janvry, Paris #123/R est:2000-2200
£1625 $2600 €2356 Lambs (41x56cm-16x22in) s. panel. 16-May-3 Skinner, Boston #46/R est:1500-2500
£1870 $2898 €2805 Peasant woman feeding sheep and hens in barn (31x41cm-12x16in) s. 9-Dec-2 Philippe Schuler, Zurich #3885/R est:4000-5000 (S.FR 4300)
£4110 $6411 €6000 Sheep in hilly landscape (130x162cm-51x64in) s. 10-Apr-3 Van Ham, Cologne #1344/R est:1800

BRISSOT, F (fl.1879) British
£1923 $3019 €3000 Traversee du fleuve (62x79cm-24x31in) s. 15-Dec-2 Mercier & Cie, Lille #339

BRISTOL, John Bunyan (1826-1909) American
£950 $1500 €1425 Mountain lake (23x41cm-9x16in) s.verso panel. 24-Apr-3 Shannon's, Milford #217/R est:2500-3500
£2400 $3936 €3600 Fisherman on an Oriental bay (75x46cm-30x18in) s. 5-Jun-3 Christie's, Kensington #669/R est:1500-2000
£4516 $7000 €6774 View of a mountain lake (46x76cm-18x30in) s.d.73 prov. 2-Nov-2 North East Auctions, Portsmouth #70/R est:6000-8000
£5031 $8000 €7547 Wooded New England landscape with stream at foreground and mountain beyond (38x58cm-15x23in) s. prov. 22-Mar-3 Nadeau, Windsor #225/R est:6000-10000
£6774 $10500 €10161 Lake Memphramagog, Vermont (46x77cm-18x30in) s.i. prov. 3-Dec-2 Phillips, New York #31/R est:8000-12000
£9740 $15000 €14610 View of the Valley (33x58cm-13x23in) s.d.78. 24-Oct-2 Shannon's, Milford #114/R est:9000-12000
£14286 $22000 €21429 View on a lake (46x76cm-18x30in) s. prov. 24-Oct-2 Shannon's, Milford #36/R est:12000-18000

BRISTOW, Edmund (1787-1876) British
£700 $1162 €1015 Dogs rabbiting in a woodland clearing, sportsman beyond (48x61cm-19x24in) s.d.1827. 12-Jun-3 Christie's, Kensington #295/R
£2200 $3344 €3300 Landscape with cattle watering, and a man on horseback with dogs (27x35cm-11x14in) s. panel. 15-Aug-2 Rupert Toovey, Partridge Green #1401/R est:2000-4000
£4518 $7500 €6551 Horse (25x30cm-10x12in) 13-Jun-3 Du Mouchelle, Detroit #2027/R est:4000-5000
£5422 $9000 €7862 Woodman a bay gelding (25x30cm-10x12in) wood panel. 13-Jun-3 Du Mouchelle, Detroit #2026/R est:4000-5000
£7500 $11625 €11250 Pointers on a heathland with Windsor Castle in distance (61x77cm-24x30in) s.indis d. 25-Sep-2 Hamptons Fine Art, Godalming #450/R est:8000-12000
£10000 $15800 €15000 Horse and groom in a stale (63x76cm-25x30in) s.i.d.1829. 28-Nov-2 Bonhams, Knightsbridge #108/R est:10000-15000
£10000 $16600 €15000 Parish clerk, Saturday evening (51x71cm-20x28in) i.verso prov. 12-Jun-3 Sotheby's, London #240/R est:10000-15000

BRISTOW, Edmund (attrib) (1787-1876) British
£400 $616 €600 Friendly chat (26x21cm-10x8in) panel. 22-Oct-2 Bonhams, Bath #261

BRITISH SCHOOL, 18th C
£23750 $38000 €35625 Seated artist painting in a landscape with a dog and distant figure (99x81cm-39x32in) 4-Jan-3 Brunk, Ashville #919/R est:3000-6000
Sculpture
£4193 $6500 €6290 Hercules resting (22x49cm-9x19in) marble prov.exhib. 29-Oct-2 Sotheby's, New York #257/R est:2500-3500

BRITISH SCHOOL, 19th C
£7143 $11000 €10715 Prize cow and sow (47x61cm-19x24in) 23-Oct-2 Doyle, New York #47/R est:7000-10000
Works on paper
£940 $1513 €1400 House party (23x38cm-9x15in) W/C set of two, after Eugene Lami. 18-Feb-3 Sotheby's, Amsterdam #1174/R

BRITOV, Kim (1925-) Russian
£276 $439 €400 Or de l'automne (18x35cm-7x14in) s.d.95 masonite. 10-Mar-3 Millon & Associes, Paris #204
£414 $658 €600 Ombres printanieres (30x40cm-12x16in) s. d.99 verso canvas on cardboard. 10-Mar-3 Millon & Associes, Paris #205
£690 $1097 €1000 Coucher de soleil sur la ville (55x67cm-22x26in) s.dd.86 cardboard. 10-Mar-3 Millon & Associes, Paris #207/R
£828 $1316 €1200 Coucher de soleil d'hiver (50x60cm-20x24in) s.d.97 masonite. 10-Mar-3 Millon & Associes, Paris #206/R

BRITTAIN, Miller Gore (1912-1968) Canadian
Works on paper
£360 $583 €540 Contemplative Head (44x30cm-17x12in) pastel pencil. 20-May-3 Bonhams, Knightsbridge #16/R
£515 $803 €773 Nude study (41x30cm-16x12in) s.d.65 graphite pastel. 25-Mar-3 Ritchie, Toronto #133 est:700-900 (C.D 1200)

BRITTAN, Charles Edward (jnr) (1870-1949) British
£950 $1501 €1425 Dartmoor Tors at twilight (34x60cm-13x24in) s. 7-Apr-3 Bonhams, Bath #99/R
Works on paper
£340 $551 €510 Sheep on a moorland landscape (26x44cm-10x17in) s. bodycol. 21-Jan-3 Bonhams, Knightsbridge #1/R
£720 $1123 €1080 Among the Dartmoor hills (33x51cm-13x20in) s.d.1902 W/C. 6-Nov-2 Bonhams, Chester #445
£1900 $2907 €2850 Moorland road to Balmoral. Rannoch moor (35x53cm-14x21in) s. W/C pair. 22-Aug-2 Bonhams, Edinburgh #1057/R est:1500-2000

BRITTAN, Charles Edward (snr) (1837-1888) British
Works on paper
£600 $978 €870 Dusk on Dartmoor (28x45cm-11x18in) s. W/C. 16-Jul-3 Sotheby's, Olympia #33/R

BRITTAN, Charles Edward (19/20th C) British
£270 $421 €405 Extensive moorland scene (25x35cm-10x14in) s. 7-Nov-2 Bonhams, Cornwall #787
Works on paper
£256 $400 €384 Study of ducks (32x41cm-13x16in) init. W/C oval. 11-Nov-2 Stephan Welz, Johannesburg #72 (SA.R 4000)
£420 $685 €630 Extensive Devonshire landscape with rocky outcrop (19x27cm-7x11in) s. W/C. 29-Jan-3 Hampton & Littlewood, Exeter #372/R
£480 $768 €720 Brendon moor, Exmoor (35x53cm-14x21in) s. W/C. 13-May-3 Bonhams, Sevenoaks #373/R
£1500 $2325 €2250 High moorland landscape with stream and distant sheep (64x99cm-25x39in) s. W/C dr. 1-Oct-2 Capes Dunn, Manchester #831/R

BRITTEN, Jack (1925-) Australian
Works on paper
£1083 $1679 €1625 Karding, where man can't climb (76x76cm-30x30in) i.verso natural pigments canvas prov. 3-Dec-2 Shapiro, Sydney #210/R est:3000-5000 (A.D 3000)

BRITTEN, William Edward Frank (1848-1916) British
Works on paper
£260 $413 €390 Ascension to heaven (83x53cm-33x21in) pastel. 29-Apr-3 Sworder & Son, Bishops Stortford #330a/R

BRITTON, Charles (1930-) British
Works on paper
£500 $780 €750 Moorland landscape (36x51cm-14x20in) s. W/C. 26-Mar-3 Woolley & Wallis, Salisbury #66/R

BRITTON, Harry (1878-1958) Canadian
£201 $317 €302 Portrait of Mr Davidson (23x18cm-9x7in) d.1915 panel. 1-Dec-2 Levis, Calgary #10a/R (C.D 500)
£489 $802 €734 Skyline, Toronto (35x25cm-14x10in) s. board. 3-Jun-3 Joyner, Toronto #423/R est:1500-2000 (C.D 1100)
£1975 $3062 €2963 Landing fish, St. Ives (22x25cm-9x10in) s. canvas on board. 3-Dec-2 Joyner, Toronto #274/R est:1200-1500 (C.D 4800)
£4889 $8018 €7334 In the harbour (75x125cm-30x49in) s.d.1911 prov. 3-Jun-3 Joyner, Toronto #116/R est:6000-8000 (C.D 11000)

BRIULLOV, Karl Pavlovich (attrib) (1799-1852) Russian
£500 $785 €750 Portrait of a lady (58x42cm-23x17in) 16-Apr-3 Christie's, Kensington #862

BRIZZI, Ary (1930-) Argentinian
£1861 $2940 €2792 Red shape (160x60cm-63x24in) s.d.57 acrylic. 15-Nov-2 Naón & Cia, Buenos Aires #14/R

BRIZZI, C (19th C) ?
£455 $677 €700 Mountain landscape with figures (62x77cm-24x30in) s.d.1853. 27-Jun-2 Neumeister, Munich #2699
£552 $822 €850 Mountain landscape with figures (62x77cm-24x30in) s.d.1855. 27-Jun-2 Neumeister, Munich #2698/R

BROADBENT, Arthur E (?) British
£300 $489 €450 Symbols of Venice (74x50cm-29x20in) init. 29-Jan-3 Hampton & Littlewood, Exeter #397

BROADLEY, Denise (1913-) British?
£320 $528 €464 Peat diggers, Galway (63x76cm-25x30in) s.d.1947. 1-Jul-3 Bonhams, Norwich #181

BROADLEY, Robert (1908-1988) South African/British
£197 $307 €296 Reclining nude (44x59cm-17x23in) s. canvasboard. 15-Oct-2 Stephan Welz, Johannesburg #456 est:2500-3500 (SA.R 3200)
£258 $415 €387 Cape courtyard (24x34cm-9x13in) s. s.i.verso canvas on board. 12-May-3 Stephan Welz, Johannesburg #207 est:2000-4000 (SA.R 3000)
Works on paper
£205 $320 €308 Pensive seated nude woman (21x23cm-8x9in) s. pen ink W/C. 11-Nov-2 Stephan Welz, Johannesburg #205 (SA.R 3200)

BROCAS, Charles (1774-1835) French
£10284 $17174 €14500 Trait d'humanite du Prince de Neuchatel (74x86cm-29x34in) exhib. 18-Jun-3 Tajan, Paris #148/R est:6000-8000

BROCAS, James Henry (c.1790-1846) British
£11000 $17600 €16500 Roller, bay hunter with hounds (63x76cm-25x30in) prov.lit. 15-May-3 Christie's, London #16/R est:7000-10000

BROCAS, Samuel Frederick (1792-1847) Irish
Works on paper
£1899 $2943 €3000 Views in the Environs of Dublin (18x27cm-7x11in) one i. W/C set of four. 25-Sep-2 James Adam, Dublin #27/R est:3000-5000

BROCAS, William (?) British?
£12500 $20000 €18750 Racehorse with jockey and attendants in a field (71x91cm-28x36in) s.i. prov. 14-May-3 Butterfields, San Francisco #1137/R est:6000-8000

BROCHART, Constant Joseph (1816-1899) French
Works on paper
£641 $1000 €962 Her new interest (69x56cm-27x22in) s. pastel oval. 9-Oct-2 Doyle, New York #18
£1218 $1900 €1827 Woman in her dressing room (61x43cm-24x17in) init. pastel. 9-Oct-2 Doyle, New York #19 est:2500-3500

BROCK, Charles Edmund (1870-1938) British
Works on paper
£280 $437 €420 Darby and Joan (23x33cm-9x13in) s.d.1915 W/C prov. 26-Mar-3 Hamptons Fine Art, Godalming #86

BROCK, Edmund (fl.1920-1950) British
£6200 $9610 €9300 Penelope, daughter of Douglas Walker (178x117cm-70x46in) s.d.1921 exhib. 3-Dec-2 Sotheby's, Olympia #195/R est:5000-7000

BROCK, Gustav (1849-1887) Danish
£2052 $3263 €3078 Landscape with the Danish Guards (43x62cm-17x24in) s.d.1881. 5-May-3 Rasmussen, Vejle #669/R est:30000 (D.KR 22000)

BROCK, Henry Matthew (1875-1960) British
Works on paper
£300 $474 €450 Huntsman seated by fireside (33x45cm-13x18in) s. W/C. 28-Nov-2 Bonhams, Knightsbridge #120/R

BROCK, William (1874-?) British
£3459 $5396 €5500 Outing in the park (165x240cm-65x94in) s.i.d.1907. 20-Sep-2 Millon & Associes, Paris #52/R est:8000-12000
Works on paper
£350 $546 €525 Gathering wood (27x46cm-11x18in) init. pencil W/C scratching out. 27-Mar-3 Christie's, Kensington #33

BROCKBANK, Albert Ernest (1862-1958) British
Works on paper
£480 $802 €696 Hedgerley, Buckinghamshire (44x29cm-17x11in) s. W/C htd white. 26-Jun-3 Mellors & Kirk, Nottingham #826/R

BROCKER, Ernst (1893-1963) German
£385 $596 €600 Aiblinger Moor (61x81cm-24x32in) s.i. 5-Dec-2 Neumeister, Munich #2770/R
£481 $745 €750 Aiblinger Moor (70x101cm-28x40in) s.i. 5-Dec-2 Neumeister, Munich #2769/R

BROCKHURST, Gerald Leslie (1890-1978) British
£7500 $11625 €11250 Portrait of Matitchka (52x45cm-20x18in) s. panel prov. 3-Dec-2 Bonhams, New Bond Street #6/R est:5000-7000
Prints
£4487 $7000 €6731 Adolescence, Kathleen Nancy Woodward (46x35cm-18x14in) s. etching edition of 90. 5-Nov-2 Christie's, Rockefeller NY #87/R est:8000-12000
£5031 $8000 €7547 Adolescence, Kathleen Nancy Woodward (37x28cm-15x11in) s. etching edition of 90. 29-Apr-3 Christie's, Rockefeller NY #426/R est:8000-10000

BROCKHUSEN, Theo von (1882-1919) German
£4167 $6458 €6500 Farmsteads (57x72cm-22x28in) s.i.d.1918 stretcher. 4-Dec-2 Lempertz, Koln #585/R est:7000
£5063 $8000 €8000 Stormy landscape with tree (64x85cm-25x33in) s.d.11. 30-Nov-2 Bassenge, Berlin #6153/R est:12000
£15823 $25000 €25000 Jetty (66x80cm-26x31in) s. i. verso exhib.lit. 29-Nov-2 Schloss Ahlden, Ahlden #1408/R est:16500
£17391 $28522 €24000 Jetty in Nieuport (80x96cm-31x38in) s.d.09 prov.lit. 31-May-3 Villa Grisebach, Berlin #162/R est:15000-20000

BROCKMAN, Ann (1899-1943) American
£2750 $4400 €4125 View of the Brooklyn Bridge (91x122cm-36x48in) s. 12-Jan-3 William Jenack, New York #254

BROCKMANN, Gottfried (1903-1983) German
£253 $400 €400 Still life (28x25cm-11x10in) mono. s.i.d.1945 verso panel. 30-Nov-2 Bassenge, Berlin #6155

BROCKTORFF, Charles Frederick de (19th C) German
Works on paper
£2273 $3500 €3410 Views of Malta (21x32cm-8x13in) i. W/C pair. 23-Oct-2 Doyle, New York #107 est:300-500

BROCKY, Karoly (attrib) (1808-1855) Hungarian
£3500 $5565 €5250 Grape harvest (61x51cm-24x20in) oval. 20-Mar-3 Christie's, Kensington #177/R est:5000-7000

BROCQUY, Louis le (1916-) Irish
£7595 $11772 €12000 Shadows (32x45cm-13x18in) s.d.1986 lithograph set of 23. 24-Sep-2 De Veres Art Auctions, Dublin #21/R est:8000-12000
£10500 $16800 €15750 Being (25x18cm-10x7in) s. si.d1957 verso canvas on board prov.exhib. 15-May-3 Christie's, London #93/R est:5000-8000
£15000 $24600 €22500 Presence (41x30cm-16x12in) s.d.47 i.on overlap. 6-Jun-3 Christie's, London #109/R est:10000-15000
£42405 $65728 €67000 Image of W. B. Yates (80x80cm-31x31in) s.d.1981 verso exhib. 24-Sep-2 De Veres Art Auctions, Dublin #59/R est:60000-80000
£48000 $76800 €72000 Human image (162x114cm-64x45in) s.d.2000 verso prov. 16-May-3 Sotheby's, London #138/R est:40000-60000
£50000 $80000 €75000 Child with flowers (40x30cm-16x12in) s.d.51 i.on overlap prov.exhib. 16-May-3 Sotheby's, London #117/R est:50000-70000
£65000 $104000 €97500 Child in spring field (76x63cm-30x25in) s.d.54 prov.exhib. 15-May-3 Christie's, London #91/R est:70000-100000
Prints
£1667 $2733 €2300 Head of W B Yeats (76x57cm-30x22in) s.num.17/100 aquatint etching. 28-May-3 Bonhams & James Adam, Dublin #136/R est:1200-1800
£1835 $2845 €2900 Head of Samuel Beckett (65x50cm-26x20in) s.num.84/100 aquatint etching. 25-Sep-2 James Adam, Dublin #142/R est:1500-2500
£1899 $2943 €3000 Head of Strinberg (77x57cm-30x22in) s.num.76/100 aquatint etching. 25-Sep-2 James Adam, Dublin #136 est:1500-2500
£2179 $3422 €3400 Procession with lilies (46x76cm-18x30in) s.num.16/75 lithograph prov. 19-Nov-2 Whyte's, Dublin #18/R est:1800-2200
£2516 $3925 €4000 Study of self (17x15cm-7x6in) s. lithograph 10 of 75 exhib. 17-Sep-2 Whyte's, Dublin #28 est:1500-2500
£2911 $4513 €4600 Head of W B Yates (77x57cm-30x22in) s.num.12/100 aquatint etching. 25-Sep-2 James Adam, Dublin #43/R est:1500-2500
£5031 $7849 €8000 Six masks for the playboy of the western world (178x43cm-70x17in) s.d.1971 num.16 aquatint rice paper on rag paper prov.lit. 17-Sep-2 Whyte's, Dublin #75/R est:3000-4000
Works on paper
£2885 $4471 €4500 Lemons (16x25cm-6x10in) init.d.1942 W/C. 3-Dec-2 Bonhams & James Adam, Dublin #107/R est:5000-7000
£3899 $6083 €6200 View in the Phoenix Park (23x14cm-9x6in) init.d.23 March 1931 W/C prov. 17-Sep-2 Whyte's, Dublin #136/R est:4000-5000
£8219 $12904 €12000 Saturday St. Stephen's Green (12x16cm-5x6in) s.d.July 1944 i.verso W/C htd white. 15-Apr-3 De Veres Art Auctions, Dublin #114/R est:9000-12000
£14557 $22563 €23000 Study of Francis Bacon (46x41cm-18x16in) s.d.81 W/C prov. 24-Sep-2 De Veres Art Auctions, Dublin #116/R est:12000-16000
£15000 $24000 €22500 Travellers (31x25cm-12x10in) s.d.45 pen ink W/C wax resist. 16-May-3 Sotheby's, London #107/R est:15000-20000
£15217 $24957 €21000 Donkey ride (24x20cm-9x8in) s.d.46 ink W/C. 28-May-3 Bonhams & James Adam, Dublin #134/R est:8000-10000
£31250 $49687 €45000 Eden (112x175cm-44x69in) s. wool tapestry prov.lit. 29-Apr 3 Whyte's, Dublin #58/R est:50000-70000
£52000 $83200 €78000 Study man with a towel (112x71cm-44x28in) s.d.51 s.i.d.verso W/C gouache col chk prov. 16-May-3 Sotheby's, London #122/R est:40000-60000
£70000 $112000 €105000 Allegory (180x225cm-71x89in) s.d.50 wool tapestry lit. 16-May-3 Sotheby's, London #113/R est:70000-100000

BRODIE, John Lamont (fl.1848-1881) British
£720 $1123 €1080 Scottish courtship - with elegant figures rowing on the loch (46x61cm-18x24in) s. indis d. s.d.1869 verso. 6-Nov-2 Bonhams, Chester #541/R

BRODIE, Kate S (fl.1891-1900) British
£500 $765 €750 By the croft (30x45cm-12x18in) s. 22-Aug-2 Bonhams, Edinburgh #1085

BRODTMANN, Joseph (1787-1862) Swiss
Prints
£1598 $2493 €2397 Elephantus Indicus - male and female (32x41cm-13x16in) lithograph two. 28-Mar-3 Koller, Zurich #3383/R est:1300-1600 (S.FR 3500)

BRODWOLF, Jurgen (1932-) Swiss
Works on paper
£897 $1364 €1400 Figure (29x21cm-11x8in) s.d.2001 mixed media. 31-Aug-2 Geble, Radolfzell #615/R

BRODZKY, Horace (1885-1969) Australian
£400 $624 €600 Return to Catania (30x25cm-12x10in) s.d.65 s.i.verso. 15-Oct-2 Bonhams, Knightsbridge #8/R
£1149 $1713 €1724 Hyde Park (26x23cm-10x9in) s.i.d.42 prov. 27-Aug-2 Christie's, Melbourne #193/R est:3000-5000 (A.D 3000)
£1300 $2028 €1950 Figures on a quay (51x41cm-20x16in) s.d.1916 s.i.verso. 12-Sep-2 Sotheby's, Olympia #72/R est:600-800
Works on paper
£242 $367 €363 Portrait of Alfred Wolmark (30x22cm-12x9in) s. pencil prov.lit. 28-Aug-2 Deutscher-Menzies, Melbourne #423/R (A.D 675)
£280 $451 €420 Rural scene (23x27cm-9x11in) s.d.41 W/C. 18-Feb-3 Bonhams, Knightsbridge #136/R
£280 $462 €406 Australian landscape (25x20cm-10x8in) s. pencil W/C. 3-Jul-3 Christie's, Kensington #278

BRODZSKY, Sandor (1819-1901) Hungarian
£1129 $1751 €1694 Rocks in the forest (31x36cm-12x14in) s. canvas on cardboard. 6-Dec-2 Kieselbach, Budapest #15/R (H.F 420000)
£1129 $1751 €1694 Waving ears (13x37cm-5x15in) cardboard. 6-Dec-2 Kieselbach, Budapest #65/R (H.F 420000)

BROE, Vern (20th C) American
£545 $850 €818 Sailing into friendship (28x41cm-11x16in) s. board. 1-Aug-2 Eldred, East Dennis #749/R

BROECK, Clemence van den (1843-1922) Belgian
£222 $350 €333 Rigging the sails (37x55cm-15x22in) s. 18-Nov-2 Waddingtons, Toronto #30/R (C.D 550)
£723 $1135 €1085 Young beauty with red hat and cherries (58x41cm-23x16in) s. 24-Jul-2 Walker's, Ottawa #5/R est:1500-2000 (C.D 1750)

BROECK, Crispin van den (1524-1588) Flemish
Works on paper
£935 $1496 €1300 Le Christ aux outrages (164x122cm-65x48in) s.d.1576 pen brown ink prov. 15-May-3 Christie's, Paris #201/R

BROECK, Crispin van den (attrib) (1524-1588) Flemish
£22973 $35838 €34000 Apollo and a muse (110x141cm-43x56in) panel prov. 27-Mar-3 Dorotheum, Vienna #172/R est:30000-50000

BROECK, Dries van den (1927-) Belgian
£440 $678 €700 Paysage (100x150cm-39x59in) s.d.1967. 22-Oct-2 Campo, Vlaamse Kaai #299

BROECK, Elias van den (1650-1708) Dutch
£44586 $69554 €70000 Forest floor still life with butterflies and snails. Forest floor still life (29x22cm-11x9in) s. panel pair. 6-Nov-2 Christie's, Amsterdam #82/R est:25000-35000
£82000 $128740 €123000 Still life of fruit, oyster, and roemer on a table (22x29cm-9x11in) panel. 12-Dec-2 Sotheby's, London #160/R est:15000-20000

BROECK, Elias van den (circle) (1650-1708) Dutch
£9000 $14040 €13500 Tulips, poppies and a daffodil and other flowers in a glass vase on a ledge (74x63cm-29x25in) 10-Apr-3 Christie's, Kensington #79/R est:7000-10000

BROECKAERDT, Herman (1878-1930) Belgian
£362 $594 €500 Promenade au bord de d'Escaut (50x70cm-20x28in) s. 27-May-3 Campo & Campo, Antwerp #41

BROEDER, Max (1903-) Belgian
£1014 $1664 €1400 Le disciple d'Emaus (50x60cm-20x24in) s. 27-May-3 Campo & Campo, Antwerp #42

BROEL, Georg (1884-1940) German
£962 $1510 €1500 Rhine landscape with Drachenfels and Nonnenwerth (75x100cm-30x39in) s.d.1929. 21-Nov-2 Van Ham, Cologne #1500

BROGE, Alfred (1870-1955) Danish
£372 $592 €558 Old farmhouse, Tibirke (46x54cm-18x21in) s. 5-Mar-3 Rasmussen, Copenhagen #1872/R (D.KR 4000)
£573 $894 €900 Extensive landscape with farm building, figure and animal (49x66cm-19x26in) s. lit. 7-Nov-2 Allgauer, Kempten #2769/R
£575 $896 €863 Interior scene with sunshine coming through window (52x63cm-20x25in) s.d.1909. 11-Nov-2 Rasmussen, Vejle #500/R (D.KR 6700)
£633 $1007 €950 Woman reading in garden (49x42cm-19x17in) s. 10-Mar-3 Rasmussen, Vejle #20/R (D.KR 6800)
£888 $1385 €1332 Interior scene with girl reading (33x41cm-13x16in) s. 11-Aug-2 Hindemae, Ullerslev #7308/R (D.KR 10500)
£1351 $2108 €2027 Interior scene with woman seated by window (47x43cm-19x17in) s. 23-Sep-2 Rasmussen, Vejle #30/R est:20000 (D.KR 16000)
£2144 $3345 €3216 Interior (50x59cm-20x23in) s. 11-Nov-2 Rasmussen, Vejle #502/R est:8000 (D.KR 25000)
£2927 $4800 €4244 By the window (52x63cm-20x25in) s.d.1909. 4-Jun-3 Christie's, Rockefeller NY #215/R est:4000-6000
£3254 $5271 €4718 Interior scene with girl looking out of window (54x52cm-21x20in) s.d.1913. 26-May-3 Rasmussen, Copenhagen #1541/R est:15000 (D.KR 34000)
£3659 $6000 €5306 Interior with white door (50x59cm-20x23in) indis.sig. 4-Jun-3 Christie's, Rockefeller NY #217/R est:6000-8000

BROGGINI, Luigi (1908-1983) Italian
Works on paper
£282 $443 €440 Figures (49x34cm-19x13in) s.d.1943 chl W/C. 19-Nov-2 Finarte, Milan #11

BROGI, Gino (1902-1989) Italian
£1622 $2530 €2400 Houses in the fields (39x55cm-15x22in) s. canvas on cardboard. 28-Mar-3 Farsetti, Prato #767/R

BROGLIA (1942-) ?
Sculpture
£503 $775 €800 Composition (65cm-26in) s. marble. 22-Oct-2 Campo & Campo, Antwerp #24

BROMBERGER, Dora (1881-1942) German
£585 $930 €860 Narrow street (56x46cm-22x18in) s. i. verso. 28-Mar-3 Bolland & Marotz, Bremen #325/R
Works on paper
£493 $769 €720 Girl in night gown sitting on chair (29x22cm-11x9in) s. W/C pencil. 11-Apr-3 Winterberg, Heidelberg #779 est:580

BROMBO, Angelo (1893-1962) Italian
£858 $1356 €1287 Venice (50x70cm-20x28in) s. 29-Nov-2 Zofingen, Switzerland #2403/R (S.FR 2000)
£1379 $2179 €2000 Venice (61x80cm-24x31in) i. verso. 5-Apr-3 Dr Fritz Nagel, Leipzig #3949/R est:2000

BROMLEY, David (1960-) Australian
£235 $364 €353 Untitled (65x98cm-26x39in) s.d.88 paper. 3-Dec-2 Shapiro, Sydney #66 (A.D 650)
£722 $1119 €1083 Turnips (86x86cm-34x34in) s. acrylic. 3-Dec-2 Shapiro, Sydney #65/R est:1500-2500 (A.D 2000)
£2183 $3623 €3719 Untitled - children cycling (115x115cm-45x45in) s. prov. 10-Jun-3 Shapiro, Sydney #81/R est:6000-8000 (A.D 5500)
£2183 $3623 €3719 Untitled - brothers in a row boat (115x115cm-45x45in) s. prov. 10-Jun-3 Shapiro, Sydney #82/R est:6000-8000 (A.D 5500)
£2183 $3623 €3719 Untitled - children on a deck at sea (115x115cm-45x45in) s. prov. 10-Jun-3 Shapiro, Sydney #83/R est:6000-8000 (A.D 5500)
£2236 $3533 €3242 Girl meets buoy (59x78cm-23x31in) s. s.i.verso board. 22-Jul-3 Lawson Menzies, Sydney #61/R est:1500-3000 (A.D 5500)
£2400 $3864 €3600 Swing (61x61cm-24x24in) s. acrylic on board. 6-May-3 Christie's, Melbourne #381/R est:2000-3000 (A.D 6000)
Works on paper
£1615 $2568 €2423 Nancy (122x91cm-48x36in) s. synthetic polymer paint canvas. 4-Mar-3 Deutscher-Menzies, Melbourne #185/R est:4000-6000 (A.D 4200)
£1628 $2588 €2442 Untitled (137x111cm-54x44in) s. synthetic polymer canvas. 5-May-3 Sotheby's, Melbourne #357/R est:3000-4000 (A.D 4200)

BROMLEY, Fred (20th C) British
£330 $525 €495 Summer's afternoon (49x54cm-19x21in) s. board. 4-May-3 Lots Road, London #357/R

BROMLEY, John Mallard (fl.1876-1904) British
Works on paper
£420 $701 €609 St. Ives Harbour (24x34cm-9x13in) s. W/C. 19-Jun-3 Lane, Penzance #40/R
£2900 $4582 €4350 Harbour at St. Ives (74x124cm-29x49in) s. W/C. 7-Apr-3 Bonhams, Bath #21/R est:800-1200

BROMLEY, Valentine Walter (1848-1877) British
Works on paper
£2400 $3792 €3600 Lord of the manor (60x90cm-24x35in) s.d.1873 W/C bodycol htd white. 7-Apr-3 Bonhams, Bath #20/R est:3000-5000
£24551 $41000 €35599 Crow family on the trail (36x48cm-14x19in) s.d.1874 W/C gouache ink prov. 18-Jun-3 Christie's, Los Angeles #39/R est:15000-25000

BROMLEY, William (19th C) British
£2250 $3645 €3263 Interior scene with woman and children (53x43cm-21x17in) s.d.1856. 26-May-3 Bukowskis, Stockholm #239a/R est:20000-25000 (S.KR 29000)
£2667 $4427 €3867 Blowing bubbles (39x34cm-15x13in) init. board prov. 16-Jun-3 Waddingtons, Toronto #169/R est:7000-9000 (C.D 6000)
£3200 $4960 €4800 Playmates (35x45cm-14x18in) s. 3-Dec-2 Sotheby's, Olympia #113/R est:3000-4000

BROMLEY, William III (fl.1843-1870) British
£3500 $5810 €5250 Waiting for a bite (36x46cm-14x18in) s. s.i.verso. 10-Jun-3 Christie's, London #115/R est:4000-6000
£12000 $19320 €18000 Knuckle down (51x62cm-20x24in) s. prov.exhib.lit. 20-Feb-3 Christie's, London #250/R est:20000

BROMS, Birgit (1924-) Swedish
£1544 $2486 €2316 Still life of bottle of wine (72x24cm-28x9in) s. 7-May-3 AB Stockholms Auktionsverk #865/R est:8000-10000 (S.KR 20000)

BRON, Achille (1867-1949) French
Works on paper
£513 $779 €800 Aux courses (21x30cm-8x12in) s.i.d.1912 W/C. 16-Aug-2 Deauville, France #11/R

BRONCHU, Jose (1912-) Spanish
£1032 $1631 €1600 Gates to the Arab area (54x65cm-21x26in) s. s.i.verso. 18-Dec-2 Ansorena, Madrid #221/R
Works on paper
£645 $1019 €1000 Yellow and black (38x64cm-15x25in) s. W/C. 18-Dec-2 Ansorena, Madrid #237/R

BRONCKHORST, Gerrit van (attrib) (1637-1673) Dutch
£2258 $3500 €3387 Diana and her attendants in classical landscape (25x36cm-10x14in) mono. panel. 2-Nov-2 North East Auctions, Portsmouth #117/R est:4000-6000

BRONDY, Matteo (1866-1944) French
Works on paper
£577 $905 €900 Cavalier de fantaisie (44x32cm-17x13in) s. W/C gouache. 10-Dec-2 Tajan, Paris #119

BRONQUART, Jean Baptiste Adolphe (19th C) French
£1304 $2035 €1956 River landscape with windmill, figures and animals (43x56cm-17x22in) s. panel. 16-Sep-2 Philippe Schuler, Zurich #3460/R est:4000-5000 (S.FR 3000)

BRONSON, Clark (1939-) American
Sculpture
£1027 $1500 €1541 Gobblers roost (36cm-14in) one of 75 bronze. 18-May-2 Altermann Galleries, Santa Fe #221/R

BRONZINO, Angelo (attrib) (1503-1572) Italian
Works on paper
£10490 $15000 €15735 Figures from Michelangelo's Last Judgement (38x22cm-15x9in) chk prov. 22-Jan-3 Doyle, New York #8/R est:7000

BROOD, Herman (1946-2001) Dutch
£1026 $1590 €1600 Bottom (119x90cm-47x35in) s.d.2000 acrylic airbrush. 3-Dec-2 Christie's, Amsterdam #133/R est:2000-3000
£1277 $2068 €1800 Wings-up yeah yeah (119x160cm-47x63in) s. acrylic. 26-May-3 Glerum, Amsterdam #319/R est:1500-2500
Works on paper
£348 $543 €550 Figure (54x36cm-21x14in) s. brush cardboard. 21-Oct-2 Bernaerts, Antwerp #758

BROODTHAERS, Marcel (1924-1976) Belgian
Prints
£4138 $6621 €6000 Animaux de la ferme, tableau A. Animaux de la ferme, tableaux B (82x60cm-32x24in) mono.d.1974 num.XVII/XX col offset lithograph board lit. two. 15-Mar-3 De Vuyst, Lokeren #566/R est:5500-6500
Sculpture
£24000 $40080 €34800 Une vipere, un vampire, une vitre (18x55x36cm-7x22x14in) acrylic canvas and suitcase executed 1974 prov. 27-Jun-3 Christie's, London #159/R est:15000-20000
Works on paper
£4000 $6680 €5800 Paquet de lettres (41x49cm-16x19in) painted canvas collage on cardboard executed 1974 prov.exhib. 27-Jun-3 Christie's, London #157/R est:5000-7000
£6259 $9951 €9200 Modele, la virgule (83x118cm-33x46in) plastic prov. 24-Mar-3 Cornette de St.Cyr, Paris #114/R

BROOK, Raymond Peter (1927-) British
£600 $936 €900 Classical Bronte landscape (76x127cm-30x50in) s.i. 27-Mar-3 Christie's, Kensington #611
£650 $1014 €975 Self portrait in Birdsroyd Lane. Northern Woolen Mills (112x127cm-44x50in) pair lit. 17-Sep-2 Bonhams, Knightsbridge #246/R
£650 $1073 €943 Looking towards Fort William from Glen Roy (51x61cm-20x24in) s.i. prov. 3-Jul-3 Christie's, Kensington #425

BROOKE, Percy (fl.1894-1916) British
Works on paper
£380 $597 €570 Lear Silverdale (25x36cm-10x14in) s.d.1914 W/C. 10-Dec-2 Capes Dunn, Manchester #776
£420 $668 €630 Homeward bound (17x27cm-7x11in) s. W/C htd white. 29-Apr-3 Bonhams, Knightsbridge #58/R
£520 $811 €780 Woman and child with a calf by a well (17x22cm-7x9in) s.d.1901 W/C htd white. 10-Apr-3 Tennants, Leyburn #903/R

BROOKER, Bertram (1888-1955) Canadian
£1794 $2870 €2691 Teapot (41x51cm-16x20in) s. s.i.verso prov. 15-May-3 Heffel, Vancouver #70/R est:5000-7000 (C.D 4000)
£1906 $3049 €2859 Country farm (29x39cm-11x15in) s. board prov. 15-May-3 Heffel, Vancouver #174/R est:3000-4000 (C.D 4250)
£3831 $6052 €5747 Still life with green bottle (38x29cm-15x11in) board prov.lit. 18-Nov-2 Sotheby's, Toronto #168/R est:4000-6000 (C.D 9500)

BROOKER, Harry (1848-1940) British
£12000 $18960 €18000 The tea party (71x91cm-28x36in) s.d.1895. 26-Nov-2 Christie's, London #98/R est:15000-20000
£15549 $25500 €22546 Young artist's (69x89cm-27x35in) s.d.1896 exhib. 30-May-3 Aspire, Cleveland #35/R est:10000-20000
£27000 $43470 €40500 Critical moment (70x91cm-28x36in) s.d.1889 prov.exhib. 20-Feb-3 Christie's, London #43/R est:35000

BROOKER, Harry (attrib) (1848-1940) British
£850 $1343 €1275 Young dentist (24x18cm-9x7in) panel. 12-Nov-2 Bonhams, Knightsbridge #289/R

BROOKES, Samuel Marsden (1816-1892) American
£1506 $2500 €2184 Still life with grapes on the vine (53x42cm-21x17in) s.d.1872 canvas on board prov. 11-Jun-3 Butterfields, San Francisco #4152/R est:3000-5000
£10828 $17000 €16242 Day's catch, three trout by a brook (51x61cm-20x24in) s. 19-Nov-2 Butterfields, San Francisco #8149/R est:15000-20000

BROOKING, Charles (1723-1759) British
£10000 $16600 €15000 Royal naval squadron of the red offshore in a heavy swell (71x91cm-28x36in) 10-Jun-3 Christie's, London #49/R est:10000-15000

BROOKS, Allan (1869-1946) Canadian
Works on paper
£609 $950 €914 Birds on branches (30x22cm-12x9in) s. gouache. 9-Nov-2 Sloan, North Bethesda #539/R

BROOKS, Cora Smalley (1885-1930) American
£569 $950 €825 On the Guidecca (30x36cm-12x14in) s. 21-Jun-3 Selkirks, St. Louis #163/R

BROOKS, Frank Leonard (1911-1989) Canadian
£356 $583 €534 Still life with pineapples (60x75cm-24x30in) s. 3-Jun-3 Joyner, Toronto #539 (C.D 800)
£422 $692 €633 Beginning of winter (19x29cm-7x11in) s. canvas on board. 3-Jun-3 Joyner, Toronto #482 est:800-1200 (C.D 950)
£533 $875 €800 York Mills, autumn (30x40cm-12x16in) s.d.38. 3-Jun-3 Joyner, Toronto #304/R est:1500-2000 (C.D 1200)
£558 $870 €837 Papaya still life (38x52cm-15x20in) s. cardboard exhib. 25-Mar-3 Iegor de Saint Hippolyte, Montreal #18 (C.D 1300)
Works on paper
£356 $583 €534 Salveterra (45x55cm-18x22in) s.i. W/C. 3-Jun-3 Joyner, Toronto #542 (C.D 800)

BROOKS, Henry Howard (1898-?) American
£287 $450 €431 Zinnias and cosmos (46x36cm-18x14in) s. canvasboard. 22-Nov-2 Skinner, Boston #170/R

BROOKS, Henry Jermyn (1865-1925) British
£4800 $7632 €7200 Portrait of the right Hon William Ewart Gladstone (20x15cm-8x6in) s.d.1889 s.verso exhib.lit. 6-Mar-3 Christie's, Kensington #378/R est:800-1200

BROOKS, Kim (1936-) British
Works on paper
£400 $624 €600 Head of a lioness (33x48cm-13x19in) s. pastel. 11-Apr-3 Keys, Aylsham #404/R

BROOKS, T (1818-1891) British
£2632 $4000 €3948 Heavenly dreams (92x69cm-36x27in) s.d.1852. 19-Aug-2 Joel, Victoria #287 est:4500-5500 (A.D 7500)

BROOKS, Thomas (1818-1891) British
£696 $1100 €1044 Consolation (36x25cm-14x10in) s.d.1859 board. 16-Nov-2 New Orleans Auction, New Orleans #550
£904 $1500 €1311 Interior with boy and animals (76x64cm-30x25in) s.d. 11-Jun-3 Boos Gallery, Michigan #530/R est:3000-5000
£8904 $13890 €13000 Sunday trip to s.d.187church (92x115cm-36x45in) 10-Apr-3 Van Ham, Cologne #1345/R est:15000

BROOM, Marion L (fl.1925-1939) British
£260 $424 €390 Apple blossom in a Doulton jug (43x33cm-17x13in) s. 14-Feb-3 Keys, Aylsham #343/R
£320 $502 €480 Vase with magnolias (50x61cm-20x24in) s. 21-Nov-2 Clevedon Sale Rooms #202
Works on paper
£250 $408 €375 Bowl of summer flowers (50x69cm-20x27in) s. W/C. 30-Jan-3 Lawrence, Crewkerne #662/R
£250 $390 €375 Still life study of mixed flowers in a blue and white vase (53x36cm-21x14in) W/C. 11-Apr-3 Keys, Aylsham #453
£275 $429 €413 Still life of mixed spring flowers in a glass bowl (43x51cm-17x20in) s. W/C. 18-Oct-2 Keys, Aylsham #347/R
£310 $518 €450 Still life of phlox in a copper jug on a table (43x30cm-17x12in) s. W/C. 20-Jun-3 Keys, Aylsham #347/R
£340 $537 €510 Study of chrysanthemums (36x56cm-14x22in) s. W/C. 17-Dec-2 Mallams, Cheltenham #214/R
£440 $686 €660 Flowers in glass bowl (56x79cm-22x31in) s. W/C. 15-Oct-2 Gorringes, Lewes #2184

£540 $853 €810 Still life study of the pick of the garden (38x51cm-15x20in) s. W/C sold with greeting card. 24-Apr-3 Richardson & Smith, Whitby #138/R

BROOME, G J (fl.1867-1873) British
£950 $1482 €1425 Still life of grapes, apples, pears, pineapple and redcurrants (51x61cm-20x24in) s. 10-Sep-2 Bonhams, Knightsbridge #231/R

BROPHY, Elizabeth (20th C) Australian/Irish
£497 $785 €775 Bowl of colourful flowers (19x24cm-7x9in) board. 12-Nov-2 Mealy's, Castlecomer #1261
£529 $836 €825 Still life of flowers (25x20cm-10x8in) 12-Nov-2 Mealy's, Castlecomer #1258
£641 $1013 €1000 Forest light (27x37cm-11x15in) board. 12-Nov-2 Mealy's, Castlecomer #1260
£641 $1013 €1000 Florist (26x20cm-10x8in) board. 12-Nov-2 Mealy's, Castlecomer #1259
£648 $1075 €920 Weary (24x18cm-9x7in) s. board. 10-Jun-3 James Adam, Dublin #110/R est:600-800
£959 $1496 €1400 Children and gulls (38x48cm-15x19in) s. board. 8-Apr-3 James Adam, Dublin #193/R
£986 $1637 €1400 Market day (24x31cm-9x12in) s. board. 10-Jun-3 James Adam, Dublin #111/R est:800-1200
£1218 $1912 €1900 Three children playing with toy buckets and boats (36x46cm-14x18in) s. board. 19-Nov-2 Whyte's, Dublin #5/R est:2000-2500
£1258 $1962 €2000 Relaxing (36x46cm-14x18in) s. board. 17-Sep-2 Whyte's, Dublin #163/R est:2000-2500
£1282 $1987 €2000 Figures in a forest. s. 3-Dec-2 Thomas Adams, Dublin #401
£1384 $2158 €2200 Beach (30x46cm-12x18in) s. i.verso board. 17-Sep-2 Whyte's, Dublin #4 est:2200-2500
£1477 $2377 €2200 Yellow umbrella (30x41cm-12x16in) s. i.verso board. 18-Feb-3 Whyte's, Dublin #228/R est:1500-2000
£1667 $2617 €2600 Lazy days (36x46cm-14x18in) s. i.verso board. 19-Nov-2 Whyte's, Dublin #113/R est:2500-3500
£1667 $2617 €2600 Fairground (36x46cm-14x18in) s. i.verso board. 19-Nov-2 Whyte's, Dublin #226/R est:2500-3500
£1879 $3026 €2800 Afternoon chat (41x51cm-16x20in) s. board. 18-Feb-3 Whyte's, Dublin #226/R est:2000-2500
£1887 $2943 €3000 Shell diggers (41x61cm-16x24in) s. i.verso board. 17-Sep-2 Whyte's, Dublin #158/R est:2500-3000

BROSAMER, Hans (?-1554) German
£9000 $14040 €13500 Portrait of Wolff Fuerleger, aged 32 (45x31cm-18x12in) mono.i. panel prov.lit. 10-Apr-3 Sotheby's, London #16/R

BROSTOLONI, Giovanni Battista (1712-1796) Italian
Prints
£48000 $74400 €72000 Le feste ducali (53x74cm-21x29in) etching album after Canaletto. 5-Dec-2 Sotheby's, London #1/R est:25000-35000

BROTAT, Joan (1920-1990) Spanish
£536 $782 €825 Figures in blue (27x35cm-11x14in) s. 17-Jun-2 Ansorena, Madrid #51/R
£789 $1279 €1200 Seen from behind (73x60cm-29x24in) s. 21-Jan-3 Ansorena, Madrid #323/R
£855 $1386 €1300 Houseproud (81x60cm-32x24in) s. 21-Jan-3 Ansorena, Madrid #314/R
£943 $1453 €1500 Women with headscarves (65x81cm-26x32in) s. 22-Oct-2 Durán, Madrid #169/R
£962 $1519 €1500 Woman and dove (81x65cm-32x26in) s. 13-Nov-2 Ansorena, Madrid #28/R
£987 $1599 €1500 Couple in landscape (65x81cm-26x32in) 21-Jan-3 Ansorena, Madrid #311/R
£1065 $1682 €1650 Three figures with flowers (73x92cm-29x36in) s. 17-Dec-2 Durán, Madrid #131/R
£1097 $1733 €1700 Woman with decorative item (41x33cm-16x13in) s. 18-Dec-2 Ansorena, Madrid #224/R
£1342 $2161 €2000 I knew it already (92x73cm-36x29in) s. lit. 18-Feb-3 Durán, Madrid #161/R
Works on paper
£292 $427 €450 Red landscape (17x24cm-7x9in) s. pastel. 17-Jun-2 Ansorena, Madrid #15/R
£308 $481 €450 Colourful woman (73x51cm-29x20in) s. wax crayon. 8-Apr-3 Ansorena, Madrid #671/R
£377 $589 €600 Figures (67x49cm-26x19in) s. mixed media. 8-Oct-2 Ansorena, Madrid #484/R

BROTHERTON, Naomi (1920-) American
£353 $550 €530 Turtle Creek (41x51cm-16x20in) canvasboard painted c.1964. 19-Oct-2 David Dike, Dallas #308/R
Works on paper
£321 $500 €482 View of lake (20x56cm-8x22in) W/C executed c.1965. 19-Oct-2 David Dike, Dallas #349/R

BROTO, Jose Manuel (1949-) Spanish
£1548 $2446 €2400 Untitled (75x50cm-30x20in) s.d.1988 acrylic paper on canvas prov. 17-Dec-2 Segre, Madrid #176/R
£18581 $29357 €28800 Fire (270x300cm-106x118in) acrylic. 18-Dec-2 Ansorena, Madrid #173b/R est:28800

BROUGH, Richard Burrell (1920-1996) American
Works on paper
£353 $550 €530 Backyard boat dock (38x56cm-15x22in) s. W/C. 12-Oct-2 Neal Auction Company, New Orleans #680
£353 $550 €530 Alabama, barge RTE, Bigbee Cty (33x51cm-13x20in) s. W/C. 12-Oct-2 Neal Auction Company, New Orleans #681
£355 $550 €533 Bass bite as dusk falls, Black Warrior River, Alabama (38x58cm-15x23in) s. W/C. 7-Dec-2 Neal Auction Company, New Orleans #512
£355 $550 €533 Bank fishermen, Guntersvill Lake, Alabama (38x56cm-15x22in) s. W/C ink. 7-Dec-2 Neal Auction Company, New Orleans #513

BROUGH, Robert (1872-1905) British
£3000 $4770 €4500 Harbour. Figures on a quay (27x35cm-11x14in) panel double-sided exhib. 6-Mar-3 Christie's, Kensington #175/R est:2000-3000

BROUSSILOVSKY, Anatoly (1932-) Russian
Works on paper
£435 $674 €653 Virgo (69x88cm-27x35in) i.d.1988 WC over Indian ink. 9-Dec-2 Philippe Schuler, Zurich #3407/R (S.FR 1000)

BROUWER, Adriaen (1606-1638) Flemish
£3648 $5691 €5800 The reader (18x25cm-7x10in) panel lit. 20-Sep-2 Schloss Ahlden, Ahlden #1058/R est:5800

BROUWER, Adriaen (attrib) (1606-1638) Flemish
£1135 $1759 €1703 Figure scene with man smoking pipe (35x23cm-14x9in) panel prov.exhib. 3-Dec-2 Bukowskis, Stockholm #458/R est:20000-25000 (S.KR 16000)
£26224 $37500 €39336 Man playing recorder (19x13cm-7x5in) copper. 22-Jan-3 Doyle, New York #128/R est:3000

BROUWER, Berend Jan (1872-1936) Dutch
£789 $1279 €1200 Country road (100x75cm-39x30in) s. 21-Jan-3 Christie's, Amsterdam #197/R est:800-1200

BROUWER, Gien (?) Dutch?
£855 $1386 €1300 La Hague (20x25cm-8x10in) s.d.1920 panel. 21-Jan-3 Thomas Adams, Dublin #375

BROUWER, Petrus Hermanus (1885-1965) Dutch
£513 $795 €800 Figures on frozen waterway (35x50cm-14x20in) s. panel. 6-Dec-2 Michael Zeller, Lindau #726/R

BROUWER, Petrus Marius (1819-1886) Dutch
£704 $1134 €1000 Landscape with abbey on a river (35x49cm-14x19in) panel. 7-May-3 Vendue Huis, Gravenhage #379/R

BROUWER, W C (?) Dutch?
Sculpture
£11538 $18115 €18000 Figure of a chameleon (74cm-29in) green grey pottery. 19-Nov-2 Christie's, Amsterdam #33/R est:3600-5500

BROUWERS, Julius (1869-1955) Dutch
£253 $395 €400 Nature morte aux fleurs (60x80cm-24x31in) s. panel. 10-Sep-2 Vanderkindere, Brussels #382
£353 $546 €550 Seascape with sailing ships (60x70cm-24x28in) s. panel. 7-Dec-2 De Vuyst, Lokeren #40
Works on paper
£458 $737 €700 Nature morte aux raies et au crabe (66x100cm-26x39in) s. W/C. 20-Jan-3 Horta, Bruxelles #306

BROVAR, Yakov Ivanovich (c.1864-1941) Russian
£5000 $8100 €7500 Bison in the woods (66x93cm-26x37in) s.d.1907. 21-May-3 Sotheby's, London #58/R est:6000-8000

BROWN, Abigail Keyes (1891-?) American
£301 $500 €436 Cabin in the autumn woods (51x53cm-20x21in) s. panel. 14-Jun-3 Jackson's, Cedar Falls #42/R

BROWN, Alex (1966-) American
£1205 $2000 €1747 Port gentil (127x152cm-50x60in) s.i.d.1999 verso prov. 11-Jun-3 Phillips, New York #348/R est:1000-1500

BROWN, Alexander Kellock (1849-1922) British
£460 $722 €690 Carradale Bay (42x52cm-17x20in) 17-Apr-3 Bonhams, Edinburgh #327
£580 $905 €870 In springtime (40x55cm-16x22in) init. 13-Sep-2 Lyon & Turnbull, Edinburgh #80/R
£1000 $1630 €1450 Winter sunset, Solway marshes (89x112cm-35x44in) init. 17-Jul-3 Thomson, Roddick & Medcalf, Carlisle #132/R
£3000 $4650 €4500 Hayfield by a village (122x165cm-48x65in) mono. 31-Oct-2 Christie's, London #88/R est:3000-5000

BROWN, Anna Wood (fl.1890-1920) American
£5380 $8500 €8070 Woman seated in a garden (46x53cm-18x21in) s. prov. 24-Apr-3 Shannon's, Milford #80/R est:8000-12000

BROWN, Benjamin Chambers (1865-1942) American
£2695 $4500 €3908 Clouds after rain (20x15cm-8x6in) i.verso board prov. 17-Jun-3 John Moran, Pasadena #6 est:4000-5500
£3106 $5000 €4659 View of Notre Dame (10x14cm-4x6in) s.i. 18-Feb-3 John Moran, Pasadena #58 est:5000-7500
£3226 $5000 €4839 Mountain landscape (41x30cm-16x12in) s. board. 29-Oct-2 John Moran, Pasadena #648 est:7000-9000
£3416 $5500 €5124 Inlet, Laguna, Cal (25x33cm-10x13in) i.d.1917 verso canvasboard prov. 18-Feb-3 John Moran, Pasadena #17 est:4000-6000
£3871 $6000 €5807 Eucalyptus landscape (28x36cm-11x14in) s. board. 29-Oct-2 John Moran, Pasadena #647 est:7000-9000
£5414 $8500 €8121 Mt Lowe and lupine (41x51cm-16x20in) s. i.verso canvasboard. 19-Nov-2 Butterfields, San Francisco #8190/R est:5000-7000
£8982 $15000 €13024 California foothill landscape (25x33cm-10x13in) s. board. 17-Jun-3 John Moran, Pasadena #48 est:6000-9000
£25449 $42500 €36901 Laguna beach coastal (81x102cm-32x40in) s.i. prov. 17-Jun-3 John Moran, Pasadena #111 est:25000-35000

BROWN, Bernard Will (1920-) Canadian
£582 $914 €873 Eastern Arctic (50x60cm-20x24in) s.i.d.1985 acrylic. 25-Nov-2 Hodgins, Calgary #347/R (C.D 1450)

BROWN, Bolton (1865-1936) American
£288 $450 €432 Silting shadows (46x66cm-18x26in) s. painted c.1916 prov. 15-Oct-2 Winter Associates, Plainville #236

BROWN, Cecily (1969-) American?
£31646 $50000 €47469 Boy trouble - rose (190x190cm-75x75in) oil on linen painted 1999 prov. 14-Nov-2 Christie's, Rockefeller NY #330/R est:50000-70000

BROWN, Charlotte Harding (1873-1951) American
Works on paper
£2174 $3500 €3261 Maude Joyce at the shrine (58x36cm-23x14in) chl gouache prov. 10-May-3 Illustration House, New York #41/R est:2500-3500

BROWN, Christy (1932-1981) Irish
£738 $1189 €1100 View down Main Street, Ballinasloe (56x69cm-22x27in) masonite board. 18-Feb-3 Whyte's, Dublin #230/R

BROWN, Clinton (20th C) American
£281 $450 €422 Coastal inlet (64x86cm-25x34in) s.d.1938 canvasboard. 8-Jan-3 Doyle, New York #40/R

BROWN, Deborah (1927-) Irish?
£440 $717 €660 Abstract (25x83cm-10x33in) s.i.verso board painted 1956. 30-Jan-3 Locke & England, Leamington Spa #202/R

BROWN, Dexter (1942-) British
£500 $775 €750 Day on the sands, Edwardian ladies and children (33x89cm-13x35in) s. panel. 26-Sep-2 Lane, Penzance #202

BROWN, E (19th C) British
£1700 $2839 €2465 Portrait of a cow in a landscape (49x64cm-19x25in) s. indis d.1882. 8-Jul-3 Bonhams, Knightsbridge #241/R est:1800-2400

BROWN, Ford Madox (1821-1893) British
£40000 $64400 €60000 Tell's son (41x37cm-16x15in) mono.d.80 prov.exhib.lit. 20-Feb-3 Christie's, London #244/R est:70000
Works on paper
£5000 $7850 €7500 Portrait of Emma Madox Brown (13x11cm-5x4in) init.d.April 53 pencil prov. 21-Nov-2 Christie's, London #78/R est:3000-5000

BROWN, Francis F (1891-1971) American
£1635 $2600 €2453 Figures in a landscape (56x76cm-22x30in) s.d. board. 4-May-3 Treadway Gallery, Cincinnati #519/R est:1500-2500

BROWN, George Henry Alan (1862-?) British
Works on paper
£340 $524 €510 Highland couple in conversation at a harbour wall (36x25cm-14x10in) s. W/C. 3-Sep-2 Gorringes, Lewes #2153
£400 $656 €600 Evening light on the road to Shotwick (34x24cm-13x9in) s.d.94 W/C. 4-Jun-3 Bonhams, Chester #289

BROWN, George Loring (1814-1889) American
£3205 $5000 €4808 Landscape with sun-tinged mountains seen across an open valley (30x48cm-12x19in) s.d.1855 panel. 1-Aug-2 Eldred, East Dennis #814/R est:5000-7000
Works on paper
£409 $650 €614 Sailing vessels (35x49cm-14x19in) s.d.06 W/C. 7-Mar-3 Skinner, Boston #322/R

BROWN, George Lunell (fl.1884) British
£1220 $2000 €1769 Gathering firewood. On the ice (102x76cm-40x30in) s. two. 4-Jun-3 Doyle, New York #20/R est:3000-5000

BROWN, Glenn (1966-) British
Sculpture
£3000 $4920 €4500 These days (20x24x20cm-8x9x8in) plaster acrylic oil paint prov.exhib. 7-Feb-3 Sotheby's, London #113/R est:3000-4000

BROWN, Grace Warner (20th C) American
Works on paper
£306 $475 €459 Club gals (46x64cm-18x25in) s. pastel chl exec.c.1940. 8-Dec-2 Toomey, Oak Park #774/R

BROWN, Grafton Tyler (1841-1918) American
£12048 $20000 €17470 View of Mt Hood from John Day Station on the Columbus River, Oregon (25x51cm-10x20in) s. i.verso canvasboard. 11-Jun-3 Butterfields, San Francisco #4006/R est:25000-35000
£20700 $32500 €31050 View of Mt Hood (41x67cm-16x26in) s.d.84 canvas on masonite prov. 19-Nov-2 Butterfields, San Francisco #8020/R est:25000-35000

BROWN, Harley (1939-) Canadian
£1186 $1886 €1779 Climbing Bear (51x38cm-20x15in) s.i.d.1979 oil pastel. 23-Mar-3 Hodgins, Calgary #27/R est:1000-1500 (C.D 2800)
Works on paper
£2130 $3450 €3089 Man from Blackfoot Crossing (46x33cm-18x13in) pastel. 23-May-3 Altermann Galleries, Santa Fe #118
£2192 $3200 €3288 Dyane (30x23cm-12x9in) pastel. 18-May-2 Altermann Galleries, Santa Fe #1/R
£4221 $6500 €6332 Bull Plume Sarcee chief (48x38cm-19x15in) pastel. 25-Oct-2 Morris & Whiteside, Hilton Head Island #28 est:7000-10000
£4259 $6900 €6176 Old lodge (43x36cm-17x14in) pastel. 23-May-3 Altermann Galleries, Santa Fe #66
£6329 $10000 €9177 Sakhsekuun (43x36cm-17x14in) s. pastel. 26-Jul-3 Coeur d'Alene, Hayden #151/R est:8000-12000

BROWN, Harrison B (1831-1915) American
£321 $500 €482 Coast of Maine (43x53cm-17x21in) 19-Oct-2 Harvey Clar, Oakland #1520
£1203 $1900 €1805 Waves crashing into triple cliffs (41x58cm-16x23in) i.stretcher. 26-Apr-3 Thomaston Place, Thomaston #53
£1840 $3000 €2760 New England landscape (33x61cm-13x24in) mono. 2-Feb-3 Grogan, Boston #62 est:2000-3000

BROWN, Harrison B (attrib) (1831-1915) American
£355 $550 €533 Coastal view (41x53cm-16x21in) 28-Sep-2 Thomaston Place, Thomaston #117
£1410 $2200 €2115 Two figures beside a calm river (66x102cm-26x40in) indis sig. 12-Apr-3 Weschler, Washington #567/R est:2000-3000

BROWN, Helen (1917-1986) New Zealander
£442 $690 €663 Landscape (74x99cm-29x39in) 6-Aug-2 Peter Webb, Auckland #1 est:2000-3000 (NZ.D 1500)
Works on paper
£251 $391 €377 City building (48x40cm-19x16in) s. W/C. 7-Nov-2 International Art Centre, Auckland #142/R (NZ.D 800)
£413 $644 €620 Camping, Coromandel (39x50cm-15x20in) s.d.1945 W/C. 6-Aug-2 Peter Webb, Auckland #56/R est:800-1600 (NZ.D 1400)

BROWN, Howard V (1869-1932) American
£1282 $2000 €1923 Poker playing gunman with pistols ablaze (48x48cm-19x19in) s. 9-Nov-2 Illustration House, New York #173/R est:3000-4500

BROWN, James (1951-1991) American

£1410 $2186 €2200 Internal order (30x40cm-12x16in) s.i.d.1999 acrylic. 3-Dec-2 Lempertz, Koln #69/R est:3000
£1859 $2919 €2900 Stabat Mater 29 (66x60cm-26x24in) s.d.1989 paper on canvas prov. 15-Dec-2 Perrin, Versailles #146/R
£2400 $3696 €3600 Stabat mater II - rose (243x196cm-96x77in) s. i.d.1986-88 verso oil paper on canvas prov. 22-Oct-2 Sotheby's, London #453/R est:3000-4000
£8844 $14061 €13000 Woman in hat (142x127cm-56x50in) s.i.d.1984 verso lacquer acrylic prov. 24-Mar-3 Cornette de St.Cyr, Paris #90/R

Works on paper

£601 $950 €950 Untitled (75x55cm-30x22in) s. pencil chk acrylic prov. 26-Nov-2 Sotheby's, Amsterdam #70/R
£2564 $3974 €4000 Egyptian series (121x91cm-48x36in) s. i.d.1984 verso pencil gouache. 3-Dec-2 Christie's, Amsterdam #297/R est:4000-6000
£2600 $4238 €3900 Untitled (127x97cm-50x38in) gouache. 3-Feb-3 Sotheby's, Olympia #151/R est:2000-3000
£2847 $4499 €4100 Egyptian serie (121x91cm-48x36in) s.d. mixed media prov. 28-Apr-3 Cornette de St.Cyr, Paris #358/R est:3000-4000

BROWN, Joan (1938-1990) American

£10256 $16000 €15384 Untitled (65x78cm-26x31in) tempera painted c.1960 prov. 14-Oct-2 Butterfields, San Francisco #2068/R est:15000-20000

BROWN, Joe (1909-1985) American

Sculpture

£1786 $2750 €2679 Boxers (23cm-9in) s.d.1935 dark green pat. bronze. 24-Oct-2 Shannon's, Milford #120/R est:2000-3000

BROWN, John (?) British

£621 $981 €900 Bord de riviere (30x42cm-12x17in) s. 2-Apr-3 Vanderkindere, Brussels #515/R

Works on paper

£300 $486 €450 Hop pickers (29x39cm-11x15in) s. W/C. 21-Jan-3 Bonhams, Knightsbridge #43/R

BROWN, John Appleton (1844-1902) American

£3437 $5500 €4984 May pastures (43x54cm-17x21in) s. prov. 16-May-3 Skinner, Boston #75/R est:6000-8000
£4687 $7500 €6796 Orchard in bloom (46x61cm-18x24in) s. 16-May-3 Skinner, Boston #128/R est:3500-4500

Works on paper

£5031 $8000 €7547 House in the woods, winter (44x55cm-17x22in) s. pastel pencil on board executed c.1885. 5-Mar-3 Sotheby's, New York #23/R est:8000-12000
£7746 $11000 €11619 Old mill (43x53cm-17x21in) pastel. 8-Aug-1 Barridorf, Portland #40/R est:8000-10000

BROWN, John Arnesby (1866-1955) British

£750 $1208 €1125 Sheep grazing (44x56cm-17x22in) s. 14-Jan-3 Bonhams, Knightsbridge #119/R
£1100 $1704 €1650 Cows in a field (27x37cm-11x15in) s. panel. 3-Dec-2 Sotheby's, Olympia #82/R est:600-800
£1700 $2839 €2465 Norfolk landscape (21x26cm-8x10in) init. panel. 17-Jun-3 Anderson & Garland, Newcastle #377 est:1000-1800

BROWN, John George (1831-1913) American

£6918 $11000 €10377 Portrait of a young girl, perhaps the artist's daughter (59x41cm-23x16in) s. 7-Mar-3 Skinner, Boston #305/R est:10000-15000
£9877 $16000 €14816 Little shoe-shine boy (36x25cm-14x10in) s.d.1878 prov. 21-May-3 Sotheby's, New York #212/R est:12000-18000
£12048 $20000 €17470 Boot black, leisure moments (61x41cm-24x16in) s.d.1885 prov. 11-Jun-3 Butterfields, San Francisco #4035/R est:25000-35000
£15924 $25000 €23886 Golden locks (58x38cm-23x15in) s.d.1880. 10-Dec-2 Doyle, New York #36/R est:25000-35000
£17742 $27500 €26613 Kite fliers (30x23cm-12x9in) s.d.1867 prov. 4-Dec-2 Sotheby's, New York #130/R est:20000-30000

Works on paper

£6250 $10000 €9375 Shoeshine boy with dog (58x46cm-23x18in) s. 15-Mar-3 Eldred, East Dennis #347/R est:12000-15000

BROWN, John George (attrib) (1831-1913) American

£3063 $4900 €4595 Boy blowing bubbles (36x25cm-14x10in) s. 11-Jan-3 James Julia, Fairfield #236a est:4500-5500

BROWN, John Lewis (1829-1890) French

£4595 $7168 €6800 Ready for hunting (30x55cm-12x22in) s. 28-Mar-3 Claude Aguttes, Neuilly #73/R

Works on paper

£464 $756 €700 Hunting scene (18x29cm-7x11in) bears sig. W/C. 3-Feb-3 Chambelland & Giafferi, Paris #319

BROWN, John Randolph (20th C) American

£417 $650 €626 Dogs (76x122cm-30x48in) 11-Apr-3 Douglas, South Deerfield #1

BROWN, Joseph (?-1923) British

£2600 $4134 €3900 Dysart Harbor, Fife (61x91cm-24x36in) s. 6-Mar-3 Christie's, Kensington #160/R est:2000-3000

BROWN, Joseph R (1861-?) American

£223 $350 €335 Seascape with sunrise over tranquil sea (13x23cm-5x9in) s.d.1931. 19-Apr-3 James Julia, Fairfield #391/R

BROWN, Leonard (1949-) Australian

Works on paper

£692 $1101 €1038 Standing (102x91cm-40x36in) init.d.92 verso synthetic polymer paint canvas. 4-Mar-3 Deutscher-Menzies, Melbourne #225/R (A.D 1800)

BROWN, Mae Bennett (20th C) American

£441 $700 €662 Still life with phlox (72x61cm-28x24in) s. 7-Mar-3 Skinner, Boston #552/R

BROWN, Mather (1761-1831) British/American

£3436 $5429 €5154 The lifeboat going out (77x92cm-30x36in) s. 27-Nov-2 Falkkloos, Malmo #77615/R est:20000 (S.KR 49000)

BROWN, Nigel (1949-) New Zealander

£940 $1467 €1410 Acrobat heart (52x35cm-20x14in) s.d.1987 board. 7-Nov-2 International Art Centre, Auckland #21/R est:2800-3600 (NZ.D 3000)
£1053 $1642 €1580 Iconic Baxter (43x31cm-17x12in) s.d.1997 board. 27-Mar-3 International Art Centre, Auckland #2/R est:2750-3500 (NZ.D 3000)
£1378 $2219 €2067 Three street scapes (46x30cm-18x12in) s.d.1980 triptych. 7-May-3 Dunbar Sloane, Auckland #16/R est:3900-6000 (NZ.D 3900)
£1498 $2308 €2247 Not merely decorative (79x59cm-31x23in) s.i.d.2000 board. 4-Sep-2 Dunbar Sloane, Wellington #28/R est:6000-9000 (NZ.D 4945)
£1515 $2333 €2273 Clairmount (120x88cm-47x35in) s.i.d.1985 acrylic on board. 4-Sep-2 Dunbar Sloane, Wellington #60 est:5000-8000 (NZ.D 5000)
£1562 $2437 €2343 House of poetry (121x80cm-48x31in) s.i.d. acrylic paper. 8-Apr-3 Peter Webb, Auckland #157/R est:6000-8000 (NZ.D 4500)
£1592 $2500 €2388 Reading (90x75cm-35x30in) s.i.d.1979 board prov. 10-Dec-2 Peter Webb, Auckland #14/R est:5000-7000 (NZ.D 5000)
£1614 $2518 €2421 Heartless voids (88x57cm-35x22in) s.d.1998. 27-Mar-3 International Art Centre, Auckland #7/R est:4500-6500 (NZ.D 4600)
£1673 $2760 €2426 Ka titirangi te maunga painting no.2 (78x58cm-31x23in) s.d.1992 board. 1-Jul-3 Peter Webb, Auckland #85/R est:4000-6000 (NZ.D 4750)
£1724 $2690 €2586 Cook as deserter (90x59cm-35x23in) s.d.1996-97. 7-Nov-2 International Art Centre, Auckland #10/R est:5000-7000 (NZ.D 5500)
£2025 $3341 €2936 Poet and words like water falling (56x45cm-22x18in) s.i.d.1981 s.i.d.verso board. 1-Jul-3 Peter Webb, Auckland #86/R est:4000-6000 (NZ.D 5750)
£2745 $4035 €4118 Home gardener painting no 14 (171x119cm-67x47in) s.d.89 acrylic board prov. 19-Jun-2 Watson's, Christchurch #25/R est:8000-15000 (NZ.D 8400)

Works on paper

£940 $1467 €1410 Urewera 87 (50x63cm-20x25in) s.i.d.1987 mixed media. 7-Nov-2 International Art Centre, Auckland #89/R est:2500-3500 (NZ.D 3000)

BROWN, Norman A (1933-) Canadian

£593 $943 €890 Valley of the ten peaks, Moraine Lake (50x40cm-20x16in) s. 23-Mar-3 Hodgins, Calgary #32/R est:1000-1200 (C.D 1400)

BROWN, Paul (19th C) American

£344 $550 €516 Seascape with sailboat and figures on a beach (20x41cm-8x16in) s. panel. 15-Mar-3 Selkirks, St. Louis #327

BROWN, Paul D (1893-1958) American
Works on paper
£633 $1000 €950 Wester ponies in front of a fence (11x36cm-4x14in) s.d.34 ink wash pencil on board. 3-Apr-3 Christie's, Rockefeller NY #183/R est:800-1200
£2848 $4500 €4272 Go ponies. Indian pony (32x38cm-13x15in) s.i. W/C pen on board pair prov. 3-Apr-3 Christie's, Rockefeller NY #187/R est:1000-1500

BROWN, Peter (fl.1758-1799) British
£233 $330 €350 Gorge in the Shotover (63x76cm-25x30in) s. board prov. 21-Nov-1 Watson's, Christchurch #68/R (NZ.D 800)

BROWN, Ralph (1928-) British
Sculpture
£2200 $3630 €3190 Head (28cm-11in) brown pat. bronze. 3-Jul-3 Christie's, Kensington #602/R est:800-1200
£2200 $3630 €3190 Girl waking (137cm-54in) st.mono.num.3/9 brown pat. bronze. 3-Jul-3 Christie's, Kensington #614/R est:2500-3500
£4200 $6930 €6090 Girl seated (119cm-47in) brown pat. bronze. 3-Jul-3 Christie's, Kensington #607/R est:2500-3500
£5500 $8689 €8250 Mother and child (100cm-39in) mono. bronze one of six executed c.1954. 27-Nov-2 Sotheby's, Olympia #173/R est:3000-4000

BROWN, Samuel John Milton (1873-1965) British
£1300 $2145 €1885 Border Bridge, Berwick (21x27cm-8x11in) init. panel. 3-Jul-3 Christie's, Kensington #446/R est:1200-1500
Works on paper
£450 $698 €675 Riding the ocean waves (38x49cm-15x19in) s. pencil W/C htd white. 31-Oct-2 Christie's, Kensington #391/R
£580 $899 €870 Brigantine racing round the lightship (33x48cm-13x19in) s. pencil W/C. 31-Oct-2 Christie's, Kensington #392/R

BROWN, Samuel Joseph (1907-1994) American
£1233 $1800 €1850 Genre scene (184x101cm-72x40in) s. canvasboard. 10-May-2 Skinner, Boston #329a/R est:1500-2500
Works on paper
£584 $900 €876 Figure in a wooded landscape (23x15cm-9x6in) s.d.1941 gouache board. 8-Sep-2 Treadway Gallery, Cincinnati #703/R

BROWN, Thomas Austen (1857-1924) British
£600 $948 €900 Loading the cart (40x60cm-16x24in) board exhib. 5-Apr-3 Shapes, Edinburgh #315
Works on paper
£1000 $1560 €1500 Highland moor (33x42cm-13x17in) s. W/C. 17-Oct-2 Bonhams, Edinburgh #193a est:1000-1500

BROWN, Vincent (1901-?) Australian
£239 $392 €347 Secrets (50x37cm-20x15in) s. i.verso hessian on board. 4-Jun-3 Deutscher-Menzies, Melbourne #362/R (A.D 600)
£407 $642 €590 Trogir (35x38cm-14x15in) s. i.verso canvas on board. 22-Jul-3 Lawson Menzies, Sydney #149/R est:800-1200 (A.D 1000)
£429 $677 €644 Seated nude (47x34cm-19x13in) s.d.42 hessian on board. 27-Nov-2 Deutscher-Menzies, Melbourne #226/R est:1500-2000 (A.D 1200)
£1385 $2202 €2078 Woman and guitar (57x44cm-22x17in) s.d.1942 canvas on board. 4-Mar-3 Deutscher-Menzies, Melbourne #256/R est:3000-4000 (A.D 3600)
Works on paper
£702 $1067 €1053 Afternoon rest (29x36cm-11x14in) s.d.1928 W/C. 19-Aug-2 Joel, Victoria #167/R est:2500-3500 (A.D 2000)

BROWN, Walter Francis (1853-1929) American
£774 $1200 €1161 Venice (30x64cm-12x25in) s. painted c.1920 prov. 8-Dec-2 Toomey, Oak Park #691/R
£1719 $2750 €2579 Ship anchored off the coast of Providence, Rhode Island (20x36cm-8x14in) s. 17-May-3 Pook & Pook, Downington #202/R est:1200-1500

BROWN, William (19th C) British
£950 $1577 €1378 Cloister, a bay racehorse in a stable (30x45cm-12x18in) s.i. 12-Jun-3 Christie's, Kensington #60/R

BROWN, William Beattie (1831-1909) British
£404 $638 €606 Moorland road, sundown (20x30cm-8x12in) s. i.verso board prov. 18-Nov-2 Waddingtons, Toronto #171/R (C.D 1000)
£667 $1107 €967 On the Findhorn (30x46cm-12x18in) s. 16-Jun-3 Waddingtons, Toronto #203/R est:1500-2000 (C.D 1500)
£949 $1500 €1424 River landscape (38x58cm-15x23in) s. 16-Nov-2 New Orleans Auction, New Orleans #312/R est:1800-2500
£950 $1482 €1425 Glen Finlas, Brig o'Turk (29x44cm-11x17in) s. 17-Oct-2 Lawrence, Crewkerne #492/R
£1000 $1590 €1500 Glen Filas, brig O'Turk (30x46cm-12x18in) s. prov. 6-Mar-3 Christie's, Kensington #77/R est:1000-1500
£1400 $2142 €2100 On Ben Ledi Burn (35x50cm-14x20in) s. 22-Aug-2 Bonhams, Edinburgh #1086 est:500-700
£1500 $2340 €2250 Water meadow (76x137cm-30x54in) s.d.1885. 7-Nov-2 Christie's, Kensington #126/R est:600-800
Works on paper
£289 $454 €434 November sunrise (38x53cm-15x21in) s.i. s.verso W/C. 24-Jul-2 Walker's, Ottawa #14/R (C.D 700)

BROWN, William Marshall (1863-1936) British
£360 $569 €540 Old salt (50x40cm-20x16in) s.d.1900. 19-Dec-2 Bonhams, Edinburgh #301
£480 $749 €720 Digging potatoes (19x24cm-7x9in) s.d.1892. 10-Apr-3 Bonhams, Edinburgh #78
£3200 $4960 €4800 Paddling in the sea (81x102cm-32x40in) s.i. 31-Oct-2 Christie's, London #114/R est:3000-5000
£4400 $6732 €6600 Loitering (19x24cm-7x9in) s. 22-Aug-2 Bonhams, Edinburgh #947/R est:1000-1500
£4500 $6975 €6750 Wading (26x20cm-10x8in) s. 31-Oct-2 Christie's, London #116/R est:5000-8000
£5500 $8525 €8250 Motor boat (25x35cm-10x14in) s. 31-Oct-2 Christie's, London #115/R est:6000-10000
£22000 $34100 €33000 Among wild roses (71x91cm-28x36in) s.d.1908. 31-Oct-2 Christie's, London #113/R est:10000-15000
Works on paper
£889 $1476 €1289 North country fisher girl (30x35cm-12x14in) s.i.verso W/C. 10-Jun-3 Ritchie, Toronto #7/R est:2000-2500 (C.D 2000)
£3000 $4860 €4500 Harvesting the elderflowers (30x35cm-12x14in) s. W/C. 21-May-3 Bonhams, Knightsbridge #129/R est:3000-4000

BROWN, William Mason (1828-1898) American
£7006 $11000 €10509 Hudson river scene with figures (43x58cm-17x23in) s.d.1886. 22-Nov-2 Eldred, East Dennis #829/R est:6000-8000
£44025 $70000 €66038 Still life with melon, grapes, peaches and black raspberries (36x61cm-14x24in) init. prov. 4-Mar-3 Christie's, Rockefeller NY #15/R est:15000-25000

BROWNE, Andrew (1960-) Australian
Works on paper
£1594 $2614 €2391 Untitled, lights (81x121cm-32x48in) s.verso synthetic polymer paint. 4-Jun-3 Deutscher-Menzies, Melbourne #172/R est:3000-4000 (A.D 4000)

BROWNE, Belmore (1880-1954) American/Canadian
£2057 $3250 €2983 Snow covered cliffs (23x28cm-9x11in) s. canvas on board. 26-Jul-3 Coeur d'Alene, Hayden #227/R est:2500-3500
£6222 $10204 €9022 Untitled - bighorn (50x40cm-20x16in) s. board. 9-Jun-3 Hodgins, Calgary #319/R est:7000-9000 (C.D 14000)

BROWNE, Byron (1907-1961) American
£926 $1500 €1343 Newspaper and candle (76x97cm-30x38in) s. s.i.d.1960 verso prov. 21-May-3 Doyle, New York #10/R est:3000-5000
Works on paper
£566 $900 €849 Abstract shapes (18x25cm-7x10in) s.d.1940 gouache. 18-Mar-3 Arthur James, Florida #60
£700 $1127 €1050 Composition (43x52cm-17x20in) s.d.1948 pen ink W/C chk. 14-Jan-3 Bonhams, Knightsbridge #124/R
£833 $1300 €1250 Sculptor and model (51x66cm-20x26in) s.d.June 3 1955 brush black ink wash. 19-Sep-2 Swann Galleries, New York #189/R
£1911 $3000 €2867 Untitled (15x10cm-6x4in) s.d. ink W/C. 19-Nov-2 Wright, Chicago #145/R est:4000-6000
£2692 $4200 €4038 Abstract composition (65x48cm-26x19in) s.d.1952 W/C gouache. 19-Sep-2 Swann Galleries, New York #188/R est:1500-2500

BROWNE, Charles Francis (1859-1920) American
£1635 $2600 €2453 Pueblo of the Zuni, New Mexico (41x31cm-16x12in) s.i.d.1895. 7-Mar-3 Skinner, Boston #351/R est:2000-3000
£2097 $3250 €3146 Pastoral landscape (66x102cm-26x40in) s.d. 8-Dec-2 Toomey, Oak Park #651/R est:6000-8000

BROWNE, George (1918-1958) American
£7111 $11662 €10311 Rocky mountain goat (50x40cm-20x16in) s. board. 9-Jun-3 Hodgins, Calgary #318/R est:7000-9000 (C.D 16000)

BROWNE, George Elmer (1871-1946) American
£449 $700 €674 Dans l'hombre (25x20cm-10x8in) s. s.i.verso board. 9-Nov-2 Sloan, North Bethesda #603/R
£774 $1200 €1161 Cluster of trees (25x36cm-10x14in) panel exhib. 2-Nov-2 North East Auctions, Portsmouth #41/R est:1200-1800

£2548 $4000 €3822 Fishing post on the Adriatic (64x76cm-25x30in) s.i. prov. 19-Nov-2 Butterfields, San Francisco #8027/R est:5000-7000
Works on paper
£382 $600 €573 North shore coast (34x48cm-13x19in) s. W/C gouache. 22-Nov-2 Skinner, Boston #126/R

BROWNE, Hablot K (1815-1892) British
Works on paper
£340 $530 €510 Beach photograph (14x22cm-6x9in) s. W/C. 25-Mar-3 Bonhams, Knightsbridge #154/R
£350 $546 €525 Miss G's mare Shies and fall (25x36cm-10x14in) s. pencil W/C. 6-Nov-2 Sotheby's, Olympia #65/R

BROWNE, Joseph (attrib) (18th C) ?
£2800 $4452 €4200 Figures in a landscape with a farmhouse beyond (71x91cm-28x36in) 6-Mar-3 Christie's, Kensington #402/R est:3000-5000

BROWNE, Joseph Archibald (1862-1948) Canadian
£267 $415 €401 Woodland - across country looking through the woods (25x35cm-10x14in) s. indis d. panel. 3-Dec-2 Joyner, Toronto #427 (C.D 650)

BROWNE, Nassau Blair (?-1940) Irish
£1667 $2650 €2400 Coastal landscape (51x61cm-20x24in) s. 29-Apr-3 Whyte's, Dublin #126/R est:1500-1800

BROWNE, Tom (19/20th C) British
Works on paper
£400 $636 €600 Shangai taxi (34x48cm-13x19in) s. pen ink W/C. 4-Mar-3 Bristol Auction Rooms #260/R

BROWNELL, Charles de Wolf (1822-1909) American
Works on paper
£88050 $140000 €132075 Studies from nature (528x76cm-208x30in) Album of 227 W/C. 30-Apr-3 Doyle, New York #117/R est:4000-6000

BROWNELL, Franklin (1856-1946) Canadian
£1240 $1946 €1860 Afternoon glow, winter (36x51cm-14x20in) s. prov. 24-Jul-2 Walker's, Ottawa #404 est:3000-3500 (C.D 3000)
£1570 $2511 €2355 Pastoral landscape with sheep (36x46cm-14x18in) s. prov. 15-May-3 Heffel, Vancouver #117/R est:3000-4000 (C.D 3500)
£2361 $3682 €3423 Rocky beach, St. Kitts (30x46cm-12x18in) s.d.13 prov.lit. 26-Mar-3 Walker's, Ottawa #264/R est:4000-5000 (C.D 5500)
£4000 $6560 €6000 Oven (28x26cm-11x10in) i. canvas on board prov. 27-May-3 Sotheby's, Toronto #41/R est:6000-8000 (C.D 9000)
£14222 $23324 €21333 Haymaking, Ile aux Coudres, Quebec (45x60cm-18x24in) s.d.1905 prov.lit. 3-Jun-3 Joyner, Toronto #57/R est:20000-30000 (C.D 32000)
Works on paper
£644 $1004 €934 Late summer (25x35cm-10x14in) s.d.21 pastel prov. 26-Mar-3 Walker's, Ottawa #201/R est:1200-1600 (C.D 1500)

BROWNHALL, Robert (1968-) American
Works on paper
£1011 $1567 €1517 Riverview from Coronation Drive (20x220cm-8x87in) s. synthetic polymer paint canvas. 3-Dec-2 Shapiro, Sydney #90 est:2500-3500 (A.D 2800)

BROWNING, Amy Katherine (1882-1978) British
£500 $780 €750 Friends in the harvest field (46x35cm-18x14in) s. board double-sided. 27-Mar-3 Christie's, Kensington #406
£1800 $2790 €2700 Glass bowl (71x91cm-28x36in) s. 4-Dec-2 Christie's, Kensington #459/R est:2000-3000
£1850 $2979 €2775 Portrait of Winston Churchill (71x61cm-28x24in) s.i.d.1951 after Oswald Birley. 18-Feb-3 Bonhams, Knightsbridge #123/R est:500-700

BROWNING, Mary (19/20th C) British
£600 $948 €900 Sicilian eve (71x102cm-28x40in) s.i. 12-Nov-2 Bonhams, Knightsbridge #95p/R

BROWNLOW, George Washington (1835-1876) British
£1300 $2054 €1950 Last stile homeward (18x22cm-7x9in) init. 12-Nov-2 Bonhams, Knightsbridge #39/R est:600-800

BROWNRIDGE, William Roy (1932-) Canadian
£169 $269 €254 Bella Coola Wharf (43x50cm-17x20in) s. acrylic on paper. 23-Mar-3 Hodgins, Calgary #115/R (C.D 400)

BROZIK, Jaroslav (1904-1986) American
£4790 $8000 €6946 Working freedom (69x91cm-27x36in) s. masonite. 18-Jun-3 Christie's, Los Angeles #105/R est:5000-7000

BRUANDET, Lazare (1755-1804) French
Works on paper
£5063 $8000 €8000 Bergers dans la foret de Fontainebleau (18x28cm-7x11in) s. gouache. 28-Nov-2 Tajan, Paris #58/R

BRUCE, Edward (1879-1943) American
£494 $800 €741 Reflections (51x61cm-20x24in) s. 24-Jan-3 Freeman, Philadelphia #187/R
£892 $1400 €1338 Forest scene with creek flowing under bridge (69x66cm-27x26in) prov. 14-Dec-2 Weschler, Washington #650/R est:2000-3000

BRUCE, Frederick William (fl.1890-1910) British
£1000 $1590 €1500 Little Breton girl (53x43cm-21x17in) s.d.92. 6-Mar-3 Christie's, Kensington #187/R est:1000-1500

BRUCE, J Christie (20th C) British
£711 $1180 €1031 Carnoustie Sand. Highland moor (30x41cm-12x16in) s.d.1922 s.d.verso board two. 10-Jun-3 Ritchie, Toronto #72/R est:500-700 (C.D 1600)

BRUCE, W (19/20th C) American
£483 $764 €725 Horseman crossing bridge on the river (43x63cm-17x25in) s. 18-Nov-2 Waddingtons, Toronto #19/R (C.D 1200)

BRUCE, William (19/20th C) American
£2229 $3500 €3344 Passing visit (46x76cm-18x30in) s.d.1910. 19-Nov-2 Butterfields, San Francisco #8033/R est:3000-5000

BRUCE, William Blair (1859-1906) Canadian
£1635 $2600 €2453 Cows watering in the mountain landscape (31x51cm-12x20in) s. 7-Mar-3 Skinner, Boston #282/R est:2500-3500
£2222 $3644 €3333 Council of three (25x33cm-10x13in) s.d.1885 prov.exhib. 27-May-3 Sotheby's, Toronto #93/R est:3000-5000 (C.D 5000)

BRUCK, Lajos (1846-1910) Hungarian
£568 $885 €824 Gate in Zboro (18x30cm-7x12in) d.84. 13-Sep-2 Mu Terem Galeria, Budapest #29/R est:120000 (H.F 220000)
£826 $1288 €1198 Washing (18x30cm-7x12in) panel. 13-Sep-2 Mu Terem Galeria, Budapest #142/R est:220000 (H.F 320000)
£1156 $1918 €1676 Young hunter (76x58cm-30x23in) s. 16-Jun-3 Waddingtons, Toronto #312/R est:1500-2500 (C.D 2600)
£1537 $2398 €2229 Painter and his model (37x45cm-15x18in) s. panel. 12-Apr-3 Mu Terem Galeria, Budapest #48/R est:350000 (H.F 550000)
£4572 $7086 €6858 Sewing woman (67x50cm-26x20in) s. 6-Dec-2 Kieselbach, Budapest #171/R (H.F 1700000)
£21928 $34208 €32892 Fruit sellars (92x73cm-36x29in) s. 11-Sep-2 Kieselbach, Budapest #161/R (H.F 8500000)

BRUCKE, Wilhelm (attrib) (19th C) German
£2857 $4257 €4400 Italian fisherman playing mandolin in Bay of Naples (37x47cm-15x19in) i. 26-Jun-2 Neumeister, Munich #696/R est:3500

BRUCKER, Edmund (1912-) American
£692 $1100 €1038 Dancer (91x71cm-36x28in) s. painted c.1960. 2-Mar-3 Toomey, Oak Park #741/R
Works on paper
£779 $1200 €1169 Indianapolis storefront (51x91cm-20x36in) s. W/C exec.c.1960. 8-Sep-2 Treadway Gallery, Cincinnati #734/R

BRUEGHEL, Abraham (1631-1690) Flemish
£9804 $16078 €15000 Roses ad other flowers (35x40cm-14x16in) s. 9-Feb-3 Anaf, Lyon #31/R
£23649 $36892 €35000 Garland of flowers around bust (119x92cm-47x36in) 26-Mar-3 Tajan, Paris #117/R est:15000
£35000 $54950 €52500 Still life of fruit and flowers with a young maidservant (130x110cm-51x43in) bears sig.d.1709. 12-Dec-2 Sotheby's, London #53/R est:35000-45000
£38000 $59280 €57000 Melons, figs, cherries and mixed flowers in a clearing (50x64cm-20x25in) 9-Apr-3 Christie's, London #93/R est:10000-15000

BRUEGHEL, Abraham (attrib) (1631-1690) Flemish
£12805 $21000 €19208 Still life of fruit and flowers resting on a stone ledge with mushrooms in the foreground (46x56cm-18x22in) 29-May-3 Sotheby's, New York #96/R est:10000-15000

BRUEGHEL, Abraham (circle) (1631-1690) Flemish
£5000 $8350 €7250 Slice of watermelon, fruits, chestnuts and upturned basket on stone ledge (43x30cm-17x12in) 9-Jul-3 Bonhams, New Bond Street #182/R est:2000-3000
£18310 $30394 €26000 Still life with grapes, melons and pomegranates (91x71cm-36x28in) prov. 11-Jun-3 Dorotheum, Vienna #11/R est:6000-8000

BRUEGHEL, Abraham and COURTOIS, Guillaume (17th C) Flemish/French
£42308 $65577 €66000 Woman with flowers in classical landscape (125x97cm-49x38in) 4-Dec-2 Christie's, Rome #487/R est:75000-100000
£42308 $65577 €66000 Woman with flowers and flute (118x97cm-46x38in) 4-Dec-2 Christie's, Rome #488/R est:75000-100000

BRUEGHEL, Abraham and SOLIMENA, Francesco (circle) (17th C) Flemish/Italian
£8500 $13175 €12750 Putti with carnations, roses and other flowers in urns (100x75cm-39x30in) 30-Oct-2 Christie's, Kensington #148/R est:7000-10000

BRUEGHEL, Ambrosius (attrib) (1617-1675) Flemish
£8387 $13252 €13000 Corbeille de fleurs et perroquet (44x60cm-17x24in) panel. 19-Dec-2 Bondu, Paris #4/R est:40000

BRUEGHEL, Ambrosius (circle) (1617-1675) Flemish
£16026 $25160 €25000 Bouquet de fleurs dans une coupe (49x64cm-19x25in) panel. 20-Nov-2 Libert, Castor, Paris #86/R est:15000-18000

BRUEGHEL, J and ROTTENHAMMER, J (16/17th C) Flemish
£400 $616 €600 Landscape with satyrs dancing in a woody glade (8x10cm-3x4in) copper panel oval. 3-Sep-2 Gorringes, Lewes #2073

BRUEGHEL, Jan (elder) (1568-1625) Flemish
Works on paper
£63291 $100000 €100000 Un paysage forestier avec une riviere. Etudes d'arbres (26x46cm-10x18in) d.1607 verso black chk pen col wash double-sided prov.lit. 27-Nov-2 Christie's, Paris #10/R est:100000-150000

BRUEGHEL, Jan (elder) and MOMPER, Joos de (16/17th C) Flemish
£34911 $56555 €50621 Mountain landscape with riders (64x93cm-25x37in) panel prov. 25-May-3 Uppsala Auktionskammare, Uppsala #40/R est:400000-500000 (S.KR 450000)
£75000 $125250 €108750 Extensive river landscape with travelers on a path (73x106cm-29x42in) prov. 9-Jul-3 Christie's, London #10/R est:20000-30000

BRUEGHEL, Jan (elder-attrib) (1568-1625) Flemish
£7424 $11729 €11136 Mary with Child and two angels (41x48cm-16x19in) tempera panel. 14-Nov-2 Stuker, Bern #114 est:20000-25000 (S.FR 17000)
£7800 $12402 €11700 Musical contest between Apollo and Pan with King Midas (41x53cm-16x21in) copper. 18-Mar-3 Capes Dunn, Manchester #526

BRUEGHEL, Jan (elder-circle) (1568-1625) Flemish
£9500 $15865 €13775 Swag of flowers decorating a silver-gilt tazza (42x33cm-17x13in) panel prov. 9-Jul-3 Bonhams, New Bond Street #50/R est:7000-10000
£15000 $23550 €22500 Landscape with peasants resting beside a road, windmill beyond (36x71cm-14x28in) panel. 12-Dec-2 Sotheby's, London #125/R est:15000-20000
£24390 $40000 €36585 Rural landscape with peasants in horse-drawn carriages on a track (13x16cm-5x6in) copper pair. 30-May-3 Christie's, Rockefeller NY #12/R est:8000-12000

BRUEGHEL, Jan (elder-studio) (1568-1625) Flemish
£28000 $43960 €42000 Coastal landscape with the Temple of Vesta (18x26cm-7x10in) bears sig. copper prov.exhib.lit. 12-Dec-2 Sotheby's, London #127/R est:30000-50000

BRUEGHEL, Jan (elder-style) (1568-1625) Flemish
£6000 $9360 €9000 Hell scene, with Devils tormenting the Souls of the Dammed (14x18cm-6x7in) copper prov. 8-Apr-3 Sotheby's, Olympia #106/R est:3000-4000
£8861 $14000 €14000 Village crossed by river with peasants in a boat (19x24cm-7x9in) panel. 27-Nov-2 Christie's, Paris #2/R est:10000-15000
£8917 $13911 €14000 Adoration of the Magi (22x33cm-9x13in) copper. 5-Nov-2 Sotheby's, Amsterdam #262/R est:8000-12000
£9500 $15865 €13775 River landscape with a fish market (39x49cm-15x19in) panel. 8-Jul-3 Sotheby's, Olympia #363/R est:6000-8000
£15000 $25050 €21750 Village by a river with a gentleman on horseback on a track (104x160cm-41x63in) prov. 8-Jul-3 Sotheby's, Olympia #362/R est:8000-12000
£18519 $30000 €27779 Mountainous landscape with travellers on a path (37x45cm-15x18in) panel. 24-Jan-3 Christie's, Rockefeller NY #4/R est:30000-50000
£30000 $47100 €45000 Village landscape with wagons on track by river (52x83cm-20x33in) bears sig. panel prov.lit. 11-Dec-2 Christie's, London #21/R est:20000-30000

BRUEGHEL, Jan (younger) (1601-1678) Flemish
£11872 $18521 €17808 Allegory of war (87x97cm-34x38in) s. copper prov. 28-Mar-3 Koller, Zurich #3031/R est:30000-50000 (S.FR 26000)
£17722 $27646 €28000 La rixe des paysans (38x59cm-15x23in) panel on panel. 20-Oct-2 Mercier & Cie, Lille #240/R est:20000-22000
£20513 $32410 €32000 Travellers stopping at mill (17x22cm-7x9in) copper. 13-Nov-2 Marc Kohn, Paris #23/R est:60000-70000
£25751 $39914 €38627 Bird concert (13x18cm-5x7in) panel prov. 3-Oct-2 Koller, Zurich #3024/R est:60000-90000 (S.FR 60000)
£27778 $45000 €41667 Calvary (15x21cm-6x8in) copper prov. 24-Jan-3 Christie's, Rockefeller NY #5/R est:30000-40000
£45000 $70650 €67500 God creating heaven and earth (70x87cm-28x34in) s. copper. 12-Dec-2 Sotheby's, London #6/R est:30000-40000
£58065 $91742 €90000 Jesus at Martha and Mary's (61x105cm-24x41in) board. 18-Dec-2 Ansorena, Madrid #84/R est:90000
£75000 $125250 €108750 Adoration of the Magi (26x34cm-10x13in) copper prov. 9-Jul-3 Christie's, London #12/R est:40000-60000
£110345 $175448 €160000 Adoration of the Magi (22x33cm-9x13in) board. 4-Mar-3 Ansorena, Madrid #54/R est:150000

BRUEGHEL, Jan (younger) and AVONT, Pieter van (circle) (17th C) Flemish
£30000 $47100 €45000 Allegory of Earth (62x88cm-24x35in) copper. 11-Dec-2 Christie's, London #22/R est:30000-50000

BRUEGHEL, Jan (younger) and FRANCKEN, Frans II (studio) (17th C) Flemish
£16000 $25120 €24000 Garland of flowers encircling an oval of the Virgin with Angles adoring the Child (1x66cm-0x26in) panel. 13-Dec-2 Christie's, Kensington #33/R est:8000-12000
£50000 $83500 €72500 Still life of flowers in sculpted parcel-gilt vase, upon stone ledge (116x91cm-46x36in) panel prov. 10-Jul-3 Sotheby's, London #13/R est:50000-80000

BRUEGHEL, Jan (younger) and JANSSENS, Abraham (17th C) Flemish
£58621 $93207 €85000 Adam and Eve in Paradise (71x89cm-28x35in) copper. 4-Mar-3 Ansorena, Madrid #65/R est:85000

BRUEGHEL, Jan (younger-attrib) (1601-1678) Flemish
£32414 $51214 €47000 Le retour du marche, paysage (37x71cm-15x28in) panel. 2-Apr-3 Marc Kohn, Paris #9/R est:60000-70000

BRUEGHEL, Jan (younger-circle) (1601-1678) Flemish
£10897 $16891 €17000 Allogory of the world (69x87cm-27x34in) copper. 4-Dec-2 Neumeister, Munich #585/R est:10000
£17949 $28179 €28000 Diane chasseresse (64x89cm-25x35in) panel. 15-Dec-2 Mercier & Cie, Lille #315/R est:40000

BRUEGHEL, Jan (younger-studio) (1601-1678) Flemish
£7042 $11690 €10000 Resting during Flight to Egypt (41x55cm-16x22in) panel prov. 11-Jun-3 Dorotheum, Vienna #107/R est:10000-15000

BRUEGHEL, Jan (younger-style) (1601-1678) Flemish
£6000 $9300 €9000 Open landscape with waggoners and drovers on track (30x41cm-12x16in) bears sig. 31-Oct-2 Sotheby's, Olympia #47/R est:6000-8000
£8000 $12560 €12000 Wooded landscape with waggoners by a river, church beyond (50x66cm-20x26in) panel prov. 12-Dec-2 Sotheby's, London #124/R est:8000-12000
£10072 $16115 €14000 Wooded landscape with figures on path (21x29cm-8x11in) pair. 13-May-3 Sotheby's, Amsterdam #1/R est:8000-12000
£12000 $18840 €18000 Allegory of earth (42x58cm-17x23in) panel. 12-Dec-2 Sotheby's, London #123/R est:8000-12000

BRUEGHEL, Jan Pieter (1628-?) Flemish
£68493 $106849 €102740 Earth. Water. Fire. Air (21x26cm-8x10in) copper four. 28-Mar-3 Koller, Zurich #3015/R est:120000-160000 (S.FR 150000)

BRUEGHEL, Pieter (16/17th C) Flemish
Prints
£2746 $4559 €3900 Alpine landscape (30x43cm-12x17in) etching copperplate after P Brueghel von Hieronymus Cock. 12-Jun-3 Hauswedell & Nolte, Hamburg #47/R est:5000

BRUEGHEL, Pieter (elder) (c.1525-1569) Flemish
Prints
£7241 $11441 €10500 The witches of Malleghem (34x47cm-13x19in) copperplate. 4-Apr-3 Venator & Hansten, Koln #1388/R est:2100

BRUEGHEL, Pieter (elder-school) (c.1525-1569) Flemish
£5769 $9058 €9000 Study of head of old woman (30x22cm-12x9in) panel prov. 21-Nov-2 Van Ham, Cologne #1318/R est:20000

BRUEGHEL, Pieter (elder-style) (c.1525-1569) Flemish
£50000 $78000 €75000 Village kermesse (76x105cm-30x41in) panel prov.exhib.lit. 10-Apr-3 Sotheby's, London #10/R est:20000-30000

BRUEGHEL, Pieter (younger) (1564-1637) Flemish
£110000 $172700 €165000 Misanthrope (19cm-7in circular) panel prov.exhib.lit. 11-Dec-2 Christie's, London #30/R est:60000-80000
£240000 $400800 €348000 Seven acts of mercy (43x57cm-17x22in) s. panel prov.lit. 9-Jul-3 Christie's, London #11/R est:180000-220000
£333333 $520000 €500000 John the Preacher (92x172cm-36x68in) i. panel prov.lit. 28-Mar-3 Koller, Zurich #3010/R est:7000-1000000 (S.FR 730000)
£450000 $751500 €652500 Spring: gardeners digging and planting a formal garden (42x57cm-17x22in) s.d.1621 panel on panel prov. 10-Jul-3 Sotheby's, London #11/R est:200000-300000
£679012 $1100000 €1018518 Winter landscape with peasants skating and playing kolf on a frozen river (41x56cm-16x22in) s.d.1621 panel prov.lit. 24-Jan-3 Christie's, Rockefeller NY #48/R est:1000000-1500000
£720000 $1130400 €1080000 Wedding dance (40x54cm-16x21in) panel prov.lit. 11-Dec-2 Christie's, London #27/R est:400000-600000
Works on paper
£1625 $2600 €2438 Landscape (15x25cm-6x10in) ink. 12-Jan-3 William Jenack, New York #308

BRUEGHEL, Pieter (younger-circle) (1564-1637) Flemish
£11728 $19000 €17592 Find the dog in the pot - a Flemish proverb (19cm-7in circular) i. panel prov. 24-Jan-3 Christie's, Rockefeller NY #46/R est:10000-15000

BRUEGHEL, Pieter (younger-studio) (1564-1637) Flemish
£8000 $12560 €12000 Collector of Tithes (72x104cm-28x41in) panel. 10-Dec-2 Bonhams, New Bond Street #296/R est:10000-15000
£25949 $41000 €41000 Paysans attables en plein air (54x69cm-21x27in) panel. 1-Dec-2 Anaf, Lyon #30/R est:12000

BRUEGHEL, Pieter (younger-style) (1564-1637) Flemish
£7500 $11775 €11250 Peasants brawling in a landscape (43x53cm-17x21in) panel. 10-Dec-2 Sotheby's, Olympia #329/R est:2500-3500

BRUENCHENHEIN, Eugene von (1910-1983) American
£1358 $2200 €2037 No.858 (60x60cm-24x24in) s.d.Feb 12 1960 masonite prov.exhib. 27-Jan-3 Christie's, Rockefeller NY #70/R est:3000-5000
Sculpture
£1235 $2000 €1853 Untitled - jar of glass arrowheads (41x13x13cm-16x5x5in) glass ceramic metal prov. 27-Jan-3 Christie's, Rockefeller NY #69/R est:800-1200

BRUESTLE, George M (1871-1939) American
£828 $1300 €1242 Rocky hillside (20x25cm-8x10in) s. board. 22-Nov-2 Skinner, Boston #234/R est:400-600
£897 $1400 €1346 Fall landscape (31x41cm-12x16in) s. 9-Nov-2 Sloan, North Bethesda #604/R
£1242 $2000 €1863 Summer landscape (18x23cm-7x9in) s.i.d.1924 board prov. 18-Feb-3 John Moran, Pasadena #3 est:1500-2000
£1274 $2000 €1911 Connecticut hills (20x25cm-8x10in) s. i.verso board. 22-Nov-2 Skinner, Boston #232/R est:400-600
£4655 $6750 €6983 Landscape with farm building (53x66cm-21x26in) painted c.1922. 1-Jun-2 Russ Antiques, Waterford #46

BRUETSCHY, François (1938-) French?
£351 $548 €520 Untitled (81x65cm-32x26in) s.d.1998 verso prov. 28-Mar-3 Charbonneaux, Paris #39

BRUFORD, Marjorie Frances (1902-1958) British
£480 $782 €720 Coastal fields (36x43cm-14x17in) s. board. 13-Feb-3 David Lay, Penzance #342/R
£680 $1108 €1020 Hounds at Eagle's Nest (36x51cm-14x20in) s. i.verso board. 13-Feb-3 David Lay, Penzance #345

BRUGES SCHOOL (16th C) Belgian
£10968 $17329 €17000 Virgin enthroned with Child, angel ad boy (91x68cm-36x27in) board. 18-Dec-2 Ansorena, Madrid #93/R est:17000

BRUGGER, Arnold (1888-1975) Swiss
£1019 $1640 €1478 Gorge with alpine stream (80x53cm-31x21in) s. 9-May-3 Dobiaschofsky, Bern #90/R (S.FR 2200)
£2347 $3850 €3403 Gletscherhubel - Mountain landscape (81x99cm-32x39in) s. 4-Jun-3 Fischer, Luzern #1246/R est:5000-6000 (S.FR 5000)

BRUGGER, Fanny (1886-1970) Swiss
£926 $1491 €1389 Street in Bevers (39x32cm-15x13in) s.i.d.1908. 7-May-3 Dobiaschofsky, Bern #3142 (S.FR 2000)

BRUGGHEN, Guillaume Anne van der (1811-1891) Dutch
£955 $1471 €1500 Pointing to prey (22x28cm-9x11in) panel. 3-Sep-2 Christie's, Amsterdam #135 est:700-900

BRUGNER, Colestin (1824-1887) German
£616 $962 €900 Lake landscape in the Alps (23x31cm-9x12in) s. bears d. 10-Apr-3 Van Ham, Cologne #1347
£828 $1308 €1200 Wooded mountain landscape with angler by stream (24x32cm-9x13in) s. 5-Apr-3 Hans Stahl, Hamburg #3/R

BRUGNOLI, Emanuele (1859-1944) Italian
Works on paper
£310 $505 €465 Venice, the Grand Canal with Doge's Palace (21x30cm-8x12in) s. W/C. 28-Jan-3 Bristol Auction Rooms #519/R
£800 $1296 €1200 Fishing boats at sea (43x60cm-17x24in) s. pencil W/C. 23-Jan-3 Christie's, Kensington #335/R
£1450 $2364 €2103 Palazzo Ducale, Venice (21x30cm-8x12in) s. W/C. 16-Jul-3 Sotheby's, Olympia #252/R est:400-600

BRUHL, Louis Burleigh (1862-1942) British
Works on paper
£300 $477 €450 Canal scene in Bruges (43x17cm-17x7in) s. W/C. 1-May-3 Locke & England, Leamington Spa #161
£620 $967 €930 Suffolk coast (62x79cm-24x31in) s. W/C. 10-Sep-2 David Duggleby, Scarborough #258

BRUIN, Cornelis de (1870-1940) Dutch
£414 $658 €600 Harderwijk (50x71cm-20x28in) s. s.i.verso. 10-Mar-3 Sotheby's, Amsterdam #200
£573 $900 €860 Cottage beside a lake in summer landscape (60x80cm-24x31in) s. masonite. 14-Dec-2 Weschler, Washington #624/R est:600-800
£1042 $1719 €1500 Windmill by a river in winter (80x60cm-31x24in) s. 1-Jul-3 Christie's, Amsterdam #163/R est:1000-1500
£2069 $3290 €3000 Volendam (90x131cm-35x52in) s. s.i.verso. 10-Mar-3 Sotheby's, Amsterdam #199/R est:1000-1500

BRUMATTI, Gianni (1901-1990) Italian
£461 $747 €650 Lavoro nei campi (17x25cm-7x10in) s. 22-May-3 Stadion, Trieste #297
£1064 $1723 €1500 Vigna in Carso (37x60cm-15x24in) s. panel. 22-May-3 Stadion, Trieste #296/R est:1200-1600

BRUMIDI, Constantino (1805-1880) American
£531 $850 €770 Young girl with golden curls (76x63cm-30x25in) s.i.d.1853 oval. 16-May-3 Skinner, Boston #89/R

BRUMMER, Benedicte (1881-1974) Danish
£531 $844 €797 Summer landscape with lake (77x94cm-30x37in) mono. 10-Mar-3 Rasmussen, Vejle #337/R (D.KR 5700)

BRUN, Annie (20th C) British?
Works on paper
£270 $451 €392 Woodland cottage with blue shutters (39x55cm-15x22in) s. W/C bodycol. 9-Jul-3 Edgar Horn, Eastbourne #282

BRUN, Edme Gustave Frederic (1817-1881) French
£4088 $6336 €6500 Sculptor's study (107x77cm-42x30in) s.d. 29-Oct-2 Finarte, Milan #399/R est:2000-3000

BRUN, Guillaume Charles (1825-1908) French
£1000 $1580 €1500 Secret rendezvous (33x27cm-13x11in) s.d.1863. 14-Nov-2 Christie's, Kensington #36/R est:1000-1500

BRUN, Louis-Auguste (1758-1815) French
£8000 $12480 €12000 Study of four dogs and an eagle. Study of seven dogs a hare and a goat (38x46cm-15x18in) one s. pair prov. 9-Apr-3 Christie's, London #79/R est:10000-15000

Works on paper
£506 $800 €759 Hunter in profile to the left carrying a rifle over his left shoulder (235x178cm-93x70in) pencil white chk. 1-Apr-3 Christie's, Rockefeller NY #382/R

BRUN, Raul (19th C) ?
£4747 $7500 €7500 Fishing huts and fishermen on the coast (94x105cm-37x41in) s.d.1883. 28-Nov-2 Dorotheum, Vienna #202/R est:7500-8500

BRUNBERG, Hakan (1905-1978) Finnish
£633 $987 €1000 Southern harbour (42x53cm-17x21in) s.d.1946. 12-Sep-2 Hagelstam, Helsinki #912/R
£849 $1308 €1350 Cat (51x40cm-20x16in) s. 24-Oct-2 Hagelstam, Helsinki #849
£1973 $3137 €2900 Paradise Beach (54x73cm-21x29in) s. 24-Mar-3 Bukowskis, Helsinki #43/R est:2500
£2278 $3600 €3600 Parisian woman (62x51cm-24x20in) s. 1-Dec-2 Bukowskis, Helsinki #307/R est:2000-2200
£2468 $3900 €3900 Summer dance (54x65cm-21x26in) s. board. 1-Dec-2 Bukowskis, Helsinki #306/R est:3500-3700
£3671 $5800 €5800 At the cafe (46x56cm-18x22in) s. 1-Dec-2 Bukowskis, Helsinki #304/R est:4500-5000

BRUNDAGE, Frances I (1854-?) American
£380 $600 €570 Portrait of a young lady (51x41cm-20x16in) s.d.99. 22-Apr-3 Arthur James, Florida #57

BRUNDRIT, Reginald Grange (1883-1960) British
£250 $390 €375 Fading light (25x35cm-10x14in) canvasboard exhib. 10-Apr-3 Tennants, Leyburn #1011
£480 $782 €696 Watermill in the Dales, winter (36x46cm-14x18in) s. 17-Jul-3 Tennants, Leyburn #864
£650 $1021 €975 Bridge at Masham, Yorkshire (46x61cm-18x24in) s. 21-Nov-2 Tennants, Leyburn #822

BRUNE, Christian (1793-1849) French
Works on paper
£317 $526 €450 Paysage a la cascade dans les Alpes (39x32cm-15x13in) s.d.1827 graphite W/C. 13-Jun-3 Rossini, Paris #69

BRUNEAU, Charles (?-1891) French
£823 $1300 €1235 Maiden milking cows (48x58cm-19x23in) s. board. 16-Nov-2 New Orleans Auction, New Orleans #973/R

BRUNEAU, Kittie (1929-) Canadian
£325 $511 €488 Sans titre (133x152cm-52x60in) s.d.73. 12-Dec-2 Iegor de Saint Hippolyte, Montreal #17 (C.D 800)

BRUNEAU, Odette (1891-1984) French
£3205 $5032 €5000 Portrait de jeune marocaine (41x33cm-16x13in) s. 16-Dec-2 Gros & Delettrez, Paris #113/R est:2200-3000
Works on paper
£612 $973 €900 Casablanca, nouvelle ville indigene (36x27cm-14x11in) s.i.d.mai 1925 W/C gouache. 24-Mar-3 Rabourdin & Choppin de Janvry, Paris #259/R

BRUNEL DE NEUVILLE (19/20th C) French
£1667 $2617 €2600 Chats (46x56cm-18x22in) s. 19-Nov-2 Servarts Themis, Bruxelles #133/R
£3205 $5032 €5000 Chats (46x56cm-18x22in) s. 19-Nov-2 Servarts Themis, Bruxelles #134/R

BRUNEL DE NEUVILLE, Alfred Arthur (1852-1941) French
£1111 $1766 €1600 Faisan et perdrix (54x65cm-21x26in) s. 30-Apr-3 Tajan, Paris #67/R
£1161 $1800 €1742 Peaches, grapes, carafes and silver cup on a marble table (27x35cm-11x14in) s. panel. 2-Oct-2 Christie's, Rockefeller NY #787/R est:2000-3000
£1300 $1976 €1950 Basket of red and white currants and plums (38x46cm-15x18in) s. 29-Aug-2 Christie's, Kensington #246/R est:1200-1800
£1370 $2000 €2055 Four kittens watching a fly in a saucer of milk (25x33cm-10x13in) s. 3-Nov-1 North East Auctions, Portsmouth #229/R
£1529 $2400 €2294 Cup of milk (38x46cm-15x18in) bears sig. 22-Nov-2 Skinner, Boston #40/R est:1000-1500
£1582 $2453 €2500 Coupe de peches et de raisins (54x65cm-21x26in) s. 29-Sep-2 Eric Pillon, Calais #35/R
£1600 $2528 €2400 Peaches, redcurrants and whitecurrants in a basket, bottle on a ledge (53x65cm-21x26in) s. 14-Nov-2 Christie's, Kensington #91/R est:1500-2000
£1600 $2592 €2400 Kittens playing (38x48cm-15x19in) indis sig. 20-May-3 Sotheby's, Olympia #388/R est:1000-1500
£1731 $2734 €2700 Ecumoire de crevetts, huitres, flasque et bouteille (46x38cm-18x15in) s. 18-Nov-2 Tajan, Paris #32/R est:1800-2100
£1781 $2778 €2600 Still life of fruit (54x66cm-21x26in) s. 10-Apr-3 Dorotheum, Vienna #260/R est:4000-5000
£1795 $2818 €2800 Assiette de poires pommes et raisins sur un entablement (54x65cm-21x26in) s. 16-Dec-2 Millon & Associes, Paris #80/R est:3000-4000
£1899 $3000 €2849 Playful kittens (25x33cm-10x13in) s. 24-Apr-3 Shannon's, Milford #221/R est:3000-5000
£1931 $3090 €2800 Kittens playing (54x65cm-21x26in) s. 15-Mar-3 De Vuyst, Lokeren #37/R est:2800-3300
£1974 $3197 €3000 Still life with prunes and berries (46x54cm-18x21in) s. 21-Jan-3 Christie's, Amsterdam #89/R est:2000-3000
£2449 $3894 €3600 Nature morte aux huitres (54x65cm-21x26in) s. canvas on panel. 26-Feb-3 Artcurial Briest, Paris #130/R est:3200-4000
£2500 $3975 €3750 Plate of peaches and a basket of grapes with a copper kettle (54x65cm-21x26in) s. 20-Mar-3 Christie's, Kensington #29/R est:3000-5000
£2600 $4212 €3900 Surprise (25x33cm-10x13in) s. i.verso board. 20-May-3 Sotheby's, Olympia #387/R est:2000-3000
£2619 $4164 €3850 Nature morte a la langouste (54x65cm-21x26in) s. canvas on panel. 26-Feb-3 Artcurial Briest, Paris #131/R est:3200-4000
£2903 $4500 €4355 New toy (54x65cm-21x26in) s. prov. 2-Oct-2 Christie's, Rockefeller NY #791/R est:4000-6000
£2911 $4600 €4600 Abricots et paniers de groseilles. Peches et paniers de raisins (38x46cm-15x18in) s. pair. 1-Dec-2 Peron, Melun #123b
£3185 $5000 €4778 Come out and play (21x26cm-8x10in) s. 10-Dec-2 Doyle, New York #207/R est:6000-8000
£3304 $4824 €4956 Still life with cherries and Johannis berries (65x92cm-26x36in) s. 17-Jun-2 Philippe Schuler, Zurich #4329/R est:4000-5000 (S.FR 7500)

BRUNERY, François (1849-1926) Italian
£6329 $10000 €9494 Rehearsal (42x33cm-17x13in) s. panel. 24-Apr-3 Sotheby's, New York #131/R est:8000-12000
£15190 $24000 €22785 Confidences (53x38cm-21x15in) s. prov. 23-Apr-3 Christie's, Rockefeller NY #114/R est:15000-20000
£20000 $31000 €30000 Interesting letter (62x51cm-24x20in) s. prov. 4-Dec-2 Christie's, London #89/R est:25000-35000
£20000 $33400 €30000 Marriage contract (65x55cm-26x22in) s. 19-Jun-3 Christie's, London #51/R est:20000-30000
£27000 $42390 €40500 Cardinal's dilemma (65x53cm-26x21in) s. panel prov. 19-Nov-2 Sotheby's, London #117/R est:30000-40000

BRUNERY, Marcel (20th C) French
£7200 $12024 €10440 Smoking companion (46x38cm-18x15in) s. 17-Jun-3 Bonhams, New Bond Street #110/R est:8000-12000

BRUNET, Adele Laure (1879-1965) American
£1538 $2400 €2307 Still life (91x74cm-36x29in) 19-Oct-2 David Dike, Dallas #240/R est:3000-5000
£3045 $4750 €4568 Galveston (43x56cm-17x22in) 19-Oct-2 David Dike, Dallas #137/R est:5500-7500

BRUNET-HOUARD, Pierre Auguste (1829-1922) French
£429 $660 €644 Untitled - cavalry soldier (22x29cm-9x11in) s. canvas on board. 3-Sep-2 Shapiro, Sydney #409 est:800-1200 (A.D 1200)

BRUNETTO, Silvio (1932-) Italian
£510 $811 €750 Susa (40x50cm-16x20in) s. card on canvas. 1-Mar-3 Meeting Art, Vercelli #208
£510 $811 €750 Villa San Secondo (30x50cm-12x20in) s. s.i.d.1981 verso masonite. 1-Mar-3 Meeting Art, Vercelli #193
£544 $865 €800 Market (24x30cm-9x12in) s. board. 1-Mar-3 Meeting Art, Vercelli #38

BRUNI, Bruno (1935-) Italian
£222 $343 €350 Pesaro harbour (69x90cm-27x35in) s.d.1958. 28-Sep-2 Ketterer, Hamburg #401/R
£353 $557 €550 Rest (80x60cm-31x24in) painted 1974. 12-Nov-2 Babuino, Rome #139/R
£462 $729 €720 Pool (60x80cm-24x31in) painted 1974. 12-Nov-2 Babuino, Rome #138/R
Sculpture
£1277 $2068 €1800 La Divina (71x11x15cm-28x4x6in) i. brown pat.bronze Cast.Venturi Arte. 24-May-3 Van Ham, Cologne #71/R
£2264 $3532 €3600 La Divina (103x21x17cm-41x8x7in) num.697/1000 gold brown pat.bronze marble socle. 11-Oct-2 Winterberg, Heidelberg #908/R est:4800

BRUNI, Laure-Stella (20th C) French
£417 $671 €626 Still life of flowers (65x81cm-26x32in) s. 7-May-3 Dobiaschofsky, Bern #3145 (S.FR 900)

BRUNI, Tatyana Georgievna (1902-1979) Russian
Works on paper
£2400 $3768 €3600 Costume designs (28x24cm-11x9in) init. W/C pencil four. 20-Nov-2 Sotheby's, London #163/R est:3500-5000

BRUNI, Umberto (1914-) Canadian
£202 $329 €303 Sous bois (35x30cm-14x12in) s. s.i.d.1978 verso. 12-Feb-3 Iegor de Saint Hippolyte, Montreal #38/R (C.D 500)

BRUNIN, Charles (1841-1887) Belgian
£1026 $1590 €1600 Composition florale sur un entablement (90x60cm-35x24in) bears sig. 9-Dec-2 Horta, Bruxelles #353 est:2000-3000

BRUNIN, Léon (1861-1949) Belgian
£288 $453 €450 Village sous la neige (29x44cm-11x17in) 16-Dec-2 Amberes, Antwerp #249
£1923 $3038 €3000 De ceremoniemeester (76x60cm-30x24in) s. 18-Nov-2 Bernaerts, Antwerp #44/R est:2000-2500

BRUNING, Max (1887-1968) German
£295 $448 €460 Spring day in Allgauer mountains near Tiefenbach in Obersdorf (80x61cm-31x24in) s. lit. 11-Jul-2 Allgauer, Kempten #2451/R

BRUNING, Peter (1929-1970) German
£2885 $4471 €4500 Nr 8.67 (93x125cm-37x49in) bears s.d.1967 acrylic canvas photo. 6-Dec-2 Hauswedell & Nolte, Hamburg #63/R est:6000
£11511 $18878 €16000 Untitled (96x124cm-38x49in) s.d. 6-Jun-3 Ketterer, Munich #103/R est:20000-30000
£26087 $42783 €36000 Nr 143 (97x130cm-38x51in) s.d.62 i. verso oil col chk. 28-May-3 Lempertz, Koln #67/R est:38000-40000
£30769 $47692 €48000 Untitled (130x171cm-51x67in) oil col chks. 3-Dec-2 Lempertz, Koln #71/R est:50000-60000
Works on paper
£1410 $2186 €2200 Untitled (49x67cm-19x26in) s.d.58 Indian ink. 3-Dec-2 Lempertz, Koln #73/R est:2500

BRUNINI, Ettore (19/20th C) French
£1548 $2446 €2400 Femmes nues (37x42cm-15x17in) s. panel. 17-Dec-2 Claude Aguttes, Neuilly #25/R est:1520-1830

BRUNKAL, Erich (1859-?) German
£493 $794 €700 Portrait of old woman with jug (21x16cm-8x6in) s. panel. 7-May-3 Michael Zeller, Lindau #653/R

BRUNNER, Antonin (1881-?) Czechoslovakian
£611 $971 €917 Spring (52cm-20in circular) s.d.1927. 8-Mar-3 Dorotheum, Prague #115/R est:15000-23000 (C.KR 28000)

BRUNNER, Carl (1796-1867) German
£415 $647 €623 Arles arena (39x56cm-15x22in) s.d.1862. 6-Nov-2 Dobiaschofsky, Bern #379/R (S.FR 950)

BRUNNER, Carl (attrib) (1796-1867) German
£371 $579 €557 Lake Thun (35x45cm-14x18in) 6-Nov-2 Dobiaschofsky, Bern #380/R (S.FR 850)

BRUNNER, Ferdinand (1870-1945) Austrian
£3239 $5215 €4600 Northern river landscape with windmill (37x31cm-15x12in) s. canvas on board. 7-May-3 Michael Zeller, Lindau #654/R est:2500
£4255 $6894 €6000 Landscape with wood and cloudy sky (20x26cm-8x10in) canvas on board prov. 20-May-3 Dorotheum, Vienna #120/R est:6000-10000
£10127 $16000 €16000 Buildings in countryside (27x36cm-11x14in) s. exhib. 27-Nov-2 Dorotheum, Vienna #118/R est:11000-16000

BRUNNER, Hattie K (1890-1982) American
Works on paper
£1731 $2700 €2597 Winter scene, skating and a sleigh ride (25x36cm-10x14in) s.d.1965 W/C prov. 19-Oct-2 Freeman, Philadelphia #121/R est:1000-2000

BRUNNER, J (19/20th C) German
£612 $973 €900 Stroll in the cart (70x100cm-28x39in) s. 1-Mar-3 Stadion, Trieste #134

BRUNNER, Ria (?) Czechoslovakian
Sculpture
£2065 $3222 €3098 Nude girl (96cm-38in) s.d. marble. 12-Oct-2 Dorotheum, Prague #296/R est:100000-150000 (C.KR 100000)

BRUNNER, Salomon (1778-1848) Swiss
£694 $1118 €1006 River landscape (34x45cm-13x18in) mono.d.1841. 9-May-3 Dobiaschofsky, Bern #6/R (S.FR 1500)

BRUNO, Francesco (1648-1726) Italian
Works on paper
£1439 $2302 €2000 Ascension of Maria (55x40cm-22x16in) i. verso ochre. 17-May-3 Lempertz, Koln #1207/R est:2000

BRUNONI, Serge (1930-) Canadian
£267 $437 €401 Montreal, Marquette Street (30x40cm-12x16in) s. acrylic prov. 3-Jun-3 Joyner, Toronto #502 (C.D 600)
£412 $638 €618 Montreal, Devant le Ritz (60x75cm-24x30in) s. 3-Dec-2 Joyner, Toronto #468 est:1000-1500 (C.D 1000)
£453 $702 €680 Kensington market, Toronto (60x75cm-24x30in) s. 3-Dec-2 Joyner, Toronto #474 est:1000-1500 (C.D 1100)
£535 $829 €803 Promenade sur sherbrooke (40x30cm-16x12in) s. acrylic. 3-Dec-2 Joyner, Toronto #296/R est:800-1200 (C.D 1300)
£565 $892 €848 Montreal, Sherbrooke Ouest (30x41cm-12x16in) s. s.i.verso acrylic prov. 14-Nov-2 Heffel, Vancouver #277 est:700-900 (C.D 1400)
£723 $1135 €1085 Certaine noblesse (75x60cm-30x24in) s.i. acrylic. 25-Nov-2 Hodgins, Calgary #285/R (C.D 1800)
£964 $1513 €1446 Montreal, Place Jaques, Cartier (60x75cm-24x30in) s.i. 25-Nov-2 Hodgins, Calgary #147/R est:1500-2000 (C.D 2400)
£988 $1531 €1482 Le Ritz Carlton, Montreal, Rue Sherbrooke (75x100cm-30x39in) s. acrylic. 3-Dec-2 Joyner, Toronto #207/R est:2500-3000 (C.D 2400)
£1512 $2389 €2268 Quebec, place d'arme (61x76cm-24x30in) s. s.i.verso acrylic prov. 14-Nov-2 Heffel, Vancouver #274/R est:1500-2000 (C.D 3750)

BRUNT, Louis (1915-1992) American
£329 $550 €477 Clipper ship on lake Michigan (64x76cm-25x30in) s. indis.i.verso. 22-Jun-3 Jeffery Burchard, Florida #54/R

BRUS, Gunter (1938-) Austrian
Works on paper
£1392 $2200 €2200 AIA (41x29cm-16x11in) mono.d.1981 col pen pencil. 27-Nov-2 Dorotheum, Vienna #309/R est:2600-3400
£1517 $2534 €2200 Tierischer ernst fall (52x36cm-20x14in) s.i.d. wax pastel chl graphite. 9-Jul-3 Cornette de St.Cyr, Paris #237/R est:3000-4000
£11392 $17658 €18000 Variations without theme (74x56cm-29x22in) s. oil chk graphite 11 lit. 24-Sep-2 Wiener Kunst Auktionen, Vienna #266/R est:18000-25000

BRUSAFERRO, Girolamo (circle) (1700-1760) Italian
£41159 $67500 €61739 Jupiter and Antiope (91x153cm-36x60in) 29-May-3 Sotheby's, New York #65/R est:25000-35000

BRUSENBAUCH, Arthur (1881-1957) German
£252 $392 €400 Female nude (42x28cm-17x11in) chk. 23-Sep-2 Dr Fritz Nagel, Stuttgart #9018/R
£414 $662 €600 Locked up (50x43cm-20x17in) s.d. panel. 11-Mar-3 Dorotheum, Vienna #117/R

BRUSSEL, Paul Theodore van (1754-1791) Dutch
£17296 $26981 €27500 Still life of flowers (50x43cm-20x17in) s. lit. 20-Sep-2 Schloss Ahlden, Ahlden #1072/R est:28500
£61728 $100000 €92592 Still lifes of flowers and fruit on a marble ledge (86x72cm-34x28in) one s.d.1779 one s. pair. 23-Jan-3 Sotheby's, New York #98/R est:120000-160000

BRUSSELMANS, Jean (1884-1953) Belgian
£2055 $3205 €3000 Coq et poules devant une dame etalant son linge dans un verger (57x66cm-22x26in) s. canvas on panel. 14-Apr-3 Horta, Bruxelles #146 est:3000-5000
£3007 $4841 €4600 Coq et poules devant une dame etalant son linge dans son verger (57x66cm-22x26in) s. canvas on panel. 20-Jan-3 Horta, Bruxelles #119/R est:7000-9000
£3019 $4679 €4800 Interior with sitting woman (62x47cm-24x19in) s.i. paper on board. 5-Oct-2 De Vuyst, Lokeren #455/R est:7000-9000
£6536 $10523 €10000 Composition au chou rouge et au journal (75x98cm-30x39in) s.d.1939 canvas on panel. 20-Jan-3 Horta, Bruxelles #118/R est:12000-15000

£7914 $12978 €11000 Farmer in a field (57x66cm-22x26in) s.d.1933 prov. 3-Jun-3 Christie's, Amsterdam #264/R est:10000-15000
£10897 $16891 €17000 Port de peche - Vissershaven (80x90cm-31x35in) s.d.1929 exhib.lit. 3-Dec-2 Christie's, Amsterdam #233/R est:12000-16000
£14483 $23172 €21000 Paysans (102x64cm-40x25in) s.d.1925 prov.lit. 15-Mar-3 De Vuyst, Lokeren #453/R
£16352 $25182 €26000 Pommiers (80x70cm-31x28in) s.d.1937. 22-Oct-2 Campo & Campo, Antwerp #25/R est:35000
£33094 $52950 €46000 Le chemin de campagne (115x99cm-45x39in) s.d.1942 exhib.lit. 13-May-3 Palais de Beaux Arts, Brussels #33/R est:45000-62000
£63291 $100000 €100000 Nature morte a la lampe (120x136cm-47x54in) s.d.1935 prov.exhib.lit. 26-Nov-2 Palais de Beaux Arts, Brussels #49/R est:100000-150000

Works on paper
£342 $540 €540 Lagne Jan, remet un mandat a Petijean (27x21cm-11x8in) ink wash. 26-Nov-2 Palais de Beaux Arts, Brussels #51/R
£949 $1481 €1500 Le grenier aux pigeons (27x36cm-11x14in) s. pencil chl htd W/C dr. 10-Sep-2 Vanderkindere, Brussels #380 est:1500-2000
£949 $1500 €1500 La phare (17x26cm-7x10in) i. ink dr. 26-Nov-2 Palais de Beaux Arts, Brussels #50/R est:750-1250
£7000 $11620 €7000 Bateaux a Ostende (50x59cm-20x23in) s.d.1937 W/C. 16-Jun-3 Horta, Bruxelles #141 est:9000-12000

BRUSSELS SCHOOL (15/16th C) Belgian
£7692 $12154 €12000 La charite (47x59cm-19x23in) panel painted c.1500. 12-Nov-2 Palais de Beaux Arts, Brussels #67/R est:15000-20000

BRUTSCH, Hans (1920-) New Zealander
£354 $552 €531 Evening at Bayly's farm (38x58cm-15x23in) s. board. 6-Aug-2 Peter Webb, Auckland #104 est:500-800 (NZ.D 1200)

BRUTT, Ferdinand (1849-1936) German
£493 $794 €700 Man in interior (38x29cm-15x11in) s. 7-May-3 Vendue Huis, Gravenhage #565/R
£80576 $128921 €112000 The stock exchange (121x155cm-48x61in) s. exhib.prov.lit. 17-May-3 Lempertz, Koln #1368/R est:40000-50000

BRUTTI, Danilo Alessandro (1969-) Italian
£851 $1379 €1200 Home sweet home (70x90cm-28x35in) s.i.d.2002 verso acrylic. 20-May-3 Porro, Milan #5/R

BRUWELL, F (?) British?
£425 $650 €638 Portrait of a young lady (36x43cm-14x17in) 16-Aug-2 Douglas, South Deerfield #4

BRUYCKER, Bernhard de (1891-1971) German
£338 $493 €520 Autumn evening paths near the Wils hills (65x93cm-26x37in) s. 15-Jun-2 Hans Stahl, Hamburg #145/R

BRUYCKER, Constant de (1823-1896) Belgian
£1224 $1947 €1800 Figures near ruins (21x17cm-8x7in) s.d.184 panel. 24-Mar-3 Bernaerts, Antwerp #10/R est:2000-2500

BRUYCKER, Jules de (1870-1945) Belgian
Prints
£2179 $3378 €3400 Montage du dragon sur le beffroi, Gand (79x61cm-31x24in) s. exec.1914 lit. 7-Dec-2 De Vuyst, Lokeren #72/R est:3000-4000

BRUYER, Léon (1827-1885) French
Sculpture
£60000 $93000 €90000 Sphinxes with putto seated on saddles holding roses (43x55x21cm-17x22x8in) s.d.1877 white marble pat bronze pair. 1-Oct-2 Christie's, London #202/R est:60000-80000

BRUYN, Barthel (elder-circle) (1493-1555) German
£4017 $6348 €6026 Portrait of woman reading (36x30cm-14x12in) panel. 14-Nov-2 Stuker, Bern #117 est:12000-16000 (S.FR 9200)

BRUYN, Barthel (younger-style) (1530-1607) German
£6173 $10000 €9260 Portrait of holding a rosary (34x25cm-13x10in) i. panel prov.exhib. 23-Jan-3 Sotheby's, New York #72/R est:15000-20000

BRUYN, D J de (?) ?
£2000 $3240 €3000 Master and the apprentice (30x24cm-12x9in) s. 21-May-3 Christie's, Kensington #632/R est:800-1200

BRUYN, Johannes Cornelis de (1800-1844) Dutch
£2302 $3683 €3200 Still life of fruit in basket on marble ledge (36x29cm-14x11in) s. 13-May-3 Sotheby's, Amsterdam #49/R est:3000-5000
£2420 $3776 €3800 Still life of grapes, lemon, prunes, roemer with white wine on marble ledge (35x28cm-14x11in) s. canvas on board. 5-Nov-2 Sotheby's, Amsterdam #307/R est:3000-5000
£2675 $4173 €4200 Still life of roses, tulips and other flowers in a vase on a marble ledge (35x27cm-14x11in) s. canvas on board. 5-Nov-2 Sotheby's, Amsterdam #308/R est:4000-6000
£4012 $6500 €5817 Still life with urn of flowers (76x64cm-30x25in) s.d.1801. 21 May-3 Doyle, New York #185/R est:8000-12000
£5594 $9343 €8000 Nature morte aux fruits et au papillon (30x25cm-12x10in) s. panel. 25-Jun-3 Sotheby's, Paris #76/R est:4000-6000

BRUYNE, Dees de (1940-) Belgian
Works on paper
£272 $433 €400 Nu allonge. s. dr. 18-Mar-3 Galerie Moderne, Brussels #117
£486 $773 €700 Touristes a Pompei (100x150cm-39x59in) s. pastel paper on canvas. 29-Apr-3 Campo, Vlaamse Kaai #68

BRUYNE, Gustaaf de (1914-1981) Belgian
Works on paper
£1923 $2981 €3000 Eva (98x68cm-39x27in) s. mixed media. 7-Dec-2 De Vuyst, Lokeren #76/R est:3000-4000
£2128 $3553 €3000 Mere et enfant (53x40cm-21x16in) W/C. 23-Jun-3 Amberes, Antwerp #85/R

BRUYNE, Joris de (20th C) Belgian
£296 $480 €450 Riviere enneigee (40x50cm-16x20in) s. panel. 21-Jan-3 Galerie Moderne, Brussels #182
£428 $693 €650 Village enneige (57x63cm-22x25in) s.d.53 panel. 21-Jan-3 Galerie Moderne, Brussels #247
£669 $1077 €950 Snowy landscape (44x49cm-17x19in) s.d.1932 s.i.d.1932 verso. 7-May-3 Vendue Huis, Gravenhage #142/R

BRUYNESTEYN, Nicolaas (1893-1950) Dutch
£478 $736 €750 Oudeschans with the Montelbaanstoren, Amsterdam (40x50cm-16x20in) s. plywood. 3-Sep-2 Christie's, Amsterdam #183

BRYAN, Richard Jenkins (1907-1986) American
£750 $1200 €1088 Summertime in the Carolinas (18x13cm-7x5in) s.d.1939 masonite. 16-May-3 Skinner, Boston #154/R est:800-1200

BRYANS, Lina (1909-2000) Australian
£876 $1437 €1314 Landscape (50x61cm-20x24in) s. board. 4-Jun-3 Deutscher-Menzies, Melbourne #310/R (A.D 2200)
£2509 $3814 €3764 Lower plenty (50x61cm-20x24in) s. s.i.d.1946 verso canvasboard. 28-Aug-2 Deutscher-Menzies, Melbourne #227/R est:3500-4500 (A.D 7000)

BRYANT, Bruce (20th C) New Zealander
£251 $391 €377 Esmeralda, Princess Wharf (50x60cm-20x24in) s. board. 7-Nov-2 International Art Centre, Auckland #202 (NZ.D 800)

BRYANT, Charles (1883-1937) Australian
£423 $659 €635 Sydney harbour (28x48cm-11x19in) s. 21-Oct-2 Australian Art Auctions, Sydney #127 (A.D 1200)
£1200 $1968 €1800 Beached vessels at St. Ives Harbour (31x39cm-12x15in) s. i.verso board. 7-Feb-3 Honiton Galleries, Honiton #273/R est:1200-1500
£1429 $2214 €2144 Three Sisters (47x57cm-19x22in) s. canvas on board. 29-Oct-2 Lawson Menzies, Sydney #56/R est:4500-5500 (A.D 4000)
£1434 $2352 €2151 HMS Hood (56x70cm-22x28in) s. canvas on board lit. 4-Jun-3 Deutscher-Menzies, Melbourne #158/R est:4000-5000 (A.D 3600)
£1667 $2533 €2501 Yacht race, Sydney Harbour (23x56cm-9x22in) s. canvas on board. 19-Aug-2 Joel, Victoria #311 est:4000-6000 (A.D 4750)
£3559 $5445 €5339 Fishing boats (63x76cm-25x30in) s. 25-Aug-2 Sotheby's, Paddington #199/R est:10000-15000 (A.D 10000)
£17558 $27741 €26337 Brixham trawlers (61x74cm-24x29in) s. s.verso prov. 2-Apr-3 Christie's, Melbourne #9/R est:8000-12000 (A.D 46000)

BRYANT, Everett L (1864-1945) American
£609 $950 €914 Floral still life with lace curtains (61x51cm-24x20in) s. 14-Sep-2 Weschler, Washington #608/R
£659 $1100 €956 Chrysanthemums (61x51cm-24x20in) s. 22-Jun-3 Freeman, Philadelphia #113/R est:1500-2500
£958 $1600 €1389 Interior (63x76cm-25x30in) s. 22-Jun-3 Freeman, Philadelphia #132/R est:2000-3000
£1948 $3000 €2922 River on a spring day (64x76cm-25x30in) est.st. verso prov. 24-Oct-2 Shannon's, Milford #164/R est:3000-5000
£1948 $3000 €2922 Amongst the water lilies (64x76cm-25x30in) s. 24-Oct-2 Shannon's, Milford #184/R est:3000-5000
£2532 $4000 €3798 Along the river (64x76cm-25x30in) s. prov. 24-Apr-3 Shannon's, Milford #183/R est:3000-5000

£3247 $5000 €4871 Fountain (64x76cm-25x30in) s. prov. 24-Oct-2 Shannon's, Milford #186/R est:3000-5000
£4221 $6500 €6332 Costume ball (89x76cm-35x30in) est.st. verso prov. 24-Oct-2 Shannon's, Milford #30/R est:6000-8000
£4430 $7000 €6645 Japanese woman amongst flowers (76x64cm-30x25in) s. prov. 24-Apr-3 Shannon's, Milford #182/R est:3000-5000
£4747 $7500 €7121 Costume party (64x76cm-25x30in) s. prov. 24-Apr-3 Shannon's, Milford #149/R est:5000-7000
£5519 $8500 €8279 At the ballet (56x71cm-22x28in) s. prov. 24-Oct-2 Shannon's, Milford #31/R est:5000-7000
£8228 $13000 €12342 The ball (76x91cm-30x36in) s. prov. 24-Apr-3 Shannon's, Milford #135/R est:10000-15000

BRYANT, H C (fl.1860-1880) British
£600 $924 €900 Feeding the chickens (53x43cm-21x17in) s.d.1866. 5-Sep-2 Christie's, Kensington #276/R
£1200 $1872 €1740 Guinea fowl. Ducks and chickens (27x29cm-11x11in) s. board pair. 13-May-3 Holloways, Banbury #665 est:400-600

BRYANT, Henry C (fl.1860-1880) British
£800 $1336 €1160 Still life with fruit, flowers, Chinese bowl and claret jug (61x73cm-24x29in) s. board. 9-Jul-3 George Kidner, Lymington #170/R

BRYANT, Maude Drein (1880-1946) American
£389 $650 €564 Landscape (30x41cm-12x16in) estate st. verso board. 22-Jun-3 Freeman, Philadelphia #151a/R
£1899 $3000 €2849 Under the arbor (41x51cm-16x20in) s. 24-Apr-3 Shannon's, Milford #151/R est:3000-5000
£4221 $6500 €6332 Summer flowers (64x76cm-25x30in) s.d.1921 prov. 24-Oct-2 Shannon's, Milford #134/R est:6000-8000

BRYANT, William (1902-1977) American
£285 $450 €428 Abandoned on shore at Port Clyde harbour (30x41cm-12x16in) s.d.1955 panel. 26-Apr-3 Thomaston Place, Thomaston #441
£380 $600 €570 Port Clyde harbour (36x46cm-14x18in) s. panel. 26-Apr-3 Thomaston Place, Thomaston #259

BRYCE, Gilbert (?) ?
£900 $1404 €1350 Maidens in an Italianate garden (35x26cm-14x10in) s. 26-Mar-3 Sotheby's, Olympia #59/R est:1000-1500

BRYCE, Gordon (1943-) British
£680 $1054 €1020 Red peppers (33x45cm-13x18in) s.i.verso board. 24-Sep-2 Anderson & Garland, Newcastle #409/R
£800 $1248 €1200 Pears and lemons (29x29cm-11x11in) s. s.i.verso board. 10-Apr-3 Bonhams, Edinburgh #38/R
£950 $1482 €1425 Yachts, Aldeburgh (29x45cm-11x18in) s.i.verso board. 10-Apr-3 Bonhams, Edinburgh #37/R
£1550 $2403 €2325 Tulips and a black tea pot (58x68cm-23x27in) s.i.verso. 24-Sep-2 Anderson & Garland, Newcastle #408/R est:2000-3000
£1600 $2480 €2400 Oranges and black tea pot (37x47cm-15x19in) s.i.verso. 24-Sep-2 Anderson & Garland, Newcastle #407/R est:1500-2500

BRYEN, Camille (1907-1977) French
£2564 $4026 €4000 Untitled (55x46cm-22x18in) s. s.i.d.1970 verso prov.lit. 24-Nov-2 Laurence Calmels, Paris #71/R
£2692 $4227 €4200 Untitled (65x54cm-26x21in) s. prov.exhib.lit. 24-Nov-2 Laurence Calmels, Paris #67/R
£2692 $4227 €4200 Untitled (61x50cm-24x20in) s. s.i.d.1974 verso prov.lit. 24-Nov-2 Laurence Calmels, Paris #72/R
£2885 $4529 €4500 Untitled (73x60cm-29x24in) s. s.i.d.1971 verso prov.lit. 24-Nov-2 Laurence Calmels, Paris #66/R
£2885 $4529 €4500 Fusee (65x54cm-26x21in) s. s.i.d.1969 verso prov.lit. 24-Nov-2 Laurence Calmels, Paris #73/R
£3125 $5156 €4500 Composition (93x73cm-37x29in) prov.exhib.lit. 1-Jul-3 Artcurial Briest, Paris #790/R est:4500-6000
£3205 $5032 €5000 Fusee (73x60cm-29x24in) s. s.i.d.1970 verso prov.lit. 24-Nov-2 Laurence Calmels, Paris #69/R
£3526 $5535 €5500 Untitled (73x60cm-29x24in) s. s.i.d.63 verso prov.exhib.lit. 24-Nov-2 Laurence Calmels, Paris #63/R
£3718 $5837 €5800 Untitled (92x73cm-36x29in) s. s.i.d.1969 verso prov.exhib.lit. 24-Nov-2 Laurence Calmels, Paris #70/R
£3846 $6038 €6000 Untitled (96x77cm-38x30in) s. s.d.1973 verso prov.exhib.lit. 24-Nov-2 Laurence Calmels, Paris #62/R
£4167 $6542 €6500 Untitled (92x73cm-36x29in) s. i.verso prov.exhib.lit. 24-Nov-2 Laurence Calmels, Paris #65/R
£4514 $7132 €6500 Mars (65x54cm-26x21in) s. prov.exhib.lit. 27-Apr-3 Perrin, Versailles #36/R est:6000-7000
£4872 $7649 €7600 Composition (81x65cm-32x26in) s. s.i.d.1962 verso prov.exhib.lit. 15-Dec-2 Perrin, Versailles #64/R
£5034 $8104 €7500 Composition (73x60cm-29x24in) s. s.i.d.1971 verso prov.lit. 23-Feb-3 Mercier & Cie, Lille #152/R
£5128 $8051 €8000 Injuste milieu (130x97cm-51x38in) s. s.d.1974 prov.exhib.lit. 24-Nov-2 Laurence Calmels, Paris #64/R
£5161 $8155 €8000 Composition (92x73cm-36x29in) s. s.i.d.1962 verso lit. 19-Dec-2 Delvaux, Paris #50/R est:11000
£5949 $9281 €9400 Composition (92x73cm-36x29in) s. s.d.1974 verso lit. 20-Oct-2 Claude Boisgirard, Paris #65/R est:10000-11000
£6090 $9561 €9500 Untitled (116x89cm-46x35in) s. s.i.d.1973 verso prov.exhib.lit. 24-Nov-2 Laurence Calmels, Paris #68/R

Works on paper
£448 $748 €650 Sans titre, racines (31x24cm-12x9in) mono. ink W/C dr exec.c.1949. 10-Jul-3 Artcurial Briest, Paris #295
£449 $704 €700 Silhouettes (43x28cm-17x11in) s. s.d.71 verso Chinese ink. 24-Nov-2 Laurence Calmels, Paris #61/R
£449 $704 €700 Silhouettes (36x30cm-14x12in) s. Chinese ink. 24-Nov-2 Laurence Calmels, Paris #59/R
£566 $877 €900 Composition (27x21cm-11x8in) studio st. W/C prov. 30-Oct-2 Artcurial Briest, Paris #644
£641 $994 €1000 Untitled (33x25cm-13x10in) s. d.Aout 54 verso W/C pastel pen ink. 3-Dec-2 Christie's, Amsterdam #119/R est:800-1200
£689 $1151 €1000 Sans titre (50x33cm-20x13in) s.i. d.nov.53 verso W/C ink. 10-Jul-3 Artcurial Briest, Paris #296
£705 $1107 €1100 Untitled (42x31cm-17x12in) init. s.d.1947 verso mixed media. 24-Nov-2 Laurence Calmels, Paris #60/R
£884 $1406 €1300 Composition (31x25cm-12x10in) s.d.62 W/C. 26-Feb-3 Artcurial Briest, Paris #551
£986 $1568 €1450 Composition no 786 (32x24cm-13x9in) s. W/C gouache. 26-Feb-3 Artcurial Briest, Paris #552
£1020 $1622 €1500 Untitled (27x21cm-11x8in) studio st. W/C. 24-Mar-3 Claude Boisgirard, Paris #111/R
£1054 $1677 €1550 Composition no 689 (37x28cm-15x11in) s. W/C gouache exec.c.1970. 26-Feb-3 Artcurial Briest, Paris #553 est:800-1000
£1224 $1947 €1800 Composition (26x20cm-10x8in) s.d.62 W/C gouache prov. 26-Feb-3 Artcurial Briest, Paris #446 est:1000-1200
£1295 $2072 €1800 Composition (31x24cm-12x9in) s. d.verso W/C. 14-May-3 Blanchet, Paris #179/R est:3000-3500
£1565 $2488 €2300 Composition no 609 (33x25cm-13x10in) s.i.d.63 s.d.avril 63 verso gouache W/C prov. 26-Feb-3 Artcurial Briest, Paris #445/R est:1000-1200
£2778 $4583 €4000 Ecorche-vide (65x76cm-26x30in) s. mixed media panel exhib. 1-Jul-3 Artcurial Briest, Paris #775/R est:4000-6000
£4762 $7571 €7000 Composition (92x73cm-36x29in) s. 26-Feb-3 Artcurial Briest, Paris #444/R est:6000-8000

BRYER, Cornelis de (17th C) Flemish
£6115 $9784 €8500 Still life with grapes, tangerine, apple, prunes and apricots on stone ledge (41x61cm-16x24in) bears sig. 13-May-3 Sotheby's, Amsterdam #46/R est:10000-15000

BRYMNER, William (1855-1925) Canadian
£9877 $15309 €14816 Frontenac receiving Sir William Phips envoy (135x195cm-53x77in) s.d.1911 exhib.lit. 3-Dec-2 Joyner, Toronto #249/R est:7000-9000 (C.D 24000)
£26210 $41411 €39315 In the orchard spring (41x30cm-16x12in) s.d.1892 board prov. 18-Nov-2 Sotheby's, Toronto #8/R est:15000-20000 (C.D 65000)

Works on paper
£533 $875 €800 Planting the fields (26x36cm-10x14in) s.d.1890 W/C. 3-Jun-3 Joyner, Toronto #535 est:1500-2000 (C.D 1200)
£1844 $2859 €2766 Washer woman at river's edge (51x34cm-20x13in) s.d.05 W/C prov. 24-Sep-2 Ritchie, Toronto #3090/R est:2500-3000 (C.D 4500)

BRYSON, Hilary (20th C) British?
Works on paper
£290 $423 €435 Early morning exercising (46x71cm-18x28in) s. pastel. 12-Jun-2 John Ross, Belfast #52
£300 $438 €450 Playing fence (33x46cm-13x18in) s. pastel. 12-Jun-2 John Ross, Belfast #274

BRYSTORP, O (19/20th C) Norwegian
£1895 $2880 €2843 Norwegian fjord landscapes (74x47cm-29x19in) s. pair. 27-Aug-2 Rasmussen, Copenhagen #1930/R est:25000 (D.KR 22000)

BUBENICEK, Jindrich (1856-1935) Czechoslovakian
£436 $694 €654 Summer landscape with building (46x33cm-18x13in) s.d.1895. 8-Mar-3 Dorotheum, Prague #89/R est:20000-30000 (C.KR 20000)

BUBENICEK, Ota (1871-1962) Czechoslovakian
£268 $424 €402 Landscape with cottage (14x19cm-6x7in) s. board. 30-Nov-2 Dorotheum, Prague #39 (C.KR 13000)
£289 $451 €434 Summer landscape in the country (17x25cm-7x10in) s. cardboard. 12-Oct-2 Dorotheum, Prague #42 est:10000-15000 (C.KR 14000)
£363 $588 €526 Landscape with cottage (24x34cm-9x13in) s. board. 24-May-3 Dorotheum, Prague #69/R est:10000-15000 (C.KR 16000)
£392 $619 €588 Pavlov at Mlada Vozice (33x50cm-13x20in) s. cardboard. 30-Nov-2 Dorotheum, Prague #44 (C.KR 19000)

£392 $619 €588 Mill on a stream (35x50cm-14x20in) s. paper on cardboard. 30-Nov-2 Dorotheum, Prague #121 (C.KR 19000)
£496 $773 €744 Early evening mood (50x65cm-20x26in) s. cardboard. 12-Oct-2 Dorotheum, Prague #50/R (C.KR 24000)
£496 $773 €744 Landscape with small church (33x50cm-13x20in) s. cardboard. 12-Oct-2 Dorotheum, Prague #55/R (C.KR 24000)
£524 $832 €786 Country house (26x36cm-10x14in) s. paper. 8-Mar-3 Dorotheum, Prague #45 est:15000-23000 (C.KR 24000)
£654 $1041 €981 Summer landscape (29x48cm-11x19in) s. board. 8-Mar-3 Dorotheum, Prague #46 est:10000-15000 (C.KR 30000)
£660 $1043 €990 Winter evening under Semberk at Mlada Vozice (33x50cm-13x20in) s. cardboard. 30-Nov-2 Dorotheum, Prague #43 (C.KR 32000)
£702 $1095 €1053 On the brook in winter (25x34cm-10x13in) s.d.18 cardboard. 12-Oct-2 Dorotheum, Prague #48/R (C.KR 34000)
£1200 $1908 €1800 Summer landscape (86x115cm-34x45in) s.d.22. 8-Mar-3 Dorotheum, Prague #50/R est:50000-75000 (C.KR 55000)
£2182 $3469 €3273 In front of a graveyard (90x100cm-35x39in) s.d.12. 8-Mar-3 Dorotheum, Prague #49/R est:80000-120000 (C.KR 100000)

BUCCI, Anselmo (1887-1955) Italian
£3481 $5430 €5500 Factory (65x92cm-26x36in) s.d.1929. 14-Sep-2 Meeting Art, Vercelli #947/R
£6803 $10816 €10000 Paris (60x80cm-24x31in) s.i.d.1916 board. 1-Mar-3 Meeting Art, Vercelli #492

BUCCI, Mario (1903-1970) Italian
£372 $580 €550 Seascape (50x60cm-20x24in) s. 28-Mar-3 Farsetti, Prato #508
£946 $1476 €1400 Still life in Paris (50x60cm-20x24in) s. painted 1960. 28-Mar-3 Farsetti, Prato #751/R

BUCCIARELLI, Daniele (1839-1911) Italian
Works on paper
£443 $700 €665 Proposal (43x23cm-17x9in) W/C. 15-Nov-2 Du Mouchelle, Detroit #2117/R

BUCHANAN, Dean (1952-) New Zealander
£408 $636 €612 Bay (82x59cm-32x23in) s.d.1999. 5-Nov-2 Peter Webb, Auckland #127 est:1200-1800 (NZ.D 1300)
£456 $711 €684 Estuaries (82x63cm-32x25in) s.d.1999. 17-Sep-2 Peter Webb, Auckland #164/R est:1800-2500 (NZ.D 1500)
£457 $700 €686 Volcano (91x107cm-36x42in) s.d.91. 21-Aug-2 Dunbar Sloane, Auckland #4/R est:1500-3000 (NZ.D 1500)
£883 $1422 €1325 Untitled (122x122cm-48x48in) s.d.88. 7-May-3 Dunbar Sloane, Auckland #14/R est:2500-3500 (NZ.D 2500)
£955 $1500 €1433 Harbour view through Nikau Trees (110x200cm-43x79in) s.d.1989. 10-Dec-2 Peter Webb, Auckland #116/R est:4000-6000 (NZ.D 3000)
£965 $1505 €1448 Circus, marionette series (141x124cm-56x49in) s. 27-Mar-3 International Art Centre, Auckland #56/R (NZ.D 2750)
£973 $1517 €1460 Kauri trees and Manukau (152x101cm-60x40in) s.d.1989. 17-Sep-2 Peter Webb, Auckland #163/R est:3500-5000 (NZ.D 3200)

BUCHANAN, George F (fl.1848-1864) British
£850 $1326 €1275 Figures in a loch landscape (51x76cm-20x30in) s.d.1855. 7-Nov-2 Christie's, Kensington #106/R
£1100 $1705 €1650 Prospect of Dumbarton and the Clyde from the south (53x89cm-21x35in) s. 5-Dec-2 Bonhams, Edinburgh #114 est:1200-1800

BUCHANAN, J P (fl.1890-1891) British
£800 $1272 €1200 Across the loch (61x91cm-24x36in) s.d.1887. 6-Mar-3 Christie's, Kensington #55/R

BUCHANAN, Peter (1855-1950) British
£455 $714 €683 Moorland, Gienfruin (46x81cm-18x32in) s.i. prov. 24-Jul-2 Walker's, Ottawa #27/R est:1000-1500 (C.D 1100)

BUCHANAN, Peter Ronald (20th C) British
Works on paper
£1050 $1659 €1575 Senior steward, E Britt. Lord Allendale. Mrs Vernet (25x18cm-10x7in) two s. pencil W/C bodycol set of three. 28-Nov-2 Christie's, Kensington #190/R est:600-800
£1350 $2255 €1958 Cartoons of Mr Edgar Wallace. Mr J H Whitney. Lord Lileen. Mr W Barnett and Joe Marshall (30x33cm-12x13in) s. W/C set of four. 20-Jun-3 Keys, Aylsham #439/R est:1000-1500

BUCHANAN, Peter S (fl.1860-1911) British
£900 $1431 €1350 Shepherd's cottage (51x76cm-20x30in) s. 6-Mar-3 Christie's, Kensington #100 est:700-1000

BUCHANAN, William Cross (19th C) ?
Works on paper
£5096 $8000 €7644 Views of Chile (24x36cm-9x14in) init. W/C ink wash set of 8. 19-Nov-2 Sotheby's, New York #67/R est:15000

BUCHE, Josef (1848-1917) Austrian
£1361 $2163 €2000 Puster valley peasant in traditional dress (63x50cm-25x20in) s. 19-Mar-3 Neumeister, Munich #521/R est:1000
£1538 $2415 €2400 Small zither player (26x21cm-10x8in) s. 10-Dec-2 Dorotheum, Vienna #210/R est:2000-2500
£4500 $7290 €6750 An interesting read (36x52cm-14x20in) bears sig d.1879. 20-May-3 Sotheby's, Olympia #403/R est:2000-3000

BUCHEL, Emmanuel (1705-1775) Swiss
Works on paper
£314 $491 €500 Basle (21x49cm-8x19in) s.i.d.1745 W/C pen lit. 20-Sep-2 Karlheinz Kaupp, Staufen #2145/R

BUCHER, Franz (1940-) Swiss
£306 $483 €459 Engadin valley (30x40cm-12x16in) s. panel. 14-Nov-2 Stuker, Bern #118 (S.FR 700)

BUCHER, Jakob Anton (1927-) Austrian
£633 $987 €1000 Memory of a landscape (95x80cm-37x31in) s. masonite. 15-Oct-2 Dorotheum, Vienna #203/R

BUCHET, Gustave (1888-1963) Swiss
£22642 $36679 €32831 Regate (81x54cm-32x21in) s.d.1950. 26-May-3 Sotheby's, Zurich #84/R est:40000-60000 (S.FR 48000)
Works on paper
£2358 $3821 €4175 Composition a la perruche (35x26cm-14x10in) W/C prov. 26-May-3 Sotheby's, Zurich #142/R est:5000-5500 (S.FR 5000)
£2575 $4069 €3863 Composition (31x22cm-12x9in) s. gouache Indian ink prov. 28-Nov-2 Christie's, Zurich #100/R est:6000-8000 (S.FR 6000)
£6987 $10969 €10481 Au port (50x35cm-20x14in) s.i.d.1933 W/C. 25-Nov-2 Sotheby's, Zurich #72/R est:8000-12000 (S.FR 16000)

BUCHET, Philippe (20th C) French?
Works on paper
£310 $490 €450 Sillage (30x21cm-12x8in) s.d.2003 ball-point pen. 7-Apr-3 Claude Aguttes, Neuilly #16/R

BUCHHEISTER, Carl (1890-1964) German
Works on paper
£496 $804 €700 Composition Choop (66x55cm-26x22in) s.i.d.58 verso gouache Indian ink. 24-May-3 Van Ham, Cologne #74/R
£1135 $1838 €1600 Composition Hoko 8/1956 (40x35cm-16x14in) s.i.d.1956 verso mixed media panel. 24-May-3 Van Ham, Cologne #73/R est:3000
£3623 $5942 €5000 Unreal space composition with red accents (47x30cm-19x12in) s.i.d.49 verso mixed media board. 29-May-3 Lempertz, Koln #555/R est:4000

BUCHHOLZ, Erich (1891-1972) German
£23718 $36763 €37000 Ordination (180x130cm-71x51in) s.i. stretcher. 7-Dec-2 Hauswedell & Nolte, Hamburg #566/R est:40000

BUCHHOLZ, Feodor Feodorovich (1857-?) Russian
£1800 $2916 €2700 Na Zdoroviye (25x30cm-10x12in) s. 21-May-3 Sotheby's, London #61 est:800-1200

BUCHHOLZ, Karl (1849-1889) German
£6507 $10151 €9500 Hunter in wooded summer landscape (33x47cm-13x19in) s. bears d.83. 10-Apr-3 Van Ham, Cologne #1349/R est:3200

BUCHHORN, Ludwig (1770-1856) German
Works on paper
£972 $1546 €1400 Portrait of young woman (8x6cm-3x2in) s. verso pastel crayon over pencil board. 5-May-3 Ketterer, Munich #278/R est:350-450

BUCHIN, Maurice (19th C) French
£676 $1054 €1000 Bord de riviere (17x21cm-7x8in) s. panel. 30-Mar-3 Anaf, Lyon #325

BUCHMAN, Arthur Avia (1904-1986) Polish
£260 $406 €390 Path in the woods (25x36cm-10x14in) s. board. 18-Sep-2 John Ross, Belfast #37

£260 $406 €390 Old stone bridge (30x41cm-12x16in) 18-Sep-2 John Ross, Belfast #63
£280 $437 €420 Female nude study (30x41cm-12x16in) board. 18-Sep-2 John Ross, Belfast #177
£300 $468 €450 In Newcastle Forest, Co. Down (30x41cm-12x16in) s.verso board. 18-Sep-2 John Ross, Belfast #1
£300 $468 €450 Trees, Barnetts Park (30x41cm-12x16in) board. 18-Sep-2 John Ross, Belfast #126
£310 $484 €465 Summer landscape (25x36cm-10x14in) board. 18-Sep-2 John Ross, Belfast #169
£320 $499 €480 Reflection on the lagan (30x41cm-12x16in) board. 18-Sep-2 John Ross, Belfast #27
£320 $499 €480 Reflections on the river Dun (30x41cm-12x16in) 18-Sep-2 John Ross, Belfast #40
£320 $499 €480 Trees by the lagan (30x41cm-12x16in) board. 18-Sep-2 John Ross, Belfast #57
£320 $499 €480 Path by the lagan (30x41cm-12x16in) 18-Sep-2 John Ross, Belfast #89/R
£320 $499 €480 Trees by the road (30x41cm-12x16in) 18-Sep-2 John Ross, Belfast #91
£320 $499 €480 Painting by the Lagan (25x36cm-10x14in) board. 18-Sep-2 John Ross, Belfast #94
£350 $546 €525 Towpath by the Lagan (25x36cm-10x14in) board. 18-Sep-2 John Ross, Belfast #174
£380 $593 €570 Haystacks in the Mournes, Co. Down (36x56cm-14x22in) s. 18-Sep-2 John Ross, Belfast #15
£380 $593 €570 Shaded path (25x36cm-10x14in) s. board. 18-Sep-2 John Ross, Belfast #21/R
£400 $624 €600 Tree reflections on the Lagan (25x36cm-10x14in) s. board. 18-Sep-2 John Ross, Belfast #54
£400 $624 €600 Cottage on the Antrim Coast (30x38cm-12x15in) board. 18-Sep-2 John Ross, Belfast #160
£420 $655 €630 Cottages, Donegal (36x61cm-14x24in) s. board. 18-Sep-2 John Ross, Belfast #87
£420 $655 €630 Farm house in the Glens (33x46cm-13x18in) 18-Sep-2 John Ross, Belfast #180
£450 $702 €675 Tree reflections on the River Lagan (25x36cm-10x14in) board. 18-Sep-2 John Ross, Belfast #186/R
£500 $795 €750 Boats at Kilkeel Harbour (33x50cm-13x20in) s. board. 5-Mar-3 John Ross, Belfast #53
£550 $858 €825 Tree reflections (30x41cm-12x16in) board. 18-Sep-2 John Ross, Belfast #198/R

Works on paper
£250 $390 €375 Path by the lagan (28x36cm-11x14in) W/C. 18-Sep-2 John Ross, Belfast #30
£250 $390 €375 Summer woodlands (33x23cm-13x9in) s. W/C. 18-Sep-2 John Ross, Belfast #7
£250 $390 €375 Still life, bottles (28x38cm-11x15in) W/C. 18-Sep-2 John Ross, Belfast #11
£250 $390 €375 Farm buildings (25x36cm-10x14in) W/C. 18-Sep-2 John Ross, Belfast #38
£250 $390 €375 Playing golf, Malone (25x36cm-10x14in) W/C. 18-Sep-2 John Ross, Belfast #55
£250 $390 €375 Summer by the lagan (25x36cm-10x14in) W/C. 18-Sep-2 John Ross, Belfast #100
£260 $406 €390 Belfast Docks (28x38cm-11x15in) pen ink W/C wash. 18-Sep-2 John Ross, Belfast #107
£260 $406 €390 Painting in Belvoir Park (23x36cm-9x14in) W/C. 18-Sep-2 John Ross, Belfast #113/R
£260 $406 €390 Old bridge by the woods (20x28cm-8x11in) W/C. 18-Sep-2 John Ross, Belfast #132
£280 $437 €420 Mountains in the mournes (30x41cm-12x16in) s. W/C. 18-Sep-2 John Ross, Belfast #20
£280 $437 €420 Still life (36x46cm-14x18in) W/C. 18-Sep-2 John Ross, Belfast #58
£280 $437 €420 Shadows over the path by the Lagan (28x38cm-11x15in) W/C. 18-Sep-2 John Ross, Belfast #97
£300 $468 €450 Summer shadows (28x36cm-11x14in) W/C. 18-Sep-2 John Ross, Belfast #4
£300 $468 €450 Winter reflection on the lagan (33x25cm-13x10in) W/C. 18-Sep-2 John Ross, Belfast #32
£300 $468 €450 Female nude study (25x36cm-10x14in) pastel. 18-Sep-2 John Ross, Belfast #143
£320 $499 €480 Still life, roses (41x30cm-16x12in) W/C. 18-Sep-2 John Ross, Belfast #8/R
£320 $499 €480 Path by a lagan (28x36cm-11x14in) W/C. 18-Sep-2 John Ross, Belfast #9
£320 $499 €480 Rocky Foreshore, Donegal (25x36cm-10x14in) W/C. 18-Sep-2 John Ross, Belfast #18
£320 $499 €480 Thatched cottage in the glens (30x41cm-12x16in) W/C. 18-Sep-2 John Ross, Belfast #59
£320 $499 €480 Still life, vase, jug and plate (33x25cm-13x10in) W/C. 18-Sep-2 John Ross, Belfast #109
£350 $546 €525 Old harbour (28x38cm-11x15in) W/C. 18-Sep-2 John Ross, Belfast #25
£350 $546 €525 Bridge at Drumbeg (28x38cm-11x15in) W/C. 18-Sep-2 John Ross, Belfast #47
£350 $546 €525 Cottages, Donegal (28x41cm-11x16in) mixed media. 18-Sep-2 John Ross, Belfast #120
£350 $546 €525 Fishing at the pier (28x38cm-11x15in) W/C. 18-Sep-2 John Ross, Belfast #142
£400 $624 €600 Harbour (28x38cm-11x15in) W/C. 18-Sep-2 John Ross, Belfast #86/R
£400 $624 €600 Female nude study (36x46cm-14x18in) pastel. 18-Sep-2 John Ross, Belfast #39
£400 $624 €600 Old farm in the Glens (30x41cm-12x16in) W/C. 18-Sep-2 John Ross, Belfast #92/R
£400 $624 €600 Farmhouse near the Co. Antrim Coast (30x41cm-12x16in) W/C. 18-Sep-2 John Ross, Belfast #159
£420 $655 €630 Farm in the Glens (30x41cm-12x16in) W/C. 18-Sep-2 John Ross, Belfast #70/R
£520 $811 €780 Female Nude study, girl reading (36x30cm-14x12in) W/C. 18-Sep-2 John Ross, Belfast #115/R
£580 $905 €870 Female nude study (46x38cm-18x15in) pastel. 18-Sep-2 John Ross, Belfast #28/R
£600 $936 €900 Portrait of Leslie Zukor (46x33cm-18x13in) mono. pastel. 18-Sep-2 John Ross, Belfast #34
£650 $1014 €975 Glengariff Bay (30x46cm-12x18in) s. W/C. 18-Sep-2 John Ross, Belfast #33
£1000 $1560 €1500 Waiting for the bus, Drumbeg (28x36cm-11x14in) W/C. 18-Sep-2 John Ross, Belfast #12/R est:150-180

BUCHNER, Carl (1821-?) German
£609 $943 €914 Portrait of two girls (65x52cm-26x20in) mono. i.d.1945 verso. 9-Dec-2 Philippe Schuler, Zurich #3887/R (S.FR 1400)

BUCHNER, Carl (1921-) South African
£243 $380 €365 Still life of flowers (44x34cm-17x13in) s. board. 11-Nov-2 Stephan Welz, Johannesburg #455 (SA.R 3800)
£276 $431 €414 White mosque with palm trees (44x58cm-17x23in) s. canvas on board. 15-Oct-2 Stephan Welz, Johannesburg #199 est:2000-2500 (SA.R 4500)
£322 $508 €483 Two boats sailing side by side (41x58cm-16x23in) s. board. 1-Apr-3 Stephan Welz, Johannesburg #487/R est:4000-6000 (SA.R 4000)
£559 $900 €839 Harlequin with a white hat (24x14cm-9x6in) s. panel. 12-May-3 Stephan Welz, Johannesburg #353 est:3000-5000 (SA.R 6500)
£1367 $2159 €2051 Harlequin musician (75x60cm-30x24in) s. 1-Apr-3 Stephan Welz, Johannesburg #489/R est:7000-10000 (SA.R 17000)
£1768 $2794 €2652 Harlequin on a green chaise longue (68x47cm-27x19in) s. board. 1-Apr-3 Stephan Welz, Johannesburg #488/R est:6000-9000 (SA.R 22000)
£1892 $3046 €2838 Portrait of a yong man in a blue vest (90x60cm-35x24in) s. board. 12-May-3 Stephan Welz, Johannesburg #453/R est:8000-12000 (SA.R 22000)

BUCHNER, Gustav Johann (1880-1951) German
£490 $784 €750 View of a lake in wooded landscape (85x125cm-33x49in) s.d.1913 lit. 10-Jan-3 Allgauer, Kempten #1556/R

BUCHNER, Hans (1856-1941) German
£828 $1292 €1300 Carnations (78x98cm-31x39in) s.i. lit. 8-Nov-2 Auktionhaus Georg Rehm, Augsburg #8028/R

BUCHNER, Rudolf (1894-1962) Austrian
£331 $540 €500 Zuidersee, Holland (86x127cm-34x50in) s.d.1940 verso plywood. 28-Jan-3 Dorotheum, Vienna #110/R
£621 $993 €900 Landscape (51x72cm-20x28in) s. bears d.5 panel. 11-Mar-3 Dorotheum, Vienna #114/R

Works on paper
£331 $540 €500 Semmering (45x60cm-18x24in) s.d.1942 W/C gouache. 28-Jan-3 Dorotheum, Vienna #125/R

BUCHS, Raymond (1878-1958) Swiss
£563 $924 €816 Le cheval blanc et le Ruckleberg (54x59cm-21x23in) s. board. 4-Jun-3 Fischer, Luzern #2020 (S.FR 1200)
£845 $1386 €1225 Still life with cup, apples and glasses (44x53cm-17x21in) s.d.40 board. 4-Jun-3 Fischer, Luzern #2021/R est:2000-3000 (S.FR 1800)
£1204 $1938 €1746 L'eglise de Tavel (62x51cm-24x20in) s. 9-May-3 Dobiaschofsky, Bern #96/R (S.FR 2600)

BUCHSEL, Elisabeth (1867-1957) German
£449 $682 €700 Man with dog on beach (20x33cm-8x13in) i. verso board. 17-Aug-2 Hans Stahl, Toestorf #67/R

BUCHSER, Frank (1828-1890) Swiss
£1870 $2898 €2805 Portrait of Franz Ludwig Flury (31x26cm-12x10in) canvas on board lit.prov. 9-Dec-2 Philippe Schuler, Zurich #3806/R est:3000-5000 (S.FR 4300)
£7075 $11462 €12524 Dark skinned boy (41x3cm-16x1in) 26-May-3 Sotheby's, Zurich #34/R est:15000-20000 (S.FR 15000)
£17467 $27424 €26201 Portrait of man and woman (115x91cm-45x36in) one s.i.d.Fev 14 two. 25-Nov-2 Sotheby's, Zurich #6/R est:40000-60000 (S.FR 40000)
£18519 $29815 €26853 Widow of Zahara (77x65cm-30x26in) mono. lit. 9-May-3 Dobiaschofsky, Bern #63/R est:60000 (S.FR 40000)

BUCHTA, Alfred (1880-1952) Italian/Austrian
£353 $554 €550 Still life with flowers and fruit (35x41cm-14x16in) s. board. 21-Nov-2 Dorotheum, Vienna #160/R

BUCHTER, C (19th C) ?
£1020 $1622 €1500 Bab el Mansour, Maroc (23x26cm-9x10in) s. canvas on cardboard. 24-Mar-3 Rabourdin & Choppin de Janvry, Paris #155/R est:1000-1200

BUCK, Adam (1759-1833) British
Miniatures
£1000 $1600 €1450 Portrait of an officer of The Light Company (5x5cm-2x2in) mono. gold pendant frame. 17-May-3 New Orleans Auction, New Orleans #1/R est:1200-1800
£3000 $4710 €4500 Young lady seated on a red covered sofa (8cm-3xin) s.d.1805 gilt metal frame prov. 10-Dec-2 Christie's, London #205/R est:1000-2000
Works on paper
£460 $764 €690 Portrait of a man quarter length (10x8cm-4x3in) d.1820 pencil wash. 10-Jun-3 Sworder & Son, Bishops Stortford #530/R
£520 $868 €754 Study of a lady holding a basket of roses (19x14cm-7x6in) s.d.1825 pencil bodycol. 23-Jun-3 Bonhams, Bath #89
£1600 $2464 €2400 Portrait of young man (38x28cm-15x11in) s.d.1801 pencil W/C. 25-Oct-2 Gorringes, Lewes #866
£3000 $4620 €4500 Portrait of Lieutenant Bradley (30x23cm-12x9in) pencil W/C. 25-Oct-2 Gorringes, Lewes #867

BUCK, Claude (1890-1974) American
£649 $1000 €974 Siren (25x20cm-10x8in) s. panel painted c.1925. 8-Sep-2 Treadway Gallery, Cincinnati #727/R
£778 $1300 €1128 Woman in blue in wooded interior. Woman in atmospheric landscape (64x25cm-25x10in) one d.1932 one i.verso board prov. 17-Jun-3 John Moran, Pasadena #122a est:800-1200
£844 $1300 €1266 Recital (81x132cm-32x52in) s.d.1929. 8-Sep-2 Treadway Gallery, Cincinnati #729/R
£844 $1300 €1266 Harvest (18x15cm-7x6in) s.d.1917 panel. 8-Sep-2 Treadway Gallery, Cincinnati #725/R
£1198 $2000 €1737 Still life of marine objects (122x53cm-48x21in) masonite prov. 17-Jun-3 John Moran, Pasadena #120b est:3000-4000
£1786 $2750 €2679 Angst (43x38cm-17x15in) s.d.1929 panel. 8-Sep-2 Treadway Gallery, Cincinnati #726/R est:1500-2500
£12579 $20000 €18869 Gossips (56x66cm-22x26in) s. board painted c.1940 exhib. 4-May-3 Treadway Gallery, Cincinnati #632/R est:8000-10000

BUCK, Evariste de (1892-1974) Belgian
£2778 $4417 €4000 Paysage avec coude de la Lys (150x200cm-59x79in) s. 29-Apr-3 Campo & Campo, Antwerp #50/R est:8000-12000

BUCK, Frederick (1771-1840) Irish
Miniatures
£1300 $2015 €1950 Militia officer, possibly Welsh (7cm-3xin) mono.verso gold frame oval. 1-Oct-2 Bonhams, New Bond Street #219/R est:800-1200
£1500 $2430 €2250 Officer, possibly of the Corneille family of Ballygarane (6cm-2xin) gilt metal frame. 22-May-3 Bonhams, New Bond Street #85/R est:500-700
£2500 $4100 €3625 Young lady in ruffled bordered white silk dress (7cm-3xin) gilt metal frame prov. 3-Jun-3 Christie's, London #140/R est:1500-2500

BUCK, Jon (1951-) British
Sculpture
£1100 $1815 €1595 Raven head (61cm-24in) s. bronze. 3-Jul-3 Christie's, Kensington #613 est:400-600
£2000 $3300 €2900 Embrace II (25cm-10in) s.num.1/9 green pat. bronze. 3-Jul-3 Christie's, Kensington #612/R est:600-800
£2800 $4620 €4060 Three figures embracing (48cm-19in) s.num.2/8 green pat. bronze. 3-Jul-3 Christie's, Kensington #605/R est:800-1200
£4000 $6600 €5800 Two men embracing (58cm-23in) s.num.1/5 green pat. bronze. 3-Jul-3 Christie's, Kensington #610/R est:1000-1500

BUCK, Rafael de (1902-1986) Belgian
Works on paper
£317 $506 €440 Ladies on the terrace (23x30cm-9x12in) s. W/C. 17-May-3 De Vuyst, Lokeren #120
£432 $691 €600 Masked ball (68x48cm-27x19in) s. W/C. 17-May-3 De Vuyst, Lokeren #117

BUCK, Samuel and Nathaniel (18th C) British
Prints
£2000 $3120 €3000 Panorama of London from the new bridge of Westminster. black white engraving five sheets framed together. 14-Apr-3 Hamilton Osborne King, Dublin #1436/R est:1000-1500

BUCK, William H (1840-1888) American
£24359 $38000 €36539 Wooden pier, Louisiana bayou (46x84cm-18x33in) s. 12-Oct-2 Neal Auction Company, New Orleans #393/R est:30000-50000
£27564 $43000 €41346 Louisiana landscape by moonlight (46x76cm-18x30in) s. exhib. prov. 20-Sep-2 New Orleans Auction, New Orleans #1226/R est:40000-60000
£90323 $140000 €135485 View of Louisiana (61x102cm-24x40in) s. indis d. 4-Dec-2 Sotheby's, New York #112/R est:75000-100000

BUCKEN, Peter (1831-1915) German
£449 $704 €700 After the storm (63x95cm-25x37in) 21-Nov-2 Van Ham, Cologne #1504

BUCKERT, M W (20th C) German
£482 $767 €700 Moored boat (35x47cm-14x19in) s.d.24 Juli 1923 board. 10-Mar-3 Sotheby's, Amsterdam #263/R

BUCKHAM, Lynn (1918-1982) American
Works on paper
£1795 $2800 €2693 Couple in Spanish interior (48x71cm-19x28in) gouache pencil board. 9-Nov-2 Illustration House, New York #122/R est:2000-3000

BUCKINGHAM, George Herbert (20th C) British
£400 $632 €600 Midsummer at Weston Mill Northampton, 1929 (26x36cm-10x14in) s. 27-Nov-2 Peter Wilson, Nantwich #59

BUCKLER, Charles E (1869-?) Canadian/American
£380 $600 €570 Sunset (30x38cm-12x15in) s. 17-Nov-2 CRN Auctions, Cambridge #40/R

BUCKLER, John Chessel (1793-1894) British
Works on paper
£800 $1304 €1160 Transept of the church of Saint Cross, near Winchester. Choir of the church of Saint Cross (37x27cm-15x11in) s.d.1829 W/C over pencil pair. 21-Jul-3 Bonhams, Bath #7/R

BUCKLER, William (fl.1836-1856) British
Works on paper
£280 $437 €420 Portrait of a lady in evening dress, holding gloves (55x39cm-22x15in) s. W/C. 18-Sep-2 Cheffins Grain & Comins, Cambridge #491/R

BUCKLEY, Maura (20th C) Irish?
£739 $1227 €1050 Finnathie, Co. Donegal (29x39cm-11x15in) s. board. 10-Jun-3 James Adam, Dublin #270/R est:800-1200

BUCKLEY, Stephen (20th C) ?
£400 $624 €600 Rothapfel (46x62cm-18x24in) s.i.d.1987 verso acrylic collage construction prov. 27-Mar-3 Christie's, Kensington #645/R

BUCKLOW, Christopher (1957-) American
Photographs
£4294 $7000 €6441 Guest (102x76cm-40x30in) s.i. dye-destruction photogram in plexi-glass. 12-Feb-3 Christie's, Rockefeller NY #118/R est:4000-6000
£5696 $9000 €8544 Guests (41x51cm-16x20in) s.i.verso cibachrome photogram prov. 24-Apr-3 Phillips, New York #216/R est:4000-6000

BUCKMASTER, E (1897-1968) Australian
£854 $1306 €1281 River valley, Pohangina (79x190cm-31x75in) s. 21-Aug-2 Dunbar Sloane, Auckland #6/R est:2800-3500 (NZ.D 2800)
£1296 $1982 €1944 Landscape, Mount Ruapehu and Ohakhu (83x150cm-33x59in) s. board. 21-Aug-2 Dunbar Sloane, Auckland #9/R est:4500-6000 (NZ.D 4250)
£1707 $2612 €2561 Floral still life (85x62cm-33x24in) s. 21-Aug-2 Dunbar Sloane, Auckland #60/R est:1000-2000 (NZ.D 5600)

BUCKMASTER, Ernest (1897-1968) Australian
£627 $978 €941 Hollyford valley (75x90cm-30x35in) s. board. 7-Nov-2 International Art Centre, Auckland #52/R est:3000-5000 (NZ.D 2000)
£717 $1090 €1076 Evening reflections (50x60cm-20x24in) s. 27-Aug-2 Goodman, Sydney #52/R (A.D 2000)
£877 $1368 €1316 Mt Ruapheu (67x100cm-26x39in) s. canvasboard prov. 27-Mar-3 International Art Centre, Auckland #75/R (NZ.D 2500)
£877 $1368 €1316 Mt Cook and Tasman Valley (65x91cm-26x36in) s. canvasboard prov. 27-Mar-3 International Art Centre, Auckland #76/R (NZ.D 2500)
£923 $1440 €1385 Vase of flowers (76x55cm-30x22in) s. 8-Apr-3 Christie's, Melbourne #271/R est:3000-5000 (A.D 2400)
£1000 $1610 €1450 Old barn (32x62cm-13x24in) s.d.26 board. 12-May-3 Joel, Victoria #265 est:1500-2000 (A.D 2500)
£1075 $1634 €1613 Early morning mist landscape (65x88cm-26x35in) s. board. 27-Aug-2 Goodman, Sydney #219/R est:3000-5000 (A.D 3000)
£1097 $1712 €1646 Mt. Tara Tara (72x97cm-28x38in) s. board. 7-Nov-2 International Art Centre, Auckland #51/R est:4000-7000 (NZ.D 3500)
£1339 $2116 €2009 By the river (54x72cm-21x28in) s. board. 18-Nov-2 Goodman, Sydney #176 est:5000-8000 (A.D 3750)
£1410 $2200 €2115 Jindabyne (71x91cm-28x36in) s.i.on stretcher. 20-Sep-2 New Orleans Auction, New Orleans #507/R est:2500-4000
£1413 $2077 €2120 Towards Akaroa (76x110cm-30x43in) s. prov. 19-Jun-2 Watson's, Christchurch #30/R est:5000-7500 (NZ.D 4325)
£1434 $2179 €2151 Still life, vase of flowers (82x64cm-32x25in) s. 27-Aug-2 Goodman, Sydney #150 est:5000-8000 (A.D 4000)
£1453 $2064 €2180 Mt Ruapehu and Ohakune (79x111cm-31x44in) s. prov. 21-Nov-1 Watson's, Christchurch #56/R est:7000-10000 (NZ.D 5000)
£1491 $2267 €2237 Afternoon light (69x92cm-27x36in) s. 19-Aug-2 Joel, Victoria #151/R est:3500-4500 (A.D 4250)
£1500 $2355 €2250 Autumn still life (53x74cm-21x29in) s.d.1933 prov. 25-Nov-2 Christie's, Melbourne #292/R est:4000-6000 (A.D 4200)
£1600 $2576 €2320 Old Bacchus Marsch quarry (68x83cm-27x33in) s. board. 12-May-3 Joel, Victoria #327 est:3000-4000 (A.D 4000)
£1916 $3008 €2874 Azaleas (77x54cm-30x21in) s. 15-Apr-3 Lawson Menzies, Sydney #56/R est:2000-3000 (A.D 5000)
£2200 $3542 €3190 Still life with bronze lion (101x75cm-40x30in) s. 12-May-3 Joel, Victoria #342/R est:6000-8000 (A.D 5500)
£2400 $3864 €3480 Coldstream landscape (66x87cm-26x34in) s. board. 12-May-3 Joel, Victoria #304 est:4000-5000 (A.D 6000)
£2456 $3733 €3684 Autumn haze, Kallista, Vic (67x91cm-26x36in) s.d.1959. 19-Aug-2 Joel, Victoria #170 est:7000-8000 (A.D 7000)
£2800 $4508 €4200 Quarry, Lilydale (64x82cm-25x32in) s. 6-May-3 Christie's, Melbourne #351a/R est:3000-5000 (A.D 7000)
£5344 $8443 €8016 Pink rhododendrons (80x57cm-31x22in) s. 2-Apr-3 Christie's, Melbourne #29/R est:4000-6000 (A.D 14000)
£9200 $14812 €13800 Morning along the Goulburn Thornton towards Eildon, Victoria (75x117cm-30x46in) s. s.i.verso canvas on board prov. 6-May-3 Christie's, Melbourne #112/R est:10000-15000 (A.D 23000)

Works on paper
£1000 $1610 €1450 Creek reflections (51x64cm-20x25in) s. W/C. 12-May-3 Joel, Victoria #382 est:2500-3500 (A.D 2500)

BUCKNER, Richard (1812-1883) British
£1500 $2340 €2250 Portrait of a boy, possibly the Viscount Newry and Morne (47x43cm-19x17in) s. painted oval. 14-Apr-3 Hamilton Osborne King, Dublin #1492/R est:1000-1500
£2623 $4250 €3803 Italian piper (74x61cm-29x24in) s. i.verso. 21-May-3 Doyle, New York #166/R est:3000-5000
£3500 $5460 €5250 Portrait of Francis Jack, 2nd Earl of Kilmorey (75x62cm-30x24in) s. 14-Apr-3 Hamilton Osborne King, Dublin #1508/R est:3000-5000
£4800 $7392 €7200 Glass of wine in the Roman campagna (82x98cm-32x39in) s. 5-Sep-2 Christie's, Kensington #310/R est:3000-5000
£25000 $39500 €37500 Portrait of Princess Marie Baden, Duchess of Hamilton (117x90cm-46x35in) prov. 28-Nov-2 Sotheby's, London #187/R est:4000-6000

BUDACH, Martha (1864-?) German
£417 $654 €650 Still life of flowers with sunflowers and dahlias in stone jug (80x60cm-31x24in) s. 21-Nov-2 Van Ham, Cologne #1502

BUDD, Rachel (1960-) British
£400 $668 €580 Sleeping in the nursery (127x117cm-50x46in) s.i.d.June 91 verso. 17-Jun-3 Bonhams, Knightsbridge #84

BUDELOT, Philippe (18/19th C) French
£714 $1043 €1100 Paysage a la clairiere avec un bucheron et son ane (18x29cm-7x11in) cardboard. 11-Jun-2 Thierry & Lannon, Brest #106/R
£839 $1325 €1300 Promeneurs et chien dans un paysage (60x47cm-24x19in) 20-Dec-2 Tajan, Paris #171
£1111 $1578 €1800 Chasse au faucon (24x32cm-9x13in) s. 16-Mar-3 Eric Pillon, Calais #37/R

BUDICIN, S (20th C) German
£962 $1462 €1500 Shepherd with flock (30x40cm-12x16in) panel. 11-Jul-2 Hugo Ruef, Munich #596

BUDT, Victor de (1886-?) Belgian
Works on paper
£613 $968 €950 Paysage a la chaumiere. s.pastel. 17-Dec-2 Galerie Moderne, Brussels #715

BUDTZ-MOLLER, Carl (1882-1953) Danish
£257 $401 €386 Church interior, Venice. s. i.d.1920 verso. 11-Nov-2 Rasmussen, Vejle #480 (D.KR 3000)
£258 $407 €387 Study of male nude (115x76cm-45x30in) s. 13-Nov-2 Kunsthallen, Copenhagen #10 (D.KR 3000)
£304 $474 €456 Mending the nets (73x99cm-29x39in) s.d.1916. 23-Sep-2 Rasmussen, Vejle #298/R (D.KR 3600)
£326 $515 €489 Mountain landscape with farm (65x76cm-26x30in) s.d.1916. 17-Nov-2 Hindemae, Ullerslev #7201 (D.KR 3800)
£340 $538 €510 Bridge of Sigh in Venice (36x48cm-14x19in) s.i.d.1933. 2-Dec-2 Rasmussen, Copenhagen #1601/R (D.KR 4000)
£512 $789 €768 Washerwomen at the waterfall in Anticoli (79x102cm-31x40in) s. 4-Sep-2 Kunsthallen, Copenhagen #163/R (D.KR 6000)
£919 $1471 €1379 From the washing place in Anticoli (78x109cm-31x43in) s. 13-Jan-3 Rasmussen, Vejle #192/R (D.KR 10500)
£991 $1506 €1487 Summer's day at Piazza della Erbe, Verona (74x64cm-29x25in) s. 27-Aug-2 Rasmussen, Copenhagen #1662/R (D.KR 11500)
£1034 $1571 €1551 Canale Grande Venezia (54x77cm-21x30in) s.d.1950. 27-Aug-2 Rasmussen, Copenhagen #1656/R est:12000-18000 (D.KR 12000)

BUEHR, Karl Albert (1866-1952) American
£2866 $4500 €4299 Winding stream (63x77cm-25x30in) s. s.i.verso. 20-Nov-2 Christie's, Los Angeles #35/R est:5000-7000
£5493 $7800 €8240 Lady with parasol (25x20cm-10x8in) board. 8-Aug-1 Barridorf, Portland #51/R est:3000-5000

BUEL, Hubert (1915-1984) American
Works on paper
£409 $650 €593 Russian river (36x53cm-14x21in) s. W/C. 3-May-3 Harvey Clar, Oakland #1203
£645 $1000 €968 Model A coupe parked near bar in landscape (36x48cm-14x19in) s.d.1945 W/C prov. 29-Oct-2 John Moran, Pasadena #770

BUELL, Alfred (1910-1996) American
£962 $1500 €1443 Couple embracing in front of fireplace (46x43cm-18x17in) s. canvasboard. 9-Nov-2 Illustration House, New York #121/R est:1500-2500
£2484 $4000 €3726 Kneeling young woman with top untied (51x38cm-20x15in) s. board painted c.1940. 10-May-3 Illustration House, New York #116/R est:4000-6000

BUENO FERRER, Pascual (1930-) Spanish
£387 $612 €600 Looking out of the window (55x45cm-22x18in) s. 17-Dec-2 Durán, Madrid #73/R
£449 $709 €700 Entering Barcelona harbour (61x73cm-24x29in) s. 19-Nov-2 Durán, Madrid #58/R

BUENO, Antonio (1918-1984) Italian
£2721 $4327 €4000 Blond girl (20x18cm-8x7in) s. cardboard on canvas. 1-Mar-3 Meeting Art, Vercelli #483
£5782 $9194 €8500 Sailor (24x18cm-9x7in) s. masonite. 1-Mar-3 Meeting Art, Vercelli #749
£6090 $9439 €9500 Little sailor (30x19cm-12x7in) s. masonite. 4-Dec-2 Finarte, Milan #283/R est:6000
£6090 $9561 €9500 Head of girl (60x51cm-24x20in) s. 20-Nov-2 Pandolfini, Florence #60/R
£7051 $11071 €11000 Girl (50x40cm-20x16in) s. masonite painted 1973. 23-Nov-2 Meeting Art, Vercelli #487/R
£7432 $11595 €11000 After Picasso (30x20cm-12x8in) s. board. 28-Mar-3 Farsetti, Prato #505/R est:13000
£7692 $11923 €12000 Girl with white hat (39x29cm-15x11in) s. s.i.verso masonite. 4-Dec-2 Finarte, Milan #295/R est:8000
£7843 $12549 €12000 Blond girl (50x40cm-20x16in) s. masonite. 4-Jan-3 Meeting Art, Vercelli #528
£8333 $13250 €12000 Girl with hat and ribbon (50x40cm-20x16in) s. masonite. 1-May-3 Meeting Art, Vercelli #111
£8861 $14000 €14000 Girl with fur hat (50x40cm-20x16in) s. painted 1973. 30-Nov-2 Farsetti, Prato #745/R est:16000
£10897 $16891 €17000 Portrait of girl (50x40cm-20x16in) s. masonite. 4-Dec-2 Finarte, Milan #324/R est:14000

Sculpture
£1154 $1788 €1800 Little sailor (47cm-19in) crystal exec.1984. 4-Dec-2 Finarte, Milan #264/R

Works on paper
£570 $889 €900 Teenager (45x33cm-18x13in) s. pencil pastel exec.1969. 14-Sep-2 Meeting Art, Vercelli #470/R

£1282 $2013 €2000 Homage to Campigli (25x16cm-10x6in) s. pastel. 23-Nov-2 Meeting Art, Vercelli #382
£1519 $2370 €2400 Sailor (38x28cm-15x11in) s. pastel pencil. 14-Sep-2 Meeting Art, Vercelli #867/R
£1667 $2650 €2400 Violin player (50x31cm-20x12in) s. pastel. 1-May-3 Meeting Art, Vercelli #90
£2014 $3202 €2900 Profile (50x35cm-20x14in) s. pastel. 1-May-3 Meeting Art, Vercelli #304
£3205 $5032 €5000 Girl with green necklace (50x35cm-20x14in) s. mixed media cardboard. 23-Nov-2 Meeting Art, Vercelli #442/R

BUENO, Pascual (1930-) Spanish
£943 $1472 €1500 Bridge in Amsterdam (60x74cm-24x29in) s. s.i.verso. 23-Sep-2 Durán, Madrid #101/R

BUENO, Pedro (1910-1993) Spanish
£2516 $3874 €4000 Girl in blue (82x62cm-32x24in) s. lit. exhib. 22-Oct-2 Durán, Madrid #194/R

BUENO, Xavier (1915-1979) Spanish
£4808 $7548 €7500 Boy on a chair (60x43cm-24x17in) s. oil tempera paper on canvas. 23-Nov-2 Meeting Art, Vercelli #236/R est:7000
£5068 $7905 €7500 Girl with red bow (25x20cm-10x8in) s. 26-Mar-3 Finarte Semenzato, Milan #359/R
£5380 $8500 €8500 Girl (55x40cm-22x16in) s. board. 27-Nov-2 Dorotheum, Vienna #62/R est:6000-8000
£6241 $10111 €8800 Young girl (40x30cm-16x12in) s. s.i.d.1966 verso canvasboard prov. 26-May-3 Christie's, Milan #125/R est:2500-3500
£6329 $9873 €10000 Profile (25x30cm-10x12in) s. cardboard on canvas painted 1972. 14-Sep-2 Meeting Art, Vercelli #987/R
£6536 $10458 €10000 Still life (40x50cm-16x20in) s. s.i.d.1966 verso lit. 4-Jan-3 Meeting Art, Vercelli #750 est:10000
£7877 $12288 €11500 Boy (30x40cm-12x16in) s. board painted 1965. 10-Apr-3 Finarte Semenzato, Rome #148/R
£8333 $13083 €13000 Girl (40x30cm-16x12in) s. cardboard on canvas painted 1974. 23-Nov-2 Meeting Art, Vercelli #484/R est:10000
£8844 $14061 €13000 Girl screamming (25x30cm-10x12in) s. cardboard on canvas. 1-Mar-3 Meeting Art, Vercelli #494 est:10000
£9615 $15096 €15000 Dancer (70x50cm-28x20in) s. prov. 20-Nov-2 Pandolfini, Florence #51/R
£9677 $15290 €15000 Boy with accordion (55x50cm-22x20in) s. 18-Dec-2 Christie's, Rome #135/R est:20000
£10256 $16103 €16000 Seated boy (70x50cm-28x20in) s. s.i.verso. 20-Nov-2 Pandolfini, Florence #56/R est:18000
£12025 $19000 €19000 Girl (59x50cm-23x20in) s. canvas on cardboard. 30-Nov-2 Farsetti, Prato #756/R est:13000
£12258 $19368 €19000 Girl with bowl (46x41cm-18x16in) s. board prov. 18-Dec-2 Christie's, Rome #137/R est:20000
£12766 $20681 €18000 Maternita (70x50cm-28x20in) s. s.i.d.1965 verso prov.exhib.lit. 26-May-3 Christie's, Milan #240/R est:15000-20000
£12821 $20128 €20000 Girl (70x50cm-28x20in) s. s.i.d.1965 verso. 20-Nov-2 Pandolfini, Florence #57/R est:20000
£15385 $24154 €24000 Maternity (70x50cm-28x20in) s. 19-Nov-2 Finarte, Milan #253/R est:16000-20000

Works on paper
£1127 $1870 €1600 Bambina (65x45cm-26x18in) s. mixed media framed paper. 10-Jun-3 Finarte Semenzato, Milan #180/R est:800-1200

BUESEM, Jan Jansz (1600-c.1649) Dutch
£760 $1239 €1140 Topers playing a violin and smoking in a barn (25x34cm-10x13in) init. panel. 11-Feb-3 Bonhams, Knowle #73/R

BUFANO, Beniamino (1888-1970) American

Sculpture
£1923 $3000 €2885 Bird (21x8cm-8x3in) s. green brown pat bronze. 14-Oct-2 Butterfields, San Francisco #2075/R est:4000-6000
£2083 $3250 €3125 Blowfish (13x13cm-5x5in) s. brown pat bronze. 14-Oct-2 Butterfields, San Francisco #2077/R est:4000-6000
£2243 $3500 €3365 Rabbit (21x9cm-8x4in) s.i. brown pat bronze. 14-Oct-2 Butterfields, San Francisco #2076/R est:4000-6000
£2243 $3500 €3365 Elephant (16x10cm-6x4in) s.i. brown pat bronze. 14-Oct-2 Butterfields, San Francisco #2078/R est:4000-6000
£10256 $16000 €15384 Large snail (73x41cm-29x16in) s. green brown pat bronze. 14-Oct-2 Butterfields, San Francisco #2079/R est:10000-15000

BUFF, Conrad (1886-1975) American
£539 $900 €782 Mountain landscape (25x33cm-10x13in) s. board. 17-Jun-3 John Moran, Pasadena #16
£745 $1200 €1118 Southwest landscape (20x25cm-8x10in) estate st. board. 18-Feb-3 John Moran, Pasadena #118a
£968 $1500 €1452 Landscape (41x61cm-16x24in) s. board. 29-Oct-2 John Moran, Pasadena #699 est:1500-2500
£968 $1500 €1452 Landscape (41x61cm-16x24in) s. board. 29-Oct-2 John Moran, Pasadena #699a est:1500-2500
£1000 $1600 €1500 Bridge over Purple Valley, possibly near Taos, New Mexico. board. 11-Jan-3 Harvey Clar, Oakland #1220
£1078 $1800 €1563 Monument Valley landscape (41x61cm-16x24in) s. board. 17-Jun-3 John Moran, Pasadena #140 est:2000-3000
£1097 $1700 €1646 Mountain landscape (38x48cm-15x19in) estate st. 29-Oct-2 John Moran, Pasadena #736b est:1800-2500
£1198 $2000 €1737 Landscape (41x61cm-16x24in) s. board double-sided. 17-Jun-3 John Moran, Pasadena #140a est:2000-3000
£1398 $2250 €2097 Southwest landscape (41x61cm-16x24in) estate st. board. 18-Feb-3 John Moran, Pasadena #106 est:2000-3000
£1398 $2250 €2097 Southwest landscape (30x41cm-12x16in) s. board prov. 18-Feb-3 John Moran, Pasadena #111 est:1500-2000
£1553 $2500 €2330 Southwest landscape (30x41cm-12x16in) s. board prov. 18-Feb-3 John Moran, Pasadena #111a est:1500-2000
£1796 $3000 €2604 Spring landscape (30x41cm-12x16in) s. board. 17 Jun-3 John Moran, Pasadena #140b est:2000-3000
£1958 $3250 €2839 Still life with roses and other flowers in a vase (76x61cm-30x24in) s. oil pencil board prov. 11-Jun-3 Butterfields, San Francisco #4263/R est:3000-5000
£3915 $6500 €5677 Mountains by the lakeside (62x76cm-24x30in) s. board prov. 11-Jun-3 Butterfields, San Francisco #4282/R est:6000-8000

BUFFAGNOTTI, Carlo Antonio (1660-1710) Italian

Works on paper
£845 $1361 €1200 Fantasia con architettura classica e fontana con figure (24x24cm-9x9in) indis.sig. pen ink brown W/C. 12-May-3 Sotheby's, Milan #44/R

BUFFET, Bernard (1928-1999) French
£5128 $8000 €7692 Vase of flowers (28x15cm-11x6in) s.d.53. 30-Mar-3 Susanin's, Chicago #6063/R est:4000-5000
£7362 $12000 €11043 Les peupliers (64x100cm-25x39in) s.d.67 prov. 12-Feb-3 Sotheby's, New York #126/R est:15000-20000
£8434 $14000 €12229 Suburban street (48x64cm-19x25in) 13-Jun-3 Du Mouchelle, Detroit #2016/R est:7000-12000
£9740 $14221 €15000 Table with fruit (60x81cm-24x32in) s.d. prov. 12-Jun-2 Castellana, Madrid #101/R est:15000
£10323 $16000 €15485 Montagne, la cascade (96x129cm-38x51in) s.d.62 i.verso prov. 26-Sep-2 Christie's, Rockefeller NY #606/R est:18000-22000
£10692 $17000 €16038 Nature morte (55x33cm-22x13in) s.d.49 oil pencil prov. 27-Feb-3 Christie's, Rockefeller NY #78/R est:20000
£10897 $17000 €16346 Bouquet (63x52cm-25x20in) s.d.66 i.verso linen prov. 14-Oct-2 Butterfields, San Francisco #2024/R est:18000-22000
£11035 $18428 €16000 Bouquet de fleurs au pichet bleu (41x27cm-16x11in) s.d.94 s.i.d.verso panel. 10-Jul-3 Artcurial Briest, Paris #226/R est:13000-15000
£11724 $19579 €17000 Bouquet de roses jaune (46x33cm-18x13in) s. s.i.d.1993 verso panel. 10-Jul-3 Artcurial Briest, Paris #225/R est:15000-18000
£12414 $20732 €18000 Bouquet de fleurs jaunes (55x46cm-22x18in) s. s.i.d.95 verso panel. 10-Jul-3 Artcurial Briest, Paris #227/R est:18000-22000
£12676 $21043 €18000 Autoportrait au chevalet (18x14cm-7x6in) s.d. prov. 12-Jun-3 Tajan, Paris #39/R est:18000-22000
£12821 $20000 €19232 Le cirque (70x55cm-28x22in) s. prov. 6-Nov-2 Sotheby's, New York #348/R est:25000-35000
£13665 $21317 €20498 Matador (66x50cm-26x20in) s.d.63. 5-Nov-2 Bukowskis, Stockholm #301/R est:125000-150000 (S.KR 195000)
£14000 $21560 €21000 Vase de soucis (35x27cm-14x11in) s. board prov. 22-Oct-2 Sotheby's, London #255/R est:10000-12000
£14000 $23380 €20300 Fleurs dans un pichet (46x65cm-18x26in) s.d.52. 25-Jun-3 Christie's, London #220/R est:14000-16000
£14000 $23380 €20300 Fleurs jaunes (46x38cm-18x15in) s.d.57 panel prov. 24-Jun-3 Sotheby's, London #206/R est:15000-20000
£14194 $22000 €21291 Nature morte avec un boite (54x65cm-21x26in) s.d.48 oil pencil prov. 26-Sep-2 Christie's, Rockefeller NY #599/R est:18000-22000
£15337 $25000 €23006 Iris noirs (65x55cm-26x22in) s.d.57 prov. 12-Feb-3 Sotheby's, New York #132/R est:20000-30000
£17949 $28179 €28000 Vue de village (54x81cm-21x32in) s.d.70 panel prov. 10-Dec-2 Pierre Berge, Paris #55/R est:30000
£18000 $29520 €27000 Cicogne (117x89cm-46x35in) s.d.61 prov. 4-Feb-3 Christie's, London #364/R est:30000
£18000 $29520 €27000 Liliums et primeveres dans un pichet (73x55cm-29x22in) s.dd.1994. 4-Feb-3 Christie's, London #363/R est:25000
£18310 $26000 €27465 Marine (74x99cm-29x39in) 8-Aug-1 Barridorf, Portland #115/R est:20000-30000
£18500 $30340 €27750 Rechaud a alcool et lampe pigeon (50x65cm-20x26in) s.d.48 oil pencil brush ink prov. 5-Feb-3 Sotheby's, London #275/R est:18000
£19231 $30000 €28847 Le chateau d'Arc (97x130cm-38x51in) s.d.58 prov. 7-Nov-2 Christie's, Rockefeller NY #359/R est:35000-45000
£20000 $30800 €30000 Rue de L'Eglise (89x130cm-35x51in) s.d.1981 prov. 22-Oct-2 Sotheby's, London #256/R est:18000-25000
£20000 $32800 €30000 Loumanch, cote du Nord (89x130cm-35x51in) s.d.1973 prov. 4-Feb-3 Christie's, London #342/R est:35000
£20000 $32200 €30000 La corbeille (72x91cm-28x36in) s.d.63 prov. 6-May-3 Christie's, Melbourne #42/R est:45000-60000 (A.D 50000)
£22436 $35000 €33654 Nature morte a la cafetiere (81x100cm-32x39in) s.d.59 prov. 6-Nov-2 Sotheby's, New York #356/R est:40000-60000
£23006 $37500 €34509 Nature morte au compotier (92x65cm-36x26in) s.d.54 prov. 12-Feb-3 Sotheby's, New York #133/R est:25000-35000
£25000 $41000 €37500 Papillon (97x130cm-38x51in) s.d.57. 4-Feb-3 Christie's, London #331/R est:35000
£25000 $41750 €36250 Les Sables d'Olonne (89x130cm-35x51in) s.d.1972 i.verso prov.lit. 25-Jun-3 Christie's, London #237/R est:25000-35000

£25540 $40863 €35500 Pot fleuri (66x55cm-26x22in) s.d. 18-May-3 Eric Pillon, Calais #149/R
£25949 $40481 €41000 Mer a Saint-Cast (98x132cm-39x52in) s.d.65. 16-Sep-2 Horta, Bruxelles #121/R est:40000-60000
£26000 $43420 €37700 Roses dans vase de galle (81x60cm-32x24in) s.d.55 prov. 24-Jun-3 Sotheby's, London #207/R est:20000-30000
£26398 $42500 €39597 Doelan , le port a maree basse (89x130cm-35x51in) s.d.1973 i.verso prov. 7-May-3 Sotheby's, New York #415/R est:30000-40000
£26582 $42000 €42000 Clown (73x61cm-29x24in) s.d.1968. 27-Nov-2 Marc Kohn, Paris #47/R est:20000-30000
£27000 $45090 €39150 Torero (81x60cm-32x24in) s.d.1994 prov.exhib. 24-Jun-3 Sotheby's, London #212/R est:25000-35000
£34000 $56780 €49300 Tete de clown fond vert (73x60cm-29x24in) s.d.68 prov. 24-Jun-3 Sotheby's, London #211/R est:20000-30000
£35000 $58450 €50750 La lampe fleurie (81x117cm-32x46in) s.d.1991 prov.exhib. 24-Jun-3 Sotheby's, London #199/R est:35000-45000
£40000 $66800 €58000 Le rhinoceros (130x295cm-51x116in) s.d.55 prov.lit. 25-Jun-3 Christie's, London #236/R est:50000-70000
£45000 $75150 €65250 La croisette, Cannes (90x130cm-35x51in) s.d.60 prov. 25-Jun-3 Christie's, London #222/R est:50000-70000
£51899 $82000 €82000 Toreador (130x97cm-51x38in) s.d.1958. 27-Nov-2 Marc Kohn, Paris #41/R est:45000-70000
£54487 $85000 €81731 La place des voges (114x195cm-45x77in) s.d.1989 prov. 7-Nov-2 Christie's, Rockefeller NY #363/R est:60000-80000
£55901 $90000 €83852 Le port Cannes (96x129cm-38x51in) s.d.57 prov. 7-May-3 Sotheby's, New York #412/R est:70000-90000

Prints

£1899 $3000 €3000 Fleurs papillons (65x48cm-26x19in) s. num.3/150 col lithograph. 29-Nov-2 Drouot Estimations, Paris #6
£1923 $3000 €2885 New York II (68x49cm-27x19in) s.num.44/150 col lithograph. 7-Nov-2 Swann Galleries, New York #567/R est:4000-6000
£2308 $3600 €3462 Paris, le Sacre-Coeur (51x66cm-20x26in) s.num.56/150 col lithograph. 7-Nov-2 Swann Galleries, New York #566/R est:4000-6000
£2331 $3800 €3497 Arc de Triomphe (52x68cm-20x27in) s. num.78/150 col lithograph. 13-Feb-3 Christie's, Rockefeller NY #23/R
£2949 $4600 €4424 Paris, Saint Germain des Pres (52x66cm-20x26in) s.num.53/150 col lithograph. 7-Nov-2 Swann Galleries, New York #565/R est:3000-5000

Works on paper

£361 $589 €520 Marin a la casquette (31x22cm-12x9in) s.i.d.1930 chl ink. 19-Jul-3 Thierry & Lannon, Brest #30
£515 $814 €773 Hanged man (40x15cm-16x6in) s. conte. 3-Apr-3 Heffel, Vancouver #11/R (C.D 1200)
£521 $849 €750 Scene de marche a Audierne (31x22cm-12x9in) s.i.d.1930 chl. 19-Jul-3 Thierry & Lannon, Brest #31
£1316 $2132 €2000 Couteau Suisse au creux d'une main (16x23cm-6x9in) s. pencil dr tracing paper. 22-Jan-3 Tajan, Paris #209 est:2000-3000
£1395 $2217 €2050 Costume de ballet (64x50cm-25x20in) s.i.d.1969 Indian ink dr. 26-Feb-3 Artcurial Briest, Paris #101/R est:1800-2200
£2848 $4415 €4500 Nature morte aux anguilles (50x65cm-20x26in) s.d. ink prov. 28-Sep-2 Cornette de St.Cyr, Paris #149/R est:5000-6000
£4430 $7000 €7000 Quatre nus (53x42cm-21x17in) W/C exec.1958. 27-Nov-2 Marc Kohn, Paris #46/R est:6000-8000
£4895 $8175 €7000 Le tapir (50x73cm-20x29in) s.d.1953 pen Indian ink dr. 26-Jun-3 Tajan, Paris #160/R est:7000-9000
£8108 $12649 €12000 Cour de l'usine (65x50cm-26x20in) s.d.52 chl dr prov. 26-Mar-3 Tajan, Paris #41/R
£9500 $15865 €14250 Plage de Bretagne (50x68cm-20x27in) s.d.63 W/C ink crayon prov. 26-Jun-3 Christie's, London #446/R est:8000-12000
£11511 $18417 €16000 Vase de fleurs (65x50cm-26x20in) s.d. W/C gouache. 18-May-3 Eric Pillon, Calais #182/R
£13669 $21871 €19000 Vase d'anemones (65x50cm-26x20in) s.d. W/C. 18-May-3 Eric Pillon, Calais #181/R
£13878 $21789 €21650 Venise, La Salute (50x64cm-20x25in) s.i. s.i.verso graphite dr. 11-Dec-2 Artcurial Briest, Paris #548/R est:12000

BUFFIN, Carlos (19th C) French

£13608 $21228 €21500 Coin de marche a Courtrai (65x100cm-26x39in) s. 20-Oct-2 Mercier & Cie, Lille #318/R est:12000-15000

BUFFO POET, Margaret (?) Italian?

£1410 $2214 €2200 Venice (70x50cm-28x20in) s. board. 10-Dec-2 Della Rocca, Turin #268/R

BUGATTI, Rembrandt (1885-1916) Italian

Sculpture

£10417 $17188 €15000 Bouledogue Francais (13x8x13cm-5x3x5in) s.num.22 brown pat bronze st.f.A.A. Hebrard exec.c.1905 lit. 2-Jul-3 Artcurial Briest, Paris #28/R est:10000-12000
£21154 $32788 €33000 Oxen in the countryside (25x83cm-10x33in) s.d.1901 dark pat bronze. 5-Dec-2 Stadion, Trieste #761/R est:36000
£24113 $39064 €34000 Puma male (31x40cm-12x16in) i.base pat plaster. 23-May-3 Camard, Paris #112/R est:30500-38000
£26950 $43660 €38000 Deux chevres du Tibet (20x33x21cm-8x13x8in) s.d.1905 brown pat bronze st.f.A.A.Hebrard. 20-May-3 Christie's, Paris #28/R est:38000-50000
£37419 $59123 €58000 Leopard (21x30x12cm-8x12x5in) s.st.f.Hebrard num.3 brown pat bronze. 18-Dec-2 Ferri, Paris #32/R est:70000
£63830 $103404 €90000 Elephant blanc (14x21cm-6x8in) s.num.B 3 black pat bronze st.f.Hebrard prov. 20-May-3 Christie's, Paris #30/R est:60000-80000
£88652 $143617 €125000 Ours brun la patte droite en avant (21x31x11cm-8x12x4in) s.num.7 black pat bronze exec.c.1913 st.f.A.A.Hebrard prov. 20-May-3 Christie's, Paris #29/R est:90000-110000
£133803 $222113 €190000 Petit leopard marchant (24x42x9cm-9x17x4in) s.i.num.5 brown pat bronze st.f.A.A. Hebrard exec.c.1910 exhib. 12-Jun-3 Tajan, Paris #10/R est:200000-250000
£295775 $490986 €420000 Lionne a la boule (34x60x20cm-13x24x8in) s.st.f.A.A. Hebrard green brown pat bronze rec. base exhib.lit. 12-Jun-3 Tajan, Paris #8/R est:340000-380000

Works on paper

£347 $573 €500 Bison (18x22cm-7x9in) st. black crayon. 1-Jul-3 Claude Aguttes, Neuilly #115/R

BUGER, Adolf (1885-?) German

£253 $392 €400 Three naked women by water (19x25cm-7x10in) s. lit. board. 27-Sep-2 Auktionhaus Georg Rehm, Augsburg #8018/R

BUGLIONI, Benedetto (1461-1521) Italian

Sculpture

£30323 $47910 €47000 Madonna and Child (71x48x5cm-28x19x2in) painted ceramic. 19-Dec-2 Semenzato, Venice #71/R est:60000

BUHAN, Jean Paul le (1946-) French

£319 $533 €450 Bouelles, bois graves et peints (52x44cm-20x17in) s. acrylic on wood engraving. 18-Jun-3 Charbonneaux, Paris #116

BUHLER, Eduard (1853-1912) Swiss

£260 $403 €390 Landscape with Eiger and cows in morning light (33x42cm-13x17in) i. verso board. 24-Sep-2 Koller, Zurich #6623 (S.FR 600)

BUHLER, Robert (1916-1989) British

£350 $553 €525 Deck chairs, Camaione (41x51cm-16x20in) s.i. d.1975 verso prov. 12-Nov-2 Rosebery Fine Art, London #680
£2500 $3900 €3750 Albert Bridge at night (63x76cm-25x30in) s. prov. 25-Mar-3 Bonhams, New Bond Street #143/R est:2000-3000

BUHLMANN, A (?) ?

£1000 $1630 €1450 Alpine landscape with waterfall. Alpine lake scene (31x42cm-12x17in) s. pair. 16-Jul-3 James Thompson, Kirby Lonsdale #201

BUHLMANN, Johann Rudolf (1802-1890) Swiss

£11321 $18113 €16982 Rome from the south west (78x110cm-31x43in) s.d. 17-Mar-3 Philippe Schuler, Zurich #4504/R est:12000-15000 (S.FR 24000)

BUHLMAYER, Conrad (1835-1883) Austrian

£1351 $2108 €2000 Returning home before the storm (50x84cm-20x33in) s. lit. 28-Mar-3 Karrenbauer, Konstanz #1718 est:800
£3096 $4829 €4644 In the field (60x84cm-24x33in) s. 11-Sep-2 Kieselbach, Budapest #28/R (H.F 1200000)

BUHOT, Felix (1847-1898) French

Prints

£2569 $4085 €3700 Japonisme. eau forte aquatint exec.1885. 29-Apr-3 Piasa, Paris #138/R est:3000

BUHOT, Louis Charles Hippolyte (1815-1865) French

Sculpture

£1200 $1860 €1800 Eagle and the Source (56cm-22in) s. pat bronze rouge marble circular socle base. 29-Oct-2 Bonhams, New Bond Street #230/R est:1000-1500

BUI XUAN PHAI (1920-1988) Vietnamese

Works on paper

£994 $1531 €1491 Actress of Cheo opera (13x9cm-5x4in) s.d.85 gouache on board. 27-Oct-2 Christie's, Hong Kong #41/R est:15000-20000 (HK.D 12000)

BUICK, Robin (20th C) British?
Sculpture
£3425 $5377 €5000 Untitled (15x46cm-6x18in) bronze. 15-Apr-3 De Veres Art Auctions, Dublin #252/R est:4000-5000

BUISSERET, Louis (1888-1956) Belgian
£962 $1490 €1500 Espagnole (57x47cm-22x19in) s. i.verso. 9-Dec-2 Horta, Bruxelles #419 est:2000-2500
£1164 $1828 €1700 Les condodines (50x40cm-20x16in) s. 15-Apr-3 Galerie Moderne, Brussels #344/R est:800-1000
£1192 $1943 €1800 Jeune femme de profil (44x37cm-17x15in) s.d.1933 panel. 17-Feb-3 Horta, Bruxelles #95
£1295 $2072 €1800 Academie feminine (180x140cm-71x55in) 19-May-3 Horta, Bruxelles #500 est:400-900
£2911 $4600 €4600 La fille au verre de vin (70x60cm-28x24in) s. panel. 26-Nov-2 Palais de Beaux Arts, Brussels #52/R est:4500-6000
Works on paper
£387 $612 €600 Jeune femme a la robe blanche (29x19cm-11x7in) s.d.1940 pencil W/C gouache. 17-Dec-2 Palais de Beaux Arts, Brussels #464
£1154 $1812 €1800 Tete de femme. s.i. pastel. 19-Nov-2 Servarts Themis, Bruxelles #124
£1274 $1987 €2000 Nu assis (47x59cm-19x23in) s. mixed media. 11-Nov-2 Horta, Bruxelles #168 est:2500-3500

BUISSON, Kasimir (1970-) French
£481 $755 €750 Untitled (50x70cm-20x28in) init.d.2000 verso acrylic. 23-Nov-2 Meeting Art, Vercelli #326/R

BUKOVAC, Vlacho (1855-1923) Yugoslavian
£11998 $19077 €17997 Portrait of Martina Lovricova (54x44cm-21x17in) s.i.d.1917. 8-Mar-3 Dorotheum, Prague #153/R est:150000-230000 (C.KR 550000)
£14194 $22000 €21291 Pharaoh's favourite (51x69cm-20x27in) s. 30-Oct-2 Christie's, Rockefeller NY #101/R est:10000-15000
£19620 $30607 €29430 Toast (59x78cm-23x31in) s. 12-Oct-2 Dorotheum, Prague #36/R est:180000-270000 (C.KR 950000)

BULCKE, Émile (1875-1963) Belgian
£2000 $3260 €3000 Portrait of a young boy holding a whip (157x89cm-62x35in) s.d.1921. 12-Feb-3 Bonhams, Knightsbridge #318/R est:2000-3000

BULCKE, Guy van den (1931-) Belgian
£667 $1060 €980 Anser Anser (159x220cm-63x87in) s.d.mai 76 verso. 24-Mar-3 Bernaerts, Antwerp #856

BULCKE, Guy van den (attrib) (1931-) Belgian
£253 $395 €400 Composition (116x89cm-46x35in) 16-Sep-2 Amberes, Antwerp #182

BULGARINI, Bartolomeo di Messer (c.1300-1378) Italian
£46000 $72220 €69000 Crucifixion with Madonna ad Saint John the Baptist (27x18cm-11x7in) oil gold ground panel. 10-Dec-2 Bonhams, New Bond Street #324/R est:15000-20000

BULL, Agnes R (fl.1913-1915) British
Works on paper
£270 $437 €392 Listen - children and fairies in woodland glade (39x29cm-15x11in) s. W/C. 29-Jul-3 Holloways, Banbury #327

BULL, Charles Livingston (1874-1932) American
Works on paper
£443 $700 €665 Great horned owl (49x32cm-19x13in) s. W/C wash ink on board. 3-Apr-3 Christie's, Rockefeller NY #206/R
£823 $1300 €1235 Black bear and cubs climbing and playing on a tree (51x36cm-20x14in) s. chl W/C prov.lit. 3-Apr-3 Christie's, Rockefeller NY #156/R est:2000-3000
£943 $1500 €1415 Allendy's calvary in Palestine (74x99cm-29x39in) s. pastel exec.c.1910. 2-Mar-3 Toomey, Oak Park #708/R est:1500-2500
£1392 $2200 €2088 Two bear cubs (28x43cm-11x17in) s. ink crayon. 3-Apr-3 Christie's, Rockefeller NY #155/R est:1000-1500
£3205 $5000 €4808 Wolves examining fallen companion, owls overhead (61x46cm-24x18in) s. pen ink chl wash en grisaille. 9-Nov-2 Illustration House, New York #43/R est:1500-2400

BULL, Knud Geelmuyden (1811-1889) Norwegian
£26718 $42214 €40077 View of Hobart Town (35x48cm-14x19in) s.d.1853 prov.exhib. 2-Apr-3 Christie's, Melbourne #22/R est:40000-60000 (A.D 70000)

BULL, Simon (?) British
Works on paper
£780 $1271 €1131 Bassenthwaite (56x74cm-22x29in) s. W/C. 17-Jul-3 Thomson, Roddick & Medcalf, Carlisle #151/R
£850 $1386 €1233 Tarn Howes (56x76cm-22x30in) s. W/C. 17-Jul-3 Thomson, Roddick & Medcalf, Carlisle #150/R

BULL, William H (1861-1940) American
£518 $850 €777 Sunrise over Mt Tamalpias (46x58cm-18x23in) s. 31-May-3 Harvey Clar, Oakland #1212

BULLEID, George Lawrence (1858-1933) British
Works on paper
£1400 $2184 €2100 Young girl reading a book, seated in an interior (49x37cm-19x15in) s.d.MCMIC pencil W/C. 27-Mar-3 Christie's, Kensington #10/R est:1000-2000

BULLMORE, Edward (1933-1978) New Zealander
£291 $413 €437 South Canterbury fishing river (60x43cm-24x17in) board prov. 21-Nov-1 Watson's, Christchurch #27/R (NZ.D 1000)
£1235 $1754 €1853 Rural sunset (43x58cm-17x23in) board prov. 21-Nov-1 Watson's, Christchurch #26/R est:5000-8000 (NZ.D 4250)
£3819 $5958 €5729 Anathema 21 (75x48cm-30x19in) mono. i.verso board. 8-Apr-3 Peter Webb, Auckland #48/R est:10000-15000 (NZ.D 11000)
£31847 $50000 €47771 Family - the beginning of survival (117x90cm-46x35in) mono. board prov.exhib. 10-Dec-2 Peter Webb, Auckland #28/R est:40000-60000 (NZ.D 100000)
Works on paper
£637 $1000 €956 Study of a woman (74x55cm-29x22in) Indian ink executed c.1966. 10-Dec-2 Peter Webb, Auckland #48/R est:2500-4000 (NZ.D 2000)
£637 $1000 €956 Study of an old man (48x31cm-19x12in) pencil prov.exhib. 10-Dec-2 Peter Webb, Auckland #49/R est:1500-2000 (NZ.D 2000)
£1389 $2167 €2084 Life study (71x51cm-28x20in) ink pastel collage. 8-Apr-3 Peter Webb, Auckland #175/R est:4000-5000 (NZ.D 4000)

BULLOCK, Edith (fl.1886-1911) British
£400 $636 €600 Bowdon Mill, watermill with man fishing (127x86cm-50x34in) s.d.1894. 18-Mar-3 Capes Dunn, Manchester #548/R
£1000 $1640 €1500 Angler by a waterfall (127x86cm-50x34in) s.d.1894. 29-May-3 Christie's, Kensington #111/R est:1000-1500

BULLOCK, George G (fl.1827-1859) British
£1600 $2560 €2400 Still life of a bird and fruit (80x70cm-31x28in) board. 7-Jan-3 Bonhams, Knightsbridge #262/R est:1500-2500

BULLOCK, Wynn (1902-1975) American
Photographs
£3481 $5500 €5222 Navigation without numbers (18x23cm-7x9in) s.i. num.1307A photograph. 23-Apr-3 Sotheby's, New York #24/R est:4000-6000
£4747 $7500 €7121 Child in forest (19x24cm-7x9in) s.d.1951 photograph. 23-Apr-3 Sotheby's, New York #100/R est:4000-6000
Prints
£1899 $3000 €2849 Woman through window (23x18cm-9x7in) s.i.d.1955 verso vintage silver gelatine print. 16-Nov-2 New Orleans Auction, New Orleans #1400/R est:3500-5000

BULMAN, Orville (20th C) American
£968 $1500 €1452 Quelle batisi (51x56cm-20x22in) i.d.1969 verso. 25-Sep-2 Doyle, New York #12/R est:800-1200
£1290 $2000 €1935 Mere et fils (25x20cm-10x8in) s. s.i.d.1973 verso board prov. 1-Oct-2 Arthur James, Florida #330
£1290 $2000 €1935 Pere et fils (25x20cm-10x8in) s. s.i.d.1972 verso board prov. 1-Oct-2 Arthur James, Florida #331
£2019 $3250 €3029 Floating tiger (25x20cm-10x8in) s. board. 20-Jan-3 Arthur James, Florida #202
£2258 $3500 €3387 Sentry (76x36cm-30x14in) s. s.i.d.1979 verso. 1-Oct-2 Arthur James, Florida #450
£3226 $5000 €4839 En garde (76x64cm-30x25in) s. i.verso. 1-Oct-2 Arthur James, Florida #452
£6129 $9500 €9194 Homme de Loi (51x56cm-20x22in) s. 1-Oct-2 Arthur James, Florida #451

BULMER, Lionel (1919-1992) British
£1200 $1860 €1800 Southwold (30x41cm-12x16in) s. acrylic board. 30-Sep-2 Bonhams, Ipswich #364/R est:1000-1500

£1200 $1860 €1800 Young mother and daughter at sea (60x61cm-24x24in) s. acrylic board. 30-Sep-2 Bonhams, Ipswich #410 est:1500-2000
£2100 $3465 €3045 Walberswick with distant lighthouse (61x76cm-24x30in) s. 1-Jul-3 Bonhams, Norwich #348/R est:2000-3000

BULOW, Agnes von (1884-?) German
£362 $554 €543 Seascape with sailing vessel (54x67cm-21x26in) s. 24-Aug-2 Rasmussen, Havnen #2069 (D.KR 4200)

BULWER, Rev James (1794-1879) British
Works on paper
£320 $528 €464 Cawston church, the west door (28x22cm-11x9in) pencil W/C. 1-Jul-3 Bonhams, Norwich #75/R

BUNCE, William Gedney (1840-1916) British
£903 $1400 €1355 Torpedo boat, Venice (23x33cm-9x13in) s. panel prov. 2-Nov-2 North East Auctions, Portsmouth #84/R est:800-1000

BUNCEY, A de (19th C) French
£360 $565 €540 Poultry in a farm yard (38x55cm-15x22in) 24-Jul-2 Hamptons Fine Art, Godalming #353

BUNCHO, Tani (1763-1840) Japanese
Works on paper
£1132 $1800 €1698 Mount Fuji in snow (27x50cm-11x20in) s. ink hanging scroll. 24-Mar-3 Christie's, Rockefeller NY #36/R est:2000-3000
£1384 $2200 €2076 Chinese scholar, flowers, butterfly - painted with Shunei and Suiran. s d.1793 ink col hanging scroll sold with one by Tani Buncho. 24-Mar-3 Christie's, Rockefeller NY #37/R
£1509 $2400 €2264 Bird on reed and rose mallow (117x32cm-46x13in) s. ink col silk hanging scroll. 24-Mar-3 Christie's, Rockefeller NY #38/R est:3000-4000
£1635 $2600 €2453 Poet, To no Enmei, Tao Yuan-Ming (94x28cm-37x11in) s.d.1797 ink hanging scroll prov.exhib. 24-Mar-3 Christie's, Rockefeller NY #40/R est:1500-2000
£1761 $2800 €2642 Ducks and reeds (104x37cm-41x15in) s. ink col silk hanging scroll. 24-Mar-3 Christie's, Rockefeller NY #39/R est:2000-3000

BUNDEL, Willem van den (1577-1655) Dutch
£9790 $16349 €14000 Paysage boise anime de personnages et un fauconnier (37x59cm-15x23in) panel two boards. 25-Jun-3 Tajan, Paris #21/R est:10000-15000
£30000 $47100 €45000 Woode river landscape with soldiers (108x164cm-43x65in) 11-Dec-2 Christie's, London #29/R est:30000-40000

BUNDY, Edgar (1862-1922) British
£580 $905 €870 Portrait of the artist's son (28x18cm-11x7in) s.i.d.1914 panel. 25-Mar-3 Gorringes, Bexhill #1146
£600 $960 €900 Two gentlemen in an interior examining documents (51x76cm-20x30in) s. 13-May-3 Bonhams, Knightsbridge #67/R
£826 $1298 €1239 Proposal (36x46cm-14x18in) s.d.1890. 24-Jul-2 Walker's, Ottawa #25/R est:1500-2000 (C.D 2000)
£1300 $2080 €1950 Cavalier on horseback (90x70cm-35x28in) 7-Jan-3 Bonhams, Knightsbridge #191/R est:1500-2000
£1333 $2213 €1933 Grandfather entertaining baby (49x39cm-19x15in) s.d.1891. 16-Jun-3 Waddingtons, Toronto #156/R est:4000-6000 (C.D 3000)
£1333 $2213 €1933 Reconciliation (46x36cm-18x14in) s.d.1891. 16-Jun-3 Waddingtons, Toronto #157/R est:4000-6000 (C.D 3000)
£1386 $2300 €2010 Young storyteller (74x99cm-29x39in) 14-Jun-3 Jackson's, Cedar Falls #198/R est:2000-2500
£2000 $3120 €3000 Wary father (71x91cm-28x36in) s.d.1888. 17-Sep-2 Sotheby's, Olympia #192/R est:1500-2000
£2357 $3865 €3418 Dispute (72x56cm-28x22in) s. 4-Jun-3 AB Stockholms Auktionsverk #2417/R est:40000-50000 (S.KR 30000)
£2800 $4452 €4200 Flirtation (51x71cm-20x28in) s.d.1907. 18-Mar-3 Bonhams, New Bond Street #112/R est:3000-5000
£2900 $4524 €4350 Found, three cavaliers in an interior (51x76cm-20x30in) s. 10-Apr-3 Tennants, Leyburn #1118/R est:2000-3000
£3500 $5635 €5250 Cavalier (99x23cm-39x9in) s.i. panel prov. 20-Feb-3 Christie's, London #278/R
£3800 $6346 €5510 Young girl and dog in a winter landscape (90x70cm-35x28in) s.d.1881. 9-Jul-3 Edgar Horn, Eastbourne #299/R est:2000-3000
£4200 $6636 €6300 In high spirits (91x72cm-36x28in) s.d.1888. 2-Dec-2 Sotheby's, London #97/R est:3000-5000
£6200 $9858 €9300 Toast to King Charles (72x92cm-28x36in) s.d.1898. 18-Mar-3 Bonhams, New Bond Street #113/R est:2000-3000
Works on paper
£1649 $2506 €2474 Sculptor's studio (67x33cm-26x13in) s.d.1895 W/C. 28-Aug-2 Deutscher-Menzies, Melbourne #287/R est:5000-8000 (A.D 4600)
£1800 $2790 €2700 Sculptor's studio (67x34cm-26x13in) s.d.1895 pencil W/C bodycol. 4-Dec-2 Christie's, Kensington #123/R est:2000-2500
£2300 $3657 €3450 Saucy look (37x53cm-15x21in) s.d.1907 W/C. 5-Mar-3 Bonhams, Bury St Edmunds #310 est:1200-1800
£2800 $4368 €4200 Three huntsman in an inn parlour (38x53cm-15x21in) s. W/C. 5-Nov-2 Bristol Auction Rooms #933/R est:800-1200

BUNDY, John Elwood (1853-1933) American
£3065 $4750 €4598 Wooded stream, sunset landscape (41x56cm-16x22in) s. prov. 29-Oct-2 John Moran, Pasadena #747 est:2000-3000

BUNEL, François (younger-attrib) (16th C) French
£1965 $3066 €2948 Victory parade (45x66cm-18x26in) panel. 6-Nov-2 Dobiaschofsky, Bern #382/R est:5500 (S.FR 4500)

BUNGARTZ, J (20th C) German
£1191 $1883 €1787 Four episodes from a horse race (35x50cm-14x20in) s. four. 2-Dec-2 Rasmussen, Copenhagen #1329/R est:12000 (D.KR 14000)

BUNIN, Narkiz Nikolaevich (1856-1912) Russian
£516 $799 €820 Cattle grazing (40x56cm-16x22in) s.d.1885. 6-Oct-2 Bukowskis, Helsinki #336/R
£1519 $2400 €2400 Cattle grazing (40x56cm-16x22in) s.d.1885. 1-Dec-2 Bukowskis, Helsinki #237/R est:1200-1400

BUNKE, Franz (1857-1939) German
£396 $633 €550 Field track (26x36cm-10x14in) s.d. board. 15-May-3 Neumeister, Munich #226/R
£573 $883 €900 A summer morning (38x55cm-15x22in) s. i.d.1934 verso. 5-Sep-2 Arnold, Frankfurt #745/R
£609 $926 €950 City with church (80x110cm-31x43in) s. 31-Aug-2 Geble, Radolfzell #616/R
£880 $1416 €1320 Warnemunde (36x65cm-14x26in) s. i. stretcher. 7-May-3 Dobiaschofsky, Bern #383/R (S.FR 1900)
£912 $1423 €1450 Old watermill on the Warnow (13x22cm-5x9in) s. panel. 21-Sep-2 Bolland & Marotz, Bremen #454/R
£959 $1496 €1400 Autumn morning (13x24cm-5x9in) s. panel. 10-Apr-3 Van Ham, Cologne #1350/R
£962 $1490 €1500 Extensive landscape (30x40cm-12x16in) s. board lit. 7-Dec-2 Bergmann, Erlangen #777/R est:1500
£2436 $3776 €3800 Extensive Mecklenburg landscape by moonlight (63x90cm-25x35in) s. 7-Dec-2 Hans Stahl, Hamburg #75/R est:3800

BUNN, George (fl.1885-1898) British
£500 $835 €725 Vessels on the beach (59x80cm-23x31in) s.d.95. 18-Jun-3 Sotheby's, Olympia #31/R
£1800 $2790 €2700 Rowing boat and fishing boats in heavy seas off a lighthouse (53x56cm-21x22in) s.d.96. 31-Oct-2 Duke & Son, Dorchester #232/R est:300-600

BUNNER, Andrew Fisher (1841-1897) American
£915 $1500 €1373 Fishing boats (36x46cm-14x18in) s. 9-Feb-3 William Jenack, New York #168 est:2000-3000
£1019 $1600 €1529 Mill beside a waterfall (36x66cm-14x26in) s.d.70. 10-Dec-2 Doyle, New York #17/R est:3000-4000
£1290 $2000 €1935 Figures in an autumn landscape (25x43cm-10x17in) 7-Dec-2 South Bay, Long Island #127/R
£5195 $8000 €7793 At East Hampton (56x81cm-22x32in) s. i.verso prov. 24-Oct-2 Shannon's, Milford #91/R est:8000-12000

BUNNETT, Henry Richard (1845-1910) Canadian
Works on paper
£658 $1021 €987 Quebec scenes (13x19cm-5x7in) two s. W/C set of three. 3-Dec-2 Joyner, Toronto #336/R est:2000-2500 (C.D 1600)

BUNNEY, John Wharlton (1828-1882) British
£1795 $2782 €2800 Interior of Palazzo Ducale, Venice (38x28cm-15x11in) s.d.1871. 4-Dec-2 Finarte, Rome #771/R
Works on paper
£300 $468 €450 St. Giorgio Maggiore from the lagoon (15x23cm-6x9in) s.d.Feb 4 1880 W/C htd white. 17-Oct-2 Christie's, Kensington #99

BUNNY, Rupert Charles Wulsten (1864-1947) Australian
£893 $1411 €1340 Farmhouse (19x24cm-7x9in) s. board prov. 27-Nov-2 Deutscher-Menzies, Melbourne #252/R est:4000-6000 (A.D 2500)
£893 $1411 €1340 Landscape (21x32cm-8x13in) board prov. 27-Nov-2 Deutscher-Menzies, Melbourne #253/R est:3500-4000 (A.D 2500)
£996 $1484 €1494 Landscape (20x23cm-8x9in) card. 27-Aug-2 Christie's, Melbourne #176/R est:2000-3000 (A.D 2600)
£1163 $1849 €1745 Mythological figures (26x28cm-10x11in) pulpboard prov. 5-May-3 Sotheby's, Melbourne #275/R est:3500-5000 (A.D 3000)
£1281 $1960 €1922 Mythological study (23x28cm-9x11in) oil on paper prov. 25-Aug-2 Sotheby's, Paddington #153 est:2000-4000 (A.D 3600)
£2135 $3267 €3203 Madame Lul Gardo in peasant costume (58x43cm-23x17in) canvas on pulpboard painted c.1917 prov.exhib. 26-Aug-2 Sotheby's, Paddington #659/R est:8000-12000 (A.D 6000)

£5357 $8464 €8036 French landscape (50x59cm-20x23in) s. on stretcher verso. 17-Nov-2 Sotheby's, Paddington #37/R est:14000-18000 (A.D 15000)
£5747 $8563 €8621 Farmhouse and olive trees, South of France (52x64cm-20x25in) mono. 27-Aug-2 Christie's, Melbourne #50/R est:15000-20000 (A.D 15000)
£8185 $12523 €12278 Le lavandou (48x63cm-19x25in) mono. 25-Aug-2 Sotheby's, Paddington #43/R est:18000-25000 (A.D 23000)
£8541 $13068 €12812 Self portrait (103x65cm-41x26in) painted c.1925-30 prov.exhib. 26-Aug-2 Sotheby's, Paddington #554/R est:18000-22000 (A.D 24000)
£9286 $14671 €13929 Botanical gardens, Melbourne (57x50cm-22x20in) mono. prov. 26-Nov-2 Sotheby's, Melbourne #29/R est:28000-38000 (A.D 26000)
£11429 $17943 €17144 Annunciation (48x63cm-19x25in) s. painted c.1895 prov. 25-Nov-2 Christie's, Melbourne #12/R est:25000-35000 (A.D 32000)
£53435 $84427 €80153 On the balcony (79x63cm-31x25in) s. i.verso prov.exhib. 2-Apr-3 Christie's, Melbourne #38/R est:120000-180000 (A.D 140000)
£76000 $122360 €114000 Sonata (80x64cm-31x25in) s. i.on stretcher painted 1909 prov.exhib. 6-May-3 Christie's, Melbourne #60/R est:180000-250000 (A.D 190000)

Works on paper
£339 $522 €509 Composition study for Nausicaa (20x12cm-8x5in) s. pencil. 3-Sep-2 Shapiro, Sydney #448/R est:1400-1600 (A.D 950)
£346 $550 €519 Interior (13x19cm-5x7in) pencil. 4-Mar-3 Deutscher-Menzies, Melbourne #239/R (A.D 900)

BUNTZEN, Heinrich (1802-1892) Danish
£345 $524 €518 Farm house by village pond (41x63cm-16x25in) 27-Aug-2 Rasmussen, Copenhagen #1850/R (D.KR 4000)
£372 $592 €558 Woman with basket on her back in front of thatched house (22x18cm-9x7in) init.d.1861. 5-Mar-3 Rasmussen, Copenhagen #1739 (D.KR 4000)
£470 $723 €705 Danish fjord landscape (17x33cm-7x13in) paper on canvas prov. 4-Sep-2 Kunsthallen, Copenhagen #38/R (D.KR 5500)
£1148 $1860 €1665 Still life of yellow and pink roses (32x28cm-13x11in) with sig.verso. 26-May-3 Rasmussen, Copenhagen #1234/R est:8000 (D.KR 12000)

Works on paper
£2830 $4415 €4245 Elbufer in Altona (26x59cm-10x23in) s.d.1826 verso W/C. 11-Nov-2 Rasmussen, Vejle #628/R est:5000 (D.KR 33000)

BUNTZEN, Sophie (19th C) Danish

Works on paper
£759 $1200 €1200 Still life of flowers (18x23cm-7x9in) s.d.1832 verso gouache board. 29-Nov-2 Schloss Ahlden, Ahlden #1159/R

BUONACCORSI, Pietro (1500-1547) Italian

Works on paper
£4938 $8000 €7407 Architectural decorations (3x8cm-1x3in) i. pen ink wash. 21-Jan-3 Sotheby's, New York #35/R est:7000

BUONACCORSI, Pietro (circle) (1500-1547) Italian

Works on paper
£1852 $3000 €2778 Hippocamp (10x18cm-4x7in) ink oval. 22-Jan-3 Christie's, Rockefeller NY #8/R

BUONGIORNO, Donatus (1865-?) Italian
£275 $450 €413 News boys (30x23cm-12x9in) s. 8-Feb-3 Neal Auction Company, New Orleans #1077

BUONO, Eugenio (1863-1954) Italian
£787 $1267 €1181 Cart on country track (35x51cm-14x20in) s. 7-May-3 Dobiaschofsky, Bern #384/R (S.FR 1700)

BUONTALENTI, Bernardo (1536-1608) Italian

Works on paper
£280 $400 €420 Architectural design for a loggia (27x16cm-11x6in) red chk. 23-Jan-3 Swann Galleries, New York #42/R

BUONTALENTI, Bernardo (attrib) (1536-1608) Italian

Works on paper
£443 $700 €700 Projet pour une fontaine. Etudes de fontaines avec des satyres (31x21cm-12x8in) graphite pen brown ink double-sided prov. 27-Nov-2 Christie's, Paris #20/R

BUORA, Giovanni di Antonio (circle) (c.1450-1513) Italian

Sculpture
£21181 $33677 €30500 Madonna and Child (153cm-60in) stone. 4-May-3 Finarte, Venice #526/R est:40000

BURAGLIO, Pierre (1939-) French

Works on paper
£1957 $3209 €2700 Gauloises (42x52cm-17x20in) collage prov. 27-May-3 Tajan, Paris #24/R est:2000-3000

BURAK, Alexander (20th C) Russian
£800 $1296 €1200 Miners (100x125cm-39x49in) s. s.i.verso. 20-May-3 Bonhams, Knightsbridge #124/R

BURBANK, E A (1858-1949) American
£6013 $9500 €8719 Standing soldier, Sioux. Chief Wolf Robe, Cheyenne (30x25cm-12x10in) s. canvas on board pair. 26-Jul-3 Coeur d'Alene, Hayden #188/R est:6000-9000

BURBANK, Elbridge Ayer (1858-1949) American
£377 $600 €566 Old church, Pueblo of Acoma (8x11cm-3x4in) s.i. board. 5-Mar-3 Sotheby's, New York #139/R
£566 $900 €849 White Swan Crow (29x24cm-11x9in) s. indis i.d.1897 canvasboard. 5-Mar-3 Christie's, Rockefeller NY #107/R
£1761 $2800 €2642 Threading the needle (20x15cm-8x6in) s. panel. 7-Mar-3 Skinner, Boston #310/R est:800-1200
£1887 $3000 €2831 Indian squaw (25x20cm-10x8in) s.d.1902 paper on board prov. 5-Mar-3 Sotheby's, New York #142/R est:1500-2500
£1946 $3250 €2822 Chief Redcloud Sioux. s. board. 28-Jun-3 Harvey Clar, Oakland #1372
£2201 $3500 €3302 Chief Geronimo, Apache (51x37cm-20x15in) s.i. board. 5-Mar-3 Sotheby's, New York #133/R est:2500-3500

Works on paper
£240 $400 €348 Blarney Castle in Ireland. s.i.d. 28-Jun-3 Harvey Clar, Oakland #1374
£329 $550 €477 Bison study. s. dr. 28-Jun-3 Harvey Clar, Oakland #1373
£357 $550 €536 Crow (30x23cm-12x9in) s.i.d.1900 crayon. 4-Sep-2 Christie's, Rockefeller NY #350/R
£455 $700 €683 Zy-You-Wah Hopi (30x23cm-12x9in) s.i.d.1898 crayon. 4-Sep-2 Christie's, Rockefeller NY #352/R
£581 $900 €872 Chief Pretty Eagle (30x25cm-12x10in) s.i.d.1898 crayon. 3-Dec-2 Christie's, Rockefeller NY #577/R

BURBRIDGE, John (fl.1862-1894) British
£650 $1008 €975 Interior of St Paul's Church, Antwerp (71x52cm-28x20in) s.d.1885. 3-Dec-2 Sotheby's, Olympia #146/R

Works on paper
£800 $1296 €1200 Cologne (71x50cm-28x20in) s.d.1881 W/C. 21-May-3 Bonhams, Knightsbridge #42/R

BURCH, Edward (1730-1814) British

Miniatures
£4200 $6930 €6090 Portrait of a young boy (7cm-3xin) init. gold frame glass oval. 1-Jul-3 Bonhams, New Bond Street #100/R est:2500-3500

BURCH, Henry Jacob (younger) (1763-1834) British

Miniatures
£1200 $1884 €1800 Mrs A Diron in a white dress (7cm-3xin) silver gilt frame oval. 10-Dec-2 Christie's, London #128/R est:600-800
£1200 $1944 €1800 Colonl Thomas William Ravenshaw, wearing uniform (14cm-6xin) i. W/C on card rectangular gilded frame. 22-May-3 Bonhams, New Bond Street #12/R est:400-600
£2000 $3240 €3000 Thomas FitzArthur Torin Ravenshaw, aged 2, seated on a stone steps holding riding crop (18cm-7xin) i.d.May 1831 W/C on card rectangular frame. 22-May-3 Bonhams, New Bond Street #9/R est:700-900

BURCH, Henry van der (19th C) Dutch
£1500 $2415 €2250 Gentleman writing a letter in an interior, cat and dog near the door (50x41cm-20x16in) init. 20-Feb-3 Christie's, Kensington #249/R est:1000-1500

BURCHARDT, Fjodor Karlowitsch (1854-1918) Russian
£8228 $13000 €13000 Extensive meadow landscape with black grouse (89x125cm-35x49in) indis.s.d.1909. 28-Nov-2 Dorotheum, Vienna #230/R est:6500-7000

BURCHARTZ, Max (1887-1961) German
£709 $1149 €1000 Binding forms (80x100cm-31x39in) s.d.58 oil sprayed plaster. 24-May-3 Van Ham, Cologne #77/R
Works on paper
£567 $919 €800 Composition (40x50cm-16x20in) s.d.58 mixed media exhib. 24-May-3 Van Ham, Cologne #78/R

BURCHFIELD, Charles (1893-1967) American
Prints
£1887 $3000 €2831 Summer Benediction (30x23cm-12x9in) lithograph exec.1951-52 one of 250. 22-Mar-3 Rachel Davis, Shaker Heights #176 est:2000-3000
£2673 $4250 €4010 Summer benediction (30x23cm-12x9in) s.i. lithograph edition of 260. 2-May-3 Sotheby's, New York #11/R est:3000-4000
£3077 $4800 €4616 Autumn wind (25x40cm-10x16in) s.i. lithograph edition of 60. 5-Nov-2 Christie's, Rockefeller NY #89/R est:3000-4000
£3145 $5000 €4718 Crows in March (34x25cm-13x10in) s.i. lithograph edition of 60. 2-May-3 Sotheby's, New York #12/R est:5000-7000
£3145 $5000 €4718 Autumn wind (19x34cm-7x13in) s.i. lithograph edition of 60. 2-May-3 Sotheby's, New York #13/R est:5000-7000
£3846 $6000 €5769 Beech tree and the Valley of the Little Beaver (24x33cm-9x13in) s.i.d. etching. 5-Nov-2 Christie's, Rockefeller NY #88/R est:4000-6000
Works on paper
£5031 $8000 €7547 Study for March wind (35x81cm-14x32in) mono.d.1926 chl pencil W/C paper on board prov.exhib.lit. 4-Mar-3 Christie's, Rockefeller NY #79/R est:12000-16000
£7547 $12000 €11321 Railroad locomotive (42x52cm-17x20in) W/C prov. 5-Mar-3 Sotheby's, New York #101a/R est:12000-18000
£10494 $17000 €15741 Along the inter urban car line (46x56cm-18x22in) s.i.d.1918 W/C pencil paper on board prov.exhib.lit. 21-May-3 Sotheby's, New York #98/R est:25000-35000
£11613 $18000 €17420 September meadows (35x51cm-14x20in) s.d.1916 W/C pencil prov.lit. 4-Dec-2 Sotheby's, New York #90/R est:12000-16000
£16129 $25000 €24194 Yellow bank (46x63cm-18x25in) mono.d.April 17.1939 W/C on board prov.lit. 4-Dec-2 Sotheby's, New York #92/R est:25000-35000
£18065 $28000 €27098 House corner (40x28cm-16x11in) mono.d.1937 W/C prov. 5-Dec-2 Christie's, Rockefeller NY #140/R est:30000-50000
£23148 $37500 €34722 Snowstorm - first snow (51x36cm-20x14in) W/C gouache executed 1916 prov.exhib.lit. 21-May-3 Sotheby's, New York #97/R est:40000-60000
£38710 $60000 €58065 Trees dancing in April sunlight (46x51cm-18x20in) s.d.Apr14.1917 W/C. 5-Dec-2 Christie's, Rockefeller NY #115/R est:40000-60000
£61290 $95000 €91935 August morning (76x102cm-30x40in) mono.d.1951-59 W/C paper on board prov.exhib.lit. 5-Dec-2 Christie's, Rockefeller NY #116/R est:120000-180000
£61728 $100000 €92592 Song of the katydids on an August morning (46x56cm-18x22in) s.d.1917 i.verso W/C chl paper on board prov.exhib.lit. 21-May-3 Sotheby's, New York #85/R est:40000-60000
£96774 $150000 €145161 Pine tree (77x57cm-30x22in) mono. W/C pencil paper on board prov.exhib.lit. 5-Dec-2 Christie's, Rockefeller NY #190/R est:200000-300000

BURCHFIELD, Mary (20th C) American
Works on paper
£488 $800 €708 Untitled - buffalo, New York (56x41cm-22x16in) W/C. 1-Jun-3 Wright, Chicago #225/R

BURCKHARD, Paul (1880-1961) Swiss
£515 $814 €773 View of Ascona with Lake Maggiore in background (55x95cm-22x37in) painted 1930. 26-Nov-2 Hans Widmer, St Gallen #1062/R (S.FR 1200)
£524 $817 €786 Sestri Levante (44x55cm-17x22in) s.d.1922. 8-Nov-2 Dobiaschofsky, Bern #146/R (S.FR 1200)
£602 $969 €873 Self portrait (68x80cm-27x31in) s.d.50. 9-May-3 Dobiaschofsky, Bern #168/R (S.FR 1300)

BURCKHARDT, Carl (1878-1923) Swiss
£568 $886 €852 Horses watering in evening landscape (60x78cm-24x31in) 6-Nov-2 Dobiaschofsky, Bern #383/R (S.FR 1300)

BURCKHARDT, Rudy (1919-) ?
Photographs
£2658 $4200 €3987 Flatiron in summer (24x19cm-9x7in) gelatin silver print prov.exhib. 25-Apr-3 Phillips, New York #91/R est:2500-3500

BURDETTE, Hattie Elizabeth (1872-1955) American
£414 $650 €621 Still life with sandwich glass dolphin candlesticks (64x76cm-25x30in) s. 23-Nov-2 Jackson's, Cedar Falls #332/R

BUREN, Raeburn van (1891-1987) American
Works on paper
£833 $1300 €1250 Young woman and sugar daddy in front of boutique window (46x58cm-18x23in) s.d.1933 chl pencil white gouache. 9-Nov-2 Illustration House, New York #100/R

BURFLEET, J M (19/20th C) British?
£1100 $1749 €1650 Romantic moment (22x28cm-9x11in) s. panel. 5-Mar-3 Bonhams, Bury St Edmunds #357/R

BURG, Adriaen van der (1693-1733) Dutch
£5755 $9209 €8000 Paradise landscape with Adam and Eve (38x29cm-15x11in) panel prov. 17-May-3 Lempertz, Koln #1016/R est:8000

BURGARITSKI, Joseph (1836-1890) Austrian
£1132 $1755 €1800 Upper Austria (42x68cm-17x27in) s. 29-Oct-2 Dorotheum, Vienna #205/R est:2000-2200
£1164 $1816 €1700 Donau valley in summer (69x105cm-27x41in) s. 10-Apr-3 Van Ham, Cologne #1351/R est:1500

BURGDORFER, Daniel David (1800-1861) Swiss
Works on paper
£280 $437 €420 Swiss village (18x26cm-7x10in) s.d.1826 W/C. 9-Oct-2 Woolley & Wallis, Salisbury #100/R

BURGDORFF, Ferdinand (1883-1975) American
£466 $750 €699 Lightship, Blunts's reef (92x122cm-36x48in) s.d.1951 board. 23-Feb-3 Butterfields, Los Angeles #7012
£487 $750 €731 California autumn landscape (41x28cm-16x11in) s. board. 8-Sep-2 DeFina, Austinburg #289
£601 $950 €902 California coastline and poppies. s. 5-Apr-3 Harvey Clar, Oakland #1518a
£898 $1500 €1302 Road in Monument Valley, Arizona (46x61cm-18x24in) i. i.verso board prov. 17-Jun-3 John Moran, Pasadena #122 est:2000-3000
£1266 $2000 €1899 Mt Tamalpais. s. 16-Nov-2 Harvey Clar, Oakland #1246
£1667 $2600 €2501 Wayfarer (36x51cm-14x20in) 19-Oct-2 David Dike, Dallas #98/R est:1500-3000
Works on paper
£422 $675 €612 Water trough in a sun-dappled setting (51x36cm-20x14in) s.d. W/C. 17-May-3 Selkirks, St. Louis #296/R

BURGE, Maude (1865-1957) New Zealander
£1148 $1849 €1722 Tulips (62x50cm-24x20in) s. board. 7-May-3 Dunbar Sloane, Auckland #51/R (NZ.D 3250)
Works on paper
£3684 $5747 €5526 Fryberg's residence at St Tropez (39x33cm-15x13in) s. W/C. 27-Mar-3 International Art Centre, Auckland #144/R est:10000-15000 (NZ.D 10500)

BURGER, Anton (1824-1905) German
£651 $1015 €950 Man's portrait (30x24cm-12x9in) 11-Apr-3 Winterberg, Heidelberg #345/R
£1282 $1987 €2000 Small girl preparing vegetables sitting in the farmer's kitchen (37x27cm-15x11in) s. 4-Dec-2 Neumeister, Munich #689/R est:1800
£2603 $4060 €3800 Peasant woman on track to farmstead (12x12cm-5x5in) s.d. panel. 11-Apr-3 Winterberg, Heidelberg #346/R est:680
£10274 $16027 €15000 Leaving church (52x39cm-20x15in) s.d. 11-Apr-3 Winterberg, Heidelberg #344/R est:2400

BURGER, Franz (1857-1940) Austrian
Works on paper
£288 $456 €450 Mountain village (31x47cm-12x19in) s. W/C. 18-Nov-2 Dorotheum, Linz #385/R

BURGER, Josef (1887-1966) German
£318 $497 €500 Birch trees on the river bank with foothills (60x80cm-24x31in) s.i. lit. 7-Nov-2 Allgauer, Kempten #2772/R
£380 $589 €600 Coach horse at blacksmiths (71x100cm-28x39in) s. 27-Sep-2 Auktionhaus Georg Rehm, Augsburg #8019/R

BURGER, Lothar (1866-1943) Austrian
£468 $748 €650 Tavern on country road (28x54cm-11x21in) s.i. 14-May-3 Dorotheum, Linz #384/R

BURGER, Willy Friedrich (1882-1964) Swiss
£377 $604 €566 Sailing club (30x39cm-12x15in) s. canvas on board. 17-Mar-3 Philippe Schuler, Zurich #8413 (S.FR 800)

BURGER-WILLING, Willi Hans (1882-1969) German
£513 $795 €800 Horses drinking (59x70cm-23x28in) s. chipboard lit. 7-Dec-2 Bergmann, Erlangen #823/R
£545 $855 €850 Hamburg harbour (47x66cm-19x26in) s. 21-Nov-2 Van Ham, Cologne #1507
£641 $1006 €1000 Two Dutch fisher boys (40x35cm-16x14in) s. 21-Nov-2 Van Ham, Cologne #1506/R
£822 $1282 €1200 Children with goats in summer landscape (60x70cm-24x28in) s. 10-Apr-3 Van Ham, Cologne #1353

BURGERS, Felix (1870-1895) German
£2069 $3269 €3000 Dachauer Moos in winter (77x103cm-30x41in) s. i. verso. 5-Apr-3 Hans Stahl, Hamburg #4/R est:3500

BURGERS, Hendricus Jacobus (1834-1899) Dutch
£573 $883 €900 Mother watching the baby. Afternoon tea (25x21cm-10x8in) s. pair. 3-Sep-2 Christie's, Amsterdam #113
£1139 $1766 €1800 Le jeune convalescent (24x31cm-9x12in) s. panel. 29-Sep-2 Eric Pillon, Calais #66/R
£2041 $3245 €3000 Le jeune lecteur (24x31cm-9x12in) s. panel. 26-Feb-3 Artcurial Briest, Paris #134/R est:2500-3000
£2390 $3681 €3800 Feeding the bird (43x31cm-17x12in) s. panel. 23-Oct-2 Christie's, Amsterdam #9/R est:3500-5000

BURGESS, A J W (1879-1957) Australian
Works on paper
£700 $1106 €1050 On the beach at Filey (23x32cm-9x13in) s.i.d.08 W/C htd white. 27-Nov-2 Hamptons Fine Art, Godalming #147

BURGESS, Arthur James Wetherall (1879-1957) Australian
£800 $1216 €1200 Tagus, a paddle steamer with a following wind (42x58cm-17x23in) s. panel. 17-Sep-2 Henry Adams, Chichester #164/R
£1100 $1782 €1650 M.V. Journalist (49x75cm-19x30in) s. 21-Jan-3 Bonhams, New Bond Street #210/R est:400-600
£1500 $2430 €2250 M.V. Craftsman 1947 (36x48cm-14x19in) s. board. 21-Jan-3 Bonhams, New Bond Street #214/R est:500-700
£1500 $2505 €2175 Tower Bridge (45x61cm-18x24in) s. s.i.on overlap. 18-Jun-3 Sotheby's, Olympia #95/R est:1500-2000
£1600 $2592 €2400 M.V Defender 1955 (30x45cm-12x18in) s.i. board. 21-Jan-3 Bonhams, New Bond Street #208/R est:500-700
£1800 $2916 €2700 M.V Defender (50x75cm-20x30in) s. 21-Jan-3 Bonhams, New Bond Street #209/R est:400-600
£1800 $2916 €2700 M.V Astronomer in the Clyde (30x46cm-12x18in) s. board. 21-Jan-3 Bonhams, New Bond Street #213/R est:300-500
£2000 $3240 €3000 M.V Crofter with the Liverpool Pilot (30x45cm-12x18in) s. board. 21-Jan-3 Bonhams, New Bond Street #212/R est:300-500
£2000 $3240 €3000 M.V. Craftsman off Holyhead (76x102cm-30x40in) s. 21-Jan-3 Bonhams, New Bond Street #215/R est:400-600
£2400 $3888 €3600 M.V Herdsman (29x44cm-11x17in) s. board. 21-Jan-3 Bonhams, New Bond Street #216/R est:300-500
£2500 $4050 €3750 M.V. Dipomat at Cape Town (60x75cm-24x30in) s. 21-Jan-3 Bonhams, New Bond Street #211/R est:400-600
£2600 $4212 €3900 M.V Inventor and Inanda on the Mersey (29x47cm-11x19in) s. board. 21-Jan-3 Bonhams, New Bond Street #207/R est:400-600
£3000 $4860 €4500 M.V. Herdsman on the Thames (63x75cm-25x30in) s. 21-Jan-3 Bonhams, New Bond Street #217/R est:400-600
£5200 $7904 €7800 Unloading convoy vessel in Holy Loch (62x75cm-24x30in) s. prov. 15-Aug-2 Bonhams, New Bond Street #453/R est:2000-3000
Works on paper
£400 $644 €600 On the early morning tide (25x35cm-10x14in) s. pastel prov. 11-May-3 Lots Road, London #331/R

BURGESS, Eliza Mary (1873-?) British
Works on paper
£360 $562 €540 Continental street scene with figures (36x25cm-14x10in) s. W/C. 18-Oct-2 Keys, Aylsham #442

BURGESS, James Howard (1817-1890) British
Works on paper
£500 $775 €750 Figures outside an Irish castle (30x48cm-12x19in) W/C. 2-Oct-2 John Ross, Belfast #179
£1040 $1612 €1560 Giants causeway (23x51cm-9x20in) s. W/C. 2-Oct-2 John Ross, Belfast #13 est:600-800
£1200 $1860 €1800 Mending the nets (30x50cm-12x20in) s. W/C. 4-Dec-2 John Ross, Belfast #236 est:1000-1250

BURGESS, John (jnr) (1814-1874) British
Works on paper
£280 $454 €420 Interior of Abbeville Cathedral (45x30cm-18x12in) s. W/C. 21-May-3 Bonhams, Knightsbridge #20/R

BURGESS, John Bagnold (1830-1897) British
£600 $948 €900 Portrait study of a gypsy girl (46x33cm-18x13in) s.d.1888. 27-Nov-2 Peter Wilson, Nantwich #44/R
£920 $1417 €1380 Moment for reflection (26x19cm-10x7in) s. panel. 22-Oct-2 Bonhams, Bath #91
£1300 $2041 €1950 La senorita (12x19cm-5x7in) init. panel. 16-Dec-2 Sotheby's, London #77/R est:800-1200
£4200 $6846 €6300 Teatime (39x34cm-15x13in) s.d.1875 panel. 30-Jan-3 Lawrence, Crewkerne #713/R
£7595 $12000 €11393 Return of the Garibaldian (86x71cm-34x28in) s.d.1860 prov. 23-Apr-3 Christie's, Rockefeller NY #86/R est:12000-18000
£10500 $16590 €15750 A Spanish post office (92x76cm-36x30in) s.d.1863 prov.exhib. 26-Nov-2 Christie's, London #167/R est:8000-12000

BURGH, Coralie de (1924-) British
£600 $930 €900 Fox hounds (63x76cm-25x30in) mono. 4-Dec-2 John Ross, Belfast #141a

BURGH, Hendrick van der (1627-c.1669) Dutch
£3846 $6077 €6000 Jeune femme a la couture (49x43cm-19x17in) 13-Nov-2 Marc Kohn, Paris #57/R

BURGH, Pieter Daniel van der (1805-1879) Dutch
£701 $1093 €1100 Stately landscape with flock of sheep (54x68cm-21x27in) s. 6-Nov-2 Vendue Huis, Gravenhage #444
£2848 $4500 €4500 Dutch harbour with boats, working horse and figures (44x36cm-17x14in) s. panel prov. 28-Nov-2 Dorotheum, Vienna #182/R est:4500-6000

BURGHARDT, Gustav (fl.1935) German
£408 $649 €600 Hamburg harbour (51x60cm-20x24in) s. 28-Mar-3 Bolland & Marotz, Bremen #545/R
£519 $830 €779 Hamburg harbour (60x80cm-24x31in) s. 17-Mar-3 Philippe Schuler, Zurich #4640 (S.FR 1100)
£586 $926 €850 Hamburg harbour (60x80cm-24x31in) s. 5-Apr-3 Hans Stahl, Hamburg #152/R
£1497 $2380 €2200 Ship "Europa" leaving Bremen harbour with tower of the old city in background (82x120cm-32x47in) s. 25-Feb-3 Dorotheum, Vienna #127/R est:2400-2800

BURGI, Jacob (1745-?) Swiss
Works on paper
£2848 $4500 €4500 Paysages du Rhin (18x27cm-7x11in) gouache vellum pair. 28-Nov-2 Tajan, Paris #103/R est:4500

BURGKMAIR, Hans (1473-c.1559) German
Prints
£3521 $5845 €5000 Aristotles and Phyllis (12x10cm-5x4in) woodcut. 12-Jun-3 Hauswedell & Nolte, Hamburg #51/R est:5000

BURGUILLOS, Jaime (1930-) Spanish
£1226 $1937 €1900 Untitled (61x50cm-24x20in) s.d.1994 prov. 17-Dec-2 Segre, Madrid #190/R
£1384 $2131 €2200 Untitled (61x50cm-24x20in) s.d.1994 prov. 28-Oct-2 Segre, Madrid #132/R

BURI, Max (1868-1915) Swiss
£8491 $13755 €15029 Houses in Brienz (33x47cm-13x19in) s. exhib. 26-May-3 Sotheby's, Zurich #42/R est:25000-30000 (S.FR 18000)
£9722 $15653 €14097 Head of girl with red hair (42x42cm-17x17in) s.d.1915 exhib. 9-May-3 Dobiaschofsky, Bern #84/R est:22000 (S.FR 21000)
£141509 $229245 €250472 Dance musicians (115x176cm-45x69in) s. prov.exhib.lit. 26-May-3 Sotheby's, Zurich #66/R est:80000-120000 (S.FR 300000)

BURI, Samuel (1935-) Swiss
Works on paper
£284 $443 €426 Portrait of small boy in night-shirt (33x41cm-13x16in) i.d.10 mars W/C bodycol pencil col pen. 6-Nov-2 Dobiaschofsky, Bern #1438 (S.FR 650)
£328 $511 €492 Le petit garcon devant l'atre (33x41cm-13x16in) d.74 bodycol col pen. 6-Nov-2 Dobiaschofsky, Bern #1434/R (S.FR 750)
£328 $511 €492 Le petit dejeuner (33x41cm-13x16in) d.6 mars 1974 W/C. 6-Nov-2 Dobiaschofsky, Bern #1437/R (S.FR 750)

£430 $702 €650 Certosa, Capri (46x61cm-18x24in) s.i. W/C exec.1983. 3-Feb-3 Cornette de St.Cyr, Paris #378
£480 $749 €720 Small boy at piano (33x41cm-13x16in) i.d.8 mars 74 bodycol pencil col pen. 6-Nov-2 Dobiaschofsky, Bern #1435/R (S.FR 1100)
£1397 $2194 €2096 Composition (50x65cm-20x26in) s. gouache. 25-Nov-2 Germann, Zurich #3/R est:3000-4000 (S.FR 3200)

BURIAN, Zdenek (1905-1981) Czechoslovakian
£908 $1471 €1362 Conscience (46x33cm-18x13in) s. board. 24-May-3 Dorotheum, Prague #113/R est:30000-45000 (C.KR 40000)
Works on paper
£330 $515 €495 Hydroplane on an iceberg, illustration for book "Biggles Flies North" (24x19cm-9x7in) s. gouache. 12-Oct-2 Dorotheum, Prague #180 (C.KR 16000)
£702 $1095 €1053 Camp by river, illustration of Vraz's Borneo (25x43cm-10x17in) s. gouache. 12-Oct-2 Dorotheum, Prague #178/R (C.KR 34000)

BURINI, Antonio (1656-1727) Italian
£20000 $31400 €30000 Saint Jerome (86x72cm-34x28in) 11-Dec-2 Christie's, London #114/R est:15000-20000
Works on paper
£3000 $5010 €4350 The Nativity (27x20cm-11x8in) pen brown ink red chk prov.lit. 9-Jul-3 Sotheby's, London #49/R est:3000-4000

BURINI, Antonio (style) (1656-1727) Italian
£14103 $22141 €22000 Adoration of the shepherds (116x132cm-46x52in) 23-Nov-2 Arnold, Frankfurt #885/R est:2000

BURK, Geraldine (20th C) American
£590 $950 €885 Sailboats and figures in harbour (30x41cm-12x16in) s. canvasboard. 18-Feb-3 John Moran, Pasadena #10a

BURKE, Augustus (c.1838-1891) British
£3774 $5887 €6000 Group of cattle, Howth Hill, with cottage in the background (46x36cm-18x14in) mono. 17-Sep-2 Whyte's, Dublin #121/R est:5000-7000
£5743 $8959 €8500 Study on the Thames (60x91cm-24x36in) s. s.verso exhib. 26-Mar-3 James Adam, Dublin #32/R est:6000-10000

BURKEL, Heinrich (1802-1869) German
£1299 $1935 €2000 Sheep and cows on country track (28x36cm-11x14in) study paper. 26-Jun-2 Neumeister, Munich #697/R
£8333 $12917 €13000 View of Civitella on the Sabiner mountains with figures and animals in foreground (21x29cm-8x11in) panel lit. 4-Dec-2 Neumeister, Munich #686 est:12000
£35256 $51474 €55000 Fight outside tavern (49x69cm-19x27in) s.d.1835 panel. 4-Jun-2 Karl & Faber, Munich #53/R est:75000-80000

BURKHALTER, Jean (1895-1982) French
Works on paper
£287 $416 €450 Echelle (50x64cm-20x25in) s. pastel. 31-May-2 Blanchet, Paris #41

BURKHARDT, Hans Gustav (1904-1994) American/Swiss
£1402 $2300 €2033 Untitled (51x71cm-20x28in) s.d.1945. 1-Jun-3 Wright, Chicago #160/R est:3000-5000
£2564 $4000 €3846 Abstract landscape (81x107cm-32x42in) s.d.57 s.i.d.verso prov. 14-Oct-2 Butterfields, San Francisco #2042/R est:6000-8000
Works on paper
£609 $950 €914 Untitled, standing nude figure (62x46cm-24x18in) s.d. pastel. 14-Oct-2 Butterfields, San Francisco #1010/R est:800-1200
£1154 $1800 €1731 Standing women. Lying woman (66x51cm-26x20in) s. one d.1973 one d.1974 pastel pair. 14-Oct-2 Butterfields, San Francisco #1011/R est:2000-4000

BURKHARDT, Louis (20th C) German
Works on paper
£449 $700 €674 Dancer with red cape (30x28cm-12x11in) s.d.1920 mixed media dr. 10-Nov-2 Selkirks, St. Louis #561

BURKI, Fernand (?) Belgian?
£256 $403 €400 Corbeille de fleurs (57x84cm-22x33in) s. 10-Dec-2 Campo, Vlaamse Kaai #60

BURLEIGH, Charles H H (1875-1956) British
£480 $763 €720 Mevagissey (46x61cm-18x24in) s. 29-Apr-3 Gorringes, Lewes #2055

BURLISON, Clement (attrib) (1815-1899) British
£500 $785 €750 Portrait of James Wilson of Hutton Rudby at a table (76x63cm-30x25in) 21-Nov-2 Tennants, Leyburn #741/R

BURLIUK, David (1882-1967) American/Russian
£645 $1000 €968 Fire and water, Ophylia (15x25cm-6x10in) s.i. panel prov. 7-Dec-2 South Bay, Long Island #177/R
£696 $1100 €1044 Eve (23x10cm-9x4in) s. canvasboard. 5-Apr-3 DeFina, Austinburg #1357
£897 $1400 €1346 Old friends (15x14cm-6x6in) s. panel. 9-Nov-2 Sloan, North Bethesda #600/R
£938 $1500 €1407 Winter landscape with barn and out buildings (38x51cm-15x20in) s. 17-May-3 Pook & Pook, Downington #397c est:1000-1200
£974 $1500 €1461 Russian man on sled pulled by horse (20x30cm-8x12in) s. painted c.1940. 8-Sep-2 Treadway Gallery, Cincinnati #673/R est:2000-3000
£1097 $1700 €1646 Barber shop. Regulars. Woman by the shore (10x10cm-4x4in) one s.d.1953 verso two s. panel three. 25-Sep-2 Doyle, New York #13/R est:1200-1800
£1274 $2000 €1911 Palisades (30x40cm-12x16in) s. canvasboard. 22-Nov-2 Skinner, Boston #253/R est:1800-2200
£1290 $2000 €1935 Da serenade (18x23cm-7x9in) board prov. 7-Dec-2 South Bay, Long Island #176/R
£1364 $2100 €2046 Oil factory (18x30cm-7x12in) s. wood painted c.1940. 8-Sep-2 Treadway Gallery, Cincinnati #660/R est:2000-3000
£1800 $2826 €2700 Portrait of 1965. Four-masted schooner (20x16cm-8x6in) s.one d.1965 one oil wood one W/C crayon. 20-Nov-2 Sotheby's, London #103/R est:1800-2200
£1911 $3000 €2867 Flowers bty water (71x41cm-28x16in) s. 10-Dec-2 Doyle, New York #133/R est:2500-3500
£2420 $3800 €3630 Flowers on the beach (53x22cm-21x9in) s.d.1949 prov. 14-Dec-2 Weschler, Washington #712/R est:1000-2000
£2683 $4400 €3890 Landscape with house and couple conversing (29x44cm-11x17in) s.d. 5-Jun-3 Swann Galleries, New York #63/R est:2000-3000
£3049 $5000 €4421 Russian farm scene (19x24cm-7x9in) s.i. board painted c.1956. 5-Jun-3 Swann Galleries, New York #65/R est:2000-3000
£3171 $5200 €4598 Village couple and cow (18x32cm-7x13in) s.d. 5-Jun-3 Swann Galleries, New York #64/R est:2000-3000
£3415 $5600 €4952 Still life, vase of flowers, Florida (60x45cm-24x18in) s.i.d. linen canvas. 5-Jun-3 Swann Galleries, New York #61/R est:1500-2500
£4500 $7066 €6750 Shells on Long Island (33x45cm-13x18in) s.d.1955 board sold with study in crayon. 20-Nov-2 Sotheby's, London #150/R est:3000-5000
£6289 $10000 €9434 Kingston, New York (39x51cm-15x20in) s.i. canvasboard prov. 27-Feb-3 Christie's, Rockefeller NY #11/R est:15000
£12000 $19440 €18000 Windows on two Worlds (66x51cm-26x20in) s.i.d.1922. 21-May-3 Sotheby's, London #202/R est:10000-15000
£13000 $20410 €19500 The orchestra (40x51cm-16x20in) s.i.d.1957 board. 20-Nov-2 Sotheby's, London #185/R est:8000-12000
£14103 $20590 €22000 Flowers in Russian spring (62x68cm-24x27in) s. exhib.lit. 4-Jun-2 Karl & Faber, Munich #189/R est:24000-26000
£16000 $25920 €24000 Saga of Positano (127x97cm-50x38in) s.d.1962. 21-May-3 Sotheby's, London #193/R est:18000-25000
£22000 $35640 €33000 Artist's wife with a still life of flowers (110x56cm-43x22in) s.i. 21-May-3 Sotheby's, London #201/R est:22000-28000
£40000 $65600 €60000 American workers (107x91cm-42x36in) s.d.1922 prov.exhib. 5-Feb-3 Sotheby's, London #167/R est:60000
£45000 $70650 €67500 The artist's house, Hampton Bay, Long Island (99x127cm-39x50in) s.d.1961 prov. 20-Nov-2 Sotheby's, London #108/R est:18000-25000
Works on paper
£406 $650 €589 By the roadside (25x32cm-10x13in) s.d.33 W/C gouache pen ink. 16-May-3 Skinner, Boston #235/R
£427 $700 €619 Happy New Year, artist at easel (18x13cm-7x5in) s.i. W/C col pencil. 5-Jun-3 Swann Galleries, New York #62/R
£671 $1100 €973 Railroad yard at riverside (25x35cm-10x14in) s.d. W/C. 5-Jun-3 Swann Galleries, New York #58/R
£671 $1100 €973 Garden scene (20x12cm-8x5in) s. W/C exec.c.1932 sold with pen ink dr. 5-Jun-3 Swann Galleries, New York #59/R
£701 $1100 €1052 Three sailors seated in a dockside pub (29x37cm-11x15in) s. W/C over pencil prov. 14-Dec-2 Weschler, Washington #711/R est:800-1200
£1037 $1700 €1504 Hampton Bays, Long Island (27x36cm-11x14in) s.i. W/C. 5-Jun-3 Swann Galleries, New York #60/R
£3400 $5508 €5100 Cowboy in the Organ mountains, New Mexico (25x36cm-10x14in) s.i.d.1949 gouache. 21-May-3 Sotheby's, London #177/R est:4000-6000

BURMAN, John (1886-1899) British
£680 $1054 €1020 Cornish bay with figures on beach (33x36cm-13x14in) s.i.verso panel. 25-Sep-2 Brightwells, Leominster #931/R

BURMAN, Sakti (1935-) Indian

£13209 $21795 €19153 Gypsies on the road (116x89cm-46x35in) s. prov.lit. 6-Jul-3 Christie's, Hong Kong #96/R est:140000-180000 (HK.D 170000)

Works on paper

£1500 $2340 €2250 Dancing figures with lion (64x54cm-25x21in) s. mixed media canvas. 17-Oct-2 Bonhams, Knightsbridge #573/R est:1800-2500

£2000 $3120 €3000 Musical harmony (53x66cm-21x26in) s. mixed media canvas. 17-Oct-2 Bonhams, Knightsbridge #572/R est:2400-3000

BURMESTER, Georg (1864-1936) German

£377 $585 €600 Kiel bay (17x29cm-7x11in) s. board. 2-Nov-2 Hans Stahl, Toestorf #61/R

£1923 $2981 €3000 Fishing boats at anchor in early morning (52x64cm-20x25in) s.d.1897. 7-Dec-2 Hans Stahl, Hamburg #92/R est:2900

£3205 $4968 €5000 Summer flowers (65x73cm-26x29in) s.d.1916. 4-Dec-2 Lempertz, Koln #591/R est:3500-4000

BURN, E (19/20th C) American

£510 $800 €765 Portrait of a bay horse, Al Farrow (48x66cm-19x26in) S. 23-Nov-2 Pook & Pook, Downington #85/R

BURN, Henry (19th C) Australian

Works on paper

£9924 $15679 €14886 Refugee from the wreck, Coast of Brighton (23x35cm-9x14in) s.d.1870 i.verso W/C htd bodycol. 2-Apr-3 Christie's, Melbourne #34/R est:10000-15000 (A.D 26000)

BURNE-JONES, Sir Edward Coley (1833-1898) British

£5346 $8500 €8019 Ariadne discrowns herself (94x71cm-37x28in) s. i.verso painted c.1865. 4-May-3 Treadway Gallery, Cincinnati #484/R est:10000-20000

Works on paper

£950 $1473 €1425 Sacrifice of Noah. pencil sketch. 24-Sep-2 Bonhams, New Bond Street #2

£1000 $1660 €1500 Studies of armour for Perseus and the Graiae (23x29cm-9x11in) black chk prov. 12-Jun-3 Sotheby's, London #202/R est:800-1200

£1100 $1826 €1650 Leg study. Studies of arm (18x9cm-7x4in) pencil two. 12-Jun-3 Sotheby's, London #206/R est:800-1200

£1500 $2490 €2250 Study one of the Hesperides (26x16cm-10x6in) i. pencil. 12-Jun-3 Sotheby's, London #208/R est:1500-2000

£1600 $2480 €2400 Study of a tree (22x13cm-9x5in) pencil sold with another similar by the same hand. 4-Dec-2 Christie's, Kensington #80 est:400-600

£2000 $3120 €3000 Study of a standing male nude for souls of the styx (10x14cm-4x6in) pencil prov. 27-Mar-3 Christie's, Kensington #15/R est:2000-3000

£2200 $3410 €3300 St Dominic (100x56cm-39x22in) false mono. W/C bodycol. 4-Dec-2 Christie's, Kensington #136/R est:1500-2000

£2800 $4340 €4200 Study for the figure of Galatea (22x17cm-9x7in) pencil exhib. 4-Dec-2 Christie's, Kensington #135/R est:3000-5000

£2800 $4648 €4200 Two head studies (32x23cm-13x9in) pencil. 12-Jun-3 Sotheby's, London #207/R est:1500-2000

£4500 $7380 €6525 Dante Gabriel Rossetti bringing cushion to Jane Morris (18x11cm-7x4in) pencil prov.lit. 5-Jun-3 Christie's, London #127/R est:5000-8000

£5500 $8635 €8250 Figure study for love's wayfaring of car of love (20x22cm-8x9in) pencil. 21-Nov-2 Christie's, London #77/R est:2500-3500

£7000 $11480 €10150 Studies for Angels in Galhad at the Shrine for Holy Grail tapestries (35x19cm-14x7in) black crayon four in two frames prov.exhib. 5-Jun-3 Christie's, London #124/R est:8000-12000

£28000 $44240 €42000 Series of highly amusing illustrated letters. album prov. 28-Nov-2 Sotheby's, London #27/R est:20000-30000

£100000 $158000 €150000 King's daughters (19x24cm-7x9in) s. pen ink. 28-Nov-2 Sotheby's, London #24/R est:40000-60000

BURNET, John (1784-1868) British

£450 $711 €675 Figures in an interior (46x56cm-18x22in) s. 12-Nov-2 Bonhams, Knightsbridge #138/R

BURNETT, Thomas Stuart (1853-1888) British

Sculpture

£38000 $58140 €57000 Rob Roy. s.d.1884 marble. 22-Aug-2 Bonhams, Edinburgh #640a/R est:20000-30000

BURNHAM, Anita (1880-?) American

Works on paper

£373 $600 €560 Flower garden (43x51cm-17x20in) s.d.1933 W/C. 19-Jan-3 Jeffery Burchard, Florida #20a/R

BURNIER, Richard (1826-1884) Dutch

£1474 $2285 €2300 Girl milking cow in barn (60x82cm-24x32in) s. prov. 7-Dec-2 Ketterer, Hamburg #90/R est:2500-3000

£2070 $3250 €3105 Beach scene with several cows and woman with sailboat in background (53x81cm-21x32in) s. 19-Apr-3 James Julia, Fairfield #176/R est:4000-6000

BURNS, Colin W (1944-) British

£1400 $2198 €2100 Wells-next-the-sea, in summer with figures (25x38cm-10x15in) s. 13-Dec-2 Keys, Aylsham #651/R est:1000-1200

£1500 $2355 €2250 Autumnal Norfolk river landscape with mallard rising from a stream (56x91cm-22x36in) s. 13-Dec-2 Keys, Aylsham #672/R est:1500-2000

£1850 $2905 €2775 Still life with white roses (43x51cm-17x20in) s. 13-Dec-2 Keys, Aylsham #663 est:1600-1800

£2500 $3950 €3750 English partridge (43x55cm-17x22in) s.i. 27-Nov-2 Christie's, London #35/R

£2500 $3925 €3750 Extensive Norfolk winter landscape with mallard in flight over river (56x89cm-22x35in) s. 13-Dec-2 Keys, Aylsham #671/R est:2000-2500

£2600 $4030 €3900 Woodcock in the dune (54x81cm-21x32in) s. i.verso. 31-Oct-2 Christie's, London #54/R est:3000-5000

£2800 $4368 €4200 Woodcock in snow (28x33cm-11x13in) s. 11-Apr-3 Keys, Aylsham #620/R est:1000-1500

£2917 $4200 €4376 Woodcock amongst brambles (38x46cm-15x18in) s. i.on stretcher. 15-Jan-3 Christie's, Rockefeller NY #180/R

£3000 $4890 €4500 Keepers Cottage, near Petersfield (36x43cm-14x17in) s. 14-Feb-3 Keys, Aylsham #640/R est:900-1200

£3000 $5010 €4350 Norfolk winter landscape with mallard in flight over a dyke (53x74cm-21x29in) s. 20-Jun-3 Keys, Aylsham #648/R est:2500-3500

£3200 $4960 €4800 Red grouse in a moorland hollows (55x66cm-22x26in) s. i.verso. 31-Oct-2 Christie's, London #55/R est:2000-3000

£4500 $6975 €6750 Red grouse crossing a burn, Rannoch Moor (77x127cm-30x50in) s. i.verso. 31-Oct-2 Christie's, London #52/R est:4000-6000

£4500 $7290 €6750 Ptarmigan in mid plumage, Cairngorms (75x95cm-30x37in) s. i.verso. 22-May-3 Christie's, London #44/R est:3000-5000

£4514 $6500 €6771 Central Park under snow (65x78cm-26x31in) s. i.on stretcher. 15-Jan-3 Christie's, Rockefeller NY #179/R

£4800 $7584 €7200 Woodcock resting in the marrams (61x91cm-24x36in) s.i. 27-Nov-2 Christie's, London #31/R

£4800 $7776 €7200 Woodcock in spring (46x62cm-18x24in) s. i.verso. 22-May-3 Christie's, London #46/R est:2000-3000

£5200 $8216 €7800 Winter in Norfolk fen (76x101cm-30x40in) s.i. 27-Nov-2 Christie's, London #32/R

£5500 $8910 €8250 Grey partridge in a winter landscape (58x76cm-23x30in) s. i.verso. 22-May-3 Christie's, London #45/R est:2500-3500

£5520 $8500 €8280 Red grouse, Beinn Laith Mhor, Wester Ross (89x149cm-35x59in) s. i.stretcher. 4-Sep-2 Christie's, Rockefeller NY #383/R est:6000-8000

£6800 $11016 €10200 Gadwall and shoveler ducks (66x117cm-26x46in) s. i.verso. 22-May-3 Christie's, London #42/R est:3000-5000

£7500 $11850 €11250 Red grouse (101x127cm-40x50in) s.i. 27-Nov-2 Christie's, London #33/R

£7500 $12150 €11250 Winter, Bacton Woods (91x127cm-36x50in) s. i.verso. 22-May-3 Christie's, London #43/R est:4000-6000

£7639 $11000 €11459 Red grouse (89x158cm-35x62in) s. 15-Jan-3 Christie's, Rockefeller NY #178/R est:10000

£7639 $11000 €11459 Pheasant drive (116x163cm-46x64in) s. i.on stretcher. 15-Jan-3 Christie's, Rockefeller NY #177/R est:8000

£8000 $12400 €12000 Ptarmigan on the slopes of Sgurr a Mhaim, Stob Ban beyond (115x150cm-45x59in) s. i.verso. 31-Oct-2 Christie's, London #51/R est:5000-8000

£8000 $13280 €11600 Keeps cottage, near Petersfield (35x44cm-14x17in) s. 12-Jun-3 Christie's, Kensington #152/R est:3000-5000

Works on paper

£520 $848 €780 Hen harrier over the Broad (15x30cm-6x12in) s. W/C. 14-Feb-3 Keys, Aylsham #629/R

£650 $1086 €943 Winterton Beach, Norfolk (18x23cm-7x9in) s. W/C. 20-Jun-3 Keys, Aylsham #599/R

£700 $1141 €1050 Lady Broad (23x46cm-9x18in) s. W/C. 14-Feb-3 Keys, Aylsham #630/R

£720 $1174 €1080 Autumn moorings (15x28cm-6x11in) s. W/C. 14-Feb-3 Keys, Aylsham #631

£780 $1303 €1131 Moonrise, Horsey (18x23cm-7x9in) s. W/C. 20-Jun-3 Keys, Aylsham #598/R

£850 $1326 €1275 Breydon South Wal and Berney Arms Mill (23x30cm-9x12in) s. W/C. 11-Apr-3 Keys, Aylsham #567/R est:500-750

£880 $1373 €1320 Winter Thompson Common, Norfolk (18x23cm-7x9in) s. W/C. 11-Apr-3 Keys, Aylsham #566

£1100 $1672 €1650 Wildfowl alighting, Horsey (33x69cm-13x27in) s. W/C. 16-Aug-2 Keys, Aylsham #571/R

£1200 $2004 €1740 Mallard alighting, Hickling (38x51cm-15x20in) s. W/C. 20-Jun-3 Keys, Aylsham #630/R est:900-1200

BURNS, Glynis R (?) British
£360 $558 €540 Feathered friends (30x18cm-12x7in) s. board. 2-Oct-2 John Ross, Belfast #184
£400 $636 €600 Cocktails with cockatiels (20x35cm-8x14in) s. board. 5-Mar-3 John Ross, Belfast #34

BURNS, Michael (20th C) Canadian
£361 $567 €542 Childhood lost (75x60cm-30x24in) s.i.d.1989. 25-Nov-2 Hodgins, Calgary #419/R (C.D 900)

BURNS, Milton J (1853-1933) American
£4403 $7000 €6605 Fisherfolk (61x102cm-24x40in) s. 7-Mar-3 Skinner, Boston #331/R est:7000-9000

BURNS, Robert (1869-1941) British
£3000 $4860 €4500 New necklace (76x63cm-30x25in) s. 23-May-3 Lyon & Turnbull, Edinburgh #43/R est:3000-5000
£6200 $9424 €9300 My Love's in Germanie, send him hame, send him hame (122x214cm-48x84in) exhib. 28-Aug-2 Sotheby's, London #928/R est:5000-7000

Works on paper
£480 $749 €720 Sheep pen (37x68cm-15x27in) s.d.1920 W/C prov. 10-Apr-3 Bonhams, Edinburgh #136
£1100 $1705 €1650 Fields under snow (47x73cm-19x29in) s. W/C. 5-Dec-2 Bonhams, Edinburgh #123 est:1000-1500

BURNS, William (1921-1972) British
£920 $1490 €1380 Railway signals (60x60cm-24x24in) s. exhib. 23-May-3 Lyon & Turnbull, Edinburgh #40
£2000 $3120 €3000 Window (76x101cm-30x40in) s. s.i.verso. 17-Oct-2 Bonhams, Edinburgh #47/R est:1200-1800

BURNS, William H (1924-) Irish
£320 $509 €480 Connemara (45x71cm-18x28in) s. 5-Mar-3 John Ross, Belfast #38
£850 $1318 €1275 Near Carna, Connemara (51x76cm-20x30in) s. 2-Oct-2 John Ross, Belfast #38

BURNSIDE, David S (20th C) American
£346 $550 €519 Scottish fisherman's cottage (23x30cm-9x12in) s.i. board painted c.1960. 2-Mar-3 Toomey, Oak Park #732/R

BURON, Henri Lucien Joseph (1880-1969) French
£500 $815 €720 Pardon a Notre Dame de la Joie (8x12cm-3x5in) s. panel. 19-Jul-3 Thierry & Lannon, Brest #107
£521 $849 €750 Jour de pardon a Ste Anne La Palue (10x15cm-4x6in) s.d.1935 cardboard. 19-Jul-3 Thierry & Lannon, Brest #308

Works on paper
£387 $624 €550 Composition au vase de roses (37x44cm-15x17in) s.d.1937 pastel. 11-May-3 Thierry & Lannon, Brest #292

BUROV, Nikolai Gerasimovich (1899-1959) Russian
£8000 $12960 €12000 Portrait of a young girl (43x34cm-17x13in) s.i.d.1874. 21-May-3 Sotheby's, London #22/R est:8000-12000

BURPEE, William P (1846-?) American
£5732 $9000 €8598 Boston fish pier (63x76cm-25x30in) one s.d.09 one s. pastel pair prov. 19-Nov-2 Butterfields, San Francisco #8023/R est:6000-8000

Works on paper
£299 $475 €449 Indian summer (15x21cm-6x8in) s. pastel. 7-Mar-3 Skinner, Boston #267/R
£312 $500 €452 Woodland winter scene (21x24cm-8x9in) s. pastel. 16-May-3 Skinner, Boston #261/R
£437 $700 €634 Nocturne, the wharf (21x23cm-8x9in) s. pastel. 16-May-3 Skinner, Boston #292/R
£1592 $2500 €2388 Dockside evening. Winter forest (22x23cm-9x9in) s. pastel pair prov. 19-Nov-2 Butterfields, San Francisco #8024/R est:3000-5000
£1807 $3000 €2620 New England coast. Rocky shoreline. Harbour view (32x44cm-13x17in) s. two pencil W/C one pastel three. 11-Jun-3 Butterfields, San Francisco #4049/R est:3000-5000
£2259 $3750 €3276 Summer woods. Winter stream. Snowy hills. Frozen river (24x36cm-9x14in) one s. pastel four. 11-Jun-3 Butterfields, San Francisco #4048/R est:3000-5000

BURR, Alexander Hohenlohe (1837-1899) British
£1000 $1530 €1500 Dressing the doll (23x23cm-9x9in) s. board arched top. 22-Aug-2 Bonhams, Edinburgh #992/R est:1200-1800
£2200 $3388 €3300 Teaching an old dog new tricks (41x59cm-16x23in) s. indis d.1875. 24-Oct-2 Christie's, Kensington #117/R est:1500-2000
£3600 $5472 €5400 Grandfather's delight (92x72cm-36x28in) 28-Aug-2 Sotheby's, London #912/R est:1500-2000
£6000 $9660 €9000 Bid man's buff (24x35cm-9x14in) mono.d. prov. 20-Feb-3 Christie's, London #339/R
£6500 $10335 €9750 Bedlam (31x49cm-12x19in) s.d.80 prov. 6-Mar-3 Christie's, Kensington #101/R est:2000-3000
£7000 $11270 €10500 Blind man's buff (46x62cm-18x24in) s. prov. 20-Feb-3 Christie's, London #338/R
£8000 $12480 €12000 Waiting an anticipation (63x51cm-25x20in) s. prov.exhib. 14-Apr-3 Sotheby's, London #56/R est:5000-7000
£9000 $14040 €13500 Obedience (51x41cm-20x16in) s.d.84 prov. 14-Apr-3 Sotheby's, London #57/R est:5000-7000
£31000 $48050 €46500 Logan Braes (83x101cm-33x40in) s.d.1860 prov.lit. 31-Oct-2 Christie's, London #61/R est:15000-20000

BURR, John (1831-1893) British
£400 $624 €600 Mother and child in a cottage interior (15x11cm-6x4in) s.d.78 panel. 10-Apr-3 Tennants, Leyburn #1108/R
£850 $1318 €1275 No weel bairn (15x20cm-6x8in) s. board. 6-Dec-2 Lyon & Turnbull, Edinburgh #28/R
£35000 $56350 €52500 Peepshow (76x64cm-30x25in) s.d.1864 prov.exhib.lit. 20-Feb-3 Christie's, London #255/R est:50000

BURRA, Edward (1905-1976) British
Works on paper
£1400 $2338 €2030 Costume design for Don Juan (63x28cm-25x11in) st.sig. W/C over pencil prov. 24-Jun-3 Bonhams, New Bond Street #31/R est:1500-2000
£3500 $5425 €5250 Saloon (56x44cm-22x17in) s.d.1928 pencil prov. 3-Dec-2 Bonhams, New Bond Street #41/R est:3000-5000
£19500 $30225 €29250 New York bar (37x51cm-15x20in) s.d.33 pen ink prov. 3-Dec-2 Bonhams, New Bond Street #40/R est:5000-7000
£80000 $131200 €116000 Figure composition, No 1 (76x132cm-30x52in) st.sig. W/C pencil. 4-Jun-3 Sotheby's, London #72/R est:80000-100000

BURRELL, Alfred Ray (1877-?) American
£566 $900 €849 California view (28x35cm-11x14in) s. canvasboard. 7-Mar-3 Skinner, Boston #355/R

BURRELL, James (fl.1859-c.1865) British
£414 $650 €621 Coastal scene (25x43cm-10x17in) s. 19-Apr-3 Susanin's, Chicago #5079

BURRI, Alberto (1915-1995) Italian
£26950 $43660 €38000 Messico (35x30cm-14x12in) i.d.64 board on plywood. 26-May-3 Christie's, Milan #189/R est:10000-15000
£45000 $70200 €67500 Combustione legno (30x40cm-12x16in) i.verso acrylic vinavil wood on masonite executed 1963 prov.lit. 21-Oct-2 Sotheby's, London #23/R est:50000-70000
£90000 $140400 €135000 Sacco bianco nero (79x50cm-31x20in) s. verso burlap cellotex oil on canvas painted 1956 prov.exhib.lit. 21-Oct-2 Sotheby's, London #48/R est:100000-150000
£187097 $295613 €290000 Big wood M (156x254cm-61x100in) s.i.d.58 wood acrylic prov.exhib.lit. 18-Dec-2 Christie's, Rome #294/R est:400000

Prints
£2838 $4427 €4200 Black D (67x96cm-26x38in) s. aquatint eau forte exec.1971 lit. 28-Mar-3 Farsetti, Prato #255/R
£4255 $6894 €6000 Cretto bianco (70x100cm-28x39in) s. num.43/90 engraving exhib.lit. 26-May-3 Christie's, Milan #19/R est:1800-2000
£14184 $22979 €20000 Combustioni (64x48cm-25x19in) s. num.11/X1 six panels eau forte aquatint exhib.lit. 26-May-3 Christie's, Milan #26 est:3000-4000

Works on paper
£2532 $3949 €4000 Cretto (67x97cm-26x38in) s. polymer card. 14-Sep-2 Meeting Art, Vercelli #120/R
£9220 $14936 €13000 Cellotex (16x14cm-6x6in) s.d.71 cellotex acrylic vinyl cardboard. 26-May-3 Christie's, Milan #29/R est:3000-4000
£12766 $20681 €18000 Combustion (16x14cm-6x6in) s.d.71 paper on cardboard. 26-May-3 Christie's, Milan #27/R est:2500-3000

BURRI, Johann-Ulrich (1802-?) Swiss
Works on paper
£798 $1309 €1157 View from Ibach of the Mythen (58x76cm-23x30in) s. W/C. 4-Jun-3 Fischer, Luzern #2592/R est:2000-2500 (S.FR 1700)

BURRINGTON, Arthur (1856-1924) British
Works on paper
£250 $398 €375 Promontogno (30x51cm-12x20in) s. W/C. 29-Apr-3 Peter Francis, Wales #33

BURROW, John H (1955-) Canadian/American
£283 $441 €471 Game in the dugout (46x61cm-18x24in) s. s.i.verso acrylic board. 13-Apr-3 Levis, Calgary #14/R (C.D 650)

BURROWS, R (1810-1883) British
£680 $1082 €1000 Cows in water (20x21cm-8x8in) s. panel pair. 20-Mar-3 Neumeister, Munich #2600/R

BURROWS, Robert (1810-1883) British
£500 $780 €750 Feeding hens. Figure on a path (30x25cm-12x10in) s. pair. 17-Oct-2 David Lay, Penzance #1055
£750 $1185 €1125 On a farm track. Returning home (32x25cm-13x10in) s. pair. 27-Nov-2 Hamptons Fine Art, Godalming #445
£800 $1240 €1200 Winter (35x51cm-14x20in) s. 30-Sep-2 Bonhams, Ipswich #450/R
£1100 $1738 €1595 Wooded landscape, with figures by cottages, windmill in distance (25x36cm-10x14in) s.d.1875. 22-Jul-3 Sworder & Son, Bishops Stortford #306/R est:400-600
£1500 $2475 €2175 Cattle and drover in wooded landscape (25x36cm-10x14in) s. 1-Jul-3 Bonhams, Norwich #252/R est:1500-2000
£1650 $2624 €2475 Lady by a cottage feeding the chickens (31x25cm-12x10in) s. sold with a companion. 5-Mar-3 Bonhams, Bury St Edmunds #404/R est:1800-2500

BURSSENS, Jan (1925-2002) Belgian
£409 $630 €650 Monsieur UBU (60x90cm-24x35in) panel. 22-Oct-2 Campo, Vlaamse Kaai #429
£903 $1435 €1300 Composition (63x180cm-25x71in) s. panel. 29-Apr-3 Campo, Vlaamse Kaai #32
£1635 $2535 €2600 Dog (100x70cm-39x28in) s.verso. 5-Oct-2 De Vuyst, Lokeren #50/R est:2000-2500

BURT, C T (1823-1902) British
£780 $1264 €1100 Highland landscape with cattle (61x89cm-24x35in) s. 20-May-3 Mealy's, Castlecomer #949/R est:700-900
£2100 $3255 €3150 Wooded landscape with figures picking bluebells by a stream (67x47cm-26x19in) s.d.1859. 1-Oct-2 Fellows & Sons, Birmingham #50/R est:1000-1500

BURT, Charles Thomas (1823-1902) British
£700 $1162 €1015 Traveller and shepherds in a highland landscape (30x46cm-12x18in) s.d.1894. 12-Jun-3 Gorringes, Lewes #1601
£956 $1500 €1434 Panoramic view with cattle watering (41x62cm-16x24in) s. 22-Nov-2 Skinner, Boston #24/R est:1000-1200
£1073 $1674 €1556 Looking out to sea (76x122cm-30x48in) s.d.1887. 26-Mar-3 Walker's, Ottawa #64/R est:3000-4000 (C.D 2500)
£3500 $5460 €5250 Partridge shoot (62x100cm-24x39in) s.d.1893. 10-Apr-3 Tennants, Leyburn #1021/R est:1500-2500

BURT, Charles Thomas (attrib) (1823-1902) British
£750 $1155 €1125 Log wagon by a pond in an extensive landscape (76x127cm-30x50in) 5-Sep-2 Christie's, Kensington #131

BURT, James (?) ?
£7143 $11000 €10715 View from Fort Putnam (53x76cm-21x30in) s.d.1838 prov. 24-Oct-2 Shannon's, Milford #47/R est:8000-12000

BURTON, Claire Eva (20th C) British
£350 $546 €525 Tight finish (40x58cm-16x23in) s.d.1985 col pastel. 6-Nov-2 Sotheby's, Olympia #106/R
Works on paper
£350 $546 €525 One man, Victory at Cheltenham (42x47cm-17x19in) s.d.97 mixed media. 6-Nov-2 Sotheby's, Olympia #108/R

BURTON, Dennis Eugène Norman (1933-) Canadian
£391 $610 €653 Macuba (30x41cm-12x16in) s.d.1963 prov. 13-Apr-3 Levis, Calgary #307/R est:1500-1700 (C.D 900)

BURTON, Henry (20th C) British
£487 $755 €770 On the road to Enniskerry (46x55cm-18x22in) s.d.48 board exhib. 24-Sep-2 De Veres Art Auctions, Dublin #160

BURTON, Jeff (1963-) ?
Photographs
£2000 $3200 €3000 Untitled no.101 - labels (101x76cm-40x30in) s.i.d.1998 num.1/3 c-print mounted on foamcore prov. 14-May-3 Sotheby's, New York #333/R est:3000-4000

BURTON, Nancy Jane (1900-1972) British
£900 $1404 €1350 Tartan jacket on Alert (35x444cm-14x175in) s. W/C pencil two. 14-Apr-3 Sotheby's, London #156/R est:1000-1500

BURTON, Ralph W (1905-1984) Canadian
£202 $319 €303 Early September (27x33cm-11x13in) s.i.d.1968 s.verso panel prov. 14-Nov-2 Heffel, Vancouver #230 (C.D 500)
£202 $319 €303 Late autumn (27x33cm-11x13in) s.i.d.1964 s.verso panel prov. 14-Nov-2 Heffel, Vancouver #231 (C.D 500)
£236 $368 €342 Autumn near Fallbrooke (27x34cm-11x13in) s.i.d.1973 panel. 26-Mar-3 Walker's, Ottawa #209/R (C.D 550)
£258 $402 €387 Spring (27x34cm-11x13in) s. i.d.1967 verso panel. 25-Mar-3 Ritchie, Toronto #111 (C.D 600)
£279 $435 €405 Autumn near Merrickville (27x34cm-11x13in) s.i.d.1974 panel. 26-Mar-3 Walker's, Ottawa #208/R (C.D 650)
£300 $469 €435 Pulp and paper, Kamiskimang, Quebec (27x34cm-11x13in) s.i.d.1955 panel. 26-Mar-3 Walker's, Ottawa #410/R (C.D 700)
£331 $519 €497 Church, North Gower, Ontario (25x36cm-10x14in) s.i.d.1975 s.verso panel. 24-Jul-2 Walker's, Ottawa #259/R (C.D 800)
£333 $546 €500 Sunlight and shadow, winter (26x34cm-10x13in) s.d.51 panel. 3-Jun-3 Joyner, Toronto #526 (C.D 750)
£343 $559 €515 Village in winter (26x34cm-10x13in) s. panel. 12-Feb-3 Iegor de Saint Hippolyte, Montreal #39 (C.D 850)
£372 $584 €558 Old log house, Lanark County, Ontario (25x36cm-10x14in) s.i.d.1973 s.verso. 24-Jul-2 Walker's, Ottawa #200/R (C.D 900)
£378 $619 €567 Spring - farmer rapids, Que (26x34cm-10x13in) s. panel. 3-Jun-3 Joyner, Toronto #586 (C.D 850)
£413 $649 €620 Creek in Lanark County, Ontario (51x66cm-20x26in) s.i.d.1973 s.verso. 24-Jul-2 Walker's, Ottawa #400/R est:1000-1500 (C.D 1000)
£422 $692 €633 Farm near Burrits Rapids, Ont (26x34cm-10x13in) s. panel prov. 3-Jun-3 Joyner, Toronto #479 est:700-900 (C.D 950)
£472 $736 €708 Old French house (27x34cm-11x13in) s. i.verso panel. 25-Mar-3 Ritchie, Toronto #110/R est:600-800 (C.D 1100)
£579 $908 €869 Spring, Burrits Rapids, Ontaio (61x76cm-24x30in) s.i.d.1971 s.verso. 24-Jul-2 Walker's, Ottawa #234/R est:1200-1600 (C.D 1400)
£730 $1138 €1059 Old farm buildings (51x66cm-20x26in) s.i.d.71. 26-Mar-3 Walker's, Ottawa #219/R est:1200-1600 (C.D 1700)
£897 $1435 €1346 Autumn near Prospect, Ontario (51x67cm-20x26in) s. s.i.d.1973 verso. 15-May-3 Heffel, Vancouver #37/R est:2250-2750 (C.D 2000)
£905 $1403 €1358 Spring on the rideau river near Carlton Lodge (60x75cm-24x30in) s. 3-Dec-2 Joyner, Toronto #290/R est:2000-2500 (C.D 2200)

BURTON, Sir Frederick William (1816-1900) British
Works on paper
£6329 $9810 €10000 La Touche family (76x61cm-30x24in) s.d.1840 W/C htd white. 24-Sep-2 De Veres Art Auctions, Dublin #157/R est:7000-10000

BURTON, Sir Frederick William (attrib) (1816-1900) British
£500 $770 €750 Going to the dairy. Wayside rest (46x81cm-18x32in) one s.d.1885 pair. 5-Sep-2 Christie's, Kensington #171/R

BURTON, William Shakespeare (1830-1916) British
£580 $905 €870 View near Blackheath (17x24cm-7x9in) mono. board. 9-Oct-2 Woolley & Wallis, Salisbury #257/R
£4000 $6440 €6000 Love letter (17x22cm-7x9in) s.i.d.1866 prov. 20-Feb-3 Christie's, London #260/R

BURWASH, Nathaniel C (1906-) American
£1613 $2500 €2420 WPA style men chopping wood (33x46cm-13x18in) s.d.36. 29-Oct-2 John Moran, Pasadena #656 est:800-1200

BURWOOD, G Vemply (19/20th C) British
£270 $410 €405 Fishing boats leaving harbour (15x20cm-6x8in) 16-Aug-2 Keys, Aylsham #449

BURY, Pol (1922-) Belgian
£256 $405 €400 Portrait d'homme (60x49cm-24x19in) panel. 15-Nov-2 Laurence Calmels, Paris #68/R
£321 $506 €500 Deux figures (50x40cm-20x16in) s. panel. 15-Nov-2 Laurence Calmels, Paris #71/R
£385 $608 €600 Untitled (49x59cm-19x23in) s. 15-Nov-2 Laurence Calmels, Paris #98
£385 $608 €600 Untitled (60x80cm-24x31in) panel. 15-Nov-2 Laurence Calmels, Paris #106
£449 $709 €700 Untitled (46x38cm-18x15in) s.d.49. 15-Nov-2 Laurence Calmels, Paris #109/R
£449 $709 €700 Untitled (69x100cm-27x39in) panel. 15-Nov-2 Laurence Calmels, Paris #105
£449 $709 €700 Untitled (50x60cm-20x24in) s. 15-Nov-2 Laurence Calmels, Paris #119/R
£513 $810 €800 Personnage dans un interieur (80x60cm-31x24in) s.d.47 panel. 15-Nov-2 Laurence Calmels, Paris #117

£513 $810 €800 Paysage (72x100cm-28x39in) panel. 15-Nov-2 Laurence Calmels, Paris #114
£641 $1013 €1000 Femme (60x49cm-24x19in) s. panel. 15-Nov-2 Laurence Calmels, Paris #86/R
£641 $1013 €1000 Femme assise (60x50cm-24x20in) s.d.46 panel. 15-Nov-2 Laurence Calmels, Paris #70/R
£641 $1013 €1000 Composition (50x60cm-20x24in) s.d.49 s.i.d.verso. 15-Nov-2 Laurence Calmels, Paris #120/R
£705 $1114 €1100 Deux figures (60x80cm-24x31in) s.d.47 panel. 15-Nov-2 Laurence Calmels, Paris #122/R
£769 $1215 €1200 Femme assise (80x60cm-31x24in) s.d.47 panel. 15-Nov-2 Laurence Calmels, Paris #73/R
£769 $1215 €1200 Untitled (60x80cm-24x31in) s. panel. 15-Nov-2 Laurence Calmels, Paris #69/R
£833 $1317 €1300 Untitled (60x49cm-24x19in) s.d.47. 15-Nov-2 Laurence Calmels, Paris #89/R
£833 $1317 €1300 Untitled (50x60cm-20x24in) s.d.47 panel. 15-Nov-2 Laurence Calmels, Paris #88/R
£833 $1317 €1300 Untitled (40x60cm-16x24in) s. 15-Nov-2 Laurence Calmels, Paris #121/R
£833 $1317 €1300 Femme assise dans un interieur (80x60cm-31x24in) panel. 15-Nov-2 Laurence Calmels, Paris #115/R
£833 $1317 €1300 Femme couchee (60x80cm-24x31in) panel lit. 15-Nov-2 Laurence Calmels, Paris #113/R
£897 $1418 €1400 Untitled (40x50cm-16x20in) s.d.47. 15-Nov-2 Laurence Calmels, Paris #36/R
£962 $1519 €1500 Untitled (70x50cm-28x20in) 15-Nov-2 Laurence Calmels, Paris #102/R
£1026 $1621 €1600 Untitled (40x34cm-16x13in) 15-Nov-2 Laurence Calmels, Paris #104/R
£1079 $1727 €1500 Movement (50x59cm-20x23in) s. exhib. 17-May-3 De Vuyst, Lokeren #60/R est:1700-2000
£1154 $1823 €1800 Deux figures (50x40cm-20x16in) s. panel. 15-Nov-2 Laurence Calmels, Paris #87/R
£1154 $1823 €1800 Voute (73x50cm-29x20in) s. 15-Nov-2 Laurence Calmels, Paris #96/R
£1282 $2026 €2000 Untitled (60x70cm-24x28in) s.d.1950. 15-Nov-2 Laurence Calmels, Paris #35/R
£1282 $2026 €2000 Untitled (81x100cm-32x39in) s.d.47. 15-Nov-2 Laurence Calmels, Paris #108/R
£1439 $2302 €2000 Landscape (72x100cm-28x39in) board painted c.1950. 17-May-3 De Vuyst, Lokeren #59/R est:2000-2600
£1603 $2532 €2500 Femme allongee (60x80cm-24x31in) panel. 15-Nov-2 Laurence Calmels, Paris #99
£1603 $2532 €2500 Untitled (81x60cm-32x24in) s. 15-Nov-2 Laurence Calmels, Paris #107/R
£1795 $2836 €2800 Paysage anime (50x60cm-20x24in) s.d.46 panel. 15-Nov-2 Laurence Calmels, Paris #72
£1795 $2836 €2800 Untitled (90x60cm-35x24in) painted c.1950. 15-Nov-2 Laurence Calmels, Paris #82/R
£1795 $2836 €2800 Traces (100x80cm-39x31in) s.d.50. 15-Nov-2 Laurence Calmels, Paris #94/R
£2051 $3241 €3200 Composition (100x70cm-39x28in) s. s.i.d.51 verso. 15-Nov-2 Laurence Calmels, Paris #34/R
£2051 $3241 €3200 Composition sur fond rouge (100x81cm-39x32in) s. i.d.1950 verso. 15-Nov-2 Laurence Calmels, Paris #33/R
£2051 $3241 €3200 Untitled (78x68cm-31x27in) s. painted 1951. 15-Nov-2 Laurence Calmels, Paris #84/R
£2244 $3545 €3500 Untitled (70x100cm-28x39in) s.d.52. 15-Nov-2 Laurence Calmels, Paris #103/R
£2244 $3545 €3500 Untitled (100x81cm-39x32in) s. 15-Nov-2 Laurence Calmels, Paris #123/R est:1500
£2564 $4051 €4000 Untitled (80x100cm-31x39in) s.d.52. 15-Nov-2 Laurence Calmels, Paris #81/R
£2564 $4051 €4000 Composition (80x100cm-31x39in) s. s.i.d.1951. 15-Nov-2 Laurence Calmels, Paris #83/R
£2878 $4604 €4000 Paysage (80x100cm-31x39in) s.d.47 exhib. 17-May-3 De Vuyst, Lokeren #57/R est:4400-5500
£3077 $4862 €4800 Untitled (80x100cm-31x39in) 15-Nov-2 Laurence Calmels, Paris #95/R
£3526 $5571 €5500 Ponctuation (80x61cm-31x24in) s.verso masonite engine. 15-Nov-2 Laurence Calmels, Paris #49/R
£3526 $5571 €5500 Ponctuation (64x64cm-25x25in) s.d.1960 verso masonite engine. 15-Nov-2 Laurence Calmels, Paris #48/R
£3526 $5571 €5500 Ponctuation (61x50cm-24x20in) masonite engine lit. 15-Nov-2 Laurence Calmels, Paris #61/R
£4167 $6583 €6500 Ponctuation carree (61x61cm-24x24in) masonite engine prov.lit. 15-Nov-2 Laurence Calmels, Paris #56/R est:2000
£4808 $7596 €7500 Ponctuation (243x46cm-96x18in) s.verso painted masonite exec.c.1960. 15-Nov-2 Laurence Calmels, Paris #10/R
£5128 $8103 €8000 Ponctuation (122x61cm-48x24in) s.verso masonite engine. 15-Nov-2 Laurence Calmels, Paris #52/R
£5449 $8609 €8500 Points blancs (61x61cm-24x24in) masonite metal engine prov.lit. 15-Nov-2 Laurence Calmels, Paris #65/R
£6090 $9622 €9500 Ponctuation (122x61cm-48x24in) i.d.1960v. masonite exhib.lit. 15-Nov-2 Laurence Calmels, Paris #2/R est:2000
£6731 $10635 €10500 Ponctuation (122x61cm-48x24in) s.d.1960 verso masonite engine. 15-Nov-2 Laurence Calmels, Paris #51/R est:3000

Sculpture

£1410 $2228 €2200 Melangeur (47x47x10cm-19x19x4in) s.i.verso painted wood engine exec.1967 exhib.lit. 15-Nov-2 Laurence Calmels, Paris #21/R
£1410 $2228 €2200 Melangeur (47x47x10cm-19x19x4in) painted wood exec.1967 prov.exhib.lit. 15-Nov-2 Laurence Calmels, Paris #40/R
£1410 $2228 €2200 Melangeur (47x47x10cm-19x19x4in) painted wood exec.1967 prov.exhib.lit. 15-Nov-2 Laurence Calmels, Paris #53/R
£1538 $2431 €2400 Melangeur (47x47x10cm-19x19x4in) s.num.6/15 verso painte wood exec.1967 exhib.lit. 15-Nov-2 Laurence Calmels, Paris #5/R
£2051 $3241 €3200 26 boucles (61x30cm-24x12in) copper exec.c.1967 lit. 15-Nov-2 Laurence Calmels, Paris #4/R
£2244 $3545 €3500 Untitled (16x76cm-6x30in) s.verso metal wood. 15-Nov-2 Laurence Calmels, Paris #3/R
£2244 $3545 €3500 Relief (30x52x20cm-12x20x8in) painted metal. 15-Nov-2 Laurence Calmels, Paris #50/R
£2244 $3545 €3500 Elements (49x30x34cm-19x12x13in) tin exec.c.1968. 15-Nov-2 Laurence Calmels, Paris #101/R
£2244 $3545 €3500 Boules dans une boite (56x12x7cm-22x5x3in) steel. 15-Nov-2 Laurence Calmels, Paris #111/R
£2308 $3646 €3600 Arcs de cercle (17x25x25cm-7x10x10in) s. metal steel engine exec.c.1969. 15-Nov-2 Laurence Calmels, Paris #110/R
£2436 $3849 €3800 Plans mobiles (71x67cm-28x26in) s.verso painted masonite. 15-Nov-2 Laurence Calmels, Paris #100/R
£2692 $4254 €4200 Relief (47x28x3cm-19x11x1in) s.verso painted metal exec.c.1953. 15-Nov-2 Laurence Calmels, Paris #1/R
£2885 $4558 €4500 Retracti;e (106x25x19cm-42x10x7in) wood engine exec.c.1960 lit. 15-Nov-2 Laurence Calmels, Paris #6/R
£3077 $4862 €4800 Boules (42x42cm-17x17in) copper exec.c.1968. 15-Nov-2 Laurence Calmels, Paris #37/R
£3165 $5065 €4400 Quinze arcs de cercle sur un plateau cylindrique (17x25x25cm-7x10x10in) s. num.1/8 metal steel motor exec.c.1969. 17-May-3 De Vuyst, Lokeren #58/R est:4400-5500
£3846 $6077 €6000 Untitled (90x88x38cm-35x35x15in) painted metal exec.1955. 15-Nov-2 Laurence Calmels, Paris #30/R
£4082 $6490 €6000 Turning squares (19x20x40cm-7x8x16in) s.num.1/8 chromed steel sold with collage. 26-Feb-3 Artcurial Briest, Paris #421/R est:3000-4000
£4167 $6583 €6500 Girouette (43x46x38cm-17x18x15in) painted metal exec.c.1955. 15-Nov-2 Laurence Calmels, Paris #7/R
£4167 $6583 €6500 Ponctuation erectile (46x78x4cm-18x31x2in) s.i.d.1961 verso masonite painted metal engine prov.exhib.lit. 15-Nov-2 Laurence Calmels, Paris #55/R est:6000
£4359 $6887 €6800 Erectile (81x81cm-32x32in) steel masonite lit. 15-Nov-2 Laurence Calmels, Paris #39/R est:5000
£4808 $7596 €7500 Oeuf sur cylindre (64cm-25in) s. stainless steel engine exec.1972 exhib.lit. 15-Nov-2 Laurence Calmels, Paris #60/R est:6000
£5449 $8609 €8500 Multiplans (64x43x17cm-25x17x7in) painted wood metal exhib.lit. 15-Nov-2 Laurence Calmels, Paris #8/R
£5769 $9115 €9000 Retractile (67x46x20cm-26x18x8in) s.verso wood exec.c.1964. 15-Nov-2 Laurence Calmels, Paris #57/R est:9000
£6410 $10064 €10000 Escalier (30x30x30cm-12x12x12in) s. num.1/8 chromed steel. 10-Dec-2 Piasa, Paris #155/R est:1500
£6410 $10128 €10000 15 points blancs (61x61cm-24x24in) s.verso painted metal wood engine prov.exhib. 15-Nov-2 Laurence Calmels, Paris #46/R est:5000
£6731 $10635 €10500 Boule rouge sur carre rouge (61x61cm-24x24in) s.verso wood engine exhib.lit. 15-Nov-2 Laurence Calmels, Paris #44/R est:9000
£7051 $11141 €11000 Plans mobiles (110cm-43in) painted masonite exec.1953 exhib.lit. 15-Nov-2 Laurence Calmels, Paris #58/R est:12000
£7372 $11647 €11500 Erectile (61x30x19cm-24x12x7in) s.i.d.63 verso aluminium wood engine exhib.lit. 15-Nov-2 Laurence Calmels, Paris #63/R
£8333 $13167 €13000 Cubes emboites (60x22x22cm-24x9x9in) wood engine exec.1966 prov.exhib.lit. 15-Nov-2 Laurence Calmels, Paris #62/R est:7000
£8974 $14179 €14000 919 points blancs (60x45x20cm-24x18x8in) s.i. wood nylon engine exec.1965 exhib.lit. 15-Nov-2 Laurence Calmels, Paris #42/R est:9000
£8974 $14179 €14000 28 boules blanches (91x91cm-36x36in) s.verso painted metal wood plastic engine exec.c.1962. 15-Nov-2 Laurence Calmels, Paris #45/R est:6000
£8974 $14179 €14000 Girouette (93x60x47cm-37x24x19in) painted metal. 15-Nov-2 Laurence Calmels, Paris #85/R est:10000
£9615 $15192 €15000 Girouette (60x65x33cm-24x26x13in) painted metal exec.1955 lit. 15-Nov-2 Laurence Calmels, Paris #16/R
£9615 $15192 €15000 Multiplans (97x47x8cm-38x19x3in) s.verso painted wood metal exec.c.1957 exhib.lit. 15-Nov-2 Laurence Calmels, Paris #41/R
£9936 $15699 €15500 Anneau en morceaux (120x22x22cm-47x9x9in) steel engine exhib.lit. 15-Nov-2 Laurence Calmels, Paris #66/R est:18000
£10256 $16205 €16000 Multiplans (91x59x29cm-36x23x11in) s.i.d.1958 verso painted wood metal exhib.lit. 15-Nov-2 Laurence Calmels, Paris #43/R est:10000
£10897 $17218 €17000 Ponctuation ronde (72x72cm-28x28in) s.verso wood nylon exec.c.1964 exhib.lit. 15-Nov-2 Laurence Calmels, Paris #47/R est:9000
£12500 $19750 €19500 Plan mobile (95x81cm-37x32in) painted wood metal lit. 15-Nov-2 Laurence Calmels, Paris #74/R
£12821 $20256 €20000 Cubes et boules (57x44x44cm-22x17x17in) s.verso wood exec.c.1964 lit. 15-Nov-2 Laurence Calmels, Paris #64/R est:8000

£19231 $30385 €30000 Girouette (86x36x38cm-34x14x15in) painted metal exec.1955. 15-Nov-2 Laurence Calmels, Paris #32/R est:8000
£21795 $34436 €34000 Plans mobiles (127cm-50in) s.verso painted masonite exec.1953 lit. 15-Nov-2 Laurence Calmels, Paris #59/R est:15000
£28846 $45577 €45000 Colonne (200x37x42cm-79x15x17in) s. wood engine exhib.lit. 15-Nov-2 Laurence Calmels, Paris #67/R est:30000-40000
£30769 $48615 €48000 Plans mobiles (153cm-60in) painted masonite exec.c.1953 exhib.lit. 15-Nov-2 Laurence Calmels, Paris #11/R est:20000

Works on paper
£816 $1298 €1200 Profil (27x21cm-11x8in) s.d.1947 ink. 24-Mar-3 Claude Boisgirard, Paris #83
£1258 $1950 €2000 Ponctuation (59cm-23in circular) s. mixed media electric motor. 30-Oct-2 Artcurial Briest, Paris #645/R est:2000-3000

BURZI, Ettore (1872-1937) Italian
£283 $453 €425 Forest clearing (25x47cm-10x19in) s.d. 17-Mar-3 Philippe Schuler, Zurich #8415 (S.FR 600)
£330 $528 €495 Study of houses (40x50cm-16x20in) s. 17-Mar-3 Philippe Schuler, Zurich #8414 (S.FR 700)
£522 $809 €783 Oleander in bloom (46x36cm-18x14in) s. 9-Dec-2 Philippe Schuler, Zurich #8707 (S.FR 1200)

BUSATO, Mario (1902-1971) Italian
Sculpture
£2821 $4428 €4400 Elephant (33x50x26cm-13x20x10in) st.f.Susse num.III/IV brown green pat bronze. 16-Dec-2 Rabourdin & Choppin de Janvry, Paris #144/R

BUSCA, Antonio (1625-1686) Italian
Works on paper
£280 $400 €420 Study of a prophet (21x16cm-8x6in) black white chk. 23-Jan-3 Swann Galleries, New York #85/R
£1149 $1792 €1700 Madonna and Child with saints (35x30cm-14x12in) chk prov. 27-Mar-3 Christie's, Paris #183/R

BUSCAGLIONE, Giuseppe (1868-1928) Italian
£696 $1085 €1044 Figures on path (43x62cm-17x24in) s. board. 16-Sep-2 Philippe Schuler, Zurich #3461 (S.FR 1600)
£962 $1510 €1500 Rural landscape (31x44cm-12x17in) s. board. 10-Dec-2 Della Rocca, Turin #288/R
£1020 $1622 €1500 Landscape covered in snow (30x43cm-12x17in) s. board. 1-Mar-3 Meeting Art, Vercelli #130
£1154 $1812 €1800 Mountainous landscape (31x44cm-12x17in) s.d.88 board. 10-Dec-2 Della Rocca, Turin #319/R
£1224 $1947 €1800 Stream in the valley (43x31cm-17x12in) s. board. 1-Mar-3 Meeting Art, Vercelli #276
£1282 $2013 €2000 Alpine lake (45x60cm-18x24in) s. 10-Dec-2 Della Rocca, Turin #277/R
£1361 $2163 €2000 Dora Riparia (42x57cm-17x22in) s. board. 1-Mar-3 Meeting Art, Vercelli #83
£1522 $2496 €2100 Strada di montagna con figure e cappellatta (45x64cm-18x25in) s. canvasboard. 27-May-3 Finarte, Milan #24/R est:1800-2000
£1594 $2614 €2200 Vecchi casolari (30x44cm-12x17in) s. panel. 27-May-3 Finarte, Milan #119/R est:1800-2000

BUSCH, Carl (1905-1973) German
£475 $750 €750 Evening landscape with bathers (74x100cm-29x39in) s. i.verso. 29-Nov-2 Bolland & Marotz, Bremen #838/R

BUSCH, Heather (20th C) New Zealander
£912 $1422 €1368 Palce cast of thought (119x93cm-47x37in) s.i.d.1981 enamel on board. 17-Sep-2 Peter Webb, Auckland #158/R est:4000-6000 (NZ.D 3000)

BUSCH, Walter (1898-1980) German
Works on paper
£318 $497 €500 Village church in Lechal (24x36cm-9x14in) s. W/C lit. 7-Nov-2 Allgauer, Kempten #2625/R

BUSCH, Wilhelm (1832-1908) German
£6329 $10000 €10000 Interior with red and blue jacket (14x18cm-6x7in) s. cardboard. 29-Nov-2 Villa Grisebach, Berlin #2/R est:10000-12000
£10256 $16205 €16000 Landscape (16x19cm-6x7in) panel prov. 16-Nov-2 Lempertz, Koln #1435/R est:10000
£11859 $18381 €18500 Peasant filling pipe (33x18cm-13x7in) s. panel lit. 7-Dec-2 Kastern, Hannover #1/R est:18500
£13768 $22580 €19000 Two children in meadow (20x20cm-8x8in) oil over pencil paper on board lit.exhib. 31-May-3 Villa Grisebach, Berlin #100/R est:9000-12000
£15580 $25551 €21500 Landscape with stream, bridge and mill (21x25cm-8x10in) s. board double-sided prov.lit. 30-May-3 Villa Grisebach, Berlin #1/R est:10000-12000

Works on paper
£897 $1310 €1400 Woodland shrine (21x16cm-8x6in) pencil. 4-Jun-2 Karl & Faber, Munich #57/R
£1346 $1965 €2100 Pipesmoker sitting at table (8x5cm-3x2in) pencil. 4-Jun-2 Karl & Faber, Munich #54/R
£1474 $2153 €2300 Study of male nude (33x21cm-13x8in) pencil double-sided. 4-Jun-2 Karl & Faber, Munich #55/R est:2300

BUSCI, Alessandro (1971-) Italian
£1090 $1689 €1700 Bicocca (69x70cm-27x28in) enamel on iron painted 2002. 4-Dec-2 Finarte, Milan #505/R
£1489 $2413 €2100 Rosso (70x70cm-28x28in) s. acrylic oil iron. 20-May-3 Porro, Milan #6/R est:2200-2400

BUSCIONI, Umberto (1931-) Italian
£1486 $2319 €2200 Fall of the rebellious angels (100x140cm-39x55in) s.d.1986-87 verso oil enamel paper on canvas. 28-Mar-3 Farsetti, Prato #435/R

BUSEK, Karl Theodor von (1803-1860) German
Works on paper
£244 $356 €380 Trier, Porta Nigra (17x23cm-7x9in) sepia wash over pencil. 4-Jun-2 Karl & Faber, Munich #58

BUSH, Charles William (1919-1989) Australian
£231 $354 €347 Road to Point Wilson (61x76cm-24x30in) s. s.i.verso painted c.1980 prov. 26-Aug-2 Sotheby's, Paddington #793 (A.D 650)
£249 $381 €374 View of You Yangs (76x55cm-30x22in) s. painted c.1981 prov. 26-Aug-2 Sotheby's, Paddington #623 (A.D 700)
£249 $381 €374 Exhibition Street at night (76x101cm-30x40in) s. s.i.verso painted c.1958 prov.exhib. 26-Aug-2 Sotheby's, Paddington #650 (A.D 700)
£498 $762 €747 Road to Point Wilson, summer rain (76x28cm-30x11in) s. s.i.d.81 verso prov. 26-Aug-2 Sotheby's, Paddington #608 est:1000-2000 (A.D 1400)
£1068 $1633 €1602 Dry landscape (75x101cm-30x40in) s.d.81 prov. 26-Aug-2 Sotheby's, Paddington #586 est:1000-2000 (A.D 3000)

BUSH, Flora (fl.1915-1930) British?
Works on paper
£400 $660 €580 Old garden (34x40cm-13x16in) s.d.1915 pencil W/C. 3-Jul-3 Christie's, Kensington #87

BUSH, Harry (1883-1957) British
£1900 $3021 €2850 Shower (56x76cm-22x30in) s. s.i.verso prov.exhib. 26-Feb-3 Sotheby's, Olympia #226/R est:600-800
£2400 $3744 €3600 Winter patchwork (53x77cm-21x30in) s.d.1926. 15-Oct-2 Bonhams, Knightsbridge #146/R est:1000-1500

BUSH, Jack (1909-1977) Canadian
£1515 $2409 €2197 Untitled (196x254cm-77x100in) s. acrylic fibre prov.exhib. 1-May-3 Heffel, Vancouver #11/R est:2500-3000 (C.D 3500)
£8065 $12742 €12098 Gay blue (61x147cm-24x58in) acrylic prov.exhib. 18-Nov-2 Sotheby's, Toronto #143/R est:25000-35000 (C.D 20000)
£8889 $14578 €13334 Bull's eye (118x94cm-46x37in) s. i.d.May-June 1969 verso acrylic prov. 27-May-3 Sotheby's, Toronto #192/R est:20000-30000 (C.D 20000)
£16889 $27698 €25334 Slope right (145x71cm-57x28in) acrylic painted 1967 prov. 3-Jun-3 Joyner, Toronto #83/R est:35000-45000 (C.D 38000)
£35556 $58311 €53334 Grey laughter (171x236cm-67x93in) s.i.d.January 1968 i.verso prov.lit. 27-May-3 Sotheby's, Toronto #144/R est:40000-60000 (C.D 80000)

Works on paper
£1008 $1593 €1512 In the woods, Thunder Bay (29x41cm-11x16in) s.i.d.1946 W/C. 14-Nov-2 Heffel, Vancouver #228/R est:3000-4000 (C.D 2500)

BUSH, Norton (1834-1894) American
£641 $1000 €962 Seashore. painted c.1891. 21-Sep-2 Harvey Clar, Oakland #1466
£5422 $9000 €7862 Boats off the California coast (51x41cm-20x16in) s.d.75 prov. 11-Jun-3 Butterfields, San Francisco #4157/R est:10000-15000
£10180 $17000 €14761 Tropical landscape (51x41cm-20x16in) s.d.1874 prov. 17-Jun-3 John Moran, Pasadena #68a est:15000-20000

BUSH, Norton (attrib) (1834-1894) American
£779 $1200 €1169 Tropical landscape (25x41cm-10x16in) board. 24-Oct-2 Shannon's, Milford #234/R

BUSH, Reginald Edgar James (1869-?) British
Works on paper
£660 $1049 €990 Mousehole (36x29cm-14x11in) s.d.1900 W/C. 4-Mar-3 Bearnes, Exeter #389/R

BUSH, Stephen (20th C) Australian
£1434 $2352 €2151 Looking for a prospect (56x71cm-22x28in) s.i.d.8/12/89 verso prov.exhib. 4-Jun-3 Deutscher-Menzies, Melbourne #2/R est:3000-4000 (A.D 3600)
£4643 $7243 €6965 Lure of Paris no 10 (183x183cm-72x72in) s.i.d.1997 verso. 11-Nov-2 Deutscher-Menzies, Melbourne #46/R est:5000-7000 (A.D 13000)

BUSHBY, Thomas (1861-1918) British
Works on paper
£270 $427 €405 Crummock water and low fell (26x36cm-10x14in) s.d.1918 W/C. 14-Nov-2 Bonhams, Edinburgh #309
£1450 $2364 €2103 On the Lowther, Westmorland (41x61cm-16x24in) s.d.1893 W/C. 17-Jul-3 Thomson, Roddick & Medcalf, Carlisle #49/R

BUSI, Adolpho (1891-?) Italian
£404 $638 €606 Lady holding a daisy (74x74cm-29x29in) s. masonite. 18-Nov-2 Waddingtons, Toronto #277/R (C.D 1000)

BUSIERI, Giovanni Battista (1698-1757) Italian
Works on paper
£700 $1099 €1050 Two figures on a path leading to a walled town. Monastery (17x23cm-7x9in) pen ink pair prov. 11-Dec-2 Sotheby's, Olympia #176/R

BUSOM, Simo (1927-) Spanish
£465 $734 €720 Arenys seen from a boat (24x33cm-9x13in) s. s.i.verso board. 17-Dec-2 Segre, Madrid #105/R
£629 $969 €1000 Carrer Pelai, Barcelona (73x60cm-29x24in) s. s.i.d.1974 verso exhib. 22-Oct-2 Durán, Madrid #149/R
£705 $1114 €1100 Roofs (33x47cm-13x19in) s. 13-Nov-2 Ansorena, Madrid #57/R
£1195 $1864 €1900 Saint Barbara Square (68x81cm-27x32in) s. s.i.d.1986 verso. 8-Oct-2 Ansorena, Madrid #444/R

BUSON, Yosa (style) (1716-1783) Japanese
Works on paper
£11000 $18370 €15950 River landscape lined with willow trees (107x50cm-42x20in) s. ink col silk hanging scroll. 10-Jul-3 Christie's, Kensington #301/R est:300-500

BUSS, Robert William (1804-1875) British
£700 $1169 €1015 Old Admiral at home, old sailors reconstructing a sea battle (19x27cm-7x11in) panel exhib. 24-Jun-3 Rowley Fine Art, Newmarket #366/R
£1400 $2184 €2100 Hogarth's first sketch (42x51cm-17x20in) s.d.1845. 26-Mar-3 Sotheby's, Olympia #137/R est:1500-2000

BUSSCHE, Jacques van den (1925-) French
£700 $1134 €1015 French garden scene (61x89cm-24x35in) s. board. 31-Jul-3 Scarborough Perry Fine Arts, Hove #830
£720 $1166 €1044 Blue vase of carnations (89x71cm-35x28in) s.d.1951 board. 31-Jul-3 Scarborough Perry Fine Arts, Hove #829

BUSSCHERE, Constant de (1876-1951) Belgian
£359 $579 €550 Chevaux de halage en hiver (16x25cm-6x10in) s. 20-Jan-3 Horta, Bruxelles #7
£1370 $2137 €2000 La charrette tiree par des chevaux (28x94cm-11x37in) s. 14-Apr-3 Horta, Bruxelles #479 est:400-600

BUSSEY, Reuben (1818-1893) British
£400 $620 €600 Figures in 16th century costume on the battlements of a castle (61x46cm-24x18in) s.d.1870. 31-Oct-2 Duke & Son, Dorchester #285

BUSSEY, Reuben (attrib) (1818-1893) British
£329 $513 €520 Scene from Henry IV (59x44cm-23x17in) s.d.1873 i. verso. 14-Sep-2 Weidler, Nurnberg #6528/R

BUSSOLINO, Vittorio (1853-1922) Italian
£1572 $2453 €2500 Landscape with courtyard (32x34cm-13x13in) s. board. 20-Sep-2 Semenzato, Venice #701/R

BUSSON, Georges (1859-1933) French
Sculpture
£3759 $6089 €5300 Retour de chasse a courre (37cm-15in) s.base pat bronze st.f.Estray. 23-May-3 Camard, Paris #6/R est:1200-1500

BUSSON, Marcel (1913-) French?
£1603 $2516 €2500 Casbah de Toundout pres de ouarzazate (54x65cm-21x26in) s. i.d.62 verso cardboard on panel. 16-Dec-2 Gros & Delettrez, Paris #71/R est:2300-3000

BUSSY, Jane Simone (20th C) ?
£380 $604 €570 Provencal landscape (33x41cm-13x16in) s. canvas on board. 26-Feb-3 Sotheby's, Olympia #236/R
£600 $954 €900 Mediterranean landscape (46x56cm-18x22in) s. 26-Feb-3 Sotheby's, Olympia #235/R

BUSSY, Simon (1869-1954) French
£1500 $2340 €2250 Baboon (74x71cm-29x28in) s. 17-Sep-2 Bonhams, Knightsbridge #148/R est:2000-3000
Works on paper
£355 $550 €533 Lemur (20x23cm-8x9in) s. pastel. 28-Sep-2 Charlton Hall, Columbia #366/R
£900 $1485 €1305 Marigold (30x25cm-12x10in) s. pastel. 3-Jul-3 Christie's, Kensington #307/R
£2000 $3120 €3000 Birds (27x19cm-11x7in) two i. pastel four. 12-Sep-2 Sotheby's, Olympia #138/R est:1000-1500
£2200 $3630 €3190 Westminster (21x15cm-8x6in) s. pastel prov. 3-Jul-3 Christie's, Kensington #309/R est:800-1200
£2500 $4125 €3625 Blue starling (23x24cm-9x9in) pastel. 3-Jul-3 Christie's, Kensington #305/R est:1000-1500
£4200 $6552 €6300 Toco toucan. Toucan (33x25cm-13x10in) one i. pastel pair. 12-Sep-2 Sotheby's, Olympia #137/R est:1500-2000
£4200 $6678 €6300 Baboon (21x21cm-8x8in) chl pastel. 26-Feb-3 Sotheby's, Olympia #173/R est:1000-1500
£4800 $7440 €7200 Grenouille (19x19cm-7x7in) i. col chks. 4-Dec-2 Sotheby's, London #15/R est:3000-4000

BUSSY, Simon (attrib) (1869-1954) French
£840 $1310 €1260 Vase of daffodils and Chinese bowl on a red table (54x44cm-21x17in) bears sig. 17-Oct-2 Lawrence, Crewkerne #524/R

BUSTAMANTE, Jean Marc (1952-) French?
Prints
£18000 $27720 €27000 Lumieres (185x140cm-73x55in) silkscreen on plexiglas executed 1990 prov. 23-Oct-2 Christie's, London #190/R est:6000-8000

BUSTARD, William (1894-1973) Australian
£420 $663 €630 Spring landscape (41x32cm-16x13in) s. painted 1939. 1-Apr-3 Lawson Menzies, Sydney #515 (A.D 1100)

BUSTOS, Hermenegildo (1832-1907) Mexican
£18902 $31000 €27408 Retrato de Juan Valdivia (41x29cm-16x11in) s.i.d.1863 verso prov.exhib. 27-May-3 Sotheby's, New York #133
£19512 $32000 €29268 Sra Da Francisca Valdivia de Chavez e hijos (71x53cm-28x21in) s.i.verso canvas on canvas painted 1862 prov.lit. 28-May-3 Christie's, Rockefeller NY #2/R est:40000-50000
£28662 $45000 €42993 Portrait of woman (41x29cm-16x11in) s.i.verso painted 1861 prov. 20-Nov-2 Christie's, Rockefeller NY #4/R est:50000-60000

BUTHAUD, René (1886-1986) French
Sculpture
£3597 $5756 €5000 Coupe trois sirenes (35cm-14in) mono. terracotta lit. 19-May-3 Tajan, Paris #177/R est:5000-6000

BUTHE, Michael (1944-1994) German
£1086 $1694 €1629 Composition (79x64cm-31x25in) s.d.1986 paper prov. 6-Nov-2 AB Stockholms Auktionsverk #925/R est:12000-15000 (S.KR 15500)
£1087 $1783 €1500 1000 and 1 nights (31x38cm-12x15in) s.i.d.1978 stretcher oil graphite wax collage paper cloth. 28-May-3 Lempertz, Koln #70/R est:1800-2000
£1087 $1783 €1500 1000 and 1 nights (33x37cm-13x15in) s.i.d.1979 stretcher oil wax paper dried grass. 28-May-3 Lempertz, Koln #71/R est:1800-2000
£1594 $2614 €2200 Tanger (54x45cm-21x18in) s.i.d.1992 oil gold silver bronze collage. 28-May-3 Lempertz, Koln #74/R est:2200

Sculpture
£1042 $1719 €1500 Ange (39x51cm-15x20in) mixed media feathers canvas. 1-Jul-3 Artcurial Briest, Paris #554/R est:1500-2000
Works on paper
£641 $994 €1000 Untitled (42x30cm-17x12in) s.d.75 gold bronze gouache paper collage board. 3-Dec-2 Lempertz, Koln #76/R
£705 $1093 €1100 Untitled (42x30cm-17x12in) s.d.75 gold bronze gouache paper collage board. 3-Dec-2 Lempertz, Koln #75/R
£2609 $4278 €3600 Marrakesh (40x50cm-16x20in) s.i.d.1986 verso collage twigs metal over acrylic. 28-May-3 Lempertz, Koln #72/R est:3600

BUTLER, Anton (1819-1874) Swiss
£786 $1226 €1179 David victor (111x89cm-44x35in) s.d.1846 lit.exhib. 20-Nov-2 Fischer, Luzern #2032/R est:2000-2500 (S.FR 1800)

BUTLER, Augustus (attrib) (19th C) British
£1600 $2640 €2320 Coronation celebrations, Fleet Street (65x30cm-26x12in) i.d.1837 panel. 2-Jul-3 Sotheby's, Olympia #109/R est:2000-3000

BUTLER, Charles Ernest (1864-?) British
£350 $539 €525 Sunlit garden (22x30cm-9x12in) s.d.18 board. 5-Sep-2 Christie's, Kensington #212/R
£1100 $1804 €1650 Portrait of a boy in a blue jacket and breeches (91x71cm-36x28in) s.d.07 framed oval. 29-May-3 Christie's, Kensington #55 est:500-800

BUTLER, David (1898-) American
£1235 $2000 €1853 Untitled - train (42x79cm-17x31in) enamel on cut tin double-sided prov. 27-Jan-3 Christie's, Rockefeller NY #87/R est:2000-3000
£1605 $2600 €2408 Untitled - man on the moon (73x79cm-29x31in) init. enamel on cut tin double-sided prov. 27-Jan-3 Christie's, Rockefeller NY #89/R est:3000-4000
£2160 $3500 €3240 Untitled - creature (70x69cm-28x27in) init. s.verso enamel on cut tin double-sided prov. 27-Jan-3 Christie's, Rockefeller NY #88/R est:3000-5000

BUTLER, Elizabeth (1846-1933) British
Works on paper
£1800 $2808 €2700 Tenr pegging (16x25cm-6x10in) W/C. 5-Nov-2 Bonhams, New Bond Street #137/R est:700-900

BUTLER, Frank (20th C) American
£357 $550 €536 Harbour view (23x30cm-9x12in) s. board painted c.1925. 8-Sep-2 Treadway Gallery, Cincinnati #607/R

BUTLER, George Edmund (1870-1936) New Zealander
£298 $474 €447 Across the fields (46x75cm-18x30in) s.d.1896. 25-Feb-3 Peter Webb, Auckland #241 (NZ.D 850)
£442 $690 €663 Seascape (60x90cm-24x35in) s.d.1903. 6-Aug-2 Peter Webb, Auckland #238/R est:2500-3500 (NZ.D 1500)
£796 $1250 €1194 Dinghy resting on the foreshore (37x61cm-15x24in) s.d.1896. 10-Dec-2 Peter Webb, Auckland #80/R est:1000-2000 (NZ.D 2500)

BUTLER, Henry (1800-1881) British
Works on paper
£253 $395 €400 Man holding a saddled horse with a dog in a courtyard (10x11cm-4x4in) pen ink dr. 15-Oct-2 Mealy's, Castlecomer #267

BUTLER, Herbert E (fl.1881-1921) British
Works on paper
£280 $448 €420 Estuary scene with boat and gulls, set in front of a coastal village. s. W/C. 10-Jan-3 Biddle & Webb, Birmingham #131
£300 $468 €450 Returning to the harbour (18x25cm-7x10in) s. W/C. 17-Oct-2 David Lay, Penzance #1442
£420 $701 €609 Fishing off a rocky headland (35x15cm-14x6in) s. W/C. 23-Jun-3 Bonhams, Bath #156
£520 $868 €754 Setting out from Polperro (35x15cm-14x6in) s. W/C. 23-Jun-3 Bonhams, Bath #155
£680 $1136 €986 Fisherfolk on the jetty at Polperro (18x26cm-7x10in) s. W/C. 23-Jun-3 Bonhams, Bath #154
£900 $1458 €1350 In shallow waters (25x36cm-10x14in) s. pencil W/C. 21-May-3 Christie's, Kensington #453/R
£900 $1503 €1305 Polperro - outer harbour (26x36cm-10x14in) s. W/C. 23-Jun-3 Bonhams, Bath #153
£920 $1536 €1334 Polperro - inner harbour (26x36cm-10x14in) s. W/C. 23-Jun-3 Bonhams, Bath #152

BUTLER, Howard Russell (1856-1934) American
£629 $1000 €944 Illuminated thunderhead Geirgia Lake (61x74cm-24x29in) d.1910. 3-May-3 Van Blarcom, South Natick #273/R
£955 $1500 €1433 Rocky coastal landscape in Maine with two-mast sailboat in distance (64x81cm-25x32in) s.d.1913 canvas on board. 19-Apr-3 James Julia, Fairfield #224/R est:3000-5000
£1032 $1600 €1548 Flat beach in evening, St Ives, 1895 (38x64cm-15x25in) s. prov.exhib. 25-Sep-2 Doyle, New York #14/R est:1200-1800
£1051 $1650 €1577 Rocky coastal landscape in Maine at sunrise (51x76cm-20x30in) s. 19-Apr-3 James Julia, Fairfield #225/R est:3000-5000
£1752 $2750 €2628 Sagaponack (66x84cm-26x33in) s. 10-Dec-2 Doyle, New York #62/R est:3000-5000
£2581 $4000 €3872 Bird Rocks, Carmel, California (36x51cm-14x20in) s. i.verso canvasboard. 29-Oct-2 John Moran, Pasadena #622 est:3000-4000
£2903 $4500 €4355 Rainy season - California (33x41cm-13x16in) s.d.1906 i.verso prov.exhib. 29-Oct-2 John Moran, Pasadena #622a est:1500-2000

BUTLER, Jacques Philip (19/20th C) American
£2323 $3670 €3600 Bord de riviere, Giverny (48x73cm-19x29in) s. 19-Dec-2 Claude Aguttes, Neuilly #158/R est:1500
£2452 $3874 €3800 The Epte in the swamp, Giverny (48x73cm-19x29in) s. i.d.1912 verso. 19-Dec-2 Claude Aguttes, Neuilly #160/R
£2452 $3874 €3800 Orak tree, Stamford (63x76cm-25x30in) s. i.d.1919 verso. 19-Dec-2 Claude Aguttes, Neuilly #159/R
£2581 $4077 €4000 Apple orchard, Hillcrest, Candor (56x86cm-22x34in) s. i.d.1916 verso. 19-Dec-2 Claude Aguttes, Neuilly #161/R est:1500

BUTLER, James (1931-) British
Sculpture
£1922 $2998 €2883 Standing dancer (53cm-21in) s.d.95 num.II/X green pat bronze marble base exhib. 11-Nov-2 Stephan Welz, Johannesburg #441/R est:30000-50000 (SA.R 30000)
£2400 $3792 €3600 Little dancer (53cm-21in) s.d.84 num.VI/X bronze with brown and green patina. 27-Nov-2 Sotheby's, Olympia #172/R est:2000-3000

BUTLER, James H (1925-) American
£1763 $2750 €2645 Autumn gold (41x51cm-16x20in) s. masonite panel prov. 9-Nov-2 Santa Fe Art, Santa Fe #46/R est:2000-2500

BUTLER, Joseph Nikolaus (1822-1885) Swiss
£1026 $1621 €1600 Swiss alpine landscape (41x60cm-16x24in) bears s. 16-Nov-2 Lempertz, Koln #1436 est:1600
£3493 $5450 €5240 Kitchen still life with cat (62x75cm-24x30in) s.d.1844. 20-Nov-2 Fischer, Luzern #1236/R est:9500-11000 (S.FR 8000)

BUTLER, Manley (20th C) American
£937 $1500 €1359 St Josephs Sound, Florida. Friendship Mission, Florida. Brick house (44x60cm-17x24in) s. i.verso canvasboard four. 16-May-3 Skinner, Boston #241/R est:800-1200

BUTLER, Mary (1865-1946) American
£562 $900 €815 Rocky coast, Maine (25x31cm-10x12in) s. i.verso board doublesided. 16-May-3 Skinner, Boston #281/R
£599 $1000 €869 Mt. Gould Glacier National Park (41x46cm-16x18in) s. canvasboard. 22-Jun-3 Freeman, Philadelphia #150/R est:1000-1500
£687 $1100 €996 Bass Rocks (26x31cm-10x12in) s.i.verso canvasboard. 16-May-3 Skinner, Boston #276/R
£710 $1100 €1065 Riverscape with mountains (61x81cm-24x32in) s. 8-Dec-2 Freeman, Philadelphia #155/R
£1097 $1700 €1646 Mount Allen (71x91cm-28x36in) s.d.1931 i.stretcher. 8-Dec-2 Freeman, Philadelphia #157/R est:1000-1500
£1656 $2600 €2484 Landscape with green hills, trees and water (61x81cm-24x32in) s. 23-Nov-2 Pook & Pook, Downington #143/R est:1000-1500
£1750 $2800 €2625 Summer landscape with large tree in foreground (58x69cm-23x27in) s. 17-May-3 Pook & Pook, Downington #326/R est:2000-3000

BUTLER, Mildred Anne (1858-1941) British
Works on paper
£167 $262 €260 Caricature sketches of military chaps and ladies (17x22cm-7x9in) s. pen. 19-Nov-2 Hamilton Osborne King, Dublin #403/R
£460 $736 €690 Tree lined country lane, possibly France (26x18cm-10x7in) s. W/C. 11-Mar-3 David Duggleby, Scarborough #143
£650 $949 €975 Cows drinking by the water's edge (36x51cm-14x20in) s. W/C. 12-Jun-2 John Ross, Belfast #260
£741 $1067 €1200 Jerpoint Abbey, Thomastown, Co Kilkenny (20x23cm-8x9in) init. W/C. 25-Apr-2 Woodwards, Cork #251
£881 $1374 €1400 Mountainous landscape (27x37cm-11x15in) W/C prov. 17-Sep-2 Whyte's, Dublin #56/R
£1500 $2385 €2250 Chair in the drawing room at Kilmurry (17x12cm-7x5in) mono. W/C. 5-Mar-3 John Ross, Belfast #82 est:1200-1400
£1600 $2608 €2400 Crows in a snowy garden (23x13cm-9x5in) s. W/C gouache. 14-Feb-3 Keys, Aylsham #493/R est:600-700

£1887 $2943 €3000 Summer garden (20x15cm-8x6in) init. W/C htd bodycol oval. 17-Sep-2 Whyte's, Dublin #195/R est:4000-5000
£2350 $3737 €3525 Winter landscape (25x17cm-10x7in) s. W/C. 5-Mar-3 John Ross, Belfast #139 est:2500-3000
£2400 $3840 €3600 Grinding wheel, Kilmurry (12x16cm-5x6in) pencil W/C prov. 15-May-3 Christie's, Kensington #229/R est:1800-2500
£2500 $4000 €3750 Sheep in a meadow (18x25cm-7x10in) s.d.1916 W/C bodycol. 15-May-3 Christie's, Kensington #228/R est:2500-3500
£2821 $4372 €4400 Summer garden (38x19cm-15x7in) s. W/C. 3-Dec-2 Bonhams & James Adam, Dublin #135/R est:1500-2000
£2826 $4635 €3900 Crows in the snow (13x18cm-5x7in) s. W/C prov. 28-May-3 Bonhams & James Adam, Dublin #39/R est:2800-3400
£2917 $4638 €4200 Flowering rhododendron (37x27cm-15x11in) s. W/C prov. 29-Apr-3 Whyte's, Dublin #90/R est:4000-5000
£3768 $6180 €5200 Snowdrop walk (28x45cm-11x18in) s. W/C. 28-May-3 Bonhams & James Adam, Dublin #31/R est:5000-8000
£6522 $10696 €9000 Cattle at rest (52x71cm-20x28in) s.d.Sept 1889 W/C. 28-May-3 Bonhams & James Adam, Dublin #34/R est:10000-15000
£7500 $10950 €11250 Cows grazing (51x36cm-20x14in) s. W/C. 12-Jun-2 John Ross, Belfast #185 est:6000-7000
£12000 $19200 €18000 Tramore Strand, low water (34x50cm-13x20in) s.i.d.89 W/C gouache prov. 16-May-3 Sotheby's, London #35/R est:12000-18000

BUTLER, Mildred Anne (attrib) (1858-1941) British
Works on paper
£621 $987 €900 Calf in a shed (26x36cm-10x14in) W/C. 4-Mar-3 Mealy's, Castlecomer #1229/R

BUTLER, Reg (1913-1981) British
Sculpture
£12500 $20500 €18750 Study for girl with a vest (56cm-22in) mono.num.4/8 dark brown pat. bronze st.f.Susse exhib. 6-Jun-3 Christie's, London #110/R est:5000-7000
£17000 $27880 €25500 Figures in space (50cm-20in) mono.num.6/8 gold brown pat. bronze st.f.Susse prov.exhib. 6-Jun-3 Christie's, London #183/R est:5000-8000
£32000 $52480 €48000 Girl looking down (148cm-58in) mono.num.4/8 dark brown pat. st.f.Susse Freres. 6-Jun-3 Christie's, London #184/R est:10000-15000
Works on paper
£2400 $3936 €3600 Cray-horse (51x60cm-20x24in) s.d.60 chl exhib. 6-Jun-3 Christie's, London #61/R est:1500-2500
£2600 $4056 €3900 Seated nude (57x42cm-22x17in) s.d.57 pencil prov. 27-Mar-3 Christie's, Kensington #550/R est:1500-2000

BUTLER, Theodore E (1861-1936) American
£6019 $9690 €9029 Avenue de l'Opera with Palais Garnier (18x29cm-7x11in) s.d.1910 paper. 7-May-3 Dobiaschofsky, Bern #385/R est:9000 (S.FR 13000)
£9677 $15290 €15000 Interior, after dinner (117x117cm-46x46in) s.d.1911 prov. 18-Dec-2 Tajan, Paris #27/R est:20000
£11321 $17660 €18000 Summer garden in bloom (42x54cm-17x21in) s.d.27 prov.lit. 20-Sep-2 Karlheinz Kaupp, Staufen #1876/R est:17000
£16129 $25000 €24194 Sunset, Giverny (65x53cm-26x21in) s. prov. 4-Dec-2 Sotheby's, New York #6/R est:30000-50000
£38710 $60000 €58065 Le bain, maison baptiste (65x81cm-26x32in) s. prov.exhib.lit. 5-Dec-2 Christie's, Rockefeller NY #77/R est:100000-150000
Works on paper
£1078 $1800 €1563 Construction workers (48x30cm-19x12in) pastel prov. 17-Jun-3 John Moran, Pasadena #80 est:2500-3500

BUTRAGUENO, Felipe (20th C) Spanish
£409 $638 €650 Mancha Real (73x92cm-29x36in) s.d.00 board. 23-Sep-2 Durán, Madrid #587/R

BUTRON, Antonio (20th C) Spanish
£411 $641 €600 Landscape with mountains (17x23cm-7x9in) init. canvas on cardboard. 8-Apr-3 Ansorena, Madrid #36/R

BUTTERFIELD, Deborah (20th C) American
Sculpture
£20570 $32500 €30855 Horse (79x84x28cm-31x33x11in) wood sticks mud wire construction executed 1978 prov. 13-Nov-2 Sotheby's, New York #142/R est:20000-30000
£21875 $35000 €32813 Goldie (197x256x104cm-78x101x41in) wood aluminum steel plastic wire executed 1980 prov. 16-May-3 Phillips, New York #204/R est:50000-70000
£38217 $60000 €57326 Rondo (76x104cm-30x41in) metal rods wire barbed wire prov. 19-Nov-2 Wright, Chicago #300/R est:40000-50000
£41139 $65000 €59652 Ismani (76cm-30in) steel prov. 26-Jul-3 Coeur d'Alene, Hayden #110/R est:45000-65000

BUTTERSACK, Bernhard (1858-1925) German
£1014 $1581 €1500 Autumn landscape, probably Dachau (43x28cm-17x11in) s.d.1889. 27-Mar-3 Dr Fritz Nagel, Stuttgart #793/R est:1900
£4403 $6868 €7000 Summer landscape (42x56cm-17x22in) s.d.95 cavnas on board. 19-Sep-2 Dr Fritz Nagel, Stuttgart #913/R est:3800

BUTTERSWORTH, James E (1817-1894) American
£3200 $5184 €4800 British First Rate in the Atlantic with Cadiz off to starboard (23x33cm-9x13in) 21-May-3 Christie's, Kensington #585/R est:4000-6000
£9868 $15000 €14802 Mouth of the Moodna on the Hudson (18x38cm-7x15in) s. canvasboard lit. 17-Aug-2 North East Auctions, Portsmouth #1098/R est:11000-14000
£14474 $22000 €21711 Schooners and merchantman (30x46cm-12x18in) prov.lit. 17-Aug-2 North East Auctions, Portsmouth #705/R est:22000-28000
£19737 $30000 €29606 British warship and fleet off a coast (18x25cm-7x10in) s. panel. 17-Aug-2 North East Auctions, Portsmouth #702/R est:25000-40000
£30864 $50000 €46296 American frigate off Gibraltar (20x30cm-8x12in) s. board prov.lit. 22-May-3 Christie's, Rockefeller NY #15/R est:60000-80000
£37829 $57500 €56744 Yachts racing under storm clouds, rounding a steamer (18x30cm-7x12in) s. panel. 17-Aug-2 North East Auctions, Portsmouth #703/R est:30000-50000
£43750 $70000 €63438 Schooner and vessels off the New England coast, with lighthouse in distance (36x56cm-14x22in) s. 16-May-3 Skinner, Boston #106/R est:40000-60000
£45161 $70000 €67742 Yacht Dauntless racing towards Victory (30x46cm-12x18in) s. prov. 5-Dec-2 Christie's, Rockefeller NY #27/R est:100000-150000
£45161 $70000 €67742 Clipper in a heavy sea (36x56cm-14x22in) s. prov. 5-Dec-2 Christie's, Rockefeller NY #28/R est:80000-120000
£50633 $80000 €80000 Regatta off Govenors Island, New York, with The Magic in the foreground (18x23cm-7x9in) s. 28-Nov-2 Dorotheum, Vienna #131/R est:35000-55000
£52632 $80000 €78948 Steady breeze off the Battery, New York harbour (18x25cm-7x10in) s. panel. 17-Aug-2 North East Auctions, Portsmouth #704/R est:30000-50000
£180645 $280000 €270968 Match between the yachts Vision and Meta with rough weather (78x103cm-31x41in) s. painted c.1873 prov. 3-Dec-2 Phillips, New York #28/R est:350000-450000

BUTTERSWORTH, James E (attrib) (1817-1894) American
£2564 $4000 €3846 Landscape with cows and stream (20x36cm-8x14in) 1-Aug-2 Eldred, East Dennis #813/R est:5000-10000
£4200 $6636 €6300 British frigate attacking a pirate lugger at night (46x61cm-18x24in) 28-Nov-2 Sotheby's, London #103/R est:2000-3000

BUTTERSWORTH, Thomas (1768-1842) British
£3200 $4864 €4800 Wreck of a British third rate with rescue at hand (51x66cm-20x26in) 15-Aug-2 Bonhams, New Bond Street #388/R est:2000-3000
£3947 $6000 €5921 Loss of the Britannia, on the Goodwins (30x41cm-12x16in) s.i.verso. 17-Aug-2 North East Auctions, Portsmouth #711/R est:7000-10000
£4800 $7776 €7200 Outward bound frigate running down the Channel (46x61cm-18x24in) 21-May-3 Christie's, Kensington #552/R est:4000-6000
£5921 $9000 €8882 British man-of-war chasing a French man-of-war (25x36cm-10x14in) 17-Aug-2 North East Auctions, Portsmouth #713/R est:10000-15000
£6579 $10000 €9869 Shipping off Dover (46x61cm-18x24in) board. 17-Aug-2 North East Auctions, Portsmouth #715/R est:10000-15000
£6579 $10000 €9869 British brig rounding the Eddystone lighthouse (30x41cm-12x16in) s.indis.d. 17-Aug-2 North East Auctions, Portsmouth #712/R est:7000-10000
£7237 $11000 €10856 Sea battle in the Mediterranean (43x53cm-17x21in) 17-Aug-2 North East Auctions, Portsmouth #720/R est:12000-18000
£8000 $13360 €11600 British Man-o-War running into Lisbon with the Belem Tower off her port bow. s. 17-Jun-3 Rosebery Fine Art, London #652/R est:4000-6000
£9211 $14000 €13817 Dell lugger approaching Admiral Gardner West, aground on Goodwin Sands (46x61cm-18x24in) prov. 17-Aug-2 North East Auctions, Portsmouth #714/R est:10000-15000

£9211 $14000 €13817 Bombardment of Copenhagen by a British fleet (30x41cm-12x16in) s. prov. 17-Aug-2 North East Auctions, Portsmouth #718/R est:15000-25000

£9211 $14000 €13817 British schooner off the White Cliffs of Dover (58x89cm-23x35in) 17-Aug-2 North East Auctions, Portsmouth #719/R est:12000-18000

£10855 $16500 €16283 British cutter and frigate at sea (51x61cm-20x24in) 17-Aug-2 North East Auctions, Portsmouth #716/R est:12000-18000

£11184 $17000 €16776 British ship and two racing yachts at sea (46x61cm-18x24in) 17-Aug-2 North East Auctions, Portsmouth #706/R est:12000-18000

£11842 $18000 €17763 Privateer in pursuit off volcanic mountain (46x61cm-18x24in) 17-Aug-2 North East Auctions, Portsmouth #717/R est:10000-15000

£15132 $23000 €22698 Marine scenes of HMS Blenheim with other ships (30x46cm-12x18in) pair. 17-Aug-2 North East Auctions, Portsmouth #707/R est:16000-24000

£16447 $25000 €24671 HMS Queen Charlotte, anchored in Cadiz Bay (46x66cm-18x26in) s. 17-Aug-2 North East Auctions, Portsmouth #708/R est:20000-28000

£21000 $34020 €31500 Nelson's patent bridge for boarding First Rates' at Battle of Cape St Vincent (63x76cm-25x30in) s. 21-May-3 Christie's, Kensington #375/R est:15000-20000

£31250 $47500 €46875 East Indiaman, Earl Balcarres, in the English Channel (81x122cm-32x48in) 17-Aug-2 North East Auctions, Portsmouth #709/R est:25000-35000

BUTTERSWORTH, Thomas (attrib) (1768-1842) British

£2000 $3100 €3000 Shipping off a coast (36x46cm-14x18in) 25-Sep-2 Hamptons Fine Art, Godalming #341 est:2000-3000

£2160 $3500 €3240 Frigate in gale (45x65cm-18x26in) 21-Jan-3 Christie's, Rockefeller NY #376/R

£2200 $3454 €3300 Shipwreck (46x61cm-18x24in) board. 16-Dec-2 Sotheby's, Olympia #9/R est:1500-2500

BUTTERSWORTH, Thomas (jnr) (early 19th C) British

£5800 $9396 €8700 Frigate running past a port. British brig and Dutch galliot off a rocky coast (43x53cm-17x21in) s. pair. 21-May-3 Christie's, Kensington #553/R est:5000-7000

BUTTERWORTH, J H (19/20th C) British

£1600 $2384 €2400 Breezy day in Douglas Bay (36x58cm-14x23in) s. 28-Jun-2 Chrystals Auctions, Isle of Man #181 est:600-900

BUTTERY, Edwin (19th C) British

£420 $680 €630 Sheep grazing at dusk (44x66cm-17x26in) s. 23-Jan-3 Christie's, Kensington #214/R

BUTTERY, Thomas (?) British

£360 $587 €540 Figures in a lakeland landscape (49x51cm-19x20in) oval. 12-Feb-3 Bonhams, Knightsbridge #285/R

BUTTGEN, Johann Peter (19th C) German

£5128 $7949 €8000 Bodensee shore with Mainau island (41x53cm-16x21in) s.d.1833 prov. 5-Dec-2 Dr Fritz Nagel, Stuttgart #643/R est:15000

BUTTINGALE, W F (20th C) British?

£650 $1001 €975 Harvesters in a river landscape (25x37cm-10x15in) indis.sig. 5-Sep-2 Christie's, Kensington #198/R

BUTTNER, Elisabeth (1807-?) German

£519 $809 €825 Grandfather playing violin to woman with baby on knee (29x27cm-11x11in) s.d.77. 9-Oct-2 Michael Zeller, Lindau #637/R

BUTTNER, Georg Heinrich (1799-1879) Baltic

£900 $1467 €1350 Preparing for the ride (16x25cm-6x10in) s.i.d.1877 panel. 13-Feb-3 Christie's, Kensington #209/R

BUTTNER, Helena (1861-?) Hungarian

£748 $1190 €1100 Hunting with falcons - elegant woman on horse with page (39x48cm-15x19in) s.i.d.1876. 20-Mar-3 Neumeister, Munich #2599/R

£980 $1529 €1470 Gentleman riding in autumn landscape (59x75cm-23x30in) s. 11-Sep-2 Kieselbach, Budapest #25/R (H.F 380000)

£1238 $1932 €1857 Indian star, 1888 (45x60cm-18x24in) s.d.1888. 11-Sep-2 Kieselbach, Budapest #23/R (H.F 480000)

BUTTNER, Werner (1954-) American

£3043 $4991 €4200 Untitled (100x100cm-39x39in) s.d.80 acrylic. 28-May-3 Lempertz, Koln #68/R est:3500

£3043 $4991 €4200 Untitled (100x100cm-39x39in) s.d.80 acrylic. 28-May-3 Lempertz, Koln #69/R est:3500

BUTTS, John (?-1764) British

£16667 $26333 €26000 Figure angling on river bank with dog (42x52cm-17x20in) 12-Nov-2 Mealy's, Castlecomer #1313/R est:25000

BUUREN, Meeuwis van (1902-1992) Dutch

£357 $521 €550 Surf (39x59cm-15x23in) s. 19-Jun-2 Vendue Huis, Gravenhage #71/R

£422 $616 €650 Breakwater in the surf (58x98cm-23x39in) s. 19-Jun-2 Vendue Huis, Gravenhage #72/R

£446 $696 €700 Choppy sea with sea gulls (59x99cm-23x39in) s. 5-Nov-2 Vendu Notarishuis, Rotterdam #93

£704 $1134 €1000 Sea view (69x118cm-27x46in) s. 7-May-3 Vendue Huis, Gravenhage #111

£1549 $2494 €2200 Seascape with sea gulls (61x100cm-24x39in) s. 6-May-3 Vendu Notarishuis, Rotterdam #126/R est:1000-1500

BUVELOT, Abram Louis (1814-1888) Swiss

£2326 $3698 €3489 Waterpool at Coleraine (23x31cm-9x12in) board prov. 5-May-3 Sotheby's, Melbourne #303/R est:1000-2000 (A.D 6000)

£3571 $5643 €5357 Ferry on the Yarra (20x30cm-8x12in) board painted c.1878-79 prov. 26-Nov-2 Sotheby's, Melbourne #96/R est:6000-10000 (A.D 10000)

£4962 $7840 €7443 At Coleraine (19x29cm-7x11in) s.d.1878 s.i.d.verso board. 2-Apr-3 Christie's, Melbourne #17/R est:8000-12000 (A.D 13000)

Works on paper

£1214 $1919 €1821 Near Oakleigh (21x27cm-8x11in) s.i. W/C. 26-Nov-2 Sotheby's, Melbourne #97/R est:3000-5000 (A.D 3400)

BUYERS, Donald (1930-) British

Works on paper

£420 $655 €630 North East landscape (54x73cm-21x29in) s. ink W/C. 10-Apr-3 Bonhams, Edinburgh #29

BUYLE, Robert (1895-1976) Belgian

£377 $591 €550 Composition (60x80cm-24x31in) s. 15-Apr-3 Galerie Moderne, Brussels #343/R

£479 $753 €700 Le'etal de fruits (50x65cm-20x26in) s. 15-Apr-3 Galerie Moderne, Brussels #377/R

BUYS, Bob (1912-1970) Dutch

£851 $1379 €1200 Figure on the quay of a port in southern France (37x49cm-15x19in) s.d.62 panel. 26-May-3 Glerum, Amsterdam #6/R

BUZEN (1734-1806) Japanese

Works on paper

£850 $1368 €1275 Kakemono (99x41cm-39x16in) s. ink silk. 19-Feb-3 Sotheby's, Olympia #2/R est:600-700

BUZON, Marius de (1879-1958) French

£513 $805 €800 Baigneuses dans le port (74x60cm-29x24in) s. 16-Dec-2 Gros & Delettrez, Paris #366

£513 $805 €800 Vue des environs de Bougies (54x65cm-21x26in) s. 16-Dec-2 Gros & Delettrez, Paris #367

£943 $1453 €1500 Kabylie (19x30cm-7x12in) s.d.1914 panel. 23-Oct-2 Rabourdin & Choppin de Janvry, Paris #202/R

£1667 $2617 €2600 Hauts d'Alger (54x65cm-21x26in) s. 22-Nov-2 Millon & Associes, Paris #73/R

BUZZI RESCHINI, Giacomo (1881-1962) Italian

Sculpture

£1154 $1812 €1800 Embrace (53x27x30cm-21x11x12in) bronze. 10-Dec-2 Della Rocca, Turin #323/R

BUZZI, Achille (19th C) Italian

Works on paper

£1800 $2808 €2700 Gondolier (43x52cm-17x20in) s. W/C. 17-Sep-2 Sotheby's, Olympia #282/R est:2000-3000

BUZZI, Andrea (1964-) Italian

Prints

£780 $1264 €1100 Untitled (50x50cm-20x20in) s.d.2002 verso. 26-May-3 Christie's, Milan #150/R

BUZZI, Federigo (19/20th C) Italian

£1282 $2013 €2000 Knife sharpener (33x35cm-13x14in) s.indis.d. 10-Dec-2 Dorotheum, Vienna #202/R est:1500-1700

BYE, Ranulph de Bayeux (1916-) American
Works on paper
£323 $500 €485 Maine lighthouse on rocky coast (33x51cm-13x20in) s. W/C. 2-Nov-2 Thomaston Place, Thomaston #163
£833 $1300 €1250 Tinicum, autumn landscape with farmhouse (25x33cm-10x13in) s.d.Oct 29 1984 W/C. 18-Sep-2 Alderfer's, Hatfield #350

BYHRE, Dale (19th C) Canadian?
£346 $526 €519 HMS Discovery and Chatham off Semiahmoo Bay (51x76cm-20x30in) 4-Jul-2 Heffel, Vancouver #3 (C.D 800)
£606 $921 €909 Empress of China, 1891 (61x76cm-24x30in) 4-Jul-2 Heffel, Vancouver #4 (C.D 1400)
£736 $1119 €1104 Port of Vancouver by moonlight, 1898 (61x76cm-24x30in) 4-Jul-2 Heffel, Vancouver #6 (C.D 1700)
£1190 $1809 €1785 Empress of Japan passing First Narrows (61x76cm-24x30in) 4-Jul-2 Heffel, Vancouver #5 est:1200-1500 (C.D 2750)

BYLANDT, Alfred Edouard van (1829-1890) Dutch
£1250 $2000 €1813 Animated shore view with distant peaks (31x45cm-12x18in) s.d.1881 panel. 16-May-3 Skinner, Boston #29/R est:2000-3000

BYLARD, Cornelis (1813-?) Dutch
£443 $691 €700 Landscape with trees near a farm (24x29cm-9x11in) panel. 21-Oct-2 Glerum, Amsterdam #135/R

BYLERT, Jan van (1603-1671) Dutch
£30769 $47692 €48000 Shepherd holding a flute (79x65cm-31x26in) prov.lit. 3-Dec-2 Sotheby's, Amsterdam #41/R est:50000-70000

BYLERT, Jan van (attrib) (1603-1671) Dutch
Works on paper
£2548 $3975 €4000 Young man in arcadian costume (19x17cm-7x7in) red chk over black chk. 5-Nov-2 Sotheby's, Amsterdam #27/R est:4000-6000

BYLES, William Hounsom (1872-c.1924) British
£550 $897 €825 Gentleman and the maid (63x56cm-25x22in) s. 12-Feb-3 Bonhams, Knightsbridge #80/R
£760 $1223 €1102 Gone away (27x38cm-11x15in) s. board. 12-May-3 Joel, Victoria #376 est:1000-1500 (A.D 1900)
£2708 $4332 €3927 Tudor cottage, Western Chichester (50x60cm-20x24in) s. i.verso. 13-May-3 Watson's, Christchurch #5/R est:8000-15000 (NZ.D 7500)
Works on paper
£2800 $4536 €4200 Grand National (27x51cm-11x20in) s. i.mount W/C bodycol. 22-May-3 Christie's, London #53/R est:4000-6000
£4000 $6240 €6000 Grand National 1927 - Valentine's Brook the second time around (28x46cm-11x18in) s. W/C bodycol. 6-Nov-2 Sotheby's, Olympia #59/R est:3000-5000

BYRNE, Bernard (20th C) Irish
£385 $596 €600 Boy in harlequinn costume (30x25cm-12x10in) s. 3-Dec-2 Bonhams & James Adam, Dublin #124/R

BYRNE, Edward Patrick (1877-1974) American
£617 $1000 €926 Untitled - movie star (15x8cm-6x3in) enamel on cardboard painted c.1966-73 prov. 27-Jan-3 Christie's, Rockefeller NY #75/R est:1500-2000
£1852 $3000 €2778 Untitled - house with two roofs (14x35cm-6x14in) enamel on cardboard painted c.1966-73 prov. 27-Jan-3 Christie's, Rockefeller NY #76/R est:2000-3000
£1975 $3200 €2963 Untitled - house with pink path (17x28cm-7x11in) enamel on cardboard prov. 27-Jan-3 Christie's, Rockefeller NY #74/R est:2000-3000
£1975 $3200 €2963 Untitled - house with checkered path (20x33cm-8x13in) enamel on cardboard painted c.1966-1973 prov. 27-Jan-3 Christie's, Rockefeller NY #77/R est:2000-3000

BYRNE, Gerard (20th C) Irish
£1130 $1774 €1650 On the canal, Warrington Place (45x74cm-18x29in) s. 15-Apr-3 De Veres Art Auctions, Dublin #37 est:1000-1500

BYRNE, John (1940-) British
£2200 $3410 €3300 Cast of Tutti Frutti (26x20cm-10x8in) s. scrapboard. 6-Dec-2 Lyon & Turnbull, Edinburgh #68/R est:2000-3000

BYRNE, John L (1906-1976) Canadian
£244 $401 €354 Summer farm (23x27cm-9x11in) s. board. 9-Jun-3 Hodgins, Calgary #7/R (C.D 550)
£301 $473 €452 Haying (39x48cm-15x19in) s. board. 25-Nov-2 Hodgins, Calgary #97/R (C.D 750)

BYRNE, Samuel (1883-1978) Australian
£464 $733 €696 Campbells Creek at the Pap's Barrier Rangers (32x43cm-13x17in) s.i. board. 18-Nov-2 Joel, Victoria #386 est:1200-1500 (A.D 1300)
£2679 $4232 €4019 Water sport, River Murray (50x77cm-20x30in) s.i. board prov. 27-Nov-2 Deutscher-Menzies, Melbourne #179/R est:4000-6000 (A.D 7500)
£2759 $4110 €4139 Bogged camels to the rescue (60x75cm-24x30in) s.i. enamel on board prov. 27-Aug-2 Christie's, Melbourne #232/R est:2500-3500 (A.D 7200)
£2857 $4429 €4286 Pernamoonta diggings (53x76cm-21x30in) s. oil metallic pyrites board. 29-Oct-2 Lawson Menzies, Sydney #32/R est:9000-12000 (A.D 8000)
£5197 $7900 €7796 Rabbit plague round up into old mine (47x60cm-19x24in) s.i. oil enamel composition board lit. 28-Aug-2 Deutscher-Menzies, Melbourne #189/R est:3000-4000 (A.D 14500)
Works on paper
£357 $564 €536 Island in a river, New Zealand (15x20cm-6x8in) gouache on card. 27-Nov-2 Deutscher-Menzies, Melbourne #180/R est:800-1200 (A.D 1000)

BYRNE, Val (?) ?
Works on paper
£420 $613 €630 Ballinakill Harbour, Co. Galway (25x36cm-10x14in) s. W/C. 12-Jun-2 John Ross, Belfast #35
£420 $651 €630 Dusk, Howth, Co. Dublin (36x51cm-14x20in) s. W/C. 2-Oct-2 John Ross, Belfast #199

BYSS, Johann Rudolf (1660-1738) Swiss
£5128 $8103 €8000 Landscape with herder and cattle by ruins (64x79cm-25x31in) s.d.1684. 16-Nov-2 Lempertz, Koln #1011a/R est:8000

BYSS, Johann Rudolf (attrib) (1660-1738) Swiss
£3041 $4743 €4500 Tarquin and Lucretia (59x73cm-23x29in) overdoor painting. 27-Mar-3 Dorotheum, Vienna #247/R est:2300-3000

BYSTROM, Johan Niklas (1783-1848) Swedish
Sculpture
£49651 $80434 €71994 Narcissus (150cm-59in) white marble incl.grey marble socle prov.lit. 26-May-3 Bukowskis, Stockholm #302/R est:200000-250000 (S.KR 640000)

BYWATERS, Jerry (1906-1989) American
Works on paper
£801 $1250 €1202 Old house (23x30cm-9x12in) W/C. 19-Oct-2 David Dike, Dallas #109/R

BYZANTIOS, Constantin (20th C) Greek?
£250 $393 €375 Figures in an interior (52x40cm-20x16in) s.i.d.55 board prov. 10-Dec-2 Rosebery Fine Art, London #637

C M (?) ?
£897 $1400 €1346 River landscape with train four cars and figures (41x66cm-16x26in) mono. 28-Mar-3 Eldred, East Dennis #815/R est:800-1200

CABAILLOT, Camille Leopold (1839-?) French
£1800 $2844 €2700 Feeding the chickens (41x32cm-16x13in) s. panel prov. 14-Nov-2 Christie's, Kensington #272/R est:1500-2000

CABAILLOT, Louis Simon (1810-?) French
£1400 $2198 €2100 Little wood gatherers (40x32cm-16x13in) s. panel. 19-Nov-2 Bonhams, New Bond Street #164/R est:2000-3000
£1962 $3041 €3100 Two peasant girls with animals walking in snow at daybreak (46x55cm-18x22in) s.d.85. 25-Sep-2 Neumeister, Munich #628/R est:2200
£2600 $4342 €3900 Dog's new trick (24x19cm-9x7in) s. panel. 18-Jun-3 Christie's, Kensington #83/R est:3000-5000
£2686 $4217 €4029 At the well (38x46cm-15x18in) s. panel. 24-Jul-2 Walker's, Ottawa #40/R est:2000-3000 (C.D 6500)

CABALLERO, Jose Luis (1916-1991) Spanish
£3097 $4893 €4800 Untitled (120x81cm-47x32in) s. s.verso. 17-Dec-2 Segre, Madrid #144/R

Works on paper
£500 $790 €780 Portrait of woman (46x31cm-18x12in) s. ink dr. 14-Nov-2 Arte, Seville #419/R
£1258 $1962 €2000 Composition (21x30cm-8x12in) s. gouache. 23-Sep-2 Durán, Madrid #123/R
£1415 $2208 €2250 Theatre scene (54x77cm-21x30in) s. gouache. 23-Sep-2 Durán, Madrid #269/R

CABALLERO, Luis (1943-1995) Colombian
Works on paper
£1573 $2438 €2500 Sans titre (73x104cm-29x41in) s.d.90 chl. 4-Oct-2 Tajan, Paris #37 est:4000-5000

CABALLERO, Maximo (1867-1951) Spanish
£2800 $4452 €4200 Musketeer (47x27cm-19x11in) s.d.1919. 20-Mar-3 Christie's, Kensington #92/R est:2000-3000
£6000 $9540 €9000 Proposal (61x73cm-24x29in) s.d.1902. 18-Mar-3 Bonhams, New Bond Street #85/R est:4000-6000
£7895 $12789 €12000 Discussing in the inn (47x39cm-19x15in) s. 21-Jan-3 Durán, Madrid #161/R est:12000
£12821 $20256 €20000 Game (54x64cm-21x25in) s. 14-Nov-2 Arte, Seville #364/R

CABANE, Edouard (1857-?) French
£3387 $5250 €5081 Portrait of a young girl holding a kitten (46x36cm-18x14in) s.d.1909. 7-Dec-2 Selkirks, St. Louis #764/R est:1500-2000

CABANEL, Alexandre (1823-1889) French
£1266 $2000 €2000 Portrait de l'actrice rachel (33x24cm-13x9in) s. canvas on board prov. 2-Dec-2 Rieunier, Paris #33/R
£2119 $3454 €3200 Bebe (32x24cm-13x9in) s. 3-Feb-3 Chambelland & Giafferi, Paris #312/R
£2390 $3704 €3800 La halte (37x56cm-15x22in) s. 30-Oct-2 Artcurial Briest, Paris #162/R est:3800-4500
£2500 $3925 €3750 Une femme nue se reposant (54x74cm-21x29in) init. 21-Nov-2 Christie's, Kensington #45/R est:3000-5000
£3028 $5027 €4300 Portrait d'Isabelle Fabre (65x54cm-26x21in) s. 16-Jun-3 Oger, Dumont, Paris #36/R est:5000-8000
£3046 $4966 €4600 Scene a l'antique (24x19cm-9x7in) s.d.1853 panel. 3-Feb-3 Chambelland & Giafferi, Paris #313/R
£3974 $6477 €6000 Etude de tete de chevalier (40x32cm-16x13in) 3-Feb-3 Chambelland & Giafferi, Paris #314/R
£10464 $17056 €15800 Venus (46x22cm-18x9in) s.d.1873 panel pair oval. 3-Feb-3 Chambelland & Giafferi, Paris #317/R est:5000
£19745 $31000 €29618 Sleeping Bacchante (76x96cm-30x38in) s. 22-Nov-2 Skinner, Boston #49/R est:5000-7000
£21854 $35623 €33000 Naissance de Venus (24x44cm-9x17in) s. panel. 3-Feb-3 Chambelland & Giafferi, Paris #318/R est:15000
£26490 $43179 €40000 Gracomica (160x76cm-63x30in) s.i.d.1871. 3-Feb-3 Chambelland & Giafferi, Paris #333/R est:20000
£483871 $750000 €725807 Birth of Venus (85x136cm-33x54in) s. painted c.1865-69 prov.exhib.lit. 30-Oct-2 Christie's, Rockefeller NY #36/R est:400000-600000
Works on paper
£2384 $3886 €3600 Nu au drap blanc (35x19cm-14x7in) s. sanguine chk. 3-Feb-3 Chambelland & Giafferi, Paris #315/R
£2781 $4534 €4200 Etude de mains et pied (22x36cm-9x14in) s. graphite. 3-Feb-3 Chambelland & Giafferi, Paris #343/R

CABAT, Louis (1812-1893) French
£2010 $3256 €2915 Le tropeau sur le Pont (40x64cm-16x25in) s. exhib.prov. 26-May-3 Rasmussen, Copenhagen #1469/R est:10000-15000 (D.KR 21000)
£2278 $3554 €3600 Le verger (28x38cm-11x15in) s. 15-Oct-2 Regis & Thiollet, Argentuil #73
Works on paper
£351 $548 €520 Paysage a Fontainebleau (23x30cm-9x12in) i.d. pen ink wash prov. 31-Mar-3 Piasa, Paris #69

CABAT, Louis (attrib) (1812-1893) French
£283 $441 €425 River landscape with viaduct (321x35cm-126x14in) s. board. 16-Sep-2 Philippe Schuler, Zurich #6432 (S.FR 650)

CABEL, Adrian van der (circle) (c.1631-1705) Dutch
£3572 $5500 €5358 Mediterranean coastal landscape (57x88cm-22x35in) i.verso. 4-Sep-2 Christie's, Rockefeller NY #246/R est:5000-7000
£8000 $12560 €12000 Mediterranean port with fishermen in the foreground, man-o-war offshore (187x156cm-74x61in) prov. 13-Dec-2 Christie's, Kensington #83/R est:8000-12000

CABIANCA, Vincenzo (1827-1902) Italian
£2900 $4727 €4350 Nun in contemplation (38x23cm-15x9in) s.d.1889 board. 29-Jan-3 Sotheby's, Olympia #312/R est:1000-1500
£9677 $15290 €15000 Murano (12x23cm-5x9in) s. board prov. 18-Dec-2 Finarte, Milan #69/R est:23000
Works on paper
£11321 $17434 €18000 Young nun meditating (34x24cm-13x9in) s.d.1865 pastel. 23-Oct-2 Finarte, Milan #72/R est:18000-20000

CABIE, L (1853-1939) French
£3310 $5263 €4800 Lake landscape (130x200cm-51x79in) s.d.1895. 4-Mar-3 Ansorena, Madrid #186/R

CABIE, Louis Alexandre (1853-1939) French
£347 $549 €500 Paysage de foret (36x51cm-14x20in) s. panel. 25-Apr-3 Piasa, Paris #60
£386 $610 €579 River landscape near Eyzies (18x29cm-7x11in) s.d.1898 board. 26-Nov-2 Hans Widmer, St Gallen #1066/R (S.FR 900)
£409 $634 €650 Matin dans les bois (45x62cm-18x24in) s. i.verso panel. 30-Oct-2 Coutau Begarie, Paris #69
£786 $1288 €1140 Coastal landscape from South of France (73x54cm-29x21in) s. 4-Jun-3 AB Stockholms Auktionsverk #2482/R (S.KR 10000)
Works on paper
£253 $400 €400 Arbre (31x38cm-12x15in) s.d.1919 gouache. 2-Dec-2 Rieunier, Paris #4

CABLE, William Lindsay (?) British
Works on paper
£400 $628 €600 Well protected (58x50cm-23x20in) pastel. 21-Nov-2 Tennants, Leyburn #690

CABRAL BEJARANO, Francisco (1824-1890) Spanish
£2244 $3522 €3500 Gypsies (58x78cm-23x31in) s. 19-Nov-2 Castellana, Madrid #540/R
£26923 $42538 €42000 Church interior during Mass (89x119cm-35x47in) s.i.d.1865. 14-Nov-2 Arte, Seville #293/R

CABRE, Manuel (1890-1983) Venezuelan
£38217 $60000 €57326 View of the Country Club in Caracas (63x110cm-25x43in) s.d.46 prov.lit. 19-Nov-2 Sotheby's, New York #29/R est:90000

CABRERA, Ben (1942-) Philippino
£27195 $44872 €39433 Brown brother's burden (75x55cm-30x22in) acrylic exhib.lit. 6-Jul-3 Christie's, Hong Kong #46/R est:150000-200000 (HK.D 350000)

CABRERA, Miguel (1695-1768) Mexican
£4878 $8000 €7317 Santisima Trinidad con la Virgen (14x13cm-6x5in) s.i.d.1761 copper prov. 28-May-3 Christie's, Rockefeller NY #62/R est:8000-12000

CABURET, Christian (20th C) French?
£298 $486 €450 Lisiere du temple (89x116cm-35x46in) acrylic. 1-Feb-3 Claude Aguttes, Neuilly #234/R

CACCIA, Guglielmo (1568-1625) Italian
£25641 $39744 €40000 Putti playing musical instruments (68x42cm-27x17in) board oval set of 4. 4-Dec-2 Christie's, Rome #458/R est:14000-18000
Works on paper
£1689 $2635 €2500 Madonna and Child (21x13cm-8x5in) chk pen ink wash. 27-Mar-3 Christie's, Paris #1/R

CACCIA, Guglielmo (attrib) (1568-1625) Italian
Works on paper
£1831 $2948 €2600 Donna con due putti (21x16cm-8x6in) pen brown ink red pencil. 12-May-3 Sotheby's, Milan #41/R est:500-700

CACCIAPUOTI, Guido (1892-1953) Italian
Sculpture
£1698 $2632 €2700 Deux elephants (12x40x10cm-5x16x4in) gold pat.bronze. 6-Oct-2 Feletin, Province #95/R

CACCIARELLI, Victor (19th C) Italian
£960 $1507 €1440 Pinch of snuff (32x24cm-13x9in) s. 16-Apr-3 Christie's, Kensington #802/R

CACERES, Jorge (1922-1949) Chilean
Works on paper
£1507 $2366 €2200 Untitled (8x14cm-3x6in) s. collage. 15-Apr-3 Laurence Calmels, Paris #4200/R
£2192 $3441 €3200 Untitled (20x14cm-8x6in) s. collage ink. 15-Apr-3 Laurence Calmels, Paris #4198/R

£2397 $3764 €3500 Idea (14x10cm-6x4in) s.i. collage. 15-Apr-3 Laurence Calmels, Paris #4196/R
£2603 $4086 €3800 Untitled (15x24cm-6x9in) s. collage. 15-Apr-3 Laurence Calmels, Paris #4199/R
£3082 $4839 €4500 Untitled (17x14cm-7x6in) s.verso collage. 15-Apr-3 Laurence Calmels, Paris #4197/R
£3425 $5377 €5000 Untitled (27x26cm-11x10in) s.d.1942 ink. 15-Apr-3 Laurence Calmels, Paris #4195/R

CACERES, L (19th C) ?
£771 $1264 €1118 Alcala de Guadaira (42x60cm-17x24in) s.d.1891. 28-May-3 Louis Morton, Mexico #90 est:10000-12000 (M.P 13000)

CACHEUX, François (1923-) French
Sculpture
£3797 $5886 €6000 L'attente (19x39cm-7x15in) s.num.4/8 col pat bronze Cast Delval. 29-Sep-2 Eric Pillon, Calais #281/R

CACHOUD, François-Charles (1866-1943) French
£850 $1394 €1275 Chemin de village de gogeat nute-de-lune (64x53cm-25x21in) s. prov. 5-Feb-3 John Nicholson, Haslemere #1068
£865 $1341 €1350 Coteaux de Saint-Alban le Montbel (21x26cm-8x10in) s. i.verso cardboard. 7-Dec-2 Martinot & Savignat, Pontoise #144
£1083 $1700 €1625 Evening, cottage scene (57x74cm-22x29in) s.d.1906. 22-Nov-2 Skinner, Boston #307/R est:1800-2200
£1341 $2200 €1944 Moonlit cottage (66x81cm-26x32in) s. 4-Jun-3 Doyle, New York #21 est:3000-5000

CADEL, Eugène (20th C) French
£417 $663 €600 Nu couche (22x27cm-9x11in) s. cardboard. 30-Apr-3 Tajan, Paris #147
£952 $1504 €1380 Blacksmith (33x41cm-13x16in) s. canvas on board. 1-Apr-3 Segre, Madrid #52/R
£1844 $2987 €2600 Le pecheur (40x60cm-16x24in) s. 21-May-3 Cornette de St.Cyr, Paris #51/R est:1000-1500

CADELL, Francis Campbell Boileau (1883-1937) British
£22000 $34100 €33000 Pier at Cove, Loch Long (44x37cm-17x15in) s. panel prov. 31-Oct-2 Christie's, London #130/R est:20000-30000
£31000 $47120 €46500 Auchnacraig, Mull (37x44cm-15x17in) s. s.i.verso panel prov. 28-Aug-2 Sotheby's, London #1081/R est:30000-40000
£35000 $55650 €52500 Still life, anemones (30x23cm-12x9in) s. s.i.verso panel prov. 6-Mar-3 Christie's, Kensington #207/R est:12000-18000
£62000 $94860 €93000 Cassis, the white villa from the balcony (45x37cm-18x15in) s. s.i.verso panel. 22-Aug-2 Bonhams, Edinburgh #1011/R est:30000-50000
£65000 $103350 €97500 Red chair (61x51cm-24x20in) s.i.verso painted c.1923-25. 6-Mar-3 Christie's, Kensington #206/R est:50000-80000
£120000 $187200 €180000 Roses (45x38cm-18x15in) s. i.verso board. 14-Apr-3 Sotheby's, London #109/R est:70000-100000
Works on paper
£7000 $10710 €10500 Haystack and crofts, Iona (16x25cm-6x10in) s. W/C. 22-Aug-2 Bonhams, Edinburgh #1039/R est:7000-10000
£7000 $10920 €10500 View of Edinburgh and the Water of Leith from no 1 Rothesay Terrace (36x44cm-14x17in) s.d.1908 W/C over pencil prov. 10-Apr-3 Bonhams, Edinburgh #149/R est:7000-10000
£7200 $11232 €10800 Iona (17x24cm-7x9in) s. i.verso W/C. 10-Apr-3 Bonhams, Edinburgh #155/R est:4000-6000
£8000 $12480 €12000 Ross of Mull (17x25cm-7x10in) s. i.verso W/C. 10-Apr-3 Bonhams, Edinburgh #156/R est:4000-6000
£10500 $16065 €15750 Milking, Lairge Farm (27x36cm-11x14in) s. W/C bodycol. 22-Aug-2 Bonhams, Edinburgh #1118/R est:5000-7000
£12500 $19875 €18750 White sands, Iona (17x24cm-7x9in) s. i.verso pencil W/C pair framed as one. 6-Mar-3 Christie's, Kensington #208/R est:4000-6000

CADELL, St John (19/20th C) British
£580 $905 €870 Water nymph (112x86cm-44x34in) s. 13-Sep-2 Lyon & Turnbull, Edinburgh #103/R
£600 $966 €900 Island of Iona (27x35cm-11x14in) s. board. 18-Feb-3 Bonhams, Ipswich #302

CADENASSO, Giuseppe (1858-1918) American
£1386 $2300 €2010 Desert clouds (38x51cm-15x20in) s. 14-Jun-3 Jackson's, Cedar Falls #13/R est:3000-5000
£2395 $4000 €3473 Wooded landscape, passing clouds (36x43cm-14x17in) s.d.92 prov.exhib. 17-Jun-3 John Moran, Pasadena #78b est:5000-7000
Works on paper
£1452 $2250 €2178 Landscape (38x48cm-15x19in) s. pastel prov. 29-Oct-2 John Moran, Pasadena #740a est:3000-5000

CADENHEAD, James (1858-1927) British
£800 $1240 €1200 Mother and child in autumn landscape, sheep and farmstead beyond (76x115cm-30x45in) s.d.1881. 31-Oct-2 Greenslade Hunt, Taunton #625/R
£2200 $3498 €3300 Figures in a pastoral landscape (76x117cm-30x46in) s.d.1881. 6-Mar-3 Christie's, Kensington #484/R est:2500-3500

CADES, Giuseppe (attrib) (1750-1799) Italian
Works on paper
£688 $1100 €1032 Apollo and Athlete (21x15cm-8x6in) pen ink gray wash. 14-May-3 Doyle, New York #18 est:1500-2000

CADMAN, Michael (1920-) British
Works on paper
£350 $581 €508 Boats at anchor, Cornish harbour (36x51cm-14x20in) s.d.1978 mixed media. 10-Jun-3 David Lay, Penzance #382

CADMUS, Paul (1904-1999) American
£11613 $18000 €17420 Ballet student (43x46cm-17x18in) egg tempera. 2-Nov-2 North East Auctions, Portsmouth #86/R est:15000-25000
Prints
£2358 $3750 €3537 Youth with kite (69x36cm-27x14in) s.d.1941 etching one of 75. 30-Apr-3 Doyle, New York #169/R est:1500-2500
£3226 $5000 €4839 Horseplay (23x13cm-9x5in) s. etching. 2-Nov-2 North East Auctions, Portsmouth #87/R est:2500-3500
£3333 $5200 €5000 Two boys on a beach no 1 (12x18cm-5x7in) s. etching edition of 75. 7-Nov-2 Swann Galleries, New York #573/R est:3000-5000
£3590 $5600 €5385 Horseplay (23x12cm-9x5in) s. etching edition of 50. 7-Nov-2 Swann Galleries, New York #571/R est:4000-6000
£3718 $5800 €5577 Going south (25x14cm-10x6in) s. etching edition of 15. 7-Nov-2 Swann Galleries, New York #568/R est:3000-5000
£3718 $5800 €5577 Y M C A locker room (17x32cm-7x13in) s.i. etching edition of 50. 7-Nov-2 Swann Galleries, New York #570/R est:5000-8000
£3846 $6000 €5769 Stewarts (20x31cm-8x12in) s. etching edition of 50. 7-Nov-2 Swann Galleries, New York #569/R est:5000-8000
£5063 $8000 €7595 Fleets in! (19x36cm-7x14in) s.i. etching executed c.1934 one of 50. 12-Nov-2 Doyle, New York #175/R est:4000-6000
Works on paper
£3302 $5250 €4953 Male nude NM98 (30x15cm-12x6in) s. col pencil prov. 3-May-3 Rachel Davis, Shaker Heights #400/R est:3000-5000
£3915 $6500 €5677 Male nude (42x31cm-17x12in) s. conte crayon prov. 11-Jun-3 Butterfields, San Francisco #4098/R est:6000-8000
£7317 $12000 €10610 Charles Eggert (25x35cm-10x14in) s.i.d. pen ink over pencil. 5-Jun-3 Swann Galleries, New York #66/R est:5000-8000

CADORET, Michel (1912-1985) French
£369 $594 €550 Formes (81x100cm-32x39in) st.sig.verso painted c.1960. 23-Feb-3 Mercier & Cie, Lille #168/R
£403 $648 €600 Valeur III (76x103cm-30x41in) s. painted c.1955. 23-Feb-3 Mercier & Cie, Lille #170/R
£403 $648 €600 Composition fond brun (101x76cm-40x30in) studio st.verso. 23-Feb-3 Mercier & Cie, Lille #173/R
£674 $1125 €950 Sans titre (76x101cm-30x40in) s.d.57. 20-Jun-3 Piasa, Paris #222/R
£1056 $1754 €1500 Sans titre (102x127cm-40x50in) bears st.sig. verso. 15-Jun-3 Anaf, Lyon #29/R est:1500-1800

CADORIN, Guido (1892-1978) Italian
£270 $437 €380 Marta Abba (228x100cm-90x39in) s. 22-May-3 Stadion, Trieste #280
£719 $1151 €1000 Carabinieri in boat going to opening of the Biennale (20x30cm-8x12in) s.d. i.d. verso panel. 15-May-3 Neumeister, Munich #689/R

CADY, Henry (1849-?) American
Works on paper
£469 $750 €680 The receding storm, a shore view (34x58cm-13x23in) s. W/C paper on board. 16-May-3 Skinner, Boston #110/R

CADY, Walter Harrison (1877-1970) American
£577 $900 €866 Village with fisherman in foreground and boat in drydock (28x23cm-11x9in) s. artist board. 15-Oct-2 Winter Associates, Plainville #122
£1410 $2200 €2115 Delaware Canal, Harrison Cady. Merry Christmas to my dear friends (41x48cm-16x19in) s. i.verso particle board pair sold with pencil sketch. 15-Oct-2 Winter Associates, Plainville #121 est:1200-1800

CAFE, Thomas Watt (1856-1925) British
£4000 $6560 €6000 Idyllis of summer (30x61cm-12x24in) s. 5-Jun-3 Christie's, Kensington #645/R est:2000-3000

CAFFE, Nino (1909-1975) Spanish

£353 $550 €530 Surrealist interior scene with two cardinals contemplating painting (18x13cm-7x5in) s. 21-Sep-2 Nadeau, Windsor #64
£375 $600 €544 Gomma a terra (14x17cm-6x7in) s. 16-May-3 Skinner, Boston #384/R
£513 $800 €770 Interior scene with two cardinals and macaw (18x13cm-7x5in) s. 21-Sep-2 Nadeau, Windsor #179
£629 $1000 €944 Santanelli (15x19cm-6x7in) s.verso. 7-Mar-3 Skinner, Boston #631/R
£650 $1021 €975 Sudden flurry (33x44cm-13x17in) panel prov. 10-Dec-2 Rosebery Fine Art, London #647
£811 $1265 €1200 Dog on the bench (14x17cm-6x7in) s. board. 28-Mar-3 Farsetti, Prato #63
£833 $1300 €1250 Surrealist interior with priests confronting demon (30x38cm-12x15in) s.d.1971. 21-Sep-2 Nadeau, Windsor #253/R
£1528 $2429 €2200 Priests at the seaside (23x37cm-9x15in) s. 1-May-3 Meeting Art, Vercelli #66
£1623 $2500 €2435 Priests sliding down a fabric chute (41x20cm-16x8in) s. i.verso panel. 7-Sep-2 Brunk, Ashville #300/R est:2000-4000
£1757 $2741 €2600 Priests (18x25cm-7x10in) s. board. 26-Mar-3 Finarte Semenzato, Milan #258/R
£1806 $2871 €2600 Priests at the Pincio (25x35cm-10x14in) s. 1-May-3 Meeting Art, Vercelli #299
£2044 $3250 €3066 Sgomento (30x40cm-12x16in) s. sold with a photo. 7-Mar-3 Skinner, Boston #633/R est:2000-3000
£2051 $3221 €3200 Snow balls (25x35cm-10x14in) s. 23-Nov-2 Meeting Art, Vercelli #180/R
£2700 $4347 €4050 Settimo Cielo (38x18cm-15x7in) s. board. 9-May-3 Mallams, Oxford #119/R est:2000-3000
£3548 $5500 €5322 Monache sulla neve (36x64cm-14x25in) s. panel. 26-Sep-2 Christie's, Rockefeller NY #558/R est:3000-5000
£3846 $6038 €6000 New air (25x30cm-10x12in) s. painted 1972 prov. 21-Nov-2 Finarte, Rome #303/R
£4167 $6542 €6500 Composition 4 (40x60cm-16x24in) s. i.verso painted 1970 exhib. 19-Nov-2 Finarte, Milan #59/R est:5000

CAFFI, Ippolito (1809-1866) Italian

£2152 $3400 €3400 View of Nizza (16x36cm-6x14in) s. panel. 28-Nov-2 Dorotheum, Vienna #101/R est:2800-3200

Works on paper

£12800 $20864 €18560 Carnival in the via del Corso, Rome (22x29cm-9x11in) s. W/C gum arabic. 16-Jul-3 Sotheby's, Olympia #147/R est:1000-1500
£12800 $20864 €18560 Fire in a Roman street (22x29cm-9x11in) s. W/C gum arabic. 16-Jul-3 Sotheby's, Olympia #150/R est:1000-1500
£13800 $22494 €20010 Carnival in the via del Campo, Rome (22x29cm-9x11in) s. W/C gum arabic. 16-Jul-3 Sotheby's, Olympia #148/R est:1000-1500
£14800 $24124 €21460 Carnival in the via del Campo, Rome (22x29cm-9x11in) s. W/C. 16-Jul-3 Sotheby's, Olympia #149/R est:1000-1500

CAFFI, Ippolito (style) (1809-1866) Italian

£349 $510 €524 Quai a Nice (16x36cm-6x14in) i. panel. 4-Jun-2 Germann, Zurich #752 (S.FR 800)

CAFFI, Margherita (c.1650-1710) Italian

£6081 $9486 €9000 Still life of flowers (61x75cm-24x30in) prov. 27-Mar-3 Dorotheum, Vienna #34/R est:7000-10000
£10759 $16677 €17000 Flowers (77x104cm-30x41in) 26-Sep-2 Castellana, Madrid #45/R

CAFFI, Margherita (attrib) (c.1650-1710) Italian

£9677 $15290 €15000 Bouquet (94x60cm-37x24in) 18-Dec-2 Piasa, Paris #12/R est:8000
£14388 $23022 €20000 Still life of flowers in field (71x88cm-28x35in) 13-May-3 Sotheby's, Amsterdam #81/R est:15000-20000
£22222 $36000 €33333 Still life of flowers in a basket. Still life of flowers in an urn (79x110cm-31x43in) pair. 23-Jan-3 Sotheby's, New York #206/R est:35000

CAFFI, Margherita (style) (c.1650-1710) Italian

£6475 $10360 €9000 Roses, tulips and other flowers in a terracotta pot (56x98cm-22x39in) 14-May-3 Christie's, Amsterdam #190/R est:9000-12000

CAFFIERI (after) (?) ?

Sculpture

£5031 $7849 €8000 L'enlevement d'Europe assise sur le taureau. black pat bronze socle. 20-Sep-2 Millon & Associes, Paris #810/R est:8000-12000

CAFFIERI, Hector (1847-1932) British

Works on paper

£780 $1225 €1170 Flowers calcolarias (32x25cm-13x10in) s.d.1871 W/C gouache. 19-Nov-2 Bonhams, Leeds #51
£1900 $3040 €2850 Carafe with calceolaria and azaleas (33x25cm-13x10in) s.d.1871 W/C bodycol. 11-Mar-3 Bonhams, New Bond Street #79/R est:1500-2000
£4500 $7425 €6525 Day's catch (36x52cm-14x20in) s. pencil W/C htd white. 3-Jul-3 Christie's, Kensington #140/R est:3000-5000

CAFFIERI, Jean Jacques (1725-1792) French

Sculpture

£10256 $15897 €16000 Portrait de Jean Restout (37x23x15cm-15x9x6in) s.d.1754 terracotta. 9-Dec-2 Rabourdin & Choppin de Janvry, Paris #40/R est:6000

CAFFREY, Yona (20th C) Irish

£288 $452 €420 Still life with flowers (29x39cm-11x15in) oil on paper. 15-Apr-3 De Veres Art Auctions, Dublin #100z

CAFFYN, Walter Wallor (?-1898) British

£300 $456 €450 Rocky river landscape (30x46cm-12x18in) s. board. 29-Aug-2 Christie's, Kensington #2
£580 $905 €870 Evening on the river Loddon, near Reading (36x61cm-14x24in) indis sig. 10-Sep-2 Sworder & Son, Bishops Stortford #778/R
£943 $1500 €1415 Shepherd tending the flock (25x36cm-10x14in) board. 22-Mar-3 New Orleans Auction, New Orleans #103/R est:1800-2500
£1244 $2066 €1804 Evening, old locks on the canal, Woking (41x69cm-16x27in) s.d.1896 s.i.verso prov. 16-Jun-3 Waddingtons, Toronto #142/R est:3000-5000 (C.D 2800)
£1948 $3019 €2922 Harvesting at Winchfield (43x53cm-17x21in) s.d.1884. 24-Sep-2 Koller, Zurich #6603/R est:3000-4000 (S.FR 4500)
£2000 $3040 €3000 Bredon View, Worcs (38x56cm-15x22in) s.d.1880. 16-Aug-2 Keys, Aylsham #665/R
£4200 $6720 €6300 Summer time by the moat near Brockham, river landscape (41x30cm-16x12in) s.d.1877-78 pair. 13-May-3 Bonhams, Knightsbridge #304/R est:1500-2000
£16000 $25120 €24000 Harvest time, Ewhurst, Surrey (61x91cm-24x36in) s.d.1891 i.verso. 19-Nov-2 Bonhams, New Bond Street #136/R est:10000-15000

CAFORIO, Fabrizio (20th C) ?

£3600 $5832 €5400 Domain (122x122cm-48x48in) s.i.d.25.8.92. 20-May-3 Sotheby's, Olympia #437/R est:3000-5000
£4000 $6480 €6000 Panthera uncia uncia (120x170cm-47x67in) s. s.i.d.20.5.94. 20-May-3 Sotheby's, Olympia #436/R est:4000-6000

CAGLI, Corrado (1910-1976) Italian

£1277 $2068 €1800 Mago Baku (54x69cm-21x27in) s.d.68 s.i.verso tempera paper on canvas prov.exhib. 26-May-3 Christie's, Milan #299/R est:1500-2000
£1702 $2757 €2400 Untitled (84x54cm-33x21in) s.d.74 s.i.d.verso card on panel. 26-May-3 Christie's, Milan #156/R est:2000-3000
£2532 $3949 €4000 Abstraction (69x67cm-27x26in) s. paper on canvas painted 1950. 14-Sep-2 Meeting Art, Vercelli #827/R
£5674 $9191 €8000 Strumenti musicali - Variazione 3 (70x45cm-28x18in) s.d.47 tempera paper on canvas prov.exhib. 26-May-3 Christie's, Milan #313/R est:3000-4000

Works on paper

£616 $962 €900 Figure in red. Woman bust (34x24cm-13x9in) wax crayon card pair. 10-Apr-3 Finarte Semenzato, Rome #113/R
£890 $1389 €1300 Totem (70x30cm-28x12in) s. s.i.verso mixed media paper on board. 10-Apr-3 Finarte Semenzato, Rome #262
£2055 $3205 €3000 Cartasole (100x40cm-39x16in) s. mixed media paper on canvas. 10-Apr-3 Finarte Semenzato, Rome #249/R
£2308 $3623 €3600 Cartasole (100x40cm-39x16in) s. s.i.verso mixed media exec.1962 prov. 21-Nov-2 Finarte, Rome #264/R

CAGNACCI, Guido (after) (1601-1681) Italian

£5517 $8772 €8000 David and Goliath (119x78cm-47x31in) lit. 5-Mar-3 Sotheby's, Milan #224/R

CAGNACCI, Guido (circle) (1601-1681) Italian

£7483 $11898 €11000 Saint with book - possibly Maria Magdalena (71x57cm-28x22in) 19-Mar-3 Neumeister, Munich #424/R est:1500

CAGNIART, Émile (1851-1911) French

Works on paper

£437 $681 €656 Woodland (45x37cm-18x15in) s.d.1890 pastel. 6-Nov-2 Dobiaschofsky, Bern #386/R (S.FR 1000)
£483 $763 €700 Busy street in Paris (43x48cm-17x19in) s. pastel lit. 5-Apr-3 Geble, Radolfzell #692/R
£586 $926 €850 Busy street in Paris (37x48cm-15x19in) s. pastel lit. 5-Apr-3 Geble, Radolfzell #693/R

CAGNONE, Angelo (1941-) Italian

£654 $1046 €1000 Objet inconnu 3 (120x120cm-47x47in) s.i.verso. 4-Jan-3 Meeting Art, Vercelli #348

CAHILL, Patrick (?) Irish

£401 $666 €570 Guitar player (51x40cm-20x16in) s. board. 10-Jun-3 James Adam, Dublin #35/R

£704 $1169 €1000 Horse against the sun, Smithfield (29x39cm-11x15in) s. board. 10-Jun-3 James Adam, Dublin #183/R est:1000-1500

£822 $1282 €1200 Trinity kiss (33x27cm-13x11in) s. board. 8-Apr-3 James Adam, Dublin #59/R

£959 $1496 €1400 Old Plod, Smithfield (48x58cm-19x23in) s. board. 8-Apr-3 James Adam, Dublin #60/R

CAHN, Marcelle (1895-1981) French

Works on paper

£304 $474 €450 Untitled (12x14cm-5x6in) collage prov. 28-Mar-3 Charbonneaux, Paris #42

£486 $773 €700 Composition (17x24cm-7x9in) s. gouache. 29-Apr-3 Artcurial Briest, Paris #118

£486 $773 €700 Sans titter (8x20cm-3x8in) s.d.62 collage felt. 29-Apr-3 Artcurial Briest, Paris #118b

CAHN, Miriam (1949-) Swiss

Works on paper

£6232 $10220 €8600 Figures (37x24cm-15x9in) mono.i.d.1.2.82 verso chl 11. 28-May-3 Lempertz, Koln #76/R est:9000-10000

CAHOON, Charles D (1861-1951) American

£223 $350 €335 Half length portrait of a man (61x51cm-24x20in) s.d.1934 verso. 22-Nov-2 Eldred, East Dennis #372/R

£573 $900 €860 Mackerel (41x20cm-16x8in) s. shingle. 22-Nov-2 Eldred, East Dennis #285/R

£2724 $4250 €4086 Landing boat, Brewster, Mass (38x51cm-15x20in) s.i. 21-Sep-2 Pook & Pook, Downington #352/R est:3000-5000

£3526 $5500 €5289 Marsh landscape (36x56cm-14x22in) s. 1-Aug-2 Eldred, East Dennis #807/R est:3500-4500

£7051 $11000 €10577 Actress (23x30cm-9x12in) s. board. 1-Aug-2 Eldred, East Dennis #809/R est:6000-8000

CAHOON, Charles D (attrib) (1861-1951) American

£1958 $2800 €2937 Swamp landscape (33x61cm-13x24in) s. 11-Dec-1 Lincoln, Orange #474/R

CAHOON, Martha (1905-1999) American

£641 $1000 €962 Portrait of a young Highlander in Scottish landscape (33x25cm-13x10in) s.d.1981 masonite. 1-Aug-2 Eldred, East Dennis #977/R

£1026 $1600 €1539 Portrait of a young girl holding a doll in a garden landscape (30x25cm-12x10in) s. masonite. 1-Aug-2 Eldred, East Dennis #978/R est:1500-2000

£1465 $2300 €2198 Woman in Swedish costume holds a lamb as she walks in field with two sheep (28x36cm-11x14in) s. masonite. 22-Nov-2 Eldred, East Dennis #846/R est:1500-2000

£4167 $6500 €6251 Portrait of a doll standing next to a toy soldier and a horse pull toy (36x46cm-14x18in) s. masonite. 1-Aug-2 Eldred, East Dennis #979/R est:3000-5000

£12179 $19000 €18269 Sailor's valentine (38cm-15in circular) s. shellwork. 28-Mar-3 Eldred, East Dennis #698/R est:3500-5000

Works on paper

£318 $500 €477 Chinese scene with figures on shore in boats (33x41cm-13x16in) s.d.1987 crayon dr. 22-Nov-2 Eldred, East Dennis #845/R

CAHOON, Ralph (1910-1982) American

£6129 $9500 €9194 Hero (53x46cm-21x18in) s. masonite. 29-Oct-2 Doyle, New York #66/R est:10000-15000

£9615 $15000 €14423 Stork transports a baby in light blue ribbon over a town and church spire (30x43cm-12x17in) s. masonite. 1-Aug-2 Eldred, East Dennis #982/R est:5000-10000

£10897 $17000 €16346 Mermaid reading on a recamier with ship and lighthouse in background (25x30cm-10x12in) s. masonite. 1-Aug-2 Eldred, East Dennis #980/R est:5000-10000

£12821 $20000 €19232 Two musicians play cello and violin on a dock as sailors and women dance (53x66cm-21x26in) s. masonite. 1-Aug-2 Eldred, East Dennis #983/R est:18000-22000

£12821 $20000 €19232 Cape Cod RR, locomotive in motion, with mermaid sitting atop (36x56cm-14x22in) s. masonite. 21-Sep-2 Pook & Pook, Downington #74/R est:20000-25000

£14103 $22000 €21155 Three mermaids feeding chickens with three hot air balloons in sky (51x61cm-20x24in) s. masonite. 1-Aug-2 Eldred, East Dennis #984/R est:18000-22000

£15385 $24000 €23078 Rockport motif No.1 (61x81cm-24x32in) s. masonite. 28-Mar-3 Eldred, East Dennis #697/R est:20000-30000

£16667 $26000 €25001 Boston Sandwich Glass Works with three mermaid glass blowers (41x51cm-16x20in) s. masonite oval. 1-Aug-2 Eldred, East Dennis #986/R est:32000-36000

£18590 $29000 €27885 Chinese harbour scene with buildings, ships and figures (46x64cm-18x25in) s. masonite. 1-Aug-2 Eldred, East Dennis #985/R est:18000-22000

£18590 $29000 €27885 Cape Cod Community College (48x61cm-19x24in) s. masonite. 28-Mar-3 Eldred, East Dennis #696/R est:20000-30000

£19108 $30000 €28662 Two sailors in hot air balloons ambush two mermaids on the back of a whale (71x91cm-28x36in) s. masonite. 22-Nov-2 Eldred, East Dennis #849/R est:40000-50000

£20513 $32000 €30770 Two mermaid mothers giving their daughters bubble baths (41x51cm-16x20in) s. masonite. 1-Aug-2 Eldred, East Dennis #981/R est:20000-30000

£22293 $35000 €33440 Widows and scrimshaw (76x104cm-30x41in) s. masonite domed vignette prov. 22-Nov-2 Eldred, East Dennis #847/R est:50000-60000

£22930 $36000 €34395 Shocking incident at the Pacific Club (51x71cm-20x28in) s. masonite exhib. 22-Nov-2 Eldred, East Dennis #848/R est:18000-22000

£42763 $65000 €64145 Hongs at Canton with ships, sailors and mermaids (56x76cm-22x30in) masonite pair. 17-Aug-2 North East Auctions, Portsmouth #691/R est:60000-90000

CAHOURS, Henry Maurice (1889-1974) French

£317 $504 €460 Plage a maree basse (46x55cm-18x22in) s. 7-Mar-3 Claude Aguttes, Neuilly #8

£1831 $2948 €2600 Marins sur les quais (46x55cm-18x22in) s. 11-May-3 Thierry & Lannon, Brest #147 est:2600-3000

CAI GUO QIANG (1957-) Chinese

£23310 $38462 €33800 Han Pillar (117x91cm-46x36in) s.i.d.1985 verso oil gunpowder. 6-Jul-3 Christie's, Hong Kong #118/R est:200000-300000 (HK.D 300000)

Sculpture

£82278 $130000 €123417 Mao (328x140x51cm-129x55x20in) wood boat sixty lanterns electric lights wire stone executed 1997. 14-Nov-2 Christie's, Rockefeller NY #306/R est:60000-80000

Works on paper

£36585 $57805 €54878 Sinking and rising-project for extraterrestrials no 27 (300x400cm-118x157in) s.i.d.1998 gunpowder ink. 28-Apr-3 Sotheby's, Hong Kong #527/R est:400000-600000 (HK.D 450000)

CAILLARD, Christian (1899-1985) French

£1007 $1621 €1500 Les arbres a Saint Philibert (60x81cm-24x32in) s. d.1947 verso. 23-Feb-3 Lesieur & Le Bars, Le Havre #22

£1199 $1882 €1750 Paysage de Provence (60x81cm-24x32in) s. 21-Apr-3 Rabourdin & Choppin de Janvry, Paris #86/R est:1800-2000

£1972 $3273 €2800 Jeune femme au panier (73x54cm-29x21in) s. prov. 13-Jun-3 Rabourdin & Choppin de Janvry, Paris #100 est:1800-2000

£3630 $5699 €5300 Jeune Marocaine allanguie (60x92cm-24x36in) s. painted c.1926. 21-Apr-3 Rabourdin & Choppin de Janvry, Paris #174/R est:5500-6500

£3846 $6038 €6000 Teinturiers (65x81cm-26x32in) s.d.27. 10-Dec-2 Tajan, Paris #121/R est:7000

CAILLAUD, Aristide (1902-1990) French

£943 $1462 €1500 Jeune fille au Rocher (55x33cm-22x13in) s.d.73. 30-Oct-2 Artcurial Briest, Paris #368/R est:2200-2500

£1761 $2730 €2800 La route du port (92x73cm-36x29in) s. 30-Oct-2 Artcurial Briest, Paris #366/R est:6000-8000

Works on paper

£629 $975 €1000 Composition (24x32cm-9x13in) s. gouache. 30-Oct-2 Artcurial Briest, Paris #372

£818 $1267 €1300 Le port (35x34cm-14x13in) s.d.55 gouache exhib. 30-Oct-2 Artcurial Briest, Paris #376

CAILLE, Léon Emile (1836-1907) French

£671 $1100 €973 Mother's little helper (20x18cm-8x7in) s.d.1866 panel. 4-Jun-3 Doyle, New York #22 est:1200-1800

£2009 $3134 €3014 Mother with child in kitchen (33x24cm-13x9in) s.d.1879 panel. 28-Mar-3 Koller, Zurich #3104/R est:3500-5500 (S.FR 4400)

CAILLEBOTTE, Gustave (1848-1894) French

£745342 $1200000 €1118013 Gateaux (54x73cm-21x29in) s. painted 1881 prov.exhib.lit. 7-May-3 Christie's, Rockefeller NY #3/R est:800000-1200000

£776398 $1250000 €1164597 Rue Halevy, vue d'un balcon (60x73cm-24x29in) st.sig. painted 1878 prov.exhib.lit. 7-May-3 Christie's, Rockefeller NY #16/R est:1200000-1600000
£2564103 $4000000 €3846155 Le pont de l'Europe (65x81cm-26x32in) st.sig. painted 1876 prov.exhib.lit. 6-Nov-2 Christie's, Rockefeller NY #26/R est:2500000-3500000

CAILLEBOTTE, Gustave (attrib) (1848-1894) French
£1223 $1907 €1835 Au bord de la mer (17x22cm-7x9in) i.d.1892 verso board prov. 20-Nov-2 Fischer, Luzern #1105/R est:2200-2500 (S.FR 2800)

CAIMI, Antonio (attrib) (1814-1878) Italian
£2893 $4455 €4600 Lunch time (74x60cm-29x24in) 23-Oct-2 Finarte, Milan #15/R est:4000-5000

CAIN, Auguste (1822-1894) French
Sculpture
£1000 $1520 €1500 Leaf tray with two sparring sparrows (26x22cm-10x9in) s. brown pat. bronze. 28-Aug-2 Sotheby's, London #864/R est:1500-2000
£1156 $1839 €1700 Lionne et lionceaux (33x45cm-13x18in) s. pat bronze. 23-Mar-3 Herbette, Doullens #153/R
£1600 $2432 €2400 Rabbits and partridges topped by a pheasant (19x21cm-7x8in) s. brown pat. bronze casket relief. 28-Aug-2 Sotheby's, London #863/R est:1000-1500
£2564 $4052 €4000 Lionne portant un sanglier a ses lioncieux (45x61x20cm-18x24x8in) s. brown pat bronze Cast Susse lit. 18-Nov-2 Tajan, Paris #78/R est:3800-4000
£3600 $5472 €5400 Brillador and fanfaron group de chiens de meute - Pair of hunting dogs (34x42cm-13x17in) s.i. dark brown pat. bronze. 28-Aug-2 Sotheby's, London #843/R est:4000-6000
£4500 $6840 €6750 Candelabra (51cm-20in) s.brown pat. bronze pair. 28-Aug-2 Sotheby's, London #862/R est:4000-6000

CAIN, Georges (1856-1919) French
£625 $1031 €900 Young beauty in a garland of flowers (75x62cm-30x24in) s. 1-Jul-3 Christie's, Amsterdam #64

CAINE, Osmund (1914-) British
Works on paper
£300 $483 €450 Brentford Fyot (35x46cm-14x18in) s.d.Aug 51 W/C. 18-Feb-3 Bonhams, Knightsbridge #196/R

CAINNING, Robert (?) Australian?
£564 $897 €846 Landscape with sheep (52x90cm-20x35in) s. 3-Mar-3 Lawson Menzies, Sydney #466 est:300-500 (A.D 1500)

CAIRATI, Gerolamo (1860-1943) Italian
£296 $476 €420 High mountain landscape in summer (32x49cm-13x19in) s.d.1893 board. 7-May-3 Michael Zeller, Lindau #661

CAIRATI, Gerolamo (attrib) (1860-1943) Italian
£748 $1190 €1100 River landscape in autumn (84x112cm-33x44in) s.d.1910. 20-Mar-3 Neumeister, Munich #2601/R

CAIRNCROSS, Sam (1913-) New Zealander
£394 $607 €591 Still life - bowl of fruit (26x36cm-10x14in) s. board. 4-Sep-2 Dunbar Sloane, Wellington #59a/R est:1500-2500 (NZ.D 1300)
£561 $876 €842 Mt Ngauruhoe from the desert road (40x90cm-16x35in) s.d.1973 board. 27-Mar-3 International Art Centre, Auckland #49/R (NZ.D 1600)
£702 $1095 €1053 Mt Ngauruhoe erupting (44x57cm-17x22in) s.d.1972 board exhib. 27-Mar-3 International Art Centre, Auckland #48/R (NZ.D 2000)
£1228 $1916 €1842 La maison, Clare (43x26cm-17x10in) s.d.1948 board. 27-Mar-3 International Art Centre, Auckland #37/R est:2800-4000 (NZ.D 3500)
£1254 $1956 €1881 At the fair, Wellington (38x45cm-15x18in) s.d.1954 board. 7-Nov-2 International Art Centre, Auckland #40/R est:3000-5000 (NZ.D 4000)

CAIRNS, John (fl.1845-1870) British
£600 $948 €870 On the coast of Ayr (23x43cm-9x17in) s. i.d.1852 verso board. 22-Jul-3 Gorringes, Lewes #1727/R

CAIRO, Francesco del (1607-1665) Italian
£18000 $30060 €26100 Lucretia (94x74cm-37x29in) 10-Jul-3 Sotheby's, London #165/R est:10000-15000
£86420 $140000 €129630 Portrait of Marchese Giovan Francesco Serra Di Cassano in armour (117x94cm-46x37in) 23-Jan-3 Sotheby's, New York #52/R est:60000-80000

CAISERMAN-ROTH, Ghitta (1923-) Canadian
£331 $519 €497 Forest interior, light effect (81x51cm-32x20in) s.d.51 board. 24-Jul-2 Walker's, Ottawa #228/R (C.D 800)

CAJETAN, Joseph (19th C) German
Works on paper
£283 $439 €450 Rebus (29x23cm-11x9in) s.i.d.846 W/C over pencil. 1-Oct-2 Dorotheum, Vienna #128/R
£283 $439 €450 Sketches for theatre paper (37x27cm-15x11in) s. W/C over pencil. 1-Oct-2 Dorotheum, Vienna #129/R

CALA Y MOYA, Jose de (1850-1891) Spanish
£20000 $31200 €30000 Presentation in the harem (38x56cm-15x22in) s.d.1879 panel. 15-Oct-2 Sotheby's, London #182/R est:20000-30000

CALABRESE, Kirstin (1968-) American
£1290 $2000 €1935 Entryway (244x244cm-96x96in) painted 1997 prov. 26-Sep-2 Christie's, Rockefeller NY #874/R est:3000-5000

CALABRIA, Ennio (1937-) Italian
£439 $685 €650 Protesters (42x37cm-17x15in) s.i.d.60 tempera Chinese ink paper. 28-Mar-3 Farsetti, Prato #152/R
£769 $1208 €1200 Figure with blackbird (70x50cm-28x20in) s.d.966 cardboard on canvas. 20-Nov-2 Pandolfini, Florence #65
£878 $1370 €1300 Man-lion (55x46cm-22x18in) s.i.d.1960. 28-Mar-3 Farsetti, Prato #203/R
£1370 $2137 €2000 Photographer (40x45cm-16x18in) s. painted 1975. 10-Apr-3 Finarte Semenzato, Rome #264
£1765 $2824 €2700 Reclining woman (70x70cm-28x28in) s. s.d.1988 verso. 4-Jan-3 Meeting Art, Vercelli #93
£1987 $3140 €3100 Figures in the night (71x46cm-28x18in) 12-Nov-2 Babuino, Rome #235/R
Works on paper
£288 $453 €450 Study for poster (75x56cm-30x22in) s. pastel card. 23-Nov-2 Meeting Art, Vercelli #3

CALACICCO, Salvatore (?) Italian?
£1200 $1872 €1800 Sailing ship, Morning Star, off Venice (59x90cm-23x35in) s. panel. 10-Sep-2 David Duggleby, Scarborough #315/R est:1000-1500

CALAME, A (19th C) Swiss
Works on paper
£784 $1255 €1200 Various landscape scenes (30x38cm-12x15in) one s. monochrome W/C lit. 10-Jan-3 Allgauer, Kempten #1389/R

CALAME, Alexandre (1810-1864) Swiss
£2581 $4000 €3872 Lake Lucerne near Brunne (32x53cm-13x21in) s. painted with studio prov.lit. 30-Oct-2 Christie's, Rockefeller NY #129/R est:12000-16000
£2620 $4114 €3930 Toreent de montagne borde de sapins (41x29cm-16x11in) paper on canvas. 25-Nov-2 Sotheby's, Zurich #21/R est:7000-9000 (S.FR 6000)
£2740 $4274 €4110 On the coast (32x39cm-13x15in) 28-Mar-3 Koller, Zurich #3164/R est:4000-7000 (S.FR 6000)
£2826 $4409 €4239 Wooded area overlooking lake (43x55cm-17x22in) i.d.Juillet 1836 paper on panel. 16-Sep-2 Philippe Schuler, Zurich #3359/R est:4000-6000 (S.FR 6500)
£3049 $5000 €4574 View of Pestarena, near Zermatt (30x33cm-12x13in) oil paper on panel lit. 29-May-3 Sotheby's, New York #48/R est:5000-7000
£4321 $7000 €6482 View by lake (32x41cm-13x16in) board lit. 23-Jan-3 Sotheby's, New York #218/R est:12000
£4878 $8000 €7317 Rocks near Murren, Switzerland (34x49cm-13x19in) s. oil paper on canvas prov.lit. 29-May-3 Sotheby's, New York #42/R est:8000-12000
£5150 $7983 €7725 Meadow with rocky outcrop and woodland (31x50cm-12x20in) prov.lit. 3-Oct-2 Koller, Zurich #3119/R est:14000-18000 (S.FR 12000)
£5488 $9000 €8232 Woods and rocky cliffs (53x42cm-21x17in) s. oil paper on panel prov.lit. 29-May-3 Sotheby's, New York #37/R est:6000-8000
£5864 $9500 €8796 View of Geneva Lake, near Evian (18x38cm-7x15in) prov. 23-Jan-3 Sotheby's, New York #230/R est:7000

£6522 $10109 €9783 Wooded landscape with foundlings (35x49cm-14x19in) paper on canvas. 9-Dec-2 Philippe Schuler, Zurich #3809/R est:6000-8000 (S.FR 15000)
£6707 $11000 €10061 Valley of Lauterbrunnen, near Geneva (45x56cm-18x22in) d.1836 oil paper on canvas prov. 29-May-3 Sotheby's, New York #44/R est:8000-12000
£7860 $12262 €11790 Route de Grimsel (30x41cm-12x16in) lit.prov. 20-Nov-2 Fischer, Luzern #1245/R est:6000-8000 (S.FR 18000)
£8681 $13803 €12500 Chevres prs d'une riviere (57x82cm-22x32in) s.i. 30-Apr-3 Tajan, Paris #56/R est:12000
£8734 $13712 €13101 Paysage de montagne avec torrent (54x81cm-21x32in) s.d.1840 prov.exhib.lit. 25-Nov-2 Sotheby's, Zurich #14/R est:25000-35000 (S.FR 20000)
£8734 $13799 €13101 Two pyramids in evening light (26x37cm-10x15in) s. 14-Nov-2 Stuker, Bern #122/R est:6000-8000 (S.FR 20000)
£8784 $13703 €13000 Mountain landscape (98x128cm-39x50in) s. 25-Mar-3 Wiener Kunst Auktionen, Vienna #108/R est:11000-20000
£9434 $15283 €16698 Trees in wide mountain valley (60x80cm-24x31in) s. 26-May-3 Sotheby's, Zurich #4/R est:20000-25000 (S.FR 20000)
£9877 $16000 €14816 Stone staircase and doorway in landscape (39x33cm-15x13in) s. paper on canvas prov.lit. 23-Jan-3 Sotheby's, New York #231/R est:15000
£10480 $16454 €15720 Lac des Quatre Cantons (34x55cm-13x22in) board. 25-Nov-2 Sotheby's, Zurich #8/R est:18000-22000 (S.FR 24000)
£12017 $18627 €18026 Thunersee (29x46cm-11x18in) paper on canvas prov.exhib.lit. 3-Oct-2 Koller, Zurich #3118/R est:12000-15000 (S.FR 28000)
£18026 $28481 €27039 Coucher de soleil (26x38cm-10x15in) board painted 1861 board prov. 26-Nov-2 Phillips, Zurich #4/R est:25000-35000 (S.FR 42000)
£18519 $29815 €26853 Vue prise de la Handeck (60x81cm-24x32in) s. lit. 9-May-3 Dobiaschofsky, Bern #36/R est:46000 (S.FR 40000)
£27397 $42740 €41096 Wetterhorn (49x40cm-19x16in) i. canvas on board. 28-Mar-3 Koller, Zurich #3099/R est:7000-9000 (S.FR 60000)
£38627 $59871 €57941 Wetterhorn (127x98cm-50x39in) s.d.1858 prov.lit. 3-Oct-2 Koller, Zurich #3120/R est:80000-120000 (S.FR 90000)

Works on paper

£217 $337 €326 Promenade en barque (7x15cm-3x6in) s. pencil htd chk. 7-Dec-2 Galerie du Rhone, Sion #302/R (S.FR 500)
£328 $511 €492 Stream in landscape with trees (15x24cm-6x9in) s.d.29.X.1841 pencil. 20-Nov-2 Fischer, Luzern #2591/R (S.FR 750)
£360 $576 €500 Mountain lake in the Alps (20x23cm-8x9in) s. pencil W/C. 17-May-3 Lempertz, Koln #1275
£448 $726 €794 Rochers et sapins (24x16cm-9x6in) mono.d.1854 W/C. 26-May-3 Sotheby's, Zurich #29/R (S.FR 950)
£699 $1090 €1049 Wooded landscape with pond (24x40cm-9x16in) s. chl. 20-Nov-2 Fischer, Luzern #2590/R est:600-800 (S.FR 1600)
£769 $1192 €1200 Cascade de la Handeck (44x34cm-17x13in) gouache. 6-Dec-2 Maigret, Paris #45
£2575 $4069 €3863 Grands arbres au bord de l'eau (28x37cm-11x15in) pencil exec.1840-1850 prov.lit. 26-Nov-2 Phillips, Zurich #6/R est:3000-5000 (S.FR 6000)
£2623 $4250 €3935 Boat caught in stormy waters near the shore (18x25cm-7x10in) s.d.1833 pen ink W/C gouache over chk prov.lit. 21-Jan-3 Sotheby's, New York #186/R
£3433 $5425 €5150 Bouquet de chenes et petit etang (30x42cm-12x17in) pencil exec.c.1840 prov.lit. 26-Nov-2 Phillips, Zurich #5/R est:3000-5000 (S.FR 8000)

CALAME, Alexandre (attrib) (1810-1864) Swiss

£2013 $3099 €3200 View of Swiss lake (47x37cm-19x15in) s. 28-Oct-2 Il Ponte, Milan #242/R
£4292 $6781 €6438 Lac des Quatre Cantons (28x37cm-11x15in) 26-Nov-2 Hans Widmer, St Gallen #1068/R est:7000-12000 (S.FR 10000)

CALAME, Alexandre (school) (1810-1864) Swiss

£568 $897 €852 Stormy skies over Well- and Wetterhorn (46x56cm-18x22in) 14-Nov-2 Stuker, Bern #123/R (S.FR 1300)

CALAME, Arthur (1843-1919) Swiss

£509 $820 €764 Beach (20x32cm-8x13in) s. canvas on board. 7-May-3 Dobiaschofsky, Bern #387/R (S.FR 1100)
£696 $1085 €1044 Wooded landscape at sunset (24x32cm-9x13in) s. 16-Sep-2 Philippe Schuler, Zurich #3360 (S.FR 1600)
£802 $1283 €1203 Promenade a Venise (13x23cm-5x9in) s. canvas on board. 17-Mar-3 Philippe Schuler, Zurich #4505 est:800-1000 (S.FR 1700)
£1397 $2180 €2096 La mare aux nympheas (36x51cm-14x20in) s.d.1883 masonite. 8-Nov-2 Dobiaschofsky, Bern #7/R est:2400 (S.FR 3200)
£8451 $13859 €12254 Un sinistre en mer - Canale de la Manche, Boulogne (104x151cm-41x59in) s. 4-Jun-3 Fischer, Luzern #1236/R est:8000-12000 (S.FR 18000)

CALAME, Arthur (attrib) (1843-1919) Swiss

£437 $681 €656 Wooded landscape with stream (85x61cm-33x24in) i.d.Sept. 1868. 6-Nov-2 Dobiaschofsky, Bern #387/R (S.FR 1000)

CALANDRUCCI, Giacinto (1646-1707) Italian

Works on paper

£577 $894 €900 Assumption (23x20cm-9x8in) i. pen ink W/C prov. 4-Dec-2 Christie's, Rome #398

CALANDRUCCI, Giacinto (attrib) (1646-1707) Italian

£5793 $9500 €8690 Archangel Michael vanquishing Satan (77x58cm-30x23in) 29-May-3 Sotheby's, New York #93/R est:6000-8000

Works on paper

£650 $1021 €975 Roman triumph, ceiling study (49x27cm-19x11in) pen ink over black chk squared prov. 11-Dec-2 Sotheby's, Olympia #70/R
£2113 $3401 €3000 Saint'Antonio che parla ad un gruppo di fedeli (39x76cm-15x30in) pen brown ink blk pencil sanguine squared. 12-May-3 Sotheby's, Milan #54/R est:3000-3500

CALBET, Antoine (1860-1944) French

Works on paper

£439 $685 €650 Scene de bal (30x23cm-12x9in) s. W/C gouache. 27-Mar-3 Maigret, Paris #34
£1899 $3000 €3000 Femme nue. Scene galante (43x28cm-17x11in) crayon dr double-sided. 27-Nov-2 Marc Kohn, Paris #12/R
£3397 $5334 €5300 Baigneuses (47x61cm-19x24in) s. pastel. 15-Dec-2 Eric Pillon, Calais #69/R

CALCAGNADORO, Antonino (1876-1935) Italian

Works on paper

£426 $689 €600 Gli amici (30x30cm-12x12in) s.d.1920 mixed media canvas. 22-May-3 Stadion, Trieste #302/R

CALCAGNO, Lawrence (1916-) American

£732 $1200 €1061 Prairie (84x61cm-33x24in) s.d.1962 oil collage on paper prov. 1-Jun-3 Wright, Chicago #298/R est:2000-3000
£1280 $2100 €1856 Mixed media 29-111-75 (53x74cm-21x29in) s.i. mixed media on canvas prov. 1-Jun-3 Wright, Chicago #296/R est:1500-2000
£3354 $5500 €4863 Earth ledend I (132x97cm-52x38in) acrylic prov.exhib. 1-Jun-3 Wright, Chicago #297/R est:2000-9000
£3659 $6000 €5306 Sunbands V (208x305cm-82x120in) acrylic oil prov. 1-Jun-3 Wright, Chicago #295/R est:4000-5000

CALCAR, Gesina (1850-1936) Dutch

£1181 $1948 €1700 Still life with flowers (48x79cm-19x31in) s. 1-Jul-3 Christie's, Amsterdam #227 est:700-900

CALDECOTT, Randolph (attrib) (1846-1886) British

Works on paper

£550 $853 €825 Dance (16x22cm-6x9in) init. W/C. 2-Oct-2 George Kidner, Lymington #125

CALDER, Alexander (1898-1976) American

£641 $1000 €962 Untitled (211x137cm-83x54in) d.1974 jute. 30-Mar-3 Susanin's, Chicago #6056/R
£23438 $37500 €35157 Rising sun (74x109cm-29x43in) s.d.70 gouache prov.exhib. 14-May-3 Sotheby's, New York #133/R est:12000-18000
£25806 $40000 €38709 Four doors and a pyramid (91x56cm-36x22in) s.d.56 prov. 26-Sep-2 Christie's, Rockefeller NY #792/R est:40000-60000
£38710 $60000 €58065 Odalisque - hommage a Matisse (51x61cm-20x24in) s.d.1945 on overlap prov.exhib. 26-Sep-2 Christie's, Rockefeller NY #789/R est:50000-70000

Prints

£2013 $3200 €3020 Boomerangs (150x117cm-59x46in) s.num.6/30 col lithograph executed c.1970. 4-Mar-3 Swann Galleries, New York #178/R est:2500-3500

Sculpture

£4403 $7000 €6605 Warrior (70cm-28in) s.d.1912 num.3 Q584 bronze st.f.Gorham. 7-Mar-3 Skinner, Boston #345/R est:5000-7000
£6500 $10660 €9750 Horse (20cm-8in) init.num.21 dark brown pat. bronze. 6-Jun-3 Christie's, London #68/R est:5000-7000
£8228 $13000 €12342 Red airplane model (16x34x47cm-6x13x19in) init. gouache on fiberglas executed 1975. 13-Nov-2 Sotheby's, New York #202/R est:15000-20000
£13000 $21710 €18850 Cheval II - horse II (12x21x12cm-5x8x5in) num.2 dark brown pat. bronze cast 1964 prov. 27-Jun-3 Christie's, London #198/R est:8000-10000
£18987 $30000 €28481 Untitled - necklace (37x37cm-15x15in) brass executed c.1950 prov. 13-Nov-2 Sotheby's, New York #200/R est:15000-20000

£19355 $30000 €29033 Untitled - light fixture (53x76x63cm-21x30x25in) tin wood light fixture executed c.1960 prov. 26-Sep-2 Christie's, Rockefeller NY #788/R est:7000-9000

£27848 $43165 €44000 Mexico No 1 (141x235x165cm-56x93x65in) acrylic fibreglass prov. 28-Sep-2 Ketterer, Hamburg #661/R est:27000-30000

£47468 $75000 €71202 Untitled (20x39cm-8x15in) init. standing mobile painted sheet metal wire executed 1976 prov. 14-Nov-2 Christie's, Rockefeller NY #160/R est:80000-120000

£48077 $75481 €75000 Black skeleton (11x29x23cm-4x11x9in) metal exec.c.1945 prov.exhib. 10-Dec-2 Piasa, Paris #220/R est:120000

£54839 $85000 €82259 Black bustle (19x15cm-7x6in) init. painted metal brass wire standing mobile prov. 26-Sep-2 Christie's, Rockefeller NY #787/R est:60000-80000

£60000 $100200 €90000 Otarie (31x21cm-12x8in) painted sheet metal stabile exc.c.1945 prov. 25-Jun-3 Sotheby's, London #34/R est:50000-70000

£60127 $95000 €90191 Untitled (48x38x30cm-19x15x12in) stabile painted sheet metal executed c.1945 prov. 14-Nov-2 Christie's, Rockefeller NY #153/R est:60000-80000

£62500 $100000 €93750 Spherical triangle (50x25cm-20x10in) painted sheet metal wire lead prov.exhib. 15-May-3 Christie's, Rockefeller NY #102/R est:100000-150000

£64103 $93590 €100000 Kitty (61x46cm-24x18in) s.d.67 painted metal prov.lit. 5-Jun-2 Il Ponte, Milan #139/R est:70000-80000

£68750 $110000 €103125 Untitled (8x11x5cm-3x4x2in) painted metal brass wire standing mobile executed c.1954. 14-May-3 Sotheby's, New York #108/R est:30000-40000

£75000 $120000 €112500 Untitled (27x47x27cm-11x19x11in) init. painted metal rod standing mobile prov. 14-May-3 Sotheby's, New York #141/R est:50000-70000

£75949 $120000 €113924 Untitled (55x46x22cm-22x18x9in) incised mono. painted sheet metal rod standing mobile. 13-Nov-2 Sotheby's, New York #323/R est:80000-120000

£87500 $140000 €131250 On one knee (113x127x51cm-44x50x20in) s. num.4/6 brown pat bronze prov.exhib.lit. 15-May-3 Christie's, Rockefeller NY #143/R est:100000-150000

£90000 $150300 €135000 Untitled (24x15x16cm-9x6x6in) painted sheet metal standing mobile exc.c.1953 prov. 25-Jun-3 Sotheby's, London #12/R est:40000-60000

£90000 $150300 €135000 Untitled (37x18cm-15x7in) painted sheet metal standing mobile exc.c.1953 prov. 25-Jun-3 Sotheby's, London #32/R est:50000-70000

£107595 $170000 €161393 Holey blue base (23x27x8cm-9x11x3in) init. painted metal brass wire standing mobile executed 1950 prov. 13-Nov-2 Sotheby's, New York #206/R est:80000-120000

£107595 $170000 €161393 Scale on yellow and blue (72x116cm-28x46in) init.d.72 standing moblie painted sheet metal wire prov. 14-Nov-2 Christie's, Rockefeller NY #183/R est:200000-300000

£125000 $200000 €187500 Object on Davit (46x51cm-18x20in) init. painted sheet metal wire exec.1938 prov.lit. 15-May-3 Christie's, Rockefeller NY #101/R est:80000-120000

£130000 $217100 €188500 Banana (32x18x15cm-13x7x6in) init. painted sheet metal wire executed 1960 prov. 27-Jun-3 Christie's, London #199/R est:80000-120000

£139241 $220000 €208862 Red pennant (50x41cm-20x16in) init. standing mobile painted sheet metal wire rocks execu.1948. 14-Nov-2 Christie's, Rockefeller NY #114/R est:200000-300000

£151899 $240000 €227849 Untitled (38x32cm-15x13in) standing mobile painted sheet metal wire executed c.1942 prov. 14-Nov-2 Christie's, Rockefeller NY #152/R est:150000-200000

£183544 $290000 €275316 Untitled (50x50x25cm-20x20x10in) painted metal standing mobile executed c.1945. 12-Nov-2 Sotheby's, New York #44/R est:150000-200000

£210000 $350700 €315000 Red I (61x91cm-24x36in) s. painted sheet metal hanging mobile exc.1950 prov.exhib. 25-Jun-3 Sotheby's, London #21/R est:180000-250000

£215190 $340000 €322785 Duck (25x40cm-10x16in) standing mobile painted wood metal executed 1943 prov.exhib. 13-Nov-2 Christie's, Rockefeller NY #7/R est:200000-300000

£256410 $400000 €384615 Lune blancher (82x176cm-32x69in) mono.d.56 hanging mobile sheet metal executed 1956 prov. 6-Nov-2 Christie's, Rockefeller NY #34/R est:400000-600000

£437500 $700000 €656250 Untitled (89cm-35in) painted metal wire exec.c.1952 prov. 14-May-3 Christie's, Rockefeller NY #6/R est:400000-600000

£518987 $820000 €778481 Untitled (107x229x76cm-42x90x30in) painted metal hanging mobile with string executed 1949 prov.exhib. 12-Nov-2 Sotheby's, New York #49/R est:800000-1200000

£696203 $1100000 €1044305 Mobile au plomb (118x104cm-46x41in) s. painted wood wire executed 1931 prov.exhib.lit. 13-Nov-2 Christie's, Rockefeller NY #13/R est:80000-120000

£1487342 $2350000 €2231013 S-Shaped vine (250x175cm-98x69in) hanging mobile painted sheet metal wire executed 1946 prov. 13-Nov-2 Christie's, Rockefeller NY #19/R est:1200000-1600000

Works on paper

£2564 $4000 €3846 Composition with five blue balloon shapes (44x32cm-17x13in) s. W/C gouache over pencil. 18-Sep-2 Swann Galleries, New York #59/R est:2000-3000

£3548 $5500 €5322 Theatrical production (50x37cm-20x15in) i. ink painted c.1976 prov.lit. 26-Sep-2 Christie's, Rockefeller NY #791/R est:7000-9000

£4167 $6500 €6251 Composition with forms (52x39cm-20x15in) s. brush ink sold with another by the same hand. 18-Sep-2 Swann Galleries, New York #57/R est:4000-6000

£4167 $6500 €6251 Composition with faces (39x58cm-15x23in) s. brush ink. 18-Sep-2 Swann Galleries, New York #58/R est:2000-3000

£4194 $6500 €6291 Toys (29x39cm-11x15in) ink executed c.1976 prov.lit. 26-Sep-2 Christie's, Rockefeller NY #797/R est:6000-8000

£4500 $7335 €6750 Oniony (56x76cm-22x30in) s.d.66 gouache prov. 3-Feb-3 Sotheby's, Olympia #57/R est:3000-5000

£4516 $7000 €6774 Yellow ringed sun (110x75cm-43x30in) s.d.69 gouache prov. 26-Sep-2 Christie's, Rockefeller NY #796/R est:8000-12000

£4777 $7500 €7166 Apogee (31x23cm-12x9in) s.d. i.verso gouache. 19-Nov-2 Wright, Chicago #199/R est:9000-12000

£5063 $8000 €8000 Untitled (74x109cm-29x43in) s.d.71 gouache. 26-Nov-2 Sotheby's, Amsterdam #248/R est:8000-12000

£5068 $7905 €7500 Composition (75x108cm-30x43in) s.d.70 gouache. 26-Mar-3 Finarte Semenzato, Milan #281/R

£5346 $8286 €8500 Fleur jaune (107x74cm-42x29in) s.i.d.64 gouache. 30-Oct-2 Artcurial Briest, Paris #421/R est:9000-12000

£5769 $8942 €9000 Untitled (75x109cm-30x43in) s.d.1970 gouache. 7-Dec-2 Hauswedell & Nolte, Hamburg #568/R est:10000

£6129 $9500 €9194 Dents de cie (78x58cm-31x23in) s.d.1969 gouache prov. 26-Sep-2 Christie's, Rockefeller NY #794/R est:7000-9000

£6500 $10010 €9750 Red and red nautilus (109x74cm-43x29in) s.d.67 gouache ink prov. 23-Oct-2 Christie's, London #115/R est:5000-7000

£6731 $10567 €10500 Ballons (106x74cm-42x29in) s.d.1970 gouache prov. 15-Dec-2 Perrin, Versailles #44/R est:10000

£6803 $10816 €10000 Echasses (74x108cm-29x43in) s.d.1972 gouache ink prov.lit. 24-Mar-3 Cornette de St.Cyr, Paris #17/R est:15000

£6950 $11189 €10425 Untitled (74x109cm-29x43in) s.d.71 gouache prov. 7-May-3 AB Stockholms Auktionsverk #1140/R est:80000-90000 (S.KR 90000)

£7200 $11088 €10800 Thin spiral (78x58cm-31x23in) s.d.68 verso gouache prov. 22-Oct-2 Sotheby's, London #471/R est:4000-6000

£7233 $11211 €11500 Fleurs noires (75x108cm-30x43in) s.d.69 gouache. 30-Oct-2 Artcurial Briest, Paris #422/R est:9000-12000

£7692 $12846 €11153 Spirale, cercle and serpent (37x56cm-15x22in) s.d.50 gouache prov. 24-Jun-3 Koller, Zurich #145/R est:17000-24000 (S.FR 17000)

£8387 $13000 €12581 Yellow meter (75x110cm-30x43in) s.d.74 gouache prov. 26-Sep-2 Christie's, Rockefeller NY #785/R est:10000-15000

£8409 $13118 €12614 Untitled (110x74cm-43x29in) s.d.71 gouache. 5-Nov-2 Bukowskis, Stockholm #312/R est:80000-100000 (S.KR 120000)

£8500 $13940 €12750 On another planet (74x108cm-29x43in) s.d.53 i.verso gouache prov. 7-Feb-3 Sotheby's, London #165/R est:4000-6000

£8597 $14357 €12466 Spirale noire et soleil rouge (54x75cm-21x30in) s.d.65 gouache prov. 24-Jun-3 Koller, Zurich #148/R est:22000-30000 (S.FR 19000)

£9677 $15000 €14516 Sigle (75x110cm-30x43in) s.d.71 gouache prov. 26-Sep-2 Christie's, Rockefeller NY #795/R est:10000-15000

£9800 $16366 €14210 Paix paix paix (56x75cm-22x30in) init.i. gouache prov. 24-Jun-3 Sotheby's, Olympia #66/R est:3000-4000

£10323 $16000 €15485 Untitled (110x75cm-43x30in) s.d.70 gouache prov. 26-Sep-2 Christie's, Rockefeller NY #784/R est:10000-15000

£10968 $17000 €16452 Pontiac (75x110cm-30x43in) s.d.70 gouache prov.exhib. 26-Sep-2 Christie's, Rockefeller NY #793/R est:10000-15000

£11000 $18040 €16500 Butterflies (108x75cm-43x30in) s.d.63 i.verso gouache prov. 7-Feb-3 Sotheby's, London #163/R est:4000-6000

£11000 $18040 €16500 Aborigine (75x108cm-30x43in) s.d.66 i.verso gouache prov. 7-Feb-3 Sotheby's, London #170/R est:4000-6000

£11000 $18370 €15950 La piste blanc (109x74cm-43x29in) s.d.72 i.verso gouache prov. 26-Jun-3 Sotheby's, London #180/R est:6000-8000

£12670 $21158 €18372 Le couple (75x109cm-30x43in) s.d.70 gouache prov. 24-Jun-3 Koller, Zurich #147/R est:30000-40000 (S.FR 28000)

£14194 $22000 €21291 Shepherd (75x110cm-30x43in) s.d.74 gouache prov. 26-Sep-2 Christie's, Rockefeller NY #790/R est:10000-15000

£15625 $25000 €23438 Blue wedge (74x109cm-29x43in) s.d.70 gouache prov.exhib. 14-May-3 Sotheby's, New York #134/R est:12000-18000

£16000 $26720 €23200 Clown with hoop (58x78cm-23x31in) s. ink executed 1931 prov. 27-Jun-3 Christie's, London #102/R est:10000-15000

CALDERARA, Antonio (1903-1978) Italian
£256 $403 €400 The Sarca (12x18cm-5x7in) d.1951 verso board. 16-Dec-2 Pandolfini, Florence #216
£704 $1169 €1000 Natura morta (15x20cm-6x8in) s. thin oil cardboard. 10-Jun-3 Finarte Semenzato, Milan #201/R
£3291 $5134 €5200 Guitti (30x20cm-12x8in) init.d.1948 board. 14-Sep-2 Meeting Art, Vercelli #973/R
Works on paper
£655 $956 €983 Sketch for portfolio: 'Nello spazio quadrato' (19x18cm-7x7in) mono.d.1974 W/C. 4-Jun-2 Germann, Zurich #70/R (S.FR 1500)
£830 $1211 €1245 Composition (15x14cm-6x6in) mono.d.1977 W/C. 4-Jun-2 Germann, Zurich #96 (S.FR 1900)
£935 $1496 €1300 Composition (18x16cm-7x6in) s.i.d. W/C pencil board prov. 15-May-3 Neumeister, Munich #690/R
£1090 $1689 €1700 Untitled (18x18cm-7x7in) init.d.1963 verso W/C prov. 3-Dec-2 Christie's, Amsterdam #154/R est:600-800
£1603 $2484 €2500 Untitled (31x28cm-12x11in) init.d.1966 s.verso W/C prov. 3-Dec-2 Christie's, Amsterdam #160/R est:1000-1500
£3205 $4968 €5000 Untitled (16x15cm-6x6in) inid.d.1972 pencil W/C eleven prov. 3-Dec-2 Christie's, Amsterdam #159/R est:2500-3000

CALDERE MARTI, Jose (20th C) Spanish
Works on paper
£395 $639 €600 Stroll in the fields (20x33cm-8x13in) s. W/C. 21-Jan-3 Ansorena, Madrid #5/R

CALDERINI, Luigi (1880-1973) Italian
£1000 $1470 €1550 Langhe's viewing (21x40cm-8x16in) 24-Jun-2 Babuino, Rome #250 est:600-900
£1154 $1812 €1800 Alpine valley (43x63cm-17x25in) s. cardboard. 10-Dec-2 Della Rocca, Turin #284

CALDERINI, Marco (1850-c.1941) Italian
£1090 $1711 €1700 Mountainous landscape (31x39cm-12x15in) s. cardboard. 10-Dec-2 Della Rocca, Turin #296/R
£1769 $2812 €2600 Houses amongst trees on the hill (16x36cm-6x14in) indis.sig. cardboard prov. 18-Mar-3 Finarte, Milan #105/R

CALDERON LOPEZ, Pedro (18th C) Mexican
£15603 $26057 €22000 Portrait de l'Archeveque de Mexico, Don Manuel Rubio y Salinas (183x126cm-72x50in) s.i. 18-Jun-3 Tajan, Paris #36/R est:10000-12000

CALDERON, Charles-Clement (1870-1906) French
£1500 $2310 €2250 Venetian scene (46x64cm-18x25in) s. 3-Sep-2 Gorringes, Lewes #2193 est:200-300
£2590 $4144 €3600 View of Doge's Palace, Venice (21x27cm-8x11in) s. panel. 17-May-3 De Vuyst, Lokeren #530/R est:3800-4400
£2838 $4428 €4257 Gondolas by the Isola di San Michele (26x35cm-10x14in) s. masonite. 6-Nov-2 Dobiaschofsky, Bern #388/R est:5500 (S.FR 6500)
£3797 $6000 €6000 Crepuscule sur le Grand Canal (46x65cm-18x26in) s. 29-Nov-2 Drouot Estimations, Paris #70/R

CALDERON, F H (19th C) ?
£950 $1472 €1425 Figure at prayer (101x139cm-40x55in) s.d.1877. 3-Dec-2 Sotheby's, Olympia #166/R est:1000-1500

CALDERON, Philip Hermogenes (1833-1898) Spanish
£460 $718 €690 Excavations at Pompeii (48x34cm-19x13in) 6-Nov-2 Bonhams, Chester #414
£1445 $2398 €2095 Mother and child in interior (46x58cm-18x23in) s.d.1889 panel. 10-Jun-3 Ritchie, Toronto #127/R est:2000-3000 (C.D 3250)
£2500 $3900 €3750 Day dream (41x36cm-16x14in) mono.d.1860. 7-Nov-2 Christie's, Kensington #236/R est:2500-3500
£4430 $7000 €6645 Sylvia (71x61cm-28x24in) s. s.i.verso. 1-Apr-3 Christie's, Rockefeller NY #188/R est:7000-9000
£11500 $18515 €17250 Moonlight serenade (42x88cm-17x35in) s.d.1872 prov.exhib.lit. 20-Feb-3 Christie's, London #66/R est:15000
£17000 $28220 €25500 Lady Betty (102x86cm-40x34in) mono.d.1890 prov.exhib. 10-Jun-3 Christie's, London #127/R est:8000-12000

CALDINI, Alfredo (19th/20th C) Italian
£516 $800 €774 Italian shore scenes (61x91cm-24x36in) pair. 7-Dec-2 South Bay, Long Island #86/R

CALDINI, Alfredo (attrib) (19th/20th C) Italian
£1100 $1716 €1650 View on the Bosphorus near Istambul (45x65cm-18x26in) indis.sig. 17-Oct-2 Lawrence, Crewkerne #481/R est:500-700

CALDWELL, Edmund (1852-1930) British
£950 $1549 €1425 Optimist (30x26cm-12x10in) mono.d.81 b,. 12-Feb-3 Bonhams, Knightsbridge #151/R

CALDWELL, Georgia Leigh (20th C) American
£377 $600 €566 Winter shadows (61x51cm-24x20in) s. painted c.1920. 2-Mar-3 Toomey, Oak Park #669/R
£755 $1200 €1133 Autumn landscape (61x51cm-24x20in) s. painted c.1920. 2-Mar-3 Toomey, Oak Park #667/R

CALDWELL, John (1942-) Australian
Works on paper
£1143 $1806 €1715 Sydneyside (91x45cm-36x18in) s. mixed media prov.exhib. 17-Nov-2 Sotheby's, Paddington #73/R est:2000-4000 (A.D 3200)

CALES, Abbe Pierre (1870-1961) French
£633 $987 €1000 Vallee du Gresivaudan (32x48cm-13x19in) s. panel. 20-Oct-2 Anaf, Lyon #78
£1014 $1581 €1500 Paysage du Dauphine (24x37cm-9x15in) mono. paper. 30-Mar-3 Anaf, Lyon #326
£1154 $1788 €1800 Meules de foin (31x47cm-12x19in) s.d.14. 5-Dec-2 Oger, Dumont, Paris #30/R
£1569 $2573 €2400 Etang au pied des montagnes (31x92cm-12x36in) s.d. cardboard. 9-Feb-3 Anaf, Lyon #33/R

CALIARI, Benedetto (1538-1598) Italian
Works on paper
£1818 $2600 €2727 Christ and the centurion (15x28cm-6x11in) pen ink wash htd white over black chk. 23-Jan-3 Swann Galleries, New York #43/R est:2000-3000

CALIARI, Carlo (1570-1596) Italian
Works on paper
£1392 $2200 €2200 La Sainte Famille avec St Jean Baptiste (23x16cm-9x6in) i. black chk pen brown ink brown wash. 27-Nov-2 Christie's, Paris #36/R est:1500-2000

CALIARI, Carlo (style) (1570-1596) Italian
£11637 $18852 €16874 Tobias and the Angel (93x118cm-37x46in) 26-May-3 Bukowskis, Stockholm #378/R est:150000-175000 (S.KR 150000)

CALIFANO, John (1864-1946) American/Italian
£380 $600 €570 Country landscape (64x76cm-25x30in) s. 3-Apr-3 Boos Gallery, Michigan #234/R
£380 $600 €570 Sunset in New Jersey (64x76cm-25x30in) s. 3-Apr-3 Boos Gallery, Michigan #235/R
£774 $1200 €1161 River landscape at sunset (61x91cm-24x36in) s. painted c.1920. 8-Dec-2 Toomey, Oak Park #653/R
£1378 $2095 €2067 English setters (59x73cm-23x29in) s. 27-Aug-2 Rasmussen, Copenhagen #1780/R est:10000 (D.KR 16000)
£1447 $2300 €2171 Leading his flock over the mountain pas (102x152cm-40x60in) s. 7-Mar-3 Skinner, Boston #272/R est:4000-6000
£1751 $2750 €2627 Livestock at watering hole with farmer and tall sunlit mountain peaks (74x107cm-29x42in) s. 19-Apr-3 James Julia, Fairfield #175/R est:2500-3500
£2591 $4250 €3757 Happy musician (152x102cm-60x40in) s. 4-Jun-3 Doyle, New York #23 est:4000-6000

CALIFORNIAN SCHOOL (20th C) American
£2019 $3250 €3029 Laguna (30x41cm-12x16in) indis.sig. masonite prov. 18-Feb-3 John Moran, Pasadena #158a est:1000-2000

CALISCH, Moritz (1819-1870) Dutch
£478 $775 €693 Portrait of gentleman with beard and black jacket (61x48cm-24x19in) s.d.1857 oval. 26-May-3 Rasmussen, Copenhagen #1441/R (D.KR 5000)
£1274 $1987 €2000 Portrait of a lady (90x70cm-35x28in) s.d.1861. 6-Nov-2 Vendue Huis, Gravenhage #477 est:2000-3000

CALKETT, Victoria S (19th C) British
£1500 $2385 €2250 Trinity Collage, Cambridge (28x41cm-11x16in) indis sig. 6-Mar-3 Christie's, Kensington #492/R est:1500-2000

CALLAHAN, Harry (1912-1999) American
Photographs
£1899 $3000 €2849 Chicago (16x24cm-6x9in) s. gelatin silver print prov.lit. 25-Apr-3 Phillips, New York #120/R est:3000-5000
£1899 $3000 €2849 Chicago (16x24cm-6x9in) s. gelatin silver print prov.lit. 25-Apr-3 Phillips, New York #143/R est:3000-5000
£2025 $3200 €3038 Chicago (16x24cm-6x9in) s. gelatin silver print prov.lit. 25-Apr-3 Phillips, New York #123/R est:3000-5000
£2110 $3250 €3165 Eleanor and Barbara, Lake Michigan (19x24cm-7x9in) s.i. photograph. 24-Oct-2 Sotheby's, New York #144/R est:3000-5000
£2110 $3250 €3165 Eleanor (20x25cm-8x10in) i.verso photograph prov.lit. 22-Oct-2 Sotheby's, New York #180/R est:4000-6000

£2215 $3500 €3323 Wisconsin (20x19cm-8x7in) s.verso photograph prov.lit. 25-Apr-3 Phillips, New York #37/R est:6000-9000
£2532 $4000 €3798 Dearborn street, Chicago (19x24cm-7x9in) s.i.verso gelatin silver print prov.lit. 25-Apr-3 Phillips, New York #106/R est:4000-6000
£2532 $4000 €3798 Rome, Italy, make darker (16x16cm-6x6in) i.verso gelatin silver print prov. 25-Apr-3 Phillips, New York #147/R est:3000-5000
£2532 $4000 €3798 New York (35x34cm-14x13in) s. gelatin silver print prov.lit. 25-Apr-3 Phillips, New York #180/R est:3000-5000
£2658 $4200 €3987 Detroit (25x20cm-10x8in) s.verso gelatin silver print prov.lit. 25-Apr-3 Phillips, New York #35/R est:5000-7000
£2658 $4200 €3987 New York (26x26cm-10x10in) s. gelatin silver print prov. 25-Apr-3 Phillips, New York #254/R est:3000-5000
£2848 $4500 €4272 Providence no.132 (14x21cm-6x8in) s. gelatin silver print prov. 25-Apr-3 Phillips, New York #146/R est:3000-5000
£3165 $5000 €4748 Circus, Chicago (16x16cm-6x6in) s.verso gelatin silver print prov.lit. 25-Apr-3 Phillips, New York #122/R est:3000-5000
£3247 $5000 €4871 Aix-en-provence (23x18cm-9x7in) s. photograph prov.lit. 22-Oct-2 Sotheby's, New York #9/R est:7000-10000
£3481 $5500 €5222 Seagram Plaza, New York (15x22cm-6x9in) embossed sig. s.verso gelatin silver print prov. 25-Apr-3 Phillips, New York #38/R
£3571 $5500 €5357 Detroit (25x34cm-10x13in) i. photograph exhib. 22-Oct-2 Sotheby's, New York #6/R est:8000-12000
£3797 $6000 €5696 Chicago (16x24cm-6x9in) s. gelatin silver print prov.exhib. 25-Apr-3 Phillips, New York #119/R est:3000-5000
£3896 $6000 €5844 Eleanor - silhouette (24x32cm-9x13in) s.i. photograph. 24-Oct-2 Sotheby's, New York #143/R est:3000-5000
£4114 $6500 €6171 Chicago (24x16cm-9x6in) s. gelatin silver print prov.lit. 25-Apr-3 Phillips, New York #145/R est:4000-6000
£4200 $6804 €6300 Eleanor (44x7cm-17x3in) s.num. gelatin silver print prov. 21-May-3 Christie's, London #195/R est:2000-3000
£4221 $6500 €6332 Cape Cod (23x24cm-9x9in) s.i. photograph. 24-Oct-2 Sotheby's, New York #140/R est:2500-3500
£4747 $7500 €7121 Alley, Chicago (31x22cm-12x9in) s.verso photograph. 23-Apr-3 Sotheby's, New York #208/R est:4000-6000
£5316 $8400 €7974 Untitled (19x24cm-7x9in) s.verso gelatin silver print prov. 25-Apr-3 Phillips, New York #115/R est:5000-7000
£5380 $8500 €8070 Wells street, Chicago (16x18cm-6x7in) s. gelatin silver print prov.lit. 25-Apr-3 Phillips, New York #105/R est:4000-6000
£5696 $9000 €8544 Bob Fine (25x20cm-10x8in) s. verso gelatin silver print prov.lit. 25-Apr-3 Phillips, New York #121/R est:3000-5000
£5844 $9000 €8766 Chicago - multiple exposure tree (17x16cm-7x6in) photograph mounted on board executed c.1964 prov.lit. 22-Oct-2 Sotheby's, New York #13/R est:7000-10000
£6013 $9500 €9020 New York (17x21cm-7x8in) s. gelatin silver print prov.lit. 25-Apr-3 Phillips, New York #36/R est:5000-7000
£6329 $10000 €9494 Chicago (18x18cm-7x7in) s.verso gelatin silver print prov.lit. 25-Apr-3 Phillips, New York #34/R est:4000-6000
£6329 $10000 €9494 Wisconsin (11x24cm-4x9in) s. gelatin silver print prov.lit. 25-Apr-3 Phillips, New York #104/R est:4000-6000
£7595 $12000 €11393 Detroit (9x14cm-4x6in) s.d.1943 verso gelatin silver print. 22-Apr-3 Christie's, Rockefeller NY #134/R est:10000-15000
£7595 $12000 €11393 Chicago (19x24cm-7x9in) s. gelatin silver print lit. 22-Apr-3 Christie's, Rockefeller NY #202/R est:5000-7000
£10759 $17000 €16139 Multiple exposure trees, Detroit (24x19cm-9x7in) gelatin silver print executed c.1942 prov. 22-Apr-3 Christie's, Rockefeller NY #90/R est:8000-10000
£12338 $19000 €18507 Studies (6x6cm-2x2in) photograph set of four prov.lit. 24-Oct-2 Sotheby's, New York #145/R est:25000-35000
£16234 $25000 €24351 Wells Street, Chicago (16x18cm-6x7in) s.verso photograph prov.exhib.lit. 22-Oct-2 Sotheby's, New York #7/R est:8000-12000
£17722 $28000 €26583 Eleanor (8x11cm-3x4in) gelatin silver print prov.lit. 22-Apr-3 Christie's, Rockefeller NY #88/R est:8000-10000

CALLAM, Edward (1904-1980) British
£300 $474 €450 Harvard (58x48cm-23x19in) s. 18-Dec-2 Mallams, Oxford #681

CALLANDE DE CHAMPMARTIN, Charles Émile (1797-1883) French
Works on paper
£922 $1540 €1300 Jeune gazelle dans un paysage (11x15cm-4x6in) s. W/C prov. 23-Jun-3 Beaussant & Lefèvre, Paris #105

CALLCOTT, Sir Augustus Wall (1779-1844) British
£340 $568 €493 Continental river scene (41x58cm-16x23in) s.d.1861. 18-Jun-3 Andrew Hartley, Ilkley #1176
£1262 $1994 €1893 Fishermen by beached boats on rocky shore (23x32cm-9x13in) panel. 27-Nov-2 Falkkloos, Malmo #77556/R est:15000 (S.KR 18000)
£1300 $2106 €1950 Fishermen congregating on the shore (23x32cm-9x13in) panel. 21-May-3 Christie's, Kensington #610/R est:1200-1800
£2000 $3040 €3000 Idle gossip on the shore (52x67cm-20x26in) s.d.1806. 29-Aug-2 Christie's, Kensington #102/R est:800-1200

CALLCOTT, William (fl.1856-1865) British
£641 $1000 €962 Windy chores (41x51cm-16x20in) 30-Mar-3 Simpson's, Houston #368

CALLCOTT, William J (19th C) British
Works on paper
£494 $765 €741 Coast of North Shields (38x63cm-15x25in) s.i.d.1890 W/C. 3-Dec-2 Ritchie, Toronto #3011/R est:1000-1500 (C.D 1200)
£2122 $3268 €3183 The breakwater at Gorleston, Yarmouth (135x202cm-53x80in) s. gouache executed 1871. 28-Oct-2 Blomqvist, Lysaker #1015/R est:20000-30000 (N.KR 25000)

CALLCOTT, William J (attrib) (19th C) British
£1150 $1829 €1725 Coastal scene with ships, boats and figures on the beach (48x86cm-19x34in) 29-Apr-3 Lawrences, Bletchingley #1432/R

CALLE, Chris (20th C) American
Works on paper
£909 $1400 €1364 Last warrior (28x36cm-11x14in) mixed media. 25-Oct-2 Morris & Whiteside, Hilton Head Island #50 est:1500-2000

CALLE, Paul (1928-) American
Works on paper
£2952 $4545 €4428 They call me Simon (33x36cm-13x14in) pencil. 25-Oct-2 Morris & Whiteside, Hilton Head Island #35 est:5000-6000
£20548 $30000 €30822 Hunting the big horn (76x102cm-30x40in) pencil. 18-May-2 Altermann Galleries, Santa Fe #219/R

CALLE, Sophie (1954-) American
Photographs
£2264 $3487 €3600 Father, mother (60x80cm-24x31in) black/white photograph exec.1990 prov. 26-Oct-2 Cornette de St.Cyr, Paris #169/R
£4500 $6930 €6750 True stories, bad breath (120x170cm-47x67in) two gelatin silver prints executed 1994 prov. 23-Oct-2 Christie's, London #185/R est:3000-5000

CALLERY, Simon (1960-) British
Works on paper
£480 $782 €720 Untitled - Cityscape (45x64cm-18x25in) s.i.d.90 chl. 3-Feb-3 Sotheby's, Olympia #129/R

CALLET, Antoine François (1741-1823) French
Works on paper
£460 $727 €690 Death of Leander (18x30cm-7x12in) red chk. 15-Nov-2 Rowley Fine Art, Newmarket #351/R
£1899 $3000 €3000 Venus demandant vengeance a Jupiter (27x20cm-11x8in) pen ink wash prov. 28-Nov-2 Tajan, Paris #93/R

CALLET, Antoine François (attrib) (1741-1823) French
£6500 $10335 €9750 King Louis VX, in full ceremonial dress (156x110cm-61x43in) after Louis Michel van Loo. 20-Mar-3 Christie's, Kensington #134/R est:6000-8000
Works on paper
£1558 $2400 €2337 Garden party with circle of women (13x18cm-5x7in) s. W/C bodycol oval. 26-Oct-2 Brunk, Ashville #991/R est:200-400

CALLIN, Isaac (fl.1881-1920) British
Works on paper
£260 $406 €390 Mr W B Purefoys Lally B Dillon up, winner of the Eclipse Stakes 1907 (25x35cm-10x14in) s.i.d.1907 W/C. 9-Oct-2 Woolley & Wallis, Salisbury #165/R

CALLINS, Charles (1887-?) Australian
£1155 $1791 €1733 Ballet practice (51x51cm-20x20in) s.i. i.d.1974 verso board. 3-Dec-2 Shapiro, Sydney #21/R est:3000-4000 (A.D 3200)

CALLIYANNIS, Manolis (1926-) Greek
£1200 $1896 €1800 Mere et enfant (30x24cm-12x9in) 1-Apr-3 Bonhams, New Bond Street #112 est:1000-1500
£1600 $2480 €2400 Sea (56x77cm-22x30in) s.d.1958 s.i.d.verso. 2-Oct-2 Sotheby's, London #107/R
£1800 $2790 €2700 Sea is blue I (88x114cm-35x45in) s. s.i.d.1954 verso prov. 2-Oct-2 Sotheby's, London #128/R
£3400 $5372 €5100 Le bateau du Roi Agamemnon (114x145cm-45x57in) 1-Apr-3 Bonhams, New Bond Street #87 est:2000-3000
£4500 $6975 €6750 La mer est bleue II (100x80cm-39x31in) s. s.i.d.1957 verso prov. 2-Oct-2 Sotheby's, London #62/R

CALLMANDER, Carl Reinhold (1840-1922) Swedish
£245 $387 €368 Sunday morning, Mother Beata's kitchen (59x48cm-23x19in) s.d.1918. 16-Nov-2 Crafoord, Lund #10/R (S.KR 3500)

CALLOIGNE, Jan Robert (1775-1830) Belgian
Sculpture
£10791 $17266 €15000 L'acteur Frans Joseph Talma (190cm-75in) stone. 13-May-3 Palais de Beaux Arts, Brussels #465/R est:5000-7000

CALLOT, Henri Eugène (1875-1956) French
£500 $835 €725 Harbour scene with sailing vessels (38x45cm-15x18in) s. 19-Jun-3 Clevedon Sale Rooms #187

CALLOT, Jacques (1592-1635) French
Prints
£6410 $10128 €10000 Le parterre de Nancy. etching. 14-Nov-2 Libert, Castor, Paris #3/R est:4000
Works on paper
£5696 $9000 €9000 Gobbi et autres monstres. Etude de jambe, d'une tete de cochon (10x14cm-4x6in) red chk pen brown ink double-sided prov.exhib.lit. 27-Nov-2 Christie's, Paris #134/R est:10000-15000
£66434 $110944 €95000 Une place de village en Lorraine (9x23cm-4x9in) pierre noire brush brown wash prov.exhib.lit. 25-Jun-3 Sotheby's, Paris #1/R est:30000-40000

CALLOT, Jacques (after) (1592-1635) French
£21795 $33782 €34000 Market at Impruneta (91x120cm-36x47in) 4-Dec-2 Christie's, Rome #449/R est:15000-20000

CALLOW, Ben (fl.1851-1869) British
£760 $1208 €1140 Figures on lane before an extensive landscape (34x51cm-13x20in) s.d.1863. 27-Feb-3 Bonhams, Chester #478

CALLOW, G D (fl.1858-1873) British
£400 $632 €600 Dovedale, Derbyshire (25x35cm-10x14in) s.d. 18-Dec-2 John Nicholson, Haslemere #1306

CALLOW, George D (fl.1858-1873) British
£360 $601 €522 Devonshire village (30x55cm-12x22in) s.d.1869. 8-Jul-3 Bonhams, Knightsbridge #130/R

CALLOW, George William (19th C) British
£419 $650 €629 Morning on the east coast (30x41cm-12x16in) s. i.verso. 25-Sep-2 Doyle, New York #15/R

CALLOW, J (19th C) British
£1200 $1824 €1800 Dutch fishing vessel off Mount Edgemont with coastal briggs beyond (66x102cm-26x40in) indis.sig. 15-Aug-2 Bonhams, New Bond Street #325 est:3000-5000

CALLOW, John (1822-1878) British
£2400 $3816 €3600 Coasters reducing sail in a heavy swell offshore (73x124cm-29x49in) s. 4-Mar-3 Bonhams, Knightsbridge #330/R est:1500-2000
£4000 $6280 €6000 Breezy day, Portsmouth Harbour (77x127cm-30x50in) s.d.1868. 21-Nov-2 Tennants, Leyburn #752/R est:4000-6000
£8500 $13345 €12750 Men-o-war, Dutch fishing boat and other shipping in the Solent (77x128cm-30x50in) s. 21-Nov-2 Tennants, Leyburn #751/R est:4000-6000
Works on paper
£250 $405 €375 Beached fishing boats below the cliffs (10x16cm-4x6in) pencil W/C prov. 21-May-3 Christie's, Kensington #424
£400 $620 €600 Channel packet running out of port (19x23cm-7x9in) s.d.69 W/C. 31-Oct-2 Christie's, Kensington #333/R
£550 $875 €825 Merchantman in French port (27x26cm-11x10in) W/C. 25-Feb-3 Bonhams, Knightsbridge #161/R
£950 $1501 €1425 Shipping off the English coast (36x51cm-14x20in) s.d.1845 W/C. 2-Dec-2 Gorringes, Lewes #2751
£1000 $1550 €1500 Figures sheltering on the beach (24x34cm-9x13in) W/C. 31-Oct-2 Christie's, Kensington #340/R est:1000-1500
£1000 $1600 €1500 Old Tadnoll Mill, Dorset (34x51cm-13x20in) W/C. 11-Mar-3 Bonhams, New Bond Street #22/R est:1000-1500
£1081 $1686 €1600 Seascape (20x30cm-8x12in) s.d. W/C gouache. 31-Mar-3 Piasa, Paris #114
£2000 $3100 €3000 Squadron running down the Channel with a flagship heaving-to (37x55cm-15x22in) s.d.1874 W/C. 31-Oct-2 Christie's, Kensington #331/R est:1200-1800

CALLOW, William (1812-1908) British
Works on paper
£250 $395 €375 Figures by a river (17x24cm-7x9in) W/C. 26-Nov-2 Bonhams, Knightsbridge #185/R
£400 $624 €600 Country scene with figures before a church (23x33cm-9x13in) W/C. 6-Nov-2 Bonhams, Chester #477
£450 $733 €675 Fisherman on a river with woodland and church in the background (17x25cm-7x10in) W/C pencil. 29-Jan-3 Sotheby's, Olympia #43/R
£600 $960 €900 Prince's house at Bonn (18x26cm-7x10in) s.i.d.63 W/C. 11-Mar-3 Bonhams, New Bond Street #9/R
£650 $1053 €975 Montrichard, Loire et Cher, France (24x33cm-9x13in) s.d.1836 W/C. 21-Jan-3 Bonhams, Knightsbridge #171/R
£700 $1092 €1050 An overshot water-mill (16x25cm-6x10in) init. W/C prov. 5-Nov-2 Bonhams, New Bond Street #64/R
£750 $1140 €1125 Towing into port, heavy weather (32x52cm-13x20in) s. W/C bodycol. 15-Aug-2 Bonhams, New Bond Street #219/R
£760 $1246 €1140 River Wharfe at Bolton Abbey (24x33cm-9x13in) s.i.d.September 30 1858 W/C. 4-Feb-3 Bonhams, Leeds #256
£950 $1482 €1425 Eastgate Street, Chester (21x32cm-8x13in) bears i. W/C. 6-Nov-2 Bonhams, Chester #323/R
£1200 $1872 €1800 Castle Maoil, Isle of Skye (12x34cm-5x13in) pencil W/C scratching out. 27-Mar-3 Christie's, Kensington #152/R est:800-1200
£1250 $1988 €1875 Street scene with church (40x31cm-16x12in) s.d.1853 W/C. 5-Mar-3 Bonhams, Bury St Edmunds #271/R est:1000-1500
£1500 $2369 €2250 Street scene, Nuremberg (40x32cm-16x13in) s. W/C over pencil bodycol prov. 28-Nov-2 Sotheby's, London #324/R est:1500-2000
£1500 $2460 €2250 Figures by a toll house in Nuremberg (26x11cm-10x4in) s. pencil W/C htd white. 4-Feb-3 Bonhams, Leeds #255 est:800-1200
£1600 $2496 €2400 Dolce aqua (25x35cm-10x14in) s.i.d.1877 pencil W/C. 17-Oct-2 Christie's, Kensington #168/R est:1500-2000
£1800 $2862 €2700 Continental market place (27x38cm-11x15in) s. W/C over pencil. 19-Mar-3 Sotheby's, London #158/R est:2000-3000
£3600 $5616 €5400 Market place, Nuremburg (40x56cm-16x22in) s.d.1888 W/C exhib. 5-Nov-2 Bonhams, New Bond Street #82/R est:2500-3500
£3600 $5868 €5400 Interior of Havre harbour (25x48cm-10x19in) s. 28-Jan-3 Gorringes, Lewes #1630/R est:3000-4000
£3600 $5976 €5400 Continental market place (21x35cm-8x14in) s. W/C over pencil htd bodycol. 12-Jun-3 Sotheby's, London #156/R est:2000-3000
£3800 $5966 €5700 Fishing boat in rough seas (24x34cm-9x13in) s.d.1841 pencil W/C scratching out. 21-Nov-2 Christie's, London #55/R est:3000-5000
£4200 $6888 €6090 Grand Canal, Venice (25x35cm-10x14in) s.i.d.12/65 pencil W/C. 5-Jun-3 Christie's, London #164/R est:3500-5500
£5800 $9628 €8700 Market square, Bologna (22x31cm-9x12in) s. W/C over pencil htd bodycol prov. 12-Jun-3 Sotheby's, London #157/R est:3000-5000
£6500 $9295 €9750 Mont Vacours, on the Seine (10x25cm-4x10in) i.d.1834 pencil W/C prov.exhib.lit. 22-Jan-3 Christie's, London #59/R
£7200 $11952 €10800 On the Riva Dei Schiavoni, Venice (23x49cm-9x19in) s. W/C over pencil htd bodycol exhib.lit. 12-Jun-3 Sotheby's, London #154/R est:6000-8000
£14000 $21980 €21000 View of the Ca' Foscari on the Grand Canal, Venice (32x47cm-13x19in) s.d.1854 pencil pen ink W/C htd bodycol. 21-Nov-2 Christie's, London #63/R est:8000-12000

CALLOWHILL, James (19th C) British
£700 $1113 €1050 On the Llugwy, North Wales (61x91cm-24x36in) s.d.1878 s.i.verso. 6-Mar-3 Christie's, Kensington #448/R

CALOGERO, Jean (1922-) Italian
£245 $400 €368 Fantastical view of Venice in festival (46x55cm-18x22in) s. i.verso. 16-Feb-3 Butterfields, San Francisco #2139
£800 $1264 €1200 Venice (46x55cm-18x22in) s. 3-Apr-3 Christie's, Kensington #194/R

CALON, Achille Augustin (?-1904) French
£915 $1500 €1327 Still life with fruit and flowers (56x46cm-22x18in) s.d.1859. 4-Jun-3 Doyle, New York #24/R est:3000-4000

CALRAET, Abraham van (1642-1722) Dutch
£7447 $11543 €11171 Still life of peaches, plums and grapes on stone ledge (76x63cm-30x25in) 8-Dec-2 Uppsala Auktionskammare, Uppsala #30/R est:100000-150000 (S.KR 105000)
£11000 $17270 €16500 Two horses and a milkmaid with cow in a landscape, with pond (38x51cm-15x20in) panel exhib. 13-Dec-2 Christie's, Kensington #115/R est:10000-15000

CALRAET, Abraham van (attrib) (1642-1722) Dutch
£1650 $2705 €2393 The white horse (30x39cm-12x15in) 4-Jun-3 AB Stockholms Auktionsverk #2568/R est:15000-20000 (S.KR 21000)
£8633 $13813 €12000 Cockerel and a hen (48x60cm-19x24in) panel prov.exhib. 14-May-3 Christie's, Amsterdam #176/R est:12000-16000

CALRAET, Barend van (1649-1737) Dutch
Works on paper
£446 $696 €700 Battle scene (28x34cm-11x13in) s. W/C over black chk vellum prov. 5-Nov-2 Sotheby's, Amsterdam #119/R

CALS, Adolphe Felix (1810-1880) French
£479 $700 €719 Route de Villerville a Honfleur (23x38cm-9x15in) s.d.71. 3-Nov-1 North East Auctions, Portsmouth #283
£1013 $1600 €1600 Portrait de Mme Cals (22x16cm-9x6in) s.d.Avril 41. 1-Dec-2 Peron, Melun #12
£2911 $4542 €4600 Promeneur dans la bocage (19x25cm-7x10in) s. panel. 15-Sep-2 Etude Bailleul, Bayeux #55

CALSINA, Ramon (1901-) Spanish
£1258 $1962 €2000 Composition with figures (60x73cm-24x29in) s. 8-Oct-2 Ansorena, Madrid #632/R
£1702 $2757 €2400 Basket with flowers (60x73cm-24x29in) s. 20-May-3 Segre, Madrid #113/R est:2400
Works on paper
£487 $711 €750 Woman (28x42cm-11x17in) s. chl dr. 17-Jun-2 Ansorena, Madrid #21/R

CALTHROP, Claude Andrew (1845-1893) British
£13000 $20540 €19500 La levee de Monseigneur (126x86cm-50x34in) s.d.1873 exhib.lit. 26-Nov-2 Christie's, London #101/R est:10000-15000

CALTHROP, Claude Andrew (attrib) (1845-1893) British
£2500 $3876 €3750 Tranquillo (80x48cm-31x19in) i.verso panel. 3-Dec-2 Sotheby's, Olympia #77/R est:3000-5000

CALUCCI, Gio (?) ?
£385 $600 €578 Modernist portrait of mother nursing baby (74x61cm-29x24in) s. 18-Sep-2 Alderfer's, Hatfield #318

CALVAERT, Dionisio (attrib) (1540-1619) Flemish
£1049 $1752 €1500 Vierge a l'Enfant (20x14cm-8x6in) htd gold copper. 27-Jun-3 Piasa, Paris #41 est:1000-1200

CALVAERT, Dionisio (circle) (1540-1619) Flemish
£5500 $8580 €8250 Mystic marriage of Saint Catherine (88x70cm-35x28in) 10-Apr-3 Christie's, Kensington #15/R est:3000-5000

CALVANI, Bruno (1904-) Italian
Works on paper
£321 $497 €500 Nude (45x35cm-18x14in) s. mixed media. 4-Dec-2 Finarte, Milan #181

CALVE, Julien (?-1924) French
£292 $475 €420 Bretonnes sur la plage de Mousterlin (35x50cm-14x20in) s.i.verso. 19-Jul-3 Thierry & Lannon, Brest #309

CALVERT, Edward (1799-1883) British
Works on paper
£450 $743 €653 The awakening of humanity (25x14cm-10x6in) mono. pencil W/C htd. white. 2-Jul-3 Sotheby's, Olympia #173/R

CALVERT, Frederick (c.1785-1845) British
£400 $620 €600 Running for shelter (25x41cm-10x16in) panel. 31-Oct-2 Christie's, Kensington #513/R
£980 $1401 €1470 Fishing craft offshore (19x31cm-7x12in) panel. 28-Feb-2 Greenslade Hunt, Taunton #417
£5500 $8910 €8250 Running for shelter. Hauling in the nets (25x36cm-10x14in) s. pair. 22-Jan-3 Bonhams, New Bond Street #373/R est:3000-5000
£6000 $9720 €8700 Shipping becalmed in a harbour. Shipping in stormy seas, off coast (28x38cm-11x15in) s. pair. 29-Jul-3 Henry Adams, Chichester #570/R est:2000-3000

CALVES, Léon Georges (1848-1924) French
Works on paper
£665 $1063 €964 Horse-drawn wagon with figures (99x70cm-39x28in) s. W/C. 18-May-3 Anders Antik, Landskrona #10 (S.KR 8500)

CALVES, Marie (1883-1957) French
£1149 $1792 €1700 Chiens s'abreuvant (16x24cm-6x9in) s. panel pair. 26-Mar-3 Rossini, Paris #122
£1169 $1777 €1800 Herdress with dogs (91x66cm-36x26in) s. 6-Jul-2 Berlinghof, Heidelberg #194/R est:1800

CALVI, Giuseppe (19/20th C) Continental
£300 $501 €435 House beside an autumn river (67x98cm-26x39in) s. 23-Jun-3 Bonhams, Bath #225

CALVO, Carmen (1950-) Spanish
£1384 $2131 €2200 Untitled (56x46cm-22x18in) s.d.1984 oil W/C prov. 28-Oct-2 Segre, Madrid #150/R

CALYO, Nicolino (1799-1884) American
Works on paper
£5263 $8000 €7895 View of New York harbour taken from Hoboken (20x33cm-8x13in) i. gouache prov. 17-Aug-2 North East Auctions, Portsmouth #838/R est:3000-5000

CALZA, Antonio (attrib) (1653-1725) Italian
Works on paper
£347 $552 €500 Landscape with rider by river (17x25cm-7x10in) i. pen prov. 5-May-3 Ketterer, Munich #395/R

CALZOLARI, Pier Paolo (1943-) Italian
£3226 $5097 €5000 Untitled (67x65cm-26x26in) s.d.70 resin tempera paper. 18-Dec-2 Christie's, Rome #123/R
£12766 $20681 €18000 Untitled (102x145cm-40x57in) tempera pastel pencil salt clover board. 26-May-3 Christie's, Milan #274/R est:18000-22000
Works on paper
£743 $1159 €1100 Untitled (50x70cm-20x28in) s.d.65 collage mixed media. 26-Mar-3 Finarte Semenzato, Milan #171
£1689 $2635 €2500 Untitled (70x102cm-28x40in) s. polymer tobacco card. 26-Mar-3 Finarte Semenzato, Milan #144/R
£1761 $2923 €2500 Untitled (75x99cm-30x39in) s.d.1968 verso mixed media board. 10-Jun-3 Finarte Semenzato, Milan #296/R est:2500-3000
£2027 $3162 €3000 Untitled (70x102cm-28x40in) sd.1968 polymer card. 26-Mar-3 Finarte Semenzato, Milan #145/R
£2258 $3568 €3500 Untitled (68x98cm-27x39in) s.d.68 pencil mixed media. 18-Dec-2 Christie's, Rome #57/R
£2394 $3975 €3400 Untitled (71x103cm-28x41in) s.d.1968 verso mixed media board. 10-Jun-3 Finarte Semenzato, Milan #297/R est:2500-3000
£3546 $5745 €5000 Untitled (72x103cm-28x41in) s. feather salt pencil prov. 26-May-3 Christie's, Milan #107/R est:4000-6000
£5493 $9118 €7800 Untitled (124x140cm-49x55in) s.d.1980 mixed media collage. 10-Jun-3 Finarte Semenzato, Milan #246/R est:3500-4500
£11538 $17885 €18000 Moon (281x200cm-111x79in) s.d.80 verso mixed media panel. 4-Dec-2 Finarte, Milan #494/R est:20000

CAMACHO, Jorge (1934-) Cuban
£2830 $4387 €4500 Le crane-de-nuit, hommage a Jean Pierre Duprey (144x114cm-57x45in) s.i.d.64 verso prov. 30-Oct-2 Artcurial Briest, Paris #491/R est:4000-5000
£3741 $5949 €5500 Avant la nuit (116x89cm-46x35in) s.i.d.1988 verso. 24-Mar-3 Claude Boisgirard, Paris #99/R
£7534 $11829 €11000 Femme de nuit (114x146cm-45x57in) s.i.d.64 verso prov.exhib.lit. 15-Apr-3 Laurence Calmels, Paris #4256/R
Works on paper
£314 $484 €500 Figures du cirque (65x50cm-26x20in) sd.1972 col dr. 22-Oct-2 Campo & Campo, Antwerp #26
£443 $700 €700 Fantasy figure (65x60cm-26x24in) s.d.92 gouache ink. 26-Nov-2 Camard, Paris #129
£1042 $1656 €1500 Personnage lunaire fous (29x22cm-11x9in) s.i.d.63 mixed media. 29-Apr-3 Artcurial Briest, Paris #600/R est:1000-1500

CAMACHO, Jose (19/20th C) Spanish
£1218 $1924 €1900 Singing in Seville (186x105cm-73x41in) 13-Nov-2 Ansorena, Madrid #289/R
£9677 $15290 €15000 Altar boy (176x100cm-69x39in) s.d.1899. 18-Dec-2 Ansorena, Madrid #161/R est:15000

CAMARENA, Jorge Gonzalez (1918-) Mexican
£3463 $5403 €5195 Cabeza de mujer (40x49cm-16x19in) s.d.1972. 17-Oct-2 Louis Morton, Mexico #109/R est:65000-70000 (M.P 55000)

CAMARGO, Sergio de (1930-1990) Brazilian
Sculpture
£11585 $19000 €17378 Sem titulo (24x14cm-9x6in) i.indis.d. verso wood on panel mounted on wood exec.c.1970 prov. 28-May-3 Christie's, Rockefeller NY #43/R est:15000-20000

£14000 $23380 €20300 Untitled (18x46x19cm-7x18x7in) white marble exec.c.1985 two parts prov. 26-Jun-3 Sotheby's, London #157/R est:12000-18000

£16000 $26720 €23200 No 344 (51x85x36cm-20x33x14in) s.i.d.71 verso painted wood prov. 26-Jun-3 Sotheby's, London #145/R est:18000-25000

£25000 $41750 €36250 Relief, opus 193 (52x36x19cm-20x14x7in) s.i.d.1968 verso painted wood prov.exhib. 26-Jun-3 Sotheby's, London #144/R est:10000-15000

CAMARLENCH, Ignacio Pinazo (1849-1916) Spanish

Works on paper

£428 $693 €650 Figures in landscape (26x21cm-10x8in) s.d.1890 sanguine. 21-Jan-3 Durán, Madrid #67/R

CAMARO, Alexander (1901-1992) German

£1835 $2900 €2900 Wooden theatre (100x70cm-39x28in) s. 30-Nov-2 Bassenge, Berlin #6164/R est:4500

£2405 $3800 €3800 Skater (32x42cm-13x17in) s. 30-Nov-2 Villa Grisebach, Berlin #360/R est:3000-4000

CAMARON Y BORONAT, Jose (style) (1730-1803) Spanish

£5000 $7850 €7500 Fete galante with elegant figures in a woodland setting (64x76cm-25x30in) 10-Dec-2 Sotheby's, Olympia #390/R est:3000-4000

CAMARON Y MELIA, Vicente (?-1864) Spanish

Works on paper

£262 $409 €393 The Tajo near Toledo (16x25cm-6x10in) s.d.1859 Indian ink brush over pencil htd white. 20-Nov-2 Fischer, Luzern #2453/R (S.FR 600)

CAMBELLOTTI, Duilio (1876-1960) Italian

Sculpture

£6164 $9616 €9000 Zodiac vase (30cm-12in) num.1/3 bronze. 10-Apr-3 Finarte Semenzato, Rome #252/R est:12000

CAMBIASO, Luca (1527-1585) Italian

Prints

£3797 $6000 €6000 Venus mourning the death of Adonis (26x30cm-10x12in) woodcut. 29-Nov-2 Bassenge, Berlin #5206/R est:6000

Works on paper

£1200 $1884 €1800 Rest on the Flight into Egypt (21x34cm-8x13in) pen ink wash prov. 11-Dec-2 Sotheby's, Olympia #19/R est:600-800

£2098 $3000 €3147 Seated philosopher (45x37cm-18x15in) pen ink wash htd white. 23-Jan-3 Swann Galleries, New York #32/R est:3000-5000

£2800 $4676 €4060 The entombent (29x19cm-11x7in) pen brown ink wash blk chk. 9-Jul-3 Sotheby's, London #28/R est:3000-4000

£3000 $5010 €4350 Putti playing (25x35cm-10x14in) pen brown ink prov. 9-Jul-3 Sotheby's, London #23/R est:3000-4000

£11486 $17919 €17000 Christ aux outrages (30x23cm-12x9in) i. pen ink wash. 27-Mar-3 Christie's, Paris #7/R

CAMBIASO, Luca (attrib) (1527-1585) Italian

£3448 $5448 €5000 Jesus in the Jetsemanih (123x98cm-48x39in) 5-Apr-3 Finarte Semenzato, Milan #71/R est:8000

Works on paper

£252 $392 €400 Composition (28x20cm-11x8in) pen. 23-Sep-2 Dr Fritz Nagel, Stuttgart #9029/R

£950 $1492 €1425 St. Sebastian (42x27cm-17x11in) pen ink wash over black chk. 11-Dec-2 Sotheby's, Olympia #5/R

£1235 $2000 €1853 Christ on the way to Calvary (21x29cm-8x11in) chk pen ink wash prov. 22-Jan-3 Christie's, Rockefeller NY #15/R

CAMBIER, Guy (1923-) French

£300 $471 €450 Landscape with a pony and trap passing a house (40x80cm-16x31in) s. 21-Nov-2 Tennants, Leyburn #832

£300 $471 €450 Portrait of a seated lady (72x53cm-28x21in) s. board. 15-Apr-3 Bonhams, Knightsbridge #122

£548 $850 €822 Mother and daughter (74x56cm-29x22in) s.d.69. 16-Jul-2 Arthur James, Florida #51

£556 $906 €800 Maternite (72x53cm-28x21in) s. panel. 19-Jul-3 Thierry & Lannon, Brest #310

CAMBIER, Juliette (1879-1949) Belgian

£250 $398 €375 Paysage (23x27cm-9x11in) s. prov. 20-Mar-3 Sotheby's, Olympia #29/R

£705 $1107 €1100 Vase de fleurs (40x35cm-16x14in) s.d.1916. 10-Dec-2 Vanderkindere, Brussels #105

£903 $1490 €1300 Fleurs d'ete (50x36cm-20x14in) s. 1-Jul-3 Christie's, Amsterdam #292/R

£966 $1526 €1400 Bouquet de fleurs (65x51cm-26x20in) s.d.1921. 2-Apr-3 Vanderkindere, Brussels #17/R

£1079 $1727 €1500 Paysage mediterraneen (46x55cm-18x22in) s.d.19. 19-May-3 Horta, Bruxelles #85 est:1500-2000

£1100 $1749 €1650 Copus au printemps (34x44cm-13x17in) s. prov. 20-Mar-3 Sotheby's, Olympia #25/R est:400-600

£1200 $1908 €1800 Le jardin (38x43cm-15x17in) s.indis.d191 prov. 20-Mar-3 Sotheby's, Olympia #28/R est:400-600

£2400 $3816 €3600 Fleurs (50x40cm-20x16in) s.indis.d.19 prov. 20-Mar-3 Sotheby's, Olympia #32/R est:100-1500

£2600 $4134 €3900 Vue d'une place (35x40cm-14x16in) s.d.1917 prov. 20-Mar-3 Sotheby's, Olympia #26/R est:500-700

CAMBIER, Louis G (1874-1949) Belgian

£269 $417 €420 Chemin en Ardennes (58x76cm-23x30in) s. 9-Dec-2 Horta, Bruxelles #449

£396 $633 €550 Autoportrait (60x50cm-24x20in) s. panel exhib. 13-May-3 Palais de Beaux Arts, Brussels #221

£1961 $3157 €3000 La scene animee dans le jardin des oliviers a Jerusalem (151x201cm-59x79in) s. 14-Jan-3 Vanderkindere, Brussels #150/R est:2000-3000

CAMBIO, A (20th C) Italian

Sculpture

£4747 $7358 €7500 Little girl (98cm-39in) i. marble. 26-Sep-2 Neumeister, Munich #2403/R est:600

CAMBOS, Jean Jules (1828-1917) French

Sculpture

£1020 $1622 €1500 Notre dame des Victoires. s. brown pat.bronze Cast.Arnault/Editeur. 24-Mar-3 Bernaerts, Antwerp #47/R est:1850-2250

CAMBOUR, Claude (?) French

£1887 $3000 €2831 Sous le soleil de Giverny (97x130cm-38x51in) s. i.verso. 7-Mar-3 Skinner, Boston #536/R est:700-900

CAMBRESIER, Jean (1856-1928) Belgian

£641 $1006 €1000 Le jeune pecheur (63x38cm-25x15in) s. 11-Dec-2 Hotel des Ventes Mosan, Brussels #222

CAMENISCH, Paul (1893-1970) Swiss

£1806 $2907 €2619 Paradies II (73x92cm-29x36in) 9-May-3 Dobiaschofsky, Bern #266/R est:4000 (S.FR 3900)

£7424 $11581 €11136 Small Wetzialp II (73x92cm-29x36in) s.d.60. 8-Nov-2 Dobiaschofsky, Bern #195/R est:7500 (S.FR 17000)

£22624 $37783 €32805 Spring landscape in Tessin (100x115cm-39x45in) s.d.30 prov. 24-Jun-3 Koller, Zurich #26/R est:50000-80000 (S.FR 50000)

CAMENZIND, Balz (1907-1989) German

£377 $611 €547 Schnaps burning (72x60cm-28x24in) s.d.73 i. stretcher acrylic prov. 24-May-3 Galerie Gloggner, Luzern #14 (S.FR 800)

£377 $611 €547 Young people (61x43cm-24x17in) s.d.66 i. stretcher prov. 24-May-3 Galerie Gloggner, Luzern #16 (S.FR 800)

£472 $764 €684 Wailing wall Israel (73x78cm-29x31in) s.d.74 i. stretcher acrylic prov. 24-May-3 Galerie Gloggner, Luzern #10/R (S.FR 1000)

£472 $764 €684 Procession (77x76cm-30x30in) s.d.85 acrylic prov. 24-May-3 Galerie Gloggner, Luzern #11/R (S.FR 1000)

£472 $764 €684 Mosque in Jerusalem (78x70cm-31x28in) s.d.74 i. stretcher acrylic prov. 24-May-3 Galerie Gloggner, Luzern #13 (S.FR 1000)

£655 $1022 €983 Homebound cowherd (64x92cm-25x36in) acrylic board prov. 9-Nov-2 Galerie Gloggner, Luzern #22 (S.FR 1500)

£751 $1232 €1089 Procession of riders (100x77cm-39x30in) s.d.69. 4-Jun-3 Fischer, Luzern #2023/R est:1800-2500 (S.FR 1600)

£1698 $2751 €2462 Three horses (78x78cm-31x31in) s.d.75 acrylic prov. 24-May-3 Galerie Gloggner, Luzern #12/R est:1200-1500 (S.FR 3600)

Works on paper

£262 $409 €393 Horse-race (42x59cm-17x23in) s. black ink W/C prov. 9-Nov-2 Galerie Gloggner, Luzern #23 (S.FR 600)

CAMERON, Douglas (19/20th C) British

£500 $795 €750 Extensive landscape with cattle on a hillside (30x43cm-12x17in) s. 29-Apr-3 Gorringes, Lewes #2174

£500 $815 €725 Highland cattle beside a loch (60x106cm-24x42in) s. 21-Jul-3 Bonhams, Bath #77/R

£620 $949 €930 Highland cattle in a misty landscape (50x75cm-20x30in) s. pair. 22-Aug-2 Bonhams, Edinburgh #1183

£2400 $4008 €3480 Highland cattle in a glen (60x90cm-24x35in) s. 26-Jun-3 Mellors & Kirk, Nottingham #907/R est:1000-1500

CAMERON, Duncan (1837-1916) British

£360 $587 €540 Harvest landscape by the river (25x40cm-10x16in) 14-Feb-3 Lyon & Turnbull, Edinburgh #23

£1500 $2385 €2250 Arthur's seat from Levenhall (41x62cm-16x24in) s. i.verso prov. 6-Mar-3 Christie's, Kensington #46/R est:1500-2000

CAMERON, Gordon Stewart (1916-1994) British
£320 $499 €480 Portrait of Ellen (100x90cm-39x35in) s. 17-Oct-2 Bonhams, Edinburgh #16
£360 $562 €540 Still life with guitar (105x128cm-41x50in) s. 17-Oct-2 Bonhams, Edinburgh #15
£500 $780 €750 Front room (23x31cm-9x12in) s. board sold with another similar. 17-Oct-2 Bonhams, Edinburgh #8/R
£580 $905 €870 Tabletop still life of flowers, fruit and picture (75x62cm-30x24in) s. 17-Oct-2 Bonhams, Edinburgh #7/R

CAMERON, Hugh (1835-1918) British
£2600 $3952 €3900 Woodland scene (38x62cm-15x24in) init. board. 28-Aug-2 Sotheby's, London #891/R est:2500-3500

CAMERON, Julia Margaret (1815-1879) British
Photographs
£1875 $3000 €2813 Ahasuerus and queen Esther (8x5cm-3x2in) with sig.i.d.1868 albumen print. 15-May-3 Swann Galleries, New York #206/R est:2000-3000
£4000 $6480 €6000 Kate Keown (35x28cm-14x11in) s.i. albumen print card lit. 22-May-3 Sotheby's, London #29/R est:4000-6000
£9146 $15000 €13719 Mrs Duckworth (28x22cm-11x9in) i. albumen print. 10-Feb-3 Swann Galleries, New York #10/R est:20000-30000
£13000 $21060 €19500 Alice Liddel, St Agnes (34x23cm-13x9in) s.i.d.Sept 1872 albumen print prov.lit. 22-May-3 Sotheby's, London #30/R est:10000-15000

CAMERON, Katherine (1874-1965) British
Works on paper
£450 $702 €675 Craig Mohr (23x33cm-9x13in) s. W/C. 13-Sep-2 Lyon & Turnbull, Edinburgh #51/R
£700 $1085 €1050 Statuette (64x47cm-25x19in) init. W/C. 5-Dec-2 Bonhams, Edinburgh #71
£1050 $1638 €1575 My wild ones (33x22cm-13x9in) s. pencil W/C bodycol. 6-Nov-2 Bonhams, Chester #436/R est:700-1000
£1450 $2262 €2175 Red roses (55x42cm-22x17in) s. W/C. 10-Apr-3 Bonhams, Edinburgh #150/R est:800-1200
£1500 $2430 €2250 Still life of late summer flowers (33x25cm-13x10in) s. pencil W/C. 23-May-3 Lyon & Turnbull, Edinburgh #70/R est:800-1200
£1900 $3135 €2755 Anemones (51x38cm-20x15in) init. pencil W/C bodycol sold with book lit. 3-Jul-3 Christie's, Kensington #38/R est:2000-3000
£3000 $4560 €4500 Roses in twilight (56x28cm-22x11in) s. W/C. 28-Aug-2 Sotheby's, London #1014/R est:2500-3500

CAMERON, Sir David Young (1865-1945) British
£340 $554 €510 Moorland (15x23cm-6x9in) 14-Feb-3 Lyon & Turnbull, Edinburgh #140
£460 $704 €690 West Highland coastal landscape (34x45cm-13x18in) board. 22-Aug-2 Bonhams, Edinburgh #1050
£1250 $1950 €1875 On the Tay (21x26cm-8x10in) init. s.i.verso canvasboard. 10-Apr-3 Bonhams, Edinburgh #128/R est:400-600
£1300 $2093 €1950 On the beach (24x33cm-9x13in) s. panel prov. 15-Jan-3 Cheffins Grain & Comins, Cambridge #439/R
£3100 $4712 €4650 Berwick Bridge (23x28cm-9x11in) s. s.i.verso board. 28-Aug-2 Sotheby's, London #991/R est:2000-3000
£6000 $9540 €9000 Snow-covered hills, Loch Goil (51x76cm-20x30in) s. 6-Mar-3 Christie's, Kensington #153/R est:4000-6000
Works on paper
£260 $434 €377 Dungoin (24x35cm-9x14in) s.i. pen blk ink. 17-Jun-3 Rosebery Fine Art, London #556
£577 $900 €866 Yarmouth herring fleet running for shelter (30x53cm-12x21in) s.i.d. W/C. 9-Nov-2 Sloan, North Bethesda #523/R
£600 $930 €900 Glen Lyon (18x25cm-7x10in) s. col wash over pencil. 24-Sep-2 Anderson & Garland, Newcastle #383
£602 $1000 €873 Sight (18x25cm-7x10in) W/C. 13-Jun-3 Du Mouchelle, Detroit #2219/R
£620 $1004 €930 Menteith (20x37cm-8x15in) s. chl col wash. 23-May-3 Lyon & Turnbull, Edinburgh #26
£1600 $2624 €2400 Cairngorms (29x55cm-11x22in) s. executed c.1921 pencil W/C. 4-Feb-3 Bonhams, Leeds #303 est:500-700

CAMIN, Joaquin Rubio (1926-) Spanish
Works on paper
£461 $746 €700 Landscapes (17x30cm-7x12in) s.d.948 W/C double-sided. 21-Jan-3 Durán, Madrid #38/R

CAMLIN, James A (1918-1982) American
Works on paper
£573 $900 €860 Tranquil Maine cove with lobster boat moored in small cove (51x74cm-20x29in) s. W/C prov. 19-Apr-3 James Julia, Fairfield #203/R

CAMMARANO, Michele (1835-c.1920) Italian
£3200 $5344 €4800 Ritratto di una ragazza (40x32cm-16x13in) mono.d.1882. 18-Jun-3 Christie's, Kensington #148/R est:1800-2200
£88608 $140000 €140000 Encouragemet to vice (267x199cm-105x78in) painted 1868 prov.exhib.lit. 26-Nov-2 Christie's, Rome #238/R est:60000-90000
Works on paper
£1384 $2131 €2200 Thief (34x23cm-13x9in) s. W/C card. 23-Oct-2 Finarte, Milan #183/R

CAMMILLIERI, Niccolo S (fl.1820-1855) Maltese
Works on paper
£1700 $2754 €2550 MC Butler Master, sailing from Malta (41x58cm-16x23in) s.i. pen black ink W/C. 21-May-3 Christie's, Kensington #426/R est:400-600
£1900 $2945 €2850 H.M ship Vengeur in Naples Bay with the Neapolitan flag at her main masthead (48x66cm-19x26in) s.i. pencil pen ink W/C. 31-Oct-2 Christie's, Kensington #360/R est:1200-1800
£1900 $3021 €2850 H.M.S. Pelican off Ricasoli Point, leaving the Grand Harbour, Malta (34x48cm-13x19in) s. bears d. May 1833 verso W/C. 29-Apr-3 Bonhams, New Bond Street #147/R est:1500-2000
£3800 $6042 €5700 The ship Anne, Captain John Colville going out to the harbour of Malta (44x56cm-17x22in) s.i.d.1814 W/C. 29-Apr-3 Bonhams, New Bond Street #146/R est:4000-6000

CAMMILLIERI, Nicolas (fl.1804-1835) Italian?
Works on paper
£2700 $4185 €4050 Ship Anne, Cptn John Colvil going out of the harbour of Malta 1814 (45x56cm-18x22in) i. pen ink W/C. 6-Dec-2 Lyon & Turnbull, Edinburgh #50/R est:1000-1500

CAMOIN, Charles (1879-1965) French
£839 $1401 €1200 Autoportrait (35x27cm-14x11in) s.d.56. 27-Jun-3 Claude Aguttes, Neuilly #83/R
£1667 $2600 €2501 Fleurs (33x37cm-13x15in) s. masonite prov. 12-Apr-3 Weschler, Washington #532/R est:4000-6000
£2568 $4005 €3800 Lecture (26x35cm-10x14in) s. paper on canvas. 30-Mar-3 Anaf, Lyon #38/R
£2619 $4164 €3850 Roses dans un vase (22x16cm-9x6in) s. panel prov. 26-Feb-3 Artcurial Briest, Paris #247/R est:3500-4000
£2658 $4438 €3800 Le Bourg (27x35cm-11x14in) s. cardboard prov. 26-Jun-3 Tajan, Paris #251/R est:4000-5000
£2756 $4190 €4300 Paturage (30x41cm-12x16in) s. 16-Aug-2 Deauville, France #98/R
£2797 $4671 €4000 Bouquet de roses (23x27cm-9x11in) s. panel. 27-Jun-3 Claude Aguttes, Neuilly #85/R est:4000-6000
£3217 $5372 €4600 Bouquet de fleurs (46x33cm-18x13in) s. paper on canvas. 27-Jun-3 Claude Aguttes, Neuilly #84/R est:8000-10000
£3401 $5408 €5000 Bouquet (41x33cm-16x13in) s. 28-Feb-3 Joron-Derem, Paris #31/R
£6013 $9320 €9500 Nature morte a la bouteille (46x38cm-18x15in) s. isorel painted c.1950 prov. 28-Sep-2 Christie's, Paris #16/R est:12000-18000
£6282 $9863 €9800 Rue de village (27x35cm-11x14in) s.panel exhib. 13-Dec-2 Piasa, Paris #56/R est:4000
£6731 $10433 €10500 Route et clocher de Courgent aux deux poules (40x55cm-16x22in) s. painted 1949 prov.lit. 9-Dec-2 Beaussant & Lefèvre, Paris #27/R est:10000-12000
£7453 $12000 €11180 Nature morte (46x55cm-18x22in) s. painted c.1960 prov. 7-May-3 Sotheby's, New York #409/R est:20000-30000
£8228 $12753 €13000 Le Baoe de Saint-Jeannet, Gairaut (46x55cm-18x22in) s. prov. 28-Sep-2 Christie's, Paris #13/R est:9000-12000
£8544 $13244 €13500 Paysage des Maures du cote du plan de la Tour (38x55cm-15x22in) s. painted c.1950 prov. 28-Sep-2 Christie's, Paris #14/R est:8000-12000
£9554 $14904 €15000 Vase de fleurs et nature morte (53x65cm-21x26in) s. 10-Nov-2 Eric Pillon, Calais #20/R
£9790 $16350 €14000 Coupe de fruits et vase de fleurs sur la terrasse de la villa (54x65cm-21x26in) s. lit. 30-Jun-3 Artcurial Briest, Paris #77/R est:18000-20000
£10494 $14901 €17000 Paris vue de Montmartre (19x27cm-7x11in) s. panel. 16-Mar-3 Eric Pillon, Calais #107/R
£12025 $18639 €19000 L'entree du port de Saint Tropez (46x55cm-18x22in) s. prov. 28-Sep-2 Christie's, Paris #43/R est:28000-38000
£12676 $21043 €18000 L'espagnole (61x46cm-24x18in) s. prov. 12-Jun-3 Tajan, Paris #22/R est:18000-22000
£13380 $22212 €19000 Champ de Vignes sur les hauteurs a Saint Tropez (33x41cm-13x16in) s. cardboard prov. 12-Jun-3 Tajan, Paris #19/R est:20000-30000
£14685 $24524 €21000 Port de Marseille (24x33cm-9x13in) s. panel. 27-Jun-3 Claude Aguttes, Neuilly #86/R est:10000-15000
£15711 $25766 €22781 Nature morte aux fruits (60x81cm-24x32in) s. 4-Jun-3 AB Stockholms Auktionsverk #2493/R est:300000-350000 (S.KR 200000)

£16000 $24640 €24000 Le port de Saint Tropez au voilier blanc (50x61cm-20x24in) s. painted c.1949 prov. 22-Oct-2 Sotheby's, London #109/R est:18000-25000
£20625 $33000 €29906 Cote d'Azur (64x84cm-25x33in) s. painted c.1910 prov. 17-May-3 CRN Auctions, Cambridge #20
£26241 $42511 €37000 Vieux port de Marseille (55x96cm-22x38in) s. 23-May-3 Binoche, Paris #53/R est:12000-15000
£30380 $47089 €48000 Coup de Mistral dans le port de Saint Tropez (56x81cm-22x32in) s. prov.exhib. 28-Sep-2 Christie's, Paris #22/R est:40000-55000

Works on paper
£479 $795 €680 Portrait de fillette (33x24cm-13x9in) s. pastel. 16-Jun-3 Oger, Dumont, Paris #19/R
£638 $1034 €900 Au parc (13x17cm-5x7in) s.d. graphite. 21-May-3 Cornette de St.Cyr, Paris #4/R
£1944 $3091 €2800 Portrait de femme (31x22cm-12x9in) s. pastel white chk exec.c.1920. 29-Apr-3 Artcurial Briest, Paris #169/R est:3000-3500

CAMOREYT, Jacques Marie Omer (19th C) French
£1572 $2421 €2500 Voilier pres de la cote (40x65cm-16x26in) s.d.1890. 27-Oct-2 Lesieur & Le Bars, Le Havre #150/R

CAMP, Jeffery (1923-) British
Works on paper
£250 $395 €363 The Lovers (45x58cm-18x23in) s. pencil. 22-Jul-3 Sotheby's, Olympia #90

CAMP, Joseph Rodefer de (1858-1923) American
Works on paper
£323 $500 €485 Reclining female nude (43x56cm-17x22in) s. W/C. 21-Jul-2 Jeffery Burchard, Florida #30a/R

CAMP, Maxime du (1822-1884) French
Photographs
£7500 $12150 €11250 Le Kaire, maison et jardin dans le Quartier Frank (21x15cm-8x6in) i.num.3 mount Blanquart-Evrard process print lit. 21-May-3 Christie's, London #83/R est:9000-12000

CAMPAGNARI, Ottorino (1910-1981) Italian
£710 $1121 €1100 Still life (40x60cm-16x24in) s. 18-Dec-2 Finarte, Milan #192/R
£1290 $2039 €2000 Grazing at Valmontei (60x40cm-24x16in) s. 18-Dec-2 Finarte, Milan #134/R est:1000

CAMPAGNE, Pierre Étienne Daniel (1851-1914) French
Sculpture
£1032 $1631 €1600 Phryne devant ses juges (60cm-24in) s. brown pat bronze lit. 19-Dec-2 Delvaux, Paris #55/R

CAMPAGNOLA, Domenico (1484-1550) Italian
Prints
£10473 $16338 €15500 Shepherds musicians (13x26cm-5x10in) engraving. 31-Mar-3 Tajan, Paris #29
Works on paper
£8642 $14000 €12963 Render unto Caesar what is Caesar's (31x44cm-12x17in) pen ink over chk pair. 21-Jan-3 Sotheby's, New York #38/R est:30000
£9000 $15030 €13050 The knight on the red horse (32x24cm-13x9in) bears i. pen brown ink prov. 9-Jul-3 Sotheby's, London #4/R est:10000-15000
£28571 $45429 €42000 Studies of horses (19x17cm-7x7in) i. pen ink prov. 24-Mar-3 Tajan, Paris #12/R est:15000

CAMPAGNOLA, Enrico (1911-1984) Italian
£690 $1097 €1000 Still life with bouquet (41x33cm-16x13in) s. 10-Mar-3 Millon & Associes, Paris #41/R

CAMPANA, Fernando and Humberto (20th C) South American
Sculpture
£6024 $10000 €8735 Screen (236x334x134cm-93x131x53in) aluminum tubes wire exhib.lit. 11-Jun-3 Phillips, New York #211/R est:6000-8000

CAMPANA, Ignace Jean Victor (attrib) (1744-1786) French
Miniatures
£10993 $17809 €15500 La reine Marie Antoinette holding rose (7cm-3in circular) ivory gilded brass surround prov. 21-May-3 Piasa, Paris #284/R est:10000-15000

CAMPANO, Miguel Angel (1948-) Spanish
£1103 $1743 €1600 Shipwreck (24x41cm-9x16in) s.i.d.84 verso prov. 1-Apr-3 Segre, Madrid #210/R
£1379 $2179 €2000 Blue composition (102x73cm-40x29in) d.1978 acrylic prov. 1-Apr-3 Segre, Madrid #193/R
Works on paper
£579 $945 €875 Candles (33x25cm-13x10in) s.d.89 s.verso gouache prov. 11-Feb-3 Segre, Madrid #295/R
£579 $945 €875 Tables with candles (32x24cm-13x9in) d.89 s.verso gouache prov. 11-Feb-3 Segre, Madrid #296/R
£759 $1199 €1100 Untitled (59x41cm-23x16in) s.d.1979 collage paint. 1-Apr-3 Segre, Madrid #187/R

CAMPBELL, Cornelius (?) ?
£500 $775 €750 Horses exercising, the Curragh, Co. Kildare (50x61cm-20x24in) s. 4-Dec-2 John Ross, Belfast #46

CAMPBELL, Cressida (1960-) Australian
Prints
£2500 $3900 €3750 Kitchen utensils (46x62cm-18x24in) init. hand painted woodblock. 11-Nov-2 Deutscher-Menzies, Melbourne #6/R est:4000-6000 (A.D 7000)
£2679 $4179 €4019 Front room (64x58cm-25x23in) s.i.d.num.2/5 woodblock. 11-Nov-2 Deutscher-Menzies, Melbourne #7/R est:3000-5000 (A.D 7500)

CAMPBELL, G F (20th C) American
£1111 $1800 €1611 Alfred and the Raleigh at sea (22x30cm-9x12in) s.i. i.verso board. 29-Jul-3 Christie's, Rockefeller NY #179/R est:800-1200

CAMPBELL, George (1917-1979) British
£1090 $1711 €1700 Retired bullfighter (121x60cm-48x24in) s. i.verso board. 19-Nov-2 Hamilton Osborne King, Dublin #433/R est:1500-3000
£1090 $1711 €1700 Woodland scene (37x45cm-15x18in) s. 19-Nov-2 Hamilton Osborne King, Dublin #467/R est:2000-3000
£2600 $4134 €3900 Botanic park, holiday at home, Hitler's War 1944 (35x40cm-14x16in) s. board. 5-Mar-3 John Ross, Belfast #163 est:1000-1200
£2609 $4278 €3600 Errigal, autumn (46x61cm-18x24in) s. i.verso board prov. 28-May-3 Bonhams & James Adam, Dublin #156/R est:4000-6000
£3043 $4991 €4200 Two fishermen resting (39x49cm-15x19in) s. board. 28-May-3 Bonhams & James Adam, Dublin #144/R est:4000-6000
£3846 $6038 €6000 Balcony and doorway, Spain (43x36cm-17x14in) s. prov. 19-Nov-2 Whyte's, Dublin #53/R est:6000-8000
£3924 $6082 €6200 Two clowns (46x59cm-18x23in) s. prov. 24-Sep-2 De Veres Art Auctions, Dublin #2/R est:4000-6000
£4151 $6475 €6600 Rugged mountains, Glengariff, County Cork (51x61cm-20x24in) s. i.verso board prov. 17-Sep-2 Whyte's, Dublin #133/R est:6000-8000
£4452 $6990 €6500 Night near Alhaurin (40x50cm-16x20in) s.i.verso board. 15-Apr-3 De Veres Art Auctions, Dublin #132 est:7000-9000
£5137 $8065 €7500 Town, Tenerife (51x41cm-20x16in) s. board prov. 15-Apr-3 De Veres Art Auctions, Dublin #168/R est:8000-10000
£5449 $8554 €8500 Roundstone (41x51cm-16x20in) s. board prov. 19-Nov-2 Whyte's, Dublin #38/R est:5000-7000
£5769 $9058 €9000 Bedroom interior with a view of Burgos Cathedral, Spain (50x39cm-20x15in) s. board prov. 19-Nov-2 Whyte's, Dublin #52/R est:7000-9000
£6597 $10490 €9500 Rocky fort of Mayo (44x102cm-17x40in) s. board prov. 29-Apr-3 Whyte's, Dublin #38/R est:10000-12000
£7609 $12478 €10500 Gweebara, Donegal (92x76cm-36x30in) s.i.verso board prov. 28-May-3 Bonhams & James Adam, Dublin #63/R est:6000-10000
£11594 $19014 €16000 Don Quixote and Sabcha Panza (74x62cm-29x24in) s. 28-May-3 Bonhams & James Adam, Dublin #150/R est:10000-15000
£13000 $20800 €19500 Clifden, Connemara (76x91cm-30x36in) s. s.i.verso board. 16-May-3 Sotheby's, London #125/R est:10000-15000
£13423 $21611 €20000 Malaga Harbour with peasants and donkey (43x56cm-17x22in) s. board exhib. 18-Feb-3 Whyte's, Dublin #32/R est:10000-12000
£18000 $28800 €27000 Tin whistle player (61x46cm-24x18in) s. board. 16-May-3 Sotheby's, London #123/R est:6000-8000
£42000 $67200 €63000 Clifden (80x105cm-31x41in) s. board prov. 16-May-3 Sotheby's, London #116/R est:15000-20000
Works on paper
£694 $1104 €1000 Standing female nude (30x17cm-12x7in) s. conte crayon. 29-Apr-3 Whyte's, Dublin #99 est:800-1000
£700 $1085 €1050 Cold night (20x25cm-8x10in) s.i.verso mixed media. 2-Oct-2 John Ross, Belfast #147
£1042 $1656 €1500 Self portrait (27x23cm-11x9in) W/C on card. 29-Apr-3 Whyte's, Dublin #92/R est:1000-1500
£1181 $1877 €1700 Connemara landscape (15x20cm-6x8in) s. W/C crayon pen ink. 29-Apr-3 Whyte's, Dublin #94/R est:1500-2000
£1181 $1877 €1700 Study of rocks in water (18x24cm-7x9in) s. W/C crayon. 29-Apr-3 Whyte's, Dublin #96 est:1200-1500

£1389 $2208 €2000 Rocky coast with wind blown tree (19x27cm-7x11in) s. i.verso W/C. 29-Apr-3 Whyte's, Dublin #93/R est:2000-2500
£1575 $2473 €2300 Landscape near Malaga (20x29cm-8x11in) s. W/C. 15-Apr-3 De Veres Art Auctions, Dublin #256/R est:1600-2000
£1667 $2650 €2400 Surreal landscape with hulk of a Viking ship and figures on a beach (18x24cm-7x9in) s. gouache board prov. 29-Apr-3 Whyte's, Dublin #8/R est:1800-2000
£1899 $2943 €3000 Still life (15x22cm-6x9in) s. mixed media prov. 24-Sep-2 De Veres Art Auctions, Dublin #169a/R est:1000-2000
£2200 $3498 €3300 Yellow moon (56x71cm-22x28in) s. mixed media. 5-Mar-3 John Ross, Belfast #182 est:1000-1500
£2222 $3533 €3200 Drilling potatoes (23x30cm-9x12in) s. W/C crayon. 29-Apr-3 Whyte's, Dublin #42/R est:2000-3000
£2692 $4173 €4200 Fishing village (22x33cm-9x13in) s. W/C. 3-Dec-2 Bonhams & James Adam, Dublin #143/R est:3000-5000
£2778 $4417 €4000 Andalucian musicians (22x30cm-9x12in) s. W/C col chk. 29-Apr-3 Whyte's, Dublin #6/R est:2500-3500
£2821 $4428 €4400 Calles de Tetuan (34x50cm-13x20in) s. i.verso W/C gouache crayon executed c.1977prov. 19-Nov-2 Whyte's, Dublin #51/R est:3000-4000

CAMPBELL, John (1855-1924) Australian
Works on paper
£2589 $4091 €3884 Stanley brewery (39x67cm-15x26in) s.i.d.1903 W/C. 26-Nov-2 Sotheby's, Melbourne #120/R est:5000-8000 (A.D 7250)

CAMPBELL, John Henry (1755-1828) Irish
Works on paper
£769 $1208 €1200 Landscape painted in a classical manner (21x28cm-8x11in) W/C prov. 19-Nov-2 Whyte's, Dublin #213/R
£1000 $1600 €1500 Bridge over the River Dodder, Upper Rathmines (15x23cm-6x9in) s.verso pen ink W/C over pencil prov.exhib. 16-May-3 Sotheby's, London #26/R est:1500-2000
£1389 $2208 €2000 On the Dargle, County Wicklow (19x30cm-7x12in) i.verso W/C. 29-Apr-3 Whyte's, Dublin #176/R est:2000-3000
£2400 $3840 €3600 View of Dublin Bay and harbour from Stillorgan (31x61cm-12x24in) s. W/C over pencil. 16-May-3 Sotheby's, London #22/R est:2500-3500

CAMPBELL, John Henry (style) (1755-1828) Irish
£4054 $6324 €6000 Figures and cattle at edge of river in woodland landscape (48x62cm-19x24in) 26-Mar-3 James Adam, Dublin #11/R est:1500-2500

CAMPBELL, Jon (1961-) Australian
£3101 $4930 €4652 Wild West comes to the drive in (244x273cm-96x107in) s.d.1989 verso. 5-May-3 Sotheby's, Melbourne #239/R est:5000-8000 (A.D 8000)

CAMPBELL, Laurence (1911-1964) British
Sculpture
£1282 $2013 €2000 Head of a girl (48cm-19in) s.d.1932 bronze one of six. 19-Nov-2 Whyte's, Dublin #180/R est:2500-3500

CAMPBELL, Reginald (1923-) Australian
£426 $626 €639 Mount Nameless, Hamersley Western Australia (58x73cm-23x29in) s. board prov. 19-Jun-2 Watson's, Christchurch #23/R est:800-1200 (NZ.D 1300)

CAMPBELL, Robert (jnr) (1944-1993) Australian
Works on paper
£1444 $2238 €2166 Untitled, emu and chicks (55x42cm-22x17in) s.d.28.6.1991 synthetic polymer paint canvas. 3-Dec-2 Shapiro, Sydney #221/R est:5000-7000 (A.D 4000)

CAMPBELL, Robert Richmond (1902-1972) Australian
£358 $545 €537 Launceston, Tasmania (61x74cm-24x29in) s. board. 27-Aug-2 Goodman, Sydney #46 (A.D 1000)
£394 $599 €591 View of Sydney harbour (12x19cm-5x7in) init. board. 27-Aug-2 Goodman, Sydney #21/R (A.D 1100)
£681 $1035 €1022 Yachts on Sydney harbour (10x20cm-4x8in) s. board. 28-Aug-2 Deutscher-Menzies, Melbourne #405/R (A.D 1900)
£720 $1159 €1044 Circus (49x60cm-19x24in) s.d.59 board. 12-May-3 Joel, Victoria #244 est:1000-1500 (A.D 1800)
£800 $1328 €1160 Boats at anchor near Sydney (25x41cm-10x16in) indis.sig. s.indis.i.verso. 10-Jun-3 David Lay, Penzance #117/R
£1819 $2765 €2729 Finger Wharves, Sydney Harbour (19x24cm-7x9in) s. board. 28-Aug-2 Deutscher-Menzies, Melbourne #221/R est:5000-7000 (A.D 5075)
£4231 $6727 €6347 Sydney harbour (15x39cm-6x15in) s. 4-Mar-3 Deutscher-Menzies, Melbourne #139/R est:9000-12000 (A.D 11000)

CAMPBELL, Steven (1953-) British
£440 $686 €660 Oeuvre 2 (28x39cm-11x15in) acrylic. 10-Apr-3 Bonhams, Edinburgh #13
£1700 $2652 €2550 Portrait of May Milton between studio and toilet (211x268cm-83x106in) oil collage. 17-Oct-2 Bonhams, Edinburgh #60 est:1500-2000
£1800 $2934 €2700 Admiral (207x148cm-81x58in) s.d.82 oil paper on board prov. 3-Feb-3 Sotheby's, Olympia #134/R est:2000-3000
£2500 $3825 €3750 Down there between a rock and a hard place (241x267cm-95x105in) s.d.1988 verso. 22-Aug-2 Bonhams, Edinburgh #1035/R est:3000-5000

CAMPBELL, Tom (1865-1943) British
£250 $405 €375 Rannoch Moor (43x59cm-17x23in) s. board. 23-Jan-3 Bonhams, Edinburgh #304
£280 $465 €406 Sheep grazing by an estuary (48x58cm-19x23in) s. board. 13-Jun-3 Lyon & Turnbull, Edinburgh #83
£340 $534 €510 Shepherd and flock on a country road (50x75cm-20x30in) 17-Apr-3 Bonhams, Edinburgh #351
Works on paper
£420 $664 €630 Old mill, near Rye, Sussex (41x53cm-16x21in) s. W/C. 2-Dec-2 Gorringes, Lewes #2702/R

CAMPBELL, Virginia (20th C) American
£3871 $6000 €5807 Cup of flowers (86x56cm-34x22in) s. 28-Sep-2 Charlton Hall, Columbia #168 est:200-400

CAMPECHE, Jose (1751-1809) Puerto Rican
£54878 $90000 €79573 Nuestra Senora de Belen (40x29cm-16x11in) s.i.d.1794 verso panel prov.exhib. 27-May-3 Sotheby's, New York #1

CAMPENDONK, Heinrich (1889-1957) German
£26582 $41468 €42000 Two girls with goose and deer (41x30cm-16x12in) mono.d.1916 tempera on glass. 18-Oct-2 Dr Fritz Nagel, Stuttgart #472/R est:23000
£920000 $1499600 €1380000 Der blaue maher (81x90cm-32x35in) i.verso painted 1914. 3-Feb-3 Christie's, London #6/R est:500000-700000
Prints
£2535 $4208 €3600 Event - girl with fish and birds (32x25cm-13x10in) s. verso woodcut. 14-Jun-3 Hauswedell & Nolte, Hamburg #1064/R est:3500
£6500 $10140 €9750 Begebenheit (32x25cm-13x10in) s. woodcut gouache. 10-Oct-2 Sotheby's, London #107/R est:8000-10000
£13380 $22211 €19000 Event - girl with fish and birds (32x25cm-13x10in) s.i. W/C woodcut. 14-Jun-3 Hauswedell & Nolte, Hamburg #1065/R est:10000
Works on paper
£7692 $11923 €12000 Tavern interior with gun (48x62cm-19x24in) mono. W/C pencil. 4-Dec-2 Lempertz, Koln #593/R est:12000-15000
£58000 $96860 €87000 Sitzender weiblicher Akt vor Spiegel (39x33cm-15x13in) s. gouache W/C exec c.1919 prov.lit. 26-Jun-3 Christie's, London #402/R est:30000-50000

CAMPESINO Y MINGO, Vicente (19th C) Spanish
£1076 $1678 €1700 Spanish scene (33x43cm-13x17in) s. panel. 18-Oct-2 Dr Fritz Nagel, Stuttgart #50/R est:1800

CAMPHUYSEN, Raphael Govertsz (1598-1657) Dutch
£1050 $1660 €1575 Moonlit landscape with figures and windmill in foreground (40x54cm-16x21in) mono. panel. 16-Nov-2 Crafoord, Lund #54/R est:15000 (S.KR 15000)
£10072 $16115 €14000 Wooded river landscape with elegant couple on path (115x165cm-45x65in) mono. 13-May-3 Sotheby's, Amsterdam #22/R est:15000-20000
£26843 $43218 €40000 Winter landscape with skaters before a cottage (47x62cm-19x24in) s. panel prov.exhib.lit. 18-Feb-3 Sotheby's, Amsterdam #234/R est:22000-28000

CAMPI, Antonio (circle) (1531-1591) Italian
£4721 $7318 €7082 Rest on the flight from Egypt (60x44cm-24x17in) 3-Oct-2 Koller, Zurich #3004/R est:12000-16000 (S.FR 11000)

CAMPI, Bernardino (1522-1592) Italian
Works on paper
£5405 $8432 €8000 Rencontre a la Porte Doree (21x27cm-8x11in) i. chk prov. 27-Mar-3 Christie's, Paris #4/R
£23148 $37500 €34722 God the Father (21x37cm-8x15in) black chk htd white squared for transfer prov.exhib.lit. 21-Jan-3 Sotheby's, New York #11/R est:30000-40000

CAMPI, Bernardino (attrib) (1522-1592) Italian
Works on paper
£5208 $8281 €7500 Angelic choir (26x16cm-10x6in) pen wash paper on board prov. 5-May-3 Ketterer, Munich #343/R est:1000-1200

CAMPI, Giacomo (1846-?) Italian
£1613 $2548 €2500 Woman at fountain (80x60cm-31x24in) s. 18-Dec-2 Finarte, Milan #35

CAMPI, Giulio (1502-1572) Italian
Works on paper
£58642 $95000 €87963 Jupiter and Astraea (16x23cm-6x9in) bears i. pen inbk grey wash point brush htd white prov.exhib.lit. 21-Jan-3 Sotheby's, New York #10/R est:80000-120000

CAMPI, Vincenzo (style) (1536-1591) Italian
£13500 $21195 €20250 Peasants brawling in a landscape (64x101cm-25x40in) 12-Dec-2 Sotheby's, London #111/R est:8000-12000

CAMPIDOGLIO, Michele di (1610-1670) Italian
£10063 $15597 €16000 Still life with melon and grapes (72x60cm-28x24in) painted c.1665. 7-Oct-2 Ansorena, Madrid #23/R est:10000

CAMPIDOGLIO, Michele di (attrib) (1610-1670) Italian
£27973 $46714 €40000 Nature morte a la coupe de figues et fruits sur un entablement (61x73cm-24x29in) 25-Jun-3 Tajan, Paris #10/R est:10000-15000

CAMPIDOGLIO, Michele di (circle) (1610-1670) Italian
£4755 $7941 €6800 Nature morte de fruits et de fleurs (65x48cm-26x19in) 25-Jun-3 Artcurial Briest, Paris #483/R est:4000-5000
£22000 $34100 €33000 Melons, grapes and other fruits on a ledge, with a lady in a blue dress and a putto (95x138cm-37x54in) 30-Oct-2 Christie's, Kensington #138/R est:12000-18000

CAMPIGLI, Massimo (1895-1971) Italian
£7092 $11489 €10000 Bozzetto (26x30cm-10x12in) 26-May-3 Christie's, Milan #137/R est:10000-15000
£32911 $52000 €52000 Changing rooms at the seaside (40x50cm-16x20in) s.d.1966. 30-Nov-2 Farsetti, Prato #644/R est:55000
£41139 $64177 €65000 Figures (28x38cm-11x15in) s.d.1971. 14-Sep-2 Meeting Art, Vercelli #989/R est:50000
£50641 $78494 €79000 Five women (27x37cm-11x15in) s.d.41. 4-Dec-2 Lempertz, Koln #27/R est:50000-60000
£51064 $82723 €72000 Composizione con figure (67x54cm-26x21in) s.d.69 prov. 26-May-3 Christie's, Milan #338/R est:60000-80000
£51899 $82000 €82000 Woman weraing necklace (46x38cm-18x15in) s.d.1950 exhib.lit. 30-Nov-2 Farsetti, Prato #728/R est:90000
£64103 $100641 €100000 Staircase with women (64x52cm-25x20in) s.d.1955. 19-Nov-2 Finarte, Milan #226/R est:96000-105000
£65000 $101400 €97500 Donne sotto l' ombrellino (55x46cm-22x18in) s. painted 1938 prov.lit. 21-Oct-2 Sotheby's, London #7/R est:45000-65000
£75949 $120000 €120000 Idols (73x92cm-29x36in) s.d.59. 30-Nov-2 Farsetti, Prato #693/R est:140000
Works on paper
£3493 $5449 €5100 Figures (40x32cm-16x13in) s. ink. 10-Apr-3 Finarte Semenzato, Rome #108/R
£4167 $6542 €6500 Tennis (11x22cm-4x9in) s.d.43 Chinese ink exhib. 19-Nov-2 Finarte, Milan #4/R est:3600
£5128 $8051 €8000 Women at the window (29x37cm-11x15in) s. mixed media prov. 21-Nov-2 Finarte, Rome #293
£10417 $17188 €15000 Personnage (54x46cm-21x18in) s.d.61 gouache prov. 1-Jul-3 Artcurial Briest, Paris #800a/R est:10000-15000

CAMPING, Simon (1928-) Canadian
Works on paper
£261 $410 €392 Creeping raspberries on a fallen log (23x30cm-9x12in) s. W/C. 25-Nov-2 Hodgins, Calgary #360/R (C.D 650)

CAMPION, George Bryant (1796-1870) British
Works on paper
£321 $506 €500 Mountain lake in Tessin or upper Italy (12x15cm-5x6in) s. w/C prov. 16-Nov-2 Lempertz, Koln #1297
£480 $778 €720 Unloading supplies on the Breton coast, with Customs men (17x29cm-7x11in) pencil W/C. 21-May-3 Christie's, Kensington #459/R
£480 $758 €696 Hasting beach (14x28cm-6x11in) W/C. 22-Jul-3 Bonhams, Knightsbridge #219/R

CAMPION, George Bryant (attrib) (1796-1870) British
Works on paper
£449 $700 €674 River landscape with figures in a boat (23x35cm-9x14in) W/C htd white prov. 14-Sep-2 Weschler, Washington #597/R

CAMPO, Federico del (19/20th C) Peruvian
£4200 $6594 €6300 Journeying through the island (39x25cm-15x10in) s.d.1885. 21-Nov-2 Christie's, Kensington #132/R est:5000-7000
£5346 $8500 €8019 Amalfi (40x29cm-16x11in) s.i.d.1898. 7-Mar-3 Skinner, Boston #226/R est:4000-6000
£29000 $48430 €43500 An afternoon in a Venetian backwater (72x48cm-28x19in) s. prov. 19-Jun-3 Christie's, London #47/R est:30000-50000
£40000 $63600 €60000 Gondolas on a Venetian canal (58x40cm-23x16in) s.d.1905 prov. 18-Mar-3 Bonhams, New Bond Street #79/R est:25000-35000
£125000 $196250 €187500 Grand Canal, Venice (56x90cm-22x35in) s.i.d.1890. 19-Nov-2 Bonhams, New Bond Street #106/R est:70000-100000

CAMPOS, Alain (1955-) French
Works on paper
£683 $1094 €950 Le paratonnerre (147x115cm-58x45in) s.d. mixed media canvas. 18-May-3 Neret-Minet, Paris #127/R

CAMPOS, Florencio Molina (20th C) South American
£920 $1500 €1380 Untitled, Argentinian landscape (41x51cm-16x20in) s.d.1943 canvasboard prov. 16-Feb-3 Butterfields, San Francisco #2119 est:3000-5000
£7927 $13000 €11494 De vuelta al rancho (35x52cm-14x20in) tempera prov.exhib.lit. 27-May-3 Sotheby's, New York #144
Works on paper
£2404 $3750 €3606 Gaucho riding with guitar (46x62cm-18x24in) s. gouache board. 5-Nov-2 Doyle, New York #9/R est:6000-8000
£2564 $4000 €3846 Gauchos with dogs (34x49cm-13x19in) s.d.943 gouache board. 5-Nov-2 Doyle, New York #8/R est:5000-7000
£2885 $4500 €4328 Gauchos playing cards (66x66cm-26x26in) s. gouache board. 5-Nov-2 Doyle, New York #7/R est:6000-8000
£4403 $7000 €6605 The chase (32x47cm-13x19in) s.d.1937 gouache. 7-Mar-3 Skinner, Boston #379/R est:3000-4000

CAMPOTOSTO, Henry (?-1910) Belgian
£480 $739 €720 Portrait of Princess Alexandra adorned with roses and heather (94x74cm-37x29in) s.d.1885. 5-Sep-2 Christie's, Kensington #73/R

CAMPOTOSTO, Octavia (fl.1870-80) Belgian
£840 $1369 €1260 Chickens and chicks. Hens feeding (25x37cm-10x15in) s.i. two. 11-Feb-3 Bonhams, Knowle #108

CAMPRIANI, Alceste (1848-1933) Italian
£943 $1453 €1500 Fishermen (25x31cm-10x12in) s. board. 23-Oct-2 Finarte, Milan #34/R

CAMPROBIN, Pedro de (1605-1674) Spanish
£80247 $130000 €120371 Still life of pears, plums and apples in a basket resting on a ledge (24x32cm-9x13in) 23-Jan-3 Sotheby's, New York #15/R est:30000-40000

CAMPS RIBERA, Francisco (1895-1949) Mexican/Spanish
£598 $933 €897 El jacal del pintor Goitia (42x58cm-17x23in) s.d.1959 temple paper. 17-Oct-2 Louis Morton, Mexico #173 est:8000-10000 (M.P 9500)
£641 $1013 €1000 Vase of flowers (59x49cm-23x19in) s. cardboard. 19-Nov-2 Durán, Madrid #45/R
Works on paper
£276 $436 €400 Portrait of lady (54x45cm-21x18in) s.d.1932 W/C gouache. 1-Apr-3 Segre, Madrid #311/R

CAMPUZANO Y AGUIRRE, Tomas (1857-1934) Spanish
£1548 $2446 €2400 Landscape (22x26cm-9x10in) s. cardboard. 17-Dec-2 Segre, Madrid #33/R
£4315 $6732 €6300 Boat trip (30x61cm-12x24in) s. 8-Apr-3 Ansorena, Madrid #220/R

CAMUS, Gustave (1914-1984) Belgian

£278	$442	€400	Nature morte (39x88cm-15x35in) s.d.1963. 29-Apr-3 Campo & Campo, Antwerp #450
£380	$600	€600	La mer sombre (22x49cm-9x19in) s.d.1965 verso. 26-Nov-2 Palais de Beaux Arts, Brussels #287
£390	$651	€550	Le chalutier (39x88cm-15x35in) s. 17-Jun-3 Palais de Beaux Arts, Brussels #515
£442	$703	€650	Chalutiers a quai (30x68cm-12x27in) s. 18-Mar-3 Vanderkindere, Brussels #42
£443	$700	€700	Les grands chardons bleus (122x55cm-48x22in) s.d.1965 verso. 26-Nov-2 Palais de Beaux Arts, Brussels #55
£478	$750	€717	Portrait of a little girl (70x59cm-28x23in) s. 22-Nov-2 Skinner, Boston #185/R
£513	$795	€800	Le chenal jaune (30x68cm-12x27in) s. 9-Dec-2 Horta, Bruxelles #326
£542	$850	€813	Beach (33x41cm-13x16in) s. board. 22-Nov-2 Skinner, Boston #387/R
£759	$1185	€1200	Quai Jaune (39x88cm-15x35in) s. 16-Sep-2 Horta, Bruxelles #66
£1042	$1656	€1500	Les chalutiers noirs (49x100cm-19x39in) s.d.1963. 29-Apr-3 Campo & Campo, Antwerp #26/R est:1000-1500
£1457	$2375	€2200	Vue de Plougrescan (80x100cm-31x39in) s.i.d.1949 verso. 17-Feb-3 Horta, Bruxelles #146
£1646	$2567	€2600	Musiciennes dans un interieur d'artiste (65x80cm-26x31in) s. 16-Sep-2 Horta, Bruxelles #63/R
£2740	$4274	€4000	Un sechoir a poissons (87x114cm-34x45in) s. 14-Apr-3 Horta, Bruxelles #153 est:1800-2200
£3165	$5065	€4400	Un guet-apens (114x146cm-45x57in) s.verso. 19-May-3 Horta, Bruxelles #45 est:2200-2800

CAMUS, Jacques (1937-) French

£468	$748	€650	Nu assis, de dos (38x31cm-15x12in) s. cardboard. 14-May-3 Blanchet, Paris #142/R
£1773	$2961	€2500	Le marche Mouffetard au petit jour (46x55cm-18x22in) s.i. i.verso. 18-Jun-3 Pierre Berge, Paris #151 est:2400-3000

Works on paper

£360	$576	€500	Le poissonnier de la rue Mouffetard (46x30cm-18x12in) s. wax pastel. 14-May-3 Blanchet, Paris #143/R

CAMUS, Jean (20th C) French

Sculpture

£892	$1400	€1338	Haute volta (59cm-23in) s.i. brown pat. bronze. 14-Dec-2 Weschler, Washington #726/R
£1656	$2600	€2484	Tam tam de man (54cm-21in) s.i. brown pat. bronze st.f.Valsuani. 14-Dec-2 Weschler, Washington #725/R

CANADIAN SCHOOL, 19th C

Works on paper

£35500	$56800	€53250	Indian chief Black Robe from Portage de Prairie (20x23cm-8x9in) W/C. 13-Mar-3 Duke & Son, Dorchester #164a/R

CANAL, Gilbert von (1849-1927) German

£637	$994	€1000	Dutch canal landscape (65x88cm-26x35in) s. 6-Nov-2 Hugo Ruef, Munich #1044/R
£1056	$1701	€1500	Kallmunz, Bavaria (43x60cm-17x24in) s. i. verso. 7-May-3 Michael Zeller, Lindau #662/R est:1500
£1410	$2214	€2200	Bruges (87x120cm-34x47in) s. 21-Nov-2 Van Ham, Cologne #1510/R est:1700
£1871	$2993	€2600	Dutch riverside town (97x151cm-38x59in) s. 17-May-3 Lempertz, Koln #1369/R est:2500

CANALETTO (1697-1768) Italian

£11151	$17842	€15500	Venice, Rialto bridge from the south (46x70cm-18x28in) bears sig. 17-May-3 Lempertz, Koln #1018/R est:5000

Prints

£1899	$3000	€3000	Riverside city (30x43cm-12x17in) etching. 29-Nov-2 Bassenge, Berlin #5589/R est:3500
£2051	$3241	€3200	La terrasse. etching. 14-Nov-2 Libert, Castor, Paris #7 est:3000
£2200	$3630	€3190	Terrace (14x21cm-6x8in) etching. 1-Jul-3 Sotheby's, London #4/R est:2000-2500
£2244	$3545	€3500	Le marche sur le Mole. etching. 14-Nov-2 Libert, Castor, Paris #6/R est:3000
£5282	$8768	€7500	Ale porte de dolo (30x43cm-12x17in) etching copperplate. 12-Jun-3 Hauswedell & Nolte, Hamburg #200/R est:10000
£5380	$8500	€8500	Le Porte del Dolo (30x43cm-12x17in) etching. 29-Nov-2 Bassenge, Berlin #5588/R est:4000
£5769	$9000	€8654	View of a town on a river bank (31x44cm-12x17in) etching exec.c.1740. 6-Nov-2 Swann Galleries, New York #97/R est:12000-18000
£9500	$14725	€14250	View of a town on a river bank (33x46cm-13x18in) etching executed c.1740. 3-Dec-2 Christie's, London #23/R est:5000-8000
£14744	$23295	€23000	Village au bord d'un fleuve. etching. 14-Nov-2 Libert, Castor, Paris #5/R est:6000

Works on paper

£60000	$100200	€87000	Arch of Janus, Rome, with the church of San Giorgio in Velabro beyond. Ceremonial boats (15x25cm-6x10in) black lead pen ink double-sided prov. 8-Jul-3 Christie's, London #46/R est:40000-60000

CANALETTO (after) (1697-1768) Italian

£8000	$13360	€11600	Grand Canal, Venice, looking east from Campo di S. Vio towards the Bacino (39x57cm-15x22in) 11-Jul-3 Christie's, Kensington #267/R est:3000-5000

CANALETTO (attrib) (1697-1768) Italian

£31469	$52552	€45000	Fete populaire sur la lagune au clair de lune (92x124cm-36x49in) 27-Jun-3 Piasa, Paris #16/R est:30000-45000

CANALETTO (circle) (1697-1768) Italian

£35000	$54250	€52500	Regatta on Ascension Day in the Grand Canal, Venice (62x91cm-24x36in) prov. 30-Oct-2 Christie's, Kensington #170/R est:15000-20000

CANALETTO (style) (1697-1768) Italian

£4375	$7000	€6563	View of the Bay of San Marco and the Doge's Palace (59x84cm-23x33in) bears sig.d.1761 canvas on board. 14-May-3 Butterfields, San Francisco #1017/R est:3000-5000
£5500	$8580	€8250	Capriccio of a Venetian canal (58x74cm-23x29in) prov. 10-Apr-3 Christie's, Kensington #297/R est:4000-6000
£7200	$11160	€10800	Venice, view of Piazzetta and Doge's Palace (63x98cm-25x39in) prov. 31-Oct-2 Sotheby's, Olympia #195/R
£7595	$12000	€12000	St Mark's Square with Doges Palace (34x55cm-13x22in) 26-Nov-2 Wiener Kunst Auktionen, Vienna #10/R est:7000-12000
£9500	$15865	€13775	Venice, view of the Molo, with the Doge's Palace, looking east (68x83cm-27x33in) 8-Jul-3 Sotheby's, Olympia #498/R est:4000-6000
£10563	$17535	€15000	View of the Piazetta, Biblioteca, St Mark's pool and Grand Canal entrance (101x143cm-40x56in) 11-Jun-3 Dorotheum, Vienna #252/R est:6000-9000
£14063	$22500	€21095	View of the Grand Canal looking north east (48x75cm-19x30in) 14-May-3 Butterfields, San Francisco #1016/R est:15000-20000
£15000	$23550	€22500	Riva Degli Schiavoni with the Palazzo Ducale, Venice (62x80cm-24x31in) 12-Dec-2 Sotheby's, London #220/R est:8000-12000
£16000	$24800	€24000	Molo, Venice, looking west with the Ducal Palace. Rio dei Mendicanti, Venice (68x92cm-27x36in) pair prov. 30-Oct-2 Christie's, Kensington #168/R est:15000-20000
£16000	$25120	€24000	Views of Venice (22x30cm-9x12in) pair. 12-Dec-2 Sotheby's, London #221/R est:8000-12000
£30488	$50000	€45732	Venice: Grand Canal looking north-west towards S Geremia (70x105cm-28x41in) prov. 30-May-3 Christie's, Rockefeller NY #52/R est:50000-70000
£30864	$50000	€46296	Venice, the Piazza San Marco from the Piazzetta (55x89cm-22x35in) prov. 24-Jan-3 Christie's, Rockefeller NY #61/R est:40000-60000
£33951	$55000	€50927	Rome, Santa Maria in Aracoeli and the Campidoglio (55x89cm-22x35in) prov. 24-Jan-3 Christie's, Rockefeller NY #60/R est:40000-60000
£52469	$85000	€78704	View of the Grand Canal, Venice, with church of San Simeone Piccolo on the left (119x203cm-47x80in) prov. 23-Jan-3 Sotheby's, New York #7/R est:50000-70000

CANALS Y LLAMBI, Ricardo (1876-1931) Spanish

Works on paper

£264	$412	€420	Study of figures (15x19cm-6x7in) s. sanguine. 8-Oct-2 Ansorena, Madrid #486/R
£8511	$13787	€12000	Taberna (45x61cm-18x24in) s. pastel gouache. 20-May-3 Segre, Madrid #266/R est:12000

CANAS, Benjamin (1937-1987) Chilean

£6098	$10000	€8842	El angel guardian (40x51cm-16x20in) s.d.76 oil gesso panel prov.exhib. 27-May-3 Sotheby's, New York #76

CANASI, Dante M (1889-?) Argentinian

£1500	$2280	€2250	Mujeres Espanolas (80x100cm-31x39in) s. 3-Jul-2 Naón & Cia, Buenos Aires #24/R est:2000-2400

CANCIANI, Jakob (c.1820-1891) Austrian

£3312	$5101	€5200	Faakersee with Mittagskogel (116x148cm-46x58in) 5-Sep-2 Arnold, Frankfurt #748/R est:1200

CANDEE, George Edward (1837-1907) American
£2656 $4250 €3984 Coming storm (51x76cm-20x30in) s. 11-Jan-3 James Julia, Fairfield #236d est:4000-6000

CANDELA VICEDO, Mario (1931-) Spanish
£268 $432 €400 Parisian street (80x65cm-31x26in) s. 18-Feb-3 Durán, Madrid #1197/R

CANDID, Peter (1548-1628) Flemish
Works on paper
£11111 $17667 €16000 Pieta (25x14cm-10x6in) i. i. verso pen wash. 5-May-3 Ketterer, Munich #200/R est:1200-1500

CANDIDO, Sal (attrib) (19th C) Italian
£11724 $18524 €17000 Chiaia coast from Mergellina. Naples from Carmine (22x32cm-9x13in) i.d.1844 paper pair. 3-Apr-3 Porro, Milan #48/R est:20000

CANE, Ella du (fl.1893-1910) British
Works on paper
£800 $1328 €1200 Children at a temple (44x29cm-17x11in) s. W/C. 12-Jun-3 Bonhams, New Bond Street #839/R
£800 $1328 €1200 Torii gate at Miyajima, Japan (41x29cm-16x11in) W/C. 12-Jun-3 Bonhams, New Bond Street #840/R
£1700 $2822 €2550 Kobai blossom (40x23cm-16x9in) s. W/C. 12-Jun-3 Bonhams, New Bond Street #838/R est:1200-1800

CANE, Louis (1943-) French
£641 $1006 €1000 Grand carre bleu (60x60cm-24x24in) s.d.1975 acrylic crayon prov. 15-Dec-2 Perrin, Versailles #137
£861 $1403 €1300 Femmes (73x54cm-29x21in) s.d.1987 paper on canvas. 1-Feb-3 Claude Aguttes, Neuilly #247/R
£1004 $1666 €1456 Still life of flowers (73x60cm-29x24in) s.d.1989 oil acrylic. 16-Jun-3 Lilla Bukowskis, Stockholm #294 est:10000-12000 (S.KR 13000)
£1191 $1858 €1787 Pins du midi (73x60cm-29x24in) s.d.87. 6-Nov-2 AB Stockholms Auktionsverk #961/R est:12000-15000 (S.KR 17000)
£1923 $3019 €3000 76B.10 (230x178cm-91x70in) s.d.1976 oil collage prov. 15-Dec-2 Perrin, Versailles #134/R
£1935 $3058 €3000 Couple (130x97cm-51x38in) s.d. 18-Dec-2 Digard, Paris #169/R
£2778 $4416 €4000 Chercheuses d'or (230x300cm-91x118in) s.i.d.Mai 78-mai 1978 verso prov. 29-Apr-3 Artcurial Briest, Paris #599/R est:6000-8000
£3125 $4969 €4500 Sans titre (230x230cm-91x91in) s.d.Nov.1980 oil collage prov. 29-Apr-3 Artcurial Briest, Paris #598/R est:6000-8000
£3261 $5348 €4500 Elvira (230x190cm-91x75in) s.i.d.1979 verso prov. 27-May-3 Tajan, Paris #30/R
£5000 $8150 €7500 Le couple (190x180cm-75x71in) s.d.1990-91. 3-Feb-3 Sotheby's, Olympia #116/R est:5000-7000
£5200 $8476 €7800 Deux figures (230x190cm-91x75in) s.d.12.2.85 oil paper collage. 3-Feb-3 Sotheby's, Olympia #117/R est:5000-7000
£5500 $8965 €8250 Deux figures (230x185cm-91x73in) s.d.85 86 88. 3-Feb-3 Sotheby's, Olympia #113/R est:5000-7000
£8844 $14061 €13000 Fleurs effacees (195x163cm-77x64in) painted 2001-02 poliptych. 3-Mar-3 Marc Kohn, Paris #46/R
Sculpture
£1042 $1646 €1500 Balancoire femme seule (40x19x13cm-16x7x5in) s.num.2/4 blue pat bronze Cast Oceane lit. 27-Apr-3 Perrin, Versailles #125/R est:1500-1800
£2083 $3292 €3000 L'effort ou la draisine (50x40x22cm-20x16x9in) s.num.5/8 blue pat bronze Cast Oceane lit. 27-Apr-3 Perrin, Versailles #105/R est:3000-3500
£2258 $3568 €3500 Petite femme au tabouret (35x15x12cm-14x6x5in) num.2/8 brown pat bronze Cast Susse. 18-Dec-2 Rieunier, Bailly-Pommery, Mathias, Paris #68/R
£4762 $7571 €7000 Femme a la crinoline (84x48x48cm-33x19x19in) s. num.4/8 polychrome bronze. 3-Mar-3 Marc Kohn, Paris #47/R
£7246 $11884 €10000 Personnage debout (103cm-41in) s. num.3/8 green pat bronze prov. 27-May-3 Tajan, Paris #28/R est:10000-12000
£9780 $15061 €15550 Grande menine (96x55cm-38x22in) s. num.1/8 Cast Barelier. 26-Oct-2 Cornette de St.Cyr, Paris #57/R
Works on paper
£329 $510 €520 Composition (78x63cm-31x25in) s.d. gouache oil canvas. 28-Sep-2 Cornette de St.Cyr, Paris #269
£442 $703 €650 Composition d'apres ucello (20x29cm-8x11in) s.d.juillet 1978 mixed media prov. 26-Feb-3 Artcurial Briest, Paris #392
£1277 $2132 €1800 Les menines d'apres Velasquez (50x52cm-20x20in) s.d. mixed media prov. 23-Jun-3 Claude Boisgirard, Paris #162/R est:1200-1500

CANE, Nicole (20th C) French
Sculpture
£2891 $4597 €4250 Ours polaire avec petit (15x48x17cm-6x19x7in) s. num.2/8 pat bronze. 3-Mar-3 Marc Kohn, Paris #50/R

CANE, Thomas (19th C) ?
Works on paper
£1943 $3129 €2915 Port Lyttelton (31x47cm-12x19in) s.d.1874 W/C. 7-May-3 Dunbar Sloane, Auckland #8/R est:5000-9000 (NZ.D 5500)

CANELLA, Giuseppe (1788-1847) Italian
£1500 $2325 €2250 Mountain landscape with hunters resting beside road (13x18cm-5x7in) s. panel. 31-Oct-2 Sotheby's, Olympia #186/R est:1500-2000
£4730 $7378 €7000 View of the Cybele fountain in Madrid (9x13cm-4x5in) s. 28-Mar-3 Delvaux, Paris #140/R est:9000
£4895 $8175 €7000 Vue des grands boulevards (20x25cm-8x10in) s.d.1828 panel. 25-Jun-3 Sotheby's, Paris #80/R est:8000-10000
Works on paper
£506 $790 €800 Old fisherman. Old bottle (13x18cm-5x7in) s. W/C two. 19-Oct-2 Semenzato, Venice #153
£566 $883 €900 Head of woman in profile (39x42cm-15x17in) s. chl. 20-Sep-2 Semenzato, Venice #218
£709 $1120 €1064 Fruit market (55x37cm-22x15in) s. W/C. 15-Nov-2 Naón & Cia, Buenos Aires #127/R
£1497 $2380 €2200 Fruit and vegetable seller (55x37cm-22x15in) s. W/C paper on cardboard. 18-Mar-3 Finarte, Milan #136/R
£5442 $8653 €8000 Parisian market. Jugglers (15cm-6in circular) s.d.1830 W/C tempera vellum pair. 18-Mar-3 Finarte, Milan #102/R
£5783 $9195 €8500 Boulevard in Paris (7x10cm-3x4in) s.d.1832 gouache. 24-Mar-3 Tajan, Paris #178/R

CANELLA, Giuseppe (attrib) (1788-1847) Italian
£2098 $3503 €3000 Vue de Saint-Cloud Prise de Meudon (11x17cm-4x7in) 25-Jun-3 Sotheby's, Paris #64/R est:3000-4000
£6500 $10335 €9750 Capriccio of a walled harbour, thought to be Valletta, Malta (48x82cm-19x32in) 20-Mar-3 Christie's, Kensington #83/R est:7000-10000

CANELLES, Pep (20th C) Spanish?
£462 $729 €720 Still life with radishes (50x65cm-20x26in) s.d.87. 13-Nov-2 Ansorena, Madrid #26/R

CANESTRARI, Carlo (1922-) Italian
Sculpture
£2821 $4372 €4400 Bust of young man (72x57x50cm-28x22x20in) s.d.69 brown pat bronze lit. 4-Dec-2 Finarte, Rome #73/R est:5000

CANEVARI, Carlo (1926-) Italian
£457 $750 €663 Pagliacci with broken lute (25x56cm-10x22in) s. panel prov. 4-Jun-3 Doyle, New York #26
£518 $850 €751 Cardinal. Nuns (36x18cm-14x7in) s. panel two. 4-Jun-3 Doyle, New York #25
£641 $1006 €1000 Saint Mary's (30x40cm-12x16in) s. painted 1953. 21-Nov-2 Finarte, Rome #355

CANEVARI, Giovanni Battista (1789-1876) Italian
Miniatures
£1000 $1560 €1500 Young lady seated holding a book in her right hand wearing a green dress (10cm-4xin) s.d.1817 gilt frame rec. 5-Nov-2 Bonhams, New Bond Street #132/R est:1000-1500

CANGEMI, Michael (20th C) American
£481 $750 €722 Prickly pear (76x61cm-30x24in) 19-Oct-2 David Dike, Dallas #161/R
£673 $1050 €1010 Bluebonnets, Ellis County (41x51cm-16x20in) 19-Oct-2 David Dike, Dallas #114/R
£705 $1100 €1058 Portrait of Quanah Parker (41x30cm-16x12in) 19-Oct-2 David Dike, Dallas #201/R

CANGIULLO, Francesco (1884-1977) Italian
£1139 $1800 €1800 Stairs in Naples (40x50cm-16x20in) s.. 26-Nov-2 Christie's, Rome #84/R

CANIFF, Milton (1907-1988) American
Works on paper
£807 $1300 €1211 Pat and Normandie chat on shipboard (13x51cm-5x20in) s. pen ink wash. 10-May-3 Illustration House, New York #32/R

CANINO, Vincenzo (1892-1978) Italian
£1038 $1619 €1650 Southern landscape near Naples (16x30cm-6x12in) s. panel. 9-Oct-2 Michael Zeller, Lindau #640/R est:1500
£1646 $2600 €2600 Market in Naples (28x38cm-11x15in) s. panel prov. 26-Nov-2 Christie's, Rome #271/R

CANITZ, George Paul (1874-1959) South African
£289 $457 €434 View of Table Mountain (101x125cm-40x49in) s. 1-Apr-3 Stephan Welz, Johannesburg #169 est:2000-3000 (SA.R 3600)

CANNATA, Antonio (1895-1960) Italian
£952 $1514 €1400 Landscape in Amalfi (50x40cm-20x16in) s. 18-Mar-3 Finarte, Milan #154/R

CANNEEL, Jean (20th C) Belgian
Sculpture
£5063 $7899 €8000 Femme nue agenouillee (86x47cm-34x19in) s. num.1/12 brown pat bronze. 15-Oct-2 Horta, Bruxelles #125/R est:8000-12000

CANNEEL, Jules Marie (1881-1953) Belgian
£411 $642 €650 Vue de Sy (77x60cm-30x24in) s. sold with another. 16-Sep-2 Horta, Bruxelles #333
£443 $691 €700 Fete nationale (84x71cm-33x28in) s.d.1928. 16-Sep-2 Horta, Bruxelles #332
£755 $1162 €1200 Mosquee de Sidi Belhioud (51x74cm-20x29in) s.d.1926 cardboard. 22-Oct-2 Campo & Campo, Antwerp #28
£1798 $2949 €2500 La mosquee de Sidi Belhioud, Maroc (52x74cm-20x29in) s.d.1926 i.verso cardboard. 4-Jun-3 Tajan, Paris #280/R est:2500-3000
Works on paper
£256 $403 €400 Le port de Casablanca (45x60cm-18x24in) s. gouache W/C. 16-Dec-2 Gros & Delettrez, Paris #443

CANNEEL, Marcel (1894-1953) Belgian
£1274 $1962 €2000 Boats in a harbour (60x70cm-24x28in) s.d.1921. 3-Sep-2 Christie's, Amsterdam #336/R est:2000-3000

CANNICCI, Nicolo (1846-1906) Italian
£16456 $26000 €26000 Back from ploughing (36x63cm-14x25in) s.i. 26-Nov-2 Christie's, Rome #181/R est:15000-18000
£42756 $67128 €66700 Harvest (60x104cm-24x41in) 10-Dec-2 Della Rocca, Turin #399/R est:50000-60000

CANNING, Criss (1941-) Australian
£2115 $3363 €3173 Nasturtiums (30x35cm-12x14in) s. exhib. 4-Mar-3 Deutscher-Menzies, Melbourne #132/R est:3000-5000 (A.D 5500)
£3187 $5227 €4781 Anthuriums (61x50cm-24x20in) s. exhib. 4-Jun-3 Deutscher-Menzies, Melbourne #183/R est:8000-12000 (A.D 8000)
£4615 $7338 €6923 Gum blossoms with poker-work vase (50x61cm-20x24in) s. exhib. 4-Mar-3 Deutscher-Menzies, Melbourne #131/R est:8000-12000 (A.D 12000)
£6786 $10585 €10179 Banksia (56x56cm-22x22in) s. i.stretcher prov.exhib. 11-Nov-2 Deutscher-Menzies, Melbourne #100/R est:6000-8000 (A.D 19000)

CANNING, Neil (1960-) British
Works on paper
£450 $738 €675 Preseli gold (54x74cm-21x29in) s. mixed media. 3-Jun-3 Sotheby's, Olympia #306/R
£450 $738 €675 Celtic landscape (54x74cm-21x29in) s. mixed media. 3-Jun-3 Sotheby's, Olympia #307/R
£450 $738 €675 Borderland (54x74cm-21x29in) s. mixed media. 3-Jun-3 Sotheby's, Olympia #308/R

CANNON, Jennie Vennerstrom (1869-1952) American
£1911 $3000 €2867 Carmel dunes (38x48cm-15x19in) s. board. 19-Nov-2 Butterfields, San Francisco #8287/R est:3000-5000

CANO, Alonso (1601-1667) Spanish
£134936 $213199 €210500 Vision of Saint Anthony of Padua (145x124cm-57x49in) 14-Nov-2 Arte, Seville #183/R

CANOGAR, Rafael (1934-) Spanish
£2516 $3975 €3900 Archeologica findings (44x44cm-17x17in) s.i.d.2001 aluminium collage cardboard. 17-Dec-2 Segre, Madrid #185/R est:3900
£4808 $7500 €7212 Pintura (81x81cm-32x32in) s.d.61 s.i.d.verso prov. 5-Nov-2 Doyle, New York #20/R est:3000-5000
£6000 $9300 €9000 Composition p-3-75 (162x130cm-64x51in) s.d.75 s.i.d.verso acrylic oil collage prov. 5-Dec-2 Christie's, Kensington #231/R est:4000-6000
£6500 $10075 €9750 P-18-76 (161x129cm-63x51in) s.d.1976 acrylic oil collage on canvas prov. 5-Dec-2 Christie's, Kensington #229/R est:4000-6000
£7000 $11690 €10150 Untitled (40x79cm-16x31in) s. s.d.1955 verso prov. 24-Jun-3 Sotheby's, Olympia #82/R est:4000-6000
£9934 $16192 €15000 Urban scene 22 (97x130cm-38x51in) s.d.1991 s.i.d.verso. 11-Feb-3 Segre, Madrid #224/R
£12000 $20040 €17400 Vida aparente en maquina preciosa (146x114cm-57x45in) s.d.63 prov. 27-Jun-3 Christie's, London #124/R est:15000-20000
£16000 $26720 €23200 Pintura no.9 (199x119cm-78x47in) s.d.58 s.i.d.verso prov.exhib. 27-Jun-3 Christie's, London #123/R est:12000-15000
£17000 $27880 €25500 Pintura 1959 (162x129cm-64x51in) s.d.59 s.i.d.1959 verso prov.exhib.lit. 6-Feb-3 Christie's, London #630/R est:12000-16000
£23000 $35420 €34500 La tolona (200x150cm-79x59in) s.d.59 s.i.d.verso prov.exhib. 23-Oct-2 Christie's, London #119/R est:8000-12000
£24000 $39360 €36000 Descabello (201x150cm-79x59in) s.d.59 s.i.d.verso prov.exhib. 6-Feb-3 Christie's, London #631/R est:15000-20000
£30272 $48133 €44500 Pintura no 70 (161x130cm-63x51in) s. s.i.d.1960 verso. 26-Feb-3 Artcurial Briest, Paris #420/R est:12000-15000
Works on paper
£1226 $1889 €1950 Untitled (19x14cm-7x6in) s. wax crayon exec.c.1962. 28-Oct-2 Segre, Madrid #131/R
£2471 $3978 €3707 Sin titulo (78x106cm-31x42in) s.d.76 mixed media. 7-May-3 AB Stockholms Auktionsverk #1146/R est:32000-35000 (S.KR 32000)

CANON, Hans (1829-1885) Austrian
£442 $703 €650 Portrait of a young man with useful objects (53x42cm-21x17in) 25-Feb-3 Dorotheum, Vienna #219/R
£471 $773 €683 Portrait of man (28x22cm-11x9in) s. cardboard. 4-Jun-3 AB Stockholms Auktionsverk #2495/R (S.KR 6000)
£641 $1006 €1000 Portrait of Arthur Schopenhauer (53x40cm-21x16in) s.d.1851 board. 10-Dec-2 Dorotheum, Vienna #165/R
£1164 $1816 €1700 Boy's portrait (21x16cm-8x6in) s. lit. 10-Apr-3 Dorotheum, Vienna #121/R est:1800-2000
£1234 $1838 €1900 Self portrait (71x58cm-28x23in) s.d.1879. 26-Jun-2 Neumeister, Munich #701/R
£1384 $2131 €2200 Portrait of a smoker (63x79cm-25x31in) s.d.862. 22-Oct-2 Wiener Kunst Auktionen, Vienna #1078/R est:2000-7200

CANON, Hans (attrib) (1829-1885) Austrian
£616 $962 €900 Portrait of Prof. Benedikt (53x42cm-21x17in) 9-Apr-3 Neumeister, Munich #655

CANOVA, Antonio (1757-1822) Italian
Sculpture
£223725 $360197 €333350 Three graces (36x15x16cm-14x6x6in) terracotta exhib.lit. 19-Feb-3 Semenzato, Venice #11/R
Works on paper
£3800 $6346 €5510 Sheet of studies. Designs for ornamental friezes and figures from the antique (34x42cm-13x17in) blk chk double-sided. 9-Jul-3 Sotheby's, London #62/R est:2500-3500
£6000 $10020 €8700 Kneeling man tying his shoe laces (13x15cm-5x6in) i.verso pen brown ink prov. 8-Jul-3 Christie's, London #57/R est:3000-5000

CANOVA, Antonio (after) (1757-1822) Italian
Sculpture
£4573 $7500 €6631 Venus (152x51x48cm-60x20x19in) grey veined marble. 7-Jun-3 Neal Auction Company, New Orleans #501/R est:7000-9000
£5161 $8155 €8000 Femme drapee a l'antique allongee sur banquette (59x82x25cm-23x32x10in) s. Carrara marble. 19-Dec-2 Bondu, Paris #97/R est:10000
£5183 $8500 €7515 Venus (152x48x48cm-60x19x19in) grey veined marble. 7-Jun-3 Neal Auction Company, New Orleans #500/R est:7000-9000
£6000 $9540 €9000 Venus (220cm-87in) white marble red scagiola column prov. 29-Apr-3 Sotheby's, Olympia #182/R est:6000-8000

CANT, James Montgomery (1911-1983) Australian
£1004 $1525 €1506 Londoner (57x48cm-22x19in) s.d.52 composition board exhib. 28-Aug-2 Deutscher-Menzies, Melbourne #319/R est:3000-4000 (A.D 2800)
£2308 $3669 €3462 Abstract still life (76x63cm-30x25in) s. 4-Mar-3 Deutscher-Menzies, Melbourne #177/R est:7000-10000 (A.D 6000)
Works on paper
£287 $436 €431 Cat (12x15cm-5x6in) W/C ink varnish exec.c.1948-49 exhib. 28-Aug-2 Deutscher-Menzies, Melbourne #427/R (A.D 800)
£3047 $4631 €4571 Durham wharf (47x67cm-19x26in) s.i.d.1937 W/C bodycol newsprint synthetic polymer paint pen ink. 28-Aug-2 Deutscher-Menzies, Melbourne #173/R est:5000-8000 (A.D 8500)

CANTAGALLINA, Remigio (1582-1628) Italian
Works on paper
£850 $1335 €1275 Two beggars sleeping (11x19cm-4x7in) pen ink. 11-Dec-2 Sotheby's, Olympia #38/R
£850 $1335 €1275 Three running figures (11x17cm-4x7in) pen ink wash over chk. 11-Dec-2 Sotheby's, Olympia #39/R
£3704 $6000 €5556 Marshy landscape with reeds (21x33cm-8x13in) i. pen ink. 21-Jan-3 Sotheby's, New York #164/R est:7000

CANTARINI, Simone (1612-1648) Italian
£30769 $47692 €48000 Saint Gerolamo meditating (130x95cm-51x37in) exhib.lit. 4-Dec-2 Christie's, Rome #484/R est:45000-55000
Works on paper
£2568 $4005 €3800 Seated man (18x17cm-7x7in) i. chk prov. 27-Mar-3 Christie's, Paris #30/R

CANTARINI, Simone (attrib) (1612-1648) Italian
£2838 $4428 €4257 Mourning of Christ (49x37cm-19x15in) 6-Nov-2 Dobiaschofsky, Bern #390/R est:5500 (S.FR 6500)

CANTATORE, Domenico (1906-1998) Italian
£1923 $3019 €3000 Interior (30x40cm-12x16in) s.d.69. 19-Nov-2 Finarte, Milan #273/R
£2838 $4427 €4200 Landscape with houses (45x55cm-18x22in) s. painted 1946. 28-Mar-3 Farsetti, Prato #376/R
£3718 $5837 €5800 Woman (58x49cm-23x19in) s. board painted c.1930. 19-Nov-2 Finarte, Milan #178/R
£4255 $6894 €6000 Figura (60x50cm-24x20in) s. s.d.1944 verso panel double-sided prov.exhib. 26-May-3 Christie's, Milan #310/R est:7000-10000
£4808 $7548 €7500 Odalisk (30x40cm-12x16in) s. 21-Nov-2 Finarte, Rome #296/R est:7000
£5063 $7899 €8000 Odalisk (30x40cm-12x16in) s. 14-Sep-2 Meeting Art, Vercelli #967/R
£5229 $8366 €8000 On the sofa (50x40cm-20x16in) s. acrylic. 4-Jan-3 Meeting Art, Vercelli #527
£5229 $8366 €8000 Red odalisk (30x40cm-12x16in) s. acrylic painted 1972. 4-Jan-3 Meeting Art, Vercelli #745
£6383 $10340 €9000 Odalisca (40x60cm-16x24in) s.d.64. 26-May-3 Christie's, Milan #333/R est:10000-12000
£7639 $12146 €11000 Odalisk (40x50cm-16x20in) s. 1-May-3 Meeting Art, Vercelli #110
£8333 $13083 €13000 Cuddles (58x53cm-23x21in) s. 23-Nov-2 Meeting Art, Vercelli #499/R est:12000
£10256 $16103 €16000 Bust of woman (77x60cm-30x24in) s. s.i.verso board painted c.1922. 21-Nov-2 Finarte, Rome #332/R est:15000-18000
Works on paper
£269 $425 €420 Woman (16x10cm-6x4in) W/C. 12-Nov-2 Babuino, Rome #213/R
£521 $828 €750 Cock (34x25cm-13x10in) s.i.d.1982 pastel. 1-May-3 Meeting Art, Vercelli #114
£833 $1308 €1300 Landscape at dawn (27x40cm-11x16in) s. W/C. 21-Nov-2 Finarte, Rome #125/R

CANTON CHECA, Miguel (1928-) Spanish
£377 $581 €600 Family (52x38cm-20x15in) s. s.i.d.1952 verso board. 22-Oct-2 Durán, Madrid #631/R

CANTRE, Jozef (1890-1957) Belgian
Sculpture
£2390 $3681 €3800 Nude (51cm-20in) s. bronze. 22-Oct-2 Campo & Campo, Antwerp #29/R
£2414 $3862 €3500 Nude sitting (32x20cm-13x8in) s. plaster lit. 15-Mar-3 De Vuyst, Lokeren #45/R est:2000-2600
£4430 $6911 €7000 Nude standing (62cm-24in) s. black pat bronze. 21-Oct-2 Bernaerts, Antwerp #570/R est:6950-7950
£5036 $8259 €7000 Er waren twee koningskinderen (37cm-15in) s. wood executed 1920 lit. 3-Jun-3 Christie's, Amsterdam #163/R est:7000-9000

CANTU, Federico (1908-1989) Mexican
£11585 $19000 €16798 Three women (115x77cm-45x30in) s. masonite. 27-May-3 Sotheby's, New York #86
Works on paper
£321 $500 €482 Allegory of the harvest (66x51cm-26x20in) s.d.60 W/C ink. 14-Sep-2 Weschler, Washington #638/R

CANU, Yvonne (1921-) French
£510 $795 €800 Chalutiers en Bretagne (33x41cm-13x16in) s. 10-Nov-2 Eric Pillon, Calais #119/R
£576 $921 €800 Marche de Provence (33x41cm-13x16in) s. s.i.verso. 14-May-3 Blanchet, Paris #131/R
£700 $1085 €1050 Fete de nuit a St. Tropez (43x35cm-17x14in) s. s.i.verso. 5-Dec-2 Christie's, Kensington #177/R
£719 $1151 €1000 L'entree du port des Glenans (24x32cm-9x13in) s. 18-May-3 Eric Pillon, Calais #252/R
£1250 $2037 €1800 Promenade en barque (55x78cm-22x31in) s. cardboard. 19-Jul-3 Thierry & Lannon, Brest #189 est:1800-2000
Works on paper
£396 $633 €550 Saint Tropez (25x35cm-10x14in) s. gouache. 14-May-3 Blanchet, Paris #130
£521 $849 €750 Le port de Concarneau (23x29cm-9x11in) s. W/C. 19-Jul-3 Thierry & Lannon, Brest #188

CANUT, Denis (1953-) French
£597 $950 €896 Paysage de Sologne (61x74cm-24x29in) s. s.i.verso. 18-Mar-3 Doyle, New York #16/R

CANUTI, Domenico Maria (1620-1684) Italian
Works on paper
£750 $1178 €1125 Studies of Venus and Cupid (15x25cm-6x10in) pen ink wash htd white chk prov. 11-Dec-2 Sotheby's, Olympia #21/R
£3200 $5024 €4800 Male nude seated, his knees drawn up (57x41cm-22x16in) i. red chk over black chk. 11-Dec-2 Sotheby's, Olympia #68/R est:3000-4000

CANZI, Auguste (19th C) ?
£1634 $2680 €2500 Jeune femme a sa fenetre (49x37cm-19x15in) s. 9-Feb-3 Anaf, Lyon #66/R

CAOUETTE, Raymond (1958-) Canadian
£267 $437 €401 Village du Nord (60x150cm-24x59in) s. 3-Jun-3 Joyner, Toronto #440/R (C.D 600)

CAP, Constant (1842-1915) Belgian
£449 $696 €700 Portrait d'un noble (90x68cm-35x27in) s. 3-Dec-2 Campo & Campo, Antwerp #36
£481 $745 €750 Portrait d'une noble (90x68cm-35x27in) s. 3-Dec-2 Campo & Campo, Antwerp #37
£2025 $3159 €3200 Faust dans la chambre de Marguerite (65x78cm-26x31in) s.d.1912. 21-Oct-2 Bernaerts, Antwerp #85/R est:3000-4000

CAPA, Joaquin (1941-) Spanish
£1136 $1659 €1750 Untitled (61x61cm-24x24in) s.d.2001. 12-Jun-2 Castellana, Madrid #269/R

CAPA, Robert (1913-1954) American/Hungarian
Photographs
£3312 $5200 €4968 Henri Matisse drawing with a bamboo pole (28x36cm-11x14in) gelatin silver print. 21-Apr-3 Phillips, New York #5/R est:800-1200
£10759 $17000 €16139 Self portrait (24x18cm-9x7in) i.verso gelatin silver print prov. 24-Apr-3 Phillips, New York #146/R est:3000-5000
£11392 $18000 €17088 Self portrait (18x24cm-7x9in) i.verso gelatin silver print prov.lit. 24-Apr-3 Phillips, New York #145/R est:3000-5000

CAPACCI, Bruno (1906-1993) French
£316 $491 €500 Ville encerclee (70x68cm-28x27in) s.d.75. 24-Sep-2 Galerie Moderne, Brussels #887
£2446 $3914 €3400 Carnaval a Venise (125x189cm-49x74in) s.d.1955 wood. 13-May-3 Galerie Moderne, Brussels #48/R est:1500-2000
Works on paper
£590 $926 €920 Composition surrealiste (55x36cm-22x14in) s. mixed media. 15-Dec-2 Thierry & Lannon, Brest #364

CAPARNE, William John (fl.1882-1893) British
Works on paper
£350 $557 €525 Near Bordeaux, Guernsey (16x31cm-6x12in) init. W/C. 20-Mar-3 Martel Maides, Guernsey #55
£420 $668 €630 View from the pine forest, Guernsey, looking towards Fermain Bay (26x35cm-10x14in) init. W/C. 20-Mar-3 Martel Maides, Guernsey #51
£650 $1028 €975 Summer blooms on Guernsey south coast cliffs (26x36cm-10x14in) init. W/C. 28-Nov-2 Martel Maides, Guernsey #28/R
£1800 $2862 €2700 Woodland stream. Clearing in the woods (55x77cm-22x30in) s. W/C double-sided exhib. 20-Mar-3 Martel Maides, Guernsey #38/R est:1000-1500

CAPDEVIELLE, Lucienne (1885-1961) French
Works on paper
£544 $865 €800 Jeune bedouine au collier (33x24cm-13x9in) s. gouache cardboard. 24-Mar-3 Raboudin & Choppin de Janvry, Paris #177/R

CAPDEVILA MASSANA, Manuel (1910-) Spanish
£1258 $2051 €1900 Path (38x46cm-15x18in) s.i.d.1946 i.verso. 11-Feb-3 Segre, Madrid #190/R

CAPDEVILA, Gines (1872-?) Spanish

£597 $932 €950 Vase of flowers (86x55cm-34x22in) s. canvas on board. 8-Oct-2 Ansorena, Madrid #308/R
£828 $1316 €1200 Roses (42x69cm-17x27in) s.d.1906. 4-Mar-3 Ansorena, Madrid #284/R

CAPDEVILLA PUIG, Genis (1860-1929) Spanish

£287 $448 €425 Flowers (35x55cm-14x22in) s. 25-Mar-3 Durán, Madrid #717/R

CAPEINICK, Jean (1838-1890) Belgian

£2303 $3730 €3500 Roses in a vase (67x51cm-26x20in) s. 21-Jan-3 Christie's, Amsterdam #122/R est:4000-6000
£4167 $6458 €6500 Still life with hollyhocks (100x80cm-39x31in) s. 7-Dec-2 De Vuyst, Lokeren #414/R est:6000-8000
£6329 $10000 €10000 Bouquets de fleurs le long d'un etang (285x190cm-112x75in) s.d.1879. 26-Nov-2 Palais de Beaux Arts, Brussels #289/R est:14000-20000
£12025 $19000 €18038 Tropical garden with assorted flowers and fruit. Tropical plants and flowers (204x208cm-80x82in) s. prov. pair. 1-Apr-3 Christie's, Rockefeller NY #192/R est:10000-15000

CAPEK, Josef (1887-1945) Czechoslovakian

£20653 $32218 €30980 Flying a kite (50x50cm-20x20in) s.d.34 canvas on canvas. 12-Oct-2 Dorotheum, Prague #140/R est:500000-750000 (C.KR 1000000)

Works on paper

£305 $486 €458 A modest one (22x30cm-9x12in) s. ink white lead. 8-Mar-3 Dorotheum, Prague #252/R est:12000-18000 (C.KR 14000)

CAPELAIN, John le (c.1814-1848) British

Works on paper

£420 $655 €630 Ship in misty weather (33x42cm-13x17in) s. W/C. 26-Mar-3 Bonhams & Langlois, Jersey #160/R
£1200 $1896 €1800 Evening coastal scene with shipping in distance (25x35cm-10x14in) s. W/C. 27-Nov-2 Bonhams, Brooks & Langlois, Jersey #95/R est:300-500

CAPELLA ARENAS, Juan (1927-) Spanish

£484 $765 €750 Landscape (62x50cm-24x20in) s.d.83. 18-Dec-2 Ansorena, Madrid #2/R

CAPELLA, Cheli (19th C) Italian

£3053 $4824 €4580 Portrait of Madame Vigee le Brun by herself (102x83cm-40x33in) s. i.verso painted c.1905 prov. 7-Apr-3 Shapiro, Sydney #510/R est:5000-7000 (A.D 8000)

CAPETTI, Cesare (?) Italian

£737 $1157 €1150 Naples harbour (31x41cm-12x16in) s. 10-Dec-2 Della Rocca, Turin #259

CAPO, Jose Cases (1906-) Spanish

£472 $736 €750 Landscape in Horta (81x100cm-32x39in) s.d.1935. 8-Oct-2 Ansorena, Madrid #430/R

CAPOGROSSI, Costanza Mennyey (20th C) Italian

£513 $805 €800 Arlequin (50x75cm-20x30in) s.i. 21-Nov-2 Finarte, Rome #299

CAPOGROSSI, Giuseppe (1900-1972) Italian

£2564 $4026 €4000 Composition (10x10cm-4x4in) tempera paper on masonite. 19-Nov-2 Finarte, Milan #156/R
£7692 $12077 €12000 Surface CP/598 (28x39cm-11x15in) tempera paper on canvas. 23-Nov-2 Meeting Art, Vercelli #117/R est:10000
£9677 $15290 €15000 Surface (50x35cm-20x14in) s. tempera paper on board prov.lit. 18-Dec-2 Christie's, Rome #239/R
£12000 $19680 €18000 Superficie 484 (49x35cm-19x14in) s.i.d.1962 verso prov.lit. 6-Feb-3 Christie's, London #637/R est:8000-12000
£18440 $29872 €26000 Superficie n.518 (45x30cm-18x12in) s.d.1961 prov.lit. 26-May-3 Christie's, Milan #370/R est:15000-20000
£23000 $35880 €34500 Superficie 346 (54x73cm-21x29in) s. s.i.d.1956 verso prov.lit. 21-Oct-2 Sotheby's, London #52/R est:25000-35000
£23611 $38958 €34000 Composition (65x54cm-26x21in) s. prov. 1-Jul-3 Artcurial Briest, Paris #490/R est:20000-25000
£43972 $71234 €62000 Superficie 286 (102x72cm-40x28in) s.d.58 i.verso exhib.lit. 26-May-3 Christie's, Milan #267/R est:5000-7000
£52000 $80080 €78000 Superficie no.27 (65x55cm-26x22in) s. i.d.1952 verso prov. 22-Oct-2 Christie's, London #24/R est:30000-40000
£100000 $154000 €150000 Superficie no. 141 (17x87cm-7x34in) s.d.55 prov.exhib.lit. 22-Oct-2 Christie's, London #33/R est:100000-130000

Works on paper

£4593 $7349 €6660 Surface CP/949 (34x26cm-13x10in) s.i.d.1961 felt-tip pen lit. 11-Mar-3 Babuino, Rome #271/R

CAPOLINO, John Joseph (1896-?) American

£449 $700 €674 Washington's headquarters, Valley Forge (61x72cm-24x28in) s. 14-Sep-2 Weschler, Washington #606/R

CAPON, Georges Émile (c.1890-1980) French

£566 $877 €900 Portrait de jeune fille sur la piste du cirque (55x46cm-22x18in) s. 6-Oct-2 Livinec, Gaudcheau & Jezequel, Rennes #65
£583 $962 €840 Nu feminin aux coussins rouges et verts (16x22cm-6x9in) s. 1-Jul-3 Rossini, Paris #78/R
£1586 $2649 €2300 Nu assis au collier (73x60cm-29x24in) s. 10-Jul-3 Artcurial Briest, Paris #163/R est:2000-3000

CAPONE, Gaetano (1845-1920) Italian

£1935 $3058 €3000 Landscape in Maiori (35x43cm-14x17in) s. i.verso prov. 18-Dec-2 Finarte, Milan #42/R est:3000

Works on paper

£2041 $3245 €3000 Pompei (48x31cm-19x12in) s. W/C. 1-Mar-3 Meeting Art, Vercelli #218

CAPONI, Dino (1920-2000) Italian

£256 $403 €400 Figure (101x70cm-40x28in) s.d.62. 16-Dec-2 Pandolfini, Florence #332/R

CAPONIGRO, Paul (1932-) American

Photographs

£2025 $3200 €3038 Revere Beach, Massachusetts (25x35cm-10x14in) s. gelatin silver print lit. 22-Apr-3 Christie's, Rockefeller NY #16/R est:4000-6000
£2373 $3750 €3560 Running white deer, Wicklow, Ireland (13x36cm-5x14in) s.d.1967 gelatin silver print. 22-Apr-3 Butterfields, San Francisco #2430/R est:3000-5000

CAPORALI, Bartolomeo (circle) (1420-1505) Italian

Works on paper

£5000 $7800 €7500 God the Father in glory with Cherubin (198x171cm-78x67in) fresco oval. 10-Apr-3 Christie's, Kensington #200/R est:6000-8000

CAPPELLI, Giovanni (1923-1994) Italian

£556 $883 €800 Souvenir of Romagna (30x40cm-12x16in) s. s.i.verso. 1-May-3 Meeting Art, Vercelli #527
£1046 $1673 €1600 Fire in the plain (80x65cm-31x26in) s.d.1973. 4-Jan-3 Meeting Art, Vercelli #211

CAPPELLO, Carmelo (1912-) Italian

£278 $442 €400 Figures (30x18cm-12x7in) s.d.1944 tempera W/C paper. 1-May-3 Meeting Art, Vercelli #8

Works on paper

£306 $487 €450 Untitled (70x50cm-28x20in) s.d.1959 mixed media. 1-Mar-3 Meeting Art, Vercelli #571
£374 $595 €550 Composition (50x70cm-20x28in) s. pastel. 1-Mar-3 Meeting Art, Vercelli #616

CAPPIA, Raffaele (19th C) Italian

£950 $1577 €950 Jesus et la Samaritaine (106x76cm-42x30in) s.d.1879 after Laviena Frontana. 16-Jun-3 Horta, Bruxelles #277

CAPPIELLO, Leonetto (1875-1942) French

Works on paper

£690 $1097 €1000 Projet d'affiche pour le Cadet Roussel (62x44cm-24x17in) s. chl W/C. 5-Mar-3 Doutrebente, Paris #78

CAPRILE, Vincenzo (1856-1936) Italian

£4516 $7000 €6774 Porta della Carta, Palazzo Ducale, Venice (47x63cm-19x25in) s.d.1909. 2-Oct-2 Christie's, Rockefeller NY #766/R est:5000-7000
£5190 $8200 €8200 Grey day in Chioggia (30x42cm-12x17in) s. board exhib. 26-Nov-2 Christie's, Rome #216a/R est:5500
£6803 $10816 €10000 Shepherds and donkeys (21x34cm-8x13in) s.d.1888 board. 18-Mar-3 Finarte, Milan #9/R est:13000
£66456 $105000 €105000 Easter market in Naples (165x259cm-65x102in) s. prov.lit. 26-Nov-2 Christie's, Rome #286/R est:110000-130000

Works on paper

£4403 $6780 €7000 Girl (53x41cm-21x16in) s.d.1906 pastel lit. 23-Oct-2 Finarte, Milan #123/R

CAPRON, Jean Pierre (1921-1997) French
£323 $500 €485 Chateau en Dordogne (64x81cm-25x32in) s.d.81 prov. 16-Jul-2 Arthur James, Florida #144
£932 $1500 €1398 Venise (145x114cm-57x45in) s.d.74. 18-Feb-3 Arthur James, Florida #413
£1439 $2302 €2000 Canal a Venise (130x97cm-51x38in) s. 18-May-3 Eric Pillon, Calais #151/R

CAPUANO, Francesco (1854-?) Italian
£768 $1129 €1190 Woodland view (68x100cm-27x39in) 24-Jun-2 Babuino, Rome #261 est:500-700
£1266 $2000 €2000 Peasant in the wood (90x155cm-35x61in) s. 26-Nov-2 Christie's, Rome #22/R

CAPULETTI, Jose Manuel (1925-1978) Spanish
£348 $550 €522 Honfleur harbour (33x56cm-13x22in) s.i. prov. 2-Apr-3 Doyle, New York #18/R
£633 $1000 €950 Surrealist still life (64x53cm-25x21in) s. 2-Apr-3 Doyle, New York #19/R
£633 $1000 €950 Plein soleil (46x66cm-18x26in) s. indis.i. prov. 2-Apr-3 Doyle, New York #20/R
£696 $1100 €1044 No man's land (51x61cm-20x24in) s. prov. 2-Apr-3 Doyle, New York #21/R
£8176 $12755 €13000 Idol woman (66x47cm-26x19in) s. prov. 23-Sep-2 Durán, Madrid #201/R est:5000

CAPULINO JAUREGUI, Joaquin (1879-1969) Spanish
Works on paper
£493 $799 €750 View of Granada (21x13cm-8x5in) s. W/C. 21-Jan-3 Ansorena, Madrid #38

CAPURRO, Sara (1922-1997) South American?
£264 $420 €396 Train (40x50cm-16x20in) s. cardboard. 2-Mar-3 Galleria Y Remates, Montevideo #42/R
£288 $460 €432 Perspective (47x59cm-19x23in) cardboard. 5-Jan-3 Galleria Y Remates, Montevideo #32
£462 $720 €693 View with port (39x50cm-15x20in) cardboard. 10-Oct-2 Galleria Y Remates, Montevideo #39/R
£833 $1300 €1250 Paisaje urbano constructivo (36x60cm-14x24in) s.d.62 cardboard. 30-Jul-2 Galleria Y Remates, Montevideo #64/R
£1375 $2200 €2063 Lady (90x55cm-35x22in) s. cardboard. 5-Jan-3 Galleria Y Remates, Montevideo #110/R

CAPUTO, Tonino (1933-) Italian
£288 $453 €450 Holy cups and magic lamp (50x40cm-20x16in) s. s.i.verso. 23-Nov-2 Meeting Art, Vercelli #406
£321 $503 €500 Untitled (60x50cm-24x20in) s. cardboard on canvas painted 1991. 23-Nov-2 Meeting Art, Vercelli #486
£449 $704 €700 Untitled (16x21cm-6x8in) s. cardboard on canvas. 23-Nov-2 Meeting Art, Vercelli #380/R
£475 $741 €750 Demolition (80x100cm-31x39in) s. s.i.verso lit. 14-Sep-2 Meeting Art, Vercelli #460/R
£475 $741 €750 Stolen piece of art (70x50cm-28x20in) s. s.i.d.1991 verso cardboard on canvas. 14-Sep-2 Meeting Art, Vercelli #895/R
£1603 $2484 €2500 Untitled (100x130cm-39x51in) s. 4-Dec-2 Finarte, Milan #539/R

CAPUTO, Ulisse (1872-1948) Italian
£377 $585 €600 Un coin de Paris (13x22cm-5x9in) s. prov. 30-Oct-2 Artcurial Briest, Paris #128
£850 $1352 €1250 Gardens in Paris (17x25cm-7x10in) s. cardboard on canvas. 1-Mar-3 Meeting Art, Vercelli #149
£1603 $2500 €2405 Moulin a Brechamps (23x33cm-9x13in) s.i.d.1913 board. 12-Oct-2 Neal Auction Company, New Orleans #160/R est:1800-2400
£1800 $2862 €2700 La couturiere (34x25cm-13x10in) s. board. 20-Mar-3 Christie's, Kensington #58/R est:2500-3500
£1905 $3029 €2800 Little lady in interior (32x23cm-13x9in) s. board. 18-Mar-3 Finarte, Milan #77/R
£4000 $6280 €6000 At the opera (40x33cm-16x13in) s. board. 21-Nov-2 Christie's, Kensington #156/R est:4000-6000
£6329 $10000 €9494 Tea time (96x74cm-38x29in) s.i. 23-Apr-3 Christie's, Rockefeller NY #125/R est:12000-16000
£11950 $19000 €17925 Two women seated at an interior table (254x330cm-100x130in) s. painted c.1910. 7-Mar-3 Jackson's, Cedar Falls #522/R est:8000-12000

CARA, Ugo (1908-) Italian
Sculpture
£922 $1494 €1300 Metamorfosi (42cm-17in) s. green pat bronze marble base. 22-May-3 Stadion, Trieste #216/R est:800-1200

CARABAIN, Jacques (1834-1892) Belgian
£680 $1082 €1000 Une rue animee a Monjoi (31x21cm-12x8in) s. d.1870 verso sold with a W/C by the same artist. 18-Mar-3 Vanderkindere, Brussels #1
£1392 $2172 €2200 Beggars before the church (39x29cm-15x11in) panel. 21-Oct-2 Bernaerts, Antwerp #733/R est:2000-2500
£1421 $2202 €2132 Biblical countryside (52x64cm-20x25in) painted c.1860. 3-Dec-2 SOGA, Bratislava #172/R est:75000 (SL.K 90000)
£1783 $2746 €2800 Mediterranean fish market (27x21cm-11x8in) s. panel. 3-Sep-2 Christie's, Amsterdam #156/R est:2000-3000
£2449 $3894 €3600 L'ancien Faubourg de Domodossola (50x35cm-20x14in) s.d.1925. 18-Mar-3 Galerie Moderne, Brussels #628/R est:4000-6000
£2532 $4000 €4000 Fontaine dans un village Italien (25x35cm-10x14in) s.i.d. 31 aout 1900 verso. 26-Nov-2 Palais de Beaux Arts, Brussels #290/R est:3000-4500
£2532 $4000 €4000 Vue de Vintmiglia (27x40cm-11x16in) s.i.d.aout 1885 verso. 26-Nov-2 Palais de Beaux Arts, Brussels #291/R est:3500-5000
£2658 $4147 €4200 View in Venice (30x37cm-12x15in) s. 21-Oct-2 Bernaerts, Antwerp #734/R est:3000-4000
£3165 $4937 €5000 Rue a San Remo, Italie (88x68cm-35x27in) s. i.d.1878 verso. 16-Sep-2 Horta, Bruxelles #105/R
£3521 $5669 €5000 Figures in the street at San Remo (88x68cm-35x27in) s. 12-May-3 Bernaerts, Antwerp #216/R est:5000-7500
£5000 $7750 €7500 Vue a Monte Corso (40x31cm-16x12in) s. 9-Dec-2 Philippe Schuler, Zurich #3889/R est:8000-12000 (S.FR 11500)
£5306 $8437 €7800 Vue de Venise (76x56cm-30x22in) s. 19-Mar-3 Hotel des Ventes Mosan, Brussels #198 est:2800-3200
£6115 $9784 €8500 Vieux puits a Westhuis (76x62cm-30x24in) s. 19-May-3 Horta, Bruxelles #135/R est:12000-15000
£6835 $10935 €9500 Rue a Monte-Rosso, bords de la Mediterranee, Italie (76x53cm-30x21in) s. 17-May-3 De Vuyst, Lokeren #529/R est:12000-15000
£7194 $11511 €10000 Vue animee a Anticouli C Italy (76x55cm-30x22in) s. i.d.1921 verso. 13-May-3 Vanderkindere, Brussels #64/R est:7000-10000
£7843 $12627 €12000 Une vieille porte a Uzerche (76x54cm-30x21in) s. 20-Jan-3 Horta, Bruxelles #183/R est:3500-4500
£7914 $12662 €11000 Rue a Monterosso, Italie (76x46cm-30x18in) s. 17-May-3 De Vuyst, Lokeren #431/R est:12000-15000
£12583 $20510 €19000 Marche a Blois (56x78cm-22x31in) s. 17-Feb-3 Horta, Bruxelles #139/R est:12000
£13699 $21507 €20000 Une vue de la Boucherie a la Madeleine a Maline, Belgique (79x63cm-31x25in) s.d.1874. 15-Apr-3 Sotheby's, Amsterdam #167/R est:25000-30000
£14570 $23748 €22000 Grand canal a Venise (70x100cm-28x39in) s.d.1913. 17-Feb-3 Horta, Bruxelles #138/R
£32704 $50365 €52000 Market day in Antwerp (78x62cm-31x24in) s. 22-Oct-2 Sotheby's, Amsterdam #158/R est:10000-15000

CARABAIN, Victor (19/20th C) Belgian
£578 $919 €850 Pont Sisto et l'Eglise St-Giovanni a Rome (61x80cm-24x31in) s. 18-Mar-3 Galerie Moderne, Brussels #516
£801 $1258 €1250 Vue animee de la Porte Zamboni a Bologne (76x103cm-30x41in) s. 19-Nov-2 Vanderkindere, Brussels #110
£986 $1587 €1400 Mediterranean harbour (67x100cm-26x39in) s. 12-May-3 Bernaerts, Antwerp #202/R

CARACCIOLO, Giovanni Battista (attrib) (1570-1637) Italian
Works on paper
£1203 $1900 €1900 Une femme nue a mi0corps (20x13cm-8x5in) i. pen brown ink. 27-Nov-2 Christie's, Paris #64/R est:2000-3000

CARACCIOLO, Niccolo d'Ardia (1941-1989) Italian
£1644 $2581 €2400 Jug of flowers (35x24cm-14x9in) 15-Apr-3 De Veres Art Auctions, Dublin #247/R est:2000-3000
£3020 $4862 €4500 Arno from Ponte San Niccolo (25x39cm-10x15in) init.d.1979 board. 18-Feb-3 Whyte's, Dublin #155/R est:5000-7000
£3038 $4709 €4800 Volterra, Italy (38x60cm-15x24in) s. prov. 24-Sep-2 De Veres Art Auctions, Dublin #72/R est:5000-7000
£6646 $10301 €10500 Still life with parasol (44x65cm-17x26in) s. 24-Sep-2 De Veres Art Auctions, Dublin #177/R est:7000-10000
£7192 $11291 €10500 Nude (84x109cm-33x43in) prov. 15-Apr-3 De Veres Art Auctions, Dublin #164/R est:10000-15000
Works on paper
£633 $981 €1000 Palm Beach (31x23cm-12x9in) s.d.89 W/C htd white prov. 24-Sep-2 De Veres Art Auctions, Dublin #152/R est:1000-1500
£696 $1079 €1100 Female nude study (38x28cm-15x11in) s. W/C prov. 24-Sep-2 De Veres Art Auctions, Dublin #128 est:900-1200

CARADEC, Louis (1936-) French
£3141 $4869 €4900 Discussion champetre en Bretagne (43x65cm-17x26in) s. 9-Dec-2 Thierry & Lannon, Brest #225

CARADEC, Marcel (1901-) French
£962 $1510 €1500 Maison de Mimi Pinson sous la neige (50x61cm-20x24in) s. 24-Nov-2 Lesieur & Le Bars, Le Havre #19

CARADOSSI, Vittorio (1861-?) Italian
Sculpture
£2038 $3200 €3057 Nymph (64cm-25in) s. alabaster. 23-Nov-2 Jackson's, Cedar Falls #246/R est:1500-2500

CARAGLIO, Giovanni Jacopo (c.1500-1570) Italian
Prints
£3797 $6000 €6000 The Annunciation (45x34cm-18x13in) copperplate after Titian. 29-Nov-2 Bassenge, Berlin #5207/R est:6000

CARALDI, P (19/20th C) Italian
Sculpture
£12658 $20000 €18987 Nude with a butterfly (155cm-61in) s. marble prov. 23-Apr-3 Christie's, Rockefeller NY #105/R est:25000-35000

CARAVAGGIO (1573-1610) Italian
£6410 $10128 €10000 Christ with soldiers and Pontius Pilate (89x120cm-35x47in) 12-Nov-2 Mealy's, Castlecomer #1059/R est:5000
£10480 $16349 €15720 The cheat (83x109cm-33x43in) 20-Nov-2 Fischer, Luzern #1012/R est:7500-8500 (S.FR 24000)

CARAVAGGIO (after) (1573-1610) Italian
£4808 $7452 €7500 Esau dealing with Jacob (97x119cm-38x47in) prov.lit. 4-Dec-2 Christie's, Rome #473/R
£5975 $9201 €9500 Saint Peter freed from jail (140x188cm-55x74in) 23-Oct-2 Finarte, Rome #510/R

CARAVAGGIO (school) (1573-1610) Italian
£5674 $9191 €8000 Judith and Holopherne (125x95cm-49x37in) 20-May-3 Babuino, Rome #21/R est:6000-8000

CARAVAGGIO (style) (1573-1610) Italian
£6164 $9616 €9000 Card players (119x150cm-47x59in) prov. 8-Apr-3 Ansorena, Madrid #107/R est:9000
£16026 $25321 €25000 Judith with Olopherne's head (107x136cm-42x54in) 13-Nov-2 Marc Kohn, Paris #32/R est:15000-20000
£280000 $467600 €406000 The flaying of Marsyas (95x136cm-37x54in) prov.lit. 10-Jul-3 Sotheby's, London #37/R est:80000-120000

CARAVANNIEZ, Alfred (1855-?) French
Sculpture
£3113 $5074 €4700 Bayard et Du Guesclin (64x66cm-25x26in) s. brown pat bronze pair. 16-Feb-3 Mercier & Cie, Lille #192/R est:4500-5500

CARAVAQUE, Louis (after) (1684-1754) Russian
£10000 $15800 €15000 Portrait of Tsar Peter the Great, wearing the order of St. Andrew (134x124cm-53x49in) i. 26-Nov-2 Christie's, Kensington #8/R est:10000-15000

CARAVIA-FLORA, Thalia (1871-1960) Greek
£4000 $6320 €6000 Portrait of a beauty (70x55cm-28x22in) 1-Apr-3 Bonhams, New Bond Street #17 est:4000-6000
£9000 $14220 €13500 View of Bebek, Constantinople (62x46cm-24x18in) painted c.1910. 1-Apr-3 Bonhams, New Bond Street #22 est:9000-11000

CARAZO, Ramon (1896-1936) Spanish
£2083 $3292 €3250 Lady with shawl (56x45cm-22x18in) s.i.d.1921. 14-Nov-2 Arte, Seville #397/R

CARBAJO, Tono (1962-) Spanish
£516 $815 €800 Ophelia's ascension (80x60cm-31x24in) s.d.1988 board prov.exhib. 17-Dec-2 Segre, Madrid #198/R

CARBEE, Scott (1860-1946) American
£292 $450 €438 Portrait of a woman seated (84x66cm-33x26in) s.d.1931. 27-Oct-2 Grogan, Boston #42/R
£552 $900 €828 Girl with flowers (69x56cm-27x22in) s. 2-Feb-3 Grogan, Boston #6

CARBONELL Y SELVA, Miguel (1855-1896) Spanish
£1763 $2768 €2750 Church interior (35x47cm-14x19in) s.i. 16-Dec-2 Castellana, Madrid #452/R

CARBONELL, Gonzales (20th C) Spanish
£350 $567 €508 Landscape with farmhouse in the distance and figures, Moncada Rio Besay (64x25cm-25x10in) s. board. 23-May-3 Dee Atkinson & Harrison, Driffield #654/R
£350 $567 €508 Landscape, Masia Canpuliou (20x25cm-8x10in) s. board. 23-May-3 Dee Atkinson & Harrison, Driffield #655

CARBONELL, Santiago (1960-) Spanish
£11650 $18174 €17475 Peras (70x92cm-28x36in) s.d.1997. 17-Oct-2 Louis Morton, Mexico #71/R est:115000-120000 (M.P 185000)

CARBONERO, Maria (1956-) Spanish
Works on paper
£710 $1121 €1100 Smoking (55x46cm-22x18in) s. gouache prov.exhib. 17-Dec-2 Segre, Madrid #222/R

CARBONI, Giovanni Bernardo (attrib) (1616-1683) Italian
£6000 $10020 €8700 Portrait of a lady, holding a fan with her moorish attendant holding a parasol (216x151cm-85x59in) prov. 8-Jul-3 Sotheby's, Olympia #327/R est:7000-10000
Works on paper
£1892 $2951 €2800 Saint Francis (32x25cm-13x10in) pen wash. 27-Mar-3 Maigret, Paris #42/R

CARBONI, Giovanni Bernardo (style) (1616-1683) Italian
£8000 $12880 €12000 Portrait of a knight of Malta (78x65cm-31x26in) 20-Feb-3 Christie's, Kensington #194/R est:1000-1500

CARBONI, Luigi (1957-) Italian
Works on paper
£1056 $1754 €1500 Bianca ombra (102x137cm-40x54in) s.i.d.1991 verso mixed media canvas. 10-Jun-3 Finarte Semenzato, Milan #363/R est:1500-2000

CARDENAS, Augustin (1927-2001) Cuban
Sculpture
£2532 $4000 €4000 Pensee volante (40x22x11cm-16x9x4in) black pat bronze exec.1982. 27-Nov-2 Tajan, Paris #64/R est:7000
£2564 $4026 €4000 Forme verticale (50x15x8cm-20x6x3in) s.d.1975 num.3/6 pat bronze Cast Tesconi. 15-Dec-2 Perrin, Versailles #123/R
£2898 $4753 €4000 Untitled (20x20x17cm-8x8x7in) s.d.1989 base white marble. 27-May-3 Tajan, Paris #43/R est:3000-4000
£3077 $4831 €4800 Forme verticale (70x13x10cm-28x5x4in) s.d. num.2/6 pat bronze Cast Tesconi. 15-Dec-2 Perrin, Versailles #124/R
£3261 $5348 €4500 Narcisse (28x18x12cm-11x7x5in) s. num.3/6 base dark pat bronze. 27-May-3 Tajan, Paris #41/R est:3000-4000
£4082 $6490 €6000 La pensee volante (40x22x11cm-16x9x4in) num.2/8 bronze. 26-Feb-3 Artcurial Briest, Paris #422/R est:3800-4200
£4268 $7000 €6189 Sin titulo (11x25x18cm-4x10x7in) s.i.d.92 black marble prov. 27-May-3 Sotheby's, New York #73
£5096 $8000 €7644 Horse (36x30x14cm-14x12x6in) st.sig.d.1985 num.4/6 brown pat bronze prov.lit. 19-Nov-2 Sotheby's, New York #98/R est:15000
£5183 $8500 €7515 Sin titulo (16x36x16cm-6x14x6in) s.d.91 white marble prov. 27-May-3 Sotheby's, New York #72
£5380 $8500 €8500 Untitled (50x32x32cm-20x13x13in) s.d.1977 white marble prov. 27-Nov-2 Tajan, Paris #63/R
£6410 $10064 €10000 Composition (70x44x16cm-28x17x6in) s.d.1970 white marble. 20-Nov-2 Binoche, Paris #44/R est:12000-13000
£7051 $11071 €11000 Untitled (75cm-30in) init. green pat bronze. 24-Nov-2 Laurence Calmels, Paris #293/R est:10000
£12195 $20000 €18293 Columna (192cm-76in) s.i.d.84 dark brown pat bronze one of 3 prov. 28-May-3 Christie's, Rockefeller NY #116/R est:20000-30000
£15000 $23700 €22500 La mer se parle (27x48cm-11x19in) s.st.f.Tesconi Pietrasanta num.1/3 brown pat bronze prov. 3-Apr-3 Christie's, Kensington #200/R est:10000-15000
£26582 $41469 €42000 Composition aux trois formes (148x64x50cm-58x25x20in) num.7/8 green white pat.bronze. 31-Jul-2 Tajan, Paris #55/R est:50000-60000

CARDENAS, Juan (1939-) Colombian
£11465 $18000 €17198 Self-portrait with cap (79x84cm-31x33in) s. painted c.1985 prov. 20-Nov-2 Christie's, Rockefeller NY #101/R est:30000-40000

CARDI, Lodovico (1559-1613) Italian
£9057 $14128 €14400 Woman, man and two putti (132x98cm-52x39in) 22-Sep-2 Semenzato, Venice #117/R est:16000-25000

CARDINAL, A (?) ?
Works on paper
£400 $624 €600 Coutances, Normandy (65x32cm-26x13in) s.i.d.91 pencil pen ink W/C. 19-Sep-2 Christie's, Kensington #130

CARDINAL-SCHUBERT, Joanne (1942-) Canadian
Works on paper
£378 $620 €548 Watchers (24x31cm-9x12in) s.d.1988 mixed media. 9-Jun-3 Hodgins, Calgary #155/R (C.D 850)

CARDISCO, Marco (c.1486-?) Italian
£6918 $10654 €11000 Mourning (100x109cm-39x43in) board. 23-Oct-2 Finarte, Rome #499/R est:12000-14000

CARDON, Claude (fl.1892-1920) British
£1800 $2880 €2700 Chickens in a stable with a puppy (18x23cm-7x9in) s. sold with a companion. 7-Jan-3 Bonhams, Knightsbridge #252/R est:1000-1500
£1800 $2952 €2700 Feeding time (29x24cm-11x9in) s. 4-Jun-3 Bonhams, Chester #409 est:1200-1600
£3200 $5184 €4800 Changing pastures (50x75cm-20x30in) s.d.16. 20-May-3 Sotheby's, Olympia #199/R est:2000-3000
£3600 $5688 €5400 Young girl carrying a pail of milk (34x52cm-13x20in) s.d.96. 18-Dec-2 John Nicholson, Haslemere #1302 est:2500-3500
£4000 $6360 €6000 Highland cattle watering (51x68cm-20x27in) s. 6-Mar-3 Christie's, Kensington #61/R est:3000-5000

CARDONA LLADOS, Juan (1877-1934) Spanish
£966 $1535 €1400 Maternity (39x30cm-15x12in) s. 4-Mar-3 Ansorena, Madrid #328/R

CARDONA TORRANDELL, Armando (1928-) Spanish
£1773 $2872 €2500 Profanacion (98x68cm-39x27in) i.verso panel. 20-May-3 Segre, Madrid #245/R est:2250

CARDOZO, Eduardo (1965-) Uruguayan
£417 $650 €626 Untitled I (90x60cm-35x24in) s. acrylic. 10-Oct-2 Galleria Y Remates, Montevideo #85/R

CARDOZO, Maria Fernanda (1963-) Colombian
Sculpture
£7643 $12000 €11465 American marble (36x360cm-14x142in) cattle bones prov.exhib.lit. 20-Nov-2 Christie's, Rockefeller NY #55/R est:15000-20000

CARDWELL, Holme (1820-?) British
Sculpture
£14500 $24215 €21025 Greyhounds playing (48x78x43cm-19x31x17in) s.d.1847 white marble. 8-Jul-3 Sotheby's, London #174/R est:15000-20000

CAREE, Georg (?) ?
£1410 $2214 €2200 Path by mountain river (48x69cm-19x27in) s. 21-Nov-2 Van Ham, Cologne #1513/R est:1400

CARELLI, Conrad (1869-?) British
Works on paper
£380 $616 €570 Boats in harbour (24x35cm-9x14in) s.d.1946 W/C. 21-Jan-3 Bonhams, Knightsbridge #91
£500 $810 €750 Venice, early morning (20x26cm-8x10in) s. W/C. 21-Jan-3 Bonhams, Knightsbridge #172/R

CARELLI, Consalve (1818-1900) Italian
£2381 $3786 €3500 Castellammare. Paestum (12cm-5in circular) s. board pair prov. 18-Mar-3 Finarte, Milan #100/R
£2454 $4000 €3681 Fishing in the Bay of Naples (18x36cm-7x14in) s. panel. 16-Feb-3 Jeffery Burchard, Florida #7
£5442 $8653 €8000 Sorrento (24x42cm-9x17in) s.i. panel. 19-Mar-3 Neumeister, Munich #529/R est:3500
£7595 $12000 €12000 Fishermen in Pozzuoli (25x39cm-10x15in) s. i.verso board. 26-Nov-2 Christie's, Rome #163/R est:7500-9000
Works on paper
£510 $811 €750 Spezzano Albanese, Kalabrien (31x42cm-12x17in) s.i. brush. 19-Mar-3 Neumeister, Munich #347
£580 $905 €870 Rural view over a lake (18x26cm-7x10in) s.d.1835 brown wash sold with a W/C by Brand. 25-Mar-3 Bonhams, Knightsbridge #183/R
£701 $1079 €1100 Street with funeral monuments, Pompeii (16x24cm-6x9in) s.d.1833 pencil brown ink W/C with work by another artist two. 3-Sep-2 Christie's, Amsterdam #126
£1880 $2932 €2970 Gulf of Naples (22x22cm-9x9in) W/C. 15-Oct-2 Babuino, Rome #250/R

CARELLI, Consalve (attrib) (1818-1900) Italian
£2500 $4175 €3750 Bay of Naples (23x39cm-9x15in) panel. 18-Jun-3 Christie's, Kensington #169/R est:1800-2200
Works on paper
£878 $1370 €1300 Tonelle (26x36cm-10x14in) s. W/C. 27-Mar-3 Maigret, Paris #213/R

CARELLI, G (19th C) Italian
£1050 $1638 €1575 Fishing in the bay of Naples (28x44cm-11x17in) s.i. 10-Apr-3 Bonhams, Edinburgh #169/R est:600-800
£1400 $2184 €2100 Figures in a Mediterranean landscape (18x32cm-7x13in) s. board. 10-Sep-2 Bonhams, Knightsbridge #22 est:300-500
£1500 $2400 €2250 Castell dell'Ovo (18x35cm-7x14in) s.indis.i. panel. 7-Jan-3 Bonhams, Knightsbridge #208/R est:1000-1500

CARELLI, Gabrielli (1820-1880) Italian
Works on paper
£480 $802 €696 View of Venice (22x13cm-9x5in) s.i. W/C. 24-Jun-3 Bonhams, Knightsbridge #17/R
£800 $1304 €1200 Bay of Naples, with monks and other figures (33x54cm-13x21in) s.d.1859 W/C. 28-Jan-3 Henry Adams, Chichester #383/R
£1300 $2158 €1950 Bay of Naples (34x55cm-13x22in) s.d.1889 W/C. 12-Jun-3 Bonhams, New Bond Street #610/R est:1000-1500
£2500 $4175 €3750 Forum, Rome (35x25cm-14x10in) s.d. pencil W/C. 18-Jun-3 Christie's, Kensington #154a/R est:1500-2000

CARELLI, Giuseppe (1858-1921) Italian
£365 $576 €548 Mediterranean coastal landscape (25x34cm-10x13in) s. board. 29-Nov-2 Zofingen, Switzerland #2409 (S.FR 850)
£1400 $2268 €2100 Above the Bay of Naples (32x16cm-13x6in) s. 23-Jan-3 Christie's, Kensington #155/R est:1200-1800
£1667 $2583 €2600 Italian fishing village (21x41cm-8x16in) s. panel. 5-Dec-2 Dr Fritz Nagel, Stuttgart #644/R est:1200
£2200 $3586 €3300 Beached fishing boats in the Bay of Naples (25x46cm-10x18in) s. 12-Feb-3 Bonhams, Knightsbridge #87/R est:2000-3000
£2635 $4111 €3900 Seascape (13x26cm-5x10in) s. cardboard on board. 28-Mar-3 Farsetti, Prato #700/R
£2867 $4500 €4301 Neapolitan view (27x48cm-11x19in) s. panel. 22-Nov-2 Skinner, Boston #139/R est:2500-3500
£4200 $6678 €6300 Vesuvius. Bay of Naples (19x34cm-7x13in) s. panel pair. 20-Mar-3 Christie's, Kensington #67/R est:2000-3000
£4200 $7014 €6300 Fishing boats on the shore by the bay of Naples (26x48cm-10x19in) s. panel. 18-Jun-3 Christie's, Kensington #168/R est:2500-3500
Works on paper
£323 $510 €500 Seascape with fishermen (16x24cm-6x9in) s. W/C. 18-Dec-2 Finarte, Milan #196
£500 $780 €750 Neopolitan coastal scene with fishing boats at sea and figures along a shore (30x48cm-12x19in) s. pencil W/C htd white. 17-Oct-2 Christie's, Kensington #114

CARELLI, Giuseppe (attrib) (1858-1921) Italian
£2000 $3240 €3000 Bay of Naples (21x41cm-8x16in) bears sig panel. 20-May-3 Sotheby's, Olympia #358/R est:2000-3000

CARELLI, Guido (19th C) Italian
Works on paper
£280 $468 €406 Goatherds by a ruined castle in Italianate landscape (30x48cm-12x19in) i.verso W/C. 25-Jun-3 Cheffins, Cambridge #677

CARELLI, Raffaele (1795-1864) Italian
£68966 $108966 €100000 Amalfi cliffs with convent (100x130cm-39x51in) s.d.1829 exhib.lit. 3-Apr-3 Porro, Milan #57/R est:150000
£82278 $130000 €130000 Tarantella at Frisio (100x128cm-39x50in) s.d.1830 lit. 26-Nov-2 Christie's, Rome #287/R est:130000-150000

CARENA, Antonio (1925-) Italian
£590 $939 €850 Sky, cut, hybrid (100x100cm-39x39in) s.i.d.1980 verso. 1-May-3 Meeting Art, Vercelli #396

CARENA, Felice (1879-1966) Italian
£4487 $6955 €7000 Bull and figures on the beach (31x62cm-12x24in) s. board. 5-Dec-2 Stadion, Trieste #864 est:8000
£5769 $8423 €9000 Still life (50x72cm-20x28in) s.d.1958. 5-Jun-2 Il Ponte, Milan #85/R est:8000-10000
Works on paper
£321 $497 €500 Apocalypse knights (24x34cm-9x13in) s.i.d.1945 Chinese ink. 4-Dec-2 Finarte, Milan #238

CARENA, Primo (1910-) Italian
£321 $503 €500 Landscape (45x60cm-18x24in) s.d.1937 board. 19-Nov-2 Finarte, Milan #115

CARESME, Jacques Philippe (1734-1796) French
Works on paper
£348 $550 €550 Bacchus couronnant Ariane (32x45cm-13x18in) col chk sold with 4 drs by other hands prov. 27-Nov-2 Christie's, Paris #179/R
£1154 $1788 €1800 Deux nymphes endormies et satyres (34x46cm-13x18in) s.d.1763 pen ink wash over crayon. 4-Dec-2 Piasa, Paris #85/R

CARETTE, Fernand (1921-) Belgian
£535 $823 €850 Printemps a Innsbruck (80x95cm-31x37in) s. exhib. 22-Oct-2 Campo & Campo, Antwerp #30

CAREY, J W (20th C) British
Works on paper
£2113 $3297 €3360 Slieve Bernagh (20x36cm-8x14in) s.d.1929 W/C. 8-Oct-2 Loughlin Bowe, Kilkenny #336

CAREY, Joseph William (1859-1937) British
Works on paper
£350 $511 €525 Molly Wards on the Lagan River, Belfast (13x20cm-5x8in) s.d.1922 W/C. 12-Jun-2 John Ross, Belfast #24
£380 $589 €600 Sundown, Loch Gill, Sligo (11x33cm-4x13in) s.d.1917 W/C prov. 24-Sep-2 De Veres Art Auctions, Dublin #13
£420 $651 €630 Kellys coal boat off Donaghadee (23x33cm-9x13in) s.d.1929 W/C. 2-Oct-2 John Ross, Belfast #4
£420 $655 €630 Near Sutton Howth (17x34cm-7x13in) s.i.d.1930 pencil W/C. 18-Sep-2 Dreweatt Neate, Newbury #8
£450 $716 €675 Lagan, near Dromore (25x50cm-10x20in) s.d.1922 W/C. 5-Mar-3 John Ross, Belfast #49
£480 $763 €720 House by the woodlands (25x35cm-10x14in) s.d.1903 W/C. 5-Mar-3 John Ross, Belfast #111/R
£480 $802 €696 Irish lake and mountain landscape (33x41cm-13x16in) s.d.1929 W/C. 20-Jun-3 Keys, Aylsham #488
£500 $775 €750 Happy valley (23x35cm-9x14in) s.d.1922 W/C. 4-Dec-2 John Ross, Belfast #2
£520 $827 €780 Cavehill, Belfast (22x50cm-9x20in) s.d.1922 W/C. 5-Mar-3 John Ross, Belfast #2
£538 $834 €850 Belfast Lough (18x35cm-7x14in) s.i.d.1918 W/C. 25-Sep-2 James Adam, Dublin #123/R
£641 $994 €1000 Near Sutton, Howth (16x33cm-6x13in) s. W/C. 3-Dec-2 Bonhams & James Adam, Dublin #7/R
£680 $1061 €1020 Howth and Ireland's Eye, Malahide (21x37cm-8x15in) s.i.d.1923 pencil W/C. 18-Sep-2 Dreweatt Neate, Newbury #9/R
£738 $1189 €1100 Near Glengariff (27x38cm-11x15in) s.i.d.1929 W/C. 18-Feb-3 Whyte's, Dublin #196/R
£780 $1303 €1131 HMS Sampson, steamship in a choppy sea with sailing ships beyond (27x44cm-11x17in) s. W/C. 25-Jun-3 Cheffins, Cambridge #724
£900 $1404 €1350 Killarney (25x38cm-10x15in) s.d.1913 W/C. 11-Apr-3 Keys, Aylsham #472/R
£950 $1511 €1425 Wind Jammer (17x12cm-7x5in) s.d.1916 W/C. 5-Mar-3 John Ross, Belfast #20
£1000 $1590 €1500 Donegal (25x35cm-10x14in) s. W/C. 5-Mar-3 John Ross, Belfast #124 est:800-1000
£1887 $2943 €3000 Dublin Bay (22x46cm-9x18in) s.i.d.1919 W/C htd bodycol. 17-Sep-2 Whyte's, Dublin #57/R est:3000-4000
£2200 $3432 €3300 View of Castle Place, Belfast. View of the high street, Belfast (26x36cm-10x14in) s.i.d.1890 pencil W/C htd white. 17-Oct-2 Christie's, Kensington #145/R est:2500-3500
£4200 $6720 €6300 Views looking across Ballyholme Bay (24x80cm-9x31in) s.i.d.1929 pencil pen ink W/C htd white pair. 15-May-3 Christie's, London #29/R est:6000

CARGALEIRO, Manuel (1927-) Portuguese
£3396 $5298 €5400 Composition jaune, bleu et noir (36x27cm-14x11in) s.d.1984 gouache. 9-Oct-2 Lombrail & Teucquam, Paris #18/R
Works on paper
£504 $806 €700 Etudes (23x16cm-9x6in) s.i.d.59 Indian ink dr. 16-May-3 Lombrail & Teucquam, Paris #160
£504 $806 €700 Etudes de formes (22x27cm-9x11in) s.d.1960 graphite dr. 16-May-3 Lombrail & Teucquam, Paris #161
£504 $806 €700 Etudes de roches (16x13cm-6x5in) s.d.59 Indian ink. 16-May-3 Lombrail & Teucquam, Paris #162
£504 $806 €700 Etudes de formes (20x13cm-8x5in) s.d.80 Indian ink dr. 16-May-3 Lombrail & Teucquam, Paris #163
£540 $863 €750 Forme abstraite (16x16cm-6x6in) s.d.59 Indian ink dr. 16-May-3 Lombrail & Teucquam, Paris #159
£1151 $1842 €1600 Fleur rougeoyante (32x24cm-13x9in) s.d.1969 wax pastel dr. 16-May-3 Lombrail & Teucquam, Paris #153/R
£1151 $1842 €1600 Fleur (32x24cm-13x9in) s.d.1969 wax pastel dr. 16-May-3 Lombrail & Teucquam, Paris #154/R
£1151 $1842 €1600 Formes florales (31x24cm-12x9in) s.d.1967 wax pastel dr. 16-May-3 Lombrail & Teucquam, Paris #155/R
£1151 $1842 €1600 Etoile et cercles (32x24cm-13x9in) s.d.1967 wax pastel dr. 16-May-3 Lombrail & Teucquam, Paris #156/R
£1151 $1842 €1600 Formes geometriques (32x24cm-13x9in) s.d.1967 wax pastel dr. 16-May-3 Lombrail & Teucquam, Paris #157/R
£1151 $1842 €1600 Formes colorees (32x24cm-13x9in) s.d.1967 wax pastel dr. 16-May-3 Lombrail & Teucquam, Paris #158/R
£1346 $2087 €2100 Composition (11x10cm-4x4in) s.d.1962 gouache. 7-Dec-2 Cornette de St.Cyr, Paris #99/R
£2436 $3776 €3800 Composition (18x14cm-7x6in) s.d.1974 gouache. 7-Dec-2 Cornette de St.Cyr, Paris #97/R
£2564 $3974 €4000 Composition (16x16cm-6x6in) s.d.1974 gouache. 7-Dec-2 Cornette de St.Cyr, Paris #98/R
£3013 $4670 €4700 Composition (25x16cm-10x6in) s.d.1974 gouache. 7-Dec-2 Cornette de St.Cyr, Paris #100/R
£3077 $4769 €4800 Composition (25x16cm-10x6in) s.d.1970 gouache. 7-Dec-2 Cornette de St.Cyr, Paris #101/R

CARGNEL, Lucio (?) Italian
£393 $613 €590 Evening on the Arno by Arrezzo (50x70cm-20x28in) s. i. verso. 6-Nov-2 Dobiaschofsky, Bern #391/R (S.FR 900)
Works on paper
£532 $862 €750 Vita di paese (58x88cm-23x35in) s. mixed media board. 22-May-3 Stadion, Trieste #397/R

CARGNEL, Vittore Antonio (1872-1931) Italian
£680 $1082 €1000 Village (25x15cm-10x6in) s. canvas on cardboard. 18-Mar-3 Finarte, Milan #197/R
£833 $1308 €1300 Market in Monte Belluno (25x30cm-10x12in) s. s.i.d.1929 verso. 16-Dec-2 Pandolfini, Florence #268/R
£952 $1514 €1400 Cadore (16x26cm-6x10in) s. i.verso cardboard painted 1927. 18-Mar-3 Finarte, Milan #194/R
£952 $1514 €1400 Riverbanks (25x40cm-10x16in) s. cardboard painted 1915. 18-Mar-3 Finarte, Milan #200/R
£6452 $10194 €10000 Mill on the Livenza (78x196cm-31x77in) s.d.1910. 18-Dec-2 Finarte, Milan #34/R est:7000

CARIANI, Giovanni de Busi (attrib) (15/16th C) Italian
£3448 $5448 €5000 Portrait of lady half length (47x36cm-19x14in) 5-Apr-3 Finarte Semenzato, Milan #27/R est:7000

CARIANI, Giovanni de Busi (studio) (15/16th C) Italian
£22152 $35000 €35000 Christ and Veronica (117x184cm-46x72in) 2-Dec-2 Finarte, Milan #183/R est:30000

CARIGIET, Alois (1902-1985) Swiss
£6438 $10172 €9657 Minca (73x60cm-29x24in) mono.i.d.68-70. 28-Nov-2 Christie's, Zurich #110/R est:15000-25000 (S.FR 15000)
£7860 $12341 €11790 Peasant and horse with sledge in snow (38x55cm-15x22in) s.d.1948. 25-Nov-2 Sotheby's, Zurich #125/R est:18000-25000 (S.FR 18000)
£25943 $42028 €45920 Zarli Carigiet (116x88cm-46x35in) mono.d.1958. 26-May-3 Sotheby's, Zurich #107/R est:60000-80000 (S.FR 55000)
Works on paper
£284 $446 €426 Untitled (11x17cm-4x7in) s.d.1961 W/C over pencil. 25-Nov-2 Germann, Zurich #696 (S.FR 650)
£386 $610 €579 Zegn furnischa leivras (22x14cm-9x6in) pencil brush lit. 26-Nov-2 Phillips, Zurich #75/R (S.FR 900)
£478 $741 €717 Standing female nude (36x25cm-14x10in) s. pencil. 4-Dec-2 Koller, Zurich #138a/R (S.FR 1100)
£601 $949 €902 Mama in Anguoscha e Pisser (22x14cm-9x6in) pencil brush lit. 26-Nov-2 Phillips, Zurich #74/R (S.FR 1400)
£783 $1213 €1175 Two owls (21x28cm-8x11in) mono.d.1966 pencil wash prov. 4-Dec-2 Koller, Zurich #127/R est:2000-3000 (S.FR 1800)
£1048 $1645 €1572 Street with street lamps - Paris (33x24cm-13x9in) s.i.d.1930 pencil col pen gouache. 25-Nov-2 Sotheby's, Zurich #80/R est:2000-3000 (S.FR 2400)
£1126 $1745 €1689 Corvatsch (22x30cm-9x12in) monno.i.d.65 W/C pencil. 24-Sep-2 Koller, Zurich #6668/R est:1600-2100 (S.FR 2600)
£1135 $1783 €1703 Street scene - Paris (33x24cm-13x9in) s.i.d.1930 pencil col pen gouache. 25-Nov-2 Sotheby's, Zurich #81/R est:2000-3000 (S.FR 2600)
£1202 $1899 €1803 Dani, tias nursas (22x18cm-9x7in) pencil W/C gouache lit. 26-Nov-2 Phillips, Zurich #76/R est:2500-3500 (S.FR 2800)
£1202 $1899 €1803 Three dancers getting dressed (20x28cm-8x11in) s. pen ink dr W/C. 29-Nov-2 Zofingen, Switzerland #2822/R est:1500 (S.FR 2800)
£1288 $2034 €1932 Aint a putschai (19x14cm-7x6in) pencil W/C gouache lit. 26-Nov-2 Phillips, Zurich #77/R est:2500-3500 (S.FR 3000)
£1310 $2044 €1965 Woman binding bessel brooms (21x17cm-8x7in) mono.d.78 pencil dr W/C. 8-Nov-2 Dobiaschofsky, Bern #242/R est:3600 (S.FR 3000)
£1509 $2445 €2672 Interior with red sofa (34x35cm-13x14in) s.d.1942 pencil Indian ink W/C. 26-May-3 Sotheby's, Zurich #127/R est:2000-2500 (S.FR 3200)

CARION, Edouard (1825-1864) Belgian
£1090 $1689 €1700 Portrait d'un couple noble (133x108cm-52x43in) s. 3-Dec-2 Campo & Campo, Antwerp #39/R est:1000-1400

CARION, Marius (1898-1949) Belgian
£922 $1540 €1300 Le village sous la neige (50x60cm-20x24in) s.d.1929. 18-Jun-3 Hotel des Ventes Mosan, Brussels #266
Works on paper
£329 $513 €520 Tete de mineur (40x30cm-16x12in) s. i.d.1931 verso mixed media. 16-Sep-2 Horta, Bruxelles #7

CARIOT, Gustave (1872-1950) French
£611 $954 €917 Summer field landscape (32x41cm-13x16in) s.d.1928 prov. 9-Nov-2 Galerie Gloggner, Luzern #24/R (S.FR 1400)
£1197 $1927 €1700 Pecheurs sur le petit pont pres de la riviere (60x80cm-24x31in) s.d.1927. 11-May-3 Thierry & Lannon, Brest #149/R est:2000-2500
£1796 $2891 €2550 Meules (60x80cm-24x31in) s.d.1927. 11-May-3 Thierry & Lannon, Brest #148/R est:2000-2500

CARL, Adolf (1814-1845) German
£7601 $11858 €11402 Fields of heather, Altona and Hamburg in the distance (55x78cm-22x31in) s. prov. 23-Sep-2 Rasmussen, Vejle #74/R est:100000 (D.KR 90000)

CARL-ROSA, Mario (1855-1913) French
£1644 $2564 €2400 Temps gris sur le bord de la Seine (32x50cm-13x20in) s. panel. 10-Apr-3 Van Ham, Cologne #1357/R est:1500

CARLANDI, Onorato (1848-1939) Italian
Works on paper
£650 $1021 €975 Young woman on the road (47x32cm-19x13in) s. pencil W/C. 16-Apr-3 Christie's, Kensington #976/R

CARLAW, William (1847-1889) British
Works on paper
£780 $1232 €1170 Quaint old village of Polperro, Cornwall (39x74cm-15x29in) s.d.1882 W/C htd white. 7-Apr-3 Bonhams, Bath #22/R

CARLBERG, Hugo (1880-1943) Swedish
£315 $498 €473 Spring landscape (100x100cm-39x39in) s.d.1916. 16-Nov-2 Crafoord, Lund #18/R (S.KR 4500)

CARLE, Pontus (1955-) ?
£392 $611 €580 Composition (61x46cm-24x18in) s. s.d.1989 verso. 28-Mar-3 Charbonneaux, Paris #47/R
£638 $1066 €900 Ouverture (65x50cm-26x20in) s. 18-Jun-3 Charbonneaux, Paris #114
£705 $1107 €1100 Composition (65x50cm-26x20in) s.d. acrylic collage. 16-Dec-2 Charbonneaux, Paris #125
£705 $1107 €1100 Composition (65x50cm-26x20in) s.d. acrylic collage. 16-Dec-2 Charbonneaux, Paris #126

CARLES, Arthur B (1882-1952) American
£1751 $2750 €2627 Seated nude woman (46x33cm-18x13in) s. board. 23-Nov-2 Pook & Pook, Downington #310/R est:3000-5000
£3145 $5000 €4718 Portrait of a woman seated before a velvet drape (62x51cm-24x20in) 7-Mar-3 Skinner, Boston #583/R est:10000-15000
£37037 $60000 €55556 French farm house (27x41cm-11x16in) painted c.1910-14 prov.exhib.lit. 21-May-3 Sotheby's, New York #39/R est:25000-35000
£92593 $150000 €138890 Still life with summer flowers (81x91cm-32x36in) s. painted c.1926 prov.exhib. 21-May-3 Sotheby's, New York #32/R est:80000-120000
£104938 $170000 €157407 Still life, flowers (174x116cm-69x46in) s. painted c.1925-26 prov.exhib.lit. 21-May-3 Sotheby's, New York #16/R est:150000-200000

CARLES, Domingo (1888-1962) Spanish
£1448 $2303 €2100 Vase of flowers (50x61cm-20x24in) s. s.d.1951 verso. 4-Mar-3 Ansorena, Madrid #12/R

CARLES, Jean Antonin (1851-1919) French
Sculpture
£1439 $2302 €2000 Bacchus, enfant (48x27cm-19x11in) s.st.f.Siot gold pat bronze. 18-May-3 Rabourdin & Choppin de Janvry, Paris #71/R est:2000-3000
£1795 $2836 €2800 Bacchus (59cm-23in) s. pat bronze Cast Siot. 18-Nov-2 Tajan, Paris #86 est:2500-2800

CARLEVARIS, Luca (1665-1731) Italian
£200000 $334000 €290000 Venice, a view of the Grand Canal with the Church of Santa Maria Della Salute (76x131cm-30x52in) prov. 10-Jul-3 Sotheby's, London #57/R est:200000-300000

CARLEVARIS, Luca (after) (1665-1731) Italian
£8000 $12400 €12000 Molo and the Riva degli Schiavoni, Venice. Molo and the Piazzetta, Venice (69x91cm-27x36in) pair. 30-Oct-2 Christie's, Kensington #167/R est:8000-12000

CARLEVARIS, Luca (circle) (1665-1731) Italian
£3871 $6000 €5807 Piazzetta de San Marco, Venice (51x60cm-20x24in) prov. 2-Oct-2 Christie's, Rockefeller NY #144/R est:10000-15000

CARLIER DE ABAUNZA (?) French?
£886 $1382 €1400 Amateurs en peinture (41x32cm-16x13in) s. s.i.verso panel after Ernest Meissoonier. 20-Oct-2 Anaf, Lyon #79/R

CARLIER, Max (1872-1938) Belgian
£514 $801 €750 Coupe garnie de raisins et de roses (45x55cm-18x22in) s. 14-Apr-3 Horta, Bruxelles #344
£586 $926 €850 Vase de roses (45x37cm-18x15in) s. 1-Apr-3 Palais de Beaux Arts, Brussels #514
£612 $978 €850 Prunes, groseilles et cruche (45x37cm-18x15in) s. 13-May-3 Palais de Beaux Arts, Brussels #222
£676 $1054 €1000 Nature morte aux fruits et aux roses (64x40cm-25x16in) s. 25-Mar-3 Campo & Campo, Antwerp #30
£680 $1082 €1000 Nature morte aux fleurs et trophee de chasse (60x46cm-24x18in) s. 18-Mar-3 Vanderkindere, Brussels #79
£1266 $1975 €2000 Nature morte aux fleurs et aux fruits (88x58cm-35x23in) s. 10-Sep-2 Vanderkindere, Brussels #409/R est:2000-3000
£1295 $2072 €1800 Composition florale sur en entablement (91x61cm-36x24in) s. 19-May-3 Horta, Bruxelles #87 est:2000-3000
£1392 $2172 €2200 Mousquetaires jouant aux echecs (85x112cm-33x44in) s. 15-Oct-2 Horta, Bruxelles #368
£1392 $2172 €2200 Mousquetaires jouant aux des (85x112cm-33x44in) s. 15-Oct-2 Horta, Bruxelles #367
£1486 $2319 €2200 Nature morte aux fleurs et aux fruits (87x57cm-34x22in) s. 25-Mar-3 Campo & Campo, Antwerp #29/R est:2400-2800
£2038 $3180 €3200 Jeune fille au bouquet de fleurs dans un paysage lacustre (110x74cm-43x29in) s. 11-Nov-2 Horta, Bruxelles #190/R est:3000-4000
£2113 $3401 €3000 Still life with white roses (66x105cm-26x41in) s. 12-May-3 Bernaerts, Antwerp #304/R est:3000-4000
£4241 $6700 €6700 Still life of flowers (60x50cm-24x20in) s.i. lit. 29-Nov-2 Schloss Ahlden, Ahlden #1222/R est:6800
£4676 $7482 €6500 Still life with flowers and fruit (80x120cm-31x47in) s. 17-May-3 De Vuyst, Lokeren #533/R est:8000-9000
£5000 $8100 €7500 Still life of a jug filled with roses and other flowers (98x68cm-39x27in) 21-May-3 Bonhams, Knightsbridge #192/R est:5000-8000

CARLIER, Modeste (1820-1878) Belgian
£355 $592 €500 Portrait d'homme assis sur une terrasse (141x106cm-56x42in) s.d. 17-Jun-3 Palais de Beaux Arts, Brussels #516

CARLIERI, Alberto (1672-1720) Italian
£18293 $30000 €27440 Capriccio of a ruined Corinthian temple with figures, landscape beyond (133x98cm-52x39in) 29-May-3 Sotheby's, New York #154/R est:20000-30000
£41379 $65793 €60000 Landscapes with ruins (98x74cm-39x29in) pair. 9-Mar-3 Semenzato, Venice #36/R est:70000

CARLIN, James (1909-) American
£323 $500 €485 Road from the village (51x71cm-20x28in) s. painted c.1940. 8-Dec-2 Toomey, Oak Park #766/R

CARLINE, George (1855-1920) British
£420 $655 €630 Capri (42x34cm-17x13in) canvasboard prov. 27-Mar-3 Christie's, Kensington #421/R
Works on paper
£400 $632 €580 Woman holding a cockerel (38x24cm-15x9in) W/C. 22-Jul-3 Bonhams, Knightsbridge #189/R

CARLINE, Sydney William (1888-1929) British
Works on paper
£500 $825 €725 Teheran, Persia the gateway of the Great Square (28x27cm-11x11in) s.i.d.1919 pencil W/C prov. 3-Jul-3 Christie's, Kensington #279/R

CARLISLE, Mary Helen (1869-1925) American
Works on paper
£314 $500 €471 Otto Kahn's house, Cedar Court, Long Island (58x46cm-23x18in) init. pastel board. 5-Mar-3 Doyle, New York #13/R

CARLO, Vittorio Maria di (1939-) Italian
£285 $444 €450 Musician (60x60cm-24x24in) s. s.verso oil collage. 14-Sep-2 Meeting Art, Vercelli #304
£294 $471 €450 Musician (50x50cm-20x20in) s. painted 1997. 4-Jan-3 Meeting Art, Vercelli #427

£316 $494 €500 Figure with sailing boat (70x50cm-28x20in) s. oil sand. 14-Sep-2 Meeting Art, Vercelli #414
£321 $503 €500 Manila girl (70x70cm-28x28in) s. s.verso. 23-Nov-2 Meeting Art, Vercelli #158/R
£327 $523 €500 Waiting (60x60cm-24x24in) s. oil sand. 4-Jan-3 Meeting Art, Vercelli #145
£327 $523 €500 Figures with vase of flowers (70x70cm-28x28in) s. painted 1994. 4-Jan-3 Meeting Art, Vercelli #474
£327 $523 €500 Figure with budgie (70x70cm-28x28in) s. 4-Jan-3 Meeting Art, Vercelli #673
£327 $523 €500 Sitar player (80x80cm-31x31in) s. painted 1991. 4-Jan-3 Meeting Art, Vercelli #685
£340 $541 €500 Sari Sari (100x70cm-39x28in) s. painted 1994. 1-Mar-3 Meeting Art, Vercelli #458
£347 $552 €500 Girl with watermelon (70x70cm-28x28in) s. painted 1995. 1-May-3 Meeting Art, Vercelli #79
£348 $543 €550 Friends (70x100cm-28x39in) s. s.verso oil collage. 14-Sep-2 Meeting Art, Vercelli #190
£353 $554 €550 Figure (70x70cm-28x28in) s. s.verso. 23-Nov-2 Meeting Art, Vercelli #405/R
£443 $691 €700 Two figures (70x100cm-28x39in) s. s.verso oil on sand. 14-Sep-2 Meeting Art, Vercelli #475
£660 $1049 €950 Love serenade (70x100cm-28x39in) s. 1-May-3 Meeting Art, Vercelli #525

CARLONE, Carlo (1686-1776) Italian
Works on paper
£7000 $11690 €10150 Baptism of Constantine (35x20cm-14x8in) pen brown ink wash traces chk. 9-Jul-3 Sotheby's, London #42/R est:4000-6000

CARLONE, Carlo (attrib) (1686-1776) Italian
£3200 $4960 €4800 Allegorical scene (23x46cm-9x18in) modello for a ceiling painting. 30-Oct-2 Christie's, Kensington #146/R est:1000-1500

CARLONI, Carlo (attrib) (fl.1800-1805) Italian
Miniatures
£2000 $3180 €2900 La meretrix, ou l'entremetteuse (12x16cm-5x6in) s. oval. 5-Mar-3 Oger, Dumont, Paris #17/R est:800-1000

CARLSEN, Bjorn (1945-) Norwegian
£1298 $2050 €1947 Study for a modern Sphinx (84x76cm-33x30in) s. 2-Dec-2 Blomqvist, Oslo #474/R est:30000-35000 (N.KR 15000)
£2602 $4059 €3903 Study - head of an object collector (98x88cm-39x35in) init.d.73 exhib. 21-Oct-2 Blomqvist, Oslo #415/R est:35000-45000 (N.KR 30000)

CARLSEN, Carl (1855-1917) Danish
£329 $514 €494 Woodland glade (53x62cm-21x24in) init. 23-Sep-2 Rasmussen, Vejle #96/R (D.KR 3900)
£1034 $1571 €1551 Still life of oranges, grapes and flowers (55x89cm-22x35in) s. 27-Aug-2 Rasmussen, Copenhagen #1821/R est:15000-20000 (D.KR 12000)
£2305 $3734 €3458 Woodland with lake and swans. s. 25-Jan-3 Rasmussen, Havnen #2110/R est:30000-40000 (D.KR 26000)
£2883 $4641 €4325 Interior from a smithy (69x105cm-27x41in) s.d.80. 22-Feb-3 Rasmussen, Havnen #2091/R est:30000 (D.KR 32000)

CARLSEN, Dines (1901-1966) American
£2516 $4000 €3774 Still life with jar and silver pieces (46x38cm-18x15in) s. masonite. 5-Mar-3 Christie's, Rockefeller NY #105/R est:3000-5000
£3145 $5000 €4718 Peones (61x50cm-24x20in) s.i. s.i.verso masonite prov. 5-Mar-3 Sotheby's, New York #39/R est:7000-10000

CARLSEN, Emil (1853-1932) American/Danish
£573 $900 €860 Northeaster, Maine. i. 13-Dec-2 Skinner, Bolton #890/R
£1282 $2000 €1923 Study of sky (18x25cm-7x10in) s. artist panel. 14-Sep-2 Selkirks, St. Louis #120/R est:1000-1500
£4717 $7500 €7076 Copper pots, lemons and grapes (38x41cm-15x16in) s. prov. 5-Mar-3 Sotheby's, New York #57/R est:10000-15000
£6369 $10000 €9554 Hillside landscape (30x40cm-12x16in) s.d.1905. 22-Nov-2 Skinner, Boston #242/R est:15000-20000
£7792 $12000 €11688 Golden afternoon (71x56cm-28x22in) s.d.29 prov. 24-Oct-2 Shannon's, Milford #20/R est:12000-18000
£17500 $27475 €26250 Still life of a copper pot and turnips (15x12cm-6x5in) s. board. 16-Dec-2 Bonhams, Bury St Edmunds #520/R est:1000-1500
£23718 $37000 €35577 Still life with iron cauldron, glass vase, garlic bulbs and teapot in background (51x41cm-20x16in) s. 12-Apr-3 Brunk, Ashville #793/R est:800-1500
£35484 $55000 €53226 Moonlight (114x94cm-45x37in) s.d.1928. 5-Dec-2 Christie's, Rockefeller NY #73/R est:60000-80000
£80247 $130000 €120371 Leeds jug (41x36cm-16x14in) s.d.1920 canvas on board prov.lit. 21-May-3 Sotheby's, New York #162/R est:40000-60000

CARLSEN, Lise Waino (1955-) Danish
£466 $740 €699 Collage (100x100cm-39x39in) mono. 10-Mar-3 Rasmussen, Vejle #633 (D.KR 5000)

CARLSEN, Peter (20th C) Danish
£947 $1469 €1421 Composition (160x135cm-63x53in) s.d.87. 4-Dec-2 Kunsthallen, Copenhagen #223/R (D.KR 11000)

CARLSON, George (1940-) American
Works on paper
£2244 $3500 €3366 Fires of twilight (51x48cm-20x19in) pastel. 9-Nov-2 Altermann Galleries, Santa Fe #29/R

CARLSON, John F (1875-1947) American
£8383 $14000 €12155 Morning on the stream (76x102cm-30x40in) s. i.verso. 21-Jun-3 Selkirks, St. Louis #174/R est:5000-7000
£11111 $18000 €16667 Woodland repose (76x102cm-30x40in) s. s.i.on stretcher painted 1915 prov.lit. 21-May-3 Sotheby's, New York #167/R est:20000-30000
£12500 $20000 €18125 Early winter (64x76cm-25x30in) s. 17-May-3 CRN Auctions, Cambridge #45

CARLSON, Ken (1937-) American
£3356 $4900 €5034 Indian summer's elk (20x30cm-8x12in) 18-May-2 Altermann Galleries, Santa Fe #214/R
£5063 $8000 €7341 Pronghorn antelope (46x61cm-18x24in) s. board prov. 26-Jul-3 Coeur d'Alene, Hayden #90/R est:10000-15000
£5696 $9000 €8259 Shoreline (33x46cm-13x18in) s. board. 26-Jul-3 Coeur d'Alene, Hayden #193/R est:8000-12000
£16026 $25000 €24039 Western foothill - Mule deer (61x102cm-24x40in) board. 9-Nov-2 Altermann Galleries, Santa Fe #235
£18987 $30000 €27531 Put to the test (51x102cm-20x40in) s. prov. 26-Jul-3 Coeur d'Alene, Hayden #224/R est:15000-25000
£20253 $32000 €29367 Rams in late light (46x91cm-18x36in) s. board. 26-Jul-3 Coeur d'Alene, Hayden #128/R est:20000-30000

CARLSON-BREDBERG, Mina (1857-1943) Swedish
£371 $615 €538 Interior scene with woman (21x30cm-8x12in) s. panel. 16-Jun-3 Lilla Bukowskis, Stockholm #165 (S.KR 4800)

CARLSTEDT, Birger (1907-1975) Finnish
£494 $770 €780 Flower vase (55x46cm-22x18in) s.d.1945. 12-Sep-2 Hagelstam, Helsinki #865
£929 $1515 €1394 Waiting (120x114cm-47x45in) s.d.1939. 17-Feb-3 Blomqvist, Lysaker #1112 (N.KR 10500)
£952 $1514 €1400 Still life of flowers (56x46cm-22x18in) s.d.1945. 27-Feb-3 Hagelstam, Helsinki #881/R
£1038 $1598 €1650 Still life (73x60cm-29x24in) s.d.1944. 24-Oct-2 Hagelstam, Helsinki #915 est:1200
£1329 $2100 €2100 Flowers in vase (73x61cm-29x24in) s. board. 1-Dec-2 Bukowskis, Helsinki #309/R est:1500-1800
£5696 $9000 €9000 Composition (44x38cm-17x15in) s.d.1950 board. 30-Nov-2 Hagelstam, Helsinki #166/R est:4000

CARLSTEDT, Mikko (1892-1964) Finnish
£340 $523 €540 Town (43x63cm-17x25in) s.d.1914. 24-Oct-2 Hagelstam, Helsinki #947
£510 $836 €780 Landscape from Tavastland (45x56cm-18x22in) s.d.19 exhib. 9-Feb-3 Bukowskis, Helsinki #208/R
£516 $815 €800 Landscape (62x80cm-24x31in) s. 19-Dec-2 Hagelstam, Helsinki #933
£544 $865 €800 Still life of flowers (65x54cm-26x21in) s.d.57. 24-Mar-3 Bukowskis, Helsinki #46/R
£597 $920 €950 Flowers (61x50cm-24x20in) s.d.1941. 24-Oct-2 Hagelstam, Helsinki #970
£791 $1298 €1100 Self-portrait (50x40cm-20x16in) s. 5-Jun-3 Hagelstam, Helsinki #832
£816 $1298 €1200 Flowers (73x60cm-29x24in) s. 27-Feb-3 Hagelstam, Helsinki #897/R
£845 $1361 €1200 Still life of apples, books and potted plant (60x73cm-24x29in) s.d.52. 10-May-3 Bukowskis, Helsinki #91/R
£884 $1406 €1300 Still life of flowers (65x55cm-26x22in) s.d.45. 24-Mar-3 Bukowskis, Helsinki #45/R
£915 $1501 €1400 Still life of flowers (66x54cm-26x21in) s.d.40. 9-Feb-3 Bukowskis, Helsinki #207/R
Works on paper
£303 $479 €440 Woman (33x24cm-13x9in) s. W/C. 3-Apr-3 Hagelstam, Helsinki #999

CARLSTROM, Gustaf (1896-1964) Swedish
£864 $1417 €1253 The sunniest point (65x81cm-26x32in) s. panel. 4-Jun-3 AB Stockholms Auktionsverk #2314/R (S.KR 11000)
£1051 $1640 €1577 Stone masons (83x62cm-33x24in) s.d.1939. 5-Nov-2 Bukowskis, Stockholm #132/R est:15000-20000 (S.KR 15000)
£1206 $1869 €1809 Girl in summer garden (55x50cm-22x20in) s. 8-Dec-2 Uppsala Auktionskammare, Uppsala #195/R est:15000-20000 (S.KR 17000)

£1358 $2199 €1969 Small girl by watercourse (46x55cm-18x22in) s. 26-May-3 Bukowskis, Stockholm #126/R est:15000-18000 (S.KR 17500)

£1414 $2319 €2050 Almost impossible to reach (65x82cm-26x32in) s. 4-Jun-3 AB Stockholms Auktionsverk #2299/R est:18000-20000 (S.KR 18000)

£1707 $2765 €2475 Girls on cliff by sea (73x82cm-29x32in) s. 25-May-3 Uppsala Auktionskammare, Uppsala #200/R est:15000-20000 (S.KR 22000)

£1915 $2968 €2873 Small girl in summer meadow (74x60cm-29x24in) s,. 3-Dec-2 Bukowskis, Stockholm #115/R est:20000-22000 (S.KR 27000)

CARLSUND, Otto (1897-1948) Swedish

£1236 $1989 €1854 Portrait de jeune femme assise les mains jointes, sur fond blanc (41x32cm-16x13in) panel. 7-May-3 AB Stockholms Auktionsverk #630/R est:30000-40000 (S.KR 16000)

£2780 $4476 €4170 Maisons le long d'une route (33x41cm-13x16in) indis.mono.i. panel. 7-May-3 AB Stockholms Auktionsverk #631/R est:50000-60000 (S.KR 36000)

£4247 $6838 €6371 Nature morte auz silhouettes (35x27cm-14x11in) panel. 7-May-3 AB Stockholms Auktionsverk #623/R est:80000-100000 (S.KR 55000)

£4942 $7957 €7413 Portrait d'une jeune femme assise les main jointes, sur fond lbeu (41x33cm-16x13in) panel. 7-May-3 AB Stockholms Auktionsverk #614/R est:80000-100000 (S.KR 64000)

£7336 $11811 €11004 Nature morte au nu et a la cruche (22x27cm-9x11in) panel. 7-May-3 AB Stockholms Auktionsverk #635/R est:25000-30000 (S.KR 95000)

£9459 $15230 €14189 Composition geometrique auc deux roses blaches (35x26cm-14x10in) panel. 7-May-3 AB Stockholms Auktionsverk #644/R est:60000-80000 (S.KR 122500)

£11197 $18027 €16796 Nu dans l'atelier - portrait presume de Fernand Leger (35x27cm-14x11in) oil pencil panel. 7-May-3 AB Stockholms Auktionsverk #627/R est:80000-100000 (S.KR 145000)

£12355 $19892 €18533 Composition a la statue, vase, paravent et tuyau (35x26cm-14x10in) init.d.24. 7-May-3 AB Stockholms Auktionsverk #619/R est:125000-150000 (S.KR 160000)

Works on paper

£347 $559 €521 Etude mecanique (24x20cm-9x8in) pencil. 7-May-3 AB Stockholms Auktionsverk #617/R (S.KR 4500)

£347 $559 €521 La terasse du Dome (24x20cm-9x8in) ink. 7-May-3 AB Stockholms Auktionsverk #640/R (S.KR 4500)

£357 $567 €536 Figural composition (8x14cm-3x6in) pencil. 3-Mar-3 Lilla Bukowskis, Stockholm #795 (S.KR 4800)

£371 $597 €557 Etudes de machines et compositions (24x20cm-9x8in) pencil. 7-May-3 AB Stockholms Auktionsverk #620/R (S.KR 4800)

£386 $622 €579 Composition a la guitare, boutelle et journal (24x20cm-9x8in) pencil. 7-May-3 AB Stockholms Auktionsverk #636/R (S.KR 5000)

£425 $684 €638 Buraliste tabac (24x20cm-9x8in) ink pencil. 7-May-3 AB Stockholms Auktionsverk #624/R (S.KR 5500)

£502 $808 €753 Trois etudes de figures (20x24cm-8x9in) pencil. 7-May-3 AB Stockholms Auktionsverk #637/R (S.KR 6500)

£656 $1057 €984 Attela tinant une charrue (11x27cm-4x11in) pencil. 7-May-3 AB Stockholms Auktionsverk #615/R (S.KR 8500)

£734 $1181 €1101 Composition (24x20cm-9x8in) ink W/C chl. 7-May-3 AB Stockholms Auktionsverk #629/R (S.KR 9500)

£811 $1305 €1217 Grouple de musciciens (24x20cm-9x8in) pencil. 7-May-3 AB Stockholms Auktionsverk #625/R (S.KR 10500)

£913 $1442 €1370 Nature morte (23x31cm-9x12in) s.d.34 W/C. 28-Apr-3 Bukowskis, Stockholm #136/R (S.KR 12000)

£2625 $4227 €3938 Etude mecanique et chiffres en marge (24x20cm-9x8in) ink pencil. 7-May-3 AB Stockholms Auktionsverk #641/R est:12000-15000 (S.KR 34000)

£2703 $4351 €4055 Composition (20x13cm-8x5in) W/C gouache pencil. 7-May-3 AB Stockholms Auktionsverk #634/R est:15000-20000 (S.KR 35000)

£2780 $4476 €4170 Composition (24x20cm-9x8in) W/C gouache pencil. 7-May-3 AB Stockholms Auktionsverk #613/R est:10000-12000 (S.KR 36000)

£4247 $6838 €6371 Etude pour un contrebassiste, etude de frise, elements decoratifs (24x20cm-9x8in) gouache pencil lit. 7-May-3 AB Stockholms Auktionsverk #622/R est:25000-30000 (S.KR 55000)

£4247 $6838 €6371 Etude au violoncelle et a la lettre R (24x20cm-9x8in) ink. 7-May-3 AB Stockholms Auktionsverk #626/R est:20000-25000 (S.KR 55000)

£5405 $8703 €8108 Roi de trefle - King of Clubs (13x12cm-5x5in) gouache. 7-May-3 AB Stockholms Auktionsverk #697/R est:12000-15000 (S.KR 70000)

CARLTON, Frederick (19th C) British

£520 $811 €780 Landscapes in Berkshire and Surrey with woodcutters and gypsy encampment (30x46cm-12x18in) s. i.verso pair. 10-Apr-3 Brightwells, Leominster #935/R

£950 $1520 €1425 Scene in the Cumbrian mountains with sheep (51x75cm-20x30in) s. 8-Jan-3 George Kidner, Lymington #196/R

CARLTON, Paddy (1936-) Australian

£728 $1143 €1092 Untitled (81x101cm-32x40in) i.verso acrylic. 15-Apr-3 Lawson Menzies, Sydney #107/R est:1800-2300 (A.D 1900)

CARLYLE, Florence (1864-1923) Canadian

£3629 $5734 €5444 Birthday (100x80cm-39x31in) s. prov. 18-Nov-2 Sotheby's, Toronto #156/R est:10000-12000 (C.D 9000)

£4839 $7645 €7259 Cottage garden with black cat (78x61cm-31x24in) s. prov.lit. 18-Nov-2 Sotheby's, Toronto #7/R est:12000-15000 (C.D 12000)

CARMASSI, Arturo (1925-) Italian

£253 $395 €400 Composition (63x51cm-25x20in) s. tempera W/C card. 14-Sep-2 Meeting Art, Vercelli #65

£6410 $10064 €10000 Composition (45x35cm-18x14in) s.i.d.1957 verso oil enamel tempera collage. 20-Nov-2 Pandolfini, Florence #103/R est:12000

£7092 $11489 €10000 Untitled (100x100cm-39x39in) s.d.54 prov. 26-May-3 Christie's, Milan #183/R est:2000-3000

CARMELO DE ARZADUN (1888-1968) Uruguayan

£535 $850 €803 Urban landscape (44x38cm-17x15in) s. cardboard. 2-Mar-3 Galleria Y Remates, Montevideo #20/R

£597 $950 €896 Montevideo from the Canteras (38x46cm-15x18in) s.d.1937 board prov. 2-Mar-3 Galleria Y Remates, Montevideo #21/R

£813 $1300 €1220 Farm (35x54cm-14x21in) s. cardboard. 5-Jan-3 Galleria Y Remates, Montevideo #78/R

£897 $1400 €1346 Girl and cat (47x37cm-19x15in) s.d.1939 cardboard. 10-Oct-2 Galleria Y Remates, Montevideo #69/R

Works on paper

£500 $800 €750 Cathedral (32x23cm-13x9in) s.d.1964 col crayon dr. 5-Jan-3 Galleria Y Remates, Montevideo #50/R

CARMI, Eugenio (1920-) Italian

£253 $395 €400 Big circle (25x25cm-10x10in) s.d.2000 s.i.d.verso. 14-Sep-2 Meeting Art, Vercelli #116/R

£313 $497 €450 Unruly square (25x25cm-10x10in) s.d.2000. 1-May-3 Meeting Art, Vercelli #40

£327 $523 €500 Crack (30x35cm-12x14in) s.d.2001. 4-Jan-3 Meeting Art, Vercelli #83

£340 $541 €500 Metaphor (25x25cm-10x10in) s.d.2000. 1-Mar-3 Meeting Art, Vercelli #401

£359 $575 €550 Transparency (30x40cm-12x16in) s.d.2001. 4-Jan-3 Meeting Art, Vercelli #591

£385 $604 €600 Square poem (30x30cm-12x12in) s. s.i.d.1998 verso. 23-Nov-2 Meeting Art, Vercelli #30/R

£442 $703 €650 Small line (35x30cm-14x12in) s.i.d.1999 verso. 1-Mar-3 Meeting Art, Vercelli #380

£458 $732 €700 Contrasts (30x35cm-12x14in) s.d.2001. 4-Jan-3 Meeting Art, Vercelli #604

£486 $773 €700 Visual noise (30x30cm-12x12in) s.i.d.1998 verso. 1-May-3 Meeting Art, Vercelli #441

£490 $784 €750 Balanced square (40x40cm-16x16in) s.i.d.2000 verso. 4-Jan-3 Meeting Art, Vercelli #399

£490 $784 €750 Unstable (40x30cm-16x12in) s.d.1999. 4-Jan-3 Meeting Art, Vercelli #606

£544 $865 €800 Escape (40x30cm-16x12in) s.d.2001. 1-Mar-3 Meeting Art, Vercelli #414

£590 $939 €850 Small magic circle (30x40cm-12x16in) s.i.d.2000 verso. 1-May-3 Meeting Art, Vercelli #195

£633 $987 €1000 Secret image (60x60cm-24x24in) s.d.1994. 14-Sep-2 Meeting Art, Vercelli #826/R

£638 $1034 €900 Ossimoro (60x60cm-24x24in) s. verso. 22-May-3 Stadion, Trieste #209/R

£641 $1006 €1000 Red Hood (60x60cm-24x24in) s.d.1998 s.i.d.verso. 23-Nov-2 Meeting Art, Vercelli #89/R

£962 $1510 €1500 Leak (60x60cm-24x24in) s.i.d.2000 acrylic. 23-Nov-2 Meeting Art, Vercelli #328/R

£980 $1569 €1500 Hope (60x60cm-24x24in) s.d.1991 acrylic. 4-Jan-3 Meeting Art, Vercelli #617

£1111 $1767 €1600 Dialogue (80x80cm-31x31in) s.i.d.2000 verso. 1-May-3 Meeting Art, Vercelli #403

£4054 $6324 €6000 Rotating circle (100x100cm-39x39in) s.d.73 s.d.verso acrylic. 26-Mar-3 Finarte Semenzato, Milan #405/R

Works on paper

£481 $745 €750 Balance (60x60cm-24x24in) s.d.88 verso mixed media on canvas. 5-Dec-2 Stadion, Trieste #717/R

£609 $944 €950 World (100x100cm-39x39in) s.d.85 verso mixed media. 5-Dec-2 Stadion, Trieste #716/R

CARMICHAEL, Franklin (1890-1945) Canadian

£339506 $526235 €509259 Frood Lake (95x120cm-37x47in) s.d.39 prov.exhib. 3-Dec-2 Joyner, Toronto #75a est:700000-800000 (C.D 825000)

Works on paper

£6568 $10443 €9852 Fraser Icefield, Jasper Park (25x23cm-10x9in) s.i. ink pencil prov. 23-Mar-3 Hodgins, Calgary #35/R est:8000-10000 (C.D 15500)

£14815 $22963 €22223 Whitefish village (21x23cm-8x9in) s.d.1924 W/C prov.lit. 3-Dec-2 Joyner, Toronto #40/R est:40000-50000 (C.D 36000)

£15121 $23891 €22682 Country home (27x32cm-11x13in) s. W/C prov. 14-Nov-2 Heffel, Vancouver #128/R est:40000-50000 (C.D 37500)

£16129 $25484 €24194 La Cloche landscape (28x34cm-11x13in) s.d.1930 W/C prov. 14-Nov-2 Heffel, Vancouver #95/R est:45000-55000 (C.D 40000)

£19556 $32071 €29334 Old maples and sumachs (26x31cm-10x12in) s.d.1925 W/C prov.exhib. 3-Jun-3 Joyner, Toronto #49/R est:45000-50000 (C.D 44000)

£22222 $36444 €33333 Grace Lake (27x32cm-11x13in) s.d.33 W/C lit. 3-Jun-3 Joyner, Toronto #31/R est:50000-60000 (C.D 50000)

CARMICHAEL, J W (1800-1868) British

£960 $1526 €1440 View of stately home with figures and carriages (33x53cm-13x21in) s.d.1803. 29-Apr-3 Lawrences, Bletchingley #1433/R

£1538 $2415 €2400 View of Cullercoats, Northumberland (24x34cm-9x13in) init. i.verso board. 19-Nov-2 Hamilton Osborne King, Dublin #474 est:1000-1500

CARMICHAEL, John Wilson (1800-1868) British

£700 $1092 €1050 Bishops Palace, Bishop Auckland (24x35cm-9x14in) inid.d.1845 s.i.verso artist board. 10-Sep-2 David Duggleby, Scarborough #348/R

£750 $1163 €1125 View on the Northumberland coast near Craster (20x29cm-8x11in) board. 24-Sep-2 Anderson & Garland, Newcastle #485/R

£1150 $1921 €1668 Cullercoats Bay (24x34cm-9x13in) panel. 17-Jun-3 Anderson & Garland, Newcastle #453/R est:1000-1800

£2500 $4175 €3625 View north towards Cullercoats Bay (24x34cm-9x13in) init.i. panel. 17-Jun-3 Anderson & Garland, Newcastle #452/R est:2000-3000

£3200 $5344 €4640 Dismasted ship on a stormy sea with rowing boat in foreground (60x90cm-24x35in) s.d.1860. 17-Jun-3 Anderson & Garland, Newcastle #484/R est:3000-5000

£3800 $6156 €5700 HMS Minden 74, off Gibraltar, moonlight (25x36cm-10x14in) s.d.1857 board. 21-May-3 Christie's, Kensington #548/R est:2000-4000

£5000 $7600 €7500 Fishing boats in harbour mouth (60x90cm-24x35in) s.d.1859 canvas on board. 15-Aug-2 Bonhams, New Bond Street #407/R est:5000-7000

£5000 $7750 €7500 Dutch river scene, evening (62x93cm-24x37in) 31-Oct-2 Christie's, Kensington #525/R est:6000-8000

£7200 $10944 €10800 Armed cutter heading for a squadron anchored offshore (30x41cm-12x16in) s.d.1844 panel. 15-Aug-2 Bonhams, New Bond Street #396/R est:6000-8000

£9000 $13950 €13500 Trading brigs passing in the Channel off Flamborough Head. Shipping becalmed in the Humber (33x46cm-13x18in) s.d.1842 pair. 31-Oct-2 Christie's, Kensington #460/R est:10000-15000

£16000 $24320 €24000 Collier briggs and a small streamer off Whitehaven (38x52cm-15x20in) s.d.1855. 15-Aug-2 Bonhams, New Bond Street #400/R est:10000-15000

£27000 $42120 €40500 Hartlepool harbour (62x92cm-24x36in) s.d.1864. 10-Apr-3 Tennants, Leyburn #948/R est:15000-20000

£55000 $86900 €82500 On the Thames at Woolwich with Buckinghamshire Indiaman going down river (75x111cm-30x44in) s.d.1842 exhib. 26-Nov-2 Christie's, London #74/R est:30000-50000

£58000 $96280 €87000 Shipping off St. Helier, Jersey (75x111cm-30x44in) s. 12-Jun-3 Sotheby's, London #235/R est:30000-50000

Works on paper

£320 $502 €480 Flamborough Head, Yorkshire (12x20cm-5x8in) s. W/C htd white prov. 19-Nov-2 Bonhams, Leeds #50/R

£520 $806 €780 Figures in boats at Newcastle quayside (20x30cm-8x12in) init.indis.i. W/C. 24-Sep-2 Anderson & Garland, Newcastle #310/R

£950 $1539 €1425 Shipping off the coast with windmills on shore (22x51cm-9x20in) s.d.1856 W/C prov. 22-Jan-3 Bonhams, New Bond Street #331/R est:600-800

£960 $1498 €1440 Breezy day in the Channel (21x31cm-8x12in) s.d.1840 W/C. 6-Nov-2 Bonhams, Chester #391

£1500 $2325 €2250 London from near Blackfriars Bridge (11x34cm-4x13in) s.i.d.Sept 2 1846 pencil wash htd white. 31-Oct-2 Christie's, Kensington #322/R est:400-600

£1605 $2600 €2327 Royal Navy brig making sail out of Portsmouth (25x39cm-10x15in) s.d.1853 pencil W/C htd white. 29-Jul-3 Christie's, Rockefeller NY #105/R est:3000-5000

£3000 $4860 €4500 Royal Naval frigate amidst other shipping at Spithead (24x32cm-9x13in) s. pencil pen brown ink W/C. 21-May-3 Christie's, Kensington #412/R est:700-900

CARMICHAEL, John Wilson (attrib) (1800-1868) British

£650 $1060 €975 Riverside village (61x81cm-24x32in) bears sig.d. 29-Jan-3 Sotheby's, Olympia #82/R

£2100 $3255 €3150 View of Balaklava, English and French men of war (51x34cm-20x13in) bears.i.verso. 1-Oct-2 Fellows & Sons, Birmingham #93 est:800-1200

£2632 $4000 €3948 Shipping off the Seven Sisters on the south coast of England (53x71cm-21x28in) 17-Aug-2 North East Auctions, Portsmouth #1073/R est:4000-6000

CARMICHAEL, John Wilson (circle) (1800-1868) British

£15000 $24900 €22500 View of London Bridge and St. Paul's Cathedral (74x122cm-29x48in) 12-Jun-3 Sotheby's, London #109/R est:15000-20000

CARMICHAEL, Lady Gibson (20th C) British?

Works on paper

£360 $594 €522 Sorrento (34x57cm-13x22in) s.d.Dec 65 W/C. 1-Jul-3 Bearnes, Exeter #454/R

CARMIENCKE, Dedo (19/20th C) German

£377 $589 €600 Inn valley with peasant woman and goats (45x69cm-18x27in) mono.d.67. 21-Sep-2 Dannenberg, Berlin #547/R

CARMIENCKE, Johan-Herman (1810-1867) Danish/American

£775 $1178 €1163 Trees in stormy weather by the coast (24x30cm-9x12in) s. panel. 27-Aug-2 Rasmussen, Copenhagen #1774/R (D.KR 9000)

CARMIENCKE, Johan-Herman (attrib) (1810-1867) Danish/American

£1191 $1883 €1787 Street scene from Blegdamsvejen with washerwoman and man (21x27cm-8x11in) indis.mono. painted c.1840. 27-Nov-2 Museumsbygningen, Copenhagen #5/R est:6000 (D.KR 14000)

CARNEO, Antonio (attrib) (17th C) Italian

£10000 $15800 €14500 Philosopher (124x108cm-49x43in) 5-Apr-3 Finarte Semenzato, Milan #32/R est:15000

CARNIER, H (?) ?

£1392 $2158 €2200 Venice (31x48cm-12x19in) s. 25-Sep-2 Neumeister, Munich #550/R est:1600

CARNOVALI, Giovanni (attrib) (1806-1873) Italian

Works on paper

£256 $397 €400 Study of figures (12x18cm-5x7in) i. pencil. 4-Dec-2 Finarte, Rome #712

CARO, Anthony (1924-) British

Sculpture

£2500 $3875 €3750 Bull (54cm-21in) s.d.54 num.dark brown pat. bronze lit. 4-Dec-2 Christie's, Kensington #496/R est:2000-3000

£2800 $4340 €4200 Cigarette smoker (32cm-13in) brown pat. bronze conceived 1957 lit. 4-Dec-2 Christie's, Kensington #500/R est:3000-5000

£14000 $21980 €21000 Redoubt (39cm-15in) bronze conceived 1988-90 lit. 22-Nov-2 Christie's, London #106/R est:8000-12000

£14000 $22960 €21000 Family book (56cm-22in) rusted iron earthenware conceived 1996-97 prov.exhib.lit. 6-Jun-3 Christie's, London #207/R est:15000-25000

£17187 $27500 €25781 Table piece CCCX-I (65x185x74cm-26x73x29in) rusted steel executed 1976-77 prov.lit. 14-May-3 Sotheby's, New York #176/R est:30000-40000

£22581 $35000 €33872 Bearing (46x124x350cm-18x49x138in) steel painted green executed 1967 prov.lit. 26-Sep-2 Christie's, Rockefeller NY #721/R est:20000-30000

£31250 $50000 €46875 Dune nectar (77x70x74cm-30x28x29in) bronze executed 1987-89 prov. 14-May-3 Sotheby's, New York #248/R est:15000-20000

Works on paper

£260 $426 €390 Nude study (50x40cm-20x16in) s.d.87 chl. 4-Feb-3 Sworder & Son, Bishops Stortford #89/R

CARO, Baldassare de (1689-c.1755) Italian
£319 $533 €450 Chien se reposant a cote d'un trophee de chasse (76x103cm-30x41in) s. 23-Jun-3 Delvaux, Paris #18/R
£1747 $2725 €2621 Hunting still life (28x47cm-11x19in) mono. 6-Nov-2 Dobiaschofsky, Bern #392/R est:4600 (S.FR 4000)

CARO, Baldassare de (attrib) (1689-c.1755) Italian
£3057 $4769 €4800 Hunting still life with dead birds and a satchel in a landscape (51x64cm-20x25in) indis.sig. 6-Nov-2 Christie's, Amsterdam #28/R est:3000-5000
£3521 $5845 €5000 Cat with fish (37x46cm-15x18in) 11-Jun-3 Dorotheum, Vienna #8/R est:4000-6000

CARO, Pierre (?) French
£385 $604 €600 Groupe d'enfants en Inde (18x25cm-7x10in) s. 15-Dec-2 Thierry & Lannon, Brest #226

CARO-DELVAILLE, Henri (1876-1926) French
£2278 $3600 €3600 Mother love (45x37cm-18x15in) s.i. panel. 28-Nov-2 Dorotheum, Vienna #55/R est:4000-4500

CAROLUS, Jean (1814-1897) Belgian
£900 $1476 €1350 Elegant figures in a garden (29x23cm-11x9in) s.d.50 panel prov. 5-Jun-3 Christie's, Kensington #623/R
£5714 $9029 €8571 Billiards match in the eighteenth century (76x97cm-30x38in) s. prov. 26-Nov-2 Sotheby's, Melbourne #189/R est:18000-28000 (A.D 16000)
£6115 $9784 €8500 Demande en mariage (82x105cm-32x41in) s.d.1866. 17-May-3 De Vuyst, Lokeren #426/R est:8500-10000

CAROLUS-DURAN, Émile Auguste (1838-1917) French
£1724 $2759 €2500 Portrait presume de Madame Delabarre (65x51cm-26x20in) s. 12-Mar-3 E & Eve, Paris #81 est:2500-3000
Works on paper
£4838 $7500 €7257 Lady in white with a fan (56x40cm-22x16in) s. W/C gouache prov. 29-Oct-2 Sotheby's, New York #65/R est:3000-4000

CARON, Aldo (1919-) Italian
Sculpture
£968 $1529 €1500 Study (90x69x55cm-35x27x22in) painted plaster exec.1965 prov.exhib. 18-Dec-2 Christie's, Rome #67

CARON, Antoine (1521-1599) French
£121951 $200000 €182927 Allegory of the Triumph of Spring (80x117cm-31x46in) prov.exhib.lit. 30-May-3 Christie's, Rockefeller NY #37/R est:200000-300000
£487805 $800000 €731708 Allegory of the Triumph of Summer (102x178cm-40x70in) prov.exhib. 30-May-3 Christie's, Rockefeller NY #33/R est:200000-300000

CARON, G (19th C) ?
£1026 $1590 €1600 Flowers in white ceramic vase (27x35cm-11x14in) s. 6-Dec-2 Michael Zeller, Lindau #730/R

CARON, Joseph (1866-1944) Belgian
£577 $894 €900 Travaux de jardinage (50x70cm-20x28in) s. panel. 9-Dec-2 Horta, Bruxelles #305
£850 $1368 €1300 Automne (107x130cm-42x51in) s. s.i.verso. 20-Jan-3 Horta, Bruxelles #77

CARON, Marcel (1890-1961) Belgian
£2436 $3824 €3800 Le paysan (60x54cm-24x21in) panel. 11-Dec-2 Hotel des Ventes Mosan, Brussels #314 est:2000-2500
£14388 $23022 €20000 Le cirque (115x90cm-45x35in) s.d.28 exhib. 13-May-3 Palais de Beaux Arts, Brussels #36/R est:19000-25000

CARON, Paul Archibald (1874-1941) Canadian
£494 $765 €741 Picken's bookshop, Beaver Hall Hill, Montreal. Study in Bonsecours market, Montreal (17x13cm-7x5in) panel two. 3-Dec-2 Joyner, Toronto #442 est:1000-1500 (C.D 1200)
£622 $1020 €933 Spring (14x17cm-6x7in) s. panel. 3-Jun-3 Joyner, Toronto #512 est:1500-2000 (C.D 1400)
£2016 $3185 €3024 Evening in the Laurentians (39x48cm-15x19in) s. s.i.d.1938 verso prov. 18-Nov-2 Sotheby's, Toronto #15/R est:5000-7000 (C.D 5000)
£2058 $3189 €3087 Early spring on the Riviere du Gouffre, Baie St. Paul, PQ Canada (30x40cm-12x16in) s. painted 1936 prov. 3-Dec-2 Joyner, Toronto #185/R est:5000-6000 (C.D 5000)
£3086 $4784 €4629 Laurentian Hill stream (37x45cm-15x18in) s. painted 1937 prov. 3-Dec-2 Joyner, Toronto #186/R est:6000-8000 (C.D 7500)
Works on paper
£236 $369 €354 Study of a male nude (32x22cm-13x9in) graphite double-sided sold with dr. by Edmond Dyonnet. 25-Mar-3 Ritchie, Toronto #150/R (C.D 550)
£329 $507 €494 Study of habitant, Murray Bay, Qc (18x13cm-7x5in) s.d.1929 i.verso col crayon. 22-Oct-2 Iegor de Saint Hippolyte, Montreal #17 (C.D 800)
£1008 $1643 €1512 View of Montreal (28x36cm-11x14in) s. W/C. 12-Feb-3 Iegor de Saint Hippolyte, Montreal #40 (C.D 2500)
£1545 $2425 €2318 Midi (19x27cm-7x11in) s. W/C prov. 10-Dec-2 Pinneys, Montreal #25 est:1500-2000 (C.D 3800)
£1893 $2934 €2840 Vieil habitant en hiver (27x21cm-11x8in) s. W/C prov. 3-Dec-2 Joyner, Toronto #9/R est:4000-6000 (C.D 4600)

CAROTO, Giovanni Francesco (1480-1555) Italian
£13580 $22000 €20370 Apostles burying the Virgin (68x106cm-27x42in) panel prov.lit. 23-Jan-3 Sotheby's, New York #63/R est:15000-20000
£17308 $27173 €27000 Madonna and Child and Saint John (122x98cm-48x39in) s. 10-Dec-2 Della Rocca, Turin #165/R est:30000

CAROZZI, Giuseppe (1864-1938) French
£2258 $3568 €3500 Troupeau au bord d'un lac du montagne (58x92cm-23x36in) s. i.verso. 17-Dec-2 Rossini, Paris #64/R

CARPACCIO, Vittore (circle) (1450-1522) Italian
£5484 $8665 €8500 Saint Jerome in the desert (104x83cm-41x33in) 20-Dec-2 Tajan, Paris #8/R est:5000

CARPANETTO, Giovanni Battista (1863-1928) Italian
£1419 $2243 €2200 Woman (65x42cm-26x17in) s.d.1915 cardboard. 18-Dec-2 Finarte, Milan #183/R
£2041 $3245 €3000 Grapes picker (120x99cm-47x39in) s. paper on canvas. 1-Mar-3 Meeting Art, Vercelli #240
£10145 $16638 €14000 Al gerbido, la corsa del Gran Premio (29x47cm-11x19in) s.d.1887 panel exhib.lit. 27-May-3 Finarte, Milan #67/R est:10000-12000

CARPANI, Ricardo R (?) Italian
£265 $432 €400 Thoughtful man (100x97cm-39x38in) s.d.1970. 11-Feb-3 Segre, Madrid #352/R

CARPANINI, David (1946-) British
£250 $390 €375 Child in a playground (27x20cm-11x8in) 27-Mar-3 Christie's, Kensington #404

CARPEAUX, J B (1827-1875) French
Sculpture
£1234 $1801 €1900 Le petit boudeur (28cm-11in) s.d.1874 terracotta socle. 11-Jun-2 Thierry & Lannon, Brest #97/R est:500-600

CARPEAUX, Jean Baptiste (1827-1875) French
£2372 $3724 €3700 Portrait presume de Henri Murger (35x27cm-14x11in) lit. 16-Dec-2 Rabourdin & Choppin de Janvry, Paris #34/R
£7097 $11000 €10646 Portrait of a man wearing a grey hat, possibly a portrait of Antoine Vollon (34x27cm-13x11in) s. prov.exhib. 29-Oct-2 Sotheby's, New York #66/R est:4000-6000
£9615 $15096 €15000 Mariage chretien (38x46cm-15x18in) s. prov.lit. 16-Dec-2 Rabourdin & Choppin de Janvry, Paris #35/R est:3000
Sculpture
£949 $1472 €1500 Buste du genie e la danse (11cm-4in) s. douce pat bronze. 29-Sep-2 Eric Pillon, Calais #110/R
£1290 $2000 €1935 Le Prince Imperial (22cm-9in) s.i. brown pat bronze prov.exhib. 29-Oct-2 Sotheby's, New York #219/R est:1500-2000
£1582 $2468 €2500 Le genie de la danse (54cm-21in) s. brown pat bronze Portor marble socle. 20-Oct-2 Mercier & Cie, Lille #151a est:2500-3000
£1731 $2717 €2700 Buste de Flore (52cm-20in) s. biscuit de Sevres. 15-Dec-2 Eric Pillon, Calais #66/R
£1911 $2981 €3000 Rieuse napolitaine (50cm-20in) s. terracotta. 10-Nov-2 Eric Pillon, Calais #41/R
£1923 $3038 €3000 La frileuse (40cm-16in) s. brown pat bronze lit. 18-Nov-2 Tajan, Paris #42/R est:2400-3000
£1923 $3019 €3000 Jeune femme a la coiffe (46cm-18in) s. marble. 15-Dec-2 Mercier & Cie, Lille #267/R
£1987 $3140 €3100 Pecheur Napolitain avec un filet (35cm-14in) s.st.f.Susse medaille pat bronze lit. 18-Nov-2 Tajan, Paris #41 est:3800-4600
£2000 $3120 €3000 Bust of Anna Foucart (32cm-13in) brown pat bronze black marble socle. 5-Nov-2 Sotheby's, London #189/R est:2000-3000
£2436 $3849 €3800 Pecheuse de vignots (72cm-28in) s.i.d.1874 brown pat bronze lit. 18-Nov-2 Tajan, Paris #90/R est:3800-5500
£2517 $4204 €3600 Flore (38cm-15in) s. brown pat bronze Cast Susse. 25-Jun-3 Artcurial Briest, Paris #52/R est:1200-1500

£2581 $4000 €3872 Neapolitan fisherboy (36cm-14in) s.i. brown pat. bronze prov.exhib.lit. 29-Oct-2 Sotheby's, New York #220/R est:5000-7000
£2600 $4056 €3900 Bust of Louis Maximilien Beauvois (26cm-10in) s.st.f.Thiebaut brown pat bronze lit. 5-Nov-2 Sotheby's, London #190/R est:3000-5000
£2692 $4253 €4200 Le genie de la danse (57cm-22in) s.d.1868 brown pat bronze lit. 18-Nov-2 Tajan, Paris #38/R est:4000-6000
£2884 $4557 €4500 Le genie de la danse (57cm-22in) s. brown pat bronze lit. 18-Nov-2 Tajan, Paris #39/R est:3800-4600
£3077 $4861 €4800 Pecheur Napolitain avec un filet (36x19x15cm-14x7x6in) s. brown pat bronze lit. 18-Nov-2 Tajan, Paris #44/R est:3000-3800
£3145 $4843 €5000 Surprised Suzanne (68cm-27in) s. pat bronze lit. 22-Oct-2 Durán, Madrid #881/R
£3205 $4968 €5000 Etude pour la jeune fille a la coquille (16x121x12cm-6x48x5in) terracotta. 4-Dec-2 Piasa, Paris #119/R est:8000
£3493 $5450 €5240 L'amour a la folie (70cm-28in) i. terracotta lit. 20-Nov-2 Fischer, Luzern #1410/R est:7500-8500 (S.FR 8000)
£3500 $5460 €5250 Ugolino and his sons (53cm-21in) s.num.4 black pat bronze st.f.A A Hebrard. 9-Apr-3 Sotheby's, London #102/R est:3000-5000
£3957 $6331 €5500 Bacchante aux roses (60x45cm-24x18in) s. rose pat terracotta. 18-May-3 Eric Pillon, Calais #38/R
£4000 $6680 €5800 Bust of Bacchante with roses (59cm-23in) s.d.1874 studio st. terracotta. 8-Jul-3 Sotheby's, London #203/R est:5000-7000
£4487 $7045 €7000 Dance (51cm-20in) wax. 13-Dec-2 Piasa, Paris #7/R
£4516 $7000 €6774 Alexandre Dumas (46cm-18in) s.d.1873 dark brown pat. lit. 29-Oct-2 Sotheby's, New York #218/R est:6000-8000
£4601 $7546 €6671 Le genie de la danse (71cm-28in) i. white marble. 4-Jun-3 Fischer, Luzern #1365/R est:10000-12000 (S.FR 9800)
£4640 $7424 €6450 La pecheuse de vignots (72x24cm-28x9in) st.eagle bronze. 18-May-3 Rabourdin & Choppin de Janvry, Paris #92/R est:6800-7000
£4808 $7452 €7500 Genie de la danse (102x36x36cm-40x14x14in) s. terracotta. 7-Dec-2 Martinot & Savignat, Pontoise #92/R est:7800
£6500 $10075 €9750 La rieur Napolitain (53cm-21in) s. white marble exec.c.1865. 1-Oct-2 Christie's, London #303/R est:4000-6000
£7407 $10519 €12000 Bacchante aux lauriers (65x47cm-26x19in) Carrara marble. 16-Mar-3 Eric Pillon, Calais #35/R
£8385 $13500 €14465 Le Genie de la danse, faun playing a tambourine (99cm-39in) s. bronze. 9-May-3 Eldred, East Dennis #612/R est:1000-1200
£9000 $14130 €13500 Norte Dame du Saint Cordon (35cm-14in) s.d.1864 terracotta lit. 10-Dec-2 Sotheby's, London #152/R est:4000-6000
£10473 $16338 €15500 Candeur (68cm-27in) s. plaster. 28-Mar-3 Neret-Minet, Paris #123/R est:6000
£12658 $20000 €18987 Bust of Jean Leon Gerome (60cm-24in) s.d.71 plaster pat. to resemble bronze prov.exhib.lit. 24-Apr-3 Sotheby's, New York #177/R est:15000-20000
£12658 $20000 €18987 La candeur (72cm-28in) white marble on square socle lit. 24-Apr-3 Christie's, Rockefeller NY #266/R est:20000-30000
£17500 $29225 €25375 Prince Imperial (46cm-18in) s.i.d.1865 dk brown pat bronze Cast Barbedienne. 8-Jul-3 Sotheby's, London #200/R est:12000-18000
£18000 $28080 €27000 Ugolino and his sons (47x36cm-19x14in) s.num.7/10 brown pat bronze st.f. Susse lit. 9-Apr-3 Sotheby's, London #103/R est:10000-15000
£19872 $31199 €31000 Ugolin et ses enfants (39cm-15in) wax. 13-Dec-2 Piasa, Paris #6/R est:15000

Works on paper

£475 $750 €750 Deux chevaux cabres et un personnage (13x16cm-5x6in) s. black chk. 27-Nov-2 Christie's, Paris #287/R
£823 $1284 €1300 Etudes de figures. chl htd white 3 in one frame. 18-Oct-2 Rabourdin & Choppin de Janvry, Paris #111/R
£823 $1284 €1300 Etudes. chl htd white in one frame. 18-Oct-2 Rabourdin & Choppin de Janvry, Paris #110/R
£1013 $1580 €1600 Etudes de figures. chl 3 in one frame. 18-Oct-2 Rabourdin & Choppin de Janvry, Paris #112/R
£2703 $4216 €4000 Groupe de cavaliers (19x26cm-7x10in) s. graphite. 27-Mar-3 Christie's, Paris #170/R
£10968 $17000 €16452 Self portrait with second study of artist at easel (46x30cm-18x12in) mono. red brown chk htd white prov.exhib. 29-Oct-2 Sotheby's, New York #67/R est:8000-12000

CARPEAUX, Jean Baptiste (after) (1827-1875) French

Sculpture

£2302 $3683 €3200 La pecheuse de Vignots (72cm-28in) s.i. gilt brown pat bronze lit. 14-May-3 Blanchet, Paris #52/R est:2500-3000

CARPEAUX, Jean Baptiste (attrib) (1827-1875) French

Sculpture

£2600 $4056 €3900 Bust of a man smoking (56cm-22in) s.d.1863 brown pat bronze marble base lit. 5-Nov-2 Sotheby's, London #191/R est:2000-3000

CARPENTER, Margaret (1793-1872) British

£8500 $13770 €12750 Portrait of Henrietta Shuckburgh (127x102cm-50x40in) s.i.indis.d.182 exhib. 23-Jan-3 Christie's, Kensington #18/R est:3000-5000

CARPENTER, Mildred Bailey (1894-?) American

Works on paper

£599 $1000 €869 Nude female floating among vines (36x23cm-14x9in) s. W/C. 21-Jun-3 Selkirks, St. Louis #162/R est:1000-1500
£833 $1300 €1250 Princess in a woodland setting (46x30cm-18x12in) s.d.1959 W/C chl dr prov. 10-Nov-2 Selkirks, St. Louis #762/R

CARPENTERO, Henri Joseph Gommarus (1820-1874) Belgian

£1205 $2000 €1747 Baby's first step (33x30cm-13x12in) s.d.1855 panel. 11-Jun-3 Boos Gallery, Michigan #528/R est:4000-6000

CARPENTIER, Evariste (1845-1922) Belgian

£353 $554 €550 Poultry with sheep and goat (18x24cm-7x9in) s.d.1872 panel. 21-Nov-2 Van Ham, Cologne #1512
£470 $756 €700 Enfants aux champs (17x25cm-7x10in) panel. 18-Feb-3 Vanderkindere, Brussels #70
£759 $1185 €1200 Les enfants au jardin (16x24cm-6x9in) s. panel. 10-Sep-2 Vanderkindere, Brussels #285
£12346 $19012 €18519 Her timid pet (66x81cm-26x32in) s. 22-Oct-2 Iegor de Saint Hippolyte, Montreal #18/R (C.D 30000)

Works on paper

£450 $738 €653 Study of an aged peasant woman, seated facing left in profile (25x25cm-10x10in) s.d.1880 W/C. 3-Jun-3 Capes Dunn, Manchester #49/R

CARPI, Aldo (1886-1973) Italian

Works on paper

£680 $1082 €1000 Figures (77x55cm-30x22in) s.d.1960 mixed media. 1-Mar-3 Meeting Art, Vercelli #511

CARPI, Girolamo da (1501-1556) Italian

Works on paper

£3200 $5344 €4640 Standing female sculptures after the antique (23x19cm-9x7in) pen brown ink brown wash double-sided corners cut. 9-Jul-3 Sotheby's, London #15/R est:1500-2000

CARPI, Girolamo da (attrib) (1501-1556) Italian

Works on paper

£1200 $1884 €1800 Draped female figure (8x10cm-3x4in) pen ink. 11-Dec-2 Sotheby's, Olympia #3/R est:1500-2000

CARPIONI, Giulio (1613-1679) Italian

£59748 $92610 €95000 Rea deceives her husband Cronus (295x209cm-116x82in) lit. 2-Oct-2 Dorotheum, Vienna #43/R est:70000-100000

Works on paper

£1486 $2319 €2200 Two heads (15x16cm-6x6in) i. chk prov. 27-Mar-3 Christie's, Paris #27/R

CARPIONI, Giulio (attrib) (1613-1679) Italian

£6000 $9300 €9000 Nurture of Bacchus (81x64cm-32x25in) prov. 30-Oct-2 Christie's, Kensington #137/R est:4000-6000

CARR, David (19/20th C) British

£440 $686 €638 Welsh mining village (16x21cm-6x8in) s. 27-Mar-3 Neales, Nottingham #1036

Works on paper

£400 $616 €600 Machine forms (22x28cm-9x11in) pencil W/C prov. 5-Sep-2 Christie's, Kensington #730/R

CARR, Emily M (1871-1945) Canadian

£15695 $25112 €23543 Treescape (29x45cm-11x18in) s. i.verso oil on paper prov.lit. 15-May-3 Heffel, Vancouver #156/R est:40000-50000 (C.D 35000)
£15695 $25112 €23543 Westcoast seashore (56x91cm-22x36in) s. paper on board painted c.1935 prov. 15-May-3 Heffel, Vancouver #154/R est:40000-50000 (C.D 35000)
£17778 $29156 €26667 Strait of Jaun de Fucca (54x83cm-21x33in) s. oil on paper prov.exhib.lit. 3-Jun-3 Joyner, Toronto #77/R est:50000-70000 (C.D 40000)

£26906 $43049 €40359 Strait and blue mountains (61x91cm-24x36in) s. oil on paper painted c.1935-36 prov. 15-May-3 Heffel, Vancouver #88/R est:50000-70000 (C.D 60000)
£28226 $44597 €42339 British Columbia coast scene (52x86cm-20x34in) s. oil paper on board prov.lit. 18-Nov-2 Sotheby's, Toronto #112/R est:70000-90000 (C.D 70000)
£28226 $44597 €42339 Mill and millpond, Crecy-En-Brie, France 1911 (41x33cm-16x13in) s. i.verso board prov.lit. 18-Nov-2 Sotheby's, Toronto #167/R est:40000-60000 (C.D 70000)
£35556 $58311 €53334 Young pine in a breeze (57x50cm-22x20in) prov. 3-Jun-3 Joyner, Toronto #26a/R est:80000-120000 (C.D 80000)
£37778 $61956 €56667 Mountain (91x59cm-36x23in) s. oil paper on board prov.exhib.lit. 27-May-3 Sotheby's, Toronto #21/R est:40000-60000 (C.D 85000)
£37778 $61956 €56667 Forest landscape (60x89cm-24x35in) s. oil paper on canvas prov. 27-May-3 Sotheby's, Toronto #69/R est:70000-90000 (C.D 85000)
£40323 $63710 €60485 Hugglegate (65x32cm-26x13in) s.i.d.1912 board prov. 14-Nov-2 Heffel, Vancouver #35/R est:80000-100000 (C.D 100000)
£48387 $76452 €72581 Somewhere (91x60cm-36x24in) s. s.i.verso oil paper on board painted c.1939 prov. 14-Nov-2 Heffel, Vancouver #31/R est:60000-80000 (C.D 120000)

Works on paper

£4036 $6457 €6054 Resting Indians (27x31cm-11x12in) i.verso W/C executed c.1907 prov.lit. 15-May-3 Heffel, Vancouver #89/R est:8000-10000 (C.D 9000)
£4115 $6379 €6173 Coastal Indian village with totems and canoe (22x30cm-9x12in) s. W/C painted c.1900 prov. 3-Dec-2 Joyner, Toronto #8/R est:10000-15000 (C.D 10000)
£15556 $25511 €23334 Parrots in a window (39x28cm-15x11in) s. W/C prov. 27-May-3 Sotheby's, Toronto #80/R est:20000-30000 (C.D 35000)

CARR, Emily M (attrib) (1871-1945) Canadian

Works on paper

£2814 $4474 €4080 Near Victoria, BC (20x27cm-8x11in) s. s.i.indis.d.1887 verso W/C prov. 1-May-3 Heffel, Vancouver #13/R est:600-800 (C.D 6500)

CARR, Hamzah (20th C) British

£1100 $1716 €1650 Can openers (26x25cm-10x10in) s. card. 12-Sep-2 Sotheby's, Olympia #161/R est:800-1200

Works on paper

£280 $437 €420 Power cartridges (24x33cm-9x13in) s. ink gouache W/C. 12-Sep-2 Sotheby's, Olympia #158/R
£320 $499 €480 Power cartridge (28x38cm-11x15in) s. ink gouache W/C. 12-Sep-2 Sotheby's, Olympia #157/R
£350 $546 €525 Fertility (36x35cm-14x14in) s. W/C. 12-Sep-2 Sotheby's, Olympia #153/R
£380 $593 €570 Perspex (18x31cm-7x12in) s. W/C. 12-Sep-2 Sotheby's, Olympia #155/R
£500 $780 €750 Research and production (22x30cm-9x12in) s. ink W/C. 12-Sep-2 Sotheby's, Olympia #156/R
£750 $1170 €1125 Gasgets (28x26cm-11x10in) s. gouache. 12-Sep-2 Sotheby's, Olympia #162/R

CARR, Sir John (attrib) (fl.1802-1807) British

Works on paper

£1014 $1581 €1500 Cork from Mardyke Walk (30x53cm-12x21in) W/C sold with an engraving of the same view. 26-Mar-3 James Adam, Dublin #20/R est:800-1200

CARR, Tom (1912-1977) British

Works on paper

£1900 $3002 €2850 Duke of Buccleuch's foxhounds (33x49cm-13x19in) s.i.d.1971 W/C htd gouache. 28-Nov-2 Bonhams, Knightsbridge #117/R est:1500-2000

CARR, Tom (1909-1999) British

£3974 $6160 €6200 Harbour (38x50cm-15x20in) s. canvasboard exhib. 3-Dec-2 Bonhams & James Adam, Dublin #90/R est:5000-7000
£5800 $8990 €8700 On the beach Newcastle, Co. Down (35x45cm-14x18in) s. 4-Dec-2 John Ross, Belfast #168 est:6000-7000
£7000 $10850 €10500 Boy with dog (61x46cm-24x18in) s. board. 2-Oct-2 John Ross, Belfast #161 est:8000-9000
£7200 $11448 €10800 Coming to shore, Ballymoran, Strangford Lough (56x45cm-22x18in) s. board. 5-Mar-3 John Ross, Belfast #152 est:6000-8000
£9615 $14904 €15000 Jetty (55x68cm-22x27in) s. 3-Dec-2 Bonhams & James Adam, Dublin #61/R est:9500-12500
£11392 $17658 €18000 Mother and child (50x45cm-20x18in) s. 24-Sep-2 De Veres Art Auctions, Dublin #74/R est:18000-22000

Works on paper

£300 $465 €450 Street study (25x33cm-10x13in) s. pen ink dr. 4-Dec-2 John Ross, Belfast #232
£400 $636 €600 Snow drops (15x10cm-6x4in) s. W/C. 5-Mar-3 John Ross, Belfast #229
£420 $651 €630 Country road (25x36cm-10x14in) s. W/C. 2-Oct-2 John Ross, Belfast #221
£480 $763 €696 Near Yetholm (36x53cm-14x21in) s.d.1973 W/C. 29-Apr-3 Gorringes, Lewes #2049
£520 $827 €780 The West, Shropshire (24x33cm-9x13in) s. pencil. 7-Mar-3 Tennants, Leyburn #69
£528 $877 €750 Main Street, Newcastle (20x29cm-8x11in) s. mixed media. 10-Jun-3 James Adam, Dublin #253/R
£600 $954 €900 Horses on the path (12x17cm-5x7in) s. W/C. 5-Mar-3 John Ross, Belfast #165
£600 $930 €900 House auction (35x25cm-14x10in) s. W/C. 4-Dec-2 John Ross, Belfast #67
£650 $1007 €975 Gate lodge , Ballydrain (28x23cm-11x9in) s. pen ink W/C wash. 2-Oct-2 John Ross, Belfast #212
£750 $1163 €1125 Cycling near Newcastle (25x36cm-10x14in) s. pen ink W/C wash. 2-Oct-2 John Ross, Belfast #137
£750 $1163 €1125 Man of God (38x28cm-15x11in) s. mixed media. 2-Oct-2 John Ross, Belfast #227
£750 $1193 €1125 Fox and geese (12x15cm-5x6in) s. W/C. 5-Mar-3 John Ross, Belfast #81
£760 $1186 €1140 Pebble beach (44x29cm-17x11in) s. pastel. 8-Apr-3 Bristol Auction Rooms #553/R
£800 $1240 €1200 Bathers (12x17cm-5x7in) s. W/C. 4-Dec-2 John Ross, Belfast #88
£1000 $1460 €1500 Harvest time by the Quoile water (25x36cm-10x14in) s.d.1939 verso pen ink W/C. 12-Jun-2 John Ross, Belfast #3 est:800-1000
£1100 $1606 €1650 Fishing (23x28cm-9x11in) s. W/C. 12-Jun-2 John Ross, Belfast #39 est:800-1000
£1300 $2015 €1950 Ballinahinch market (25x30cm-10x12in) s. mixed media. 4-Dec-2 John Ross, Belfast #97 est:1250-1500
£1400 $2184 €2100 Blossom study (36x55cm-14x22in) s. W/C. 17-Oct-2 Lawrence, Crewkerne #425/R est:1500-2000
£1410 $2186 €2200 Still life of flowers in a white jug (22x15cm-9x6in) s. pastel. 3-Dec-2 Bonhams & James Adam, Dublin #136/R est:2000-3000
£1689 $2635 €2500 Roses and Staffordshire figure (25x33cm-10x13in) s. W/C pencil prov. 26-Mar-3 James Adam, Dublin #139/R est:1500-2500
£2800 $4088 €4200 Cows grazing, near Newcastle (28x36cm-11x14in) s. W/C. 12-Jun-2 John Ross, Belfast #137 est:2500-2800
£2800 $4340 €4200 Still life, roses (28x38cm-11x15in) s. W/C. 2-Oct-2 John Ross, Belfast #151 est:2750-3000
£3500 $5110 €5250 Reeds (48x66cm-19x26in) s. W/C. 12-Jun-2 John Ross, Belfast #129 est:3500-3750
£4500 $6975 €6750 Swans (75x56cm-30x22in) s. W/C. 4-Dec-2 John Ross, Belfast #207 est:4000-5000
£6000 $9540 €9000 Snow scene (56x76cm-22x30in) s.d.1984 verso W/C. 5-Mar-3 John Ross, Belfast #114 est:4000-5000

CARR-HARRIS, Ian (1941-) Canadian

Sculpture

£3778 $6196 €5667 Nov 25 1966 (254cm-100in) i.d.1971 painted wood letraset text rope. 27-May-3 Sotheby's, Toronto #142/R est:4000-6000 (C.D 8500)

CARRA, Carlo (1881-1966) Italian

£19858 $32170 €28000 Still life (35x45cm-14x18in) s.d.963 s.verso prov.lit. 26-May-3 Christie's, Milan #336/R est:25000-30000
£36879 $59745 €52000 Mare (41x51cm-16x20in) s.d.947 prov.lit. 26-May-3 Christie's, Milan #244/R est:50000-70000
£38462 $60385 €60000 Sailing boat (40x50cm-16x20in) s.d.947. 19-Nov-2 Finarte, Milan #245/R est:45000-55000
£42553 $68936 €60000 Marina (40x51cm-16x20in) s. s.d.1962 verso. 26-May-3 Christie's, Milan #281/R est:60000-80000
£88608 $140000 €140000 Houses by the lake (70x90cm-28x35in) s.d.927 exhib.lit. 30-Nov-2 Farsetti, Prato #731/R est:180000
£147436 $215256 €230000 Mother and daughter (90x70cm-35x28in) s.d.1939 exhib.lit. 5-Jun-2 Il Ponte, Milan #99/R est:100000-120000

Works on paper

£1644 $2564 €2400 Seated man (29x20cm-11x8in) s.d.923 Chinese ink. 10-Apr-3 Finarte Semenzato, Rome #273/R
£2027 $3162 €3000 Room (24x16cm-9x6in) s.d.945 W/C over lithograph. 26-Mar-3 Finarte Semenzato, Milan #261/R
£2270 $3677 €3200 Don Chisciotte fra le donne (39x28cm-15x11in) s.i.d.1943 chl paper on canvas prov.lit. 26-May-3 Christie's, Milan #37/R est:2700-3000
£2468 $3851 €3900 Untitled (23x15cm-9x6in) dr. exec.1917. 15-Oct-2 Babuino, Rome #287/R
£3846 $6038 €6000 Landscape in Tuscany (33x48cm-13x19in) s.d.1965 wax crayon. 23-Nov-2 Meeting Art, Vercelli #393/R
£22000 $35860 €33000 Solitude (43x34cm-17x13in) s.d.1917 pencil vellum prov.exhib.lit. 3-Feb-3 Christie's, London #151/R est:30000
£51613 $81548 €80000 Homage to Betuda (28x24cm-11x9in) s.d.1915 collage W/C. 18-Dec-2 Tajan, Paris #37/R est:20000-30000

£129747 $205000 €205000 Horse galloping (27x36cm-11x14in) s. pencil pastel ink W/C exec.1913 exhib.lit. 30-Nov-2 Farsetti, Prato #682/R est:200000-250000

CARRACCI, Agostino (1557-1602) Italian
Works on paper
£9877 $16000 €14816 Female nude reclining (10x12cm-4x5in) i. pen ink. 22-Jan-3 Christie's, Rockefeller NY #22/R est:20000

CARRACCI, Agostino (attrib) (1557-1602) Italian
Works on paper
£1200 $1884 €1800 Fallen soldier holding a shield (19x19cm-7x7in) pen ink prov. 11-Dec-2 Sotheby's, Olympia #46/R est:600-800

CARRACCI, Agostino (style) (1557-1602) Italian
£5500 $8579 €8250 Galatea and Polyphemus (41x55cm-16x22in) panel. 19-Sep-2 Christie's, Kensington #230/R est:2000-3000

CARRACCI, Annibale (1560-1609) Italian
£700000 $1169000 €1015000 Holy Family with the Infant Saint John the Baptist; the Montalto Madonna (35x27cm-14x11in) i.verso copper prov.lit. 10-Jul-3 Sotheby's, London #35/R est:300000-500000
Prints
£2600 $4030 €3900 Holy Family with St. John the Baptist (116x22cm-46x9in) etching. 5-Dec-2 Sotheby's, London #4/R est:2000-3000
Works on paper
£1500 $2355 €2250 River valley seen through a double rock arch (19x28cm-7x11in) pen ink corners cut prov.lit. 11-Dec-2 Sotheby's, Olympia #42/R est:2000-3000
£6790 $11000 €10185 Study of standing satyr (18x7cm-7x3in) pen ink wash prov. 21-Jan-3 Sotheby's, New York #22/R est:6000

CARRACCI, Annibale (after) (1560-1609) Italian
£629 $975 €1000 Homme au singe (60x48cm-24x19in) panel. 1-Oct-2 Palais de Beaux Arts, Brussels #402

CARRACCI, Annibale (attrib) (1560-1609) Italian
Works on paper
£822 $1282 €1200 Mary and St Elisabeth with Infant Jesus and St John (14x19cm-6x7in) pen ochre wash. 11-Apr-3 Winterberg, Heidelberg #64/R
£2063 $3445 €2950 La Vierge a l'Enfant avec Saint Jean Baptiste (25x19cm-10x7in) i. pen brown ink brown wash prov. 27-Jun-3 Claude Aguttes, Neuilly #4/R est:4000-6000
£11000 $18370 €15950 Male academy (41x27cm-16x11in) indis.i. red chk. 9-Jul-3 Sotheby's, London #31/R est:3000-4000

CARRACCI, Annibale (circle) (1560-1609) Italian
£13500 $21060 €20250 Saint Jerome (75x62cm-30x24in) 10-Apr-3 Sotheby's, London #77/R est:8000
Works on paper
£676 $1054 €1000 Landscape with figures by bridge (18x27cm-7x11in) i. pen ink prov. 27-Mar-3 Christie's, Paris #186/R

CARRACCI, Annibale (studio) (1560-1609) Italian
£7000 $10920 €10500 Ecce Homo (56x40cm-22x16in) panel prov. 9-Apr-3 Christie's, London #105/R est:7000-10000

CARRACCI, Annibale (style) (1560-1609) Italian
£26000 $40560 €39000 Landscape with a cloaked figure riding a donkey (53x68cm-21x27in) prov. 9-Apr-3 Christie's, London #103/R est:5000-8000

CARRACCI, Antonio (attrib) (1583-1618) Italian
£19753 $32000 €29630 Christ at the sea of Galilee (16x32cm-6x13in) oval prov. 23-Jan-3 Sotheby's, New York #2/R est:10000-15000

CARRAND, Louis (1821-1899) French
£483 $768 €700 La brouette (31x40cm-12x16in) s. panel. 5-Mar-3 Doutrebente, Paris #40/R

CARRE, Ben (1883-1978) American
£484 $750 €726 Sunset landscape (56x71cm-22x28in) s. masonite. 29-Oct-2 John Moran, Pasadena #737
£2866 $4500 €4299 Artist's garden, Santa Monica (61x76cm-24x30in) s. masonite. 19-Nov-2 Butterfields, San Francisco #8293/R est:5000-7000

CARRE, Franciscus (1630-1669) Dutch
£1911 $2981 €3000 Temptation of St. Anthony (36x31cm-14x12in) s.d.1656 panel prov. 5-Nov-2 Sotheby's, Amsterdam #53/R est:4000-6000
£2500 $4175 €3625 Temptation of Saint Anthony (16x16cm-6x6in) s.d.1663 panel. 11-Jul-3 Christie's, Kensington #106/R est:3000-4000
£2866 $4471 €4500 Temptation of St. Anthony (16x17cm-6x7in) s.d.1663 panel. 5-Nov-2 Sotheby's, Amsterdam #322/R est:5000-7000
£3022 $4835 €4200 Interior with a woman seated by the fire holding a child upon her lap (36x32cm-14x13in) s.d.1647 prov.exhib. 14-May-3 Christie's, Amsterdam #145/R est:3500-5000

CARRE, Gerda (1872-?) German
£345 $548 €500 Still life with fish, lemon and onions (76x130cm-30x51in) s.d.1902 board. 8-Mar-3 Arnold, Frankfurt #561/R

CARRE, Ketty (1882-1964) French
£538 $850 €850 Paradis terrestre (30x21cm-12x8in) s.d.1922 paper on cardboard. 28-Nov-2 Piasa, Paris #30/R
£1295 $2124 €1800 Conversation sur une terrasse (27x33cm-11x13in) s.i. cardboard. 4-Jun-3 Tajan, Paris #246/R est:1800-2000
Works on paper
£506 $800 €800 Jardin a Alger (23x18cm-9x7in) s.d.1913 W/C crayon. 28-Nov-2 Piasa, Paris #27
£570 $900 €900 Patio (26x35cm-10x14in) s.d.1928 gouache. 28-Nov-2 Piasa, Paris #24
£665 $1050 €1050 Courtisane (29x25cm-11x10in) s.d.1918 gouache paper on cardboard. 28-Nov-2 Piasa, Paris #28/R
£1013 $1600 €1600 Interieur arabe (23x31cm-9x12in) s.d.1931 stump paper on cardboard. 28-Nov-2 Piasa, Paris #23/R
£1013 $1600 €1600 Femmes dans une maison mauresque (26x33cm-10x13in) s.d.1926 gouache paper on cardboard. 28-Nov-2 Piasa, Paris #22/R

CARRE, Léon (1878-1942) French
£440 $678 €700 Village d'orient (30x40cm-12x16in) s.i.d.1946 cardboard. 23-Oct-2 Rabourdin & Choppin de Janvry, Paris #141
£1103 $1843 €1600 15 jours a Londres, Billets speciaux pour fetes de Paques (55x45cm-22x18in) s.d.08 cardboard. 9-Jul-3 Millon & Associes, Paris #127 est:600-800
Works on paper
£426 $689 €600 Le paradis terrestre (38x32cm-15x13in) s. gouache. 26-May-3 Joron-Derem, Paris #33
£647 $1062 €900 Cavalier de fantasia. Berger et son ane dans une oasis (30x21cm-12x8in) s. gouache pair. 4-Jun-3 Tajan, Paris #170/R
£823 $1300 €1300 Dancer (20x14cm-8x6in) i. gouache htd gold. 28-Nov-2 Piasa, Paris #33/R
£1076 $1700 €1700 Idyll (35x25cm-14x10in) s. gouache. 28-Nov-2 Piasa, Paris #29

CARREE, Michiel (1657-1747) Dutch
£2069 $3290 €3000 Shepherdess with cattle (31x36cm-12x14in) s.d.1694. 10-Mar-3 Sotheby's, Amsterdam #8/R est:1500-2000

CARREE, Michiel (attrib) (1657-1747) Dutch
£828 $1316 €1200 Couple sitting under a tree with their cattle (38x45cm-15x18in) 10-Mar-3 Sotheby's, Amsterdam #6 est:600-900

CARREE, Michiel (circle) (1657-1747) Dutch
£7200 $11304 €10800 Italianate landscape with horsemen at a fountain (73x100cm-29x39in) i.verso. 10-Dec-2 Bonhams, New Bond Street #123/R est:4000-6000

CARRENO DE MIRANDA, Juan (1614-1685) Spanish
£5655 $8992 €8200 Atocha Virgin (43x33cm-17x13in) 4-Mar-3 Ansorena, Madrid #70/R

CARRENO DE MIRANDA, Juan (attrib) (1614-1685) Spanish
Works on paper
£935 $1496 €1300 Head of St Francis of Assissi (23x17cm-9x7in) ochre prov. 17-May-3 Lempertz, Koln #1212

CARRENO DE MIRANDA, Juan (studio) (1614-1685) Spanish
£4803 $7493 €7205 Portrait of Charles II of Spain (183x118cm-72x46in) 20-Nov-2 Fischer, Luzern #1008/R est:12000-18000 (S.FR 11000)

CARRENO, Mario (1913-1999) Cuban
£4403 $6780 €7000 Untitled (55x42cm-22x17in) s.d.1953 cardboard on canvas prov. 28-Oct-2 Segre, Madrid #127/R est:7000
£9615 $15000 €14423 Untitled, naturaleza muerta (51x42cm-20x17in) s.d.43 canvasboard. 14-Oct-2 Butterfields, San Francisco #2135/R est:18000-22000
£12805 $21000 €18567 Pescadora ensardinada (81x54cm-32x21in) s.d.82 s.i.d.verso prov. 27-May-3 Sotheby's, New York #67
£19817 $32500 €28735 The river (30x41cm-12x16in) s.d.40. prov.exhib. 27-May-3 Sotheby's, New York #81

£31847 $50000 €47771 Nude (60x48cm-24x19in) s.d.43 stucco panel prov. 20-Nov-2 Christie's, Rockefeller NY #21/R est:60000-80000
£243902 $400000 €353658 Guitar player (73x63cm-29x25in) pyroxylin panel prov.exhib. 27-May-3 Sotheby's, New York #5

CARRERA PASCUAL, Maria (1937-) Spanish
£377 $581 €600 View of Madrid roofs (70x100cm-28x39in) s.d.66 s.i.d.verso. 22-Oct-2 Durán, Madrid #90/R

CARRERE, F Ouillon (20th C) ?
Sculpture
£2000 $3200 €3000 Sword dance (54cm-21in) s. bronze. 15-May-3 Christie's, Kensington #412/R est:800-1200

CARRERE, René (19/20th C) French
Works on paper
£1603 $2484 €2500 Portrait presume de Mistinguette (106x137cm-42x54in) s. pastel. 5-Dec-2 Gros & Delettrez, Paris #32/R

CARRERO Y TAULET, Juan (1860-?) Spanish
£1118 $1812 €1700 View of Ceuta (32x88cm-13x35in) s.d.1881. 21-Jan-3 Ansorena, Madrid #257/R

CARRESSE, Pierre (20th C) French
£2302 $3683 €3200 La cafetiere rouge (81x65cm-32x26in) s. wood. 18-May-3 Neret-Minet, Paris #191/R est:980-1100

CARREY, Georges (1902-1953) French
£609 $944 €950 Composition au Figaro (70x92cm-28x36in) i.verso. 9-Dec-2 Horta, Bruxelles #187
£886 $1382 €1400 Jeune femme nue de face (91x61cm-36x24in) 16-Sep-2 Horta, Bruxelles #21
£1076 $1678 €1700 Composition (55x46cm-22x18in) s. 16-Sep-2 Horta, Bruxelles #22
£1154 $1823 €1800 Composition bleu, rouge et gris (80x130cm-31x51in) s. s.d.40 verso. 15-Nov-2 Laurence Calmels, Paris #97/R

CARREY, Louis Jacques (1822-1871) French
Works on paper
£6173 $10000 €9260 Bouquet of flowers on marble ledge (56x43cm-22x17in) s.d.1843 gouache over pencil. 21-Jan-3 Sotheby's, New York #187/R est:6000

CARRICK, Desmond (1930-) Irish
£478 $745 €750 Mountain goat (41x53cm-16x21in) s. 6-Nov-2 James Adam, Dublin #80/R
£637 $994 €1000 Men in a field (46x60cm-18x24in) s. board. 6-Nov-2 James Adam, Dublin #147/R
£669 $1043 €1050 On the canal (28x38cm-11x15in) s. board. 6-Nov-2 James Adam, Dublin #45/R
£1074 $1729 €1600 Mountain goat (41x53cm-16x21in) s. 18-Feb-3 Whyte's, Dublin #63/R est:1200-1500
£1370 $2137 €2000 Evening at Fresnoy-La-Riviere, Oise (39x50cm-15x20in) s. 8-Apr-3 James Adam, Dublin #130/R est:1000-1500
£1582 $2453 €2500 Spanish Marina (65x85cm-26x33in) s. board. 25-Sep-2 James Adam, Dublin #36/R est:2500-3500
£1806 $2871 €2600 An overcast day, Burriana Beach, Nerja (46x61cm-18x24in) s. i.verso canvasboard. 29-Apr-3 Whyte's, Dublin #164/R est:1500-2000
£1884 $3090 €2600 Ducks in a meadow after a shower at Rusheen, Inishbofin (46x61cm-18x24in) s. board. 28-May-3 Bonhams & James Adam, Dublin #94/R est:2000-3000
£2138 $3336 €3400 Marshland below Caherdaniel, County Kerry (46x61cm-18x24in) s. i.verso board. 17-Sep-2 Whyte's, Dublin #6/R est:2000-3000

CARRICK, John Mulcaster (1833-?) British
£580 $905 €870 Dinan, Brittany (18x13cm-7x5in) s.i. d.1888 verso board. 15-Oct-2 Bearnes, Exeter #423/R
£1964 $3104 €2946 Street scenes (21x26cm-8x10in) s.d.1887 board pair. 27-Nov-2 Deutscher-Menzies, Melbourne #267/R est:8000-10000 (A.D 5500)
£2000 $3160 €3000 Street in Newlyn (21x25cm-8x10in) s. i.d.1882 verso board. 27-Nov-2 Hamptons Fine Art, Godalming #352/R est:1200-1500
£3200 $5024 €4800 St. Michael's Mount (56x97cm-22x38in) s.d.1876. 16-Dec-2 Sotheby's, Olympia #39/R est:2500-3500

CARRICK, Robert (19th C) British
£17000 $27370 €25500 Weary life (102x82cm-40x32in) s. prov.exhib.lit. 20-Feb-3 Christie's, London #55/R est:18000

CARRICK, William (1879-1964) British
£560 $879 €840 Loch Eport, North Uist (52x79cm-20x31in) 17-Apr-3 Bonhams, Edinburgh #353
£950 $1511 €1425 Highlands games at Kingussie (34x53cm-13x21in) s. board. 6-Mar-3 Christie's, Kensington #213/R
£2000 $3180 €3000 Old trawler, Pennan, Aberdeenshire (41x56cm-16x22in) s. prov. 6-Mar-3 Christie's, Kensington #143/R est:1000-1500

CARRIER DE ABAUNZA (?) Spanish?
£2318 $3778 €3500 Art lovers (41x32cm-16x13in) s. panel. 31-Jan-3 Raboundin & Choppin de Janvry, Paris #91/R

CARRIER, A (19th C) French
Sculpture
£1900 $2945 €2850 Female nymph standing filling an oil lamp (53cm-21in) i. bronze. 3-Dec-2 Sworder & Son, Bishops Stortford #583/R est:1800-2200

CARRIER, Louis (1925-1976) Canadian
Works on paper
£193 $302 €290 Portrait de Francois Desrochers (51x35cm-20x14in) s. chl. 25-Mar-3 Iegor de Saint Hippolyte, Montreal #19 (C.D 450)

CARRIER-BELLEUSE (19/20th C) French
Sculpture
£2548 $3975 €4000 Fileuse (46cm-18in) s. ivory pat bronze marble base. 6-Nov-2 Tajan, Paris #16/R

CARRIER-BELLEUSE, A (1824-1887) French
Sculpture
£962 $1490 €1500 Fileuse (54x15x15cm-21x6x6in) s. pat bronze marble base. 4-Dec-2 Anaf, Lyon #26
£1700 $2686 €2550 The reader (47cm-19in) s. bronze. 14-Nov-2 Christie's, Kensington #280/R est:800-1000

CARRIER-BELLEUSE, Albert (1824-1887) French
Sculpture
£1389 $2194 €2000 La liseuse (41cm-16in) s.i. ivory silver pat bronze round socle. 25-Apr-3 Drouot Estimations, Paris #26 est:2000-3000
£1451 $2250 €2177 Bust of Beethoven (41cm-16in) s. terracotta on wooden base prov.exhib.lit. 29-Oct-2 Sotheby's, New York #223/R est:2500-3500
£1451 $2250 €2177 Bust of Beethoven (44cm-17in) s. terracotta on wooden base lit. 29-Oct-2 Sotheby's, New York #224/R est:3000-4000
£1500 $2340 €2250 Bust of a woman (65cm-26in) s. terracotta ebonised wood socle lit. 9-Apr-3 Sotheby's, London #209/R est:2000-3000
£1572 $2437 €2500 Liseuse (41cm-16in) s.i. pat bronze ivory. 30-Oct-2 Coutau Begarie, Paris #129/R
£1799 $2878 €2500 Le messie (79x39cm-31x15in) rose pat terracotta. 18-May-3 Rabourdin & Choppin de Janvry, Paris #78/R est:2500-2800
£1800 $3006 €2610 Figure of a young girl (61cm-24in) s. terracotta. 18-Jun-3 Henry Adams, Chichester #296/R est:2000-3000
£1899 $2943 €3000 Suzanne surprise (64x23x22cm-25x9x9in) terracotta. 27-Sep-2 Rabourdin & Choppin de Janvry, Paris #115/R est:3000-3200
£2098 $3504 €3000 Bacchante et ses chevres (52cm-20in) s. terracotta. 25-Jun-3 Artcurial Briest, Paris #711/R est:3000-4000
£2158 $3453 €3000 La liseuse (60cm-24in) s. silver bronze. 13-May-3 Galerie Moderne, Brussels #1523/R est:3000-3500
£2500 $4175 €3625 Bust of Dante (49cm-19in) s. dk brown pat bronze htd gilding incl red marble base. 8-Jul-3 Sotheby's, London #209/R est:3000-5000
£2600 $4056 €3900 Allegorical figure of night (64cm-25in) s. terracotta ebonised wood plinth. 5-Nov-2 Sotheby's, London #193/R est:3000-5000
£2800 $4368 €4200 Triton and bacchante (66cm-26in) s. terracotta lit. 5-Nov-2 Sotheby's, London #152/R est:3000-5000
£2800 $4368 €4200 Bust of Dante (54cm-21in) s. terracotta ceramic tile ebonised wood socle. 5-Nov-2 Sotheby's, London #154/R est:3000-5000
£2857 $4543 €4200 Melodie (81cm-32in) s. green brown pat bronze marble socle. 18-Mar-3 Vanderkindere, Brussels #189/R est:2500-4000
£3000 $4710 €4500 Bust of a woman (45cm-18in) s.d.1868 white marble on mottled red marble socle. 10-Dec-2 Sotheby's, London #176/R est:3000-5000
£3019 $4679 €4800 Jeune femme drapee tenant un vase (88cm-35in) pat bronze marble socle. 1-Oct-2 Palais de Beaux Arts, Brussels #384/R est:6000-8000
£3226 $5000 €4839 Virgile (44cm-17in) s. brown pat. bronze prov.exhib. 29-Oct-2 Sotheby's, New York #230/R est:5000-7000
£3310 $5297 €4800 Buste d'elegante avec coiffure fleurie (54cm-21in) s. verso terracotta. 17-Mar-3 Horta, Bruxelles #133 est:5000-7000
£3526 $5535 €5500 La liseuse (58cm-23in) s. ivory gilt bronze. 19-Nov-2 Galerie Moderne, Brussels #1517/R est:5000-5500

£3548 $5500 €5322 Bust of a woman, possibly Marguerite Bellanger (69cm-27in) s. terracotta on wooden base prov.lit. 29-Oct-2 Sotheby's, New York #227/R est:8000-12000
£3741 $5949 €5500 La fileuse (46cm-18in) s. ivory bronze marble base. 18-Mar-3 Campo, Vlaamse Kaai #21/R est:2800-3300
£3800 $5928 €5700 Allegorical figure of night (61cm-24in) s. white marble. 5-Nov-2 Sotheby's, London #167/R est:4000-6000
£3846 $6423 €5500 Jeune femme a la lecture (61cm-24in) bronze ivory. 25-Jun-3 Artcurial Briest, Paris #709 est:6000-7000
£4000 $6200 €6000 Bust of America with feathers and shell in her plaited hair (66cm-26in) terracotta exec.c.1885. 1-Oct-2 Christie's, London #286/R est:4000-6000
£4500 $7515 €6525 Innocence tormented by cupid (69cm-27in) s. terrracotta incl ebonised wooden socle. 8-Jul-3 Sotheby's, London #202/R est:5000-7000
£4516 $7000 €6774 Bust of Velasquez (52cm-20in) s. terrracotta on wooden base prov.exhib.lit. 29-Oct-2 Sotheby's, New York #222/R est:5000-7000
£4557 $7063 €7200 Amazone (56x19x17cm-22x7x7in) black brown pat bronze exec.c.1880. 27-Sep-2 Rabourdin & Choppin de Janvry, Paris #105/R est:7600-7800
£5161 $8000 €7742 Bust of Bartolome Esteban Murillo (54cm-21in) s. terracotta on wooden base prov.exhib.lit. 29-Oct-2 Sotheby's, New York #221/R est:5000-7000
£5500 $8580 €8250 Woman with a cat (83cm-33in) s. brown pat bronze. 5-Nov-2 Sotheby's, London #146/R est:6000-8000
£7000 $10920 €10500 Torquato Tasso seated (67cm-26in) s.st.Gautier et Cie brown pat bronze. 9-Apr-3 Sotheby's, London #143/R est:8000-12000
£7000 $10920 €10500 Moliere seated (60cm-24in) s.indis.num.843 brown pat bronze st.Gautier et Cie. 9-Apr-3 Sotheby's, London #146/R est:8000-12000
£7800 $13026 €11310 Nymph and Satyr (58cm-23in) s. terracotta. 8-Jul-3 Sotheby's, London #205/R est:4000-6000
£7911 $12500 €12500 Enlevement de Dejanire (65cm-26in) s. green pat bronze. 29-Nov-2 Drouot Estimations, Paris #133/R est:3200
£9677 $15000 €14516 Orpheus (49cm-19in) s. brown pat. bronze. 29-Oct-2 Sotheby's, New York #228/R est:6000-8000
£14000 $21700 €21000 Scantily clad lady holding a ribbon with a cat at her feet (29cm-11in) s. ivory gilt bronze onyx circular base exec.c.1880. 1-Oct-2 Christie's, London #289/R est:14000-18000
£14839 $23000 €22259 Torchbearer (180cm-71in) s. bronze marble base. 29-Oct-2 Sotheby's, New York #103/R est:18000-25000

CARRIER-BELLEUSE, Louis (1848-1913) French
£11268 $18141 €16000 Serenade (140x200cm-55x79in) s. lit. 9-May-3 Schloss Ahlden, Ahlden #1385/R est:18500
Works on paper
£633 $1000 €1000 Deux ramoneurs (59x40cm-23x16in) s.d.1887 crayon chk. 28-Nov-2 Tajan, Paris #190/R

CARRIER-BELLEUSE, Pierre (1851-1932) French
£764 $1215 €1100 Elegante dans sous-bois (21x27cm-8x11in) s. panel. 30-Apr-3 Tajan, Paris #138
£6475 $10360 €9000 Elegante dans l'atelier du peintre (45x38cm-18x15in) s.d.1880. 14-May-3 Rabourdin & Choppin de Janvry, Paris #52/R est:10000-13000
£13380 $22211 €19000 Hotel des Amis des Arts (28x46cm-11x18in) s. panel. 11-Jun-3 Beaussant & Lefèvre, Paris #8/R est:6000-8000
Works on paper
£488 $800 €708 Portrait of a woman (91x74cm-36x29in) s.d.1927 pastel. 4-Jun-3 Doyle, New York #27
£2200 $3454 €3300 Un instant de surprise (100x64cm-39x25in) s. pastel on linen. 21-Nov-2 Christie's, Kensington #42/R est:1500-2000
£2740 $4274 €4000 Deux jeunes femmes dansant (72x58cm-28x23in) s.d.1926 pastel. 14-Apr-3 Horta, Bruxelles #176 est:5000-7000
£2800 $4676 €4060 Summer bonnet (70x52cm-28x20in) s.d.1893 pastel. 17-Jun-3 Bonhams, New Bond Street #120/R est:3000-5000
£5161 $8155 €8000 Jeune ballerine (81x64cm-32x25in) s. pastel on canvas. 19-Dec-2 Claude Aguttes, Neuilly #76/R
£6203 $9676 €9800 Lavandiere en bord de mer (54x81cm-21x32in) s.i.d. pastel. 20-Oct-2 Mercier & Cie, Lille #296/R est:7500-8000
£16456 $26000 €26000 Partie de cartes (120x170cm-47x67in) s.d.1905 pastel. 1-Dec-2 Anaf, Lyon #52/R est:35000
£25806 $40000 €38709 La premiere pose (100x65cm-39x26in) s.d.1900 pastel. 30-Oct-2 Christie's, Rockefeller NY #194/R est:10000-15000

CARRIERA, Rosalba (1675-1757) Italian
Works on paper
£1241 $1961 €1800 Portrait of lady (65x54cm-26x21in) pastel paper on canvas. 5-Apr-3 Finarte Semenzato, Milan #2/R
£6500 $10855 €9425 Portrait of Lewis Watson, 2nd Earl of Rockingham (19x13cm-7x5in) s.i. black chk brown ink prov.lit. 8-Jul-3 Christie's, London #43/R est:3000-5000
£18987 $30000 €30000 Portrait of gentleman (56x44cm-22x17in) pastel. 2-Dec-2 Finarte, Milan #82/R est:40000
£23000 $38410 €33350 Allegorical female figure possibly Spring (45x34cm-18x13in) bears i. stretcher pastel prov. 9-Jul-3 Sotheby's, London #58/R est:20000-30000
£47552 $79413 €68000 Portrait de femme en costume Turc (64x52cm-25x20in) pastel prov. 25-Jun-3 Sotheby's, Paris #21/R est:40000-60000

CARRIERA, Rosalba (attrib) (1675-1757) Italian
Works on paper
£1200 $1848 €1800 Portrait of lady as Venus (71x56cm-28x22in) col chk oval. 25-Oct-2 Gorringes, Lewes #882

CARRIERE, Eugène (1849-1906) French
£513 $805 €800 Femme portant son enfant (60x50cm-24x20in) s.d.1887. 10-Dec-2 Vanderkindere, Brussels #164
£1039 $1600 €1559 Etiennette Chausson (65x42cm-26x17in) st.sig. prov. 4-Sep-2 Christie's, Rockefeller NY #316/R est:3000-5000
£1389 $2209 €2000 Femme assise (46x36cm-18x14in) 30-Apr-3 Tajan, Paris #115 est:2500
£1440 $2218 €2160 Sophie Carriere, wife of the artist (65x55cm-26x22in) 26-Oct-2 Heffel, Vancouver #6 est:5000-7000 (C.D 3500)
£2484 $4000 €3726 Sphie Carriere, wife of the artist (66x53cm-26x21in) studio st. prov. 19-Feb-3 Doyle, New York #71 est:3000-5000
£2516 $3925 €4000 Femme assise (45x38cm-18x15in) prov. 11-Oct-2 Binoche, Paris #124/R
£3226 $5000 €4839 Conversation (33x41cm-13x16in) st.sig. 2-Oct-2 Christie's, Rockefeller NY #778/R est:6000-8000
£4194 $6500 €6291 Portrait of a woman (88x70cm-35x28in) s. 2-Oct-2 Christie's, Rockefeller NY #775/R est:8000-12000
Works on paper
£385 $642 €550 Etude d'enfants (22x32cm-9x13in) bears st.sig. dr. 26-Jun-3 Tajan, Paris #32
£422 $700 €612 Mother and child (33x30cm-13x12in) pencil. 13-Jun-3 Du Mouchelle, Detroit #2424/R
£823 $1300 €1235 Maternite (23x30cm-9x12in) st.sig. chl. 1-Apr-3 Christie's, Rockefeller NY #190/R

CARRILLO, Antonio (20th C) Mexican
Works on paper
£409 $639 €614 Torso masculino (87x51cm-34x20in) s.d.1995 sanguine paper prov. 17-Oct-2 Louis Morton, Mexico #2 est:8000-10000 (M.P 6500)

CARRINGTON, Dora (1893-1932) British
£2600 $4264 €3900 Gypsy horse stealers (63x80cm-25x31in) i. plywood exhib. 3-Jun-3 Sotheby's, Olympia #81/R est:2000-3000
£21000 $34440 €31500 Cyclamen in a pot. Scaffolding (39x30cm-15x12in) board double-sided. 6-Jun-3 Christie's, London #21/R est:6000-8000
Works on paper
£700 $1092 €1050 Shoe shop (20x20cm-8x8in) pencil pen ink wash prov.exhib. 27-Mar-3 Christie's, Kensington #277
£1150 $1794 €1725 Landscape at Yegen, Spain (22x26cm-9x10in) pencil. 27-Mar-3 Christie's, Kensington #279 est:200-300

CARRINGTON, James Yates (1857-1892) British
£3125 $5000 €4688 Moment's anticipation (94x74cm-37x29in) s.d.1886. 14-May-3 Butterfields, San Francisco #1161/R est:5000-7000

CARRINGTON, Joy (1907-1999) American
£385 $600 €578 Bluebonnets (41x51cm-16x20in) canvasboard. 19-Oct-2 David Dike, Dallas #15/R

CARRINGTON, Leonora (1917-) British
£4082 $6531 €5919 Caballos (21x60cm-8x24in) s.d.1960 tempera ceramic. 15-May-3 Louis Morton, Mexico #25/R est:14000-35000 (M.P 66000)
£7643 $12000 €11465 Bull (20x25cm-8x10in) s.i.d.1959 tempera gold leaf board. 19-Nov-2 Sotheby's, New York #94/R est:20000
£47771 $75000 €71657 Venus landscape (59x91cm-23x36in) s. tempera panel painted 1954 prov.lit. 19-Nov-2 Sotheby's, New York #17/R est:100000
£67073 $110000 €100610 Nativity (61x138cm-24x54in) s. egg tempera masonite triptych painted 1989 prov.exhib. 28-May-3 Christie's, Rockefeller NY #15/R est:120000-160000
£76433 $120000 €114650 Syssigy (56x50cm-22x20in) s.d.1957 board prov.lit. 19-Nov-2 Sotheby's, New York #25/R est:120000

CARROL, Robert (1934-) American
£654 $1046 €1000 Pima Point (54x65cm-21x26in) s. 4-Jan-3 Meeting Art, Vercelli #391
£694 $1104 €1000 Rake in light (50x65cm-20x26in) s. s.i.verso acrylic board. 1-May-3 Meeting Art, Vercelli #99

£1923 $3019 €3000 After summer rain (81x100cm-32x39in) s. 23-Nov-2 Meeting Art, Vercelli #324/R
£1961 $3137 €3000 Tension (82x100cm-32x39in) s. 4-Jan-3 Meeting Art, Vercelli #229

CARROLL, John (1892-1959) American
Works on paper
£438 $700 €657 Portrait of young girl (15x9cm-6x4in) pencil. 14-Mar-3 Du Mouchelle, Detroit #2270/R
£500 $800 €750 Nude female figure lounging on chair (10x13cm-4x5in) pencil. 14-Mar-3 Du Mouchelle, Detroit #2272/R
£563 $900 €845 Three dancers (8x14cm-3x6in) pencil. 14-Mar-3 Du Mouchelle, Detroit #2271/R

CARROLL, Lawrence (1954-) American
Works on paper
£5063 $8000 €7595 Return (251x122cm-99x48in) s.i.d.88 verso mixed media prov.exhib. 13-Nov-2 Sotheby's, New York #594/R est:8000-12000

CARROLL, Lewis (1832-1898) British
Photographs
£2400 $3888 €3600 John, Johnnie Henry Joshua Ellison (20x15cm-8x6in) albumen print card prov.lit. 22-May-3 Sotheby's, London #28/R est:2000-3000

CARROLL, Marie (20th C) British?
£250 $365 €375 Sailing, Howth (30x36cm-12x14in) s. board. 12-Jun-2 John Ross, Belfast #45
£260 $380 €390 Bewley's cafe (30x36cm-12x14in) s. board. 12-Jun-2 John Ross, Belfast #101
£280 $434 €420 Night out in O'Shea's bar, Dublin (36x30cm-14x12in) s. board. 2-Oct-2 John Ross, Belfast #223
£340 $541 €510 At the Shelbourne Hotel, Dublin (35x30cm-14x12in) s. board. 5-Mar-3 John Ross, Belfast #95
£345 $552 €500 River Liffey with the gasometer in the distance (58x74cm-23x29in) s.d.93 card. 11-Mar-3 Thomas Adams, Dublin #446
£400 $620 €600 Around the Maypole (73x45cm-29x18in) s. board. 4-Dec-2 John Ross, Belfast #108
£420 $651 €630 Fishing boats off Westport (41x51cm-16x20in) s. board. 2-Oct-2 John Ross, Belfast #270
£440 $682 €660 In the Shelbourne Hotel, Dublin (71x45cm-28x18in) s. board. 4-Dec-2 John Ross, Belfast #258
£480 $701 €720 Stroll in the park (56x61cm-22x24in) s. board. 12-Jun-2 John Ross, Belfast #97
£500 $775 €750 Mulligans Bar, Dublin (46x66cm-18x26in) s. board. 2-Oct-2 John Ross, Belfast #57
£500 $795 €750 Duck pond (91x61cm-36x24in) s. board. 5-Mar-3 John Ross, Belfast #112
£520 $806 €780 Dublin (71x45cm-28x18in) s. board. 4-Dec-2 John Ross, Belfast #45
£550 $803 €825 Sailing off Dublin (53x71cm-21x28in) s. board. 12-Jun-2 John Ross, Belfast #146
£550 $875 €825 Thatched cottage, Donegal (50x71cm-20x28in) s. board. 5-Mar-3 John Ross, Belfast #46
£580 $899 €870 In the bunker (56x71cm-22x28in) s. board. 2-Oct-2 John Ross, Belfast #37
£650 $949 €975 High waves off Dublin (51x74cm-20x29in) s. board. 12-Jun-2 John Ross, Belfast #140
£950 $1511 €1425 Mulligans Bar (61x86cm-24x34in) s. board. 5-Mar-3 John Ross, Belfast #121
£1200 $1908 €1800 At the Shelbourne Hotel, Dublin (96x66cm-38x26in) s. board. 5-Mar-3 John Ross, Belfast #115 est:500-600

CARROLL, Patrick (1949-) Australian
£393 $621 €590 Big event - city to surf (90x75cm-35x30in) s.i.d.1979 oil collage on board. 17-Nov-2 Sotheby's, Paddington #88 est:800-1200 (A.D 1100)

CARROLL, William Joseph (19/20th C) British
£1056 $1700 €1584 Portrait of a young maiden (76x56cm-30x22in) s. 22-Feb-3 Pook & Pook, Downington #402/R est:800-1000
Works on paper
£1500 $2430 €2250 Portraits of beautiful young ladies (35x25cm-14x10in) W/C htd white pair. 21-Jan-3 Bonhams, Knightsbridge #16/R est:1000-1500

CARSE, James Howe (1819-1900) Australian/British
£349 $555 €524 Waterfall (51x40cm-20x16in) s.indis.d. prov. 5-May-3 Sotheby's, Melbourne #352 (A.D 900)
£650 $1040 €975 Extensive landscape with figures on a lane and deer (38x71cm-15x28in) s.d.1860 board pair. 11-Mar-3 Gorringes, Lewes #2445

CARSE, William (19th C) British
£1000 $1660 €1450 Cattle watering with a cowherd and a dog looking on (43x58cm-17x23in) panel. 16-Jun-3 Duke & Son, Dorchester #194 est:800-1600

CARSLEY, Gary (1957-) Australian
£245 $382 €425 Blue rape (199x199cm-78x78in) 31-Mar-3 Goodman, Sydney #58 (A.D 650)
£264 $412 €458 The flames are cold and made of glass (105x84cm-41x33in) i.d.1984 verso oil spraypaint prov. 31-Mar-3 Goodman, Sydney #73/R (A.D 700)

CARSON, Gerald J A (?) Irish?
£360 $601 €522 Irish harbour, estuary scene (28x74cm-11x29in) s. 20-Jun-3 Keys, Aylsham #340

CARSON, Robert Taylor (1919-) British
£519 $804 €820 River scene (29x40cm-11x16in) s. board. 24-Sep-2 De Veres Art Auctions, Dublin #125
£621 $901 €1000 On the road near the beach (30x38cm-12x15in) s. 3-May-2 Woodwards, Cork #229
£962 $1510 €1500 Figure on a west coastal road, West of Ireland (41x51cm-16x20in) s. canvasboard. 19-Nov-2 Whyte's, Dublin #223 est:1500-2000
£1258 $1962 €2000 Downings Strand (51x64cm-20x25in) s. i.verso. 17-Sep-2 Whyte's, Dublin #221 est:2000-3000
£1611 $2593 €2400 Outside Ryan's bar (30x41cm-12x16in) s. i.d.1983 verso board. 18-Feb-3 Whyte's, Dublin #223/R est:2500-3500
£1667 $2617 €2600 Galway door (41x30cm-16x12in) s. i.verso board. 19-Nov-2 Whyte's, Dublin #221/R est:2500-3500
£1761 $2747 €2800 Figures on the Strand (64x76cm-25x30in) s. 17-Sep-2 Whyte's, Dublin #188/R est:2000-3000
£2000 $3160 €3000 Cottages, Co. Donegal (51x64cm-20x25in) s. i.verso. 13-Nov-2 Halls, Shrewsbury #379/R est:500-700
£3600 $5580 €5400 Paddy the cooper (61x91cm-24x36in) s.d.Oct 68 verso. 4-Dec-2 John Ross, Belfast #153 est:1500-2000
Works on paper
£1384 $2158 €2200 Ashford Castle (51x61cm-20x24in) s. prov. 17-Sep-2 Whyte's, Dublin #11/R est:2000-3000

CARSON, W A (20th C) American
£637 $1000 €956 Expansive western landscape with Native American figure (61x91cm-24x36in) s. canvasboard. 23-Nov-2 Jackson's, Cedar Falls #91/R

CARSTENSEN, Andreas Christian Riis (1844-1906) Danish
£380 $586 €570 Lots of boats at Sundet, Swedish coast in background (39x56cm-15x22in) s. 26-Oct-2 Rasmussen, Havnen #3010/R (D.KR 4500)
£408 $649 €600 Sailing boat (76x109cm-30x43in) s. 24-Mar-3 Bukowskis, Helsinki #395/R
£426 $672 €639 Man in kayak in fjord by Vajgattet (29x46cm-11x18in) mono. 2-Dec-2 Rasmussen, Copenhagen #1424/R (D.KR 5000)
£474 $720 €711 Seascape with sailing vessels (40x60cm-16x24in) s. 27-Aug-2 Rasmussen, Copenhagen #1757/R (D.KR 5500)
£1278 $1980 €1917 View with icebergs and polar bears, Greenland (56x81cm-22x32in) s. 28-Sep-2 Rasmussen, Havnen #3617/R est:15000-20000 (D.KR 15000)
£1435 $2325 €2081 Harbour scene in Constantinople (33x68cm-13x27in) init. 26-May-3 Rasmussen, Copenhagen #1358/R est:15000 (D.KR 15000)

CARSTENSEN, Claus (1957-) Danish
£836 $1322 €1254 The emblems used again as articles (110x150cm-43x59in) s.i.d.1986 verso. 1-Apr-3 Rasmussen, Copenhagen #266 (D.KR 9000)
£914 $1453 €1371 Yes, Dad (90x75cm-35x30in) s.d.1997 verso. 26-Feb-3 Kunsthallen, Copenhagen #178/R (D.KR 10000)

CARSTENSEN, Ebba (1885-1967) Danish
£270 $417 €405 Interior scene with still life on table (85x87cm-33x34in) s.d.49. 23-Oct-2 Kunsthallen, Copenhagen #4 (D.KR 3200)
£279 $441 €419 Carpenter in backyard (70x90cm-28x35in) s. d.39 stretcher. 1-Apr-3 Rasmussen, Copenhagen #601 (D.KR 3000)
£304 $469 €456 Wooded landscape (90x87cm-35x34in) s. 23-Oct-2 Kunsthallen, Copenhagen #117 (D.KR 3600)
£368 $588 €552 Wooded landscape with figure and deer (112x119cm-44x47in) s.d.1947. 13-Jan-3 Rasmussen, Vejle #2225 (D.KR 4200)
£423 $651 €635 Autumn scene (86x100cm-34x39in) s. 23-Oct-2 Kunsthallen, Copenhagen #82 (D.KR 5000)
£524 $876 €760 Portrait of young woman seated, wearing blue dress (73x57cm-29x22in) sketch verso. 17-Jun-3 Rasmussen, Copenhagen #89/R (D.KR 5500)
£651 $1028 €977 Wooded landscape (95x71cm-37x28in) s. s.d.54 verso exhib. 1-Apr-3 Rasmussen, Copenhagen #530/R (D.KR 7000)

£838 $1332 €1257 Autumn landscape (60x79cm-24x31in) s.d.1924 exhib. 10-Mar-3 Rasmussen, Vejle #575 (D.KR 9000)

CARTE, Antoine (1886-1954) Belgian
£545 $855 €850 Paysage fluvial (29x36cm-11x14in) s. cardboard. 19-Nov-2 Servarts Themis, Bruxelles #110
£1027 $1613 €1500 Fleurs. Paysage (33x40cm-13x16in) s. panel double-sided. 15-Apr-3 Galerie Moderne, Brussels #328/R est:2000-3000
£1282 $2013 €2000 Etude pour haleurs (39x39cm-15x15in) s.d. paper. 19-Nov-2 Servarts Themis, Bruxelles #137/R
£6115 $9784 €8500 Allegorie de l'abondance (90x90cm-35x35in) s.d.1914. 19-May-3 Horta, Bruxelles #136 est:5000-7000
£7914 $12662 €11000 Maternite (125x114cm-49x45in) 19-May-3 Horta, Bruxelles #137/R est:2000-3000
£10067 $16208 €15000 Maternite (79cm-31in) tempera plaster. 18-Feb-3 Galerie Moderne, Brussels #392/R est:20000-30000
£20253 $32000 €32000 L'accordeoniste (64x49cm-25x19in) s. exhib. 26-Nov-2 Palais de Beaux Arts, Brussels #296/R est:20000-30000
£28846 $45288 €45000 Haleur. s.i.d. 19-Nov-2 Servarts Themis, Bruxelles #113/R est:18000
£53237 $85180 €74000 La fuite en Egypte (80x100cm-31x39in) s. 13-May-3 Palais de Beaux Arts, Brussels #41/R est:50000-62000
£54430 $86000 €86000 Mere et enfant devant le village (105x100cm-41x39in) s.d.1928. 26-Nov-2 Palais de Beaux Arts, Brussels #297/R est:50000-75000
£63309 $101295 €88000 L'orgue de Barbarie (125x90cm-49x35in) s. exhib.lit. 13-May-3 Palais de Beaux Arts, Brussels #44/R est:62000-75000
Works on paper
£2302 $3683 €3200 Le dieu Mercure (63x43cm-25x17in) s. mixed media. 13-May-3 Palais de Beaux Arts, Brussels #34/R est:3200-4800
£7639 $12146 €11000 Maternite (48x34cm-19x13in) s. gouache. 29-Apr-3 Campo, Vlaamse Kaai #34/R est:10000-12000

CARTER, Clarence Holbrook (1904-2000) American
£1442 $2250 €2163 Consolation. Still life (56x71cm-22x28in) s.d.1927 board double-sided. 28-Mar-3 Aspire, Cleveland #24/R est:1000-2000
£2258 $3500 €3387 Landscape (61x102cm-24x40in) s.d.1941. 8-Dec-2 Toomey, Oak Park #769/R est:4000-6000
Works on paper
£305 $500 €442 Industrial study (35x43cm-14x17in) s. conte crayon exec.c.1922 exhib. 5-Jun-3 Swann Galleries, New York #67/R

CARTER, Frank Thomas (1853-1934) British
£750 $1170 €1125 Mountain torrent (81x112cm-32x44in) board. 10-Apr-3 Tennants, Leyburn #999
£850 $1326 €1275 River landscape with sheep (76x127cm-30x50in) s. 10-Apr-3 Tennants, Leyburn #998/R

CARTER, Gary (1939-) American
£1923 $3000 €2885 The big step (36x56cm-14x22in) 9-Nov-2 Altermann Galleries, Santa Fe #151

CARTER, Henry (fl.1866-1873) British
£950 $1473 €1425 Hare and curlew (46x61cm-18x24in) s. 30-Sep-2 Bonhams, Ipswich #486

CARTER, Henry Barlow (1803-1867) British
Works on paper
£260 $408 €390 Hull, fishing boats off the coast (16x24cm-6x9in) W/C bodycol over pencil scratching. 21-Nov-2 Tennants, Leyburn #541
£280 $442 €420 Old Scarborough figure with fishing boat to the fore (15x20cm-6x8in) init.i. W/C. 7-Apr-3 David Duggleby, Scarborough #360
£340 $568 €493 Scarbro - figures on a jetty (18x26cm-7x10in) s.d.1834 W/C scratching out. 23-Jun-3 Bonhams, Bath #36
£350 $550 €525 North Bay, Scarborough (17x26cm-7x10in) W/C bodycol scratching. 21-Nov-2 Tennants, Leyburn #652
£360 $569 €540 Fishing boats off the Scarborough coast (8x18cm-3x7in) W/C. 7-Apr-3 David Duggleby, Scarborough #313
£380 $600 €570 Whitby Abbey (25x36cm-10x14in) s. monochrome W/C. 24-Apr-3 Richardson & Smith, Whitby #233
£500 $780 €750 Bempton cliffs (44x58cm-17x23in) s.d.1847 W/C. 10-Apr-3 Tennants, Leyburn #816
£500 $810 €725 Off Whitby (15x23cm-6x9in) W/C. 22-May-3 Richardson & Smith, Whitby #470
£1250 $1975 €1875 Boat unloading at Robin Hoods Bay. Three views of South Bay Scarborough (12x20cm-5x8in) one s. W/C five. 7-Apr-3 David Duggleby, Scarborough #310/R est:700-1000
£2000 $3260 €2900 Staithes (31x45cm-12x18in) s.i.d.1851 pencil W/C scratching out. 17-Jul-3 Tennants, Leyburn #696/R est:2000-3000

CARTER, Henry Barlow (attrib) (1803-1867) British
Works on paper
£300 $468 €450 Fishermen on a beach at sunset (12x16cm-5x6in) W/C. 15-Oct-2 Bearnes, Exeter #351/R

CARTER, J N (19th C) British
Works on paper
£650 $988 €975 Scarborough Lodge, Torquay. Coastal scene (30x48cm-12x19in) d.1866 one s.i. W/C pair. 14-Aug-2 Andrew Hartley, Ilkley #638

CARTER, Jack (?-1992) British
Works on paper
£420 $685 €609 Still life of roses within a glass vase (49x44cm-19x17in) s.d.56 W/C over pencil. 16-Jul-3 Rupert Toovey, Partridge Green #5/R
£560 $874 €840 Still life of anemones in a pewter jug beside a bowl (31x41cm-12x16in) s.d.1981 W/C. 7-Nov-2 Rupert Toovey, Partridge Green #1448/R

CARTER, Joseph Newington (1835-1871) British
Works on paper
£260 $421 €390 Dunstanborough Castle from the sea (11x17cm-4x7in) s. W/C. 21-Jan-3 Bonhams, Knightsbridge #27/R
£620 $1017 €930 Lifeboats and wreck in Cornelian Bay, Scarborough (25x36cm-10x14in) s.d.November 30th 67. 10-Feb-3 David Duggleby, Scarborough #558/R
£680 $1115 €1020 Castle headland, the Baths and harbour from Scarborough Peir (24x36cm-9x14in) d.1863 W/C. 2-Jun-3 David Duggleby, Scarborough #304/R

CARTER, Norman (1875-1963) Australian
£687 $1085 €1031 Nude (25x19cm-10x7in) s.d.1918. 1-Apr-3 Lawson Menzies, Sydney #458 (A.D 1800)

CARTER, Richard Harry (1839-1911) British
Works on paper
£260 $434 €377 Church Cove, Cornwall (23x46cm-9x18in) init.i. W/C. 24-Jun-3 Bonhams, Knightsbridge #169/R
£270 $443 €405 Ship in distress at the harbour mouth (31x45cm-12x18in) s. W/C scratching out. 10-Feb-3 David Duggleby, Scarborough #546
£310 $493 €465 Watching the gulls (49x83cm-19x33in) s. W/C. 4-Mar-3 Bristol Auction Rooms #363/R
£500 $775 €750 Cornish fishing cove, Portloe (36x58cm-14x23in) s. W/C bodycol. 31-Oct-2 Duke & Son, Dorchester #159
£700 $1134 €1050 Day's catch (53x94cm-21x37in) s. W/C. 20-May-3 Sotheby's, Olympia #279/R
£880 $1470 €1276 Fisherwomen on a rocky cliff path (51x94cm-20x37in) s. W/C. 19-Jun-3 Lane, Penzance #325

CARTER, Robert Radcliffe (1867-?) British
£2200 $3432 €3300 Children playing by a river (61x91cm-24x36in) s. 10-Sep-2 Bonhams, Knightsbridge #81/R est:2000-3000

CARTER, Samuel (19th C) British
£380 $593 €570 Portrait of a young boy and the horse Greatshot (70x90cm-28x35in) s.d.1888. 8-Oct-2 Bonhams, Knightsbridge #58/R
Works on paper
£680 $1054 €1020 Cattle and sheep in a landscape (44x62cm-17x24in) s.d.1853 black white chk. 30-Sep-2 Bonhams, Ipswich #488

CARTER, Samuel John (1835-1892) British
£1350 $2241 €1958 Greatshot, held by a groom (71x91cm-28x36in) s.d.1888. 12-Jun-3 Christie's, Kensington #74/R est:1000-1500

CARTER, Sydney (1874-1945) British
£197 $307 €296 Evening (24x33cm-9x13in) s.i.verso board. 15-Oct-2 Stephan Welz, Johannesburg #169 est:1800-2400 (SA.R 3200)
£418 $660 €627 Cape village (49x59cm-19x23in) s. canvasboard. 1-Apr-3 Stephan Welz, Johannesburg #248 est:3000-5000 (SA.R 5200)
Works on paper
£258 $415 €387 Figures outside rondavels (36x27cm-14x11in) s. W/C. 12-May-3 Stephan Welz, Johannesburg #299 est:1200-1800 (SA.R 3000)
£275 $443 €413 Sea view (31x38cm-12x15in) s. W/C. 12-May-3 Stephan Welz, Johannesburg #74 est:1800-2400 (SA.R 3200)
£275 $443 €413 Man and dog on a road (34x47cm-13x19in) s. W/C. 12-May-3 Stephan Welz, Johannesburg #136 est:1800-2400 (SA.R 3200)
£275 $443 €413 Winter landscape (26x36cm-10x14in) s. W/C. 12-May-3 Stephan Welz, Johannesburg #156 est:2000-3000 (SA.R 3200)
£327 $526 €491 Buildings and trees (35x27cm-14x11in) s. gouache. 12-May-3 Stephan Welz, Johannesburg #190 est:1500-2000 (SA.R 3800)
£480 $750 €720 Cape house with Signal Hill in the background (44x62cm-17x24in) s. gouache pastel. 11-Nov-2 Stephan Welz, Johannesburg #454 (SA.R 7500)

CARTER, William Sylvester (1909-) American
Works on paper
£519 $800 €779 Jester with mandolin (28x20cm-11x8in) s. ink dr exec.c.1950. 8-Sep-2 Treadway Gallery, Cincinnati #732/R

CARTER, Z A (20th C) American
£446 $700 €669 Autumn landscape (64x76cm-25x30in) s. 28-Jul-2 Butterfields, San Francisco #3075

CARTERET, Jean Albert Grand (1903-) French
Works on paper
£500 $805 €750 Portrait of a lady, in fur (36x28cm-14x11in) s.d.32 pastel. 18-Feb-3 Bonhams, Knightsbridge #120/R

CARTIER, T (20th C) French
Sculpture
£2038 $3180 €3200 Pierrot descendant des marches (47cm-19in) s. ivory gilt bronze. 11-Nov-2 Horta, Bruxelles #57 est:2500-3700

CARTIER-BRESSON, Henri (1908-) French
Photographs
£1646 $2600 €2600 Turkey (25x17cm-10x7in) i. verso silver gelatin. 28-Nov-2 Villa Grisebach, Berlin #1130/R est:1000-1500
£1948 $3000 €2922 Lovers, Paris (36x24cm-14x9in) s. photograph. 24-Oct-2 Sotheby's, New York #153/R est:2500-3500
£2057 $3250 €3086 Siphnos, Greece (24x36cm-9x14in) s. photograph. 23-Apr-3 Sotheby's, New York #125/R est:3000-5000
£2147 $3500 €3221 Paris (24x36cm-9x14in) s. gelatin silver print. 12-Feb-3 Christie's, Rockefeller NY #199/R est:2000-3000
£2597 $4000 €3896 Rue mouffetard (36x24cm-14x9in) s. photograph. 24-Oct-2 Sotheby's, New York #150/R est:4000-6000
£2800 $4536 €4200 Brussels (30x40cm-12x16in) s. silver print. 22-May-3 Sotheby's, London #91/R est:1500-2000
£4114 $6500 €6171 Baroda, India (25x17cm-10x7in) i. gelatin silver print prov. 24-Apr-3 Phillips, New York #147/R est:4000-6000
£7595 $12000 €11393 Behind the gare St. Lazare, Paris (35x24cm-14x9in) i. i.verso gelatin silver print executed c.1956 prov. 24-Apr-3 Phillips, New York #18/R est:6000-8000

CARTON, Jean (1912-1988) French
Sculpture
£3871 $6000 €5807 Jeune homme (74cm-29in) s.num.3/6 black pat bronze st.f.Bisceglia exhib. 3-Dec-2 Christie's, Rockefeller NY #32/R est:800-1200

CARTOTTO, Ercole (1889-1946) American/Italian
£1372 $2250 €2058 Portrait of Mrs Beatrice Schoellkops Penn (137x102cm-54x40in) s. 8-Feb-3 Neal Auction Company, New Orleans #34/R est:3000-5000

CARTWRIGHT, Joseph (1789-1829) British
Works on paper
£360 $572 €540 Low tide (20x29cm-8x11in) s.d.1813 grey wash. 30-Apr-3 Hampton & Littlewood, Exeter #418/R

CARTWRIGHT, William (18/19th C) British
£700 $1113 €1050 Shipping off the cliffs (62x51cm-24x20in) s.i.verso. 5-Mar-3 Bonhams, Bury St Edmunds #403

CARUELLE D'ALIGNY, Theodore (attrib) (1798-1871) French
Works on paper
£449 $696 €700 Cerfs au bord de riviere (20x27cm-8x11in) wash. 4-Dec-2 Piasa, Paris #122

CARUS, Carl Gustav (1789-1869) German
£70000 $108500 €105000 Phantasie aus der Alpenwelt, Adler, die auf einem Alpenhorn nisten (52x67cm-20x26in) painted 1822 prov.exhib.lit. 4-Dec-2 Christie's, London #71/R est:70000-100000

CARUSO, Bruno (1927-) Italian
£310 $518 €450 Homme dans la rue (39x27cm-15x11in) s.d.1953 wood palette. 10-Jul-3 Artcurial Briest, Paris #230
£310 $518 €450 Tutti frutti and skyline (45x35cm-18x14in) s.d.9.53 panel. 10-Jul-3 Artcurial Briest, Paris #231
£1026 $1621 €1600 Compositions (36x50cm-14x20in) s.d.1950 tempera paper pair. 15-Nov-2 Farsetti, Prato #270/R
Works on paper
£1026 $1610 €1600 Profile of young woman (54x47cm-21x19in) s. mixed media card exec.1996. 21-Nov-2 Finarte, Rome #40/R

CARUSO, Enrico (19/20th C) ?
Sculpture
£2258 $3500 €3387 Laughing Buddha (15cm-6in) s.d.1909 brown pat. bronze. 29-Oct-2 Sotheby's, New York #254/R est:300-500

CARVER, Robert (attrib) (?-1791) British
£1900 $3002 €2850 Irish scene with red coated soldier and other figuers (76x64cm-30x25in) s. 18-Dec-2 John Nicholson, Haslemere #1244/R est:1500-2000

CARWARDINE, Penelope (1730-1801) British
Miniatures
£1200 $1872 €1800 Young lady wearing black Tudor costume and bonnet (5cm-2xin) gold frame oval. 5-Nov-2 Bonhams, New Bond Street #28/R est:600-800

CARY, Francis Stephen (1808-1880) British
£600 $954 €900 Waiting (113x86cm-44x34in) s. 2-Mar-3 Lots Road, London #347

CARY, William de la Montagne (1840-1922) American
£14744 $23000 €22116 Negotiation (25x41cm-10x16in) s. prov.lit. 9-Nov-2 Santa Fe Art, Santa Fe #88/R est:25000-35000

CARZOU (1907-2000) French
Works on paper
£1655 $2764 €2400 La Bretonne (63x47cm-25x19in) s.d.61 W/C. 8-Jul-3 Gioffredo, Nice #35/R

CARZOU, Jean (1907-2000) French
£1194 $1886 €1850 Garden (50x64cm-20x25in) s.d.58 prov. 18-Dec-2 Rieunier, Bailly-Pommery, Mathias, Paris #64/R
£1397 $2040 €2096 Paysage fantastique (41x33cm-16x13in) s.d.1948. 4-Jun-2 Germann, Zurich #10/R est:3500-4500 (S.FR 3200)
£1481 $2104 €2400 Maison dans la vallee (40x33cm-16x13in) s.d.1948. 16-Mar-3 Eric Pillon, Calais #256/R
£1975 $2805 €3200 Jardin pres de la maison (50x65cm-20x26in) s.d.1958. 16-Mar-3 Eric Pillon, Calais #258/R
£2166 $3378 €3400 Paysage (46x55cm-18x22in) s.d.1955 panel. 10-Nov-2 Eric Pillon, Calais #198/R
£2658 $4438 €3800 Paysage surrealiste (46x56cm-18x22in) s.d.50. 26-Jun-3 Tajan, Paris #317/R est:4600-6000
£15705 $24657 €24500 Paysage fantastique (97x130cm-38x51in) s.d.51. 13-Dec-2 Piasa, Paris #21/R est:15000
Works on paper
£839 $1325 €1300 Bateau (41x55cm-16x22in) s.d.1959 Chinese ink W/C dr. 18-Dec-2 Ferri, Paris #37/R
£1457 $2375 €2200 Portrait de femme (26x20cm-10x8in) s. pencil W/C. 1-Feb-3 Claude Aguttes, Neuilly #194/R est:800-1220
£1678 $2803 €2400 Femme au bouquet (63x49cm-25x19in) s. felt tip. 26-Jun-3 Tajan, Paris #166/R est:2400-3000
£2695 $4501 €3800 La mer emeraude (51x65cm-20x26in) s.d. gouache paper on canvas. 23-Jun-3 Claude Boisgirard, Paris #192/R est:3500-4000

CASADO DEL ALISAL, Jose (1830-1886) Spanish
£6081 $9486 €9000 Chapel interior (56x76cm-22x30in) s. lit. 25-Mar-3 Durán, Madrid #196/R est:5500
Works on paper
£2800 $4368 €4200 Odalisque (25x36cm-10x14in) s. W/C. 15-Oct-2 Sotheby's, London #136/R est:1000-1500

CASAMADA, Alberto Rafols (1923-) Spanish
£1164 $1816 €1700 Accent (35x27cm-14x11in) s.d.1989 s.i.verso. 8-Apr-3 Ansorena, Madrid #277/R
£2069 $3269 €3000 Painting (42x42cm-17x17in) s.d.1972 s.i.d.verso prov.lit. 1-Apr-3 Segre, Madrid #192/R
£2328 $3678 €3375 Harbour (46x55cm-18x22in) s.d.1959 prov. 1-Apr-3 Segre, Madrid #191/R
£4717 $7264 €7500 Marine structure (100x100cm-39x39in) s.d.1992 s.i.d.verso prov. 28-Oct-2 Segre, Madrid #142/R est:6000
£7092 $11489 €10000 Llum Blava (100x100cm-39x39in) s.d.1981 s.i.d.verso. 20-May-3 Segre, Madrid #149/R est:9500
Prints
£11538 $18231 €18000 Forms (40x28cm-16x11in) num.6/16 serigraph. 13-Nov-2 Ansorena, Madrid #389/R

Works on paper
£265 $432 €400 Untitled (27x21cm-11x8in) s.d.1991 ink wash. 11-Feb-3 Segre, Madrid #208/R

CASANOVA Y ESTORACH, Antonio (1847-1896) Spanish
£316 $491 €500 Le moine (9x6cm-4x2in) panel. 29-Sep-2 Eric Pillon, Calais #85/R
£380 $589 €600 Le cardinal (9x6cm-4x2in) panel. 29-Sep-2 Eric Pillon, Calais #84/R
£816 $1298 €1200 Portrait de moine (6x3cm-2x1in) panel. 26-Feb-3 Artcurial Briest, Paris #135
£1013 $1570 €1600 Les moines joueurs et buveurs (9x11cm-4x4in) panel pair. 29-Sep-2 Eric Pillon, Calais #82/R
£1139 $1766 €1800 Portraits de cardinaux (10x7cm-4x3in) panel pair. 29-Sep-2 Eric Pillon, Calais #83/R
£1149 $1792 €1700 Priest drinking (26x14cm-10x6in) 25-Mar-3 Durán, Madrid #79/R
£3290 $5199 €5100 Monk holding wine bottles (31x25cm-12x10in) s.d.1896. 17-Dec-2 Segre, Madrid #61/R est:6500
£3290 $5199 €5100 Monk with cricket box (31x25cm-12x10in) s.d.1896. 17-Dec-2 Segre, Madrid #62/R
£9615 $15192 €15000 Playing the violin (50x41cm-20x16in) s. 13-Nov-2 Ansorena, Madrid #123/R
£14151 $22075 €22500 Tolerance (25x33cm-10x13in) s. 23-Sep-2 Durán, Madrid #212/R
Works on paper
£4054 $6324 €6000 New shoes (37x28cm-15x11in) s.i.d.1873 W/C. 25-Mar-3 Durán, Madrid #187/R

CASANOVA, Carlo (1871-1950) Italian
£1087 $1783 €1500 Giogaie dello Spluga (34x62cm-13x24in) s. 27-May-3 Finarte, Milan #3 est:2000-2200

CASANOVA, Francesco Giuseppe (1727-1802) Italian
Works on paper
£252 $390 €400 Soldiers riding horses (16x22cm-6x9in) pen wash htd white. 29-Oct-2 Artcurial Briest, Paris #5
£2414 $3862 €3500 Cavaliers vus de dos et de profil (18x12cm-7x5in) col wash pierre noire pair dr. 12-Mar-3 E & Eve, Paris #24/R est:2500-3500

CASANOVA, Francesco Giuseppe (attrib) (1727-1802) Italian
£699 $1090 €1049 Herder driving cattle through gate (40x32cm-16x13in) i. verso. 6-Nov-2 Dobiaschofsky, Bern #397/R est:2800 (S.FR 1600)

CASARELLI, B (20th C) Italian
£1056 $1701 €1500 Venice with St Marks Square (60x80cm-24x31in) s. panel. 9-May-3 Schloss Ahlden, Ahlden #1391/R est:1200

CASAS, Fernando (20th C) Mexican
Works on paper
£204 $331 €306 Tianguis (37x48cm-15x19in) s.d.1966 W/C. 21-Jan-3 Louis Morton, Mexico #89/R (M.P 3500)

CASATI, Alexandre (19th C) Italian
£833 $1300 €1250 Retour de la pache (43x65cm-17x26in) s.d.1836 i.d.stretcher. 9-Nov-2 Sloan, North Bethesda #583/R

CASAUS, Jesus (1926-) Spanish
£629 $969 €1000 Cadaques (58x92cm-23x36in) s. board. 22-Oct-2 Durán, Madrid #163/R

CASCELLA, Andrea (1920-1990) Italian
Sculpture
£1736 $2760 €2500 Birth of Venus (27x67x29cm-11x26x11in) marble three parts prov. 29-Apr-3 Artcurial Briest, Paris #603/R est:2500-3000

CASCELLA, Michele (1892-1989) Italian
£1701 $2704 €2500 View of Paraggi (32x47cm-13x19in) s. tempera paper on cardboard. 1-Mar-3 Meeting Art, Vercelli #692
£2049 $3257 €2950 Sailing boats (35x50cm-14x20in) s. s.verso. 1-May-3 Meeting Art, Vercelli #109
£2051 $3221 €3200 Path amongst brooms (20x30cm-8x12in) s. 19-Nov-2 Finarte, Milan #286/R
£2115 $3321 €3300 Brooms (20x30cm-8x12in) s. s.i.verso. 23-Nov-2 Meeting Art, Vercelli #463/R
£2614 $4183 €4000 Vase of flowers (50x35cm-20x14in) s. s.verso. 4-Jan-3 Meeting Art, Vercelli #736
£3503 $5500 €5255 Anemones and orange marigolds (24x36cm-9x14in) s. prov. 10-Dec-2 Doyle, New York #235/R est:10000-15000
£5000 $8000 €7250 Autumn in Central Park (70x91cm-28x36in) s.i.d.1959. 16-May-3 Skinner, Boston #321/R est:6000-8000
£5448 $8500 €8172 Mandorlo fiorito (61x91cm-24x36in) s. prov. 14-Oct-2 Butterfields, San Francisco #2035/R est:5000-7000
£5448 $8500 €8172 Daffodils and poppies with poplar trees (70x100cm-28x39in) s. i.verso linen prov. 14-Oct-2 Butterfields, San Francisco #2033/R est:6000-8000
£6250 $9938 €9000 Portofino (40x60cm-16x24in) s. 1-May-3 Meeting Art, Vercelli #582 est:8000
£6410 $10000 €9615 Autumn field at San Gimignano (61x91cm-24x36in) s. prov. 14-Oct-2 Butterfields, San Francisco #2034/R est:10000-15000
£6875 $11000 €10313 Bouquet of flowers (102x76cm-40x30in) s. 14-May-3 Butterfields, San Francisco #1182/R est:12000-15000
£7692 $12077 €12000 Portofino in summer (60x90cm-24x35in) s. painted c.1982. 23-Nov-2 Meeting Art, Vercelli #247/R
£9615 $15000 €14423 Pont on the Seine (76x102cm-30x40in) s. 30-Mar-3 Susanin's, Chicago #6061/R est:6000-8000
£10968 $17329 €17000 Opera (61x77cm-24x30in) s.d.1950 prov. 18-Dec-2 Christie's, Rome #237/R est:20000
£16667 $26167 €26000 House with wall clock (70x110cm-28x43in) s. s.i.verso board painted c.1946-48 prov. 21-Nov-2 Finarte, Rome #324/R est:26000-28000
Works on paper
£676 $1054 €1000 Certosa (21x34cm-8x13in) s. pastel ball-point pen. 26-Mar-3 Finarte Semenzato, Milan #68
£897 $1400 €1346 Venezia la salute (30x41cm-12x16in) s.d.51 W/C pen ink. 30-Mar-3 Susanin's, Chicago #6072/R
£1090 $1711 €1700 Storm on the lake (58x47cm-23x19in) s. pastel chl. 20-Nov-2 Pandolfini, Florence #4/R
£1667 $2617 €2600 Landscape with trees (49x64cm-19x25in) s. gouache. 19-Nov-2 Finarte, Milan #181/R
£2436 $3824 €3800 Schio's church (24x32cm-9x13in) s.d.1917 pastel lit. 19-Nov-2 Finarte, Milan #255/R
£2500 $3875 €3750 Portofino (29x42cm-11x17in) s. gouache on card. 5-Dec-2 Christie's, Kensington #91/R est:2500-3500
£2848 $4443 €4500 Le lac majeur (68x100cm-27x39in) s. pastel. 31-Jul-2 Tajan, Paris #29/R est:3000-4000
£6410 $10064 €10000 Venice (55x77cm-22x30in) s.d.1928 s.i.verso Chinese ink tempera card. 19-Nov-2 Finarte, Milan #29/R est:9000-11000
£8974 $14090 €14000 Spring evening (63x91cm-25x36in) s.d.1912 pastel card prov. 21-Nov-2 Finarte, Rome #180/R est:14000-16000

CASCELLA, Michele (attrib) (1892-1989) Italian
£570 $900 €900 Back to the vilage (20x28cm-8x11in) s.d.1919 board. 26-Nov-2 Christie's, Rome #36

CASCELLA, Pietro (1921-) Italian
Sculpture
£2466 $3847 €3600 Sculpture (30x30x25cm-12x12x10in) st.sig. marble exec.1972. 10-Apr-3 Finarte Semenzato, Rome #220/R

CASCELLA, Tommaso (1951-) Italian
Works on paper
£367 $580 €580 Composition (62x62cm-24x24in) mixed media collage board. 29-Nov-2 Farsetti, Prato #29
£521 $828 €750 Bullet between teeth (40x40cm-16x16in) s.i.d.1995 mixed media collage board. 1-May-3 Meeting Art, Vercelli #401
£822 $1282 €1200 Untitled (61x61cm-24x24in) s.d.88 verso polymer board. 10-Apr-3 Finarte Semenzato, Rome #224/R
£1410 $2214 €2200 Mother (60x60cm-24x24in) s.i.d.1990 polymer board exhib. 20-Nov-2 Pandolfini, Florence #149/R

CASCELLA, Tommaso (1890-1968) Italian
£2381 $3786 €3500 Storm in Pescara (47x61cm-19x24in) s. 24-Mar-3 Finarte Semenzato, Rome #295/R
Works on paper
£2055 $3205 €3000 Shepherds in Guardiagrele (98x68cm-39x27in) s. wax crayon card. 10-Apr-3 Finarte Semenzato, Rome #126

CASCIARO, G (20th C) Italian
Works on paper
£1384 $2131 €2200 View of lake with terrace (22x31cm-9x12in) s.i.d.1907 pastel. 28-Oct-2 Il Ponte, Milan #320

CASCIARO, Giuseppe (1861-1943) Italian
£629 $969 €1000 Italian mountain village (20x31cm-8x12in) s. 23-Oct-2 Neumeister, Munich #625/R
£1103 $1754 €1600 View of village (50x40cm-20x16in) s.d.1901 board. 5-Mar-3 Sotheby's, Milan #52
£1266 $1975 €2000 Houses by Ischia (35x62cm-14x24in) s.d. prov. 19-Oct-2 Semenzato, Venice #329/R
£1548 $2400 €2322 Waves breaking on a rocky coastline (50x70cm-20x28in) s.indis.d. board. 2-Oct-2 Christie's, Rockefeller NY #798/R est:3000-5000
£2177 $3461 €3200 Spring (24x15cm-9x6in) s.d.1885 board. 1-Mar-3 Meeting Art, Vercelli #252

Works on paper
£510 $811 €750 Houses amongst trees (24x16cm-9x6in) s.d.1953 pastel tempera. 1-Mar-3 Meeting Art, Vercelli #179
£641 $994 €1000 Landscape with trees (18x30cm-7x12in) s.d.1916 mixed media card. 5-Dec-2 Stadion, Trieste #751/R
£1013 $1600 €1600 Garden in Capri (27x19cm-11x7in) s. pastel card lit. 26-Nov-2 Christie's, Rome #246/R
£1032 $1631 €1600 Marine in Naples (13x35cm-5x14in) s.d.1910 pastel cardboard. 18-Dec-2 Finarte, Milan #5/R
£1051 $1639 €1660 Tivoli (45x49cm-18x19in) pastel. 15-Oct-2 Babuino, Rome #307/R
£1203 $1900 €1900 Road to Nusco (21x27cm-8x11in) s.d.911 pastel card. 26-Nov-2 Christie's, Rome #243/R
£1266 $2000 €2000 View of Capri (45x51cm-18x20in) s.d. pastel card. 26-Nov-2 Christie's, Rome #20/R
£1531 $2434 €2250 Landscape with figures (29x38cm-11x15in) s.d.1913 pastel card. 1-Mar-3 Meeting Art, Vercelli #157
£1531 $2434 €2250 Road in the Roman countryside (23x30cm-9x12in) s.d.1900 pastel card. 1-Mar-3 Meeting Art, Vercelli #209
£1804 $2814 €2850 Landscape (45x48cm-18x19in) pastel. 15-Oct-2 Babuino, Rome #340/R
£1804 $2814 €2850 Tivoli (45x49cm-18x19in) pastel. 15-Oct-2 Babuino, Rome #361/R
£2658 $4200 €4200 Csciaro's villa. s. pastel card. 26-Nov-2 Christie's, Rome #245/R
£3165 $5000 €5000 Seiano, coastal view (44x50cm-17x20in) s.i. pastel card lit. 26-Nov-2 Christie's, Rome #248/R
£3797 $6000 €6000 Landscape with trees (38x71cm-15x28in) s. pastel card. 26-Nov-2 Christie's, Rome #250/R est:7500
£5063 $8000 €8000 Beach and sea (70x100cm-28x39in) s. pastel card. 26-Nov-2 Christie's, Rome #247/R

CASCIARO, Giuseppe (attrib) (1861-1943) Italian
£590 $931 €885 Untitled (12x30cm-5x12in) s.d.1903. 17-Nov-2 Koller, Geneva #1238/R (S.FR 1350)
Works on paper
£568 $897 €852 Venice (18x37cm-7x15in) s.d.1901 pastel. 17-Nov-2 Koller, Geneva #1237 (S.FR 1300)

CASCIARO, Guido (1900-1963) Italian
£252 $387 €400 Capri - Marina piccola (19x29cm-7x11in) s. i. verso. 23-Oct-2 Neumeister, Munich #626
£449 $704 €700 Dusk in Abruzzo (34x51cm-13x20in) s.d.1924. 16-Dec-2 Pandolfini, Florence #295/R
£1290 $2000 €1935 Path to the beach (50x70cm-20x28in) s. board. 2-Oct-2 Christie's, Rockefeller NY #796/R est:1000-1500

CASE, Edmund E (1840-1919) American
£932 $1500 €1398 Fall landscape (61x46cm-24x18in) s. 15-Jan-3 Boos Gallery, Michigan #573/R est:3000-4000
£962 $1500 €1443 River landscape at sunset (29x41cm-11x16in) 14-Sep-2 Weschler, Washington #600/R est:700-900

CASEBERE, James (1953-) American?
Photographs
£3374 $5500 €5061 Converging hallways from right (122x183cm-48x72in) s. dye-destruction print mounted on aluminum. 12-Feb-3 Christie's, Rockefeller NY #137/R est:6000-8000
£7097 $11000 €10646 Asylum (122x152cm-48x60in) s.i.d.1994 num.5/5 dye destruction print prov.exhib.lit. 26-Sep-2 Christie's, Rockefeller NY #839/R est:10000-15000

CASELLI, S (?) Italian
£256 $403 €400 View of park (42x57cm-17x22in) s.d.45. 16-Dec-2 Pandolfini, Florence #236

CASFORD, Michael (1940-) British/Norwegian
£1150 $1818 €1725 Havsuler - composition with birds (170x120cm-67x47in) s. 28-Apr-3 Blomqvist, Oslo #395/R (N.KR 13000)

CASILE, Alfred (1847-1909) French
£1310 $2070 €1900 Environs de Marseille (23x34cm-9x13in) s. cardboard. 4-Apr-3 Tajan, Paris #134
£1310 $2070 €1900 Silhouette sur la plage en Normandie (21x27cm-8x11in) s. cardboard. 4-Apr-3 Tajan, Paris #132/R

CASILEAR, John W (1811-1893) American
£31847 $50000 €47771 View of the Catskills at sunset (48x41cm-19x16in) init.d.55 painted oval prov. 19-Nov-2 Butterfields, San Francisco #8004/R est:20000-30000
Works on paper
£955 $1500 €1433 Trees on a hillside (25x36cm-10x14in) pencil dr. double-sided prov. 10-Dec-2 Doyle, New York #9/R est:2000-3000

CASISSA, Nicola (?-1730) Italian
£7500 $11775 €11250 Spaniel flushing duck with flowers in a sculpted urn and a fountain (37x102cm-15x40in) s. 10-Dec-2 Bonhams, New Bond Street #270/R est:7000-10000

CASISSA, Nicola (attrib) (?-1730) Italian
£20645 $32619 €32000 Still life of flowers and fruit in landscape (177x127cm-70x50in) bears mono. 18-Dec-2 Piasa, Paris #13/R est:35000

CASLEY, William (fl.1891-1912) British
Works on paper
£250 $408 €375 Bishops Rock and Asparagus Island, Mullion (20x36cm-8x14in) s. i.verso W/C. 13-Feb-3 David Lay, Penzance #256
£300 $468 €450 Pentreath, The Lizard (25x43cm-10x17in) s. W/C. 17-Oct-2 David Lay, Penzance #1032
£320 $534 €464 Hen - Scathe Point Mullion Cornwall (49x59cm-19x23in) s. W/C. 17-Jun-3 Rosebery Fine Art, London #456/R
£600 $978 €900 Lizard Beach (25x43cm-10x17in) s.d.1883. 13-Feb-3 David Lay, Penzance #420
£2050 $3198 €2973 Mousehole - sorting the catch (65x39cm-26x15in) s. W/C. 27-Mar-3 Lane, Penzance #255/R est:1500-2000

CASNELLI, Victor (1867-1961) American
£2673 $4250 €4010 Indian encampment (51x76cm-20x30in) s. 5-Mar-3 Sotheby's, New York #126/R est:4000-6000
Works on paper
£275 $450 €413 Farmyard (28x53cm-11x21in) s. W/C. 8-Feb-3 Neal Auction Company, New Orleans #566

CASOLANI, Alessandro (1552-1606) Italian
Works on paper
£6329 $10000 €10000 Head of woman (16x12cm-6x5in) i. sanguine. 28-Nov-2 Tajan, Paris #1/R est:5000-6000

CASORATI, Felice (1883-1963) Italian
£8974 $14090 €14000 Nude (42x25cm-17x10in) s.d.1926 paper on canvas exhib.lit. 23-Nov-2 Meeting Art, Vercelli #490/R est:14000
£14103 $22141 €22000 Rest (48x33cm-19x13in) s. tempera card on cardboard lit. 23-Nov-2 Meeting Art, Vercelli #240/R est:20000
£21935 $34658 €34000 Seated nude (70x50cm-28x20in) s. tempera paper on canvas painted 1961 prov.exhib.lit. 18-Dec-2 Christie's, Rome #270/R est:30000
£35461 $57447 €50000 Studio per 'conversatione platonica' (43x63cm-17x25in) s.d.1925 dry oil board prov.lit. 26-May-3 Christie's, Milan #203/R est:20000-30000
£36129 $57084 €56000 Village in Liguria (50x48cm-20x19in) s. board painted 1928 prov.exhib.lit. 18-Dec-2 Christie's, Rome #233/R est:80000
£50633 $80000 €80000 Fruit in the bowl (38x45cm-15x18in) s. painted 1941 lit. 30-Nov-2 Farsetti, Prato #637/R est:80000
£58228 $92000 €92000 Eggs in green background (70x47cm-28x19in) s. board painted 1956 lit. 30-Nov-2 Farsetti, Prato #699/R est:90000
Prints
£3205 $4968 €5000 Two nudes (25x32cm-10x13in) s. num.48/75 eau forte drypoint exec.1927. 4-Dec-2 Finarte, Milan #47/R est:6000
Sculpture
£14184 $22979 €20000 Ada (28x16x22cm-11x6x9in) painted terracotta prov. 26-May-3 Christie's, Milan #62/R est:8000-12000
Works on paper
£2365 $3689 €3500 Figure (32x22cm-13x9in) pencil dr exec.1928. 28-Mar-3 Farsetti, Prato #349/R

CASPEL, Johann Georg van (1870-1928) Dutch
£461 $746 €700 Girl doing needlework (69x47cm-27x19in) s.d.12. 21-Jan-3 Christie's, Amsterdam #176
£1831 $2948 €2600 Mother with baby (87x64cm-34x25in) s.d.10. 7-May-3 Vendue Huis, Gravenhage #563/R est:3000-5000

CASPERS, R (20th C) ?
£1050 $1670 €1575 Fruit on a ledge (76x63cm-30x25in) s. wood. 27-Feb-3 Bonhams, Chester #432 est:800-1200

CASS, George Nelson (1831-1882) American
£1019 $1600 €1529 Ice fishing in New England (36x56cm-14x22in) s. sold with framed Louis Prang chromolitho. 14-Dec-2 CRN Auctions, Cambridge #19/R

CASS, M L (19th C) American
£2742 $4250 €4113 Winter landscape (66x91cm-26x36in) s. 29-Oct-2 Doyle, New York #43 est:1500-2000

CASSAB, Judy (1920-) Australian/Austrian
£246 $385 €369 Devil's marbles (36x53cm-14x21in) s. board. 21-Oct-2 Australian Art Auctions, Sydney #77 (A.D 700)
£260 $408 €390 Composition (62x49cm-24x19in) s.d.1958 oil on paper. 15-Apr-3 Bonhams, Knightsbridge #189a
£265 $414 €398 Abstracted desert landscape (91x71cm-36x28in) i.verso. 6-Aug-2 Peter Webb, Auckland #147 (NZ.D 900)
£329 $524 €494 Houses (24x30cm-9x12in) s. board. 5-May-3 Sotheby's, Melbourne #209 (A.D 850)
£339 $529 €509 Abstracted desert landscape (91x71cm-36x28in) 6-Aug-2 Peter Webb, Auckland #148 est:500-1000 (NZ.D 1150)
£423 $659 €635 Kimberley remembrance (68x84cm-27x33in) s. 21-Oct-2 Australian Art Auctions, Sydney #143 (A.D 1200)
£643 $1003 €965 Monkey forest, Bali (36x52cm-14x20in) s.d.76 board. 11-Nov-2 Deutscher-Menzies, Melbourne #125/R est:2500-4000 (A.D 1800)
£714 $1107 €1071 Abstract with figures (49x63cm-19x25in) s.d.1964 board. 29-Oct-2 Lawson Menzies, Sydney #131 (A.D 2000)
£717 $1090 €1076 Artist at easel (39x29cm-15x11in) s.d.1955. 27-Aug-2 Goodman, Sydney #66 (A.D 2000)
£873 $1449 €1488 Untitled - figures and chickens (37x55cm-15x22in) s. board. 10-Jun-3 Shapiro, Sydney #9 est:2000-4000 (A.D 2200)
£893 $1411 €1340 Abstract (45x47cm-18x19in) s. board. 18-Nov-2 Goodman, Sydney #88 (A.D 2500)
£1200 $1932 €1800 Retreat (100x88cm-39x35in) s.d.67 oil mixed media canvas on board. 6-May-3 Christie's, Melbourne #268 est:3000-5000 (A.D 3000)

Works on paper
£264 $412 €396 Mother and child (45x59cm-18x23in) s. mixed media. 21-Oct-2 Australian Art Auctions, Sydney #142 (A.D 750)
£649 $1025 €1124 Portrait of a girl (60x46cm-24x18in) s. W/C gouache. 1-Apr-3 Goodman, Sydney #93/R (A.D 1700)

CASSANA, Giovanni Agostino (attrib) (1658-1720) Italian
Works on paper
£699 $1000 €1049 Vegetable still life (9x19cm-4x7in) red black chk. 23-Jan-3 Swann Galleries, New York #111/R est:1500-2500

CASSANDRE, Adolphe (1901-1968) French
£26531 $42184 €39000 Composition surrealiste (88x116cm-35x46in) s.d.1952. 28-Feb-3 Joron-Derem, Paris #37/R est:12000

CASSAS, Louis-François (1756-1827) French
Prints
£4965 $8291 €7000 Vue de theatre de Taormina (55x78cm-22x31in) engraving htd W/C. 23-Jun-3 Beaussant & Lefèvre, Paris #64/R est:2000-3000
£5674 $9475 €8000 Le monument de Philopappus a Athenes (55x78cm-22x31in) engraving htd W/C. 23-Jun-3 Beaussant & Lefèvre, Paris #68/R est:2000-3000

Works on paper
£7500 $12525 €10875 View of the Val di Noto in Sicily (54x76cm-21x30in) pen brown ink W/C gum arabic. 9-Jul-3 Sotheby's, London #79/R est:4000-6000
£10000 $16700 €14500 View of the Emperor Diocletian's palace at Split (49x79cm-19x31in) s.d.1783 i. black chk ink wash squared in black chk prov. 8-Jul-3 Christie's, London #84/R est:6000-8000
£10063 $15698 €16000 Vue des ruines de Palmyre (53x77cm-21x30in) chk pen ink W/C. 8-Oct-2 Christie's, Paris #18/R est:30000
£16000 $24960 €24000 Acropolis (58x98cm-23x39in) W/C grey ink squared for transfer. 15-Oct-2 Sotheby's, London #1/R est:8000-10000

CASSAS, Louis-François (attrib) (1756-1827) French
Works on paper
£3800 $5928 €5700 Evocation of Ancient Athens (47x61cm-19x24in) W/C ink pencil. 15-Oct-2 Sotheby's, London #29/R est:2000-3000

CASSATT, Mary (1844-1926) American
£967742 $1500000 €1451613 Sara seated, leaning on her left hand (73x55cm-29x22in) s. prov.exhib.lit. 5-Dec-2 Christie's, Rockefeller NY #78/R est:2000000-3000000
£1153846 $1800000 €1730769 Maternite (81x65cm-32x26in) s. painted c.1906 prov.exhib.lit. 5-Nov-2 Sotheby's, New York #15/R est:2000000-3000000

Prints
£3012 $5000 €4367 Mere avec enfant sur les genouse (15x13cm-6x5in) drypoint. 13-Jun-3 Du Mouchelle, Detroit #2078/R est:500-800
£6597 $10424 €9500 Helene (31x24cm-12x9in) drypoint. 25-Apr-3 Piasa, Paris #2/R est:6000
£6944 $10972 €10000 Sollicitude (27x18cm-11x7in) drypoint exec.c.1889. 25-Apr-3 Piasa, Paris #1/R est:6000
£8228 $13000 €12342 Party dress (22x15cm-9x6in) s. drypoint. 22-Apr-3 Butterfields, San Francisco #2026/R est:4000-6000
£8333 $13000 €12500 Picture book (31x19cm-12x7in) s. drypoint prov. 14-Oct-2 Butterfields, San Francisco #1013/R est:8000-10000
£11538 $18000 €17307 Reflection (31x24cm-12x9in) st.mono. brownish black drypoint exec.c.1889-90 prov. 5-Nov-2 Christie's, Rockefeller NY #90/R est:10000-15000
£16026 $25000 €24039 Crocheting lesson (48x33cm-19x13in) s.num.2/50 drypoint prov. 14-Oct-2 Butterfields, San Francisco #1014/R est:15000-25000
£19497 $31000 €29246 Reine and Margot seated on a sofa (43x33cm-17x13in) s.num.11 drypoint edition of 25 exec.c.1902. 2-May-3 Sotheby's, New York #15/R est:25000-30000

Works on paper
£1623 $2500 €2435 Portrait of a cavalier. Study of a girls head (20x8cm-8x3in) pencil double-sided prov. 27-Oct-2 Grogan, Boston #11 est:1000-1500
£5031 $8000 €7547 Sketch of nurse seated on a bench, baby standing beside her (25x16cm-10x6in) pencil prov.exhib.lit. 4-Mar-3 Christie's, Rockefeller NY #24/R est:5000-7000
£5422 $9000 €7862 Mother and child (13x20cm-5x8in) pencil sketch. 13-Jun-3 Du Mouchelle, Detroit #2019/R est:4000-6000
£6410 $10064 €10000 Portrait of woman with muff (30x25cm-12x10in) s. pastel. 23-Nov-2 Arnold, Frankfurt #698/R est:15000
£85106 $142128 €120000 Femme et enfant (46x37cm-18x15in) s. drawing vellum paper. 20-Jun-3 Piasa, Paris #13/R est:20000-30000
£745342 $1200000 €1118013 Reine Lefebvre with blond baby and Sara holding cat (81x65cm-32x26in) s.i. pastel paper on board prov.exhib.lit. 6-May-3 Sotheby's, New York #3/R est:1000000-1500000

CASSAVETTI-ZAMBACCO, Marie (1843-?) Greek
Sculpture
£4600 $7130 €6900 Armour irresistible (65cm-26in) s. brown pat bronze verde antico circular base. 29-Oct-2 Bonhams, New Bond Street #166/R est:1500-2000

CASSELL, Frank (?) British
£900 $1368 €1350 Interior of stable one with Old English spaniel in liver and white and other with King Charles (15x23cm-6x9in) s. pair. 13-Aug-2 Canterbury Auctions, UK #95/R

CASSELLI, Henry (1946-) American
Works on paper
£705 $1100 €1058 Black man and his son beside a quilt (25x36cm-10x14in) s.d.72 graphite prov. 12-Oct-2 Neal Auction Company, New Orleans #652/R
£3165 $5000 €4748 Mother and child (71x51cm-28x20in) s. W/C. 16-Nov-2 New Orleans Auction, New Orleans #1583/R est:4000-7000

CASSETTI, Marino (1947-) Italian
Works on paper
£224 $348 €350 Speed (33x43cm-13x17in) s.d.74 mixed media on canvas. 5-Dec-2 Stadion, Trieste #713

CASSIDY, Ira Diamond Gerald (1879-1934) American
£3247 $5000 €4871 Day's end, desert sunset no.3 (41x51cm-16x20in) s. prov. 24-Oct-2 Shannon's, Milford #236/R est:5000-7000

Works on paper
£5769 $9000 €8654 Pueblo Indian (25x15cm-10x6in) s. W/C prov. 9-Nov-2 Santa Fe Art, Santa Fe #94/R est:10000-12000

CASSIE, James (1819-1879) British
£1400 $2170 €2100 Culter burn (41x52cm-16x20in) 5-Dec-2 Bonhams, Edinburgh #107 est:1500-2000
£1600 $2496 €2400 Culter Burn at Peterculter, Aberdeenshire (41x52cm-16x20in) 18-Sep-2 Cheffins Grain & Comins, Cambridge #548/R est:800-1000
£2000 $3240 €3000 Pet rabbits (35x30cm-14x12in) s.d.1860 board. 23-May-3 Lyon & Turnbull, Edinburgh #74/R est:2000-3000

CASSIERS, Henry (1858-1944) Belgian
£346 $533 €550 A la sortie de l'eglise (27x42cm-11x17in) s. 22-Oct-2 Campo, Vlaamse Kaai #433
£2400 $3984 €2400 Depart des bateaux de peche (33x40cm-13x16in) s. board. 16-Jun-3 Horta, Bruxelles #185 est:1500-2000
£2830 $4358 €4500 View of a canal in Venice (62x72cm-24x28in) s. tempera on cardboard. 23-Oct-2 Christie's, Amsterdam #27/R est:5000-7000

Works on paper

£345 $552 €500 Enterrement a Kocke (13x21cm-5x8in) s.d.84 W/C. 15-Mar-3 De Vuyst, Lokeren #52
£359 $579 €550 Le pont a bascule (16x34cm-6x13in) s.d.81 W/C. 20-Jan-3 Horta, Bruxelles #336
£406 $650 €589 Harbour view with ketches and windmills (28x37cm-11x15in) s. W/C gouache graphite paperboard. 16-May-3 Skinner, Boston #28/R
£432 $691 €600 Lac aux voiliers (14x33cm-6x13in) s. W/C. 13-May-3 Vanderkindere, Brussels #24
£448 $717 €650 Retour a la ferme (20x10cm-8x4in) s. W/C. 17-Mar-3 Horta, Bruxelles #247
£605 $944 €950 Pecheurs par temps calme (29x50cm-11x20in) s. W/C. 11-Nov-2 Horta, Bruxelles #497
£719 $1151 €1000 La fenaison (59x99cm-23x39in) s. mixed media. 19-May-3 Horta, Bruxelles #372
£728 $1135 €1150 Marine (33x48cm-13x19in) s. W/C. 15-Oct-2 Vanderkindere, Brussels #63
£949 $1481 €1500 Zelandaise devant une fermette (30x47cm-12x19in) s. gouache. 15-Oct-2 Horta, Bruxelles #46
£1678 $2701 €2500 Rue d'Amsterdam animee (37x37cm-15x15in) s. gouache. 18-Feb-3 Vanderkindere, Brussels #222/R
£1800 $2988 €1800 Le porche (22x22cm-9x9in) s. mixed media W/C sold with W/C by F van Ackers. 16-Jun-3 Horta, Bruxelles #186 est:700-900
£2069 $3310 €3000 Sunny scene in Zeeland (30x47cm-12x19in) s. gouache. 15-Mar-3 De Vuyst, Lokeren #424/R est:2800-3600

CASSIGNEUL, Jean Pierre (1935-) French

£2069 $3269 €3000 Couple dans la clairiere (35x24cm-14x9in) s. 4-Apr-3 Tajan, Paris #245/R
£7975 $13000 €11963 Le banc (81x60cm-32x24in) s. prov. 12-Feb-3 Sotheby's, New York #128/R est:12000-18000
£10429 $17000 €15644 Deux femmes aux parc (92x73cm-36x29in) s. prov. 12-Feb-3 Sotheby's, New York #103/R est:10000-15000
£19355 $30000 €29033 La ballon (81x65cm-32x26in) s. s.i.d.1969 verso prov. 26-Sep-2 Christie's, Rockefeller NY #589/R est:20000-30000
£24516 $38000 €36774 La loge (81x60cm-32x24in) s. s.i.verso prov. 26-Sep-2 Christie's, Rockefeller NY #580/R est:20000-30000

CASSINARI, Bruno (1912-1992) Italian

£2980 $4737 €4470 Bull fighter (73x60cm-29x24in) s.indis.d.51 or 58. 10-Mar-3 Rasmussen, Vejle #694/R est:40000-60000 (D.KR 32000)
£7453 $12000 €11180 Natura morta (70x100cm-28x39in) s. painted 1952 prov.lit. 7-May-3 Sotheby's, New York #363/R est:15000-20000
£7595 $12000 €12000 Moira (60x50cm-24x20in) s.d.71 s.i.d.verso. 30-Nov-2 Farsetti, Prato #667/R est:15000
£8333 $13083 €13000 Landscape with nude (70x80cm-28x31in) s.d.1969. 20-Nov-2 Pandolfini, Florence #119/R
£9032 $14271 €14000 Blue window (80x90cm-31x35in) s. s.i.d.84 verso prov.exhib. 18-Dec-2 Christie's, Rome #140/R
£9574 $15511 €13500 Le amiche (140x100cm-55x39in) s.d.64 s.i.d.verso prov.exhib.lit. 26-May-3 Christie's, Milan #331/R est:15000-20000
£15484 $24465 €24000 Harbour (69x100cm-27x39in) s.d.54 s.i.d.verso prov.exhib. 18-Dec-2 Christie's, Rome #283/R est:16000

Works on paper

£680 $1082 €1000 Figure (65x47cm-26x19in) s. W/C lit. 1-Mar-3 Meeting Art, Vercelli #520
£1056 $1754 €1500 Nudo femminile (70x40cm-28x16in) s.d.1961 ink W/C framed paper. 10-Jun-3 Finarte Semenzato, Milan #181/R est:1500-1800
£1076 $1678 €1700 Figures (70x50cm-28x20in) s.d.1978 W/C card on canvas. 14-Sep-2 Meeting Art, Vercelli #911/R
£1307 $2092 €2000 Seated figure (66x48cm-26x19in) s. mixed media paper on canvas. 4-Jan-3 Meeting Art, Vercelli #210
£1346 $2113 €2100 Figure (70x50cm-28x20in) s. mixed media paper on canvas. 23-Nov-2 Meeting Art, Vercelli #291/R
£2297 $3674 €3330 Horses (55x82cm-22x32in) s. Chinese ink W/C. 11-Mar-3 Babuino, Rome #341/R
£2452 $3874 €3800 Horse. Composition (48x66cm-19x26in) s. gouache pair. 18-Dec-2 Christie's, Rome #38/R

CASSON, Alfred Joseph (1898-1992) Canadian

£3086 $4784 €4629 Old ice house - Baptiste (24x28cm-9x11in) s. board prov. 3-Dec-2 Joyner, Toronto #51/R est:7000-9000 (C.D 7500)
£3587 $5740 €5381 Grey autumn day, Grenville, Quebec (30x38cm-12x15in) s. s.i.d.1969 verso panel prov. 15-May-3 Heffel, Vancouver #40/R est:8000-10000 (C.D 8000)
£3704 $5741 €5556 Marsh at Elephant Lake (23x27cm-9x11in) s. board prov. 3-Dec-2 Joyner, Toronto #115/R est:10000-12000 (C.D 9000)
£4032 $6371 €6048 Barn, Grenville, Quebec (30x38cm-12x15in) s.i.d.1971 panel prov. 14-Nov-2 Heffel, Vancouver #152/R est:9000-12000 (C.D 10000)
£4222 $6924 €6333 Autumn, Grenville, Que (30x37cm-12x15in) s. board prov. 3-Jun-3 Joyner, Toronto #248/R est:10000-12000 (C.D 9500)
£4435 $7008 €6653 Fog fingers (30x38cm-12x15in) s. prov. 18-Nov-2 Sotheby's, Toronto #103/R est:8000-10000 (C.D 11000)
£4435 $7008 €6653 Long Lake (30x38cm-12x15in) s.d.1976 s.verso panel prov. 14-Nov-2 Heffel, Vancouver #88/R est:9000-12000 (C.D 11000)
£4444 $7289 €6666 Madawaska Valley, 1958 (30x37cm-12x15in) s. board prov. 3-Jun-3 Joyner, Toronto #123/R est:10000-15000 (C.D 10000)
£4444 $7289 €6666 Rocky Point, Penn Lake (30x37cm-12x15in) s. board painted 1980. 3-Jun-3 Joyner, Toronto #152/R est:10000-15000 (C.D 10000)
£4484 $7175 €6726 October, South Portage Road (30x38cm-12x15in) s. s.i.d.1972 verso panel prov. 15-May-3 Heffel, Vancouver #96/R est:9000-12000 (C.D 10000)
£4484 $7175 €6726 Pine, poplar, spruce, Combermere, Ontario (31x38cm-12x15in) s. s.i.verso panel prov. 15-May-3 Heffel, Vancouver #113/R est:10000-12000 (C.D 10000)
£4527 $7016 €6791 Sunlit outcropping (30x37cm-12x15in) s. board painted July 1983. 3-Dec-2 Joyner, Toronto #107/R est:12000-15000 (C.D 11000)
£4889 $8018 €7334 Farm at Fairmount (30x37cm-12x15in) s. board. 3-Jun-3 Joyner, Toronto #147/R est:10000-15000 (C.D 11000)
£5242 $8282 €7863 Sombre day (24x29cm-9x11in) s.i.d.1945 s.verso panel prov. 14-Nov-2 Heffel, Vancouver #241/R est:10000-15000 (C.D 13000)
£5333 $8747 €8000 Barns (24x28cm-9x11in) s. i.verso canvas on panel prov. 27-May-3 Sotheby's, Toronto #112/R est:10000-12000 (C.D 12000)
£5350 $8292 €8025 Georgian Bay (30x37cm-12x15in) s. board painted September 1981. 3-Dec-2 Joyner, Toronto #11/R est:12000-15000 (C.D 13000)
£5652 $8817 €9425 Rock Island, Quebec (30x37cm-12x15in) s. s.i.d.1974 verso prov. 13-Apr-3 Levis, Calgary #14a est:14000-18000 (C.D 13000)
£5778 $9476 €8667 Summer day, Haliburton (23x28cm-9x11in) s. board prov. 3-Jun-3 Joyner, Toronto #15/R est:10000-15000 (C.D 13000)
£5778 $9476 €8667 October rain - Bark Lake (30x38cm-12x15in) s. s.i.verso board prov.exhib. 27-May-3 Sotheby's, Toronto #215/R est:10000-15000 (C.D 13000)
£6222 $10204 €9333 Port Caldwell. Lake Superior (25x30cm-10x12in) s. s.i.d.1928 verso panel prov.lit. 27-May-3 Sotheby's, Toronto #19/R est:12000-15000 (C.D 14000)
£6584 $10206 €9876 Buttermilk Falls, Haliburton (24x28cm-9x11in) s. board. 3-Dec-2 Joyner, Toronto #29/R est:15000-20000 (C.D 16000)
£6667 $10933 €10001 From the desert road (30x38cm-12x15in) s. s.i.d.1970 verso board prov. 27-May-3 Sotheby's, Toronto #67/R est:12000-15000 (C.D 15000)
£7111 $11662 €10667 On the Madawaska (30x38cm-12x15in) s. s.i.verso board prov.exhib. 27-May-3 Sotheby's, Toronto #153/R est:10000-12000 (C.D 16000)
£7556 $12391 €11334 Palmer rapids- Madawaska River (30x38cm-12x15in) s.i.verso board prov. 27-May-3 Sotheby's, Toronto #151/R est:12000-15000 (C.D 17000)
£8969 $14350 €13454 Farmhouse near Terra Cotta (23x29cm-9x11in) s. s.verso panel prov. 15-May-3 Heffel, Vancouver #109/R est:12000-15000 (C.D 20000)
£9073 $14335 €13610 Madawaska River near Whitney (24x29cm-9x11in) s.i. s.verso panel painted c.1930 prov.lit. 14-Nov-2 Heffel, Vancouver #1/R est:12000-15000 (C.D 22500)
£10700 $16584 €16050 October flurry, Mud lake, East End, Algon-Quin Park (24x28cm-9x11in) s. board. 3-Dec-2 Joyner, Toronto #85/R est:15000-20000 (C.D 26000)
£12346 $19136 €18519 Little country church (60x75cm-24x30in) s. prov. 3-Dec-2 Joyner, Toronto #93/R est:30000-40000 (C.D 30000)
£14222 $23324 €21333 Holiday country (50x60cm-20x24in) s. painted 1979 prov. 3-Jun-3 Joyner, Toronto #78/R est:20000-30000 (C.D 32000)
£14444 $23689 €21666 Typical homestead in Eastern Canada (86x70cm-34x28in) s. canvasboard prov. 27-May-3 Sotheby's, Toronto #207/R est:20000-25000 (C.D 32500)
£15111 $24782 €22667 Northern homestead (60x90cm-24x35in) s. prov. 3-Jun-3 Joyner, Toronto #59/R est:30000-40000 (C.D 34000)
£16129 $25484 €24194 Winter window (76x61cm-30x24in) s.i.d.1970 s.verso prov. 14-Nov-2 Heffel, Vancouver #116/R est:40000-50000 (C.D 40000)
£16667 $27333 €25001 Ottawa River at Hawkesbury (51x61cm-20x24in) s. s.i.d.1975 verso masonite prov. 27-May-3 Sotheby's, Toronto #68/R est:30000-40000 (C.D 37500)
£24194 $38226 €36291 Autumn morning - Oxtongue Lake (76x96cm-30x38in) s. prov. 18-Nov-2 Sotheby's, Toronto #52/R est:35000-45000 (C.D 60000)
£24444 $40089 €36666 Valley farm, March (87x114cm-34x45in) s. prov.exhib. 27-May-3 Sotheby's, Toronto #170/R est:40000-60000 (C.D 55000)
£24664 $39462 €36996 October rains (76x91cm-30x36in) s. s.i.d.1979 verso prov. 15-May-3 Heffel, Vancouver #131/R est:50000-60000 (C.D 55000)
£32258 $50968 €48387 Wapomeo Island (61x76cm-24x30in) s.i. s.verso prov.lit. 14-Nov-2 Heffel, Vancouver #81/R est:70000-90000 (C.D 80000)
£34274 $54153 €51411 Still morning (61x76cm-24x30in) s.i.d.1962 verso board prov.exhib.lit. 14-Nov-2 Heffel, Vancouver #80/R est:70000-90000 (C.D 85000)

£35556 $58311 €53334 Casson Lake, 1976 (75x115cm-30x45in) s. prov.lit. 3-Jun-3 Joyner, Toronto #22/R est:80000-100000 (C.D 80000)
£35874 $57399 €53811 Autumn panorama (41x104cm-16x41in) s. s.i.d.1975 verso prov.lit. 15-May-3 Heffel, Vancouver #38/R est:50000-60000 (C.D 80000)

Works on paper
£472 $736 €684 Tree on Lee Farm (20x15cm-8x6in) s.d.74 graphite dr. prov. 26-Mar-3 Walker's, Ottawa #448 est:900-1200 (C.D 1100)

CASSON, Sir Hugh (1910-) British

Works on paper
£260 $434 €377 Langstone harbour (7x12cm-3x5in) init.i. W/C. 17-Jun-3 Bonhams, Knightsbridge #105
£300 $480 €450 Woman seated in a chapel (13x8cm-5x3in) ink W/C. 11-Mar-3 Gorringes, Lewes #2458
£380 $627 €551 Laid up Shioggia (10x15cm-4x6in) mono.i. W/C. 3-Jul-3 Duke & Son, Dorchester #113
£400 $620 €600 Seminar on Victorian studies, Canada (28x19cm-11x7in) init.i. pen black ink htd col crayon. 4-Dec-2 Christie's, Kensington #267
£480 $787 €720 St. Maxime, South of France (8x13cm-3x5in) init.i. pen ink W/C prov. 6-Jun-3 Christie's, London #82/R
£650 $1047 €975 Somerset House (24x22cm-9x9in) s.d.79 W/C. 18-Feb-3 Bonhams, Knightsbridge #1/R
£700 $1105 €1050 Town scene (10x20cm-4x8in) s.i. pen ink gouache. 27-Nov-2 Sotheby's, Olympia #17/R
£750 $1163 €1125 Persepolis (10x23cm-4x9in) init.i. W/C sold with other by same hand. 3-Dec-2 Bonhams, Knightsbridge #357
£750 $1163 €1125 Calle (10x9cm-4x4in) init. pencil W/C and another by the same artist. 4-Dec-2 Christie's, Kensington #275/R
£800 $1232 €1200 Design for the Coronation decorations on Shaftesbury Avenue (37x52cm-15x20in) s. W/C bodycol two tracing paper overlays. 5-Sep-2 Christie's, Kensington #675/R
£1000 $1550 €1500 Exercising, Wittering beach (5x15cm-2x6in) init.i. W/C htd white and another by the same hand. 4-Dec-2 Christie's, Kensington #264/R est:600-800
£1000 $1550 €1500 Pensioners bench, Place de la Tour (8x14cm-3x6in) init. pencil W/C and another by the same artist. 4-Dec-2 Christie's, Kensington #273/R est:600-800
£1400 $2170 €2100 Original architectural plan for the Festival of Britain 1951 (53x75cm-21x30in) pencil col crayon sold with other drs and memorabilia. 4-Dec-2 Christie's, Kensington #276/R est:1500-2000

CASTAGNOLA, Gabriele (1828-1883) Italian
£1699 $2736 €2600 Jeune fille au balcon. mono.i.d.1865 panel double-sided. 20-Jan-3 Horta, Bruxelles #244 est:2500-3500

CASTAING, Henry Joseph (1860-1918) French

Works on paper
£285 $450 €450 Vierge a l'Enfant (34x47cm-13x19in) s. pastel. 26-Nov-2 Camard, Paris #5

CASTAN, Gustave-Eugène (1823-1892) Swiss
£374 $547 €561 Stream (38x59cm-15x23in) s. paper on masonite. 17-Jun-2 Philippe Schuler, Zurich #4262 (S.FR 850)
£435 $674 €653 Wooded landscape with faggot gatherer (38x58cm-15x23in) paper on masonite. 9-Dec-2 Philippe Schuler, Zurich #3810 (S.FR 1000)
£1111 $1789 €1611 Wooded landscape with woman in clearing (38x58cm-15x23in) s. board on masonite. 9-May-3 Dobiaschofsky, Bern #41/R (S.FR 2400)
£1509 $2445 €2672 Woodsmen on lakeshore (38x54cm-15x21in) s. 26-May-3 Sotheby's, Zurich #14/R est:3000-5000 (S.FR 3200)
£1509 $2445 €2672 Pecheur en Bretagne (39x58cm-15x23in) s. board. 26-May-3 Sotheby's, Zurich #22/R est:3000-5000 (S.FR 3200)
£1528 $2460 €2216 A Concarneau (37x57cm-15x22in) s. i.verso masonite. 9-May-3 Dobiaschofsky, Bern #54/R est:3600 (S.FR 3300)
£2643 $3859 €3965 Mountain landscape with stream (64x98cm-25x39in) s. 17-Jun-2 Philippe Schuler, Zurich #4259/R est:6000-8000 (S.FR 6000)
£2838 $4485 €4257 Paysage avec pere et fils allumant feu (90x129cm-35x51in) s. 17-Nov-2 Koller, Geneva #1240/R (S.FR 6500)
£3043 $4717 €4565 Soleil couchant, souvenir du Bourbonnais (104x161cm-41x63in) s. init.verso lit. 7-Dec-2 Galerie du Rhone, Sion #451/R est:10000-15000 (S.FR 7000)
£3648 $5764 €5472 River landscape in autumn (90x130cm-35x51in) s. 28-Nov-2 Christie's, Zurich #9/R est:8000-12000 (S.FR 8500)
£4292 $6781 €6438 Woodland path (38x59cm-15x23in) s. s.i. verso paper on panel. 28-Nov-2 Christie's, Zurich #8/R est:5000-7000 (S.FR 10000)
£6438 $10172 €9657 Debut Dorage sur le lac (80x130cm-31x51in) s. prov. 26-Nov-2 Phillips, Zurich #3/R est:10200-13300 (S.FR 15000)
£7174 $11191 €10761 Paysage d'automne (133x198cm-52x78in) s. 16-Sep-2 Philippe Schuler, Zurich #3361/R est:8000-12000 (S.FR 16500)
£8297 $13026 €12446 Landscape in autumn with peasants (89x147cm-35x58in) s. 25-Nov-2 Sotheby's, Zurich #20/R est:10000-15000 (S.FR 19000)
£10480 $16349 €15720 Autumn landscape (133x198cm-52x78in) s. 20-Nov-2 Fischer, Luzern #1258/R est:24000-28000 (S.FR 24000)

CASTAN, Pierre Jean Edmond (1817-?) French
£2009 $3134 €3014 Family in Norman interior (26x35cm-10x14in) s.d.1863 panel. 28-Mar-3 Koller, Zurich #3109/R est:3000-5000 (S.FR 4400)

CASTANEDA, Felipe (1933-) Mexican

Sculpture
£10366 $17000 €15031 Insight (69x69x46cm-27x27x18in) s.d.1984 num.VI/VII brown pat bronze prov.lit. 27-May-3 Sotheby's, New York #104

CASTBERG, Johan (1911-) Norwegian
£355 $543 €533 Le pont (67x84cm-26x33in) s. 26-Aug-2 Blomqvist, Lysaker #1061 (N.KR 4100)

CASTEELE, Auguste van de (1889-1969) Belgian
£276 $436 €400 Vue de Lisseweghe (80x75cm-31x30in) s. 2-Apr-3 Vanderkindere, Brussels #554

CASTEELS, Peter (attrib) (17/18th C) Flemish
£31000 $48670 €46500 Still life of fowl, with cat chasing bantams from a chicken coop (96x117cm-38x46in) d.1712. 12-Dec-2 Sotheby's, London #207/R est:15000-20000

CASTEELS, Peter Franz (attrib) (17th C) Flemish
£2700 $4185 €4050 Flowers in a copper vase on a stone ledge (56x43cm-22x17in) 30-Oct-2 Bonhams, New Bond Street #163/R est:3000-5000

CASTEELS, Peter II (fl.1690-1699) Flemish
£9859 $16366 €14000 Floral bouquet in potter vase (92x108cm-36x43in) 11-Jun-3 Dorotheum, Vienna #75/R est:14000-16000
£37415 $59490 €55000 Vue du Pont-Neuf. Vue du Louvre (30x43cm-12x17in) pair. 21-Mar-3 Rieunier, Bailly-Pommery, Mathias, Paris #60/R est:60000

CASTEELS, Peter II (attrib) (fl.1690-1699) Flemish
£11408 $18367 €17000 Still lifes of flowers in gilt urns, upon stone plinths (61x49cm-24x19in) pair prov. 18-Feb-3 Sotheby's, Amsterdam #242/R est:7000-9000

CASTEELS, Peter III (1684-1749) Flemish
£3379 $5271 €5000 Still life with garland of flowers (40x49cm-16x19in) 26-Mar-3 Tajan, Paris #153/R
£8392 $14014 €12000 Scenes de ports mediterraneens (32x43cm-13x17in) pair. 25-Jun-3 Tajan, Paris #32/R est:12000-15000
£78000 $129480 €117000 Demoiselle crane, pheasants, duck and other birds in an Italianate garden (203x128cm-80x50in) 10-Jun-3 Christie's, London #6/R est:40000-60000

CASTEELS, Peter III (attrib) (1684-1749) Flemish
£14423 $22788 €22500 Vase of flowers on table (91x67cm-36x26in) 13-Nov-2 Marc Kohn, Paris #48/R est:22000-25000

CASTEELS, Peter III (circle) (1684-1749) Flemish
£5183 $8500 €7515 Capriccio of a Mediterranean harbour scene (38x51cm-15x20in) 4-Jun-3 Christie's, Rockefeller NY #185/R est:4000-6000

CASTEL, Moshe (1909-1992) Israeli
£7692 $12077 €12000 Composition (65x50cm-26x20in) s. oil sand collage. 12-Dec-2 Rabourdin & Choppin de Janvry, Paris #155/R est:12000

Works on paper
£1897 $3034 €2750 Figure (28x22cm-11x9in) s. mixed media on canvas. 12-Mar-3 Rabourdin & Choppin de Janvry, Paris #147/R
£3077 $4831 €4800 Rouleaux de la Mer Morte (50x38cm-20x15in) s. s.i.d.1976-80 verso mixed media on canvas. 12-Dec-2 Rabourdin & Choppin de Janvry, Paris #153/R
£4483 $7172 €6500 Alleluia (46x36cm-18x14in) s. 12-Mar-3 Rabourdin & Choppin de Janvry, Paris #148/R

CASTELLAN, Antoine Laurent (1772-1838) French

Works on paper
£270 $422 €400 Femme au pied de rocher (20x13cm-8x5in) i. W/C. 31-Mar-3 Piasa, Paris #81
£304 $474 €450 Paysage compose (16x22cm-6x9in) pen ink wash. 31-Mar-3 Piasa, Paris #80

£439 $685 €650 Paysage compose (17x23cm-7x9in) pen ink wash. 31-Mar-3 Piasa, Paris #79/R
£608 $949 €900 Femme assise (14x19cm-6x7in) W/C. 31-Mar-3 Piasa, Paris #83
£1284 $2003 €1900 Arbres (14x19cm-6x7in) W/C. 31-Mar-3 Piasa, Paris #82

CASTELLANI, Enrico (1930-) Italian
£4167 $6542 €6500 Silver surface (56x77cm-22x30in) s.d.1980 enamel paper. 19-Nov-2 Finarte, Milan #65/R est:6500
£13462 $21135 €21000 Blue surface (80x100cm-31x39in) s.i.d.1991. 23-Nov-2 Meeting Art, Vercelli #119/R
£15823 $24684 €25000 White surface (120x80cm-47x31in) s.i.d.1998 tempera. 14-Sep-2 Meeting Art, Vercelli #834/R est:20000
£17904 $28109 €26856 Superficie bianca (100x100cm-39x39in) s.i.d.1988 verso acrylic canvas relief prov. 23-Nov-2 Burkhard, Luzern #46/R est:40000-60000 (S.FR 41000)
£20000 $31200 €30000 Superficie rossa (68x68cm-27x27in) s.d.1964 on stretcher shaped canvas prov. 21-Oct-2 Sotheby's, London #24/R est:30000-40000
£25000 $41750 €36250 Superficie bianca (120x150cm-47x59in) s.i.d.1998 on stretcher shaped canvas prov. 27-Jun-3 Christie's, London #161/R est:30000-50000
£35000 $54600 €52500 Superficie bianca (70x80cm-28x31in) s.d.1965 stretcher shaped canvas prov. 21-Oct-2 Sotheby's, London #46/R est:30000-40000
£43871 $69316 €68000 White surface (180x151cm-71x59in) s.i.d.1968 verso prov. 18-Dec-2 Christie's, Rome #292/R est:80000
£55000 $84700 €82500 Superficie bianca (120x124cm-47x49in) shaped canvas prov.exhib. 22-Oct-2 Christie's, London #36/R est:40000-60000
£60000 $92400 €90000 Superficie bianca (150x150cm-59x59in) s.i.d.1983 on overlap prov. 22-Oct-2 Christie's, London #39/R est:60000-80000

Works on paper
£3846 $5962 €6000 White surface (118x88cm-46x35in) s.d.74 card. 5-Dec-2 Stadion, Trieste #805/R

CASTELLANI, Mario (1914-) Italian
£353 $554 €550 Marialba (90x60cm-35x24in) s. s.i.d.1958 verso. 23-Nov-2 Meeting Art, Vercelli #134

CASTELLANO, Carmelo (20th C) ?
£397 $648 €600 Lumiere d'ete (81x60cm-32x24in) s. acrylic. 31-Jan-3 Charbonneaux, Paris #67
£699 $1168 €1000 Mirage (80x65cm-31x26in) s. acrylic. 25-Jun-3 Claude Aguttes, Neuilly #103/R

CASTELLANOS, Carlos Alberto (1881-1945) Uruguayan
£1875 $3000 €2813 Granny and kid at the park (40x32cm-16x13in) s.i.d.1911 cardboard. 5-Jan-3 Galleria Y Remates, Montevideo #69/R

CASTELLANOS, Roberto (1871-1942) South American
£481 $750 €722 Playa de Costa Azul (36x50cm-14x20in) s. 30-Jul-2 Galleria Y Remates, Montevideo #23/R
£609 $950 €914 Pirate ship (35x45cm-14x18in) s.d.1921. 10-Oct-2 Galleria Y Remates, Montevideo #47/R

CASTELLI, Carmen Dede Bischoff (1936-) Swiss
£1389 $2236 €2014 Siesta (69x100cm-27x39in) s.d.86. 9-May-3 Dobiaschofsky, Bern #263/R est:5000 (S.FR 3000)

CASTELLI, Luciano (1951-) Swiss
£725 $1188 €1000 Untitled (70x49cm-28x19in) s.d.86 acrylic W/C chl. 28-May-3 Lempertz, Koln #83/R
£995 $1662 €1443 Small blue nude (66x50cm-26x20in) s.d.89 paper prov. 24-Jun-3 Koller, Zurich #82/R est:2600-3500 (S.FR 2200)
£2516 $3899 €4000 Sans titre (200x70cm-79x28in) s. acrylic. 30-Oct-2 Artcurial Briest, Paris #477/R est:4000-5000

Works on paper
£1651 $2675 €2922 Self portrait (74x55cm-29x22in) s.i.d.2000 W/C oil prov. 26-May-3 Sotheby's, Zurich #140/R est:5000-6000 (S.FR 3500)

CASTELLO, Bernardo (1557-1629) Italian
Works on paper
£5500 $8525 €8250 Narcissus (21x15cm-8x6in) d.1613 pen ink wash htd white prov. 9-Dec-2 Bonhams, New Bond Street #63/R est:5000-7000

CASTELLO, Bernardo (attrib) (1557-1629) Italian
Works on paper
£2199 $3672 €3100 Un pape entoure d'eveques et de cardinaux sur une barque (19x29cm-7x11in) pen brown ink brown wash black crayon prov. 19-Jun-3 Piasa, Paris #15/R est:3000

CASTELLO, Castellino (c.1579-1649) Italian
Works on paper
£1892 $2951 €2800 Allegory of Charity (14x20cm-6x8in) i. pen ink wash. 27-Mar-3 Christie's, Paris #19/R

CASTELLO, Giovanni Battista (1547-1637) Italian
Works on paper
£7500 $12525 €10875 Psyche telling her sister of her lover (30x28cm-12x11in) i.verso black chk ink wash square in black. 8-Jul-3 Christie's, London #23/R est:3000-5000

CASTELLO, Valerio (1625-1659) Italian
£10000 $15600 €15000 Orpheus attacked by the Maenads of Ciconia, a bozzetto (37x45cm-15x18in) oil on paper on canvas prov. 9-Apr-3 Christie's, London #104/R est:10000-15000

CASTELLO, Valerio (circle) (1625-1659) Italian
£9434 $14623 €15000 Adoration of the Shepherds (152x203cm-60x80in) 2-Oct-2 Dorotheum, Vienna #264/R est:15000-20000

CASTELLS CAPURRO, Enrique (1913-1987) Uruguayan
£781 $1250 €1172 Horses (58x78cm-23x31in) s.d.73. 5-Jan-3 Galleria Y Remates, Montevideo #117/R
£1474 $2300 €2211 Escena de campo (60x80cm-24x31in) s.d.70 prov. 30-Jul-2 Galleria Y Remates, Montevideo #75/R est:2200-2700

Works on paper
£344 $540 €516 Riding (34x47cm-13x19in) s.d.50 ink W/C. 20-Nov-2 Galleria Y Remates, Montevideo #7/R
£344 $540 €516 Waiting for noon (33x47cm-13x19in) s.d.54 ink W/C. 20-Nov-2 Galleria Y Remates, Montevideo #6/R

CASTELUCHO, Claudio (1870-1927) Spanish
£900 $1431 €1350 Portrait of a Spanish woman holding a fan. Harbour scene (72x60cm-28x24in) s. card double-sided. 29-Apr-3 Henry Adams, Chichester #285

CASTEX-DEGRANGE, Adolphe Louis (1840-1918) French
£6803 $10816 €10000 Grande composition au potiron, faisan et fleurs (138x165cm-54x65in) s.d.1888. 2-Mar-3 Lombrail & Teucquam, Paris #160/R

CASTIGLIONE, Giovanni Benedetto (1616-1670) Italian
£16049 $26000 €24074 Saint Catherine of Alexandria (37x27cm-15x11in) paper prov. 22-Jan-3 Christie's, Rockefeller NY #37/R est:50000

Works on paper
£664 $950 €996 Hagar and the Angel (19x14cm-7x6in) black chk brown wash. 23-Jan-3 Swann Galleries, New York #73/R
£1600 $2512 €2400 Crucifixion with God the Father (39x29cm-15x11in) point col wash prov. 11-Dec-2 Sotheby's, Olympia #89/R est:1200-1500
£2246 $3750 €3257 Angel in flight (23x13cm-9x5in) ink htd gouache. 21-Jun-3 Selkirks, St. Louis #1047/R est:2500-3500
£35802 $58000 €53703 Portrait of man with turban (22x15cm-9x6in) i. pen ink prov. 22-Jan-3 Christie's, Rockefeller NY #36/R est:50000

CASTIGLIONE, Giovanni Francesco (attrib) (1641-1710) Italian
£5000 $7750 €7500 Finding of the Infant Cyrus (83x102cm-33x40in) i.verso. 30-Oct-2 Christie's, Kensington #118/R est:4000-6000

CASTIGLIONE, Giuseppe (1829-1908) Italian
£1537 $2490 €2306 L'attente (41x32cm-16x13in) s. panel. 27-Jan-3 Blomqvist, Lysaker #1030/R est:12000-15000 (N.KR 17000)

CASTILIAN SCHOOL (?) Spanish
£1948 $2844 €3000 Scenes from a holy man's life (90x70cm-35x28in) board pair. 17-Jun-2 Ansorena, Madrid #190/R

CASTILIAN SCHOOL (16th C) Spanish
£17000 $26690 €25500 Saint Ursula and the Virgins (117x47cm-46x19in) panel painted c.1500. 12-Dec-2 Sotheby's, London #107/R est:14000-18000

CASTILLO, Jorge (1933-) Spanish
£1039 $1517 €1600 Figures and animals (36x46cm-14x18in) s. board. 17-Jun-2 Ansorena, Madrid #323/R
£1103 $1743 €1600 Figures in interior (33x41cm-13x16in) s. 1-Apr-3 Segre, Madrid #173/R
£1258 $1962 €2000 Untitled (41x33cm-16x13in) s. 17-Sep-2 Segre, Madrid #176/R
£1258 $1962 €2000 Composition with figures and animals (33x81cm-13x32in) s. board. 8-Oct-2 Ansorena, Madrid #636/R

£1277 $2068 €1800 Personages (33x41cm-13x16in) s.d.1967. 20-May-3 Segre, Madrid #189/R est:1400
£1509 $2325 €2400 Untitled (43x36cm-17x14in) s. board. 28-Oct-2 Segre, Madrid #177/R
£1987 $3238 €3000 Figures and bird (91x73cm-36x29in) s. 11-Feb-3 Segre, Madrid #251/R
Works on paper
£256 $405 €400 Flight (27x38cm-11x15in) s.i.d.82 W/C ink. 13-Nov-2 Ansorena, Madrid #242/R
£256 $405 €400 Untitled (35x42cm-14x17in) s.d.78 mixed media. 13-Nov-2 Ansorena, Madrid #246/R
£256 $405 €400 Woman (23x29cm-9x11in) s.d.75 W/C. 13-Nov-2 Ansorena, Madrid #243/R
£283 $436 €450 Cat with string and beheaded bird (17x55cm-7x22in) s.d.72 Chinese ink gouache. 22-Oct-2 Durán, Madrid #233/R
£288 $456 €450 Girl (29x43cm-11x17in) s.d.78 W/C. 13-Nov-2 Ansorena, Madrid #241/R
£308 $486 €480 Erotic scene (23x32cm-9x13in) s.d.78 mixed media. 13-Nov-2 Ansorena, Madrid #245/R
£345 $548 €500 Flight (27x38cm-11x15in) s.i.d.82 W/C ink. 4-Mar-3 Ansorena, Madrid #777/R
£346 $533 €550 Still life (16x44cm-6x17in) s.d.81 W/C. 22-Oct-2 Durán, Madrid #232/R
£506 $800 €800 Los mejores artistas (39x57cm-15x22in) i. verso W/C over pen. 29-Nov-2 Villa Grisebach, Berlin #540/R
£839 $1325 €1300 Racins (57x78cm-22x31in) s.d.1983 gouache pencil. 17-Dec-2 Segre, Madrid #214/R
£1132 $1766 €1800 Still life (43x61cm-17x24in) s.d.83 gouache. 8-Oct-2 Ansorena, Madrid #589/R
£2051 $3241 €3200 Taggio en la mesa de cafe (80x120cm-31x47in) s.d.1977 i. verso spray wash col over Indian ink htd bodycol. 15-Nov-2 Reiss & Sohn, Konigstein #778/R est:4000

CASTILLO, Jose del (attrib) (1737-1793) Spanish
£2922 $4266 €4500 Figures in the field (20x35cm-8x14in) board. 17-Jun-2 Ansorena, Madrid #162/R

CASTILLO, Juan del (1584-1640) Spanish
£16026 $25321 €25000 Saint Joseph's death (129x158cm-51x62in) 14-Nov-2 Arte, Seville #163/R

CASTLE, Barry (20th C) British
£2603 $4086 €3800 Skimmers (61x84cm-24x33in) init.d.97 board. 15-Apr-3 De Veres Art Auctions, Dublin #240/R est:3000-6000
£2639 $4196 €3800 Boy and moths (61x34cm-24x13in) init.d.1995 board. 29-Apr-3 Whyte's, Dublin #139/R est:2500-3500
Works on paper
£1076 $1668 €1700 Wild geese (38x29cm-15x11in) init.d.96 W/C. 24-Sep-2 De Veres Art Auctions, Dublin #61/R est:1000-1500

CASTLE, Florence E (1867-?) British
£550 $858 €825 Maiden in a moonlit wood (91x72cm-36x28in) s. 7-Nov-2 Christie's, Kensington #228/R

CASTLE, James (1900-1977) American
Works on paper
£3704 $6000 €5556 Untitled - house (29x34cm-11x13in) W/C prov. 27-Jan-3 Christie's, Rockefeller NY #62/R est:6000-8000
£8642 $14000 €12963 Untitled - bird (12x18cm-5x7in) W/C carboard paper string executed c.1955-65 prov. 27-Jan-3 Christie's, Rockefeller NY #58/R est:12000-18000

CASTLE, Phillip (20th C) British
£2000 $3140 €3000 Fiesta del mare (127x86cm-50x34in) exhib. 16-Dec-2 Sotheby's, London #90/R est:500-1000

CASTLE, Wendell (1932-) American
Sculpture
£5484 $8500 €8226 Wall sculpture (12x109x49cm-5x43x19in) walnut brass prov. 8-Dec-2 Wright, Chicago #183/R est:10000-15000

CASTLEDEN, George Frederick (1869-1945) American/British
Works on paper
£705 $1100 €1058 Sailboat on Lake Ponchartrain (43x30cm-17x12in) s.d.34 pastel. 12-Oct-2 Neal Auction Company, New Orleans #1323

CASTONGUAY, Claudette (1949-) Canadian
£402 $631 €603 Madame Recoit (60x90cm-24x35in) s.i.d.2002. 25-Nov-2 Hodgins, Calgary #264/R (C.D 1000)
£412 $638 €618 First concert (60x75cm-24x30in) s. 3-Dec-2 Joyner, Toronto #318/R est:1000-1200 (C.D 1000)
£522 $820 €783 Letter (60x45cm-24x18in) s.i.d.2000. 25-Nov-2 Hodgins, Calgary #323/R (C.D 1300)
£533 $875 €773 Le quai de San Antonio (75x60cm-30x24in) s.i.d.2003. 9-Jun-3 Hodgins, Calgary #65/R est:800-1200 (C.D 1200)
£609 $950 €1015 Trio d'adois (91x61cm-36x24in) s.i.d.2002 acrylic. 13-Apr-3 Levis, Calgary #15/R est:1200-1500 (C.D 1400)
£711 $1166 €1067 Variations pour piano (75x100cm-30x39in) s.d.2000. 3-Jun-3 Joyner, Toronto #447/R est:800-1200 (C.D 1600)

CASTONGUAY, Gerard (1933-) Canadian
£884 $1387 €1326 Grandeur d'ame (60x45cm-24x18in) s.i. 25-Nov-2 Hodgins, Calgary #365/R est:1500-1750 (C.D 2200)

CASTRES, Edouard (1838-1902) Swiss
£606 $939 €909 Army convoy in gully (20x37cm-8x15in) mono. panel. 24-Sep-2 Koller, Zurich #6632/R (S.FR 1400)
£708 $1132 €1062 Japanese woman in kimono (35x24cm-14x9in) mono. 17-Mar-3 Philippe Schuler, Zurich #4506 est:1500-2000 (S.FR 1500)

CASTRO CIRES, Raimundo (1894-1970) Spanish
£629 $981 €1000 Laredo beach (150x150cm-59x59in) s.d.1954. 23-Sep-2 Durán, Madrid #10/R

CASTRO ORTEGA, Pedro (1956-) Spanish
£548 $866 €850 Eclosion XIV (73x60cm-29x24in) s.d.1986 s.i.d.verso prov.exhib. 17-Dec-2 Segre, Madrid #200/R

CASTRO, Gabriel Henriques de (1808-1853) Dutch
£3521 $5669 €5000 Still life of flowers (85x70cm-33x28in) s.d.1840. 7-May-3 Vendue Huis, Gravenhage #428/R est:6000-7000

CASTRO, Sergio de (1922-) Argentinian
£2128 $3553 €3000 Objets (73x92cm-29x36in) s.d. exhib. 18-Jun-3 Charbonneaux, Paris #81/R est:3500-4000
£4255 $7106 €6000 L'hiver, nature morte (81x100cm-32x39in) s.d. exhib. 18-Jun-3 Charbonneaux, Paris #80/R est:4000-4500

CASTY, Gian (20th C) Swiss
£300 $475 €450 Jockey on a horse (36x40cm-14x16in) s. col glass. 29-Nov-2 Zofingen, Switzerland #2823 (S.FR 700)

CASWELL, Stuart (20th C) American
Works on paper
£566 $900 €821 Chain link II (76x102cm-30x40in) pencil dr exec.c.1984. 4-May-3 Treadway Gallery, Cincinnati #652/R

CAT, Roland (1943-) French
Works on paper
£577 $906 €900 Davidson au pre (54x44cm-21x17in) s.d.1972 mixed media. 21-Nov-2 Neret-Minet, Paris #49
£769 $1208 €1200 Rescape (49x62cm-19x24in) s.d.1972 mixed media. 21-Nov-2 Neret-Minet, Paris #50
£1026 $1610 €1600 Amants (61x49cm-24x19in) s.d.1975 mixed media cardboard prov. 21-Nov-2 Neret-Minet, Paris #51

CATALANO, R G (20th C) Italian?
£1400 $2170 €2100 On the Amalfi coast. Capri (46x66cm-18x26in) indis sig. panel pair. 31-Oct-2 Christie's, Kensington #503/R est:1000-1500

CATANI, Ugo (19/20th C) Italian
£444 $701 €666 At the water pump (16x11cm-6x4in) s. board. 18-Nov-2 Waddingtons, Toronto #276/R (C.D 1100)

CATANO, F (19th C) Italian
Works on paper
£260 $408 €390 View of Constantinople with figures (30x46cm-12x18in) s. W/C. 21-Nov-2 Tennants, Leyburn #648

CATARSINI, Alfredo (1899-1993) Italian
£316 $494 €500 Angler (60x40cm-24x16in) s. s.i.verso. 14-Sep-2 Meeting Art, Vercelli #450/R
£316 $494 €500 Rest room (50x47cm-20x19in) s. s.i.verso board. 14-Sep-2 Meeting Art, Vercelli #860/R
£633 $987 €1000 Mediterranean bay (50x70cm-20x28in) s. s.i.verso. 14-Sep-2 Meeting Art, Vercelli #495/R
£641 $1006 €1000 Composition (47x60cm-19x24in) s.d.1960 masonite. 23-Nov-2 Meeting Art, Vercelli #395/R
£641 $1006 €1000 Model (80x48cm-31x19in) s.d.1950 board. 23-Nov-2 Meeting Art, Vercelli #420/R
£654 $1046 €1000 Engines (70x50cm-28x20in) s.d.1959 board exhib.lit. 4-Jan-3 Meeting Art, Vercelli #221
£654 $1046 €1000 Composition (70x50cm-28x20in) s.d.1951 oil collage masonite. 4-Jan-3 Meeting Art, Vercelli #512
£1020 $1622 €1500 Landscape in the North (69x110cm-27x43in) s. masonite painted 1959 lit. 1-Mar-3 Meeting Art, Vercelli #734

CATASSE, Carlos (1944-) ?

£915 $1474 €1300 Landscape (43x70cm-17x28in) s.d.72. 10-May-3 Bukowskis, Helsinki #297/R

CATEL, Franz Ludwig (1778-1856) German

£14138 $22338 €20500 Genre scene in Pozzuoli Bay (24x33cm-9x13in) 3-Apr-3 Porro, Milan #51/R est:30000

£34532 $55252 €48000 The explorers. The Gulf of Naples (31x44cm-12x17in) s. verso prov. 17-May-3 Lempertz, Koln #1370/R est:50000

Works on paper

£897 $1310 €1400 Landscape with trees (23x16cm-9x6in) s.i. pencil. 4-Jun-2 Karl & Faber, Munich #59

CATEL, Franz Ludwig (attrib) (1778-1856) German

£450 $684 €675 Convent in Capri (71x97cm-28x38in) bears indis.sig.d. 4-Jul-2 Duke & Son, Dorchester #191

CATEL, Ludwig Friedrich (1776-1819) German

Works on paper

£380 $600 €600 Classical palace in hilly landscape (29x41cm-11x16in) s.d.1812 pencil wash. 29-Nov-2 Bassenge, Berlin #5850

CATHELIN, Bernard (1919-) French

£3200 $4960 €4800 Les faisans (89x140cm-35x55in) s.d.57. 5-Dec-2 Christie's, Kensington #183/R est:2500-3500

£3459 $5500 €5189 Bouquet rouge au pot blanc (36x27cm-14x11in) s.d.81 paper on board prov. 27-Feb-3 Christie's, Rockefeller NY #85/R est:7000

£5128 $8000 €7692 Bouquet dr roses au fond gris clair (130x89cm-51x35in) s. s.i.d.1977 verso prov. 14-Oct-2 Butterfields, San Francisco #2031/R est:5000-7000

£5128 $8000 €7692 Boquet d'anemones (65x46cm-26x18in) s.d.69 s.i.d.fevrier 1969 verso prov. 14-Oct-2 Butterfields, San Francisco #2032/R est:3000-5000

£7000 $10780 €10500 Pagode a nikko (115x146cm-45x57in) s.d.71 s.i.d.verso prov. 22-Oct-2 Sotheby's, London #254/R est:8000-12000

£11321 $17547 €18000 Bouquet de roses d'Inde et achillees (100x50cm-39x20in) s.d.78 s.i.d.1978 verso. 5-Oct-2 De Vuyst, Lokeren #503/R est:9500-12000

Prints

£2700 $4239 €4050 Grand tokonoma aux roses blanches (231x113cm-91x44in) s.num.VIII/X col lithograph. 17-Apr-3 Christie's, Kensington #212/R est:1000-1300

CATHERINE, Norman (1949-) South African

£1089 $1699 €1634 Man with pipe (100x75cm-39x30in) s.d.97 oil stick paper. 11-Nov-2 Stephan Welz, Johannesburg #509 est:5000-7000 (SA.R 17000)

£5125 $7995 €7688 Room service (146x150cm-57x59in) s.d.1997 wood. 11-Nov-2 Stephan Welz, Johannesburg #510/R est:25000-35000 (SA.R 80000)

£6449 $10383 €9674 Negotiator (89x148cm-35x58in) s.d.1990 prov.lit. 12-May-3 Stephan Welz, Johannesburg #538/R est:40000-60000 (SA.R 75000)

Works on paper

£1075 $1730 €1613 Morning storm (34x41cm-13x16in) s.i.d.76 air brush pastel. 12-May-3 Stephan Welz, Johannesburg #170 est:5000-7000 (SA.R 12500)

CATLIN, George (1796-1872) American

Works on paper

£480 $750 €720 Portrait of Charles White (18x15cm-7x6in) i.verso W/C. 12-Oct-2 Neal Auction Company, New Orleans #495/R

CATOIR, L (19th C) German

£652 $1017 €978 Moonlit lake with boats, figures and castle (37x47cm-15x19in) s.d.1841 panel. 16-Sep-2 Philippe Schuler, Zurich #3462/R (S.FR 1500)

CATS, Jacob (1741-1799) Dutch

Works on paper

£4189 $6535 €6200 Paysage entre Haarlem et Overveen (13x17cm-5x7in) s.i.d.1786 verso pen ink wash. 31-Mar-3 Piasa, Paris #48

CATTANEO, Achille (1872-1931) Italian

£839 $1325 €1300 Naviglio in Milan. s. board 3 in one frame. 18-Dec-2 Finarte, Milan #137/R

£1087 $1783 €1500 Naviglio al ponte de Porta Romana (60x50cm-24x20in) s. panel lit. 27-May-3 Finarte, Milan #22/R est:1000-1500

CATTAPAN, Jon (1956-) Australian

£677 $1111 €1016 Study (61x91cm-24x36in) s.d.89 verso linen diptych prov. 4-Jun-3 Deutscher-Menzies, Melbourne #179/R (A.D 1700)

£1964 $3064 €2946 Interruption (197x197cm-78x78in) s.i.d.1990 verso. 11-Nov-2 Deutscher-Menzies, Melbourne #47/R est:6000-8000 (A.D 5500)

£4464 $7009 €6696 Pill city (198x167cm-78x66in) s.i.d.95 verso linen prov. 25-Nov-2 Christie's, Melbourne #41/R est:10000-12000 (A.D 12500)

CATTELAN, Maurizo (1960-) Italian

Photographs

£2436 $3824 €3800 Errotin, the true rabbit (85x60cm-33x24in) s.i.verso cibachrome on plexiglas prov. 11-Dec-2 Artcurial Briest, Paris #776/R

Sculpture

£1429 $2271 €2100 AC furniture sud (17x23x17cm-7x9x7in) s.i. paper plexiglas. 24-Mar-3 Cornette de St.Cyr, Paris #190/R

£3077 $4769 €4800 Oblomov Foundation (5x5cm-2x2in) s.verso carved glass exec.1992 lit. 4-Dec-2 Finarte, Milan #474/R

£41139 $65000 €61709 Spermini (172x8x10cm-68x3x4in) painted latex rubber mask exec.1995 set of 25 prov.exhib.lit. 13-Nov-2 Sotheby's, New York #448/R est:60000-80000

£76923 $120000 €115385 Spermini - little sperms. 50 painted latex rubber masks. 11-Nov-2 Phillips, New York #3/R est:100000-150000

£100000 $167000 €150000 Turisti. twenty taxidermied pigeons exc.1997 prov.exhib.lit. 25-Jun-3 Sotheby's, London #3/R est:100000-150000

£218750 $350000 €328125 Untitled (250x10x20cm-98x4x8in) taxidermied white rabbit with extended ears executed 1996 prov. 15-May-3 Christie's, Rockefeller NY #329/R est:200000-300000

Works on paper

£1633 $2596 €2400 Comic strip (32x41cm-13x16in) s. graphite exec. with Manfrin prov. 24-Mar-3 Cornette de St.Cyr, Paris #189/R

£44872 $70000 €67308 Super noi - Torino (30x21cm-12x8in) ink on acetate in 50 parts executed 1996 prov.exhib.lit. 11-Nov-2 Phillips, New York #8/R est:80000-120000

CATTELL, Raymond Victor (1921-) Canadian

£329 $510 €494 Christmas birthday, 1966 (105x80cm-41x31in) s. prov. 3-Dec-2 Joyner, Toronto #380 (C.D 800)

CATTERMOLE, Charles (1832-1900) British

Works on paper

£250 $388 €375 Knights and a Cardinal on the return to the castle (20x45cm-8x18in) s. W/C. 4-Dec-2 Christie's, Kensington #18

£250 $398 €375 Banquet, with Henry VII and courtiers (17x40cm-7x16in) s. W/C. 27-Feb-3 Bonhams, Chester #455

£320 $499 €480 Forward the guns (45x58cm-18x23in) s. W/C gouache over pencil. 17-Oct-2 Lawrence, Crewkerne #405

£400 $616 €600 Card players (38x59cm-15x23in) s.d.1865 W/C htd white. 22-Oct-2 Bonhams, Knightsbridge #49/R

£410 $668 €615 Lecture (14x44cm-6x17in) s.i. W/C htd white. 11-Feb-3 Bonhams, Knowle #31

£540 $842 €810 Alchemist (33x46cm-13x18in) s.d.69 W/C. 15-Oct-2 Canterbury Auctions, UK #190/R

£1863 $3000 €2795 The Order, arrest of the Royalist by the Roundheads (46x66cm-18x26in) 19-Jan-3 Jeffery Burchard, Florida #58/R

CATTERMOLE, George (1800-1868) British

£320 $496 €480 Interior of Jacobean house with figures by fire (33x46cm-13x18in) mono.d.1890. 1-Oct-2 Gildings, Market Harborough #280

Works on paper

£360 $554 €540 Guard room (25x37cm-10x15in) W/C. 23-Oct-2 Hamptons Fine Art, Godalming #90/R

£560 $890 €840 Interior with lady and gentleman inspecting an artist's work (19x29cm-7x11in) mono. W/C bodycol. 27-Feb-3 Bonhams, Chester #454

£620 $967 €930 Historical scene (32x47cm-13x19in) mixed media. 18-Sep-2 James Thompson, Kirby Lonsdale #81

£700 $1134 €1050 Illustration from a book on Cromwell by Richard Cattermole (36x49cm-14x19in) W/C. 21-May-3 Bonhams, Knightsbridge #208/R

CATTLEY, Major George A (1896-1978) British

£491 $800 €737 What's that (23x11cm-9x4in) s.d.1958 masonite. 11-Feb-3 Bonhams & Doyles, New York #137

CATULLE, Claude (1929-) French
Works on paper
£481 $745 €750 Cancan de la vie parisienne (46x36cm-18x14in) s. ink pastel gouache. 9-Dec-2 Artcurial Briest, Paris #26

CAUCHIE, Paul (1875-1952) Belgian
£258 $408 €400 Entree de ferme (68x77cm-27x30in) s. 17-Dec-2 Galerie Moderne, Brussels #807
£276 $441 €400 Serenite (90x70cm-35x28in) s. 17-Mar-3 Horta, Bruxelles #32
Works on paper
£396 $633 €550 Le vieux Zoute (55x75cm-22x30in) s. gouache. 13-May-3 Palais de Beaux Arts, Brussels #223

CAUCHOIS, Eugène-Henri (1850-1911) French
£671 $1081 €1000 Vase garni de fleurs (65x50cm-26x20in) s. 18-Feb-3 Galerie Moderne, Brussels #274/R
£833 $1375 €1200 Fleurs dans un panier (38x46cm-15x18in) s. 1-Jul-3 Christie's, Amsterdam #53
£886 $1400 €1400 Bunch of roses in a ceramic jug (47x55cm-19x22in) s. 30-Nov-2 Berlinghof, Heidelberg #299/R
£927 $1511 €1400 Nature morte aux gibiers (56x41cm-22x16in) s. 16-Feb-3 Mercier & Cie, Lille #287 est:1500-1800
£1203 $1900 €1900 Still life with various coloured dahlias (46x55cm-18x22in) s. 30-Nov-2 Berlinghof, Heidelberg #298/R est:890
£1258 $1962 €2000 Asters in white dish (54x64cm-21x25in) s. lit. 20-Sep-2 Karlheinz Kaupp, Staufen #1881/R est:1800
£1400 $2226 €2100 Summer flowers in a basket (35x41cm-14x16in) s. canvas on panel. 20-Mar-3 Christie's, Kensington #28/R est:1500-2000
£1519 $2370 €2400 Still life with rabbit and poultry (135x87cm-53x34in) s.d.1884. 21-Oct-2 Bernaerts, Antwerp #714 est:2500-3000
£1600 $2608 €2400 Still life of summer flowers in a vase (45x36cm-18x14in) indis sig. 29-Jan-3 Sotheby's, Olympia #306/R est:1500-2000
£1899 $2943 €3000 Vase de roses (33x41cm-13x16in) s. 29-Sep-2 Eric Pillon, Calais #112/R
£1900 $3097 €2755 Still life of fruit, pewter plate and other objects (56x70cm-22x28in) s. 17-Jul-3 Tennants, Leyburn #902/R est:1500-2000
£2069 $3290 €3000 Vase de fleurs (46x38cm-18x15in) s. 7-Mar-3 Rabourdin & Choppin de Janvry, Paris #13/R est:3000-3500
£2215 $3456 €3500 Bouquet de dalhias (41x27cm-16x11in) s. 15-Sep-2 Feletin, Province #77
£2405 $3728 €3800 Nature morte au livre et a la jardiniere de fleurs des champs (52x75cm-20x30in) s. panel. 29-Sep-2 Eric Pillon, Calais #33/R
£2500 $4175 €3625 Summer flowers in a basket (46x55cm-18x22in) s. 17-Jun-3 Bonhams, New Bond Street #119/R est:3000-5000
£2949 $4629 €4600 Bouquet (65x50cm-26x20in) s. 15-Dec-2 Lombrail & Teucquam, Paris #4/R
£3000 $4890 €4500 Still life of roses (44x53cm-17x21in) s. 29-Jan-3 Sotheby's, Olympia #308/R est:2000-3000
£3000 $4680 €4500 Vase of peonies (46x55cm-18x22in) s. prov. 26-Mar-3 Sotheby's, Olympia #246/R est:1800-2500
£3006 $4750 €4509 Chrysanthemums in a copper vase (33x41cm-13x16in) s. 5-Apr-3 Neal Auction Company, New Orleans #170/R est:5000-7000
£3275 $5175 €4913 Animated river landscape (73x92cm-29x36in) s. 14-Nov-2 Stuker, Bern #131/R est:8000-10000 (S.FR 7500)
£3600 $5868 €5400 Still life of daisies and pansies in a vase (50x73cm-20x29in) s. panel. 29-Jan-3 Sotheby's, Olympia #342/R est:3000-4000
£4194 $6626 €6500 Corbeille de fleurs (55x65cm-22x26in) s. 19-Dec-2 Claude Aguttes, Neuilly #53/R
£4700 $7284 €7050 Jete de fleurs (46x61cm-18x24in) s. 3-Dec-2 Sotheby's, Olympia #295/R est:2500-3500
£5484 $8665 €8500 Bouquet de roses (46x55cm-18x22in) s. 19-Dec-2 Claude Aguttes, Neuilly #52/R
£6419 $10014 €9500 Nature morte aux fleurs et aux grenades (100x120cm-39x47in) s. 28-Mar-3 Claude Aguttes, Neuilly #92/R

CAUCIG, Franz (attrib) (1762-1828) Austrian
£4088 $6336 €6500 Leda and the swan (55x69cm-22x27in) prov. 2-Oct-2 Dorotheum, Vienna #381/R est:3000-5000

CAUD, Marcel Henri Leonce (1883-?) French
£13836 $21585 €22000 Tasting (145x114cm-57x45in) s.d.1909. 20-Sep-2 Millon & Associes, Paris #344/R est:20000-35000

CAUER, Friedrich (1874-1945) German
Works on paper
£417 $654 €650 Kriel Cathedral in Cologne (17x23cm-7x9in) s. W/C. 21-Nov-2 Van Ham, Cologne #1514/R

CAULA, Sigismondo (1637-1713) Italian
Works on paper
£377 $588 €550 Abigail kneeling before David and his soldiers (18x13cm-7x5in) wash pen. 11-Apr-3 Winterberg, Heidelberg #65/R

CAULDWELL, Cecil (20th C) Irish?
£288 $453 €450 Annalong harbour with trawler (54x49cm-21x19in) s. board. 19-Nov-2 Hamilton Osborne King, Dublin #455

CAULFIELD, Patrick (1936-) British
£4200 $6552 €6300 Curtain and bottle (59x80cm-23x31in) i. oil pencil on card prov. 25-Mar-3 Bonhams, New Bond Street #145/R est:2000-3000

CAULLERY, Louis de (16/17th C) French/Flemish
£4321 $7000 €6482 Road to Calvary (39x56cm-15x22in) panel. 24-Jan-3 Christie's, Rockefeller NY #13/R est:15000-20000
£5743 $8959 €8500 Crucifixion (84x62cm-33x24in) panel prov. 28-Mar-3 Piasa, Paris #11/R
£6918 $10723 €11000 Duel (40x56cm-16x22in) 2-Oct-2 Dorotheum, Vienna #170/R est:10000-13000
£209459 $326757 €310000 Scene de carnaval en hiver sur la place d'une ville flamande (45x67cm-18x26in) copper. 26-Mar-3 Tajan, Paris #138/R est:12000

CAULLERY, Louis de (circle) (16/17th C) French/Flemish
£5000 $7750 €7500 Virgin and Child (24x14cm-9x6in) copper arched top prov. 31-Oct-2 Sotheby's, Olympia #29/R est:2500-3500

CAUSSE, Marie Louise (19th C) French
£1200 $1872 €1800 He loves me, he loves me not (31x20cm-12x8in) s. 21-Sep-2 Lacy Scott, Bury St.Edmunds #378/R

CAUVIN, Louis Edouard Isidore (1816-1900) French
£3333 $5200 €5300 Rade de Toulon (83x150cm-33x59in) s. 9-Oct-2 Marc Kohn, Paris #25/R

CAUVY, Léon (1874-1933) French
£409 $634 €650 Paysage (31x53cm-12x21in) s.d.06 canvas on cardboard prov. 30-Oct-2 Artcurial Briest, Paris #131
£4808 $7548 €7500 Le marche sur les quais (54x72cm-21x28in) s. exhib. 16-Dec-2 Gros & Delettrez, Paris #301/R est:7500-9000
£7211 $11465 €10600 Femmes dans un palais Oriental (46x55cm-18x22in) s. 24-Mar-3 Rabourdin & Choppin de Janvry, Paris #148/R est:8000-10000

CAUWER, Émile Pierre Joseph de (1828-1873) Belgian
£2051 $3179 €3200 Interieur d'une cathedrale (45x32cm-18x13in) s. panel. 3-Dec-2 Campo & Campo, Antwerp #62/R est:3000-4000

CAUWER, Leopold de (19th C) German
£600 $978 €900 Labourers returning home (51x68cm-20x27in) s.d.56. 13-Feb-3 Christie's, Kensington #211/R

CAVAEL, Rolf (1898-1979) German
£225 $328 €350 Composition (34x25cm-13x10in) mono.d.65 oil chk pencil. 4-Jun-2 Karl & Faber, Munich #197
£818 $1259 €1300 Untitled (11x17cm-4x7in) s.d.1951 oil on monotype. 26-Oct-2 Dr Lehr, Berlin #69/R
£886 $1400 €1400 No 50/153 (26x32cm-10x13in) s.i.d.Juni 1950 paper. 29-Nov-2 Villa Grisebach, Berlin #541/R est:700-800
£2069 $3269 €3000 Composition - 59/Ja.6 (55x40cm-22x16in) mono. s.i. verso masonite exhib. 2-Apr-3 Dr Fritz Nagel, Stuttgart #9325/R est:4000
£2244 $3478 €3500 Composition No 77/F 1 (32x36cm-13x14in) mono. s.i. verso masonite. 3-Dec-2 Lempertz, Koln #85/R est:3500-4000
£2405 $3728 €3800 56/Jn 16 (50x38cm-20x15in) mono. i.d.1956 verso board on canvas prov.lit. 28-Sep-2 Ketterer, Hamburg #350/R est:4000-6000
£2899 $4754 €4000 Composition IK 4 (32x45cm-13x18in) mono. board on panel. 28-May-3 Lempertz, Koln #88/R est:6000
£4114 $6377 €6500 69/Ja 1 (68x58cm-27x23in) mono. s.i. verso prov.exhib. 28-Sep-2 Ketterer, Hamburg #354/R est:7000-8000
Works on paper
£256 $397 €400 Composition (16x13cm-6x5in) mono. s. verso mixed media board. 7-Dec-2 Ketterer, Hamburg #586/R
£321 $497 €500 Composition (24x39cm-9x15in) s.mono.d.1953 mixed media. 7-Dec-2 Ketterer, Hamburg #588/R
£507 $832 €700 Composition 77/77 (23x19cm-9x7in) mono.d.77 W/C Indian ink. 28-May-3 Lempertz, Koln #91/R

CAVAGLIERI, Mario (1887-1969) Italian
£5161 $8155 €8000 Hommage a Cezanne (65x54cm-26x21in) s.d.37 verso prov. 18-Dec-2 Christie's, Rome #169/R est:12000

CAVAILLES, F (?) French?
£1709 $2700 €2700 Portrait d'enfant au dessin (46x38cm-18x15in) s. 1-Dec-2 Livinec, Gaudcheau & Jezequel, Rennes #88/R

CAVAILLES, Jules (1901-1977) French
£2500 $3850 €3750 Port de Cannes (73x46cm-29x18in) s. s.i.verso prov. 23-Oct-2 Sotheby's, Olympia #800/R est:3000-4000

£3548 $5500 €5322 Nature morte aux fruits (61x61cm-24x24in) s. 2-Oct-2 Christie's, Rockefeller NY #85/R est:7000-9000
£4730 $7378 €7000 Hommage a Raoul Dufy (78x78cm-31x31in) s. i.verso. 26-Mar-3 Millon & Associes, Paris #88/R
£5479 $8603 €8000 Le port de Cassis (55x38cm-22x15in) s. s.i.verso. 21-Apr-3 Rabourdin & Choppin de Janvry, Paris #122/R est:8000-9000
£6500 $10270 €9750 Potiche jaune (81x65cm-32x26in) s. s.i.verso prov. 3-Apr-3 Christie's, Kensington #132/R
£7742 $12000 €11613 Norte Dame (81x64cm-32x25in) s. s.i.verso prov. 26-Sep-2 Christie's, Rockefeller NY #587/R est:8000-10000
£8333 $13167 €12000 Port mediterraneen (65x46cm-26x18in) s. 23-Apr-3 Rabourdin & Choppin de Janvry, Paris #42/R est:18000
Works on paper
£1300 $2054 €1950 Vase of flowers on a table with a chair behind (60x44cm-24x17in) s.d.42 gouache over pencil. 7-Apr-3 Bonhams, Bath #52/R est:800-1200
£1972 $3175 €2800 Nature morte au bouquet (62x36cm-24x14in) s. mixed media. 11-May-3 Thierry & Lannon, Brest #244 est:2500-3000

CAVALERI, Ludovico (1867-1942) Italian
£1069 $1647 €1700 Landscape (28x31cm-11x12in) s.d.1925 s.i.d.verso cardboard. 23-Oct-2 Finarte, Milan #10
£7483 $11898 €11000 Dusk, Lerici (61x111cm-24x44in) s.d.1890. 18-Mar-3 Finarte, Milan #23/R

CAVALIERI, Luigi (19th C) Italian
£3803 $6313 €5400 Promenade dans le parc (26x45cm-10x18in) s.i.d.1892. 13-Jun-3 Rabourdin & Choppin de Janvry, Paris #99/R est:6000-7000

CAVALLA, Giuseppe (1859-1935) Italian
£774 $1223 €1200 Figures in the wood (31x44cm-12x17in) s.d.25 cardboard. 18-Dec-2 Finarte, Milan #78/R

CAVALLERI, Vittorio (1860-1938) Italian
£1154 $1812 €1800 Alassio (34x44cm-13x17in) s. cardboard. 10-Dec-2 Della Rocca, Turin #309/R
£1701 $2704 €2500 Medieval village (35x45cm-14x18in) s. cardboard. 1-Mar-3 Meeting Art, Vercelli #261

CAVALLI, Emanuele (1904-1981) Italian
£1370 $2137 €2000 Still life (15x20cm-6x8in) s. cardboard on canvas. 10-Apr-3 Finarte Semenzato, Rome #188/R

CAVALLI, Mirko (1962-) Italian
£359 $575 €550 Cloud nine (90x80cm-35x31in) s. s.i.verso acrylic. 4-Jan-3 Meeting Art, Vercelli #637

CAVALLINO, Bernardo (attrib) (1622-1654) Italian
£132075 $213962 €191509 Ariadne on Naxos (215x169cm-85x67in) prov. 24-May-3 Galerie Gloggner, Luzern #17/R est:30000-50000 (S.FR 280000)

CAVALLON, Giorgio (1904-) American
£7595 $12000 €11393 Untitled (107x138cm-42x54in) s.d.80 s.d.verso prov. 13-Nov-2 Sotheby's, New York #216/R est:18000-22000

CAVALLUCCI, Antonio (attrib) (1752-1795) Italian
Works on paper
£1000 $1670 €1450 Kneeling angel presenting a salver, with subsidiary studies of his head (35x31cm-14x12in) black white chk. 8-Jul-3 Christie's, London #15/R est:1000-1500

CAVE, Peter le (fl.1769-1810) British
Works on paper
£360 $572 €540 Off to market (21x32cm-8x13in) s.d.1799 W/C. 27-Feb-3 Bonhams, Chester #452
£420 $668 €630 Country scene with figures, cattle and sheep before a barn (17x23cm-7x9in) s. W/C. 27-Feb-3 Bonhams, Chester #451
£700 $1120 €1050 Going to market (10x13cm-4x5in) W/C. 11-Mar-3 Bonhams, New Bond Street #40/R
£840 $1378 €1260 Figures, horse, cattle, pigs and a goat near a thatched barn (33x48cm-13x19in) s.d.1802 ink W/C. 4-Feb-3 Bonhams, Leeds #284
£1300 $2028 €1950 To market. Haycart (18x25cm-7x10in) s.d.1800 W/C two. 5-Nov-2 Bonhams, New Bond Street #54/R est:1000-1500
£2000 $3180 €3000 Figures on horseback by Lake Windermere, Belle Isle beyond (20x28cm-8x11in) s.i. pen ink W/C over pencil. 19-Mar-3 Sotheby's, London #147/R est:1000-1500

CAVE, Peter le (attrib) (fl.1769-1810) British
£480 $782 €720 Goat and two sheep in a landscape (12x15cm-5x6in) s. board oval. 13-Feb-3 Christie's, Kensington #216/R

CAVEDONE, Giacomo (1577-1660) Italian
Works on paper
£2200 $3454 €3300 Head of a bearded man (27x20cm-11x8in) chl htd white chk prov. 11-Dec-2 Sotheby's, Olympia #30/R est:1200-1800
£2593 $4200 €3890 Conversion of Constantine (27x23cm-11x9in) chk ink htd white prov.lit. 22-Jan-3 Christie's, Rockefeller NY #24/R

CAVEDONE, Giacomo (attrib) (1577-1660) Italian
£4200 $7014 €6090 Saint Peter (45x34cm-18x13in) i. canvas on panel. 11-Jul-3 Christie's, Kensington #193/R est:3000-5000

CAVIEZEL, Ratus (1893-1980) Swiss
£421 $665 €632 Village in Zillis (70x90cm-28x35in) s.i.verso. 29-Nov-2 Zofingen, Switzerland #2825 (S.FR 980)

CAVIGLIONI, Angelo (1887-?) Italian
£7692 $12077 €12000 Concert (80x90cm-31x35in) sd.30 board exhib. 21-Nov-2 Finarte, Rome #255/R est:12000-14000

CAVIN, Marylin (20th C) French
Works on paper
£468 $748 €650 L'aspiration d'une perspective (50x50cm-20x20in) s. mixed media. 18-May-3 Neret-Minet, Paris #185

CAWEN, Alvar (1886-1935) Finnish
£327 $507 €520 Sunday stroll in Paris (42x32cm-17x13in) 6-Oct-2 Bukowskis, Helsinki #152/R
£1961 $3216 €3000 Coastal town (46x42cm-18x17in) s.d.18. 9-Feb-3 Bukowskis, Helsinki #209/R est:3000
£3873 $6236 €5500 Time for reading (61x73cm-24x29in) s. 10-May-3 Bukowskis, Helsinki #56/R est:6000-8000
Works on paper
£1197 $1927 €1700 Meditation (56x51cm-22x20in) s.d.29 gouache. 10-May-3 Bukowskis, Helsinki #115/R est:1200-1500

CAWSE, John (1779-1862) British
£3000 $4920 €4500 On her Spanish guitar, she played a ditty which lulled her old guardian (61x76cm-24x30in) 29-May-3 Christie's, Kensington #249/R est:1800-2000

CAWSTON, Mick (1959-) British
£300 $471 €450 Fox (23x28cm-9x11in) s. 13-Dec-2 Keys, Aylsham #751
£1900 $3154 €2755 Pointers (61x91cm-24x36in) s. 12-Jun-3 Christie's, Kensington #305/R est:1500-2000

CAWTHORNE, Edward (1849-1914) British
£270 $432 €405 Cattle watering on the rivers edge (58x89cm-23x35in) s.d.1909 board. 11-Mar-3 David Duggleby, Scarborough #259

CAWTHORNE, Neil (1936-) British
£350 $546 €525 Foal (34x44cm-13x17in) s. canvasboard. 6-Nov-2 Sotheby's, Olympia #110/R
£380 $543 €570 Huntsman and hounds in a sun dappled wood (46x61cm-18x24in) s.d.81. 28-Feb-2 Heathcote Ball, Leicester #490
£460 $713 €690 Atherstone Hunt Kennels at Witherley (51x76cm-20x30in) s.d.79. 3-Oct-2 Heathcote Ball, Leicester #586
£650 $929 €975 Fernie with huntsman Bruce Durno away from Gumley Wood (51x76cm-20x30in) s.d.1971. 28-Feb-2 Heathcote Ball, Leicester #489
£900 $1422 €1350 All out, Newmarket, July course (46x66cm-18x26in) s. 28-Nov-2 Christie's, Kensington #202/R
£1000 $1550 €1500 Crackaseal - racehorse with jockey up (19x29cm-7x11in) s.i.d.71 prov. 1-Oct-2 Gildings, Market Harborough #284/R
£1000 $1580 €1500 First morning out (46x61cm-18x24in) s. 28-Nov-2 Christie's, Kensington #105/R est:1000-1500
£1400 $2212 €2100 Homeward bound (35x46cm-14x18in) s. 28-Nov-2 Christie's, Kensington #104/R est:600-800
£1600 $2528 €2400 Full cry (41x61cm-16x24in) s. 28-Nov-2 Christie's, Kensington #106/R est:800-1200
£1600 $2656 €2320 Waiting (46x66cm-18x26in) s. 12-Jun-3 Christie's, Kensington #256/R est:1200-1800
£1700 $2652 €2550 Over the first, Cheltenham (51x76cm-20x30in) s. 6-Nov-2 Sotheby's, Olympia #117/R est:1800-2500
£1700 $2652 €2550 Our heritage (46x66cm-18x26in) s. 6-Nov-2 Sotheby's, Olympia #118/R est:1200-1800
£1700 $2652 €2550 At the start, Goodwood (51x76cm-20x30in) s. 6-Nov-2 Sotheby's, Olympia #119/R
£1800 $2988 €2610 View holloa (46x61cm-18x24in) s. 12-Jun-3 Christie's, Kensington #29/R est:1200-1800
£1900 $3154 €2755 Full cry (46x66cm-18x26in) s. 12-Jun-3 Christie's, Kensington #27/R est:1200-1800
£1900 $3154 €2755 Moving off (46x66cm-18x26in) s. 12-Jun-3 Christie's, Kensington #28/R est:1200-1800

£2600 $4316 €3770 Eye of the storm (30x61cm-12x24in) s. 12-Jun-3 Christie's, Kensington #113/R est:1000-1200

CAYLEY, Neville (19/20th C) Australian
Works on paper
£643 $1016 €965 Shot duck (66x51cm-26x20in) s.i.d.1894 W/C. 18-Nov-2 Joel, Victoria #395a est:1800-2000 (A.D 1800)

CAYLEY, Neville William (1887-1950) Australian
Works on paper
£179 $282 €269 Quails (46x72cm-18x28in) s.d.1912 W/C. 18-Nov-2 Goodman, Sydney #42 (A.D 500)
£260 $434 €377 Stone curlews (24x18cm-9x7in) s. W/C. 25-Jun-3 Cheffins, Cambridge #715
£325 $514 €471 Sparrows in a nest (53x23cm-21x9in) s. W/C. 22-Jul-3 Lawson Menzies, Sydney #187/R (A.D 800)
£717 $1090 €1076 War cry, Kookaburra (47x36cm-19x14in) s.d.1894 W/C. 27-Aug-2 Goodman, Sydney #165/R (A.D 2000)
£772 $1173 €1158 Gun dog and quarry (33x49cm-13x19in) s. W/C. 19-Aug-2 Joel, Victoria #262 est:1500-2500 (A.D 2200)

CAYRE, J Mario (20th C) French
£1295 $2072 €1800 Porteuse d'eau (147x51cm-58x20in) s.d.46. 19-May-3 Tajan, Paris #203/R est:2000-3000

CAZANAVE, Charles Antoine (1882-1957) French
Works on paper
£566 $900 €849 Still life with glazed Chinese dancing figures (218x180cm-86x71in) s. pastel. 7-Mar-3 Jackson's, Cedar Falls #526/R est:600-1200

CAZAUBON, Pierre Louis (1872-?) French
£855 $1386 €1300 Seascape with boat (35x28cm-14x11in) s. board. 21-Jan-3 Ansorena, Madrid #63/R

CAZAUX, Edouard (1889-1974) French
Sculpture
£3022 $4835 €4200 Orphee endormi tenant sa lyre (36x39cm-14x15in) i. brown pat bronze 1 of 4 prov. 16-May-3 Lombrail & Teucquam, Paris #55/R

CAZES, Pierre-Jacques (attrib) (1676-1754) French
£692 $1065 €1100 Vierge en buste (23x18cm-9x7in) 25-Oct-2 Tajan, Paris #112/R

CAZET, Louis M (19/20th C) French
£463 $745 €671 Dans l'atelier (58x50cm-23x20in) s. 7-May-3 Dobiaschofsky, Bern #397/R (S.FR 1000)

CAZIN, Jean Charles (1841-1901) French
£2013 $3200 €3020 After the harvest (38x46cm-15x18in) s. 5-Mar-3 Christie's, Rockefeller NY #73/R est:4000-6000
£3593 $6000 €5210 Castle by night (55x74cm-22x29in) s. 22-Jun-3 Freeman, Philadelphia #41/R est:6000-8000
£5484 $8500 €8226 Houses in the dunes (60x74cm-24x29in) s. prov.exhib. 30-Oct-2 Christie's, Rockefeller NY #130/R est:10000-15000

CAZIN, Jean Charles (attrib) (1841-1901) French
£943 $1472 €1500 Landscape near Barbizon (53x42cm-21x17in) s. canvas on panel. 19-Sep-2 Dr Fritz Nagel, Stuttgart #914/R est:1900

CAZZANIGA, Enrico (1966-) Italian
Works on paper
£1135 $1838 €1600 Togliere a Largo Cairoli (70x100cm-28x39in) s.verso bleach pastel blk fustian. 20-May-3 Porro, Milan #8/R est:1300-1500

CAZZANIGA, Giancarlo (1930-) Italian
£380 $592 €600 Brooms (30x40cm-12x16in) s. 14-Sep-2 Meeting Art, Vercelli #715/R
£680 $1082 €1000 Brooms (50x40cm-20x16in) s. painted 1997. 1-Mar-3 Meeting Art, Vercelli #766
£962 $1510 €1500 Landscape (73x92cm-29x36in) s.d.1963. 23-Nov-2 Meeting Art, Vercelli #319/R
Works on paper
£278 $442 €400 Fruit (34x49cm-13x19in) s.d.1989 mixed media. 1-May-3 Meeting Art, Vercelli #30
£321 $503 €500 Brooms at Conero (47x35cm-19x14in) s.i. W/C. 23-Nov-2 Meeting Art, Vercelli #141/R
£321 $503 €500 Brooms (47x35cm-19x14in) s. W/C. 23-Nov-2 Meeting Art, Vercelli #184/R

CECCARELLI, Simona (1975-) Italian
£638 $1034 €900 Pesi a terra (50x50cm-20x20in) s.i.d.2002 verso. 26-May-3 Christie's, Milan #149/R

CECCHI, Adriano (1850-1936) Italian
£366 $600 €531 My kingdom for a kiss (23x25cm-9x10in) s. panel. 4-Jun-3 Doyle, New York #28
£3000 $5010 €4350 Italian flower seller (60x29cm-24x11in) indis sig. 17-Jun-3 Bonhams, New Bond Street #100/R est:3000-5000
£5106 $8068 €7659 Two courtesans in pink and pale blue dresses (35x26cm-14x10in) s. pair. 2-Dec-2 Rasmussen, Copenhagen #1526/R est:75000 (D.KR 60000)
£30000 $49200 €45000 Old fashioned gallantry (60x100cm-24x39in) s.i. prov. 3-Jun-3 Sotheby's, London #167/R est:30000-50000

CECCHI, Carlo (1890-?) Italian
£490 $804 €750 Mountainous landscape (60x75cm-24x30in) s. i.verso. 5-Feb-3 Il Ponte, Milan #576

CECCHI, Giulia (19th C) Italian
Works on paper
£290 $475 €435 Cathedral interior with monks (36x61cm-14x24in) s. W/C. 9-Feb-3 William Jenack, New York #268

CECCHI, Sergio (1921-1986) Italian
£352 $515 €528 Horse (50x80cm-20x31in) s. 17-Jun-2 Philippe Schuler, Zurich #7321 (S.FR 800)
£391 $610 €587 Harbour with sailing ships at dusk (35x128cm-14x50in) s. 16-Sep-2 Philippe Schuler, Zurich #6435 (S.FR 900)
£881 $1286 €1322 Venice at night (80x130cm-31x51in) s. 17-Jun-2 Philippe Schuler, Zurich #4367/R (S.FR 2000)
£1145 $1672 €1718 Doges Palace and Ponte della Paglia, Venice (80x130cm-31x51in) s. 17-Jun-2 Philippe Schuler, Zurich #4368/R est:3500-4000 (S.FR 2600)

CECCHI, V E (20th C) Italian
£1087 $1685 €1631 St John (92x67cm-36x26in) s. verso. 9-Dec-2 Philippe Schuler, Zurich #8628 est:3500-4000 (S.FR 2500)

CECCHINI, Eugène Prichard (1831-?) Italian
£2400 $3768 €3600 G. Helena's island, Venice (32x50cm-13x20in) s. 16-Apr-3 Christie's, Kensington #567/R est:800-1200

CECCOBELLI, Bruno (1952-) Italian
£327 $523 €500 Kids' mouths (35x25cm-14x10in) s.i.d.1999 paper. 4-Jan-3 Meeting Art, Vercelli #670
£1282 $2013 €2000 Egg clock (56x72cm-22x28in) s.i.d.1986 board. 21-Nov-2 Finarte, Rome #276/R
£1497 $2380 €2200 By laughing God (72x50cm-28x20in) s.i.d.1995 verso mixed media paper on canvas. 1-Mar-3 Meeting Art, Vercelli #659
Works on paper
£253 $395 €400 Raising eyes (28x276cm-11x109in) s.i.d.1994 verso mixed media collage cardboard. 14-Sep-2 Meeting Art, Vercelli #794
£321 $503 €500 Re-born, re-thought (50x36cm-20x14in) s.i.d.1999 mixed media collage cardboard. 23-Nov-2 Meeting Art, Vercelli #266/R
£327 $523 €500 From start to end (40x30cm-16x12in) s.i.d.2001 mixed media card on canvas. 4-Jan-3 Meeting Art, Vercelli #325
£340 $541 €500 Happiness pots (32x25cm-13x10in) s.i.d.1993 mixed media collage cardboard. 1-Mar-3 Meeting Art, Vercelli #412
£340 $541 €500 Column (33x28cm-13x11in) s.i.d.1999 verso mixed media collage cardboard. 1-Mar-3 Meeting Art, Vercelli #587
£340 $541 €500 Immortal (31x23cm-12x9in) s.i.d.1999 verso mixed media collage cardboard. 1-Mar-3 Meeting Art, Vercelli #607
£353 $554 €550 Composition (37x54cm-15x21in) s.d.1965 pastel card. 23-Nov-2 Meeting Art, Vercelli #21
£380 $592 €600 Two hearts man (57x46cm-22x18in) s.i.d.1996 mixed media collage cardboard on card. 14-Sep-2 Meeting Art, Vercelli #726
£451 $718 €650 Lovely (44x37cm-17x15in) mixed media card. 1-May-3 Meeting Art, Vercelli #13
£458 $732 €700 Killing time (45x38cm-18x15in) s.i.d.2000 mixed media collage card. 4-Jan-3 Meeting Art, Vercelli #467
£506 $790 €800 You are me! (35x35cm-14x14in) s.i.d.1989 mixed media panel glove. 14-Sep-2 Meeting Art, Vercelli #822/R
£521 $828 €750 Centre of force (48x26cm-19x10in) s. i.d.2001 verso mixed media collage on fabric. 1-May-3 Meeting Art, Vercelli #223
£1181 $1877 €1700 Dance (80x60cm-31x24in) s.i.d.1998 mixed media gold leaf on canvas. 1-May-3 Meeting Art, Vercelli #416
£1233 $1923 €1800 Ignoring (60x40cm-24x16in) init.i.verso polymer board. 10-Apr-3 Finarte Semenzato, Rome #295

CECCONI, Eugenio (1842-1903) Italian
£3871 $6116 €6000 Tuscan landscape (25x35cm-10x14in) s. board prov. 18-Dec-2 Finarte, Milan #73/R
£13924 $22000 €22000 Reverie (36x60cm-14x24in) s. exhib.lit. 26-Nov-2 Christie's, Rome #179/R est:15000-25000

CECCONI, Eugenio (attrib) (1842-1903) Italian
£503 $775 €800 Plein air (13x10cm-5x4in) board. 28-Oct-2 Il Ponte, Milan #267

CECCONI, Niccolo (1835-?) Italian
£609 $956 €950 View of Venice with gondola (44x31cm-17x12in) s. 10-Dec-2 Della Rocca, Turin #349

CECILE, Antoine (fl.1798-1809) French
Works on paper
£1486 $2319 €2200 Figures et costumes du Temple de Denderah. i. graphite pen ink wash seven in one frame. 27-Mar-3 Christie's, Paris #128/R est:3500
£1892 $2951 €2800 Frise du Temple d'Edfou (19x82cm-7x32in) s.i. graphite pen ink wash. 27-Mar-3 Christie's, Paris #127/R
£1892 $2951 €2800 Bas-reliefs pour le Temple de Karnak (26x43cm-10x17in) i. graphite pen ink wash. 27-Mar-3 Christie's, Paris #129/R est:5000
£1892 $2951 €2800 Releves hieroglyphiques (28x41cm-11x16in) i. graphite ink pen wash. 27-Mar-3 Christie's, Paris #130/R
£2365 $3689 €3500 Bas-relief de l'edifice sud du Temple de l'Ile d'Elephantine (13x40cm-5x16in) s.i. graphite pen ink wash. 27-Mar-3 Christie's, Paris #126/R est:6000
£3041 $4743 €4500 Decoration interieure de deux murs (25x21cm-10x8in) s.i. graphite. 27-Mar-3 Christie's, Paris #125/R est:7000
£5405 $8432 €8000 Pilier hathorique (56x38cm-22x15in) i. graphite pen ink wash. 27-Mar-3 Christie's, Paris #131/R

CEDANNE (1944-) French
£878 $1370 €1300 Petite Provence (46x38cm-18x15in) s. 28-Mar-3 Charbonneaux, Paris #50

CEDERBERG, Karl (1861-1904) Swedish
£824 $1252 €1236 View of Gamleby Harbour, Smaaland (105x153cm-41x60in) s.d.1894. 16-Aug-2 Lilla Bukowskis, Stockholm #876 (S.KR 12000)
£892 $1419 €1338 Inlet (48x72cm-19x28in) s. 3-Mar-3 Lilla Bukowskis, Stockholm #405 (S.KR 12000)

CEDERBERG, S (19th C) ?
£1437 $2400 €2084 Drawing room scene (86x117cm-34x46in) s. 21-Jun-3 Susanin's, Chicago #5002/R est:1600-2000

CEDERGREN, Per Vilhelm (1823-1896) Swedish
£294 $482 €450 Sailing in moonlight (28x39cm-11x15in) s. 9-Feb-3 Bukowskis, Helsinki #401/R

CEDERSTROM, Eva (1909-1995) Finnish
£314 $515 €480 Landscape from Kilpisjarvi (24x33cm-9x13in) s.i.d.1953. 9-Feb-3 Bukowskis, Helsinki #211/R
£340 $541 €500 Horse chestnut (32x40cm-13x16in) s.d.1971. 27-Feb-3 Hagelstam, Helsinki #815
£1646 $2600 €2600 Self portrait (56x46cm-22x18in) s.d.1941 exhib.lit. 30-Nov-2 Hagelstam, Helsinki #163/R est:2000
£2535 $4082 €3600 The artist's studio (70x100cm-28x39in) s.d.1978. 10-May-3 Bukowskis, Helsinki #262/R est:4000-5000
£2658 $4200 €4200 Town by the Mediterranean (81x100cm-32x39in) s.d.1976. 1-Dec-2 Bukowskis, Helsinki #310/R est:4000-5000
Works on paper
£324 $512 €470 Landscape (30x44cm-12x17in) s.d.1966 pastel. 3-Apr-3 Hagelstam, Helsinki #1954

CEESEPE (1958-) Spanish
Works on paper
£789 $1279 €1200 Musiciann jockey (51x36cm-20x14in) s. W/C. 21-Jan-3 Ansorena, Madrid #1/R

CEIST, P (19th C) German
£321 $487 €500 Young gilr on quayside with sailing ships beyond (22x18cm-9x7in) s.d.1845. 11-Jul-2 Hugo Ruef, Munich #605

CEJUDO NOGALES, Ricardo (1952-) Spanish
£503 $785 €800 Landscape in Old Colmenar (107x166cm-42x65in) s.i.d.1996. 23-Sep-2 Durán, Madrid #44/R

CELADA DA VIRGILIO, Ugo (1895-1995) Italian
£968 $1529 €1500 Portrait of man (107x84cm-42x33in) s. board. 18-Dec-2 Finarte, Milan #49
£2194 $3466 €3400 Still life (44x35cm-17x14in) s. 18-Dec-2 Finarte, Milan #191/R est:2200

CELEBRANO, Francesco (1729-1814) Italian
£2000 $3120 €3000 Madonna at the tomb of Christ (71x62cm-28x24in) oval. 9-Apr-3 Bonhams, New Bond Street #74/R est:2000-3000

CELESTI, Andrea (1637-1706) Italian
£13462 $20865 €21000 Jesus and the Samaritan (110x149cm-43x59in) 4-Dec-2 Christie's, Rome #442/R est:12000-18000

CELIBERTI, Giorgio (1929-) Italian
£481 $745 €750 Paris (24x35cm-9x14in) s.d.952 tempera board. 4-Dec-2 Finarte, Milan #211
£886 $1382 €1400 Landscape with trees (60x80cm-24x31in) s.d.1955 s.verso. 19-Oct-2 Semenzato, Venice #146/R
£922 $1494 €1300 Still life (60x73cm-24x29in) s.i. verso s.d.1960 stretcher prov. 26-May-3 Christie's, Milan #308
£949 $1481 €1500 Landscape (60x80cm-24x31in) s.d.1957. 19-Oct-2 Semenzato, Venice #107/R
£949 $1481 €1500 Still life (45x45cm-18x18in) s. canvas on canvas. 14-Sep-2 Meeting Art, Vercelli #823/R
£1135 $1838 €1600 Tavolino e bicchiere (60x70cm-24x28in) s. prov. 26-May-3 Christie's, Milan #312/R est:1800-2200
£3056 $4858 €4400 Civil inheritance (110x130cm-43x51in) s.i.d.1997 verso oil mixed media canvas on board. 1-May-3 Meeting Art, Vercelli #466
Works on paper
£256 $397 €400 Horse (23x31cm-9x12in) s. ink. 5-Dec-2 Stadion, Trieste #782
£541 $843 €800 Wall (40x30cm-16x12in) s.i.d.1977 fresco. 26-Mar-3 Finarte Semenzato, Milan #105
£680 $1082 €1000 Figure (40x30cm-16x12in) s.d.1973 fresco on canvas. 1-Mar-3 Meeting Art, Vercelli #322
£884 $1406 €1300 Untitled (50x40cm-20x16in) s.d.1994 mixed media board. 1-Mar-3 Meeting Art, Vercelli #422
£2245 $3569 €3300 Happy thoughts (107x78cm-42x31in) s.i.d.1993 verso fresco board. 1-Mar-3 Meeting Art, Vercelli #427
£2885 $4529 €4500 Soul scaffolding (110x90cm-43x35in) s.i.d.1998 fresco board. 23-Nov-2 Meeting Art, Vercelli #338/R
£3197 $5084 €4700 Love bundles (70x100cm-28x39in) s.i.d.1994 verso fresco board. 1-Mar-3 Meeting Art, Vercelli #635
£3205 $4968 €5000 Double exhibition (120x140cm-47x55in) s.i.d.1990 verso mixed media on canvas. 4-Dec-2 Finarte, Milan #548/R

CELIE, Pieter (1942-) Dutch
Works on paper
£694 $1104 €1000 Figures et nuages (75x238cm-30x94in) s.d.1996 mixed media. 29-Apr-3 Campo, Vlaamse Kaai #35/R

CELLE, Edmond Carl de (1889-1957) American
£258 $400 €387 Heavy seas on Gulf (64x76cm-25x30in) s.d.1938. 7-Dec-2 Neal Auction Company, New Orleans #483

CELMINS, Vija (1939-) American
£300000 $480000 €450000 Untitled - Ocean (38x40cm-15x16in) on linen painted 1990-95 prov.exhib.lit. 13-May-3 Sotheby's, New York #5/R est:200000-300000
Photographs
£4200 $6468 €6300 Untitled - galaxy (32x42cm-13x17in) s.d.1975 num.33/75 lithograph. 24-Oct-2 Christie's, Kensington #209/R est:2000-3000
£4800 $7392 €7200 Untitled - sky (32x42cm-13x17in) s.d.1975 num.33/75 beige black lithograph. 24-Oct-2 Christie's, Kensington #208/R est:2000-3000
Prints
£1887 $3000 €2831 Saturn (6x6cm-2x2in) s.num.5/50 offset lithograph. 2-May-3 Sotheby's, New York #409/R est:2500-3500
£2642 $4200 €3963 Untitled, sky (34x42cm-13x17in) s.d.num.17/75 col lithograph. 2-May-3 Sotheby's, New York #407/R est:4000-6000
£2642 $4200 €3963 Untitled, desert (31x41cm-12x16in) s.d.num.17/75 col lithograph. 2-May-3 Sotheby's, New York #408/R est:4000-6000
£3145 $5000 €4718 Comet (52x58cm-20x23in) s.num.40/80 linocut. 2-May-3 Sotheby's, New York #411/R est:2500-3500
£3400 $5236 €5100 Untitled - desert (30x42cm-12x17in) s.d.1975 num.33/75 beige black lithograph. 24-Oct-2 Christie's, Kensington #207/R est:2000-3000
£4194 $6500 €6291 Untitled (43x35cm-17x14in) s.num.23/60 mezzotint. 25-Sep-2 Christie's, Rockefeller NY #253/R est:4000-6000
£5660 $9000 €8490 Untitled, desert (53x70cm-21x28in) s.i.d. col lithograph. 29-Apr-3 Christie's, Rockefeller NY #599/R est:6000-8000
£5800 $8932 €8700 Untitled - ocean (32x42cm-13x17in) s.d.1975 beige black lithograph. 24-Oct-2 Christie's, Kensington #206/R est:2000-3000
£11321 $18000 €16982 Ocean surface (22x30cm-9x12in) s.d.num.26/50 woodcut. 2-May-3 Sotheby's, New York #410/R est:12000-15000
Sculpture
£28125 $45000 €42188 To fix the image in memory XII (11x9x11cm-4x4x4in) stone painted cast bronze in two parts prov. 14-May-3 Sotheby's, New York #171/R est:30000-40000

Works on paper

£100000 $160000 €150000 Double galaxy - coma bernices (32x58cm-13x23in) s.d.1974-75 verso pencil acrylic ground on paper prov.exhib. 14-May-3 Sotheby's, New York #172/R est:80000-120000
£137500 $220000 €206250 Long Ocean 5 (75x111cm-30x44in) s.i.d.1972 verso graphite acrylic prov.exhib. 13-May-3 Sotheby's, New York #6/R est:150000-200000
£260000 $426400 €390000 Untitled - sea 10 (30x38cm-12x15in) s.d.1975 verso graphite acrylic prov. 6-Feb-3 Sotheby's, London #11/R est:80000

CELOMMI, Pasquale (1860-1928) Italian
£6962 $11000 €11000 Fishermen coming back (63x113cm-25x44in) s. 26-Nov-2 Christie's, Rome #167/R est:12000-14000

CELOS, Julien (1884-?) Belgian
£417 $654 €650 Le mont St Michel (46x55cm-18x22in) s. 19-Nov-2 Vanderkindere, Brussels #147
£440 $678 €700 Figure by town gate (65x55cm-26x22in) s. 22-Oct-2 Campo & Campo, Antwerp #34
£464 $756 €700 Le Beguinage de Tournai en hiver (63x52cm-25x20in) 17-Feb-3 Amberes, Antwerp #178
£1701 $2704 €2500 Village anime sous la neige (81x131cm-32x52in) s. 19-Mar-3 Hotel des Ventes Mosan, Brussels #297/R est:2000-2200

CEMICKY, Ladislav (1909-2000) Czechoslovakian
£347 $492 €521 Woman seated (40x52cm-16x20in) oil tempera paper painted 1948. 26-Mar-2 SOGA, Bratislava #115/R (SL.K 22000)
£379 $587 €569 Portrait of a lady (70x45cm-28x18in) painted 1946. 3-Dec-2 SOGA, Bratislava #245/R (SL.K 24000)

CEMIN, Saint Clair (1951-) American

Sculpture

£9554 $15000 €14331 Monument to the Iberic orator (153x75x75cm-60x30x30in) st.sig.st.f.Empire d.94 num.1/3 bronze enamel coated steel prov. 19-Nov-2 Sotheby's, New York #141/R est:18000

CENICEROS, Guillermo (20th C) Mexican?

Works on paper

£398 $606 €577 Paisaje (79x99cm-31x39in) s. mixed media canvas. 24-Jul-2 Louis Morton, Mexico #69/R (M.P 6000)

CENNI DI FRANCESCO DI SER CENNI (fl.1410-1415) Italian
£27028 $42163 €40000 Madonna and Child with saints. Crucifixion. Saint Christopher (61x25cm-24x10in) panel triptych. 26-Mar-3 Tajan, Paris #8/R est:45000

CERACCHINI, Gisberto (1899-1982) Italian

Works on paper

£897 $1409 €1400 Tuscan landscape (70x30cm-28x12in) s. wax crayon. 21-Nov-2 Finarte, Rome #41/R
£1603 $2516 €2500 Study for 'The dove' (65x55cm-26x22in) s. graphite exec.1934. 21-Nov-2 Finarte, Rome #69/R

CERAGIOLI, Giorgio (1861-1947) Italian
£1474 $2315 €2300 Vase with dahlias (48x64cm-19x25in) s. masonite. 10-Dec-2 Della Rocca, Turin #377/R

CERAMANO, Charles Ferdinand (1829-1909) Belgian
£478 $745 €750 Paysage (65x92cm-26x36in) s.d.1898. 7-Nov-2 Claude Aguttes, Neuilly #20
£545 $850 €818 Shepherd with flock in a barn (53x81cm-21x32in) s. 14-Sep-2 Selkirks, St. Louis #700/R
£786 $1226 €1179 Stable interior (26x35cm-10x14in) s. masonite. 6-Nov-2 Dobiaschofsky, Bern #400/R est:3800 (S.FR 1800)
£1081 $1795 €1567 Souvenir de Belle Croix (50x65cm-20x26in) s. 16-Jun-3 Lilla Bukowskis, Stockholm #497 (S.KR 14000)
£1646 $2600 €2600 Berger et ses moutons (65x80cm-26x31in) s. 26-Nov-2 Palais de Beaux Arts, Brussels #292/R est:1500-2000
£1935 $3000 €2903 Sheep grazing in a wooded landscape (65x81cm-26x32in) s. 2-Oct-2 Christie's, Rockefeller NY #774/R est:4000-6000

CERESA, Carlo (circle) (1609-1679) Italian
£6000 $9300 €9000 Portrait of a nobleman, standing by a table (199x118cm-78x46in) prov. 30-Oct-2 Bonhams, New Bond Street #87/R est:3000-5000

CERIA, Edmond (1884-1955) French
£486 $768 €700 Paysage du Midi (73x92cm-29x36in) s. 25-Apr-3 Piasa, Paris #64
£540 $863 €750 La pergola a Evian (50x61cm-20x24in) s. s.i.verso. 14-May-3 Blanchet, Paris #79/R
£577 $894 €900 Mediterranean harbour town (33x45cm-13x18in) s. prov. 7-Dec-2 Ketterer, Hamburg #186/R
£604 $972 €900 Nu allonge (24x41cm-9x16in) s. 23-Feb-3 Lesieur & Le Bars, Le Havre #24
£772 $1243 €1150 Village au bord de l'eau (38x46cm-15x18in) s. 23-Feb-3 Lesieur & Le Bars, Le Havre #23/R
£833 $1317 €1200 Village breton, Guininec (33x46cm-13x18in) s. exhib. 25-Apr-3 Piasa, Paris #65
£937 $1528 €1350 Bigoudenes a la plage (24x33cm-9x13in) s. 19-Jul-3 Thierry & Lannon, Brest #109/R
£1007 $1641 €1450 Bigoudenes rue de la Tour a St Guenole (28x41cm-11x16in) s. panel. 19-Jul-3 Thierry & Lannon, Brest #110/R
£2109 $3353 €3100 Plage de Saint-Guenole (33x41cm-13x16in) s. exhib. 21-Mar-3 Rieunier, Bailly-Pommery, Mathias, Paris #122/R

CERMAKOVA, Alena (1926-) Czechoslovakian
£413 $644 €620 Still life with bouquet and fruit (95x92cm-37x36in) s.d.82 cardboard. 12-Oct-2 Dorotheum, Prague #137/R (C.KR 20000)

CEROLI, Mario (1938-) Italian

Sculpture

£725 $1188 €1000 Untitled (28x38cm-11x15in) s.i.d.70 wooden relief prov. 28-May-3 Lempertz, Koln #92/R
£1026 $1590 €1600 Profiles (45x60cm-18x24in) s.d.1969 num.34/100 board. 4-Dec-2 Finarte, Milan #53
£1282 $1987 €2000 Profiles (70x100cm-28x39in) s.d.1970 num.85/90 board on card. 4-Dec-2 Finarte, Milan #52/R
£1282 $1987 €2000 After Leonardo (70x100cm-28x39in) s.d.70 board on card. 4-Dec-2 Finarte, Milan #51/R
£1282 $1987 €2000 Profiles (70x100cm-28x39in) s.d.70 board on card. 4-Dec-2 Finarte, Milan #50/R
£4783 $7413 €7175 Mariposa (85x98cm-33x39in) s.d.67 wood metal pencil prov.exhib. 4-Dec-2 Koller, Zurich #191/R est:6000-8000 (S.FR 11000)
£8654 $12635 €13500 Seated figure (133x135x40cm-52x53x16in) s. wood prov.lit. 5-Jun-2 Il Ponte, Milan #160/R
£10000 $15600 €15000 Fiori (210x100x33cm-83x39x13in) wood oil executed 1967 prov. 21-Oct-2 Sotheby's, London #45/R est:10000-15000
£32000 $49280 €48000 Gloria eterna ai caduti per la pittura (204x130cm-80x51in) wood bronze prov. 22-Oct-2 Christie's, London #51/R est:20000-30000

Works on paper

£282 $468 €400 Volti (24x34cm-9x13in) s. shaped cloth on canvas. 10-Jun-3 Finarte Semenzato, Milan #29/R
£962 $1510 €1500 Horse (73x103cm-29x41in) s. wood cardboard. 21-Nov-2 Finarte, Rome #74
£1410 $2214 €2200 Sun (73x103cm-29x41in) s.i.d.1980 wood cardboard. 21-Nov-2 Finarte, Rome #73/R

CERQUOZZI, Michelangelo (1602-1660) Italian
£680 $1082 €1000 The Holy Family (49x64cm-19x25in) s.d.1653 verso. 27-Feb-3 Hagelstam, Helsinki #938
£10490 $17518 €15000 Herminie chez les bergers (50x67cm-20x26in) 25-Jun-3 Tajan, Paris #6/R est:10000-12000

CERQUOZZI, Michelangelo (attrib) (1602-1660) Italian
£3333 $5167 €5000 Pastoral landscapes (20x16cm-8x6in) oval pair. 4-Dec-2 AB Stockholms Auktionsverk #2007/R est:40000-50000 (S.KR 47000)
£55172 $87172 €80000 Still life of fruit under arches (185x265cm-73x104in) lit. 5-Apr-3 Finarte Semenzato, Milan #109/R est:120000

CERQUOZZI, Michelangelo (circle) (1602-1660) Italian
£9500 $15295 €14250 Adoration of the shepherds (103x145cm-41x57in) 20-Feb-3 Christie's, Kensington #165/R est:4000-6000

CERRAJERIA, Inaki (1957-) Spanish
£516 $815 €800 Known figures (145x122cm-57x48in) s.d.1982 canvas on board prov. 17-Dec-2 Segre, Madrid #211/R

CERUTI, Giacomo (1698-1767) Italian
£351724 $555724 €510000 Spinner (121x157cm-48x62in) prov.exhib.lit. 5-Apr-3 Finarte Semenzato, Milan #143/R

CERUTI, Giacomo (circle) (1698-1767) Italian
£5000 $7800 €7500 Portrait of a lady in a white blouse with a ribbon in her hair (42x32cm-17x13in) 10-Apr-3 Christie's, Kensington #206/R est:5000-7000
£5031 $7799 €8000 Portrait of young nobleman with hoe (84x63cm-33x25in) 2-Oct-2 Dorotheum, Vienna #327/R est:8000-12000

CERVANTES, Dorothy (20th C) American
£484 $750 €726 Martinez Street, Sunday morning, Colorado. s.verso painted c.1940. 8-Dec-2 Toomey, Oak Park #707/R
£548 $850 €822 Colorado town. s.verso painted c.1940. 8-Dec-2 Toomey, Oak Park #709/R

CERVELLI, Federico (1625-1700) Italian

£12000 $18840 €18000 Allegory of Victory (200x145cm-79x57in) 12-Dec-2 Sotheby's, London #187/R est:10000-15000

CERVEROS, Juste (19th C) Italian?

£1132 $1743 €1800 Fishermen at sunset (12x21cm-5x8in) s.d.82 board. 23-Oct-2 Finarte, Milan #7/R

CERVI, Giulio (19th C) Italian

Works on paper

£800 $1304 €1200 The tell tale letter (70x53cm-28x21in) s.i.d.1884 W/C. 29-Jan-3 Sotheby's, Olympia #262/R

CESAR, Baldaccini (1921-1998) French

Sculpture

£1013 $1600 €1600 Compression (6x2x2cm-2x1x1in) s. lids. 29-Nov-2 Drouot Estimations, Paris #95

£1076 $1668 €1700 Conserve expansion (25x51x14cm-10x20x6in) jam jar polyurethane foam lit. 28-Sep-2 Cornette de St.Cyr, Paris #272a est:1500-2000

£1154 $1788 €1800 Boite de cigarette brulee (33x26cm-13x10in) s. cigarette box cardboard. 7-Dec-2 Cornette de St.Cyr, Paris #105/R

£1206 $2013 €1700 Poule (35x25x20cm-14x10x8in) s.num.40/100 white resin. 18-Jun-3 Charbonneaux, Paris #125 est:2000-2500

£1250 $1975 €1800 Mehari compressee (33x43cm-13x17in) s. num.16/50 compressed toy. 28-Apr-3 Cornette de St.Cyr, Paris #367/R est:2000-3000

£1250 $1988 €1800 Expansion rouge (41x33cm-16x13in) red polyurethane tinned conserve. 29-Apr-3 Artcurial Briest, Paris #369/R est:1800-2000

£1255 $1983 €1883 Expansion au pot au lait (14cm-6in) s.num.111/150 white epoxy metal. 28-Apr-3 Bukowskis, Stockholm #967/R est:12000-15000 (S.KR 16500)

£1355 $2141 €2100 Poule blanche. s. num.66 resin. 18-Dec-2 Digard, Paris #154

£1410 $2186 €2200 Compression (30x20x20cm-12x8x8in) s. num.58/150 plexiglas. 7-Dec-2 Cornette de St.Cyr, Paris #104/R

£1519 $2400 €2400 Untitled (20x36x24cm-8x14x9in) s. wood plexiglas one of 30. 26-Nov-2 Camard, Paris #138/R est:2200

£1682 $2624 €2523 L'Oiseau (34cm-13in) s.num.60/100 black metal. 6-Nov-2 AB Stockholms Auktionsverk #752/R est:15000-20000 (S.KR 24000)

£1765 $2824 €2700 Untitled (50x42cm-20x17in) s. num.EA10/10 motorbike compression. 4-Jan-3 Meeting Art, Vercelli #562

£1822 $2842 €2733 Compression plastique (30cm-12in) s.num.56/150 shaped plexiglas. 6-Nov-2 AB Stockholms Auktionsverk #730/R est:18000-20000 (S.KR 26000)

£2327 $3584 €3700 Compression pop pendentif (6x2x2cm-2x1x1in) s. lids. 26-Oct-2 Cornette de St.Cyr, Paris #65/R

£2412 $3738 €3618 Animal (10x12x12cm-4x5x5in) s.num.8/9 bronze st.f.Valsuani cire perdue. 4-Dec-2 Kunsthallen, Copenhagen #84/R est:30000 (D.KR 28000)

£2468 $3875 €3850 Mini pouce or (4cm-2in) st.sig. num.19/100 gold. 11-Dec-2 Artcurial Briest, Paris #652/R

£2658 $4200 €4200 Petite plaque hommage (27x18cm-11x7in) s.st.f.Barelier num.7/8 welded bronze prov.lit. 27-Nov-2 Tajan, Paris #15/R

£2692 $4227 €4200 Sein (3cm-1in) st.sig. num.27 gold diamond. 11-Dec-2 Artcurial Briest, Paris #648/R

£2903 $4587 €4500 Mouche (12x17x14cm-5x7x6in) s. num.2/8 gilt pat bronze lit. 18-Dec-2 Digard, Paris #193/R

£3125 $4938 €4500 Trophee des Cesar (29x7x7cm-11x3x3in) s. gilt bronze Cast Blanchet. 27-Apr-3 Perrin, Versailles #96/R est:3000-3500

£4487 $7045 €7000 Chandelier a sept branches (46cm-18in) s. iron. 12-Dec-2 Rabourdin & Choppin de Janvry, Paris #105/R

£5000 $7700 €7500 Morceau de la tour Eiffel (37x36x22cm-15x14x9in) s.d.6.86 steel nails wooden base. 22-Oct-2 Sotheby's, London #348/R est:5000-7000

£5346 $8286 €8500 Pouce (43cm-17in) num.114/300 cristal baccarat. 30-Oct-2 Artcurial Briest, Paris #646/R est:9000-12000

£5500 $8965 €8250 Compression d;or (5cm-2in) s. compresse 18 carat gold with 6 diamonds executed 1977 prov. 3-Feb-3 Sotheby's, Olympia #71/R est:3000-4000

£5903 $9326 €8500 Compression (28x28x6cm-11x11x2in) s. compressed steel bumper prov.lit. 27-Apr-3 Perrin, Versailles #95/R est:10000-12000

£6973 $11087 €10250 Plaque (41x24x15cm-16x9x6in) s.num.3/8 bronze st.f.Romain Barelier lit. 26-Feb-3 Artcurial Briest, Paris #411/R est:8000-12000

£7226 $11417 €11200 Echassier (28x25x19cm-11x10x7in) s. num.5/9 gilt pat bronze lit. 18-Dec-2 Digard, Paris #208/R

£7308 $11473 €11400 Mini pouce plein (6x4cm-2x2in) st.sig. num.13/100 gold. 11-Dec-2 Artcurial Briest, Paris #649/R

£7547 $11698 €12000 Compression (40x40x10cm-16x16x4in) s.i.d.1970 compressed moped. 30-Oct-2 Artcurial Briest, Paris #451/R est:10000-15000

£8163 $12980 €12000 Pouce (43cm-17in) s. num.104/300 crystal exhib. 24-Mar-3 Cornette de St.Cyr, Paris #74/R

£8681 $13803 €12500 Compression Coca-Cola (27x11x11cm-11x4x4in) compressed cans. 29-Apr-3 Artcurial Briest, Paris #355/R est:6000-8000

£8696 $14261 €12000 Femme nue debout (45x15x17cm-18x6x7in) s.base num.8/8 bronze f.Barrelier lit. 27-May-3 Tajan, Paris #4/R est:12000-15000

£9057 $13947 €14400 Compression de boite de magnesium (35x35x12cm-14x14x5in) s. exec.1969. 26-Oct-2 Cornette de St.Cyr, Paris #51/R est:15000

£9780 $15061 €15550 Insecte africain (33x23x17cm-13x9x7in) s. num.4/8 welded bronze Cast Bocquel exec.c.1980. 26-Oct-2 Cornette de St.Cyr, Paris #56/R

£13475 $21830 €19000 Compression (80x60x12cm-31x24x5in) s.d.76 jute canvas prov. 26-May-3 Christie's, Milan #263/R est:10000-15000

£18000 $27720 €27000 L'homme de villetaneuse (42x74x22cm-17x29x9in) s. bronze i.f.Valsuani lit. 22-Oct-2 Sotheby's, London #426/R est:20000-30000

£18750 $30937 €27000 Cathy (40x22x34cm-16x9x13in) s.d.86 num.3/8 soldered bronze Cast Bocquel. 1-Jul-3 Artcurial Briest, Paris #535/R est:25000-30000

£19310 $30897 €28000 Untitled (36x11x7cm-14x4x3in) welded iron exec.c.1956 lit. 11-Mar-3 Christie's, Paris #429/R

£19728 $31367 €29000 Parisienne (76cm-30in) s. num.4/8 welded bronze Cast Bocquel lit. 24-Mar-3 Cornette de St.Cyr, Paris #47/R est:40000

£20833 $32917 €30000 Poule Julie (37x41x17cm-15x16x7in) s.num.7/8 green brown pat bronze Cast Bocquel prov.lit. 27-Apr-3 Perrin, Versailles #91/R est:30000-35000

£26000 $43420 €37700 Grand valentin (91x160x42cm-36x63x17in) s.num.3/8 bronze st.f.Bocquel prov.lit. 26-Jun-3 Sotheby's, London #231/R est:30000-40000

£26101 $40195 €41500 Julie (39x42x20cm-15x17x8in) s. num.4/8 welded bronze Cast Bocquel exec.1991. 26-Oct-2 Cornette de St.Cyr, Paris #58/R est:40000

£27000 $41580 €40500 Le pied (61x28x36cm-24x11x14in) s.d.58 welded iron prov.exhib.lit. 22-Oct-2 Sotheby's, London #403/R est:30000-40000

£30612 $48673 €45000 Poule Andree (52x65x30cm-20x26x12in) s. num.HC1/2 welded bronze Cast Bocquel exhib. 24-Mar-3 Cornette de St.Cyr, Paris #65/R est:55000

£46202 $73000 €73000 Poule a limes (110x126x54cm-43x50x21in) s. num.2/8 welded bronze Cast Bocquel prov. 27-Nov-2 Tajan, Paris #31/R est:85000-100000

£60000 $92400 €90000 Le centaure, hommage a Picasso (73x53x31cm-29x21x12in) s.i.num.7/8 bronze i.f.Bocquel prov.exhib.lit. 22-Oct-2 Sotheby's, London #398/R est:30000-40000

£110283 $169836 €175350 Pouce (140cm-55in) s.verso gilt pat bronze one of 8. 26-Oct-2 Cornette de St.Cyr, Paris #55/R est:180000

£174403 $268580 €277300 Fanny, Fanny (245x123x233cm-96x48x92in) s. num.1/8 welded bronze Cast Bocquel exec.1981-1991. 26-Oct-2 Cornette de St.Cyr, Paris #54/R est:300000

Works on paper

£400 $620 €600 Tete (18x14cm-7x6in) s.i.d.1963 black felt tipped pen ballpoint pen ink prov. 5-Dec-2 Christie's, Kensington #206/R

£709 $1184 €1000 Compression de tissus (26x21cm-10x8in) s.i.d.1975 collage crayon. 20-Jun-3 Piasa, Paris #207/R

£836 $1322 €1254 Napoleon on horseback (12x21cm-5x8in) s.i.d.86 frament picture cut paper. 1-Apr-3 Rasmussen, Copenhagen #283/R (D.KR 9000)

£1022 $1615 €1533 Tw omen at a gallery (10x26cm-4x10in) s.i. fragment photo cut paper. 1-Apr-3 Rasmussen, Copenhagen #284/R (D.KR 11000)

£2000 $3340 €2900 Untitled (41x30cm-16x12in) s.d.1972 burnt matchsticks paper on cardboard. 24-Jun-3 Sotheby's, Olympia #74/R est:2000-3000

£2025 $3200 €3200 Poulette (62x43cm-24x17in) s. crayon ink dr. 26-Nov-2 Camard, Paris #137/R est:3800

£2041 $3245 €3000 Portrait de compression (44x34cm-17x13in) s.d.1977 tampons jex pencil panel prov. 26-Feb-3 Artcurial Briest, Paris #410/R est:2500-3000

£2949 $4571 €4600 Arrachages (99x65cm-39x26in) s. ink exec.1962 prov.lit. 7-Dec-2 Cornette de St.Cyr, Paris #102/R

CESARI, Bernardino (?-1614) Italian

£48000 $80160 €69600 Destruction of the children of Niobe (69x55cm-27x22in) indis sig. panel prov. 9-Jul-3 Christie's, London #89/R est:20000-30000

CESARI, Giuseppe (1568-1640) Italian

£10266 $16631 €14475 The stoning of Saint Stephen (71x57cm-28x22in) i.verso lit. 20-May-3 Babuino, Rome #14/R est:15000-20000

£25786 $39711 €41000 Romans against Veientes and Fidenates (79x108cm-31x43in) lit. 23-Oct-2 Finarte, Rome #496/R est:45000-55000

Works on paper

£625 $994 €900 Foolish young woman (14x9cm-6x4in) s. pen wash. 5-May-3 Ketterer, Munich #347/R
£5556 $8833 €8000 Josua crossing river (40x27cm-16x11in) i. verso pen wash htd white. 5-May-3 Ketterer, Munich #344/R est:1200-1400
£27000 $45090 €39150 Angel seated on clouds, praying and looking down to it's right (26x18cm-10x7in) blk chk prov.lit. 9-Jul-3 Sotheby's, London #13/R est:15000-20000

CESARI, Giuseppe (attrib) (1568-1640) Italian

Works on paper

£694 $1104 €1000 Head of boy (17x15cm-7x6in) i. verso chk. 5-May-3 Ketterer, Munich #345/R
£1600 $2512 €2400 Allegorical female figure (17x10cm-7x4in) red black chk htd white prov. 11-Dec-2 Sotheby's, Olympia #28/R est:700-900

CESARI, Roberto (1949-) Italian

£472 $736 €750 Landscape in Venice (46x61cm-18x24in) s. board. 8-Oct-2 Ansorena, Madrid #427/R
£503 $775 €800 View of Venice (50x61cm-20x24in) s. canvas on board. 22-Oct-2 Durán, Madrid #660/R
£503 $785 €800 View of Venice (50x61cm-20x24in) s. canvas on board. 23-Sep-2 Durán, Madrid #150/R
£642 $1001 €950 View of Venice (50x61cm-20x24in) s. canvas on board. 25-Mar-3 Durán, Madrid #110/R
£818 $1275 €1300 View of Venie (46x61cm-18x24in) s. canvas on board. 23-Sep-2 Durán, Madrid #151/R
£1208 $1945 €1800 View of Venice (54x65cm-21x26in) s. canvas on board. 18-Feb-3 Durán, Madrid #147/R

CESBRON, Achille (1849-1915) French

£1195 $1900 €1793 Young girl with flowers (76x46cm-30x18in) s. painted c.1880. 4-May-3 Treadway Gallery, Cincinnati #463/R est:2500-4500
£1689 $2635 €2500 Jetee de roses (50x80cm-20x31in) s. 28-Mar-3 Claude Aguttes, Neuilly #97/R

CESETTI, Giuseppe (1902-1990) Italian

£1603 $2516 €2500 Still life (50x60cm-20x24in) s. 23-Nov-2 Meeting Art, Vercelli #243/R
£1765 $2824 €2700 Still life (40x50cm-16x20in) s. 4-Jan-3 Meeting Art, Vercelli #742
£2115 $3321 €3300 Three jockeys (40x50cm-16x20in) s. painted 1989 lit. 19-Nov-2 Finarte, Milan #44/R
£2258 $3568 €3500 Horses at pasture (60x60cm-24x24in) s. prov. 18-Dec-2 Christie's, Rome #229/R
£2564 $4026 €4000 Jockeys (50x65cm-20x26in) s. 19-Nov-2 Finarte, Milan #189/R
£2778 $4417 €4000 Landscape (47x56cm-19x22in) s. 1-May-3 Meeting Art, Vercelli #103
£2837 $4596 €4000 La Giudecca (24x24cm-9x9in) s.i.d.1930 verso. 26-May-3 Christie's, Milan #122/R est:4000-6000
£2952 $4723 €4280 Cassano d'Adda seen from South (74x100cm-29x39in) s. 11-Mar-3 Babuino, Rome #300/R
£3401 $5408 €5000 Ox and tree (40x50cm-16x20in) s. painted 1982. 1-Mar-3 Meeting Art, Vercelli #490
£3472 $5521 €5000 Horse grazing (60x80cm-24x31in) s. 1-May-3 Meeting Art, Vercelli #347
£3716 $5797 €5500 Vase of flowers (81x60cm-32x24in) s. lit. 28-Mar-3 Farsetti, Prato #534/R
£3772 $6036 €5470 View of Como from Villa Molteni (73x100cm-29x39in) s. 11-Mar-3 Babuino, Rome #301/R
£5903 $9385 €8500 Horses grazing (80x100cm-31x39in) s. painted 1969. 1-May-3 Meeting Art, Vercelli #586

Works on paper

£287 $459 €415 Study of foals (35x35cm-14x14in) s.i. ink. 11-Mar-3 Babuino, Rome #220/R
£513 $810 €800 Jockeys (30x38cm-12x15in) s. W/C pencil. 15-Nov-2 Farsetti, Prato #299/R
£949 $1481 €1500 Derby, arrival (55x75cm-22x30in) s. W/C paper on board exec.1974. 14-Sep-2 Meeting Art, Vercelli #933/R

CESTARO, Jacopo (attrib) (?) Italian?

£7500 $11775 €11250 Laban, Jacob, Rachel and lea (68x91cm-27x36in) 10-Dec-2 Bonhams, New Bond Street #107/R est:8000-12000

CEYTAIRE, Jean-Pierre (1946-) French

£513 $831 €780 Tete rouge (26x40cm-10x16in) s. 27-Jan-3 Millon & Associes, Paris #22
£855 $1386 €1300 Lutteur luttant pour la belle endormie (72x59cm-28x23in) s. 27-Jan-3 Millon & Associes, Paris #23
£1448 $2303 €2100 Femme au bras dans un bas (98x44cm-39x17in) s. i.verso. 10-Mar-3 Millon & Associes, Paris #129/R
£1792 $2778 €2850 Douce langue fait le sillon (73x60cm-29x24in) s. 3-Nov-2 Feletin, Province #101
£2014 $3223 €2800 Madame Spa Phile (146x97cm-57x38in) s. 16-May-3 Lombrail & Teucquam, Paris #196
£2403 $3652 €3700 Nude (100x50cm-39x20in) 7-Jul-2 Lombrail & Teucquam, Paris #101/R
£3907 $6369 €5900 Collant-collant fond dore (150x150cm-59x59in) s.d.2000 verso decoupe collants wood. 1-Feb-3 Claude Aguttes, Neuilly #217/R est:9900-10700

Works on paper

£345 $548 €500 Se deshabillant (41x30cm-16x12in) s.d.96 crayon. 10-Mar-3 Millon & Associes, Paris #126/R

CEZANNE, Paul (1839-1906) French

£179487 $280000 €269231 Portrait d'achille emperaire (43x41cm-17x16in) painted 1867-68 prov.exhib.lit. 6-Nov-2 Christie's, Rockefeller NY #15/R est:400000-600000
£180000 $293400 €270000 Portrait de Paul Cezanne, fils de l'artiste (26x20cm-10x8in) painted c.1885 prov.exhib.lit. 3-Feb-3 Christie's, London #61/R est:350000
£243590 $380000 €365385 Baigneur, vu de dos (24x19cm-9x7in) painted 1877-78 prov.exhib.lit. 6-Nov-2 Christie's, Rockefeller NY #1/R est:400000-600000
£260000 $434200 €377000 Le vase de fleurs (40x29cm-16x11in) painted c.1897-1898 prov.exhib.lit. 24-Jun-3 Christie's, London #58/R est:280000-350000
£512821 $800000 €769232 La faience Italienne (42x55cm-17x22in) painted 1872-73 prov.exhib.lit. 6-Nov-2 Christie's, Rockefeller NY #6/R est:600000-800000
£1153846 $1800000 €1730769 Le potager de Pissarro a pontoise (50x60cm-20x24in) painted 1877 prov.exhib.lit. 5-Nov-2 Sotheby's, New York #8/R est:2000000-2500000
£2564103 $4000000 €3846155 L'estaque vu a travers les arbres (45x53cm-18x21in) painted July 1878 prov.exhib.lit. 6-Nov-2 Christie's, Rockefeller NY #16/R est:4000000-6000000
£9627330 $15500000 €14440995 Portrait de Paul Cezanne (55x46cm-22x18in) painted c.1895 prov.exhib.lit. 7-May-3 Christie's, Rockefeller NY #14/R est:15000000-20000000

Prints

£8333 $13000 €12500 Les baigneurs (26x33cm-10x13in) col lithograph. 14-Oct-2 Butterfields, San Francisco #1088/R est:7000-9000

Works on paper

£4200 $7014 €6300 Soldat au bain (6x11cm-2x4in) pen ink executed c.1864-68 after Michel-Ange prov.exhib.lit. 26-Jun-3 Christie's, London #319/R est:1500-2500
£6000 $10020 €9000 Les musiciens. Personnage devant des arches, Marie, soeur de l'artiste et buste d'homme (12x21cm-5x8in) pencil ink exec c.1862-1869 double-sided prov.lit. 26-Jun-3 Christie's, London #349/R est:3000-4000
£6500 $10855 €9750 Femme agenouillee. Etude de personnage accoude (27x22cm-11x9in) W/C pencil exec 1894-98 inside covers two prov.exhib.lit. 26-Jun-3 Christie's, London #332/R est:5000-7000
£7000 $10780 €10500 Le meutre (13x15cm-5x6in) pencil executed 1868-71 prov.exhib.lit. 22-Oct-2 Sotheby's, London #121/R est:6000-8000
£7000 $11690 €10500 Lucius Verus. Esquisse de tete d'enfant (20x12cm-8x5in) pencil executed 1888-1894 double-sided prov.exhib.lit. 26-Jun-3 Christie's, London #320/R est:600-800
£7500 $12525 €11250 Piece d'eau au dauphin du Jas de Bouffan. Tete d'un homme au chapeau (19x12cm-7x5in) pencil executed c.1883-1886 double-sided prov.exhib.lit. 26-Jun-3 Christie's, London #341/R est:4000-6000
£8000 $13360 €12000 Homme assis. Three handwritten addresses (27x21cm-11x8in) pencil executed c.1893-96 double-sided prov.exhib.lit. 26-Jun-3 Christie's, London #348/R est:800-1200
£8500 $14195 €12750 Bords de riviere. Etude de baigneur (21x27cm-8x11in) pencil executed c.1880-1990 double-sided prov.lit. 26-Jun-3 Christie's, London #347/R est:10000-15000
£10000 $16700 €15000 Deux etudes de baigneuse. Nu masculin vu de dos (12x19cm-5x7in) pencil executed c.1871-1879 double-sided prov.exhib.lit. 26-Jun-3 Christie's, London #344/R est:12000-15000
£11000 $18370 €16500 Brouillon de lettre et etudes de baigneurs. Pecheur et scene avec personnages (31x20cm-12x8in) ink pencil executed c.1871-1877 double-sided prov.lit. 26-Jun-3 Christie's, London #336/R est:4000-6000
£12422 $20000 €18633 Etude d'une figure d'une garniture de cheminee (32x27cm-13x11in) pencil executed c.1881-84 prov.exhib.lit. 7-May-3 Sotheby's, New York #124/R est:30000-40000
£13000 $21710 €19500 Mise au tombeau (15x14cm-6x6in) pencil executed c.1877-80 after Caravage prov.exhib.lit. 26-Jun-3 Christie's, London #328/R est:4000-6000
£14000 $23380 €21000 L'amour (30x20cm-12x8in) pencil executed c.1886-1889 attrib Puget prov.exhib.lit. 26-Jun-3 Christie's, London #337/R est:400-600

£15000 $25050 €22500 Vue de Pantheon. Etudes avec personnages et colonnade (23x12cm-9x5in) pencil executed c.1871-82 double-sided prov.exhib.lit. 26-Jun-3 Christie's, London #333/R est:8000-12000
£15000 $25050 €22500 Dans la carriere de Bibemus (21x27cm-8x11in) pencil executed c.1900 prov.exhib.lit. 26-Jun-3 Christie's, London #338/R est:7000-10000
£15528 $25000 €23292 Paysage vaste avec maison. Apres Puget Hurcules au repos (15x22cm-6x9in) pencil double-sided prov.lit. 7-May-3 Sotheby's, New York #118/R est:30000-40000
£15528 $25000 €23292 Vue de L'Estaque (31x45cm-12x18in) pencil executed c.1881-84 pencil prov.exhib.lit. 7-May-3 Sotheby's, New York #119/R est:30000-40000
£16000 $26720 €24000 Etude pour la montagne Sainte-Victoire. Etude d'homme allonge lisant (21x27cm-8x11in) pencil W/C executed c.1886-1896 double-sided prov.exhib.lit. 26-Jun-3 Christie's, London #329/R est:8000-12000
£18000 $30060 €27000 Paysage au maison et arbres. Etude d'une eglise (12x19cm-5x7in) pencil executed c.1876-1892 double-sided prov.exhib.lit. 26-Jun-3 Christie's, London #307/R est:18000-25000
£19000 $31730 €28500 Une tasse. Clemence Isaure (19x12cm-7x5in) pencil exec c.1880-83 double-sided after A Preault prov.exhib.lit. 26-Jun-3 Christie's, London #301/R est:15000-20000
£21000 $35070 €31500 Venus et Psyche (22x12cm-9x5in) pencil executed c.1877-1880 after Raphael prov.exhib.lit. 26-Jun-3 Christie's, London #306/R est:8000-12000
£22000 $36740 €33000 Etude pour Leda et Etude de tete. Deux etudes de Paul Cezanne fils (12x22cm-5x9in) pencil executed c.1877-1882 double-sided prov.exhib.lit. 26-Jun-3 Christie's, London #302/R est:12000-16000
£22000 $36740 €33000 Tete d'un garcon (19x12cm-7x5in) pencil executed c.1886-1887 prov.exhib.lit. 26-Jun-3 Christie's, London #340/R est:10000-15000
£22000 $36740 €33000 Etude de jambes. Etudes: Une oreille et figure d'un homme (19x12cm-7x5in) pencil exec c.1877-86 double-sided after Signorelli prov.lit. 26-Jun-3 Christie's, London #343/R est:7000-12000
£22000 $36740 €33000 Ambroise Vollard. Bethsabee et baigneur debout (27x21cm-11x8in) pencil W/C executed c.1894-99 double-sided prov.exhib.lit. 26-Jun-3 Christie's, London #346/R est:12000-16000
£23000 $38410 €34500 Paysage aux arbres. Etudes de personnages feminins (21x26cm-8x10in) pencil executed c.1892-1900 double-sided prov.exhib.lit. 26-Jun-3 Christie's, London #312/R est:6000-9000
£24000 $40080 €36000 Jeune homme assoupi. Etudes, pot et cruche en terre et baigneuse (19x12cm-7x5in) pen ink pencil exec c.1884-1894 double-sided prov.exhib.lit. 26-Jun-3 Christie's, London #315/R est:18000-25000
£25000 $41750 €37500 Paysage fantastique. Etude d'une femme et d'un faune (8x14cm-3x6in) pencil executed c.1869-73 double-sided prov.exhib.lit. 26-Jun-3 Christie's, London #321/R est:6000-8000
£26000 $43420 €39000 Venus accroupie. Etude de tete et etude pour La Tentation de Saint-Antoine (20x12cm-8x5in) pencil executed c.1875-97 double-sided prov.exhib.lit. 26-Jun-3 Christie's, London #326/R est:4000-6000
£27000 $44280 €40500 Tete (17x23cm-7x9in) pencil prov. 6-Feb-3 Christie's, London #405/R est:30000
£28000 $46760 €42000 Deux baigneurs. Caryatide (21x12cm-8x5in) pencil executed c.1875-1880 double-sided prov.exhib.lit. 26-Jun-3 Christie's, London #325/R est:25000-35000
£29503 $47500 €44255 Arbres (49x32cm-19x13in) pencil executed c.1892-95 prov.exhib.lit. 7-May-3 Sotheby's, New York #125/R est:60000-80000
£30000 $50100 €45000 Paysage le mur. D'apres L'Ecorche (21x27cm-8x11in) W/C pencil executed c.1890-1896 double-sided prov.exhib.lit. 26-Jun-3 Christie's, London #310/R est:20000-30000
£30000 $50100 €45000 Boileau-Despreaux, after F Girardon. Hercule, vue de dos, after P Puget (27x21cm-11x8in) pencil exec c.1892-97 double-sided prov.exhib.lit. 26-Jun-3 Christie's, London #314/R est:8000-12000
£30000 $50100 €45000 Venus et amours. Diane Chasseresse (12x19cm-5x7in) pencil executed c.1887-1890 double-sided prov.exhib.lit. 26-Jun-3 Christie's, London #316/R est:12000-16000
£30000 $50100 €45000 Baigneur descendant dans l'eau (20x12cm-8x5in) pencil pen ink executed c.1886-1889 prov.exhib.lit. 26-Jun-3 Christie's, London #324/R est:40000-60000
£30000 $50100 €45000 Tete de Cezanne fils, Ceres, d'apres Rubens. Paysage aux arbres et aux maisons (22x12cm-9x5in) pencil executed c.1880-86 double-sided prov.exhib.lit. 26-Jun-3 Christie's, London #339/R est:15000-20000
£35000 $58450 €52500 Milon de Crotone (20x12cm-8x5in) pencil executed c.1882-1885 prov.exhib.lit. after P Puget. 26-Jun-3 Christie's, London #313/R est:20000-30000
£38000 $63460 €57000 Academie d'homme, vue do dos (62x43cm-24x17in) s.d.1862 verso pencil prov.exhib.lit. 26-Jun-3 Christie's, London #304/R est:20000-25000
£38000 $63460 €57000 Nino espulgandose (19x12cm-7x5in) pencil executed c.1882-1885 after E Murillo prov.exhib.lit. 26-Jun-3 Christie's, London #305/R est:15000-20000
£38000 $63460 €57000 Profil du Roc de Chere, Lac d'Annecy. Homme vu de dos (21x27cm-8x11in) W/C pencil executed c.1886-1896 double-sided prov.exhib.lit. 26-Jun-3 Christie's, London #309/R est:20000-30000
£42000 $70140 €63000 Baigneurs et etude de caryatide. Nature morte (12x22cm-5x9in) pencil executed c.1877-86 double-sided prov.exhib.lit. 26-Jun-3 Christie's, London #323/R est:14000-18000
£44872 $70000 €67308 Madame Cezanne - le dormeuse (31x47cm-12x19in) W/C pencil executed 1897-1900 prov.exhib.lit. 7-Nov-2 Christie's, Rockefeller NY #113/R est:70000-90000
£45000 $75150 €67500 Deux arbres (21x26cm-8x10in) W/C pencil executed c.1890 prov.lit. 26-Jun-3 Christie's, London #342/R est:35000-45000
£48000 $80160 €72000 Portrait de Mme Cezanne, profil gauche. Esclave enchaine, after Michel-Ange (19x12cm-7x5in) pencil exec c.1883-1887 double-sided prov.exhib.lit. 26-Jun-3 Christie's, London #317/R est:35000-45000
£65000 $108550 €97500 Paysage aux rochers et arbres, Bibemus. Page d'etudes (21x26cm-8x10in) pencil executed c.1890-1894 double-sided prov.exhib.lit. 26-Jun-3 Christie's, London #303/R est:10000-15000
£70513 $110000 €105770 Baigneur les bras etendus. Tete du jeune baigneur, nombres (22x12cm-9x5in) pencil double-sided executed 1883-86 prov.exhib.lit. 7-Nov-2 Christie's, Rockefeller NY #101/R est:35000-45000
£85000 $141950 €127500 Emile Zola lisant. Tete de Paul Cezanne fils (22x12cm-9x5in) pencil executed c.1879-1884 double-sided prov.exhib.lit. 26-Jun-3 Christie's, London #311/R est:40000-60000
£92000 $153640 €138000 Carnet de dessins dit 'Chappuis II' (12x21cm-5x8in) pencil W/C executed 1872-1896 sketchbook 27 studies prov.exhib.li. 26-Jun-3 Christie's, London #330/R est:130000-150000
£108974 $170000 €163461 Sous bois aux grands troncs. Lisiere de foret (45x59cm-18x23in) W/C pencil double-sided prov.exhib.lit. 7-Nov-2 Christie's, Rockefeller NY #106/R est:180000-250000
£120000 $200400 €180000 La tranchee. Nature mortes aux pommes. Portrait d'un peintre espagnole et personnages (26x31cm-10x12in) W/C ink pencil exec c.1867-1877 double-sided prov.exhib.lit. 26-Jun-3 Christie's, London #345/R est:50000-7
£125000 $208750 €187500 Portrait de Madame Cezanne. Six pommes sur une assiette (27x21cm-11x8in) W/C pencil executed c.1891-1900 double-sided prov.exhib.lit. 26-Jun-3 Christie's, London #335/R est:50000-70000
£170000 $283900 €255000 Table de toilette avec essuie-mains et cuvette. Paysage (26x21cm-10x8in) W/C pencil executed c.1880-1895 double-sided prov.exhib.lit. 26-Jun-3 Christie's, London #318/R est:40000-80000
£180000 $300600 €270000 Lit defait. Arbres au-dessus d'un ruisseau (27x21cm-11x8in) W/C pencil executed c.1885-95 double-sided prov.exhib.lit. 26-Jun-3 Christie's, London #327/R est:40000-60000
£220000 $367400 €330000 Crane sur une table. Arbre denude (21x27cm-8x11in) pencil executed c.1892-1900 double-sided prov.exhib.lit. 26-Jun-3 Christie's, London #308/R est:18000-25000
£220000 $367400 €330000 Baigneur aux bras ecartes. Paysage (22x12cm-9x5in) pencil executed c.1880-86 double-sided prov.exhib.lit. 26-Jun-3 Christie's, London #322/R est:40000-60000
£390000 $651300 €585000 Autoportrait. Tete de Cezanne fils, une femme et un homme, trois baigneuses (22x12cm-9x5in) pencil executed c.1871-1883 double-sided prov.exhib.lit. 26-Jun-3 Christie's, London #334/R est:60000-80000

CHABANIAN, Arsene (1864-1949) French
£1944 $3091 €2800 Scene de plage (32x44cm-13x17in) oil pastel cardboard. 29-Apr-3 Artcurial Briest, Paris #174/R est:3000-4000

CHABAS, Maurice (1862-1947) French
£699 $1168 €1000 L'innocence (46x33cm-18x13in) s. 26-Jun-3 Tajan, Paris #295
£1338 $2087 €2100 Paysanne bretonne (31x41cm-12x16in) s. painted c.1903. 7-Nov-2 Chochon-Barre & Allardi, Paris #92/R
£2113 $3401 €3000 Paysage a la riviere (80x91cm-31x36in) s. 11-May-3 Thierry & Lannon, Brest #338 est:3400-3800
£2420 $3776 €3800 Reverie (33x41cm-13x16in) s. 7-Nov-2 Chochon-Barre & Allardi, Paris #93/R

CHABAS, Paul (1869-1937) French
£5405 $8432 €8000 Femmes a l'etang (73x116cm-29x46in) s. 25-Mar-3 Claude Aguttes, Neuilly #100/R

CHABAUD LA TOUR, Raymond de (1865-1930) French
£443 $691 €700 Femme assise au compotier (45x60cm-18x24in) s. 18-Oct-2 Raboudin & Choppin de Janvry, Paris #2

CHABAUD, Auguste (1882-1955) French
£903 $1435 €1300 Interieur (27x32cm-11x13in) s. paper on isorel panel. 29-Apr-3 Artcurial Briest, Paris #218 est:1500-1800
£903 $1435 €1300 La moisson (47x38cm-19x15in) s. cardboard. 29-Apr-3 Artcurial Briest, Paris #219 est:1200-1500
£1592 $2309 €2500 Oliviers (53x76cm-21x30in) s. i.verso cardboard. 31-May-2 Blanchet, Paris #58/R
£1911 $2771 €3000 Mas en Provence (53x76cm-21x30in) s. cardboard. 31-May-2 Blanchet, Paris #56/R
£3057 $4433 €4800 Pres du Lourmarin (53x76cm-21x30in) s. cardboard. 31-May-2 Blanchet, Paris #49/R
£3312 $4803 €5200 Chapelle romane en Provence (37x53cm-15x21in) s. i.verso cardboard. 31-May-2 Blanchet, Paris #57/R
£3648 $5654 €5800 Champ d'oliviers (60x92cm-24x36in) s. exhib. 4-Oct-2 Tajan, Paris #46 est:6000-7500
£4140 $6003 €6500 Carriole sur chemin (46x61cm-18x24in) s. i.verso. 31-May-2 Blanchet, Paris #48/R
£40000 $63200 €62000 Couple rentrant au cabaret (67x52cm-26x20in) s. cardboard painted c.1907 prov. 18-Dec-2 Ferri, Paris #40 est:20000

CHABOT, Hendrik (1894-1949) Dutch
£4140 $6459 €6500 View of mountains in the summer (70x78cm-28x31in) s. prov.exhib. 6-Nov-2 Vendue Huis, Gravenhage #570/R est:8000-10000
£13462 $20865 €21000 Landscape with green houses (73x84cm-29x33in) s.d.45. 3-Dec-2 Christie's, Amsterdam #225/R est:6000-8000

Works on paper
£292 $481 €420 Farmhouses in winter (35x52cm-14x20in) s. W/C gouache. 1-Jul-3 Christie's, Amsterdam #399

CHABRIER, Gilles (20th C) French
£272 $433 €400 Untitled (46x33cm-18x13in) s. 24-Mar-3 Claude Boisgirard, Paris #201

CHADWICK, Emma (1855-1932) Swedish
£477 $753 €716 Interior scene with woman reading (80x64cm-31x25in) s,. 30-Nov-2 Goteborg Auktionsverk, Sweden #160/R (S.KR 6800)

CHADWICK, Ernest Albert (1876-1955) British

Works on paper
£380 $597 €570 Cottage gardens, Savoys (18x26cm-7x10in) s. W/C over pencil. 15-Apr-3 Bonhams, Knowle #97
£1200 $1992 €1800 Beaudesert Lane, Henley in Arden, Warwickshire (24x27cm-9x11in) s. W/C. 12-Jun-3 Bonhams, New Bond Street #673/R est:800-1200

CHADWICK, Lynn (1914-2003) British

Sculpture
£1401 $2200 €2102 Seated female figure from the miniature figure series (11cm-4in) num.C858 bronze i.f. 14-Dec-2 Weschler, Washington #601/R est:3000-5000
£1500 $2325 €2250 Miniature lion IV (13cm-5in) num.51/8/20 dark brown pat. bronze lit. 4-Dec-2 Christie's, Kensington #510/R est:1500-2000
£1500 $2325 €2250 Miniature lion IV (13cm-5in) num.51/10/20 brown pat. bronze lit. 4-Dec-2 Christie's, Kensington #512/R est:1500-2000
£1800 $2772 €2700 Miniature lion IV (13cm-5in) num.c/c51/5/20 brown pat bronze lit. 5-Sep-2 Christie's, Kensington #649/R est:1000-1500
£2500 $3875 €3750 Miniature figure III (9cm-4in) d.1986 num.9/30 black pat. bronze lit. 4-Dec-2 Christie's, Kensington #511/R est:2500-3500
£2500 $3951 €3750 Miniture figure III (9cm-4in) i.num.29/30 bronze lit. 27-Nov-2 Sotheby's, Olympia #174/R est:2500-3500
£2600 $4004 €3900 Miniature figure III (9cm-4in) d.1986 num.5/30.C41 black pat bronze lit. 5-Sep-2 Christie's, Kensington #651/R est:2500-3500
£2600 $4056 €3900 Miniature figure III (9cm-4in) d.1986 num.3/30 black pat. bronze lit. 27-Mar-3 Christie's, Kensington #584/R est:2500-3500
£5500 $8635 €8250 Maquette VII high wind (30cm-12in) init.num.8/9 black pat. bronze cast 1984 lit. 22-Nov-2 Christie's, London #72/R est:6000-8000
£5500 $8965 €8250 Maquette II (26x39cm-10x15in) s.d.68 num.560 0/4 black pat. bronze prov.lit. 3-Feb-3 Sotheby's, Olympia #54/R est:3000-4000
£6000 $9420 €9000 Pair of cloaked figures III (18cm-7in) s.d.77 num.5/8 dark brown pat. bronze prov.exhib.lit. 22-Nov-2 Christie's, London #70/R est:6000-8000
£7500 $12300 €11250 Winged figure (55cm-22in) mono.d.76 num.733/5/8 black pat. bronze lit. 6-Jun-3 Christie's, London #40/R est:8000-12000
£8000 $12560 €12000 Bird IX (49cm-19in) s.num.0/6 green blue pat bronze st.f.Brotal cast 1959 prov.lit. 22-Nov-2 Christie's, London #73/R est:12000-18000
£8000 $13120 €12000 Two reclining figures. mono.d.76 num.739 and 4/8 bronze two parts prov.lit. 7-Feb-3 Sotheby's, London #238/R est:8000-12000
£8500 $13940 €12750 Cloaked figure VIII (26cm-10in) init.d.76 num.755S/2/8 black pat. bronze lit. 6-Jun-3 Christie's, London #42/R est:6000-8000
£9000 $14760 €13500 Maquette IV, two reclining figures (22x30x43cm-9x12x17in) mono.d.73 num.675 and 1/8 bronze prov.lit. 7-Feb-3 Sotheby's, London #246/R est:12000-15000
£9500 $15865 €13775 Trig III (45cm-18in) s.num.4/4 358 brown pat bronze prov.lit. 24-Jun-3 Bonhams, New Bond Street #117/R est:7000-10000
£10000 $15700 €15000 Sitting woman in robes II (31cm-12in) d.1987 num.2/9 black pat. bronze lit. 22-Nov-2 Christie's, London #69/R est:10000-15000
£10000 $16400 €15000 Sitting elektra maquette VI (33cm-13in) s.d.70 num.584/0/6 brown pat. bronze st.f.Morris Singer lit. 6-Jun-3 Christie's, London #175/R est:8000-12000
£11000 $18040 €16500 Cloaked figure IV (23cm-9in) init.num.746 6/8 black pat. bronze polished face lit. 6-Jun-3 Christie's, London #177/R est:7000-10000
£12000 $20040 €17400 Winged figures (39x21cm-15x8in) s.d.71 num.630 and 6/6 bronze prov.lit. 26-Jun-3 Sotheby's, London #238/R est:12000-15000
£12500 $20875 €18125 Figures. s.d.76 numbers 718 and 14/30 bronze twenty parts prov.lit. 26-Jun-3 Sotheby's, London #235/R est:14000-18000
£13500 $21195 €20250 Three sitting figures (30cm-12in) st.num.634 5/7/8 grey pat. bronze conceived 1976 lit. 22-Nov-2 Christie's, London #105/R est:15000-20000
£14000 $21560 €21000 Two lying figures on base II (24x34x56cm-9x13x22in) mono.num.4/8 bronze polished bronze executed 1974 prov.lit. 22-Oct-2 Sotheby's, London #442/R est:12000-15000
£14000 $22960 €21000 Two lying figures on base (24x34x59cm-9x13x23in) s.d.1974 num.4/8 bronze prov.lit. 7-Feb-3 Sotheby's, London #239/R est:10000-15000
£14063 $22500 €21095 Maquette II two winged figures (25x23x11cm-10x9x4in) mono.d.73 num.669-5/6 dark brown pat. bronze in two parts. 14-May-3 Sotheby's, New York #175/R est:15000-20000
£16000 $25120 €24000 Maquette VI two winged figures (49cm-19in) init.num.3/8 dark grey pat. bronze two conceived 1973 lit. 22-Nov-2 Christie's, London #68/R est:18000-25000
£16000 $26240 €23200 Watcher (43cm-17in) num.1/9 mid-brown pat bronze st.f. one of nine exec.1959 exhib. 4-Jun-3 Sotheby's, London #80/R est:12000-16000
£18000 $29520 €27000 Two winged figures (51cm-20in) init.num.76/735s/3/8 light grey pat. bronze polished faces lit. 6-Jun-3 Christie's, London #176/R est:20000-30000
£18000 $30060 €26100 Sitting elektra IV (61x43x37cm-24x17x15in) s.d.68 num.577 and 2/4 bronze polished bronze lit. 26-Jun-3 Sotheby's, London #230/R est:12000-15000
£22000 $36080 €33000 Maquette diamond wing (69cm-27in) s.d.70 num.2/6 green pat. bronze lit. 6-Jun-3 Christie's, London #38/R est:25000-35000
£22000 $36080 €33000 Maquette I jubilee III (52cm-20in) init.num.4/9 dark brown pat. bronze polished faces lit. 6-Jun-3 Christie's, London #174/R est:20000-30000
£24528 $38019 €39000 Five sitting figures (14x16cm-6x6in) mono.d.76 num.6/8 dark brown pat bronze prov.lit. five. 5-Oct-2 De Vuyst, Lokeren #497/R
£26000 $42640 €39000 Cloaked couple IV (49cm-19in) init.d.1977 num.2/9 black pat. bronze polished faces lit. 6-Jun-3 Christie's, London #39/R est:18000-25000
£26250 $42000 €39375 Stranger V (46x46x16cm-18x18x6in) s. num.3/3 black green pat bronze exec.1959 lit. 15-May-3 Christie's, Rockefeller NY #147/R est:18000-25000
£62500 $100000 €93750 Maquette for Jubilee II (90x66x112cm-35x26x44in) s.d.1983 num.2/9 black brown pat bronze two prov.lit. 15-May-3 Christie's, Rockefeller NY #142/R est:100000-150000

Works on paper
£550 $891 €798 Abstract study in black, grey and brown (56x33cm-22x13in) s.d.61 ink W/C pen. 20-May-3 Dreweatt Neate, Newbury #215/R
£700 $1078 €1050 Study for sculpture (57x79cm-22x31in) s.d.69 W/C. 5-Sep-2 Christie's, Kensington #652/R
£2200 $3586 €3300 Untitled (76x55cm-30x22in) s.d.68 W/C ball point pen pencil paper on cardboard. 3-Feb-3 Sotheby's, Olympia #187/R est:2000-3000

CHADWICK, William (1879-1962) American/British

£1006 $1600 €1509 Springtime (35x45cm-14x18in) s. 7-Mar-3 Skinner, Boston #391/R est:700-900
£1447 $2300 €2171 Autumn trees (41x50cm-16x20in) s. board. 7-Mar-3 Skinner, Boston #443/R est:1000-1500
£3503 $5500 €5255 Summer landscape with a girl walking along a wooded path (61x51cm-24x20in) s. 23-Nov-2 Pook & Pook, Downington #400/R est:5000-6000
£8448 $12250 €12672 Autumn in Lyme (71x91cm-28x36in) 1-Jun-2 Russ Antiques, Waterford #55

CHAFFEE, Samuel R (19/20th C) American

Works on paper

£267 $425 €401 At low tide (29x54cm-11x21in) s. W/C. 7-Mar-3 Skinner, Boston #469/R
£311 $500 €467 Windy winter farm scene (48x71cm-19x28in) s. W/C bodycol. 22-Feb-3 Brunk, Ashville #314/R

CHAGALL, Marc (1887-1985) French/Russian

£5449 $8500 €8174 Moon pierrot (76x54cm-30x21in) s.i. col lithograph edition of 50. 5-Nov-2 Christie's, Rockefeller NY #128/R est:6000-8000
£19231 $30000 €28847 Le plateau de fruits (13x18cm-5x7in) st.sig. oil pencil pen ink on panel painted c.1960 prov. 7-Nov-2 Christie's, Rockefeller NY #294/R est:30000-40000
£25316 $40000 €37974 Bouquet a chatel (26x25cm-10x10in) s.i.d.1927 oil gouache on paper. 27-Apr-3 Sotheby's, Tel Aviv #21/R est:40000-60000
£41925 $67500 €62888 La tendresse (24x19cm-9x7in) s. oil India ink crayon board painted c.1978 prov. 7-May-3 Sotheby's, New York #371/R est:50000-70000
£45000 $73800 €67500 Ame de la ville (24x19cm-9x7in) s. oil brush ink painted c.1970. 5-Feb-3 Sotheby's, London #253/R est:70000
£45000 $75150 €65250 La famille et l'ane vert (33x22cm-13x9in) s.verso tempera brush ink canvas on board painted c.1980. 24-Jun-3 Sotheby's, London #191/R est:35000-45000
£53000 $86920 €79500 Village en rouge (35x27cm-14x11in) st.sig. canvas on board prov. 5-Feb-3 Sotheby's, London #254/R est:90000
£57692 $90000 €86538 Le mariage (33x24cm-13x9in) s. d.23 Sept 1964 verso masonite. 7-Nov-2 Christie's, Rockefeller NY #353/R est:100000-150000
£64220 $107248 €93119 Couple sous le baldaquin (27x19cm-11x7in) st.sig. canvas on board prov. 20-Jun-3 Kornfeld, Bern #21/R est:100000 (S.FR 140000)
£73718 $115737 €115000 Place du Tertre, esquisse (28x35cm-11x14in) s. 12-Dec-2 Rabourdin & Choppin de Janvry, Paris #74/R est:130000-150000
£74534 $120000 €111801 Nu a l'ane rouge (41x32cm-16x13in) s. s.verso tempera on masonite painted 1981 prov. 8-May-3 Christie's, Rockefeller NY #222/R est:70000-90000
£80745 $130000 €121118 Souvenirs de deux bouquets (41x33cm-16x13in) s. board painted c.1978 prov. 7-May-3 Sotheby's, New York #357/R est:100000-150000
£84000 $140280 €121800 Bouquets et fruits sur la table (33x41cm-13x16in) st.sig oil tempera pastel painted c.1982. 24-Jun-3 Sotheby's, London #193/R est:80000-100000
£96154 $150000 €144231 L'offrande des fleurd aux maries (35x27cm-14x11in) s. s.verso painted 1981 prov. 7-Nov-2 Christie's, Rockefeller NY #360/R est:120000-160000
£96330 $160872 €139679 Bouquet sur fond bleu (35x27cm-14x11in) s. verso canvas on board prov. 20-Jun-3 Kornfeld, Bern #20/R est:125000 (S.FR 210000)
£100000 $164000 €150000 Peintre et grand nu (65x54cm-26x21in) st.sig. oil ink painted 1984. 4-Feb-3 Christie's, London #302/R est:180000
£145000 $242150 €210250 Muguets et bouquet rouge (55x38cm-22x15in) st.sig oil gouache on canvas painted 1972. 24-Jun-3 Sotheby's, London #179/R est:120000-150000
£145963 $235000 €218945 Les amoureux au bouquet de fleurs (73x60cm-29x24in) s. s.verso painted c.1970 prov. 8-May-3 Christie's, Rockefeller NY #226/R est:250000-350000
£179487 $280000 €269231 Le bouquet dans le ciel bleu (73x50cm-29x20in) s. s.verso painted c.1980 prov. 7-Nov-2 Christie's, Rockefeller NY #318/R est:250000-350000
£198718 $310000 €298077 Le couple au bouquet (81x60cm-32x24in) s. s.verso prov. 6-Nov-2 Sotheby's, New York #332/R est:300000-400000
£198758 $320000 €298137 Les maries aux deux bouquets (65x54cm-26x21in) s. s.verso painted c.1980 prov. 7-May-3 Sotheby's, New York #321/R est:250000-350000
£199367 $315000 €315000 Mere a la robe rouge (38x46cm-15x18in) s. painted 1965-68 exhib.lit. 30-Nov-2 Farsetti, Prato #720/R est:350000
£200000 $328000 €300000 Nu sur fond rouge (73x92cm-29x36in) s. oil ink painted 1967 exhib. 4-Feb-3 Christie's, London #339/R est:350000
£210000 $344400 €315000 Bouquets dans le ciel (73x92cm-29x36in) s.d.1981 verso prov. 5-Feb-3 Sotheby's, London #173/R est:350000
£220000 $360800 €330000 Peintre au dessus de Vitebsk (91x60cm-36x24in) s. s.verso painted 1982 prov.exhib.lit. 4-Feb-3 Sotheby's, London #53/R est:350000
£220000 $367400 €330000 Le coq dans le bouquet bleu (60x81cm-24x32in) st.sig. oil gouache painted c.1980 prov. 23-Jun-3 Sotheby's, London #35/R est:200000-300000
£224359 $350000 €336539 Le cheval vert (95x75cm-37x30in) s.d.1956 s. verso prov.exhib.lit. 6-Nov-2 Sotheby's, New York #323/R est:300000-400000
£230000 $377200 €345000 Scene paysanne (92x73cm-36x29in) s. s.verso oil gouache ink painted 1974 exhib. 4-Feb-3 Christie's, London #334/R est:280000
£240000 $400800 €360000 Confidence dans le paysage bleu (100x80cm-39x31in) s.i. s.verso oil gouache painted c.1978 prov. 23-Jun-3 Sotheby's, London #33/R est:300000-400000
£254658 $410000 €381987 Couple aux quatre bouquets (81x54cm-32x21in) s. s.d.1980-82 verso prov. 7-May-3 Sotheby's, New York #184/R est:375000-425000
£300000 $492000 €450000 Au-dessus du village (116x89cm-46x35in) s. painted c.1980 prov. 4-Feb-3 Sotheby's, London #55/R est:600000
£301282 $470000 €451923 La piste du cirque (86x50cm-34x20in) s. s.verso panel painted c.1967 prov. 7-Nov-2 Christie's, Rockefeller NY #344/R est:350000-450000
£320000 $521600 €480000 Trois acrobates (99x66cm-39x26in) s. painted 1959 lit. 3-Feb-3 Christie's, London #79/R est:600000
£360000 $601200 €522000 L'oiseau rouge (72x60cm-28x24in) s. painted c.1968-72 prov. 24-Jun-3 Christie's, London #73/R est:280000-350000
£380734 $635826 €552064 La branche (146x114cm-57x45in) s. s. verso prov.exhib. 20-Jun-3 Kornfeld, Bern #22/R (S.FR 830000)
£448718 $700000 €673077 Les amis (116x81cm-46x32in) s. s.verso painted 1968-71 prov.lit. 5-Nov-2 Sotheby's, New York #54/R est:800000-1200000
£520000 $868400 €754000 L'ane a la tour Eiffel (46x38cm-18x15in) s. prov. sold with a photo-certificate. 24-Jun-3 Christie's, London #8/R est:180000-240000
£1474359 $2300000 €2211539 La grande roue (60x89cm-24x35in) s.d.1911-12 prov.exhib.lit. 6-Nov-2 Christie's, Rockefeller NY #36/R est:2500000-3500000

Prints

£1698 $2700 €2547 Female rider (33x23cm-13x9in) s.num.IV/XXV etching exec.1926. 3-May-3 Rachel Davis, Shaker Heights #73/R est:2000-3000
£1740 $2750 €2610 Moses (64x41cm-25x16in) s.num.M114 col lithograph. 24-Apr-3 Shannon's, Milford #222/R est:2000-3000
£1761 $2923 €2500 Passage de la mer rouge (53x39cm-21x15in) init. acquaforte W/C num.74/100 lit. 10-Jun-3 Finarte Semenzato, Milan #50/R est:1500-2000
£1887 $3000 €2831 Prophete tue par un lion (32x22cm-13x9in) init.etching aquatint hand col W/C. 4-Mar-3 Swann Galleries, New York #200/R est:2500-3500
£1887 $3000 €2831 Village (31x23cm-12x9in) s.num.16/26 woodcut. 4-Mar-3 Swann Galleries, New York #207/R est:2000-3000
£1887 $3000 €2831 La maison de mon village (32x25cm-13x10in) s.num.26/40 col lithograph. 1-May-3 Swann Galleries, New York #421/R est:4000-6000
£1887 $3000 €2831 Moses receiving the Ten Commandments (21x14cm-8x6in) s.num.24/40 etching in black and orange. 1-May-3 Swann Galleries, New York #426/R est:2500-3500
£1899 $3000 €3000 Ma mere (32x24cm-13x9in) s. woodcut. 30-Nov-2 Bassenge, Berlin #6169/R est:3250
£1923 $3000 €2885 Syrinx fable (42x32cm-17x13in) col lithograph edition of 250. 5-Nov-2 Christie's, Rockefeller NY #112/R est:3000-4000
£1923 $3000 €2885 Twelve sketches for windows of Jerusalem (38x33cm-15x13in) s.num.43/50 col lithograph. 7-Nov-2 Swann Galleries, New York #594/R est:3500-5000
£1923 $3000 €2885 L'artiste et son modele (21x15cm-8x6in) s. etching. 7-Nov-2 Swann Galleries, New York #605/R est:2000-3000
£1931 $3013 €2800 Little peasants II (35x29cm-14x11in) s. num.13/50 col lithograph. 26-Mar-3 Walker's, Ottawa #45/R est:3000-4000 (C.D 4500)
£1963 $3200 €2945 Green Eiffel Tower (29x30cm-11x12in) s. num.53/90 col lithograph exec.1957. 13-Feb-3 Christie's, Rockefeller NY #40/R
£2000 $3300 €2900 L'ane au bouquet de fleurs (34x39cm-13x15in) s.num.V/X etching drypoint. 2-Jul-3 Christie's, London #58/R est:2500-3500
£2013 $3200 €3020 Abraham pleurant Sara (29x24cm-11x9in) init.num.74/100 etching aquatint hand col W/C. 4-Mar-3 Swann Galleries, New York #201/R est:2500-3500
£2013 $3200 €3020 Maternity with centaur (23x23cm-9x9in) s.num.15/90 col lithograph. 4-Mar-3 Swann Galleries, New York #203/R est:3000-5000
£2013 $3200 €3020 La mort de saul (28x23cm-11x9in) num.74/100 etching aquatint hand col W/C. 1-May-3 Swann Galleries, New York #16/R est:3000-5000

£2065 $3200 €3098 De mauvais (43x33cm-17x13in) s.num.1/9 etching aquatint. 25-Sep-2 Christie's, Rockefeller NY #57/R est:1500-2000
£2083 $3292 €3000 Job en priere (52x38cm-20x15in) s.num.33/50 col lithograph. 26-Apr-3 Cornette de St.Cyr, Paris #22/R est:3000-4000
£2089 $3300 €3300 Le cirque (33x25cm-13x10in) s. col lithograph. 30-Nov-2 Bassenge, Berlin #6181/R est:3200
£2138 $3400 €3207 Promesse a Jerusalem (32x22cm-13x9in) init.num.57/100 etching hand col W/C. 1-May-3 Swann Galleries, New York #416/R est:2000-3000
£2147 $3500 €3221 Moses (38x26cm-15x10in) s. num.65/75 col lithograph. 13-Feb-3 Christie's, Rockefeller NY #38/R
£2172 $3389 €3258 Les Amoureux (40x59cm-16x23in) s.num.14/50 col lithograph 1951 lit. 6-Nov-2 AB Stockholms Auktionsverk #982/R est:30000-40000 (S.KR 31000)
£2179 $3400 €3269 Moise (61x42cm-24x17in) s.num.48/50 col lithograph. 7-Nov-2 Swann Galleries, New York #579/R est:4000-6000
£2180 $3422 €3400 Les amoureux en gris (27x22cm-11x9in) s. col lithograph. 22-Nov-2 Tajan, Paris #208/R est:2000-2400
£2183 $3428 €3275 Vision de Paris (35x52cm-14x20in) s. num.4/75 col lithograph prov.lit. 25-Nov-2 Germann, Zurich #270 est:5000-6000 (S.FR 5000)
£2200 $3410 €3300 Mein leben, der vater (28x22cm-11x9in) s.num.25/110 etching drypoint. 5-Dec-2 Sotheby's, London #93/R est:2500-3000
£2200 $3410 €3300 Mein leben Speisezimmer (28x22cm-11x9in) s.num.25/110 etching drypoint. 5-Dec-2 Sotheby's, London #100/R est:2000-2500
£2200 $3630 €3190 Le cirque fantastique (24x31cm-9x12in) s.num.2/35 etching aquatint. 2-Jul-3 Christie's, London #57/R est:2500-3500
£2215 $3500 €3323 Vision d'Ezechiel, from la Bible (33x26cm-13x10in) init.num.74/100 hand col etching. 22-Apr-3 Butterfields, San Francisco #2103/R est:2500-3500
£2215 $3500 €3323 Entree en piste (48x25cm-19x10in) s.num.XXI/XXV col lithograph. 22-Apr-3 Butterfields, San Francisco #2106/R est:4000-6000
£2243 $3500 €3365 Le repas chez Dryas (41x64cm-16x25in) col lithograph edition of 250. 14-Oct-2 Butterfields, San Francisco #1094/R est:4000-5000
£2258 $3500 €3387 De mauvais sujets (43x32cm-17x13in) s.num.1/9 col etching aquatint. 25-Sep-2 Christie's, Rockefeller NY #58/R est:1500-2000
£2264 $3600 €3396 Tamar daughter-in-law of Judah (36x27cm-14x11in) s.num.21/50 col lithograph. 3-Mar-3 Swann Galleries, New York #83/R est:3000-5000
£2264 $3600 €3396 Ruth Gleaning (36x27cm-14x11in) s.num.4/50 col lithograph. 3-Mar-3 Swann Galleries, New York #84/R est:3000-5000
£2264 $3600 €3396 Anne invoque l'eternel (27x23cm-11x9in) init. num.74/100 etching aquatine hand col W/C. 1-May-3 Swann Galleries, New York #15/R est:3000-5000
£2281 $3605 €3422 Les anemones (32x25cm-13x10in) s.num.32/50 col lithograph lit. 28-Apr-3 Bukowskis, Stockholm #376/R est:30000-40000 (S.KR 30000)
£2300 $3565 €3450 Mein leben, pokrowskaja in Witebsk (18x21cm-7x8in) s.num.25/110 etching drypoint. 5-Dec-2 Sotheby's, London #98/R est:2200-2800
£2308 $3600 €3462 Sacrifice d'Abraham (31x24cm-12x9in) init.num.44/100 hand col W/C etching aquatint. 7-Nov-2 Swann Galleries, New York #576a/R est:2500-3500
£2308 $3577 €3600 Evocation (49x34cm-19x13in) s. col lithograph exec.1983 one of 50. 4-Dec-2 Finarte, Milan #55/R est:3000
£2317 $3730 €3476 Jonah I (34x482cm-13x190in) s.num.11/50 col.lithograph lit. 7-May-3 AB Stockholms Auktionsverk #1179/R est:35000-40000 (S.KR 30000)
£2373 $3750 €3560 Samson renverse les colonnes, from la Bible (30x25cm-12x10in) init. hand col etching. 22-Apr-3 Butterfields, San Francisco #2102/R est:2500-3500
£2390 $3800 €3585 Sarah and the angels (36x27cm-14x11in) s.num.21/50 col lithograph. 3-Mar-3 Swann Galleries, New York #82/R est:2500-3500
£2405 $3752 €3800 Angel of music (31x22cm-12x9in) s.i. col lithograph. 15-Oct-2 Dorotheum, Vienna #164/R est:4700-5500
£2405 $3800 €3800 Self portrait (31x24cm-12x9in) s. col lithograph. 30-Nov-2 Bassenge, Berlin #6179/R est:4500
£2411 $3738 €3617 La tribu de Levi - from Douze maquettes de vitraux pour Jerusalem (61x46cm-24x18in) s. col lithograph lit. 8-Dec-2 Uppsala Auktionskammare, Uppsala #317/R est:30000-35000 (S.KR 34000)
£2436 $3556 €3800 De mauvais sujets III (37x27cm-15x11in) s. col etching with aquatint. 4-Jun-2 Karl & Faber, Munich #200/R est:5000-6000
£2436 $3800 €3654 Ruth aux pieds de booz (36x27cm-14x11in) s.i. col lithograph. 18-Sep-2 Swann Galleries, New York #83/R est:4000-6000
£2436 $3800 €3654 Grey crucifixion (72x57cm-28x22in) s.num.29/50 col lithograph. 5-Nov-2 Christie's, Rockefeller NY #130/R est:2000-3000
£2436 $3800 €3654 Cantique de l'arc (32x24cm-13x9in) init.num.74/100 hand col etching aquatint. 7-Nov-2 Swann Galleries, New York #577a/R est:2500-3500
£2436 $3800 €3654 Le prophete Daniel avec les lions (36x27cm-14x11in) s.num.15/75 col lithograph. 7-Nov-2 Swann Galleries, New York #580/R est:3000-5000
£2436 $3849 €3800 Capricorn (55x40cm-22x16in) col lithograph. 12-Nov-2 Babuino, Rome #224/R
£2452 $3800 €3678 De mauvais sujets (43x32cm-17x13in) s. col etching aquatint. 25-Sep-2 Christie's, Rockefeller NY #59/R est:1500-2000
£2453 $3826 €3680 Jonah I (34x26cm-13x10in) s.num.13/50 col lithograph 1972 lit. 6-Nov-2 AB Stockholms Auktionsverk #981/R est:35000-40000 (S.KR 35000)
£2483 $4022 €3600 Composition with figures and animals (100x75cm-39x30in) s.num.21/50 lithograph. 25-May-3 Uppsala Auktionskammare, Uppsala #339/R est:30000-40000 (S.KR 32000)
£2500 $3875 €3750 Mein leben, Hochzeit (14x16cm-6x6in) s.num.25/110 etching drypoint. 5-Dec-2 Sotheby's, London #102/R est:3000-3500
£2500 $4125 €3625 Bible, Jeremiah (35x26cm-14x10in) s.num.23/75 col lithograph card. 1-Jul-3 Sotheby's, London #65/R est:3000-5000
£2516 $4000 €3774 Circus riders (65x48cm-26x19in) s.num.5/30 lithograph. 4-Mar-3 Swann Galleries, New York #208/R est:5000-8000
£2516 $4000 €3774 Mein leben, speisezimmer (21x27cm-8x11in) s.num.109/110 drypoint etching prov.exhib. 2-May-3 Sotheby's, New York #91/R est:5000-7000
£2533 $3976 €3800 The painter by the village (41x29cm-16x11in) s. num.26/75 col lithograph. 23-Nov-2 Burkhard, Luzern #131/R est:6000-8000 (S.FR 5800)
£2536 $4159 €3500 Bateau mouche menu (25x16cm-10x6in) s. col lithograph. 29-May-3 Lempertz, Koln #565/R est:3000
£2564 $4000 €3846 Moise sauve des eaux (41x34cm-16x13in) init.num.38/100 hand col etching. 14-Oct-2 Butterfields, San Francisco #1089/R est:2000-3000
£2564 $4000 €3846 Still life with flowers (43x36cm-17x14in) s.num.37/50 col lithograph. 14-Oct-2 Butterfields, San Francisco #1098/R est:1500-2500
£2564 $4000 €3846 Recontre de Ruth et de Booz (36x27cm-14x11in) s.i. col lithograph. 18-Sep-2 Swann Galleries, New York #82/R est:4000-6000
£2564 $4000 €3846 Sorrel horse (38x56cm-15x22in) s.num.103/200 col lithograph. 5-Nov-2 Christie's, Rockefeller NY #103/R est:3500-4500
£2581 $4000 €3872 De mauvais sujets (43x32cm-17x13in) s.num.1/9 col etching aquatint. 25-Sep-2 Christie's, Rockefeller NY #60/R est:1500-2000
£2586 $4085 €3879 Le songe du peintre (74x57cm-29x22in) s.num.40/50 col lithograph lit. 28-Apr-3 Bukowskis, Stockholm #373a/R est:40000-45000 (S.KR 34000)
£2587 $4165 €3881 Le Pierrot (62x45cm-24x18in) s.num.24/50 etching aquatint lit. 7-May-3 AB Stockholms Auktionsverk #1176/R est:35000-40000 (S.KR 33500)
£2600 $4030 €3900 Mein leben, die grossvater (28x21cm-11x8in) s.num.25/110 etching drypoint. 5-Dec-2 Sotheby's, London #95/R est:2500-3000
£2600 $4030 €3900 Mein leben, selbstportait (27x21cm-11x8in) s.num.25/110 etching drypoint. 5-Dec-2 Sotheby's, London #108/R est:2500-3000
£2600 $4030 €3900 Lovers in grey (27x22cm-11x9in) s.i. col lithograph. 4-Dec-2 Bonhams, New Bond Street #165/R est:1500-2000
£2621 $4036 €3932 Musicians with green background (36x30cm-14x12in) s. col lithograph. 27-Oct-2 Anders Antik, Landskrona #522/R est:15000-20000 (S.KR 38000)
£2642 $4200 €3963 Ruth at the feet of Boaz (36x27cm-14x11in) s.num.21/50 col lithograph. 3-Mar-3 Swann Galleries, New York #85/R est:3500-5000
£2692 $4200 €4038 Green tree with lovers (64x48cm-25x19in) s.num.45/50 col lithograph. 5-Nov-2 Christie's, Rockefeller NY #131/R est:4000-6000
£2692 $4200 €4038 Young Methymneans (43x32cm-17x13in) s.num.39/60 col lithograph. 7-Nov-2 Swann Galleries, New York #591/R est:7000-10000
£2710 $4200 €4065 Martyr (76x59cm-30x23in) s.num.7/50 col lithograph. 25-Sep-2 Christie's, Rockefeller NY #69/R est:3500-4500
£2710 $4200 €4065 David (30x25cm-12x10in) s.num.108/150 col lithograph. 25-Sep-2 Christie's, Rockefeller NY #70/R est:2400-2800
£2710 $4200 €4065 De mauvais sujets (43x32cm-17x13in) s. col etching aquatint. 25-Sep-2 Christie's, Rockefeller NY #61/R est:1500-2000
£2715 $4534 €3937 Rencontre de Ruth et de Booz (52x38cm-20x15in) s. col lithograph. 24-Jun-3 Koller, Zurich #329/R est:4800-6800 (S.FR 6000)
£2724 $4250 €4086 Artist II (48x39cm-19x15in) s.num.37/50 col lithograph. 14-Oct-2 Butterfields, San Francisco #1101/R est:3000-5000
£2767 $4400 €4151 Planche de cartes de voeux (65x50cm-26x20in) s,num.5/10 lithograph. 1-May-3 Swann Galleries, New York #417/R est:6000-9000
£2771 $4239 €4157 In the land of Gods - For a woman, what remains (45x38cm-18x15in) s.num.62/75 col lithograph. 26-Aug-2 Blomqvist, Lysaker #1062/R est:45000-50000 (N.KR 32000)
£2800 $4340 €4200 Mein leben, der rabbi (25x19cm-10x7in) s.num.20/110 etching drypoint. 5-Dec-2 Sotheby's, London #106/R est:3500-4500

£2800 $4340 €4200 Mein leben, an der staffele (25x19cm-10x7in) s.num.25/110 etching. 5-Dec-2 Sotheby's, London #109/R est:3000-3500
£2817 $4676 €4000 Talmud teacher (25x18cm-10x7in) s. drypoint etching. 14-Jun-3 Hauswedell & Nolte, Hamburg #1072/R est:4000
£2821 $4400 €4232 Couple noir au musicien (32x25cm-13x10in) s.i. col lithograph. 7-Nov-2 Swann Galleries, New York #589/R est:6000-9000
£2821 $4400 €4232 Hymenee (35x26cm-14x10in) s.num.6/50 col lithograph. 7-Nov-2 Swann Galleries, New York #607/R est:5000-8000
£2830 $4500 €4245 Couple with angels (36x47cm-14x19in) s.num.11/50 lithograph. 2-May-3 Sotheby's, New York #113 est:3000-4000
£2848 $4500 €4500 Creation (36x27cm-14x11in) s. col lithograph. 30-Nov-2 Villa Grisebach, Berlin #383/R est:3500-4500
£2848 $4500 €4272 Blue sky (69x53cm-27x21in) s.num.82/90 col lithograph. 22-Apr-3 Butterfields, San Francisco #2105/R est:6000-8000
£2885 $4500 €4328 Chloe (42x32cm-17x13in) col lithograph edition of 250. 5-Nov-2 Christie's, Rockefeller NY #115/R est:4000-6000
£2885 $4500 €4328 XX siecle homage to March Chagall (50x36cm-20x14in) s.i. col lithograph edition of 75. 5-Nov-2 Christie's, Rockefeller NY #127/R est:3500-4500
£2893 $4600 €4340 Ruth gleaning (36x27cm-14x11in) s.num.21/50 col lithograph. 1-May-3 Swann Galleries, New York #420/R est:3000-5000
£2899 $4754 €4000 Eve damned by God (36x27cm-14x11in) s. col lithograph. 31-May-3 Villa Grisebach, Berlin #310/R est:3500-4500
£2945 $4800 €4418 David and Bathsheba (35x30cm-14x12in) s. num.41/50 col lithograph. 13-Feb-3 Christie's, Rockefeller NY #46/R
£2949 $4600 €4424 Bezaleel fit deux cherubins d'or (48x35cm-19x14in) s.i. col lithograph. 7-Nov-2 Swann Galleries, New York #595/R est:4000-6000
£2956 $4611 €4700 Man with samovar (41x27cm-16x11in) s. num.9/35 lithograph. 11-Oct-2 Winterberg, Heidelberg #928/R est:6500
£3038 $4800 €4800 Ruth glaneuse (36x27cm-14x11in) s. col lithograph. 30-Nov-2 Villa Grisebach, Berlin #384/R est:3500-4500
£3043 $4717 €4565 Vitraux pour Jerusalem - La tribu de Gad (61x46cm-24x18in) s.i. lithograph. 4-Dec-2 Koller, Zurich #332/R est:5800-8000 (S.FR 7000)
£3045 $4750 €4568 Artist I (49x39cm-19x15in) s.num.37/50 col lithograph. 14-Oct-2 Butterfields, San Francisco #1100/R est:3000-5000
£3045 $4750 €4568 Appearance of King David (60x47cm-24x19in) s.num.32/50 col lithograph. 14-Oct-2 Butterfields, San Francisco #1104/R est:3000-5000
£3077 $4800 €4616 Circus with yellow clown (67x49cm-26x19in) s.num.27/150 col lithograph. 19-Sep-2 Waddingtons, Toronto #165/R est:7000-9000 (C.D 7600)
£3077 $4769 €4800 Peasant with flower bouquet (32x24cm-13x9in) s. col lithograph. 4-Dec-2 Lempertz, Koln #606/R est:5000-6000
£3097 $4800 €4646 Place de la Concorde (36x27cm-14x11in) s.num.12/75 lithograph. 25-Sep-2 Christie's, Rockefeller NY #54/R est:2500-3500
£3141 $4931 €4900 Affiche (64x50cm-25x20in) s.i.d.1954 num.52.130 col lithograph. 12-Dec-2 Rabourdin & Choppin de Janvry, Paris #77/R est:6000
£3200 $4960 €4800 L'oiseau-peintre (65x46cm-26x18in) s.num.48/50 col lithograph. 3-Dec-2 Christie's, London #99 est:2000-3000
£3200 $4960 €4800 Mein leben, haus des Grossvaters (21x16cm-8x6in) s.num.25/110 etching drypoint. 5-Dec-2 Sotheby's, London #107/R est:2200-2800
£3200 $5280 €4640 Creation (95x60cm-37x24in) s.num.5/50 lithograph. 2-Jul-3 Christie's, London #234/R est:3000-5000
£3205 $5000 €4808 Roofs (7x51cm-3x20in) s.num.35/75 col lithograph. 14-Oct-2 Butterfields, San Francisco #1091/R est:7000-9000
£3205 $5000 €4808 Elie's chariot (57x42cm-22x17in) s.num.37/50 lithograph. 14-Oct-2 Butterfields, San Francisco #1099/R est:3000-5000
£3205 $5000 €4808 Painter in front of the picture (62x47cm-24x19in) s.num.37/50 col lithograph. 14-Oct-2 Butterfields, San Francisco #1103/R est:3000-5000
£3205 $5000 €4808 Noemie et ses belles-filles (36x27cm-14x11in) s.i. col lithograph. 18-Sep-2 Swann Galleries, New York #81/R est:4000-6000
£3205 $5000 €4808 L'artiste II (34x26cm-13x10in) s.i. col lithograph. 18-Sep-2 Swann Galleries, New York #100/R est:6000-9000
£3205 $5000 €4808 Hymen (42x64cm-17x25in) col lithograph edition of 250. 5-Nov-2 Christie's, Rockefeller NY #119/R est:5000-7000
£3224 $5029 €4836 Sur la Terre des Dieux - Amour est un Dieu mes enfants (65x50cm-26x20in) s.num.19/75 col lithograph 1967 lit. 6-Nov-2 AB Stockholms Auktionsverk #979/R est:50000-70000 (S.KR 46000)
£3226 $5000 €4839 La nymphe bleue (59x50cm-23x20in) s.num.5/50 col lithograph. 25-Sep-2 Christie's, Rockefeller NY #64/R est:2000-3000
£3247 $5000 €4871 David and Bathsheba (36x25cm-14x10in) s. num.65/75 col lithograph prov. 24-Oct-2 Shannon's, Milford #161/R est:4000-6000
£3270 $5200 €4905 Naomi and her daughters-in-law (36x27cm-14x11in) s.num.21/50 col lithograph. 1-May-3 Swann Galleries, New York #419/R est:4000-6000
£3300 $5117 €4950 L' arbre de Jesse (48x32cm-19x13in) s.num.88/90 col lithograph. 4-Dec-2 Bonhams, New Bond Street #166/R est:2000-3000
£3422 $5407 €5133 La joie de vivre (36x56cm-14x22in) s.num.3/50 col lithograph. 28-Apr-3 Bukowskis, Stockholm #372/R est:40000-50000 (S.KR 45000)
£3440 $5504 €4988 Sirene et Poisson (73x53cm-29x21in) s.i. col. lithograph. 18-May-3 Anders Antik, Landskrona #102 est:40000 (S.KR 44000)
£3459 $5500 €5189 Le concert (39x56cm-15x22in) s.num.2/90 col lithograph. 2-May-3 Sotheby's, New York #96/R est:3500-4500
£3459 $5500 €5189 Nude with flowers (49x65cm-19x26in) s.num.9/30 lithograph. 2-May-3 Sotheby's, New York #107/R est:3000-5000
£3472 $5486 €5000 Assuerus chasse Vashti (52x38cm-20x15in) s.num.17/50 col lithograph. 26-Apr-3 Cornette de St.Cyr, Paris #20/R est:3000-4000
£3478 $5391 €5217 Bouquet a l'arc en ciel (54x43cm-21x17in) s. lithograph. 4-Dec-2 Koller, Zurich #331/R est:3800-5000 (S.FR 8000)
£3481 $5500 €5222 David's tower (34x25cm-13x10in) s.num.24/100 col lithograph. 22-Apr-3 Butterfields, San Francisco #2112/R est:6000-8000
£3500 $5425 €5250 Le profil et l'enfant rouge (47x32cm-19x13in) s.num.11/40 col lithograph. 3-Dec-2 Christie's, London #98/R est:2000-3000
£3525 $5500 €5288 Echo (64x42cm-25x17in) col lithograph edition of 250. 14-Oct-2 Butterfields, San Francisco #1095/R est:4000-6000
£3525 $5500 €5288 Interior (57x42cm-22x17in) s.num.37/50 col lithograph. 14-Oct-2 Butterfields, San Francisco #1102/R est:3000-5000
£3526 $5500 €5289 Chloe's judgement (42x64cm-17x25in) col lithograph edition of 250. 5-Nov-2 Christie's, Rockefeller NY #105/R est:3000-5000
£3526 $5500 €5289 Chloe's kiss (42x32cm-17x13in) col lithograph edition of 250. 5-Nov-2 Christie's, Rockefeller NY #106/R est:3000-5000
£3526 $5500 €5289 Bird chase (42x64cm-17x25in) col lithograph edition of 250. 5-Nov-2 Christie's, Rockefeller NY #110/R est:5000-8000
£3526 $5500 €5289 Circus with yellow clown (77x58cm-30x23in) s.num.57/150 col lithograph. 5-Nov-2 Christie's, Rockefeller NY #122/R est:5500-6500
£3526 $5465 €5500 Aleko (47x52cm-19x20in) s. aquatint etching. 7-Dec-2 Hauswedell & Nolte, Hamburg #584/R est:1200
£3597 $5754 €5216 Avenue de la Victoire a Nice (61x46cm-24x18in) s.num.70/150 col lithograph. 18-May-3 Anders Antik, Landskrona #138 est:40000 (S.KR 46000)
£3644 $5685 €5466 Les amoureux sous l'arbre (44x64cm-17x25in) s.num.12/50 col etching aquatint lit. 5-Nov-2 Bukowskis, Stockholm #515/R est:50000-60000 (S.KR 52000)
£3648 $5800 €5472 Acrobats at play (46x32cm-18x13in) s.num.9/40 col lithograph. 2-May-3 Sotheby's, New York #103/R est:4000-5000
£3718 $5763 €5800 Trick rider on horseback (33x25cm-13x10in) s. col lithograph. 4-Dec-2 Lempertz, Koln #600/R est:5000-6000
£3774 $6000 €5661 Night in Paris (33x28cm-13x11in) s.num.52/75 col lithograph. 2-May-3 Sotheby's, New York #94/R est:4500-5500
£3802 $6008 €5703 Trapeziste a l'oiseau (28x22cm-11x9in) s.num.28/75 col lithograph lit. 28-Apr-3 Bukowskis, Stockholm #373/R est:40000-45000 (S.KR 50000)
£3861 $6216 €5792 Aleko (47x52cm-19x20in) s.num.170/300 col etching aquatint. 7-May-3 AB Stockholms Auktionsverk #1181/R est:40000-50000 (S.KR 50000)
£3901 $6319 €5500 Notre Dame in grey (68x53cm-27x21in) s. lithograph. 24-May-3 Van Ham, Cologne #87/R est:3800
£3974 $6200 €5961 Adam et Eve et le fruit defendu (36x27cm-14x11in) s.i. col lithograph. 18-Sep-2 Swann Galleries, New York #80/R est:5000-8000
£4088 $6500 €6132 Port (117x91cm-46x36in) s.d.1966 col lithograph. 30-Apr-3 Doyle, New York #173/R est:5000-7000
£4114 $6500 €6171 Springtime on the meadow, from Daphnis and Chloe (39x64cm-15x25in) s.num.60/250 col lithograph. 22-Apr-3 Butterfields, San Francisco #2104/R est:5000-6000
£4194 $6626 €6500 Champs Elysees (71x47cm-28x19in) col lithograph exec.1954 lit. 19-Dec-2 Delvaux, Paris #1/R est:8000
£4200 $6510 €6300 Couple au panier de fruits (66x53cm-26x21in) s.num.12/50 col lithograph. 3-Dec-2 Christie's, London #100/R est:2000-3000
£4200 $6510 €6300 Mein leben, haus in Witesk (19x25cm-7x10in) s.num.25/110 etching drypoint. 5-Dec-2 Sotheby's, London #101/R est:2000-2500
£4205 $6559 €6308 Le jeu (65x47cm-26x19in) s.i. col lithograph lit. 5-Nov-2 Bukowskis, Stockholm #513/R est:60000-80000 (S.KR 60000)
£4225 $6803 €6000 Musique (30x23cm-12x9in) s.num.20/50 col.etching lit. 10-May-3 Bukowskis, Helsinki #322/R est:5500-6000
£4403 $7000 €6605 Little red horse (71x61cm-28x24in) s.d.1975 num.23/50 col lithograph. 30-Apr-3 Doyle, New York #174/R est:2500-3500
£4430 $7000 €6645 Anemones (54x41cm-21x16in) s.num.3/4 col lithograph. 22-Apr-3 Butterfields, San Francisco #2111/R est:6000-8000
£4487 $7000 €6731 Daphnis and Gnathon (42x32cm-17x13in) col lithograph edition of 250. 5-Nov-2 Christie's, Rockefeller NY #117/R est:4000-6000
£4551 $7100 €6827 Daphnis and Chloe, Pans banquet (42x32cm-17x13in) s.num.55/60 col lithograph. 20-Sep-2 Sloan, North Bethesda #294/R est:1500-2500
£4577 $7599 €6500 Offrande de fleurs (62x47cm-24x19in) s.i. col lithograph. 14-Jun-3 Hauswedell & Nolte, Hamburg #1081/R est:6000
£4648 $7715 €6600 Les Champs Elysees (61x43cm-24x17in) s. col lithograph. 14-Jun-3 Hauswedell & Nolte, Hamburg #1082/R est:4000

£4655 $7541 €6750 Le Printemps (76x56cm-30x22in) s.num.14/75 col lithograph lit. 25-May-3 Uppsala Auktionskammare, Uppsala #338/R est:50000-70000 (S.KR 60000)
£4700 $7332 €7050 Le nuage aux amoureux (57x50cm-22x20in) s.num.35/50 etching aquatint. 25-Mar-3 Sotheby's, London #72/R est:4000-5000
£4717 $7500 €7076 Dorcon's strategy (42x32cm-17x13in) s.num.54/60 col lithograph. 1-May-3 Swann Galleries, New York #422/R est:10000-15000
£4800 $7920 €6960 Pierrot (61x44cm-24x17in) s.num.38/50 col etching aquatint. 1-Jul-3 Sotheby's, London #67/R est:2500-3500
£4808 $7500 €7212 Wedding feast in the nymphs' grotto (42x64cm-17x25in) col lithograph edition of 250. 5-Nov-2 Christie's, Rockefeller NY #118/R est:6000-8000
£4808 $7500 €7212 Joy of life (54x75cm-21x30in) s.num.VI/XV col lithograph. 5-Nov-2 Christie's, Rockefeller NY #123/R est:5000-7000
£4808 $7500 €7212 Selbstbildnis mit lachendem Gesicht (28x22cm-11x9in) s.i.num.85/100 etching drypoint. 7-Nov-2 Swann Galleries, New York #576/R est:10000-15000
£4808 $7500 €7212 Dorcon's strategy (43x32cm-17x13in) s.num.39/60 col lithograph. 7-Nov-2 Swann Galleries, New York #590/R est:10000-15000
£4867 $7690 €7301 Le cecle rouge (49x63cm-19x25in) s.num.29/50 col lithograph. 28-Apr-3 Bukowskis, Stockholm #371/R est:60000-80000 (S.KR 64000)
£4965 $8043 €7000 L'atelier a Saint-Paul (54x76cm-21x30in) s. num.40/50 col lithograph lit. 23-May-3 Camard, Paris #128/R est:7500-8500
£5031 $8000 €7547 Young girl with bouquet (32x24cm-13x9in) s.num.X/XXV col lithograph. 29-Apr-3 Christie's, Rockefeller NY #459/R est:4000-6000
£5031 $8000 €7547 Adam and Eve and the forbidden fruit (36x27cm-14x11in) s.num.8/50 col lithograph. 1-May-3 Swann Galleries, New York #418/R est:5000-8000
£5031 $8000 €7547 Couple a l'eventail (64x45cm-25x18in) s.num.4/50 col lithograph. 1-May-3 Swann Galleries, New York #423/R est:12000-18000
£5128 $8000 €7692 Young Methymneans. Chloe is dressed and braided by Cleariste (42x32cm-17x13in) col lithograph edition of 250 pair. 5-Nov-2 Christie's, Rockefeller NY #109/R est:5000-7000
£5128 $8000 €7692 Woman by a window (76x56cm-30x22in) s.num.XIII/XXV col lithograph. 5-Nov-2 Christie's, Rockefeller NY #121/R est:8000-10000
£5128 $7949 €8000 Clown a la chevre jaune (67x52cm-26x20in) s.i. num.29/50 col lithograph. 7-Dec-2 Ketterer, Hamburg #340/R est:12000-14000
£5200 $8112 €7800 Autoportrait (59x45cm-23x18in) s.num.40/50 col lithograph. 10-Oct-2 Sotheby's, London #19/R est:5000-7000
£5323 $8411 €7985 Offrande a la Tour Eiffel (65x49cm-26x19in) s.num.39/50 col lithograph. 28-Apr-3 Bukowskis, Stockholm #369/R est:60000-80000 (S.KR 70000)
£5346 $8500 €8019 Recollection of a spring (50x33cm-20x13in) s.i. col lithograph. 29-Apr-3 Christie's, Rockefeller NY #466/R est:6000-8000
£5385 $8400 €8078 Daphnis and Chloe, arrival of Dionysophanes (42x32cm-17x13in) s.num.40/60 col lithograph. 20-Sep-2 Sloan, North Bethesda #297/R est:6000-8000
£5449 $8500 €8174 Wine harvest (54x38cm-21x15in) col lithograph. 5-Nov-2 Christie's, Rockefeller NY #108/R est:7000-10000
£5449 $8500 €8174 Light of the circus (51x67cm-20x26in) s.i. col lithograph edition of 50. 5-Nov-2 Christie's, Rockefeller NY #126/R est:5000-7000
£5660 $9000 €8490 Circus performer with a fan (42x32cm-17x13in) col lithograph. 1-May-3 Swann Galleries, New York #424/R est:8000-12000
£5755 $9439 €8000 Le bouquet (64x50cm-25x20in) s.i. col lithograph. 6-Jun-3 Ketterer, Munich #125/R est:7500-8500
£5786 $9026 €9200 La poetesse (44x34cm-17x13in) s. num.19/50 col lithograph. 11-Oct-2 Winterberg, Heidelberg #942/R est:11500
£5797 $9507 €8000 Bonjour sur Paris (41x53cm-16x21in) s.i. col lithograph. 31-May-3 Villa Grisebach, Berlin #314/R est:9000-12000
£6026 $9400 €9039 Le cirque (42x32cm-17x13in) s.num.22/24 lithograph. 20-Sep-2 Sloan, North Bethesda #295/R est:7000-9000
£6090 $9500 €9135 Dorcon's strategy (54x38cm-21x15in) s.num.14/60 col lithograph. 5-Nov-2 Christie's, Rockefeller NY #107/R est:8000-10000
£6178 $9946 €9267 Couple a l'Eventail (64x44cm-25x17in) s.i. col. lithograph lit. 7-May-3 AB Stockholms Auktionsverk #1175/R est:80000-100000 (S.KR 80000)
£6329 $10000 €9494 Intimacy (76x51cm-30x20in) s.num.35/50 col lithograph. 22-Apr-3 Butterfields, San Francisco #2108/R est:12000-15000
£6475 $10619 €9000 Le ciel bleu (67x52cm-26x20in) s.i. col lithograph. 6-Jun-3 Ketterer, Munich #124/R est:8500-9500
£6918 $11000 €10377 When Abdullah got the net ashore (37x29cm-15x11in) s.i.num.6/90 col lithograph. 29-Apr-3 Christie's, Rockefeller NY #457/R est:8000-12000
£6918 $11000 €10377 Light of the circus (40x55cm-16x22in) s.num.44/50 col lithograph. 29-Apr-3 Christie's, Rockefeller NY #460/R est:7000-9000
£7051 $11000 €10577 So I cam forth out of the sea (43x33cm-17x13in) s.num.89/90 col lithograph. 14-Oct-2 Butterfields, San Francisco #1090/R est:10000-15000
£7200 $11880 €10440 Circus girl rider (63x50cm-25x20in) s.num.41/50 col lithograph. 1-Jul-3 Sotheby's, London #69/R est:4000-5000
£7692 $11923 €12000 Creation (116x75cm-46x30in) s. num.4/50 lithograph exec.1980 lit. 7-Dec-2 Cornette de St.Cyr, Paris #12/R est:12000-15000
£7692 $11923 €12000 Paysage bleu (50x66cm-20x26in) s. col lithograph. 4-Dec-2 Lempertz, Koln #603/R est:15000
£7708 $12025 €11562 Daphnis et Gnathon (42x32cm-17x13in) s.num.41/60 col lithograph 1961 lit. 6-Nov-2 AB Stockholms Auktionsverk #980/R est:100000-120000 (S.KR 110000)
£7975 $13000 €11963 Then he spent the night with her embracing and clipping (36x28cm-14x11in) s.i. num.50/90 col lithograph. 13-Feb-3 Christie's, Rockefeller NY #32/R
£8000 $12480 €12000 Painter's bouquet (75x57cm-30x22in) s.num.36/75 col lithograph. 25-Mar-3 Sotheby's, London #74/R est:10000-12000
£8333 $13000 €12500 L'arc-en-ciel (70x70cm-28x28in) s.num.72/75 col lithograph. 7-Nov-2 Swann Galleries, New York #599/R est:15000-20000
£8491 $13160 €13500 Les amoureux de la Tour Eiffel (65x49cm-26x19in) s.num.20/50 col lithograph. 30-Oct-2 Artcurial Briest, Paris #506/R est:11000-12000
£8494 $13676 €12741 Le bouquet rouge et jaune (64x48cm-25x19in) s.num.15/50 col lithograph lit. 7-May-3 AB Stockholms Auktionsverk #1180/R est:100000-150000 (S.KR 110000)
£8500 $13175 €12750 Autoportrait (59x45cm-23x18in) s.num.40/50 col lithograph. 5-Dec-2 Sotheby's, London #116/R est:10000-12000
£8500 $14025 €12325 Les deux rives (94x60cm-37x24in) s.num.7/50 col lithograph. 2-Jul-3 Christie's, London #237/R est:10000-15000
£8500 $14025 €12325 Les lilas (93x60cm-37x24in) s.num.15/50 col lithograph. 2-Jul-3 Christie's, London #238/R est:10000-15000
£8500 $14025 €12325 La parade (96x62cm-38x24in) s.num.15/50 col lithograph. 2-Jul-3 Christie's, London #241/R est:10000-15000
£8734 $13712 €13101 Les lilas (116x75cm-46x30in) s. col lithograph lit. 25-Nov-2 Germann, Zurich #271/R est:15000-20000 (S.FR 20000)
£8734 $13712 €13101 Les amoureux a l'Isba (75x116cm-30x46in) s. col lithograph lit. 25-Nov-2 Germann, Zurich #272/R est:20000-25000 (S.FR 20000)
£8805 $14000 €13208 Arc de Triomphe (80x56cm-31x22in) s.num.35/50 col lithograph. 29-Apr-3 Christie's, Rockefeller NY #463/R est:6000-8000
£8805 $14000 €13208 Blue bouquet (76x60cm-30x24in) s.num.24/50 col lithograph. 2-May-3 Sotheby's, New York #111/R est:18000-24000
£8974 $14000 €13461 Daphnis and Chloe, noon in summer (42x32cm-17x13in) s.num.22/60 col lithograph. 20-Sep-2 Sloan, North Bethesda #298/R est:3000-5000
£8974 $14000 €13461 Les amoureux a l'Isba (76x117cm-30x46in) s.num.19/50 col lithograph. 7-Nov-2 Swann Galleries, New York #606/R est:12000-18000
£8974 $13910 €14000 Paysage bleu (50x66cm-20x26in) s.i. num.59/90 col lithograph. 7-Dec-2 Ketterer, Hamburg #339/R est:15000-20000
£9110 $14212 €13665 Le printemps - Daphnis et Chloe (42x65cm-17x26in) s.num.30/60 col lithograph lit. 5-Nov-2 Bukowskis, Stockholm #510/R est:140000-160000 (S.KR 130000)
£9202 $15000 €13803 Angel violinist (494x403cm-194x159in) s. num.I/XII col lithograph exec.1974. 13-Feb-3 Christie's, Rockefeller NY #44/R est:12000
£9434 $15000 €14151 Banquet de pan (42x32cm-17x13in) s.num.55/60 col lithograph. 3-Mar-3 Swann Galleries, New York #87/R est:12000-18000
£9460 $14758 €14190 Festin nuptial dans la grotte des nymphes (42x64cm-17x25in) s.num.30/60 col lithograph lit. 5-Nov-2 Bukowskis, Stockholm #511/R est:140000-160000 (S.KR 135000)
£9615 $15000 €14423 Daphnis and Chloe, Megacles recongnizes his dauhter during the feast (42x64cm-17x25in) s.num.35/60 col lithograph. 20-Sep-2 Sloan, North Bethesda #296/R est:5000-7000
£9615 $15000 €14423 Les deux rives (94x60cm-37x24in) s.num.27/50 col lithograph. 7-Nov-2 Swann Galleries, New York #603/R est:20000-30000
£10000 $16500 €14500 L'envolee magique (95x60cm-37x24in) s.num.17/50 col lithograph. 2-Jul-3 Christie's, London #61/R est:8000-12000
£10000 $16500 €14500 Le couple au crepuscule (95x61cm-37x24in) s.num.5/50 col lithograph. 2-Jul-3 Christie's, London #235/R est:12000-18000
£10063 $16000 €15095 Louis Aragon, celui qui dit les choses sans rien dire (48x36cm-19x14in) col etching aquatint set of 25 portfolio box. 29-Apr-3 Christie's, Rockefeller NY #462/R est:18000-22000
£10563 $17535 €15000 Decouverte de Daphnis par Lamon. s. col lithograph. 14-Jun-3 Hauswedell & Nolte, Hamburg #1080/R est:5000
£10692 $17000 €16038 Rose bouquet (67x60cm-26x24in) s.num.13/50 col lithograph. 29-Apr-3 Christie's, Rockefeller NY #464/R est:12000-18000
£10870 $17826 €15000 Quai des Celestins (62x47cm-24x19in) s. col lithograph. 31-May-3 Villa Grisebach, Berlin #312/R est:7000-9000

£10897 $17000 €16346 Daphne discovers Chloe (54x38cm-21x15in) s.num.59/60 col lithograph. 14-Oct-2 Butterfields, San Francisco #1092/R est:10000-15000
£10897 $17000 €16346 Circus with an angel (60x49cm-24x19in) s.num.12/50 col lithograph. 7-Nov-2 Swann Galleries, New York #598/R est:18000-22000
£11000 $17160 €16500 Arabian nights, then he spent the night with her embracing and clipping (43x33cm-17x13in) s.i.num.57/90 lithograph. 10-Oct-2 Sotheby's, London #18/R est:12000-14000
£11212 $17491 €16818 Bouquet de la Tour Eiffel (46x61cm-18x24in) s.num.83/90 col lithograph 1958 lit. 6-Nov-2 AB Stockholms Auktionsverk #978/R est:180000-200000 (S.KR 160000)
£11321 $18000 €16982 Le corsage violet (63x45cm-25x18in) s.num.47/50 col lithograph. 1-May-3 Swann Galleries, New York #425/R est:20000-30000
£11538 $18000 €17307 Bible (46x35cm-18x14in) etchings edition of 275 collection of 31. 7-Nov-2 Swann Galleries, New York #577/R est:14000-16000
£12000 $19800 €17400 Aurore a Saint Paul (57x38cm-22x15in) s.num.24/75 col lithograph. 2-Jul-3 Christie's, London #233/R est:8000-12000
£12025 $19000 €18038 Blue bouquet (62x48cm-24x19in) s.num.23/50 col lithograph. 22-Apr-3 Butterfields, San Francisco #2109/R est:10000-12000
£12025 $19000 €18038 Red acrobat (81x62cm-32x24in) s.num.48/50 col lithograph. 22-Apr-3 Butterfields, San Francisco #2110/R est:12000-15000
£12263 $19131 €18395 Maternite rouge (94x60cm-37x24in) s.num.18/50 col lithograph lit. 5-Nov-2 Bukowskis, Stockholm #517/R est:200000-300000 (S.KR 175000)
£12614 $19678 €18921 Quai de la Tournelle - Regards sur Paris (39x60cm-15x24in) s.i. col lithograph lit. 5-Nov-2 Bukowskis, Stockholm #512/R est:200000-300000 (S.KR 180000)
£12821 $19872 €20000 Deux rives (116x75cm-46x30in) s. num.4/50 col lithograph exec.1980 lit. 7-Dec-2 Cornette de St.Cyr, Paris #14/R est:20000-22000
£12821 $19872 €20000 Clowns magiciens (116x75cm-46x30in) s. num.4/50 col lithograph exec.1980 lit. 7-Dec-2 Cornette de St.Cyr, Paris #13/R est:20000-22000
£12821 $20000 €19232 Magician of Paris (90x62cm-35x24in) s.i. col lithograph. 7-Nov-2 Swann Galleries, New York #600/R est:18000-22000
£13000 $21450 €18850 Les clowns musiciens (96x60cm-38x24in) s.num.7/50 col lithograph. 2-Jul-3 Christie's, London #240/R est:10000-15000
£13291 $21000 €21000 La Bastille (51x66cm-20x26in) s. col lithograph. 30-Nov-2 Villa Grisebach, Berlin #385/R est:7000-9000
£14103 $21859 €22000 Couple au crepuscule (116x75cm-46x30in) s num.4/50 col lithograph exec.1980 lit. 7-Dec-2 Cornette de St.Cyr, Paris #17/R est:20000-25000
£14423 $22356 €22500 Lilas (116x75cm-46x30in) s. num.4/50 col lithograph exec.1980 lit. 7-Dec-2 Cornette de St.Cyr, Paris #16/R est:20000-22000
£15094 $24000 €22641 Magician of Paris II (91x67cm-36x26in) s.i. col lithograph. 29-Apr-3 Christie's, Rockefeller NY #461/R est:15000-20000
£15209 $24030 €22814 Les quinze dernieres lithographs de Marc Chagall 1984-1985 (90x61cm-35x24in) st.sig.num.12/50 portfolio of 15 col lithographs lit. 28-Apr-3 Bukowskis, Stockholm #378a/R est:150000-200000 (S.KR 200000)
£15217 $24957 €21000 La Bastille (51x66cm-20x26in) s. col lithograph. 31-May-3 Villa Grisebach, Berlin #311/R est:14000-18000
£15596 $26046 €22614 Nu a l'eventail (21x28cm-8x11in) s.i. etching drypoint W/C. 20-Jun-3 Kornfeld, Bern #17/R est:25000 (S.FR 34000)
£16000 $26400 €23200 La joie (95x60cm-37x24in) s.num.21/50 col lithograph. 2-Jul-3 Christie's, London #60/R est:10000-15000
£16055 $26812 €23280 Homere. L'Odyssee (45x35cm-18x14in) s. lithograph two. 20-Jun-3 Kornfeld, Bern #23/R est:40000 (S.FR 35000)
£16352 $26000 €24528 Red maternity (94x60cm-37x24in) s.num.13/50 col lithograph. 29-Apr-3 Christie's, Rockefeller NY #465/R est:20000-30000
£17431 $29110 €25275 Le violoniste (21x16cm-8x6in) s. etching W/C. 20-Jun-3 Kornfeld, Bern #16/R est:25000 (S.FR 38000)
£17490 $27635 €26235 From - Four tales from the Arabian Nights, plate 13 (37x28cm-15x11in) s.num.IV/10 col lithograph. 28-Apr-3 Bukowskis, Stockholm #365/R est:140000-160000 (S.KR 230000)
£18000 $29700 €26100 Dans le ciel de l'opera (96x61cm-38x24in) s.num.5/50 col lithograph. 2-Jul-3 Christie's, London #236 est:12000-18000
£18239 $29000 €27359 Story of the Exodus. s.num.12 col lithograph text 24 portfolio box. 2-May-3 Sotheby's, New York #108/R est:30000-40000
£19000 $31350 €27550 La joie (94x62cm-37x24in) s.num.5/50 col lithograph. 2-Jul-3 Christie's, London #239/R est:10000-15000
£20513 $32000 €30770 Orchard (54x75cm-21x30in) s.num.19/60 col lithograph. 5-Nov-2 Christie's, Rockefeller NY #116/R est:40000-60000
£24000 $37200 €36000 Bible (47x35cm-19x14in) etching album. 5-Dec-2 Sotheby's, London #110/R est:20000-25000
£26606 $44431 €38579 Musician (27x21cm-11x8in) s.i. etching bodycol W/C. 20-Jun-3 Kornfeld, Bern #15/R est:40000 (S.FR 58000)
£28846 $45000 €43269 Circus. col lithograph thirteen of 38 incomplete album. 14-Oct-2 Butterfields, San Francisco #1097/R est:35000-45000
£28846 $45000 €43269 Screen, paravent (193x188cm-76x74in) s.num.38/100 col lithographs four oak panel folding screen. 5-Nov-2 Christie's, Rockefeller NY #120/R est:40000-60000
£30000 $46500 €45000 De mauvais sujets (43x33cm-17x13in) etching aquatint set of ten. 5-Dec-2 Sotheby's, London #112/R est:25000-35000
£34591 $55000 €51887 Die erscheinung (37x27cm-15x11in) s. hand col etching aquatint edition of 4. 29-Apr-3 Christie's, Rockefeller NY #456/R est:40000-50000
£74074 $119259 €111111 Cirque. folio of 38 lithographs some col. 7-May-3 Dobiaschofsky, Bern #2129/R est:100000 (S.FR 160000)
£89744 $140000 €134616 March Chagall, Cirque, Paris, Teriade Editeur. col lithographs set of 23 black lithographs 15 portfolio. 5-Nov-2 Christie's, Rockefeller NY #125/R est:120000-150000
£240000 $372000 €360000 Four tales from the Arabian Nights (44x33cm-17x13in) i. col lithograph album of 13. 3-Dec-2 Christie's, London #101/R est:230000-250000

Works on paper

£1659 $2605 €2489 Homme au bouquet de fleurs (27x21cm-11x8in) s. pastel Indian ink on letter. 25-Nov-2 Germann, Zurich #5/R est:4000-5000 (S.FR 3800)
£2436 $3776 €3800 L'ange au violin (38x25cm-15x10in) s. Indian ink brush col chk. 4-Dec-2 Lempertz, Koln #594/R est:5000-7000
£4808 $7500 €7212 Moses receiving the Tables of the Law (32x25cm-13x10in) s.i.d. col crayon. 18-Sep-2 Swann Galleries, New York #98/R est:4000-6000
£5097 $8053 €7900 Vase de fleurs et palette (29x21cm-11x8in) s. W/C dr. 18-Dec-2 Digard, Paris #109/R
£6730 $10431 €10700 Le peintre tour-eiffel au chevalet (28x22cm-11x9in) s. Indian ink wash pastel pencil exec.c.1980-82. 30-Oct-2 Artcurial Briest, Paris #9/R est:8000-10000
£7192 $11291 €10500 Profil de femme avec fleurs (29x30cm-11x12in) s.i.d. Indian ink col crayon prov. 21-Apr-3 Rabourdin & Choppin de Janvry, Paris #96/R est:12000-14000
£9679 $14713 €15100 New York, bouquet de fleurs (27x19cm-11x7in) s.i. W/C exec.1967. 16-Aug-2 Deauville, France #60/R est:15000
£11000 $16940 €16500 Autoportrait au chevalet (18x22cm-7x9in) s.d.1966 col crayon prov. 22-Oct-2 Sotheby's, London #234/R est:12000-15000
£15172 $23972 €22000 Bouquet (27x20cm-11x8in) s. i. verso pastel biro. 2-Apr-3 Dr Fritz Nagel, Stuttgart #9322/R est:35000
£15652 $24261 €23478 David et Bethsabee (27x22cm-11x9in) s. pastel chk ink pencil prov. 4-Dec-2 Koller, Zurich #122/R est:33000-38000 (S.FR 36000)
£16000 $26240 €24000 Esquisse pour jeune fille a cheval (13x18cm-5x7in) s. gouache W/C pencil exec.c.1929. 6-Feb-3 Christie's, London #435/R est:24000
£18000 $29520 €27000 Scene de ferme (18x27cm-7x11in) s.i. sanguine exec.c.1925 prov. 6-Feb-3 Christie's, London #453/R
£18310 $30394 €26000 Les profils (41x33cm-16x13in) s.i. col chk. 14-Jun-3 Hauswedell & Nolte, Hamburg #1070/R est:30000
£19000 $31160 €28500 Moise recevant les Tables de la Loi (37x29cm-15x11in) s. gouache ink brush wash exec.c.1955. 6-Feb-3 Christie's, London #480/R est:15000
£20183 $33706 €29265 Ruth aux pieds de Booz (33x26cm-13x10in) s. W/C Indian ink. 20-Jun-3 Kornfeld, Bern #18/R est:30000 (S.FR 44000)
£24000 $39360 €36000 Rayon de soleil (40x30cm-16x12in) s. gouache ink pencil exec.1937 prov. 6-Feb-3 Christie's, London #479/R est:15000
£25000 $41750 €37500 La visite de l'ange (43x66cm-17x26in) s. pastel col.crayons pen exec c.1969. 26-Jun-3 Christie's, London #416/R est:20000-30000
£25000 $41750 €36250 Le berger (67x51cm-26x20in) s.d.1959 gouache over red crayon exhib. 24-Jun-3 Sotheby's, London #270/R est:25000-35000
£26451 $41793 €41000 Chant de l'espoir (35x27cm-14x11in) s.i.d.1947 ink W/C prov. 18-Dec-2 Tajan, Paris #64/R est:22000
£34000 $56780 €49300 Le voile (77x56cm-30x22in) s. brush ink wash gouache executed 1964 prov.exhib. 24-Jun-3 Sotheby's, London #289/R est:35000-45000
£35000 $57400 €52500 Joueurs de cartes (48x64cm-19x25in) s. W/C wash ink brush exec.c.1925 prov. 6-Feb-3 Christie's, London #452/R est:60000
£38462 $60000 €57693 Les amoureux (41x29cm-16x11in) s. crayon col pencil prov.exhib. 6-Nov-2 Sotheby's, New York #222/R est:60000-80000
£42000 $70140 €63000 Le Christ en croix (65x50cm-26x20in) s. gouache indian ink pastel crayon exec c.1954-60 prov.exhib. 26-Jun-3 Christie's, London #403/R est:50000-70000
£44872 $70000 €67308 Bucolique (76x56cm-30x22in) s. pen ink wash W/C. 6-Nov-2 Sotheby's, New York #259/R est:80000-120000
£45000 $73800 €67500 Nu (30x24cm-12x9in) s.i. gouache W/C exec.c.1912-13 prov. 6-Feb-3 Christie's, London #437/R est:65000
£50000 $83500 €75000 Le musicien et les maries (38x28cm-15x11in) s.i.d.1975 W/C indian ink col.crayon. 26-Jun-3 Christie's, London #394/R est:55000-75000
£52174 $80870 €78261 Au bord de la Mediterranee (28x24cm-11x9in) s. mixed media exec.1949 prov.exhib. 4-Dec-2 Koller, Zurich #45/R est:120000-160000 (S.FR 120000)

£55000 $91850 €82500 Acrobates au cheval (68x53cm-27x21in) s. gouache pastel exec 1958 exhib. 26-Jun-3 Christie's, London #393/R est:40000-60000
£61728 $100000 €89506 Peintre et le Christ (56x46cm-22x18in) s. gouache chl col chk laid paper c.1938-40 prov.lit. 21-May-3 Doyle, New York #46/R est:140000-180000
£62000 $101680 €93000 Ecuyere a la jupe fleurie (35x35cm-14x14in) s. gouache India ink col crayon exec.1976 prov. 6-Feb-3 Christie's, London #475/R est:60000
£65385 $103308 €102000 Vase de fleurs (54x49cm-21x19in) s. mixed media board. 14-Nov-2 Neumeister, Munich #527/R est:140000-150000
£70000 $116900 €105000 Fleurs et fruits (65x50cm-26x20in) W/C crayon wash pen ink pencil. 26-Jun-3 Christie's, London #392/R est:60000-80000
£72000 $118080 €108000 Aubade (64x50cm-25x20in) s. gouache pastel col crayon pen ink prov. 6-Feb-3 Christie's, London #493/R est:100000
£74534 $120000 €111801 Composition avec fleurs (50x40cm-20x16in) s.d.1971 s.d.verso W/C gouache col wax crayon prov.exhib. 8-May-3 Christie's, Rockefeller NY #131/R est:120000-160000
£83333 $129167 €130000 REncontre avec le nu (67x49cm-26x19in) s. W/C col crayon pastel exec.c.1980. 7-Dec-2 Cornette de St.Cyr, Paris #44/R est:130000-180000
£90000 $150300 €130500 Les fiances devant l'isba (66x51cm-26x20in) s. W/C gouache pen ink executed 1925-26 prov. 24-Jun-3 Sotheby's, London #236/R est:120000-150000
£92949 $145000 €139424 Maternite Mexicaine (67x50cm-26x20in) s. gouache W/C brush India ink executed c.1943 prov. 6-Nov-2 Sotheby's, New York #271/R est:160000-220000
£95000 $146300 €142500 Le bouquet sur le toit (50x32cm-20x13in) s. brush ink pastel oil gouache executed 1968 prov.exhib. 22-Oct-2 Sotheby's, London #231/R est:90000-120000
£95000 $155800 €142500 Peintre et oiseau (58x50cm-23x20in) s. gouache pastel col crayon exec.1973 prov. 6-Feb-3 Christie's, London #474/R est:150000
£98000 $160720 €147000 Amoureux a Paris (68x53cm-27x21in) s.d.1959 gouache W/C prov. 6-Feb-3 Christie's, London #496/R est:150000
£108974 $170000 €163461 Composition aux deux bouquets (65x50cm-26x20in) s.d.1958-59 gouache W/C pastel col wax crayon brush pen prov. 7-Nov-2 Christie's, Rockefeller NY #140/R est:150000-200000
£121118 $195000 €181677 Place de la concorde ou Tour Eiffel, bouquet de fleurs et amants (52x34cm-20x13in) s. W/C gouache pastel executed 1969 prov.exhib. 8-May-3 Christie's, Rockefeller NY #136/R est:100000-150000
£140000 $233800 €210000 Les promis au soleil jaune (90x62cm-35x24in) s. gouache W/C col.crayons pastel india ink pencil exec 1971 prov. 26-Jun-3 Christie's, London #434/R est:140000-150000
£142202 $237477 €206193 Le traineau sur Sils Maria (65x50cm-26x20in) s. s.i. verso W/C bodycol pencil prov.lit. 20-Jun-3 Kornfeld, Bern #19/R est:300000 (S.FR 310000)
£185000 $308950 €277500 Le cavalier violet (91x62cm-36x24in) s. W/C gouache pastel crayon india ink pencil prov.exhib. 26-Jun-3 Christie's, London #417/R est:160000-220000

CHAGALL, Marc (after) (1887-1985) French/Russian
Prints
£2821 $4400 €4232 Jerusalem windows, the Tribe of Zabulon (63x47cm-25x19in) s.num.87/150 col lithograph. 7-Nov-2 Swann Galleries, New York #609/R est:5000-8000
£3270 $5200 €4905 Jerusalem windows (62x46cm-24x18in) s.num.43/150 col lithograph. 1-May-3 Swann Galleries, New York #427/R est:5000-8000
£3462 $5400 €5193 Bouquet (64x50cm-25x20in) s.num.225/300 col lithograph. 19-Sep-2 Swann Galleries, New York #243/R est:4000-6000
£4200 $6510 €6300 L'oiseau bleu (71x52cm-28x20in) s.i. col lithograph. 3-Dec-2 Christie's, London #102/R est:4000-6000
£4487 $7000 €6731 Femme au bouquet (63x47cm-25x19in) s.num.147/150 col lithograph. 7-Nov-2 Swann Galleries, New York #611/R est:8000-12000
£4516 $7000 €6774 Tribe of Gad (61x46cm-24x18in) s.num.145/150 col lithograph. 25-Sep-2 Christie's, Rockefeller NY #71/R est:4000-6000
£4717 $7500 €7076 Bouquet (64x50cm-25x20in) s.num.225/300 col lithograph. 4-Mar-3 Swann Galleries, New York #215/R est:3000-5000
£4808 $7500 €7212 Sirene with pine (74x53cm-29x21in) s.num.XXIX/LXXV col lithograph. 5-Nov-2 Christie's, Rockefeller NY #135/R est:7000-9000
£5031 $8000 €7547 Sierene au poete (62x46cm-24x18in) s.num.33/150 col lithograph. 1-May-3 Swann Galleries, New York #429/R est:8000-12000
£5606 $8746 €8409 Le Cantique des Cantiques (52x43cm-20x17in) s.num.71/200 col lithograph 1975 lit. 6-Nov-2 AB Stockholms Auktionsverk #986/R est:40000-50000 (S.KR 80000)
£5627 $8891 €8441 Aleco (47x52cm-19x20in) s.num.166/300 col aquatint executed c.1950 lit.prov. 28-Apr-3 Bukowskis, Stockholm #381/R est:50000-60000 (S.KR 74000)
£6410 $10000 €9615 Couple in mimosa (62x46cm-24x18in) s.i. col lithograph. 18-Sep-2 Swann Galleries, New York #93/R est:8000-12000
£6410 $10000 €9615 Avenue de la Victoire at Nice (74x53cm-29x21in) s.num.113/150 col lithograph. 5 Nov-2 Christie's, Rockefeller NY #134/R est:10000-12000
£6410 $10000 €9615 Fiances in the sky at Nice (75x53cm-30x21in) s.num.55/450 col lithograph. 5-Nov-2 Christie's, Rockefeller NY #136/R est:8000-10000
£7051 $11000 €10577 Carnival of flowers (63x45cm-25x18in) s.i. col lithograph. 18-Sep-2 Swann Galleries, New York #94/R est:12000-16000

CHAIGNEAU, J F (1830-1906) French
£1197 $1927 €1700 Landscape with two women minding cattle (22x44cm-9x17in) s.d. 10-May-3 Berlinghof, Heidelberg #202/R est:1500

CHAIGNEAU, Jean Ferdinand (1830-1906) French
£10127 $16000 €15191 Shepherd (58x81cm-23x32in) s.d.1880. 24-Apr-3 Sotheby's, New York #99/R est:15000-20000

CHAIGNEAU, Paul (20th C) French
£894 $1404 €1341 Soleil couchant (21x27cm-8x11in) s. panel or possibly by Jean F Chaigneau. 12-Dec-2 Iegor de Saint Hippolyte, Montreal #18 (C.D 2200)
£1831 $2948 €2600 Berger et troupeau de moutons sous un ciel orageux (21x26cm-8x10in) s. panel. 11-May-3 Lombrail & Teucquam, Paris #159/R
£2420 $3776 €3800 Berger et moutons au soleil couchant (22x27cm-9x11in) s. panel. 11-Nov-2 Horta, Bruxelles #653 est:2000-3000
£2532 $4000 €4000 Le troupeau (22x27cm-9x11in) s. panel. 1-Dec-2 Peron, Melun #177
£3354 $5300 €5300 Berger et ses moutons pres de Chailly (46x55cm-18x22in) s. 1-Dec-2 Peron, Melun #110

CHAILLOUX, Robert (1913-) French
£440 $682 €660 Still life of roses (38x30cm-15x12in) s. board. 3-Dec-2 Sotheby's, Olympia #205/R
£600 $954 €900 Still life with blue and white tureen, apples and nuts (28x36cm-11x14in) s. panel. 20-Mar-3 Ewbank, Send #405
£1230 $1894 €1845 Nature morte, tomats (44x53cm-17x21in) s. 22-Oct-2 Bonhams, Bath #26 est:400-600
£1350 $2079 €2025 Chardons bleus. Les olives (33x25cm-13x10in) s. board pair. 22-Oct-2 Bonhams, Bath #27 est:300-500

CHAISSAC, Gaston (1910-1964) French
£870 $1348 €1305 Untitled (21x10cm-8x4in) s. collage. 9-Dec-2 Philippe Schuler, Zurich #3412/R est:2000-3000 (S.FR 2000)
£3401 $5408 €5000 Untitled (33x17cm-13x7in) s. cardboard painted 1959. 24-Mar-3 Claude Boisgirard, Paris #96/R
£4430 $6911 €7000 Sans titre (36x50cm-14x20in) i. felt painted c.1962-63 prov. 20-Oct-2 Charbonneaux, Paris #110/R est:8000-10000
£16000 $24640 €24000 Personnage a la pipe (63x49cm-25x19in) s.d.Mars 1950 oil paper on canvas prov.exhib. 22-Oct-2 Sotheby's, London #421/R est:5000-7000

Works on paper
£962 $1490 €1500 Auto-portrait (11x7cm-4x3in) s. ink exec.1948. 7-Dec-2 Cornette de St.Cyr, Paris #38/R
£1056 $1754 €1500 Personaggi (41x27cm-16x11in) s. i.verso ink acrylic exhib. 10-Jun-3 Finarte Semenzato, Milan #222/R est:1800-2200
£1497 $2380 €2200 Composition (22x17cm-9x7in) s.i. felt exec.c.1963. 26-Feb-3 Artcurial Briest, Paris #432/R est:2000-3000
£2083 $3313 €3000 Tete-collage (27x18cm-11x7in) studio st.verso collage cardboard exec.c.1955-57. 29-Apr-3 Artcurial Briest, Paris #604/R est:3500-4000
£2174 $3565 €3000 Untitled - Mylene Demongeot (25x24cm-10x9in) s.d.1960 Indian ink brush over reproduction newspaper prov. 28-May-3 Lempertz, Koln #94/R est:5000
£2857 $4543 €4200 Composition (27x21cm-11x8in) s.d.12.10.52 Indian ink dr. 26-Feb-3 Artcurial Briest, Paris #434/R est:4000-5000
£2857 $4543 €4200 Composition au personnage (24x31cm-9x12in) s. Indian ink dr exec.c.1941 lit. 26-Feb-3 Artcurial Briest, Paris #437/R est:4000-5000
£3546 $5922 €5000 Sans titre (32x22cm-13x9in) s. collage Indian ink craft paper. 20-Jun-3 Piasa, Paris #218/R est:4000-6000
£3548 $5500 €5322 Composition (50x65cm-20x26in) s.d.61 gouache prov.exhib. 26-Sep-2 Christie's, Rockefeller NY #745/R est:7000-9000
£5000 $7700 €7500 Croix (63x47cm-25x19in) s. ink wallpaper on paper executed 1960 prov. 22-Oct-2 Sotheby's, London #413/R est:5000-7000

£6918 $10723 €11000 Sans titre (50x64cm-20x25in) s. gouache collage col felt exec.c.1962/63. 30-Oct-2 Artcurial Briest, Paris #419a/R est:12000-15000
£7200 $11088 €10800 Composition a deux personnages (50x64cm-20x25in) s.i.d.20.1.61 gouache ink prov.exhib. 22-Oct-2 Sotheby's, London #415/R est:7000-9000
£9000 $13860 €13500 Untitled (36x29cm-14x11in) i.d.24.8.62 gouache pastel paper collage on paper prov. 22-Oct-2 Sotheby's, London #427/R est:5000-7000
£9500 $14630 €14250 Personnage (58x41cm-23x16in) s. ink felt tip pen gouache wallpaper collage on board exec.1962. 22-Oct-2 Sotheby's, London #401/R est:8000-12000
£14500 $22330 €21750 Composition a un visage (64x90cm-25x35in) s. ink varnish wallpaper collage on paper executed 1961 prov. 22-Oct-2 Sotheby's, London #400/R est:10000-15000

CHAIX, Louis (18th C) French
Works on paper
£574 $896 €850 Portrait de jeune garcon (21x17cm-8x7in) crayon htd gouache exhib. 27-Mar-3 Maigret, Paris #141

CHAKLADHAR, Amol (1922-) Indian
£1000 $1560 €1500 Jungle of lotus (27x36cm-11x14in) s.d. tempera board. 17-Oct-2 Bonhams, Knightsbridge #608/R est:1000-1500

CHALEYE, Jean (1878-1960) French
£710 $1100 €1065 Les trois nus dans la prairie (46x56cm-18x22in) s.i.d.1932 board prov. 16-Jul-2 Arthur James, Florida #52
£745 $1200 €1118 Bouquet mystique (74x61cm-29x24in) s. i.d.1931 verso panel prov. 20-Jan-3 Arthur James, Florida #812

CHALGRIN, Jean François (1739-1811) French
Works on paper
£5247 $8500 €7871 View of classical ruin with figures in antique dress (55x90cm-22x35in) pen ink W/C prov. 21-Jan-3 Sotheby's, New York #189/R est:7000

CHALIAPINE, Fyodor (1873-1938) Russian
Works on paper
£2000 $3240 €3000 Self portraits (15x12cm-6x5in) s. pencil set of four. 21-May-3 Sotheby's, London #141/R est:2000-3000

CHALLE, Charles Michelange (1718-1778) French
Works on paper
£2848 $4500 €4500 Une femme nue etendue sur un lit (32x42cm-13x17in) col chk. 27-Nov-2 Christie's, Paris #170/R est:5000-7000

CHALLE, Charles Michelange (attrib) (1718-1778) French
Works on paper
£2244 $3522 €3500 Fantaisie architecturale (49x64cm-19x25in) pen ink wash. 13-Dec-2 Pierre Berge, Paris #31/R

CHALLE, Charles Michelange (circle) (1718-1778) French
£5674 $9475 €8000 Minerve apparaissant a un guerrier (105x132cm-41x52in) 18-Jun-3 Tajan, Paris #119/R est:5000-7000

CHALLE, Simon (1719-1765) French
Works on paper
£2778 $4500 €4167 Bacchante seated in the clouds (35x43cm-14x17in) chk. 21-Jan-3 Sotheby's, New York #116/R

CHALLENER, Frederick (1869-1959) Canadian
Works on paper
£378 $619 €567 Geraniums in a vase (17x22cm-7x9in) s.d.1889 W/C. 3-Jun-3 Joyner, Toronto #608 (C.D 850)

CHALLIE, Jean Laurent (1880-1943) French
£986 $1587 €1400 Embarcadere sur la riviere (64x80cm-25x31in) s. 11-May-3 Thierry & Lannon, Brest #339
£2500 $3975 €3750 Maternite (48x65cm-19x26in) s. 20-Mar-3 Sotheby's, Olympia #52/R est:3000-4000
£2817 $4676 €4000 Devant le fenetre (55x46cm-22x18in) s. 13-Jun-3 Rabourdin & Choppin de Janvry, Paris #158/R est:4000-4500

CHALMERS, C P (1890-?) ?
£318 $500 €477 Portrait of a boy playing a Jew's harp (41x30cm-16x12in) indis.sig. oil zinc. 28-Jul-2 Butterfields, San Francisco #3034

CHALMERS, George Paul (1833-1878) British
£320 $522 €480 Study of an old woman knitting (25x18cm-10x7in) 14-Feb-3 Lyon & Turnbull, Edinburgh #85
£420 $655 €630 Club sketch (29x22cm-11x9in) bears init.i. board prov. 17-Oct-2 Bonhams, Edinburgh #216
£880 $1461 €1276 Cottage interior (60x48cm-24x19in) 13-Jun-3 Lyon & Turnbull, Edinburgh #72
£1500 $2280 €2250 Anglers on a loch (61x107cm-24x42in) indis sig. 28-Aug-2 Sotheby's, London #888/R est:1500-2000

CHALMERS, Hector (c.1849-1943) British
£300 $474 €450 Children on a shore (32x46cm-13x18in) s. 27-Nov-2 Hamptons Fine Art, Godalming #351
£550 $858 €825 Sorting the catch (35x25cm-14x10in) s. 17-Sep-2 Sotheby's, Olympia #79/R
£750 $1170 €1125 Cottage door (51x41cm-20x16in) s.d.1877 prov. 17-Sep-2 Sotheby's, Olympia #7/R
£940 $1476 €1410 Chopping wood (24x35cm-9x14in) 17-Apr-3 Bonhams, Edinburgh #372

CHALMERS, John (19th C) British
£2600 $4342 €3770 Seaweed gatherers (66x99cm-26x39in) s.d.1874. 20-Jun-3 Keys, Aylsham #685/R est:2500-3500
Works on paper
£260 $408 €390 Fishing boats at dawn (41x56cm-16x22in) s. paper on canvas. 16-Dec-2 Sotheby's, Olympia #117/R
£311 $516 €451 Fishing boats with distant fleet (47x67cm-19x26in) s. W/C. 16-Jun-3 Waddingtons, Toronto #80/R (C.D 700)

CHALMERS, Victoria (1970-) British?
£1500 $2310 €2250 Untitled (152x140cm-60x55in) s.d.93 prov. 23-Oct-2 Christie's, London #232/R est:2000-3000

CHALON, Alfred Edward (1780-1860) British
£3800 $6118 €5700 Study for 'Autumn' (29x49cm-11x19in) s.d.1848 panel prov. 20-Feb-3 Christie's, London #73/R
Works on paper
£440 $678 €660 Portrait of a young lady with a toy cat (22x18cm-9x7in) s.d.1826 W/C. 22-Oct-2 Bonhams, Knightsbridge #175/R

CHALON, Alfred Edward (attrib) (1780-1860) British
Works on paper
£1300 $2119 €1885 Portrait of Miss Angerstein, riding side saddle on a pony (34x24cm-13x9in) W/C prov. 21-Jul-3 Sotheby's, London #134/R est:800-1200

CHALON, F (19th C) French?
£2500 $4175 €3625 Four seasons, landscapes (6x12cm-2x5in) three s.d.1820 oil on ivory set of four. 11-Jul-3 Christie's, Kensington #119/R est:2500-3500

CHALON, Henry Bernard (1770-1849) British
£2000 $3260 €2900 African antelope (49x60cm-19x24in) s. 21-Jul-3 Sotheby's, London #514/R est:3000-5000

CHALON, Louis (1866-?) French
£833 $1375 €1200 Le poete et sa muse (36x24cm-14x9in) s. panel. 2-Jul-3 Artcurial Briest, Paris #29/R
£1800 $2862 €2700 Une jeune femme deshabillant (41x27cm-16x11in) s. 20-Mar-3 Christie's, Kensington #122/R est:2000-3000
Sculpture
£2128 $3447 €3000 Valquiria (55cm-22in) s. bronze green marble base. 21-May-3 Segre, Madrid #706/R est:3000
£12448 $20787 €17800 La pieuvre (53cm-21in) s. gilt pat bronze. 25-Jun-3 Tajan, Paris #17/R est:10000-12000

CHALON, Maria A (1800-1867) British
Miniatures
£1300 $2028 €1950 Lady Susan Reeve (9cm-4in circular) gilt metal frame executed c.1845 oval. 8-Oct-2 Sotheby's, Olympia #445/R est:300-400
£2000 $3120 €3000 Colonel John Reeve and sister Emma both half length (11cm-4in circular) gilt metal frames executed c.1860 prov. pair. 8-Oct-2 Sotheby's, Olympia #447/R est:1000-1500

CHALON, T (?) French
£7800 $12090 €11700 Exotic interior with court dancers and fountain (97x119cm-38x47in) s. 18-Jul-2 Neales, Nottingham #704/R est:4000-6000

CHALOPIN, Albert (19/20th C) French
£596 $972 €900 Panier de pommes renverse (59x73cm-23x29in) panel. 13-Feb-3 Muizon & Le Coent, Paris #2

CHAMAILLARD, Ernest (1862-1930) French
£5449 $8554 €8500 Paysage breton (73x92cm-29x36in) s. i.verso. 10-Dec-2 Renaud, Paris #21/R
Works on paper
£387 $624 €550 Le Mont St Michel en Cornouaille (20x27cm-8x11in) s. W/C. 11-May-3 Thierry & Lannon, Brest #318
£458 $737 €650 Vitre en Bretagne (17x23cm-7x9in) s. W/C. 11-May-3 Thierry & Lannon, Brest #320

CHAMAROFF, Paul (20th C) French?
£6289 $9748 €10000 Baigneuse aux trois arbres (55x84cm-22x33in) s. 7-Oct-2 Claude Aguttes, Neuilly #290/R est:12200

CHAMBAS, Jean Paul (1947-) French
£545 $855 €850 Untitled (98x66cm-39x26in) s.d.87 oil mixed media paper. 15-Dec-2 Perrin, Versailles #168/R

CHAMBERLAIN, Brenda (1912-1971) British
£440 $686 €660 Seated woman (51x41cm-20x16in) s.indis.d.55. 23-Sep-2 Bonhams, Chester #1005
Works on paper
£540 $886 €810 Portrait study 'Peter Gimpel'. Study of two trout (25x33cm-10x13in) s.i. pen ink s.d.1950 W/C two. 4-Jun-3 Bonhams, Chester #303

CHAMBERLAIN, John (1927-) American
£2609 $4278 €3600 Maab No 360 (21x21cm-8x8in) s.i. verso exhib. 28-May-3 Lempertz, Koln #95/R est:3600
Sculpture
£7595 $12000 €11393 Untitled (20x25x25cm-8x10x10in) aluminum foil polyester resin paint executed 1974 prov.exhib. 13-Nov-2 Sotheby's, New York #291/R est:12000-18000
£9375 $15000 €14063 Untitled (13x15x14cm-5x6x6in) aluminum foil acrylic lacquer polyester resin executed 1973 prov. 14-May-3 Sotheby's, New York #223/R est:6000-8000
£16774 $26000 €25161 Untitled (91x144x84cm-36x57x33in) painted chromium plated steel executed 1971 prov. 26-Sep-2 Christie's, Rockefeller NY #763/R est:15000-20000
£81250 $130000 €121875 Bags down, bags down II (94x89x71cm-37x35x28in) painted chromium-plated steel prov.exhib.lit. 15-May-3 Christie's, Rockefeller NY #173/R est:100000-150000
£83333 $130000 €125000 Tippecanoe (101x106x91cm-40x42x36in) galvanized stainless steel executed 1967 prov.exhib.lit. 11-Nov-2 Phillips, New York #34/R est:80000-100000
£118750 $190000 €178125 Carmen Miranda's shoes (230cm-91in) chrome plated painted steel executed 1989 prov. 15-May-3 Phillips, New York #29/R est:150000-250000
£162500 $260000 €243750 White thumb four (182x286x81cm-72x113x32in) painted chromium-plated steel exec.1978 prov.exhib.lit. 13-May-3 Sotheby's, New York #9/R est:250000-350000
£177215 $280000 €265823 J.J.J.J. (129x127x122cm-51x50x48in) painted steel executed c.1963 prov.lit. 14-Nov-2 Christie's, Rockefeller NY #137/R est:100000-150000
£180000 $300600 €270000 Hollywood John (163x152x109cm-64x60x43in) painted chromium-plated steel exc.1962 prov.exhib.lit. 26-Jun-3 Christie's, London #4/R est:80000-120000
£250000 $400000 €375000 Sprayed myopia (221x145x127cm-87x57x50in) painted steel exec.1988 prov.exhib. 14-May-3 Christie's, Rockefeller NY #33/R est:120000-180000

CHAMBERLAIN, Trevor (1933-) British
£1500 $2430 €2250 Big top, Hertford (25x35cm-10x14in) s.d.87 sold with three others by same hand. 20-May-3 Sotheby's, Olympia #160/R est:500-700
Works on paper
£480 $763 €696 Beach scene (13x23cm-5x9in) s.d.77 W/C. 29-Apr-3 Gorringes, Lewes #2091

CHAMBERLAYNE, William John (1821-1910) British
Works on paper
£550 $869 €825 British Military station in the West Indies. Village by the sea (36x51cm-14x20in) s. W/C over pencil htd bodycol pair. 15-Nov-2 Sotheby's, London #80

CHAMBERLIN, Mason (elder) (1727-1787) British
£850 $1326 €1275 Portrait of William Elliott (76x64cm-30x25in) s.d.1778 prov. 8-Oct-2 Sotheby's, Olympia #383/R
£2000 $3160 €3000 Portrait of General Allanby, Governor of Santa Lucia (75x62cm-30x24in) 28-Nov-2 Sotheby's, London #169 est:2000-3000

CHAMBERLIN, William Benjamin (fl.1880-1895) British
Works on paper
£360 $598 €522 At Perugia, Italy (36x53cm-14x21in) s.d.84 W/C. 12-Jun-3 Gorringes, Lewes #1686

CHAMBERLIN, William Benjamin (attrib) (fl.1880-1895) British
£1050 $1733 €1523 Orford Castle, Suffolk (23x19cm-9x7in) init. pair. 1-Jul-3 Bonhams, Norwich #269/R est:700-900

CHAMBERS, Charles Edward (1883-1942) American
£932 $1500 €1398 Seated man seeking divine enlightenment (76x51cm-30x20in) en grisialle. 20-Feb-3 Illustration House, New York #23 est:2000-3000
£1763 $2750 €2645 Portrait of a lady, at rest with a parasol (84x33cm-33x13in) s. masonite. 14-Sep-2 Selkirks, St. Louis #121/R est:1000-1500

CHAMBERS, George (attrib) (19th C) British
£2500 $3900 €3750 Shipping off Portsmouth (76x122cm-30x48in) 9-Oct-2 Woolley & Wallis, Salisbury #222/R est:2500-3000

CHAMBERS, George (jnr) (fl.1848-1868) British
£650 $1021 €975 Off Greenwich (24x37cm-9x15in) s. s.i.verso. 16-Dec-2 Sotheby's, Olympia #24/R
£700 $1085 €1050 Shipping on the Thames before the Tower of London (29x45cm-11x18in) mono. board. 31-Oct-2 Christie's, Kensington #538/R
£2000 $3140 €3000 Shipping off a headland in heavy seas (30x43cm-12x17in) s. 16-Dec-2 Sotheby's, Olympia #23/R est:2000-3000
£3000 $4860 €4500 Guardship at the Nore (41x67cm-16x26in) indis i. verso. 22-Jan-3 Bonhams, New Bond Street #396/R est:3000-5000
£24000 $38880 €36000 Shipping off Greenwich (85x144cm-33x57in) s.d.67 prov. 22-Jan-3 Bonhams, New Bond Street #390/R est:10000-15000

CHAMBERS, George (jnr-attrib) (fl.1848-1868) British
£800 $1336 €1160 Fishing vessel at sea (31x44cm-12x17in) indis sig. 18-Jun-3 Sotheby's, Olympia #35/R

CHAMBERS, George (snr) (1803-1840) British
£250 $390 €375 Shipwreck on the coast (20x43cm-8x17in) s. 20-Sep-2 Richardson & Smith, Whitby #84
£3800 $6308 €5700 View of the Mansion House, London. View of the Royal Exchange, London (9x20cm-4x8in) board pair. 10-Jun-3 Christie's, London #78/R est:1500-2000
£4000 $6480 €6000 Trading brigs offshore (30x43cm-12x17in) s. panel. 21-May-3 Christie's, Kensington #590/R est:3000-5000
£5200 $8216 €7800 Fishing boats in a squall off a harbour (81x97cm-32x38in) s. 7-Apr-3 Bonhams, Bath #88/R est:3000-5000
£10000 $15700 €15000 Fresh breeze, Portsmouth (81x122cm-32x48in) i.on stretcher. 16-Dec-2 Sotheby's, Olympia #25/R est:10000-15000

CHAMBERS, George (19th C) British
£800 $1216 €1200 Two master in distress with ship coming up astern (21x28cm-8x11in) board. 15-Aug-2 Bonhams, New Bond Street #302/R

CHAMBERS, George W (19th C) American
£994 $1600 €1491 Pastoral landscape with two cows in a green pasture and barns in background (25x33cm-10x13in) panel. 22-Feb-3 Pook & Pook, Downington #172/R est:500-1000

CHAMBERS, John (1852-1928) British
£280 $437 €420 Three masted sailing boat by the quayside (23x29cm-9x11in) board. 10-Sep-2 David Duggleby, Scarborough #305

CHAMBERS, Richard (?) British?
£350 $550 €525 Navajo Country, New Mexico (25x37cm-10x15in) s.i. W/C on board. 14-Dec-2 Weschler, Washington #675/R

CHAMBERS, Robert William (1865-1933) American
£629 $1000 €944 Gathering wood (60x50cm-24x20in) s.d.93. 7-Mar-3 Skinner, Boston #306/R

CHAMBERS, Thomas (1808-1866) American
£9868 $15000 €14802 Shipping in New York harbour with castle garden (46x61cm-18x24in) 17-Aug-2 North East Auctions, Portsmouth #931/R est:15000-20000
£26316 $40000 €39474 Black X Packet off Sandy Hook, New Jersey (46x61cm-18x24in) painted c.1834-1840 prov. 17-Aug-2 North East Auctions, Portsmouth #605/R est:20000-40000

CHAMBERS, Thomas (attrib) (1808-1866) American
£1227 $2000 €1841 Two men on hillside of mount Holyoke above Northampton. 1-Feb-3 Thomaston Place, Thomaston #32
£1433 $2250 €2150 Monastery by the sea (46x61cm-18x24in) prov. 23-Nov-2 Pook & Pook, Downington #82/R est:2500-3500
£1575 $2300 €2363 River encampment (69x86cm-27x34in) 3-Nov-1 North East Auctions, Portsmouth #868/R
£3947 $6000 €5921 Frigates, United States and Macedonia (61x74cm-24x29in) 17-Aug-2 North East Auctions, Portsmouth #679/R
£9938 $16000 €14907 Threatening sky, Bay of New York (46x61cm-18x24in) 23-Feb-3 Skinner, Boston #20/R

CHAMBON, Emile François (1905-1993) Swiss
£327 $526 €500 La toilette au lever du lit (81x65cm-32x26in) s. 19-Jan-3 Feletin, Province #132
£694 $1118 €1041 Love games (23x40cm-9x16in) s.d.68 board. 7-May-3 Dobiaschofsky, Bern #401/R (S.FR 1500)
£1092 $1714 €1638 Oranges et cartes (46x55cm-18x22in) s.d.1932 prov. 25-Nov-2 Sotheby's, Zurich #128/R est:2500-3500 (S.FR 2500)
£1397 $2208 €2096 Manege a Geneve (35x58cm-14x23in) s. 17-Nov-2 Koller, Geneva #1314/R (S.FR 3200)
£1659 $2622 €2489 Trois Graces (80x100cm-31x39in) s.d.51. 17-Nov-2 Koller, Geneva #1313/R (S.FR 3800)
Works on paper
£328 $517 €492 Nu assis (26x37cm-10x15in) s.d.49 dr. 17-Nov-2 Koller, Geneva #1310 (S.FR 750)

CHAMPAGNE, Horace (1937-) Canadian
Works on paper
£207 $324 €311 Green water, St. Joseph de la Riviere, Quebec (30x38cm-12x15in) s.i.d.March 29/83 pastel. 24-Jul-2 Walker's, Ottawa #206/R (C.D 500)
£412 $638 €618 Late winter colour, St. Ferreol Les Neiges, Que (22x30cm-9x12in) s. pastel prov. 3-Dec-2 Joyner, Toronto #366 est:800-1200 (C.D 1000)
£502 $788 €753 Roaring winds, les eboulements, PQ (20x25cm-8x10in) s.i.d.1989 pastel. 25-Nov-2 Hodgins, Calgary #146/R (C.D 1250)
£522 $820 €783 Sunrise at Rue St Oliver, Quebec City (42x56cm-17x22in) s.i.d.1982 pastel. 25-Nov-2 Hodgins, Calgary #104/R (C.D 1300)
£533 $831 €800 A l'entree des montagnes de la Gatineau (41x61cm-16x24in) pastel s. i.verso. 10-Sep-2 Iegor de Saint Hippolyte, Montreal #15 (C.D 1300)
£602 $946 €903 Corner store (44x59cm-17x23in) s. pastel. 25-Nov-2 Hodgins, Calgary #103/R est:1200-1500 (C.D 1500)
£889 $1458 €1334 Incoming tide (40x50cm-16x20in) s. pastel. 3-Jun-3 Joyner, Toronto #109/R est:2500-3000 (C.D 2000)
£978 $1604 €1418 Late afternoon light (43x58cm-17x23in) s. pastel prov. 9-Jun-3 Hodgins, Calgary #47/R est:2000-2500 (C.D 2200)
£1229 $1954 €1844 December, Point-au-pic (41x56cm-16x22in) s.i. pastel. 23-Mar-3 Hodgins, Calgary #100/R est:1200-1500 (C.D 2900)
£1289 $2114 €1869 250 year old barn. les Eboulements, PQ (45x60cm-18x24in) s.i.d.1988 pastel. 9-Jun-3 Hodgins, Calgary #48/R est:2000-2500 (C.D 2900)
£1399 $2169 €2099 Quiet times for a caeche ride, Place d'armes vieux Quebec (46x60cm-18x24in) s. pastel. 3-Dec-2 Joyner, Toronto #30/R est:3000-4000 (C.D 3400)
£1511 $2478 €2191 After school, Sutherland Street, Quebec City (53x73cm-21x29in) s. pastel. 9-Jun-3 Hodgins, Calgary #172/R est:3000-3500 (C.D 3400)
£1864 $2964 €2796 Racing the sun Gleam, St. Irenee (60x45cm-24x18in) s.i.d.2000 pastel. 23-Mar-3 Hodgins, Calgary #39/R est:2000-2500 (C.D 4400)
£3602 $5727 €5403 Lake Agnes, Canadian Rockies near Lake Louise (75x100cm-30x39in) s.i. pastel. 23-Mar-3 Hodgins, Calgary #50/R est:3000-4000 (C.D 8500)
£5556 $9111 €8056 Arriving at Lake O'Hara Lodge, Yoho National Park (120x180cm-47x71in) s. pastel prov. 9-Jun-3 Hodgins, Calgary #321/R est:9000-12000 (C.D 12500)

CHAMPAIGNE, Philippe de (attrib) (1602-1674) Flemish
£1006 $1570 €1600 Portrait of man (79x61cm-31x24in) 21-Sep-2 Bolland & Marotz, Bremen #431/R

CHAMPAIGNE, Philippe de (style) (1602-1674) Flemish
£6918 $10654 €11000 Portrait de Jean Baptiste Colbert assis a son bureau (116x88cm-46x35in) prov. 25-Oct-2 Tajan, Paris #2/R est:3000-3800

CHAMPIERRE, Elisabeth (20th C) French
£489 $783 €680 La tannerie de Fez (50x50cm-20x20in) s. 18-May-3 Neret-Minet, Paris #181/R

CHAMPION, Theo (1887-1952) German
£780 $1264 €1100 By the wall (13x16cm-5x6in) mono.d.1946 canvas on board prov. 24-May-3 Van Ham, Cologne #90/R
£833 $1292 €1300 Lower Rhine landscape (25x37cm-10x15in) s.d.1946 board prov. 4-Dec-2 Lempertz, Koln #615/R
£942 $1545 €1300 Evening landscape (25x34cm-10x13in) canvas on panel. 29-May-3 Lempertz, Koln #571/R
£1087 $1783 €1500 Church - Lower Kassel (21x25cm-8x10in) s.d.1937 i. verso canvas on panel prov. 29-May-3 Lempertz, Koln #570/R est:1400
£1159 $1901 €1600 Between the trees (40x50cm-16x20in) s. i. verso canvas on panel. 29-May-3 Lempertz, Koln #572/R est:2000
£1232 $2020 €1700 Cows in meadow (36x42cm-14x17in) s.d.1913 prov. 29-May-3 Lempertz, Koln #569/R est:1800
Works on paper
£321 $497 €500 Landscape with peasant woman and livestock (11x15cm-4x6in) s. gouache. 4-Dec-2 Lempertz, Koln #616/R

CHAMPION-METADIER, Isabelle (1947-) French
£306 $487 €450 Taiwan (390x387cm-154x152in) s. i.d.1982 verso diptych. 3-Mar-3 Marc Kohn, Paris #26/R
£612 $973 €900 Oiseau du futur (195x175cm-77x69in) s.i.d.1983 verso acrylic. 3-Mar-3 Marc Kohn, Paris #127/R

CHAMPNEY, Benjamin (1817-1907) American
£938 $1500 €1407 Landscape with a woman walking on a path with mountains in background (28x38cm-11x15in) s. 17-May-3 Pook & Pook, Downington #201/R est:2500-3500
£1299 $2000 €1949 Study of rocks and trees (25x25cm-10x10in) s. arched prov. 24-Oct-2 Shannon's, Milford #204/R est:2000-3000
£1761 $2800 €2642 North Conway (24x16cm-9x6in) init.d.84 panel prov. 7-Mar-3 Skinner, Boston #288/R est:400-600
£2548 $4000 €3822 Forest stream (53x43cm-21x17in) s. 22-Nov-2 Skinner, Boston #74/R est:4000-6000
£3639 $5750 €5459 Landscape with seated figure (25x46cm-10x18in) s. 17-Nov-2 CRN Auctions, Cambridge #50/R
£4221 $6500 €6332 Afternoon in New Hampshire (61x91cm-24x36in) s. prov. 24-Oct-2 Shannon's, Milford #183/R est:5000-7000

CHAMPNEY, Benjamin (attrib) (1817-1907) American
£255 $400 €383 Echo Lake, Cathedral Rock, North Conway (20x26cm-8x10in) 22-Nov-2 Skinner, Boston #79/R
£566 $900 €849 Pond in Woburn, Massachusetts (36x46cm-14x18in) s. 7-Mar-3 Skinner, Boston #278/R

CHAMPNEY, James Wells (1843-1903) American
£2343 $3750 €3515 Never too late to mend (33x23cm-13x9in) s. panel. 11-Jan-3 James Julia, Fairfield #236b est:4000-6000
Works on paper
£1006 $1600 €1509 Portrait of a young lady (56x46cm-22x18in) s. pastel. 7-Mar-3 Skinner, Boston #307/R est:700-900
£2031 $3250 €2945 Lilith (61x51cm-24x20in) pastel canvas. 16-May-3 Skinner, Boston #93/R est:4500-5500

CHAN, Henry (?) ?
£680 $1082 €1000 Marche aux poissons a Menton (92x73cm-36x29in) s. i.verso. 24-Mar-3 Coutau Begarie, Paris #283
£755 $1170 €1200 Amaryllis roses (73x60cm-29x24in) s. i.verso. 30-Oct-2 Coutau Begarie, Paris #148

CHANCO, Roland (1914-) French
£987 $1599 €1500 Portrait de vielle femme (61x50cm-24x20in) s.d.1948 isorel. 27-Jan-3 Millon & Associes, Paris #33
£1348 $2250 €1900 La geisha (91x72cm-36x28in) s. cardboard. 23-Jun-3 Claude Boisgirard, Paris #207/R est:2000-2200
£1447 $2345 €2200 L'heure du the (97x130cm-38x51in) s. 27-Jan-3 Millon & Associes, Paris #35
£1678 $2718 €2550 Partie de belote (130x97cm-51x38in) s. 27-Jan-3 Millon & Associes, Paris #36
£2368 $3837 €3600 Petit navire (120x80cm-47x31in) s.d.1973. 27-Jan-3 Millon & Associes, Paris #34
Works on paper
£276 $448 €420 Portrait bras croises (64x50cm-25x20in) s. pastel. 27-Jan-3 Millon & Associes, Paris #30
£428 $693 €650 Portrait femme a chapeau (61x50cm-24x20in) s. pastel. 27-Jan-3 Millon & Associes, Paris #31

CHANCOURTOIS, René Louis Beguyer de (1757-1817) French
Works on paper
£680 $1082 €1000 Vue du Lac d'Albano (55x79cm-22x31in) s.i. pen ink wash over crayon. 24-Mar-3 Tajan, Paris #93
£1300 $2041 €1950 View of the Zingheri cave at Vicovaro (50x65cm-20x26in) s.i. pen ink wash over black chk. 11-Dec-2 Sotheby's, Olympia #205/R est:1500-2000

CHANCOURTOIS, René Louis Beguyer de (attrib) (1757-1817) French
Works on paper
£3497 $5839 €5000 Deux vues de paysages de montagnes (49x64cm-19x25in) sepia wash pair. 25-Jun-3 Pierre Berge, Paris #2/R est:1000-1500

CHANDELIER, Jules Michel (1813-1871) French
Works on paper
£347 $566 €500 Marine Hollandaise (17x26cm-7x10in) s. W/C. 19-Jul-3 Thierry & Lannon, Brest #258

CHANDLER, Joseph Goodhue (1813-1880) American
Works on paper
£215 $335 €323 Sunset over the lake (35x70cm-14x28in) s. pastel. 25-Mar-3 Iegor de Saint Hippolyte, Montreal #20 (C.D 500)

CHANDLER, R (17th C) ?
£6475 $10619 €9000 Vanitas still life (73x61cm-29x24in) s.d.1695. 4-Jun-3 Reiss & Sohn, Konigstein #130/R est:10000

CHANDLER, William (1854-1928) American
Works on paper
£306 $475 €459 Mountain landscape with lake, barn and birch trees (69x43cm-27x17in) s. pastel. 29-Sep-2 Provenance, Pittstown #130

CHANEY, Lester Joseph (1907-) American
£584 $900 €876 Surf at dawn (56x71cm-22x28in) s.d.1938. 8-Sep-2 Treadway Gallery, Cincinnati #610/R

CHANG SHUSEN (1954-) Chinese
Works on paper
£11655 $19231 €16900 Oxen (119x223cm-47x88in) s.i. ink scroll. 6-Jul-3 Christie's, Hong Kong #280/R est:100000-150000 (HK.D 150000)

CHANG WAN-CHUAN (1909-) Chinese
£13986 $23077 €20280 Feast (49x60cm-19x24in) s.d.83. 6-Jul-3 Christie's, Hong Kong #142/R est:200000-300000 (HK.D 180000)

CHANG YU SHU (1900-1966) Chinese
Works on paper
£2580 $4024 €4050 Reclining female nude (39x56cm-15x22in) s. Chinese ink. 10-Nov-2 Eric Pillon, Calais #161/R

CHANTREY, Sir Francis (1781-1842) British
Sculpture
£78000 $124020 €117000 Bust of James Watts (68cm-27in) i.verso marble on socle. 20-Mar-3 Sotheby's, London #57/R est:20000-30000
Works on paper
£3000 $4770 €4500 Portrait of James Watt (17x11cm-7x4in) pencil. 20-Mar-3 Sotheby's, London #64/R est:600-800

CHANTREY, Sir Francis (after) (1781-1842) British
Sculpture
£9000 $14310 €13500 Bust of James Watt (23cm-9in) s.d.1842 marble after Sir Francis Chantrey. 20-Mar-3 Sotheby's, London #58/R est:2000-3000
£9500 $15105 €14250 Bust of James Watt (18cm-7in) s.d.1841 ivory after Sir Francis Cheverton. 20-Mar-3 Sotheby's, London #59/R est:2000-3000

CHAPAUD, Marc (1914-) French
£460 $718 €690 Rue de village (54x45cm-21x18in) s. s.i.verso. 12-Sep-2 Rupert Toovey, Partridge Green #1450/R
£1346 $2100 €2019 La Place aux Herbs (89x117cm-35x46in) s. 18-Sep-2 Jackson's, Cedar Falls #928/R

CHAPEL, Guy Martin (1871-1929) American
£366 $600 €531 French quarter courtyard (33x25cm-13x10in) s. board. 7-Jun-3 Neal Auction Company, New Orleans #364

CHAPELAIN-MIDY, Roger (1904-1992) French
£409 $634 €650 Nature morte aux oranges (27x46cm-11x18in) s. oil metal plaque prov. 30-Oct-2 Artcurial Briest, Paris #410b
£457 $750 €663 Maree Basse a l'lile de re (61x91cm-24x36in) s. indis d. 4-Jun-3 Doyle, New York #30
£854 $1400 €1238 Rue a Nazare, Portugal (64x51cm-25x20in) s.d.64. 4-Jun-3 Doyle, New York #29 est:800-1200
£1655 $2647 €2300 La serviette pervenche (73x60cm-29x24in) s. 16-May-3 Lombrail & Teucquam, Paris #135/R
£1795 $2782 €2800 Marine (54x73cm-21x29in) s.d.47. 9-Dec-2 Beaussant & Lefevre, Paris #28/R
£2302 $3683 €3200 Nature morte a l'orange coupee (66x81cm-26x32in) s. 16-May-3 Lombrail & Teucquam, Paris #136/R
Works on paper
£288 $460 €400 Poupee articulee au miroir (64x48cm-25x19in) s. gouache. 14-May-3 Blanchet, Paris #128/R
£538 $850 €850 Venise (48x59cm-19x23in) s. W/C. 27-Nov-2 Blanchet, Paris #76

CHAPELET, Roger (1902-1995) French
Works on paper
£900 $1395 €1350 Cutty Sark and a French paddle steamer in a Mediterranean harbour (44x63cm-17x25in) s.i. bodycol. 31-Oct-2 Christie's, Kensington #400/R
£2200 $3410 €3300 Sagres at Hong Kong (45x60cm-18x24in) s.i. bodycol. 31-Oct-2 Christie's, Kensington #401/R est:800-1200

CHAPELLE, Dominique (1941-) French
£372 $569 €580 Courses a Deauville (46x55cm-18x22in) s. 23-Aug-2 Deauville, France #170

CHAPIN, Bryant (1859-1927) American
£3323 $5250 €4985 Still life with fruit (30x38cm-12x15in) s.d.1901. 17-Nov-2 CRN Auctions, Cambridge #34/R
£3437 $5500 €4984 Still life with apples (33x43cm-13x17in) s.d.1908. 16-May-3 Skinner, Boston #98/R est:6000-8000
£4140 $6500 €6210 Still life with fruit (30x41cm-12x16in) s.d.1901. 22-Nov-2 Skinner, Boston #112/R est:7000-9000

CHAPIN, Charles H (19th C) American
£625 $1000 €938 River valley landscape (38x56cm-15x22in) s. board. 15-Mar-3 Jeffery Burchard, Florida #48/R

CHAPIN, Francis (1899-1965) American
Works on paper
£355 $550 €533 Nude (46x30cm-18x12in) s. W/C. 8-Dec-2 Toomey, Oak Park #788/R

CHAPIRO, Jacques (1887-1972) Russian
£385 $604 €600 Paysan dans la campagne (38x46cm-15x18in) s. s.verso. 12-Dec-2 Rabourdin & Choppin de Janvry, Paris #117
£962 $1510 €1500 Reve (100x73cm-39x29in) 12-Dec-2 Rabourdin & Choppin de Janvry, Paris #124/R
£1058 $1661 €1650 Moise sauve des eaux (73x60cm-29x24in) studio st.verso. 12-Dec-2 Rabourdin & Choppin de Janvry, Paris #119
£1154 $1812 €1800 Toreador (91x64cm-36x25in) studio st. 12-Dec-2 Rabourdin & Choppin de Janvry, Paris #116/R
£1282 $2013 €2000 Peintre dans l'atelier (53x73cm-21x29in) s.d.1953. 12-Dec-2 Rabourdin & Choppin de Janvry, Paris #118
£1859 $2919 €2900 Auto-portrait (46x38cm-18x15in) s. 12-Dec-2 Rabourdin & Choppin de Janvry, Paris #120
£2414 $3862 €3500 Landscapes (100x114cm-39x45in) double-sided triptych. 12-Mar-3 Rabourdin & Choppin de Janvry, Paris #123/R

CHAPLIN, Charles (1825-1891) French
£500 $800 €750 Farmer and pigs in a landscape (11x19cm-4x7in) s. 11-Mar-3 Bonhams, Knightsbridge #200/R
£968 $1529 €1500 Jeune femme en Diane (75x41cm-30x16in) s. 18-Dec-2 Rieunier, Bailly-Pommery, Mathias, Paris #56
£1310 $2044 €1965 Portrait of young woman with dog (30x24cm-12x9in) s. masonite. 6-Nov-2 Dobiaschofsky, Bern #402/R est:3600 (S.FR 3000)
£3000 $5010 €4500 Sleeping child (38x56cm-15x22in) s. 18-Jun-3 Christie's, Kensington #158/R est:3000-5000
£3200 $4992 €4800 Flown away (46x29cm-18x11in) s. 17-Sep-2 Sotheby's, Olympia #257/R est:2000-3000
£3500 $5565 €5250 Coy look (46x38cm-18x15in) s. prov. 20-Mar-3 Christie's, Kensington #119/R est:4000-6000
£3500 $5845 €5250 Portrait of a young beauty (65x55cm-26x22in) s. 18-Jun-3 Christie's, Kensington #125/R est:4000-6000
£3797 $6000 €6000 Jeune fille lisant (33x23cm-13x9in) s.indis.d. 27-Nov-2 Christie's, Paris #70/R est:6000-8000
£5696 $9000 €8544 Blowing bubbles (29x23cm-11x9in) s. 24-Apr-3 Sotheby's, New York #142/R est:10000-15000
£6200 $9610 €9300 Her favourite dog (46x33cm-18x13in) s. 3-Dec-2 Sotheby's, Olympia #260/R est:3000-4000

£9677 $15000 €14516 Head of a young beauty with a basket of flowers (65x46cm-26x18in) s.d.1891 prov. 30-Oct-2 Christie's, Rockefeller NY #187/R est:15000-20000

Works on paper

£3399 $5370 €5099 Jeune femme au repos (43x25cm-17x10in) s. W/C. 15-Nov-2 Naón & Cia, Buenos Aires #79/R

CHAPLIN, Charles (attrib) (1825-1891) French

Works on paper

£3200 $5024 €4800 Portrait of an elegant beauty (62x49cm-24x19in) s. pastel. 21-Nov-2 Christie's, Kensington #37/R est:3000-5000

CHAPLIN, Elisabeth (1890-1982) French

£609 $957 €950 Seascape (75x56cm-30x22in) s. card. 16-Dec-2 Pandolfini, Florence #234/R
£1090 $1711 €1700 Autumn landscape (47x40cm-19x16in) s. card. 16-Dec-2 Pandolfini, Florence #235 est:1400

CHAPMAN, Carlton Theodore (1860-1925) American

£1250 $2000 €1875 Summer landscape (30x41cm-12x16in) s. board. 11-Jan-3 James Julia, Fairfield #593 est:1800-2200
£1461 $2250 €2192 Golden morning (15x25cm-6x10in) s. board prov. 24-Oct-2 Shannon's, Milford #209/R est:1200-1800

Works on paper

£240 $375 €360 Goat Island, The Dolphin (18x25cm-7x10in) i.d.1909 W/C pencil gouache. 28-Mar-3 Eldred, East Dennis #89/R

CHAPMAN, Charles S (1879-1962) American

£475 $750 €713 Chinese New Year (18x20cm-7x8in) s. masonite. 26-Apr-3 Jeffery Burchard, Florida #41

CHAPMAN, Conrad Wise (1842-1910) American

£5161 $8000 €7742 Beach scene (15x23cm-6x9in) s.d.1880 panel. 2-Nov-2 North East Auctions, Portsmouth #45/R est:8000-12000
£5346 $8500 €8019 Skating scene (16x20cm-6x8in) mono.d.1876 panel. 5-Mar-3 Sotheby's, New York #18/R est:8000-12000
£10692 $17000 €16038 At the beach (22x41cm-9x16in) mono. panel. 5-Mar-3 Sotheby's, New York #17/R est:10000-15000
£17296 $27500 €25944 Skating in the Bois de Boulogne (22x41cm-9x16in) mono.d.1877 panel. 5-Mar-3 Sotheby's, New York #16/R est:15000-25000
£38000 $60040 €57000 Figures in the fields outside Mexico City (22x40cm-9x16in) 15-Nov-2 Sotheby's, London #83/R est:25000-35000
£89172 $140000 €133758 Mexican valley (63x126cm-25x50in) s.i.d.1894 prov.exhib.lit. 20-Nov-2 Christie's, Rockefeller NY #5/R est:140000-180000

CHAPMAN, George (20th C) American

£521 $740 €782 Cairo (50x60cm-20x24in) s.d.1929 board. 20-Mar-2 Watson's, Christchurch #48/R est:1500-4000 (NZ.D 1700)

CHAPMAN, John Gadsby (1808-1889) American

£1100 $1749 €1650 Sabine (36x25cm-14x10in) mono.d.1869 s.i.verso board. 29-Apr-3 Bonhams, New Bond Street #205/R est:1000-1500

CHAPMAN, John Linton (1839-1905) American

£10390 $16000 €15585 Excavations on the Campagna (79x142cm-31x56in) prov.exhib. 24-Oct-2 Shannon's, Milford #170/R est:5000-7000

Works on paper

£750 $1215 €1125 Whitbread greys, Royal Lancashire show (19x29cm-7x11in) s. W/C. 21-May-3 James Thompson, Kirby Lonsdale #225

CHAPMAN, John Watkins (1832-1903) British

£850 $1386 €1233 Musician's interlude (22x17cm-9x7in) s. 21-Jul-3 Bonhams, Bath #84/R
£2000 $3120 €3000 Gypsy dancer (71x91cm-28x36in) 10-Sep-2 Bonhams, Knightsbridge #48/R est:2000-3000

CHAPMAN, Margaret (20th C) British

£280 $442 €420 On the prom, Edwardian seaside scene (46x61cm-18x24in) s.d.73 board. 28-Nov-2 Morphets, Harrogate #553
£280 $459 €420 Schoolyard (27x31cm-11x12in) s. wood. 4-Jun-3 Bonhams, Chester #317

CHAPOVAL (1919-1951) French/Russian

£6090 $9561 €9500 Gladiateur (65x92cm-26x36in) s.d.1949 s.i.d.verso. 20-Nov-2 Binoche, Paris #41/R est:10000-11000

CHAPOVAL, Youla (1919-1951) French/Russian

£633 $987 €1000 Composition (35x27cm-14x11in) s. panel prov. 20-Oct-2 Claude Boisgirard, Paris #67
£1348 $2250 €1900 Homme au verre (73x60cm-29x24in) s. 17-Jun-3 Claude Boisgirard, Paris #34/R est:2000-3000
£1773 $2961 €2500 Composition (37x45cm-15x18in) s.d.50 VIII exhib. 18-Jun-3 Pierre Berge, Paris #98 est:1000-1500
£3473 $5521 €5000 Composition a la bouteille et au verre (56x38cm-22x15in) s.d.1948-7 prov. 29-Apr-3 Artcurial Briest, Paris #210/R est:3000-4000
£4082 $6490 €6000 Composition (22x33cm-9x13in) s.d.4/7/1949 d.4 juillet 1949 verso. 26-Feb-3 Artcurial Briest, Paris #554 est:3500-4500

Works on paper

£571 $909 €840 Composition (38x46cm-15x18in) d.25.XII.49 chl dr. 26-Feb-3 Artcurial Briest, Paris #448/R

CHAPPEL, E (1859-1946) Belgian

£949 $1500 €1500 Nature morte au panier de fleurs (59x48cm-23x19in) 2-Dec-2 Amberes, Antwerp #1333

CHAPPEL, Edouard (1859-1946) Belgian

£680 $1082 €1000 Still life with hydrangea (46x56cm-18x22in) s. 24-Mar-3 Bernaerts, Antwerp #134/R est:600-750
£3846 $5962 €6000 Fleurs dans un vase de Delft (180x140cm-71x55in) s. 3-Dec-2 Campo & Campo, Antwerp #44/R est:6000-7000

CHAPPELL, Reuben (1870-1940) British

£500 $785 €750 Ada Dews of Leeds Captain Samuel Sheard, off the coast (52x76cm-20x30in) s.i. 21-Nov-2 Tennants, Leyburn #753
£650 $1040 €975 Madby Ann of Falmouth (33x51cm-13x20in) s.i. 14-Mar-3 Gardiner & Houlgate, Bath #85/R
£2449 $3894 €3600 August Julius von Pernau (35x54cm-14x21in) 27-Feb-3 Hagelstam, Helsinki #998 est:2500

Works on paper

£270 $417 €405 Ship's portrait of Jorgensen of Ronne (34x51cm-13x20in) s.d.06 pencil W/C. 26-Oct-2 Rasmussen, Havnen #3081 (D.KR 3200)
£402 $651 €583 Ship's portrait of Rossing (37x53cm-15x21in) s. W/C. 24-May-3 Rasmussen, Havnen #2079/R (D.KR 4200)
£465 $716 €698 Concordia of Thuro off a coast (35x54cm-14x21in) s. W/C pen. 26-Oct-2 Rasmussen, Havnen #3018 (D.KR 5500)
£465 $716 €698 Emilie of Thoro on rough seas (35x52cm-14x20in) s. W/C pen. 26-Oct-2 Rasmussen, Havnen #3019 (D.KR 5500)
£475 $750 €750 Christa von Bremen (37x55cm-15x22in) s.i. gouache. 29-Nov-2 Bolland & Marotz, Bremen #675/R
£549 $846 €824 Ship's portrait of Alma of Thuro (38x54cm-15x21in) s.i.d.1905 pencil W/C. 26-Oct-2 Rasmussen, Havnen #3082/R (D.KR 6500)
£550 $870 €825 Sidney of Guernsey (36x55cm-14x22in) s.i. W/C. 28-Nov-2 Martel Maides, Guernsey #26/R
£850 $1386 €1275 Portrait of the Falmouth built ketch, "Kindly Light", of Bude (48x71cm-19x28in) s.i. W/C. 13-Feb-3 David Lay, Penzance #100/R
£900 $1413 €1350 Seaforth of Bristol. S.S. Calgaria of Workington (36x56cm-14x22in) s.i. W/C bodycol pair. 16-Dec-2 Sotheby's, Olympia #116/R
£980 $1529 €1470 Progress, of Bideford (36x49cm-14x19in) s.i. W/C pair. 15-Oct-2 Bearnes, Exeter #373/R
£1100 $1716 €1650 Vixen of Pentewan (32x55cm-13x22in) s.i. pencil W/C. 18-Sep-2 Dreweatt Neate, Newbury #75 est:300-500

CHAPPLE, David (20th C) American

£599 $1000 €869 Landscape, Tuolumne River (30x41cm-12x16in) s. 17-Jun-3 John Moran, Pasadena #178a est:1200-1800
£1018 $1700 €1476 Landscape, evening eucalyptus (30x41cm-12x16in) s. 17-Jun-3 John Moran, Pasadena #178 est:1200-1800

CHAPPUIS, B (19th C) French

£2800 $4396 €4200 Fine glass of red (53x42cm-21x17in) s. 21-Nov-2 Christie's, Kensington #49/R est:3000-5000

CHAPU, Henri Michel Antoine (1833-1891) French

Sculpture

£1032 $1600 €1548 Seated muse (62cm-24in) s. brown pat. bronze St.f.Thiebaut Freres. 29-Oct-2 Sotheby's, New York #229/R est:800-1200
£1226 $1900 €1839 Seated muse (62cm-24in) s. brown pat. bronze. 29-Oct-2 Sotheby's, New York #231/R est:800-1200
£1242 $1999 €1900 Jeanne d'Arc assise (56cm-22in) s.st.f.F.Barbedienne brown pat bronze. 20-Jan-3 Horta, Bruxelles #84 est:2500-3000
£1392 $2172 €2200 Late 19th century seated Jeanne d'Arc (70x50cm-28x20in) s. num.794 brown pat bronze Cast Collas lit. 21-Oct-2 Bernaerts, Antwerp #37/R est:3000-3800
£1948 $3000 €2922 Woman reading (74x51cm-29x20in) s. brown pat. bronze relief st.f.Fumiere Thiebaut. 27-Oct-2 Grogan, Boston #119 est:1500-2000

CHAPUIS, Maurice (?) ?
£503 $810 €750 Bord de riviere (65x50cm-26x20in) s. 23-Feb-3 Lesieur & Le Bars, Le Havre #25

CHAPUIS, Pierre Marie Alfred (1863-1942) French
£1862 $2979 €2700 Elegantes dans un parc (48x34cm-19x13in) s.d.mai 1909 cardboard. 12-Mar-3 Libert, Castor, Paris #55 est:450-600
£2432 $3795 €3600 Jardin du Luxembourg (54x80cm-21x31in) s. 28-Mar-3 Delvaux, Paris #19/R

CHAPUS, Henri (?) Belgian?
Sculpture
£962 $1510 €1500 Internat (95cm-37in) s. brown pat bronze. 15-Dec-2 Mercier & Cie, Lille #294

CHARAVEL, Paul (1877-1961) French
£630 $977 €945 Summer landscape (38x47cm-15x19in) s.d.1939 panel. 9-Dec-2 Philippe Schuler, Zurich #3943 (S.FR 1450)
£870 $1348 €1305 Wooded riverbank with figures (38x55cm-15x22in) s. 9-Dec-2 Philippe Schuler, Zurich #3944 (S.FR 2000)
£915 $1473 €1400 Le peintre et sa palette (92x70cm-36x28in) s.d.1932. 20-Jan-3 Horta, Bruxelles #98
£1847 $2882 €2900 Aubade a Saint-Tropez (81x65cm-32x26in) s. panel. 7-Nov-2 Chochon-Barre & Allardi, Paris #97/R
£38710 $61161 €60000 Elegantes sur la falaise (170x266cm-67x105in) s.d.1909 lit. 19-Dec-2 Claude Aguttes, Neuilly #86/R est:60000

CHARBERT, E (?) ?
£514 $801 €750 Small city (60x50cm-24x20in) s. board. 9-Apr-3 Neumeister, Munich #656

CHARBONIER, Jean (16th C) French
£8387 $13251 €13000 Destruction des Niobides (87x114cm-34x45in) s.i.d.1551 panel prov.lit. 18-Dec-2 Tajan, Paris #37/R est:12000-15000

CHARBONNIER, Pierre (attrib) (1897-1978) French
£704 $1134 €1000 Paysage boise avec barques sur une riviere (60x80cm-24x31in) s. 11-May-3 Thierry & Lannon, Brest #340

CHARCHOUNE, Serge (1888-1975) Russian
£795 $1295 €1200 Composition (16x25cm-6x10in) s. paper on canvas. 3-Feb-3 Cornette de St.Cyr, Paris #289/R
£1321 $2034 €2100 Composition a la croix (12x22cm-5x9in) s. 26-Oct-2 Cornette de St.Cyr, Paris #5/R
£1667 $2617 €2600 Weber conc (46x65cm-18x26in) s.d.64 s.i.d.verso. 24-Nov-2 Laurence Calmels, Paris #75/R
£1859 $2937 €2789 Composition inspire par la music portugise (50x65cm-20x26in) s.d.60 s.d.XI 60 verso prov. 1-Apr-3 Rasmussen, Copenhagen #173/R est:25000-30000 (D.KR 20000)
£2436 $3824 €3800 Impressionisme ornamental 4 (23x24cm-9x9in) s.d.1939 i.verso prov. 15-Dec-2 Perrin, Versailles #51/R
£2482 $4021 €3500 Francesca da Rimini de Tschaikowsky (46x55cm-18x22in) s.d.54 i.d.verso prov. 26-May-3 Christie's, Milan #321/R est:4000-6000
£2817 $4676 €4000 Fond gris ardoise (20x29cm-8x11in) s.d.44. 18-Jun-3 Anaf, Lyon #44/R est:1000-1200
£3020 $4862 €4500 Hautbois et cordes (40x80cm-16x31in) s. s.i.verso. 23-Feb-3 Mercier & Cie, Lille #128/R
£3205 $5032 €5000 Untitled (65x46cm-26x18in) s.d.50 s.i.d.verso. 24-Nov-2 Laurence Calmels, Paris #76/R
£3526 $5535 €5500 Beethoven V numero 2 (54x73cm-21x29in) s.d.54 s.i.d.verso. 24-Nov-2 Laurence Calmels, Paris #74/R
£3774 $5849 €6000 Nature morte blanche (38x46cm-15x18in) s.d.44-45 panel prov.exhib.lit. 30-Oct-2 Artcurial Briest, Paris #423/R est:7500-10000
£3774 $5849 €6000 Nature morte au violon (38x61cm-15x24in) s. painted c.1945. 30-Oct-2 Artcurial Briest, Paris #424/R est:7500-10000
£3819 $6073 €5500 Adam, Gisele, II acte (98x130cm-39x51in) s. s.i.verso exhib. 29-Apr-3 Artcurial Briest, Paris #556/R est:6000-8000
£3924 $6200 €6200 Composition musicaliste (97x162cm-38x64in) 2-Dec-2 Tajan, Paris #197/R
£7292 $12031 €10500 Composition (35x24cm-14x9in) s.d.46 s.verso. 1-Jul-3 Artcurial Briest, Paris #771/R est:6000-8000
Works on paper
£709 $1184 €1000 Composition blanche et verte (34x27cm-13x11in) s. gouache exhib. 23-Jun-3 Claude Boisgirard, Paris #133/R

CHARDIGNY, Barthelemy Francois (1757-1813) French
Sculpture
£18590 $28814 €29000 Bacchus allonge sur la depouille du lion de Nemee (38x57x24cm-15x22x9in) bears sig. terracotta exec.1802 lit. 9-Dec-2 Rabourdin & Choppin de Janvry, Paris #112/R est:22000
Works on paper
£483 $772 €700 Carle Vernet a Rome (30x18cm-12x7in) i. black pencil. 12-Mar-3 E & Eve, Paris #42

CHARDIN, Jean Baptiste Simeon (1699-1779) French
£20062 $32500 €30093 Still life with ray-fish, onions, eggs, mortar and pestle (41x32cm-16x13in) prov.lit. 23-Jan-3 Sotheby's, New York #203a/R est:40000

CHARDIN, Leon (19th C) French
Works on paper
£316 $494 €500 Le bal masque (52x32cm-20x13in) s. pastel exec.c.1900. 10-Sep-2 Vanderkindere, Brussels #355

CHAREMOURE, Charchoume (20th C) Belgian?
Works on paper
£625 $994 €900 Composition (25x30cm-10x12in) s. gouache. 29-Apr-3 Campo, Vlaamse Kaai #36

CHARETTE-DUVAL, François (fl.1836-1878) Belgian
Works on paper
£755 $1170 €1200 Bouquet de fleurs, fruits et vases sur un entablement (99x69cm-39x27in) s. W/C. 1-Oct-2 Palais de Beaux Arts, Brussels #439

CHARLEMAGNE, Adolf-Jossifowitsch (1826-1901) Russian
Works on paper
£7500 $11774 €11250 Funeral procession of H.I.H. Alexander II (29x43cm-11x17in) s. pencil W/C. 20-Nov-2 Sotheby's, London #36/R est:5000-7000

CHARLEMAGNE, Iosef Iosefovich (1824-1870) Russian
Works on paper
£4000 $6480 €6000 Topographical vignettes of the Imperial residence Alexandria near St. Petersburg (32x46cm-13x18in) s.d.1859 W/C over pencil. 21-May-3 Sotheby's, London #3/R est:4000-6000
£4200 $6804 €6300 Celebrations on the marsovoyo pol'ye St Petersburg (27x41cm-11x16in) s.d.1859 pencil W/C. 21-May-3 Sotheby's, London #4/R est:4000-6000

CHARLEMONT, Hugo (1850-1939) Austrian
£600 $936 €900 Wooded garden (43x36cm-17x14in) s. board. 17-Sep-2 Bonhams, Knightsbridge #122/R
£1307 $2144 €2000 Still life with peaches, pears and dish on table (19x26cm-7x10in) s. panel. 29-Mar-3 Dannenberg, Berlin #553/R est:2000
£1497 $2380 €2200 Still life with flowers and ornamental objects (60x47cm-24x19in) s. 25-Feb-3 Dorotheum, Vienna #10/R est:2500-2800
Works on paper
£270 $422 €400 Garden (31x42cm-12x17in) s.i. oil chk htd white. 28-Mar-3 Dorotheum, Vienna #106
£676 $1054 €1000 Landscape (34x52cm-13x20in) s.i.d.1907 W/C paper on board. 28-Mar-3 Dorotheum, Vienna #314/R

CHARLEMONT, Theodor (?) Austrian
Sculpture
£2819 $4538 €4200 Young woman holding a box of onyx, Pandora (70x52x41cm-28x20x16in) s. 18-Feb-3 Sotheby's, Amsterdam #311/R est:4500-7500

CHARLES, James (1851-1906) British
£2000 $3120 €3000 Figures in a cafe interior (42x44cm-17x17in) s. board. 8-Oct-2 Bonhams, Knightsbridge #287/R est:300-400
£22000 $35420 €33000 Darby and Joan (78x81cm-31x32in) mono.d.1893 prov.exhib. 20-Feb-3 Christie's, London #272/R est:18000

CHARLES, Michael Ray (1967-) American
£8750 $14000 €13125 Rewopetihw (117x131cm-46x52in) s.d.94 acrylic latex oil wash copper penny panel prov.exhib. 15-May-3 Christie's, Rockefeller NY #389a/R est:12000-18000

CHARLESWORTH, Rod (20th C) Canadian?
£326 $509 €544 Kluane September (30x36cm-12x14in) s. s.i.verso board. 13-Apr-3 Levis, Calgary #16b (C.D 750)
£348 $543 €580 Okanagan headwaters (28x36cm-11x14in) s. s.i.verso board. 13-Apr-3 Levis, Calgary #16a (C.D 800)

£361 $571 €542 Icicles (46x61cm-18x24in) hardboard. 1-Dec-2 Levis, Calgary #13/R (C.D 900)
£422 $666 €633 September light on the Adams River (28x36cm-11x14in) hardboard. 1-Dec-2 Levis, Calgary #15/R (C.D 1050)
£442 $694 €663 Reid Lake, Northern Ontario (28x35cm-11x14in) s.i. board. 25-Nov-2 Hodgins, Calgary #166/R (C.D 1100)
£467 $765 €677 Similkameen (28x35cm-11x14in) s.i. board. 9-Jun-3 Hodgins, Calgary #79/R est:750-950 (C.D 1050)
£482 $761 €723 Colours of the autumn, near Chase (30x61cm-12x24in) hardboard. 1-Dec-2 Levis, Calgary #14/R (C.D 1200)
£602 $946 €903 After school greetings (38x75cm-15x30in) s.i. board. 25-Nov-2 Hodgins, Calgary #6/R (C.D 1500)
£667 $1093 €967 Western dusk, Beaver Lake (40x50cm-16x20in) s.i. board. 9-Jun-3 Hodgins, Calgary #26/R est:900-1200 (C.D 1500)
£1044 $1639 €1566 Galina Bay view (100x60cm-39x24in) s.i. board. 25-Nov-2 Hodgins, Calgary #41/R est:2500-3000 (C.D 2600)

CHARLET, Émile (1851-?) Belgian
£548 $855 €800 Sunny Norwegian fjord landscape (45x51cm-18x20in) s. 10-Apr-3 Schopman, Hamburg #699

CHARLET, Frans (1862-1928) Belgian
£1923 $3019 €3000 Jeune orientale au perroquet (72x54cm-28x21in) s. 16-Dec-2 Gros & Delettrez, Paris #115/R est:3000-4500
Works on paper
£3121 $5211 €4400 Deux fillettes assises (55x67cm-22x26in) s. W/C. 17-Jun-3 Palais de Beaux Arts, Brussels #531/R est:2000-3000

CHARLET, Nicolas Toussaint (1792-1845) French
£961 $1518 €1442 After the Battle of Waterloo (43x59cm-17x23in) 14-Nov-2 Stuker, Bern #137/R est:2500-3000 (S.FR 2200)

CHARLET, Nicolas Toussaint (attrib) (1792-1845) French
Works on paper
£2128 $3553 €3000 Une place un jour de carnaval (23x34cm-9x13in) pen black ink col wash W/C. 19-Jun-3 Piasa, Paris #157 est:1000

CHARLEY, Thelma (20th C) New Zealander?
Works on paper
£1064 $1660 €1596 Studio types (84x81cm-33x32in) s.i. s.i.verso. 17-Sep-2 Peter Webb, Auckland #194/R est:3500-5000 (NZ.D 3500)

CHARLIER, Jacques (attrib) (1720-1790) French
Works on paper
£1486 $2319 €2200 Mercure (54x39cm-21x15in) gouache. 26-Mar-3 Piasa, Paris #49/R

CHARLIER, Jacques (1939-) Belgian
£1042 $1656 €1500 Alienation (110x107cm-43x42in) 29-Apr-3 Campo, Vlaamse Kaai #37 est:1500-1800

CHARLOT, Jean (1898-1979) Mexican/French
£3045 $4750 €4568 Hammock (41x51cm-16x20in) s.d.37 prov. 5-Nov-2 Doyle, New York #10/R est:3000-5000
Works on paper
£962 $1500 €1443 Kneeling woman (21x16cm-8x6in) s.i.d. col pastel. 18-Sep-2 Swann Galleries, New York #61/R est:2000-3000

CHARLOT, Louis (1878-1951) French
£962 $1490 €1500 Uchon sous la neige (46x55cm-18x22in) s. panel. 4-Dec-2 Pierre Berge, Paris #134

CHARLOT, Raymond (20th C) ?
£1258 $2051 €1900 Gitane au violon (121x91cm-48x36in) s.d.1924. 17-Feb-3 Horta, Bruxelles #208

CHARLTON, Alan (1948-) British
£7800 $12792 €11700 Untitled no 5 (187x156cm-74x61in) s.i.d.1975 verso acrylic two parts prov.exhib. 7-Feb-3 Sotheby's, London #144/R est:4000-6000

CHARLTON, Daphne (20th C) British
£320 $499 €480 Self portrait (60x50cm-24x20in) s. canvasboard. 15-Oct-2 Bonhams, Knightsbridge #21/R

CHARLTON, Evan (1904-) British
£1800 $2826 €2700 View from the window (62x46cm-24x18in) s.d.47. 20-Nov-2 Sotheby's, Olympia #86/R est:1200-1800

CHARLTON, George J (attrib) (1899-1979) British
£477 $750 €716 Nude seated in red chair (76x63cm-30x25in) 14-Dec-2 Weschler, Washington #600/R

CHARLTON, J (1849-1917) British
£982 $1493 €1473 Just in time - fox hunt (33x54cm-13x21in) s.d.1902 s.i.d.verso. 19-Aug-2 Joel, Victoria #260/R est:1500-2500 (A.D 2800)

CHARLTON, John (1849-1917) British
£600 $948 €900 Stable companions (15x19cm-6x7in) mono.d.74. 28-Nov-2 Bonhams, Knightsbridge #101/R
£1400 $2198 €2100 Afternoon nap (51x68cm-20x27in) s. 21-Nov-2 Tennants, Leyburn #771/R est:600-800
£2600 $4316 €3770 Going to ground (35x55cm-14x22in) s.d.1902. 12-Jun-3 Christie's, Kensington #16/R est:2000-3000

CHARLTON, Maria (20th C) Irish?
£949 $1472 €1500 Crimson landscape (75x60cm-30x24in) s.d.2001 verso board. 24-Sep-2 De Veres Art Auctions, Dublin #30 est:1500-2000

CHARMAN, Clifford (1910-1993) British
£700 $1092 €1050 Double Saturday (102x122cm-40x48in) s. board. 27-Mar-3 Christie's, Kensington #572/R
£700 $1092 €1050 Signs of the times (86x122cm-34x48in) s. board. 27-Mar-3 Christie's, Kensington #573/R

CHARMAN, Rodney (1944-) American
£380 $597 €570 Passing the Sevenstones (76x102cm-30x40in) s.d.79. 10-Dec-2 Capes Dunn, Manchester #893

CHAROY, Bernard (1929-) French
£625 $994 €900 Nu assis (73x60cm-29x24in) cardboard. 29-Apr-3 Campo & Campo, Antwerp #28
£629 $969 €1000 Maisons dans un paysage enneige (55x46cm-22x18in) s. 22-Oct-2 Campo & Campo, Antwerp #35/R
£1258 $1937 €2000 Femme assise (65x54cm-26x21in) s. acrylic. 22-Oct-2 Campo & Campo, Antwerp #37/R
£2075 $3217 €3300 Verger (72x60cm-28x24in) s. lit. 5-Oct-2 De Vuyst, Lokeren #586/R est:3600-4200

CHARPENTIER, Alexandre (1856-1909) French
Sculpture
£1531 $2434 €2250 Femme allongee (20cm-8in) s. num.6 pat bronze. 23-Mar-3 Herbette, Doullens #155/R
£2692 $4227 €4200 Joueuse de violon. Joueuse de violoncelle (33x35cm-13x14in) st.mono. pat plaster relief pair. 11-Dec-2 Piasa, Paris #21/R

CHARPENTIER, Auguste (1813-1880) French
£1631 $2724 €2300 La Napolitaine en buste (74x60cm-29x24in) s. 21-Jun-3 Bretagne Encheres, St Malo #49

CHARPENTIER, Eugène (1811-1890) French
£3077 $4861 €4800 Vase de fleurs, coupe en porcelaine et grenade sur un chale Indien (122x90cm-48x35in) s. 18-Nov-2 Tajan, Paris #167/R est:4600-6000

CHARPENTIER, Felix (1858-1924) French
Sculpture
£7051 $11071 €11000 Matinado (107cm-42in) s.i. marble. 15-Dec-2 Mercier & Cie, Lille #295/R est:15000

CHARPENTIER, Georges Emile (19th C) French
£3169 $5102 €4500 Thoniers sous voiles a Concarneau (73x92cm-29x36in) s. 11-May-3 Thierry & Lannon, Brest #150/R est:2000-2500

CHARPENTIER, Jean Baptiste (elder-attrib) (1728-1806) French
£9804 $16078 €15000 Jeune garcon nourissant des oisillons. Jeune fille tenant un pot de fleurs (55x45cm-22x18in) pair oval prov. 9-Feb-3 Anaf, Lyon #68/R est:16000

CHARPENTIER, Michel (20th C) French
£285 $444 €450 Nu (100x65cm-39x26in) s.d.1963 ink wash paper on canvas. 20-Oct-2 Claude Boisgirard, Paris #93
Works on paper
£285 $444 €450 Nu (100x65cm-39x26in) s.d.1963 ink wash paper on canvas. 20-Oct-2 Claude Boisgirard, Paris #94

CHARPIN, Albert (1842-1924) French
£709 $1099 €1064 Bergere et ses moutons (52x72cm-20x28in) s. 4-Dec-2 AB Stockholms Auktionsverk #1857/R (S.KR 10000)
£766 $1210 €1149 Meadow with cattle (33x46cm-13x18in) s. exhib. 2-Dec-2 Rasmussen, Copenhagen #1338/R (D.KR 9000)

CHARPIN, Albert (attrib) (1842-1924) French
£466 $740 €699 Shepherd with sheep and cattle (28x46cm-11x18in) s. 5-Mar-3 Rasmussen, Copenhagen #1638 (D.KR 5000)

CHARRETON, Victor (1864-1937) French
£608 $949 €900 Jetee de roses (22x32cm-9x13in) s. 26-Mar-3 Rieunier, Paris #20
£1266 $1975 €2000 Paysage au lac (26x34cm-10x13in) s. cardboard. 20-Oct-2 Anaf, Lyon #102/R
£4747 $7500 €7500 Jardin public (50x61cm-20x24in) s. lit. 27-Nov-2 Marc Kohn, Paris #19/R est:9000
£4937 $7800 €7800 Vase de fleurs (40x60cm-16x24in) s. 2-Dec-2 Tajan, Paris #55/R
£5000 $7850 €7800 Hameau sous la neige (46x58cm-18x23in) s. cardboard. 13-Dec-2 Piasa, Paris #68/R est:8000
£6207 $9931 €9000 Montagnes a Murols (37x47cm-15x19in) bears sig. cardboard prov.lit. 12-Mar-3 E & Eve, Paris #104/R est:4000-5000
£6329 $9810 €10000 Paysage vallonne (38x55cm-15x22in) s. panel prov. 29-Sep-2 Eric Pillon, Calais #196/R
£6790 $9642 €11000 Maison dans les arbres (50x73cm-20x29in) s. 16-Mar-3 Eric Pillon, Calais #103/R
£6790 $9642 €11000 Vase de fleurs (40x60cm-16x24in) s. 16-Mar-3 Eric Pillon, Calais #113/R
£7095 $11068 €10500 Paysage de Provence (54x65cm-21x26in) s. lit. 26-Mar-3 Millon & Associes, Paris #86/R est:10000
£7692 $12077 €12000 Paysage aux arbres (46x64cm-18x25in) s. cardboard. 13-Dec-2 Piasa, Paris #70/R est:10000
£8013 $12580 €12500 Clocher d'eglise (47x61cm-19x24in) s. cardboard. 13-Dec-2 Piasa, Paris #69/R est:10000
£9936 $15599 €15500 Chemin sous la neige (59x72cm-23x28in) s. panel lit. 15-Dec-2 Eric Pillon, Calais #104/R
£10191 $15898 €16000 Paysage pres de la Crouze de Chambord (60x73cm-24x29in) s. panel lit. 10-Nov-2 Eric Pillon, Calais #32/R
£12230 $19568 €17000 Maison dans le vallon (60x72cm-24x28in) s. panel. 18-May-3 Eric Pillon, Calais #75/R
£14331 $22357 €22500 Allee de rhododendrons (69x92cm-27x36in) s. 10-Nov-2 Eric Pillon, Calais #47/R
£20144 $32230 €28000 Jardin en fleurs a Saint-Amant (60x73cm-24x29in) s. 18-May-3 Eric Pillon, Calais #30/R

CHARRIER, Henri (1859-1950) French
£507 $791 €750 Reflets d'arbres, bord de riviere (40x49cm-16x19in) studio st.verso panel. 31-Mar-3 Rossini, Paris #55

CHARRIN, Fanny (?-1854) French
Miniatures
£1600 $2592 €2400 Madame de Sevigne, wearing white dress (4cm-2xin) enamel. 22-May-3 Bonhams, New Bond Street #27/R est:1000-1500

CHARTRAN, Theobald (1849-1907) French
£1500 $2445 €2175 Elegante lisante (39x31cm-15x12in) s.d.1885-88. 16-Jul-3 Sotheby's, Olympia #237/R est:1500-2000

CHASE, Asa (?) ?
£286 $450 €429 Whale hunt (41x58cm-16x23in) s. 26-Jul-2 Eldred, East Dennis #248/R

CHASE, Frank M (fl.1880-1898) British
£320 $499 €480 On the Mediterranean coast (31x46cm-12x18in) s. 23-Sep-2 Bonhams, Chester #976

CHASE, Harry (1853-1889) American
£1375 $2200 €2063 Fresh day (33x51cm-13x20in) s. painted c.1876. 15-Mar-3 Selkirks, St. Louis #335/R est:1800-2400
£1730 $2750 €2595 Still life with grapes (61x36cm-24x14in) s. prov. 5-Mar-3 Sotheby's, New York #58/R est:800-1200

CHASE, John (1810-1879) British
Works on paper
£877 $1368 €1316 Abbey by moonlight (28x38cm-11x15in) s.d.1871 W/C. 27-Mar-3 International Art Centre, Auckland #188/R (NZ.D 2500)

CHASE, Marian (1844-1905) British
Works on paper
£800 $1248 €1200 At Clovelly, North Devon (26x36cm-10x14in) W/C. 26-Mar-3 Hamptons Fine Art, Godalming #65/R
£2500 $4075 €3750 Wild orchid and ferns (33x23cm-13x9in) s.d.1884 W/C. 28-Jan-3 Gorringes, Lewes #1731/R est:500-800

CHASE, Sidney March (1877-1957) American
£1263 $1985 €1895 Maine coastal scene with evergreen trees and two seagulls (41x51cm-16x20in) s. 19-Apr-3 James Julia, Fairfield #261/R est:3000-4000

CHASE, William Merritt (1849-1916) American
£1266 $2000 €1899 Still life of three freshly caught fish lying atop a net (61x102cm-24x40in) s. 26-Apr-3 Thomaston Place, Thomaston #30
£8917 $14000 €13376 Portrait of a lady with red bead necklace (61x43cm-24x17in) s. 10-Dec-2 Doyle, New York #55/R est:8000-10000
£9063 $14500 €13595 Still life with fish and shrimp (66x97cm-26x38in) s. prov. 11-Jan-3 James Julia, Fairfield #48 est:15000-25000
£16561 $26000 €24842 Portrait of Hope (65x53cm-26x21in) s. prov.lit. 20-Nov-2 Christie's, Los Angeles #49/R est:15000-25000
£49383 $80000 €74075 Gondola in Venice (20x29cm-8x11in) s. panel painted 1913 prov. 22-May-3 Christie's, Rockefeller NY #35/R est:60000-80000
£90323 $140000 €135485 Young girl (76x63cm-30x25in) s. prov.lit. 5-Dec-2 Christie's, Rockefeller NY #82/R est:150000-250000
Works on paper
£1225806 $1900000 €1838709 Afternoon in the park (48x37cm-19x15in) s. pastel executed c.1889 prov.exhib.lit. 4-Dec-2 Sotheby's, New York #29/R est:200000-300000

CHASE, William Merritt (attrib) (1849-1916) American
£481 $745 €750 Half-figure portrait of a man in three-quarters profile (75x60cm-30x24in) masonite. 4-Dec-2 Neumeister, Munich #694/R

CHASSELAT, Henri Jean Saint Ange (attrib) (1813-1880) French
£14000 $23380 €21000 Parrot on a ledge with a vase of tulips and other summer flowers. Melon, grapes with flowers on ledg (105x80cm-41x31in) s. oval pair. 18-Jun-3 Christie's, Kensington #37/R est:12000-18000

CHASSERIAU, Theodore (1819-1856) French
£25316 $40000 €37974 Study for saint Francis Xavier Baptising the Indians (49x51cm-19x20in) prov.exhib.lit. 24-Apr-3 Sotheby's, New York #40/R est:20000-30000
Works on paper
£633 $1000 €1000 Une femme debout, pour La Romance du Saule (18x10cm-7x4in) graphite brown wash prov. 27-Nov-2 Christie's, Paris #284/R
£1076 $1700 €1700 Soldat romain vu de dos (21x14cm-8x6in) st.sig. graphite prov.lit. 29-Nov-2 Claude Boisgirard, Paris #14/R
£2885 $4471 €4500 Etude de pecheur (22x13cm-9x5in) crayon. 4-Dec-2 Piasa, Paris #148/R est:10000
£3704 $6000 €5556 Hero and Leander (24x21cm-9x8in) s.d.1839 pencil htd white prov.lit. 22-Jan-3 Christie's, Rockefeller NY #108a/R est:8000
£3871 $6000 €5807 Study of a youth (17x12cm-7x5in) d.1844 pencil prov.exhib. 29-Oct-2 Sotheby's, New York #19/R est:1500-2000
£19753 $32000 €29630 Susanna at the bath (19x14cm-7x6in) s. pencil prov.exhib.lit. 22-Jan-3 Christie's, Rockefeller NY #109/R est:30000

CHASTEL, Roger (1897-1981) French
£748 $1190 €1100 Le bistro (46x55cm-18x22in) s.d.1954 i.verso. 26-Feb-3 Artcurial Briest, Paris #556

CHASTELLUS, Jacques de (1894-1957) Belgian
£1538 $2385 €2400 Petit port Breton (59x55cm-23x22in) s. 7-Dec-2 De Vuyst, Lokeren #78/R est:2000-3000

CHATAUD, Marc Alfred (1833-1908) French
£3237 $5309 €4500 Vues de la mosquee avec personnages et chamelier (50x39cm-20x15in) s. cardboard pair. 4-Jun-3 Tajan, Paris #245/R est:4500-6000
£3517 $5628 €5100 Jeune femme se regardant dans la glace (30x107cm-12x42in) 12-Mar-3 E & Eve, Paris #83/R est:1500-2000
£5000 $7800 €7500 Woman of the Casbah (70x43cm-28x17in) s. 15-Oct-2 Sotheby's, London #210/R est:5000-7000
Works on paper
£503 $775 €800 Jeune arabe et son ane (18x24cm-7x9in) mono. W/C. 23-Oct-2 Raboudin & Choppin de Janvry, Paris #142

CHATEAU, Yves (20th C) French
£288 $453 €450 Corsage vert (53x70cm-21x28in) s. panel. 19-Nov-2 Galerie Moderne, Brussels #317

CHATEIGNON, Ernest (1851-?) French
£4000 $6280 €6000 La moisson (60x46cm-24x18in) s. 19-Nov-2 Sotheby's, London #178/R est:4000-6000
£9677 $15290 €15000 Fenaison (60x80cm-24x31in) s. 19-Dec-2 Claude Aguttes, Neuilly #25/R est:12000

CHATELAIN, Jean Baptiste Claude (1710-1771) French
Works on paper
£320 $499 €480 Estuary scene (19x28cm-7x11in) chk prov. 19-Sep-2 John Bellman, Billingshurst #1430

CHATELET, Claude Louis (1753-1794) French
Works on paper
£994 $1570 €1550 Church in park (17x27cm-7x11in) bears mono. pen W/C prov. 16-Nov-2 Lempertz, Koln #1208/R est:1500

CHATELET, Claude Louis (attrib) (1753-1794) French
£8742 $14599 €12500 Paysage rocheux animes de pecheurs (71x91cm-28x36in) pair. 25-Jun-3 Tajan, Paris #67/R est:12000-15000
Works on paper
£629 $900 €944 Italianate landscape with a farm building, a bridge and peasants (18x26cm-7x10in) pen ink W/C. 23-Jan-3 Swann Galleries, New York #277/R
£1418 $2369 €2000 Personnages au bord d'un lac en Italie (26x34cm-10x13in) W/C gouache pen brown ink. 23-Jun-3 Delvaux, Paris #1/R est:2000-2500

CHATELET, Claude Louis (circle) (1753-1794) French
£10000 $16000 €15000 Capriccio landscape with figures by a waterfall (146x199cm-57x78in) 14-May-3 Butterfields, San Francisco #1040/R est:4000-6000

CHATERA, Makhan (?) Indian
Works on paper
£892 $1293 €1400 Portrait of Jaswant Singh of Jodhpur (36x24cm-14x9in) s. gouache. 31-May-2 Blanchet, Paris #17

CHATFIELD, Thomas F (1921-) Canadian
£244 $401 €366 Fall's End (40x50cm-16x20in) s. board. 3-Jun-3 Joyner, Toronto #555 (C.D 550)

CHATHAM, Russell (1940-) American
£3313 $5500 €4804 Sea near Pacifica (51x41cm-20x16in) mono.d.1985 canvasboard prov. 11-Jun-3 Butterfields, San Francisco #4095/R est:6000-8000
£4459 $7000 €6689 Fall fields (46x51cm-18x20in) mono.i.d.1984. 19-Nov-2 Butterfields, San Francisco #8107/R est:7000-10000

CHATILLON, Pierre (1885-1974) Swiss
Works on paper
£349 $545 €524 Brunngasshalde (45x37cm-18x15in) s.i. W/C over pencil. 8-Nov-2 Dobiaschofsky, Bern #189/R (S.FR 800)
£556 $894 €806 Rathausgasse with town hall (44x36cm-17x14in) s.i.d.24 W/C over pencil. 9-May-3 Dobiaschofsky, Bern #111/R (S.FR 1200)
£602 $969 €873 Untertorbrucke (37x45cm-15x18in) s.i. W/C over pencil. 9-May-3 Dobiaschofsky, Bern #110/R (S.FR 1300)
£655 $1022 €983 Unterorbrucke with view of Nydegg church (51x41cm-20x16in) s.i. W/C over pencil. 8-Nov-2 Dobiaschofsky, Bern #191/R (S.FR 1500)

CHATILLON, Zoe Laure de (1826-1908) French
Works on paper
£1667 $2533 €2600 Les deux soeurs (89x69cm-35x27in) s.d.1856 pastel oval. 10-Jul-2 Rabourdin & Choppin de Janvry, Paris #37/R est:3200-3500

CHATTEN, Geoffrey (?) British
£260 $434 €377 Oulton Broad (56x76cm-22x30in) 20-Jun-3 Keys, Aylsham #538
£300 $471 €450 Gorleston (23x15cm-9x6in) s. 13-Dec-2 Keys, Aylsham #480/R
£360 $601 €522 Mautby landscape, Norfolk (76x117cm-30x46in) s. i.verso. 20-Jun-3 Keys, Aylsham #519
£390 $612 €585 Busy harbour scene in rough weather (58x117cm-23x46in) s. 13-Dec-2 Keys, Aylsham #286/R
£400 $668 €580 Herringfleet (76x56cm-30x22in) s. 20-Jun-3 Keys, Aylsham #540/R

CHATZIS, Vasilios (1870-1915) Greek
£2000 $3100 €3000 Rest in Constantinople (23x30cm-9x12in) s. paper on canvas. 2-Oct-2 Sotheby's, London #77/R

CHAUD, Munkund (?) Indian
Works on paper
£1083 $1570 €1700 Portrait of mado Singh of Jaipur (25x19cm-10x7in) s. gouache. 31-May-2 Blanchet, Paris #19

CHAUDET, Louis Alfred (1812-1891) French
Works on paper
£567 $948 €800 L'Odeon d'Herodes Atticus a Athenes (16x30cm-6x12in) s.i.d.1847 W/C prov. 23-Jun-3 Beaussant & Lefèvre, Paris #90/R

CHAUVEAU, François (1613-1676) French
Works on paper
£1852 $3000 €2778 Design for frontespiece of atlas (37x26cm-15x10in) pen ink wash. 21-Jan-3 Sotheby's, New York #117/R

CHAUVEL, Georges (1886-1962) French
Sculpture
£2041 $3245 €3000 Femme agenouillee (48cm-19in) s. marble. 24-Mar-3 Digard, Paris #76/R

CHAUVIN, Jean (1889-1976) French
Sculpture
£7639 $12604 €11000 Sur un air d'accordeon (46x20x20cm-18x8x8in) s.num.1/5 brown pat bronze st.f.Godard. 2-Jul-3 Artcurial Briest, Paris #667/R est:12000-15000
£9500 $14630 €14250 Forme ailee (51cm-20in) i. lacquered wood on wooden base prov. 22-Oct-2 Sotheby's, London #142/R est:3000-4000
£18000 $27720 €27000 Fertilite (48cm-19in) i. lacquered wood on wooden base prov. 22-Oct-2 Sotheby's, London #143/R est:3000-4000

CHAUVIN, Pierre Athanase (1774-1832) French
£10976 $18000 €16464 View of the convent of San Antonio near Posilippo, Naples (63x84cm-25x33in) s.d.1810 prov. 29-May-3 Sotheby's, New York #46/R est:20000-30000
£19000 $29830 €28500 Italianate landscape with travellers (61x75cm-24x30in) d.1805 prov. 11-Dec-2 Christie's, London #85/R

CHAVANNES, Alfred (1836-1894) Swiss
£1223 $1907 €1835 Mountain landscape in summer (21x26cm-8x10in) s. exhib. 8-Nov-2 Dobiaschofsky, Bern #32/R est:3400 (S.FR 2800)
£2146 $3391 €3219 Lake Geneva with Vevey and the Alps (47x62cm-19x24in) s.d.84. 29-Nov-2 Falk & Falk, Zurich #498/R est:6000 (S.FR 5000)

CHAVAZ, Albert (1907-1990) Swiss
£566 $906 €849 Le trimardeur (39x55cm-15x22in) s. i. verso board. 17-Mar-3 Philippe Schuler, Zurich #4508 est:1200-1600 (S.FR 1200)
£1792 $2868 €2688 Vignes a Montorges (49x64cm-19x25in) s.d. i. verso board. 17-Mar-3 Philippe Schuler, Zurich #4507 est:2500-3000 (S.FR 3800)
£3043 $4717 €4565 Michele au chapeau de paille (34x23cm-13x9in) s.d.64 canvas on panel prov.lit. 7-Dec-2 Galerie du Rhone, Sion #473/R est:7000-9000 (S.FR 7000)
Works on paper
£655 $1022 €983 Still life with flowers in white vase (27x37cm-11x15in) s.d.58 W/C. 8-Nov-2 Dobiaschofsky, Bern #105/R (S.FR 1500)

CHAVAZ, Jose de (?) Spanish?
£480 $778 €696 Spanish lady seated, reading (44x33cm-17x13in) 20-May-3 Dreweatt Neate, Newbury #334

CHAVAZ, Valencia (20th C) ?
£500 $815 €750 Prized commodity at the slave market (126x93cm-50x37in) s.d.1926. 13-Feb-3 Christie's, Kensington #8/R

CHAVEPEYER, Albert (1899-1986) Belgian
£255 $397 €400 Vase fleuri de glaieuls (60x50cm-24x20in) s. 11-Nov-2 Horta, Bruxelles #477

CHAVET, Victor Joseph (1822-1906) French
£4800 $7536 €7200 Gentleman connoisseurs (19x15cm-7x6in) s.d.53 panel. 19-Nov-2 Bonhams, New Bond Street #170/R est:2000-3000

CHAVEZ LOPEZ, Gerardo (1937-) Peruvian
£694 $1104 €1000 Composition surrealiste aux figures (33x42cm-13x17in) s. 29-Apr-3 Campo, Vlaamse Kaai #38

CHAVIGNAUD, Georges (1865-1944) Canadian
Works on paper
£201 $315 €302 At the river's edge (43x33cm-17x13in) s.d.1923 W/C. 25-Nov-2 Hodgins, Calgary #16/R (C.D 500)
£246 $384 €369 Ferme (19x26cm-7x10in) s.d.1907 W/C. 10-Sep-2 Iegor de Saint Hippolyte, Montreal #17 (C.D 600)
£258 $402 €374 Children in a courtyard (27x32cm-11x13in) s. W/C prov. 26-Mar-3 Walker's, Ottawa #470 (C.D 600)
£444 $729 €666 Figures on a farm road (37x51cm-15x20in) s.d.1937 W/C. 3-Jun-3 Joyner, Toronto #532 est:1500-1800 (C.D 1000)

CHAZAL, Antoine (1793-1854) French
£2346 $3800 €3519 Study of primulas, camellias and prunus (24x32cm-9x13in) paper on canvas. 23-Jan-3 Sotheby's, New York #212/R
£2469 $4000 €3704 Study of anemones, veronica and other flowers (45x31cm-18x12in) paper on canvas. 23-Jan-3 Sotheby's, New York #211/R est:5000
£2593 $4200 €3890 Study of camellias (38x26cm-15x10in) s.d.1845. 23-Jan-3 Sotheby's, New York #210/R

CHAZAL, Louis (20th C) French
£403 $657 €580 Dechargement du poisson a Concarneau (17x25cm-7x10in) s. panel. 19-Jul-3 Thierry & Lannon, Brest #313

CHEADLE, Henry (1852-1910) British
£980 $1519 €1470 Rural landscape with cattle resting by a riverbank (64x39cm-25x15in) s. 1-Oct-2 Fellows & Sons, Birmingham #73/R
£1300 $2015 €1950 River landscape with grazing sheep two figures (47x26cm-19x10in) s.d.1876. 1-Oct-2 Fellows & Sons, Birmingham #71/R est:800-1200
£1700 $2635 €2550 Avon at Hadbury - river landscape with cattle grazing (52x34cm-20x13in) s.d.92. 1-Oct-2 Fellows & Sons, Birmingham #72/R est:1000-1500

CHECA Y SANZ, Ulpiano (1860-1916) Spanish
Prints
£2564 $4026 €4000 L'Andalousie au temps des Maures (131x354cm-52x139in) s. lithograph lit. 16-Dec-2 Gros & Delettrez, Paris #35/R est:3500-4500

Works on paper
£577 $912 €900 Cart (32x43cm-13x17in) s. chl dr. 13-Nov-2 Ansorena, Madrid #436/R
£2534 $3953 €3750 View of Venice (38x24cm-15x9in) s. W/C. 25-Mar-3 Durán, Madrid #705/R
£2724 $4304 €4250 Shepherdess (54x37cm-21x15in) s. W/C. 19-Nov-2 Durán, Madrid #225/R

CHECA, Jose Luis (1950-) Spanish
£258 $408 €400 Valencia harbour (33x55cm-13x22in) s. 17-Dec-2 Durán, Madrid #61/R
£277 $432 €440 El Negret beach (11x18cm-4x7in) s. s.i.verso board. 17-Sep-2 Segre, Madrid #226/R
£306 $484 €475 Beach (20x25cm-8x10in) s. board. 17-Dec-2 Durán, Madrid #30/R
£314 $491 €500 Sailing boat (11x18cm-4x7in) s. s.i.verso. 17-Sep-2 Segre, Madrid #227/R
£324 $512 €470 Venice (11x18cm-4x7in) s. s.i.verso board. 1-Apr-3 Segre, Madrid #374/R
£336 $540 €500 Beach (14x22cm-6x9in) s. 18-Feb-3 Durán, Madrid #596/R
£346 $540 €550 Silla little harbour (27x42cm-11x17in) s. 8-Oct-2 Ansorena, Madrid #594/R
£379 $599 €550 Venice (11x18cm-4x7in) s. s.i.verso board. 1-Apr-3 Segre, Madrid #371/R
£414 $654 €600 Fishermen (46x65cm-18x26in) s. s.i.verso. 1-Apr-3 Segre, Madrid #366/R
£414 $654 €600 Cazorla Sierra (65x45cm-26x18in) s. s.i.verso. 1-Apr-3 Segre, Madrid #365/R
£453 $706 €720 Cataroja harbour (73x50cm-29x20in) s. s.i.verso. 17-Sep-2 Segre, Madrid #225/R
£453 $706 €720 Sierra Espadan (65x46cm-26x18in) s. s.i.verso. 17-Sep-2 Segre, Madrid #224/R
£472 $726 €750 Autumn in Albarracin (46x65cm-18x26in) s. s.i.verso. 28-Oct-2 Segre, Madrid #285/R
£645 $1019 €1000 River Jucar (46x65cm-18x26in) s. s.i.verso. 17-Dec-2 Durán, Madrid #60/R
£662 $1079 €1000 Gree sea, Javea (73x116cm-29x46in) s. s.i.verso. 11-Feb-3 Segre, Madrid #336/R
£662 $1079 €1000 Looking for shelter (73x116cm-29x46in) s. s.i.verso. 11-Feb-3 Segre, Madrid #335/R

CHECKWITCH, Robert (20th C) Canadian
£667 $1093 €967 Jack fish inlet (164x104cm-65x41in) s.i. acrylic. 9-Jun-3 Hodgins, Calgary #189/R est:1000-1500 (C.D 1500)

CHEEK, Carl (20th C) British
£650 $1047 €975 Still life on a table (105x71cm-41x28in) s.d.60. 14-Jan-3 Bonhams, Knightsbridge #84/R

CHEESWRIGHT, Ethel S (1874-?) British
Works on paper
£280 $437 €420 Jersey coastal scene (28x45cm-11x18in) s. pencil W/C. 10-Sep-2 Sworder & Son, Bishops Stortford #737/R
£300 $468 €450 View of harbour and sailing vessels off rocky coastline (37x26cm-15x10in) s. W/C gouache over pencil. 12-Sep-2 Rupert Toovey, Partridge Green #1406/R
£300 $474 €450 Sark coastal scene (34x51cm-13x20in) s. W/C. 28-Nov-2 Martel Maides, Guernsey #10
£320 $531 €464 Continental coastal town (16x28cm-6x11in) s. W/C. 12-Jun-3 Martel Maides, Guernsey #22
£340 $530 €510 View of rocky cove with gulls (44x36cm-17x14in) s. W/C htd gouache over pencil. 12-Sep-2 Rupert Toovey, Partridge Green #1405/R
£360 $601 €522 Coastal view of Sark (38x58cm-15x23in) s.d.1910 W/C. 9-Jul-3 George Kidner, Lymington #130/R
£450 $749 €653 Sark coastal scene (35x52cm-14x20in) s. W/C. 12-Jun-3 Martel Maides, Guernsey #24
£480 $797 €696 View of Creux harbour, Sark from the clifftop (38x27cm-15x11in) s. W/C. 12-Jun-3 Martel Maides, Guernsey #23
£480 $797 €696 Cove on the Sark coast (45x36cm-18x14in) s. W/C. 12-Jun-3 Martel Maides, Guernsey #28
£520 $827 €780 Les Autelets and west coast of Sark (23x35cm-9x14in) s. W/C. 20-Mar-3 Martel Maides, Guernsey #47/R
£520 $827 €780 Clifftop view of Le Creux Harbour, Sark (34x24cm-13x9in) s. W/C. 20-Mar-3 Martel Maides, Guernsey #49
£620 $1029 €899 Sark coastal scene (38x52cm-15x20in) s. W/C. 12-Jun-3 Martel Maides, Guernsey #27
£650 $1034 €975 Cove at Gull's Chapel, Sark (31x26cm-12x10in) s. W/C. 20-Mar-3 Martel Maides, Guernsey #50
£800 $1272 €1200 Sark coastal scenes (16x24cm-6x9in) s. W/C pair. 20-Mar-3 Martel Maides, Guernsey #36/R
£1300 $2054 €1950 Les Autelets Sark (36x52cm-14x20in) s. W/C. 28-Nov-2 Martel Maides, Guernsey #12 est:1000-1200
£1300 $2067 €1950 Guernsey (29x38cm-11x15in) s. W/C. 4-Mar-3 Bearnes, Exeter #337/R est:300-500
£1700 $2686 €2550 Sark coastline looking towards Brecqhou (34x51cm-13x20in) s. W/C. 28-Nov-2 Martel Maides, Guernsey #13/R est:1000-1500
£1800 $2862 €2700 Stormy day at Sark (26x52cm-10x20in) s.d.1913 W/C. 20-Mar-3 Martel Maides, Guernsey #63/R est:1500-2000

CHEFFER, Henry (1860-1957) French?
Works on paper
£451 $736 €650 Cote Bretonne (53x73cm-21x29in) s. chl W/C. 19-Jul-3 Thierry & Lannon, Brest #34
£669 $1077 €950 Sortie de procession devant la chapelle en Bretagne (36x30cm-14x12in) s. W/C gouache. 11-May-3 Thierry & Lannon, Brest #82

CHELAZZI, Tito (1835-1892) Italian
£770 $1224 €1155 Still life of iris and roses (33x23cm-13x9in) s. panel. 30-Apr-3 Hampton & Littlewood, Exeter #480/R

CHELMINSKI, Jan van (1851-1925) Polish
£2000 $3180 €3000 Cavalryman accepting a drink at the roadside (28x20cm-11x8in) s. panel. 29-Apr-3 Gorringes, Lewes #2029
£3526 $5465 €5500 Elegant figures out riding (29x37cm-11x15in) s.d.79 panel lit. 7-Dec-2 Kastern, Hannover #2/R est:2200
£10000 $16400 €15000 Retreat from Moscow (65x81cm-26x32in) s. 3-Jun-3 Sotheby's, London #37/R est:10000-15000

CHEMELLIER, Georges de (attrib) (?-c.1908) French
Sculpture
£1154 $1788 €1800 Man and dog (39cm-15in) s. dark pat bronze. 5-Dec-2 Stadion, Trieste #125/R

CHEMIAKIN, Mikhail (1943-) Russian
£5000 $7750 €7500 Carnaval de Saint Petersbourg (132x132cm-52x52in) s.d.91. 5-Dec-2 Christie's, Kensington #266/R est:5000-7000
£5556 $8833 €8000 Les trois personnages grotesques (115x89cm-45x35in) s. d.1992 verso exhib. 29-Apr-3 Campo & Campo, Antwerp #33/R est:10000-12000
£5755 $9209 €8000 Composition fantastique (132x132cm-52x52in) s.d. 18-May-3 Eric Pillon, Calais #296/R
Sculpture
£1667 $2617 €2600 Carnival in Saint-Petersburg (17cm-7in) num.1/12 precious stones. 16-Dec-2 Eric Coutrier, Paris #113
£2830 $4387 €4500 Carnaval a Saint Petersbourg (57cm-22in) s.num.4/8 green pat bronze. 30-Oct-2 Artcurial Briest, Paris #650 est:5000-6000
£2830 $4387 €4500 Carnaval de Saint Petersbourg (59cm-23in) s.num.4/8 green pat bronze. 30-Oct-2 Artcurial Briest, Paris #651 est:5000-6000
Works on paper
£658 $1065 €1000 Le soleil (21x21cm-8x8in) s.d.95 col ink. 22-Jan-3 Tajan, Paris #237 est:1000-1500
£694 $1104 €1000 Etude pour le bestiaire III (28x21cm-11x8in) s.d.1989 Indian ink W/C dr. 29-Apr-3 Artcurial Briest, Paris #323
£723 $1172 €1100 Rendez-vous avec la lune (21x21cm-8x8in) s.d.95 col ink. 22-Jan-3 Tajan, Paris #236
£764 $1215 €1100 Illustration pour le bestiaire I (28x21cm-11x8in) s.d.1989 Indian ink W/C dr. 29-Apr-3 Artcurial Briest, Paris #321

£764 $1215 €1100 Illustration pour le bestiaire II (28x21cm-11x8in) s. Indian ink W/C dr. 29-Apr-3 Artcurial Briest, Paris #322
£1000 $1550 €1500 Carnaval de Saint Petersbourg (30x30cm-12x12in) s.i.d.1977 pen ink col crayons W/C on card. 5-Dec-2 Christie's, Kensington #265/R est:1000-1500
£1006 $1560 €1600 Composition (24x31cm-9x12in) s.d.80 gouache. 5-Oct-2 De Vuyst, Lokeren #58/R est:1750-2000
£2075 $3217 €3300 Petrouchka (110x75cm-43x30in) s.d.85 pastel. 30-Oct-2 Artcurial Briest, Paris #649 est:3000-3500

CHEMIELINSKI, W T (20th C) European
£2422 $3900 €3633 Winter cityscape (36x51cm-14x20in) s. 22-Feb-3 Brunk, Ashville #313/R

CHEMIELINSKY, Wladyslaw (1895-1978) Polish
£2419 $3823 €3629 Warsaw Square in winter (62x91cm-24x36in) s. prov. 18-Nov-2 Waddingtons, Toronto #292/R est:6000-7000 (C.D 6000)

CHEMIN, Joseph Victor (1825-1901) French
Sculpture
£1800 $2808 €2700 Monkey riding a circus horse (30x33cm-12x13in) s.indis.num. brown pat bronze marble base. 5-Nov-2 Sotheby's, London #112/R est:2000-3000

CHEN CHENG-PO (1895-1947) Chinese
£271950 $448718 €394328 Returning home (72x90cm-28x35in) s.d.1933 prov.lit. 6-Jul-3 Christie's, Hong Kong #130/R est:2200000-4200000 (HK.D 3500000)

CHEN CHI (1912-) Chinese/American
Works on paper
£288 $450 €432 Absinthe House, New Orleans, Louisiana (25x28cm-10x11in) s.d.50 W/C. 12-Oct-2 Neal Auction Company, New Orleans #1390

CHEN HAI XIA (20th C) Chinese
Works on paper
£345 $548 €500 Herd of buffalo by lake. s.d.1960 ink polychrome. 7-Mar-3 Piasa, Paris #303

CHEN JIRU (1558-1639) Chinese
Works on paper
£13986 $23077 €20280 Landscape after the Mi style (82x28cm-32x11in) s.i.d.1596 ink satin hanging scroll. 7-Jul-3 Christie's, Hong Kong #523/R est:120000-150000 (HK.D 180000)

CHEN PEIQIAN (20th C) Chinese
Works on paper
£870 $1426 €1200 Bird in tree (69x45cm-27x18in) s. seals Indian ink col hanging scroll. 30-May-3 Dr Fritz Nagel, Stuttgart #1143/R

CHEN PEIQIU (1922-) Chinese
Works on paper
£2602 $4111 €3903 Peach blossom (17x48cm-7x19in) s.i.d.1980 i.verso ink col folding fan. 28-Apr-3 Sotheby's, Hong Kong #535/R est:7000-9000 (HK.D 32000)
£3659 $5780 €5489 Orchid (67x28cm-26x11in) s.i.d.1964 ink col silk. 28-Apr-3 Sotheby's, Hong Kong #620/R est:60000-80000 (HK.D 45000)

CHEN PING (1960-) Chinese
Works on paper
£362 $594 €500 Houses in hilly landscape (68x68cm-27x27in) i. seals Indian ink col hanging scroll. 30-May-3 Dr Fritz Nagel, Stuttgart #1289/R

CHEN QIKUAN (1921-) Chinese
Works on paper
£4715 $7450 €7073 Eggplant (22x28cm-9x11in) s. ink col hanging scroll exhib. 28-Apr-3 Sotheby's, Hong Kong #522/R est:30000-40000 (HK.D 58000)
£8130 $12846 €12195 Shangrila (22x120cm-9x47in) s. ink col handscroll. 28-Apr-3 Sotheby's, Hong Kong #524/R est:60000-80000 (HK.D 100000)

CHEN QONGQIANG (1948-) Chinese
Works on paper
£2486 $4103 €3605 Flowers (137x69cm-54x27in) s.i.d.2001 ink scroll. 6-Jul-3 Christie's, Hong Kong #272/R est:30000-40000 (HK.D 32000)

CHEN SHAOMEI (1909-1954) Chinese
Works on paper
£3659 $5780 €5489 Deep in the jungle (54x33cm-21x13in) seal ink hanging scroll. 28-Apr-3 Sotheby's, Hong Kong #589/R est:50000-70000 (HK.D 45000)
£9756 $15415 €14634 Copy of Legendary figure Chang E by Tang Yin (142x65cm-56x26in) i. ink col. 28-Apr-3 Sotheby's, Hong Kong #663/R est:120000-180000 (HK.D 120000)
£34146 $53951 €51219 Boating along the gorge (73x33cm-29x13in) s.i.d.1938 ink col hanging scroll. 28-Apr-3 Sotheby's, Hong Kong #644/R est:65000-80000 (HK.D 420000)
£36585 $57805 €54878 Landscape (68x37cm-27x15in) s. ink col hanging scroll style of GUO XI prov. 28-Apr-3 Sotheby's, Hong Kong #643/R est:60000-80000 (HK.D 450000)

CHEN SHUN (1483-1544) Chinese
Works on paper
£7770 $12821 €11267 Admiring the moon. s.i. ink col silk handscroll. 6-Jul-3 Christie's, Hong Kong #412/R est:120000-150000 (HK.D 100000)

CHEN XIONGLI (20th C) Chinese
Works on paper
£2720 $4487 €3944 Deer (97x180cm-38x71in) s.i. ink scroll. 6-Jul-3 Christie's, Hong Kong #279/R est:35000-40000 (HK.D 35000)

CHEN YINPI (1913-1995) Chinese
Works on paper
£15540 $25641 €22533 Composition in ancient calligraphy (121x75cm-48x30in) s. mixed media canvas exec.c.1950-1960. 6-Jul-3 Christie's, Hong Kong #126/R est:220000-320000 (HK.D 200000)

CHEN YUAN (14th C) Chinese
Works on paper
£1014 $1664 €1400 Three immortals (131x80cm-52x31in) seal Indian ink col silk hanging scroll. 30-May-3 Dr Fritz Nagel, Stuttgart #1158/R

CHEN ZHEN (1955-) Chinese
Sculpture
£4082 $6490 €6000 Citizen LC510 (69x40x15cm-27x16x6in) s. num.8/33 water light prov. 24-Mar-3 Cornette de St.Cyr, Paris #164/R

CHEN ZHIFO (1895-1962) Chinese
Works on paper
£6504 $10276 €9756 White parrot (156x45cm-61x18in) s.i.d.1957 ink col hanging scroll. 28-Apr-3 Sotheby's, Hong Kong #571/R est:80000-120000 (HK.D 80000)

CHEN ZIZHUANG (1913-1976) Chinese
Works on paper
£616 $1010 €850 Demon conqueror Zhongkui with wine jug (61x46cm-24x18in) s. seal Indian ink col hanging scroll. 30-May-3 Dr Fritz Nagel, Stuttgart #1200/R
£13821 $21837 €20732 Kingfisher resting in a lotus pond (187x81cm-74x32in) s.i. ink col hanging scroll. 28-Apr-3 Sotheby's, Hong Kong #629/R est:25000-35000 (HK.D 170000)

CHENE DE VERE, H du (19th C) French
£620 $967 €930 Musical interlude (34x24cm-13x9in) s. 17-Sep-2 Bonhams, Oxford #41

CHENEY, Robert Henry (1801-1866) British
Works on paper
£1300 $2132 €1950 Roman forum (53x74cm-21x29in) i. pencil W/C. 5-Jun-3 Christie's, Kensington #956/R est:800-1200

CHENG SHIFA (1921-) Chinese
Works on paper
£616 $1010 €850 Two fishes (60x85cm-24x33in) i. seal Indian ink. 30-May-3 Dr Fritz Nagel, Stuttgart #1134/R
£1709 $2821 €2478 Opera figures (56x41cm-22x16in) s. col ink scroll. 6-Jul-3 Christie's, Hong Kong #223/R est:25000-35000 (HK.D 22000)
£1789 $2826 €2684 Opera figures (70x35cm-28x14in) s.i.d.1961 ink col hanging scroll. 28-Apr-3 Sotheby's, Hong Kong #564/R est:20000-30000 (HK.D 22000)
£2953 $4872 €4282 Crane (65x53cm-26x21in) s. col ink scroll. 6-Jul-3 Christie's, Hong Kong #221/R est:25000-30000 (HK.D 38000)
£3623 $5942 €5000 Women feeding deer (69x136cm-27x54in) s.d.1973 seals Indian ink seals hanging scroll. 30-May-3 Dr Fritz Nagel, Stuttgart #1151/R est:1800-2800
£4472 $7065 €6708 Zhong kui (27x142cm-11x56in) s. ink col handscroll. 28-Apr-3 Sotheby's, Hong Kong #566/R est:40000-60000 (HK.D 55000)
£4662 $7692 €6760 Landscape (34x136cm-13x54in) s.i. col ink scroll. 6-Jul-3 Christie's, Hong Kong #220/R est:40000-50000 (HK.D 60000)

CHENG WU FEI (?) Chinese
Works on paper
£380 $604 €570 My Pekingese dog, Jill (37x44cm-15x17in) s. W/C. 26-Feb-3 Cheffins Grain & Comins, Cambridge #566/R

CHENOWETH, Joseph G (fl.1920) American
£2244 $3500 €3366 Couple in kitchen with bankbook (66x61cm-26x24in) s. 9-Nov-2 Illustration House, New York #162/R est:3000-4000

CHENYEVIERE, Cecile (19/20th C) French
Works on paper
£1013 $1600 €1520 Love's offering (53x38cm-21x15in) s. W/C. 3-Apr-3 Boos Gallery, Michigan #229/R est:600-800

CHEPFER, Emile (20th C) French
£625 $987 €900 Militaire posant (46x38cm-18x15in) s.d.1892 panel. 25-Apr-3 Piasa, Paris #66

CHERCHI, Sandro (1911-) Italian
£510 $811 €750 Still life on blue table (40x50cm-16x20in) s.d.1970. 1-Mar-3 Meeting Art, Vercelli #716

CHERET, Auguste (20th C) French
Works on paper
£680 $1081 €1000 Enfants a l'ombrelle (38x31cm-15x12in) s. W/C gouache over crayon. 24-Mar-3 Tajan, Paris #189/R

CHERET, Jules (1836-1933) French
£2603 $4060 €3800 Portrait de jeune fille (36x22cm-14x9in) 8-Apr-3 Gioffredo, Nice #172
£2877 $4488 €4200 Portrait de jeune fille au chapeau fleuri et foulard noir (36x22cm-14x9in) 8-Apr-3 Gioffredo, Nice #171
£14744 $23147 €23000 Le carnaval (60x125cm-24x49in) s. 16-Dec-2 Millon & Associes, Paris #171/R est:15000-20000
£18269 $28683 €28500 Moulin Rouge en fete (125x75cm-49x30in) s.d.19 pastel on canvas. 22-Nov-2 Millon & Associes, Paris #14/R est:15000-20000
Works on paper
£278 $447 €417 Seated woman with basket (34x22cm-13x9in) s. ochre. 7-May-3 Dobiaschofsky, Bern #1471 (S.FR 600)
£304 $474 €450 Danseuses (20x10cm-8x4in) W/C. 26-Mar-3 Millon & Associes, Paris #21/R
£449 $704 €700 La lettre (34x25cm-13x10in) s.i.d.25/6/97 sanguine htd white chk. 16-Dec-2 Millon & Associes, Paris #17/R
£463 $745 €695 Elegant woman (37x22cm-15x9in) s. chl. 7-May-3 Dobiaschofsky, Bern #1473 (S.FR 1000)
£541 $845 €850 Jeune femme (32x22cm-13x9in) crayon chk. 6-Nov-2 Gioffredo, Nice #4/R
£545 $855 €850 Elegantes (36x23cm-14x9in) s. chl htd white dr pair. 13-Dec-2 Piasa, Paris #64/R
£839 $1401 €1200 La farandole, projet d'affiche (60x38cm-24x15in) s. blue crayon dr. 26-Jun-3 Tajan, Paris #37/R
£901 $1279 €1450 Arlequine (25x35cm-10x14in) s. crayon bistre gouache. 20-Mar-2 Chayette & Cheval, Paris #12/R
£1613 $2548 €2420 Belle epoque beauties (61x52cm-24x20in) s.d.1910 pastel. 18-Nov-2 Waddingtons, Toronto #212/R est:8000-12000 (C.D 4000)
£4110 $6411 €6000 Tete de jeune femme, jeune femme a la coiffe (23x20cm-9x8in) pastel. 8-Apr-3 Gioffredo, Nice #170
£4400 $7128 €6600 Masked ball (35x22cm-14x9in) s. pastel. 20-May-3 Sotheby's, Olympia #411/R est:3000-5000
£5248 $8135 €7872 Flirting (24x70cm-9x28in) s. pastel. 3-Dec-2 Bukowskis, Stockholm #331/R est:50000-60000 (S.KR 74000)
£6383 $10660 €9000 Danseuse au tambourin (60x38cm-24x15in) s.i.d.11-95 pastel. 20-Jun-3 Rieunier, Paris #41/R est:6000-8000
£8784 $13703 €13000 Carnaval (60x32cm-24x13in) s. pastel on canvas. 26-Mar-3 Millon & Associes, Paris #19/R
£9177 $14500 €14500 Jeune femme avec moulin (61x35cm-24x14in) s. pastel. 2-Dec-2 Rieunier, Paris #13/R est:12000
£22759 $36414 €33000 Le bal masque (160x80cm-63x31in) s.d.94. 12-Mar-3 Libert, Castor, Paris #56/R est:8000-10000

CHERET, Jules (attrib) (1836-1933) French
£1613 $2548 €2500 Portrait de femme (41x33cm-16x13in) 18-Dec-2 Ferri, Paris #42/R

CHERIANE (1900-?) French
£1419 $2213 €2129 Bouquet of Lilies (64x92cm-25x36in) s. 11-Sep-2 Kieselbach, Budapest #41/R (H.F 550000)

CHERIER, Bruno Joseph (1819-1880) French
£503 $775 €800 Portrait d'homme. Portrait de femme (100x81cm-39x32in) s.d.1867 pair. 27-Oct-2 Muizon & Le Coent, Paris #29/R

CHERIOT, L (?) ?
£3500 $5705 €5250 Seated doberman pinscher (41x61cm-16x24in) s. 12-Feb-3 Bonhams, Knightsbridge #154/R est:1000-1500

CHERPIN, Alexina (1834-?) French
£2397 $3764 €3500 Still life with pink and white roses (60x51cm-24x20in) s. 15-Apr-3 Sotheby's, Amsterdam #72/R est:4000-6000

CHERRY, Kathryn (1880-1931) American
£781 $1250 €1132 Landscape with house and trees (28x36cm-11x14in) s. canvasboard. 17-May-3 Selkirks, St. Louis #303
£1410 $2200 €2115 Landscape with house and figures (28x36cm-11x14in) s. artist board prov. 10-Nov-2 Selkirks, St. Louis #772/R est:2500-3000
£1474 $2300 €2211 Rural landscape (36x28cm-14x11in) s. canvas on board prov. 10-Nov-2 Selkirks, St. Louis #766/R est:2500-3500
£1603 $2500 €2405 Wooded landscape (46x41cm-18x16in) s. prov. 10-Nov-2 Selkirks, St. Louis #767/R est:3000-4000
£1603 $2500 €2405 Landscape with blooming flowers and trees (36x28cm-14x11in) s. masonite prov. 10-Nov-2 Selkirks, St. Louis #768/R est:3000-4000
£1883 $2900 €2825 Gloucester harbour (28x30cm-11x12in) s. canvas on board painted c.1920. 8-Sep-2 Treadway Gallery, Cincinnati #561/R est:3000-4000
£1923 $3000 €2885 Wooded landscape with house (48x43cm-19x17in) s. canvasboard prov. 10-Nov-2 Selkirks, St. Louis #769/R est:3000-4000
£2628 $4100 €3942 Wooded forest scene (46x41cm-18x16in) s. canvasboard prov. 10-Nov-2 Selkirks, St. Louis #771/R est:5000-6000
£2821 $4400 €4232 Winter scene with bridge (51x61cm-20x24in) s. prov. 10-Nov-2 Selkirks, St. Louis #770/R est:4000-5000
£11538 $18000 €17307 Field flowers in a purple ceramic vase (91x102cm-36x40in) s. prov. 10-Nov-2 Selkirks, St. Louis #774/R est:10000-15000

CHERRY-GARRARD, Apsley George Benet (1886-1959) British
Works on paper
£500 $795 €750 Sunset (17x21cm-7x8in) s.d.1933 W/C. 29-Apr-3 Bonhams, New Bond Street #180/R

CHERSICLA, Bruno (20th C) Italian
Works on paper
£686 $1084 €1070 Earth with red sign (137x108cm-54x43in) mixed media on canvas exec.1962. 12-Nov-2 Babuino, Rome #265/R

CHERSON, David Davidovich (1882-1967) American/Russian
£478 $750 €717 Stylized flowers (89x30cm-35x12in) s. 28-Jul-2 William Jenack, New York #211

CHERUBINI, Carlo (1890-1978) Italian
£475 $741 €750 Nature morte au bouquet de roses blanches (48x63cm-19x25in) s. 20-Oct-2 Charbonneaux, Paris #111
£782 $1244 €1150 Flowers (50x36cm-20x14in) s. 1-Mar-3 Stadion, Trieste #552
£3481 $5500 €5500 Carnival in Venice (133x195cm-52x77in) s. 26-Nov-2 Christie's, Rome #132a/R est:1500-2000

CHERVIN, Louis (1905-1969) French?
£260 $411 €390 Jetee, Mer du Nord (60x73cm-24x29in) s.d.1948. 1-Dec-2 Lots Road, London #334

CHESTER, George (1813-1897) British
£260 $406 €390 River landscape with reed, woodland cottage and bridge (46x72cm-18x28in) s.d.1883. 17-Sep-2 Rosebery Fine Art, London #669/R

CHEVALIER, Andree (20th C) French
£861 $1403 €1300 Vase de fleurs des champs (100x81cm-39x32in) s. 31-Jan-3 Rabourdin & Choppin de Janvry, Paris #110

CHEVALIER, Henry (?) French
£897 $1364 €1400 Frozen lake (48x73cm-19x29in) s. 28-Aug-2 Castellana, Madrid #23/R
£897 $1364 €1400 Skaters on frozen lake (48x73cm-19x29in) s. 28-Aug-2 Castellana, Madrid #22/R

CHEVALIER, Jacques le (20th C) French
Sculpture
£19231 $29808 €30000 Lampe (42cm-17in) aluminium metal. 5-Dec-2 Gros & Delettrez, Paris #147/R est:20000

CHEVALIER, Jean (c.1725-c.1790) French
£12739 $19873 €20000 Portrait of an elegant lady and her daughter drinking chocolate (92x73cm-36x29in) s.d.1755. 5-Nov-2 Sotheby's, Amsterdam #335/R est:15000-20000

CHEVALIER, Nicholas (1828-1902) Australian
£580 $911 €870 An Asian maiden (23x18cm-9x7in) 17-Apr-3 Bonhams, Edinburgh #331
£627 $978 €941 Mt. Egmont (19x35cm-7x14in) s. board. 7-Nov-2 International Art Centre, Auckland #126/R est:3000-6000 (NZ.D 2000)
£4626 $7078 €6939 Approaching storm (62x91cm-24x36in) s.d.1884. 25-Aug-2 Sotheby's, Paddington #245/R est:4000-6000 (A.D 13000)
Works on paper
£630 $976 €945 Royal barges on the Ganges (18x30cm-7x12in) s.d.1866 W/C htd bodycol. 3-Dec-2 Sotheby's, Olympia #109/R
£3203 $4900 €4805 Beauties by a well (51x38cm-20x15in) s.d.1883 W/C gouache pencil. 26-Aug-2 Sotheby's, Paddington #658/R est:8000-12000 (A.D 9000)

CHEVALIER, Peter (1953-) German
£471 $772 €650 Untitled (31x35cm-12x14in) s.d.85 verso prov. 28-May-3 Lempertz, Koln #96/R
£769 $1192 €1200 Cyclops (63x92cm-25x36in) s.i.d.87 lit. 3-Dec-2 Lempertz, Koln #86/R
£3261 $5348 €4500 Garten Ronzano (165x135cm-65x53in) s.i.d.83 verso. 31-May-3 Villa Grisebach, Berlin #385/R est:5000-7000

CHEVALIER, Robert Magnus (fl.1876-1911) British
£1313 $2100 €1970 St Mark's, Venice (61x91cm-24x36in) s.d. 15-Mar-3 Selkirks, St. Louis #88/R est:1800-2400
Works on paper
£350 $567 €525 Figures on a street in Cairo (52x22cm-20x9in) s. W/C. 20-May-3 Sotheby's, Olympia #236/R

CHEVALIER, Roberte Jeanne Aimee (1907-) French
£346 $533 €550 Nu couche (46x61cm-18x24in) s. 22-Oct-2 Campo & Campo, Antwerp #38

CHEVALIER, Vincent (1770-1841) French
Photographs
£9615 $15192 €15000 Pantheon (19x13cm-7x5in) daguerrotype. 13-Nov-2 Beaussant & Lefèvre, Paris #45/R est:15000-20000

CHEVALLERIE, Friedrich Wilhelm von (?-1758) German
Works on paper
£1538 $2431 €2400 Bacchanal (24x27cm-9x11in) gouache. 16-Nov-2 Lempertz, Koln #1254/R est:1500

CHEVILLIARD, Vincent Jean Baptiste (1841-1904) French
£1633 $2596 €2400 Nest of chickens (44x64cm-17x25in) s. 24-Mar-3 Bernaerts, Antwerp #265/R est:2500-3000
£1796 $3000 €2604 Pause in the day (24x18cm-9x7in) s. panel. 22-Jun-3 Freeman, Philadelphia #32/R est:2000-3000

CHEVIOT, Lilian (fl.1894-1930) British
£3125 $4750 €4688 Pick of the horse fair (122x153cm-48x60in) 3-Jul-2 Naón & Cia, Buenos Aires #3/R est:4000-6000
£13497 $22000 €20246 Wake up England (71x86cm-28x34in) s. 11-Feb-3 Bonhams & Doyles, New York #212/R est:10000-15000

CHEVOLLEAU, Jean (1924-1996) French
£348 $550 €550 Deux chevaux de course (14x50cm-6x20in) s. i.verso. 27-Nov-2 Blanchet, Paris #117
£380 $600 €600 Peche au filet (24x41cm-9x16in) s. s.i.verso. 27-Nov-2 Blanchet, Paris #118
£662 $1079 €1000 Le marche, a peniscola, Espagne (81x60cm-32x24in) s. i.d.verso. 31-Jan-3 Charbonneaux, Paris #69
£739 $1190 €1050 Tolede (65x50cm-26x20in) s. 12-May-3 Lesieur & Le Bars, Le Havre #17/R
£1007 $1612 €1400 Nature morte au homard (21x38cm-8x15in) s. 18-May-3 Eric Pillon, Calais #226/R
£1060 $1727 €1600 Marine (50x65cm-20x26in) s. 31-Jan-3 Charbonneaux, Paris #68/R est:1300-1500
£1195 $1852 €1900 Peniscola (92x65cm-36x26in) s. painted 1974. 7-Oct-2 Claude Aguttes, Neuilly #187
£1409 $2269 €2100 L'arrivee (65x92cm-26x36in) s. d.1977 verso. 23-Feb-3 Lesieur & Le Bars, Le Havre #29/R
£1583 $2532 €2200 Nature morte a l'aiguiere (60x73cm-24x29in) s. s.i.d.90 verso. 18-May-3 Charbonneaux, Paris #136/R est:2000-2500
£1678 $2701 €2500 Nature morte a l'aiguiere (60x73cm-24x29in) s. 23-Feb-3 Lesieur & Le Bars, Le Havre #28/R
£1763 $2820 €2450 Combat de coqs (114x148cm-45x58in) s. s.i.d.75 verso. 18-May-3 Charbonneaux, Paris #137/R est:2500-3000

CHEVRIER, Ferdinando (1920-) Italian
£353 $557 €550 Concentric pattern (50x35cm-20x14in) s. tempera paper on cardboard. 15-Nov-2 Farsetti, Prato #260
£353 $557 €550 Purple and yellow (50x35cm-20x14in) s. tempera paper on cardboard. 15-Nov-2 Farsetti, Prato #261
£385 $608 €600 Axes (50x35cm-20x14in) s. tempera paper on cardboard. 15-Nov-2 Farsetti, Prato #259
£506 $790 €800 Abstract composition (96x57cm-38x22in) s. s.v. 19-Oct-2 Semenzato, Venice #141/R

CHEVTSOV, Igor (1963-) Russian
£268 $432 €400 Sunny Sunday (20x61cm-8x24in) s. canvas on cardboard. 18-Feb-3 Durán, Madrid #670/R
£275 $426 €413 Sunday at sea (12x37cm-5x15in) s. oil argillite. 29-Sep-2 John Nicholson, Haslemere #3/R
£275 $426 €413 On the beach in Caber (12x31cm-5x12in) s. board. 29-Sep-2 John Nicholson, Haslemere #5/R
£290 $459 €450 Summer at the seaside (20x61cm-8x24in) s. canvas on cardboard. 17-Dec-2 Durán, Madrid #662/R
£362 $586 €550 Beach (12x40cm-5x16in) s. cardboard. 21-Jan-3 Durán, Madrid #723/R
£362 $586 €550 Windy day (12x40cm-5x16in) s. cardboard. 21-Jan-3 Durán, Madrid #724/R
£369 $594 €550 Holiday at the beach (12x40cm-5x16in) s. cardboard. 18-Feb-3 Durán, Madrid #671/R
£439 $685 €650 Saint Mark"s (19x27cm-7x11in) s. 25-Mar-3 Durán, Madrid #733/R

CHEYNE, Ian Alec Johnson (1895-1955) British
£300 $468 €450 Shells (34x42cm-13x17in) s/. 17-Oct-2 Bonhams, Edinburgh #98

CHIA, Sandro (1946-) Italian
£2113 $3507 €3000 Figure (66x50cm-26x20in) s.d.1991 tempera paper. 10-Jun-3 Finarte Semenzato, Milan #262/R est:3000-3800
£7800 $13026 €11310 Untitled (91x107cm-36x42in) s.d.1982 oil pastel pencil. 24-Jun-3 Sotheby's, Olympia #111/R est:4000-6000
£9722 $15458 €14000 Two figures (105x71cm-41x28in) s. oil mixed media paper. 1-May-3 Meeting Art, Vercelli #120 est:12000
£13924 $22000 €22000 Arlequin (77x102cm-30x40in) acrylic cardboard. 29-Nov-2 Farsetti, Prato #303/R est:25000
£15603 $25277 €22000 Questo e l'autunno o questa e la notte (97x72cm-38x28in) i. prov.exhib. 26-May-3 Christie's, Milan #284/R est:25000-30000
£16026 $24840 €25000 Figure (92x73cm-36x29in) s. oil acrylic. 4-Dec-2 Finarte, Milan #470/R est:32000
£22000 $36740 €31900 Drinker (99x75cm-39x30in) s.d.84 prov.exhib. 27-Jun-3 Christie's, London #177/R est:12000-18000
£23000 $35420 €34500 Sisyphe (152x101cm-60x40in) s.d.84 oil pastel on board prov. 22-Oct-2 Christie's, London #55/R est:18000-22000
£25695 $40855 €37000 Ragazzo con bandie Italiani (111x108cm-44x43in) s. s.d.84 verso prov. 29-Apr-3 Artcurial Briest, Paris #485/R est:12000-15000
£28000 $45920 €42000 Sul Collo (86x91cm-34x36in) s.i.d.1981 verso prov.exhib. 6-Feb-3 Christie's, London #651/R est:20000-30000
£34375 $55000 €51563 Figure looking in landscape - The Tempest (198x218cm-78x86in) s.i.verso painted c.1983 prov. 14-May-3 Sotheby's, New York #425/R est:30000-40000
£55556 $91667 €80000 Diretto direttore (130x162cm-51x64in) s.i.d.1981 prov.lit. 3-Jul-3 Christie's, Paris #13/R est:80000-120000
Sculpture
£950 $1548 €1425 Seated nude (35x23x30cm-14x9x12in) s.num.X/X green pat. bronze executed c.1990 prov. 3-Feb-3 Sotheby's, Olympia #98/R est:800-1200
£1500 $2325 €2250 L'ange (37cm-15in) st.sig.num.IV/IX gold blue black pat. bronze marble base. 5-Dec-2 Christie's, Kensington #276/R est:1500-2000
£2200 $3586 €3300 Winged figure (62cm-24in) s.num.39/50 green pat. bronze executed 1997. 3-Feb-3 Sotheby's, Olympia #97/R est:1500-2000

£2532 $4000 €4000 Sitting man with grapes (44cm-17in) i.num.32/50 bronze on marble base executed c.1990. 26-Nov-2 Sotheby's, Amsterdam #79/R est:4000-5000
£3000 $4890 €4500 Man holding heart (48cm-19in) s. num.III/X black gold pat. bronze. 3-Feb-3 Sotheby's, Olympia #58/R est:4000-6000
£3000 $4920 €4500 Untitled (63x28x28cm-25x11x11in) st.sig.num.PA 7/10 painted bronze exec.c.1990 prov. 7-Feb-3 Sotheby's, London #280/R est:4000-6000
£3056 $4858 €4400 Angel (35x30x24cm-14x12x9in) s. num.I/X green pat bronze. 1-May-3 Meeting Art, Vercelli #450
£6500 $10595 €9750 Blue angel (36cm-14in) s.i. num.5/10 blue black pat. bronze on marble base. 3-Feb-3 Sotheby's, Olympia #59/R est:4000-6000
£10759 $16785 €17000 Angel (65x25x20cm-26x10x8in) s. bronze. 14-Sep-2 Meeting Art, Vercelli #806/R est:15000

Works on paper

£276 $460 €400 Personnage dans la foret (27x21cm-11x8in) s. graphite dr prov. 10-Jul-3 Artcurial Briest, Paris #338
£1736 $2760 €2500 Untitled (28x20cm-11x8in) s. mixed media exec.2000. 1-May-3 Meeting Art, Vercelli #191
£2703 $4216 €4000 Figure (91x63cm-36x25in) s.d.89 col pencil paper on canvas. 28-Mar-3 Farsetti, Prato #105/R
£2800 $4564 €4200 Untitled (30x22cm-12x9in) s.d.85 W/C gouache pen ink. 3-Feb-3 Sotheby's, Olympia #94/R est:3000-4000
£2821 $4372 €4400 Figure (76x59cm-30x23in) s.d.1987 mixed media. 4-Dec-2 Finarte, Milan #515/R est:4500
£3205 $5032 €5000 Untitled (75x55cm-30x22in) s.d.90 mixed media. 20-Nov-2 Pandolfini, Florence #135/R
£3562 $5556 €5200 Two figures and a centaure (50x37cm-20x15in) s. mixed media paper on canvas. 10-Apr-3 Finarte Semenzato, Rome #64/R
£3750 $6000 €5625 Untitled (72x54cm-28x21in) s.d.87 gouache paperboard prov. 14-May-3 Sotheby's, New York #423/R est:7000-9000
£4051 $6400 €6400 Untitled (65x52cm-26x20in) s. mixed media collage card exec.1993. 29-Nov-2 Farsetti, Prato #273/R est:6700
£4114 $6500 €6500 Figure (63x50cm-25x20in) s. gouache wax crayon exec.2000. 27-Nov-2 Tajan, Paris #96/R
£4861 $8021 €7000 Giovane artista preso dalla scultura (30x30cm-12x12in) s.d.1982 i.verso chl pastel gouache prov. 3-Jul-3 Christie's, Paris #12/R est:3000-4000
£8125 $13000 €12188 Untitled (118x103cm-46x41in) s.d.84 gouache W/C. 16-May-3 Phillips, New York #162/R est:15000-20000
£8333 $13250 €12000 Untitled (81x73cm-32x29in) s.d.1989 mixed media paper on canvas. 1-May-3 Meeting Art, Vercelli #478 est:10000
£8974 $14090 €14000 Untitled (83x60cm-33x24in) s. mixed media. 23-Nov-2 Meeting Art, Vercelli #368/R est:10000
£9500 $15865 €13775 Untitled (89x81cm-35x32in) s.d.87 pencil pastel chl prov. 27-Jun-3 Christie's, London #184/R est:8000-12000
£9615 $14904 €15000 Figure seen from the back (100x70cm-39x28in) s.d.1988 pastel card lit. 4-Dec-2 Finarte, Milan #486/R est:16000
£10000 $16400 €15000 Man (123x90cm-48x35in) pastel prov. 7-Feb-3 Sotheby's, London #266/R est:7000-10000

CHIACIGH, Giuseppe (1895-1967) Italian

£612 $973 €900 White horse (30x49cm-12x19in) s. board. 1-Mar-3 Stadion, Trieste #5
£612 $973 €900 In the desert (50x60cm-20x24in) s. board. 1-Mar-3 Stadion, Trieste #106

CHIALIVA, Luigi (1842-1914) Swiss

£9434 $15000 €14151 Shepherdess (52x40cm-20x16in) s. 7-Mar-3 Skinner, Boston #235/R est:8000-12000
£10625 $17000 €15938 Shepherdess and flock resting beside a lake (46x36cm-18x14in) s. 15-Mar-3 Selkirks, St. Louis #675/R est:10000-15000

Works on paper

£739 $1146 €1109 Troupeau de moutons (28x44cm-11x17in) s. W/C gouache. 7-Dec-2 Galerie du Rhone, Sion #316/R (S.FR 1700)
£806 $1274 €1250 Moutons (11x16cm-4x6in) s. W/C. 17-Dec-2 Rossini, Paris #17
£962 $1519 €1500 Pecheur (29x46cm-11x18in) s. W/C prov. 18-Nov-2 Sotheby's, Paris #65/R

CHIANA, Epaminanua (19/20th C) ?

£260 $411 €377 Still life of fruit (30x51cm-12x20in) s.d.1918. 22-Jul-3 Gorringes, Lewes #1719

CHIANG, Anita (20th C) New Zealander

£632 $1004 €948 Baby face (79x120cm-31x47in) s.i. board. 25-Feb-3 Peter Webb, Auckland #79 est:500-700 (NZ.D 1800)

CHIAPORELLA, Luigi (18/19th C) Italian

Sculpture

£1200 $1884 €1800 Allegory of painting (28x3cm-11x1in) s. terracotta prov. 10-Dec-2 Sotheby's, London #134/R est:1000-1500

CHIAPORY, Bernard Charles (19th C) French

Works on paper

£1600 $2656 €2400 In the harem (61x71cm-24x28in) s. indis d. pastel. 12-Jun-3 Bonhams, New Bond Street #603/R est:1200-1800

CHIAPPINI, Ludovico (attrib) (17th C) Italian

Sculpture

£33557 $54027 €50000 Angels (130cm-51in) painted wood pair. 19-Feb-3 Semenzato, Venice #80/R est:60000

CHIARI, Giuseppe (1926-) Italian

Works on paper

£316 $494 €500 Guitar and music (70x100cm-28x39in) s. mixed media collage card. 14-Sep-2 Meeting Art, Vercelli #791
£321 $503 €500 Music (70x50cm-28x20in) s. mixed media collage cardboard. 23-Nov-2 Meeting Art, Vercelli #56
£392 $627 €600 Paino (70x100cm-28x39in) s. mixed media. 4-Jan-3 Meeting Art, Vercelli #336
£425 $680 €650 Guitar (100x70cm-39x28in) s. mixed media collage cardboard. 4-Jan-3 Meeting Art, Vercelli #579
£451 $718 €650 Guitar (100x38cm-39x15in) s.d.1998 verso mixed media collage on guitar. 1-May-3 Meeting Art, Vercelli #34
£472 $751 €680 Music (26x19cm-10x7in) s. Chinese ink pen. 1-May-3 Meeting Art, Vercelli #72
£641 $1006 €1000 Serenade (119x77cm-47x30in) s. mixed media. 20-Nov-2 Pandolfini, Florence #157/R
£884 $1406 €1300 Violin (70x70cm-28x28in) s. mixed media collage violin board. 1-Mar-3 Meeting Art, Vercelli #402

CHIARI, Giuseppe Bartolomeo (attrib) (1654-1727) Italian

£3800 $6346 €5510 Holy Family in glory with putti (68x51cm-27x20in) 11-Jul-3 Christie's, Kensington #224/R est:2000-4000
£11511 $18417 €16000 Venus and Adonis (34x27cm-13x11in) copper oval prov. 13-May-3 Christie's, Amsterdam #44/R est:7000-10000

CHIARI, Giuseppe Bartolomeo (style) (1654-1727) Italian

£22000 $34540 €33000 Massacre of the innocents (136x100cm-54x39in) prov. 13-Dec-2 Christie's, Kensington #255/R est:5000-7000

CHIAROMONTE, Gaetano (1872-1962) Italian

Sculpture

£1013 $1600 €1600 Bust o Master Orsi (60cm-24in) s.st.f.Chiurazzi pat bronze. 26-Nov-2 Christie's, Rome #12/R

CHIBOURG, Pierre Justin Leopold (1823-?) French

£633 $1000 €1000 Levee du soleil. Coucher de soleil (15x21cm-6x8in) s. panel pair. 1-Dec-2 Peron, Melun #157

CHICCO, Riccardo (1910-1973) Italian

£353 $554 €550 Cavour Gardens (40x50cm-16x20in) s.d.1969 cardboard. 23-Nov-2 Meeting Art, Vercelli #132

CHICHARRO Y AGUERA, Eduardo (1873-1949) Spanish

£439 $685 €650 Sunset, Avila (54x65cm-21x26in) s.d.1938. 25-Mar-3 Durán, Madrid #722/R
£1935 $3058 €3000 Garden corner (84x44cm-33x17in) s.d. i.verso. 17-Dec-2 Segre, Madrid #88/R
£2212 $3494 €3450 Woman (61x50cm-24x20in) s.d.1945. 14-Nov-2 Arte, Seville #399/R
£10000 $15700 €15000 Gitana - gypsy girl (83x98cm-33x39in) s.d.1906 prov. 19-Nov-2 Sotheby's, London #66/R est:10000-15000

CHICO PRATS, Joseph Manuel (1916-) Spanish

Works on paper

£503 $775 €800 Rue Norvin, Paris (34x45cm-13x18in) s.d.1956 gouache prov. 28-Oct-2 Segre, Madrid #112/R

CHICOTE, Victoriano (1874-1945) Spanish

£2534 $3953 €3801 Interior scene with young woman wearing red party dress (198x115cm-78x45in) s. 23-Sep-2 Rasmussen, Vejle #133/R est:30000-40000 (D.KR 30000)

CHIERICI, Gaetano (1838-1920) Italian

£83871 $130000 €125807 Feeding time (28x38cm-11x15in) s. 30-Oct-2 Christie's, Rockefeller NY #49/R est:140000-180000

CHIESA, Pietro (1876-1959) Swiss

£2402 $3747 €3603 Alberi fioriti a Cortivalle (50x60cm-20x24in) s.d.51. 8-Nov-2 Dobiaschofsky, Bern #171/R est:7500 (S.FR 5500)

Works on paper

£3057 $4769 €4586 Garden landscape at Lugan lake in the summer (30x46cm-12x18in) s.i.d.1901 W/C bodycol. 8-Nov-2 Dobiaschofsky, Bern #181/R est:6000 (S.FR 7000)

CHIESA, Renato (1947-) Italian
Works on paper
£556 $883 €800 Fourth dimension (25x50cm-10x20in) s. mixed media on canvas. 1-May-3 Meeting Art, Vercelli #82
£833 $1308 €1300 Fobos (50x70cm-20x28in) s.verso mixed media on canvas exec.2000. 23-Nov-2 Meeting Art, Vercelli #327/R
£903 $1435 €1300 Creation (50x70cm-20x28in) s. mixed media exec.c.2000. 1-May-3 Meeting Art, Vercelli #148

CHIESI, Giorgio (1941-) Italian
£261 $418 €400 Business man (30x20cm-12x8in) s. enamel board. 4-Jan-3 Meeting Art, Vercelli #331
£641 $1006 €1000 Clown (70x50cm-28x20in) s. enamel. 23-Nov-2 Meeting Art, Vercelli #45/R
£949 $1481 €1500 Picking the apple (70x60cm-28x24in) s. mixed media on canvas. 14-Sep-2 Meeting Art, Vercelli #321
Works on paper
£253 $395 €400 Phone call (60x70cm-24x28in) s. mixed media on canvas. 14-Sep-2 Meeting Art, Vercelli #89
£316 $494 €500 Warrior (100x70cm-39x28in) s. mixed media on canvas exec.2000. 14-Sep-2 Meeting Art, Vercelli #430/R
£316 $494 €500 Night ward (100x90cm-39x35in) s. mixed media on canvas. 14-Sep-2 Meeting Art, Vercelli #465/R
£327 $523 €500 Yellow bike (70x60cm-28x24in) s. mixed media on canvas. 4-Jan-3 Meeting Art, Vercelli #182
£327 $523 €500 Free style (60x90cm-24x35in) s. mixed media collage. 4-Jan-3 Meeting Art, Vercelli #492
£347 $552 €500 Ghost sailing boat (100x70cm-39x28in) s. mixed media on canvas. 1-May-3 Meeting Art, Vercelli #278
£359 $575 €550 Metaphysical cock (80x70cm-31x28in) s. mixed media on canvas. 4-Jan-3 Meeting Art, Vercelli #184
£380 $592 €600 Bringing peace (80x90cm-31x35in) s. mixed media on canvas. 14-Sep-2 Meeting Art, Vercelli #741/R
£443 $691 €700 Got to destination (80x90cm-31x35in) s. mixed media on canvas. 14-Sep-2 Meeting Art, Vercelli #703/R
£521 $828 €750 Easy adventure (110x120cm-43x47in) s. 1-May-3 Meeting Art, Vercelli #559
£556 $889 €850 Wandering knight (120x110cm-47x43in) s. mixed media on canvas. 4-Jan-3 Meeting Art, Vercelli #68
£570 $889 €900 Stressed (120x100cm-47x39in) s. mixed media on canvas. 14-Sep-2 Meeting Art, Vercelli #932/R
£633 $987 €1000 Summer feeling (100x70cm-39x28in) s. mixed media on canvas. 14-Sep-2 Meeting Art, Vercelli #340/R
£759 $1185 €1200 Visiting a friend (60x70cm-24x28in) s. mixed media on canvas. 14-Sep-2 Meeting Art, Vercelli #279

CHIESI, Pietro (19th C) Italian
£1781 $2778 €2600 Capri (71x109cm-28x43in) s. 10-Apr-3 Van Ham, Cologne #1360/R est:2800

CHIGOT, Alphonse (19th C) French
£16667 $26167 €26000 Cavaliers au pied des remparts (200x138cm-79x54in) s. 16-Dec-2 Gros & Delettrez, Paris #448/R est:30000-40000

CHIGOT, Eugène (1860-1927) French
£252 $390 €400 Port de Quimper (24x32cm-9x13in) s. 30-Oct-2 Coutau Begarie, Paris #140
£348 $539 €522 House in park landscape (44x55cm-17x22in) s. 9-Dec-2 Philippe Schuler, Zurich #8629 (S.FR 800)
£660 $1042 €950 Bord de riviere (35x26cm-14x10in) s.d.1912. 25-Apr-3 Piasa, Paris #67
£950 $1492 €1425 Lake in autumn, Versailles (66x88cm-26x35in) s. 15-Apr-3 Bonhams, Knightsbridge #220/R
£1900 $3002 €2850 Clair de lune (18x22cm-7x9in) s. board. 3-Apr-3 Christie's, Kensington #24/R

CHIGUSA, Kitani (1895-1947) Japanese
Works on paper
£5660 $9000 €8490 Beauty sewing (70x82cm-28x32in) s. ink col gold silk hanging scroll. 24-Mar-3 Christie's, Rockefeller NY #206/R est:6000-8000
£15094 $24000 €22641 Beauty at her toilette (170x218cm-67x86in) s. ink col gold silk two-panel screen. 24-Mar-3 Christie's, Rockefeller NY #207/R est:30000-40000

CHIHUNG YANG (20th C) Chinese
Works on paper
£876 $1367 €1314 Woman in sentiment (127x96cm-50x38in) s.d.85 mixed media. 6-Nov-2 AB Stockholms Auktionsverk #963/R (S.KR 12500)

CHIKANOBU, Kano and MINENOBU, Kano (17th C) Japanese
Works on paper
£10692 $17000 €16038 Pine, plum, flowers and grasses of the four seasons (107x306cm-42x120in) s. ink col gold leaf six-panel screens double-sided pair. 24-Mar-3 Christie's, Rockefeller NY #87/R est:12000-18000

CHILCOTT, Gavin (1950-) New Zealander
£634 $1046 €919 Vessel (55x75cm-22x30in) s.d.1995 acrylic W/C paper. 1-Jul-3 Peter Webb, Auckland #56/R est:2000-3000 (NZ.D 1800)
£972 $1516 €1458 At the tandoori restaurant and later that night (91x137cm-36x54in) s.i.d.January 1986 verso acrylic. 5-Nov-2 Peter Webb, Auckland #9/R est:3000-4000 (NZ.D 3100)
Works on paper
£442 $690 €663 New ceramics III (29x83cm-11x33in) s.d.1995 W/C. 6-Aug-2 Peter Webb, Auckland #76 est:1000-2000 (NZ.D 1500)
£560 $874 €840 Vases (55x74cm-22x29in) s.d.1995 W/C. 6-Aug-2 Peter Webb, Auckland #75/R est:1800-2500 (NZ.D 1900)
£1220 $1866 €1830 Revised ideal standard from - homage to Ed Allington (115x95cm-45x37in) s.d.August 1987 verso mixed media. 21-Aug-2 Dunbar Sloane, Auckland #30/R est:2500-5000 (NZ.D 4000)

CHILCOTT, Gavin and HAMMOND, Bill (20th C) New Zealander
£1520 $2372 €2280 Untitled (27x45cm-11x18in) s.verso board. 7-Nov-2 International Art Centre, Auckland #27/R est:4000-6000 (NZ.D 4850)
£1754 $2737 €2631 Plate (85x85cm-33x33in) s.d.1991 board. 27-Mar-3 International Art Centre, Auckland #67/R est:5000-8000 (NZ.D 5000)

CHILD, Edwin Burge (1868-1937) American
£20700 $32500 €31050 Squash blossoms (127x91cm-50x36in) s. exhib. 19-Nov-2 Butterfields, San Francisco #8059/R est:10000-15000

CHILDS, Jamie (20th C) American
Works on paper
£1032 $1600 €1548 Standing male nude (50x32cm-20x13in) s.d.1974 pencil sold with two others. 29-Oct-2 Sotheby's, New York #301 est:400-600

CHILLIDA BELZUNCE, Eduardo (1964-) Spanish
£865 $1367 €1350 Interior (73x60cm-29x24in) s. 13-Nov-2 Ansorena, Madrid #47/R

CHILLIDA, Eduardo (1924-2002) Spanish
Prints
£1899 $3000 €3000 Gau at night (90x62cm-35x24in) s. eau forte. 29-Nov-2 Drouot Estimations, Paris #11
£2128 $3447 €3000 Colympic Centennial (90x56cm-35x22in) s. num.18/50 serigraph lit. 20-May-3 Segre, Madrid #219/R est:3000
£2446 $3914 €3400 Grande modulation (55x58cm-22x23in) s. num.26/50 aquatint etching. 15-May-3 Neumeister, Munich #691/R est:1000-1200
£2536 $4159 €3500 Leizaran (91x64cm-36x25in) s. aquatint etching. 31-May-3 Villa Grisebach, Berlin #323/R est:3000-4000
£2564 $3974 €4000 Columbus (12x56cm-5x22in) s.num.I/XXXIX silk screen print exec.1992. 7-Dec-2 Van Ham, Cologne #101 est:2500
£4839 $7645 €7500 Banatu II (123x161cm-48x63in) s. num.42/50 eau forte lit. 17-Dec-2 Segre, Madrid #151/R est:3500
£7595 $12000 €12000 Banatu III (122x100cm-48x39in) s. aquatint. 30-Nov-2 Villa Grisebach, Berlin #392/R est:5000-6000
Sculpture
£42000 $64680 €63000 Larra (30x25x31cm-12x10x12in) mono. terracotta executed 1984 prov.exhib. 23-Oct-2 Christie's, London #123/R est:40000-60000
£60000 $92400 €90000 Estudio peine del viento III (11cm-4in) mono. iron wooden base executed c.1965 prov.exhib. 23-Oct-2 Christie's, London #122/R est:50000-70000
£220000 $367400 €330000 Hierros de tremblor II (29x24x63cm-11x9x25in) st.mono. iron exc.1956 prov.exhib.lit. 25-Jun-3 Sotheby's, London #24/R est:150000-200000
Works on paper
£3205 $4968 €5000 Composition (15x14cm-6x6in) s.mono.d.1992 Indian ink brush. 6-Dec-2 Hauswedell & Nolte, Hamburg #82/R est:2000
£4800 $7584 €7200 Untitled (11x12cm-4x5in) mono. brush ink exec.1967 exhib. 3-Apr-3 Christie's, Kensington #207/R
£13930 $22707 €21035 Portrait of Pablo Palazuelo (21x27cm-8x11in) s.d.1949 pencil prov.exhib.lit. 11-Feb-3 Segre, Madrid #233/R est:24000
£17949 $27821 €28000 Untitled (31x39cm-12x15in) s. Indian ink collage prov. 3-Dec-2 Lempertz, Koln #87/R est:20000-22000
£19000 $31730 €27550 Untitled (40x30cm-16x12in) s. pencil cut out paper collage prov. 26-Jun-3 Sotheby's, London #211/R est:8000-12000
£25000 $38500 €37500 Gravitacion (38x56cm-15x22in) s. ink paper string executed 1990 prov. 23-Oct-2 Christie's, London #121/R est:25000-35000
£29000 $47560 €43500 Untitled (40x73cm-16x29in) s.i. black ink pencil prov.exhib. 6-Feb-3 Christie's, London #628/R est:12000-16000
£29000 $48430 €42050 Untitled (70x100cm-28x39in) s. ink exec.c.1970. 26-Jun-3 Sotheby's, London #215/R est:18000-25000
£37179 $57628 €58000 Gravitacion (59x79cm-23x31in) s. i. verso Indian ink brush prov. 3-Dec-2 Lempertz, Koln #88/R est:55000-60000

£75000 $125250 €112500 Gravitacion (111x119cm-44x47in) mono.i. ink handmade paper string exc.1989 prov.exhib. 26-Jun-3 Christie's, London #34/R est:60000-80000

CHILONE, Vincenzo (1758-1839) Italian
£57927 $95000 €86891 View of the flooded Piazza San Marco, Venice, December 9 1825 (60x79cm-24x31in) prov. 29-May-3 Sotheby's, New York #157/R est:50000-70000

CHILTIAN, Grigor (20th C) Russian
£3910 $6139 €6100 Vase with carnations (55x38cm-22x15in) s. 12-Dec-2 Rabourdin & Choppin de Janvry, Paris #26/R
£4615 $7246 €7200 Nature morte de fleurs et fruits (73x54cm-29x21in) s.d.31. 12-Dec-2 Rabourdin & Choppin de Janvry, Paris #22/R est:3000

CHILVERS, Robert (20th C) New Zealander
£239 $349 €359 Summer Harbour, Picton (59x71cm-23x28in) s.d.66. 12-Sep-1 Watson's, Christchurch #21 (NZ.D 800)

CHIMENTI, Jacopo (1554-1640) Italian
£613 $901 €950 Jesus Christ (21x17cm-8x7in) s. 24-Jun-2 Babuino, Rome #47

CHIMENTI, Jacopo (attrib) (1554-1640) Italian
Works on paper
£610 $1000 €885 Study for a fresco (23x28cm-9x11in) red ink wash. 30-May-3 Aspire, Cleveland #68/R est:1500-2500

CHINA TRADE SCHOOL
£3947 $6000 €5921 Portrait of the Gleanros of London, approaching Hong Kong (46x61cm-18x24in) i. 17-Aug-2 North East Auctions, Portsmouth #808/R est:7000-10000
£5137 $7500 €7706 Shipping at Whampoa Anchorage, Dane's Island cemetery in foreground (46x79cm-18x31in) 3-Nov-1 North East Auctions, Portsmouth #1037/R est:7000-10000
£6507 $9500 €9761 Whampoa Anchorage and Danes Island (10x15cm-4x6in) copper painted c.1810 prov. 3-Nov-1 North East Auctions, Portsmouth #1105/R est:6000-9000
£9589 $14000 €14384 Port scene of Praya Grande at Macao (46x79cm-18x31in) 3-Nov-1 North East Auctions, Portsmouth #1038/R est:10000-15000
£9868 $15000 €14802 View of Whampoa Reach from Dane's Island (46x58cm-18x23in) 17-Aug-2 North East Auctions, Portsmouth #807/R est:15000-25000
£19863 $29000 €29795 Shipping off Table Mountain and Bay, Cape Town, S Africa (28x56cm-11x22in) prov. 3-Nov-1 North East Auctions, Portsmouth #1107/R est:12000-16000
£46053 $70000 €69080 Months of the year. reverse paintings on glass nine. 17-Aug-2 North East Auctions, Portsmouth #626/R
£46053 $70000 €69080 Extensive view of the Bund at Shanghai (41x94cm-16x37in) 17-Aug-2 North East Auctions, Portsmouth #750/R est:70000-90000
£47368 $72000 €71052 Memorial to George Washington (71x51cm-28x20in) i. reverse painting on glass lit. 17-Aug-2 North East Auctions, Portsmouth #601/R est:20000-40000
Works on paper
£5592 $8500 €8388 Hong Kong harbour (15x28cm-6x11in) W/C. 17-Aug-2 North East Auctions, Portsmouth #1062/R est:9000-15000

CHINA TRADE SCHOOL, 19th C
£8904 $13000 €13356 Hong Kong from the east (23x28cm-9x11in) painted c.1850-1860 prov. 3-Nov-1 North East Auctions, Portsmouth #1108/R est:14000-18000
£16447 $25000 €24671 Hong Kong from the harbour (46x74cm-18x29in) painted c.1865. 17-Aug-2 North East Auctions, Portsmouth #673/R est:20000-30000
£19178 $28000 €28767 Chinese Ports and scenes (10x15cm-4x6in) painted c.1800-1810 four prov. 3-Nov-1 North East Auctions, Portsmouth #1109/R est:12000-18000
£22368 $34000 €33552 Views of the Boca Tigris and the Hongs at Canton (46x58cm-18x23in) painted c.1810-1815. 17-Aug-2 North East Auctions, Portsmouth #1015/R est:30000-50000

CHINARD, Joseph (1756-1813) French
Sculpture
£3846 $5962 €6000 Portrait du Comte de Bondy (73x51x29cm-29x20x11in) s. plaster exec.1812. 9-Dec-2 Rabourdin & Choppin de Janvry, Paris #90/R
£4167 $6458 €6500 Portrait du General Duhesme (20x20cm-8x8in) s. terracotta relief. 9-Dec-2 Rabourdin & Choppin de Janvry, Paris #85/R
£4808 $7452 €7500 Portrait d'Alexandre-Antoine Regny (71x46x30cm-28x18x12in) s. pat bronze. 9-Dec-2 Rabourdin & Choppin de Janvry, Paris #88/R
£7051 $10929 €11000 Portrait d'homme de profil (31x31cm-12x12in) s.d.1809 terracotta relief. 9-Dec-2 Rabourdin & Choppin de Janvry, Paris #84/R
£9615 $14904 €15000 Portrait de Felix Bacchiochi (28x17x9cm-11x7x4in) s. terracotta. 9-Dec-2 Rabourdin & Choppin de Janvry, Paris #81/R
£11189 $18685 €16000 L'hiver et l'ete (30cm-12in) one s.d.1777 one st. terracotta onyx socle pair. 25-Jun-3 Sotheby's, Paris #92/R est:18000-25000
£12179 $18878 €19000 Portrait du Prince Eugene. s. terracotta. 9-Dec-2 Rabourdin & Choppin de Janvry, Paris #82/R
£15385 $24308 €24000 Napoleon en buste (65cm-26in) terracotta sold with base. 17-Nov-2 Osenat, Fontainebleau #280/R est:30000
£19551 $30304 €30500 Portrait presume de madame de Stael (76x49x28cm-30x19x11in) plaster pat. terracotta. 9-Dec-2 Rabourdin & Choppin de Janvry, Paris #83/R

CHINARD, Joseph (attrib) (1756-1813) French
Sculpture
£2098 $3503 €3000 Portrait presume de Madame de Stael (74cm-29in) plaster lit. 25-Jun-3 Sotheby's, Paris #93/R est:6000-8000

CHINARD, Joseph (studio) (1756-1813) French
Sculpture
£5128 $7949 €8000 Portrait d'inconnue (67x41x20cm-26x16x8in) plaster terracotta lit. 9-Dec-2 Rabourdin & Choppin de Janvry, Paris #80/R

CHINESE SCHOOL, 18th C
£8805 $14000 €13208 Figures within a landscape (63x94cm-25x37in) prov. 30-Apr-3 Sotheby's, New York #676/R est:6000-8000

CHINESE SCHOOL, 18th/19th C
Works on paper
£714 $1043 €1100 Noblemen (137x180cm-54x71in) W/C pair. 17-Jun-2 Ansorena, Madrid #325a/R

CHINESE SCHOOL, 19th C
£4000 $6480 €6000 S.S. Historian in Chinese waters (44x58cm-17x23in) 21-Jan-3 Bonhams, New Bond Street #220/R est:500-700
£5556 $9000 €8056 American three masted clipper Borneo (65x89cm-26x35in) 29-Jul-3 Christie's, Rockefeller NY #173/R est:12000-18000
£6452 $10000 €9678 View of the Port of Macao, from the south looking north (46x53cm-18x21in) 2-Oct-2 Christie's, Rockefeller NY #175/R est:10000-15000
£10256 $16000 €15384 Foreign factories, Canton (43x76cm-17x30in) 27-Mar-3 Sotheby's, New York #93/R est:18000-25000
£20513 $32000 €30770 Meeting of the Shanghai regatta club (30x47cm-12x19in) 27-Mar-3 Sotheby's, New York #92/R est:25000-35000
£46296 $75000 €69444 Bund at Shanghai (44x118cm-17x46in) prov. 21-Jan-3 Christie's, Rockefeller NY #353/R est:20000

CHINESE SCHOOL, 20th C
Works on paper
£4472 $7065 €6708 Various subjects (17x50cm-7x20in) s. ink col folding fan. 28-Apr-3 Sotheby's, Hong Kong #554/R est:20000-30000 (HK.D 55000)

CHING, Raymond (1939-) New Zealander
£3797 $6000 €5696 Perched kestrel (37x26cm-15x10in) s. board lit. 3-Apr-3 Christie's, Rockefeller NY #221/R est:6000-8000
Works on paper
£1123 $1752 €1685 Tufted duck and mallard (46x38cm-18x15in) s.d.1975 pencil lit. 27-Mar-3 International Art Centre, Auckland #101/R est:3500-5500 (NZ.D 3200)
£1754 $2737 €2631 European common coutts (45x58cm-18x23in) s.d.1966 W/C. 27-Mar-3 International Art Centre, Auckland #100/R est:7000-10000 (NZ.D 5000)
£2229 $3500 €3344 Razor-bill, Alca Torda (51x70cm-20x28in) s.i.d.1966 W/C exhib. 10-Dec-2 Peter Webb, Auckland #61/R est:7000-10000 (NZ.D 7000)

£2456 $3832 €3684 Hammerhead (49x41cm-19x16in) s.d.1978 W/C pencil lit. 27-Mar-3 International Art Centre, Auckland #84/R est:10000-15000 (NZ.D 7000)

£4211 $6568 €6317 Pukeko chick (51x36cm-20x14in) s. W/C lit. 27-Mar-3 International Art Centre, Auckland #85/R est:10000-15000 (NZ.D 12000)

£4459 $7000 €6689 Male and female Huia (41x32cm-16x13in) s.d.1972 pencil dr. pair. 10-Dec-2 Peter Webb, Auckland #58/R est:15000-20000 (NZ.D 14000)

£5329 $8313 €7994 Kiri Te Kanawa (62x55cm-24x22in) s. W/C. 7-Nov-2 International Art Centre, Auckland #94/R est:20000-30000 (NZ.D 17000)

£8150 $12715 €12225 Kiwi and Weta (52x38cm-20x15in) s. W/C. 7-Nov-2 International Art Centre, Auckland #104/R est:15000-25000 (NZ.D 26000)

CHINI, Galileo (1873-1956) Italian

£611 $954 €917 Una via di Firenze - street in Firenze (35x21cm-14x8in) s.i. verso masonite. 6-Nov-2 Dobiaschofsky, Bern #405/R (S.FR 1400)

£3200 $5120 €4640 Pine grove in Viareggio (31x41cm-12x16in) init.d.1929 board. 11-Mar-3 Babuino, Rome #274/R

£3205 $4968 €5000 Model (60x90cm-24x35in) s.d.32. 5-Dec-2 Stadion, Trieste #822/R

£3226 $5097 €5000 Houses (36x44cm-14x17in) s. board prov. 18-Dec-2 Christie's, Rome #141/R

£3438 $5500 €4985 Studio di nude (61x48cm-24x19in) s. board. 17-May-3 CRN Auctions, Cambridge #13

£4113 $6664 €5800 Marina versiliese (55x70cm-22x28in) s.d.21 panel prov. 22-May-3 Stadion, Trieste #259/R est:5000-7000

CHINNERY, George (1774-1852) British

£1200 $1920 €1800 Portrait of a gentleman (28x20cm-11x8in) 11-Mar-3 Gorringes, Lewes #2345 est:1200-1500

£2632 $4000 €3948 Portrait of a lady, possibly Mrs Davis (10x8cm-4x3in) lit. 17-Aug-2 North East Auctions, Portsmouth #782/R est:4000-5000

£4200 $6636 €6300 Portrait of a gentleman (24x20cm-9x8in) 28-Nov-2 Sotheby's, London #190/R est:4000-6000

£4200 $6678 €6300 Portrait of Andrew Stirling esquire at his desk (40x32cm-16x13in) prov.exhib. 29-Apr-3 Bonhams, New Bond Street #47/R est:2000-3000

£7500 $12450 €11250 Indian watchman and his goat (32x39cm-13x15in) prov. 12-Jun-3 Sotheby's, London #103/R est:7000-10000

£7500 $12450 €11250 Chinese junk at sea (15x17cm-6x7in) prov.exhib.lit. 12-Jun-3 Sotheby's, London #102/R est:6000-8000

£18000 $28260 €27000 Chinese family at the sea-shore, near Macau (17x23cm-7x9in) prov. 16-Dec-2 Sotheby's, London #64/R est:20000-30000

Miniatures

£1500 $2355 €2250 Young girl in a white dress (7cm-3xin) silver gilt frame oval. 10-Dec-2 Christie's, London #240/R est:400-600

Works on paper

£550 $875 €825 Studies of Chinese figures (18x11cm-7x4in) i. pencil. 19-Mar-3 Sotheby's, London #181/R

£550 $875 €825 Chinese barber (8x7cm-3x3in) i. pencil exhib. 29-Apr-3 Bonhams, New Bond Street #42

£620 $973 €930 Nanny goat and kids (14x16cm-6x6in) i.d.1811 pencil. 16-Dec-2 Sotheby's, London #67/R

£1600 $2544 €2400 My good little squib (4x8cm-2x3in) i. pencil sold with two other painting. 29-Apr-3 Bonhams, New Bond Street #46/R est:700-1000

£2000 $3180 €3000 Cattle resting by a cart, Bengal, India (15x18cm-6x7in) i.verso W/C exhib. 29-Apr-3 Bonhams, New Bond Street #51/R est:2000-3000

£2200 $3454 €3300 Water carriers and other Indians figures. Indian figures and cattle outside a hut (17x25cm-7x10in) pencil pen ink pair prov. 21-Nov-2 Christie's, London #71/R est:2500-3500

£3500 $5565 €5250 Terrace, Macao (25x18cm-10x7in) d.1835 W/C over pencil htd bodycol. 19-Mar-3 Sotheby's, London #162/R est:4000-6000

CHINTREUIL, Antoine (1816-1873) French

£993 $1619 €1500 Paysage (24x43cm-9x17in) s. 16-Feb-3 Mercier & Cie, Lille #240/R est:1200-1500

£1935 $3058 €3000 Ru a Igny (42x34cm-17x13in) s. painted c.1850-57 prov.lit. 18-Dec-2 Ferri, Paris #43

£2414 $3838 €3500 Paysan sur la route du village (19x24cm-7x9in) s. 5-Mar-3 Doutrebente, Paris #41/R est:1700-2300

£6993 $11678 €10000 La promenade (64x82cm-25x32in) s. 27-Jun-3 Claude Aguttes, Neuilly #28/R est:8000-10000

£11538 $18231 €18000 Chevreuil a l'oree du bois (69x55cm-27x22in) s. 18-Nov-2 Tajan, Paris #89/R est:10000-15000

Works on paper

£608 $949 €900 Cerf dans la campagne. s.i.d.1868 W/C. 27-Mar-3 Maigret, Paris #222

CHINZAN, Tsubaki (1801-1854) Japanese

Works on paper

£1006 $1600 €1509 Beautiful as jade, calm as an immortal. Abundance of grain and fruit (126x55cm-50x22in) s. ink col silk hanging scroll two. 24-Mar-3 Christie's, Rockefeller NY #61/R est:2000-3000

£3019 $4800 €4529 Rooster and praying mantis (38x70cm-15x28in) s. ink col silk hanging scroll sold with two others. 24-Mar-3 Christie's, Rockefeller NY #59/R est:3500-4500

CHIOSTRI, Carlo (19th C) Italian

£1050 $1638 €1575 Grand Canal, Venice (72x98cm-28x39in) s. 17-Sep-2 Rosebery Fine Art, London #681/R est:800-1200

CHIPARUS, D (1888-1950) Rumanian

Sculpture

£1200 $1920 €1800 Figure of a girl (19cm-7in) s. gilt bronze ivory. 15-May-3 Christie's, Kensington #446/R est:600-800

£2100 $3360 €3150 Equilibrium (46cm-18in) i. bronze lit. 15-May-3 Christie's, Kensington #434/R est:2000-3000

£3200 $5056 €4800 Lazzarone (24cm-9in) i. gilt bronze. 14-Nov-2 Christie's, Kensington #303/R est:2500-3500

£5500 $8800 €8250 Squall (31cm-12in) s. gilt bronze ivory. 15-May-3 Christie's, Kensington #452/R est:6000-8000

£15000 $24000 €22500 Ayouta (47cm-19in) i. cold pat. bronze ivory lit. 15-May-3 Christie's, Kensington #461/R est:10000-12000

£17000 $27200 €25500 Tanara (65cm-26in) i. cold pat. bronze ivory lit. 15-May-3 Christie's, Kensington #463/R est:15000-20000

£18000 $29340 €27000 Dancer of Kapurthala (22cm-9in) s. art deco bronze ivory with onyx base. 12-Feb-3 Andrew Hartley, Ilkley #248/R est:12000-15000

CHIPARUS, Demetre (1888-1950) Rumanian

Sculpture

£1064 $1777 €1500 La fille genee (14cm-6in) s. ivory firegilt bronze marble stand Cast Etling. 23-Jun-3 Bernaerts, Antwerp #203/R est:1500-2000

£1449 $2377 €2000 Young girls (28cm-11in) s. bronze. 27-May-3 Campo & Campo, Antwerp #47/R est:2500-3500

£1553 $2500 €2330 Faetalliana (20cm-8in) pat bronze marble base. 15-Jan-3 Boos Gallery, Michigan #543/R est:2000-3000

£1622 $2530 €2400 Dancer of Olynthus (32cm-13in) s. emaille a froid bronze lit. 25-Mar-3 Campo & Campo, Antwerp #33/R est:2500-3500

£2014 $3304 €2800 L'eternelle histoire (41x13cm-16x56in) s. ivory col gold silver bronze onyx Portor marble socle. 3-Jun-3 Piasa, Paris #33/R est:3000-4000

£2484 $4000 €3726 Mother Therese of Little Flower (46cm-18in) s.i. ivory bronze marble base. 15-Jan-3 Boos Gallery, Michigan #529/R est:4000-6000

£2553 $4264 €3600 La fille genee. s. ivory gilt bronze marble stand Cast Etling. 23-Jun-3 Bernaerts, Antwerp #202/R est:2800-3200

£2564 $4051 €4000 Le coup de vent (18cm-7in) s. ivory col pat bronze onyx base. 12-Nov-2 Palais de Beaux Arts, Brussels #476/R est:3000-4000

£2581 $3794 €4000 Hindu dancer (60cm-24in) bronze ivory marble socle. 20-Jun-2 Dr Fritz Nagel, Stuttgart #205/R est:5000

£2878 $4719 €4000 Dourga (26cm-10in) s. ivory gold pat bronze sold with onyx socle. 3-Jun-3 Piasa, Paris #26/R est:2000-2500

£3165 $5000 €5000 Amis de toujours (54x65x19cm-21x26x7in) s. gilt pat bronze onyx socle lit. 26-Nov-2 Tajan, Paris #54/R

£4138 $6579 €6000 Rameses entertainer (72cm-28in) s. pat.bronze marble socle. 8-Mar-3 Arnold, Frankfurt #239/R est:6000

£4194 $6500 €6291 Little sad one (30cm-12in) st.sig. carved ivory gilt bronze marble. 6-Dec-2 Sotheby's, New York #156/R est:5000-8000

£4487 $7090 €7000 L'eternelle histoire (40x76x22cm-16x30x9in) s. synthetic resin metal col pat bronze marble base. 12-Nov-2 Palais de Beaux Arts, Brussels #491/R est:5000-7500

£4487 $7090 €7000 Jeune femme dans le vent (31cm-12in) s. ivory pat bronze sold with socle. 13-Nov-2 Fraysse & Associes, Paris #140/R

£4800 $7632 €7200 Balancing act (44cm-17in) s. bronze. 27-Feb-3 Sotheby's, Olympia #200/R est:5000-5500

£5063 $8000 €8000 Petit dourga (35cm-14in) s. pat bronze ivory onyx socle lit. 26-Nov-2 Tajan, Paris #13/R

£5625 $8550 €8438 Despues de la lectura (37cm-15in) ivory bronze. 3-Jul-2 Naón & Cia, Buenos Aires #567/R est:5000-5500

£6500 $10335 €9750 Phoenician dancer (29cm-11in) s. green pat. bronze marble base. 27-Feb-3 Sotheby's, Olympia #198/R est:4000-5000

£6646 $10500 €10500 Danseuse (29cm-11in) s. pat bronze ivory onyx socle. 26-Nov-2 Tajan, Paris #12/R

£6962 $11000 €11000 Solo (55cm-22in) ivory pat bronze wooden socle lit. 26-Nov-2 Tajan, Paris #45/R

£7000 $11130 €10500 Young woman lifting her skirt to adjust her garter (30cm-12in) bronze lit. 27-Feb-3 Sotheby's, Olympia #199/R est:7500-8500

£7595 $12000 €12000 Danseuse au gilet (34cm-13in) s. pat bronze ivory onyx base lit. 26-Nov-2 Tajan, Paris #14/R

£9722 $16041 €14000 Danseuse Hindoue (43cm-17in) s. ivory gilt bronze black marble base prov.lit. 2-Jul-3 Artcurial Briest, Paris #33/R est:8000-12000
£9722 $16041 €14000 Danseuse a trois cerceaux (34cm-13in) s. ivory gilt bronze onyx base prov. 2-Jul-3 Artcurial Briest, Paris #34/R est:6000-8000
£10897 $17218 €17000 Les amis de toujours (42x42x13cm-17x17x5in) s.i. ivory col pat bronze onyx socle. 12-Nov-2 Palais de Beaux Arts, Brussels #493/R est:12500-17500
£10897 $16891 €17000 Ayouta (46cm-18in) s. bronze ivory onyx base Cast Etling prov.lit. 9-Dec-2 Artcurial Briest, Paris #90/R est:25000
£11392 $18000 €18000 Danseuse de Kapurthala (54cm-21in) s. pat bronze ivory onyx socle lit. 26-Nov-2 Tajan, Paris #40/R est:18000
£17742 $27500 €26613 Russian dancers (56x43x15cm-22x17x6in) s.i. cold painted ivory bronze. 29-Sep-2 Butterfields, Los Angeles #4058/R est:22000-26000
£27778 $43889 €40000 Danseurs russes (46cm-18in) s. ivory silver gold pat bronze sold with marble socle lit. 25-Apr-3 Drouot Estimations, Paris #27 est:38000-40000

CHIPARUS, Demetre (attrib) (1888-1950) Rumanian
Sculpture
£1407 $2252 €2040 Woman and deer (41x50cm-16x20in) s. bronze incl.marble socle. 18-May-3 Anders Antik, Landskrona #159 est:20000 (S.KR 18000)
£6255 $10008 €9070 A slight accident (40cm-16in) s. bronze incl. socle. 18-May-3 Anders Antik, Landskrona #158 est:80000 (S.KR 80000)

CHIPLEY, Ida (20th C) American
£256 $400 €384 Will Rogers, jnr (25x20cm-10x8in) canvasboard. 19-Oct-2 David Dike, Dallas #195/R

CHIRICO, Giorgio de (1888-1978) Italian
£8511 $13787 €12000 Ritratto di Isa (15x12cm-6x5in) s.i.d.1930. 26-May-3 Christie's, Milan #242/R est:12000-18000
£8511 $13787 €12000 Cavalli nella campagna romana (23x34cm-9x13in) s. s.i.verso tempera paper on board prov.exhib. 26-May-3 Christie's, Milan #290/R est:10000-15000
£11613 $18348 €18000 Prothee. tempera wax crayon paper on card painted 1938 lit. 18-Dec-2 Christie's, Rome #246/R est:24000
£13699 $21370 €20000 Little horse in landscape (20x27cm-8x11in) s. canvas on board. 10-Apr-3 Finarte Semenzato, Rome #312/R est:25000
£17647 $28235 €27000 Silent life (25x30cm-10x12in) s. painted 1972 lit. 4-Jan-3 Meeting Art, Vercelli #749 est:25000
£17730 $28723 €25000 Cavallo in un paese (20x28cm-8x11in) s. s.i.verso canvas on panel c.1957-58 prov. 26-May-3 Christie's, Milan #286/R est:18000-20000
£20253 $31595 €32000 Le cheval de Sultan (23x31cm-9x12in) s. i. verso canvas on board lit. 31-Jul-2 Tajan, Paris #20/R est:35000-40000
£22436 $35224 €35000 Sunset on the Ticino (30x40cm-12x16in) s. s.i.verso cardboard. 19-Nov-2 Finarte, Milan #203/R est:34000-40000
£30000 $49200 €45000 Self-portrait (50x40cm-20x16in) s. masonite painted 1954. 4-Feb-3 Christie's, London #324/R est:50000
£31646 $50000 €50000 Lonely knight (40x50cm-16x20in) s. painted c.1942. 30-Nov-2 Farsetti, Prato #642/R est:60000
£42308 $66423 €66000 La Salute (30x40cm-12x16in) s. cardboard. 21-Nov-2 Finarte, Rome #360/R est:65000-70000
£47742 $75432 €74000 Venice (40x50cm-16x20in) s. si.verso. 18-Dec-2 Christie's, Rome #252/R est:120000
£52402 $76507 €78603 Office interior (50x40cm-20x16in) s. prov. 4-Jun-2 Germann, Zurich #19/R est:80000-100000 (S.FR 120000)
£56738 $91915 €80000 Cavali in un paese con bosco e marina (50x70cm-20x28in) s. 26-May-3 Christie's, Milan #279/R est:80000-120000
£60000 $98400 €90000 Italian square, summer afternoon (50x40cm-20x16in) s.d.1971. 4-Feb-3 Christie's, London #321/R est:45000
£65248 $105702 €92000 Piazza d'Italia (30x40cm-12x16in) s. s.i.verso prov. 26-May-3 Christie's, Milan #337/R est:60000-80000
£85000 $132600 €127500 Vita silenta di mele, arance e fragole (27x34cm-11x13in) s. tempera board painted c.1922 prov.exhib.lit. 21-Oct-2 Sotheby's, London #5/R est:80000-120000
£101266 $160000 €160000 Arianna's dream (60x50cm-24x20in) s.d.1972 lit. 30-Nov-2 Farsetti, Prato #726/R est:180000
£139241 $220000 €220000 Hector and Andromaca (55x40cm-22x16in) s. i.verso painted c.1950. 30-Nov-2 Farsetti, Prato #736/R est:210000
£140000 $228200 €210000 Skyscraper enigma (40x60cm-16x24in) s.d.1960 prov.exhib.lit. 3-Feb-3 Christie's, London #189/R est:120000
£164557 $260000 €260000 Horses on seashore, castle in background (60x77cm-24x30in) s.d.1927 exhib.lit. 30-Nov-2 Farsetti, Prato #729/R est:300000
£192308 $300000 €288462 Il Trovatore (80x60cm-31x24in) s. s.i.verso painted 1963 prov.exhib.lit. 6-Nov-2 Sotheby's, New York #211/R est:250000-350000
£224359 $350000 €336539 Autorittrato (62x49cm-24x19in) s.d.1919 prov.exhib.lit. 5-Nov-2 Sotheby's, New York #60/R est:300000-400000
Prints
£1923 $2981 €3000 Melancholy (100x70cm-39x28in) s. col lithograph exec.1972 lit. 4-Dec-2 Finarte, Milan #65/R
Sculpture
£1282 $2013 €2000 Gladiator (31x9x7cm-12x4x3in) s.i. num.LXIV/100 gilt pat bronze. 23-Nov-2 Meeting Art, Vercelli #170/R
£1731 $2717 €2700 Painter (25x14x14cm-10x6x6in) s. num.LXXXII/100 polished bronze exec.1998. 23-Nov-2 Meeting Art, Vercelli #464/R
£5449 $8554 €8500 Holding a horse (30cm-12in) s.st.f.Cavallari brown pat bronze exec.1978 lit. 21-Nov-2 Finarte, Rome #224/R
£10127 $16000 €16000 Troubador (29cm-11in) s. num.1/6 gilt pat bronze lit. 30-Nov-2 Farsetti, Prato #625/R est:16000
£12025 $19000 €19000 Penelope and Telemaco (41cm-16in) s.i. dark pat bronze exec.1970 lit. 30-Nov-2 Farsetti, Prato #626/R est:18000
Works on paper
£1986 $3217 €2800 Horse (17x23cm-7x9in) s. s.i.verso col.crayons. 26-May-3 Christie's, Milan #42/R est:2200-2800
£2258 $3568 €3500 Horse and rider (40x28cm-16x11in) s. pencil exec.c.1972. 18-Dec-2 Christie's, Rome #24/R
£2400 $3720 €3600 Palafreniere -Atto I Quadro I (16x12cm-6x5in) i. W/C pencil paper on board. 5-Dec-2 Christie's, Kensington #153/R est:800-1200
£3000 $4890 €4500 Cavaliere antico all attacco (12x14cm-5x6in) s.i. pencil prov. 3-Feb-3 Bonhams, New Bond Street #68/R est:800-1200
£3200 $5216 €4800 Angelo berniniano. Studio di Ulvio (12x9cm-5x4in) s. pencil two framed as one. 3-Feb-3 Bonhams, New Bond Street #67/R est:800-1200
£5769 $9058 €9000 Self-portrait (27x20cm-11x8in) s. chl exec.1948 lit. 23-Nov-2 Meeting Art, Vercelli #466/R
£6000 $9780 €9000 La battaglia (20x24cm-8x9in) s. chl. 3-Feb-3 Bonhams, New Bond Street #69/R est:2000-3000
£8654 $13587 €13500 Furniture in the valley (33x53cm-13x21in) s. mixed media exec.1971. 19-Nov-2 Finarte, Milan #186/R est:9000-12000
£10811 $16865 €16000 Study for archeologists. Study for metaphysical figures (25x32cm-10x13in) s. pencil double-sided. 26-Mar-3 Finarte Semenzato, Milan #262a/R est:15000
£11644 $18164 €17000 Bridge of Sighs. i. chl set of 12. 10-Apr-3 Finarte Semenzato, Rome #78/R est:20000
£13475 $21830 €19000 Testa di cavallo (40x30cm-16x12in) s. W/C pencil cardboard prov.lit. 26-May-3 Christie's, Milan #49/R est:10000-15000
£40000 $61600 €60000 Hector at andromaque. les adieux (44x35cm-17x14in) s. pencil W/C executed 1968 prov.exhib. 22-Oct-2 Sotheby's, London #186/R est:20000-30000

CHIRKOV, Aleksandr Inokentevich (1865-1913) Russian
£516 $847 €748 Hayrick (37x28cm-15x11in) s. board. 4-Jun-3 Fischer, Luzern #2029/R (S.FR 1100)

CHISTOVSKY, L (19/20th C) Russian
Works on paper
£10000 $16200 €15000 Reclining nude (44x92cm-17x36in) s.i. gouache. 21-May-3 Sotheby's, London #56 est:2000-3000

CHITI, Guido (1918-) Italian
£1418 $2298 €2000 Tavola da cucina (80x100cm-31x39in) s.d.62 prov.exhib. 26-May-3 Christie's, Milan #360/R est:500-700

CHITTENDEN, Alice B (1859-1934) American
£875 $1400 €1313 Purple Mountain Valley. s. canvas on board. 11-Jan-3 Harvey Clar, Oakland #1356

CHITTUSSI, Anton (1847-1891) Czechoslovakian
£3709 $5897 €5564 Late afternoon landscape with pathway (19x24cm-7x9in) s. panel. 8-Mar-3 Dorotheum, Prague #12/R est:150000-230000 (C.KR 170000)
£6000 $9840 €9000 Landscape in Normandy (44x31cm-17x12in) s. prov. 3-Jun-3 Sotheby's, London #46/R est:7000-10000

CHIU TENG-HIOK (1903-1972) American/Chinese
£3263 $5385 €4731 Landscape of the rice field (32x40cm-13x16in) s.d.1929 panel. 6-Jul-3 Christie's, Hong Kong #167/R est:30000-40000 (HK.D 42000)

CHMAROFF, Paval (1874-1950) Russian
£532 $888 €750 Les ombres dans la nuit (18x16cm-7x6in) panel. 17-Jun-3 Claude Boisgirard, Paris #3
£1064 $1777 €1500 Scenes au bord d'un etang (12x18cm-5x7in) s. three. 17-Jun-3 Claude Boisgirard, Paris #1/R est:1500-1800
£1135 $1895 €1600 Scene de plage I (11x18cm-4x7in) s. paper. 17-Jun-3 Claude Boisgirard, Paris #8 est:1000-1500
£1277 $2132 €1800 Scene de plage II (11x18cm-4x7in) s. panel. 17-Jun-3 Claude Boisgirard, Paris #9/R est:1000-1500

£1986 $3316 €2800 Quatre femmes (27x16cm-11x6in) panel. 17-Jun-3 Claude Boisgirard, Paris #7 est:1500-1800
£3401 $5408 €5000 Nu assis (50x73cm-20x29in) s. 3-Mar-3 Claude Boisgirard, Paris #5 est:1500-1800
£3404 $5515 €4800 Baigneuses (53x80cm-21x31in) s. canvas on panel. 23-May-3 Camard, Paris #97/R est:4500-5300
£3741 $5949 €5500 Deux femmes au bord d'une fleuve (49x76cm-19x30in) s. canvas on cardboard. 3-Mar-3 Claude Boisgirard, Paris #2 est:1500-1800
£3901 $6514 €5500 Six baigneuses (26x40cm-10x16in) panel. 17-Jun-3 Claude Boisgirard, Paris #6 est:2000-3000
£4113 $6870 €5800 Enfant a cheval avec une femme (31x26cm-12x10in) s. canvas on panel. 17-Jun-3 Claude Boisgirard, Paris #4/R est:1500-2000
£4762 $7571 €7000 Trois femmes au bouquet de fleurs (50x73cm-20x29in) s. double-sided. 3-Mar-3 Claude Boisgirard, Paris #1 est:1200-1500
£4762 $7571 €7000 Fille aux violettes (48x35cm-19x14in) s. isorel. 3-Mar-3 Claude Boisgirard, Paris #3 est:1000-1200
£5106 $8528 €7200 Autoportrait (43x23cm-17x9in) s.verso. 17-Jun-3 Claude Boisgirard, Paris #2/R est:1500-1800
£5306 $8437 €7800 Nature morte aux pommes et bananes (50x73cm-20x29in) s. 3-Mar-3 Claude Boisgirard, Paris #4/R est:1000-1200
£5442 $8653 €8000 Nature morte au bouquet de fleurs (81x60cm-32x24in) s. 3-Mar-3 Claude Boisgirard, Paris #21/R est:1500-2000
£5578 $8869 €8200 Trois filles aux bougies (50x73cm-20x29in) s. 3-Mar-3 Claude Boisgirard, Paris #9/R est:1500
£6259 $9951 €9200 Nature morte aux peches et raisins (50x73cm-20x29in) s. 3-Mar-3 Claude Boisgirard, Paris #10 est:1000-1200
£7143 $11357 €10500 Trois paysannes avec un bebe (46x65cm-18x26in) s. 3-Mar-3 Claude Boisgirard, Paris #6/R est:1500-1800
£7143 $11357 €10500 Femmes aux bougies (54x73cm-21x29in) s. 3-Mar-3 Claude Boisgirard, Paris #7 est:1500-1800
£7823 $12439 €11500 Au couchee de soleil (50x73cm-20x29in) s. 3-Mar-3 Claude Boisgirard, Paris #13 est:1000-1200
£8503 $13520 €12500 Trois baigneuses (50x72cm-20x28in) s. 3-Mar-3 Claude Boisgirard, Paris #8 est:1200-1500
£8844 $14061 €13000 Orchidees et lilas (60x92cm-24x36in) 3-Mar-3 Claude Boisgirard, Paris #15/R est:1200-1500
£9220 $15397 €13000 Dix baigneuses avec un chien (50x73cm-20x29in) s. 17-Jun-3 Claude Boisgirard, Paris #11/R est:6000-8000
£9524 $15143 €14000 Bord de mer en famille (39x56cm-15x22in) isorel. 3-Mar-3 Claude Boisgirard, Paris #11 est:1200-1500
£12245 $19469 €18000 Trois jeunes filles avec garcon (65x92cm-26x36in) s. 3-Mar-3 Claude Boisgirard, Paris #16 est:1200-1500
£13475 $22504 €19000 Nature morte aux fruits et a la langouste (119x48cm-47x19in) s. 17-Jun-3 Claude Boisgirard, Paris #10/R est:8000-10000
£13605 $21633 €20000 Enfants dans un jardin (60x91cm-24x36in) s. 3-Mar-3 Claude Boisgirard, Paris #19 est:1500-1800
£14286 $22714 €21000 Baignade au lac (50x71cm-20x28in) s. 3-Mar-3 Claude Boisgirard, Paris #12 est:1500
£15646 $24878 €23000 Trois nymphes (65x92cm-26x36in) s. 3-Mar-3 Claude Boisgirard, Paris #18/R est:1800-2000
£16327 $25959 €24000 Procession de femmes (60x92cm-24x36in) s. 3-Mar-3 Claude Boisgirard, Paris #14/R est:1800-2000
£17730 $29610 €25000 Cinq femmes avec un bebe (65x92cm-26x36in) s. 17-Jun-3 Claude Boisgirard, Paris #12/R est:12000-14000
£18367 $29204 €27000 Baigneuse au lac I (60x92cm-24x36in) s. 3-Mar-3 Claude Boisgirard, Paris #17 est:1800-2000
£18367 $29204 €27000 Baigneuses au lac II (60x92cm-24x36in) s. 3-Mar-3 Claude Boisgirard, Paris #20/R est:1800-2000

Works on paper

£355 $592 €500 Baigneuses (23x21cm-9x8in) W/C. 17-Jun-3 Claude Boisgirard, Paris #5

CHMIELINSKI, W T (1911-1979) Polish

£296 $461 €444 Town scene with church (35x25cm-14x10in) s. 23-Sep-2 Rasmussen, Vejle #2043 (D.KR 3500)
£306 $496 €444 Winter landscape with figure by church (35x25cm-14x10in) s. 24-May-3 Rasmussen, Havnen #2152 (D.KR 3200)
£309 $482 €464 Monastery interior with watchman (35x25cm-14x10in) s. 11-Nov-2 Rasmussen, Vejle #684/R (D.KR 3600)
£383 $620 €555 Street scene with figures (50x35cm-20x14in) s. 24-May-3 Rasmussen, Havnen #2161 (D.KR 4000)
£388 $589 €582 Winter's day in an East European town with horses and sleighs at market (25x35cm-10x14in) with sig. 27-Aug-2 Rasmussen, Copenhagen #1865 (D.KR 4500)
£557 $870 €836 Street scene, Copenhagen, winter (35x50cm-14x20in) s. 11-Nov-2 Rasmussen, Vejle #689/R (D.KR 6500)
£560 $890 €840 Two horses and wagons at full speed on outskirts of town (50x60cm-20x24in) s. 5-May-3 Rasmussen, Vejle #289 (D.KR 6000)
£621 $1005 €900 Horse and carriage. Horses watering (18x25cm-7x10in) pair panel. 25-May-3 Uppsala Auktionskammare, Uppsala #100/R (S.KR 8000)
£670 $1085 €972 Sleigh ride in winter landscape (26x36cm-10x14in) s. panel. 26-May-3 Rasmussen, Copenhagen #1482/R (D.KR 7000)
£732 $1113 €1098 Street scene from Store Kannikestraede (54x66cm-21x26in) s. 27-Aug-2 Rasmussen, Copenhagen #1834/R (D.KR 8500)
£1007 $1611 €1511 Troika with Cossacks in snowstorm (50x70cm-20x28in) s. 13-Jan-3 Rasmussen, Vejle #208/R (D.KR 11500)
£1071 $1703 €1607 From Warsaw in winter (35x50cm-14x20in) s. 10-Mar-3 Rasmussen, Vejle #556/R (D.KR 11500)
£1138 $1821 €1707 Eastern European street scene with figures (35x51cm-14x20in) s. 13-Jan-3 Rasmussen, Vejle #212/R est:6000 (D.KR 13000)
£2703 $4216 €4055 Street scenes from Warsaw in winter (35x50cm-14x20in) s. pair. 23-Sep-2 Rasmussen, Vejle #192/R est:10000 (D.KR 32000)

CHMIELINSKI, Wladyslaw (1895-?) Polish

£1258 $1962 €2000 Wintry Schlossplatz in Warsaw (35x25cm-14x10in) s. 20-Sep-2 Karlheinz Kaupp, Staufen #1957/R est:2300
£9494 $15000 €14241 Winter day in Warsaw. Carriage ride in Warsaw (35x50cm-14x20in) s. pair. 23-Apr-3 Christie's, Rockefeller NY #91/R est:10000-15000

CHOCARNE-MOREAU, Paul Charles (1855-1931) French

£7547 $11623 €12000 Heureuse rencontre (46x55cm-18x22in) s.i. 27-Oct-2 Muizon & Le Coent, Paris #47/R

Works on paper

£2384 $3886 €3600 Le petit marmiton (30x43cm-12x17in) s. gouache. 16-Feb-3 Mercier & Cie, Lille #235/R est:2500-3000

CHOCHON, Andre (1910-) French

£304 $480 €480 View of Pors Hir (38x55cm-15x22in) s. 1-Dec-2 Livinec, Gaudcheau & Jezequel, Rennes #76

CHODOWIECKI, Daniel (1726-1801) German

Miniatures

£2000 $3280 €2900 Young gentleman in a light grey coat (3cm-1xin) gilt metal frame oval prov. 3-Jun-3 Christie's, London #95/R est:400-600

Works on paper

£253 $400 €400 Three men lounging on the ground (9x11cm-4x4in) d.July 10.a.62 pencil. 29-Nov-2 Bassenge, Berlin #5602
£348 $550 €550 Four people in conversation (15x9cm-6x4in) pen wash. 29-Nov-2 Bassenge, Berlin #5601
£349 $552 €524 Blind man's buff (24x37cm-9x15in) W/C pen. 14-Nov-2 Stuker, Bern #9541 (S.FR 800)
£352 $585 €500 Calas saying farewell to his family (17x19cm-7x7in) pencil. 12-Jun-3 Hauswedell & Nolte, Hamburg #203/R
£367 $580 €580 Two men in conversation: 'I hate you' (15x9cm-6x4in) pen wash. 29-Nov-2 Bassenge, Berlin #5600
£396 $633 €550 Male nude (53x41cm-21x16in) chk prov.lit. 17-May-3 Lempertz, Koln #1213
£396 $633 €550 Standing male nude with outstretched right arm (54x31cm-21x12in) chk prov.lit. 17-May-3 Lempertz, Koln #1214
£570 $900 €900 Apollo and Neptune on clouds (25x21cm-10x8in) i. 29-Nov-2 Bassenge, Berlin #5598

CHOKI, Eishosai (fl.c.1785-1805) Japanese

Prints

£2692 $4200 €4038 Confessions of Takao (28x25cm-11x10in) s. print. 25-Mar-3 Christie's, Rockefeller NY #50/R est:2500-3500

CHOLODKOV, Nikolaj Ivanovic (1925-) Czechoslovakian

£442 $685 €663 On a sledge (36x57cm-14x22in) painted c.1950. 3-Dec-2 SOGA, Bratislava #158/R (SL.K 28000)

CHOPARD, Henri (1914-1990) Swiss

£419 $624 €629 Vase with flowers. s.d.77 pavatex. 25-Jun-2 Koller, Zurich #6033 (S.FR 950)

CHOUDHARY, Bijan (1931-) Indian

£800 $1248 €1200 Offering prayer (46x53cm-18x21in) s.d.63. 17-Oct-2 Bonhams, Knightsbridge #616/R

CHOULTSE, Ivan Fedorovich (1874-1939) Russian

£1646 $2551 €2600 Sous bois (24x32cm-9x13in) s. panel. 29-Sep-2 Eric Pillon, Calais #163/R
£3546 $5745 €5000 Derniers rayons (32x40cm-13x16in) s.d.22 board. 23-May-3 Camard, Paris #99/R est:4500-6000
£6500 $10205 €9750 Deer in a snowy landscape at dusk (48x73cm-19x29in) s.i. 21-Nov-2 Christie's, Kensington #118/R est:3000-5000
£9500 $15865 €13775 Moonlit seascape (66x100cm-26x39in) s. 17-Jun-3 Bonhams, New Bond Street #20/R est:3000-5000
£13121 $20337 €19682 Winter landscape with waterway, afternoon light (89x113cm-35x44in) s. 3-Dec-2 Bukowskis, Stockholm #328/R est:40000-50000 (S.KR 185000)

CHOUN, Yamazaki (1867-1954) Japanese

Sculpture

£7000 $11060 €10500 Tanomura Chikuden seated with a gourd at his side (25cm-10in) s.i. wood table stand wood box. 13-Nov-2 Christie's, London #134/R est:3000-4000

CHOVAN, Lorant (1913-) Czechoslovakian
£583 $903 €875 Party (100x70cm-39x28in) painted c.1940. 1-Oct-2 SOGA, Bratislava #133/R est:25000 (SL.K 37000)

CHOW KWA (fl.1850-1880) Chinese
£14474 $22000 €21711 Bininger Hong at 10 Canton Road, Shanghai (51x76cm-20x30in) i. prov.lit. 17-Aug-2 North East Auctions, Portsmouth #672/R est:20000-30000

CHOWDHURY, Jogen (1939-) Indian
Works on paper
£2486 $4103 €3605 Nude (58x89cm-23x35in) s.d.19.9.98 pastel. 6-Jul-3 Christie's, Hong Kong #100/R est:32000-40000 (HK.D 32000)

CHOWNE, Gerard (1875-?) British
Works on paper
£260 $413 €390 Ronda (23x35cm-9x14in) s.i.d.1913 W/C. 26-Feb-3 Sotheby's, Olympia #72/R

CHRETIEN, Auguste Clement (1835-?) French
£5975 $9321 €9500 Famille de pecheurs (115x147cm-45x58in) s.d.1882. 11-Oct-2 Pierre Berge, Paris #22/R est:10000-12000

CHRETIEN, René Louis (1867-1942) French
£280 $443 €420 Hunting still life (16x22cm-6x9in) s. panel. 16-Nov-2 Crafoord, Lund #2/R (S.KR 4000)

CHRISP, Richard (20th C) ?
£526 $821 €789 Driving Creek, Coromandel (81x122cm-32x48in) s. acrylic paper. 27-Mar-3 International Art Centre, Auckland #185 (NZ.D 1500)

CHRISSA (1923-) Greek
Works on paper
£10000 $15500 €15000 Today's special (137x244cm-54x96in) neonlights acrylic asbestos in 2 parts prov. 2-Oct-2 Sotheby's, London #123/R est:10000-15000

CHRIST, Martin Alfred (1900-1979) Swiss
Works on paper
£283 $453 €425 Standing female nude (43x31cm-17x12in) s. pastel chk. 17-Mar-3 Philippe Schuler, Zurich #4299 (S.FR 600)

CHRIST, Pieter Casper and VERBOECKHOVEN, Eugene (19th C) Dutch
£3500 $5845 €5250 Animals watering in a wooded lake landscape (63x77cm-25x30in) s. 18-Jun-3 Christie's, Kensington #53/R est:4000-6000

CHRISTAUX, F (19/20th C) ?
£4085 $6454 €6128 Small girls walking with bare feet in shallow water (122x91cm-48x36in) s. 2-Dec-2 Rasmussen, Copenhagen #1431/R est:30000 (D.KR 48000)

CHRISTENBERRY, William (1936-) American
Photographs
£1899 $3000 €2849 Door of auto repair shop, near Tuscaloosa, Alabama (38x48cm-15x19in) s.i.d.1981 verso dye transfer print prov. 25-Apr-3 Phillips, New York #192/R est:1500-2500
£3165 $5000 €4748 Door of cotton warehouse (44x56cm-17x22in) s. verso dye transfer print prov. 25-Apr-3 Phillips, New York #191/R est:3000-5000

CHRISTENSEN, Antonore (1849-1926) Danish
£388 $589 €582 Agave (33x26cm-13x10in) mono. 27-Aug-2 Rasmussen, Copenhagen #1793/R (D.KR 4500)
£622 $1008 €902 Flowering honeysuckle and butterfly (37x32cm-15x13in) mono. 26-May-3 Rasmussen, Copenhagen #1246/R (D.KR 6500)
£681 $1076 €1022 Mountain landscape from the Alps (46x61cm-18x24in) mono. 2-Dec-2 Rasmussen, Copenhagen #1546/R (D.KR 8000)
£689 $1047 €1034 From Palatin in Rome (33x48cm-13x19in) mono.i.d.1902. 27-Aug-2 Rasmussen, Copenhagen #1713/R (D.KR 8000)
£745 $1184 €1118 White lilies (44x25cm-17x10in) mono. 5-Mar-3 Rasmussen, Copenhagen #1842/R (D.KR 8000)
£1277 $2017 €1916 White cacti (41x54cm-16x21in) mono.d.1914 exhib. 2-Dec-2 Rasmussen, Copenhagen #1449/R est:15000 (D.KR 15000)
£1702 $2689 €2553 Flowers in basket (40x55cm-16x22in) mono.d.1883. 2-Dec-2 Rasmussen, Copenhagen #1453/R est:25000 (D.KR 20000)
£8176 $12591 €13000 Flower bouquet on a forest floor (46x39cm-18x15in) mono.d.1882. 22-Oct-2 Sotheby's, Amsterdam #82/R est:8000-12000

CHRISTENSEN, Antonore (attrib) (1849-1926) Danish
£392 $623 €588 Still life of white anemones (29x22cm-11x9in) 5-May-3 Rasmussen, Vejle #583/R (D.KR 4200)
£513 $816 €770 Woodland ground with flowers (31x21cm-12x8in) 5-May-3 Rasmussen, Vejle #577/R (D.KR 5500)
£513 $816 €770 Wood anemones and violets with dead leaves by tree trunk (42x30cm-17x12in) 5-May-3 Rasmussen, Vejle #581/R (D.KR 5500)

CHRISTENSEN, Chr I (?) Danish
£442 $689 €663 Copenhagen street scene with flower seller (61x70cm-24x28in) s. 5-Aug-2 Rasmussen, Vejle #279/R (D.KR 5200)

CHRISTENSEN, Finn (1920-) Norwegian
£363 $606 €526 A GATEWAY (60x73cm-24x29in) s. s.i.stretcher. 18-Jun-3 Grev Wedels Plass, Oslo #159 (N.KR 4200)

CHRISTENSEN, Godfred (1845-1928) Danish
£257 $401 €386 Southern landscape with large stones on beach (31x44cm-12x17in) mono.d.1874. 11-Nov-2 Rasmussen, Vejle #672/R (D.KR 3000)
£272 $430 €408 Coastal landscape with jetty and figures (30x41cm-12x16in) init.d.87. 30-Nov-2 Rasmussen, Havnen #2070/R (D.KR 3200)
£279 $444 €419 Liren near Salten Langso, Silkeborg (27x37cm-11x15in) init.d.11. 10-Mar-3 Rasmussen, Vejle #261 (D.KR 3000)
£300 $468 €450 Landscape from Munkebjerg (22x29cm-9x11in) init.d.23 i.verso. 11-Nov-2 Rasmussen, Vejle #649/R (D.KR 3500)
£372 $592 €558 Danish summer landscape (42x63cm-17x25in) init.d.92. 10-Mar-3 Rasmussen, Vejle #318/R (D.KR 4000)
£426 $672 €639 Landscape idyll near Kildeport (35x52cm-14x20in) init.d.28. 2-Dec-2 Rasmussen, Copenhagen #1476/R (D.KR 5000)
£438 $701 €657 Heath landscape with children and sheep near Silkeborg (32x53cm-13x21in) init.d.1865. 13-Jan-3 Rasmussen, Vejle #135/R (D.KR 5000)
£440 $677 €660 Alpine landscape with lake (33x45cm-13x18in) init.d.1877. 26-Oct-2 Rasmussen, Havnen #2156/R (D.KR 5200)
£515 $814 €773 Small boy in the Sabin Mountains (46x63cm-18x25in) s.i.d.sept.1873. 13-Nov-2 Kunsthallen, Copenhagen #80/R (D.KR 6000)
£521 $829 €782 Coastal landscape with fishing boat (30x41cm-12x16in) init.d.87. 10-Mar-3 Rasmussen, Vejle #477/R (D.KR 5600)
£591 $922 €887 Italian girl (34x21cm-13x8in) s.d.1874 study. 23-Sep-2 Rasmussen, Vejle #215/R (D.KR 7000)
£606 $964 €909 Landscape from Albana (30x44cm-12x17in) init.i.d.1894-1907. 5-May-3 Rasmussen, Vejle #569/R (D.KR 6500)
£643 $1003 €965 Hazy landscape near Himmelbjerget (42x63cm-17x25in) s. 11-Nov-2 Rasmussen, Vejle #676/R (D.KR 7500)
£652 $1036 €978 Vegetation behind a thatched house (30x45cm-12x18in) s. 5-Mar-3 Rasmussen, Copenhagen #1879/R (D.KR 7000)
£851 $1345 €1277 Summer landscape with river and reeds (52x50cm-20x20in) s.d.1868. 2-Dec-2 Rasmussen, Copenhagen #1247/R (D.KR 10000)
£861 $1395 €1292 Coastal landscape from Nettuno in Italy (31x44cm-12x17in) init.i.d.1874. 21-May-3 Museumsbygningen, Copenhagen #14 (D.KR 9000)

CHRISTENSEN, John (1896-1940) Danish
£485 $771 €728 Wild flowers (25x18cm-10x7in) s.d.37 cardboard. 29-Apr-3 Kunsthallen, Copenhagen #249 (D.KR 5200)
£1120 $1736 €1680 The drunkard - the day after (68x48cm-27x19in) s.d.1933 cardboard exhib.prov. 4-Dec-2 Kunsthallen, Copenhagen #314/R est:15000 (D.KR 13000)

CHRISTENSEN, Kay (1899-1981) Danish
£254 $391 €381 Girl and cat (50x65cm-20x26in) s. 23-Oct-2 Kunsthallen, Copenhagen #32 (D.KR 3000)
£342 $551 €513 Mother and child (46x55cm-18x22in) s. 22-Feb-3 Rasmussen, Havnen #2285 (D.KR 3800)
£406 $625 €609 The Christmas tree and the days after Christmas Eve (46x55cm-18x22in) s. painted 1964. 23-Oct-2 Kunsthallen, Copenhagen #81 (D.KR 4800)
£459 $738 €689 Franciska's flowers (65x50cm-26x20in) s.i.d.1951. 19-Jan-3 Hindemae, Ullerslev #7524/R (D.KR 5200)
£483 $764 €725 The unreal goes over a scene (46x55cm-18x22in) s. s.i.d.august 1965 verso. 1-Apr-3 Rasmussen, Copenhagen #505 (D.KR 5200)
£548 $872 €822 Murnau am Staffelsee, Ober Bayern (57x70cm-22x28in) s.d.1957. 26-Feb-3 Kunsthallen, Copenhagen #297/R (D.KR 6000)
£549 $846 €824 Banegarden (51x66cm-20x26in) s. painted 1959. 23-Oct-2 Kunsthallen, Copenhagen #105/R (D.KR 6500)
£596 $924 €894 The precious times (47x55cm-19x22in) s,. 28-Sep-2 Rasmussen, Havnen #2000/R (D.KR 7000)

CHRISTENSEN, N H (?) Danish?
£253 $395 €380 Mountain landscape with water, vessels and houses (62x92cm-24x36in) s. 23-Sep-2 Rasmussen, Vejle #2488 (D.KR 3000)

CHRISTENSEN, Otto (1898-1982) Danish
£743 $1175 €1115 Model resting (61x83cm-24x33in) s.stretcher. 1-Apr-3 Rasmussen, Copenhagen #518/R (D.KR 8000)

CHRISTENSEN, Torben (1950-) Danish
£390 $639 €585 Composition (60x70cm-24x28in) s.d.1991 acrylic. 27-May-3 Museumsbygningen, Copenhagen #520 (D.KR 4000)

CHRISTIANSEN, G Sand (1913-) Danish
£545 $884 €790 Danish street life with figures (98x108cm-39x43in) s. masonite. 24-May-3 Rasmussen, Havnen #4190 (D.KR 5700)

CHRISTIANSEN, Jesper (1955-) Danish
£836 $1322 €1254 Debut painting no.2 (84x73cm-33x29in) s.d.1995 verso. 1-Apr-3 Rasmussen, Copenhagen #335/R (D.KR 9000)

CHRISTIANSEN, N H (19th C) Danish
£426 $672 €639 Norwegian fjord landscape (61x93cm-24x37in) s. 2-Dec-2 Rasmussen, Copenhagen #1586/R (D.KR 5000)

CHRISTIANSEN, Nils (19th C) Scandinavian
£313 $489 €470 Landscape with cottages and river (24x49cm-9x19in) s. board. 7-Nov-2 International Art Centre, Auckland #169/R est:1500-2500 (NZ.D 1000)

CHRISTIANSEN, Nils H (1850-1922) Danish
£360 $576 €540 Lake, Wanstead Park (30x40cm-12x16in) s. 13-May-3 Bonhams, Knightsbridge #53/R
£431 $655 €647 Winter landscape with deer (69x93cm-27x37in) s.d.74. 27-Aug-2 Rasmussen, Copenhagen #1923/R (D.KR 5000)
£530 $880 €795 Highland lake scene with figures. Winter landscape. pair. 10-Jun-3 Lawrences, Bletchingley #1266
£550 $858 €825 Fjord scenes (15x23cm-6x9in) s. board pair. 10-Apr-3 Tennants, Leyburn #954a
£580 $905 €870 Skaters on a frozen lake by moonlight (30x45cm-12x18in) s.i. board. 26-Mar-3 Sotheby's, Olympia #201/R
£600 $942 €900 Stag in winter woodland (51x76cm-20x30in) s. pair. 16-Dec-2 Bonhams, Bury St Edmunds #512
£620 $1011 €930 Fjord landscapes (23x32cm-9x13in) s. board pair. 29-Jan-3 Sotheby's, Olympia #255/R
£851 $1319 €1277 Winter landscape with avenue of trees (69x89cm-27x35in) s.d.1883. 8-Dec-2 Uppsala Auktionskammare, Uppsala #109/R (S.KR 12000)
£1200 $1896 €1800 Country landscape with figures walking down a tree lined road (65x96cm-26x38in) s. 12-Nov-2 Bonhams, Knightsbridge #25 est:1000-1500
£1809 $2749 €2714 Winter's day in the woods with stag (117x152cm-46x60in) s.d.76. 27-Aug-2 Rasmussen, Copenhagen #1925/R est:8000-12000 (D.KR 21000)

CHRISTIANSEN, Professor Hans (1866-1945) German
£1127 $1814 €1600 Water garden (33x40cm-13x16in) mono. i. verso board. 10-May-3 Berlinghof, Heidelberg #204/R est:3000
£1824 $2845 €2900 Schloss Montfort - Langenargen-Bodensee (69x89cm-27x35in) i.d.1926 verso prov.lit. 20-Sep-2 Karlheinz Kaupp, Staufen #1932/R est:4500

CHRISTIANSEN, Rasmus (1863-1940) Danish
£271 $434 €407 Cows by Hjarbaek fjord (64x94cm-25x37in) s.i.d.juli 1918. 13-Jan-3 Rasmussen, Vejle #2057 (D.KR 3100)
£298 $474 €447 Farmer and cattle in meadow (49x70cm-19x28in) init. 10-Mar-3 Rasmussen, Vejle #90 (D.KR 3200)
£317 $511 €476 Boy and cattle by the coast of Jylland (51x72cm-20x28in) s. 19-Jan-3 Hindemae, Ullerslev #7479/R (D.KR 3600)
£652 $1043 €978 Royal inspection of the military regiment (48x56cm-19x22in) init. 16-Mar-3 Hindemae, Ullerslev #385/R (D.KR 7000)
£6052 $9623 €9078 Morning sunshine on a hill, girl picking flowers, man resting, Benzon (75x120cm-30x47in) init.d.1885 exhib. 5-Mar-3 Rasmussen, Copenhagen #1551/R est:75000 (D.KR 65000)

CHRISTIANSEN, Soren (1858-1937) Danish
£288 $464 €432 Children surrounding women musicians in winter (39x53cm-15x21in) mono. 22-Feb-3 Rasmussen, Havnen #2102/R (D.KR 3200)
£495 $798 €743 From Nytorn with figures, horse and wagon (42x55cm-17x22in) s.d.1900. 22-Feb-3 Rasmussen, Havnen #2015/R (D.KR 5500)

CHRISTIANSEN, Ursula Reuter (1943-) Danish
£1487 $2349 €2231 Il gigante degli montagni - a-d (230x135cm-91x53in) s.d.1988 stretcher four exhib. 1-Apr-3 Rasmussen, Copenhagen #308/R est:15000 (D.KR 16000)

CHRISTIE, James Elder (1847-1914) British
£400 $624 €600 Lonely furrow (25x33cm-10x13in) s. paper on canvas. 13-Sep-2 Lyon & Turnbull, Edinburgh #58/R
£2200 $3498 €3300 Autumn (26x21cm-10x8in) init.d.82. 6-Mar-3 Christie's, Kensington #190/R est:600-800

CHRISTIE, Lorraine (1967-) British
£500 $775 €750 Summer in Provence (41x51cm-16x20in) s. 2-Oct-2 John Ross, Belfast #271
£600 $954 €900 Still life (50x40cm-20x16in) s. 5-Mar-3 John Ross, Belfast #15
£600 $930 €900 Still life (40x50cm-16x20in) s. 4-Dec-2 John Ross, Belfast #135
£700 $1085 €1050 Still life (41x51cm-16x20in) s. 2-Oct-2 John Ross, Belfast #82

CHRISTIE, Robert (fl.1887-1926) British
£1991 $3047 €2987 Garden scene with sun-dial and Cupid (159x113cm-63x44in) s. 26-Aug-2 Blomqvist, Lysaker #1067/R est:12000-15000 (N.KR 23000)

CHRISTIE, Robert Duncan (1946-) Canadian
£267 $437 €387 Rolling pink (94x71cm-37x28in) acrylic. 1-Jun-3 Levis, Calgary #30/R (C.D 600)

CHRISTMAN, John Christopher (18/19th C) British
£980 $1588 €1470 Falcon (30x25cm-12x10in) s. 20-May-3 Sotheby's, Olympia #208/R

CHRISTMANN, Gunther (1936-) German
Works on paper
£319 $523 €479 Untitled (51x35cm-20x14in) s.d.83 pastel prov. 4-Jun-3 Deutscher-Menzies, Melbourne #322/R (A.D 800)

CHRISTMAS, Ernest W (1863-1918) Australian
£298 $465 €447 Early morning calm, Sunshine Bay, Lake Wakatipou (13x37cm-5x15in) s. board. 27-Mar-3 International Art Centre, Auckland #152/R (NZ.D 850)
£807 $1259 €1211 Southern landscape (74x120cm-29x47in) s. 27-Mar-3 International Art Centre, Auckland #186 (NZ.D 2300)

CHRISTO (1935-) American/Bulgarian
£28000 $45920 €42000 The umbrellas (60x109cm-24x43in) s.i.d.1988 acrylic wax crayon topographical dr. board two parts. 6-Feb-3 Christie's, London #666/R est:25000-35000
Prints
£1717 $2712 €2576 Wrapped monument to Victor Emmanuele, Piazza del Duomo, Milan (71x55cm-28x22in) s.d.1975 num.55/75 lithograph collage. 3-Apr-3 Heffel, Vancouver #13/R est:4500-5500 (C.D 4000)
£2115 $3088 €3300 Wrapped building - Project for No 1 Times Square (108x71cm-43x28in) s. col lithograph collage photo. 4-Jun-2 Karl & Faber, Munich #204/R est:3400
£2166 $3400 €3249 Pont Alexandre III, wrapped, project for Paris (69x74cm-27x29in) s.i.num.9/35 col lithograph collage. 21-Nov-2 Swann Galleries, New York #28/R est:2000-3000
£2383 $3717 €3575 Two lower Manhattan wrapped buildings, project for New York (70x55cm-28x22in) s.num.10/99 col lithograph collage lit. 5-Nov-2 Bukowskis, Stockholm #535/R est:25000-30000 (S.KR 34000)
£2642 $4200 €3963 Wrapped building (102x66cm-40x26in) s.num.112/125 col lithograph collage thread tape. 29-Apr-3 Christie's, Rockefeller NY #600/R est:4000-6000
£3552 $5719 €5328 Wrapped Opera House, project for the Opera House, Sidney (76x62cm-30x24in) s.num.60/120 col lithograph collage lit. 7-May-3 AB Stockholms Auktionsverk #1187/R est:45000-50000 (S.KR 46000)
£4015 $6465 €6023 Lower Manhattan wrapped building, project for 2 Broadway, New York (71x56cm-28x22in) s.num.97/110 col lithograph collage lit. 7-May-3 AB Stockholms Auktionsverk #1186/R est:45000-50000 (S.KR 52000)
£4088 $6500 €6132 Lower Manhattan wrapped buildings, project for 2 Broadway (102x66cm-40x26in) s.num.2/125 col lithograph collage. 2-May-3 Sotheby's, New York #412/R est:5000-7000
Sculpture
£2083 $3312 €3000 Roses empaquettees (60x17x10cm-24x7x4in) s.num.10/75 multiple. 29-Apr-3 Campo, Vlaamse Kaai #40 est:400-500
£2564 $4051 €4000 Look magazine (56x46cm-22x18in) paper magazine string plastic. 15-Nov-2 Laurence Calmels, Paris #20/R

£32000	$52480	€48000	Wrapped can (20x8x8cm-8x3x3in) can painted fabric wire on painted can. 6-Feb-3 Christie's, London #685/R est:25000-35000
£65000	$108550	€97500	Packed supermarket cart (105x78x42cm-41x31x17in) s.d.63 mixed media prov.exhib.lit. 25-Jun-3 Sotheby's, London #10/R est:60000-80000

Works on paper

£3205	$4968	€5000	441 barrels construction (32x40cm-13x16in) s.i.d.1967 W/C gouache pencil. 6-Dec-2 Hauswedell & Nolte, Hamburg #83/R est:7500
£3797	$5886	€6000	Wrapped Reichstag (36x28cm-14x11in) oil col chk pen pencil over photo photocopy collage. 28-Sep-2 Ketterer, Hamburg #781/R est:5000-6000
£4747	$7500	€7500	Wrapped Reichstag - Project for Berlin (29x36cm-11x14in) s.d.1993 collage photosenamel colours col chk pencil board panel. 30-Nov-2 Villa Grisebach, Berlin #480/R est:6000-8000
£6604	$10236	€10500	Surrounded islands, project for Biscayne Bay, Greater Miami. s.d.83 mixed media photo collage. 30-Oct-2 Artcurial Briest, Paris #448/R est:6000-8000
£9266	$14919	€13899	Running fence- project for Sonoma and Marin County, State of California (55x71cm-22x28in) s.d.1974 pencil collage. 7-May-3 AB Stockholms Auktionsverk #989/R est:150000-200000 (S.KR 120000)
£10145	$16638	€14000	Store front's - project part I and II (65x46cm-26x18in) s.i.d.64-65 graphite chk transparent paper on board. 31-May-3 Villa Grisebach, Berlin #353/R est:4000-6000
£10145	$16638	€14000	Texas mastaba (71x56cm-28x22in) s.i.d.1977 graphite col chks varnish collage board. 31-May-3 Villa Grisebach, Berlin #354/R est:9000-12000
£10862	$16945	€16293	Adu Dhabi Mastaba - project for United Arab Emirates (71x56cm-28x22in) s.d.1978 crayon pencil prov. 5-Nov-2 Bukowskis, Stockholm #442/R est:80000-100000 (S.KR 155000)
£10897	$16891	€17000	Store front part 4 - project 9F (48x38cm-19x15in) s. i.d.1965 mixed media paper on plywood. 3-Dec-2 Christie's, Amsterdam #296/R est:8000-12000
£12000	$19680	€18000	Project for united Arab Emirates (80x61cm-31x24in) s.d.1980 chl pastel crayon collage cardboard plexiglass. 7-Feb-3 Sotheby's, London #190a/R est:10000-15000
£13000	$21710	€18850	Project for United Arab Emirates (79x61cm-31x24in) s.i.d.1979 chl pastel crayon map collage on cardboard plexiglass. 26-Jun-3 Sotheby's, London #258/R est:10000-15000
£13014	$20301	€19000	Cubic feet (80x65cm-31x26in) s.i.d.1966 mixed media collage paper on card. 10-Apr-3 Finarte Semenzato, Rome #245/R est:22000
£13043	$21391	€18000	Red store front - project (71x56cm-28x22in) s.i.d.1977 graphite pencil varnish wrapping paper board. 31-May-3 Villa Grisebach, Berlin #352/R est:7000-9000
£15484	$24000	€23226	Package on dolly collage (71x56cm-28x22in) s.i.d.1975 pencil plastified fabric twine wax crayon chl. 26-Sep-2 Christie's, Rockefeller NY #770/R est:28000-35000
£17187	$27500	€25781	Wrapped tree (56x71cm-22x28in) s.i.d.1971 pencil tarpaulin twine polyethylene chl glue. 14-May-3 Sotheby's, New York #194/R est:20000-30000
£18987	$30000	€30000	Wrapped Reichstag - project for Berlin (56x71cm-22x28in) s.i.d.1987 crayon over silkscreen perspex collage in 2 parts. 29-Nov-2 Villa Grisebach, Berlin #90/R est:30000-40000
£21277	$34468	€30000	Packed Coast, project for Little Bay, near Sidney, Australia (71x36cm-28x14in) s.i.d.1969 pencil pastel material string map paper on board prov. 26-May-3 Christie's, Milan #235/R est:30000-40000
£21528	$34014	€31000	Wrapped pont neuf, project for Paris (28x71cm-11x28in) s.i.d. graphite chl crayon pastel collage prov. 27-Apr-3 Perrin, Versailles #92/R est:30000-35000
£22000	$36080	€33000	The Pont Neuf wrapped - Project for Paris (72x85cm-28x33in) s.i.d.1980 pastel photo collage pastel pencil in two parts. 6-Feb-3 Christie's, London #665/R est:25000-35000
£22152	$35000	€33228	Valley curtain - project for Colorado (71x56cm-28x22in) s.i.d.71 graphite fabric pastel aerial photograph. 14-Nov-2 Christie's, Rockefeller NY #223/R est:25000-35000
£26899	$42500	€40349	Puerta de alcala wrapped, project for Madrid (71x56cm-28x22in) s. chl pencil string fabric collage on board executed 1976 prov. 13-Nov-2 Sotheby's, New York #295/R est:25000-30000
£31884	$52290	€44000	Store front project (108x81cm-43x32in) s.i.d.64 chk varnish wrapping paper nettle plastic film board. 30-May-3 Villa Grisebach, Berlin #76/R est:40000-60000
£50000	$82000	€75000	The Pont Neuf wrapped - Project for Paris (148x245cm-58x96in) s.i.d.1980 pastel pencil paper collage on board two parts. 6-Feb-3 Christie's, London #673/R est:50000-70000

CHRISTO and Jeanne Claude (20th C) American

Works on paper

£11000	$18370	€15950	Abu Dhabi mastaba - project for the United Arab Emirates (95x60cm-37x24in) s.i.d.1978 pencil pastel chl wax crayon photograph on board. 27-Jun-3 Christie's, London #176/R est:12000-15000
£16000	$26720	€23200	Valley Curtain - project for Colorado (71x56cm-28x22in) s.d.1972 pencil pastel wax crayon chl fabric on card. 27-Jun-3 Christie's, London #172/R est:10000-15000
£48000	$80160	€69600	Umbrellas - joint project for Japan and USA (77x67cm-30x26in) pencil oil pastel photograph on board executed 1991 prov. 27-Jun-3 Christie's, London #166/R est:25000-35000

CHRISTOFFERSEN, Frede (1919-1987) Danish

£392	$623	€588	Evening III, Humlebaek (42x63cm-17x25in) init.d.57 exhib. 29-Apr-3 Kunsthallen, Copenhagen #207/R (D.KR 4200)
£426	$707	€618	Evening VI, Humlebaek (42x63cm-17x25in) init.d.57 verso exhib. 12-Jun-3 Kunsthallen, Copenhagen #115/R (D.KR 4500)
£524	$807	€786	Autumn (46x64cm-18x25in) init.d.45. 23-Oct-2 Kunsthallen, Copenhagen #338/R (D.KR 6200)
£560	$890	€840	Thunder storm at night (48x54cm-19x21in) init.d.51. 29-Apr-3 Kunsthallen, Copenhagen #2/R (D.KR 6000)
£653	$1038	€980	Sun (54x60cm-21x24in) init.d.51. 29-Apr-3 Kunsthallen, Copenhagen #1/R (D.KR 7000)
£715	$1194	€1037	Morning (68x60cm-27x24in) init.d.53 i.verso exhib. 17-Jun-3 Rasmussen, Copenhagen #114/R (D.KR 7500)
£732	$1135	€1098	Evening (37x55cm-15x22in) init.d.54. 4-Dec-2 Kunsthallen, Copenhagen #11/R (D.KR 8500)
£803	$1237	€1205	Autumn (50x71cm-20x28in) init.d.50. 23-Oct-2 Kunsthallen, Copenhagen #16/R (D.KR 9500)
£1101	$1706	€1652	Evening in March (45x52cm-18x20in) init.d.72 verso exhib. 1-Oct-2 Rasmussen, Copenhagen #205/R est:7000 (D.KR 13000)
£1355	$2100	€2033	Evening, Skagen, summer (47x65cm-19x26in) init.d.60. 1-Oct-2 Rasmussen, Copenhagen #247/R est:10000 (D.KR 16000)

CHRISTOFFERSEN, Uffe (1947-) Danish

£517	$801	€776	Elephant on the hill (72x95cm-28x37in) s.d.1977. 4-Dec-2 Kunsthallen, Copenhagen #168 (D.KR 6000)
£1371	$2180	€2057	Mistralen and winter light (114x146cm-45x57in) s.d.1997 verso. 26-Feb-3 Kunsthallen, Copenhagen #204/R est:8000 (D.KR 15000)

CHRISTOFOROU, John (1921-) British

£480	$744	€720	Crucifixion (83x55cm-33x22in) s. paper on board prov. 3-Dec-2 Bonhams, Knightsbridge #383/R
£513	$810	€800	Portrait rouge de profil (55x46cm-22x18in) painted 1985. 12-Nov-2 Babuino, Rome #142/R
£532	$841	€830	Portrait de temoin (73x60cm-29x24in) painted 1971. 12-Nov-2 Babuino, Rome #97/R
£532	$841	€830	Portrait noir au gilet rouge (57x46cm-22x18in) painted 1984. 12-Nov-2 Babuino, Rome #245/R
£532	$841	€830	Homme bleu au casque (55x46cm-22x18in) painted 1985. 12-Nov-2 Babuino, Rome #98/R
£554	$875	€831	Clown (48x32cm-19x13in) s.d.1949 board. 18-Nov-2 Goodman, Sydney #251 (A.D 1550)
£629	$1025	€950	Man with black ad white hat (59x71cm-23x28in) s. i.d.1985 verso. 3-Feb-3 Cornette de St.Cyr, Paris #382
£647	$1023	€1010	Chevalier jaune (55x46cm-22x18in) painted 1975. 12-Nov-2 Babuino, Rome #277/R
£647	$1023	€1010	Savant ensorcelle (130x97cm-51x38in) 12-Nov-2 Babuino, Rome #238/R
£800	$1256	€1200	Seated figure (70x48cm-28x19in) s. board. 15-Apr-3 Bonhams, Knightsbridge #77/R
£1325	$2107	€1988	L'acrobate (73x60cm-29x24in) s. 26-Feb-3 Kunsthallen, Copenhagen #170/R est:15000 (D.KR 14500)
£1497	$2380	€2200	Portrait de prophete bleu (80x65cm-31x26in) s. i.d.1988 verso acrylic. 26-Feb-3 Artcurial Briest, Paris #513 est:1200-1500
£1603	$2516	€2500	Homme vert (80x65cm-31x26in) s. s.i.d.1964 verso. 24-Nov-2 Laurence Calmels, Paris #77/R

CHRISTOFOROU, John (attrib) (1921-) British

£250	$393	€375	Seated male nude (74x51cm-29x20in) s. board prov. 10-Dec-2 Rosebery Fine Art, London #723/R

CHRISTOPH, Hans (1901-1992) German

£1319	$2085	€1900	Untitled abstract landscape (46x67cm-18x26in) s. panel double-sided. 26-Apr-3 Dr Lehr, Berlin #101/R est:1000

CHRISTOPHE (?) ?

Works on paper

£517	$817	€750	Intrigant (30x21cm-12x8in) s. Chinese ink. 7-Apr-3 Claude Aguttes, Neuilly #120/R

£690 $1090 €1000 Comment Lolo fit de gros pates (30x21cm-12x8in) s. Chinese ink. 7-Apr-3 Claude Aguttes, Neuilly #119/R

CHRISTOPHE, Pierre Robert (1880-1971) French
Sculpture
£1795 $2782 €2800 Hamadryas (19x21x8cm-7x8x3in) s. num.9 brown green pat bronze. 7-Dec-2 Martinot & Savignat, Pontoise #86/R

CHRISTOPHER, Ken (20th C) ?
£261 $407 €435 Will-o-the-Whisp (61x84cm-24x33in) s.d.1979 acrylic. 13-Apr-3 Levis, Calgary #422/R (C.D 600)

CHRISTOPHERSEN, Alejandro (1866-1946) Norwegian
£2800 $4368 €4200 Orange seller (175x155cm-69x61in) s.d.1909. 26-Mar-3 Sotheby's, Olympia #283/R est:800-1200

CHRISTOPHERSON, John (1921-1996) British
£300 $495 €435 Courtyard, Westgrove Lane, Greenwich (30x24cm-12x9in) init. board exhib. 3-Jul-3 Christie's, Kensington #706

CHRISTY, F Earl (20th C) American
Works on paper
£932 $1500 €1398 Couple about to kiss against orange background (38x23cm-15x9in) s. 20-Feb-3 Illustration House, New York #24 est:1800-2600

CHRISTY, Howard Chandler (1872-1952) American
£281 $450 €407 Skipper (59x49cm-23x19in) s. board. 16-May-3 Skinner, Boston #151/R
£1235 $2000 €1791 Portrait of Blanche d'Arville Fellner (102x76cm-40x30in) s.i. indis d.19.. 21-May-3 Doyle, New York #157/R est:4000-6000
£9259 $15000 €13426 Shaded from the midday sun (102x76cm-40x30in) s.d.1940. 21-May-3 Doyle, New York #156/R est:10000-15000

CHRISVALAIN (20th C) French?
Works on paper
£833 $1358 €1200 Marche aux bestiaux a Gourin (48x62cm-19x24in) s. pastel. 19-Jul-3 Thierry & Lannon, Brest #191/R

CHTEMBER, Viktor Karlovich (1863-1917) Russian
£10915 $17574 €15500 Eve (107x187cm-42x74in) s. 10-May-3 Bukowskis, Helsinki #380/R est:4000-6000

CHU TEH CHUN (1920-) Chinese
£3165 $5000 €5000 Untitled (50x65cm-20x26in) s.d.1973 acrylic paper on panel. 29-Nov-2 Drouot Estimations, Paris #122/R
£6605 $10897 €9577 Abstraction no 473 (60x80cm-24x31in) s. 6-Jul-3 Christie's, Hong Kong #129/R est:60000-80000 (HK.D 85000)
£9494 $15000 €15000 Composition (73x100cm-29x39in) s.d.1962 s.d.verso prov. 27-Nov-2 Tajan, Paris #34/R est:12000-15000
£9677 $15290 €15000 Composition abstraite (114x146cm-45x57in) s.d.91 prov. 18-Dec-2 Digard, Paris #168/R
£11218 $17612 €17500 Composition (92x65cm-36x26in) s. s.i.d.1960 verso prov. 15-Dec-2 Perrin, Versailles #67/R
£12279 $19523 €18050 Poetique boreale no 1 (60x120cm-24x47in) s. s.i.d.verso prov. 26-Feb-3 Artcurial Briest, Paris #447/R est:15000-20000
£15000 $23100 €22500 Lumiere centrale (162x130cm-64x51in) s.d.89 s.i.d.verso acrylic on canvas. 22-Oct-2 Sotheby's, London #422/R est:8000-12000
£23310 $38462 €33800 Esperance naissante (120x60cm-47x24in) s. exhib. 6-Jul-3 Christie's, Hong Kong #128/R est:300000-400000 (HK.D 300000)
£32634 $53846 €47319 Dans un sentier sous bois no 42 (120x60cm-47x24in) s. 6-Jul-3 Christie's, Hong Kong #127/R est:350000-450000 (HK.D 420000)
Works on paper
£1250 $1988 €1800 Composition (40x54cm-16x21in) s. Indian ink wash dr. 29-Apr-3 Artcurial Briest, Paris #557/R est:2000-3000
£1923 $2981 €3000 Composition (35x53cm-14x21in) s. Chinese ink gouache prov. 4-Dec-2 Pierre Berge, Paris #7
£2244 $3522 €3500 Composition (56x38cm-22x15in) s. s.d.1961 verso gouache ink prov. 15-Dec-2 Perrin, Versailles #32/R
£2722 $4246 €4300 Composition (55x36cm-22x14in) s. mixed media paper on canvas. 20-Oct-2 Claude Boisgirard, Paris #56/R est:4500-5000
£3205 $5032 €5000 Untitled (62x48cm-24x19in) s.d.66 gouache. 24-Nov-2 Laurence Calmels, Paris #78/R

CHUBB, Lee (1904-) American
£346 $550 €519 Abstract construction (71x97cm-28x38in) s. oil board 3-D painted c.1960. 2-Mar-3 Toomey, Oak Park #802/R
£346 $550 €519 Abstract composition (76x102cm-30x40in) s. board painted c.1960. 2-Mar-3 Toomey, Oak Park #820/R

CHUCK, Carl (?) ?
£280 $442 €406 Still life of a table setting (51x58cm-20x23in) s.d.52. 23-Jul-3 Mallams, Oxford #227

CHUGHTAI, Abdur Rahman (1894-1975) Indian
Works on paper
£3000 $4680 €4500 Lady holding a flower (48x27cm-19x11in) s.d. W/C pencil htd bodycol. 17-Oct-2 Bonhams, Knightsbridge #599/R est:4000-6000

CHURBERG, Fanny Maria (1845-1892) Finnish
£12658 $20000 €20000 Summer landscape (32x45cm-13x18in) s.d.79. 1-Dec-2 Bukowskis, Helsinki #33/R est:12000-14000
£14085 $22676 €20000 The road to town (32x26cm-13x10in) s.d.79 cardboard. 10-May-3 Bukowskis, Helsinki #111/R est:14000-17000

CHURCH, Frederic Edwin (1826-1900) American
£101852 $165000 €152778 Setting sun (24x36cm-9x14in) s.i.d.64 panel prov.lit. 21-May-3 Sotheby's, New York #191/R est:150000-200000
£245161 $380000 €367742 Study for 'The iceberg' (21x33cm-8x13in) paperboard on canvas prov.exhib.lit. 3-Dec-2 Phillips, New York #18/R est:250000-350000
£432099 $700000 €648149 Lumber mill, Mount desert Island (36x51cm-14x20in) s. painted c.1850 lit. 21-May-3 Sotheby's, New York #197/R est:700000-900000

CHURCH, Frederick Stuart (1842-1923) American
£4037 $6500 €6056 Young lady seated on river bank near flamingos (38x61cm-15x24in) s.d.1909 prov. 18-Feb-3 Arthur James, Florida #75
Works on paper
£2019 $3250 €3029 The tease (36x28cm-14x11in) s.d.99 i.verso W/C paper on board prov. 18-Feb-3 John Moran, Pasadena #139 est:1000-2000

CHURCH, Katharine (1910-1999) British
£2000 $3180 €3000 Still life a rubber plant (76x91cm-30x36in) 1937verso. 26-Feb-3 Sotheby's, Olympia #237/R est:600-800
Works on paper
£520 $827 €780 Tarrant Hinton (36x55cm-14x22in) s.d.48 W/C gouache. 26-Feb-3 Sotheby's, Olympia #238/R est:200-400

CHURCHER, Peter (1964-) Australian
£460 $722 €690 Study of a woman (38x33cm-15x13in) s. 15-Apr-3 Lawson Menzies, Sydney #95/R est:900-1000 (A.D 1200)

CHURCHILL, John Spencer (1909-) British
£2200 $3432 €3300 Portrait of Sir Winston Churchill (56x45cm-22x18in) s. 27-Mar-3 Christie's, Kensington #405/R est:2000-3000
Works on paper
£1500 $2490 €2175 Retreat to Dunkirk (31x44cm-12x17in) s.i.d.30 May '40 ink grey wash. 10-Jun-3 Mellors & Kirk, Nottingham #836/R est:300-400

CHURCHILL, Sir Winston (1874-1965) British
£53000 $83210 €79500 Trees in the eastern counties, near Beccles (63x76cm-25x30in) painted c.1936 prov.exhib.lit. 22-Nov-2 Christie's, London #84/R est:40000-60000
£58000 $95120 €84100 Calanques, near Marseilles (61x76cm-24x30in) prov.lit. 4-Jun-3 Sotheby's, London #56/R est:30000-40000
£85000 $133450 €127500 Rocky seascape (56x68cm-22x27in) init. painted 1940 prov.exhib.lit. 22-Nov-2 Christie's, London #48/R est:60000-100000

CHURCHYARD, Charles (19th C) British
Works on paper
£250 $418 €363 Tidemill at Woodbridge (21x44cm-8x17in) W/C. 24-Jun-3 Rowley Fine Art, Newmarket #394/R

CHURCHYARD, Thomas (1798-1865) British
£680 $1122 €986 River with church beyond (18x14cm-7x6in) board pair. 1-Jul-3 Bonhams, Norwich #250/R
£950 $1482 €1425 Study of trees in the park at Campsey Ash (22x22cm-9x9in) s.i. panel. 18-Sep-2 Cheffins Grain & Comins, Cambridge #513/R
£1500 $2325 €2250 Maidavale Gardens, Ipswich Road, Woodbridge (16x12cm-6x5in) i.verso panel sold with a companion. 30-Sep-2 Bonhams, Ipswich #506/R est:800-1200
£2300 $3565 €3450 Kyson Point, Woodbridge (22x34cm-9x13in) i.verso panel. 30-Sep-2 Bonhams, Ipswich #497/R est:1000-1500
Works on paper
£360 $594 €522 Walled garden (12x17cm-5x7in) W/C. 1-Jul-3 Bonhams, Norwich #60

£600 $990 €870 View of the shore at Southwold, Suffolk (10x12cm-4x5in) pencil W/C. 3-Jul-3 Christie's, Kensington #136/R

CHURCHYARD, Thomas (attrib) (1798-1865) British
£400 $668 €580 Lock near Beccles (20x26cm-8x10in) board. 8-Jul-3 Bonhams, Knightsbridge #129/R
£520 $816 €780 Cottage by moonlight (28x23cm-11x9in) 13-Dec-2 Keys, Aylsham #659
Works on paper
£300 $471 €450 Fishing on the River Deben (14x19cm-6x7in) W/C prov. 19-Nov-2 Bonhams, Leeds #18

CHWALA, Adolf (1836-1900) Czechoslovakian
£685 $1068 €1000 Donau landscape with man and horse and cart (37x58cm-15x23in) s. canvas on canvas lit. 10-Apr-3 Allgauer, Kempten #2744/R
£1361 $2163 €2000 River landscape with figures (45x58cm-18x23in) s. 25-Feb-3 Dorotheum, Vienna #2/R est:2400-2600
£1384 $2145 €2200 Summer morning in Salzach valley (49x81cm-19x32in) s. i. verso. 29-Oct-2 Dorotheum, Vienna #273/R est:2600-2700
£2013 $3119 €3200 Storm over landscape with waterfall (53x41cm-21x16in) s. panel. 29-Oct-2 Dorotheum, Vienna #2/R est:3200-3400
£2148 $3458 €3200 Raven tower near Frain on the River Thaya, lower Austrai (79x116cm-31x46in) s. prov.exhib. 18-Feb-3 Sotheby's, Amsterdam #289/R est:1200-1800
£9615 $15096 €15000 Calm summer's day near Eisgrub in Mahren (79x156cm-31x61in) s. 21-Nov-2 Van Ham, Cologne #1517/R est:8000

CHWALA, Adolf (attrib) (1836-1900) Czechoslovakian
£1136 $1772 €1704 Sunset over a lake (24x43cm-9x17in) bears sig. 12-Oct-2 Dorotheum, Prague #26/R est:40000-60000 (C.KR 55000)

CHWALA, Fritz (1872-1936) Austrian
£2793 $4524 €4050 Lake landscape with rowing boat (67x103cm-26x41in) s. 25-May-3 Uppsala Auktionskammare, Uppsala #99/R est:10000-12000 (S.KR 36000)

CHWAT, Molli (1888-1979) Russian/French
£272 $433 €400 Paysage (49x54cm-19x21in) s. 26-Feb-3 Artcurial Briest, Paris #186
£408 $649 €600 Village au pied d'un chateau (46x61cm-18x24in) s. 3-Mar-3 Claude Boisgirard, Paris #34/R

CIACELLI, Arturo (1883-1966) Italian
Works on paper
£743 $1159 €1100 Air routes (34x45cm-13x18in) init.d.1942 pencil prov. 26-Mar-3 Finarte Semenzato, Milan #250/R

CIAMPELLI, Agostini (1578-1640) Italian
Works on paper
£26235 $42500 €39353 Stoning of St. Stephen (35x52cm-14x20in) pen brown ink over black chk squared for transfer prov.exhib. 21-Jan-3 Sotheby's, New York #18/R est:25000-35000

CIAMPI, Alimondo (1876-1939) Italian
Sculpture
£4600 $7130 €6900 Seated girl with clasped hands, and kneeling boy (83cm-33in) s.i. brown pat bronze oval base. 29-Oct-2 Bonhams, New Bond Street #138/R est:2000-3000

CIAN, Fernand (19/20th C) Italian
Sculpture
£1200 $1872 €1800 Bust of Wagner (24cm-9in) s.d.1923 terracotta marble base. 9-Apr-3 Sotheby's, London #208/R est:1500-2500

CIANGOTTINI, Giovanni (1912-) Italian
£633 $987 €1000 Landscape (60x75cm-24x30in) s.d.1958 acrylic. 19-Oct-2 Semenzato, Venice #122/R

CIANI, Cesare (1854-1925) Italian
£510 $811 €750 Portrait of woman (34x26cm-13x10in) s. 1-Mar-3 Meeting Art, Vercelli #182
£633 $1000 €1000 Donkey with cart (20x25cm-8x10in) board. 26-Nov-2 Christie's, Rome #175/R
£1646 $2600 €2600 Woman in profile (19x9cm-7x4in) s.d.1899 board prov. 26-Nov-2 Christie's, Rome #189/R est:4000
£1772 $2800 €2800 View of village with figures (8x16cm-3x6in) s. board. 26-Nov-2 Christie's, Rome #193/R
£2405 $3800 €3800 Florence, market (12x35cm-5x14in) s. cardboard on canvas. 26-Nov-2 Christie's, Rome #192/R
£5031 $7748 €8000 Maternity (31x20cm-12x8in) s. i.verso cardboard exhib.lit. 23-Oct-2 Finarte, Milan #127/R est:6000-7000
Works on paper
£417 $650 €626 Man with ox drawn cart (27x38cm-11x15in) s.i.d.1920 W/C. 19-Sep-2 Swann Galleries, New York #255/R

CIAPPA, Carlo (19/20th C) Italian
£506 $800 €759 Coastal view of Capri from a veranda (61x91cm-24x36in) s. 26-Apr-3 Jeffery Burchard, Florida #51a

CIAPPA, Frederico (fl.1830-1840) Italian
£466 $740 €699 Portrait of gentleman (70x55cm-28x22in) 5-Mar-3 Rasmussen, Copenhagen #1613/R (D.KR 5000)

CIAPPA, Mario (20th C) Italian
£680 $1082 €1000 Peasant woman in stable (68x49cm-27x19in) s.d.1924 canvas on board. 18-Mar-3 Finarte, Milan #159/R
£680 $1082 €1000 Farmer feeding hens (69x49cm-27x19in) s. board. 18-Mar-3 Finarte, Milan #158/R

CIAPPA, Vincenzo (?) Italian
£1282 $2013 €2000 Clio ou la muse de la poesie epique (103x76cm-41x30in) s. 10-Dec-2 Vanderkindere, Brussels #5/R est:2000-3000

CIAPPORI-PUCHE, Claudius Joseph (1822-c.1887) French
Works on paper
£340 $541 €500 Christ as Saviour of the World (49x58cm-19x23in) s.d.1856 pencil wash sold with another. 19-Mar-3 Neumeister, Munich #348

CIARALLO, Antonio (1957-) Italian
£256 $403 €400 Untitled (40x30cm-16x12in) s.i.d.1998 tar board lit. 23-Nov-2 Meeting Art, Vercelli #60
Works on paper
£253 $395 €400 Untitled (94x40cm-37x16in) s.i.d.1997 verso mixed media board. 14-Sep-2 Meeting Art, Vercelli #337
£590 $939 €850 Timeless (124x44cm-49x17in) s.i.d.1996 verso mixed media board lit. 1-May-3 Meeting Art, Vercelli #384
£646 $1028 €950 Shovel (121x44cm-48x17in) s.i.d.1997 verso mixed media board. 1-Mar-3 Meeting Art, Vercelli #585

CIARDI, Beppe (1875-1932) Italian
£3481 $5500 €5500 Lagoon (18x26cm-7x10in) s. board. 26-Nov-2 Christie's, Rome #205/R
£3871 $6116 €6000 Boat in the lagoon (24x31cm-9x12in) s. s.verso board prov. 18-Dec-2 Finarte, Milan #43/R est:6000
£4110 $6452 €6000 Venetian sunset (22x32cm-9x13in) s. board. 15-Apr-3 Sotheby's, Amsterdam #67/R est:5000-7000
£4516 $7135 €7000 Canove, Asiago (20x49cm-8x19in) s. s.d.1905 verso cardboard. 18-Dec-2 Finarte, Milan #6/R est:8000
£4516 $7135 €7000 Boats on the seashore (25x38cm-10x15in) s. board. 18-Dec-2 Finarte, Milan #18/R
£5161 $8155 €8000 Harvest (30x39cm-12x15in) s. s.verso cardboard. 18-Dec-2 Finarte, Milan #75/R
£6918 $10654 €11000 Venice (30x39cm-12x15in) s. cardboard. 23-Oct-2 Finarte, Milan #58/R
£10884 $17306 €16000 Boat (29x39cm-11x15in) s. cardboard. 1-Mar-3 Meeting Art, Vercelli #244 est:15000
£11321 $17434 €18000 Along the Sile (74x72cm-29x28in) s. lit. 23-Oct-2 Finarte, Milan #59/R est:20000-24000

CIARDI, Emma (1879-1933) Italian
£2516 $3874 €4000 Morning in the park (27x20cm-11x8in) s. board. 23-Oct-2 Finarte, Milan #14/R est:4000-5000
£2600 $4342 €3900 Gente elegante nel giardino (23x37cm-9x15in) s.d.09 board crescent shape. 18-Jun-3 Christie's, Kensington #145/R est:3000-5000
£2899 $4754 €4000 La fontana della Najadi (32x27cm-13x11in) s. prov. 27-May-3 Finarte, Milan #18/R est:4000-5000
£2908 $4711 €4100 Pomeriggio d'agosto (20x30cm-8x12in) s. board. 22-May-3 Stadion, Trieste #394/R est:4000-5000
£3038 $4800 €4800 Lake with swans (27x37cm-11x15in) s. s.i.verso board. 26-Nov-2 Christie's, Rome #209/R
£3188 $5229 €4400 Bisbigli d'autumno (28x28cm-11x11in) s. board prov. 27-May-3 Finarte, Milan #17/R est:4000-5000
£4747 $7500 €7121 Elegant ladies in front of a stagecoach (62x74cm-24x29in) s. panel prov. 1-Apr-3 Christie's, Rockefeller NY #201/R est:4000-6000

CIARDI, G (1842-1917) Italian
£922 $1494 €1300 Santa Maria de la Salute from the canal (13x18cm-5x7in) s. panel prov. 20-May-3 Mealy's, Castlecomer #983/R est:800-1200

CIARDI, Guglielmo (1842-1917) Italian
£5031 $7748 €8000 Linen in the sun (22x34cm-9x13in) s. 23-Oct-2 Finarte, Milan #68/R est:10000-12000
£8228 $13000 €13000 Calm river (29x37cm-11x15in) s. s.i.verso prov. 26-Nov-2 Christie's, Rome #208/R est:8000-12000
£15823 $25000 €23735 Paesaggio alpino con torrente (43x79cm-17x31in) s. 23-Apr-3 Christie's, Rockefeller NY #75/R est:10000-15000
£91772 $145000 €137658 Fishermen along the canal (55x100cm-22x39in) s.i.d.1893. 24-Apr-3 Sotheby's, New York #88/R est:40000-60000

CIARDI, Guglielmo (attrib) (1842-1917) Italian
£881 $1356 €1400 Snowfall (17x22cm-7x9in) s.indis.d. paper on cardboard prov. 28-Oct-2 Il Ponte, Milan #261

CIARDIELLO, Carmine (1871-?) Italian
£633 $1000 €1000 Young peasant woman (25x40cm-10x16in) s. 26-Nov-2 Christie's, Rome #27/R

CIARDIELLO, Michele (1839-?) Italian
£1885 $3092 €2733 Flirt (28x46cm-11x18in) s. 4-Jun-3 AB Stockholms Auktionsverk #2420/R est:18000-20000 (S.KR 24000)

CIARDO, Vincenzo (1894-1970) Italian
£449 $704 €700 Autumn (20x14cm-8x6in) s. i.verso board. 21-Nov-2 Finarte, Rome #301
£769 $1208 €1200 View of Lucrino lake (21x26cm-8x10in) s. s.i.d.1946 verso board. 21-Nov-2 Finarte, Rome #329
£1206 $1953 €1700 Casa di campagna (30x41cm-12x16in) s. panel. 22-May-3 Stadion, Trieste #289 est:700-1000

CIARROCCHI, Arnoldo (1916-) Italian
£1154 $1812 €1800 Landscape (50x40cm-20x16in) s. 21-Nov-2 Finarte, Rome #218/R
Works on paper
£417 $654 €650 View of Navona Square (50x35cm-20x14in) s. Chinese ink. 21-Nov-2 Finarte, Rome #173
£609 $956 €950 Female bust (70x50cm-28x20in) s.d.1973 col pastel. 21-Nov-2 Finarte, Rome #168

CIBO, Gherardo (1512-1597) Italian
Works on paper
£40123 $65000 €60185 Study of tree (28x19cm-11x7in) i. pen ink wash htd white prov. 21-Jan-3 Sotheby's, New York #29/R est:30000

CICCOTELLI, Beniamino (1937-) Italian
£253 $395 €400 Grapes in a bowl (50x50cm-20x20in) s. s.i.verso. 14-Sep-2 Meeting Art, Vercelli #849
£545 $855 €850 Half a melon in steel bowl (60x80cm-24x31in) s. s.i.verso. 23-Nov-2 Meeting Art, Vercelli #175/R

CICERI, Ernest (1817-1866) American
Works on paper
£613 $968 €950 Ruines romaines (15x27cm-6x11in) s. W/C. 19-Dec-2 Claude Aguttes, Neuilly #2/R
£920 $1500 €1334 Jerusalem at night (15x27cm-6x11in) s. W/C. 16-Jul-3 Sotheby's, Olympia #161/R

CICERI, Eugène (1813-1890) French
£809 $1277 €1214 Grape pickers (27x41cm-11x16in) s. 30-Nov-2 Rasmussen, Havnen #2008/R (D.KR 9500)
£1500 $2370 €2250 Figures by a wooden bridge (35x55cm-14x22in) s.d.75 panel. 14-Nov-2 Christie's, Kensington #289/R est:1800-2200
Works on paper
£654 $1052 €1000 Navires de peche sur la plage en Pays de Caux (19x26cm-7x10in) s. W/C. 18-Jan-3 Neret-Minet, Paris #183/R

CICERI, Pierre Luc Charles (1782-1868) French
£280 $434 €420 Continental town square (8x13cm-3x5in) s.d.1831. 1-Oct-2 Capes Dunn, Manchester #841
Works on paper
£1026 $1620 €1600 Cerfs et biches sur un chemin montagneux (32x46cm-13x18in) s.d. W/C. 18-Nov-2 Tajan, Paris #76 est:700-800

CICERI, Pierre Luc Charles (attrib) (1782-1868) French
Works on paper
£1678 $2400 €2517 Picnic on a hill overlooking Rome (14x20cm-6x8in) gouache. 23-Jan-3 Swann Galleries, New York #290/R est:2000-3000

CICVAREK, Miloslav (1927-) Czechoslovakian
£1439 $2360 €2000 Picture of Salzburg from Mulln (120x115cm-47x45in) s. 5-Jun-3 Dorotheum, Salzburg #645/R est:2000-2400

CIDONCHA, Rafael (1952-) Spanish
£641 $1006 €1000 Cactus (33x24cm-13x9in) s.d.83 canvas on board. 19-Nov-2 Castellana, Madrid #61/R

CIESLEWSKI, Thaddaus (1870-1950) Polish
Works on paper
£613 $950 €920 Winter street scene (46x58cm-18x23in) s. W/C. 16-Jul-2 Arthur James, Florida #339

CIGNANI, Carlo (1628-1719) Italian
Works on paper
£823 $1300 €1300 Tete de bacchus (14x12cm-6x5in) red chk prov. 27-Nov-2 Christie's, Paris #67/R
£2568 $4005 €3800 Young girl in landscape with two putti (16x17cm-6x7in) i. pen ink wash htd white prov. 27-Mar-3 Christie's, Paris #31/R

CIGNAROLI, Vittorio Amedeo (c.1747-1793) Italian
£6690 $10771 €9500 River landscape with big bridge (73x99cm-29x39in) 11-May-3 Finarte, Venice #36/R est:12000
£9615 $14904 €15000 River landscape with peasants fishing (225x90cm-89x35in) 4-Dec-2 Christie's, Rome #464/R est:9000-12000
£16026 $24840 €25000 Peasants playing and dancing (223x100cm-88x39in) 4-Dec-2 Christie's, Rome #463/R
£19872 $30801 €31000 Couple playing on a swing in the woods (224x127cm-88x50in) 4-Dec-2 Christie's, Rome #466/R est:20000
£21795 $33782 €34000 Hunters and hounds resting (225x108cm-89x43in) 4-Dec-2 Christie's, Rome #467/R est:15000-20000
£78205 $121218 €122000 Deer hunt (226x187cm-89x74in) 4-Dec-2 Christie's, Rome #468/R est:40000-60000

CIGNAROLI, Vittorio Amedeo (circle) (c.1747-1793) Italian
£29000 $48430 €42050 Landscape with shepherdess and her flock. Landscape with girls and man collecting firewood (55x70cm-22x28in) pair. 8-Jul-3 Sotheby's, Olympia #437/R est:10000-15000

CIKOVSKY, Nicolai (1894-1984) American
£375 $600 €563 Still life in blue (41x51cm-16x20in) s. canvasboard. 8-Jan-3 Doyle, New York #48/R
Works on paper
£457 $750 €663 St Mark's church, 2nd Avenue and 10th Street (31x42cm-12x17in) s.i.d. pen ink col pastel. 5-Jun-3 Swann Galleries, New York #71/R

CILA, Otakar (1894-?) Czechoslovakian
£305 $486 €458 Pheasants (24x31cm-9x12in) s. paper. 8-Mar-3 Dorotheum, Prague #109/R est:6000-9000 (C.KR 14000)
£785 $1249 €1178 Girl semi nude (65x51cm-26x20in) s.d.1922. 8-Mar-3 Dorotheum, Prague #82/R est:26000-37000 (C.KR 36000)
£1310 $2031 €1965 Portrait of a young Indian woman (43x35cm-17x14in) painted 1937. 3-Dec-2 SOGA, Bratislava #217/R est:38000 (SL.K 83000)

CIMAROLI, Giovanni Battista (attrib) (17/18th C) Italian
£8844 $14061 €13000 River landscape in Veneto (51x66cm-20x26in) 19-Mar-3 Neumeister, Munich #425/R est:7000
£10000 $15500 €15000 Pastoral landscape with figures and cattle rested (27x41cm-11x16in) 31-Oct-2 Sotheby's, Olympia #142/R est:7000-10000

CIMAROLI, Giovanni Battista (circle) (17/18th C) Italian
£24000 $37440 €36000 Italianate landscapes with figures and cattle, fishermen in a town (35x48cm-14x19in) pair. 10-Apr-3 Christie's, Kensington #301/R est:8000-12000

CIMIOTTI, Gustave (1875-1969) American
£1097 $1700 €1646 Rockport home. Lake Champlain (33x41cm-13x16in) s. i.verso canvasboard masonite with work by another hand three. 25-Sep-2 Doyle, New York #18/R est:2000-3000

CINALLI, Ricardo (1948-) Argentinian
Works on paper
£1772 $2800 €2658 Untitled. s.d.MCMLXXXVIII pastel. 15-Nov-2 Naón & Cia, Buenos Aires #21/R

CINGRIA, Alexandre (1879-1945) Swiss
Works on paper
£1616 $2553 €2424 Bateau de Leman (43x75cm-17x30in) s. gouache cardboard. 17-Nov-2 Koller, Geneva #1201/R (S.FR 3700)

CINI, Alfred (1887-1970) Swiss
£262 $414 €393 Wallis landscape (50x62cm-20x24in) s. 14-Nov-2 Stuker, Bern #139 (S.FR 600)
£417 $671 €626 Sleeping nude (75x112cm-30x44in) s.d.31 i. verso. 7-May-3 Dobiaschofsky, Bern #3165 (S.FR 900)
£849 $1358 €1274 La Benedicit (80x62cm-31x24in) s. s.i. verso. 17-Mar-3 Philippe Schuler, Zurich #4509 est:2000-2500 (S.FR 1800)

CINTO, Sandra (1968-) Brazilian
Photographs
£4573 $7500 €6860 Sem titulo (70x127cm-28x50in) cibachrome print on panel one of five exec.1998 prov.exhib.lit. 28-May-3 Christie's, Rockefeller NY #56/R est:5000-7000

CIOLINA, Tonio (1898-?) Swiss
£480 $749 €720 Country house near Colombier (42x42cm-17x17in) s.d.20. 6-Nov-2 Dobiaschofsky, Bern #407/R (S.FR 1100)

CIOTTI, Giuseppe (1889-1991) Italian
£642 $1001 €950 Future Itaalian landscape (23x32cm-9x13in) s.i. oil tempera. 28-Mar-3 Farsetti, Prato #117/R

CIPOLLA, Fabio (1854-?) Italian
£5479 $8548 €8219 Serenade on the southern Italian coast (65x99cm-26x39in) s. 28-Mar-3 Koller, Zurich #3161/R est:12000-18000 (S.FR 12000)

CIPPER, Giacomo Francesco (c.1670-1738) Italian
£2830 $4387 €4500 Portrait of young man scaling fish (81x62cm-32x24in) prov. 2-Oct-2 Dorotheum, Vienna #403/R est:4500-6000
£7692 $12077 €12000 Concert paysan (74x93cm-29x37in) 13-Dec-2 Rossini, Paris #148/R est:8000

CIPPER, Giacomo Francesco (attrib) (c.1670-1738) Italian
£1200 $1884 €1800 Brawl over a market stall (46x34cm-18x13in) arched top prov. 11-Dec-2 Sotheby's, Olympia #170/R est:1500-2000
£1800 $2808 €2700 Boy with cloves of garlic, bread and jug of water (77x64cm-30x25in) 10-Apr-3 Christie's, Kensington #285/R est:2000-3000
£2402 $3747 €3603 Young beggar eating stew (65x54cm-26x21in) 20-Nov-2 Fischer, Luzern #1036/R est:3000-4000 (S.FR 5500)
£3459 $5362 €5500 Old man with mandolin and pipe (97x74cm-38x29in) 2-Oct-2 Dorotheum, Vienna #317/R est:1800-2600

CIPRIANI, A (19th C) Italian
Sculpture
£823 $1276 €1235 Venus (74cm-29in) s. white marble. 3-Dec-2 Ritchie, Toronto #3132/R est:800-1200 (C.D 2000)

CIPRIANI, C (19th C) ?
Sculpture
£1700 $2686 €2550 Woman in middle eastern dress (59cm-23in) i. alabaster. 14-Nov-2 Christie's, Kensington #122/R est:2000-3000

CIPRIANI, Giovanni Battista (1727-1785) Italian
Works on paper
£552 $850 €828 Four female figures with a small child (197x254cm-78x100in) black chk pen ink W/C oval. 4-Sep-2 Christie's, Rockefeller NY #270/R est:700-1000
£559 $800 €839 Standing female nude with two putti (43x32cm-17x13in) red black chk. 23-Jan-3 Swann Galleries, New York #141/R
£1250 $1988 €1875 Untitled (18cm-7in circular) W/C dr. 19-Mar-3 John Nicholson, Haslemere #1048/R est:500-750
£2000 $3140 €3000 Venus with putti (37x48cm-15x19in) black red chk oval. 11-Dec-2 Sotheby's, Olympia #137/R est:2000-3000
£2600 $3718 €3900 Girls and angler on river bank (14x22cm-6x9in) i. pencil ink wash prov.exhib. 22-Jan-3 Christie's, London #9/R

CIPRIANI, Giovanni Battista (attrib) (1727-1785) Italian
£1965 $3066 €2948 Personification of music inspired by love (64x54cm-25x21in) pastel. 20-Nov-2 Fischer, Luzern #1064/R est:4500-6000 (S.FR 4500)

CIPRIANI, Giovanni Pinotti (attrib) (19/20th C) French
Sculpture
£1474 $2315 €2300 Love cuddles (42cm-17in) s. marble. 16-Dec-2 Pandolfini, Florence #198/R

CIPRIANI, Nazzarreno (1843-1925) Italian
Works on paper
£1100 $1727 €1650 He is coming Venice (32x48cm-13x19in) pencil W/C. 16-Apr-3 Christie's, Kensington #999/R est:400-600

CIRCIELLO, Michele (1944-) Italian
Works on paper
£316 $494 €500 Dawn (90x50cm-35x20in) s. mixed media board exec.2001. 14-Sep-2 Meeting Art, Vercelli #732/R
£868 $1380 €1250 Rocky light (93x68cm-37x27in) s. sand marble powder. 1-May-3 Meeting Art, Vercelli #281

CIRIA, Jose Manuel (1960-) British
£567 $919 €800 Untitled (70x50cm-28x20in) s. acrylic paper. 20-May-3 Segre, Madrid #178/R
£1631 $2643 €2300 Vanitas (100x100cm-39x39in) s.i.d.1994 verso coated plastic canvas. 20-May-3 Segre, Madrid #175/R est:1800

CIRINO, Antonio (1889-1983) American
£285 $450 €428 Hammond Castle, Magnolia, MA (36x46cm-14x18in) s. 17-Nov-2 CRN Auctions, Cambridge #51/R

CIROU, Paul (19/20th C) French
£949 $1481 €1500 Marche sous la neige (59x69cm-23x27in) s. isorel. 15-Sep-2 Etude Bailleul, Bayeux #59/R
£2884 $4529 €4500 Jour de marche a Nedroma (35x55cm-14x22in) s.i.d.1928 panel. 10-Dec-2 Tajan, Paris #129/R est:6000

CIRQUET, Franky (20th C) French
£336 $561 €480 Femme montant a cheval (162x44cm-64x17in) s. diptych. 25-Jun-3 Claude Aguttes, Neuilly #120

CIRY, Michel (1919-) French
£417 $654 €650 Verger (36x68cm-14x27in) s.d.1960. 15-Dec-2 Eric Pillon, Calais #267/R
£510 $795 €800 Paysage de neige (92x60cm-36x24in) s.d.1965. 10-Nov-2 Eric Pillon, Calais #197/R
£1401 $2186 €2200 Portrait de femme (38x46cm-15x18in) s.d.1959. 10-Nov-2 Eric Pillon, Calais #201/R
£1646 $2567 €2600 La resurrection (200x70cm-79x28in) s.d.1957 i.verso. 20-Oct-2 Charbonneaux, Paris #113 est:3000-4000
£1655 $2632 €2400 Les baux de Provence (40x40cm-16x16in) s.d.61. 10-Mar-3 Thierry & Lannon, Brest #161/R
Works on paper
£823 $1300 €1300 Paysage de neige (27x31cm-11x12in) s. W/C. 27-Nov-2 Blanchet, Paris #93/R
£880 $1416 €1320 L'avenue des tilleuls a Chatou (51x73cm-20x29in) s.d.63 W/C prov. 7-May-3 Dobiaschofsky, Bern #412/R est:2500 (S.FR 1900)

CISCO, Theo (20th C) French
Works on paper
£800 $1272 €1200 Nouba II (120x120cm-47x47in) s.i.verso mixed media on canvas. 18-Mar-3 Bonhams, Knightsbridge #54

CISTERNA, Eugenio (1862-1933) Italian
Works on paper
£417 $646 €650 Saint Joseph and Jesus (82cm-32in circular) mixed media exec.c.1920. 4-Dec-2 Finarte, Rome #9/R

CITROEN, Paul (1896-1983) Dutch
£263 $426 €400 Flowering garden. portrait (40x30cm-16x12in) s. double-sided. 21-Jan-3 Christie's, Amsterdam #417
£705 $1093 €1100 Frivolite I (43x24cm-17x9in) s.i.d.X.34 verso oil collage prov. 4-Dec-2 Lempertz, Koln #618/R
£1772 $2800 €2800 Ballet (42x52cm-17x20in) s. s.i.d.1937/38 verre eglomisee lit. 26-Nov-2 Sotheby's, Amsterdam #105/R est:2500-3500

CITTADINI, Pier Francesco (circle) (1616-1681) Italian
£4430 $7000 €7000 Portrait of lady (196x114cm-77x45in) 2-Dec-2 Finarte, Milan #161/R
£6993 $11678 €10000 Nature morte (96x102cm-38x40in) painted c.1700. 27-Jun-3 Claude Aguttes, Neuilly #21/R est:10000-12000
£11000 $18370 €15950 Double portrait of a lady and her daughter (202x122cm-80x48in) 11-Jul-3 Christie's, Kensington #233/R est:6000-8000

CITTADINI, Tito (1886-1960) Argentinian
£2192 $3419 €3200 Mountain view (24x33cm-9x13in) s.d.1930 cardboard. 8-Apr-3 Ansorena, Madrid #212/R
£3082 $4777 €4900 Landscape in Majorca (39x48cm-15x19in) s. cardboard. 7-Oct-2 Ansorena, Madrid #65/R est:4500
£3618 $5862 €5500 House in Minorca (27x35cm-11x14in) s. 21-Jan-3 Ansorena, Madrid #191/R
£6918 $10654 €11000 Pollensa (50x62cm-20x24in) s. 22-Oct-2 Durán, Madrid #136/R est:1500

CIUSSI, Carlo (1930-) Italian
Works on paper
£423 $701 €600 Composition (70x50cm-28x20in) s.verso mixed media. 10-Jun-3 Finarte Semenzato, Milan #244/R

CIVITARESE, Goffredo (1938-) Italian
£359 $575 €550 Teenager with jewel (70x50cm-28x20in) s. s.i.verso. 4-Jan-3 Meeting Art, Vercelli #714
£425 $680 €650 Oriental women (70x50cm-28x20in) s. s.verso. 4-Jan-3 Meeting Art, Vercelli #513
£490 $784 €750 Armaneide (80x80cm-31x31in) s. 4-Jan-3 Meeting Art, Vercelli #203
£490 $784 €750 Chanel (80x80cm-31x31in) s. 4-Jan-3 Meeting Art, Vercelli #710
£513 $805 €800 Still life and blue images (100x70cm-39x28in) s. s.i.verso. 23-Nov-2 Meeting Art, Vercelli #451/R
£521 $828 €750 White shawl (80x80cm-31x31in) s. painted 2000. 1-May-3 Meeting Art, Vercelli #291
£544 $865 €800 Far East (80x80cm-31x31in) s. 1-Mar-3 Meeting Art, Vercelli #743
£625 $994 €900 Chapeau noir (60x50cm-24x20in) s. s.i.verso. 1-May-3 Meeting Art, Vercelli #551

CLAEISSINS, Anthonis (circle) (1536-1613) Flemish
£11321 $17660 €18000 Orpheus charming the animals (99x126cm-39x50in) panel. 20-Sep-2 Millon & Associes, Paris #315/R est:25000-40000

CLAEISSINS, Pieter I (attrib) (1500-1576) Flemish
£4730 $7378 €7000 Adoration of the Magi (127x89cm-50x35in) panel prov. 27-Mar-3 Dorotheum, Vienna #152/R est:8000-12000

CLAEISSINS, Pieter II (attrib) (1532-1623) Flemish
£4167 $6542 €6500 La descente de croix (77x77cm-30x30in) panel. 19-Nov-2 Vanderkindere, Brussels #155/R est:7000-10000

CLAERHOUT, Frans (1919-) South African
£522 $814 €783 Labourers in a landscape (50x60cm-20x24in) s. board. 15-Oct-2 Stephan Welz, Johannesburg #493 est:5000-8000 (SA.R 8500)
£737 $1150 €1106 Workers loading a cart (49x58cm-19x23in) s. board. 15-Oct-2 Stephan Welz, Johannesburg #492 est:4000-6000 (SA.R 12000)
£764 $1207 €1146 Labourer (49x60cm-19x24in) s. board. 1-Apr-3 Stephan Welz, Johannesburg #481 est:7000-10000 (SA.R 9500)
£946 $1523 €1419 Figure near a church (45x58cm-18x23in) s. board. 12-May-3 Stephan Welz, Johannesburg #500/R est:8000-12000 (SA.R 11000)
£1229 $1916 €1844 Donkey cart (78x121cm-31x48in) s. board. 15-Oct-2 Stephan Welz, Johannesburg #494/R est:12000-16000 (SA.R 20000)
£2251 $3556 €3377 Walking figure in a landscape with three birds (71x91cm-28x36in) s. board. 1-Apr-3 Stephan Welz, Johannesburg #482/R est:10000-15000 (SA.R 28000)
Works on paper
£288 $450 €432 Woman carrying goods (76x56cm-30x22in) s. mixed media. 11-Nov-2 Stephan Welz, Johannesburg #589 (SA.R 4500)

CLAES, Constant Guillaume (1826-1905) Belgian
£823 $1284 €1300 L'etude. La recompense (36x25cm-14x10in) s. panel pair. 15-Oct-2 Vanderkindere, Brussels #109

CLAESSENS, Artus (fl.1640-1649) Flemish
£5031 $7799 €8000 Basket of grapes (46x58cm-18x23in) panel lit. 2-Oct-2 Dorotheum, Vienna #370/R est:8000-10000

CLAESZ, Jan (fl.1594-1616) Dutch
£115000 $192050 €166750 Portrait of Wouter Gael aged four. Portrait of Marijke Gael aged six (56x45cm-22x18in) i.d.1604 panel pair prov. 9-Jul-3 Christie's, London #28/R est:50000-70000

CLAESZ, Pieter (1590-1661) Dutch
£18293 $30000 €27440 Still life of a Dutch silver beaker, a roemer and skull on a draped table (48x74cm-19x29in) indis sig. panel prov. 29-May-3 Sotheby's, New York #117/R est:30000-40000
£40000 $66800 €58000 Oysters in earthenware dish, half filled roemer and other objects on a ledge (39x55cm-15x22in) mono.d.1657 panel prov. 9-Jul-3 Bonhams, New Bond Street #51/R est:10000-15000
£50000 $78500 €75000 Still life of a roemer, pewter plates, olives, lemons and watch (37x55cm-15x22in) mono.indis.d.162 panel prov. 12-Dec-2 Sotheby's, London #23/R est:60000-80000

CLAEYS, Albert (1889-1967) Belgian
£1727 $2763 €2400 Paysage de la Lys (40x58cm-16x23in) s. 13-May-3 Palais de Beaux Arts, Brussels #38/R est:2500-3500
£2158 $3453 €3000 Paysage de la Lys en hiver (60x91cm-24x36in) s. 13-May-3 Palais de Beaux Arts, Brussels #42/R est:3000-4000
£2158 $3453 €3000 Paysage de la Lys avec fermes (80x100cm-31x39in) s. 13-May-3 Palais de Beaux Arts, Brussels #45/R est:3000-4000
£2276 $3641 €3300 Leieoever (65x90cm-26x35in) s. 15-Mar-3 De Vuyst, Lokeren #57/R est:2800-3500
£6250 $9938 €9000 Enfants qui jouent sur un etang gele (80x100cm-31x39in) s. 29-Apr-3 Campo & Campo, Antwerp #35/R est:8250-9250
Works on paper
£252 $387 €400 De Leie en de Tempelhoeve te Latem (22x30cm-9x12in) s. 22-Oct-2 Campo, Vlaamse Kaai #437

CLAGETT, Jean (20th C) French
Sculpture
£2179 $3335 €3400 Silvermine et sa pouliche (24x47cm-9x19in) s. num.2/5 bronze. 23-Aug-2 Deauville, France #233

CLAGUE, Richard (1816-1878) American
£15244 $25000 €22104 Fishermen on the Louisiana Bayou (38x51cm-15x20in) s. prov. 7-Jun-3 Neal Auction Company, New Orleans #336/R est:20000-30000
£103658 $170000 €155487 Backyard in Algiers (41x61cm-16x24in) s. prov. 8-Feb-3 Neal Auction Company, New Orleans #356/R est:120000-150000

CLAIR, Charles (1860-1930) French
£1026 $1600 €1539 Sheep and chickens in a stable (81x101cm-32x40in) s. 12-Apr-3 Weschler, Washington #527/R est:3000-5000
£1800 $2826 €2700 Rentree a la Bergerie (46x55cm-18x22in) s. 19-Nov-2 Bonhams, Leeds #101 est:1000-1500
£2800 $4368 €4200 Sheep watering (51x66cm-20x26in) s.d.1909. 9-Oct-2 Woolley & Wallis, Salisbury #312/R est:1500-2500
£3125 $5000 €4531 Working the fields (38x46cm-15x18in) s. 16-May-3 Skinner, Boston #47/R est:4000-6000

CLAIRIN, Georges (1843-1919) French
£2742 $4250 €4113 Mars (62x45cm-24x18in) s. prov. 29-Oct-2 Sotheby's, New York #61/R est:3000-4000
£4200 $6552 €6300 Ramparts of a fortified city (85x130cm-33x51in) s. 15-Oct-2 Sotheby's, London #201/R est:5000-7000
£4803 $7493 €7205 Portrait of the dancer Virginia Zucchi (65x44cm-26x17in) s. i. verso. 6-Nov-2 Dobiaschofsky, Bern #408/R est:9000 (S.FR 11000)
£5000 $8350 €7500 Don Quixote (60x120cm-24x47in) s. panel. 18-Jun-3 Christie's, Kensington #174/R est:5000-7000
£17949 $28359 €28000 La melancolie d'automne (77x44cm-30x17in) s. 18-Nov-2 Tajan, Paris #173/R est:25000-30000
£38710 $60000 €58065 On the balcony (95x111cm-37x44in) s. 29-Oct-2 Sotheby's, New York #90/R est:60000-80000
Works on paper
£897 $1418 €1400 Chemin boise a Belle-Ile (36x53cm-14x21in) s.i. pastel. 18-Nov-2 Sotheby's, Paris #68/R
£1361 $2163 €2000 Le guerrier (44x29cm-17x11in) s.d.1905 wash crayon htd white chk. 24-Mar-3 Rabourdin & Choppin de Janvry, Paris #60/R est:2000-2500

CLAIRIN, Pierre Eugène (1897-1980) French
£317 $510 €450 Portrait de jeune femme (38x49cm-15x19in) s. 11-May-3 Thierry & Lannon, Brest #343
£333 $543 €480 Paysage a la chapelle (45x63cm-18x25in) s. 19-Jul-3 Thierry & Lannon, Brest #316
£775 $1247 €1100 Fleurs des champs (61x50cm-24x20in) s. 11-May-3 Thierry & Lannon, Brest #151
£775 $1286 €1100 Paysage aux arbres fleuris (53x80cm-21x31in) s. 16-Jun-3 Oger, Dumont, Paris #39/R
£786 $1219 €1250 Vachere (81x65cm-32x26in) s. 6-Oct-2 Livinec, Gaudcheau & Jezequel, Rennes #63/R
£1013 $1661 €1550 Port sur riviere (38x55cm-15x22in) s. 7-Feb-3 Oger, Dumont, Paris #63/R
£1319 $2151 €1900 Paysage a la barriere (54x65cm-21x26in) s. 19-Jul-3 Thierry & Lannon, Brest #111 est:1800-2000
£1831 $2948 €2600 Paysage printannier, le pecheur en barque (81x65cm-32x26in) s. 11-May-3 Thierry & Lannon, Brest #341 est:1500-1800

CLAIRMONT, Philip (1949-1984) New Zealander
Works on paper
£912 $1451 €1368 Vase (26x21cm-10x8in) init.i. mixed media. 25-Feb-3 Peter Webb, Auckland #143 est:1500-2500 (NZ.D 2600)
£1128 $1760 €1692 Study for " Cathedral Attacked by Demons" (37x24cm-15x9in) s. s.i.d.1973 verso mixed media. 8-Apr-3 Peter Webb, Auckland #29/R est:2500-3500 (NZ.D 3250)
£1408 $2324 €2042 Corner of studio with swing light bulb and vase (76x63cm-30x25in) i.d.Jun 3 1977. 1-Jul-3 Peter Webb, Auckland #61/R est:4500-6500 (NZ.D 4000)

£1831 $3021 €2655 Through the window (83x58cm-33x23in) s.i.d.1975 W/C pastel prov. 1-Jul-3 Peter Webb, Auckland #60/R est:4500-6500 (NZ.D 5200)
£1997 $3115 €2996 Composition with chair and cushions (54x37cm-21x15in) s.d.1976 ink W/C. 8-Apr-3 Peter Webb, Auckland #28/R est:3000-5000 (NZ.D 5750)
£4340 $6771 €6510 Departure in search of spiritual knowledge through the window (155x111cm-61x44in) s.i.d.1979 wax crayon ink W/C. 8-Apr-3 Peter Webb, Auckland #91/R est:8000-12000 (NZ.D 12500)
£4823 $7476 €7235 Self portrait, listening to music (155x75cm-61x30in) i.d. mixed media board. 4-Dec-2 Dunbar Sloane, Auckland #24/R est:20000-35000 (NZ.D 15000)

CLAISSE, Genevieve (1935-) French
Works on paper
£1179 $1851 €1769 Formes en mouvement (22x27cm-9x11in) s.d.10.58 gouache. 23-Nov-2 Burkhard, Luzern #43/R est:1800-2200 (S.FR 2700)

CLAPP, Margaret A (1887-1978) American
£255 $400 €383 California landscape with eucalyptus trees (56x71cm-22x28in) s. canvasboard. 23-Nov-2 Jackson's, Cedar Falls #96/R
£276 $425 €414 Late summer landscape (43x58cm-17x23in) s. board. 8-Sep-2 DeFina, Austinburg #170

CLAPP, William H (1879-1954) Canadian
£806 $1274 €1209 Fishing boats near the harbour (38x30cm-15x12in) s.d.December 1897 board prov. 14-Nov-2 Heffel, Vancouver #227 est:1000-1200 (C.D 2000)
£1121 $1794 €1682 Apple orchard (41x51cm-16x20in) i.verso prov. 15-May-3 Heffel, Vancouver #30/R est:2500-3500 (C.D 2500)
£2395 $4000 €3473 Landscape (38x46cm-15x18in) s.d.46 board. 17-Jun-3 John Moran, Pasadena #76 est:5000-7000
£2691 $4305 €4037 Washing women (26x34cm-10x13in) s. s.verso panel prov. 15-May-3 Heffel, Vancouver #17/R est:2500-3500 (C.D 6000)
£5280 $8500 €7920 Abandoned farm (18x24cm-7x9in) s.d.47 i.verso board prov. 18-Feb-3 John Moran, Pasadena #74 est:10000-15000

CLARAMUNT, Luis (1951-2000) Spanish
£377 $581 €600 Goat (17x24cm-7x9in) s.d.86. 28-Oct-2 Segre, Madrid #152/R

CLARE, George (1835-c.1890) British
£420 $680 €630 Grapes, apples and a strawberry on a mossy bank (25x20cm-10x8in) s. 23-Jan-3 Christie's, Kensington #180
£460 $731 €690 Still life of primroses on a mossy bank (24x29cm-9x11in) s. 4-Mar-3 Bearnes, Exeter #461
£680 $1054 €1020 Spring blossom and flowers and bird's nest (15x20cm-6x8in) s. 2-Oct-2 Bonhams, Knowle #95
£705 $1100 €1058 Flowers and nest (15x20cm-6x8in) s. 30-Mar-3 Susanin's, Chicago #6076/R
£897 $1400 €1346 Still life with fruit (15x20cm-6x8in) s. 30-Mar-3 Susanin's, Chicago #6077/R
£1400 $2268 €2100 Still life of apples , plums and strawberries in basket (38x23cm-15x9in) s. canvas on board. 20-May-3 Sotheby's, Olympia #259/R est:1500-2500
£1500 $2340 €2250 Still life studies, wild roses, birds nests and grapes (25x23cm-10x9in) s. pair. 7-Nov-2 Mallams, Cheltenham #354 est:700-1000
£3000 $4710 €4500 Grapes in a basket, and other fruit against a mossy bank (46x61cm-18x24in) s. 15-Apr-3 Bonhams, Knowle #125/R est:4000-6000
£3200 $5088 €4800 Primrose, primulas, apple blossom with a bird's nest with eggs and wicker basket on mossy bank (30x25cm-12x10in) s. 6-Mar-3 Christie's, Kensington #635/R est:3000-5000

CLARE, Henry (19/20th C) British?
£818 $1300 €1227 Still life with fruit, flowers and bird's nest on a mossy bank (30x61cm-12x24in) s. 18-Mar-3 Doyle, New York #20/R

CLARE, Oliver (1853-1927) British
£375 $615 €563 Still life composition with fruit and flowers (20x25cm-8x10in) s. board. 7-Feb-3 Biddle & Webb, Birmingham #343
£460 $768 €667 Strawberries on a cabbage leaf and other fruit on a mossy bank (14x20cm-6x8in) s. board. 24-Jun-3 Bonhams, Knowle #49
£520 $816 €780 Plums, white currants, a peach and a strawberry (14x21cm-6x8in) s. board. 15-Apr-3 Bonhams, Knowle #140
£530 $822 €795 Green plums, black grapes and gooseberries (15x25cm-6x10in) s. 2-Oct-2 Bonhams, Knowle #72/R
£600 $924 €900 Apples, peach, plum and strawberry on a mossy bank (23x30cm-9x12in) s.d.91. 5-Sep-2 Christie's, Kensington #344/R
£620 $1017 €930 Still life, plums, apples and strawberries on a mossy bank (22x29cm-9x11in) s.d.90 board. 10-Feb-3 David Duggleby, Scarborough #591/R
£660 $1102 €957 Strawberries on a cabbage leaf and other fruit on a bank (20x25cm-8x10in) s. card. 24-Jun-3 Bonhams, Knowle #47
£700 $1134 €1050 Grapes, gooseberries and an apple on a mossy bank (18x23cm-7x9in) s. 23-Jan-3 Christie's, Kensington #183/R
£764 $1192 €1146 Still life with fruit and leaves (37x29cm-15x11in) s. pair. 8-Apr-3 Peter Webb, Auckland #120/R (NZ.D 2200)
£800 $1272 €1200 Still life of plums and apples on mossy bank (25x20cm-10x8in) 30-Apr-3 Brightwells, Leominster #969/R
£800 $1296 €1200 Still life with fruit (33x28cm-13x11in) s. board. 21-May-3 James Thompson, Kirby Lonsdale #130
£800 $1312 €1200 Still life with peaches, plums, gooseberries on a mossy bank (19x24cm-7x9in) s.d.89. 3-Jun-3 Bonhams, Oxford #76/R
£880 $1399 €1320 Still life of plums and gooseberries on a mossy bank (29x23cm-11x9in) s. 4-Mar-3 Bearnes, Exeter #462/R
£900 $1404 €1350 Still lives of grapes and other fruit (19x17cm-7x7in) s. board pair. 10-Oct-2 Rupert Toovey, Partridge Green #1535/R
£960 $1517 €1440 Black grapes, greengages, pear and strawberry on a ledge (30x23cm-12x9in) s. board. 27-Nov-2 Bonhams, Knowle #205
£980 $1529 €1470 Still life (26x20cm-10x8in) s. 17-Sep-2 Sotheby's, Olympia #196/R
£1000 $1560 €1500 Still life of a peaches, strawberries on a mossy bank (14x19cm-6x7in) 8-Oct-2 Bonhams, Knightsbridge #154/R est:800-1200
£1304 $2022 €1956 Still life with apples, grapes, raspberries and peach (33x28cm-13x11in) s. paper on canvas. 9-Dec-2 Philippe Schuler, Zurich #3890/R est:3500-4000 (S.FR 3000)
£1400 $2268 €2100 Apples and grapes (18x23cm-7x9in) s. 20-May-3 Sotheby's, Olympia #262/R est:800-1200
£1500 $2370 €2250 Still life with apples, grapes and strawberries on mossy bank. Damson a peach and strawberries (18x23cm-7x9in) s. board pair. 13-Nov-2 Halls, Shrewsbury #396/R est:700-1000
£1500 $2385 €2250 Still life of black grapes, greengages, peach and strawberries (21x16cm-8x6in) s. card. 4-Mar-3 Bearnes, Exeter #463/R est:1000-1200
£1500 $2505 €2175 Flowers and berries by a bird's nest against a bank (14x19cm-6x7in) s. 24-Jun-3 Bonhams, Knowle #60/R est:1200-1800
£1566 $2600 €2271 Still life of fruit (20x25cm-8x10in) s. pair. 14-Jun-3 Jackson's, Cedar Falls #219/R est:2500-4000
£1600 $2608 €2400 Grapes and apples (17x20cm-7x8in) s.d.1903 panel. 29-Jan-3 Sotheby's, Olympia #210/R est:600-800
£1800 $2790 €2700 Still life with strawberries and grapes (14x26cm-6x10in) s. board. 3-Dec-2 Sotheby's, Olympia #87/R est:800-1200
£1800 $2934 €2700 Still life study of black grapes, apples and other fruit on a mossy bank (19x13cm-7x5in) s. board. 11-Feb-3 Fellows & Sons, Birmingham #19/R est:700-900
£2050 $3424 €2973 Plums, gooseberries and other fruit on a mossy bank (46x35cm-18x14in) s.d.99. 24-Jun-3 Bonhams, Knowle #46/R est:1800-2500
£2100 $3045 €3150 Still life of fruit (23x30cm-9x12in) s. 3-May-2 Biddle & Webb, Birmingham #340/R est:2000-2400
£2100 $3402 €3150 Still life of plums. grapes and strawberries (26x20cm-10x8in) s. 20-May-3 Sotheby's, Olympia #260/R est:1000-1500
£2108 $3500 €3057 Still life of fruit (30x23cm-12x9in) board. 13-Jun-3 Du Mouchelle, Detroit #2041/R est:2000-2500
£2108 $3500 €3057 Still life of fruit (30x23cm-12x9in) board. 13-Jun-3 Du Mouchelle, Detroit #2042/R est:2000-2500
£2200 $3586 €3300 Still life study of black grapes, apples and two strawberries, on a mossy bank (23x15cm-9x6in) s. board. 11-Feb-3 Fellows & Sons, Birmingham #15/R est:1200-1500
£2200 $3674 €3190 Various fruits against mossy banks (24x18cm-9x7in) s. board pair. 24-Jun-3 Bonhams, Knowle #53 est:1800-2500
£2300 $3749 €3450 Still life study of raspberries held in a cabbage leaf, together with other fruit (23x15cm-9x6in) s. board. 11-Feb-3 Fellows & Sons, Birmingham #16/R est:1200-1500
£2400 $3912 €3600 Still life study of black grapes, apples, gooseberries and raspberry on mossy bank (24x19cm-9x7in) s. 11-Feb-3 Fellows & Sons, Birmingham #20/R est:1500-1800
£2500 $3875 €3750 Still life of grapes and other fruit on a mossy bank (22x17cm-9x7in) s. board. 1-Oct-2 Fellows & Sons, Birmingham #19/R est:700-1000
£2600 $4030 €3900 Black grapes, greengages, white currants and peach. Green grapes, plums (14x19cm-6x7in) s.d.1920 board canvas board pair. 2-Oct-2 Bonhams, Knowle #77/R est:1500-2500
£2600 $4316 €3900 Blossom and a bird's nest with eggs on a mossy bank. Still life (14x22cm-6x9in) s.d.91 two. 10-Jun-3 Bonhams, Knightsbridge #277/R est:1200-1800
£2900 $4843 €4205 Black grapes, peaches and other fruit on a mossy bank (23x30cm-9x12in) 24-Jun-3 Bonhams, Knowle #44/R est:2500-3500
£2900 $4843 €4205 Flowers against a mossy bank. Fruit against a mossy bank (25x20cm-10x8in) s.d.97 pair. 24-Jun-3 Bonhams, Knowle #56/R est:3000-5000
£3000 $4680 €4500 Apples, grapes and strawberries. Peaches and plums (20x25cm-8x10in) s. pair. 26-Mar-3 Sotheby's, Olympia #104/R est:2500-3500

£3049 $5000 €4421 Fruit by a mossy bank. Flowers by a nest with eggs on a mossy bank (15x20cm-6x8in) s. pair. 4-Jun-3 Christie's, Rockefeller NY #253/R est:3000-4000
£3097 $4800 €4646 Pink, red, white and purple violets, with bird's nest (20x25cm-8x10in) s. pair. 2-Oct-2 Christie's, Rockefeller NY #789/R est:4000-6000
£3100 $5053 €4650 Still life study of black grapes, apples and other fruit on a mossy bank (29x34cm-11x13in) s. 11-Feb-3 Fellows & Sons, Birmingham #17/R est:2000-3000
£3300 $5511 €4785 Fruit on a mossy bank (23x31cm-9x12in) s.d.1908. 24-Jun-3 Bonhams, Knowle #42/R est:3000-5000
£3400 $5542 €4930 Still life of mixed fruit on a mossy bank (35x29cm-14x11in) s. 21-Jul-3 Bonhams, Bath #101/R est:2000-3000
£3500 $5845 €5075 Punnet of greengages and fruit on a mossy bank (46x38cm-18x15in) s. 24-Jun-3 Bonhams, Knowle #41/R est:3500-4500
£3500 $5845 €5075 Punnet of gooseberries and other fruit on a mossy bank (41x56cm-16x22in) s.d.1920. 24-Jun-3 Bonhams, Knowle #50/R est:3500-4500
£3800 $6346 €5510 Plums, apples, peaches, raspberries, currents and greengages (35x46cm-14x18in) s. 24-Jun-3 Bonhams, Knowle #39/R est:2800-3500
£3900 $6045 €5850 Still life of strawberries, gooseberries and other fruit on a mossy bank (22x18cm-9x7in) s. board pair. 1-Oct-2 Fellows & Sons, Birmingham #17/R est:1800-2500
£4000 $6520 €6000 Still life study of plums, green grapes, and other fruit on a mossy bank (29x34cm-11x13in) s. 11-Feb-3 Fellows & Sons, Birmingham #18/R est:2000-3000
£4000 $6480 €6000 Apples and grapes. Apples and plums (29x23cm-11x9in) s. indis d. board pair. 20-May-3 Sotheby's, Olympia #225/R est:2500-3500
£4000 $6480 €6000 Peaches, grapes and raspberries (38x30cm-15x12in) s.d.1922 board. 20-May-3 Sotheby's, Olympia #258/R est:2500-3500
£4100 $6355 €6150 Still life of grapes, peaches and other fruit on a mossy bank (23x14cm-9x6in) s. board pair. 1-Oct-2 Fellows & Sons, Birmingham #18/R est:2000-2800
£4200 $6846 €6300 Still lifes of pears and strawberries on a mossy bank (18x24cm-7x9in) s. board pair. 29-Jan-3 Wintertons, Lichfield #368a/R est:2500-3500
£4200 $6846 €6090 Still life of fruit (13x21cm-5x8in) s. board pair. 16-Jul-3 Sotheby's, Olympia #57/R est:2500-3500
£4400 $7348 €6380 Various fruit on mossy banks (16x23cm-6x9in) pair. 24-Jun-3 Bonhams, Knowle #48/R est:3800-4500
£4500 $6975 €6750 Still life of blossom, birds nest and eggs (24x17cm-9x7in) s. board pair. 1-Oct-2 Fellows & Sons, Birmingham #16/R est:2000-2800
£5000 $7800 €7500 Still life of grapes and apples. Still life of raspberries and grapes (15x21cm-6x8in) s. one board pair. 17-Sep-2 Sotheby's, Olympia #170/R est:2000-3000
£5000 $8000 €7500 Still life with bird's nest and flowers on a mossy bank. Companion (30x25cm-12x10in) s. one d.1914 board pair. 14-May-3 Butterfields, San Francisco #1164/R est:4000-6000
£5100 $8517 €7395 Various fruits on a stone ledge (29x23cm-11x9in) s. board pair. 24-Jun-3 Bonhams, Knowle #52/R est:4000-6000
£6200 $10044 €9300 Still life of fruit (30x22cm-12x9in) s. oil on card pair. 20-May-3 Sotheby's, Olympia #224/R est:3000-4000
£8000 $12720 €12000 Primrose and apple blossom, bird's nest with eggs on mossy bank. Grapes and other fruit on a bank (46x36cm-18x14in) s.d.98 pair. 6-Mar-3 Christie's, Kensington #634/R est:8000-12000

Works on paper

£1550 $2403 €2325 Still life study of plums and other fruit. s. W/C. 6-Dec-2 Biddle & Webb, Birmingham #108

CLARE, Vincent (1855-1930) British

£450 $747 €675 Still life of flowers in a basket (33x27cm-13x11in) s. 10-Jun-3 Bonhams, Knightsbridge #285/R
£500 $780 €750 Still life with grapes (20x25cm-8x10in) s. 15-Oct-2 Canterbury Auctions, UK #157/R
£692 $1100 €1038 Still life with bird's nest and spring blossoms on a mossy bank (23x30cm-9x12in) s. 5-Mar-3 Doyle, New York #15/R
£840 $1403 €1218 Green grapes in a punnet with other fruits on a mossy bank (23x30cm-9x12in) s. 24-Jun-3 Bonhams, Knowle #62
£1300 $2132 €1950 Spring flowers on a mossy bank (23x30cm-9x12in) s. 29-May-3 Christie's, Kensington #318/R est:1500-2000
£1350 $2133 €2025 Still life of strawberries and apples by a mossy bank. Flower basket (23x33cm-9x13in) pair. 26-Nov-2 Rogers Jones, Clwyd #177
£1475 $2463 €2139 Fruit against a mossy bank (35x25cm-14x10in) s. 24-Jun-3 Bonhams, Knowle #61 est:1500-2000
£1600 $2608 €2400 Still life study of basket of black grapes and other fruit on mossy bank (29x21cm-11x8in) s. 11-Feb-3 Fellows & Sons, Birmingham #21/R est:1500-2500
£1950 $3179 €2925 Primrose, yellow rose and spring flowers, birds nest (19x23cm-7x9in) s. 11-Feb-3 Bonhams, Knowle #144 est:1000-1500
£2000 $3140 €3000 Spring flowers (23x30cm-9x12in) s. 19-Nov-2 Bonhams, New Bond Street #111/R est:2000-3000
£2000 $3200 €3000 Still life of flowers and a bird's nest (61x51cm-24x20in) s. 11-Mar-3 Bonhams, Knightsbridge #94/R est:2000-3000
£2600 $4004 €3900 May blossom in a basket, with bird's nest. Plums and grapes on a bank (23x30cm-9x12in) s. pair. 5-Sep-2 Christie's, Kensington #351/R est:2500-3500
£2744 $4500 €3979 Flowers and nest with eggs on a mossy bank. Fruit on a bank (25x20cm-10x8in) s. pair. 4-Jun-3 Christie's, Rockefeller NY #254/R est:4000-6000
£3200 $4992 €4800 Still life with a basket and fruit. Still life with a basket and flowers (31x25cm-12x10in) s. pair. 26-Mar-3 Sotheby's, Olympia #109/R est:3000-4000
£3500 $5565 €5250 Grapes and other fruit on a mossy bank (51x77cm-20x30in) s. 6-Mar-3 Christie's, Kensington #636/R est:3000-5000
£3500 $5740 €5250 Flowers on a mossy bank (50x70cm-20x28in) s. 29-May-3 Christie's, Kensington #316/R est:3000-5000
£4000 $6680 €5800 Still life with blossom and a bird's nest. Still life of fruit (23x30cm-9x12in) s. i.verso pair. 17-Jun-3 Bonhams, New Bond Street #53/R est:3000-5000
£4500 $7065 €6750 Still life with fruit and flowers (25x20cm-10x8in) s.i.d.93 verso pair. 19-Nov-2 Bonhams, New Bond Street #110/R est:2500-3500
£5300 $8639 €7685 Potted polyanthus with a bird's nest and primroses (40x60cm-16x24in) s. 21-Jul-3 Bonhams, Bath #102/R est:4000-5000

Works on paper

£260 $424 €390 Still life study of grapes, plums and apples on a mossy bank (25x16cm-10x6in) s.i. W/C. 11-Feb-3 Fellows & Sons, Birmingham #85/R
£260 $406 €390 Still life of apples, plums and grapes (15x23cm-6x9in) indis.sig. W/C. 26-Mar-3 Hamptons Fine Art, Godalming #59/R
£360 $562 €540 Still life of plums on a mossy bank (18x25cm-7x10in) s. W/C bodycol. 10-Apr-3 Tennants, Leyburn #896/R
£380 $593 €570 Still life with blossom and other flowers on mossy bank (21x29cm-8x11in) s. W/C htd white. 27-Mar-3 Christie's, Kensington #51/R
£800 $1272 €1200 Still life composition with cherry blossom and primroses. Grapes and plums (10x15cm-4x6in) s. W/C oval pair. 30-Apr-3 Halls, Shrewsbury #225/R
£1500 $2445 €2250 Still life of primroses and bird's nest. Still life of plums and grapes (17x25cm-7x10in) s. W/C htd bodycol pair. 30-Jan-3 Lawrence, Crewkerne #633/R est:500-800

CLARENBACH, Max (1880-1952) German

£1379 $2179 €2000 Lower Rhine landscape with fisherman in boat (56x72cm-22x28in) s. 2-Apr-3 Dr Fritz Nagel, Stuttgart #9320/R est:2700
£5479 $8548 €8000 The Rhine and Burg Gutenfels in the snow (33x45cm-13x18in) s.d.1900 lit. 10-Apr-3 Van Ham, Cologne #1363/R est:5000
£13014 $20301 €19000 Winter on the Erft (95x121cm-37x48in) s. 10-Apr-3 Van Ham, Cologne #1362/R est:13000

CLARENCE, Arderne (fl.1908-1937) British

Works on paper

£320 $506 €464 Market scene (24x35cm-9x14in) s. W/C. 22-Jul-3 Bonhams, Knightsbridge #239/R

CLARENCE, H (19th C) British

Works on paper

£600 $966 €870 Bringing the herd home (44x74cm-17x29in) s.d.99 W/C. 12-May-3 Joel, Victoria #290 est:2500-3500 (A.D 1500)

CLARIS, Antoine Gabriel Gaston (1844-1899) French

£1437 $2300 €2084 Battle plan (60x81cm-24x32in) s.d.1879. 16-May-3 Skinner, Boston #51/R est:2500-3500

CLARK, Albert (19th C) British

£620 $1035 €899 Study of a horse in loose box (48x61cm-19x24in) s.d.1868. 20-Jun-3 Keys, Aylsham #676/R
£830 $1294 €1245 Horse (50x61cm-20x24in) s.d.1860. 6-Nov-2 Dobiaschofsky, Bern #409/R est:1800 (S.FR 1900)
£850 $1343 €1275 Tethered brown hunter in a stable (42x53cm-17x21in) s. canvas on board. 28-Nov-2 Christie's, Kensington #156a/R
£920 $1490 €1380 Maritana (51x61cm-20x24in) s.d.1884. 20-May-3 Sotheby's, Olympia #205/R
£920 $1490 €1380 Spot (51x61cm-20x24in) s.d.1885. 20-May-3 Sotheby's, Olympia #206/R

£1000 $1570 €1500 Bay hunter in a stable interior (51x61cm-20x24in) s.d.1868. 16-Dec-2 Bonhams, Bury St Edmunds #509 est:500-700
£1500 $2340 €2250 Chestnut hunter, Norfolk Gentleman, in a stable (51x61cm-20x24in) s.d.1888. 10-Apr-3 Tennants, Leyburn #1036/R est:600-800
£1800 $2808 €2700 Rosador, a champion Hackney stallion in a stable (51x61cm-20x24in) s. 10-Apr-3 Tennants, Leyburn #1035/R est:600-800
£2000 $3280 €3000 Portrait of a piebald pony in a landscape (49x64cm-19x25in) s.d.1882. 3-Jun-3 Bonhams, Knightsbridge #44/R est:2000-3000
£4000 $6320 €6000 Bury Victor Chief a heavy horse. Bindsall Menestrel a heavy horse (51x61cm-20x24in) s. pair. 28-Nov-2 Christie's, Kensington #115/R est:600-800

CLARK, Alison (attrib) (19th C) British
£350 $546 €525 Portrait of a gentleman, possibly of the Cunard family (18x13cm-7x5in) i.verso panel prov. 7-Nov-2 Christie's, Kensington #64

CLARK, Alson Skinner (1876-1949) American
£3503 $5500 €5255 Portrait of Mrs Frieseke (63x48cm-25x19in) exhib. 20-Nov-2 Christie's, Los Angeles #73/R est:6000-8000
£3822 $6000 €5733 Archway, Cuernavaca (19x24cm-7x9in) s.i. canvas on board prov. 20-Nov-2 Christie's, Los Angeles #16/R est:3000-5000
£4658 $7500 €6987 Toward the Mazatlan, Mexico (18x22cm-7x9in) s. canvas on board prov. 18-Feb-3 John Moran, Pasadena #64 est:5500-7500
£6627 $11000 €9609 Portrait of Katherine Hall (65x53cm-26x21in) s.d.25 prov. 11-Jun-3 Butterfields, San Francisco #4221/R est:7000-10000
£7453 $12000 €11180 Figures at a courtyard entrance, probably Toledo, Spain (53x64cm-21x25in) s. prov. 18-Feb-3 John Moran, Pasadena #107 est:15000-20000
£9032 $14000 €13548 Landscape, Owen's Valley, CA (64x76cm-25x30in) estate st. prov. 29-Oct-2 John Moran, Pasadena #731 est:15000-20000

CLARK, Alvan (1804-1887) American
Miniatures
£3416 $5500 €5124 Portrait of David Murray Hoffman and Mary Murray Ogden Hoffman (8x5cm-3x2in) one s. W/C two painted with N Carlsen prov. 23-Feb-3 Skinner, Boston #22/R est:1500-2500

CLARK, Benton (1895-1964) American
£566 $900 €849 King Charles spaniels (16x20cm-6x8in) s.d. board. 4-May-3 Treadway Gallery, Cincinnati #561/R
£1420 $2300 €2059 Fighting cowboys (76x84cm-30x33in) 23-May-3 Altermann Galleries, Santa Fe #90
£1923 $3000 €2885 Quarry captured in the desert (91x97cm-36x38in) s.d.1937 en grisaille. 9-Nov-2 Illustration House, New York #164/R est:4000-6000
£2830 $4500 €4245 Winfield scout treatying with the Indians (61x91cm-24x36in) s. painted c.1920 prov. 5-Mar-3 Sotheby's, New York #152/R est:6000-8000
£16149 $26000 €24224 Cowboy riding bronc as cowgirl and others look on (91x91cm-36x36in) s.d. lit. 10-May-3 Illustration House, New York #172/R est:16000-24000

CLARK, C Myron (1876-1925) American
£309 $500 €464 Autumn landscape with stream (38x51cm-15x20in) s. board. 24-Jan-3 Freeman, Philadelphia #166/R
£633 $1000 €950 The signal, nocturnal marine scene. s.d.1883. 26-Apr-3 Thomaston Place, Thomaston #58
£968 $1500 €1452 Path through autumn woods (46x53cm-18x21in) s. painted c.1900 prov. 8-Dec-2 Toomey, Oak Park #689/R est:1500-2500
£1250 $2000 €1813 The day's catch, a still life with trout and rod (56x61cm-22x24in) s.d.1918 board. 16-May-3 Skinner, Boston #95/R est:2000-4000
£2166 $3400 €3249 Inlet scene with sailboats and lighthouse (46x71cm-18x28in) s. 14-Dec-2 Weschler, Washington #647/R est:1500-2500

CLARK, Christopher (1875-1942) British
Works on paper
£250 $385 €375 Drum Major (51x37cm-20x15in) s. W/C. 3-Sep-2 Bristol Auction Rooms #490/R

CLARK, Claude L (19th C) British
£2300 $3611 €3450 At work. near Chilton, Folkstone. Smoke after dinner, Chilton woods (25x35cm-10x14in) s.i. pair. 19-Nov-2 Bonhams, Leeds #234 est:1200-1800

CLARK, Dixon (1849-1944) British
£270 $419 €405 High light, North Shields (75x62cm-30x24in) s. board. 24-Sep-2 Anderson & Garland, Newcastle #488

CLARK, Eliot (1883-1980) American
£344 $550 €499 Autumn leaves (29x41cm-11x16in) s. board. 16-May-3 Skinner, Boston #253/R
£1043 $1700 €1565 Pueblo near Santa-Fe (43x48cm-17x19in) board. 31-Jan-3 Douglas, South Deerfield #21

CLARK, Frederick Albert (fl.1888-1909) British
£1800 $2952 €2700 Billy Boy (51x61cm-20x24in) s.i.d.1903. 3-Jun-3 Bonhams, Knightsbridge #45/R est:2000-3000

CLARK, Gordon Matta (1945-1978) American
Photographs
£11392 $18000 €17088 Bingo (150x53cm-59x21in) st.sig.i.d.1973 num.1/9 verso col coupler print prov. 14-Nov-2 Christie's, Rockefeller NY #433/R est:12000-18000

CLARK, James (fl.1858-1909) British
£700 $1141 €1050 Bay hunter in a stable (42x51cm-17x20in) s.d.89. 29-Jan-3 Sotheby's, Olympia #102/R
£900 $1368 €1350 Runaway horse with hunt in the distance (48x61cm-19x24in) s. 16-Aug-2 Keys, Aylsham #660
£1200 $1896 €1800 Runaway (51x61cm-20x24in) s. canvas on board. 28-Nov-2 Christie's, Kensington #139/R est:1200-1800
£1500 $2475 €2175 Prize shorthorn in a landscape (62x75cm-24x30in) 2-Jul-3 Sotheby's, Olympia #134/R est:2000-3000
£1558 $2322 €2400 Portrait of a gentleman on horseback (46x61cm-18x24in) s. 28-Jun-2 Woodwards, Cork #197
£2200 $3652 €3190 Meet. At the end of the day (41x61cm-16x24in) s. pair. 12-Jun-3 Christie's, Kensington #8/R est:1500-2000
£9500 $14630 €14250 Prize sows in a sty (25x46cm-10x18in) s. 5-Sep-2 Christie's, Kensington #145/R est:300-500

CLARK, James (1858-1943) British
£625 $1000 €938 Portrait of a horse in a stable (48x64cm-19x25in) s.i. 15-Mar-3 Selkirks, St. Louis #84/R
£1200 $1896 €1800 Strawberry roan horse in a landscape (62x74cm-24x29in) s. 28-Nov-2 Sotheby's, London #204 est:1500-2500
£1250 $2088 €1813 Bay hunter in a landscape (49x59cm-19x23in) s. 25-Jun-3 Cheffins, Cambridge #797/R est:700-1000

CLARK, James Lippitt (1883-1957) American
Sculpture
£1392 $2200 €2088 Standing buffalo (11cm-4in) i. brown pat. bronze prov. 3-Apr-3 Christie's, Rockefeller NY #132/R est:2000-4000
£1772 $2800 €2658 Cape buffalo skull and horse (15cm-6in) i. dark brown marble base prov. 3-Apr-3 Christie's, Rockefeller NY #141/R est:1500-2000
£2273 $3500 €3410 Rhinoceros (38cm-15in) s.i.d.24 mottled brown pat. bronze prov. 24-Oct-2 Shannon's, Milford #118/R est:3000-5000
£3165 $5000 €4748 Ovis poli (43cm-17in) i. reddish brown pat. bronze prov. 3-Apr-3 Christie's, Rockefeller NY #130/R est:7000-10000
£3165 $5000 €4748 Kodiak (30cm-12in) i. brown pat. bronze prov.exhib. 3-Apr-3 Christie's, Rockefeller NY #159/R est:5000-7000
£6962 $11000 €10443 Charging rhino (43cm-17in) i.d.1949 dark brown pat. bronze prov. 3-Apr-3 Christie's, Rockefeller NY #148/R est:6000-8000

CLARK, Joseph (1834-1926) British
£2600 $4056 €3900 Favourite grandfather (61x50cm-24x20in) s.indis.d.1886. 10-Apr-3 Tennants, Leyburn #1109/R est:1000-1500
£7000 $11060 €10500 Charity (61x46cm-24x18in) s. 2-Dec-2 Sotheby's, London #15/R est:7000-10000
Works on paper
£260 $406 €390 Two girls sitting on a fence (17x12cm-7x5in) s. W/C. 9-Oct-2 Woolley & Wallis, Salisbury #135/R

CLARK, Larry (1943-) American
Photographs
£2078 $3200 €3117 Dead, Billy Mann, Tulsa (36x28cm-14x11in) s.i. gelatin silver print exec.c.1970 prov.lit. 25-Oct-2 Phillips, New York #133/R est:2000-3000

CLARK, Lygia (1920-1988) Brazilian
£30488 $50000 €45732 Superficie modulada no 6 (44x109cm-17x43in) industrial paint panel on masonite painted 1956 prov.lit. 28-May-3 Christie's, Rockefeller NY #42/R est:50000-60000

CLARK, Malcolm (20th C) British?
£300 $477 €450 Still life, fish (38x28cm-15x11in) s.d.02 board. 5-Mar-3 John Ross, Belfast #211

CLARK, Octavius T (1850-1921) British
£320 $496 €480 Rustic corner near Dorking (58x38cm-23x15in) s.d.verso. 4-Oct-2 Mallams, Oxford #534/R
£320 $525 €480 Country riverscape with two figures by cottage (49x75cm-19x30in) s. 5-Jun-3 Locke & England, Leamington Spa #255/R
£400 $640 €600 River landscape with a church tower beyond (51x76cm-20x30in) s. 13-May-3 Bonhams, Knightsbridge #79/R
£540 $842 €810 Autumn country scene with sheep on a track by cottage (75x50cm-30x20in) s. 5-Nov-2 Bristol Auction Rooms #972/R
£550 $880 €825 Country landscape with house and children on lane (49x75cm-19x30in) 11-Mar-3 Bonhams, Knightsbridge #291/R
£560 $862 €840 Country cottage with children on the lane (51x76cm-20x30in) s. 22-Oct-2 Bonhams, Bath #157
£605 $950 €908 Rural landscape with figures (51x76cm-20x30in) s. 20-Nov-2 Boos Gallery, Michigan #524/R
£700 $1106 €1050 Shepherd with his flock by a pond (63x107cm-25x42in) s. 14-Nov-2 Christie's, Kensington #172
£938 $1500 €1360 Man fishing at a country lake (51x76cm-20x30in) s. 17-May-3 New Orleans Auction, New Orleans #1077/R est:2000-4000

CLARK, Paraskeva (1898-1986) Canadian
Works on paper
£403 $637 €605 Rocky shore - Muskoka (62x42cm-24x17in) s.d.1970 s.i.d.verso W/C prov.exhib. 14-Nov-2 Heffel, Vancouver #65 est:1200-1500 (C.D 1000)
£444 $701 €666 Summer holidays, Joe Lake (49x67cm-19x26in) s.d.1963 s.i.verso pastel W/C. 14-Nov-2 Heffel, Vancouver #19 est:1200-1500 (C.D 1100)
£785 $1233 €1178 Landscape near canoe lake station (56x76cm-22x30in) i.d.1956 s.verso W/C. 24-Jul-2 Walker's, Ottawa #230/R est:2000-2500 (C.D 1900)

CLARK, Roland (?) ?
£5063 $8000 €7595 Rising black ducks (51x41cm-20x16in) s. prov. 3-Apr-3 Christie's, Rockefeller NY #195/R est:2000-3000

CLARK, Rose (1853-1942) American
£1573 $2500 €2360 Maternite (83x63cm-33x25in) i.verso. 7-Mar-3 Skinner, Boston #559/R est:2500-3500

CLARK, Russell (1905-1966) New Zealander
£9119 $14225 €13679 Tourists and guide (51x46cm-20x18in) s.i.verso board. 17-Sep-2 Peter Webb, Auckland #104/R est:25000-35000 (NZ.D 30000)
£9848 $15167 €14772 Milford Mural I, 1953 (27x37cm-11x15in) s.i.d.1953 acrylic. 4-Sep-2 Dunbar Sloane, Wellington #27/R est:15000-25000 (NZ.D 32500)
Sculpture
£2120 $3413 €3180 Model sculpture (29x43x14cm-11x17x6in) plaster bronze. 7-May-3 Dunbar Sloane, Auckland #22/R est:6000-8000 (NZ.D 6000)
£4861 $7583 €7292 Maori woman's head (23x16x15cm-9x6x6in) s.verso limestone wooden base exec.c.1954 prov. 8-Apr-3 Peter Webb, Auckland #36/R est:13000-18000 (NZ.D 14000)
Works on paper
£2424 $3733 €3636 Wrecked Jap planes, Rekata Bay, Sta Isabel (22x35cm-9x14in) i. W/C. 4-Sep-2 Dunbar Sloane, Wellington #19/R est:8000-12000 (NZ.D 8000)
£3030 $4667 €4545 Torokina strip, Bouganville (22x35cm-9x14in) i. W/C. 4-Sep-2 Dunbar Sloane, Wellington #18/R est:10000-15000 (NZ.D 10000)
£3125 $4875 €4688 Rapaki, Lyttleton Harbour (34x55cm-13x22in) s. i.verso ink W/C. 8-Apr-3 Peter Webb, Auckland #144/R est:9000-12000 (NZ.D 9000)
£9028 $14083 €13542 Three figures (43x31cm-17x12in) s. s.i.verso ink W/C wax exec.c.1954 prov. 8-Apr-3 Peter Webb, Auckland #35/R est:20000-25000 (NZ.D 26000)
£10417 $16250 €15626 Field workers, Urerewa (38x46cm-15x18in) s. s.i.verso ink W/C crayon exec.c.1950 prov. 8-Apr-3 Peter Webb, Auckland #34/R est:20000-25000 (NZ.D 30000)

CLARK, S J (19/20th C) British
£1100 $1793 €1650 Country scene with team of horses pulling wood cart through stream (28x38cm-11x15in) 29-Jan-3 Brightwells, Leominster #867/R est:300-500

CLARK, S Joseph (19th C) British
£700 $1141 €1050 Landscape with cattle watering (35x61cm-14x24in) s. 29-Jan-3 Sotheby's, Olympia #107/R
£851 $1319 €1277 Pastoral landscape with girl and calves (50x75cm-20x30in) s. 8-Dec-2 Uppsala Auktionskammare, Uppsala #79/R (S.KR 12000)
£1100 $1672 €1650 Early morning (35x44cm-14x17in) mono.d.1878 s.i.stretcher. 4-Jul-2 Mellors & Kirk, Nottingham #820/R est:800-1200
£1410 $2200 €2115 Logging (50x76cm-20x30in) mono.d.1879. 7-Nov-2 Christie's, Kensington #189/R est:1500-2000
£1500 $2430 €2250 Cattle on the cliffs. Horses and cattle on the cliffs (30x36cm-12x14in) mono pair. 23-Jan-3 Christie's, Kensington #73/R est:2000-3000
£1600 $2496 €2400 Livestock by the village pond (35x53cm-14x21in) s. 26-Mar-3 Sotheby's, Olympia #117/R est:1000-2000

CLARK, W A (19/20th C) British
£1600 $2544 €2400 Old Berkeley (56x76cm-22x30in) s.d.1926. 6-Mar-3 Christie's, Kensington #589/R est:2000-3000

CLARK, William (1803-1883) British
£2127 $3360 €3191 Chestnut hunter. Brown hunter in stable (30x35cm-12x14in) s.d.1826 pair. 15-Nov-2 Naón & Cia, Buenos Aires #68/R
£4000 $6120 €6000 Steamship and sailing in the Firth of Clyde (49x75cm-19x30in) s.d.1849. 22-Aug-2 Bonhams, Edinburgh #1003/R est:2000-3000
£4000 $6280 €6000 Arran from the Ayrshire Coast (32x47cm-13x19in) s.d.1858. 16-Dec-2 Sotheby's, Olympia #47/R est:4000-6000
£7000 $10710 €10500 Auxiliary iron paddle steamer Atrato passing Ailsa Craig (107x183cm-42x72in) s.d.1854. 22-Aug-2 Bonhams, Edinburgh #956/R est:10000-15000
£8000 $12400 €12000 An outward bound barque off the Firth of Clyde (35x49cm-14x19in) s.d.1832. 31-Oct-2 Christie's, Kensington #461/R est:8000-12000
£20000 $31800 €30000 Crossing the finishing line at the royal northern yacht club's regatta at Greenock, 1835 (38x56cm-15x22in) s. prov.lit. 19-Mar-3 Sotheby's, London #5/R est:20000-30000

CLARK, William Albert (20th C) British
£340 $524 €510 Barr Amelia, pedigree Ayrshire cow at Barr Farm, Dumfriesshire (49x60cm-19x24in) s.d.1923. 22-Oct-2 Bonhams, Bath #271
£1000 $1540 €1500 Lessnessock Miss Viola III (50x60cm-20x24in) s.d.1939 sold with three companions. 22-Oct-2 Bonhams, Bath #272 est:800-1200
£1650 $2574 €2475 Old Berkeley (52x75cm-20x30in) s.d.1926. 15-Oct-2 Bearnes, Exeter #417/R est:1000-1500

CLARKE, Carey (fl.1957-1979) Irish?
£548 $860 €800 River landscape (45x50cm-18x20in) s. s.d.1973 verso. 15-Apr-3 De Veres Art Auctions, Dublin #19
£956 $1500 €1434 Rain, Brittas Lakes, Co Wicklow, Ireland (61x76cm-24x30in) s. i.verso. 22-Nov-2 Skinner, Boston #250/R est:2000-4000
£2568 $4005 €3800 Still life with roses and silver tray (60x74cm-24x29in) s. 26-Mar-3 James Adam, Dublin #105/R est:4000-5000

CLARKE, David (20th C) Irish
Works on paper
£601 $932 €950 Path through the woods at Delphi (43x57cm-17x22in) s.i.d. gouache prov. 24-Sep-2 De Veres Art Auctions, Dublin #101/R

CLARKE, Frank (19/20th C) British
£380 $604 €570 Lady gathering sticks from a river bank. Lady walking on a riverside path (44x29cm-17x11in) s. pair. 19-Mar-3 Wintertons, Lichfield #491/R

CLARKE, Geoffrey (1924-) British
Sculpture
£3600 $5688 €5400 Head of faun (10cm-4in) bronze executed c.1951. 27-Nov-2 Sotheby's, Olympia #175/R est:600-800

CLARKE, Harry (1889-1931) British
£520 $806 €780 Woodland scene with sunlight on the path in the foreground (34x41cm-13x16in) s. canvasboard. 1-Oct-2 Bonhams, Leeds #270
Works on paper
£764 $1192 €1200 Cartoon (20x15cm-8x6in) init. indian ink W/C. 6-Nov-2 James Adam, Dublin #105/R

CLARKE, Harry Harvey (1869-?) British
Works on paper
£250 $418 €363 Old trees in a wood (15x18cm-6x7in) s.d.97 W/C. 20-Jun-3 Keys, Aylsham #901

CLARKE, Joseph Clayton (fl.1883-1885) British
Works on paper
£300 $456 €450 Young boy in bed, cowering from a spider (27x19cm-11x7in) s. W/C ink. 15-Aug-2 Rupert Toovey, Partridge Green #1480/R

CLARKE, Margaret (1888-1961) Irish
£5128 $7949 €8000 Ann (90x71cm-35x28in) prov.exhib. 3-Dec-2 Bonhams & James Adam, Dublin #38/R est:8000-12000

CLARKE, Patricia Cleland (20th C) British?
£500 $795 €750 Ballyhornan tide coming in (76x68cm-30x27in) s.d.16/9/02 board. 5-Mar-3 John Ross, Belfast #105

CLARKE, William Hanna (1882-1924) British
£1250 $1950 €1875 Galloway landscape with cattle (45x60cm-18x24in) s. 28-Mar-3 Bonhams, Edinburgh #126 est:800-1200
£3200 $5024 €4800 Girl gathering flowers in a glade (40x51cm-16x20in) s.d.1920. 10-Dec-2 Rosebery Fine Art, London #677/R est:1000-1500

CLARKSON, Robert (fl.1880-1914) British
£550 $891 €825 Resting by the haystack (40x76cm-16x30in) s.d.1877. 20-May-3 Sotheby's, Olympia #227/R
Works on paper
£250 $400 €375 Cottages on the cliff top, Robin Hoods Bay (24x33cm-9x13in) d.Sept 12 1914 W/C. 11-Mar-3 David Duggleby, Scarborough #126

CLAROS GARCIA, Alfredo (1893-1965) Spanish
£252 $387 €400 Still life with eels (46x56cm-18x22in) s.d.1947. 28-Oct-2 Segre, Madrid #244/R

CLAROT, Alexander (1796-1842) Austrian
Works on paper
£3041 $4743 €4500 Portrait of young woman in green dress (19x15cm-7x6in) s.d.1835 W/C. 28-Mar-3 Dorotheum, Vienna #210/R est:1200-1500

CLAROT, Alexander (attrib) (1796-1842) Austrian
Works on paper
£636 $1030 €922 Portrait of young man (12x10cm-5x4in) i. W/C board. 24-May-3 Dorotheum, Prague #217/R est:15000-23000 (C.KR 28000)

CLAROT, René (1882-1972) Belgian
£327 $526 €500 Retour de la barque de peche a Ostende (66x78cm-26x31in) s.d.38. 20-Jan-3 Horta, Bruxelles #448
£353 $536 €550 Vue de ville (50x60cm-20x24in) s.d.47. 27-Aug-2 Galerie Moderne, Brussels #286
£380 $592 €600 Ruelle bruxelloise (60x50cm-24x20in) s.d.59. 16-Sep-2 Horta, Bruxelles #283
£397 $648 €600 Ane tirant une charrette (90x120cm-35x47in) s.d.29. 17-Feb-3 Horta, Bruxelles #241
£481 $745 €750 Ane tirant une charrette devant un moulin (90x120cm-35x47in) s.d.29. 9-Dec-2 Horta, Bruxelles #322
£755 $1170 €1200 Blankenberg harbour (59x61cm-23x24in) s.d.23. 5-Oct-2 De Vuyst, Lokeren #61
Works on paper
£276 $441 €400 Place Saint Jacques animee (32x44cm-13x17in) s. W/C. 17-Mar-3 Horta, Bruxelles #11

CLART, Max Ernest (1916-) Belgian
£256 $403 €400 Portrait de jeune fille (120x90cm-47x35in) s. 10-Dec-2 Campo, Vlaamse Kaai #74

CLARY-BAROUX, Albert Adolphe (1865-1933) French
£304 $474 €450 Butte Montmartre (51x61cm-20x24in) s. 26-Mar-3 Peschetau-Badin Godeau & Leroy, Paris #25
£473 $738 €700 Le Sacre Coeur vu de la banlieue (46x55cm-18x22in) s. 25-Mar-3 Chochon-Barre & Allardi, Paris #76
£541 $843 €800 Bord de Seine (50x61cm-20x24in) s. i.verso. 30-Mar-3 Anaf, Lyon #349
£541 $843 €800 Apres-midi d'automne (38x55cm-15x22in) s. i.verso. 30-Mar-3 Anaf, Lyon #348
£764 $1192 €1200 Bord de riviere (54x73cm-21x29in) s. 10-Nov-2 Eric Pillon, Calais #4/R

CLARYS, Alexandre (1857-1912) Belgian
£253 $395 €400 Biche et son faon dans une clairiere (62x85cm-24x33in) s. 16-Sep-2 Horta, Bruxelles #509
£340 $541 €500 Chevaux au pre (32x46cm-13x18in) s. 18-Mar-3 Vanderkindere, Brussels #69
£621 $1000 €950 Chien (100x75cm-39x30in) s. 14-Jan-3 Vanderkindere, Brussels #471
£705 $1093 €1100 Le petit Brabancon (31x23cm-12x9in) s. panel oval lit. 9-Dec-2 Horta, Bruxelles #52
£755 $1162 €1200 Chien de berger et troupeau (90x130cm-35x51in) 22-Oct-2 Campo & Campo, Antwerp #39
£2092 $3367 €3200 Travaux de debardage en foret (98x123cm-39x48in) s. 20-Jan-3 Horta, Bruxelles #242 est:3500-4500
Works on paper
£448 $717 €650 Apres la glissade (41x57cm-16x22in) s.d.1908 W/C. 17-Mar-3 Horta, Bruxelles #50

CLATWORTHY, Robert (1928-) British
Sculpture
£1200 $1860 €1800 Horse and rider (35cm-14in) brown pat. bronze. 4-Dec-2 Christie's, Kensington #513/R est:1000-1500

CLAUDE, Eugène (1841-1923) French
£1596 $2618 €2314 Still life with oysters and lobster (54x65cm-21x26in) s. prov. 4-Jun-3 Fischer, Luzern #1074/R est:2500-3500 (S.FR 3400)
£2500 $3900 €3750 Still life of flowers in a basket (54x65cm-21x26in) s. 17-Sep-2 Sotheby's, Olympia #242/R est:2500-3500

CLAUDE, Eugène (attrib) (1841-1923) French
£1652 $2577 €2478 Still life with flowers and orange (90x45cm-35x18in) s. 16-Sep-2 Philippe Schuler, Zurich #3463/R est:2000-2500 (S.FR 3800)

CLAUDE, Jean Maxime (1824-1904) French
£8800 $13728 €13200 End of the day (56x43cm-22x17in) s.d.1866. 6-Nov-2 Sotheby's, Olympia #72/R est:3000-5000

CLAUDEL, Camille (1864-1943) French
Sculpture
£9028 $14896 €13000 La jeune fille a la gerbe ou jeune fille assise (35x20x20cm-14x8x8in) s.num.III/IV black pat bronze st.f.Coubertin lit. 2-Jul-3 Artcurial Briest, Paris #633/R est:15000-20000
£12821 $20128 €20000 L'homme penche (42cm-17in) s.st.f.Delval num.5/8 bronze prov. 10-Dec-2 Pierre Berge, Paris #8/R est:22000
£32051 $50000 €48077 L'implorante (28cm-11in) i.num.38 dark brown pat. bronze st.f.Eug Blot cast 1937 prov.lit. 6-Nov-2 Sotheby's, New York #113/R est:60000-80000
£77465 $128592 €110000 L'aurore (33cm-13in) s.num.3 pat bronze Cast Eugene Blot prov.exhib.lit. 12-Jun-3 Tajan, Paris #3/R est:55000-60000
£118012 $190000 €177018 L'abandon - Sakountala Sucountala Vertumne et Pomone (62cm-24in) i.num.6. black pat. bronze st.f.Eug Blot prov.lit. 7-May-3 Sotheby's, New York #123/R est:180000-220000
£136646 $220000 €204969 La valse (46cm-18in) i. black pat. bronze st.f.Eug Blot prov.lit. 7-May-3 Sotheby's, New York #117/R est:200000-300000
£187180 $293872 €292000 Abandon (62x57x27cm-24x22x11in) s.st.f.Blot num.15 bronze exec.c.1905 lit. 16-Dec-2 Rabourdin & Choppin de Janvry, Paris #60/R est:120000-180000

CLAUDET, Antoine (19th C) British
Photographs
£4000 $6480 €6000 Chess players. stereoscopic daguerreotype stereo viewer exec.c.1850. 21-May-3 Christie's, London #12/R est:3000-4000

CLAUDIUS, Wilhelm (1854-1942) German
£379 $599 €550 Sunny forest clearing in early autumn (28x18cm-11x7in) s.i. board. 5-Apr-3 Hans Stahl, Hamburg #116
£627 $971 €990 Sunlit forest clearing in early autumn (28x18cm-11x7in) s.i. board. 28-Sep-2 Hans Stahl, Hamburg #136

CLAUDOT, Andre (1892-1982) French
£1384 $2145 €2200 Paysage d'ete (65x81cm-26x32in) s.i.d.23 verso. 30-Oct-2 Coutau Begarie, Paris #103/R

CLAUDOT, Jean-Baptiste-Charles (1733-1805) French
£105634 $175352 €150000 Various views (102x121cm-40x48in) s. five. 13-Jun-3 Rabourdin & Choppin de Janvry, Paris #48/R

CLAUS, Carl Friedrich (1930-1998) Austrian
£486 $768 €700 Figures on beach II (40x55cm-16x22in) s. s.i.d.1976 verso. 26-Apr-3 Dr Lehr, Berlin #85/R

CLAUS, Émile (1849-1924) Belgian

£5063 $8000 €8000 La fenaison (22x33cm-9x13in) s. s.i.verso. 26-Nov-2 Palais de Beaux Arts, Brussels #57/R est:7500-10000
£9353 $14964 €13000 Bathers (24x33cm-9x13in) s. 17-May-3 De Vuyst, Lokeren #458/R est:12000-16000
£12230 $19568 €17000 Thames under snow (28x41cm-11x16in) i.verso painted 1916 lit. 17-May-3 De Vuyst, Lokeren #457/R est:18000-22000
£12658 $19747 €20000 Flandres (46x46cm-18x18in) s. s.i.verso. 15-Oct-2 Horta, Bruxelles #106/R est:20000-25000
£13924 $22000 €22000 La lagune de Venise (10x60cm-4x24in) s. 26-Nov-2 Palais de Beaux Arts, Brussels #58/R est:20000-25000
£14184 $23688 €20000 Sunset (46x55cm-18x22in) s. painted c.1910. 23-Jun-3 Bernaerts, Antwerp #184/R est:20000-30000
£24828 $39724 €36000 Ouvrieres entre des meules de foin (49x72cm-19x28in) mono. 17-Mar-3 Amberes, Antwerp #195/R
£26582 $41468 €42000 Portrait of a young Arab at Clemcen (36x32cm-14x13in) s.d.1879 exhib. 21-Oct-2 Bernaerts, Antwerp #643/R est:15000-20000
£41509 $64340 €66000 Embankment (48x43cm-19x17in) s.i.d.16. 5-Oct-2 De Vuyst, Lokeren #454/R

Works on paper

£417 $646 €650 View of village surrounding Astene (23x28cm-9x11in) mono. pencil dr exec.c.1880. 7-Dec-2 De Vuyst, Lokeren #55
£700 $1099 €1050 Study of old woman (33x25cm-13x10in) s.d.1898. 10-Dec-2 Capes Dunn, Manchester #777
£2553 $4264 €3600 Plage animee a la Panne (22x29cm-9x11in) mono.d.20 sept 16 i.verso pastel. 17-Jun-3 Palais de Beaux Arts, Brussels #521/R est:2000-3000
£5063 $7899 €8000 Heyst (29x43cm-11x17in) s.i. W/C. 21-Oct-2 Bernaerts, Antwerp #628/R est:10000-12500
£9028 $14354 €13000 Hiver sur la Lys (48x65cm-19x26in) s. pastel paper on canvas. 29-Apr-3 Campo, Vlaamse Kaai #41/R est:12000-15000

CLAUS, Emile (attrib) (1849-1924) Belgian

£360 $587 €540 Figures in a gallery (30x38cm-12x15in) s. 28-Jan-3 Gorringes, Lewes #1786

CLAUS, Hugo (1929-) Belgian

Works on paper

£409 $630 €650 Nu (34x48cm-13x19in) s. pastel. 22-Oct-2 Campo, Vlaamse Kaai #43

CLAUS, Wilhelm (1882-?) German

£320 $515 €480 View through the trees (90x67cm-35x26in) s.d.07 board. 18-Feb-3 Bonhams, Knightsbridge #125/R

CLAUS, William A J (1862-?) American

£1195 $1900 €1793 Springtime landscape (56x46cm-22x18in) s. 7-Mar-3 Skinner, Boston #389/R est:1000-1500

CLAUSADES, Pierre de (1910-1976) French

£380 $600 €570 Vessels at the mouth of the estuary on a calm day (38x55cm-15x22in) s. 14-Nov-2 Christie's, Kensington #116
£387 $600 €581 Riverscape (38x46cm-15x18in) s. 25-Sep-2 Doyle, New York #22/R
£400 $652 €580 Coastal scene (39x55cm-15x22in) s. 16-Jul-3 Sotheby's, Olympia #271/R
£414 $650 €621 Winter landscape (33x41cm-13x16in) s. 14-Dec-2 Weschler, Washington #615/R
£420 $647 €630 Dans le Bassin d'Arcachon (38x55cm-15x22in) s. i.on stretcher. 24-Oct-2 Christie's, Kensington #177
£480 $768 €720 Sailing dinghy pulled up on a beach with dunes beyond (38x46cm-15x18in) s. 13-Mar-3 Duke & Son, Dorchester #205/R
£550 $880 €825 Extensive view of a beach with trees on rising ground beyond (61x91cm-24x36in) s. 13-Mar-3 Duke & Son, Dorchester #206/R
£570 $883 €900 Le Cap Griz Nez (65x55cm-26x22in) s. 29-Sep-2 Eric Pillon, Calais #219/R
£700 $1169 €1015 Neige au quai d'Orfevres, Paris (45x55cm-18x22in) s.i.d.75 verso prov. 17-Jun-3 Bonhams, Knightsbridge #7/R
£800 $1272 €1200 Summer clouds over a cornfield (37x44cm-15x17in) s. 29-Apr-3 Henry Adams, Chichester #329/R
£900 $1404 €1350 Cote corses (51x62cm-20x24in) s. i.d.67 verso. 26-Mar-3 Hamptons Fine Art, Godalming #204/R
£1000 $1630 €1450 River landscape (45x80cm-18x31in) s. 16-Jul-3 Sotheby's, Olympia #270/R est:1000-2000
£1100 $1782 €1650 Summer meadow, Beauceron (46x55cm-18x22in) s. i.verso. 23-Jan-3 Christie's, Kensington #269/R est:700-1000
£1700 $2771 €2550 Coteaux de la Loire (48x98cm-19x39in) s. 29-Jan-3 Sotheby's, Olympia #347/R est:1000-2000
£2500 $3875 €3750 Loire estuary (82x116cm-32x46in) s. 1-Nov-2 Moore Allen & Innocent, Cirencester #463/R est:1000-1500

CLAUSELL, Joaquin (1866-1935) Mexican

£4268 $7000 €6189 Entrada al Puerto de Manzanillo (14x23cm-6x9in) s.i.verso board painted c.1906-1910 prov. 27-May-3 Sotheby's, New York #141
£7730 $12369 €11209 Paisaje con roca (14x17cm-6x7in) s. board. 15-May-3 Louis Morton, Mexico #70/R est:130000-140000 (M.P 125000)
£8280 $13000 €12420 Sea (17x22cm-7x9in) s.i. painted c.1915 prov.lit. 20-Nov-2 Christie's, Rockefeller NY #68/R est:12000-15000
£30488 $50000 €45732 Paisaje de noche (62x83cm-24x33in) s.verso painted c.1925 prov. 28-May-3 Christie's, Rockefeller NY #34/R est:60000-80000
£47771 $75000 €71657 Marine (100x150cm-39x59in) s.d.1920 verso prov. 20-Nov-2 Christie's, Rockefeller NY #6/R est:80000-100000

Works on paper

£3557 $5833 €5158 Marina (47x35cm-19x14in) s. mixed media. 28-May-3 Louis Morton, Mexico #86/R est:70000-100000 (M.P 60000)

CLAUSEN, Christian (1862-1911) Danish

£276 $419 €414 Marie Grubbe (29x23cm-11x9in) mono.d.1891. 27-Aug-2 Rasmussen, Copenhagen #1878/R (D.KR 3200)
£1292 $1964 €1938 Reading aloud in lamp light (65x82cm-26x32in) mono.d.1903. 27-Aug-2 Rasmussen, Copenhagen #1876/R est:10000 (D.KR 15000)
£2401 $3746 €3602 Interior scene with two girls reading at table (66x82cm-26x32in) mono. 11-Nov-2 Rasmussen, Vejle #504/R est:30000 (D.KR 28000)
£2793 $4441 €4190 Interior scene with girl by window (52x38cm-20x15in) mono. 5-Mar-3 Rasmussen, Copenhagen #1515/R est:30000-50000 (D.KR 30000)
£26701 $40586 €40052 Sitting room in sunshine - interior with girl putting her hat on (62x49cm-24x19in) mono. exhib. 27-Aug-2 Rasmussen, Copenhagen #1455/R est:30000-50000 (D.KR 310000)

Works on paper

£296 $459 €444 Composition (8x10cm-3x4in) crayon prov. 1-Oct-2 Rasmussen, Copenhagen #173/R (D.KR 3500)

CLAUSEN, Franciska (1899-1986) Danish

£339 $525 €509 Dynamic shape in green, white and red (7x7cm-3x3in) prov. 1-Oct-2 Rasmussen, Copenhagen #7/R (D.KR 4000)

Works on paper

£292 $480 €438 Concrete composition (11x8cm-4x3in) init. gouache. 27-May-3 Museumsbygningen, Copenhagen #424 (D.KR 3000)
£293 $454 €440 Icon self portrait (23x17cm-9x7in) W/C prov. 4-Dec-2 Kunsthallen, Copenhagen #132/R (D.KR 3400)
£466 $722 €699 Cubist composition (10x8cm-4x3in) init. pencil cardboard prov. 1-Oct-2 Rasmussen, Copenhagen #11/R (D.KR 5500)
£467 $729 €701 Park with Chinese couple and cat (54x43cm-21x17in) gouache. 5-Aug-2 Rasmussen, Vejle #297 (D.KR 5500)
£511 $808 €767 Neoplastic composition (8x7cm-3x3in) init. gouache executed c.1930 prov. 1-Apr-3 Rasmussen, Copenhagen #301/R (D.KR 5500)
£594 $945 €891 Neo-plastic composition. Composition (24x18cm-9x7in) init. one exec.c.1925 one d.1930 pastel pair prov. 26-Feb-3 Kunsthallen, Copenhagen #104/R (D.KR 6500)
£960 $1526 €1440 Still life - Academie Moderne, Paris (29x21cm-11x8in) pencil. 26-Feb-3 Kunsthallen, Copenhagen #65/R (D.KR 10500)
£1016 $1575 €1524 Neo plastic composition (78x58cm-31x23in) i. gouache Indian ink pencil executed c.1930 prov.exhib.lit. 1-Oct-2 Rasmussen, Copenhagen #31/R est:12000-15000 (D.KR 12000)
£1267 $1976 €1901 Plastic composition (19x10cm-7x4in) init.i. gouache executed c.1930 pair prov. 18-Sep-2 Kunsthallen, Copenhagen #198/R est:15000 (D.KR 15000)
£1270 $1969 €1905 Neoplastic composition (80x60cm-31x24in) i. gouache Indian ink pencil executed c.1930 prov.exhib.lit. 1-Oct-2 Rasmussen, Copenhagen #16/R est:15000 (D.KR 15000)
£1270 $1969 €1905 Variation of Clair de lune (19x13cm-7x5in) s. gouache Indian ink prov.exhib.lit. 1-Oct-2 Rasmussen, Copenhagen #17/R est:15000-20000 (D.KR 15000)
£1863 $2887 €2795 Circles and verticals (16x13cm-6x5in) s. gouache Indian ink pencil executed c.1930 prov.exhib. 1-Oct-2 Rasmussen, Copenhagen #18/R est:12000-15000 (D.KR 22000)
£2202 $3412 €3303 Neo plastic composition (81x60cm-32x24in) i.d.1928 gouache Indian ink pencil prov.exhib.lit. 1-Oct-2 Rasmussen, Copenhagen #6/R est:15000 (D.KR 26000)
£2540 $3937 €3810 Neo plastic composition (9x8cm-4x3in) s.d.1930 gouache pencil prov.exhib.lit. 1-Oct-2 Rasmussen, Copenhagen #4/R est:8000 (D.KR 30000)
£2618 $4084 €3927 Composition (19x13cm-7x5in) gouache painted c.1925. 18-Sep-2 Kunsthallen, Copenhagen #7/R est:20000 (D.KR 31000)

£3810 $5906 €5715 Cubist composition with walking stick, chair and vase (37x28cm-15x11in) init.d.1925 gouache prov. 1-Oct-2 Rasmussen, Copenhagen #3/R est:50000-75000 (D.KR 45000)

CLAUSEN, Sir George (1852-1944) British

£950 $1492 €1425 Farmyard entrance (33x33cm-13x13in) s. 13-Dec-2 Keys, Aylsham #653/R

£2000 $3160 €3000 Apple blossom (41x31cm-16x12in) s. 26-Nov-2 Bonhams, Oxford #37 est:2000-3000

£2800 $4312 €4200 Flowers in a vase (30x37cm-12x15in) s. panel prov. 5-Sep-2 Christie's, Kensington #584/R est:3000-5000

£3500 $5845 €5075 Pottery (20x26cm-8x10in) init. s.i.verso. 25-Jun-3 Bonhams, Bury St Edmunds #608 est:3000-4000

£5000 $7800 €7500 Apple blossom (35x46cm-14x18in) s. exhib. 27-Mar-3 Christie's, Kensington #527/R est:6000-8000

£100000 $166000 €150000 In the street (25x17cm-10x7in) s.d.1880 i.d.verso prov.exhib.lit. 11-Jun-3 Christie's, London #10/R est:100000-150000

Works on paper

£450 $702 €675 Cows in a lane (26x31cm-10x12in) pastel. 27-Mar-3 Christie's, Kensington #316/R

£640 $1018 €960 Pony and cart with figures by a hayrick (17x25cm-7x10in) s. W/C over pencil. 4-Mar-3 Bearnes, Exeter #362/R

£1100 $1771 €1650 Saltfleetby (15x24cm-6x9in) s.d.1887 i.verso pastel W/C prov. 14-Jan-3 Bonhams, Knightsbridge #214/R est:1200-1800

£4800 $7536 €7200 Harvesting (45x31cm-18x12in) s.d.1879 pencil W/C gum arabic scratching out. 21-Nov-2 Christie's, London #104/R est:5000-7000

£16456 $26000 €24684 Little Rose (51x36cm-20x14in) s.d.1889 pastel paper on board. 24-Apr-3 Sotheby's, New York #36/R est:40000-60000

CLAVE, Antoni (1913-) Spanish

£9028 $14896 €13000 Le guerrier a la feuille (87x66cm-34x26in) oil resin collage zinc plaque. 1-Jul-3 Artcurial Briest, Paris #800b/R est:13000-15000

£9500 $15865 €13775 Le roi (23x19cm-9x7in) s.i. enamel glass pebbles copper exec.c.1960. 26-Jun-3 Sotheby's, London #203/R est:6000-8000

£10000 $15400 €15000 Roi (27x22cm-11x9in) s. s.i.verso oil mixed media collage on board prov. 22-Oct-2 Sotheby's, London #435/R est:10000-15000

£11218 $17612 €17500 Guerrier sur fond noir (145x130cm-57x51in) s.d.1978 oil collage prov. 15-Dec-2 Perrin, Versailles #102/R est:25000

£15000 $25050 €21750 Hommage au Greco (100x73cm-39x29in) s.i. oil pastel paper on canvas prov. 26-Jun-3 Sotheby's, London #207/R est:18000-25000

£16026 $25000 €24039 Nature morte (61x72cm-24x28in) s. prov. 14-Oct-2 Butterfields, San Francisco #2023/R est:22000-28000

£16556 $26987 €25000 La plage a Honfleur (15x38cm-6x15in) s. 2-Feb-3 Muizon & Le Coent, Paris #72

£17949 $28179 €28000 Points rouges et verts (116x89cm-46x35in) s.d.66 prov.lit. 11-Dec-2 Artcurial Briest, Paris #728/R est:40000

£20290 $33275 €28000 Roi de cartes (76x56cm-30x22in) s. oil Indian ink brush over chl paper on board prov. 31-May-3 Villa Grisebach, Berlin #376/R est:6000-8000

£24558 $39047 €36100 Nature morte (55x38cm-22x15in) s. oil mixed media panel. 26-Feb-3 Artcurial Briest, Paris #423/R est:15000-20000

£30000 $50100 €43500 Petit arlequin (73x60cm-29x24in) s.d.53 init.i.d.1953 verso prov. 26-Jun-3 Sotheby's, London #208/R est:20000-30000

£55000 $91850 €79750 Rois face a face (99x73cm-39x29in) i.verso oil paper on canvas painted 1956 prov.exhib. 27-Jun-3 Christie's, London #118/R est:40000-60000

£140000 $233800 €210000 Le peintre flamand (130x145cm-51x57in) s. exc.1955 prov.exhib.lit. 25-Jun-3 Sotheby's, London #25/R est:80000-120000

Sculpture

£2517 $4102 €3800 Woman (31cm-12in) s. num.EA gilt pat bronze. 3-Feb-3 Cornette de St.Cyr, Paris #384/R

£4097 $6474 €5900 Guerrier a la lance (57x24x11cm-22x9x4in) s.num.6/8 green pat bronze Cast Guyot exhib.lit. 27-Apr-3 Perrin, Versailles #103/R est:5000-6000

£10417 $16563 €15000 On dirait un guerrier (102x48x17cm-40x19x7in) s. soldered bronze Cast Parallaba lit. 29-Apr-3 Artcurial Briest, Paris #550/R est:15000-20000

Works on paper

£314 $487 €500 Composition (65x50cm-26x20in) s.i. mixed media. 30-Oct-2 Coutau Begarie, Paris #32a/R

£1528 $2429 €2200 Etude de decors pour le ballet Carmen (34x55cm-13x22in) s. Indian ink dr exec.c.1940 prov. 29-Apr-3 Artcurial Briest, Paris #140/R est:1800-2000

£1736 $2760 €2500 Autoportrait. Etude de tete de femme (44x32cm-17x13in) Indian ink dr double-sided exec.c.1950 prov. 29-Apr-3 Artcurial Briest, Paris #141 est:1500-1800

£2516 $3899 €4000 Composition (26x20cm-10x8in) s. mixed media. 7-Oct-2 Claude Aguttes, Neuilly #282

£3145 $4843 €5000 Warrior (32x22cm-13x9in) s.d.1960 mixed media collage cardboard. 28-Oct-2 Segre, Madrid #136/R est:3500

£3214 $5079 €4821 Portrait of Moya Dyring (32x25cm-13x10in) s.i. gouache prov. 26-Nov-2 Sotheby's, Melbourne #147/R est:9000-12000 (A.D 9000)

£3681 $5815 €5300 Ficelle bleue (48x35cm-19x14in) s. mixed media collage aluminium panel exec.c.1980. 27-Apr-3 Perrin, Versailles #70/R est:5000-6000

£4306 $6803 €6200 Retour du japon (78x56cm-31x22in) s.d. mixed media collage. 27-Apr-3 Perrin, Versailles #68/R est:4000-5000

£4487 $7045 €7000 Deux punaises rouges (52x40cm-20x16in) s.d.1980 mixed media collage aluminium panel. 15-Dec-2 Perrin, Versailles #90/R

£4861 $7681 €7000 Deux ficelles rouges (65x50cm-26x20in) s.d. s.i.d.verso mixed media collage panel. 27-Apr-3 Perrin, Versailles #71/R est:5000-6000

£5000 $7900 €7200 Avec trois cordes (64x81cm-25x32in) s.d. s.i.d.verso mixed media collage aluminium panel. 27-Apr-3 Perrin, Versailles #72/R est:6000-8000

£5449 $8554 €8500 Punaise rouge (75x55cm-30x22in) s.d.1982 mixed media collage cardboard on canvas. 15-Dec-2 Perrin, Versailles #89/R

£5556 $9000 €8056 Jeune fille au coq (56x33cm-22x13in) s. gouache India ink chk. 21-May-3 Doyle, New York #28/R est:14000-18000

£5577 $8756 €8700 Tampons ministeriaux (50x34cm-20x13in) s.d.1981 s.i.d.verso mixed media collage panel. 15-Dec-2 Perrin, Versailles #92/R

£5769 $9058 €9000 Untitled (65x50cm-26x20in) s.d.1976 mixed media collage panel. 15-Dec-2 Perrin, Versailles #91/R

£10577 $16606 €16500 Vu a New York (132x99cm-52x39in) s.d.1990 s.i.d.verso mixed media collage on canvas prov. 15-Dec-2 Perrin, Versailles #101/R est:25000

£34000 $56780 €49300 Roi a la pipe et a la fleur (65x50cm-26x20in) s.d.58 gouache pastel ink collage prov. 26-Jun-3 Sotheby's, London #204/R est:15000-20000

CLAVE, Pelegrin (1810-1880) Spanish

£24390 $40000 €35366 Portrait of a lady (124x95cm-49x37in) s.d.1849 prov. 27-May-3 Sotheby's, New York #34

CLAVERIE, Jules Justin (1859-1932) French

£881 $1365 €1400 Carriole sur route en bord de mer (46x61cm-18x24in) s. 30-Oct-2 Coutau Begarie, Paris #160

CLAVO, Javier (1918-1994) Spanish

£483 $768 €700 Landscape (30x19cm-12x7in) s. board. 4-Mar-3 Ansorena, Madrid #248/R

£513 $810 €800 Venice (33x25cm-13x10in) s.i.d.1985 board. 19-Nov-2 Durán, Madrid #55/R

£1724 $2724 €2500 Saint Francis the Great's, Madrid (52x62cm-20x24in) s. board. 1-Apr-3 Segre, Madrid #313/R

£1776 $2878 €2700 Urban view (40x91cm-16x36in) s.d.91. 21-Jan-3 Ansorena, Madrid #78/R

Works on paper

£346 $533 €550 Westminster Abbey (25x35cm-10x14in) s.i. W/C. 22-Oct-2 Durán, Madrid #81/R

CLAXTON, Marshall (1812-1881) British

£650 $1060 €975 Lady with mother and child (72x91cm-28x36in) s. 29-Jan-3 Sotheby's, Olympia #201/R

£680 $1061 €1020 Morning prayer (56x44cm-22x17in) s.i.d.58 verso board. 9-Oct-2 Woolley & Wallis, Salisbury #344/R

CLAY, Elizabeth C Fisher (fl.1927-1938) American/British

£420 $659 €630 Continental sunlit street scene with figures (14x20cm-6x8in) s. s.verso panel. 19-Nov-2 Bonhams, Leeds #157

£3145 $5000 €4718 Ring-o-roses (61x66cm-24x26in) prov. 5-Mar-3 Christie's, Rockefeller NY #100/R est:3000-5000

CLAYDEN, Phillippa (1955-) British

Works on paper

£280 $445 €420 Travellers (60x60cm-24x24in) collage mixed media. 18-Mar-3 Bonhams, Knightsbridge #51

CLAYES, Alice des (1890-?) Canadian

£2790 $4352 €4046 Merripet farm, Postbridge (30x41cm-12x16in) s.i. canvasboard prov. 26-Mar-3 Walker's, Ottawa #200/R est:2000-3000 (C.D 6500)

£2889 $4738 €4189 Poor pastures - tired workers (40x50cm-16x20in) s.i. 9-Jun-3 Hodgins, Calgary #371/R est:6000-8000 (C.D 6500)

Works on paper

£222 $364 €333 Riders in an English village (16x24cm-6x9in) s. W/C htd white. 3-Jun-3 Joyner, Toronto #536 (C.D 500)

£356 $583 €534 Ploughing (16x24cm-6x9in) s. W/C prov. 3-Jun-3 Joyner, Toronto #361/R est:800-1200 (C.D 800)

£400 $656 €600 Forest en France, summer. En France, autumn (32x24cm-13x9in) s. pastel pair. 3-Jun-3 Joyner, Toronto #568 est:1200-1500 (C.D 900)
£815 $1272 €1182 Loading the cart. Landscape studies (23x19cm-9x7in) s. gouache graphite dr. double-sided. 26-Mar-3 Walker's, Ottawa #263/R est:1500-2000 (C.D 1900)

CLAYES, Berthe des (1877-1968) Canadian
£930 $1460 €1395 Autumn ploughing (30x41cm-12x16in) s. canvasboard. 24-Jul-2 Walker's, Ottawa #252/R est:2000-2500 (C.D 2250)
£1033 $1622 €1550 Boaters at ponds edge (36x46cm-14x18in) s. 24-Jul-2 Walker's, Ottawa #211/R est:2000-2500 (C.D 2500)
£1244 $2041 €1866 Early summer, Melbourne (30x40cm-12x16in) canvas on board prov. 3-Jun-3 Joyner, Toronto #175/R est:2500-3500 (C.D 2800)
£1707 $2680 €2561 Winter, Como, Quebec (31x39cm-12x15in) s. prov. 10-Dec-2 Pinneys, Montreal #169 est:1500-2000 (C.D 4200)
£1728 $2679 €2592 On the road at st. Agathe, Pro, Quebec (26x34cm-10x13in) s. panel. 3-Dec-2 Joyner, Toronto #124/R est:2500-3000 (C.D 4200)
Works on paper
£289 $454 €434 Historic buildings at river's edge (28x30cm-11x12in) s. pastel. 24-Jul-2 Walker's, Ottawa #432/R (C.D 700)
£494 $760 €741 Moulin a eau (11x9cm-4x4in) s. pastel. 22-Oct-2 Iegor de Saint Hippolyte, Montreal #29 (C.D 1200)
£622 $1020 €933 Church in Knowlton, Eastern townships (24x29cm-9x11in) s. pastel prov. 3-Jun-3 Joyner, Toronto #433/R est:800-1200 (C.D 1400)
£650 $1021 €975 Young girl amongst the geese (27x19cm-11x7in) s. mixed media. 10-Dec-2 Pinneys, Montreal #135 (C.D 1600)
£756 $1239 €1134 Gathering firewood, winter (22x22cm-9x9in) s. pastel. 3-Jun-3 Joyner, Toronto #336/R est:1200-1500 (C.D 1700)

CLAYES, Berthe des (attrib) (1877-1968) Canadian
Works on paper
£620 $942 €930 Autumnal woodland landscape with lake and hills beyond (34x39cm-13x15in) s. pastel dr. 15-Aug-2 Rupert Toovey, Partridge Green #1145/R
£1150 $1748 €1725 Winter woodland landscape with horse-drawn sleigh (35x39cm-14x15in) s. pastel dr. 15-Aug-2 Rupert Toovey, Partridge Green #1444/R est:300-500

CLAYETTE, Pierre (20th C) French
£629 $975 €1000 Flying Dutchman (80x100cm-31x39in) s. s.d.1977 verso. 4-Oct-2 Paul Kieffer, Pforzhiem #9160/R

CLAYS, Paul Jean (1819-1900) Belgian
£521 $859 €750 Busy harbour (18x28cm-7x11in) studio st. board. 1-Jul-3 Christie's, Amsterdam #28
£1000 $1520 €1500 Shipping on an estuary (24x36cm-9x14in) s.d.1856 panel prov. 29-Aug-2 Christie's, Kensington #214/R est:800-1200
£1154 $1812 €1800 Bateaux de peche en Hollande (26x50cm-10x20in) studio st. 10-Dec-2 Vanderkindere, Brussels #1 est:1000-1500
£1500 $2340 €2250 Unloading the catch (58x47cm-23x19in) s. panel. 25-Mar-3 Bonhams, Leeds #647/R est:1500-2000
£2278 $3554 €3600 Bateaux de peche sous toile (24x35cm-9x14in) s.d.1856 panel. 15-Oct-2 Horta, Bruxelles #131
£2600 $4056 €3900 Beached fishing vessels (49x73cm-19x29in) s. panel. 8-Oct-2 Bonhams, Knightsbridge #81/R est:2000-4000
£3200 $4864 €4800 Calm weather at Kinderdyck (43x63cm-17x25in) s. board. 15-Aug-2 Bonhams, New Bond Street #317/R est:2000-3000
£3819 $6073 €5500 Shipping on a calm (28x42cm-11x17in) s.d.75 panel prov. 29-Apr-3 Christie's, Amsterdam #23/R est:3000-5000
£9500 $15770 €9500 Le retour au port des trois-mats (95x126cm-37x50in) s.d.1838. 16-Jun-3 Horta, Bruxelles #118/R est:10000-12000
£11950 $19000 €17925 Harbour view (64x106cm-25x42in) s.d.1866 panel. 7-Mar-3 Skinner, Boston #334/R est:4000-6000
Works on paper
£276 $439 €400 Bateaux de peche en mer (24x33cm-9x13in) s. wash gouache. 4-Mar-3 Palais de Beaux Arts, Brussels #294

CLAYTON, Harold (1896-1979) British
£2200 $3630 €3190 Still life with roses (62x52cm-24x20in) s. 3-Jul-3 Christie's, Kensington #479/R est:2000-3000
£4000 $6200 €6000 Flowers in a vase (51x41cm-20x16in) prov. 4-Dec-2 Christie's, Kensington #465/R est:2000-2500
£4500 $6975 €6750 Still life roses, narcissi and polyanthus (35x29cm-14x11in) s. 4-Dec-2 Christie's, Kensington #461/R est:2500-3500
£4500 $7155 €6750 Still life of a vase of mixed summer flowers (30x25cm-12x10in) s. 29-Apr-3 Henry Adams, Chichester #308/R est:5000-7000
£5159 $8306 €7739 Flower piece (54x64cm-21x25in) s. prov. 12-May-3 Stephan Welz, Johannesburg #434/R est:60000-80000 (SA.R 60000)
£6000 $9360 €9000 Still life with roses, phlox and campanlas (46x41cm-18x16in) s. 27-Mar-3 Christie's, Kensington #528/R est:4000-6000
£6500 $10855 €9425 Summer fragrance (56x66cm-22x26in) s. prov. 24-Jun-3 Bonhams, New Bond Street #18/R est:7000-9000
£11000 $17050 €16500 Still life with summer roses in a glass vase (63x76cm-25x30in) s. prov. 3-Dec-2 Bonhams, New Bond Street #12/R est:6000-8000

CLAYTON, J Hughes (fl.1891-1929) British
Works on paper
£250 $393 €375 Coastal scene with two figures (24x49cm-9x19in) s. W/C. 21-Nov-2 Tennants, Leyburn #622
£250 $390 €375 Chequers Inn, Helmdon (27x39cm-11x15in) s. W/C. 6-Nov-2 Bonhams, Chester #338
£340 $530 €510 By the sunlit sea, Cemaes Bay, Anglesea (20x40cm-8x16in) s. s.i.verso W/C. 6-Nov-2 Bonhams, Chester #343
£360 $562 €540 Sailing boats off a rocky shore (18x26cm-7x10in) s. W/C. 11-Sep-2 Bonhams, Newport #224
£380 $623 €551 Thatched cottage and figure on lane, view of bay and fishing boats beyond (18x38cm-7x15in) s. W/C. 3-Jun-3 Capes Dunn, Manchester #40/R
£400 $668 €580 Towyn, River Conway (24x41cm-9x16in) s. W/C. 19-Jun-3 Clevedon Sale Rooms #156
£450 $734 €675 Old houses near Shottery (28x46cm-11x18in) s. W/C. 13-Feb-3 David Lay, Penzance #168
£450 $716 €675 Near Wesford, thatched cottage with figures, cattle and trees (28x43cm-11x17in) s. W/C dr. 18-Mar-3 Capes Dunn, Manchester #462/R
£500 $835 €725 Fisherfolk unloading boats on a beach (19x40cm-7x16in) s. W/C. 17-Jun-3 Anderson & Garland, Newcastle #284
£540 $842 €810 Fishing boats off the Anglesey Coast, probably Bay (35x55cm-14x22in) s. W/C pair. 6-Nov-2 Bonhams, Chester #342
£550 $897 €825 Anglesey coastal scene with boat and figures (28x46cm-11x18in) s. W/C. 28-Jan-3 Rogers Jones, Clwyd #115/R
£560 $874 €840 Shore scene with beached fishing boat and figures (32x53cm-13x21in) s. W/C. 23-Sep-2 Bonhams, Chester #871
£980 $1558 €1470 Country cottage near Camaes with figure on a lane (28x44cm-11x17in) s. W/C pair. 27-Feb-3 Bonhams, Chester #334/R
£1600 $2544 €2400 Shore scene with fisherfolk. Coastal scene with fishing boats (27x65cm-11x26in) s. W/C pair. 27-Feb-3 Bonhams, Chester #340 est:1000-1500
£4600 $7314 €6900 Girls collecting flowers, Cameaes Bay, Angelsey (58x109cm-23x43in) s.d.1900 W/C. 30-Apr-3 Halls, Shrewsbury #257/R est:4000-5000

CLAYTON, Matthew Thomas (1831-1922) New Zealander
£298 $465 €447 Barque in the southern ocean (44x90cm-17x35in) s.d.1919. 10-Nov-2 Dunbar Sloane, Auckland #9 (NZ.D 950)

CLAYTON, W J M (20th C) British
£400 $640 €600 Butch Cassidy (50x39cm-20x15in) s.d.1971. 13-May-3 Sotheby's, Olympia #94/R

CLAYTON, William J M (20th C) British
£600 $930 €900 Trompe l'oeil of theatre programme (46x36cm-18x14in) s.d.1975. 3-Dec-2 Bonhams, Knightsbridge #108/R

CLEALOR, W (19th C) Canadian?
£6140 $9149 €9210 Ship Bucephelus 1196 registor (61x91cm-24x36in) s.i. prov. 26-Jun-2 Iegor de Saint Hippolyte, Montreal #17/R (C.D 14000)

CLEARY, Manon (20th C) American
Works on paper
£692 $1100 €1038 Self portrait with Randy no.5 (66x94cm-26x37in) s.d.1978 graphite. 22-Mar-3 New Orleans Auction, New Orleans #1072/R est:600-900

CLEARY, Michael H (1930-) Canadian
Works on paper
£301 $473 €452 Morrison's shack (25x35cm-10x14in) s.d.1974 W/C prov. 25-Nov-2 Hodgins, Calgary #102/R (C.D 750)

CLEEMPUT, Jean van (1881-?) Belgian
£625 $994 €900 Pecheur (48x40cm-19x16in) s. canvas on panel. 30-Apr-3 Tajan, Paris #102

CLEENEWERCK, Henry (19th C) French
£1205 $2000 €1747 Cows grazing by a Sierra lake (18x34cm-7x13in) s. canvas on board prov. 11-Jun-3 Butterfields, San Francisco #4167/R est:3000-5000

CLEET, J (19th C) British
£2200 $3344 €3300 Paddle sloop HMS Bulldog in amongst Baltic Fleet (61x91cm-24x36in) s.i.d.1890. 15-Aug-2 Bonhams, New Bond Street #417/R est:1200-1800

CLEGG and GUTTMAN (20th C) American
Photographs
£3042 $4806 €4563 The cripple (231x167cm-91x66in) C-print on acrylic glass two parts. 28-Apr-3 Bukowskis, Stockholm #948/R est:35000-40000 (S.KR 40000)

CLELAND, Patricia (20th C) British?
£450 $698 €675 Sunflowers (61x61cm-24x24in) s.d.2002 verso board. 2-Oct-2 John Ross, Belfast #145
£500 $730 €750 Sunflowers (61x61cm-24x24in) s.d.2001 verso board. 12-Jun-2 John Ross, Belfast #301

CLELAND, Thomas Maitland (1880-1964) American
Works on paper
£764 $1200 €1146 Sport Phaeton (53x38cm-21x15in) s.i.d.1943 ink W/C. 20-Nov-2 Boos Gallery, Michigan #542

CLELLAND, Mary Alberta (1876-1919) Canadian
£261 $410 €392 Shoreline at sunset (25x28cm-10x11in) s. board. 25-Nov-2 Hodgins, Calgary #320/R (C.D 650)

CLEM, Robert Verity (20th C) American
Works on paper
£1302 $1900 €1953 Junco (26x20cm-10x8in) s.d.1956 W/C gouache graphite paperboard. 10-May-2 Skinner, Boston #139/R
£2707 $4250 €4061 Bluebirds (43x64cm-17x25in) s.d.1965 gouache. 22-Nov-2 Skinner, Boston #154/R est:4000-6000
£2812 $4500 €4077 Black bellied plovers (46x62cm-18x24in) s.d.1976 gouache. 16-May-3 Skinner, Boston #134/R est:5000-7000
£4110 $6000 €6165 Blue jay perched on an oak bough (57x44cm-22x17in) s.d.1956 W/C graphite gouache paperboard. 10-May-2 Skinner, Boston #141/R
£4687 $7500 €6796 Flock of eiders (40x74cm-16x29in) s.d.1971 W/C gouache. 16-May-3 Skinner, Boston #136/R est:5000-7000

CLEMENS, Curt (1911-1947) Swedish
£760 $1202 €1140 Autumn in the town (67x93cm-26x37in) s.d.1940. 28-Apr-3 Bukowskis, Stockholm #77/R (S.KR 10000)
£2934 $4724 €4401 Boy sitting in flowering summer meadow - the artist's son Lennart (55x90cm-22x35in) s.d.1944. 7-May-3 AB Stockholms Auktionsverk #768/R est:30000-35000 (S.KR 38000)

CLEMENS, G A (1870-1918) Danish
£300 $468 €450 A poodle (27x26cm-11x10in) init.d.1910. 11-Nov-2 Rasmussen, Vejle #515 (D.KR 3500)
£426 $672 €639 Road through the dunes near Tannishus (33x65cm-13x26in) s.i.d.1937. 2-Dec-2 Rasmussen, Copenhagen #1310/R (D.KR 5000)
£652 $1036 €978 Interior scene with lady sewing (57x45cm-22x18in) s. 10-Mar-3 Rasmussen, Vejle #19/R (D.KR 7000)

CLEMENS, Paul Lewis (1911-1992) American
£2229 $3500 €3344 Woman reading a letter in a garden (46x38cm-18x15in) s. prov. 19-Nov-2 Butterfields, San Francisco #8347/R est:3000-5000

CLEMENT, A (20th C) French
£818 $1292 €1227 Landscape with cattle and donkey (60x74cm-24x29in) indis sig. 5-Apr-3 Rasmussen, Havnen #2159/R (D.KR 8800)

CLEMENT, Alain (1941-) French
£2564 $3744 €4000 Composition (122x94cm-48x37in) s.i.d.98 verso. 4-Jun-2 Karl & Faber, Munich #205/R est:4500

CLEMENT, Felix Auguste (1826-1888) French
£113904 $186803 €165161 Odalisque (120x197cm-47x78in) s.i.d.1858. 4-Jun-3 AB Stockholms Auktionsverk #2406/R est:200000-300000 (S.KR 1450000)

CLEMENT, Max (20th C) Swiss
£415 $647 €623 Black Forest landscape (22x60cm-9x24in) s. i.d.1973 verso masonite. 6-Nov-2 Dobiaschofsky, Bern #411/R (S.FR 950)

CLEMENT, Therese (1889-1984) French
£256 $403 €400 Dans les souks (8x13cm-3x5in) s. panel. 21-Nov-2 Neret-Minet, Paris #48
£417 $654 €650 Port du Nord (60x73cm-24x29in) s. 21-Nov-2 Neret-Minet, Paris #43
£449 $704 €700 Carriole sous la pluie (50x61cm-20x24in) s. 21-Nov-2 Neret-Minet, Paris #44
£577 $906 €900 Canal a Venise (46x38cm-18x15in) s. 21-Nov-2 Neret-Minet, Paris #45
£962 $1510 €1500 Sierra Nevada (96x135cm-38x53in) s. 21-Nov-2 Neret-Minet, Paris #42

CLEMENTE PEREZ, Salvador (1859-1909) Spanish
£285 $450 €428 Covered wagon, Seville (10x18cm-4x7in) init.i. panel. 2-Apr-3 Doyle, New York #53/R

CLEMENTE, Francesco (1952-) Italian
£12658 $20000 €18987 Untitled (38x57cm-15x22in) gouache exec.1982 prov. 13-Nov-2 Sotheby's, New York #529/R est:25000-35000
£60000 $92400 €90000 Untitled (199x238cm-78x94in) painted 1983 prov.lit. 22-Oct-2 Christie's, London #54/R est:60000-80000
Works on paper
£1600 $2624 €2400 Oil slick an abstract (71x97cm-28x38in) i.verso W/C. 5-Feb-3 John Nicholson, Haslemere #1055 est:1000-1500
£3125 $5000 €4688 Nameless (61x46cm-24x18in) pastel executed 1980 prov.exhib. 14-May-3 Sotheby's, New York #421/R est:6000-8000
£4688 $7500 €7032 Astronomy (67x48cm-26x19in) s.i.verso col chk executed 1994-95 prov.exhib. 15-May-3 Christie's, Rockefeller NY #382/R est:15000-20000
£7000 $11690 €10150 My lover (67x48cm-26x19in) s.i.d.1994 verso pastel prov. 27-Jun-3 Christie's, London #175/R est:8000-12000
£7595 $12000 €11393 Weight of water (61x46cm-24x18in) pastel exec.1981 prov.exhib.lit. 13-Nov-2 Sotheby's, New York #523/R est:8000-12000
£7800 $13026 €11310 Untitled (66x48cm-26x19in) s.d.MCMLXXXVI verso prov. 26-Jun-3 Sotheby's, London #264/R est:7000-10000
£8750 $14000 €13125 Two (67x48cm-26x19in) col chk executed 1994 prov.exhib. 15-May-3 Christie's, Rockefeller NY #386/R est:15000-20000
£8750 $14000 €13125 Lover's wing (36x51cm-14x20in) s.i.d.1996 verso W/C prov.exhib. 14-May-3 Sotheby's, New York #424/R est:12000-18000
£11250 $18000 €16875 Body (67x48cm-26x19in) s.i.d.1994 verso col chk prov.exhib. 15-May-3 Christie's, Rockefeller NY #384/R est:15000-20000
£12500 $20000 €18750 Flying (67x48cm-26x19in) s.i.d.1994-95 col chk prov.exhib. 15-May-3 Christie's, Rockefeller NY #383/R est:15000-20000
£12500 $20000 €18750 Tree (67x48cm-26x19in) s.i.verso col chk executed 1994-95 prov.exhib. 15-May-3 Christie's, Rockefeller NY #385/R est:15000-20000
£15000 $24600 €22500 Fifty-one days on a mountain (54x71cm-21x28in) W/C prov. 6-Feb-3 Christie's, London #655/R est:8000-12000
£16000 $26720 €23200 Untitled - self portrait (46x61cm-18x24in) s.d.1990 verso W/C prov.exhib. 27-Jun-3 Christie's, London #186/R est:15000-20000
£17500 $28000 €26250 Unstained hill (67x48cm-26x19in) s.i.d.1988 verso pastel prov.exhib.lit. 16-May-3 Phillips, New York #164/R est:25000-35000
£18000 $30060 €26100 Men and women no.12 (108x51cm-43x20in) W/C pastel on three sheets prov.exhib. 27-Jun-3 Christie's, London #174/R est:12000-18000
£38462 $60000 €57693 Untitled (238x330cm-94x130in) gouache paper on canvas executed 1985 prov.lit. 11-Nov-2 Phillips, New York #40/R est:90000-120000

CLEMENTI, Maria Giovanna (1690-1761) Italian
£8974 $14179 €14000 Girl and her page. s.d.1725. 15-Nov-2 Beaussant & Lefèvre, Paris #38/R est:10000-12000

CLEMENTS, Grace (1905-1969) American
£548 $850 €822 Tea lady (61x51cm-24x20in) s.d. painted c.1948. 8-Dec-2 Toomey, Oak Park #814/R
£4459 $7000 €6689 Warehouse district (72x87cm-28x34in) s.d.31 s.i.stretcher prov.exhib. 20-Nov-2 Christie's, Los Angeles #119/R est:8000-12000

CLEMENTZ, Hermann (1852-?) German
£6452 $10000 €9678 Feeble dismissal (56x75cm-22x30in) s.d.77. 30-Oct-2 Christie's, Rockefeller NY #150/R est:15000-20000

CLEMINSON, J (19/20th) British?
£1494 $2225 €2300 Saddled horses in paddock (51x61cm-20x24in) s. 28-Jun-2 Woodwards, Cork #201/R

CLEMINSON, R (19th C) British
£700 $1085 €1050 Spaniel amongst reeds and rushes flushing out ducks (29x40cm-11x16in) s. 25-Sep-2 Wintertons, Lichfield #562/R

CLEMINSON, Robert (19th C) British
£750 $1155 €1125 Otter with a salmon. Otter bringing salmon to its young (51x76cm-20x30in) one s. pair. 5-Sep-2 Christie's, Kensington #264/R
£820 $1263 €1230 Highland deer (75x61cm-30x24in) s. 23-Oct-2 Hampton & Littlewood, Exeter #461

£850 $1343 €1275 Setters retrieving partridges (41x61cm-16x24in) s. 28-Nov-2 Christie's, Kensington #348/R

£950 $1473 €1425 Study of a terrier dog (74x64cm-29x25in) s. 26-Sep-2 Lane, Penzance #85/R

£950 $1558 €1425 Gundogs with dead game in a highland landscape. Deer (69x90cm-27x35in) s. pair. 3-Jun-3 Bonhams, Oxford #60

£2083 $3000 €3125 Resting after the hunt. Waiting for master (59x49cm-23x19in) pair. 15-Jan-3 Christie's, Rockefeller NY #162/R

CLEMINSON, Robert (attrib) (19th C) British

£2000 $3160 €3000 Setters on a moor (71x96cm-28x38in) 28-Nov-2 Christie's, Kensington #351/R

CLEMMER, John (1921-) American

Works on paper

£1026 $1600 €1539 View from Fermo (66x81cm-26x32in) s. W/C gouache. 12-Oct-2 Neal Auction Company, New Orleans #664 est:1000-1500

CLENNELL, Luke (1781-1840) British

Works on paper

£440 $691 €660 Low tide on the river, probably the Thames (11x21cm-4x8in) W/C. 16-Dec-2 Bonhams, Bury St Edmunds #378/R

£600 $930 €900 Fisher folk in a bay beneath cliffs with castle and houses (32x52cm-13x20in) W/C. 25-Sep-2 John Nicholson, Haslemere #910/R

CLEOPAS, Olav (?) ?

£780 $1303 €1100 Nature morte aux cruches en gres. (50x64cm-20x25in) 23-Jun-3 Amberes, Antwerp #77

£1560 $2606 €2200 Nature morte aux cruches en gres (50x64cm-20x25in) 23-Jun-3 Amberes, Antwerp #78

CLERC, Jean le (attrib) (1587-c.1633) French

£5500 $9185 €7975 Two young men playing tric-trac, lady and bearded looking on (22x17cm-9x7in) copper. 9-Jul-3 Bonhams, New Bond Street #19/R est:5000-7000

CLERC, Philippe le (1755-1826) German

Works on paper

£540 $837 €810 Andromaque and Astyanax (22x16cm-9x6in) pen ink sold with another by different hand. 9-Dec-2 Bonhams, New Bond Street #51/R

CLERC, Pierre Thomas le (1740-?) French

Works on paper

£1899 $3000 €3000 Elegant en redingote bleue dans un paysage. Elegant portant l'epee (25x18cm-10x7in) pen brown ink W/C pair prov. 27-Nov-2 Christie's, Paris #217/R est:3000-5000

CLERCK, Hendrick de (1570-1629) Flemish

£29268 $48000 €43902 Continence of Scipio (156x260cm-61x102in) 30-May-3 Christie's, Rockefeller NY #11/R est:50000-70000

CLERCK, Hendrick de (attrib) (1570-1629) Flemish

£12414 $19614 €18000 Holy Family with Saint John (151x112cm-59x44in) 5-Apr-3 Finarte Semenzato, Milan #129/R est:25000

CLERCK, Hendrick de (circle) (1570-1629) Flemish

£6000 $10020 €8700 Charity (54x41cm-21x16in) panel. 11-Jul-3 Christie's, Kensington #10/R est:2000-3000

CLERCK, Hendrick de (style) (1570-1629) Flemish

£8511 $14214 €12000 Le banquet des dieux (46x55cm-18x22in) 18-Jun-3 Tajan, Paris #66/R est:8000-10000

CLERCK, Jan de (1881-1962) Belgian

Works on paper

£822 $1282 €1200 Vue de la mer du Nord (48x69cm-19x27in) s. pastel. 14-Apr-3 Horta, Bruxelles #130

CLERCQ, Alphonse de (1868-1945) Belgian

£298 $486 €450 Beguinage dans l'hiver (68x49cm-27x19in) 17-Feb-3 Amberes, Antwerp #185

£468 $748 €650 L'allee a Bornem (100x130cm-39x51in) s. 19-May-3 Horta, Bruxelles #26

£690 $1103 €1000 L'allee a Bornem (100x130cm-39x51in) s. 17-Mar-3 Horta, Bruxelles #71

£1126 $1835 €1700 Pecheur dans un paysage lacustre au coucher du soleil (65x99cm-26x39in) 17-Feb-3 Amberes, Antwerp #186/R

£1418 $2369 €2000 Barques de peche dans un paysage fluvial (100x150cm-39x59in) 23-Jun-3 Amberes, Antwerp #86

CLERCQ, P de (19th C) Belgian?

£3623 $5942 €5000 Gibier sur une table partiellement drapee (100x148cm-39x58in) s.d.1854. 27-May-3 Palais de Beaux Arts, Brussels #434/R est:5000-7500

CLERCQ, Pieter Jan de (1891-1964) Belgian

£346 $533 €550 Concarneau (44x59cm-17x23in) s. panel. 22-Oct-2 Campo & Campo, Antwerp #64

£380 $592 €600 Fisherman at the quay (50x60cm-20x24in) s. 21-Oct-2 Bernaerts, Antwerp #13/R

£696 $1086 €1100 Vue hivernale sur l'Escaut (73x83cm-29x33in) 16-Sep-2 Amberes, Antwerp #187

CLERGET, Hubert (1818-1899) French

Works on paper

£3165 $5000 €5000 Hotel Continental a Paris. W/C crayon pen set of 10. 28-Nov-2 Tajan, Paris #153/R est:1500

£3165 $5000 €5000 Hotel de la Legion d'Honneur. crayon W/C wash set of 5. 28-Nov-2 Tajan, Paris #147/R

CLERICI, Fabrizio (1913-1993) Italian

£7742 $12232 €12000 Untitled (100x150cm-39x59in) s. 18-Dec-2 Christie's, Rome #245/R

Works on paper

£833 $1317 €1300 Artist (53x40cm-21x16in) mixed media. 12-Nov-2 Babuino, Rome #307/R

£897 $1409 €1400 Eye (50x60cm-20x24in) s. mixed media card exec.1985. 23-Nov-2 Meeting Art, Vercelli #286/R

CLERISSEAU, Charles Louis (1721-1820) French

Works on paper

£570 $900 €900 Projet pour un plafond a caisson (36x45cm-14x18in) i.verso black chk pen black ink grey wash. 27-Nov-2 Christie's, Paris #183/R

CLERISSEAU, Charles Louis (attrib) (1721-1820) French

£4545 $7591 €6500 Personnages dans un paysage de ruines (47x60cm-19x24in) 25-Jun-3 Sotheby's, Paris #28/R est:7000-10000

Works on paper

£676 $1054 €1000 Fantaisie architecturale (18cm-7in circular) pen ink wash. 31-Mar-3 Piasa, Paris #34

£1948 $3000 €2922 Ruined classical villa with figures dancing (597x483cm-235x190in) bodycol. 4-Sep-2 Christie's, Rockefeller NY #272/R est:3000-4000

£3228 $5100 €5100 Capriccio with classic Roman memorials (61x43cm-24x17in) W/C pen. 29-Nov-2 Bassenge, Berlin #5613/R est:7500

CLERK, A de (?) ?

£950 $1539 €1425 Danish topsail schooner Valborg of Viele off the Noord Hinder lightship (63x96cm-25x38in) i. 21-May-3 Christie's, Kensington #642/R

Works on paper

£300 $465 €450 Topsil schooner Fairy King of Padstow in Belgian waters (58x93cm-23x37in) i. W/C bodycol. 31-Oct-2 Christie's, Kensington #363a/R

£650 $1053 €975 Barquentine Gladstone off a lighthouse with the Deal pilot astern (51x70cm-20x28in) i. W/C bodycol. 21-May-3 Christie's, Kensington #647/R

CLERK, Pierre Jean (1928-) Canadian

£205 $318 €308 Composition (66x76cm-26x30in) s.d.63 prov. 24-Sep-2 Ritchie, Toronto #3201/R (C.D 500)

CLERK, William F (19th C) American

£854 $1400 €1281 Waterfall (30x46cm-12x18in) s.d.1880 canvas on masonite. 8-Feb-3 Neal Auction Company, New Orleans #920 est:1000-2500

CLESINGER, J B (1814-1883) French

Sculpture

£1450 $2248 €2175 Classical woman in flowering robes with lyre (27cm-11in) s. bronze Cast.Barbedienne Fondeur. 30-Oct-2 Mallams, Oxford #588/R

CLESINGER, Jean Baptiste (1814-1883) French
£1410 $2228 €2200 Paysage d'Italie (12x48cm-5x19in) init.d. panel. 18-Nov-2 Tajan, Paris #109/R est:2400-2600
£1539 $2431 €2400 Soir sur les ruines de Prima Porta (19x46cm-7x18in) s. panel. 18-Nov-2 Tajan, Paris #110 est:2400-2600

CLESSE, Louis (1889-1961) Belgian
£316 $494 €500 Trompe l'oeil au perdreau (39x29cm-15x11in) s. panel. 15-Oct-2 Horta, Bruxelles #23
£321 $503 €500 Nature morte (48x38cm-19x15in) s. panel. 10-Dec-2 Campo, Vlaamse Kaai #76
£345 $552 €500 Boathouse (30x39cm-12x15in) s. panel. 15-Mar-3 De Vuyst, Lokeren #60
£440 $678 €700 Fermette (30x45cm-12x18in) s. 22-Oct-2 Campo & Campo, Antwerp #41
£503 $785 €800 Voliers a lestacade (54x64cm-21x25in) board. 14-Oct-2 Amberes, Antwerp #139
£535 $829 €850 Bridge near Bruges (55x65cm-22x26in) st.sig. panel. 5-Oct-2 De Vuyst, Lokeren #63
£633 $987 €1000 Petit pont (36x49cm-14x19in) s. panel. 21-Oct-2 Bernaerts, Antwerp #512/R
£696 $1086 €1100 Vase fleuri de roses (48x39cm-19x15in) s.d.1947 panel. 15-Oct-2 Horta, Bruxelles #22
£759 $1200 €1200 Bord d'etang en automne (45x65cm-18x26in) s. panel. 26-Nov-2 Palais de Beaux Arts, Brussels #59/R
£795 $1295 €1200 Passerelle sur la riviere (67x86cm-26x34in) s. panel. 17-Feb-3 Horta, Bruxelles #46
£823 $1284 €1300 Village au bord de l'eau (40x50cm-16x20in) s. panel. 21-Oct-2 Bernaerts, Antwerp #513/R
£897 $1391 €1400 Fermette a Oudenburg (40x50cm-16x20in) s.d.1938 panel. 9-Dec-2 Horta, Bruxelles #349
£1020 $1622 €1500 Still life with fruit and flowers (70x75cm-28x30in) s.d.1938 panel. 24-Mar-3 Bernaerts, Antwerp #640/R est:2000-3000
£1139 $1777 €1800 Etang en automne (75x100cm-30x39in) s.d.1934. 15-Oct-2 Horta, Bruxelles #21
£1203 $1876 €1900 Fermette au bord de cours d'eau (71x76cm-28x30in) s.d.1932 panel. 16-Sep-2 Horta, Bruxelles #68
£4138 $6538 €6000 Facade de la vieille maison d'Oudenburg (45x65cm-18x26in) s. panel. 2-Apr-3 Vanderkindere, Brussels #321/R est:700-1200
Works on paper
£544 $865 €800 Chemin de campagne par temps de pluie (66x78cm-26x31in) s. W/C. 18-Mar-3 Campo, Vlaamse Kaai #26/R

CLEVE, Corneille van (1645-1735) French
Sculpture
£8000 $13360 €11600 Three adorned putti (40cm-16in) i.d.1705 terracotta. 8-Jul-3 Sotheby's, London #136/R est:8000-12000

CLEVE, Hendrick van III (attrib) (1525-1589) Flemish
£90000 $141300 €135000 Tower of Babel (74x107cm-29x42in) panel prov.lit. 12-Dec-2 Sotheby's, London #1/R est:40000-60000

CLEVE, Hendrick van III (studio) (1525-1589) Flemish
£20000 $31400 €30000 Tower of Babel (49x70cm-19x28in) panel. 12-Dec-2 Sotheby's, London #126/R est:10000-15000

CLEVE, Joos van (1485-1540) Dutch
£42000 $70140 €60900 Virgin and Child (81x56cm-32x22in) panel prov.lit. 9-Jul-3 Christie's, London #16/R est:15000-20000
£140000 $219800 €210000 Madonna of the cherries (71x51cm-28x20in) panel painted with studio prov.exhib.lit. 16-Dec-2 Sotheby's, London #27/R est:150000-200000

CLEVE, Marten van (1527-1581) Flemish
£16975 $27500 €25463 Wedding procession (43x79cm-17x31in) panel prov. 23-Jan-3 Sotheby's, New York #250/R est:30000
£29032 $45871 €45000 Gluttony (95x77cm-37x30in) board. 18-Dec-2 Ansorena, Madrid #87/R est:45000
£29487 $46590 €46000 Market (104x232cm-41x91in) prov. 16-Nov-2 Lempertz, Koln #1016/R est:35000
£40000 $66800 €58000 Interior, mother and father visiting their child in the house of a wet-nurse (73x102cm-29x40in) oak panel prov. 10-Jul-3 Sotheby's, London #114/R est:30000-40000

CLEVE, Marten van (circle) (1527-1581) Flemish
£5850 $9302 €8600 Kitchen scene (91x117cm-36x46in) indis.sig. 26-Feb-3 Marc Kohn, Paris #3/R est:12000
£67308 $104327 €105000 Farmer's feast in the barn (72x105cm-28x41in) mono. panel. 4-Dec-2 Neumeister, Munich #586/R est:8000

CLEVE, Marten van (style) (1527-1581) Flemish
£6500 $10205 €9750 Kings drinks (71x104cm-28x41in) panel. 10-Dec-2 Sotheby's, Olympia #329a/R est:5000-7000
£6690 $11106 €9500 The fat kitchen (56x75cm-22x30in) 11-Jun-3 Dorotheum, Vienna #301/R est:2000-3000
£11000 $17270 €16500 Peasants feasting and making music in an inn (21x28cm-8x11in) panel. 13-Dec-2 Christie's, Kensington #6/R est:6000-8000

CLEVE-JONAND, Agnes (1876-1951) Swedish
£931 $1508 €1350 Southern garden scene (31x36cm-12x14in) s.d.27 glass prov. 25-May-3 Uppsala Auktionskammare, Uppsala #221/R (S.KR 12000)
£1051 $1640 €1577 The old ferry station, Kallviken, Dragsmark (49x62cm-19x24in) s.d.44 canvas on panel. 5-Nov-2 Bukowskis, Stockholm #65/R est:15000-20000 (S.KR 15000)
£1081 $1741 €1622 Woman with red hairband (41x37cm-16x15in) s.d.14. 7-May-3 AB Stockholms Auktionsverk #869/R est:20000-25000 (S.KR 14000)
£1141 $1802 €1712 Still life of flowers in vase (56x47cm-22x19in) s. 28-Apr-3 Bukowskis, Stockholm #24/R est:20000-25000 (S.KR 15000)
£1236 $2051 €1792 Nude (71x55cm-28x22in) s. 16-Jun-3 Lilla Bukowskis, Stockholm #150 est:10000-12000 (S.KR 16000)
£1612 $2514 €2418 From Strommarna, Bohuslan (52x54cm-20x21in) s.d.30. 5-Nov-2 Bukowskis, Stockholm #91/R est:35000-40000 (S.KR 23000)
£1892 $2952 €2838 Spring in Bohuslan (64x49cm-25x19in) s.d.29 panel. 5-Nov-2 Bukowskis, Stockholm #92/R est:25000-30000 (S.KR 27000)
£2523 $3936 €3785 Red twilight and sailing boat (59x47cm-23x19in) s.d.39 panel. 5-Nov-2 Bukowskis, Stockholm #198/R est:25000-30000 (S.KR 36000)
£3083 $4810 €4625 The harbour (52x64cm-20x25in) s. 5-Nov-2 Bukowskis, Stockholm #58/R est:30000-35000 (S.KR 44000)
£5792 $9324 €8688 The steam launch - view from a coastal town (82x61cm-32x24in) s. panel. 7-May-3 AB Stockholms Auktionsverk #701/R est:70000-80000 (S.KR 75000)
Works on paper
£1369 $2163 €2054 View from Stockholm (42x53cm-17x21in) s.d.29 W/C. 28-Apr-3 Bukowskis, Stockholm #155/R est:25000-30000 (S.KR 18000)
£1483 $2343 €2225 Out walking, Paris (38x36cm-15x14in) s.i.d.23 chk. 28-Apr-3 Bukowskis, Stockholm #53/R est:12000-15000 (S.KR 19500)
£1822 $2842 €2733 New York (49x64cm-19x25in) s.d.36 gouache. 6-Nov-2 AB Stockholms Auktionsverk #570/R est:35000-40000 (S.KR 26000)
£2281 $3605 €3422 New York (52x67cm-20x26in) s.i.d.36 mixed media. 28-Apr-3 Bukowskis, Stockholm #46/R est:30000-35000 (S.KR 30000)

CLEVELAND, William (1777-1845) American
£1974 $3000 €2961 Ship portrait (56x71cm-22x28in) s.d.1843 oil on sailcloth. 30-Aug-2 Thomaston Place, Thomaston #10

CLEVELEY, John (jnr) (1747-1786) British
Works on paper
£6500 $10530 €9750 HMS Carcass with the young Nelson aboard and another vessel (36x45cm-14x18in) s.i. pencil pen grey ink W/C. 21-May-3 Christie's, Kensington #359/R est:2000-3000

CLEVELEY, John (snr-attrib) (?-1792) British
Works on paper
£300 $486 €450 Execution of Admiral John Byng (7x12cm-3x5in) pencil pen grey ink wash. 21-May-3 Christie's, Kensington #355/R

CLEVELEY, Robert (1747-1809) British
Works on paper
£380 $593 €570 Royal Yacht with the Royal Barge with numerous boats (11x17cm-4x7in) s. W/C. 9-Oct-2 Woolley & Wallis, Salisbury #55/R

CLEVENBERGH, Antoine (1755-1810) Flemish
£3928 $6441 €5696 Hunting still life with hare and birds (62x51cm-24x20in) s. panel. 4-Jun-3 AB Stockholms Auktionsverk #2541/R est:60000-80000 (S.KR 50000)

CLEVENBERGH, Charles-Antoine (c.1791-?) Flemish
£1064 $1777 €1500 Lievre dans un paysage (84x72cm-33x28in) s.d.1836. 17-Jun-3 Palais de Beaux Arts, Brussels #522 est:800-1200

CLIFFORD, Charles (c.1819-1863) American
Photographs
£1923 $3038 €3000 Temple dy Cayo Julio Lacer (40x31cm-16x12in) st.sig. albumin print. 16-Nov-2 Christie's, Paris #113/R est:2000-2500
£6000 $9720 €9000 Oviedo (43x33cm-17x13in) i.mount num.A 14 verso albumen print exec.c.1860. 21-May-3 Christie's, London #78/R est:1500-2000

CLIFFORD, Edward C (1858-1910) British
Works on paper
£550 $836 €825 View of cottages and distant town from a poppy field (50x33cm-20x13in) s. W/C. 15-Aug-2 Rupert Toovey, Partridge Green #1420/R

CLIFFORD, Henry Charles (1861-?) British
Works on paper
£450 $752 €653 Beached boats at Whitby (33x48cm-13x19in) s.d.06 W/C. 20-Jun-3 Keys, Aylsham #515

CLIFTON, Hewitt (19th C) British?
Works on paper
£700 $1092 €1050 Fairy Glen, Bettesy-Coed. Penrhyn, Wales (61x48cm-24x19in) s.d.1879 W/C pair. 18-Oct-2 Keys, Aylsham #659/R

CLIME, Winfield Scott (1881-1958) American
£1006 $1600 €1509 Near Issoudun, France (17x24cm-7x9in) mono.d.1918 i.verso board. 7-Mar-3 Skinner, Boston #523/R est:300-500
£1379 $2000 €2069 Old homestead, Old Lyme (51x61cm-20x24in) 1-Jun-2 Russ Antiques, Waterford #150
£2138 $3100 €3207 Monhegan Island (64x76cm-25x30in) 1-Jun-2 Russ Antiques, Waterford #149
Works on paper
£1103 $1600 €1655 Library Lane, Old Lyme (36x38cm-14x15in) W/C. 1-Jun-2 Russ Antiques, Waterford #18

CLINEDINST, Benjamin West (1860-1931) American
£1751 $2750 €2627 Summer landscape (30x23cm-12x9in) init.d.1908 panel prov. 19-Nov-2 Butterfields, San Francisco #8052/R est:2000-3000
Works on paper
£288 $450 €432 Getting grandma's pension. gouache. 21-Sep-2 Harvey Clar, Oakland #1464

CLINT, Alfred (attrib) (1807-1883) British
£570 $900 €855 Sailboats by the shore (41x56cm-16x22in) 17-Nov-2 CRN Auctions, Cambridge #54/R

CLINTON, F (19th C) British?
£1100 $1804 €1650 Fisherman's cottages on a coastline. Beach scene with village beyond (51x76cm-20x30in) s. pair. 29-May-3 Christie's, Kensington #200/R est:1000-1500

CLOAR, Carroll (1913-1993) American
£8805 $14000 €13208 Good Friday (51x63cm-20x25in) s. tempera on board prov.exhib. 4-Mar-3 Christie's, Rockefeller NY #112/R est:5000-7000

CLODION (1738-1814) French
Sculpture
£1027 $1603 €1500 Classical scene (63cm-25in) bronze. 8-Apr-3 Ansorena, Madrid #937/R
£1486 $2319 €2200 Satyre feminine aux enfants (49cm-19in) s. bronze. 25-Mar-3 Campo & Campo, Antwerp #34/R est:1800-2200
£1583 $2532 €2200 Pair of dancing Menads with Pan (41cm-16in) s. bronze. 17-May-3 Hagelstam, Helsinki #448/R est:2000
£2532 $4000 €3798 Group of la famille (68cm-27in) i. bronze on marble plinth. 24-Apr-3 Christie's, Rockefeller NY #221/R est:4000-6000
£2593 $3681 €4200 Libations de Bacchus (53cm-21in) s. brown pat bronze. 16-Mar-3 Eric Pillon, Calais #58/R
£3445 $5478 €5168 Bacchante and pan dancing (59cm-23in) s.i. gilded bronze. 10-Mar-3 Rasmussen, Vejle #1192/R est:30000 (D.KR 37000)
£4218 $6706 €6200 Bacchanal (59cm-23in) s. fire gilt bronze marble socle lit. 24-Mar-3 Bernaerts, Antwerp #109/R est:5000-6000
£4225 $6803 €6000 Two young women and a child (66cm-26in) s. brown pat bronze. 12-May-3 Bernaerts, Antwerp #56/R est:7000-8000
£5170 $8220 €7600 Bacchanal (78cm-31in) s. fire gilt bronze Cast.Raingo F lit. 24-Mar-3 Bernaerts, Antwerp #111/R est:5000-6000
£173077 $268269 €270000 Caton (39x10x10cm-15x4x4in) s. terracotta exec.1804 prov.lit. 9-Dec-2 Rabourdin & Choppin de Janvry, Paris #99/R

CLODION (after) (1738-1814) French
Sculpture
£5449 $8446 €8500 Satyresse tendant une grappe a un satyre enfant (28x17x20cm-11x7x8in) s. terracotta prov.lit. 9-Dec-2 Rabourdin & Choppin de Janvry, Paris #101/R est:9000
£6410 $9936 €10000 Bacchanale (28x61cm-11x24in) s. terracotta relief. 9-Dec-2 Rabourdin & Choppin de Janvry, Paris #102/R est:4500

CLODION (attrib) (1738-1814) French
Works on paper
£321 $497 €500 Study for relief with ancient gods (30x45cm-12x18in) sanguine dr. 4-Dec-2 Libert, Castor, Paris #17
£837 $1222 €1256 Neriade with Delphin (23x26cm-9x10in) chk htd white. 17-Jun-2 Philippe Schuler, Zurich #4789 (S.FR 1900)

CLOKE, Rene (20th C) ?
Works on paper
£1000 $1540 €1500 Goblin market (25x32cm-10x13in) s. W/C. 23-Oct-2 Hamptons Fine Art, Godalming #61/R est:1000-1500

CLOSE, Chuck (1940-) American
£812500 $1300000 €1218750 Cindy II (183x152cm-72x60in) s.i.d.1988 verso prov.exhib.lit. 14-May-3 Christie's, Rockefeller NY #15/R est:1200000-1600000
Photographs
£6329 $10000 €9494 Jasper (75x56cm-30x22in) s.d.1997 polaroid prov. 13-Nov-2 Sotheby's, New York #263/R est:15000-20000
£12658 $20000 €18987 Self portrait (71x57cm-28x22in) s.i.d.1991 polaroid photo oil ink masking tape prov.exhib.lit. 14-Nov-2 Christie's, Rockefeller NY #462/R est:30000-40000
£16456 $26000 €24684 Nat (54x268cm-21x106in) s.i. dye transfer col ink set of five executed 1971 prov. 14-Nov-2 Christie's, Rockefeller NY #461/R est:40000-60000
Prints
£1887 $3000 €2831 Self portrait (17x12cm-7x5in) s.d.num.11/70aquatint. 2-May-3 Sotheby's, New York #417/R est:2000-3000
£1935 $3000 €2903 Phil spit bite (71x51cm-28x20in) s.d.1995 num.45/60 spitbite aquatint. 25-Sep-2 Christie's, Rockefeller NY #256/R est:2500-3500
£2013 $3200 €3020 Lucas (37x32cm-15x13in) s.d.num.14/50 sepia linoleum cut. 2-May-3 Sotheby's, New York #416/R est:2500-3500
£2516 $4000 €3774 Leslie (62x54cm-24x21in) s.i.d.num.71/150 col woodcut. 2-May-3 Sotheby's, New York #415/R est:3000-4000
£2642 $4200 €3963 Self portrait, spitbite/white on black (53x40cm-21x16in) s.d.num.15/50 black aquatint. 2-May-3 Sotheby's, New York #418/R est:3000-4000
£3145 $5000 €4718 Robert I (64x49cm-25x19in) s.d.num.18/20 col handmade pressed paper pulp. 2-May-3 Sotheby's, New York #414/R est:3000-4000
£4088 $6500 €6132 Keith II, white (86x68cm-34x27in) s.d.num.2/20 col handmade pressed paper pulp. 2-May-3 Sotheby's, New York #413/R est:4000-6000
£7692 $12000 €11538 Alex/reduction print (176x153cm-69x60in) s.d.num.AP AA/XV screenprint carved linoleum edition of 35. 5-Nov-2 Christie's, Rockefeller NY #362/R est:15000-20000
Works on paper
£5414 $8500 €8121 Robert manipulated (85x67cm-33x26in) s.d.1982 num.11/25 col paper pulp. 21-Nov-2 Swann Galleries, New York #29/R est:5000-8000
£43750 $70000 €65625 Keith/random fingerprint (76x57cm-30x22in) s.i.d.1980 stamp pad ink prov. 15-May-3 Christie's, Rockefeller NY #334/R est:70000-90000

CLOSS, Gustav Paul (1840-1870) German
£1266 $2000 €2000 Autumnal forest landscape by moonlight (73x59cm-29x23in) s. canvas on canvas. 30-Nov-2 Berlinghof, Heidelberg #303/R est:2500
£2564 $3974 €4000 Sunlit ruins of Reussenstein (61x51cm-24x20in) s.d.1861. 5-Dec-2 Dr Fritz Nagel, Stuttgart #645/R est:3800

CLOSTERMAN, Johann Baptist (1660-1713) German
£2800 $4452 €4200 Portrait of a gentleman, probably Sir Henry Monson (123x99cm-48x39in) prov. 19-Mar-3 Sotheby's, London #34/R est:3000-4000
£6500 $10335 €9750 Portrait of Margaret Watson, Lady Monson (122x99cm-48x39in) prov. 19-Mar-3 Sotheby's, London #35/R est:3000-4000
£9000 $14310 €13500 Portrait of Hon George Monson (124x100cm-49x39in) prov. 19-Mar-3 Sotheby's, London #36/R est:3000-4000

CLOUARD, Albert (1866-1952) French
£269 $423 €420 Nature morte a la bouteille (10x16cm-4x6in) cardboard. 15-Dec-2 Thierry & Lannon, Brest #369
£1824 $2827 €2900 Jeune femme nue surprise dans son bain (26x40cm-10x16in) panel. 6-Oct-2 Livinec, Gaudcheau & Jezequel, Rennes #53/R

CLOUET, François (circle) (1522-1572) French
£16084 $26860 €23000 Portrait presume de Martin du Hardaz (27x20cm-11x8in) panel oval. 27-Jun-3 Piasa, Paris #66/R est:20000-25000

CLOUET, François (studio) (1522-1572) French
£5063 $8000 €8000 Portrait presume du Vicomte Sebastien de Luxembourg (31x23cm-12x9in) i. panel prov. 27-Nov-2 Christie's, Paris #32/R est:8000-12000

CLOUGH, George L (1824-1901) American
£1266 $2000 €1836 Trapper's camp (36x46cm-14x18in) s. 26-Jul-3 Coeur d'Alene, Hayden #238/R est:2000-3000

CLOUGH, Prunella (1919-2000) British
£9000 $14760 €13500 Industrial landscape (24x21cm-9x8in) s. board prov.exhib. 6-Jun-3 Christie's, London #188/R est:5000-8000
£32000 $52480 €46400 Lorry with ladder (87x65cm-34x26in) s. painted c.1953 prov.lit. 4-Jun-3 Sotheby's, London #35/R est:8000-12000

Works on paper
£300 $471 €450 Urban detail (23x34cm-9x13in) s. W/C. 15-Apr-3 Bonhams, Knightsbridge #96
£460 $731 €690 Structural studies (30x39cm-12x15in) s. pencil W/C. 26-Feb-3 Sotheby's, Olympia #192/R
£480 $773 €720 Abstract in black and red (37x25cm-15x10in) s. gouache. 14-Jan-3 Bonhams, Knightsbridge #210/R
£500 $785 €750 Agitate (9x8cm-4x3in) collage aluminium paint executed c.1970 prov. 15-Apr-3 Bonhams, Knightsbridge #234/R
£750 $1193 €1125 Mechanical studies (38x28cm-15x11in) chl W/C. 26-Feb-3 Sotheby's, Olympia #197/R
£850 $1351 €1275 Untitled (24x24cm-9x9in) s. ink white chk. 26-Feb-3 Sotheby's, Olympia #193/R est:400-600
£950 $1510 €1425 Figures studies (39x30cm-15x12in) indis i. chl ink wash. 26-Feb-3 Sotheby's, Olympia #198/R est:600-800
£3200 $5248 €4800 Industrial landscape (52x44cm-20x17in) s. chl gouache W/C prov. 3-Jun-3 Sotheby's, Olympia #294/R est:1500-2000

CLOUGH, Tom (1867-1943) British

Works on paper
£1000 $1670 €1450 Fishing harbour (26x44cm-10x17in) s.d.99 pencil W/C. 26-Jun-3 Mellors & Kirk, Nottingham #814/R est:400-600
£1100 $1716 €1650 Robins Hoods Bay (44x64cm-17x25in) s. W/C. 18-Sep-2 James Thompson, Kirby Lonsdale #65
£1200 $1872 €1800 Village lane, with woman carrying a pail (44x60cm-17x24in) s. W/C. 6-Nov-2 Bonhams, Chester #319 est:700-900

CLOUTIER, Albert Edward (1902-1965) Canadian
£756 $1239 €1134 Payasge D'Ete, Co Charlevoix (60x71cm-24x28in) s. 3-Jun-3 Joyner, Toronto #335/R est:1000-1500 (C.D 1700)
£773 $1205 €1121 Making maple syrup (22x27cm-9x11in) s. panel. 26-Mar-3 Walker's, Ottawa #228/R est:500-700 (C.D 1800)

CLOVER, Joseph (1779-1853) British
£2517 $3600 €3776 Portraitof barbara, Baroness Grey de Ruthyn (76x63cm-30x25in) i.verso. 22-Jan-3 Doyle, New York #157/R

CLOWES, Daniel (1774-1829) British
£4000 $6640 €5800 Bay hunter in an extensive landscape (58x84cm-23x33in) s. prov. 12-Jun-3 Christie's, Kensington #49/R est:4000-6000
£6000 $9360 €9000 Bay racehorse with jockey, Trainer and groom (56x84cm-22x33in) 6-Nov-2 Sotheby's, Olympia #35/R est:6000-9000

CLOWES, Daniel (attrib) (1774-1829) British
£1761 $2800 €2642 Portrait of a horse (59x73cm-23x29in) s.d.1820. 7-Mar-3 Skinner, Boston #237/R est:2000-3000
£1800 $2772 €2700 Pointers on the scent (47x58cm-19x23in) 5-Sep-2 Christie's, Kensington #256/R est:2000-3000

CLOWES, Henry (jnr) (1834-?) British
£300 $477 €450 Chestnut hunter in a loose box (28x38cm-11x15in) s.d.1860. 27-Feb-3 Bonhams, Chester #341

CLUTTERBUCK, Violet (19/20th C) British?

Works on paper
£290 $484 €421 Walsinham (33x48cm-13x19in) s.d.06 W/C. 20-Jun-3 Keys, Aylsham #405

CLUVER, Bernt (1897-1941) Norwegian
£561 $937 €813 Autumn landscape, Hadeland (46x53cm-18x21in) s.indis.d.29 i.verso. 18-Jun-3 Grev Wedels Plass, Oslo #160 (N.KR 6500)

CLUYSENAAR, Andre (1872-1939) Belgian
£291 $454 €460 Jeune fille de profil (55x40cm-22x16in) s.d.1924. 16-Sep-2 Horta, Bruxelles #384

CLYMER, John Ford (1907-1989) American
£2244 $3500 €3366 Saffloer red, dying in China (76x102cm-30x40in) 9-Nov-2 Altermann Galleries, Santa Fe #145
£3526 $5500 €5289 Early spinning, dying and weaving in Peru (66x97cm-26x38in) 9-Nov-2 Altermann Galleries, Santa Fe #144
£7877 $11500 €11816 Pony soldier no.two (51x91cm-20x36in) 18-May-2 Altermann Galleries, Santa Fe #81/R
£50633 $80000 €73418 Beaver pond - Upper Green River, Wyoming (25x51cm-10x20in) s. board. 26-Jul-3 Coeur d'Alene, Hayden #150/R est:30000-50000
£50633 $80000 €73418 Home in the clouds (61x102cm-24x40in) s. 26-Jul-3 Coeur d'Alene, Hayden #162/R est:50000-75000
£82192 $120000 €123288 Long ago winter (61x102cm-24x40in) 18-May-2 Altermann Galleries, Santa Fe #78/R

Works on paper
£1923 $3000 €2885 Frontier man in dugout canoe (18x28cm-7x11in) pen ink. 9-Nov-2 Altermann Galleries, Santa Fe #53

CLYMES, John (20th C) British
£448 $700 €650 Figures on a country path (61x46cm-24x18in) s. 13-Apr-3 Butterfields, Los Angeles #7029

COADY, Tony (20th C) Irish?

Works on paper
£288 $449 €420 Tennis, Howth (60x50cm-24x20in) init. W/C. 8-Apr-3 James Adam, Dublin #13/R

COAT, Jo (20th C) ?
£556 $906 €800 La cale verte (22x27cm-9x11in) s. cardboard. 19-Jul-3 Thierry & Lannon, Brest #317

COATES, Andrew (?) New Zealander
£1534 $2178 €2301 Lions Head, Milford Sound (26x41cm-10x16in) s. prov. 20-Mar-2 Watson's, Christchurch #9/R est:5000-7000 (NZ.D 5000)

COATES, Tom (1941-) British
£320 $515 €480 Restorers at the Amber Palace (25x30cm-10x12in) mono. board. 14-Jan-3 Bonhams, Knightsbridge #9/R
£480 $744 €720 Summer landscape (91x126cm-36x50in) init. 3-Dec-2 Bonhams, Knightsbridge #119/R
£550 $869 €825 Amateur (24x19cm-9x7in) init. canvas on board. 27-Nov-2 Sotheby's, Olympia #154/R
£700 $1105 €1050 Saddling up at Lockinge Point to Point, Berks (18x25cm-7x10in) init. canvasboard. 27-Nov-2 Sotheby's, Olympia #116/R
£700 $1105 €1050 Market stall (29x24cm-11x9in) init. canvas on board. 27-Nov-2 Sotheby's, Olympia #155/R
£800 $1264 €1200 Market day (29x21cm-11x8in) init. canvas on board. 27-Nov-2 Sotheby's, Olympia #156/R

Works on paper
£350 $574 €508 Reflections of India (49x59cm-19x23in) mono. W/C prov. 1-Jun-3 Lots Road, London #363
£450 $711 €675 At the bar (24x11cm-9x4in) init. pencil W/C with work by Frank Archer two. 27-Nov-2 Sotheby's, Olympia #152/R

COATS, Randolph (1891-?) American
£1572 $2500 €2358 Quiet pool (66x91cm-26x36in) s. painted c.1915. 4-May-3 Treadway Gallery, Cincinnati #518/R est:4500-6500
£1572 $2500 €2358 Weed Patch Hill, Brown County, Indiana (66x81cm-26x32in) s. painted c.1920. 4-May-3 Treadway Gallery, Cincinnati #524/R est:4500-6500

COBB, Charles David (1921-) British
£280 $437 €420 Evening seascape with yachts and single masted sailing vessel (45x66cm-18x26in) s. 18-Sep-2 Dreweatt Neate, Newbury #184
£300 $474 €450 Evening seascape with yachts and a single masted sailing vessel (45x66cm-18x26in) s. 27-Nov-2 Hamptons Fine Art, Godalming #457

COBB, Darius (1834-1919) American
£1935 $3000 €2903 Back Bay, Boston (13x38cm-5x15in) s. exhib. 3-Dec-2 Christie's, Rockefeller NY #51/R est:1000-1500

COBB, David (19th C) British?
£310 $496 €465 Breaking sea (51x76cm-20x30in) indis sig. verso. 14-Mar-3 Gardiner & Houlgate, Bath #165/R

COBBAERT, Jan (1909-1995) Belgian
£818 $1259 €1300 Figures (73x54cm-29x21in) s.d.1952. 22-Oct-2 Campo, Vlaamse Kaai #439/R
£959 $1496 €1400 Poupees (70x50cm-28x20in) s. 14-Apr-3 Horta, Bruxelles #133

£1258 $1937 €2000 Witte mineralen (100x80cm-39x31in) s. 22-Oct-2 Campo, Vlaamse Kaai #441/R
£1410 $2186 €2200 Good morning (70x60cm-28x24in) s. i.verso. 7-Dec-2 De Vuyst, Lokeren #57/R est:2600-3300
£1439 $2302 €2000 Composition (73x55cm-29x22in) s.d.52 paper on canvas. 17-May-3 De Vuyst, Lokeren #75/R est:1800-2000
£3019 $4649 €4800 Figures (150x140cm-59x55in) s.verso. 22-Oct-2 Campo & Campo, Antwerp #42/R est:4250

Works on paper
£347 $552 €500 Composition (62x54cm-24x21in) s.d.1960 ink dr. 29-Apr-3 Campo, Vlaamse Kaai #44
£576 $921 €800 Personnages (72x54cm-28x21in) s. gouache. 13-May-3 Vanderkindere, Brussels #167

COBBETT, Edward John (1815-1899) British
£636 $1011 €954 Fern gatherer (51x61cm-20x24in) s. canvas on board. 18-Mar-3 Maynards, Vancouver #61/R (C.D 1500)
£680 $1136 €986 Bracken gatherers (37x48cm-15x19in) s.d.1898. 17-Jun-3 Bristol Auction Rooms #556/R
£1300 $2028 €1950 Sweet hearts we shall be rich ere we depart (61x71cm-24x28in) s.i.verso panel. 7-Nov-2 Christie's, Kensington #213/R est:800-1200
£1397 $2263 €2096 Hilly coastal landscape with figures (51x76cm-20x30in) s. 3-Feb-3 Lilla Bukowskis, Stockholm #919 est:12000-15000 (S.KR 19500)
£1600 $2608 €2320 Bird's nest (43x36cm-17x14in) s.d.1855. 16-Jul-3 Sotheby's, Olympia #43/R est:800-1200
£1974 $3119 €2961 Honest pupil - girl playing with her dog (58x45cm-23x18in) s.d.1857. 29-Nov-2 Zofingen, Switzerland #2322/R est:3200 (S.FR 4600)
£5242 $8282 €7863 Fern gatherers (93x118cm-37x46in) s.d.1868 prov. 18-Nov-2 Waddingtons, Toronto #155/R est:10000-15000 (C.D 13000)

COBBETT, Hilary (1885-?) British
£700 $1099 €1050 French fishing boat in harbour (51x61cm-20x24in) s. 10-Dec-2 Rosebery Fine Art, London #601/R

COBELLE, Charles (1902-1998) French
£239 $375 €359 Harbour scene with buildings and boats (23x30cm-9x12in) s. board. 19-Apr-3 James Julia, Fairfield #148/R

COBO, Chema (1952-) Spanish
Works on paper
£1258 $1962 €2000 Enigma (45x32cm-18x13in) s.i.d.1980 col crayon prov. 17-Sep-2 Segre, Madrid #281/R
£2579 $3971 €4100 Fire (152x196cm-60x77in) s.d.1984 pastel paper on board exhib.lit. 28-Oct-2 Segre, Madrid #159/R
£6028 $9766 €8500 Sodoma (135x160cm-53x63in) s.d.1983 pastel col wax crayons paper on panel prov. 20-May-3 Segre, Madrid #170/R est:8000

COBO, Mariano (20th C) Spanish
£436 $702 €650 Landscape (200x288cm-79x113in) s.d.1995 triptych exhib. 18-Feb-3 Durán, Madrid #92/R

COBO, Raymundo (20th C) Mexican?
Sculpture
£917 $1450 €1376 Bull (36cm-14in) bronze. 14-Nov-2 Louis Morton, Mexico #71 est:25000 (M.P 15000)

COBURN, Alvin Langdon (1882-1966) American
Photographs
£1899 $3000 €2849 Two trees, Rothenberg (37x28cm-15x11in) s. photograph prov.lit. 23-Apr-3 Sotheby's, New York #107/R est:3000-5000
£1948 $3000 €2922 Brighton piers (9x12cm-4x5in) s.d.1904 warm toned photograph prov. 22-Oct-2 Sotheby's, New York #123/R est:3000-5000
£2057 $3250 €3086 Gateway, Dinklesbuhl (36x28cm-14x11in) s.d.1908 hand pulled photogravure prov. 23-Apr-3 Sotheby's, New York #108/R est:2500-3500
£2215 $3500 €3323 Rotterdam (30x39cm-12x15in) s.d.1908 large hand pulled photogravue prov.lit. 23-Apr-3 Sotheby's, New York #110/R est:4000-6000
£2435 $3750 €3653 Twilight study (16x20cm-6x8in) gum platinum print. 22-Oct-2 Sotheby's, New York #126/R est:6000-9000
£3718 $5800 €5577 London. photogravures 20. 21-Oct-2 Swann Galleries, New York #107/R est:6000-9000
£9146 $15000 €13719 London. s.i. photogravures 20 folio. 10-Feb-3 Swann Galleries, New York #26/R est:7000-10000
£11392 $18000 €17088 Niagara Falls (40x30cm-16x12in) d.1910 verso large format gum platinum print prov.lit. 23-Apr-3 Sotheby's, New York #113/R est:20000-30000
£33766 $52000 €50649 Colorado River from Hermit Point (31x40cm-12x16in) platinum print prov. 22-Oct-2 Sotheby's, New York #40/R est:70000-100000
£55000 $89100 €82500 Vortograph (28x21cm-11x8in) gelatin silver print prov. 21-May-3 Christie's, London #122/R est:40000-60000
£75000 $121500 €112500 Vortograph (20x26cm-8x10in) gelatin silver print prov. 21-May-3 Christie's, London #123/R est:30000-50000
£85000 $137700 €127500 Vortograph (28x20cm-11x8in) s.mount gelatin silver print prov. 21-May-3 Christie's, London #121/R est:60000-80000
£120000 $194400 €180000 Vortograph (27x20cm-11x8in) s.mount gelatin silver print prov. 21-May-3 Christie's, London #120/R est:60000-80000

COBURN, Frank (1866-1931) American
£1218 $1900 €1827 Rainy sidewalk. board. 21-Sep-2 Harvey Clar, Oakland #1495
£1347 $2250 €1953 Still life of corn and pumpkin (41x51cm-16x20in) s. card on board prov. 17-Jun-3 John Moran, Pasadena #120c est:2000-3000
£1774 $2750 €2661 Sail ship and tug, LA Harbour (30x25cm-12x10in) s. masonite prov. 29-Oct-2 John Moran, Pasadena #607 est:2500-3500
£2548 $4000 €3822 Sunset, the last glow (46x71cm-18x28in) s. canvas over board painted c.1920-1925. 19-Nov-2 Butterfields, San Francisco #8212/R est:3000-5000
£2903 $4500 €4355 Shepherd and flock in sunset landscape (46x61cm-18x24in) s. prov. 29-Oct-2 John Moran, Pasadena #735 est:3000-5000
£5120 $8500 €7424 Los Angeles park scene with sprinkler action on lawn (51x61cm-20x24in) s. prov.lit. 11-Jun-3 Butterfields, San Francisco #4238/R est:12000-16000
£47771 $75000 €71657 Wet night, Sixth and Hill, Los Angeles (51x76cm-20x30in) s. paperboard on board painted c.1930 prov.exhib.lit. 19-Nov-2 Butterfields, San Francisco #8224/R est:40000-50000

COBURN, Frederick Simpson (1871-1960) Canadian
£667 $1093 €1001 Panoramic landscape (30x42cm-12x17in) s.d.16. 3-Jun-3 Joyner, Toronto #299/R est:2000-3000 (C.D 1500)
£1556 $2551 €2334 Winter landscape (28x32cm-11x13in) s.d.24 prov. 27-May-3 Sotheby's, Toronto #203/R est:3000-4000 (C.D 3500)
£1564 $2424 €2346 Venetian canal at night (39x27cm-15x11in) s. oil paper on cardboard. 3-Dec-2 Joyner, Toronto #315/R est:2000-3000 (C.D 3800)
£1600 $2624 €2400 Washer woman in a cottage interior (34x24cm-13x9in) s. panel. 3-Jun-3 Joyner, Toronto #349/R est:5000-7000 (C.D 3600)
£2675 $4146 €4013 Figure on a country road, summer (35x26cm-14x10in) s. oil on card. 3-Dec-2 Joyner, Toronto #224/R est:2000-3000 (C.D 6500)
£3226 $5097 €4839 Laurentian scene, winter day (38x46cm-15x18in) s.d.27 prov. 18-Nov-2 Sotheby's, Toronto #14/R est:10000-12000 (C.D 8000)
£3909 $6060 €5864 Washing day (34x26cm-13x10in) s.d.22 board. 3-Dec-2 Joyner, Toronto #181/R est:5000-7000 (C.D 9500)
£6667 $10933 €10001 Hauling logs on a sunny day (57x80cm-22x31in) s.d.45 prov. 3-Jun-3 Joyner, Toronto #54/R est:20000-30000 (C.D 15000)
£7258 $11468 €10887 Drawing firewood (46x39cm-18x15in) s.d.28 prov.lit. 18-Nov-2 Sotheby's, Toronto #13/R est:10000-15000 (C.D 18000)
£7407 $11481 €11111 Hauling wood on a sunny day (38x50cm-15x20in) s.d.47. 3-Dec-2 Joyner, Toronto #103/R est:10000-15000 (C.D 18000)
£8658 $13766 €12554 Hauling logs, winter (61x76cm-24x30in) s.d.1948 prov. 1-May-3 Heffel, Vancouver #14/R est:20000-25000 (C.D 20000)
£8889 $14578 €13334 Winter fuel (51x82cm-20x32in) s.d.33 prov. 27-May-3 Sotheby's, Toronto #180/R est:15000-20000 (C.D 20000)
£9053 $14033 €13580 Red sleigh (37x50cm-15x20in) s.d.47. 3-Dec-2 Joyner, Toronto #34/R est:10000-15000 (C.D 22000)
£10667 $17493 €16001 Logging in winter (63x81cm-25x32in) s.d.45 prov. 27-May-3 Sotheby's, Toronto #179/R est:20000-25000 (C.D 24000)
£14667 $24053 €22001 Logging team at rest (47x63cm-19x25in) s.d.32 prov. 3-Jun-3 Joyner, Toronto #20/R est:30000-40000 (C.D 33000)
£21459 $33476 €31116 Friendly chat (51x81cm-20x32in) s.d.43 prov. 26-Mar-3 Walker's, Ottawa #233/R est:25000-35000 (C.D 50000)

Works on paper
£1070 $1658 €1605 Country mill. Near boast's schoolhouse, Upper Melbourne, Que. Hauling firewood (11x19cm-4x7in) s. col pencil dr. set of three. 3-Dec-2 Joyner, Toronto #444 est:700-900 (C.D 2600)
£1646 $2551 €2469 Country doctor (22x27cm-9x11in) s. col crayon prov. 3-Dec-2 Joyner, Toronto #129/R est:1500-2000 (C.D 4000)

COBURN, John (1925-) Australian
£996 $1484 €1494 Untitled (65x52cm-26x20in) s. acrylic paper on board. 27-Aug-2 Christie's, Melbourne #153/R est:3000-5000 (A.D 2600)
£1071 $1682 €1607 White bird in the garden II (50x39cm-20x15in) s. i.verso acrylic canvasboard. 25-Nov-2 Christie's, Melbourne #361/R est:3500-5000 (A.D 3000)
£1429 $2243 €2144 Untitled (51x69cm-20x27in) s. acrylic paper on board. 25-Nov-2 Christie's, Melbourne #313/R est:4000-6000 (A.D 4000)
£1429 $2257 €2144 Dry country (51x69cm-20x27in) s. acrylic board. 18-Nov-2 Goodman, Sydney #59/R est:4000-6000 (A.D 4000)
£1842 $2800 €2763 Picadors (31x48cm-12x19in) s. board. 19-Aug-2 Joel, Victoria #261 est:2000-3000 (A.D 5250)

£2671 $4141 €4007 November (67x122cm-26x48in) s. board prov. 3-Dec-2 Shapiro, Sydney #87/R est:8000-12000 (A.D 7400)
£3203 $4900 €4805 Procession (53x71cm-21x28in) s. board painted c.1980 prov. 26-Aug-2 Sotheby's, Paddington #677/R est:6000-8000 (A.D 9000)
£3943 $5993 €5915 Walkabout (75x91cm-30x36in) s. s.i.d.1982 verso. 28-Aug-2 Deutscher-Menzies, Melbourne #8/R est:7000-10000 (A.D 11000)
£3943 $5993 €5915 Summertime (76x91cm-30x36in) s. s.i.d.1982 verso. 28-Aug-2 Deutscher-Menzies, Melbourne #9/R est:7000-10000 (A.D 11000)
£4070 $6471 €6105 Dry country (76x45cm-30x18in) s. i.verso board. 5-May-3 Sotheby's, Melbourne #302/R est:6000-8000 (A.D 10500)
£4720 $7175 €7080 Abstract (60x76cm-24x30in) s. canvas on board. 27-Aug-2 Goodman, Sydney #132/R est:7000-10000 (A.D 13170)
£4960 $8234 €8452 Reaching for the moon (61x61cm-24x24in) i.verso. 10-Jun-3 Shapiro, Sydney #32/R est:8000-12000 (A.D 12500)
£5054 $7834 €7581 Barrier reef (61x76cm-24x30in) s. board prov. 3-Dec-2 Shapiro, Sydney #83/R est:15000-20000 (A.D 14000)
£5200 $8372 €7800 Basilisk (90x90cm-35x35in) s. s.i.d.1974 verso acrylic prov. 6-May-3 Christie's, Melbourne #138/R est:8000-12000 (A.D 13000)
£5714 $8914 €8571 Babinda (130x110cm-51x43in) s. s.i.d.2001 verso exhib. 11-Nov-2 Deutscher-Menzies, Melbourne #9/R est:12000-16000 (A.D 16000)
£5754 $9552 €9782 Bushland after fire (83x91cm-33x36in) s. lit. 10-Jun-3 Shapiro, Sydney #22a/R est:18000-25000 (A.D 14500)
£6897 $10276 €10346 Dark mountain (91x121cm-36x48in) s. i.d.1987 verso. 27-Aug-2 Christie's, Melbourne #85/R est:18000-25000 (A.D 18000)
£7800 $12558 €11700 Combat (54x94cm-21x37in) s. board prov. 6-May-3 Christie's, Melbourne #86/R est:9000-12000 (A.D 19500)
£9722 $16139 €16565 Homage to Matisse at the Grand Palais (161x130cm-63x51in) s. i.verso prov.lit. 10-Jun-3 Shapiro, Sydney #36/R est:20000-25000 (A.D 24500)
£10000 $15800 €15000 Resurrection (138x71cm-54x28in) s.d.59 board exhib. 17-Nov-2 Sotheby's, Paddington #2/R est:15000-20000 (A.D 28000)
£11382 $17984 €16504 Tree of life - maquette for tapestry (90x110cm-35x43in) s. i.d.11.67 verso. 22-Jul-3 Lawson Menzies, Sydney #99/R est:25000-35000 (A.D 28000)
£14286 $22286 €21429 Riches of the earth (152x213cm-60x84in) s.d.86 s.i.d.1986 verso lit. 11-Nov-2 Deutscher-Menzies, Melbourne #29/R est:30000-40000 (A.D 40000)

Works on paper

£678 $1065 €1017 Study (31x27cm-12x11in) s. gouache. 25-Nov-2 Christie's, Melbourne #262/R (A.D 1900)
£797 $1307 €1196 Study for dark forest (30x37cm-12x15in) s.i. synthetic polymer paint prov. 4-Jun-3 Deutscher-Menzies, Melbourne #164/R (A.D 2000)
£890 $1361 €1335 Study for desert moon (22x28cm-9x11in) s.i. gouache. 25-Aug-2 Sotheby's, Paddington #177 est:2500-4500 (A.D 2500)
£1075 $1634 €1613 Bangara (50x70cm-20x28in) s. W/C pastel prov. 28-Aug-2 Deutscher-Menzies, Melbourne #325/R est:3200-3600 (A.D 3000)
£1083 $1679 €1625 Study for Uluru (30x40cm-12x16in) s.i. W/C crayon prov. 3-Dec-2 Shapiro, Sydney #45 est:4000-6000 (A.D 3000)
£1116 $1829 €1674 Study for exotic garden (30x37cm-12x15in) s.i. synthetic polymer paint prov. 4-Jun-3 Deutscher-Menzies, Melbourne #163/R est:2000-3000 (A.D 2800)
£1138 $1798 €1650 Echidna, etude, lakes entrance, Vic (38x33cm-15x13in) s.i. pastel gouache. 22-Jul-3 Lawson Menzies, Sydney #216/R est:2000-3000 (A.D 2800)
£1149 $1713 €1724 Study for rainforest II (26x33cm-10x13in) s.i.d.68 W/C. 27-Aug-2 Christie's, Melbourne #154/R est:3000-4000 (A.D 3000)
£1286 $2031 €1929 Study for field II (39x34cm-15x13in) s.i. gouache pastel. 27-Nov-2 Deutscher-Menzies, Melbourne #150/R est:2000-3000 (A.D 3600)
£1385 $2202 €2078 Untitled (76x56cm-30x22in) s. pastel. 4-Mar-3 Deutscher-Menzies, Melbourne #221/R est:1800-2200 (A.D 3600)
£1456 $2286 €2184 Study for yellow landscape (35x40cm-14x16in) s.d.2001 W/C pastel. 15-Apr-3 Lawson Menzies, Sydney #12/R est:2000-3000 (A.D 3800)
£1505 $2288 €2258 Tree of life (49x69cm-19x27in) s. W/C. 28-Aug-2 Deutscher-Menzies, Melbourne #242/R est:4500-6000 (A.D 4200)
£1514 $2483 €2271 Study for Yuendumu (37x31cm-15x12in) s. synthetic polymer paint col pencil prov. 4-Jun-3 Deutscher-Menzies, Melbourne #357/R est:2000-3000 (A.D 3800)
£1594 $2614 €2391 Study for tree of life II (37x31cm-15x12in) s.i. synthetic polymer paint prov. 4-Jun-3 Deutscher-Menzies, Melbourne #356/R est:2000-3000 (A.D 4000)
£2214 $3476 €3321 Maquette for tapestry Sydney Summer, for Sydney County Council (42x74cm-17x29in) s.i.d.1977 gouache. 25-Nov-2 Christie's, Melbourne #442/R est:3000-5000 (A.D 6200)
£3559 $5445 €5339 Autumn landscape (52x70cm-20x28in) s. gouache on board prov. 25-Aug-2 Sotheby's, Paddington #146/R est:7000-9000 (A.D 10000)
£4874 $7554 €7311 Image of night II (100x115cm-39x45in) s. i.d.1/65 verso synthetic polymer paint board prov. 3-Dec-2 Shapiro, Sydney #30/R est:12000-18000 (A.D 13500)
£13077 $20792 €19616 Tree of life IV (120x120cm-47x47in) s. s.i.d.1973 verso synthetic polymer paint gold leaf lit. 4-Mar-3 Deutscher-Menzies, Melbourne #90/R est:28000-35000 (A.D 34000)

COCCAPANI, Sigismondo (attrib) (1583-1642) Italian

Works on paper

£664 $950 €996 Cosmos and Damian replacing the leg (22x14cm-9x6in) red chk wash. 23-Jan-3 Swann Galleries, New York #63/R

COCCAPANI, Sigismondo (style) (1583-1642) Italian

£7000 $10920 €10500 Saint John the Baptist (35x26cm-14x10in) 8-Apr-3 Sotheby's, Olympia #213/R est:3000-5000

COCCO, Francesco di (1900-1989) Italian

£769 $1208 €1200 Fantastic vision (43x63cm-17x25in) board. 16-Dec-2 Pandolfini, Florence #371

COCCORANTE, Leonardo (1680-1750) Italian

£4483 $7128 €6500 Seascape. Seascape with ruins (55x101cm-22x40in) pair. 9-Mar-3 Semenzato, Venice #8/R
£24691 $40000 €37037 Figures amongst ruins in a moonlit Mediterranean port (131x208cm-52x82in) init. 24-Jan-3 Christie's, Rockefeller NY #156/R est:40000-60000

COCCORANTE, Leonardo (circle) (1680-1750) Italian

£5484 $8500 €8226 Architectural capriccios (68x35cm-27x14in) one indis.sig. pair. 2-Oct-2 Christie's, Rockefeller NY #145/R est:6000-8000

COCCORANTE, Leonardo and PO, Giacomo del (17th C) Italian

£48276 $76276 €70000 Architecture (152x111cm-60x44in) 3-Apr-3 Porro, Milan #32/R est:65000

COCHIN, Charles-Nicolas (18th C) French

Works on paper

£1795 $2782 €2800 Tete d'homme de profil (10cm-4in circular) crayon htd sanguine. 4-Dec-2 Piasa, Paris #91/R

COCHIN, Charles-Nicolas (younger) (1715-1790) French

Works on paper

£577 $906 €900 Laureata messis pressa resurgunt (35x33cm-14x13in) s.d.1776 crayon. 21-Nov-2 Neret-Minet, Paris #57
£629 $975 €1000 Etude pour eveque. Etude pour garde-maison (17x13cm-7x5in) pierre noire htd white. 29-Oct-2 Artcurial Briest, Paris #6/R
£800 $1256 €1200 Design for a book illustration, the glutton (5x7cm-2x3in) s.i. black chk framing lines. 11-Dec-2 Sotheby's, Olympia #160/R
£823 $1300 €1300 Renaud et Armide (25x17cm-10x7in) black chk prov.lit. 27-Nov-2 Christie's, Paris #173/R
£28000 $46760 €40600 Seated couple playing backgammon by candlelight (15x18cm-6x7in) black chk prov.exhib. 8-Jul-3 Christie's, London #76/R est:10000-15000

COCHIN, Charles-Nicolas (younger-attrib) (1715-1790) French

Works on paper

£222 $350 €350 Deux figures en habit (13x9cm-5x4in) i. pen ink wash crayon. 28-Nov-2 Tajan, Paris #52

COCHRAN, Allen Dean (1888-1935) American

£1946 $3250 €2822 Winter landscape (20x25cm-8x10in) canvasboard prov. 17-Jun-3 John Moran, Pasadena #3 est:500-700

COCHRANE, Constance (1888-?) American

£1198 $2000 €1737 Fishing boats, Monhegan (30x41cm-12x16in) s. 21-Jun-3 Selkirks, St. Louis #165 est:600-800
£3846 $6000 €5769 Gift of the garden (76x91cm-30x36in) s. exhib. 18-Sep-2 Alderfer's, Hatfield #343/R est:2000-3000

COCK, Cesar de (1823-1904) Flemish

£1164 $1885 €1688 River landscape (98x138cm-39x54in) s.d.1900. 26-May-3 Bukowskis, Stockholm #247/R est:30000-35000 (S.KR 15000)
£4335 $6850 €6850 Chemin pres des chaumieres (47x67cm-19x26in) s.d.1864. 1-Dec-2 Peron, Melun #170
£5161 $8000 €7742 Landscape with cottage (43x64cm-17x25in) s.d.1872 prov. 29-Oct-2 Sotheby's, New York #31/R est:4000-6000

COCK, Gilbert de (1928-) Belgian
£1223 $1957 €1700 Priene (65x92cm-26x36in) s.d.64 i.verso. 17-May-3 De Vuyst, Lokeren #123/R est:1800-2000

COCK, Lucas de (19th C) French
Works on paper
£535 $823 €850 Landscape with trunk (27x42cm-11x17in) s.d.1878 W/C. 27-Oct-2 Muizon & Le Coent, Paris #37

COCKAYNE, Kathleen (20th C) British
£380 $578 €570 Saddled hunter (56x66cm-22x26in) s.d.1939. 16-Aug-2 Keys, Aylsham #676

COCKBURN, Major General James Pattison (1778-1847) British
Works on paper
£1100 $1694 €1650 London from Greenwich Park (31x46cm-12x18in) mono.d.36 W/C. 8-Sep-2 Lots Road, London #339 est:300-500

COCKERELL, Christabel A (1863-1951) British
£346 $540 €550 Naked girl (71x91cm-28x36in) s. 20-Sep-2 Schloss Ahlden, Ahlden #1274/R

COCKRAM, George (1861-1950) British
Works on paper
£280 $437 €420 Ploughing the field (22x28cm-9x11in) s.d.88 pencil W/C htd white. 27-Mar-3 Christie's, Kensington #102
£360 $558 €540 Evening glow (33x51cm-13x20in) s. W/C dr. 1-Oct-2 Capes Dunn, Manchester #820
£700 $1092 €1050 Pool at the Lledr, Bettws-y-Coed. Llyn Ogwen, Nant Ffancon (29x46cm-11x18in) s. W/C pair. 26-Mar-3 Hamptons Fine Art, Godalming #112
£800 $1240 €1200 Coastal scene (28x46cm-11x18in) s. W/C dr. 1-Oct-2 Capes Dunn, Manchester #819
£1200 $1848 €1800 Oriental poppies (30x45cm-12x18in) s. W/C. 22-Oct-2 Bonhams, Knightsbridge #53/R est:1000-1500

COCKRILL, Maurice (1936-) British
£400 $656 €600 Pines of Rome (20x25cm-8x10in) s.d.1989 i.verso. 3-Jun-3 Sotheby's, Olympia #271/R
£500 $770 €750 Portable kingdom (22x30cm-9x12in) init.d.96 verso board sold with another by the same artist. 5-Sep-2 Christie's, Kensington #703
£1000 $1560 €1500 Portable Kingdom (52x61cm-20x24in) i.d.1996 verso panel. 26-Mar-3 Hamptons Fine Art, Godalming #219/R est:1500-1800
£1800 $2808 €2700 Fold back (61x66cm-24x26in) i.d.1998 verso. 26-Mar-3 Hamptons Fine Art, Godalming #227/R est:1800-2500

COCKS, William Pennington (1791-1878) British
Works on paper
£291 $460 €460 Pope's agent watering protestant soil (12x13cm-5x5in) ink monochrome wash. 27-Nov-2 James Adam, Dublin #139/R
£411 $650 €650 Members of the Fenian Brotherhood 1865 (8x21cm-3x8in) pen ink monochrome wash. 27-Nov-2 James Adam, Dublin #140/R
£475 $750 €750 Irish agitator (26x19cm-10x7in) pen ink monochrome wash. 27-Nov-2 James Adam, Dublin #143/R
£487 $770 €770 General Stephens and a coward (15x11cm-6x4in) pen ink two. 27-Nov-2 James Adam, Dublin #135/R
£570 $900 €900 Fenian pike man 1865 (25x19cm-10x7in) W/C pen ink. 27-Nov-2 James Adam, Dublin #136/R
£601 $950 €950 Invincible Fenian armed at all points (26x18cm-10x7in) pen ink monochrome wash. 27-Nov-2 James Adam, Dublin #137/R

COCKX, F (19th C) Dutch?
£1000 $1580 €1500 Extensive winter river landscape (75x126cm-30x50in) s.d.1875. 2-Dec-2 Bonhams, Bath #158/R est:1500-2500

COCKX, Marcel (1930-) Belgian
£411 $650 €650 Kinderwereld (90x110cm-35x43in) s. 26-Nov-2 Palais de Beaux Arts, Brussels #61

COCKX, Philibert (1879-1949) Belgian
£445 $695 €650 Village au bord de l'etang (33x41cm-13x16in) s. 14-Apr-3 Horta, Bruxelles #371
£451 $718 €650 Nature morte aux fleurs (60x50cm-24x20in) s. d.1948 verso. 29-Apr-3 Campo & Campo, Antwerp #466
£481 $745 €750 Eglise a la campagne (40x47cm-16x19in) s.d.41 panel. 9-Dec-2 Horta, Bruxelles #29
£625 $994 €900 Nature morte aux fleurs et vase (80x80cm-31x31in) s.d.1943. 29-Apr-3 Campo & Campo, Antwerp #463

COCLERS, Jean Baptiste Pierre (c.1696-1772) Dutch
Works on paper
£709 $1184 €1000 Le jugement dernier (32x20cm-13x8in) pierre noire pen wash. 23-Jun-3 Beaussant & Lefèvre, Paris #201/R

COCLERS, Louis Bernard (attrib) (1741-1817) Flemish
£2390 $3704 €3800 Marchande de legumes (60x48cm-24x19in) bears sig. 29-Oct-2 Artcurial Briest, Paris #38/R

COCQ, Suzanne (1894-1979) Belgian
Works on paper
£342 $538 €500 Les Lys. s.d.1950 gouache. 15-Apr-3 Galerie Moderne, Brussels #317
£526 $853 €800 Les lys. s.d.50 gouache. 21-Jan-3 Galerie Moderne, Brussels #271/R

COCTEAU, Jean (1889-1963) French
£573 $853 €860 Mentonnaise (21x13cm-8x5in) feltpen. 25-Jun-2 Koller, Zurich #6034/R (S.FR 1300)
Sculpture
£2308 $3623 €3600 Profile (6x5cm-2x2in) st.sig. gold lit. 11-Dec-2 Artcurial Briest, Paris #612/R
£2308 $3623 €3600 Losange (11cm-4in) st.sig. gold lit. 11-Dec-2 Artcurial Briest, Paris #616/R
£4231 $6642 €6600 Grande masque (8x8cm-3x3in) st.sig. gold lit. 11-Dec-2 Artcurial Briest, Paris #608/R
£5000 $7850 €7800 Taureau (11cm-4in) st.sig. gold lit. 11-Dec-2 Artcurial Briest, Paris #609/R
Works on paper
£333 $530 €490 Les ailes du demon, l'ange de la poesie (15x11cm-6x4in) s.d.1956 pen. 28-Mar-3 Bolland & Marotz, Bremen #594
£348 $550 €550 Composition (13x9cm-5x4in) s. pen. 30-Nov-2 Arnold, Frankfurt #88/R
£370 $596 €555 Man's head (28x22cm-11x9in) s.i.d.1942 pencil. 7-May-3 Dobiaschofsky, Bern #1481 (S.FR 800)
£371 $542 €557 Visage (20x21cm-8x8in) s. pencil on two sheets. 4-Jun-2 Germann, Zurich #754 (S.FR 850)
£414 $658 €600 La coupe (37x27cm-15x11in) s. col crayon. 9-Mar-3 Feletin, Province #162
£417 $663 €600 Deux figures de profil. Etude de visage (28x38cm-11x15in) s. ink dr double-sided. 29-Apr-3 Artcurial Briest, Paris #143
£417 $671 €626 Letter with fantasy figures (27x21cm-11x8in) s.d.27 Jan 1957 biro col pen. 7-May-3 Dobiaschofsky, Bern #1482 (S.FR 900)
£449 $700 €674 Untitled. drawings two. 22-Sep-2 Susanin's, Chicago #5071/R
£463 $745 €695 Man's head (29x21cm-11x8in) s.i.d.1938 pencil. 7-May-3 Dobiaschofsky, Bern #1483 (S.FR 1000)
£504 $806 €700 Le rappel a l'orde (18x12cm-7x5in) i.d.1950 dr edition stock. 18-May-3 Eric Pillon, Calais #201/R
£516 $815 €800 Untitled (44x32cm-17x13in) s.d.1960 felt-tip pen. 18-Dec-2 Christie's, Rome #33/R
£563 $900 €845 Le fils de l'air (23x18cm-9x7in) s. pen ink. 18-May-3 Jeffery Burchard, Florida #53/R
£563 $900 €845 Portrait of self at masquerade (18x15cm-7x6in) s. i.verso pen ink. 18-May-3 Jeffery Burchard, Florida #53a/R
£603 $1007 €850 Couple dans un lit (19x17cm-7x7in) s. pen. 18-Jun-3 Hotel des Ventes Mosan, Brussels #249
£610 $957 €915 Homme tenant une branche de houx (30x23cm-12x9in) s. feltpen col crayon. 12-Dec-2 Iegor de Saint Hippolyte, Montreal #20 (C.D 1500)
£638 $1034 €900 Politesse exquise (19x13cm-7x5in) i. Indian ink. 20-May-3 Dorotheum, Vienna #20/R
£705 $1107 €1100 Ce ne sont que festons, ce ne sont qu'astragales (31x24cm-12x9in) s.d.36 crayon dr. 13-Dec-2 Piasa, Paris #75
£764 $1215 €1100 Le peintre Anglais Frances Rose (26x20cm-10x8in) ink dr exec.c.1926. 29-Apr-3 Artcurial Briest, Paris #83/R
£880 $1416 €1320 Marianne with Jacobean hat (30x23cm-12x9in) s.d.1966 Indian ink pencil. 7-May-3 Dobiaschofsky, Bern #1480 (S.FR 1900)
£886 $1382 €1400 Boy's head with tunic (51x42cm-20x17in) s.d.1959 col pencil. 21-Oct-2 Bernaerts, Antwerp #654
£961 $1500 €1442 Untitled, profile (42x29cm-17x11in) s.d. col pencil prov. 14-Oct-2 Butterfields, San Francisco #1108/R est:1000-1500
£1014 $1664 €1400 Medieval - chevalier a la tour (42x26cm-17x10in) s.d.57 col pen. 29-May-3 Lempertz, Koln #575/R
£1034 $1655 €1500 Tristan et Yseult (26x20cm-10x8in) init.d.1960 felt on paper. 12-Mar-3 Libert, Castor, Paris #57 est:500-600
£1051 $1723 €1450 Les enfants terribles (25x13cm-10x5in) one mono. Indian ink prov. two. 29-May-3 Lempertz, Koln #574/R est:500
£1069 $1657 €1700 Deux visages (34x26cm-13x10in) s. graphite dr exec.c.1956-58. 30-Oct-2 Artcurial Briest, Paris #221 est:600-800
£1100 $1738 €1650 Embrassade (20x20cm-8x8in) pen ink. 3-Apr-3 Christie's, Kensington #89/R
£1132 $1755 €1800 Baigneur au soleil (23x21cm-9x8in) init. graphite dr exec.c.1956-58. 30-Oct-2 Artcurial Briest, Paris #225 est:750-900
£1138 $1821 €1650 Le sphinx (26x20cm-10x8in) init.d.60 felt on paper. 12-Mar-3 Libert, Castor, Paris #58 est:500-600
£1139 $1800 €1800 Esquisse de visage (25x19cm-10x7in) s.d.1962 chl dr prov. 29-Nov-2 Drouot Estimations, Paris #98

£1154 $1812 €1800 Auto-portrait a l'eloge de l'opium (25x21cm-10x8in) s.d.1924 Chinese ink dr. 11-Dec-2 Piasa, Paris #8/R
£1184 $1918 €1800 Untitled (62x48cm-24x19in) s.d.1959 col dr. 21-Jan-3 Ansorena, Madrid #839/R
£1189 $1986 €1700 Personnage (21x27cm-8x11in) s.d.6 avril 1956 pencil dr. 26-Jun-3 Tajan, Paris #118 est:800-1000
£1195 $1852 €1900 Gondoliers a Venise (21x27cm-8x11in) s.d.1956 col crayon dr prov. 30-Oct-2 Artcurial Briest, Paris #225a est:750-900
£1258 $1950 €2000 Horticulture comparee (54x37cm-21x15in) s.i.d.1961 black marker. 30-Oct-2 Artcurial Briest, Paris #223/R est:750-950
£1282 $2000 €1923 Untitled, profile (53x32cm-21x13in) s. magic marker pastel. 14-Oct-2 Butterfields, San Francisco #1109 est:1000-1500
£1282 $2013 €2000 Croquis erotique (27x24cm-11x9in) crayon dr. 13-Dec-2 Piasa, Paris #79
£1282 $2013 €2000 Prisonniers de Jason (27x24cm-11x9in) s.i.d.36 crayon dr. 13-Dec-2 Piasa, Paris #74
£1290 $2039 €2000 Fauconnier (45x37cm-18x15in) s. col dr prov. 18-Dec-2 Beaussant & Lefèvre, Paris #43/R
£1316 $2132 €2000 Profil affronte (27x21cm-11x8in) s.d.18 juillet 1956 col crayon dr. 22-Jan-3 Tajan, Paris #161 est:2000-3000
£1316 $2132 €2000 Tete de profil (20x13cm-8x5in) s.i. ink dr. 22-Jan-3 Tajan, Paris #162 est:1200-2000
£1316 $2132 €2000 Visages de France (46x41cm-18x16in) s.d.1954 col dr. 21-Jan-3 Ansorena, Madrid #840/R
£1438 $2358 €2200 Fou (35x28cm-14x11in) init.d. col crayon dr. 9-Feb-3 Anaf, Lyon #71/R
£1481 $2385 €2222 Maison hantee (35x22cm-14x9in) s.i.d.1938 Indian ink. 7-May-3 Dobiaschofsky, Bern #1484/R est:2600 (S.FR 3200)
£1485 $2346 €2228 Abstract woman's portrait (27x21cm-11x8in) s.d.14 Juillet 1958 biro. 14-Nov-2 Stuker, Bern #143 est:2000-3000 (S.FR 3400)
£1572 $2437 €2500 Etude pour un hommage a Raoul Dufy (27x21cm-11x8in) s.i. graphite dr. 30-Oct-2 Artcurial Briest, Paris #224 est:900-1100
£1603 $2516 €2500 Etude pour 'La querelle de Brest' (25x18cm-10x7in) s. crayon. 10-Dec-2 Renaud, Paris #58
£1799 $2950 €2500 Le sphinx (41x31cm-16x12in) col crayon dr. 4-Jun-3 Marc Kohn, Paris #15 est:2000-2500
£1887 $2925 €3000 Orphee (64x49cm-25x19in) s.i.d.1950 black marker dr. 30-Oct-2 Artcurial Briest, Paris #219/R est:2300-3000
£1921 $3130 €2900 Shinge (41x32cm-16x13in) s. pastel graphite. 3-Feb-3 Cornette de St.Cyr, Paris #286/R
£1923 $3019 €3000 Profil aux lunettes (30x22cm-12x9in) s.i. crayon dr. 13-Dec-2 Piasa, Paris #81
£1944 $3072 €2800 Profile (29x21cm-11x8in) s.d.5.April 1959 col pen. 24-Apr-3 Dorotheum, Vienna #160/R est:2000-3000
£1974 $3197 €3000 Profil (19x12cm-7x5in) s.d.1958 col crayon on letterhead paper. 22-Jan-3 Tajan, Paris #160/R est:1200-1500
£2000 $3160 €3000 Jeune soldat apres avoir lu ses lettres d'amour (20x28cm-8x11in) pen ink. 3-Apr-3 Christie's, Kensington #88/R
£2000 $3160 €3000 DEux hommes (27x20cm-11x8in) pen ink. 3-Apr-3 Christie's, Kensington #85/R
£2200 $3410 €3300 Deux hommes s'allongeant (19x25cm-7x10in) pen ink. 5-Dec-2 Christie's, Kensington #118/R est:1500-2000
£2200 $3410 €3300 Deux hommes au lit (26x20cm-10x8in) pencil pen ink. 5-Dec-2 Christie's, Kensington #120/R est:1200-1800
£2200 $3410 €3300 L'extase (32x23cm-13x9in) pen ink. 5-Dec-2 Christie's, Kensington #121/R est:1200-1800
£2200 $3476 €3300 Deux femmes et un homme (26x20cm-10x8in) pen ink. 3-Apr-3 Christie's, Kensington #87/R
£2292 $3621 €3300 Portrait presume de Roland Petit (48x31cm-19x12in) s.d.37 col crayon dr. 23-Apr-3 Rabourdin & Choppin de Janvry, Paris #40/R
£2390 $3704 €3800 Je suis la jeune fille bleue (31x25cm-12x10in) s.i. blue marker col wax crayon dr exec.c.1960. 30-Oct-2 Artcurial Briest, Paris #222/R est:1500-1800
£2436 $3824 €3800 Souvenir de Diche Maron (44x33cm-17x13in) Chinese ink pen dr. 13-Dec-2 Piasa, Paris #76
£2516 $3899 €4000 Profil pendentif (31x23cm-12x9in) s. gouache on cardboard. 30-Oct-2 Artcurial Briest, Paris #226/R est:4000-5000
£2564 $4026 €4000 Circus (27x24cm-11x9in) s.d.36 crayon dr. 13-Dec-2 Piasa, Paris #73/R
£2885 $4471 €4500 Buste d'homme (27x21cm-11x8in) Chinese ink exec.c.1930. 4-Dec-2 Christie's, Paris #75/R
£2908 $4711 €4100 Portrait de Nijinski (26x20cm-10x8in) s.i. crayon. 26-May-3 Joron-Derem, Paris #19/R est:2000-2300
£3000 $4740 €4500 Groupe d'hommes (25x19cm-10x7in) pen ink. 3-Apr-3 Christie's, Kensington #86/R
£3239 $5377 €4600 Oedipe. Profil (22x15cm-9x6in) init.i.d.56 col crayon double-sided. 11-Jun-3 Beaussant & Lefèvre, Paris #16/R est:1500
£3472 $5729 €5000 Mantonnaise et pecheurs (48x63cm-19x25in) s.d. crayon dr exec.c.1956-57. 2-Jul-3 Artcurial Briest, Paris #693/R est:6000-8000
£3548 $5606 €5500 Vent (34x26cm-13x10in) indis.sig. ink wash sepia ink prov. 18-Dec-2 Beaussant & Lefèvre, Paris #42/R
£3774 $5849 €6000 Baigneur. Arlequin dansant (75x54cm-30x21in) s.d.1956 col wax crayon brown paint dr double-sided. 30-Oct-2 Artcurial Briest, Paris #217/R est:6000-8000
£4088 $6336 €6500 Portrait de Carole Wesweiler (65x50cm-26x20in) s.d.1954 pastel. 30-Oct-2 Artcurial Briest, Paris #216/R est:7000-9000
£5769 $9058 €9000 Naissance de mandragore (44x55cm-17x22in) s.i.d.35 Chinese ink dr. 13-Dec-2 Piasa, Paris #78/R
£6410 $10064 €10000 Souvenir de Diche Maron (27x22cm-11x9in) s. Chinese ink wash dr set of 4. 13-Dec-2 Piasa, Paris #77 est:3000

COCTEAU, Jean and MORETTI, Raymond (20th C) French
Works on paper
£530 $864 €800 Untitled (51x66cm-20x26in) s.d.1962 gouache collage. 3-Feb-3 Cornette de St.Cyr, Paris #288
£1060 $1727 €1600 Promenade des Anglais (65x50cm-26x20in) s.d.1962 ink col crayon. 3-Feb-3 Cornette de St.Cyr, Paris #287/R

CODAZZI, Niccolo (1648-1693) Italian
£9574 $14840 €14361 Classic landscape with ruins and figures (95x124cm-37x49in) 4-Dec-2 AB Stockholms Auktionsverk #2009/R est:80000-100000 (S.KR 135000)

CODAZZI, Viviano (circle) (1603-1672) Italian
£5844 $9000 €8766 Architectural cappriccio (135x100cm-53x39in) 23-Oct-2 Doyle, New York #92/R est:8000-12000
£7500 $11625 €11250 Capriccio of classical ruins with the statue of Marcus Aurelius, draughtsman and other figures (95x132cm-37x52in) 30-Oct-2 Christie's, Kensington #140/R est:8000-10000
£8000 $13360 €11600 Capriccio of Roman ruins with peasants amongst the ruins (94x69cm-37x27in) 11-Jul-3 Christie's, Kensington #269/R est:8000-12000

CODAZZI, Viviano (studio) (1603-1672) Italian
£8228 $13000 €13000 Architectonic capriccios (75x100cm-30x39in) pair. 27-Nov-2 Finarte, Milan #87/R est:12000-15000

CODAZZI, Viviano (style) (1603-1672) Italian
£9000 $14040 €13500 Capriccio of classical ruins and Renaissance buildings with cattle gathering around an obelisk (80x105cm-31x41in) 10-Apr-3 Christie's, Kensington #298/R est:10000-15000

CODAZZI, Viviano and GARGIULIO, Domenico (17th C) Italian
£105000 $164850 €157500 Rome, capriccio view of the Piazza del Popolo (175x254cm-69x100in) bears d.1660 prov.lit. 12-Dec-2 Sotheby's, London #59/R est:80000-120000

CODAZZI, Viviano and GARGIULIO, Domenico (circle) (17th C) Italian
£7000 $11690 €10150 Architectural capriccio with the rape of Helen (70x87cm-28x34in) 8-Jul-3 Sotheby's, Olympia #436/R est:3000-5000

CODAZZI, Viviano and GINER, Vicente (attrib) (17th C) Italian
£51282 $79487 €80000 Ruins in Mediterranean landscape (98x123cm-39x48in) pair. 4-Dec-2 Christie's, Rome #477/R est:80000-100000

CODDE, Pieter (1599-1678) Dutch
£16522 $25609 €24783 Music making (40x54cm-16x21in) panel prov. 9-Dec-2 Philippe Schuler, Zurich #3893/R est:30000-40000 (S.FR 38000)
£38462 $59615 €60000 Lady and servant in Dutch interior (36x44cm-14x17in) bears sig. 5-Dec-2 Gros & Delettrez, Paris #11/R est:55000

CODDE, Pieter (attrib) (1599-1678) Dutch
£10861 $17595 €15748 Interior scene with card players (30x37cm-12x15in) panel. 26-May-3 Bukowskis, Stockholm #417/R est:60000-80000 (S.KR 140000)

CODDRON, Oscar (1881-1960) Belgian
£863 $1381 €1200 Hay making (40x49cm-16x19in) s. panel. 17-May-3 De Vuyst, Lokeren #78/R

CODE, Ernva (20th C) Canadian
£289 $474 €419 Overlooking the valley (30x40cm-12x16in) s. board prov. 9-Jun-3 Hodgins, Calgary #392/R (C.D 650)
£1244 $2041 €1804 Two homes overlooking an inlet (65x80cm-26x31in) s. 9-Jun-3 Hodgins, Calgary #359/R est:3000-4000 (C.D 2800)

CODINA Y LANGLIN, Victoriano (1844-1911) Spanish
£881 $1356 €1400 Landscape (26x44cm-10x17in) s. board. 22-Oct-2 Durán, Madrid #242/R

CODRON, Jef (1882-?) Belgian
£753 $1175 €1100 Chemin en foret (120x145cm-47x57in) s. 14-Apr-3 Horta, Bruxelles #476

COEDES, Louis Eugène (1810-1906) French
Works on paper
£506 $800 €800 Portrait de gentilhomme (72x59cm-28x23in) s.d.1870 pastel oval. 2-Dec-2 Cornette de St.Cyr, Paris #57

COEFFIN (?) ?
Works on paper
£1348 $2183 €1900 Abstract composition (61x43cm-24x17in) s. gouache prov. 24-May-3 Van Ham, Cologne #106/R est:600

COELENBIER, Jan (1630-1677) Dutch
£4500 $7065 €6750 River landscape with a horse drawn cart and figures on a bank (37x55cm-15x22in) s.d.1646 panel oval prov.lit. 10-Dec-2 Sotheby's, Olympia #368/R est:3000-4000

COELLO, Claudio (circle) (1630-1693) Spanish
£5369 $8644 €8000 Immaculate Conception (153x120cm-60x47in) 18-Feb-3 Durán, Madrid #229/R est:1300

COENE, Constantinus Fidelio (1780-1841) Flemish
£1528 $2429 €2200 Galanterie dans la cuisine (58x70cm-23x28in) s. panel. 30-Apr-3 Tajan, Paris #2/R
£2207 $3509 €3200 Interieur de cuisine avec paysans mangeant des moules (39x49cm-15x19in) s.d.1828 panel. 4-Mar-3 Palais de Beaux Arts, Brussels #295/R est:2500-3500
£2580 $4153 €3870 Tavern scene (33x49cm-13x19in) s. panel. 12-May-3 Stephan Welz, Johannesburg #416/R est:9000-12000 (SA.R 30000)

COENE, Jean Baptiste (1805-1850) Belgian
£256 $403 €400 Nature morte (50x62cm-20x24in) s. 10-Dec-2 Campo, Vlaamse Kaai #80
£543 $891 €750 Deballage du service (93x64cm-37x25in) s. panel. 27-May-3 Campo & Campo, Antwerp #52
£2405 $3752 €3800 Conversation pres de la chaumiere (47x40cm-19x16in) s. 16-Sep-2 Horta, Bruxelles #184

COENE, Jean Henri de (1798-1866) Flemish
£566 $872 €900 Old man with cigarette holder (26x20cm-10x8in) s.d.1831 panel. 22-Oct-2 Wiener Kunst Auktionen, Vienna #1077/R

COENEN, Otto (1907-1971) German
Works on paper
£385 $596 €600 Landscape with houses - Upper Kassel (25x40cm-10x16in) s.d.37 prov. 4-Dec-2 Lempertz, Koln #620/R

COENRAETS, Ferdinand (19th C) Belgian?
Works on paper
£319 $533 €450 L'Eglise de Knokke (33x21cm-13x8in) W/C. 23-Jun-3 Amberes, Antwerp #79
£709 $1184 €1000 La cursale d'Ostende (12x33cm-5x13in) W/C. 23-Jun-3 Amberes, Antwerp #80
£1410 $2186 €2200 Snowy landscape (34x49cm-13x19in) s.d.88 W/C. 7-Dec-2 De Vuyst, Lokeren #58/R est:700-900
£1560 $2606 €2200 La Meuse a Huy (31x16cm-12x6in) W/C. 23-Jun-3 Amberes, Antwerp #81

COESSIN DE LA FOSSE, Charles Alexandre (1829-1910) French
£5063 $8000 €7595 Nouvelle inattendue (54x65cm-21x26in) s. 23-Apr-3 Christie's, Rockefeller NY #129/R est:12000-16000

COETZEE, Christo (1929-2001) South African
£480 $763 €720 Visitors (335x30cm-132x12in) s.indis.d. board. 18-Mar-3 Rosebery Fine Art, London #849/R
£641 $999 €962 Renaissance head in colour (120x120cm-47x47in) s.d.97 s.i.d.97 verso board. 11-Nov-2 Stephan Welz, Johannesburg #506/R (SA.R 10000)
£769 $1199 €1154 Infanta, flora 2 (121x120cm-48x47in) s.d.96 s.i.d.96 verso board. 11-Nov-2 Stephan Welz, Johannesburg #507/R (SA.R 12000)
£2923 $4707 €4385 Rose head (121x120cm-48x47in) s. s.i.d.92 verso board. 12-May-3 Stephan Welz, Johannesburg #561/R est:15000-20000 (SA.R 34000)

Works on paper
£243 $380 €365 Tubular baroque image (50x62cm-20x24in) s.d.77 i.verso mixed media. 11-Nov-2 Stephan Welz, Johannesburg #516 (SA.R 3800)
£301 $485 €452 Abstract composition (98x48cm-39x19in) s. mixed media on canvas. 12-May-3 Stephan Welz, Johannesburg #409 est:2000-3000 (SA.R 3500)
£482 $762 €723 Untitled (91x91cm-36x36in) s.d.56 verso mixed media. 1-Apr-3 Stephan Welz, Johannesburg #499/R est:3000-5000 (SA.R 6000)
£523 $826 €785 After Japan (152x102cm-60x40in) s.d.1960 i.verso mixed media on canvas lit. 1-Apr-3 Stephan Welz, Johannesburg #500/R est:7000-10000 (SA.R 6500)
£688 $1107 €1032 Untitled (102x102cm-40x40in) s.d.1956 verso mixed media on canvas. 12-May-3 Stephan Welz, Johannesburg #509/R est:5000-7000 (SA.R 8000)
£961 $1499 €1442 Violet (152x102cm-60x40in) s.d.1960 i.verso mixed media prov. 11-Nov-2 Stephan Welz, Johannesburg #515/R est:4000-6000 (SA.R 15000)
£1089 $1699 €1634 Composition with found objects (100x100cm-39x39in) s.d.62 s.i.d.1962 verso mixed media. 11-Nov-2 Stephan Welz, Johannesburg #577/R est:5000-7000 (SA.R 17000)
£1376 $2215 €2064 Untitled (152x130cm-60x51in) s.d.1962 i.verso mixed media on canvas prov.lit. 12-May-3 Stephan Welz, Johannesburg #510/R est:10000-15000 (SA.R 16000)

COETZER, Willem H (1900-1983) South African
£327 $526 €491 Farm beneath the Drakensberg (38x54cm-15x21in) s.d.28.11.45. 12-May-3 Stephan Welz, Johannesburg #90 est:3000-5000 (SA.R 3800)
£327 $526 €491 Sentinel amphitheatre, Drakensberg (20x25cm-8x10in) s.i.d.44 i.verso board. 12-May-3 Stephan Welz, Johannesburg #130 est:3000-5000 (SA.R 3800)
£344 $554 €516 Eastern buttress amphitheatre, Drakensberg (22x26cm-9x10in) s.d.46 i.verso canvas on board. 12-May-3 Stephan Welz, Johannesburg #131 est:3000-5000 (SA.R 4000)
£344 $554 €516 Three figures in a landscape (17x25cm-7x10in) s.i.d.63 s.verso board. 12-May-3 Stephan Welz, Johannesburg #290 est:2000-4000 (SA.R 4000)
£372 $580 €558 Naby ohrigstad (29x44cm-11x17in) s.d.63 i.verso board. 11-Nov-2 Stephan Welz, Johannesburg #549 (SA.R 5800)
£387 $623 €581 Retief se bottel (33x26cm-13x10in) s.d.45 canvas on board. 12-May-3 Stephan Welz, Johannesburg #380 est:5000-7000 (SA.R 4500)
£418 $660 €627 Drakensberg (27x33cm-11x13in) s.d.49 i.verso board. 1-Apr-3 Stephan Welz, Johannesburg #453 est:3500-5000 (SA.R 5200)
£420 $655 €630 Coastal landscape (10x51cm-4x20in) s.d.56 board. 17-Sep-2 Bonhams, Knightsbridge #64
£545 $849 €818 Blydevooruitzicht naby oliviershoekpas (39x49cm-15x19in) s. i.verso canvasboard. 11-Nov-2 Stephan Welz, Johannesburg #548 (SA.R 8500)
£645 $1038 €968 Extensive mountainous landscape with figures on a path near anthills (39x49cm-15x19in) s. canvas on board. 12-May-3 Stephan Welz, Johannesburg #303 est:6000-8000 (SA.R 7500)
£1032 $1661 €1548 Umzimkulu River, Oribi Gorge (49x70cm-19x28in) s.d.65 i.verso canvas on board. 12-May-3 Stephan Welz, Johannesburg #473/R est:7000-10000 (SA.R 12000)

Works on paper
£774 $1246 €1161 Farm at sunset (21x29cm-8x11in) s.d.62 pastel. 12-May-3 Stephan Welz, Johannesburg #301 est:6000-8000 (SA.R 9000)

COFFA, Andrea (19th C) Italian
£1572 $2453 €2500 Mother, father and child on sunny day (52x31cm-20x12in) s. 9-Oct-2 Michael Zeller, Lindau #648/R est:2500

COFFERMANS, Marcellus (16th C) Flemish
£110000 $183700 €159500 Visitation. Virgin annunciate. Angel of the Annunciation (64x101cm-25x40in) panel triptych. 9-Jul-3 Christie's, London #23/R est:40000-60000

COFFEY, Alfred (1869-1950) Australian
£250 $395 €375 Village fete (26x34cm-10x13in) s. board. 18-Nov-2 Goodman, Sydney #215 (A.D 700)
£411 $637 €617 Fishing boats, Tuggerah (22x29cm-9x11in) s.d.1920 board. 29-Oct-2 Lawson Menzies, Sydney #277 (A.D 1150)
£1088 $1795 €1578 Floating bridge over the Lygergract (50x35cm-20x14in) s. 6-Jul-3 Christie's, Hong Kong #15/R est:16000-20000 (HK.D 14000)

COFFIN, William A (1855-1925) American
£617 $950 €926 Meadow pool (36x51cm-14x20in) s. painted c.1900. 8-Sep-2 Treadway Gallery, Cincinnati #542/R

COFFIN, William H (1837-1898) American
£3571 $5500 €5357 Clipper ship off Boston Light (84x132cm-33x52in) s.d.87 prov. 27-Oct-2 Grogan, Boston #65 est:4000-6000

COGGESHALL, John I (attrib) (1856-1927) American
£271 $425 €407 Seascape with two schooners near shore (25x41cm-10x16in) s.d.1891. 22-Nov-2 Eldred, East Dennis #624

COGHUF (1905-1976) Swiss
£1092 $1703 €1638 Jura landscape in winter (31x52cm-12x20in) s.d.39. 6-Nov-2 Hans Widmer, St Gallen #139/R est:1200-2800 (S.FR 2500)
£4148 $6472 €6222 Fields in extensive Jura landscape (75x100cm-30x39in) s.d.1948. 6-Nov-2 Hans Widmer, St Gallen #113/R est:8500-14000 (S.FR 9500)

Works on paper
£524 $817 €786 Concours hippique a Saignelegier (21x14cm-8x6in) s. Indian ink W/C. 6-Nov-2 Dobiaschofsky, Bern #1467 (S.FR 1200)
£1048 $1635 €1572 Evening party (47x62cm-19x24in) s.d.43 W/C. 6-Nov-2 Dobiaschofsky, Bern #413/R est:2400 (S.FR 2400)

COGLE, Henry George (1875-1957) British
£340 $568 €493 Restaurant interior with a lady and gentleman at a table (21x25cm-8x10in) s. board. 17-Jun-3 Anderson & Garland, Newcastle #359/R

COGNAL, Jean Baptiste (?) French?
£612 $978 €850 La visite du sultan a Venise (39x65cm-15x26in) s. 18-May-3 Charbonneaux, Paris #138

COGNATA, Giovanni la (1954-) Italian
£1712 $2671 €2500 Landscape (70x60cm-28x24in) s. 10-Apr-3 Finarte Semenzato, Rome #236/R

COGNEE, Philippe (1957-) French
£833 $1317 €1200 Sans titre (150x160cm-59x63in) acrylic paper on canvas diptych. 28-Apr-3 Cornette de St.Cyr, Paris #369/R

COGNIET, Léon (1794-1880) French
£4838 $7500 €7257 Brigand's wife (36x27cm-14x11in) s.d1825 prov. 29-Oct-2 Sotheby's, New York #38/R est:2000-3000

Works on paper
£372 $580 €550 Tete d'homme (21x21cm-8x8in) i. pen ink wash. 27-Mar-3 Maigret, Paris #14
£3064 $4750 €4596 Seated angel (55x41cm-22x16in) init.i. pencil chl. htd white prov. 29-Oct-2 Sotheby's, New York #23/R est:2000-3000

COGNIET, Léon (attrib) (1794-1880) French

Works on paper
£317 $500 €500 Jeune garcon assis portant un chapeau (21x29cm-8x11in) crayon sanguine htd gouache. 28-Nov-2 Tajan, Paris #150

COHELEACH, Guy Joseph (1933-) American
£31646 $50000 €45887 Victoria Falls, twilight Leopard (122x91cm-48x36in) s. exhib. 26-Jul-3 Coeur d'Alene, Hayden #153/R est:40000-60000

COHEN, Alfred (1920-) American

Works on paper
£280 $462 €406 Flowers in a jug (30x24cm-12x9in) s. W/C bodycol. 1-Jul-3 Bonhams, Norwich #148/R

COHEN, Bernard (1933-) British
£760 $1216 €1140 Untitled (53x97cm-21x38in) s.d.57 board. 15-May-3 Lawrence, Crewkerne #1017

COHEN, George (20th C) American?
£671 $1100 €973 Cubiculum (30x30cm-12x12in) init. oil gesso on plywood exhib. 1-Jun-3 Wright, Chicago #316/R est:600-800

COHEN, Gil (attrib) (20th C) American

Works on paper
£248 $400 €372 Man prepares to bury slain woman (61x33cm-24x13in) init. gouache. 20-Feb-3 Illustration House, New York #27/R

COHEN, Harold (1928-) British
£1300 $2145 €1885 Bayeux (107x137cm-42x54in) s.i.d.1963 verso prov. 3-Jul-3 Christie's, Kensington #745/R est:300-500

COHEN, Larry (20th C) American
£1139 $1800 €1709 View from Taft Avenue in the fog (168x112cm-66x44in) s.on stretcher painted 1986 prov. 13-Nov-2 Sotheby's, New York #611/R
£4430 $7000 €6645 View from Oriole Way (167x111cm-66x44in) s.on stretcher painted 1987 prov. 13-Nov-2 Sotheby's, New York #612/R est:3000-5000

COHEN, Minnie Agnes (1864-?) British
£1050 $1649 €1575 Untitled (35x30cm-14x12in) 15-Apr-3 Bonhams, Chester #1015
£5000 $7950 €7500 Fisherwomen gossiping on the beach (71x105cm-28x41in) s. 6-Mar-3 Christie's, Kensington #121/R est:5000-7000

COHEN, P (20th C) American
£1899 $3000 €2754 Construction workers (64x109cm-25x43in) s.d.1948. 5-Apr-3 DeFina, Austinburg #1337

COHEN, Rachel (20th C) American
£271 $425 €407 Landscape (36x25cm-14x10in) s.verso. 28-Jul-2 William Jenack, New York #119

COHEN, Yvonne Frankel (1914-) Australian
£323 $490 €485 Magnolias (50x40cm-20x16in) s. canvas on board. 28-Aug-2 Deutscher-Menzies, Melbourne #385/R (A.D 900)

COHN, Benny (1896-?) Danish
£1185 $1837 €1778 Modern dancing (36x44cm-14x17in) s.d.1917 prov. 1-Oct-2 Rasmussen, Copenhagen #304/R est:5000 (D.KR 14000)

COHN, Ola (1892-1964) Australian

Works on paper
£214 $338 €321 We love to play we're soldiers (19x14cm-7x6in) s.i.d.1915 W/C pen ink. 27-Nov-2 Deutscher-Menzies, Melbourne #241/R (A.D 600)
£214 $338 €321 I did em! (19x14cm-7x6in) s. W/C pen ink. 27-Nov-2 Deutscher-Menzies, Melbourne #242/R (A.D 600)

COHN, Philip (1923-) American
£247 $400 €371 By the sea (51x61cm-20x24in) s.d.90. 24-Jan-3 Freeman, Philadelphia #190/R
£247 $400 €371 Summertime (51x61cm-20x24in) s. 24-Jan-3 Freeman, Philadelphia #201/R

COIGNARD (?) ?
£706 $1108 €1024 Cattle in landscape. 15-Dec-2 Anders Antik, Landskrona #288 (S.KR 10000)

COIGNARD, James (1925-1997) French
£379 $633 €550 Nature morte (55x33cm-22x13in) s. 9-Jul-3 Cornette de St.Cyr, Paris #248
£449 $696 €700 Composition (27x41cm-11x16in) s. oil spray paper on board. 7-Dec-2 Ketterer, Hamburg #641/R
£494 $765 €780 Composition (46x35cm-18x14in) s. acrylic collage paper. 28-Sep-2 Cornette de St.Cyr, Paris #277
£545 $845 €850 Composition (57x33cm-22x13in) s. oil gouache spray masonite. 7-Dec-2 Ketterer, Hamburg #640/R
£759 $1267 €1100 Nature morte aux poissons (50x65cm-20x26in) s. painted c.1960. 10-Jul-3 Artcurial Briest, Paris #237
£833 $1342 €1250 Children in market (50x29cm-20x11in) s. 7-May-3 Dobiaschofsky, Bern #415/R (S.FR 1800)
£1135 $1783 €1703 Vertical jaune (35x25cm-14x10in) s. s.i.d.1986 verso acrylic mixed media prov. 25-Nov-2 Germann, Zurich #108/R est:2000-3000 (S.FR 2600)
£1489 $2487 €2100 Bouquet de fleurs et lampe a petrole (116x89cm-46x35in) s. painted c.1965 prov. 18-Jun-3 Pierre Berge, Paris #167/R est:2000-3000
£1736 $2760 €2500 Chevaliers (50x61cm-20x24in) s. s.i.d.verso. 29-Apr-3 Artcurial Briest, Paris #287/R est:2500
£2053 $3244 €3080 Proposition dualisee (80x110cm-31x43in) s. 28-Apr-3 Bukowskis, Stockholm #336/R est:15000-20000 (S.KR 27000)
£2780 $4476 €4170 Espace rouge (100x81cm-39x32in) s. 7-May-3 AB Stockholms Auktionsverk #1137/R est:45000-50000 (S.KR 36000)
£3930 $6170 €5895 Hommage a Brett (137x183cm-54x72in) s. i.d.1987 verso acrylic collage prov. 25-Nov-2 Germann, Zurich #42/R est:12000-16000 (S.FR 9000)
£4803 $7013 €7205 Bipolarisation Aet B - dyptique (81x65cm-32x26in) s. i. verso acrylic two prov. 4-Jun-2 Germann, Zurich #24/R est:8000-12000 (S.FR 11000)

Works on paper
£461 $719 €692 Otage et stratification (59x34cm-23x13in) s. mixed media exhib. 15-Oct-2 Stephan Welz, Johannesburg #411 est:8000-12000 (SA.R 7500)
£520 $828 €780 Paysage aux barques (50x100cm-20x39in) s. mixed media. 3-Mar-3 Lilla Bukowskis, Stockholm #16 (S.KR 7000)

£538 $839 €850 Composition (48x60cm-19x24in) s. mixed media collage. 20-Oct-2 Charbonneaux, Paris #49 est:1200-1500
£562 $877 €843 Rai (66x52cm-26x20in) s. mixed media. 13-Sep-2 Lilla Bukowskis, Stockholm #795 (S.KR 8200)
£633 $987 €1000 Untitled (23x50cm-9x20in) mixed media pair. 30-Jul-2 Gioffredo, Nice #122
£663 $1041 €995 Spirale et rouge (100x66cm-39x26in) s. mixed media. 16-Dec-2 Lilla Bukowskis, Stockholm #626 (S.KR 9400)
£849 $1368 €1274 Composition (48x61cm-19x24in) s. mixed media. 7-May-3 AB Stockholms Auktionsverk #1118/R (S.KR 11000)
£1051 $1640 €1577 Composition (91x66cm-36x26in) s. mixed media. 6-Nov-2 AB Stockholms Auktionsverk #947/R est:10000-12000 (S.KR 15000)
£1682 $2624 €2523 Trois elements en bleu (65x55cm-26x22in) s. mixed media. 5-Nov-2 Bukowskis, Stockholm #328/R est:12000-15000 (S.KR 24000)

COIGNARD, Louis (1810-1883) French
£774 $1138 €1200 Cowherd resting under tree (50x65cm-20x26in) s. 20-Jun-2 Dr Fritz Nagel, Stuttgart #758/R

COIGNET (?) French
£1120 $1702 €1680 Hilly landscape with cattle on road (65x97cm-26x38in) s. 27-Aug-2 Rasmussen, Copenhagen #1678/R est:15000 (D.KR 13000)

COIGNET, Jules Louis Philippe (1798-1860) French
£870 $1400 €1305 View of Lebanon (23x33cm-9x13in) 19-Feb-3 Doyle, New York #13
£1310 $1913 €1965 Summer landscape (41x65cm-16x26in) s.d.1841. 4-Jun-2 Germann, Zurich #44/R est:2000-3000 (S.FR 3000)
£2695 $4366 €3800 Rocky landscape with figures (41x65cm-16x26in) s.d.1841. 22-May-3 Dorotheum, Vienna #118/R est:3000-4000

Works on paper
£350 $567 €508 Travellers on road (14x22cm-6x9in) s. W/C. 29-Jul-3 Holloways, Banbury #325
£2979 $4974 €4200 Paysage d'Italie avec la vasque Medicis (32x46cm-13x18in) s. W/C gouache black crayon. 19-Jun-3 Piasa, Paris #205/R est:3000

COIGNET, Jules Louis Philippe (attrib) (1798-1860) French
£525 $830 €788 Mountain landscape with watermill (32x37cm-13x15in) s. 16-Nov-2 Crafoord, Lund #57/R (S.KR 7500)
£1064 $1777 €1500 La boulangerie de la grande chartreuse (29x38cm-11x15in) i.d.1838 paper on cardboard. 23-Jun-3 Delvaux, Paris #22 est:1200-1500
£1892 $2951 €2800 Paysages aux moulins (22x30cm-9x12in) cardboard pair. 28-Mar-3 Piasa, Paris #63

COIGNET, Marie (19th C) French
£1548 $2400 €2322 Bowl of grapes and pears, and an apple on a ledge (60x81cm-24x32in) s. 3-Dec-2 Christie's, Rockefeller NY #632/R est:4000-6000

COJAN, Aurel (1914-) Rumanian
£448 $749 €650 Sans titre (92x65cm-36x26in) s. 9-Jul-3 Cornette de St.Cyr, Paris #250

COKER, Peter (1926-) British
£600 $936 €900 Windbreakers, Aldeburgh (18x13cm-7x5in) s. board. 27-Mar-3 Christie's, Kensington #515/R
£1000 $1660 €1450 Beach, Aldeburgh (20x38cm-8x15in) s.d.1971 board. 12-Jun-3 Gorringes, Lewes #1738 est:1000-1500
£4000 $6200 €6000 Dewley Fell near Alston (122x91cm-48x36in) s. s.verso. 4-Dec-2 Christie's, Kensington #545/R est:2000-3000
£5000 $8350 €7250 Sunflowers (121x81cm-48x32in) s. board prov. 24-Jun-3 Bonhams, New Bond Street #108/R est:5000-7000
£7800 $12090 €11700 Apple tree (128x153cm-50x60in) s. i.d.Oct 1965 verso. 1-Nov-2 Moore Allen & Innocent, Cirencester #501/R est:3000-5000

Works on paper
£280 $468 €406 Artist's wife and son at a table (51x36cm-20x14in) init.d.55-56 red chk. 17-Jun-3 Bonhams, Knightsbridge #73/R
£320 $499 €480 Shore scene, Aldeburgh (14x37cm-6x15in) init. W/C two sheets joined. 17-Sep-2 Bonhams, Ipswich #368
£460 $759 €667 Track down to valley farm (50x77cm-20x30in) s.i. pencil col chks. 1-Jul-3 Bonhams, Norwich #157
£600 $936 €900 Frozen fields in winter, Higham, Essex (71x53cm-28x21in) s.d. s.i.d.verso pastel. 27-Mar-3 Christie's, Kensington #622/R

COL, Jan David (1822-1900) Belgian
£574 $896 €850 Vue sur l'atelier (34x42cm-13x17in) 25-Mar-3 Campo & Campo, Antwerp #35
£1100 $1716 €1650 Fisherman (15x11cm-6x4in) s. panel. 10-Sep-2 Bonhams, Knightsbridge #138/R est:1200-1800
£1154 $1788 €1800 Cour de la maison (32x38cm-13x15in) panel prov. 3-Dec-2 Campo & Campo, Antwerp #50/R est:1750-2250
£6962 $10861 €11000 Fumeur (19x16cm-7x6in) s. i.verso panel. 15-Oct-2 Horta, Bruxelles #132/R est:12000-15000
£14000 $21980 €21000 Finishing tough (46x37cm-18x15in) s. panel. 19-Nov-2 Bonhams, New Bond Street #11/R est:6000-8000

COL, Jan David and MAES, E R (19th C) Belgian
£6013 $9500 €8719 Feeding the chicken (58x94cm-23x37in) s. i.verso. 5-Apr-3 DeFina, Austinburg #1287 est:6000-9000

COL, Jan David and MAES, Eugène Remy (19th C) Belgian
£8000 $13360 €12000 Finest poultry (60x95cm-24x37in) s.i.verso. 18-Jun-3 Christie's, Kensington #44/R est:8000-12000

COLACICCHI, Giovanni (1900-1993) Italian
£400 $636 €600 Pathway through an olive grove with hill top village in the distance (60x76cm-24x30in) s. 18-Mar-3 Rosebery Fine Art, London #797
£1420 $2300 €2059 Sera di autunno (76x99cm-30x39in) s.d.1931 exhib. 21-May-3 Doyle, New York #7/R est:4000-6000
£3108 $4849 €4600 Sea woman (50x40cm-20x16in) s. cardboard on canvas. 26-Mar-3 Finarte Semenzato, Milan #121/R
£4054 $6324 €6000 Reclining female nude (51x70cm-20x28in) s. 26-Mar-3 Finarte Semenzato, Milan #367/R

COLACICCO, Salvatore (1935-) British/Italian
£2097 $3250 €3146 British man-of-war off Malta (61x91cm-24x36in) s. s.i.verso. 1-Oct-2 Arthur James, Florida #116
£2097 $3250 €3146 Shipping at anchor off Malta (61x91cm-24x36in) s.i.verso panel. 1-Oct-2 Arthur James, Florida #117

COLAGROSSI, Angelo (1960-) Italian
£694 $1104 €1000 Loneliness (60x80cm-24x31in) s.s.i.verso acrylic. 1-May-3 Meeting Art, Vercelli #452

COLAHAN, Colin (1897-1987) Australian
£609 $926 €914 Still life with Oriental doll (50x61cm-20x24in) s. 28-Aug-2 Deutscher-Menzies, Melbourne #404/R (A.D 1700)

COLAO, Domenico (1881-1943) Italian
Works on paper
£959 $1496 €1400 Boy (42x30cm-17x12in) s. pastel card. 10-Apr-3 Finarte Semenzato, Rome #95/R

COLAO, Rudy (?) ?
£1282 $2000 €1923 Lilacs (61x76cm-24x30in) 9-Nov-2 Altermann Galleries, Santa Fe #217

COLAS, Alphonse (1818-1887) French
£1519 $2370 €2400 Portrait de femme (98x80cm-39x31in) s. 20-Oct-2 Mercier & Cie, Lille #321/R est:2300-2500

COLBY, George E (1859-?) American
£688 $1100 €1032 Missouri river landscape (38x28cm-15x11in) s.d. 15-Mar-3 Selkirks, St. Louis #337/R

COLDSTREAM, Sir William (1908-1987) British
£3500 $5775 €5075 Portrait of David Ropner (91x71cm-36x28in) s.d.81 exhib. 3-Jul-3 Christie's, Kensington #409/R est:1000-1500

COLE, Augusta (fl.1856-1859) British
Miniatures
£1600 $2544 €2400 Mrs H S Leigh Hunt with her son Shelley in a interior (25cm-10xin) arched mount exhib. 4-Mar-3 Bearnes, Exeter #313/R est:800-1200

COLE, Carolyn (20th C) American
Works on paper
£813 $1300 €1179 Colour abstractions (36x25cm-14x10in) s. mixed media three. 17-May-3 Selkirks, St. Louis #304/R

COLE, G (1810-1883) British
£550 $847 €825 Racehorse in a stable (43x51cm-17x20in) s. 3-Sep-2 Gorringes, Lewes #2215

COLE, George (1810-1883) British
£1800 $3006 €2610 Fisherman and cattle by the river with Windsor Castle beyond (78x103cm-31x41in) 25-Jun-3 Bonhams, Bury St Edmunds #584 est:2000-4000
£2800 $4452 €4200 Wooded river landscape with sailing vessels (30x46cm-12x18in) s.d.1876 panel. 29-Apr-3 Gorringes, Lewes #2169

£3281 $5250 €4922 English landscape with lake (36x53cm-14x21in) s. 1-Jan-3 Nadeau, Windsor #80/R est:4000-7000
£3500 $5565 €5250 Harvesting (37x51cm-15x20in) s.d.1874 oil paper on canvas. 6-Mar-3 Christie's, Kensington #433/R est:4000-6000
£4400 $6996 €6600 Horse, recumbent cow and sheep in a lowland landscape (46x76cm-18x30in) indis.sig. 18-Mar-3 Capes Dunn, Manchester #527
£5000 $7950 €7500 Carting timber (61x91cm-24x36in) s.d.1877 prov. 6-Mar-3 Christie's, Kensington #463/R est:6000-8000
£5031 $8000 €7547 Bay racehorse held by a groom (51x61cm-20x24in) s.d.1844 prov. 30-Apr-3 Sotheby's, New York #563/R est:8000-12000
£7500 $11700 €11250 Burnham Overy, Norfolk, seen from the Norton Marshes (61x96cm-24x38in) s.d.1865. 10-Apr-3 Tennants, Leyburn #977/R est:4000-6000
£28000 $46480 €42000 Last load (52x77cm-20x30in) 10-Jun-3 Christie's, London #135/R est:15000-20000

COLE, George Vicat (1833-1893) British
£250 $415 €363 Landscape with a figure (30x61cm-12x24in) 10-Jun-3 David Lay, Penzance #369
£1200 $1920 €1800 Wooded landscape with figures seated beside a felled tree (39x60cm-15x24in) s.d.1858. 13-May-3 Bonhams, Knightsbridge #65/R est:1500-2000
£1300 $2080 €1950 Arun near Arundel (36x54cm-14x21in) mono.indis d. 11-Mar-3 Bonhams, Knightsbridge #320/R est:800-1200
£3000 $4860 €4500 Cattle watering with Windsor Castle in the background (51x76cm-20x30in) s.d.1870. 20-May-3 Sotheby's, Olympia #201/R est:3000-5000
£4000 $6200 €6000 Near Dolgelly, North Wales (74x121cm-29x48in) s.d.1859. 4-Oct-2 ELR Auctions, Sheffield #305/R est:5000-7000
£8865 $14362 €12500 Figures in a cornfield (49x75cm-19x30in) s.d.1886 prov. 20-May-3 Mealy's, Castlecomer #1260/R est:6000-8000
£14000 $22120 €21000 Haymaking (46x61cm-18x24in) s. prov. 26-Nov-2 Christie's, London #89/R est:12000-18000
£25000 $39500 €37500 Windsor Castle from a backwater (99x152cm-39x60in) mono.d.1892 prov.lit. 26-Nov-2 Christie's, London #91/R est:25000-35000

Works on paper
£350 $574 €508 Summer landscape with approaching rainstorm and shepherd with sheep (23x33cm-9x13in) mono.d.1886 W/C. 3-Jun-3 Capes Dunn, Manchester #52
£540 $886 €810 Wooded landscape with a distant view of a farm and cottage (36x51cm-14x20in) s.d.1876 W/C htd white. 4-Feb-3 Bonhams, Leeds #262

COLE, Herbert R (19/20th C) ?
Works on paper
£316 $493 €474 Sailing ships (38x58cm-15x23in) s. W/C. 27-Mar-3 International Art Centre, Auckland #200 (NZ.D 900)

COLE, J (19/20th C) British
£580 $905 €870 Returning home - Rustic landscape with family at a cottage gate (30x61cm-12x24in) s. 17-Sep-2 Holloways, Banbury #334

COLE, James William (19th C) British
£380 $608 €570 Shire horse beside a barrow with figures working in a field beyond and an extensive landscape (30x43cm-12x17in) s. board. 13-Mar-3 Duke & Son, Dorchester #241

COLE, John Vicat (1903-1975) British
£500 $775 €750 Study of 17-18 Nassau street, W1 (30x41cm-12x16in) s. board. 4-Dec-2 Christie's, Kensington #539/R
£3200 $4992 €4800 Antique shop (75x101cm-30x40in) s.d.48. 25-Mar-3 Bonhams, New Bond Street #8/R est:2000-3000

COLE, Joseph Foxcroft (1837-1892) American
£1410 $2200 €2115 Landscape with cows (46x66cm-18x26in) s. 1-Aug-2 Eldred, East Dennis #915/R est:2000-3000

COLE, Max (20th C) American
£2751 $4319 €4127 Malachi (76x95cm-30x37in) s.i.d.1999 verso acrylic prov. 23-Nov-2 Burkhard, Luzern #61/R est:6000-8000 (S.FR 6300)

COLE, Peter (1946-) Australian
Sculpture
£1169 $1824 €2027 New friend no 17 (100x70cm-39x28in) s.d.1999 mixed media. 31-Mar-3 Goodman, Sydney #153/R (A.D 3100)

COLE, Peter D (1947-) Australian
Sculpture
£1227 $1903 €1841 Night (77cm-30in) painted steel bronze. 3-Dec-2 Shapiro, Sydney #82/R est:3000-5000 (A.D 3400)
£1916 $2854 €2874 Campaspe river, evening (113cm-44in) s. bronze brass enamel executed 1994 prov. 27-Aug-2 Christie's, Melbourne #194/R est:4000-6000 (A.D 5000)
£2500 $3900 €3750 Landscape (69x121x40cm-27x48x16in) enamel paint green oxide steel. 11-Nov-2 Deutscher-Menzies, Melbourne #85/R est:8000-12000 (A.D 7000)
£3187 $5227 €4781 Musical balance (247cm-97in) painted pat brass wood prov. 4-Jun-3 Deutscher-Menzies, Melbourne #18/R est:10000-15000 (A.D 8000)
£4643 $7243 €6965 Campaspe landscape (211x90x28cm-83x35x11in) s.i.d.1995 bronze brass steel enamel paint. 11-Nov-2 Deutscher-Menzies, Melbourne #33/R est:15000-20000 (A.D 13000)
£5357 $8411 €8036 Winter solstice (221x73x19cm-87x29x7in) bronze brass enamel prov. 25-Nov-2 Christie's, Melbourne #65/R est:10000-15000 (A.D 15000)

Works on paper
£690 $1083 €1035 Untitled - Langley landscape (80x120cm-31x47in) s.d.99 gouache pastel prov. 15-Apr-3 Lawson Menzies, Sydney #96/R est:2000-3000 (A.D 1800)

COLE, Philip Tennyson (fl.1880-1930) British
Works on paper
£250 $408 €375 Portrait of a lady (56x39cm-22x15in) indis sig.i. W/C. 2-Feb-3 Lots Road, London #359a/R

COLE, Rex Vicat (1870-1940) British
£1050 $1638 €1575 Springtime in Wasing Woods (48x38cm-19x15in) s.d.1903. 17-Sep-2 Bonhams, Oxford #36/R est:800-1000
£2308 $3600 €3462 Harvesting in Sussex (117x140cm-46x55in) s.d.1908. 12-Apr-3 Weschler, Washington #509/R est:7000-10000

COLE, Ruth (20th C) New Zealander
£304 $474 €456 Street scene with Mt. Eden in the distance (55x74cm-22x29in) oil chk pastel. 17-Sep-2 Peter Webb, Auckland #162/R est:1200-1800 (NZ.D 1000)
£1306 $2050 €1959 Coromandel coastal (125x142cm-49x56in) s.d.1994. 10-Dec-2 Peter Webb, Auckland #107/R est:3000-5000 (NZ.D 4100)

COLE, Solomon (fl.1845-1859) British
£300 $480 €450 Portrait of Hannah Cooke, daughter of Charles Cooke of Stockton, Worcestershire (20x15cm-8x6in) s.d.1842 i.verso metal. 15-May-3 Lawrence, Crewkerne #914
£1050 $1670 €1575 Portrait of Mrs Savage in black dress (33x23cm-13x9in) s.d.1846 panel. 27-Feb-3 Brightwells, Leominster #851/R est:500-800

COLE, T (1801-1848) American
£1375 $2200 €2063 Italian landscape (28x41cm-11x16in) s. 17-May-3 Pook & Pook, Downington #397d est:500-1000

COLE-WILLIS, James (19th C) British
£1200 $2004 €1740 Happiness (26x36cm-10x14in) s.d.1865. 25-Jun-3 Bonhams, Bury St Edmunds #545 est:800-1200

COLEMAN, Charles (1807-1874) British
£3500 $5495 €5250 Buffaloes watering in the roman campagna. Shepherd girl washing her clothes (43x68cm-17x27in) s.d.1852 pair. 21-Nov-2 Christie's, Kensington #164/R est:4000-6000

COLEMAN, Charles Caryl (1840-1928) American
£25806 $40000 €38709 Summer flowers, Capri (53x105cm-21x41in) mono.i.d.1906 prov.exhib. 5-Dec-2 Christie's, Rockefeller NY #65/R est:50000-70000
£49383 $80000 €74075 Blossoming pink branches. Blossoming white branches (74x20cm-29x8in) mono.d.1875 pair. 22-May-3 Christie's, Rockefeller NY #41/R est:40000-60000
£77844 $130000 €112874 Primavera (66x194cm-26x76in) s.i.d.1877 prov. 18-Jun-3 Christie's, Los Angeles #28/R est:100000-150000

COLEMAN, E (19th C) British
Works on paper
£4487 $7000 €6731 Buffalos near Tivoli (41x58cm-16x23in) s. i.verso W/C. 30-Mar-3 Susanin's, Chicago #6067/R est:800-1200

COLEMAN, Edward (?-1867) British

£1800	$2844	€2700	Day's bag (58x68cm-23x27in) s. 28-Nov-2 Christie's, Kensington #43/R est:1500-2000

COLEMAN, Ellen H (19th C) American

£427	$700	€619	Crotched mountain landscape with sunset (43x33cm-17x13in) s. 30-May-3 Aspire, Cleveland #53/R

COLEMAN, Enrico (1846-1911) Italian

£2006	$3250	€2909	Italian women carrying firewood (51x71cm-20x28in) s. W/C paper on board. 21-May-3 Doyle, New York #190/R est:3000-5000

Works on paper

£400	$656	€600	Girl in a wood, Marino (43x27cm-17x11in) s.i. pencil W/C. 5-Jun-3 Christie's, Kensington #944
£550	$787	€825	Oxen watering at a trough (9x13cm-4x5in) s.i.d.1873 pair. 28-Feb-2 Greenslade Hunt, Taunton #385/R
£1371	$2167	€2057	Oxen pulling a hay cart (21x34cm-8x13in) s. W/C. 18-Nov-2 Waddingtons, Toronto #273/R est:2000-2500 (C.D 3400)
£2692	$4173	€4200	Villa d'Este, Tivoli (32x46cm-13x18in) s.d.1908 W/C. 4-Dec-2 Finarte, Rome #716/R

COLEMAN, Francesco (1851-1918) Italian

Works on paper

£215	$335	€323	Drummer (35x24cm-14x9in) s.d.1875 W/C. 15-Oct-2 Stephan Welz, Johannesburg #383/R est:4000-6000 (SA.R 3500)
£350	$539	€525	Afternoon walk (43x30cm-17x12in) s.d.1877 W/C. 24-Oct-2 Richardson & Smith, Whitby #462/R
£420	$655	€630	Young couple conversing in a street (40x26cm-16x10in) s.i. W/C. 10-Apr-3 Tennants, Leyburn #895/R
£429	$670	€622	Vanity (53x37cm-21x15in) s.i. W/C prov. 26-Mar-3 Walker's, Ottawa #31/R est:1200-1600 (C.D 1000)

COLEMAN, Francesco (attrib) (1851-1918) Italian

£320	$509	€480	Challenge (43x56cm-17x22in) canvas laid down board. 30-Apr-3 Halls, Shrewsbury #271/R

COLEMAN, George (?) British

£1300	$2041	€1950	River landscape with cattle and distant castle ruin (61x107cm-24x42in) s.d.87. 21-Nov-2 Tennants, Leyburn #798/R est:600-800

COLEMAN, George Sumner (1881-1934) American

£581	$900	€872	Coastal inlet, shack and skiff (71x86cm-28x34in) s. 29-Oct-2 John Moran, Pasadena #736
£2194	$3400	€3291	Flying cloud, fourth of July Cove (30x41cm-12x16in) s. s.i.verso. 20-Jul-2 New Orleans Auction, New Orleans #800/R est:700-1000

COLEMAN, H (?) ?

£4300	$6536	€6450	Landscape with sheep, figures, distant buildings and mountains (33x61cm-13x24in) s. 28-Aug-2 Brightwells, Leominster #1087/R est:300-500

COLEMAN, Harvey B (1884-1959) American

£256	$400	€384	Desert view. s. canvasboard. 9-Aug-2 Skinner, Bolton #835

COLEMAN, J (19/20th C) British

£520	$811	€780	Still life dead game (62x75cm-24x30in) s. 10-Sep-2 Sworder & Son, Bishops Stortford #805/R
£1500	$2490	€2175	Day's catch (65x76cm-26x30in) s. 12-Jun-3 Christie's, Kensington #165/R est:1500-2000
£1600	$2656	€2320	Day's catch and a creel on a river bank (64x77cm-25x30in) s. 12-Jun-3 Christie's, Kensington #166/R est:2000-3000

COLEMAN, John (?) British

£1500	$2280	€2250	Study of carp, pike, trout, perch and roach - the days catch (56x71cm-22x28in) s. 16-Aug-2 Keys, Aylsham #641/R

COLEMAN, Mary Dartes (1894-?) American

£224	$350	€336	Mountain landscape. canvasboard. 9-Aug-2 Skinner, Bolton #565a
£256	$400	€384	Cows grazing at the mountains foot. s. canvasboard. 9-Aug-2 Skinner, Bolton #665

COLEMAN, Michael (1946-) American

£2388	$3750	€3582	Cottage with dirt road (51x41cm-20x16in) s. masonite prov. 19-Nov-2 Butterfields, San Francisco #8120/R est:4000-6000
£3425	$5000	€5138	In the woods (30x18cm-12x7in) 18-May-2 Altermann Galleries, Santa Fe #107/R
£3767	$5500	€5651	Mother bear and cubs (36x43cm-14x17in) 18-May-2 Altermann Galleries, Santa Fe #227/R
£4747	$7500	€6883	Lion Rock, Zimbabwe (61x76cm-24x30in) s. board. 26-Jul-3 Coeur d'Alene, Hayden #134/R est:10000-15000
£5844	$9000	€8766	High country camp (51x102cm-20x40in) 25-Oct-2 Morris & Whiteside, Hilton Head Island #149 est:13000-15000
£6962	$11000	€10095	Indian encampment (51x76cm-20x30in) s. board. 26-Jul-3 Coeur d'Alene, Hayden #36/R est:8000-12000
£8904	$13000	€13356	Canadian sunset (51x76cm-20x30in) 18-May-2 Altermann Galleries, Santa Fe #108/R
£12658	$20000	€18354	Summer camp on the bitterroot (61x76cm-24x30in) s. board. 26-Jul-3 Coeur d'Alene, Hayden #213/R est:10000-20000
£21154	$33000	€31731	Golden moment - Indian encampment (122x91cm-48x36in) 9-Nov-2 Altermann Galleries, Santa Fe #79

Works on paper

£4452	$6500	€6678	Indian encampment (28x43cm-11x17in) gouache. 18-May-2 Altermann Galleries, Santa Fe #105/R

COLEMAN, Nicholas (1978-) American

£3526	$5500	€5289	Woodland fire (51x76cm-20x30in) 9-Nov-2 Altermann Galleries, Santa Fe #37
£3904	$6325	€5661	Marshland sunset (51x76cm-20x30in) board. 23-May-3 Altermann Galleries, Santa Fe #57
£4110	$6000	€6165	Green river camp (61x91cm-24x36in) 18-May-2 Altermann Galleries, Santa Fe #27/R

COLEMAN, Ralph Pallen (1892-1968) American

£641	$1000	€962	Lord's supper (76x61cm-30x24in) s. board sold with a book. 18-Sep-2 Boos Gallery, Michigan #282/R
£6211	$10000	€9317	Couple in flat-bottomed boat afloat on a lily pond (71x89cm-28x35in) s.d. board. 10-May-3 Illustration House, New York #55/R est:5000-8000

COLEMAN, Simon (1916-) Irish

£2568	$4005	€3800	Summer (40x51cm-16x20in) s. board. 26-Mar-3 James Adam, Dublin #142/R est:1000-1500

COLEMAN, William (1922-1993) Australian

£398	$653	€577	Mother and child (50x39cm-20x15in) s. board. 3-Jun-3 Lawson Menzies, Sydney #971 (A.D 1000)
£421	$640	€632	Landscape with car (32x39cm-13x15in) s. board. 19-Aug-2 Joel, Victoria #298 est:1000-1500 (A.D 1200)
£520	$790	€780	Sitting nude (37x29cm-15x11in) s. kodak board. 27-Aug-2 Goodman, Sydney #11 (A.D 1450)
£573	$872	€860	Family group (34x26cm-13x10in) s. board exhib. 28-Aug-2 Deutscher-Menzies, Melbourne #338/R (A.D 1600)
£573	$872	€860	Bill poster (40x34cm-16x13in) s. canvas on board. 28-Aug-2 Deutscher-Menzies, Melbourne #380/R (A.D 1600)
£789	$1199	€1184	Walking home (45x61cm-18x24in) s.d.74 canvasboard. 28-Aug-2 Deutscher-Menzies, Melbourne #368/R (A.D 2200)
£797	$1307	€1196	Abstract (48x32cm-19x13in) s. composition board. 4-Jun-3 Deutscher-Menzies, Melbourne #292/R (A.D 2000)
£928	$1467	€1392	Bus stop (45x61cm-18x24in) s. canvas on board. 27-Nov-2 Deutscher-Menzies, Melbourne #219/R est:2000-3000 (A.D 2600)
£932	$1416	€1398	Promenade (43x29cm-17x11in) s. canvasboard exhib. 28-Aug-2 Deutscher-Menzies, Melbourne #369/R est:1800-2200 (A.D 2600)
£1000	$1590	€1500	Sisters (54x44cm-21x17in) s. canvas on board exhib. 4-Mar-3 Deutscher-Menzies, Melbourne #259/R est:2000-3000 (A.D 2600)
£1491	$2267	€2237	Nude on a couch (44x59cm-17x23in) s. board. 19-Aug-2 Joel, Victoria #255/R est:2000-3000 (A.D 4250)
£2143	$3386	€3215	Reclining nude (71x91cm-28x36in) s.d.74 canvas on board. 27-Nov-2 Deutscher-Menzies, Melbourne #133e/R est:6000-9000 (A.D 6000)
£3585	$5880	€5378	Woman bedside wine table (76x61cm-30x24in) s. canvas on composition board. 4-Jun-3 Deutscher-Menzies, Melbourne #186/R est:5000-6000 (A.D 9000)

Works on paper

£400	$644	€580	Family. W/C. 12-May-3 Joel, Victoria #225 (A.D 1000)
£537	$817	€806	Chess players (33x44cm-13x17in) s. pastel. 28-Aug-2 Deutscher-Menzies, Melbourne #261/R (A.D 1500)
£1149	$1805	€1724	Street scene with figures (39x50cm-15x20in) s. mixed media on canvas. 15-Apr-3 Lawson Menzies, Sydney #226/R est:2500-3000 (A.D 3000)

COLEMAN, William Stephen (1829-1904) British

£347	$549	€602	Seated nude (24x36cm-9x14in) s. i.verso paper. 1-Apr-3 Goodman, Sydney #24/R (A.D 910)
£2000	$3260	€2900	On the sea shore (76x51cm-30x20in) s. 16-Jul-3 Sotheby's, Olympia #114/R est:2000-3000
£10638	$17234	€15000	Sleepy tune (65x42cm-26x17in) s. 22-May-3 Dorotheum, Vienna #31/R est:15000-16000
£10638	$17234	€15000	Winding wool (65x42cm-26x17in) s. 22-May-3 Dorotheum, Vienna #32/R est:15000-16000

Works on paper

£250	$395	€375	Blue ball (38x30cm-15x12in) s. mixed media oil gouache. 18-Nov-2 Goodman, Sydney #17 (A.D 700)
£360	$601	€522	Sunset over a river landscape (14x21cm-6x8in) W/C prov. 24-Jun-3 Bonhams, Knightsbridge #39/R
£2400	$3840	€3600	Children approaching a brickworks (20x31cm-8x12in) mono. W/C bodycol. 11-Mar-3 Bonhams, New Bond Street #66/R est:2000-4000

COLERIDGE, F G (fl.1866-1914) British

Works on paper

£1100	$1793	€1650	Near Dover with mother and child and ducks on a lane (25x33cm-10x13in) s. W/C. 28-Jan-3 Gorringes, Lewes #1583 est:500-700
£1300	$2027	€1950	Sunrise at Windsor during the floods (34x72cm-13x28in) s. W/C. 19-Sep-2 Christie's, Kensington #77/R est:500-800

COLERIDGE, Frederick G (fl.1866-1914) British

Works on paper

£650	$1014	€975	View on the Thames (24x36cm-9x14in) s. gouache. 26-Mar-3 Woolley & Wallis, Salisbury #93/R

COLES, Cowper Phipps (19th C) British

Works on paper

£800	$1336	€1160	H.M.S Phaeton at Lisbon 1851. Well done Phaeton (34x51cm-13x20in) s.d.1850 pencil bodycol wash two. 18-Jun-3 Sotheby's, Olympia #17/R

COLESCOTT, Robert (1925-) American

£10759	$17000	€16139	Egg foo yung to go (201x150cm-79x59in) s. acrylic painted 1971 prov.exhib. 14-Nov-2 Christie's, Rockefeller NY #253/R est:15000-20000

COLETTE, Marie (20th C) American

£258	$400	€387	Manayunk (63x81cm-25x32in) s. 8-Dec-2 Freeman, Philadelphia #187/R
£452	$700	€678	Philadelphia cricket club (50x61cm-20x24in) s.d.84. 8-Dec-2 Freeman, Philadelphia #186/R

COLIN, G (19th C) French

Sculpture

£1034	$1655	€1500	Marin. green pat bronze marble base. 17-Mar-3 Amberes, Antwerp #426

COLIN, Gerard-Philippe (18th C) Belgian

£2009	$3134	€3014	Horses in the Schelde (42x49cm-17x19in) s. i. verso panel. 6-Nov-2 Dobiaschofsky, Bern #414/R est:6500 (S.FR 4600)

COLIN, Gustave (1828-1910) French

£378	$609	€567	Portrait of woman (77x62cm-30x24in) s. 11-May-3 Hindemae, Ullerslev #165 (D.KR 4000)
£417	$671	€626	Roman bridge (37x55cm-15x22in) s. panel. 7-May-3 Dobiaschofsky, Bern #416/R (S.FR 900)
£833	$1342	€1250	Young Italian woman with water jug (46x37cm-18x15in) s. panel. 7-May-3 Dobiaschofsky, Bern #417/R (S.FR 1800)
£3355	$5301	€5200	Vendanges a Chalasse (27x41cm-11x16in) s. 18-Dec-2 Ferri, Paris #46
£3846	$6038	€6000	View of village (82x115cm-32x45in) s. 15-Dec-2 Mercier & Cie, Lille #347/R est:8000
£7742	$12232	€12000	Rue animee au Pays Basque (68x52cm-27x20in) s. prov. 18-Dec-2 Ferri, Paris #45/R est:4500

COLIN, Jean (1881-1961) Belgian

£256	$403	€400	Scene de rue (37x30cm-15x12in) s.i. 11-Dec-2 Hotel des Ventes Mosan, Brussels #262

COLIN, Paul (1892-1985) French

£601	$950	€950	Nu debout (100x65cm-39x26in) s. 29-Nov-2 Drouot Estimations, Paris #43

Works on paper

£252	$390	€400	Danseur (31x18cm-12x7in) s. wax pastel dr exec.c.1925. 30-Oct-2 Artcurial Briest, Paris #239
£380	$600	€600	Etude pour affiche (40x29cm-16x11in) s. chl crayon. 26-Nov-2 Camard, Paris #75
£759	$1200	€1200	Trois femmes (91x72cm-36x28in) s.d.1925 gouache. 29-Nov-2 Drouot Estimations, Paris #85
£1800	$2772	€2700	Tumulte noir, Josephine Baker (26x22cm-10x9in) s. gouache pastel col crayon exec.c.1930 prov. 23-Oct-2 Sotheby's, Olympia #698/R est:600-800

COLIN, Paul-Émile (1867-1949) French

£372	$580	€550	Cavalier arme sur un ane (32x41cm-13x16in) s. panel. 26-Mar-3 Millon & Associes, Paris #80/R
£828	$1382	€1200	Chevre dans la montagne (66x31cm-26x12in) 9-Jul-3 Millon & Associes, Paris #122/R

COLINET, C J R (fl.1913-1945) French

Sculpture

£1126	$1835	€1700	Danseuse et serpent (50cm-20in) bronze alabaster socle. 29-Jan-3 Tajan, Paris #62
£12500	$20000	€18750	Dance of Carthage (55cm-22in) s. cold pat. enameled bronze. 15-May-3 Christie's, Kensington #386/R est:8000-12000

COLINET, Claire Jeanne Roberte (fl.1913-1945) French

Sculpture

£2244	$3522	€3500	Danseuse espagnole (22x18x7cm-9x7x3in) s. brown black pat bronze ivory onyx socle. 20-Nov-2 Claude Boisgirard, Paris #49/R
£3226	$5000	€4839	Towards the unknown (48cm-19in) st.sig. parcel gilt bronze carved ivory stone lit. 6-Dec-2 Sotheby's, New York #153/R est:6000-9000
£9797	$15284	€14500	Walkyrie (70x70cm-28x28in) s. brown pat bronze ivory. 26-Mar-3 Millon & Associes, Paris #166/R est:18000
£12500	$19875	€18750	Warrior sitting astride the running horse (47x41cm-19x16in) s. gilt bronze. 27-Feb-3 Sotheby's, Olympia #194/R est:8000-10000

COLINET, Paul (1898-1957) French

Works on paper

£753	$1183	€1100	Ligne brisee (36x27cm-14x11in) s.d.1947 ink. 15-Apr-3 Laurence Calmels, Paris #4201/R

COLKETT, Samuel David (1806-1863) British

£807	$1300	€1211	Seascape (46x61cm-18x24in) s.d.1844 i.stretcher prov. 19-Feb-3 Doyle, New York #37
£826	$1298	€1239	Field activity at sunrise (33x48cm-13x19in) s.d.1837 panel. 24-Jul-2 Walker's, Ottawa #26/R est:3000-3500 (C.D 2000)
£1050	$1754	€1523	Postwick Grove (28x38cm-11x15in) prov. 20-Jun-3 Keys, Aylsham #641/R est:1000-1500
£1500	$2280	€2250	Norfolk landscape with drover and cow by an old stone cottage (33x41cm-13x16in) 16-Aug-2 Keys, Aylsham #637/R
£2000	$3260	€3000	Norfolk landscape with figures, horse, dog and sheep (23x33cm-9x13in) prov. 14-Feb-3 Keys, Aylsham #652/R est:1000-1500
£3500	$5425	€5250	River scene with harvesting beyond (30x41cm-12x16in) s.d.1839. 30-Sep-2 Bonhams, Ipswich #490/R est:2000-3000
£4400	$6908	€6600	Harvest landscape with windmill (35x61cm-14x24in) panel. 16-Dec-2 Bonhams, Bury St Edmunds #515 est:3000-5000

COLKETT, Samuel David (attrib) (1806-1863) British

£900	$1431	€1350	Old lady feeding chickens outside a woodland cottage (30x38cm-12x15in) panel. 30-Apr-3 Halls, Shrewsbury #281/R

COLKETT, Victoria S (1840-1926) British

Works on paper

£620	$973	€930	View of Lincoln Cathedral (65x48cm-26x19in) s.i.d.1888 W/C. 16-Dec-2 Bonhams, Bury St Edmunds #441

COLL, Joseph Clement (1881-1921) American

Works on paper

£745	$1200	€1118	Begging for quarter at swordpoint (33x23cm-13x9in) s. pen ink. 10-May-3 Illustration House, New York #163/R

COLLA, Ettore (1896-1968) Italian

Sculpture

£30000	$46200	€45000	Rilievo con ovali e bulloni (96x140x14cm-38x55x6in) recycled iron prov.exhib.lit. 22-Oct-2 Christie's, London #28/R est:30000-40000
£50000	$78000	€75000	Saturno (315x144x90cm-124x57x35in) iron executed 1962 prov.exhib.lit. 21-Oct-2 Sotheby's, London #50/R est:50000-70000

COLLADO, Juan (1948-) Spanish

£586	$932	€850	Cibeles (46x55cm-18x22in) s. 4-Mar-3 Ansorena, Madrid #245/R
£645	$1019	€1000	Urban view (50x65cm-20x26in) s. 18-Dec-2 Ansorena, Madrid #217/R

COLLADON, Germain (attrib) (1698-1747) Swiss
Miniatures
£3200 $5248 €4640 Venus and Cupid (8cm-3xin) enamel on copper oval prov. 3-Jun-3 Christie's, London #26/R est:2000-3000

COLLART, Marie (1842-1911) Belgian
£1079 $1727 €1500 Sieste au paturage (37x53cm-15x21in) s. 19-May-3 Horta, Bruxelles #223 est:1500-2000

COLLE, Michel-Auguste (1872-1949) French
£728 $1150 €1150 Grands arbres Turenne (77x52cm-30x20in) s.d.1909. 26-Nov-2 Camard, Paris #59/R
£1139 $1800 €1800 Gargouilles (77x52cm-30x20in) s.d.1906. 26-Nov-2 Camard, Paris #61/R
£1266 $2000 €2000 Allee pres de Nancy (52x77cm-20x30in) s.d.1907. 26-Nov-2 Camard, Paris #62/R
£2128 $3447 €3000 Gargouilles ' Vue de la cathedrale de Toul' (77x52cm-30x20in) s.d.1906. 23-May-3 Camard, Paris #91/R est:1200-1500
£2270 $3677 €3200 Place Carriere Nancy (77x52cm-30x20in) s.d.1906 i.verso. 23-May-3 Camard, Paris #88/R est:2000-2500
£2979 $4826 €4200 Propriete de Madame G a Nancy (103x77cm-41x30in) s.d.1906. 23-May-3 Camard, Paris #86/R est:1500-2000
£3354 $5300 €5300 Place du chateau. Chambery. Savoie (75x150cm-30x59in) s.i.d.1911 triptych. 26-Nov-2 Camard, Paris #58/R est:5300
£3546 $5745 €5000 Bon coin (52x77cm-20x30in) s.d.1906 i.d.1905 verso. 23-May-3 Camard, Paris #89/R est:1200-1500
£5696 $9000 €9000 Place des Carrieres (44x57cm-17x22in) s.d.1909 cardboard. 26-Nov-2 Camard, Paris #51/R

COLLET, Beatrice Vial (20th C) British?
£380 $619 €570 Floral still life (71x58cm-28x23in) s.d.91. 2-Feb-3 Lots Road, London #356a/R

COLLETT, Frederik (1839-1914) Norwegian
£1305 $2089 €1958 Boggy landscape, possibly Flatanger (40x58cm-16x23in) init.d.94. 17-Mar-3 Blomqvist, Oslo #366/R est:20000-25000 (N.KR 15000)
£1735 $2706 €2603 Autumn in Aasgaardstrand (40x32cm-16x13in) s.d.85 lit. 21-Oct-2 Blomqvist, Oslo #347/R est:20000-25000 (N.KR 20000)
£7163 $11747 €10386 Mesna outlet in Mjosa (40x60cm-16x24in) init.d.07 exhib. 2-Jun-3 Blomqvist, Oslo #180/R est:40000-50000 (N.KR 78000)
£7806 $12177 €11709 Landscape from the outlet of Mesna river (65x90cm-26x35in) init.d.09 lit. 21-Oct-2 Blomqvist, Oslo #338/R est:70000-90000 (N.KR 90000)

COLLETTE, Joan (1889-1958) Dutch
£355 $574 €500 Mary washes the feet of Christ (115x90cm-45x35in) s.d.1948 board. 26-May-3 Glerum, Amsterdam #16

COLLIANDER, Ina (1908-1985) Finnish
£443 $691 €700 The harbour (50x60cm-20x24in) s.d.45. 15-Sep-2 Bukowskis, Helsinki #174/R

COLLIE, George (fl.1922-1940) British
£521 $859 €750 Still life of a carved Japanese ivory figure (60x50cm-24x20in) 7-Jul-3 Hamilton Osborne King, Dublin #216/R
£1233 $1923 €1800 Shoulder length portrait of Sybil Connolly (42x29cm-17x11in) s. board. 8-Apr-3 James Adam, Dublin #21/R est:400-500
£4514 $7448 €6500 Still life of flowers in a vase, with Chinese ornaments on a table (88x66cm-35x26in) s. canvasboard. 7-Jul-3 Hamilton Osborne King, Dublin #215/R est:2000-3000
£8228 $12013 €13000 Tea rooms at Jammets (75x87cm-30x34in) s. 21-May-2 Thomas Adams, Dublin #318

COLLIER, Alan Caswell (1911-1990) Canadian
£372 $584 €558 South of Boharm, Sask (30x41cm-12x16in) s.i. s.verso board prov. 24-Jul-2 Walker's, Ottawa #418/R (C.D 900)
£413 $644 €689 Autumn Tangle, Popineau Lake Road, Madawaska Valley Ont (30x41cm-12x16in) s. paper board prov. 13-Apr-3 Levis, Calgary #20 est:1000-1200 (C.D 950)
£533 $875 €800 In the Ogilvie Mountains, Yukon Territory (30x40cm-12x16in) s. board. 3-Jun-3 Joyner, Toronto #490 est:1500-1800 (C.D 1200)
£535 $829 €803 Shrinkage stope, delnite mine, Timmins, ONT (40x50cm-16x20in) s. board. 3-Dec-2 Joyner, Toronto #356 est:400-600 (C.D 1300)
£535 $829 €803 St. Martin's N.B (30x40cm-12x16in) s. board prov. 3-Dec-2 Joyner, Toronto #371 est:400-800 (C.D 1300)
£538 $861 €807 Out from the bush, Ontario (30x41cm-12x16in) s. s.i.verso board prov. 15-May-3 Heffel, Vancouver #223/R est:1500-2000 (C.D 1200)
£615 $953 €923 Newfoundland cove (61x81cm-24x32in) s. prov. 24-Sep-2 Ritchie, Toronto #3160/R (C.D 1500)
£662 $1047 €993 Barnes Lake above Ashcroft, BC (30x41cm-12x16in) d.1974 paperboard. 1-Dec-2 Levis, Calgary #16/R (C.D 1650)
£667 $1093 €1001 Low water on the Skeena River (30x40cm-12x16in) s. board prov. 3-Jun-3 Joyner, Toronto #281/R est:800-1200 (C.D 1500)
£739 $1153 €1233 South of Cache Creek, B.C (30x41cm-12x16in) s.i.d.1970 paper board prov. 13-Apr-3 Levis, Calgary #19/R est:1000-1200 (C.D 1700)
£1067 $1749 €1601 Magdalen Island (45x60cm-18x24in) s. 3-Jun-3 Joyner, Toronto #179/R est:1500-2000 (C.D 2400)
£1200 $1968 €1800 Labrador iceberg no.8 (45x60cm-18x24in) s. board prov. 3-Jun-3 Joyner, Toronto #163/R est:2000-3000 (C.D 2700)
£1285 $2018 €1928 Letnikof Cannery (50x75cm-20x30in) s.i. board. 25-Nov-2 Hodgins, Calgary #117/R est:2750-3250 (C.D 3200)
£2111 $3462 €3061 Logging roads, near Gold River, Vancouver Island, BC (60x80cm-24x31in) s.i. 9-Jun-3 Hodgins, Calgary #128/R est:4500-5500 (C.D 4750)
£3284 $5221 €4926 Tide is low, Grice inlet near Tofino, Vancouver Island (75x125cm-30x49in) s.i. painted c.1982 prov. 23-Mar-3 Hodgins, Calgary #41/R est:3500-4500 (C.D 7750)
£4343 $6906 €6515 Evening light from Bob Russell's farm, Northwest of Drumheller, Alta (60x90cm-24x35in) s.i. board. 23-Mar-3 Hodgins, Calgary #18/R est:3000-4000 (C.D 10250)
Works on paper
£578 $948 €867 From Rogers Pass, B.C (27x36cm-11x14in) s. W/C. 3-Jun-3 Joyner, Toronto #366/R est:800-1200 (C.D 1300)

COLLIER, Arthur Bevan (fl.1855-1899) British
£300 $495 €435 West country coastal view (34x52cm-13x20in) s. 1-Jul-3 Bearnes, Exeter #488/R

COLLIER, Evert (1640-1706) Dutch
£3185 $4968 €5000 Portrait of a young lady, aged 23 (12x11cm-5x4in) s.d.1673 panel prov.exhib.lit. 5-Nov-2 Sotheby's, Amsterdam #109/R est:6000-8000
£9259 $15000 €13889 Vanitas still life (75x63cm-30x25in) s.i.d.1707. 23-Jan-3 Sotheby's, New York #207/R est:20000
£11511 $18417 €16000 Vanitas still life with an hour glass (34x31cm-13x12in) s.d.1693 prov. 14-May-3 Christie's, Amsterdam #196/R est:20000-30000
£12000 $18720 €18000 Vanitas still life of court jewels in casket (97x124cm-38x49in) s.d.1705 prov. 10-Apr-3 Sotheby's, London #49/R est:18000
£16547 $26475 €23000 Vanitas still life with books, globes, beaker, roemer (104x108cm-41x43in) i.d.1665. 13-May-3 Sotheby's, Amsterdam #12/R est:20000-30000
£30000 $47100 €45000 Vanitas still life of violin, recorder, books, etching and jewellery (100x124cm-39x49in) mono. prov. 12-Dec-2 Sotheby's, London #157/R est:20000-30000
£32000 $50240 €48000 Letter rack (48x61cm-19x24in) s. trompe l'oeil prov.exhib.lit. 16-Dec-2 Sotheby's, London #42/R est:7000-10000
£82517 $137804 €118000 Nature morte aux globes terrestres et celestes (80x106cm-31x42in) s.d.1664. 27-Jun-3 Piasa, Paris #23/R est:40000-60000

COLLIER, Evert (style) (1640-1706) Dutch
£15000 $23700 €22500 Letters, magnifying glass, watch, dividers and other items (45x60cm-18x24in) trompe l'oeil panel. 4-Apr-3 Moore Allen & Innocent, Cirencester #659/R est:1000-2000

COLLIER, Imogen (fl.1898-1904) British
£300 $480 €450 Portrait of a bay hunter in a field (35x45cm-14x18in) s. 15-May-3 Lawrence, Crewkerne #949/R
£310 $496 €465 Two grooms with four horses in a field (19x29cm-7x11in) s.d.1921 indis.i.verso panel. 15-May-3 Lawrence, Crewkerne #951/R
£320 $512 €480 Africa: country bred polo pony (22x32cm-9x13in) s.i.d.1930 verso panel. 15-May-3 Lawrence, Crewkerne #953/R
£380 $608 €570 Miss Bayly: a bay hunter in a stable (28x36cm-11x14in) s.i. 15-May-3 Lawrence, Crewkerne #955
£450 $711 €675 Chestnut hunter in a wood (46x56cm-18x22in) s. 28-Nov-2 Christie's, Kensington #160/R
£1700 $2686 €2550 Chestnut hunter with a lady up (38x49cm-15x19in) s. 28-Nov-2 Christie's, Kensington #159/R est:1000-1500
£1700 $2822 €2465 Derby 1898, Jeddah wins! (20x35cm-8x14in) s.i. panel. 12-Jun-3 Christie's, Kensington #108 est:1000-1500

COLLIER, John (1708-1786) British
£535 $850 €803 Portrait of a woman (66x51cm-26x20in) s. 5-Mar-3 Doyle, New York #16/R

COLLIER, The Hon John (1850-1934) British
£280 $437 €420 Portrait of Alice Crowder, standing in a interior (238x148cm-94x58in) s.d.1900 s.i.on stretcher. 8-Oct-2 Bonhams, Knightsbridge #26b

£4140 $6500 €6210 Grand lady (60x48cm-24x19in) s.d.1920 prov. 10-Dec-2 Doyle, New York #217/R est:10000-15000
£4516 $7000 €6774 Shopping for silks (102x127cm-40x50in) s. 3-Dec-2 Christie's, Rockefeller NY #624/R est:6000-8000
£14000 $22540 €21000 Trouble (101x122cm-40x48in) prov.exhib. 20-Feb-3 Christie's, London #111/R est:10000
£15000 $24900 €22500 Water nymph (127x102cm-50x40in) s.d.1923. 12-Jun-3 Sotheby's, London #258/R est:10000-15000

COLLIER, Thomas (1840-1891) British
Works on paper
£460 $741 €690 Cattle grazing in a landscape (33x48cm-13x19in) s. W/C. 19-Feb-3 Mallams, Oxford #393/R
£1150 $1898 €1668 Going home (18x25cm-7x10in) s. pencil W/C prov.exhib. 3-Jul-3 Christie's, Kensington #82/R est:800-1200

COLLIER, Thomas Frederick (fl.1848-1874) British
Works on paper
£450 $702 €675 Still life with pears, plums and grapes (27x38cm-11x15in) s.d.1871 pencil W/C htd white. 27-Mar-3 Christie's, Kensington #50
£700 $1113 €1050 Still life of roses (24x35cm-9x14in) s. W/C. 29-Apr-3 Henry Adams, Chichester #222
£920 $1435 €1380 Still life of fruit (28x37cm-11x15in) s.d.1874 W/C. 26-Mar-3 Sotheby's, Olympia #107/R
£2200 $3586 €3300 Still life of bird's nest with primroses and ivy (28x39cm-11x15in) s.d.1881 W/C. 29-Jan-3 Sotheby's, Olympia #115/R est:800-1200

COLLIER, Thomas Frederick (attrib) (fl.1848-1874) British
£250 $410 €375 Grapes, an apple, strawberries and bird's nest on mossy bank (21x32cm-8x13in) mono. board. 5-Jun-3 Christie's, Kensington #801/R

COLLIGNON, Eugène (1876-1961) Belgian
£276 $427 €430 Vue d'eglise sur fond de paysage fluvial (66x50cm-26x20in) s. 9-Dec-2 Horta, Bruxelles #452

COLLIGNON, Georges (1923-2002) Belgian
£629 $975 €1000 Composition (32x46cm-13x18in) s.d.59 paper lit. 5-Oct-2 De Vuyst, Lokeren #64
£1392 $2200 €2200 Nocturne (97x130cm-38x51in) s.d.1965 verso exhib. 26-Nov-2 Palais de Beaux Arts, Brussels #244/R est:2000-3000
£2041 $3245 €3000 Composition (65x81cm-26x32in) s. s.d.1950 verso. 26-Feb-3 Artcurial Briest, Paris #449 est:1500-1800
Works on paper
£266 $420 €420 Composition bleue (60x49cm-24x19in) s. W/C. 26-Nov-2 Palais de Beaux Arts, Brussels #245
£278 $442 €400 Composition (64x49cm-25x19in) s.d.1955 ink dr. 29-Apr-3 Campo, Vlaamse Kaai #49
£380 $592 €600 Composition abstraite (33x48cm-13x19in) s. mixed media. 16-Oct-2 Hotel des Ventes Mosan, Brussels #294
£791 $1266 €1100 Ville Saite (64x48cm-25x19in) s. mixed media exhib. 19-May-3 Horta, Bruxelles #461
£1667 $2650 €2400 Plaisir d'armures (118x150cm-46x59in) s. d.1984 verso mixed media. 29-Apr-3 Campo, Vlaamse Kaai #48/R est:2500-2800

COLLIN, Alberic (1886-1962) Belgian
Sculpture
£1325 $2159 €2000 Fennec couche (15x30cm-6x12in) s. pat bronze. 17-Feb-3 Horta, Bruxelles #133
£3038 $4800 €4800 Groupe de trois pelicans (25x23x16cm-10x9x6in) s. pat bronze Cast Valsuani. 26-Nov-2 Palais de Beaux Arts, Brussels #64/R est:1800-2500
£4967 $7997 €7600 Cerf se grattant (29x33cm-11x13in) s.st.f.Valsuani dark pat bronze. 20-Jan-3 Horta, Bruxelles #127/R est:3000-4000
£9353 $14964 €13000 Bison (51x66x23cm-20x26x9in) s. bronze Cast Valsuani exhib. 13-May-3 Palais de Beaux Arts, Brussels #49/R est:12500-17500
£10692 $16679 €17000 Le dernier fiacre (53x121cm-21x48in) s. num.2/4 brown pat.bronze Cast.C. Valsuani. 14-Oct-2 Amberes, Antwerp #375

COLLIN, Andre (1862-1930) Belgian
£570 $889 €900 Attelage. s. panel. 10-Sep-2 Vanderkindere, Brussels #342
£10884 $17306 €16000 Les deux gamines (116x82cm-46x32in) s.d.1890. 24-Mar-3 Bernaerts, Antwerp #77 est:10000-15000

COLLIN, Georges (19th C) ?
Sculpture
£993 $1619 €1500 Ours assis (12cm-5in) s. num.1/8 green pat bronze. 17-Feb-3 Horta, Bruxelles #134

COLLIN, Marcus (1882-1966) Finnish
£449 $714 €660 Boda (40x46cm-16x18in) s.d.1917. 27-Feb-3 Hagelstam, Helsinki #845
£1069 $1657 €1700 Picking potatoes (50x61cm-20x24in) s.d.43. 6-Oct-2 Bukowskis, Helsinki #155/R est:2000
£1439 $2302 €2000 Country scene (65x55cm-26x22in) s.d.1932. 17-May-3 Hagelstam, Helsinki #152/R est:2000
£1799 $2878 €2500 By the Seine (34x70cm-13x28in) s.d.1909. 17-May-3 Hagelstam, Helsinki #149/R est:3000
£1901 $3061 €2700 Still life of bottles (47x58cm-19x23in) s.d.18 exhib. 10-May-3 Bukowskis, Helsinki #78/R est:2500-2800
Works on paper
£286 $454 €420 Beggars (32x24cm-13x9in) s.d.39 pastel. 24-Mar-3 Bukowskis, Helsinki #49/R
£316 $494 €500 The pig market (24x32cm-9x13in) s.d.51 pastel. 15-Sep-2 Bukowskis, Helsinki #176/R
£317 $519 €440 Wagons in the market (24x32cm-9x13in) s.d.51 pastel. 4-Jun-3 Bukowskis, Helsinki #265/R
£354 $562 €520 Time for reading (32x24cm-13x9in) s.d.39 pastel. 24-Mar-3 Bukowskis, Helsinki #50/R
£540 $863 €750 Market scene, Paris (24x32cm-9x13in) s.d.1958 pastel. 17-May-3 Hagelstam, Helsinki #151/R
£612 $973 €900 Hymn-book (32x24cm-13x9in) s. pastel. 27-Feb-3 Hagelstam, Helsinki #910/R
£719 $1179 €1100 After a day's work (33x25cm-13x10in) s.d.52 pastel. 9-Feb-3 Bukowskis, Helsinki #215/R
£759 $1200 €1200 Archway (56x47cm-22x19in) s.d.1930 pastel exhib. 30-Nov-2 Hagelstam, Helsinki #141/R
£1367 $2187 €1900 Washing the steps (65x49cm-26x19in) s.d.1927 pastel. 17-May-3 Hagelstam, Helsinki #150/R est:1800

COLLIN, Paul Louis (1834-?) French
£3148 $4628 €4880 Self portrait (98x76cm-39x30in) init. 24-Jun-2 Babuino, Rome #291 est:1500-2000

COLLIN, Raphael (1850-1916) French
£1032 $1600 €1548 Portrait of Constantin (40x32cm-16x13in) s.i.d.1881 panel prov. 29-Oct-2 Sotheby's, New York #59/R est:1000-1500

COLLINA, Alberto (19th C) Italian
Works on paper
£440 $700 €660 Near the Coliseum (117x91cm-46x36in) s.i.d.1903 W/C. 7-Mar-3 Jackson's, Cedar Falls #527/R

COLLINASSY, Juraj (1907-1963) Czechoslovakian
£378 $586 €567 Portrait of a girl (62x50cm-24x20in) 1-Oct-2 SOGA, Bratislava #245/R est:24000 (SL.K 24000)
£441 $626 €662 Hamlet (70x24cm-28x9in) board painted c.1960. 26-Mar-2 SOGA, Bratislava #232/R (SL.K 28000)

COLLINGRIDGE, George de Tourcey (1847-1931) Australian
£321 $498 €482 View of Cumberland Street (24x15cm-9x6in) s. panel painted c.1880. 29-Oct-2 Lawson Menzies, Sydney #159 (A.D 900)

COLLINGS, Albert Harry (?-1947) British
£500 $780 €750 Semi-naked gypsy on a rug (16x20cm-6x8in) board. 9-Oct-2 Woolley & Wallis, Salisbury #242/R
£1000 $1560 €1500 Nude study of a lady (51x61cm-20x24in) 9-Oct-2 Woolley & Wallis, Salisbury #243/R est:1000-1500
£1700 $2652 €2550 Study of a female nude (20x16cm-8x6in) board. 9-Oct-2 Woolley & Wallis, Salisbury #241/R est:300-500
£3200 $4992 €4800 Gabrielle in fancy dress (109x86cm-43x34in) s. 9-Oct-2 Woolley & Wallis, Salisbury #244/R est:1500-2500
£15000 $23400 €22500 Yasmin (211x127cm-83x50in) s. with kutani vase. 9-Oct-2 Woolley & Wallis, Salisbury #245/R est:4000-6000

COLLINGS, Charles John (1848-1931) British
£3139 $5022 €4709 Autumn birch trees on the lake (97x72cm-38x28in) mono.d.1920 s.verso prov. 15-May-3 Heffel, Vancouver #10/R est:8000-10000 (C.D 7000)
Works on paper
£151 $241 €219 Street scene (21x30cm-8x12in) init. W/C. 1-May-3 Heffel, Vancouver #15/R (C.D 350)

COLLINGWOOD, Leicester (19th C) ?
£1500 $2325 €2250 Haymaking (48x137cm-19x54in) s. 6-Dec-2 Chrystals Auctions, Isle of Man #196a est:2000-3000

COLLINGWOOD, William (1819-1903) British
Works on paper
£260 $413 €390 Figures resting on the shore of an alpine lake (13x18cm-5x7in) mono.d.1875 W/C. 4-Mar-3 Bearnes, Exeter #335/R
£500 $835 €725 Fisherfolk on the beach (33x49cm-13x19in) s.d.1852 W/C. 24-Jun-3 Bonhams, Knightsbridge #20/R
£1100 $1760 €1650 Rural idyll (47x77cm-19x30in) init.d.1853 W/C. 11-Mar-3 Bonhams, New Bond Street #120/R est:1000-1500

COLLINI, Paolo (1950-) Italian
£347 $552 €500 Appearances (30x24cm-12x9in) s.i.d.2001 verso. 1-May-3 Meeting Art, Vercelli #424
£389 $618 €560 Places (24x30cm-9x12in) s.i.d.2001 verso. 1-May-3 Meeting Art, Vercelli #389

COLLINS, Cecil (1908-1989) British
£8000 $12640 €12000 Figure reading (58x43cm-23x17in) s.d.1955 board. 27-Nov-2 Sotheby's, Olympia #296/R est:5000-7000
£8000 $13120 €11600 Head of a fool (30x32cm-12x13in) s. s.i.d.1963 verso board prov.exhib. 4-Jun-3 Sotheby's, London #78/R est:3000-4000
Works on paper
£4800 $7488 €7200 Charming birds out of trees (23x31cm-9x12in) s.d.1942 pencil pen ink W/C. 27-Mar-3 Christie's, Kensington #298/R est:4000-6000

COLLINS, Charles (c.1680-1744) British
£1418 $2199 €2127 In the Maytime - landscape with cattle (51x77cm-20x30in) s. 3-Dec-2 Bukowskis, Stockholm #318/R est:30000-35000 (S.KR 20000)
£1688 $2600 €2532 King Charles spaniel in a landscape (38x41cm-15x16in) s. 4-Sep-2 Christie's, Rockefeller NY #379/R est:3000-5000

COLLINS, Charles (1851-1921) British
£1600 $2672 €2320 River scene with cattle near Mickleham (34x49cm-13x19in) s.i.verso. 9-Jul-3 George Kidner, Lymington #175/R est:600-800
£2500 $4100 €3750 Summertime (51x76cm-20x30in) s.d.1879. 29-May-3 Christie's, Kensington #158/R est:3000-5000
Works on paper
£520 $801 €780 Cattle resting beside a stream (34x53cm-13x21in) s.d.1889 W/C. 22-Oct-2 Sworder & Son, Bishops Stortford #698/R
£1456 $2271 €2300 Brining in the harvest (35x52cm-14x20in) s. W/C. 30-Jul-2 Hamilton Osborne King, Dublin #253/R est:1500-2500

COLLINS, Charles (19/20th C) American
£346 $550 €519 Shepherd (61x81cm-24x32in) s.d. 2-Mar-3 Toomey, Oak Park #680/R
£455 $700 €683 Shepherd (61x81cm-24x32in) s.d.1896. 8-Sep-2 Treadway Gallery, Cincinnati #568/R

COLLINS, Earl (20th C) American
£318 $500 €477 Fully rigged ship (61x91cm-24x36in) s. 22-Nov-2 Eldred, East Dennis #618/R

COLLINS, George Edward (1880-1968) British
£360 $601 €522 Sheep at rest beneath oak trees (12x35cm-5x14in) s. panel. 23-Jun-3 Bonhams, Bath #161

COLLINS, Hannah (1956-) British
Works on paper
£1803 $2866 €2650 Passage (197x156cm-78x61in) argentique on cotton prov. 26-Feb-3 Artcurial Briest, Paris #366/R est:2000-3000

COLLINS, Hugh (fl.1868-1892) British
£600 $936 €900 Young child in an interior. s.d.1867. 8-Apr-3 Bonhams, Knightsbridge #244/R
£900 $1485 €1305 Portrait of J G Paton Esq. Portrait of his wife (127x101cm-50x40in) s.d.1881 s.d.1891 pair. 2-Jul-3 Sotheby's, Olympia #307/R
£2128 $3447 €3000 Feeding the pigeons (42x62cm-17x24in) s.d.1864. 21-May-3 James Adam, Dublin #30/R est:1500-2500
£3000 $4650 €4500 Young boys bathing (119x178cm-47x70in) s. 3-Dec-2 Sotheby's, Olympia #154/R est:3000-5000

COLLINS, Kreigh L (1908-1974) American
£283 $450 €425 Still life with kettle and bottle (36x48cm-14x19in) s. painted c.1928. 7-Mar-3 Jackson's, Cedar Falls #646/R

COLLINS, Majella (20th C) Irish
£1164 $1828 €1700 Passage (76x41cm-30x16in) exhib. 15-Apr-3 De Veres Art Auctions, Dublin #100o est:700-1000

COLLINS, Marnie A (1959-) Canadian
£311 $510 €451 Summer's colour (43x33cm-17x13in) s.i. acrylic. 9-Jun-3 Hodgins, Calgary #135/R (C.D 700)
£763 $1198 €1145 Friends and family at Bowness Park (123x118cm-48x46in) s. wall hanging acrylic. 25-Nov-2 Hodgins, Calgary #404/R est:1750-2250 (C.D 1900)

COLLINS, Patrick (1911-1994) British
£2568 $4005 €3800 Chinese kite (48x41cm-19x16in) s.d.1985 i.verso prov. 26-Mar-3 James Adam, Dublin #140/R est:3000-5000
£7500 $12000 €11250 Pierrot (51x41cm-20x16in) s. board. 16-May-3 Sotheby's, London #115/R est:6000-8000
£8500 $13600 €12750 Druid's altar (45x60cm-18x24in) s. i.verso board. 16-May-3 Sotheby's, London #121/R est:8000-12000
£9494 $14715 €15000 Mediterranean landscape (30x40cm-12x16in) s. board. 25-Sep-2 James Adam, Dublin #80/R est:15000-20000
£9932 $15592 €14500 Sheep resting (24x46cm-9x18in) s. prov. 15-Apr-3 De Veres Art Auctions, Dublin #180/R est:12000-14000
£14103 $22141 €22000 Shepherd (41x51cm-16x20in) s. i.verso board prov.exhib. 19-Nov-2 Whyte's, Dublin #41/R est:25000-35000
£14744 $23147 €23000 Rain on the hill (41x51cm-16x20in) s. i.verso prov.exhib. 19-Nov-2 Whyte's, Dublin #45/R est:25000-35000
£15823 $24525 €25000 Landscape (38x51cm-15x20in) s. board prov.exhib. 24-Sep-2 De Veres Art Auctions, Dublin #64/R est:25000-35000
£27673 $43170 €44000 Sun on the bog (46x61cm-18x24in) s.d.1964 board prov.exhib. 17-Sep-2 Whyte's, Dublin #41/R est:40000-60000
£42405 $65728 €67000 Patrick Kavanagh from Baggot Street Bridge (64x50cm-25x20in) s. i.verso board prov.exhib.lit. 24-Sep-2 De Veres Art Auctions, Dublin #22/R est:3500-4500

COLLINS, W W (1862-1952) British
Works on paper
£400 $608 €600 Old Dick Whittington, Cloth Fair, with figures (26x17cm-10x7in) s. W/C. 15-Aug-2 Rupert Toovey, Partridge Green #1430

COLLINS, William (1788-1847) British
£2397 $3500 €3596 Seascape with waves in headland with figures (58x91cm-23x36in) s. panel. 3-Nov-1 North East Auctions, Portsmouth #1189/R
£2400 $3720 €3600 Blowing bubbles (48x61cm-19x24in) s.d.1846. 2-Oct-2 Bonhams, Knowle #71/R est:3000-5000
£2900 $4843 €4205 Coastal scene with figures in the foreground (64x89cm-25x35in) s.d.1839. 17-Jun-3 Anderson & Garland, Newcastle #486/R est:1200-1800
£3500 $5390 €5250 Down by the stream (35x46cm-14x18in) s. panel. 5-Sep-2 Christie's, Kensington #178/R est:4000-6000
£4268 $7000 €6189 Decoy pond at Hendon (43x35cm-17x14in) s.i. verso panel prov. 4-Jun-3 Christie's, Rockefeller NY #238/R est:3000-5000
£10500 $16590 €15750 Wooded landscape with figures by cottage (161x79cm-63x31in) with sig.d.1863 unlined canvas. 26-Nov-2 Christie's, London #70/R est:10000-15000

COLLINS, William (attrib) (1788-1847) British
£280 $437 €420 Fisherfolk on a rocky coast (36x46cm-14x18in) bears sig. 13-Sep-2 Lyon & Turnbull, Edinburgh #81/R
£400 $632 €600 Fisherfolk on the shore (20x18cm-8x7in) init.d.1838. 18-Dec-2 John Nicholson, Haslemere #1280

COLLINS, William Wiehe (1862-1952) British
Works on paper
£520 $858 €754 Bockhampton, Dorset (18x25cm-7x10in) s. W/C. 3-Jul-3 Duke & Son, Dorchester #134/R

COLLINSON, James (1825-1881) British
£3221 $5282 €4670 Sisters (61x51cm-24x20in) s. 4-Jun-3 AB Stockholms Auktionsverk #2453/R est:20000-25000 (S.KR 41000)
£17000 $27370 €25500 Holy Family (110x85cm-43x33in) i. prov.lit. 20-Feb-3 Christie's, London #296/R est:25000
£50000 $80500 €75000 To let (51x47cm-20x19in) oval prov.exhib.lit. 20-Feb-3 Christie's, London #97/R est:100000

COLLINSON, Robert (1832-?) British
£10500 $16905 €15750 Playing with the kitten (49x69cm-19x27in) s. prov. 20-Feb-3 Christie's, London #44a/R est:10000

COLLIS, Peter (1929-) Irish
£556 $883 €800 Mountainside, Wicklow (13x19cm-5x7in) s. i.verso board. 29-Apr-3 Whyte's, Dublin #11/R
£1096 $1721 €1600 Vico Road (20x22cm-8x9in) s. board. 15-Apr-3 De Veres Art Auctions, Dublin #105/R est:900-1200
£1275 $2053 €1900 Melting snow, Glencullen (25x30cm-10x12in) s. board painted c.1978. 18-Feb-3 Whyte's, Dublin #154/R est:1500-2500
£1500 $2325 €2250 Road in glencree (36x46cm-14x18in) s. board. 2-Oct-2 John Ross, Belfast #168 est:1000-1200
£2416 $3890 €3600 Wicklow woods (28x32cm-11x13in) s. paper prov. 18-Feb-3 Whyte's, Dublin #45/R est:2000-3000
£2416 $3890 €3600 Looking towards Bray from Rocky Valley (56x71cm-22x28in) s. canvasboard. 18-Feb-3 Whyte's, Dublin #151/R est:4000-5000
£2819 $4538 €4200 Wicklow Road (38x39cm-15x15in) s. board. 18-Feb-3 Whyte's, Dublin #59/R est:3000-4000
£2953 $4754 €4400 Studio still life (36x41cm-14x16in) s. 18-Feb-3 Whyte's, Dublin #137/R est:4000-5000
£5616 $8818 €8200 Large still life (87x87cm-34x34in) s. 15-Apr-3 De Veres Art Auctions, Dublin #246/R est:6000-8000

COLLISHAW, Mat (1966-) British
Photographs
£4000 $6160 €6000 Self portrait (49x41cm-19x16in) 3d col transparency in lightbox executed 1997 prov. 22-Oct-2 Sotheby's, London #497/R est:2000-3000
Sculpture
£3200 $5248 €4800 Self portrait (51x43x7cm-20x17x3in) num.6/10 verso 3D col transparency lightbox prov. 7-Feb-3 Sotheby's, London #288/R est:2000-3000

COLLISTER, Alfred James (fl.1895-1939) British
Works on paper
£280 $448 €420 River landscape with boats moored (41x55cm-16x22in) s. i.verso W/C. 11-Mar-3 Bonhams, Oxford #46

COLLOMB, Paul (1921-) French
£450 $711 €675 L'arbre en fleurs (72x59cm-28x23in) s. 6-Apr-3 Lots Road, London #367

COLLON, Jean Roch (1894-1951) Belgian
£411 $641 €600 Miarka (63x71cm-25x28in) s.d.1925. 14-Apr-3 Horta, Bruxelles #480

COLLS, Ebenezer (1812-1887) British
£605 $950 €908 Maritime scene (55x79cm-22x31in) s. 22-Nov-2 Skinner, Boston #119/R est:1000-1500
£2500 $3875 €3750 Off Harwich (39x61cm-15x24in) s. 31-Oct-2 Christie's, Kensington #516/R est:1500-2500

COLLS, Harry (19th C) British
£368 $600 €552 Homeward bound (30x47cm-12x19in) s. board. 16-Feb-3 Butterfields, San Francisco #2056

COLLYER, Margaret (fl.1897-1910) British
£1300 $2028 €1950 Chestnut hunter in an extensive landscape (64x85cm-25x33in) s.d.1908. 10-Apr-3 Tennants, Leyburn #1038a est:800-1200
£2000 $3120 €3000 Dog portrait, terrier Bobby (20x33cm-8x13in) s. 11-Apr-3 Keys, Aylsham #678/R est:500-800
£2100 $3318 €3150 Oyster gatherers (81x114cm-32x45in) s.indis.d.32 exhib. 29-Nov-2 Dee Atkinson & Harrison, Driffield #825/R est:2000-3000

COLMAN, Roi Clarkson (1884-1945) American
£479 $800 €695 Evening sea - La Jolla, California (13x15cm-5x6in) i.verso canvasboard prov. 17-Jun-3 John Moran, Pasadena #6a
£750 $1200 €1125 Evening Tide, Laguna Beach, California (31x41cm-12x16in) s. 18-May-3 Butterfields, Los Angeles #7026 est:1500-2000
£1398 $2250 €2097 Western sea (24x30cm-9x12in) s. i.d.1919 stretcher bar. 18-Feb-3 John Moran, Pasadena #63 est:2000-3000
£1911 $3000 €2867 Golden sunset (26x76cm-10x30in) s.d.1941 i.stretcher. 19-Nov-2 Butterfields, San Francisco #8215/R est:3000-5000
£2108 $3500 €3057 Opal Sea, Laguna Beach (56x76cm-22x30in) s.d.1941 i. on stretcher. 11-Jun-3 Butterfields, San Francisco #4293/R est:3000-5000
£2795 $4500 €4193 Moonlight serenade (24x30cm-9x12in) s. s.i.stretcher. 18-Feb-3 John Moran, Pasadena #62a est:2500-3500
Works on paper
£1807 $3000 €2620 Golden sunset (56x76cm-22x30in) s.d.1941 i. on stretcher. 11-Jun-3 Butterfields, San Francisco #4294/R est:3000-5000

COLMAN, Samuel (1832-1920) American
£3875 $6200 €5813 Panoramic western landscape (46x79cm-18x31in) s. prov. 12-Jan-3 William Jenack, New York #190
£4459 $7000 €6689 Riverscape (20x38cm-8x15in) s.d.64 i.on stretcher. 10-Dec-2 Doyle, New York #19/R est:4000-6000
£9494 $15000 €13766 Mt. McDonell - Glacier park (112x152cm-44x60in) s. prov. 26-Jul-3 Coeur d'Alene, Hayden #119/R est:25000-35000
£61290 $95000 €91935 View on the Hudson (38x76cm-15x30in) s. painted c.1865 prov.exhib.lit. 3-Dec-2 Phillips, New York #15/R est:75000-125000
Works on paper
£535 $850 €803 Herders and goats before ruins, a Middle Eastern scene (22x50cm-9x20in) s.d.1895 W/C. 7-Mar-3 Skinner, Boston #341b/R
£2013 $3200 €3020 Mountains landscape (23x36cm-9x14in) s. W/C. 5-Mar-3 Christie's, Rockefeller NY #87/R est:3000-5000

COLMEIRO, Manuel (1901-1999) Spanish
Works on paper
£582 $908 €850 Man and animals (32x25cm-13x10in) ink dr lit. 8-Apr-3 Ansorena, Madrid #641/R
£592 $959 €900 Figures (32x25cm-13x10in) s. ink dr lit. 21-Jan-3 Ansorena, Madrid #795/R

COLMEIRO, Manuel (attrib) (1901-1999) Spanish
Works on paper
£419 $663 €650 Entry (31x22cm-12x9in) s. W/C. 18-Dec-2 Ansorena, Madrid #265

COLMO, Giovanni (1867-1947) Italian
£272 $433 €400 Mountainous landscape (10x16cm-4x6in) s. card. 1-Mar 3 Meeting Art, Vercelli #2
£578 $919 €850 Coming storm (23x18cm-9x7in) s. cardboard. 1-Mar-3 Meeting Art, Vercelli #29
£680 $1082 €1000 Cottages in the mountains (26x37cm-10x15in) s.d.1933 cardboard. 1-Mar-3 Meeting Art, Vercelli #98
£680 $1082 €1000 River in the under-growth (40x29cm-16x11in) s. cardboard. 1-Mar-3 Meeting Art, Vercelli #274
£714 $1136 €1050 Garessio (37x26cm-15x10in) s.dd.1941 card. 1-Mar-3 Meeting Art, Vercelli #206
£870 $1426 €1200 Viottolo di montagna con figure (35x27cm-14x11in) s. board. 27-May-3 Finarte, Milan #126/R
£1020 $1622 €1500 Cottages (29x37cm-11x15in) s. cardboard. 1-Mar-3 Meeting Art, Vercelli #96
£1020 $1622 €1500 Summer in the hills (26x37cm-10x15in) s. cardboard. 1-Mar-3 Meeting Art, Vercelli #129

COLMORE, Nina (1889-1973) British
£1200 $1992 €1740 Up-Rooter, a liver chestnut hunter (63x81cm-25x32in) s.i.d.27. 12-Jun-3 Christie's, Kensington #51/R est:1200-1800

COLNOT, Arnout (1887-1983) Dutch
£1053 $1705 €1600 Still life with flowers and fruit (50x60cm-20x24in) s. 21-Jan-3 Christie's, Amsterdam #402 est:800-1200
£3448 $5482 €5000 View of the Voert, Bergen (40x60cm-16x24in) s. 10-Mar-3 Sotheby's, Amsterdam #275/R est:3000-5000
£3546 $5745 €5000 Polder landscape with farm in the background (48x62cm-19x24in) s. canvas on panel. 26-May-3 Glerum, Amsterdam #26/R est:4500-5500
Works on paper
£496 $804 €700 View of a canal with moored boats and farm in the background (47x61cm-19x24in) s. chk. 26-May-3 Glerum, Amsterdam #31/R
£1899 $3000 €3000 Stilleven met geranium (90x65cm-35x26in) s. W/C prov. 26-Nov-2 Sotheby's, Amsterdam #6/R est:3000-4000

COLNOT, Karel (1921-) Dutch
£481 $755 €750 Avenue along the willows (59x49cm-23x19in) s. 25-Nov-2 Glerum, Amsterdam #113/R
£724 $1172 €1100 Landscape with corn sheafs (80x65cm-31x26in) s. 21-Jan-3 Christie's, Amsterdam #384 est:900-1200

COLOGNE SCHOOL (15th C) German
£47297 $73784 €70000 Saint Anne with Mary and Infant Jesus, Saint Agnes and St Catherine (92x61cm-36x24in) d.1481 panel. 27-Mar-3 Dorotheum, Vienna #223/R est:58000-65000

COLOM Y AGUSTI, Juan (1879-1969) Spanish
Works on paper
£403 $648 €600 Catalan interior (45x54cm-18x21in) s. W/C. 18-Feb-3 Durán, Madrid #115/R
£403 $648 €600 Aragona (40x55cm-16x22in) s. i.verso W/C. 18-Feb-3 Durán, Madrid #116/R

COLOMBI, Plinio (1873-1951) Swiss
£330 $528 €495 Autumnal river landscape (65x68cm-26x27in) s.d. 17-Mar-3 Philippe Schuler, Zurich #8416 (S.FR 700)
£463 $745 €695 Lakeshore (60x76cm-24x30in) s.d.1940. 7-May-3 Dobiaschofsky, Bern #3173 (S.FR 1000)
£696 $1085 €1044 Lake Thun in summer (77x100cm-30x39in) s.d.1934. 16-Sep-2 Philippe Schuler, Zurich #3363/R (S.FR 1600)
£708 $1146 €1253 River bank (69x56cm-27x22in) s.d.1915 panel. 26-May-3 Sotheby's, Zurich #40/R (S.FR 1500)
£881 $1313 €1322 River landscape in winter (95x68cm-37x27in) s.d.1915. 25-Jun-2 Koller, Zurich #6710/R est:2000-3000 (S.FR 2000)
£2083 $3354 €3125 Winter landscape in the mountains (70x85cm-28x33in) s.d.1945 panel. 7-May-3 Dobiaschofsky, Bern #418/R est:1400 (S.FR 4500)
£2318 $3662 €3477 Winter magic (65x80cm-26x31in) i.verso. 29-Nov-2 Zofingen, Switzerland #2829 est:2200 (S.FR 5400)
Works on paper
£301 $484 €452 Autumn landscape (40x58cm-16x23in) s.d.1935 W/C over pencil. 7-May-3 Dobiaschofsky, Bern #3172/R (S.FR 650)
£371 $579 €557 Landscape in the Alps (51x69cm-20x27in) s.d.1918 W/C over pencil. 6-Nov-2 Dobiaschofsky, Bern #3230 (S.FR 850)

COLOMBO, A (19/20th C) Italian
£1824 $2809 €2900 Landscape with lake in Lombardy (52x110cm-20x43in) s. 23-Oct-2 Finarte, Milan #103/R

COLOMBO, Ambrogio (1821-?) Italian
£818 $1300 €1227 On the shores of Bosphorus (56x102cm-22x40in) s. panel pair. 7-Mar-3 Jackson's, Cedar Falls #534/R est:1000-2000

COLOMBO, Gianni (1937-1993) Italian
£8000 $12320 €12000 Spazio elastico (60x60cm-24x24in) s. acrylic elastic band nails on panel prov.lit. 22-Oct-2 Christie's, London #37/R est:8000-11000

Sculpture
£18000 $28080 €27000 Spazio elastico (125x125cm-49x49in) s.d.1975 verso painted wood nails elastic bands acrylic on board. 21-Oct-2 Sotheby's, London #28/R est:18000-25000

COLOMBO, Giovanni Battista Innocenzo (1717-1793) Italian
£37037 $60000 €55556 Architectural capriccio with figures by a fountain and column (103x147cm-41x58in) s.i. pair. 24-Jan-3 Christie's, Rockefeller NY #59/R est:80000-120000

COLOMES, F (19th C) ?
£1042 $1656 €1500 View of Grenoble (41x54cm-16x21in) s.d.1859 panel. 30-Apr-3 Tajan, Paris #106

COLONIA, Adam de (attrib) (1634-1685) Dutch
£1006 $1550 €1600 Paysans au clair de lune (26x38cm-10x15in) 25-Oct-2 Tajan, Paris #20 est:1500-1800

COLONIAL SCHOOL (18th C)
£3831 $5594 €5900 Bull fight (92x151cm-36x59in) 17-Jun-2 Ansorena, Madrid #165/R

COLQUHOUN, Alexander (1862-1941) Australian
£1085 $1726 €1628 Fizroy Gardens, Melbourne (29x24cm-11x9in) s. board painted c.1920. 5-May-3 Sotheby's, Melbourne #318 est:2000-3000 (A.D 2800)

COLQUHOUN, Amalie Sara (?-1974) Australian
£251 $381 €377 Looking down to the beach, Lorne (26x34cm-10x13in) s. canvas on board. 28-Aug-2 Deutscher-Menzies, Melbourne #416/R (A.D 700)
£304 $463 €456 Seaside pastures, evening, Lorne (38x45cm-15x18in) s. composition board. 28-Aug-2 Deutscher-Menzies, Melbourne #415/R (A.D 850)

COLQUHOUN, Brett (1958-) Australian

Works on paper
£589 $907 €884 Split second (167x167cm-66x66in) s.d.1990 i.verso synthetic polymer. 8-Sep-2 Sotheby's, Melbourne #16 est:1500-2000 (A.D 1650)
£1071 $1650 €1607 Awaken (213x152cm-84x60in) s. i.d.1992 verso synthetic polymer on canvas. 8-Sep-2 Sotheby's, Melbourne #57/R est:2000-3000 (A.D 3000)
£1143 $1760 €1715 Still (155x208cm-61x82in) s. i.d.1991 synthetic polymer on canvas. 8-Sep-2 Sotheby's, Melbourne #87/R est:2000-3000 (A.D 3200)

COLQUHOUN, Ithell (1906-1988) British
£300 $498 €435 Oil on a wet road (74x66cm-29x26in) mono.d.1963 i.verso. 10-Jun-3 David Lay, Penzance #501/R
£600 $972 €900 Exposed on the mountains of the heart (30x43cm-12x17in) board sold with another by same hand. 20-May-3 Bonhams, Knightsbridge #133/R

COLQUHOUN, Robert and MACBRYDE, Robert (20th C) British
£1300 $2015 €1950 Composition (30x34cm-12x13in) panel. 6-Dec-2 Lyon & Turnbull, Edinburgh #72/R est:1000-1500

Works on paper
£450 $711 €675 Goat man (33x24cm-13x9in) s.i. gouache black chk. 27-Nov-2 Sotheby's, Olympia #24/R

COLSON, Jaime (20th C) American
£2908 $4856 €4100 Maternite (60x50cm-24x20in) s.d.37 paper on panel. 18-Jun-3 Pierre Berge, Paris #169/R est:1000-1500

COLSON, Jean François (after) (1733-1803) French
£8500 $13685 €12750 Portrait of a girl sleeping on a chair (92x73cm-36x29in) 20-Feb-3 Christie's, Kensington #333/R est:1500-2500

COLSOUL, Louis (1907-) Belgian
£316 $494 €500 Pichet fleuri de jonquilles (80x70cm-31x28in) s. 16-Sep-2 Horta, Bruxelles #385

COLUCCI, Gio (1892-1974) Italian?

Works on paper
£503 $800 €755 Abstracted face (102x61cm-40x24in) s. mixed media exec.c.1950. 2-Mar-3 Toomey, Oak Park #822/R
£552 $883 €800 Le village (31x41cm-12x16in) s. gouache W/C. 12-Mar-3 Libert, Castor, Paris #59

COLUCCI, Vincenzo (1898-1970) Italian
£1613 $2548 €2500 Paris (60x81cm-24x32in) s.i.d.1937. 18-Dec-2 Christie's, Rome #77/R

COLVILLE, Alex (1920-) Canadian

Prints
£1399 $2169 €2099 Sleeper (42x52cm-17x20in) s.d.1975 num.68/70 serigraph print lit. 3-Dec-2 Joyner, Toronto #134/R est:4000-5000 (C.D 3400)

Works on paper
£1244 $2041 €1866 Study for dog and priest (14x21cm-6x8in) s.d.31 May 78 pencil ink lit. 3-Jun-3 Joyner, Toronto #6/R est:2500-3500 (C.D 2800)

COLVILLE, G (?) British?
£600 $954 €900 Melrose Abbey (51x68cm-20x27in) s.i. 6-Mar-3 Christie's, Kensington #83/R

COLVILLE, George Garden (1887-1970) Australian
£440 $708 €638 Riverside farm (39x49cm-15x19in) s. canvas on board. 12-May-3 Joel, Victoria #315 est:1500-2000 (A.D 1100)
£731 $1162 €1097 Sydney harbour (15x20cm-6x8in) s.d.1956 i.verso canvas on board. 4-Mar-3 Deutscher-Menzies, Melbourne #253/R (A.D 1900)

COLVIN, J M (?) ?
£280 $437 €420 Portrait of a young girl in a hat (51x41cm-20x16in) s. 10-Sep-2 Bonhams, Knightsbridge #73/R

COMAN, Charlotte Buell (1833-1925) American
£500 $800 €725 New Jersey hills, possibly Elizabethtown (29x26cm-11x10in) s. i.verso. 16-May-3 Skinner, Boston #214/R

COMBA, Juan (1852-1924) Spanish
£655 $1035 €950 Prince Eugenio's coat (15x13cm-6x5in) i. 1-Apr-3 Segre, Madrid #46/R
£1034 $1634 €1500 Royal Palace Chapel (23x15cm-9x6in) s. i.verso. 1-Apr-3 Segre, Madrid #44/R

Works on paper
£353 $557 €550 Young woman (31x22cm-12x9in) W/C. 14-Nov-2 Arte, Seville #317/R

COMBA, Pierre (?-1934) French

Works on paper
£276 $439 €400 L'arrivee des soldats dans la ville (17x34cm-7x13in) s. W/C. 4-Mar-3 Livinec, Gaudcheau & Jezequel, Rennes #15
£308 $481 €450 Chasseurs alpins sur une route du Midi (19x35cm-7x14in) W/C. 8-Apr-3 Gioffredo, Nice #179
£317 $504 €460 Vue de Trayas, Mediterranee (16x34cm-6x13in) s. W/C. 4-Mar-3 Livinec, Gaudcheau & Jezequel, Rennes #16/R
£439 $685 €650 General des garets (45x25cm-18x10in) s.i. W/C. 28-Mar-3 Delvaux, Paris #14
£507 $791 €750 Le rivage a Theoule au pied de l'Esterel (27x51cm-11x20in) s. W/C. 31-Mar-3 Rossini, Paris #35/R

COMBAS, Pierre (?) French

Works on paper
£403 $648 €600 Patrouille de chasseurs alpins dans un defile le long d'un torrent (52x35cm-20x14in) W/C. 19-Feb-3 Tajan, Paris #65

COMBAS, Robert (1957-) French
£377 $585 €600 Totem (42cm-17xin) s. acrylic brush rubber. 30-Oct-2 Artcurial Briest, Paris #597

£477 $777 €720 Abricot peche (35x27cm-14x11in) s.d.1989 paper. 3-Feb-3 Cornette de St.Cyr, Paris #385
£497 $810 €750 Fruit courant (34x23cm-13x9in) s.d.1999 paper. 3-Feb-3 Cornette de St.Cyr, Paris #386
£516 $815 €800 Herpes (33x24cm-13x9in) s. 18-Dec-2 Digard, Paris #155
£629 $969 €1000 Martien vert (33x23cm-13x9in) s. 22-Oct-2 Campo & Campo, Antwerp #44
£641 $1006 €1000 Figure couronnee (33x23cm-13x9in) s. acrylic emaillee. 16-Dec-2 Charbonneaux, Paris #131/R
£692 $1072 €1100 Composition (30cm-12in circular) s.d.94 sig. acrylic gramophone record. 5-Oct-2 De Vuyst, Lokeren #65
£1509 $2325 €2400 Romains (32x21cm-13x8in) s.d.1984 acrylic. 26-Oct-2 Cornette de St.Cyr, Paris #115/R
£1887 $2906 €3000 Guerrier (32x22cm-13x9in) s.d.1984 acrylic. 26-Oct-2 Cornette de St.Cyr, Paris #116/R
£2041 $3245 €3000 Maurice Chevalier (55x46cm-22x18in) s. acrylic. 26-Feb-3 Artcurial Briest, Paris #397/R est:2500-3000
£2431 $3840 €3500 Portrait d'Henri Maculot (65x50cm-26x20in) s.d. acrylic prov. 27-Apr-3 Perrin, Versailles #136/R est:2500-3000
£2532 $3949 €4000 Gladiateur (85x52cm-33x20in) s. s. verso acrylic. 20-Oct-2 Claude Boisgirard, Paris #70/R est:4500-5000
£2532 $3949 €4000 Guerrier (85x52cm-33x20in) s.d.2002 s. verso acrylic. 20-Oct-2 Claude Boisgirard, Paris #71/R est:4500-5000
£3125 $4969 €4500 Le pelerin St Geremin a l'oreille attentive et au copain au corps (100x81cm-39x32in) s.d.96 acrylic. 29-Apr-3 Artcurial Briest, Paris #537/R est:5000-6000
£3145 $4874 €5000 Poule royale (100x92cm-39x36in) s. acrylic prov. 30-Oct-2 Artcurial Briest, Paris #482/R est:5000-6000
£3265 $5192 €4800 Le guitariste (66x56cm-26x22in) s. acrylic. 26-Feb-3 Artcurial Briest, Paris #396/R est:3000-3800
£3472 $5486 €5000 Sans titre (100x74cm-39x29in) s. acrylic prov. 27-Apr-3 Perrin, Versailles #135/R est:4500-5000
£3472 $5486 €5000 Sans titre (108x75cm-43x30in) s. acrylic paper on canvas prov. 27-Apr-3 Perrin, Versailles #137/R est:4000-5000
£3526 $5535 €5500 Attak, Amazona (150x116cm-59x46in) s.d. acrylic exhib. 16-Dec-2 Charbonneaux, Paris #236/R est:5500-6000
£3774 $5849 €6000 Autoportrait et Genevieve (73x92cm-29x36in) s. acrylic. 30-Oct-2 Artcurial Briest, Paris #589/R est:6000-7000
£4722 $7461 €6800 La Nana, c'est un homme (162x130cm-64x51in) s.d. acrylic. 28-Apr-3 Cornette de St.Cyr, Paris #370/R est:8000-10000
£5208 $8594 €7500 L'attaque provient du ciel (126x160cm-50x63in) s.d.87 acrylic. 1-Jul-3 Artcurial Briest, Paris #849/R est:8000-10000
£5319 $8617 €7500 Combat (169x124cm-67x49in) s.d. acrylic. 23-May-3 Binoche, Paris #68/R est:6000-8000
£5634 $9352 €8000 Hommage a munch, le cri (106x123cm-42x48in) s. acrylic. 18-Jun-3 Anaf, Lyon #43/R est:12000-15000
£5935 $9378 €9200 Amitie franco-allemande (44x94cm-17x37in) s. acrylic prov. 18-Dec-2 Digard, Paris #88/R
£6000 $10020 €8700 Revolution Francaise (163x205cm-64x81in) s.d.Decembre 82 dispersion fabric on board prov.exhib.lit. 26-Jun-3 Sotheby's, London #245/R est:6000-8000
£6038 $9298 €9600 Head (92x73cm-36x29in) s.d.1988 acrylic. 26-Oct-2 Cornette de St.Cyr, Paris #109/R
£7639 $12604 €11000 David Bowie dans toute sa plendeur heterogene et jolie (142x127cm-56x50in) s.d.83 prov.exhib. 3-Jul-3 Christie's, Paris #41/R est:6000-8000
£8696 $14261 €12000 Nature morte (134x105cm-53x41in) s.d.1987 prov. 27-May-3 Tajan, Paris #61/R est:9000-12000
£8725 $14047 €13000 Diner (97x162cm-38x64in) s.d.1988 acrylic. 23-Feb-3 Mercier & Cie, Lille #157/R est:15000
£8974 $13910 €14000 Danseur a la tulipe jaune (180x114cm-71x45in) s.d.1984 acrylic. 7-Dec-2 Cornette de St.Cyr, Paris #121/R est:12000-15000
£11232 $18420 €15500 Le Roi et le Pape (158x115cm-62x45in) s.d.1986 prov. 27-May-3 Tajan, Paris #63/R est:15000-18000
£11258 $18351 €17000 Reggae (212x161cm-83x63in) s. s.d.verso acrylic painted 2002. 3-Feb-3 Cornette de St.Cyr, Paris #391/R est:18000
£12000 $19680 €18000 Bataille (223x237cm-88x93in) s.d.83 acrylic fabric prov. 7-Feb-3 Sotheby's, London #265/R est:6000-8000
£14245 $21938 €22650 Musee de Chateauroux (203x170cm-80x67in) s.d.2002 acrylic panel. 26-Oct-2 Cornette de St.Cyr, Paris #122/R
£15278 $25208 €22000 Black Gabrielle d'estree et sa quatrieme soeur (148x172cm-58x68in) s.d.85 acrylic canvas on canvas prov.lit. 1-Jul-3 Artcurial Briest, Paris #558/R est:25000-30000
£17201 $26490 €27350 Battle (183x203cm-72x80in) s. acrylic painted 1984. 26-Oct-2 Cornette de St.Cyr, Paris #110/R
£17201 $26490 €27350 Poty de tulipes chaudes (208x100cm-82x39in) s. acrylic painted 1991. 26-Oct-2 Cornette de St.Cyr, Paris #117/R
£22390 $34481 €35600 Serenade (180x177cm-71x70in) s. acrylic. 26-Oct-2 Cornette de St.Cyr, Paris #113/R

Sculpture

£1795 $2818 €2800 La triade antiraciste (88x51x28cm-35x20x11in) s.d.num.4/8 painted resin. 16-Dec-2 Charbonneaux, Paris #312/R est:3000-3500
£3145 $4843 €5000 Saint-Raymond (180x92x60cm-71x36x24in) wood mixed media exhib.lit. 26-Oct-2 Cornette de St.Cyr, Paris #114/R

Works on paper

£347 $552 €500 Le chien est un serpent (32x23cm-13x9in) s.d.1997 mixed media. 29-Apr-3 Campo & Campo, Antwerp #36
£374 $595 €550 Elle a mit une queue en plastiue (31x23cm-12x9in) s.d.1997 felt-tip pen dr. 24-Mar-3 Cornette de St.Cyr, Paris #138/R
£390 $651 €550 Composition (27x20cm-11x8in) s. felt tip acrylic photo. 18-Jun-3 Pierre Berge, Paris #57
£503 $780 €800 Personnage au cigare (31x24cm-12x9in) s. col wax crayon. 30-Oct-2 Artcurial Briest, Paris #595
£535 $834 €850 Maries (24x17cm-9x7in) s. gouache felt-tip pen over photograph. 11-Oct-2 Binoche, Paris #142
£581 $917 €900 L'archer (48x34cm-19x13in) s.i. black ink. 17-Dec-2 Rossini, Paris #18
£780 $1303 €1100 Serie sacho mado (31x25cm-12x10in) mixed media. 18-Jun-3 Charbonneaux, Paris #71
£816 $1298 €1200 Malrau l'elephant sado maso (23x31cm-9x12in) s.d.86 ink prov. 26-Feb-3 Artcurial Briest, Paris #557
£1135 $1895 €1600 Un avion de guerre (33x36cm-13x14in) s.d.verso mixed media paper canvas. 18-Jun-3 Pierre Berge, Paris #104/R est:1300-1500
£1327 $2109 €1950 Inspecteur Karate, joue par Yul Bruner (50x70cm-20x28in) s. ink prov. 26-Feb-3 Artcurial Briest, Paris #395/R est:1500-2000
£1447 $2242 €2300 Personnage dans une chaussure (34x27cm-13x11in) s.d.87 col wax pastel graphite. 30-Oct-2 Artcurial Briest, Paris #591/R est:2700-3300
£2857 $4543 €4200 Mur (57x77cm-22x30in) mixed media painted 2000 exhib. 3-Mar-3 Marc Kohn, Paris #44/R

COMBAZ, Ghisbert (1869-1941) Belgian

£321 $503 €500 Projet d'affiche, pour le 75eme anniversaire de la Belgique (102x62cm-40x24in) s.d.1905. 10-Dec-2 Vanderkindere, Brussels #465
£673 $1057 €1050 Dans les rochers (50x75cm-20x30in) s.d.1914. 10-Dec-2 Vanderkindere, Brussels #480
£1509 $2325 €2400 Village en Bretagne (50x62cm-20x24in) s.d.1913 cardboard. 22-Oct-2 Campo & Campo, Antwerp #47

Works on paper

£342 $534 €500 L'embarcadere (49x59cm-19x23in) s. mixed media double-sided. 14-Apr-3 Horta, Bruxelles #297

COMBER, Melanie (1970-) British

£900 $1467 €1305 Pond (137x171cm-54x67in) s.i.d.1988 oil pigment. 15-Jul-3 Bonhams, Knightsbridge #129/R

COMBES, Andre (20th C) French

£426 $672 €639 Table with cloth and dinner service (49x55cm-19x22in) s. 2-Dec-2 Rasmussen, Copenhagen #1762/R (D.KR 5000)

COMBETTE, Joseph Marcellin (1770-1840) French

£1826 $2849 €2739 Portrait of seated man (141x109cm-56x43in) s.d.1795. 28-Mar-3 Koller, Zurich #3095/R est:7000-12000 (S.FR 4000)

COMBLAT, A de (19/20th C) French?

£1439 $2360 €2000 Le cerisier sauvage (92x60cm-36x24in) s. exhib. 4-Jun-3 Marc Kohn, Paris #18 est:1500-2000

COMENSOLI, Mario (1922-1993) Italian

£300 $475 €450 Landscape in Ticino (31x41cm-12x16in) d.1943 s.i.verso tempera panel. 29-Nov-2 Zofingen, Switzerland #2831 (S.FR 700)
£365 $576 €548 Self-portrait of the artist (60x49cm-24x19in) board double-sided. 29-Nov-2 Zofingen, Switzerland #2836 (S.FR 850)
£429 $678 €644 Lugano quay (40x50cm-16x20in) d.1943 s.i.verso masonite. 29-Nov-2 Zofingen, Switzerland #2834 (S.FR 1000)
£472 $746 €708 Still life with fish (34x39cm-13x15in) s.d.1944 board. 29-Nov-2 Zofingen, Switzerland #2830 (S.FR 1100)
£558 $882 €837 Coastal landscape in Tessin (40x50cm-16x20in) s.d.1945 board. 29-Nov-2 Zofingen, Switzerland #2833 (S.FR 1300)
£1629 $2720 €2362 Still life with fishes (53x55cm-21x22in) s. pavatex. 24-Jun-3 Koller, Zurich #77/R est:3000-5000 (S.FR 3600)
£3654 $5773 €5700 Working woman (95x60cm-37x24in) painted 1964. 12-Nov-2 Babuino, Rome #349/R

Works on paper

£429 $678 €644 Winter in Zurich (40x50cm-16x20in) s.i.verso mixed media double-sided. 29-Nov-2 Zofingen, Switzerland #2832 (S.FR 1000)
£611 $960 €917 Untitled (47x36cm-19x14in) s.d.1988 chl. 25-Nov-2 Germann, Zurich #699 (S.FR 1400)
£696 $1078 €1044 Time for tenderness (63x45cm-25x18in) s.d.1992 mixed media. 9-Dec-2 Philippe Schuler, Zurich #3526/R est:800-1000 (S.FR 1600)
£2643 $3859 €3965 Pizza baker (121x78cm-48x31in) s.d.1970 mixed media masonite. 17-Jun-2 Philippe Schuler, Zurich #4263/R est:7000-9000 (S.FR 6000)

COMERRE, Léon (1850-1916) French

£265 $432 €400 Etude de plantes (49x41cm-19x16in) st.sig. 3-Feb-3 Chambelland & Giafferi, Paris #124
£265 $432 €400 Songe (23x34cm-9x13in) st.sig. panel double-sided. 3-Feb-3 Chambelland & Giafferi, Paris #154
£265 $432 €400 Vieillard (27x17cm-11x7in) st.sig. panel double-sided. 3-Feb-3 Chambelland & Giafferi, Paris #150
£298 $486 €450 Homme a la casquette (41x31cm-16x12in) st.sig. 3-Feb-3 Chambelland & Giafferi, Paris #34

£298 $486 €450 Etude de femme endormie (24x63cm-9x25in) st.sig. 3-Feb-3 Chambelland & Giafferi, Paris #49
£298 $486 €450 Etude de Neptune (37x74cm-15x29in) st.sig. 3-Feb-3 Chambelland & Giafferi, Paris #119
£331 $540 €500 Chat (35x27cm-14x11in) st.sig. 3-Feb-3 Chambelland & Giafferi, Paris #56
£331 $540 €500 ACtrice (75x30cm-30x12in) st.sig. 3-Feb-3 Chambelland & Giafferi, Paris #71
£331 $540 €500 Jeanne d'Arc (52x28cm-20x11in) st.sig. 3-Feb-3 Chambelland & Giafferi, Paris #140
£364 $594 €550 Etude de visage (55x46cm-22x18in) st.sig. 3-Feb-3 Chambelland & Giafferi, Paris #103
£364 $594 €550 Taverne (61x49cm-24x19in) st.sig. 3-Feb-3 Chambelland & Giafferi, Paris #123
£364 $594 €550 Village en bord de mer (16x31cm-6x12in) st.sig. panel. 3-Feb-3 Chambelland & Giafferi, Paris #148
£397 $648 €600 Chien noir (58x44cm-23x17in) st.sig. 3-Feb-3 Chambelland & Giafferi, Paris #73
£397 $648 €600 Etude d'Apollon (50x37cm-20x15in) st.sig. 3-Feb-3 Chambelland & Giafferi, Paris #76
£430 $702 €650 Etude de femme pensante (23x63cm-9x25in) st.sig. oil graphite. 3-Feb-3 Chambelland & Giafferi, Paris #50
£430 $702 €650 Neptune (55x130cm-22x51in) st.sig. 3-Feb-3 Chambelland & Giafferi, Paris #61
£464 $756 €700 Bebe endormi (30x27cm-12x11in) st.sig. canvas on panel. 3-Feb-3 Chambelland & Giafferi, Paris #15
£464 $756 €700 Portrait de Geo en clown (41x33cm-16x13in) st.sig. cardboard on canvas. 3-Feb-3 Chambelland & Giafferi, Paris #25
£464 $756 €700 Etude de feuilles (59x80cm-23x31in) st.sig. 3-Feb-3 Chambelland & Giafferi, Paris #36/R
£464 $756 €700 Gondole (26x16cm-10x6in) st.sig. panel. 3-Feb-3 Chambelland & Giafferi, Paris #143
£464 $756 €700 Patio de l'Alhambra (29x18cm-11x7in) st.sig. panel. 3-Feb-3 Chambelland & Giafferi, Paris #146
£497 $810 €750 Bebe eveille (28x30cm-11x12in) st.sig. canvas on panel. 3-Feb-3 Chambelland & Giafferi, Paris #35
£497 $810 €750 Projet pour plafond (79x36cm-31x14in) st.sig. 3-Feb-3 Chambelland & Giafferi, Paris #37
£497 $810 €750 Etude de femmes allongees (24x63cm-9x25in) st.sig. oil graphite. 3-Feb-3 Chambelland & Giafferi, Paris #51
£497 $810 €750 Etude de reine (61x46cm-24x18in) st.sig. 3-Feb-3 Chambelland & Giafferi, Paris #52
£497 $810 €750 Patio de l'Alhambra (33x18cm-13x7in) st.sig. panel. 3-Feb-3 Chambelland & Giafferi, Paris #147
£497 $810 €750 Route (16x25cm-6x10in) st.sig. panel. 3-Feb-3 Chambelland & Giafferi, Paris #158
£530 $864 €800 POrte du jardin (55x38cm-22x15in) st.sig. 3-Feb-3 Chambelland & Giafferi, Paris #14
£563 $918 €850 Venice (17x28cm-7x11in) st.sig. panel. 3-Feb-3 Chambelland & Giafferi, Paris #144
£596 $972 €900 Portrait de petite fille (35x27cm-14x11in) s. 3-Feb-3 Chambelland & Giafferi, Paris #9
£596 $972 €900 Pierrot (55x46cm-22x18in) st.sig. 3-Feb-3 Chambelland & Giafferi, Paris #26
£629 $1025 €950 Femme et enfant au bord de la mer (12x33cm-5x13in) s. panel. 3-Feb-3 Chambelland & Giafferi, Paris #1/R
£629 $1025 €950 Femme et enfants dans un jardin (38x61cm-15x24in) st.sig. 3-Feb-3 Chambelland & Giafferi, Paris #10
£629 $1025 €950 Etude de nu (46x24cm-18x9in) s. panel. 3-Feb-3 Chambelland & Giafferi, Paris #70
£629 $1025 €950 Petit garcon blond (46x38cm-18x15in) st.sig. 3-Feb-3 Chambelland & Giafferi, Paris #75/R
£662 $1079 €1000 Bebe endormi (24x33cm-9x13in) st.sig. 3-Feb-3 Chambelland & Giafferi, Paris #16
£662 $1079 €1000 Clin d'oeil (55x38cm-22x15in) s. 3-Feb-3 Chambelland & Giafferi, Paris #12
£662 $1079 €1000 Portrait de femme au chien (52x52cm-20x20in) s. 3-Feb-3 Chambelland & Giafferi, Paris #43/R
£662 $1079 €1000 Esquisse pour 'Venus triomphante' (63x150cm-25x59in) st.sig. lit. 3-Feb-3 Chambelland & Giafferi, Paris #83/R
£662 $1079 €1000 Etudes (51x121cm-20x48in) s. 3-Feb-3 Chambelland & Giafferi, Paris #85/R
£662 $1079 €1000 Femme au chevalet (27x17cm-11x7in) st.sig. panel double-sided. 3-Feb-3 Chambelland & Giafferi, Paris #152
£695 $1133 €1050 Chien au noeud rouge (24x19cm-9x7in) st.sig. 3-Feb-3 Chambelland & Giafferi, Paris #5
£728 $1187 €1100 Pierrot (35x27cm-14x11in) st.sig. 3-Feb-3 Chambelland & Giafferi, Paris #24
£728 $1187 €1100 Vierge (77x58cm-30x23in) st.sig. 3-Feb-3 Chambelland & Giafferi, Paris #58
£728 $1187 €1100 Etude (73x116cm-29x46in) st.sig. 3-Feb-3 Chambelland & Giafferi, Paris #60
£728 $1187 €1100 Etude de femme habillee a l'orientale (81x65cm-32x26in) st.sig. 3-Feb-3 Chambelland & Giafferi, Paris #62/R
£728 $1187 €1100 Portrait de femme en tenue de bal blanche (89x69cm-35x27in) s. 3-Feb-3 Chambelland & Giafferi, Paris #67
£728 $1187 €1100 Portrait de jeune femme (66x53cm-26x21in) s. 3-Feb-3 Chambelland & Giafferi, Paris #94/R
£728 $1187 €1100 Fee (30x38cm-12x15in) st.sig. cardboard on canvas. 3-Feb-3 Chambelland & Giafferi, Paris #135
£762 $1241 €1150 Portrait d'enfant (11cm-4in circular) s. panel. 3-Feb-3 Chambelland & Giafferi, Paris #6/R
£795 $1295 €1200 Bouquet de roses (63x40cm-25x16in) s. 3-Feb-3 Chambelland & Giafferi, Paris #13
£795 $1295 €1200 Blonde denudee (83x60cm-33x24in) st.sig. 3-Feb-3 Chambelland & Giafferi, Paris #42/R
£828 $1349 €1250 Lili (35x25cm-14x10in) s.i. 3-Feb-3 Chambelland & Giafferi, Paris #27/R
£861 $1403 €1300 Alhambra (40x22cm-16x9in) st.sig. panel. 3-Feb-3 Chambelland & Giafferi, Paris #31/R
£861 $1403 €1300 Etude de ballerine (150x53cm-59x21in) st.sig. 3-Feb-3 Chambelland & Giafferi, Paris #57
£861 $1403 €1300 Etude de Venus triomphante (67x152cm-26x60in) st.sig. oil graphite. 3-Feb-3 Chambelland & Giafferi, Paris #53/R
£861 $1403 €1300 Portrait de Mademoiselle Achille Fould a l'eventail (25x18cm-10x7in) s. panel. 3-Feb-3 Chambelland & Giafferi, Paris #82
£861 $1403 €1300 Femme a l'eventail (98x69cm-39x27in) s. 3-Feb-3 Chambelland & Giafferi, Paris #125/R
£894 $1457 €1350 Portrait de napolitaine au tambourin (22x17cm-9x7in) s.d.1879 panel. 16-Feb-3 Mercier & Cie, Lille #267
£927 $1511 €1400 Paysanne accoudee (66x27cm-26x11in) st.sig. 3-Feb-3 Chambelland & Giafferi, Paris #55
£927 $1511 €1400 Buste de jeune fille (65x50cm-26x20in) st.sig. 3-Feb-3 Chambelland & Giafferi, Paris #100/R
£927 $1511 €1400 Tete bonnet blanc (35x27cm-14x11in) st.sig. panel lit. 3-Feb-3 Chambelland & Giafferi, Paris #116
£927 $1511 €1400 Madonna and Child (96x72cm-38x28in) st.sig. oil collage. 3-Feb-3 Chambelland & Giafferi, Paris #126
£993 $1619 €1500 Madonna and Child (66x66cm-26x26in) s. 3-Feb-3 Chambelland & Giafferi, Paris #19
£993 $1619 €1500 Jeune orientale (46x33cm-18x13in) s. 3-Feb-3 Chambelland & Giafferi, Paris #30/R
£1060 $1727 €1600 Bord de riviere (48x27cm-19x11in) s. 3-Feb-3 Chambelland & Giafferi, Paris #3
£1060 $1727 €1600 Femme au chapeau noir (61x46cm-24x18in) s. 3-Feb-3 Chambelland & Giafferi, Paris #18/R
£1126 $1835 €1700 Jetee de roses (38x55cm-15x22in) s. 3-Feb-3 Chambelland & Giafferi, Paris #46
£1126 $1835 €1700 Etude de Venus (72x115cm-28x45in) st.sig. 3-Feb-3 Chambelland & Giafferi, Paris #91/R
£1126 $1835 €1700 Petit canal a Venise (26x16cm-10x6in) st.sig. panel. 3-Feb-3 Chambelland & Giafferi, Paris #138/R
£1126 $1835 €1700 Jeune femme revant (61x50cm-24x20in) st.sig. 3-Feb-3 Chambelland & Giafferi, Paris #134/R
£1126 $1835 €1700 Jeune fille de profil (40x31cm-16x12in) st.sig. 3-Feb-3 Chambelland & Giafferi, Paris #133
£1192 $1943 €1800 Etude pour pluie d'or (33x46cm-13x18in) st.sig. 3-Feb-3 Chambelland & Giafferi, Paris #72
£1192 $1943 €1800 Etude de Vierge a l'Enfant (67x67cm-26x26in) st.sig. oil collage. 3-Feb-3 Chambelland & Giafferi, Paris #122
£1258 $2051 €1900 Deux jeunes filles a la pomme (46x55cm-18x22in) st.sig. 3-Feb-3 Chambelland & Giafferi, Paris #7/R
£1325 $2159 €2000 Ballerine rose et blanche (64x33cm-25x13in) s. 3-Feb-3 Chambelland & Giafferi, Paris #23/R
£1325 $2159 €2000 Assemblee (93x41cm-37x16in) s. 3-Feb-3 Chambelland & Giafferi, Paris #128
£1391 $2267 €2100 Apparition. s.i.d.1876 panel. 3-Feb-3 Chambelland & Giafferi, Paris #45/R
£1391 $2267 €2100 NU assis (115x85cm-45x33in) st.sig. 3-Feb-3 Chambelland & Giafferi, Paris #89
£1391 $2267 €2100 Family (22x58cm-9x23in) st.sig. 3-Feb-3 Chambelland & Giafferi, Paris #137
£1457 $2375 €2200 Portrait de femme et chien au noeud bleu (52x52cm-20x20in) s. 3-Feb-3 Chambelland & Giafferi, Paris #81/R
£1457 $2375 €2200 Rachel (82x57cm-32x22in) s.d.1904. 3-Feb-3 Chambelland & Giafferi, Paris #86/R
£1457 $2375 €2200 Etude de Geo (60x75cm-24x30in) st.sig. 3-Feb-3 Chambelland & Giafferi, Paris #107/R
£1457 $2375 €2200 Fountain (22x40cm-9x16in) st.sig. panel. 3-Feb-3 Chambelland & Giafferi, Paris #156
£1523 $2483 €2300 Saluant (61x50cm-24x20in) st.sig. lit. 3-Feb-3 Chambelland & Giafferi, Paris #17/R
£1722 $2807 €2600 Auto-portrait (32x25cm-13x10in) i.d.1877 verso. 3-Feb-3 Chambelland & Giafferi, Paris #4/R
£1722 $2807 €2600 Ballerine bleue (58x43cm-23x17in) s. 3-Feb-3 Chambelland & Giafferi, Paris #20/R
£1722 $2807 €2600 Ballerine rose (65x46cm-26x18in) s. 3-Feb-3 Chambelland & Giafferi, Paris #21/R
£1722 $2807 €2600 Etude de Venus (31x64cm-12x25in) s. lit. 3-Feb-3 Chambelland & Giafferi, Paris #136
£1724 $2741 €2500 Gitane a la guitare (56x47cm-22x19in) s.d.74. 7-Mar-3 Rabourdin & Choppin de Janvry, Paris #30/R est:3000-3500
£1854 $3023 €2800 Aveugles (49x34cm-19x13in) s.i. 3-Feb-3 Chambelland & Giafferi, Paris #2/R
£1854 $3023 €2800 Madame Gayrard Pacini (142x83cm-56x33in) s. lit. 3-Feb-3 Chambelland & Giafferi, Paris #118/R
£1854 $3023 €2800 Orientale (20x10cm-8x4in) s.i.d.1879 panel. 3-Feb-3 Chambelland & Giafferi, Paris #139/R
£1921 $3130 €2900 Ballerine au voile blanc (81x54cm-32x21in) st.sig. 3-Feb-3 Chambelland & Giafferi, Paris #22/R
£1987 $3238 €3000 Etude de femme a la bougie (81x65cm-32x26in) st.sig. 3-Feb-3 Chambelland & Giafferi, Paris #90/R
£2119 $3454 €3200 Etude de couple (75x73cm-30x29in) st.sig. 3-Feb-3 Chambelland & Giafferi, Paris #88
£2119 $3454 €3200 Orientale (51x70cm-20x28in) st.sig. 3-Feb-3 Chambelland & Giafferi, Paris #99/R
£2119 $3454 €3200 Femme au chat (92x73cm-36x29in) st.sig. 3-Feb-3 Chambelland & Giafferi, Paris #130/R
£2252 $3670 €3400 Etude de femme se maquillant (67x67cm-26x26in) st.sig. 3-Feb-3 Chambelland & Giafferi, Paris #105/R
£2318 $3778 €3500 Femme blonde au chat (55x33cm-22x13in) s. 3-Feb-3 Chambelland & Giafferi, Paris #74/R

£2450	$3994	€3700	Promenade en barque (46x38cm-18x15in) st.sig. 3-Feb-3 Chambelland & Giafferi, Paris #132
£2649	$4318	€4000	Nu au drap (123x76cm-48x30in) st.sig. 3-Feb-3 Chambelland & Giafferi, Paris #96/R
£2715	$4426	€4100	Portrait de jeune fille rousse (70x48cm-28x19in) s. 3-Feb-3 Chambelland & Giafferi, Paris #11
£2715	$4426	€4100	Sortie de bain (77x58cm-30x23in) st.sig. 3-Feb-3 Chambelland & Giafferi, Paris #101/R
£2781	$4534	€4200	Mariage (51x68cm-20x27in) s. 3-Feb-3 Chambelland & Giafferi, Paris #44/R
£2781	$4534	€4200	Fee a la lampe a huile (102x68cm-40x27in) st.sig. 3-Feb-3 Chambelland & Giafferi, Paris #87/R
£2914	$4750	€4400	Repos (31x40cm-12x16in) st.sig. 3-Feb-3 Chambelland & Giafferi, Paris #8/R
£2914	$4750	€4400	Nu allonge (54x73cm-21x29in) st.sig. 3-Feb-3 Chambelland & Giafferi, Paris #102/R
£3000	$5010	€4350	Study for la Ville de Lyon (71x180cm-28x71in) s. oil over pencil arched top. 17-Jun-3 Bonhams, New Bond Street #118/R est:3000-5000
£3046	$4966	€4600	Gout. Vue. Ouie. Odorat (32x57cm-13x22in) st.sig. lit. set of 4. 3-Feb-3 Chambelland & Giafferi, Paris #77/R
£3311	$5397	€5000	Madonna and Child (87x65cm-34x26in) st.sig. 3-Feb-3 Chambelland & Giafferi, Paris #129
£3311	$5397	€5000	Nu allonge (200x140cm-79x55in) st.sig. 3-Feb-3 Chambelland & Giafferi, Paris #162
£3444	$5613	€5200	Fuite en Egypte (114x145cm-45x57in) st.sig. 3-Feb-3 Chambelland & Giafferi, Paris #97/R
£3444	$5613	€5200	Dams, or et rose (41x32cm-16x13in) st.sig. lit. 3-Feb-3 Chambelland & Giafferi, Paris #131/R
£3576	$5829	€5400	Jeune fille a la bicyclette (51x29cm-20x11in) s. 3-Feb-3 Chambelland & Giafferi, Paris #109/R
£3642	$5937	€5500	Bulle (73x60cm-29x24in) st.sig. 3-Feb-3 Chambelland & Giafferi, Paris #106/R
£3709	$6045	€5600	Bebe bonnet rose (33x30cm-13x12in) s.i. lit. 3-Feb-3 Chambelland & Giafferi, Paris #115/R est:5000
£3974	$6477	€6000	Jeune fille dans un jardin (106x68cm-42x27in) st.sig. 3-Feb-3 Chambelland & Giafferi, Paris #66/R
£4040	$6585	€6100	Jeune orientaliste (62x42cm-24x17in) st.sig. 3-Feb-3 Chambelland & Giafferi, Paris #28/R
£4371	$7125	€6600	Femme dans les vagues (45x78cm-18x31in) st.sig. 3-Feb-3 Chambelland & Giafferi, Paris #41/R
£4503	$7340	€6800	Pierrot (25x14cm-10x6in) s. panel. 3-Feb-3 Chambelland & Giafferi, Paris #26a/R
£4967	$8096	€7500	Jeune femme a la tasse de the (82x60cm-32x24in) s. 3-Feb-3 Chambelland & Giafferi, Paris #93/R
£5166	$8420	€7800	Femme, chien et chat (64x46cm-25x18in) s. 3-Feb-3 Chambelland & Giafferi, Paris #40/R
£5960	$9715	€9000	Family (270x158cm-106x62in) s. oil graphite. 3-Feb-3 Chambelland & Giafferi, Paris #59/R
£6604	$10170	€10500	Dream (90x89cm-35x35in) s. oval. 23-Oct-2 Finarte, Milan #1/R est:3000-4000
£6623	$10795	€10000	Marcelle Souty (106x60cm-42x24in) st.sig. lit. 3-Feb-3 Chambelland & Giafferi, Paris #64/R
£6623	$10795	€10000	Repos (37x68cm-15x27in) s. 3-Feb-3 Chambelland & Giafferi, Paris #108 est:1500
£6954	$11334	€10500	Etude pour 'Le manteau legendaire' (40x67cm-16x26in) s. 3-Feb-3 Chambelland & Giafferi, Paris #29/R
£7285	$11874	€11000	Mousseline Liberty (150x70cm-59x28in) s. lit. 3-Feb-3 Chambelland & Giafferi, Paris #111/R est:10000
£8609	$14033	€13000	Chapeau a plumes (150x85cm-59x33in) st.sig. lit. 3-Feb-3 Chambelland & Giafferi, Paris #112/R est:10000
£9603	$15652	€14500	Geo infante (125x65cm-49x26in) s.i. lit. 3-Feb-3 Chambelland & Giafferi, Paris #35a/R est:18000
£9934	$16192	€15000	Etude pour 'Le manteau legendaire' (74x115cm-29x45in) s. 3-Feb-3 Chambelland & Giafferi, Paris #68/R
£10596	$17272	€16000	Petite fille au cerceau (46x86cm-18x34in) S.D.1886. 3-Feb-3 Chambelland & Giafferi, Paris #39/R
£10596	$17272	€16000	Etude de Sardanapale (450x386cm-177x152in) st.sig. 3-Feb-3 Chambelland & Giafferi, Paris #98/R est:18000
£11258	$18351	€17000	Petit crapaud (137x98cm-54x39in) s. lit. 3-Feb-3 Chambelland & Giafferi, Paris #69/R est:8000
£11921	$19430	€18000	Nu au collier de perles (108x195cm-43x77in) s. 3-Feb-3 Chambelland & Giafferi, Paris #113/R est:10000
£13907	$22669	€21000	Pierrot, Coolombine et Arlequin (146cm-57in circular) s. 3-Feb-3 Chambelland & Giafferi, Paris #47/R est:12000
£15563	$25368	€23500	Marchande de fleurs (117x76cm-46x30in) s. 3-Feb-3 Chambelland & Giafferi, Paris #95/R
£17219	$28066	€26000	Lion amoureux (273x205cm-107x81in) s.i. lit. 3-Feb-3 Chambelland & Giafferi, Paris #63/R est:15000
£22152	$35000	€33228	Flower seller (117x76cm-46x30in) s. prov. 24-Apr-3 Sotheby's, New York #79/R est:35000-50000
£23179	$37781	€35000	Capeline velours vert (125x65cm-49x26in) s.i. lit. 3-Feb-3 Chambelland & Giafferi, Paris #110/R est:10000
£26490	$43179	€40000	Jezabel devoree par les chiens (152x247cm-60x97in) s. 3-Feb-3 Chambelland & Giafferi, Paris #38/R est:18000
£36424	$59371	€55000	En l'absence du peintre (216x158cm-85x62in) s. 3-Feb-3 Chambelland & Giafferi, Paris #85a/R est:18000
Works on paper			
£265	$432	€400	Silene (62x61cm-24x24in) s. chl htd chk. 3-Feb-3 Chambelland & Giafferi, Paris #234a
£278	$453	€420	Hiver (46x30cm-18x12in) s. chl lit. 3-Feb-3 Chambelland & Giafferi, Paris #277
£298	$486	€450	Sanson et Dalila (14x11cm-6x4in) s. graphite W/C gouache. 3-Feb-3 Chambelland & Giafferi, Paris #212
£305	$497	€460	Etude (32x23cm-13x9in) st.sig. ink W/C gouache. 3-Feb-3 Chambelland & Giafferi, Paris #211a/R
£318	$518	€480	Destin (62x48cm-24x19in) st.sig. chl double-sided. 3-Feb-3 Chambelland & Giafferi, Paris #199
£338	$551	€510	Etude d'africaine (64x49cm-25x19in) st.sig. chl. 3-Feb-3 Chambelland & Giafferi, Paris #249
£344	$561	€520	Figures (27x18cm-11x7in) s.i.d.1877 ink wash. 3-Feb-3 Chambelland & Giafferi, Paris #201a/R
£344	$561	€520	Etude de petites filles (61x47cm-24x19in) st.sig. chl lit. 3-Feb-3 Chambelland & Giafferi, Paris #289
£364	$594	€550	Sortie de theatre (35x27cm-14x11in) st.sig. pastel chl. 3-Feb-3 Chambelland & Giafferi, Paris #208
£397	$648	€600	Etude (47x61cm-19x24in) s. chl. 3-Feb-3 Chambelland & Giafferi, Paris #195
£397	$648	€600	Petit faune (27x34cm-11x13in) s. chl dr lit. 3-Feb-3 Chambelland & Giafferi, Paris #207
£437	$712	€660	Etyude d'africaine (48x62cm-19x24in) st.sig. chl. 3-Feb-3 Chambelland & Giafferi, Paris #259
£450	$734	€680	Love (48x62cm-19x24in) st.sig. chl lit. 3-Feb-3 Chambelland & Giafferi, Paris #201
£477	$777	€720	Etude de Arachne (27x45cm-11x18in) st.sig. graphite lit. 3-Feb-3 Chambelland & Giafferi, Paris #211
£530	$864	€800	Etudes (31x47cm-12x19in) st.sig. chl htd chk pair. 3-Feb-3 Chambelland & Giafferi, Paris #205/R
£609	$993	€920	Femmes nues (47x31cm-19x12in) st.sig. chl lit. 3-Feb-3 Chambelland & Giafferi, Paris #200
£728	$1187	€1100	Etude d'africaine (62x48cm-24x19in) st.sig. chl. 3-Feb-3 Chambelland & Giafferi, Paris #252
£927	$1511	€1400	Etudes (48x61cm-19x24in) st.sig. chl set of 3. 3-Feb-3 Chambelland & Giafferi, Paris #204/R
£960	$1565	€1450	Etude pour 'Jezabel devoree par les chiens' (8x12cm-3x5in) s.d.1876 graphite ink W/C gouache. 3-Feb-3 Chambelland & Giafferi, Paris #213/R
£1325	$2159	€2000	Nu de dos (29x22cm-11x9in) s.d.1878 W/C. 3-Feb-3 Chambelland & Giafferi, Paris #209/R
£1523	$2483	€2300	Croquis pour foyer. st.sig. chl lit. 3-Feb-3 Chambelland & Giafferi, Paris #272/R
£1755	$2861	€2650	Etude pour lion amoureux (20x15cm-8x6in) s.i.d.1877 graphite W/C gouache. 3-Feb-3 Chambelland & Giafferi, Paris #214/R

COMERRE-PATON, Jacqueline (1859-?) French

£993	$1619	€1500	Etude pour paysanne (73x43cm-29x17in) 3-Feb-3 Chambelland & Giafferi, Paris #338
£14570	$23748	€22000	Paysanne (228x128cm-90x50in) s. 3-Feb-3 Chambelland & Giafferi, Paris #334/R est:2500

COMERY, Gilles (20th C) French

£662	$1079	€1000	Deux nus dans un paysage (40x40cm-16x16in) s.verso. 1-Feb-3 Claude Aguttes, Neuilly #197

COMFORT, Charles Fraser (1900-) Canadian

£978	$1604	€1467	Roseate haze, Lake Clear (30x40cm-12x16in) s. panel prov. 3-Jun-3 Joyner, Toronto #17/R est:2500-3000 (C.D 2200)
£1033	$1622	€1550	Rocky promontory, Starr's Channel, Georgian Bay (30x41cm-12x16in) s. panel. 24-Jul-2 Walker's, Ottawa #204/R est:2500-3000 (C.D 2500)
£1233	$1973	€1850	Outer Island, Georgian Bay (30x41cm-12x16in) s.d.1950 i.verso board. 15-May-3 Heffel, Vancouver #111 est:2000-3000 (C.D 2750)
£1681	$2690	€2522	Monument Channel, Georgian Bay (30x41cm-12x16in) s.d.1950 i.verso board. 15-May-3 Heffel, Vancouver #31 est:2000-3000 (C.D 3750)
£2000	$3280	€3000	Mountain peaks (61x76cm-24x30in) s.d.30 prov.exhib. 27-May-3 Sotheby's, Toronto #169/R est:5000-7000 (C.D 4500)
£2018	$3229	€3027	Glacial boulders on a limestone beach, Ingonish, Cape Breton (30x41cm-12x16in) s. i.verso board prov. 15-May-3 Heffel, Vancouver #29/R est:2500-3500 (C.D 4500)
£2466	$3946	€3699	As the fog lifted, Georgian Bay (51x66cm-20x26in) s. i.verso prov. 15-May-3 Heffel, Vancouver #172/R est:3500-4500 (C.D 5500)
£2575	$4017	€3863	August sunrise, Georgian Bay (50x66cm-20x26in) s.i.d.1972 prov. 25-Mar-3 Ritchie, Toronto #98/R est:2000-2500 (C.D 6000)
£3498	$5422	€5247	Line storm approaching Split Rock Island, Georgian Bay (60x80cm-24x31in) s. board prov. 3-Dec-2 Joyner, Toronto #155/R est:6000-8000 (C.D 8500)

COMINETTI, Ernesto (1900-1990) Italian

£340	$541	€500	Entreves (60x45cm-24x18in) s. d.1962 verso. 1-Mar-3 Meeting Art, Vercelli #159

COMMENT, Jean-François (1919-2002) Swiss

£830	$1303	€1245	Composition (74x85cm-29x33in) s.d.70 prov. 23-Nov-2 Burkhard, Luzern #195/R (S.FR 1900)
£1266	$1988	€1899	Le nuage rouge (80x100cm-31x39in) s.d.81-84 prov. 23-Nov-2 Burkhard, Luzern #196/R est:3000-4000 (S.FR 2900)

COMMERE, Jean Yves (1920-1986) French
£340 $541 €500 Petit dejeuner (30x30cm-12x12in) s. 28-Feb-3 Joron-Derem, Paris #41
£690 $1152 €1000 Paysage de Loire (27x35cm-11x14in) s. 9-Jul-3 Millon & Associes, Paris #189
£1329 $2100 €2100 Nu au chapeau de paille (40x80cm-16x31in) s. exhib. 27-Nov-2 Blanchet, Paris #91/R
£1358 $1928 €2200 Petit coin de village (60x81cm-24x32in) s. 16-Mar-3 Eric Pillon, Calais #176/R
Works on paper
£833 $1308 €1300 Chausey (92x72cm-36x28in) s. W/C. 11-Dec-2 Maigret, Paris #169

COMMICHAU, Armin Felix (1889-1961) Polish
£270 $422 €400 Autumn landscape (35x43cm-14x17in) s. 26-Mar-3 Hugo Ruef, Munich #291/R

COMMUNAL, Joseph (1876-1962) French
£440 $682 €700 Les montagnes bleues (27x35cm-11x14in) s. panel prov. 30-Oct-2 Artcurial Briest, Paris #132

COMOLLI, Angelo (1863-1943) Italian
£1548 $2446 €2400 Hydrangeas (44x54cm-17x21in) s.d.1930 cardboard. 18-Dec-2 Finarte, Milan #32

COMOLLI, Gigi (1893-1976) Italian
£1161 $1835 €1800 Mottarone (40x63cm-16x25in) s. 18-Dec-2 Finarte, Milan #15/R
£5797 $9507 €8000 Paesaggio con la Rocca di Angera (91x116cm-36x46in) s.d.1921. 27-May-3 Finarte, Milan #25/R est:8000-9000
Works on paper
£1572 $2421 €2500 View of lake (60x70cm-24x28in) s. pastel card. 28-Oct-2 Il Ponte, Milan #308

COMPARD, Émile (1900-1977) French
£538 $855 €780 Le bouquet devant la fenetre (75x54cm-30x21in) s. 10-Mar-3 Thierry & Lannon, Brest #96/R
£1444 $2324 €2050 La mulatresse ou nu aux voiliers (73x60cm-29x24in) s. 11-May-3 Thierry & Lannon, Brest #153 est:2500-2800
Works on paper
£574 $896 €850 Portrait d'Alfred Flechteim (31x25cm-12x10in) s.d.1921 sanguine. 31-Mar-3 Piasa, Paris #125

COMPTE-CALIX, François Claudius (1813-1880) French
£11392 $18000 €17088 Les jeunes bressanes (100x81cm-39x32in) s. exhib. 24-Apr-3 Sotheby's, New York #154/R est:12000-15000
Works on paper
£321 $503 €500 Portrait d'une elegante en bleu (32x22cm-13x9in) s. W/C. 11-Dec-2 Maigret, Paris #156/R

COMPTON, Charles (1828-1884) British
£3500 $5635 €5250 Study in the National Gallery (25x30cm-10x12in) s.d.1855 prov.exhib. 20-Feb-3 Christie's, London #42/R

COMPTON, Edward Harrison (1881-1960) British
£280 $448 €420 River valley from the hills (23x36cm-9x14in) s.d.1914. 14-Mar-3 Gardiner & Houlgate, Bath #104/R
£449 $704 €700 Mountain pass in south Tyrol (20x32cm-8x13in) mono. pencil W/C. 21-Nov-2 Dorotheum, Vienna #415/R
£544 $865 €800 Mountain landscape (50x60cm-20x24in) s. linen lit. 21-Mar-3 Auktionhaus Georg Rehm, Augsburg #8013
£774 $1138 €1200 Vierwaldstatter See in summer (40x64cm-16x25in) s.d.1942. 20-Jun-2 Dr Fritz Nagel, Stuttgart #759/R
£1224 $1947 €1800 Lautersee (41x58cm-16x23in) s.i.verso. 25-Feb-3 Dorotheum, Vienna #173/R est:2000-2400
£1258 $1962 €2000 Mountain stream (62x89cm-24x35in) s.d.1924 canvas on panel. 19-Sep-2 Dr Fritz Nagel, Stuttgart #915/R est:2500
£1529 $2385 €2400 Ortler mountains (60x80cm-24x31in) s. 6-Nov-2 Hugo Ruef, Munich #1049/R est:1600
£1538 $2415 €2400 Landscape near Murnau (40x50cm-16x20in) s. i.d.1948 verso canvas on chipboard. 21-Nov-2 Dorotheum, Vienna #308/R est:4000-6000
£1761 $2747 €2800 Mountain storm brewing (61x78cm-24x31in) s. lit. 20-Sep-2 Schloss Ahlden, Ahlden #1145/R est:2400
£1923 $2981 €3000 Mountain landscape with St Gotthard, Hospenthal (70x97cm-28x38in) s.i. 5-Dec-2 Dr Fritz Nagel, Stuttgart #646/R est:2800
£1923 $3019 €3000 View of Alps from Kitzsteinhorn (60x80cm-24x31in) s. 10-Dec-2 Dorotheum, Vienna #90/R est:4500-5000
£2102 $3237 €3300 Summer's day in the Alps (90x121cm-35x48in) s. 5-Sep-2 Arnold, Frankfurt #749 est:2500
£5577 $8644 €8700 Sunny winters day in the mountains with children and sledges on a path (61x90cm-24x35in) s.d.1906. 4-Dec-2 Neumeister, Munich #696/R est:6000
£18000 $27900 €27000 Sheep in a winter landscape (76x140cm-30x55in) s.d.1905. 31-Oct-2 Christie's, London #108/R est:3000-5000
Works on paper
£283 $442 €450 Fortress and tower (24x30cm-9x12in) mono.i. W/C over pencil. 9-Oct-2 Michael Zeller, Lindau #651
£382 $596 €600 Boats on southern coast (19x30cm-7x12in) s. 6-Nov-2 Hugo Ruef, Munich #1357/R
£417 $646 €650 View of Inntal in Tyrol (25x38cm-10x15in) s. W/C htd white. 4-Dec-2 Neumeister, Munich #507
£503 $785 €800 City view (21x17cm-8x7in) s.d.1956 W/C lit. 20-Sep-2 Schloss Ahlden, Ahlden #1195/R
£513 $795 €800 Rocky mountain path (22x28cm-9x11in) s. lit. gouache. 6-Dec-2 Karlheinz Kaupp, Staufen #2096/R
£629 $981 €1000 Wartburg (23x32cm-9x13in) mono.i.d.09 W/C over pencil. 9-Oct-2 Michael Zeller, Lindau #650/R
£811 $1265 €1200 Lermoos (22x30cm-9x12in) s.i.d. W/C. 28-Mar-3 Dorotheum, Vienna #248/R
£1519 $2400 €2400 Coastal landscape (27x37cm-11x15in) s.i.d.01 W/C. 28-Nov-2 Dorotheum, Vienna #228/R est:2200-2600
£2420 $3776 €3800 Sun terrace with mountain view (17x55cm-7x22in) s. W/C. 6-Nov-2 Hugo Ruef, Munich #1358/R est:600

COMPTON, Edward Theodore (1849-1921) British
£1384 $2158 €2200 Val di Mitramonio, Capri (33x51cm-13x20in) s.i.d.May 1874 lit. 20-Sep-2 Karlheinz Kaupp, Staufen #1909/R est:1200
£1603 $2532 €2500 On the coast of Lofoten (48x68cm-19x27in) s. 16-Nov-2 Lempertz, Koln #1442/R est:4500
£11594 $19014 €16000 Monte Civetta (43x60cm-17x24in) s. 27-May-3 Wiener Kunst Auktionen, Vienna #28/R est:8000-20000
£14557 $23000 €23000 Lienz, eastern Tyrol (110x150cm-43x59in) s. 26-Nov-2 Wiener Kunst Auktionen, Vienna #46/R est:14000-25000
Works on paper
£500 $775 €750 Mountain landscape (18x15cm-7x6in) W/C grisaille. 4-Dec-2 Neal & Fletcher, Woodbridge #230
£514 $801 €750 At Chiemsee (21x30cm-8x12in) s. W/C. 10-Apr-3 Allgauer, Kempten #2599/R
£580 $905 €870 Mountain landscape with goatherd and castle ruins (31x49cm-12x19in) s.d.1878 W/C. 10-Apr-3 Tennants, Leyburn #851/R
£925 $1442 €1350 In the mountains (17x27cm-7x11in) s.d.1899 W/C lit. 10-Apr-3 Allgauer, Kempten #2598/R
£1069 $1657 €1700 Durrensee and Monte Cristallo (16x24cm-6x9in) mono. grisaille W/C board. 1-Oct-2 Dorotheum, Vienna #233/R est:1700-2000
£1761 $2730 €2800 Scluderbach (18x25cm-7x10in) mono.i. grisaille W/C board. 1-Oct-2 Dorotheum, Vienna #234/R est:1700-2000
£6289 $9748 €10000 Mountain landscape (47x33cm-19x13in) s. W/C. 1-Oct-2 Dorotheum, Vienna #232/R est:6000-8000

COMPTON, Mildred N (1912-1976) American
£3686 $5750 €5529 Pink granite rocks (76x91cm-30x36in) masonite exhib. 19-Oct-2 David Dike, Dallas #129/R est:6000-8000

COMTE DE GRAUVILLE (18th C) French
Works on paper
£2027 $3162 €3000 Forge de Vulcain (23x27cm-9x11in) s.d.1782 gouache. 26-Mar-3 Piasa, Paris #54/R

COMTE, Pierre Charles (1823-1895) French
£6500 $10205 €9750 Catherine de Medici in the Chateau Chaumont (32x22cm-13x9in) s. prov. 16-Apr-3 George Kidner, Lymington #106/R est:7000-10000
£8000 $12400 €12000 Rendezvous (73x54cm-29x21in) s. panel. 4-Dec-2 Christie's, London #87/R est:8000-12000

COMTOIS, Ulysse (20th C) Canadian
Works on paper
£285 $425 €428 Composition (21x30cm-8x12in) s.d.54 ink W/C. 26-Jun-2 Iegor de Saint Hippolyte, Montreal #18 (C.D 650)

CONANT, Lucy Scarborough (1867-1921) American
£605 $950 €908 Shorse of Etretat (43x53cm-17x21in) s. 22-Nov-2 Skinner, Boston #302/R est:600-800

CONCA, Sebastiano (attrib) (1676-1764) Italian
£3797 $6000 €6000 Madonna and Child (35x25cm-14x10in) 27-Nov-2 Finarte, Milan #111/R
£9310 $14897 €13500 Sanson and Dalial (31x41cm-12x16in) pair. 17-Mar-3 Pandolfini, Florence #589/R est:18000
Works on paper
£352 $567 €500 Accademia maschile (35x38cm-14x15in) red pencil htd white. 12-May-3 Sotheby's, Milan #21

CONCA, Sebastiano (circle) (1676-1764) Italian

£5000 $7750 €7500 Madonna of the Rosary with Saint Catherine of Siena, Saint Dominic and members (64x40cm-25x16in) 30-Oct-2 Christie's, Kensington #160/R est:5000-7000

CONCONI, Luigi (1852-1917) Italian

Works on paper

£1548 $2446 €2400 Portrait of girl (25x22cm-10x9in) init. W/C card. 18-Dec-2 Finarte, Milan #61/R

£2464 $4041 €3400 Volto femminile di profilo (43x32cm-17x13in) s.d.1900 W/C. 27-May-3 Finarte, Milan #70/R est:3500-4000

£3774 $6000 €5661 In the garden (27x56cm-11x22in) s.i.d.89 W/C gouache paperboard. 7-Mar-3 Skinner, Boston #594/R est:1500-3000

CONCONNAN, Hugh (19/20th C) British

£300 $480 €450 Pretty Polly, Newmarket (56x76cm-22x30in) s.d.02. 14-Mar-3 Gardiner & Houlgate, Bath #185/R

CONDAMY, Charles Fernand de (1855-?) French

Prints

£2759 $4386 €4000 Cavalier lisant une pancarte. i. print. 10-Mar-3 Coutau Begarie, Paris #87/R

Works on paper

£629 $975 €1000 Joueurs de polo (29x23cm-11x9in) s. W/C. 6-Oct-2 Livinec, Gaudcheau & Jezequel, Rennes #17

£818 $1267 €1300 Coqs. Chiens (12x16cm-5x6in) s. W/C three in one frame. 6-Oct-2 Livinec, Gaudcheau & Jezequel, Rennes #18

£1486 $2319 €2200 Cerf poursuivi par meute (24x32cm-9x13in) W/C. 27-Mar-3 Maigret, Paris #228/R

£3481 $5500 €5500 Le relais de chiens (33x24cm-13x9in) s. W/C. 1-Dec-2 Peron, Melun #14

CONDE, Miguel (20th C) American

Works on paper

£839 $1325 €1300 Walker (50x33cm-20x13in) s.d.1984 W/C ink prov. 17-Dec-2 Segre, Madrid #163/R

CONDER, Charles (1868-1909) British

£714 $1129 €1071 Au bord du lac (29x39cm-11x15in) oil W/C on silk prov. 26-Nov-2 Sotheby's, Melbourne #156 est:1000-2000 (A.D 2000)

£5179 $8494 €7769 Apres le bal (52x44cm-20x17in) prov. 4-Jun-3 Deutscher-Menzies, Melbourne #143/R est:14000-18000 (A.D 13000)

£7000 $11130 €10500 Dejeuner sur l'herbe (49x74cm-19x29in) lit. 26-Feb-3 Sotheby's, Olympia #40/R est:8000-12000

£30357 $47964 €45536 Quayside 1893 (53x73cm-21x29in) s. prov. 27-Nov-2 Deutscher-Menzies, Melbourne #31/R est:100000-150000 (A.D 85000)

£80000 $131200 €116000 The Beach, Pourville (46x55cm-18x22in) s.d.1895 prov. 4-Jun-3 Sotheby's, London #9/R est:80000-120000

Works on paper

£360 $569 €540 Venetian masquerade (15x24cm-6x9in) s. W/C over pencil. 2-Dec-2 Bonhams, Bath #33/R

£651 $970 €977 Nude and dog (16x25cm-6x10in) s. pencil prov. 27-Aug-2 Christie's, Melbourne #204 est:1000-2000 (A.D 1700)

£1286 $2031 €1929 Love's arrow (38x42cm-15x17in) s.verso pastel prov.exhib.lit. 17-Nov-2 Sotheby's, Paddington #15/R est:2000-3000 (A.D 3600)

£1300 $2067 €1950 Nude woman on a sofa (25x35cm-10x14in) s. red conte two lit. 26-Feb-3 Sotheby's, Olympia #42/R est:800-1200

£1400 $2226 €2100 The trellis. The orchard (55x42cm-22x17in) mixed media double-sided lit. 26-Feb-3 Sotheby's, Olympia #44/R est:500-700

£1500 $2355 €2250 Woman sitting in a park (23x16cm-9x6in) s.d.1897 pencil W/C gouache. 25-Nov-2 Christie's, Melbourne #456 est:3000-5000 (A.D 4200)

£1500 $2340 €2175 Theatrical scenes, design for fans (11x19cm-4x7in) s.i.d.1905 W/C pair. 27-Mar-3 Neales, Nottingham #928 est:250-300

£2286 $3611 €3429 Ladies in a garden (75x86cm-30x34in) W/C on silk prov.exhib. 26-Nov-2 Sotheby's, Melbourne #151 est:6000-10000 (A.D 6400)

£3000 $4650 €4500 Mythological scene (23x42cm-9x17in) s. W/C silk. 4-Dec-2 Christie's, Kensington #229/R est:2000-3000

£4200 $6678 €6300 Lady in blue (56x44cm-22x17in) W/C pastel lit. 26-Feb-3 Sotheby's, Olympia #45/R est:1000-1500

CONDO, George (1957-) American

£3125 $5000 €4688 Untitled (41x36cm-16x14in) s.d.89 verso prov. 14-May-3 Sotheby's, New York #450/R est:4000-6000

£3291 $5200 €4937 Grace (51x41cm-20x16in) init.d.93 verso prov. 12-Nov-2 Phillips, New York #239/R est:5000-7000

£5380 $8500 €8070 Green and white figure composition (61x46cm-24x18in) s.d.93 s.i.d.verso linen prov. 13-Nov-2 Sotheby's, New York #577/R est:6000-8000

£12658 $20000 €18987 Seated black figure nude (195x179cm-77x70in) painted 1988 prov.exhib. 12-Nov-2 Phillips, New York #143/R est:20000-30000

£12658 $20000 €18987 Untitled - Sir Alfred Chipmunk (202x202cm-80x80in) painted 1996 prov. 14-Nov-2 Christie's, Rockefeller NY #396/R est:25000-35000

Works on paper

£3484 $5505 €5400 Nude with green hat (104x74cm-41x29in) s.d.1988 pastel wax cr cardboard exhib.lit. 17-Dec-2 Segre, Madrid #169/R est:5400

£7500 $12000 €11250 Ballet blank (213x306cm-84x120in) s.d.98 s.i.d.verso col pencil graphite acrylic oil paper collage. 15-May-3 Christie's, Rockefeller NY #389/R est:15000-20000

£11111 $18333 €16000 5/ISM (180x110cm-71x43in) col crayons graphite wax polish acrylic oil prov.lit. 3-Jul-3 Christie's, Paris #31/R est:15000-20000

CONDOPOULOS, Alecos (1905-1975) Greek

£14000 $21700 €21000 Enangalismos (140x125cm-55x49in) s. s.i.d.1974. prov. 2-Oct-2 Sotheby's, London #64/R est:15000-20000

£15000 $23700 €22500 Composition in black and green (100x70cm-39x28in) 1-Apr-3 Bonhams, New Bond Street #96 est:6000-8000

CONDOY, Honorio Garcia (1900-1953) Spanish

Works on paper

£441 $626 €662 Sathyr and nymph (43x29cm-17x11in) ink exec.1948. 26-Mar-2 SOGA, Bratislava #192/R (SL.K 28000)

£441 $626 €662 Three figures (43x29cm-17x11in) ink exec.1948. 26-Mar-2 SOGA, Bratislava #193/R (SL.K 28000)

CONDY, Nicholas (1793-1857) British

Works on paper

£280 $445 €420 Boats of HMS Undaunted in the Marseilles Bay (12x18cm-5x7in) i.verso pen ink sepia. 25-Feb-3 Bonhams, Knightsbridge #181/R

£500 $810 €750 Offloading the catch (12x16cm-5x6in) W/C. 21-May-3 Bonhams, Knightsbridge #233/R

£860 $1410 €1290 Obelisk, near mount Edgcumbe, Plymouth (10x14cm-4x6in) W/C htd white. 4-Feb-3 Bonhams, Leeds #261

CONDY, Nicholas (attrib) (1793-1857) British

Works on paper

£260 $424 €377 Shipping in an estuary (5x7cm-2x3in) W/C. 21-Jul-3 Sotheby's, London #822

£660 $1030 €990 Fishing boat and rowing boat off the coast (11x15cm-4x6in) s. W/C htd white. 10-Sep-2 David Duggleby, Scarborough #266/R

CONDY, Nicholas Matthew (1816-1851) British

£1800 $2916 €2700 H.M.S. Polyphemus, Mediterranean , 1841, Richard S Rundle 2nd master (18x23cm-7x9in) board. 22-Jan-3 Bonhams, New Bond Street #395/R est:1000-1500

£5000 $8100 €7500 Royal yacht squadron's schooner Fair Rosamond running up the Channel (30x41cm-12x16in) s.d.1848 i.board board prov. 22-Jan-3 Bonhams, New Bond Street #309/R est:5000-8000

£7500 $12150 €11250 Cutter yachts racing at Plymouth (19x32cm-7x13in) init. board prov. 22-Jan-3 Bonhams, New Bond Street #321/R est:5000-8000

£11000 $17050 €16500 Royal Naval brig heaving to the wake of a Royal Yacht Squadron topsail schooner racing to windward (30x41cm-12x16in) s.d.1836 board prov. 31-Oct-2 Christie's, Kensington #435/R est:10000-15000

Works on paper

£480 $778 €720 British frigate off a Chilean fortress and other vessels (30x45cm-12x18in) brown wash. 21-May-3 Christie's, Kensington #405/R

CONE, Marvin D (1891-1964) American

£9036 $15000 €13102 Still life with bowl and ginger jar (46x38cm-18x15in) painted c.1929 prov.exhib. 14-Jun-3 Jackson's, Cedar Falls #3/R est:15000-22000

£10828 $17000 €16242 Summer farmscape (33x38cm-13x15in) s. i.verso painted c.1940-45 canvasboard prov. 23-Nov-2 Jackson's, Cedar Falls #47/R est:12000-15000

£11111 $18000 €16667 Plant with woman (43x33cm-17x13in) prov. 21-May-3 Sotheby's, New York #115/R est:15000-25000

£18471 $29000 €27707 Still life with fruit flowers (41x46cm-16x18in) s. painted c.1929-1930 prov.exhib. 23-Nov-2 Jackson's, Cedar Falls #46/R est:30000-35000

£39809 $62500 €59714 Cloud bank number 4 (46x56cm-18x22in) s. painted c.1931 prov.exhib.lit. 23-Nov-2 Jackson's, Cedar Falls #45/R est:40000-50000
£44578 $74000 €64638 Hills and river (28x46cm-11x18in) s. canvasboard prov.exhib.lit. 14-Jun-3 Jackson's, Cedar Falls #1/R est:60000-80000

CONGNET, Gillis (circle) (1538-1599) Dutch
£8000 $12480 €12000 Nativity (108x168cm-43x66in) panel. 9-Apr-3 Christie's, London #16/R est:8000-12000

CONINCK, David de (1636-1699) Flemish
£18622 $29609 €27933 Hunting scene, dog watching the day's catch (99x117cm-39x46in) prov. 5-Mar-3 Rasmussen, Copenhagen #1651/R est:200000-250000 (D.KR 200000)

CONINCK, Gregorius (c.1631-?) Dutch
£16547 $26475 €23000 Still life with ham on silver plate, fruit, mustard jar, jug, flutes (136x108cm-54x43in) bears sig. 13-May-3 Sotheby's, Amsterdam #14/R est:15000-20000

CONINCK, Octave de (1894-1974) Dutch
£955 $1490 €1500 Parkheuvel in Rotterdam on a sunny day (54x69cm-21x27in) s. board. 5-Nov-2 Vendu Notarishuis, Rotterdam #237 est:1000-1500

CONINCK, Pierre Louis Joseph de (1828-1910) French
£2158 $3453 €3000 Elegante au bois (32x23cm-13x9in) s. panel. 14-May-3 Blanchet, Paris #43/R est:3000-4000

CONINXLOO, Gillis van III (circle) (1544-1607) Flemish
£9790 $16350 €14000 Paysage avec scene de chasse (51x67cm-20x26in) panel. 25-Jun-3 Pierre Berge, Paris #26/R est:12000-15000

CONINXLOO, Jan van II (attrib) (c.1489-1560) Flemish
£47256 $77500 €70884 Saint Francis renouncing the world for the Cloister (114x84cm-45x33in) panel prov.exhib.lit. 29-May-3 Sotheby's, New York #28/R est:60000-80000

CONJOLA, Carl (1773-1831) German
£2436 $3703 €3800 Southern Tyrol landscape (54x67cm-21x26in) s.d.1812. 11-Jul-2 Hugo Ruef, Munich #607/R est:1800

CONKEY, Samuel (1830-1904) American
£404 $638 €606 River landscape at sunset (30x40cm-12x16in) s. canvas on masonite. 18-Nov-2 Waddingtons, Toronto #14/R (C.D 1000)

CONN, Budwin (20th C) American
£320 $499 €480 Portrait of Yuki standing in green and blue lined robe (77x56cm-30x22in) i. board. 6-Nov-2 Dreweatt Neate, Newbury #320/R

CONNARD, Philip (1875-1958) British
£350 $546 €525 Thames at Richmond (25x35cm-10x14in) board. 27-Mar-3 Christie's, Kensington #425
£1200 $1860 €1800 Still life with tulips (61x51cm-24x20in) exhib. 4-Dec-2 Christie's, Kensington #457/R est:1500-2000
£9000 $14760 €13050 The mirror (63x51cm-25x20in) s. prov. 4-Jun-3 Sotheby's, London #14/R est:6000-8000

CONNAVALE, Robert (20th C) American
£255 $400 €383 Haley's dock, Maine (64x76cm-25x30in) s.d.43. 14-Dec-2 CRN Auctions, Cambridge #65/R

CONNAWAY, Jay Hall (1893-1970) American
£377 $600 €566 Windy tress (28x23cm-11x9in) board. 8-Mar-3 Harvey Clar, Oakland #1197
£881 $1400 €1322 Head Harbour Island, Maine (38x61cm-15x24in) s. board. 7-Mar-3 Skinner, Boston #486/R est:1800-2200
£903 $1400 €1355 Monhegan surf (41x51cm-16x20in) s.d.42 board. 25-Sep-2 Doyle, New York #19/R
£1032 $1600 €1548 Outer surf (30x41cm-12x16in) s. board. 2-Nov-2 North East Auctions, Portsmouth #42/R est:800-1200
£1063 $1700 €1595 Seascape (23x28cm-9x11in) s. board. 11-Jan-3 James Julia, Fairfield #320 est:1500-2500
£1156 $1850 €1734 Hot weather, Lobster Cove (38x51cm-15x20in) s.i. board. 11-Jan-3 James Julia, Fairfield #321 est:3000-5000
£1774 $2750 €2661 Fine Vermont Hills mountain winter clearing (51x76cm-20x30in) s. s.i.d.1965 verso board. 21-Jul-2 Jeffery Burchard, Florida #46/R

CONNELL, Bunny (20th C) American
Sculpture
£2215 $3500 €3323 Turning the play (33cm-13in) i. brown pat. bronze prov. 3-Apr-3 Christie's, Rockefeller NY #162/R est:600-800

CONNER, Angela (20th C) British
£550 $869 €825 East River, New York, from Dag Hammerskold's flat (34x80cm-13x31in) s.d.1978 canvas on board. 27-Nov-2 Sotheby's, Olympia #168/R

CONNER, Charles (1857-1905) American
£3822 $6000 €5733 San Antonio ranch near Los Angeles (25x41cm-10x16in) s. i.verso board prov. 19-Nov-2 Butterfields, San Francisco #8188/R est:4000-6000

CONNER, John Anthony (1892-1971) American
£315 $500 €473 In the California desert (23x30cm-9x12in) s. canvasboard. 7-Mar-3 Skinner, Boston #356/R
£581 $900 €872 Eagle Rock, California (61x91cm-24x36in) s.i. painted c.1950. 8-Dec-2 Toomey, Oak Park #677/R
£633 $1000 €950 Near Palm Springs (61x76cm-24x30in) s. i.stretcher. 22-Apr-3 Arthur James, Florida #177
£955 $1500 €1433 Desert verbena (61x76cm-24x30in) s. prov. 19-Nov-2 Butterfields, San Francisco #8318/R est:3000-5000

CONNER, John Ramsey (1867-1952) American
£457 $750 €686 Houses and trees (23x33cm-9x13in) s. canvasboard. 5-Feb-3 Doyle, New York #13/R
£968 $1500 €1452 Twilight (35x37cm-14x15in) s. exhib. 8-Dec-2 Freeman, Philadelphia #107/R est:700-1000

CONNER, McCauley (1913-) American
Works on paper
£435 $700 €653 Lounging nude smelling flower (51x58cm-20x23in) s. gouache. 10-May-3 Illustration House, New York #137/R

CONNER, Paul (1881-1968) American
£621 $1000 €932 Flowering dunes (76x91cm-30x36in) s. exhib. 18-Feb-3 John Moran, Pasadena #91b

CONNERLEY, Brian (20th C) British
£300 $468 €450 Portrait of David Horner (57x36cm-22x14in) s.d.1954 tempera on board. 15-Oct-2 Bonhams, Knightsbridge #14/R

CONNOR, Arthur Bentley (fl.1903-1918) British
£2300 $3680 €3450 Prospero releasing Ariel from the tree (152x94cm-60x37in) s.d.1911 prov. 14-Mar-3 Gardiner & Houlgate, Bath #174/R est:2000-4000

CONNOR, Kevin (1932-) Australian
£956 $1568 €1434 Figure in a garden (61x61cm-24x24in) s.d.70 s.i.d.70 verso composition board prov. 4-Jun-3 Deutscher-Menzies, Melbourne #284/R (A.D 2400)
£1071 $1693 €1607 Poet and city (150x185cm-59x73in) s.d.1978 i.verso prov. 17-Nov-2 Sotheby's, Paddington #60/R est:5000-8000 (A.D 3000)
£1073 $1684 €1610 Landing (92x122cm-36x48in) s.d.02 board prov. 15-Apr-3 Lawson Menzies, Sydney #119/R est:3000-5000 (A.D 2800)

CONOR (?) ?
£1400 $2296 €2100 Young shawlie (33x30cm-13x12in) s. canvas on board. 7-Feb-3 Biddle & Webb, Birmingham #230/R

CONOR, William (1881-1968) Irish
£1139 $1766 €1800 Portrait of a boy in a suit and tie (46x33cm-18x13in) s. prov. 25-Sep-2 James Adam, Dublin #118/R est:1000-2000
£1700 $2720 €2550 Still life with cinerarias (51x40cm-20x16in) s. board. 16-May-3 Sotheby's, London #96/R est:4000-6000
£7000 $10220 €10500 Connemara mother and child (76x61cm-30x24in) s. canvas on board. 12-Jun-2 John Ross, Belfast #176 est:8000-9000
£8000 $12400 €12000 Patience (25x30cm-10x12in) board. 2-Oct-2 John Ross, Belfast #159 est:8000-10000
£18000 $26280 €27000 Melodian player (36x46cm-14x18in) s. 12-Jun-2 John Ross, Belfast #184 est:20000-22500
Works on paper
£268 $378 €440 Seated gentleman (30x20cm-12x8in) s. pastel. 7-Feb-2 Woodwards, Cork #243
£1081 $1686 €1600 Child writing a letter - Happy Christmas and all the best (12x10cm-5x4in) s. ink col pencil. 26-Mar-3 James Adam, Dublin #87/R est:600-800
£1081 $1686 €1600 Fiddler (15x12cm-6x5in) s.i. ink W/C. 26-Mar-3 James Adam, Dublin #86/R est:800-1200

£1250 $1825 €1875 Accordian player (10x10cm-4x4in) s. mixed media. 12-Jun-2 John Ross, Belfast #26 est:1000-1200
£1800 $2862 €2700 Playing the fiddle (33x25cm-13x10in) s. wax crayon. 5-Mar-3 John Ross, Belfast #59 est:1000-1200
£2639 $4196 €3800 Three women at Smithfield (29x24cm-11x9in) s.i. crayon. 29-Apr-3 Whyte's, Dublin #80/R est:4000-5000
£2639 $4196 €3800 Dredger - York Docks (17x27cm-7x11in) s. W/C exhib. 29-Apr-3 Whyte's, Dublin #85/R est:3000-5000
£3600 $5256 €5400 Digging turf (23x20cm-9x8in) s. wax crayon. 12-Jun-2 John Ross, Belfast #64 est:4000-5000
£3819 $6073 €5500 Seated woman with sack and basket (29x24cm-11x9in) s. crayon dr. 29-Apr-3 Whyte's, Dublin #79/R est:4000-6000
£3846 $5962 €6000 Workers with their hay cart (20x23cm-8x9in) s. crayon. 3-Dec-2 Bonhams & James Adam, Dublin #121/R est:4000-6000
£4000 $5840 €6000 Riveter (43x33cm-17x13in) wax crayon. 12-Jun-2 John Ross, Belfast #12 est:4000-5000
£4000 $5840 €6000 Reading (30x25cm-12x10in) s.d.1907 verso wax crayon. 12-Jun-2 John Ross, Belfast #298 est:5000-7500
£4000 $6400 €6000 Ballyhalbert (34x42cm-13x17in) s. pastel double-sided. 15-May-3 Christie's, London #72/R est:6000
£4000 $6400 €6000 Picking potatoes (29x22cm-11x9in) s. pen black ink crayon. 15-May-3 Christie's, Kensington #158/R est:4000-6000
£4800 $7440 €7200 On the turf cart (36x30cm-14x12in) s. wax crayon. 2-Oct-2 John Ross, Belfast #162 est:6000-8000
£6500 $9490 €9750 Launch (48x36cm-19x14in) s. wax crayon. 12-Jun-2 John Ross, Belfast #33 est:7500-8500
£6500 $10400 €9750 Fiddler (38x28cm-15x11in) s. pastel. 15-May-3 Christie's, London #71/R est:6000
£10738 $17289 €16000 Three choir girls (47x39cm-19x15in) s. crayon. 18-Feb-3 Whyte's, Dublin #79/R est:15000-20000
£12500 $20000 €18750 Accordian players (38x47cm-15x19in) s. chl wax crayon. 15-May-3 Christie's, London #70/R est:7000-10000
£16438 $25808 €24000 Collecting potatoes, Ardglass (49x37cm-19x15in) s. wax crayon prov. 15-Apr-3 De Veres Art Auctions, Dublin #141/R est:20000-25000
£22000 $34980 €33000 Mill girls (50x35cm-20x14in) s. wax crayon. 5-Mar-3 John Ross, Belfast #150 est:17500-20000

CONRAD, Charles (1912-) Belgian
Sculpture
£1923 $2981 €3000 Accolade (19x32x10cm-7x13x4in) s. brown pat bronze. 7-Dec-2 Martinot & Savignat, Pontoise #134/R

CONRAD, Christina (?) ?
£634 $1046 €919 After the exhibition (120x119cm-47x47in) s.d.1984 s.i.d.verso board. 1-Jul-3 Peter Webb, Auckland #89/R est:3500-4500 (NZ.D 1800)

CONRAD, George (1916-) American
£346 $550 €519 Judgement of Paris (102x76cm-40x30in) s. i.verso painted c.1960 prov. 2-Mar-3 Toomey, Oak Park #785/R
£346 $550 €519 Susanna (91x122cm-36x48in) s. i.verso painted c.1960 prov. 2-Mar-3 Toomey, Oak Park #788/R

CONRADE, Alfred Charles (1863-1955) British
£700 $1113 €1050 Elegant figures in a parkland, Greenwich beyond (51x76cm-20x30in) s.d.1902. 6-Mar-3 Christie's, Kensington #531/R
Works on paper
£420 $668 €630 Horse and cart in a continental town (25x17cm-10x7in) s.d.1913 W/C over pencil. 25-Feb-3 Bonhams, Knightsbridge #44/R

CONRARDY, Georges (1908-1978) Belgian
£435 $713 €600 Artistes du cirque (74x60cm-29x24in) s. 27-May-3 Campo & Campo, Antwerp #56

CONROY, Stephen (1964-) British
£25000 $41750 €36250 Mirror (152x102cm-60x40in) s.d.1994 overlap linen prov.exhib. 26-Jun-3 Sotheby's, London #227/R est:10000-15000

CONSADORI, Silvio (1909-1996) Italian
£654 $1046 €1000 Red shirt (50x40cm-20x16in) s. s.i.d.1944 verso board. 4-Jan-3 Meeting Art, Vercelli #506

CONSAGRA, Pietro (1920-) Italian
Sculpture
£3205 $5032 €5000 Giano's door (10x39cm-4x15in) s. num.3/3 bronze. 23-Nov-2 Meeting Art, Vercelli #92/R
£3526 $5147 €5500 Composition (42x38cm-17x15in) s.num.3/3/ bronze. 5-Jun-2 Il Ponte, Milan #124 est:6000-8000
£3546 $5745 €5000 Untitled (33x28x6cm-13x11x2in) s.d.70 num.1/3 base iron. 26-May-3 Christie's, Milan #145/R est:2500-3000

CONSTABLE, John (1776-1837) British
£4902 $7500 €7353 Old Cramond Bridge on the Almond near Barnton, Edwingshire (64x43cm-25x17in) 16-Aug-2 Douglas, South Deerfield #3
£8000 $13200 €11600 Portrait of Ramsay Richard Reinagle (76x63cm-30x25in) i.verso lit. 2-Jul-3 Sotheby's, Olympia #42/R est:2000-3000
£29000 $48140 €43500 Portrait of Elizabeth, Lady Croft, wearing a white dress with pink sash, in a landscape (63x77cm-25x30in) i. prov.lit. 11-Jun-3 Christie's, London #3/R est:30000-50000
£40000 $63200 €60000 Edge of the heath by moonlight (17x27cm-7x11in) panel prov.exhib.lit. 28-Nov-2 Sotheby's, London #14/R est:40000-60000
£80000 $126400 €120000 Dedham Vale (16x23cm-6x9in) canvas on panel prov.lit. 28-Nov-2 Sotheby's, London #12/R est:80000-120000
£85000 $141100 €127500 Harvest field (49x66cm-19x26in) prov.exhib.lit. 12-Jun 3 Sotheby's, London #11/R est:50000-70000
£130000 $205400 €195000 Cloudy study (13x16cm-5x6in) oil on paper prov. 28-Nov-2 Sotheby's, London #13/R est:40000-60000
£200000 $316000 €300000 Gothic house, Sillwood place, Brighton (25x30cm-10x12in) i.verso oil on paper prov.lit. 28-Nov-2 Sotheby's, London #15/R est:200000-300000
Works on paper
£6000 $9420 €9000 Landscape with country folk (17x20cm-7x8in) pen ink wash prov.lit. 21-Nov-2 Christie's, London #25/R est:3000-5000
£7700 $12012 €11550 Heavey swell (8x11cm-3x4in) d.3 Aug 13 W/C over pencil prov. 5-Nov-2 Bonhams, New Bond Street #48/R est:5000-8000
£8000 $12480 €12000 Stoke-by-Nayland Church from the South East, Suffolk (8x10cm-3x4in) pencil prov. 5-Nov-2 Bonhams, New Bond Street #49/R est:4000-6000
£9000 $14310 €13500 Horse and cart (9x17cm-4x7in) pencil prov. 19-Mar-3 Sotheby's, London #172/R est:4000-6000
£34000 $54060 €51000 Broadside view of H.M.S Victory in the Medway (20x25cm-8x10in) indis i. pencil prov.lit. 19-Mar-3 Sotheby's, London #138/R est:15000-20000
£80000 $127200 €120000 Stern view of H.M.S Victory in the Medway (25x20cm-10x8in) pencil prov.lit. 19-Mar-3 Sotheby's, London #140/R est:10000-15000
£188000 $298920 €282000 Bow view of H.M.S Victory in the Medway (25x20cm-10x8in) pencil prov.lit. 19-Mar-3 Sotheby's, London #139/R est:15000-20000

CONSTABLE, John (attrib) (1776-1837) British
£847 $1338 €1271 Dedham village, Suffolk (31x36cm-12x14in) bears sig.indis.d.1809 i.verso prov. 18-Nov-2 Waddingtons, Toronto #98/R est:3000-5000 (C.D 2100)
£1509 $2325 €2400 Lock scene (35x30cm-14x12in) boardprov. 28-Oct-2 Il Ponte, Milan #273
£9434 $14528 €15000 Deedham Vale (72x96cm-28x38in) s. 28-Oct-2 Il Ponte, Milan #221/R est:8000
£9877 $16000 €14816 Stormy sky at night (15x25cm-6x10in) paper on canvas prov.exhib. 23-Jan-3 Sotheby's, New York #247/R est:12000
Works on paper
£700 $1120 €1050 Jetty, Yarmouth (26x35cm-10x14in) i.d.Nov 18 1831 ink wash. 8-Jan-3 George Kidner, Lymington #148/R

CONSTABLE, Lionel (1828-1884) British
£6000 $9480 €9000 On the Brent (30x33cm-12x13in) prov.exhib. 28-Nov-2 Sotheby's, London #112/R est:7000-9000

CONSTABLE, Lionel (attrib) (1828-1887) British
£1500 $2385 €2250 Coastal landscape (18x32cm-7x13in) 19-Mar-3 Sotheby's, London #82/R est:1000-1500

CONSTABLE, Michael (20th C) British
£1227 $2000 €1841 Rowley, a spaniel in a landscape. Portrait of a Blenheim King Charles Spaniel (27x33cm-11x13in) s. panel two. 11-Feb-3 Bonhams & Doyles, New York #135 est:600-800

CONSTANT (1920-) Dutch
£12950 $21237 €18000 Untitled (122x45cm-48x18in) s. prov. 6-Jun-3 Ketterer, Munich #97/R est:18000-24000
Works on paper
£897 $1391 €1400 Preliminary drawing for Casanova (21x25cm-8x10in) s. pen ink executed 1975. 3-Dec-2 Christie's, Amsterdam #127/R est:1800-2200
£6041 $9545 €9062 Figure and fantasy animal (27x21cm-11x8in) s.i.d.1949 Indian ink ballpoint pen exhib.prov. 1-Apr-3 Rasmussen, Copenhagen #128/R est:75000 (D.KR 65000)
£7595 $12000 €12000 La famille (57x42cm-22x17in) s.d.90 W/C prov. 26-Nov-2 Sotheby's, Amsterdam #258/R est:12000-15000
£21154 $32788 €33000 Chantier (55x76cm-22x30in) s.d.72 brush ink W/C pastel prov.lit. 3-Dec-2 Christie's, Amsterdam #290/R est:20000-30000

CONSTANT, Benjamin (1845-1902) French
£299 $475 €449 Une fille de l'Orient (12x8cm-5x3in) s.i.d.1884 i.verso canvas on panel. 7-Mar-3 Skinner, Boston #247/R
£1948 $2903 €3000 In the harem (30x45cm-12x18in) s. i. verso study. 26-Jun-2 Neumeister, Munich #704 est:3000
£2414 $3814 €3500 Portrait d'une espagnole (78x65cm-31x26in) s. oval. 4-Apr-3 Tajan, Paris #125/R
£2436 $3824 €3800 Autoportrait (29x21cm-11x8in) s.d.1892 cardboard. 16-Dec-2 Millon & Associes, Paris #101/R est:1000-1500
£2885 $4529 €4500 Diane (54x42cm-21x17in) s. panel. 16-Dec-2 Millon & Associes, Paris #104/R est:5000-6000
£3205 $5032 €5000 Portrait de Marguerite Hignette au manchon (114x73cm-45x29in) s. 16-Dec-2 Millon & Associes, Paris #103/R est:5000-7000
£4000 $6480 €6000 Seated Arab (89x64cm-35x25in) s. 20-May-3 Sotheby's, Olympia #401/R est:4000-6000
£5128 $8051 €8000 Portrait de Marguerite Hignette a 17 ans (72x54cm-28x21in) s. 16-Dec-2 Millon & Associes, Paris #102/R est:8000-10000
£7097 $11000 €10646 Herodiade (129x95cm-51x37in) s.d.1881 prov.exhib. 30-Oct-2 Christie's, Rockefeller NY #84/R est:40000-60000
£12500 $19500 €18750 On the terrace (54x102cm-21x40in) indis sig. 15-Oct-2 Sotheby's, London #162/R est:15000-20000
£13000 $21060 €19500 Afternoon languor (88x70cm-35x28in) s. panel. 20-May-3 Sotheby's, Olympia #402/R est:10000-15000

CONSTANT, Benjamin (circle) (1845-1902) French
£12258 $19000 €18387 Guarding the chieftain (61x49cm-24x19in) panel prov. 30-Oct-2 Christie's, Rockefeller NY #93/R est:10000-15000

CONSTANTIN, Auguste Aristide Fernand (1824-1895) French
£961 $1519 €1500 Gibier, poissons, victuailles et chat (100x81cm-39x32in) s. 18-Nov-2 Tajan, Paris #11 est:1500-2000

CONSTANTIN, Jean Antoine (1756-1844) French
Works on paper
£385 $608 €600 Martigues (25x37cm-10x15in) PEN WASH P. 16-Nov-2 Lempertz, Koln #1300/R
£439 $685 €650 Nature morte au lievre (20x18cm-8x7in) sanguine. 26-Mar-3 Rieunier, Paris #31/R

CONSTANTIN, Jean Antoine (attrib) (1756-1844) French
Works on paper
£348 $550 €550 Figures dessinant dans les ruines (17x23cm-7x9in) pen ink wash W/C. 28-Nov-2 Tajan, Paris #54

CONSTANTINE, G Hamilton (1875-1967) British
£1260 $2016 €1890 Farmstead with working horse returning home (24x34cm-9x13in) s. board. 11-Mar-3 David Duggleby, Scarborough #225/R est:1000-1500
Works on paper
£300 $492 €450 Gathering firewood (23x26cm-9x10in) s.i. W/C. 4-Jun-3 Bonhams, Chester #365
£320 $525 €480 Shepherd and sheep by trees (17x25cm-7x10in) s. W/C. 4-Jun-3 Bonhams, Chester #367
£380 $623 €570 Country land with horse drawn cart (26x36cm-10x14in) s. W/C. 4-Jun-3 Bonhams, Chester #369
£500 $795 €750 River landscape (32x48cm-13x19in) s. W/C. 4-Mar-3 Bearnes, Exeter #399/R
£720 $1130 €1080 Poor catch, near Fowey (34x24cm-13x9in) s.i. W/C gouache. 19-Nov-2 Bonhams, Leeds #77/R
£720 $1166 €1080 Moorland camp (25x35cm-10x14in) s.i. W/C. 21-Jan-3 Bonhams, Knightsbridge #22/R
£750 $1163 €1125 Winter morning (18x24cm-7x9in) s.i. W/C. 25-Sep-2 Hamptons Fine Art, Godalming #281/R
£760 $1246 €1140 Nr Storrington, harvesting scene with men loading farm cart (23x31cm-9x12in) s.i. W/C. 4-Jun-3 Bonhams, Chester #366
£860 $1410 €1290 In the meadows, Hathersage, with cattle grazing (27x37cm-11x15in) s.i. W/C. 4-Jun-3 Bonhams, Chester #370
£900 $1413 €1350 View of York Minster from an ancient gateway (35x25cm-14x10in) s. W/C. 19-Nov-2 Bonhams, Leeds #78
£900 $1404 €1350 Hunting scenes (15x10cm-6x4in) s. W/C set of four. 6-Nov-2 Bonhams, Chester #494
£1200 $1884 €1800 Grey day. Misty morning (17x24cm-7x9in) s. W/C pair prov. 16-Apr-3 George Kidner, Lymington #82/R est:1200-1500
£1300 $2132 €1950 Landing herrings, Great Yarmouth (23x50cm-9x20in) s.i. W/C. 4-Jun-3 Bonhams, Chester #364 est:1000-1500
£1350 $2106 €2025 Scotch fisher girls, Scarbro (34x25cm-13x10in) s.i. W/C htd white. 10-Sep-2 David Duggleby, Scarborough #257/R est:1000-1500
£1500 $2460 €2250 Yarmouth (23x50cm-9x20in) s.i. W/C. 4-Jun-3 Bonhams, Chester #363/R est:1000-1500
£2800 $4480 €4200 On the mussel beds. Across the moor to Bakewell Fort (24x35cm-9x14in) s. W/C pair. 8-Jan-3 George Kidner, Lymington #165/R est:2000-3000

CONSTANTINEAU, Fleurimond (1905-) Canadian
£246 $384 €369 Un coin Pangnintung, Ils de Baffin (25x30cm-10x12in) s.i.d.1972 s.i.verso isorel. 10-Sep-2 Iegor de Saint Hippolyte, Montreal #21 (C.D 600)
£287 $448 €431 Couple esquimau au marche a poisson du Godthab, Groenland (40x50cm-16x20in) s.d. s.i.verso isorel. 10-Sep-2 Iegor de Saint Hippolyte, Montreal #19 (C.D 700)
£287 $448 €431 Cap au meules, Iles de la Madeleine, PQc (20x25cm-8x10in) s.i.d. s.i.verso isorel. 10-Sep-2 Iegor de Saint Hippolyte, Montreal #20 (C.D 700)
£290 $453 €435 L'Eglise St Jaques, Montreal (40x30cm-16x12in) s.d.65 i.verso isorel. 30-Jul-2 Iegor de Saint Hippolyte, Montreal #33 (C.D 720)
£363 $573 €545 Preparation au voyage maricourt (61x91cm-24x36in) s.d.1968 s.i.d.verso board prov. 14-Nov-2 Heffel, Vancouver #135 est:600-800 (C.D 900)
£645 $1019 €968 Fox Point - N. Ecosse (41x51cm-16x20in) s. s.i.verso board. 14-Nov-2 Heffel, Vancouver #258/R est:600-800 (C.D 1600)
£5242 $8544 €7863 Deportation of the Acadians (12x15cm-5x6in) s.d.31. 12-Feb-3 Iegor de Saint Hippolyte, Montreal #42 (C.D 13000)
Works on paper
£215 $335 €323 L'igloo arctique (51x61cm-20x24in) s. s.i.d.verso isorel. 25-Mar-3 Iegor de Saint Hippolyte, Montreal #25 (C.D 500)

CONSTANTINI, Virgile (1882-1940) Italian
£58065 $90000 €87098 Nu (120x68cm-47x27in) s.d.11 prov.lit. 30-Oct-2 Christie's, Rockefeller NY #77/R est:60000-80000

CONTANT D'IVRY, Pierre (1698-1777) French
Works on paper
£440 $687 €700 Projet d'eelevation d'eglise (36x25cm-14x10in) s. chk pen ink wash. 8-Oct-2 Christie's, Paris #13/R

CONTE, Dante Mose (1885-1919) Italian
£535 $823 €850 Palace entry (46x55cm-18x22in) s.verso. 28-Oct-2 Il Ponte, Milan #338

CONTE, Hortense (fl.1870-1881) French
£5800 $9454 €8410 Still life of grapes (61x51cm-24x20in) s.d.1848. 16-Jul-3 Sotheby's, Olympia #213/R est:3000-5000

CONTEL, Jean Charles (1895-1928) French
£385 $596 €600 Vieille rue a Rouen (65x46cm-26x18in) s. 8-Dec-2 Feletin, Province #221
£425 $684 €650 Amiens. Rue du milieu de la Vieillerie (65x53cm-26x21in) s. pair. 19-Jan-3 Feletin, Province #78
£981 $1530 €1550 Vieille cour a Lisieux (66x54cm-26x21in) s. 15-Sep-2 Etude Bailleul, Bayeux #101/R

CONTENCIN, Charles Henry (20th C) French
£1699 $2633 €2650 Chalet dans la neige (47x52cm-19x20in) 8-Dec-2 Teitgen, Nancy #26/R
£1923 $2981 €3000 Aguille du geant (46x51cm-18x20in) 8-Dec-2 Teitgen, Nancy #25

CONTENOT, H D (19/20th C) French
Sculpture
£1935 $3000 €2903 Seated Roman (159cm-63in) s.num. bronze marble pedestal exec.c.1890 st.f. 2-Oct-2 Christie's, Rockefeller NY #738/R est:3000-4000

CONTENT, Marjorie (1895-1984) American
Photographs
£2278 $3600 €3417 Washington Square (11x9cm-4x4in) s.d.1928 gelatin silver print prov. 25-Apr-3 Phillips, New York #79/R est:2000-3000
£2405 $3800 €3608 Untitled (14x11cm-6x4in) s.d.1930 verso gelatin silver print prov.lit. 25-Apr-3 Phillips, New York #78/R est:2000-3000
£2468 $3800 €3702 New England barn with window reflections (7x9cm-3x4in) s.verso gold toned gelatin silver print prov. 25-Oct-2 Phillips, New York #9/R est:2500-3500
£2658 $4200 €3987 Untitled (10x7cm-4x3in) s.d.1932 verso gelatin silver print prov.lit. 25-Apr-3 Phillips, New York #7/R est:3000-4000
£3165 $5000 €4748 From Doctors Hospital (17x12cm-7x5in) s.d.1933 verso gelatin silver print prov.exhib. 25-Apr-3 Phillips, New York #6/R est:2500-3500

CONTI, Andrea (1921-) Italian
£316 $494 €500 At the window (70x50cm-28x20in) s.d.1983. 14-Sep-2 Meeting Art, Vercelli #896/R

CONTI, Bernardino de (circle) (1450-1525) Italian
£12000 $18600 €18000 Study of Head of Christ (41x30cm-16x12in) panel. 31-Oct-2 Sotheby's, Olympia #13/R est:6000-8000

CONTI, Eugenio (19/20th C) Italian
£1842 $2984 €2800 Consuming chianti (18x12cm-7x5in) s. panel prov. 21-Jan-3 Christie's, Amsterdam #101/R est:1500-2000

CONTI, Eugenio Giuseppe (1842-1909) Italian
£2338 $3553 €3600 Washerwoman (76x48cm-30x19in) s.i. 7-Jul-2 Lombrail & Teucquam, Paris #49/R

CONTI, Primo (1900-1989) Italian
£2436 $3849 €3800 Mother (60x50cm-24x20in) painted 1934. 12-Nov-2 Babuino, Rome #358/R
£5128 $8103 €8000 Still life with fish (91x66cm-36x26in) s.d.1931. 15-Nov-2 Farsetti, Prato #609/R

CONTI, Regina (1890-1960) Swiss
£602 $969 €873 Italian woman (60x42cm-24x17in) s. indis.i. 9-May-3 Dobiaschofsky, Bern #70/R (S.FR 1300)

CONTI, Tito (1842-1924) Italian
£900 $1476 €1350 Young beauty (33x25cm-13x10in) s. canvasboard. 5-Jun-3 Christie's, Kensington #613/R
£1500 $2340 €2250 Boy playing a flute (36x31cm-14x12in) s. canvas on board. 10-Apr-3 Tennants, Leyburn #1114/R est:400-600

CONTI, Tito and GEORGE, W (19th C) Italian/British
£5161 $8000 €7742 Fashionable couple on a grand stairway (123x93cm-48x37in) s.d.02. 2-Oct-2 Christie's, Rockefeller NY #786/R est:5000-7000

CONTICH, K van (?) Dutch
£1076 $1700 €1614 Untitled (43x51cm-17x20in) 1-Dec-2 Susanin's, Chicago #5069/R

CONTINENTAL SCHOOL
£5975 $9201 €9500 Vase of flowers (51x42cm-20x17in) board. 28-Oct-2 Il Ponte, Milan #148 est:1500
£10759 $16677 €17000 Mater Dolorosa (81x67cm-32x26in) 26-Sep-2 Neumeister, Munich #2884 est:400

CONTINENTAL SCHOOL, 16th C
Works on paper
£14744 $22853 €23000 Christ presented at the temple (41x21cm-16x8in) pen ink wash. 4-Dec-2 Piasa, Paris #35/R

CONTINENTAL SCHOOL, 17th C
£4487 $6551 €7000 Madonna and Child with Saints (230x165cm-91x65in) i. 5-Jun-2 Il Ponte, Milan #351 est:4000-5000
£9615 $14038 €15000 The sultan visiting a fortified town (124x238cm-49x94in) 5-Jun-2 Il Ponte, Milan #311/R est:6000-7000
£11935 $18858 €18500 Saint Magdalene (20x129cm-8x51in) paper lit. 18-Dec-2 Beaussant & Lefèvre, Paris #14/R est:8000

CONTINENTAL SCHOOL, 18th C
£8280 $12752 €13000 Bacchanalian views with putti and goats (111x107cm-44x42in) pair. 4-Sep-2 James Adam, Dublin #82/R est:15000-20000
£20513 $31795 €32000 Landscape with market scene (152x108cm-60x43in) 4-Dec-2 Finarte, Rome #868/R est:7000

CONTINENTAL SCHOOL, 19th C
£6200 $9796 €8990 Lake scene with figures on horseback in foreground (51x79cm-20x31in) 23-Jul-3 Brightwells, Leominster #982/R est:400-600
£7500 $11700 €11250 Palazzo Madonna in the Piazza Castello in Turin (23x33cm-9x13in) indis.sig.i. paper. 17-Sep-2 Sotheby's, Olympia #252/R est:400-600
£12987 $20000 €19481 St Bernard carrying a terrier in a mountainous landscape (123x133cm-48x52in) 4-Sep-2 Christie's, Rockefeller NY #242/R est:5000-7000
Sculpture
£9032 $14000 €13548 Before the bath (152cm-60in) marble. 30-Oct-2 Christie's, Rockefeller NY #195/R est:15000-20000
Miniatures
£5500 $8635 €8250 Putto flying amongst the clouds, holding open blue curtain revealing a right eye (5cm-2xin) gold brooch frame rec. 10-Dec-2 Christie's, London #294/R est:3000-5000

CONTINENTAL SCHOOL, 20th C
Sculpture
£8228 $13000 €12342 Sphinx (124x157x58cm-49x62x23in) grey marble. 24-Apr-3 Christie's, Rockefeller NY #225/R est:10000-15000

CONTOIT, Louis (19/20th C) European
£1994 $3250 €2991 Back off (46x77cm-18x30in) s. indis d. 11-Feb-3 Bonhams & Doyles, New York #145 est:1500-2500
£2914 $4750 €4371 English setters working (40x51cm-16x20in) s. pair. 11-Feb-3 Bonhams & Doyles, New York #118/R est:2000-3000

CONTRERAS, Jesus Fructuoso (1867-1902) Mexican
Sculpture
£9000 $14040 €13500 Awakening (74cm-29in) s. white marble. 5-Nov-2 Sotheby's, London #166/R est:5000-7000

CONWAY, Douglas (20th C) ?
£223 $350 €335 Two boats in grass lined canal at lock with building (38x28cm-15x11in) s. board. 19-Apr-3 James Julia, Fairfield #412/R

CONWAY, Fred (1900-1972) American
Works on paper
£256 $400 €384 Venice (36x48cm-14x19in) s.d.1957 W/C. 10-Nov-2 Selkirks, St. Louis #784

CONWAY, George L (19/20th C) American
£304 $475 €456 Rustic and gold (30x41cm-12x16in) s.d.1908 board. 18-Sep-2 Alderfer's, Hatfield #302

CONWAY, Richard (19th C) British
£400 $656 €600 Returning home (51x76cm-20x30in) s. 29-May-3 Christie's, Kensington #118/R

CONYERS, Matilda (1753-1803) British
Works on paper
£4196 $6000 €6294 Amaryllis vitata. Pancutium aboinense (39x30cm-15x12in) W/C pair. 22-Jan-3 Doyle, New York #68/R

COOK OF PLYMOUTH, William (fl.1870-1880) British
Works on paper
£250 $408 €375 Wreckers on the coast (20x33cm-8x13in) mono.d.1882 W/C. 13-Feb-3 David Lay, Penzance #110
£320 $496 €480 Breach at Newquay (64x99cm-25x39in) mono.d.1883 W/C. 26-Sep-2 Lane, Penzance #83
£320 $525 €480 Shepherd with sheep on a stone bridge (24x41cm-9x16in) init. W/C. 7-Feb-3 Honiton Galleries, Honiton #357
£340 $541 €510 An overshot mill (43x33cm-17x13in) mono.d.73 W/C. 4-Mar-3 Bearnes, Exeter #338
£440 $726 €638 New stone, near Plymouth (25x42cm-10x17in) mono.d.74 W/C. 1-Jul-3 Bearnes, Exeter #460/R
£460 $750 €690 Cattle at the water's edge (29x43cm-11x17in) init.d.81 W/C over pencil htd white. 11-Feb-3 Bonhams, Knowle #19
£1000 $1580 €1450 Anchored off the South Coast (38x58cm-15x23in) init.d.74 W/C. 22-Jul-3 Bonhams, Knightsbridge #160/R est:800-1200

COOK OF PLYMOUTH, William (attrib) (fl.1870-1880) British
Works on paper
£725 $1146 €1088 At Tintagel, Cornwall, King Arthur's Castle, a wreck (36x54cm-14x21in) mono.d.72 W/C. 18-Dec-2 John Nicholson, Haslemere #1137

COOK, Arthur M (1931-) American
Works on paper
£696 $1100 €1044 Snow geese coming in (55x74cm-22x29in) s. W/C gouache on board prov. 3-Apr-3 Christie's, Rockefeller NY #197/R est:2500-3500

COOK, Beryl (1926-) British
£4200 $6636 €6300 Dusting the cat (20x33cm-8x13in) init. board prov. 27-Nov-2 Sotheby's, Olympia #184/R est:2500-3500
£5000 $8350 €7250 Granny on television (54x54cm-21x21in) s. board prov. 24-Jun-3 Bonhams, New Bond Street #101/R est:5000-7000
£8200 $12710 €12300 Car full of dogs (43x60cm-17x24in) s. i.verso board. 3-Dec-2 Bonhams, New Bond Street #102/R est:5000-7000
£18000 $30060 €26100 Street in Soho (84x61cm-33x24in) s. i.d.1987 verso board prov.exhib. 24-Jun-3 Bonhams, New Bond Street #100/R est:7000-10000
Works on paper
£1500 $2505 €2175 Farewell to arms (36x33cm-14x13in) gouache. 24-Jun-3 Bonhams, New Bond Street #102/R est:2000-3000

COOK, Charles Bailey (?) ?
£710 $1100 €1065 Portland waterfront in winter (61x76cm-24x30in) s. 2-Nov-2 Thomaston Place, Thomaston #38

COOK, Ebenezer Wake (1843-1926) British
Works on paper
£250 $405 €363 Merry moments (21x16cm-8x6in) s.d.95 W/C. 20-May-3 Dreweatt Neate, Newbury #171/R
£285 $444 €450 Largo Maggiore (27x37cm-11x15in) s.d.92 W/C. 30-Jul-2 Hamilton Osborne King, Dublin #304
£287 $436 €431 Man with horses and cart (13x12cm-5x5in) s.d.79 W/C. 28-Aug-2 Deutscher-Menzies, Melbourne #328/R (A.D 800)
£320 $515 €464 On the lagoons Venice (40x57cm-16x22in) s. W/C prov. 12-May-3 Joel, Victoria #254 (A.D 800)
£380 $635 €551 Merry moments, Florence (21x16cm-8x6in) s.d.95 W/C. 24-Jun-3 Bonhams, Knightsbridge #74/R
£520 $827 €780 Lake Como (14x21cm-6x8in) s. W/C. 4-Mar-3 Bearnes, Exeter #374/R
£620 $1004 €930 Old town, Mentone (17x25cm-7x10in) s.d.91 W/C htd white. 21-May-3 Bonhams, Knightsbridge #201/R
£800 $1304 €1160 Loch Katrine from above the Silver Strand (25x35cm-10x14in) s.d.88 W/C. 16-Jul-3 Sotheby's, Olympia #46/R
£900 $1458 €1350 Loch Achray and Ben Venue, Perthshire (30x45cm-12x18in) s. W/C. 21-Jan-3 Bonhams, Knightsbridge #156/R
£1200 $1920 €1800 River Vire at St Lo, Normandy (81x56cm-32x22in) s. W/C exhib. 11-Mar-3 Bonhams, New Bond Street #83/R est:1000-1500
£1434 $2179 €2151 Mountain landscape (33x46cm-13x18in) s.d.80 W/C. 28-Aug-2 Deutscher-Menzies, Melbourne #181/R est:4000-6000 (A.D 4000)
£1900 $3040 €2850 Richmond, North Wales. Rydal Water, Cumbria (22x12cm-9x5in) s.d.86 W/C pair. 11-Mar-3 Bonhams, New Bond Street #80/R est:1000-1500
£1900 $3059 €2755 Lake Como (55x80cm-22x31in) s. W/C prov. 12-May-3 Joel, Victoria #358/R est:6000-8000 (A.D 4750)

COOK, Emily Annie (fl.1880-1909) British
£442 $690 €663 Portrait of a young girl in a pink dress (47x34cm-19x13in) s. 6-Aug-2 Peter Webb, Auckland #195/R est:1200-1800 (NZ.D 1500)

COOK, Frederick T W (1907-1982) British
Works on paper
£260 $434 €377 Polperro Harbour (24x30cm-9x12in) s. W/C bodycol. 19-Jun-3 Lane, Penzance #399

COOK, Henry (1819-c.1890) British
£350 $550 €525 Young lady resting on a hillside before a mountain range (216x114cm-85x45in) s.d.1882. 16-Apr-3 Christie's, Kensington #663

COOK, Herbert Moxon (1844-c.1920) British
£300 $477 €450 Winter landscape (33x43cm-13x17in) s. 29-Apr-3 Gorringes, Lewes #2205

COOK, Howard (1901-1980) American
Works on paper
£1282 $2000 €1923 Sangre de Christo (43x104cm-17x41in) s. pastel on board prov.lit. 9-Nov-2 Santa Fe Art, Santa Fe #229/R est:3000-5000

COOK, J A (20th C) American
Works on paper
£288 $450 €432 Gloucester Harbour (33x23cm-13x9in) s. 1-Aug-2 Eldred, East Dennis #163

COOK, J D (?) ?
£500 $760 €750 Haymaking scene with figures, horses, cart and dog in hayfield (43x76cm-17x30in) s.d.88. 16-Aug-2 Keys, Aylsham #528/R

COOK, John A (1870-1936) American
Works on paper
£478 $750 €717 Gloucester harbor views (18x28cm-7x11in) s. W/C two. 22-Nov-2 Skinner, Boston #366/R

COOK, May E (19th C) British
£300 $477 €450 Portrait of a terrier (30x25cm-12x10in) s.d.1894. 18-Mar-3 Sworder & Son, Bishops Stortford #411a/R

COOK, Otis (1900-1980) American
£1156 $1850 €1734 Gloucester Harbor scene (51x61cm-20x24in) 11-Jan-3 James Julia, Fairfield #223 est:2500-3000

COOK, Paul Rodda (1897-1972) American
£14103 $22000 €21155 Bear grass yucca, West Texas (102x102cm-40x40in) 19-Oct-2 David Dike, Dallas #226/R est:20000-30000

COOK, William Delafield (jnr) (1936-) Australian
£36822 $58547 €55233 Bundanon 3 (94x166cm-37x65in) s.d.98 prov. 5-May-3 Sotheby's, Melbourne #131/R est:60000-90000 (A.D 95000)
Works on paper
£17794 $27224 €26691 Bend (71x183cm-28x72in) s.d.92 synthetic polymer paint prov. 26-Aug-2 Sotheby's, Paddington #526/R est:35000-40000 (A.D 50000)
£44643 $70535 €66965 Homage to Ingres (127x137cm-50x54in) s.d.1972 chl conte paper on canvas prov.exhib. 27-Nov-2 Deutscher-Menzies, Melbourne #22/R est:24000-28000 (A.D 125000)

COOK, Winifred H (20th C) British
Works on paper
£400 $668 €580 Portrait of a man in profile (44x32cm-17x13in) s. W/C. 17-Jun-3 Bonhams, Knightsbridge #80

COOKA, Philip P (20th C) American Indian
£406 $650 €609 Kachina dancers of the Hopi country (30x46cm-12x18in) s.i. 13-Jan-3 Christie's, Rockefeller NY #57/R

COOKE, Arthur Claude (1867-?) British
Works on paper
£850 $1343 €1275 Collie (21x22cm-8x9in) s.d.1928 pencil W/C. 28-Nov-2 Christie's, Kensington #326/R

COOKE, Barrie (1931-) British
£2215 $3434 €3500 Untitled (140x127cm-55x50in) s.d.68-70. 24-Sep-2 De Veres Art Auctions, Dublin #104 est:4000-6000
£6159 $10101 €8500 Stones, lake 3 (81x122cm-32x48in) s.d.79-80 i.verso. 28-May-3 Bonhams & James Adam, Dublin #66/R est:6000-10000
Works on paper
£704 $1169 €1000 Study for bog figure (11x19cm-4x7in) mixed media prov. 10-Jun-3 James Adam, Dublin #277/R est:1000-1500
£725 $1188 €1000 Bone no.5, 1973 (38x17cm-15x7in) s.d.71 pencil W/C. 28-May-3 Bonhams & James Adam, Dublin #158/R est:1000-1500
£943 $1472 €1500 Bone, no 23 (51x38cm-20x15in) s.d.1972 W/C over pencil exhib. 17-Sep-2 Whyte's, Dublin #95/R est:1200-1500

COOKE, E Wake (fl.1870s) British
Works on paper
£353 $554 €550 View of Knaresborough, Yorkshire (25x35cm-10x14in) s. W/C. 19-Nov-2 Hamilton Osborne King, Dublin #416

COOKE, Edward William (1811-1880) British
£19000 $31540 €28500 Dutch boats on a river in Holland (99x136cm-39x54in) s. 12-Jun-3 Sotheby's, London #46/R est:12000-18000
£70000 $110600 €105000 Vinegia, vinegia, chi non te vede, ei non te pregia (68x106cm-27x42in) s.d.1852 prov.lit. 27-Nov-2 Christie's, London #23/R est:60000-80000
£70000 $110600 €105000 San Giorgio Maggiore and Salute, Venice, with fishing crafts of Chioggia (70x102cm-28x40in) s.i. prov.exhib.lit. 27-Nov-2 Christie's, London #24/R est:60000-80000
Works on paper
£320 $506 €464 Dutch boats on the Suyder Zee (13x18cm-5x7in) s.d.11 Feb 1871 pencil dr. 23-Jul-3 Mallams, Oxford #179/R
£500 $779 €750 Whale skeleton on the shore (21x29cm-8x11in) s.d.1867 pastel. 19-Sep-2 Christie's, Kensington #146
£500 $800 €750 Sail barges in a heavy sea (23x33cm-9x13in) mono.d.1840 W/C. 11-Mar-3 Gorringes, Lewes #2363
£600 $990 €870 San Clemente, Venice (12x18cm-5x7in) s.i.d.1862 pencil brown wash prov. 3-Jul-3 Christie's, Kensington #134/R

COOKE, Edward William (attrib) (1811-1880) British
£600 $990 €870 Unloading cargo (19x14cm-7x6in) init. panel. 1-Jul-3 Bearnes, Exeter #516/R

COOKE, Ernest Owen (?-1937) British
£450 $707 €675 Cattle watering at a pool in wooded landscape (48x61cm-19x24in) s.d.1928. 13-Dec-2 Keys, Aylsham #711
£620 $1004 €930 Storm clouds rising (34x39cm-13x15in) s.d.1917. 20-May-3 Sotheby's, Olympia #286/R

COOKE, Isaac (1846-1922) British
£340 $537 €510 Sunshine showers, Lwyn Idwal (49x72cm-19x28in) s. 27-Nov-2 Peter Wilson, Nantwich #12
Works on paper
£300 $465 €450 On the country road (29x49cm-11x19in) s. W/C. 25-Sep-2 Hamptons Fine Art, Godalming #238
£440 $686 €660 Highland farmers dipping sheep (30x48cm-12x19in) s. W/C. 15-Oct-2 Gorringes, Lewes #2290

COOKE, Roger (1941-) American
£3165 $5000 €4589 Phantons of the forest (56x76cm-22x30in) s. 26-Jul-3 Coeur d'Alene, Hayden #234/R est:3000-6000

COOKE, William Edward (fl.1880-1886) British
£280 $437 €420 Village street (22x30cm-9x12in) mono.d.1878 board. 26-Mar-3 Sotheby's, Olympia #116/R

COOKESLEY, Margaret Murray (?-1927) British
£457 $750 €663 In the harem (91x46cm-36x18in) mono. prov. 4-Jun-3 Doyle, New York #32

COOKMAN, Charles Edwin (1856-1913) American
£353 $550 €530 Elegant woman with her dog (66x41cm-26x16in) s. 9-Oct-2 Doyle, New York #25
Works on paper
£239 $375 €359 Summer (21x26cm-8x10in) s. W/C. 22-Nov-2 Skinner, Boston #233/R

COOKSEY, May Louise Greville (1878-1943) British
£620 $955 €930 Lady holding a bunch of honesty (56x38cm-22x15in) s. board. 3-Sep-2 Gorringes, Lewes #2123/R
Works on paper
£620 $961 €930 Dutch market scene (52x37cm-20x15in) s.d.1908 W/C. 25-Sep-2 Peter Wilson, Nantwich #134

COOLE, Brian (19th C) British
£962 $1500 €1443 Steam boat, R E Lee (30x46cm-12x18in) s. 20-Oct-2 Jeffery Burchard, Florida #32/R
£1053 $1600 €1580 Riverboat, Mississippi (28x51cm-11x20in) s. 17-Aug-2 North East Auctions, Portsmouth #571/R

COOLIDGE, John Earle (1882-1947) American
£898 $1500 €1302 Oaks and eucalyptus in landscape (30x41cm-12x16in) s.d.21. 17-Jun-3 John Moran, Pasadena #199 est:1000-1500

COOMANS, Auguste (1855-?) Belgian
£544 $865 €800 Landscape with sheep, lamb and chickens (19x24cm-7x9in) s. panel. 28-Mar-3 Bolland & Marotz, Bremen #431a
£1060 $1727 €1600 Quatre moutons dans un paysage (17x30cm-7x12in) indis.sig. s.verso. 17-Feb-3 Horta, Bruxelles #93
£1410 $2214 €2200 Wooded mountain landscape (48x72cm-19x28in) s.d.1865. 21-Nov-2 Van Ham, Cologne #1523/R est:2200
£1433 $2250 €2150 Lady in an interior (46x36cm-18x14in) panel. 13-Dec-2 Du Mouchelle, Detroit #2179/R est:1500-2000

COOMANS, Diana (19th C) Belgian
£2500 $3925 €3750 After the wedding (49x69cm-19x27in) s. 21-Nov-2 Christie's, Kensington #209/R est:3000-5000

COOMANS, Pierre Olivier Joseph (1816-1889) Belgian
£1399 $2169 €2099 Portrait of a woman holding a fan (74x58cm-29x23in) s.d.1888. 3-Dec-2 Ritchie, Toronto #3064/R est:3000-5000 (C.D 3400)
£1860 $2919 €2790 Portrait of a young beauty (74x58cm-29x23in) s.i.d.1888. 24-Jul-2 Walker's, Ottawa #47/R est:7000-9000 (C.D 4500)
£3268 $5261 €5000 Jeune femme narrant une histoire a l'heure de la sieste (20x26cm-8x10in) s. panel. 20-Jan-3 Horta, Bruxelles #181/R est:5000-7000
£4487 $7045 €7000 Beaute revassant (80x65cm-31x26in) s. 10-Dec-2 Campo, Vlaamse Kaai #84/R est:4000-5000
£6000 $9840 €9000 Odalisque (81x66cm-32x26in) s.d.1865 prov. 3-Jun-3 Sotheby's, London #158/R est:7000-10000
£6329 $10000 €9494 Praising the Virtues of Athena (56x42cm-22x17in) s.d.1875 panel prov. 23-Apr-3 Christie's, Rockefeller NY #112/R est:10000-15000

COOMBS, Daniel (1971-) British
£1000 $1630 €1500 Room II - falling (200x200cm-79x79in) oil ac, painted 1995 prov. 3-Feb-3 Sotheby's, Olympia #16/R est:1000-1500

COOMBS, Delbert Dana (1850-1938) American
£1006 $1600 €1509 Mt Washington Valley (61x46cm-24x18in) s.d.1885 prov. 7-Mar-3 Skinner, Boston #295/R est:600-800
£3185 $5000 €4778 Rounding the island (51x77cm-20x30in) s.d.1887. 22-Nov-2 Skinner, Boston #85/R est:2000-3000

COON, Howard A (20th C) American
£248 $400 €372 Gloucester dock scene (66x53cm-26x21in) s.d.60 board. 19-Jan-3 Jeffery Burchard, Florida #48/R

COONEY, Albert (?) ?
£309 $444 €500 Fenian gun runner Erins Hope (127x102cm-50x40in) s. 25-Apr-2 Woodwards, Cork #249

COOP, Hubert (1872-1953) British
Works on paper
£280 $448 €420 Castle beside an estuary, probably Conway (25x41cm-10x16in) mono. W/C. 13-Mar-3 Duke & Son, Dorchester #80
£750 $1140 €1125 Canal with windmill behind and thatched cottage (34x52cm-13x20in) s. W/C. 13-Aug-2 Gildings, Market Harborough #242/R
£750 $1193 €1088 Misty harbour scene with sailing craft and Caernarfan Castle beyond (48x36cm-19x14in) s. W/C. 1-May-3 Amersham Auction Rooms, UK #244
£850 $1326 €1233 Evening sunshine (13x19cm-5x7in) s. W/C. 27-Mar-3 Neales, Nottingham #909/R
£920 $1463 €1334 Whitby Harbour with moored sailing craft (36x66cm-14x26in) s. W/C. 1-May-3 Amersham Auction Rooms, UK #243
£1100 $1705 €1650 Chalk cliff (36x54cm-14x21in) s. W/C. 25-Sep-2 John Nicholson, Haslemere #898 est:500-1000
£1350 $2106 €2025 Extensive view from Bogg Hall at low tide with fishing boats (28x57cm-11x22in) s. W/C. 10-Sep-2 David Duggleby, Scarborough #118/R est:1000-1500
£1800 $2916 €2700 Southwold Harbour, Suffolk (58x75cm-23x30in) s. W/C. 23-Jan-3 Christie's, Kensington #367/R est:700-1000
£3200 $4864 €4800 Thames at Westminster, with a sailing barge in the foreground (56x77cm-22x30in) s. W/C. 13-Aug-2 Gildings, Market Harborough #241/R est:1000-1500

COOPER, A C (19th C) British
£1266 $1975 €2000 Cattle (40x65cm-16x26in) s. 16-Sep-2 Horta, Bruxelles #84

COOPER, A E (1883-1974) British
£3200 $4864 €4800 Portrait of a chef, half length, standing in his kitchen (76x64cm-30x25in) s.d.1923. 29-Aug-2 Christie's, Kensington #75/R est:600-800

COOPER, Abraham (1787-1868) British
£2000 $3160 €3000 Saddled grey hunter in landscape (51x60cm-20x24in) 27-Nov-2 Christie's, London #6/R

COOPER, Alfred Egerton (1883-1974) British
£260 $411 €390 Portrait of Arthur Annesley (126x100cm-50x39in) s.i.d.1926 verso after Lely. 12-Nov-2 Bonhams, Knightsbridge #298/R
£4115 $6379 €6173 Sir Edward Mountain Bart, landing a salmon at Minister's Pool, Stanley Waters, River Tay (77x101cm-30x40in) init. s.d.1947 verso. 3-Dec-2 Ritchie, Toronto #3048/R est:5000-7000 (C.D 10000)

COOPER, Alfred Heaton (1864-1929) British
Works on paper
£320 $518 €480 Wastwater (24x34cm-9x13in) s.i.d.1910 W/C. 21-May-3 Bonhams, Knightsbridge #257
£350 $567 €525 Lakeland landscape with arched beidge (19x37cm-7x15in) W/C. 21-May-3 James Thompson, Kirby Lonsdale #11
£420 $655 €630 Middle Eastern street scene (54x38cm-21x15in) s. W/C. 17-Sep-2 Sotheby's, Olympia #115/R
£650 $1053 €975 Scandinavian coastal scene (54x36cm-21x14in) s. W/C. 21-May-3 James Thompson, Kirby Lonsdale #154/R
£740 $1147 €1110 Mountainous view with trees and sheep in foreground (25x33cm-10x13in) s. W/C. 30-Oct-2 Wingetts, Wrexham #256
£850 $1369 €1275 Sweden Bridge near Ambleside (36x26cm-14x10in) s. W/C. 15-Jan-3 James Thompson, Kirby Lonsdale #71
£850 $1326 €1275 Heart of Borrowdale (36x53cm-14x21in) s. W/C. 25-Mar-3 Bonhams, Knightsbridge #163/R
£900 $1413 €1350 Haunt of the wild duck, Urswick Farm (38x55cm-15x22in) s. W/C. 21-Nov-2 Clevedon Sale Rooms #256/R
£1100 $1716 €1650 Rowing boat on a lake (38x55cm-15x22in) s. W/C. 17-Sep-2 Sotheby's, Olympia #138/R est:500-700
£1200 $1860 €1800 Falling leaves, sheep in a paddock (97x142cm-38x56in) s. W/C exhib. 26-Sep-2 Lane, Penzance #369 est:1000-1200
£1450 $2306 €2175 Charcoal burners (53x75cm-21x30in) s.d.1908 W/C. 27-Feb-3 Bonhams, Chester #338 est:900-1200

COOPER, Astley D M (1865-1924) American
£1090 $1700 €1635 Panoramic landscape with buffalo and native American (74x122cm-29x48in) s.d.1894. 18-Sep-2 Boos Gallery, Michigan #194/R est:1500-2500
£1159 $1900 €1739 California redwoods (107x33cm-42x13in) s. 31-May-3 Harvey Clar, Oakland #1421
£1218 $1900 €1827 Panoramic landscape with buffalo (36x43cm-14x17in) s.d.1894. 18-Sep-2 Boos Gallery, Michigan #195/R est:1500-2500
£1572 $2500 €2358 Danae (107x178cm-42x70in) s. painted c.1890 prov. 4-May-3 Treadway Gallery, Cincinnati #494/R est:3000-5000
£2044 $3250 €3066 Cherubs at play. s.d.1882. 8-Mar-3 Harvey Clar, Oakland #1318
£2724 $4250 €4086 Panoramic winter landscape with buffalo (102x152cm-40x60in) s.d.1895. 18-Sep-2 Boos Gallery, Michigan #193/R est:4000-6000
£2830 $4500 €4245 Pursuit (41x51cm-16x20in) s.d.1916 canvas on masonite. 4-Mar-3 Christie's, Rockefeller NY #31/R est:6000-8000
£5031 $8000 €7547 Trompe l'oeil od artist's palette with Indians (43x59cm-17x23in) s. board on panel prov.exhib. 4-Mar-3 Christie's, Rockefeller NY #29/R est:10000-15000

COOPER, Byron (1850-1933) British
£650 $1034 €975 Warm moonshine. Port Nigel, sunset (28x74cm-11x29in) indis sig. i.verso pair. 6-Mar-3 Christie's, Kensington #476/R
Works on paper
£350 $574 €508 Spring morning, Morcambe Bay (30x46cm-12x18in) s.d.1886 W/C. 3-Jun-3 Capes Dunn, Manchester #3

COOPER, Cheape (19th C) British?
Works on paper
£2700 $4428 €4050 Devil's Bridge, Cornwall, country house in Cornwall (44x60cm-17x24in) bodycol. 4-Feb-3 Bonhams, Leeds #230/R est:500-700

COOPER, Colin Campbell (1856-1937) American
£1050 $1649 €1575 Continental town scene with figures (20x14cm-8x6in) s. board. 16-Dec-2 Bonhams, Bury St Edmunds #518/R est:800-1200
£1613 $2500 €2420 Distant freighter in moderate seas (15x23cm-6x9in) s. board. 29-Oct-2 John Moran, Pasadena #619a est:1200-2000
£20253 $32000 €30380 Harbor at Dordrecht, Holland (109x147cm-43x58in) s. canvas on plywood prov. 24-Apr-3 Shannon's, Milford #148/R est:20000-30000
£27848 $44000 €41772 New York cityscape (76x51cm-30x20in) i.verso. 16-Nov-2 New Orleans Auction, New Orleans #1109/R est:2500-4000
Works on paper
£599 $1000 €869 Spanish residence in landscape (10x18cm-4x7in) s. W/C gouache. 17-Jun-3 John Moran, Pasadena #59a est:1500-2000
£778 $1300 €1128 View of the Forum, Rome (13x18cm-5x7in) s.d.May 16 1929 W/C gouache prov. 17-Jun-3 John Moran, Pasadena #8 est:1000-2000
£4969 $8000 €7454 San Francisco exposition (23x28cm-9x11in) s. gouache prov. 18-Feb-3 John Moran, Pasadena #28 est:4500-6000

COOPER, Edwin (1785-1833) British
£800 $1240 €1200 Horse standing in a landscape (66x88cm-26x35in) 30-Sep-2 Bonhams, Ipswich #502
£1900 $3040 €2850 Chestnut hunter in a landscape (51x61cm-20x24in) s. indis d. 13-May-3 Bonhams, Knightsbridge #311 est:1500-2000
£3000 $4950 €4350 Groom feeding a horse in a landscape (69x85cm-27x33in) 2-Jul-3 Sotheby's, Olympia #145/R est:3000-5000
£4200 $6930 €6090 Grey hunter in a wooded landscape (45x59cm-18x23in) s.d.1803. 2-Jul-3 Sotheby's, Olympia #150/R est:2000-3000

COOPER, Edwin (attrib) (1785-1833) British
£5600 $8848 €8400 Gentleman with his greyhounds in a landscape (61x74cm-24x29in) 28-Nov-2 Sotheby's, London #203/R est:4000-6000

COOPER, Eileen (1953-) British
£450 $743 €653 Egg (46x56cm-18x22in) s.i.d.1992 verso prov. 3-Jul-3 Christie's, Kensington #642/R
£750 $1155 €1125 The onlookers (94x165cm-37x65in) s. 5-Sep-2 Christie's, Kensington #739/R
Works on paper
£250 $388 €375 Feet first (33x25cm-13x10in) s.i.d.1997 pastel prov. 4-Dec-2 Christie's, Kensington #307

COOPER, Emma Lampert (1860-1920) American
£340 $554 €510 The Square, Abbeville, France (21x26cm-8x10in) 14-Feb-3 Lyon & Turnbull, Edinburgh #135
£1000 $1600 €1450 Rocky shallows and quiet harbour (46x66cm-18x26in) s.d.1890. 16-May-3 Skinner, Boston #286/R est:1500-2000
£1210 $1900 €1815 Brittany scene (30x41cm-12x16in) s. 23-Nov-2 Jackson's, Cedar Falls #60/R est:1400-1600

COOPER, George Gordon Byron (?-1933) British
£400 $640 €600 Rough sea, the Lizard, Cornwall (45x60cm-18x24in) s. 15-May-3 Lawrence, Crewkerne #1000

COOPER, Henry (19/20th C) British
£280 $442 €406 Mountains landscape with a figure punting on a river in the foreground (49x74cm-19x29in) s. 22-Jul-3 Sworder & Son, Bishops Stortford #310/R
£340 $527 €510 Port Madoc (51x76cm-20x30in) s. 25-Sep-2 Hamptons Fine Art, Godalming #452
£500 $815 €750 Fishing from the riverbank (30x46cm-12x18in) s. 29-Jan-3 Sotheby's, Olympia #35/R
£760 $1155 €1140 River landscapes, Christchurch on the Avon. Christchurch on the road to New Forest (51x76cm-20x30in) s.i. pair. 13-Aug-2 Canterbury Auctions, UK #109/R

COOPER, John Horace (fl.1877-1899) British
£1872 $2958 €2808 After a shower - English landscape with house by road (92x71cm-36x28in) s. 2-Dec-2 Rasmussen, Copenhagen #1568/R est:15000-20000 (D.KR 22000)

COOPER, Julian (1947-) British
£250 $383 €375 Point of no return (90x64cm-35x25in) s. paper painted c.1988. 25-Aug-2 Lots Road, London #338

COOPER, Margaret Miles (1874-1965) American
£441 $700 €662 Nantucket (28x35cm-11x14in) s. i.verso canvasboard. 7-Mar-3 Skinner, Boston #502/R
£688 $1100 €1032 Devils Hop Yard Lyme, Conn (61x74cm-24x29in) s. s.d.1947 verso. 17-Mar-3 Winter Associates, Plainville #130

COOPER, Mario Ruben (1905-1995) American
Works on paper
£373 $600 €560 Waving Cleopatra carried in procession (36x56cm-14x22in) s. gouache W/C. 20-Feb-3 Illustration House, New York #30/R

COOPER, Robert (19th C) British
Works on paper
£250 $398 €375 Highland cattle (40x67cm-16x26in) s. bodycol. 29-Apr-3 Bonhams, Knightsbridge #153/R

COOPER, Samuel (1609-1672) British
Miniatures
£3200 $4992 €4800 Lady wearing decollete blue dress with white underslip (7cm-3xin) init.d.1645 vellum silver gilt frame oval. 5-Nov-2 Bonhams, New Bond Street #20/R est:3000-5000

COOPER, Thomas George (1836-1901) British
£800 $1248 €1200 Sheep in an open landscape (26x41cm-10x16in) s.d.68. 10-Apr-3 Tennants, Leyburn #976/R
£1300 $2028 €1950 Sheep on a cliff top. Cattle in a water meadow (30x46cm-12x18in) monod.71 pair. 7-Nov-2 Christie's, Kensington #185/R est:1000-1500
£4000 $6240 €6000 Shepherd and flock before Salisbury Cathedral (61x91cm-24x36in) s.d.1893. 15-Oct-2 Gorringes, Lewes #2215/R est:4000-6000
Works on paper
£580 $922 €870 Sheep in a rural landscape (29x46cm-11x18in) s.d.1880 W/C. 29-Apr-3 Bonhams, Knightsbridge #82/R

COOPER, Thomas Sidney (1803-1902) British
£701 $1100 €1052 Cow in repose and sheep in a landscape (43x61cm-17x24in) s.d.1885. 10-Dec-2 Doyle, New York #164/R est:2000-3000
£770 $1201 €1155 Near East Grinstead (35x45cm-14x18in) s.i.d.34. 10-Apr-3 Tennants, Leyburn #970/R
£932 $1500 €1398 Cattle and sheep at pasture (41x61cm-16x24in) s.d.1842. 20-Feb-3 Skinner, Bolton #999/R est:1050-1750
£1000 $1550 €1500 Highland scene with sheep and a Highland cow (17x25cm-7x10in) s.i.d.1853 verso panel. 3-Dec-2 Sotheby's, Olympia #145/R est:1000-2000
£1000 $1580 €1500 Grazing stock - Cumberland (29x46cm-11x18in) i.verso panel exhib. 7-Apr-3 Bonhams, Bath #109/R est:2000-3000
£1150 $1829 €1725 Landscape with cattle and sheep grazing near water, trees behind (48x58cm-19x23in) s. 30-Apr-3 Brightwells, Leominster #939/R est:1000-1500

£2200	$3476	€3300	Fir trees (61x45cm-24x18in) prov. 2-Dec-2 Bonhams, Bath #88/R est:2000-3000
£2344	$3750	€3516	Landscape with three cows over looking a river (30x41cm-12x16in) s. board. 17-May-3 Pook & Pook, Downington #325/R est:4000-6000
£2600	$4056	€3900	Cattle and sheep in a landscape (44x60cm-17x24in) s.d.1865 panel. 8-Oct-2 Bonhams, Knightsbridge #188b/R est:2500-3500
£3000	$4830	€4500	Cockerel (16x11cm-6x4in) i.d.1857 board. 15-Jan-3 Cheffins Grain & Comins, Cambridge #422/R
£3172	$4886	€4758	Landscape with cattle and sheep, couple in background (51x64cm-20x25in) s.d.1856 panel. 27-Oct-2 Anders Antik, Landskrona #191/R est:30000-40000 (S.KR 46000)
£3400	$5440	€5100	Cattle resting in landscape (32x27cm-13x11in) s.d.1883 panel. 13-May-3 Bonhams, Knightsbridge #303/R est:2000-3000
£3500	$5530	€5250	Cattle on a river bank (25x35cm-10x14in) s.d.1862 panel. 2-Dec-2 Bonhams, Bath #82/R est:4000-6000
£3593	$6000	€5210	Panoramic landscape of cows grazing with sheep and livestock (51x76cm-20x30in) s. 22-Jun-3 Jeffery Burchard, Florida #61/R
£4000	$6320	€6000	Sheep in a landscape under a stormy sky (24x19cm-9x7in) s.i.d.1873. 12-Nov-2 Bonhams, Knightsbridge #196/R est:2000-3000
£4000	$6640	€6000	Three cows in a pasture (34x28cm-13x11in) s.d.1879 board. 10-Jun-3 Bonhams, Leeds #151/R est:4000-6000
£4800	$7632	€7200	Bull and two cows in a landscape (48x43cm-19x17in) s.d.1840 panel prov. 18-Mar-3 Bonhams, New Bond Street #42/R est:6000-8000
£5000	$7950	€7500	Cattle resting in a landscape (53x43cm-21x17in) s. indis d. prov. 18-Mar-3 Bonhams, New Bond Street #46/R est:6000-8000
£6000	$9540	€9000	Highland landscape with sheep grazing (79x104cm-31x41in) s.d.1852. 29-Apr-3 Gorringes, Lewes #2305
£7000	$11060	€10500	Six cows on the banks of a river (42x37cm-17x15in) s.d.1855 panel. 2-Dec-2 Bonhams, Bath #91/R est:5000-7000
£7200	$11376	€10800	The old mill (48x69cm-19x27in) s.d.1834 prov.exhib. 26-Nov-2 Christie's, London #124/R est:8000-12000
£8000	$12640	€12000	Cattle resting beside a river (41x61cm-16x24in) s.d.1873 panel. 2-Dec-2 Sotheby's, London #2/R est:8000-12000
£8000	$13280	€12000	Sheep in a highland landscape (43x53cm-17x21in) s.d.1860 panel. 10-Jun-3 Christie's, London #152/R est:8000-12000
£8200	$12956	€12300	Watering place (66x91cm-26x36in) bears sigd.1852. 2-Dec-2 Bonhams, Bath #98/R est:5000-7000
£9000	$15030	€13050	Sheep and cattle on a hillock, resting in the shade of three trees (74x62cm-29x24in) s.d.1884 panel. 17-Jun-3 Anderson & Garland, Newcastle #476/R est:3000-5000
£10000	$16300	€15000	Cattle at a pool on a heath (49x69cm-19x27in) panel. 30-Jan-3 Lawrence, Crewkerne #729/R est:5000-7000
£10000	$15900	€15000	Group in an interior (45x61cm-18x24in) s.d.1855 panel prov.exhib.lit. 18-Mar-3 Bonhams, New Bond Street #35/R est:6000-8000
£10500	$17430	€15750	Lane scene, with a peasant driving cattle (23x28cm-9x11in) s.d.1831 panel prov. 10-Jun-3 Christie's, London #97/R est:4000-6000
£11000	$17380	€16500	Sheep in moorland landscape (23x28cm-9x11in) s.d.1839 panel. 26-Nov-2 Christie's, London #138/R est:5000-7000
£12500	$19500	€18750	Cattle by a stream (51x76cm-20x30in) s.d.1891 prov. 8-Oct-2 Sotheby's, Olympia #379/R est:10000-15000
£13000	$20670	€19500	Cattle, sheep and a goat (61x45cm-24x18in) s.d.1838 panel prov. 18-Mar-3 Bonhams, New Bond Street #34/R est:12000-18000
£14000	$21980	€21000	In the marshes (46x61cm-18x24in) s.d.1856 panel prov. 19-Nov-2 Bonhams, New Bond Street #67/R est:7000-10000
£14000	$22260	€21000	Cow, calf and sheep (48x58cm-19x23in) s.d.1842 panel prov. 18-Mar-3 Bonhams, New Bond Street #43/R est:8000-12000
£18000	$30060	€26100	Farm animals at rest (61x91cm-24x36in) s. 17-Jun-3 Bonhams, New Bond Street #41/R est:18000-25000
£20000	$31400	€30000	Cattle and sheep being driven through an archway (91x71cm-36x28in) s.d.1834 prov. 19-Nov-2 Bonhams, New Bond Street #56/R est:15000-20000
£32000	$50240	€48000	Cattle, sheep and a goat at rest in an extensive landscape (71x122cm-28x48in) s.d.1857 prov.exhib. 19-Nov-2 Bonhams, New Bond Street #68/R est:25000-35000
£35000	$58100	€52500	Approaching storm (122x183cm-48x72in) s. prov. 10-Jun-3 Christie's, London #151/R est:40000-60000
£150000	$241500	€225000	Reposing on God's acre (122x163cm-48x64in) s.d.1875 prov.exhib.lit. 20-Feb-3 Christie's, London #299/R est:100000

Works on paper

£253	$400	€380	Cows by a lake (41x61cm-16x24in) s.d.1892 W/C. 17-Nov-2 CRN Auctions, Cambridge #21/R
£260	$421	€390	Eiverside house (18x25cm-7x10in) s.d.Aug 20 1886 pencil. 21-May-3 Bonhams, Knightsbridge #33/R
£680	$1074	€1020	Cattle, sheep and goats in a landscape (20x32cm-8x13in) W/C prov. 2-Dec-2 Bonhams, Bath #10/R
£880	$1426	€1276	Sheep resting in a meadow (23x28cm-9x11in) s.d.1877 W/C. 1-Aug-3 Dee Atkinson & Harrison, Driffield #684
£1500	$2490	€2250	Cattle watering (30x45cm-12x18in) s.d.1863 W/C. 10-Jun-3 Bonhams, Leeds #69/R est:1500-2000
£1688	$2600	€2532	Cattle grazing in Sandwich Meadows, Kent (41x56cm-16x22in) s.d.Dec 29 1897 W/C prov. 4-Sep-2 Christie's, Rockefeller NY #382/R est:400-600
£2700	$4266	€3915	Sheep in a landscape (23x41cm-9x16in) s.d.1868 W/C. 22-Jul-3 Gorringes, Lewes #1646/R est:1500-2000
£2800	$4620	€4060	Cattle resting in the meadows, Sandwich, Kent (41x57cm-16x22in) s.d.1879 pencil W/C gum arabic. 3-Jul-3 Christie's, Kensington #128/R est:2000-3000
£3100	$4836	€4650	Sheep in landscape (37x52cm-15x20in) s.d. W/C. 9-Oct-2 Woolley & Wallis, Salisbury #138/R est:1000-1500

COOPER, Thomas Sidney (attrib) (1803-1902) British

£310	$475	€465	Canterbury meadows (23x28cm-9x11in) panel. 23-Aug-2 York Town, York #550
£400	$640	€600	Old horse (16x22cm-6x9in) bears sig.indis.d. panel. 7-Jan-3 Bonhams, Knightsbridge #285h/R

COOPER, Thomas Sidney and LEE, Frederick Richard (19th C) British

£140000	$225400	€210000	Chequered shade (200x168cm-79x66in) s.d.1854 prov.exhib.lit. 20-Feb-3 Christie's, London #47/R est:70000-100000

COOPER, Thornhill (19/20th C) New Zealander

Works on paper

£343	$549	€497	Jacksons Hotel, west coast (29x44cm-11x17in) s.i.d.1909 W/C. 13-May-3 Watson's, Christchurch #38/R (NZ.D 950)

COOPER, W (19th C) ?

£1364	$2032	€2100	Horse in a field with two hunting dogs (51x61cm-20x24in) s.d.1826. 28-Jun-2 Woodwards, Cork #205

COOPER, W H (1903-) British

£807	$1300	€1211	Pastoral wooded landscape (28x43cm-11x17in) s. 22-Feb-3 Pook & Pook, Downington #183/R

COOPER, W S (1854-1927) British

£5200	$8112	€7800	Sheep grazing with Canterbury Cathedral beyond (25x30cm-10x12in) s.d.1917. 12-Oct-2 Hogben, Folkstone #165

COOPER, W Savage (fl.1880-1926) British

£274	$450	€397	Head of a cavalier (25x20cm-10x8in) s.d.1884 board. 4-Jun-3 Doyle, New York #33
£380	$597	€570	Arab warrior (49x39cm-19x15in) s.d.1882. 24-Jul-2 Hamptons Fine Art, Godalming #309
£2000	$3120	€3000	Portrait of a man smoking a hookah (51x40cm-20x16in) s. 15-Oct-2 Sotheby's, London #170/R est:1000-1500

COOPER, William (1923-) British

£500	$835	€725	Safe harbour (39x49cm-15x19in) s.i.d.verso. 19-Jun-3 Lane, Penzance #67

COOPER, William Heaton (1903-) British

£260	$395	€390	Lakeland backwater with figure in sailing boat (33x23cm-13x9in) W/C. 16-Aug-2 Keys, Aylsham #737

Works on paper

£420	$655	€630	Lakeland scene (53x35cm-21x14in) s. W/C. 10-Sep-2 David Duggleby, Scarborough #248
£480	$749	€720	In a Yorkshire dale (24x37cm-9x15in) s. W/C. 12-Sep-2 Sotheby's, Olympia #46/R
£700	$1148	€1050	Spring pasture (37x55cm-15x22in) s. W/C. 3-Jun-3 Sotheby's, Olympia #143/R
£980	$1637	€1421	Loch Coruisk, Isle of Skye (38x56cm-15x22in) s. W/C. 17-Jun-3 Anderson & Garland, Newcastle #154/R
£1050	$1670	€1575	Pillar mountain from haystack (37x55cm-15x22in) s. pastel. 5-Mar-3 Bonhams, Bury St Edmunds #257
£1150	$1794	€1725	Morning mist above Crummock (38x53cm-15x21in) s. W/C. 6-Nov-2 Bonhams, Chester #310 est:1200-1800
£1300	$2132	€1950	Ashness farm, Derwentwater (38x55cm-15x22in) s. W/C. 4-Feb-3 Sworder & Son, Bishops Stortford #113/R est:600-800
£1400	$2296	€2100	Reflections, Crummock Water (38x55cm-15x22in) s. W/C. 4-Feb-3 Sworder & Son, Bishops Stortford #114/R est:500-700
£1400	$2212	€2100	Study of a lakeland view (38x56cm-15x22in) s. W/C. 24-Apr-3 Mallams, Cheltenham #247/R est:200-300
£1600	$2624	€2400	Shap Fells and granite quarry (38x53cm-15x21in) s. pencil W/C. 4-Feb-3 Bonhams, Leeds #310 est:400-600
£1750	$2730	€2625	Lakeland landscape with sunshine and shadow on the Fells (37x55cm-15x22in) s. W/C. 18-Sep-2 James Thompson, Kirby Lonsdale #170

COOPER, William Sidney (1854-1927) British

£320	$496	€480	Sheep in a meadow by a river, church in the distance (18x28cm-7x11in) s. board. 3-Oct-2 Ewbank, Send #499
£400	$632	€600	An East Kent farm (26x36cm-10x14in) s.d.1907 board. 18-Dec-2 John Nicholson, Haslemere #1165
£480	$749	€720	Sheep on grassy bank (18x33cm-7x13in) s.d.1902. 15-Oct-2 Canterbury Auctions, UK #159/R
£500	$785	€750	Sheep by a river with church beyond (15x25cm-6x10in) s. board. 12-Dec-2 Richardson & Smith, Whitby #415

£2200 $3520 €3300 Cattle watering (63x11cm-25x4in) s.d.1892. 13-May-3 Bonhams, Knightsbridge #311b/R est:1500-2000
£2300 $3588 €3450 Autumn in Kent (51x91cm-20x36in) s.d.1906. 15-Oct-2 Canterbury Auctions, UK #160/R
£2800 $4424 €4200 Near Broomfield, Kent (41x61cm-16x24in) s.d.1917. 27-Nov-2 Bonhams, Knowle #239 est:3000-5000
£6000 $9420 €9000 River landscape with cattle (51x91cm-20x36in) s.d.1905. 21-Nov-2 Tennants, Leyburn #816/R est:1500-2500

Works on paper

£267 $443 €387 Sheep and drover on country road (13x18cm-5x7in) s.d.1925 W/C. 16-Jun-3 Waddingtons, Toronto #77/R (C.D 600)
£300 $468 €450 Sheep resting by an old oak (25x35cm-10x14in) s.d.1914 W/C. 17-Sep-2 Bonhams, Ipswich #360
£310 $496 €465 Cattle in marshland (23x37cm-9x15in) s.d.83 W/C. 11-Mar-3 David Duggleby, Scarborough #144
£320 $534 €464 Cattle on a country path with figures, sailing ships on sea beyond (28x36cm-11x14in) s. W/C. 25-Jun-3 Goldings, Lincolnshire #339
£756 $1254 €1096 At Mashside, Kent (25x35cm-10x14in) s.d.1915 i.verso W/C. 16-Jun-3 Waddingtons, Toronto #81/R est:1000-1500 (C.D 1700)
£800 $1256 €1200 Near Pangbourne, Berkshire. At Herne, Kent (13x18cm-5x7in) s.d.1926 pencil W/C pair. 16-Apr-3 Christie's, Kensington #1027/R
£980 $1539 €1470 Near Hearne Bay (24x34cm-9x13in) s.d.1925 pencil W/C. 19-Nov-2 Bonhams, Leeds #42
£1550 $2434 €2325 At Sturry Kent. At Highstead, Kent (20x28cm-8x11in) s.d.1914 W/C pair. 13-Dec-2 Keys, Aylsham #604/R est:1000-1500
£2200 $3454 €3300 In the meadows. Cattle at pasture (24x34cm-9x13in) s.d.1913 pencil W/C two. 19-Nov-2 Bonhams, Leeds #41/R est:1800-2200

COOPSE, Pieter (?-1677) Dutch

£5696 $8829 €9000 Dutch threemaster and other shipping in a stiff breeze with Middelburg (83x118cm-33x46in) 24-Sep-2 Christie's, Amsterdam #138/R est:10000-15000

COORTE, Adriaen (fl.1685-1723) Dutch

£180000 $300600 €261000 Stawberries in a pot on stone ledge with butterfly (22x17cm-9x7in) s.d.1704. 9-Jul-3 Christie's, London #42/R est:60000-80000

COOSEMANS, J (1828-1904) Belgian

£2411 $3906 €3400 Vacher dans un paysage fluvial (39x79cm-15x31in) 26-May-3 Amberes, Antwerp #23/R

COOSEMANS, Joseph (1828-1904) Belgian

£1583 $2532 €2200 Promeneurs dans un chemin de campagne (23x42cm-9x17in) s. panel. 19-May-3 Horta, Bruxelles #75 est:1500-2500
£4029 $6446 €5600 Mere et enfant se promenant dans un paysage ensoleille (75x48cm-30x19in) s. 13-May-3 Palais de Beaux Arts, Brussels #50/R est:3000-4000

Works on paper

£353 $554 €550 Paysage (13x22cm-5x9in) s. W/C. 10-Dec-2 Vanderkindere, Brussels #4

COPE, Charles West (1811-1890) British

£780 $1287 €1131 Moment on the stairs (54x36cm-21x14in) mono.d.1880. 1-Jul-3 Bearnes, Exeter #508
£1509 $2355 €2400 PO. of boy (78x63cm-31x25in) s. painted 1835. 17-Sep-2 Segre, Madrid #79/R
£2721 $4327 €4000 Lost wager (72x92cm-28x36in) s. 19-Mar-3 Neumeister, Munich #531/R est:1800
£3600 $5724 €5400 Taming the shrew - meat was well, if you were so contented (77x103cm-30x41in) init.d.1874 exhib. 18-Mar-3 Bonhams, New Bond Street #62/R est:4000-6000

Works on paper

£350 $546 €525 Nude (28x18cm-11x7in) s.d.March 1853 pen ink prov. 26-Mar-3 Sotheby's, Olympia #26/R

COPE, Elizabeth (1952-) Irish

£962 $1490 €1500 Shelling peas (63x51cm-25x20in) s. board. 3-Dec-2 Bonhams & James Adam, Dublin #130/R est:1500-2500
£1195 $1864 €1900 Still life with fruit dish and tea things on a patterned cloth (61x76cm-24x30in) s.d.1996 verso board. 17-Sep-2 Whyte's, Dublin #175/R est:2000-3000
£1410 $2214 €2200 Interior with houseplants and cat (75x61cm-30x24in) s.d.1996 verso board. 19-Nov-2 Whyte's, Dublin #120/R est:2000-3000
£1887 $2943 €3000 Farm scene with geese and sheep (61x76cm-24x30in) s. board. 17-Sep-2 Whyte's, Dublin #7/R est:2000-3000
£3478 $5704 €4800 Interior with still life (124x155cm-49x61in) s.d.99 board. 28-May-3 Bonhams & James Adam, Dublin #157/R est:4000-6000

COPE, George (1855-1929) American

£2250 $3600 €3375 Still life with nautilus shell (36x30cm-14x12in) i. panel. 17-May-3 Pook & Pook, Downington #358/R est:4000-5000
£2484 $4000 €3726 River scene with 2 men in canoes and cabin on tree-lined shore (25x20cm-10x8in) init. painted 1916. 21-Feb-3 York Town, York #1225
£3464 $5300 €5196 Dead canvasback duck suspended from a nail (41x71cm-16x28in) s.d.1912. 23-Aug-2 York Town, York #520
£7742 $12000 €11613 Hanging duck (72x43cm-28x17in) s.d.1912 prov. 8-Dec-2 Freeman, Philadelphia #103/R est:7000-10000
£87097 $135000 €130646 Ace hunter's door (198x84cm-78x33in) s.d.1910 prov.exhib. 5-Dec-2 Christie's, Rockefeller NY #163/R est:50000-70000

COPE, Gordon Nicholson (1906-1970) American

£2695 $4500 €3908 Utah canyon river landscape (102x132cm-40x52in) s. masonite. 17-Jun-3 John Moran, Pasadena #93a est:5000-7000

COPE, Leslie (1913-) American

Works on paper

£347 $570 €503 Hitching rail, scene from Farmerstown (23x33cm-9x13in) s.d.1973 pastel. 30-May-3 Aspire, Cleveland #105/R

COPELAND, Charles (1858-1945) American

£1250 $2000 €1813 Hunter (46x61cm-18x24in) s.d.07. 16-May-3 Skinner, Boston #127/R

Works on paper

£1656 $2600 €2484 Cowboys shooting (42x27cm-17x11in) s. gouache chl board exhib. 20-Nov-2 Christie's, Los Angeles #99/R est:3000-5000
£2038 $3200 €3057 Cowboys roping a steer (42x27cm-17x11in) s. gouache chl exhib. 20-Nov-2 Christie's, Los Angeles #98/R est:3000-5000
£2229 $3500 €3344 Cowboys at work (42x27cm-17x11in) s. gouache chl board exhib. 20-Nov-2 Christie's, Los Angeles #97/R est:3000-5000

COPIEUX, Albert (19/20th C) French

£408 $649 €600 Cheval a l'ecurie (54x65cm-21x26in) 23-Mar-3 Herbette, Doullens #1/R

Works on paper

£288 $453 €450 Dechargement a Le Havre (49x64cm-19x25in) s. W/C. 24-Nov-2 Lesieur & Le Bars, Le Havre #23
£288 $453 €450 Cargo a quai (23x35cm-9x14in) s. W/C. 24-Nov-2 Lesieur & Le Bars, Le Havre #24
£340 $541 €500 Etudes de lapins (38x70cm-15x28in) s. chl W/C. 23-Mar-3 Herbette, Doullens #2/R
£442 $703 €650 Cheval de trait (70x38cm-28x15in) s. chl W/C. 23-Mar-3 Herbette, Doullens #3/R
£503 $775 €800 Le paquebot Colombie a quai (52x63cm-20x25in) s. W/C gouache. 27-Oct-2 Lesieur & Le Bars, Le Havre #202

COPLEY, John Singleton (school) (1738-1815) American

£4605 $7000 €6908 Watson and the shark (91x76cm-36x30in) prov.lit. 17-Aug-2 North East Auctions, Portsmouth #1014/R est:7000-10000

COPLEY, William Nelson (1919-1996) American

£3526 $5465 €5500 Bullfight (38x46cm-15x18in) s.d.56. 3-Dec-2 Christie's, Amsterdam #149/R est:3000-5000
£4839 $7500 €7259 Dig we must (76x61cm-30x24in) s. i.d.63 on stretcher prov.lit. 26-Sep-2 Christie's, Rockefeller NY #743/R est:6000-8000

COPNALL, Frank T (1870-1949) British

£400 $652 €580 View of Liverpool from the water (17x18cm-7x7in) board. 15-Jul-3 Bonhams, Knightsbridge #8/R

COPNALL, John (1928-) British

£350 $543 €525 Rockscape (63x82cm-25x32in) s.d.61 board. 4-Dec-2 Christie's, Kensington #561

COPNALL, Theresa Norah (1882-1972) British

£550 $858 €825 Still life of flowers in a vase (76x63cm-30x25in) s. 9-Oct-2 Woolley & Wallis, Salisbury #231/R

COPPEDGE, Fern Isabel (1888-1951) American

£2419 $3750 €3629 Burnetts Mound, Topeka, Kas (30x41cm-12x16in) s. i.verso board. 29-Oct-2 John Moran, Pasadena #715 est:1000-2000
£6452 $10000 €9678 Skytop (30x30cm-12x12in) s. canvasboard prov.exhib. 8-Dec-2 Freeman, Philadelphia #198/R est:15000-25000
£9554 $15000 €14331 Spring reflections, view of a town (30x25cm-12x10in) s. i.d.1924 verso canvasboard prov. 19-Nov-2 Butterfields, San Francisco #8036/R est:5000-7000
£12903 $20000 €19355 Old boat house, Gloucester (41x51cm-16x20in) s. i.on stretcher prov. 4-Dec-2 Sotheby's, New York #46/R est:25000-35000
£13924 $22000 €20886 House by the river (30x30cm-12x12in) s. prov. 24-Apr-3 Shannon's, Milford #33/R est:3000-5000
£13924 $22000 €20886 Delaware, October (30x30cm-12x12in) s. i.d.1946 verso prov. 24-Apr-3 Shannon's, Milford #34/R est:3000-5000
£17284 $28000 €25062 Winter on the Delaware (30x23cm-12x9in) s. canvas on board. 21-May-3 Doyle, New York #126/R est:8000-10000

£22436 $35000 €33654 Delaware in winter (61x61cm-24x24in) s. 18-Sep-2 Alderfer's, Hatfield #363/R est:30000-40000
£26946 $45000 €39072 Autumn gold, Lumberville (61x61cm-24x24in) s. prov. 22-Jun-3 Freeman, Philadelphia #151/R est:50000-80000
£29677 $46000 €44516 After Christmas, near Carversville, PA (51x61cm-20x24in) s. board prov. 8-Dec-2 Freeman, Philadelphia #172/R est:30000-50000
£38710 $60000 €58065 New Hope, early spring (41x51cm-16x20in) s. prov. 8-Dec-2 Freeman, Philadelphia #185/R est:30000-50000
£42208 $65000 €63312 Bucks County village (61x61cm-24x24in) s. prov. 24-Oct-2 Shannon's, Milford #72/R est:40000-60000
£83871 $130000 €125807 By the Delaware, winter (51x61cm-20x24in) s. prov. 8-Dec-2 Freeman, Philadelphia #171/R est:30000-50000

COPPEL, Jeanne (1896-1971) French
£1088 $1731 €1600 Composition (60x92cm-24x36in) s.d.1956. 24-Mar-3 Claude Boisgirard, Paris #133

COPPENOLLE, Edmon van (1846-1914) Belgian
£2365 $3689 €3500 Coquelicots et marguerites (50x61cm-20x24in) s. 28-Mar-3 Claude Aguttes, Neuilly #90/R
£3497 $5839 €5000 Bouquet de pivoines et de roses sauvages (74x92cm-29x36in) s. 27-Jun-3 Claude Aguttes, Neuilly #50/R est:4500-6000

COPPENOLLE, Jacques van (1878-1915) French
£1304 $2073 €1956 Poultry feeding (19x25cm-7x10in) s. pair. 5-Mar-3 Rasmussen, Copenhagen #1860/R est:15000 (D.KR 14000)
£4516 $7135 €7000 Roses, pavots et lilas (73x92cm-29x36in) s. 19-Dec-2 Claude Aguttes, Neuilly #50/R
£4516 $7135 €7000 Composition aux pavots tricolores (73x92cm-29x36in) s. 19-Dec-2 Claude Aguttes, Neuilly #49/R

COPPENS, Frans (1895-1975) Belgian
£705 $1093 €1100 Farm in the snow (38x46cm-15x18in) s. 7-Dec-2 De Vuyst, Lokeren #59

COPPENS, Jean Baptist (1865-?) Belgian
£264 $407 €420 Artiste Joseph Moerenhout dans son atelier (46x38cm-18x15in) s. panel. 22-Oct-2 Campo & Campo, Antwerp #49

COPPENS, Omer (1864-1926) Belgian
£425 $684 €650 Papallo (24x32cm-9x13in) s. panel. 20-Jan-3 Horta, Bruxelles #314
£443 $691 €700 Pont a bRuges (33x24cm-13x9in) s. panel. 15-Oct-2 Horta, Bruxelles #254
£461 $770 €650 Scene de rue orientale (34x25cm-13x10in) s. 17-Jun-3 Palais de Beaux Arts, Brussels #523
£497 $810 €750 Pont a Malines (24x32cm-9x13in) s.d.1917 panel. 17-Feb-3 Horta, Bruxelles #466
£503 $780 €800 Evening in Dordrecht (39x30cm-15x12in) s.i. panel. 5-Oct-2 De Vuyst, Lokeren #66
£576 $921 €800 Bord de mer en Italie (24x32cm-9x13in) s. panel. 13-May-3 Vanderkindere, Brussels #168
£833 $1308 €1300 Coucher de soleil sur la mer (70x100cm-28x39in) s. 10-Dec-2 Vanderkindere, Brussels #20
£980 $1578 €1500 Le pont sur l'Adige, Italy (41x71cm-16x28in) s. 14-Jan-3 Vanderkindere, Brussels #90 est:1000-1500
£6028 $10067 €8500 Aube au lac c'Amour, Bruges (124x155cm-49x61in) s.d.1913 lit. 17-Jun-3 Palais de Beaux Arts, Brussels #546/R est:8000-12000
£6250 $9875 €9000 Venice Mars (99x69cm-39x27in) 28-Apr-3 Amberes, Antwerp #266/R

COPPERMAN, Mildred Tuner (1906-) American
£574 $900 €861 Gloucester Harbor (33x38cm-13x15in) s. 22-Nov-2 Skinner, Boston #345/R est:400-600

COPPIER, Andre Charles (1867-?) French
£476 $757 €700 Young girl with baby birds in nest (57x35cm-22x14in) s. lit. 21-Mar-3 Auktionhaus Georg Rehm, Augsburg #8014/R

COPPING, Harold (1863-1932) British
Works on paper
£440 $717 €638 Story teller (53x34cm-21x13in) s. W/C. 16-Jul-3 Sotheby's, Olympia #109/R

COPPING, Ronald (20th C) British
£500 $790 €725 Cafes in Montmarte (45x60cm-18x24in) s.d.64 board. 27-Jul-3 Lots Road, London #331

COPPINGER, Frances (19th C) British
Works on paper
£350 $571 €525 Tomb (37x56cm-15x22in) s.d.1882 W/C. 29-Jan-3 Sotheby's, Olympia #117/R

COPPOLA, Antonio (1839-?) Italian
£2025 $3200 €3200 Naples seen from Posilipo (70x110cm-28x43in) s. 26-Nov-2 Christie's, Rome #15/R
Works on paper
£320 $506 €480 Capri from a stormy sea (41x61cm-16x24in) s. gouache. 26-Nov-2 Bonhams, Knightsbridge #81/R

COPPOLA-CASTALDO, Francesco (c.1845-1916) Italian
Works on paper
£550 $897 €798 Castella Donna Anna, Posilippo (36x59cm-14x23in) s.i. gouache on board. 16-Jul-3 Sotheby's, Olympia #158/R

COPSON, Amy (attrib) (20th C) British
£650 $1014 €975 Still life of an azalea, pineapple, grapes and a sarcophagus (55x74cm-22x29in) 9-Apr-3 Cheffins Grain & Comins, Cambridge #729/R

COPUS, A (19th C) German
£516 $759 €800 Teacher admonishing little boy (24x17cm-9x7in) s. panel. 20-Jun-2 Dr Fritz Nagel, Stuttgart #760/R

COQUES, Gonzales (1614-1684) Flemish
£4304 $6714 €6800 Portrait d'homme en pied dans un paysage (43x33cm-17x13in) panel. 20-Oct-2 Mercier & Cie, Lille #246/R est:6000-7000

COQUES, Gonzales (attrib) (1614-1684) Flemish
£612 $978 €850 Portrait de femme a la collerette de dentelle (60x53cm-24x21in) 13-May-3 Galerie Moderne, Brussels #338/R
£6410 $10064 €10000 Portrait of Johannes Couchet (24x22cm-9x9in) i. lit. panel. 21-Nov-2 Van Ham, Cologne #1322/R est:6000

COQUES, Gonzales and PEETERS, Jan (17th C) Flemish
£42000 $65940 €63000 Portuguese commander beneath a portico, a view of warships beyond (79x61cm-31x24in) prov. 12-Dec-2 Sotheby's, London #146/R est:10000-15000

CORBAUX, Fanny (1812-1883) British
Works on paper
£800 $1264 €1160 Portraits of a young lady (38x30cm-15x12in) s.d.1839 W/C two. 22-Jul-3 Gorringes, Lewes #1663

CORBAUX, Marie (attrib) (19th C) British
Works on paper
£714 $1129 €1035 Four girls. init.d.1854 W/C. 18-Nov-2 Goodman, Sydney #253/R (A.D 2000)

CORBAZ, Aloise (1886-1964) French
Works on paper
£13014 $20432 €19000 Hymne a la terre (40x27cm-16x11in) init. col crayon exhib.lit. 15-Apr-3 Laurence Calmels, Paris #4245/R est:15000
£18493 $28849 €27000 Reine Victoria dans le manteau imperial pontifical (58x44cm-23x17in) i. col crayon. 14-Apr-3 Laurence Calmels, Paris #4024/R est:15000
£20548 $32055 €30000 Aristoloches (49x66cm-19x26in) col crayon. 14-Apr-3 Laurence Calmels, Paris #4023/R est:15000

CORBELLA, Tito (1885-1966) Italian
Works on paper
£381 $594 €572 Young woman applying lipstick (51x47cm-20x19in) s. pastel. 15-Oct-2 Stephan Welz, Johannesburg #393 est:2500-4000 (SA.R 6200)

CORBELLI, Edgardo (1918-1989) Italian
£340 $541 €500 Marie Claire (50x40cm-20x16in) s.i.d.1971 board. 1-Mar-3 Meeting Art, Vercelli #722

CORBELLINI, Luigi (1901-1968) French
£260 $424 €390 Portrait of Nicole Ratier, aged 4 years (61x46cm-24x18in) s. i.stretcher. 13-Feb-3 Christie's, Kensington #52
£986 $1587 €1400 Reve bleu (33x24cm-13x9in) s. 11-May-3 Thierry & Lannon, Brest #245

CORBERO, Xavier (1935-) Spanish
Sculpture
£1195 $1840 €1900 Sevillan bird (40x40x25cm-16x16x10in) s. num.5/7 bronze iron exec.1987 prov.exhib. 28-Oct-2 Segre, Madrid #162/R

CORBIERE, Roger de la (?) French
£260 $429 €377 Coastal landscape at sunset (46x56cm-18x22in) s. 3-Jul-3 Ewbank, Send #301
£350 $585 €508 Sunset on the coast (44x53cm-17x21in) s.i. prov. 26-Jun-3 Mellors & Kirk, Nottingham #923
£400 $660 €580 Moonlight at La Turballe, Brittany, coastal landscape with jetty and vessels (61x91cm-24x36in) s. 3-Jul-3 Ewbank, Send #302

CORBIN, Peter (20th C) ?
£20570 $32500 €29827 Evening encounter (61x102cm-24x40in) s. 26-Jul-3 Coeur d'Alene, Hayden #209/R est:10000-15000

CORBINEAU, Charles August (1835-1901) French
£1117 $1777 €1676 Italian family (47x61cm-19x24in) s. 5-Mar-3 Rasmussen, Copenhagen #1718/R est:15000 (D.KR 12000)
£1719 $2750 €2579 La baigneuse et les cignes (61x47cm-24x19in) s. prov. 14-May-3 Butterfields, San Francisco #1110/R est:3000-5000

CORBINO, Jon (1905-1964) American
£2564 $4000 €3846 Black cat with goldfish and poppies (70x60cm-28x24in) s. board prov. 12-Apr-3 Weschler, Washington #579/R est:3000-5000

CORBOULD, Aster R C (1812-1882) British
£440 $691 €660 Returning to the marshes (31x46cm-12x18in) s. i.stretcher. 10-Dec-2 Rosebery Fine Art, London #524

CORBOULD, Edward Henry (1815-1905) British
Works on paper
£1000 $1560 €1500 Offering to the Mayan Gods (46x59cm-18x23in) s.d.1891 W/C. 17-Sep-2 Sotheby's, Olympia #120/R est:1000-1500
£1500 $2310 €2250 Picture sale (33x26cm-13x10in) s.d.1839 pencil brown ink W/C. 23-Oct-2 Hamptons Fine Art, Godalming #84 est:1500-1800
£3500 $5740 €5075 Salome dancing before Herod (75x105cm-30x41in) s.d.1868 pencil W/C bodycol gum arabic prov.exhib. 5-Jun-3 Christie's, London #151/R est:4000-6000
£8000 $12880 €12000 Dream of fair women (101x140cm-40x55in) s.i.d.1859 mixed media paper on panel prov. 20-Feb-3 Christie's, London #230/R est:15000
£10000 $16100 €15000 Cold (29x41cm-11x16in) s.i.d.1869 pencil pen ink W/C bodycol gum arabic arched top prov. 20-Feb-3 Christie's, London #112/R est:6000

CORBOULD, Richard (1757-1831) British
£4268 $7000 €6402 View in Suffolk with figure in the foreground (69x63cm-27x25in) s.d.1971 prov. 29-May-3 Sotheby's, New York #15/R est:7000-10000

CORBUSIER, Jean Francois (1810-1852) French
£3400 $5644 €3400 Jeune garcon et son singe sur fond de paysage (62x52cm-24x20in) s. 16-Jun-3 Horta, Bruxelles #229 est:1200-1800

CORBUSIER, le (1887-1965) French
£2115 $3279 €3300 Nude female model (51x36cm-20x14in) mono.d.29 lit. 7-Dec-2 Bergmann, Erlangen #843/R est:1800
£6962 $11000 €11000 Femme nue debout, mains derriere la tete (41x23cm-16x9in) s.d.33 prov. 2-Dec-2 Tajan, Paris #107/R
£9220 $14936 €13000 Femme et taureau (27x57cm-11x22in) mono. enamel. 20-May-3 Dorotheum, Vienna #48/R est:13000-15000
£12000 $19680 €18000 Figures (34x45cm-13x18in) init.d.48 masonite prov. 5-Feb-3 Sotheby's, London #274/R est:15000
Prints
£3275 $5142 €4913 Les musiciens (68x97cm-27x38in) s. col lithograph lit. 25-Nov-2 Germann, Zurich #283/R est:5000-7000 (S.FR 7500)
Sculpture
£16190 $25743 €23800 Composition (65x55x2cm-26x22x1in) mono.i. plaque lit. 24-Mar-3 Digard, Paris #38/R est:18000
Works on paper
£648 $1044 €940 View of a bay in south of France (31x40cm-12x16in) s.indis.d. mixed media board. 9-May-3 Dobiaschofsky, Bern #167/R (S.FR 1400)
£987 $1599 €1500 Devinez vous meme (47x47cm-19x19in) mono.d.62 and 1930 caseine on rhodoid. 22-Jan-3 Tajan, Paris #167/R est:1500-2000
£987 $1599 €1500 Vagues (47x47cm-19x19in) mono. caseine on rhodoid. 22-Jan-3 Tajan, Paris #174 est:1500-2000
£1184 $1918 €1800 L'enfant est la (47x47cm-19x19in) mono.d.62 and 1941 caseine on rhodoid. 22-Jan-3 Tajan, Paris #171 est:1500-2000
£1184 $1918 €1800 La famille cocasse (47x47cm-19x19in) mono.i.d.62 and 1942 caseine on rhodoid. 22-Jan-3 Tajan, Paris #172 est:1500-2000
£1204 $1938 €1746 Peintre et modele (20x18cm-8x7in) ink scratching out prov. 9-May-3 Dobiaschofsky, Bern #276/R est:4000 (S.FR 2600)
£1250 $2025 €1900 Le verre a cotes (47x47cm-19x19in) mono.d.62 and 1927 caseine on rhodoid. 22-Jan-3 Tajan, Paris #165 est:1500-2000
£1316 $2132 €2000 Danseuse (47x47cm-19x19in) mono.d.62 caseine on rhodoid. 22-Jan-3 Tajan, Paris #168 est:1500-2000
£1316 $2132 €2000 Bonsoir (47x47cm-19x19in) mono.d.62 caseine on rhodoid. 22-Jan-3 Tajan, Paris #169 est:1500-2000
£1316 $2132 €2000 Assise (47x47cm-19x19in) mono.d.62 and 1940-43 caseine on rhodoid. 22-Jan-3 Tajan, Paris #170 est:1500-2000
£1316 $2132 €2000 Long Island (47x47cm-19x19in) mono.d.62 and 1947 caseine on rhodoid. 22-Jan-3 Tajan, Paris #173 est:1500-2000
£1400 $2224 €2100 Tete (13x21cm-5x8in) init.i. brush ink collage exec.c.1953-54. 20-Mar-3 Sotheby's, Olympia #89/R est:1500-2000
£1513 $2452 €2300 Sans titre, ca-ma-ao (43x32cm-17x13in) mono.d. caseine on rhodoid. 22-Jan-3 Tajan, Paris #177/R est:1500-2000
£1645 $2665 €2500 Sans titre, ca-ma-ao (43x33cm-17x13in) mono.d. caseine on rhodoid. 22-Jan-3 Tajan, Paris #182 est:1500-2000
£1710 $2771 €2600 Sans titre, ca-ma-ao (43x35cm-17x14in) caseine on rhodoid. 22-Jan-3 Tajan, Paris #178 est:1500-2000
£1747 $2742 €2621 Nature morte (14x21cm-6x8in) mono. pencil. 25-Nov-2 Sotheby's, Zurich #156/R est:3000-5000 (S.FR 4000)
£1842 $2984 €2800 Sans titre, ca-ma-ao (43x32cm-17x13in) mono.d. caseine on rhodoid. 22-Jan-3 Tajan, Paris #176/R est:1500-2000
£1842 $2984 €2800 Sans titre, ca-ma-ao (43x32cm-17x13in) mono.d. caseine on rhodoid. 22-Jan-3 Tajan, Paris #180/R est:1500-2000
£1843 $2858 €2765 Two cows and bird (43x34cm-17x13in) mono.d.53 prov. 4-Dec-2 Koller, Zurich #187/R est:7000-10000 (S.FR 4240)
£1974 $3197 €3000 Sans titre, ca-ma-ao (43x32cm-17x13in) mono.d. caseine on rhodoid. 22-Jan-3 Tajan, Paris #175/R est:1500-2000
£1974 $3197 €3000 Sans titre, ca-ma-ao (43x32cm-17x13in) mono.d. caseine on rhodoid. 22-Jan-3 Tajan, Paris #179 est:1500-2000
£2041 $3245 €3000 Composition (49x32cm-19x13in) s.i.d.1963 graphite lit. 24-Mar-3 Digard, Paris #36/R
£2237 $3624 €3400 La cruche (47x47cm-19x19in) mono.d.62 and 1925 caseine on rhodoid. 22-Jan-3 Tajan, Paris #166/R est:1500-2000
£2335 $3409 €3503 Untitled composition (50x64cm-20x25in) s.d.1923-1940 W/C. 17-Jun-2 Philippe Schuler, Zurich #4195/R est:4000-6000 (S.FR 5300)
£2453 $3826 €3680 Trois femmes et une vache (20x30cm-8x12in) s.d.1934 pencil crayon prov.lit. 6-Nov-2 AB Stockholms Auktionsverk #934/R est:20000-25000 (S.KR 35000)
£2564 $4051 €4000 Nature morte (24x32cm-9x13in) mono.d.56 ink cardboard prov. 15-Nov-2 Laurence Calmels, Paris #21a/R
£3782 $5862 €5900 Femme devant une porte (30x21cm-12x8in) s.d.1933 pastel graphite. 6-Dec-2 Rieunier, Bailly-Pommery, Mathias, Paris #75/R
£4808 $7500 €7212 Josephine Baker (42x25cm-17x10in) init.d.Nov 29 brush orange ink over pencil. 18-Sep-2 Swann Galleries, New York #63/R est:8000-12000
£5019 $8081 €7529 Femme (21x35cm-8x14in) d.27 april 53 W/C Indian ink pastel. 7-May-3 AB Stockholms Auktionsverk #1124/R est:8000-10000 (S.KR 65000)
£5677 $8856 €8516 Figure (41x32cm-16x13in) s.i.d.53 pen ink over collage. 8-Nov-2 Dobiaschofsky, Bern #232/R est:16000 (S.FR 13000)
£6154 $9662 €9600 Composition (21x27cm-8x11in) s.d.29 col crayon dr. 11-Dec-2 Artcurial Briest, Paris #540/R
£6289 $9811 €10000 Sans titre (62x47cm-24x19in) init.d.2/56 and 23 mai 59 mixed media prov. 10-Oct-2 Ribeyre & Baron, Paris #59/R est:10000-12000
£6604 $10698 €11688 Deux algeriennes (21x26cm-8x10in) s.d. silver pen. 26-May-3 Sotheby's, Zurich #139/R est:14000-18000 (S.FR 14000)
£10377 $16811 €18368 Femme et cordage (47x30cm-19x12in) mono. gouache oil. 26-May-3 Sotheby's, Zurich #145/R est:26000-32000 (S.FR 22000)
£11915 $19302 €16800 Violon et boite a violon rouge (20x22cm-8x9in) s.d. col crayon tracing paper lit. 21-May-3 Cornette de St.Cyr, Paris #86/R est:8000-10000
£19149 $31021 €27000 La main (69x49cm-27x19in) init. gouache collage prov. 21-May-3 Cornette de St.Cyr, Paris #87/R est:30000-40000

CORCK, Albert (20th C) American
£500 $800 €725 Rockport, motif number one (46x56cm-18x22in) s. 16-May-3 Skinner, Boston #285/R

CORCOS, Vittorio (1859-1933) Italian
£4082 $6490 €6000 Portrait of lady (41x32cm-16x13in) s.d.1901 board. 18-Mar-3 Finarte, Milan #37/R
£12903 $20000 €19355 Portrait of a girl in a yellow shawl (61x46cm-24x18in) s.d.90 prov. 29-Oct-2 Sotheby's, New York #73/R est:20000-30000
£64516 $100000 €96774 New kitten (109x61cm-43x24in) s.d.98. 30-Oct-2 Christie's, Rockefeller NY #79/R est:70000-90000
Works on paper
£6757 $10541 €10000 Couple by a beach (23x14cm-9x6in) s. W/C gouache over crayon. 26-Mar-3 Piasa, Paris #129/R

CORDA, Mauro (1960-) French
Sculpture
£1418 $2369 €2000 Metamorphose (70cm-28in) num.3/8 bronze. 21-Jun-3 Bretagne Encheres, St Malo #198
£1773 $2961 €2500 L'elegante (73cm-29in) num. 2/8 blue pat bronze. 21-Jun-3 Bretagne Encheres, St Malo #195
£1773 $2961 €2500 Mannequin (69cm-27in) num.4/8 bronze. 21-Jun-3 Bretagne Encheres, St Malo #196
£3582 $5981 €5050 Vierge a l'enfant (73cm-29in) num.2/8 bronze sold with socle. 21-Jun-3 Bretagne Encheres, St Malo #199

CORDES, Johann Wilhelm (1824-1869) German
£1092 $1703 €1638 Small Norwegian goat shepherd in Rondane mountains near Gudbrandsdal (60x81cm-24x32in) s.d.1851 prov. 9-Nov-2 Galerie Gloggner, Luzern #27/R est:3800-4500 (S.FR 2500)

CORDEY, Frederic (1854-1911) French
£1500 $2325 €2250 Un paysage au soleil couchant (42x56cm-17x22in) s. 5-Dec-2 Christie's, Kensington #11/R est:1500-2000

CORDIER, Charles Henri Joseph (1827-1905) French
Sculpture
£103226 $160000 €154839 L'aurore et le crepuscule (133cm-52in) s. white marble pair prov.exhib.lit. 29-Oct-2 Sotheby's, New York #105/R est:150000-200000

CORDIER, Nicolas (circle) (1567-1612) French
Sculpture
£251724 $400241 €365000 Allegory of Fortune (180x59x56cm-71x23x22in) polychrome marble. 9-Mar-3 Semenzato, Venice #105/R

CORDIER, Thierry de (1954-) Belgian
Sculpture
£4430 $7000 €6645 Untitled (145x226x13cm-57x89x5in) steel fish skeletons concrete paper wire exec.1987 prov. 13-Nov-2 Sotheby's, New York #593/R

CORDIVIOLA, Luis Adolfo (1892-1967) Argentinian
£1033 $1694 €1498 Extensive landscape with cow (55x66cm-22x26in) s.d.934 board. 4-Jun-3 Fischer, Luzern #1100/R est:2500-3500 (S.FR 2200)

CORDREY, John (fl.1765-1825) British
£2639 $3800 €3959 Stagecoach in extensive landscape (55x91cm-22x36in) 15-Jan-3 Christie's, Rockefeller NY #154/R

CORECORIO, de (19th C) Italian
£400 $624 €600 Young lady and music teacher (36x25cm-14x10in) panel. 15-Oct-2 Gorringes, Lewes #2248

CORELLI (?) Italian
£288 $453 €450 Portrait de femme (45x40cm-18x16in) s. panel. 19-Nov-2 Galerie Moderne, Brussels #202
Works on paper
£700 $1099 €1050 Bay of Naples (27x44cm-11x17in) gouache two. 16-Dec-2 Bonhams, Bury St Edmunds #391/R

CORELLI, Augusto (1853-1910) Italian
£2400 $3792 €3600 Sunny street in Capri (80x60cm-31x24in) s. 14-Nov-2 Christie's, Kensington #304/R est:1500-2000
Works on paper
£858 $1356 €1287 Winter in the countryside (65x99cm-26x39in) s.i. W/C. 29-Nov-2 Zofingen, Switzerland #2411 (S.FR 2000)
£3311 $5165 €4900 Italian shepherd and sheep with girl and goats (52x78cm-20x31in) s.i. W/C. 26-Mar-3 Hugo Ruef, Munich #351/R est:4900
£5000 $8000 €7500 The sermon (56x86cm-22x34in) s. pencil W/C paper on board. 14-May-3 Butterfields, San Francisco #1051/R est:6000-8000

CORELLI, Conrad H R (1869-?) Italian
Works on paper
£600 $954 €900 View of Cairo (35x25cm-14x10in) s.i. W/C. 29-Apr-3 Bonhams, Knightsbridge #10/R

CORELLI, G (19/20th C) Italian
£5000 $8000 €7500 Fishing boats on the Mediterranean coast (28x46cm-11x18in) one s. panel pair. 11-Mar-3 Gorringes, Lewes #2465 est:4000-6000

CORELLI, Rosa (19th C) Italian
Works on paper
£550 $897 €798 Bay of Naples (10x46cm-4x18in) s. gouache. 16-Jul-3 Sotheby's, Olympia #159/R

COREY, Bernard (20th C) American
£535 $850 €803 In the cove (19x30cm-7x12in) s. i.verso board. 7-Mar-3 Skinner, Boston #467/R
£828 $1300 €1242 Summer pasture (31x50cm-12x20in) s. masonite. 22-Nov-2 Skinner, Boston #248/R est:800-1200
£1000 $1600 €1500 Seascape with waves crashing on rocks (18x28cm-7x11in) 14-Mar-3 Douglas, South Deerfield #5
Works on paper
£250 $400 €375 Low tide, fisherman painting his boat (25x33cm-10x13in) s. 15-Mar-3 Eldred, East Dennis #121/R

CORINTH, Lovis (1858-1925) German
£1528 $2429 €2200 Nature morte aux tournesols (65x92cm-26x36in) s. 29-Apr-3 Campo & Campo, Antwerp #469
£3957 $6489 €5500 Flowers - fragment (18x55cm-7x22in) canvas on board prov. 6-Jun-3 Ketterer, Munich #9/R est:5000-7000
£4200 $7014 €6090 Im bett (38x48cm-15x19in) s.i.d.1903 oil on card prov.exhib.lit. 25-Jun-3 Christie's, London #143/R est:4000-6000
£6944 $11042 €10000 Female nude (25x13cm-10x5in) s. pencil. 5-May-3 Ketterer, Munich #830/R est:400-600
£27027 $42162 €40000 Sleeping Silen with nymph (84x100cm-33x39in) s.d.1899 exhib. 25-Mar-3 Wiener Kunst Auktionen, Vienna #118/R est:50000-120000
£99548 $166244 €144345 Mother and child (80x95cm-31x37in) s.d.1906 prov.exhib.lit. 24-Jun-3 Koller, Zurich #120/R est:150000-200000 (S.FR 220000)
£700000 $1092000 €1050000 Walchensee, aufgehender mond - Walchensee, rising moon (80x101cm-31x40in) s.d.1922 prov.exhib.lit. 9-Oct-2 Sotheby's, London #7/R est:400000-600000
Prints
£1795 $2621 €2800 Extensive landscape (25x38cm-10x15in) s. lithograph. 4-Jun-2 Karl & Faber, Munich #206/R est:3000
£1944 $3092 €2800 Walchensee (25x32cm-10x13in) s. num.4/50 col lithograph. 5-May-3 Ketterer, Munich #844/R est:1500-2000
£2025 $3200 €3200 Self portrait (40x25cm-16x10in) s. lithograph prov. 30-Nov-2 Villa Grisebach, Berlin #157/R est:4000-5000
£2264 $3600 €3396 Blick auf den Walchensee (24x32cm-9x13in) s.num.72/75 drypoint. 1-May-3 Swann Galleries, New York #432/R est:2500-3500
£2405 $3800 €3800 In the studio (32x26cm-13x10in) s. drypoint prov. 30-Nov-2 Villa Grisebach, Berlin #161/R est:2500-3500
£2658 $4200 €4200 Large Walchensee landscape (30x49cm-12x19in) s. drypoint. 30-Nov-2 Villa Grisebach, Berlin #160/R est:5000-6000
Works on paper
£316 $500 €500 Animal studies (34x25cm-13x10in) chk board prov. 29-Nov-2 Villa Grisebach, Berlin #549/R
£358 $559 €570 Male nude (47x30cm-19x12in) pencil. 11-Oct-2 Winterberg, Heidelberg #975
£362 $594 €500 Knight with lance (31x25cm-12x10in) s.d.1919 pencil sketch verso prov. 31-May-3 Villa Grisebach, Berlin #514/R
£481 $760 €750 Lovers - Weislingen and Marie (24x17cm-9x7in) s. pencil. 14-Nov-2 Neumeister, Munich #531/R
£755 $1177 €1200 Einer Dirne schon gesicht muss allgemein sein wie's Sonnenlicht (22x14cm-9x6in) s.i.d.18 Marz 1922 pen brush ink prov. 9-Oct-2 Sotheby's, London #180/R est:2000-3000
£769 $1192 €1200 Female nude (35x48cm-14x19in) s. pencil board. 7-Dec-2 Van Ham, Cologne #113/R
£905 $1511 €1312 Portrait of Charlotte Behrend Corinth (15x14cm-6x6in) s. ochre. 24-Jun-3 Koller, Zurich #119a/R est:2000-3000 (S.FR 2000)
£962 $1490 €1500 Seated female nude (50x34cm-20x13in) s.i.d.1887 pencil. 4-Dec-2 Lempertz, Koln #621/R est:2000-2500
£962 $1490 €1500 Aline's downfall (25x23cm-10x9in) chk. 7-Dec-2 Hauswedell & Nolte, Hamburg #586/R est:1500
£1127 $1870 €1600 Luneburger Heide (25x34cm-10x13in) s.i. pencil. 14-Jun-3 Hauswedell & Nolte, Hamburg #1085/R est:1400
£1258 $1962 €2000 Lover - shepherd scene (22x14cm-9x6in) s.d.1923 pen ink prov. 9-Oct-2 Sotheby's, London #179/R est:3000-4000
£1582 $2500 €2500 Reclining figure (26x44cm-10x17in) s.d.1903 pencil lit. 29-Nov-2 Villa Grisebach, Berlin #548/R est:2500-3000
£1635 $2551 €2600 Standing female nude (34x24cm-13x9in) s.d.1912 chl prov.lit. 9-Oct-2 Sotheby's, London #185/R est:3000-4000
£1772 $2800 €2800 Trees (25x32cm-10x13in) s.i.d.Juni 1917 pencil col chk prov. 30-Nov-2 Villa Grisebach, Berlin #162/R est:3500-4500
£2254 $3741 €3200 Reclining nude (28x20cm-11x8in) s. pencil. 14-Jun-3 Hauswedell & Nolte, Hamburg #1084/R est:3000
£2778 $4417 €4000 Study for 'Spring' (26x24cm-10x9in) s.i.d. pencil. 5-May-3 Ketterer, Munich #821/R est:500-600
£4167 $6625 €6000 Nude girl standing (42x17cm-17x7in) s.mono. pencil. 5-May-3 Ketterer, Munich #820/R est:600-700
£4717 $7358 €7500 Seated man playing the lute (48x31cm-19x12in) s.d.1895 pencil prov. 9-Oct-2 Sotheby's, London #187/R est:4500-6500
£5031 $7849 €8000 Self portrait - torso (31x25cm-12x10in) s.d.1922 chl prov.exhib. 9-Oct-2 Sotheby's, London #175/R est:8000-12000

£12821 $19872 €20000 Portrait of Thomas Corinth (21x24cm-8x9in) s.d.1922 chk. 7-Dec-2 Hauswedell & Nolte, Hamburg #587/R est:25000
£15278 $24292 €22000 Revellers returning home (34x44cm-13x17in) s.i.d. W/C opaque white over pencil sketch verso. 5-May-3 Ketterer, Munich #822/R est:3000-4000
£85000 $132600 €127500 Selbstbildnis - Self portrait (47x31cm-19x12in) s.d.13 Sep 1924 black crayon prov.lit. 9-Oct-2 Sotheby's, London #8/R est:10000-15000
£140000 $218400 €210000 Walchensee (34x50cm-13x20in) s.i.d.1925 W/C prov.exhib. 9-Oct-2 Sotheby's, London #9/R est:40000-60000

CORKE, C Essenhigh (19/20th C) British
Works on paper
£3100 $4929 €4650 Knole from her ladyship seat. Knole, north front autumn sunset (25x72cm-10x28in) s.i. W/C pair. 18-Mar-3 Bonhams, Sevenoaks #226 est:1000-1500

CORMACK, Neil (fl.1818-1837) British
Works on paper
£850 $1352 €1275 Delhi gate of the Shaniwarwada Palace, Pune India (34x47cm-13x19in) W/C prov. 29-Apr-3 Bonhams, New Bond Street #55/R

CORMAIN, Jean (?) French?
£346 $536 €550 Saint-Jacut-de-la Mer, les doris (37x46cm-15x18in) s.i. panel. 6-Oct-2 Livinec, Gaudcheau & Jezequel, Rennes #56

CORMON, Fernand (1854-1924) French
£348 $550 €522 Untitled (89x64cm-35x25in) s. 5-Apr-3 DeFina, Austinburg #1299
£2878 $4719 €4000 Femmes au bain (90x54cm-35x21in) s.d.1920. 4-Jun-3 Tajan, Paris #248/R est:3500-4500

CORNEILLE (1922-) Belgian
£966 $1535 €1400 Figure (9x17cm-4x7in) s.d.54. 10-Mar-3 Sotheby's, Amsterdam #391 est:800-1200
£2692 $4173 €4200 Corps person (29x25cm-11x10in) s.d.55 s.i.d.verso. 3-Dec-2 Christie's, Amsterdam #257/R est:4000-6000
£2738 $4325 €4107 La Corneille et la Marguerite (33x42cm-13x17in) s.d.91 prov. 28-Apr-3 Bukowskis, Stockholm #330/R est:20000-22000 (S.KR 36000)
£3165 $5000 €5000 Ellen. Caroline (70x60cm-28x24in) s.d.98 acrylic two prov. 26-Nov-2 Sotheby's, Amsterdam #49/R est:2500-3500
£5346 $8286 €8500 Personnage (33x22cm-13x9in) s.d.55 lit. 30-Oct-2 Artcurial Briest, Paris #429/R est:7000-10000
£8044 $12468 €12066 Aux abords d'une ville (46x55cm-18x22in) s.d.55 exhib.prov. 1-Oct-2 Rasmussen, Copenhagen #62/R est:100000-125000 (D.KR 95000)
£9220 $14936 €13000 Table que derange le chien (54x65cm-21x26in) s.d.69 s.i.d.verso acrylic prov. 26-May-3 Christie's, Milan #345/R est:10000-15000
£12821 $19872 €20000 Zonning Amsterdam - sunny Amsterdam (40x50cm-16x20in) s.d.48 s.i.d.verso exhib.lit. 3-Dec-2 Christie's, Amsterdam #262/R est:20000-30000
£15000 $25050 €21750 Promenade dans la montagne (81x81cm-32x32in) s.d.60 s.i.d.60 verso prov.exhib. 26-Jun-3 Sotheby's, London #237/R est:20000-30000
£18581 $28986 €27872 Vert paturage et soleil rose (100x73cm-39x29in) s.d.63 i.verso exhib. 18-Sep-2 Kunsthallen, Copenhagen #4/R est:300000 (D.KR 220000)
£24164 $38178 €36246 La reine de Saba I et II (100x138cm-39x54in) s.d.77 acrylic diptych exhib.prov. 1-Apr-3 Rasmussen, Copenhagen #127/R est:300000 (D.KR 260000)
£30405 $47432 €45608 Images du quotidien (65x100cm-26x39in) s.d.62 prov. 18-Sep-2 Kunsthallen, Copenhagen #41/R est:300000 (D.KR 360000)
Prints
£1918 $2992 €2800 Perrault's fairy tales (150x280cm-59x110in) s.d.1977 serigraph on canvas. 10-Apr-3 Finarte Semenzato, Rome #24/R
Sculpture
£1139 $1800 €1800 Bird and cat (29x32x7cm-11x13x3in) s.d.2000 num.2/150 wood. 27-Nov-2 Dorotheum, Vienna #341/R est:1800-2000
£1394 $2203 €2091 Femme couronnee (65x50x10cm-26x20x4in) s.num.43/60 laminated painted wood sold with catalogue lit. 1-Apr-3 Rasmussen, Copenhagen #257/R est:15000 (D.KR 15000)
£1580 $2496 €2370 Le doux felins de l'ete (51x73cm-20x29in) s.d.98 st.num.24/40 verso stone ware. 1-Apr-3 Rasmussen, Copenhagen #254/R est:15000-18000 (D.KR 17000)
£1582 $2500 €2500 Sculpture sur bois XVII (83cm-33in) s. painted wood executed 1993. 26-Nov-2 Sotheby's, Amsterdam #51/R est:2500-3500
£9615 $14904 €15000 Sculpture sur bois (210x190x115cm-83x75x45in) s. painted wood in four parts executed 1993. 3-Dec-2 Christie's, Amsterdam #77/R est:15000-20000
Works on paper
£440 $682 €700 Sans titre (20x29cm-8x11in) s.d.84 ink gouache. 30-Oct-2 Artcurial Briest, Paris #652
£647 $1062 €900 Arnhem - de stad herrijst (71x50cm-28x20in) s.i.d.94 gouache chl over painted base. 3-Jun-3 Christie's, Amsterdam #125/R
£887 $1383 €1331 Reve de chat I (18x24cm-7x9in) s.d.94 crayon. 18-Sep-2 Kunsthallen, Copenhagen #84/R (D.KR 10500)
£929 $1449 €1394 L'appel de l'Afrique (35x50cm-14x20in) s.d.98 gouache W/C. 18-Sep-2 Kunsthallen, Copenhagen #210/R (D.KR 11000)
£935 $1534 €1300 Couple under a palm tree (31x25cm-12x10in) s.d.98 black chk W/C gouache. 3-Jun-3 Christie's, Amsterdam #119/R est:1200-1600
£1117 $1777 €1676 Cat and bird (18x24cm-7x9in) s.d.2000 W/C. 10-Mar-3 Rasmussen, Vejle #773/R est:12000-15000 (D.KR 12000)
£1141 $1802 €1712 Le corps de l'oiseau sur le corps de la femme (32x24cm-13x9in) s.d.89 W/C. 28-Apr-3 Bukowskis, Stockholm #331/R est:8000-10000 (S.KR 15000)
£1282 $1987 €2000 Il reve de la marine (27x21cm-11x8in) s.i.d.1950 Indian ink. 3-Dec-2 Lempertz, Koln #104/R est:2000-2500
£1430 $2388 €2074 Figure composition with whale (100x70cm-39x28in) s.d.73-88 gouache. 17-Jun-3 Rasmussen, Copenhagen #33/R est:15000 (D.KR 15000)
£1439 $2360 €2000 Bird (65x50cm-26x20in) s.d.73 W/C col crayon over painted base. 3-Jun-3 Christie's, Amsterdam #120/R est:2000-3000
£1633 $2596 €2400 Nu allonge a l'oiseau (52x42cm-20x17in) s.d.1975 gouache. 18-Mar-3 Galerie Moderne, Brussels #532/R est:2000-3000
£1923 $3019 €3000 Soleils sur l'Afrique (17x28cm-7x11in) s.d.1957 ink pastel prov. 15-Dec-2 Perrin, Versailles #36/R
£2051 $3179 €3200 Untitled (23x22cm-9x9in) s.d.67 brush ink gouache. 3-Dec-2 Christie's, Amsterdam #115/R est:2000-3000
£2146 $3411 €3219 Femme, oiseau et arbre (29x21cm-11x8in) s.d.69 gouache. 29-Apr-3 Kunsthallen, Copenhagen #152/R est:30000 (D.KR 23000)
£2800 $4676 €4060 Composition (28x38cm-11x15in) s.d.58 gouache. 24-Jun-3 Sotheby's, Olympia #86/R est:3000-4000
£2949 $4571 €4600 Untitled - aerienne comme un papillon (25x32cm-10x13in) s.d.49 Indian ink col chks. 3-Dec-2 Lempertz, Koln #103/R est:4000-5000
£3000 $4620 €4500 Parole de chair (38x28cm-15x11in) s.d.85 gouache paper on canvas. 22-Oct-2 Sotheby's, London #449/R est:4000-6000
£3030 $5030 €4394 Composition (22x24cm-9x9in) s.d.57 gouache. 12-Jun-3 Kunsthallen, Copenhagen #26/R est:25000 (D.KR 32000)
£3481 $5430 €5500 Les femmes du port (23x30cm-9x12in) s.d. mixed media. 16-Oct-2 Hotel des Ventes Mosan, Brussels #279/R est:6100-8500
£4717 $7311 €7500 Composition with woman and bird (64x49cm-25x19in) s.d.77 gouache. 5-Oct-2 De Vuyst, Lokeren #494/R est:5000-6000
£5161 $8155 €8000 Untitled (150x280cm-59x110in) s.d.77 serigraph. 18-Dec-2 Christie's, Rome #19/R
£5705 $9185 €8500 Composition (45x32cm-18x13in) s.d.1960 W/C ink. 23-Feb-3 Mercier & Cie, Lille #71/R
£6962 $11000 €11000 Untitled (50x65cm-20x26in) s.d.84 gouache black chk paper on canvas. 26-Nov-2 Sotheby's, Amsterdam #238/R est:8000-10000
£7708 $12025 €11562 Jardin au bord de l'azur Mediterraneen (49x66cm-19x26in) s.d.64 gouache. 5-Nov-2 Bukowskis, Stockholm #319/R est:30000-40000 (S.KR 110000)

CORNEILLE DE LYON (?-1574) Flemish
£18000 $28260 €27000 Portrait of a bearded man in a black slashed doublet (17x15cm-7x6in) panel marble tabernacle frame. 12-Dec-2 Sotheby's, London #143/R est:20000-30000

CORNEILLE DE LYON (attrib) (?-1574) Flemish
£6867 $10644 €10301 Portrait of man wearing black beret (19x15cm-7x6in) panel prov. 3-Oct-2 Koller, Zurich #3002/R est:20000-28000 (S.FR 16000)

CORNEILLE DE LYON (circle) (?-1574) Flemish
£6000 $9360 €9000 Portrait of a bearded gentleman in a black velvet doublet (30x23cm-12x9in) panel prov. 9-Apr-3 Christie's, London #67/R est:7000-10000

CORNEILLE DE LYON (style) (?-1574) Flemish
£5000 $7800 €7500 Portrait of man wearing black (16x13cm-6x5in) panel on canvas. 10-Apr-3 Sotheby's, London #15/R est:8000

CORNEILLE, Jean Baptiste (1649-1695) French
£2113 $3507 €3000 La traversee de la mer rouge (40x33cm-16x13in) oval. 16-Jun-3 Claude Aguttes, Neuilly #5/R est:3000-4000
£5594 $9343 €8000 Allegories des Victoires de la France (32x40cm-13x16in) 25-Jun-3 Sotheby's, Paris #11/R est:7000-9000

CORNEILLE, Michel (17th C) French
Works on paper
£353 $546 €550 Paysage classique anime (31x49cm-12x19in) sanguine. 4-Dec-2 Piasa, Paris #48
£4255 $7106 €6000 Putto portant un casque (21x14cm-8x6in) black crayon prov. 19-Jun-3 Piasa, Paris #80/R est:6000-8000

CORNEILLE, Michel (attrib) (17th C) French
Works on paper
£577 $894 €900 Scene de labours (25x46cm-10x18in) sanguine chk. 4-Dec-2 Piasa, Paris #47a

CORNEILLE, Michel (elder) (1602-1664) French
Works on paper
£1216 $1897 €1800 Putto a mi-corps (13x20cm-5x8in) chk. 27-Mar-3 Christie's, Paris #84/R

CORNEILLE, Michel (younger) (1642-1708) French
Works on paper
£405 $632 €600 Bacchanale (26x41cm-10x16in) i. pen ink wash. 26-Mar-3 Piasa, Paris #37
£1646 $2600 €2600 Jeune fille a mi-corps tenant un couple de colombes (20cm-8in circular) red chk prov. 27-Nov-2 Christie's, Paris #153/R est:1500-2000

CORNELISZ, Adriaen (16/17th C) German
£922 $1429 €1383 Gundogs (54x45cm-21x18in) 4-Dec-2 AB Stockholms Auktionsverk #1925/R (S.KR 13000)

CORNELISZ, Cornelis van Haarlem (1562-1638) Dutch
£1921 $2997 €2882 Woman's head (32x25cm-13x10in) mono.d.1621 panel lit.prov. 20-Nov-2 Fischer, Luzern #1031/R est:4000-5000 (S.FR 4400)
£4000 $6240 €6000 Bust of a man wearing a laurel crown (11x10cm-4x4in) mono.d.1621 panel. 9-Apr-3 Bonhams, New Bond Street #82/R est:3000-5000

CORNELIUS, G (?) ?
£1603 $2484 €2500 Le baiser (73x57cm-29x22in) panel. 8-Dec-2 Teitgen, Nancy #30/R

CORNELIUS, J G (1880-1963) French
£1282 $1987 €2000 Atlas (81x57cm-32x22in) P. 8-Dec-2 Teitgen, Nancy #73

CORNELIUS, Jean Georges (1880-1963) French
£1268 $2041 €1800 Scene symboliste (81x58cm-32x23in) s. 11-May-3 Thierry & Lannon, Brest #154/R est:1500-1800
£1690 $2721 €2400 Meditation en bord de mer (60x73cm-24x29in) board. 11-May-3 Thierry & Lannon, Brest #345 est:2000-2500
£2254 $3628 €3200 Vue de New York City (81x65cm-32x26in) s. painted 1937. 11-May-3 Thierry & Lannon, Brest #344/R est:1800-2200
£2394 $3855 €3400 Deux femmes de I'lle de Sein (60x91cm-24x36in) panel. 11-May-3 Thierry & Lannon, Brest #155/R est:2800-3200

CORNELIUS, Marie Lucie (fl.1885-1893) French
£2703 $4216 €4000 Bouquet de roses (112x72cm-44x28in) s. 28-Mar-3 Claude Aguttes, Neuilly #89/R

CORNELIUS, Peter (attrib) (1783-1867) German
Works on paper
£253 $392 €400 Portrait of woman (49x39cm-19x15in) s. chk. 27-Sep-2 Venator & Hansten, Koln #1234/R

CORNELIUS, Robert (19th C) American
Photographs
£11538 $18000 €17307 Solomon Andrews. i. daguerreotype. 21-Oct-2 Swann Galleries, New York #18/R est:20000-25000

CORNELL, Joseph (1903-1972) American
£22000 $35860 €33000 Magister study (30x23cm-12x9in) s.i. tempera pencil collage paper masonite exec.1966 prov.exhib. 3-Feb-3 Christie's, London #186/R est:30000
Sculpture
£9375 $15000 €14063 Untitled - homaga to Magritte (10cm-4in) s.d.56 ink glass cut printed paper collaged cardboard. 14-May-3 Sotheby's, New York #107/R est:10000-15000
£34375 $55000 €51563 Via parmigianino - for allegra (31x21x9cm-12x8x4in) s.i.d.1956 painted wood box construction prov.exhib. 14-May-3 Sotheby's, New York #301/R est:50000-70000
£42188 $67500 €63282 Nearest star, an allegory of time (40x24x11cm-16x9x4in) s.verso painted wood construction oil metal rings stamp prov. 14-May-3 Sotheby's, New York #313/R est:60000-80000
£44304 $70000 €66456 Villa Violetta no.1 (46x60x11cm-18x24x4in) s. i.d.1950 verso box construction oil paper glass prov.exhib. 13-Nov-2 Sotheby's, New York #104/R est:60000-80000
£47468 $75000 €71202 Grand hotel de l'univers (49x33x9cm-19x13x4in) s. wood box construction paper collage oil executed c.1950. 14-Nov-2 Christie's, Rockefeller NY #116/R est:60000-80000
£50000 $80000 €75000 Untitled - celestial navigation (29x17x8cm-11x7x3in) s.verso painted wood box construction oil metal rings exec.1960. 14-May-3 Sotheby's, New York #300/R est:50000-70000
£50633 $80000 €75950 Untitled - yellow bird with watch spring (22x16x9cm-9x6x4in) s.verso box construction gouache wood sea shells prov. 13-Nov-2 Sotheby's, New York #152/R est:40000-60000
£75000 $120000 €112500 Untitled -abandoned cage (48x32x19cm-19x13x7in) s.verso wood box metal coil wood mirror prov.exhib. 13-May-3 Sotheby's, New York #23/R est:90000-120000
£187500 $300000 €281250 Mademoiselle Faretti (28x20x5cm-11x8x2in) s.i.d.1933 verso wood box photograph mirror foil prov. 14-May-3 Christie's, Rockefeller NY #7/R est:300000-400000
£187500 $300000 €281250 Untitled (45x28x11cm-18x11x4in) s.i. wood box plastic metal paper mirror tempera prov.exhib. 14-May-3 Christie's, Rockefeller NY #40/R est:300000-400000
£227848 $360000 €341772 Aviary - for Giuiditta pasta (52x32x18cm-20x13x7in) s. box construction with wood executed c.1953-57 prov. 12-Nov-2 Sotheby's, New York #16/R est:250000-350000
Works on paper
£10000 $16000 €15000 Untitled (39x23cm-15x9in) s. ink gouache collage exec.1942 prov. 15-May-3 Christie's, Rockefeller NY #145/R est:12000-18000
£16667 $26167 €26000 Mathematics music (30x24cm-12x9in) s.i.verso collage crayon double-sided prov. 10-Dec-2 Pierre Berge, Paris #53/R est:20000
£18987 $30000 €28481 Untitled - how to grow a rainbow series (30x23cm-12x9in) s.d.12-19-69 i.verso ink printed collage on paper prov. 13-Nov-2 Sotheby's, New York #330/R est:20000-30000

CORNET, Jacobus Ludovicus (1815-1882) Dutch
£1233 $1923 €1800 Violinist in interior (35x29cm-14x11in) s. 14-Apr-3 Glerum, Amsterdam #1/R est:1000-1500

CORNIENTI, Cherubino (attrib) (1816-1860) Italian
£461 $747 €650 Contadino vicino alla roggia (26x29cm-10x11in) board. 22-May-3 Stadion, Trieste #237
£496 $804 €700 Armigero (23x12cm-9x5in) panel. 22-May-3 Stadion, Trieste #242

CORNINI, Marco (1966-) Italian
Sculpture
£3901 $6319 €5500 Presenza (33x56x20cm-13x22x8in) s. base terracotta. 20-May-3 Porro, Milan #9/R est:3000-3300

CORNISH, Norman (1919-) British
Works on paper
£450 $698 €675 Workman smoking a cigarette by a bus stop (29x20cm-11x8in) s. felt tip pen. 1-Oct-2 Bonhams, Leeds #349
£450 $698 €675 Street scene with traffic lights and figures. Workman resting against a post (18x13cm-7x5in) s. dr. double-sided. 1-Oct-2 Bonhams, Leeds #350
£600 $930 €900 Figures walking on a wet footpath (20x30cm-8x12in) s. felt tip pen. 1-Oct-2 Bonhams, Leeds #348
£3600 $6012 €5220 Whitworth colliery, demolished 1975 (20x60cm-8x24in) s.i.verso W/C prov. 17-Jun-3 Anderson & Garland, Newcastle #304/R est:1800-2600

CORNO, Johanne (1952-) Canadian
£193 $302 €290 Two friends (51x61cm-20x24in) s. 25-Mar-3 Iegor de Saint Hippolyte, Montreal #29 (C.D 450)
£215 $335 €323 Prego 1-2-3 (81x133cm-32x52in) s. acrylic. 25-Mar-3 Iegor de Saint Hippolyte, Montreal #26 (C.D 500)

CORNOYER, Paul (1864-1923) American
£2372 $3700 €3558 Horse in a field (36x30cm-14x12in) s.d. 14-Sep-2 Selkirks, St. Louis #122 est:1800-2400
£7042 $10000 €10563 Madison Square on a sunny day (20x25cm-8x10in) board. 8-Aug-1 Barridorf, Portland #60/R est:6000-9000
£7746 $11000 €11619 Rainy day, New York (20x25cm-8x10in) board. 8-Aug-1 Barridorf, Portland #57/R est:6000-9000
£9375 $15000 €14063 Lights in the window (91x81cm-36x32in) s. 11-Jan-3 James Julia, Fairfield #201 est:15000-25000

CORNU, Pierre (1895-1996) French
£638 $1034 €900 Entree du port (49x64cm-19x25in) s. 21-May-3 Cornette de St.Cyr, Paris #99/R
£791 $1266 €1100 Modele sur le canape (38x55cm-15x22in) s. i.verso. 14-May-3 Blanchet, Paris #125/R
£823 $1300 €1300 Bas blancs (55x38cm-22x15in) s. 27-Nov-2 Blanchet, Paris #96/R

CORNU, Vital (1851-?) French
Sculpture
£5500 $8525 €8250 Victoire triumphante (92cm-36in) s.st.f.Societe des Bronzes golden brown pat bronze rockwork base. 29-Oct-2 Bonhams, New Bond Street #163/R est:6000-8000
£6500 $10140 €9750 Victoire triumphante (97cm-38in) s.num.5010 brown pat bronze gilt bronze st.f.Societe des Bronzes. 9-Apr-3 Sotheby's, London #135/R est:6000-8000

CORNUT, Roger (?) American?
£252 $400 €365 Along the quay (84x64cm-33x25in) s. 3-May-3 Harvey Clar, Oakland #1200

CORNWELL, Dean (1892-1960) American
£311 $500 €467 Perry at the North pole (36x46cm-14x18in) oi. on glassine. 20-Feb-3 Illustration House, New York #32/R
£4348 $7000 €6522 Confrontation in cabin, with young woman holding candle (56x91cm-22x36in) init. board on panel. 10-May-3 Illustration House, New York #86/R est:9000-12000
£4808 $7500 €7212 Cowboys meeting, one on horse (51x97cm-20x38in) init.d.1918. 9-Nov-2 Illustration House, New York #175/R est:9000-12000
£5280 $8500 €7920 Men gathered around antique keg (89x94cm-35x37in) painted c.1940. 10-May-3 Illustration House, New York #65/R est:9000-12000
£5769 $9000 €8654 Before the jude (74x85cm-29x33in) s.d.1938 paper on board. 20-Sep-2 Sloan, North Bethesda #499/R est:12000-18000
£8974 $14000 €13461 Woman at ball surrounded by potential dance partners (76x99cm-30x39in) init.d.1925 panel. 9-Nov-2 Illustration House, New York #98/R est:12000-18000
£13665 $22000 €20498 Couple on a patterned couch (61x76cm-24x30in) s.d. 10-May-3 Illustration House, New York #85/R est:24000-32000
Works on paper
£248 $400 €372 War correspondent pausing at battlefield grave (51x36cm-20x14in) W/C chl. 20-Feb-3 Illustration House, New York #31/R

CORONA, Vittorio (1901-1966) Italian
£7051 $10929 €11000 Bugatti at 1000 km per hour (39x47cm-15x19in) s. 5-Dec-2 Stadion, Trieste #787/R est:15000

CORONEL, Pedro (1923-1985) Mexican
£41401 $65000 €62102 Peasant loneliness (88x124cm-35x49in) s.d.51 verso masonite prov.exhib.lit. 20-Nov-2 Christie's, Rockefeller NY #23/R est:50000-70000

CORONEL, Rafael (1932-) Mexican
£8658 $13853 €12554 Peregrino (100x125cm-39x49in) s. 15-May-3 Louis Morton, Mexico #69/R est:140000-150000 (M.P 140000)
£12739 $20000 €19109 Water carrier (103x103cm-41x41in) s. painted 1971. 19-Nov-2 Sotheby's, New York #105/R est:35000
Works on paper
£416 $650 €624 Still life with fish (63x49cm-25x19in) s.d.58 W/C. 14-Sep-2 Weschler, Washington #656/R
£3401 $5442 €4931 Personaje (102x76cm-40x30in) s. pastel crayon. 15-May-3 Louis Morton, Mexico #118/R est:60000-64000 (M.P 55000)

COROT, Jean Baptiste Camille (1796-1875) French
£3939 $6067 €5909 Bord d' Etang - Bucheronne a la lisiere d'un bois (12x21cm-5x8in) s. panel prov. 4-Sep-2 Dunbar Sloane, Wellington #91/R est:4000-6000 (NZ.D 13000)
£26923 $42269 €42000 Inondation (23x35cm-9x14in) s. prov. 13-Dec-2 Piasa, Paris #2/R est:70000
£29032 $45000 €43548 Paysage au bord du lac (39x53cm-15x21in) s. painted c.1865-70 prov.lit. 30-Oct-2 Christie's, Rockefeller NY #27/R est:40000-60000
£37975 $60000 €56963 Environs d'Amsterdam, petite ferme des bords de I'Amstel (21x14cm-8x6in) s. painted 1854 prov.lit. 23-Apr-3 Christie's, Rockefeller NY #66/R est:20000-30000
£41139 $65000 €61709 Vaches au marais, le matin (31x44cm-12x17in) s. panel painted c.1850 prov.lit. 23-Apr-3 Christie's, Rockefeller NY #39/R est:70000-90000
£47468 $75000 €71202 Quatre paysannes au bord de la mare (60x51cm-24x20in) s. painted c.1860-65 prov. 24-Apr-3 Sotheby's, New York #15/R est:80000-120000
£53165 $84000 €79748 Paturages marecageux (27x45cm-11x18in) s. prov.lit. 24-Apr-3 Sotheby's, New York #17/R est:60000-80000
£54839 $85000 €82259 Saint Quentin des pres oise, pres Gournay-en-Bray (44x33cm-17x13in) s. prov.exhib.lit. 29-Oct-2 Sotheby's, New York #140/R est:80000-120000
£64516 $100000 €96774 Le batelier quittant la rive avec une femme et un enfant assis dans sa barque, soleil couchant (80x63cm-31x25in) s. prov.lit. 29-Oct-2 Sotheby's, New York #141/R est:80000-120000
£66901 $95000 €100352 Portrait of a young woman in a landscape (30x20cm-12x8in) s.d.1927. 8-Aug-1 Barridorf, Portland #124/R est:75000-125000
£80645 $125000 €120968 Souvenir de la Rotte, pres Rotterdam (52x75cm-20x30in) s. painted c.1860-65 prov.lit. 30-Oct-2 Christie's, Rockefeller NY #24/R est:60000-80000
£83871 $130000 €125807 Les d'enicheurs Toscans (75x65cm-30x26in) s. painted c.1855-65 prov.exhib.lit. 30-Oct-2 Christie's, Rockefeller NY #23/R est:100000-150000
£129032 $200000 €193548 Fillette a l'etude, en train d'ecricre (42x37cm-17x15in) s. panel prov.exhib.lit. 30-Oct-2 Christie's, Rockefeller NY #15/R est:250000-350000
£170000 $266900 €255000 Carrefour dans la campagne - environs de marcoussis (37x56cm-15x22in) s. prov.exhib.lit. 19-Nov-2 Sotheby's, London #156/R est:150000-200000
£189873 $300000 €284810 L'atelier de Corot (46x32cm-18x13in) s. painted c.1865-68 exhib. 23-Apr-3 Christie's, Rockefeller NY #40/R est:300000-400000
£202532 $320000 €303798 Un bord de riviere aux arbres coupes (36x46cm-14x18in) s. prov.exhib.lit. 24-Apr-3 Sotheby's, New York #25/R est:120000-180000
£880000 $1443200 €1320000 Reveuse a la fontaine (64x44cm-25x17in) s. painted c.1860-70 prov.exhib.lit. 4-Feb-3 Sotheby's, London #6/R est:700000
Works on paper
£935 $1496 €1300 Trees (29x16cm-11x6in) chk prov. double-sided. 17-May-3 Lempertz, Koln #1278/R
£2041 $3245 €3000 Landscape with trees and ruins (18x18cm-7x7in) s. pencil. 28-Mar-3 Bolland & Marotz, Bremen #432/R est:800
£2264 $3600 €3396 Paysage avec deux femmes (23x30cm-9x12in) brush ink wash pencil. 3-Mar-3 Swann Galleries, New York #5/R est:3000-5000
£3056 $4859 €4400 Personnages lisant sous les grands arbres (29x21cm-11x8in) s. chl dr lit. 29-Apr-3 Artcurial Briest, Paris #20/R est:5000-7000
£3901 $6514 €5500 Civitella, vue prese du Chemin de Rocca San Stefano (21x25cm-8x10in) lead pencil c.1825-1828 prov.exhib.lit. 20-Jun-3 Piasa, Paris #44/R est:6000-8000
£4000 $6680 €5800 Wooded landscape with a shepherd by a lake (30x25cm-12x10in) s. stumped black chk prov. 8-Jul-3 Christie's, London #92/R est:4000-6000
£17284 $28000 €25926 Landscape with figures and trees (47x34cm-19x13in) s.i.d.1862 chk htd white prov. 22-Jan-3 Christie's, Rockefeller NY #113/R est:30000

COROT, Jean Baptiste Camille (attrib) (1796-1875) French
£2013 $3099 €3200 Sur la rotable (18x25cm-7x10in) s. paper on canvas. 28-Oct-2 Il Ponte, Milan #228/R
£2013 $3099 €3200 Moonlight (24x27cm-9x11in) s. 28-Oct-2 Il Ponte, Milan #240/R
£2673 $4250 €4010 Return from battle (13x13cm-5x5in) board prov. 5-Mar-3 Doyle, New York #90/R est:700-900
£3200 $5216 €4640 Landscape Idyll (46x61cm-18x24in) i.verso. 17-Jul-3 Thomson, Roddick & Medcalf, Carlisle #40/R
£3899 $6005 €6200 Paysage au soleil couchant (32x40cm-13x16in) s. board prov. 28-Oct-2 Il Ponte, Milan #250/R

Works on paper
£583 $950 €875 Head of a dog (14x23cm-6x9in) bears sig verso black chk htd white. 11-Feb-3 Bonhams & Doyles, New York #69/R

CORPAATO (1950-) Swiss
£262 $414 €393 Red cello and small dog with bone with yellow background (60x30cm-24x12in) s.d.78. 26-Nov-2 Hans Widmer, St Gallen #1078 (S.FR 610)

CORPORA, Antonio (1909-) Italian
£1346 $2113 €2100 Abstract composition (76x63cm-30x25in) s.verso painted 1961. 16-Dec-2 Eric Coutrier, Paris #104
£2048 $3277 €2970 Lagoon in Venice (60x73cm-24x29in) s. 11-Mar-3 Babuino, Rome #289/R
£2405 $3752 €3800 Old Mediterranean (81x65cm-32x26in) painted 1973. 15-Oct-2 Babuino, Rome #313/R
£2449 $3894 €3600 Paysage de Tunisie (44x54cm-17x21in) s. 24-Mar-3 Rabourdin & Choppin de Janvry, Paris #237/R est:2500-3000
£2532 $3949 €4000 Eastern legend (81x60cm-32x24in) s. s.i.verso acrylic painted 1997. 14-Sep-2 Meeting Art, Vercelli #810/R
£2614 $4183 €4000 Morning (70x60cm-28x24in) s. acrylic painted 1990. 4-Jan-3 Meeting Art, Vercelli #407
£2658 $4200 €4200 Flying carpet (65x81cm-26x32in) s. painted 1973. 29-Nov-2 Farsetti, Prato #473/R est:2700
£2778 $4417 €4000 Trip in the East (70x60cm-28x24in) s.s id.1998 verso acrylic. 1-May-3 Meeting Art, Vercelli #454
£3846 $6038 €6000 Bay (60x73cm-24x29in) s.d.74 s.i.d.verso. 21-Nov-2 Finarte, Rome #348/R
£4200 $6636 €6300 Untitled (107x140cm-42x55in) s. 3-Apr-3 Christie's, Kensington #210/R
£4487 $7045 €7000 Trinita' dei Monti (70x50cm-28x20in) s.d.46. 21-Nov-2 Finarte, Rome #336/R est:6000
£5229 $8366 €8000 Surface (100x80cm-39x31in) s.d.1964. 4-Jan-3 Meeting Art, Vercelli #623
£5417 $8558 €8450 Seaside (130x98cm-51x39in) painted 1949. 12-Nov-2 Babuino, Rome #325/R
£5449 $8554 €8500 Composition (81x100cm-32x39in) s.d.1968. 23-Nov-2 Meeting Art, Vercelli #114/R
£5674 $9191 €8000 Pietra miliare (65x81cm-26x32in) s.d.59 prov. 26-May-3 Christie's, Milan #162/R est:9000-13000
£6500 $10270 €9750 Composition (146x144cm-57x57in) s.i.d.1960 on stretcher exhib. 3-Apr-3 Christie's, Kensington #212/R
£9589 $14959 €14000 Stone age (114x146cm-45x57in) s. s.verso painted 1956 exhib. 10-Apr-3 Finarte Semenzato, Rome #244/R

Works on paper
£382 $607 €550 Composition (42x32cm-17x13in) s. gouache. 29-Apr-3 Artcurial Briest, Paris #629
£490 $784 €750 African sea (51x36cm-20x14in) s. W/C card. 4-Jan-3 Meeting Art, Vercelli #380
£490 $784 €750 Curtain (51x36cm-20x14in) s. W/C exec.1997. 4-Jan-3 Meeting Art, Vercelli #379
£490 $784 €750 Eastern river (36x51cm-14x20in) s. W/C card. 4-Jan-3 Meeting Art, Vercelli #378
£490 $784 €750 Toreador (51x36cm-20x14in) s. s.i.verso W/C. 4-Jan-3 Meeting Art, Vercelli #594
£510 $811 €750 Untitled (51x36cm-20x14in) s. W/C card. 1-Mar-3 Meeting Art, Vercelli #348
£513 $805 €800 Middle Ages (51x36cm-20x14in) s. W/C exec.1997. 23-Nov-2 Meeting Art, Vercelli #69/R
£513 $805 €800 Trip to the East (51x36cm-20x14in) s. W/C exec.1999. 23-Nov-2 Meeting Art, Vercelli #306/R
£544 $865 €800 Sea and desert tales (51x36cm-20x14in) s. W/C card. 1-Mar-3 Meeting Art, Vercelli #613
£577 $906 €900 Untitled (50x35cm-20x14in) s. W/C. 21-Nov-2 Finarte, Rome #21
£590 $939 €850 Untitled (36x48cm-14x19in) s. W/C. 1-May-3 Meeting Art, Vercelli #135
£612 $973 €900 Composition (65x50cm-26x20in) s. pastel paper on canvas. 1-Mar-3 Meeting Art, Vercelli #383
£665 $1037 €1050 Southern sea (51x36cm-20x14in) s. s.i.d.1999 verso W/C card. 14-Sep-2 Meeting Art, Vercelli #774/R
£769 $1208 €1200 Untitled (33x24cm-13x9in) s. pastel W/C. 19-Nov-2 Finarte, Milan #131/R
£801 $1258 €1250 Composition (41x33cm-16x13in) s. wax pastel. 19-Nov-2 Finarte, Milan #81/R
£897 $1310 €1400 Scirocco (36x51cm-14x20in) s.i.d.2001 W/C. 4-Jun-2 Karl & Faber, Munich #212/R
£1032 $1631 €1600 Untitled (67x47cm-26x19in) s.d.61 mixed media cardboard. 18-Dec-2 Christie's, Rome #49/R
£1266 $1975 €2000 East (76x57cm-30x22in) s.i.d.1989 W/C pastel card. 14-Sep-2 Meeting Art, Vercelli #802/R
£1389 $2208 €2000 Composition (50x65cm-20x26in) s. pastel. 1-May-3 Meeting Art, Vercelli #199
£2245 $3569 €3300 Untitled (67x48cm-26x19in) s. mixed media cardboard. 1-Mar-3 Meeting Art, Vercelli #612

CORRADI, Konrad (1813-1878) Swiss
Works on paper
£510 $795 €800 View of Eiger, Monch and Jungfrau (33x47cm-13x19in) s.i. gouache. 5-Nov-2 Hartung & Hartung, Munich #5030/R
£961 $1499 €1442 Brienz lake (31x46cm-12x18in) s. gouache. 8-Nov-2 Dobiaschofsky, Bern #2/R (S.FR 2200)
£1717 $2661 €2576 Urnersee, Brunnen and Schwyz with Seelisberg (32x46cm-13x18in) s. gouache. 3-Oct-2 Koller, Zurich #3220 est:4000-6000 (S.FR 4000)

CORRAL, Imeldo (1889-1976) Spanish
£3947 $6395 €6000 Landscape with houses (65x81cm-26x32in) s. 21-Jan-3 Ansorena, Madrid #231/R

CORREGGIO (after) (1494-1534) Italian
£4930 $7937 €7000 Madonna and Saint Jerome (213x140cm-84x55in) 11-May-3 Finarte, Venice #6/R
£5800 $9048 €8700 Madonna of Saint Jerome (185x129cm-73x51in) 9-Apr-3 Bonhams, New Bond Street #90/R est:5000-7000
£6000 $9660 €9000 Madonna and Child with Saints Jerome and Mary Magdalene and Angles (147x113cm-58x44in) fragment. 20-Feb-3 Christie's, Kensington #143/R est:6000-8000

CORREGGIO (circle) (1494-1534) Italian
£5660 $8830 €9000 Female angel and putto (132x75cm-52x30in) 23-Sep-2 Wiener Kunst Auktionen, Vienna #34/R est:7500-14000

CORREGGIO (style) (1494-1534) Italian
£8228 $13000 €13000 Ecce Homo (99x78cm-39x31in) board. 28-Nov-2 Semenzato, Venice #234/R est:8000

CORREGGIO, Ludwig (1846-1920) German
£318 $497 €500 Moor landscape (28x40cm-11x16in) s. board. 6-Nov-2 Hugo Ruef, Munich #1050
£318 $497 €500 Mountain pastures (30x42cm-12x17in) board. 6-Nov-2 Hugo Ruef, Munich #1051/R
£386 $617 €590 Mountain village with trees and figures (19x28cm-7x11in) s. lit. 10-Jan-3 Allgauer, Kempten #1562/R

CORREGIO, Max (1854-1908) German
£13000 $20540 €19500 Regent of Bavaria and entourage shooting pheasants (70x120cm-28x47in) s.i.d.1892 prov. 27-Nov-2 Christie's, London #39/R est:8000-12000

CORRERO, Rubello (19th/20th C) ?
£5000 $7750 €7500 Scared of the sea (54x70cm-21x28in) indis sig. 5-Dec-2 Christie's, Kensington #85/R est:4000-6000

CORRODI, Arnaldo (1846-1874) Italian
£9607 $14987 €14411 Roman harvest scene (46x61cm-18x24in) s.i.d.1868 prov.lit. 9-Nov-2 Galerie Gloggner, Luzern #28/R est:9000-12000 (S.FR 22000)

CORRODI, Hermann David Salomon (1844-1905) Italian
£3863 $6103 €5795 Chapel by the sea (37x71cm-15x28in) s. 3-Apr-3 Heffel, Vancouver #15/R est:10000-12000 (C.D 9000)
£5000 $7850 €7500 On the lagoon, Venice (37x69cm-15x27in) s.d.73. 19-Nov-2 Sotheby's, London #113/R est:5000-7000
£7000 $10920 €10500 Busy market, Cairo (65x123cm-26x48in) 17-Oct-2 Bonhams, Knightsbridge #485/R est:8000-12000
£11348 $17589 €17022 Town scene with figures by well (100x64cm-39x25in) s. 3-Dec-2 Bukowskis, Stockholm #191/R est:70000-80000 (S.KR 160000)
£12000 $18720 €18000 Fishing at sunset, Rome in the distance (56x98cm-22x39in) s.i.d.73. 17-Sep-2 Sotheby's, Olympia #221/R est:5000-7000
£12766 $19787 €19149 Figures outside the church in Jerusalem (100x64cm-39x25in) s.i. 3-Dec-2 Bukowskis, Stockholm #188/R est:50000-60000 (S.KR 180000)
£23270 $35836 €37000 Landscape by Rome (180x140cm-71x55in) s. lit. 23-Oct-2 Finarte, Milan #172/R est:38000-45000
£42958 $69162 €61000 Holy spring in Jerusalem (127x75cm-50x30in) s.i. lit.prov. 9-May-3 Schloss Ahlden, Ahlden #1398/R est:38000
£43478 $71304 €60000 Via del Cairo (67x156cm-26x61in) s. 27-May-3 Finarte, Milan #85/R est:65000-85000
£188387 $297652 €292000 Pont de Galata au crepuscule (86x165cm-34x65in) s.i. prov.lit. 19-Dec-2 Claude Aguttes, Neuilly #114/R est:200000

CORRODI, Salomon (1810-1892) Swiss
£8811 $12863 €13217 View towards Hammergut near Cham (44x59cm-17x23in) s.d.1837. 17-Jun-2 Philippe Schuler, Zurich #4264/R est:4000-6000 (S.FR 20000)

Works on paper
£2957 $4583 €4436 Rome from Monte Mario (25x37cm-10x15in) s.d.1858. 9-Dec-2 Philippe Schuler, Zurich #4153/R est:4000-5000 (S.FR 6800)

£3609 $5593 €5414 Naples from Posillipo with Palazzo Donn'Anna (24x37cm-9x15in) s.d.1898 W/C. 9-Dec-2 Philippe Schuler, Zurich #4152/R est:4000-5000 (S.FR 8300)
£5800 $8990 €8700 On the Appian Way, looking toward Rome (42x63cm-17x25in) s.i.d.1869 W/C. 31-Oct-2 Greenslade Hunt, Taunton #575/R est:2000-3000
£9692 $14150 €14538 Villa Mattei veduta dall'Appia fino ai colli Albani (43x60cm-17x24in) s.d.1869 W/C. 17-Jun-2 Philippe Schuler, Zurich #4790/R est:6000-8000 (S.FR 22000)

CORSAUT, Jesse (1929-) American
£484 $750 €726 Nude reclining on Victorian settee (51x61cm-20x24in) s.d.66 masonite prov. 29-Oct-2 John Moran, Pasadena #764

CORSELLIS, Jane (1940-) British
£750 $1230 €1125 Don Giovanni at the English National Opera (24x34cm-9x13in) s. canvasboard. 3-Jun-3 Sotheby's, Olympia #188/R

CORSETTI, Carlo (1825-1903) Italian
£313 $500 €470 Sailing boats (19x35cm-7x14in) s. canvas on cardboard. 5-Jan-3 Galleria Y Remates, Montevideo #43/R

CORSI, Carlo (1879-1966) Italian
£641 $936 €1000 Sunset (24x34cm-9x13in) s.d.1902 board. 5-Jun-2 Il Ponte, Milan #166

CORSI, Nicolas de (1882-1956) Italian
£380 $600 €600 Night view in Venice (12x17cm-5x7in) s. board. 26-Nov-2 Christie's, Rome #274
£952 $1514 €1400 Port (20x25cm-8x10in) s. board. 1-Mar-3 Meeting Art, Vercelli #16a
£1097 $1700 €1646 Sailboats in the Bay of Naples, Vesuvius beyond (39x50cm-15x20in) s. board. 2-Oct-2 Christie's, Rockefeller NY #801/R est:2000-3000

CORSIA, Gilbert (1915-) French
£255 $397 €400 Still life with two jugs with flowers (50x58cm-20x23in) s. board. 5-Nov-2 Vendu Notarishuis, Rotterdam #121/R

CORSSEN, Johann (20th C) ?
£410 $598 €615 Mountain lake (70x95cm-28x37in) 4-Jun-2 SOGA, Bratislava #165/R est:30000 (SL.K 26000)

CORTAZZO, Oreste (1836-?) Italian
£3000 $4680 €4500 Musician (28x19cm-11x7in) s. board. 17-Sep-2 Sotheby's, Olympia #267/R est:3000-5000

Works on paper
£897 $1391 €1400 Village (85x145cm-33x57in) s. mixed media. 5-Dec-2 Stadion, Trieste #773

CORTES Y AGUILAR, Andres (1810-1879) Spanish
£436 $702 €650 Cows (38x46cm-15x18in) s. 18-Feb-3 Durán, Madrid #84/R
£662 $1079 €1000 Herd at river (54x65cm-21x26in) s. 17-Feb-3 Horta, Bruxelles #482

CORTES Y CORDERO, Antonio (1826-1908) Spanish
£793 $1300 €1150 Cows in a landscape (28x36cm-11x14in) s. 4-Jun-3 Doyle, New York #34 est:800-1200
£1761 $2747 €2800 Landscape with cows (32x40cm-13x16in) s.d.1892. 17-Sep-2 Segre, Madrid #84/R
£1761 $2747 €2800 Landscape with sheep (32x40cm-13x16in) s.i.d.1891. 17-Sep-2 Segre, Madrid #85/R

CORTES Y CORDERO, Eduardo (1837-1903) Spanish
£1730 $2664 €2750 Roses and carnations (23x30cm-9x12in) s.d.1901 board lit. 22-Oct-2 Durán, Madrid #255/R

CORTES, A (?) ?
£793 $1300 €1190 Flowers with a bee on a stone ledge (65x60cm-26x24in) s.d.1967. 5-Feb-3 Christie's, Rockefeller NY #195/R est:1000-1500
£1081 $1686 €1600 Toreador with boy (66x54cm-26x21in) s.d.1865. 25-Mar-3 Durán, Madrid #141/R

CORTES, Andre (1815-1880) Spanish
£1008 $1593 €1512 Drover on country path (81x65cm-32x26in) s. board prov. 18-Nov-2 Waddingtons, Toronto #297/R est:2000-3000 (C.D 2500)
£1266 $2000 €1899 Tending the livestock (20x41cm-8x16in) s. panel. 17-Nov-2 CRN Auctions, Cambridge #60/R
£12690 $20177 €18400 Boys playing (125x96cm-49x38in) s. 4-Mar-3 Ansorena, Madrid #170/R

CORTES, Antonio (19th C) Spanish
£2848 $4500 €4500 Berger et son troupeau a l'approche de l'orage (63x108cm-25x43in) s. 1-Dec-2 Peron, Melun #129

CORTES, Edouard (1882-1969) French
£3000 $4680 €4500 By the fireside (16x22cm-6x9in) s. panel. 26-Mar-3 Sotheby's, Olympia #264/R est:2000-3000
£4038 $6340 €6300 Retour de fenaison (23x33cm-9x13in) s. panel. 13-Dec-2 Peschetau-Badin Godeau & Leroy, Paris #62/R
£4684 $7306 €7400 27 rue Saint Jean a Caen (27x22cm-11x9in) s. panel lit. 15-Sep-2 Etude Bailleul, Bayeux #60/R
£6111 $9717 €8800 Cuivre (22x27cm-9x11in) st.sig. panel prov.exhib.lit. 30-Apr-3 Tajan, Paris #163/R est:7000
£6598 $10490 €9500 Soupe en Bretagne, effet de lampe (38x46cm-15x18in) s. prov.lit. 30-Apr-3 Tajan, Paris #162/R est:4600
£8974 $14000 €13461 Moulin Rouge (33x46cm-13x18in) s. 12-Apr-3 Weschler, Washington #538/R est:20000-30000
£9615 $15000 €14423 Le Grande Boulevard, Paris (33x43cm-13x17in) s. 23-Sep-2 Aspire, Cleveland #5 est:20000-30000
£9936 $15500 €14904 Boulevard de la Madeleine (25x46cm-10x18in) 9-Nov-2 Altermann Galleries, Santa Fe #223
£10959 $16000 €16439 Paris Boulevard (46x53cm-18x21in) 18-May-2 Altermann Galleries, Santa Fe #234/R
£11538 $18000 €17307 Paris le soir (23x33cm-9x13in) 9-Nov-2 Altermann Galleries, Santa Fe #221
£12258 $19368 €19000 Marche aux fleurs (27x35cm-11x14in) s. lit. 18-Dec-2 Digard, Paris #161/R est:8000
£12821 $20000 €19232 Rue de Lyon (33x46cm-13x18in) s. prov. 22-Sep-2 Susanin's, Chicago #5072/R est:20000-25000
£13782 $21500 €20673 Boulevard du Capucine (51x64cm-20x25in) 9-Nov-2 Altermann Galleries, Santa Fe #224
£13889 $22083 €20000 Paris, Madeleine, Rue Royale (16x21cm-6x8in) s. panel lit. 30-Apr-3 Tajan, Paris #164/R est:18000
£14063 $22500 €21095 Paris street scene at dusk (33x46cm-13x18in) s. 11-Jan-3 James Julia, Fairfield #116 est:17500-25000
£14189 $22135 €21000 Avenue de l'Opera (46x55cm-18x22in) s. painted c.1964 prov. 26-Mar-3 Peschetau-Badin Godeau & Leroy, Paris #41/R
£14194 $22000 €21291 Place Pigalle in winter (38x46cm-15x18in) s. 30-Oct-2 Christie's, Rockefeller NY #225/R est:15000-20000
£14557 $23000 €21836 Flower market, near la Madeleine (16x22cm-6x9in) s. panel. 24-Apr-3 Sotheby's, New York #148/R est:10000-15000
£15385 $24000 €23078 View of Notre Dame at dusk (33x46cm-13x18in) s. prov. 12-Apr-3 Weschler, Washington #537/R est:25000-35000
£17000 $26520 €25500 Rue de Madeleine (33x46cm-13x18in) s. 17-Sep-2 Sotheby's, Olympia #294/R est:6000-8000
£17197 $27000 €25796 Une nuit Parisienne (33x46cm-13x18in) s. prov. 14-Dec-2 Weschler, Washington #609/R est:30000-40000
£18065 $28000 €27098 Cafe de la paix, place de l'opera (33x46cm-13x18in) s. 30-Oct-2 Christie's, Rockefeller NY #226/R est:20000-30000
£18471 $29000 €27707 Place Vendome (33x46cm-13x18in) 13-Dec-2 Du Mouchelle, Detroit #2044/R est:20000-30000
£18519 $30000 €26853 Port St Denis (33x46cm-13x18in) s. 21-May-3 Doyle, New York #238/R est:20000-30000
£18519 $30000 €26853 Place de l'Opera (33x46cm-13x18in) s. 21-May-3 Doyle, New York #239/R est:20000-30000
£19445 $30917 €28000 Arc de Triomphe et Champs Elysees (33x46cm-13x18in) s. prov. 30-Apr-3 Tajan, Paris #161/R est:45000
£20000 $32800 €30000 Paris, place de la Republique (55x38cm-22x15in) s. painted c.1940-45. 3-Jun-3 Sotheby's, London #179/R est:10000-15000
£20645 $32000 €30968 Parisian street scene (33x46cm-13x18in) s. 7-Dec-2 Selkirks, St. Louis #769/R est:20000-25000
£23899 $38000 €35849 La porte st. Denis a Paris (84x91cm-33x36in) s. 7-Mar-3 Jackson's, Cedar Falls #521/R est:20000-25000
£26582 $42000 €39873 Paris at dusk (40x79cm-16x31in) s. panel prov. 23-Apr-3 Christie's, Rockefeller NY #21/R est:30000-40000
£28936 $45719 €43404 Parisian street scene, winter (46x65cm-18x26in) s. 2-Dec-2 Rasmussen, Copenhagen #1197/R est:100000-125000 (D.KR 340000)
£33333 $52667 €52000 Paris la Madeleine, Boulevard des Capucines le soir sour la neige (50x65cm-20x26in) s. painted c.1960 prov.lit. 18-Nov-2 Tajan, Paris #195/R est:38000-40000
£37975 $60000 €56963 La place de la Republique (50x65cm-20x26in) s. 23-Apr-3 Christie's, Rockefeller NY #23/R est:50000-70000
£40000 $62000 €60000 Arc de Triomphe in winter (50x65cm-20x26in) s. 3-Dec-2 Sotheby's, Olympia #305/R est:20000-30000
£54795 $85479 €80000 Boulevard Parisien sous la neige (64x90cm-25x35in) s. 14-Apr-3 Horta, Bruxelles #170/R est:15000-20000

Works on paper
£1282 $2013 €2000 Femme pres de l'atre (15x21cm-6x8in) s. W/C. 16-Dec-2 Rabourdin & Choppin de Janvry, Paris #25/R
£3462 $5469 €5400 Biercy-sur-Morin (22x34cm-9x13in) s.i.d.Mars 18 prov.lit. 18-Nov-2 Tajan, Paris #197/R est:3000-3500
£4152 $6561 €6228 Evening by Madeleine Church in Paris (27x46cm-11x18in) s/ gouache. 2-Dec-2 Blomqvist, Oslo #323/R est:40000-50000 (N.KR 48000)
£4730 $7378 €7000 Boulevard La Madeleine (29x55cm-11x22in) s. gouache. 25-Mar-3 Durán, Madrid #192/R
£5068 $7905 €7500 Place de la Madeleine (26x45cm-10x18in) s. gouache. 28-Mar-3 Claude Aguttes, Neuilly #30/R
£6531 $10384 €9600 Meule en bordure de chemin (20x26cm-8x10in) s. gouache lit. 26-Feb-3 Artcurial Briest, Paris #129/R est:4500-6000

£10959 $16000 €16439 Porte St Denis (18x28cm-7x11in) gouache. 18-May-2 Altermann Galleries, Santa Fe #233/R

CORTESE, Federico (1829-1913) Italian

£1250 $1975 €1875 Duck shoot; wooded lake scene with two men in a boat (38x66cm-15x26in) s. 5-Apr-3 Finan Watkins & Co, Mere #202/R

CORTESE, G (1625-1679) Italian

£2000 $3160 €3000 Coast of Capri. Fishermen in the Bay of Naples (51x71cm-20x28in) s. pair. 14-Nov-2 Christie's, Kensington #123/R est:1200-1800

CORTHALS, Léon (1877-1935) Belgian

£759 $1185 €1200 Ruisseau en sous-bois (130x100cm-51x39in) s. 16-Sep-2 Horta, Bruxelles #510

CORTIELLO, Mario (1907-1982) Italian

£513 $749 €800 View of Paris (50x60cm-20x24in) s.i. 5-Jun-2 Il Ponte, Milan #12

Works on paper

£545 $796 €850 Pulcinella escaping (50x60cm-20x24in) s.d.70 mixed media. 5-Jun-2 Il Ponte, Milan #15

CORTIJO, Francisco (1936-) Spanish

£1218 $1924 €1900 Untitled (75x47cm-30x19in) s.d.1989 acrylicpastel cardboard on board. 14-Nov-2 Arte, Seville #437/R

CORTONA, Pietro da (1596-1669) Italian

£5769 $8942 €9000 Moses' sacrifice (50x65cm-20x26in) lit. 4-Dec-2 Christie's, Rome #455/R est:5000-8000

CORTONA, Pietro da (attrib) (1596-1669) Italian

£16000 $25120 €24000 Guardian Angel (67x44cm-26x17in) prov.exhib.lit. 12-Dec-2 Sotheby's, London #181/R est:10000-15000

CORTONA, Pietro da (circle) (1596-1669) Italian

£24000 $37200 €36000 Venus disguised as a huntress appearing to Aeneas and Achates (112x119cm-44x47in) prov. 30-Oct-2 Christie's, Kensington #136/R est:10000-15000

Works on paper

£1268 $2104 €1800 Angels making music at saint's death bed (21x16cm-8x6in) pen wash chk htd white. 12-Jun-3 Hauswedell & Nolte, Hamburg #60/R est:2400

CORTONA, Pietro da (style) (1596-1669) Italian

£8000 $12480 €12000 Jacob and Laban (200x178cm-79x70in) 10-Apr-3 Christie's, Kensington #272/R est:8000-12000

CORTOT, Jean (1925-) French

Works on paper

£380 $623 €551 Ville, architectures grises (62x47cm-24x19in) W/C exec.1958 prov. 1-Jun-3 Lots Road, London #359

CORVER, J (19th C) Dutch?

£2051 $3241 €3200 Dutch summer. Winter landscape (46x65cm-18x26in) s. pair. 16-Nov-2 Lempertz, Koln #1443/R est:2000

CORWIN, Charles Abel (1857-1938) American

£1506 $2500 €2184 Sun-dappled path in the woods (51x76cm-20x30in) s. prov. 11-Jun-3 Butterfields, San Francisco #4058/R est:3000-5000

CORZAS, Francisco (1936-1983) Mexican

Works on paper

£278 $445 €403 Personaje (30x41cm-12x16in) s.d.1976 Indian ink. 15-May-3 Louis Morton, Mexico #2 (M.P 4500)
£2834 $4421 €4251 Mujer (48x33cm-19x13in) s.d.1963 gouache prov. 17-Oct-2 Louis Morton, Mexico #52/R est:55000-65000 (M.P 45000)

COSGROVE, J R (20th C) American

£903 $1400 €1355 House in eucalyptus landscape (51x61cm-20x24in) s. masonite. 29-Oct-2 John Moran, Pasadena #772 est:1000-1500

COSGROVE, Stanley Morel (1911-2002) Canadian

£389 $607 €584 Le Mexicain (29x26cm-11x10in) inid.d.1943. 10-Sep-2 Iegor de Saint Hippolyte, Montreal #24 (C.D 950)
£779 $1207 €1169 Annunciation angel (41x30cm-16x12in) s.d.51 board prov. 24-Sep-2 Ritchie, Toronto #3196/R est:1200-1600 (C.D 1900)
£1235 $1901 €1853 Sentier dans la foret (12x16cm-5x6in) s. cardboard. 22-Oct-2 Iegor de Saint Hippolyte, Montreal #20/R (C.D 3000)
£1373 $2142 €2060 Rose forest (37x46cm-15x18in) s. s.d.verso panel. 25-Mar-3 Iegor de Saint Hippolyte, Montreal #31 (C.D 3200)
£1395 $2176 €2023 Mexican water carriers (35x42cm-14x17in) init.d.43 board prov.lit. 26-Mar-3 Walker's, Ottawa #225/R est:3500-4500 (C.D 3250)
£1457 $2332 €2186 Trees (41x51cm-16x20in) s. prov. 15-May-3 Heffel, Vancouver #224/R est:3500-4500 (C.D 3250)
£1502 $2343 €2253 River in winter (30x40cm-12x16in) s. isorel. 25-Mar-3 Iegor de Saint Hippolyte, Montreal #33 (C.D 3500)
£1557 $2430 €2336 Ete 1981 (61x51cm-24x20in) s. s.i.verso panel. 10-Sep-2 Iegor de Saint Hippolyte, Montreal #22/R (C.D 3800)
£2146 $3348 €3112 Girl with shawl (33x28cm-13x11in) s.d.48 board prov.exhib. 26-Mar-3 Walker's, Ottawa #224/R est:4000-5000 (C.D 5000)
£2177 $3397 €3266 Nature morte (40x50cm-16x20in) s. cardboard. 30-Jul-2 Iegor de Saint Hippolyte, Montreal #35 (C.D 5400)
£2675 $4146 €4013 Forest clearing (36x42cm-14x17in) s.d.47 oil paper on canvas. 3-Dec-2 Joyner, Toronto #55/R est:4000-6000 (C.D 6500)
£3049 $4787 €4574 La Tuque (56x76cm-22x30in) s.d.48 board prov. 10-Dec-2 Pinneys, Montreal #147 est:8000-12000 (C.D 7500)
£3292 $5103 €4938 Reclining nude (24x45cm-9x18in) s.d.50 board prov. 3-Dec-2 Joyner, Toronto #32/R est:6000-8000 (C.D 8000)
£3292 $5103 €4938 Foret en ocre (52x61cm-20x24in) s. painted c.1953 prov.exhib. 3-Dec-2 Joyner, Toronto #74/R est:10000-15000 (C.D 8000)
£3556 $5831 €5334 Still life (50x75cm-20x30in) s.d.59. 3-Jun-3 Joyner, Toronto #105/R est:8000-12000 (C.D 8000)
£5350 $8292 €8025 Nature morte aux deux pommes (36x43cm-14x17in) s.d.47 oil paper on canvas prov.exhib. 3-Dec-2 Joyner, Toronto #54/R est:4000-6000 (C.D 13000)
£5778 $9476 €8667 La tuque (55x75cm-22x30in) s.d.48 board prov. 3-Jun-3 Joyner, Toronto #130/R est:15000-20000 (C.D 13000)
£6048 $9556 €9072 Trees (63x81cm-25x32in) s. prov. 14-Nov-2 Heffel, Vancouver #273/R est:6000-8000 (C.D 15000)
£7175 $11480 €10763 Femme en gris (61x51cm-24x20in) s.d.1952 i.verso board prov. 15-May-3 Heffel, Vancouver #79/R est:10000-12000 (C.D 16000)
£15111 $24782 €22667 Nature morte au pot (90x120cm-35x47in) s.d.52-55 board prov.exhib. 3-Jun-3 Joyner, Toronto #18/R est:20000-30000 (C.D 34000)

Works on paper

£328 $511 €492 Mexican head (27x23cm-11x9in) mono.d.41 pencil. 10-Sep-2 Iegor de Saint Hippolyte, Montreal #23 (C.D 800)
£496 $779 €744 Seated nude (33x25cm-13x10in) s. conte dr. 24-Jul-2 Walker's, Ottawa #215/R est:1000-1500 (C.D 1200)

COSLIE, Michel (attrib) (16th C) ?

£2308 $3623 €3600 Crucifixion (100x76cm-39x30in) panel. 10-Dec-2 Vanderkindere, Brussels #14/R est:2500-4000

COSOMATI, Ettore (1873-1960) Italian

£952 $1514 €1400 Ampollino Lake, Sila (60x75cm-24x30in) init. board. 18-Mar-3 Finarte, Milan #181/R

COSSAAR, J (1874-1966) Dutch

£900 $1368 €1350 Carriages and omnibuses on a busy London street, thought to be Piccadilly (71x91cm-28x36in) s. 29-Aug-2 Christie's, Kensington #117
£1438 $2244 €2100 Entree d'un port du nord (61x79cm-24x31in) 8-Apr-3 Gioffredo, Nice #59/R

COSSAAR, Jan (1874-1966) Dutch

£255 $397 €400 Moored boats in fishing harbour (28x37cm-11x15in) s. 6-Nov-2 Vendue Huis, Gravenhage #58/R
£318 $497 €500 Our Dear Lady Church in Bruges (39x29cm-15x11in) s. 6-Nov-2 Vendue Huis, Gravenhage #46/R
£382 $596 €600 St Bartholomew in London (49x39cm-19x15in) s. 6-Nov-2 Vendue Huis, Gravenhage #125/R
£478 $745 €750 Church in the square (35x26cm-14x10in) s. panel. 6-Nov-2 Vendue Huis, Gravenhage #45
£566 $872 €900 Waterloo Road, National Theatre, London (30x40cm-12x16in) s. painted c.1904. 22-Oct-2 Campo, Vlaamse Kaai #449
£637 $994 €1000 Church interior (92x67cm-36x26in) s. 6-Nov-2 Vendue Huis, Gravenhage #13/R
£789 $1279 €1200 Fountain on Trafalgar Square, London (91x70cm-36x28in) s. oil paper on board. 21-Jan-3 Christie's, Amsterdam #156 est:1500-2000

Works on paper

£318 $490 €500 Forum Romanum, Rome (61x48cm-24x19in) s.i. brown chk W/C. 3-Sep-2 Christie's, Amsterdam #217
£329 $533 €500 Busy market square (37x47cm-15x19in) s. black chk W/C. 21-Jan-3 Christie's, Amsterdam #128
£330 $515 €495 Noon school (54x40cm-21x16in) s.i. col wash. 9-Oct-2 Woolley & Wallis, Salisbury #124/R

COSSARD, Adolphe Auguste Edouard (1880-1952) French
£493 $794 €700 Fortin de l'ile Port-Cros (55x46cm-22x18in) s. 11-May-3 Thierry & Lannon, Brest #346
£1761 $2835 €2500 Animation devant la Koutoubia a Marrakech (61x50cm-24x20in) s. 11-May-3 Thierry & Lannon, Brest #347/R est:2000-2500

COSSIERS, Jan (attrib) (1600-1671) Flemish
£5793 $9211 €8400 Salome with the head of the Baptist (149x233cm-59x92in) 4-Mar-3 Ansorena, Madrid #44/R est:8400

COSSIO, Pancho (1898-1970) Spanish
£13449 $21249 €19500 Matelots (92x73cm-36x29in) s.d.31. 4-Apr-3 Tajan, Paris #200/R est:22000
£16129 $25484 €25000 Still life (66x82cm-26x32in) s. 17-Dec-2 Durán, Madrid #214/R est:18000

COSSON, Helier (19/20th C) French
£952 $1514 €1400 Elegant (64x54cm-25x21in) s. 19-Mar-3 Claude Boisgirard, Paris #28/R

COSSON, Marcel (1878-1956) French
£1161 $1835 €1800 Attente des ballerines (33x41cm-13x16in) s. masonite. 18-Dec-2 Digard, Paris #101/R
£1361 $2163 €2000 Flamenco (38x46cm-15x18in) s. panel. 26-Feb-3 Artcurial Briest, Paris #267 est:1800-2500
£1565 $2488 €2300 Scene de bal (33x41cm-13x16in) s. panel. 2-Mar-3 Lombrail & Teucquam, Paris #173/R
£1736 $2743 €2500 Opera (25x30cm-10x12in) s. cardboard. 25-Apr-3 Piasa, Paris #69
£1795 $2728 €2800 Foyer (22x27cm-9x11in) s. 16-Aug-2 Deauville, France #103/R
£1897 $3016 €2750 La repetition (33x41cm-13x16in) s. 9-Mar-3 Feletin, Province #99
£1911 $2981 €3000 Dans la loge des ballerines (22x27cm-9x11in) s. panel. 10-Nov-2 Eric Pillon, Calais #74/R
£1911 $2981 €3000 Dans la loge (22x27cm-9x11in) s. panel. 10-Nov-2 Eric Pillon, Calais #90/R
£2000 $3160 €3100 Bal masque, arlequin et colombine (55x46cm-22x18in) s. 17-Dec-2 Rossini, Paris #67/R
£2057 $3435 €2900 Au cafe (35x27cm-14x11in) s. panel. 20-Jun-3 Piasa, Paris #155/R est:2000-3000
£2166 $3378 €3400 Ballerines et abilleuse dans la loge (42x33cm-17x13in) s. 10-Nov-2 Eric Pillon, Calais #78/R
£2407 $3419 €3900 Ballerines dans le foyer (24x33cm-9x13in) s. panel. 16-Mar-3 Eric Pillon, Calais #132/R
£3057 $4769 €4800 Ballerines dans le foyer (46x55cm-18x22in) s. 10-Nov-2 Eric Pillon, Calais #75/R
£4691 $6662 €7600 Ballerines a l'entreacte (38x60cm-15x24in) s. 16-Mar-3 Eric Pillon, Calais #133/R
£4877 $6925 €7900 Cours de danse (38x45cm-15x18in) s. 16-Mar-3 Eric Pillon, Calais #134/R
£6500 $10335 €9750 Deux danseuses (73x60cm-29x24in) s. prov. 20-Mar-3 Sotheby's, Olympia #20/R est:7000-9000
Works on paper
£280 $467 €400 Femme au coquelicot (56x26cm-22x10in) s. pastel. 25-Jun-3 Claude Aguttes, Neuilly #282
£611 $965 €917 Untitled, the cafe. Untitled, the orchestra (46x61cm-18x24in) gouache W/C pencil double-sided. 7-Apr-3 Shapiro, Sydney #527 (A.D 1600)

COSTA BEIRO, Alfonso (1943-) Spanish
£252 $387 €400 Head (60x39cm-24x15in) s. cardboard on board. 28-Oct-2 Segre, Madrid #187/R
Works on paper
£258 $408 €400 Man with fish (31x19cm-12x7in) s. W/C ink. 17-Dec-2 Segre, Madrid #227/R

COSTA BURES, Eduardo (1919-) Spanish
£270 $422 €400 Still life with dead game (73x92cm-29x36in) s. 25-Mar-3 Durán, Madrid #617/R

COSTA VILLA, Jose (1953-) Spanish
Works on paper
£472 $736 €750 Sitting-room with sofa (81x64cm-32x25in) s. mixed media on canvas. 8-Oct-2 Ansorena, Madrid #618/R

COSTA, Antonio (1847-1915) Italian
£943 $1453 €1500 Pastoral duet (66x42cm-26x17in) 28-Oct-2 Il Ponte, Milan #293/R

COSTA, Emanuele (1833-1913) French/Italian
Works on paper
£9032 $14271 €14000 Le port de Nice (48x80cm-19x31in) s. W/C. 17-Dec-2 Claude Boisgirard, Paris #12/R est:10000-12000

COSTA, Giacomo (1970-) Italian
Photographs
£2908 $4711 €4100 Megalopoli 35 (200x100cm-79x39in) s.d.2002 verso ed.1/3 digital photo. 20-May-3 Porro, Milan #10/R est:4000-4200

COSTA, Giovanni (1833-1903) Italian
£962 $1510 €1500 Cheers! (60x46cm-24x18in) s.indis.d. 16-Dec-2 Pandolfini, Florence #83

COSTA, Hans (?) ?
£327 $523 €500 Former with horse and cart (50x60cm-20x24in) s. 10-Jan-3 Allgauer, Kempten #1563/R

COSTA, John da (1866-1931) British
£2200 $3432 €3300 Portrait of the artist's second wife, Christine Bonnar (76x63cm-30x25in) 27-Mar-3 Christie's, Kensington #408/R est:3000-5000

COSTA, Lorenzo (1460-1535) Italian
£25000 $39250 €37500 Virgin annunciate (42x29cm-17x11in) gold ground panel lit. 12-Dec-2 Sotheby's, London #106/R est:15000-20000

COSTA, Olga (1913-1993) Mexican/German
£2516 $4000 €3774 Cabeza de Maya (20x16cm-8x6in) s. board painted c.1960. 4-May-3 Treadway Gallery, Cincinnati #574/R est:5000-7000

COSTA, Oreste (1851-?) Italian
£1154 $1800 €1731 Still life after the hunt (67x55cm-26x22in) s.d.1874. 20-Sep-2 Sloan, North Bethesda #378/R est:1000-1500

COSTANTINI, Virgile (1882-1940) Italian
£2069 $3269 €3000 Mother and child (81x60cm-32x24in) s. 4-Apr-3 Tajan, Paris #169/R

COSTANZI, Placido (1690-1759) Italian
£16049 $26000 €24074 Justices and Temperance triumphant over Vice (62x74cm-24x29in) prov.lit. 24-Jan-3 Christie's, Rockefeller NY #158/R est:15000-20000

COSTELLO, Eileen (1911-1976) Irish
£604 $972 €900 Spring. Autumn 2. landscape winter (36x43cm-14x17in) s. board three prov.exhib. 18-Feb-3 Whyte's, Dublin #47/R

COSTER, Adam de (1586-1643) Flemish
£19512 $32000 €29268 Denial of Saint Peter (124x100cm-49x39in) prov.lit. 29-May-3 Sotheby's, New York #30/R est:30000-40000

COSTER, Jan Herman (1846-1920) Dutch
£402 $647 €615 Crepuscule (80x60cm-31x24in) s.d.1882. 14-Jan-3 Vanderkindere, Brussels #81

COSTETTI, Giovanni (1875-1949) Italian
£2179 $3422 €3400 Woman (27x16cm-11x6in) s.d.18 card. 16-Dec-2 Pandolfini, Florence #219/R
£5128 $8051 €8000 View of village (100x68cm-39x27in) card. 16-Dec-2 Pandolfini, Florence #213/R
£5128 $8051 €8000 Three graces (54x70cm-21x28in) s.d.XXX board. 16-Dec-2 Pandolfini, Florence #222/R est:9000
£16026 $25160 €25000 Reclining female nude with vase (101x30cm-40x12in) s. 16-Dec-2 Pandolfini, Florence #212/R est:30000
Works on paper
£1456 $2271 €2300 Portrait of woman (41x28cm-16x11in) s.d.1944-45 pencil. 19-Oct-2 Semenzato, Venice #51/R

COSTIGAN, John E (1888-1972) American
£1226 $1900 €1839 Figure in wooded landscape (30x41cm-12x16in) s. canvasboard. 16-Jul-2 Arthur James, Florida #405
£2742 $4250 €4113 Figure bathing outdoors (51x61cm-20x24in) s. 16-Jul-2 Arthur James, Florida #406
£3704 $6000 €5371 Mother and children with their goat (46x53cm-18x21in) s. canvasboard. 21-May-3 Doyle, New York #127/R est:8000-10000

COSWAY, Maria (1759-1838) British
£3000 $4770 €4500 Angel and putti accompanying a child's soul to Heaven (59x48cm-23x19in) 19-Mar-3 Sotheby's, London #98/R est:1500-2000

COSWAY, Patrick (18th C) British
£1795 $2800 €2693 Portrait of a lady (102x76cm-40x30in) 30-Mar-3 Susanin's, Chicago #6033/R est:2000-4000

COSWAY, Richard (1742-1821) British

£1951 $3200 €2829 Portrait of a lady, in a black dress with a girl in a pink bonnet (76x53cm-30x21in) prov. 4-Jun-3 Christie's, Rockefeller NY #171/R est:3000-5000

Miniatures

£1100 $1727 €1650 Young lady in a white dress (4cm-2xin) gold bracelet clasp frame oval. 10-Dec-2 Christie's, London #123/R est:800-1200
£1800 $2952 €2610 Young lady in a red dress (2cm-1xin) gold bracelet frame oval prov. 3-Jun-3 Christie's, London #78/R est:1800-2200
£2000 $3120 €3000 Sacrifice to love, young lady draped across a bed, sobbing cupid at her feet (17cm-7xin) pencil ink paper card W/C border rec. 5-Nov-2 Bonhams, New Bond Street #60/R est:2000-3000
£2500 $3850 €3750 Gentleman in turquoise and black doublet (5cm-2xin) gilt metal frame oval exec.c.1780. 24-Oct-2 Sotheby's, Olympia #10/R est:1500-2000
£3000 $4710 €4500 Young gentleman wearing a blue coat (7cm-3xin) s.d.1799 oval prov. 10-Dec-2 Christie's, London #68/R est:3000-5000
£4200 $6594 €6300 Sir William Twysden 7th Bt. (6cm-2xin) silver gilt oval prov.exhib.lit. 10-Dec-2 Christie's, London #70/R est:3000-5000
£9500 $14915 €14250 William, 3rd Viscount Courtenay, later 9th Earl of Devon (7cm-3xin) silver gilt frame oval prov.exhib.lit. 10-Dec-2 Christie's, London #120/R est:5000-7000
£21000 $34020 €31500 Portrait of George IV, as Prince of Wales (7cm-3xin) i.verso prov.exhib.lit. 22-May-3 Bonhams, New Bond Street #131/R est:6000-8000
£26000 $41340 €39000 Lady Elizabeth Foster, later Duchess of Devonshire (7cm-3xin) s.i.d.1790 fishskin case. 6-Mar-3 Sotheby's, Olympia #10/R est:4000-6000

Works on paper

£385 $550 €578 Belle courtesane (17x11cm-7x4in) graphite W/C. 22-Jan-3 Doyle, New York #44

COSWAY, Richard (attrib) (1742-1821) British

£4573 $7500 €6631 Portrait of an officer in uniform (77x64cm-30x25in) oval prov.exhib. 4-Jun-3 Christie's, Rockefeller NY #165/R est:6000-8000

Miniatures

£1600 $2544 €2400 John Williams with brown hair, wearing Vandyke costume (3cm-1xin) painted c.1770. 6-Mar-3 Sotheby's, Olympia #4/R est:1500-2000

Works on paper

£750 $1170 €1125 Mrs Elizabeth Merry, ne death, wife of Anthony Merry (25x16cm-10x6in) s.i.d.1793 i.verso pencil W/C prov. 27-Mar-3 Christie's, Kensington #7/R
£1500 $2340 €2250 Portrait of a young man standing by a stone pedestal (23x14cm-9x6in) pencil W/C. 26-Mar-3 Hamptons Fine Art, Godalming #90/R est:1500-1800

COSYNS, Gies (1920-1997) Belgian

£544 $865 €800 Chaumiere sous la neige (50x60cm-20x24in) s. 18-Mar-3 Campo, Vlaamse Kaai #27
£629 $981 €1000 Vue de plage (48x68cm-19x27in) 14-Oct-2 Amberes, Antwerp #141

COTALILLO, Salvatore (20th C) American?

£255 $400 €383 American ship in China (23x36cm-9x14in) s. board. 22-Nov-2 Eldred, East Dennis #1059/R

COTANDA, Vicente Nicolau (1852-1898) Spanish

£1250 $2025 €1900 Mother and girl (93x78cm-37x31in) s. cardboard. 21-Jan-3 Durán, Madrid #119/R
£2013 $3099 €3200 Woman from Valencia (32x19cm-13x7in) s. board. 22-Oct-2 Durán, Madrid #174/R
£2400 $3912 €3600 Sharing the light (65x40cm-26x16in) s. 29-Jan-3 Sotheby's, Olympia #279/R est:1000-1500

COTE, Bruno (1940-) Canadian

£329 $507 €494 Coucher de soleil sur le village (51x61cm-20x24in) s. isorel. 22-Oct-2 Iegor de Saint Hippolyte, Montreal #22 (C.D 800)
£482 $757 €723 Ste Rose du Nord on Saguenay River (40x50cm-16x20in) s.i.d.1983 board. 25-Nov-2 Hodgins, Calgary #270/R (C.D 1200)
£601 $937 €871 Near Carleton, Quebec (51x61cm-20x24in) s.i.d.85 board prov. 26-Mar-3 Walker's, Ottawa #212/R est:1000-1500 (C.D 1400)
£988 $1531 €1482 Gorges, rivier Malbaie (50x60cm-20x24in) s. board prov. 3-Dec-2 Joyner, Toronto #201/R est:2000-2500 (C.D 2400)
£1048 $1656 €1572 Campement, Riviere manicouagan (91x102cm-36x40in) s. i.verso board. 14-Nov-2 Heffel, Vancouver #262/R est:3000-3500 (C.D 2600)
£1244 $2041 €1866 Spring reflections (50x60cm-20x24in) s. board. 3-Jun-3 Joyner, Toronto #305/R est:2000-2500 (C.D 2800)
£1411 $2230 €2117 The sea, Mingan (61x76cm-24x30in) s. s.i.verso board. 14-Nov-2 Heffel, Vancouver #240/R est:2000-2500 (C.D 3500)
£1457 $2332 €2186 Et du jaune (51x61cm-20x24in) s. s.i.verso board. 15-May-3 Heffel, Vancouver #35/R est:1800-2200 (C.D 3250)

COTEAU, Jean (attrib) (c.1739-1812) Swiss

Works on paper

£532 $888 €750 Scenes de chasse a courre (24x36cm-9x14in) s.d.1791 black crayon estompe white chk pair. 19-Jun-3 Piasa, Paris #148

COTELLE, Jean (younger-attrib) (1642-1708) French

£32051 $50321 €50000 Moise et les filles de Jethro (93x66cm-37x26in) panel pair. 14-Dec-2 Artcurial Briest, Paris #49/R est:30000

COTES, Francis (1726-1770) British

£9000 $14940 €13500 Portrait of Admiral Thomas Craven (74x62cm-29x24in) painted oval prov.lit. 12-Jun-3 Sotheby's, London #65/R est:10000-15000
£18000 $28440 €27000 Portrait of Mrs William Colquhound of Wrotham by urn in landscape (236x143cm-93x56in) s.i.d.1768 prov.exhib.lit. 26-Nov-2 Christie's, London #30/R est:20000-30000

Works on paper

£1300 $2028 €1950 Portrait of a lady (58x43cm-23x17in) s.d.1762 pastel. 17-Oct-2 Christie's, Kensington #10/R est:700-1000
£1829 $3000 €2744 Portrait of a lady said to be Henrietta Conyers (61x45cm-24x18in) pastel prov. 29-May-3 Sotheby's, New York #98/R est:4000-6000

COTES, Francis (attrib) (1726-1770) British

£580 $951 €870 Waist length portrait of a young lady wearing a blue dress (73x58cm-29x23in) 3-Jun-3 Bonhams, Oxford #74/R

COTES, Samuel (1734-1818) British

Miniatures

£1600 $2464 €2400 Young girl, her hair decorated with flowers (3cm-1xin) gold slide frame garnets oval exec.c.1760 with matching piece. 24-Oct-2 Sotheby's, Olympia #1/R est:1500-2000

COTMAN, Frederick George (1850-1920) British

£320 $499 €480 Broadland landscape with village and windmills in distance (28x41cm-11x16in) s. 11-Apr-3 Keys, Aylsham #614/R
£1900 $3097 €2850 In the box (53x41cm-21x16in) s. 29-Jan-3 Sotheby's, Olympia #216/R est:2000-3000
£4400 $6820 €6600 Rural landscape with seated figure and children in front of a thatched cottage (94x64cm-37x25in) s.d.1872. 4-Dec-2 Neal & Fletcher, Woodbridge #229/R est:2500-3500

Works on paper

£320 $518 €480 River Waveney (24x17cm-9x7in) s.d.1896 W/C. 21-Jan-3 Bonhams, Knightsbridge #196/R
£600 $936 €900 Witon near Ross (20x30cm-8x12in) s. i.verso W/C. 27-Mar-3 Christie's, Kensington #78/R
£650 $1021 €975 Figure mending sails near a wherry on the Norfolk Broads (28x43cm-11x17in) s.d.1904 W/C. 13-Dec-2 Keys, Aylsham #639/R

COTMAN, John Joseph (1814-1878) British

Works on paper

£380 $635 €551 Travelers resting beside a copse (13x30cm-5x12in) init. pen ink col chk. 24-Jun-3 Rowley Fine Art, Newmarket #391
£780 $1287 €1131 Wooded landscape at sunset (22x333cm-9x131in) W/C. 2-Jul-3 Sotheby's, Olympia #228/R
£1000 $1590 €1500 Country track with a cottage and windmill beyond (24x32cm-9x13in) s. W/C over pencil two. 19-Mar-3 Sotheby's, London #209 est:600-800
£1300 $2158 €1950 Norwich from the North Walsham Road (29x19cm-11x7in) W/C. 12-Jun-3 Bonhams, New Bond Street #635/R est:1000-1500
£1350 $2093 €2025 Bramerton (38x77cm-15x30in) s.d.1871 W/C over pencil. 30-Sep-2 Bonhams, Ipswich #347/R est:1000-1500
£1700 $2839 €2465 Wherry on the Norfolk Broads (25x41cm-10x16in) s.d.1874 W/C. 20-Jun-3 Keys, Aylsham #615/R est:1800-2500
£4100 $6765 €5945 Thorpe Reach (38x74cm-15x29in) s. W/C. 1-Jul-3 Bonhams, Norwich #89 est:2000-3000

COTMAN, John Joseph (attrib) (1814-1878) British

£1800 $2862 €2700 Suffolk landscape, with mother and child on a country road (73x61cm-29x24in) bears sig exhib. 19-Mar-3 Sotheby's, London #73 est:2000-3000

Works on paper

£380 $592 €570 Distant view of Norwich (22x37cm-9x15in) s.d.1874 pencil W/C. 19-Sep-2 Christie's, Kensington #143

COTMAN, John Sell (1782-1842) British

£1319 $2137 €1913 Wooded landscape with stags resting (65x84cm-26x33in) s.d.1834. 25-May-3 Uppsala Auktionskammare, Uppsala #72/R est:20000-25000 (S.KR 17000)

£4000 $6200 €6000 Lauffenberg on the Rhine (51x81cm-20x32in) exhib. 30-Sep-2 Bonhams, Ipswich #476/R est:4000-6000

Works on paper

£280 $437 €420 Portrait of an old gentleman (10x13cm-4x5in) pencil sketch prov. 11-Apr-3 Keys, Aylsham #588

£480 $782 €720 Haymaking (10x12cm-4x5in) chl white chk exhib. 30-Jan-3 Lawrence, Crewkerne #608

£1600 $2528 €2400 Child playing in a river below a cottage, Guildford, Surrey (27x21cm-11x8in) s.verso pencil. 28-Nov-2 Sotheby's, London #304/R est:1500-2000

£1800 $2988 €2700 Slingsby Castle, Yorkshire (24x19cm-9x7in) s.i. pencil prov. 12-Jun-3 Bonhams, New Bond Street #636/R est:1000-1500

£2600 $4264 €3770 Study of farm buildings (21x16cm-8x6in) s. pencil wash prov. 5-Jun-3 Christie's, London #88/R est:2000-3000

£3800 $6004 €5700 Angler on bridge. Rabbit catcher in wooded landscape (38x21cm-15x8in) indis.sig. W/C oil over pencil board pair. 26-Nov-2 Christie's, London #69/R est:4000-6000

£4500 $7111 €6750 In the park of sir Robert Reade, Barsham, Suffolk (16x18cm-6x7in) s. brown washes prov. 28-Nov-2 Sotheby's, London #263/R est:4000-6000

£4500 $7470 €6750 Chepstow Castle (30x24cm-12x9in) i.verso W/C stopping out prov. 12-Jun-3 Bonhams, New Bond Street #629/R est:5000-8000

£8200 $11726 €12300 Church of Saint Michael lloking across the Waveneey, Suffolk (16x29cm-6x11in) s.i.d.1818 pencil wash prov.exhib.lit. 22-Jan-3 Christie's, London #16/R

£11000 $17380 €16500 Milton's paradise regained (32x44cm-13x17in) i.verso grey brown wash over pencil prov. 28-Nov-2 Sotheby's, London #262/R est:4000-6000

£11500 $18285 €17250 Shipping off Cromer, Norfolk (23x32cm-9x13in) s. W/C over pencil htd stopping out prov.exhib. 19-Mar-3 Sotheby's, London #165/R est:12000-18000

£12000 $17160 €18000 Windmill, Blackheath (16x28cm-6x11in) init.i. pencil W/C prov. 22-Jan-3 Christie's, London #15/R est:12000

COTMAN, John Sell (attrib) (1782-1842) British

£1500 $2445 €2250 River estuary with boats by a cottage (25x33cm-10x13in) 14-Feb-3 Keys, Aylsham #645/R est:800-1000

COTMAN, Miles Edmund (1810-1858) British

Works on paper

£900 $1494 €1350 Billingford church, Norfolk (18x29cm-7x11in) s. W/C prov. 12-Jun-3 Bonhams, New Bond Street #630

£950 $1549 €1425 River landscape scene with distant town, possibly Boston, Lincolnshire (12x26cm-5x10in) W/C pencil. 30-Jan-3 Lawrence, Crewkerne #609/R

£2200 $3388 €3300 Loaded barges in an estuary (23x33cm-9x13in) W/C. 22-Oct-2 Bonhams, Knightsbridge #29/R est:200-300

COTMAN, Miles Edmund (attrib) (1810-1858) British

£1500 $2355 €2250 Sailing boats with a brig in the background (19x27cm-7x11in) 16-Dec-2 Sotheby's, Olympia #28/R est:800-1200

Works on paper

£320 $493 €480 Chepstow Castle (20x18cm-8x7in) W/C. 5-Sep-2 Clevedon Sale Rooms #143

COTTAAR, Piet (1878-1950) Dutch

£577 $900 €866 Still life with flowers in a vase. s. 19-Oct-2 Harvey Clar, Oakland #1549

COTTAVOZ, Andre (1922-) French

£556 $878 €800 Sophie et la poupee (34x24cm-13x9in) s.d. s.i.d.verso panel. 28-Apr-3 Cornette de St.Cyr, Paris #250

£566 $877 €900 Nature morte au vase de fleurs (23x30cm-9x12in) s. panel. 30-Oct-2 Artcurial Briest, Paris #353/R

£724 $1144 €1050 Mer (27x35cm-11x14in) s.d.62 s.i.d.verso. 4-Apr-3 Tajan, Paris #244/R

£759 $1185 €1200 Orage en Toscane (50x66cm-20x26in) s.d.61 s.i.d.verso. 20-Oct-2 Anaf, Lyon #105

£818 $1267 €1300 Le depart pour l'ecole (24x35cm-9x14in) s. s.i.d.68 verso. 30-Oct-2 Artcurial Briest, Paris #354

£828 $1308 €1200 Muriel (55x38cm-22x15in) s.d.64 s.i.d.verso. 4-Apr-3 Tajan, Paris #243/R

£884 $1406 €1300 Portrait d'Anne-Marie (81x54cm-32x21in) s. s.i.d.4-60 verso prov. 26-Feb-3 Artcurial Briest, Paris #326

£939 $1540 €1362 Le portail rouge (50x73cm-20x29in) s. d.64 verso. 4-Jun-3 Fischer, Luzern #1085/R est:2500-3500 (S.FR 2000)

£943 $1462 €1500 La famille sur la terrase (38x46cm-15x18in) s.d.70 s.i.d.1970 verso. 30-Oct-2 Artcurial Briest, Paris #357 est:2000-2500

£1079 $1727 €1500 Autoportrait devant le miroir (81x65cm-32x26in) s. 18-May-3 Eric Pillon, Calais #287/R

£1517 $2534 €2200 Nu au repos (52x76cm-20x30in) s.d.76 paper on canvas. 10-Jul-3 Artcurial Briest, Paris #260/R est:2500-3000

£1582 $2468 €2500 Bouquet de fleurs (35x25cm-14x10in) s. panel. 20-Oct-2 Anaf, Lyon #106

£1633 $2596 €2400 Nu assis (100x73cm-39x29in) s.d.72. 26-Feb-3 Artcurial Briest, Paris #323/R est:2000-3000

£1667 $2367 €2700 Vase de fleurs (38x28cm-15x11in) s. panel. 16-Mar-3 Eric Pillon, Calais #252/R

Works on paper

£290 $475 €421 Le jardin (76x94cm-30x37in) s. W/C. 7-Jun-3 Susanin's, Chicago #5027/R

£833 $1317 €1200 Baigneurs (24x35cm-9x14in) s. d.55 verso mixed media on canvas. 25-Apr-3 Piasa, Paris #63

COTTER, Arthur (?) British

£353 $550 €530 Harvest time (61x91cm-24x36in) 22-Sep-2 Susanin's, Chicago #5033/R

COTTET, Charles (1863-1924) French

£417 $679 €600 Vue d'Alger (14x41cm-6x16in) s. cardboard. 19-Jul-3 Thierry & Lannon, Brest #112

£897 $1409 €1400 Retour des pecheurs (21x29cm-8x11in) s. paper. 21-Nov-2 Neret-Minet, Paris #39

£1255 $1996 €1820 Barques de peche sous voiles pres de camaret (35x50cm-14x20in) s. cardboard. 10-Mar-3 Thierry & Lannon, Brest #99/R

£1446 $2271 €2169 Sailing at sunset (41x56cm-16x22in) s. board prov. 24-Jul-2 Walker's, Ottawa #46/R est:3500-4000 (C.D 3500)

£2676 $4308 €3800 Village pres de la baie en Bretagne (41x54cm-16x21in) s. board. 11-May-3 Thierry & Lannon, Brest #156/R est:3800-4200

COTTINGHAM, Robert (1935-) American

£5128 $8000 €7692 Ritz hotel (53x79cm-21x31in) s.i.d.1982 verso acrylic prov. 5-Nov-2 Doyle, New York #47/R est:10000-15000

£17500 $28000 €26250 Keen Kottons (81x81cm-32x32in) s.i.d.1981 verso prov.exhib.lit. 15-May-3 Christie's, Rockefeller NY #166/R est:20000-30000

COTTON, Olive Edith (1911-) Australian

Photographs

£1512 $2314 €2268 Interior (26x35cm-10x14in) s.i. silver gelatin print. 25-Aug-2 Sotheby's, Paddington #101 est:1500-3000 (A.D 4250)

£4982 $7623 €7473 Tea cup ballet (35x28cm-14x11in) s.i.d.1935/1993 num.31/50 silver gelatin print. 25-Aug-2 Sotheby's, Paddington #92/R est:1500-3000 (A.D 14000)

COTTON, Shane (1964-) New Zealander

£1736 $2708 €2604 Untitled (36x55cm-14x22in) s.d.1994 acrylic. 8-Apr-3 Peter Webb, Auckland #24/R est:4500-6500 (NZ.D 5000)

£1937 $3195 €2809 Kupapa (28x35cm-11x14in) init.d.1997. 1-Jul-3 Peter Webb, Auckland #18/R est:5000-8000 (NZ.D 5500)

£4091 $6300 €6137 Untitled (25x50cm-10x20in) s. i.d.1994 verso. 4-Sep-2 Dunbar Sloane, Wellington #41/R est:8000-12000 (NZ.D 13500)

£4823 $7476 €7235 Kowaikoe (73x90cm-29x35in) s.d.1994. 4-Dec-2 Dunbar Sloane, Auckland #3/R est:16000-26000 (NZ.D 15000)

£7042 $11620 €10211 Koroniti IV (50x60cm-20x24in) init.d.1998 exhib. 1-Jul-3 Peter Webb, Auckland #17/R est:10000-15000 (NZ.D 20000)

COTTON, Will (1965-) American

£1582 $2500 €2373 Sprout (51x51cm-20x20in) painted 1997 prov. 12-Nov-2 Phillips, New York #219/R est:4000-6000

£9494 $15000 €14241 Candy houses (150x196cm-59x77in) s.d.1998 overlap exhib. 13-Nov-2 Sotheby's, New York #589/R est:12000-18000

COTTON, William (1880-1958) American

Works on paper

£4037 $6500 €6056 Young woman primping in museum's armour gallery (36x28cm-14x11in) s. pastel sold with magazine cover. 10-May-3 Illustration House, New York #7/R est:5000-7000

COTTRELL, H S (fl.1840-1860) British

£2000 $3320 €2900 Setting off for a day's shooting (22x30cm-9x12in) s. prov. 12-Jun-3 Christie's, Kensington #120/R est:1000-1500

COUASNON, Jean Louis (1747-1812) French

Sculpture

£16026 $24840 €25000 Portrait de mademoiselle Charlotte de Grouchy (47x23x21cm-19x9x8in) s.d.1775 marble lit. 9-Dec-2 Rabourdin & Choppin de Janvry, Paris #50/R est:30000

COUBINE, Othon (1883-1969) Czechoslovakian

£2759 $4607 €4000 Nature morte aux figues (38x46cm-15x18in) s. 10-Jul-3 Artcurial Briest, Paris #152/R est:4500-5000

£3481 $5500 €5500 Vue du village de Simiane (40x65cm-16x26in) s. 2-Dec-2 Tajan, Paris #114/R

£3924 $6121 €5886 Still life with bouquet and cactus (46x55cm-18x22in) s. 12-Oct-2 Dorotheum, Prague #105/R est:180000-270000 (C.KR 190000)

£4500 $6975 €6750 Irises with summer flowers in a vase (65x54cm-26x21in) s. prov. 5-Dec-2 Christie's, Kensington #93/R est:3000-4000

£5370 $8377 €8055 Winter landscape (60x75cm-24x30in) s. 12-Oct-2 Dorotheum, Prague #159/R est:260000-400000 (C.KR 260000)

£9294 $14498 €13941 Landscape in the Lower Alps (53x64cm-21x25in) s. exhib. 12-Oct-2 Dorotheum, Prague #157/R est:300000-450000 (C.KR 450000)

COUCH, Henry (19/20th C) British?

£320 $486 €480 Wartime scene of numerous army personnel and loved ones (43x66cm-17x26in) s.d.1918. 16-Aug-2 Keys, Aylsham #419/R

COUDER, Alexandre (1808-1879) French

£432 $691 €600 Le tendre amour (21x15cm-8x6in) s. panel. 18-May-3 Charbonneaux, Paris #139

£1004 $1567 €1506 Still life with peaches and wine glass (22x27cm-9x11in) s.d.1871. 20-Nov-2 Fischer, Luzern #1128/R est:2200-2500 (S.FR 2300)

£1096 $1710 €1600 Still life with fruit and flowers in a vase (46x55cm-18x22in) s. lit. 10-Apr-3 Allgauer, Kempten #2745/R est:1500

£1122 $1761 €1750 Nature morte aux fleurs (65x44cm-26x17in) s. 19-Nov-2 Vanderkindere, Brussels #151/R est:1750-2500

£1410 $2144 €2200 Interieur de cuisine (23x31cm-9x12in) s. panel. 10-Jul-2 Rabourdin & Choppin de Janvry, Paris #48/R est:2400-2600

COUDOUR, Henry (19/20th C) French

£267 $425 €401 Dans un parc (19x22cm-7x9in) i.verso. 7-Mar-3 Skinner, Boston #538/R

£283 $450 €425 Hillside landscape (26x27cm-10x11in) i.verso board. 7-Mar-3 Skinner, Boston #534/R

COUDRAY, Georges Charles (fl.1883-1903) French

Sculpture

£943 $1453 €1500 Serena (53cm-21in) s. bronze pat bronze. 22-Oct-2 Galerie Moderne, Brussels #1523/R

£1151 $1842 €1600 Buste de jeune fille (64cm-25in) s. white marble. 13-May-3 Vanderkindere, Brussels #162 est:800-1200

£1800 $2808 €2700 Lute player (74cm-29in) s.num.E 6793 red brown pat bronze st.f.Societe des Bronzes. 9-Apr-3 Sotheby's, London #204/R est:2000-3000

£3304 $5155 €4956 Art nouveau bust of a girl (63cm-25in) i. marble. 12-Oct-2 Dorotheum, Prague #300/R est:80000-120000 (C.KR 160000)

COULDERY, Horatio H (1832-1893) British

£1104 $1800 €1656 Dog in a manger (11x9cm-4x4in) s. paper on board. 11-Feb-3 Bonhams & Doyles, New York #186/R est:800-1200

£1200 $1956 €1800 Their first experience (46x69cm-18x27in) 12-Feb-3 Bonhams, Knightsbridge #121/R est:1000-1500

£1900 $3002 €2850 Pug (27x23cm-11x9in) s. i.verso canvas on board. 28-Nov-2 Christie's, Kensington #341/R est:1500-2000

£3200 $5344 €4640 Dispute (41x60cm-16x24in) s.d.1869. 17-Jun-3 Bonhams, New Bond Street #72/R est:4000-6000

£5200 $8684 €7540 Puppies playing with a doll (45x61cm-18x24in) s. 17-Jun-3 Bonhams, New Bond Street #71/R est:4000-6000

£5500 $8470 €8250 Stalking the pet mouse (30x36cm-12x14in) s. 5-Sep-2 Christie's, Kensington #263/R est:4000-6000

£6000 $9540 €9000 Captured audience (51x83cm-20x33in) s. 6-Mar-3 Christie's, Kensington #583/R est:6000-8000

£8200 $13120 €12300 Off guard (49x67cm-19x26in) s. 15-May-3 Lawrence, Crewkerne #996/R est:4000-6000

Works on paper

£1474 $2300 €2211 Head of a bull mastiff (42x20cm-17x8in) mono. chk pastel. 15-Oct-2 Stephan Welz, Johannesburg #380 est:6000-10000 (SA.R 24000)

COULENTIANOS, Costas (20th C) French

Sculpture

£4930 $8183 €7000 Totem (179cm-70in) soldered iron lead gold. 18-Jun-3 Anaf, Lyon #25/R est:3000-4000

£5000 $8300 €7100 Silhouettes (209x88cm-82x35in) gilt metal on two doors. 18-Jun-3 Anaf, Lyon #24/R est:3000-4000

COULON, George (1854-1922) American

£3125 $5000 €4531 Portrait of a black woman with a headkerchief (64x38cm-25x15in) s. 17-May-3 New Orleans Auction, New Orleans #927/R est:6000-9000

COULON, George D (1822-1904) American

£641 $1000 €962 Old church tower in Jamestown, Va (8x8cm-3x3in) init. i.verso paper. 12-Oct-2 Neal Auction Company, New Orleans #395/R

£671 $1100 €1007 Southern landscape (15x25cm-6x10in) 8-Feb-3 Neal Auction Company, New Orleans #340/R

£1053 $1705 €1527 Early morning on a Bayou (24x32cm-9x13in) s.d.1881 i.verso panel. 24-May-3 Rasmussen, Havnen #2268/R (D.KR 11000)

£1282 $2000 €1923 Louisiana bayou landscape (8x8cm-3x3in) init. i.verso paper. 12-Oct-2 Neal Auction Company, New Orleans #394/R est:2000-3000

COULON, Pauline (fl.1840-1875) American

Works on paper

£488 $800 €732 Nature morte of birds (41x33cm-16x13in) s. pastel. 8-Feb-3 Neal Auction Company, New Orleans #341

COULTER, Sam (1925-) British

£282 $468 €400 Bringing home the turf (39x50cm-15x20in) s. board. 10-Jun-3 James Adam, Dublin #100/R

COULTER, William Alexander (1849-1936) American

£1592 $2500 €2388 Ship in full sail (54x28cm-21x11in) s. canvas on board prov. 19-Nov-2 Butterfields, San Francisco #8140/R est:3000-5000

£1958 $3250 €2839 Off the rocks (29x44cm-11x17in) bears sig. canvasboard prov. 11-Jun-3 Butterfields, San Francisco #4191/R est:3000-5000

£4487 $7000 €6731 Moonlit by the bay. s.d.1874 board. 21-Sep-2 Harvey Clar, Oakland #1496

£11465 $18000 €17198 Boats in a harbour (36x61cm-14x24in) s. prov. 19-Nov-2 Butterfields, San Francisco #8138/R est:5000-7000

COUMONT, Charles (1822-1889) Flemish

£769 $1192 €1200 Famille napolitaine se deplacant au champ (60x92cm-24x36in) s. 9-Dec-2 Horta, Bruxelles #122

£1006 $1570 €1600 Shepherdess with sheep holding spindle (60x93cm-24x37in) s. lit. 20-Sep-2 Karlheinz Kaupp, Staufen #1950/R est:1600

COUNHAYE, Charles (1884-1971) Belgian

£284 $474 €400 Portrait d'homme (99x65cm-39x26in) s.d.55 panel. 18-Jun-3 Hotel des Ventes Mosan, Brussels #261

£616 $962 €900 Vase sur fond de fenetre ouverte (87x80cm-34x31in) s.d.35 exhib. 14-Apr-3 Horta, Bruxelles #322

£918 $1432 €1450 Grande soeur (56x45cm-22x18in) s.d.30. 16-Sep-2 Horta, Bruxelles #44

COUNIHAN, Noel Jack (1913-1986) Australian

£5179 $8494 €7769 Soldier (68x86cm-27x34in) s.d.66 composition board exhib. 4-Jun-3 Deutscher-Menzies, Melbourne #119/R est:14000-18000 (A.D 13000)

£21352 $32669 €32028 Wife (61x87cm-24x34in) s.d.55 board prov.exhib. 25-Aug-2 Sotheby's, Paddington #6/R est:40000-60000 (A.D 60000)

Works on paper

£304 $480 €456 Young woman (75x55cm-30x22in) s.d.1973 s.i.verso chl prov. 17-Nov-2 Sotheby's, Paddington #44/R (A.D 850)

£1068 $1633 €1602 Good life (21x28cm-8x11in) s.d.78 synthetic polymer paint prov. 26-Aug-2 Sotheby's, Paddington #582/R est:3000-5000 (A.D 3000)

COUNTESS DAUBIGNY DAFOY (19th C) French

Works on paper

£2000 $3340 €2900 Bouquet of peonies and tulips (40x31cm-16x12in) s.d.1835 W/C blk chk. 9-Jul-3 Sotheby's, London #118/R est:2000-2500

COUNTESS OF ABERDEEN, Ishbel Maria (19/20th C) British?

Works on paper

£201 $317 €302 Edmonton (13x23cm-5x9in) d.1894 W/C. 1-Dec-2 Levis, Calgary #1/R (C.D 500)

COUPE, Louise (1877-1915) Belgian

£461 $747 €650 Nature morte aux chrysanthemes (88x58cm-35x23in) 26-May-3 Amberes, Antwerp #24

COUPER, William (1853-1942) American

£778 $1300 €1128 Fishing boats in harbour, probably Rockport (51x61cm-20x24in) s. canvasboard prov. 17-Jun-3 John Moran, Pasadena #207 est:800-1200

COUPIN DE LA COUPERIE, Marie Philippe (attrib) (1773-1851) French

£2390 $3681 €3800 Diane de Poitiers implorant Francois Ier. 25-Oct-2 Tajan, Paris #146/R est:4000-5000

COUR, Janus la (1837-1909) Danish

£354 $563 €531 Wooded landscape (37x55cm-15x22in) indis sig.i.d.1869 i.stretcher. 10-Mar-3 Rasmussen, Vejle #290/R (D.KR 3800)
£359 $552 €539 Forest in spring (36x43cm-14x17in) prov. 4-Sep-2 Kunsthallen, Copenhagen #87 (D.KR 4200)
£474 $725 €711 Mountain landscape with waterfall (46x75cm-18x30in) s.d.1897. 24-Aug-2 Rasmussen, Havnen #2068/R (D.KR 5500)
£511 $807 €767 View across the water (27x39cm-11x15in) indis.i.d.1911. 27-Nov-2 Museumsbygningen, Copenhagen #86 (D.KR 6000)
£512 $814 €768 Mountain landscape (25x33cm-10x13in) init.d.5 Juni 1874. 5-Mar-3 Rasmussen, Copenhagen #1699 (D.KR 5500)
£523 $841 €785 Hilly heath landscape with flowering heather (42x68cm-17x27in) s.d.4 oktbr 1886. 26-Feb-3 Museumsbygningen, Copenhagen #8 (D.KR 5800)
£552 $862 €828 Fjord landscape (23x40cm-9x16in) mono.d.juli 1873. 5-Aug-2 Rasmussen, Vejle #198/R (D.KR 6500)
£555 $899 €833 Hilly heath landscape (21x28cm-8x11in) indis sig. verso. 21-May-3 Museumsbygningen, Copenhagen #6/R (D.KR 5800)
£657 $1051 €986 Landscape from Silkeborg Islands (63x100cm-25x39in) s. 13-Jan-3 Rasmussen, Vejle #140/R (D.KR 7500)
£718 $1163 €1041 Coastal landscape, Aarhus Bay (46x76cm-18x30in) s.d.19 Aug 1894. 26-May-3 Rasmussen, Copenhagen #1413/R (D.KR 7500)
£772 $1204 €1158 Coastal landscape from Moesgaard (44x70cm-17x28in) s.d.1 aug.1886. 11-Nov-2 Rasmussen, Vejle #640/R (D.KR 9000)
£861 $1309 €1292 Marshy landscape with trees (30x50cm-12x20in) s.d.1859. 27-Aug-2 Rasmussen, Copenhagen #1938/R (D.KR 10000)
£1053 $1705 €1527 Transporting ice across Storebaelt (32x57cm-13x22in) init.d.20 Januar 1861 prov. 26-May-3 Rasmussen, Copenhagen #1364/R (D.KR 11000)
£1184 $1965 €1717 View towards Monte Rosa, Switzerland (44x76cm-17x30in) s.d.17-8-98. 12-Jun-3 Kunsthallen, Copenhagen #357/R est:15000 (D.KR 12500)
£1914 $3100 €2775 Winter landscape with thatched farm near Snekkersten (60x94cm-24x37in) s.d.1888. 24-May-3 Rasmussen, Havnen #2167/R est:8000-10000 (D.KR 20000)
£2679 $4341 €3885 Coastal landscape with storm approaching and reflection of sun in water (88x123cm-35x48in) s.d.1883-1886. 26-May-3 Rasmussen, Copenhagen #1171/R est:20000-25000 (D.KR 28000)
£2756 $4189 €4134 Landscape by Juel Lake, summer evening in June (46x70cm-18x28in) s.d.1876 exhib.prov. 27-Aug-2 Rasmussen, Copenhagen #1416/R est:12000-15000 (D.KR 32000)
£3828 $6201 €5551 Sunset over field landscape with trees by river (82x132cm-32x52in) s.d.1861. 26-May-3 Rasmussen, Copenhagen #1147/R est:15000-25000 (D.KR 40000)

Works on paper

£605 $962 €908 Les hautes Pyrenees Arreau (32x42cm-13x17in) init.i.d.30 juli 1865 pen W/C exhib. 5-Mar-3 Rasmussen, Copenhagen #2076/R (D.KR 6500)

COUR, Janus la (attrib) (1837-1909) Danish

£325 $527 €488 Coastal landscape with beach and dunes (13x34cm-5x13in) prov. 21-May-3 Museumsbygningen, Copenhagen #5 (D.KR 3400)

COURANT, Maurice (1847-1925) French

£352 $567 €500 La cote sauvage (73x100cm-29x39in) s. 12-May-3 Lesieur & Le Bars, Le Havre #19
£750 $1185 €1125 Calm day on the river with a busy town beyond (38x56cm-15x22in) s. 14-Nov-2 Christie's, Kensington #176/R
£2372 $3724 €3700 Plage de Sainte-Adresse (38x56cm-15x22in) s.d.1904. 24-Nov-2 Lesieur & Le Bars, Le Havre #25/R

COURBET, G (1819-1877) French

£949 $1500 €1500 Village montagnard anime de personnages (65x54cm-26x21in) s. 26-Nov-2 Palais de Beaux Arts, Brussels #404 est:1500-2000

COURBET, Gustave (1819-1877) French

£5240 $8175 €7860 Landscape study (40x32cm-16x13in) s. 20-Nov-2 Fischer, Luzern #1092/R est:5500-6500 (S.FR 12000)
£6389 $10094 €9200 Chute d'eau (23x23cm-9x9in) mono. a. lit. 23-Apr-3 Rabourdin & Choppin de Janvry, Paris #15/R
£7692 $12077 €12000 Petit pont (86x20cm-34x8in) bears sig. painted 1876 prov.lit. 10-Dec-2 Artcurial Briest, Paris #460/R est:12000-15000
£12658 $19620 €20000 Bord de mer avec barque echouee sous ciel orageux (50x60cm-20x24in) s. lit. 24-Sep-2 Galerie Moderne, Brussels #879/R est:20000-30000
£14583 $23042 €21000 Tete de biche (31x50cm-12x20in) mono. 23-Apr-3 Rabourdin & Choppin de Janvry, Paris #13/R est:15000
£25641 $40256 €40000 Paysage avec un pecheur (65x81cm-26x32in) s. prov.exhib.lit. 16-Dec-2 Millon & Associes, Paris #156/R est:20000-30000
£29032 $45000 €43548 Le glacier (27x41cm-11x16in) s. prov.exhib. 30-Oct-2 Christie's, Rockefeller NY #20/R est:35000-45000
£40000 $65600 €60000 La petite bergere - young shepherdess (51x66cm-20x26in) s.d.76 prov. 3-Jun-3 Sotheby's, London #143/R est:40000-60000
£44304 $70000 €66456 Portrait of Madame Frond (65x51cm-26x20in) s. prov.exhib.lit. 24-Apr-3 Sotheby's, New York #33/R est:100000-150000
£60897 $95609 €95000 Marine a Deauville (50x73cm-20x29in) exhib. 13-Dec-2 Piasa, Paris #3/R est:80000
£63291 $100000 €94937 La grotte humide (50x60cm-20x24in) s. painted 1864 prov. 23-Apr-3 Christie's, Rockefeller NY #37/R est:50000-70000
£72917 $115208 €105000 Cerfs a la neige (43x59cm-17x23in) s. painted c.1866. 23-Apr-3 Rabourdin & Choppin de Janvry, Paris #14/R est:30000-50000
£113924 $180000 €170886 Jeune fille dormant (39x47cm-15x19in) s. painted 1847 prov.exhib.lit. 23-Apr-3 Christie's, Rockefeller NY #42/R est:200000-300000
£126582 $200000 €189873 Rendez-vous de chasse (59x72cm-23x28in) painted 1862 prov.exhib.lit. 23-Apr-3 Christie's, Rockefeller NY #35/R est:200000-300000
£126582 $200000 €189873 Portrait of Urbain Cuenot (95x75cm-37x30in) s. prov.exhib.lit. 24-Apr-3 Sotheby's, New York #32/R est:200000-300000
£139241 $220000 €208862 La vague (25x54cm-10x21in) s. 24-Apr-3 Sotheby's, New York #19/R est:100000-150000
£154839 $240000 €232259 Family of deer in a landscape with a waterfall (81x60cm-32x24in) s. prov.exhib. 30-Oct-2 Christie's, Rockefeller NY #14/R est:300000-400000
£202532 $320000 €303798 Le moulin de Longeville (80x130cm-31x51in) s.d.68 prov.exhib.lit. 24-Apr-3 Sotheby's, New York #18/R est:400000-600000
£250000 $410000 €375000 Les bords de la mer, Palavas (48x65cm-19x26in) s. prov.exhib.lit. 3-Jun-3 Sotheby's, London #139/R est:150000-200000

Sculpture

£9494 $15000 €14241 La dame a la mouette - woman with the seagull (70cm-28in) s. white plaster prov. 24-Apr-3 Sotheby's, New York #23/R est:20000-30000

COURBET, Gustave (attrib) (1819-1877) French

£450 $702 €675 Alpine township by a lakeside (48x71cm-19x28in) s. 20-Sep-2 Richardson & Smith, Whitby #58
£786 $1226 €1179 Hunting scene (37x37cm-15x15in) i. 6-Nov-2 Dobiaschofsky, Bern #423/R est:2400 (S.FR 1800)
£5660 $8830 €9000 Rocky landscape with ruin (48x59cm-19x23in) bears sig. 20-Sep-2 Millon & Associes, Paris #241/R est:12000-20000

Works on paper

£339 $540 €500 Forteresse (15x22cm-6x9in) crayon prov.exhib. 24-Mar-3 Tajan, Paris #183
£339 $540 €500 Plantes au bord de ruisseau (18x31cm-7x12in) crayon prov.exhib. 24-Mar-3 Tajan, Paris #196
£840 $1328 €1260 Study for The stone cutters (33x42cm-13x17in) bears sig.i.indis.d.1867 mixed media prov. 16-Nov-2 Crafoord, Lund #45/R est:8000 (S.KR 12000)

COURBET, Gustave (circle) (1819-1877) French

£5714 $8514 €8800 Woman's portrait (46x37cm-18x15in) i. prov. 26-Jun-2 Neumeister, Munich #705/R est:3500

COURBET, Gustave (style) (1819-1877) French

£392 $620 €620 Riviere de montagne (58x51cm-23x20in) panel. 27-Nov-2 Lemoine & Ferrando, Paris #71

COURBET, Gustave and ORDINAIRE, Marcel (19th C) French

£2222 $3511 €3200 Maison dans un paysage de montagne suisse (37x49cm-15x19in) bears sig. 23-Apr-3 Rabourdin & Choppin de Janvry, Paris #11/R
£4306 $6803 €6200 Bord de riviere dans le Jura francais (32x45cm-13x18in) s. 23-Apr-3 Rabourdin & Choppin de Janvry, Paris #8/R

COURBET, Gustave and PATA, Cherubino (19th C) French

£2014 $3182 €2900 Paysage d'automne (50x61cm-20x24in) s. 23-Apr-3 Rabourdin & Choppin de Janvry, Paris #6/R
£2292 $3621 €3300 Paysage du Jura (50x61cm-20x24in) s.d.77. 23-Apr-3 Rabourdin & Choppin de Janvry, Paris #7/R
£2778 $4389 €4000 Chute d'eau en foret (35x23cm-14x9in) mono. canvas on panel. 23-Apr-3 Rabourdin & Choppin de Janvry, Paris #9/R

COURBIER, Marcel Louis Maurice (1898-1976) French
Sculpture
£9353 $14964 €13000 Femme nue (110x39x32cm-43x15x13in) s. stone. 19-May-3 Tajan, Paris #175/R est:12000-15000

COURDOUAN, Vincent-Joseph-François (1810-1893) French
Works on paper
£1465 $2285 €2300 Bedouins (11x15cm-4x6in) s. dr pair. 10-Nov-2 Deauville, France #23/R

COURMES, Alfred (1898-1993) French
£9014 $14332 €13250 Persee delivrera Andromede (54x65cm-21x26in) s.d.43. 26-Feb-3 Artcurial Briest, Paris #303/R est:10000-12000
Works on paper
£2313 $3678 €3400 Escadron d'Amazones au repos (90x70cm-35x28in) s.i.d.1975 pencil tracing paper two parts prov. 26-Feb-3 Artcurial Briest, Paris #514/R est:3000-3300

COURREAU, Paul (19th C) French
£298 $471 €447 Apres midi d'Ete (32x47cm-13x19in) s. panel. 2-Dec-2 Rasmussen, Copenhagen #1289/R (D.KR 3500)

COURT, Joseph-Desire (1797-1865) French
£2837 $4738 €4000 Portrait de femme assise pres d'un bouquet de fleurs (130x97cm-51x38in) s.d.1841. 23-Jun-3 Beaussant & Lefèvre, Paris #282/R est:3000-4000

COURT, Lee Winslow (1903-) American
£938 $1500 €1407 Mt. Washington winter scene (46x81cm-18x32in) s. init.d.52 verso. 11-Jan-3 James Julia, Fairfield #196b est:1000-2000
£1063 $1700 €1595 Freedom from disturbance (51x86cm-20x34in) s. 11-Jan-3 James Julia, Fairfield #196a est:1000-2000

COURTEN, Comte Angelo de (1848-1925) Italian
£6481 $10435 €9397 Diana and lion (65x83cm-26x33in) s. 7-May-3 Dobiaschofsky, Bern #423/R est:17000 (S.FR 14000)

COURTENS, Alfred (1889-1967) Belgian
£5346 $8286 €8500 Coucher de soleil (76x110cm-30x43in) s.d.76. 5-Oct-2 De Vuyst, Lokeren #432/R est:8500-9500
Sculpture
£1655 $2615 €2400 Profils des cinq premiers souverains de Belgique (18x30cm-7x12in) s.i.d.1956 gold bronze bas relief black marble socle. 2-Apr-3 Vanderkindere, Brussels #181/R est:200-300
£1724 $2724 €2500 Profils des cinq premiers souverains de Belgique (18x30cm-7x12in) s.i.d.1956 gold bronze bas relief black marble socle. 2-Apr-3 Vanderkindere, Brussels #180/R est:200-300
£3529 $5682 €5400 Pecheur de la mer du Nord sur son ane (50cm-20in) s.d.1924 gilt pat bronze st.f.Petterman a St Gilles. 20-Jan-3 Horta, Bruxelles #130/R est:3500-4500
£4114 $6418 €6500 Jeune orientale a l'ombrelle (59cm-23in) s. 15-Oct-2 Horta, Bruxelles #164/R

COURTENS, Franz (1854-1943) Belgian
£426 $689 €600 Dreve (45x31cm-18x12in) 26-May-3 Amberes, Antwerp #25
£870 $1400 €1305 Sheep on country lane (81x61cm-32x24in) s. 20-Jan-3 Arthur James, Florida #696
£968 $1529 €1500 Vue de village (35x26cm-14x10in) s. panel. 17-Dec-2 Palais de Beaux Arts, Brussels #478 est:1500-2000
£1899 $2962 €3000 La gardienne de troupeau (70x51cm-28x20in) s. 10-Sep-2 Vanderkindere, Brussels #280 est:2000-3000
£3957 $6331 €5500 Lever de soleil, l'hiver (76x111cm-30x44in) s. 13-May-3 Vanderkindere, Brussels #26/R est:5000-7500
£4676 $7482 €6500 Voiliers en Mer du Nord (44x68cm-17x27in) s. 13-May-3 Palais de Beaux Arts, Brussels #51/R est:6000-8000
£6897 $11034 €10000 Vaches au bord d'un cours d'eau (112x180cm-44x71in) s.d.29. 17-Mar-3 Horta, Bruxelles #141/R est:6500-8500

COURTENS, Hermann (1884-1956) Belgian
£355 $592 €500 Still life with flowers (39x47cm-15x19in) s. 23-Jun-3 Bernaerts, Antwerp #409/R
£380 $592 €600 Nature morte aux fruits sur en entablement (35x25cm-14x10in) s. panel. 10-Sep-2 Vanderkindere, Brussels #351
£472 $726 €750 Still life with cherries (62x81cm-24x32in) s. 22-Oct-2 Campo & Campo, Antwerp #51/R
£544 $865 €800 Bouquet de fleurs (60x80cm-24x31in) s. 19-Mar-3 Hotel des Ventes Mosan, Brussels #300
£1151 $1842 €1600 Etain et chrysanthemes (115x97cm-45x38in) s. 13-May-3 Palais de Beaux Arts, Brussels #228 est:1500-2000
£1854 $3023 €2800 Elegante admirant son collier (47x38cm-19x15in) s. panel. 17-Feb-3 Horta, Bruxelles #165/R
£3576 $5829 €5400 Composition aux fleurs et aux oranges (80x105cm-31x41in) s. 17-Feb-3 Horta, Bruxelles #166
£13924 $21722 €22000 Femme au perroquet (141x108cm-56x43in) s. 20-Oct-2 Mercier & Cie, Lille #319/R est:12000-14000

COURTICE, Rody Kenny (1895-?) Canadian
£356 $583 €534 Weather bird (72x52cm-28x20in) board. 3-Jun-3 Joyner, Toronto #363/R (C.D 800)
£578 $948 €867 Butternut and pears (27x36cm-11x14in) s. board prov. 3-Jun-3 Joyner, Toronto #424/R est:500-700 (C.D 1300)

COURTIN, Pierre (1921-) French
Works on paper
£897 $1409 €1400 UN. (66x51cm-26x20in) s. gouache exec.1970. 15-Dec-2 Perrin, Versailles #10/R

COURTOIS, Albert de (19th C) French?
£331 $530 €480 Street peddlers (56x46cm-22x18in) s.d.1860. 15-Mar-3 De Vuyst, Lokeren #79

COURTOIS, Jacques (1621-1676) French
£5240 $8279 €7860 Battle scenes (23x35cm-9x14in) pair prov. 17-Nov-2 Koller, Geneva #1247/R est:15000 (S.FR 12000)
£7432 $11595 €11000 Cavalry engagement between Christian and Turkish troops (57x73cm-22x29in) 27-Mar-3 Dorotheum, Vienna #314/R est:2000-3000

COURTOIS, Jacques (attrib) (1621-1676) French
£4655 $7541 €6750 Old Testament scene with Moses and the Israelites leaving Egypt (92x142cm-36x56in) 26-May-3 Bukowskis, Stockholm #429/R est:80000-100000 (S.KR 60000)

COURTOIS, Jacques (circle) (1621-1676) French
£4340 $6771 €6510 Cavalry skirmish (35x67cm-14x26in) 19-Sep-2 Christie's, Kensington #188/R est:1000-1500
£6962 $10791 €11000 Turkish slaughter (99x134cm-39x53in) 25-Sep-2 Neumeister, Munich #470/R est:2500
£7134 $11129 €11200 Battle scenes (29x72cm-11x28in) two. 6-Nov-2 Hugo Ruef, Munich #946/R est:3000
£7447 $11543 €11171 Battle scene (69x141cm-27x56in) 3-Dec-2 Bukowskis, Stockholm #473/R est:30000-35000 (S.KR 105000)

COURTOIS, Jacques (style) (1621-1676) French
£9000 $15030 €13050 Battle scene with Turks and Christians before a bridge (72x135cm-28x53in) 8-Jul-3 Sotheby's, Olympia #427/R est:6000-8000

COURTONNE, Jean (attrib) (1671-1739) French
Works on paper
£355 $592 €500 Projet d'un pavillon aux armes du duc d'Antin (33x21cm-13x8in) i.verso pen wash. 23-Jun-3 Beaussant & Lefèvre, Paris #270

COURTRIGHT, Robert (1926-) American
£288 $456 €450 Composition in blue (76x16cm-30x6in) s.d.90. 18-Nov-2 Rieunier, Paris #160
£417 $658 €650 Composition in red (140x71cm-55x28in) s.d.90. 18-Nov-2 Rieunier, Paris #170
Works on paper
£256 $405 €400 Composition (92cm-36in circular) s.d.90 torn newspapers collage. 18-Nov-2 Rieunier, Paris #169
£288 $456 €450 Red composition (70x70cm-28x28in) s.d.90 mixed media. 18-Nov-2 Rieunier, Paris #165
£288 $456 €450 Composition in blue and red (70x70cm-28x28in) mixed media. 18-Nov-2 Rieunier, Paris #164
£346 $550 €519 Porta San Lorenzo, Rome (36x74cm-14x29in) s.d.55 collage prov. 18-Mar-3 Doyle, New York #60/R
£617 $1000 €895 Untitled (76x56cm-30x22in) s.d.76 white paper collage pencil prov. 21-May-3 Doyle, New York #41/R
£962 $1510 €1500 Relief (50x35cm-20x14in) s.d.62 collage relief. 24-Nov-2 Laurence Calmels, Paris #79/R

COUSE, E Irving (1866-1936) American
£2548 $4000 €3822 Sketch for Beacon blanket (26x19cm-10x7in) sold with a letter. 22-Nov-2 Skinner, Boston #146/R est:6000-8000
£2556 $4140 €3706 Landscape (23x30cm-9x12in) 23-May-3 Altermann Galleries, Santa Fe #196
£3822 $6000 €5733 Dedication to the sun of a newborn child (24x20cm-9x8in) 22-Nov-2 Skinner, Boston #148/R est:5000-7000
£4088 $6500 €6132 Clouds over Taos Valley (25x20cm-10x8in) s.i. s.d.1911 verso board. 5-Mar-3 Sotheby's, New York #137/R est:7000-10000
£7911 $12500 €11867 Figures at the seashore (58x71cm-23x28in) s. canvas on board. 26-Apr-3 Jeffery Burchard, Florida #100

£16975 $27500 €25463 Indian woman with child in blanket (117x51cm-46x20in) s. painted c.1916-24 prov.lit. 21-May-3 Sotheby's, New York #222/R est:20000-30000
£23734 $37500 €34414 New pipe (20x25cm-8x10in) s. board prov. 26-Jul-3 Coeur d'Alene, Hayden #123/R est:15000-25000
£24038 $37500 €36057 Indian by fireside (23x28cm-9x11in) s. board prov. 9-Nov-2 Santa Fe Art, Santa Fe #85/R est:35000-55000
£32051 $50000 €48077 Moonlight resting (41x30cm-16x12in) s. s.i.verso board prov.lit. 9-Nov-2 Santa Fe Art, Santa Fe #36/R est:40000-50000
£34414 $55750 €49900 Quiver maker (25x30cm-10x12in) 23-May-3 Altermann Galleries, Santa Fe #68
£61644 $90000 €92466 Mountain birds (91x76cm-36x30in) 18-May-2 Altermann Galleries, Santa Fe #34/R
£68364 $110750 €99128 Tomahawk pipe (51x61cm-20x24in) 23-May-3 Altermann Galleries, Santa Fe #74
£111111 $180000 €166667 Indian boy and brave looking at a blanket (125x149cm-49x59in) s. painted c.1916-24 prov.lit. 21-May-3 Sotheby's, New York #218/R est:150000-250000
£197531 $320000 €296297 Indian examining a blanket (118x117cm-46x46in) s. painted 1922 prov.lit. 21-May-3 Sotheby's, New York #219/R est:125000-175000

Works on paper
£2885 $4500 €4328 Across the dunes (36x53cm-14x21in) W/C. 9-Nov-2 Altermann Galleries, Santa Fe #179

COUSE, William Percy (1898-?) American
£497 $800 €746 Young man and older couple in interior (5x91cm-2x36in) s.d.1925. 20-Feb-3 Illustration House, New York #33/R

COUSIN, Charles (19/20th C) French
£350 $553 €525 Villa on the Mediterranean coast (54x65cm-21x26in) s. 14-Nov-2 Christie's, Kensington #133/R
£490 $804 €750 View of Venice (35x26cm-14x10in) s. panel. 7-Feb-3 Oger, Dumont, Paris #65
£828 $1382 €1200 Cap d'Antibes, barques de pecheurs (50x100cm-20x39in) s. 8-Jul-3 Gioffredo, Nice #30/R
£1006 $1560 €1600 View of Venice (16x22cm-6x9in) s. board. 29-Oct-2 Finarte, Milan #453
£1603 $2516 €2500 Venise (73x54cm-29x21in) s. pair. 16-Dec-2 Millon & Associes, Paris #124/R est:2500-3500
£1740 $2750 €2610 Canal in Venice (56x46cm-22x18in) s. canvas on canvas. 5-Apr-3 Neal Auction Company, New Orleans #168 est:4000-6000

COUSIN, Jean I (attrib) (1490-1560) French
Works on paper
£61728 $100000 €92592 Destruction of the servants and flocks of Job (20x49cm-8x19in) pen ink wash htd white prov. 21-Jan-3 Sotheby's, New York #23a/R est:70000

COUSINS, Albert H (20th C) British
Works on paper
£280 $431 €420 Nude in a romantic landscape (33x21cm-13x8in) s.d.19 W/C. 22-Oct-2 Bonhams, Knightsbridge #58/R

COUSSEE (?) ?
Sculpture
£1400 $2212 €2100 Diana (66cm-26in) s. bronze. 14-Nov-2 Christie's, Kensington #199/R est:1000-1500

COUSTOU, Jean (attrib) (1719-1791) French
£8392 $14014 €12000 Allegorie de l'Amerique. Allegorie de l'Afrique (96x135cm-38x53in) pair. 25-Jun-3 Sotheby's, Paris #30/R est:12000-15000

COUSTURIER, Lucie (1876-1925) French
£2138 $3314 €3400 Fleurs et statuettes (46x55cm-18x22in) s. prov. 30-Oct-2 Artcurial Briest, Paris #178/R est:4000-6000

COUTACHE, Benjamin (19th C) ?
£690 $1097 €1000 Figures in the desert (41x60cm-16x24in) s.d.1846. 4-Mar-3 Ansorena, Madrid #138/R

COUTAN, Jules Felix (1848-1939) French
Sculpture
£2564 $4000 €3846 Union travail paix (69x38x36cm-27x15x14in) s.i. pat bronze lit. 12-Oct-2 Neal Auction Company, New Orleans #569/R est:4000-6000

COUTAUD, Lucien (1904-1977) French
£276 $441 €400 Les deux pecheurs honfleurais (50x61cm-20x24in) s. s.i.d.3.11.68 verso paper. 14-Mar-3 Millon & Associes, Paris #272
£276 $441 €400 Fauteuil et canape (32x38cm-13x15in) s.d. s.i.d.1968 verso paper. 14-Mar-3 Millon & Associes, Paris #284
£276 $441 €400 Dans la nuit (25x32cm-10x13in) s.d. s.i.d.2.11.68 verso paper. 14-Mar-3 Millon & Associes, Paris #285
£276 $441 €400 Nimois et nimoise (61x50cm-24x20in) s.d.70 paper. 14-Mar-3 Millon & Associes, Paris #296
£276 $441 €400 Proche d'un depart (60x51cm-24x20in) s.d. s.i.d.11.68 verso paper. 14-Mar-3 Millon & Associes, Paris #297
£297 $474 €430 Personnage solitaire (38x31cm-15x12in) s.d.68 i.verso oil gouache paper. 14-Mar-3 Millon & Associes, Paris #121/R
£310 $497 €450 L'un deux possedait le cheval (51x60cm-20x24in) s.d. s.i.d.12.68 verso paper. 14-Mar-3 Millon & Associes, Paris #300
£310 $497 €450 Bientot octobre (16x21cm-6x8in) s.d. s.i.d.9.75 verso. 14-Mar-3 Millon & Associes, Paris #309
£345 $552 €500 Filles de la campagne (50x61cm-20x24in) s.d.68 s.i.verso paper. 14-Mar-3 Millon & Associes, Paris #270
£345 $552 €500 Quelques mains de plus (33x40cm-13x16in) s.d. s.i.d.16.12.68 verso paper. 14-Mar-3 Millon & Associes, Paris #291
£345 $552 €500 La nuit des deux fauteuils (51x60cm-20x24in) s.d. s.i.11.68 verso paper. 14-Mar-3 Millon & Associes, Paris #302
£379 $607 €550 Il va pleuvoir (16x21cm-6x8in) s.d. s.i.d.avril 73 verso. 14-Mar-3 Millon & Associes, Paris #307
£414 $662 €600 Deux femmes de pecheurs (50x61cm-20x24in) s.d.68 s.i.verso paper. 14-Mar-3 Millon & Associes, Paris #268
£414 $662 €600 Elle ecoutait (50x61cm-20x24in) s.d.69 paper. 14-Mar-3 Millon & Associes, Paris #280
£448 $717 €650 Lys estival (46x38cm-18x15in) s.d. s.i.d.14.7.66 verso. 14-Mar-3 Millon & Associes, Paris #288/R
£469 $750 €680 Elles sont en avance (49x64cm-19x25in) s.d. s.i.d.11.74 verso paper. 14-Mar-3 Millon & Associes, Paris #298
£483 $772 €700 Discussion maritime (50x61cm-20x24in) s. s.i.d.11.68 verso paper. 14-Mar-3 Millon & Associes, Paris #274
£517 $828 €750 Le soleil disparaissait (50x61cm-20x24in) s.d. s.i.d.68 verso. 14-Mar-3 Millon & Associes, Paris #299/R
£538 $861 €780 Villervilloise de Mer (60x50cm-24x20in) s.d.68 i.verso oil gouache paper. 14-Mar-3 Millon & Associes, Paris #125/R
£552 $883 €800 La plage du cheval de Brique (50x61cm-20x24in) s.d.68 s.i.verso paper. 14-Mar-3 Millon & Associes, Paris #266
£552 $883 €800 Trois dames de dirigeant vers la mer (38x46cm-15x18in) s.d.58 paper. 14-Mar-3 Millon & Associes, Paris #282
£552 $883 €800 Trois personnages (16x21cm-6x8in) s. s.d.2 aout 73 verso. 14-Mar-3 Millon & Associes, Paris #306
£552 $883 €800 Les deux maisons (62x50cm-24x20in) s.d. s.i.d.70 verso. 14-Mar-3 Millon & Associes, Paris #323
£552 $883 €800 A mains basses (45x55cm-18x22in) s.d.69 s.i.d.verso. 14-Mar-3 Millon & Associes, Paris #339/R
£566 $877 €900 Nue (22x14cm-9x6in) s. s.i.d.1973 verso. 30-Oct-2 Artcurial Briest, Paris #404
£586 $938 €850 Fin d'un mois de decembre (50x61cm-20x24in) s. s.i.d.12.1968 verso paper. 14-Mar-3 Millon & Associes, Paris #276
£586 $938 €850 Un deux aout (48x54cm-19x21in) s.d. s.i.d.75 verso. 14-Mar-3 Millon & Associes, Paris #319
£621 $993 €900 Agglomeration (46x38cm-18x15in) s.d. s.i.d.3.71 verso. 14-Mar-3 Millon & Associes, Paris #314/R
£690 $1103 €1000 Un 15.8.75 (54x73cm-21x29in) s.d. s.i.d.verso. 14-Mar-3 Millon & Associes, Paris #327
£690 $1103 €1000 Fleurs des champs et d'ailleurs (46x54cm-18x21in) s.d. s.i.d.4.6.67 verso. 14-Mar-3 Millon & Associes, Paris #332
£690 $1103 €1000 Conversation champetre (18x15cm-7x6in) s. i.d.1955 verso. 14-Mar-3 Millon & Associes, Paris #344
£759 $1214 €1100 Deux personnage d'ete (65x92cm-26x36in) s.d.76 s.i.d.verso. 14-Mar-3 Millon & Associes, Paris #333/R
£759 $1214 €1100 Quelques personnages (55x46cm-22x18in) s.d. s.i.d.9.4.73 verso. 14-Mar-3 Millon & Associes, Paris #349
£793 $1269 €1150 Le fauteuil de Pentecote (73x92cm-29x36in) s.d.76 s.i.d.verso. 14-Mar-3 Millon & Associes, Paris #335/R
£828 $1324 €1200 Une fois de plus (55x46cm-22x18in) s.d. s.i.d.8.9.68 verso. 14-Mar-3 Millon & Associes, Paris #305/R
£897 $1434 €1300 Sans titre (46x56cm-18x22in) s.d. s.i.d.29.8.71 verso. 14-Mar-3 Millon & Associes, Paris #324/R
£897 $1434 €1300 Reunion champetre (54x73cm-21x29in) s.d. s.i.d.Juillet 1975 verso. 14-Mar-3 Millon & Associes, Paris #337/R
£897 $1434 €1300 Quelques bonnes idees (46x56cm-18x22in) s.d. s.i.d.9.8.70 verso. 14-Mar-3 Millon & Associes, Paris #350/R
£931 $1490 €1350 Ils attendent (45x61cm-18x24in) s.d. i.d.12.44 verso. 14-Mar-3 Millon & Associes, Paris #331
£931 $1490 €1350 Trois etudes de nus (56x46cm-22x18in) s.d. s.i.d.25.8.1971 verso. 14-Mar-3 Millon & Associes, Paris #334/R
£949 $1500 €1500 Derniere de toutes (73x60cm-29x24in) s.d.72 s.i.d.verso. 27-Nov-2 Blanchet, Paris #55/R
£966 $1545 €1400 Ou vont-elles (48x54cm-19x21in) s.d. s.i.d.8.75 verso. 14-Mar-3 Millon & Associes, Paris #320
£1000 $1600 €1450 Personnages lunaires (50x61cm-20x24in) s.d. s.i.d.1.70 verso. 14-Mar-3 Millon & Associes, Paris #281/R
£1000 $1600 €1450 Elles ne voulaient pas s'asseoir (38x55cm-15x22in) s.d. s.i.d.21.8.69 verso. 14-Mar-3 Millon & Associes, Paris #346/R
£1034 $1655 €1500 Quelques fleurs (48x54cm-19x21in) s.d. s.i.d.juillet 75 verso. 14-Mar-3 Millon & Associes, Paris #318
£1034 $1655 €1500 Demoiselles de l'estuaire (54x73cm-21x29in) s. s.i.d.8.7.1975 verso. 14-Mar-3 Millon & Associes, Paris #329
£1138 $1821 €1650 Nu aux trois soufflets (54x48cm-21x19in) s.i.d.27.7.57 verso. 14-Mar-3 Millon & Associes, Paris #315
£1241 $1986 €1800 Les trois poissons (55x44cm-22x17in) s.d. s.i.d.12.56. 14-Mar-3 Millon & Associes, Paris #269/R

£1380 $2180 €2000 Jeune chasseur (92x73cm-36x29in) s. 4-Apr-3 Tajan, Paris #234/R
£1448 $2317 €2100 Elles arrivent en septembre (73x92cm-29x36in) s.d.75 s.i.d.verso. 14-Mar-3 Millon & Associes, Paris #322/R
£1456 $2300 €2300 Autre Normandie (65x100cm-26x39in) s.d.71 s.i.d.verso. 27-Nov-2 Blanchet, Paris #56/R
£1497 $2380 €2200 L'ile enchantee (190x335cm-75x132in) s.d.39 grisaille. 28-Feb-3 Tajan, Paris #14/R est:2500-3000
£1517 $2428 €2200 Femmes (54x73cm-21x29in) s.d.77. 14-Mar-3 Millon & Associes, Paris #325
£1724 $2759 €2500 En souvenir de nombreux mois de Mai (98x130cm-39x51in) s.d. s.i.d.31.4.73 verso. 14-Mar-3 Millon & Associes, Paris #343/R
£1759 $2814 €2550 Paysage estival (92x73cm-36x29in) s.d.76 s.i.d.verso. 14-Mar-3 Millon & Associes, Paris #352/R
£1793 $2869 €2600 Aux cinq poissons (61x73cm-24x29in) s.d.68 s.i.d.verso. 14-Mar-3 Millon & Associes, Paris #277/R
£1793 $2869 €2600 Elle l'etrangle (73x60cm-29x24in) s.d. s.i.d.7.9.72 verso. 14-Mar-3 Millon & Associes, Paris #310/R
£1793 $2869 €2600 Apparition de l'epave (60x73cm-24x29in) s.d. s.i.d.1.8.72 verso. 14-Mar-3 Millon & Associes, Paris #312/R
£1931 $3090 €2800 Il y avait une jambe (60x73cm-24x29in) s.d. s.i.d.27.8.70 verso. 14-Mar-3 Millon & Associes, Paris #283/R
£2069 $3310 €3000 La nuit ne tardera pas (65x92cm-26x36in) s.d.73 s.i.d.verso. 14-Mar-3 Millon & Associes, Paris #328/R
£2207 $3531 €3200 L'eau de mer (60x73cm-24x29in) s.d.55 i.d.verso. 14-Mar-3 Millon & Associes, Paris #273/R
£2885 $4529 €4500 Quelques porteuses de pain (130x97cm-51x38in) s.d. s.i.d.23-8-66 verso prov.exhib. 16-Dec-2 Charbonneaux, Paris #238 est:8000
£3449 $5449 €5000 Pluie (282x72cm-111x28in) s.d.46. 4-Apr-3 Tajan, Paris #226/R
£3449 $5449 €5000 Neige (288x70cm-113x28in) s.d.46. 4-Apr-3 Tajan, Paris #227/R
£3449 $5449 €5000 Taureau blanc de la plage au cheval de bois (145x113cm-57x44in) s. i.verso. 4-Apr-3 Tajan, Paris #233/R

Works on paper

£241 $403 €350 Composition marine (18x25cm-7x10in) s. gouache. 10-Jul-3 Artcurial Briest, Paris #58
£276 $441 €400 Etudes darmarbres (31x45cm-12x18in) s.i.d.65 wash. 14-Mar-3 Millon & Associes, Paris #27/R
£276 $441 €400 Trois personnages (40x33cm-16x13in) s. gouache. 14-Mar-3 Millon & Associes, Paris #167
£276 $441 €400 Dames du nuit (49x64cm-19x25in) s. s.i.d.11.74 verso. 14-Mar-3 Millon & Associes, Paris #190
£276 $441 €400 Elles ne savent pas (49x64cm-19x25in) s.d. s.i.d.11.74 verso gouache. 14-Mar-3 Millon & Associes, Paris #195
£276 $441 €400 Cinq femmes (49x64cm-19x25in) s.d.5.76 gouache. 14-Mar-3 Millon & Associes, Paris #203
£283 $452 €410 Personnage debout (46x38cm-18x15in) s.d.58 gouache. 14-Mar-3 Millon & Associes, Paris #87
£290 $463 €420 Deuxieme fragment de plage (49x64cm-19x25in) s.d. s.i.d.74 verso gouache. 14-Mar-3 Millon & Associes, Paris #197
£290 $463 €420 Toujours Pazac (38x46cm-15x18in) s.d.75 i.d.verso gouache. 14-Mar-3 Millon & Associes, Paris #254/R
£310 $497 €450 Deux dames de Gisors (28x42cm-11x17in) s.d.66 i.verso gouache. 14-Mar-3 Millon & Associes, Paris #69/R
£310 $497 €450 L'une d'elle pouvait ecouter (37x26cm-15x10in) s.i.d.67 gouache cardboard. 14-Mar-3 Millon & Associes, Paris #152
£310 $497 €450 Dames mauves (49x64cm-19x25in) s.i.d.juillet 76 gouache. 14-Mar-3 Millon & Associes, Paris #189
£310 $497 €450 Elles ramassent des moules (49x64cm-19x25in) s.d. s.i.d.74 verso gouache. 14-Mar-3 Millon & Associes, Paris #193/R
£340 $541 €500 La femme fleur (45x30cm-18x12in) s. W/C. 18-Mar-3 Galerie Moderne, Brussels #508/R
£345 $552 €500 Toujours Lundi de Pentecote (41x51cm-16x20in) s.d. i.d.1968 verso gouache. 14-Mar-3 Millon & Associes, Paris #73/R
£345 $552 €500 Quatre femmes (38x46cm-15x18in) s.d.75 gouache. 14-Mar-3 Millon & Associes, Paris #114/R
£345 $552 €500 Quatre personnages (50x65cm-20x26in) s.d.76 gouache. 14-Mar-3 Millon & Associes, Paris #118/R
£345 $552 €500 Projet pour l'exposition de gouaches de L Coutaude a la Galerie (55x46cm-22x18in) s.d.75 gouache. 14-Mar-3 Millon & Associes, Paris #149
£345 $552 €500 Fleurs et poissons (33x25cm-13x10in) s. gouache. 14-Mar-3 Millon & Associes, Paris #156
£345 $552 €500 Etude de tete (38x46cm-15x18in) s.i.d.56 s.i.d.verso gouache. 14-Mar-3 Millon & Associes, Paris #256
£359 $574 €520 Cinq personnages (50x64cm-20x25in) s.d.24.6.75 gouache. 14-Mar-3 Millon & Associes, Paris #26
£359 $574 €520 Par temps gris (26x39cm-10x15in) s.d.1.52 i.d.verso gouache. 14-Mar-3 Millon & Associes, Paris #255
£379 $607 €550 Trois anges de mer (45x55cm-18x22in) s.d. s.i.d.4.75 verso gouache. 14-Mar-3 Millon & Associes, Paris #209
£411 $642 €650 Personnages (45x55cm-18x22in) s.d.1969 gouache. 20-Oct-2 Charbonneaux, Paris #51 est:600-800
£414 $662 €600 Personnage (40x33cm-16x13in) s.d.66 gouache. 14-Mar-3 Millon & Associes, Paris #47/R
£414 $662 €600 Un Dimanche de Pentecote (46x38cm-18x15in) s.d.68 s.i.verso gouache. 14-Mar-3 Millon & Associes, Paris #107/R
£414 $662 €600 Le plage etait presque vide (49x64cm-19x25in) s. s.i.d.8.74 verso gouache. 14-Mar-3 Millon & Associes, Paris #191
£414 $662 €600 Quatre dames (45x55cm-18x22in) s.d.21.6.76 gouache. 14-Mar-3 Millon & Associes, Paris #210
£483 $772 €700 Deux femmes fleurs (46x38cm-18x15in) s.d.59 wash. 14-Mar-3 Millon & Associes, Paris #51/R
£483 $772 €700 Souvenir d'un phare (37x45cm-15x18in) s.d. i.d.1975 verso gouache. 14-Mar-3 Millon & Associes, Paris #105
£483 $772 €700 Les autres ne tarderont pas (49x64cm-19x25in) s. s.i.d.74 verso gouache. 14-Mar-3 Millon & Associes, Paris #192
£483 $772 €700 Au crepuscule elles viennent (49x64cm-19x25in) s.i.d.8.74 verso gouache. 14-Mar-3 Millon & Associes, Paris #196
£483 $772 €700 Cygnes et poissons sur la plage (53x72cm-21x28in) s.d.9.7.69 gouache. 14-Mar-3 Millon & Associes, Paris #265
£517 $828 €750 Elles cherchent la transparence (38x46cm-15x18in) s.d.75 i.d.verso gouache. 14-Mar-3 Millon & Associes, Paris #100/R
£552 $883 €800 Simple rencontre (46x38cm-18x15in) s.d.75 i.d.verso gouache. 14-Mar-3 Millon & Associes, Paris #103
£552 $883 €800 Deux dames bleues (48x63cm-19x25in) s.d. s.i.d.11.68 verso gouache. 14-Mar-3 Millon & Associes, Paris #260
£621 $993 €900 Deux dames sur la plage (53x76cm-21x30in) s.d.73 gouache. 14-Mar-3 Millon & Associes, Paris #187
£690 $1103 €1000 La rencontre (27x17cm-11x7in) s.d.74 i.verso gouache. 14-Mar-3 Millon & Associes, Paris #24
£690 $1103 €1000 Etude de nus (63x48cm-25x19in) s.i. i.d.1974 verso gouache. 14-Mar-3 Millon & Associes, Paris #79/R
£690 $1103 €1000 Pecheur (38x46cm-15x18in) d.1956 verso gouache. 14-Mar-3 Millon & Associes, Paris #91/R
£690 $1103 €1000 Six personnages (50x61cm-20x24in) s.d.67-5 gouache. 14-Mar-3 Millon & Associes, Paris #145
£690 $1103 €1000 Dans un instant elles sortent (48x63cm-19x25in) s.d. i.d.1975 verso gouache. 14-Mar-3 Millon & Associes, Paris #258
£724 $1159 €1050 Ils etaient sept sur la plage (33x40cm-13x16in) s.d.54 i.verso. 14-Mar-3 Millon & Associes, Paris #83/R
£862 $1379 €1250 Vetues de nuit elles viennent (48x63cm-19x25in) s. i.d.1974 verso gouache. 14-Mar-3 Millon & Associes, Paris #96/R
£897 $1434 €1300 Les deux du Cheval de Brique (49x64cm-19x25in) s.d.74 i.verso gouache. 14-Mar-3 Millon & Associes, Paris #137/R
£897 $1434 €1300 La mare (50x64cm-20x25in) s.d.74 s.i.d.verso gouache. 14-Mar-3 Millon & Associes, Paris #144/R
£986 $1568 €1450 L'aeroplane (24x46cm-9x18in) s. i.d.37 verso gouache cardboard. 26-Feb-3 Artcurial Briest, Paris #71
£1241 $1986 €1800 Quelques dames fleurs (38x46cm-15x18in) s.d.75 i.verso gouache. 14-Mar-3 Millon & Associes, Paris #140/R
£1448 $2317 €2100 Dames des planches (48x62cm-19x24in) s. i.d.1974 verso gouache. 14-Mar-3 Millon & Associes, Paris #264/R
£1469 $2453 €2100 Le mythe de Proserpine (40x80cm-16x31in) s.d. gouache cardboard. 26-Jun-3 Tajan, Paris #173 est:1000-1200
£1724 $2759 €2500 Elles parlaient (54x73cm-21x29in) s.d.73 gouache. 14-Mar-3 Millon & Associes, Paris #133/R

COUTENIL, Louis (19th C) French

£7000 $11690 €10500 Rembrandt's studio (75x58cm-30x23in) panel. 18-Jun-3 Christie's, Kensington #99/R est:8000-12000

COUTTS, Alice Gray (1880-1973) American

£1090 $1700 €1635 American Indian baby in woven crib. 21-Sep-2 Harvey Clar, Oakland #1485
£1863 $3000 €2795 Sea murmurs, chicken crying (7x8cm-3x3in) s. i.verso prov. 18-Feb-3 John Moran, Pasadena #73a est:3000-5000
£2373 $3750 €3560 Young native American girl bringing poppies home to mother (33x25cm-13x10in) board. 16-Nov-2 Harvey Clar, Oakland #1392
£2419 $3750 €3629 Turning turtle (18x25cm-7x10in) s. board. 29-Oct-2 John Moran, Pasadena #704a est:2000-3000

COUTTS, Gordon (1868-1937) British/American

£484 $750 €726 Market day at North African Village. 7-Dec-2 Harvey Clar, Oakland #1175
£683 $1100 €1025 Cattle in a landscape (36x51cm-14x20in) s.indis.d. 23-Feb-3 Butterfields, Los Angeles #7000
£1161 $1800 €1742 Mexican village scene (38x48cm-15x19in) s. canvas on masonite prov. 29-Oct-2 John Moran, Pasadena #754 est:2500-3500
£1218 $1900 €1827 Market day in North African village. 21-Sep-2 Harvey Clar, Oakland #1497
£1923 $3000 €2885 Market day in Marrakesh. 21-Sep-2 Harvey Clar, Oakland #1498
£2246 $3750 €3257 Cattle watering in sunset landscape (36x51cm-14x20in) s. indis d. 17-Jun-3 John Moran, Pasadena #54c est:2000-3000
£4037 $6500 €6056 Self portrait (71x61cm-28x24in) s. 18-Feb-3 John Moran, Pasadena #100 est:6000-8000

Works on paper

£387 $600 €581 Near Salinas (23x36cm-9x14in) s. i.verso W/C. 29-Oct-2 John Moran, Pasadena #686a

COUTTS, Hubert (1851-1921) British

Works on paper

£800 $1248 €1200 Windermere from Loughrigg Fells (63x100cm-25x39in) s. W/C. 10-Apr-3 Tennants, Leyburn #853/R

COUTURE, Thomas (1815-1879) French

£1266 $1975 €2000 Portrait de Monsieur Gilbert (55x46cm-22x18in) mono.d.1859 prov. 18-Oct-2 Rabourdin & Choppin de Janvry, Paris #10/R

£3548 $5500 €5322 Portrait of Philip Ricord (62x51cm-24x20in) init. prov.lit. 29-Oct-2 Sotheby's, New York #41/R est:3000-5000
£3548 $5500 €5322 Woman in a white cap (56x47cm-22x19in) init. oil sketch prov. 29-Oct-2 Sotheby's, New York #42/R est:2500-3500
Works on paper
£567 $948 €800 Etude pour une branche de lierre (27x41cm-11x16in) black crayon white chk. 19-Jun-3 Piasa, Paris #149
£1613 $2500 €2420 Portrait of a man (51x41cm-20x16in) init. chl htd white. 29-Oct-2 Sotheby's, New York #44/R est:2000-3000
£2419 $3750 €3629 Portrait of Monginot with unfinished. Portrait of a woman (61x43cm-24x17in) init. pencil black chk htd white prov. 29-Oct-2 Sotheby's, New York #43/R est:2000-3000
£2903 $4500 €4355 Portrait of woman in a bonnet (55x43cm-22x17in) init.i. pencil chl htd white prov. 29-Oct-2 Sotheby's, New York #45/R est:2000-3000
£29032 $45000 €43548 Two politicians (43x55cm-17x22in) init. pencil black white chk prov.exhib.lit. 29-Oct-2 Sotheby's, New York #39/R est:25000-35000

COUTURIER, Philibert Léon (1823-1901) French
£704 $1169 €1000 Le basse-cour (27x44cm-11x17in) s. panel. 11-Jun-3 Beaussant & Lefèvre, Paris #18
£2468 $3900 €3900 La basse cour (56x96cm-22x38in) s.d.1863. 1-Dec-2 Peron, Melun #133

COUTY, Jean (1907-1991) French
£2817 $4676 €4000 Lyon, le pont Bonaparte et la Cathedrale Saint Jean (73x60cm-29x24in) s.d.64. 15-Jun-3 Anaf, Lyon #56/R est:3000-4000

COUTY, Jean Frederic (1829-1904) French
£1899 $2962 €3000 Saone (61x46cm-24x18in) s.d.1932 panel double-sided. 20-Oct-2 Anaf, Lyon #107/R
£3038 $4800 €4800 Paysage du Magrehb (60x73cm-24x29in) s. 1-Dec-2 Anaf, Lyon #58/R
£3503 $5500 €5255 Still life with tableware (27x35cm-11x14in) s. panel. 22-Nov-2 Skinner, Boston #45/R est:4500-5500
£8784 $13703 €13000 La Saone aux glacons (100x81cm-39x32in) s. 30-Mar-3 Anaf, Lyon #350/R

COUVER, Jan van (1836-1909) Dutch
£460 $768 €667 River scene with windmill (33x49cm-13x19in) s. 25-Jun-3 Bonhams, Bury St Edmunds #537
£500 $775 €750 Riverside village and jetty (51x79cm-20x31in) s. board. 26-Sep-2 Lane, Penzance #267
£1400 $2282 €2100 Barge moored by a windmill before a Dutch town (46x61cm-18x24in) s. 13-Feb-3 Christie's, Kensington #172/R est:800-1200
£1823 $2881 €2735 Fruit trees in blossom by waterway, town in background (52x76cm-20x30in) s. 27-Nov-2 Falkkloos, Malmo #77562/R est:20000 (S.KR 26000)
£2357 $3865 €3418 Coastal landscape with boat and mill (61x92cm-24x36in) s/. 4-Jun-3 AB Stockholms Auktionsverk #2468/R est:35000-40000 (S.KR 30000)
Works on paper
£311 $516 €451 Oudenaarde (32x51cm-13x20in) s. W/C prov. 16-Jun-3 Waddingtons, Toronto #217/R (C.D 700)
£380 $593 €570 On the Spaaen, Holland. Nr Muiden, Holland (18x26cm-7x10in) s. W/C gouache pair. 18-Sep-2 Dreweatt Neate, Newbury #89
£620 $986 €899 Views of Holland. s. W/C pair. 26-Feb-3 John Bellman, Billingshurst #1793

COUWENBERG, Christiaan van (1604-1667) Dutch
£10000 $15700 €15000 Warrior kneeling before a woman on a throne (160x180cm-63x71in) prov.lit. 10-Dec-2 Bonhams, New Bond Street #181/R est:12000-18000

COUWENBERG, Christiaan van (style) (1604-1667) Dutch
£6000 $9360 €9000 Interior with a merry toper seated at a table smoking a pipe (89x74cm-35x29in) init.d.1627 panel. 8-Apr-3 Sotheby's, Olympia #199/R est:2000-3000

COVARRUBIAS, Miguel (1904-1957) Mexican
Works on paper
£7407 $12000 €10740 Girl in a hammock (38x58cm-15x23in) s. W/C gouache pencil prov. 21-May-3 Doyle, New York #53/R est:10000-15000
£14024 $23000 €20335 Tehuanas banandose en el rio (35x23cm-14x9in) s. casein prov. 27-May-3 Sotheby's, New York #82
£41401 $65000 €62102 Gentleman (36x26cm-14x10in) s. casein. 19-Nov-2 Sotheby's, New York #1/R est:22000
£147630 $243590 €214064 Two Balinese girls (60x41cm-24x16in) s. col ink. 6-Jul-3 Christie's, Hong Kong #23/R est:550000-750000 (HK.D 1900000)

COVENTRY, Gertrude Mary (1886-1964) British
£1700 $2652 €2550 Anstruther Fair (46x61cm-18x24in) s. 14-Apr-3 Sotheby's, London #152/R est:1200-1800

COVENTRY, Keith (1958-) British
£4000 $6160 €6000 Eton schoolboys (54x80cm-21x31in) s.i.d.96 verso oil canvasboard wood gesso glass painted. 23-Oct-2 Christie's, London #237/R est:4000-6000
Sculpture
£7000 $11690 €10150 Loughborough estate (166x127x8cm-65x50x3in) i. s.i.d.1996 verso oil canvas wood gesso glass prov. 26-Jun-3 Sotheby's, London #295/R est:8000-12000

COVENTRY, Robert McGown (1855-1914) British
£460 $722 €690 Market place, Bruges (19x24cm-7x9in) 17-Apr-3 Bonhams, Edinburgh #304
£4200 $6384 €6300 Winter river scene (82x101cm-32x40in) s. 28-Aug-2 Sotheby's, London #997/R est:4000-6000
Works on paper
£400 $632 €600 Figures with a hay cart on a country road (13x23cm-5x9in) s. W/C. 13-Nov-2 Halls, Shrewsbury #355/R
£750 $1163 €1125 Fisher girl (28x20cm-11x8in) s. W/C. 6-Dec-2 Lyon & Turnbull, Edinburgh #92

COVERLEY-PRICE, A Victor (1901-) British
£550 $908 €798 Downing Street (51x61cm-20x24in) s.d.1945. 3-Jul-3 Christie's, Kensington #498
£600 $936 €900 Florence (29x39cm-11x15in) s. board. 12-Sep-2 Sotheby's, Olympia #120/R

COWARD, Malcolm (20th C) British
£360 $565 €540 Tethered white bull (28x33cm-11x13in) s. 13-Dec-2 Keys, Aylsham #755

COWARD, Sir Noel (1899-1973) British
£2000 $3300 €2900 Cow parsley (51x41cm-20x16in) s.d.66. 3-Jul-3 Christie's, Kensington #475/R est:800-1200
Works on paper
£3800 $6232 €5700 Two fishermen (35x30cm-14x12in) s. mixed media canvas on board. 3-Jun-3 Sotheby's, Olympia #116/R est:2000-3000

COWELL, William Wilson (1856-?) American
£6494 $10000 €9741 View of Marblehead (23x69cm-9x27in) s. 24-Oct-2 Shannon's, Milford #17/R est:6000-8000

COWEN, Lionel J (1847-1895) British
£382 $603 €573 Untitled, mother and child (24x19cm-9x7in) panel. 7-Apr-3 Shapiro, Sydney #534 (A.D 1000)

COWIE, James (1886-1956) British
£260 $413 €390 Doors in the woods (20x24cm-8x9in) oil on paper exhib. 6-Mar-3 Christie's, Kensington #202
Works on paper
£580 $905 €870 Girl in a gym slip (38x19cm-15x7in) pencil exhib. 13-Sep-2 Lyon & Turnbull, Edinburgh #132/R

COWLES, Russell (1887-1979) American
£719 $1200 €1043 Horses in wooded landscape, after rain (46x61cm-18x24in) s. i.verso panel prov. 17-Jun-3 John Moran, Pasadena #168 est:2000-3500
£1911 $3000 €2867 Summer wind (103x92cm-41x36in) s. i.verso prov. 19-Nov-2 Butterfields, San Francisco #8327/R est:4000-6000

COWLEY, Reta (1910-) Canadian
£281 $444 €422 Friesen pasture and road across the river (18x30cm-7x12in) d.1984 hardboard. 1-Dec-2 Levis, Calgary #306/R (C.D 700)
£636 $1011 €954 Friesen pasture, October (20x29cm-8x11in) s.i.d.1982 board. 23-Mar-3 Hodgins, Calgary #108/R est:1000-1400 (C.D 1500)
Works on paper
£304 $475 €508 East and North of Osler in evening (56x71cm-22x28in) s.d.1988 W/C. 13-Apr-3 Levis, Calgary #21/R (C.D 700)
£321 $508 €482 Friesen thicket (51x64cm-20x25in) d.1977 W/C. 1-Dec-2 Levis, Calgary #307/R (C.D 800)
£400 $656 €600 Under a prairie sky (56x75cm-22x30in) s.d.Aug 8 1980 W/C. 3-Jun-3 Joyner, Toronto #312/R est:1000-1500 (C.D 900)
£636 $1011 €954 Friesen pasture (56x75cm-22x30in) s.i.d.1981 W/C prov. 23-Mar-3 Hodgins, Calgary #55/R est:800-1200 (C.D 1500)

COWLEY-BROWN, Patrick George (1918-) British

£2419 $3823 €3629 The Sound, British Columbia (72x84cm-28x33in) s.i.d.1947 prov. 14-Nov-2 Heffel, Vancouver #233/R est:4500-6500 (C.D 6000)

COWPER, Frank Cadogan (1877-1958) British

£148387 $230000 €222581 Titania sleeps, midsummer night's dream (95x116cm-37x46in) s.d.1928 prov.exhib.lit. 30-Oct-2 Christie's, Rockefeller NY #35/R est:250000-350000

COX, Charles Edward (fl.1879-1901) British

£1400 $2128 €2100 Barges and other traffic in the pool of London (32x92cm-13x36in) s.d.1893. 15-Aug-2 Bonhams, New Bond Street #335/R est:1500-2000

COX, Charles T (?) British

Works on paper

£260 $424 €390 Perry Barr Church (69x102cm-27x40in) s.d.1909 W/C. 14-Feb-3 Keys, Aylsham #439

COX, D (1783-1859) British

£320 $493 €480 Wooded landscape with figure and horse (28x38cm-11x15in) s.d.1845. 6-Sep-2 Biddle & Webb, Birmingham #116

COX, David (jnr) (1809-1885) British

Works on paper

£250 $389 €375 Landscape with castle in the distance (21x20cm-8x8in) indis.studio st. pencil W/C. 19-Sep-2 Christie's, Kensington #71

£300 $464 €450 Clouds gathering in the mountains (45x65cm-18x26in) W/C. 3-Dec-2 Sotheby's, Olympia #40/R

£320 $499 €480 Travellers beside hay stooks with castle on a hill beyond (29x37cm-11x15in) studio st. pencil W/C. 19-Sep-2 Christie's, Kensington #87

£350 $585 €508 Fisherman on a highland river (33x47cm-13x19in) s. W/C. 24-Jun-3 Bonhams, Knightsbridge #3

£351 $550 €527 Near Dolgelly (18x23cm-7x9in) s. W/C. 23-Nov-2 Jackson's, Cedar Falls #22/R

£440 $735 €638 Cattle watering in an upland river (27x37cm-11x15in) s. indis d. W/C over pencil. 23-Jun-3 Bonhams, Bath #209

£450 $698 €675 Two ladies strolling in the garden of a country house (21x26cm-8x10in) W/C prov. 3-Dec-2 Sotheby's, Olympia #39/R

£450 $720 €675 Extensive rural landscape with mountains and bridge in mid ground (46x74cm-18x29in) s. W/C. 10-Jan-3 Biddle & Webb, Birmingham #32

£900 $1476 €1350 On the Wharfe (31x46cm-12x18in) bears sig panel W/C. 4-Feb-3 Bonhams, Leeds #216

£1050 $1638 €1575 At Drislyn, North Wales (46x73cm-18x29in) s.d.1843. 6-Nov-2 Bonhams, Chester #336 est:600-800

COX, David (jnr-attrib) (1809-1885) British

Works on paper

£769 $1215 €1200 Bord de mer (28x45cm-11x18in) bears sig.d.1857 W/C. 15-Nov-2 Beaussant & Lefèvre, Paris #8/R

COX, David (1783-1859) British

£940 $1532 €1410 Harvest landscape with figures on a track (27x43cm-11x17in) panel. 17-Feb-3 Bonhams, Bath #63

£1000 $1570 €1500 Figure in windswept landscape approaching storm (13x18cm-5x7in) s. 13-Dec-2 Keys, Aylsham #532/R est:800-1000

£1100 $1749 €1650 Shepherd with his flock on a path beside a thatched cottage (41x51cm-16x20in) s.d.1850 panel prov. 30-Apr-3 Halls, Shrewsbury #269/R est:1000-1500

£1157 $1828 €1736 Harvesters returning from market (21x26cm-8x10in) s.indis.d.70. 27-Nov-2 Falkkloos, Malmo #77717/R est:20000 (S.KR 16500)

£2500 $4050 €3750 Angler on the river Llugwy, Bettws-y-Coed (39x28cm-15x11in) s.verso prov. 22-May-3 Christie's, London #27/R est:2500-3500

£2600 $4134 €3900 Landscape with a figure sawing wood beneath a tree (23x25cm-9x10in) s. panel. 18-Mar-3 Bonhams, New Bond Street #33/R est:2000-3000

£3300 $5280 €4950 Landscape of view in North Wales (33x43cm-13x17in) i.verso board. 8-Jan-3 Brightwells, Leominster #1001/R est:2000-3000

£4500 $7155 €6750 Peat cutters in a landscape (20x30cm-8x12in) s.d.1850 panel prov. 18-Mar-3 Bonhams, New Bond Street #41/R est:2000-3000

£7500 $11850 €11250 The fisherman - view at Bettws-y-Coed (46x36cm-18x14in) s.d.1852 prov.exhib. 26-Nov-2 Christie's, London #63/R est:8000-12000

£20000 $32200 €30000 Conway castle (64x92cm-25x36in) prov.exhib.lit. 20-Feb-3 Christie's, London #345/R est:20000

Works on paper

£250 $413 €363 Cottage amongst trees (16x25cm-6x10in) blk chk stump. 2-Jul-3 Sotheby's, Olympia #216/R

£280 $437 €420 Lane near Hereford (15x20cm-6x8in) s.i.d.1834 W/C. 20-Sep-2 Richardson & Smith, Whitby #121

£305 $466 €458 Landscape scene with horse and cart (28x51cm-11x20in) s.d.1858 W/C. 21-Aug-2 Dunbar Sloane, Auckland #85 est:1000-1500 (NZ.D 1000)

£400 $628 €600 Rural landscape (10x20cm-4x8in) s.d.1848 W/C. 10-Dec-2 Capes Dunn, Manchester #766

£550 $869 €825 Mountainscape with figures by a river (25x46cm-10x18in) s.i.verso W/C. 26-Nov-2 Rogers Jones, Clwyd #151

£600 $978 €900 Gathering hay, study of horses and figures in a landscape (49x32cm-19x13in) s.d. W/C. 29-Jan-3 Wintertons, Lichfield #351a

£600 $1002 €870 Travelers in a Welsh landscape (12x16cm-5x6in) W/C prov. 17-Jun-3 Anderson & Garland, Newcastle #273

£1200 $1872 €1800 Snowdon (30x42cm-12x17in) W/C. 5-Nov-2 Bonhams, New Bond Street #63/R est:1200-1500

£1800 $2826 €2700 On the Scheldt, Holland (18x25cm-7x10in) s.d.1832 pencil W/C scratching out prov. 21-Nov-2 Christie's, London #56/R est:2000-3000

£1850 $3016 €2775 Kenilwoth Castle (18x26cm-7x10in) i. W/C pencil. 11-Feb-3 Bonhams, Knowle #49 est:1500-2000

£2200 $3652 €3300 Cattle watering at a pool (13x15cm-5x6in) s. W/C prov. 12-Jun-3 Bonhams, New Bond Street #625/R est:1000-1500

£2200 $3608 €3190 Figures receiving alms at the church door (27x19cm-11x7in) black chk W/C htd bodycol. 5-Jun-3 Christie's, London #69/R est:1500-2000

£2200 $3652 €3190 Harlech Castle (13x20cm-5x8in) s.d.1826 W/C. 16-Jun-3 Duke & Son, Dorchester #139/R est:500-1000

£2800 $4424 €4200 Horsemen approaching Windsor Castle (17x25cm-7x10in) W/C over pencil htd bodycol stopping out. 28-Nov-2 Sotheby's, London #293/R est:3000-4000

£3000 $4740 €4500 French street (15x11cm-6x4in) s. W/C over pencil htd bodycol. 28-Nov-2 Sotheby's, London #291/R est:3000-4000

£3500 $5005 €5250 Distant view of a castle (15x22cm-6x9in) pencil W/C double-sided prov.exhib.lit. 22-Jan-3 Christie's, London #33/R est:6000

£3500 $5005 €5250 Child with dog outside cottage (19x27cm-7x11in) chk W/C prov.exhib.lit. 22-Jan-3 Christie's, London #32/R est:2000

£3600 $5760 €5400 Lane at Harborne, Staffordshire (27x19cm-11x7in) s. W/C over pencil prov.exhib. 11-Mar-3 Bonhams, New Bond Street #42/R est:2000-3000

£3800 $6232 €5510 Haddon Hall, Derbyshire (21x28cm-8x11in) init.d.1845 black chk W/C prov.exhib. 5-Jun-3 Christie's, London #68/R est:2500-3500

£4000 $6640 €6000 Sheep grazing by a windmill, storm approaching (49x72cm-19x28in) W/C over pencil. 12-Jun-3 Sotheby's, London #139/R est:3000-5000

£4100 $6519 €6150 Landscape with traveller's camp (25x36cm-10x14in) s. 30-Apr-3 Brightwells, Leominster #951/R est:500-700

£4800 $7632 €7200 Hay on Wye (20x31cm-8x12in) W/C over pencil htd stopping out. 19-Mar-3 Sotheby's, London #197/R est:4000-6000

£4800 $7968 €7200 Retreat of John Graham of Claverhouse to the castle of Tillietudlem (46x61cm-18x24in) W/C over pencil htd bodycol. 12-Jun-3 Sotheby's, London #144a/R est:5000-7000

£5000 $7850 €7500 Figures on a beach near Rye, Sussex (16x25cm-6x10in) pencil W/C prov. 21-Nov-2 Christie's, London #49/R est:6000-8000

£5500 $7865 €8250 Figures in wooded lane (25x18cm-10x7in) chk wash prov.exhib.lit. 22-Jan-3 Christie's, London #35/R est:6000

£6000 $8580 €9000 Cottages in woodland (36x27cm-14x11in) i. chk W/C prov.exhib.lit. 22-Jan-3 Christie's, London #34/R est:10000

£6000 $9600 €9000 Distant view of Harlech Castle, North Wales (21x28cm-8x11in) W/C prov.exhib. 11-Mar-3 Bonhams, New Bond Street #14/R est:3000-5000

£6500 $9295 €9750 Soldiers below Stirling Castle (12x18cm-5x7in) s.d.1836 pencil W/C scratching out prov.exhib.lit. 22-Jan-3 Christie's, London #31/R

£7500 $10725 €11250 Landscape at dusk with woman and child walking home (17x35cm-7x14in) s.d.1812 pencil W/C scratching out prov.exhib.lit. 22-Jan-3 Christie's, London #25/R

£8000 $11440 €12000 The Thames estuary with vessels (11x15cm-4x6in) s.d.1827 pencil W/C scartching out prov.exhib.lit. 22-Jan-3 Christie's, London #26/R est:6000

£8500 $13600 €12750 Going to market (27x37cm-11x15in) s. W/C over black chk. 11-Mar-3 Bonhams, New Bond Street #51/R est:3000-5000

£9500 $15200 €14250 Pack horse (19x28cm-7x11in) W/C. 11-Mar-3 Bonhams, New Bond Street #35/R est:2000-3000

£11000 $15730 €16500 Rue Vivienne, Paris (22x15cm-9x6in) s. pencil W/C gum scratching out prov.exhib.lit. 22-Jan-3 Christie's, London #61/R est:18000

£15000 $21450 €22500 Early morning on the French coast (16x24cm-6x9in) s. pencil W/C scratching out prov.exhib.lit. 22-Jan-3 Christie's, London #30/R est:15000
£19000 $27170 €28500 Greenwich Hospital from the Thames (15x24cm-6x9in) s. pencil W/C scratching out prov.exhib.lit. 22-Jan-3 Christie's, London #27/R est:15000
£19000 $27170 €28500 Crossing the sands (22x32cm-9x13in) pencil W/C scratching out prov.exhib.lit. 22-Jan-3 Christie's, London #28/R est:25000
£28000 $40040 €42000 Laugharne Castle (25x35cm-10x14in) s.d.1849 pencil W/C scartching out prov.exhib.lit. 22-Jan-3 Christie's, London #29/R est:15000
£36000 $56520 €54000 Rhyl Sands (27x37cm-11x15in) s. pencil W/C prov. 21-Nov-2 Christie's, London #47/R est:20000-30000

COX, David (attrib) (1783-1859) British
£380 $589 €570 Welsh landscape with figure on a bridge (30x36cm-12x14in) 31-Oct-2 Duke & Son, Dorchester #228/R
£400 $620 €600 Haystacks and carts in a field (16x24cm-6x9in) board. 24-Sep-2 Anderson & Garland, Newcastle #426/R

Works on paper
£242 $382 €363 Wayfarers and cattle in an extensive landscape (16x22cm-6x9in) bears sig. W/C gouache. 18-Nov-2 Waddingtons, Toronto #53/R (C.D 600)
£300 $489 €450 Roxburgh Abbey (35x25cm-14x10in) bears sig.i. W/C. 11-Feb-3 Fellows & Sons, Birmingham #118
£350 $557 €525 Angler in river landscape (36x52cm-14x20in) s. W/C. 5-Mar-3 Wingetts, Wrexham #458
£580 $934 €870 Kenilworth Castle (15x20cm-6x8in) W/C. 9-May-3 Mallams, Oxford #52
£1300 $2132 €1885 Manchester cathedral from the River Irwell (20x26cm-8x10in) i.verso pencil W/C prov.exhib. 5-Jun-3 Christie's, London #101/R est:1500-2000

COX, David and TAYLER, John Frederick (19th C) British

Works on paper
£1200 $1896 €1800 Figures crossing the sands (18x28cm-7x11in) s. W/C over pencil htd bodycol. 28-Nov-2 Sotheby's, London #297/R est:1500-2000

COX, E A (1876-1955) British
£550 $858 €825 Avenue (40x55cm-16x22in) s. board. 17-Sep-2 Bonhams, Knightsbridge #273/R

COX, F (19th C) British
£2200 $3564 €3300 S.S. Traveller off the South Stack (29x61cm-11x24in) s. board. 21-Jan-3 Bonhams, New Bond Street #218/R est:1000-1500

COX, Frank E (1850-?) British
£1064 $1649 €1596 Love will find out the way - man giving letter to maid at brick wall (110x60cm-43x24in) s.d.1893. 8-Dec-2 Uppsala Auktionskammare, Uppsala #82/R est:10000-12000 (S.KR 15000)

COX, Garstin (1892-1933) British
£320 $534 €464 St. Michael's Mount viewed across in inland pond (25x35cm-10x14in) s. 23-Jun-3 Bonhams, Bath #132
£400 $620 €600 Carphillian, the Lizard coastline (48x61cm-19x24in) board. 26-Sep-2 Lane, Penzance #207
£700 $1078 €1050 Cliffs off the Cornish coast (51x61cm-20x24in) board. 5-Sep-2 Christie's, Kensington #574/R
£769 $1192 €1200 Hilly coastal landscape (71x91cm-28x36in) s. 6-Dec-2 Michael Zeller, Lindau #736/R
£769 $1192 €1200 View over heathland to sea (72x94cm-28x37in) s. 6-Dec-2 Michael Zeller, Lindau #737/R
£1750 $2748 €2625 Lizard coastline (127x101cm-50x40in) 10-Dec-2 Lane, Penzance #347 est:2000-2500
£2400 $3768 €3600 On the Lizard coast, Cornwall (100x127cm-39x50in) 10-Dec-2 Lane, Penzance #346 est:2500-3000
£6700 $11189 €9715 Departing day (102x127cm-40x50in) s. 19-Jun-3 Lane, Penzance #450/R est:5500-6500

Works on paper
£318 $497 €500 Bord de ruisseau (49x89cm-19x35in) s. pastel cardboard. 11-Nov-2 Horta, Bruxelles #494

COX, Gerard (20th C) Irish?

Sculpture
£1127 $1870 €1600 Eclipse (33cm-13in) bronze. 10-Jun-3 James Adam, Dublin #200/R est:1400-1800

COX, Jack (?) ?
£290 $452 €435 North Norfolk river estuary scene with boats (43x69cm-17x27in) s. 11-Apr-3 Keys, Aylsham #572
£310 $484 €465 Boats in the harbour at Blakeney (41x74cm-16x29in) s. 11-Apr-3 Keys, Aylsham #574
£310 $484 €465 Wells harbour (43x64cm-17x25in) s. 11-Apr-3 Keys, Aylsham #577
£320 $499 €480 Off Stiffkey church (43x69cm-17x27in) s. i.verso. 11-Apr-3 Keys, Aylsham #573
£320 $534 €464 Boats at Burnham, Overy Staithe (38x48cm-15x19in) s. 20-Jun-3 Keys, Aylsham #533
£350 $532 €525 North Norfolk river estuary with figures and boats (43x69cm-17x27in) s. 16-Aug-2 Keys, Aylsham #316/R
£360 $562 €540 Wooden bridge across the marshes, possibly at Morston (3x61cm-1x24in) s. 11-Apr-3 Keys, Aylsham #576
£400 $648 €580 Marsh landscape at sunset (61x122cm-24x48in) board. 20-May-3 Dreweatt Neate, Newbury #340/R
£400 $624 €600 Wells Harbour (43x69cm-17x27in) s. 11-Apr-3 Keys, Aylsham #575/R
£580 $905 €870 East End, Wells (61x91cm-24x36in) s. 11-Apr-3 Keys, Aylsham #578/R

COX, Jan (1919-1980) Belgian
£1538 $2385 €2400 Chairs in my studio (50x40cm-20x16in) s.d.44 exhib.lit. 7-Dec-2 De Vuyst, Lokeren #481/R est:2500-3000
£1727 $2763 €2400 Rest (44x61cm-17x24in) s.d.49 wash Indian ink dr prov.lit. 17-May-3 De Vuyst, Lokeren #487/R est:2000-2500
£3165 $5065 €4400 Jois des branches (100x60cm-39x24in) s.d.51 prov.exhib.lit. 17-May-3 De Vuyst, Lokeren #486/R est:5000-6000
£4167 $6625 €6000 Elisa en Belinda (153x153cm-60x60in) s.d.1967. 29-Apr-3 Campo, Vlaamse Kaai #61 est:6000-8000

Works on paper
£633 $987 €1000 Still life with table (33x17cm-13x7in) s.d.42 W/C oil. 21-Oct-2 Bernaerts, Antwerp #646/R

COX, Marjorie (20th C) British

Works on paper
£250 $395 €375 Tim, fox terrier (47x35cm-19x14in) s.i.d.1967 col chk. 28-Nov-2 Christie's, Kensington #291
£300 $474 €450 Two Pekinese (42x42cm-17x17in) s. col chk. 28-Nov-2 Christie's, Kensington #339/R
£320 $486 €480 Poppet, Jonathan and Tinkerbell (41x58cm-16x23in) s.i.d.1965 pastel W/C. 14-Aug-2 Andrew Hartley, Ilkley #586

COX, Neil (?) British

Works on paper
£400 $664 €580 Peregrine falcon on a cliff top (25x35cm-10x14in) s. W/C bodycol. 12-Jun-3 Christie's, Kensington #159/R
£600 $996 €870 Two springer spaniels (34x49cm-13x19in) s. W/C. 12-Jun-3 Christie's, Kensington #307/R
£650 $1079 €943 Spaniel in a wood (25x35cm-10x14in) s. W/C htd white. 12-Jun-3 Christie's, Kensington #302/R
£700 $1162 €1015 Grouse on a moor (34x49cm-13x19in) s. W/C. 12-Jun-3 Christie's, Kensington #155/R
£700 $1162 €1015 English partridge in snow (39x60cm-15x24in) s. pencil W/C. 12-Jun-3 Christie's, Kensington #162/R
£800 $1328 €1160 Fox cubs in a wood (46x68cm-18x27in) s. pencil W/C htd white. 12-Jun-3 Christie's, Kensington #35/R
£800 $1328 €1160 Grouse in an extensive landscape (53x72cm-21x28in) s. pencil W/C htd white. 12-Jun-3 Christie's, Kensington #163/R
£950 $1577 €1378 Cock and hen pheasant in leaf litter (34x49cm-13x19in) s. W/C bodycol. 12-Jun-3 Christie's, Kensington #161/R
£1100 $1826 €1595 Partridge and daisies (30x41cm-12x16in) s. W/C htd white. 12-Jun-3 Christie's, Kensington #158/R est:500-700
£1900 $3154 €2755 Woodcock in leaf litter (32x42cm-13x17in) s. W/C. 12-Jun-3 Christie's, Kensington #164/R est:600-800

COX, Palmer (1840-1924) American

Works on paper
£1410 $2200 €2115 Brownies marvelling at Brooklyn bridge (28x23cm-11x9in) s. pen ink. 9-Nov-2 Illustration House, New York #49/R est:2000-3000
£1410 $2200 €2115 Brownies riding steam locomotive (20x20cm-8x8in) pen ink. 9-Nov-2 Illustration House, New York #50/R est:1500-2500

COX, Patrick Douglass (1953-) Canadian
£978 $1526 €1631 Cow boss, Bob Hale near Finnigan (29x69cm-11x27in) s.d.1992 acrylic on paper prov. 13-Apr-3 Levis, Calgary #22/R est:3000-3500 (C.D 2250)

COX, Tim (1957-) American

Works on paper
£357 $550 €536 Driving snow (25x36cm-10x14in) s. W/C exec.c.1970. 8-Sep-2 Treadway Gallery, Cincinnati #588/R

COXCIE, Michiel (attrib) (16/17th C) Flemish
£288 $460 €400 Le Christ (38x26cm-15x10in) panel. 13-May-3 Galerie Moderne, Brussels #462/R

COXON, Raymond (1896-1997) British
£650 $1007 €975 View of the Grand Canyon (37x45cm-15x18in) s. 3-Dec-2 Bonhams, Knightsbridge #195/R

COYLE, John (1928-) British
£1201 $1826 €1850 Portrait of Jane (53x36cm-21x14in) s. 2-Jul-2 Thomas Adams, Dublin #358
Works on paper
£462 $702 €720 Girl in black skirt in ladder back chair (61x51cm-24x20in) chl. 27-Aug-2 Thomas Adams, Dublin #2

COYNE, Rod (20th C) Irish?
£296 $491 €420 Hay bale in summer meadow (65x40cm-26x16in) s.d.02. 10-Jun-3 James Adam, Dublin #129/R

COYPEL, Antoine (1661-1722) French
Works on paper
£1014 $1581 €1500 Figure debout (23x12cm-9x5in) chk prov.. 27-Mar-3 Christie's, Paris #89/R
£4730 $7378 €7000 Ombre de Saul (42x55cm-17x22in) chk. 27-Mar-3 Christie's, Paris #88/R

COYPEL, Antoine (attrib) (1661-1722) French
£3930 $6131 €5895 La gloire du roi (89x116cm-35x46in) 6-Nov-2 Dobiaschofsky, Bern #425/R est:12000 (S.FR 9000)
Works on paper
£500 $800 €750 Susanna accused by the Elders (15x22cm-6x9in) pen ink gray wash. 14-May-3 Doyle, New York #28

COYPEL, Charles Antoine (1694-1752) French
£7097 $11213 €11000 Jesus au berceau (37x49cm-15x19in) oval. 18-Dec-2 Tajan, Paris #39/R est:10000
Works on paper
£968 $1500 €1452 Putto with an outstretched arm (24x23cm-9x9in) black col chk. 3-Dec-2 Christie's, Rockefeller NY #64/R est:2000-3000

COYPEL, Charles Antoine (attrib) (1694-1752) French
£7692 $12846 €11000 Scene de l'histoire antique (152x172cm-60x68in) prov. 25-Jun-3 Sotheby's, Paris #19/R est:8000-12000

COYPEL, Noel (1628-1707) French
Works on paper
£5106 $8528 €7200 Apollon courronne par la Victoire (34x18cm-13x7in) pen brown ink grey wash gouache. 19-Jun-3 Piasa, Paris #125/R est:2500-3000

COZAR, Jose (1944-) Spanish
£943 $1472 €1500 Losa del Obispo (70x130cm-28x51in) s. s.i.d.1970 verso. 8-Oct-2 Ansorena, Madrid #457/R
£943 $1472 €1500 Landscape near Valencia (70x130cm-28x51in) s. s.i.d.1970 verso. 8-Oct-2 Ansorena, Madrid #460/R

COZENS, Alexander (c.1717-1786) British
Works on paper
£3800 $5434 €5700 Coastal landscape with ruined tower (9x15cm-4x6in) s. pencil brush ink wash prov.exhib. 22-Jan-3 Christie's, London #1/R est:5000

COZENS, John Robert (1752-1799) British
Works on paper
£7000 $11480 €10150 Hannibal's march over the Alps (26cm-10in circular) pencil grey wash prov.exhib.lit. 5-Jun-3 Christie's, London #25/R est:8000-12000
£200000 $316000 €300000 Between Chamonix and Martigny - the aiguille verte (44x61cm-17x24in) W/C over pencil prov.exhib.lit. 28-Nov-2 Sotheby's, London #11/R est:200000-300000

COZZARELLI, Giacomo di Bartolomeo di Marco (1453-1515) Italian
£67901 $110000 €101852 Madonna and Child enthroned with angels (62x38cm-24x15in) tempera gold ground panel shaped top prov. 24-Jan-3 Christie's, Rockefeller NY #24/R est:100000-150000

COZZENS, Frederick Schiller (1846-1928) American
Works on paper
£255 $400 €383 Dutch fisherman (33x25cm-13x10in) s. 26-Jul-2 Eldred, East Dennis #246/R
£287 $450 €431 Dutch ell boats (33x23cm-13x9in) s. W/C. 26-Jul-2 Eldred, East Dennis #378/R
£287 $450 €431 To the rescue (28x48cm-11x19in) s. 22-Nov-2 Eldred, East Dennis #674/R
£313 $500 €470 Long Island Sound seascape with cutter on starboard tack. s. W/C. 1-Jan-3 Nadeau, Windsor #121
£382 $600 €573 Coastal scene of a beached steamship (38x66cm-15x26in) s. W/C. 23-Nov-2 Pook & Pook, Downington #338/R
£701 $1100 €1052 Spanish galleons (33x51cm-13x20in) s. W/C. 26-Jul-2 Eldred, East Dennis #376/R est:700-900
£741 $1200 €1074 Fishing off the coast at calm (30x55cm-12x22in) s.d.08 W/C on board. 29-Jul-3 Christie's, Rockefeller NY #112/R est:2000-3000
£839 $1300 €1217 Sailing ships racing around buoy in strong wind (25x36cm-10x14in) W/C. 7-Dec-2 South Bay, Long Island #180a/R
£938 $1500 €1407 Seascape with fully rigged boat depicted bow on starboard track. s. W/C. 1-Jan-3 Nadeau, Windsor #217/R est:1000-2000
£3503 $5500 €5255 Sailing near shore (51x74cm-20x29in) s.d.91 W/C htd white over pencil paper on board. 10-Dec-2 Doyle, New York #31/R est:2500-3500

CRACKING ART (20th C) Italian
Sculpture
£3401 $5408 €5000 S.O.S. World. turtles exec.2001 exhib.lit. 1-Mar-3 Meeting Art, Vercelli #645 est:5000

CRACO, Arthur (1869-?) Belgian
Works on paper
£252 $390 €400 Prise de becs (31x41cm-12x16in) s.i. W/C pen dr. 5-Oct-2 De Vuyst, Lokeren #68
£506 $785 €800 Nativity. ink W/C. 24-Sep-2 Galerie Moderne, Brussels #718
£886 $1373 €1400 Sainte Famille et pelerins. ink graphite dr htd gouache. 24-Sep-2 Galerie Moderne, Brussels #693/R

CRADOCK, Marmaduke (1660-1717) British
£6500 $10725 €9425 Assemblies of fowl (29x62cm-11x24in) pair. 2-Jul-3 Sotheby's, Olympia #138/R est:3500-4500

CRADOCK, Marmaduke (style) (1660-1717) British
£13000 $20670 €19500 Ducks and chickens by a river. Peacocks, a cockerel and doves by a pond (35x44cm-14x17in) pair. 6-Mar-3 Christie's, Kensington #617/R est:5000-8000

CRAESBEECK, Joos van (1606-1654) Flemish
£1510 $2325 €2400 Jeune garcon prisant du tabac (16x13cm-6x5in) panel. 25-Oct-2 Tajan, Paris #55/R est:3000-4000

CRAESBEECK, Joos van (attrib) (1606-1654) Flemish
£1100 $1715 €1650 Man trimming his moustache (25x20cm-10x8in) panel. 19-Sep-2 Christie's, Kensington #34/R est:1200-1800
£5500 $9185 €7975 Man counting money (65x50cm-26x20in) panel. 11-Jul-3 Christie's, Kensington #74/R est:4000-6000

CRAFFONARA, Giuseppe (1790-1837) Italian
£2041 $3245 €3000 Kids (49x60cm-19x24in) s.d.1827 board. 18-Mar-3 Finarte, Milan #145/R

CRAFT, Percy R (1856-1934) British
£650 $1060 €975 Mitsey (28x23cm-11x9in) s.i.d. 12-Feb-3 Bonhams, Knightsbridge #152/R
£1300 $2132 €1885 Setting sail (33x48cm-13x19in) s.d.26. 6-Jun-3 Halls, Shrewsbury #720 est:600-800
£2000 $3120 €3000 Old Bosham (51x77cm-20x30in) s. 26-Mar-3 Hamptons Fine Art, Godalming #238/R est:2000-3000
£2500 $4175 €3625 Garden in bloom (61x35cm-24x14in) s. 24-Jun-3 Bonhams, Knowle #93/R est:2500-3500
£4397 $7343 €6200 Vendeur turque d'oranges (60x90cm-24x35in) 23-Jun-3 Amberes, Antwerp #115/R
£15000 $23250 €22500 New song, boy in a fish loft playing a pipe to a caged bird (193x130cm-76x51in) s.d.1887 prov. 26-Sep-2 Lane, Penzance #300/R est:20000-35000
Works on paper
£1300 $2028 €1950 Street in Jerusalem (44x34cm-17x13in) s. canvas on board exhib. 15-Oct-2 Sotheby's, London #127/R est:1500-2000

CRAFT, William (18th C) British
£1634 $2631 €2500 Anglo-French ship battle (62x90cm-24x35in) s. s.i.verso. 18-Jan-3 Neret-Minet, Paris #181/R

CRAGG, Tony (1949-) British
Sculpture
£25000 $41000 €37500 Liverpool stop (79x220x205cm-31x87x81in) mixed media six parts prov.exhib.lit. 7-Feb-3 Sotheby's, London #159/R est:15000-20000
£29000 $44660 €43500 Spill (90x330x115cm-35x130x45in) bronze executed 1987 prov.lit. 23-Oct-2 Christie's, London #163/R est:30000-50000
£42000 $68880 €63000 Fruit bottles (66x585x260cm-26x230x102in) bronze seven parts prov.exhib.lit. 7-Feb-3 Sotheby's, London #158/R est:20000-30000
Works on paper
£2222 $3534 €3200 Sans titre (29x42cm-11x17in) s. gouache prov. 29-Apr-3 Artcurial Briest, Paris #487/R est:2000-2500
£2222 $3534 €3200 Sans titre (29x42cm-11x17in) s. gouache prov. 29-Apr-3 Artcurial Briest, Paris #488/R est:2000-2500

CRAGLIETTO, Giovanni (1889-1975) Italian
£2051 $3179 €3200 Concert amongst friends (170x250cm-67x98in) s.d.1926. 5-Dec-2 Stadion, Trieste #737/R est:4500

CRAHAY, Albert (1881-1914) Belgian
£478 $745 €750 Pecheurs de crevettes et leurs chevaux a la mer du Nord (45x55cm-18x22in) s. panel. 11-Nov-2 Horta, Bruxelles #523

CRAIG, Charles (1846-1931) American
£1398 $2250 €2097 Indian brave and horse in a landscape (23x33cm-9x13in) s. 18-Feb-3 John Moran, Pasadena #114b est:1500-2000
£6289 $10000 €9434 Indians hunting buffalo (56x91cm-22x36in) s.i.d.92 prov. 5-Mar-3 Sotheby's, New York #116/R est:12000-18000
£7547 $12000 €11321 Indians on horses riding along a trail (46x62cm-18x24in) s. 5-Mar-3 Sotheby's, New York #121/R est:8000-12000

CRAIG, David (fl.1934-1939) British
£450 $707 €675 Harmony in yellow (51x61cm-20x24in) s.d.1935 board. 15-Apr-3 Bonhams, Knightsbridge #24/R

CRAIG, Henry Robertson (1916-1984) British
£380 $604 €570 Male nude study (40x17cm-16x7in) s. board. 5-Mar-3 John Ross, Belfast #164
£1507 $2366 €2200 Place du France, Tangier (46x69cm-18x27in) s. board. 15-Apr-3 De Veres Art Auctions, Dublin #220 est:2500-3500
£1635 $2551 €2600 Unloading the catch, Portimao, Algarve (24x34cm-9x13in) s. canvasboard prov. 17-Sep-2 Whyte's, Dublin #155/R est:2500-3000
£1667 $2617 €2600 Spectators on a bridge, Portimao, Algarve (30x41cm-12x16in) s. canvasboard prov. 19-Nov-2 Whyte's, Dublin #230/R est:2500-3000
£2405 $3728 €3800 Early morning (23x76cm-9x30in) s.i. s.verso. 24-Sep-2 De Veres Art Auctions, Dublin #71/R est:4000-6000
£2500 $3975 €3600 Sunday in the park (30x46cm-12x18in) s. panel prov. 29-Apr-3 Whyte's, Dublin #125/R est:3000-4000
£3600 $5868 €5400 In the Tuileries Gardens (60x50cm-24x20in) s. 2-Feb-3 Lots Road, London #334/R est:2500-4000
£4700 $7614 €7050 At play in the garden (64x76cm-25x30in) s. 21-May-3 Bonhams, Knightsbridge #164/R est:5000-7000

CRAIG, J H (1878-1944) Irish
£3000 $4560 €4500 In Glendun (23x33cm-9x13in) s. i.verso board. 14-Aug-2 Andrew Hartley, Ilkley #663 est:700-900

CRAIG, J Humbert (1878-1944) Irish
£1200 $1908 €1800 Parkmore, County Antrim (25x30cm-10x12in) s. board. 5-Mar-3 John Ross, Belfast #60a est:1500-1800
£1800 $2862 €2700 Driving cattle, France (35x30cm-14x12in) s. board. 5-Mar-3 John Ross, Belfast #61 est:2000-2500
£2100 $3339 €3150 River in the glens (25x40cm-10x16in) s. board. 5-Mar-3 John Ross, Belfast #120 est:2000-2500
£2200 $3498 €3300 Fishing, Donegal (25x32cm-10x13in) s. board. 5-Mar-3 John Ross, Belfast #26 est:1500-1750
£2564 $4051 €4000 Cattle at evening (33x28cm-13x11in) s. board. 12-Nov-2 Mealy's, Castlecomer #1241
£2800 $4340 €4200 Red Bay Castle, Co. Antrim (32x44cm-13x17in) board prov. 4-Dec-2 Christie's, Kensington #437/R est:2000-3000
£2800 $4452 €4200 Behind the school, Glendun (22x30cm-9x12in) s. board. 5-Mar-3 John Ross, Belfast #23 est:2000-2500
£3400 $5406 €5100 In Bloody Foreland Donegal (25x35cm-10x14in) s. board. 5-Mar-3 John Ross, Belfast #188 est:2500-2800
£3986 $6536 €5500 Near Letterkenny (25x35cm-10x14in) s. i.verso panel prov. 28-May-3 Bonhams & James Adam, Dublin #172/R est:3000-5000
£4295 $6743 €6700 Glens of Antrim (38x51cm-15x20in) s. board. 19-Nov-2 Whyte's, Dublin #73/R est:8000-10000
£4305 $7017 €6500 Fisherman in punt, on rocky shore (12x17cm-5x7in) s. 29-Jan-3 Woodwards, Cork #195
£4500 $6570 €6750 Fishing boats at Cushendun, Co. Antrim (25x38cm-10x15in) s. board prov. 12-Jun-2 John Ross, Belfast #182 est:3000-3500
£4795 $7527 €7000 Lake and mountain landscape, West of Ireland (51x61cm-20x24in) s. board. 15-Apr-3 De Veres Art Auctions, Dublin #227/R est:7000-9000
£4800 $7632 €7200 Bringing home the turf (38x50cm-15x20in) s. board exhib. 5-Mar-3 John Ross, Belfast #158 est:2500-3500
£5800 $9280 €8700 Meandering river (30x43cm-12x17in) s. board. 15-May-3 Christie's, London #35 est:6000
£6000 $9540 €9000 Ardglass (40x56cm-16x22in) s. 5-Mar-3 John Ross, Belfast #147 est:5000-6000
£6090 $9439 €9500 Turf mountain, Connemara (29x42cm-11x17in) s. s.i.verso board. 3-Dec-2 Bonhams & James Adam, Dublin #110/R est:6000-10000
£6159 $10101 €8500 Dervock, Co. Antrim (37x49cm-15x19in) s. 28-May-3 Bonhams & James Adam, Dublin #110/R est:6000-8000
£7000 $11130 €10500 Cattle grazing, Red Bay, Country Antrim (50x61cm-20x24in) s. 5-Mar-3 John Ross, Belfast #73 est:3500-4000
£7372 $11426 €11500 Building turf near Glengesh, Donegal (46x60cm-18x24in) canvasboard. 3-Dec-2 Bonhams & James Adam, Dublin #76/R est:12000-18000
£7700 $12705 €11165 Lough landscape, Donegal (51x61cm-20x24in) s. painted c.1939. 3-Jul-3 Christie's, Kensington #463/R est:2500-3500
£8446 $13176 €12500 Donegal mountain landscape with figure on pathway (52x62cm-20x24in) s. 26-Mar-3 James Adam, Dublin #88/R est:12000-15000
£8696 $14261 €12000 Glenveigh, Co. Donegal (59x69cm-23x27in) s. 28-May-3 Bonhams & James Adam, Dublin #131/R est:12000-18000
£12000 $17520 €18000 Carrig Pin, Connemara (38x51cm-15x20in) s. 12-Jun-2 John Ross, Belfast #177 est:12000-14000
Works on paper
£550 $875 €825 Barge on the River Lagan (22x28cm-9x11in) s. W/C. 5-Mar-3 John Ross, Belfast #242

CRAIG, James Stevenson (fl.1854-1870) British
£3800 $5852 €5700 Blacksmith's cottage (91x71cm-36x28in) s.d.1873. 5-Sep-2 Christie's, Kensington #328/R est:3000-5000
£8889 $14756 €12889 After rain in the Rosses (41x51cm-16x20in) s. s.i.verso panel. 16-Jun-3 Waddingtons, Toronto #192/R est:7000-9000 (C.D 20000)

CRAIG, Sybil (1901-1989) Australian
Works on paper
£299 $490 €449 Banksia (34x44cm-13x17in) s.i. gouache. 4-Jun-3 Deutscher-Menzies, Melbourne #390/R (A.D 750)
£518 $849 €777 Beach, near Black Rock (36x45cm-14x18in) s. gouache. 4-Jun-3 Deutscher-Menzies, Melbourne #389/R (A.D 1300)
£518 $849 €777 Boats (34x43cm-13x17in) s. gouache pencil. 4-Jun-3 Deutscher-Menzies, Melbourne #391/R (A.D 1300)

CRAIG, Thomas (19th C) ?
£1282 $2000 €1923 Pastoral landscape with cows in river (48x41cm-19x16in) s. 18-Sep-2 Alderfer's, Hatfield #354/R est:1200-1500

CRAIG, Thomas Bigelow (1849-1924) American
£1563 $2500 €2345 Quiet retreat (46x66cm-18x26in) s. 15-Mar-3 Selkirks, St. Louis #334 est:1800-2200
£2258 $3500 €3387 Road by the brook (41x51cm-16x20in) s. i.verso prov. 2-Nov-2 North East Auctions, Portsmouth #82/R est:1500-2500
£2308 $3600 €3462 Summer and autumn (36x23cm-14x9in) s.d.1876 on e s. canvas on board pair. 12-Apr-3 Weschler, Washington #568/R est:2000-3000
£4192 $7000 €6078 Figures in a forest interior, autumn (128x91cm-50x36in) s.d.1876 canvas on board. 22-Jun-3 Freeman, Philadelphia #108/R est:3000-5000
Works on paper
£219 $350 €318 Flock at pasture (26x36cm-10x14in) s. W/C. 16-May-3 Skinner, Boston #64/R
£220 $350 €330 Cows watering (34x58cm-13x23in) s. W/C. 7-Mar-3 Skinner, Boston #264/R

CRAIG, William Marshall (fl.1788-1828) British
Works on paper
£850 $1352 €1275 Cupid sleeping on a bed of roses (30x43cm-12x17in) s.i.verso W/C prov. 30-Apr-3 Halls, Shrewsbury #236

CRAIG-MARTIN, Michael (1941-) Irish
£5500 $8470 €8250 Untitled (41x36cm-16x14in) acrylic on canvas executed 1996 prov. 22-Oct-2 Sotheby's, London #316/R est:4000-6000
Sculpture
£3500 $5740 €5250 Half box, green (62x181x171cm-24x71x67in) blockboard gloss paint prov.exhib. 7-Feb-3 Sotheby's, London #133/R est:5000-7000

CRAIGMILE, William (fl.1905-1931) British
Works on paper
£400 $624 €600 Swan lake (24x36cm-9x14in) s. pencil W/C. 19-Sep-2 Christie's, Kensington #65

CRALI, Tullio (1910-2000) Italian
Works on paper
£348 $543 €550 Little nude (16x10cm-6x4in) s. Chinese ink W/C. 14-Sep-2 Meeting Art, Vercelli #129
£548 $855 €800 Abstraction (25x17cm-10x7in) s. mixed media. 10-Apr-3 Finarte Semenzato, Rome #278

CRAM, Allen G (1886-1947) American
£1321 $2100 €1982 Cattle country (50x61cm-20x24in) s. i.verso canvasboard. 7-Mar-3 Skinner, Boston #346/R est:3000-5000

CRAMER, Konrad (1888-1963) American
Works on paper
£732 $1200 €1061 Modernist nude (29x13cm-11x5in) s.d. W/C gouache wax resist. 5-Jun-3 Swann Galleries, New York #73/R

CRAMER, Konrad (1888-1963) American
£9877 $16000 €14816 Tulips in a light vase (61x51cm-24x20in) s.d.1924 masonite prov. 21-May-3 Sotheby's, New York #42/R est:15000-25000
£18519 $30000 €27779 Hollyhocks (53x33cm-21x13in) s.d.1928 board prov.exhib. 21-May-3 Sotheby's, New York #41/R est:20000-30000
Works on paper
£701 $1100 €1052 Ink well (8x11cm-3x4in) s. ink chk wash prov. 19-Nov-2 Wright, Chicago #113/R

CRAMER, Rie (20th C) Dutch
Works on paper
£855 $1386 €1300 Feeding the ducks (18x26cm-7x10in) s. ink W/C. 21-Jan-3 Christie's, Amsterdam #260/R est:600-800

CRAMOYSAN, Marcel (1915-) French
£353 $554 €550 Niege a Saint-Arnoult (52x72cm-20x28in) s. 24-Nov-2 Lesieur & Le Bars, Le Havre #26
£403 $648 €600 Bouquet de fleurs (46x33cm-18x13in) s. 23-Feb-3 Lesieur & Le Bars, Le Havre #31

CRANACH, Lucas (elder) (1472-1553) German
£75000 $117750 €112500 Adam (51x44cm-20x17in) panel prov.exhib.lit. 12-Dec-2 Sotheby's, London #45/R est:60000-80000
£175676 $274054 €260000 Portrait of Princess Margaret of Saxony (48x32cm-19x13in) panel prov.lit. 27-Mar-3 Dorotheum, Vienna #303/R
£192308 $298077 €300000 Hercules and Antaeus (26x17cm-10x7in) panel prov.lit.exhib. 5-Dec-2 Dr Fritz Nagel, Stuttgart #593/R
Prints
£3004 $4657 €4506 Tournament (26x37cm-10x15in) mono.i. woodcut. 3-Oct-2 Koller, Zurich #3373/R est:7000-9000 (S.FR 7000)
£20253 $32000 €32000 Luther as an Augustinian Friar with doctoral cap (20x14cm-8x6in) copperplate. 29-Nov-2 Bassenge, Berlin #5210/R est:15000

CRANACH, Lucas (elder-after) (1472-1553) German
£5500 $8580 €8250 Hercules at a court of Omphale (79x120cm-31x47in) i. panel. 10-Apr-3 Christie's, Kensington #142/R est:6000-8000
£6419 $10014 €9500 Portrait of Melanchthon (48x59cm-19x23in) prov. 27-Mar-3 Dorotheum, Vienna #291/R est:1700-2500

CRANACH, Lucas (elder-circle) (1472-1553) German
£6500 $10205 €9750 Nobleman and his retinue outside a town (30x47cm-12x19in) panel. 13-Dec-2 Christie's, Kensington #139/R est:7000-10000

CRANACH, Lucas (elder-studio) (1472-1553) German
£18519 $30000 €27779 Holy Family with angels in a landscape (40x25cm-16x10in) panel prov. 24-Jan-3 Christie's, Rockefeller NY #31/R est:30000-50000

CRANACH, Lucas (elder-style) (1472-1553) German
£14000 $21700 €21000 Adam and Eve in the Garden of Eden - taking forbidden fruit (42x40cm-17x16in) bears serpent device d.1597 panel. 31-Oct-2 Sotheby's, Olympia #27/R est:5000-7000
£15000 $25050 €21750 Madonna and Child (58x35cm-23x14in) i.d.1536 panel. 9-Jul-3 Bonhams, New Bond Street #150/R est:15000-20000
£31963 $49863 €47945 Lucretia (95x58cm-37x23in) i.d.1537 panel. 28-Mar-3 Koller, Zurich #3067/R est:20000-30000 (S.FR 70000)

CRANACH, Lucas (studio) (15/16th C) German
£11613 $18348 €18000 Madonna and Child (49x4cm-19x2in) board. 18-Dec-2 Ansorena, Madrid #92/R est:18000

CRANACH, Lucas (younger) (1515-1586) German
£61728 $100000 €92592 Lucretia (75x56cm-30x22in) panel prov. 24-Jan-3 Christie's, Rockefeller NY #33/R est:150000-250000
£70000 $109900 €105000 Virgin and child with seven angels (50x35cm-20x14in) s. panel prov.exhib.lit. 12-Dec-2 Sotheby's, London #47/R est:80000-120000

CRANACH, Lucas (younger-circle) (1515-1586) German
£12000 $18840 €18000 Christ and the adulteress (87x120cm-34x47in) i.d.1540 panel. 13-Dec-2 Christie's, Kensington #137/R est:12000-18000

CRANACH, Lucas (younger-style) (1515-1586) German
£5660 $8830 €9000 Ridicule of Christ (86x58cm-34x23in) panel. 21-Sep-2 Berlinghof, Heidelberg #116/R est:6600

CRANE, Bruce (1857-1937) American
£750 $1200 €1125 Golden hills (23x30cm-9x12in) s. board. 11-Jan-3 James Julia, Fairfield #31a est:2500-4000
£1400 $2198 €2100 Farmstead in the fall (27x23cm-11x9in) s. board. 16-Dec-2 Bonhams, Bury St Edmunds #524/R est:1000-1500
£1419 $2200 €2129 November landscape (56x76cm-22x30in) s. 2-Nov-2 North East Auctions, Portsmouth #53/R
£1452 $2250 €2178 Landscape (25x33cm-10x13in) s. panel prov. 29-Oct-2 John Moran, Pasadena #626a est:2000-3000
£2160 $3500 €3132 Hamptons cottage at sunset (64x76cm-25x30in) s. 21-May-3 Doyle, New York #80/R est:3000-5000
£2258 $3500 €3387 November study (30x42cm-12x17in) s. s.i.stretcher. 3-Dec-2 Christie's, Rockefeller NY #583/R est:3000-5000
£2867 $4500 €4301 Sunset scene with a cottage (63x76cm-25x30in) s. 22-Nov-2 Skinner, Boston #225/R est:3000-5000
£3797 $6000 €5696 Grey October (36x51cm-14x20in) s. i.verso. 24-Apr-3 Shannon's, Milford #224/R est:4000-6000
£4037 $6500 €6056 Mohawk Hills (38x61cm-15x24in) s. 18-Feb-3 Arthur James, Florida #74
£5128 $8000 €7692 Road through the dunes (51x76cm-20x30in) s. prov. 12-Apr-3 Weschler, Washington #562/R est:6000-8000
£6013 $9500 €9020 Tranquil landscape (46x61cm-18x24in) s. prov. 24-Apr-3 Shannon's, Milford #23/R est:6000-8000
£7143 $11000 €10715 Winter sunset (64x76cm-25x30in) s. prov. 24-Oct-2 Shannon's, Milford #207/R est:12000-18000
£7595 $12000 €11393 Marshes at sunset (51x86cm-20x34in) s. 24-Apr-3 Shannon's, Milford #153/R est:9000-12000
£9938 $16000 €14907 Autumn landscape (28x36cm-11x14in) s.d.33. 18-Feb-3 John Moran, Pasadena #70a est:18000-22500
£10313 $16500 €15470 Indian river, Conn (41x61cm-16x24in) s. 11-Jan-3 James Julia, Fairfield #31 est:6000-8000
Works on paper
£350 $550 €525 Fading tints (33x41cm-13x16in) s. W/C paper on board. 10-Dec-2 Doyle, New York #40/R

CRANE, Grace (20th C) American
£440 $700 €638 Beach shacks (20x24cm-8x9in) s.d. 4-May-3 Treadway Gallery, Cincinnati #602/R

CRANE, Walter (1845-1915) British
£80000 $127200 €120000 Freedom (183x122cm-72x48in) s.i.d.1885 exhib.lit. 19-Mar-3 Sotheby's, London #274/R est:80000-120000
Works on paper
£600 $930 €900 Valle de Molini (44x29cm-17x11in) i.d.Sept 23 1872 pencil. 4-Dec-2 Christie's, Kensington #119a/R
£650 $1007 €975 Winds of the World - design for the frontispiece (38x27cm-15x11in) W/C bodycol. 24-Sep-2 Bonhams, New Bond Street #7/R
£1000 $1550 €1500 Pandora (20x15cm-8x6in) W/C bodycol. 24-Sep-2 Bonhams, New Bond Street #8/R
£17000 $27370 €25500 Lohengrin (91x56cm-36x22in) s.d.1895 pe col chk htd bodycol prov.exhib. 20-Feb-3 Christie's, London #236/R est:15000

CRANSTON, Toller (1949-) Canadian
Works on paper
£218 $358 €327 Female head (48x36cm-19x14in) s.d.1970 mixed media. 6-Feb-3 Heffel, Vancouver #011/R (C.D 550)

CRAPELET, Louis-Amable (1822-1867) French
£1500 $2430 €2250 Oriental bazaar (44x30cm-17x12in) s.i.d.1863. 20-May-3 Sotheby's, Olympia #399/R est:1500-2000
Works on paper
£317 $500 €500 Interior of castle room (16x21cm-6x8in) pen ink crayon W/C. 28-Nov-2 Tajan, Paris #151
£1218 $1924 €1900 Interieur de mosquee (25x31cm-10x12in) s. W/C. 18-Nov-2 Sotheby's, Paris #102/R

CRAS, Monique (1910-) French
£4167 $6542 €6500 Femmes Touareg (73x92cm-29x36in) s.i.d.1942. 10-Dec-2 Tajan, Paris #135/R est:7800

CRAVEN, William 2nd Earl (1809-1866) British
Photographs
£2885 $4558 €4500 Etude d'un arbre (37x29cm-15x11in) albumin print cardboard exec.c.1855 prov. 16-Nov-2 Christie's, Paris #154/R est:1200-1800
£9295 $14686 €14500 Sentier dans les arbres (29x24cm-11x9in) albumin print cardboard exec.c.1855 prov. 16-Nov-2 Christie's, Paris #153/R est:1000-1500
£15385 $24308 €24000 Wild Dayrell, vainqueur de Derby (23x30cm-9x12in) one i.verso albumin print exec.c.1856 two prov. 16-Nov-2 Christie's, Paris #155/R est:1500-2000
£23077 $36462 €36000 Jeune femme, probablement Lady Evelyn Mary Craven (23x18cm-9x7in) st.sig. albumin print exec.c.1855 prov. 16-Nov-2 Christie's, Paris #256/R est:1000-1500

CRAVO NETO, Mario (1947-) ?
Photographs
£2564 $4000 €3846 Ode (40x40cm-16x16in) s.d.num.5/25 gelatin silver print. 14-Oct-2 Butterfields, San Francisco #1519/R est:1500-2500

CRAWFORD, Edmund Thornton (1806-1885) British
£580 $916 €870 Crossing the ford (25x40cm-10x16in) s.d.1882 panel. 2-Dec-2 Bonhams, Bath #131/R
£780 $1232 €1170 Entrance to the port of Rotterdam (22x59cm-9x23in) s. indis d. panel. 7-Apr-3 Bonhams, Bath #83
£2000 $3040 €3000 Edinburgh from Inchcolm (41x81cm-16x32in) canvas on panel. 28-Aug-2 Sotheby's, London #875/R est:2000-3000
£2800 $4340 €4200 Watering the horses (41x58cm-16x23in) s.d.1869. 6-Dec-2 Lyon & Turnbull, Edinburgh #7/R est:1500-2000

CRAWFORD, Edmund Thornton (attrib) (1806-1885) British
£700 $1099 €1050 Hauling in the nets (30x43cm-12x17in) s.d.1836 panel. 16-Dec-2 Sotheby's, Olympia #29/R

CRAWFORD, Esther Mabel (1872-1958) American
£1774 $2750 €2661 Coastal (38x56cm-15x22in) s. prov. 29-Oct-2 John Moran, Pasadena #668 est:2000-3000

CRAWFORD, Hugh Adana (1898-1982) British
£380 $600 €570 Christ, portrait head (55x46cm-22x18in) s. board. 5-Apr-3 Shapes, Edinburgh #316

CRAWFORD, Isabel (20th C) American
£325 $475 €488 Lake Louise (39x30cm-15x12in) s. d.1939 verso board. 10-May-2 Skinner, Boston #133/R

CRAWFORD, Ralston (1906-1978) American
Photographs
£2179 $3400 €3269 Queen Mary (15x23cm-6x9in) s. verso silver. 21-Oct-2 Swann Galleries, New York #111/R est:4000-6000
Works on paper
£9756 $16000 €14146 Study for Maitland Bridge (30x38cm-12x15in) s.d.1939 W/C. 1-Jun-3 Wright, Chicago #214/R est:5000-7000

CRAWFORD, Robert C (1842-1924) British
£1500 $2460 €2250 On Loch Long side (98x68cm-39x27in) s.d.1877 exhib. 29-May-3 Christie's, Kensington #97 est:2000-3000

CRAWFORD, Susan L (1941-) British
£272 $425 €408 Morning workout with race horses (37x61cm-15x24in) s.d.1992 board. 13-Apr-3 Butterfields, Los Angeles #7016

CRAWFORD, William Caldwell (fl.1898-1936) British
£1333 $2213 €1933 Cottage window (76x63cm-30x25in) s.d.1933 prov. 10-Jun-3 Ritchie, Toronto #82/R est:2000-3000 (C.D 3000)

CRAWHALL, Joseph (1821-1896) British
£480 $782 €720 Three foxhounds in full flight (19x60cm-7x24in) s.d.187. 28-Jan-3 Bristol Auction Rooms #539/R
Works on paper
£640 $1043 €960 Buff, a coursing greyhound in landscape with quarry (31x41cm-12x16in) s.i.d.1882 W/C. 28-Jan-3 Bristol Auction Rooms #509/R

CRAWHALL, Joseph (1861-1913) British
Works on paper
£1100 $1782 €1650 En plein air (20x14cm-8x6in) init.i.d.80 pencil col wash. 23-May-3 Lyon & Turnbull, Edinburgh #12/R est:1000-1500
£5500 $8525 €8250 Camel (18x23cm-7x9in) W/C prov.exhib.lit. 6-Dec-2 Lyon & Turnbull, Edinburgh #4/R est:1000-1500
£20000 $30400 €30000 Bullfight (44x35cm-17x14in) s. W/C prov.exhib. 28-Aug-2 Sotheby's, London #1062/R est:20000-30000

CRAWHALL, W (fl.1858-1894) British
£1950 $3101 €2925 Coastal scene (120x72cm-47x28in) s.i. 19-Mar-3 Anthemion, Cardiff #426/R est:1500-2000

CRAWHALL, William (fl.1858-1894) British
£750 $1155 €1125 Rest on the coast. Figures on the coast (19x30cm-7x12in) board pair. 5-Sep-2 Christie's, Kensington #228/R

CRAWLEY, Michael (?) British
Works on paper
£320 $506 €480 Low tide, Whitby (23x36cm-9x14in) s. i.verso W/C. 24-Apr-3 Richardson & Smith, Whitby #41
£350 $560 €525 Pool of London (30x58cm-12x23in) s. W/C. 10-Jan-3 Biddle & Webb, Birmingham #405

CRAWSHAW, Alwyn (1934-) British
£440 $695 €660 Pastoral landscape (58x89cm-23x35in) s. 17-Dec-2 Gorringes, Lewes #1402

CRAWSHAW, Lionel Townsend (1864-1949) British
£480 $749 €720 Children playing by beached fishing boat (11x16cm-4x6in) i.verso panel. 10-Sep-2 David Duggleby, Scarborough #313
£1800 $3006 €2610 La Place de la Concorde, Paris (20x26cm-8x10in) i.verso artist's board. 17-Jun-3 Gildings, Market Harborough #461 est:200-300
£3557 $5584 €5336 Young girl seated near some trees (21x27cm-8x11in) s. board. 10-Dec-2 Pinneys, Montreal #51 est:2000-3000 (C.D 8750)
£4900 $7644 €7350 Children playing on the sands, Whitby harbour (34x24cm-13x9in) s. panel. 10-Sep-2 David Duggleby, Scarborough #285/R est:2000-3000

CRAXTON, John (1922-) British
£8300 $12948 €12450 Greek panorama in winter (28x185cm-11x73in) s.d.58 tempora hardboard exhib. 9-Oct-2 Woolley & Wallis, Salisbury #180/R est:3000-5000
£12000 $18960 €18000 Man and cat at cafe (56x45cm-22x18in) s.d.54 paper prov. 27-Nov-2 Sotheby's, Olympia #62/R est:3000-5000
Works on paper
£2600 $4030 €3900 House by the sea (44x61cm-17x24in) s.d.20.8.46 W/C paper on board. 3-Dec-2 Bonhams, Knightsbridge #224/R est:1000-2000
£3600 $5616 €5400 Still life with cat and child (36x46cm-14x18in) s.d.57 gouache on board. 25-Mar-3 Bonhams, New Bond Street #86/R est:4000-6000

CRAYER, Gaspar de (1584-1669) Flemish
£3688 $5716 €5532 The Penitent Magdalene (37x24cm-15x9in) s.d.1630 panel. 3-Dec-2 Bukowskis, Stockholm #432/R est:50000-60000 (S.KR 52000)
£32000 $49920 €48000 Martyrdom of Saint Dorothea (173x133cm-68x52in) prov.lit. 9-Apr-3 Christie's, London #7/R est:12000-18000

CRAYER, Gaspar de (attrib) (1584-1669) Flemish
£1307 $2105 €2000 St Dominique recevant la scapulaire de la Vierge (85x127cm-33x50in) 14-Jan-3 Vanderkindere, Brussels #409 est:2500-4000

CREALOCK, John (1871-1959) British
£500 $785 €750 St Margaret's Church, Westminster (63x78cm-25x31in) s.d.1921. 24-Nov-2 Lots Road, London #339

CREAN, Emma (20th C) Irish?
£342 $534 €500 Tarifa (88x61cm-35x24in) s.d.00 acrylic paper. 8-Apr-3 James Adam, Dublin #140/R

CREDI, Lorenzo di (circle) (1459-1537) Italian
£68987 $106930 €109000 Holy Family with Infant St John the Baptist (85cm-33in circular) mono.verso panel. 25-Sep-2 Neumeister, Munich #478/R est:45000

CREER, Deirdre Henty (?) ?
Works on paper
£550 $875 €798 Children skating on a frozen river (48x58cm-19x23in) s. W/C. 19-Mar-3 John Nicholson, Haslemere #1136
£550 $875 €798 Line up for sleigh haul (48x64cm-19x25in) s. W/C board. 19-Mar-3 John Nicholson, Haslemere #1137/R

CREFFIELD, Dennis (1931-) British
Works on paper
£360 $572 €540 Winchester from the South-East (92x101cm-36x40in) chl exhib. 26-Feb-3 Sotheby's, Olympia #370/R
£550 $908 €798 York Minster, east window (85x61cm-33x24in) chl prov.exhib. 3-Jul-3 Christie's, Kensington #663/R

CREGAN, Martin (1788-1870) Irish
£900 $1395 €1350 Portrait of Richard Ward (76x63cm-30x25in) s.d.1826 i.verso. 30-Sep-2 Bonhams, Ipswich #501/R

CREGAN, Martin (attrib) (1788-1870) Irish
£1200 $1920 €1800 Portrait of Mr Mitchell, wearing a black jacket (71x59cm-28x23in) 16-May-3 Sotheby's, London #13 est:1500-2000

CREIFELDS, Richard (1853-1939) American
£692 $1100 €1038 Checkmate (36x41cm-14x16in) s. prov.exhib. 5-Mar-3 Doyle, New York #17/R

CREIXAMS, Pierre (1893-1965) Spanish
£380 $600 €600 Jeune fille au chale colore (55x46cm-22x18in) s. 2-Dec-2 Tajan, Paris #90
£676 $1054 €1000 Nature morte au bouquet de fleurs (58x47cm-23x19in) s. 26-Mar-3 Millon & Associes, Paris #108/R
£1145 $1820 €1660 Little beggar (41x33cm-16x13in) s. 4-Mar-3 Ansorena, Madrid #331/R
£1438 $2244 €2100 Femme au foulard (63x41cm-25x16in) s. 13-Apr-3 Feletin, Province #92
£1709 $2700 €2700 Famille (90x73cm-35x29in) s. 2-Dec-2 Tajan, Paris #91/R
£2830 $4387 €4500 Antequera fair (38x55cm-15x22in) s. 7-Oct-2 Ansorena, Madrid #68/R

CRELL, Rudolf (1833-1904) German
£298 $471 €447 Coastal breakers (60x90cm-24x35in) s. 2-Dec-2 Rasmussen, Copenhagen #1383/R (D.KR 3500)
£553 $874 €830 Sunset over the sea (67x95cm-26x37in) s. 2-Dec-2 Rasmussen, Copenhagen #1379/R (D.KR 6500)

CREMA, Giovanni Battista (1883-1964) Italian
£2770 $4322 €4100 Still life (30x49cm-12x19in) s. board. 28-Mar-3 Farsetti, Prato #692/R
£23077 $36230 €36000 Nude (120x100cm-47x39in) s. panel. 10-Dec-2 Tajan, Paris #136/R est:40000

CREMER, Jan (1940-) Dutch
£1603 $2484 €2500 Nachtgevecht (63x78cm-25x31in) s.d.58 s.d.on stretcher oil lacquer exhib. 3-Dec-2 Christie's, Amsterdam #132/R est:1500-2000

CREMONA, Tranquillo (1837-1878) Italian
£4613 $6781 €7150 Mail (63x50cm-25x20in) 24-Jun-2 Babuino, Rome #320 est:3000-4000
£7092 $11489 €10000 Three-quarter length portrait of a girl in decorative dress (80x48cm-31x19in) i.verso panel. 22-May-3 Dorotheum, Vienna #6/R est:10000-12000
Works on paper
£750 $1140 €1125 Tres figuras femeninas (23x17cm-9x7in) init. W/C. 3-Jul-2 Naón & Cia, Buenos Aires #31
£3270 $5036 €5200 Girl (16x9cm-6x4in) mono. W/C. 28-Oct-2 Il Ponte, Milan #236/R est:3200

CREMONA, Tranquillo (attrib) (1837-1878) Italian
Works on paper
£690 $1097 €1000 The King vittorio Emanuele II meeting Radetzky (29x20cm-11x8in) W/C prov. 7-Mar-3 Semenzato, Venice #537/R

CREMONINI, Leonardo (1925-) Italian
Works on paper
£506 $800 €759 Kicking bull (28x40cm-11x16in) s.d.52 pen ink prov.exhib. 24-Apr-3 Sotheby's, New York #174/R

CREMP, Erminio (20th C) Italian
£443 $700 €700 Italian coastal landscape with figures on a path and fishing boats (68x120cm-27x47in) s.i. 30-Nov-2 Geble, Radolfzell #658
£475 $750 €750 Palmermo harbour with fishermen and their boats (68x120cm-27x47in) s.i. 30-Nov-2 Geble, Radolfzell #659
£1474 $2241 €2300 Gulf of Palermo (50x76cm-20x30in) s.i. board. 31-Aug-2 Geble, Radolfzell #618
£2244 $3410 €3500 Gulf of Naples with Vesuvius (72x115cm-28x45in) s. 31-Aug-2 Geble, Radolfzell #619 est:100

CREPAX, Guido (20th C) Italian?
£513 $805 €800 Dreams under accusation (50x72cm-20x28in) s.i.verso tempera Chinese ink card. 16-Dec-2 Pandolfini, Florence #377/R
Works on paper
£513 $805 €800 Lonely woman (58x41cm-23x16in) s.i.verso Chinese ink card. 16-Dec-2 Pandolfini, Florence #378
£704 $1169 €1000 Valentina (51x37cm-20x15in) s.d.81 Indian ink. 10-Jun-3 Finarte Semenzato, Milan #216/R

CREPAZ, Hans (1938-) Austrian?
£331 $540 €500 Bunch of flowers and butterfly (25x20cm-10x8in) s. panel. 28-Jan-3 Dorotheum, Vienna #227/R

CREPIN D'ORLEANS (18th C) French
£11149 $17392 €16500 Paysages de riviere (37x46cm-15x18in) pair. 28-Mar-3 Piasa, Paris #48 est:4000-6000

CREPIN, Joseph (1875-1948) French
£3526 $5571 €5500 Numero 62 (34x23cm-13x9in) s.i.d.1940 prov. 15-Nov-2 Laurence Calmels, Paris #11a/R
£5479 $8548 €8000 Numero 164 (63x51cm-25x20in) s.i. painted 1941 exhib. 14-Apr-3 Laurence Calmels, Paris #4010/R
£5822 $9140 €8500 Numero 83 (33x29cm-13x11in) s.i. painted 1940 exhib. 15-Apr-3 Laurence Calmels, Paris #4205/R
£7877 $12366 €11500 Numero 88 (34x27cm-13x11in) i. exhib. 15-Apr-3 Laurence Calmels, Paris #4206/R
£9932 $15592 €14500 Numero 103 (34x51cm-13x20in) i.d.1940 exhib. 15-Apr-3 Laurence Calmels, Paris #4207/R est:5000
£10959 $17205 €16000 Numero 50 (52x35cm-20x14in) s.i. prov.exhib. 15-Apr-3 Laurence Calmels, Paris #4204/R
£13699 $21507 €20000 Numero 110 (56x73cm-22x29in) s.i.d.1940 prov.exhib. 15-Apr-3 Laurence Calmels, Paris #4208/R est:10000
£17123 $26884 €25000 Numero 11 (57x73cm-22x29in) i. prov.exhib.lit. 15-Apr-3 Laurence Calmels, Paris #4203/R

CREPIN, Louis Philippe (1772-1851) French
£4000 $6280 €6000 River landscape with fishermen in the foreground. River landscape with cottages (24x32cm-9x13in) with sig.d.1815 panel pair. 10-Dec-2 Sotheby's, Olympia #406/R est:4000-6000

CREPIN, Louis Philippe (attrib) (1772-1851) French
£1899 $3000 €3000 Landscape with figures (61x72cm-24x28in) 2-Dec-2 Finarte, Milan #143/R
£2585 $4110 €3800 Paysage anime (71x85cm-28x33in) 28-Feb-3 Joron-Derem, Paris #15/R

CRESCIMANNO, Nicola F (19th C) Italian
£2000 $3100 €3000 Luzzu passing St. Paul's Island in St. Paul's Bay. Luzzu in a squall off Maltese coast (17x29cm-7x11in) s.d.1874 panel pair. 31-Oct-2 Christie's, Kensington #468/R est:1000-1500

CRESCIMBENI, Angelo (1734-1781) Italian
£4690 $7410 €6800 Portrait of gentleman in black coat (105x80cm-41x31in) 5-Apr-3 Finarte Semenzato, Milan #108/R est:12000

CRESPI, Giuseppe Maria (1665-1747) Italian
£20000 $31400 €30000 Portrait of artist in black coat and white shirt (56x44cm-22x17in) 11-Dec-2 Christie's, London #115/R est:20000-30000

CRESPI, Giuseppe Maria (attrib) (1665-1747) Italian
£692 $1079 €1100 Maria with sleeping child (49x38cm-19x15in) panel. 9-Oct-2 Michael Zeller, Lindau #554/R
£4839 $7645 €7259 Dancing figure with a lute (22x16cm-9x6in) copper. 18-Nov-2 Waddingtons, Toronto #286/R est:20000-30000 (C.D 12000)

CRESPI, Giuseppe Maria (circle) (1665-1747) Italian
£8387 $13251 €13000 Judith presenting Olophernes' head (114x151cm-45x59in) 20-Dec-2 Tajan, Paris #17/R est:18000

CRESPIGNY, Rose de (fl.1891-1929) British
Works on paper
£700 $1092 €1050 View of St. Paul's Cathedral from the River Thames (25x36cm-10x14in) s. pencil W/C. 17-Oct-2 Christie's, Kensington #52

CRESS, Fred (1938-) Australian/Indian
Works on paper
£321 $498 €482 Secrets no 31 (56x92cm-22x36in) s.d.85 mixed media. 29-Oct-2 Lawson Menzies, Sydney #146 (A.D 900)
£619 $978 €1073 Among friends (77x112cm-30x44in) i.d.83 pastel. 1-Apr-3 Goodman, Sydney #76/R (A.D 1620)

CRESSWELL, William Nichol (1822-1888) Canadian
£956 $1500 €1434 Shooting party, White Mountains (94x75cm-37x30in) s. 22-Nov-2 Skinner, Boston #81 est:3000-5000
£1400 $2282 €2100 Home coming (39x65cm-15x26in) s.d.1864. 29-Jan-3 Hampton & Littlewood, Exeter #402/R est:800-1000
Works on paper
£348 $540 €522 Sheep and farmhands by a canal (24x48cm-9x19in) s.d.1884 W/C prov. 24-Sep-2 Ritchie, Toronto #3097/R (C.D 850)
£723 $1135 €1085 Wreck on the Pacific Coast (26x51cm-10x20in) s.d.1886 W/C prov.exhib. 25-Nov-2 Hodgins, Calgary #111/R est:2000-2500 (C.D 1800)

CRESTI, Domenico (1558-1638) Italian
£9929 $16085 €14000 Lute player with dog and landscape in the background (116x97cm-46x38in) lit. 20-May-3 Babuino, Rome #8/R est:10000-15000

CRESTI, Domenico (attrib) (1558-1638) Italian
Works on paper
£833 $1325 €1200 Mary with child on clouds with five saints below (26x20cm-10x8in) pen. 5-May-3 Ketterer, Munich #367/R

CRESWICK, Thomas (1811-1869) British
£276 $450 €414 English countryside with cows (30x41cm-12x16in) s. 2-Feb-3 Simpson's, Houston #142
£304 $475 €441 English countryside with cows (30x41cm-12x16in) s. 30-Mar-3 Simpson's, Houston #62
£450 $702 €675 Angler on a footbridge in a wooded landscape (35x46cm-14x18in) board. 7-Nov-2 Christie's, Kensington #120
£500 $770 €750 Mill Pool (29x24cm-11x9in) s. 22-Oct-2 Bonhams, Bath #259
£550 $897 €825 Dovedale (46x66cm-18x26in) indis.s.d.1873. 14-Feb-3 Keys, Aylsham #662/R
£600 $966 €900 Pastoral landscape (15x22cm-6x9in) board prov. 15-Jan-3 Cheffins Grain & Comins, Cambridge #420/R
£962 $1490 €1500 Summer landscape with mother and her child on bank of the stream (86x112cm-34x44in) s.d.1852. 4-Dec-2 Neumeister, Munich #698/R est:1800
£4000 $6320 €6000 River landscape with mother and child seated on the bank (53x71cm-21x28in) s. prov.exhib. 26-Nov-2 Christie's, London #79/R est:5000-8000
£13000 $21580 €19500 Anglers by a waterfall (69x100cm-27x39in) s.d.1840 prov. 10-Jun-3 Christie's, London #69/R est:10000-15000

CRESWICK, Thomas (attrib) (1811-1869) British
£400 $628 €600 Figure on a riverbank with church beyond (20x16cm-8x6in) mono. panel. 16-Apr-3 Christie's, Kensington #608/R
£3800 $6004 €5700 By a ford (71x91cm-28x36in) bears sig.d.1832. 2-Dec-2 Bonhams, Bath #103/R est:4000-6000

CRETEN, Victor (1878-1966) Belgian
£691 $1105 €960 Paysages Ardennais (45x57cm-18x22in) panel pair. 19-May-3 Horta, Bruxelles #115
Works on paper
£432 $691 €600 Paysage architectural (70x80cm-28x31in) s.verso gouache cardboard. 19-May-3 Horta, Bruxelles #114
£791 $1266 €1100 Promenade dans un parc (50x60cm-20x24in) s. gouache paper on canvas. 19-May-3 Horta, Bruxelles #113

CRETEN-GEORGES (1887-1966) Belgian
£2564 $3974 €4000 Mannequin (70x58cm-28x23in) s.d.48 paper on board exhib. 7-Dec-2 De Vuyst, Lokeren #67/R est:2500-3000
Works on paper
£272 $433 €400 Fleurs des champs. s. W/C. 18-Mar-3 Galerie Moderne, Brussels #115

CRETI, Donato (1671-1749) Italian
£46000 $71760 €69000 Still life of flowers in urn with young boy. Still life with basket of grapes with young girl (124x90cm-49x35in) pair. 10-Apr-3 Sotheby's, London #84/R est:40000
Works on paper
£839 $1200 €1259 Youth and old age (15x17cm-6x7in) pen brown ink. 23-Jan-3 Swann Galleries, New York #116/R est:1500-2500
£850 $1377 €1275 Designs for the monument to Giovan Guiseppe Sbaraglia (35x23cm-14x9in) s. pen sepia ink. 21-Jan-3 Bonhams, Knightsbridge #269/R
£2703 $4216 €4000 Femme au turban (14x22cm-6x9in) i.pen ink. 27-Mar-3 Christie's, Paris #79/R
£2778 $4417 €4000 Hieronymus (15x10cm-6x4in) pen paper on board prov. 5-May-3 Ketterer, Munich #382/R est:2000-3000
£5556 $8833 €8000 Mary in the Temple (23x30cm-9x12in) s. pen. 5-May-3 Ketterer, Munich #383/R est:1300-1600

CRETI, Donato (attrib) (1671-1749) Italian
Works on paper
£2207 $3509 €3200 Head of boy in profile (35x26cm-14x10in) chl lead. 5-Mar-3 Sotheby's, Milan #230/R est:3000

CREUZ, Serge (1924-1996) Belgian
£348 $543 €550 Voilier en carenage (46x55cm-18x22in) s. 16-Sep-2 Horta, Bruxelles #254
Works on paper
£464 $756 €700 Vue de Greolieres (56x76cm-22x30in) s.d.1975 verso W/C. 17-Feb-3 Horta, Bruxelles #376

CREVANI, A (?) ?
£2200 $3564 €3190 Street scene in Seville (67x104cm-26x41in) 21-May-3 Outhwaite & Litherland, Liverpool #208/R

CREVEL, René (20th C) French
£1844 $2987 €2600 Le cavalier (49x61cm-19x24in) s.d.1934 canvas on isorel. 23-May-3 Camard, Paris #132/R est:500-600

CREWDSON, Gregory (1962-) American
Photographs
£2468 $3900 €3702 Natural wonder (51x61cm-20x24in) s.i.d.1990 verso cibachrome print prov. 13-Nov-2 Sotheby's, New York #496/R
£3006 $4750 €4509 Natural wonder (51x61cm-20x24in) s.d.1990 verso cibachrome print prov. 13-Nov-2 Sotheby's, New York #495/R
£6250 $10000 €9375 Untitled (46x56cm-18x22in) s.d.1997 num.6/6 gelatin silver print prov.lit. 14-May-3 Sotheby's, New York #329/R est:3500-4500
£8442 $13000 €12663 Untitled (127x152cm-50x60in) s.d.1998 num.2/10 verso col chromogenic print prov.lit. 25-Oct-2 Phillips, New York #67/R est:10000-15000
£9375 $15000 €14063 Untitled - twilight series (122x152cm-48x60in) c-print mounted on aluminum executed 1998-2002 prov.exhib. 16-May-3 Phillips, New York #113/R est:15000-20000
£9740 $15000 €14610 Untitled (127x152cm-50x60in) col chromogenic print 3 of 10 prov.lit. 25-Oct-2 Phillips, New York #195/R est:10000-15000
£12500 $20000 €18750 Untitled - sod man (127x152cm-50x60in) s. laser direct col coupler print mounted on cintra executed 1999. 15-May-3 Christie's, Rockefeller NY #337/R est:15000-20000
£16456 $26000 €24684 Untitled - sewer mystery (122x152cm-48x60in) s. laser direct col coupler print executed 1999 prov. 14-Nov-2 Christie's, Rockefeller NY #470/R est:12000-18000
£17722 $28000 €26583 Untitled - awake (122x152cm-48x60in) s.verso chromogenic col print prov.lit. 24-Apr-3 Phillips, New York #67/R est:15000-20000
£22152 $35000 €33228 Untitled - beer dreams (127x152cm-50x60in) s.d.1998 laser direct col coupler print prov.exhib.lit. 14-Nov-2 Christie's, Rockefeller NY #469/R est:12000-18000

CREYTENS, Julien (1897-1972) Belgian
£486 $773 €700 Vase blanc aux fleurs (82x65cm-32x26in) s.d.1943. 29-Apr-3 Campo & Campo, Antwerp #46
£833 $1325 €1200 Nature morte au jambon (81x100cm-32x39in) s.d.1942. 29-Apr-3 Campo & Campo, Antwerp #45/R est:1600-2000
£1528 $2429 €2200 Nature morte aux fruits (82x97cm-32x38in) s.d.1943. 29-Apr-3 Campo & Campo, Antwerp #44/R est:1800-2400

CRICK, Alfred Egide (1858-1931) Belgian
Sculpture
£1090 $1689 €1700 Gavroche (56x16cm-22x6in) s.d.1891 brown pat bronze Cast Petermann. 7-Dec-2 De Vuyst, Lokeren #68 est:1600-1800

CRIPPA, Roberto (1921-1972) Italian
£769 $1208 €1200 Untitled (28x20cm-11x8in) s.i.d.1955 verso board. 19-Nov-2 Finarte, Milan #83/R
£1090 $1711 €1700 Spiral (70x50cm-28x20in) s. acrylic card. 23-Nov-2 Meeting Art, Vercelli #303/R
£1139 $1777 €1800 Totem (71x50cm-28x20in) s. paper on canvas painted 1970. 14-Sep-2 Meeting Art, Vercelli #730/R
£1631 $2643 €2300 Untitled (66x83cm-26x33in) s. board. 26-May-3 Christie's, Milan #182/R est:2000-3000
£2179 $3422 €3400 Totem (81x60cm-32x24in) s.d.54 masonite. 19-Nov-2 Finarte, Milan #92/R
£2188 $3478 €3150 Spirals (30x40cm-12x16in) s.d.1952 verso. 1-May-3 Meeting Art, Vercelli #19
£2308 $3623 €3600 Sunset (73x60cm-29x24in) s.verso collage cork board. 23-Nov-2 Meeting Art, Vercelli #353/R
£2703 $4216 €4000 Spirals (70x50cm-28x20in) s.d.1951 verso acrylic. 26-Mar-3 Finarte Semenzato, Milan #376/R
£2949 $4659 €4600 Spirals (50x60cm-20x24in) s.d.54. 15-Nov-2 Farsetti, Prato #291/R
£2993 $4759 €4400 Spiral (50x60cm-20x24in) s.d.1952 verso. 1-Mar-3 Meeting Art, Vercelli #603
£3056 $4858 €4400 Spiral (38x54cm-15x21in) s.d.1952. 1-May-3 Meeting Art, Vercelli #471
£3378 $5270 €5000 Spirals (65x55cm-26x22in) s.d.1952 verso acrylic. 26-Mar-3 Finarte Semenzato, Milan #278/R
£3401 $5408 €5000 Spirals (50x70cm-20x28in) s.d.1951. 1-Mar-3 Meeting Art, Vercelli #655
£3546 $5745 €5000 Groviglio 129 (50x70cm-20x28in) s.d.52 s.d.52 verso prov. 26-May-3 Christie's, Milan #344/R est:4000-6000
£4937 $7800 €7800 Tangle (80x59cm-31x23in) s.d.952. 29-Nov-2 Farsetti, Prato #547/R est:4000
£5128 $8051 €8000 Spiral (50x100cm-20x39in) s.d.1951 verso. 23-Nov-2 Meeting Art, Vercelli #362/R
£11111 $17667 €16000 Spacial concept (115x145cm-45x57in) s.i.d.1954 verso. 1-May-3 Meeting Art, Vercelli #211 est:10000
Sculpture
£1667 $2433 €2600 Untitled (51x28x28cm-20x11x11in) bronze. 5-Jun-2 Il Ponte, Milan #120
Works on paper
£574 $896 €850 Lizard (49x69cm-19x27in) s. collage mixed media paper on canvas. 26-Mar-3 Finarte Semenzato, Milan #138/R
£705 $1093 €1100 Arc-en-ciel (35x27cm-14x11in) s.verso cork enamel board prov. 5-Dec-2 Stadion, Trieste #697/R
£748 $1190 €1100 Mountains and sun (40x30cm-16x12in) s. collage cardboard. 1-Mar-3 Meeting Art, Vercelli #416
£922 $1494 €1300 Disegni (27x35cm-11x14in) s.i.d.71 mixed media board on panel prov. 26-May-3 Christie's, Milan #52
£993 $1609 €1400 Aereopittura (40x32cm-16x13in) s.i.d.1970 verso mixed media panel prov. 26-May-3 Christie's, Milan #159/R est:1500-2000
£1154 $1685 €1800 Spiral (100x75cm-39x30in) mixed media exec.1955. 5-Jun-2 Il Ponte, Milan #18
£1351 $2108 €2000 Oiseau (35x27cm-14x11in) s.i.d.1972 cork collage. 26-Mar-3 Finarte Semenzato, Milan #404/R
£1533 $2500 €2300 Cielo giallo (72x68cm-28x27in) s.i.d.1964 verso mixed media cork newspaper panel prov. 16-Feb-3 Butterfields, San Francisco #2134 est:2000-3000
£1795 $2818 €2800 Composition (54x40cm-21x16in) s.verso exec.1960 cork board. 19-Nov-2 Finarte, Milan #259/R
£1892 $2951 €2800 Sea (46x55cm-18x22in) s.i.d.70 verso collage cork board. 28-Mar-3 Farsetti, Prato #372/R
£1899 $3000 €3000 Sun origin (46x55cm-18x22in) s.i.d.1969 verso cork collage board. 29-Nov-2 Farsetti, Prato #271/R
£2115 $3321 €3300 Composition (69x60cm-27x24in) s.i.d.1965 mixed media cork board. 19-Nov-2 Finarte, Milan #283/R
£2329 $3633 €3400 Composition (62x70cm-24x28in) s.verso cork board. 10-Apr-3 Finarte Semenzato, Rome #180/R
£2342 $3700 €3700 Space bird (65x54cm-26x21in) s.d.1971 verso cork collage board. 29-Nov-2 Farsetti, Prato #231/R est:3900
£2436 $3849 €3800 Untitled (73x91cm-29x36in) s.d.70 verso cork collage. 15-Nov-2 Farsetti, Prato #46/R
£2692 $4227 €4200 Composition (88x126cm-35x50in) s.i.d.1965 cork board. 19-Nov-2 Finarte, Milan #133/R
£5449 $8609 €8500 Icarus' dream (135x162cm-53x64in) s.i.d.1962 cork collage. 15-Nov-2 Farsetti, Prato #351/R est:12000
£5696 $9000 €9000 Landscape (116x76cm-46x30in) s.i.d.61 cork collage board. 29-Nov-2 Farsetti, Prato #477/R est:8000
£6013 $9500 €9500 Homme (145x114cm-57x45in) s.d.1960 verso cork collage board. 29-Nov-2 Farsetti, Prato #539/R
£6944 $11042 €10000 Landscape (130x97cm-51x38in) s.i.d.1961 verso mixed media collage cork board. 1-May-3 Meeting Art, Vercelli #437 est:8000
£7770 $12122 €11500 Giant (200x200cm-79x79in) s.i.d.1960 cork collage board. 28-Mar-3 Farsetti, Prato #342/R est:12000
£8544 $13500 €13500 Head at window (200x200cm-79x79in) s.d.1961 cork collage. 29-Nov-2 Farsetti, Prato #315/R est:9000

CRISCIMANNO, Nicola (19th C) Italian
£1700 $2754 €2550 Luzzo off Valetta by moonlight. Luzzo off the coast at dawn (19x28cm-7x11in) one s.d.1890 board oval pair. 21-May-3 Christie's, Kensington #656/R est:1000-1500

CRISCONIO, Luigi (1893-1946) Italian
£578 $919 €850 Portrait of the sculptor Ferrara di Napoli (29x33cm-11x13in) s. board. 18-Mar-3 Finarte, Milan #206/R

CRISCUOLO, Renato (1954-) Italian
£288 $453 €450 Pomegranates and mimosas (20x55cm-8x22in) s. s.i.verso. 23-Nov-2 Meeting Art, Vercelli #138
£759 $1185 €1200 Mimosas (70x40cm-28x16in) s. s.i.verso. 14-Sep-2 Meeting Art, Vercelli #440/R
£949 $1481 €1500 Rural road (70x70cm-28x28in) s. 14-Sep-2 Meeting Art, Vercelli #400/R

CRISP, George (19/20th C) British
£320 $499 €480 Still life of apples, grapes and a plum (22x29cm-9x11in) s.d.1870. 26-Mar-3 Woolley & Wallis, Salisbury #159/R
£360 $562 €540 Still life of chillies and fruit on a mossy bank (27x36cm-11x14in) s.d.1887. 8-Oct-2 Bonhams, Knightsbridge #115b
£380 $635 €551 Still life with fruit (26x36cm-10x14in) s.d.77. 8-Jul-3 Bonhams, Knightsbridge #186/R
£800 $1248 €1200 Still life with flowers and butterfly (25x36cm-10x14in) s. 9-Apr-3 Andrew Hartley, Ilkley #946/R

CRISS, Bert E (20th C) American
£1840 $3000 €2760 French bulldog (54x47cm-21x19in) s. i.d.Oct 10 39 verso shaped board. 11-Feb-3 Bonhams & Doyles, New York #216 est:1500-2500

CRISS, Francis (1901-1973) American
£11321 $18000 €16982 Window reflection no.2 (46x61cm-18x24in) s. prov. 5-Mar-3 Sotheby's, New York #78/R est:8000-12000

CRISTALL, Joshua (1767-1847) British
Works on paper
£400 $624 €600 Girl and boy resting beneath a tree (30x23cm-12x9in) indis.sig.d. W/C over pencil. 10-Apr-3 Tennants, Leyburn #890
£1800 $2952 €2610 Beach at Ventnor, Isle of Wight (20x52cm-8x20in) i.verso pencil W/C on two joined sheets prov. 5-Jun-3 Christie's, London #97/R est:2000-3000

CRISTESCO, Constantin (fl.1911) French
Sculpture
£4777 $7452 €7500 Deux chevaux sautant la barriere (38x35x22cm-15x14x9in) s. brown pat bronze Cast Susse. 10-Nov-2 Eric Pillon, Calais #37/R

CRITCHER, Catherine Carter (1868-1964) American
£70064 $110000 €105096 Portrait of Star Road (94x81cm-37x32in) prov.lit. 14-Dec-2 Weschler, Washington #672/R est:80000-120000

CRIVELLI, Angelo Maria (17/18th C) Italian
£13000 $20280 €19500 Hounds putting up duck from a river (131x110cm-52x43in) 9-Apr-3 Christie's, London #111/R est:10000-15000

CRIVELLI, Angelo Maria (attrib) (17/18th C) Italian
£3000 $4650 €4500 Cockerel, hen, chicks and owl in landscape (98x74cm-39x29in) i.verso. 31-Oct-2 Sotheby's, Olympia #118/R est:3000-4000

CROATTO, Bruno (1875-1945) Italian
£1538 $2385 €2400 Queen of Saba (70x90cm-28x35in) s.d.1923 lit. 5-Dec-2 Stadion, Trieste #826/R
£3019 $4649 €4800 Vase and pomegranates (50x40cm-20x16in) s.d.1938 canvas on cardboard lit. 23-Oct-2 Finarte, Milan #3/R est:5000-6000
£3333 $5167 €5200 Still life with pomegranates (38x48cm-15x19in) s.i.d.1935 board. 4-Dec-2 Finarte, Rome #733/R est:6000
£3526 $5465 €5500 Venice (35x55cm-14x22in) s. 5-Dec-2 Stadion, Trieste #709/R est:7000
£4747 $7500 €7500 Via Appia, Rome (70x86cm-28x34in) s.i.d.1941. 26-Nov-2 Christie's, Rome #213/R
£5816 $9421 €8200 Melograni e porcellana (69x57cm-27x22in) s.d.1941 panel. 22-May-3 Stadion, Trieste #354/R est:5500-7500

CROCHEPIERRE, Andre (1860-?) French
£1724 $2741 €2500 Cottage interior with old woman spinning (81x65cm-32x26in) s.d.1901. 4-Mar-3 Mealy's, Castlecomer #969/R est:1200-1500

CROCIANI, Émile (1902-1979) French
£1083 $1689 €1700 Bouquet (64x49cm-25x19in) s. panel. 5-Nov-2 Tajan, Paris #67/R

£1083 $1689 €1700 Cirque Pinder. La diligence (54x65cm-21x26in) s. panel double-sided. 5-Nov-2 Tajan, Paris #68/R

CROCKER, J H (?) ?

£480 $750 €720 House on Old Queen Anne Road, Chatham (41x51cm-16x20in) s. 1-Aug-2 Eldred, East Dennis #920/R

CROCKER, John Denison (1823-1907) American

£764 $1200 €1146 Her flock (36x31cm-14x12in) s.d.1880. 22-Nov-2 Skinner, Boston #82a/R est:1200-1800

CROCKFORD, Duncan (1920-1991) Canadian

£321 $504 €482 Rocks (30x45cm-12x18in) s.i.d.1957 board. 25-Nov-2 Hodgins, Calgary #159/R (C.D 800)
£361 $567 €542 River in winter (40x50cm-16x20in) s.d.1954 board. 25-Nov-2 Hodgins, Calgary #312/R (C.D 900)
£482 $757 €723 Clipper North America (65x90cm-26x35in) s.i.d.1966. 25-Nov-2 Hodgins, Calgary #163/R (C.D 1200)
£482 $757 €723 Landscape (50x60cm-20x24in) s. board. 25-Nov-2 Hodgins, Calgary #407/R (C.D 1200)
£482 $761 €723 Off the Cornish coast (61x76cm-24x30in) d.1984. 1-Dec-2 Levis, Calgary #18/R (C.D 1200)
£667 $1093 €967 Three sisters (39x49cm-15x19in) s. board. 9-Jun-3 Hodgins, Calgary #329/R est:1500-2000 (C.D 1500)
£763 $1198 €1145 Mt John Laurie, Seebe, Alt. (60x75cm-24x30in) s.i.d.1963. 25-Nov-2 Hodgins, Calgary #188/R est:2500-3000 (C.D 1900)
£763 $1198 €1145 Rundle mountains from Cascade Mountain, Banff, Alberta (50x40cm-20x16in) s.i.d.1986. 25-Nov-2 Hodgins, Calgary #293/R est:1600-2000 (C.D 1900)
£1044 $1650 €1566 Three sisters in winter (61x76cm-24x30in) d.1956 hardboard. 1-Dec-2 Levis, Calgary #17/R est:2500-3500 (C.D 2600)
£1205 $1892 €1808 On the road to Turner Valley (60x75cm-24x30in) s.i.d.1963. 25-Nov-2 Hodgins, Calgary #98/R est:3000-3500 (C.D 3000)
£1333 $2187 €1933 Near Exshaw, Alberta, Pidgeon Mountain (60x75cm-24x30in) s.i. board. 9-Jun-3 Hodgins, Calgary #55/R est:2500-3000 (C.D 3000)
£1687 $2648 €2531 Three Sister's (60x75cm-24x30in) s.d.1963. 25-Nov-2 Hodgins, Calgary #43/R est:2500-3000 (C.D 4200)

CRODEL, Charles (1894-1973) French

£580 $951 €800 Three girls in drawing class (29x41cm-11x16in) s. 31-May-3 Villa Grisebach, Berlin #529/R

CROEGAERT VAN BREE, Jan Jakob (1818-1897) Flemish

£329 $513 €520 Garde forestier en hiver (40x33cm-16x13in) s.d.1886. 15-Oct-2 Horta, Bruxelles #1

CROEGAERT, Georges (1848-1923) Belgian

£4167 $6458 €6500 Cardinal qui peint (25x19cm-10x7in) s. i.verso panel. 3-Dec-2 Campo & Campo, Antwerp #54/R est:4500-6000
£6772 $10565 €10700 Middle-class interior with seated cardinal (34x26cm-13x10in) s. 21-Oct-2 Bernaerts, Antwerp #87/R est:3750-5000
£7000 $11690 €10500 Good news (33x24cm-13x9in) s. panel prov. 18-Jun-3 Christie's, Kensington #156/R est:7000-10000
£7500 $12300 €11250 Letter (35x27cm-14x11in) s.i. panel. 3-Jun-3 Sotheby's, London #174/R est:6000-8000
£11465 $17885 €18000 Prelat a la lecture (33x25cm-13x10in) s.i. panel. 11-Nov-2 Horta, Bruxelles #187/R est:8000-12000
£15000 $25050 €22500 Quiet read in a chinoiserie interior (37x29cm-15x11in) s.d.1887 panel. 19-Jun-3 Christie's, London #27/R est:15000-20000
£19000 $29830 €28500 Cardinal's pets (26x22cm-10x9in) s. panel. 19-Nov-2 Bonhams, New Bond Street #25/R est:7000-10000

CROEGAERT, Jacques (19th C) ?

£3600 $5976 €3600 Patineurs pres de la chaumiere (41x54cm-16x21in) s.d.1838. 16-Jun-3 Horta, Bruxelles #142 est:3500-4500

CROFT, Arthur (1828-?) British

Works on paper

£268 $432 €400 Castle by a lake (30x63cm-12x25in) s.d.1888 W/C gouache. 18-Feb-3 Sotheby's, Amsterdam #287/R
£300 $471 €450 Mountains pass with figures entering a tunnel (55x43cm-22x17in) s.d.1891 W/C. 21-Nov-2 Tennants, Leyburn #625
£320 $506 €480 Fisherfolk by a lake, with town and Swiss Alps beyond (24x39cm-9x15in) s.d.1874 W/C. 26-Nov-2 Bonhams, Oxford #11/R
£800 $1304 €1200 Early morning from the Schynuge platte (53x74cm-21x29in) s.d.1872 W/C. 29-Jan-3 Sotheby's, Olympia #116/R
£2201 $3390 €3500 Halte de chameliers (25x65cm-10x26in) s.i.d.1880 W/C. 23-Oct-2 Raboudin & Choppin de Janvry, Paris #102/R

CROFT, Richard (1935-) British

£370 $574 €555 Venetian blind series (91x76cm-36x30in) s.d.82. 2-Oct-2 John Ross, Belfast #231
£450 $716 €675 Black beach, Dundrum (45x45cm-18x18in) s.d.1999. 5-Mar-3 John Ross, Belfast #76

CROFTS, Ernest (1847-1911) British

£346 $550 €519 Fallen soldier of the Imperial Guard, Waterloo (18x32cm-7x13in) init. canvasboard. 7-Mar-3 Skinner, Boston #239a/R
£2000 $3160 €3000 Cromwell's ironsides (42x33cm-17x13in) s.d.1901 i.mount. 27-Nov-2 Bonhams, Knowle #244 est:1000-1200
£3500 $5845 €5075 Searching for rebels (35x25cm-14x10in) s.d.1895. 17-Jun-3 Bonhams, New Bond Street #62/R est:2000-3000
£4600 $7222 €6900 Elopement (97x75cm-38x30in) s.d.1886. 19-Nov-2 Bonhams, New Bond Street #150/R est:5000-7000
£18000 $28440 €27000 The surrender of the City of York to the Roundheads (177x133cm-70x52in) s.d.1908 exhib. 26-Nov-2 Christie's, London #115/R est:20000-30000
£40000 $64400 €60000 Whitehall, January 30th, 1649 (168x129cm-66x51in) s.d.1890 prov.exhib.lit. 20-Feb-3 Christie's, London #67/R est:80000

CROIN, Joseph (1894-1949) Dutch

£423 $680 €600 Nude standing (80x45cm-31x18in) s. 7-May-3 Vendue Huis, Gravenhage #206/R
£641 $1006 €1000 Small square in Paris (54x65cm-21x26in) s. 25-Nov-2 Glerum, Amsterdam #171/R

CROISSANT, Michael (1928-) German

Sculpture

£3237 $5180 €4500 Head (22x16x18cm-9x6x7in) bronze exhib. 15-May-3 Neumeister, Munich #692/R est:2000-2500

Works on paper

£254 $416 €350 Figure (57x42cm-22x17in) s.d.75 gouache. 31-May-3 Villa Grisebach, Berlin #780/R

CROIX, François Grenier de la (attrib) (1700-c.1782) French

£3846 $5962 €6000 Southern harbour (43x72cm-17x28in) s.i.d.1763. 5-Dec-2 Dr Fritz Nagel, Stuttgart #606/R est:5000
£21000 $35070 €30450 Mediterranean port with figures on the shore (34x43cm-13x17in) prov. 11-Jul-3 Christie's, Kensington #186/R est:6000-8000

CROIX, Pierre Frederik de la (1709-1782) French

Works on paper

£1146 $1789 €1800 Portrait of Martinus van Toulon. Portrait of Adriana Maria van Toulon (33x26cm-13x10in) s.d.1771 pastel prov. pair. 6-Nov-2 Christie's, Amsterdam #46/R est:2000-3000

CROIX, Pierre Frederik de la (attrib) (1709-1782) French

£7500 $11775 €11250 Ordonnance du Roi (55x45cm-22x18in) s.d.1773 trompe l'oeil prov. 16-Dec-2 Sotheby's, London #47/R est:5000-7000

CROLA, Georg Heinrich (1804-1879) German

£2734 $4374 €3800 Harz landscape (25x31cm-10x12in) s. board. 17-May-3 Lempertz, Koln #1376/R est:7000

CROMBEKE, Cecile (20th C) British

£340 $554 €510 Sunflowers (65x86cm-26x34in) s. board. 17-Feb-3 Bonhams, Bath #106
£720 $1202 €1044 Waterlillies (58x89cm-23x35in) s. board. 23-Jun-3 Bonhams, Bath #143
£920 $1500 €1380 Brent Knoll, Somerset, viewed from the south (73x105cm-29x41in) s. board. 17-Feb-3 Bonhams, Bath #107

CROMBRUGGE, J van (?) Belgian

Works on paper

£294 $474 €450 Paysanne au panier devant Durbuy (401x141cm-158x56in) s. gouache mixed media. 14-Jan-3 Vanderkindere, Brussels #88

CROME, John (1768-1821) British

£519 $820 €779 Sprowston old mill (33x47cm-13x19in) cardboard exhib. 27-Nov-2 Falkkloos, Malmo #78010/R (S.KR 7400)
£1026 $1600 €1539 Pollard Oaks (48x58cm-19x23in) painted c.1790-1800. 28-Mar-3 Aspire, Cleveland #14/R est:1000-2000

Works on paper

£663 $1100 €961 Cottage among trees. pencil. 13-Jun-3 Du Mouchelle, Detroit #2094/R

CROME, John (attrib) (1768-1821) British

£450 $698 €675 Figures resting by a country lane (63x76cm-25x30in) prov. 30-Sep-2 Bonhams, Ipswich #503
£2025 $3200 €3200 Spreading oaks (92x124cm-36x49in) 27-Nov-2 James Adam, Dublin #98/R est:3000-4000

CROME, John Berney (1794-1842) British

£500 $815 €750 Moonrise on the Bure, Norfolk (30x40cm-12x16in) panel prov. 29-Jan-3 Sotheby's, Olympia #14/R
£2800 $4620 €4060 Yarmouth jetty, moonlight (40x54cm-16x21in) s.d.1824 panel. 1-Jul-3 Bonhams, Norwich #200/R est:2000-3000

CROME, John Berney (attrib) (1794-1842) British
£505 $798 €758 Figures and horses by windmill at dawn (57x63cm-22x25in) 27-Nov-2 Falkkloos, Malmo #77993/R (S.KR 7200)

CROME, Vivian (fl.1858-1894) British
£650 $1014 €975 Farm scene (51x66cm-20x26in) s.d.1885. 26-Mar-3 Sotheby's, Olympia #8/R

CROME, William Henry (1806-1873) British
£550 $836 €825 Norfolk river landscape with figures near cottages by moonlight (43x56cm-17x22in) s. 16-Aug-2 Keys, Aylsham #636/R
£3200 $5248 €4800 Figures by a cottage in a wooded landscape, windmill beyond (66x94cm-26x37in) indis.sig. 29-May-3 Christie's, Kensington #82/R est:2000-3000

CROMMELYNCK, Robert (1895-1968) Belgian
£530 $864 €800 Paysage des Fagnes (100x100cm-39x39in) s. 17-Feb-3 Horta, Bruxelles #69

CROMPTON, Mabel Ann Elizabeth (fl.1901-1930) British
£280 $459 €406 Summer flowers in a wicker basket on a stone ledge (61x51cm-24x20in) s. panel. 3-Jun-3 Capes Dunn, Manchester #121

CROMWELL, Joane (1889-1966) American
£266 $425 €399 Where mountains and desert meet (20x25cm-8x10in) s. i. verso canvasboard. 18-May-3 Butterfields, Los Angeles #7008
£342 $550 €513 Point Happy, Indian Wells, Cal (30x41cm-12x16in) s. canvasboard prov. 18-Feb-3 John Moran, Pasadena #175
£375 $600 €563 Fisherman's Cove (41x51cm-16x20in) s. 18-May-3 Butterfields, Los Angeles #7045
£449 $750 €651 Sunset landscape (18x18cm-7x7in) s. canvasboard prov. 17-Jun-3 John Moran, Pasadena #5
£503 $800 €755 Coast royal (30x41cm-12x16in) s. board painted c.1950. 2-Mar-3 Toomey, Oak Park #649/R
£898 $1500 €1302 Coastal, Seal Rock (51x61cm-20x24in) s. i.on stretcher prov. 17-Jun-3 John Moran, Pasadena #177 est:1000-1500

CRONAU, Rudolf Daniel Ludwig (1855-1939) German
Works on paper
£2866 $4500 €4299 Giant cactus in the Gila Desert (20x11cm-8x4in) s.d.82 i.d.1882 verso ink graphite prov. 20-Nov-2 Christie's, Los Angeles #56/R est:5000-7000
£9554 $15000 €14331 Tatanka Iyotake, Sitting Bull (39x31cm-15x12in) s.i.d.25/10/1881 graphite ink wash. 20-Nov-2 Christie's, Los Angeles #21/R est:15000-25000

CRONEAU, Alphonse (1818-?) French
£833 $1292 €1300 I'm waiting - young girl in national costume sitting on bank of lake (35x27cm-14x11in) s.d.1836 paper. 4-Dec-2 Neumeister, Munich #700/R

CRONHJELM (?) Finnish?
£345 $566 €480 Jean Sibelius (50x40cm-20x16in) s. 5-Jun-3 Hagelstam, Helsinki #926

CRONQVIST, Lena (1938-) Swedish
£1158 $1923 €1679 Flowering heather on the west coast (35x35cm-14x14in) s. 16-Jun-3 Lilla Bukowskis, Stockholm #958 est:8000-10000 (S.KR 15000)
£1445 $2283 €2168 The flight to the south (92x116cm-36x46in) s.d.64. 28-Apr-3 Bukowskis, Stockholm #1021/R est:20000-25000 (S.KR 19000)
£1682 $2624 €2523 Landscape from Koster (34x37cm-13x15in) s.d.1966. 5-Nov-2 Bukowskis, Stockholm #410/R est:20000-25000 (S.KR 24000)
£2625 $4227 €3938 Untitled (81x98cm-32x39in) s.d.1966. 7-May-3 AB Stockholms Auktionsverk #1027/R est:20000-25000 (S.KR 34000)
£3118 $4926 €4677 In Arabia (110x100cm-43x39in) s.d.65 exhib.lit. 28-Apr-3 Bukowskis, Stockholm #1021a/R est:50000-60000 (S.KR 41000)
£3644 $5685 €5466 Girl with dolls in buckets (39x48cm-15x19in) s.d.1996 prov. 6-Nov-2 AB Stockholms Auktionsverk #806/R est:35000-40000 (S.KR 52000)
£10512 $16398 €15768 Girls and clouds (150x200cm-59x79in) s.d.1996 verso exhib. 6-Nov-2 AB Stockholms Auktionsverk #804/R est:150000-200000 (S.KR 150000)
£13900 $22378 €20850 Girl with swan (167x150cm-66x59in) s.d.93 exhib. 7-May-3 AB Stockholms Auktionsverk #960/R est:175000-200000 (S.KR 180000)
Sculpture
£2453 $3826 €3680 Girls with skipping rope (19x31x22cm-7x12x9in) s.num.4/5 pat.bronze wood panel base prov. 6-Nov-2 AB Stockholms Auktionsverk #805/R est:40000-50000 (S.KR 35000)
Works on paper
£849 $1368 €1274 Two men (59x43cm-23x17in) s.d.86 pastel. 7-May-3 AB Stockholms Auktionsverk #1029/R (S.KR 11000)

CROOK, D (?) ?
£420 $647 €630 Rural landscape with cattle by a stream (102x74cm-40x29in) s. 5-Sep-2 Clevedon Sale Rooms #154

CROOKE, Ray Austin (1922-) Australian
£426 $678 €639 Outback landscape (12x19cm-5x7in) card prov. 5-May-3 Sotheby's, Melbourne #325 (A.D 1100)
£496 $784 €744 Girl with water (20x15cm-8x6in) s. acrylic oil glaze hardboard prov. 7-Apr-3 Shapiro, Sydney #431b (A.D 1300)
£690 $1083 €1035 Outback landscape (17x25cm-7x10in) s. painted c.1962 prov. 15-Apr-3 Lawson Menzies, Sydney #128/R est:2000-3000 (A.D 1800)
£704 $1099 €1056 Beachside hut (20x25cm-8x10in) s. 21-Oct-2 Australian Art Auctions, Sydney #87/R (A.D 2000)
£717 $1176 €1040 Palmer river landscape (35x45cm-14x18in) i.verso board. 3-Jun-3 Lawson Menzies, Sydney #817 (A.D 1800)
£789 $1199 €1184 Mother and children, Northern Queensland (23x30cm-9x12in) s. composition board prov. 28-Aug-2 Deutscher-Menzies, Melbourne #355/R (A.D 2200)
£876 $1437 €1314 Islanders (15x22cm-6x9in) s. canvas on board painted c.1970 prov. 4-Jun-3 Deutscher-Menzies, Melbourne #283/R (A.D 2200)
£1032 $1579 €1548 West Australian landscape (61x76cm-24x30in) s. canvas on board painted c.1970 prov. 26-Aug-2 Sotheby's, Paddington #678/R est:7000-10000 (A.D 2900)
£1068 $1633 €1602 Hammersley, WA (76x101cm-30x40in) i.verso board painted c.1970 prov. 26-Aug-2 Sotheby's, Paddington #664/R est:7000-10000 (A.D 3000)
£1069 $1689 €1604 Untitled, North Queensland camp with figure in a red dress (30x38cm-12x15in) s. board prov. 7-Apr-3 Shapiro, Sydney #431a est:3000-5000 (A.D 2800)
£1075 $1634 €1613 Queensland workers (59x90cm-23x35in) s. board. 27-Aug-2 Goodman, Sydney #113 est:3000-6000 (A.D 3000)
£1084 $1712 €1626 Melbourne Zoo (30x37cm-12x15in) s.d.57 board. 27-Nov-2 Deutscher-Menzies, Melbourne #212/R est:3000-4000 (A.D 3035)
£1163 $1849 €1745 Landscape (28x23cm-11x9in) s. i.verso canvasboard exhib. 5-May-3 Sotheby's, Melbourne #223 est:3000-5000 (A.D 3000)
£1210 $1851 €1815 Ferntree gully (58x73cm-23x29in) s.d.58 board prov. 26-Aug-2 Sotheby's, Paddington #581/R est:6000-8000 (A.D 3400)
£1336 $2110 €2313 Island village Fiji (22x29cm-9x11in) s. board. 1-Apr-3 Goodman, Sydney #3 est:3000-5000 (A.D 3500)
£1456 $2286 €2184 Cape York (28x36cm-11x14in) s. board. 15-Apr-3 Lawson Menzies, Sydney #145/R est:3000-5000 (A.D 3800)
£1585 $2472 €2378 Island interior (41x51cm-16x20in) s. 21-Oct-2 Australian Art Auctions, Sydney #128/R (A.D 4500)
£1607 $2491 €2411 Landscape with figures (34x44cm-13x17in) s. board. 29-Oct-2 Lawson Menzies, Sydney #17/R est:5000-7500 (A.D 4500)
£1613 $2452 €2420 Figures in town (20x27cm-8x11in) s. board. 27-Aug-2 Goodman, Sydney #180/R est:4000-6000 (A.D 4500)
£1622 $2563 €2352 Islander in tropical garden (50x40cm-20x16in) s. 7-Apr-3 Australian Art Auctions, Sydney #103 (A.D 4250)
£1779 $2722 €2669 Rocks, Sydney Harbour (57x87cm-22x34in) s. board. 25-Aug-2 Sotheby's, Paddington #121 est:5000-7000 (A.D 5000)
£1829 $2891 €2652 Rocky landscape, Central Australia (58x89cm-23x35in) s. board. 22-Jul-3 Lawson Menzies, Sydney #106/R est:6000-8000 (A.D 4500)
£1938 $3081 €2907 Mornington Island camp (22x30cm-9x12in) s. i.verso board. 5-May-3 Sotheby's, Melbourne #333/R est:5000-7000 (A.D 5000)
£1957 $2995 €2936 Islander (29x39cm-11x15in) s. canvas on board. 25-Aug-2 Sotheby's, Paddington #180 est:3000-5000 (A.D 5500)
£2099 $3317 €3044 Island morning (50x50cm-20x20in) s. 7-Apr-3 Australian Art Auctions, Sydney #136/R (A.D 5500)
£2135 $3267 €3203 Stockman and pack horse (43x48cm-17x19in) s. board. 25-Aug-2 Sotheby's, Paddington #145/R est:6000-8000 (A.D 6000)
£2299 $3609 €3449 Islander painting no.3 (57x46cm-22x18in) s. 15-Apr-3 Lawson Menzies, Sydney #146/R est:5000-7000 (A.D 6000)
£2321 $3668 €3482 Frangipane and native women (39x49cm-15x19in) s. 26-Nov-2 Sotheby's, Melbourne #129/R est:7000-9000 (A.D 6500)
£2776 $4247 €4164 Island girls (44x39cm-17x15in) s. oil tempera on board prov. 25-Aug-2 Sotheby's, Paddington #213/R est:3000-5000 (A.D 7800)
£2789 $4573 €4184 Tobacco ovens flat (61x76cm-24x30in) s. i.verso composition board prov. 4-Jun-3 Deutscher-Menzies, Melbourne #148/R est:8000-12000 (A.D 7000)
£2857 $4486 €4286 Islanders (60x80cm-24x31in) s. 25-Nov-2 Christie's, Melbourne #308/R est:8000-12000 (A.D 8000)
£2905 $4415 €4358 Island girl with fruit bowl (50x40cm-20x16in) s. 27-Aug-2 Goodman, Sydney #149/R est:7000-10000 (A.D 8104)
£3101 $4930 €4652 Island still life (39x49cm-15x19in) s. canvasboard prov. 5-May-3 Sotheby's, Melbourne #359/R est:8000-12000 (A.D 8000)

£3187 $5227 €4781 Islanders (50x40cm-20x16in) s. 4-Jun-3 Deutscher-Menzies, Melbourne #138/R est:9000-12000 (A.D 8000)
£3295 $5238 €4943 Natives on homestead (22x29cm-9x11in) s. board prov. 5-May-3 Sotheby's, Melbourne #33/R est:8000 (A.D 8500)
£3571 $5607 €5357 Weaving the lei (60x76cm-24x30in) s. canvasboard. 25-Nov-2 Christie's, Melbourne #99/R est:10000-15000 (A.D 10000)
£3737 $5717 €5606 Native stockman and river (34x49cm-13x19in) s. board. 25-Aug-2 Sotheby's, Paddington #210/R est:6000-8000 (A.D 10500)
£3876 $6163 €5814 Island girl with flowers (54x44cm-21x17in) s. board. 5-May-3 Sotheby's, Melbourne #317/R est:9000-11000 (A.D 10000)
£4286 $6771 €6429 Three figures (56x43cm-22x17in) s.d.56 board. 18-Nov-2 Joel, Victoria #317 est:16000-20000 (A.D 12000)
£4598 $6851 €6897 Towards the mission, Cape York (44x60cm-17x24in) s. board painted c.1959 prov. 27-Aug-2 Christie's, Melbourne #2/R est:12000-15000 (A.D 12000)
£4615 $7338 €6923 Arthur Bay (51x76cm-20x30in) s. prov.exhib. 4-Mar-3 Deutscher-Menzies, Melbourne #113/R est:10000-15000 (A.D 12000)
£4615 $7338 €6923 Women and forest pool (44x61cm-17x24in) s. composition board. 4-Mar-3 Deutscher-Menzies, Melbourne #162/R est:8000-12000 (A.D 12000)
£5446 $8279 €8169 Island man with bowl (75x59cm-30x23in) s. 27-Aug-2 Goodman, Sydney #138/R est:12000-16000 (A.D 15195)
£5658 $8827 €9803 Waiting for the start (60x76cm-24x30in) s. prov. 31-Mar-3 Goodman, Sydney #166/R (A.D 15000)
£6670 $10605 €10005 Fijian studies (102x76cm-40x30in) init. linen prov. 4-Mar-3 Deutscher-Menzies, Melbourne #20/R est:20000-30000 (A.D 17340)
£7168 $10896 €10752 Still life with bananas (63x83cm-25x33in) s. prov.exhib. 28-Aug-2 Deutscher-Menzies, Melbourne #19/R est:18000-24000 (A.D 20000)
£7168 $10896 €10752 Station, North Queensland (91x121cm-36x48in) s. painted c.1972-74. 28-Aug-2 Deutscher-Menzies, Melbourne #71/R est:20000-25000 (A.D 20000)
£7885 $11986 €11828 Islanders (76x101cm-30x40in) s. 28-Aug-2 Deutscher-Menzies, Melbourne #84/R est:20000-25000 (A.D 22000)
£8571 $13457 €12857 Arrival at blue lagoon (77x91cm-30x36in) s. prov. 25-Nov-2 Christie's, Melbourne #29/R est:15000-20000 (A.D 24000)
£8897 $13612 €13346 Chillagoe (61x91cm-24x36in) s. canvas on board painted c.1970. 26-Aug-2 Sotheby's, Paddington #644/R est:10000-15000 (A.D 25000)
£8897 $13612 €13346 Island village (75x100cm-30x39in) s. prov. 25-Aug-2 Sotheby's, Paddington #62/R est:25000-35000 (A.D 25000)
£8929 $14018 €13394 Pink hibiscus (54x68cm-21x27in) s. board prov. 25-Nov-2 Christie's, Melbourne #5/R est:25000-35000 (A.D 25000)
£8929 $14107 €13394 Still life with figure (110x90cm-43x35in) s. 26-Nov-2 Sotheby's, Melbourne #5/R est:25000-35000 (A.D 25000)
£9609 $14701 €14414 Island girls with bowl of fruit (61x75cm-24x30in) s. oil over synthetic polymer. 25-Aug-2 Sotheby's, Paddington #8/R est:15000-25000 (A.D 27000)
£10357 $16364 €15536 Tropical still life (105x75cm-41x30in) s. prov. 26-Nov-2 Sotheby's, Melbourne #49/R est:20000-30000 (A.D 29000)
£10728 $16843 €16092 Island scene, Tahiti (75x59cm-30x23in) s. painted c.1972 prov.exhib. 15-Apr-3 Lawson Menzies, Sydney #27/R est:19000-28000 (A.D 28000)
£10853 $17256 €16280 Boy with Sepik mask (101x75cm-40x30in) s.d.64 i.verso prov.exhib.lit. 5-May-3 Sotheby's, Melbourne #5/R est:35000 (A.D 28000)
£13008 $20553 €18862 Untitled - Islanders (74x100cm-29x39in) s. 22-Jul-3 Lawson Menzies, Sydney #23/R est:40000-50000 (A.D 32000)
£13523 $20690 €20285 Natives near Lagoon (90x120cm-35x47in) s. canvasboard prov. 25-Aug-2 Sotheby's, Paddington #15/R est:30000-40000 (A.D 38000)
£14947 $22868 €22421 Island town (59x90cm-23x35in) s. board prov. 25-Aug-2 Sotheby's, Paddington #2/R est:28000-38000 (A.D 42000)
£20000 $31800 €30000 Island interior (76x101cm-30x40in) s. canvas on board prov. 4-Mar-3 Deutscher-Menzies, Melbourne #80/R est:38000-45000 (A.D 52000)
£20000 $32200 €30000 Islanders (61x76cm-24x30in) s.d.59 oil tempera board prov. 6-May-3 Christie's, Melbourne #4/R est:50000-60000 (A.D 50000)
£20384 $32411 €30576 Island song (74x100cm-29x39in) s.d.65 i.verso canvas on board prov.exhib.lit. 4-Mar-3 Deutscher-Menzies, Melbourne #35/R est:40000-60000 (A.D 53000)

Works on paper
£575 $856 €863 Study (22x30cm-9x12in) s.i. gouache paper on board. 27-Aug-2 Christie's, Melbourne #160/R est:1500-2000 (A.D 1500)
£600 $966 €900 Study (22x30cm-9x12in) s.i. gouache on board. 6-May-3 Christie's, Melbourne #219 est:1500-2000 (A.D 1500)
£929 $1467 €1394 Island boy (41x29cm-16x11in) s.d.57 mixed media. 18-Nov-2 Joel, Victoria #179/R est:2500-3000 (A.D 2600)
£1073 $1684 €1610 Thursday Island (14x21cm-6x8in) s. gouache executed c.1965. 15-Apr-3 Lawson Menzies, Sydney #129/R est:3000-5000 (A.D 2800)
£3203 $4900 €4805 Victorian landscape (45x61cm-18x24in) s. synthetic polymer paint board painted c.1960 prov. 26-Aug-2 Sotheby's, Paddington #630/R est:12000-18000 (A.D 9000)

CROOS, Anthony Jansz van der (1606-1662) Dutch
£11511 $18417 €16000 Extensive landscape with peasants conversing by a dead tree (36x35cm-14x14in) s.d.1644 panel prov.lit. 14-May-3 Christie's, Amsterdam #181/R est:12000-16000

CROOS, Anthony Jansz van der (attrib) (1606-1662) Dutch
£3205 $5032 €5000 Canal landscape with boats, bridge and buildings (53x88cm-21x35in) mono. 21-Nov-2 Van Ham, Cologne #1324/R est:8000

CROOS, Anthony Jansz van der (circle) (1606-1662) Dutch
£5096 $7949 €8000 River landscape with fishermen hauling in their catch near a village, view of Haarlem (45x59cm-18x23in) panel. 5-Nov-2 Sotheby's, Amsterdam #315/R est:8000-12000

CROOS, Jacob van der (17th C) Dutch
£1875 $3000 €2813 River landscape with a bridge (44x32cm-17x13in) s.d.1659 panel prov. 14-May-3 Doyle, New York #88/R est:6000-8000
£19108 $29809 €30000 View of Rijswijk Castle (34x60cm-13x24in) mono. panel prov.exhib.lit. 6-Nov-2 Christie's, Amsterdam #68/R est:15000-20000

CROOS, Pieter van der (1610-1677) Dutch
£22000 $34320 €33000 Shipping in a stiff sea breeze (29x65cm-11x26in) s. panel prov. 9-Apr-3 Christie's, London #47/R est:10000-15000

CROPSEY, Jasper Francis (1823-1900) American
£13291 $21000 €19937 Boating in Autumn on Lake Wawayanda (10x25cm-4x10in) s.indis.d.188 prov. 16-Nov-2 New Orleans Auction, New Orleans #1110/R est:15000-25000
£16129 $25000 €24194 Greenwood Notch, New Jersey (58x43cm-23x17in) s.d.1879 W/C on board prov.exhib.lit. 4-Dec-2 Sotheby's, New York #109/R est:15000-25000
£30573 $48000 €45860 Greenwood lake in the autumn (30x51cm-12x20in) s.d.1890 i.on stretcher prov. 14-Dec-2 Weschler, Washington #663/R est:30000-50000
£43210 $70000 €64815 On the Susquahana River (30x56cm-12x22in) s.d.1880 prov.exhib.lit. 21-May-3 Sotheby's, New York #103/R est:60000-80000
£96774 $150000 €145161 Hazy afternoon (30x51cm-12x20in) s.d.1873 prov. 3-Dec-2 Phillips, New York #21/R est:100000-150000
£103226 $160000 €154839 View near Sherburne (61x105cm-24x41in) s.d.1853 prov.lit. 3-Dec-2 Phillips, New York #7/R est:200000-300000

CROS, Cesar Isidore Henri (1840-1907) French
Sculpture
£5903 $9740 €8500 Felicitee (43cm-17in) s. terracotta polychrome wood socle exec.c.1899 lit. 1-Jul-3 Claude Aguttes, Neuilly #181/R est:150-200

CROSATO, Giovanni Battista (1697-1756) Italian
£25641 $40256 €40000 Madeleine aux pieds du Christ (121x88cm-48x35in) prov.lit. 14-Dec-2 Artcurial Briest, Paris #16/R

CROSBIE, William (1915-1999) British
£950 $1444 €1425 Buchlyvie (49x59cm-19x23in) s.i.indis d.56 verso. 28-Aug-2 Sotheby's, London #1026/R
£1500 $2430 €2250 Bristol blue (22x23cm-9x9in) s.d.LXV board. 23-May-3 Lyon & Turnbull, Edinburgh #45/R est:600-800
£3200 $4896 €4800 Pittenweem (25x30cm-10x12in) s. panel. 22-Aug-2 Bonhams, Edinburgh #1182/R est:2000-3000
£8000 $12640 €12000 Orchestra (78x107cm-31x42in) s. board. 27-Nov-2 Sotheby's, Olympia #326/R est:7000-9000
Works on paper
£5500 $8525 €8250 Cessnock in summer (48x66cm-19x26in) s.d.44 W/C prov. 31-Oct-2 Christie's, London #165/R est:1500-2000

CROSBY, Frederick Gordon (1885-1943) British
£400 $636 €600 Battleships in line ahead (33x38cm-13x15in) s.d.1911 board. 4-Mar-3 Bonhams, Knightsbridge #273/R
£2500 $3850 €3750 Confirmed kill (90x70cm-35x28in) s.d.1941. 6-Sep-2 Bonhams, Knightsbridge #45/R est:3000-5000
Works on paper
£1400 $2156 €2100 1934 Lagonda Rapier, bare chassis study. s.d.15.9.33 pencil htd white. 6-Sep-2 Bonhams, Knightsbridge #36/R est:1200-1500
£3800 $5852 €5700 Irish Grand Prix 1931, Phoenix Park, Dublin (43x71cm-17x28in) s. chl htd white. 6-Sep-2 Bonhams, Knightsbridge #35/R est:4000-6000

£5200 $8008 €7800 Le Mans 1939, 4.5 litre V12 Lagonda team car leads the sister car (50x70cm-20x28in) s.d.39 chl htd white. 6-Sep-2 Bonhams, Knightsbridge #38/R est:5500-7500
£11000 $16940 €16500 Isle of Man TT 1914, Kennelm Lee Guiness on the winning GP Sunbeam (70x44cm-28x17in) s. W/C lit. 6-Sep-2 Bonhams, Knightsbridge #40/R est:12000-18000

CROSBY, William (1830-1910) British
£310 $505 €465 Coast scene at Ryhope, Seaham harbour in the distance (18x35cm-7x14in) i. s.d.1863 stretcher. 13-Feb-3 Christie's, Kensington #119

CROSIO, Luigi (1835-1915) Italian
£2553 $3957 €3830 Scene from Carmen (54x77cm-21x30in) s,. 8-Dec-2 Uppsala Auktionskammare, Uppsala #89/R est:40000-50000 (S.KR 36000)
£2930 $4571 €4600 Interior with elegant lady, dog and parrot (40x30cm-16x12in) s.d.1975. 5-Nov-2 Vendu Notarishuis, Rotterdam #158/R est:4000-5000
£7012 $11500 €10167 Helping hand (33x25cm-13x10in) s.d.1878 panel. 4-Jun-3 Christie's, Rockefeller NY #222/R est:8000-12000

CROSS, Frederick George (1881-1941) Canadian
Works on paper
£489 $802 €709 Hailed out (38x54cm-15x21in) s. W/C. 9-Jun-3 Hodgins, Calgary #295/R est:1200-1500 (C.D 1100)

CROSS, Henri Edmond (1856-1910) French
£355 $592 €500 Paysage (13x18cm-5x7in) panel. 20-Jun-3 Piasa, Paris #91
£3291 $5134 €5200 Docteur Soin dans son cabinet (46x33cm-18x13in) s.i.d.1883 panel exhib.lit. 18-Oct-2 Rabourdin & Choppin de Janvry, Paris #11/R
£5500 $8525 €8250 Paysage (21x13cm-8x5in) canvas on board prov.exhib. 5-Dec-2 Christie's, Kensington #15/R est:1500-2000
£185897 $290000 €278846 Quai de Passy (65x90cm-26x35in) painted c.1899 prov.exhib.lit. 7-Nov-2 Christie's, Rockefeller NY #220/R est:300000-400000
£210000 $350700 €315000 Un pin (65x50cm-26x20in) s. painted c.1905 prov.lit. 23-Jun-3 Sotheby's, London #7/R est:120000-180000
Prints
£4366 $7248 €6200 La promenade, ou les Cypres (28x41cm-11x16in) s.num. col lithograph edition of 100. 12-Jun-3 Piasa, Paris #43/R
Works on paper
£252 $392 €400 Au bord d'un fleuve (20x30cm-8x12in) st.mono. pencil. 11-Oct-2 Winterberg, Heidelberg #498
£462 $729 €720 Scenes de jardin public (13x8cm-5x3in) W/C. 14-Nov-2 Credit Municipal, Paris #40
£1250 $1988 €1800 Sous-bois en Bretagne (22x33cm-9x13in) st.init. W/C graphite prov. 29-Apr-3 Artcurial Briest, Paris #3/R est:1800-2200
£1736 $2760 €2500 Lande en bord de mer (16x23cm-6x9in) init. W/C exec.c.1904 lit. 29-Apr-3 Artcurial Briest, Paris #2/R est:3500-4500

CROSS, Henry H (1837-1918) American
£1370 $2000 €2055 Rattling runner (91x74cm-36x29in) 18-May-2 Altermann Galleries, Santa Fe #53/R
£1370 $2000 €2055 Great singer (91x74cm-36x29in) 18-May-2 Altermann Galleries, Santa Fe #54/R
£1849 $2700 €2774 Buy with stone (91x74cm-36x29in) 18-May-2 Altermann Galleries, Santa Fe #55/R
£1923 $3000 €2885 Perils of the chase (61x91cm-24x36in) 9-Nov-2 Altermann Galleries, Santa Fe #233
£2055 $3000 €3083 Buffalo by the river (71x117cm-28x46in) 18-May-2 Altermann Galleries, Santa Fe #56/R
£2308 $3600 €3462 Yellowstone River (76x114cm-30x45in) 9-Nov-2 Altermann Galleries, Santa Fe #234
£2466 $3600 €3699 E-Tey-Hoo-Taye, face (91x74cm-36x29in) 18-May-2 Altermann Galleries, Santa Fe #52/R
£2740 $4000 €4110 Coming haze (91x74cm-36x29in) 18-May-2 Altermann Galleries, Santa Fe #51/R

CROSS, Penni Anne (1939-) American
£4430 $7000 €6424 Reflections (102x76cm-40x30in) s. board. 26-Jul-3 Coeur d'Alene, Hayden #32/R est:8000-12000

CROSS, William Amos (?) British?
£400 $596 €600 Basse Auvergne (46x30cm-18x12in) s. panel. 28-Jun-2 Chrystals Auctions, Isle of Man #170a

CROSSE, Malcolm (20th C) British
Works on paper
£500 $815 €750 Looe and Trevaunance Cove (36x23cm-14x9in) s.i. W/C pair. 13-Feb-3 David Lay, Penzance #284

CROSSE, Peter Lawrence (attrib) (c.1645-1724) British
Works on paper
£480 $802 €696 Portrait of a lady in blue dress (7x5cm-3x2in) W/C. 25-Jun-3 Cheffins, Cambridge #679

CROSSE, Richard (1742-1810) British
Miniatures
£2000 $3240 €3000 Gentleman wearing red coat (4cm-2xin) clasp frame. 22-May-3 Bonhams, New Bond Street #48/R est:2000-3000
£3800 $5928 €5700 King George IV as Reagent holding a tricorn hat and leaning against his horse (65cm-26xin) s.d.1788 pencil on paper black frame rec. prov. 5-Nov-2 Bonhams, New Bond Street #4/R est:2000-3000
£3800 $5928 €5700 Officer wearing scarlet coat with yellow facings and silver lace (4cm-2xin) gilt and gold frame pierced ribbon surmount oval. 5-Nov-2 Bonhams, New Bond Street #50/R est:3500-5500
£4500 $7380 €6525 James Daniell in blue coat with gold buttons (6cm-2xin) silver gilt frame lit. 3-Jun-3 Christie's, London #117/R est:1000-1500

CROSSLAND, J H (1852-1939) British
£580 $916 €870 Shepherd with sheep and dog crossing a bridge in a mountainous landscape (49x74cm-19x29in) s. 26-Nov-2 Bonhams, Oxford #61/R

CROSSLAND, James Henry (1852-1939) British
£720 $1174 €1044 Shaft of sunlight in the Lake District (71x122cm-28x48in) s. 17-Jul-3 Thomson, Roddick & Medcalf, Carlisle #19/R
£750 $1185 €1125 Mount Beinn near Cille - in the Scottish Highlands (61x91cm-24x36in) s. 2-Dec-2 Bonhams, Bath #110/R
£750 $1223 €1125 Highland stream (45x35cm-18x14in) s. 29-Jan-3 Sotheby's, Olympia #77/R
£2600 $4056 €3900 Landscape in Wales (51x76cm-20x30in) s. 26-Mar-3 Sotheby's, Olympia #13/R est:1000-1500

CROTTI, Jean (1878-1958) French
£1156 $1839 €1700 Fleurs (35x27cm-14x11in) s.d. panel. 3-Mar-3 Claude Boisgirard, Paris #37/R est:800-1000
£3123 $4966 €4500 Composition (55x46cm-22x18in) s.d.43 panel. 29-Apr-3 Artcurial Briest, Paris #212 est:5000-6000
£5605 $8744 €8800 Deroulement (60x73cm-24x29in) s. 7-Nov-2 Claude Aguttes, Neuilly #22/R est:9000-11000
Works on paper
£935 $1496 €1300 Couple assis (39x27cm-15x11in) s. gouache. 18-May-3 Eric Pillon, Calais #153/R
£2500 $3950 €3750 Harmonie nait du chaos (58x47cm-23x19in) s.d.1916 gouache card prov. 3-Apr-3 Christie's, Kensington #124/R

CROUBIE, William (?) British?
Works on paper
£3300 $5379 €4950 Within the music we begat (53x33cm-21x13in) s.d.42 W/C. 14-Feb-3 Keys, Aylsham #500/R est:200-300

CROUCH, Brian (1929-) British
£350 $557 €525 Winchelsea Beach (34x65cm-13x26in) s. painted 1960. 4-May-3 Lots Road, London #358/R

CROUCH, William (fl.1817-1850) British
Works on paper
£380 $585 €570 Figures on a country lane (8x13cm-3x5in) bears sig. W/C. 22-Oct-2 Bonhams, Knightsbridge #200/R
£850 $1352 €1275 Arcadian landscape (12x15cm-5x6in) W/C pair. 25-Feb-3 Bonhams, Knightsbridge #1/R

CROUSE, M (fl.1889-1907) British
£1400 $2226 €2100 Tower of refuge, Douglas, Isle of Man. Castle Rushden, Castletown (16x23cm-6x9in) s. board pair. 4-Mar-3 Bonhams, Knightsbridge #289/R est:500-700

CROW, Derek Walter (1928-) British
Works on paper
£480 $749 €720 Seymour Tower (58x76cm-23x30in) s.d.1987 gouache. 26-Mar-3 Bonhams & Langlois, Jersey #137
£480 $749 €720 Explosive sunshine beyond Seymour Tower (37x56cm-15x22in) s.d.1988 gouache. 26-Mar-3 Bonhams & Langlois, Jersey #138

CROW, W M (20th C) British
£320 $512 €464 Billiards: the ripped baize (40x29cm-16x11in) s. 17-May-3 Thomson Roddick & Medcalf, Edinburgh #674/R

CROWE, Eyre (1824-1910) British
£25000 $40250 €37500 Foundry (152x238cm-60x94in) s.d.1869 prov.exhib.lit. 20-Feb-3 Christie's, London #58/R est:50000

CROWE, Victoria (1945-) British
Works on paper
£320 $496 €480 Silver icon (75x55cm-30x22in) s.d.71 mixed media on card. 1-Oct-2 Bonhams, Leeds #366/R
£420 $655 €630 Interrupting the dialogue (40x51cm-16x20in) s. s.i.verso mixed media. 17-Oct-2 Bonhams, Edinburgh #110/R

CROWELL, A Elmer (1862-1952) American
Sculpture
£3519 $5700 €5103 Ducks. st.i. painted carvings wire exec.c.1920 three prov. 22-May-3 Sotheby's, New York #739
£4074 $6600 €5907 Ducks. st.i. painted carvings wire exec.c.1920 three prov. 22-May-3 Sotheby's, New York #742
£4444 $7200 €6444 Upland gamebirds. one st. i. painted carvings wire exec.c.1920 two prov. 22-May-3 Sotheby's, New York #741
£5556 $9000 €8056 Songbirds. three st. painted carvings wire exec.c.1920 five prov. 22-May-3 Sotheby's, New York #736
£5926 $9600 €8593 Upland gamebirds. painted carvings wire exec.c.1920 two prov. 22-May-3 Sotheby's, New York #740
£6296 $10200 €9129 Birds. four st. one i. painted carvings wire exec.c.1920 five prov. 22-May-3 Sotheby's, New York #737
£6667 $10800 €9667 Birds. st.i. painted carvings wire exec.c.1920 four prov. 22-May-3 Sotheby's, New York #738

CROWL, Robert and MELCARTH, Edward (20th C) American
Works on paper
£580 $900 €870 View of male nudes (30x23cm-12x9in) s. i.verso black chk two prov. 29-Oct-2 Sotheby's, New York #294/R est:400-600

CROWLEY, Donald (20th C) American
£7099 $11500 €10294 Contemporary Paiute (61x61cm-24x24in) 23-May-3 Altermann Galleries, Santa Fe #42
£15068 $22000 €22602 Firewood (102x76cm-40x30in) 18-May-2 Altermann Galleries, Santa Fe #28/R
Works on paper
£2244 $3500 €3366 Jingle dancer (41x51cm-16x20in) pencil. 9-Nov-2 Altermann Galleries, Santa Fe #55
£2808 $4100 €4212 John H Holliday No.11301 (41x51cm-16x20in) pencil. 18-May-2 Altermann Galleries, Santa Fe #169/R

CROWLEY, Nicholas Joseph (1813-1857) British
£5000 $8000 €7500 Portrait of a mother and child, woman standing wearing a white gown, the girl seated (204x133cm-80x52in) 16-May-3 Sotheby's, London #15/R est:6000-8000

CROWTHER, Henry (19/20th C) British?
£1043 $1700 €1565 Head of an Irish wolfhound (30x38cm-12x15in) s.d.1913. 11-Feb-3 Bonhams & Doyles, New York #122 est:1000-1500
£1380 $2250 €2070 Stedfast, a red setter in a landscape (30x38cm-12x15in) s.i. 11-Feb-3 Bonhams & Doyles, New York #121/R est:1200-1800

CROXFORD, William Edwards (19/20th C) British
£2100 $3276 €3150 Harbour scenes (18x23cm-7x9in) s.d.84 one d.90 pair. 26-Mar-3 Sotheby's, Olympia #115/R est:1000-2000
Works on paper
£300 $468 €450 End of the headland, Newquay (18x26cm-7x10in) s.d.22 i.d.1922 verso pencil W/C. 17-Oct-2 Christie's, Kensington #62/R
£350 $546 €525 St Ives (25x36cm-10x14in) s.d.1912 W/C. 17-Oct-2 David Lay, Penzance #1242/R
£380 $619 €570 Crossing the river (30x46cm-12x18in) s.d.1908 W/C. 13-Feb-3 David Lay, Penzance #87
£400 $628 €600 Washing fish Polperro (25x37cm-10x15in) s.d.1919 i.verso W/C. 10-Dec-2 Lane, Penzance #27
£420 $659 €630 Outer harbour Polperro (25x37cm-10x15in) s.d.1919 W/C. 10-Dec-2 Lane, Penzance #28
£600 $930 €900 Landing the catch at Great Yarmouth (35x44cm-14x17in) s. pencil W/C htd bodycol. 31-Oct-2 Christie's, Kensington #349/R

CROXFORD, William Edwards (attrib) (19/20th C) British
£440 $686 €660 Newlyn port scene (74x36cm-29x14in) i. 27-Mar-3 Ambrose, Loughton #798/R

CROYDON, Michael (20th C) American
Sculpture
£915 $1500 €1327 Horse head I (36x51x20cm-14x20x8in) s. green pat. bronze cast stone. 1-Jun-3 Wright, Chicago #309/R est:2000-3000

CROZIER, William (1930-) British
£633 $981 €1000 Untitled (51x41cm-20x16in) s.d.1960 oil on paper. 24-Sep-2 De Veres Art Auctions, Dublin #150 est:1000-1500
£800 $1224 €1200 Landscape (78x72cm-31x28in) board. 22-Aug-2 Bonhams, Edinburgh #1099/R
£1069 $1668 €1700 Landscape with blue sky (50x37cm-20x15in) s.d.1960 paper prov. 17-Sep-2 Whyte's, Dublin #78 est:1600-1800
£1090 $1711 €1700 Abstract (64x50cm-25x20in) s.d.1969 card. 19-Nov-2 Whyte's, Dublin #47/R est:1800-2200
£1500 $2385 €2250 Sex wilderness (66x86cm-26x34in) board prov. 26-Feb-3 Sotheby's, Olympia #383/R est:800-1200
£2027 $3162 €3000 Vase and bottle (39x49cm-15x19in) s. s.i.verso. 26-Mar-3 James Adam, Dublin #64/R est:3000-4000
£2372 $3724 €3700 Stone way (99x99cm-39x39in) s. i.verso canvas on board painted c.1963 prov. 19-Nov-2 Whyte's, Dublin #28/R est:4000-6000
£2400 $3936 €3600 Dark field, Essex (60x52cm-24x20in) s.d.1968 i.verso board prov. 3-Jun-3 Sotheby's, Olympia #290/R est:700-900
£2500 $3975 €3600 Empty hill, 1959 (66x89cm-26x35in) s. board. 29-Apr-3 Whyte's, Dublin #49/R est:3000-4000
£2500 $4000 €3750 Cornfield (35x46cm-14x18in) s. prov. 15-May-3 Christie's, Kensington #243/R est:2500-3500
£2532 $3924 €4000 Lisheen (36x46cm-14x18in) s.verso prov. 24-Sep-2 De Veres Art Auctions, Dublin #94/R est:3500-4500
£3826 $6159 €5700 Landscape (76x91cm-30x36in) s. i.verso prov. 18-Feb-3 Whyte's, Dublin #44/R est:6000-8000
£4557 $7063 €7200 Haystack, West Cork (61x78cm-24x31in) s. 24-Sep-2 De Veres Art Auctions, Dublin #28/R est:6000-7000
£5031 $7849 €8000 Painting (152x122cm-60x48in) s. hardboard prov.exhib. 17-Sep-2 Whyte's, Dublin #80/R est:6000-8000
£6164 $9678 €9000 Winter field (80x100cm-31x39in) s. exhib. 15-Apr-3 De Veres Art Auctions, Dublin #179/R est:9000-12000
Works on paper
£420 $655 €630 Floral still life (52x37cm-20x15in) s.i.d.1980 W/C. 17-Sep-2 Rosebery Fine Art, London #621
£1026 $1610 €1600 Still life, Carway Road (53x38cm-21x15in) s.i.d.1980 W/C. 19-Nov-2 Whyte's, Dublin #133/R est:1200-1500

CRUICKSHANK, William (1848-1922) British
Works on paper
£280 $462 €406 Still life with pineapple, plums and hazelnuts (24x37cm-9x15in) s.d.1865 pencil W/C htd white. 3-Jul-3 Christie's, Kensington #39/R
£300 $465 €450 Still life of white wild rose, birds with eggs (10x13cm-4x5in) W/C. 6-Dec-2 Chrystals Auctions, Isle of Man #272y
£450 $698 €675 Still life with a bird's nest and blossom (19x23cm-7x9in) s. bodycol. 24-Sep-2 Bonhams, Knightsbridge #32/R
£500 $780 €750 Still life of birds (6x8cm-2x3in) s. W/C on ivorine pair. 25-Mar-3 Bonhams, Knightsbridge #108
£600 $936 €900 Still life of birds nest with eggs and flowers. Birds nest with moss and flowers (18x25cm-7x10in) s. W/C bodycol pair. 10-Sep-2 Sworder & Son, Bishops Stortford #750/R
£1050 $1649 €1575 Game larder (11x15cm-4x6in) s. on ivorine pair. 16-Dec-2 Bonhams, Bury St Edmunds #400/R est:1000-1500

CRUIKSHANK, George (1792-1878) British
£6200 $9982 €9300 Study for 'The Highland whisky-still' (28x21cm-11x8in) panel. 20-Feb-3 Christie's, London #356/R

CRUIKSHANK, Isaac (1756-1811) British
Works on paper
£240 $374 €360 Rowdy crowd (18x11cm-7x4in) d.Oct 16th 1781 pen ink W/C. 19-Sep-2 Christie's, Kensington #23
£300 $471 €450 Yorkshire Irishman (15x22cm-6x9in) pen ink W/C. 16-Dec-2 Bonhams, Bury St Edmunds #431
£400 $668 €580 An Irishman, Covent Garden market (15x21cm-6x8in) W/C. 24-Jun-3 Bonhams, Knightsbridge #30/R

CRUSSENS, Anton (17th C) Flemish
Works on paper
£613 $968 €950 Drinkers. s. ink pair. 17-Dec-2 Galerie Moderne, Brussels #923/R

CRUTE, Harry E (20th C) British
£600 $978 €900 Coastal scenes (23x28cm-9x11in) s. pair. 13-Feb-3 David Lay, Penzance #52

CRUYS, Cornelis (attrib) (17th C) Dutch
£13000 $21710 €18850 Roemer of white wine, lobster on a salver and other foods on draped table (39x61cm-15x24in) panel. 9-Jul-3 Bonhams, New Bond Street #76/R est:5000-7000

CRUZ HERRERA, Jose Herrerilla (1890-1972) Spanish
£1565 $2488 €2300 Jeune Andalouse (36x29cm-14x11in) s. panel. 26-Feb-3 Artcurial Briest, Paris #142 est:1800-2200

£1613 $2548 €2500 Woman with shawl (53x44cm-21x17in) s. 17-Dec-2 Durán, Madrid #163/R
£1763 $2768 €2750 Dark-haired girl (55x46cm-22x18in) s. 16-Dec-2 Castellana, Madrid #55/R
£2089 $3300 €3300 Aveugle au Mellah, Maroc (102x80cm-40x31in) s. i.verso. 28-Nov-2 Piasa, Paris #70/R
£2365 $3689 €3500 Bust of lady (52x36cm-20x14in) s. 25-Mar-3 Durán, Madrid #145/R
£3597 $5900 €5000 Nu aux fruits (22x35cm-9x14in) s. isorel. 4-Jun-3 Tajan, Paris #250/R est:3000-4000
£4403 $6780 €7000 Young woman with blue and pink scarf (34x27cm-13x11in) s. 23-Oct-2 Rabourdin & Choppin de Janvry, Paris #180/R

CRUZ, Diego de la (attrib) (fl.1487-1496) Spanish
£7927 $13000 €11891 Immaculate conception (98x63cm-39x25in) gold ground tempera panel prov. 29-May-3 Sotheby's, New York #76/R est:15000-20000

CRUZ, Pedro (?) ?
£1000 $1660 €1500 Summer landscape (96x129cm-38x51in) s. 10-Jun-3 Bonhams, Knightsbridge #151/R est:1200-1800

CRUZ-DIEZ, Carlos (1923-) Venezuelan
£4777 $7500 €7166 Physicrome 2147 (102x102cm-40x40in) s.i.d.1984 acrylic panel prov. 19-Nov-2 Sotheby's, New York #107/R est:18000
Sculpture
£3275 $5142 €4913 Physiochrome 155 (38x70x7cm-15x28x3in) s.i.d.1965 verso materials colours wooden box. 23-Nov-2 Burkhard, Luzern #158/R est:8000-12000 (S.FR 7500)

Works on paper
£3481 $5500 €5500 Physichromie 460 (40x40cm-16x16in) s.i.d.1969 verso mixed media. 26-Nov-2 Camard, Paris #128/R est:2700
£4516 $7135 €7000 Physiochromie (60x75cm-24x30in) i.d.66 s.verso mixed media. 18-Dec-2 Digard, Paris #251/R est:3500
£9058 $14855 €12500 Physichromie No 337 (61x121cm-24x48in) s.i.d.Juin 1967 verso plastic gouache painted wood. 28-May-3 Lempertz, Koln #106/R est:9000

CSAKY, Josef (1888-1971) French/Hungarian
Sculpture
£1959 $3057 €2900 Jeune fille aux raisins (49x18x13cm-19x7x5in) s.st.f.Blanchet num.2/8 green pat bronze. 26-Mar-3 Millon & Associes, Paris #174/R
£2917 $4638 €4200 Femme agenouillee (27x25x15cm-11x10x6in) plaster exec.c.1929 lit. 29-Apr-3 Artcurial Briest, Paris #204/R est:4500-5000
£3077 $4831 €4800 Nu allonge (22x39cm-9x15in) s. num.7/8 brown pat bronze. 15-Dec-2 Thierry & Lannon, Brest #18/R
£3846 $6038 €6000 Visage ovoide (30x12cm-12x5in) s. num.4/8 brown pat bronze. 15-Dec-2 Thierry & Lannon, Brest #16/R
£4294 $7000 €6441 Femme debout (36cm-14in) i.d.64 num.8/8 gold pat. bronze i.f.L Thinot. 12-Feb-3 Sotheby's, New York #117/R est:2000-3000
£4392 $6851 €6500 Architecture (72x22x14cm-28x9x6in) s. num.8/8 brown pat bronze. 26-Mar-3 Millon & Associes, Paris #173/R est:8000
£12414 $19738 €18000 Nu (64cm-25in) s.d. plaster prov. 4-Mar-3 Livinec, Gaudcheau & Jezequel, Rennes #131/R
£18354 $29000 €29000 Tete (38x21x12cm-15x8x5in) s.d.1914 num.3/8 brown pat bronze lit. 27-Nov-2 Marc Kohn, Paris #26/R est:25000-30000
£23742 $37987 €33000 Nu assis, bras leve (73x83x33cm-29x33x13in) s. stone lit.exhib. 19-May-3 Tajan, Paris #82/R est:35000-40000
Works on paper
£563 $935 €800 Trois femmes a l'enfant (48x29cm-19x11in) s.d.51 black crayon estompe. 11-Jun-3 Beaussant & Lefèvre, Paris #17/R
£1410 $2200 €2115 Sculpture study of woman standing (25x23cm-10x9in) s. W/C ink dr. 10-Nov-2 Selkirks, St. Louis #575/R est:800-1000
£2083 $3438 €3000 Femme assise au livre (34x24cm-13x9in) s. W/C pencil exec.c.1925-30. 2-Jul-3 Artcurial Briest, Paris #36/R est:3000-4000
£7194 $11799 €10000 Composition cubiste (34x25cm-13x10in) s. Indian ink W/C. 3-Jun-3 Piasa, Paris #7/R est:5000-6000

CSERNUS, Tibor (1927-) Hungarian
£1509 $2400 €2264 Belvedere (96x130cm-38x51in) s.d.1980 prov. 27-Feb-3 Christie's, Rockefeller NY #122/R est:9000

CSOK, Istvan (1865-1961) Hungarian
£2151 $3335 €3227 Girl in front of the mirror (61x50cm-24x20in) s. board. 6-Dec-2 Kieselbach, Budapest #183/R (H.F 800000)
£2322 $3622 €3367 Housemaid (50x40cm-20x16in) s.d.1903 panel. 13-Sep-2 Mu Terem Galeria, Budapest #120/R est:850000 (H.F 900000)
£3354 $5232 €5031 Lake Balaton (38x47cm-15x19in) s. board. 11-Sep-2 Kieselbach, Budapest #17/R (H.F 1300000)
£3496 $5419 €5244 Hon y soit mal y pense, 1915 bad who is thinking of bad (21x27cm-8x11in) s. board. 6-Dec-2 Kieselbach, Budapest #10/R (H.F 1300000)
£3496 $5419 €5244 Erzsebet Bathory (60x50cm-24x20in) s. 6-Dec-2 Kieselbach, Budapest #139/R (H.F 1300000)
£3765 $5836 €5648 Zuzu on the beach (64x83cm-25x33in) s. 6-Dec-2 Kieselbach, Budapest #1141/R (H.F 1400000)
£3870 $6037 €5805 Magdelene (61x44cm-24x17in) s. 11-Sep-2 Kieselbach, Budapest #202/R (H.F 1500000)
£5030 $7847 €7294 Thamar (32x40cm-13x16in) s. panel. 12-Apr-3 Mu Terem Galeria, Budapest #29/R est:1500000 (H.F 1800000)
£5676 $8854 €8514 In a bower, 1943 (65x87cm-26x34in) s.d.1943. 11-Sep-2 Kieselbach, Budapest #139/R (H.F 2200000)
£8383 $13078 €12575 Girls in red dresses (84x93cm-33x37in) s.d.1917. 11-Apr-3 Kieselbach, Budapest #178/R est:2800000-3000000 (H.F 3000000)
£8942 $13950 €12966 Still life of flowers (50x60cm-20x24in) s. 12-Apr-3 Mu Terem Galeria, Budapest #26/R est:1200000 (H.F 3200000)
£10319 $16098 €14963 At the lido (55x65cm-22x26in) s. 13-Sep-2 Mu Terem Galeria, Budapest #123/R est:1800000 (H.F 4000000)
£11737 $18309 €17019 Zuzu is ill (59x77cm-23x30in) s. 12-Apr-3 Mu Terem Galeria, Budapest #182/R est:2500000 (H.F 4200000)
£29582 $45852 €42894 Corner of the studio at the end of the 1920s (65x81cm-26x32in) s. panel. 9-Dec-2 Mu Terem Galeria, Budapest #85/R est:3000000 (H.F 11000000)

Works on paper
£1677 $2616 €2432 Playing cards (50x40cm-20x16in) s. chl paperboard lit. 12-Apr-3 Mu Terem Galeria, Budapest #126/R est:250000 (H.F 600000)
£5851 $9361 €8777 Young girl with roses (41x44cm-16x17in) s. mixed media. 16-May-3 Kieselbach, Budapest #43/R (H.F 2000000)

CSONT, Ferenc (1888-1969) Hungarian
£645 $1006 €968 Boy leaning against fireplace (49x66cm-19x26in) s. 11-Sep-2 Kieselbach, Budapest #151/R (H.F 250000)

CSORDAK, Ludovit (1864-1937) Czechoslovakian
Works on paper
£378 $552 €567 Landscape (45x36cm-18x14in) W/C. 4-Jun-2 SOGA, Bratislava #38/R est:24000 (SL.K 24000)

CSUK, Jeno (1887-1927) Hungarian
£8255 $12878 €12383 Afternoon rest, 1910 (115x96cm-45x38in) s. 11-Sep-2 Kieselbach, Budapest #49/R (H.F 3200000)

CUARTIELLES, Ramon (19th C) Spanish
£1689 $2635 €2500 Seascape (20x35cm-8x14in) s. board. 25-Mar-3 Durán, Madrid #46/R

CUBASCH, Constanze (19th C) Swiss?
Works on paper
£524 $828 €786 Thun (24x38cm-9x15in) s.d.1837 gouache. 14-Nov-2 Stuker, Bern #9086 (S.FR 1200)

CUBELLS Y RUIZ, Enrique Martinez (1874-1947) Spanish
£5519 $8058 €8500 Back from the market (23x29cm-9x11in) s. 17-Jun-2 Ansorena, Madrid #170/R
£10284 $15940 €15426 Sailing boats in harbour (28x38cm-11x15in) s. canvas on panel. 3-Dec-2 Bukowskis, Stockholm #189/R est:30000-40000 (S.KR 145000)
£11409 $18369 €17000 Breton woman (47x37cm-19x15in) s. 18-Feb-3 Durán, Madrid #241/R est:6000
Works on paper
£308 $481 €450 Classical figure (34x29cm-13x11in) s.d.01 chl dr. 8-Apr-3 Ansorena, Madrid #677/R

CUBLEY, Henry Hadfield (fl.1882-1904) British
£250 $395 €375 Oncoming storm (36x53cm-14x21in) s.i.verso. 14-Nov-2 Christie's, Kensington #179
£300 $489 €450 Driving geese (44x65cm-17x26in) s. board. 13-Feb-3 Mellors & Kirk, Nottingham #813
£340 $486 €510 Highland cattle in a misty glen (35x26cm-14x10in) s.d.1905 s.i. panel. 11-Apr-2 Mellors & Kirk, Nottingham #554
£400 $656 €600 Wooded landscape (45x35cm-18x14in) s. 10-Feb-3 David Duggleby, Scarborough #612
£400 $660 €580 Near Torquay (37x53cm-15x21in) s. s.i.d.1927 verso board. 1-Jul-3 Bearnes, Exeter #532/R
£420 $659 €630 Untitled (76x64cm-30x25in) 15-Apr-3 Bonhams, Chester #993
£466 $750 €699 Landscape with cows in field (36x61cm-14x24in) s. 22-Feb-3 Brunk, Ashville #477/R

CUBLEY, William Harold (1816-1896) British
£3500 $5705 €5075 Sketching beside a mountain stream in Westmorland (61x101cm-24x40in) s.d.1859. 16-Jul-3 Sotheby's, Olympia #26/R est:3000-4000

CUCARO, Pascal (1915-) American
£409 $650 €614 Fisherman, San Francisco (41x51cm-16x20in) s. board painted c.1960. 2-Mar-3 Toomey, Oak Park #763/R

CUCCHI, Enzo (1949-) Italian
£4681 $7583 €6600 Untitled (54x72cm-21x28in) s.d.1996 verso tempera mixed media collage paper prov. 26-May-3 Christie's, Milan #36/R est:4000-5000
£7595 $12000 €11393 Age of Jesus (76x111cm-30x44in) oil tempera paper on board exec.1996 prov.exhib. 13-Nov-2 Sotheby's, New York #528/R est:12000-18000
£60000 $93600 €90000 Cani con la lingua a spasso (180x205cm-71x81in) s.i.d.1980 verso pencil. 21-Oct-2 Sotheby's, London #63/R est:25000-35000

Works on paper
£1859 $2881 €2900 Italian suns (40x29cm-16x11in) s.i.d.1982 chl pencil. 4-Dec-2 Finarte, Milan #481/R
£3176 $4954 €4700 Untitled (24x31cm-9x12in) s.d.1979 wax crayon card. 26-Mar-3 Finarte Semenzato, Milan #155/R
£4194 $6626 €6500 Strolling with de Chirico (79x68cm-31x27in) s.i.d.1982 verso mixed media prov. 18-Dec-2 Christie's, Rome #128/R

CUCUEL, Edward (1875-1951) American
£2866 $4500 €4299 View of the Hudson River from the artist studio (36x64cm-14x25in) i. s.verso board. 10-Dec-2 Doyle, New York #140/R est:6000-8000
£4500 $6975 €6750 Bescheite buchen (65x80cm-26x31in) s. s.verso. 5-Dec-2 Christie's, Kensington #59/R est:5000-7000
£5449 $8500 €8174 Pier scene with boats and figures (25x36cm-10x14in) s. i.verso board. 22-Sep-2 Jeffery Burchard, Florida #59
£5500 $8525 €8250 Beschneite buchen (80x80cm-31x31in) s. 5-Dec-2 Christie's, Kensington #58/R est:6000-8000
£7971 $13072 €11000 Coastline near Menton (40x50cm-16x20in) s. s.i. verso panel. 29-May-3 Lempertz, Koln #581/R est:12000
£20144 $33036 €28000 Two women on lake shore watching sailing boats (65x130cm-26x51in) s. prov. 6-Jun-3 Ketterer, Munich #17/R est:35000-45000
£28571 $44000 €42857 Afternoon tea (81x81cm-32x32in) s. prov. 24-Oct-2 Shannon's, Milford #80/R est:40000-60000
£30216 $48345 €42000 Lakeside villa (110x100cm-43x39in) s. i. stretcher. 15-May-3 Neumeister, Munich #235a/R est:40000-50000
£32051 $49679 €50000 Her boat (80x80cm-31x31in) s. s.i.d.verso painted c.1920/25 prov. 6-Dec-2 Ketterer, Munich #37/R est:50000-70000
£38462 $59615 €60000 Tree mermaid (98x100cm-39x39in) s. painted c.1911/12 prov. 6-Dec-2 Ketterer, Munich #34/R est:40000-60000
£42000 $68880 €63000 Bathers (92x110cm-36x43in) s. prov. 3-Jun-3 Sotheby's, London #84/R est:50000-70000
£45161 $70000 €67742 At the lake (81x81cm-32x32in) s. s.on stretcher. 4-Dec-2 Sotheby's, New York #30/R est:40000-60000
£46296 $75000 €69444 Boat (80x80cm-31x31in) s. s.i.verso. 21-May-3 Sotheby's, New York #164/R est:60000-80000
£50000 $77500 €75000 Unter dem Rotdorn (80x80cm-31x31in) s. i.verso. 4-Dec-2 Christie's, London #67/R est:60000-80000
£55000 $85250 €82500 Sommermorgen (100x100cm-39x39in) s. s.i.verso prov. 4-Dec-2 Christie's, London #66/R est:60000-80000

Works on paper
£5036 $8259 €7000 Regatta (40x34cm-16x13in) s. W/C over pencil prov. 6-Jun-3 Ketterer, Munich #16/R est:8000-10000

CUDENNEC, Patrice (20th C) French
£269 $423 €420 Maisons au clocher (27x35cm-11x14in) s. 15-Dec-2 Thierry & Lannon, Brest #228
£288 $453 €450 Clowns a l'ecuyere (27x35cm-11x14in) init. 15-Dec-2 Thierry & Lannon, Brest #230
£417 $679 €600 Deux pecheurs au Bono (27x35cm-11x14in) s. 19-Jul-3 Thierry & Lannon, Brest #195
£556 $906 €800 Ecce homo (46x55cm-18x22in) s. 19-Jul-3 Thierry & Lannon, Brest #193/R
£694 $1132 €1000 Retour de peche sacre (60x73cm-24x29in) s. 19-Jul-3 Thierry & Lannon, Brest #197/R
£1410 $2214 €2200 Dechargement du poisson (54x195cm-21x77in) init. 15-Dec-2 Thierry & Lannon, Brest #229

CUDWORTH, Jack (1930-) British
£300 $495 €435 Meadow (35x58cm-14x23in) s.d.74 board exhib. 3-Jul-3 Christie's, Kensington #419
£366 $608 €520 Still life with vase of flowers and pear (27x22cm-11x9in) s. board. 10-Jun-3 James Adam, Dublin #14/R
£450 $743 €653 Beach scene (33x59cm-13x23in) s.d.74 exhib. 3-Jul-3 Christie's, Kensington #431
£520 $806 €780 Forest (33x43cm-13x17in) s. board. 2-Oct-2 John Ross, Belfast #43
£1013 $1570 €1600 Washing (38x38cm-15x15in) s. board. 24-Sep-2 De Veres Art Auctions, Dublin #1/R est:800-1200
£1087 $1783 €1500 Forest (29x39cm-11x15in) s. board. 28-May-3 Bonhams & James Adam, Dublin #111/R est:1200-1600
£1164 $1828 €1700 Behind the houses (42x54cm-17x21in) s. board. 15-Apr-3 De Veres Art Auctions, Dublin #188/R est:1500-2000

CUECO, Henri (1929-) French
£385 $642 €550 Plage (61x46cm-24x18in) s. 25-Jun-3 Claude Aguttes, Neuilly #134/R
£596 $972 €900 Le couple (46x33cm-18x13in) s. 1-Feb-3 Claude Aguttes, Neuilly #325/R
£633 $987 €1000 Les baigneuses (46x51cm-18x20in) s. prov. 20-Oct-2 Claude Boisgirard, Paris #90

CUENI, August (1883-1966) Swiss
£2146 $3391 €3219 Castle Angenstein (62x77cm-24x30in) s.d.1930. 29-Nov-2 Zofingen, Switzerland #2838/R est:6000 (S.FR 5000)

CUERDA, Abel (1943-) Spanish?
£414 $658 €600 Untitled (74x60cm-29x24in) s.indis.d. 4-Mar-3 Ansorena, Madrid #211/R
£448 $713 €650 Untitled (74x60cm-29x24in) s.d.72. 4-Mar-3 Ansorena, Madrid #209/R
£552 $877 €800 Composition (92x64cm-36x25in) s.d.74. 4-Mar-3 Ansorena, Madrid #212/R
£552 $877 €800 Untitled (100x81cm-39x32in) 4-Mar-3 Ansorena, Madrid #210/R
£690 $1097 €1000 Fishtank (101x73cm-40x29in) s.d.1973. 4-Mar-3 Ansorena, Madrid #208/R

CUEVAS, Ivan (20th C) Mexican
£292 $473 €438 Three figures (79x100cm-31x39in) s. 21-Jan-3 Louis Morton, Mexico #75/R (M.P 5000)

CUEVAS, Jose Luis (1934-) Mexican

Works on paper
£252 $390 €400 Malformaciones congenitas no 3 (28x21cm-11x8in) i.d.31.V.1980 s.i.verso ink W/C. 30-Oct-2 Artcurial Briest, Paris #657
£3185 $5000 €4778 Vigil (48x61cm-19x24in) s.d.52 mixed media prov. 20-Nov-2 Christie's, Rockefeller NY #132/R

CUEVAS, Raymond (1932-) American
£497 $800 €746 California landscape (51x61cm-20x24in) s. 18-Feb-3 John Moran, Pasadena #108

CUGAT, Delia (1935-) Argentinian
£6051 $9500 €9077 Afternoon (129x97cm-51x38in) s. painted c.1990 diptych prov. 20-Nov-2 Christie's, Rockefeller NY #124/R

CUGNOT, Louis-Léon (1835-1894) French

Sculpture
£3797 $6000 €5696 Greek warrior with drawn sword (94cm-37in) s. bronze circular plinth. 26-Nov-2 Christie's, Rockefeller NY #194/R est:5000-8000

CUI RUZUO (1944-) Chinese

Works on paper
£725 $1188 €1000 Lotos (88x96cm-35x38in) s.d.1986 seals Indian ink col hanging scroll. 30-May-3 Dr Fritz Nagel, Stuttgart #1192/R

CUI ZHENKUAN (1935-) Chinese

Works on paper
£362 $594 €500 Temple of Sima Qian (136x68cm-54x27in) i.d.1988 seals Indian ink col hanging scroll. 30-May-3 Dr Fritz Nagel, Stuttgart #1268/R

CUI ZIFAN (1915-) Chinese

Works on paper
£1297 $2050 €1946 Cranes and cherry blossom (89x61cm-35x24in) s.d.1982 Indian ink red mineral colour. 27-Nov-2 Falkkloos, Malmo #77929/R est:15000 (S.KR 18500)

CUITT, George (jnr) (1779-1854) British
£3000 $4890 €4350 Marske Hall, Yorkshire, the seat of John Hutton Esq (35x48cm-14x19in) s.i.d.1833 verso panel. 17-Jul-3 Tennants, Leyburn #826/R est:3000-3500

Works on paper
£360 $562 €540 River estuary with figures near a cottage (18x33cm-7x13in) s.d.1831 W/C. 10-Apr-3 Tennants, Leyburn #840
£400 $628 €600 Extensive river landscape (24x33cm-9x13in) s.d.1851 W/C. 21-Nov-2 Tennants, Leyburn #613

CUIXART, Modest (1925-) Spanish

Works on paper

£3546 $5745 €5000 Composition (80x30cm-31x12in) s.d.verso mixed media. 23-May-3 Binoche, Paris #72 est:5000-6000

£3600 $5868 €5400 Composition (98x79cm-39x31in) s.d.1959 verso mixed media. 3-Feb-3 Bonhams, New Bond Street #89/R est:3000-5000

CULBERTSON, Josephine M (1852-1939) American

£1129 $1750 €1694 Landscape (61x76cm-24x30in) s. canvas on masonite. 29-Oct-2 John Moran, Pasadena #667 est:2500-3500

CULLBERG, Erland (1931-) Swedish

£315 $498 €473 Self portrait in the evening (89x60cm-35x24in) s. prov.exhib. 16-Nov-2 Crafoord, Lund #21/R (S.KR 4500)

£798 $1262 €1197 Drama in the backyard (97x69cm-38x27in) s. 28-Apr-3 Bukowskis, Stockholm #1022/R (S.KR 10500)

£824 $1252 €1236 Figure composition (144x178cm-57x70in) s. 16-Aug-2 Lilla Bukowskis, Stockholm #686 (S.KR 12000)

£841 $1312 €1262 Untitled (120x100cm-47x39in) s. 5-Nov-2 Bukowskis, Stockholm #380/R (S.KR 12000)

£1051 $1640 €1577 Woodland reflection (130x140cm-51x55in) s. 5-Nov-2 Bukowskis, Stockholm #381/R est:25000-30000 (S.KR 15000)

CULLEN, Adam (1965-) Australian

£794 $1317 €1353 Hippie head - for the new millenium (45x38cm-18x15in) s.verso enamel on board. 10-Jun-3 Shapiro, Sydney #85 est:1500-2500 (A.D 2000)

Works on paper

£1036 $1699 €1554 Playstation (122x244cm-48x96in) s.d.1998 verso synthetic polymer paint ink enamel foam prov.exhib. 4-Jun-3 Deutscher-Menzies, Melbourne #102/R est:3000-5000 (A.D 2600)

CULLEN, Maurice Galbraith (1866-1934) Canadian

£2469 $3827 €3704 Paysage (25x40cm-10x16in) init. prov. 3-Dec-2 Joyner, Toronto #216/R est:7000-9000 (C.D 6000)

£3580 $5514 €5370 Riviere en hiver (11x21cm-4x8in) s. 22-Oct-2 Iegor de Saint Hippolyte, Montreal #23/R (C.D 8700)

£4222 $6924 €6333 Evening star, Grez, France (54x43cm-21x17in) s. painted c.1904 prov. 3-Jun-3 Joyner, Toronto #99a/R est:10000-15000 (C.D 9500)

£9130 $14243 €15225 Devil River (46x39cm-18x15in) s.i. prov. 13-Apr-3 Levis, Calgary #23/R est:12000-15000 (C.D 21000)

£14444 $23689 €21666 Early snowfall, Cache River (45x61cm-18x24in) s.d.circa 1928 prov.exhib.lit. 27-May-3 Sotheby's, Toronto #181/R est:35000-45000 (C.D 32500)

£16129 $25484 €24194 Moonlight landscape (74x168cm-29x66in) mono. canvas on board prov. 18-Nov-2 Sotheby's, Toronto #31/R est:50000-70000 (C.D 40000)

£24194 $38226 €36291 Early spring, Cache River (43x62cm-17x24in) s.verso prov. 14-Nov-2 Heffel, Vancouver #30/R est:30000-35000 (C.D 60000)

£74074 $114815 €111111 Quebec from Levis (59x80cm-23x31in) s.d.97 prov.lit. 3-Dec-2 Joyner, Toronto #95/R est:200000-250000 (C.D 180000)

Works on paper

£806 $1274 €1209 War sketch (13x18cm-5x7in) s.d.1918 chl prov. 14-Nov-2 Heffel, Vancouver #46 est:600-800 (C.D 2000)

£3498 $5422 €5247 Evening on the Cache River (30x40cm-12x16in) s. pastel prov. 3-Dec-2 Joyner, Toronto #1/R est:10000-15000 (C.D 8500)

£5381 $8610 €8072 Bend in river cache (46x56cm-18x22in) s.i.verso pastel prov. 15-May-3 Heffel, Vancouver #9/R est:12000-15000 (C.D 12000)

£6667 $10933 €10001 Autumn view of Northmount - Westmount hump of Mount Royal (60x73cm-24x29in) s. pastel prov. 3-Jun-3 Joyner, Toronto #149/R est:20000-25000 (C.D 15000)

£7661 $12105 €11492 Sunglow on the hills, Ste Margaret's (43x58cm-17x23in) s. pastel prov. 18-Nov-2 Sotheby's, Toronto #165/R est:12000-15000 (C.D 19000)

CULLEN, Michael (1946-) Irish

£1644 $2581 €2400 Ludwig in a panama - portrait of self (80x70cm-31x28in) 15-Apr-3 De Veres Art Auctions, Dublin #211/R est:2000-3000

£2740 $4301 €4000 Painting with gun man - classical figure and painter etc (140x150cm-55x59in) i.d.1990. 15-Apr-3 De Veres Art Auctions, Dublin #184/R est:4000-5000

CULLEN, Stephen (20th C) Irish?

£338 $561 €480 Tug boat at Coliemore harbour (39x59cm-15x23in) s. acrylic. 10-Jun-3 James Adam, Dublin #34/R

£548 $860 €800 In the park (48x61cm-19x24in) 15-Apr-3 De Veres Art Auctions, Dublin #8

CULLEY, Cathy B (fl.1908-1928) British?

Works on paper

£250 $388 €375 Portrait of a young woman holding a basket of flowers (72x51cm-28x20in) s.d.1907 W/C. 22-Jul-2 Bonhams, Bury St Edmunds #345

CULLIN, Isaac (fl.1881-1920) British

£400 $624 €600 Roddy Owen reading the Pink-un (20x15cm-8x6in) s. 17-Sep-2 Bonhams, Oxford #52

Works on paper

£280 $437 €420 Flat racing at Epsom, city and suburban (25x35cm-10x14in) s.i. W/C. 25-Mar-3 Bonhams, Knightsbridge #245/R

£550 $869 €825 Molecomb Stakes 1914 (26x35cm-10x14in) s.i.d.1915 pencil W/C. 28-Nov-2 Christie's, Kensington #197/R

£600 $978 €900 Zoedene, chestnut horse with Count Kinsky up and trainer alongside. s. bears another sig. W/C prov. 29-Jan-3 Hampton & Littlewood, Exeter #367/R

£700 $1162 €1015 Mr W.B Purefoy's Lully with B Dillon up, and Sancy (25x36cm-10x14in) s.i.d.1907 pencil W/C. 12-Jun-3 Christie's, Kensington #110/R

CULVER, Charles (1908-1967) American

Works on paper

£392 $650 €568 Two guinea hens (38x53cm-15x21in) W/C. 13-Jun-3 Du Mouchelle, Detroit #2269/R

CULVERHOUSE, Johann Mongels (1820-1892) Dutch

£1646 $2600 €2600 Supplicant beforeMagarete II of Parma (47x65cm-19x26in) s. panel lit. 29-Nov-2 Schloss Ahlden, Ahlden #1161/R est:1500

CUMBERWORTH, Charles (1811-1852) French

Sculpture

£1600 $2464 €2400 Classical muses (34cm-13in) s. bronze pair. 28-Oct-2 Sotheby's, Olympia #77/R est:1200-1800

CUMBERWORTH, Charles (style) (1811-1852) French

Sculpture

£12579 $19623 €20000 Africains, un jongleur et un charmeur de serpent (194x48x48cm-76x19x19in) brown pat bronze round base pair. 20-Sep-2 Millon & Associes, Paris #182/R est:20000-40000

CUMBRAE-STEWART, Janet Agnes (1883-1960) Australian

£842 $1280 €1263 Hobart Harbour (20x25cm-8x10in) board. 19-Aug-2 Joel, Victoria #246/R est:2000-3000 (A.D 2400)

£842 $1280 €1263 Jones's cottage by the beach, 1910 (40x27cm-16x11in) 19-Aug-2 Joel, Victoria #251/R est:1500-2500 (A.D 2400)

£912 $1387 €1368 Hot day at Garfield, 1910 (20x28cm-8x11in) s. s.i.verso board. 19-Aug-2 Joel, Victoria #248/R est:2000-3000 (A.D 2600)

£1193 $1813 €1790 Lower paddock, Montrose (16x31cm-6x12in) 19-Aug-2 Joel, Victoria #250/R est:2000-3000 (A.D 3400)

£2105 $3200 €3158 Henley on the Yarra (22x29cm-9x11in) board. 19-Aug-2 Joel, Victoria #249/R est:6000-8000 (A.D 6000)

£2281 $3467 €3422 Gathering wildflowers (37x54cm-15x21in) 19-Aug-2 Joel, Victoria #247/R est:5000-7000 (A.D 6500)

Works on paper

£1221 $1930 €1832 Little cockney (37x26cm-15x10in) s. pastel. 2-Apr-3 Christie's, Melbourne #25/R est:1000-2000 (A.D 3200)

£1607 $2539 €2411 Prague (45x38cm-18x15in) s. pastel. 18-Nov-2 Joel, Victoria #264 est:5000-7000 (A.D 4500)

£2115 $3363 €3173 Seated nude (74x53cm-29x21in) s. pastel. 4-Mar-3 Deutscher-Menzies, Melbourne #145/R est:6000-9000 (A.D 5500)

£3053 $4824 €4580 Standing nude with waterpot (54x36cm-21x14in) s.d.25 pastel prov. 2-Apr-3 Christie's, Melbourne #58/R est:8000-12000 (A.D 8000)

£3571 $5643 €5357 Seated nude (54x33cm-21x13in) s.d.17 pastel. 27-Nov-2 Deutscher-Menzies, Melbourne #47/R est:10000-15000 (A.D 10000)

£3596 $5467 €5394 Woman with green urn (54x37cm-21x15in) s. pastel. 19-Aug-2 Joel, Victoria #154/R est:8000-12000 (A.D 10250)

£3785 $6207 €5678 Yellow shawl (52x26cm-20x10in) s.d.16 pastel. 4-Jun-3 Deutscher-Menzies, Melbourne #156/R est:8000-12000 (A.D 9500)

£5200 $8372 €7800 Loving cup (63x48cm-25x19in) s.d.26 pastel prov. 6-May-3 Christie's, Melbourne #388/R est:8000-12000 (A.D 13000)

CUMING, Frederick G R (1930-) British

£520 $842 €780 Apples in a box (45x38cm-18x15in) s. board. 20-May-3 Bonhams, Knightsbridge #119/R

£550 $891 €825 Rye Harbour I (23x33cm-9x13in) s. board sold with sketch of a skull by same hand. 20-May-3 Sotheby's, Olympia #149/R

£650 $1053 €975 Swing bridge, Littlehampton (30x35cm-12x14in) s. board. 20-May-3 Sotheby's, Olympia #148/R

£800 $1288 €1200 Figures at a table (30x31cm-12x12in) s. board. 14-Jan-3 Bonhams, Knightsbridge #6/R
£900 $1404 €1350 Port at twilight (51x61cm-20x24in) s.d.65. 27-Mar-3 Christie's, Kensington #521/R
£1500 $2340 €2250 Hilltop view at sunset (41x51cm-16x20in) 27-Mar-3 Christie's, Kensington #520/R est:1500-2000
£2000 $3280 €3000 Thames and the Tower of London (30x35cm-12x14in) s. board. 3-Jun-3 Sotheby's, Olympia #159/R est:2000-3000

CUMMING, Charles Atherton (1858-1932) American
£2229 $3500 €3344 Neva (91x69cm-36x27in) s. canvas laid down prov.exhib. 23-Nov-2 Jackson's, Cedar Falls #52/R est:5000-7500

CUMMING, Frederick (20th C) American
£270 $425 €405 Shoreside cottage (51x41cm-20x16in) s. 22-Nov-2 Skinner, Boston #372/R

CUMMING, James (1922-1991) British
£1600 $2480 €2400 Astronomer (71x91cm-28x36in) s. lit. 6-Dec-2 Lyon & Turnbull, Edinburgh #67/R est:1000-1500

CUMMING, Liz (1956-) Australian
£650 $1007 €975 Hawkesbury (122x288cm-48x113in) s.d.89 i.verso diptych prov. 3-Dec-2 Shapiro, Sydney #114/R est:4000-6000 (A.D 1800)

CUMMING, Peter (1916-) British
£340 $541 €510 Still life with flowers in a vase on a wooden chair (72x62cm-28x24in) init. i.verso. 18-Mar-3 Rosebery Fine Art, London #850/R

CUMMING, William Skeoch (fl.1885-1906) British
£9800 $14896 €14700 Prayer for Victory, Battle of Prestonpans (162x251cm-64x99in) prov. 28-Aug-2 Sotheby's, London #927/R est:4000-6000

Works on paper
£720 $1152 €1080 Transvaal 1900: the Kopje, enemy retiring. S Africa, 1901: Tommy Atkins (25x35cm-10x14in) s.i. W/C pencil prov. two. 15-May-3 Lawrence, Crewkerne #853/R

CUMMINGS, Vera (1891-1949) New Zealander
£251 $391 €377 Guide Sophia with pipe (59x44cm-23x17in) s.i. verso board. 5-Nov-2 Peter Webb, Auckland #11 (NZ.D 800)
£702 $1095 €1053 Guide Sophia (34x24cm-13x9in) s. 27-Mar-3 International Art Centre, Auckland #104/R (NZ.D 2000)
£815 $1271 €1223 Maria Tikitiki (25x19cm-10x7in) s. 7-Nov-2 International Art Centre, Auckland #161/R est:2000-3000 (NZ.D 2600)

CUNAEUS, Conradyn (1828-1895) Dutch
£1899 $3000 €3000 Horse with saddle (43x62cm-17x24in) s.d.1860 board. 26-Nov-2 Christie's, Rome #43/R
£6748 $11000 €10122 Leonburger by the steps of a country house (43x59cm-17x23in) s. panel. 11-Feb-3 Bonhams & Doyles, New York #203/R est:10000-15000

CUNAEUS, Conradyn (attrib) (1828-1895) Dutch
£3400 $5406 €4930 Waiting for their master (46x64cm-18x25in) s. panel. 29-Apr-3 Gorringes, Lewes #2079

CUNDALL, Charles (1890-1971) British
£300 $468 €450 On the Seine, Paris (29x55cm-11x22in) 26-Mar-3 Hamptons Fine Art, Godalming #222/R
£550 $858 €825 Cottage flowers (60x41cm-24x16in) s. 26-Mar-3 Hamptons Fine Art, Godalming #130/R
£700 $1085 €1050 View (42x57cm-17x22in) s.d.1923. 3-Dec-2 Sworder & Son, Bishops Stortford #926/R
£850 $1326 €1275 At the quayside Dieppe (29x56cm-11x22in) s. 26-Mar-3 Hamptons Fine Art, Godalming #178/R
£850 $1394 €1275 View of Preston (50x63cm-20x25in) studio st.verso board prov. 3-Jun-3 Sotheby's, Olympia #71/R
£1700 $2788 €2550 Tuscan landscape (38x52cm-15x20in) studio st. paper sold with two landscapes prov. 3-Jun-3 Sotheby's, Olympia #74/R est:500-700
£2000 $3340 €2900 Ludlow Bridge (41x56cm-16x22in) s.d.1923. 19-Jun-3 Lane, Penzance #180/R est:3000-3500
£2857 $4514 €4286 Spanish steps (64x77cm-25x30in) s. exhib. 26-Nov-2 Sotheby's, Melbourne #234/R est:10000-15000 (A.D 8000)

CUNDERLIK, Marian (1926-1983) Czechoslovakian

Works on paper
£315 $488 €473 Head of a woman (49x32cm-19x13in) Indian ink W/C. 1-Oct-2 SOGA, Bratislava #278/R est:12000 (SL.K 20000)

CUNEO, Jose (1887-1977) Uruguayan
£929 $1450 €1394 Ombu a la luz de la luna (63x48cm-25x19in) cardboard. 30-Jul-2 Galleria Y Remates, Montevideo #81/R
£2642 $4200 €3963 Landscape (50x61cm-20x24in) s.d.1916. 2-Mar-3 Galleria Y Remates, Montevideo #60/R

Works on paper
£478 $750 €717 Ostrich and cattle (40x32cm-16x13in) s.d.1945 W/C ink. 20-Nov-2 Galleria Y Remates, Montevideo #36/R
£764 $1200 €1146 Cattle (51x33cm-20x13in) s.d.1935 Chinese ink W/C. 20-Nov-2 Galleria Y Remates, Montevideo #35/R
£781 $1250 €1172 Las Caronas (59x6cm-23x2in) s. W/C ink. 5-Jan-3 Galleria Y Remates, Montevideo #49/R
£1051 $1650 €1577 Moon (52x35cm-20x14in) s. ink W/C. 20-Nov-2 Galleria Y Remates, Montevideo #33/R
£1795 $2800 €2693 Venecia (48x64cm-19x25in) s.d.38 W/C. 30-Jul-2 Galleria Y Remates, Montevideo #79/R est:3800-4200

CUNEO, Nell Marion (fl.1893-1940) British
£756 $1254 €1096 Undercliff, Hayle (40x30cm-16x12in) s. canvasboard. 10-Jun-3 Ritchie, Toronto #83 est:800-1200 (C.D 1700)

CUNEO, Rinaldo (1877-1935) American
£1592 $2500 €2388 Marina on a sunny day (40x51cm-16x20in) s. board prov. 19-Nov-2 Butterfields, San Francisco #8309/R est:3000-5000
£1592 $2500 €2388 Extensive landscape with town and lake in the distance (38x46cm-15x18in) s. canvas on board prov. 19-Nov-2 Butterfields, San Francisco #8310/R est:3000-5000
£1911 $3000 €2867 Marin county general store (35x42cm-14x17in) s. board prov. 19-Nov-2 Butterfields, San Francisco #8179/R est:3000-5000
£7097 $11000 €10646 View of Sausalito (51x61cm-20x24in) s.i.d.1920 verso exhib. 29-Oct-2 John Moran, Pasadena #765 est:7000-9000

CUNEO, Terence (1907-1996) British
£600 $936 €900 Polythene (35x50cm-14x20in) canvasboard. 12-Sep-2 Sotheby's, Olympia #213/R
£950 $1558 €1425 Warwick air and sea rescue (61x51cm-24x20in) s.d.Nov 44 prov.exhib. 3-Jun-3 Sotheby's, Olympia #151/R
£1200 $1872 €1800 Anthony and Cleopatra (35x25cm-14x10in) s.d.1974 pair prov. 27-Mar-3 Christie's, Kensington #447/R est:800-1200
£1300 $2054 €1950 Boats and washing (25x35cm-10x14in) s.d.Jan 1989. 7-Apr-3 Bonhams, Bath #69/R est:800-1200
£1400 $2212 €2100 View of Chiswick (61x101cm-24x40in) s.d.70. 27-Nov-2 Sotheby's, Olympia #100/R est:1500-2000
£1800 $2808 €2700 Radar (35x50cm-14x20in) s.d.1948 canvasboard. 12-Sep-2 Sotheby's, Olympia #227/R est:2000-3000
£3800 $6346 €5510 Boat builders (64x77cm-25x30in) s.d.May 1952. 25-Jun-3 Bonhams, Bury St Edmunds #599 est:2500-4000
£4000 $6600 €5800 Gas light (76x101cm-30x40in) s.d.1953. 3-Jul-3 Christie's, Kensington #412/R est:2000-3000
£7500 $11625 €11250 Interior of a plane making factory (51x71cm-20x28in) s.d.1943 canvas on board. 4-Dec-2 Christie's, Kensington #541/R est:2000-3000
£7500 $11700 €11250 Steam train at the station (31x41cm-12x16in) s. 27-Mar-3 Christie's, Kensington #500/R est:3000-5000
£26000 $40040 €39000 Racing cars (60x50cm-24x20in) s.d.Sept 1950. 6-Sep-2 Bonhams, Knightsbridge #42/R

Works on paper
£420 $655 €630 Radio contact (51x38cm-20x15in) s. chl gouache. 12-Sep-2 Sotheby's, Olympia #201/R

CUNNINGHAM, Edward Francis (c.1742-1795) British

Works on paper
£4000 $6280 €6000 Reception given for the Duchess of Kingston, by Paul, son of Catherine the Great (48x69cm-19x27in) s.d.1783 pencil pen ink htd white prov. 21-Nov-2 Christie's, London #22/R est:4000-6000

CUNNINGHAM, Imogen (1883-1976) American

Photographs
£1899 $3000 €2849 Tea at Foster's (19x18cm-7x7in) s.d.1950 gelatin silver print prov. 25-Apr-3 Phillips, New York #124/R est:2000-3000
£2025 $3200 €3038 Alone (20x19cm-8x7in) s.d.1950 gelatin silver print prov. 25-Apr-3 Phillips, New York #125/R est:2000-3000
£2083 $3250 €3125 Alfred Stieglitz at an American Place (24x19cm-9x7in) s.d. gelitan silver print. 14-Oct-2 Butterfields, San Francisco #1450/R est:2500-3500
£2658 $4200 €3987 Self portrait on Geary Streey (22x19cm-9x7in) s.d.1958 gelatin silver print prov. 25-Apr-3 Phillips, New York #126/R est:3000-4000
£2690 $4250 €4035 Unmade bed (27x35cm-11x14in) s.d.1957 photograph. 23-Apr-3 Sotheby's, New York #23/R est:4000-6000
£2848 $4500 €4272 Twin boy's - rondal and padraic (20x25cm-8x10in) d.1923 warm tone photograph. 23-Apr-3 Sotheby's, New York #149/R est:5000-7000

£5844 $9000 €8766 Triangles (9x7cm-4x3in) s.i.d.1928 photograph prov. 24-Oct-2 Sotheby's, New York #137/R est:6000-9000
£6494 $10000 €9741 Agave design 2 (36x28cm-14x11in) s.d.1920 gelatin silver print prov.lit. 25-Oct-2 Phillips, New York #11/R est:30000-50000
£7975 $13000 €11963 Two callas (34x27cm-13x11in) s.d.1929 gelatin silver print. 12-Feb-3 Christie's, Rockefeller NY #73/R est:9000-12000
£12987 $20000 €19481 Nude (18x24cm-7x9in) s.d.1932 photograph. 24-Oct-2 Sotheby's, New York #136/R est:20000-30000
£35443 $56000 €53165 Tower of jewels (24x19cm-9x7in) warm toned photograph prov.lit. 23-Apr-3 Sotheby's, New York #150/R est:30000-50000

CUNNINGHAM, John (1926-1999) British
£1000 $1580 €1500 By the river (30x40cm-12x16in) s. panel prov. 27-Nov-2 Sotheby's, Olympia #85/R est:1000-1500
£1000 $1550 €1500 Castlebay, Barra (44x54cm-17x21in) s. 6-Dec-2 Lyon & Turnbull, Edinburgh #74 est:1000-1500
£2000 $3120 €3000 Anemones and lamp (44x39cm-17x15in) s. 10-Apr-3 Bonhams, Edinburgh #55/R est:2000-3000
£3300 $5148 €4950 North end of Skye from Gairloch (40x71cm-16x28in) s. 10-Apr-3 Bonhams, Edinburgh #53/R est:2500-4000
£4400 $6864 €6600 West coast landscape (39x75cm-15x30in) s. 10-Apr-3 Bonhams, Edinburgh #39/R est:2000-3000

CUNNINGHAM, William (?) British?
£350 $511 €525 Galway Bay (25x30cm-10x12in) s. board. 12-Jun-2 John Ross, Belfast #263
£520 $806 €780 Galway hooker (36x36cm-14x14in) s. board. 2-Oct-2 John Ross, Belfast #42

CUNZ, Martha (1876-1961) Swiss
£1073 $1695 €1610 New snow at Glogghus, Melchsee-Frutt (31x58cm-12x23in) mono. pavatex painted 1909. 26-Nov-2 Hans Widmer, St Gallen #1079/R est:2400-3600 (S.FR 2500)
£6550 $10284 €9825 Tree on Untersee shore (59x66cm-23x26in) s. 25-Nov-2 Sotheby's, Zurich #97/R est:8000-12000 (S.FR 15000)
Works on paper
£742 $1166 €1113 Bernina massif (33x45cm-13x18in) mono. pastel. 25-Nov-2 Sotheby's, Zurich #103/R (S.FR 1700)

CUPRIEN, Frank W (1871-1948) American
£2419 $3750 €3629 Silvery sea and a grey day (28x36cm-11x14in) s. i.verso board prov.exhib. 29-Oct-2 John Moran, Pasadena #756 est:2500-3500
£7186 $12000 €10420 On radiant sea (91x127cm-36x50in) s. mono.i.verso prov. 18-Jun-3 Christie's, Los Angeles #100/R est:15000-25000

CURIA, Francesco (attrib) (1538-c.1610) Italian
£5579 $8648 €8369 Madonna with child and St Anna (76x52cm-30x20in) panel prov. 3-Oct-2 Koller, Zurich #3032/R est:15000-25000 (S.FR 13000)

CURLING, Peter (1955-) Irish
£5405 $8432 €8000 Cattle at Camus Bridge, Tipperary (50x75cm-20x30in) s. 26-Mar-3 James Adam, Dublin #93/R est:10000-15000
£12162 $18973 €18000 Turning to go down to the start (47x70cm-19x28in) s. 26-Mar-3 James Adam, Dublin #92/R est:15000-20000
£12319 $20203 €17000 Saratoga, summer 1989, Shug McHaigey's barn (76x102cm-30x40in) s. s.i.verso. 28-May-3 Bonhams & James Adam, Dublin #126/R est:18000-22000
Works on paper
£459 $715 €720 Racehorse in landscape (27x38cm-11x15in) s.d.1976 W/C. 6-Nov-2 James Adam, Dublin #82/R
£759 $1177 €1200 Sketches of horses exercising (53x70cm-21x28in) s.d.72 W/C. 25-Sep-2 James Adam, Dublin #41 est:1000-2000

CURNOCK, James Jackson (1839-1891) British
Works on paper
£300 $477 €450 Walking home from church (12x19cm-5x7in) s. W/C bodycol. 25-Feb-3 Bonhams, Knightsbridge #166/R
£420 $689 €630 Idwal stream, North Wales (54x74cm-21x29in) s.d.1889 W/C. 3-Jun-3 Bonhams, Oxford #14
£580 $916 €870 Beech wood at Capel Curig, North Wales (54x69cm-21x27in) s. i.verso W/C htd white scratching out. 7-Apr-3 Bonhams, Bath #17/R
£1200 $1872 €1800 Brook (62x44cm-24x17in) s. pencil W/C scratching out. 17-Oct-2 Christie's, Kensington #91/R est:1200-1800
£2200 $3630 €3190 Watermill in a wooded landscape (66x84cm-26x33in) s.d.1880 pencil W/C scratching out. 3-Jul-3 Christie's, Kensington #92/R est:1500-2000

CURNOCK, James Jackson and WAINEWRIGHT, Thomas Francis (19th C) British
Works on paper
£1500 $2340 €2250 Cattle watering in a copes (35x53cm-14x21in) s.i.d.1860 pencil W/C scratching out. 17-Oct-2 Christie's, Kensington #92/R est:1500-2000

CURNOE, Greg (1936-) Canadian
Prints
£6222 $10204 €9333 Superleggero (108x172cm-43x68in) s.d.1979 num.9/30 serigraph on plexiglass prov. 27-May-3 Sotheby's, Toronto #137/R est:8000-10000 (C.D 14000)

CUROS, Jordi (1930-) Spanish
£298 $486 €450 The Seine in Paris (73x93cm-29x37in) s. 11-Feb-3 Castellana, Madrid #23/R
£597 $932 €950 Santa Maria del Mar (100x81cm-39x32in) s. 8-Oct-2 Ansorena, Madrid #429/R

CURRADI, Francesco (attrib) (1570-1661) Italian
£755 $1162 €1200 Le Christ ressuscite (45x37cm-18x15in) 25-Oct-2 Tajan, Paris #23/R

CURRAN, Charles Courtney (1861-1942) American
£962 $1500 €1443 Study for sunshine of youth (20x14cm-8x6in) i.verso canvasboard. 9-Nov-2 Sloan, North Bethesda #543/R est:800-1000
£1592 $2500 €2388 Cows in the pasture, Wengen (30x46cm-12x18in) s.i.d.1900 prov. 19-Nov-2 Butterfields, San Francisco #8039/R est:5000-7000
£2830 $4500 €4245 Cloud study with two figures at background (64x76cm-25x30in) s. 22-Mar-3 Nadeau, Windsor #230/R est:4000-5000
£3503 $5500 €5255 An elegant woman (23x15cm-9x6in) s.d.1911. 22-Nov-2 Skinner, Boston #110/R est:5000-7000
£3822 $6000 €5733 Deer on the hilltop (38x28cm-15x11in) s. i.verso board. 23-Nov-2 Pook & Pook, Downington #302/R est:10000-15000
£7042 $10000 €10563 Bacchanal (25x38cm-10x15in) 8-Aug-1 Barridorf, Portland #1/R est:12000-18000
£22013 $35000 €33020 Sunlit valley (77x51cm-30x20in) s.d.1920 i.stretcher exhib. 7-Mar-3 Skinner, Boston #573/R est:20000-40000

CURRIE, Ken (20th C) ?
£14000 $21700 €21000 Tree of liberty (218x386cm-86x152in) exhib.lit. 6-Dec-2 Lyon & Turnbull, Edinburgh #61/R est:15000-20000

CURRIE, William (19th C) British
£250 $395 €375 Panoramic mountain scene. River scene with figures. d.1875 one oil one W/C two. 5-Apr-3 Hogben, Folkstone #206

CURRIER and IVES (19th C) American
Prints
£1975 $3100 €2963 Life of a fireman - the Metropolitan system (58x76cm-23x30in) col lithograph. 22-Nov-2 Eldred, East Dennis #1034/R est:3000-4000

CURRIER, Nathaniel (1813-1888) American
Prints
£1887 $3000 €2831 Life of a fireman (71x91cm-28x36in) hand col lithograph. 1-Mar-3 North East Auctions, Portsmouth #256/R est:3000-4000
£2293 $3600 €3440 Life of a fireman (43x66cm-17x26in) i. col lithograph. 23-Nov-2 Pook & Pook, Downington #132/R est:1000-1500

CURRIN, John (1962-) American
£82278 $130000 €123417 Architecture student (122x96cm-48x38in) s.d.92 on overlap prov. 12-Nov-2 Sotheby's, New York #57/R est:250000-350000
£113924 $180000 €170886 Flag (86x76cm-34x30in) s.d.90 prov.exhib.lit. 14-Nov-2 Christie's, Rockefeller NY #326/R est:100000-150000
Works on paper
£15190 $24000 €22785 Mrs So-and So (35x27cm-14x11in) s.d.2000 verso ink gouache prov. 14-Nov-2 Christie's, Rockefeller NY #331/R est:40000-60000
£16250 $26000 €24375 Hobo (22x19cm-9x7in) gouache executed 1996 prov. 16-May-3 Phillips, New York #111/R est:20000-30000

CURRY, John Steuart (1897-1946) American
£92593 $150000 €138890 Preliminary study for a mural, Oklahoma land rush (72x150cm-28x59in) prov. 22-May-3 Christie's, Rockefeller NY #83/R est:150000-250000
Prints
£1887 $3000 €2831 Baptism in Big Stranger Creek (25x34cm-10x13in) s. lithograph. 4-Mar-3 Swann Galleries, New York #239/R est:1000-1500
£2435 $3750 €3653 John Brown (13x28cm-5x11in) s. num.250 lithograph prov. 24-Oct-2 Shannon's, Milford #163/R est:2500-3500

£3797 $6000 €5506 Our good Earth (25x33cm-10x13in) s. lithograph sold with Thomas Hart Benton, Arkansas evening. 26-Jul-3 Coeur d'Alene, Hayden #58/R est:3000-5000

Works on paper

£755 $1200 €1133 Pigs (16x32cm-6x13in) s. graphite. 7-Mar-3 Skinner, Boston #298/R

£1296 $2100 €1879 Ballet Designs (76x56cm-30x22in) s.i. s.d.Nov. 8th 40 s.i. blk red chk three. 21-May-3 Doyle, New York #21/R est:1500-2500

CURRY, Robert F (1872-1945) American

£352 $515 €528 Winter landscape with stream (40x50cm-16x20in) s. board. 17-Jun-2 Philippe Schuler, Zurich #7322 (S.FR 800)

£385 $562 €600 Moor landscape (56x68cm-22x27in) s. 4-Jun-2 Karl & Faber, Munich #214

£414 $654 €600 Village with church and fortress (60x74cm-24x29in) s. 5-Apr-3 Hans Stahl, Hamburg #5/R

£446 $696 €700 Sunny winter landscape (50x80cm-20x31in) s. 6-Nov-2 Hugo Ruef, Munich #1052

£753 $1175 €1100 Winter in the forest (60x74cm-24x29in) s. lit. 10-Apr-3 Allgauer, Kempten #2747/R

£833 $1292 €1300 Snow-covered mountain landscape (80x100cm-31x39in) s. lit. 7-Dec-2 Bergmann, Erlangen #808/R

£1039 $1548 €1600 Steinach am Brenner, Tyrol in winter (76x87cm-30x34in) s. i. stretcher. 26-Jun-2 Neumeister, Munich #707/R

£1234 $1838 €1900 River in winter valley (105x126cm-41x50in) s. 26-Jun-2 Neumeister, Munich #706/R

£1258 $1950 €2000 Faggot gatherer in autumn wood (69x100cm-27x39in) s. 29-Oct-2 Dorotheum, Vienna #69/R est:3200-3400

£1923 $2923 €3000 Sunny winter day in Italian mountains (80x100cm-31x39in) s. lit. 11-Jul-2 Allgauer, Kempten #2458/R

CURSITER, Stanley (1887-1976) British

£4500 $6975 €6750 Girl in white (46x41cm-18x16in) s.d.1923 prov. 31-Oct-2 Christie's, London #166/R est:5000-8000

£32000 $48960 €48000 Two girls by a window (46x41cm-18x16in) s.d.1923. 22-Aug-2 Bonhams, Edinburgh #1091/R est:18000-25000

Works on paper

£3800 $5928 €5700 View from the artist's bed in the canvas hospital (15x22cm-6x9in) s.d.1916 W/C prov. 10-Apr-3 Bonhams, Edinburgh #84/R est:1000-1500

CURTIS, Calvin (1822-1893) American

£292 $450 €438 Portrait of a man (17x14cm-7x6in) s.d.1873. 9-Sep-2 Schrager Galleries, Milwaukee #1037/R

CURTIS, David (20th C) American

£780 $1217 €1170 Quiet moment, Helsey Hall (29x39cm-11x15in) s.indis.d.98. 10-Sep-2 David Duggleby, Scarborough #379

CURTIS, Edward S (1868-1952) American

£2147 $3500 €3221 Homeward (28x35cm-11x14in) s. orotone. 12-Feb-3 Christie's, Rockefeller NY #21/R est:3000-5000

Photographs

£1875 $3000 €2813 Before the storm (14x19cm-6x7in) s. sepia toned silver border print executed c.1906. 15-May-3 Swann Galleries, New York #316/R est:1500-2000

£1899 $3000 €2849 Vanishing race (36x43cm-14x17in) s.i. orotone. 23-Apr-3 Sotheby's, New York #37/R est:5000-7000

£2308 $3600 €3462 Chief Joseph (34x27cm-13x11in) s. verso sepia silver copy. 21-Oct-2 Swann Galleries, New York #114/R est:4000-5000

£2500 $4000 €3750 Vanishing race (26x34cm-10x13in) with sig. orotone. 15-May-3 Swann Galleries, New York #321/R est:6000-9000

£2532 $4000 €3798 Vanishing race - Navaho (8x25cm-3x10in) s. orotone. 22-Apr-3 Christie's, Rockefeller NY #5/R est:4000-6000

£2848 $4500 €4272 Vanishing race - Navaho (27x34cm-11x13in) s. gelatin silver print. 22-Apr-3 Christie's, Rockefeller NY #8/R est:5000-7000

£2922 $4500 €4383 Vash gon - jicarilla (40x23cm-16x9in) s. platinum print. 24-Oct-2 Sotheby's, New York #23/R est:7000-10000

£3067 $5000 €4601 Canon del Muerto, Navajo (36x28cm-14x11in) s. orotone. 12-Feb-3 Christie's, Rockefeller NY #19/R est:6000-8000

£4063 $6500 €6095 Canon del Muerto (36x28cm-14x11in) with sig. orotone. 15-May-3 Swann Galleries, New York #317/R est:6000-9000

£4167 $6500 €6251 Portrait of a man in head-dress (39x28cm-15x11in) s. platinum. 21-Oct-2 Swann Galleries, New York #115/R est:4000-5000

£4487 $7000 €6731 Waiting in the forest - Cheyenne (39x28cm-15x11in) i. verso photogravure. 21-Oct-2 Swann Galleries, New York #119/R est:9000-12000

£4573 $7500 €6860 Vanishing race (26x34cm-10x13in) s. orotone. 10-Feb-3 Swann Galleries, New York #22/R est:7000-10000

£4750 $7600 €7125 Scout Apache (18x23cm-7x9in) s. orotone photograph. 11-Jan-3 James Julia, Fairfield #19 est:2000-3000

£5313 $8500 €7970 Vash Gon Jicarilla (41x22cm-16x9in) with sig. platinum print. 15-May-3 Swann Galleries, New York #322/R est:6000-9000

£5380 $8500 €8070 Chief of the desert - Navaho (42x32cm-17x13in) s. silver toned platinum print. 22-Apr-3 Christie's, Rockefeller NY #6/R est:10000-15000

£6962 $11000 €10443 Maid of dreams (36x28cm-14x11in) s. orotone photo. 22-Apr-3 Butterfields, San Francisco #2395/R est:7000-10000

£7595 $12000 €11393 Oasis in the Badlands - Sioux (36x28cm-14x11in) s. orotone lit. 22-Apr-3 Christie's, Rockefeller NY #2/R est:10000-15000

£7595 $12000 €11393 Canon de Chelly, Navaho (28x36cm-11x14in) s.num.1012 orotone photo lit. 22-Apr-3 Butterfields, San Francisco #2393/R est:10000-12000

£8750 $14000 €13125 Walpi-hopi (39x27cm-15x11in) with sig. platinum print. 15-May-3 Swann Galleries, New York #313/R est:7000-10000

£8861 $14000 €13292 North American Indian (37x27cm-15x11in) photograph 36 in portfolio. 22-Apr-3 Christie's, Rockefeller NY #226/R est:12000-18000

£9494 $15000 €14241 North American Indian (38x27cm-15x11in) photgraph 39 inn portfolio. 22-Apr-3 Christie's, Rockefeller NY #212/R est:18000-22000

£9494 $15000 €14241 North American Indian (40x27cm-16x11in) 36 bound portfolio. 23-Apr-3 Sotheby's, New York #39/R est:15000-25000

£10127 $16000 €15191 North American Indian (37x27cm-15x11in) photograph 36 in portfolio. 22-Apr-3 Christie's, Rockefeller NY #227/R est:18000-22000

£10625 $17000 €15938 Zuni Governor (41x25cm-16x10in) with sig platinum print. 15-May-3 Swann Galleries, New York #315/R est:6000-9000

£10759 $17000 €16139 Chief of the desert - Navaho (28x36cm-11x14in) s. orotone lit. 22-Apr-3 Christie's, Rockefeller NY #1/R est:15000-20000

£10759 $17000 €16139 North American Indian (37x27cm-15x11in) photograph 36 in portfolio. 22-Apr-3 Christie's, Rockefeller NY #215/R est:18000-22000

£10759 $17000 €16139 North American Indian (37x27cm-15x11in) photograph 36 in portfolio. 22-Apr-3 Christie's, Rockefeller NY #228/R est:18000-22000

£10759 $17000 €15601 Prayer to the great mystery (33x25cm-13x10in) s. orontone prov.lit. 26-Jul-3 Coeur d'Alene, Hayden #104/R est:10000-15000

£11250 $18000 €16875 Son of the desert Navaho (40x30cm-16x12in) with sig. platinum print. 15-May-3 Swann Galleries, New York #312/R est:7000-10000

£11392 $18000 €17088 North American Indian (37x27cm-15x11in) photograph 37 in portfolio. 22-Apr-3 Christie's, Rockefeller NY #218/R est:20000-30000

£12658 $20000 €18987 North American Indian (37x27cm-15x11in) photograph 36 in portfolio. 22-Apr-3 Christie's, Rockefeller NY #222/R est:25000-35000

£13291 $21000 €19937 North American Indian (40x27cm-16x11in) portfolio of 36 photograph. 23-Apr-3 Sotheby's, New York #40/R est:15000-25000

£24051 $38000 €36077 North American Indian (37x27cm-15x11in) photograph 36 in portfolio. 22-Apr-3 Christie's, Rockefeller NY #217/R est:30000-40000

£29114 $46000 €43671 North American Indian (37x27cm-15x11in) photograph 36 in portfolio. 22-Apr-3 Christie's, Rockefeller NY #214/R est:50000-70000

£29114 $46000 €43671 North American Indian (37x27cm-15x11in) photograph 36 in portfolio. 22-Apr-3 Christie's, Rockefeller NY #216/R est:60000-80000

£30380 $48000 €45570 North American Indian. photograph 36 in portfolio. 22-Apr-3 Christie's, Rockefeller NY #213/R est:60000-80000

£32911 $52000 €49367 North American Indian (38x27cm-15x11in) photographs 39 in portfolio. 22-Apr-3 Christie's, Rockefeller NY #211/R est:50000-70000

£39241 $62000 €58862 North American Indian (40x27cm-16x11in) portfolio of 39 photographs. 23-Apr-3 Sotheby's, New York #41/R est:40000-60000

£53797 $85000 €80696 North American Indian. photograph 18 volumes. 22-Apr-3 Christie's, Rockefeller NY #229/R est:60000-80000

Prints

£5128 $8000 €7692 Vanishing race (28x36cm-11x14in) s.i. orotone print prov. 9-Nov-2 Santa Fe Art, Santa Fe #80/R est:10000-12000

Works on paper

£859 $1400 €1246 Oath (30x36cm-12x14in) sepia. 18-Jul-3 Du Mouchelle, Detroit #2226/R est:500-600

CURTIS, George V (19th C) British

£1358 $1928 €2200 Jeune femme dans le jardin (55x46cm-22x18in) s. 16-Mar-3 Eric Pillon, Calais #26/R

CURTIS, Howard Parker (1848-1920) British?

£360 $601 €522 Venetian scene (73x117cm-29x46in) 25-Jun-3 Cheffins, Cambridge #779/R

CURTIS, J W (1839-1901) Australian
£1971 $2996 €2957 Murray River landscapes (19x44cm-7x17in) one s.verso board pair. 28-Aug-2 Deutscher-Menzies, Melbourne #121/R est:4000-5000 (A.D 5500)

CURTIS, James Waltham (1839-1901) Australian
£1429 $2257 €2144 Murray below Echuca (42x70cm-17x28in) s.d.99 s.i. 18-Nov-2 Joel, Victoria #349/R est:6000-8000 (A.D 4000)

CURTIS, Leland (1897-?) American
£1032 $1600 €1548 Snowy Creek (30x41cm-12x16in) s. i.verso board. 29-Oct-2 John Moran, Pasadena #613 est:800-1200
£3915 $6500 €5677 Antarctica (71x104cm-28x41in) s.i.d.1939-1940 prov. 11-Jun-3 Butterfields, San Francisco #4134/R est:3000-5000
Works on paper
£240 $374 €360 Mountainous landscape with a river (46x63cm-18x25in) s. W/C. 13-Apr-3 Butterfields, Los Angeles #7036
£488 $800 €708 Neall lake (15x18cm-6x7in) s. gouache. 5-Jun-3 Swann Galleries, New York #75/R

CURTIS, Sidney W (19/20th C) American
£720 $1130 €1080 Faggot gatherers (22x16cm-9x6in) board. 16-Dec-2 Bonhams, Bury St Edmunds #523/R

CURVAL, Lopes (20th C) Spanish?
£1181 $1865 €1700 La femme au saphir (150x150cm-59x59in) s.d. s.i.d.verso acrylic. 28-Apr-3 Cornette de St.Cyr, Paris #373/R est:1000-1500

CUSACHS Y CUSACHS, Jose (1851-1908) Spanish
£2368 $3837 €3600 Soldier (34x20cm-13x8in) s.d.1899 board. 21-Jan-3 Ansorena, Madrid #202/R est:3000
£5449 $8609 €8500 Battle scene (20x30cm-8x12in) s. 13-Nov-2 Ansorena, Madrid #182/R
£6410 $10128 €10000 Portrait of woman (80x66cm-31x26in) s.d.1896. 13-Nov-2 Ansorena, Madrid #112/R est:9000
£8974 $14179 €14000 Horse and rider (46x35cm-18x14in) s. 13-Nov-2 Ansorena, Madrid #115/R est:11000
£13208 $20472 €21000 Military parade (53x97cm-21x38in) s. 7-Oct-2 Ansorena, Madrid #59/R est:21000
Works on paper
£472 $736 €750 Soldier (24x16cm-9x6in) s.d.1888 ink dr. 8-Oct-2 Ansorena, Madrid #482/R
£535 $834 €850 Soldier (24x15cm-9x6in) s. ink dr. 8-Oct-2 Ansorena, Madrid #483/R
£2069 $3290 €3000 Soldier (27x15cm-11x6in) s.d.1889 mixed media. 4-Mar-3 Ansorena, Madrid #181/R

CUSACK, Ralph (1912-) British?
Works on paper
£331 $549 €470 Autumn leaves (29x42cm-11x17in) s.d.44 W/C. 10-Jun-3 James Adam, Dublin #232/R

CUSATI, Gaetano (circle) (18th C) Italian
£8621 $13621 €12500 Still life with pomegranates, figs and grapes (63x50cm-25x20in) 5-Apr-3 Finarte Semenzato, Milan #150/R est:8000

CUSTER, W (19th C) ?
£912 $1440 €1368 The communication (63x58cm-25x23in) s.d.1852. 27-Nov-2 Falkkloos, Malmo #77792/R (S.KR 13000)

CUSTIS, Eleanor Parke (1897-1983) American
Works on paper
£385 $600 €578 Artist's studio (55x46cm-22x18in) s. W/C. 9-Nov-2 Sloan, North Bethesda #544/R

CUSTIS, Jane R (19th C) American
Works on paper
£5000 $8000 €7500 Basket of fruit (18x23cm-7x9in) s. W/C pencil. 17-May-3 Pook & Pook, Downington #90b/R est:3000-3500

CUTHBERTSON, Arch (1924-) Australian
£1434 $2179 €2151 Abstract (121x136cm-48x54in) s.d.71. 28-Aug-2 Deutscher-Menzies, Melbourne #391/R est:2000-3000 (A.D 4000)

CUTLER, Carl Gordon (1873-1945) American
£350 $550 €525 Portrait of a young girl (53x46cm-21x18in) 22-Nov-2 Skinner, Boston #160/R

CUTLER, Cecil (?-1934) British
Works on paper
£500 $830 €725 Huntsman on a grey (42x30cm-17x12in) s.d.1900 W/C bodycol prov. 12-Jun-3 Christie's, Kensington #84

CUTTING, Francis Harvey (1872-1964) American
£538 $850 €807 Landscape with sequoias and mountains (114x183cm-45x72in) 16-Nov-2 Harvey Clar, Oakland #1298
£719 $1200 €1043 Flower garden by the sea (41x51cm-16x20in) s. canvasboard. 17-Jun-3 John Moran, Pasadena #23 est:1500-2000

CUTTS, Gertrude Spurr (1858-1941) Canadian
£1689 $2770 €2534 Farmstead by a river (30x60cm-12x24in) s. board. 3-Jun-3 Joyner, Toronto #369/R est:1000-1500 (C.D 3800)

CUTTS, William Malcolm (1857-1943) Canadian
£393 $616 €590 Pastoral stream (56x41cm-22x16in) s. 24-Jul-2 Walker's, Ottawa #245/R (C.D 950)

CUVELIER, Hippolyte Joseph (1803-1876) French
£1456 $2271 €2300 Le joueur de flute (92x73cm-36x29in) 20-Oct-2 Mercier & Cie, Lille #315/R est:1500-2300

CUYCK VAN MIERHOP, Franz (c.1640-1690) Flemish
£5660 $8774 €9000 Hunting still life with game birds and dog (66x85cm-26x33in) bears sig. prov. 2-Oct-2 Dorotheum, Vienna #149/R est:9000-14000

CUYLENBORCH, Abraham van (1620-1658) Dutch
£4500 $7515 €6525 Interior of a grotto with nymphs bathing (60x84cm-24x33in) panel. 11-Jul-3 Christie's, Kensington #61/R est:5000-8000
£4800 $7440 €7200 Diana and Actaeon (50x74cm-20x29in) s.d.1643 panel. 31-Oct-2 Sotheby's, Olympia #68/R est:5000-7000

CUYLENBORCH, Abraham van (attrib) (1620-1658) Dutch
£2098 $3503 €3000 Bain de nymphes pres d'une grotte (60x83cm-24x33in) panel. 27-Jun-3 Piasa, Paris #53/R est:3000-4000
£4196 $7007 €6000 Couple de bergers pres de tombeaux dans un grotte (44x68cm-17x27in) panel. 27-Jun-3 Piasa, Paris #51/R est:4000-6000

CUYP, Benjamin Gerritsz (1612-1652) Dutch
£3535 $5797 €5126 Interior scene with figures at an inn (51x38cm-20x15in) panel prov. 4-Jun-3 AB Stockholms Auktionsverk #2592/R est:40000-50000 (S.KR 45000)
£6707 $11000 €10061 Conversion of Saul (75x92cm-30x36in) bears sig. 5-Feb-3 Christie's, Rockefeller NY #266/R est:6000-8000
£8500 $13175 €12750 Annunciation of the Angels to the Shepherds (124x180cm-49x71in) rem.sig. prov. 31-Oct-2 Sotheby's, Olympia #72/R est:8000-12000
£8917 $13911 €14000 Liberation of St. Peter (75x106cm-30x42in) panel prov.exhib.lit. 5-Nov-2 Sotheby's, Amsterdam #56/R est:12000-18000

CUYP, Benjamin Gerritsz (attrib) (1612-1652) Dutch
£305 $500 €442 Road thieves in a landscape (53x70cm-21x28in) marouflaged panel. 4-Jun-3 Christie's, Rockefeller NY #186/R
£1493 $2448 €2165 Interior scene with figures playing cards (41x51cm-16x20in) panel. 4-Jun-3 AB Stockholms Auktionsverk #2590/R est:20000-25000 (S.KR 19000)

CUYP, Jacob Gerritsz (style) (1594-1651) Dutch
£6000 $9300 €9000 Portrait of a girl in a red dress, pink flowers in her right hand (75x60cm-30x24in) panel prov. 30-Oct-2 Christie's, Kensington #43/R est:3000-5000

CUYPER, Alfons de (1887-1950) Belgian
£256 $403 €400 Nature morte aux lys et aux roses (38cm-15in circular) s. panel. 11-Dec-2 Hotel des Ventes Mosan, Brussels #304
£674 $1125 €950 De Veergrep te Gent (46x65cm-18x26in) s. canvas laid down. 17-Jun-3 Palais de Beaux Arts, Brussels #530

CUZCO SCHOOL (18th C) South American
£6051 $9500 €9077 Virgin (107x82cm-42x32in) prov.lit. 19-Nov-2 Sotheby's, New York #61/R est:15000

CUZZI, Virgilio (?) Italian
Works on paper
£374 $595 €550 Saint Mark's square, Venice (50x70cm-20x28in) s. W/C. 1-Mar-3 Stadion, Trieste #557

CYLKOW, Ludwik (1877-?) Polish

£284 $474 €400 Les Rochers en Bretagne (30x40cm-12x16in) s. panel. 17-Jun-3 Claude Boisgirard, Paris #35

CZACHORSKI, Ladislaus von (1850-1911) Polish

£15686 $25725 €24000 Woman in drawing-room (34x48cm-13x19in) s.d.1897. 5-Feb-3 Neumeister, Munich #692/R est:400

£40000 $63600 €60000 Song (36x50cm-14x20in) s.d.1902. 20-Mar-3 Christie's, Kensington #104/R est:10000-15000

CZAPSKI, Jozef (1896-1993) Polish

£2183 $3406 €3275 Rue Jacues Callot (60x38cm-24x15in) s.d.83. 6-Nov-2 Dobiaschofsky, Bern #428/R est:2400 (S.FR 5000)

£3493 $5450 €5240 Carafe et orange (65x50cm-26x20in) s.d.84. 6-Nov-2 Dobiaschofsky, Bern #429/R est:2600 (S.FR 8000)

CZECH, Emil (1862-1929) Austrian

£1871 $2974 €2750 Spring time (90x50cm-35x20in) s.d.1903. 25-Feb-3 Dorotheum, Vienna #19/R est:3200-3400

CZECH, Emil (attrib) (1862-1929) Austrian

£500 $780 €750 Mother and child on wayside (61x99cm-24x39in) s.d.1928. 15-Oct-2 Gorringes, Lewes #2304

CZEDEKOWSKI, Jan Boleslaw (1885-1969) Austrian

£1100 $1694 €1650 Nude reading (32x41cm-13x16in) s. canvas on board. 24-Oct-2 Christie's, Kensington #178/R est:800-1200

CZERMANSKI, Zolzislaw (1900-1970) American/Polish

Works on paper

£355 $592 €500 D'apres Jan Matejko (63x48cm-25x19in) s. graphite chl gouache. 17-Jun-3 Claude Boisgirard, Paris #38/R

£496 $829 €700 Fille au cerceau (46x33cm-18x13in) s.d. graphite W/C gouache. 17-Jun-3 Claude Boisgirard, Paris #39

£567 $948 €800 Marechal Pilsudski entoure de personnages (48x38cm-19x15in) s. graphite Indian ink W/C. 17-Jun-3 Claude Boisgirard, Paris #36/R

£745 $1244 €1050 Fille au lit (44x35cm-17x14in) s.d. Indian ink W/C. 17-Jun-3 Claude Boisgirard, Paris #37

CZERNOTZKY, Ernst (1869-1939) Austrian

£285 $444 €450 Still life with nautilus cup (25x20cm-10x8in) s. panel. 14-Sep-2 Weidler, Nurnberg #308/R

£1761 $2730 €2800 Books and antiquities. Fruit and antiquities (27x21cm-11x8in) s. panel two. 29-Oct-2 Dorotheum, Vienna #170/R est:2800-3200

£2368 $3671 €3552 Still life (27x21cm-11x8in) panel painted c.1890. 3-Dec-2 SOGA, Bratislava #162/R est:140000 (SL.K 150000)

CZESCHKA, Carl Otto (1878-?) Austrian

Works on paper

£1042 $1656 €1500 Drawings (23x15cm-9x6in) mono. Indian ink board three. 29-Apr-3 Wiener Kunst Auktionen, Vienna #226/R est:1500-4000

CZIGANY, Dezso (1883-1937) Hungarian

£21514 $33347 €31195 Still life (57x48cm-22x19in) s. canvas on card exhib. 9-Dec-2 Mu Terem Galeria, Budapest #129/R est:4000000 (H.F 8000000)

£28378 $44269 €42567 Muser, 1903 (76x60cm-30x24in) s.d.1903. 11-Sep-2 Kieselbach, Budapest #128/R (H.F 11000000)

CZIMRA, Gyula (1901-1966) Hungarian

£1397 $2180 €2096 Table still life (50x40cm-20x16in) s. 11-Apr-3 Kieselbach, Budapest #114/R est:180000-500000 (H.F 500000)

CZINOBER, Nicolas (1899-1984) Hungarian/French

£1892 $2951 €2800 Nature morte aux fleurs (60x50cm-24x20in) init. 26-Mar-3 Millon & Associes, Paris #121/R

£2162 $3373 €3200 Place de la Republique (50x72cm-20x28in) studio st.verso. 26-Mar-3 Millon & Associes, Paris #116/R

Works on paper

£338 $527 €500 Scene de rue (24x26cm-9x10in) studio st. ink. 26-Mar-3 Millon & Associes, Paris #118/R

£419 $654 €620 Paysage (34x27cm-13x11in) studio st. crayon. 26-Mar-3 Millon & Associes, Paris #117/R

CZOBEL, Bela (1883-1974) Hungarian

£446 $696 €700 Toits rouges auux grands arbres (45x27cm-18x11in) s. paper. 7-Nov-2 Chochon-Barre & Allardi, Paris #108/R

£1064 $1777 €1500 Village aux toits rouges (21x34cm-8x13in) s. 17-Jun-3 Claude Boisgirard, Paris #43 est:1800-2000

£1064 $1777 €1500 Le petit port (22x30cm-9x12in) s. paper. 17-Jun-3 Claude Boisgirard, Paris #44/R est:1800-2000

£2794 $4359 €4051 In the garden (26x39cm-10x15in) s. paperboard. 12-Apr-3 Mu Terem Galeria, Budapest #218/R est:650000 (H.F 1000000)

£4586 $7154 €7200 Tete de femme (48x33cm-19x13in) s. 6-Nov-2 Claude Boisgirard, Paris #11 est:4000-5000

£5266 $8425 €7899 Landscape in Szentendre (73x56cm-29x22in) 16-May-3 Kieselbach, Budapest #23/R (H.F 1800000)

£6191 $9659 €9287 Still life of flowers (101x73cm-40x29in) s. paper. 11-Sep-2 Kieselbach, Budapest #84/R (H.F 2400000)

£7962 $12420 €12500 Jeune femme au fichu rouge (65x50cm-26x20in) s. 6-Nov-2 Claude Boisgirard, Paris #12 est:6000-7000

£8255 $12878 €11970 Still life with lilacs (61x50cm-24x20in) s. 13-Sep-2 Mu Terem Galeria, Budapest #198/R est:3000000 (H.F 3200000)

£8383 $13078 €12575 Still life with flowers and books (79x59cm-31x23in) s. 11-Apr-3 Kieselbach, Budapest #48/R est:2500000-3000000 (H.F 3000000)

£10060 $15694 €14587 Elbowing lady (54x65cm-21x26in) s. 12-Apr-3 Mu Terem Galeria, Budapest #189/R est:2800000 (H.F 3600000)

£10319 $16098 €14963 Girl playing the guitar (82x61cm-32x24in) s. 13-Sep-2 Mu Terem Galeria, Budapest #74/R est:3000000 (H.F 4000000)

£11737 $18309 €17019 Still life of flowers (72x59cm-28x23in) s. canvas on board prov.exhib. 12-Apr-3 Mu Terem Galeria, Budapest #166/R est:3400000 (H.F 4200000)

£14791 $22926 €22187 Blue dressed girl in the studio (73x60cm-29x24in) s. 6-Dec-2 Kieselbach, Budapest #178/R (H.F 5500000)

£14791 $22926 €21447 Still life of geranium and book (73x60cm-29x24in) s. 9-Dec-2 Mu Terem Galeria, Budapest #128/R est:3000000 (H.F 5500000)

£128545 $200531 €186390 Street in Paris (73x100cm-29x39in) s. 12-Apr-3 Mu Terem Galeria, Budapest #152/R est:6000000 (H.F 46000000)

Works on paper

£255 $397 €400 Bouquet (30x22cm-12x9in) s. W/C. 7-Nov-2 Chochon-Barre & Allardi, Paris #111

£539 $874 €820 Sous le parasol (62x46cm-24x18in) s. W/C. 22-Jan-3 Tajan, Paris #155

£861 $1334 €1292 Girl in a blue skirt, sitting in an armchair (59x46cm-23x18in) s. mixed media. 6-Dec-2 Kieselbach, Budapest #46/R (H.F 320000)

£877 $1368 €1316 House among the trees (38x48cm-15x19in) s. mixed media. 11-Sep-2 Kieselbach, Budapest #36/R (H.F 340000)

£1156 $1839 €1700 Paysage avec un pont (35x27cm-14x11in) s. gouache W/C. 3-Mar-3 Claude Boisgirard, Paris #38 est:1500-2000

£2064 $3220 €3096 Still life of flowers (78x64cm-31x25in) s. mixed media. 11-Sep-2 Kieselbach, Budapest #74/R (H.F 800000)

£2200 $3608 €3300 Landscape with trees (39x28cm-15x11in) s. gouache W/C. 3-Jun-3 Sotheby's, London #101/R est:2000-3000

£3511 $5617 €5267 Woman with blue hair band (65x50cm-26x20in) s. mixed media. 16-May-3 Kieselbach, Budapest #9/R (H.F 1200000)

DAALHOFF, Hermanus Antonius van (1867-1953) Dutch

£255 $397 €400 Farm (23x34cm-9x13in) s. panel. 6-Nov-2 Vendue Huis, Gravenhage #36

£362 $586 €550 Bij de boerderij (27x39cm-11x15in) s. panel prov. 21-Jan-3 Christie's, Amsterdam #251

DABADIE, Henri (1867-1949) French

£748 $1190 €1100 Mosquee de Bab Doukala, Marrakech (19x24cm-7x9in) s.i. panel prov. 24-Mar-3 Rabourdin & Choppin de Janvry, Paris #260/R

D'ACCARDI, Gian Rodolfo (1906-1993) Italian

£256 $403 €400 Horse in the woods (40x50cm-16x20in) s. 23-Nov-2 Meeting Art, Vercelli #76

£294 $471 €450 Little horses (60x70cm-24x28in) s. s.verso. 4-Jan-3 Meeting Art, Vercelli #654

£316 $494 €500 Horses in the woods (70x60cm-28x24in) s. 14-Sep-2 Meeting Art, Vercelli #905

£385 $604 €600 Clown (60x70cm-24x28in) s. s.verso. 23-Nov-2 Meeting Art, Vercelli #400/R

£608 $949 €900 Snowfall (70x60cm-28x24in) s. 26-Mar-3 Finarte Semenzato, Milan #108/R

£633 $987 €1000 Rural scene with figures (30x40cm-12x16in) s.d.1830 board. 14-Sep-2 Meeting Art, Vercelli #875/R

DADAMAINO (1935-) Italian

Sculpture

£5380 $8500 €8500 Volume (70x50x3cm-28x20x1in) plastic exec.1960. 29-Nov-2 Farsetti, Prato #423/R est:5700

Works on paper

£2179 $3378 €3400 Il movimento delle cose No 5 (360x100cm-142x39in) s.i.d.1995 permanent pen astralon. 3-Dec-2 Lempertz, Koln #108/R est:3500

£6709 $10600 €10600 Volume (70x60cm-28x24in) waterpaint on canvas exec.1959. 29-Nov-2 Farsetti, Prato #256/R est:5700

DADD, Frank (1851-1929) British
£1000 $1630 €1500 Sunny street scene overlooking the sea. Figures on a road (12x22cm-5x9in) s.d.1922 two. 11-Feb-3 Bonhams, Knowle #79 est:200-300
Works on paper
£660 $1023 €990 After a hard day (26x36cm-10x14in) s.d. W/C over pencil. 2-Oct-2 Bonhams, Knowle #38

DADD, Richard (1819-1887) British
£40000 $64400 €60000 Haunt of the fairies (61x51cm-24x20in) oval prov.exhib.lit. 20-Feb-3 Christie's, London #86/R est:60000

DADDI, Bernardo (1312-1350) Italian
£180645 $285419 €280000 Madonna of the Birth (93x58cm-37x23in) tempera board lit. 19-Dec-2 Semenzato, Venice #28/R est:250000

DADE, Ernest (1864-1935) British
Works on paper
£1100 $1727 €1650 Fishing boats off the coast at dusk (34x52cm-13x20in) s.d.88 W/C. 21-Nov-2 Tennants, Leyburn #662/R est:600-800

DADE, Frederick (1874-1908) British
Works on paper
£500 $815 €725 Whitby (18x47cm-7x19in) s.i. W/C bodycol. 17-Jul-3 Tennants, Leyburn #703

DADELBEEK, G (18th C) Dutch
£3500 $5460 €5250 Grapes, peaches and other fruits, cabbage and walnut on a stone ledge, vase of flowers (68x51cm-27x20in) s.d.1766. 10-Apr-3 Christie's, Kensington #131/R est:4000-6000

DADO, Miodrag Djuric (1933-) Yugoslavian
£1582 $2500 €2500 Personnage sur fond bleu (92x65cm-36x26in) s.d.1963. 27-Nov-2 Lemoine & Ferrando, Paris #85/R est:3000-4000
£3526 $5465 €5500 Untitled (243x123cm-96x48in) panel painted 1997. 7-Dec-2 Cornette de St.Cyr, Paris #133/R
£5064 $7951 €7900 Untitled (30x70cm-12x28in) painted c.1953 prov. 15-Dec-2 Perrin, Versailles #81/R est:8000
Works on paper
£556 $878 €800 Les bebes (37x53cm-15x21in) pencil dr exec.c.1953 prov. 27-Apr-3 Perrin, Versailles #61/R

DAEL, Jan Frans van (attrib) (1764-1840) Dutch
£3000 $4830 €4500 Mixed flowers in a glass vase on a ledge (33x27cm-13x11in) s.d.1798 panel. 20-Feb-3 Christie's, Kensington #71/R est:2000-3000

DAELE, Casimir van den (1818-1880) Belgian
£1006 $1600 €1509 Bed time (127x107cm-50x42in) s. 7-Mar-3 Jackson's, Cedar Falls #525/R est:1750-2500

DAELE, Friedrich van den (1861-?) German
£1887 $2943 €3000 Two lambs heads (23x62cm-9x24in) s. board. 9-Oct-2 Michael Zeller, Lindau #656/R est:700

DAEMS, Ferdinand (c.1809-1875) Belgian
£641 $1013 €1000 Monks in the cloister (53x42cm-21x17in) s.d.1848 panel. 18-Nov-2 Bernaerts, Antwerp #43/R
£769 $1215 €1200 Letter (35x27cm-14x11in) s. panel. 18-Nov-2 Bernaerts, Antwerp #46/R

DAENS, Antoine (1871-1946) Belgian
£369 $594 €550 Vue d'Alger (38x45cm-15x18in) s. canvas on panel. 18-Feb-3 Vanderkindere, Brussels #7

DAFFINGER, Moritz Michael (1790-1849) Austrian
Miniatures
£2400 $3768 €3600 Prince Charles Joseph de Ligne (6cm-2xin) s. gilt metal mount. 10-Dec-2 Christie's, London #274/R est:800-1200
£4800 $7392 €7200 Lady in a purple dress, seated before a column (12cm-5xin) s. gilt metal bezel rec. exec.c.1840. 24-Oct-2 Sotheby's, Olympia #46/R est:2500-3500
£6000 $9420 €9000 Young lady in black and blue dress, landscape beyond (8x7cm-3x3in) s. gilt metal rec prov. 10-Dec-2 Christie's, London #264/R est:6000-8000
£6289 $9748 €10000 Portrait of Graf Kark von Lanckoronski (9x7cm-4x3in) s. W/C ivory. 1-Oct-2 Dorotheum, Vienna #368/R est:11000-15000

D'AGAR, Charles (attrib) (1669-1723) French
£1000 $1580 €1500 Portrait of a young man in blue coat (76x63cm-30x25in) prov. 12-Nov-2 Bonhams, Knightsbridge #161/R est:800-1200

DAGLEY, Arthur (20th C) New Zealander
£295 $460 €443 Reclamation no.3 (46x92cm-18x36in) s. s.i.verso board. 6-Aug-2 Peter Webb, Auckland #163 est:400-600 (NZ.D 1000)

DAGO, Herman (19th C) Spanish?
£2083 $3292 €3250 Still lives of fruit (40x75cm-16x30in) s. pair. 14-Nov-2 Arte, Seville #341/R

DAGONET, Ernest (1856-1926) French
Sculpture
£1259 $2102 €1800 Astarte (70cm-28in) s. medaille pat bronze socle. 25-Jun-3 Tajan, Paris #15/R est:1800-2000

D'AGUILAR, Michael (20th C) ?
£470 $771 €705 Eastern Mediterranean shoreline scene (99x122cm-39x48in) s. board. 5-Jun-3 Amersham Auction Rooms, UK #233
£720 $1174 €1044 Sur la promenade - un coup du vent (45x60cm-18x24in) s. canvas on board. 21-Jul-3 Bonhams, Bath #44/R
£1000 $1640 €1500 Portrait of Antonio, Spanish interior scene (109x97cm-43x38in) s.d.55. 5-Jun-3 Amersham Auction Rooms, UK #232

DAHL, Anton (19th C) Scandinavian
£392 $623 €588 Wooded landscape with bridge across river (92x131cm-36x52in) s.d.93. 5-May-3 Rasmussen, Vejle #694/R (D.KR 4200)
£426 $672 €639 Coastal landscape, moonlight (92x131cm-36x52in) s.d.87. 30-Nov-2 Rasmussen, Havnen #2262 (D.KR 5000)

DAHL, Carl (1813-1862) German
£1761 $2835 €2500 Romantic high mountain landscape with cows, figures and buildings (42x57cm-17x22in) s.d.1853. 10-May-3 Hans Stahl, Toestorf #32/R est:2500
£3000 $4860 €4500 Shipping off Kronberg Castle (48x74cm-19x29in) init. 22-Jan-3 Bonhams, New Bond Street #386/R est:3000-5000
£3445 $5237 €5168 Sailing vessels at anchor by large warehouse (37x50cm-15x20in) prov. 27-Aug-2 Rasmussen, Copenhagen #1428/R est:40000 (D.KR 40000)

DAHL, Hans (1849-1937) Norwegian
£354 $577 €531 Head of girl (21x18cm-8x7in) s.d.1876 panel. 17-Feb-3 Blomqvist, Lysaker #1025/R (N.KR 4000)
£770 $1255 €1155 Fisherman kissing girl wearing national costume (35x23cm-14x9in) s,. 17-Feb-3 Blomqvist, Lysaker #1024/R (N.KR 8700)
£785 $1233 €1178 Farm in evening light (28x51cm-11x20in) s/ panel. 25-Nov-2 Blomqvist, Lysaker #1038 (N.KR 9000)
£1990 $3144 €2985 Two girls in rowing boat (41x68cm-16x27in) s.indis.i.d.3 Juli 1901 canvas on panel. 2-Dec-2 Blomqvist, Oslo #333/R est:20000-25000 (N.KR 23000)
£2392 $3876 €3468 Girl from Fjaerland (67x47cm-26x19in) s.i. 26-May-3 Rasmussen, Copenhagen #1302/R est:25000-35000 (D.KR 25000)
£3165 $5000 €4748 Flower gatherer (69x49cm-27x19in) s.i. 1-Apr-3 Christie's, Rockefeller NY #207/R est:5000-7000
£3578 $5617 €5367 Too late (47x65cm-19x26in) s. 25-Nov-2 Blomqvist, Lysaker #1039/R est:45000-55000 (N.KR 41000)
£5000 $8200 €7500 Vikingskipenes tilvakekomst - return of the Viking ships (46x74cm-18x29in) s.i. s.on stretcher. 3-Jun-3 Sotheby's, London #268/R est:5000-7000
£5696 $9000 €8544 Spring time (71x53cm-28x21in) s. 5-Apr-3 Neal Auction Company, New Orleans #192/R est:10000-15000
£7483 $11898 €11000 Young girl by fjord (93x144cm-37x57in) s. 28-Mar-3 Bolland & Marotz, Bremen #434/R est:13000
£7500 $11775 €11250 Love letter (125x100cm-49x39in) s. 21-Nov-2 Christie's, Kensington #120/R est:4000-6000
£9000 $13950 €13500 Summer day by the fjord (89x140cm-35x55in) s.i. 4-Dec-2 Christie's, London #91/R est:5000-7000
£9974 $15559 €14961 Voyage in fresh breeze (74x51cm-29x20in) s.i. 21-Oct-2 Blomqvist, Oslo #356/R est:100000-120000 (N.KR 115000)
£10860 $17593 €16290 Vestland fjord landscape with figures (92x144cm-36x57in) s. 26-May-3 Grev Wedels Plass, Oslo #46/R est:150000-200000 (N.KR 120000)
£14000 $21700 €21000 Secret embrace (81x121cm-32x48in) s. 4-Dec-2 Christie's, London #90/R est:5000-7000
£18000 $27900 €27000 Rowing ashore (65x97cm-26x38in) s.i. 4-Dec-2 Christie's, London #92/R est:12000-18000
£19639 $32207 €28477 Boat trip on the fjord (84x125cm-33x49in) s. 4-Jun-3 AB Stockholms Auktionsverk #2478/R est:250000-300000 (S.KR 250000)

DAHL, Hans Andreas (1881-1919) Norwegian
£265 $433 €398 Fjord on the west coast of Norway (30x40cm-12x16in) s. panel. 17-Feb-3 Blomqvist, Lysaker #1027/R (N.KR 3000)
£320 $490 €480 Spring in Sogn (30x40cm-12x16in) s, panel. 26-Aug-2 Blomqvist, Lysaker #1069/R (N.KR 3700)
£1900 $3079 €2850 Fjord landscape with figures (24x36cm-9x14in) s. panel. 26-May-3 Grev Wedels Plass, Oslo #84/R est:12000-15000 (N.KR 21000)
£3246 $5128 €4869 Fjord landscape (100x66cm-39x26in) s. 17-Dec-2 Grev Wedels Plass, Oslo #143/R est:30000-40000 (N.KR 37000)
£3800 $5966 €5700 Admiring the view (92x71cm-36x28in) s. 16-Apr-3 Christie's, Kensington #796/R est:1500-2000
£5625 $9000 €8438 Extensive fjord view with girl resting on the shore (71x102cm-28x40in) s. 14-May-3 Butterfields, San Francisco #1098/R est:6000-8000

DAHL, Johan Christian Clausen (1788-1857) Norwegian
£3046 $4874 €4569 Portrait study of an old man seen in profile (34x27cm-13x11in) painted c.1813 lit. 17-Mar-3 Blomqvist, Oslo #318/R est:40000-50000 (N.KR 35000)
£6140 $9702 €9210 Study of stones from Nystuen, Filefjell (37x45cm-15x18in) s.d.27 aug.1850 i.verso panel. 17-Dec-2 Grev Wedels Plass, Oslo #144/R est:50000-70000 (N.KR 70000)
£6460 $9819 €9690 Large trees in a park, Dresden (32x39cm-13x15in) d.22 Septbr.1822. 27-Aug-2 Rasmussen, Copenhagen #1417/R est:100000-125000 (D.KR 75000)
£24433 $38360 €36650 Mountain farm (33x49cm-13x19in) s.d.1854 exhib.lit. 21-Nov-2 Grev Wedels Plass, Oslo #19/R est:300000-400000 (N.KR 280000)
£39792 $62872 €59688 Slindebirken, winter - large tree on mound (26x38cm-10x15in) s.d.1838 prov.exhib.lit. 2-Dec-2 Blomqvist, Oslo #331/R est:500000-600000 (N.KR 460000)
£42064 $65620 €63096 Street in a town - possibly Wachwitz near Dresden (57x67cm-22x26in) s.d.Oct 6 1832 prov.lit. 21-Oct-2 Blomqvist, Oslo #326/R est:475000-525000 (N.KR 485000)

Works on paper
£1280 $1997 €1920 Evening - Die Elbe (15x20cm-6x8in) s. pencil W/C executed 1833. 23-Sep-2 Blomqvist, Lysaker #1022/R est:8000-12000 (N.KR 15000)
£3309 $5427 €4600 Landscape (10x14cm-4x6in) s.i.d.1838 pencil htd white. 4-Jun-3 Reiss & Sohn, Konigstein #219/R est:5500

DAHL, Johan Christian Clausen (attrib) (1788-1857) Norwegian
£3000 $4710 €4500 Waterfall in Morgenbach, Germany (26x38cm-10x15in) s.d.28 Aug 33 paper on canvas. 21-Nov-2 Christie's, Kensington #123/R est:3000-5000

DAHL, Johan Vilhelm Ludvig (1818-1885) Danish
£270 $422 €405 Staubach Waterfall near Lautenbrunne, Switzerland (57x50cm-22x20in) s. 23-Sep-2 Rasmussen, Vejle #272/R (D.KR 3200)

DAHL, Jorgen (1825-1890) Danish
£1034 $1571 €1551 Several sailing vessels off Skagen's new lighthouse (58x83cm-23x33in) s.d.1885. 27-Aug-2 Rasmussen, Copenhagen #1476/R est:15000-20000 (D.KR 12000)

DAHL, Karl (1869-1942) German
£331 $526 €480 Market place (24x35cm-9x14in) s. 8-Mar-3 Arnold, Frankfurt #566

DAHL, Michael (1656-1743) Swedish
£488 $800 €732 Portrait of a gentleman, said to be Sir Henry Temple (76x63cm-30x25in) painted oval prov. 5-Feb-3 Christie's, Rockefeller NY #243/R
£3000 $4620 €4500 Portrait of Sarah Jennings (74x61cm-29x24in) oval. 25-Oct-2 Gorringes, Lewes #870
£3262 $5057 €4893 Portrait of Charles, Duke of Marlborough when Earl of Sunderland (233x145cm-92x57in) prov.lit. 3-Dec-2 Bukowskis, Stockholm #507/R est:40000-50000 (S.KR 46000)
£12000 $19920 €18000 Portrait of the Duke of Schomberg in armour, holding a baton in his right hand (130x102cm-51x40in) prov.exhib.lit. 10-Jun-3 Christie's, London #25/R est:15000-20000
£22000 $36520 €33000 Portrait of Dorothy Brudenell, countess of Westmoreland, seated in an ochre dress, in an landscape (127x112cm-50x44in) i. prov. 10-Jun-3 Christie's, London #24/R est:15000-20000
£28000 $46480 €42000 Portrait of a young gentleman in a green coat, with gold frogging, holding a bow in his left hand (77x65cm-30x26in) i. prov.exhib.lit. 10-Jun-3 Christie's, London #22/R est:7000-10000

DAHL, Michael (attrib) (1656-1743) Swedish
£1844 $2858 €2766 Portrait of young man (64x47cm-25x19in) 4-Dec-2 AB Stockholms Auktionsverk #1695/R est:20000-25000 (S.KR 26000)
£2766 $4287 €4149 Portrait of mother and two children (142x120cm-56x47in) 3-Dec-2 Bukowskis, Stockholm #508/R est:50000-60000 (S.KR 39000)
£3688 $5716 €5532 Portrait of lady (126x102cm-50x40in) 4-Dec-2 AB Stockholms Auktionsverk #1696/R est:35000-40000 (S.KR 52000)

DAHL, Olaf (1842-1895) Norwegian
£905 $1466 €1358 Landscape from Sandvigs river (36x57cm-14x22in) s.d.78 i.stretcher. 26-May-3 Grev Wedels Plass, Oslo #98/R (N.KR 10000)

DAHL, Peter (1934-) Swedish/Norwegian
£631 $984 €947 Self portrait (47x39cm-19x15in) s.d.70. 5-Nov-2 Bukowskis, Stockholm #372/R (S.KR 9000)
£771 $1203 €1157 View of a town (34x33cm-13x13in) s.d.63. 5-Nov-2 Bukowskis, Stockholm #371/R (S.KR 11000)
£772 $1243 €1158 Sawmill (50x60cm-20x24in) s.d.59. 7-May-3 AB Stockholms Auktionsverk #969/R (S.KR 10000)
£2317 $3730 €3476 Portrait (70x80cm-28x31in) s.d.75. 7-May-3 AB Stockholms Auktionsverk #1068/R est:30000-40000 (S.KR 30000)
£5019 $8081 €7529 Forest (100x80cm-39x31in) s. 7-May-3 AB Stockholms Auktionsverk #1037/R est:50000-60000 (S.KR 65000)
£15067 $23504 €22601 Winter view from Aspudden towards North (110x150cm-43x59in) s.d.1993. 6-Nov-2 AB Stockholms Auktionsverk #857/R est:100000-125000 (S.KR 215000)

Works on paper
£310 $503 €450 Figures resting in landscape (45x35cm-18x14in) s.d.80 W/C. 25-May-3 Uppsala Auktionskammare, Uppsala #280 (S.KR 4000)
£334 $540 €484 Portrait of unknown woman (24x16cm-9x6in) s. W/C. 25-May-3 Uppsala Auktionskammare, Uppsala #302 (S.KR 4300)
£340 $564 €493 Seated woman (21x17cm-8x7in) s. pencil. 16-Jun-3 Lilla Bukowskis, Stockholm #232 (S.KR 4400)
£1081 $1741 €1622 Lovers (31x21cm-12x8in) s. chl. 7-May-3 AB Stockholms Auktionsverk #967/R est:10000-12000 (S.KR 14000)
£1962 $3061 €2943 Gota cellars (65x49cm-26x19in) s. W/C. 6-Nov-2 AB Stockholms Auktionsverk #862/R est:15000-18000 (S.KR 28000)
£3042 $4806 €4563 Dancers (50x72cm-20x28in) s. W/C. 28-Apr-3 Bukowskis, Stockholm #1009/R est:25000-30000 (S.KR 40000)
£3498 $5527 €5247 Couple dancing (53x72cm-21x28in) s. W/C. 28-Apr-3 Bukowskis, Stockholm #1010/R est:25000-30000 (S.KR 46000)

DAHL, Poul (1899-?) Danish
£408 $636 €612 Female nude reclining (70x100cm-28x39in) mono. 5-Aug-2 Rasmussen, Vejle #64/R (D.KR 4800)

DAHL, Sigwald Johannes (1827-1902) Norwegian
£1044 $1671 €1566 Oxen and cart, Florence (74x110cm-29x43in) s.d.1854. 17-Mar-3 Blomqvist, Oslo #346/R (N.KR 12000)
£1840 $3000 €2760 Blue ribbon (24x33cm-9x13in) s.d.58. 11-Feb-3 Bonhams & Doyles, New York #86 est:3000-5000

DAHL, Thomas (19th C) American
Sculpture
£4304 $6800 €6456 Bust of Napoleon (81x58x188cm-32x23x74in) s. white marble pedestal prov. 26-Nov-2 Christie's, Rockefeller NY #300 est:2500-3500

DAHL-WOLFE, Louise (1895-1989) American
Photographs
£5380 $8500 €8070 Japanese bath (35x28cm-14x11in) gelatin silver print prov.lit. 22-Apr-3 Christie's, Rockefeller NY #65/R est:6000-8000
£6013 $9500 €9020 Orson Welles (26x27cm-10x11in) i.d.verso gelatin silver print prov.lit. 22-Apr-3 Christie's, Rockefeller NY #173/R est:3000-5000

DAHLBOM, Wilhelm (1855-1928) Swedish
£302 $476 €453 Summer's day (72x92cm-28x36in) s. exhib. 27-Nov-2 Falkkloos, Malmo #78013/R (S.KR 4300)

DAHLEN, Paul (1881-?) German
£428 $667 €680 Old Rhine landscape (20x30cm-8x12in) s.d.1915 board. 11-Oct-2 Winterberg, Heidelberg #993

DAHLGREN, Carl Christian (1841-1920) American
£964 $1600 €1398 Clear lake (52x77cm-20x30in) s. 11-Jun-3 Butterfields, San Francisco #4195/R est:3000-5000

DAHLMAN, Helge (1924-1979) Finnish
£377 $581 €600 Mallard (18x22cm-7x9in) s.d.70. 27-Oct-2 Bukowskis, Helsinki #150/R
£619 $1015 €860 Umbrellas (22x27cm-9x11in) s. 5-Jun-3 Hagelstam, Helsinki #994/R
£633 $1000 €1000 Munksnas Bridge (38x46cm-15x18in) s. board. 1-Dec-2 Bukowskis, Helsinki #39/R
£665 $1037 €1050 Landscape (38x46cm-15x18in) s. 12-Sep-2 Hagelstam, Helsinki #885
£719 $1179 €1100 Autumn evening, Kytaja (23x41cm-9x16in) s.d.67. 9-Feb-3 Bukowskis, Helsinki #216/R
£1013 $1600 €1600 Lady wearing blue dress (55x38cm-22x15in) s.d.1947. 30-Nov-2 Hagelstam, Helsinki #158/R est:2000
£1439 $2302 €2000 Winter (44x55cm-17x22in) s. 17-May-3 Hagelstam, Helsinki #190/R est:1800

DAHLQVIST, Karl (1900-1971) Swedish
£1825 $2884 €2738 Summer's day at Soder (104x110cm-41x43in) s.d.32. 28-Apr-3 Bukowskis, Stockholm #81/R est:10000-12000 (S.KR 24000)

DAHLSKOG, Evald (1894-1950) Swedish
£337 $545 €506 Composition (73x60cm-29x24in) s.d.1932 panel. 3-Feb-3 Lilla Bukowskis, Stockholm #627 (S.KR 4700)
£379 $584 €569 Karthago's ruins (81x100cm-32x39in) s.verso exhib. 27-Oct-2 Anders Antik, Landskrona #504/R (S.KR 5500)
£494 $776 €716 Still life. 15-Dec-2 Anders Antik, Landskrona #1130 (S.KR 7000)
£494 $776 €716 Cartage's ruins. 15-Dec-2 Anders Antik, Landskrona #1190 (S.KR 7000)
£586 $903 €879 Still life (90x52cm-35x20in) s.d.1927. 27-Oct-2 Anders Antik, Landskrona #503/R (S.KR 8500)
£1313 $2114 €1970 Storm (114x79cm-45x31in) s.d.33. 7-May-3 AB Stockholms Auktionsverk #671/R est:20000-25000 (S.KR 17000)
£6084 $9612 €9126 Canal Grande, Venice (72x92cm-28x36in) s.i.d.1920 exhib.lit. 28-Apr-3 Bukowskis, Stockholm #15/R est:60000-70000 (S.KR 80000)

Works on paper
£760 $1202 €1140 San Gimignano (46x63cm-18x25in) s.d.1920 pastel. 28-Apr-3 Bukowskis, Stockholm #23/R (S.KR 10000)

DAHLSTROM, O W (?) ?
£1250 $2000 €1875 Sailors in a boat (91x66cm-36x26in) 14-Mar-3 Douglas, South Deerfield #2
£1250 $2000 €1875 Sailors in a boat (91x66cm-36x26in) 14-Mar-3 Douglas, South Deerfield #28

DAHM, H P C (1787-1844) Danish
Works on paper
£2847 $4669 €4128 Ship's portrait Frue Birthe Cathrine (44x55cm-17x22in) s.i. go pen. 2-Jun-3 Blomqvist, Oslo #2/R est:12000-15000 (N.KR 31000)
£4040 $6626 €5858 The vessels Providentia and Osterrisoer Praie in rough seas (45x57cm-18x22in) s. gouache. 2-Jun-3 Blomqvist, Oslo #1/R est:18000-22000 (N.KR 44000)

DAHM, Helen (1878-1968) Swiss
£655 $1022 €983 Still life with geraniums (36x29cm-14x11in) s. panel. 8-Nov-2 Dobiaschofsky, Bern #167/R (S.FR 1500)
£849 $1358 €1274 Still life with vase, dish and cat (56x40cm-22x16in) behind glass. 17-Mar-3 Philippe Schuler, Zurich #4301/R est:2800-3400 (S.FR 1800)
£1087 $1685 €1631 Water carrier (72x47cm-28x19in) s. canvas on pavatex. 4-Dec-2 Koller, Zurich #163/R est:2500-3500 (S.FR 2500)
£3004 $4747 €4506 Farmstead with flower garden (63x83cm-25x33in) s. pavatex. 29-Nov-2 Falk & Falk, Zurich #499/R est:8000 (S.FR 7000)
£3396 $5434 €5094 Three nuns with lilies (102x31cm-40x12in) s. panel. 17-Mar-3 Philippe Schuler, Zurich #4510/R est:6000-8000 (S.FR 7200)

Works on paper
£365 $576 €548 Water-lilies (25x37cm-10x15in) s. pencil col pencil dr. 29-Nov-2 Zofingen, Switzerland #2841 (S.FR 850)
£926 $1491 €1343 Guelder-rose (114x68cm-45x27in) s. mixed media. 9-May-3 Dobiaschofsky, Bern #224/R (S.FR 2000)

DAHMEN, Karl-Fred (1917-1981) German
£253 $395 €400 Abstract composition (79x50cm-31x20in) s. 14-Sep-2 Weidler, Nurnberg #4464
£2949 $4571 €4600 Cathedral (95x52cm-37x20in) s. s.i.d.1955 verso. 6-Dec-2 Hauswedell & Nolte, Hamburg #91/R est:6000
£25641 $39744 €40000 Azur hour (136x115cm-54x45in) s. s.i.d.1957 sand prov. 7-Dec-2 Van Ham, Cologne #120/R est:45000

Sculpture
£1957 $3209 €2700 Object shrine in landscape (51x43x270cm-20x17x106in) s. s.i.d.Juli 73 verso cushion objects prov. 28-May-3 Lempertz, Koln #109/R est:3500

Works on paper
£1135 $1838 €1600 Aretha (40x30cm-16x12in) s. collage col pen board. 20-May-3 Dorotheum, Vienna #221/R est:1400-1600
£1603 $2484 €2500 Composition (35x25cm-14x10in) s. collage board on panel. 6-Dec-2 Hauswedell & Nolte, Hamburg #93/R est:2500
£3901 $6319 €5500 Untitled (100x81cm-39x32in) bears i. verso mixed media exhib. 24-May-3 Van Ham, Cologne #119/R est:6000

DAHMS, Paul W (1913-1988) Swedish
£253 $392 €400 Fox stalking ducks (81x120cm-32x47in) 26-Sep-2 Neumeister, Munich #2699/R
£588 $941 €900 Autumn landscape with fox and ducks being hunted (50x60cm-20x24in) s. lit. 10-Jan-3 Allgauer, Kempten #1566/R
£612 $973 €900 Wild ducks flying up out of reeds (70x100cm-28x39in) s. 21-Mar-3 Auktionhaus Georg Rehm, Augsburg #8015/R

DAHN, Walter (1954-) German
£2949 $4571 €4600 Another intimate dialogue (180x150cm-71x59in) s.i.d.1981 verso acrylic prov. 3-Dec-2 Lempertz, Koln #109/R est:6000

Sculpture
£1304 $2139 €1800 The owner of Hell (33cm-13in) mono.d.84 num.1/4 black pat.bronze Cast.Noack Berlin exhib. 28-May-3 Lempertz, Koln #110/R est:2500

Works on paper
£270 $422 €400 Pyramid (29x21cm-11x8in) s.d.1976 W/C pencil. 28-Mar-3 Ketterer, Hamburg #276/R

DAI XI (1801-1860) Chinese
Works on paper
£7724 $12203 €11586 Admiring the waterfall (33x123cm-13x48in) s.i.d.1847 ink handscroll. 28-Apr-3 Sotheby's, Hong Kong #640/R est:700000-900000 (HK.D 95000)

DAILE, C van den (19th C) ?
£1200 $1848 €1800 Tempting treat (70x91cm-28x36in) s.d.1868. 24-Oct-2 Christie's, Kensington #40/R est:800-1200

DAILLON, H (?) Belgian?
Sculpture
£1090 $1689 €1700 Aurore (78cm-31in) s.i. bronze. 3-Dec-2 Campo & Campo, Antwerp #56/R est:2000-3000

DAIMLER, Elise (1875-?) German
£755 $1177 €1200 Flowers and green jug (36x40cm-14x16in) s. board. 19-Sep-2 Dr Fritz Nagel, Stuttgart #918/R

DAIN, Michael (20th C) British
£350 $546 €525 Spanish village on an autumn evening. s.verso. 13-Apr-3 Lots Road, London #346

DAINGERFIELD, Elliott (1859-1932) American
£1687 $2700 €2446 Full moon (14x21cm-6x8in) s. i.verso panel. 16-May-3 Skinner, Boston #224/R est:2500-3500
£7317 $12000 €10976 Spirit of the canyon (69x53cm-27x21in) s. 8-Feb-3 Neal Auction Company, New Orleans #263/R est:20000-30000
£24691 $40000 €37037 Storm breaking up (77x91cm-30x36in) painted c.1912 prov.exhib.lit. 21-May-3 Sotheby's, New York #171/R est:10000-15000

DAINI, Augusto (1860-1920) Italian
£2500 $3925 €3900 Overheard message (47x64cm-19x25in) s. 23-Nov-2 Arnold, Frankfurt #701/R est:1000

DAINTREY, Adrian (1902-1988) British
£250 $388 €375 South Kensington (102x127cm-40x50in) s. s.i.verso. 4-Dec-2 Christie's, Kensington #506
£550 $858 €825 Metropolitan square (50x61cm-20x24in) init. 15-Oct-2 Bonhams, Knightsbridge #22/R
£1200 $1896 €1800 Weir on the Thames (62x75cm-24x30in) s.d.1937. 27-Nov-2 Sotheby's, Olympia #128/R est:1200-1800

DAIWAILLE, Alexander Joseph and VERBOECKHOVEN, Eugène (19th C) Dutch/Belgian
£13000 $21580 €13000 Berger et son troupeau au bord de l'etang (64x91cm-25x36in) s. 16-Jun-3 Horta, Bruxelles #120/R est:14000-16000

DAKE, Carel Lodewijk (jnr) (1886-1946) Dutch
£318 $497 €500 Indian landscape with rice fields (58x79cm-23x31in) s. board. 6-Nov-2 Vendue Huis, Gravenhage #274/R

DAKEN, Sidney Tilden (1876-1935) American
£539 $900 €782 Cattle in pastoral landscape (46x61cm-18x24in) s.i. 17-Jun-3 John Moran, Pasadena #72

DAKIN, Joseph (19/20th C) British
£350 $532 €525 Children picking flowers in a wooded glade (58x43cm-23x17in) s. 16-Aug-2 Keys, Aylsham #663/R
£1200 $1956 €1740 Wooded river landscape with a fisherman (53x81cm-21x32in) mono.i.d.1872. 17-Jul-3 Tennants, Leyburn #854/R est:900-1100

DALBERG, Ake (1910-) Swedish
£351 $554 €527 Interior scene with model (108x91cm-43x36in) s. panel. 30-Nov-2 Goteborg Auktionsverk, Sweden #526/R (S.KR 5000)

DALBY OF YORK, D (1794-1836) British
£750 $1155 €1125 Hunting scene at full cry (25x30cm-10x12in) s. board. 5-Sep-2 Morphets, Harrogate #356

DALBY OF YORK, David (1794-1836) British
£4500 $7155 €6750 Whittington, a favourite bay hunter in a stable (59x73cm-23x29in) s.i. prov. 19-Mar-3 Sotheby's, London #111/R est:4000-6000
£7586 $12138 €11000 Negro (63x76cm-25x30in) s.d.1820. 11-Mar-3 Castellana, Madrid #335/R est:15000
£8000 $12640 €12000 Jerry, winner of the 1824 Saint-Leger with Ben Smith up by post at Doncaster (58x76cm-23x30in) i. prov. 27-Nov-2 Christie's, London #45/R est:7000-10000
£9032 $14271 €14000 Arrival of the Epson Derby (51x75cm-20x30in) s.d.1821. 18-Dec-2 Castellana, Madrid #41/R est:6000

DALBY OF YORK, David (attrib) (1794-1836) British
£900 $1494 €1305 Bloomsbury, a bay racehorse (61x76cm-24x30in) 12-Jun-3 Christie's, Kensington #55/R
£1800 $2808 €2700 Hunter and rider in open landscape (61x71cm-24x28in) i.stretcher. 9-Oct-2 Woolley & Wallis, Salisbury #208/R est:2000-3000

DALBY, John (fl.1826-1853) British
£1050 $1712 €1523 Floss, a hunter in loose box (31x41cm-12x16in) s.i.d.1839. 21-Jul-3 Bonhams, Bath #80/R est:1200-1800
£3300 $5214 €4785 Huntsmen with a bay hunter in a landscape (30x38cm-12x15in) s. 23-Jul-3 Mallams, Oxford #244/R est:3500-4000
£7000 $11060 €10500 Horse drawn chaise on the road to York (30x47cm-12x19in) s. panel. 28-Nov-2 Sotheby's, London #207/R est:8000-12000

DALE, H (?) British
£520 $790 €780 Windsor Castle on the Thames (71x119cm-28x47in) s. 16-Aug-2 Keys, Aylsham #667/R

DALEN, Jan van I (fl.1632-1641) Dutch
£115108 $184173 €160000 Allegory of the four elements (179x224cm-70x88in) s.d.1653. 13-May-3 Sotheby's, Amsterdam #39/R est:20000-30000

DALEN, Willem (attrib) (?-1675) Dutch
£6000 $9420 €9000 View of Delft from the north with the Leiden ferry (59x82cm-23x32in) init. panel. 13-Dec-2 Christie's, Kensington #97/R est:8000-12000

DALENS, Dirk (attrib) (17/18th C) Dutch
£2516 $3875 €4000 Personnages sur un chemin dans un paysage de marais (39x61cm-15x24in) panel. 25-Oct-2 Tajan, Paris #85/R est:4500-5000

DALENS, Dirk III (attrib) (1688-1753) Dutch
£4810 $7792 €6975 Landscape with view of a Dutch town (66x99cm-26x39in) 26-May-3 Bukowskis, Stockholm #467/R est:40000-50000 (S.KR 62000)

D'ALESI, Hugo (1849-1906) French
£3597 $5900 €5000 Passage des troupeaux au pied de la citadelle (48x73cm-19x29in) s. 4-Jun-3 Tajan, Paris #254/R est:2000-3000

DALGLISH, William (1860-1909) British
Works on paper
£318 $500 €477 Harbour townscape with fishermen (24x34cm-9x13in) s. W/C. 10-Dec-2 Peter Webb, Auckland #155/R est:1200-1800 (NZ.D 1000)

D'ALHEIM, Jean (1840-1894) Russian
£629 $981 €1000 Southern coast with fishing boat (36x27cm-14x11in) s. prov. 19-Sep-2 Dr Fritz Nagel, Stuttgart #917/R

DALI, Louis (20th C) French?
£1090 $1700 €1635 Aling the Seine (51x61cm-20x24in) s. 20-Sep-2 Sloan, North Bethesda #386/R est:1500-2500

DALI, Salvador (1904-1989) Spanish
£2098 $3503 €3000 Gala (34x42cm-13x17in) acrylic collage tissue on photograph. 30-Jun-3 Artcurial Briest, Paris #224/R est:4000-6000
£2098 $3503 €3000 D'apres Meissonnier (41x30cm-16x12in) s. acrylic photograph. 30-Jun-3 Artcurial Briest, Paris #231/R est:6000-8000
£3497 $5839 €5000 Composition numerique (31x42cm-12x17in) acrylic. 30-Jun-3 Artcurial Briest, Paris #451/R est:6000-8000
£5594 $9343 €8000 Cupidon (25x21cm-10x8in) canvas on canvas. 30-Jun-3 Artcurial Briest, Paris #184/R est:8000-10000
£6294 $10510 €9000 Etude pour "Le Toreador Hallucinogene" (33x41cm-13x16in) acrylic collage decoupage photographic sheet exhib. 30-Jun-3 Artcurial Briest, Paris #223/R est:3000-4000
£11189 $18685 €16000 Villabertran (9x14cm-4x6in) mono. cardboard on wood exhib.lit. 30-Jun-3 Artcurial Briest, Paris #183/R est:3000-4000
£11189 $18685 €16000 Tachisme surrealiste (100x73cm-39x29in) oil W/C Indian ink cardboard on canvas exhib. 30-Jun-3 Artcurial Briest, Paris #452/R est:15000-20000
£20548 $32260 €30000 Revolver a cheveux blancs (17x11cm-7x4in) copper plate. 15-Apr-3 Laurence Calmels, Paris #4257/R
£52000 $85280 €78000 Gala (23x19cm-9x7in) s.d.1934 silver point card prov. 6-Feb-3 Christie's, London #482/R est:50000
£52000 $86840 €75400 Diamond head (61x46cm-24x18in) mono.d.1979 oil gouache ink. 25-Jun-3 Christie's, London #225/R est:25000-35000
£134615 $210000 €201923 Temple de Diane a Epheseus (22x43cm-9x17in) s. painted c.1954 prov. 7-Nov-2 Christie's, Rockefeller NY #334/R est:150000-200000
£155844 $227532 €240000 Peche aux gouaches (47x35cm-19x14in) s. cardboard. 17-Jun-2 Ansorena, Madrid #65/R
£160839 $268601 €230000 Sans titre connu comme Suenos en la playa (9x7cm-4x3in) s. mahagony panel exhib. 30-Jun-3 Artcurial Briest, Paris #6/R est:130000-180000
£251748 $420420 €360000 La plage du Llane a Cadaques (67x92cm-26x36in) s. cardboard on panel exhib.lit. 30-Jun-3 Artcurial Briest, Paris #34/R est:250000-350000
£384615 $600000 €576923 Trois femmes imitant les mouvements d'un voilier (54x65cm-21x26in) s.i.d.1940 prov.exhib.lit. 5-Nov-2 Sotheby's, New York #64/R est:600000-800000
£700000 $1148000 €1050000 Naissance du nouveau monde (43x53cm-17x21in) s.d.1942 prov.exhib.lit. 4-Feb-3 Sotheby's, London #46/R est:900000
£1200000 $1968000 €1800000 Jeune vierge autosodomisee par les cornes de sa propre chastete (40x30cm-16x12in) s.d.1954 prov.lit. 4-Feb-3 Sotheby's, London #43/R est:1800000

Photographs
£8000 $12400 €12000 Mujer con fruta (32x21cm-13x8in) s. photograph montage gouache pen. 5-Dec-2 Christie's, Kensington #152/R est:8000-12000

Prints
£2179 $3378 €3400 Artus - mythologie (40x50cm-16x20in) s. col etching. 4-Dec-2 Lempertz, Koln #635/R est:1800
£5822 $9140 €8500 Tamanoir (4x6cm-2x2in) engraving. 15-Apr-3 Laurence Calmels, Paris #4258/R
£5975 $9500 €8963 Cranes et harpe cranienne (37x30cm-15x12in) etching. 3-Mar-3 Swann Galleries, New York #48/R est:10000-15000
£6410 $10000 €9615 St George and the Dragon (46x28cm-18x11in) s.d.1947 etching edition of 250. 21-Sep-2 Rachel Davis, Shaker Heights #474/R est:8000-12000
£7547 $12000 €11321 Grasshopper child (36x29cm-14x11in) s.num.85/100 engraving. 1-May-3 Swann Galleries, New York #434/R est:10000-15000
£8333 $13000 €12500 Twelve tribes of Israel (66x50cm-26x20in) s.num.8/195 col drypoint etching 13 blue leather portfolio. 14-Oct-2 Butterfields, San Francisco #1114/R est:7000-9000
£8805 $14000 €13208 Les Caprices de Goya de Dali. s.num.39/200 col drypoint 80 portfolio. 2-May-3 Sotheby's, New York #124/R est:5000-7000
£8974 $14000 €13461 Cranes mous et harpe cranienne (37x31cm-15x12in) etching. 7-Nov-2 Swann Galleries, New York #620a/R est:12000-18000
£10063 $16000 €15095 Three plays by the Marquis de Sade (65x50cm-26x20in) s.num. col lithograph set of 25 portfolio box. 29-Apr-3 Christie's, Rockefeller NY #469/R est:8000-12000
£12579 $20000 €18869 Carmen, Michelier Lopsinger (69x52cm-27x20in) s.num.123/125 col lithograph text 25 vinyl portfolio. 2-May-3 Sotheby's, New York #120/R est:10000-14000
£14423 $22500 €21635 La divine comedie (33x27cm-13x11in) s.i. col wood engraving 100 in three volumes. 14-Oct-2 Butterfields, San Francisco #1111/R est:10000-15000

£16352 $26000 €24528 Twelve Tribes of Israel (69x54cm-27x21in) s.num. pochoir col drypoint set of 13 portfolio case. 29-Apr-3 Christie's, Rockefeller NY #470/R est:18000-25000

Sculpture

£1013 $1570 €1600 Venus a la girafe (56x27x9cm-22x11x4in) s.sig.i. silver pat.bronze Cast. Venturi Arte Bologna. 28-Sep-2 Ketterer, Hamburg #772/R

£1069 $1668 €1700 Menorah (51cm-20in) s. num.44/350 silvered metal Jerusalem marble socle. 9-Oct-2 Lombrail & Teucquam, Paris #10/R

£1258 $1950 €2000 Les Trois Graces (46x36cm-18x14in) i.num.68/150 green pat bronze plaque. 30-Oct-2 Artcurial Briest, Paris #405 est:2200-3000

£1313 $2114 €1970 Venus a la Girafe (57cm-22in) mono.num.1214/1500 polished bronze. 7-May-3 AB Stockholms Auktionsverk #1089/R est:18000-20000 (S.KR 17000)

£1402 $2186 €2103 Le cabinet antropomorphe (22cm-9in) s.num.055/330 sterling silver sold with stone socle st.f.Mibrosa. 5-Nov-2 Bukowskis, Stockholm #242b/R est:20000-22000 (S.KR 20000)

£1552 $2514 €2250 Le cabinet antropomorphe (16x22cm-6x9in) s.num.101/330 sterling silver incl. marble socle Cast Mibrosa. 25-May-3 Uppsala Auktionskammare, Uppsala #385/R est:20000-25000 (S.KR 20000)

£1646 $2567 €2600 La croix de Leibnitz (52x36cm-20x14in) s.num.25/150 green pat exec.c.1968-1970. 20-Oct-2 Charbonneaux, Paris #188 est:3000-3500

£1691 $2705 €2350 Montre molle (53cm-21in) s. bronze. 16-May-3 Lombrail & Teucquam, Paris #59/R

£1700 $2652 €2550 Venus a la girafe (56x27cm-22x11in) inscised sig. num.964/1000 silver pat. bronze. 25-Mar-3 Sotheby's, London #76/R est:2000-3000

£1709 $2666 €2700 La fleur du mal (37x19cm-15x7in) s.num.26/150 green pat. 20-Oct-2 Charbonneaux, Paris #189 est:2500-3000

£1747 $2742 €2621 The surrealist angel (44x25x6cm-17x10x2in) i. black pat.bronze Cast.Strehle. 25-Nov-2 Germann, Zurich #29/R est:4000-5000 (S.FR 4000)

£1748 $2920 €2500 Le gladiateur (16cm-6in) s. silvered bronze incl. socle. 30-Jun-3 Artcurial Briest, Paris #203/R est:3000-4000

£1748 $2920 €2500 Gala (16cm-6in) s.verso brown pat bronze Cast Valsuani cire perdue. 30-Jun-3 Artcurial Briest, Paris #213/R est:3000-4000

£1761 $2712 €2800 Jerusalem stone (52cm-20in) silver. 22-Oct-2 Campo & Campo, Antwerp #58/R

£1772 $2764 €2800 Femme dehanchee (45x33x18cm-18x13x7in) s. num.314/350 gilded brass. 31-Jul-2 Tajan, Paris #80/R est:1500-2000

£1875 $2850 €2813 Homenaje a Newton (35cm-14in) s.num.119/350 black pat bronze grained black marble socle. 3-Jul-2 Naón & Cia, Buenos Aires #551 est:3000-3500

£1887 $2906 €3000 Saint Narcissus (12cm-5in) s.d.1974 num.281/300 gold. 22-Oct-2 Durán, Madrid #1563/R

£1899 $3000 €3000 Porte-manteau Montre (63cm-25in) s.d.1971 num.141/150 glass bronze lit. 26-Nov-2 Camard, Paris #120/R

£1921 $3017 €2882 Christ (37x15x15cm-15x6x6in) i. verso gold pat.bronze Cast.C. 25-Nov-2 Germann, Zurich #109/R est:4000-5000 (S.FR 4400)

£1931 $3225 €2800 Cabinet anthropomorphique (25x23x6cm-10x9x2in) s.num.102/330-A silver bronze st.f.Foneria Mibrosa. 10-Jul-3 Artcurial Briest, Paris #245/R est:3500-4500

£2051 $3179 €3200 Surreal angel (44cm-17in) i. verso dark pat.bronze brass socle Cast.Strehle. 7-Dec-2 Ketterer, Hamburg #498/R est:2500-3000

£2069 $3310 €3000 Persistance de la Memoire (36cm-14in) s.i. green pat.bronze Cast.Camblest. 11-Mar-3 Dorotheum, Vienna #189/R est:3000-4000

£2081 $3476 €3017 La vision de l'ange (44x34x36cm-17x13x14in) s.d.1977 brown green gold pat.bronze. 24-Jun-3 Koller, Zurich #347 est:4500-6500 (S.FR 4600)

£2089 $3237 €3300 Surreal eyes (34x22x5cm-13x9x2in) s.i. verso silver pat.bronze plastic Cast.Venturi Arte. 28-Sep-2 Ketterer, Hamburg #773/R est:2800-3200

£2100 $3255 €3150 Homage to Newton (39cm-15in) s.num.155/350 bronze st.f.Camblest. 3-Dec-2 Bonhams, Knightsbridge #182/R est:1500-2500

£2152 $3357 €3400 Poisson malebranche (44cm-17in) s.num.31/150 green pat. 20-Oct-2 Charbonneaux, Paris #190/R est:2000-2500

£2152 $3357 €3400 Guitare (60x30cm-24x12in) s.num.48/150 green pat exec.c.1968-70. 20-Oct-2 Charbonneaux, Paris #191 est:3500-4000

£2400 $3744 €3600 Persistence of time (41cm-16in) s.num.305/350 green pat bronze marble base. 17-Sep-2 Bonhams, Knightsbridge #291/R est:2500-3500

£2400 $3720 €3600 Vision of angels (42cm-17in) s.num.86/350 green pat. bronze st.f.Jemelton. 3-Dec-2 Bonhams, Knightsbridge #184/R est:1800-2200

£2446 $3914 €3400 Menorah de la paix (53x32cm-21x13in) s.num. silver bronze socle. 18-May-3 Charbonneaux, Paris #223 est:3000-4000

£2448 $4087 €3500 Cygne elephant (13x14cm-5x6in) silvered pat bronze exhib. 30-Jun-3 Artcurial Briest, Paris #208/R est:2000-3000

£2448 $4087 €3500 Chevalier (38x38cm-15x15in) mono. green grey pat bronze exhib. 30-Jun-3 Artcurial Briest, Paris #212/R est:2000-3000

£2484 $4000 €3726 Jeune Trajan (11cm-4in) i.num1 18 carat gold cast 1973. 7-May-3 Sotheby's, New York #317/R est:6000-8000

£2600 $4030 €3900 St. George and the dragon (50x45cm-20x18in) num.126/350 green pat. bronze st.f.Jemelton. 3-Dec-2 Bonhams, Knightsbridge #181/R est:2800-3200

£2600 $4212 €3900 Elephant (93cm-37in) s.num.349/350 green pat. bronze resin obelisk. 20-May-3 Bonhams, Knightsbridge #174/R est:1000-1500

£2700 $4185 €4050 Profile of time (51cm-20in) s.num.337/350 brown pat. bronze st.f.Corti. 3-Dec-2 Bonhams, Knightsbridge #186/R est:2000-2500

£2715 $4534 €3937 Profil de temps (35x35cm-14x14in) s.d.1977 num.315/350 brown green pat.bronze. 24-Jun-3 Koller, Zurich #340 est:4000-6000 (S.FR 6000)

£2722 $4218 €4300 Alice au pays des merveilles (90x45x20cm-35x18x8in) s.i. green gold pat bronze brass Cast.Cera/Perseo84/Persa. 28-Sep-2 Ketterer, Hamburg #774/R est:3000-4000

£2740 $4274 €4000 Arlequin (86x48cm-34x19in) s. num.97/99 painted ceramic. 8-Apr-3 Ansorena, Madrid #932/R

£2797 $4671 €4000 John Kennedy, buste aux trombones (46cm-18in) brown pat bronze incl. socle. 30-Jun-3 Artcurial Briest, Paris #202/R est:4000-6000

£2937 $4905 €4200 Le Toreador (45cm-18in) s. num.193/500 gilded brn pat bronze incl. socle Cast Bologne. 30-Jun-3 Artcurial Briest, Paris #217/R est:4000-6000

£3000 $4650 €4500 Elephant (93cm-37in) s.num.349/350 green pat. bronze resin obelisk st.f.Camblest. 3-Dec-2 Bonhams, Knightsbridge #185/R est:3000-5000

£3200 $4928 €4800 La persistance de la memoire (37x14cm-15x6in) s.num.200/350 bronze prov.lit. 23-Oct-2 Sotheby's, Olympia #789/R est:1500-2500

£3205 $4968 €5000 Cabinet antropomorphique (31x63x20cm-12x25x8in) i. num.77/330 brown pat bronze removable drawer keys exec.1973. 6-Dec-2 Ketterer, Munich #114/R est:6000-8000

£3333 $5167 €5200 Spatial elephant (90x14x27cm-35x6x11in) i. green pat.bronze plexiglass marble socle. 7-Dec-2 Ketterer, Hamburg #497/R est:5000-7000

£3357 $5606 €4800 Edifice surrealiste (34x28x12cm-13x11x5in) s. num.29/999 verso silvered pat bronze incl. socle. 30-Jun-3 Artcurial Briest, Paris #216/R est:2000-3000

£3472 $5729 €5000 Le desir hyperrationnel (40cm-16in) s. blue glass gold bronze. 2-Jul-3 Artcurial Briest, Paris #120 est:5000-6000

£3497 $5839 €5000 La femme a la tete de rose (44cm-17in) s. num.127/350 gilded pat bronze. 30-Jun-3 Artcurial Briest, Paris #204/R est:4000-6000

£3846 $6423 €5500 Tete de Beatrice (38cm-15in) brn pat bronze gilded silvered green stones incl. socle exhib. 30-Jun-3 Artcurial Briest, Paris #206/R est:6000-8000

£4000 $6160 €6000 Venus a la girafe (56cm-22in) s.num.259/1500 bronze conceived 1973 lit. 23-Oct-2 Sotheby's, Olympia #791/R est:2000-3000

£4000 $6240 €6000 La femme en flammes (84x38cm-33x15in) inscised sig.num.182/350 silver pat. bronze. 25-Mar-3 Sotheby's, London #75/R est:4000-6000

£4196 $7007 €6000 Le Mannequin Javanais (20x32x15cm-8x13x6in) s. num.EA base gilded pat bronze exhib.lit. 30-Jun-3 Artcurial Briest, Paris #308/R est:2000-3000

£4895 $8175 €7000 Buste de dante (26cm-10in) s.d.1964 num.EA pat bronze gold exhib.lit. 30-Jun-3 Artcurial Briest, Paris #205/R est:8000-12000

£5000 $8150 €7500 Cabinet Anthromorphique (64cm-25in) s.num.148/330 bronze f.st.Foneria Mibrosa. 3-Feb-3 Bonhams, New Bond Street #78/R est:6000-8000

£5200 $8008 €7800 Cheval a la montre (56x22cm-22x9in) s.num.36/500 bronze prov.lit. 23-Oct-2 Sotheby's, Olympia #788/R est:3000-5000

£5245 $8759 €7500 Cheval a la montre molle (42x56x16cm-17x22x6in) s.num.41/350 silvered pat bronze. 30-Jun-3 Artcurial Briest, Paris #207/R est:5000-7000

£5245 $8759 €7500 Venus a la tete de rose (83x54x36cm-33x21x14in) s. gilded bronze on electricity exhib. 30-Jun-3 Artcurial Briest, Paris #306/R est:6000-8000

£5594 $9343 €8000 Masque funebre de Napoleon (22x19x28cm-9x7x11in) s. num.2/9 gilded pat bronze two parts exhib. 30-Jun-3 Artcurial Briest, Paris #303/R est:6000-8000

£	$	€	Description
£5594	$9343	€8000	Homme oiseau (20cm-8in) s. num.EA blk pat bronze Cast Valsuani cire perdue exhib. 30-Jun-3 Artcurial Briest, Paris #434/R est:10000-12000
£6500	$10335	€9750	Cabinet anthropomorphique (64cm-25in) s.num.146/330 bronze conceived 1973 st.f.Foneria Mibrosa. 20-Mar-3 Sotheby's, Olympia #194/R est:6000-8000
£6787	$11335	€9841	La venus spatiale (65x35x32cm-26x14x13in) s.d.1977 num.259/350 brown pat.bronze. 24-Jun-3 Koller, Zurich #346/R est:900-12000 (S.FR 15000)
£7500	$11550	€11250	Femme en flammes (83cm-33in) s.d.1981 num.325/350bronze st.f.Artistica Battaglia prov.lit. 23-Oct-2 Sotheby's, Olympia #793/R est:5000-7000
£7595	$11848	€12000	Venus spatiale (66x32x35cm-26x13x14in) s. verso num.66/350 brown pat.bronze gilded brass. 31-Jul-2 Tajan, Paris #66/R est:10000-12000
£7975	$12600	€12600	The woman aflame (88cm-35in) s.num.110/350 gilt bronze. 30-Nov-2 Hagelstam, Helsinki #1/R est:3500
£8993	$14388	€12500	Alice in Wonderland (93cm-37in) s.num.62/350 gilt bronze exhib. 17-May-3 Hagelstam, Helsinki #1/R est:3500
£9500	$15105	€14250	Alice in Wonderland (90cm-35in) s.d.1984 num.20/350 bronze st.f.Perseo prov.lit. 20-Mar-3 Sotheby's, Olympia #187/R est:4000-6000
£11000	$17490	€16500	St George and the dragon (46cm-18in) s.d.1984 num.157/350 bronze st.f.Perseo prov.lit. 20-Mar-3 Sotheby's, Olympia #193/R est:3000-5000
£15000	$23850	€22500	L'elephant spatial (91cm-36in) s.d.1981 num.314/350 bronze plexiglass prov.lit. 20-Mar-3 Sotheby's, Olympia #188/R est:4000-6000
£38000	$62320	€57000	Vision de l'ange (139cm-55in) s. num.2/7 green brown pat bronze exec.1977-84 lit. 4-Feb-3 Christie's, London #325/R est:60000
£38462	$64231	€55000	Cybelle (97cm-38in) s. num.1/8 green pat bronze exec.1972-1973 Cast Bologne exhib. 30-Jun-3 Artcurial Briest, Paris #30/R est:60000-80000
£39161	$65399	€56000	Venus a la girafe (156x66x23cm-61x26x9in) s. num.HC white painted bronze Cast Venturi Arte exhib.lit. 30-Jun-3 Artcurial Briest, Paris #36/R est:60000-80000
£45455	$75909	€65000	Ballerine, hommage a Margot Fonteyn ou femme a la Souris (200x45x45cm-79x18x18in) s. num.1/8 base pat bronze Cast Venturi Arte exhib. 30-Jun-3 Artcurial Briest, Paris #40/R est:80000-120000
£50000	$83500	€72500	Hommage a Terpsichore (187cm-74in) s.num.2/7 green pat. polished bronze prov.lit. 25-Jun-3 Christie's, London #202/R est:50000-70000
£52448	$87587	€75000	Le soulier de gala, objet surrealiste a fonctionnement symbolique (49cm-19in) s. num.3/8 shoe various objects executed 1932-1973 lit. 30-Jun-3 Artcurial Briest, Paris #14/R est:80000-120000
£55696	$86886	€88000	Hommage a terpsichore (187x103x55cm-74x41x22in) s. num.3/3 bronze exhib. 31-Jul-2 Tajan, Paris #62/R est:90000-120000
£55901	$90000	€83852	La noblesse du temps (154x89x70cm-61x35x28in) s.num.3/7 green gold pat. bronze cast 1984 prov.exhib.lit. 8-May-3 Christie's, Rockefeller NY #208/R est:80000-100000
£65000	$106600	€97500	Profil du temps (151x100x77cm-59x39x30in) s. num.6/7 gren polished pat bronze exec.1977-84 lit. 4-Feb-3 Christie's, London #322/R est:70000
£80000	$133600	€116000	Venus de Milo aux tiroirs (218cm-86in) s.num. green pat. bronze st.f.C. Valsuani lit. 25-Jun-3 Christie's, London #212/R est:80000-120000
£98601	$164664	€141000	Femme en flamme (176x46x56cm-69x18x22in) s. base num.EA 2/3 pat bronze Cast D'Arte Tesconi lit. 30-Jun-3 Artcurial Briest, Paris #29/R est:180000-250000
£170000	$277100	€255000	Hommage a Newton (132cm-52in) s.st.f.Valsuani num.6/8 brown gren pat bronze prov.lit. 3-Feb-3 Christie's, London #180/R est:200000
£209790	$350350	€300000	Reconstitution du buste de femme - La femme au pain (71cm-28in) s.d.1933-1977 num.2/8 painted bronze beads plastic exhib.lit. 30-Jun-3 Artcurial Briest, Paris #13/R est:180000-250000
£256410	$400000	€384615	Newton de Gala (38cm-15in) i.num.7 black pat. bronze st.f.E.Capa cast 1985 prov.lit. 5-Nov-2 Sotheby's, New York #53/R est:400000-500000

Works on paper

£280	$467	€400	Etude pour le tableau "le Crane de Zurbaran" (23x16cm-9x6in) Indian ink. 30-Jun-3 Artcurial Briest, Paris #430/R
£350	$584	€500	Etude pour "l'enigme sans fin" (23x17cm-9x7in) lead pencil htd col crayons. 30-Jun-3 Artcurial Briest, Paris #127/R
£350	$584	€500	Rhinoceros (26x18cm-10x7in) ball pen hotel headed paper. 30-Jun-3 Artcurial Briest, Paris #371/R
£350	$584	€500	Etude pour le numero de Vogue Decembre 1971 (23x25cm-9x10in) lead pencil. 30-Jun-3 Artcurial Briest, Paris #415/R
£350	$584	€500	La danse (25x16cm-10x6in) lead pencil. 30-Jun-3 Artcurial Briest, Paris #416/R
£420	$701	€600	Marie Madeleine (12x7cm-5x3in) ball pen. 30-Jun-3 Artcurial Briest, Paris #252/R
£420	$701	€600	Etude de portrait (15x11cm-6x4in) s. lead pencil. 30-Jun-3 Artcurial Briest, Paris #300/R
£420	$701	€600	Etude pour une composition cubique corpusculaire (26x21cm-10x8in) ball pen. 30-Jun-3 Artcurial Briest, Paris #319/R
£420	$701	€600	Etude de Christ (17x10cm-7x4in) ball pen felt pen. 30-Jun-3 Artcurial Briest, Paris #432/R
£490	$817	€700	Etude pour jeune vierge autosodomisee (17x24cm-7x9in) s. apocryphe lead pencil ball pen. 30-Jun-3 Artcurial Briest, Paris #253/R
£490	$817	€700	Personnages etude pour le galacidalacidesoxyribonucleicacid (27x21cm-11x8in) ball pen. 30-Jun-3 Artcurial Briest, Paris #315/R
£490	$817	€700	Etude pour le galacidalacidesoxyribonucleicacid (26x18cm-10x7in) lead pencil. 30-Jun-3 Artcurial Briest, Paris #316/R
£490	$817	€700	Etude pour le galacidalacidesoxyribonucleicacid (22x18cm-9x7in) ball pen. 30-Jun-3 Artcurial Briest, Paris #320/R
£490	$817	€700	Etude de Madonne avec ange annonciateur (26x18cm-10x7in) ball pen. 30-Jun-3 Artcurial Briest, Paris #424/R
£513	$800	€770	Elongated figure holding a staff (23x18cm-9x7in) s.indis.d.1942 ink dr. 10-Nov-2 Selkirks, St. Louis #618/R
£550	$847	€825	Sans titre (51x30cm-20x12in) s.indis.i.d.1963 pen ink frontispiece prov. 23-Oct-2 Sotheby's, Olympia #786/R
£559	$934	€800	Portrait d'Edward James (18x14cm-7x6in) lead pencil. 30-Jun-3 Artcurial Briest, Paris #138/R
£559	$934	€800	Personnages (18x17cm-7x7in) lead pencil tracing paper. 30-Jun-3 Artcurial Briest, Paris #248/R
£559	$934	€800	Etudes de formes modernes (20x11cm-8x4in) ball pen lead pencil sketches verso. 30-Jun-3 Artcurial Briest, Paris #257/R
£559	$934	€800	Sans titre, etude pour une composition cubique corpusculaire (26x21cm-10x8in) ball pen. 30-Jun-3 Artcurial Briest, Paris #318/R
£559	$934	€800	Projet d'ecusson pour le chateau de Pubol (18x13cm-7x5in) lead pencil. 30-Jun-3 Artcurial Briest, Paris #335/R
£559	$934	€800	Etude pour le portrait de Madam X (20x15cm-8x6in) lead pencil. 30-Jun-3 Artcurial Briest, Paris #421/R
£559	$934	€800	Etude pour le tableau "Dali nu en contemplation devant cinq corps" (14x11cm-6x4in) lead pencil. 30-Jun-3 Artcurial Briest, Paris #422/R
£559	$934	€800	Architecture (15x13cm-6x5in) blk ball pen. 30-Jun-3 Artcurial Briest, Paris #428/R
£629	$1051	€900	Sponge skeleton (9x6cm-4x2in) Indian ink. 30-Jun-3 Artcurial Briest, Paris #171/R
£629	$1051	€900	Etude de personnage (10x6cm-4x2in) ball pen lead pencil. 30-Jun-3 Artcurial Briest, Paris #258/R
£629	$1051	€900	Strates geologique (27x21cm-11x8in) ball pen. 30-Jun-3 Artcurial Briest, Paris #446/R
£629	$1051	€900	Etude pour "Dali nu en contemplation de cinq corps" (23x21cm-9x8in) ball pen. 30-Jun-3 Artcurial Briest, Paris #454/R
£699	$1168	€1000	Erotique no. 10 (10x7cm-4x3in) ball pen. 30-Jun-3 Artcurial Briest, Paris #96/R
£699	$1168	€1000	Etude de mise en place pour le tableau "La peche au Thon" (15x20cm-6x8in) felt pen tracing paper. 30-Jun-3 Artcurial Briest, Paris #241/R
£699	$1168	€1000	Etude de nu au Vieillard (25x21cm-10x8in) ball pen. 30-Jun-3 Artcurial Briest, Paris #259/R
£699	$1168	€1000	Spirale (15x12cm-6x5in) ball pen. 30-Jun-3 Artcurial Briest, Paris #265/R
£699	$1168	€1000	Homme torture (6x10cm-2x4in) sig. apocryphe ball pen after Bracelli. 30-Jun-3 Artcurial Briest, Paris #301/R
£699	$1168	€1000	Etude pour le galacidalacidesoxyribonucleicacid (22x18cm-9x7in) lead pencil. 30-Jun-3 Artcurial Briest, Paris #317/R
£699	$1168	€1000	Etude pour un crucifixion (26x20cm-10x8in) lead pencil ball pen. 30-Jun-3 Artcurial Briest, Paris #425/R
£699	$1168	€1000	Etude pour le tableau "Nature morte Vivante" (16x9cm-6x4in) ball pen lead pencil sketches verso. 30-Jun-3 Artcurial Briest, Paris #458/R
£769	$1285	€1100	Erotique no. 16 (10x6cm-4x2in) blue blk ball pen exhib. 30-Jun-3 Artcurial Briest, Paris #104/R
£769	$1285	€1100	Les secrets magiques (14x18cm-6x7in) Indian ink. 30-Jun-3 Artcurial Briest, Paris #162/R
£769	$1285	€1100	Dali et Gala assis sur une coquille (14x11cm-6x4in) ball pen. 30-Jun-3 Artcurial Briest, Paris #270/R
£769	$1285	€1100	Nu d'homme (17x8cm-7x3in) lead pencil. 30-Jun-3 Artcurial Briest, Paris #299/R
£769	$1285	€1100	Etude pour galacidalacidesoxyribonucleicacid (23x19cm-9x7in) ball pen. 30-Jun-3 Artcurial Briest, Paris #321/R
£769	$1285	€1100	Etude pour le tableau "Les Trois Ages" (23x17cm-9x7in) lead pencil sketches verso. 30-Jun-3 Artcurial Briest, Paris #325/R
£769	$1285	€1100	Autographe (13x25cm-5x10in) d.1939 Indian ink. 30-Jun-3 Artcurial Briest, Paris #329/R
£769	$1285	€1100	Portraits ajoutes sur un profil de Dali (8x6cm-3x2in) ball pen. 30-Jun-3 Artcurial Briest, Paris #420/R
£779	$1138	€1200	Untitled (23x32cm-9x13in) s.d.1977 ink dr. 17-Jun-2 Ansorena, Madrid #115/R

£839	$1401	€1200	Erotique no. 18 (12x7cm-5x3in) lead pencil. 30-Jun-3 Artcurial Briest, Paris #106/R
£839	$1401	€1200	Groupe de personnages (26x42cm-10x17in) chl sanguine. 30-Jun-3 Artcurial Briest, Paris #243/R
£839	$1401	€1200	Nus (13x10cm-5x4in) i. verso ball pen blk crayon. 30-Jun-3 Artcurial Briest, Paris #296/R est:3000-4000
£839	$1401	€1200	Personnage (23x10cm-9x4in) sig. apocryphe lead pencil. 30-Jun-3 Artcurial Briest, Paris #322/R est:2000-3000
£839	$1401	€1200	D'Apres Goya - La Caida (7x9cm-3x4in) col crayons. 30-Jun-3 Artcurial Briest, Paris #330/R
£839	$1401	€1200	Etude pour le portrait de Gala. Symptome rhinoceromptic galatea (22x18cm-9x7in) ball pen two. 30-Jun-3 Artcurial Briest, Paris #447/R
£909	$1518	€1300	Erotique no. 14 (6x11cm-2x4in) sanguine drawing exhib. 30-Jun-3 Artcurial Briest, Paris #102/R
£909	$1518	€1300	Erotique no. 15 (12x4cm-5x2in) lead pencil exhib. 30-Jun-3 Artcurial Briest, Paris #103/R
£909	$1518	€1300	Erotique no. 20 (8x6cm-3x2in) blk ball pen exhib. 30-Jun-3 Artcurial Briest, Paris #108/R
£909	$1518	€1300	Etude pour le "Tricorne" (27x19cm-11x7in) lead pencil. 30-Jun-3 Artcurial Briest, Paris #290/R
£909	$1518	€1300	Nu assis de face (31x30cm-12x12in) lead pencil. 30-Jun-3 Artcurial Briest, Paris #346/R
£979	$1635	€1400	Etude d'homme pour "La peche au Thon" (14x18cm-6x7in) lead pencil. 30-Jun-3 Artcurial Briest, Paris #240/R
£979	$1635	€1400	Etude puor le tableau "Les Trois Ages" (23x17cm-9x7in) i. verso lead pencil sketches verso. 30-Jun-3 Artcurial Briest, Paris #324/R
£979	$1635	€1400	Projet d'architecture pour le Parc du Chateau de Pubol (17x13cm-7x5in) s. lead pencil. 30-Jun-3 Artcurial Briest, Paris #333/R
£979	$1635	€1400	Etude pour le tableau "Apparition d'un visage et d'un compotier sur une plage" (18x22cm-7x9in) lead pencil col crayons. 30-Jun-3 Artcurial Briest, Paris #423/R
£1049	$1752	€1500	Erotique no. 11 - Penetration (11x7cm-4x3in) ball pen exhib. 30-Jun-3 Artcurial Briest, Paris #101/R est:4000-6000
£1049	$1752	€1500	La sieste du moine pour le livre "les 50 secrets magiques" (16x8cm-6x3in) Indian ink. 30-Jun-3 Artcurial Briest, Paris #147/R est:3000-4000
£1049	$1752	€1500	Les palmiers se cherissent d'un amour vehement (14x10cm-6x4in) Indian ink. 30-Jun-3 Artcurial Briest, Paris #163/R est:1000-1500
£1049	$1752	€1500	Oursin (6x9cm-2x4in) mono.d.1947 Indian ink. 30-Jun-3 Artcurial Briest, Paris #164/R est:1000-1500
£1049	$1752	€1500	Olive pour le livre "les 50 secrets magiques" (9x7cm-4x3in) s.d.1947 Indian ink. 30-Jun-3 Artcurial Briest, Paris #167/R est:1000-1500
£1049	$1752	€1500	Homme etonne (15x11cm-6x4in) lead pencil. 30-Jun-3 Artcurial Briest, Paris #276/R est:2000-3000
£1049	$1752	€1500	Homere (14x9cm-6x4in) lead pencil. 30-Jun-3 Artcurial Briest, Paris #277/R est:2000-3000
£1049	$1752	€1500	Tete d'enfant (17x8cm-7x3in) lead pencil. 30-Jun-3 Artcurial Briest, Paris #298/R est:1000-1500
£1049	$1752	€1500	Etude de Cygne-Elephant (12x11cm-5x4in) ball pen. 30-Jun-3 Artcurial Briest, Paris #364/R est:1500-2000
£1049	$1752	€1500	Etude pour l'anamorphose de nu (23x31cm-9x12in) ball pen. 30-Jun-3 Artcurial Briest, Paris #372/R
£1049	$1752	€1500	Etude de nu (23x15cm-9x6in) s. lead pencil. 30-Jun-3 Artcurial Briest, Paris #439/R est:2000-3000
£1119	$1869	€1600	Etude pour "Le lion du tableau Espana" (19x27cm-7x11in) lead pencil. 30-Jun-3 Artcurial Briest, Paris #129/R est:4000-6000
£1119	$1869	€1600	Etue pour le "Tableau le concile oecumenique" (23x20cm-9x8in) ball pen. 30-Jun-3 Artcurial Briest, Paris #244/R est:2000-3000
£1119	$1869	€1600	Architecture paranoiaque (20x18cm-8x7in) lead pencil. 30-Jun-3 Artcurial Briest, Paris #332/R est:2000-3000
£1189	$1985	€1700	Me encuentro exatame (20x24cm-8x9in) ball pen. 30-Jun-3 Artcurial Briest, Paris #256/R est:2000-3000
£1189	$1985	€1700	Etude pour le tableau "Les Trois Ages" (23x17cm-9x7in) lead pencil manuscript sketches verso. 30-Jun-3 Artcurial Briest, Paris #327/R est:1500-2000
£1237	$1991	€1856	Untitled (64x38cm-25x15in) s. ink W/C. 7-May-3 Dunbar Sloane, Auckland #69 est:500-1000 (NZ.D 3500)
£1259	$2102	€1800	Erotique no. 19 Nu de dos (11x6cm-4x2in) blk blue ball pen exhib. 30-Jun-3 Artcurial Briest, Paris #110/R est:3000-4000
£1259	$2102	€1800	Etude de tete de Nitscheen eclatee (21x21cm-8x8in) lead pencil. 30-Jun-3 Artcurial Briest, Paris #247/R est:1000-2000
£1259	$2102	€1800	Dali et Gala a la piscine de Port Lligat (28x23cm-11x9in) s.d.1975 felt pen cardboard. 30-Jun-3 Artcurial Briest, Paris #331/R est:2000-3000
£1259	$2102	€1800	Trois personnages (21x30cm-8x12in) sanguine. 30-Jun-3 Artcurial Briest, Paris #417/R est:3000-4000
£1399	$2336	€2000	Erotique no. 17 (11x6cm-4x2in) ball pen sanguine exhib. 30-Jun-3 Artcurial Briest, Paris #105/R est:3000-4000
£1399	$2336	€2000	Etude pour le tableau la Turbie, Sir James Dunn assis (28x24cm-11x9in) lead pencil on tracing paper. 30-Jun-3 Artcurial Briest, Paris #135/R est:2000-3000
£1399	$2336	€2000	Maternite (26x15cm-10x6in) lead pencil. 30-Jun-3 Artcurial Briest, Paris #136/R est:2000-3000
£1399	$2336	€2000	Regard a travers les oursins (17x22cm-7x9in) ball pen. 30-Jun-3 Artcurial Briest, Paris #153/R est:2000-3000
£1399	$2336	€2000	Sea urchin, Aristote's lantern, Aristothe's lantern (9x8cm-4x3in) Indian ink. 30-Jun-3 Artcurial Briest, Paris #159/R est:2000-3000
£1399	$2336	€2000	Hommage au rhinoceros (37x29cm-15x11in) gouache photograph. 30-Jun-3 Artcurial Briest, Paris #230/R est:3000-4000
£1399	$2336	€2000	Nu d'homme (25x20cm-10x8in) ball pen lead pencil. 30-Jun-3 Artcurial Briest, Paris #260/R est:3000-4000
£1399	$2336	€2000	Etude de main, pour le dessin "scene hysterique" (21x18cm-8x7in) ball pen. 30-Jun-3 Artcurial Briest, Paris #261/R est:3000-4000
£1399	$2336	€2000	Etude de lunettes (21x18cm-8x7in) lead pencil collage. 30-Jun-3 Artcurial Briest, Paris #269/R est:3000-4000
£1399	$2336	€2000	Nu d'homme (50x35cm-20x14in) lead pencil exhib. 30-Jun-3 Artcurial Briest, Paris #275/R est:3000-4000
£1399	$2336	€2000	Cavalier et buste (16x11cm-6x4in) s. Indian ink wash. 30-Jun-3 Artcurial Briest, Paris #278/R est:2000-3000
£1399	$2336	€2000	D'apres Bracelli (12x7cm-5x3in) sig. apocryphe Indian ink. 30-Jun-3 Artcurial Briest, Paris #294/R est:3000-4000
£1399	$2336	€2000	L'ange etude pour le galacidalacidesoxyribonucleicacid (27x21cm-11x8in) ball pen. 30-Jun-3 Artcurial Briest, Paris #312/R est:3000-4000
£1399	$2336	€2000	Buste de femme au bras allonge (25x34cm-10x13in) d.67 lead pencil. 30-Jun-3 Artcurial Briest, Paris #339/R est:2000-3000
£1399	$2336	€2000	Crane - Etude pour "Le Crane de Zurbaran" (17x27cm-7x11in) lead pencil blue paper. 30-Jun-3 Artcurial Briest, Paris #426/R est:1000-1500
£1399	$2336	€2000	Crane et architecture (20x19cm-8x7in) sig. apocryphe blk ball pen. 30-Jun-3 Artcurial Briest, Paris #427/R est:1000-1500
£1399	$2336	€2000	Etude pour "Dali en contemplation de cinq corps" (20x15cm-8x6in) lead pencil. 30-Jun-3 Artcurial Briest, Paris #441/R est:2000-3000
£1399	$2336	€2000	Etudes pour les tableaux "Nature morte Vivante" et "Le Crane de Zurbaran" (19x25cm-7x10in) ball pen. 30-Jun-3 Artcurial Briest, Paris #457/R est:3000-4000
£1413	$2276	€2120	Homage to Quedo (50x36cm-20x14in) s. ink W/C. 7-May-3 Dunbar Sloane, Auckland #67 est:500-1000 (NZ.D 4000)
£1469	$2452	€2100	Etude pour le tableau "Les Trois Ages" (17x23cm-7x9in) i. verso lead pencil drawings verso. 30-Jun-3 Artcurial Briest, Paris #326/R est:1500-2000
£1538	$2569	€2200	Erotique no. 5 arlequin nu (16x7cm-6x3in) ball pen. 30-Jun-3 Artcurial Briest, Paris #91/R est:3000-4000
£1538	$2569	€2200	Buste de femme au bras leve (26x21cm-10x8in) lead pencil. 30-Jun-3 Artcurial Briest, Paris #337/R est:3000-4000
£1538	$2569	€2200	Etudes pour les tableaux, Nature morte Vivante et Le Crane de Zurbaran (19x25cm-7x10in) ball pen two. 30-Jun-3 Artcurial Briest, Paris #456/R est:500-1000
£1700	$2635	€2550	Sans titre - elephant et cornac (29x53cm-11x21in) s.d.1971 red felt tipped pen. 5-Dec-2 Christie's, Kensington #150/R est:2000-3000
£1748	$2920	€2500	Etude pour "ll'enigme sans fin" (22x13cm-9x5in) lead pencil exhib. 30-Jun-3 Artcurial Briest, Paris #124/R est:3000-4000
£1748	$2920	€2500	Etude pour la Cene (21x28cm-8x11in) ball pen. 30-Jun-3 Artcurial Briest, Paris #133/R est:3000-4000
£1748	$2920	€2500	La couronne de lait Dalinienne, pour le livre "les 50 secrets magiques" (22x30cm-9x12in) Indian ink W/C collage strong paper. 30-Jun-3 Artcurial Briest, Paris #141/R est:2000-3000
£1748	$2920	€2500	Empreintes fleuries (30x20cm-12x8in) s. gouache on photograph. 30-Jun-3 Artcurial Briest, Paris #222/R est:3000-4000
£1748	$2920	€2500	Etude pour let projet de film avec les Marx Brothers, Horseback Salad (24x22cm-9x9in) s. lead pencil. 30-Jun-3 Artcurial Briest, Paris #362/R est:2000-3000
£1748	$2920	€2500	Fleur surrealiste (73x60cm-29x24in) s. col glass. 30-Jun-3 Artcurial Briest, Paris #465/R est:2000-3000
£1888	$3153	€2700	Etude pour la Gare de Perpignan (11x13cm-4x5in) ball pen exhib. 30-Jun-3 Artcurial Briest, Paris #455/R est:1000-2000
£1958	$3270	€2800	Nu de dos et portrait d'homme erotique (11x6cm-4x2in) ball pen blk crayon. 30-Jun-3 Artcurial Briest, Paris #92/R est:3000-4000
£1958	$3270	€2800	Erotique no. 12 (15x23cm-6x9in) ball pen lead pencil exhib. 30-Jun-3 Artcurial Briest, Paris #99/R est:6000-8000
£1958	$3270	€2800	Erotique no. 13 (10x6cm-4x2in) ball pen col crayons exhib. 30-Jun-3 Artcurial Briest, Paris #100/R est:4000-6000
£1958	$3270	€2800	Nu debout et nu allonge (25x33cm-10x13in) sanguine lead pencil. 30-Jun-3 Artcurial Briest, Paris #114/R est:4000-6000
£1958	$3270	€2800	Galacidalacidesoxyribonucleicacid (27x21cm-11x8in) blk ball pen exhib. 30-Jun-3 Artcurial Briest, Paris #314/R est:2000-3000
£1958	$3270	€2800	Decor pour Don Juan Tenorio (19x28cm-7x11in) s. ball pen htd W/C. 30-Jun-3 Artcurial Briest, Paris #363/R est:2000-3000
£2098	$3503	€3000	Erotique no. 3 (19x14cm-7x6in) lead pencil. 30-Jun-3 Artcurial Briest, Paris #88/R est:3000-4000

£2098 $3503 €3000 Erotique no. 22 - Masturbation (9x6cm-4x2in) ball pen exhib. 30-Jun-3 Artcurial Briest, Paris #107/R est:4000-6000

£2098 $3503 €3000 Nu aux jambes ecartes (27x37cm-11x15in) lead pencil. 30-Jun-3 Artcurial Briest, Paris #109/R est:4000-6000

£2098 $3503 €3000 Etude pour le tableau - Gala avec des symptomes rhynocerontiques (27x21cm-11x8in) lead pencil ball pen. 30-Jun-3 Artcurial Briest, Paris #120/R est:2000-3000

£2098 $3503 €3000 Portrait de Madame Franco (15x10cm-6x4in) lead pencil. 30-Jun-3 Artcurial Briest, Paris #137/R est:2000-3000

£2098 $3503 €3000 Personnage au parapluie et a la Bequille (18x10cm-7x4in) Indian ink. 30-Jun-3 Artcurial Briest, Paris #142/R est:4000-6000

£2098 $3503 €3000 Excellent position of a perfect painter from "les 50 secrets magiques" (19x23cm-7x9in) Indian ink. 30-Jun-3 Artcurial Briest, Paris #144/R est:4000-6000

£2098 $3503 €3000 Transformation d'un album pour enfant "petit a petit" (21x15cm-8x6in) Indian ink lead pencil fond d'impression. 30-Jun-3 Artcurial Briest, Paris #154/R est:3000-4000

£2098 $3503 €3000 Daliesque is pour le livre "les 50 secrets magiques" (15x21cm-6x8in) Indian ink. 30-Jun-3 Artcurial Briest, Paris #172/R est:2000-3000

£2098 $3503 €3000 Le gladiateur, etude pour "La peche au Thon" (13x19cm-5x7in) lead pencil Indian ink. 30-Jun-3 Artcurial Briest, Paris #239/R est:3000-4000

£2098 $3503 €3000 Epaule et Sein de Gala (28x16cm-11x6in) Indian ink htd col exhib. 30-Jun-3 Artcurial Briest, Paris #264/R est:3000-4000

£2098 $3503 €3000 Nu a la Grecque (38x12cm-15x5in) lead pencil. 30-Jun-3 Artcurial Briest, Paris #273/R est:2000-3000

£2098 $3503 €3000 Nu de face (37x27cm-15x11in) lead pencil double-sided. 30-Jun-3 Artcurial Briest, Paris #407/R est:4000-6000

£2098 $3503 €3000 Les clous. Composition (18x12cm-7x5in) s. Indian ink two. 30-Jun-3 Artcurial Briest, Paris #445/R est:2000-3000

£2120 $3413 €3180 Untitled (42x32cm-17x13in) s. ink W/C. 7-May-3 Dunbar Sloane, Auckland #68/R est:500-1000 (NZ.D 6000)

£2238 $3737 €3200 Young and adult sea-urchin (19x13cm-7x5in) Indian ink on fond d'impression. 30-Jun-3 Artcurial Briest, Paris #151/R est:2000-3000

£2238 $3737 €3200 D'apres Raphael, personnage et profil (13x14cm-5x6in) lead pencil htd white. 30-Jun-3 Artcurial Briest, Paris #251/R est:2000-3000

£2238 $3737 €3200 Architecture (25x20cm-10x8in) ball pen exhib. 30-Jun-3 Artcurial Briest, Paris #429/R est:1000-1500

£2238 $3737 €3200 Nu de face (34x27cm-13x11in) felt pen double-sided. 30-Jun-3 Artcurial Briest, Paris #448/R est:3000-4000

£2308 $3854 €3300 Carmen (12x11cm-5x4in) sig. apocryphe Indian ink wash ink. 30-Jun-3 Artcurial Briest, Paris #354/R est:6000-8000

£2378 $3971 €3400 Etude pour le tableau (11x15cm-4x6in) i. ball pen blk crayon. 30-Jun-3 Artcurial Briest, Paris #295/R est:2000-3000

£2400 $3696 €3600 Sans titre (36x26cm-14x10in) s. ballpoint pen frontispiece sold with a book prov. 23-Oct-2 Sotheby's, Olympia #787/R est:2000-3000

£2448 $4087 €3500 Etude pour le tableau (22x16cm-9x6in) indis.sig. lead pencil white gouache. 30-Jun-3 Artcurial Briest, Paris #121/R est:5000-7000

£2448 $4087 €3500 Alexandre le grand (45x31cm-18x12in) lead pencil exhib. 30-Jun-3 Artcurial Briest, Paris #250/R est:4000-6000

£2448 $4087 €3500 Decor pour le don Juan Tenorio (16x36cm-6x14in) Indian ink two sheets peeled paper. 30-Jun-3 Artcurial Briest, Paris #254/R est:2000-3000

£2448 $4087 €3500 L'ovocipede (14x11cm-6x4in) sig. apocryphe lead pencil ball pen. 30-Jun-3 Artcurial Briest, Paris #268/R est:3000-4000

£2448 $4087 €3500 Etude pour le Galacidalacidesoxyribonuclicacid (27x21cm-11x8in) ball pen exhib. 30-Jun-3 Artcurial Briest, Paris #311/R est:3000-4000

£2448 $4087 €3500 Ange aux trompettes (27x21cm-11x8in) i. blk ball pen. 30-Jun-3 Artcurial Briest, Paris #323/R est:2000-3000

£2448 $4087 €3500 Nu assis (39x28cm-15x11in) sig. apocryphe sanguine Indian ink cardboard. 30-Jun-3 Artcurial Briest, Paris #359/R est:4000-6000

£2448 $4087 €3500 Etude pour "Torero Hallucinogene" (29x44cm-11x17in) ball pen. 30-Jun-3 Artcurial Briest, Paris #443/R est:3000-5000

£2448 $4087 €3500 Sommaire (19x27cm-7x11in) s.d.1969 Indian ink. 30-Jun-3 Artcurial Briest, Paris #467/R est:4000-6000

£2453 $3826 €3680 Figure studies (21x16cm-8x6in) s. Indian ink pencil prov. 5-Nov-2 Bukowskis, Stockholm #310/R est:30000-35000 (S.KR 35000)

£2657 $4438 €3800 Etude d'yeux (15x21cm-6x8in) sanguine. 30-Jun-3 Artcurial Briest, Paris #128/R est:1500-2000

£2657 $4438 €3800 Sans titre, voiture Americaine (32x37cm-13x15in) gouache photograph collage. 30-Jun-3 Artcurial Briest, Paris #228/R est:4000-6000

£2657 $4438 €3800 Etude de personnage, rhinoceros et elephant (20x24cm-8x9in) ball pen. 30-Jun-3 Artcurial Briest, Paris #255/R est:3000-4000

£2657 $4438 €3800 Etude pour "Le Toreador Hallucinogene" (17x8cm-7x3in) gouache tracing paper exhib. 30-Jun-3 Artcurial Briest, Paris #360/R est:4000-6000

£2797 $4671 €4000 Erotique no. 7 (16x25cm-6x10in) lead pencil blue ball pen exhib. 30-Jun-3 Artcurial Briest, Paris #95/R est:5000-7000

£2797 $4671 €4000 Erotique no. 8 (25x35cm-10x14in) ball pen. 30-Jun-3 Artcurial Briest, Paris #97/R est:5000-7000

£2797 $4671 €4000 Etude pour le tableau (22x16cm-9x6in) lead pencil exhib. 30-Jun-3 Artcurial Briest, Paris #125/R est:4000-6000

£2797 $4671 €4000 Etude pour la Cene (20x24cm-8x9in) ball pen. 30-Jun-3 Artcurial Briest, Paris #132/R est:2000-3000

£2797 $4671 €4000 Etude pour la Cene, le Christ et les Apotres (10x12cm-4x5in) i. verso ball pen exhib. 30-Jun-3 Artcurial Briest, Paris #134/R est:1000-1500

£2797 $4671 €4000 L'heure de la monarchie (54x43cm-21x17in) s. lead pencil ink wash sketch verso. 30-Jun-3 Artcurial Briest, Paris #310/R est:3000-4000

£2800 $4452 €4200 Esquisse pour Veronique (30x27cm-12x11in) i. felt tip pen. 20-Mar-3 Sotheby's, Olympia #198/R est:2000-3000

£2937 $4905 €4200 La danse des Aiguilles (9x11cm-4x4in) Indian ink five in same frame. 30-Jun-3 Artcurial Briest, Paris #267/R est:5000-7000

£3147 $5255 €4500 Le coq pour le livre "les 50 secrets magiques" (11x18cm-4x7in) Indian ink fond d'impression. 30-Jun-3 Artcurial Briest, Paris #155/R est:3000-4000

£3147 $5255 €4500 Intra-atomic machine for imagination (21x10cm-8x4in) s. Indian ink fond d'impression. 30-Jun-3 Artcurial Briest, Paris #157/R est:2000-3000

£3147 $5255 €4500 Hypnotic dont! pour le livre "les 50 secrets magiques" (11x9cm-4x4in) Indian ink. 30-Jun-3 Artcurial Briest, Paris #168/R est:2000-3000

£3147 $5255 €4500 The golden section (22x14cm-9x6in) s.d.1947 Indian ink. 30-Jun-3 Artcurial Briest, Paris #170/R est:2000-3000

£3147 $5255 €4500 Etude pour "l'Ascension de Sainte Cecile" (36x20cm-14x8in) drawing on squared plastic. 30-Jun-3 Artcurial Briest, Paris #274/R est:2000-3000

£3147 $5255 €4500 Etude de nu (35x28cm-14x11in) s. chl stiff cloth. 30-Jun-3 Artcurial Briest, Paris #358/R est:7000-9000

£3147 $5255 €4500 Les trois graces (75x57cm-30x22in) s.i.d.1974 lead pencil. 30-Jun-3 Artcurial Briest, Paris #453/R est:6000-8000

£3147 $5255 €4500 L'iris (73x51cm-29x20in) s. col glass. 30-Jun-3 Artcurial Briest, Paris #466/R est:2000-3000

£3217 $5372 €4600 Etude pour le tableau "La Guerre esthetique" (10x10cm-4x4in) i. verso lead pencil sketches verso. 30-Jun-3 Artcurial Briest, Paris #328/R est:2000-3000

£3357 $5606 €4800 Apparition d'une infante de Velasquez au sommet d'un temple Hindou (23x17cm-9x7in) gouache photograph exhib. 30-Jun-3 Artcurial Briest, Paris #234/R est:5000-7000

£3497 $5839 €5000 Gala (11x9cm-4x4in) s. lead pencil exhib. 30-Jun-3 Artcurial Briest, Paris #262/R est:6000-8000

£3497 $5839 €5000 Nu, bras leve (68x43cm-27x17in) s. i.verso lead pencil. 30-Jun-3 Artcurial Briest, Paris #357/R est:4000-6000

£3497 $5839 €5000 Maquette Cadillac (18x24cm-7x9in) W/C. 30-Jun-3 Artcurial Briest, Paris #374/R est:3000-4000

£3636 $6073 €5200 Erotique no. 6 (18x15cm-7x6in) Indian ink exhib. 30-Jun-3 Artcurial Briest, Paris #93/R est:6000-8000

£3700 $5883 €5550 Esquisse pour floris (23x31cm-9x12in) s.i.d.1960 ballpoint pen. 20-Mar-3 Sotheby's, Olympia #197/R est:2000-3000

£3846 $6423 €5500 La danseuse (24x16cm-9x6in) Indian ink wash exhib. 30-Jun-3 Artcurial Briest, Paris #122/R est:5000-7000

£3846 $6423 €5500 Etude pour "le Toreador Hallucinogene" (21x9cm-8x4in) gouache Indian ink. 30-Jun-3 Artcurial Briest, Paris #173/R est:6000-8000

£3846 $6423 €5500 Etude de portrait d'homme et scene erotiques (29x40cm-11x16in) ball pen htd col crayons. 30-Jun-3 Artcurial Briest, Paris #266/R est:5000-7000

£3846 $6423 €5500 Composition aux oiseaux (42x42cm-17x17in) s. W/C gouache. 30-Jun-3 Artcurial Briest, Paris #343/R est:6000-8000

£3846 $6423 €5500 Composition aux soleils (42x42cm-17x17in) s. W/C gouache. 30-Jun-3 Artcurial Briest, Paris #345/R est:6000-8000

£3947 $6394 €6000 Eclatement cranien (14x10cm-6x4in) ink dr envelope. 22-Jan-3 Tajan, Paris #219/R est:7000-9000

£4000 $6200 €6000 Femme et cheval (23x28cm-9x11in) s.i.d.1968 pen ink two sheet. 5-Dec-2 Christie's, Kensington #154/R est:4000-6000

£4056 $6773 €5800 Les apotres (35x46cm-14x18in) s. ink wash Indian ink. 30-Jun-3 Artcurial Briest, Paris #334/R est:3000-4000

£4196 $7007 €6000 Etudes pour le tableau - twist dans l'atelier de Velasquez (27x21cm-11x8in) drawings five crayon one ball pen six exhib. 30-Jun-3 Artcurial Briest, Paris #38/R est:8000-12000

£4196 $7007 €6000 Unusual shadows from "les 50 secrets magiques" (16x9cm-6x4in) mono.i.s.d.1947 Indian ink. 30-Jun-3 Artcurial Briest, Paris #149/R est:5000-7000

£4196 $7007 €6000 Nu agenouille (55x41cm-22x16in) s. lead pencil gold spray. 30-Jun-3 Artcurial Briest, Paris #347/R est:8000-10000

£4403	$6824	€7000	Cavalier et personnages (33x26cm-13x10in) s. blue ink exec.c.1962. 30-Oct-2 Artcurial Briest, Paris #253/R est:7000-9000
£4545	$7591	€6500	Pour le livre "les 50 secrets magiques" (15x10cm-6x4in) s. Indian ink traces wash fond d'impression. 30-Jun-3 Artcurial Briest, Paris #166/R est:3000-4000
£4545	$7591	€6500	Etude pour "L'heure de la Monarchie" plafond du Palais Albeniz de Monjuic, Barcelone (39x51cm-15x20in) s. lead pencil. 30-Jun-3 Artcurial Briest, Paris #291/R est:6000-8000
£4795	$7527	€7000	Le docteur et son assistante (47x35cm-19x14in) s.d. orange felt tip pencil. 21-Apr-3 Rabourdin & Choppin de Janvry, Paris #125/R est:8500-9500
£4895	$8175	€7000	Etudes pour le tableau - twist dans l'atelier de Velasquez (27x21cm-11x8in) ink ball pen lead pencil sanguine nine. 30-Jun-3 Artcurial Briest, Paris #39/R est:10000-15000
£4895	$8175	€7000	Monogramme Galasalvadordali (28x34cm-11x13in) Indian ink exhib. 30-Jun-3 Artcurial Briest, Paris #130/R est:6000-8000
£4895	$8175	€7000	Plate XV, Star-Polyhedra after Leonardo (14x23cm-6x9in) s.d.1947 Indian ink fond d'impression. 30-Jun-3 Artcurial Briest, Paris #161/R est:3000-4000
£4895	$8175	€7000	La peche au thon (21x28cm-8x11in) gouache collage photograph exhib. 30-Jun-3 Artcurial Briest, Paris #236/R est:10000-12000
£4895	$8175	€7000	Etude pour "le portrait de Velasquez" (30x23cm-12x9in) s.d.1974 crayon. 30-Jun-3 Artcurial Briest, Paris #245/R est:5000-7000
£5245	$8759	€7500	Etude pour le tableau (22x17cm-9x7in) col crayons Indian ink. 30-Jun-3 Artcurial Briest, Paris #126/R est:6000-8000
£5245	$8759	€7500	Dalinien manner to paint the finest details from "les 50 secrets magiques" (21x22cm-8x9in) s. Indian ink. 30-Jun-3 Artcurial Briest, Paris #148/R est:5000-7000
£5245	$8759	€7500	Hidden faces (25x17cm-10x7in) htd Indian ink on photograph. 30-Jun-3 Artcurial Briest, Paris #225/R est:10000-15000
£5245	$8759	€7500	Composition aux fleches (42x42cm-17x17in) s. W/C gouache. 30-Jun-3 Artcurial Briest, Paris #342/R est:6000-8000
£5594	$9343	€8000	The way to wash abdomen (9x18cm-4x7in) s.d.1947 Indian ink. 30-Jun-3 Artcurial Briest, Paris #160/R est:4000-6000
£5594	$9343	€8000	Le sommeil (30x39cm-12x15in) decoupage collage htd gouache on photographic sheet exhib. 30-Jun-3 Artcurial Briest, Paris #218/R est:5000-7000
£5594	$9343	€8000	Composition aux yeux (42x42cm-17x17in) s. W/C gouache. 30-Jun-3 Artcurial Briest, Paris #340/R est:6000-8000
£5594	$9343	€8000	Composition a l'etoile de mer (48x48cm-19x19in) s. W/C gouache. 30-Jun-3 Artcurial Briest, Paris #341/R est:6000-8000
£5734	$9576	€8200	Tete de Beatrice (40x46cm-16x18in) chl blotting paper exhib. 30-Jun-3 Artcurial Briest, Paris #249/R est:4000-6000
£5734	$9576	€8200	Galacidalacidesoxyribonucleicacid (28x35cm-11x14in) ball pen sketches verso. 30-Jun-3 Artcurial Briest, Paris #313/R est:4000-6000
£5944	$9927	€8500	The ideal studio built after a Icosahedron (20x20cm-8x8in) st.sig. Indian ink printed plank. 30-Jun-3 Artcurial Briest, Paris #158/R est:4000-6000
£6000	$9540	€9000	Heaume de chevalier (27x19cm-11x7in) s.i. pen ink W/C gold paint exec.c.1967 prov. 20-Mar-3 Sotheby's, Olympia #201/R est:7000-9000
£6294	$10510	€9000	Variation autour de la gare de Perpignan (24x32cm-9x13in) gouache photograph executed 1965-1966 exhib. 30-Jun-3 Artcurial Briest, Paris #235/R est:8000-12000
£6410	$10000	€9615	Happening with Salvador Dali (48x34cm-19x13in) s.d.1966 ink collage prov. 14-Oct-2 Butterfields, San Francisco #2022/R est:30000-50000
£6619	$10855	€9200	Composition surrealiste (21x32cm-8x13in) s.d. W/C ink pastel exhib. 4-Jun-3 Marc Kohn, Paris #52/R est:9000-12000
£6643	$11094	€9500	Composition aux guitares (42x42cm-17x17in) s. W/C gouache. 30-Jun-3 Artcurial Briest, Paris #344/R est:8000-12000
£6835	$10935	€9500	Erotic composition (19x17cm-7x7in) bears i. pencil. 15-May-3 Neumeister, Munich #240/R est:8000-10000
£6918	$11000	€10377	Imagination (23x22cm-9x9in) s. pen ink. 3-Mar-3 Swann Galleries, New York #49/R est:12000-18000
£6993	$11678	€10000	Le regne du mou, le regne du dur (20x9cm-8x4in) s.d.1946 Indian ink. 30-Jun-3 Artcurial Briest, Paris #146/R est:3000-4000
£6993	$11678	€10000	Gala lisant, etude pour un vitrail (54x54cm-21x21in) s. Indian ink. 30-Jun-3 Artcurial Briest, Paris #373/R est:6000-8000
£7089	$11200	€11200	Figures et composition (43x30cm-17x12in) s. ink W/C. 29-Nov-2 Drouot Estimations, Paris #87/R
£7343	$12262	€10500	Macbeth (18x14cm-7x6in) s.i.d.1946 gouache Indian ink collage fond d'impression. 30-Jun-3 Artcurial Briest, Paris #181/R est:6000-8000
£7692	$12846	€11000	Etude de tete eclatee d'apres Leonard De Vinci (22x17cm-9x7in) Indian ink ball pen lead pencil on rodhoid exhib. 30-Jun-3 Artcurial Briest, Paris #131/R est:4000-6000
£7692	$12846	€11000	Nu, le bras et la jambe leves (57x78cm-22x31in) s.d.1972 lead pencil. 30-Jun-3 Artcurial Briest, Paris #272/R est:6000-8000
£7692	$12846	€11000	Nu allonge de dos (59x89cm-23x35in) s.d.1968 lead pencil exhib. 30-Jun-3 Artcurial Briest, Paris #414/R est:15000-20000
£8000	$12640	€12000	Queen (31x20cm 12x8in) s. gouache collage. 3-Apr-3 Christie's, Kensington #143/R est:12000
£8000	$12640	€12000	King (33x21cm-13x8in) s. gouache collage. 3-Apr-3 Christie's, Kensington #142/R est:12000
£8392	$14014	€12000	Nu allonge de dos (59x89cm-23x35in) s.d.1976 lead pencil exhib. 30-Jun-3 Artcurial Briest, Paris #98/R est:10000-15000
£8392	$14014	€12000	Reve provoque par un repas d'oursins pour le livre "les 50 secrets magiques" (13x22cm-5x9in) mono.i. Indian ink. 30-Jun-3 Artcurial Briest, Paris #143/R est:4000-6000
£8392	$14014	€12000	Flesh wheel barrow pour le livre "les 50 secrets magiques" (15x9cm-6x4in) s. Indian ink. 30-Jun-3 Artcurial Briest, Paris #145/R est:6000-8000
£8392	$14014	€12000	Les 50 secrets (22x15cm-9x6in) Indian ink fond d'impression. 30-Jun-3 Artcurial Briest, Paris #169/R est:3000-4000
£8392	$14014	€12000	Colon et Lull, projet pour le hall du Musee de Figueras (40x51cm-16x20in) s. apocryphe gouache W/C chl cardboard. 30-Jun-3 Artcurial Briest, Paris #179/R est:15000-20000
£8392	$14014	€12000	Couple et nu allonge (57x78cm-22x31in) sig. apocryphe i.d.1968 lead pencil. 30-Jun-3 Artcurial Briest, Paris #271/R est:6000-8000
£8741	$14598	€12500	The eye glass of the painter (16x16cm-6x6in) s. Indian ink. 30-Jun-3 Artcurial Briest, Paris #150/R est:5000-7000
£8741	$14598	€12500	L'Angelus (25x29cm-10x11in) s. i.verso gouache photograph exhib. 30-Jun-3 Artcurial Briest, Paris #233/R est:6000-8000
£9091	$15182	€13000	Costume de l'an 2000 (47x35cm-19x14in) s.d.1966 gouache W/C exhib. 30-Jun-3 Artcurial Briest, Paris #178/R est:15000-20000
£9091	$15182	€13000	Couverts a poisson (18x24cm-7x9in) s.d.1959 i.verso chl gouache cardboard sketches verso exhib. 30-Jun-3 Artcurial Briest, Paris #351/R est:10000-15000
£9790	$16350	€14000	Museo Dali, maquette pour panneau publicitaire du musee de figueras (26x49cm-10x19in) W/C gouache lead pencil cardboard. 30-Jun-3 Artcurial Briest, Paris #180/R est:10000-15000
£9790	$16350	€14000	L'as de carreau (53x36cm-21x14in) s. gouache felt pen. 30-Jun-3 Artcurial Briest, Paris #198/R est:20000-30000
£9790	$16350	€14000	Le filet du pecheur etude pour "La peche au Thon" (57x76cm-22x30in) s.d.1967 Indian ink exhib. 30-Jun-3 Artcurial Briest, Paris #238/R est:12000-15000
£9790	$16350	€14000	Le Pere Lucas, Meunier (45x32cm-18x13in) s. W/C gouache felt cardboard c.1958-1959 exhib. 30-Jun-3 Artcurial Briest, Paris #279/R est:15000-20000
£10000	$15400	€15000	Cavalier a la Brosse (18x13cm-7x5in) s.i.d.1955 ballpoint pen folded sheets. 22-Oct-2 Sotheby's, London #185/R est:10000-15000
£10490	$17517	€15000	Saint-Jean de la Croix (17x9cm-7x4in) s.d.1947 Indian ink exhib. 30-Jun-3 Artcurial Briest, Paris #246/R est:4000-6000
£10490	$17517	€15000	La dame a la lumiere (33x23cm-13x9in) s.d.1958-69 sanguine lead pencil exhib. 30-Jun-3 Artcurial Briest, Paris #348/R est:25000-35000
£11189	$18685	€16000	L'homme labyrinthe (20x28cm-8x11in) W/C Indian ink exhib. 30-Jun-3 Artcurial Briest, Paris #26/R est:15000-20000
£11189	$18685	€16000	Romulus et Remus pour le livre "les 50 secrets magiques" (15x10cm-6x4in) s. Indian ink fond d'impression. 30-Jun-3 Artcurial Briest, Paris #165/R est:4000-6000
£11538	$18000	€17307	Statue et homme dormant (40x28cm-16x11in) s. pencil. 18-Sep-2 Swann Galleries, New York #50/R est:25000-35000
£11538	$19269	€16500	L'Alguazil (41x31cm-16x12in) s. W/C Indian ink felt pen cardboard c.1958-1959 exhib. 30-Jun-3 Artcurial Briest, Paris #283/R est:20000-30000
£11888	$19853	€17000	La soeur de Dali et sa poupee (47x29cm-19x11in) d.1923 pastel. 30-Jun-3 Artcurial Briest, Paris #350/R est:5000-7000
£12587	$21021	€18000	Dahlia rapax (49x36cm-19x14in) s.i.d.1967 W/C gouache felt pen exhib. 30-Jun-3 Artcurial Briest, Paris #177/R est:25000-30000
£12587	$21021	€18000	La Corregidora, elle qui aurait aime etre religieuse (45x32cm-18x13in) s.d.1959 W/C gouache felt pen cardboard exhib. 30-Jun-3 Artcurial Briest, Paris #284/R est:20000-30000
£12587	$21021	€18000	1805, Les Pyrenees autre muraille de Chine (45x32cm-18x13in) s.d.1958 W/C Indian ink felt pen cardboard exhib. 30-Jun-3 Artcurial Briest, Paris #285/R est:20000-25000
£12587	$21021	€18000	La maison surrealiste (25x34cm-10x13in) s.d.1949 sketches verso. 30-Jun-3 Artcurial Briest, Paris #410/R est:5000-7000
£12587	$21021	€18000	Sigismond enchaine (28x21cm-11x8in) s.d.1962 Indian ink ball pen cardboard exhib. 30-Jun-3 Artcurial Briest, Paris #449/R est:6000-8000

£13287 $22189 €19000 Kniphofia aphrodisiaca (56x38cm-22x15in) s.d.1967 gouache felt pen exhib. 30-Jun-3 Artcurial Briest, Paris #175/R est:25000-30000
£13287 $22189 €19000 Allium chrisophi pilique pubescentes aux bequilles (56x39cm-22x15in) s.d.1967 W/C felt pen exhib. 30-Jun-3 Artcurial Briest, Paris #174/R est:25000-30000
£13287 $22189 €19000 Etude pour "La peche au Thon" (37x49cm-15x19in) ball pen col crayons paper on cardboard exhib. 30-Jun-3 Artcurial Briest, Paris #242/R est:6000-8000
£13287 $22189 €19000 Pinona et Liviana, les Anesses du Meunier et de la Meunier (41x32cm-16x13in) s.d.1958 W/C Indian ink felt pen cardboard exhib. 30-Jun-3 Artcurial Briest, Paris #280/R est:20000-30000
£13986 $23357 €20000 C'est une statue de l'Antiquite Hellenique (45x32cm-18x13in) s. W/C felt pen cardboard c.1958-1959 exhib. 30-Jun-3 Artcurial Briest, Paris #282/R est:18000-25000
£14000 $22120 €21000 Illustration pour la Sainte Bible (50x34cm-20x13in) s.d.1964 pen ink W/C gouache collage. 3-Apr-3 Christie's, Kensington #138/R est:18000
£14110 $23000 €21165 Classical scene (41x76cm-16x30in) s.d.1956 India ink wash pen pencil on board. 12-Feb-3 Sotheby's, New York #91/R est:25000-35000
£14685 $24524 €21000 Le triomphe de Cesar (20x25cm-8x10in) s.i.d.1946 Indian ink exhib. 30-Jun-3 Artcurial Briest, Paris #140/R est:8000-12000
£14685 $24524 €21000 Madonne a l'enfant (22x13cm-9x5in) s.d.1947 Indian ink exhib. 30-Jun-3 Artcurial Briest, Paris #152/R est:6000-8000
£15000 $23700 €22500 Chevalier (31x46cm-12x18in) s.i. pen ink. 3-Apr-3 Christie's, Kensington #147/R est:12000
£15000 $23700 €22500 Gluttony (43x30cm-17x12in) s.d.1950 W/C gouache. 3-Apr-3 Christie's, Kensington #148/R est:20000
£15064 $23349 €23500 Grotte invertebree (23x14cm-9x6in) i.verso gouache exec.1935 prov.exhib. 7-Dec-2 Cornette de St.Cyr, Paris #49/R est:30000
£15827 $25324 €22000 La chute d'Icare (27x20cm-11x8in) s.d.1933 Indian ink pencil double-sided prov. 15-May-3 Neumeister, Munich #239/R est:18000-20000
£15827 $25324 €22000 From: Comte de Lautreament - Chants de Maldoror (28x21cm-11x8in) s. pencil Indian ink prov. 15-May-3 Neumeister, Munich #238/R est:12000-14000
£16783 $28028 €24000 L'atelier imaginaire (20x21cm-8x8in) s.d.1949 W/C Indian ink exhib. 30-Jun-3 Artcurial Briest, Paris #156/R est:10000-15000
£17483 $29196 €25000 The wood of Birnam (25x17cm-10x7in) mono.d.1932 Indian ink exhib. 30-Jun-3 Artcurial Briest, Paris #139/R est:10000-15000
£17483 $29196 €25000 Cycle systematique de conferences surrealistes (70x50cm-28x20in) s. gouache collage c.1935-1936. 30-Jun-3 Artcurial Briest, Paris #352/R est:35000-45000
£18000 $30060 €27000 El caballo y el caballero esqueletico (37x26cm-15x10in) s. pen pencil exec 1977 prov. 26-Jun-3 Christie's, London #441/R est:18000-25000
£20979 $35035 €30000 Les tortues pour le livre - Les diners de gala (33x50cm-13x20in) s. Indian ink W/C. 30-Jun-3 Artcurial Briest, Paris #15/R est:25000-35000
£20979 $35035 €30000 La Sena Frasquita a la recherche de Lucas (40x30cm-16x12in) s. W/C Indian ink felt pen cardboard c.1958-1959 exhib. 30-Jun-3 Artcurial Briest, Paris #286/R est:20000-25000
£20979 $35035 €30000 L'Anesse, L'Eveque, La Meuniere Frasquita et le Meunier Lucas (45x32cm-18x13in) s.d.1958 W/C Indian ink felt pen cardboard exhib. 30-Jun-3 Artcurial Briest, Paris #287/R est:20000-25000
£21739 $35000 €32609 L'Eglise (51x76cm-20x30in) s.d.1950 pen red ink pencil on card prov. 7-May-3 Sotheby's, New York #322/R est:20000-30000
£22028 $36787 €31500 Les chanoines (43x30cm-17x12in) s.d.1959 W/C Indian ink felt pen cardboard exhib. 30-Jun-3 Artcurial Briest, Paris #21/R est:20000-30000
£22378 $37371 €32000 La Corrigedora Mercedes (45x32cm-18x13in) s.d.1958 W/C felt pen cardboard exhib. 30-Jun-3 Artcurial Briest, Paris #2/R est:25000-35000
£23000 $36340 €34500 Elephant spatiale (37x25cm-15x10in) s.d.1966 pencil pen ink W/C acrylic. 3-Apr-3 Christie's, Kensington #137/R est:15000
£25175 $42042 €36000 La meuniere et l'Alcade (43x30cm-17x12in) s.d.1959 W/C India ink felt pen cardboard exhib. 30-Jun-3 Artcurial Briest, Paris #1/R est:20000-30000
£25641 $40000 €38462 Creation de Eve Rendre du sommeil de 'homme la nature vivante reddoublee (30x24cm-12x9in) s.i.d.1950 pen ink sanguine W/C prov.exhib. 6-Nov-2 Sotheby's, New York #276/R est:50000-70000
£25874 $43210 €37000 Le meunier Lucas dans le costume du corregidor (49x34cm-19x13in) s. W/C Indian ink felt cardboard c.1958-1959 exhib. 30-Jun-3 Artcurial Briest, Paris #22/R est:25000-35000
£26573 $44378 €38000 La meuniere frasquita (41x32cm-16x13in) s.d.1958 W/C Indian ink felt pen cardboard exhib. 30-Jun-3 Artcurial Briest, Paris #19/R est:25000-35000
£26573 $44378 €38000 Le corregidor Doneugenio de Zuniga et son Alguazil Garduna (44x29cm-17x11in) s.d.1958 W/C Indian ink felt pen cardboard exhib. 30-Jun-3 Artcurial Briest, Paris #23/R est:25000-35000
£26573 $44378 €38000 Le filtre de l'amour, Tristan et Iseult (61x61cm-24x24in) s.d.1973 paint collage panel exhib. 30-Jun-3 Artcurial Briest, Paris #32/R est:40000-60000
£26923 $42000 €40385 Projet pour une conference surrealiste (46x50cm-18x20in) s. gouache black paper on board executed c.1937 prov. 7-Nov-2 Christie's, Rockefeller NY #143/R est:30000-40000
£28671 $47881 €41000 La Meuniere Frasquita (41x31cm-16x12in) s.d.1959 W/C felt pen ball pen cardboard exhib. 30-Jun-3 Artcurial Briest, Paris #3/R est:25000-35000
£28671 $47881 €41000 Roma a Cadaques (41x47cm-16x19in) s.d.1934 W/C Indian ink exhib. 30-Jun-3 Artcurial Briest, Paris #4/R est:25000-30000
£30000 $49200 €45000 Reve de Venus (49x35cm-19x14in) st.mono. gouache brush ink exec.1939. 6-Feb-3 Christie's, London #511/R est:30000
£30070 $50217 €43000 Composition surrealiste, mannequin javanais, connu aussi comme hommage a quevedo (24x18cm-9x7in) s.d.1934 Indian ink panel exhib. 30-Jun-3 Artcurial Briest, Paris #5/R est:50000-70000
£31469 $52552 €45000 La mort du taureau (30x40cm-12x16in) s.i.d.1966 Indian ink felt pen on fond d'impression. 30-Jun-3 Artcurial Briest, Paris #24/R est:18000-22000
£32867 $54888 €47000 Le cavalier de l'apocalypse (18x17cm-7x7in) s.d.1943 W/C Indian ink exhib. 30-Jun-3 Artcurial Briest, Paris #16/R est:20000-30000
£33333 $52000 €50000 Biblia sacra (50x34cm-20x13in) s.d.1964 gouache oil W/C lit. 7-Nov-2 Christie's, Rockefeller NY #149/R est:40000-60000
£34615 $53654 €54000 Marie, l'egyptienne (92x63cm-36x25in) s.d.1963 gouache w ink prov.exhib. 7-Dec-2 Cornette de St.Cyr, Paris #50/R est:40000-60000
£34965 $58392 €50000 Cycle systematique de conferences surrealistes (78x50cm-31x20in) s. gouache collage exhib. 30-Jun-3 Artcurial Briest, Paris #353/R est:45000-65000
£36364 $60727 €52000 Dada, surrealism and their heritage (95x63cm-37x25in) s.d.1968 W/C Indian ink wash col crayons collage exhib. 30-Jun-3 Artcurial Briest, Paris #12/R est:40000-60000
£38000 $63460 €57000 Le Roi Soleil (55x44cm-22x17in) s.d.1971 gouache W/C pen ink prov. 26-Jun-3 Christie's, London #444/R est:35000-45000
£40559 $67734 €58000 Autoportrait d'un tres grand dessinateur admirateur d'ingres, l'oeil de Salvador Dali (32x25cm-13x10in) s.d.1943 lead pencil cardboard exhib. 30-Jun-3 Artcurial Briest, Paris #17/R est:25000-35000
£40881 $63365 €65000 Mostra oggetto da virgilio (27x40cm-11x16in) s.d.1969 W/C Indian ink chl pencil gold felt-pen double-sided. 5-Oct-2 De Vuyst, Lokeren #488/R
£42000 $68880 €63000 Spellbound (15x20cm-6x8in) i. pen bbrush ink over pencil prov.lit. 5-Feb-3 Sotheby's, London #196/R est:35000
£43357 $72406 €62000 Nu a la fenetre (77x57cm-30x22in) s.d.1970 lead pencil W/C wash exhib. 30-Jun-3 Artcurial Briest, Paris #25/R est:35000-45000
£45000 $75150 €67500 Lady Godiva (57x42cm-22x17in) mono.d.1971 gouache W/C pen ink exec 1971 prov. 26-Jun-3 Christie's, London #442/R est:25000-35000
£50000 $83500 €72500 Interpretation paranoiaque critique de la charite d'apes Saint Augustin (40x32cm-16x13in) s.i.d.1959 pen brush ink wash collage prov.lit. 24-Jun-3 Sotheby's, London #246/R est:40000-60000
£59441 $99266 €85000 Le concile oecumenique connu aussi comme archeveque et pelerins apres le concil (76x102cm-30x40in) s.i.d.1960 W/C Indian ink exhib. 30-Jun-3 Artcurial Briest, Paris #8/R est:45000-65000
£62937 $105105 €90000 Portrait de Harpo Marx avec girafes en feu (62x48cm-24x19in) s.d.1937 W/C lead pencil exhib. 30-Jun-3 Artcurial Briest, Paris #7/R est:70000-100000
£62937 $105105 €90000 Le rhinoceros, hommage a Albrecht Durer (58x76cm-23x30in) s.d.1968 gouache pen exhib. 30-Jun-3 Artcurial Briest, Paris #28/R est:60000-80000
£71329 $119119 €102000 Le petit tigre hallucinogene (52x60cm-20x24in) s.d.1963 apocryphe gouache cardboard exhib. 30-Jun-3 Artcurial Briest, Paris #18/R est:100000-150000
£80000 $130400 €120000 Visage aux fourmis (24x13cm-9x5in) gouache ink exec.c.1936 prov.lit. 3-Feb-3 Christie's, London #158/R est:70000
£92000 $153640 €133400 Infanta velazquena (94x62cm-37x24in) s.i.d.1961 gouache brush ink ball point pen prov.exhib. 24-Jun-3 Sotheby's, London #242/R est:75000-95000

£100000 $167000 €150000 Femme avec papillons (55x30cm-22x12in) s.d.1954 W/C. 26-Jun-3 Christie's, London #443/R est:80000-120000
£136986 $213699 €200000 Melancolie extatique des chiens, gateuse comme une vertigineuse descente en ski (14x9cm-6x4in) i. s.i.verso collage gouache card prov.exhib.lit. 14-Apr-3 Laurence Calmels, Paris #4017/R est:80000

DALI, Salvador (attrib) (1904-1989) Spanish
Works on paper
£22378 $37371 €32000 Etude pour le tableau - le peche originel (48x63cm-19x25in) s.i.d.1941 lead pencil Indian ink. 30-Jun-3 Artcurial Briest, Paris #9/R est:20000-30000

DALIFARD, Raymond (1901-1976) French
£1600 $2528 €2400 Provencal landscape (56x47cm-22x19in) s. board. 27-Nov-2 Sotheby's, Olympia #303/R est:400-600

DALIPHARD, Edouard (1833-1877) French
£903 $1435 €1300 Paysage au ruisseau (25x33cm-10x13in) s.d.1868. 30-Apr-3 Tajan, Paris #95
£1348 $2250 €1900 Bord de riviere (40x28cm-16x11in) s. 20-Jun-3 Rieunier, Paris #34/R est:1500

DALL, Hans (1862-1920) Danish
£559 $894 €839 Two children playing by large trees in bloom (45x68cm-18x27in) s. 16-Mar-3 Hindemae, Ullerslev #373/R (D.KR 6000)

DALLAIRE, Jean Guy (1943-) Canadian
Sculpture
£1282 $1987 €2000 Life is fragile (53x12x12cm-21x5x5in) s.i.d.1980 brown pat.bronze marble socle. 7-Dec-2 Ketterer, Hamburg #704/R est:2500-2800

DALLAIRE, Jean Philippe (1916-1965) Canadian
£6173 $9568 €9260 Buche alpine (45x54cm-18x21in) s. board prov. 3-Dec-2 Joyner, Toronto #122/R est:25000-30000 (C.D 15000)
£6996 $10844 €10494 CAVALIER. le cheval de l'etable ronde (20x25cm-8x10in) s. board painted June 1954 prov. 3-Dec-2 Joyner, Toronto #130/R est:10000-12000 (C.D 17000)
£9333 $15307 €14000 Calcul lunaire (85x65cm-33x26in) s.i.d.1957. 3-Jun-3 Joyner, Toronto #79/R est:15000-20000 (C.D 21000)
£11789 $18508 €17684 Painting (50x65cm-20x26in) s. s.i.d.1963 verso prov. 12-Dec-2 Iegor de Saint Hippolyte, Montreal #23 (C.D 29000)
£18930 $29342 €28395 Still life (37x50cm-15x20in) s.d.1953 i.verso board prov. 3-Dec-2 Joyner, Toronto #89/R est:15000-20000 (C.D 46000)
Works on paper
£407 $638 €611 Riviere (48x61cm-19x24in) s. W/C. 12-Dec-2 Iegor de Saint Hippolyte, Montreal #24 (C.D 1000)
£1475 $2302 €2213 Nature morte au soleil (9x14cm-4x6in) s.d.57 gouache W/C. 10-Sep-2 Iegor de Saint Hippolyte, Montreal #26 (C.D 3600)
£2444 $4009 €3666 Fantaisie (25x24cm-10x9in) s.d.58 W/C gouache. 3-Jun-3 Joyner, Toronto #2/R est:3000-4000 (C.D 5500)
£3024 $4778 €4536 Les convives (14x23cm-6x9in) s.i.d.1947 s.d.verso gouache prov.lit. 18-Nov-2 Sotheby's, Toronto #74/R est:7000-9000 (C.D 7500)
£3556 $5831 €5334 Le guignol (25x19cm-10x7in) s.d.62 gouache prov. 3-Jun-3 Joyner, Toronto #161/R est:8000-10000 (C.D 8000)
£4000 $6560 €6000 Two figures in the sun (27x17cm-11x7in) s.d.46 gouache. 3-Jun-3 Joyner, Toronto #127/R est:8000-12000 (C.D 9000)
£4527 $7016 €6791 Fencer (17x22cm-7x9in) s.d.1952 gouache. 3-Dec-2 Joyner, Toronto #174/R est:12000-15000 (C.D 11000)
£6584 $10206 €9876 La petanque (45x60cm-18x24in) s.d.61-62 W/C. 3-Dec-2 Joyner, Toronto #157/R est:25000-30000 (C.D 16000)
£7556 $12391 €11334 Two figures (25x23cm-10x9in) s.d.59 gouache. 3-Jun-3 Joyner, Toronto #169/R est:4000-6000 (C.D 17000)
£20179 $32287 €30269 Le collaborateur (66x53cm-26x21in) s.i. s.d.1946 verso gouache on board prov.exhib.lit. 15-May-3 Heffel, Vancouver #63/R est:35000-45000 (C.D 45000)

DALL'AVA, Augustine (1950-) Australian/French
Sculpture
£1600 $2576 €2400 If only Carl knew (121x103x38cm-48x41x15in) painted wood metal stone wire prov. 6-May-3 Christie's, Melbourne #239 est:1500-2500 (A.D 4000)

DALLEAS, Jacques (1910-1997) French
£272 $433 €400 Vase brise. paper. 24-Mar-3 Rieunier, Paris #23
£306 $487 €450 Etude de vases (28x20cm-11x8in) s. 24-Mar-3 Rieunier, Paris #27/R
£306 $487 €450 Pinede (54x65cm-21x26in) s. paper. 24-Mar-3 Rieunier, Paris #26/R
£306 $487 €450 Usines a Longwy (19x27cm-7x11in) cardboard on canvas. 24-Mar-3 Rieunier, Paris #125
£340 $541 €500 Canard dans la neige (33x41cm-13x16in) s. painted c.1940. 24-Mar-3 Rieunier, Paris #5/R
£340 $541 €500 Composition (27x41cm-11x16in) s. painted c.1964. 24-Mar-3 Rieunier, Paris #28/R
£340 $541 €500 Paysage (25x21cm-10x8in) s. paper. 24-Mar-3 Rieunier, Paris #54
£340 $541 €500 Composition aux flacons (41x24cm-16x9in) s. 24-Mar-3 Rieunier, Paris #98/R
£408 $649 €600 Bord de lac (23x30cm-9x12in) paper. 24-Mar-3 Rieunier, Paris #107
£476 $757 €700 Nature morte a la raie (45x55cm-18x22in) s. painted c.1965. 24-Mar-3 Rieunier, Paris #55/R
£476 $757 €700 Ecorche. s.d.1942 panel. 24-Mar-3 Rieunier, Paris #9/R
£476 $757 €700 Paysage irrationnel (23x14cm-9x6in) s.d.66 paper. 24-Mar-3 Rieunier, Paris #70/R
£476 $757 €700 Nature morte a l'artichaut (46x61cm-18x24in) painted 1980. 24-Mar-3 Rieunier, Paris #120
£544 $865 €800 Composition au vase (29x20cm-11x8in) s. paper. 24-Mar-3 Rieunier, Paris #77/R
£680 $1082 €1000 Composition au clair de lune (32x49cm-13x19in) canvas on panel exhib. 24-Mar-3 Rieunier, Paris #59/R
£680 $1082 €1000 Composition au poron cubisante (24x41cm-9x16in) s. 24-Mar-3 Rieunier, Paris #88
£748 $1190 €1100 Avannt les labours a Courteilles (66x81cm-26x32in) painted 1955. 24-Mar-3 Rieunier, Paris #19
£748 $1190 €1100 Etude de vase (65x54cm-26x21in) s.d.69. 24-Mar-3 Rieunier, Paris #66/R
£748 $1190 €1100 La Dordogne a Courtebotte (24x33cm-9x13in) painted c.1980. 24-Mar-3 Rieunier, Paris #113
£816 $1298 €1200 Vase (65x54cm-26x21in) s. 24-Mar-3 Rieunier, Paris #63
£884 $1406 €1300 Vue de port (40x80cm-16x31in) s. 24-Mar-3 Rieunier, Paris #123
£1020 $1622 €1500 Nature morte a la raie (54x65cm-21x26in) s. 24-Mar-3 Rieunier, Paris #50/R
£1020 $1622 €1500 Chevremont (40x80cm-16x31in) 24-Mar-3 Rieunier, Paris #104/R
£1224 $1947 €1800 Moissons a Courteilles (54x76cm-21x30in) s.d.55 verso panel. 24-Mar-3 Rieunier, Paris #18/R
£1497 $2380 €2200 Vue de Tillieres vers Verneuil (73x116cm-29x46in) s. 24-Mar-3 Rieunier, Paris #64/R

DALLEVES, Raphy (1878-1940) Swiss
Works on paper
£10435 $16174 €15653 Portrait of girl in traditional dress (58x46cm-23x18in) s.d.1924 mixed media. 9-Dec-2 Philippe Schuler, Zurich #3530/R est:4000-6000 (S.FR 24000)
£21459 $33906 €32189 Jeune fille de Vex (112x49cm-44x19in) s.d.1906 W/C lit. 26-Nov-2 Phillips, Zurich #16/R est:18000-25000 (S.FR 50000)

DALLIN, Cyrus Edwin (1861-1944) American
Sculpture
£6918 $11000 €10377 Appeal to the Great spirit (23cm-9in) i.d.1913 brown pat. bronze. 4-Mar-3 Christie's, Rockefeller NY #95/R est:6000-8000
£10127 $16000 €15191 Scout (56x58cm-22x23in) bronze. 15-Nov-2 Du Mouchelle, Detroit #2010/R est:18000-22000

DALLIN, Cyrus Edwin (attrib) (1861-1944) American
Sculpture
£1132 $1743 €1800 Red Indian on horseback (47x49x29cm-19x19x11in) s. bronze green stone socle. 22-Oct-2 Wiener Kunst Auktionen, Vienna #1055/R est:300-1000

DALLIN, Norman (1948-) Canadian
£339 $539 €509 Plant and fruit bowl (56x51cm-22x20in) s. oil on paper. 23-Mar-3 Hodgins, Calgary #7/R (C.D 800)

DALLINGER VON DALLING, Alexander Johann (1783-1844) Austrian
£816 $1298 €1200 Landscape with bull (29x37cm-11x15in) s.d.1826. 25-Feb-3 Dorotheum, Vienna #112
£3797 $6000 €6000 Grazing scene (47x39cm-19x15in) s. panel. 28-Nov-2 Dorotheum, Vienna #180/R est:5500-6000

DALL'OCA BIANCA, Angelo (1858-1942) Italian
£2041 $3245 €3000 Portrait of woman (50x34cm-20x13in) s. i.verso cardboard. 18-Mar-3 Finarte, Milan #78/R
£2313 $3678 €3400 Sailing on the lake (49x35cm-19x14in) s. 18-Mar-3 Finarte, Milan #112/R
£4422 $7031 €6500 Portrait of young woman (48x34cm-19x13in) s. cardboard. 18-Mar-3 Finarte, Milan #121/R

Works on paper
£408 $649 €600 Portrait of girl (29x22cm-11x9in) s. pencil. 18-Mar-3 Finarte, Milan #113/R
£476 $757 €700 Portrait of man in profile (35x24cm-14x9in) s. pencil. 18-Mar-3 Finarte, Milan #118/R
£476 $757 €700 Portrait of lady with hat (28x20cm-11x8in) s. pencil. 18-Mar-3 Finarte, Milan #117/R
£578 $919 €850 Portrait of woman (27x21cm-11x8in) s. pencil. 18-Mar-3 Finarte, Milan #114/R
£816 $1298 €1200 Portrait of Matilda Olivieri (21x18cm-8x7in) s. pencil. 18-Mar-3 Finarte, Milan #120/R
£1701 $2704 €2500 Portrait of woman in profile (26x19cm-10x7in) s. pencil. 18-Mar-3 Finarte, Milan #119/R

DALL'OLIO, Luca (1958-) Italian
£438 $701 €670 Pink light wrapping the earth (50x70cm-20x28in) s.d.2002 s.i.d.verso. 4-Jan-3 Meeting Art, Vercelli #159

DALMATIAN SCHOOL (15th C) European
£13423 $21611 €20000 Madonna and Child and Crucifixion (43x19cm-17x7in) tempera gold panel lit. 19-Feb-3 Semenzato, Venice #17/R est:22000

DALMBERT, Daniel (1918-) French
£288 $460 €400 Nature morte au violon (60x81cm-24x32in) s.d.verso. 18-May-3 Eric Pillon, Calais #145/R

D'ALOISIO, Aniello (1775-1855) Italian
£4000 $6320 €5800 San Carlo's Theatre, Naples (15x23cm-6x9in) tempera paper. 3-Apr-3 Porro, Milan #59/R est:8000
£26207 $41407 €38000 Naples Duomo, interior (164x115cm-65x45in) s. lit. 3-Apr-3 Porro, Milan #55/R est:40000-50000

DALOU, Aime Jules (1838-1902) French
Sculpture
£993 $1619 €1500 Maternite (51cm-20in) s. Sevres biscuit. 3-Feb-3 Camard, Paris #235
£1000 $1560 €1500 Resting labourer (13cm-5in) s. brown pat bronze. 9-Apr-3 Sotheby's, London #214/R est:1200-1500
£1000 $1590 €1500 Bineur retroussant sa manche droite (15cm-6in) s.num.5 brown pat bronze st.f.Susse. 29-Apr-3 Sotheby's, Olympia #101/R est:1000-1500
£1000 $1590 €1500 Ramasseuse de fagots (10cm-4in) s.st.f.Susse green black pat bronze. 29-Apr-3 Sotheby's, Olympia #103/R est:1200-1500
£1007 $1621 €1500 Homme allant au travail, pelle sur l'epaule (14cm-6in) num.148 green brown pat bronze Cast Susse. 23-Feb-3 Lesieur & Le Bars, Le Havre #32
£1007 $1621 €1500 Terrassier levant sa pelle (14cm-6in) num.118 green brown pat bronze Cast Susse. 23-Feb-3 Lesieur & Le Bars, Le Havre #33/R
£1100 $1749 €1650 Ramasseusse de foin. s.num.5 brown pat bronze st.f.Susse. 29-Apr-3 Sotheby's, Olympia #104/R est:1000-1500
£1100 $1749 €1650 Pavementeur (15cm-6in) s.st.f.Susse brown pat bronze. 29-Apr-3 Sotheby's, Olympia #106/R est:1200-1500
£1100 $1749 €1650 Terrassier levant sa pelle horizontalement (13cm-5in) s.num.2 green brown pat bronze st.f.Susse. 29-Apr-3 Sotheby's, Olympia #108/R est:1000-1500
£1111 $1833 €1600 Travaux des champs (22x18cm-9x7in) s. brown pat bronze bas relief Cast A.A. Hebrard. 1-Jul-3 Rossini, Paris #49
£1200 $1908 €1800 Terrassier (9cm-4in) s.st.f.Susse brown pat bronze. 29-Apr-3 Sotheby's, Olympia #98/R est:1200-1800
£1200 $1956 €1740 Bust of a young boy (26cm-10in) s. stoneware. 15-Jul-3 Sotheby's, Olympia #97/R est:1200-1600
£1300 $2028 €1950 Woman carrying straw (13cm-5in) s.st.f.Susse brown pat bronze. 9-Apr-3 Sotheby's, London #218/R est:1000-1200
£1300 $2067 €1950 Batteur de faux (12cm-5in) s.num.2 green brown pat bronze st.f.Susse. 29-Apr-3 Sotheby's, Olympia #109/R est:1500-2000
£1400 $2184 €2100 Woman picking potatoes (8cm-3in) s.st.f.Susse brown pat bronze. 9-Apr-3 Sotheby's, London #215/R est:1000-1500
£1400 $2184 €2100 Woman carrying water (11cm-4in) s.st.f.Susse brown pat bronze. 9-Apr-3 Sotheby's, London #217/R est:1000-1200
£1400 $2226 €2100 Terassier s'appuyant sur sa pelle (19cm-7in) s.st.f.Susse brown pat bronze. 29-Apr-3 Sotheby's, Olympia #100/R est:1200-1500
£1400 $2226 €2100 Dans la forge (21cm-8in) s.num.8 green black pat bronze st.f.Susse. 29-Apr-3 Sotheby's, Olympia #111/R est:1500-2000
£1500 $2340 €2250 Woman carrying firewood (10cm-4in) s.st.f.Susse brown pat bronze. 9-Apr-3 Sotheby's, London #216/R est:800-1200
£1727 $2763 €2400 Le miroir casse, nu assis (14x12x7cm-6x5x3in) s. bronze Cast Susse. 13-May-3 Palais de Beaux Arts, Brussels #181/R est:1000-1500
£2200 $3498 €3300 Femme nue surprise (21cm-8in) s.st.num.9 brown pat bronze. 29-Apr-3 Sotheby's, Olympia #112/R est:1500-2000
£2781 $4534 €4200 Le terrassier (44cm-17in) brown pat bronze Cast Susse. 16-Feb-3 Mercier & Cie, Lille #196/R est:4200-4500
£4516 $7000 €6774 Angel of Death (30cm-12in) s. brown pat. bronze i.f.Hebrard prov.exhib.lit. 29-Oct-2 Sotheby's, New York #211/R est:4000-6000
£5000 $7800 €7500 Head of sleeping infant (26cm-10in) s.st.f.A A Hebrard brown pat bronze marble plinth. 9-Apr-3 Sotheby's, London #220/R est:3000-5000
£6090 $9622 €9500 Les chatiments (36x26cm-14x10in) s.st.f.Susse bas relief pat bronze prov.exhib. 18-Nov-2 Tajan, Paris #46/R est:4600-6000
£6452 $10000 €9678 Charity (34cm-13in) s. black bronze st.f.Hebrard prov.exhib. 29-Oct-2 Sotheby's, New York #212/R est:6000-8000
£6500 $10140 €9750 Le grand paysan (60cm-24in) s.st.f.Susse green brown pat bronze lit. 5-Nov-2 Sotheby's, London #206/R est:5000-7000
£6500 $10855 €9425 Study for the figure of the Republic from 'The Triumph of the Republic' (50cm-20in) s. dk brown pat bronze incl white marble base st.f.Hebrard. 8-Jul-3 Sotheby's, London #235/R est:7000-9000
£7000 $10920 €10500 Truth acknowledged (33x29cm-13x11in) s.st.f.Susse brown pat bronze. 9-Apr-3 Sotheby's, London #219/R est:4000-6000
£11000 $17270 €16500 La charite - Homage to carpe aux's Notre Dame du Saint Cordon (35cm-14in) s.num.C-9 black pat. bronze prov.lit. 10-Dec-2 Sotheby's, London #153/R est:8000-12000
£15000 $23400 €22500 Labour's child from the Triumph of the Republic (45x26cm-18x10in) s.st.f.A A Hebrard brown pat bronze lit. 9-Apr-3 Sotheby's, London #221/R est:18000-25000
£19000 $31730 €27550 Study of a male nude from the 'Triumph of Silenus' (42cm-17in) s.i. dk brown pat bronze st.f.Hebrard. 8-Jul-3 Sotheby's, London #236/R est:15000-20000
£44000 $68640 €66000 Bather, called before the bath (54cm-21in) s.num.B-3 brown black pat bronze wood plinth st.f.A.A.Hebrard. 5-Nov-2 Sotheby's, London #208/R est:25000-35000

DALSGAARD, Christen (1824-1907) Danish
£258 $393 €387 Religious scene (39x52cm-15x20in) 27-Aug-2 Rasmussen, Copenhagen #1946/R (D.KR 3000)
£372 $592 €558 Elisabeth greeting Mary (28x25cm-11x10in) init. 5-Mar-3 Rasmussen, Copenhagen #1782/R (D.KR 4000)
£420 $667 €630 Boat at water's edge (31x24cm-12x9in) init.d.October 1951. 5-May-3 Rasmussen, Vejle #720/R (D.KR 4500)
£1420 $2358 €2059 A chat on the heath (37x47cm-15x19in) init.d.1866. 12-Jun-3 Kunsthallen, Copenhagen #334/R est:15000 (D.KR 15000)
£3828 $6201 €5551 Young girl waiting for her boyfriend (69x53cm-27x21in) s.i.d.1874 exhib. 26-May-3 Rasmussen, Copenhagen #1169/R est:40000 (D.KR 40000)

DALSGAARD, Christen (attrib) (1824-1907) Danish
£258 $407 €387 Elisabeth paying homage to Maria (28x25cm-11x10in) 13-Nov-2 Kunsthallen, Copenhagen #67/R (D.KR 3000)
£818 $1244 €1227 Ditch with wild flowers and weeds (27x36cm-11x14in) with init. 27-Aug-2 Rasmussen, Copenhagen #1829/R (D.KR 9500)

DALSGAARD, Sven (1914-1999) Danish
£325 $514 €488 Certificate (40x30cm-16x12in) s. d.1970 verso painting stones gold leaf silver exhib.lit. 1-Apr-3 Rasmussen, Copenhagen #292/R (D.KR 3500)
£325 $514 €488 12.3 kilo (30x30cm-12x12in) s.d.1970 exhib.lit. 1-Apr-3 Rasmussen, Copenhagen #336/R (D.KR 3500)
£390 $617 €585 Happy people II (40x40cm-16x16in) s.d.1960 exhib.lit. 1-Apr-3 Rasmussen, Copenhagen #315/R (D.KR 4200)
£524 $817 €786 Sven Dalsgaard: Composition with poetry (65x50cm-26x20in) s.d.August 1946. 23-Sep-2 Rasmussen, Vejle #2417/R (D.KR 6200)
£689 $1068 €1034 SituaSDtion 2-1-67 (64x96cm-25x38in) s.d.1967 oil with stuck on bows. 4-Dec-2 Kunsthallen, Copenhagen #44/R (D.KR 8000)
£720 $1116 €1080 The horse (37x50cm-15x20in) s.d.1956 prov. 1-Oct-2 Rasmussen, Copenhagen #180/R (D.KR 8500)
£775 $1202 €1163 The Japanese machine (65x42cm-26x17in) s. prov. 4-Dec-2 Kunsthallen, Copenhagen #116/R (D.KR 9000)
£1117 $1777 €1676 Cape Farewell (122x93cm-48x37in) s.d.1959 masonite. 10-Mar-3 Rasmussen, Vejle #677 est:12000-15000 (D.KR 12000)
£1170 $1918 €1755 Kiss to Sarajevo (72x72cm-28x28in) s.d.16.8.1993 varnish metal handles crayon acrylic. 27-May-3 Museumsbygningen, Copenhagen #545/R est:12000-15000 (D.KR 12000)
£1206 $1869 €1809 Meeting at 7 o'clock (54x65cm-21x26in) s.d.1964 exhib. 4-Dec-2 Kunsthallen, Copenhagen #135/R est:15000 (D.KR 14000)
£2534 $4156 €3801 Occasional meeting with the old (98x63cm-39x25in) s.d.maj 1944 i.d.1944 verso prov.exhib.lit. 27-May-3 Museumsbygningen, Copenhagen #542/R est:25000-30000 (D.KR 26000)
£3216 $5275 €4824 The night is burning (102x65cm-40x26in) s.d.19.12.54 - 24.1.55 i.verso prov.exhib.lit. 27-May-3 Museumsbygningen, Copenhagen #540/R est:25000-30000 (D.KR 33000)

Sculpture
£1866 $2966 €2799 The Three Sisters (250cm-98in) sculpture in three parts sold with photo exhib. 29-Apr-3 Kunsthallen, Copenhagen #184/R est:30000 (D.KR 20000)

Works on paper
£333 $532 €500 All beginnings are (60x60cm-24x24in) s.d.1991 verso mixed media panel. 13-Jan-3 Rasmussen, Vejle #298 (D.KR 3800)
£651 $1028 €977 Emballage II (28x36cm-11x14in) s.d.1966 verso mixed media. 1-Apr-3 Rasmussen, Copenhagen #297/R (D.KR 7000)
£653 $1038 €980 Souvenir No.1. Rubber. s.i.d.17-7-76 pencil two. 29-Apr-3 Kunsthallen, Copenhagen #136/R (D.KR 7000)

DALTON, Ernest Alfred (1887-?) Canadian
£206 $319 €309 Country road, winter (60x75cm-24x30in) s. canvasboard. 3-Dec-2 Joyner, Toronto #452 (C.D 500)
£489 $802 €734 Autumn in Muskoka (60x75cm-24x30in) s. canvasboard. 3-Jun-3 Joyner, Toronto #346/R est:1500-2000 (C.D 1100)

DALVIT, Oskar (1911-1975) Swiss
£401 $642 €602 Composition (112x65cm-44x26in) s. i.d. verso exhib. 17-Mar-3 Philippe Schuler, Zurich #4516 (S.FR 850)
£419 $611 €629 Morning prelude (59x49cm-23x19in) s.d.1947 i. verso canvas on board. 17-Jun-2 Philippe Schuler, Zurich #4265 (S.FR 950)
£613 $981 €920 Fragment (65x72cm-26x28in) s.d. i. verso. 17-Mar-3 Philippe Schuler, Zurich #4515/R (S.FR 1300)
£699 $1090 €1049 Meditation sur la croix I (101x81cm-40x32in) s.d.58 i.verso. 8-Nov-2 Dobiaschofsky, Bern #240/R (S.FR 1600)

Works on paper
£420 $689 €630 Vehicle (30x34cm-12x13in) s.d.1948 gouache prov. 3-Jun-3 Sotheby's, Olympia #279/R

DALY, Kathleen (1898-1995) Canadian
£964 $1513 €1446 Indian portrait, Montagaris Tribe (60x53cm-24x21in) s.i. exhib. 25-Nov-2 Hodgins, Calgary #34/R est:2500-3000 (C.D 2400)

DALY, Matthew A (1860-1937) American
£818 $1300 €1227 Stream in early autumn (61x76cm-24x30in) s.d. 2-Mar-3 Toomey, Oak Park #678/R

DAM VAN ISSELT, Lucie van (1871-1949) Dutch
£3947 $6395 €6000 Meizoentjes in een kommetje (24x25cm-9x10in) s. plywood. 21-Jan-3 Christie's, Amsterdam #248/R est:2000-3000

DAM, Jan van (1857-?) Dutch
£1690 $2721 €2400 Churchgoers in front of St Petrus church in Leiden (117x83cm-46x33in) s.d.1903. 7-May-3 Vendue Huis, Gravenhage #569/R est:2500-3000
£2420 $3727 €3800 Putti disporting with vines, grapes and Bacchus (114x84cm-45x33in) s. three. 3-Sep-2 Christie's, Amsterdam #72/R est:1000-1500

D'AMARO, Valentina (1966-) Italian
£577 $894 €900 Modern still life I (59x70cm-23x28in) s.d.1999 verso. 4-Dec-2 Finarte, Milan #464/R

DAMBERG, Alexander Konstantinovitch (1843-?) Finnish
£1712 $2671 €2500 Guitar player (78x54cm-31x21in) s.d.1917. 10-Apr-3 Dorotheum, Vienna #132/R est:3200-3600

DAMBERGER, Josef (1867-1951) German
£304 $474 €450 Girl knitting (40x31cm-16x12in) s. panel. 26-Mar-3 Hugo Ruef, Munich #89
£629 $981 €1000 Peasant and peasant woman (40x36cm-16x14in) s. panel prov. 19-Sep-2 Dr Fritz Nagel, Stuttgart #919/R

DAMBEZA, Léon (1865-?) French
£256 $403 €400 La gardienne de moutons au bord de l'eau (16x22cm-6x9in) s. cardboard. 16-Dec-2 Millon & Associes, Paris #152

DAMERON, E (19th C) Continental

Works on paper
£918 $1422 €1450 Portrait d'Orientale (74x58cm-29x23in) s. pastel. 29-Sep-2 Eric Pillon, Calais #74/R

DAMERON, Émile Charles (1848-1908) French
£1203 $1900 €1900 Gardien de troupeau (38x55cm-15x22in) s. 29-Nov-2 Drouot Estimations, Paris #63

DAMGAARD-SORENSEN, Henning (1928-) Danish
£593 $919 €890 Composition (70x100cm-28x39in) s.d.1988-89 verso prov. 1-Oct-2 Rasmussen, Copenhagen #5/R (D.KR 7000)

DAMIAN, Horia (20th C) Rumanian
£943 $1462 €1500 Le colisee blanc (72x123cm-28x48in) s.d.1988 i.verso white bas relief paint wood. 30-Oct-2 Artcurial Briest, Paris #662 est:2000-2500

DAMIANI, Jorge (1931-) Italian
£1094 $1750 €1641 Night scene (73x60cm-29x24in) s.d.86. 5-Jan-3 Galleria Y Remates, Montevideo #119/R

Works on paper
£1813 $2900 €2720 House by the sea (74x93cm-29x37in) s.d.78 collage on canvas. 5-Jan-3 Galleria Y Remates, Montevideo #118/R

DAMIANO, Bernard (1926-) ?
£408 $649 €600 Femme a la bougie (116x89cm-46x35in) s. mono.i.d.1988 verso. 24-Mar-3 Claude Boisgirard, Paris #183
£408 $649 €600 Bon Aventura (97x128cm-38x50in) s. mono.i.verso. 24-Mar-3 Claude Boisgirard, Paris #184
£452 $714 €700 Village (114x146cm-45x57in) s. 17-Dec-2 Gioffredo, Nice #10/R
£566 $877 €900 Autorttrato (92x73cm-36x29in) s.i.d.1968 verso. 30-Oct-2 Artcurial Briest, Paris #663

DAMIEN, Joseph (1879-1973) Belgian
£458 $737 €650 The dance (50x40cm-20x16in) s. oval. 12-May-3 Bernaerts, Antwerp #687/R
£504 $806 €700 Vase fleuri (55x70cm-22x28in) s. 19-May-3 Horta, Bruxelles #310
£1013 $1580 €1600 Sous la caresse des derniers rayons de soleil (70x80cm-28x31in) s. 16-Sep-2 Horta, Bruxelles #461
£1096 $1710 €1600 Jeune femme au bassin a poisson (52cm-20in circular) s. canvas on panel. 14-Apr-3 Horta, Bruxelles #155 est:1500-2000

DAMIN, Georges (?) French
£541 $843 €800 Rue a Lyon (46x61cm-18x24in) s. 30-Mar-3 Anaf, Lyon #352

DAMIOLI, Aldo (1952-) Italian
£4577 $7599 €6500 Venezia New York (70x90cm-28x35in) s.i.d.1997 verso acrylic. 10-Jun-3 Finarte Semenzato, Milan #359/R est:2800-3500

DAMIS Y CORTES, Joaquin (19th C) Spanish
£353 $557 €550 Portrait of girl (47x36cm-19x14in) oval. 14-Nov-2 Arte, Seville #328/R
£1026 $1621 €1600 Young woman in a garden (77x57cm-30x22in) s.i.d.1879. 14-Nov-2 Arte, Seville #327/R

DAMISCH, Gunter (1958-) Austrian
£609 $962 €950 Oval world (30x40cm-12x16in) s.d.89. 12-Nov-2 Dorotheum, Vienna #291/R
£897 $1434 €1300 Head (70x40cm-28x16in) s.d.89 verso. 11-Mar-3 Dorotheum, Vienna #261/R
£993 $1619 €1500 Untitled (45x30cm-18x12in) 28-Jan-3 Dorotheum, Vienna #273/R est:900-1200
£1159 $1901 €1600 Figure with animal (65x50cm-26x20in) 27-May-3 Wiener Kunst Auktionen, Vienna #225/R est:1500-2500
£1266 $1975 €2000 Untitled (60x40cm-24x16in) mono. verso. 15-Oct-2 Dorotheum, Vienna #253/R est:2000-2800
£1457 $2375 €2200 Untitled (45x30cm-18x12in) 28-Jan-3 Dorotheum, Vienna #274/R est:900-1200
£2162 $3373 €3200 Worlds (80x80cm-31x31in) s.i.d.88 verso. 25-Mar-3 Wiener Kunst Auktionen, Vienna #23/R est:3000-6000
£2345 $3752 €3400 Untitled (110x70cm-43x28in) s.d.1998 verso. 11-Mar-3 Dorotheum, Vienna #292/R est:3000-4000
£2564 $4051 €4000 Green field stand (110x70cm-43x28in) s.d.1991/92 i. verso. 12-Nov-2 Dorotheum, Vienna #282/R est:3000-4000
£4747 $7358 €7500 Yellow field (249x180cm-98x71in) s.i.d.1988 verso. 24-Sep-2 Wiener Kunst Auktionen, Vienna #309/R est:7000-14000

Works on paper
£265 $432 €400 Untitled (82x53cm-32x21in) s.d.88/9 chk graphite. 28-Jan-3 Dorotheum, Vienna #265/R
£430 $702 €650 Untitled (78x53cm-31x21in) s. mixed media exec.c.1985. 28-Jan-3 Dorotheum, Vienna #268/R
£795 $1295 €1200 Untitled (64x104cm-25x41in) s.d.84 mixed media. 28-Jan-3 Dorotheum, Vienna #262/R
£1064 $1723 €1500 Standing figure with animal (100x85cm-39x33in) s.i.d.90/91 verso mixed media paper on Mollino. 20-May-3 Dorotheum, Vienna #292/R est:1500-1900

DAMM, Bertil (1887-1942) Swedish
£631 $984 €947 Bull fighting (28x42cm-11x17in) init.i.d.1919 exhib. 5-Nov-2 Bukowskis, Stockholm #12/R (S.KR 9000)

DAMM, Per (1929-) Danish
£604 $954 €906 Early morning, Skarvens, Lille Dimun in background (81x100cm-32x39in) s.d.74 s.i.d.1974 verso. 1-Apr-3 Rasmussen, Copenhagen #578/R (D.KR 6500)

DAMMASCH, Willy (1887-?) German
£1164 $1815 €1850 Entrance to Finkenwarder (56x68cm-22x27in) s. i. verso. 21-Sep-2 Bolland & Marotz, Bremen #342/R est:2000

DAMME, Frans van (1858-1925) Belgian
£288 $460 €400 Le repos des pecheurs (22x40cm-9x16in) s. 19-May-3 Horta, Bruxelles #4
£346 $536 €550 La moisson (30x39cm-12x15in) s. 1-Oct-2 Palais de Beaux Arts, Brussels #536
£443 $691 €700 Scene de peche (40x54cm-16x21in) s. 15-Oct-2 Vanderkindere, Brussels #116
£596 $972 €900 Quai aux Foins (31x28cm-12x11in) s. panel. 17-Feb-3 Horta, Bruxelles #356
£823 $1300 €1300 Bateaux en Mer du Nord (55x98cm-22x39in) s. 26-Nov-2 Palais de Beaux Arts, Brussels #170

DAMME, Suzanne van (1901-1986) Belgian
£360 $576 €500 Ronde des signes (42x65cm-17x26in) s. panel. 17-May-3 De Vuyst, Lokeren #356
£753 $1183 €1100 Les heritieres du rose (65x80cm-26x31in) s. panel. 15-Apr-3 Galerie Moderne, Brussels #326/R
£823 $1275 €1300 Receptacle de la memoire (121x102cm-48x40in) s. panel. 24-Sep-2 Galerie Moderne, Brussels #823
£1139 $1766 €1800 Solitude a coeur d'homme (97x195cm-38x77in) s. 24-Sep-2 Galerie Moderne, Brussels #963/R

DAMME-SYLVA, Émile van (1853-1935) Belgian
£1400 $2156 €2100 Cattle watering in a Flemish landscape (49x75cm-19x30in) s. 5-Sep-2 Morphets, Harrogate #358/R est:1800-2400
£4828 $7724 €7000 Rural scene (97x114cm-38x45in) s. 15-Mar-3 De Vuyst, Lokeren #417/R est:6500-7500

DAMMERON, C (?) ?
Works on paper
£306 $487 €450 Jeune fille aux bijoux (68x48cm-27x19in) s. pastel. 24-Mar-3 Rabourdin & Choppin de Janvry, Paris #21/R
£340 $541 €500 Femme au voile mauve (59x47cm-23x19in) s. pastel. 24-Mar-3 Rabourdin & Choppin de Janvry, Paris #19
£476 $757 €700 Femme Ouled-Nail a l'amande (69x49cm-27x19in) s.i. pastel. 24-Mar-3 Rabourdin & Choppin de Janvry, Paris #16
£476 $757 €700 Les enfants a la fontaine (64x50cm-25x20in) s. pastel. 24-Mar-3 Rabourdin & Choppin de Janvry, Paris #18
£503 $775 €800 Jeune fille berbere (31x29cm-12x11in) s. pastel. 23-Oct-2 Rabourdin & Choppin de Janvry, Paris #63/R
£566 $872 €900 Jeune fille a la tunique blanche (63x53cm-25x21in) s. pastel. 23-Oct-2 Rabourdin & Choppin de Janvry, Paris #59
£692 $1065 €1100 Portrait de jeune fille (86x60cm-34x24in) s. pastel. 23-Oct-2 Rabourdin & Choppin de Janvry, Paris #60
£881 $1356 €1400 Portrait de femme en rouge (67x48cm-26x19in) s. pastel. 23-Oct-2 Rabourdin & Choppin de Janvry, Paris #57/R
£1069 $1647 €1700 Jeune marocaine aux bijoux (71x53cm-28x21in) s. pastel. 23-Oct-2 Rabourdin & Choppin de Janvry, Paris #58/R

DAMNISIER, R (?) ?
£368 $588 €552 Street scene in Tyrol with figures (57x68cm-22x27in) s. 13-Jan-3 Rasmussen, Vejle #2223 (D.KR 4200)
£425 $663 €638 Street scene from Tyrol with figures (57x68cm-22x27in) s. 5-Aug-2 Rasmussen, Vejle #126/R (D.KR 5000)

DAMOYE, Pierre Emmanuel (1847-1916) French
£961 $1461 €1442 River landscape (63x77cm-25x30in) s.d.1903. 16-Aug-2 Lilla Bukowskis, Stockholm #1003 est:12000-15000 (S.KR 14000)
£1081 $1686 €1600 Bord de mer en Normandie (45x73cm-18x29in) s. 27-Mar-3 Maigret, Paris #331/R
£1258 $1962 €2000 Landscape with small lake (18x44cm-7x17in) s. panel lit. 20-Sep-2 Schloss Ahlden, Ahlden #1172/R est:1800
£2500 $4000 €3625 Open fields (50x73cm-20x29in) s.d.1900. 16-May-3 Skinner, Boston #325/R est:8000-12000
£3521 $5845 €5000 Lavandiere et gardeuse de troupeau (46x73cm-18x29in) s.d.82. 13-Jun-3 Rossini, Paris #97/R est:5000-6000
£3797 $6000 €6000 Extensive valley (43x77cm-17x30in) canvas on board. 28-Nov-2 Dorotheum, Vienna #152/R est:5500-5800
£13291 $21000 €19937 Landscape with windmill (67x111cm-26x44in) s.d.94. 24-Apr-3 Sotheby's, New York #107/R est:25000-35000

DAMOYE, Pierre Emmanuel (attrib) (1847-1916) French
£929 $1478 €1394 Heath landscape (51x73cm-20x29in) s.d.1901. 3-Mar-3 Lilla Bukowskis, Stockholm #851 (S.KR 12500)

DAMROW, Charles (1916-1989) American
£745 $1200 €1118 Indians on horseback (41x48cm-16x19in) s. prov. 18-Feb-3 John Moran, Pasadena #169

DAMSCHROEDER, Jan Jac Matthys (1825-1905) German
£458 $737 €650 Mother and child by artist's easel (44x36cm-17x14in) init. 7-May-3 Vendue Huis, Gravenhage #364/R

DAN, Lars (1960-) Danish
£379 $587 €569 Composition (110x70cm-43x28in) s.d.89-90 verso. 4-Dec-2 Kunsthallen, Copenhagen #139 (D.KR 4400)
£743 $1175 €1115 Composition (96x96cm-38x38in) s.d.96. 1-Apr-3 Rasmussen, Copenhagen #309/R (D.KR 8000)

DANBY, J (19th C) British
£250 $408 €375 Coastal scene with figures on the beach (36x53cm-14x21in) s.d.1869. 28-Jan-3 Riddetts, Bournemouth #611/R

DANBY, James Francis (1816-1875) British
£8500 $13260 €12750 Steam tug towing sailing ship off Mont Orgueil Castle (57x93cm-22x37in) s.d.1875. 26-Mar-3 Bonhams & Langlois, Jersey #139/R est:3000-5000
£26000 $41860 €39000 Rescue (76x102cm-30x40in) s. prov.exhib. 20-Feb-3 Christie's, London #213/R est:18000

DANBY, James Francis (attrib) (1816-1875) British
£390 $605 €585 Sun setting over a man of war (34x59cm-13x23in) 1-Oct-2 Bristol Auction Rooms #489/R

DANBY, Ken (1940-) Canadian
Works on paper
£1008 $1593 €1512 Fenced in (51x71cm-20x28in) s.d.67 W/C prov. 18-Nov-2 Sotheby's, Toronto #66/R est:3000-4000 (C.D 2500)

D'ANCONA, Edward (20th C) American
£1553 $2500 €2330 Shapely brunette rolling hoop (84x66cm-33x26in) s. 20-Feb-3 Illustration House, New York #35/R est:3500-5000

D'ANCONA, Vito (1825-1884) Italian
£1258 $1937 €2000 Woman in the garden (27x21cm-11x8in) cardboard prov. 28-Oct-2 Il Ponte, Milan #247/R
£13406 $21986 €18500 Profilo femminile (25x18cm-10x7in) prov.lit. 27-May-3 Finarte, Milan #77/R est:16000-18000

D'ANCONA, Vito (attrib) (1825-1884) Italian
£472 $726 €750 In the rain (10x6cm-4x2in) board. 28-Oct-2 Il Ponte, Milan #211

DANDELOT, Elisabeth (20th C) French
Works on paper
£385 $604 €600 Fez (27x37cm-11x15in) s.i.d.1928 W/C dr. 10-Dec-2 Tajan, Paris #146

DANDINI, Cesare (1595-1658) Italian
£3226 $5097 €5000 Philosopher (74x58cm-29x23in) 19-Dec-2 Semenzato, Venice #123/R est:6500

DANDINI, Cesare (attrib) (1595-1658) Italian
£38994 $60050 €62000 La muse de la sculpture (72x58cm-28x23in) 25-Oct-2 Tajan, Paris #22/R est:12000-15000
£51000 $85170 €73950 Madonna and Child with the Infant Saint John the Baptist (79x62cm-31x24in) 11-Jul-3 Christie's, Kensington #214/R est:3000-4000

DANDINI, Ottaviano (18th C) Italian
Works on paper
£550 $919 €798 Head of a youth turned to the left (17x18cm-7x7in) mono. red chk prov. 9-Jul-3 Bonhams, Knightsbridge #29/R
£1800 $2826 €2700 Figures of day from the Lorenzo de Medici Tomb (36x28cm-14x11in) init. black white chk after Michelangelo. 11-Dec-2 Sotheby's, Olympia #129/R est:1000-1500

DANDINI, Pietro (1646-1712) Italian
£6500 $10855 €9425 The Holy Family (45x34cm-18x13in) 8-Jul-3 Sotheby's, Olympia #387/R est:6000-8000
Works on paper
£2800 $4340 €4200 Study of bulldog. init. black red chk prov.exhib. 9-Dec-2 Bonhams, New Bond Street #73/R est:700-1000

DANDOY, Armand (1834-1898) Flemish
£950 $1482 €1425 White forest (59x90cm-23x35in) s. prov. 9-Apr-3 Cheffins Grain & Comins, Cambridge #748/R

DANDRE BARDON, Michel (attrib) (1700-1778) French
Works on paper
£1277 $2132 €1800 Samson et Dalila (19x24cm-7x9in) pen black ink brown wash gouache. 19-Jun-3 Piasa, Paris #89 est:2000-2500

DANDRIDGE, Bartholomew (17/18th C) British
£550 $913 €798 Portrait of a young lady wearing an ivory satin gown (28x23cm-11x9in) panel. 16-Jun-3 Duke & Son, Dorchester #174

DANEDI, Stefano (1608-1689) Italian
Works on paper
£2365 $3689 €3500 Femme en buste (20x11cm-8x4in) chk prov. 27-Mar-3 Christie's, Paris #63/R

DANELUND, Sven (1916-) Danish
£557 $870 €836 From Skagen Harbour (75x94cm-30x37in) s. 11-Nov-2 Rasmussen, Vejle #61/R (D.KR 6500)
£1147 $1789 €1721 Crane at Skagen Gasworks (72x112cm-28x44in) s. painted juli 1962. 5-Aug-2 Rasmussen, Vejle #2481 est:2000 (D.KR 13500)

DANGELO, Sergio (1931-) Italian
Works on paper
£288 $472 €400 L'oasis en dentelle (60x80cm-24x31in) s.d.1961 s.i.d.verso gouache collage on canvas. 3-Jun-3 Christie's, Amsterdam #94/R
£868 $1380 €1250 Six windows for the heart. s. mixed media collage on canvas. 1-May-3 Meeting Art, Vercelli #107

DANGER, Henri (1857-1937) French
£943 $1453 €1500 Muses (65x81cm-26x32in) s. d.1932 verso. 27-Oct-2 Muizon & Le Coent, Paris #40/R
£1923 $3019 €3000 Muses (65x81cm-26x32in) s. 15-Dec-2 Mercier & Cie, Lille #398/R

D'ANGERS, David (19th C) ?
Sculpture
£1451 $2250 €2177 Philopoemene (36cm-14in) s. brown pat. bronze prov.exhib.lit. 29-Oct-2 Sotheby's, New York #240/R est:4000-6000

D'ANGERS, David (attrib) (19th C) ?
Sculpture
£1774 $2750 €2661 Bust of a man (56cm-22in) terracotta prov.exhib. 29-Oct-2 Sotheby's, New York #226/R est:3000-5000

DANHAUSER, Josef (1805-1845) Austrian
£4610 $7468 €6500 Head of a girl with brown locks (46x39cm-18x15in) 22-May-3 Dorotheum, Vienna #22/R est:5000-6000

DANIEL, Abraham (?-1806) British
Miniatures
£1000 $1650 €1450 Lady wearing a white dress with frilled collar (4cm-2xin) gold mount rec. ivory toothpick box oval. 1-Jul-3 Bonhams, New Bond Street #89/R

DANIEL, Elekne (20th C) Czechoslovakian
£1496 $2319 €2244 Lake in a forest (60x84cm-24x33in) painted c.1930. 1-Oct-2 SOGA, Bratislava #131 est:28000 (SL.K 95000)

DANIEL, Mary Reed (1946-) American
£962 $1500 €1443 Nature study No.20 (56x49cm-22x19in) s. tempera. 20-Sep-2 Sloan, North Bethesda #456/R est:2000-3000

DANIEL, William Swift (1865-1933) American
£569 $950 €825 Summer coastal (30x41cm-12x16in) s. 17-Jun-3 John Moran, Pasadena #77 est:1000-1500

DANIELI, Giuseppe (1865-1931) Italian
£1497 $2380 €2200 Landscape by the lagoon (27x40cm-11x16in) s. board. 1-Mar-3 Meeting Art, Vercelli #110

DANIELL, William (1769-1837) British
£6200 $9796 €9300 View of Clovelly North Devon (42x66cm-17x26in) exhib. 28-Nov-2 Sotheby's, London #110/R est:6000-8000
Works on paper
£580 $922 €870 Sanky Droog - an pool near a hill top fort (33x54cm-13x21in) i. monochrome wash over pencil. 29-Apr-3 Bonhams, New Bond Street #62/R
£1000 $1600 €1500 Shipping on a river. cattle watering (28x36cm-11x14in) s.d.1806 verso W/C double-sided. 11-Mar-3 Bonhams, New Bond Street #33a/R est:1000-1500
£1800 $2988 €2700 Entrance to Fingal's cave, Staffordshire, Scotland (16x23cm-6x9in) W/C over pencil htd white prov. 12-Jun-3 Sotheby's, London #131/R est:2000-3000
£3200 $5312 €4640 Hindu temple at Permabor, India. 1792 (30x46cm-12x18in) i.verso W/C over pencil. 16-Jun-3 Duke & Son, Dorchester #145/R est:1500-3000
£50000 $83000 €75000 Jama Masjid, Delhi (47x75cm-19x30in) s. i.verso W/C over pencil. 12-Jun-3 Sotheby's, London #14/R est:50000-70000

DANIELS, Alfred (1924-) British
£1250 $1963 €1875 Magdalen College, Oxford (40x51cm-16x20in) s. board. 15-Apr-3 Bonhams, Knightsbridge #2/R est:1500-2000

DANIELS, Andries (attrib) (c.1580-1640) Flemish
£2113 $3507 €3000 Virgin and Child wreathed in flowers (24x21cm-9x8in) copper. 11-Jun-3 Dorotheum, Vienna #354/R est:1000-1500
£6646 $10500 €10500 Medaillon, la Sainte Famille entouree d'un bouquet de fleurs (124x93cm-49x37in) panel. 2-Dec-2 Amberes, Antwerp #1336

DANIELS, Andries and FRANCKEN, Frans II (17th C) Flemish
£6154 $9723 €9600 Garland of flowers (24x19cm-9x7in) copper. 13-Nov-2 Marc Kohn, Paris #6/R

DANIELS, René (1950-) Dutch
£50360 $82590 €70000 Salles pacifiques (90x120cm-35x47in) s.i.d.1984 prov.exhib.lit. 3-Jun-3 Christie's, Amsterdam #376/R est:60000-80000
Works on paper
£2564 $3974 €4000 Man with watering can (29x21cm-11x8in) pen brush ink W/C executed 1981. 3-Dec-2 Christie's, Amsterdam #377/R est:3000-5000

DANIELSON, Carl Johan (1866-1945) Finnish
£331 $523 €480 Boats (66x100cm-26x39in) s. after Herman af Sillen. 3-Apr-3 Hagelstam, Helsinki #827
£680 $1082 €1000 The artist Ali Munsterhjelm (32x41cm-13x16in) s. 27-Feb-3 Hagelstam, Helsinki #859
Works on paper
£1266 $2000 €2000 Fox hunting butterfly (39x50cm-15x20in) s.d.1938 W/C. 30-Nov-2 Hagelstam, Helsinki #79/R est:500

DANIELSON, Carl Otto (1883-1944) Finnish
£286 $454 €420 Eckero postal pier (25x48cm-10x19in) s.i.d.1926. 24-Mar-3 Bukowskis, Helsinki #53/R
£816 $1298 €1200 Kastelholm (45x86cm-18x34in) s.d.1926. 24-Mar-3 Bukowskis, Helsinki #54/R
£1701 $2704 €2500 Bridge across Aura river (71x92cm-28x36in) s. 24-Mar-3 Bukowskis, Helsinki #55/R est:1200

DANIELSON-GAMBOGI, Elin (1861-1919) Finnish
£7194 $11511 €10000 Morning twilight at Aaland (31x41cm-12x16in) s. 17-May-3 Hagelstam, Helsinki #101/R est:12000
£7911 $12500 €12500 In light of the oil lamp (20x25cm-8x10in) s. canvas on board. 1-Dec-2 Bukowskis, Helsinki #41/R est:6000-8000
£14029 $22446 €19500 Poppies (40x24cm-16x9in) s.d.1886. 17-May-3 Hagelstam, Helsinki #102/R est:17000
£20567 $31879 €30851 By the window - young woman sewing (51x61cm-20x24in) s.d.1890. 8-Dec-2 Uppsala Auktionskammare, Uppsala #128/R est:150000-200000 (S.KR 290000)
£26619 $42590 €37000 Reclaiming land at Onningeby (50x68cm-20x27in) s.d.1886. 17-May-3 Hagelstam, Helsinki #100/R est:40000
Works on paper
£15823 $25000 €25000 The apple girl (40x17cm-16x7in) s. W/C. 1-Dec-2 Bukowskis, Helsinki #42/R est:5000-6000

DANIFER, Sigurd (1894-1958) Norwegian
£262 $411 €393 Still life of bowls and bottles (48x58cm-19x23in) s. 25-Nov-2 Blomqvist, Lysaker #1042/R (N.KR 3000)
£372 $606 €558 Aasgaardstrand (50x61cm-20x24in) s. panel. 17-Feb-3 Blomqvist, Lysaker #1029/R (N.KR 4200)
£433 $662 €650 Nude seen from behind (35x30cm-14x12in) s. 26-Aug-2 Blomqvist, Lysaker #1073/R (N.KR 5000)
Works on paper
£312 $477 €468 Sunbathers (56x73cm-22x29in) s. gouache canvas. 26-Aug-2 Blomqvist, Lysaker #1072/R (N.KR 3600)

DANILEVSKY, Evgueni (1928-) Russian
£463 $745 €671 Lenin with working class family (85x104cm-33x41in) s.i.d.1956. 7-May-3 Dobiaschofsky, Bern #3178/R (S.FR 1000)

DANINO, A (?) Italian
£1346 $2087 €2100 Airfight (60x50cm-24x20in) s. 5-Dec-2 Stadion, Trieste #788/R

DANIOTH, Heinrich (1896-1953) German
£939 $1540 €1362 Face - mosaic design (27x34cm-11x13in) s.d.38 tempera prov. 4-Jun-3 Fischer, Luzern #2605/R est:800-1200 (S.FR 2000)
Works on paper
£437 $681 €656 Head of soldier from Urne (27x19cm-11x7in) i. W/C pen ink exec.c.1940. 9-Nov-2 Galerie Gloggner, Luzern #32/R (S.FR 1000)
£556 $894 €834 Couple (52x36cm-20x14in) Indian ink col pen. 7-May-3 Dobiaschofsky, Bern #1526/R (S.FR 1200)
£611 $954 €917 Cats (47x62cm-19x24in) s.d.32 W/C prov.lit. 9-Nov-2 Galerie Gloggner, Luzern #29/R (S.FR 1400)

DANISH SCHOOL, 17th C
£4928 $7687 €7392 Prince Christian of Denmark seated on a black horse (63x83cm-25x33in) painted c.1690 lit. 5-Aug-2 Rasmussen, Vejle #145/R est:40000-60000 (D.KR 58000)

DANISH SCHOOL, 19th C
£7656 $12402 €11101 Interior scene with young man studying Thorvaldsen's sculpture Venus with apple (33x28cm-13x11in) 26-May-3 Rasmussen, Copenhagen #1152/R est:15000-25000 (D.KR 80000)

DANK, Walter (?) German?
£387 $612 €600 Seascape (30x61cm-12x24in) s. 18-Dec-2 Finarte, Milan #170

DANKMEYER, Carel Bernardus (1861-1923) Dutch
£414 $646 €650 Country residence near Noordwijkerhout (23x34cm-9x13in) s. 6-Nov-2 Vendue Huis, Gravenhage #2/R
£510 $785 €800 Boats on the water, Venice beyond (29x40cm-11x16in) s. plywood. 3-Sep-2 Christie's, Amsterdam #229
£1401 $2186 €2200 City on the river (69x99cm-27x39in) s. 6-Nov-2 Vendue Huis, Gravenhage #47/R est:1000-1500

DANLER, Herbert (1928-) Austrian
£1203 $1876 €1900 Plagott, Vinschgau (18x33cm-7x13in) mono. s.i.d.2000 verso panel. 15-Oct-2 Dorotheum, Vienna #270/R est:1500-2000
£1258 $2051 €1900 Building in Proveis, South Tyrol (27x41cm-11x16in) mono. s.i.d.2000 verso chipboard. 28-Jan-3 Dorotheum, Vienna #316/R est:1500-2000

DANLOUX, Henri Pierre (1753-1809) French
£36364 $60727 €52000 Les petits gourmands (16x12cm-6x5in) panel pair prov.lit. 25-Jun-3 Sotheby's, Paris #41/R est:15000-20000

DANLOUX, Henri Pierre (attrib) (1753-1809) French
£2229 $3500 €3344 Comtesse de Romagnesi en Diane (81x66cm-32x26in) 13-Dec-2 Du Mouchelle, Detroit #2091/R est:5000-7000
£5532 $8962 €7800 Portrait presume de Louis XVII (54x44cm-21x17in) oval prov. 21-May-3 Piasa, Paris #377/R est:4000-6000

DANN, Frode N (1892-?) American/Danish
£745 $1200 €1118 Outside the artist's home in Talpa NM near Tao (61x76cm-24x30in) init.d.57 prov. 18-Feb-3 John Moran, Pasadena #112

D'ANNA, Alessandro (18th C) Italian
£3165 $5000 €5000 Innocence. Contemplation. Brotherly charity (31x23cm-12x9in) s.i.d.1793 tempera card three. 26-Nov-2 Christie's, Rome #115/R

D'ANNA, Giulio (1908-1978) Italian
£3205 $5032 €5000 Monn idyll (27x24cm-11x9in) s. tempera paper painted 1937 exhib. 21-Nov-2 Finarte, Rome #252/R
£4110 $6411 €6000 Moon over the Ammiraglio bridge (29x29cm-11x11in) s.d.930 tempera card exhib. 10-Apr-3 Finarte Semenzato, Rome #287/R
£4167 $6458 €6500 Futuristic view of a sea town (50x43cm-20x17in) s.d.1930 tempera. 5-Dec-2 Stadion, Trieste #789/R
£12838 $20027 €19000 Plane (47x71cm-19x28in) s. tempera lit. 26-Mar-3 Finarte Semenzato, Milan #249/R est:19000

D'ANNA, Vito (1718-1769) Italian
Works on paper
£1410 $2186 €2200 Allegory of Knowledge. Allegory of Geometry (20x47cm-8x19in) pencil pen ink W/C prov.lit. pair. 4-Dec-2 Christie's, Rome #396/R

DANNECKER, Arnold (1939-) German
£599 $994 €850 Shepherd with his flock (13x17cm-5x7in) s. panel. 14-Jun-3 Arnold, Frankfurt #721

DANNECKER, Johan Heinrich von (1758-1841) German
Sculpture
£12821 $19872 €20000 Minerva (30cm-12in) marble prov. 5-Dec-2 Dr Fritz Nagel, Stuttgart #770/R

DANNECKER, Johan Heinrich von (attrib) (1758-1841) German
Sculpture
£1154 $1788 €1800 Portrait probably of Friedrich Schiller (10x9cm-4x4in) plaster prov. 5-Dec-2 Dr Fritz Nagel, Stuttgart #771/R est:2000
£1282 $1987 €2000 Relief portrait probably of Nicolas Guibal (11x8cm-4x3in) plaster prov. 5-Dec-2 Dr Fritz Nagel, Stuttgart #772/R est:2000

DANNET, Charles (19th C) French
Works on paper
£507 $800 €800 Berger sonnant le rappel de son troupeau (46x56cm-18x22in) s.d.1867 pastel. 28-Nov-2 Tajan, Paris #157

DANPT, J (19/20th C) French?
Sculpture
£3145 $4906 €5000 Buste d'une jeune femme (46x51x26cm-18x20x10in) s.d.1910 white marble. 20-Sep-2 Millon & Associes, Paris #510/R est:7000-12000

DANS, Maria Antonia (1932-1988) Spanish
£9929 $16085 €14000 La frutera (96x162cm-38x64in) s. lit. 20-May-3 Segre, Madrid #131/R est:6000
Works on paper
£1103 $1754 €1600 Landscape with houses (28x36cm-11x14in) s. wax crayon board. 4-Mar-3 Ansorena, Madrid #144/R
£1241 $1974 €1800 Night scene (29x35cm-11x14in) s. wax crayon board. 4-Mar-3 Ansorena, Madrid #143/R
£1776 $2878 €2700 House with figure (48x68cm-19x27in) s. gouache. 21-Jan-3 Ansorena, Madrid #305/R

DANSAERT, Léon (1830-1909) Belgian
£5769 $8942 €9000 La visite du Loubre en galante compagnie (67x53cm-26x21in) s. panel. 9-Dec-2 Horta, Bruxelles #117/R est:10000-12000
£6013 $9380 €9500 Sunday in the country (38x56cm-15x22in) s. 21-Oct-2 Bernaerts, Antwerp #94/R est:5500-7000

DANTI, Amleto (?) Italian
£270 $422 €400 Peasants (25x40cm-10x16in) s. s.verso. 28-Mar-3 Farsetti, Prato #610

DANTU, Georges (19/20th C) French
£1218 $1851 €1900 Passerelle sous les cerisiers roses au Japon (65x54cm-26x21in) s. s.i.verso. 10-Jul-2 Rabourdin & Choppin de Janvry, Paris #42/R est:2300-2500

D'ANTY, Henry (1910-1998) French
£276 $461 €400 Paysage sous la neige (53x43cm-21x17in) s. 9-Jul-3 Cornette de St.Cyr, Paris #154
£278 $439 €400 Bouquet (46x55cm-18x22in) s. s.d.verso. 25-Apr-3 Piasa, Paris #49
£279 $441 €419 Winter landscape with houses (14x18cm-6x7in) s. 1-Apr-3 Rasmussen, Copenhagen #559/R (D.KR 3000)
£359 $599 €520 La caleche (44x53cm-17x21in) s. 9-Jul-3 Cornette de St.Cyr, Paris #153/R
£360 $576 €500 Le village aux toits rouges (22x35cm-9x14in) s. 18-May-3 Eric Pillon, Calais #231/R
£414 $691 €600 Fleurs (62x50cm-24x20in) s. s.i.verso. 9-Jul-3 Cornette de St.Cyr, Paris #151
£503 $841 €730 La vieille eglise (57x72cm-22x28in) s. s.i.verso. 9-Jul-3 Cornette de St.Cyr, Paris #152
£517 $864 €750 Neige (72x60cm-28x24in) s. s.i.verso. 9-Jul-3 Cornette de St.Cyr, Paris #155
£552 $921 €800 Maternite (100x50cm-39x20in) s. 9-Jul-3 Cornette de St.Cyr, Paris #157
£566 $944 €820 Arrivee de la diligence (80x65cm-31x26in) s. s.i.verso. 9-Jul-3 Cornette de St.Cyr, Paris #156
£658 $980 €987 Le hameau (56x46cm-22x18in) s. 26-Jun-2 Iegor de Saint Hippolyte, Montreal #20a/R (C.D 1500)
£694 $1118 €1006 Clown with cello (55x45cm-22x18in) s. 7-May-3 Dobiaschofsky, Bern #321/R (S.FR 1500)
£741 $1193 €1074 Still life of flowers (80x100cm-31x39in) s. 7-May-3 Dobiaschofsky, Bern #322/R (S.FR 1600)

£877 $1307 €1316 Le combat de Don Quichotte (152x51cm-60x20in) s. 26-Jun-2 Iegor de Saint Hippolyte, Montreal #20b (C.D 2000)
£1026 $1590 €1600 Clown (100x50cm-39x20in) s. pair. 8-Dec-2 Feletin, Province #152/R
£1026 $1590 €1600 Villlage aux toits rouges (50x100cm-20x39in) s. 8-Dec-2 Feletin, Province #154

D'ANTY, Rene (20th C) French
£302 $468 €480 Rabbins avec la Torah (65x54cm-26x21in) s. 7-Oct-2 Claude Aguttes, Neuilly #313

DANVIN, Victor Marie Felix (1802-1842) French
£2200 $3476 €3300 Figures and boats in a river landscape (66x54cm-26x21in) s. 12-Nov-2 Bonhams, Knightsbridge #93/R est:2000-3000

DAPLYN, Alfred James (1844-1926) Australian
£1792 $2724 €2688 Pioneers (73x56cm-29x22in) s. 28-Aug-2 Deutscher-Menzies, Melbourne #348/R est:4000-6000 (A.D 5000)

DARAIO, Innocenzo (1903-) American?
£1274 $2000 €1911 Area of Worthington Glacier, Alaska (61x75cm-24x30in) s.d.1931 i.verso masonite. 19-Nov-2 Butterfields, San Francisco #8098/R est:3000-5000
£1347 $2250 €1953 Pebble beach (61x76cm-24x30in) s. canvasboard. 17-Jun-3 John Moran, Pasadena #179 est:1500-2500

DARBES, Joseph (1747-1810) German
£4255 $6723 €6383 Portrait of Friedrich Wilhelm III of Preussen wearing blue uniform (70x55cm-28x22in) prov. 2-Dec-2 Rasmussen, Copenhagen #1696/R est:30000-40000 (D.KR 50000)

DARBOUR, Marguerite Mary (19/20th C) French
£355 $592 €500 Fillette dans un pre (61x46cm-24x18in) s. 23-Jun-3 Delvaux, Paris #195

Works on paper
£451 $736 €650 Le port de Concarneau (31x47cm-12x19in) s. chl W/C. 19-Jul-3 Thierry & Lannon, Brest #401

DARBOVEN, Hanne (1941-) German

Works on paper
£8500 $13940 €12750 49 variante. i.num.1-16 ink printed paper collage 16 parts prov.exhib. 7-Feb-3 Sotheby's, London #161/R est:3000-4000
£50000 $80000 €75000 Ein jahrhundert 365 366 indices one century (126x30cm-50x12in) s.i.d.1971 typewriter ink pencil in 61 panel prov. 14-May-3 Sotheby's, New York #216/R est:80000-120000

D'ARCANGELO, Allan (1930-) American
£3481 $5500 €5222 NYC (180x216cm-71x85in) s.i.d.1967 verso acrylic prov. 22-Apr-3 Butterfields, San Francisco #6062/R est:2500-3500

D'ARCEVIA, Bruno (20th C) Italian
£1282 $2013 €2000 Before sunrise (70x50cm-28x20in) s.i.d.1992 verso. 21-Nov-2 Finarte, Rome #61/R
£3797 $6000 €6000 Atalanata and Hyppomenes (180x130cm-71x51in) s.d.87. 2-Dec-2 Finarte, Milan #145

DARCY-DUMOULIN, Alexis Auguste (1815-1864) French
£1923 $2981 €3000 Marche aux legumes (24x36cm-9x14in) s. 5-Dec-2 Gros & Delettrez, Paris #16/R
£2179 $3378 €3400 Marche aux chevaux (24x36cm-9x14in) s.d.52. 5-Dec-2 Gros & Delettrez, Paris #15/R

DARDE, Paul (1888-1963) French

Sculpture
£2158 $3453 €3000 Les pleureuses (200x86cm-79x34in) s. plaster lit. 16-May-3 Beaussant & Lefèvre, Paris #83/R est:1000-1500

DARDEL, Fritz von (1817-1901) Swedish
£284 $440 €426 Coastal landscape with sailing vessel by cliffs (31x39cm-12x15in) s.d.1857 panel. 8-Dec-2 Uppsala Auktionskammare, Uppsala #40 (S.KR 4000)

DARDEL, Nils (1888-1943) Swedish
£2162 $3481 €3243 Seated blonde model (92x73cm-36x29in) s.d.1930 prov.exhib.lit. 7-May-3 AB Stockholms Auktionsverk #704/R est:25000-30000 (S.KR 28000)
£3422 $5407 €5133 The coalman (84x57cm-33x22in) exhib.lit. 28-Apr-3 Bukowskis, Stockholm #158/R est:30000-35000 (S.KR 45000)

Works on paper
£950 $1510 €1425 Isadora Duncan and Clive Bell (46x60cm-18x24in) s.i. pencil W/C. 26-Feb-3 Sotheby's, Olympia #181/R est:300-500
£1673 $2643 €2510 Ali (49x38cm-19x15in) s.d.1936 W/C exhib. 28-Apr-3 Bukowskis, Stockholm #61/R est:20000-25000 (S.KR 22000)
£1931 $3108 €2897 Arab standing wearing blue jacket and fez (61x43cm-24x17in) s.d.1936 W/C exhib. 7-May-3 AB Stockholms Auktionsverk #656/R est:25000-30000 (S.KR 25000)
£2281 $3605 €3422 Dudja (49x39cm-19x15in) s.d.1936 W/C exhib. 28-Apr-3 Bukowskis, Stockholm #60/R est:20000-25000 (S.KR 30000)

DARDEL, Robert Guillaume (attrib) (1749-1821) French

Sculpture
£8974 $13910 €14000 Couple de romains priant la deesse Athena pour le repos des ames de leurs enfants morts (26x23x17cm-10x9x7in) terracotta lit. 9-Dec-2 Rabourdin & Choppin de Janvry, Paris #55/R est:15000

DARDENNE, Léon (1865-1912) Belgian
£396 $633 €550 Allee ensoleillee (58x98cm-23x39in) s. panel. 19-May-3 Horta, Bruxelles #24
£417 $646 €650 Tram attele a la tombee du jour (27x45cm-11x18in) s. panel. 9-Dec-2 Horta, Bruxelles #445
£818 $1267 €1300 Hanging out the washing (55x67cm-22x26in) s. 5-Oct-2 De Vuyst, Lokeren #72/R

DARDOIZE, Émile (1826-1901) French
£566 $872 €900 Landscape (61x38cm-24x15in) s. 27-Oct-2 Muizon & Le Coent, Paris #38/R

DARGE, Fred (1900-1979) American
£321 $500 €482 Sundown (41x51cm-16x20in) canvasboard. 19-Oct-2 David Dike, Dallas #202/R
£449 $700 €674 Mare with foal (20x25cm-8x10in) board. 19-Oct-2 David Dike, Dallas #93a
£1065 $1725 €1544 Afternoon shadows (30x41cm-12x16in) board. 23-May-3 Altermann Galleries, Santa Fe #91
£1282 $2000 €1923 After the rain (30x41cm-12x16in) canvasboard. 19-Oct-2 David Dike, Dallas #290a est:2000-3000
£1571 $2450 €2357 Little Sierra Blanca (30x41cm-12x16in) canvasboard painted c.1919. 19-Oct-2 David Dike, Dallas #93/R est:1500-3000

DARGELAS, Andre Henri (1828-1906) French
£2803 $4372 €4400 Le retour des ecoliers (41x31cm-16x12in) s. panel. 11-Nov-2 Horta, Bruxelles #240/R est:5500-6500
£3000 $4680 €4500 Le saut a la corde (39x32cm-15x13in) s. panel. 26-Mar-3 Sotheby's, Olympia #208/R est:3000-4000

DARGER, Henry (20th C) French

Works on paper
£18519 $30000 €27779 At sunbeam creek - at wickey sansia (47x91cm-19x36in) W/C graphite collage painted c.1950-1960 prov. 27-Jan-3 Christie's, Rockefeller NY #72/R est:35000-55000
£21605 $35000 €32408 Violet goes on a dangerous mission. Surprised again (47x235cm-19x93in) W/C graphite collage double-sided prov.lit. 27-Jan-3 Christie's, Rockefeller NY #73/R est:40000-60000
£46296 $75000 €69444 While inside they await developments, they are cleverly outwitted (61x272cm-24x107in) W/C graphite collage double-sided prov.lit. 27-Jan-3 Christie's, Rockefeller NY #71/R est:50000-70000

DARGIE, Sir William (1912-) Australian
£396 $606 €594 Landscape (29x34cm-11x13in) s. board. 21-Aug-2 Dunbar Sloane, Auckland #69/R est:1000-2000 (NZ.D 1300)
£464 $733 €696 Hitchhiker, Country Road (27x34cm-11x13in) s. board. 18-Nov-2 Joel, Victoria #180 est:1000-1200 (A.D 1300)

DARGIS, Alfons (1909-1996) German?
£1083 $1689 €1700 Friend (58x45cm-23x18in) s. 6-Nov-2 Hugo Ruef, Munich #1055

DARIEN, Henri Gaston (1864-1926) French
£513 $811 €800 Les pecheurs de crevettes (81x65cm-32x26in) s.d.91. 18-Nov-2 Tajan, Paris #49
£1701 $2704 €2500 Falaise de Vaucotte (32x55cm-13x22in) s. prov. 24-Mar-3 Coutau Begarie, Paris #198/R
£2077 $3345 €2950 Jeune femme sur la falaise (55x46cm-22x18in) s. 11-May-3 Lombrail & Teucquam, Paris #168/R
£6000 $9540 €9000 Un jardin en ete (72x99cm-28x39in) s. 20-Mar-3 Christie's, Kensington #17/R est:6000-8000

DARJOU, A (19th C) French
£632 $960 €948 Refusal (39x31cm-15x12in) s. panel. 19-Aug-2 Joel, Victoria #196 est:2000-3000 (A.D 1800)

DARLEY, Felix O C (1822-1888) American
Works on paper
£419 $650 €629 Pifferari (33x23cm-13x9in) s.d.1867 W/C paper on board prov. 29-Oct-2 Doyle, New York #49
£7097 $11000 €10646 Oak openings (47x37cm-19x15in) s.i. brush ink wash over pencil oval. 3-Dec-2 Phillips, New York #1/R est:4000-6000

DARLEY, Jesse (19th C) American
£641 $1000 €962 Children at a cottage door (81x58cm-32x23in) indis sig. panel. 20-Sep-2 Freeman, Philadelphia #120/R est:800-1200

DARLING, Sanford (1894-1974) American
£1852 $3000 €2778 House of one thousand paintings no.008 (101x26cm-40x10in) panel painted c.1963-1973 prov.exhib. 27-Jan-3 Christie's, Rockefeller NY #61/R est:2000-3000
£1975 $3200 €2963 House of one thousand paintings no.064 (63x27cm-25x11in) masonite painted c.1973 prov.exhib. 27-Jan-3 Christie's, Rockefeller NY #60/R est:2500-3500

DARLING, Wilder M (1856-1933) American
£602 $1000 €873 Shoreline at Marblehead. Impressionist painting (25x33cm-10x13in) s. composition board double-sided. 14-Jun-3 Jackson's, Cedar Falls #21/R

DARLING, William S (1882-1963) American
£1553 $2500 €2330 Palm Canyon Way (46x56cm-18x22in) s. i.verso canvas on board. 18-Feb-3 John Moran, Pasadena #96a est:1500-2500
£1553 $2500 €2330 Young cottonwood (41x51cm-16x20in) s. i.verso masonite prov. 18-Feb-3 John Moran, Pasadena #96b est:1500-2000
£4140 $6500 €6210 Clearing skies (76x102cm-30x40in) s. masonite prov.exhib. 19-Nov-2 Butterfields, San Francisco #8312/R est:7000-10000

D'ARLOY, Irene (19/20th C) French
£481 $750 €697 Lady on a terrace (28x38cm-11x15in) s. porcelain. 30-Mar-3 Simpson's, Houston #325

DARMANA, Margaretha (20th C) German
Works on paper
£304 $475 €441 Bullfight (25x33cm-10x13in) s.i. gouache. 30-Mar-3 Simpson's, Houston #74

DARNAUT, Hugo (1851-1937) Austrian
£629 $975 €1000 Mountain stream (36x48cm-14x19in) s. board. 29-Oct-2 Dorotheum, Vienna #79/R
£943 $1462 €1500 Thatched cottage (12x18cm-5x7in) s. W/C pencil. 1-Oct-2 Dorotheum, Vienna #266/R est:1100-1200
£1899 $3000 €3000 Water-meadow landscape (27x37cm-11x15in) s. board on board. 28-Nov-2 Dorotheum, Vienna #48/R est:4500-5500
£2837 $4596 €4000 Part of the Rugen Island (47x38cm-19x15in) s. 22-May-3 Dorotheum, Vienna #173/R est:4000-5500
£2848 $4500 €4500 Autumn woods (27x19cm-11x7in) s. board. 28-Nov-2 Dorotheum, Vienna #178/R est:3000-4000
£3165 $5000 €5000 In the Lainzer Tiergarten (53x43cm-21x17in) s. board. 28-Nov-2 Dorotheum, Vienna #141/R est:5000-6500
£4167 $6542 €6500 Summer landscape (46x61cm-18x24in) s. board. 10-Dec-2 Dorotheum, Vienna #98/R est:4500-6000
£5704 $9184 €8500 Roadside chapel in the snow (45x61cm-18x24in) s. panel prov. 18-Feb-3 Sotheby's, Amsterdam #334/R est:3000-5000
£7246 $11884 €10000 Village pond in Lower Austria (48x64cm-19x25in) s. board. 27-May-3 Hassfurther, Vienna #27/R est:9000-10000
£21277 $34468 €30000 Twig collectors in Buchenwald (55x39cm-22x15in) s.d.1889 panel. 22-May-3 Dorotheum, Vienna #111/R est:30000-36000
Works on paper
£321 $503 €500 Church in autumn landscape (22x30cm-9x12in) s. W/C. 21-Nov-2 Dorotheum, Vienna #411/R
£1986 $3217 €2800 Spring landscape (24x37cm-9x15in) s. W/C. 22-May-3 Dorotheum, Vienna #166/R est:3000-3400
£2000 $3320 €3000 Austrian town (34x49cm-13x19in) s.d.1882 W/C. 12-Jun-3 Bonhams, New Bond Street #601/R est:2000-4000
£2885 $4529 €4500 Summer landscape (30x40cm-12x16in) s. W/C. 25-Nov-2 Hassfurther, Vienna #30/R est:3500-4500
£5975 $9261 €9500 May wood (50x70cm-20x28in) s.d.1900 mixed media. 1-Oct-2 Dorotheum, Vienna #248/R est:4500-5000

DARONDEAU, Stanislas Henri Benoit (1807-1841) French
£1613 $2500 €2420 Woman with dog gazing at the sea. 7-Dec-2 Harvey Clar, Oakland #1328

DARRAH, Ann Sophia Towne (1819-1881) American
£5469 $8750 €8204 Hall's mill at the head of Devil's Gully (64x76cm-25x30in) 12-Jan-3 William Jenack, New York #311

DARRICAU, Henry Leonce (1870-?) French
£34965 $58392 €50000 Les presents (133x147cm-52x58in) s.d. prov.exhib. 27-Jun-3 Claude Aguttes, Neuilly #137/R est:50000-60000

DARRO (20th C) American
£1615 $2600 €2423 Young woman artist at the easel (76x61cm-30x24in) s. 20-Feb-3 Illustration House, New York #36/R est:3000-4000

DARROCH, Duncan (1888-1967) New Zealander
£436 $619 €654 Port Lyttelton (39x49cm-15x19in) s. board prov. 21-Nov-1 Watson's, Christchurch #52/R (NZ.D 1500)

DARRU, Louise (19th C) French
£1437 $2400 €2084 Mixed flower in a vase (87x69cm-34x27in) s. indis d. 22-Jun-3 Freeman, Philadelphia #29/R est:1000-1500

D'ARTHOIS, Jacques (1613-1686) Flemish
£5031 $7799 €8000 Flanders river landscape with boatmen (51x61cm-20x24in) 2-Oct-2 Dorotheum, Vienna #130/R est:8000-12000
£11511 $18417 €16000 Wooded landscape with elegant figures on a path (67x93cm-26x37in) 14-May-3 Christie's, Amsterdam #126/R est:3000-5000

D'ARTHOIS, Jacques (attrib) (1613-1686) Flemish
£822 $1282 €1200 Maria with Infant Jesus and putti before wooded landscape (28x40cm-11x16in) panel. 10-Apr-3 Van Ham, Cologne #1150/R

D'ARTHOIS, Jacques (circle) (1613-1686) Flemish
£5000 $7800 €7500 Wooded landscape with a drover and his cattle crossing a ford and figure on a track (81x118cm-32x46in) 10-Apr-3 Christie's, Kensington #92/R est:5000-7000
£5396 $8633 €7500 Extensive wooded landscape with travellers resting on path (106x143cm-42x56in) 13-May-3 Sotheby's, Amsterdam #23/R est:7000-9000

DARWIN, Sir Robin (1910-1974) British
Works on paper
£280 $437 €420 Castle Howard (24x36cm-9x14in) s. pen ink W/C. 26-Mar-3 Hamptons Fine Art, Godalming #71

DASBURG, Andrew (1887-1979) American
£19231 $30000 €28847 Pinons (41x56cm-16x22in) s. painted c.1933 prov.lit. 9-Nov-2 Santa Fe Art, Santa Fe #122/R est:40000-60000
Works on paper
£11538 $18000 €17307 Taos landscape (46x64cm-18x25in) s.d.71 pastel ink prov.lit. 9-Nov-2 Santa Fe Art, Santa Fe #117/R est:20000-30000

DASH, Robert and MORGAN, Howard (20th C) American
£709 $1100 €1064 View. Portrait of a young man (81cm-32in circular) s. two prov. 29-Oct-2 Sotheby's, New York #290/R est:500-700

DASHWOOD, Jeffrey (1947-) British
Sculpture
£1200 $1992 €1740 Black-tailed godwit (33x33cm-13x13in) s.num.8/12 bronze. 12-Jun-3 Christie's, Kensington #220/R est:500-700
£1300 $2106 €1950 Woodpecker (17cm-7in) s.num7/12 bronze. 20-May-3 Sotheby's, Olympia #123/R est:1000-2000
£1300 $2158 €1885 Eagle (51x15cm-20x6in) s.num.12/12 bronze. 12-Jun-3 Christie's, Kensington #213/R est:600-800
£1700 $2822 €2465 Herring gull (38x53cm-15x21in) s.num.4/12 painted bronze. 12-Jun-3 Christie's, Kensington #217/R est:600-800
£1900 $3154 €2755 Goshawk (51x16cm-20x6in) s.num.9/12 painted bronze. 12-Jun-3 Christie's, Kensington #215/R est:600-800
£2200 $3652 €3190 Baillon's crake (28x28cm-11x11in) s.num.1/12 bronze. 12-Jun-3 Christie's, Kensington #216/R est:600-800
£2200 $3652 €3190 Peahen (46x41cm-18x16in) s.num.7/12 bronze. 12-Jun-3 Christie's, Kensington #221/R est:600-800
£3000 $4860 €4500 Owl (17cm-7in) s.num.7/12 bronze. 20-May-3 Sotheby's, Olympia #124/R est:1500-2500
£3200 $5312 €4640 Red-throated diver (20x55cm-8x22in) s.num.7/12 bronze. 12-Jun-3 Christie's, Kensington #218/R est:600-800
£3800 $6308 €5510 Pheasant (30x96cm-12x38in) s.num.5/12 bronze. 12-Jun-3 Christie's, Kensington #219/R est:600-800

DASHWOOD, Susan Alice (19th C) British
Works on paper
£2000 $3260 €2900 Sir William Rowley of Tendring, 2BT and his wife Susannah (19x16cm-7x6in) s.d.1879 i.verso pastel oval pair after Richard Cosway. 21-Jul-3 Sotheby's, London #137 est:200-300

DASNOY, Albert (1901-1992) Belgian
£563 $918 €850 Jardin des Richir (110x90cm-43x35in) 17-Feb-3 Horta, Bruxelles #101

DASPHER, Julian (20th C) New Zealander
Works on paper
£821 $1280 €1232 Abstract (100x80cm-39x31in) mixed media. 17-Sep-2 Peter Webb, Auckland #136/R est:2500-3000 (NZ.D 2700)

DASSEN, Pieke (1926-) Dutch
£1274 $1987 €2000 Still life with carnival attributes (166x125cm-65x49in) s.d.75. 6-Nov-2 Vendue Huis, Gravenhage #141/R est:2000-3000

DASSI, Antonio (18th C) Italian
£541 $844 €860 Virgin Mary praying (26x20cm-10x8in) s.i. verso panel. 9-Oct-2 Michael Zeller, Lindau #555/R

DASSON, Henri (1825-1896) French
Sculpture
£3481 $5430 €5500 Allegorie de la mer (59cm-23in) s.d.1886 brown pat bronze. 20-Oct-2 Mercier & Cie, Lille #122/R est:5500-6000

DASSONVILLE, William E (20th C) American?
Photographs
£2436 $3800 €3654 Eucalyptus tees and San Francisco skyline (25x20cm-10x8in) s. silver. 21-Oct-2 Swann Galleries, New York #121/R est:4000-5000

D'ASTE, Joseph (20th C) Italian
Sculpture
£1667 $2617 €2600 Groupe enfants jouant sur un arbre (34x62cm-13x24in) s. bronze exec.c.1900. 10-Dec-2 Vanderkindere, Brussels #455/R est:2000-3000

DATER, Judy (1941-) American
Photographs
£2215 $3500 €3323 Imogen and Twinka at Yosemite (24x19cm-9x7in) s.d.1974 verso photograph prov. 23-Apr-3 Sotheby's, New York #123/R est:2500-3500
£4294 $7000 €6441 Imogen and Twinka (25x20cm-10x8in) s. i.d.1974 verso gelatin silver print. 12-Feb-3 Christie's, Rockefeller NY #48/R est:2500-3500

DATSENKO, Lidya (1946-) Russian
£400 $620 €600 Still life with strawberry (40x45cm-16x18in) s. 8-Dec-2 John Nicholson, Haslemere #107/R
£400 $620 €600 Still life with cherries (40x45cm-16x18in) s. 8-Dec-2 John Nicholson, Haslemere #106/R

DAUBAN, Jules Joseph (1822-1908) French
£256 $397 €400 Crucifixion (58x26cm-23x10in) 6-Dec-2 Maigret, Paris #118
Works on paper
£1282 $2013 €2000 Etude pour Marie Madeleine (39x43cm-15x17in) crayon chl htd white. 13-Dec-2 Pierre Berge, Paris #39/R

DAUBEIL, Jules (19th C) French
£1097 $1733 €1700 Campement nomade devant la ville, Gabes (27x35cm-11x14in) s.i.d. 17-Dec-2 Rossini, Paris #68/R

DAUBIGNY, Charles François (1817-1878) French
£1000 $1570 €1500 Wooded landscape with woodcutter (11x24cm-4x9in) s. panel. 21-Nov-2 Tennants, Leyburn #804/R est:1000-1500
£1519 $2400 €2400 Homme a la pipe (40x32cm-16x13in) s. lit. 2-Dec-2 Tajan, Paris #1/R
£2058 $3169 €3087 Deux cerfs dans la foret (18x29cm-7x11in) panel. 26-Oct-2 Heffel, Vancouver #10 est:6000-8000 (C.D 5000)
£6000 $9780 €8700 L'ike de bezons (22x34cm-9x13in) i. panel. 17-Jul-3 Tennants, Leyburn #869/R est:5000-7000
£7500 $11775 €11250 Aux bords de l'Oise (34x58cm-13x23in) s.d.1844 panel prov. 21-Nov-2 Christie's, Kensington #6/R est:3000-5000
£7742 $12232 €12000 Moulins au bord de l'eau a Dordrecht (35x58cm-14x23in) s. painted 1872. 19-Dec-2 Claude Aguttes, Neuilly #29/R est:10000
£7911 $12500 €12500 Arc en ciel a Corbigny (22x35cm-9x14in) s. panel. 1-Dec-2 Peron, Melun #40b
£15000 $23250 €22500 Paysage (40x67cm-16x26in) s.d.1874 panel prov. 4-Dec-2 Christie's, London #97/R est:15000-20000
£17722 $27468 €28000 River landscape - possibly the Oise (38x66cm-15x26in) s.d.1867 panel prov.lit. 25-Sep-2 Neumeister, Munich #553/R est:17000
£24051 $38000 €36077 Les bords de l'Oise (32x59cm-13x23in) s. panel painted c.1864 prov.exhib.lit. 23-Apr-3 Christie's, Rockefeller NY #34/R est:40000-60000
£26899 $42500 €40349 Bateaux sur l'Oise (38x67cm-15x26in) s.d.1867 panel prov.lit. 24-Apr-3 Sotheby's, New York #26/R est:30000-40000
£29032 $45000 €43548 Les lles vierges a Bezons (52x82cm-20x32in) s. canvas on panel prov.exhib.lit. 30-Oct-2 Christie's, Rockefeller NY #25/R est:40000-60000
Works on paper
£816 $1298 €1200 Chemin (49x34cm-19x13in) chl prov. 24-Mar-3 Tajan, Paris #177
£816 $1298 €1200 Campement militaire. Canards sur l'Oise (11x19cm-4x7in) crayon ink chl pair prov. 24-Mar-3 Tajan, Paris #175
£816 $1298 €1200 Village au bord de l'Oise (28x44cm-11x17in) chl. 24-Mar-3 Tajan, Paris #176
£1225 $1948 €1800 Vaches pres de l'Oise (28x43cm-11x17in) sanguine prov. 24-Mar-3 Tajan, Paris #168/R
£1701 $2704 €2500 Bords de l'Oise (32x49cm-13x19in) chl prov. 24-Mar-3 Tajan, Paris #166/R

DAUBIGNY, Charles François (attrib) (1817-1878) French
£473 $738 €700 Paysage en bord de foret (31x47cm-12x19in) s. 27-Mar-3 Maigret, Paris #332
Works on paper
£1329 $2100 €2100 Parc du Chateau de Saint-Cloud (21x31cm-8x12in) mono.i. W/C. 2-Dec-2 Rieunier, Paris #38/R

DAUBIGNY, Karl (1846-1886) French
£1092 $1703 €1638 River landscape in summer (25x40cm-10x16in) s. 6-Nov-2 Dobiaschofsky, Bern #433/R est:3500 (S.FR 2500)

DAUCHEZ, Andre (1870-1943) French
£986 $1587 €1400 Moulin a mer au pays bigouden (65x92cm-26x36in) s. 11-May-3 Thierry & Lannon, Brest #157 est:1400-1600
Works on paper
£278 $453 €400 Bord de mer (18x25cm-7x10in) s. chl. 19-Jul-3 Thierry & Lannon, Brest #404

DAUCHOT, Gabriel (1927-) French
£335 $550 €503 Sad lover (79x41cm-31x16in) s. i.verso. 5-Feb-3 Doyle, New York #57/R
£633 $987 €1000 L'atelier de l'artiste (54x73cm-21x29in) s.d.1953. 20-Oct-2 Claude Boisgirard, Paris #91/R
Works on paper
£283 $439 €450 L'homme au bouquet de fleurs (49x31cm-19x12in) s. W/C ink. 30-Oct-2 Artcurial Briest, Paris #269

DAUDELIN, Charles (1920-) Canadian
£887 $1446 €1331 Untitled (33x51cm-13x20in) s.d.65 acrylic. 12-Feb-3 Iegor de Saint Hippolyte, Montreal #51/R (C.D 2200)

DAUDET, Henri (19th C) French
£1572 $2452 €2358 Views of Paris (21x33cm-8x13in) s. panel two. 6-Nov-2 Dobiaschofsky, Bern #434/R est:4500 (S.FR 3600)

DAUMIER, Honore (1808-1879) French
£51282 $80000 €76923 Le premier bain (15x23cm-6x9in) init. panel prov.exhib.lit. 7-Nov-2 Christie's, Rockefeller NY #207/R est:100000-150000
Prints
£2432 $3795 €3600 Ventre legislatif (28x43cm-11x17in) lithograph. 31-Mar-3 Tajan, Paris #300
£3397 $5368 €5300 Grand escalier du Palais de justive. Vue de face. lithograph. 14-Nov-2 Libert, Castor, Paris #69/R est:1500
£4595 $7168 €6800 Rue Transnonain (29x44cm-11x17in) lithograph. 31-Mar-3 Tajan, Paris #299/R
£6731 $10635 €10500 Le ventre legislatif. lithograph. 14-Nov-2 Libert, Castor, Paris #62 est:3500
£8013 $12660 €12500 Rue Transnonain, le 15 avril 1834. lithograph. 14-Nov-2 Libert, Castor, Paris #63/R est:7000
£32051 $50000 €48077 Untitled. col lithograph woodcut 3000 exec.c.1822-72 sold with a catalogue. 14-Oct-2 Butterfields, San Francisco #1116/R est:80000-100000
Sculpture
£3333 $5500 €4800 L'avocat saluant (15cm-6in) s.num.20/30 brown pat bronze st.f.Valsuani exec.c.1840-45 lit. 2-Jul-3 Artcurial Briest, Paris #629/R est:4500-6000
£3423 $5512 €5135 Bust of Charles Merlot Francois Lameth (14cm-6in) num.20/30 lit. 26-Feb-3 Museumsbygningen, Copenhagen #45/R est:40000-50000 (D.KR 38000)

£3604 $5802 €5406 Bust of Jaques Antoine Adrian Delors (22cm-9in) num.25/25 bronze lit. 26-Feb-3 Museumsbygningen, Copenhagen #44/R est:40000-50000 (D.KR 40000)
£4808 $7452 €7500 Le rieur edente (16x12x9cm-6x5x4in) 7-Dec-2 Hauswedell & Nolte, Hamburg #619/R est:10000
£14103 $22000 €21155 Ratapoil (44cm-17in) s. brown pat. bronze st.f.Alexis Rudier cast c.1925 prov.lit. 7-Nov-2 Christie's, Rockefeller NY #208/R est:25000-35000
£35484 $55000 €53226 Le portier parisien. Bourgeois en promenade. L'elegant. Lamateur surpris (17cm-7in) brown pat. bronze set of four cast 1963-64. 4-Nov-2 Phillips, New York #22/R est:80000-120000
£322581 $500000 €483872 Bustes de trente-six parlementaires. bronze conceived c.1832-1835 cast 1955-1960 prov.exhib.lit. 4-Nov-2 Phillips, New York #23/R est:650000-850000

Works on paper
£3019 $4800 €4529 Etude d'homme accroupi (9x11cm-4x4in) init. chk wash prov.exhib.lit. 27-Feb-3 Christie's, Rockefeller NY #6/R
£9032 $14000 €13548 Homme (8x6cm-3x2in) init. pen ink wash lit. 26-Sep-2 Christie's, Rockefeller NY #504/R est:2000-3000
£14815 $24000 €22223 Violoniste chantant (30x22cm-12x9in) s. pencil chk pen ink wash. 22-Jan-3 Christie's, Rockefeller NY #112/R est:30000
£24845 $40000 €37268 Le boucher (31x25cm-12x10in) init. brush wash conte crayon chl executed c.1860 prov.exhib. 8-May-3 Christie's, Rockefeller NY #116/R est:50000-70000

DAUMIER, Honore (attrib) (1808-1879) French
£1950 $3003 €3100 Palace de Justice (31x24cm-12x9in) board prov. 28-Oct-2 Il Ponte, Milan #218/R

Works on paper
£449 $700 €674 First class cougar. pen ink. 21-Sep-2 Harvey Clar, Oakland #1014
£481 $750 €722 Two spectators. 21-Sep-2 Harvey Clar, Oakland #1412
£766 $1240 €1111 Group of three figures looking at a servant (29x22cm-11x9in) init.i. crayon pen. 26-May-3 Rasmussen, Copenhagen #1601/R (D.KR 8000)
£1731 $2683 €2700 Scene de requisitoire (8x14cm-3x6in) mono. pen ink wash over crayon. 4-Dec-2 Piasa, Paris #120/R

DAUMIER, Jean (20th C) French
£250 $388 €375 By the riverbank (61x90cm-24x35in) s. 3-Nov-2 Lots Road, London #355
£705 $1100 €1058 Summer landscape with figures (61x91cm-24x36in) s. 12-Apr-3 Weschler, Washington #541/R est:700-900

DAUPHIN, Eugène Baptiste Emile (1857-1930) French
£524 $828 €786 Paysage de Provence (46x65cm-18x26in) s. 17-Nov-2 Koller, Geneva #1297 (S.FR 1200)

Works on paper
£426 $711 €600 Vue presumee de la Rade de Toulon (16x25cm-6x10in) s.d.1886 W/C prov. 20-Jun-3 Piasa, Paris #43

DAUR, Hermann (1870-1925) Swiss
£1887 $2943 €3000 Early spring in Oetlingen (50x63cm-20x25in) s. prov.lit. 20-Sep-2 Karlheinz Kaupp, Staufen #2099/R est:3000

DAUVERGNE, Anatole (1812-1870) Belgian
£552 $877 €800 Personnage assis (47x81cm-19x32in) s.d.1838. 9-Mar-3 Feletin, Province #140

DAUVERGNE, Louis (1828-1899) French
£2500 $3925 €3750 Midday rest (93x74cm-37x29in) s. 21-Nov-2 Christie's, Kensington #15/R est:3000-5000

DAUZATS, Adrien (1804-1868) French
£1800 $2808 €2700 Cairo bazaar (25x18cm-10x7in) s.d.1839 panel. 15-Oct-2 Sotheby's, London #160/R est:2000-3000
£9259 $15000 €13889 Jerusalem, a view of the city walls with the gate of Jaffa and the tower of David (33x41cm-13x16in) s.i. prov.exhib.lit. 24-Jan-3 Christie's, Rockefeller NY #128/R est:18000-22000

Works on paper
£608 $949 €900 Interieur d'eglise (25x18cm-10x7in) W/C over crayon prov. 31-Mar-3 Piasa, Paris #75

DAVANZO, Marco (1872-?) Italian
£385 $596 €600 Loreto seen from Porto Recanati (26x37cm-10x15in) s.i.d.1919 board. 4-Dec-2 Finarte, Rome #802

DAVENPORT, Hayward M (fl.1898-1904) British
£2500 $3900 €3750 H.M.S Ophir leaving Portsmouth, March 15th 1901 (75x151cm-30x59in) s.d.1901 sold with letters and book. 23-Apr-3 Rupert Toovey, Partridge Green #85/R est:2500-3500

DAVENPORT, Ian (1966-) British
£2500 $4175 €3625 Poured painting, black (91x91cm-36x36in) gloss paint board prov.exhib. 26-Jun-3 Sotheby's, London #300/R est:2500-3500

DAVENPORT, William Slocum (1868-?) American
£352 $550 €528 Audenarde, Belguim. s.i. 9-Aug-2 Skinner, Bolton #844

DAVEY, Randall (1887-1964) American
£5031 $8000 €7547 Portrait of a girl with a yellow hat (61x51cm-24x20in) s. prov. 5-Mar-3 Sotheby's, New York #26/R est:7000-10000

DAVID, Annick (20th C) ?
£705 $1114 €1100 Composition (130x162cm-51x64in) s. 18-Nov-2 Rieunier, Paris #161

DAVID, Gerard (studio) (1460-1523) Flemish
£555556 $900000 €833334 Holy Family (41x33cm-16x13in) panel prov.exhib.lit. 24-Jan-3 Christie's, Rockefeller NY #36/R est:700000-900000

DAVID, Giovanni (1743-1790) Italian
£12346 $20000 €18519 Allegory of winter, an old man warming his hands on a brazier (88x63cm-35x25in) prov. 24-Jan-3 Christie's, Rockefeller NY #148/R est:10000-15000

DAVID, Gustave (1824-1891) French

Works on paper
£258 $408 €400 Le violoniste (23x17cm-9x7in) s. W/C gouache. 17-Dec-2 Rossini, Paris #20

DAVID, Hermine (1886-1971) French
£331 $529 €460 Les moissons (22x27cm-9x11in) s. prov. 18-May-3 Charbonneaux, Paris #248
£426 $711 €600 Personnages au bout de la jetee (33x22cm-13x9in) s. wood. 23-Jun-3 Claude Boisgirard, Paris #76
£590 $944 €820 Petit port de peche (22x27cm-9x11in) s. panel prov. 18-May-3 Charbonneaux, Paris #249/R
£780 $1303 €1100 Les remparts de St Paul (78x58cm-31x23in) s.i.d. 17-Jun-3 Claude Boisgirard, Paris #46/R

Works on paper
£243 $386 €350 Village au moulin (12x19cm-5x7in) s. graphite col crayon dr. 29-Apr-3 Artcurial Briest, Paris #229
£284 $474 €400 Portrait de fillette (33x25cm-13x10in) s.d.fevrier 1937 sanguine. 18-Jun-3 Charbonneaux, Paris #38/R
£360 $576 €500 Cuba, port de peche (21x26cm-8x10in) st.sig. pencil dr prov. 18-May-3 Charbonneaux, Paris #240
£360 $576 €500 Dromadaires a Carthage (18x27cm-7x11in) s.d.1921 W/C prov. 18-May-3 Charbonneaux, Paris #241
£360 $576 €500 Cotes de Saint-Vaast-La-Hougue (27x42cm-11x17in) s.d.1947 W/C prov. 18-May-3 Charbonneaux, Paris #247
£432 $691 €600 Saint-Vaast-La-Hougue (25x39cm-10x15in) s. W/C prov. 18-May-3 Charbonneaux, Paris #243
£453 $725 €630 Personnages orientaux pres de la grotte (20x29cm-8x11in) st.sig. W/C prov. 18-May-3 Charbonneaux, Paris #242
£461 $770 €650 Les meules de foin (24x31cm-9x12in) s.d. W/C. 23-Jun-3 Claude Boisgirard, Paris #72/R
£576 $921 €800 Jungle cubaine (24x34cm-9x13in) st.sig. pencil W/C prov. 18-May-3 Charbonneaux, Paris #239
£590 $944 €820 Cafe du Dome a Montparnasse (18x27cm-7x11in) s. pencil dr prov. 18-May-3 Charbonneaux, Paris #238
£662 $1059 €920 Autoportrait (26x19cm-10x7in) s. W/C pencil prov. 18-May-3 Charbonneaux, Paris #244/R
£791 $1266 €1100 Saint-Vaast-La-Hougue (25x33cm-10x13in) s.d.1947 W/C gouache prov. 18-May-3 Charbonneaux, Paris #246
£833 $1308 €1300 Portugal, rue de village (65x50cm-26x20in) s. mixed media cardboard prov. 11-Dec-2 Maigret, Paris #103/R

DAVID, Jacques-Louis (1748-1825) French
£12903 $20000 €19355 Venitienne a sa toilette (148x96cm-58x38in) s.d.1860 exhib. 29-Oct-2 Sotheby's, New York #100/R est:20000-30000

Works on paper
£16892 $26351 €25000 Etde pour le Sacre (11x18cm-4x7in) i. i.verso pen ink crayon prov.lit. 26-Mar-3 Piasa, Paris #86/R est:15000

DAVID, Jean-Louis (1792-1868) French

Works on paper
£316 $491 €500 Mother and child by castle pond (27x21cm-11x8in) s. W/C over pencil htd white. 25-Sep-2 Neumeister, Munich #392/R

DAVID, Jose Maria (1944-) ?
Sculpture
£2000 $3180 €3000 Pug dog (39cm-15in) s.i.num.111/121 brown pat bronze st.f. 29-Apr-3 Sotheby's, Olympia #170/R est:2000-3000
£2000 $3180 €3000 Boar (36cm-14in) s.i.num.4/8 brown pat bronze s.t.f. 29-Apr-3 Sotheby's, Olympia #171/R est:2000-3000
£5036 $8259 €7000 Les kangourous (31x64x22cm-12x25x9in) s.d.27.4.88 num.2/8 brown pat bronze. 4-Jun-3 Marc Kohn, Paris #73/R est:12000-15000
£28000 $44520 €42000 Hippopotamus (40x100cm-16x39in) s.num.3/7 brown pat bronze. 29-Apr-3 Sotheby's, Olympia #174/R est:6000-8000

DAVID, Leonie (19/20th C) French
£522 $814 €783 Family of dolls (32x46cm-13x18in) s. 16-Sep-2 Philippe Schuler, Zurich #3464/R (S.FR 1200)

DAVID, Pierre Jean (1788-1856) French
Sculpture
£1346 $2127 €2100 General Napoleon Bonaparte (16x16cm-6x6in) s.i.d. pat bronze medallion exhib.lit. 18-Nov-2 Tajan, Paris #6/R est:1500-1800
£3269 $5133 €5100 Talma (44x19x31cm-17x7x12in) i. plaster. 13-Dec-2 Peschetau-Badin Godeau & Leroy, Paris #35/R

DAVID, R B (19th C) British
£241 $380 €380 Winter landscape with figures by a windmill (29x24cm-11x9in) s. 27-Nov-2 James Adam, Dublin #128/R
£304 $480 €480 Pastoral landscape with sheep drover (29x24cm-11x9in) s. 27-Nov-2 James Adam, Dublin #130/R

DAVID, Villiers (1906-1985) British
£600 $984 €870 Still life with tulips and hat (39x49cm-15x19in) s. 9-Jun-3 Bonhams, Bath #101/R

DAVIDSON, Allan Douglas (1873-1932) British
£400 $620 €600 Portrait of a scantily clad young woman with long hair (61x51cm-24x20in) s. 30-Sep-2 Bonhams, Ipswich #379/R
£400 $620 €600 Portrait of a young girl (41x35cm-16x14in) s. 3-Dec-2 Bonhams, Knightsbridge #61
£520 $868 €754 Standing female nude (30x15cm-12x6in) s. board. 24-Jun-3 Bonhams, Knowle #82
£533 $885 €773 Solitude (23cm-9in circular) s. s.i.verso panel. 16-Jun-3 Waddingtons, Toronto #105a/R est:800-1200 (C.D 1200)
£550 $897 €825 Head and shoulders portrait of a young lady with blond hair (51x41cm-20x16in) s. 14-Feb-3 Keys, Aylsham #372/R
£700 $1099 €1050 Highland soldier and sailor in whites (77x50cm-30x20in) s. 10-Dec-2 Rosebery Fine Art, London #611
£1829 $3000 €2652 Artist's model (36x18cm-14x7in) s. board. 4-Jun-3 Doyle, New York #38 est:2000-3000

DAVIDSON, Bessie (1879-1965) Australian
£3400 $5474 €4930 Bowl of flowers (40x31cm-16x12in) s. s.d.1952 verso board. 12-May-3 Joel, Victoria #370 est:10000-15000 (A.D 8500)
£4345 $7256 €6300 Bouquet de fleurs (46x38cm-18x15in) s. panel. 10-Jul-3 Artcurial Briest, Paris #154/R est:8000-10000
£17176 $27137 €25764 Still life with blossoms and books (63x91cm-25x36in) s. board. 2-Apr-3 Christie's, Melbourne #16/R est:30000-40000 (A.D 45000)

DAVIDSON, C (19th C) British
Works on paper
£640 $992 €960 Red hill, rural landscape with figures (15x25cm-6x10in) s.i. W/C. 1-Nov-2 Moore Allen & Innocent, Cirencester #225/R

DAVIDSON, Charles (1824-1902) British
Works on paper
£550 $852 €825 Deer in Knole Park (44x60cm-17x24in) W/C prov. 3-Dec-2 Sotheby's, Olympia #108/R

DAVIDSON, Charles Topham (1848-?) British
Works on paper
£700 $1141 €1015 Evening, mooring seine boat (46x74cm-18x29in) s. indis d.1893 pencil W/C. 17-Jul-3 Tennants, Leyburn #698/R
£800 $1272 €1200 Regent's canal (40x29cm-16x11in) s. W/C. 26-Feb-3 Cheffins Grain & Comins, Cambridge #523/R
£3200 $5216 €4640 Early morning Seine boats going out (60x90cm-24x35in) s.d.1889 W/C. 17-Jul-3 Tennants, Leyburn #699/R est:1000-1500

DAVIDSON, Colin (1968-) Irish
£650 $1007 €975 Harbour at Roundstone (30x41cm-12x16in) s. board. 2-Oct-2 John Ross, Belfast #41
£800 $1272 €1200 Boat reflection, Roundstone (30x28cm-12x11in) s. board. 5-Mar-3 John Ross, Belfast #160
£2800 $4340 €4200 Reclining nude study (71x127cm-28x50in) s. 2-Oct-2 John Ross, Belfast #123 est:2200-2500

DAVIDSON, Daniel Pender (1885-1933) British
£850 $1326 €1275 Hollyhocks (54x36cm-21x14in) s.d.1919. 17-Sep-2 Sotheby's, Olympia #52/R

DAVIDSON, Jeremiah (1695-1745) British
£3000 $4950 €4350 Portrait of Elizabeth Dunch, Lady Bishop of Parham and her daughter Mary (109x129cm-43x51in) s.i.d.1730 prov. 2-Jul-3 Sotheby's, Olympia #6/R est:3000-5000

DAVIDSON, Jo (1883-1952) American
Sculpture
£1392 $2200 €2088 Bust of Dorothy Hirshon (46x20x20cm-18x8x8in) s.d.1933 plaster black marble stand prov. 26-Nov-2 Christie's, Rockefeller NY #29/R est:1200-1800

DAVIDSON, Lilian Lucy (1879-1954) Irish
£12000 $18600 €18000 Market day (71x91cm-28x36in) mono. 2-Oct-2 John Ross, Belfast #116 est:15000-20000
£26087 $42783 €36000 Fashions at the fair (71x92cm-28x36in) s. 28-May-3 Bonhams & James Adam, Dublin #87/R est:20000-25000
Works on paper
£423 $701 €600 Figure on a turf cart (21x28cm-8x11in) s. mixed media print. 10-Jun-3 James Adam, Dublin #267/R
£1000 $1590 €1500 Pots and pans (45x20cm-18x8in) mono. pastel. 5-Mar-3 John Ross, Belfast #27 est:1200-1500

DAVIDSON, Nora (fl.1926-1927) British
Works on paper
£300 $464 €450 Street scene (28x42cm-11x17in) s. W/C. 30-Sep-2 Sotheby's, Olympia #163/R

DAVIDSON, Patrick (?) ?
Works on paper
£283 $436 €450 Le canot de sauvetage Bailli de Suffren II de la SNSM (40x59cm-16x23in) s.i.d. W/C. 27-Oct-2 Lesieur & Le Bars, Le Havre #91

DAVIDSON, Rowland (20th C) British
£650 $1007 €975 Cobbler (41x30cm-16x12in) s. 2-Oct-2 John Ross, Belfast #35
£950 $1511 €1425 Play time (56x45cm-22x18in) s. 5-Mar-3 John Ross, Belfast #93
£1154 $1812 €1800 Young girl holding dog (51x41cm-20x16in) s. 19-Nov-2 Whyte's, Dublin #118/R est:1000-1200

DAVIDSON, Thomas (19th C) British
£1400 $2184 €2100 Street encounter, Ancient Rome (91x71cm-36x28in) s.d.1886. 6-Nov-2 Bonhams, Chester #398/R est:1500-2000

DAVIDSON, Willy (1890-1933) German
£2436 $3776 €3800 Venice (57x79cm-22x31in) s. 7-Dec-2 Ketterer, Hamburg #171/R est:4000-4500

DAVIE, Alan (1920-) British
£968 $1500 €1452 Untitled (53x41cm-21x16in) s.d.60 oil paper on masonite prov.exhib. 26-Sep-2 Christie's, Rockefeller NY #733/R est:3000-5000
£2979 $4826 €4200 Implements for a sweet sorcery (55x75cm-22x30in) s.d.64 tempera cardboard prov. 26-May-3 Christie's, Milan #296/R est:3000-4000
£3046 $4966 €4600 He-he wheel (41x52cm-16x20in) s.i. paper painted 1961 prov.exhib. 3-Feb-3 Cornette de St.Cyr, Paris #399
£3546 $5745 €5000 Lla (42x53cm-17x21in) s.d.59 paper on panel prov.exhib. 26-May-3 Christie's, Milan #349/R est:3000-4000
£5000 $7750 €7500 All-seeing fish No.2 (51x61cm-20x24in) s.d.July 1967 verso prov. 3-Dec-2 Bonhams, New Bond Street #118/R est:6000-8000
£5161 $8000 €7742 Silver serpent (122x152cm-48x60in) s. i.d.July 79 verso prov. 26-Sep-2 Christie's, Rockefeller NY #735/R est:4000-6000
£7500 $11624 €11250 Witch gong no.12 (152x183cm-60x72in) painted May 1974 lit. 4-Dec-2 Sotheby's, London #87/R est:8000-12000
Works on paper
£280 $465 €406 12964B (29x23cm-11x9in) s. pen ink. 13-Jun-3 Lyon & Turnbull, Edinburgh #126

£950 $1500 €1425 Glass for snake juice (49x76cm-19x30in) s.d.July 1963 gouache prov. 22-Apr-3 Butterfields, San Francisco #6067/R est:2500-3500
£1200 $1908 €1800 Drawing no.85 (27x42cm-11x17in) s.d.8.67 brush ink prov. 6-Mar-3 Christie's, Kensington #256/R est:600-800
£1550 $2449 €2325 Game for moonlight (55x76cm-22x30in) s.i.d.1968 ink gouache wash prov.exhib. 27-Nov-2 Sotheby's, Olympia #225/R est:1500-2000
£2000 $3180 €3000 Studies for a figure-mask no.3 (57x82cm-22x32in) s.i.d.1975 gouache. 6-Mar-3 Christie's, Kensington #255/R est:2500-3500
£2400 $3816 €3600 Bird fingers (57x82cm-22x32in) s.d.Sept 75 gouache. 6-Mar-3 Christie's, Kensington #254/R est:2500-3500
£3000 $4770 €4500 Abstract (27x38cm-11x15in) s.d.Nov 68 gouache W/C. 26-Feb-3 Sotheby's, Olympia #345/R est:3000-5000

DAVIE, Karen (1965-) American
£13924 $22000 €20886 Hysteric (183x244cm-72x96in) s. i.d.1998 verso prov.exhib.lit. 14-Nov-2 Christie's, Rockefeller NY #341/R est:12000-18000
£14375 $23000 €21563 Relapse (183x244cm-72x96in) s.i.d.2000 prov. 15-May-3 Christie's, Rockefeller NY #342/R est:12000-18000

DAVIEL, Leon (20th C) French
£250 $410 €363 Portrait of Sir Lovelace T Stainer, Bishop of Shrewsbury (122x91cm-48x36in) s. 6-Jun-3 Halls, Shrewsbury #825

DAVIES, A B (1862-1928) American
Works on paper
£531 $850 €797 Rural landscape (28x38cm-11x15in) s. W/C. 12-Jan-3 William Jenack, New York #343

DAVIES, Albert Webster (1890-?) American
£2097 $3250 €3146 White Inn (46x61cm-18x24in) s. 29-Oct-2 Doyle, New York #67/R est:3000-4000
£2419 $3750 €3629 Summers day (46x61cm-18x24in) s. masonite. 29-Oct-2 Doyle, New York #68/R est:3000-4000
£2419 $3750 €3629 Antiques for sale (41x51cm-16x20in) s. canvasboard. 29-Oct-2 Doyle, New York #68a/R est:3000-4000

DAVIES, Arthur B (1862-1928) American
£1951 $3200 €2829 Study of two female nudes in a landscape (34x39cm-13x15in) canvas on board. 5-Jun-3 Swann Galleries, New York #76/R est:1500-2500
£15432 $25000 €23148 Heart's hansel (41x28cm-16x11in) s. i.verso tempera on gessoed panel prov. 21-May-3 Sotheby's, New York #158/R est:15000-25000
Works on paper
£247 $400 €371 Kneeling figure (36x25cm-14x10in) st.sig. i. pastel. 24-Jan-3 Freeman, Philadelphia #129/R
£313 $500 €470 Landscape (15x23cm-6x9in) i.verso pastel. 15-Mar-3 Jeffery Burchard, Florida #14/R
£519 $800 €779 Female nude (36x23cm-14x9in) s. chl pencil crayon. 4-Sep-2 Christie's, Rockefeller NY #359/R
£793 $1300 €1190 Bathers by a river (51x36cm-20x14in) bears sig.i.d.1921 W/C htd white. 5-Feb-3 Doyle, New York #17/R est:1500-2000
£4938 $8000 €7407 Tiger (25x39cm-10x15in) s. W/C gouache executed c.1890 prov.exhib. 21-May-3 Sotheby's, New York #62/R est:5000-7000

DAVIES, Arthur E (1893-1988) British
£460 $764 €667 Runham Mill, near Gt Yarmouth (15x20cm-6x8in) s. board. 12-Jun-3 Gorringes, Lewes #1745
£500 $785 €750 Horning Mill, Norfolk (13x20cm-5x8in) s. 13-Dec-2 Keys, Aylsham #723/R
£700 $1092 €1050 Blakeney, Norfolk (23x30cm-9x12in) s. exhib. 18-Oct-2 Keys, Aylsham #772
£800 $1304 €1200 Thorpe Old Hall (33x41cm-13x16in) s. 14-Feb-3 Keys, Aylsham #642/R
Works on paper
£250 $380 €375 Happisburgh Church, Norfolk (28x38cm-11x15in) s. W/C. 16-Aug-2 Keys, Aylsham #566
£250 $418 €363 Runton Church, Norfolk (23x30cm-9x12in) s. W/C. 20-Jun-3 Keys, Aylsham #601
£280 $440 €420 Norfolk landscape with church in distance (30x38cm-12x15in) s. W/C. 13-Dec-2 Keys, Aylsham #595
£420 $655 €630 Three Mills Runham Marshes. s.d.1972 W/C. 18-Oct-2 Keys, Aylsham #621
£420 $701 €609 Cardiganshire farm (30x46cm-12x18in) s.d.1968 W/C. 20-Jun-3 Keys, Aylsham #606/R
£480 $749 €720 Racing yachts on a corner of the Broads (25x33cm-10x13in) s. W/C. 18-Oct-2 Keys, Aylsham #619
£500 $780 €750 Cromer from the beach (28x38cm-11x15in) s. W/C. 11-Apr-3 Keys, Aylsham #558/R
£500 $825 €725 Kimberley Green, Norfolk (23x35cm-9x14in) s.i.d.May 27th 1960 W/C. 1-Jul-3 Bonhams, Norwich #86/R
£520 $858 €754 Mousehold Heath, Norwich (31x40cm-12x16in) s. W/C. 1-Jul-3 Bonhams, Norwich #85
£600 $936 €900 Cathedral Close, Norwich (28x38cm-11x15in) s. W/C. 18-Oct-2 Keys, Aylsham #623
£650 $1060 €975 Ash Tree Farm MIll (28x38cm-11x15in) s. W/C. 14-Feb-3 Keys, Aylsham #608/R
£680 $1061 €1020 Fye Bridge, Norwich (30x38cm-12x15in) s. W/C. 18-Oct-2 Keys, Aylsham #622
£680 $1068 €1020 Bishop Palace entrance gate, Norwich (28x38cm-11x15in) s. W/C. 13-Dec-2 Keys, Aylsham #593

DAVIES, Brian (20th C) ?
£380 $593 €570 Still life study of shrimps, lemon, glass, bread and pewter jug on stone ledge (29x24cm-11x9in) s. 12-Sep-2 Rupert Toovey, Partridge Green #1445/R
£650 $1014 €975 Still life study of violin on table surrounded by various objects (49x74cm-19x29in) s. 12-Sep-2 Rupert Toovey, Partridge Green #1444/R

DAVIES, David (1864-1939) Australian
£2000 $3220 €2900 Evening, Dieppe (35x45cm-14x18in) s. 12-May-3 Joel, Victoria #245 est:6000-8000 (A.D 5000)
£4600 $7682 €6670 Street scene, Naples (44x59cm-17x23in) i.verso. 25-Jun-3 Cheffins, Cambridge #814
£11388 $17423 €17082 Cottages in snow, North Wales (51x61cm-20x24in) s. i.verso painted 1906 prov.exhib. 26-Aug-2 Sotheby's, Paddington #545/R est:40000-60000 (A.D 32000)
Works on paper
£1724 $2569 €2586 Still life (37x30cm-15x12in) s. W/C. 27-Aug-2 Christie's, Melbourne #284 est:3000-5000 (A.D 4500)
£1908 $3015 €2862 Moonrise (35x48cm-14x19in) s. W/C pastel prov. 2-Apr-3 Christie's, Melbourne #26/R est:5000-7000 (A.D 5000)
£2481 $3920 €3722 Peasant woman in a French village (36x30cm-14x12in) s. W/C. 2-Apr-3 Christie's, Melbourne #41/R est:4000-6000 (A.D 6500)

DAVIES, Gordon (1926-) British
£350 $546 €525 Pair of boots and plant on a window ledge (20x31cm-8x12in) s.d.73 panel. 9-Oct-2 Woolley & Wallis, Salisbury #234/R

DAVIES, Harold Christopher (1891-1976) American
£209 $350 €303 Untitled (51x61cm-20x24in) s. indis d.1968 oil tempera on canvasboard prov. 29-Jun-3 Butterfields, Los Angeles #7092/R

DAVIES, Ivon (20th C) British
£360 $562 €540 Stalin, Roosevelt and Churchill at Tehran. 18-Sep-2 Hobbs Parker, Ashford #464

DAVIES, James Hey (1844-1930) British
£313 $500 €470 Snow scene with elderly man and girl feeding chickens (53x36cm-21x14in) s. 15-Mar-3 Eldred, East Dennis #416/R
£600 $930 €900 Rural landscape with pond, geese and farmhouse (48x64cm-19x25in) 4-Dec-2 Neal & Fletcher, Woodbridge #244
£900 $1467 €1350 Harvesting scene (41x56cm-16x22in) s. 28-Jan-3 Peter Francis, Wales #22/R est:600-900

DAVIES, Kenneth Southworth (1925-) American
£2922 $4500 €4383 Butterpress (23x23cm-9x9in) s. board. 24-Oct-2 Shannon's, Milford #212/R est:2000-3000

DAVIES, Norman Prescott (1862-1915) British
£800 $1256 €1200 Portrait of a young girl (38x28cm-15x11in) s.d.1896. 19-Nov-2 Bonhams, Leeds #207/R
£8861 $14000 €13292 Grecian muse (33x25cm-13x10in) s.d.1892 panel prov. 23-Apr-3 Christie's, Rockefeller NY #132/R est:10000-15000

DAVIES, Roland (1904-1993) British
£450 $729 €675 Knightsbridge (30x41cm-12x16in) s. 23-Jan-3 Christie's, Kensington #246/R

DAVIES, Shona Rapira (20th C) New Zealander?
£273 $420 €410 His role for woman (119x88cm-47x35in) s. acrylic on board. 4-Sep-2 Dunbar Sloane, Wellington #161 (NZ.D 900)

DAVIES, William (1826-1910) British
£3125 $5000 €4688 View of Glen Finart, Argyleshire with sheep in the foreground (36x51cm-14x20in) s.d.1894 i.d.verso prov. 14-May-3 Butterfields, San Francisco #1144/R est:3000-5000

DAVILA, Alberto (1912-) Peruvian
£342 $550 €513 Abstract landscape with figures (81x64cm-32x25in) masonite. 15-Jan-3 Boos Gallery, Michigan #261

DAVILA, Juan (1946-) Chilean
£4821 $7425 €7232 Love (99x90cm-39x35in) s. i.d.1993 verso prov.exhib. 8-Sep-2 Sotheby's, Melbourne #5/R est:15000-25000 (A.D 13500)
£5520 $8390 €8280 Hybrid Venus (67x57cm-26x22in) s.d.89 wood prov. 28-Aug-2 Deutscher-Menzies, Melbourne #146/R est:15000-20000 (A.D 15400)

Works on paper
£2308 $3669 €3462 Portrait of Bungaree (242x160cm-95x63in) s.d.1991 W/C screenprint exhib. 4-Mar-3 Deutscher-Menzies, Melbourne #186/R est:7000-9000 (A.D 6000)

DAVIS, Arthur A (fl.1877-1905) British
£759 $1200 €1139 Fox hounds (51x76cm-20x30in) s.d.1910. 17-Nov-2 CRN Auctions, Cambridge #31/R
£6135 $10000 €9203 Entering the cover. At fault. The Chase (61x91cm-24x36in) s.d.1886 set of three. 11-Feb-3 Bonhams & Doyles, New York #111/R est:10000-15000

Works on paper
£270 $432 €405 Hunting scene with riders and hounds in dense rural setting (25x36cm-10x14in) s. W/C. 10-Jan-3 Biddle & Webb, Birmingham #224

DAVIS, Brad (1942-) American
£1392 $2200 €2088 Dusk-hanging lake falls II (147x137cm-58x54in) s. i.d.1987 verso acrylic prov. 13-Nov-2 Sotheby's, New York #608/R

DAVIS, C (?) ?
£1763 $2750 €2645 Landscape (71x91cm-28x36in) 11-Apr-3 Du Mouchelle, Detroit #2051/R est:1000-2000

DAVIS, Charles Harold (1856-1933) American
£1321 $2100 €1982 Autumn woods (33x40cm-13x16in) s. exhib. 7-Mar-3 Skinner, Boston #447/R est:1800-2200
£2564 $4000 €3846 Summer landscape, cows in foreground (36x43cm-14x17in) s. 15-Oct-2 Winter Associates, Plainville #68 est:2500-5000
£3045 $4750 €4568 Autumn landscape with boulders in foreground (30x41cm-12x16in) s. 15-Oct-2 Winter Associates, Plainville #67 est:3000-6000
£3097 $4800 €4646 Spring (51x69cm-20x27in) s.i.on stretcher exhib. 2-Nov-2 North East Auctions, Portsmouth #68/R est:4000-6000
£5937 $9500 €8609 Grey twilight (51x69cm-20x27in) s. i. on stretcher prov. 16-May-3 Skinner, Boston #80/R est:10000-15000

DAVIS, Edward Thompson (1833-1867) British
£680 $1081 €1020 Words of peace (66x81cm-26x32in) i.verso paper on canvas. 5-Mar-3 Bonhams, Bury St Edmunds #359/R

DAVIS, Frederic (1919-1996) French
£811 $1265 €1200 Composition (50x65cm-20x26in) s. paint paper on panel. 31-Mar-3 Rossini, Paris #111/R

DAVIS, Frederick (fl.1853-1892) British
Works on paper
£401 $633 €625 Kells Castle (25x47cm-10x19in) s.d.1869 W/C. 12-Nov-2 Mealy's, Castlecomer #1228

DAVIS, Frederick William (1862-1919) British
£520 $822 €780 Merry toper (41x30cm-16x12in) s.d.1889. 27-Nov-2 Bonhams, Knowle #240

DAVIS, Gene (1920-1985) American
£1667 $2600 €2501 Royal wagon (91x79cm-36x31in) i.d.1979 s.verso acrylic. 30-Mar-3 Susanin's, Chicago #6090/R est:3000-4000

DAVIS, Gerald (?) ?
£255 $397 €400 Form in flight (39x29cm-15x11in) s.d.86 mixed media. 6-Nov-2 James Adam, Dublin #36/R
£282 $468 €400 Man in landscape (30x20cm-12x8in) s.d.1977 board. 10-Jun-3 James Adam, Dublin #78/R
£315 $492 €460 Night (15x40cm-6x16in) s.d.87 board. 8-Apr-3 James Adam, Dublin #148/R
£338 $561 €480 In the shimmering dusk (40x51cm-16x20in) s.d.1977 board. 10-Jun-3 James Adam, Dublin #69/R
£342 $534 €500 Master of Mister J (40x30cm-16x12in) s.d.86 board. 8-Apr-3 James Adam, Dublin #7/R
£352 $585 €500 From the west (30x40cm-12x16in) s.d.80 board. 10-Jun-3 James Adam, Dublin #83/R
£423 $701 €600 Desert hills (48x58cm-19x23in) s.d.1977 board. 10-Jun-3 James Adam, Dublin #103/R
£425 $662 €620 Study for James Joyce (40x30cm-16x12in) s. board. 8-Apr-3 James Adam, Dublin #8/R
£479 $753 €700 City skyline (29x38cm-11x15in) s.d.74. 15-Apr-3 De Veres Art Auctions, Dublin #39
£493 $818 €700 Presence (40x31cm-16x12in) s.d. board. 10-Jun-3 James Adam, Dublin #84/R
£493 $818 €700 Evening forms (46x56cm-18x22in) s.d.1972 board. 10-Jun-3 James Adam, Dublin #102/R
£563 $935 €800 Olympus (48x38cm-19x15in) s.d.1974 board. 10-Jun-3 James Adam, Dublin #70/R
£613 $1017 €870 Nightscape (61x76cm-24x30in) s.d.1971. 10-Jun-3 James Adam, Dublin #248/R
£1477 $2377 €2200 Forms in a landscape (41x51cm-16x20in) s.d.1977 board prov. 18-Feb-3 Whyte's, Dublin #43/R est:1200-1700

DAVIS, Gerald Vivian (1899-1987) American
£11709 $18500 €17564 Hesitation (130x81cm-51x32in) s.d.24 s.i.d.verso exhib. 24-Apr-3 Shannon's, Milford #136/R est:20000-30000

DAVIS, H B (19/20th C) British
£300 $468 €450 Loch Lomond (50x75cm-20x30in) s.d.1925. 23-Sep-2 Bonhams, Chester #934

DAVIS, H W B (1833-1914) British
£1500 $2325 €2250 Cattle in riverside meadow (50x75cm-20x30in) s. 25-Sep-2 Wintertons, Lichfield #565/R est:1000-1500

DAVIS, Henry William Banks (1833-1914) British
£2600 $4082 €3900 Coastal landscape with sheep (20x30cm-8x12in) s. board. 19-Nov-2 Bonhams, Leeds #215/R est:2000-3000
£4600 $7268 €6670 Shadow of Evening, near Presteigne with cattle in apple orchard (152x79cm-60x31in) s.i.d.1890. 23-Jul-3 Brightwells, Leominster #983/R est:3000-4000
£8500 $13260 €12750 Coastal scene with cattle and sheep (50x75cm-20x30in) s.d.1887 exhib. 17-Oct-2 Lawrence, Crewkerne #489/R est:8000-10000
£30000 $47400 €45000 A spring morning (76x152cm-30x60in) s.i.d.1866 prov. 26-Nov-2 Christie's, London #119/R est:30000-50000

Works on paper
£16000 $25760 €24000 Portraits. pen ink oil on fan painted with other artists prov.exhib.lit. 20-Feb-3 Christie's, London #125/R est:15000

DAVIS, J Valentine (1854-1930) British
£740 $1214 €1110 Fenland (23x35cm-9x14in) s. 28-May-3 Mallams, Oxford #367/R

DAVIS, Jack (1924-) American
Works on paper
£1603 $2500 €2405 Children and dog assaulted by movie images (53x36cm-21x14in) s. ink W/C dyes. 9-Nov-2 Illustration House, New York #130/R est:2500-3500

DAVIS, John Scarlett (1804-1845) British
Works on paper
£1000 $1580 €1500 Rue St. Dennis, Paris (25x31cm-10x12in) grey blue wash pencil. 28-Nov-2 Sotheby's, London #289/R est:1000-1500
£1500 $2369 €2250 Rue St. Martin, Paris (15x11cm-6x4in) i. pencil htd bodycol prov. 28-Nov-2 Sotheby's, London #328/R est:1200-1800
£7500 $10725 €11250 Figures and dog on quayside in Paris (16x11cm-6x4in) s.i.d.1831 pencil ink W/C prov.exhib.lit. 22-Jan-3 Christie's, London #60/R est:10000

DAVIS, Kenn (20th C) American
£255 $400 €383 Student of a strange science (71x51cm-28x20in) s.d.55 i.verso. 28-Jul-2 Butterfields, San Francisco #3087

DAVIS, Laurence (1879-?) British
Works on paper
£260 $408 €390 Lowestoft (18x27cm-7x11in) s.i. W/C. 24-Jul-2 Hamptons Fine Art, Godalming #100/R

DAVIS, Lucien (1860-1941) British
Works on paper
£380 $623 €570 Lady in 17th century interior (34x23cm-13x9in) s. W/C. 2-Jun-3 David Duggleby, Scarborough #299

DAVIS, Lynn (1944-) American
Photographs
£4908 $8000 €7362 Indian Ocean, Zanzibar, Tanzania (70x70cm-28x28in) s.i.d.1997/98 num.4/10 gelatin silver print. 12-Feb-3 Christie's, Rockefeller NY #142/R est:6000-8000

DAVIS, Nicolaus (19/20th C) ?
£500 $785 €750 Two masted bargue in full sail (30x40cm-12x16in) s.i. canvas on board. 16-Apr-3 Christie's, Kensington #911/R

DAVIS, Noel Denholm (fl.1899-1939) British
Works on paper
£250 $418 €363 Distant thoughts (26x17cm-10x7in) s. pencil W/C. 26-Jun-3 Mellors & Kirk, Nottingham #836

DAVIS, Richard Barrett (attrib) (1782-1854) British
£974 $1500 €1461 Huntsman with his hunter in a landscape (62x83cm-24x33in) s. 4-Sep-2 Christie's, Rockefeller NY #374/R est:3000-5000

DAVIS, Roger (1898-1935) American
£304 $475 €456 Flowers (46x35cm-18x14in) s. i.d.1930 verso. 20-Sep-2 Sloan, North Bethesda #446/R

DAVIS, Ron (1937-) American
Works on paper
£961 $1500 €1442 Checkerboard cube (31x23cm-12x9in) s.i.d.1979 cel vinyl ink line acetate ragboard prov. 14-Oct-2 Butterfields, San Francisco #2092/R est:2500-3500

DAVIS, Stan (1942-) American
£7099 $11500 €10294 Warrior's prayer (71x86cm-28x34in) 23-May-3 Altermann Galleries, Santa Fe #58
£20548 $30000 €30822 Autumn morning (107x152cm-42x60in) 18-May-2 Altermann Galleries, Santa Fe #95/R

DAVIS, Stuart (1894-1964) American
£270968 $420000 €406452 Breakfast table (123x87cm-48x34in) s. prov.exhib.lit. 5-Dec-2 Christie's, Rockefeller NY #197/R est:100000-150000
£451613 $700000 €677420 Anchors (56x81cm-22x32in) s. s.i.verso prov.exhib.lit. 5-Dec-2 Christie's, Rockefeller NY #207/R est:600000-800000
Prints
£2548 $4000 €3822 Spawn time (15x19cm-6x7in) s.i.d.55 num.15/25 screenprint. 19-Nov-2 Wright, Chicago #164/R est:4000-5000
£15924 $25000 €23886 Barber shop chord (35x48cm-14x19in) s.num.11/25 lithograph prov. 14-Dec-2 Weschler, Washington #764/R est:20000-30000
Works on paper
£29321 $47500 €43982 Pennsylvania (37x34cm-15x13in) s. pencil executed c.1946 prov.exhib. 21-May-3 Sotheby's, New York #14/R est:50000-75000
£516129 $800000 €774194 Eggbeater no.4 (36x50cm-14x20in) s. s.i.d.March 1928 verso gouache on board prov.exhib.lit. 5-Dec-2 Christie's, Rockefeller NY #120/R est:500000-700000

DAVIS, Warren B (1865-1928) American
£1656 $2600 €2484 Ripple (41x30cm-16x12in) i.verso prov. 14-Dec-2 Weschler, Washington #683/R est:1200-1800
£2057 $3250 €3086 Nude in a landscape (51x41cm-20x16in) s. prov. 24-Apr-3 Shannon's, Milford #193/R est:2500-3500

DAVIS, William Henry (?-1865) British
£5500 $8745 €8250 Study of three prize sheep in a landscape (56x76cm-22x30in) s.d.1856. 18-Mar-3 Bonhams, New Bond Street #44/R est:6000-8000

DAVIS, William M (1829-1920) American
£5312 $8500 €7702 Lady behind the door (27x33cm-11x13in) s. 16-May-3 Skinner, Boston #60/R est:2500-3500

DAVIS, William R (1952-) American
£2293 $3600 €3440 Prepare to tack (33x43cm-13x17in) s. 26-Jul-2 Eldred, East Dennis #522/R est:3500-4000

DAVISON, Francis (1919-1984) British
Works on paper
£380 $597 €570 Blue and green squares and holes (91x72cm-36x28in) init. i.verso collage prov. 10-Dec-2 Rosebery Fine Art, London #695/R
£420 $647 €630 Earth circles (51x53cm-20x21in) s.i.d.1952 verso collage exhib. 5-Sep-2 Christie's, Kensington #705
£600 $990 €870 Blue and green squares and holes (91x71cm-36x28in) i.d.72 verso collage exhib. 3-Jul-3 Christie's, Kensington #680
£750 $1155 €1125 Brilliant yellow and dark green (89x90cm-35x35in) collage exec.c.1972. 5-Sep-2 Christie's, Kensington #743/R

DAVISON, Nora (fl.1881-1905) British
£286 $421 €429 Spencer range from Hanmer (39x49cm-15x19in) s. board. 19-Jun-2 Watson's, Christchurch #114/R (NZ.D 875)
Works on paper
£320 $496 €480 Sailmakers loft (23x34cm-9x13in) s. W/C. 24-Sep-2 Bonhams, Knightsbridge #151/R
£400 $624 €600 At Whitstable (22x33cm-9x13in) s. W/C. 15-Oct-2 Bearnes, Exeter #376
£740 $1184 €1073 Native clematis (53x44cm-21x17in) s. W/C. 13-May-3 Watson's, Christchurch #75/R (NZ.D 2050)

DAVRINGHAUSEN, Heinrich Maria (1894-1970) German
£278 $441 €400 Sans titre (51x66cm-20x26in) s.d.60 oil pastel paper on canvas. 29-Apr-3 Artcurial Briest, Paris #562
£382 $607 €550 Sans titre (30x21cm-12x8in) mono. painted engraved slate. 29-Apr-3 Artcurial Briest, Paris #560
£625 $994 €900 Sans titre (30x21cm-12x8in) mono. painted engraved slate double-sided. 29-Apr-3 Artcurial Briest, Paris #558
£972 $1546 €1400 Sans titre (29x21cm-11x8in) painted engraved slate double-sided. 29-Apr-3 Artcurial Briest, Paris #559 est:800-1000

DAWBARN, J Y (attrib) (fl.1890-1930) British
Works on paper
£420 $685 €630 Shipping off Scarborough (41x56cm-16x22in) init.i.d.1874 W/C. 30-Jan-3 Richardson & Smith, Whitby #570

DAWS, F T (1878-?) British
£780 $1232 €1170 Crescendo (75x63cm-30x25in) s. 28-Nov-2 Christie's, Kensington #340/R
£2200 $3542 €3300 Three terriers standing in a landscape (38x49cm-15x19in) s.d. 20-Feb-3 Thos Mawer, Lincoln #429/R est:400-600

DAWS, Frederick Thomas (1878-?) British
£1840 $3000 €2760 English cocker spaniels at rest in a wood (25x36cm-10x14in) s. i.verso board. 11-Feb-3 Bonhams & Doyles, New York #133 est:2000-3000

DAWS, Lawrence (1927-) Australian
£423 $659 €635 Melbourne shrine (45x56cm-18x22in) s. exhib. 21-Oct-2 Australian Art Auctions, Sydney #147 (A.D 1200)
£702 $1067 €1053 Anakie (56x53cm-22x21in) s. board. 19-Aug-2 Joel, Victoria #240/R est:2000-2500 (A.D 2000)
£714 $1129 €1071 Sketch for happy Jack (44x59cm-17x23in) s. board. 18-Nov-2 Joel, Victoria #366/R est:2000-3000 (A.D 2000)
£813 $1285 €1179 Finders light (51x61cm-20x24in) s. i.verso board. 22-Jul-3 Lawson Menzies, Sydney #173/R est:2400-3000 (A.D 2000)
£1200 $1932 €1800 Sun over landscape (55x55cm-22x22in) s. board. 6-May-3 Christie's, Melbourne #229/R est:3000-5000 (A.D 3000)
£1857 $2879 €2786 Landscape with mandala (62x61cm-24x24in) s. 29-Oct-2 Lawson Menzies, Sydney #4/R est:5000-8000 (A.D 5200)
£10064 $15902 €15096 Yuendumu (91x121cm-36x48in) s. board prov.exhib.lit. 27-Nov-2 Deutscher-Menzies, Melbourne #18/R est:9000-12000 (A.D 28180)
Works on paper
£5735 $8717 €8603 Clare landscape (152x152cm-60x60in) s. synthetic polymer paint board prov. 28-Aug-2 Deutscher-Menzies, Melbourne #110/R est:18000-24000 (A.D 16000)

DAWSON, Alfred (fl.1860-1894) British
£745 $1200 €1118 On the Thames (41x61cm-16x24in) s.d.1878 i.d.verso. 19-Feb-3 Doyle, New York #40
£2200 $3388 €3300 Hoping for a safe return (56x66cm-22x26in) s.d.1891. 23-Oct-2 Hamptons Fine Art, Godalming #165/R est:2500-3500

DAWSON, Elizabeth Rumley (fl.1851-1876) British
£450 $702 €675 Winter berries (30x25cm-12x10in) mono.d.1858. 7-Nov-2 Christie's, Kensington #247

DAWSON, G (1870-?) American
£2000 $3080 €3000 Peril of whisky (61x51cm-24x20in) s. 5-Sep-2 Christie's, Kensington #296/R est:2000-3000

DAWSON, Henry (1811-1878) British
£450 $733 €675 Figure in a punt (23x33cm-9x13in) mono. 29-Jan-3 Sotheby's, Olympia #80/R
£550 $847 €825 Trent Lock and Colwick Hill (25x37cm-10x15in) panel. 5-Sep-2 Christie's, Kensington #177
£750 $1163 €1125 Self portrait as a young man (33x26cm-13x10in) 2-Oct-2 George Kidner, Lymington #143/R
£4600 $7130 €6900 Children playing with a model boat on a pond before a farm (71x91cm-28x36in) mono.d.1855. 3-Oct-2 Heathcote Ball, Leicester #593/R
Works on paper
£1000 $1650 €1450 Riverside scenes (28x51cm-11x20in) mono.d.1866 W/C pair. 2-Jul-3 Sotheby's, Olympia #347/R est:1200-1500

DAWSON, Henry (style) (1811-1878) British
£4067 $6750 €5897 Harbour sunset (61x61cm-24x24in) inid.d.09. 14-Jun-3 Jackson's, Cedar Falls #215/R est:1000-1500

DAWSON, Henry Thomas (fl.1860-1896) British
£800 $1232 €1200 Sunset on the Thames, near Windsor (16x20cm-6x8in) i. panel on board. 5-Sep-2 Christie's, Kensington #182/R

DAWSON, J (?) ?
£800 $1264 €1200 Rataplan. Nutwith (15x20cm-6x8in) s.d.1857 canvas on panel pair after Harry Hall. 28-Nov-2 Christie's, Kensington #129/R

DAWSON, Janet (1935-) Australian
£1116 $1829 €1674 Abstract (60x63cm-24x25in) s.verso. 4-Jun-3 Deutscher-Menzies, Melbourne #320/R est:1000-2000 (A.D 2800)
£1571 $2420 €2357 Shadows (104x122cm-41x48in) s.d.68 verso oil on linen exhib. 8-Sep-2 Sotheby's, Melbourne #40 est:2000-4000 (A.D 4400)
£2236 $3533 €3242 Abstract (91x122cm-36x48in) s.verso. 22-Jul-3 Lawson Menzies, Sydney #174/R est:2500-3500 (A.D 5500)
Works on paper
£2143 $3300 €3215 Shadows III (122x122cm-48x48in) s.i.d.9/75 synthetic polymer. 8-Sep-2 Sotheby's, Melbourne #20 est:1500-2500 (A.D 6000)
£3393 $5225 €5090 Moon and Pepper's ghost (214x336cm-84x132in) s.i.d.79 verso synthetic polymer on three panel. 8-Sep-2 Sotheby's, Melbourne #29/R est:7000-9000 (A.D 9500)

DAWSON, Lucy (20th C) British
Works on paper
£280 $434 €420 Study of a German shepherd (17x24cm-7x9in) s. W/C bodycol. 24-Sep-2 Bonhams, Knightsbridge #5/R

DAWSON, Manierre (1887-1969) American
£33951 $55000 €50927 Coordinate escape (48x37cm-19x15in) s.d.10 board prov.exhib.lit. 21-May-3 Sotheby's, New York #89/R est:20000-30000

DAWSON, Montague (1895-1973) British
£1300 $2171 €1885 British destroyer on her lawful occasions (23x36cm-9x14in) board prov. 18-Jun-3 Sotheby's, Olympia #131/R est:1000-1500
£1900 $2945 €2850 Portrait of Mary Dawson (76x50cm-30x20in) s. 2-Oct-2 George Kidner, Lymington #147/R est:2000-3000
£2564 $4000 €3846 Whales ahoy (33x53cm-13x21in) s. masonite. 22-Sep-2 Susanin's, Chicago #5005 est:15000-20000
£4321 $7000 €6265 On patrol (25x61cm-10x24in) board prov. 29-Jul-3 Christie's, Rockefeller NY #97/R est:8000-12000
£6173 $10000 €8951 H.M.S Illustrious landing on in difficult condition (47x63cm-19x25in) s. i.verso board prov. 29-Jul-3 Christie's, Rockefeller NY #98/R est:10000-15000
£6173 $10000 €8951 Lorna Doone (51x76cm-20x30in) s. prov. 29-Jul-3 Christie's, Rockefeller NY #99/R est:12000-15000
£8500 $13175 €12750 Arrival of the Queen Mary at Southampton after her maiden voyage (46x91cm-18x36in) s. lit. 31-Oct-2 Christie's, Kensington #561/R est:5000-7000
£15060 $25000 €21837 Evening sun (51x61cm-20x24in) 13-Jun-3 Du Mouchelle, Detroit #2029/R est:30000-40000
£15674 $24451 €23511 Trade winds, clipper ship Elizabeth cushing (50x75cm-20x30in) s. 10-Nov-2 Dunbar Sloane, Auckland #15 est:60000-90000 (NZ.D 50000)
£16049 $26000 €24074 Horn a beam (46x61cm-18x24in) s. boardprov. 21-Jan-3 Christie's, Rockefeller NY #400/R est:50000
£16049 $26000 €24074 One rail under (61x92cm-24x36in) s. 21-Jan-3 Christie's, Rockefeller NY #401/R est:50000
£18519 $30000 €27779 Racing clipper Winged Racer (66x76cm-26x30in) s. prov. 21-Jan-3 Christie's, Rockefeller NY #399/R est:50000
£21000 $32760 €31500 Crossing the bar (70x90cm-28x35in) s. 15-Oct-2 Bearnes, Exeter #437/R est:15000-25000
£21605 $35000 €31327 Clipper with stun's sail set (61x73cm-24x29in) s. 29-Jul-3 Christie's, Rockefeller NY #192/R est:40000-60000
£24691 $40000 €35802 Yarmouth one's heading for the finish line in the Royal Solent yacht clubs (51x76cm-20x30in) s. prov. 29-Jul-3 Christie's, Rockefeller NY #190/R est:40000-60000
£30000 $48600 €45000 American full rigger Abner Coburn running before the wind (51x76cm-20x30in) s. 22-Jan-3 Bonhams, New Bond Street #392/R est:30000-50000
£30063 $47500 €43591 Eyes of the fleet (61x91cm-24x36in) s. prov. 26-Jul-3 Coeur d'Alene, Hayden #109/R est:40000-60000
£34810 $55000 €50475 Grainship - British Isles (69x104cm-27x41in) s. prov. 26-Jul-3 Coeur d'Alene, Hayden #108/R est:50000-70000
£37037 $60000 €53704 Yachting scene, spanking inshore breeze the Solent (51x61cm-20x24in) s. prov. 29-Jul-3 Christie's, Rockefeller NY #189/R est:40000-60000
£37975 $60000 €55064 Argonaut off the Wolf Lighthouse (51x76cm-20x30in) s. prov. 26-Jul-3 Coeur d'Alene, Hayden #107/R est:35000-55000
£43210 $70000 €62655 Crossing Mayflowers II bound for Plymouth, Massachusetts, in 1957 (100x125cm-39x49in) s. 29-Jul-3 Christie's, Rockefeller NY #191/R est:60000-80000
£58642 $95000 €87963 The U.S.S. Constellation in action (60x91cm-24x36in) s. prov. 21-Jan-3 Christie's, Rockefeller NY #402/R est:80000
£64286 $101571 €96429 Trafalgar (102x127cm-40x50in) s. prov. 26-Nov-2 Sotheby's, Melbourne #239/R est:180000-220000 (A.D 180000)
Works on paper
£3200 $5184 €4800 Alter course (37x82cm-15x32in) s. gouache. 22-Jan-3 Bonhams, New Bond Street #354/R est:3000-5000
£4375 $7000 €6344 Coastal craft on rough seas (44x69cm-17x27in) s. W/C gouache. 16-May-3 Skinner, Boston #293/R est:3000-5000
£6164 $9000 €9246 Three yachts in race (28x43cm-11x17in) s. W/C. 3-Nov-1 North East Auctions, Portsmouth #38/R est:9000-12000
£6500 $10205 €9750 Yachting days (46x58cm-18x23in) s. W/C. 16-Dec-2 Sotheby's, Olympia #160/R est:3000-5000
£8000 $12560 €12000 Heavy weather V and W class destroyer (45x76cm-18x30in) s. gouache. 16-Dec-2 Sotheby's, Olympia #161/R est:3000-5000

DAWSON, Neil (1948-) New Zealander
Sculpture
£2113 $3486 €3064 Arch rivals (68x123x200cm-27x48x79in) welded steel rods mesh kiwi flute aluminium. 1-Jul-3 Peter Webb, Auckland #49/R est:6000-8000 (NZ.D 6000)
£4225 $6972 €6126 Impact II (43x95x131cm-17x37x52in) painted wire mesh plastic ball acrylic. 1-Jul-3 Peter Webb, Auckland #48/R est:7000-9000 (NZ.D 12000)
Works on paper
£1408 $2324 €2042 Mirror, rock (92x119cm-36x47in) painted wire mesh. 1-Jul-3 Peter Webb, Auckland #47/R est:5000-7000 (NZ.D 4000)

DAX, Adrien and ELLEOUET, Yves (20th C) French
Sculpture
£8904 $13890 €13000 Untitled (27x25x37cm-11x10x15in) wood exec. with Charles Estienne and Toyen. 14-Apr-3 Laurence Calmels, Paris #4003/R est:1000

DAXHELET, Paul (1905-1993) Belgian
£253 $395 €400 Vue d'une vallee (60x80cm-24x31in) s. 16-Oct-2 Hotel des Ventes Mosan, Brussels #296
£269 $423 €420 Zaire, un marche (30x62cm-12x24in) s. i.verso panel. 11-Dec-2 Hotel des Ventes Mosan, Brussels #323
£298 $497 €420 Nu couche (60x80cm-24x31in) s. 18-Jun-3 Hotel des Ventes Mosan, Brussels #285
£340 $541 €500 Maroc, Marrakech, les teinturiers (50x60cm-20x24in) s. i. verso. 19-Mar-3 Hotel des Ventes Mosan, Brussels #335
£340 $541 €500 Sri Lanka: la famille singhalaise (80x60cm-31x24in) s. i. verso. 19-Mar-3 Hotel des Ventes Mosan, Brussels #340
£380 $592 €600 Groupe du nus feminins (60x50cm-24x20in) s. 16-Oct-2 Hotel des Ventes Mosan, Brussels #290
£387 $600 €581 Et des fleurs jailli rent du sol (51x102cm-20x40in) s. painted c.1960. 8-Dec-2 Toomey, Oak Park #816/R
£449 $704 €700 Jeune femme aux oiseaux (70x100cm-28x39in) s. 11-Dec-2 Hotel des Ventes Mosan, Brussels #328
£481 $755 €750 Baigneuses, Bora-Bora (30x62cm-12x24in) s.i.verso panel. 11-Dec-2 Hotel des Ventes Mosan, Brussels #326
£513 $795 €800 Port mediterraneen (50x60cm-20x24in) s. 9-Dec-2 Horta, Bruxelles #302
£578 $919 €850 La procession au flambeaux, Lourdes (70x100cm-28x39in) s. i. verso. 19-Mar-3 Hotel des Ventes Mosan, Brussels #326
£680 $1082 €1000 Indonesie: procession de Bonzes (60x100cm-24x39in) s. i. verso. 19-Mar-3 Hotel des Ventes Mosan, Brussels #331
£1076 $1678 €1700 Marche a Cuzco, Perou (130x195cm-51x77in) s. i.verso lit. 16-Oct-2 Hotel des Ventes Mosan, Brussels #307 est:1500-2000
£1370 $2151 €2000 Marche aux fleurs en Afrique (50x60cm-20x24in) s. 15-Apr-3 Galerie Moderne, Brussels #336/R est:1000-1200
£3472 $5521 €5000 Quatre femmes Africaines (100x100cm-39x39in) s. 5-May-3 Bernaerts, Antwerp #66/R
Works on paper
£284 $474 €400 Le football (24x44cm-9x17in) s. W/C drawing. 18-Jun-3 Hotel des Ventes Mosan, Brussels #302
£353 $554 €550 La danseuse Africaine (35x50cm-14x20in) s. W/C graphite. 11-Dec-2 Hotel des Ventes Mosan, Brussels #329
£461 $770 €650 Le sporting (50x70cm-20x28in) s.d.70 mixed media. 18-Jun-3 Hotel des Ventes Mosan, Brussels #298
£567 $948 €800 Danseuses Zairoises (54x68cm-21x27in) s. mixed media. 18-Jun-3 Hotel des Ventes Mosan, Brussels #288

DAY, Maurice (1892-1983) American
Works on paper
£710 $1100 €1065 Lobsterman resting in a chair on his dock near his boat (20x30cm-8x12in) s. W/C. 28-Sep-2 Thomaston Place, Thomaston #1
£774 $1200 €1161 Low tide and red buoys (33x43cm-13x17in) s.i. W/C. 28-Sep-2 Thomaston Place, Thomaston #2

DAY, Melvin (1923-) New Zealander
£804 $1246 €1206 Still life arrangement (57x76cm-22x30in) s.d.1990 paper. 4-Dec-2 Dunbar Sloane, Auckland #36/R est:2000-4000 (NZ.D 2500)
£892 $1400 €1338 Abstract (61x61cm-24x24in) s.d.1970. 10-Dec-2 Peter Webb, Auckland #21/R est:2000-3000 (NZ.D 2800)

DAY, Nancy (20th C) Canadian
£348 $543 €580 Many colors (81x122cm-32x48in) s. s.i.d.1993 verso prov. 13-Apr-3 Levis, Calgary #24/R (C.D 800)

DAY, Worden (1916-1986) American
£610 $1000 €885 Arcana I (114x84cm-45x33in) s.d.1955 cassein on masonite prov.exhib. 1-Jun-3 Wright, Chicago #273/R est:2000-3000

DAYES, Edward (1763-1804) British
Works on paper
£1500 $2369 €2250 Wooded river landscape with cows crossing a bridge (34x59cm-13x23in) s. W/C over pencil prov.lit. 28-Nov-2 Sotheby's, London #222/R est:1500-2000

DAYES, Edward (attrib) (1763-1804) British
Works on paper
£650 $1079 €943 View of Winchester with the cathedral in the distance. Figures and cattle in distance (41x56cm-16x22in) W/C two. 16-Jun-3 Duke & Son, Dorchester #132

DAYEZ, Georges (1907-1991) French
£285 $450 €450 Nature morte (28x47cm-11x19in) s. 27-Nov-2 Blanchet, Paris #68
£440 $682 €700 La falaise de Varengeville (60x120cm-24x47in) s.d.54 s.i.d.54 verso. 30-Oct-2 Artcurial Briest, Paris #383
Works on paper
£863 $1416 €1200 Still life with flowers on a table (61x47cm-24x19in) s.d.48 gouache. 3-Jun-3 Christie's, Amsterdam #70/R est:1400-1600

DAZE (1963-) American
£380 $600 €600 Dream of Meduse (107x107cm-42x42in) s. d.1988 verso acrylic. 2-Dec-2 Tajan, Paris #250

DEACON, Richard and SCHUTTE, Thomas (20th C) British/German
Sculpture
£10759 $17000 €16139 Them and us (45x60x69cm-18x24x27in) aluminum felt animal hair executed 1995 prov.exhib. 14-Nov-2 Christie's, Rockefeller NY #320/R est:15000-20000

DEAGOSTINI, Carlo (20th C) Italian
£256 $403 €400 Still life (38x45cm-15x18in) s. 10-Dec-2 Della Rocca, Turin #330

DEAK EBNER, Lajos (1850-1934) Hungarian
£727 $1133 €1091 Fruit harvest (34x46cm-13x18in) s. 11-Apr-3 Kieselbach, Budapest #24/R est:240000-260000 (H.F 260000)
£833 $1292 €1300 Hungarian market scene (50x70cm-20x28in) s. 5-Dec-2 Dorotheum, Graz #9/R
£1537 $2398 €2306 Market in Szolnok (47x71cm-19x28in) s. canvas on board. 11-Apr-3 Kieselbach, Budapest #67/R est:550000 (H.F 550000)
£1614 $2501 €2340 Melon market (44x64cm-17x25in) s. panel. 9-Dec-2 Mu Terem Galeria, Budapest #139/R est:500000 (H.F 600000)
£1806 $2817 €2709 After rain (77x118cm-30x46in) s. 11-Sep-2 Kieselbach, Budapest #85/R (H.F 700000)
£2633 $4213 €3950 Sunlit grove (28x18cm-11x7in) s. panel. 16-May-3 Kieselbach, Budapest #3/R (H.F 900000)

DEAK, Adrienne (1895-?) Hungarian
£1022 $1584 €1533 Bunch of wild flowers (86x70cm-34x28in) s. 6-Dec-2 Kieselbach, Budapest #113/R (H.F 380000)
£1748 $2709 €2622 Still life of roses (80x100cm-31x39in) s. 6-Dec-2 Kieselbach, Budapest #112/R (H.F 650000)

DEAKIN, Edwin (1838-1923) American
£266 $425 €399 Portals of the past, Golden Gate Park. 11-Jan-3 Harvey Clar, Oakland #1212
£641 $1000 €962 Portals of the past, Golden Gate Park. 21-Sep-2 Harvey Clar, Oakland #1499
£897 $1400 €1346 Hills overlooking north, San Francisco. painted c.1872. 21-Sep-2 Harvey Clar, Oakland #1500
£1807 $3000 €2620 Village church (91x61cm-36x24in) s. 11-Jun-3 Boos Gallery, Michigan #524/R est:4000-6000
£1958 $3250 €2839 Castle of Chillon, Switzerland (76x51cm-30x20in) s.d.1897 i.verso. 11-Jun-3 Butterfields, San Francisco #4204/R est:3000-5000

DEAKIN, Peter (fl.1855-1879) British
£450 $716 €675 North Wales (59x89cm-23x35in) s. 27-Feb-3 Bonhams, Chester #479
Works on paper
£400 $636 €600 Porlock, Somersetshire (33x53cm-13x21in) s. W/C. 4-Mar-3 Bearnes, Exeter #375

DEAKIN, Peter (attrib) (fl.1855-1879) British
£2100 $3423 €3150 Taking the catch to market (41x61cm-16x24in) bears sig. 11-Feb-3 Bonhams, Knowle #93 est:800-1200

DEAN, Frank (1865-1946) British
£700 $1120 €1050 Landscape with sheep being penned in foreground (43x71cm-17x28in) 11-Mar-3 Gorringes, Lewes #2557
Works on paper
£1280 $1997 €1920 French drawing room (51x38cm-20x15in) s. W/C. 2-Aug-2 Biddle & Webb, Birmingham #407

DEAN, Walter Lofthouse (1854-1912) American
£649 $1000 €974 Old shepherd farm, Pawnage Place (51x61cm-20x24in) s. i.on stretcher. 27-Oct-2 Grogan, Boston #78 est:1000-1500

DEANGELIS, Paulo Andrea (19th C) Italian
£2200 $3498 €3300 Marsamaxett Harbour, Malta (19x28cm-7x11in) s.i.d.1855. 29-Apr-3 Bonhams, New Bond Street #142/R est:1200-1800
Works on paper
£1900 $3021 €2850 Battery overlooking the Grand Harbour, Valletta, Malta (19x27cm-7x11in) init.d.1856 gouache. 29-Apr-3 Bonhams, New Bond Street #141/R est:1200-1800
£4200 $6678 €6300 Black Watch on Floriana Parade, Malta (27x35cm-11x14in) s. bear d.1846 verso gouache. 29-Apr-3 Bonhams, New Bond Street #140/R est:2000-3000

DEANS, A A (1915-) New Zealander
Works on paper
£895 $1307 €1343 Two Thumb Range (59x90cm-23x35in) s.d.1963 W/C. 12-Sep-1 Watson's, Christchurch #35 est:1500-3500 (NZ.D 3000)

DEANS, Austin A (1915-) New Zealander
£276 $392 €414 New snow and shed (28x21cm-11x8in) s. prov. 20-Mar-2 Watson's, Christchurch #11/R est:200-500 (NZ.D 900)
£313 $489 €470 Mt. Peel, from Peel Forest Road, Canterbury, N.Z (49x74cm-19x29in) s.d.1971 i.verso board. 5-Nov-2 Peter Webb, Auckland #226/R est:1000-1600 (NZ.D 1000)
£458 $674 €687 Dull day, Kenepuru Sounds (43x34cm-17x13in) s.d.1991. 19-Jun-2 Watson's, Christchurch #37/R est:600-1000 (NZ.D 1400)
£482 $748 €723 Misty morning, Mayfield (39x85cm-15x33in) s.d.1968 board. 4-Dec-2 Dunbar Sloane, Auckland #47/R (NZ.D 1500)
£915 $1345 €1373 Barossa Station (72x89cm-28x35in) s.d.1961 board prov. 19-Jun-2 Watson's, Christchurch #3/R est:2500-4500 (NZ.D 2800)
Works on paper
£328 $480 €492 Mt. Peele, South Canterbury (25x36cm-10x14in) s.d.1991 W/C. 12-Sep-1 Watson's, Christchurch #76/R est:350-650 (NZ.D 1100)
£433 $632 €650 Pudding Hill, Rangitata Valley (27x9cm-11x4in) s.d.1973 W/C. 12-Sep-1 Watson's, Christchurch #61 est:500-1000 (NZ.D 1450)
£727 $1032 €1091 Winter 1992, Darfield (48x64cm-19x25in) s. W/C prov. 21-Nov-1 Watson's, Christchurch #1/R est:2000-4000 (NZ.D 2500)

DEARDEN, Harold (1888-1969) British
£650 $1014 €975 Cornish fishermen with their catch (74x74cm-29x29in) 18-Oct-2 Keys, Aylsham #723/R

DEARLE, John H (fl.1853-1891) British
Works on paper
£750 $1163 €1125 Pirbright common, ducks on the common by a pond (47x64cm-19x25in) s. W/C. 25-Sep-2 John Nicholson, Haslemere #907/R

DEARMAN, John (?-1857) British
£550 $869 €825 Landscape with cattle and sheep (9x12cm-4x5in) indis sig. panel. 2-Dec-2 Bonhams, Bath #79/R
£1400 $2226 €2100 Shepherd with his flock in an extensive landscape (9x13cm-4x5in) s. board. 6-Mar-3 Christie's, Kensington #482/R est:600-800

DEARN, Raymond (?) British
£260 $403 €390 Glenfaber Bridge, Peel (38x56cm-15x22in) s.i.verso. 6-Dec-2 Chrystals Auctions, Isle of Man #272m

£798 $1300 €1197 Dog in a landscape (76x96cm-30x38in) s. 11-Feb-3 Bonhams & Doyles, New York #41 est:1500-2000

£2000 $3100 €3000 Sheep by cottage, Sulby. Sheep on track, Sulby (46x61cm-18x24in) s.d.1920 board pair. 6-Dec-2 Chrystals Auctions, Isle of Man #156 est:1000-1500

DEARTH, Henry Golden (1864-1918) American

£1923 $3000 €2885 Storm on the Brittany coast (51x61cm-20x24in) s. panel exhib. 14-Sep-2 Selkirks, St. Louis #123/R est:3000-3500

DEAS, Charles (1818-1867) American

£96774 $150000 €145161 Dragoons crossing river (30x46cm-12x18in) prov.exhib.lit. 5-Dec-2 Christie's, Rockefeller NY #168/R est:200000-300000

£419355 $650000 €629033 Winnebagos playing checkers (32x37cm-13x15in) i.d.1842 prov.exhib.lit. 3-Dec-2 Phillips, New York #41/R est:350000-550000

D'EAUBONNE, Louis Lucien (1834-1894) French

£600 $948 €900 River landscape with barge in the foreground and a townscape beyond (27x40cm-11x16in) s. 12-Nov-2 Bonhams, Knightsbridge #127/R

DEBAT-PONSAN, Edouard-Bernard (1847-1913) French

£563 $907 €800 River landscape with woman and washing board (11x20cm-4x8in) s.i.d.1906 panel. 7-May-3 Vendue Huis, Gravenhage #570

£1333 $2213 €1933 Going to pasture (66x92cm-26x36in) s.d.1891. 10-Jun-3 Ritchie, Toronto #116/R est:4000-6000 (C.D 3000)

£2500 $3950 €3750 Old, old story (65x50cm-26x20in) s. 14-Nov-2 Christie's, Kensington #28/R est:3000-5000

£3226 $5000 €4839 Leading the herd to drink (65x92cm-26x36in) s.d.1912. 2-Oct-2 Christie's, Rockefeller NY #773/R est:6000-8000

DEBATTICE, Jean (1919-1979) Belgian

£346 $543 €540 La fin des conquistadores (122x122cm-48x48in) s.d.62 i.verso panel. 11-Dec-2 Hotel des Ventes Mosan, Brussels #320

DEBAY, Auguste Hyacinth (1804-1865) French

Sculpture

£32000 $49920 €48000 First cradle (50cm-20in) terracotta lit. 9-Apr-3 Sotheby's, London #106/R est:6000-8000

DEBERITZ, Per (1880-1945) Norwegian

£1653 $2711 €2397 Landscape from Skaatoy (59x67cm-23x26in) s.d.1924 exhib. 2-Jun-3 Blomqvist, Oslo #183/R est:20000-25000 (N.KR 18000)

£3122 $4871 €4683 From Tvedestrand - Bakke towards Osterklev (59x69cm-23x27in) s. 21-Oct-2 Blomqvist, Oslo #380/R est:35000-40000 (N.KR 36000)

DEBICKI, Stanislaw (1866-1924) Polish

£968 $1500 €1452 Market scene (15x23cm-6x9in) board exhib. 7-Dec-2 South Bay, Long Island #54/R

DEBRE, Olivier (1920-1999) French

£643 $1003 €965 Petit sous blue Royal (22x27cm-9x11in) s.d.82 verso. 11-Nov-2 Rasmussen, Vejle #143/R (D.KR 7500)

£1329 $2073 €2100 Bleu gris de Cherbourg (16x22cm-6x9in) s.i.d.1994 verso acrylic. 20-Oct-2 Claude Boisgirard, Paris #44/R est:1500-1800

£1384 $2145 €2200 Composition (19x27cm-7x11in) s.d.58 verso. 30-Oct-2 Artcurial Briest, Paris #665 est:2300-3000

£1572 $2437 €2500 Rose et vert (34x46cm-13x18in) s. i.d.88 verso prov. 30-Oct-2 Artcurial Briest, Paris #442/R est:3000-4000

£1582 $2468 €2500 Petite bleu fonce oblique (19x27cm-7x11in) s.i.d.1992 verso acrylic. 20-Oct-2 Claude Boisgirard, Paris #51/R est:1500-1800

£1772 $2765 €2800 Bleu pale taches vertes (24x33cm-9x13in) s.i.d.1996 verso acrylic. 20-Oct-2 Claude Boisgirard, Paris #49/R est:2800-3000

£1923 $3019 €3000 Paysage (55x46cm-22x18in) s.d.43. 24-Nov-2 Laurence Calmels, Paris #87/R

£1962 $3061 €3100 Temple a Bangkok (24x16cm-9x6in) s.i.d.1997 verso acrylic. 20-Oct-2 Claude Boisgirard, Paris #45/R est:1500-1800

£2025 $3159 €3200 Daikakuji jaune (38x46cm-15x18in) s.i.d.1991 verso acrylic. 20-Oct-2 Claude Boisgirard, Paris #48/R est:3000-4000

£2025 $3159 €3200 Petit rose de Dakar (22x27cm-9x11in) s.i.d.1986 verso acrylic. 20-Oct-2 Claude Boisgirard, Paris #50/R est:1800-2000

£2051 $3221 €3200 Automne ocre vert (65x81cm-26x32in) s.i.d.64 verso. 24-Nov-2 Laurence Calmels, Paris #85/R

£2215 $3456 €3500 Petite ocre de Loire (22x27cm-9x11in) s.i.d.1988 verso acrylic. 20-Oct-2 Claude Boisgirard, Paris #47/R est:1800-2000

£2452 $3874 €3800 Bord de Loire aux taches foncees. s.i.d.83-84. 19-Dec-2 Ruellan, Paris #136/R

£2516 $3899 €4000 Macerata, petit vert et rouge (35x50cm-14x20in) s.i.d.73 verso. 30-Oct-2 Artcurial Briest, Paris #666/R est:3000-4000

£2564 $4026 €4000 Paysage (60x73cm-24x29in) init.d.48. 24-Nov-2 Laurence Calmels, Paris #80/R

£3165 $5000 €5000 Chamarante rose rouge, trace bleu clair (34x54cm-13x21in) s. i.verso painted 1992. 27-Nov-2 Tajan, Paris #51/R est:2500-3000

£3459 $5362 €5500 A la tache rose, loire (100x100cm-39x39in) i.d.84 s.verso prov. 30-Oct-2 Artcurial Briest, Paris #667/R est:6000-9000

£3490 $5619 €5200 Bleu du haut chemin (38x46cm-15x18in) s.i.d.1979 verso. 23-Feb-3 Mercier & Cie, Lille #127/R

£3526 $5535 €5500 Rouge clair de Loire (60x81cm-24x32in) s.i.d.87 verso. 24-Nov-2 Laurence Calmels, Paris #88/R

£3718 $5837 €5800 HK petite 6 (54x73cm-21x29in) init.i. verso. 24-Nov-2 Laurence Calmels, Paris #86/R

£3846 $6038 €6000 Loire d'automne pres d'Amboise (100x100cm-39x39in) s.i.d.70 verso. 24-Nov-2 Laurence Calmels, Paris #82/R

£4167 $6542 €6500 Bleu leger aux taches lourdes (100x100cm-39x39in) init. s.i.d.65 verso prov. 24-Nov-2 Laurence Calmels, Paris #81/R

£4167 $6625 €6000 Rose des tilleuls, touraine (60x73cm-24x29in) s.i.d.93 verso. 29-Apr-3 Artcurial Briest, Paris #563/R est:6000-8000

£4214 $6489 €6700 Port bleu (65x81cm-26x32in) s.d.1963 s.i.d.verso. 26-Oct-2 Cornette de St.Cyr, Paris #23/R

£4359 $6844 €6800 Untitled (54x73cm-21x29in) s.d.1948 s.d.verso. 15-Dec-2 Perrin, Versailles #54/R

£4557 $7109 €7200 Rouge du rideau Hong Kong (60x92cm-24x36in) s.i.d.1988 verso. 20-Oct-2 Claude Boisgirard, Paris #52/R est:5000-6000

£4717 $7311 €7500 Grise legere coulee de Loire (100x100cm-39x39in) s. i.d.88 verso. 30-Oct-2 Artcurial Briest, Paris #444/R est:8000-12000

£4967 $8096 €7500 Royan blanc barres rouges (73x92cm-29x36in) s.i.d.1972 verso. 3-Feb-3 Cornette de St.Cyr, Paris #401/R

£5072 $8319 €7000 Blanche de Royan (100x100cm-39x39in) s.i.d.aout 88. 27-May-3 Tajan, Paris #47/R est:7500-9000

£5769 $9058 €9000 Gris rose d'Urbisagha (100x100cm-39x39in) s.i.d.77 verso. 24-Nov-2 Laurence Calmels, Paris #83/R

£6012 $9500 €9500 Amboise rose (101x101cm-40x40in) s.i.d.1979 verso. 27-Nov-2 Tajan, Paris #55/R est:7000-9000

£8333 $13083 €13000 Auvermi sombre (100x100cm-39x39in) init. s.i.d.1974 verso. 24-Nov-2 Laurence Calmels, Paris #84/R

£9220 $15397 €13000 Personnages en gris et faune, hiver (162x130cm-64x51in) s.i.d.verso. 18-Jun-3 Pierre Berge, Paris #96/R est:10000-120000

£9524 $15143 €14000 Composition (162x97cm-64x38in) s.d.1948 exhib. 24-Mar-3 Claude Boisgirard, Paris #105/R est:15000

£10204 $16224 €15000 Still life (95x108cm-37x43in) s. s.i.d.1955 verso. 24-Mar-3 Claude Boisgirard, Paris #115/R

£14744 $23147 €23000 Saint-Geroges de Didonne (81x100cm-32x39in) s. s.i.d.1955 verso prov. 11-Dec-2 Artcurial Briest, Paris #710/R

£18590 $29186 €29000 Jaune dore d'automne (180x250cm-71x98in) s.i.verso lit. 16-Dec-2 Charbonneaux, Paris #239/R est:15000-18000

Works on paper

£1266 $1975 €2000 Tiro - musiciens chanteurs (14x23cm-6x9in) mono.d.1949 i. verso gouache. 20-Oct-2 Claude Boisgirard, Paris #43/R est:1500-1800

DEBRUS, Alexandre (19th C) French

£958 $1600 €1389 Still life with roses (33x25cm-13x10in) s.d.1882. 29-Jun-3 Butterfields, Los Angeles #7037/R est:1200-1800

DEBRUS, Alexandre (attrib) (19th C) French

£288 $453 €450 Bouquet de roses (32x25cm-13x10in) s.d.1895. 10-Dec-2 Vanderkindere, Brussels #124

DEBUCOURT, Philibert Louis (1755-1832) French

£3459 $5362 €5500 Amoureux en voyage (22x27cm-9x11in) init.d.1810 panel prov.exhib. 29-Oct-2 Artcurial Briest, Paris #47/R

£4317 $6906 €6000 Harem scene (43x33cm-17x13in) mono. panel. 17-May-3 Lempertz, Koln #1029/R est:7000

Works on paper

£18919 $29514 €28000 Portraits de femmes (6cm-2in circular) wash htd W/C pair. 27-Mar-3 Maigret, Paris #110/R est:1500

DEBUS-DIGNEFFE, Maria (1876-1956) German

£1266 $1962 €2000 Dachau peasant woman with daughter (70x60cm-28x24in) s. 25-Sep-2 Neumeister, Munich #554/R est:1000

DEBUSK, Kelly (20th C) American

£385 $600 €578 Cactus, Carrizo Springs, TX (61x30cm-24x12in) 19-Oct-2 David Dike, Dallas #234/R

DEBUT, J-D (1824-1893) French

£633 $987 €1000 Clair de lune (64x53cm-25x21in) 30-Jul-2 Gioffredo, Nice #100

DEBUT, Jean-Didier (1824-1893) French

Sculpture

£1026 $1610 €1600 Porteur d'eau tunisien (32cm-13in) s. pat bronze. 10-Dec-2 Tajan, Paris #204/R

DEBUT, Marcel (1865-1933) French

£360 $565 €540 St Valery sur Soberine (33x23cm-13x9in) s.i. panel. 10-Dec-2 Rosebery Fine Art, London #519/R

Sculpture

£1511 $2478 €2100 Le fauconnier (65cm-26in) s. bronze. 4-Jun-3 Tajan, Paris #249/R est:1800-2000

£2138 $3421 €3100 Untitled (71x34x26cm-28x13x10in) s. silver pat. 14-Mar-3 Libert, Castor, Paris #66/R
£2170 $3515 €3147 Dancing nymph (110cm-43in) s. pat.bronze prov. 24-May-3 Galerie Gloggner, Luzern #22/R est:3500-3800 (S.FR 4600)
£7241 $11586 €10500 Untitled (59x41x25cm-23x16x10in) s.st.f.Blot bronze pair. 14-Mar-3 Libert, Castor, Paris #65/R

DECAISNE, Henri (1799-1852) Belgian
£650 $1007 €975 Girl reading a letter (54x45cm-21x18in) s. 3-Nov-2 Lots Road, London #350/R

DECAMPS, Alexandre Gabriel (1803-1860) French
£910 $1447 €1320 Interior scene (34x42cm-13x17in) s. 4-Mar-3 Ansorena, Madrid #326/R
£11218 $17388 €17500 Les murs de Jericho (25x34cm-10x13in) panel on canvas. 9-Dec-2 Beaussant & Lefèvre, Paris #32/R est:7000
Works on paper
£450 $702 €675 Monkey duet (17x25cm-7x10in) s. W/C. 26-Mar-3 Sotheby's, Olympia #267/R
£520 $868 €754 Turkish gentleman and child feeding their horse before a castle (27x35cm-11x14in) W/C bodycol. 25-Jun-3 Bonhams, Bury St Edmunds #485/R

DECAMPS, Alexandre Gabriel (attrib) (1803-1860) French
£1006 $1600 €1509 Before the temple (29x45cm-11x18in) paper. 7-Mar-3 Skinner, Boston #340/R est:800-1200
£1481 $2400 €2222 Battle of Independence (36x33cm-14x13in) 24-Jan-3 New Orleans Auction, New Orleans #1384/R est:2500-4000
£2405 $3800 €3608 Pointing the way (35x65cm-14x26in) 1-Apr-3 Christie's, Rockefeller NY #202/R est:1500-2000

DECAMPS, Maurice (1892-1953) French
£452 $714 €700 Bouquet de fleurs a la corbeille de faience (46x55cm-18x22in) s. 17-Dec-2 Rossini, Paris #69
£550 $902 €825 Still life of flowers in a basket vase (44x54cm-17x21in) s. 3-Jun-3 Bonhams, Oxford #72/R
£650 $988 €975 Gladioli in porcelain basket (54x81cm-21x32in) s. 29-Aug-2 Christie's, Kensington #205/R
£700 $1092 €1050 Still life of roses (46x56cm-18x22in) s. prov. 17-Sep-2 Bonhams, Knightsbridge #121/R

DECANIS, Theophile (1847-1917) French
£274 $427 €400 Stream in sunny landscape (45x68cm-18x27in) s. 10-Apr-3 Van Ham, Cologne #1366

DECARAVA, Roy (1919-) American
Photographs
£6962 $11000 €10443 Man in window (33x22cm-13x9in) s.d.1978 photograph. 23-Apr-3 Sotheby's, New York #230/R est:4000-6000
£8228 $13000 €12342 Untitled (26x33cm-10x13in) s.i. gelatin silver print prov.exhib. 25-Apr-3 Phillips, New York #270/R est:3000-5000

DECARIS, Albert (attrib) (1901-1988) French
£1837 $2920 €2700 Kore (135x100cm-53x39in) 21-Mar-3 Rieunier, Bailly-Pommery, Mathias, Paris #133/R

DECCAN SCHOOL (17/18th C) Indian
Works on paper
£7500 $11925 €11250 Portrait of Shah Jahan (42x26cm-17x10in) i.verso gouache gold silver exec.c.1695-1700 lit. 2-May-3 Christie's, Kensington #500/R est:1500-2000

DECHELETTE, Louis Auguste (1894-1964) French
£310 $490 €450 Bouquet (41x33cm-16x13in) s. 4-Apr-3 Tajan, Paris #29/R
£350 $547 €550 Utopie (31x43cm-12x17in) mono.d.1941 panel. 5-Nov-2 Tajan, Paris #2/R

DECK, Leo (1908-1997) Swiss
£258 $407 €387 Lakeside (38x46cm-15x18in) s.i.verso masonite. 29-Nov-2 Zofingen, Switzerland #2844 (S.FR 600)
£262 $409 €393 Flowers (54x46cm-21x18in) s. i. verso panel. 6-Nov-2 Dobiaschofsky, Bern #438 (S.FR 600)
£262 $409 €393 Anglers by lake in summer (54x44cm-21x17in) s. board. 6-Nov-2 Dobiaschofsky, Bern #3244/R (S.FR 600)
£278 $447 €417 La Parisienne (54x45cm-21x18in) s. i. verso panel. 7-May-3 Dobiaschofsky, Bern #433 (S.FR 600)
£284 $443 €426 Autumn landscape with river (84x103cm-33x41in) s.d.67 panel. 6-Nov-2 Dobiaschofsky, Bern #439 (S.FR 650)
£348 $539 €522 River in spring (69x87cm-27x34in) s.d.1960 panel. 9-Dec-2 Philippe Schuler, Zurich #8708 (S.FR 800)
£349 $545 €524 November (84x103cm-33x41in) s. i.d.1970 verso panel. 6-Nov-2 Dobiaschofsky, Bern #440 (S.FR 800)
£480 $749 €720 Iseltwald (60x72cm-24x28in) s.d.65 i. verso. 6-Nov-2 Dobiaschofsky, Bern #436/R (S.FR 1100)
£611 $954 €917 Mammern, Bodensee (55x45cm-22x18in) s.d.64 i. verso. 6-Nov-2 Dobiaschofsky, Bern #437/R (S.FR 1400)

DECKER, Albert (1817-1871) French
Works on paper
£473 $738 €700 Little soldiers (16x21cm-6x8in) s.d.855 W/C pencil. 28-Mar-3 Dorotheum, Vienna #180/R

DECKER, Cornelis (1651-1709) Dutch
£6329 $9873 €10000 Paysage anime de personnages (78x109cm-31x43in) s.d.1656. 20-Oct-2 Mercier & Cie, Lille #264/R est:10000-12000
£8108 $12649 €12000 River landscape with old farmhouse and angler (49x65cm-19x26in) bears s.d. panel prov.lit. 27-Mar-3 Dorotheum, Vienna #129/R est:13000-18000

DECKER, Cornelis Gerritsz (attrib) (1625-1678) Dutch
£766 $1119 €1180 Paysage a la riviere flamande avec des pecheurs (38x32cm-15x13in) panel. 11-Jun-2 Thierry & Lannon, Brest #107/R
£3691 $5942 €5500 River landscape with fishermen in a boat before a house (41x36cm-16x14in) bears sig panel prov. 18-Feb-3 Sotheby's, Amsterdam #235/R est:7000-9000

DECKER, Jos de (1912-2000) Belgian
Sculpture
£1379 $2207 €2000 Ros Beiaard (14x34cm-6x13in) s.num.I/IV dark brown pat bronze stone base lit. 15-Mar-3 De Vuyst, Lokeren #80 est:2000-2500
£2014 $3223 €2800 Motherhood (80x37cm-31x15in) s. num.1/8 st.f.Bonvici brown pat bronze. 17-May-3 De Vuyst, Lokeren #126/R est:2800-3300

DECKER, Joseph (1853-1924) American
£2075 $3238 €3300 Still life with dahlias and figure (67x50cm-26x20in) s. 21-Sep-2 Bolland & Marotz, Bremen #460/R est:4900
£5346 $8500 €8019 Still life of strawberries (23x30cm-9x12in) 5-Mar-3 Sotheby's, New York #10/R est:8000-12000

DECKER, Luc de (1907-1982) Belgian
£544 $865 €800 Roses (80x100cm-31x39in) s.d.1941. 18-Mar-3 Galerie Moderne, Brussels #265
£855 $1386 €1300 Vase garni de roses (80x100cm-31x39in) s. 21-Jan-3 Galerie Moderne, Brussels #251

DECKER, Robert M (1847-1921) American
£253 $400 €380 Distant mountain landscape with lake and cows (51x76cm-20x30in) s. 17-Nov-2 CRN Auctions, Cambridge #67/R
£633 $1000 €950 Wooded hillside landscape (76x51cm-30x20in) s. 17-Nov-2 Jeffery Burchard, Florida #28/R

DECKERS, Edouard (1873-1956) Belgian
Sculpture
£1905 $3029 €2800 Two labourers near blast furnace (60x86x40cm-24x34x16in) s. black pat.bronze. 24-Mar-3 Bernaerts, Antwerp #35/R est:3000-4000

DECKERS, Émile (1885-1968) Belgian
£10256 $16103 €16000 Homme du sud au poignard (84x56cm-33x22in) s.i.d.1947. 16-Dec-2 Gros & Delettrez, Paris #163/R est:10000-15000
£10256 $16103 €16000 Bergere Kabyle (80x100cm-31x39in) s.i.d.1929 lit. 16-Dec-2 Gros & Delettrez, Paris #429/R est:15000-22000

DECKERS, Jan (?) Belgian
£601 $938 €950 Nature morte au melon et aux raisins (50x73cm-20x29in) s. 15-Oct-2 Vanderkindere, Brussels #78
£816 $1298 €1200 Nature morte au homard (60x85cm-24x33in) s. 18-Mar-3 Campo, Vlaamse Kaai #60

DECLEVA, Mario (1930-1979) Austrian
Works on paper
£321 $506 €500 Untitled (21x29cm-8x11in) s.d.51 gouache. 12-Nov-2 Dorotheum, Vienna #173/R

DECONINCK, P (19th C) ?
£3396 $5298 €5400 Portrait de dame au bouquet de fleurs (76x58cm-30x23in) 14-Oct-2 Amberes, Antwerp #148

DEDREUX, Pierre Anne (1788-1849) French
Works on paper
£2308 $3646 €3600 Villa Medici in Rome (16x26cm-6x10in) pencil wash prov. 16-Nov-2 Lempertz, Koln #1302/R est:3000

DEELEMAN, Frederik Charles Theodorus (1823-1884) Dutch
Works on paper
£696 $1079 €1100 Figures watching an Indian play (26x40cm-10x16in) s.d.1837 pencil W/C. 24-Sep-2 Christie's, Amsterdam #139/R est:700-900

DEFAUX, Alexandre (1826-1900) French
£1048 $1635 €1572 Garden landscape with hedges and trees (49x65cm-19x26in) s. 6-Nov-2 Dobiaschofsky, Bern #441/R est:4800 (S.FR 2400)
£2009 $3134 €3014 Landscape with farmstead (51x70cm-20x28in) s.d.1883 prov. 20-Nov-2 Fischer, Luzern #1096/R est:3000-3500 (S.FR 4600)
£4177 $6600 €6600 Coq et poules, bord d'eau, journee de printemps (50x73cm-20x29in) s. 1-Dec-2 Peron, Melun #167
£5845 $9703 €8300 Printemps, poules sous le pommier en fleurs (58x85cm-23x33in) s. 11-Jun-3 Beaussant & Lefèvre, Paris #23/R est:7000-8000
£7595 $12000 €11393 Les laveuses (100x81cm-39x32in) s. 23-Apr-3 Christie's, Rockefeller NY #67/R est:15000-20000

DEFER, Jean Joseph Jules (1803-?) French
£2759 $4607 €4000 Vue de l'entree du port de Nice animme de personnages (26x42cm-10x17in) 8-Jul-3 Gioffredo, Nice #55/R
£3448 $5759 €5000 Pecheurs quai des Ponchettes (26x42cm-10x17in) 8-Jul-3 Gioffredo, Nice #54/R
Works on paper
£420 $600 €630 Landscape with a family resting a horse drawn cart (24x32cm-9x13in) s. pen ink wash. 23-Jan-3 Swann Galleries, New York #313/R
£559 $800 €839 Landscape with a hunter and his dog and a herd of goats (23x30cm-9x12in) init.d.1897 pen ink htd white. 23-Jan-3 Swann Galleries, New York #312/R

DEFERT, Maxime (1944-) French
£264 $409 €420 Composition (114x89cm-45x35in) s.verso painted 1974. 7-Oct-2 Claude Aguttes, Neuilly #262

DEFFREGER, N (19th C) French?
£2244 $3478 €3500 Scene galante sur barque (52x67cm-20x26in) s. 5-Dec-2 Gros & Delettrez, Paris #27/R

DEFOREST, Lockwood (1850-1932) American
£1250 $1925 €1875 Lompoc - California (23x35cm-9x14in) init.i. board prov. 3-Sep-2 Shapiro, Sydney #369/R est:1500-2500 (A.D 3500)
£1260 $1990 €1890 Santa Barbara coastline (23x34cm-9x13in) board painted c.1903 prov. 7-Apr-3 Shapiro, Sydney #514/R est:3500-4500 (A.D 3300)
£1374 $2171 €2061 Cyrpess Point (23x34cm-9x13in) s.i.d.Mar 3/11 board prov. 7-Apr-3 Shapiro, Sydney #512/R est:4000-5000 (A.D 3600)
£1374 $2171 €2061 Santa Barbara area (23x35cm-9x14in) s. board prov. 7-Apr-3 Shapiro, Sydney #513/R est:4000-5000 (A.D 3600)
£1929 $2970 €2894 Carmel (24x35cm-9x14in) init.i.d.5/9 prov. 3-Sep-2 Shapiro, Sydney #368/R est:1500-2500 (A.D 5400)
£2395 $4000 €3473 Sunset (24x36cm-9x14in) init.d.20/06 board prov. 18-Jun-3 Christie's, Los Angeles #23/R est:2500-3500
£2515 $4200 €3647 Palm Springs (25x36cm-10x14in) init.i.d.apr 9.07 board prov. 18-Jun-3 Christie's, Los Angeles #24/R est:2500-3500
£2515 $4200 €3647 California landscape (14x25cm-6x10in) init.d.Mar 23.1903 board prov. 18-Jun-3 Christie's, Los Angeles #25/R est:2500-3500
£4518 $7500 €6551 Flowerfields of Lompoc. Poppies along the Carmel coast (25x36cm-10x14in) one init.i.d.1924 one init.i.d.09 masonite two. 11-Jun-3 Butterfields, San Francisco #4213/R est:5000-8000

DEFREGGER, F von (1835-1921) German
Works on paper
£918 $1460 €1350 Peasant girl (17x14cm-7x6in) s.d.2.6.10 pencil. 19-Mar-3 Neumeister, Munich #350 est:300

DEFREGGER, Franz von (1835-1921) German
£1698 $2649 €2700 Peasant kitchen interior (38x47cm-15x19in) 11-Oct-2 Winterberg, Heidelberg #500/R est:2800
£2143 $3193 €3300 Let the children come unto me (29x36cm-11x14in) s. study lit. 26-Jun-2 Neumeister, Munich #710/R est:1600
£3741 $5949 €5500 Peasant portrait (24x18cm-9x7in) s. bears i.d. verso panel. 19-Mar-3 Neumeister, Munich #535/R est:3500
£7643 $11924 €12000 Tyrolean girl (35x28cm-14x11in) s. 6-Nov-2 Hugo Ruef, Munich #1057/R est:12000
£8228 $13000 €13000 Young girl (18x15cm-7x6in) s. board prov.lit. 28-Nov-2 Dorotheum, Vienna #87/R est:13000-15000
£9091 $13545 €14000 Tyrolean woman in traditional costume (66x55cm-26x22in) s.d.99 lit. 26-Jun-2 Neumeister, Munich #709/R est:12000
£15108 $24173 €21000 Young peasant woman with beer mug sitting at tavern table (75x52cm-30x20in) s.d.1895 panel. 17-May-3 Lempertz, Koln #1380/R est:15000
£33094 $52950 €46000 Girl playing zither (71x54cm-28x21in) s.d.94 panel prov.lit. 17-May-3 Lempertz, Koln #1379/R est:15000
Works on paper
£417 $663 €600 Portrait of smoking Tyrolean (9x8cm-4x3in) s. pencil double-sided. 5-May-3 Ketterer, Munich #279/R
£440 $687 €700 Portrait of young Tyrolean woman (18x15cm-7x6in) s.d.1865 pencil. 21-Sep-2 Bolland & Marotz, Bremen #461
£510 $795 €800 Old man with beard (25x17cm-10x7in) s. ochre. 6-Nov-2 Hugo Ruef, Munich #1363
£1216 $1897 €1800 Village. one s.d.8.Aug 68 i. pencil two. 28-Mar-3 Dorotheum, Vienna #111/R est:1000-1200
£1258 $1950 €2000 Peasant (20x16cm-8x6in) s. pencil. 1-Oct-2 Dorotheum, Vienna #144/R est:1900-2200
£1622 $2530 €2400 Tyrolean woman wearing hat (15x15cm-6x6in) s. pencil. 28-Mar-3 Dorotheum, Vienna #161/R est:1800-2000
£5479 $8548 €8000 Bust portrait of a young girl (77x57cm-30x22in) s. pastel lit. 10-Apr-3 Allgauer, Kempten #2600/R est:5500

DEFREGGER, Franz von (attrib) (1835-1921) German
£780 $1264 €1170 Portrait of a woman (24x17cm-9x7in) bears sig board. 20-May-3 Sotheby's, Olympia #396/R
£19858 $32170 €28000 Zither player (95x79cm-37x31in) 22-May-3 Dorotheum, Vienna #155/R est:20000-30000

DEGALLAIX, Louis (19/20th C) French
£3718 $5837 €5800 Bat l'eau, scene de chasse (120x150cm-47x59in) s.d.1879. 15-Dec-2 Mercier & Cie, Lille #392

DEGAS, Edgar (1834-1917) French
£19000 $29260 €28500 La fille de jephte (36x28cm-14x11in) st.sig. painted c.1861-64 prov.lit. 22-Oct-2 Sotheby's, London #105/R est:20000-30000
£22297 $34784 €33000 Portrait de Rene Hilaire Degas (46x38cm-18x15in) painted c.1853-55 prov. 31-Mar-3 Ribeyre & Baron, Paris #45/R
£294872 $460000 €442308 Portrait de femme (59x49cm-23x19in) st.sig. painted c.1867-72 prov.exhib.lit. 6-Nov-2 Christie's, Rockefeller NY #12/R est:400000-600000
Prints
£2436 $3800 €3654 Au Louvre, la peinture, Mary Cassatt (30x13cm-12x5in) etching drypoint edition of 150 exec.c.1879-80. 7-Nov-2 Swann Galleries, New York #423/R est:1500-2500
£5769 $9115 €9000 Chanteuse de cafe concert (7x8cm-3x3in) monotype. 14-Nov-2 Libert, Castor, Paris #80/R est:7500
£10000 $15500 €15000 La famille cardinal. Pauline and Virgine conversing with admirers (16x21cm-6x8in) monotype. 5-Dec-2 Sotheby's, London #118/R est:15000-20000
£14103 $22282 €22000 Sur la scene. vernis mou drypoint. 14-Nov-2 Libert, Castor, Paris #77/R est:15000
£14679 $24514 €21285 Femme mettant les bas (16x12cm-6x5in) monotype. 20-Jun-3 Kornfeld, Bern #27/R est:40000 (S.FR 32000)
£22936 $38303 €33257 Manet en buste (13x10cm-5x4in) etching prov. 20-Jun-3 Kornfeld, Bern #26/R est:60000 (S.FR 50000)
£24359 $38487 €38000 Aux ambassadeurs: Mlle Becat. lithograph. 14-Nov-2 Libert, Castor, Paris #78 est:45000
£41667 $65833 €65000 Femme nue debout, a sa toilette. lithograph. 14-Nov-2 Libert, Castor, Paris #79/R est:35000
£142202 $237477 €206193 Manet assis, tourne a gauche (17x12cm-7x5in) etching. 20-Jun-3 Kornfeld, Bern #25/R est:150000 (S.FR 310000)
Sculpture
£1572 $2421 €2500 Danseuse regardant pied droit (41cm-16in) s. bronze. 22-Oct-2 Campo & Campo, Antwerp #69/R
£6211 $10000 €9317 Tete etude pour le portrait de Madame S (16cm-6in) i.num.7/L dark green pat. lit. 7-May-3 Sotheby's, New York #127/R est:12000-18000
£41667 $65000 €62501 Femme enceinte (43cm-17in) st.sig.num.24/C brown pat. bronze st.f.AA Hebrard prov.exhib.lit. 7-Nov-2 Christie's, Rockefeller NY #237/R est:50000-70000
£54487 $85000 €81731 L'ecolier or Jeune fille a la natte (27cm-11in) st.sig. brown pat. bronze st.f.A.A. Hebrard conceived c.1880 prov. 7-Nov-2 Christie's, Rockefeller NY #215/R est:60000-80000
£93168 $150000 €139752 Cheval au galop sur le pied droit, le pied gauche arriere seul touchant terre, jockey monte sur (25x33cm-10x13in) st.sig.num.25 brown pat. bronze st.f. Hebrard cire perdue prov. 8-May-3 Christie's, Rockefeller NY #137
£99379 $160000 €149069 Cheval sautant un obstacle (30cm-12in) i.num.48 brown pat. bronze prov.lit. 7-May-3 Sotheby's, New York #111/R est:150000-200000

£100853	$163382	€146237	Danseuse attachant le cordon de son Maillot (43cm-17in) s.num.33/L dark pat.bronze Cast Hebrard cire perdue prov.lit. 26-May-3 Bukowskis, Stockholm #309/R est:700000-800000 (S.KR 1300000)
£111801	$180000	€167702	Danseuse regardant la plante de son pied droit (46cm-18in) st.sig. brown pat. bronze st.f.Hebrard prov.exhib.lit. 8-May-3 Christie's, Rockefeller NY #163/R est:180000-220000
£120000	$196800	€180000	Cheval au galop (29cm-11in) s.st.f.Hebrard brown pat bronze prov.exhib.lit. 4-Feb-3 Christie's, London #229/R est:180000
£125000	$203750	€187500	Danseuse mettant son bas (46cm-18in) st.sig.st.f.Hebrard brown pat bronze prov.exhib.lit. 3-Feb-3 Christie's, London #51/R est:140000-180000
£186335	$300000	€279503	Position de quatrieme devant sur la jambe gauche (57cm-22in) s.st.f.Hebrard num.5/B brown pat bronze prov.exhib.lit. 6-May-3 Sotheby's, New York #5/R est:400000
£223602	$360000	€335403	Arabesque sur la jambe droite (44cm-17in) s.st.f.Hebrard brown pat bronze prov.exhib.lit. 6-May-3 Sotheby's, New York #1/R est:400000
£5714286	$9200000	€8571429	Petite danseuse de quatorze ans (98cm-39in) s.st.f.Hebrard brown pat bronze prov.exhib.lit. 7-May-3 Christie's, Rockefeller NY #11/R est:8000000-12000000

Works on paper

£3916	$6500	€5678	Etude de paysage (23x15cm-9x6in) pencil. 13-Jun-3 Du Mouchelle, Detroit #2022/R est:8000-10000
£5405	$8432	€8000	Etude d'un jeune spartiate (34x20cm-13x8in) s. chl exec.c.1860. 31-Mar-3 Rossini, Paris #52/R
£9494	$14810	€15000	Jockey a cheval (21x12cm-8x5in) graphite prov.exhib. 31-Jul-2 Tajan, Paris #2/R est:12000-15000
£10256	$16000	€15384	Etude de draperie (32x24cm-13x9in) st.sig. pencil paper on board executed 1856-58 prov.exhib. 7-Nov-2 Christie's, Rockefeller NY #157/R est:20000-30000
£12000	$20040	€17400	Copie d'apres les funeralles de St. Bernadin de pinturicchio (28x21cm-11x8in) st.sig. sanguine executed c.1857-58 prov.exhib.lit. 24-Jun-3 Sotheby's, London #216/R est:15000-20000
£12179	$19000	€18269	Tete de femme (29x24cm-11x9in) pencil executed c.1865 prov.exhib. 7-Nov-2 Christie's, Rockefeller NY #159/R est:20000-30000
£12422	$20000	€18633	Etude pour le jockey blesse, un cheval deleste de son cavalier un cheval monte (19x29cm-7x11in) pencil prov. 7-May-3 Sotheby's, New York #110/R est:25000-35000
£17000	$26180	€25500	Cheval de selle et cheval monte par un jockey (30x20cm-12x8in) studio st. chl pencil prov. 22-Oct-2 Sotheby's, London #122/R est:16000-18000
£19231	$30000	€28847	Apres le bain - femme s'essuyant (26x18cm-10x7in) st.sig. pencil prov.exhib.lit. 7-Nov-2 Christie's, Rockefeller NY #123/R est:30000-40000
£22436	$35000	€33654	Buste de jeune homme, etudes pour la fille de jephte (33x21cm-13x8in) st.sig. pencil executed 1859-60 prov.exhib.lit. 7-Nov-2 Christie's, Rockefeller NY #105/R est:35000-45000
£24648	$40916	€35000	Danseuse (27x22cm-11x9in) bears st.sig. chl dr prov. 12-Jun-3 Tajan, Paris #1/R est:30000-40000
£32000	$53440	€48000	Deux etudes d'un jockey (48x30cm-19x12in) st.sig. studio st.verso chl. pencil. 26-Jun-3 Christie's, London #359/R est:40000-60000
£32051	$50321	€50000	Tete de femme (26x23cm-10x9in) crayon dr prov. 16-Dec-2 Rabourdin & Choppin de Janvry, Paris #17/R est:13000-15000
£35256	$55000	€52884	Cavaliers en habit, etude d'apres Carle Vernet's la chasse au cerf, le jour de Saint-Hubert (23x36cm-9x14in) st.sig. pencil prov.exhib. 7-Nov-2 Christie's, Rockefeller NY #114/R est:70000-90000
£35484	$55000	€53226	Standing male youth (30x21cm-12x8in) indis sig.i. pencil prov.exhib.lit. 29-Oct-2 Sotheby's, New York #21/R est:20000-30000
£44872	$70000	€67308	Danseuses (18x19cm-7x7in) st.sig. pencil executed c.1879 prov.exhib.lit. 7-Nov-2 Christie's, Rockefeller NY #104/R est:40000-60000
£48077	$75000	€72116	Apres le bain - femme nue (48x44cm-19x17in) st.sig. chl paper on board prov.lit. 7-Nov-2 Christie's, Rockefeller NY #102/R est:60000-80000
£64103	$100000	€96155	Danseuses au repos (87x83cm-34x33in) st.sig. chl htd white chk paper on board prov. 7-Nov-2 Christie's, Rockefeller NY #112/R est:100000-150000
£72000	$118080	€108000	Femme au bain (31x41cm-12x16in) st.sig. chl chk prov. 6-Feb-3 Christie's, London #410/R est:120000
£82051	$128000	€123077	Danseuse debout (30x23cm-12x9in) st.sig. i.verso black crayon htd white prov.exhib.lit. 5-Nov-2 Phillips, New York #107/R est:90000-120000
£135000	$225450	€202500	Deux danseuses (69x57cm-27x22in) st.sig. chl. sanguine exec c.1890 prov. 26-Jun-3 Christie's, London #360/R est:80000-120000
£176282	$276763	€275000	Apres le bain, femme s'essuyant (33x50cm-13x20in) studio st. pastel chl exec.c.1884 prov.lit. 10-Dec-2 Artcurial Briest, Paris #473/R est:150000-230000
£190000	$317300	€275500	Danseuse au repos (54x44cm-21x17in) st.sig. pastel counterproof exec.c.1897-1900 prov.exhib.lit. 24-Jun-3 Christie's, London #49/R est:160000-220000
£195000	$319800	€292500	Danseuse a l'eventail (47x62cm-19x24in) st.sig. pastel paper on canvas prov.lit. 4-Feb-3 Sotheby's, London #4/R est:350000
£256410	$400000	€384615	Femme a sa toilette (110x84cm-43x33in) st.sig. chl pastel paper on board executed c.1895 prov.lit. 7-Nov-2 Christie's, Rockefeller NY #126/R est:350000-450000
£384615	$600000	€576923	Apres le bain, femme s'essuyant (97x83cm-38x33in) st.sig. chl executed c.1905-07 pexhib. 5-Nov-2 Sotheby's, New York #13/R est:600000-800000
£434783	$700000	€652175	Portrait de femme (61x46cm-24x18in) s. pastel paper on canvas exec.c.1885 prov.exhib.lit. 7-May-3 Christie's, Rockefeller NY #12/R est:900000-1200000
£850000	$1385500	€1275000	Danseuse (40x27cm-16x11in) s. pastel paper on card exec.1896 prov.exhib.lit. 3-Feb-3 Christie's, London #59/R est:1200000
£1153846	$1800000	€1730769	La toilette (59x51cm-23x20in) s. pastel executed c.1897 prov.exhib.lit. 5-Nov-2 Sotheby's, New York #57/R est:1800000-2500000
£2173913	$3500000	€3260870	Danseuses pres d'un portant (59x46cm-23x18in) s. pastel paper on cardboard prov.exhib.lit. 6-May-3 Sotheby's, New York #10/R est:2500000-3500000
£5900621	$9500000	€8850932	Danseuse (77x45cm-30x18in) s. pastel paper on cardboard prov.exhib.lit. 6-May-3 Sotheby's, New York #11/R est:9000000-12000000

DEGAS, Edgar (attrib) (1834-1917) French

Works on paper

£2297	$3584	€3400	Etude de cavaliers et academie d'homme (25x19cm-10x7in) crayon stump chk prov. 26-Mar-3 Piasa, Paris #88

DEGAS, Edgar and THORNLEY, Georges W (19/20th C) French

Prints

£4277	$6800	€6416	Danseuse pres de la poele (33x25cm-13x10in) mauve ink lithograph. 3-Mar-3 Swann Galleries, New York #13/R est:5000-8000
£5769	$9000	€8654	Le bain (23x32cm-9x13in) s. col lithograph edition of 25 exec.c.1888. 7-Nov-2 Swann Galleries, New York #424/R est:7000-10000

DEGEN, Paul (1941-) American

Works on paper

£2564	$4000	€3846	Stepping rails on staircase (36x25cm-14x10in) s. ink col pencil. 9-Nov-2 Illustration House, New York #82/R est:2500-4000

DEGENEVE, Robert (1919-) Belgian

£1722	$2807	€2600	Pecheur a la pipe (60x50cm-24x20in) s. cardboard. 17-Feb-3 Horta, Bruxelles #461

DEGENHARD, Hugo (1866-1901) German

£324	$522	€486	Country landscape with farmstead (59x70cm-23x28in) s. panel. 7-May-3 Dobiaschofsky, Bern #435/R (S.FR 700)

DEGLUME, Henri (1865-1940) Belgian

£304	$474	€480	Village enneige (52x70cm-20x28in) s. 15-Oct-2 Horta, Bruxelles #278
£306	$487	€450	Sous-bois (56x85cm-22x33in) s. 18-Mar-3 Campo, Vlaamse Kaai #61
£340	$541	€500	Sous-bois a l'etang (50x72cm-20x28in) s. 18-Mar-3 Campo, Vlaamse Kaai #62
£379	$607	€550	Rayons de soleil sur le village (47x70cm-19x28in) s. 17-Mar-3 Horta, Bruxelles #246

DEGN, Ernst (1904-1995) Austrian

Works on paper

£694	$1104	€1000	Fendels (37x44cm-15x17in) s. W/C. 29-Apr-3 Wiener Kunst Auktionen, Vienna #616/R

DEGODE, Wilhelm (1862-1931) German

£3200	$5344	€4800	Kaiserwert (100x150cm-39x59in) s.d.97. 18-Jun-3 Christie's, Kensington #70/R est:2500-3500

DEGOTTEX, Jean (1918-1988) French
£288 $453 €450 Ecriture noire sur rouge (24x17cm-9x7in) s.d. acrylic Indian ink. 16-Dec-2 Charbonneaux, Paris #134
£897 $1409 €1400 Ecriture sur fond jaune (38x10cm-15x4in) s.d.verso siorel. 16-Dec-2 Charbonneaux, Paris #240
£1773 $2961 €2500 L'ephemere (100x50cm-39x20in) s.d. 18-Jun-3 Pierre Berge, Paris #89/R est:2000-3000
£2215 $3434 €3500 Composition (45x68cm-18x27in) s. oil collage panel. 28-Sep-2 Cornette de St.Cyr, Paris #287/R est:2000-3000
£6289 $9748 €10000 Horsphere romane (280x130cm-110x51in) s. prov.lit. 30-Oct-2 Artcurial Briest, Paris #465/R est:10000-15000
£7292 $11594 €10500 Ken Do (130x97cm-51x38in) s.d.69 s.i.d.14 avril 1969 verso prov.lit. 29-Apr-3 Artcurial Briest, Paris #490 est:10000-15000
£11392 $18000 €18000 Sabi II (195x97cm-77x38in) s.d.61 prov.exhib. 27-Nov-2 Blanchet, Paris #141/R est:30000
Works on paper
£395 $640 €600 Sans titre (12x12cm-5x5in) felt crayon dr. 22-Jan-3 Tajan, Paris #246
£861 $1403 €1300 Metasphere bleue (62x49cm-24x19in) s.d.66 frottage gouache. 3-Feb-3 Cornette de St.Cyr, Paris #402
£903 $1435 €1300 Composition (24x17cm-9x7in) s.d.1965 mixed media ink. 29-Apr-3 Artcurial Briest, Paris #489/R est:1500-2000
£1111 $1833 €1600 Suit IBN, III (105x75cm-41x30in) s.d.1.8.62 Indian ink prov. 1-Jul-3 Artcurial Briest, Paris #860/R est:2000-2500
£1139 $1766 €1800 Composition (48x62cm-19x24in) s.d. ink W/C. 28-Sep-2 Cornette de St.Cyr, Paris #288/R est:1500-1800
£1181 $1948 €1700 Suite JSHET (105x75cm-41x30in) s.d.25.4.62 Indian ink. 1-Jul-3 Artcurial Briest, Paris #861/R est:2000-2500
£1389 $2194 €2000 Entre-acte II (50x64cm-20x25in) s.i.d.25/2/74 Indian ink prov.exhib.lit. 27-Apr-3 Perrin, Versailles #112/R est:2500-3000
£1586 $2649 €2300 Sans titre (74x104cm-29x41in) s.d.54 W/C ink. 10-Jul-3 Artcurial Briest, Paris #300/R est:2500-3000
£1806 $2854 €2800 Composition (65x50cm-26x20in) s. W/C Chinese ink. 19-Dec-2 Ruellan, Paris #139/R
£1879 $3026 €2800 Composition (32x49cm-13x19in) mono. W/C. 23-Feb-3 Mercier & Cie, Lille #59/R
£2222 $3534 €3200 NM I (45x100cm-18x39in) s.d.verso ink wash prov. 29-Apr-3 Artcurial Briest, Paris #491/R est:2500-3000

DEGOUVE DE NUNCQUES, William (1867-1935) Belgian
£818 $1267 €1300 Old farm (49x59cm-19x23in) mono.d.18. 5-Oct-2 De Vuyst, Lokeren #85/R
£10072 $16115 €14000 Paysage de montagne dans la brume, Espagne (54x67cm-21x26in) mono.d.02. 13-May-3 Palais de Beaux Arts, Brussels #60/R est:9000-12000
Works on paper
£382 $607 €550 Esquisse pour un cavalier (11x18cm-4x7in) mono. mixed media. 29-Apr-3 Campo & Campo, Antwerp #61/R
£641 $1006 €1000 Paysage montagneux (16x31cm-6x12in) mono. col crayon dr sold with a lithograph. 10-Dec-2 Vanderkindere, Brussels #92
£903 $1435 €1300 Riviere dans le parc (35x45cm-14x18in) mono. pastel. 29-Apr-3 Campo & Campo, Antwerp #58/R
£1319 $2098 €1900 Esquisse pour une vue de parc (40x49cm-16x19in) mono.d.1909 mixed media. 29-Apr-3 Campo & Campo, Antwerp #60/R est:400-500
£16767 $26156 €25151 Street in Magent (34x52cm-13x20in) s. pastel. 11-Apr-3 Kieselbach, Budapest #55/R est:5600000-6000000 (H.F 6000000)

DEGREEF, Amedee (1878-1968) Belgian
£2166 $3378 €3400 Jeune fille au bouquet de fleuri (58x52cm-23x20in) s. 11-Nov-2 Horta, Bruxelles #60 est:1500-2000

DEGREEF, Jean (1852-1894) Belgian
£400 $664 €400 Vue d'etang (20x29cm-8x11in) s. panel. 16-Jun-3 Horta, Bruxelles #373
£481 $745 €750 Maison de maitre dans un paysage (20x25cm-8x10in) s. 3-Dec-2 Campo & Campo, Antwerp #67
£490 $789 €750 L'arrivee au moulin (28x40cm-11x16in) s. panel. 14-Jan-3 Vanderkindere, Brussels #37
£823 $1284 €1300 Arrivee au moulin (28x40cm-11x16in) s. panel. 16-Sep-2 Horta, Bruxelles #60
£1583 $2532 €2200 Le repos du forestier (85x70cm-33x28in) s. 19-May-3 Horta, Bruxelles #84 est:3000-4000
£1727 $2763 €2400 Avenue of beech trees in autumn (107x144cm-42x57in) s. 17-May-3 De Vuyst, Lokeren #130/R est:2500-3600

DEGROSSI, Adelchi (19th C) Italian
£866 $1343 €1299 Ponte Rialto (21x18cm-8x7in) painted c.1880. 1-Oct-2 SOGA, Bratislava #181/R est:55000 (SL.K 55000)

DEHN, Adolf (1895-1968) American
Works on paper
£427 $700 €619 The wall (47x69cm-19x27in) s. W/C. 5-Jun-3 Swann Galleries, New York #79/R
£1463 $2400 €2121 Burlesque dancers (34x51cm-13x20in) s.d. W/C gouache. 5-Jun-3 Swann Galleries, New York #77/R est:2500-3500
£2404 $3750 €3606 Ouray, Colorado (51x71cm-20x28in) W/C executed c.1941. 19-Oct-2 David Dike, Dallas #354/R est:3000-6000
£3774 $6000 €5661 Breakers, Palm Beach (37x55cm-15x22in) s.d.1951 gouache pencil. 5-Mar-3 Christie's, Rockefeller NY #108/R est:1200-1800

DEHNER, Dorothy (1901-1994) American
Works on paper
£641 $1000 €962 Abstract composition (51x79cm-20x31in) s.d.1975 pen ink W/C. 19-Sep-2 Swann Galleries, New York #297/R

DEHODENCQ, Alfred (1822-1882) French
£16340 $26797 €25000 Danse des negres a Tanger (61x97cm-24x38in) s. exhib.lit. 7-Feb-3 Oger, Dumont, Paris #79/R
Works on paper
£380 $600 €600 Etudes d'orientaux a cheval (20x29cm-8x11in) pen ink. 28-Nov-2 Tajan, Paris #158
£405 $632 €600 Assemblee de personnages (19x30cm-7x12in) bears mono. crayon pen ink wash. 27-Mar-3 Maigret, Paris #123/R
£1097 $1700 €1646 Othello recounting his battles (35x45cm-14x18in) s.i. pencil W/C ink prov.lit. 29-Oct-2 Sotheby's, New York #16/R est:1000-1500

DEHOY, Charles (1872-1940) Belgian
£548 $855 €800 Vase fleuri de tulipes (60x51cm-24x20in) s.d.1931. 14-Apr-3 Horta, Bruxelles #25
£753 $1175 €1100 Nature morte aux peches et a la cruche (70x60cm-28x24in) s.d.1930. 14-Apr-3 Horta, Bruxelles #24
£1069 $1657 €1700 Walkers on the beach (17x21cm-7x8in) s. board. 5-Oct-2 De Vuyst, Lokeren #86/R est:1400-1600
Works on paper
£1474 $2285 €2300 Still life with fruit dish and jug (96x66cm-38x26in) s.d.1921 W/C. 7-Dec-2 De Vuyst, Lokeren #550/R est:2500-3000

DEIBL, Anton (1833-1883) German
£1634 $2614 €2500 Child in blue dress with trumpet (115x60cm-45x24in) s.d.1879 lit. 10-Jan-3 Allgauer, Kempten #1568/R est:2500

DEIBLER, Anatole (1863-1939) French
Photographs
£55556 $91111 €85000 Untitled. photograph album. 5-Feb-3 Beaussant & Lefèvre, Paris #9/R

DEIKE, Clara (1881-1964) American
£4088 $6500 €6132 Gloucester harbour (61x53cm-24x21in) s.d. board. 2-Mar-3 Toomey, Oak Park #569/R est:1500-2500
Works on paper
£415 $680 €602 Lake Erie scene (23x30cm-9x12in) s.d.1911 W/C. 30-May-3 Aspire, Cleveland #95/R

DEIKER, Carl (1879-1958) German
Works on paper
£414 $638 €650 Pheasant (30x41cm-12x16in) s.d.1919. 5-Sep-2 Arnold, Frankfurt #751/R

DEIKER, Carl Friedrich (1836-1892) German
£1218 $1912 €1900 Fox (71x91cm-28x36in) s. 21-Nov-2 Van Ham, Cologne #1526 est:3500
£2138 $3336 €3400 Hunting dog with dead hare (56x45cm-22x18in) s.d.1867. 21-Sep-2 Bolland & Marotz, Bremen #462/R est:1300

DEINEKA, Alexander (1899-1969) Russian
Works on paper
£7042 $11338 €10000 Ships in harbour (43x72cm-17x28in) s.d.35 gouache. 10-May-3 Bukowskis, Helsinki #393/R est:2000-3000

DEITERS, Heinrich (1840-1916) German
£616 $962 €900 Dutch dyke landscape with windmills (31x60cm-12x24in) s.d.93. 10-Apr-3 Van Ham, Cologne #1367
£4359 $6844 €6800 Angler in summer river landscape (65x107cm-26x42in) s. 21-Nov-2 Van Ham, Cologne #1527/R est:3300

DEIX, Manfred (1949-) Austrian
£321 $506 €500 Ass violinist (45x51cm-18x20in) s.d.1974 i. verso. 12-Nov-2 Dorotheum, Vienna #224/R
Works on paper
£633 $981 €1000 Untitled (24x18cm-9x7in) s. mixed media. 24-Sep-2 Wiener Kunst Auktionen, Vienna #336/R

DEKEN, Albert de (1915-2003) Belgian

£278 $442 €400 Paysage (35x45cm-14x18in) s. 29-Apr-3 Campo & Campo, Antwerp #496
£278 $442 €400 Allee dans un village (35x50cm-14x20in) s. 29-Apr-3 Campo & Campo, Antwerp #501
£313 $497 €450 Promenade sur la plage (34x48cm-13x19in) s. panel. 29-Apr-3 Campo & Campo, Antwerp #55
£313 $497 €450 Nature morte aux oranges (35x44cm-14x17in) s. 29-Apr-3 Campo & Campo, Antwerp #498
£347 $552 €500 Vue de la ville (51x68cm-20x27in) paper. 29-Apr-3 Campo & Campo, Antwerp #506
£355 $592 €500 Still life with coffee pot (46x59cm-18x23in) s. paper. 23-Jun-3 Bernaerts, Antwerp #428
£486 $773 €700 Mer du Nord (35x45cm-14x18in) s. 29-Apr-3 Campo & Campo, Antwerp #500
£545 $845 €850 Town view (50x60cm-20x24in) s. 7-Dec-2 De Vuyst, Lokeren #82/R
£556 $883 €800 Roulotte (35x44cm-14x17in) s. 29-Apr-3 Campo & Campo, Antwerp #497
£590 $939 €850 Carrosse (35x45cm-14x18in) s. 29-Apr-3 Campo & Campo, Antwerp #502
£625 $994 €900 Vue sur les polders en Flandre (60x73cm-24x29in) s. 29-Apr-3 Campo & Campo, Antwerp #504
£764 $1215 €1100 Nature morte a la cafetiere (50x64cm-20x25in) s. paper. 29-Apr-3 Campo & Campo, Antwerp #56/R
£1111 $1767 €1600 Royal Yacht Club, Ostende (50x60cm-20x24in) s. 29-Apr-3 Campo, Vlaamse Kaai #72/R est:800-1000
£1132 $1743 €1800 Nature morte (60x82cm-24x32in) s. 22-Oct-2 Campo, Vlaamse Kaai #471/R
£1172 $1876 €1700 Jachthaven (50x60cm-20x24in) s. 15-Mar-3 De Vuyst, Lokeren #81 est:750-1000
£1944 $3092 €2800 Vue sur Plage-Albert a Knokke (35x45cm-14x18in) s. 29-Apr-3 Campo & Campo, Antwerp #54 est:700-900

Works on paper

£347 $552 €500 Fleurs (55x41cm-22x16in) s. W/C. 29-Apr-3 Campo, Vlaamse Kaai #73

DEKKER, Henk (1897-1957) Dutch

£528 $850 €750 Sea ship on the river (29x49cm-11x19in) s. 6-May-3 Vendu Notarishuis, Rotterdam #220/R
£658 $1066 €1000 Sailing vessels in open water (60x80cm-24x31in) s. 21-Jan-3 Christie's, Amsterdam #190/R est:1200-1600
£789 $1279 €1200 Shipping on a river, town beyond (40x60cm-16x24in) s.d.31. 21-Jan-3 Christie's, Amsterdam #185 est:1200-1600
£833 $1308 €1300 Sailing boats in evening sun (25x41cm-10x16in) s.d.30. 25-Nov-2 Glerum, Amsterdam #82
£1090 $1689 €1700 Fishing port of Ostend (50x70cm-20x28in) s. 7-Dec-2 De Vuyst, Lokeren #84/R est:1800-2500
£1197 $1927 €1700 Fishing boats in Schevening (77x97cm-30x38in) s. 6-May-3 Vendu Notarishuis, Rotterdam #83/R est:1000-1500
£1210 $1888 €1900 Fishing boats in the surf (49x69cm-19x27in) s.d.31. 6-Nov-2 Vendue Huis, Gravenhage #653/R est:1200-1600
£1408 $2268 €2000 Wild sea with the "Scheveningen 14" (78x48cm-31x19in) s. 7-May-3 Vendue Huis, Gravenhage #94/R est:2200-2600
£1620 $2608 €2300 Schevening fisherwoman on the quay (49x69cm-19x27in) s. 7-May-3 Vendue Huis, Gravenhage #36/R est:2000-3000
£1831 $2948 €2600 Entrance of the fleet (60x100cm-24x39in) s. 7-May-3 Vendue Huis, Gravenhage #89/R est:1000-1500

DEKKERS, Ad (1938-) Dutch

£7595 $12000 €12000 Houtgrafiek No.1 (120x120cm-47x47in) s.d.1970 verso white painted wood exhib.lit. 26-Nov-2 Sotheby's, Amsterdam #268/R est:12000-15000

DEKKERT, Eugène (1865-1956) German

£316 $500 €500 Farming family on the field, near Stettin (50x75cm-20x30in) s. double-sided. 29-Nov-2 Bolland & Marotz, Bremen #679/R
£321 $506 €500 Garmisch with Zugspitze (54x68cm-21x27in) s.i. stretcher. 12-Nov-2 Dorotheum, Vienna #103/R
£409 $638 €650 Stettin harbour (62x91cm-24x36in) s. 21-Sep-2 Bolland & Marotz, Bremen #463/R
£1000 $1560 €1500 Fishing fleet setting off (30x35cm-12x14in) s. 10-Apr-3 Bonhams, Edinburgh #159 est:800-1200
£1800 $2808 €2700 Unloading the catch (30x34cm-12x13in) s. 10-Apr-3 Bonhams, Edinburgh #160 est:800-1200
£2000 $3120 €3000 Fishing boats in the harbour at Pittenweem (45x51cm-18x20in) s. 14-Apr-3 Sotheby's, London #83/R est:1200-1500

DELABANO, Barney (1926-1997) American

£577 $900 €866 Old house (51x61cm-20x24in) painted c.1948. 19-Oct-2 David Dike, Dallas #245/R

DELABRIERE, P E (1829-1912) French

Sculpture

£1000 $1550 €1500 Model of a hunting dog (30cm-12in) s. bronze with oval base. 4-Nov-2 Brightwells, Leominster #969/R est:800-1200

DELABRIERE, Paul Edouard (1829-1912) French

Sculpture

£1060 $1727 €1600 Chien a l'arret devant un perdrix (17x29cm-7x11in) s.num.37 green pat bronze. 2-Feb-3 Muizon & Le Coent, Paris #76
£2532 $3949 €4000 Etalon de course selle (28x40cm-11x16in) s. brown pat bronze. 20-Oct-2 Mercier & Cie, Lille #130/R est:4500-5000
£5800 $9048 €8700 Pheasants with their chicks (43x54cm-17x21in) s. golden brown pat bronze lit. 5-Nov-2 Sotheby's, London #103/R est:6000-8000

DELACAZETTE, Sophie Clemence (1774-1854) French

Miniatures

£3800 $5966 €5700 Young lady, formerly called Queen Therese of Bavaria (7cm-3xin) s.d.1815 gilt metal mount oval prov.lit. 10-Dec-2 Christie's, London #204/R est:2000-3000

DELACHAUX, Léon (1850-1918) Swiss

£1408 $2338 €2000 L'heureuse famille (32x24cm-13x9in) s. panel. 13-Jun-3 Rabourdin & Choppin de Janvry, Paris #82/R est:3000-4000

DELACROIX (19th C) French

£7447 $11543 €11171 Classical coastal landscape with figures (14x22cm-6x9in) indis.sig.indis.d.1784 copper. 4-Dec-2 AB Stockholms Auktionsverk #1923/R est:8000-10000 (S.KR 105000)

DELACROIX (attrib) (19th C) French

Works on paper

£315 $526 €450 Etudes de personnages (18x28cm-7x11in) black crayon W/C. 27-Jun-3 Claude Aguttes, Neuilly #16/R

DELACROIX, Andre (?-1934) French

£2244 $3522 €3500 Coin de jardin pres de la fontaine, Sidi Bou Said, au matin (22x33cm-9x13in) s. s.i.verso. 16-Dec-2 Gros & Delettrez, Paris #79/R est:3000-4000

DELACROIX, Auguste (1809-1868) French

£1834 $2861 €2751 River landscape with windmill (36x61cm-14x24in) s. 20-Nov-2 Fischer, Luzern #1071/R est:4400-5200 (S.FR 4200)

Works on paper

£641 $994 €1000 Quatre dames en discussion (35x47cm-14x19in) s. W/C. 3-Dec-2 Campo & Campo, Antwerp #71/R

DELACROIX, Eugène (1798-1863) French

£23585 $36557 €37500 Jeune tigre couche (23x37cm-9x15in) pen w/C. 3-Nov-2 Feletin, Province #97
£41958 $70070 €60000 Lelia pleurant sur le corps de Stenio (46x39cm-18x15in) s. 25-Jun-3 Sotheby's, Paris #84/R est:60000-80000

Works on paper

£629 $900 €944 Sheet of studies with figures and a bench (15x9cm-6x4in) pencil ink wash. 23-Jan-3 Swann Galleries, New York #292/R
£962 $1500 €1443 Etude pour des Lunettes, l'Hotel de Ville de Paris (17x28cm-7x11in) artist st. i.d.verso pencil. 19-Sep-2 Swann Galleries, New York #299/R est:1000-1500
£1172 $1876 €1700 Mirabeau et Dreux Breze devant le Tiers-Etat (29x23cm-11x9in) st. graphite. 12-Mar-3 E & Eve, Paris #38/R est:1500-2000
£1282 $1987 €2000 Trois figures Renaissance (16x30cm-6x12in) pen ink wash. 4-Dec-2 Piasa, Paris #134/R
£1500 $2385 €2250 Political caricatures, who are you? non mi Ricordo? (15x25cm-6x10in) init. pen ink prov. 20-Mar-3 Christie's, Kensington #137/R est:3000-5000
£1519 $2400 €2400 Homme nu debout, d'apres Durieu (19x16cm-7x6in) i.d.5 oct 55 graphite. 27-Nov-2 Christie's, Paris #244/R est:1500-2000
£1698 $2632 €2700 Etude de femme endormie (29x46cm-11x18in) st.sig. crayon dr. 6-Oct-2 Livinec, Gaudcheau & Jezequel, Rennes #21/R
£1905 $3029 €2800 Projet de decor pour le Salon de la Paix (29x36cm-11x14in) mono. crayon dr. 21-Mar-3 Rieunier, Bailly-Pommery, Mathias, Paris #46/R
£2096 $3250 €3144 Bust of a bearded man (14x15cm-6x6in) st. pencil prov.lit. 29-Oct-2 Sotheby's, New York #20/R est:5000-7000
£2128 $3553 €3000 Etude de chats et de jeune romain (17x20cm-7x8in) st.d.25 mars 1844. 23-Jun-3 Beaussant & Lefèvre, Paris #298/R est:2500-3000
£2405 $3800 €3800 Etude d'un bra tenant un baton et une etude de la main (20x30cm-8x12in) graphite prov.lit. 27-Nov-2 Christie's, Paris #243/R est:4000-6000
£2564 $3974 €4000 Etude de lion (9x13cm-4x5in) studio st. W/C over crayon prov. 4-Dec-2 Piasa, Paris #136/R

£3200 $5344 €4640 Figure riding a horse, three horse studies. Figures dueling and other studies (24x31cm-9x12in) pencil double-sided prov. 8-Jul-3 Christie's, London #89/R est:2500-3500
£3205 $5032 €5000 Palais marocain (8x10cm-3x4in) ink wash crayon. 20-Nov-2 Binoche, Paris #53/R est:5000-6000
£4800 $7536 €7200 Une jeune fille marocaine (20x14cm-8x6in) init. pencil wash prov.exhib.lit. 19-Nov-2 Sotheby's, London #173/R est:3000-4000
£5000 $8200 €7500 Un roulier a l'auberge (20x13cm-8x5in) s. sepia pen ink prov.lit. 3-Jun-3 Sotheby's, London #131/R est:6000-8000
£5128 $7949 €8000 Etudes de figures arabes (20x29cm-8x11in) d.29 pen ink prov. 4-Dec-2 Piasa, Paris #135/R
£6419 $10014 €9500 Deux amants dans la foret (15x12cm-6x5in) s.i. W/C gouache htd gum arabic prov.lit. 27-Mar-3 Christie's, Paris #156a/R
£12000 $19680 €18000 Les bergers chaldeens - the chaldean shepherds (22x25cm-9x10in) pastel prov.lit. 3-Jun-3 Sotheby's, London #133/R est:12000-18000
£12346 $20000 €18519 Studies of cats and female nudes (23x32cm-9x13in) i. pencil pen ink wash prov. 22-Jan-3 Christie's, Rockefeller NY #104a/R est:35000
£22517 $36702 €34000 Orientale assise (19x20cm-7x8in) st.init. W/C graphite ink. 3-Feb-3 Chambelland & Giafferi, Paris #327/R est:30000
£32407 $52500 €48611 Study for 'The education of Achilles' (20x33cm-8x13in) d.1845 i.verso pen ink prov.lit. 21-Jan-3 Sotheby's, New York #176/R est:16000
£35897 $56359 €56000 Etude de hampes de rose tremiere (48x30cm-19x12in) chl pastel prov. 13-Dec-2 Pierre Berge, Paris #51/R est:8000
£49383 $80000 €74075 Stallion in profile (18x23cm-7x9in) s.d.1825 graphite prov. 22-Jan-3 Christie's, Rockefeller NY #104/R est:50000

DELACROIX, Eugène (attrib) (1798-1863) French
£1258 $1937 €2000 Abidos' fiancee (39x30cm-15x12in) 28-Oct-2 Il Ponte, Milan #238/R
£3673 $5841 €5400 Etude de cheval a l'attache (20x26cm-8x10in) i.verso. 24-Mar-3 Coutau Begarie, Paris #106/R
£8387 $13252 €13000 Assassinat de Jean san Peur au pont de Montereau (83x121cm-33x48in) prov.exhib.lit. 18-Dec-2 Piasa, Paris #98/R est:30000
Works on paper
£851 $1421 €1200 Feuille d'etudes. Tete de dindon (20x23cm-8x9in) pen brown ink double-sided. 19-Jun-3 Piasa, Paris #172/R

DELACROIX, Henry Eugène (1845-1929) French
£2096 $3500 €3039 Amongst the trees (46x62cm-18x24in) s.d.1904 prov. 22-Jun-3 Freeman, Philadelphia #36/R est:3000-5000

DELACROIX, Victor (1842-?) Belgian
£1731 $2734 €2700 La confidence (95x78cm-37x31in) s.i.d.1848 panel. 18-Nov-2 Tajan, Paris #16 est:3000-4600

DELACROIX-GARNIER, Pauline (1863-1912) French
£1337 $2086 €2006 Girl reading (65x54cm-26x21in) s.d.1893. 13-Sep-2 Lilla Bukowskis, Stockholm #52 est:8000-10000 (S.KR 19500)

DELAFOSSE, Jean Charles (1734-1789) French
Works on paper
£696 $1100 €1100 Etudes de deux chapiteaux et un fronton ornementes de trophes (18x30cm-7x12in) i. pen brown ink grey wash prov. 27-Nov-2 Christie's, Paris #186/R
£2069 $3290 €3000 Allegoire de La Boheme et la Hongrie (35x19cm-14x7in) s.i. pierre noire grey wash. 4-Mar-3 Livinec, Gaudcheau & Jezequel, Rennes #33/R
£5068 $7905 €7500 Portrait de marie Delafosse (20x26cm-8x10in) i. crayon. 26-Mar-3 Piasa, Paris #51/R

DELAFOSSE, Jean Charles (attrib) (1734-1789) French
Works on paper
£265 $432 €400 Etude (21x12cm-8x5in) pen wash. 3-Feb-3 Chambelland & Giafferi, Paris #308
£1361 $2164 €2000 Projet pour porte de prison (23x35cm-9x14in) W/C pen ink. 24-Mar-3 Tajan, Paris #58/R

DELAGE, Pierre (?) ?
£2600 $4212 €3900 Fine vintage (39x47cm-15x19in) s. board. 23-Jan-3 Christie's, Kensington #123/R est:1500-2000

DELAGE, R (20th C) Austrian
£2009 $3134 €3014 Chess game (63x74cm-25x29in) s. 6-Nov-2 Dobiaschofsky, Bern #443/R est:4800 (S.FR 4600)

DELAGRANGE, Léon Noel (1872-1910) French
Sculpture
£3291 $5232 €4937 Young couple embracing by spring (92cm-36in) indis.sig. white marble. 25-Feb-3 Rasmussen, Copenhagen #876/R est:30000-40000 (D.KR 36000)

DELAHAUT, Jo (1911-1992) Belgian
£443 $691 €700 Coin de rue en hiver (50x46cm-20x18in) s. 16-Sep-2 Horta, Bruxelles #485
£674 $1125 €950 Composition abstraite (42x31cm-17x12in) s.d.47 board. 18-Jun-3 Hotel des Ventes Mosan, Brussels #287
£833 $1292 €1300 Couleur no.25 (40x61cm-16x24in) s.i.d.1971 verso panel prov. 3-Dec-2 Christie's, Amsterdam #278/R est:1600-2000
£1727 $2763 €2400 Chant (64x49cm-25x19in) s.d.57 board. 17-May-3 De Vuyst, Lokeren #134/R est:2200-2600
£2405 $3800 €3800 Vert noir (91x72cm-36x28in) s.d.87. 26-Nov-2 Palais de Beaux Arts, Brussels #247/R est:3750-5000
£2621 $4193 €3800 Signe vert (64x98cm-25x39in) s.i.d.1955 verso panel lit. 15-Mar-3 De Vuyst, Lokeren #480/R est:3000-3600
£2911 $4542 €4600 Rythmes nouveaux (48x70cm-19x28in) s.d.53. 15-Oct-2 Horta, Bruxelles #29
Sculpture
£1931 $3090 €2800 Cinetic Nr 3 (65x51cm-26x20in) s.d.63 verso wood white laquer. 15-Mar-3 De Vuyst, Lokeren #481/R est:3000-3600
Works on paper
£709 $1184 €1000 Composition (24x23cm-9x9in) s.d.47 gouache. 17-Jun-3 Palais de Beaux Arts, Brussels #537

DELAHOGUE, Alexis-Auguste (1867-1936) French
£314 $484 €500 Tirailleurs senegalais en campagne (27x35cm-11x14in) s.verso panel. 23-Oct-2 Rabourdin & Choppin de Janvry, Paris #159
£2177 $3461 €3200 Les lavandieres au bord de l'oued (19x24cm-7x9in) s.d.1917. 24-Mar-3 Rabourdin & Choppin de Janvry, Paris #219/R est:2500-2800
£2903 $4587 €4500 Biskra 1910 (46x33cm-18x13in) s. 17-Dec-2 Gioffredo, Nice #13/R

DELAISTRE, François Nicolas (1746-1832) French
Sculpture
£4196 $7007 €6000 Buste d'enfant (40cm-16in) s. terracotta exec.c.1798-1799. 25-Jun-3 Sotheby's, Paris #74/R est:5000-8000

DELALEUF, Martine (20th C) French
Works on paper
£5172 $8638 €7500 Lisa, sur une idee de Leonard de Vinci (120x120cm-47x47in) s. s.d.verso mixed media. 9-Jul-3 Cornette de St.Cyr, Paris #271/R est:8000-10000

DELAMAIN, Paul (1821-1882) French
£9615 $15096 €15000 Guerrier et son cheval (65x54cm-26x21in) s. 16-Dec-2 Gros & Delettrez, Paris #455/R est:15000-23000

DELAMAR, David (?) Belgian?
£1027 $1613 €1500 La jeune fermiere (82x57cm-32x22in) s.d.1888. 15-Apr-3 Galerie Moderne, Brussels #400/R est:2000-3000

DELAMARE, R (?) French
Sculpture
£2548 $3975 €4000 Tete de femme au chignon (50x16x16cm-20x6x6in) s. pat bronze sold with socle. 6-Nov-2 Tajan, Paris #17/R

DELAMARRE, Jacques Barthelemy (18th C) French
£1277 $2132 €1800 Nature morte aux radis, navets et verre de vin sur un entablement (25x32cm-10x13in) s. 18-Jun-3 Tajan, Paris #132 est:2500-3500

DELAMARRE, Theodore (19th C) French
£1497 $2380 €2200 Chinese in conversation (24x19cm-9x7in) s. 28-Mar-3 Bolland & Marotz, Bremen #436/R est:2300

DELAMART, Richard (attrib) (?) ?
£915 $1520 €1300 Portrait de Claude Bougitat de Chanay (22x17cm-9x7in) oval. 16-Jun-3 Oger, Dumont, Paris #73/R

DELAMME, Paul (?) French?
£390 $605 €585 Money lender (50x68cm-20x27in) s. 30-Oct-2 Bonhams, Knowle #276

DELAMONCE, Ferdinand-Pierre-Joseph-Ignace (1678-1753) French
Works on paper
£475 $750 €750 L'adoration des Mages, avec une etude subsidiaire d'un mage (15x20cm-6x8in) pen brown ink prov. 27-Nov-2 Christie's, Paris #176/R

DELAMORINIERE, Marc Raymond (1904-) French
£442 $703 €650 Ville du M'zab (60x50cm-24x20in) cardboard. 24-Mar-3 Rabourdin & Choppin de Janvry, Paris #94/R

DELAMOTTE, William (attrib) (1775-1863) British
£2600 $4160 €3900 Shepherd resting with sheep overlooking a river plain with mountains beyond (59x90cm-23x35in) 11-Mar-3 Bonhams, Oxford #67 est:2000-2500

DELANCE, Paul (1848-1924) French
£480 $749 €720 Town in hazy sunshine (17x27cm-7x11in) s.d.1911 verso panel prov. 13-Sep-2 Lilla Bukowskis, Stockholm #418 (S.KR 7000)
£1600 $2496 €2400 Marie et Marguerite sur L'ille D'Adam (23x14cm-9x6in) s. i.verso panel prov. 9-Oct-2 Woolley & Wallis, Salisbury #281/R est:1000-1500
£2900 $4727 €4350 St. Malo (50x81cm-20x32in) s.i. 29-Jan-3 Dreweatt Neate, Newbury #161/R est:3500-4500

DELANEY, Arthur (1927-1987) British
£480 $754 €720 Still life (61x46cm-24x18in) s. board. 10-Dec-2 Capes Dunn, Manchester #729
£2600 $4212 €3770 Street scene with figures, terraced houses with a mill (17x6cm-7x2in) s. board. 29-Jul-3 Capes Dunn, Manchester #8/R
£2700 $4185 €4050 Royal exchange, Manchester (23x15cm-9x6in) s. board. 1-Oct-2 Bonhams, Leeds #351/R est:3000-5000
£3800 $6156 €5510 Street scenes with terraced buildings, figures (9x6cm-4x2in) s. board pair. 29-Jul-3 Capes Dunn, Manchester #7/R
£4200 $6804 €6090 Manchester with figures, two trams and a cathedral in the background (11x8cm-4x3in) s. board. 29-Jul-3 Capes Dunn, Manchester #6/R
£4600 $7452 €6670 Oxford Street, Manchester (9x12cm-4x5in) s. board. 29-Jul-3 Capes Dunn, Manchester #10/R
£4700 $7614 €6815 Manchester street scenes with trams (10x8cm-4x3in) s. pair. 29-Jul-3 Capes Dunn, Manchester #11
£5200 $8060 €7800 Oxford Street (30x28cm-12x11in) s. board. 25-Sep-2 Peter Wilson, Nantwich #81/R est:4000-5000
£5800 $9048 €8700 Albert Square, Manchester (21x24cm-8x9in) s. board. 6-Nov-2 Bonhams, Chester #361/R est:3000-5000
£6800 $10608 €10200 Rates protest (37x29cm-15x11in) s. board. 6-Nov-2 Bonhams, Chester #360/R
£9200 $15088 €13800 St Peter's Square, Manchester (38x41cm-15x16in) s. board. 4-Jun-3 Bonhams, Chester #326/R est:4000-6000
£9800 $16072 €14700 Albert Square, Manchester (36x45cm-14x18in) s. i.verso board prov. 4-Jun-3 Bonhams, Chester #325/R est:6000-8000

DELANEY, Edward (?) ?
Sculpture
£725 $1188 €1000 Mother and child (15cm-6in) bronze. 28-May-3 Bonhams & James Adam, Dublin #165/R est:1000-1500
£942 $1545 €1300 Queen Maeve (16cm-6in) bronze. 28-May-3 Bonhams & James Adam, Dublin #164/R est:1000-1500
£2027 $3162 €3000 Aran fisherman (51cm-20in) bronze green marble base. 26-Mar-3 James Adam, Dublin #35/R est:3000-5000

DELANEY, Joseph (1904-1981) American
Works on paper
£1465 $2300 €2198 Untitled (7x5cm-3x2in) one s. one st.verso pen ink drs exec.c.1935 pair. 19-Nov-2 Wright, Chicago #129/R est:2500-3000

DELANO, Gerard Curtis (1890-1972) American
£2051 $3200 €3077 Totem pole (18x13cm-7x5in) 9-Nov-2 Altermann Galleries, Santa Fe #100
£5449 $8500 €8174 Maroon bells (76x61cm-30x24in) s. i.verso masonite panel prov.lit. 9-Nov-2 Santa Fe Art, Santa Fe #106/R est:12000-18000
£5679 $9200 €8235 In canyon de Chelly (30x38cm-12x15in) board. 23-May-3 Altermann Galleries, Santa Fe #82
£6410 $10000 €9615 Solitude. 9-Nov-2 Altermann Galleries, Santa Fe #101
£7742 $12000 €11613 Trappers with red river cart (39x50cm-15x20in) s. s.i.verso masonite prov. 5-Dec-2 Christie's, Rockefeller NY #188/R est:20000-30000
£14151 $22500 €21227 Evening campfire (56x102cm-22x40in) s. prov. 5-Mar-3 Sotheby's, New York #146/R est:15000-25000
£14423 $22500 €21635 How! (30x38cm-12x15in) i. board i.verso prov.lit. 9-Nov-2 Santa Fe Art, Santa Fe #177/R est:15000-20000
£18590 $29000 €27885 Where distance lends enchantment (51x61cm-20x24in) 9-Nov-2 Altermann Galleries, Santa Fe #99
£18868 $30000 €28302 Lone scout (56x102cm-22x40in) s.i. s.verso prov. 5-Mar-3 Sotheby's, New York #148/R est:25000-35000
£30645 $47500 €45968 Indian trapper (56x103cm-22x41in) s.i. s.i.verso prov. 4-Dec-2 Sotheby's, New York #149/R est:20000-30000
£51282 $80000 €76923 Vermillion cliffs (76x91cm-30x36in) s. prov. 9-Nov-2 Santa Fe Art, Santa Fe #147/R est:80000-120000
£61644 $90000 €92466 Peace or war (56x102cm-22x40in) 18-May-2 Altermann Galleries, Santa Fe #103/R
Works on paper
£7692 $12000 €11538 Two Indians on horseback (46x51cm-18x20in) W/C. 9-Nov-2 Altermann Galleries, Santa Fe #102
£9615 $15000 €14423 Navajo riders (38x66cm-15x26in) s. W/C prov.lit. 9-Nov-2 Santa Fe Art, Santa Fe #77/R est:15000-25000

DELAP, Tony (1927-) American
£2564 $4000 €3846 Apport medium (148x107cm-58x42in) s.i.d.1976 verso acrylic canvas over wood prov.exhib. 14-Oct-2 Butterfields, San Francisco #2089 est:3000-5000

DELAPEINE, Charles-Samuel (1826-1894) Swiss
£463 $745 €695 Sunny coast in southern France (18x30cm-7x12in) s. paper on board. 7-May-3 Dobiaschofsky, Bern #436/R (S.FR 1000)

DELAPLACE, Jacques (1767-?) French
Miniatures
£2400 $3768 €3600 Gentleman in grey coat (6cm-2xin) s.d.1817 gilt metal frame oval. 10-Dec-2 Christie's, London #276/R est:1000-1500

DELAPLANCHE, Eugène (1836-1891) French
Sculpture
£2113 $3507 €3000 Apres le bain (92x19x19cm-36x7x7in) s. white marble. 18-Jun-3 Anaf, Lyon #94/R est:3000-3500

DELAPUENTE, Fernando (1909-1975) Spanish
£581 $917 €900 Fly (31x43cm-12x17in) s.i.d.1957 paper. 17-Dec-2 Durán, Madrid #47/R
£1132 $1743 €1800 View of Segovia (33x46cm-13x18in) s.d.74 board exhib. 22-Oct-2 Durán, Madrid #154/R

DELARMO, J (19/20th C) Belgian?
£3957 $6489 €5500 La favorite du harem (72x46cm-28x18in) s. 4-Jun-3 Tajan, Paris #261/R est:6000-7000

DELAROCHE, Paul (1797-1856) French
Works on paper
£1032 $1600 €1548 Marie Antoinette and double portrait for a medallion (13cm-5in circular) i.d.1843 pencil two. 29-Oct-2 Sotheby's, New York #9/R est:800-1200
£1139 $1800 €1800 Le President Duranti resistant a la force armee (18x15cm-7x6in) s.d.1826 graphite, w/c prov. 27-Nov-2 Christie's, Paris #246/R est:2000-3000
£1290 $2000 €1935 Studies of Napoleon and figures (14x20cm-6x8in) mono. pencil ink set of four. 29-Oct-2 Sotheby's, New York #3/R est:2500-3500
£1290 $2000 €1935 Portrait of Charles Burton and Edouard Odier (31x25cm-12x10in) i. pencil chl col chk two prov. 29-Oct-2 Sotheby's, New York #5/R est:1500-2000
£1774 $2750 €2661 Portrait of the artist Eugene Lami (27x22cm-11x9in) i.d.1834 pencil chl col chk prov. 29-Oct-2 Sotheby's, New York #6/R est:3000-4000
£1844 $3079 €2600 Portrait de Giacomo Meyerbeer (21x17cm-8x7in) black crayon sanguine white chk. 19-Jun-3 Piasa, Paris #200/R est:3000-3500
£1935 $3000 €2903 Portraits of Anthony van Dyck and Peter Paul Rubens in the hemicycle of the ecole des beaux arts (24x17cm-9x7in) mono. pencil chl htd white two. 29-Oct-2 Sotheby's, New York #7/R est:1000-1500
£4838 $7500 €7257 Oliver Cromwell (13x13cm-5x5in) indis sig. pencil black red chk htd white prov. 29-Oct-2 Sotheby's, New York #4/R est:1000-1500
£9032 $14000 €13548 Portrait of the actress Marie Dorval (38x28cm-15x11in) s.d.1831 pencil chl chk prov.exhib. 29-Oct-2 Sotheby's, New York #8/R est:2000-3000

DELAROCHE, Paul (attrib) (1797-1856) French
£314 $484 €500 Ensevelissement du Christ (45x60cm-18x24in) s. 22-Oct-2 Galerie Moderne, Brussels #703/R

Works on paper
£507 $800 €800 Portrait de napoleon vu de profil (18x12cm-7x5in) crayon. 28-Nov-2 Tajan, Paris #149

DELASPRE, Henri (?) French
Works on paper
£497 $706 €800 Vin Mariani, force, sante (27x38cm-11x15in) pen brush Indian ink gouache pair. 20-Mar-2 Chayette & Cheval, Paris #93

DELAUNAY, Robert (1885-1941) French
£13462 $21135 €21000 Fleurs (53x34cm-21x13in) s. prov. 24-Nov-2 Laurence Calmels, Paris #89/R
£23077 $36231 €36000 Ecarteuse de goemon (63x59cm-25x23in) s.d.06 s.i.verso prov.exhib.lit. 10-Dec-2 Piasa, Paris #203/R est:25000
£26923 $42269 €42000 Bretonne (46x38cm-18x15in) s.d.1904 prov.exhib.lit. 10-Dec-2 Piasa, Paris #204/R est:25000
£27950 $45000 €41925 Marche Breton (28x35cm-11x14in) s.d.05 canvasboard exhib. 8-May-3 Christie's, Rockefeller NY #168/R est:30000-40000
£256410 $400000 €384615 Hommage a bleriot - esquisse (26x26cm-10x10in) s.verso oil paper on canvas painted 1914 prov.exhib.lit. 5-Nov-2 Sotheby's, New York #24/R est:275000-350000
Prints
£2658 $4200 €4200 Eglise Saint-Severin (57x42cm-22x17in) s.i. lithograph. 29-Nov-2 Drouot Estimations, Paris #13

DELAUNAY, Sonia (1885-1979) French/Russian
£345 $548 €500 Composition (65x50cm-26x20in) s. 9-Mar-3 Feletin, Province #154
£2278 $3600 €3600 Untitled (65x50cm-26x20in) s.d.1961 pochoir parchment. 27-Nov-2 Dorotheum, Vienna #49/R est:3500-4000
£128205 $201282 €200000 Rythme couleur (97x130cm-38x51in) s.d.1954 prov.exhib. 24-Nov-2 Laurence Calmels, Paris #91/R est:200000
£532051 $835321 €830000 Prisme electrique (81x64cm-32x25in) s.d.1913 prov.exhib. 24-Nov-2 Laurence Calmels, Paris #90/R est:350000-450000
Prints
£42000 $68880 €63000 Auto-portrait (33x22cm-13x9in) s.d.1916 pochoir gouache encaustic paint prov.lit. 5-Feb-3 Sotheby's, London #156/R est:15000
Works on paper
£472 $750 €708 Fashion study (18x9cm-7x4in) s. col pastel. 4-Mar-3 Swann Galleries, New York #258/R
£496 $829 €700 Croisees noirs (9x12cm-4x5in) wash. 18-Jun-3 Charbonneaux, Paris #45
£1158 $1865 €1737 Fleurs sur fond jaune (25x19cm-10x7in) stamped sig. i.verso W/C. 7-May-3 AB Stockholms Auktionsverk #1141/R est:6000-8000 (S.KR 15000)
£1350 $2255 €1958 Curvilinear geometric composition (33x25cm-13x10in) s. i.verso gouache buff paper prov. 17-Jun-3 Rosebery Fine Art, London #441/R est:300-500
£1418 $2298 €2000 Compositions, coulleurs, idees (38x28cm-15x11in) gouache pencil prov. 24-May-3 Van Ham, Cologne #140/R est:2000
£1702 $2757 €2400 Composition with semi circles (53x37cm-21x15in) s. pochoir col pencil. 20-May-3 Dorotheum, Vienna #84/R est:2500-2800
£1871 $2993 €2600 Dessin (15x13cm-6x5in) s.i. mono.d.1956 verso Indian ink brush col chk. 15-May-3 Neumeister, Munich #241/R est:1300-1500
£2244 $3478 €3500 Projets de tissus (25x19cm-10x7in) st.sig. gouache pair. 9-Dec-2 Artcurial Briest, Paris #105/R
£2436 $3824 €3800 Composition (11x11cm-4x4in) s.d.1926 verso gouache Chinese ink. 20-Nov-2 Binoche, Paris #36/R
£2553 $4136 €3600 Projet de robe et chapeau (31x23cm-12x9in) s.d.1924 W/C paper on board prov. 26-May-3 Christie's, Milan #292/R est:2000-2500
£2979 $4826 €4200 Projet de tissus (31x23cm-12x9in) s.d.1926 W/C paper on board prov. 26-May-3 Christie's, Milan #295/R est:1800-2200
£3145 $4906 €5000 Composition (27x21cm-11x8in) s.d.1923 crayon ink wash prov. 11-Oct-2 Binoche, Paris #146/R
£3378 $5270 €5067 Composition (65x45cm-26x18in) s.i.d.1961 gouache. 18-Sep-2 Kunsthallen, Copenhagen #14/R est:30000 (D.KR 40000)
£4114 $6500 €6500 Rhthme couleur (56x40cm-22x16in) s.d.1970 gouache pencil board prov.exhib. 27-Nov-2 Dorotheum, Vienna #53/R est:2500-3000
£6090 $9561 €9500 Maquette (57x38cm-22x15in) s. gouache. 24-Nov-2 Laurence Calmels, Paris #97/R
£8974 $14090 €14000 Untitled (42x23cm-17x9in) s.d.1962 gouache. 24-Nov-2 Laurence Calmels, Paris #92/R
£9295 $14593 €14500 Rythme couleur (41x29cm-16x11in) s. gouache. 24-Nov-2 Laurence Calmels, Paris #96/R
£9317 $15000 €13976 Rythme colore (27x15cm-11x6in) s.d.1935 W/C gouache brush ink paper on card prov.exhib. 7-May-3 Sotheby's, New York #199/R est:18000-25000
£9615 $15096 €15000 Rythme couleur (57x39cm-22x15in) s.d.71 gouache. 24-Nov-2 Laurence Calmels, Paris #94/R est:12000
£9615 $15096 €15000 Gouache 1897 (50x32cm-20x13in) s.d.73 gouache. 24-Nov-2 Laurence Calmels, Paris #93/R
£9655 $15255 €14000 Composition (77x56cm-30x22in) s.d.72 gouache chl. 2-Apr-3 Christie's, Paris #6/R est:9000
£10000 $15400 €15000 Projet d'album no.1 (23x21cm-9x8in) s.i.d.1916 gouache over pencil. 22-Oct-2 Sotheby's, London #177/R est:12000-15000
£10646 $16928 €15650 Composition (65x48cm-26x19in) s.i.d.1961 gouache. 26-Feb-3 Artcurial Briest, Paris #80/R est:13000-15000
£16000 $26720 €23200 Rythme couleur (57x77cm-22x30in) s.d.1959 gouache chl prov. 24-Jun-3 Sotheby's, London #232/R est:18000-25000
£21154 $33212 €33000 Rythme couleur 972 (57x77cm-22x30in) s.d.62 gouache. 24-Nov-2 Laurence Calmels, Paris #95/R est:20000
£22000 $36080 €33000 Boulevard Saint-Michel (34x17cm-13x7in) s.i.d.1913-14 pastel chl prov. 5-Feb-3 Sotheby's, London #158/R est:18000
£23000 $37720 €34500 Etude lumiere (39x27cm-15x11in) s.d.13-14 pastel chl prov.exhib.lit. 5-Feb-3 Sotheby's, London #159/R est:20000

DELAVALLEE, Henri (1862-1943) French
£1923 $3019 €3000 Jeunes enfants prs de la chaumiere (34x45cm-13x18in) s. 15-Dec-2 Thierry & Lannon, Brest #128
£2222 $3622 €3200 La belle Angele (55x46cm-22x18in) s. 19-Jul-3 Thierry & Lannon, Brest #112a est:3000-4000
£2973 $4638 €4400 Jeune femme dans la lande (55x38cm-22x15in) s. 28-Mar-3 Claude Aguttes, Neuilly #131c
£3077 $4831 €4800 Bord de mer en Turquie (54x73cm-21x29in) s. 15-Dec-2 Thierry & Lannon, Brest #a
£4054 $6324 €6000 Bateau reposant a l'entree de l'Aven (50x65cm-20x26in) s. 28-Mar-3 Claude Aguttes, Neuilly #131b/R
£6090 $9561 €9500 Homme assis de dos (29x25cm-11x10in) s. canvas on board painted c.1886. 15-Dec-2 Thierry & Lannon, Brest #125
£14000 $22960 €21000 Portrait de jeune fille (41x33cm-16x13in) s.d.88 prov.exhib.lit. 4-Feb-3 Christie's, London #255/R est:18000
Works on paper
£2254 $3628 €3200 Bretonne au parapluie. Bretonne sur la dune (29x47cm-11x19in) chl htd chk two. 11-May-3 Thierry & Lannon, Brest #55 est:2500-3000
£3380 $5442 €4800 Grand paysage de Bretagne (51x47cm-20x19in) s.d.1891 pastel. 11-May-3 Thierry & Lannon, Brest #56/R est:4500-5000

DELAWARR, Val (19th C) Australian
£421 $662 €632 Alpine river landscape (44x29cm-17x11in) s. board. 15-Apr-3 Lawson Menzies, Sydney #213/R est:1200-1800 (A.D 1100)
£464 $720 €696 Colo Creek, Hawkesbury river (20x30cm-8x12in) s. painted c.1880. 29-Oct-2 Lawson Menzies, Sydney #486 (A.D 1300)
£491 $747 €737 Mountain stream (43x58cm-17x23in) s.d.94 board. 19-Aug-2 Joel, Victoria #347 est:1500-2500 (A.D 1400)

DELAYE, Theophile Jean (1896-1973) French
Works on paper
£759 $1200 €1200 Vue panoramique de Marrakech (27x38cm-11x15in) s.i. W/C gouache. 28-Nov-2 Piasa, Paris #65/R

DELBOS, Julius (1879-1967) American
£548 $850 €822 Boats in a harbour (51x61cm-20x24in) s. painted c.1920. 8-Dec-2 Toomey, Oak Park #700/R
Works on paper
£457 $750 €686 La plage (20x23cm-8x9in) s. W/C over pencil exhib. 5-Feb-3 Doyle, New York #76/R

DELCOL, Roland (1942-) Belgian
£380 $589 €600 Nue chaussee (60x80cm-24x31in) s.d. 28-Sep-2 Cornette de St.Cyr, Paris #290

DELCROIX, Giacomo (1894-1972) Italian
£705 $1107 €1100 View of Tuscan countryside (38x57cm-15x22in) s. board. 16-Dec-2 Pandolfini, Florence #275/R

DELDERENE, Léon (1864-1921) Belgian
£403 $648 €600 Paysage boise au bord de l'eau (30x50cm-12x20in) s.d.1892. 24-Feb-3 Bernaerts, Antwerp #177
£952 $1514 €1400 Landscape with figure near farmhouse (51x67cm-20x26in) s.d.1903. 24-Mar-3 Bernaerts, Antwerp #73/R est:1000-1200
£1014 $1581 €1500 Chasseur dans la foret (90x75cm-35x30in) s. 25-Mar-3 Campo & Campo, Antwerp #53/R est:1500-2000
£1026 $1590 €1600 Flemish village street (60x89cm-24x35in) s.d.1900 prov. 7-Dec-2 Ketterer, Hamburg #162/R est:2500-3000

DELECHAUX, Marcelin (1902-) French
£1900 $2983 €2850 Reading lesson (55x47cm-22x19in) s. prov. 21-Nov-2 Christie's, Kensington #22/R est:1500-2000

DELECLUSE, Eugène (1882-?) French
£256 $403 €400 La Seine a Meudon (26x24cm-10x9in) s. cardboard on canvas. 24-Nov-2 Lesieur & Le Bars, Le Havre #32
£417 $654 €650 Douarnenez (24x32cm-9x13in) s. cardboard on canvas. 24-Nov-2 Lesieur & Le Bars, Le Havre #31

£449 $704 €700 Charge de cavallerie (81x100cm-32x39in) s. 24-Nov-2 Lesieur & Le Bars, Le Havre #30

DELEHAYE, Jos (?) ?

£253 $395 €400 Nature morte aux fruits (44x54cm-17x21in) 16-Sep-2 Amberes, Antwerp #193

£382 $630 €550 Still life with fruit, roemer and golden goblet on a table (60x80cm-24x31in) s. 1-Jul-3 Christie's, Amsterdam #31

DELEN, Dirk van (1605-1671) Dutch

£75000 $117750 €112500 Interior of church with sermon in progress (57x70cm-22x28in) s. panel. 11-Dec-2 Christie's, London #68/R est:20000-30000

DELEN, Dirk van (circle) (1605-1671) Dutch

£8000 $12560 €12000 Elegant company, dogs and a beggar in a Renaissance interior (26x33cm-10x13in) panel. 13-Dec-2 Christie's, Kensington #40/R est:6000-8000

DELESCLUSE, Jean (1871-1947) Belgian

£414 $662 €600 Interior with nude (90x56cm-35x22in) s. 15-Mar-3 De Vuyst, Lokeren #84

£478 $745 €750 Jeune femme au jardin (22x27cm-9x11in) s. panel. 11-Nov-2 Horta, Bruxelles #719

Works on paper

£705 $1135 €1050 Femme assise (74x58cm-29x23in) s.pastel. 18-Feb-3 Vanderkindere, Brussels #51

DELESCLUZE, Edmond (1905-1993) Belgian

£360 $576 €500 Barques de peche entre les Ducs d'Albe (32x46cm-13x18in) s. 19-May-3 Horta, Bruxelles #51

£1223 $1957 €1700 Jeune femme nue allongee (100x900cm-39x354in) s.d.1938. 19-May-3 Horta, Bruxelles #49 est:2200-2800

Works on paper

£321 $503 €500 La massacre des Saints Innocents (51x55cm-20x22in) s.d.1932 W/C gouache. 19-Nov-2 Vanderkindere, Brussels #41

DELESTRE, Eugène (1862-1919) French

£350 $560 €525 Table et pot des fleurs a contre jour (43x60cm-17x24in) s.d.1907. 13-Jan-3 Rasmussen, Vejle #288/R (D.KR 4000)

DELEURRE, A (20th C) ?

Works on paper

£608 $949 €900 Sarah Bernhardt (67x100cm-26x39in) s.d.1906 W/C. 26-Mar-3 Millon & Associes, Paris #24/R

DELFF, Cornelis Jacobsz (1571-1643) Dutch

£37736 $58491 €60000 Culinary still life (76x126cm-30x50in) s. panel lit. 2-Oct-2 Dorotheum, Vienna #121/R est:60000-80000

DELFF, Jacob Willemsz (elder-attrib) (1550-1601) Dutch

£3546 $5496 €5319 Portrait of lady (103x75cm-41x30in) i.d.1593 panel. 4-Dec-2 AB Stockholms Auktionsverk #1993/R est:50000-70000 (S.KR 50000)

DELFGAAUW, Gerard Johannes (1882-1947) Dutch

£324 $522 €460 Polder landscape with little water (53x63cm-21x25in) s. 6-May-3 Vendu Notarishuis, Rotterdam #113

£342 $534 €500 Winter afternoon near Rijswijk (24x33cm-9x13in) s. canvas on panel. 10-Apr-3 Van Ham, Cologne #1369

£387 $624 €550 Hens feeding near farm with blossom trees (33x43cm-13x17in) s. 7-May-3 Vendue Huis, Gravenhage #16

£611 $966 €917 Two cargo ships in Rotterdam harbour (60x100cm-24x39in) s. 14-Nov-2 Stuker, Bern #157 (S.FR 1400)

£725 $1131 €1088 Dutch polder landscape with windmills and dykes (39x59cm-15x23in) s. 16-Oct-2 Mervyn Carey, Tenterden #162/R

£828 $1275 €1300 Milking time in the polder (50x70cm-20x28in) s. 3-Sep-2 Christie's, Amsterdam #182

£955 $1490 €1500 Harbour scene with many ship and cranes (58x98cm-23x39in) s. 5-Nov-2 Vendu Notarishuis, Rotterdam #67/R est:1000-1500

£1274 $1987 €2000 Harbour with cranes (24x44cm-9x17in) s. 6-Nov-2 Vendue Huis, Gravenhage #652/R est:1400-1600

£1290 $1897 €2000 Rotterdam harbour (59x100cm-23x39in) s. 20-Jun-2 Dr Fritz Nagel, Stuttgart #761/R est:1800

£1528 $2521 €2200 Daily activities at the harbour of Rotterdam (49x70cm-19x28in) s. 1-Jul-3 Christie's, Amsterdam #136/R est:2000-3000

£1529 $2385 €2400 River scene with mills and view of town in distance (54x98cm-21x39in) s. 5-Nov-2 Vendu Notarishuis, Rotterdam #266/R est:2000-2500

£1644 $2564 €2400 View of Rotterdam Harbour (60x100cm-24x39in) s. 14-Apr-3 Glerum, Amsterdam #112/R est:1500-1800

£2038 $3180 €3200 View of Zierikszee (58x79cm-23x31in) s. 6-Nov-2 Vendue Huis, Gravenhage #650/R est:3000-4000

£2293 $3577 €3600 Blokzijl port (48x58cm-19x23in) s. 6-Nov-2 Vendue Huis, Gravenhage #484/R est:2000-3000

£2830 $4358 €4500 View of Dordrecht (61x81cm-24x32in) s. 22-Oct-2 Sotheby's, Amsterdam #98/R est:5000-7000

DELFOSSE, Georges Marie Joseph (1869-1939) Canadian

£193 $301 €280 Laurentian hills, Quebec (23x30cm-9x12in) s. canvas on panel. 26-Mar-3 Walker's, Ottawa #408/R (C.D 450)

£282 $460 €423 Convent on Gouin Boulevard (36x71cm-14x28in) s. 12-Feb-3 Iegor de Saint Hippolyte, Montreal #54 (C.D 700)

£307 $457 €461 Maison Canadienne (18x25cm-7x10in) s. 26-Jun-2 Iegor de Saint Hippolyte, Montreal #26 (C.D 700)

£439 $654 €659 Vue d'une cour interieure (30x18cm-12x7in) s. wood. 26-Jun-2 Iegor de Saint Hippolyte, Montreal #22 (C.D 1000)

£766 $1249 €1149 Chateau Ramezay (11x18cm-4x7in) s. d.1892 verso panel. 12-Feb-3 Iegor de Saint Hippolyte, Montreal #55/R (C.D 1900)

Works on paper

£351 $523 €527 Village (33x25cm-13x10in) s. gouache W/C. 26-Jun-2 Iegor de Saint Hippolyte, Montreal #25 (C.D 800)

£514 $792 €771 Three sisters (22x15cm-9x6in) s. pencil. 22-Oct-2 Iegor de Saint Hippolyte, Montreal #28/R (C.D 1250)

£526 $784 €789 Transport de bois a traineau (23x32cm-9x13in) s. pastel sec. 26-Jun-2 Iegor de Saint Hippolyte, Montreal #23 (C.D 1200)

£1184 $1764 €1776 Le coucher de soleil (23x32cm-9x13in) s. pastel sec. 26-Jun-2 Iegor de Saint Hippolyte, Montreal #24/R (C.D 2700)

DELGADO RAMOS, Alvaro (1922-) Spanish

£299 $460 €475 Alvaro Delgado and the Spanish golden age. s. 22-Oct-2 Durán, Madrid #652/R

£671 $1081 €1000 Saint Joseph (55x46cm-22x18in) s.i.d.45. 18-Feb-3 Durán, Madrid #138/R

£1132 $1743 €1800 Portrait of Carmen Espinosa (81x65cm-32x26in) s.d.1946. 22-Oct-2 Durán, Madrid #128/R

£1379 $2193 €2000 Female nudes (46x38cm-18x15in) s. board. 4-Mar-3 Ansorena, Madrid #207/R

£2500 $3800 €3750 Descargando barcas pesqueras (64x120cm-25x47in) s. 3-Jul-2 Naón & Cia, Buenos Aires #4/R est:1500-2000

£3020 $4862 €4500 Still life with fish (80x100cm-31x39in) s. 18-Feb-3 Durán, Madrid #208/R

£3901 $6319 €5500 Paisaje con carro (38x46cm-15x18in) s. panel. 20-May-3 Segre, Madrid #126/R est:3500

£4088 $6377 €6500 Still life with fish (80x100cm-31x39in) s. exhib. 23-Sep-2 Durán, Madrid #210/R

Works on paper

£537 $864 €800 Village (49x36cm-19x14in) s. W/C. 18-Feb-3 Durán, Madrid #95/R

£943 $1472 €1500 Rouault's friend (46x38cm-18x15in) s.i.d.1975 verso mixed media board. 8-Oct-2 Ansorena, Madrid #637/R

DELGADO, Desiderio (1955-) Spanish

£597 $932 €950 Landscape (117x90cm-46x35in) s. 23-Sep-2 Durán, Madrid #86/R

DELHOMMEAU, Charles (1883-?) French

Sculpture

£1154 $1788 €1800 Cochon d'Inde angora (9x13x7cm-4x5x3in) s. num.4/8 black pat bronze. 7-Dec-2 Martinot & Savignat, Pontoise #87/R

D'ELIA, Alessio (18th C) Italian

£6000 $9300 €9000 Elegant company in an interior with a gentleman sitting for his portrait (42x65cm-17x26in) 30-Oct-2 Christie's, Kensington #163/R est:7000-10000

D'ELIA, Emilio (1958-) ?

Works on paper

£837 $1222 €1256 Nicchia luminosa. Guardiani de tempio (177x91cm-70x36in) s.i.d.1989 verso mixed media paper on panel two. 17-Jun-2 Philippe Schuler, Zurich #4019 (S.FR 1900)

DELINCOURT, L G (19/20h C) French

£1424 $2250 €2136 Sultan and his harem (81x130cm-32x51in) s. 18-Nov-2 Schrager Galleries, Milwaukee #1248

DELIOTTI, Walter (1925-) Uruguayan

£256 $400 €384 Constructivo con pez verde (20x25cm-8x10in) s. cardboard. 30-Jul-2 Galleria Y Remates, Montevideo #16

£263 $420 €395 Building site (20x25cm-8x10in) s. cardboard. 5-Jan-3 Galleria Y Remates, Montevideo #20/R

£325 $520 €488 Marine elements (20x25cm-8x10in) s. cardboard. 5-Jan-3 Galleria Y Remates, Montevideo #21/R

£375 $600 €563 Red boat (24x33cm-9x13in) s. 5-Jan-3 Galleria Y Remates, Montevideo #18/R

£417 $650 €626 Canal Street, New York (41x3cm-16x1in) s.i.d.90 cardboard. 10-Oct-2 Galleria Y Remates, Montevideo #32/R

£513 $800 €770 Barco con grua (33x41cm-13x16in) s. 30-Jul-2 Galleria Y Remates, Montevideo #62/R

£1250 $2000 €1875 Harbour (60x73cm-24x29in) s. cardboard. 5-Jan-3 Galleria Y Remates, Montevideo #107/R
Works on paper
£256 $400 €384 Couple (31x25cm-12x10in) s. mixed media relief cardboard. 10-Oct-2 Galleria Y Remates, Montevideo #33/R

DELL, Etheline (fl.1885-1923) British
Works on paper
£400 $624 €600 Figures before a country cottage (17x24cm-7x9in) s. pencil W/C htd white. 19-Sep-2 Christie's, Kensington #145

DELL, G (19th C) British
£3057 $4769 €4586 Barque "Alfred Hawley" outward bound in the Channel, Beachy Head beyond (51x77cm-20x30in) s.d.1860 canvas on canvas prov. 9-Nov-2 Galerie Gloggner, Luzern #35/R est:1200-1500 (S.FR 7000)
£5000 $8100 €7500 Barque Alfred Hawley off the Skerries on her way into Liverpool (51x76cm-20x30in) s.d.1860 prov. 21-May-3 Christie's, Kensington #568/R est:4000-6000

DELL, J H (1836-1888) British
£762 $1166 €1143 Pet rabbit (19x15cm-7x6in) s. board. 21-Aug-2 Dunbar Sloane, Auckland #91/R est:1500-2000 (NZ.D 2500)
£915 $1399 €1373 Feeding the rabbit (16x18cm-6x7in) s. board. 21-Aug-2 Dunbar Sloane, Auckland #89/R est:1500-2000 (NZ.D 3000)
£915 $1399 €1373 Pet kid (18x15cm-7x6in) s. board. 21-Aug-2 Dunbar Sloane, Auckland #90/R est:1500-2000 (NZ.D 3000)

DELL, John H (1836-1888) British
£350 $557 €525 Moonlight, the Norfolk coast (27x51cm-11x20in) s.i.verso panel painted lunette. 6-Mar-3 Christie's, Kensington #424/R
£750 $1170 €1125 Cattle watering in a river landscape (20x25cm-8x10in) mono.d.65 panel prov. 7-Nov-2 Christie's, Kensington #102/R
£1400 $2310 €2030 Feeding rabbits. Tidying the hutch (11x15cm-4x6in) mono. panel pair. 1-Jul-3 Bearnes, Exeter #481/R est:400-600

DELL, Juan (?) American?
Sculpture
£1218 $1900 €1827 Following the bison (33x51x15cm-13x20x6in) bronze. 9-Nov-2 Altermann Galleries, Santa Fe #54

DELL'ACQUA, Cesare Felix Georges (1821-1904) Italian
£1210 $1888 €1900 Elegante a la balustrade (50x39cm-20x15in) s. 11-Nov-2 Horta, Bruxelles #590 est:2000-3000
£1887 $2906 €3000 Cavaliers Arabes (50x55cm-20x22in) s.d.1851. 22-Oct-2 Campo, Vlaamse Kaai #482/R
£7200 $11664 €10800 Her favourite pet (92x71cm-36x28in) s.d.1871 panel. 20-May-3 Sotheby's, Olympia #364/R est:3000-4000
£85000 $141950 €127500 La charmeuse (117x84cm-46x33in) s.d.1873 s.i.verso prov. 19-Jun-3 Christie's, London #8/R est:15000-20000
Works on paper
£510 $811 €750 Lady with umbrella and little dog (54x42cm-21x17in) s.d.1872 W/C. 24-Mar-3 Bernaerts, Antwerp #5/R

DELL'AMICO, Carlo (1954-) Italian
£348 $543 €550 Figures (80x100cm-31x39in) s. 14-Sep-2 Meeting Art, Vercelli #877/R

DELL'ARZERE, Stefano (attrib) (16th C) Italian
Works on paper
£2568 $4005 €3800 Deposition (17x32cm-7x13in) pen ink over crayon. 27-Mar-3 Maigret, Paris #9/R est:1500-2000

DELLEANI, Lorenzo (1840-1908) Italian
£6289 $9686 €10000 Wood (31x45cm-12x18in) s.d.92 board. 23-Oct-2 Finarte, Milan #63/R est:10000-12000
£8974 $14090 €14000 Fierce sunset (31x44cm-12x17in) s.i.d.86 board lit. 10-Dec-2 Della Rocca, Turin #395/R est:12000
£10204 $16224 €15000 Snowfall (26x37cm-10x15in) s.d.1900 board. 1-Mar-3 Meeting Art, Vercelli #243 est:15000

DELLEANI, Nina (1868-?) Italian
£1020 $1622 €1500 River in winter (80x60cm-31x24in) s.d.1910 board. 18-Mar-3 Finarte, Milan #155/R

DELLEPIANE, David (1866-c.1932) French/Italian
£1613 $2548 €2500 Jeune bergere a la flute (42x130cm-17x51in) panel. 19-Dec-2 Claude Aguttes, Neuilly #231/R est:3500
Works on paper
£1173 $1853 €1700 Village provencal (11x36cm-4x14in) pastel dr. 4-Apr-3 Tajan, Paris #135/R

DELLSCHAU, Charles A A (1830-1923) American
Works on paper
£4321 $7000 €6482 Untitled (42x43cm-17x17in) d.October 29 1919 W/C ink graphite collage executed 1919 prov. 27-Jan-3 Christie's, Rockefeller NY #9/R est:8000-12000
£4630 $7500 €6945 Untitled (39x43cm-15x17in) d. January 14 1920 W/C ink graphite collage prov.exhib. 27-Jan-3 Christie's, Rockefeller NY #8/R est:8000-12000

DELMONTE, Alberto (1933-) Argentinian
£570 $900 €855 Middle of 1997 (50x60cm-20x24in) s. 15-Nov-2 Naón & Cia, Buenos Aires #7/R

DELMOTTE, Marcel (1901-1984) Belgian
£532 $888 €750 Paysage surrealiste avec personnages (60x50cm-24x20in) s.d.1966 panel. 17-Jun-3 Palais de Beaux Arts, Brussels #566/R
£641 $994 €1000 La porte s'ouvre (75x60cm-30x24in) s.d.1951 panel. 9-Dec-2 Horta, Bruxelles #300
£1438 $2315 €2200 Composition fantastique (60x80cm-24x31in) s.d.69 panel. 20-Jan-3 Horta, Bruxelles #241 est:2500-3000
Works on paper
£1409 $2269 €2100 Paysage fantastique (50x63cm-20x25in) s. gouache. 23-Feb-3 Mercier & Cie, Lille #292

DELOBBE, F A (1835-1920) French
£705 $1100 €1058 Coastal scene with figures (3x8cm-1x3in) s. panel. 9-Nov-2 Sloan, North Bethesda #572/R

DELOBBE, François Alfred (1835-1920) French
£2866 $4500 €4299 Return from the fields (51x30cm-20x12in) s. 10-Dec-2 Doyle, New York #206/R est:6000-8000
£5161 $8000 €7742 Moment of reflection (65x43cm-26x17in) s. 30-Oct-2 Christie's, Rockefeller NY #173/R est:10000-15000

DELORMOZ, Paul (1895-1980) French
£556 $906 €800 Lesconil (27x41cm-11x16in) s. panel. 19-Jul-3 Thierry & Lannon, Brest #319
£704 $1134 €1000 Chapelle pres du Guilvinec (33x46cm-13x18in) 11-May-3 Thierry & Lannon, Brest #173e
£3028 $4875 €4300 Plage de Loctudy (21x40cm-8x16in) panel c.1946. 11-May-3 Thierry & Lannon, Brest #173c est:2500-3000

DELORT, Charles Edouard (1841-1895) French
£5128 $8000 €7692 Untimely visit (65x91cm-26x36in) s. 9-Nov-2 Sloan, North Bethesda #578/R est:10000-12000
£22581 $35000 €33872 Place la Concord, Paris (78x100cm-31x39in) s. 30-Oct-2 Christie's, Rockefeller NY #216/R est:25000-35000

DELPECH, Hermann (1865-1918) French
£596 $972 €900 Voiliers dans le bassin (46x55cm-18x22in) s. 31-Jan-3 Rabourdin & Choppin de Janvry, Paris #71/R

DELPLACE, Rupert (1896-1951) Belgian?
£276 $436 €400 Sous le masque (50x61cm-20x24in) s. 1-Apr-3 Palais de Beaux Arts, Brussels #524
£276 $436 €400 Mere et enfants a la fenetre (56x46cm-22x18in) s. 1-Apr-3 Palais de Beaux Arts, Brussels #525

DELPORTE, Charles (1928-) Belgian
£278 $442 €400 Les fleurs de l'esprit (100x80cm-39x31in) s. d.1969 verso panel. 29-Apr-3 Campo & Campo, Antwerp #68/R
£486 $773 €700 Untitled (120cm-47in circular) s. unalite. 5-May-3 Bernaerts, Antwerp #400/R

DELPY, H C (1842-1910) French
£4118 $6300 €6177 Bords de la Seine (99x69cm-39x27in) s.d.1901 board. 23-Aug-2 York Town, York #519

DELPY, Hippolyte Camille (1842-1910) French
£1300 $2054 €1950 Maisons enneigees (50x65cm-20x26in) s. 3-Apr-3 Christie's, Kensington #11/R
£2469 $4000 €3580 Washerwomen at dusk (33x61cm-13x24in) s.d.85 st.init.verso panel prov.exhib. 21-May-3 Doyle, New York #194/R est:4000-6000
£3179 $5181 €4800 Les moulins a vent, effet de neige (50x100cm-20x39in) s. painted c.1879. 16-Feb-3 Mercier & Cie, Lille #241/R est:6000-7000
£3380 $5442 €4800 Paysans sur le chemin pres du village (30x53cm-12x21in) s. 11-May-3 Thierry & Lannon, Brest #158/R est:4000-5000
£3861 $6100 €6100 Lavandiere et barque, soleil couchant (45x71cm-18x28in) s. panel. 1-Dec-2 Peron, Melun #123
£3901 $6046 €5852 Bord de riviere (48x80cm-19x31in) s.d.03 panel. 4-Dec-2 AB Stockholms Auktionsverk #1887/R est:25000-30000 (S.KR 55000)

£4808 $7452 €7500 Lavandiere au coucher du soleil (55x97cm-22x38in) s. 9-Dec-2 Horta, Bruxelles #186/R est:7000-9000
£7013 $11080 €10520 Les Laveuses - French river landscape with washerwomen (60x100cm-24x39in) s.d.1902 exhib. 27-Nov-2 Falkkloos, Malmo #77577/R est:100000 (S.KR 100000)
£7500 $12300 €11250 Lavandiere au soleil couchant (45x71cm-18x28in) s. panel. 3-Jun-3 Sotheby's, London #138/R est:8000-12000
£10127 $16000 €15191 Washerwoman by the lake. s.d.98 panel. 24-Apr-3 Sotheby's, New York #94/R est:20000-30000
£14557 $23000 €21836 Washerwomen at sunset (56x100cm-22x39in) s. 24-Apr-3 Sotheby's, New York #95/R est:12000-15000
£15823 $25000 €23735 Moonrise over the lake (29x53cm-11x21in) s. panel. 24-Apr-3 Sotheby's, New York #93/R est:10000-15000
£18987 $30000 €28481 Matinees d'ete a Rueil (61x101cm-24x40in) s.d.1902. 23-Apr-3 Christie's, Rockefeller NY #54/R est:20000-30000

DELPY, Hippolyte Camille (attrib) (1842-1910) French
£3265 $5192 €4800 French river landscape (40x70cm-16x28in) i.d.1900 mono. verso panel. 19-Mar-3 Neumeister, Munich #536/R est:1250

DELPY, Jacques-Henry (1877-1957) French
£260 $413 €390 Lake scene (12x21cm-5x8in) s. card. 23-Mar-3 Lots Road, London #355/R
£328 $511 €492 Washer woman (27x46cm-11x18in) s. 10-Sep-2 Iegor de Saint Hippolyte, Montreal #28 (C.D 800)
£449 $704 €700 Oise a Cergy (14x18cm-6x7in) s. panel. 13-Dec-2 Piasa, Paris #85
£523 $858 €800 Barque sur etang (23x41cm-9x16in) s. panel. 7-Feb-3 Oger, Dumont, Paris #83
£683 $1094 €950 La Seine animee (25x40cm-10x16in) s.d.1921 cardboard. 19-May-3 Horta, Bruxelles #174
£719 $1151 €1000 Vase d'anemones (18x31cm-7x12in) s. panel. 18-May-3 Eric Pillon, Calais #54/R
£1379 $2193 €2000 Washerwomen by river at dusk (54x81cm-21x32in) s. 8-Mar-3 Arnold, Frankfurt #568/R est:1000
£1905 $3029 €2800 Village at dusk (39x61cm-15x24in) 25-Feb-3 Dorotheum, Vienna #207/R est:2800-3000
£1905 $3029 €2800 River landscape with figures (46x62cm-18x24in) s. panel. 19-Mar-3 Neumeister, Munich #537/R est:2500
£2000 $3180 €3000 Summer river landscape (46x62cm-18x24in) s. 20-Mar-3 Christie's, Kensington #1/R est:2000-3000
£3205 $5032 €5000 River landscape at dusk (21x35cm-8x14in) s. panel. 10-Dec-2 Dorotheum, Vienna #83/R est:3200-3600

DELPY, Lucien Victor (1898-1966) French
£1157 $1863 €1678 Sunny harbour (45x54cm-18x21in) s. panel. 7-May-3 Dobiaschofsky, Bern #437/R est:3000 (S.FR 2500)
£1218 $1912 €1900 Tas de pois (27x91cm-11x36in) s.d.1949. 15-Dec-2 Thierry & Lannon, Brest #130
£1250 $2037 €1800 Retour de peche (22x27cm-9x11in) s. panel. 19-Jul-3 Thierry & Lannon, Brest #320 est:500-600
£1408 $2268 €2000 Retour de peche a Concarneau (38x46cm-15x18in) s. 11-May-3 Thierry & Lannon, Brest #160/R est:2000-2500
£2115 $3321 €3300 Camaret (84x81cm-33x32in) s. 15-Dec-2 Thierry & Lannon, Brest #129
£2222 $3622 €3200 Le port de Concarneau (54x65cm-21x26in) s. 19-Jul-3 Thierry & Lannon, Brest #114/R est:3000-4000
£3239 $5215 €4600 Les goemoniers au pays bigouden (50x100cm-20x39in) s. 11-May-3 Thierry & Lannon, Brest #159/R est:2500-3000
Works on paper
£1620 $2608 €2300 Concarneau, voiliers et thoniers pres du paysage Lanriec (46x65cm-18x26in) s. gouache. 11-May-3 Thierry & Lannon, Brest #120/R est:2600-2800

DELRUE, Ronny (20th C) ?
Works on paper
£348 $550 €550 Gesprek (101x72cm-40x28in) s.d.1990 mixed media. 26-Nov-2 Palais de Beaux Arts, Brussels #80

DELSARTE, Louis (1944-) American
Works on paper
£641 $1000 €962 Ocean of time (49x63cm-19x25in) s.d.77 chl white chk exhib. 20-Sep-2 Sloan, North Bethesda #340/R est:1500-2000

DELSAUX, Willem (1862-1945) Belgian
£348 $543 €550 Parc Royal de Laeken en automne (104x96cm-41x38in) s. 16-Sep-2 Horta, Bruxelles #327
£647 $1036 €900 Paysage de bord de mer avec moulin. s.d.1896. 19-May-3 Horta, Bruxelles #348
£816 $1298 €1200 City view by night (140x100cm-55x39in) s. 24-Mar-3 Bernaerts, Antwerp #175 est:1250-1500
£962 $1490 €1500 Bord de canal anime (65x100cm-26x39in) s.d.1909. 9-Dec-2 Horta, Bruxelles #346 est:2000-3000
Works on paper
£2192 $3419 €3200 Les champs de fleurs (80x100cm-31x39in) s.d.1905 mixed media. 14-Apr-3 Horta, Bruxelles #241 est:800-1200

DELVAUX, Edouard (1806-1862) Belgian
£5517 $8828 €8000 Passant a l'autre rive (87x124cm-34x49in) s.d.46 panel. 15-Mar-3 De Vuyst, Lokeren #405/R est:8000-9500

DELVAUX, Laurent (1696-1778) Flemish
Sculpture
£4167 $6583 €6500 Bust of emperor Nero as a child (49cm-19in) s. marble incl. base. 18-Nov-2 Bernaerts, Antwerp #107/R est:7000-7500

DELVAUX, Paul (1897-1994) Belgian
£3034 $4855 €4400 Amies (24x17cm-9x7in) chl dr. 15-Mar-3 De Vuyst, Lokeren #92/R est:3600-4000
£120000 $200400 €174000 La legenda Egyptienne (119x150cm-47x59in) s.d.11.53 panel prov.exhib.lit. 24-Jun-3 Sotheby's, London #172/R est:100000-150000
£340000 $554200 €510000 Fin du voyage (160x140cm-63x55in) s.d.68 s.i.d.on stretcher prov.exhib.lit. 3-Feb-3 Christie's, London #168/R est:500000
£750000 $1252500 €1087500 Les courtisanes rouges (122x186cm-48x73in) s.d.43 prov.exhib.lit. 24-Jun-3 Christie's, London #39/R est:700000-1000000
£1500000 $2505000 €2175000 Le nu et le mannequin (156x225cm-61x89in) s.d.47 prov.exhib.lit. 24-Jun-3 Christie's, London #37/R est:800000-1200000
Prints
£1923 $2981 €3000 Femme a la boule (49x31cm-19x12in) s. num.9/75 lithograph. 7-Dec-2 Cornette de St.Cyr, Paris #9/R
£1923 $3000 €2885 Seven dialogues with Paul Delvaux (30x21cm-12x8in) s.num.15/150 col etching. 7-Nov-2 Swann Galleries, New York #626/R est:2000-3000
£1935 $3058 €3000 Trois femmes dans un interieur. s. lithograph. 17-Dec-2 Galerie Moderne, Brussels #759
£2069 $3310 €3000 Sommeil (46x65cm-18x26in) s.num.33/50 d.70 lithograph lit. 15-Mar-3 De Vuyst, Lokeren #88/R est:3000-3600
£2115 $3279 €3300 Fenetre (58x78cm-23x31in) s.d.71 num.45/50 lithograph lit. 7-Dec-2 De Vuyst, Lokeren #89 est:3500-4000
£2200 $3432 €3300 Mauve curtains (36x27cm-14x11in) s.num.7/100 col lithograph. 10-Oct-2 Sotheby's, London #23/R est:2200-2800
£2358 $3750 €3537 Lover (50x66cm-20x26in) s.num.60/75 black beige lithograph. 2-May-3 Sotheby's, New York #127/R est:3000-4000
£2484 $3999 €3800 Eve (40x27cm-16x11in) s.num.12/30 col etching. 20-Jan-3 Horta, Bruxelles #158 est:4200-4500
£2500 $3875 €3750 By the town (48x65cm-19x26in) s.num.33/75 lithograph. 5-Dec-2 Sotheby's, London #121/R est:3000-4000
£2510 $3965 €3765 The clairvoyant (79x59cm-31x23in) s.num.25/75 col lithograph lit. 28-Apr-3 Bukowskis, Stockholm #402/R est:35000-45000 (S.KR 33000)
£2564 $4000 €3846 Phryne (31x24cm-12x9in) s.num.47/75 col lithograph. 7-Nov-2 Swann Galleries, New York #625/R est:3000-5000
£2700 $4455 €3915 Window (58x78cm-23x31in) s.num.72/75 col lithograph. 2-Jul-3 Christie's, London #68/R est:3000-4000
£2857 $4543 €4200 La robe de dimanche (63x51cm-25x20in) s.i.d.6-6-67 num.35/75 col lithograph board. 19-Mar-3 Hotel des Ventes Mosan, Brussels #276/R est:4000-4500
£3000 $4680 €4500 Locomobile (60x80cm-24x31in) s.num.65/75 lithograph. 10-Oct-2 Sotheby's, London #24/R est:3000-3500
£3595 $5788 €5500 Chapeau 1900 (58x39cm-23x15in) s.num.14/75 col lithograph. 20-Jan-3 Horta, Bruxelles #157/R est:7000-9000
£3644 $5685 €5466 La fenetre (58x78cm-23x31in) s.num.10/75 col lithograph lit. 5-Nov-2 Bukowskis, Stockholm #545/R est:50000-60000 (S.KR 52000)
£3822 $5962 €6000 Paiolive (59x77cm-23x30in) s.d.74/75 num.51/75 engraving lithograph. 11-Nov-2 Horta, Bruxelles #146 est:5000-7000
£4138 $6621 €6000 Anne Songeuse (65x51cm-26x20in) s.d.66 num.51/75 lit. 15-Mar-3 De Vuyst, Lokeren #560/R est:7000-8000
£4717 $7500 €7076 Paiolive (59x79cm-23x31in) s.num.21/100 col lithograph. 2-May-3 Sotheby's, New York #128/R est:6000-8000
£4902 $7892 €7500 La voute (60x80cm-24x31in) s.num.56/75 col lithograph. 20-Jan-3 Horta, Bruxelles #156/R est:10000-12000
£5031 $7799 €8000 Fenetre (58x78cm-23x31in) s.d.71 num.62/75 col lith lit. 5-Oct-2 De Vuyst, Lokeren #567/R est:8000-9000
£5128 $8000 €7692 Rivals (78x58cm-31x23in) s.i. col lithograph edition of 75. 5-Nov-2 Christie's, Rockefeller NY #142/R est:9000-11000
£5517 $8828 €8000 Robe du dimanche (63x51cm-25x20in) s.d.67 col lithograph lit. 15-Mar-3 De Vuyst, Lokeren #485/R est:7000-8000
£5769 $9000 €8654 Le jardin (56x76cm-22x30in) s.num.61/75 col lithograph. 7-Nov-2 Swann Galleries, New York #627/R est:8000-12000
Works on paper
£1410 $2186 €2200 Dialogue (18x13cm-7x5in) ballpoint pen dr lit. 7-Dec-2 De Vuyst, Lokeren #85/R est:2000-2500
£1589 $2591 €2400 Nude (26x17cm-10x7in) chl exec.c.1920. 28-Jan-3 Dorotheum, Vienna #19/R est:2400-2600
£2115 $3279 €3300 Nu feminin (41x34cm-16x13in) pencil dr. 7-Dec-2 De Vuyst, Lokeren #469/R est:3800-4400
£2264 $3509 €3600 Nu couche (21x26cm-8x10in) s. wash Indian ink. 5-Oct-2 De Vuyst, Lokeren #560/R est:4000-5000
£2600 $4108 €3900 Vive Linkador !! (24x20cm-9x8in) s.i.d.78 pe ink. 3-Apr-3 Christie's, Kensington #76/R

£2692 $4173 €4200 Nu debout (31x23cm-12x9in) chl dr. 7-Dec-2 De Vuyst, Lokeren #555/R est:4000-5000
£3165 $5000 €5000 Jeune fille au chapeau (27x21cm-11x8in) s.i.d.26.7.81 prov. 26-Nov-2 Palais de Beaux Arts, Brussels #82/R est:3000-3700
£3333 $5167 €5200 Gare du Luxembourg a Bruxelles (31x41cm-12x16in) s. W/C Indian ink. 7-Dec-2 De Vuyst, Lokeren #474/R est:4800-5500
£3448 $5517 €5000 Femmes dans un jardin (19x28cm-7x11in) s.d.1957 Indian ink dr. 15-Mar-3 De Vuyst, Lokeren #559/R est:5000-6000
£3597 $5755 €5000 Premiere motrice electrique des Tramways Bruxellois (20x27cm-8x11in) i. Indian ink W/C prov. 13-May-3 Palais de Beaux Arts, Brussels #63/R est:5000-7500
£3793 $6069 €5500 Maternite (30x22cm-12x9in) mono.d.1930 chl pencil dr exhib.lit. 15-Mar-3 De Vuyst, Lokeren #542/R est:5500-6500
£4800 $7584 €7200 Nu feminin (41x33cm-16x13in) init. wax crayon. 3-Apr-3 Christie's, Kensington #74/R est:4000
£4808 $7452 €7500 Diana Melly (12x19cm-5x7in) s.d.38 Chinese ink. 7-Dec-2 Cornette de St.Cyr, Paris #61/R est:10000
£4808 $7452 €7500 Femme a la lampe (40x32cm-16x13in) s. Indian ink wash. 7-Dec-2 De Vuyst, Lokeren #473/R est:6500-7500
£5208 $8281 €7500 Les deux amantes (21x27cm-8x11in) s.d.1940 wash. 29-Apr-3 Campo & Campo, Antwerp #74/R est:8000-10000
£6475 $10360 €9000 Amies (75x56cm-30x22in) s.d.87 Indian ink wash. 17-May-3 De Vuyst, Lokeren #507/R est:12000-14000
£8725 $14047 €13000 Jeune femme (50x41cm-20x16in) ink wash prov. 23-Feb-3 Mercier & Cie, Lille #47/R
£8861 $14000 €14000 Hommes et femmes dans un paysage (57x76cm-22x30in) s.d.6-34 Indian ink wash W/C. 26-Nov-2 Palais de Beaux Arts, Brussels #312/R est:15000-20000
£8974 $13910 €14000 Tete de femme (60x46cm-24x18in) s.d.4-30 W/C wash dr exhib. 9-Dec-2 Horta, Bruxelles #121/R est:25000-35000
£10072 $16115 €14000 Amies devant un rideau rouge (45x59cm-18x23in) s. W/C Indian ink dr. 17-May-3 De Vuyst, Lokeren #563/R est:16000-20000
£10127 $16000 €16000 La liseuse (106x76cm-42x30in) s.d.25.2.89 and 31.3.89 verso Indian ink W/C gouache prov. 26-Nov-2 Palais de Beaux Arts, Brussels #83/R est:17500-25000
£10759 $17000 €17000 Jeune femme de profil (72x53cm-28x21in) s.d.8-83 Indian ink wash. 26-Nov-2 Palais de Beaux Arts, Brussels #313/R est:17500-23000
£11392 $18000 €18000 Jeune femme a la fenetre (37x27cm-15x11in) s.i.d.20 octobre 1979 Indian ink wash prov. 26-Nov-2 Palais de Beaux Arts, Brussels #85/R est:12500-17500
£11392 $18000 €18000 Le tram de Wilrijck (18x27cm-7x11in) i. Indian ink W/C. 26-Nov-2 Palais de Beaux Arts, Brussels #311/R est:17500-25000
£12658 $20000 €20000 Jeune femme nue assise (29x21cm-11x8in) s.d.1972 Indian ink wash W/C prov. 26-Nov-2 Palais de Beaux Arts, Brussels #84/R est:12500-17500
£13497 $22000 €20246 Nu (29x37cm-11x15in) s.i.d.25-8-48 India ink W/C wash prov. 12-Feb-3 Sotheby's, New York #64/R est:10000-15000
£17000 $27880 €25500 Projet pour 'Aube sur ville' (21x27cm-8x11in) init.i.d.1940 verso gouache W/C pen ink prov.exhib. 6-Feb-3 Christie's, London #488/R est:20000
£20253 $32000 €32000 Nu au chapeau (42x34cm-17x13in) s.d.55 Indian ink wash prov. 26-Nov-2 Palais de Beaux Arts, Brussels #86/R est:15000-23000
£33987 $54719 €52000 Elegante nue au chapeau. Elegante habillee au chapeau (77x40cm-30x16in) W/C double-sided. 20-Jan-3 Horta, Bruxelles #155/R est:60000-70000
£65000 $108550 €94250 Femme couchee (60x80cm-24x31in) s.d.22.7.46 W/C pen brush ink over pencil prov. 24-Jun-3 Sotheby's, London #243/R est:70000-90000
£240000 $391200 €360000 Courtisanes d'Alexandrie (74x110cm-29x43in) s.i.d.49 W/C pen ink prov.exhib.lit. 3-Feb-3 Christie's, London #175/R est:350000

DELVILLE, Jean (1867-1953) Belgian
£449 $704 €700 Abraham and Sarah (51x64cm-20x25in) canvas on panel. 16-Dec-2 Bernaerts, Antwerp #75/R
£2055 $3226 €3000 La procession (54x67cm-21x26in) s. 15-Apr-3 Galerie Moderne, Brussels #330/R est:3000-4000
Works on paper
£6475 $10360 €9000 Tete de jeune femme au diademe de perles (42x29cm-17x11in) s.d.1896 pencil htd white gouache exhib. 13-May-3 Palais de Beaux Arts, Brussels #66/R est:8700-12500

DELVOYE, Wim (1965-) Dutch?
Photographs
£5500 $8470 €8250 Swiss Mountain (131x195cm-52x77in) digital iris print executed 1996 prov.lit. 23-Oct-2 Christie's, London #214/R est:4000-6000
Sculpture
£3019 $4649 €4800 Pas tenakia (161x43cm-63x17in) s.i.d.1991 verso painted shovel. 26-Oct-2 Cornette de St.Cyr, Paris #141/R

DEMACHY, Pierre Antoine (1723-1807) French
£2903 $4587 €4500 Destruction devant la Colonnade du Louvre (21x31cm-8x12in) 18-Dec-2 Piasa, Paris #97/R
£3846 $6423 €5500 Vue de parc de Saint-Cloud (21x14cm-8x6in) panel. 25-Jun-3 Sotheby's, Paris #38/R est:5000-6000
Works on paper
£372 $580 €550 Femme et enfants (9x19cm-4x7in) pen ink wash. 31-Mar-3 Piasa, Paris #71
£929 $1441 €1450 Figures dans les ruines (13x16cm-5x6in) pen ink wash over crayon. 4-Dec-2 Piasa, Paris #102/R

DEMACHY, Pierre Antoine (attrib) (1723-1807) French
Works on paper
£1905 $3029 €2800 Fosses de la Concorde (36x50cm-14x20in) pen ink wash. 24-Mar-3 Tajan, Paris #46/R

DEMAN, Albert (1929-) French
£955 $1490 €1500 Portrait de pierrot (92x73cm-36x29in) s. 10-Nov-2 Eric Pillon, Calais #282/R
£2357 $3676 €3700 Vase de fleurs (92x65cm-36x26in) s. 10-Nov-2 Eric Pillon, Calais #279/R

DEMAND, Thomas (1964-) German
Photographs
£20000 $32800 €30000 Untitled (142x223cm-56x88in) num.1/3 cibachrome print exec.1993 prov.exhib. 6-Feb-3 Sotheby's, London #44/R est:30000
£28000 $43120 €42000 Flugel - grand piano (62x155cm-24x61in) s.d.1992 verso cibachrome print prov. 22-Oct-2 Sotheby's, London #309/R est:20000-30000
£34810 $55000 €52215 Prking garage (135x165cm-53x65in) s.d.1996 num.1/5 chromographic paper diasec. 14-Nov-2 Christie's, Rockefeller NY #408/R est:30000-40000
£55000 $91850 €82500 Fenster (183x286cm-72x113in) C-Print on diasec exc.1998 3/6 prov.exhib.lit. 25-Jun-3 Sotheby's, London #1/R est:40000-60000

DEMANET, Victor (1895-1964) Belgian
Sculpture
£949 $1481 €1500 Haleurs. s. green pat bronze. 16-Sep-2 Horta, Bruxelles #139

DEMARCHELIER, Patrick (1943-) ?
Photographs
£3988 $6500 €5982 Princess Diana, London (50x35cm-20x14in) s.d.1997 num.4/25 platinum print. 12-Feb-3 Christie's, Rockefeller NY #167/R est:3000-5000

DEMARMELS, Ludwig (1917-1992) Swiss
£1092 $1703 €1638 Summer flowers in garden (47x59cm-19x23in) s.d.75 board. 6-Nov-2 Hans Widmer, St Gallen #143/R est:2500-4000 (S.FR 2500)

DEMARNE, Jean Louis (1744-1829) French
£2158 $3453 €3000 Mountain landscape with castle (17x24cm-7x9in) mono. panel. 17-May-3 Lempertz, Koln #1077/R est:4000
£2848 $4443 €4500 La visite aux ruches (28x39cm-11x15in) i.verso panel. 20-Oct-2 Galerie de Chartres, Chartres #106 est:6000-9000
£7693 $12847 €11000 Bergere et son troupeau dans un paysage (37x55cm-15x22in) s. prov.lit. 25-Jun-3 Tajan, Paris #82/R est:12000-15000

DEMARNE, Jean Louis (attrib) (1744-1829) French
£649 $1000 €974 Travelers halting at an inn (34x41cm-13x16in) 23-Oct-2 Doyle, New York #61 est:1000-1500
£1224 $1947 €1800 Berger et troupeau (6cm-2in circular) indis.sig. paper. 24-Mar-3 Fraysse & Associes, Paris #31

DEMARTEAU, Gilles (1722-1776) Flemish
Prints
£2552 $4083 €3700 Femme a l'oiseau (36x24cm-14x9in) engraving. 13-Mar-3 Artcurial Briest, Paris #8/R

DEMAY, Jean François (attrib) (1798-1850) French
£968 $1529 €1500 Bergers sur un chemin (23x32cm-9x13in) panel. 20-Dec-2 Tajan, Paris #169

DEMEL, Franz (1878-1947) Austrian
Works on paper
£566 $877 €900 Dreimaderlhaus on the Molkerbastei (24x33cm-9x13in) s. w/C. 1-Oct-2 Dorotheum, Vienna #285/R

DEMENKO, Vladimir (1943-) Russian
£275 $426 €413 Copy from American impressionism (62x64cm-24x25in) s. 29-Sep-2 John Nicholson, Haslemere #18

DEMESTER, Eugène (?) French?
£480 $787 €720 Audierne Bretagne (60x100cm-24x39in) s. 5-Jun-3 Christie's, Kensington #749/R
£480 $787 €720 Fishing vessels at the Golfe du Morbihan (60x100cm-24x39in) s. 5-Jun-3 Christie's, Kensington #750/R

DEMIN, Giovanni (1786-1859) Italian
£19355 $30000 €29033 Solomon and the Queen of Sheba (105x138cm-41x54in) lit. 29-Oct-2 Sotheby's, New York #48/R est:30000-40000

DEMING, Edwin Willard (1860-1942) American
£920 $1500 €1380 Resting at dusk (79x112cm-31x44in) mono. prov. 16-Feb-3 Butterfields, San Francisco #2053 est:3000-5000
Works on paper
£481 $750 €722 Wyoming cowboy roping a steer. Buffalo skin hunters (10x13cm-4x5in) s. W/C pair. 9-Nov-2 Santa Fe Art, Santa Fe #131/R
£503 $800 €755 Long voyage (18x25cm-7x10in) s.i.verso W/C gouache pencil board. 5-Mar-3 Sotheby's, New York #144/R

DEMMIN, Erich (1911-) German
£258 $402 €410 Pre-alpine landscape in summer (11x25cm-4x10in) s. panel. 21-Sep-2 Dannenberg, Berlin #548/R
£316 $500 €500 Flowers by window (49x52cm-19x20in) mono. i.d.1958 verso panel. 29-Nov-2 Schloss Ahlden, Ahlden #1387/R
£538 $850 €850 Southern Italian beach on sunny day (60x80cm-24x31in) s. 29-Nov-2 Schloss Ahlden, Ahlden #1344/R

DEMONCHY, Andre (1914-) French
£414 $654 €600 Semur en Auxois, Cote d'Or (50x61cm-20x24in) s. i.verso. 4-Apr-3 Tajan, Paris #97/R
£1507 $2366 €2200 Petit pont (33x41cm-13x16in) s. 15-Apr-3 Laurence Calmels, Paris #4210/R
£2397 $3764 €3500 Auxerre, horloge (46x38cm-18x15in) s.d.55. 15-Apr-3 Laurence Calmels, Paris #4211/R

DEMORY, Charles Theophile (1833-1895) French
£566 $883 €900 Breton fishing couple on beach (80x60cm-31x24in) s. lit. 20-Sep-2 Sigalas, Stuttgart #1004/R

DEMUTH, Charles (1883-1935) American
Works on paper
£103226 $160000 €154839 Jazz singer (33x20cm-13x8in) s.d.1916 i.verso W/C prov.exhib.lit. 4-Dec-2 Sotheby's, New York #81/R est:60000-80000
£148148 $240000 €222222 Rooftops (25x38cm-10x15in) s.d.1918 W/C pencil prov.exhib.lit. 21-May-3 Sotheby's, New York #36/R est:100000-150000
£197531 $320000 €296297 Daisies and tomatoes (35x30cm-14x12in) i.d.1925 verso W/C pencil prov.exhib.lit. 21-May-3 Sotheby's, New York #2/R est:250000-350000

DEMUTH, William (studio) (19th C) American
Sculpture
£35257 $55000 €52886 Indian maiden (206cm-81in) cast painted zinc round plinth exec.c.1880 prov.exhib. 21-Sep-2 Pook & Pook, Downington #134/R est:30000-40000

DENAHY, John (1922-) British
£400 $616 €600 Summer at Danbury (34x41cm-13x16in) board exhib. 5-Sep-2 Christie's, Kensington #687

DENCKER, August (1882-?) German
£250 $385 €375 Summer in the woods (74x99cm-29x39in) s.d.1940. 22-Oct-2 Peter Francis, Wales #13

DENEUX, Gabriel Charles (1856-?) French
£315 $488 €500 Marche aux fleurs (17x20cm-7x8in) s. panel. 4-Oct-2 Tajan, Paris #61
Works on paper
£629 $969 €1000 Vues d'Alger (18x26cm-7x10in) s.i.d.1900 W/C pair. 23-Oct-2 Rabourdin & Choppin de Janvry, Paris #130

DENG FEN (1892-1968) Chinese
Works on paper
£1943 $3205 €2817 Two beauties (95x36cm-37x14in) s.i. ink scroll. 6-Jul-3 Christie's, Hong Kong #381/R est:40000-50000 (HK.D 25000)

DENIS, Maurice (1870-1943) French
£500 $790 €750 Contemplation (50x36cm-20x14in) init.d.17 board prov. 3-Apr-3 Christie's, Kensington #38/R
£828 $1292 €1300 Maternite (19x15cm-7x6in) s. wash. 7-Nov-2 Claude Aguttes, Neuilly #24
£7092 $11844 €10000 Printemps a assise, la porte San Pietro (46x33cm-18x13in) cardboard painted c.1936 lit. 23-Jun-3 Delvaux, Paris #127/R est:9000-12000
£8621 $13793 €12500 Eglise (39x54cm-15x21in) s.d.1927. 12-Mar-3 Libert, Castor, Paris #62/R est:6000-8000
£10897 $17000 €16346 Bois de hetres a Loguivy (46x65cm-18x26in) s.d.26 prov.exhib. 7-Nov-2 Christie's, Rockefeller NY #261/R est:18000-22000
£12500 $19250 €18750 La chapelle de kernivinen (28x37cm-11x15in) s.d.09 board on panel prov. 22-Oct-2 Sotheby's, London #172/R est:10000-12000
£14000 $23380 €20300 La Salute, Venise (50x70cm-20x28in) s.d.1922 prov. 25-Jun-3 Christie's, London #126/R est:12000-18000
£20000 $33400 €29000 Tente de plage aux trois baigneuses devant une tente (45x53cm-18x21in) s. painted 1933 prov. 24-Jun-3 Sotheby's, London #205/R est:22000-28000
£25641 $40256 €40000 Maternite rose (20x15cm-8x6in) s.d.11 cardboard prov.lit. 10-Dec-2 Artcurial Briest, Paris #472/R est:40000-60000
£26490 $43179 €40000 Nymphes des hortensias (48x73cm-19x29in) s.d.1912. 3-Feb-3 Cornette de St.Cyr, Paris #291/R est:12000
£43871 $69316 €68000 Partie de plage (88x125cm-35x49in) s.d.1913 prov. 18-Dec-2 Tajan, Paris #26/R est:90000
£54487 $85000 €81731 Mystere catholique (27x40cm-11x16in) mono.d.90 prov.lit. 7-Nov-2 Christie's, Rockefeller NY #222/R est:70000-90000
Prints
£3239 $5377 €4600 Le reflet dans la fontaine (41x25cm-16x10in) s.num. col lithograph edition of 100. 12-Jun-3 Piasa, Paris #56/R
£10563 $17535 €15000 Amour. s.i. folio col lithograph vellum exec.c.1892-1899. 12-Jun-3 Piasa, Paris #57/R
Works on paper
£1418 $2369 €2000 Le pinet (13x21cm-5x8in) s.i. W/C. 20-Jun-3 Piasa, Paris #108 est:2000-2200
£1418 $2298 €2000 Spes, Fides et Caritas (53x58cm-21x23in) s. col chk. 20-May-3 Dorotheum, Vienna #130/R est:2200-2500
£1486 $2319 €2200 Jeune homme tendant le bras vers une femme assoupie (39x31cm-15x12in) s. crayon chk prov. 26-Mar-3 Piasa, Paris #125/R
£1911 $2981 €3000 Village de Provence (11x18cm-4x7in) mono. W/C. 10-Nov-2 Eric Pillon, Calais #59/R
£2000 $3160 €3000 Rue de temptation (50x70cm-20x28in) gouache board prov. 3-Apr-3 Christie's, Kensington #37/R
£7500 $11550 €11250 Etude pour la ronde de psyche (89x108cm-35x43in) s.d.1908 sanguine white chk over pencil prov.exhib. 22-Oct-2 Sotheby's, London #127/R est:8000-12000

DENIS, Simon Joseph Alexander Clement (1755-1813) Flemish
£2941 $4824 €4500 Danseur napolitain (25x26cm-10x10in) d.1809 paper. 7-Feb-3 Piasa, Paris #215 est:1000

DENMARK (1950-) Belgian
Works on paper
£2361 $3754 €3400 Persarchief (24x150cm-9x59in) s.d.1995 mixed media. 29-Apr-3 Campo, Vlaamse Kaai #102 est:3500-4000
£2778 $4417 €4000 Newspaper cut up, burned (66x92cm-26x36in) s.d.1977 verso mixed media. 29-Apr-3 Campo, Vlaamse Kaai #101/R est:5000-5500

DENNEHY, Douglas Manson (1927-) Irish
£1111 $1767 €1600 Poppies (46x36cm-18x14in) s. canvasboard. 29-Apr-3 Whyte's, Dublin #217/R est:1800-2200
£2500 $3975 €3600 Farmstead, Donegal (30x61cm-12x24in) s. board. 29-Apr-3 Whyte's, Dublin #118/R est:1800-2200

DENNER, Balthasar (1685-1749) German
£2000 $3100 €3000 Portrait of gentleman wearing black jacket (37x30cm-15x12in) prov. 31-Oct-2 Sotheby's, Olympia #166/R est:2000-3000

DENNER, Balthasar (attrib) (1685-1749) German
£851 $1319 €1277 Portrait of elderly man (63x48cm-25x19in) 4-Dec-2 AB Stockholms Auktionsverk #1980/R (S.KR 12000)

DENNIS, Morgan (1892-1960) American
Works on paper
£224 $350 €336 Depicting a German shepherd dog (38x46cm-15x18in) s. pastel. 1-Aug-2 Eldred, East Dennis #136/R

DENNIS, Roger Wilson (1902-1996) American
£2414 $3500 €3621 Main Street, New London (41x30cm-16x12in) 1-Jun-2 Russ Antiques, Waterford #156
£4207 $6100 €6311 Watch Hill carousel (41x51cm-16x20in) 1-Jun-2 Russ Antiques, Waterford #107

DENNY, Gideon Jacques (1830-1886) American
£675 $1100 €1013 Sailing ship on rough seas (41x76cm-16x30in) s.d.1882. 16-Feb-3 Butterfields, San Francisco #2090
£1290 $2000 €1935 Evening on the Pacific coast, 1880 (51x91cm-20x36in) s.d.1880 prov. 29-Oct-2 John Moran, Pasadena #645 est:3000-5000

DENON, Vivant Dominique (1747-1825) French
Works on paper
£884 $1406 €1300 Scene galante (13x10cm-5x4in) pen ink wash. 24-Mar-3 Tajan, Paris #92
£1700 $2839 €2465 Seated man in a hat. Man by a chair holding a fan and handkerchief (22x16cm-9x6in) s. black chk pen ink wash two. 8-Jul-3 Christie's, London #86/R est:1500-2000

DENONNE, Alexander (1879-1953) Belgian
£380 $592 €600 Dame a la lecture (50x60cm-20x24in) s. 16-Sep-2 Horta, Bruxelles #355
£612 $978 €850 La fillette sur le pas de la porte (80x60cm-31x24in) s. 19-May-3 Horta, Bruxelles #441
£782 $1244 €1150 Jeune femme cousant dans un interieur. La table dressee (60x80cm-24x31in) s. double-sided. 18-Mar-3 Vanderkindere, Brussels #43
£1054 $1677 €1550 Le marche de la place Ste Catherine a Bruxelles (80x70cm-31x28in) s. 18-Mar-3 Vanderkindere, Brussels #29
£2930 $4571 €4600 Cabines a la mer du Nord (62x68cm-24x27in) s. 11-Nov-2 Horta, Bruxelles #547 est:2500-3700

DENTON, Kenneth (1932-) British
£280 $454 €420 Paddlers at Gorleston (30x51cm-12x20in) s. s.i.verso board. 20-May-3 Sotheby's, Olympia #162/R
£280 $454 €420 Haystack on the marsh, Norfolk (30x50cm-12x20in) s.i.verso board. 20-May-3 Sotheby's, Olympia #163/R
£300 $480 €435 Heavy weather off Harwich (19x29cm-7x11in) s. board. 18-May-3 Lots Road, London #357
£320 $496 €480 Departure at sunrise (41x61cm-16x24in) s. s.i.verso cardboard. 30-Sep-2 Bonhams, Ipswich #407
£320 $496 €480 Early morning, river Blackwater (41x61cm-16x24in) s. s.i.verso cardboard. 30-Sep-2 Bonhams, Ipswich #408
£420 $651 €630 Winter sunlight, Rochester (41x61cm-16x24in) s. s.i.verso cardboard. 30-Sep-2 Bonhams, Ipswich #433

DENTON, Troy (1949-) American
£309 $500 €464 Indian and buffalo (58x48cm-23x19in) 24-Jan-3 Douglas, South Deerfield #6
£783 $1300 €1135 On the trail (102x76cm-40x30in) s. 14-Jun-3 Jackson's, Cedar Falls #35/R
£1195 $1900 €1793 Hunting party (122x61cm-48x24in) s. 7-Mar-3 Jackson's, Cedar Falls #625/R est:1200-1800

DENTON, William (fl.1789-1795) British
Miniatures
£1500 $2385 €2250 Officer, probably of the 12th Light Dragoons (7cm-3xin) s.d.1794 gold frame plaited hair. 4-Mar-3 Bonhams, New Bond Street #131/R est:700-900

D'ENTRAYGUES, Charles Bertrand (1851-?) French
£7407 $12000 €10740 Fierce competition (46x61cm-18x24in) s. 21-May-3 Doyle, New York #211/R est:7000-9000
£7595 $12000 €11393 La lecon de patience (178x130cm-70x51in) s.d.1888 exhib. 24-Apr-3 Sotheby's, New York #161/R est:15000-20000

DEPERO, Fortunato (1892-1960) Italian
£4730 $7378 €7000 Study for advertisement (52x73cm-20x29in) s. tempera paper on canvas prov. 26-Mar-3 Finarte Semenzato, Milan #247/R
£5449 $8554 €8500 Woman with red hat (60x50cm-24x20in) s. tempera paper on cardboard. 20-Nov-2 Pandolfini, Florence #18/R est:9000
£7097 $11213 €11000 Masked figure (62x42cm-24x17in) s. cardboard painted 1940. 18-Dec-2 Christie's, Rome #152/R est:15000
£7317 $12000 €10610 Ballerina (51x30cm-20x12in) s. 1-Jun-3 Wright, Chicago #123/R est:5000-7000
£12766 $20681 €18000 Giocoliere-Mandarino (59x46cm-23x18in) s.d.1919 marquetry in col.wool cloth stitched exhib.lit. 26-May-3 Christie's, Milan #209/R est:18000-24000
£14103 $22141 €22000 Alpine view (37x46cm-15x18in) s.d.1945 board. 19-Nov-2 Finarte, Milan #241/R est:20000-24000
Sculpture
£2128 $3447 €3000 Chiocce con pulcini (28x55cm-11x22in) bas-relief painted gypsum exec.1913-1915. 26-May-3 Christie's, Milan #208/R est:3000-4000
£4808 $7548 €7500 Campari lamp (38x27x15cm-15x11x6in) s. wood vellum exec.c.1932. 19-Nov-2 Finarte, Milan #163/R est:9000
Works on paper
£878 $1370 €1300 Landscape (17x24cm-7x9in) init. ink W/C pencil. 26-Mar-3 Finarte Semenzato, Milan #57/R
£1042 $1656 €1500 Study for carving (27x21cm-11x8in) init. pencil. 1-May-3 Meeting Art, Vercelli #303
£1056 $1754 €1500 Insetti (23x18cm-9x7in) s. Indian ink W/C. 10-Jun-3 Finarte Semenzato, Milan #197/R est:1000-1400
£2581 $4077 €4000 Knight (120x40cm-47x16in) s. W/C ink pencil paper on canvas. 18-Dec-2 Christie's, Rome #29/R
£3526 $5465 €5500 Love cup (25x25cm-10x10in) s.i.d.1945 ink W/C. 4-Dec-2 Finarte, Milan #198/R
£4103 $6441 €6400 Untitled (27x14cm-11x6in) s.d.1917 pencil prov. 20-Nov-2 Pandolfini, Florence #16/R
£4167 $6542 €6500 Motorbike rider (19x25cm-7x10in) s. i.verso. 19-Nov-2 Finarte, Milan #24/R est:2500
£4487 $7045 €7000 Metropolitan realities (44x42cm-17x17in) s. Chinese ink chl exec.c.1944. 19-Nov-2 Finarte, Milan #160/R
£6028 $9766 €8500 Lo sciatore (80x70cm-31x28in) W/C tempera pencil prov. 26-May-3 Christie's, Milan #215/R est:6000-8000
£6383 $10340 €9000 La donne e l'asino (28x22cm-11x9in) s.d.1916 pencil chl htd.white prov.exhib. 26-May-3 Christie's, Milan #294/R est:9000-10000

DEPETRIS, Giovanni (attrib) (1890-1940) Italian
£493 $750 €740 Alpine village (56x71cm-22x28in) s.indis.d. i.on stretcher. 15-Aug-2 Doyle, New York #110

DEPEW, Viola (1894-?) Canadian
£444 $729 €666 Corner of sun life - from an upper window (45x35cm-18x14in) s. board exhib. 3-Jun-3 Joyner, Toronto #435/R est:800-1200 (C.D 1000)

D'EPINAY, Prosper (1830-1914) French
Sculpture
£1736 $2743 €2500 Portrait posthume du prince imperial (45x30cm-18x12in) pat plaster. 23-Apr-3 Rabourdin & Choppin de Janvry, Paris #89/R
£4000 $6240 €6000 Bust of Hadrian de Bosmelet as the infant Emperor Hadrian (41cm-16in) s.i. polychrome terracotta wooden base lit. 9-Apr-3 Sotheby's, London #96/R est:4000-6000

DEPONIRT, K S L (?) ?
Sculpture
£1987 $3238 €3000 Esclave, porteuse d'eau (108cm-43in) i.verso pat plaster. 17-Feb-3 Horta, Bruxelles #110

DEPONTI, Barbara (1975-) Italian
Works on paper
£922 $1494 €1300 Untitled (100x140cm-39x55in) s.d.2002 verso mixed media dusted paper. 20-May-3 Porro, Milan #15/R est:1200-1400

DEPPE, Gustav (1913-) German
£513 $810 €800 Tower impression (39x28cm-15x11in) mono.d.1958 s.i.d. verso oil tempera panel. 14-Nov-2 Neumeister, Munich #761/R

DEPRE, Albert (1861-1937) French
£316 $494 €500 Soleil couchant aux environs de Paris (54x81cm-21x32in) s. 20-Oct-2 Chayette & Cheval, Paris #18

DEPUYDT, Pierre (20th C) Belgian
£252 $387 €400 Lady in interior (140x120cm-55x47in) s.d.1979. 22-Oct-2 Campo & Campo, Antwerp #468

DERAIN, Andre (1880-1954) French
£230 $373 €350 Homme nu debout tenant un baton (22x15cm-9x6in) studio st. black crayon. 22-Jan-3 Tajan, Paris #126
£612 $973 €900 Female head (45x37cm-18x15in) s.i. 27-Feb-3 Hagelstam, Helsinki #811
£2000 $3080 €3000 Pichet et corbeille de fruits sur une nappe (11x28cm-4x11in) s. painted c.1948-50 prov. 23-Oct-2 Sotheby's, Olympia #703/R est:2500-3500

£3191	$4947	€4787	Bateaux sur la plage, maree basse (40x61cm-16x24in) s. 4-Dec-2 AB Stockholms Auktionsverk #1890/R est:50000-60000 (S.KR 45000)
£3500	$5390	€5250	Chasseur et chiens (32x26cm-13x10in) st.sig. painted c.1946-50 prov.lit. 23-Oct-2 Sotheby's, Olympia #706/R est:4000-5000
£3548	$5500	€5322	Panier avec cerises (24x25cm-9x10in) s. 26-Sep-2 Christie's, Rockefeller NY #575/R est:7000-9000
£4194	$6500	€6291	Portrait de Tela-Tchai (33x33cm-13x13in) s. painted c.1929-30 prov.exhib.lit. 26-Sep-2 Christie's, Rockefeller NY #600/R est:10000-15000
£4908	$8000	€7362	Tete de femme (27x22cm-11x9in) s. panel painted c.1928 prov. 12-Feb-3 Sotheby's, New York #94/R est:10000-15000
£5000	$7700	€7500	Citrons et couteau (19x30cm-7x12in) panel painted c.1936-38 prov.lit. 23-Oct-2 Sotheby's, Olympia #702/R est:6000-8000
£5321	$8087	€8300	Portrait du fils de l'artiste (29x34cm-11x13in) bears sig. 16-Aug-2 Deauville, France #85/R est:10000
£5556	$8834	€8000	Nymphes, chiens et cerf dans un paysage (16x27cm-6x11in) s. canvas on cardboard painted c.1942-1945 lit. 29-Apr-3 Artcurial Briest, Paris #217/R est:5000-6000
£5660	$9000	€8490	Paysage d'Ile-de-France (35x34cm-14x13in) s. painted 1936-38 prov.lit. 27-Feb-3 Christie's, Rockefeller NY #59/R est:10000
£6000	$9540	€9000	Buste de femme (71x32cm-28x13in) s.stretcher painted c.1914 prov.exhib.lit. 20-Mar-3 Sotheby's, Olympia #60/R est:12000-15000
£8451	$14028	€12000	Les baigneuses (34x33cm-13x13in) s. 11-Jun-3 Beaussant & Lefèvre, Paris #19/R est:10000-12000
£11304	$17522	€16956	Paysage (33x41cm-13x16in) s. prov.lit. 4-Dec-2 Koller, Zurich #124/R est:25000-40000 (S.FR 26000)
£14000	$21700	€21000	Nature morte avec pichet (32x41cm-13x16in) s. painted 1911 prov.exhib.lit. 5-Dec-2 Christie's, Kensington #47/R est:7000-10000
£17949	$28000	€26924	Portrait de femme (52x48cm-20x19in) painted c.1946-50 prov.lit. 7-Nov-2 Christie's, Rockefeller NY #277/R est:30000-40000
£44515	$70334	€66773	Buste de femme aux seins nus (55x46cm-22x18in) s. prov.exhib.lit. 27-Nov-2 Deutscher-Menzies, Melbourne #34/R est:80000-120000 (A.D 124640)
£220000	$367400	€330000	Nature morte a la lampe (64x92cm-25x36in) s. painted c.1900-01 prov.lit. 23-Jun-3 Sotheby's, London #8/R est:120000-150000
£339744	$530000	€509616	Le jardin (75x89cm-30x35in) s.d.99 prov.exhib.lit. 7-Nov-2 Christie's, Rockefeller NY #246/R est:250000-350000

Sculpture

£1000	$1540	€1500	Masque aux grands yeux (75x75cm-30x30in) s.num.1/11 bronze exec.c.1938 prov.lit. 23-Oct-2 Sotheby's, Olympia #778/R est:1500-2000
£2500	$3850	€3750	Femme etonnee aux boucles d'oreilles (13x13cm-5x5in) num.3/11 bronze prov.lit. 23-Oct-2 Sotheby's, Olympia #779/R est:3000-4000
£4294	$7000	€6441	L'enigme and la vieux (17cm-7in) i. num.6/11 two prov.lit. 12-Feb-3 Sotheby's, New York #116/R est:7000-10000
£8589	$14000	€12884	L'homme aux cheveux plaques (20cm-8in) i.num.6/11 brown pat. bronze prov.lit. 12-Feb-3 Sotheby's, New York #110/R est:8000-12000
£14110	$23000	€21165	Personnage sans menton (26cm-10in) i.num.6/11 brown pat. bronze prov.lit. 12-Feb-3 Sotheby's, New York #109/R est:12000-18000

Works on paper

£241	$403	€350	Homme a cheval (21x27cm-8x11in) bears studio st. graphite dr. 10-Jul-3 Artcurial Briest, Paris #24
£252	$390	€400	Jeune garcon en habit (24x17cm-9x7in) st.sig. graphite dr. 30-Oct-2 Artcurial Briest, Paris #250
£252	$390	€400	Trois personnages dans un paysage (19x23cm-7x9in) st.sig. graphite dr. 30-Oct-2 Artcurial Briest, Paris #251
£263	$427	€400	Visage de profil gauche (14x13cm-6x5in) studio st. black crayon. 22-Jan-3 Tajan, Paris #129
£264	$419	€380	Nu de face (19x12cm-7x5in) st.sig. pencil dr tracing paper. 29-Apr-3 Artcurial Briest, Paris #46
£278	$441	€400	Femme nue de dos (24x20cm-9x8in) st.sig. pencil estompe dr. 29-Apr-3 Artcurial Briest, Paris #48
£278	$458	€400	Tetes feminines de face et de profil (27x15cm-11x6in) studio st. black ink. 1-Jul-3 Rossini, Paris #3
£288	$460	€400	Les baigneurs sur la plage (20x30cm-8x12in) studio st. graphite dr. 18-May-3 Eric Pillon, Calais #89/R
£308	$477	€480	Tetes (22x15cm-9x6in) dr. 8-Dec-2 Feletin, Province #18
£312	$496	€450	Jeune homme costume (24x16cm-9x6in) st.sig. graphite dr. 29-Apr-3 Artcurial Briest, Paris #47
£312	$496	€450	Personnage de dos (48x12cm-19x5in) studio st. pencil dr. 29-Apr-3 Artcurial Briest, Paris #49
£312	$496	€450	Chouette (16x12cm-6x5in) st.sig. blue ball point pen dr. 29-Apr-3 Artcurial Briest, Paris #50
£321	$503	€500	Etude de femme nue (28x18cm-11x7in) studio st. crayon. 10-Dec-2 Renaud, Paris #51/R
£321	$487	€500	Nu debout (30x21cm-12x8in) studio st. crayon dr. 16-Aug-2 Deauville, France #4/R
£321	$487	€500	Nu au bras leve (29x16cm-11x6in) studio st. crayon dr. 16-Aug-2 Deauville, France #8/R
£329	$533	€500	La femme qui marche (24x14cm-9x6in) studio st. black crayon. 22-Jan-3 Tajan, Paris #125
£348	$550	€550	Etude de nu feminin assis (29x20cm-11x8in) studio st. chl. 28-Nov-2 Tajan, Paris #216
£350	$584	€500	Deux visages de femme (33x21cm-13x8in) bears studio st. dr. 26-Jun-3 Tajan, Paris #80
£385	$585	€600	Nu debout (29x15cm-11x6in) studio st. crayon dr. 16-Aug-2 Deauville, France #2
£395	$640	€600	Cheval (26x38cm-10x15in) studio st. black crayon dr. 22-Jan-3 Tajan, Paris #123
£395	$640	€600	Femme assise (20x31cm-8x12in) studio st. Indian ink pen dr. 22-Jan-3 Tajan, Paris #130
£408	$649	€600	Quatre personnages dans un interieur (20x23cm-8x9in) st.sig. graphite dr. 26-Feb-3 Artcurial Briest, Paris #37
£411	$650	€650	Nu de face (29x20cm-11x8in) s. crayon. 27-Nov-2 Blanchet, Paris #64
£417	$663	€600	Portrait de jeune femme (13x12cm-5x5in) st.sig. graphite dr. 29-Apr-3 Artcurial Briest, Paris #45
£428	$693	€650	Femme, jambe levee (26x21cm-10x8in) studio st. chl. 22-Jan-3 Tajan, Paris #131
£433	$676	€680	Nu de face (26x20cm-10x8in) st.sig. crayon prov. 7-Nov-2 Chochon-Barre & Allardi, Paris #116/R
£440	$683	€700	Vue de village (9x28cm-4x11in) studio st. black pencil dr. 4-Oct-2 Tajan, Paris #62
£490	$779	€720	Femme nue allongee (13x23cm-5x9in) st.sig. graphite dr. 26-Feb-3 Artcurial Briest, Paris #42
£507	$800	€800	Etude de nu feminin (29x19cm-11x7in) studio st. chl. 28-Nov-2 Tajan, Paris #201/R
£513	$805	€800	Nu (26x20cm-10x8in) st.sig. graphite prov. 16-Dec-2 Chochon-Barre & Allardi, Paris #31
£513	$805	€800	Nu assis (26x20cm-10x8in) st.sig. graphite prov. 16-Dec-2 Chochon-Barre & Allardi, Paris #32
£527	$853	€800	Profils (37x25cm-15x10in) studio st. graphite dr. 22-Jan-3 Tajan, Paris #122
£531	$844	€780	Femme nue allongee (28x42cm-11x17in) st.sig. chl dr. 26-Feb-3 Artcurial Briest, Paris #36
£538	$850	€850	Nu au bras leve (26x20cm-10x8in) s. crayon. 27-Nov-2 Blanchet, Paris #65
£545	$828	€850	Femme en buste au collier (22x18cm-9x7in) studio st. crayon dr. 16-Aug-2 Deauville, France #1/R
£552	$877	€800	Nu assis (38x28cm-15x11in) s. sanguine estompe. 5-Mar-3 Doutrebente, Paris #29/R
£571	$909	€840	Femme nue de dos (25x18cm-10x7in) st.sig. chl dr. 26-Feb-3 Artcurial Briest, Paris #39
£577	$906	€900	Composition (27x30cm-11x12in) studio st. gouache W/C. 22-Nov-2 Millon & Associes, Paris #29
£600	$954	€900	Nu debout (24x20cm-9x8in) pencil prov. 20-Mar-3 Sotheby's, Olympia #75/R
£609	$956	€950	Nu de dos (26x20cm-10x8in) st.sig. graphite prov. 16-Dec-2 Chochon-Barre & Allardi, Paris #33
£629	$1051	€900	Raymond Knaublich de profil. Etude de poupee (25x20cm-10x8in) bears studio st. black crayon estompe dr double-sided prov. 26-Jun-3 Tajan, Paris #78/R
£629	$1051	€900	Portrait de femme. Modele nu (25x20cm-10x8in) bears studio st. black crayon ink dr double-sided prov. 26-Jun-3 Tajan, Paris #79
£633	$1058	€918	Stylised woman's head (24x16cm-9x6in) pencil. 24-Jun-3 Koller, Zurich #158/R (S.FR 1400)
£641	$1006	€1000	Cheval (25x42cm-10x17in) s. crayon. 14-Dec-2 Deauville, France #88
£696	$1079	€1100	Femme pensive (25x19cm-10x7in) studio st. graphite. 28-Sep-2 Cornette de St.Cyr, Paris #155
£696	$1100	€1100	Nu de face (26x20cm-10x8in) s. graphite. 27-Nov-2 Blanchet, Paris #63/R
£735	$1168	€1080	Profil de femme (18x14cm-7x6in) st.sig. chl dr. 26-Feb-3 Artcurial Briest, Paris #43
£750	$1193	€1125	Nu allonge (15x22cm-6x9in) pencil prov. 20-Mar-3 Sotheby's, Olympia #76/R
£789	$1279	€1200	Modele nu debout (35x13cm-14x5in) studio st. black crayon dr. 22-Jan-3 Tajan, Paris #124/R
£800	$1272	€1200	Femme debout (22x17cm-9x7in) pencil prov. 20-Mar-3 Sotheby's, Olympia #73/R
£865	$1315	€1350	Portrait de jeune femme de profil (18x11cm-7x4in) st.sig. graphite dr. 16-Aug-2 Deauville, France #9/R
£886	$1400	€1400	Seated female nude (58x39cm-23x15in) ochre. 27-Nov-2 Dorotheum, Vienna #143/R
£900	$1431	€1350	Nu au repos (15x22cm-6x9in) pencil prov. 20-Mar-3 Sotheby's, Olympia #72/R
£921	$1492	€1400	Deux etudes de modeles nus (34x24cm-13x9in) studio st. chl tracing paper. 22-Jan-3 Tajan, Paris #121/R est:800
£986	$1568	€1450	Femme nue debout de face (24x16cm-9x6in) studio st. Indian ink tracing paper. 26-Feb-3 Artcurial Briest, Paris #40
£1026	$1600	€1539	Jeune femme (36x27cm-14x11in) studio st. pencil. 19-Sep-2 Swann Galleries, New York #304/R est:2000-3000
£1026	$1559	€1600	Femme nue se tenant la jambe. st.sig. crayon dr. 16-Aug-2 Deauville, France #6/R
£1161	$1835	€1800	Modele assis (62x47cm-24x19in) studio st. crayon stump. 19-Dec-2 Delvaux, Paris #14/R
£1250	$2025	€1900	Femme nue debout, la main droite sur la hanche (36x25cm-14x10in) studio st. black crayon tracing paper. 22-Jan-3 Tajan, Paris #128/R est:1000-1200

£1400 $2156 €2100 Etude de femme (25x19cm-10x7in) bears estate st. pencil prov. 23-Oct-2 Sotheby's, Olympia #684/R est:600-800
£1500 $2370 €2250 Etude de nu feminin (66x51cm-26x20in) s. chk. 3-Apr-3 Christie's, Kensington #52/R
£1600 $2480 €2400 Etude pour fontaine ornementale. Pecheur et poisson (21x35cm-8x14in) st.sig. pen ink brush two. 5-Dec-2 Christie's, Kensington #97/R est:1000-1500
£1700 $2618 €2550 Nu allonge (13x19cm-5x7in) bears estate st. pencil prov. 23-Oct-2 Sotheby's, Olympia #686/R est:600-800
£1736 $2865 €2500 Personnage de comedie (21x16cm-8x6in) W/C. 2-Jul-3 Artcurial Briest, Paris #697/R est:3000-5000
£1944 $3091 €2800 Femme nue de dos (30x23cm-12x9in) studio st. pencil estompe dr. 29-Apr-3 Artcurial Briest, Paris #44/R est:1500-2000
£1944 $3208 €2800 Personnage de comedie (21x16cm-8x6in) W/C. 2-Jul-3 Artcurial Briest, Paris #696/R est:3000-5000
£1957 $3209 €2700 Young woman (60x48cm-24x19in) s. ochre. 31-May-3 Villa Grisebach, Berlin #532/R est:1800-2400
£2200 $3388 €3300 Femme debout (21x15cm-8x6in) bears estate st. pencil prov. 23-Oct-2 Sotheby's, Olympia #685/R est:600-800
£2200 $3388 €3300 Nature morte (16x23cm-6x9in) studio st. W/C gouache exec.c.1945-48. 23-Oct-2 Sotheby's, Olympia #695/R est:2000-3000
£2710 $4200 €4065 Nu debout (63x47cm-25x19in) st. red chk prov. 26-Sep-2 Christie's, Rockefeller NY #612/R est:2000-4000
£4000 $6360 €6000 Nuque aux nattes (55x46cm-22x18in) s. chl prov. 20-Mar-3 Sotheby's, Olympia #15/R est:4000-6000
£4965 $8291 €7000 Ballerines (60x47cm-24x19in) s. sanguine c.1926-27. 20-Jun-3 Piasa, Paris #84/R est:7000-8000
£6410 $10064 €10000 Nu (43x30cm-17x12in) s.i. graphite dr. 10-Dec-2 Piasa, Paris #266 est:1500
£22000 $36740 €31900 Les baigneuses (32x48cm-13x19in) s. gouache W/C pencil prov. 24-Jun-3 Christie's, London #3/R est:6000-9000
£27891 $44347 €41000 Les naiades (47x61cm-19x24in) s. W/C exec.c.1905. 26-Feb-3 Fraysse & Associes, Paris #13/R est:10000-15000

DERBY, Alfred Thomas (1821-1873) British
£450 $720 €675 Smuggler (28x39cm-11x15in) s. 7-Jan-3 Bonhams, Knightsbridge #227h/R

DERCKSEN, Marinus Hendrikus (1814-1866) Dutch
£1126 $1835 €1700 Dutch family in interior (50x43cm-20x17in) s.d.49. 17-Feb-3 Horta, Bruxelles #479

DEREDIA, Jimenez (1954-) Costa Rican
Sculpture
£6369 $10000 €9554 Guard (35x37cm-14x15in) brown pat bronze exec.1999 prov. 20-Nov-2 Christie's, Rockefeller NY #96/R

DERFLA, Alfred (?) ?
£274 $428 €411 Town scene with horses (15x31cm-6x12in) s. panel. 13-Sep-2 Lilla Bukowskis, Stockholm #313 (S.KR 4000)
£659 $1042 €989 Market scene with horses and riders (15x31cm-6x12in) s. panel. 27-Nov-2 Falkkloos, Malmo #78378/R (S.KR 9400)

DERGES, Susan (1955-) British
Photographs
£3797 $6000 €5696 Shoreline, 7 October 1998 (98x242cm-39x95in) cibachrome photogram prov.lit. 24-Apr-3 Phillips, New York #56/R est:6000-8000
£5000 $8350 €7250 Shoreline (105x241cm-41x95in) cibachrome photogram prov.lit. 26-Jun-3 Sotheby's, London #276/R est:5000-7000
£6329 $10000 €9494 River Taw - leaf fall (168x61cm-66x24in) s.i.d.1998 dye destruction photogram prov. 22-Apr-3 Christie's, Rockefeller NY #115/R est:6000-8000

DERHAM, Frances Alexandra Mabel Letitia (1894-1987) Australian
£286 $440 €429 Nude sitting (65x49cm-26x19in) s. 7-Sep-2 Goodman, Sydney #85 (A.D 800)
£429 $677 €644 Seated nude (49x34cm-19x13in) init.d.1953 canvas on board. 27-Nov-2 Deutscher-Menzies, Melbourne #228/R est:800-1200 (A.D 1200)

DERIANS, A (19th C) French
£500 $780 €790 Le troupeau (63x48cm-25x19in) s. 15-Sep-2 Feletin, Province #95

DERKERT, Siri (1888-1973) Swedish
£837 $1322 €1256 Woman standing (111x48cm-44x19in) s. 28-Apr-3 Bukowskis, Stockholm #67/R (S.KR 11000)
£837 $1322 €1256 Carlo reading art history (63x48cm-25x19in) s. panel painted 1942 exhib.lit. 28-Apr-3 Bukowskis, Stockholm #74/R (S.KR 11000)
£981 $1530 €1472 Girl asleep (47x59cm-19x23in) s.d.1933 tempera cardboard. 5-Nov-2 Bukowskis, Stockholm #112/R est:20000-25000 (S.KR 14000)
£1179 $1862 €1769 Portrait of Elsa Thorling (24x18cm-9x7in) canvas on panel painted 1911. 28-Apr-3 Bukowskis, Stockholm #73/R est:8000-10000 (S.KR 15500)
£1369 $2163 €2054 Woman from Algier (39x33cm-15x13in) s. canvas on panel lit. 28-Apr-3 Bukowskis, Stockholm #69/R est:15000-18000 (S.KR 18000)
£3118 $4926 €4677 Sara's head (36x32cm-14x13in) s. panel painted 1930 exhib.lit. 28-Apr-3 Bukowskis, Stockholm #72/R est:15000-20000 (S.KR 41000)

Works on paper
£272 $433 €400 Carlo (43x32cm-17x13in) s. dr. 27-Feb-3 Hagelstam, Helsinki #957
£278 $461 €403 View from my window (45x58cm-18x23in) s. W/C exhib. 16-Jun-3 Lilla Bukowskis, Stockholm #389 (S.KR 3600)
£324 $538 €470 Self-portrait (78x58cm-31x23in) s. pastel exhib. 16-Jun-3 Lilla Bukowskis, Stockholm #388 (S.KR 4200)

DERKOVITS, Gyula (1894-1934) Hungarian
Works on paper
£1419 $2213 €2058 Farewell (34x36cm-13x14in) W/C. 13-Sep-2 Mu Terem Galeria, Budapest #190/R est:180000 (H.F 550000)
£8606 $13339 €12909 In the boat (34x33cm-13x13in) s. mixed media. 6-Dec-2 Kieselbach, Budapest #47/R (H.F 3200000)

DEROME, Albert Thomas (1885-1959) American
£1774 $2750 €2661 After storm, Monterey Bay (15x20cm-6x8in) s. i.d.46 verso prov. 29-Oct-2 John Moran, Pasadena #735a est:1500-2000
£2329 $3750 €3494 El Toro Creek, Monterey-Salinas Canyon (46x61cm-18x24in) s. i.d.1955 verso canvasboard prov.exhib. 18-Feb-3 John Moran, Pasadena #137 est:5000-7000
£4194 $6500 €6291 Glen Una Meadow, Los Gatos (46x61cm-18x24in) s. i.d.1951 verso masonite prov.exhib. 29-Oct-2 John Moran, Pasadena #734 est:5000-7000
£4348 $7000 €6522 Los Gatos Creek picnic grounds (46x61cm-18x24in) s. i.d.1944 verso canvasboard prov.exhib. 18-Feb-3 John Moran, Pasadena #136 est:5000-7000
£5484 $8500 €8226 Alisomar Beach and Point from Spanish Beach, Monterey Bay (46x61cm-18x24in) s. canvasboard painted c.1942 prov. 29-Oct-2 John Moran, Pasadena #637 est:5000-7000
£6024 $10000 €8735 Above the picnic grounds, Los Gatos (41x50cm-16x20in) s. i.verso canvasboard. 11-Jun-3 Butterfields, San Francisco #4215/R est:10000-15000

Works on paper
£745 $1200 €1118 Morro Rock, Giant Forest, minnerets on left in Sawtooth Range (8x20cm-3x8in) s. s.i.d.1918 verso W/C prov. 18-Feb-3 John Moran, Pasadena #88

DEROY, Isidore (1797-1886) French
Works on paper
£278 $440 €440 Storm gathering over lake (5x8cm-2x3in) mono. w/C. 29-Nov-2 Bassenge, Berlin #5861/R

DERUET, Claude (attrib) (1588-1662) French
£2885 $4529 €4500 Portrait de jeune femme en noir (33x25cm-13x10in) panel. 20-Nov-2 Libert, Castor, Paris #48/R
£3077 $4831 €4800 Portrait de jeune femme en rouge (34x25cm-13x10in) panel. 20-Nov-2 Libert, Castor, Paris #71/R
£4196 $7007 €6000 Portrait d'un jeune couple (51x62cm-20x24in) 25-Jun-3 Artcurial Briest, Paris #493/R est:2300-2500
£8803 $14613 €12500 Assemblee galante dans un interieur clair-obscur (55x89cm-22x35in) 15-Jun-3 Anaf, Lyon #58/R est:5000-6000

DERUET, Claude (circle) (1588-1662) French
£38000 $63460 €55100 Allegory of love, twelve noblewomen seated in a garden, each holding an arrow (71x112cm-28x44in) prov. 9-Jul-3 Christie's, London #63/R est:30000-50000

DESAN, Charles (19th C) ?
£1266 $1975 €2000 Troupeau de vaches dans un paysage (25x35cm-10x14in) s. panel. 16-Sep-2 Horta, Bruxelles #150

DESANI, Pietro (1595-1657) Italian
£10473 $16338 €15500 Saint Vincent Ferrer (122x172cm-48x68in) 25-Mar-3 Finarte Semenzato, Rome #128/R est:14000-16000

DESATNICK, Mike (1943-) American?
£3526 $5500 €5289 Deer dancers (76x102cm-30x40in) 9-Nov-2 Altermann Galleries, Santa Fe #31

DESBOIS, Jules (1851-1935) French
Sculpture
£9375 $14812 €13500 Eve (33cm-13in) s. terracotta. 25-Apr-3 Piasa, Paris #30/R est:1500

DESBOUTIN, Marcelin Gilbert (1823-1902) French
£567 $919 €800 Enfant au bonnet blanc (39x25cm-15x10in) canvas on board prov. 23-May-3 Camard, Paris #29
£1709 $2700 €2700 Portrait d'enfant (41x33cm-16x13in) s. paper on canvas. 1-Dec-2 Peron, Melun #84

DESBROSSES, Jean-Alfred (1835-1906) French
£325 $514 €488 Southern landscape with ruins (56x36cm-22x14in) s.d.1886. 5-Apr-3 Rasmussen, Havnen #2018/R (D.KR 3500)
£577 $900 €866 Horse and rider in the valley (28x43cm-11x17in) s. 5-Nov-2 Arthur James, Florida #361
£759 $1185 €1200 Cavalier sur un chemin de montagne (56x34cm-22x13in) s. 20-Oct-2 Mercier & Cie, Lille #335

DESCAMPS, Guillaume-Desire-Joseph (1779-1858) French
£11321 $17660 €18000 Jeunes amoureux lisant une lettre devant Naples (92x75cm-36x30in) s.d.1812. 8-Oct-2 Christie's, Paris #32/R est:12000

DESCHAMPS, Gabriel (1919-) French
£261 $421 €400 Port de La Rochelle (38x55cm-15x22in) s. masonite. 18-Jan-3 Neret-Minet, Paris #152
£1384 $2131 €2200 Scene mediterraneene (65x82cm-26x32in) s. 22-Oct-2 Campo, Vlaamse Kaai #486/R
£1400 $2338 €2030 View in Provence (50x61cm-20x24in) s. indis.i.verso. 17-Jun-3 Bonhams, Knightsbridge #79/R est:1000-1500
£1600 $2624 €2400 Near Grasse (47x55cm-19x22in) s. 4-Feb-3 Sworder & Son, Bishops Stortford #115/R est:600-800
£1700 $2771 €2550 Mas fleuri, campagne de grasse (46x55cm-18x22in) s. 3-Feb-3 Bonhams, New Bond Street #92/R est:1000-1500
£1700 $2788 €2550 Vieux moulin (61x73cm-24x29in) s. 4-Feb-3 Sworder & Son, Bishops Stortford #116/R est:800-1000
£1800 $2934 €2700 Un pont en provence (45x55cm-18x22in) s. 3-Feb-3 Bonhams, New Bond Street #91/R est:800-1200
£2100 $3423 €3045 Marinaon the Mediterranean (34x26cm-13x10in) s. 21-Jul-3 Bonhams, Bath #43/R est:400-600
£3205 $5000 €4808 Untitled, coastal scene (74x91cm-29x36in) 18-Oct-2 Du Mouchelle, Detroit #63/R est:1000-1500
£8500 $13260 €12750 Paysage provincal, Cap Ferrat and Villefranche (54x46cm-21x18in) s. exhib. 9-Oct-2 Woolley & Wallis, Salisbury #286/R est:2500-3500

DESCHAMPS, Gerard (1937-) French
£1100 $1738 €1650 Grasse mae - study of a country villa. 15-Nov-2 Moore Allen & Innocent, Cirencester #1033
£2014 $3182 €2900 Bache de signalisation (48x56cm-19x22in) s.i.d.verso. 27-Apr-3 Perrin, Versailles #85/R est:1000-1200
Sculpture
£1736 $2865 €2500 Sans titre (70x80cm-28x31in) s.d.verso fabric plexiglas. 1-Jul-3 Artcurial Briest, Paris #828/R est:3000-4000
£11258 $17337 €17900 Dessous au plastique bleu (156x136x31cm-61x54x12in) s.i.d.1961 verso underwera plastic bags plexiglas. 26-Oct-2 Cornette de St.Cyr, Paris #39/R est:8000

DESCHAMPS, Louis Henri (1846-1902) French
£2468 $3800 €3702 Young girl holding a violin (55x39cm-22x15in) s. 4-Sep-2 Christie's, Rockefeller NY #315/R est:4000-6000

DESCHWANDEN, Melchior Paul von (1811-1881) Swiss
£1572 $2484 €2358 Portrait of girl in traditional costume with guitar (72x58cm-28x23in) mono. 14-Nov-2 Stuker, Bern #160/R est:4200-4700 (S.FR 3600)

DESCHWANDEN, Theodor von (attrib) (1826-1861) Swiss
£742 $1158 €1113 Still life (32x89cm-13x35in) s. verso. 6-Nov-2 Dobiaschofsky, Bern #444/R est:2000 (S.FR 1700)

DESCLABISSAC, Alexander (1868-c.1938) German
£288 $449 €420 Gathering in the tavern (37x41cm-15x16in) s. lit. 10-Apr-3 Allgauer, Kempten #2752/R
£392 $627 €600 Strand cafe in English garden (44x59cm-17x23in) s. board lit. 10-Jan-3 Allgauer, Kempten #1569/R

DESCOMPS, Joe (1869-1950) French
Sculpture
£994 $1560 €1550 Femme nue bras croisees (16cm-6in) s. ivory onyx base. 20-Nov-2 Claude Boisgirard, Paris #53/R

DESFOSSEZ, Charles Henri (1764-1809) French
Miniatures
£2979 $4826 €4200 La reine Marie Antoinette (4x3cm-2x1in) s. ivory oval pendant lock of hair exhib. 21-May-3 Piasa, Paris #278/R est:3000-4000

DESFRICHES, Aignan (1715-1800) French
Works on paper
£748 $1190 €1100 Paysage anime (18x26cm-7x10in) s. crayon. 24-Mar-3 Tajan, Paris #83

DESGOFFE, Alexandre (attrib) (1805-1885) French
£2162 $3373 €3200 Trophee militaire devant un portrait de gentilhomme dans un oeil de boeuf sculpte (107x69cm-42x27in) panel. 28-Mar-3 Delvaux, Paris #141/R est:4000

DESGOFFE, Blaise (1830-1901) French
£500 $835 €725 Life of a crystal jug and other artifacts in a gallery (44x34cm-17x13in) s. prov. 9-Jul-3 George Kidner, Lymington #169/R
£764 $1200 €1146 Casque Italian 16e Siecle (23x21cm-9x8in) s.d.1883 i.verso board. 22-Nov-2 Skinner, Boston #27/R est:600-800
£2070 $3250 €3105 Still life of ewer, plate of red raspberries and grapes (28x38cm-11x15in) s. panel. 23-Nov-2 Pook & Pook, Downington #341/R est:2000-2500
£7595 $12000 €11393 Silver mounted ivory tankard, a renaissance silver gilt mounted agate cup on a draped marble ledge (56x62cm-22x24in) s.d.1868 prov. 23-Apr-3 Christie's, Rockefeller NY #101/R est:15000-20000

DESHAIES, Jacques (1941-) French
£253 $395 €400 Baie du Rozel, La Hague (73x93cm-29x37in) s. i.d.1979 verso. 15-Sep-2 Etude Bailleul, Bayeux #156
£316 $500 €500 Dans mon atelier (163x114cm-64x45in) s.d.63 s.i.d.Juillet 63 verso. 27-Nov-2 Lemoine & Ferrando, Paris #87

DESHAYES, Charles Felix Edouard (1831-1895) French
£526 $853 €800 Hilly landscape with cattle (90x130cm-35x51in) s.d.1889. 21-Jan-3 Christie's, Amsterdam #64
£828 $1382 €1200 Bord de riviere (25x44cm-10x17in) s. panel. 8-Jul-3 Gioffredo, Nice #37/R
£1139 $1800 €1800 Chasseur et ses chiens en foret (32x42cm-13x17in) s. 1-Dec-2 Peron, Melun #3

DESHAYES, Eugène (1828-1890) French
£481 $755 €750 Ruines islamiques, Algerie (19x27cm-7x11in) s. 16-Dec-2 Gros & Delettrez, Paris #363
£1346 $2113 €2100 Femme et enfants marchant (27x100cm-11x39in) s. 20-Nov-2 Claude Boisgirard, Paris #34/R
£1410 $2214 €2200 Derniers rayons sur Biskra (55x45cm-22x18in) s. cardboard. 16-Dec-2 Gros & Delettrez, Paris #464 est:2300-3000
£1603 $2516 €2500 Scene de campement (31x55cm-12x22in) s.d.05 panel. 10-Dec-2 Tajan, Paris #142/R est:3300

DESHAYES, Frederic Léon (1883-1970) French
£318 $462 €500 Bouquet de pivoines et amarantes (81x60cm-32x24in) s. 31-May-2 Blanchet, Paris #38/R
£318 $462 €500 Atelier du peintre (55x47cm-22x19in) s. 31-May-2 Blanchet, Paris #54/R
£382 $554 €600 Entree du village (49x73cm-19x29in) s. 31-May-2 Blanchet, Paris #53/R
£446 $646 €700 Bouquet d'arum (81x60cm-32x24in) s. 31-May-2 Blanchet, Paris #39/R
£446 $646 €700 Regate (24x33cm-9x13in) s. cardboard. 31-May-2 Blanchet, Paris #47
£573 $831 €900 Village en Provence (60x81cm-24x32in) s. 31-May-2 Blanchet, Paris #51/R
£1019 $1478 €1600 Paysage cubiste (75x100cm-30x39in) s. 31-May-2 Blanchet, Paris #44
£4331 $6280 €6800 Nature morte aux pommes (27x41cm-11x16in) s. 31-May-2 Blanchet, Paris #46
Works on paper
£255 $369 €400 Quais de Paris (25x35cm-10x14in) s. ink W/C gouache. 31-May-2 Blanchet, Paris #52

DESI HUBER, Istvan (1895-1944) Hungarian
Works on paper
£671 $1046 €973 Trees (61x45cm-24x18in) s.d.936 chl. 13-Sep-2 Mu Terem Galeria, Budapest #195/R est:180000 (H.F 260000)

DESIDE, Ramon (1935-) Spanish
£387 $612 €600 Composition (80x65cm-31x26in) s. 17-Dec-2 Durán, Madrid #21/R
£497 $785 €775 Composition in grey (85x70cm-33x28in) s.d.94 board. 19-Nov-2 Durán, Madrid #115/R

DESIDERIO DA FIRENZE (studio) (16th C) Italian
Sculpture
£27097 $42813 €42000 Satyre (19cm-7in) black pat bronze lit. 18-Dec-2 Beaussant & Lefèvre, Paris #72/R est:10000-12000

DESILLAS, Stelios (1873-?) Greek
£1220 $2000 €1769 Still life with cherries in a glass bowl by a basket (44x68cm-17x27in) s. card prov. 4-Jun-3 Christie's, Rockefeller NY #255/R est:2500-3500

DESIRE, Henry (?) French?
£880 $1365 €1400 La lagune a Venise (35x45cm-14x18in) s. cardboard. 4-Oct-2 Tajan, Paris #64/R est:500-600

DESIRE-LUCAS, Louis-Marie (1869-1949) French
£481 $755 €750 Florence, Ponte Vecchio (15x14cm-6x6in) s. paper. 15-Dec-2 Thierry & Lannon, Brest #123
£486 $773 €700 Petite eglise en Bretagne (92x73cm-36x29in) s.d.1913. 29-Apr-3 Campo & Campo, Antwerp #80
£641 $1006 €1000 Eglise (19x22cm-7x9in) s. 15-Dec-2 Thierry & Lannon, Brest #31
£1090 $1711 €1700 Vue du Ponte Vecchio, Florence (54x65cm-21x26in) s.d.1899. 15-Dec-2 Mercier & Cie, Lille #416/R
£1188 $1900 €1782 Bridge (52x63cm-20x25in) s. 5-Jan-3 Galleria Y Remates, Montevideo #89/R
£1218 $1912 €1900 Ponts d'Espalion (38x45cm-15x18in) s. 15-Dec-2 Thierry & Lannon, Brest #122
£1410 $2214 €2200 Village breton au bord de fleuve (59x73cm-23x29in) 15-Dec-2 Mercier & Cie, Lille #414/R
£1458 $2377 €2100 Barques amarrees sur le quai, St Cado (32x40cm-13x16in) s. panel. 19-Jul-3 Thierry & Lannon, Brest #322 est:2200-2400
£1806 $2943 €2600 Le bourg de Locronan (38x46cm-15x18in) s. 19-Jul-3 Thierry & Lannon, Brest #115/R est:1800-2200
£2628 $4126 €4100 Cote rocheuse (54x65cm-21x26in) s. 15-Dec-2 Thierry & Lannon, Brest #121

DESMARQUAIS, C H (1823-?) French
£316 $480 €474 Woodland in autumn with figures (36x54cm-14x21in) s. 16-Aug-2 Lilla Bukowskis, Stockholm #149 (S.KR 4600)

DESMARQUAIS, Charles Hippolyte (1823-?) French
£823 $1300 €1235 Marshland landscape (28x46cm-11x18in) s. 16-Nov-2 New Orleans Auction, New Orleans #310/R

DESMOND, Maurice (?) ?
Works on paper
£1154 $1788 €1800 Earth rhythm (51x66cm-20x26in) s.d. chl acrylic W/C. 17-Jul-2 Woodwards, Cork #237

DESNOS, Ferdinand (1901-1958) French
£377 $585 €600 Le village (33x41cm-13x16in) s. 30-Oct-2 Artcurial Briest, Paris #378
£417 $663 €600 Le papillon (17x23cm-7x9in) s. isorel panel. 29-Apr-3 Artcurial Briest, Paris #263
£573 $894 €900 Portrait de jeune homme (41x33cm-16x13in) s.i. panel. 5-Nov-2 Tajan, Paris #38/R
£1905 $3029 €2800 Nu a la mouette (55x55cm-22x22in) s. 28-Feb-3 Joron-Derem, Paris #35/R
£4452 $6990 €6500 Portrait d'Andre Breton (36x26cm-14x10in) s. i.verso cardboard. 15-Apr-3 Laurence Calmels, Paris #4209/R
£6203 $9800 €9800 Biches dans la clairiere (97x146cm-38x57in) s. s.i.verso exhib. 27-Nov-2 Marc Kohn, Paris #49/R est:9000-10000
Works on paper
£483 $762 €700 Auto-portrait (49x38cm-19x15in) s. chl dr. 4-Apr-3 Tajan, Paris #3/R

DESNOS, Louise Adelaide (1807-?) French
£4085 $6576 €5800 Two children (75x61cm-30x24in) s.d.1848. 7-May-3 Michael Zeller, Lindau #673/R est:5800

DESNOYER, François (1894-1972) French
£382 $600 €573 Douarnenez bateaux a Quai, Brittany (44x62cm-17x24in) s. i.on stretcher prov. 24-Nov-2 Butterfields, San Francisco #2673/R
£629 $975 €1000 Fleurs (38x55cm-15x22in) s. 30-Oct-2 Artcurial Briest, Paris #358
£1026 $1610 €1600 Modele allonge a la robe bayadere (30x54cm-12x21in) s. 11-Dec-2 Maigret, Paris #110/R est:1000-1200
£1450 $2349 €2103 Plage de Magaluf (30x43cm-12x17in) s. board. 23-May-3 Dee Atkinson & Harrison, Driffield #656 est:1500-2000
£2000 $3340 €2900 Lagune (33x65cm-13x26in) s. 9-Jul-3 Millon & Associes, Paris #196/R est:2000-2500
£2908 $4856 €4100 Marine (33x55cm-13x22in) s. 23-Jun-3 Claude Boisgirard, Paris #106/R est:1200-1500
£3401 $5408 €5000 Village (46x65cm-18x26in) s. 3-Mar-3 Claude Boisgirard, Paris #43/R est:4500-5000
£6918 $10792 €11000 San Giorgio vu du quai de la Guidecca (60x92cm-24x36in) s.d.1962 prov.exhib. 10-Oct-2 Ribeyre & Baron, Paris #65/R est:4000-4500

DESORIA, Jean-Baptiste-François (1758-1832) French
£878 $1370 €1300 Jeune paysanne et sa fille (40x32cm-16x13in) s.d.1790 paper on canvas. 26-Mar-3 Tajan, Paris #75

DESORMEAUX, Jean Baptiste (attrib) (17/18th C) French
£2643 $3859 €3965 Young nobleman with umbrella. Young nobleman with dog (81x65cm-32x26in) pair. 17-Jun-2 Philippe Schuler, Zurich #4333/R est:2500-3000 (S.FR 6000)

DESOUTTER, Roger (1923-) British
£950 $1539 €1425 Moonlight and mist (61x91cm-24x36in) s. 21-May-3 Christie's, Kensington #675/R

D'ESPAGNAT, Georges (1870-1950) French
£704 $1155 €1021 Male nude study model (81x65cm-32x26in) s.d.98. 4-Jun-3 Fischer, Luzern #2069/R est:1200-1500 (S.FR 1500)
£1862 $2979 €2700 Maison dans un paysage (46x38cm-18x15in) init. 12-Mar-3 Libert, Castor, Paris #73 est:2000-2500
£2315 $3750 €3357 Nude with flowers (53x33cm-21x13in) init. 21-May-3 Doyle, New York #227/R est:6000-8000
£2767 $4262 €4400 Dormeuse (37x54cm-15x21in) mono. prov. 27-Oct-2 Muizon & Le Coent, Paris #53/R
£2885 $4529 €4500 Vue de Cagnes (24x34cm-9x13in) init. panel painted c.1906. 22-Nov-2 Millon & Associes, Paris #72/R
£3145 $4874 €5000 Paysage (55x73cm-22x29in) mono. exhib. 30-Oct-2 Artcurial Briest, Paris #300/R est:5000-6000
£3448 $5517 €5000 Femme au chapeau (39x31cm-15x12in) init. canvas on panel. 12-Mar-3 Libert, Castor, Paris #76 est:2000-2500
£3526 $5535 €5500 Bateaux sur la greve (38x45cm-15x18in) init. cardboard. 16-Dec-2 Millon & Associes, Paris #178/R est:1800-2300
£4194 $6626 €6500 Lecon de piano (33x24cm-13x9in) mono. 18-Dec-2 Ferri, Paris #50/R
£4483 $7172 €6500 Le tango (46x38cm-18x15in) init. 12-Mar-3 Libert, Castor, Paris #77 est:2500-3000
£4552 $7283 €6600 Mere et enfant dans un verger (46x55cm-18x22in) init. 12-Mar-3 Libert, Castor, Paris #79 est:6000-7000
£4690 $7503 €6800 Paysage (31x39cm-12x15in) init. panel. 12-Mar-3 Libert, Castor, Paris #78/R est:3000-3500
£5068 $7905 €7500 Bouquet de fleurs dans un interieur (73x60cm-29x24in) mono. 30-Mar-3 Anaf, Lyon #98/R
£5405 $8432 €8000 Paysage du Midi (26x35cm-10x14in) mono. panel. 25-Mar-3 Chochon-Barre & Allardi, Paris #104/R est:8000-8500
£6250 $10000 €9375 Study for enfants dans le parc - young boy with fancy yellow hat (36x25cm-14x10in) init. 11-Jan-3 James Julia, Fairfield #117 est:10000-20000
£7692 $12077 €12000 Madame D'Espagnat devant la mer (54x65cm-21x26in) mono. painted c.1922 lit. 11-Dec-2 Artcurial Briest, Paris #529/R est:13000
£7917 $12508 €11400 Vase de fleurs (81x65cm-32x26in) mono. 23-Apr-3 Rabourdin & Choppin de Janvry, Paris #38/R est:18000
£9864 $15684 €14500 Les bas noirs (65x55cm-26x22in) init. 26-Feb-3 Fraysse & Associes, Paris #17/R est:15000-18000
£11000 $16940 €16500 Musique a la campagne (46x38cm-18x15in) init. canvasboard painted c.1906. 22-Oct-2 Sotheby's, London #201/R est:8000-12000
£11043 $18000 €16565 Bouquets de fleurs sur un gueridon (81x65cm-32x26in) s. prov. 12-Feb-3 Sotheby's, New York #24/R est:20000-25000
£16139 $25500 €25500 Hamac (66x54cm-26x21in) init. painted 1906 prov. 27-Nov-2 Marc Kohn, Paris #16/R est:18000-22000
Works on paper
£516 $815 €800 Mme d'Espagnat et son fils (13x21cm-5x8in) W/C. 17-Dec-2 Gioffredo, Nice #2/R
£567 $948 €800 Nu vu de dos (29x19cm-11x7in) init. sanguine. 18-Jun-3 Charbonneaux, Paris #49
£612 $973 €900 Scene de port (22x30cm-9x12in) mono. W/C. 24-Mar-3 Coutau Begarie, Paris #184/R
£645 $1019 €1000 Petit garcon a la chemise rose (21x14cm-8x6in) mono. chl W/C. 18-Dec-2 Ferri, Paris #49/R
£774 $1223 €1200 Les voiliers (25x32cm-10x13in) W/C. 17-Dec-2 Gioffredo, Nice #3/R
£774 $1223 €1200 Voiliers a Concarneau (25x32cm-10x13in) W/C. 17-Dec-2 Gioffredo, Nice #4/R
£931 $1490 €1350 La ronde (19x23cm-7x9in) init. W/C graphite. 12-Mar-3 Libert, Castor, Paris #74 est:300-450
£1258 $2051 €1900 Les quais du port de Collioure (23x28cm-9x11in) mono. W/C. 2-Feb-3 Muizon & Le Coent, Paris #52

D'ESPAGNAT, Georges (attrib) (1870-1950) French
£976 $1600 €1464 Fresh picked flowers (28x18cm-11x7in) bears init. i.verso panel. 5-Feb-3 Doyle, New York #23/R est:800-1200

D'ESPARBES, Jean (1898-1968) French
£308 $483 €480 Noce au village (55x47cm-22x19in) s. 15-Dec-2 Lombrail & Teucquam, Paris #18/R
£714 $1136 €1050 To be or not to be (116x89cm-46x35in) s. 18-Mar-3 Vanderkindere, Brussels #58

DESPIAU, Charles (1874-1946) French
Sculpture
£13924 $21722 €22000 La bacchante (57x46x50cm-22x18x20in) s. num.3/5 verso black pat.bronze prov. 20-Oct-2 Claude Boisgirard, Paris #34/R est:22000-25000

DESPIERRE, Jacques (1912-1995) French
£377 $572 €580 Saumur castle on the Loire (30x30cm-12x12in) s. 6-Jul-2 Berlinghof, Heidelberg #199/R
£483 $806 €700 Les baigneurs (64x81cm-25x32in) s. 9-Jul-3 Millon & Associes, Paris #211

DESPORTES, Alexandre-François (1661-1743) French
£65000 $108550 €94250 Plums in a basket ans apricots in a blue and white bowl, and other fruits, partridge on marble shelf (74x92cm-29x36in) panel. 9-Jul-3 Christie's, London #65/R est:15000-25000
£92593 $150000 €138890 Still life with game, a dog, cat and a hare on a table decorated with a bas relief (100x130cm-39x51in) s.d.1730 prov.exhib.lit. 23-Jan-3 Sotheby's, New York #96/R est:150000-200000
Works on paper
£1000 $1570 €1500 Studies of dogs (15x18cm-6x7in) black chk htd white double-sided. 11-Dec-2 Sotheby's, Olympia #188/R est:600-800

DESPORTES, Alexandre-François (attrib) (1661-1743) French
£5380 $8392 €8500 Oiseaux sur fond de paysage (67x72cm-26x28in) 18-Oct-2 Rabourdin & Choppin de Janvry, Paris #128/R
£16129 $25484 €25000 Nature morte au paanier de raisins, abricots et perdrix (96x131cm-38x52in) prov. 18-Dec-2 Tajan, Paris #51/R est:15000

D'ESPOSITO (19/20th C) ?
Works on paper
£400 $632 €600 Sailing boats with steam funnel off the coast (31x48cm-12x19in) s.d.1890 W/C. 18-Dec-2 John Nicholson, Haslemere #1129

D'ESPOSITO, G (19/20th C) ?
Works on paper
£900 $1431 €1350 Steamship (30x48cm-12x19in) i.verso W/C bodycol. 6-Mar-3 Christie's, Kensington #501/R

DESPOULAIN, Jean Claude (1945-) French
Sculpture
£1007 $1621 €1500 Marmotte (18cm-7in) st.f.Royaume num.5/8 brown pat bronze. 23-Feb-3 Mercier & Cie, Lille #182/R
£1282 $1987 €2000 Hermine (21x29x11cm-8x11x4in) s. num.2/8 brown red pat bronze. 7-Dec-2 Martinot & Savignat, Pontoise #131
£1667 $2583 €2600 Hippopotame (12x17x7cm-5x7x3in) s. num.1/8 brown red pat bronze. 7-Dec-2 Martinot & Savignat, Pontoise #132/R

DESPREY, A (?) French?
£304 $474 €450 Bateaux a quai (54x65cm-21x26in) s.d.60. 26-Mar-3 Millon & Associes, Paris #106/R

DESPREZ, Louis Jean (1743-1804) French
Works on paper
£3299 $5411 €4784 Alexandria's foundations (63x98cm-25x39in) W/C line-etching prov. 4-Jun-3 AB Stockholms Auktionsverk #2136/R est:25000-30000 (S.KR 42000)
£5886 $9300 €9300 Scene de combat antique (45x71cm-18x28in) pen W/C prov. 29-Nov-2 Claude Boisgirard, Paris #12/R
£10811 $16865 €16000 Cortege des antiquites d'Hercolanum (21x36cm-8x14in) i. W/C pen ink. 26-Mar-3 Piasa, Paris #48/R
£16543 $23491 €26800 Projet de monument a la gloire d'un prince (56x38cm-22x15in) pen ink over crayon. 17-Mar-2 Galerie de Chartres, Chartres #31

DESPREZ, Louis Jean (attrib) (1743-1804) French
Works on paper
£1793 $2869 €2600 Parade militaire (21x36cm-8x14in) ink dr W/C. 14-Mar-3 Libert, Castor, Paris #19/R

DESPUJOLS, Jean (1886-1965) French
£1013 $1600 €1520 Landscape (53x74cm-21x29in) s. 5-Apr-3 Neal Auction Company, New Orleans #337/R
Works on paper
£892 $1391 €1400 Pique-nique interrompu (39x50cm-15x20in) graphite dr. 10-Nov-2 Eric Pillon, Calais #61/R

DESRAIS, Claude Louis (1746-1816) French
Works on paper
£541 $843 €800 Pensionnaires (20x29cm-8x11in) pen ink wash over sanguine. 26-Mar-3 Piasa, Paris #56
£603 $1007 €850 Frise de putti (6x14cm-2x6in) s.d.1774 pen brown ink brown wash gouache prov. 19-Jun-3 Piasa, Paris #90
£1014 $1581 €1500 Scenes galantes (18x12cm-7x5in) pen ink W/C set of 5. 26-Mar-3 Piasa, Paris #53/R

DESROSIERS, Jean Guy (1934-) Canadian
£201 $317 €302 Fleurs des poires et du vin (51x41cm-20x16in) 1-Dec-2 Levis, Calgary #21/R (C.D 500)
£337 $553 €506 L'enjeux est de taille (61x76cm-24x30in) s. i.verso board. 6-Feb-3 Heffel, Vancouver #012/R (C.D 850)

DESSAIN, Emile Francois (1808-1882) French
£574 $930 €832 Salesmen with their wares, South of France (21x17cm-8x7in) s. pair. 26-May-3 Rasmussen, Copenhagen #1536/R (D.KR 6000)

DESSAIN, Emile Francois (attrib) (1808-1882) French
£578 $919 €850 Scene galante dans un parc (24x38cm-9x15in) 18-Mar-3 Vanderkindere, Brussels #52

DESSAR, Louis Paul (1867-1952) American
£641 $1000 €962 Evening on the lake (36x25cm-14x10in) s. 9-Nov-2 Sloan, North Bethesda #613/R
£964 $1600 €1398 Shepherdess with sheep (30x41cm-12x16in) 13-Jun-3 Du Mouchelle, Detroit #2224/R est:800-1000
£20645 $32000 €30968 Departure of the fishermen in the early morning (161x205cm-63x81in) s.d.1891 prov.exhib. 3-Dec-2 Phillips, New York #45/R est:25000-45000

DESSERPRIT, Roger (1923-1985) French
£316 $494 €500 Composition (38x52cm-15x20in) s.d.1948 panel. 20-Oct-2 Charbonneaux, Paris #123 est:500-600
£340 $541 €500 Composition (75x107cm-30x42in) s.d.1972 card on canvas. 1-Mar-3 Meeting Art, Vercelli #633
£477 $777 €720 Composition (54x64cm-21x25in) s.d.1948 panel. 3-Feb-3 Cornette de St.Cyr, Paris #405
£497 $810 €750 Composition (38x53cm-15x21in) s. panel painted 1948. 3-Feb-3 Cornette de St.Cyr, Paris #406
£621 $1037 €900 Composition (37x52cm-15x20in) s.d. panel. 9-Jul-3 Cornette de St.Cyr, Paris #273
£759 $1185 €1200 Composition (146x98cm-57x39in) s.d.1971. 20-Oct-2 Charbonneaux, Paris #119 est:1200-1500
Works on paper
£3901 $6514 €5500 Composition a fond jaune (129x89cm-51x35in) s.d.64 mixed media panel. 18-Jun-3 Charbonneaux, Paris #82/R est:5000-6000

DESSI, Gianni (1955-) Italian
£1046 $1673 €1600 Untitled (41x41cm-16x16in) s.d.1991 verso panel. 4-Jan-3 Meeting Art, Vercelli #347
£1667 $2617 €2600 Face (80x70cm-31x28in) s.d.1983 verso. 21-Nov-2 Finarte, Rome #274
£1750 $2765 €2730 Treshold (67x72cm-26x28in) painted 1980. 12-Nov-2 Babuino, Rome #328/R

DESSONS, Pierre (1936-) French
Works on paper
£288 $460 €400 Maternite (56x76cm-22x30in) s. W/C gouache. 18-May-3 Neret-Minet, Paris #154
£561 $898 €780 Le pied de nez (60x73cm-24x29in) s. mixed media canvas. 18-May-3 Neret-Minet, Paris #113/R

D'ESTIENNE, Henri (1872-1949) French
£446 $696 €700 Source (27x35cm-11x14in) s. panel. 7-Nov-2 Chochon-Barre & Allardi, Paris #140/R
£845 $1361 €1200 Sortie de messe en Bretagne (25x23cm-10x9in) s. 11-May-3 Thierry & Lannon, Brest #177
£2703 $4216 €4000 Jeune femme bercant son enfant (69x81cm-27x32in) s. 28-Mar-3 Charbonneaux, Paris #72/R
£4528 $6974 €7200 Portrait de jeune fille nue au voile (50x34cm-20x13in) s. panels. 23-Oct-2 Rabourdin & Choppin de Janvry, Paris #100

Works on paper
£324 $506 €480 Bohemienne (49x24cm-19x9in) s. col crayon. 27-Mar-3 Maigret, Paris #146

DESTOUCHES, Johanna von (1869-1956) German
£1146 $1789 €1800 White roses in vase (73x92cm-29x36in) s. 6-Nov-2 Hugo Ruef, Munich #1059/R est:800

DESTREE, Johannes Josephus (1827-1888) Belgian
£915 $1474 €1300 Woman doing laundry and tramp at outskirts of a village (39x60cm-15x24in) s.d.1888. 12-May-3 Bernaerts, Antwerp #27/R

DESUBLEO, Michele (1601-1676) Flemish
£13514 $21081 €20000 Death of Cleopatra (97x123cm-38x48in) canvas on panel prov. 27-Mar-3 Dorotheum, Vienna #19/R est:20000-30000

DESVARREUX, Raymond (1876-1963) French
£2885 $4558 €4500 Depart en campagne (46x38cm-18x15in) s. 17-Nov-2 Osenat, Fontainebleau #225 est:4000
Works on paper
£602 $969 €903 Napoleon and his troops (14x30cm-6x12in) s. gouache horn. 7-May-3 Dobiaschofsky, Bern #440/R (S.FR 1300)

DESVARREUX-LARPENTEUR, James (1847-1937) American
£864 $1400 €1296 Tending the flock (20x33cm-8x13in) s. 24-Jan-3 New Orleans Auction, New Orleans #177/R est:1000-1500

DESVIGNES, Gabrielle Marie Therese (attrib) (19th C) French
£363 $573 €545 Untitled, girl dressing up a dog (25x22cm-10x9in) 7-Apr-3 Shapiro, Sydney #535 (A.D 950)

DETAILLE, Edouard (1848-1912) French
£377 $581 €600 Study for soldiers' heads (22x30cm-9x12in) prov.lit. 28-Oct-2 Il Ponte, Milan #253
£2885 $4471 €4500 Soldat russe (67x21cm-26x8in) on tin. 4-Dec-2 Libert, Castor, Paris #66/R
£3226 $5000 €4839 Infantry in snow (36x43cm-14x17in) s. 7-Dec-2 South Bay, Long Island #131/R
£9797 $15284 €14500 Carabinier a cheval (55x41cm-22x16in) s.d.1880. 28-Mar-3 Neret-Minet, Paris #8/R
£18868 $29434 €30000 Hussard a cheval (66x55cm-26x22in) mono. st.sig.verso. 8-Oct-2 Christie's, Paris #49/R est:18000
£22152 $35000 €33228 Skirmish between Cossacks and the Imperial bodyguard, 1814 (100x81cm-39x32in) s.d.1870 prov.exhib.lit. 23-Apr-3 Christie's, Rockefeller NY #28/R est:30000-40000
£54000 $84780 €81000 Napoleon (194x107cm-76x42in) s.d.1908. 19-Nov-2 Sotheby's, London #201/R est:15000-20000
Works on paper
£324 $506 €480 Campagne de Medeah (20x26cm-8x10in) pen ink wash over crayon. 28-Mar-3 Delvaux, Paris #116
£417 $650 €626 Soldiers with horse (15x20cm-6x8in) s.d.1887 W/C. 30-Mar-3 Susanin's, Chicago #6069/R
£545 $850 €818 Soldier (33x20cm-13x8in) s.d.1899 W/C. 30-Mar-3 Susanin's, Chicago #6068/R
£2000 $3240 €3000 French cavalry on horseback (34x26cm-13x10in) s.d.1900 pencil W/C htd bodycol. 23-Jan-3 Christie's, Kensington #353/R est:1200-1800

DETHLEFFS-EDELMANN, Fridel (1899-?) German
£321 $497 €500 View from my studio window (32x40cm-13x16in) s.i.d.1950 board. 6-Dec-2 Michael Zeller, Lindau #740/R
£1763 $2732 €2750 Winter in Allgau, landscape near Isny (75x99cm-30x39in) s.d.1942 i. verso. 6-Dec-2 Michael Zeller, Lindau #743/R est:2500

DETMOLD, Edward Julian (1883-1957) British
Works on paper
£280 $434 €420 Phoenix (23x13cm-9x5in) mono. sepia pen ink W/C wash. 24-Sep-2 Bonhams, New Bond Street #16/R

DETMOLD, Henry E (1854-1924) British
£800 $1248 €1200 Seaweed gatherer (61x87cm-24x34in) s. 8-Oct-2 Bonhams, Knightsbridge #138/R

DETROY, Léon (1857-1955) French
£321 $503 €500 Nature morte a la coupe de fruits (46x38cm-18x15in) s. 16-Dec-2 Rabourdin & Choppin de Janvry, Paris #2/R
£705 $1107 €1100 Nature morte aux fruits (38x55cm-15x22in) s. 16-Dec-2 Rabourdin & Choppin de Janvry, Paris #1/R
£769 $1208 €1200 Village sous la neige (74x50cm-29x20in) s. 16-Dec-2 Rabourdin & Choppin de Janvry, Paris #4/R
£833 $1308 €1300 Rochers a Camaret (50x61cm-20x24in) s. 16-Dec-2 Rabourdin & Choppin de Janvry, Paris #7/R
£884 $1406 €1300 Bouquet de lilas au vase orange (74x100cm-29x39in) s. cardboard. 26-Feb-3 Fraysse & Associes, Paris #16
£962 $1510 €1500 Paysage du Midi (57x74cm-22x29in) s. 16-Dec-2 Rabourdin & Choppin de Janvry, Paris #29/R
£1060 $1727 €1600 Paysage au torrent et aux rochers (72x92cm-28x36in) s. 31-Jan-3 Rabourdin & Choppin de Janvry, Paris #66/R
£1090 $1711 €1700 Village pres de la riviere (91x72cm-36x28in) s. 16-Dec-2 Rabourdin & Choppin de Janvry, Paris #38/R
£1126 $1835 €1700 Hameau dans la vallee (75x100cm-30x39in) s. cardboard. 31-Jan-3 Rabourdin & Choppin de Janvry, Paris #65/R
£1126 $1835 €1700 Village sous la neige (65x97cm-26x38in) s. 31-Jan-3 Rabourdin & Choppin de Janvry, Paris #63/R
£1268 $2104 €1800 Partie de peche (25x33cm-10x13in) s. 11-Jun-3 Beaussant & Lefèvre, Paris #29/R est:1500-2000
£1325 $2159 €2000 Paysage au torrent (54x73cm-21x29in) s. 31-Jan-3 Rabourdin & Choppin de Janvry, Paris #62/R
£1391 $2267 €2100 Paysage enneige (73x92cm-29x36in) s. 31-Jan-3 Rabourdin & Choppin de Janvry, Paris #64/R
£1709 $2666 €2700 Paysage de riviere aux grands arbres (73x73cm-29x29in) s. 18-Oct-2 Rabourdin & Choppin de Janvry, Paris #4/R
£1899 $2962 €3000 Marine (34x57cm-13x22in) s. 18-Oct-2 Rabourdin & Choppin de Janvry, Paris #6/R
£1899 $2962 €3000 Mediterranee, pecheur remontant l'ancre (82x118cm-32x46in) s. 16-Oct-2 Fraysse & Associes, Paris #42 est:4000-5000
£2051 $3221 €3200 Riviere ombragee (60x73cm-24x29in) s. 16-Dec-2 Rabourdin & Choppin de Janvry, Paris #30/R
£2308 $3623 €3600 Paysage lacustre (68x92cm-27x36in) s. 16-Dec-2 Rabourdin & Choppin de Janvry, Paris #47/R
£2436 $3824 €3800 Village sous la neige (86x110cm-34x43in) s. 16-Dec-2 Rabourdin & Choppin de Janvry, Paris #39/R
£2848 $4443 €4500 Paysage fluvial (60x73cm-24x29in) s. prov. 18-Oct-2 Rabourdin & Choppin de Janvry, Paris #5/R
£3145 $5000 €4718 Ville au Maroc (47x66cm-19x26in) s. oil over pencil prov. 27-Feb-3 Christie's, Rockefeller NY #102/R est:7000
Works on paper
£903 $1427 €1400 Profil feminin (32x40cm-13x16in) s. black pencil. 17-Dec-2 Rossini, Paris #21
£1241 $1986 €1800 Marocaines dans leur interieur (47x62cm-19x24in) s. chl pastel. 12-Mar-3 E & Eve, Paris #92 est:500-800
£1392 $2172 €2200 Fillette au grenouilles, portrait de Mademoiselle Osterling (64x53cm-25x21in) s. pastel prov. 16-Oct-2 Fraysse & Associes, Paris #46 est:1500-1800

DETTHOW, Eric (1888-1952) Swedish
£295 $465 €443 Southern scene (52x61cm-20x24in) s. 30-Nov-2 Goteborg Auktionsverk, Sweden #139/R (S.KR 4200)
£1390 $2238 €2085 Parisian woman (46x37cm-18x15in) s.d.1931 exhib. 7-May-3 AB Stockholms Auktionsverk #674/R est:10000-12000 (S.KR 18000)
£2242 $3498 €3363 Nature morte (38x61cm-15x24in) s.d.1921. 5-Nov-2 Bukowskis, Stockholm #199/R est:30000-40000 (S.KR 32000)

DETTI, Cesare Auguste (1847-1914) Italian
£5484 $8500 €8226 Secret correspondence (67x56cm-26x22in) s. 2-Oct-2 Christie's, Rockefeller NY #780/R est:8000-12000
£174194 $270000 €261291 Musical interlude (98x152cm-39x60in) s.d.80. 30-Oct-2 Christie's, Rockefeller NY #83/R est:180000-250000
Works on paper
£1524 $2500 €2286 Kiss at the gate (43x61cm-17x24in) s. W/C. 9-Feb-3 William Jenack, New York #291 est:3000-4000

DETTMANN, Ludwig Julius Christian (1865-1944) German
£1379 $2179 €2000 Ducks in orchard (32x34cm-13x13in) s.d.94. 5-Apr-3 Hans Stahl, Hamburg #95/R est:2200

DETWILLER, Frederick (1882-1953) American
£395 $600 €593 Steamboat at wharf (79x132cm-31x52in) s. exhib. 17-Aug-2 North East Auctions, Portsmouth #560/R

DEUEL, Austin (1939-) American
Works on paper
£1006 $1600 €1509 Pursuers (36x102cm-14x40in) s. W/C pencil on board prov. 4-Mar-3 Christie's, Rockefeller NY #90/R est:2000-3000

DEULLY, Eugène Auguste Francois (1860-?) French
£611 $954 €917 Venice at night (30x37cm-12x15in) s. board. 6-Nov-2 Dobiaschofsky, Bern #446/R (S.FR 1400)
£137931 $220690 €200000 Berger et son troupeau (60x81cm-24x32in) s. 13-Mar-3 Artcurial Briest, Paris #56/R

DEURS, Caroline van (1860-1932) Danish
£1021 $1614 €1532 Grandmother's spinning wheel (53x38cm-21x15in) mono.d.1913. 2-Dec-2 Rasmussen, Copenhagen #1306/R est:8000-10000 (D.KR 12000)

DEUSS, Hans (1948-) Dutch
£758 $1206 €1100 Levenslijn (55x70cm-22x28in) s.d.81. 10-Mar-3 Sotheby's, Amsterdam #307 est:1300-1500

DEUTERS, Janet (attrib) (1940-) British?
£323 $500 €485 Interior with muffin stand over looking Brompton Oratory (91x71cm-36x28in) 28-Sep-2 Charlton Hall, Columbia #156/R

DEUTMANN, Frans (1867-1915) Dutch
£329 $533 €500 Sisters strolling (28x20cm-11x8in) s. 21-Jan-3 Christie's, Amsterdam #144

DEUTSCH, Boris (1892-1978) American
£224 $375 €325 Portrait of an old man (71x56cm-28x22in) s.d.1962. 29-Jun-3 Butterfields, Los Angeles #7095/R
£352 $550 €528 Reading the Torah (48x65cm-19x26in) s.d.1959 board. 13-Apr-3 Butterfields, Los Angeles #7110

DEUTSCH, Eileen Rita (20th C) American
Works on paper
£318 $500 €477 Coastal inlet, Eureka (12x14cm-5x6in) s. pastel board prov. 19-Nov-2 Wright, Chicago #307/R

DEUTSCH, Hans Emile (1927-) ?
£1048 $1635 €1572 Sailing boats by shore (53x75cm-21x30in) s.d.71. 6-Nov-2 Hans Widmer, St Gallen #2/R est:1000-2000 (S.FR 2400)

DEUTSCH, Ludwig (1855-1935) French
Works on paper
£1122 $1705 €1750 Oriental scene (27x18cm-11x7in) s. W/C painted 1896. 28-Aug-2 Castellana, Madrid #4/R

DEUTSCHMANN, Joseph (1717-1787) German
Sculpture
£2273 $3386 €3500 Angel head (34x45cm-13x18in) gilded wood lit. 26-Jun-2 Neumeister, Munich #30/R est:750

DEUX, Fred (1924-) French
Works on paper
£476 $757 €700 Viatique (32x25cm-13x10in) s.i.d.1993 graphite col crayon. 26-Feb-3 Artcurial Briest, Paris #519
£510 $811 €750 Untitled (41x30cm-16x12in) s.d.1966 graphite exhib. 24-Mar-3 Claude Boisgirard, Paris #95
£578 $919 €850 Les trois voiles du dehors (26x33cm-10x13in) s.i.d.1993 graphite col crayon. 26-Feb-3 Artcurial Briest, Paris #517
£612 $973 €900 Dostoeivski (57x37cm-22x15in) s.i. graphite col crayon. 26-Feb-3 Artcurial Briest, Paris #518
£646 $1028 €950 Les perdants (57x38cm-22x15in) s.i.d.1995 graphite col crayon. 26-Feb-3 Artcurial Briest, Paris #516

DEVAMBEZ, Andre (1867-1943) French
£780 $1264 €1100 Ulysse et le cyclope (46x55cm-18x22in) s. 23-May-3 Camard, Paris #23
£1013 $1580 €1600 Une ruelle (12x17cm-5x7in) s. cardboard. 16-Oct-2 Hotel des Ventes Mosan, Brussels #182 est:1000-1200
£1543 $2191 €2500 Enfant dans le parc (16x22cm-6x9in) s. 16-Mar-3 Eric Pillon, Calais #152/R
£1728 $2454 €2800 Lecture au jeune malade (30x33cm-12x13in) s. 16-Mar-3 Eric Pillon, Calais #153/R
£2564 $4026 €4000 Le bouge du Papagallo (22x28cm-9x11in) s. cardboard. 16-Dec-2 Millon & Associes, Paris #175 est:1800-2500
Works on paper
£1700 $2822 €1700 L'orchestre (25x20cm-10x8in) s. mixed media. 16-Jun-3 Horta, Bruxelles #228 est:1500-2000

DEVAS, Anthony (1911-1958) British
£400 $624 €600 Portrait of a lady (81x61cm-32x24in) s.d.40. 27-Mar-3 Christie's, Kensington #403/R

DEVAUD, Patrick (1954-) French
£544 $865 €800 Nature morte aux abricots et aux cerises (24x33cm-9x13in) s. 24-Mar-3 Coutau Begarie, Paris #307/R

DEVAULX, François Theodore (1808-1870) French
Sculpture
£1200 $1848 €1800 Sleeping bacchante (41x26cm-16x10in) s. bronze. 28-Oct-2 Sotheby's, Olympia #3/R est:1200-1800

DEVE, Eugène (1826-1867) French
£1299 $1896 €2000 La ramasseuse de fagots dans la clairiere (60x73cm-24x29in) s. 11-Jun-2 Thierry & Lannon, Brest #108/R est:1000-1500

DEVENTER, Jan Frederik van (1822-1886) Dutch
£5313 $8500 €7970 Farmyard scene with cows in the foreground (53x89cm-21x35in) s. 14-May-3 Butterfields, San Francisco #1062/R est:3000-5000

DEVENTER, Willem Anthonie van (1824-1893) Dutch
£1736 $2865 €2500 Tending to the rigging in an extensive river landscape (34x46cm-13x18in) s. paper on panel. 1-Jul-3 Christie's, Amsterdam #2 est:1500-2000
Works on paper
£278 $458 €400 Looking out to sea from the fortress (35x58cm-14x23in) s.d.22/25 pencil W/C. 1-Jul-3 Christie's, Amsterdam #32

DEVENYNS, Steve (1953-) American
£4795 $7000 €7193 Yellowstone straggler (61x107cm-24x42in) 18-May-2 Altermann Galleries, Santa Fe #155/R

DEVERELL, Walter Howell (1827-1854) British
£540000 $869400 €810000 Twelfth night (102x132cm-40x52in) prov.exhib.lit. 19-Feb-3 Christie's, London #36/R est:800000-1200000

DEVERIA, Achille (1800-1857) French
Works on paper
£475 $750 €750 Raphael et la Fornarina (21x17cm-8x7in) s.d.1825 crayon wash gouache. 28-Nov-2 Tajan, Paris #130
£2128 $3553 €3000 Portrait presume de la famille de Victor Hugo pendant une promenade (25x32cm-10x13in) s. W/C prov.exhib. 19-Jun-3 Piasa, Paris #152/R est:3000

DEVERIA, Eugène (1808-1865) French
£1538 $2385 €2400 Portrait (65x54cm-26x21in) s.d.1838. 9-Dec-2 Thierry & Lannon, Brest #226
Works on paper
£451 $700 €677 Milk seller (39x31cm-15x12in) s.d.1835 W/C prov. 29-Oct-2 Sotheby's, New York #36/R
£645 $1000 €968 Three figures conversing (26x35cm-10x14in) s. W/C prov. 29-Oct-2 Sotheby's, New York #35/R est:600-800

DEVETTA, Edoardo (1912-1993) Italian
£1282 $1987 €2000 Still life of flowers, fruit and painting (94x67cm-37x26in) s. 5-Dec-2 Stadion, Trieste #688

DEVILLE, Jean (1872-?) French
£3077 $4769 €4800 Landscape with cypresses (50x51cm-20x20in) s. cardboard prov.lit. 3-Dec-2 Christie's, Amsterdam #44/R est:4000-6000

DEVILLE, Joseph Henri (1803-1857) Swiss
Works on paper
£306 $477 €459 Two girls doing a swap (24x29cm-9x11in) s. W/C. 20-Nov-2 Fischer, Luzern #2456/R (S.FR 700)

DEVILLE-CHABROLLE, Marie Paule (1952-) French
Sculpture
£4403 $6824 €7000 Baiser (60x45x25cm-24x18x10in) num.3/8 blue pat bronze Cast Deval. 30-Oct-2 Coutau Begarie, Paris #132/R est:8000-9000

DEVIS, Anthony (1729-1817) British
Works on paper
£450 $711 €653 Fisherman in a romantic landscape (24x37cm-9x15in) s. W/C. 22-Jul-3 Bonhams, Knightsbridge #92/R
£800 $1248 €1200 Hornby Castle, near Lancaster (25x38cm-10x15in) pen ink monochrome wash. 6-Nov-2 Bonhams, Chester #335
£1900 $3116 €2755 Extensive landscape, Gloucestershire. probably Wooton-under-edge (26x38cm-10x15in) pencil pen ink W/C prov. 5-Jun-3 Christie's, London #86/R est:1500-2000

DEVIS, Anthony (attrib) (1729-1817) British
£1200 $1872 €1800 Portrait of Henry St Paul (76x62cm-30x24in) 9-Oct-2 Woolley & Wallis, Salisbury #273/R est:1000-1500

DEVIS, Arthur (1711-1787) British
£8000 $13280 €12000 Portrait of Anthony Devis (12x9cm-5x4in) i. canvas on panel oval prov.lit. 12-Jun-3 Sotheby's, London #82/R est:8000-12000

DEVIS, Arthur (attrib) (1711-1787) British
Works on paper
£260 $424 €390 Figures in open landscape (13x20cm-5x8in) pen ink wash dr. 14-Feb-3 Keys, Aylsham #473

DEVIS, Arthur William (1763-1822) British
£1800 $2826 €2700 Portrait of Henry Heneage St. Paul, M P for Berwick (76x63cm-30x25in) lit. 10-Dec-2 Bonhams, New Bond Street #237/R est:2000-3000
£30000 $47400 €45000 Portrait of a lady said to be Emily Shalespear, seated beneath a tree (91x71cm-36x28in) 13-Nov-2 Halls, Shrewsbury #413/R est:8000-12000

DEVIS, Arthur William (attrib) (1763-1822) British
£6500 $10270 €9750 Portrait of gentleman holding hat and cane (75x63cm-30x25in) 26-Nov-2 Christie's, London #33/R est:5000-8000

DEVOLL, Frederick Usher (1873-1941) American
£1026 $1600 €1539 Providence Rhode Island in the snow (36x25cm-14x10in) s. stretcher. 21-Sep-2 Nadeau, Windsor #63/R est:2000-3000
£1563 $2500 €2266 Potter's Dock, Noank, CT (41x51cm-16x20in) s. 17-May-3 CRN Auctions, Cambridge #55

DEVOOGHT, Robertine (1904-1979) Belgian
£346 $536 €550 Still life (65x75cm-26x30in) s. 5-Oct-2 De Vuyst, Lokeren #103

DEVOS, Albert (1868-1950) Belgian
£563 $907 €800 Fishermen with sloop in stormy seas (90x120cm-35x47in) s. 12-May-3 Bernaerts, Antwerp #622/R
£805 $1297 €1200 Moored yachts in French port (70x110cm-28x43in) s. 24-Feb-3 Bernaerts, Antwerp #768/R
£972 $1546 €1400 Marine impressionniste (70x90cm-28x35in) s. 29-Apr-3 Campo & Campo, Antwerp #91

DEVOS, Léon (1897-1974) Belgian
£284 $474 €400 Portrait d'enfant (40x30cm-16x12in) s. 18-Jun-3 Hotel des Ventes Mosan, Brussels #255
£313 $497 €450 Harengs (32x40cm-13x16in) s. panel. 29-Apr-3 Campo & Campo, Antwerp #92
£380 $600 €600 Bouquet de fleurs (41x34cm-16x13in) s. 26-Nov-2 Palais de Beaux Arts, Brussels #315/R
£481 $755 €750 Nature morte aux poissons (69x82cm-27x32in) s. i.verso. 11-Dec-2 Hotel des Ventes Mosan, Brussels #285
£573 $894 €900 Nature morte au gres de Raeren (48x38cm-19x15in) s. 11-Nov-2 Horta, Bruxelles #520
£651 $1022 €950 Dunes (65x80cm-26x31in) s. panel. 15-Apr-3 Galerie Moderne, Brussels #401/R
£685 $1075 €1000 Cavaliers sur la plage (33x60cm-13x24in) s. panel. 15-Apr-3 Galerie Moderne, Brussels #335/R
£753 $1183 €1100 Nu dans un jardin (65x50cm-26x20in) s. panel. 15-Apr-3 Galerie Moderne, Brussels #398/R
£897 $1434 €1300 Bateaux de peche dans un estuaire (50x60cm-20x24in) s. 17-Mar-3 Horta, Bruxelles #77
£1076 $1700 €1700 Regates a Menton (53x68cm-21x27in) s. cardboard. 26-Nov-2 Palais de Beaux Arts, Brussels #314/R est:1500-2000
£1392 $2172 €2200 Sieste au jardin (65x50cm-26x20in) s. 16-Sep-2 Horta, Bruxelles #45
£1918 $3011 €2800 Nu dans un interieur (93x70cm-37x28in) s. 15-Apr-3 Galerie Moderne, Brussels #366/R est:2000-2500
£1987 $3238 €3000 Dernier voyage en hiver (51x55cm-20x22in) s.d.23 panel. 17-Feb-3 Horta, Bruxelles #159
£2353 $3788 €3600 La baie de St Tropez (65x80cm-26x31in) s. 20-Jan-3 Horta, Bruxelles #230/R est:3000-4000
£4317 $6906 €6000 Nude seated (130x81cm-51x32in) s. 17-May-3 De Vuyst, Lokeren #569/R est:5000-6000
£6962 $10861 €11000 Two standing nudes (130x80cm-51x31in) s. 21-Oct-2 Bernaerts, Antwerp #574/R est:5000-6000

DEVRIENT, Charles (19th C) French
£303 $467 €455 Aristocratic gentleman drinking wine in interior (43x38cm-17x15in) s. 27-Oct-2 Anders Antik, Landskrona #81/R (S.KR 4400)

DEWASNE, Jean (1921-1999) French
£2051 $3179 €3200 Ladyrinth (50x65cm-20x26in) s.d.1952 s.i.on stretcher. 3-Dec-2 Christie's, Amsterdam #280/R est:2000-3000
£2152 $3400 €3400 Les astres (49x65cm-19x26in) s. panel. 26-Nov-2 Palais de Beaux Arts, Brussels #271/R est:3000-4000
£2323 $3671 €3485 Composition (50x82cm-20x32in) masonite painted c.1962 prov. 1-Apr-3 Rasmussen, Copenhagen #190/R est:20000-25000 (D.KR 25000)
£3810 $6020 €5715 Peinture murale (65x91cm-26x36in) s.d.48 exhib. 1-Apr-3 Rasmussen, Copenhagen #184/R est:30000 (D.KR 41000)
£4205 $6686 €6308 Jeux de pure (37x67cm-15x26in) s.d.1949 verso plywood exhib.prov. 26-Feb-3 Kunsthallen, Copenhagen #6/R est:30000 (D.KR 46000)
Works on paper
£1239 $2070 €1797 Concrete composition (50x35cm-20x14in) s.d.1953 gouache. 17-Jun-3 Rasmussen, Copenhagen #20/R est:10000-15000 (D.KR 13000)

DEWEHRT, Friedrich (1808-?) German
£1164 $1816 €1700 Children playing (56x44cm-22x17in) s.d.1850 board. 10-Apr-3 Dorotheum, Vienna #161/R est:3000-3500

DEWEY, David (1946-) American
Works on paper
£1720 $2700 €2580 Pemaquid point lighthouse, New Harbor, Maine (72x102cm-28x40in) s.d.84 W/C. 22-Nov-2 Skinner, Boston #379/R est:3000-5000

DEWHURST, Wynford (1864-1941) British
£1350 $2174 €2025 May tree (74x61cm-29x24in) s. 18-Feb-3 Bonhams, Knightsbridge #180/R est:600-800
£3200 $5280 €4640 Apple blossom before a cottage (93x72cm-37x28in) s. 3-Jul-3 Christie's, Kensington #452/R est:1500-2500
Works on paper
£400 $636 €600 Foothills of the Alps (24x34cm-9x13in) s.d.1922 pastel. 27-Feb-3 Bonhams, Chester #435
£500 $825 €725 Couple fishing (30x48cm-12x19in) s. pastel. 3-Jul-3 Christie's, Kensington #288/R

DEWING, Thomas W (1851-1938) American
£2000000 $3100000 €3000000 Song (67x86cm-26x34in) s.d.1891. 4-Dec-2 Sotheby's, New York #37/R est:200000-300000

DEWS, J Steven (1949-) British
£9259 $15000 €13426 Beached brig on the sands at Scarborough (61x91cm-24x36in) s. 29-Jul-3 Christie's, Rockefeller NY #187/R est:15000-20000
£21605 $35000 €31327 Valsheda racing Endeavor and Shamrock in Christ Church bay (61x91cm-24x36in) s. i.d.2001 on stretcher. 29-Jul-3 Christie's, Rockefeller NY #185/R est:40000-50000
£50000 $78500 €75000 Vigilant racing Valkyrie for the America's Cup off Rhode Island (101x152cm-40x60in) s. 16-Dec-2 Sotheby's, Olympia #175/R est:50000-70000

DEXEL, Walter (1890-1973) German
£7246 $11884 €10000 Trapeze composition (75x53cm-30x21in) s. s.i.d.23/64 verso prov. 29-May-3 Lempertz, Koln #585/R est:10000-12000
£9615 $14904 €15000 Glass picture 1928 II or blue slice (42x35cm-17x14in) s.d.1928 verso prov.exhib. 4-Dec-2 Lempertz, Koln #650/R est:15000-18000
£11218 $17388 €17500 Green week - head series (65x50cm-26x20in) s.i. tempera board exhib.lit. 4-Dec-2 Lempertz, Koln #652/R est:14000-16000
Works on paper
£769 $1192 €1200 Sketch for interlacing black-red (39x29cm-15x11in) s.d.66 W/C Indian ink over pencil squares prov. 4-Dec-2 Lempertz, Koln #653/R

DEXTER, Walter (1876-1958) British
£300 $468 €450 West Lynn from common Staithe (23x28cm-9x11in) s.d.1944 verso. 11-Apr-3 Keys, Aylsham #563/R
£580 $911 €870 Fruits of our labours (22x34cm-9x13in) mono. board. 15-Apr-3 Bonhams, Knightsbridge #136/R
£29000 $45820 €43500 Carpenter's workshop (76x63cm-30x25in) s.d.1904. 26-Nov-2 Christie's, London #152/R est:18000-25000

DEXTER, William (1818-1860) Australian
Works on paper
£702 $1067 €1053 Bird's nest (22x33cm-9x13in) s.i. W/C exhib. 19-Aug-2 Joel, Victoria #145 est:2000-3000 (A.D 2000)

DEYEMA (20th C) French?
£11644 $18281 €17000 Untitled (100x81cm-39x32in) s. 15-Apr-3 Laurence Calmels, Paris #4273/R est:5000-6000

DEYNUM, Guilliam van (attrib) (17th C) Flemish
£9259 $15000 €13889 Still life with pipe and tumbler (33x45cm-13x18in) 23-Jan-3 Sotheby's, New York #217/R est:20000

DEYROLLE, Jean (1911-1967) French

£1301 $2056 €1952 Gens (65x54cm-26x21in) s. i.verso tempera prov. 1-Apr-3 Rasmussen, Copenhagen #265/R est:15000 (D.KR 14000)
£1580 $2496 €2370 Olive (59x81cm-23x32in) s. s.d.1946 verso exhib.prov. 1-Apr-3 Rasmussen, Copenhagen #280/R est:15000 (D.KR 17000)
£1761 $2835 €2500 Nature morte au potiron (65x46cm-26x18in) st. c.1943. 11-May-3 Thierry & Lannon, Brest #162/R est:2200-2500
£2146 $3411 €3219 Nuits - Opus 279 (81x54cm-32x21in) s. tempera prov.exhib.lit. 29-Apr-3 Kunsthallen, Copenhagen #28/R est:25000 (D.KR 23000)
£2178 $3616 €3158 Composition (73x54cm-29x21in) tempera cardboard prov. 12-Jun-3 Kunsthallen, Copenhagen #99/R est:25000 (D.KR 23000)
£2534 $3953 €3801 Gaudens - Opus 589 (73x100cm-29x39in) s. i.verso tempera painted 1958-1959 exhib.lit. 18-Sep-2 Kunsthallen, Copenhagen #20/R est:40000 (D.KR 30000)
£2885 $4529 €4500 Untitled (37x57cm-15x22in) s. paper on canvas. 24-Nov-2 Laurence Calmels, Paris #99/R
£3810 $6020 €5715 Olier (120x60cm-47x24in) s. s.i.verso tempera exhib.lit. 1-Apr-3 Rasmussen, Copenhagen #175/R est:30000-40000 (D.KR 41000)
£4054 $6324 €6000 Nino (81x100cm-32x39in) s. i.d.1965 verso tempera exhib.lit. 28-Mar-3 Charbonneaux, Paris #90/R est:7000
£4307 $6720 €6461 Riom - opus 408 (100x60cm-39x24in) s. i.verso tempera painted 1954-55 prov.exhib.lit. 18-Sep-2 Kunsthallen, Copenhagen #54/R est:45000 (D.KR 51000)
£4500 $6975 €6750 Garsende opus 590 (113x77cm-44x30in) s. s.i.verso painted 1959 prov. 5-Dec-2 Christie's, Kensington #192/R est:5000-7000
£4808 $7548 €7500 Ronan (100x50cm-39x20in) s. i.verso. 24-Nov-2 Laurence Calmels, Paris #98/R
£5112 $8076 €7668 Floxel - composition (115x88cm-45x35in) s. i.verso exhib.lit. 1-Apr-3 Rasmussen, Copenhagen #156/R est:50000-75000 (D.KR 55000)
£5576 $8810 €8364 Guijean - composition (116x89cm-46x35in) s. s.i.verso tempera exhib.prov. 1-Apr-3 Rasmussen, Copenhagen #168/R est:80000 (D.KR 60000)
£7051 $11071 €11000 Vinicio (92x73cm-36x29in) s. s.i.d.1953 verso prov.exhib. 24-Nov-2 Laurence Calmels, Paris #100/R

Works on paper

£915 $1474 €1300 Fauteuil devant la cheminee (29x46cm-11x18in) st. pastel c.1943. 11-May-3 Thierry & Lannon, Brest #57
£1213 $1928 €1820 Composition (31x24cm-12x9in) s. gouache. 29-Apr-3 Kunsthallen, Copenhagen #3/R est:3000 (D.KR 13000)

DEYROLLE, Theophile-Louis (1844-1923) French

£359 $590 €550 Gitane au tambourin (65x50cm-26x20in) s. 7-Feb-3 Oger, Dumont, Paris #85
£764 $1260 €1100 Young woman on the beach (46x35cm-18x14in) s. 1-Jul-3 Christie's, Amsterdam #66/R
£1528 $2490 €2200 La gardienne de moutons au bord de la mer (40x60cm-16x24in) s. 19-Jul-3 Thierry & Lannon, Brest #119/R est:2000-2500
£2083 $3396 €3000 La cueillette des pommes (96x71cm-38x28in) s.d.1905. 19-Jul-3 Thierry & Lannon, Brest #121 est:3000-3500

DEZAUNAY, Émile (1854-1940) French

£347 $566 €500 Bouquet de fleurs (24x18cm-9x7in) s. panel. 19-Jul-3 Thierry & Lannon, Brest #325
£1079 $1727 €1500 Portrait de Maxime Maufra (46x38cm-18x15in) s.i. 18-May-3 Eric Pillon, Calais #56/R
£2158 $3453 €3000 Barques sur la berge en bord de riviere (32x46cm-13x18in) s.i. 18-May-3 Eric Pillon, Calais #33/R
£2756 $4328 €4300 Nantes, pont transbordeur (46x55cm-18x22in) s. 15-Dec-2 Thierry & Lannon, Brest #133
£2817 $4535 €4000 Animation sur la cale du port de Merrien (47x55cm-19x22in) s. 11-May-3 Thierry & Lannon, Brest #163/R est:5000-6000
£2958 $4762 €4200 Jeune Bretonne sous la porte cintree (55x46cm-22x18in) s. 11-May-3 Thierry & Lannon, Brest #169 est:4500-5000
£3333 $5233 €5200 Petite bretonne en coiffe (46x38cm-18x15in) s. 15-Dec-2 Thierry & Lannon, Brest #131
£3380 $5442 €4800 Barque a l'entree de St Giles Croix de Vie (46x55cm-18x22in) s. 11-May-3 Thierry & Lannon, Brest #164/R est:4000-5000
£3521 $5669 €5000 Jeune Bretonne assise pres du rivage (38x46cm-15x18in) s. 11-May-3 Thierry & Lannon, Brest #168/R est:5000-6000
£3846 $6038 €6000 Jeune bretonne et sa petite fille (44x53cm-17x21in) s. 15-Dec-2 Thierry & Lannon, Brest #132
£5986 $9637 €8500 Soleil couchant sur la mer (46x53cm-18x21in) s. board. 11-May-3 Thierry & Lannon, Brest #165/R est:6000-8000

Works on paper

£1479 $2381 €2100 Scene d'interieur, les brodeuses (31x39cm-12x15in) s. W/C. 11-May-3 Thierry & Lannon, Brest #83/R est:2200-2500

DEZEUZE, Daniel (1942-) French

Works on paper

£472 $751 €680 Sans titre (27x37cm-11x15in) s.d.76 Indian ink prov. 29-Apr-3 Artcurial Briest, Paris #454
£782 $1244 €1150 Composition (51x50cm-20x20in) s.d.1986 col pastel. 26-Feb-3 Artcurial Briest, Paris #367/R

D'HAESE, Reinhoud (1928-) Belgian

Sculpture

£1603 $2484 €2500 Creature (61cm-24in) welded copper executed c.1959-60 prov. 3-Dec-2 Christie's, Amsterdam #70/R est:1000-1500
£1887 $2925 €3000 Pantomime (27x39cm-11x15in) i.d.1986 brass stone base. 5-Oct-2 De Vuyst, Lokeren #509/R est:2500-3000
£1887 $2925 €3000 Le cousin de l'ambassadeur (29x26cm-11x10in) i.d.1988 copper stone base. 5-Oct-2 De Vuyst, Lokeren #510/R est:2500-3000
£2230 $3479 €3345 The pitcher (86cm-34in) bronze incl. stone socle. 11-Nov-2 Rasmussen, Vejle #129/R est:25000-30000 (D.KR 26000)
£2326 $3605 €3489 Figure (35cm-14in) copper. 4-Dec-2 Kunsthallen, Copenhagen #101/R est:35000 (D.KR 27000)
£2436 $3776 €3800 Cest difficile d'etre different (43cm-17in) i. welded copper. 3-Dec-2 Christie's, Amsterdam #69/R est:3000-5000
£2710 $4200 €4065 Untitled (65cm-26in) pat.bronze incl. wood socle prov. 1-Oct-2 Rasmussen, Copenhagen #97/R est:30000 (D.KR 32000)
£3022 $4955 €4200 Mythical figure (36cm-14in) welded copper. 3-Jun-3 Christie's, Amsterdam #179/R est:3500-4500
£3453 $5663 €4800 Auto defense (70cm-28in) welded copper executed 1972. 3-Jun-3 Christie's, Amsterdam #180/R est:5000-7000
£3793 $6069 €5500 I had a hard time (43x40cm-17x16in) brass stone base exec.1978. 15-Mar-3 De Vuyst, Lokeren #563/R est:4500-5500
£4167 $6458 €6500 Tout est dans le geste (68x60cm-27x24in) bronze exec.1970 exhib. 7-Dec-2 De Vuyst, Lokeren #485/R est:6500-8500
£4321 $7000 €6265 Metaphor of an insect (53x53cm-21x21in) welded copper stone base. 21-May-3 Doyle, New York #16/R est:4000-6000

D'HAESE, Roel (1921-) Belgian

Works on paper

£314 $487 €500 Fete nocturne (66x51cm-26x20in) s.i.d.11.78 black pencil. 30-Oct-2 Artcurial Briest, Paris #661

D'HAVELOOSE, Marnix (1885-1973) Belgian

Sculpture

£3425 $5342 €5000 Danseuse Art Deco (84x60cm-33x24in) s. brown pat bronze. 14-Apr-3 Horta, Bruxelles #96 est:8000-10000
£5063 $7899 €8000 Danseuse (85cm-33in) s. gilt pat bronze. 16-Sep-2 Horta, Bruxelles #118/R est:10000-12000

D'HEUR, Emile (1827-1906) Belgian

£704 $1134 €1000 Portrait de Monsieur Close (69x62cm-27x24in) s. s.i.d.verso. 12-May-3 Bernaerts, Antwerp #41

D'HONT, Piet (1917-1997) Dutch

Sculpture

£955 $1471 €1500 Het geslaagde zakenaccoord (22cm-9in) bronze. 3-Sep-2 Christie's, Amsterdam #405/R est:1500-2000
£1529 $2354 €2400 Rape of Europe (37cm-15in) bronze. 3-Sep-2 Christie's, Amsterdam #406/R est:2500-3000

DIACOMIDIS, Dimitris (1911-1969) Greek

£750 $1185 €1125 Port of Hydra (25x33cm-10x13in) 1-Apr-3 Bonhams, New Bond Street #85

DIAGO, Roberto (1920-1957) Cuban

£14634 $24000 €21951 Mujer (70x50cm-28x20in) s.d.1944 prov. 28-May-3 Christie's, Rockefeller NY #93/R est:30000-40000

DIAL, Thornton (1928-) American

£17284 $28000 €25926 Making friends (175x175cm-69x69in) painted 1990 prov.exhib. 27-Jan-3 Christie's, Rockefeller NY #91/R est:18000-24000

Works on paper

£466 $750 €699 Figure of woman (46x30cm-18x12in) s. W/C pastel. 22-Feb-3 Brunk, Ashville #315/R
£745 $1200 €1118 Figure of woman (46x30cm-18x12in) s. W/C pastel. 22-Feb-3 Brunk, Ashville #316/R

DIAMANTINI, Giuseppe (1621-1705) Italian

Works on paper

£350 $500 €525 Bacchant and a satyr dancing (17x11cm-7x4in) red chk. 23-Jan-3 Swann Galleries, New York #94/R

DIANA, Benedetto (15/16th C) Italian

£15000 $25050 €21750 Rest on the flight into Egypt with the Penitent Saint Jerome in a wooded river landscape (108x168cm-43x66in) prov.exhib.lit. 11-Jul-3 Christie's, Kensington #188/R est:10000-15000

DIAZ CASTILLA, Luciano (1940-) Spanish
£535 $834 €850 In the field (33x46cm-13x18in) s. 17-Sep-2 Segre, Madrid #218/R
£822 $1282 €1200 Yellow flowers (41x60cm-16x24in) s. 8-Apr-3 Ansorena, Madrid #14/R
£855 $1386 €1300 Navagrande (50x61cm-20x24in) s. 21-Jan-3 Ansorena, Madrid #308/R
£865 $1367 €1350 Jockey (60x73cm-24x29in) s. 19-Nov-2 Durán, Madrid #214/R
£871 $1376 €1350 Girl (73x60cm-29x24in) lit. 18-Dec-2 Ansorena, Madrid #145/R
£878 $1370 €1300 Horizon (60x73cm-24x29in) s. 25-Mar-3 Durán, Madrid #135/R
£1006 $1550 €1600 Reclining bulls (65x81cm-26x32in) s. 22-Oct-2 Durán, Madrid #180/R
£1226 $1937 €1900 Bulls (73x92cm-29x36in) s. 17-Dec-2 Segre, Madrid #102/R
£1241 $1974 €1800 Winter (73x92cm-29x36in) s. 4-Mar-3 Ansorena, Madrid #218/R
£1258 $1988 €1950 Yellow tree (81x100cm-32x39in) s. 17-Dec-2 Durán, Madrid #170/R
£1510 $2431 €2250 Celebrating in the fields (73x100cm-29x39in) s. 18-Feb-3 Durán, Madrid #163/R

DIAZ DE LA PENA, Narcisse-Virgile (1807-1876) French
£500 $835 €725 Personnages dans une clairere (10x14cm-4x6in) panel. 17-Jun-3 Bonhams, New Bond Street #112/R
£574 $896 €850 Moise sauve des eaux (29x45cm-11x18in) s. 31-Mar-3 Rossini, Paris #17/R
£692 $1100 €1038 Fetching water (30x40cm-12x16in) s. 7-Mar-3 Skinner, Boston #231/R
£1154 $1812 €1800 Jete de fleurs (22x14cm-9x6in) s. panel. 16-Dec-2 Rabourdin & Choppin de Janvry, Paris #8/R
£1397 $2180 €2096 Woodland pond (53x34cm-21x13in) s. board. 20-Nov-2 Fischer, Luzern #1070/R est:2500-3000 (S.FR 3200)
£1644 $2548 €2466 Nymphs (27x19cm-11x7in) s. panel. 3-Oct-2 Koller, Zurich #3138/R est:4000-7000 (S.FR 3830)
£2199 $3408 €3299 Still life of flowers (22x15cm-9x6in) panel lit. 3-Dec-2 Bukowskis, Stockholm #363/R est:20000-25000 (S.KR 31000)
£3000 $4890 €4500 L'amour desarmee (42x23cm-17x9in) s.d.38. 13-Feb-3 Christie's, Kensington #1/R est:1200-1800
£3038 $4739 €4800 Le sous-bois (40x32cm-16x13in) panel. 15-Oct-2 Regis & Thiollet, Argentuil #74
£3082 $4839 €4500 Artist with his grandchildren (54x44cm-21x17in) s. canvas on panel. 15-Apr-3 Sotheby's, Amsterdam #74/R est:7000-9000
£3377 $5505 €5100 Apres midi orageux (19x40cm-7x16in) s. panel. 16-Feb-3 Mercier & Cie, Lille #238/R est:3600-4000
£3448 $5483 €5000 Figures in wood (39x51cm-15x20in) s. panel. 8-Mar-3 Arnold, Frankfurt #569/R est:7000
£3500 $5565 €5250 Un foret (25x16cm-10x6in) indis i. 20-Mar-3 Christie's, Kensington #23/R est:1500-2000
£3526 $5571 €5500 Figure in Fontainebleau wood (33x23cm-13x9in) s. panel prov. 15-Nov-2 Reiss & Sohn, Konigstein #20/R est:8000
£4545 $7000 €6818 Mystical marriage of St Catherine (65x46cm-26x18in) s.d.58. 4-Sep-2 Christie's, Rockefeller NY #308/R est:7000-9000
£4959 $7785 €7439 Les confidences de L'Amour (46x28cm-18x11in) s.d.70 panel prov. 24-Jul-2 Walker's, Ottawa #41/R est:12000-16000 (C.D 12000)
£5380 $8500 €8070 Woodcutters in forest of Fontainebleau (94x69cm-37x27in) s. 5-Apr-3 Harvey Clar, Oakland #1516
£5500 $8745 €8250 Cinq orientales fumant le narguile sous les arbres dans un jardin (23x30cm-9x12in) s.d.70 panel. 20-Mar-3 Christie's, Kensington #21/R est:3000-5000
£5844 $8708 €9000 Roses (37x46cm-15x18in) s. panel. 26-Jun-2 Neumeister, Munich #711/R est:10000
£6338 $10521 €9000 Landscape with peasant women (23x33cm-9x13in) s. panel. 12-Jun-3 Hauswedell & Nolte, Hamburg #338/R est:12000
£6962 $11000 €10443 Conversation sous les arbres (24x33cm-9x13in) s. 23-Apr-3 Christie's, Rockefeller NY #52/R est:12000-16000
£15823 $25000 €23735 Storyteller (51x61cm-20x24in) exhib. 24-Apr-3 Sotheby's, New York #51/R est:30000-40000
£25806 $40000 €38709 En foret de Fontainebleau (62x82cm-24x32in) s.d.70 panel prov.exhib.lit. 30-Oct-2 Christie's, Rockefeller NY #19/R est:30000-40000

Works on paper
£1795 $2782 €2800 Three women and a boy (25x17cm-10x7in) s. W/C over crayon htd gouache. 4-Dec-2 Piasa, Paris #177/R

DIAZ DE LA PENA, Narcisse-Virgile (attrib) (1807-1876) French
£515 $782 €773 Woman with bouquet of flowers (23x18cm-9x7in) panel. 16-Aug-2 Lilla Bukowskis, Stockholm #28 (S.KR 7500)
£556 $894 €834 Wooded landscape with clearing (16x22cm-6x9in) bears i. panel. 7-May-3 Dobiaschofsky, Bern #453/R (S.FR 1200)
£629 $969 €1000 Deiseuse de bonne venture (22x27cm-9x11in) s. 28-Oct-2 Il Ponte, Milan #277
£694 $1118 €1041 Still life with landscape (46x38cm-18x15in) i. panel. 7-May-3 Dobiaschofsky, Bern #451/R (S.FR 1500)
£719 $1180 €1000 Hut in wood near Fontainebleau with clearing (25x34cm-10x13in) i. verso board. 4-Jun-3 Reiss & Sohn, Konigstein #134/R
£1258 $1937 €2000 Woman (30x22cm-12x9in) 28-Oct-2 Il Ponte, Milan #229/R

Works on paper
£1384 $2131 €2200 Harem (44x36cm-17x14in) s. pastel tempera. 28-Oct-2 Il Ponte, Milan #271/R

DIAZ DE LA REQUERA, Francisco (attrib) (16th C) Spanish
Works on paper
£13548 $21000 €20322 Perseus and Andromeda (25x15cm-10x6in) gouache on vellum. 2-Nov-2 North East Auctions, Portsmouth #99/R est:4000-6000

DIAZ FERRER, Jose (1922-) Spanish
£277 $432 €440 Water lilies (64x81cm-25x32in) s. 17-Sep-2 Segre, Madrid #186/R

Works on paper
£395 $639 €600 Fishing boat (67x97cm-26x38in) mono.d.88 gouache cardboard. 21-Jan-3 Ansorena, Madrid #338/R

DIAZ Y VALERA, Jose (1827-1903) Spanish
£566 $883 €900 Bandits (41x34cm-16x13in) s.d.1868. 8-Oct-2 Ansorena, Madrid #436/R

DIAZ, Domingo Garcia (fl.1880s) Spanish
£3546 $5745 €5000 Siesta in the inner courtyard (89x69cm-35x27in) s.d.1880 canvas on board. 22-May-3 Dorotheum, Vienna #132/R est:8000-9000

DIAZ, Jose (?) Spanish
£323 $510 €500 Plain (92x75cm-36x30in) s. 17-Dec-2 Durán, Madrid #10/R
£355 $561 €550 Dawn (81x100cm-32x39in) s. 17-Dec-2 Durán, Madrid #9/R

DIBBETS, Jan (1941-) Dutch
£4487 $6955 €7000 Voor Morandi (122x130cm-48x51in) s.d.65 verso s.i.d.on stretcher. 3-Dec-2 Christie's, Amsterdam #344/R est:7000-9000

Photographs
£12500 $20000 €18750 Untitled (59x59cm-23x23in) s.num.i-x 35/40 c-print in ten parts executed 1998. 14-May-3 Sotheby's, New York #353/R est:25000-35000
£26250 $42000 €39375 Panorama bloemendaal (155x142cm-61x56in) s.i.d.1971 gelatin silver print graphite 144 on paper. 15-May-3 Christie's, Rockefeller NY #312/R est:30000-40000

DIBDIN, Thomas Colman (1810-1893) British
Works on paper
£260 $424 €390 Carshalton Road (23x36cm-9x14in) s.i. 14-Feb-3 Keys, Aylsham #899
£323 $510 €485 Abbeville (54x37cm-21x15in) s.i.d.1875 W/C htd white. 18-Nov-2 Waddingtons, Toronto #74/R (C.D 800)
£400 $644 €600 Continental town scene with cathedral (51x33cm-20x13in) W/C. 19-Feb-3 Mallams, Oxford #351/R
£580 $905 €870 Village life (36x26cm-14x10in) s.d.1869 W/C. 25-Mar-3 Bonhams, Knightsbridge #32/R
£1102 $1752 €1653 Courtyard scene (74x51cm-29x20in) s.d.1873 W/C. 18-Mar-3 Maynards, Vancouver #29/R est:2000-3000 (C.D 2600)
£1400 $2324 €2100 Street scenes in Northern France (37x28cm-15x11in) s. one d.1877 W/C htd bodycol pair. 12-Jun-3 Bonhams, New Bond Street #647/R est:1200-1800

DICHTL, Erich (1890-1955) Austrian
£382 $603 €550 Stags fighting (65x83cm-26x33in) s. jute on board. 24-Apr-3 Dorotheum, Vienna #84/R
£696 $1100 €1100 Deer (52x66cm-20x26in) s. board. 26-Nov-2 Wiener Kunst Auktionen, Vienna #132/R
£1457 $2375 €2200 Chamois in the snow (120x101cm-47x40in) s. 28-Jan-3 Dorotheum, Vienna #100/R est:1800-2400
£1517 $2428 €2200 Deer in winter wood (94x84cm-37x33in) s. 11-Mar-3 Dorotheum, Vienna #76/R est:1500-2000

DICHTL, Martin (fl.1660-1690) German
£4730 $7378 €7000 Scissors grinder and old woman in town square (112x94cm-44x37in) prov. 27-Mar-3 Dorotheum, Vienna #274/R est:7000-10000
£6757 $10541 €10000 Still life with mouse (39x31cm-15x12in) 27-Mar-3 Dorotheum, Vienna #282/R est:6000-8000

DICK, Karl Theophil (1884-1967) German

£266	$420	€399	Still life with Chinese figure, carafe and plate with fruit (45x34cm-18x13in) s. 29-Nov-2 Zofingen, Switzerland #2848 (S.FR 620)
£563	$924	€816	The Rhine at Grenzach (50x66cm-20x26in) s.d.35. 4-Jun-3 Fischer, Luzern #2051/R (S.FR 1200)

DICK, Sir William Reid (1879-1961) British
Sculpture

£5500	$8855	€8250	Catapult (34cm-13in) s. bronze exhib.lit. 20-Feb-3 Christie's, London #280/R

DICK, Walter (1950-) Swiss?
Works on paper

£217	$337	€326	Hameau sous la neige, janvier (50x66cm-20x26in) s.d.1977 ink pencil white chk. 7-Dec-2 Galerie du Rhone, Sion #378 (S.FR 500)
£304	$472	€456	Paysage des Prealpes (77x54cm-30x21in) s.d.1976 ink. 7-Dec-2 Galerie du Rhone, Sion #377/R (S.FR 700)

DICKENS, W (19th C) ?

£1500	$2280	€2250	Congestion at the harbour mouth (66x91cm-26x36in) s. 29-Aug-2 Christie's, Kensington #68/R est:700-1000

DICKER, Charles William Hamilton (1855-1912) Australian
Works on paper

£308	$489	€462	Flora at Twofold Bay (16x23cm-6x9in) i. W/C exhib. 4-Mar-3 Deutscher-Menzies, Melbourne #142/R (A.D 800)

DICKERHOF, Urs (1941-) Swiss

£284	$443	€426	Peniscola VI (59x82cm-23x32in) s.d.64 i. stretcher. 6-Nov-2 Dobiaschofsky, Bern #3282 (S.FR 650)
£328	$511	€492	Painting 1965/16 (85x85cm-33x33in) s.d. i. stretcher. 6-Nov-2 Dobiaschofsky, Bern #3283 (S.FR 750)

DICKERSON, Robert (1924-) Australian

£717	$1090	€1076	Two faces (51x68cm-20x27in) s. chl. 27-Aug-2 Goodman, Sydney #44 (A.D 2000)
£1714	$2709	€2571	Face (29x24cm-11x9in) s. 26-Nov-2 Sotheby's, Melbourne #93 est:5000-7000 (A.D 4800)
£3386	$5554	€5079	Two figures (34x24cm-13x9in) s. composition board painted c.1966 exhib. 4-Jun-3 Deutscher-Menzies, Melbourne #7/R est:7500-9500 (A.D 8500)
£6944	$10833	€10416	Head of portrait of a woman (40x33cm-16x13in) s.d.60 board prov. 8-Apr-3 Peter Webb, Auckland #113/R est:7000-9000 (NZ.D 20000)
£9962	$15640	€14943	Figure in the bush, Brookfield (100x74cm-39x29in) s. acrylic prov. 15-Apr-3 Lawson Menzies, Sydney #35/R est:27000-35000 (A.D 26000)
£10000	$15800	€15000	Man in hospital. Mother and child (100x75cm-39x30in) s. i.verso board prov. 26-Nov-2 Sotheby's, Melbourne #11/R est:30000-50000 (A.D 28000)
£10676	$16335	€16014	Across the nullabor (91x91cm-36x36in) s. i.verso prov. 25-Aug-2 Sotheby's, Paddington #38/R est:30000-40000 (A.D 30000)
£10753	$16344	€16130	Woman with flowers (122x91cm-48x36in) s. composition board prov.lit. 28-Aug-2 Deutscher-Menzies, Melbourne #12/R est:36000-45000 (A.D 30000)
£11155	$18295	€16733	Early morning Randwick (152x152cm-60x60in) s. oil synthetic polymer paint prov.exhib. 4-Jun-3 Deutscher-Menzies, Melbourne #91/R est:20000-30000 (A.D 28000)
£16000	$25760	€24000	Mother and child (120x90cm-47x35in) i. board prov.exhib. 6-May-3 Christie's, Melbourne #125/R est:38000-45000 (A.D 40000)
£16923	$26908	€25385	Into the subway (183x122cm-72x48in) s. composition board prov.exhib.lit. 4-Mar-3 Deutscher-Menzies, Melbourne #26/R est:50000-70000 (A.D 44000)
£17143	$27086	€25715	Woolloomooloo (121x182cm-48x72in) s. board prov. 26-Nov-2 Sotheby's, Melbourne #47/R est:35000-45000 (A.D 48000)
£19929	$30491	€29894	Night traffic (121x122cm-48x48in) enamel on board painted 1958 prov.exhib. 26-Aug-2 Sotheby's, Paddington #556/R est:70000-100000 (A.D 56000)
£20609	$31326	€30914	Punters (180x120cm-71x47in) s. board painted c.1966. 27-Aug-2 Goodman, Sydney #133/R est:70000-90000 (A.D 57500)

Works on paper

£643	$1016	€965	Female head (37x27cm-15x11in) s. chl. 18-Nov-2 Goodman, Sydney #6 (A.D 1800)
£675	$1120	€1150	Untitled - Portrait (18x14cm-7x6in) s. chl. 10-Jun-3 Shapiro, Sydney #92 est:1200-2500 (A.D 1700)
£687	$1085	€1190	Face (35x32cm-14x13in) s. chl. 1-Apr-3 Goodman, Sydney #2 (A.D 1800)
£714	$1129	€1071	Woman at the market (34x25cm-13x10in) s. chl. 18-Nov-2 Goodman, Sydney #84/R (A.D 2000)
£766	$1203	€1149	Two figures (26x19cm-10x7in) s. chl. 15-Apr-3 Lawson Menzies, Sydney #267/R est:1000-2000 (A.D 2000)
£894	$1413	€1296	Baby (55x36cm-22x14in) s. chl. 22-Jul-3 Lawson Menzies, Sydney #182/R est:2500-4000 (A.D 2200)
£932	$1416	€1398	Nude standing (36x27cm-14x11in) s. pastel. 27-Aug-2 Goodman, Sydney #117 (A.D 2600)
£1000	$1590	€1500	Spring festival (27x21cm-11x8in) s. chl. 4-Mar-3 Deutscher-Menzies, Melbourne #153/R est:3000-4000 (A.D 2600)
£1013	$1601	€1520	Girl in red (38x28cm-15x11in) s. pastel. 18-Nov-2 Goodman, Sydney #123 est:4000-6000 (A.D 2835)
£1071	$1693	€1607	Face (100x64cm-39x25in) s. chl. 26-Nov-2 Sotheby's, Melbourne #91 est:3000-5000 (A.D 3000)
£1111	$1689	€1667	Indecision (36x27cm-14x11in) s. pastel. 27-Aug-2 Goodman, Sydney #22 est:2500-3500 (A.D 3100)
£1145	$1809	€1718	Farmer (15x22cm-6x9in) s. chl. 7-Apr-3 Australian Art Auctions, Sydney #84 (A.D 3000)
£1200	$1932	€1740	Learned friends (18x28cm-7x11in) s. pastel. 12-May-3 Joel, Victoria #258 est:2500-3000 (A.D 3000)
£1221	$1929	€2115	Female study (36x26cm-14x10in) s. chl. 1-Apr-3 Goodman, Sydney #60k est:3000-6000 (A.D 3200)
£1290	$1961	€1935	Ralph (56x38cm-22x15in) s. pastel. 27-Aug-2 Goodman, Sydney #186 est:3600-5600 (A.D 3600)
£1316	$2080	€2280	Ballerina (38x29cm-15x11in) s. chl. 1-Apr-3 Goodman, Sydney #106/R est:2800-3800 (A.D 3450)
£1431	$2261	€2147	Art critic (38x28cm-15x11in) s. pastel. 7-Apr-3 Australian Art Auctions, Sydney #135 (A.D 3750)
£1434	$2179	€2151	Boy sitting (75x55cm-30x22in) s. chl. 27-Aug-2 Goodman, Sydney #71 est:4000-6000 (A.D 4000)
£1495	$2287	€2243	Face (55x37cm-22x15in) s. chl prov. 25-Aug-2 Sotheby's, Paddington #186 est:1500-2500 (A.D 4200)
£1526	$2411	€2645	Young boy (75x54cm-30x21in) s. chl. 1-Apr-3 Goodman, Sydney #15 est:4000-7000 (A.D 4000)
£1526	$2411	€2645	Female study (36x26cm-14x10in) s. chl. 1-Apr-3 Goodman, Sydney #60n/R est:3000-6000 (A.D 4000)
£1533	$2406	€2300	Two heads (46x66cm-18x26in) s. chl executed c.1966. 15-Apr-3 Lawson Menzies, Sydney #144/R est:5000-7000 (A.D 4000)
£1545	$2441	€2240	Winner (54x37cm-21x15in) s. chl. 22-Jul-3 Lawson Menzies, Sydney #185/R est:3500-4500 (A.D 3800)
£1577	$2397	€2366	Young child (75x51cm-30x20in) s. chl paper on board. 28-Aug-2 Deutscher-Menzies, Melbourne #306/R est:4500-6000 (A.D 4400)
£1600	$2576	€2400	Young girl III (36x26cm-14x10in) s. pastel. 6-May-3 Christie's, Melbourne #347 est:3000-5000 (A.D 4000)
£1600	$2576	€2400	Jockeys (32x36cm-13x14in) s. pastel. 6-May-3 Christie's, Melbourne #382 est:4000-6000 (A.D 4000)
£1649	$2506	€2474	Jockey (30x22cm-12x9in) s. pastel. 28-Aug-2 Deutscher-Menzies, Melbourne #324/R est:1500-2000 (A.D 4600)
£1714	$2691	€2571	Portrait (37x27cm-15x11in) s. pastel. 25-Nov-2 Christie's, Melbourne #263/R est:2500-3500 (A.D 4800)
£1718	$2714	€2577	As I know. s. pastel. 7-Apr-3 Australian Art Auctions, Sydney #80b (A.D 4500)
£1719	$2715	€2579	Girl with long hair (76x56cm-30x22in) s. chl. 18-Nov-2 Goodman, Sydney #175 est:2000-3000 (A.D 4810)
£1769	$2813	€2654	Geisha (36x27cm-14x11in) s. chl. 4-Mar-3 Deutscher-Menzies, Melbourne #196/R est:2500-3500 (A.D 4600)
£1786	$2821	€2679	Two faces (38x56cm-15x22in) s. pastel. 18-Nov-2 Goodman, Sydney #66 est:1500-3000 (A.D 5000)
£1786	$2821	€2679	Face of a girl (37x27cm-15x11in) s. pastel. 18-Nov-2 Goodman, Sydney #167 est:2800-3800 (A.D 5000)
£1800	$2898	€2700	Young girl II (37x27cm-15x11in) s. pastel. 6-May-3 Christie's, Melbourne #298 est:3000-5000 (A.D 4500)
£1829	$2891	€2652	Face (36x26cm-14x10in) s. chl. 22-Jul-3 Lawson Menzies, Sydney #10/R est:2000-4000 (A.D 4500)
£1875	$2963	€2813	Girl with daisies (55x37cm-22x15in) s. i.verso pastel. 26-Nov-2 Sotheby's, Melbourne #66/R est:3000-5000 (A.D 5250)
£1912	$3136	€2868	Crouching child in street (34x38cm-13x15in) s. pastel paper on board. 4-Jun-3 Deutscher-Menzies, Melbourne #137/R est:5500-7000 (A.D 4800)
£1938	$3081	€2907	Children on the street (37x55cm-15x22in) s. pastel paper on board. 5-May-3 Sotheby's, Melbourne #297/R est:2000-3000 (A.D 5000)
£1964	$3045	€2946	Portrait of a boy (72x52cm-28x20in) s. chl. 29-Oct-2 Lawson Menzies, Sydney #37/R est:5500-6000 (A.D 5500)
£1971	$2996	€2957	Thoughts (37x27cm-15x11in) s. pastel. 28-Aug-2 Deutscher-Menzies, Melbourne #354/R est:4000-5000 (A.D 5500)
£2000	$3220	€3000	Young girl I (37x27cm-15x11in) s. pastel. 6-May-3 Christie's, Melbourne #289/R est:3000-5000 (A.D 5000)
£2061	$3132	€3092	Young girl (37x25cm-15x10in) s. pastel paper on board. 28-Aug-2 Deutscher-Menzies, Melbourne #351/R est:3500-4500 (A.D 5750)
£2107	$3140	€3161	Man in hat and overcoat (76x55cm-30x22in) s. pastel. 27-Aug-2 Christie's, Melbourne #197/R est:5000-7000 (A.D 5500)
£2115	$3363	€3173	Face (37x28cm-15x11in) s. pastel paper on board. 4-Mar-3 Deutscher-Menzies, Melbourne #161/R est:4500-6500 (A.D 5500)
£2135	$3267	€3203	Boy with a broom (74x54cm-29x21in) s. chl. 25-Aug-2 Sotheby's, Paddington #214/R est:4000-6000 (A.D 6000)

£2143 $3321 €3215 Infant, Sam Dickerson (73x53cm-29x21in) s. chl exec.c.1971. 29-Oct-2 Lawson Menzies, Sydney #16/R est:6000-9000 (A.D 6000)
£2151 $3269 €3227 Children (73x54cm-29x21in) s. chl exec.c.1972. 28-Aug-2 Deutscher-Menzies, Melbourne #187/R est:7000-9000 (A.D 6000)
£2191 $3593 €3287 Young boy, Sam (76x56cm-30x22in) s. i.verso chl prov. 4-Jun-3 Deutscher-Menzies, Melbourne #189/R est:6000-9000 (A.D 5500)
£2289 $3617 €3966 Twins (52x72cm-20x28in) s. chl. 1-Apr-3 Goodman, Sydney #60a/R est:6000-9000 (A.D 6000)
£2299 $3425 €3449 Two figures (56x37cm-22x15in) s. pastel. 27-Aug-2 Christie's, Melbourne #303 est:6000-8000 (A.D 6000)
£2321 $3668 €3482 Lining up (56x37cm-22x15in) s. i.verso pastel. 27-Nov-2 Deutscher-Menzies, Melbourne #140/R est:5500-7500 (A.D 6500)
£2330 $3541 €3495 Man with hat (75x55cm-30x22in) s. i.verso pastel. 28-Aug-2 Deutscher-Menzies, Melbourne #81/R est:9000-12000 (A.D 6500)
£2600 $4186 €3900 Lovers (65x51cm-26x20in) s. pastel chl. 6-May-3 Christie's, Melbourne #222/R est:4000-6000 (A.D 6500)
£2632 $4000 €3948 Female face (75x54cm-30x21in) s. chl. 19-Aug-2 Joel, Victoria #303/R est:6000-8000 (A.D 7500)
£2642 $4175 €3831 Sailing (56x77cm-22x30in) s. paste executed c.1974. 22-Jul-3 Lawson Menzies, Sydney #9/R est:4500-6500 (A.D 6500)
£2688 $4085 €4032 Seated girl (54x36cm-21x14in) s. pastel. 28-Aug-2 Deutscher-Menzies, Melbourne #133/R est:6000-8000 (A.D 7500)
£2778 $4611 €4733 Untitled - Lawyers (74x54cm-29x21in) s. pastel crayons. 10-Jun-3 Shapiro, Sydney #94/R est:3000-5000 (A.D 7000)
£2789 $4573 €4184 Winter warmth (74x54cm-29x21in) s. pastel. 4-Jun-3 Deutscher-Menzies, Melbourne #188/R est:6000-8000 (A.D 7000)
£2800 $4508 €4200 Streetscape (76x64cm-30x25in) s. pastel chl. 6-May-3 Christie's, Melbourne #209/R est:8000-10000 (A.D 7000)
£2884 $4586 €4326 Sisters (54x74cm-21x29in) s. i.verso pastel prov. 4-Mar-3 Deutscher-Menzies, Melbourne #51/R est:8000-12000 (A.D 7500)
£2907 $4622 €4361 What have I done (56x38cm-22x15in) s. i.verso pastel paper on board. 5-May-3 Sotheby's, Melbourne #316/R est:4000-6000 (A.D 7500)
£3000 $4830 €4500 Lady with flowers (73x53cm-29x21in) s. pastel. 6-May-3 Christie's, Melbourne #242/R est:6000-8000 (A.D 7500)
£3049 $4817 €4421 Thoughtful girl (55x36cm-22x14in) s. pastel executed c.1980. 22-Jul-3 Lawson Menzies, Sydney #128/R est:6000-8000 (A.D 7500)
£3077 $4892 €4616 Mother and child (76x55cm-30x22in) s. chl. 4-Mar-3 Deutscher-Menzies, Melbourne #161a/R est:9000-12000 (A.D 8000)
£3143 $4966 €4715 Portrait of a girl (56x38cm-22x15in) s. pastel. 26-Nov-2 Sotheby's, Melbourne #125/R est:5500-7500 (A.D 8800)
£3187 $5227 €4781 Girl (78x55cm-31x22in) s. chl exec.c.1960-65. 4-Jun-3 Deutscher-Menzies, Melbourne #94/R est:7500-9500 (A.D 8000)
£3269 $5198 €4904 Child in a lane (55x75cm-22x30in) s. pastel paper on board. 4-Mar-3 Deutscher-Menzies, Melbourne #160/R est:5500-8000 (A.D 8500)
£3297 $5012 €4946 Girl with flowers (51x35cm-20x14in) s. pastel. 27-Aug-2 Goodman, Sydney #167/R est:5000-7000 (A.D 9200)
£3338 $5274 €5784 Girl with daisies (72x52cm-28x20in) s. chl. 1-Apr-3 Goodman, Sydney #60f/R est:6000-9000 (A.D 8750)
£3400 $5474 €5100 Sisters (77x56cm-30x22in) s. pastel executed c.1975. 6-May-3 Christie's, Melbourne #257/R est:6000-8000 (A.D 8500)
£3640 $5715 €5460 Before the race (75x55cm-30x22in) s. pastel prov. 15-Apr-3 Lawson Menzies, Sydney #266/R est:12000-15000 (A.D 9500)
£3750 $5925 €5625 Two girls (64x36cm-25x14in) s. pastel executed 1980 prov. 26-Nov-2 Sotheby's, Melbourne #64/R est:6000-9000 (A.D 10500)
£3831 $6015 €5747 Two children (55x37cm-22x15in) s. pastel executed c.1969. 15-Apr-3 Lawson Menzies, Sydney #127/R est:6000-9000 (A.D 10000)
£4200 $6762 €6300 Couple (63x100cm-25x39in) s. pastel. 6-May-3 Christie's, Melbourne #65/R est:9000-12000 (A.D 10500)
£4231 $6727 €6347 Best of friends (76x55cm-30x22in) s. i.verso pastel prov. 4-Mar-3 Deutscher-Menzies, Melbourne #15/R est:7000-9000 (A.D 11000)
£4231 $6727 €6347 Local girl (76x56cm-30x22in) s. synthetic polymer paint canvas exhib. 4-Mar-3 Deutscher-Menzies, Melbourne #112/R est:14000-18000 (A.D 11000)
£5018 $7627 €7527 Single girl (73x106cm-29x42in) s. pastel exhib.lit. 28-Aug-2 Deutscher-Menzies, Melbourne #132/R est:12000-15000 (A.D 14000)

DICKINSON, Anson (1779-1852) American
Miniatures
£6579 $10000 €9869 Portraits of General and Mrs Jacob Jennings Brown. pair prov.lit. 17-Aug-2 North East Auctions, Portsmouth #603/R est:6000-9000

DICKINSON, Edwin (1891-1978) American
Works on paper
£1774 $2750 €2661 Athens study, porch of the maidens and a Olive (22x30cm-9x12in) s.i.d.1961 pencil. 29-Oct-2 Sotheby's, New York #278/R est:700-900

DICKINSON, J (19/20th C) British
£8328 $12992 €12492 Ormonde (122x177cm-48x70in) s. prov. 11-Nov-2 Stephan Welz, Johannesburg #409 est:80000-120000 (SA.R 130000)

DICKINSON, Jeremy (20th C) German
£705 $1100 €1058 Trailer home (107x81cm-42x32in) s.i.d.2000 verso oil acrylic prov. 14-Oct-2 Butterfields, San Francisco #2119a/R est:3000-5000

DICKINSON, Maud Elizabeth (1868-c.1945) British
£260 $406 €390 Study of a donkey (31x24cm-12x9in) init. 26-Mar-3 Woolley & Wallis, Salisbury #148/R

DICKINSON, Preston (1891-1930) American
£24691 $40000 €37037 Village by the sea (30x41cm-12x16in) s. board painted c.1918 prov.exhib. 21-May-3 Sotheby's, New York #83/R est:12000-18000

DICKMAN, Charles John (1863-1943) American
£723 $1200 €1048 Rural landscape with figure (69x94cm-27x37in) s. 11-Jun-3 Boos Gallery, Michigan #583/R est:400-600

DICKMEIS, Gerhard (1918-1978) German
£897 $1409 €1400 Regal figures in park (80x70cm-31x28in) s. 21-Nov-2 Van Ham, Cologne #1562

DICKSEE, Frank (1853-1928) British
£9000 $14130 €13500 Reverie (35x25cm-14x10in) board. 19-Nov-2 Bonhams, New Bond Street #149/R est:10000-15000
£30000 $49800 €45000 Spring maiden (41x30cm-16x12in) s.d.1884. 12-Jun-3 Sotheby's, London #269/R est:10000-15000
£280000 $464800 €420000 Symbol - Is it nothing to you, all ye that pass by ? (182x141cm-72x56in) s.d.1881 prov.exhib.lit. 11-Jun-3 Christie's, London #7/R est:300000-500000
£350000 $563500 €525000 Chivalry (183x137cm-72x54in) indis sig.d.1885 prov.exhib.lit. 19-Feb-3 Christie's, London #35/R est:600000-800000
Works on paper
£850 $1309 €1275 Funeral of a Viking (39x63cm-15x25in) W/C htd gouache. 23-Oct-2 Hamptons Fine Art, Godalming #91/R
£1100 $1705 €1650 European man (33x23cm-13x9in) s.d.1900 chl chk sketch. 3-Dec-2 Sworder & Son, Bishops Stortford #906/R est:100-200
£1300 $2158 €1950 Study of a heavily draped figure (49x30cm-19x12in) s.d.June 12 1873 black white chk. 12-Jun-3 Sotheby's, London #204/R est:1000-1500
£5500 $8855 €8250 Untitled. s.i. pen ink dr on fan exec. with other artists prov. 20-Feb-3 Christie's, London #126/R
£14000 $22540 €21000 Composition study for 'Chivalry' (34x25cm-13x10in) pencil W/C bodycol gum arabic scratching out prov. 20-Feb-3 Christie's, London #82/R est:12000
£34000 $54740 €51000 Study for head of damsel in 'Chivalry' (25x19cm-10x7in) pencil chk prov.lit. 20-Feb-3 Christie's, London #83/R est:12000

DICKSEE, Thomas Francis (1819-1895) British
£253 $400 €380 Grief of Constance (34x26cm-13x10in) init.d.1865 oval board. 1-Apr-3 Christie's, Rockefeller NY #186/R

DICORCIA, Philip Lorca (1953-) American
Photographs
£1948 $3000 €2922 Untitled (39x58cm-15x23in) s.num.verso ilfochrome cibachrome print 25 of 25 prov. 25-Oct-2 Phillips, New York #188/R est:3000-5000
£2600 $4342 €3770 Edward Earl Windsor, 20 years old, Atlanta, Georgia (38x58cm-15x23in) s.num.3/5 verso col coupler print exec.c.1990-92. 24-Jun-3 Sotheby's, Olympia #133/R est:2000-3000
£3165 $5000 €4748 London (63x94cm-25x37in) s.verso chromogenic co print prov.lit. 24-Apr-3 Phillips, New York #218/R est:9000-12000
£3797 $6000 €5696 Los Angeles (62x95cm-24x37in) s.verso col coupler print prov. 22-Apr-3 Christie's, Rockefeller NY #104/R est:7000-9000
£4430 $7000 €6645 New York (63x94cm-25x37in) s.verso chromogenic col print prov. 24-Apr-3 Phillips, New York #66/R est:9000-12000
£4800 $8016 €6960 London (65x96cm-26x38in) s. ektacolor print executed 1995 prov.lit. 27-Jun-3 Christie's, London #253/R est:5000-7000
£5625 $9000 €8438 Mexico City, 1998 (76x101cm-30x40in) s.verso c-print executed 1998 prov. 14-May-3 Sotheby's, New York #331/R est:10000-15000

£6250 $10000 €9375 London (76x101cm-30x40in) s.verso col coupler print mounted on board executed 1993 prov. 15-May-3 Christie's, Rockefeller NY #405/R est:8000-12000
£6329 $10000 €9494 Marilyn (50x61cm-20x24in) s.d.1990 num.10/20 verso prov.lit. 13-Nov-2 Sotheby's, New York #450/R est:14000-18000
£8000 $13360 €11600 London (76x101cm-30x40in) s.num118.12 ektacolour print prov.lit. 27-Jun-3 Christie's, London #254/R est:10000-15000
£10390 $16000 €15585 New York (76x102cm-30x40in) s.verso col chromogenic print edition of 20 prov.lit. 25-Oct-2 Phillips, New York #60/R est:15000-20000
£11039 $17000 €16559 London (76x102cm-30x40in) s.verso col chromogenic print edition of 15 prov.lit. 25-Oct-2 Phillips, New York #189/R est:15000-20000
£11688 $18000 €17532 Eddie Anderson, 21 years old, Houston, Texas (76x102cm-30x40in) s.verso col chromogenic print edition of 20 prov.lit. 25-Oct-2 Phillips, New York #59/R est:18000-25000

DIDAY, François (1802-1877) Swiss
£1739 $2696 €2609 Paysage de montagne (34x49cm-13x19in) s. prov. 7-Dec-2 Galerie du Rhone, Sion #453/R est:3000-4000 (S.FR 4000)
£2000 $3100 €3000 Le pont de St Maurice (23x28cm-9x11in) i.verso cardboard. 7-Dec-2 Galerie du Rhone, Sion #452/R est:5000-7000 (S.FR 4600)
£2052 $3243 €3078 Chateau Saint-Saphorin (42x58cm-17x23in) 17-Nov-2 Koller, Geneva #1287/R est:6000 (S.FR 4700)
£6987 $10900 €10481 Grande Sceidegg et le Wetterhorn (37x50cm-15x20in) s.i.d.77. 8-Nov-2 Dobiaschofsky, Bern #29/R est:15000 (S.FR 16000)
£8491 $13755 €15029 Handeck (42x53cm-17x21in) s. panel exhib. 26-May-3 Sotheby's, Zurich #21/R est:18000-25000 (S.FR 18000)

DIDAY, François (attrib) (1802-1877) Swiss
£271 $422 €407 Horses in river by house (34x50cm-13x20in) i. paper on canvas. 20-Nov-2 Fischer, Luzern #2050/R (S.FR 620)

DIDIER, Clovis François Auguste (1858-?) French
£8403 $13277 €12605 Breakfast (116x88cm-46x35in) s.d.1903. 16-Nov-2 Crafoord, Lund #42/R est:75000 (S.KR 120000)

DIDIER, Jules (1831-1892) French
£946 $1476 €1400 Paysage italien aux boeufs (29x48cm-11x19in) s. 28-Mar-3 Claude Aguttes, Neuilly #52
£7233 $11138 €11500 Rencontre avec amazone (146x114cm-57x45in) s. oval. 27-Oct-2 Muizon & Le Coent, Paris #36/R

DIDIER-POUGET, William (1864-1959) French
£957 $1483 €1436 Paysage fluvial (53x100cm-21x39in) s. prov. 7-Dec-2 Galerie du Rhone, Sion #506/R est:3000-4000 (S.FR 2200)
£1076 $1700 €1700 Brume et rosee (38x46cm-15x18in) s. i.verso. 29-Nov-2 Drouot Estimations, Paris #61

DIEBENKORN, Richard (1922-1993) American
£348101 $550000 €522152 Cups (41x46cm-16x18in) init.d.57 s.i.d.1957 verso prov.exhib. 12-Nov-2 Sotheby's, New York #4/R est:400000-600000
Prints
£1899 $3000 €2849 From eight by eight - Untitled (102x69cm-40x27in) init.d.1981-82 col lithograph. 22-Apr-3 Butterfields, San Francisco #2261/R est:4000-5000
£2404 $3750 €3606 Untitled, club spade (102x69cm-40x27in) init.d.num.212/250 col lithograph. 14-Oct-2 Butterfields, San Francisco #1240/R est:3000-4000
£5346 $8500 €8019 Untitled, ocean park (61x48cm-24x19in) init.d.num.69/90 col lithograph. 2-May-3 Sotheby's, New York #420/R est:4000-5000
£5414 $8500 €8121 Fulsom Street variations I, black (32x53cm-13x21in) init.d.1986 num.44/60 col aquatint soap ground. 21-Nov-2 Swann Galleries, New York #34/R est:5000-8000
£8974 $14000 €13461 Softgrounds (101x67cm-40x26in) init.d. three i. one num.25/35 etching drypoint four. 5-Nov-2 Christie's, Rockefeller NY #364/R est:10000-15000
£10692 $17000 €16038 Tri-color II (48x45cm-19x18in) init.d.num.34/35 col etching aquatint. 2-May-3 Sotheby's, New York #421/R est:6000-8000
Works on paper
£34810 $55000 €52215 Untitled (28x43cm-11x17in) init.d.62 chl brush black ink wash prov.exhib. 14-Nov-2 Christie's, Rockefeller NY #187/R est:40000-60000

DIEDEREN, Jef (1920-) Dutch
Works on paper
£504 $826 €700 Untitled (79x105cm-31x41in) s.d.67 gouache collage prov. 3-Jun-3 Christie's, Amsterdam #86/R
£504 $826 €700 Untitled (78x105cm-31x41in) s.d.67 gouache collage prov. 3-Jun-3 Christie's, Amsterdam #88
£1266 $2000 €2000 Untitled (72x52cm-28x20in) s.d.81 W/C. 26-Nov-2 Sotheby's, Amsterdam #62/R est:2000-2500

DIEDERICHS, Peter (1923-1982) German
£886 $1400 €1400 Abstract composition (155x130cm-61x51in) s.d.1967 board exhib. 30-Nov-2 Geble, Radolfzell #661/R est:1400

DIEFENBACH, Lucidus (1886-1958) German
£285 $450 €450 Wiessee with church (70x60cm-28x24in) s. 29-Nov-2 Bolland & Marotz, Bremen #1374

DIEGHEM, J van (19th C) Dutch
£1700 $2686 €2550 Sheep with two lambs on a grassy river bank (17x25cm-7x10in) s. panel pair. 7-Apr-3 David Duggleby, Scarborough #414/R est:1200-1500

DIEGHEM, Jacob van (19th C) Dutch
£560 $918 €840 Sheep in a meadow (21x29cm-8x11in) s. 4-Jun-3 Bonhams, Chester #339
£820 $1279 €1230 Sheep and lambs in a meadow (18x25cm-7x10in) s. panel pair. 6-Nov-2 Bonhams, Chester #409a
£1274 $2000 €1911 In the pasture (24x32cm-9x13in) s.d.64 panel. 22-Nov-2 Skinner, Boston #20/R est:800-1200

DIEGHEM, Joseph van (19th C) Belgian
£479 $748 €700 Landscape with sheep and ducks (22x29cm-9x11in) s.d.1867 panel. 10-Apr-3 Dorotheum, Vienna #203/R
£788 $1277 €1182 Landscape with sheep and chickens (41x30cm-16x12in) s.d.1880. 3-Feb-3 Lilla Bukowskis, Stockholm #917 (S.KR 11000)
£962 $1500 €1443 Moutons dans paysage (15x23cm-6x9in) s.d.73 panel. 5-Nov-2 Arthur James, Florida #403

DIEGO, Julio de (1900-1979) Spanish
£1647 $2750 €2388 History of medicine (33x48cm-13x19in) s. panel painted c.1940. 29-Jun-3 Butterfields, Los Angeles #7047/R est:2000-3000

DIEHL, Arthur (1870-1929) American
£337 $525 €506 Freighter at sea (15x25cm-6x10in) s. board. 1-Aug-2 Eldred, East Dennis #926/R
£385 $600 €578 Fishing boats and figures on flats (28x25cm-11x10in) s. 1-Aug-2 Eldred, East Dennis #1089/R
£570 $900 €855 Ships dockside on the river Thames (13x25cm-5x10in) s. panel. 26-Apr-3 Thomaston Place, Thomaston #192
£600 $912 €900 Figures before windmills aside a Dutch waterway (25x20cm-10x8in) s. 29-Aug-2 Christie's, Kensington #9
£769 $1200 €1154 Provincetown harbour (15x30cm-6x12in) s. board. 1-Aug-2 Eldred, East Dennis #1083/R
£897 $1400 €1346 Village by the lake (56x85cm-22x33in) s.d.1923 board. 9-Nov-2 Sloan, North Bethesda #595/R
£962 $1500 €1443 Dune scene (15x30cm-6x12in) s. board. 1-Aug-2 Eldred, East Dennis #929/R est:1100-1300
£1090 $1700 €1635 Boats at twilight (30x46cm-12x18in) s. board. 1-Aug-2 Eldred, East Dennis #927/R est:1500-1800
£1274 $2000 €1911 Fishing boats (43x36cm-17x14in) s. board. 10-Dec-2 Doyle, New York #82/R est:2500-3500
£1859 $2900 €2789 Dune scene (51x79cm-20x31in) s. board. 1-Aug-2 Eldred, East Dennis #924/R est:3000-4000
£6329 $10000 €9494 Provincetown docks (43x76cm-17x30in) s.d.1927 board. 24-Apr-3 Shannon's, Milford #87/R est:3000-5000

DIEHL, Gosta (1899-1964) Finnish
£478 $736 €760 Landscape (64x49cm-25x19in) s.d.1939. 24-Oct-2 Hagelstam, Helsinki #817
Works on paper
£523 $858 €800 Storm shore (49x66cm-19x26in) s.d.57 W/C. 9-Feb-3 Bukowskis, Helsinki #217/R

DIELEN, Adrian Jacob Willem van (1772-1812) Dutch
Works on paper
£350 $539 €550 Extensive landscape with shepherd and his flock on a path (40x53cm-16x21in) s.d.1798 black chk W/C. 3-Sep-2 Christie's, Amsterdam #88/R

DIELMANN, Jakob Furchtegott (1809-1885) German
£10432 $16691 €14500 Village musician (17x13cm-7x5in) s.d.1840 panel. 17-May-3 Lempertz, Koln #1387/R est:4000
Works on paper
£282 $468 €400 Talking over the fence (28x23cm-11x9in) W/C pencil. 14-Jun-3 Arnold, Frankfurt #728/R
£577 $912 €900 Girl in traditional costume of Hessen (13x10cm-5x4in) s.d.1841 W/C pencil. 15-Nov-2 Reiss & Sohn, Konigstein #259/R

£634 $1052 €900 Promising beginning in the summer swell (15x19cm-6x7in) s. W/C htd white. 14-Jun-3 Arnold, Frankfurt #727/R

DIEM-TILP, Ida (1877-1957) Austrian

£256 $397 €400 Reclining female nude (46x68cm-18x27in) s. lit. 6-Dec-2 Auktionhaus Georg Rehm, Augsburg #8019

DIEMEN, Jan van (20th C) Dutch?

£513 $805 €800 American football player (95x80cm-37x31in) s.d.88 acrylic. 25-Nov-2 Glerum, Amsterdam #356/R
£526 $853 €800 Football player (95x80cm-37x31in) s.d.82 acrylic. 21-Jan-3 Christie's, Amsterdam #509/R
£789 $1279 €1200 Skier (115x100cm-45x39in) s.d.82 acrylic. 21-Jan-3 Christie's, Amsterdam #507/R est:800-1200
£855 $1386 €1300 Golf player (130x150cm-51x59in) s.d.85 s.on stretcher. 21-Jan-3 Christie's, Amsterdam #500/R est:1000-1500
£1053 $1705 €1600 Racing cyclist (100x125cm-39x49in) s.d.84 acrylic. 21-Jan-3 Christie's, Amsterdam #501/R est:800-1200
£1379 $2193 €2000 Golfplayer (110x160cm-43x63in) s.d.86. 10-Mar-3 Sotheby's, Amsterdam #396/R est:2000-3000

DIEMER, Michael Zeno (1867-1939) German

£252 $392 €400 Southern fishing harbour (16x19cm-6x7in) canvas on board. 9-Oct-2 Michael Zeller, Lindau #663/R
£950 $1520 €1425 Sailing vessels in choppy seas (69x95cm-27x37in) s. 11-Mar-3 David Duggleby, Scarborough #232
£1000 $1620 €1450 Sailing ship foundering off a coast (70x95cm-28x37in) s. 21-May-3 Edgar Horn, Eastbourne #264 est:800-1200
£1027 $1603 €1500 Steamship at sea (59x83cm-23x33in) s. 10-Apr-3 Van Ham, Cologne #1397 est:800
£1410 $2186 €2200 Ships on Mediterranean (38x45cm-15x18in) s.d.1931 prov. 7-Dec-2 Ketterer, Hamburg #30/R est:2500-3000
£1690 $2721 €2400 Sailing by the Sicilian coast (59x83cm-23x33in) s. 10-May-3 Bukowskis, Helsinki #362/R est:1500-2000
£2100 $3339 €3150 Men o war passing on the open sea (109x142cm-43x56in) s. 4-Mar-3 Bonhams, Knightsbridge #308/R est:2000-3000
£2400 $3816 €3600 On the open sea (100x145cm-39x57in) s. 4-Mar-3 Bonhams, Knightsbridge #307/R est:2000-3000
£2500 $3875 €3750 Approaching the headland (60x84cm-24x33in) s. 31-Oct-2 Christie's, Kensington #462/R est:3000-5000
£3205 $5000 €4808 Two masted ship on the Mediterranean (81x109cm-32x43in) s. 21-Sep-2 Pook & Pook, Downington #21/R est:4000-6000
£3704 $6000 €5371 Norwegian lobster boat (59x83cm-23x33in) s. 29-Jul-3 Christie's, Rockefeller NY #176/R est:6000-8000

Works on paper

£1000 $1560 €1500 View of Hydra (31x48cm-12x19in) s. W/C gouache. 15-Oct-2 Sotheby's, London #57/R est:1500-2000

DIEMER, Zeno (19/20th C) German

£1795 $2782 €2800 Sailing ship in front of the coast of Albania (45x60cm-18x24in) s. i.verso. 4-Dec-2 Neumeister, Munich #713/R est:2000
£1923 $2981 €3000 Seascape with fishing boat in front of a mountainous coast (89x126cm-35x50in) s. 4-Dec-2 Neumeister, Munich #712/R est:2500
£3247 $4838 €5000 Seascape (91x120cm-36x47in) s. 26-Jun-2 Neumeister, Munich #712/R est:2600
£3481 $5396 €5500 Seascape (85x110cm-33x43in) s. 25-Sep-2 Neumeister, Munich #559/R est:2500

DIENER-DENOS, Rudolph (1889-1956) Hungarian

£1816 $2834 €2724 Still life with mirror and fruit (57x46cm-22x18in) s. board. 11-Apr-3 Kieselbach, Budapest #207/R est:450000-650000 (H.F 650000)

DIENES, Janos (20th C) ?

£1397 $2180 €2026 Tea in the garden (67x87cm-26x34in) s. 12-Apr-3 Mu Terem Galeria, Budapest #200/R est:220000 (H.F 500000)

DIENST, Rolf Gunter (1942-) German

£379 $599 €550 Epitaph for Ad Reinhardt Nr 77 (50x40cm-20x16in) s.i.d. verso lit. 2-Apr-3 Dr Fritz Nagel, Stuttgart #9037/R

DIENZ, Herm (1891-1980) German

£25362 $41594 €35000 The red bridge (67x41cm-26x16in) s.d.1920 board prov.lit. 29-May-3 Lempertz, Koln #587/R est:15000

DIEPENBECK, Abraham van (1596-1675) Flemish

£8387 $13252 €13000 Resting during the Flight into Egypt (39x31cm-15x12in) board en grisaille. 17-Dec-2 Segre, Madrid #64/R est:12000

Works on paper

£909 $1300 €1364 Virgin as the woman of the Apocalypse (42x35cm-17x14in) s.d.1650 black red chk. 23-Jan-3 Swann Galleries, New York #186/R est:2500-3500
£1206 $2013 €1700 Le martyre des dix-mille (38x27cm-15x11in) pen brown ink black crayon col wash. 19-Jun-3 Piasa, Paris #63 est:1000-1200

DIEPRAAM, Abraham (1622-1670) Dutch

£5000 $8350 €7250 Interior with a boor drinking and smoking (29x22cm-11x9in) mono. panel. 8-Jul-3 Sotheby's, Olympia #373/R est:3500-4500
£8766 $13850 €13149 The country doctor performing a back operation (40x32cm-16x13in) s. panel exhib. 27-Nov-2 Falkkloos, Malmo #77592/R est:40000 (S.KR 125000)

DIERA, G L (20th C) ?

£943 $1453 €1500 Foule devant les remparts (33x46cm-13x18in) s. panel. 23-Oct-2 Rabourdin & Choppin de Janvry, Paris #213/R
£943 $1453 €1500 Arrivvee de la fantasia (47x64cm-19x25in) s.d.1948 panel. 23-Oct-2 Rabourdin & Choppin de Janvry, Paris #223/R

DIERCKX, Pierre Jacques (1854-1947) Belgian

£665 $1037 €1050 Interieur de ferme anime (33x41cm-13x16in) s. 15-Oct-2 Vanderkindere, Brussels #55
£1438 $2315 €2200 Interieur hollandais (54x60cm-21x24in) s. 20-Jan-3 Horta, Bruxelles #4 est:400-600
£16026 $25160 €25000 Le souper des enfants a l'orphelinat (69x91cm-27x36in) s. 10-Dec-2 Vanderkindere, Brussels #50/R est:7500-10000

DIERICKX, Karel (1940-) Belgian

£791 $1266 €1100 Composition (55x45cm-22x18in) s. 17-May-3 De Vuyst, Lokeren #157
£1151 $1842 €1600 Larylight (100x100cm-39x39in) s.i.d.1986 verso prov.exhib. 17-May-3 De Vuyst, Lokeren #156/R est:1200-1400
£1727 $2763 €2400 Secretly relation (180x160cm-71x63in) s.d.1988 s.i.d.1988 verso. 17-May-3 De Vuyst, Lokeren #155/R est:1600-1800

DIERS, Thierry (1954-) French

£949 $1481 €1500 Nature morte a l'horaire de train (70x100cm-28x39in) s. s.i.d.sept 77 verso exhib.lit. 20-Oct-2 Charbonneaux, Paris #125/R est:1500-2000

DIESNER, Gerhild (1915-1995) Austrian

£1218 $1912 €1900 Rose (25x16cm-10x6in) s.d.69. 21-Nov-2 Dorotheum, Vienna #313/R est:2200-3000
£4828 $7724 €7000 Fish and lemons (33x51cm-13x20in) s.d.56 prov. 11-Mar-3 Dorotheum, Vienna #149/R est:7000-10000
£7971 $13072 €11000 Still life (69x47cm-27x19in) s.d.57. 27-May-3 Wiener Kunst Auktionen, Vienna #182/R est:11000-18000
£8511 $13787 €12000 Still life with melon, maize, lemons, red bottle and red chair (95x95cm-37x37in) s.d.58. 20-May-3 Dorotheum, Vienna #191/R est:10000-16000
£14184 $22979 €20000 Southern reeds (120x110cm-47x43in) s.d.58 i. verso. 20-May-3 Dorotheum, Vienna #192/R est:13000-18000

DIEST, Adriaen van (1655-1704) Dutch

£2000 $3340 €2900 English man-o-war off the coast (66x141cm-26x56in) 18-Jun-3 Sotheby's, Olympia #3/R est:2000-3000
£2229 $3478 €3500 Italianate landscape with a bull in the foreground (40x40cm-16x16in) s. prov. 5-Nov-2 Sotheby's, Amsterdam #38/R est:4000-6000

DIEST, Frans van (?) Belgian

£314 $491 €500 Chasseur dans un paysage hivernal (77x117cm-30x46in) 14-Oct-2 Amberes, Antwerp #214
£709 $1184 €1000 Landscape in the Ardennes, near the river Maas (80x120cm-31x47in) s. 23-Jun-3 Bernaerts, Antwerp #32/R

DIETER, Hans (1881-1968) German

£577 $877 €900 Back yard (49x40cm-19x16in) s. canvas on panel. 31-Aug-2 Geble, Radolfzell #625/R
£1282 $1949 €2000 Bodensee landscape (67x83cm-26x33in) s. 31-Aug-2 Geble, Radolfzell #624/R est:1300
£1959 $3057 €2900 Window with lake view (61x50cm-24x20in) s. lit. 28-Mar-3 Karrenbauer, Konstanz #1721 est:2900
£2609 $3704 €4200 Bodensee landscape (80x91cm-31x36in) s. 23-Mar-2 Geble, Radolfzell #533/R est:1280

DIETERLE, Marie (1856-1935) French

£1290 $2000 €1935 At the brookside (25x38cm-10x15in) s. panel prov. 2-Nov-2 North East Auctions, Portsmouth #32/R est:2000-3000
£1813 $2900 €2720 Cows at a watering hole (43x61cm-17x24in) s. prov. 15-Mar-3 Eldred, East Dennis #342/R est:5000-7000
£1974 $3197 €3000 Midday break (69x100cm-27x39in) s.i. 21-Jan-3 Christie's, Amsterdam #129/R est:3500-4500
£3503 $5465 €5500 Cows on track (80x65cm-31x26in) s. 6-Nov-2 Hugo Ruef, Munich #1060/R est:5500

DIETERLE, Pierre Georges (1844-1937) French

£478 $745 €750 Troupeau pres d'une riviere (55x81cm-22x32in) s. 7-Nov-2 Chochon-Barre & Allardi, Paris #121

DIETLER, Johann Friedrich (1804-1874) Swiss

Works on paper

£305 $500 €442 Portraits of Mr and Mrs D'Ivernois (26x19cm-10x7in) s.d.1856 and 1859 W/C pair. 4-Jun-3 Fischer, Luzern #2606/R (S.FR 650)

DIETMANN, Erik (1937-2002) Swedish

£347 $552 €521 Chloroformalisme - man's breakfast (51x58cm-20x23in) s.d.74-75 verso oil paper with cotton wool. 26-Feb-3 Kunsthallen, Copenhagen #210/R (D.KR 3800)

£911 $1421 €1367 Ils voulaient faire (120x120cm-47x47in) oil collage panel. 6-Nov-2 AB Stockholms Auktionsverk #881/R est:8000-12000 (S.KR 13000)

Sculpture

£1051 $1640 €1577 Almost 1 meter plaster around an environmental destruction (20cm-8in) s.d.1964 spray pot plaster. 5-Nov-2 Bukowskis, Stockholm #351/R est:8000-10000 (S.KR 15000)

£1051 $1640 €1577 Un vampire anemique est un ennemi, un salami (28cm-11in) one of 20 green pat.bronze prov. 5-Nov-2 Bukowskis, Stockholm #437/R est:18000-20000 (S.KR 15000)

£1261 $1968 €1892 Figure (117cm-46in) pat.bronze with metal executed 1986-88. 6-Nov-2 AB Stockholms Auktionsverk #882/R est:20000-25000 (S.KR 18000)

£1261 $1968 €1892 Composition (36x55cm-14x22in) green pat.bronze wood executed 1986-88. 6-Nov-2 AB Stockholms Auktionsverk #884/R est:20000-25000 (S.KR 18000)

£1371 $2180 €2057 Untitled (190cm-75in) s. copper granite glass pearls. 26-Feb-3 Kunsthallen, Copenhagen #218/R est:18000 (D.KR 15000)

£1892 $2952 €2838 Untitled (14x71x37cm-6x28x15in) green pat.bronze executed 1986-88. 6-Nov-2 AB Stockholms Auktionsverk #883/R est:25000-30000 (S.KR 27000)

Works on paper

£274 $436 €411 Recherche du pfain, Lecas sec.Route au vingt (45x50cm-18x20in) s.d.75 mixed media. 26-Feb-3 Kunsthallen, Copenhagen #211/R (D.KR 3000)

£278 $441 €400 49,4 cm of taylors zinc oxide plaster BPC (20x12cm-8x5in) s. collage sparadrap ink. 29-Apr-3 Artcurial Briest, Paris #631/R

£335 $529 €503 Untitled (105x151cm-41x59in) s.d.1988-89 verso mixed media. 28-Apr-3 Bukowskis, Stockholm #987/R (S.KR 4400)

£335 $529 €503 Untitled (75x156cm-30x61in) s.d.1988-89 verso mixed media. 28-Apr-3 Bukowskis, Stockholm #988/R (S.KR 4400)

£335 $529 €503 Untitled (74x128cm-29x50in) s.d.88 mixed media. 28-Apr-3 Bukowskis, Stockholm #989/R (S.KR 4400)

£374 $595 €550 Burroughs and Ginsberg (17x20cm-7x8in) s.d.1983 ink prov. 24-Mar-3 Cornette de St.Cyr, Paris #155/R

£570 $901 €855 Untitled (118x90cm-46x35in) s.d.1988-89 verso mixed media. 28-Apr-3 Bukowskis, Stockholm #993/R (S.KR 7500)

£646 $1021 €969 Untitled (75x179cm-30x70in) s.d.1988-89 verso mixed media. 28-Apr-3 Bukowskis, Stockholm #990/R (S.KR 8500)

£722 $1141 €1083 Indian summer (57x77cm-22x30in) s.d.79 mixed media collage. 28-Apr-3 Bukowskis, Stockholm #992/R (S.KR 9500)

DIETRICH, Adelheid (1827-?) German

£1146 $1766 €1800 Still life of flowers (21x17cm-8x7in) s.d.1866. 5-Sep-2 Arnold, Frankfurt #754/R est:2000

£1538 $2415 €2400 Still life of mixed flowers (23x18cm-9x7in) mono.d.1872. 23-Nov-2 Arnold, Frankfurt #705/R est:2000

£1800 $2862 €2700 Summer bouquet (21x17cm-8x7in) s.d.1866 panel. 20-Mar-3 Christie's, Kensington #31/R est:2000-3000

£6090 $9622 €9500 Still life of flowers (23x18cm-9x7in) s. board. 16-Nov-2 Lempertz, Koln #1451/R est:10000

£58065 $90000 €87098 Floral still lifes (23x18cm-9x7in) s.i.d.1870 pair. 5-Dec-2 Christie's, Rockefeller NY #1/R est:40000-60000

DIETRICH, Adolf (1877-1957) Swiss

£14151 $22925 €25047 Woodland path with deer (38x58cm-15x23in) s.d.1925 board lit. 26-May-3 Sotheby's, Zurich #124/R est:30000-40000 (S.FR 30000)

£25751 $40687 €38627 Ornamental gourds (34x39cm-13x15in) s.d.1936 board on plywood exhib.lit. 26-Nov-2 Phillips, Zurich #46/R est:50000-60000 (S.FR 60000)

£25751 $40687 €38627 Daisies in jug with yellow canary (54x56cm-21x22in) s.d.1954 board prov.lit. 28-Nov-2 Christie's, Zurich #92/R est:80000-120000 (S.FR 60000)

£43668 $68559 €65502 Woodpecker (30x24cm-12x9in) s.d.1937 board lit. 25-Nov-2 Sotheby's, Zurich #112/R est:70000-80000 (S.FR 100000)

£104803 $164541 €157205 Berlingen and the Reichenau (53x66cm-21x26in) s.d.1932 board exhib.lit. 25-Nov-2 Sotheby's, Zurich #100/R est:240000-280000 (S.FR 240000)

£107296 $169528 €160944 Winter at Untersee (29x40cm-11x16in) s.d.1933 board lit. 26-Nov-2 Phillips, Zurich #47/R est:200000-250000 (S.FR 250000)

£107296 $169528 €160944 Blue winter's day with Schienerberg (40x60cm-16x24in) s.d.1940 board prov.exhib.lit. 28-Nov-2 Christie's, Zurich #87/R est:250000-300000 (S.FR 250000)

Works on paper

£870 $1348 €1305 Untersee (10x13cm-4x5in) pencil prov. double-sided. 4-Dec-2 Koller, Zurich #139a/R est:2000-3000 (S.FR 2000)

£1717 $2712 €2576 Dog lying down (48x36cm-19x14in) s. chl. 28-Nov-2 Christie's, Zurich #83/R est:2500-3500 (S.FR 4000)

£1803 $2848 €2705 Untersee landscape (18x26cm-7x10in) s.d.1947 pencil prov.exhib.lit. 28-Nov-2 Christie's, Zurich #84/R est:3000-5000 (S.FR 4200)

£2489 $3933 €3734 Two squirrels (27x20cm-11x8in) s.d.1948 lithographic pen prov.exhib.lit. 28-Nov-2 Christie's, Zurich #85/R est:4000-6000 (S.FR 5800)

£7860 $12341 €11790 Seagull in storm (36x48cm-14x19in) s.d.1900 W/C prov.lit. 25-Nov-2 Sotheby's, Zurich #120/R est:6000-9000 (S.FR 18000)

£17167 $27124 €25751 Footbridge at Untersee (25x34cm-10x13in) s. exhib. 26-Nov-2 Phillips, Zurich #45/R est:12000-15000 (S.FR 40000)

DIETRICH, Christian Wilhelm Ernst (1712-1774) German

£500 $715 €750 Portrait of an elderly man (24x19cm-9x7in) 28-Feb-2 Greenslade Hunt, Taunton #413/R

£1500 $2415 €2250 Portrait of a beard old man, wearing a turban and red mantle (29x24cm-11x9in) 20-Feb-3 Christie's, Kensington #245/R est:1000-1500

£4000 $6240 €6000 Wooed landscape with highwaymen holding up a carriage. Wooded landscape with capture of highwaymen (30x36cm-12x14in) s.d.1742 panel pair. 9-Apr-3 Bonhams, New Bond Street #105/R est:4000-5000

£8108 $12649 €12000 Ange avec betail et figures (82x98cm-32x39in) s. 25-Mar-3 Campo & Campo, Antwerp #60/R est:8000-10000

£9000 $14130 €13500 Bearded Oriental in a turban. Bearded Oriental in a feathered turban (83x70cm-33x28in) pair. 10-Dec-2 Bonhams, New Bond Street #312/R est:10000-15000

£10490 $17517 €15000 Jeune berger apercevant des baigneuses dans un paysage (67x84cm-26x33in) s.d.1761. 27-Jun-3 Piasa, Paris #75/R est:15000-20000

£13380 $19000 €20070 Landscapes with figures (28x36cm-11x14in) s. panel pair. 8-Aug-1 Barridorf, Portland #54/R est:30000-40000

£14839 $23445 €23000 Dancing scene in garden (110x139cm-43x55in) 18-Dec-2 Tajan, Paris #35/R est:30000

£15962 $26178 €23145 Southern landscape with herders and cattle (58x67cm-23x26in) s.d.1762 pair. 4-Jun-3 Fischer, Luzern #1109/R est:18000-25000 (S.FR 34000)

DIETRICH, Christian Wilhelm Ernst (attrib) (1712-1774) German

£252 $388 €400 Portrait de Platon (26x20cm-10x8in) panel. 25-Oct-2 Tajan, Paris #86

£837 $1222 €1256 Ruins in landscape with rider and beggars (36x27cm-14x11in) panel. 17-Jun-2 Philippe Schuler, Zurich #4334/R (S.FR 1900)

£1295 $2072 €1800 Portrait of man in Oriental costume (38x27cm-15x11in) panel after Rembrandt. 17-May-3 Hagelstam, Helsinki #23/R est:2000

£2800 $4340 €4200 Shepherds playing with a caged bird. Shepherds courting (29x22cm-11x9in) panel pair. 30-Oct-2 Bonhams, New Bond Street #92/R est:3000-5000

£3546 $5922 €5000 Deux putti jouant dans un paysage architecture (45x36cm-18x14in) 18-Jun-3 Tajan, Paris #102/R est:3000-5000

£8108 $12649 €12000 Christ on Mount of Olives (42x32cm-17x13in) bears sig. panel. 27-Mar-3 Dorotheum, Vienna #252/R est:12000-25000

DIETRICH, Friedrich August Theodor (1817-?) Bosnian

Sculpture

£1753 $2700 €2630 Bust of a Russian soldier (33x18x10cm-13x7x4in) s.st.f.Nikolaus I silver. 26-Oct-2 Brunk, Ashville #354/R est:1500-2500

£2727 $4064 €4200 Czar Nikolaus I or Alexander II of Russia (59cm-23in) i. gold pat.bronze. 26-Jun-2 Neumeister, Munich #33/R est:1200

DIETRICH, Gustave (1860-?) German

£900 $1467 €1350 Waterfall in a forest, Alps in background (36x44cm-14x17in) s. 29-Jan-3 Sotheby's, Olympia #258/R est:800-1000

DIETRICH-MOHR (1924-) German

Sculpture

£1795 $2818 €2800 Untitled (56x17cm-22x7in) init. tin. 24-Nov-2 Laurence Calmels, Paris #294/R

DIETRICHSON, Mathilde (1837-1921) Norwegian
£1828 $2924 €2742 Evening in Granada - woman on terrace (41x28cm-16x11in) s.d.1885 i.verso panel. 17-Mar-3 Blomqvist, Oslo #301/R est:25000-30000 (N.KR 21000)
£2388 $3916 €3463 Woman on verandah (100x80cm-39x31in) s.indis.d.1889. 2-Jun-3 Blomqvist, Oslo #210/R est:30000-40000 (N.KR 26000)
£4363 $6850 €6545 Woman sewing (98x71cm-39x28in) s.d.1891. 21-Nov-2 Grev Wedels Plass, Oslo #54/R est:50000-70000 (N.KR 50000)

DIETZ, Gundi (1942-) Austrian
Sculpture
£1646 $2567 €2600 Jane (86x35x45cm-34x14x18in) mono.d.1990 col gold ceramic metal table. 15-Oct-2 Dorotheum, Vienna #231/R est:2800-4000
£1899 $2962 €3000 Dancer, after Degas (10x40x40cm-4x16x16in) s.d.18.4.89 col gold ceramic metal table. 15-Oct-2 Dorotheum, Vienna #232/R est:2800-4000

DIETZSCH, Johann Christoph (1710-1769) German
Works on paper
£979 $1400 €1469 Shepherd and his flock in a landscape with a valley and a hamlet at sunset (12x18cm-5x7in) gouache. 23-Jan-3 Swann Galleries, New York #341/R est:2000-3000
£1295 $2072 €1800 Italian landscape with washerwomen and couple resting (21x26cm-8x10in) s. Indian ink brush bodycol prov. 17-May-3 Lempertz, Koln #1220/R est:2000

DIEU, Antoine (attrib) (1662-1727) French
£4196 $7007 €6000 Louix XIV assistant aux funerailles du Grand Dauphin Louis de France (97x129cm-38x51in) 27-Jun-3 Piasa, Paris #70/R est:6000-8000

DIEUDONNE, Emmanuel de (19th C) French
£2201 $3390 €3500 Procession dans les rues du Caire (68x50cm-27x20in) s.i. 23-Oct-2 Rabourdin & Choppin de Janvry, Paris #110/R

DIEVENBACH, Hendricus Anthonius (1872-1946) Dutch
£284 $475 €412 Visit (36x30cm-14x12in) s. 28-Jun-3 Harvey Clar, Oakland #1151
£605 $944 €950 Interior with man reading by candle light (53x46cm-21x18in) s. 5-Nov-2 Vendu Notarishuis, Rotterdam #252/R
£741 $1148 €1112 Helping mother (51x61cm-20x24in) s. 3-Dec-2 Ritchie, Toronto #3063/R est:2000-3000 (C.D 1800)
£826 $1298 €1239 Mother's happiness (51x61cm-20x24in) s. 24-Jul-2 Walker's, Ottawa #6/R est:2500-3000 (C.D 2000)

DIEY, Yves (1892-1984) French
£283 $439 €450 Nu (61x92cm-24x36in) s. 3-Nov-2 Feletin, Province #153
£288 $453 €450 Portrait de M. Chacon (90x116cm-35x46in) s.d.1947. 22-Nov-2 Millon & Associes, Paris #58

DIEZ DE SANTOS, Vicente (1899-1993) Spanish
£331 $523 €480 Carts (27x39cm-11x15in) s. cardboard. 1-Apr-3 Segre, Madrid #144/R

DIEZ, Anton (1914-1992) Belgian
£472 $731 €750 Mother and child (80x60cm-31x24in) s. 5-Oct-2 De Vuyst, Lokeren #110

DIEZ, Samuel (1803-1873) Swiss
Works on paper
£833 $1292 €1300 Portrait of a lady with Belvedere castle near Weimar in background (40x33cm-16x13in) s.d.1850 W/C over pencil htd white. 4-Dec-2 Neumeister, Munich #509/R

DIEZ, Wilhelm von (1839-1907) German
£301 $470 €440 Soldiers in market (16x21cm-6x8in) mono. panel. 9-Apr-3 Neumeister, Munich #661/R
£405 $632 €600 Rider with two horses (26x12cm-10x5in) s. panel. 27-Mar-3 Dr Fritz Nagel, Stuttgart #803/R
£566 $883 €900 Humorous scene from soldier's life (22x30cm-9x12in) s. panel. 19-Sep-2 Dr Fritz Nagel, Stuttgart #921/R
£1000 $1520 €1500 Rest on the journey (31x44cm-12x17in) s.d.1889 panel. 29-Aug-2 Christie's, Kensington #141/R est:1200-1800
£1154 $1788 €1800 Meeting at horse trough (14x16cm-6x6in) s. lit. 6-Dec-2 Karlheinz Kaupp, Staufen #2374/R est:1800

DIGGING, Yam (1978-) Australian
Works on paper
£1372 $2126 €2058 Untitled (25x35cm-10x14in) synthetic polymer paint board exhib. 3-Dec-2 Shapiro, Sydney #233/R est:3500-5000 (A.D 3800)

DIGHTON, Joshua (fl.1820-1840) British
Works on paper
£600 $936 €900 Sir Watkin Williams Wynn Bt astride his horse (22x18cm-9x7in) i.d.1859 W/C. 11-Sep-2 Bonhams, Newport #200
£1400 $2324 €2030 Jockey up (27x24cm-11x9in) pencil W/C htd white prov. 12-Jun-3 Christie's, Kensington #105/R est:300-400

DIGHTON, Richard (1785-1880) British
Works on paper
£330 $538 €495 Admiral Rous and Mr George Pane, fathers of the turf (21x15cm-8x6in) W/C. 2-Feb-3 Lots Road, London #354a/R
£400 $632 €600 Portrait of George Hawkes, holding a Doncaster sale catalogue held at Tattersalls (25x15cm-10x6in) pencil W/C. 28-Nov-2 Christie's, Kensington #191/R
£500 $775 €750 Portrait of a gentleman (48x41cm-19x16in) s.d.1805 W/C. 6-Oct-2 Lots Road, London #354

DIGNAM, Mary Ella Williams (1860-1938) Canadian
£215 $335 €323 Canal Venice (30x24cm-12x9in) s.i.d.1910 verso canvasboard. 25-Mar-3 Ritchie, Toronto #68/R (C.D 500)
£658 $1021 €987 Harbour scene (35x45cm-14x18in) s. 3-Dec-2 Joyner, Toronto #498 est:1000-1500 (C.D 1600)

DIGNIMONT, Andre (1891-1965) French
£3734 $5826 €6470 Bordello scene (22x27cm-9x11in) s. paper prov. 31-Mar-3 Goodman, Sydney #199/R (A.D 9900)
Works on paper
£270 $422 €400 Vase de fleurs (65x50cm-26x20in) s. W/C. 28-Mar-3 Neret-Minet, Paris #1
£284 $474 €400 Femme accoudee (57x45cm-22x18in) s. W/C. 23-Jun-3 Delvaux, Paris #192
£345 $576 €500 Nu debout a l'eventail (64x50cm-25x20in) W/C. 9-Jul-3 Millon & Associes, Paris #206a
£411 $650 €650 Jeune femme a l'eventail (44x24cm-17x9in) s. W/C. 27-Nov-2 Blanchet, Paris #22
£414 $646 €650 Decor de theatre (33x41cm-13x16in) s. gouache W/C. 10-Nov-2 Eric Pillon, Calais #117/R
£420 $655 €630 Seated lady (48x63cm-19x25in) s.i.d.1942 W/C pen. 15-Oct-2 Bonhams, Knightsbridge #108/R
£434 $673 €690 Portrait de femme (62x48cm-24x19in) s.d.35 pastel. 3-Nov-2 Feletin, Province #125
£475 $741 €750 Bouquet de fleurs (64x49cm-25x19in) s. gouache. 20-Oct-2 Claude Boisgirard, Paris #7
£510 $795 €800 Elegante au chapeau rouge (50x60cm-20x24in) s.i. W/C. 7-Nov-2 Chochon-Barre & Allardi, Paris #122
£2449 $3894 €3600 Retour de peche (42x35cm-17x14in) s.i. W/C gouache. 26-Feb-3 Artcurial Briest, Paris #53/R est:3000-3500

DIJKSTRA, Rineke (1959-) Dutch
Photographs
£1840 $3000 €2760 Tiergarten, Berlin, July (29x24cm-11x9in) s.i.d.num.31/32 verso color coupler print. 12-Feb-3 Christie's, Rockefeller NY #123/R est:3000-5000
£5063 $8000 €7595 Kolobzeg, Poland (35x28cm-14x11in) s.i.d.July 23 1992 verso chromogenic col print prov.lit. 24-Apr-3 Phillips, New York #217/R est:9000-12000
£6500 $10855 €9425 Evora, Portugal. Villa Franca, Portugal (26x20cm-10x8in) s.i.d.May 1994 one num.4/20 one num.12/20 verso col photo 2 prov. 26-Jun-3 Sotheby's, London #287/R est:5000-7000
£13750 $22000 €20625 Evors. Portugal May 1 1994. Villa Franca, Portugal May 1994 (27x20cm-11x8in) s.i.d.1.May 1994 num.20 two col photograph. 16-May-3 Phillips, New York #122/R est:15000-20000
£18000 $29520 €27000 Asylum Centre Leiden. Almerisa Wormer. Almerisa Wormer (35x28cm-14x11in) s.i.d.1997 1996 1998 Cibachrome prints three from edition of three pro. 6-Feb-3 Christie's, London #745/R est:18000-24000
£20253 $32000 €30380 Almerisa, asielzoekerscentrum, Leiden, the Netherlands (120x100cm-47x39in) three col coupler prints set of three executed 1994-98 prov. 14-Nov-2 Christie's, Rockefeller NY #420/R est:20000-30000
£20570 $32500 €30855 Tiergarten, Berlin (153x129cm-60x51in) s.i. c-print one of 10 prov.exhib.lit. 13-Nov-2 Sotheby's, New York #436/R est:20000-30000
£28000 $45920 €42000 Julie, den haag, Netherlands, February 29 1994 (153x129cm-60x51in) c-print executed 1994 prov.exhib.lit. 5-Feb-3 Christie's, London #26/R est:25000-35000

£31646 $50000 €47469 Dubrovnik, Croatia, July 13 1996 (116x119cm-46x47in) s.d.1999 col coupler print prov.lit. 14-Nov-2 Christie's, Rockefeller NY #419/R est:35000-45000
£51282 $80000 €76923 Self portrait, Marnixbad, Amsterdam (152x129cm-60x51in) s. col coupler print executed 1991. 11-Nov-2 Phillips, New York #2/R est:60000-80000

DIJSSELHOF, Gerrit Willem (1866-1924) Dutch
£828 $1316 €1200 Stilleven met kabeljauw (31x24cm-12x9in) mono. panel. 10-Mar-3 Sotheby's, Amsterdam #140/R est:1500-2000
£943 $1453 €1500 Lobster (42x59cm-17x23in) mono. 23-Oct-2 Christie's, Amsterdam #155/R est:2000-3000
£2069 $3290 €3000 Lobster in an aquarium (52x70cm-20x28in) mono. canvas on panel. 10-Mar-3 Sotheby's, Amsterdam #133/R est:2200-2400
£2390 $3681 €3800 Turtle (29x30cm-11x12in) mono. prov. 23-Oct-2 Christie's, Amsterdam #154/R est:1500-2000
Works on paper
£318 $490 €500 School of fish (21x24cm-8x9in) mono. black ink chl. 3-Sep-2 Christie's, Amsterdam #259

DIKE, Philip Latimer (1906-1990) American
Works on paper
£2388 $3750 €3582 Approach to the sea (121x61cm-48x24in) s. i.verso mixed media masonite prov. 19-Nov-2 Butterfields, San Francisco #8350/R est:3000-5000

DILGER, Richard (20th C) German
£248 $353 €400 Woman's head (34x28cm-13x11in) s. board. 23-Mar-2 Geble, Radolfzell #536
£422 $600 €680 Still life with pot plant (61x66cm-24x26in) s.d.33 board. 23-Mar-2 Geble, Radolfzell #534/R

DILL, Laddie John (1943-) American
£967 $1500 €1451 Untitled (122x218cm-48x86in) st.verso. 29-Sep-2 Butterfields, Los Angeles #4418/R est:1500-2000

DILL, Ludwig (1848-1940) German
£233 $365 €350 Seascape with jetty with sailboat docked beside (25x33cm-10x13in) s. 19-Apr-3 James Julia, Fairfield #291/R
£516 $759 €800 Fishing boat off Gioggia (20x29cm-8x11in) s. i. verso board. 20-Jun-2 Dr Fritz Nagel, Stuttgart #762/R
£828 $1292 €1300 Fishermen near Gioggia (20x28cm-8x11in) s. board lit. 7-Nov-2 Allgauer, Kempten #2785/R
£1088 $1731 €1600 Fishing boat in evening (25x35cm-10x14in) s. panel. 28-Mar-3 Bolland & Marotz, Bremen #439/R est:1400
£1146 $1789 €1800 Fishing boats in Chioggia (51x65cm-20x26in) s. panel. 6-Nov-2 Hugo Ruef, Munich #1061 est:1800
£1210 $1864 €1900 Sailing ship by town (27x31cm-11x12in) s. 5-Sep-2 Arnold, Frankfurt #756/R est:800
£1301 $2030 €1900 Fishing boats in Chioggia Lagoon (40x54cm-16x21in) s. s.i. verso board. 11-Apr-3 Winterberg, Heidelberg #909/R est:2600
£1389 $2208 €2000 Sailing boats in Mediterranean waters (49x33cm-19x13in) s. panel. 29-Apr-3 Wiener Kunst Auktionen, Vienna #631/R
£2564 $3974 €4000 Dachau landscape in autumn (32x48cm-13x19in) s. i. verso panel. 5-Dec-2 Dr Fritz Nagel, Stuttgart #649/R est:2500
£3766 $5612 €5800 Birch trees on lake shore (75x95cm-30x37in) s.d.1925. 26-Jun-2 Neumeister, Munich #714/R est:4500
£7051 $11071 €11000 Fishing boats off Venice (59x100cm-23x39in) s. 21-Nov-2 Van Ham, Cologne #1564/R est:2000

DILL, Otto (1884-1957) German
£619 $997 €929 Shipping (27x18cm-11x7in) s. board. 12-May-3 Stephan Welz, Johannesburg #25 est:2500-4000 (SA.R 7200)
£822 $1282 €1200 Two women from Bernhardin (27x36cm-11x14in) board. 11-Apr-3 Sigalas, Stuttgart #435
£1370 $2137 €2000 Lioness (34x23cm-13x9in) s. W/C chl. 11-Apr-3 Winterberg, Heidelberg #912/R est:1450
£1923 $2923 €3000 Homebound farmer with sheep and cows (32x51cm-13x20in) s. lit. 11-Jul-2 Allgauer, Kempten #2463/R
£2365 $3689 €3500 Fight (60x80cm-24x31in) s. 26-Mar-3 Hugo Ruef, Munich #90/R est:3500
£2830 $4415 €4500 Returning home from the fields (61x80cm-24x31in) s.d.1934 i. verso panel. 19-Sep-2 Dr Fritz Nagel, Stuttgart #922/R est:2900
£3077 $4769 €4800 Carthorses in meadow (36x49cm-14x19in) s.d.1908 board. 4-Dec-2 Lempertz, Koln #655/R est:2000
£3145 $4906 €5000 Cows drawing cart through wood (50x70cm-20x28in) s. board. 19-Sep-2 Dr Fritz Nagel, Stuttgart #923/R est:2700
£3205 $5032 €5000 Four horses drawing cart (36x50cm-14x20in) s.d.17 board. 21-Nov-2 Van Ham, Cologne #1565/R est:5500
£3654 $5663 €5700 Jockeys on race track (50x70cm-20x28in) s.d.1922 prov. 7-Dec-2 Ketterer, Hamburg #158/R est:8000-9000
£4214 $6489 €6700 Peasant with horses (69x80cm-27x31in) s. board. 26-Oct-2 Quittenbaum, Hamburg #7/R est:4500
£8000 $12560 €12000 Der stierkampf - bull fight (60x70cm-24x28in) s.indis d.1923. 19-Nov-2 Sotheby's, London #186/R est:6000-8000
£8099 $13039 €11500 Horse racing (50x70cm-20x28in) s. board. 10-May-3 Berlinghof, Heidelberg #210/R est:11500
Works on paper
£411 $650 €650 Horse tamers (23x31cm-9x12in) s.d.1919. 30-Nov-2 Bassenge, Berlin #6220/R
£435 $713 €600 Horse racing (24x31cm-9x12in) s. chk graphite. 29-May-3 Lempertz, Koln #588/R
£504 $826 €700 Bullfight (21x29cm-8x11in) s.d.1926 W/C Indian ink brush. 4-Jun-3 Reiss & Sohn, Konigstein #354/R
£541 $843 €800 Desert scene (30x41cm-12x16in) s. W/C prov. 27-Mar-3 Dr Fritz Nagel, Stuttgart #802/R
£897 $1426 €1300 Young fox (33x25cm-13x10in) s. gouache. 8-Mar-3 Arnold, Frankfurt #571/R
£1206 $1953 €1700 Men leading two horses (30x42cm-12x17in) s. i. verso Indian ink. 24-May-3 Van Ham, Cologne #147/R est:1800

DILLENIUS, Johan Kaspar Anton (attrib) (1791-1869) German
£2887 $4649 €4100 Still life of flowers (36x28cm-14x11in) 10-May-3 Hans Stahl, Toestorf #3/R est:3800

DILLENS, Adolphe Alexander (1821-1877) Belgian
£252 $387 €400 Fillette a l'echarpe (18x15cm-7x6in) s.verso panel. 22-Oct-2 Campo, Vlaamse Kaai #97
£355 $561 €550 Woman wearing hat (33x28cm-13x11in) s.d.1876 panel. 19-Dec-2 Delvaux, Paris #39/R
£1242 $1999 €1900 Fillettes et leur poupees (40x32cm-16x13in) s. 14-Jan-3 Vanderkindere, Brussels #47 est:1500-2500

DILLENS, Albert (1844-?) Belgian
£609 $944 €950 Pecheurs de crevettes a Blankenberge (68x52cm-27x20in) s.i.d.19 avril 1880 canvas on cardboard. 9-Dec-2 Horta, Bruxelles #350

DILLENS, Hendrick Joseph (1812-1872) Belgian
£1384 $2145 €2200 Listener (53x42cm-21x17in) s.d.1849 panel. 5-Oct-2 De Vuyst, Lokeren #111/R est:2200-2600
£2113 $3401 €3000 Animated village (18x23cm-7x9in) s.d.59 panel. 12-May-3 Bernaerts, Antwerp #50/R est:3000-3500
£5000 $8150 €7500 Lady of the house (57x42cm-22x17in) s.d.1856 panel. 29-Jan-3 Sotheby's, Olympia #299/R est:3000-5000

DILLENS, Hendrick Joseph (attrib) (1812-1872) Belgian
£1600 $2528 €2400 Time with the children (61x45cm-24x18in) bears sig.d.1854 panel. 2-Dec-2 Bonhams, Bath #146/R est:1200-1800

DILLENS, Henri (19th C) ?
£6200 $9734 €9300 Centre of attention (53x73cm-21x29in) s.d.1855 panel. 19-Nov-2 Sotheby's, London #194/R est:6000-8000

DILLER, F (?) ?
Sculpture
£1069 $1668 €1700 Boar (52cm-20in) i. 23-Sep-2 Dr Fritz Nagel, Stuttgart #8044/R est:250

DILLEY, Ramon (1933-) French
£299 $475 €449 Plage du Charlton (36x28cm-14x11in) s.d.82 s.i.verso cardboard on canvas. 18-Mar-3 Arthur James, Florida #35

D'ILLIERS, Gaston (1876-1952) French
Sculpture
£1410 $2158 €2200 Avant la course (19cm-7in) s.i. bronze. 23-Aug-2 Deauville, France #288/R
£1500 $2340 €2250 Huntsman on horseback in winter (27x21cm-11x8in) s.st.f.Jaboef and Rouard brown pat bronze. 5-Nov-2 Sotheby's, London #102/R est:1800-2500
£2057 $3332 €2900 Le saut d'obstacle (34cm-13in) s. brown pat. bronze oak base. 23-May-3 Camard, Paris #5/R est:2800-3500

DILLIS, Cantius (attrib) (1779-1856) German
£943 $1472 €1500 Cattle drinking in Miesbach valley near Traunstein (32x43cm-13x17in) panel. 11-Oct-2 Winterberg, Heidelberg #504/R
£1154 $1788 €1800 Mountain valley with stone bridge over the water, with farmhouse (24x32cm-9x13in) panel. 4-Dec-2 Neumeister, Munich #714/R est:1500

DILLIS, Johann Georg von (1759-1841) German
£3401 $5408 €5000 Lake Nemi with view of Genzano (18x23cm-7x9in) oil study over pencil paper on canvas. 19-Mar-3 Neumeister, Munich #543/R est:6000
Works on paper
£321 $468 €500 Near Schneitzlreuth (21x26cm-8x10in) i.d.1832 chk pencil htd white. 4-Jun-2 Karl & Faber, Munich #63

£737 $1077 €1150 Italian peasant on horse with animals (19x16cm-7x6in) W/C over pencil. 4-Jun-2 Karl & Faber, Munich #64/R
£833 $1217 €1300 Gurnwande neaar Ruhpolding (21x26cm-8x10in) i.d.1817 chk pencil htd white. 4-Jun-2 Karl & Faber, Munich #62
£886 $1373 €1400 Landscape with building in Munchen-Harlaching (21x30cm-8x12in) mono.i. pencil pen wash study verso. 27-Sep-2 Venator & Hansten, Koln #1262 est:1900
£1042 $1656 €1500 Landscape with riverbank (17x21cm-7x8in) pen over pencil. 5-May-3 Ketterer, Munich #287/R est:700-900
£1101 $1717 €1750 Alpine landscape near Kleinweil near the Kochelsee (33x41cm-13x16in) chk htd white. 11-Oct-2 Winterberg, Heidelberg #505/R est:1800
£1181 $1877 €1700 Trees and bushes (20x28cm-8x11in) brush ink over pencil wash htd white. 5-May-3 Ketterer, Munich #289/R est:400-600
£1346 $1965 €2100 Portrait of Joseph Dillis (15x11cm-6x4in) i. W/C over pencil. 4-Jun-2 Karl & Faber, Munich #65/R est:1800

DILLIS, Johann Georg von (attrib) (1759-1841) German
Works on paper
£285 $450 €450 Landscape (15x20cm-6x8in) pencil wash double-sided. 29-Nov-2 Bassenge, Berlin #5625
£322 $502 €470 Southern mountain town with riders and travellers on road (33x48cm-13x19in) W/C chl pencil. 11-Apr-3 Winterberg, Heidelberg #364/R
£616 $962 €900 Riding party with dog (18x22cm-7x9in) W/C pen. 11-Apr-3 Winterberg, Heidelberg #363/R
£1806 $2871 €2600 Boy enveloped in travelling rug with another boy (18x14cm-7x6in) W/C over pencil. 5-May-3 Ketterer, Munich #286/R est:800-1000

DILLIS, Johann Georg von (circle) (1759-1841) German
£7692 $11000 €11538 Study of the sky after a sunset, Rome. Evening clouds above a dark tree lined ridge (11x22cm-4x9in) i. oil on paper two. 23-Jan-3 Swann Galleries, New York #359/R est:800-1200

DILLMANN, Hilmar (1940-) German
£321 $497 €500 Romantic extensive landscape in Normandy with windmills and figures (11x25cm-4x10in) s. i.verso panel. 7-Dec-2 Bergmann, Erlangen #781/R

DILLON, Frank (1823-1909) British
£5800 $9048 €8700 Arabs at prayer on the banks of the Nile (79x135cm-31x53in) s.d.1888. 17-Sep-2 Sotheby's, Olympia #167/R est:2000-3000
£8500 $13685 €12750 Pyramids of Gyzeh at sunrise (43x73cm-17x29in) init.d.1855 exhib. 20-Feb-3 Christie's, London #287/R
Works on paper
£2600 $4316 €3900 Saimon of the Kiyumizu-dera temple, Kyoto, Japan (36x51cm-14x20in) W/C bodycol. 12-Jun-3 Bonhams, New Bond Street #843/R est:1200-1800

DILLON, Gerard (1917-1971) Irish
£1042 $1656 €1500 Fish and profiles (23x33cm-9x13in) init. oil sand. 29-Apr-3 Whyte's, Dublin #41/R est:3000-4000
£4717 $7358 €7500 Back view, Roundstone (45x64cm-18x25in) s. i.verso board prov. 17-Sep-2 Whyte's, Dublin #43/R est:8000-10000
£5072 $8319 €7000 Reclining nude (41x51cm-16x20in) s. 28-May-3 Bonhams & James Adam, Dublin #114/R est:5000-8000
£7432 $11595 €11000 Long woman's dream (50x68cm-20x27in) s. prov. 26-Mar-3 James Adam, Dublin #53/R est:10000-15000
£7500 $12000 €11250 Bird's nest (91x61cm-36x24in) s. oil sand board prov. 15-May-3 Christie's, London #86/R est:8000-12000
£7500 $12000 €11250 Masked figure and nude (85x120cm-33x47in) s. s.i.verso board. 16-May-3 Sotheby's, London #136/R est:8000-12000
£9615 $14904 €15000 Whispering (58x41cm-23x16in) s. board prov.exhib. 3-Dec-2 Bonhams & James Adam, Dublin #93/R est:12000-16000
£11000 $17600 €16500 Untitled (152x91cm-60x36in) s. 16-May-3 Sotheby's, London #142/R est:10000-15000
£13000 $20800 €19500 Spectator (30x51cm-12x20in) prov. 16-May-3 Sotheby's, London #104/R est:10000-15000
£13208 $20604 €21000 Blue hoop (44x58cm-17x23in) s. i.verso board exhib. 17-Sep-2 Whyte's, Dublin #87/R est:20000-25000
£14557 $22563 €23000 Unassuming (60x75cm-24x30in) s. exhib. 25-Sep-2 James Adam, Dublin #99/R est:10000-15000
£18239 $28453 €29000 Mac Dara's yard (36x47cm-14x19in) s. i.verso canvas on board prov.exhib. 17-Sep-2 Whyte's, Dublin #46/R est:30000-40000
£21739 $35652 €30000 Farmer in landscape (37x53cm-15x21in) s. board prov. 28-May-3 Bonhams & James Adam, Dublin #106/R est:14000-18000
£37848 $62071 €56772 Boys catching crabs in Connemara (56x82cm-22x32in) s. board painted c.1948 prov.lit. 4-Jun-3 Deutscher-Menzies, Melbourne #42/R est:90000-120000 (A.D 95000)

Works on paper
£450 $698 €675 Figures (12x17cm-5x7in) s. mixed media. 4-Dec-2 John Ross, Belfast #110
£550 $803 €825 Mother and child (13x13cm-5x5in) mono. mixed media. 12-Jun-2 John Ross, Belfast #94
£550 $853 €825 Three wise men (15x22cm-6x9in) s. W/C. 4-Dec-2 John Ross, Belfast #165
£709 $1107 €1050 Brown and green abstract (24x33cm-9x13in) s. mixed media prov. 26-Mar-3 James Adam, Dublin #50/R est:1000-1500
£755 $1177 €1200 Nativity scene (13x18cm-5x7in) i.verso W/C wax crayon pen ink card. 17-Sep-2 Whyte's, Dublin #88/R
£890 $1398 €1300 Fossilised forms (45x62cm-18x24in) mixed media prov. 15-Apr-3 De Veres Art Auctions, Dublin #100d est:900-1200
£1081 $1686 €1600 Personnages (24x33cm-9x13in) s.d.61 mixed media. 26-Mar-3 James Adam, Dublin #130/R est:1000-1500
£1500 $2385 €2250 Figure study (30x35cm-12x14in) s. pencil. 5-Mar-3 John Ross, Belfast #184 est:1250-1500
£2095 $3268 €3100 Fisherman (18x24cm-7x9in) Indian ink prov. 26-Mar-3 James Adam, Dublin #52/R est:1000-1500
£3425 $5377 €5000 Head and lanscape (30x40cm-12x16in) s. mixed media prov. 15-Apr-3 De Veres Art Auctions, Dublin #181/R est:5000-7000
£3500 $5600 €5250 Harbour (24x34cm-9x13in) s. W/C prov. 16-May-3 Sotheby's, London #146/R est:2000-3000
£3600 $5580 €5400 Listening and watching (76x64cm-30x25in) s.verso mixed media. 2-Oct-2 John Ross, Belfast #181 est:3500-4500

DIMMEL, Herbert (1894-1980) Austrian
Works on paper
£321 $506 €500 Composition (28x42cm-11x17in) mono.i. pen. 18-Nov-2 Dorotheum, Linz #479/R

DIMOVSKI, Zoran (20th C) Yugoslavian
Works on paper
£250 $400 €363 Generator of shapes (70x100cm-28x39in) s.d.2001 verso col pencil graphite. 13-May-3 Sotheby's, Tel Aviv #32/R
£250 $400 €363 Generator of shapes (70x100cm-28x39in) s.d.2001 verso col pencil graphite. 13-May-3 Sotheby's, Tel Aviv #37/R
£250 $400 €363 Generator of shapes (70x100cm-28x39in) s.d.2001 col pencil graphite. 13-May-3 Sotheby's, Tel Aviv #43/R
£250 $400 €363 Generator of shapes (70x100cm-28x39in) s.d.2001 col pencil graphite. 13-May-3 Sotheby's, Tel Aviv #35/R
£250 $400 €363 Generator of shapes (70x100cm-28x39in) s.d.2001 verso col pencil graphite. 13-May-3 Sotheby's, Tel Aviv #40/R
£250 $400 €363 Generator of shapes (70x100cm-28x39in) s.d.2001 verso col pencil graphite. 13-May-3 Sotheby's, Tel Aviv #46/R
£250 $400 €363 Generator of shapes (70x100cm-28x39in) s.d.2001 verso col. pencil graphite. 13-May-3 Sotheby's, Tel Aviv #58/R
£250 $400 €363 Generator of shapes (70x100cm-28x39in) s.d.2001 verso col pencil graphite. 13-May-3 Sotheby's, Tel Aviv #64/R
£250 $400 €363 Generator of shapes (70x100cm-28x39in) s.d.2001 verso col pencil graphite. 13-May-3 Sotheby's, Tel Aviv #50/R
£250 $400 €363 Generator of shapes (70x100cm-28x39in) s.d.2001 verso col pencil graphite. 13-May-3 Sotheby's, Tel Aviv #60/R
£250 $400 €363 Generator of shapes (70x100cm-28x39in) s.d.2001 verso col pencil graphite. 13-May-3 Sotheby's, Tel Aviv #65/R

DINARDO, A (19th C) Italian
£2000 $3040 €3000 Mediterranean fishing boats coming into port (66x104cm-26x41in) s. 15-Aug-2 Bonhams, New Bond Street #320/R est:2000-3000

DINE, Jim (1935-) American
£37500 $60000 €56250 Double plaette for R.M (122x244cm-48x96in) s.d.1963 verso prov. 14-May-3 Sotheby's, New York #213/R est:80000-120000
£51282 $80000 €76923 Our dreams still point north (243x348cm-96x137in) s. i.d.1979 verso diptych prov.exhib.lit. 11-Nov-2 Phillips, New York #38/R est:100000-150000
£68750 $110000 €103125 Study for 'This sovereign life' (122x185cm-48x73in) i.d.1985 verso oil sand diptych prov. 15-May-3 Christie's, Rockefeller NY #176/R est:140000-180000
£72785 $115000 €109178 Full sleeves, empty eyes (183x122cm-72x48in) s.d.1996 wood prov. 13-Nov-2 Sotheby's, New York #276/R est:120000-180000
Prints
£2000 $3140 €3000 Blue on the North Continent (161x205cm-63x81in) s.d.1994 num.5/20 blue black etching. 17-Apr-3 Christie's, Kensington #261/R est:2000-3000
£2000 $3300 €2900 Nine views of winter (133x94cm-52x37in) s.d.num.5/24 col screenprint woodcut. 2-Jul-3 Christie's, London #244/R est:1500-2500
£2201 $3500 €3302 Wall chart I (109x76cm-43x30in) s.d.num.34/75 col lithograph. 2-May-3 Sotheby's, New York #425/R est:4000-6000
£2400 $3744 €3600 Two dark robes (70x98cm-28x39in) s.num.13/18 handcol etching. 10-Oct-2 Sotheby's, London #233/R est:2000-3000
£2400 $3744 €3600 Robe in Los Angeles (137x89cm-54x35in) s.d.1984 num.34/50 col lithograph. 25-Mar-3 Sotheby's, London #161/R est:2000-2500

£2564 $4000 €3846 Fresh, French and beautiful (56x43cm-22x17in) s.i.d. hand col woodcut lithograph. 14-Oct-2 Butterfields, San Francisco #1244/R est:4000-6000
£2593 $4045 €3890 The hand-coloured Viennese hearts VI (79x76cm-31x30in) s.d.1990 num.20/40 silkscreen hand col in acrylic etching. 5-Nov-2 Bukowskis, Stockholm #555/R est:40000-45000 (S.KR 37000)
£2692 $4200 €4038 Two red hearts (76x109cm-30x43in) s.d.num.104/120 col woodcut photoengraving two sheets. 5-Nov-2 Christie's, Rockefeller NY #366/R est:5000-8000
£2800 $4620 €4060 Self portrait, the landscape (135x96cm-53x38in) s.i. col lithograph. 2-Jul-3 Christie's, London #70/R est:3000-5000
£2885 $4500 €4328 The world, for Anne Waldman, Williams College 38 (77x102cm-30x40in) s.i.d.1972 num.69/100 col lithograph woodcut screen-print collage. 5-Nov-2 Christie's, Rockefeller NY #365/R est:5000-7000
£3057 $4800 €4586 Self portrait, the landscape (135x96cm-53x38in) s.d.1969 num.41/75 col lithograph. 21-Nov-2 Swann Galleries, New York #38/R est:6000-9000
£3057 $4799 €4586 Hammer (113x157cm-44x62in) s.d.1982 num.5/46 lithograph W/C lit. 25-Nov-2 Germann, Zurich #306/R est:7000-10000 (S.FR 7000)
£3200 $5280 €4640 Five paint brushes (60x89cm-24x35in) s.d.num.30/75 etching. 1-Jul-3 Sotheby's, London #169/R est:2500-3500
£3459 $5500 €5189 Self portrait, the landscape (135x96cm-53x38in) s.i.d. col lithograph. 2-May-3 Sotheby's, New York #422/R est:5000-7000
£3800 $6270 €5510 Heart and the wall (227x177cm-89x70in) s.d.num.16/28 col etching. 1-Jul-3 Sotheby's, London #170/R est:3000-4000
£3800 $6270 €5510 Kindergarten robe (139x91cm-55x36in) s.d.num.6/75 col woodcut diptych. 2-Jul-3 Christie's, London #72/R est:5000-7000
£4088 $6500 €6132 Heart on the Rue de Grenelle (57x69cm-22x27in) s.d.num.8/36 col etching aquatint. 2-May-3 Sotheby's, New York #428/R est:8000-12000
£4600 $7176 €6900 Viennese hearts VII (88x73cm-35x29in) s.num.33/40 silkscreen etching acrylic. 10-Oct-2 Sotheby's, London #234/R est:3500-4500
£5240 $8227 €7860 The handkerchief (70x58cm-28x23in) s.d.1993 num.11/36 col woodcut etching lit. 25-Nov-2 Germann, Zurich #303/R est:8000-12000 (S.FR 12000)
£5346 $8500 €8019 Kindergarten robe (152x187cm-60x74in) s.d. num.21/75 col woodcut. 29-Apr-3 Christie's, Rockefeller NY #606/R est:8000-10000
£6090 $9500 €9135 Yellow watercolors (148x109cm-58x43in) s.d.num.6/24 col woodcut. 5-Nov-2 Christie's, Rockefeller NY #367/R est:12000-18000
£6114 $9598 €9171 The hand-coloured Viennese hearts I (119x92cm-47x36in) s.d.1990 num.30/40 col etching serigraph prov. 23-Nov-2 Burkhard, Luzern #116/R est:14000-18000 (S.FR 14000)
£6500 $10725 €9425 Two hearts for the moment (44x87cm-17x34in) s.i.d.1984 offset lithograph col etching engraving. 2-Jul-3 Christie's, London #71/R est:7000-10000

Sculpture
£17405 $27500 €26108 Venus with tools (156x81x76cm-61x32x30in) bronze executed 1983 prov.exhib.lit. 13-Nov-2 Sotheby's, New York #277/R est:40000-60000

Works on paper
£5380 $8500 €8070 Sitting with me (135x100cm-53x39in) s.d.1966 num.21/30 cardboard col relief intaglio. 12-Nov-2 Doyle, New York #199/R est:3000-4000
£6500 $10855 €9425 Untitled (42x59cm-17x23in) s.i.d.1968 W/C pencil tracing paper prov. 27-Jun-3 Christie's, London #204/R est:8000-12000
£11000 $18370 €15950 Atheism VII (110x96cm-43x38in) s.i.d.1986 W/C pencil prov. 27-Jun-3 Christie's, London #205/R est:10000-15000
£13924 $22000 €20886 Untitled - two robes (80x116cm-31x46in) s.d.1976 col pastel chl prov. 13-Nov-2 Sotheby's, New York #278/R est:20000-30000

DINE, Jim and FRIEDLANDER, Lee (20th C) American
Photographs
£12579 $19497 €20000 Portfolio (46x76cm-18x30in) s.i. photographs etchings 16 lit. 2-Nov-2 Lempertz, Koln #421/R est:12000-14000

DINET, Étienne (1861-1929) French
£75540 $123884 €105000 Invocation et encens (53x77cm-21x30in) s. 4-Jun-3 Tajan, Paris #257/R est:45000-60000

Works on paper
£645 $1019 €1000 Palmiers (24x21cm-9x8in) st.sig. W/C lit. 19-Dec-2 Delvaux, Paris #13/R
£4430 $7000 €7000 Fillettes regardant une fete du haut d'une terrasse (20x15cm-8x6in) s. crayon W/C gouache. 28-Nov-2 Piasa, Paris #37/R est:7500

DING YANYONG (1902-1978) Chinese
£9756 $15415 €14634 Chinese opera, farewell to concubine (61x45cm-24x18in) s.d.Oct.23 1971 board prov. 28-Apr-3 Sotheby's, Hong Kong #516/R est:120000-150000 (HK.D 120000)
£18699 $29545 €28049 Portrait of a lady (89x60cm-35x24in) s.d.Oct.515 23 1971 prov. 28-Apr-3 Sotheby's, Hong Kong #514/R est:220000-350000 (HK.D 230000)

Works on paper
£2176 $3590 €3155 Zhong Kui (53x69cm-21x27in) s.d.1971 ink scroll. 6-Jul-3 Christie's, Hong Kong #348/R est:30000-40000 (HK.D 28000)
£3730 $6154 €5409 Lotus and frogs (119x59cm-47x23in) s.d.1978 ink scroll. 6-Jul-3 Christie's, Hong Kong #349/R est:50000-70000 (HK.D 48000)
£10569 $16699 €15854 Still life (58x37cm-23x15in) s.d.1965 W/C prov. 28-Apr-3 Sotheby's, Hong Kong #515/R est:65000-80000 (HK.D 130000)

DINGEMANS, Jan (1921-2001) South African
£192 $300 €288 Four Congolese women in a landscape (55x37cm-22x15in) s. canvas on board. 11-Nov-2 Stephan Welz, Johannesburg #198 (SA.R 3000)
£205 $320 €308 Congolese women in a landscape (34x58cm-13x23in) s. board. 11-Nov-2 Stephan Welz, Johannesburg #200 (SA.R 3200)
£243 $380 €365 Five Congolese women in a landscape (55x37cm-22x15in) s. canvas on board. 11-Nov-2 Stephan Welz, Johannesburg #199 (SA.R 3800)
£275 $443 €413 Still life with a white vase and a bowl of fruit (22x27cm-9x11in) s. board. 12-May-3 Stephan Welz, Johannesburg #377 est:1800-2400 (SA.R 3200)

DINGER, Otto (1860-?) German
£680 $1082 €1000 Two peasants in tavern (16x21cm-6x8in) s. panel lit. 21-Mar-3 Auktionhaus Georg Rehm, Augsburg #8021/R
£1224 $1947 €1800 Farmer with slaves and ox carts in field (37x63cm-15x25in) s. i. verso board. 20-Mar-3 Neumeister, Munich #2607/R est:1600

DINGLE, Adrian (1911-1974) Canadian
£558 $870 €809 Cleaning the catch, Ingonish Harbour (46x61cm-18x24in) s. board prov. 26-Mar-3 Walker's, Ottawa #417/R est:1200-1600 (C.D 1300)
£823 $1276 €1235 Momento di Pausa, Rome, Italy (60x75cm-24x30in) s. board prov. 3-Dec-2 Joyner, Toronto #269/R est:1500-2000 (C.D 2000)

DINGLE, Edward von Siebold (20th C) American
Works on paper
£480 $700 €720 Perched in the magnolia, portrait of a cardinal (33x25cm-13x10in) s. W/C gouache. 10-May-2 Skinner, Boston #140/R

DINGLE, Florence Nellie (1907-) British
Works on paper
£300 $477 €450 Interior scene with table lamp and paintings (68x52cm-27x20in) s. W/C. 26-Feb-3 Cheffins Grain & Comins, Cambridge #538/R

DINGLI, Edward Caruana (1876-1950) Maltese
£4400 $7348 €6380 Lady on a terrace above the Grand Harbour, Venice (21x32cm-8x13in) s.d.1927. 17-Jun-3 Bristol Auction Rooms #547/R est:200-300

Works on paper
£6000 $9360 €9000 Fort St Angelo, Valetta (32x50cm-13x20in) s. W/C sold with an oil by T Booth. 17-Sep-2 Sotheby's, Olympia #249/R est:700-900
£6500 $10140 €9750 St Julians Bay, Malta. St Pauls Bay, Malta (26x37cm-10x15in) s. W/C pair. 17-Sep-2 Sotheby's, Olympia #250/R est:600-900

DINKEL, Ernest Michael (1894-1983) British
Works on paper
£620 $1004 €930 Portrait of Canton di Switz, half length. Portrait of Canton di Solure (18x13cm-7x5in) s.i. pencil W/C pair. 23-Jan-3 Christie's, Kensington #292a

DINNERSTEIN, Harvey (1928-) American
£556 $900 €834 Pink scarf (71x76cm-28x30in) s. oil pastel. 24-Jan-3 Freeman, Philadelphia #249/R

DINSDALE, John Bentham (19th C) British
£310 $493 €465 Yacht "Shianne" at sea with other vessels. s. i.verso. 7-Mar-3 Biddle & Webb, Birmingham #301

DIOFEBI, Francesco (19th C) Italian
£4200 $6594 €6300 Troupe of Commedia sell arte actors in Roman Piazza (38x47cm-15x19in) s.d.1822. 10-Dec-2 Bonhams, New Bond Street #249/R est:3000-5000
£10502 $16384 €15753 Baron Otto Magnus von Stackelberg at desk in Rome (41x31cm-16x12in) s. i.d. verso. 28-Mar-3 Koller, Zurich #3121/R est:12000-16000 (S.FR 23000)

DIOGG, Felix Maria (1764-1834) Swiss
£348 $539 €522 Portrait of J J L Steinegger, doctor in Lachen (27x33cm-11x13in) s.d.1789 lit. 9-Dec-2 Philippe Schuler, Zurich #8711 (S.FR 800)

DIOSI, Ernest Charles (1881-?) French
Sculpture
£2581 $4000 €3872 Athlete with hoop (70cm-28in) st.sig. brown patinated bronze. 6-Dec-2 Sotheby's, New York #168/R est:5000-8000

DIRANIAN, Serkis (19th C) Turkish
£506 $785 €800 Jeune femme aux coquelicots (35x28cm-14x11in) s. 27-Sep-2 Rabourdin & Choppin de Janvry, Paris #55

DIRCKINCK-HOLMFELD, H (1835-1912) Danish
£364 $589 €528 Fjord landscape from Svendborg (52x72cm-20x28in) s.i.d.75 prov. 24-May-3 Rasmussen, Havnen #2183 (D.KR 3800)

DIRCKX, Anton (1878-1927) Dutch
£276 $439 €400 Moored boat in a canal (22x16cm-9x6in) s. panel. 10-Mar-3 Sotheby's, Amsterdam #131
£318 $497 €500 River view (40x59cm-16x23in) s.d.1898 i.verso. 5-Nov-2 Vendu Notarishuis, Rotterdam #73
£1911 $2981 €3000 Rotterdam harbour with buildings and figures on boats (34x49cm-13x19in) d.1910. 6-Nov-2 Vendue Huis, Gravenhage #133/R est:1000-1500

DIRIKS, Edvard Karl (1855-1930) Norwegian
£271 $439 €407 Reading in bed (59x72cm-23x28in) s. 27-Jan-3 Blomqvist, Lysaker #1046 (N.KR 3000)
£393 $616 €590 Autumn day (45x53cm-18x21in) s. panel. 25-Nov-2 Blomqvist, Lysaker #1046 (N.KR 4500)
£446 $678 €669 Landscape from South of France (53x74cm-21x29in) s. cardboard. 16-Aug-2 Lilla Bukowskis, Stockholm #866 (S.KR 6500)
£764 $1177 €1146 Collioure - Pyrenees Orientales (46x55cm-18x22in) s. painted 1918. 28-Oct-2 Blomqvist, Lysaker #1029 (N.KR 9000)
£904 $1465 €1356 Drobak straight in summer (70x58cm-28x23in) s. 27-Jan-3 Blomqvist, Lysaker #1048/R (N.KR 10000)
£918 $1506 €1331 Sailing (73x54cm-29x21in) s. 2-Jun-3 Blomqvist, Oslo #97/R (N.KR 10000)
£1396 $2192 €2094 Avenue in autumn landscape (40x60cm-16x24in) s. 25-Nov-2 Blomqvist, Lysaker #1048/R est:15000-18000 (N.KR 16000)
£1571 $2466 €2357 Winter in Drobak (73x60cm-29x24in) s. 25-Nov-2 Blomqvist, Lysaker #1047/R est:20000-25000 (N.KR 18000)
£1837 $3012 €2664 Village street scene, possibly Drobak (56x46cm-22x18in) s. 2-Jun-3 Blomqvist, Oslo #178/R est:30000-40000 (N.KR 20000)

DIRIX, Jos (1958-) Dutch
Sculpture
£1203 $1900 €1900 Horse (38cm-15in) init. bronze on stone base. 26-Nov-2 Sotheby's, Amsterdam #37/R est:1200-1500

DIRK, Nathaniel (1895-1961) American
Works on paper
£220 $350 €330 On the coast (19x25cm-7x10in) s. W/C. 7-Mar-3 Skinner, Boston #484/R

DIRKS, Andreas (1866-1922) German
£545 $855 €850 Sailing boat on Dutchcanal (39x61cm-15x24in) s. 21-Nov-2 Van Ham, Cologne #1566

DISCANNO, G (?) ?
£889 $1476 €1289 San Cleto (64x78cm-25x31in) s.i. indis d. 10-Jun-3 Ritchie, Toronto #173/R est:2000-2500 (C.D 2000)

DISCART, Jean (19th C) French
£70968 $110000 €106452 Arab smoker (34x23cm-13x9in) s.d.1889 panel prov. 30-Oct-2 Christie's, Rockefeller NY #88/R est:100000-150000
£85000 $133450 €127500 Three Arab musicians (49x30cm-19x12in) s. panel. 19-Nov-2 Bonhams, New Bond Street #93/R est:50000-70000

DISCEPOLI, Giovanni Battista (1590-1660) Italian
£16456 $26000 €26000 Ecce Homo (75x59cm-30x23in) exhib.lit. 2-Dec-2 Finarte, Milan #158/R

DISCHLER, Hermann (1866-1935) German
£818 $1275 €1300 Snow covered pine trees before Black Forest peaks (26x18cm-10x7in) s.d.17 lit. 20-Sep-2 Karlheinz Kaupp, Staufen #2047
£1284 $2003 €1900 Winter landscape (27x35cm-11x14in) s.d.08 i. verso board. 26-Mar-3 Hugo Ruef, Munich #92
£1442 $2236 €2250 Farmsteads in landscape (31x45cm-12x18in) s.d.X.13 board lit. 6-Dec-2 Karlheinz Kaupp, Staufen #2097/R est:2500

DISEN, Andreas (1845-1923) Norwegian
£442 $721 €663 High mountains and water (49x73cm-19x29in) s.d.1909. 17-Feb-3 Blomqvist, Lysaker #1035/R (N.KR 5000)
£1557 $2460 €2336 Sawmill in the high mountains (33x49cm-13x19in) s.d.85 i.stretcher. 2-Dec-2 Blomqvist, Oslo #302/R est:18000-22000 (N.KR 18000)

DISLER, Martin (1949-1996) Swiss
£742 $1084 €1113 Untitled (75x106cm-30x42in) s.d.1983 acrylic mixed media. 4-Jun-2 Germann, Zurich #93/R (S.FR 1700)
£830 $1211 €1245 Untitled (100x65cm-39x26in) s.d.1983 mixed media prov. 4-Jun-2 Germann, Zurich #94/R (S.FR 1900)
Works on paper
£742 $1158 €1113 Untitled (74x55cm-29x22in) s.d.83 col crayon chl dr. 8-Nov-2 Dobiaschofsky, Bern #272/R (S.FR 1700)
£1572 $2468 €2358 Derniere valse (177x62cm-70x24in) s.i.d.1984 gouache. 25-Nov-2 Germann, Zurich #12/R est:4000-5000 (S.FR 3600)

DISMORR, Jessica (1885-1939) British
£800 $1320 €1160 Portrait of a farmer with a pipe (62x47cm-24x19in) board. 3-Jul-3 Christie's, Kensington #565/R
£1300 $2145 €1885 Man reading (62x47cm-24x19in) board. 3-Jul-3 Christie's, Kensington #567/R est:600-800
£1300 $2145 €1885 Portrait of Katherine Dawson Giles (63x49cm-25x19in) board exhib. 3-Jul-3 Christie's, Kensington #568/R est:500-700
£1500 $2475 €2175 Woman seated at a piano (62x46cm-24x18in) 3-Jul-3 Christie's, Kensington #566/R est:600-800

DISTON, J Swinton (fl.1890-1930) Australian
Works on paper
£324 $506 €486 Coastal landscape (39x26cm-15x10in) W/C. 6-Aug-2 Peter Webb, Auckland #92 est:250-350 (NZ.D 1100)

DITCHFIELD, Arthur (1842-1888) British
Works on paper
£1300 $2028 €1950 View of the Acropolis (30x47cm-12x19in) W/C. 15-Oct-2 Sotheby's, London #8/R est:700-900

DITSCHEINER, Adolf (1846-1904) Austrian
£578 $919 €850 Spring in Pitten (24x44cm-9x17in) 25-Feb-3 Dorotheum, Vienna #216/R
Works on paper
£507 $791 €750 Mountain plateau (15x20cm-6x8in) s.d.89 W/C. 28-Mar-3 Dorotheum, Vienna #252/R

DITTEN, Johannes van (1848-1924) Norwegian
£606 $927 €909 From Akershus (35x54cm-14x21in) s. 26-Aug-2 Blomqvist, Lysaker #1075/R (N.KR 7000)

DITTMER, A (19th C) German
£1132 $1766 €1800 Scene from the Franco-German war (84x65cm-33x26in) s.d.1873. 20-Sep-2 Schloss Ahlden, Ahlden #1133/R est:1900

DITTRICH, Anette (20th C) German?
£443 $700 €700 Fortress (30x40cm-12x16in) s.d.77. 29-Nov-2 Sigalas, Stuttgart #1178

DIULGHEROFF, Nicolas (1901-1982) Italian/Bulgarian
£347 $552 €500 Composition (31x47cm-12x19in) s.i.d.1978 verso paper on canvas. 1-May-3 Meeting Art, Vercelli #427

DIX, Charles Temple (1838-1873) American

£6000 $10020 €8700 Flying Dutchman (59x94cm-23x37in) mono. 18-Jun-3 Sotheby's, Olympia #57/R est:6000-8000

DIX, Otto (1891-1969) German

£1443 $2106 €2250 Clouds hanging over valley (25x49cm-10x19in) mono.d.1933 pen over pencil. 4-Jun-2 Karl & Faber, Munich #221/R est:4500

£41727 $68432 €58000 Bodensee landscape with potato harvest and Reichenau (65x85cm-26x33in) mono.d. panel prov. 6-Jun-3 Ketterer, Munich #77/R est:50000-70000

Prints

£2051 $3179 €3200 Battlescene (24x29cm-9x11in) s.i.d. etching. 4-Dec-2 Lempertz, Koln #661/R est:3100

£2468 $3751 €3850 Fisherman and child (60x49cm-24x19in) s.i.d.61 num.45/60 col lithograph. 31-Aug-2 Geble, Radolfzell #704/R est:3850

£2489 $4156 €3609 Cockerel, before barn (71x51cm-28x20in) s.i.d.68 col lithograph. 24-Jun-3 Koller, Zurich #359/R est:2200-3200 (S.FR 5500)

£2532 $3924 €4000 Masks (56x54cm-22x21in) s.i.d.1963 num.4/70 col lithograph. 28-Sep-2 Ketterer, Hamburg #304/R est:5000-6000

£2564 $3974 €4000 Cat and cockerel (43x60cm-17x24in) s.i.d. lithograph. 7-Dec-2 Hauswedell & Nolte, Hamburg #631/R est:4000

£2759 $4414 €4000 Visiting Madame Germaine in Mericourt (26x20cm-10x8in) s.i. etching. 11-Mar-3 Dorotheum, Vienna #54/R est:3400-4500

£2848 $4500 €4500 Burial (28x35cm-11x14in) s.i.d. drypoint prov. 30-Nov-2 Villa Grisebach, Berlin #183/R est:3500-4500

£2878 $4719 €4000 Petrus and the cock (57x46cm-22x18in) s. col lithograph. 6-Jun-3 Ketterer, Munich #44/R est:4000-5000

£3028 $5027 €4300 Front soldier in Brussels (29x20cm-11x8in) s.i. etching. 14-Jun-3 Hauswedell & Nolte, Hamburg #1125/R est:4500

£3165 $5000 €5000 Pregnancy (35x28cm-14x11in) s.i.d. drypoint prov. 30-Nov-2 Villa Grisebach, Berlin #181/R est:5000-6000

£3165 $5000 €5000 Dead soldier (28x35cm-11x14in) s.i.d. drypoint prov. 30-Nov-2 Villa Grisebach, Berlin #184/R est:5000-6000

£3521 $5845 €5000 Reclining nude - seated with cigarette (56x43cm-22x17in) s.i.d. lithograph. 14-Jun-3 Hauswedell & Nolte, Hamburg #1127/R est:6000

£3623 $5942 €5000 Woman from Rome (57x36cm-22x14in) s.i.d. col lithograph. 31-May-3 Villa Grisebach, Berlin #283/R est:5000-7000

£3797 $6000 €6000 Contessa (62x40cm-24x16in) s.i.d. col lithograph. 30-Nov-2 Villa Grisebach, Berlin #320/R est:6000-7000

£4710 $7725 €6500 Maud Arizona - Suleika, the tatooed wonder (30x20cm-12x8in) s.i.d. drypoint prov. 31-May-3 Villa Grisebach, Berlin #226/R est:6500-7500

£4747 $7500 €7500 Balancing act (30x20cm-12x8in) s.i.d. drypoint prov. 30-Nov-2 Villa Grisebach, Berlin #180/R est:6000-7000

£5063 $8000 €8000 Contessa (62x40cm-24x16in) s.i.d.62 col lithograph. 30-Nov-2 Bassenge, Berlin #6231/R est:7500

£5063 $8000 €8000 International riding act (40x30cm-16x12in) s.i. drypoint prov. 30-Nov-2 Villa Grisebach, Berlin #275/R est:6000-8000

£5253 $8300 €8300 Harbour worker with child (72x54cm-28x21in) s. col lithograph exec.1968 one of 80 lit. 30-Nov-2 Geble, Radolfzell #751 est:7900

£5280 $7497 €8500 Cat in poppy field (56x45cm-22x18in) s.d.66 col lithograph lit. 23-Mar-2 Geble, Radolfzell #621/R est:6500

£5380 $8500 €8500 Cat and hen (44x63cm-17x25in) s.d.1966 num.58/80 col lithograph lit. 30-Nov-2 Geble, Radolfzell #750 est:7500

£5380 $8500 €8500 Two children with sunflower (43x59cm-17x23in) s.i.d. col lithograph. 30-Nov-2 Villa Grisebach, Berlin #325/R est:8500-9500

£5769 $8942 €9000 Cat in poppy field (56x49cm-22x19in) s.i.d.1968 col lithograph. 4-Dec-2 Lempertz, Koln #667/R est:10000-12000

£6159 $10101 €8500 International riding act (40x29cm-16x11in) s.i.d. drypoint prov. 31-May-3 Villa Grisebach, Berlin #227/R est:8500-9500

£7595 $12000 €12000 American riding act (35x31cm-14x12in) s.i.d. drypoint prov. 30-Nov-2 Villa Grisebach, Berlin #179/R est:10000-12000

£7595 $12000 €12000 The suicide - hung (35x28cm-14x11in) s.i.d. drypoint prov. 30-Nov-2 Villa Grisebach, Berlin #182/R est:7000-8000

£12676 $21042 €18000 The street (25x22cm-10x9in) s.i.d. drypoint etching. 14-Jun-3 Hauswedell & Nolte, Hamburg #1123/R est:20000

£28986 $47536 €40000 Death and resurrection (50x43cm-20x17in) s.i.d. drypoint portfolio eight prov. 30-May-3 Villa Grisebach, Berlin #45/R est:45000-55000

£50000 $81500 €75000 Mieze II (49x36cm-19x14in) s.i.num.156 lithograph prov.lit. 3-Feb-3 Christie's, London #26/R est:50000-70000

Works on paper

£308 $481 €450 Letter to an artist friend with a female nude (29x21cm-11x8in) exec.1967 lit. 10-Apr-3 Allgauer, Kempten #2602/R

£570 $883 €900 Foreplay (30x21cm-12x8in) i. pencil feltpen letter paper. 28-Sep-2 Ketterer, Hamburg #301/R

£705 $1093 €1100 Seated female nude (33x44cm-13x17in) s.d.1926 pencil. 6-Dec-2 Michael Zeller, Lindau #749/R

£949 $1472 €1500 Erotica (21x29cm-8x11in) s. pencil biro chk ink. 28-Sep-2 Ketterer, Hamburg #302/R est:1000-1500

£1667 $2600 €2501 Weiblicher Ruckenakt (43x33cm-17x13in) s. pencil. 19-Sep-2 Swann Galleries, New York #309/R est:2500-3500

£2089 $3300 €3300 Self in erotic scene (30x21cm-12x8in) pencil. 30-Nov-2 Bassenge, Berlin #6221/R est:3500

£2532 $4000 €4000 Reclining nude (41x59cm-16x23in) s. pencil. 30-Nov-2 Villa Grisebach, Berlin #322/R est:3500-4000

£2817 $4676 €4000 The widow (17x22cm-7x9in) s.d. pencil. 14-Jun-3 Hauswedell & Nolte, Hamburg #1122/R est:4000

£3012 $4278 €4850 Findeisen portrait (39x29cm-15x11in) mono.d.1958 chl. 23-Mar-2 Geble, Radolfzell #586/R est:4850

£3597 $5755 €5000 Cockerel and swan by farmstead (15x21cm-6x8in) s. i. verso W/C col chk over pencil. 15-May-3 Neumeister, Munich #244/R est:5000-6000

£3774 $5887 €6000 Reclining female nude (24x32cm-9x13in) s. chl over pencil. 11-Oct-2 Winterberg, Heidelberg #1016/R est:7800

£3797 $5924 €6000 Reclining nude before landscape (59x96cm-23x38in) i. verso chl htd bodycol. 18-Oct-2 Dr Fritz Nagel, Stuttgart #484/R est:7500

£4200 $6676 €6300 Female nude (49x32cm-19x13in) s.d.20 pencil. 20-Mar-3 Sotheby's, Olympia #79/R est:4000-6000

£4241 $6700 €6700 Female nude standing, Erna II (56x38cm-22x15in) s. pencil dr exec.1931. 30-Nov-2 Geble, Radolfzell #712 est:6700

£5128 $7949 €8000 Erlenloh (38x48cm-15x19in) mono.d.1944. 7-Dec-2 Hauswedell & Nolte, Hamburg #624/R est:10000

£5310 $8390 €7700 Reclining nude on sofa (37x54cm-15x21in) s. chl wash. 5-Apr-3 Geble, Radolfzell #741/R est:7700

£7278 $11500 €11500 Bodensee landscape (38x56cm-15x22in) mono.d.5DX3 W/C. 30-Nov-2 Villa Grisebach, Berlin #324/R est:7000-9000

£7372 $11426 €11500 Sachsen landscape - Lichthain (47x57cm-19x22in) mono.d. i. verso pen over pencil bodycol. 7-Dec-2 Hauswedell & Nolte, Hamburg #623/R est:10000

£7595 $12000 €12000 Portrait of child (43x31cm-17x12in) s.d.26 W/C over pencil. 30-Nov-2 Villa Grisebach, Berlin #326/R est:14000-16000

£8696 $12348 €14000 Female nude on chair hugging knees (60x31cm-24x12in) s. chl. 23-Mar-2 Geble, Radolfzell #585/R est:11800

DIXON, Alfred (1842-1919) British

£250 $395 €363 Finishing touch (25x20cm-10x8in) mono. panel. 22-Jul-3 Sworder & Son, Bishops Stortford #394/R

DIXON, Anna (1873-1959) British

Works on paper

£580 $963 €841 Market place, Concarneau (37x56cm-15x22in) s. W/C. 13-Jun-3 Lyon & Turnbull, Edinburgh #79

DIXON, Annie (1817-1901) British

Miniatures

£4200 $6552 €6300 Four members of the Browne family (9cm-4xin) one d.1854 others d.1856 all set in red leather cases oval four. 5-Nov-2 Bonhams, New Bond Street #164/R est:4000-6000

DIXON, Arthur A (fl.1892-1927) British

Works on paper

£6000 $9840 €8700 Queen of clubs (37x26cm-15x10in) s.d.1902 pencil W/C prov. 5-Jun-3 Christie's, London #128/R est:6000-8000

DIXON, Charles Edward (1872-1934) British

£1800 $2826 €2700 C.S Faraday in a gale (122x244cm-48x96in) s.d.1930. 16-Dec-2 Sotheby's, Olympia #172/R est:2000-4000

£2821 $4401 €4232 Homeward bound off Start point, English channel (49x75cm-19x30in) s.d.1927. 10-Nov-2 Dunbar Sloane, Auckland #10 est:7000-10000 (NZ.D 9000)

£42000 $68040 €63000 Off Billingsgate (109x191cm-43x75in) s.d.1922. 22-Jan-3 Bonhams, New Bond Street #393/R est:20000-30000

Works on paper

£260 $413 €390 Barfleur (41x56cm-16x22in) s.d.31 bodycol. 25-Feb-3 Bonhams, Knightsbridge #160/R

£360 $601 €522 Tugged out of port (16x12cm-6x5in) s.d.90 W/C. 18-Jun-3 Sotheby's, Olympia #101/R

£440 $686 €660 SS Cameron (18x25cm-7x10in) s.d.1914 w/C. 15-Oct-2 Gorringes, Lewes #2183

£475 $793 €689 Approaching showers (43x58cm-17x23in) i.d.1879 mount. 18-Jun-3 Andrew Hartley, Ilkley #1010

£650 $1001 €975 Off the Palace, Alexandria (18x38cm-7x15in) s.i.d.09 W/C. 23-Oct-2 Hamptons Fine Art, Godalming #47/R

£700 $1113 €1050 Rowing out past steam ships (39x58cm-15x23in) s.d.1898 W/C htd white. 25-Feb-3 Bonhams, Knightsbridge #162/R

£900 $1503 €1305 Above Greenwich (26x37cm-10x15in) s.i.d.1911 W/C. 18-Jun-3 Sotheby's, Olympia #94/R

£900 $1467 €1305 Ships, tug and other vessels in a river (47x33cm-19x13in) s.d.92 W/C. 21-Jul-3 Bonhams, Bath #19/R

£1282 $1987 €2000 Paquebot sortant du port (20x34cm-8x13in) s.d.95 W/C gouache. 9-Dec-2 Beaussant & Lefèvre, Paris #29/R

£1300 $2028 €1950 Lowestoft trawlers (46x76cm-18x30in) s.d.1920 W/C htd white. 10-Sep-2 Sworder & Son, Bishops Stortford #718/R est:1000-1500

£1300 $2106 €1950 Steamer and other shipping in the Lower Pool (20x15cm-8x6in) s.d.90 pen brown ink W/C. 21-May-3 Christie's, Kensington #484/R est:300-500
£1391 $2157 €2087 Off Tilbury (27x76cm-11x30in) s.i.d.1912 W/C. 9-Dec-2 Philippe Schuler, Zurich #3423/R est:4000-6000 (S.FR 3200)
£1400 $2170 €2100 Wapping on Thames dock scene with steamer, tugs and residences (25x53cm-10x21in) s.d.1891. 25-Sep-2 Brightwells, Leominster #916/R est:900-1200
£1728 $2800 €2506 King's arrival at Cowes (17x20cm-7x8in) s.i.d.08 W/C gouache prov. 29-Jul-3 Christie's, Rockefeller NY #115/R est:1000-1500
£1800 $2808 €2700 Houses of Parliament, from the river Thames (14x23cm-6x9in) s.d.04 pencil W/C htd white. 19-Sep-2 Christie's, Kensington #179/R est:500-800
£1800 $2790 €2700 Steam boat with barges in the foreground (26x28cm-10x11in) s.d.09 pencil W/C htd bodycol. 4-Dec-2 Christie's, Kensington #115/R est:2000-3000
£2000 $3120 €3000 Off the Royal Albert Docks, Thames, London (26x76cm-10x30in) s.d.09 W/C with white. 5-Nov-2 Bristol Auction Rooms #953 est:400-500
£2000 $3240 €3000 Below Blackwall (27x72cm-11x28in) s.i.d.99 ink W/C htd white. 22-Jan-3 Bonhams, New Bond Street #338/R est:2000-3000
£2500 $3875 €3750 Off Tilbury (27x77cm-11x30in) s.i.d.03 pen ink W/C htd white. 31-Oct-2 Christie's, Kensington #385 est:1500-2500
£2600 $4134 €3900 Moonrise (51x38cm-20x15in) s. W/C bodycol. 29-Apr-3 Gorringes, Lewes #2233
£3000 $4860 €4500 Busy day in the Pool of London (34x52cm-13x20in) s.d.97 pen brown ink W/C. 21-May-3 Christie's, Kensington #487/R est:1500-2000
£3000 $4860 €4500 Steamer of the Castle Line on the Thames (34x52cm-13x20in) s.d.97 pen brown ink W/C. 21-May-3 Christie's, Kensington #488/R est:1500-2500
£3030 $4667 €4545 Beating down off Gravesend (26x70cm-10x28in) s.i.d.1913 W/C. 4-Sep-2 Dunbar Sloane, Wellington #82/R est:10000-15000 (NZ.D 10000)
£3900 $5928 €5850 Off Gravesend (27x79cm-11x31in) s.d.03 W/C. 17-Sep-2 Henry Adams, Chichester #109/R est:1500-2000
£3900 $6045 €5850 Thames dock scene with steamer, tug and tall ships (36x56cm-14x22in) s.d.1897. 25-Sep-2 Brightwells, Leominster #917/R est:1200-1500
£4000 $6480 €6000 Off to the fishing grounds (44x74cm-17x29in) s.d.1920 pen ink W/C htd white. 22-Jan-3 Bonhams, New Bond Street #345/R est:4000-6000
£4000 $6600 €5800 London Bridge (33x78cm-13x31in) s.i.d.1915 W/C prov. 1-Jul-3 Bearnes, Exeter #457/R est:2000-3000
£4600 $7452 €6900 Bustling river (27x74cm-11x29in) s.i.d.02 W/C htd white. 22-Jan-3 Bonhams, New Bond Street #340/R est:2000-3000
£5500 $9075 €7975 Tower Bridge from the Pool (33x78cm-13x31in) s.i.d.15 W/C prov. 1-Jul-3 Bearnes, Exeter #458/R est:2000-3000
£14000 $21280 €21000 Houses of Parliament. Tower Bridge. St Paul's Cathedral. Westminster Abbey (31x52cm-12x20in) s.d.1923 W/C over pencil htd bodycol four. 15-Aug-2 Bonhams, New Bond Street #436/R est:12000-18000

DIXON, David J (19/20th C) British?
£700 $1099 €1050 S.S. Manora in high seas (30x61cm-12x24in) s.d.1886. 16-Dec-2 Sotheby's, Olympia #124/R

DIXON, Francis Stillwell (1872-1967) American
£240 $375 €360 Winter landscape with red barn (30x41cm-12x16in) s. 14-Sep-2 Weschler, Washington #601/R
£297 $475 €446 Evening landscape (30x41cm-12x16in) s. 12-Jan-3 William Jenack, New York #170

DIXON, Frank (19th C) British
Works on paper
£350 $581 €508 St. Bernard (39x29cm-15x11in) col chk. 12-Jun-3 Christie's, Kensington #279/R
£360 $562 €540 Fishermen rowing out to his boat (50x84cm-20x33in) s. W/C. 25-Mar-3 Bonhams, Knightsbridge #206/R

DIXON, Geoff (20th C) New Zealander
£426 $664 €639 Journey (104x59cm-41x23in) i. s.d.1992 verso enamel on board. 17-Sep-2 Peter Webb, Auckland #180/R est:1000-2000 (NZ.D 1400)
£541 $850 €812 Self portrait with helleconias and cyclone (122x80cm-48x31in) i. s.i.d.1976 verso enamel on board. 10-Dec-2 Peter Webb, Auckland #100/R est:1500-2000 (NZ.D 1700)

DIXON, Harry (1861-1942) British
£1600 $2496 €2400 Study of a tiger (62x108cm-24x43in) s. 26-Mar-3 Woolley & Wallis, Salisbury #254/R est:300-500

DIXON, James (1887-1970) British?
£1812 $2971 €2500 Sea birds resting (38x56cm-15x22in) s.i.d.22.10.1967 oil on paper. 28-May-3 Bonhams & James Adam, Dublin #140/R est:2400-2800
£2200 $3476 €3300 Shepherd driving his flock to the sheepfold to the west end, Tory Island (56x76cm-22x30in) s.i.d.60 board. 27-Nov-2 Sotheby's, Olympia #55/R est:1800-2500
£4600 $7314 €6900 Whaling boats (21x65cm-8x26in) s.d.21.5.65 board. 26-Feb-3 Sotheby's, Olympia #214/R est:3000-5000

DIXON, Joseph Kossuth (19/20th C) American
Photographs
£3049 $5000 €4574 Four Crow scouts that guided General Custer to the Sioux Camp (72x98cm-28x39in) bromide print exec.c.1909. 10-Feb-3 Swann Galleries, New York #25/R est:7000-10000

DIXON, Leng (1916-1968) South African
Works on paper
£430 $692 €645 Washday in a Cape courtyard (21x29cm-8x11in) s. pen ink W/C. 12-May-3 Stephan Welz, Johannesburg #210 est:3000-5000 (SA.R 5000)
£553 $862 €830 District six (36x25cm-14x10in) s. pen ink W/C exhib. 15-Oct-2 Stephan Welz, Johannesburg #487 est:4000-6000 (SA.R 9000)

DIXON, Maynard (1875-1946) American
£2484 $4000 €3726 Gunfight between two groups of banditos (15x43cm-6x17in) s. gouache en grisaille painted c.1905. 10-May-3 Illustration House, New York #173/R est:6000-9000
£13174 $22000 €19102 Rain in Dobe town (28x35cm-11x14in) init.i.d.15 s.i.d.verso canvas on masonite. 18-Jun-3 Christie's, Los Angeles #59/R est:8000-12000
£17964 $30000 €26048 In old Tucson (23x30cm-9x12in) i.d.Aug 1907 verso prov. 18-Jun-3 Christie's, Los Angeles #58/R est:8000-12000
£22293 $35000 €33440 Arizona pastures (30x41cm-12x16in) s.i.d.1943 board prov. 20-Nov-2 Christie's, Los Angeles #55/R est:40000-60000
£23952 $40000 €34730 Horse corral (38x51cm-15x20in) s.d.1945 W/C gouache prov. 18-Jun-3 Christie's, Los Angeles #73/R est:50000-70000
£30063 $47500 €43591 Mt. Carmel, Utah, White Mesa (30x41cm-12x16in) s. canvas on board. 26-Jul-3 Coeur d'Alene, Hayden #103/R est:25000-35000
£55556 $90000 €83334 Running buffalo with hunters, sketch for a mural (43x102cm-17x40in) init.d.1939 tempera on board prov.lit. 22-May-3 Christie's, Rockefeller NY #82/R est:80000-120000
£216867 $360000 €314457 The Monument, Navajo Reservation, Arizona (64x76cm-25x30in) s.i.d.1922 i.verso prov.exhib.lit. 11-Jun-3 Butterfields, San Francisco #4108/R est:300000-500000

Works on paper
£675 $1100 €1013 Female nude study (28x22cm-11x9in) init.d.Aug 1939 brown pencil. 16-Feb-3 Butterfields, San Francisco #2096
£1274 $2000 €1911 Taos, New Mexico. Cloud study. Horse studies (12x18cm-5x7in) one init.i.d.Aug 1931 one init.i.d.1944 graphite 3 prov.lit. 20-Nov-2 Christie's, Los Angeles #27/R est:2500-3500
£1582 $2500 €2294 Cowboy profile (13x10cm-5x4in) d.1901 pencil prov. 26-Jul-3 Coeur d'Alene, Hayden #61/R est:1000-2000
£4747 $7500 €6883 Old adobe. San Goronio Range (33x36cm-13x14in) init.d.1926 mixed media pair. 26-Jul-3 Coeur d'Alene, Hayden #59/R est:5000-10000
£5090 $8500 €7381 Charro (42x23cm-17x9in) init.d.42 ink W/C on board prov. 18-Jun-3 Christie's, Los Angeles #59a/R est:5000-7000
£7831 $13000 €11355 The car was at his hip, almost (74x51cm-29x20in) s.d.13 i.verso gouache paperboard prov.lit. 11-Jun-3 Butterfields, San Francisco #4129/R est:8000-12000
£8280 $13000 €12420 Three godfathers (74x51cm-29x20in) s.d.1913 i.verso mixed media paperboard prov. 19-Nov-2 Butterfields, San Francisco #8083/R est:5000-7000
£9228 $14950 €13381 It's dead easy, kid (56x36cm-22x14in) gouache. 23-May-3 Altermann Galleries, Santa Fe #92
£11180 $18000 €16770 Cowboys roping horses (33x43cm-13x17in) s.d.1940 mixed media prov. 18-Feb-3 John Moran, Pasadena #113 est:15000-20000

DIXON, Percy (1862-1924) British
Works on paper
£241 $381 €362 Snow-capped mountains (25x33cm-10x13in) W/C. 1 Dec-2 Levis, Calgary #213/R (C.D 600)
£660 $1076 €990 Moorland river (34x52cm-13x20in) s. W/C. 17-Feb-3 Bonhams, Bath #142
£660 $1049 €990 Mist rolling over a highland lake (35x52cm-14x20in) s. W/C. 4-Mar-3 Bearnes, Exeter #328/R
£900 $1467 €1350 Lock Maree from above Conee Bay. Graig Tollie (34x52cm-13x20in) s.d.1902 W/C two. 29-Jan-3 Dreweatt Neate, Newbury #84/R
£2000 $3200 €3000 Among the tumbled fragments of the hills (66x102cm-26x40in) s. W/C. 11-Mar-3 Gorringes, Lewes #2423/R est:1500-2000

DIZIANI, Antonio (1737-1797) Italian
Works on paper
£633 $1000 €1000 Jacob et Rachel au puits (24x38cm-9x15in) i. pen ink wash. 28-Nov-2 Tajan, Paris #41

DIZIANI, Antonio (attrib) (1737-1797) Italian
£4500 $7020 €6750 Mountain river landscape with a shepherd and shepherdess (116x89cm-46x35in) 10-Apr-3 Christie's, Kensington #295/R est:3000-5000

DIZIANI, Gaspare (1689-1767) Italian
£6757 $10541 €10000 The story of Aaron and Miriam (33x49cm-13x19in) prov. 27-Mar-3 Dorotheum, Vienna #10/R est:12000-18000
£19000 $29640 €28500 Adoration of the shepherds (116x131cm-46x52in) 10-Apr-3 Sotheby's, London #83/R est:18000
£19753 $32000 €29630 Rest on the Flight to Egypt (56x47cm-22x19in) shaped prov. 24-Jan-3 Christie's, Rockefeller NY #157/R est:15000-20000
£59748 $92610 €95000 The judgement of Midas (97x131cm-38x52in) 2-Oct-2 Dorotheum, Vienna #42/R est:75000-100000
Works on paper
£3716 $5797 €5500 Study for garden sculpture (29x28cm-11x11in) chk pen ink wash. 27-Mar-3 Christie's, Paris #66/R

DIZIANI, Gaspare (attrib) (1689-1767) Italian
£1690 $2806 €2400 Putti in landscape (40x63cm-16x25in) prov. 11-Jun-3 Dorotheum, Vienna #232/R est:1200-2500

DIZIANI, Gaspare (circle) (1689-1767) Italian
£10000 $15600 €15000 Alexander with his physician Philip (135x106cm-53x42in) 10-Apr-3 Christie's, Kensington #278/R est:2500-3500

DJAGAMARA, Old Mick (20th C) Australian
Works on paper
£279 $457 €405 Carpet snake design (60x91cm-24x36in) synthetic polymer linen. 3-Jun-3 Lawson Menzies, Sydney #807 (A.D 700)

DJAMIN, Nasjah (1924-1997) Indonesian
£4557 $7017 €6836 Wanita nelayan - women selling fish (85x110cm-33x43in) s.d.89 acrylic. 27-Oct-2 Christie's, Hong Kong #91/R est:22000-32000 (HK.D 55000)

DJIRNA, I Made (1957-) Balinese
£2720 $4487 €3944 Figures (131x131cm-52x52in) s.d.1996 s.i.d.verso. 6-Jul-3 Christie's, Hong Kong #50/R est:45000-65000 (HK.D 35000)

DMITRIENKO, Pierre (1925-1974) French
£962 $1510 €1500 Composition (60x73cm-24x29in) s.d.1954 prov. 15-Dec-2 Perrin, Versailles #33/R
£972 $1536 €1400 Composition (27x45cm-11x18in) s.d.54. 25-Apr-3 Piasa, Paris #73
£2083 $3292 €3000 Composition (115x148cm-45x58in) s.d.verso. 28-Apr-3 Cornette de St.Cyr, Paris #382 est:3000-5000
Works on paper
£340 $541 €500 Composition (49x32cm-19x13in) s.d.51 gouache. 18-Mar-3 Galerie Moderne, Brussels #630/R
£486 $773 €700 Composition (36x54cm-14x21in) s.d.1948 mixed media. 29-Apr-3 Artcurial Briest, Paris #566/R

DOANE, W E (19/20th C) American?
£796 $1250 €1194 America's cup race with white racing yacht in full sail (46x66cm-18x26in) 19-Apr-3 James Julia, Fairfield #103/R

DOAR, M Wilson (1898-?) British
£300 $471 €450 Mixed flowers in a vase (54x44cm-21x17in) s. 16-Apr-3 Christie's, Kensington #888/R

DOARES, Robert (20th C) American
£932 $1500 €1398 Policeman coaching boys how to box (48x43cm-19x17in) casein. 19-Feb-3 Illustration House, New York #224/R est:2000-3000

DOBASHI, Jun (1917-) Japanese/French
Works on paper
£430 $702 €650 Composition abstraite (38x53cm-15x21in) s.i.d.1956 mixed media. 3-Feb-3 Cornette de St.Cyr, Paris #412/R

DOBBIN, John (1815-1888) British
Works on paper
£400 $620 €600 Craigmillar castle (36x51cm-14x20in) s.d.1851 W/C. 24-Sep-2 Anderson & Garland, Newcastle #363/R
£840 $1319 €1260 Anglers by a mountain river, a stone bridge beyond (55x89cm-22x35in) s.d.1874 W/C over pencil. 15-Apr-3 Bonhams, Knowle #85

DOBBIN, Lady Kate (1868-c.1948) Irish
Works on paper
£350 $508 €550 Hellebores (14x17cm-6x7in) s. W/C. 29-May-2 Woodwards, Cork #186

DOBELI, Johann Othmar (1874-1922) Swiss
£255 $410 €383 Thatched cottage in Aargau with peasant woman (24x28cm-9x11in) s.d.1911 board. 7-May-3 Dobiaschofsky, Bern #461 (S.FR 550)
£262 $409 €393 Farmstead, Safenwil near Zofingen (24x28cm-9x11in) s.d.1914 i. verso board. 6-Nov-2 Dobiaschofsky, Bern #3292 (S.FR 600)
£262 $409 €393 Oftringen Farmstead (24x29cm-9x11in) s.d.1914 i. verso board. 6-Nov-2 Dobiaschofsky, Bern #3293/R (S.FR 600)
£284 $448 €426 Aargau farmstead in spring (23x28cm-9x11in) s. panel. 14-Nov-2 Stuker, Bern #174 (S.FR 650)

DOBELL, Sir William (1899-1970) Australian
£3484 $5504 €5226 Study for portrait of W S Robinson Esquire (31x38cm-12x15in) board prov. 27-Nov-2 Deutscher-Menzies, Melbourne #69/R est:9000-12000 (A.D 9755)
£6000 $9660 €9000 Gossip (15x25cm-6x10in) s. board. 6-May-3 Christie's, Melbourne #118a/R est:18000-25000 (A.D 15000)
£7143 $11286 €10715 Study for self portrait no.1 (19x40cm-7x16in) board painted 1966 prov.lit. 17-Nov-2 Sotheby's, Paddington #8/R est:30000-50000 (A.D 20000)
£7171 $11761 €10757 Beach carnival (61x76cm-24x30in) s. i.d.1961 verso composition. 4-Jun-3 Deutscher-Menzies, Melbourne #118/R est:20000-30000 (A.D 18000)
£9286 $14579 €13929 Old Joe, Julian Ashton School portrait (59x45cm-23x18in) s. canvasboard prov.exhib. 25-Nov-2 Christie's, Melbourne #81/R est:20000-30000 (A.D 26000)
£14559 $21693 €21839 Frandam (22x19cm-9x7in) s.i. board painted 1953 prov.exhib.lit. 27-Aug-2 Christie's, Melbourne #16/R est:40000-60000 (A.D 38000)
£36585 $57805 €53048 Study for the Titivators (77x88cm-30x35in) hardboard painted c.1968 prov. 22-Jul-3 Lawson Menzies, Sydney #39/R est:90000-120000 (A.D 90000)
£53640 $84215 €80460 Student (108x72cm-43x28in) s. prov.exhib.lit. 15-Apr-3 Lawson Menzies, Sydney #44/R est:150000-180000 (A.D 140000)
Works on paper
£464 $720 €696 New Guinea mountain sketch (11x16cm-4x6in) s. W/C. 29-Oct-2 Lawson Menzies, Sydney #301 (A.D 1300)
£972 $1517 €1458 Concrete works (22x16cm-9x6in) s.d.1944 ink prov. 8-Apr-3 Peter Webb, Auckland #111/R est:2000-3000 (NZ.D 2800)

DOBELL, Sir William (attrib) (1899-1970) Australian
Works on paper
£268 $421 €402 War impressions (16x24cm-6x9in) pen. 15-Apr-3 Lawson Menzies, Sydney #209/R (A.D 700)

DOBES, Milan (1929-) Czechoslovakian
£647 $1003 €971 Cathedral in Bratislava (71x45cm-28x18in) painted c.1955. 3-Dec-2 SOGA, Bratislava #291/R (SL.K 41000)
Works on paper
£1263 $1958 €1895 Optic collage (43x43cm-17x17in) mixed media exec.1971. 3-Dec-2 SOGA, Bratislava #292/R est:59000 (SL.K 80000)
£1733 $2685 €2600 Optical object I (26x26cm-10x10in) mixed media exec.c.1965. 1-Oct-2 SOGA, Bratislava #300/R est:70000 (SL.K 110000)

£1733 $2685 €2600 Optical object II (26x26cm-10x10in) mixed media exec.c.1965. 1-Oct-2 SOGA, Bratislava #301/R est:70000 (SL.K 110000)
£1890 $2930 €2835 Optical object III (21x21cm-8x8in) mixed media exec.c.1965. 1-Oct-2 SOGA, Bratislava #299/R est:90000 (SL.K 120000)

DOBIE, Beatrix Charlotte (1887-?) New Zealander
£526 $837 €789 Maori woman and children beside Lake Taupo (25x22cm-10x9in) s. board. 25-Feb-3 Peter Webb, Auckland #20 est:800-1200 (NZ.D 1500)

DOBLHOFF, Robert Heinrich (1880-1960) Austrian
£753 $1175 €1100 The Mandarin Kunpah T King, Peking (54x43cm-21x17in) i.d.1911 verso board. 10-Apr-3 Dorotheum, Vienna #118/R est:1500-1800

DOBLOUG, Jorgen (1945-) German
£1206 $1869 €1809 Christiania quadrature (120x130cm-47x51in) s.d.96 verso acrylic. 4-Dec-2 Kunsthallen, Copenhagen #237/R est:10000 (D.KR 14000)

DOBOSIEWICZ, Eugeniusz (20th C) American
£513 $800 €770 Along the shore (41x51cm-16x20in) s.d.57. 20-Sep-2 Sloan, North Bethesda #470/R
£545 $850 €818 Port scene (30x41cm-12x16in) s. s.i.d.1957 verso. 20-Sep-2 Sloan, North Bethesda #469/R

DOBOUJINSKY, Mstislav (1875-1957) Russian
£14000 $22680 €21000 View of the circus at Mariampule, Lithuania (46x56cm-18x22in) s.i.d.1930 prov. 21-May-3 Sotheby's, London #146/R est:15000-20000
£26000 $40820 €39000 View of Kaunas (46x55cm-18x22in) mono.d.1933. 20-Nov-2 Sotheby's, London #135/R est:14000-18000
Works on paper
£4000 $6480 €6000 Baltic townscape (38x66cm-15x26in) bears sig gouache on board. 21-May-3 Sotheby's, London #199/R est:4000-6000

DOBRINSKY, Yitzhak (1891-1973) Russian
£414 $662 €600 Interior (60x73cm-24x29in) s.i.d.68. 12-Mar-3 Rabourdin & Choppin de Janvry, Paris #41
£480 $749 €720 Portrait of a lady in a red dress (80x64cm-31x25in) s. 15-Oct-2 Bonhams, Knightsbridge #243/R
£828 $1324 €1200 Boutiques sur le boulevard (50x65cm-20x26in) s. 12-Mar-3 Rabourdin & Choppin de Janvry, Paris #125/R

DOBROWSKY, Josef (1889-1964) Austrian
£4054 $6324 €6000 Flowers in vase (52x36cm-20x14in) s.d.34. 25-Mar-3 Wiener Kunst Auktionen, Vienna #144/R est:6000-8000
£5435 $8913 €7500 Self portrait in 48th year (75x60cm-30x24in) s.d.1937. 27-May-3 Hassfurther, Vienna #29/R est:1800-2500
£5769 $9058 €9000 Gladiolii (67x54cm-26x21in) mono. 25-Nov-2 Hassfurther, Vienna #34 est:8000-11000
£5797 $9507 €8000 Lady in waiting (79x67cm-31x26in) panel. 27-May-3 Wiener Kunst Auktionen, Vienna #58/R est:8000-14000
£7092 $11489 €10000 Burial (100x74cm-39x29in) panel prov. 20-May-3 Dorotheum, Vienna #141/R est:13000-18000
£11594 $19014 €16000 Frau W, the model (99x74cm-39x29in) s.d.42 board. 27-May-3 Hassfurther, Vienna #28/R est:2500-3500
Works on paper
£288 $456 €450 Reclining female nude (49x65cm-19x26in) pastel. 12-Nov-2 Dorotheum, Vienna #94/R
£382 $603 €550 Female nude (49x66cm-19x26in) mono. gouache. 24-Apr-3 Dorotheum, Vienna #110/R
£414 $662 €600 Seated woman (61x44cm-24x17in) mono. pastel. 11-Mar-3 Dorotheum, Vienna #129/R
£497 $810 €750 Female nude sitting (68x49cm-27x19in) pastel. 28-Jan-3 Dorotheum, Vienna #77/R
£764 $1207 €1100 Summer landscape (45x56cm-18x22in) s.d.42 mixed media. 24-Apr-3 Dorotheum, Vienna #140/R
£1192 $1943 €1800 Last snow (45x59cm-18x23in) s.d.37 mixed media. 28-Jan-3 Dorotheum, Vienna #79/R est:2500-3600
£1528 $2414 €2200 St Margarethen, Burgenland (47x61cm-19x24in) mono. pastel. 24-Apr-3 Dorotheum, Vienna #136/R est:2200-3200
£1538 $2431 €2400 Cross roads in autumn landscape (48x62cm-19x24in) mono.d.1950 mixed media. 12-Nov-2 Dorotheum, Vienna #168/R est:1900-2600
£1667 $2633 €2400 Steiermark landscape (33x45cm-13x18in) s.d.1934 gouache. 24-Apr-3 Dorotheum, Vienna #79/R est:2400-3200
£1793 $2869 €2600 Landscape with yellow house (50x70cm-20x28in) mono. i. verso pastel. 11-Mar-3 Dorotheum, Vienna #124/R est:2600-3600
£2083 $3292 €3000 Blue jug of flowers (70x52cm-28x20in) s.d.61 mixed media. 24-Apr-3 Dorotheum, Vienna #183/R est:3000-4000
£2152 $3357 €3400 Ybbs (48x62cm-19x24in) s. gouache. 15-Oct-2 Dorotheum, Vienna #57/R est:3200-4000
£2278 $3600 €3600 Landscape in early spring (43x56cm-17x22in) s.d.38 chl W/C. 27-Nov-2 Dorotheum, Vienna #171/R est:2800-4000
£2483 $3972 €3600 Flowers (61x44cm-24x17in) s.d.1939 gouache. 11-Mar-3 Dorotheum, Vienna #58/R est:2000-3000
£2695 $4366 €3800 Yellow and orange jugs with flowers and fruit on plate (74x50cm-29x20in) s.d.1935 gouache. 20-May-3 Dorotheum, Vienna #163/R est:4000-6000
£3378 $5270 €5000 Peonies (61x47cm-24x19in) s.d.45 W/C. 25-Mar-3 Wiener Kunst Auktionen, Vienna #143/R est:5000-8000

DOBSON, Cowan (1893-1980) British
£270 $419 €405 Portrait of Admiral Lord Beatty (62x51cm-24x20in) init. 2-Oct-2 Bonhams, Knowle #75
£420 $655 €630 Still life with red roses (40x50cm-16x20in) s. 13-Sep-2 Lyon & Turnbull, Edinburgh #12/R
£1200 $1980 €1740 Flowers in a vase (46x35cm-18x14in) s.d.16. 2-Jul-3 Sotheby's, Olympia #360/R est:700-1000

DOBSON, Cowan (attrib) (1893-1980) British
£650 $1053 €975 His pet St. Bernard (100x118cm-39x46in) 23-May-3 Lyon & Turnbull, Edinburgh #55

DOBSON, Frank (1886-1963) British
£400 $632 €580 Three nude studies (41x30cm-16x12in) board. 24-Jul-3 John Nicholson, Haslemere #1124
£9500 $15675 €13775 Figures in a landscape. Family interior (31x39cm-12x15in) s.d.15 double-sided board. 3-Jul-3 Christie's, Kensington #515/R est:3000-5000
Works on paper
£315 $500 €473 Shrike, a bird study (36x48cm-14x19in) s.i.d.53 pen ink pastel. 7-Mar-3 Skinner, Boston #364/R
£315 $500 €473 Common hangnest (35x47cm-14x19in) s.d.54 pen ink pastel. 7-Mar-3 Skinner, Boston #365/R
£315 $500 €473 Splendid sunbird (35x48cm-14x19in) s.i.d.53 pen ink pastel. 7-Mar-3 Skinner, Boston #366/R
£350 $543 €525 Reclining female nude, nature reserve (51x61cm-20x24in) W/C on board. 25-Sep-2 John Nicholson, Haslemere #996
£500 $795 €750 Head and shoulders of a pretty young girl (51x41cm-20x16in) s. W/C board. 19-Mar-3 John Nicholson, Haslemere #1130/R
£650 $1073 €943 Study of a seated woman (39x36cm-15x14in) s.d.21 pencil. 3-Jul-3 Christie's, Kensington #259/R
£750 $1170 €1125 Reclining female nude (34x49cm-13x19in) s.d.27 pencil. 25-Mar-3 Bonhams, New Bond Street #58/R
£800 $1240 €1200 Seated female nude (33x25cm-13x10in) s.d.1931 red chk. 4-Dec-2 Christie's, Kensington #320/R
£800 $1320 €1160 Reclining nude (30x46cm-12x18in) s.d.47 brown chk. 3-Jul-3 Christie's, Kensington #258/R
£850 $1318 €1275 Two female torsos (41x33cm-16x13in) s.d.43 pen black ink W/C bodycol. 4-Dec-2 Christie's, Kensington #279/R
£900 $1413 €1350 Standing female nude (51x34cm-20x13in) s.d.35 pen ink chk. 21-Nov-2 Christie's, London #148/R
£900 $1485 €1305 Study of a pregnant woman (39x28cm-15x11in) s.d.21 pencil bodycol ex. 3-Jul-3 Christie's, Kensington #256/R
£920 $1500 €1380 Reclining female nude (31x46cm-12x18in) s.d.47 col chk sold with painting by Emmanuel Levy. 29-Jan-3 Dreweatt Neate, Newbury #198/R

DOBSON, Henry John (1858-1928) British
£900 $1395 €1350 Silent sympathy (39x48cm-15x19in) s.i.stretcher. 5-Dec-2 Bonhams, Edinburgh #58
£950 $1473 €1425 Morning service (40x30cm-16x12in) s. 6-Dec-2 Lyon & Turnbull, Edinburgh #99/R
£950 $1473 €1425 Reading aloud (23x29cm-9x11in) s. 5-Dec-2 Bonhams, Edinburgh #90
£1200 $1836 €1800 Knitting by the fire (30x41cm-12x16in) s. 22-Aug-2 Bonhams, Edinburgh #1161 est:1200-1400
£1550 $2449 €2325 Quiet read (60x45cm-24x18in) s. 2-Dec-2 Bonhams, Bath #159/R est:800-1200
£1700 $2652 €2550 Guiding light (30x35cm-12x14in) s.d.1915. 13-Sep-2 Lyon & Turnbull, Edinburgh #10/R est:700-1000
£2025 $3200 €3038 Critical move (43x48cm-17x19in) s. exhib. 16-Nov-2 New Orleans Auction, New Orleans #966/R est:3000-5000

DOBSON, Henry Raeburn (1901-) British
Works on paper
£525 $877 €761 Garden path (33x28cm-13x11in) s. 18-Jun-3 Andrew Hartley, Ilkley #1057/R

DOBSON, William Charles Thomas (1817-1898) British
£3000 $4830 €4500 Study for 'David bade them teach the children of Judah the use of the bow' (18x16cm-7x6in) s.i. card double-sided prov. 20-Feb-3 Christie's, London #148/R
£5500 $8855 €8250 Study for 'David bade them teach the children of Judah the use of the bow' (23x20cm-9x8in) mono.d.1859 panel prov. 20-Feb-3 Christie's, London #147/R

Works on paper
£800 $1248 €1200 Portrait of a young in a landscape (44x34cm-17x13in) mono.d.1879 pencil W/C. 17-Oct-2 Christie's, Kensington #9/R
£800 $1248 €1200 Madonna di Foligno (28x18cm-11x7in) pencil W/C htd bodycol after Sanzio Raffaello. 17-Oct-2 Christie's, Kensington #17/R
£800 $1240 €1200 Portrait of a young girl seated. Sketch of a hilltop village (23x14cm-9x6in) i. pencil double-sided. 9-Dec-2 Bonhams, New Bond Street #81/R

DOBYASCHOFSKY, Franz Joseph (1818-1867) Austrian
£1408 $2268 €2000 Man's portrait (113x86cm-44x34in) s.d.1860 lit. 9-May-3 Schloss Ahlden, Ahlden #1364/R est:2500

DOCHARTY, A Brownlie (1862-1940) British
£420 $659 €630 Carradale Bay (24x34cm-9x13in) 17-Apr-3 Bonhams, Edinburgh #373
£580 $916 €870 Castle in Dailly (40x50cm-16x20in) s.d.97. 19-Dec-2 Bonhams, Edinburgh #318
£650 $1060 €943 Wooded Scottish glen with waterfall (102x51cm-40x20in) s. 17-Jul-3 Tennants, Leyburn #851/R
£750 $1170 €1125 Shepherd and his flock on a woodland track (62x75cm-24x30in) s. 17-Oct-2 Bonhams, Edinburgh #160
£800 $1248 €1200 Loch Clair, Glen Torridon (41x61cm-16x24in) s. prov. 14-Apr-3 Sotheby's, London #141/R
£992 $1557 €1488 Highland river (46x61cm-18x24in) s. prov. 24-Jul-2 Walker's, Ottawa #19/R est:1200-1600 (C.D 2400)
£1200 $1872 €1800 Sunlight on the loch, Ben Lomond (48x79cm-19x31in) s. 14-Apr-3 Sotheby's, London #123/R est:1200-1800
£1400 $2170 €2100 Autumn river landscape (45x60cm-18x24in) s. 5-Dec-2 Bonhams, Edinburgh #116 est:1500-2000
£1600 $2496 €2400 Woodland stream (63x76cm-25x30in) s. 14-Apr-3 Sotheby's, London #124/R est:1000-1500
£1700 $2652 €2550 River in autumn (71x91cm-28x36in) s. 14-Apr-3 Sotheby's, London #125/R est:1500-2000
£1900 $2964 €2850 Log cart (99x126cm-39x50in) s. 17-Sep-2 Sotheby's, Olympia #54/R est:2000-3000

DOCHARTY, James (1829-1878) British
£343 $536 €497 Heading home (36x53cm-14x21in) s. prov. 26-Mar-3 Walker's, Ottawa #70/R (C.D 800)
£370 $596 €555 Children fishing off rocks (34x49cm-13x19in) s. 20-Feb-3 Bonhams, Edinburgh #322
£780 $1217 €1170 Angler (21x29cm-8x11in) s.i.verso board. 17-Oct-2 Bonhams, Edinburgh #171
£1800 $2736 €2700 Cadzow Forest, autumn (50x69cm-20x27in) s.d.1866 s.i.on stretcher. 28-Aug-2 Sotheby's, London #917/R est:2000-3000
£2000 $3040 €3000 In the highlands (66x91cm-26x36in) S. 28-Aug-2 Sotheby's, London #920/R est:2000-3000

DOCKERY, Susanna Roope (fl.1895-1901) British
Works on paper
£580 $928 €870 Threshing maize, Portugal (32x48cm-13x19in) s. W/C over pencil scratching out exhib. 15-May-3 Lawrence, Crewkerne #849
£680 $1088 €1020 Ploughing (32x48cm-13x19in) s. W/C over pencil. 15-May-3 Lawrence, Crewkerne #848
£820 $1312 €1230 Wine making, filling the grape vats (24x34cm-9x13in) s. W/C pencil. 15-May-3 Lawrence, Crewkerne #851
£900 $1440 €1350 Wine making, in the vineyard (32x48cm-13x19in) s. W/C. 15-May-3 Lawrence, Crewkerne #850/R

DOCKING, Shay (1928-) Australian
£1000 $1580 €1500 Port fairy image (45x61cm-18x24in) s.d.57 hessian on board. 27-Nov-2 Deutscher-Menzies, Melbourne #152/R est:3500-5000 (A.D 2800)
Works on paper
£357 $554 €536 Hill over plain I (76x94cm-30x37in) s. pastel. 29-Oct-2 Lawson Menzies, Sydney #200 (A.D 1000)

DODD, Charles Tattershall (snr) (1815-1878) British
£5500 $8634 €8250 Ship building at Penmaenpool (54x87cm-21x34in) s.d.1857. 20-Nov-2 Sotheby's, Olympia #11/R est:6000-9000

DODD, Joseph Josiah (1809-1880) British
£1550 $2527 €2248 Milan Cathedral (70x90cm-28x35in) s.i.d.1878. 21-Jul-3 Bonhams, Bath #86/R est:1500-2000

DODD, Lamar (?) ?
£11111 $18000 €16667 Cotton pickers (76x112cm-30x44in) s.d.45 prov.exhib. 24-Jan-3 Freeman, Philadelphia #196/R est:2000-3000

DODD, Robert (1748-1816) British
£2532 $3924 €4000 Coastal scene with ships at anchor and fishing boats returning home (64x76cm-25x30in) s.d.1779. 28-Sep-2 Hans Stahl, Hamburg #195/R est:4500
£17000 $26350 €25500 Capture of the Guillaume Tell, 31 March 1800 (56x76cm-22x30in) s.d.1800 prov. 31-Oct-2 Christie's, Kensington #431/R est:18000-25000

DODEIGNE, Eugène (1923-) French
Sculpture
£1439 $2360 €2000 Figure (30cm-12in) init.num.9/9 bronze prov. 3-Jun-3 Christie's, Amsterdam #184/R est:2000-3000
£3957 $6331 €5500 Tete (44x22cm-17x9in) mono. iron sold with base prov.exhib. 17-May-3 De Vuyst, Lokeren #497a/R est:6000-8000
£31034 $49655 €45000 Figure debout, sur le chemin (180x44cm-71x17in) mono. exec.1972 prov.lit. 15-Mar-3 De Vuyst, Lokeren #491/R est:20000-25000
Works on paper
£377 $585 €600 Three figures (106x73cm-42x29in) s. black chk dr. 5-Oct-2 De Vuyst, Lokeren #113
£486 $773 €700 Personnage (64x49cm-25x19in) s. chl dr. 29-Apr-3 Artcurial Briest, Paris #632
£1054 $1677 €1550 Sans titre (75x54cm-30x21in) s.d.12-1997 chl prov. 26-Feb-3 Artcurial Briest, Paris #520 est:450-600

DODEL, Wilhelm (1907-1944) Russian
£6289 $9686 €10000 Elbe Venus (146x100cm-57x39in) s.d.1940 panel. 26-Oct-2 Dr Lehr, Berlin #90/R est:10000
£11806 $18653 €17000 Portrait of E S (105x100cm-41x39in) s. panel. 26-Apr-3 Dr Lehr, Berlin #114/R est:8000

DODENHOFF, Heinz (1889-?) German
£506 $800 €800 Autumn evening by canal (43x55cm-17x22in) s. board. 29-Nov-2 Bolland & Marotz, Bremen #496/R

DODERO, Pietro (1882-1967) Italian
Works on paper
£321 $503 €500 Pause (40x40cm-16x16in) s. graphite exec.1927. 21-Nov-2 Finarte, Rome #145

DODSON, Tom (1910-1991) British
£3000 $4770 €4500 Gold Hill, Shaftesbury, Dorset (33x43cm-13x17in) s.d.1989 canvasboard. 18-Mar-3 Capes Dunn, Manchester #408

DODWELL, Edward (1767-1832) British
Works on paper
£11000 $18040 €15950 Mount Vesuvius, Italy (61x101cm-24x40in) pencil W/C prov. 5-Jun-3 Christie's, London #31/R est:8000-12000

DODWELL, Edward (attrib) (1767-1832) British
Works on paper
£355 $592 €500 La tour des Vents a Athenes (19x26cm-7x10in) W/C prov. 23-Jun-3 Beaussant & Lefèvre, Paris #74

DOELEMAN, Johan Hendrik (1848-1913) Dutch
£282 $454 €400 Farm and mill at the water (28x37cm-11x15in) s. board. 7-May-3 Vendue Huis, Gravenhage #14/R
£288 $450 €432 Dutch pastoral scene. s. board. 19-Oct-2 Harvey Clar, Oakland #1402
£1197 $1927 €1700 Farmer's wife with cows along a canal (16x24cm-6x9in) s. panel. 7-May-3 Vendue Huis, Gravenhage #474/R est:1500-2000

DOEPLER, Karl Emil (elder) (1824-1905) German
£1111 $1822 €1700 Roccocco woman with suitor in palace garden (70x58cm-28x23in) s.d.94. 29-Mar-3 Dannenberg, Berlin #561/R est:250

DOERR, Carl (1777-1842) German
£870 $1348 €1305 Paysages lacustres (25x35cm-10x14in) one s.d.1809 copper pair. 7-Dec-2 Galerie du Rhone, Sion #100 (S.FR 2000)

DOES, Jacob van der (attrib) (17th C) Dutch
£692 $1079 €1100 Extensive landscape with animals (25x28cm-10x11in) panel. 19-Sep-2 Dr Fritz Nagel, Stuttgart #867/R

DOES, Jacob van der (elder) (1623-1673) Dutch
£3020 $4862 €4500 Landscape with a shepherd and his flock (51x63cm-20x25in) init.d.1657 prov.lit. 18-Feb-3 Sotheby's, Amsterdam #219/R est:6000-8000

DOES, Jacob van der (elder-attrib) (1623-1673) Dutch
£1611 $2593 €2400 Southern landscape with drover and animals resting beside classical ruins (38x53cm-15x21in) panel prov. 18-Feb-3 Sotheby's, Amsterdam #218/R est:3000-5000

DOES, Simon van der (attrib) (1653-1717) Dutch
£2516 $3899 €4000 Shepherd couple in southern landscape (31x40cm-12x16in) panel prov. one of pair. 2-Oct-2 Dorotheum, Vienna #342/R est:4000-6000
£2516 $3899 €4000 Herdsman playing the shawm with shepherdess in southern landscape (31x40cm-12x16in) panel prov. one of pair. 2-Oct-2 Dorotheum, Vienna #343/R est:4000-6000

DOES, Willem van der (1889-1966) Dutch
£573 $894 €900 Fishing boats in Japanese harbour (42x57cm-17x22in) s. 6-Nov-2 Vendue Huis, Gravenhage #277
£701 $1093 €1100 On the path (58x44cm-23x17in) s. 6-Nov-2 Vendue Huis, Gravenhage #280

DOESBURG, Theo van and SCHWITTERS, Kurt (20th C) Dutch
Prints
£4194 $6500 €6291 Kleine dada soiree (30x30cm-12x12in) offset lithograph with cental folds. 25-Sep-2 Christie's, Rockefeller NY #215/R est:2000-3000

DOESER, Jacobus (1884-1969) Dutch
£315 $492 €460 Cows by a river (50x70cm-20x28in) s. 14-Apr-3 Glerum, Amsterdam #124
£390 $632 €550 Still life of flowers with tulips (80x60cm-31x24in) s. 26-May-3 Glerum, Amsterdam #134
£414 $646 €650 Farmhouse near a ditch (86x16cm-34x6in) s. 6-Nov-2 Vendue Huis, Gravenhage #103/R

DOGARTH, Oskar Robert (1898-1961) Austrian
£881 $1365 €1400 Roses in glass vase (51x41cm-20x16in) s. masonite. 29-Oct-2 Dorotheum, Vienna #237/R

DOHANOS, Stevan (1907-1994) American
£823 $1300 €1235 Venice (20x25cm-8x10in) s. s.i.d.1981 verso. 3-Apr-3 Christie's, Rockefeller NY #165/R est:1000-1500
£1321 $2100 €1982 Man's best friend (61x76cm-24x30in) s. 3-May-3 Rachel Davis, Shaker Heights #176/R est:800-1200

DOHLMANN, Augusta (1847-1914) Austrian
£681 $1076 €1022 Beech leaves and fruit blossom (29x24cm-11x9in) mono. 2-Dec-2 Rasmussen, Copenhagen #1439/R (D.KR 8000)

DOIG, Peter (1959-) British
£12658 $20000 €18987 Surfer (98x77cm-39x30in) paper painted 2000 prov. 13-Nov-2 Sotheby's, New York #401/R est:20000-30000
£14000 $23380 €20300 Surfer (29x21cm-11x8in) s.i.d.2002 verso oil chl on paper prov. 27-Jun-3 Christie's, London #275/R est:7000-10000
£85000 $139400 €127500 Alpine hotel (145x114cm-57x45in) oil zinc paint painted 1992 prov.exhib. 5-Feb-3 Christie's, London #10/R est:70000-90000
£200000 $334000 €300000 Grasshopper (200x250cm-79x98in) s.i.d.March/April/May 1990 prov. 25-Jun-3 Sotheby's, London #7/R est:120000-150000

DOIGNEAU, Edouard Edmond de (1865-1954) French
£1410 $2214 €2200 Gardians en Camargue (54x81cm-21x32in) s. 13-Dec-2 Piasa, Paris #92
£2516 $3874 €4000 Caravane au soleil (55x81cm-22x32in) s. i.verso. 23-Oct-2 Rabourdin & Choppin de Janvry, Paris #89/R
Works on paper
£414 $658 €600 La charrette (37x48cm-15x19in) bears st.sig. W/C. 4-Mar-3 Livinec, Gaudcheau & Jezequel, Rennes #122
£449 $704 €700 Chasse a courre (51x64cm-20x25in) s. W/C. 11-Dec-2 Maigret, Paris #145
£451 $736 €650 Moulin dans le Golfe du Morbihan (33x45cm-13x18in) studio st. gouache. 19-Jul-3 Thierry & Lannon, Brest #86
£563 $935 €800 Jeune Bretonne et son chien (30x30cm-12x12in) s. W/C gouache. 11-Jun-3 Beaussant & Lefèvre, Paris #27
£641 $1006 €1000 Les guardians (51x60cm-20x24in) s. W/C. 11-Dec-2 Maigret, Paris #144

DOISNEAU, Robert (1912-1994) French
Photographs
£1800 $2916 €2700 Giacometti dans son atelier (31x40cm-12x16in) s. init.i.d.verso silver print. 22-May-3 Sotheby's, London #96/R est:1800-2200
£2025 $3200 €3038 Le baiser de l'Hotel de Ville (24x27cm-9x11in) s.i.d.1950/1980 gelatin silver print. 22-Apr-3 Christie's, Rockefeller NY #50/R est:5000-7000
£2147 $3500 €3221 Baiser Blotto (32x24cm-13x9in) s. i.d.1950 verso gelatin silver print. 12-Feb-3 Christie's, Rockefeller NY #116/R est:2000-3000
£2147 $3500 €3221 Photographie aerienne (29x24cm-11x9in) s. i.d.1950 verso gelatin silver print. 12-Feb-3 Christie's, Rockefeller NY #117/R est:2000-3000
£2200 $3564 €3300 La derniere valse du 14 juillet (40x30cm-16x12in) s. init.i.d.verso silver print lit. 22-May-3 Sotheby's, London #99/R est:1800-2200
£2331 $3800 €3497 La Dame Indignee (23x30cm-9x12in) s.i.d.1948 init.i.d.verso gelatin silver print. 12-Feb-3 Christie's, Rockefeller NY #273/R est:2000-3000
£2500 $4050 €3750 La voiture fondue (30x40cm-12x16in) s. init.i.d.verso silver print lit. 22-May-3 Sotheby's, London #102/R est:1500-2000
£2761 $4500 €4142 Le baiser de L'Hotel de ville (24x27cm-9x11in) s. init.i.d.1950 verso gelatin silver print. 12-Feb-3 Christie's, Rockefeller NY #274/R est:4000-6000
£2800 $4536 €4200 Picasso et Francoise Gilot (30x40cm-12x16in) s. init.i.d.verso silver print. 22-May-3 Sotheby's, London #97/R est:1800-2200
£3000 $4860 €4500 Le manege de Monsieur Barre (40x30cm-16x12in) s. init.i.d.verso silver print lit. 22-May-3 Sotheby's, London #94/R est:1800-2200
£3500 $5670 €5250 Fernand Leger dans ses oeuvres (40x30cm-16x12in) s. init.i.d.verso silver print lit. 22-May-3 Sotheby's, London #98/R est:2000-3000
£4000 $6480 €6000 Les enfants de la Place Herbert (40x30cm-16x12in) s. init.i.d.verso silver print lit. 22-May-3 Sotheby's, London #104/R est:1500-2000
£4294 $7000 €6441 Le Baiser de l'Hotel de Ville (36x44cm-14x17in) s. gelatin silver print. 12-Feb-3 Christie's, Rockefeller NY #115/R est:8000-10000
£6000 $9720 €9000 Un regard oblique (30x40cm-12x16in) s. init.i.d.verso silver print lit. 22-May-3 Sotheby's, London #105/R est:3000-5000
£7000 $11340 €10500 Le baiser de l'Hotel de Ville (30x40cm-12x16in) s. init.i.d.verso silver print lit. 22-May-3 Sotheby's, London #100/R est:2500-3500

DOKOUPIL, Jiri Georg (1954-) Czechoslovakian
£2581 $4000 €3872 Mother and child, embrace (163x102cm-64x40in) acrylic candle soot varnish prov. 26-Sep-2 Christie's, Rockefeller NY #823/R est:7000-9000
Sculpture
£2365 $3689 €3500 12 bananas (73cm-29in) mono. pat.bronze exhib.lit. 25-Mar-3 Wiener Kunst Auktionen, Vienna #50/R est:3500-5500
Works on paper
£5696 $9000 €8544 Lavabo (113x162cm-44x64in) candle soot on canvas executed 1989 prov.exhib. 13-Nov-2 Sotheby's, New York #139/R est:6000-8000

DOLAN, Patrick (1926-1980) British
£3056 $4858 €4400 Ex machina (91x81cm-36x32in) s.d.July 1967 verso acrylic mixed media prov. 29-Apr-3 Whyte's, Dublin #50/R est:2000-3000

DOLBY, Edwin (fl.1849-1865) British
Works on paper
£280 $442 €420 St Maclou Rouen (25x17cm-10x7in) mono.d.1885 W/C. 7-Apr-3 David Duggleby, Scarborough #337
£780 $1264 €1100 Corrida en la Real Maestranza de Sevilla (17x25cm-7x10in) s.i.d.1893 W/C. 20-May-3 Segre, Madrid #25/R est:850

DOLCI, Carlo (1616-1686) Italian
£457719 $741505 €663693 Allegorical figure representing Patience (71x54cm-28x21in) s.d.1677 oval prov.lit. 26-May-3 Bukowskis, Stockholm #379/R est:800000-1000000 (S.KR 5900000)

DOLCI, Carlo (after) (1616-1686) Italian
£10191 $15694 €16000 La Poesia (58x44cm-23x17in) 3-Sep-2 Christie's, Amsterdam #9/R est:5000-7000

DOLCI, Carlo (attrib) (1616-1686) Italian
£1351 $2108 €2000 Christ with thorn crown (80x65cm-31x26in) 31-Mar-3 Finarte Semenzato, Milan #454/R
£1351 $2108 €2000 St Bernard (83x66cm-33x26in) 27-Mar-3 Dorotheum, Vienna #362/R est:2000-4000
£2308 $3854 €3300 Vierge en priere (56x43cm-22x17in) 27-Jun-3 Piasa, Paris #3/R est:2000-2500

DOLE, William (1917-1983) American
Works on paper
£938 $1500 €1407 Fanfare (43x36cm-17x14in) s. collage prov. 12-Jan-3 William Jenack, New York #437
£961 $1500 €1442 Noble thoughts (21x26cm-8x10in) s.d.1967 i.verso newsprint collage col ink prov. 14-Oct-2 Butterfields, San Francisco #2054/R est:2000-3000
£2006 $3250 €2909 Sign for a foggy night (51x66cm-20x26in) s.d.1962 collage ink W/C prov. 21-May-3 Doyle, New York #42/R est:2000-3000

DOLEZAL, Frantisek (1910-1989) Czechoslovakian
£654 $1041 €981 Remembrance of Venice (99x80cm-39x31in) s.d.72. 8-Mar-3 Dorotheum, Prague #91/R est:30000-45000 (C.KR 30000)

DOLEZEL, Jenny (1964-) New Zealander
£2194 $3423 €3291 Ship of fools (50x79cm-20x31in) s.i.d.1991 oil paper. 7-Nov-2 International Art Centre, Auckland #63/R est:7000-10000 (NZ.D 7000)
£3215 $4984 €4823 Study for the Circus of Life (71x91cm-28x36in) s. 4-Dec-2 Dunbar Sloane, Auckland #40/R est:5000-10000 (NZ.D 10000)
Works on paper
£1641 $2560 €2462 Figures in a landscape or hello darling (67x100cm-26x39in) s.i.d.1992 chk pastel. 17-Sep-2 Peter Webb, Auckland #119/R est:4000-6000 (NZ.D 5400)
£1929 $2990 €2894 Natural encounters I 4 (51x86cm-20x34in) s.d.1990 mixed media. 4-Dec-2 Dunbar Sloane, Auckland #37/R est:6500-8500 (NZ.D 6000)

DOLICE, Leon (1892-1960) American
£419 $650 €629 Back alley (30x20cm-12x8in) s. canvasboard. 25-Sep-2 Doyle, New York #23/R

DOLL, Anton (1826-1887) German
£513 $805 €800 Upper Bavarian lake in winter (13x26cm-5x10in) s. panel. 21-Nov-2 Van Ham, Cologne #1568/R
£1266 $1962 €2000 Alpine hut on mountain pasture (20x31cm-8x12in) s.i. 25-Sep-2 Neumeister, Munich #562/R est:2500
£2000 $3340 €3000 Skaters on a frozen river (76x91cm-30x36in) s. 18-Jun-3 Christie's, Kensington #63/R est:3000-5000
£2115 $3279 €3300 Esslingen on the Neckar with view of the Dominican church choir (40x30cm-16x12in) s.i. i.verso panel. 4-Dec-2 Neumeister, Munich #716/R est:2800
£2324 $3858 €3300 Group of children in a village street in winter (31x25cm-12x10in) s.i. 14-Jun-3 Arnold, Frankfurt #731/R est:2000
£2958 $4910 €4200 Market day in a town in winter with an equestrian statue (31x25cm-12x10in) s.i. 14-Jun-3 Arnold, Frankfurt #730/R est:3000
£3378 $5270 €5000 Hay harvest in mountain valley (51x65cm-20x26in) s.i. 27-Mar-3 Dr Fritz Nagel, Stuttgart #805/R est:8200
£5128 $8103 €8000 Tegernsee castle (43x66cm-17x26in) s. 16-Nov-2 Lempertz, Koln #1453/R est:10000
Works on paper
£974 $1451 €1500 Garden in Glockenstrasse, Munich (29x27cm-11x11in) s.i. i. verso W/C. 26-Jun-2 Neumeister, Munich #573/R
£1384 $2131 €2200 Scene paysanne Bavaroise (23x18cm-9x7in) s. W/C. 22-Oct-2 Campo, Vlaamse Kaai #487

DOLL, Anton (attrib) (1826-1887) German
£513 $795 €800 Winter meeting (21x15cm-8x6in) i. lit. 6-Dec-2 Karlheinz Kaupp, Staufen #2356/R

DOLLA, Noel (1945-) French
Works on paper
£476 $757 €700 Sans titre (110x40cm-43x16in) mono.d.84 col paste black ink. 26-Feb-3 Artcurial Briest, Paris #412
£556 $884 €800 Les silences de la fumee no 9 (56x76cm-22x30in) s.i.d.6.90 black smoke acrylic prov. 29-Apr-3 Artcurial Briest, Paris #493/R
£1528 $2429 €2200 Croix (116x96cm-46x38in) s.verso pigments prov. 29-Apr-3 Artcurial Briest, Paris #492/R est:2000-2500

DOLLERSCHELL, Eduard (1887-1948) German
£355 $574 €500 Ebbe beach, Normandy (33x41cm-13x16in) s.d.29 s.i. verso panel. 24-May-3 Van Ham, Cologne #154
£638 $1034 €900 Provence (50x58cm-20x23in) s.i.d.28 s.i. verso. 24-May-3 Van Ham, Cologne #153
£993 $1609 €1400 Boy from Mallorca (60x48cm-24x19in) s.d.28 s.i. stretcher. 24-May-3 Van Ham, Cologne #152/R

DOLLMAN, Herbert P (1856-?) British
£5405 $8703 €8108 Children playing in circus wagon (46x36cm-18x14in) s. 22-Feb-3 Rasmussen, Havnen #2088/R est:5000-7000 (D.KR 60000)

DOLLMAN, John Charles (1851-1934) British
£14000 $22820 €21000 The chase. The refuge (76x127cm-30x50in) s.d.1901 pair. 29-Jan-3 Sotheby's, Olympia #225a/R est:12000-18000

DOLLOND, W Anstey (fl.1880-1911) British
£1200 $1848 €1800 Lost in thought (51x41cm-20x16in) s. 5-Sep-2 Christie's, Kensington #307/R est:1500-2000
Works on paper
£500 $780 €750 Connoisseur. Duet (20x28cm-8x11in) s. W/C htd bodycol pair. 17-Sep-2 Sotheby's, Olympia #122/R
£823 $1300 €1235 Classical maiden (41x31cm-16x12in) s. W/C paper on card. 1-Apr-3 Christie's, Rockefeller NY #185/R
£1250 $1938 €1875 Scene in ancient Greece with young women on a balcony (34x21cm-13x8in) s. W/C. 24-Sep-2 Anderson & Garland, Newcastle #342/R est:600-900
£2400 $3936 €3600 Grecian maiden in a classical building (33x22cm-13x9in) s. W/C pair. 5-Jun-3 Locke & England, Leamington Spa #227/R est:2500-3500

DOLPH, John Henry (1835-1903) American
£1121 $1750 €1682 Cattle in farmyard (30x51cm-12x20in) s. 1-Aug-2 Eldred, East Dennis #937b est:2000-3000
£2690 $4250 €4035 Unsure kitten (20x28cm-8x11in) s. canvasboard prov. 24-Apr-3 Shannon's, Milford #223/R est:3000-5000
£4870 $7500 €7305 Young girl with dog (56x46cm-22x18in) s. prov. 24-Oct-2 Shannon's, Milford #144/R est:4000-6000

DOLPHIN, Willem (1935-) Belgian
£3038 $4800 €4800 Stilleven (50x39cm-20x15in) s.d.1984 panel. 26-Nov-2 Sotheby's, Amsterdam #82/R est:2500-3500

DOLPHYN, Victor (1909-1992) Belgian
£252 $387 €400 Landscape (33x50cm-13x20in) s. 22-Oct-2 Campo & Campo, Antwerp #91
£417 $663 €600 Vaches dans un paysage (55x31cm-22x12in) s. 29-Apr-3 Campo & Campo, Antwerp #98

DOLTON, Percy (20th C) British?
Works on paper
£400 $624 €600 Porth, yacht in full sail (39x54cm-15x21in) s. pencil W/C htd white. 18-Sep-2 Dreweatt Neate, Newbury #78

DOM, Paulus Ludovicus Carolus (1885-?) Dutch
Works on paper
£793 $1158 €1190 Carnaval (31x37cm-12x15in) s.d.1933 i. verso mixed meida board. 17-Jun-2 Philippe Schuler, Zurich #4020 (S.FR 1800)

DOMBROWSKI, Carl Ritter von (1872-1951) German
£409 $634 €650 Deer in wooded mountain landscape (63x83cm-25x33in) s. 4-Oct-2 Paul Kieffer, Pforzhiem #9194
£596 $972 €900 Deer in wood (60x79cm-24x31in) s. 14-Feb-3 Paul Kieffer, Pforzhiem #7053
Works on paper
£541 $843 €800 Deer in clearing (64x84cm-25x33in) s. pastel mixed media. 28-Mar-3 Dorotheum, Vienna #324/R

DOMELA, Cesar (1900-1992) Dutch
Works on paper
£288 $460 €400 Untitled (19x12cm-7x5in) s.d.1956 pencil bodycol transparent paper. 15-May-3 Neumeister, Munich #694/R
£360 $576 €500 Composition with circle (23x12cm-9x5in) s.d. pencil. 15-May-3 Neumeister, Munich #696/R
£1389 $2292 €2000 Sans titre (61x47cm-24x19in) s. W/C gouache. 1-Jul-3 Artcurial Briest, Paris #764/R est:2000-3000
£2083 $3313 €3000 Composition (59x44cm-23x17in) s.d.1967 gouache collage. 29-Apr-3 Artcurial Briest, Paris #122/R est:1500-2000
£2083 $3437 €3000 Sans titre (76x57cm-30x22in) s.d.1953 gouache exhib. 1-Jul-3 Artcurial Briest, Paris #769/R est:2000-3000
£2222 $3667 €3200 Sans titre (60x45cm-24x18in) s.d.1972 verso gouache collage exhib. 1-Jul-3 Artcurial Briest, Paris #763/R est:2000-3000
£4321 $7000 €6265 Composition (61x46cm-24x18in) s. s.d.1949 verso gouache prov. 21-May-3 Doyle, New York #2/R est:1500-2500
£8013 $12580 €12500 Untitled (62x48cm-24x19in) s.d.1949 mixed media. 24-Nov-2 Laurence Calmels, Paris #101/R est:12000
£9028 $14896 €13000 Relief no 149 (110x75cm-43x30in) s.d.Decembre 1997 verso plexiglas duralumin wood relief prov.lit. 1-Jul-3 Artcurial Briest, Paris #766/R est:13000-18000
£9028 $14896 €13000 Relief no 72 (122x80cm-48x31in) s.d.Janvier 1961 verso paint wood brass relief prov.lit. 1-Jul-3 Artcurial Briest, Paris #767/R est:13000-18000

£10417 $17188 €15000 Relief, courbes enfermees no 55 (100x73cm-39x29in) s.d.1955 verso painted wood brass relief lit. 1-Jul-3 Artcurial Briest, Paris #761/R est:16000-20000

DOMELA, Jan Marinus (1894-1973) American
£559 $900 €839 California harbour scene with fishing boats and figures (41x51cm-16x20in) s. masonite. 18-Feb-3 John Moran, Pasadena #171a

DOMENGE, Melcior (1871-1939) Spanish
£604 $972 €900 Rural landscape (48x70cm-19x28in) s. 18-Feb-3 Durán, Madrid #89/R

DOMENICHINO (1581-1641) Italian
Works on paper
£3593 $6000 €5210 Three figural studies depicting a putto, bust of a woman (20x25cm-8x10in) chl chk. 21-Jun-3 Selkirks, St. Louis #1049/R est:4000-6000

DOMENICHINO (after) (1581-1641) Italian
£13699 $21370 €20549 Rinaldo and Armida (114x156cm-45x61in) 28-Mar-3 Koller, Zurich #3041/R est:8000-14000 (S.FR 30000)

DOMENICHINO (attrib) (1581-1641) Italian
Works on paper
£1538 $2385 €2400 Travellers on mountain path (27x20cm-11x8in) pen ink prov. 4-Dec-2 Piasa, Paris #2/R

DOMENICI, Carlo (1898-1981) Italian
£510 $811 €750 Ploughing (30x40cm-12x16in) s. board. 1-Mar-3 Meeting Art, Vercelli #95
£513 $805 €800 Men on horseback (35x50cm-14x20in) s. board. 16-Dec-2 Pandolfini, Florence #326/R
£680 $1082 €1000 Good harvest (35x50cm-14x20in) s. s.i.verso board. 1-Mar-3 Meeting Art, Vercelli #20
£680 $1082 €1000 Tuscan cowboy (35x50cm-14x20in) s. board. 1-Mar-3 Meeting Art, Vercelli #153
£769 $1208 €1200 Boats at harbour (50x70cm-20x28in) masonite. 16-Dec-2 Pandolfini, Florence #318/R
£1090 $1711 €1700 Mazzini Square in Livorno (45x50cm-18x20in) board. 16-Dec-2 Pandolfini, Florence #293/R
£1346 $2113 €2100 Ploughing (60x80cm-24x31in) s. board. 16-Dec-2 Pandolfini, Florence #294/R
£1361 $2163 €2000 Landscape with oxen (50x70cm-20x28in) s. board. 18-Mar-3 Finarte, Milan #53/R
£1486 $2319 €2200 Shepherdess (34x50cm-13x20in) s.d.1924 board. 28-Mar-3 Farsetti, Prato #463/R
£1538 $2415 €2400 Tuscan cow-boys (49x69cm-19x27in) s.i. masonite. 16-Dec-2 Pandolfini, Florence #296
£1538 $2415 €2400 Regina Margherita Avenue (13x21cm-5x8in) s. s.i. board. 16-Dec-2 Pandolfini, Florence #319/R
£1633 $2596 €2400 Landscape with horses (50x70cm-20x28in) s. board. 18-Mar-3 Finarte, Milan #58/R
£3784 $5903 €5600 Boat keepers (51x63cm-20x25in) s. board. 28-Mar-3 Farsetti, Prato #636/R

DOMENJOZ, Raoul (1896-1978) Swiss
Works on paper
£377 $611 €668 Femme marocaine (27x22cm-11x9in) s. gouache W/C. 26-May-3 Sotheby's, Zurich #131/R (S.FR 800)

DOMERGUE, J G (1889-1962) French
£1824 $2846 €2700 Baghera (24x19cm-9x7in) s. panel. 25-Mar-3 Chochon-Barre & Allardi, Paris #97 est:3000-3500

DOMERGUE, Jean Gabriel (1889-1962) French
£696 $1100 €1100 Femme assise priant a l'eglise (54x46cm-21x18in) s.d.1906. 29-Nov-2 Drouot Estimations, Paris #101
£705 $1093 €1100 Young woman undressing at window (50x60cm-20x24in) i. lit. 6-Dec-2 Auktionhaus Georg Rehm, Augsburg #8021
£1310 $2044 €1965 Nina (24x19cm-9x7in) s. i. verso panel. 6-Nov-2 Dobiaschofsky, Bern #464/R est:5000 (S.FR 3000)
£1379 $2193 €2000 Portrait de femme (46x38cm-18x15in) s. 7-Mar-3 Rabourdin & Choppin de Janvry, Paris #40/R est:2700-3000
£1389 $2194 €2000 Jacqueline (24x19cm-9x7in) s. masonite. 25-Apr-3 Piasa, Paris #6/R
£1418 $2369 €2000 Portrait de femme de profil (24x19cm-9x7in) s. panel. 20-Jun-3 Piasa, Paris #220 est:2500-3000
£1481 $2385 €2222 Nane (24x19cm-9x7in) s. i. verso panel. 7-May-3 Dobiaschofsky, Bern #465/R est:2000 (S.FR 3200)
£1519 $2400 €2400 Baghera (24x19cm-9x7in) s. masonite. 2-Dec-2 Tajan, Paris #106
£1701 $2704 €2500 Nadia (23x18cm-9x7in) s. i.verso isorel. 2-Mar-3 Lombrail & Teucquam, Paris #172/R
£1772 $2765 €2800 Adele (19x24cm-7x9in) s. i.verso panel. 20-Oct-2 Anaf, Lyon #128/R
£1850 $3034 €2775 Girl in yellow hat. Girl in yellow headscarf (24x18cm-9x7in) s. panel pair. 4-Feb-3 Sworder & Son, Bishops Stortford #104/R est:1500-1800
£1852 $2630 €3000 Portrait de Nadine (24x19cm-9x7in) s. i.verso panel. 16-Mar-3 Eric Pillon, Calais #194/R
£1899 $3000 €3000 Portrait d'elegante en buste (80x64cm-31x25in) s.d31. 29-Nov-2 Drouot Estimations, Paris #100
£1911 $2981 €3000 Portrait de Fernande (24x19cm-9x7in) s. panel. 10-Nov-2 Eric Pillon, Calais #150/R
£1986 $3316 €2800 Portrait de femme (24x19cm-9x7in) s. panel. 20-Jun-3 Piasa, Paris #221 est:2500-3000
£2051 $3221 €3200 Elegante au chapeau (38x27cm-15x11in) s. canvas on panel. 10-Dec-2 Vanderkindere, Brussels #95/R est:1500-2500
£2065 $3200 €3098 Femme (55x46cm-22x18in) s. 26-Sep-2 Christie's, Rockefeller NY #583/R est:4000-5000
£2102 $3279 €3300 Portrait de femme au foulard rose (23x18cm-9x7in) s. panel. 10-Nov-2 Eric Pillon, Calais #148/R
£2109 $3353 €3100 Jeune femme a la voilette (24x18cm-9x7in) s. 21-Mar-3 Rieunier, Bailly-Pommery, Mathias, Paris #117/R
£2115 $3321 €3300 Natacha (24x19cm-9x7in) s. panel. 16-Dec-2 Chochon-Barre & Allardi, Paris #40/R est:2700-3000
£2160 $3068 €3500 Portrait de Claudie (24x19cm-9x7in) s. panel. 16-Mar-3 Eric Pillon, Calais #190/R
£2229 $3478 €3500 Julia, nu en buste (33x24cm-13x9in) s. panel. 10-Nov-2 Eric Pillon, Calais #156/R
£2230 $3658 €3100 Portrait de Flossie (24x31cm-9x12in) s. i.verso panel. 4-Jun-3 Marc Kohn, Paris #48/R est:2200-2500
£2308 $3623 €3600 Femme a la voilette (41x33cm-16x13in) s. 11-Dec-2 Maigret, Paris #153/R est:3800-4500
£2315 $3727 €3473 Belle de Cafe (60x49cm-24x19in) s. board. 7-May-3 Dobiaschofsky, Bern #464/R est:9000 (S.FR 5000)
£2338 $3741 €3250 Le bouquet de liliums (73x91cm-29x36in) s. i.verso prov. 14-May-3 Blanchet, Paris #103/R est:5000-6000
£2402 $3747 €3603 Young woman wearing transparent hat with flower (60x50cm-24x20in) s. 6-Nov-2 Hans Widmer, St Gallen #78/R est:5000-9500 (S.FR 5500)
£2420 $3776 €3800 Portrait de Lily (24x19cm-9x7in) s. panel. 10-Nov-2 Eric Pillon, Calais #146/R
£2620 $4087 €3930 Nadine (54x46cm-21x18in) s. i. verso panel. 6-Nov-2 Dobiaschofsky, Bern #463/R est:8000 (S.FR 6000)
£2710 $4200 €4065 Femme a l'etole de boa (45x37cm-18x15in) s. masonite prov. 26-Sep-2 Christie's, Rockefeller NY #623/R est:4000-6000
£2866 $4471 €4500 Jeune femme au bibi et a la robe rose (33x24cm-13x9in) s. panel. 10-Nov-2 Eric Pillon, Calais #153/R
£3472 $5590 €5208 La douce Flossie (61x50cm-24x20in) s. i. verso. 7-May-3 Dobiaschofsky, Bern #466/R est:8500 (S.FR 7500)
£3503 $5465 €5500 Anita (46x38cm-18x15in) s. panel. 10-Nov-2 Eric Pillon, Calais #154/R
£3694 $5763 €5800 Jeune femme aux cheveux roux cendres. s. panel. 10-Nov-2 Eric Pillon, Calais #151/R
£4000 $6320 €6200 Modele au canape Louis XV (46x38cm-18x15in) s. panel. 19-Dec-2 Claude Aguttes, Neuilly #172/R
£4113 $6664 €5800 Marylin (55x46cm-22x18in) s. panel. 23-May-3 Camard, Paris #172/R est:6000-8000
£4194 $6626 €6500 Portrait de femme (55x46cm-22x18in) s. 19-Dec-2 Claude Aguttes, Neuilly #174/R est:9000
£4331 $6757 €6800 Ida au bar (41x33cm-16x13in) s. i.verso panel. 10-Nov-2 Eric Pillon, Calais #155/R
£4586 $7154 €7200 Nu allonge (33x41cm-13x16in) s. panel. 10-Nov-2 Eric Pillon, Calais #152/R
£5123 $7275 €8300 Portrait de Dinah en buste (33x24cm-13x9in) s. i.verso panel. 16-Mar-3 Eric Pillon, Calais #197/R
£5287 $8247 €8300 Femme a l'etole de boa (45x37cm-18x15in) s. panel. 10-Nov-2 Eric Pillon, Calais #145/R
£5370 $7626 €8700 Elegante au chapeau bleu (41x33cm-16x13in) s. 16-Mar-3 Eric Pillon, Calais #198/R
£6051 $9439 €9500 Ombrelle (33x24cm-13x9in) s. panel. 10-Nov-2 Eric Pillon, Calais #143/R
£6943 $10831 €10900 Elegante au bibi de plumes roses et bleues (65x54cm-26x21in) s. 10-Nov-2 Eric Pillon, Calais #144/R
£6993 $11678 €10000 Jeune femme enlevant sa chemise (73x92cm-29x36in) s. i.verso. 27-Jun-3 Claude Aguttes, Neuilly #99/R est:12000-15000
£8176 $12673 €13000 Portrait de Nita Raya (80x65cm-31x26in) s. prov. 30-Oct-2 Artcurial Briest, Paris #309/R est:14000-18000
£8861 $13823 €14000 French cancan (46x38cm-18x15in) s. isorel prov. 31-Jul-2 Tajan, Paris #45/R est:8500-10000
£11290 $17500 €16935 Jeune femme aux fleurs (100x80cm-39x31in) s. 6-Dec-2 Sotheby's, New York #145/R est:10000-12000
£32168 $53720 €46000 Aux courses (116x90cm-46x35in) s. 27-Jun-3 Claude Aguttes, Neuilly #98/R est:40000-50000
Works on paper
£862 $1440 €1250 Elegante au chapeau (16x13cm-6x5in) s. gouache pastel. 9-Jul-3 Cornette de St.Cyr, Paris #160/R
£1135 $1838 €1600 L'espagnole (28x22cm-11x9in) s. pastel prov. 21-May-3 Cornette de St.Cyr, Paris #16/R est:1500-1800
£1392 $2200 €2200 Femme aux rideaux verts (31x24cm-12x9in) mono. W/C gouache. 27-Nov-2 Lemoine & Ferrando, Paris #88/R est:2300-3000
£2100 $3507 €3045 Study of Russian ballet dancers Vrouska and Alperoff (32x23cm-13x9in) pastel. 19-Jun-3 Clevedon Sale Rooms #145/R est:1000-1500
£2564 $4026 €4000 Venise, masque enleve (50x64cm-20x25in) s. W/C. 13-Dec-2 Piasa, Paris #102/R

£2838 $4427 €4200 Elegante aux cacatoes (25x48cm-10x19in) s. W/C. 31-Mar-3 Pierre Berge, Paris #32/R est:3800-4500

DOMINGO Y FALLOLA, Roberto (1867-1956) Spanish
£1226 $1913 €1950 Mass (50x65cm-20x26in) s. 8-Oct-2 Ansorena, Madrid #461/R
£4200 $6636 €6300 Bull fight (36x51cm-14x20in) s. 3-Apr-3 Christie's, Kensington #59/R
Works on paper
£258 $408 €400 Saturio Joron (15x21cm-6x8in) s. pen dr. 17-Dec-2 Durán, Madrid #1310
£274 $433 €425 Praising the toreador (13x21cm-5x8in) s. pen dr. 17-Dec-2 Durán, Madrid #1312
£304 $474 €450 Bull (20x15cm-8x6in) s. dr. 25-Mar-3 Durán, Madrid #586/R
£329 $513 €480 Bull scene (12x20cm-5x8in) s. ink dr. 8-Apr-3 Ansorena, Madrid #673/R
£346 $540 €550 Dancer (17x13cm-7x5in) s. ink dr. 23-Sep-2 Durán, Madrid #677/R
£419 $663 €650 Bull scene (15x21cm-6x8in) s. pen dr. 17-Dec-2 Durán, Madrid #1314
£974 $1422 €1500 Bull fight (12x23cm-5x9in) s. gouache. 17-Jun-2 Ansorena, Madrid #302/R
£1480 $2398 €2250 Bull fight (50x65cm-20x26in) s. i.verso gouache. 21-Jan-3 Durán, Madrid #108/R
£1747 $2725 €2621 Bullfight (49x62cm-19x24in) s. gouache. 6-Nov-2 Dobiaschofsky, Bern #465/R est:4500 (S.FR 4000)
£2358 $3679 €3750 Triumph exit (35x22cm-14x9in) s. gouache. 23-Sep-2 Durán, Madrid #200/R
£3446 $5376 €5100 Conducteurs de taureaux (34x54cm-13x21in) s. gouache. 27-Mar-3 Maigret, Paris #287/R

DOMINGO Y MARQUES, Francisco (1842-1920) Spanish
£1034 $1634 €1500 Goya and two people (45x33cm-18x13in) s.d.1909 on palette. 1-Apr-3 Segre, Madrid #118/R
£3797 $6000 €6000 Telegram (46x38cm-18x15in) s.i. 28-Nov-2 Dorotheum, Vienna #217/R est:7000-9000
£4258 $6728 €6600 Merlin and the magic pan (55x42cm-22x17in) s. board. 17-Dec-2 Segre, Madrid #72/R
Works on paper
£310 $489 €480 Portrait of boy (13x10cm-5x4in) s. pastel chl. 17-Dec-2 Segre, Madrid #24/R
£1316 $2132 €2000 Mosquetaires meeting (19x26cm-7x10in) s.i.d.1904 gouache. 21-Jan-3 Ansorena, Madrid #54/R

DOMINGO, Francesc (1893-1974) Spanish
£294 $482 €450 Portrait of boy (24x21cm-9x8in) board. 5-Feb-3 Arte, Seville #757/R

DOMINGO, Roberto (1883-1956) Spanish
Works on paper
£780 $1264 €1100 Rafael Vega de los Reyes, viendo caer sin puntilla al tercer toro (15x21cm-6x8in) s. pencil pen. 20-May-3 Segre, Madrid #21/R est:390
£780 $1264 €1100 Marcial Lalanda en un quite en el cuarto toro (15x21cm-6x8in) s.d.28 pencil pen. 20-May-3 Segre, Madrid #22/R est:390
£811 $1265 €1200 Fishing harbour (22x40cm-9x16in) s. gouache. 31-Mar-3 Ribeyre & Baron, Paris #35
£1554 $2424 €2300 Bateau de peche devant la jetee (29x47cm-11x19in) s. gouache. 31-Mar-3 Ribeyre & Baron, Paris #36
£1622 $2530 €2400 Bullfight (30x41cm-12x16in) s. gouache. 31-Mar-3 Ribeyre & Baron, Paris #37
£2759 $4414 €4000 Cow-boys (34x42cm-13x17in) s. gouache. 11-Mar-3 Castellana, Madrid #51/R

DOMINGUEZ (?) ?
£374 $591 €561 Still life (38x28cm-15x11in) s.d.1987 masonite. 26-Nov-2 Louis Morton, Mexico #110/R (M.P 6000)

DOMINGUEZ BECQUER, Jose (1805-1841) Spanish
£1379 $2179 €2000 Genre scene (56x42cm-22x17in) 7-Apr-3 Castellana, Madrid #54/R est:500

DOMINGUEZ, Benjamin (20th C) Mexican
£12369 $19790 €17935 El mago (110x100cm-43x39in) s. 15-May-3 Louis Morton, Mexico #74/R est:250000-300000 (M.P 200000)

DOMINGUEZ, Oscar (1906-1958) Spanish
£5283 $8242 €8400 Fenetre (22x14cm-9x6in) s.d.1953. 17-Sep-2 Segre, Madrid #156/R
£9353 $14964 €13000 Nature morte au chandeleir et aux fruits (46x61cm-18x24in) s.d. canvas on cardboard. 18-May-3 Eric Pillon, Calais #272/R
£14448 $21094 €22250 Composition (38x46cm-15x18in) s.d.1950. 12-Jun-2 Castellana, Madrid #97/R est:18000
£15000 $23250 €22500 Paysage (72x114cm-28x45in) s.d.56 prov.exhib. 5-Dec-2 Christie's, Kensington #193/R est:10000-15000
£16234 $23701 €25000 Untitled (38x45cm-15x18in) s. painted 1950. 12-Jun-2 Castellana, Madrid #278/R est:15000
£16981 $26321 €27000 Mujer con carro (39x48cm-15x19in) i. cardboard painted c.1947. 30-Oct-2 Artcurial Briest, Paris #336/R est:20000-25000
£17177 $27311 €25250 Mujer con carro (39x48cm-15x19in) i. cardboard painted c.1947. 26-Feb-3 Artcurial Briest, Paris #305/R est:20000-25000
£17419 $27523 €27000 Fight (28x36cm-11x14in) mono.d.1948 prov. 19-Dec-2 Ruellan, Paris #93/R est:22000
£17857 $26071 €27500 Cocks (61x50cm-24x20in) s.i.d.47. 12-Jun-2 Castellana, Madrid #270/R est:25000
£20513 $32205 €32000 Tour (65x54cm-26x21in) prov. 24-Nov-2 Laurence Calmels, Paris #102/R est:15000
£22727 $33182 €35000 Untitled (38x46cm-15x18in) s.d.1946. 12-Jun-2 Castellana, Madrid #266/R est:25000
£26923 $42269 €42000 Composition au phonographe (65x46cm-26x18in) s. s.verso prov. 24-Nov-2 Laurence Calmels, Paris #103/R est:20000
£32877 $51616 €48000 Femme bleue (27x46cm-11x18in) s.d.46 exhib. 15-Apr-3 Laurence Calmels, Paris #4263/R
£45278 $71539 €65200 Scene de tauromachie (60x92cm-24x36in) s.d.1950. 23-Apr-3 Rabourdin & Choppin de Janvry, Paris #39/R est:6500
£58000 $96860 €84100 Taureaux (60x73cm-24x29in) s.d.51 prov. 24-Jun-3 Sotheby's, London #168/R est:40000-60000
£60000 $100200 €87000 Les femmes (73x60cm-29x24in) s.d.1949 prov. 24-Jun-3 Sotheby's, London #166/R est:50000-70000
£82192 $129041 €120000 Nature morte a la poire (89x116cm-35x46in) s.d.49 prov.exhib. 15-Apr-3 Laurence Calmels, Paris #4264/R est:40000
£219178 $341918 €320000 Untitled (107x77cm-42x30in) painted c.1934-35 exhib.lit. 14-Apr-3 Laurence Calmels, Paris #4009/R est:100000
Works on paper
£828 $1382 €1200 Le crabe (21x15cm-8x6in) mono. W/C Indian ink. 9-Jul-3 Cornette de St.Cyr, Paris #161/R
£1058 $1661 €1650 Oiseaux dans la nuit (34x26cm-13x10in) s. gouache. 24-Nov-2 Lesieur & Le Bars, Le Havre #36/R
£1783 $2782 €2800 Composition au taureau (30x40cm-12x16in) s. Chinese ink. 7-Nov-2 Chochon-Barre & Allardi, Paris #123/R
£2611 $4074 €4100 Composition au taureau sur fond jaune (23x33cm-9x13in) s. ink W/C prov. 7-Nov-2 Chochon-Barre & Allardi, Paris #125/R
£2866 $4471 €4500 Composition au pistolet et citron (26x25cm-10x10in) s. gouache. 7-Nov-2 Chochon-Barre & Allardi, Paris #124/R
£3846 $6038 €6000 Untitled (37x48cm-15x19in) mixed media. 24-Nov-2 Laurence Calmels, Paris #104/R
£5036 $8058 €7000 Le couple (30x19cm-12x7in) s. Indian ink dr. 18-May-3 Eric Pillon, Calais #291/R

DOMINICI, Carlo (1897-1981) Italian
£737 $1157 €1150 Countryside (35x50cm-14x20in) s. board. 10-Dec-2 Della Rocca, Turin #291/R

DOMINICIS, Gino de (1947-1998) Italian
£10759 $16785 €17000 Untitled (33x33cm-13x13in) s.verso board. 14-Sep-2 Meeting Art, Vercelli #837/R
£12671 $19767 €18500 Untitled (65x48cm-26x19in) s.verso paint collage board. 10-Apr-3 Finarte Semenzato, Rome #302/R
£13548 $21406 €21000 Planets (50x50cm-20x20in) s.verso oil collage. 18-Dec-2 Christie's, Rome #309/R est:15000
£75000 $115500 €112500 Untitled (272x176cm-107x69in) household paint golf leaf on board executed 1992 prov.exhib. 22-Oct-2 Christie's, London #53/R est:50000-70000

DOMINIQUE, John August (1893-1984) American
£304 $475 €456 Mountains near Ojai. s.d.1948 masonite. 19-Oct-2 Harvey Clar, Oakland #1424
£314 $500 €471 Pt. Lobos (30x41cm-12x16in) s.i.d.1953 canvas on board. 8-Mar-3 Harvey Clar, Oakland #1200
£1553 $2500 €2330 Eucalyptus landscape (22x28cm-9x11in) s.indis.d.1921. 18-Feb-3 John Moran, Pasadena #71 est:2000-3000
£3185 $5000 €4778 Ventura river (76x96cm-30x38in) s.d.1973. 19-Nov-2 Butterfields, San Francisco #8304/R est:4000-6000

DOMMELEN, Theodorus van (c.1770-?) Dutch
£828 $1292 €1300 Herdsman with cattle on forest edge (61x64cm-24x25in) s. 6-Nov-2 Vendue Huis, Gravenhage #358/R

DOMMERSEN, Cornelis Christian (1842-1928) Dutch
£2083 $3437 €3000 Taking the tender to shore (51x77cm-20x30in) s. canvas on board. 1-Jul-3 Christie's, Amsterdam #128 est:3000-5000
£3459 $5327 €5500 Fishermen unloading a bomschuit (36x27cm-14x11in) s.d.96 panel. 23-Oct-2 Christie's, Amsterdam #17/R est:5000-7000
£4808 $7596 €7500 Cityscape with church with two spires (38x31cm-15x12in) s. bears i. verso. 16-Nov-2 Lempertz, Koln #1454/R est:8000
£5031 $7748 €8000 View of the Overtoom, Amsterdam (38x65cm-15x26in) s.d.1890 i.verso. 22-Oct-2 Sotheby's, Amsterdam #154/R est:15000-20000
£5660 $8717 €9000 Shipping in an estuary (56x83cm-22x33in) s.d.1861 canvas on panel. 22-Oct-2 Sotheby's, Amsterdam #182/R est:9000-12000
£6962 $10861 €11000 Jewish area in Amsterdam (31x25cm-12x10in) s.d.89 panel. 15-Oct-2 Horta, Bruxelles #171/R est:6000-6500
£7186 $12000 €10420 Evening at Maassluis Holland (52x79cm-20x31in) s. s.i.verso. 22-Jun-3 Freeman, Philadelphia #11/R est:4000-6000

£8000 $12560 €12000 Views of the Bay of Naples (11x17cm-4x7in) s. paper on board set of eight. 19-Nov-2 Bonhams, New Bond Street #26/R est:7000-10000
£8228 $12835 €13000 Amsterdam (33x25cm-13x10in) s.d.89 panel. 15-Oct-2 Horta, Bruxelles #170/R est:7000-9000
Works on paper
£510 $795 €800 View of town by the water (12x19cm-5x7in) s.d.1881/91 W/C. 6-Nov-2 Vendue Huis, Gravenhage #374

DOMMERSEN, Pieter Christian (1834-1908) Dutch
£1233 $1923 €1800 Ships on choppy waters in front of the town of Hoorn (29x38cm-11x15in) panel. 14-Apr-3 Glerum, Amsterdam #11/R est:2000-3000
£1700 $2652 €2550 Coastal scene, with fishermen in their catch (27x37cm-11x15in) indis sig. 8-Oct-2 Bonhams, Knightsbridge #257/R est:1000-1500
£2069 $3290 €3000 Sailing vessel in heavy weather (41x30cm-16x12in) s.d.1908 panel. 10-Mar-3 Sotheby's, Amsterdam #116/R est:3000-5000
£2692 $4173 €4200 View of Biervliet in Zeeland in Holland with fishing family and boats (27x37cm-11x15in) s.d.1893 i.verso panel. 4-Dec-2 Neumeister, Munich #717/R est:2000
£3000 $4650 €4500 Fishing boat with figures (41x61cm-16x24in) s.d.1875. 25-Sep-2 John Nicholson, Haslemere #1022/R est:3000-4000
£3390 $5390 €5085 Isle of Terschellingen, Holland (28x38cm-11x15in) s. panel. 18-Mar-3 Maynards, Vancouver #24a est:9000-12000 (C.D 8000)
£3500 $5670 €5250 Oosthuizen on the Zuiderzee, Holland (20x30cm-8x12in) s.d.1892 panel prov. 20-May-3 Sotheby's, Olympia #359/R est:3000-5000
£5000 $7950 €7500 Figures in a street in Utrecht (49x39cm-19x15in) s.d.1904 panel prov. 18-Mar-3 Bonhams, New Bond Street #10/R est:5000-8000
£6000 $9720 €9000 Maassluis, Holland (41x61cm-16x24in) s.d.1882 i.verso panel. 21-May-3 Christie's, Kensington #659/R est:3000-5000
£6198 $9731 €9297 Shipping on the Zuider Zee (51x76cm-20x30in) i. s.d.1905 verso prov. 24-Jul-2 Walker's, Ottawa #10/R est:15000-20000 (C.D 15000)
£12000 $19680 €18000 Canal in Amsterdam (51x41cm-20x16in) s.d.1874 prov. 3-Jun-3 Sotheby's, London #156/R est:10000-15000

DOMMERSEN, Pieter Christian (attrib) (1834-1908) Dutch
£1800 $2790 €2700 Fishermen setting their lobster pots, with sailing vessels (38x26cm-15x10in) i. panel. 1-Oct-2 Fellows & Sons, Birmingham #80/R est:1800-2500

DOMMERSEN, W (1850-1927) Dutch
£1600 $2384 €2400 Bellagio Lago Como. Belem Castle, Lisbon (41x61cm-16x24in) s.i.verso pair. 28-Jun-2 Chrystals Auctions, Isle of Man #167 est:800-1200
£1650 $2607 €2475 Fisher folk on the Schelett (40x61cm-16x24in) s. 28-Nov-2 Morphets, Harrogate #573/R est:1000-1500
£1700 $2686 €2550 Vollerokoven on the Schelett, Holland (40x61cm-16x24in) s. 28-Nov-2 Morphets, Harrogate #572/R est:1000-1500
£1900 $2945 €2850 View of Conway Castle (40x60cm-16x24in) 31-Oct-2 Locke & England, Leamington Spa #135/R est:1250-2000

DOMMERSEN, William (1850-1927) Dutch
£300 $477 €450 Evening on the Jure (26x1cm-10x0in) s. i.verso. 5-Mar-3 Bonhams, Bury St Edmunds #373
£430 $684 €645 Cattaro, Italy (30x51cm-12x20in) s. i.verso. 5-Mar-3 Bonhams, Bury St Edmunds #372
£705 $1107 €1100 Riverside ruins at dusk (30x41cm-12x16in) s. 21-Nov-2 Van Ham, Cologne #1571
£884 $1397 €1326 Three figures in a sail boat. Three figures in rowing boat (21x29cm-8x11in) s. s.i.verso pair. 1-Apr-3 Stephan Welz, Johannesburg #421 est:8000-12000 (SA.R 11000)
£884 $1397 €1326 Sailing and shipping on a calm estuary (39x59cm-15x23in) s. 1-Apr-3 Stephan Welz, Johannesburg #422/R est:10000-15000 (SA.R 11000)
£1350 $2133 €2025 Cattaro, Italy (30x40cm-12x16in) s. i.verso pair. 7-Apr-3 Bonhams, Bath #122/R est:1000-1500
£1392 $2172 €2200 Thames at Greenwich (50x77cm-20x30in) s.i.d.1893. 21-Oct-2 Glerum, Amsterdam #44/R est:2500-3000
£1408 $2268 €2000 On the Schelde, Holland (49x75cm-19x30in) s. 7-May-3 Vendue Huis, Gravenhage #384/R est:2000-2500
£1633 $2596 €2400 River landscapes (20x41cm-8x16in) s. pair. 19-Mar-3 Neumeister, Munich #547/R est:2200
£2100 $3486 €3150 Rue St. Margaret, Dieppe (46x35cm-18x14in) s. prov. 10-Jun-3 Bonhams, Leeds #160 est:1200-1500
£2138 $3314 €3400 Southern city (41x61cm-16x24in) s. i. verso. 29-Oct-2 Dorotheum, Vienna #267/R est:3800-4000
£2400 $3744 €3600 Maastricht on the Maas (51x74cm-20x29in) s. s.i.verso. 26-Mar-3 Sotheby's, Olympia #213/R est:1200-1800
£2600 $3952 €3900 On the river Amstel, Amsterdam (51x41cm-20x16in) s. s.i.verso. 29-Aug-2 Christie's, Kensington #28/R est:1500-2000
£2813 $4500 €4220 Dutch town scene with figure and card and children fishing (51x41cm-20x16in) s. 14-May-3 Butterfields, San Francisco #1061/R est:3000-5000
£6000 $9540 €9000 Flemish market place (97x144cm-38x57in) s. prov. 18-Mar-3 Bonhams, New Bond Street #7/R est:4000-6000
£11806 $18771 €17000 Street in the Jews quarter, Amsterdam (48x37cm-19x15in) s.d.1883 i.verso panel. 29-Apr-3 Christie's, Amsterdam #88/R est:10000-15000

DOMMERSEN, William (attrib) (1850-1927) Dutch
£960 $1488 €1440 Dutch town scene with figures (51x41cm-20x16in) s.d.1883. 1-Nov-2 Moore Allen & Innocent, Cirencester #428/R

DOMOTO, Hisao (1928-) Japanese
£2786 $4458 €4040 Gold green (110x110cm-43x43in) s.i.d.1963 verso canvas on board exhib. 11-Mar-3 Babuino, Rome #325/R
Works on paper
£411 $650 €617 Cirrus (25x36cm-10x14in) s.d.1958 i.verso gouache prov. 2-Apr-3 Doyle, New York #73a/R

DOMSAITIS, Pranas (1880-1965) South African
£307 $479 €461 Figure outside a rondavel (37x35cm-15x14in) mono. board. 15-Oct-2 Stephan Welz, Johannesburg #422 est:4000-6000 (SA.R 5000)
£516 $831 €774 Karoo landscape (36x49cm-14x19in) s. oil paper on board. 12-May-3 Stephan Welz, Johannesburg #580 est:6000-8000 (SA.R 6000)
£799 $1246 €1199 Flowers in a vase (57x72cm-22x28in) mono. board. 15-Oct-2 Stephan Welz, Johannesburg #424/R est:8000-12000 (SA.R 13000)
£1044 $1629 €1566 Yellow sunset over a settlement (38x59cm-15x23in) s. board. 15-Oct-2 Stephan Welz, Johannesburg #423/R est:8000-12000 (SA.R 17000)
£1167 $1821 €1751 Hibiscus flowers in a white jug (62x51cm-24x20in) s. board. 15-Oct-2 Stephan Welz, Johannesburg #425/R est:10000-15000 (SA.R 19000)
£1333 $2146 €2000 Three figures in a landscape (46x62cm-18x24in) s. board. 12-May-3 Stephan Welz, Johannesburg #448/R est:10000-15000 (SA.R 15500)
£1345 $2099 €2018 Still life of roses (57x73cm-22x29in) board. 11-Nov-2 Stephan Welz, Johannesburg #518/R est:8000-12000 (SA.R 21000)
£1376 $2215 €2064 Family near a stable (55x45cm-22x18in) init. 12-May-3 Stephan Welz, Johannesburg #513/R est:7000-10000 (SA.R 16000)
£1806 $2907 €2709 Flight into Egypt (54x52cm-21x20in) mono. board. 12-May-3 Stephan Welz, Johannesburg #449/R est:15000-20000 (SA.R 21000)

DOMSCHAT, Julius (20th C) German?
£411 $641 €600 Lago Maggiore with Isola Bella (65x100cm-26x39in) s. 10-Apr-3 Van Ham, Cologne #1404

DOMY, Eve (1951-) French
£397 $648 €600 Composition (128x99cm-50x39in) s.d.2002 oil ink pastel. 3-Feb-3 Cornette de St.Cyr, Paris #413

DONA, Lydia (20th C) American
Works on paper
£3200 $5216 €4800 Mechanisms on nomadism and the folds of fluidity (122x122cm-48x48in) s.d.1994 mixed media on canvas. 3-Feb-3 Sotheby's, Olympia #173/R est:1200-1500

DONADONI, Stefano (1844-1911) Italian
£1266 $2000 €2000 Castel Sant'Angelo, Rome (20x27cm-8x11in) s cardboard. 26-Nov-2 Christie's, Rome #152/R
Works on paper
£318 $497 €500 Rome (13x22cm-5x9in) s. W/C. 6-Nov-2 Hugo Ruef, Munich #1366/R

DONALD, John Milne (1819-1866) British
£1600 $2592 €2400 Greenock from Helensburgh (19x27cm-7x11in) s.d.60 i.verso panel. 23-May-3 Lyon & Turnbull, Edinburgh #6/R est:800-1200

DONALDSON, Andrew (1790-1846) British
Works on paper
£520 $811 €780 Back view of the old Baronial hall, Gorbals, Glasgow (16x21cm-6x8in) s.d.1832 pencil. 10-Apr-3 Bonhams, Edinburgh #91

DONALDSON, David Abercrombie (1916-1996) British
£8000 $12400 €12000 Still life with mussels (76x81cm-30x32in) s. 31-Oct-2 Christie's, London #172/R est:8000-12000

DONALDSON, Kim (1952-) Zimbabwean
Works on paper
£450 $698 €675 Zambesi river (53x74cm-21x29in) s. pastel col chk. 24-Sep-2 Rowley Fine Art, Newmarket #360/R
£480 $758 €696 Bushbank Bokkeloof Autumn (56x76cm-22x30in) pastel. 23-Jul-3 Brightwells, Leominster #899
£900 $1422 €1305 Jungle cat (74x109cm-29x43in) s. pastel. 23-Jul-3 Brightwells, Leominster #900/R

DONALDSON, Marysia (20th C) British?
£480 $782 €720 Still life with a basket of fruit upon a table (48x43cm-19x17in) indis sig. board. 29-Jan-3 Dreweatt Neate, Newbury #201

DONAT, Friederich Reginald (1830-1907) Belgian
£377 $600 €566 Good cheer (41x53cm-16x21in) s. 7-Mar-3 Jackson's, Cedar Falls #846/R
£915 $1501 €1400 An indiscreet question (53x41cm-21x16in) s. i. verso panel. 29-Mar-3 Dannenberg, Berlin #562/R est:1500
£961 $1499 €1442 Marriage broker on the beach (52x41cm-20x16in) s. panel. 20-Nov-2 Fischer, Luzern #1089/R est:2200-2400 (S.FR 2200)
£1048 $1635 €1572 Net mending lesson (52x41cm-20x16in) s. panel. 20-Nov-2 Fischer, Luzern #1088/R est:2200-2400 (S.FR 2400)

DONATI, Enrico (1909-) American/Italian
£23973 $37637 €35000 Sang gazeux (46x35cm-18x14in) s.d.48. 15-Apr-3 Laurence Calmels, Paris #4265/R
£23973 $37637 €35000 Coqs de bruyere (76x63cm-30x25in) s.d.45 exhib. 15-Apr-3 Laurence Calmels, Paris #4267/R est:10000
£27397 $43014 €40000 Disait Giovanni di Paolo (51x61cm-20x24in) s.i.d.1942. 15-Apr-3 Laurence Calmels, Paris #4268/R
Works on paper
£2174 $3370 €3261 Fossil series - Le Noir (77x64cm-30x25in) s. mixed media prov. 4-Dec-2 Koller, Zurich #190/R est:5000-7000 (S.FR 5000)
£2397 $3764 €3500 Untitled (28x33cm-11x13in) s.d.46 ink. 15-Apr-3 Laurence Calmels, Paris #4266/R
£3165 $4937 €5000 Moon view (50x70cm-20x28in) s.i.d.1953 verso mixed media terracotta on canvas. 19-Oct-2 Semenzato, Venice #13/R

DONATO, Veneziano (fl.1344-1386) Italian
£49057 $76528 €78000 San Donato (25x16cm-10x6in) i. tempera gold. 21-Sep-2 Semenzato, Venice #139/R est:60000-70000

DONCKER, Maurice den (20th C) Belgian?
£268 $432 €400 Pont sur la Zenne (79x100cm-31x39in) s. painted 1948. 24-Feb-3 Bernaerts, Antwerp #15/R

DONELLI, Carlo (1660-1715) Italian
Works on paper
£12346 $20000 €18519 Seated man looking up (30x22cm-12x9in) i. chk. 22-Jan-3 Christie's, Rockefeller NY #46/R est:15000

DONG SHOUPING (1904-) Chinese
Works on paper
£543 $891 €750 Bamboo (55x50cm-22x20in) s. seal Indian ink hanging scroll. 30-May-3 Dr Fritz Nagel, Stuttgart #1136/R
£932 $1538 €1351 Prunus (68x68cm-27x27in) s.d.1988 ink scroll. 6-Jul-3 Christie's, Hong Kong #380/R est:15000-25000 (HK.D 12000)
£1232 $2020 €1700 Chrysanthemums and bamboo on rock (118x43cm-46x17in) s. seals Indian ink col. 30-May-3 Dr Fritz Nagel, Stuttgart #1138/R est:500-800

DONGEN, Dionys van (1748-1819) Dutch
£4430 $6867 €7000 Dutch yacht and a rowing boat in choppy waters, other shipping beyond (32x40cm-13x16in) s.d.17.9 panel prov. 24-Sep-2 Christie's, Amsterdam #99/R est:7000-10000

DONGEN, Kees van (1877-1968) French/Dutch
£10000 $16400 €15000 Roses dans un verre (28x22cm-11x9in) s. board painted c.1920 prov. 5-Feb-3 Sotheby's, London #269/R est:15000
£20645 $32619 €32000 Deer (24x33cm-9x13in) s. s.verso. 19-Dec-2 Claude Aguttes, Neuilly #189/R est:15000
£20833 $32917 €30000 Oiseau solitaire (46x38cm-18x15in) s. i.d.1908 verso. 25-Apr-3 Piasa, Paris #8/R est:35000
£28000 $46760 €40600 Poulain dans la prairie Hollandaise (33x46cm-13x18in) s. s.i.verso painted 1937 prov. 25-Jun-3 Christie's, London #152/R est:25000-35000
£66879 $104331 €105000 Portrait of Putti Geene (54x45cm-21x18in) s. s.d.1949 verso. 5-Nov-2 Vendu Notarishuis, Rotterdam #200/R est:40000-60000
£70513 $110705 €110000 Champs-Elysees (24x19cm-9x7in) s. cardboard painted 1902 lit. 10-Dec-2 Artcurial Briest, Paris #479/R est:120000-180000
£90909 $151818 €130000 La Marquise Luisa Casati (46x38cm-18x15in) s. lit. 30-Jun-3 Artcurial Briest, Paris #75/R est:100000-150000
£120000 $200400 €174000 Champ de courses a Mandelieu - Alpes Maritimes (81x99cm-32x39in) s. painted 1924 exhib.lit. 25-Jun-3 Christie's, London #181/R est:120000-160000
£124224 $200000 €186336 Deauville (100x81cm-39x32in) s. painted c.1920 prov.lit. 7-May-3 Sotheby's, New York #364/R est:150000-200000
£135000 $221400 €202500 Portrait de femme (55x46cm-22x18in) s. init.i.d.1949 on stretcher prov. 5-Feb-3 Sotheby's, London #137/R est:120000
£140000 $229600 €210000 Couple dans un bois (61x46cm-24x18in) s. s.i. verso lit. 5-Feb-3 Sotheby's, London #144/R est:180000
£142857 $230000 €214286 La plage de Deauville (46x56cm-18x22in) s. painted c.1935. 7-May-3 Sotheby's, New York #180/R est:220000-280000
£150000 $250500 €217500 Kaia Metis (55x46cm-22x18in) init. i.verso panel prov. 25-Jun-3 Christie's, London #173/R est:130000-160000
£165000 $275550 €239250 Les arums (147x115cm-58x45in) s. painted 1912 prov.exhib. 25-Jun-3 Christie's, London #169/R est:80000-120000
£170000 $283900 €246500 Porteuse d'eau, Egypte (100x81cm-39x32in) s. i.on stretcher painted 1913 prov.lit. 24-Jun-3 Sotheby's, London #144/R est:180000-250000
£176056 $292254 €250000 Ariana Gedeonov (147x130cm-58x51in) s. prov.exhib.lit. 12-Jun-3 Tajan, Paris #34/R est:300000-400000
£177019 $285000 €265529 Vase de fleurs (81x54cm-32x21in) s. s.on stretcher prov. 8-May-3 Christie's, Rockefeller NY #188/R est:140000-180000
£180000 $300600 €261000 La Piazzetta, Venise (92x74cm-36x29in) s. painted 1921 prov.lit. 25-Jun-3 Christie's, London #172/R est:180000-240000
£189103 $295000 €283655 Place des Doges, Venise (100x81cm-39x32in) s. prov.exhib. 7-Nov-2 Christie's, Rockefeller NY #290/R est:180000-220000
£201923 $315000 €302885 Le polo a Deauville (54x83cm-21x33in) s. painted 1955 prov.exhib. 7-Nov-2 Christie's, Rockefeller NY #357/R est:350000-450000
£224359 $350000 €336539 Portrait de Lucie Valore (147x114cm-58x45in) s. s.on stretcher painted c.1947 prov.lit. 7-Nov-2 Christie's, Rockefeller NY #319/R est:400000-600000
£240385 $375000 €360578 Harem (65x54cm-26x21in) s. i.d.1911 verso prov. 6-Nov-2 Sotheby's, New York #181/R est:400000-600000
£250000 $417500 €375000 Au Cabaret Negre (98x95cm-39x37in) s. s.i.verso painted c.1925 prov. 23-Jun-3 Sotheby's, London #27/R est:250000-350000
£258065 $400000 €387098 Femme au collier (55x46cm-22x18in) s. painted c.1908 prov.exhib. 4-Nov-2 Phillips, New York #32/R est:500000-700000
£380000 $623200 €570000 Portrait de Guus (100x81cm-39x32in) s. painted c.1906-07 prov.lit. 4-Feb-3 Sotheby's, London #20/R est:600000
£400000 $668000 €600000 Aux courses (65x54cm-26x21in) s. painted c.1910 prov.exhib. 23-Jun-3 Sotheby's, London #9/R est:400000-600000
£434783 $700000 €652175 Deux femmes nues a la fenetre (129x96cm-51x38in) s. s.i.verso painted c.1922 prov. 6-May-3 Sotheby's, New York #24/R est:700000-900000
Works on paper
£1603 $2484 €2500 La porteuse d'eau, Maroc (21x16cm-8x6in) s. pencil. 3-Dec-2 Christie's, Amsterdam #21/R est:2500-3500
£1986 $3217 €2800 Scene de bal (20x13cm-8x5in) s. graphite. 21-May-3 Cornette de St.Cyr, Paris #40/R est:3000-4000
£2436 $3776 €3800 Femme en profile. La fenetre (14x9cm-6x4in) s. i.verso pencil wasx crayon double-sided. 3-Dec-2 Christie's, Amsterdam #18/R est:3500-4500
£2692 $4227 €4200 Tete de femme (20x10cm-8x4in) init. ink dr. paper on cardboard lit. 11-Dec-2 Artcurial Briest, Paris #514/R
£3526 $5535 €5500 Femme de Zandstraat (44x27cm-17x11in) init. chl W/C lit. 11-Dec-2 Artcurial Briest, Paris #513/R
£3767 $5914 €5500 Femme et cygne. s. W/C. 15-Apr-3 Galerie Moderne, Brussels #131/R est:800-1200
£4167 $6583 €6000 A bas la Rue Lafitte (46x38cm-18x15in) s.i. ink gouache crayon dr. 25-Apr-3 Piasa, Paris #7/R est:7000
£5484 $8500 €8226 Personnages (24x32cm-9x13in) s. brush India ink over chl over gouache prov. 26-Sep-2 Christie's, Rockefeller NY #516/R est:6000-8000
£5769 $9058 €9000 Femme assise (23x15cm-9x6in) s. ink. 10-Dec-2 Renaud, Paris #63/R
£9615 $15000 €14423 Le kiosque a musique (25x33cm-10x13in) s. gouache W/C black crayon brush ink executed 1900. 6-Nov-2 Sotheby's, New York #198/R est:15000-20000
£11000 $16940 €16500 Les meres au bal (39x56cm-15x22in) s. brush ink. 22-Oct-2 Sotheby's, London #131/R est:8000-10000
£11538 $17538 €18000 Femme accoudee a une table (26x19cm-10x7in) s. W/C ink lit. 16-Aug-2 Deauville, France #51/R est:21000
£11728 $16654 €19000 Two kids on the beach (19x28cm-7x11in) s. pen W/C. 17-Mar-2 Galerie de Chartres, Chartres #140b

£13000 $21710 €18850 Portrait de jeune fille (30x23cm-12x9in) s. brush ink wash W/C prov. 24-Jun-3 Sotheby's, London #276/R est:6000-8000

£14493 $23768 €20000 Scene d'exterieur, femmes de dos (31x27cm-12x11in) s. chk W/C. 29-May-3 Lempertz, Koln #593/R est:25000

£19000 $31160 €28500 Portrait de femme de profil (64x40cm-25x16in) s. W/C pen ink. 6-Feb-3 Christie's, London #420/R est:25000

£20000 $32800 €30000 Sommeil des fleurs (24x21cm-9x8in) st.sig. gouache W/C pencil exec.1947. 6-Feb-3 Christie's, London #434/R est:15000

£22000 $36740 €33000 Deux enfants sur la plage (28x36cm-11x14in) s. W/C pen ink. 26-Jun-3 Christie's, London #383/R est:16000-20000

£23077 $36231 €36000 Rendez-vous avec des elegantes au Jardin du Luxembourg (23x18cm-9x7in) s. W/C gouache crayon prov. 10-Dec-2 Pierre Berge, Paris #30/R est:30000

£35256 $55353 €55000 Femme allongee (47x63cm-19x25in) mono. ink wash W/C prov. 10-Dec-2 Pierre Berge, Paris #33/R est:90000

£48000 $80160 €69600 Le prince de sagan au bois (24x21cm-9x8in) st.sig. W/C gouache over pencil executed c.1946-47 prov.lit. 24-Jun-3 Sotheby's, London #238/R est:35000-45000

£58621 $93793 €85000 Portrait de Madame Renee Albouy (49x31cm-19x12in) s. gouache. 12-Mar-3 Libert, Castor, Paris #202/R est:30000-45000

DONKERSLOOT, Peter (1959-) Dutch

£284 $460 €400 Portrait of a man (100x78cm-39x31in) s.d.90 acrylic. 26-May-3 Glerum, Amsterdam #280/R

DONNA, Porfirio di (1942-1986) American

Works on paper

£605 $950 €908 Wavy lines (106x76cm-42x30in) s.d.1984 mixed media. 21-Nov-2 Swann Galleries, New York #44/R

DONNAY, Auguste (1862-1921) Belgian

Works on paper

£496 $829 €700 Paysages (50x69cm-20x27in) s.d.1901 pastel board. 18-Jun-3 Hotel des Ventes Mosan, Brussels #238

£567 $948 €800 Vue de verger (38x27cm-15x11in) s.d.1888 W/C. 18-Jun-3 Hotel des Ventes Mosan, Brussels #267

£709 $1184 €1000 Le mois de fevrier (25x16cm-10x6in) mono. crayon. 18-Jun-3 Hotel des Ventes Mosan, Brussels #231

DONNE, Benjamin John Merifield (1831-1928) British

Works on paper

£250 $398 €375 Track in the Austrian Alps (68x104cm-27x41in) s.d.88 W/C. 18-Mar-3 Rosebery Fine Art, London #747

£300 $477 €450 Temple of Bacchus in the Campagna (22x34cm-9x13in) s.d.1877 W/C. 26-Feb-3 Cheffins Grain & Comins, Cambridge #493

£400 $624 €600 Peaceful moment within an ancient ruin (43x66cm-17x26in) s.d.1883 W/C. 25-Mar-3 Bonhams, Knightsbridge #195/R

DONNE, Col Henry Richard Beadon (fl.1906-1939) British

Works on paper

£360 $562 €540 Winkelmatten, a chalet in the mountains (23x35cm-9x14in) s.i.d.8.7.20 W/C. 25-Mar-3 Bonhams, Knightsbridge #227/R

DONNE, Walter J (1867-?) British

Works on paper

£300 $480 €450 Evening in the Dolomites (25x51cm-10x20in) s.d.1882 W/C bodycol. 11-Mar-3 Gorringes, Lewes #2317

£700 $1078 €1050 Red Rocks (33x48cm-13x19in) s.d.78 pencil W/C htd bodycol. 25-Oct-2 Gorringes, Lewes #892

DONNE, Winifred (fl.1910-1922) British

Works on paper

£280 $456 €420 Girl with alsation (70x50cm-28x20in) s.d.1911 W/C. 2-Feb-3 Lots Road, London #350/R

DONNELLY, Deborah (1978-) Irish

£2051 $3221 €3200 Irish cow (91x91cm-36x36in) s. s.i.d.2002 verso. 19-Nov-2 Whyte's, Dublin #239/R est:1500-2000

DONNER, Carl (?) ?

Works on paper

£300 $477 €450 Woodcock in flight in snow covered wood (47x71cm-19x28in) s. W/C. 18-Mar-3 Sworder & Son, Bishops Stortford #450/R

£300 $468 €450 Grouse in highland setting (51x36cm-20x14in) s. W/C. 11-Apr-3 Keys, Aylsham #542/R

£300 $498 €435 Great grey shrike (33x23cm-13x9in) s. pencil W/C bodycol. 12-Jun-3 Christie's, Kensington #160/R

£400 $668 €580 Cock and hen pheasants in a Norfolk landscape (33x51cm-13x20in) s. W/C. 20-Jun-3 Keys, Aylsham #568

£650 $1079 €943 Falcon on a rocky outcrop (36x29cm-14x11in) s. pencil W/C. 12-Jun-3 Christie's, Kensington #157/R

DONNER, Diego (1959-) Uruguayan

Works on paper

£865 $1350 €1298 Confluence (110x130cm-43x51in) s. mixed media. 10-Oct-2 Galleria Y Remates, Montevideo #86/R

DONNY, Desire (1798-1861) Flemish

£600 $936 €900 Sailing boat off the beach (25x36cm-10x14in) s. board. 26-Mar 3 Sotheby's, Olympia #197/R

£1076 $1678 €1700 Chatelain au bord de cascade (76x100cm-30x39in) s. 15-Oct-2 Horta, Bruxelles #153

DONOVAN, Phoebe (1902-1998) British

£850 $1360 €1275 Cottages by the coast (27x41cm-11x16in) s. board. 15-May-3 Christie's, Kensington #191/R

Works on paper

£270 $422 €400 Cottages in wooded landscape (23x30cm-9x12in) s. W/C. 26-Mar-3 James Adam, Dublin #143

DONZE, Numa (1885-1952) Swiss

£1397 $2194 €2096 Self portrait with hat (61x50cm-24x20in) s. s.i. stretcher. 25-Nov-2 Sotheby's, Zurich #126/R est:1500-1800 (S.FR 3200)

DONZEL, Charles (1824-1889) French

Works on paper

£1013 $1580 €1600 Bords de riviere (54x73cm-21x29in) one s. one s.d.1855 pastel oval pair. 20-Oct-2 Galerie de Chartres, Chartres #107 est:1800-2500

DONZELLI, Bruno (1941-) Italian

£321 $503 €500 Porto Miro' (25x25cm-10x10in) s.i. s.i.verso acrylic painted 2000. 23-Nov-2 Meeting Art, Vercelli #25/R

£321 $503 €500 Italian postcard (40x50cm-16x20in) s.d.1984. 23-Nov-2 Meeting Art, Vercelli #34

£327 $523 €500 Breakfast at Matisse's (25x25cm-10x10in) s. acrylic painted 2000. 4-Jan-3 Meeting Art, Vercelli #728

£340 $541 €500 Palette (40x50cm-16x20in) s. 1-Mar-3 Meeting Art, Vercelli #717

£340 $541 €500 Breakfast at Burri's (30x35cm-12x14in) s. oil collage. 1-Mar-3 Meeting Art, Vercelli #524

£340 $541 €500 Window with Depero (40x50cm-16x20in) s. s.i.verso. 1-Mar-3 Meeting Art, Vercelli #715

£347 $552 €500 Print (40x50cm-16x20in) s. oil mixed media collage. 1-May-3 Meeting Art, Vercelli #313

£347 $549 €500 Morandiana, su paesaggio ll'Italiana (100x100cm-39x39in) s.d. s.i.d.verso acrylic prov. 27-Apr-3 Perrin, Versailles #156/R

£694 $1104 €1000 Imitating De Chirico (70x60cm-28x24in) s. s.i.verso acrylic. 1-May-3 Meeting Art, Vercelli #52

£1026 $1610 €1600 Atelier Miro' (100x100cm-39x39in) s. s.i.verso. 23-Nov-2 Meeting Art, Vercelli #88/R

£1042 $1656 €1500 Picasso mirror (100x90cm-39x35in) s. 1-May-3 Meeting Art, Vercelli #446

£2353 $3765 €3600 Homage to De Chirico (100x100cm-39x39in) s. acrylic painted 1988 lit. 4-Jan-3 Meeting Art, Vercelli #401

Works on paper

£316 $494 €500 Ormare, Alberto Burri (20x20cm-8x8in) s. s.i.verso mixed media collage on canvas. 14-Sep-2 Meeting Art, Vercelli #290/R

£321 $503 €500 Still life with tropical fruit (40x50cm-16x20in) s. s.i.verso mixed media collage on canvas. 23-Nov-2 Meeting Art, Vercelli #20

DOOMER, Lambert (1623-1700) Dutch

Works on paper

£4938 $8000 €7407 Study of goat (12x17cm-5x7in) pen ink wash htd white prov. 21-Jan-3 Sotheby's, New York #143/R est:3000

DOOMS, Vic (1912-1994) Belgian

£586 $938 €850 Still life (42x36cm-17x14in) s. panel. 15-Mar-3 De Vuyst, Lokeren #104

£1379 $2207 €2000 Landscape (30x40cm-12x16in) s. panel. 15-Mar-3 De Vuyst, Lokeren #103/R est:800-1000

DOOREN, Edmond van (1895-1965) Belgian

£403 $648 €600 Paysage des Ardennes (50x70cm-20x28in) 24-Feb-3 Bernaerts, Antwerp #899/R

£629 $969 €1000 Paysage ensoleille en Flandres (70x95cm-28x37in) s. 22-Oct-2 Campo & Campo, Antwerp #289

£680 $1082 €1000 Night time (88x95cm-35x37in) s. 24-Mar-3 Bernaerts, Antwerp #820/R est:1200-1500

£1667 $2650 €2400 Steen der Wijzen (145x135cm-57x53in) s.d.1948. 29-Apr-3 Campo & Campo, Antwerp #315/R est:2250-2750

Works on paper

£1582 $2468 €2500 Futurist city (70x51cm-28x20in) s. ink dr. 21-Oct-2 Bernaerts, Antwerp #638 est:1000-1500

DOOREN, Émile van (attrib) (20th C) Belgian
£374 $595 €550 Le jeune fermier (60x90cm-24x35in) 18-Mar-3 Galerie Moderne, Brussels #195

DOORMAAL, Theo van (?) Belgian?
£532 $862 €750 Interieur d'eglise (59x69cm-23x27in) 26-May-3 Amberes, Antwerp #88

DOORN, Adriaan van (1825-1903) Dutch
£387 $569 €600 Woman leading cow through meadow (36x54cm-14x21in) s. 20-Jun-2 Dr Fritz Nagel, Stuttgart #763/R
£552 $877 €800 Cows in a meadow (43x35cm-17x14in) s. 10-Mar-3 Sotheby's, Amsterdam #101

DOORN, Jan van (1916-) Dutch
£3800 $5928 €5700 Extensive river landscape with windmills and a ferry boat (44x57cm-17x22in) s.d.1734 panel prov. 8-Apr-3 Sotheby's, Olympia #167/R est:4000-6000

DOORN, Tinus van (1905-1940) Dutch
£2270 $3677 €3200 Death by rabbit (75x100cm-30x39in) mono.d.34. 26-May-3 Glerum, Amsterdam #153/R est:3000-5000

DOORNBOS, Abraham R (fl.1670-1679) Dutch
£3836 $5984 €5600 Herders and cattle in landscape (32x40cm-13x16in) s. panel. 10-Apr-3 Van Ham, Cologne #1187/R est:2800

DOORNIK, Jan van (attrib) (18th C) Dutch
£964 $1600 €1398 Travelers along a road with windmill in the background (33x46cm-13x18in) panel. 14-Jun-3 Jackson's, Cedar Falls #188/R est:1500-2000

DOOYEWAARD, Jacob (1876-1969) Dutch
£301 $475 €452 Untitled (25x18cm-10x7in) s.d.66. 1-Dec-2 Susanin's, Chicago #5073/R
£411 $650 €617 Untitled (41x33cm-16x13in) s.d.66 board. 1-Dec-2 Susanin's, Chicago #5064/R
£489 $812 €709 Interior with young girl tending open hearth (17x24cm-7x9in) s. panel. 10-Jun-3 Ritchie, Toronto #133/R est:1500-2000 (C.D 1100)
£538 $850 €807 Untitled (41x48cm-16x19in) s.d.1968 board. 1-Dec-2 Susanin's, Chicago #5067/R

DORAZIO, Piero (1927-) Italian
£458 $760 €650 Untitled (21x28cm-8x11in) s.d.1996 tempera paper. 10-Jun-3 Finarte Semenzato, Milan #232/R
£833 $1308 €1300 Ebla (18x24cm-7x9in) s.i.d.1999. 23-Nov-2 Meeting Art, Vercelli #269/R
£1090 $1711 €1700 Blue notes I (25x35cm-10x14in) s.i.d.2001 verso. 23-Nov-2 Meeting Art, Vercelli #44/R
£1250 $1987 €1800 See (35x25cm-14x10in) s.i.d.1999 verso. 1-May-3 Meeting Art, Vercelli #23
£1361 $2163 €2000 Terina (25x30cm-10x12in) s.i.d.2000. 1-Mar-3 Meeting Art, Vercelli #617
£1503 $2405 €2300 Untitled (30x37cm-12x15in) s.d.1979 tempera paper. 4-Jan-3 Meeting Art, Vercelli #389
£1503 $2405 €2300 Eleusi (25x35cm-10x14in) s.i.verso. 4-Jan-3 Meeting Art, Vercelli #592
£1837 $2920 €2700 Gonia Azur I (42x36cm-17x14in) s.i.d.1996 verso hexagonal. 1-Mar-3 Meeting Art, Vercelli #381
£1923 $2981 €3000 Asmask (35x50cm-14x20in) s.i.d.1996 verso acrylic. 4-Dec-2 Finarte, Milan #259/R
£2026 $3242 €3100 Phoenix (50x35cm-20x14in) s.i.d.2000 verso. 4-Jan-3 Meeting Art, Vercelli #595
£2089 $3258 €3300 Taliesin I (40x60cm-16x24in) s.i.d.2000. 14-Sep-2 Meeting Art, Vercelli #763/R
£2244 $3522 €3500 Ex light II (50x35cm-20x14in) s.i.verso. 21-Nov-2 Finarte, Rome #231/R
£2292 $3644 €3300 Heplis (40x60cm-16x24in) s.i.d.1999 verso. 1-May-3 Meeting Art, Vercelli #474
£2653 $4218 €3900 Allaxi II (50x35cm-20x14in) s.i. painted 2001. 1-Mar-3 Meeting Art, Vercelli #628
£2692 $4227 €4200 Grace (40x60cm-16x24in) s.i.d.2001 acrylic. 19-Nov-2 Finarte, Milan #48/R
£2692 $4254 €4200 Composition (39x51cm-15x20in) s.d.1950 tempera paper. 15-Nov-2 Farsetti, Prato #266/R
£3425 $5342 €5000 Composition (47x30cm-19x12in) s. tempera paper painted 1957. 10-Apr-3 Finarte Semenzato, Rome #62/R
£3595 $5752 €5500 Mekan (60x80cm-24x31in) s.i.d.1996. 4-Jan-3 Meeting Art, Vercelli #373
£4487 $7045 €7000 Composition (50x32cm-20x13in) s.d.1957 tempera card. 21-Nov-2 Finarte, Rome #152/R
£4514 $7177 €6500 Clear night II (70x40cm-28x16in) s.i.d.1989 verso lit. 1-May-3 Meeting Art, Vercelli #218
£4514 $7177 €6500 Malouf (75x75cm-30x30in) s.i.d.2002 verso. 1-May-3 Meeting Art, Vercelli #408
£6114 $9598 €9171 Summacum II (100x81cm-39x32in) s.i.d.1991 verso prov. 25-Nov-2 Germann, Zurich #85/R est:14000-18000 (S.FR 14000)
£8511 $13787 €12000 Scaletta II (55x38cm-22x15in) s.i.d.1968 verso exhib.lit. 26-May-3 Christie's, Milan #260/R est:12000-16000
£8974 $14090 €14000 REd reflection (75x95cm-30x37in) s.i.d.1990. 19-Nov-2 Finarte, Milan #174/R est:10000-14000
£8974 $13910 €14000 Hard I (70x120cm-28x47in) s.i.d.1973 verso lit. 4-Dec-2 Finarte, Milan #306/R est:14000
£10638 $17234 €15000 Ascensione C and V (72x93cm-28x37in) s.i.d.1965 verso prov.exhib.lit. 26-May-3 Christie's, Milan #329/R est:1000-12000
£10897 $15910 €17000 Points (120x200cm-47x79in) s.i.d.1984 verso. 5-Jun-2 Il Ponte, Milan #116/R est:15000-20000
£17000 $28390 €24650 A latere (61x50cm-24x20in) s.i.d.1962 verso prov.exhib. 26-Jun-3 Sotheby's, London #131/R est:8000-12000
£18367 $29204 €27000 Pride (120x200cm-47x79in) s.i.d.1984 verso. 1-Mar-3 Meeting Art, Vercelli #364 est:25000
£18710 $29561 €29000 Nice look (180x90cm-71x35in) s.i.d.1964 verso prov.exhib.lit. 18-Dec-2 Christie's, Rome #290/R est:30000
£32000 $49920 €48000 Rosso di sotto (81x100cm-32x39in) s. i.d.1961 verso prov.exhib.lit. 21-Oct-2 Sotheby's, London #53/R est:35000-45000

Sculpture
£1418 $2298 €2000 Untitled (16x22cm-6x9in) bas-relief bronze prov. 26-May-3 Christie's, Milan #140/R est:2000-2500

Works on paper
£577 $900 €866 Senza titolo (28x22cm-11x9in) s.d.1957 W/C. 19-Sep-2 Swann Galleries, New York #311/R
£1944 $3092 €2800 Composition (25x33cm-10x13in) s.d.1964 W/C. 1-May-3 Meeting Art, Vercelli #160
£2129 $3364 €3300 Untitled (106x145cm-42x57in) collage. 18-Dec-2 Christie's, Rome #183/R
£2692 $4254 €4200 Composition (40x26cm-16x10in) s.d.47 W/C ink. 15-Nov-2 Farsetti, Prato #281/R
£2903 $4587 €4500 Untitled (50x70cm-20x28in) s.d.64 gouache prov. 18-Dec-2 Christie's, Rome #191/R
£2903 $4587 €4500 Untitled (58x72cm-23x28in) s.d.1965 gouache prov. 18-Dec-2 Christie's, Rome #190/R
£5797 $9507 €8000 Untitled (56x78cm-22x31in) s.d.63 gouache board prov. 28-May-3 Lempertz, Koln #121/R est:5500

DORDA RODRIGUEZ, Enrique (19/20th C) Spanish

Works on paper
£472 $736 €750 Portrait of lady (60x45cm-24x18in) s.d.1911 pastel. 23-Sep-2 Durán, Madrid #115/R

DORE, Gustave (1832-1883) French
£2564 $4052 €4000 Les sommets enneiges (21x33cm-8x13in) s.d.57 panel. 18-Nov-2 Tajan, Paris #129/R est:4600-6000
£26923 $42539 €42000 L'aigle noir de prusse (129x195cm-51x77in) s.d.1871 prov.lit. 18-Nov-2 Tajan, Paris #94/R est:30000-33000
£44872 $70897 €70000 L'aigle d'ecosse (110x185cm-43x73in) s.d. prov. 18-Nov-2 Tajan, Paris #93/R est:30000-38000

Works on paper
£478 $741 €717 Evening lake (32x47cm-13x19in) s.i. W/C. 9-Dec-2 Philippe Schuler, Zurich #4154 (S.FR 1100)
£609 $944 €950 Jeune peintre de la Renaissance (17x8cm-7x3in) s. sepia ink wash graphite dr. 4-Dec-2 Libert, Castor, Paris #37
£900 $1404 €1350 Old fortress, Villeneuve les Avignon (71x51cm-28x20in) s. W/C. 26-Mar-3 Woolley & Wallis, Salisbury #98/R
£1119 $1600 €1679 London street scene (37x67cm-15x26in) pencil stumping. 23-Jan-3 Swann Galleries, New York #311/R est:2000-3000
£1304 $2022 €1956 Matterhorn (43x33cm-17x13in) s. W/C. 9-Dec-2 Philippe Schuler, Zurich #4155/R est:2000-3000 (S.FR 3000)
£1646 $2600 €2600 Personnages accroches au mat d'un bateau naufrage (21x30cm-8x12in) s. pen brown ink brown wash. 27-Nov-2 Christie's, Paris #282/R est:1500-2000
£1959 $3057 €2900 Course de bateaux (46x33cm-18x13in) s.i.d.1870 pen ink wash over crayon. 26-Mar-3 Piasa, Paris #99
£2027 $3162 €3000 View of Scotland (23x32cm-9x13in) s.i.d.1873 W/C over crayon. 26-Mar-3 Piasa, Paris #97/R
£2244 $3545 €3500 Portrait presume d'un des freres de l'artiste, General de Brigade (46x31cm-18x12in) s.d. W/C gouache prov. 18-Nov-2 Tajan, Paris #95/R est:3800-4600
£3165 $5000 €5000 Promeneuse assise au pied d'un arbre (21x29cm-8x11in) s. W/C prov. 28-Nov-2 Tajan, Paris #156/R
£3526 $5465 €5500 Diseuse de bonne aventure (55x74cm-22x29in) studio st. crayon W/C. 4-Dec-2 Piasa, Paris #165/R
£3846 $6077 €6000 Le Rhin Allemand (65x91cm-26x36in) s.i. wash gouache prov.lit. 18-Nov-2 Tajan, Paris #96/R est:6000-7000
£8013 $12580 €12500 Autoportrait (46x30cm-18x12in) s. W/C exhib. 16-Dec-2 Millon & Associes, Paris #10/R est:10000-12000

DORE, Gustave (attrib) (1832-1883) French

Works on paper
£2793 $4441 €4190 In the wizard's grotto (33x24cm-13x9in) s. W/C. 5-Mar-3 Rasmussen, Copenhagen #2082/R est:5000 (D.KR 30000)

DORE, Jacques (?) French
£290 $475 €400 Portrait de dame (38x40cm-15x16in) s. 27-May-3 Campo, Vlaamse Kaai #83
£290 $475 €400 Portrait de dame (38x30cm-15x12in) s. 27-May-3 Campo, Vlaamse Kaai #84
£503 $775 €800 Lady (38x30cm-15x12in) s. pair. 22-Oct-2 Galerie Moderne, Brussels #1716

DORELL, Arnost Gustav (1832-1877) Czechoslovakian?
£1032 $1630 €1548 Northern Bohemian landscape with castle ruins (18x22cm-7x9in) s.d.1873 oval. 30-Nov-2 Dorotheum, Prague #36 (C.KR 50000)
£1088 $1731 €1600 Outside the farmhouse (21x28cm-8x11in) s. paper on board. 25-Feb-3 Dorotheum, Vienna #133/R est:1500-1600

DOREN, Émile van (1865-1949) Belgian
£420 $659 €630 Woodland pond (66x61cm-26x24in) s. 10-Dec-2 Rosebery Fine Art, London #557/R
£503 $810 €750 Paysage (26x36cm-10x14in) s. panel. 18-Feb-3 Vanderkindere, Brussels #66
£784 $1263 €1200 Soir au marais (30x49cm-12x19in) s. s.i.verso. 20-Jan-3 Horta, Bruxelles #29

DORFLES, Gillo (1910-) Italian
Prints
£2051 $3221 €3200 Composition (49x55cm-19x22in) s.d.1953 monotype prov.lit. 20-Nov-2 Pandolfini, Florence #94

DORFMEISTER, Johann Evangelist (1742-1765) Austrian
£335 $540 €500 Rocky woodland path with a traveller resting (31x23cm-12x9in) panel prov.lit. 18-Feb-3 Sotheby's, Amsterdam #283/R

D'ORGEIX, Christian (20th C) French
£1346 $2113 €2100 Tentation de Saint-Antoine (65x50cm-26x20in) s. paper on panel. 15-Dec-2 Perrin, Versailles #79/R
Works on paper
£577 $906 €900 Untitled (8x5cm-3x2in) s. mixed media exec.c.1956. 15-Dec-2 Perrin, Versailles #82/R

DORIES, L (?) ?
£1679 $2653 €2519 Last rehearsal (40x50cm-16x20in) s. board prov. 7-Apr-3 Shapiro, Sydney #525/R est:3000-5000 (A.D 4400)

DORIGNY, Louis (1654-1742) French
Works on paper
£1076 $1700 €1700 Scenes from Saint Frances's life (16x23cm-6x9in) pen ink wash crayon dr pair. 28-Nov-2 Tajan, Paris #19/R

DORIGNY, Michel (attrib) (1617-1665) French
£769 $1215 €1200 Vierge de l'Annonciation (32x24cm-13x9in) 15-Nov-2 Beaussant & Lefèvre, Paris #33
£26000 $40820 €39000 Judgement of Paris (99x134cm-39x53in) 10-Dec-2 Bonhams, New Bond Street #65/R est:6000-8000

DORING, Adam Lude (1925-) German
£385 $596 €600 Table tennis player (41x17cm-16x7in) s.d.68/70 s.i.d.72 verso board. 6-Dec-2 Karlheinz Kaupp, Staufen #2076
£414 $654 €600 Woman with cigarettes (26x25cm-10x10in) s.d. s.d. verso tempera masonite. 2-Apr-3 Dr Fritz Nagel, Stuttgart #9044/R
£486 $773 €700 Kopf (25x25cm-10x10in) s. d.1977 verso acrylic. 29-Apr-3 Campo & Campo, Antwerp #99
£513 $795 €800 Female nude on horseback (54x37cm-21x15in) s.d.68 s.d.68 verso. 6-Dec-2 Karlheinz Kaupp, Staufen #2080/R
£586 $926 €850 Hands (42x42cm-17x17in) s.d. tempera masonite. 2-Apr-3 Dr Fritz Nagel, Stuttgart #9045/R
Works on paper
£345 $545 €500 Couple (14x10cm-6x4in) s. W/C ballpen. 2-Apr-3 Dr Fritz Nagel, Stuttgart #9047/R
£517 $817 €750 Black head (56x56cm-22x22in) s.d. s.d. verso gouache graphite board. 2-Apr-3 Dr Fritz Nagel, Stuttgart #9043/R
£886 $1382 €1400 Untitled (40x40cm-16x16in) s.d.1969 mixed media board. 18-Oct-2 Dr Fritz Nagel, Stuttgart #75/R

DORING, Walter (1914-1975) ?
Works on paper
£253 $392 €400 Visage abstrait (28x28cm-11x11in) s.verso graphite col crayon gouache cardboard. 28-Sep-2 Cornette de St.Cyr, Paris #293

DORNBERGER, Karl Johannes (1864-1940) Norwegian
£2531 $3973 €3797 Winter in Soon (60x101cm-24x40in) s. 25-Nov-2 Blomqvist, Lysaker #1050/R est:20000-25000 (N.KR 29000)
£3306 $5421 €4794 Leaving Grand Cafe (55x60cm-22x24in) s.d.1919 i.d.verso panel. 2-Jun-3 Blomqvist, Oslo #179/R est:35000-40000 (N.KR 36000)

DORNER, Johann Jakob (younger) (1775-1852) German
£1538 $2385 €2400 Farmhouse in Eichenwald with farmer, his son and dog (24x29cm-9x11in) mono.d.1835 panel. 4-Dec-2 Neumeister, Munich #719/R est:1200
£10759 $16677 €17000 Delling and the Pilsensee (44x62cm-17x24in) 25-Sep-2 Neumeister, Munich #563/R est:15000
Works on paper
£513 $749 €800 Landscape study (22x28cm-9x11in) s.i. W/C pencil. 4-Jun-2 Karl & Faber, Munich #67
£755 $1177 €1200 Woodland (32x20cm-13x8in) W/C bodycol. 11-Oct-2 Winterberg, Heidelberg #506/R
£828 $1292 €1300 Harlaching, beginning of 19th C (24x37cm-9x15in) s.i. W/C pencil. 5-Nov-2 Hartung & Hartung, Munich #5049/R
£1181 $1877 €1700 Farmstead in the mountains (19x29cm-7x11in) s.i. pen brush Indian ink wash. 5-May-3 Ketterer, Munich #293/R est:1000-1200

DORNER, Max (1870-1939) German
£256 $390 €400 Moor landscape with lake (60x70cm-24x28in) s. 11-Jul-2 Hugo Ruef, Munich #619

DORPH, Anton (1831-1914) Danish
£298 $471 €447 Dinghy by stone pier (23x32cm-9x13in) init. 2-Dec-2 Rasmussen, Copenhagen #1389/R (D.KR 3500)
£298 $477 €447 Sunday in the country (28x45cm-11x18in) init.d.1868. 16-Mar-3 Hindemae, Ullerslev #378/R (D.KR 3200)
£630 $996 €945 Dog and cat by food dish (26x32cm-10x13in) s.d.1874. 16-Nov-2 Crafoord, Lund #4/R (S.KR 9000)

DORREE, Émile (1885-1959) French
Works on paper
£617 $877 €1000 View of Fez (19x50cm-7x20in) s.i.d.1936 gouache. 16-Mar-3 Eric Pillon, Calais #73/R

DORRELL, Edmund (1778-1857) British
Works on paper
£1900 $3135 €2755 Village scene, Devonshire (18x25cm-7x10in) s. W/C. 2-Jul-3 Sotheby's, Olympia #212/R est:800-1200

DORS, Mirabelle and LUCA, Gherasim (20th C) Russian
Works on paper
£1712 $2688 €2500 Dialogue (35x41cm-14x16in) assemblage. 15-Apr-3 Laurence Calmels, Paris #4270/R

DORSCH, Ferdinand (1875-1938) German
£552 $877 €800 Still life of roses, peach wine bottle and goblet (45x60cm-18x24in) s.i.d.1935 panel. 8-Mar-3 Arnold, Frankfurt #576/R
£577 $894 €900 Terraced landscape near Dresden (91x130cm-36x51in) i. 9-Dec-2 Dr Fritz Nagel, Stuttgart #6969/R
£962 $1490 €1500 Interior of Dresden castle (98x80cm-39x31in) i. 9-Dec-2 Dr Fritz Nagel, Stuttgart #6970/R est:1000

DORSEY, William (1942-) American
£466 $750 €699 Eucalyptus coastal (23x30cm-9x12in) s. prov. 18-Feb-3 John Moran, Pasadena #10
£621 $1000 €932 Flower field, coastal (20x25cm-8x10in) s. 18-Feb-3 John Moran, Pasadena #29a
£683 $1100 €1025 Flowering eucalyptus coastal (20x25cm-8x10in) s. masonite prov. 18-Feb-3 John Moran, Pasadena #2
£692 $1100 €1038 Untitled, landscape (58x89cm-23x35in) 28-Feb-3 Douglas, South Deerfield #10
£745 $1200 €1118 Ojai (61x41cm-24x16in) s. prov. 18-Feb-3 John Moran, Pasadena #155a
£1018 $1700 €1476 Eucalyptus coastal (41x51cm-16x20in) s. 17-Jun-3 John Moran, Pasadena #18 est:1500-2500
£1138 $1900 €1650 Flower field eucalyptus coastal (51x61cm-20x24in) s. 17-Jun-3 John Moran, Pasadena #54a est:2000-3000
£1198 $2000 €1737 Foothill landscape (76x61cm-30x24in) s. 17-Jun-3 John Moran, Pasadena #63 est:2500-3500
£1708 $2750 €2562 Eucalyptus landscape (46x61cm-18x24in) s. 18-Feb-3 John Moran, Pasadena #29
£1774 $2750 €2661 Flowered field and eucalyptus coastal (81x76cm-32x30in) s. masonite. 29-Oct-2 John Moran, Pasadena #712 est:3000-4000
£1783 $2800 €2675 Valley in bloom (51x61cm-20x24in) s. prov. 20-Nov-2 Christie's, Los Angeles #11/R est:3000-5000
£1863 $3000 €2795 Landscape flower fields (20x24cm-8x9in) s. 18-Feb-3 John Moran, Pasadena #75b est:1500-2500
£2581 $4000 €3872 Flowered field and eucalyptus (76x61cm-30x24in) s. 29-Oct-2 John Moran, Pasadena #640 est:3000-4000
£2861 $4750 €4148 Coast in bloom (76x102cm-30x40in) s. 11-Jun-3 Butterfields, San Francisco #4344/R est:3000-5000

DORT, Willem van (jnr-attrib) (1905-1996) Dutch
£338 $544 €480 Winter landscape with sailing ships (42x56cm-17x22in) 6-May-3 Vendu Notarishuis, Rotterdam #122/R

DORT, Willem van (snr) (1875-1949) Dutch
Works on paper
£350 $539 €550 Daily activities in a harbour (96x97cm-38x38in) s.d.1917 pencil col chk W/C htd white. 3-Sep-2 Christie's, Amsterdam #325

DOSHIN, Kaigetsudo (fl.1700-1716) Japanese
Works on paper
£9434 $15000 €14151 Beauty looking over her shoulder (86x42cm-34x17in) s. ink col hanging scroll. 24-Mar-3 Christie's, Rockefeller NY #26/R est:8000-10000

DOSQUE, Raoul (19/20th C) Spanish
£266 $420 €399 Country road in Cenon, Gironde (27x19cm-11x7in) s.indis.i. 13-Nov-2 Kunsthallen, Copenhagen #54/R (D.KR 3100)

DOSSENA, Alceo (1878-1937) Italian
Sculpture
£1635 $2518 €2600 Elisabetta d'Este (40cm-16in) s.d.35 alabaster. 23-Oct-2 Finarte, Rome #578/R

DOSSI, Battista (1474-1548) Italian
£95000 $149150 €142500 Adoration of the Magi (55x69cm-22x27in) panel prov.lit. 11-Dec-2 Christie's, London #97/R est:70000-100000

DOSSI, Battista (attrib) (1474-1548) Italian
£6962 $11000 €11000 Circumcision (36x73cm-14x29in) board. 2-Dec-2 Finarte, Milan #122/R est:12000

DOSWALD, Oskar (1887-?) Swiss?
£376 $616 €545 Hortensia in glass vase (60x50cm-24x20in) s.d.1951. 4-Jun-3 Fischer, Luzern #2052/R (S.FR 800)

DOTREMONT, Christian (1922-1979) Belgian
Works on paper
£818 $1268 €1227 Peut-etre bien apres tout (27x21cm-11x8in) init.d.1965 red chk lit. 4-Dec-2 Kunsthallen, Copenhagen #18/R (D.KR 9500)
£844 $1308 €1266 Peut-etre bien apres tout (27x21cm-11x8in) init.d.1965 black chk lit. 4-Dec-2 Kunsthallen, Copenhagen #19/R (D.KR 9800)
£2011 $3197 €3017 Order and thunder (35x26cm-14x10in) blue W/C. 26-Feb-3 Kunsthallen, Copenhagen #33/R est:18000 (D.KR 22000)
£8410 $13371 €12615 Fandenivolsk - composition (97x60cm-38x24in) s.d.1972 Indian ink Japan paper on canvas exhib. 26-Feb-3 Kunsthallen, Copenhagen #48/R est:70000 (D.KR 92000)

DOTTORI, Gerardo (1884-1977) Italian
£3472 $5521 €5000 Untitled (25x16cm-10x6in) s.verso cardboard. 1-May-3 Meeting Art, Vercelli #85
£12821 $20128 €20000 Lake vision (50x50cm-20x20in) s. board painted 1932 exhib. 21-Nov-2 Finarte, Rome #253/R est:9000-10000

DOU, Gerard (1613-1675) Dutch
£645 $1019 €968 Scholar (27x23cm-11x9in) panel on masonite prov. 18-Nov-2 Waddingtons, Toronto #195/R (C.D 1600)

DOU, Gerard (style) (1613-1675) Dutch
£3957 $6331 €5500 Still life with armour, shield, gun, helmet, sword, jacket and drum (32x46cm-13x18in) panel. 13-May-3 Sotheby's, Amsterdam #41/R est:3000-5000

DOUAIHY, Saliba (1912-1994) Lebanese
Works on paper
£1300 $2067 €1950 Al Hamra-Grenada (33x28cm-13x11in) s.i.d.1981 W/C over pencil htd bodycol. 30-Apr-3 Sotheby's, London #128/R est:1500-2000

DOUBLEDAY, Matthew (?) ?
Works on paper
£220 $348 €330 Trent Bridge (32x60cm-13x24in) W/C htd white. 28-Nov-2 Martel Maides, Guernsey #41/R

DOUCET, Henri (1883-1915) French
£971 $1554 €1350 Paysage a la riviere (59x81cm-23x32in) s.d.1909. 14-May-3 Blanchet, Paris #70/R

DOUCET, Jacques (1924-1994) French
£1693 $2625 €2540 Abstraction (43x57cm-17x22in) s. paper on canvas. 1-Oct-2 Rasmussen, Copenhagen #60/R est:20000 (D.KR 20000)
£1795 $2782 €2800 Composition (50x41cm-20x16in) s. cardboard painted 1970. 7-Dec-2 Cornette de St.Cyr, Paris #90/R
£2152 $3400 €3400 Regards des forets (92x60cm-36x24in) s. s.i.d.verso lit. 1-Dec-2 Anaf, Lyon #70/R
£2482 $4021 €3500 Lucca (55x46cm-22x18in) s. s.i.verso prov. 26-May-3 Christie's, Milan #348/R est:3000-4000
£3237 $5309 €4500 Soleil et quelques fantomes (100x73cm-39x29in) s. s.i.d.1969 verso prov.exhib.lit. 3-Jun-3 Christie's, Amsterdam #69/R est:5000-7000
£3265 $5192 €4800 Diluance d'aout (64x99cm-25x39in) s. s.i.verso lit. 26-Feb-3 Artcurial Briest, Paris #452/R est:3000-4000
£3846 $6038 €6000 Naissance du mouvement (73x60cm-29x24in) s. lit. 24-Nov-2 Laurence Calmels, Paris #105/R
£4114 $6418 €6500 Poeme des traboules (61x50cm-24x20in) s. s.i. verso lit. 20-Oct-2 Claude Boisgirard, Paris #61/R est:6500-7000
£4422 $7031 €6500 Regard des forets (92x60cm-36x24in) s. s.i.d.1984 verso lit. 24-Mar-3 Claude Boisgirard, Paris #100/R
£5903 $9385 €8500 Voyage autour de ma tete (114x195cm-45x77in) s. s.i.verso exhib.lit. 29-Apr-3 Artcurial Briest, Paris #567/R est:9000-12000
Works on paper
£477 $796 €692 Composition (60x43cm-24x17in) s. crayon prov. 17-Jun-3 Rasmussen, Copenhagen #8/R (D.KR 5000)
£696 $1100 €1100 Composition (52x40cm-20x16in) s. pastel lit. 1-Dec-2 Anaf, Lyon #66/R
£886 $1400 €1400 Composition (40x50cm-16x20in) s. gouache lit. 1-Dec-2 Anaf, Lyon #68/R
£1250 $2063 €1800 Composition (31x43cm-12x17in) s. mixed media collage exhib.lit. 1-Jul-3 Artcurial Briest, Paris #794d/R est:2200-3000
£1266 $2000 €2000 Composition (44x70cm-17x28in) s. pastel gouache collage lit. 1-Dec-2 Anaf, Lyon #69/R
£1352 $2082 €2150 Composition (60x37cm-24x15in) s. gouache exec.1983 lit. 26-Oct-2 Cornette de St.Cyr, Paris #24/R
£1384 $2145 €2200 Composition (62x40cm-24x16in) s. gouache lit. 30-Oct-2 Artcurial Briest, Paris #669/R est:2300-3000
£1389 $2292 €2000 Composition (36x23cm-14x9in) s. mixed media collage exhib. 1-Jul-3 Artcurial Briest, Paris #794a/R est:2200-3000
£1410 $2186 €2200 Composition (59x42cm-23x17in) s. gouache. 7-Dec-2 Cornette de St.Cyr, Paris #93/R
£1572 $2437 €2500 Poeme des migrations (30x20cm-12x8in) s. collage newspaper cardboard exhib.lit. 30-Oct-2 Artcurial Briest, Paris #430/R est:2200-3000
£1795 $2782 €2800 Composition (65x50cm-26x20in) s. gouache. 7-Dec-2 Cornette de St.Cyr, Paris #92/R
£1887 $2906 €3000 Composition (54x37cm-21x15in) s. collage gouache exec.1982 lit. 26-Oct-2 Cornette de St.Cyr, Paris #25/R
£2201 $3412 €3500 Sans titre (40x56cm-16x22in) s. gouache cardboard lit. 30-Oct-2 Artcurial Briest, Paris #431/R est:2000-3000
£3958 $6254 €5700 Composition (34x54cm-13x21in) s. gouache prov. 27-Apr-3 Perrin, Versailles #8/R est:2000-2500

DOUGHERTY, Parke Custis (1867-?) American
£4321 $7000 €6265 Winter morning, Quai Voltaire (66x81cm-26x32in) s.d.09 exhib. 21-May-3 Doyle, New York #96/R est:6000-8000

DOUGHERTY, Paul (1877-1947) American
£838 $1400 €1215 Rocky peak (33x41cm-13x16in) s. panel prov. 18-Jun-3 Christie's, Los Angeles #67/R est:3000-5000
£964 $1600 €1398 Snowstorm on the Jungfrau (32x40cm-13x16in) st.sig. panel. 11-Jun-3 Butterfields, San Francisco #4318/R est:3000-5000
£1018 $1700 €1476 Boats in a harbour (30x41cm-12x16in) s. canvasboard prov. 18-Jun-3 Christie's, Los Angeles #46/R est:3000-5000
£1205 $2000 €1747 Stormy day over the sea (33x41cm-13x16in) st sig. panel. 11-Jun-3 Butterfields, San Francisco #4287/R est:3000-5000
£1935 $3000 €2903 Canyon after rain (51x61cm-20x24in) s. i.verso masonite exhib. 29-Oct-2 John Moran, Pasadena #738 est:2500-3500
£2201 $3500 €3302 Coastal landscape (33x41cm-13x16in) s. panel. 8-Mar-3 Harvey Clar, Oakland #1397
£2246 $3750 €3257 Rocks and surf (38x46cm-15x18in) s. i.verso masonite. 17-Jun-3 John Moran, Pasadena #45 est:3000-4000
£2389 $3750 €3584 Crashing waves, rugged coastline (91x86cm-36x34in) s. prov. 10-Dec-2 Doyle, New York #107/R est:3000-4000
£2410 $4000 €3495 Rocky coast (33x41cm-13x16in) st.sig. panel. 11-Jun-3 Butterfields, San Francisco #4286/R est:3000-5000
£3145 $5000 €4718 Surf in sunlight (30x41cm-12x16in) s. panel. 8-Mar-3 Harvey Clar, Oakland #1396
£3614 $6000 €5240 Looking down to the sea (33x41cm-13x16in) st.sig. panel prov. 11-Jun-3 Butterfields, San Francisco #4051/R est:3000-5000
£4140 $6500 €6210 Inflowing tide (91x122cm-36x48in) s. prov. 10-Dec-2 Doyle, New York #122/R est:10000-15000
£4348 $7000 €6522 Morning-outer ledges Carmel highland, Calif (15x18cm-6x7in) s. i.d.September 1932 verso board. 18-Feb-3 John Moran, Pasadena #77 est:4000-6000
£4459 $7000 €6689 Crashing waves (94x119cm-37x47in) s.d.1906 prov. 10-Dec-2 Doyle, New York #108/R est:3000-4000

DOUGHTY, Thomas (1793-1856) American
£9434 $15000 €14151 Early winter, Hiawatha Island, Owego, New York (49x71cm-19x28in) s. painted c.1853 prov.exhib.lit. 5-Mar-3 Sotheby's, New York #8/R est:15000-25000
£12676 $18000 €19014 Silver cascade, White Mountains, new Hampshire (91x71cm-36x28in) 8-Aug-1 Barridorf, Portland #24/R est:9000-12000
£37037 $60000 €55556 On the river (66x91cm-26x36in) s. prov. 21-May-3 Sotheby's, New York #210/R est:40000-60000

DOUGLAS, Andrew A (1870-1935) British
£580 $945 €870 Cattle grazing in a mountainous landscape (27x38cm-11x15in) 14-Feb-3 Lyon & Turnbull, Edinburgh #66

DOUGLAS, Cameron (1957-) Canadian?
£280 $442 €420 Landscape with highland cattle (59x49cm-23x19in) 1-Apr-3 Patersons, Paisley #528
Sculpture
£844 $1385 €1266 Splendid team (42cm-17in) s.d.02 num.2/6 bronze. 3-Jun-3 Joyner, Toronto #214/R est:2000-2500 (C.D 1900)
£988 $1531 €1482 Girl without a basket (42cm-17in) s.d.00 num.2/6 bronze. 3-Dec-2 Joyner, Toronto #304/R est:1200-1500 (C.D 2400)
£1440 $2233 €2160 Front step (49cm-19in) s.d.01 num.2/6 bronze. 3-Dec-2 Joyner, Toronto #176/R est:3500-4000 (C.D 3500)

DOUGLAS, Earl Graham (1879-1954) American
£352 $550 €510 Mountain landscape (71x81cm-28x32in) s. 13-Apr-3 Butterfields, Los Angeles #7022

DOUGLAS, Edward Algernon Stuart (1850-c.1920) British
£1200 $1872 €1800 Study of a bay horse (41x56cm-16x22in) s. 6-Nov-2 Sotheby's, Olympia #75/R est:600-900
£9000 $14580 €13500 View halloo. Returning to kennels (41x61cm-16x24in) s.d.1875. 22-May-3 Christie's, London #17/R est:8000-12000
Works on paper
£4500 $6975 €6750 Meet (28x50cm-11x20in) s.d.1914 W/C four. 6-Dec-2 Lyon & Turnbull, Edinburgh #112/R est:4000-6000

DOUGLAS, Edwin (1848-1914) British
£1048 $1656 €1572 Venus and the hounds of Adonis (71x91cm-28x36in) s. 18-Nov-2 Waddingtons, Toronto #181/R est:2500-3000 (C.D 2600)
£3500 $5495 €5250 Ferreters (95x52cm-37x20in) mono.d.1902. 16-Dec-2 Bonhams, Bury St Edmunds #510/R est:2000-3000
£5800 $9106 €8700 Collie in the snow (61x51cm-24x20in) s. 16-Dec-2 Bonhams, Bury St Edmunds #506/R est:5000-8000
£7000 $11130 €10500 Bagged fox (91x71cm-36x28in) init. 18-Mar-3 Bonhams, New Bond Street #54/R est:6000-8000
£9500 $14440 €14250 Roused (51x61cm-20x24in) s.d.1873. 28-Aug-2 Sotheby's, London #808/R est:10000-15000

DOUGLAS, Hope Toulmin (1883-?) British
£310 $471 €465 Old pensioner, study of a grey horse at a five bar gate (24x34cm-9x13in) s. i.verso panel. 13-Aug-2 Gildings, Market Harborough #254
£310 $481 €465 Equestrian study, the old pensioner (23x33cm-9x13in) s. panel. 6-Dec-2 Biddle & Webb, Birmingham #253

DOUGLAS, James (1858-1911) British
£480 $782 €720 Harvest time (18x35cm-7x14in) 14-Feb-3 Lyon & Turnbull, Edinburgh #88
Works on paper
£350 $546 €525 Priory garden (20x30cm-8x12in) s.d.1897 pencil W/C. 19-Sep-2 Christie's, Kensington #74

DOUGLAS, Jessie (fl.1903-1928) British
Works on paper
£1087 $1783 €1500 Brittany maid (28x20cm-11x8in) s. W/C exhib. 28-May-3 Bonhams & James Adam, Dublin #42/R est:1200-1800

DOUGLAS, R (?) ?
£513 $800 €770 Fisherman (38x28cm-15x11in) two. 30-Mar-3 Susanin's, Chicago #6017/R

DOUGLAS, Sir William Fettes (1822-1891) British
£1000 $1550 €1500 Serenade (26x31cm-10x12in) mono.d.66. 5-Dec-2 Bonhams, Edinburgh #55 est:1200-1800

DOUGLAS, Stan (1960-) Canadian
Photographs
£37975 $60000 €56963 Untitled - Detroit series (52x99cm-20x39in) s.d.num. 25 photographs executed 1998 prov. 14-Nov-2 Christie's, Rockefeller NY #432/R est:40000-60000

DOUGLAS, William (1780-1832) British
Miniatures
£3000 $4680 €4500 Thomas Henry Duthie wearing uniform of 72nd Duke of Albany's Highlanders (11cm-4xin) s.i.d.1828 verso inner gilt mount in red leather case rec. prov. 5-Nov-2 Bonhams, New Bond Street #153/R est:2500-3500

DOUTHWAITE, Patricia (1939-2002) British
£640 $998 €960 Red goblets (64x48cm-25x19in) s.d.90 col chk. 10-Apr-3 Bonhams, Edinburgh #23
£2800 $4368 €4200 Woman possessed by a cheetah (153x121cm-60x48in) s.stretcher. 17-Oct-2 Bonhams, Edinburgh #106/R est:800-1200
Works on paper
£280 $437 €420 Oriental figure (73x54cm-29x21in) conte. 17-Oct-2 Bonhams, Edinburgh #68
£320 $499 €480 Head of a child (54x41cm-21x16in) s.d.89 col chk. 10-Apr-3 Bonhams, Edinburgh #3
£340 $541 €510 Abstract female (69x44cm-27x17in) pastel. 1-Mar-3 Shapes, Edinburgh #419
£720 $1123 €1080 Whitby, July (28x21cm-11x8in) s.i. col chk. 17-Oct-2 Bonhams, Edinburgh #64
£850 $1326 €1275 Woman with a reptile (74x55cm-29x22in) s.d.69 conte wax crayon. 17-Oct-2 Bonhams, Edinburgh #62/R
£1350 $2106 €2025 Vavarra with a kite (30x22cm-12x9in) s.d.94 conte W/C. 17-Oct-2 Bonhams, Edinburgh #63 est:500-700
£1400 $2170 €2100 Geisha (59x40cm-23x16in) col chk. 5-Dec-2 Bonhams, Edinburgh #106 est:1000-1500

DOUTRELEAU, Pierre (1938-) French
£993 $1619 €1500 Sans titre (27x22cm-11x9in) s.verso. 1-Feb-3 Claude Aguttes, Neuilly #195

DOUVEN, Jac (1908-) Belgian
£481 $745 €750 Kemp landscape (60x90cm-24x35in) s. 7-Dec-2 De Vuyst, Lokeren #108
£633 $987 €1000 Alongside the river Ourthe near Durbuy (50x70cm-20x28in) s. 21-Oct-2 Bernaerts, Antwerp #16/R
£823 $1284 €1300 Hechtelt landscape (50x70cm-20x28in) s. 21-Oct-2 Bernaerts, Antwerp #622
£828 $1308 €1200 Limburgse Kempen (40x50cm-16x20in) s.d.1955. 2-Apr-3 Vanderkindere, Brussels #76
£1076 $1678 €1700 View at Pery in the Ardens (80x100cm-31x39in) s. 21-Oct-2 Bernaerts, Antwerp #624 est:800-900

DOUVEN, Jan Frans van (1656-1727) German
£2308 $3646 €3600 Portrait of nobleman (86x67cm-34x26in) s.d.1714 verso. 16-Nov-2 Lempertz, Koln #1024/R est:3000

DOUVEN, Jan Frans van (studio) (1656-1727) German
£8904 $13890 €13000 Jan Wellem (132x100cm-52x39in) 10-Apr-3 Van Ham, Cologne #1188/R est:10000

DOUW, Simon Johannes van (1630-1677) Flemish
£4200 $6510 €6300 Cavalry skirmish between Christians and Turks (58x84cm-23x33in) s. panel. 30-Oct-2 Christie's, Kensington #46/R est:4000-6000
£5096 $7949 €8000 Cavalry battle near a tower (29x28cm-11x11in) s. copper prov. 5-Nov-2 Sotheby's, Amsterdam #33/R est:6000-8000
£6129 $9684 €9500 Rendez-vous de chasse (79x122cm-31x48in) s. prov. 18-Dec-2 Piasa, Paris #38/R est:12000
£9554 $14904 €15000 Return after the hunt (45x77cm-18x30in) s.d.16 panel prov. 5-Nov-2 Sotheby's, Amsterdam #330/R est:10000-15000
£9929 $15390 €14894 Hunting party (103x155cm-41x61in) s. 4-Dec-2 AB Stockholms Auktionsverk #1928/R est:150000-200000 (S.KR 140000)

DOUZETTE, Louis (1834-1924) German
£943 $1472 €1500 Harbour entrance by moonlight (41x33cm-16x13in) s. i. verso board. 21-Sep-2 Bolland & Marotz, Bremen #468/R est:1100
£1519 $2400 €2400 Waves breaking on the shore (36x60cm-14x24in) s. 30-Nov-2 Villa Grisebach, Berlin #110/R est:3000-4000
£1667 $2617 €2600 Lakeshore in evening (24x40cm-9x16in) s. panel. 21-Nov-2 Van Ham, Cologne #2040 est:350

DOVA, Gianni (1925-1991) Italian
£1081 $1686 €1600 Composition (37x50cm-15x20in) s. tempera paper. 26-Mar-3 Finarte Semenzato, Milan #70/R
£1519 $2370 €2400 Paradise bird (49x37cm-19x15in) s.d.1971 acrylic card. 14-Sep-2 Meeting Art, Vercelli #776/R
£1667 $2583 €2600 Bittany landscape (48x74cm-19x29in) s. tempera paper on canvas. 4-Dec-2 Finarte, Milan #233/R
£1955 $3070 €3050 Fish tank (75x50cm-30x20in) s.d. tempera paper on canvas. 23-Nov-2 Meeting Art, Vercelli #360/R
£2297 $3584 €3400 Protecting the nest (50x40cm-20x16in) s. painted 1985. 28-Mar-3 Farsetti, Prato #373/R

£3205 $5032 €5000 Vortix (81x60cm-32x24in) s.i.d.1952 verso oil enamel. 23-Nov-2 Meeting Art, Vercelli #81/R
£3291 $5200 €5200 View of gardenm (60x50cm-24x20in) s. i.verso. 29-Nov-2 Farsetti, Prato #431/R est:6000
£4167 $6625 €6000 Flowers at window in the Maldives (92x73cm-36x29in) s.i.verso painted 1982 lit. 1-May-3 Meeting Art, Vercelli #456
£4808 $7452 €7500 Nuclear (100x100cm-39x39in) s.d.52-53. 4-Dec-2 Finarte, Milan #332/R est:12000
£5063 $7899 €8000 Target (85x110cm-33x43in) s. painted 1962. 14-Sep-2 Meeting Art, Vercelli #809/R est:8000
£6774 $10703 €10500 Bird (70x60cm-28x24in) enamel painted 1960 prov. 18-Dec-2 Christie's, Rome #184/R est:10000

Sculpture

£1149 $1792 €1700 Untitled (28x28cm-11x11in) s.d.55 verso polychrome terracotta. 26-Mar-3 Finarte Semenzato, Milan #178/R

Works on paper

£625 $994 €900 Composition (15x29cm-6x11in) s.d.1952 mixed media. 1-May-3 Meeting Art, Vercelli #105
£654 $1046 €1000 Untitled (70x50cm-28x20in) s.d.1962 mixed media card. 4-Jan-3 Meeting Art, Vercelli #683
£897 $1409 €1400 Untitled (50x70cm-20x28in) s.d.50 ink paper on canvas. 20-Nov-2 Pandolfini, Florence #89/R
£1081 $1686 €1600 National Gallery (150x100cm-59x39in) s. pastel paper on canvas exec.1978. 26-Mar-3 Finarte Semenzato, Milan #403/R
£1389 $2208 €2000 Composition (50x64cm-20x25in) s.d.1962 verso felt-tip pen. 1-May-3 Meeting Art, Vercelli #198
£1497 $2380 €2200 Fish (90x70cm-35x28in) s. mixed media paper on canvas. 1-Mar-3 Meeting Art, Vercelli #611

DOVASTON, Margaret (1884-?) British

£24648 $35000 €36972 Recording the weight (51x71cm-20x28in) 8-Aug-1 Barridorf, Portland #90/R est:15000-25000

DOVE, Arthur G (1880-1946) American

Works on paper

£1778 $2951 €2578 Eadle over cliffs (13x18cm-5x7in) s. W/C paper on board. 16-Jun-3 Waddingtons, Toronto #3/R est:4000-6000 (C.D 4000)
£12579 $20000 €18869 Two horses (12x17cm-5x7in) s. W/C paper on board prov. 4-Mar-3 Christie's, Rockefeller NY #74/R est:5000-7000
£18065 $28000 €27098 Brow cow (14x23cm-6x9in) s. W/C pen ink prov.exhib. 3-Dec-2 Phillips, New York #71/R est:30000-50000
£22013 $35000 €33020 Sunset (13x18cm-5x7in) s. W/C paper on board prov. 4-Mar-3 Christie's, Rockefeller NY #73/R est:7000-9000

DOVE, Thomas (?-1887) British

£300 $465 €450 Cunard liner Lucania making headway in a heavy Atlantic swell (61x91cm-24x36in) s.d.1898. 31-Oct-2 Christie's, Kensington #504/R

DOVERA, Achille (1838-1895) Italian

£2041 $3245 €3000 Portrait of woman (105x69cm-41x27in) s. 1-Mar-3 Meeting Art, Vercelli #241

DOW, Arthur W (1857-1922) American

£12025 $19000 €18038 Blue Dragon, Ipswich (23x38cm-9x15in) s. board prov. 24-Apr-3 Shannon's, Milford #99/R est:12000-18000

DOW, Jim (1942-) American

Photographs

£2078 $3200 €3117 Dairy Queen at night, US 6, Iowa City (40x51cm-16x20in) s.i.d.num.3 verso col chromogenic print exec.1988 prov. 25-Oct-2 Phillips, New York #144/R est:1000-1500

DOW, Thomas Millie (1848-1919) British

£550 $897 €825 Spring time (34x46cm-13x18in) 14-Feb-3 Lyon & Turnbull, Edinburgh #100

DOWLING, Robert (1827-1886) British

£2546 $4100 €3819 First advances (76x63cm-30x25in) s. i.d.1873. 7-May-3 Dobiaschofsky, Bern #467/R est:7500 (S.FR 5500)
£4000 $6360 €6000 Third class carriage (53x107cm-21x42in) s. 6-Mar-3 Christie's, Kensington #574/R est:3000-5000

DOWLING, William Paul (c.1824-1877) Australian

Works on paper

£1708 $2614 €2562 Portrait of a young woman (36x30cm-14x12in) s. W/C prov. 25-Aug-2 Sotheby's, Paddington #148/R est:3000-4000 (A.D 4800)

DOWNES, John Ireland Howe (1861-1933) American

£749 $1250 €1086 Convent (71x51cm-28x20in) mono. 21-Jun-3 Selkirks, St. Louis #173/R est:2000-2500

DOWNIE, John P (1871-1945) British

£1400 $2184 €2100 Fresh fodder (53x66cm-21x26in) s.d.1915 exhib. 7-Nov-2 Christie's, Kensington #223/R est:1200-1800

DOWNIE, Patrick (1854-1945) British

£400 $648 €600 Sun setting over the coast (18x25cm-7x10in) s.d.1916 board. 20-May-3 Bonhams, Knightsbridge #18/R
£700 $1162 €1015 Coastal scene with boats in foreground (23x33cm-9x13in) s. board. 10-Jun-3 Louis Taylor, Stoke on Trent #914
£759 $1177 €1200 Lifting seaweed - Ayrshire coast (25x35cm-10x14in) s. i.d.1928 verso canvas on board. 25-Sep-2 Neumeister, Munich #564/R
£800 $1328 €1160 Coastal scene with boats (43x58cm-17x23in) s. board. 10-Jun-3 Louis Taylor, Stoke on Trent #913
£1000 $1560 €1500 Balcraig farm, Renfrewshire (51x61cm-20x24in) s. board. 14-Apr-3 Sotheby's, London #130/R est:1000-1500
£1923 $3038 €3000 Noon day rest (37x55cm-15x22in) exhib. 12-Nov-2 Mealy's, Castlecomer #1051/R
£2100 $3276 €3150 Ducks on a pond (26x33cm-10x13in) s. board. 26-Mar-3 Sotheby's, Olympia #165/R est:1000-2000
£2400 $3744 €3600 Lifting seaweed, Ayrshire coat (25x35cm-10x14in) s.i.d.1929 board. 14-Apr-3 Sotheby's, London #76/R est:1500-2000
£2675 $4146 €4013 Summer day, Ballantrae (30x46cm-12x18in) s.i.d.1918. 3-Dec-2 Ritchie, Toronto #3030/R est:4000-6000 (C.D 6500)

Works on paper

£320 $499 €480 Winter, Greenock (31x40cm-12x16in) s.i. W/C. 10-Apr-3 Tennants, Leyburn #862
£680 $1115 €1020 Off the coast (36x51cm-14x20in) s. W/C. 7-Jun-3 Shapes, Edinburgh #432/R
£820 $1369 €1189 Fresh breeze, off Gourock (35x53cm-14x21in) s.d.1918 W/C. 18-Jun-3 Sotheby's, Olympia #100/R
£1200 $1860 €1800 Fishing boats (19x32cm-7x13in) s. gouache. 6-Dec-2 Lyon & Turnbull, Edinburgh #31 est:600-800
£1500 $2340 €2250 Coming home with the catch (35x53cm-14x21in) s. i.verso W/C. 14-Apr-3 Sotheby's, London #78/R est:1500-2000

DOWNING, Delapoer (fl.1886-1902) British

£1000 $1630 €1450 Make a wish (75x49cm-30x19in) s. 16-Jul-3 Sotheby's, Olympia #80/R est:800-1200
£1281 $1973 €1922 Elderly gentleman escorting young lady in garden of flowers (78x53cm-31x21in) s. 4-Sep-2 Kunsthallen, Copenhagen #16/R est:20000 (D.KR 15000)
£1300 $2028 €1950 Milkmaids (81x58cm-32x23in) s. 17-Sep-2 Sotheby's, Olympia #162/R est:1000-1500

DOWNMAN, John (1750-1824) British

£6000 $9360 €9000 Portrait of Right Honourable William George Monckton-Arundell half length (21x17cm-8x7in) with another work two. 8-Oct-2 Sotheby's, Olympia #381/R est:2000-3000

Miniatures

£2600 $4030 €3900 Mother and daughter, Anne and Charlotte Cooper (23cm-9xin) s. one d.1792 one d.1794 i.verso paper rec.wood frame oval 2 lit. 1-Oct-2 Bonhams, New Bond Street #47/R est:1500-2200
£6500 $10140 €9750 Officer believed to be Francis Hepburn of the 3rd regiment of Foot Guards (8cm-3xin) gold frame oval. 5-Nov-2 Bonhams, New Bond Street #92/R est:6500-7500

Works on paper

£700 $1092 €1050 Portrait of a lady facing right (23x16cm-9x6in) pencil W/C col chk oval. 26-Mar-3 Hamptons Fine Art, Godalming #75
£800 $1304 €1200 Portrait of a lady, believed to be Lady Elizabeth Compton (22x19cm-9x7in) mono.d.1780 pencil W/C oval. 29-Jan-3 Dreweatt Neate, Newbury #77/R
£800 $1248 €1160 Portrait of a lady in blue dress with blue ribbon in her hair (30x24cm-12x9in) s.indis.d. W/C. 13-May-3 Holloways, Banbury #623/R
£949 $1500 €1500 Portrait of young boy (23x19cm-9x7in) s.d.1792 crayon W/C. 28-Nov-2 Tajan, Paris #107/R
£1013 $1600 €1600 Portrait of Clara-Louise Middleton (22x19cm-9x7in) s.d.1792 crayon W/C. 28-Nov-2 Tajan, Paris #106/R
£1456 $2300 €2300 Portrait of young girl (23x18cm-9x7in) s. crayon W/C. 28-Nov-2 Tajan, Paris #108/R
£2848 $4500 €4500 Portraits of Pierre Middleton and his sisters (32x28cm-13x11in) d.1792 verso crayon W/C. 28-Nov-2 Tajan, Paris #109/R est:3500

DOWNMAN, John (attrib) (1750-1884) British

£400 $652 €580 Portrait of R.P. Mendham, Esq (34x29cm-13x11in) 21-Jul-3 Sotheby's, London #563

DOWNS, Edgar (1876-1963) British
£620 $986 €930 Cattle and other farm animals feeding (24x30cm-9x12in) s.d.26 panel. 5-Mar-3 Bonhams, Bury St Edmunds #370/R

DOWNS, J F (?) ?
£280 $450 €420 Landscape view of a traveller. i. 20-Feb-3 Skinner, Bolton #689/R

DOWNS, Jarinyanu David (c.1925-1995) Australian
£8000 $12880 €12000 Dance of Kurtal (198x137cm-78x54in) s. acrylic ochres on linen prov.exhib. 6-May-3 Christie's, Melbourne #70/R est:20000-30000 (A.D 20000)

DOWNTON, John C (1939-) Australian
£251 $364 €377 Boys of the bush (90x120cm-35x47in) s. 10-Dec-1 Goodman, Sydney #403 (A.D 700)

DOWSON, Russell (fl.1880-1911) British
£350 $574 €508 Thames near Oxford (37x54cm-15x21in) s. 1-Jun-3 Lots Road, London #333

DOYEN, Gabriel François (1726-1806) French
£9146 $15000 €13719 Study for a head of Neptune. Academic study of a seated male nude (55x41cm-22x16in) paper double-sided prov.exhib. 30-May-3 Christie's, Rockefeller NY #35/R est:10000-15000

DOYEN, Gustave (1837-?) French
£9032 $14000 €13548 Young beauty wearing a red veil (59x46cm-23x18in) s.d.1880. 30-Oct-2 Christie's, Rockefeller NY #171/R est:12000-16000

DOYLE, D'Arcy (1932-2001) Australian
£1221 $1929 €2115 Long haul (24x29cm-9x11in) s. board. 1-Apr-3 Goodman, Sydney #60m est:3000-6000 (A.D 3200)
£3405 $5176 €5108 High flyer (34x27cm-13x11in) s. board prov. 27-Aug-2 Goodman, Sydney #131/R est:7000-10000 (A.D 9500)
£3600 $5796 €5400 High country chase (44x60cm-17x24in) s. board. 6-May-3 Christie's, Melbourne #110/R est:9000-12000 (A.D 9000)
£4674 $7384 €8097 Brumby run (38x49cm-15x19in) s. board. 1-Apr-3 Goodman, Sydney #60j/R est:10000-15000 (A.D 12245)
£5976 $9801 €8964 Cricketers (61x91cm-24x36in) s. composition board prov. 4-Jun-3 Deutscher-Menzies, Melbourne #293/R est:10000-15000 (A.D 15000)
£9600 $15456 €14400 Cricket after the rain (60x90cm-24x35in) s. board. 6-May-3 Christie's, Melbourne #63/R est:16000-24000 (A.D 24000)

DOYLE, John (1928-) British
£300 $480 €450 Les baux, Provence (30x41cm-12x16in) s.d.1966. 11-Mar-3 Gorringes, Lewes #2426

Works on paper
£300 $465 €450 Harvest time at Eton (15x23cm-6x9in) mono. gouache. 25-Sep-2 Hamptons Fine Art, Godalming #151

DOYLE, Richard (1824-1883) British

Works on paper
£9000 $14310 €13500 Dragon slayer (35x50cm-14x20in) mono.d.1876 i.verso W/C prov.exhib.lit. 19-Mar-3 Sotheby's, London #223/R est:6000-8000

DOYLE, Sam (1906-1985) American
£4321 $7000 €6482 Go down (98x53cm-39x21in) s. enamel on wood panel prov.lit. 27-Jan-3 Christie's, Rockefeller NY #92/R est:8000-12000

DOYLY-JOHN, C R (1906-1993) British
£250 $390 €375 Barbados, West Indies (23x30cm-9x12in) s. 18-Oct-2 Keys, Aylsham #520
£260 $421 €390 Continental square (55x68cm-22x27in) 20-May-3 Bonhams, Knightsbridge #91
£280 $437 €420 Mediterranean market scene (41x53cm-16x21in) s. 11-Apr-3 Keys, Aylsham #300/R
£290 $452 €435 Poznia, village in south Spain near Costa Brava (23x33cm-9x13in) s. 18-Oct-2 Keys, Aylsham #519/R
£300 $468 €450 Valanus, village between Cannes and Nice, S France (23x33cm-9x13in) s. 18-Oct-2 Keys, Aylsham #521
£300 $492 €450 Fishermen on the Cape de Antibes (29x50cm-11x20in) s. 7-Feb-3 Honiton Galleries, Honiton #278
£350 $585 €508 View of Cannes Bay from the summer casino (35x71cm-14x28in) s.i.verso. 17-Jun-3 Bonhams, Knightsbridge #3/R
£360 $572 €522 Venice, side street off the Grand Canal (36x71cm-14x28in) s. 29-Apr-3 Gorringes, Lewes #2144
£387 $623 €581 Coastal landscape with fishermen (43x58cm-17x23in) s. 12-May-3 Stephan Welz, Johannesburg #39 est:1500-2000 (SA.R 4500)
£450 $707 €675 Cannes harbour (43x63cm-17x25in) s. i.verso. 11-Dec-2 Rupert Toovey, Partridge Green #117/R

Works on paper
£260 $426 €390 Figures chatting in a continental town square (25x70cm-10x28in) s. W/C. 7-Feb-3 Honiton Galleries, Honiton #284/R

DOZIER, Otis (1904-1987) American
£1571 $2450 €2357 Margaret (61x46cm-24x18in) masonite. 19-Oct-2 David Dike, Dallas #296/R est:3000-6000
£2083 $3250 €3125 Self portrait (61x64cm-24x25in) masonite. 19-Oct-2 David Dike, Dallas #191/R est:4000-6000
£2885 $4500 €4328 Owl (61x61cm-24x24in) masonite painted c.1963. 19-Oct-2 David Dike, Dallas #187/R est:5000-8000

DRACHKOVITCH, Thomas Albert (1928-) French/Yugoslavian
£833 $1292 €1300 Winter landscape (46x39cm-18x15in) s. panel. 5-Dec-2 Gros & Delettrez, Paris #90
£886 $1373 €1400 Paysage de neige (27x35cm-11x14in) s.d.1967 panel. 29-Sep-2 Eric Pillon, Calais #233/R

DRACHMANN, Holger (1846-1908) Danish
£444 $684 €666 Sailing boats off coastal cliffs (13x22cm-5x9in) s.i.d.1905 panel. 4-Sep-2 Kunsthallen, Copenhagen #11 (D.KR 5200)
£596 $941 €894 Seascape with fishing boat, Mediterranean (25x33cm-10x13in) mono.d.68 prov. 27-Nov-2 Museumsbygningen, Copenhagen #30 (D.KR 7000)
£947 $1440 €1421 Coastal landscape with steep cliffs, fishing boats on the way to beach (19x29cm-7x11in) mono.d.65. 27-Aug-2 Rasmussen, Copenhagen #1767/R (D.KR 11000)
£1292 $1964 €1938 View of the sea at Skagen (29x38cm-11x15in) with sig.i.verso. 27-Aug-2 Rasmussen, Copenhagen #1484/R est:20000 (D.KR 15000)
£1435 $2325 €2081 Seascape with sailing vessels (42x53cm-17x21in) s.d.1873. 26-May-3 Rasmussen, Copenhagen #1368/R est:15000 (D.KR 15000)
£2128 $3362 €3192 Sailing vessels at entrance to Frederikshavn Harbour (42x62cm-17x24in) s.i.d.Dec.1902. 2-Dec-2 Rasmussen, Copenhagen #1385/R est:15000 (D.KR 25000)
£2723 $4303 €4085 Coastal landscape near Nysted (32x47cm-13x19in) s.d.73. 2-Dec-2 Rasmussen, Copenhagen #1387/R est:20000 (D.KR 32000)
£3259 $5182 €4889 Sailing vessels in rough seas off Skagen (35x51cm-14x20in) s.i.d.1906. 10-Mar-3 Rasmussen, Vejle #464/R est:20000 (D.KR 35000)
£3451 $5488 €5177 Coastal landscape from Skagen Strand (41x51cm-16x20in) s.i.d.1906. 5-May-3 Rasmussen, Vejle #253/R est:40000-50000 (D.KR 37000)
£4936 $7799 €7404 Fishing boats off Scheveningen (45x69cm-18x27in) s.i.d.1883. 2-Dec-2 Rasmussen, Copenhagen #1420/R est:50000 (D.KR 58000)
£5277 $8337 €7916 Fishing boats and gondolas, Grand Canal, Venice (36x56cm-14x22in) s.i.d.Juli 84. 2-Dec-2 Rasmussen, Copenhagen #1152/R est:50000 (D.KR 62000)

DRAGO, Antonio del (18th C) Italian

Works on paper
£5484 $8500 €8226 Pantheon in Rome with obelisk (64x89cm-25x35in) s. W/C. 2-Nov-2 North East Auctions, Portsmouth #61/R

DRAHONET, Alexandre Jean Dubois (1791-1834) French
£461 $770 €650 Incroyable (35x25cm-14x10in) canvas on panel. 18-Jun-3 Piasa, Paris #9
£10000 $15800 €15000 Portrait of a young man in Greek costume standing before the acropolis (35x25cm-14x10in) 1-Apr-3 Bonhams, New Bond Street #1 est:7000-10000

Works on paper
£2642 $4121 €4200 Capriccio (45x37cm-18x15in) s.d.1807 gouache. 8-Oct-2 Christie's, Paris #17/R

DRAHONOVSKY, Josef (1877-1938) Czechoslovakian

Sculpture
£1547 $2445 €2321 Toilette of a young woman (37cm-15in) s.d.1914 Cast Anyz bronze wood base. 30-Nov-2 Dorotheum, Prague #224/R est:50000-75000 (C.KR 75000)

DRAIJER, Rein (1899-1986) Dutch
£2548 $3975 €4000 Harbour mouth (90x120cm-35x47in) s.i. 5-Nov-2 Vendu Notarishuis, Rotterdam #143/R est:600-800

DRAKE, Elizabeth (1866-1954) British
Works on paper
£280 $462 €406 St. Margaret's church, King's Lynn (34x24cm-13x9in) s.d.1928 W/C. 1-Jul-3 Bonhams, Norwich #153

DRAKE, Nathan (1728-1778) British
£650 $1014 €975 Portrait of a lady. Portrait of a gentleman (76x63cm-30x25in) mono.verso pair. 17-Sep-2 Sotheby's, Olympia #86/R
£700 $1092 €1050 Portrait of Henrietta Maria (67x49cm-26x19in) mono.verso after Sir Anthony van Dyck. 17-Sep-2 Sotheby's, Olympia #85/R

DRAMARD, Georges de (1839-1900) ?
£541 $843 €800 Nature morte aux poissons (32x46cm-13x18in) s.i. 26-Mar-3 Peschetau-Badin Godeau & Leroy, Paris #57

DRAPER, Herbert James (1864-1920) British
£2200 $3674 €3190 Study for the foam sprite (27x20cm-11x8in) i. canvasboard prov. 17-Jun-3 Bonhams, New Bond Street #95/R est:1200-1800
£13000 $20930 €19500 Study for sea maiden (15x28cm-6x11in) board prov. 20-Feb-3 Christie's, London #140/R est:10000

DRAPER, Kenneth (1944-) British
Works on paper
£300 $468 €450 White wanes (55x65cm-22x26in) s.i.d.89 W/C. 17-Sep-2 Bonhams, Knightsbridge #23/R

DRAPER, William Franklin (1912-) American
£18868 $30000 €28302 View of New York City looking South (112x107cm-44x42in) s. painted c.1984 exhib. 5-Mar-3 Sotheby's, New York #97/R est:20000-30000

DRAPPIER, Edmond (19th C) French
Sculpture
£2431 $3865 €3500 Cavalier chargeant (41x21x20cm-16x8x8in) s. brown pat bronze. 30-Apr-3 Tajan, Paris #44/R
£2517 $4102 €3800 Homme faisant reculer un cheval (33x47cm-13x19in) pat bronze. 16-Feb-3 Mercier & Cie, Lille #190/R est:2200-3000

DRAVER, Orrin (1895-1964) American
£577 $900 €866 Autumn river landscape (51x61cm-20x24in) s. 14-Sep-2 Weschler, Washington #615/R

DRAWBRIDGE, John (1930-) New Zealander
Works on paper
£784 $1223 €1176 Daybreak South Coast (78x57cm-31x22in) s. W/C pastel. 7-Nov-2 International Art Centre, Auckland #92/R est:2500-3500 (NZ.D 2500)

DREANY, Edward Joseph (1908-) Canadian
£700 $1084 €1050 Tilling their garden (90x100cm-35x39in) s. 3-Dec-2 Joyner, Toronto #332/R est:1500-2000 (C.D 1700)

DREBER, Heinrich (1822-1875) German
£513 $795 €800 Girl harvesting grapes for wine with coastal landscape in background (37x24cm-15x9in) lit. 4-Dec-2 Neumeister, Munich #720/R
Works on paper
£274 $427 €400 Wood (16x28cm-6x11in) wash pencil htd bodycol. 11-Apr-3 Winterberg, Heidelberg #368
£274 $427 €400 Grounds of the Villa Borghese (45x60cm-18x24in) i. 11-Apr-3 Winterberg, Heidelberg #369/R
£453 $706 €720 Castel Gondolfo and Albaner See (28x44cm-11x17in) pencil sold with another. 11-Oct-2 Winterberg, Heidelberg #507

DRECHSLER, Johann Baptist (style) (1756-1811) Austrian
£11500 $17940 €17250 Still life with various flowers and fruit (69x49cm-27x19in) panel prov. 8-Apr-3 Sotheby's, Olympia #197/R est:6000-8000

DREGER, Tom von (1868-1949) Austrian
£1132 $1755 €1800 Portrait of Arthur Schopenhauer (83x71cm-33x28in) s. 29-Oct-2 Dorotheum, Vienna #189/R est:1800-2200
Works on paper
£513 $810 €800 Portrait of Johann Wolfgang von Goethe (50x39cm-20x15in) s.mono.d.1931 mixed media canvas on board. 12-Nov-2 Dorotheum, Vienna #101/R

DREHER, Peter (1932-) German
£353 $546 €550 View of Black Forest from St Margen (24x28cm-9x11in) s.d.1972 board. 6-Dec-2 Karlheinz Kaupp, Staufen #2142
£486 $768 €700 Glass (25x20cm-10x8in) d.1.4.81 canvas on panel. 26-Apr-3 Dr Lehr, Berlin #115/R

DREI, Ercole (1886-1973) Italian
Sculpture
£3767 $5877 €5500 Dancer with masks (62cm-24in) s. brown pat bronze. 10-Apr-3 Finarte Semenzato, Rome #251/R

DREIBHOLZ, Cristiaan Lodewyck Willem (1799-1874) Dutch
£1026 $1590 €1600 Voilier pendant l'orage (40x46cm-16x18in) mono. panel. 3-Dec-2 Campo & Campo, Antwerp #80 est:1400-1800
£1056 $1701 €1500 Ships near harbour mouth (29x41cm-11x16in) s. panel. 7-May-3 Vendue Huis, Gravenhage #402/R est:1500-2000
£1911 $2943 €3000 Shipping near Dordrecht (34x47cm-13x19in) s. panel. 3-Sep-2 Christie's, Amsterdam #286/R

DREIFUSS, Willy (1897-?) Swiss
Works on paper
£283 $438 €425 Conductor, Rafael Kubelik (20x14cm-8x6in) s.d.12.12.60 pencil chk. 4-Dec-2 Koller, Zurich #107b/R (S.FR 650)
£522 $809 €783 Clara Haskil at the piano (14x10cm-6x4in) mono.d.7.12.45 pencil. 4-Dec-2 Koller, Zurich #107a/R (S.FR 1200)
£870 $1348 €1305 Igor Strawinsky conducting (28x16cm-11x6in) mono.d.Dr38 pencil. 4-Dec-2 Koller, Zurich #107/R est:1500-2000 (S.FR 2000)

DRENDEL, Graeme (1953-) Australian?
£1429 $2229 €2144 Degree of difficulty (73x68cm-29x27in) s.d.98 s.i.d.98/99 verso. 11-Nov-2 Deutscher-Menzies, Melbourne #138/R est:2500-3500 (A.D 4000)
Works on paper
£286 $446 €429 Observer (26x34cm-10x13in) s.d.99 gouache. 11-Nov-2 Deutscher-Menzies, Melbourne #139/R (A.D 800)

DRESSE, Fernand (1916-) Belgian
£417 $654 €650 Nature morte au vase de Chine (99x124cm-39x49in) s. exhib. 19-Nov-2 Vanderkindere, Brussels #42

DRESSER, Rod (20th C) American
Photographs
£2229 $3500 €3344 Four French tulips, Carmel, California (61x51cm-24x20in) artist st.verso gelatin silver print edition of 15. 21-Apr-3 Phillips, New York #18/R est:2000-3000

DRESSLER, August Wilhelm (1886-1970) German
Works on paper
£399 $654 €550 Seated female nude (41x30cm-16x12in) mono. pen. 31-May-3 Villa Grisebach, Berlin #541/R

DRESSLER, Conrad (1856-1940) British
Sculpture
£5500 $8525 €8250 Bust of Henry Morton Stanley (70cm-28in) bronze. 24-Sep-2 Christie's, London #108/R est:2000-3000

DREUX, Alfred de (1810-1860) French
£14103 $22141 €22000 Chasse a courre (33x24cm-13x9in) s. 13-Dec-2 Piasa, Paris #4/R est:28000
£16000 $24800 €24000 Deux amazone (38x28cm-15x11in) one s. one mono. board pair. 4-Dec-2 Christie's, London #85/R est:15000-20000
£104167 $165625 €150000 Cheval en main (65x81cm-26x32in) s. prov. 30-Apr-3 Tajan, Paris #32/R est:50000-60000

DREUX, Alfred de (after) (1810-1860) French
£4167 $6625 €6000 Amazone de fantaisie (65x54cm-26x21in) bears sig. prov. 30-Apr-3 Tajan, Paris #33/R
£4514 $7178 €6500 Amazone de fantaisie (65x54cm-26x21in) prov. 30-Apr-3 Tajan, Paris #35/R

DREW, Clement (1806-1889) American
£599 $1000 €869 Water scene with lighthouse (36x56cm-14x22in) s.d.1873. 21-Jun-3 Charlton Hall, Columbia #544/R est:1500-2500
£1316 $2000 €1974 Eddystone light (23x30cm-9x12in) s.i. panel oval. 17-Aug-2 North East Auctions, Portsmouth #970/R est:2000-3000

DREW, Clement (attrib) (1806-1889) American
£541 $850 €812 Minot's light, Boston Harbour (20x30cm-8x12in) i.verso. 26-Jul-2 Eldred, East Dennis #230/R

DREW, Dudley (1924-) Australian
£596 $907 €894 Lilac (79x59cm-31x23in) s. 19-Aug-2 Joel, Victoria #297 est:800-1200 (A.D 1700)
£714 $1129 €1071 White and yellow roses (94x75cm-37x30in) s. 18-Nov-2 Joel, Victoria #377 est:2400-2800 (A.D 2000)

DREW, George H (c.1830-?) American
£562 $900 €815 Twilight along the river (24x31cm-9x12in) s, board. 16-May-3 Skinner, Boston #67/R

DREW, George W (1875-1968) American
£409 $650 €614 Mountain top cabin (46x61cm-18x24in) s.d.1958. 7-Mar-3 Skinner, Boston #430a/R
£573 $950 €831 Summer cottage by the pond (61x91cm-24x36in) s. 14-Jun-3 Jackson's, Cedar Falls #19/R
£750 $1200 €1088 Lakeside cottage (51x76cm-20x30in) s. 16-May-3 Skinner, Boston #62/R
£1304 $2100 €1956 Landscape with pond and cherry tree (61x91cm-24x36in) s. 15-Jan-3 Boos Gallery, Michigan #476/R est:800-1200
£1364 $2100 €2046 Lake cottage (61x91cm-24x36in) s. painted c.1910. 8-Sep-2 Treadway Gallery, Cincinnati #534/R est:2000-3000

DREW, Pamela (1910-1989) British
£260 $419 €390 Looms (51x61cm-20x24in) s.d.1935 board. 18-Feb-3 Bonhams, Knightsbridge #43

DREWES, Werner (1899-1985) American
£897 $1400 €1346 Untitled. 12-Oct-2 Fallon, Copake #81
Works on paper
£366 $600 €531 View of Central Park, New York (23x41cm-9x16in) s.d. pen ink pencil. 5-Jun-3 Swann Galleries, New York #81/R
£801 $1250 €1202 Lake through trees (38x53cm-15x21in) s.d.1949 W/C dr. 10-Nov-2 Selkirks, St. Louis #796/R

DREWS, Kaj (1884-1964) Danish
£244 $383 €366 Fresh snow along the river bank (27x39cm-11x15in) s.d.1923. 10-Dec-2 Pinneys, Montreal #74 (C.D 600)
£346 $550 €519 Landscape with river. s. 22-Mar-3 Fallon, Copake #180/R

DREWS, Svend (1919-) Danish
£297 $470 €446 River landscape (65x55cm-26x22in) s. 5-Apr-3 Rasmussen, Havnen #2052 (D.KR 3200)
£377 $600 €566 Norsk landskab (64x53cm-25x21in) 28-Feb-3 Douglas, South Deerfield #5

DREXEL, Francis Martin (1792-1863) American
£1615 $2600 €2423 Portrait of Mary Joanna Drexel as a child sitting atop a feathery pillow (61x46cm-24x18in) prov. 22-Feb-3 Pook & Pook, Downington #240/R est:2500-3500
£1708 $2750 €2562 Self portrait of the artist sitting at an easel with canvas and his palette (48x36cm-19x14in) prov. 22-Feb-3 Pook & Pook, Downington #241/R est:2000-2500
£124225 $200000 €186338 Family portrait of artist at his easel, his wife and young daughter (137x112cm-54x44in) prov. 22-Feb-3 Pook & Pook, Downington #200/R est:15000-20000

DREXEL, Hans Christoph (1886-1979) German
£1582 $2500 €2500 Still life with observer at window (93x82cm-37x32in) s. verso. 30-Nov-2 Villa Grisebach, Berlin #323/R est:3000-4000
Works on paper
£1887 $2943 €3000 Untitled (62x48cm-24x19in) chl executed c.1911-14 prov. 9-Oct-2 Sotheby's, London #229/R est:4500-6500

DREXEL, Norbert (1933-) Austrian
£903 $1435 €1300 Woman with fruit bowl (34x28cm-13x11in) s.d.1988. 29-Apr-3 Wiener Kunst Auktionen, Vienna #454/R

DREYER, Dankvart (1816-1852) Danish
£10213 $16136 €15320 Landscape from Brandsoe with large stones (46x61cm-18x24in) exhib. 2-Dec-2 Rasmussen, Copenhagen #1130/R est:150000 (D.KR 120000)

DREYFUS, Bernardo (1940-) Nicaraguan
£577 $900 €866 Untitled (121x121cm-48x48in) s.d.78 acrylic polymer resin board. 14-Sep-2 Weschler, Washington #657/R

DRI, Primo (?) Italian
£340 $541 €500 White house (50x65cm-20x26in) s.d.47. 1-Mar-3 Stadion, Trieste #8

DRIAN, Étienne (1885-1961) French
£481 $755 €750 Deux statuettes (38x30cm-15x12in) s. 13-Dec-2 Piasa, Paris #113

DRIBEN, Peter (c.1903-1968) American
£2174 $3500 €3261 Voluptuous woman tying strap of red stilletto (74x51cm-29x20in) s. board. 20-Feb-3 Illustration House, New York #44/R est:4000-8000

DRIDAN, David Clyde (1932-) Australian
£249 $381 €374 Coorong (91x122cm-36x48in) s. painted c.1973 prov. 26-Aug-2 Sotheby's, Paddington #615 (A.D 700)
£440 $700 €660 Lincoln Gap Hills (61x91cm-24x36in) s.d.62 board. 18-Mar-3 Rosebery Fine Art, London #769

DRIELST, Egbert van (1746-1818) Dutch
Works on paper
£780 $1303 €1100 Paysans et fermes dans un paysage (22x31cm-9x12in) s.d.1780 verso col wash black pencil. 19-Jun-3 Piasa, Paris #53
£2420 $3776 €3800 Figure on the Petit Pont Suisse, in the park at Elswout, near Haarlem (36x52cm-14x20in) brush grey wash over black chk. 5-Nov-2 Sotheby's, Amsterdam #164/R est:2500-3500

DRIELST, Egbert van and LELIE, Adriaen de (18th C) Dutch
£46763 $74820 €65000 Group portrait of a gentleman and a lady seated on a bench, with theie two children (81x111cm-32x44in) s.indis d. painted c.1799 prov.lit. 14-May-3 Christie's, Amsterdam #205/R est:10000-15000

DRIESSCHE, Ernest van den (1894-1985) Belgian
£629 $975 €1000 La fanfare (34x47cm-13x19in) s. panel. 1-Oct-2 Palais de Beaux Arts, Brussels #533
£1223 $1957 €1700 La rencontre des cavaliers (56x66cm-22x26in) s. 13-May-3 Palais de Beaux Arts, Brussels #324/R est:1250-2000

DRIESSCHE, Lucien van den (1926-1991) Belgian
£764 $1215 €1100 Eglise pres de la Lys (70x85cm-28x33in) s.d.1947. 29-Apr-3 Campo & Campo, Antwerp #308/R
Works on paper
£1007 $1612 €1400 La ville (78x122cm-31x48in) s. mixed media panel. 13-May-3 Vanderkindere, Brussels #98

DRIESSCHE, Marcel van (1925-) Belgian
£347 $552 €500 Nature morte aux tulipes jaunes (104x83cm-41x33in) s. d.1974 verso. 29-Apr-3 Campo & Campo, Antwerp #900
£382 $607 €550 Dame dans un interieur (107x89cm-42x35in) s. 29-Apr-3 Campo & Campo, Antwerp #897

DRIESTEN, Arend Jan van (1878-1969) Dutch
£271 $422 €425 Kakatoe (37x50cm-15x20in) s. board exhib. 6-Nov-2 Vendue Huis, Gravenhage #603
£317 $510 €450 Haystack (21x32cm-8x13in) 7-May-3 Vendue Huis, Gravenhage #579/R
£318 $497 €500 In de Pan, Wassenaar (30x49cm-12x19in) s. 6-Nov-2 Vendue Huis, Gravenhage #595/R
£318 $497 €500 View of farmyard (29x48cm-11x19in) s. 6-Nov-2 Vendue Huis, Gravenhage #612/R
£350 $546 €550 Farm with haystack (27x37cm-11x15in) s. 6-Nov-2 Vendue Huis, Gravenhage #604
£350 $546 €550 Wild rabbits against fence (52x32cm-20x13in) s. exhib. 6-Nov-2 Vendue Huis, Gravenhage #607/R
£350 $546 €550 Bloaters (30x50cm-12x20in) s. 6-Nov-2 Vendue Huis, Gravenhage #610/R
£446 $696 €700 Country-house, Rijksdorp in Wassenaar (18x30cm-7x12in) s. 6-Nov-2 Vendue Huis, Gravenhage #613/R
£541 $845 €850 By the limestone factory on the waters edge of Utrechts tow-path (32x49cm-13x19in) s. 6-Nov-2 Vendue Huis, Gravenhage #596
£541 $845 €850 Study of mills near Giessen, Nieuwkoop (23x32cm-9x13in) s. two. 6-Nov-2 Vendue Huis, Gravenhage #608/R
£573 $894 €900 Study of Oegstgeest canal near Katwijk (29x50cm-11x20in) s. studio st. 6-Nov-2 Vendue Huis, Gravenhage #593/R
£828 $1292 €1300 Blossoming tree near farm (34x48cm-13x19in) s. 6-Nov-2 Vendue Huis, Gravenhage #590/R
£955 $1490 €1500 Sand boat on the waters edge (33x53cm-13x21in) s. 6-Nov-2 Vendue Huis, Gravenhage #606/R est:1000-1500
Works on paper
£255 $397 €400 Our house, Utrechts tow-path (41x27cm-16x11in) s. pastel. 6-Nov-2 Vendue Huis, Gravenhage #594/R
£271 $422 €425 Mill near Weipoort (35x25cm-14x10in) s. chl pastel. 6-Nov-2 Vendue Huis, Gravenhage #598/R
£287 $447 €450 House with flower garden (32x21cm-13x8in) s. W/C pencil. 6-Nov-2 Vendue Huis, Gravenhage #600/R

DRING, James (1905-1985) British

£600 $966 €900 Harrods from the Hammersmith Bridge (95x60cm-37x24in) s. board. 18-Feb-3 Bonhams, Knightsbridge #32/R

DRINKARD, David (20th C) American

£2244 $3500 €3366 Windmill Covey (61x91cm-24x36in) 9-Nov-2 Altermann Galleries, Santa Fe #240

DRISCOLL, H A (1872-1944) American

£1233 $1800 €1850 Hooked pickerel (30x51cm-12x20in) s. masonite. 3-Nov-1 North East Auctions, Portsmouth #230/R

£1410 $2200 €2115 Trout taking a fly (36x25cm-14x10in) s. 21-Sep-2 Pook & Pook, Downington #351/R est:1500-2000

DRIVIER, Leon-Ernest (1878-1951) French

Sculpture

£5833 $9217 €9100 Couple nu enlace (38cm-15in) s. black pat bronze. 17-Nov-2 Herbette, Doullens #118/R est:5000

Works on paper

£1139 $1777 €1800 Personnage au bord de cours d'eau (30x47cm-12x19in) s. pastel. 18-Oct-2 Rabourdin & Choppin de Janvry, Paris #24

DROHAN, Walter (1932-) Canadian

£1111 $1822 €1611 Red on white (90x124cm-35x49in) s.i.d.1987 prov. 9-Jun-3 Hodgins, Calgary #264/R est:2500-3000 (C.D 2500)

£1667 $2733 €2417 Meeting of the seasons (100x160cm-39x63in) s.i.d.1997. 9-Jun-3 Hodgins, Calgary #81/R est:4000-6000 (C.D 3750)

£3178 $5053 €4767 Channel sortie (105x138cm-41x54in) s.i. 23-Mar-3 Hodgins, Calgary #119/R est:3000-5000 (C.D 7500)

DROLLING, Martin (1752-1817) French

£903 $1400 €1355 Washerwoman in an interior with a child blowing a bubble (13x16cm-5x6in) panel. 2-Oct-2 Christie's, Rockefeller NY #167/R est:5000-7000

£3262 $5448 €4600 La correction paternelle (17x19cm-7x7in) s. panel. 20-Jun-3 Rieunier, Paris #25/R est:3000-4000

£10127 $16000 €16000 Les enfants de l'artiste conversant pres d'une cheminee (28x36cm-11x14in) i.verso panel prov. 27-Nov-2 Christie's, Paris #61/R est:13500-18000

£11486 $17919 €17000 Jeune fille assise pres de fontaine (64x54cm-25x21in) s.d.1807 prov. 28-Mar-3 Delvaux, Paris #139/R est:8000-10000

Works on paper

£743 $1159 €1100 Studies of heads (27x37cm-11x15in) crayon chk prov. 26-Mar-3 Piasa, Paris #98

DROLLING, Michel Martin (1786-1851) French

Works on paper

£1139 $1800 €1800 Jeune homme debout de profil (42x28cm-17x11in) crayon stump wash. 28-Nov-2 Tajan, Paris #94/R

DROLLING, Michel Martin (attrib) (1786-1851) French

£1549 $2447 €2400 Portrait of elderly woman (45x38cm-18x15in) 20-Dec-2 Tajan, Paris #147/R est:4000

DRONSFIELD, John (1900-1951) British/South African

Works on paper

£387 $623 €581 Crucifixion (57x46cm-22x18in) pastel. 12-May-3 Stephan Welz, Johannesburg #275 est:3000-5000 (SA.R 4500)

DROOCHSLOOT, Cornelis (1630-1673) Dutch

£5895 $9197 €8843 Lively village street (34x52cm-13x20in) mnoo.d.1664 panel prov. 20-Nov-2 Fischer, Luzern #1048/R est:15000-20000 (S.FR 13500)

DROOCHSLOOT, Joost Cornelisz (1586-1666) Dutch

£1732 $2684 €2598 Pool in Bethesda with angel (59x76cm-23x30in) panel. 24-Sep-2 Koller, Zurich #6430/R est:3000-4000 (S.FR 4000)

£2000 $3340 €2900 Village with peasants gathered around a speaker (41x53cm-16x21in) s. panel. 11-Jul-3 Christie's, Kensington #79/R est:4000-6000

£5096 $7949 €8000 Landscape with figures entering a village, other figures with dogs in the foreground (26x36cm-10x14in) mono.d.1652 panel. 5-Nov-2 Sotheby's, Amsterdam #217/R est:8000-12000

£9615 $15096 €15000 Halte du vin chaud sur le canal gele (30x51cm-12x20in) panel. 16-Dec-2 Rabourdin & Choppin de Janvry, Paris #193/R est:22000

£12950 $20719 €18000 Wooded landscape with figures and dogs outside tavern (24x34cm-9x13in) mono.d.1642 panel. 13-May-3 Sotheby's, Amsterdam #26/R est:8000-12000

£13986 $23357 €20000 La rue d'un village Flamand (49x70cm-19x28in) panel. 25-Jun-3 Artcurial Briest, Paris #474/R est:20000-25000

£14000 $21980 €21000 Wooded landscape with skirmish (77x108cm-30x43in) s.d.1641. 11-Dec-2 Christie's, London #61/R est:12000-18000

£17986 $28777 €25000 Village festivities (64x88cm-25x35in) s.d.1642 panel prov. 17-May-3 Lempertz, Koln #1037/R est:25000

DROST, Willem (1630-1678) Dutch

£400000 $668000 €580000 Portrait of the artist's as Saint John (81x71cm-32x28in) prov.lit. 9-Jul-3 Christie's, London #34/R est:120000-180000

DROUAIS, François Hubert (1727-1775) French

£839 $1300 €1259 Portrait of Madame Sophie daughter of Louis XV (76x61cm-30x24in) 2-Nov-2 North East Auctions, Portsmouth #947/R

£60839 $101601 €87000 Portrait du Marquis de Briges enfant (71x57cm-28x22in) s.d.1768 oval prov. 25-Jun-3 Sotheby's, Paris #37/R est:50000-70000

DROUAIS, François Hubert (after) (1727-1775) French

£4294 $7000 €6441 Portrait of la Mse de Pompadour (51x64cm-20x25in) oval. 2-Feb-3 Simpson's, Houston #365

DROUAIS, François Hubert (attrib) (1727-1775) French

£6383 $10660 €9000 Portrait de Madame du Barry en costume de chasse (55x45cm-22x18in) oval prov. 23-Jun-3 Beaussant & Lefèvre, Paris #276/R est:6000-8000

DROUAIS, François Hubert (studio) (1727-1775) French

£6383 $9894 €9575 Portrait of Ludvig XV of France as Dauphin (73x59cm-29x23in) prov.lit. 3-Dec-2 Bukowskis, Stockholm #515/R est:70000-90000 (S.KR 90000)

DROUILLARD (19th C) French?

£2564 $4026 €4000 Femmes de Constantinople (32x46cm-13x18in) s.d.85. 10-Dec-2 Tajan, Paris #148/R

DROUIN, Patrick (1948-) French

Sculpture

£1129 $1784 €1750 Desir (27x22x30cm-11x9x12in) s. chestnut brown pat.bronze Cast.Susse. 17-Dec-2 Gioffredo, Nice #38/R

DROUOT, E (1859-1945) French

Sculpture

£1119 $1869 €1600 Athlete et lionne (52cm-20in) s. brown pat bronze green marble socle. 25-Jun-3 Artcurial Briest, Paris #48/R est:1200-1500

DROUOT, Edouard (1859-1945) French

Sculpture

£830 $1361 €1204 Figura de hombre sentado, Victor Hugo ? (48cm-19in) brown pat bronze green marble base. 28-May-3 Louis Morton, Mexico #44/R est:14000-16000 (M.P 14000)

£1895 $3052 €2900 Cheval de trait au travail (34x54cm-13x21in) s. brown pat bronze. 20-Jan-3 Horta, Bruxelles #89/R est:3000-3500

£3020 $4862 €4500 La caravane Egyptienne (89x18x36cm-35x7x14in) black brown gold pat bronze exec.c.1930 Cast Edling. 23-Feb-3 Lesieur & Le Bars, Le Havre #36/R

£3185 $5000 €4778 Figure of a warrior (91cm-36in) s. bronze. 21-Nov-2 Sotheby's, New York #118/R est:5000-7000

£4747 $7500 €7121 Figure of soldier (44cm-17in) i. marble. 24-Apr-3 Christie's, Rockefeller NY #217/R est:6000-8000

£5679 $8064 €9200 Caravane dans le desert (36x86cm-14x34in) s. brown pat bronze. 16-Mar-3 Eric Pillon, Calais #72/R

DRTIKOL, Frantisek (1883-1961) Czechoslovakian

£611 $971 €917 Landscape with two trees (27x26cm-11x10in) s.d.1941 board. 8-Mar-3 Dorotheum, Prague #139/R est:10000-15000 (C.KR 28000)

Photographs

£1829 $3000 €2744 La danse (20x10cm-8x4in) s.d. st.verso bromoil. 10-Feb-3 Swann Galleries, New York #31/R est:3500-4500

£2532 $4000 €4000 Nude study (30x24cm-12x9in) s. i. verso col bromide lit.exhib. 28-Nov-2 Villa Grisebach, Berlin #1157/R est:4000-6000

£2600 $4212 €3900 Nude study (30x24cm-12x9in) s. i.verso col bromoil print lit. 22-May-3 Sotheby's, London #67/R est:2800-3200

£9494 $15000 €14241 Composition (29x23cm-11x9in) s.d.1930 warm toned pigment print prov.lit. 23-Apr-3 Sotheby's, New York #187/R est:15000-25000

£16250 $26000 €24375 Nue (28x22cm-11x9in) s.d.1931 pigment print. 15-May-3 Swann Galleries, New York #331/R est:14000-18000
£17089 $27000 €25634 Composition (29x23cm-11x9in) s.d.1927 warm tones pigment print prov.lit. 23-Apr-3 Sotheby's, New York #179/R est:20000-30000
£24051 $38000 €36077 Half nude (28x22cm-11x9in) s.i. warm toned pigment print lit. 23-Apr-3 Sotheby's, New York #171/R est:30000-50000
£36709 $58000 €55064 Step II (22x28cm-9x11in) pigment print prov.lit. 22-Apr-3 Christie's, Rockefeller NY #59/R est:30000-50000
£41558 $64000 €62337 The bow (22x28cm-9x11in) s.d.1928 verso pigment print prov.exhib.lit. 22-Oct-2 Sotheby's, New York #29/R est:40000-60000

Works on paper
£595 $988 €1015 Untitled (22x17cm-9x7in) i. s.verso sepia photograph. 10-Jun-3 Shapiro, Sydney #103/R est:1000-1500 (A.D 1500)

DRUBI, Hafiz (1914-1991) Iraqi
£4200 $6678 €6300 Melon sellers (61x41cm-24x16in) s.d.69. 30-Apr-3 Sotheby's, London #152/R est:2000-3000

DRUM, David Clayton (1944-) Canadian
£348 $540 €522 Field of poppies (56x66cm-22x26in) s. s.i.d.2000 verso oil pastel panel. 24-Sep-2 Ritchie, Toronto #3194 (C.D 850)

DRUMAUX, Angelina (1881-1959) Luxembourger
£308 $477 €480 Les genets en fleur (32x40cm-13x16in) s. panel. 9-Dec-2 Horta, Bruxelles #276
£1282 $2013 €2000 Bouquet de roses (100x80cm-39x31in) s. 11-Dec-2 Hotel des Ventes Mosan, Brussels #315 est:2500-3000
£2000 $3240 €3000 Anemones (64x49cm-25x19in) s. 21-May-3 Bonhams, Knightsbridge #181/R est:2000-3000

DRUME, Auguste (20th C) Belgian
£523 $842 €800 Vase fleuri de roses (50x40cm-20x16in) s. 20-Jan-3 Horta, Bruxelles #422

DRUMMOND, Arthur (1871-1951) British
£1986 $3078 €2979 A beauty by the pond (48x40cm-19x16in) s.indis.d.1911 panel. 4-Dec-2 AB Stockholms Auktionsverk #1840/R est:25000-30000 (S.KR 28000)
£3300 $5247 €4950 Reflections (46x38cm-18x15in) s. panel. 19-Mar-3 John Nicholson, Haslemere #1185/R est:3000-4000

DRUMMOND, Charlotte (?-1793) British
Works on paper
£3800 $5928 €5700 Birdsfoot telfoil. Floral studies (30x24cm-12x9in) i. W/C on vellum set of eight. 5-Nov-2 Bonhams, New Bond Street #77/R est:4000-6000

DRUMMOND, J (19th C) British
£244 $344 €400 Portrait of John Lee Esquire (43x36cm-17x14in) 7-Feb-2 Woodwards, Cork #266

DRUMMOND, James (1816-1877) British
£6800 $10880 €10200 Cromwell in Edinburgh; Cromwell and troops overlooking the city in snow (89x123cm-35x48in) s.indis.d.186. 11-Mar-3 Bonhams, Oxford #50/R est:2000-3000

Works on paper
£400 $620 €600 Stag hunting in the Highlands (41x69cm-16x27in) s. W/C bodycol. 31-Oct-2 Duke & Son, Dorchester #165/R
£700 $1162 €1015 Old sea captain (49x37cm-19x15in) s.d.1878 W/C. 13-Jun-3 Lyon & Turnbull, Edinburgh #66

DRUMMOND, Samuel (1765-1844) British
£1300 $2015 €1950 Portrait of Sir Robert Williams Vaughan (89x69cm-35x27in) i.d.1825 v,. 5-Oct-2 Finan Watkins & Co, Mere #210/R
£3600 $5580 €5400 Portrait of Sir Robert Williams Vaughan, Baronet, M.P (89x69cm-35x27in) i.verso. 5-Oct-2 Finan Watkins & Co, Mere #209/R

DRURY, A (19/20th C) British
Sculpture
£2300 $3634 €3335 Bust of a young girl (48cm-19in) s. green bronze on green plinth. 22-Jul-3 Sworder & Son, Bishops Stortford #137/R est:300-400

DRURY, Alfred (1856-1944) British
Sculpture
£1100 $1793 €1595 Griselda - portrait bust of lady wearing Aesthetic costume (27cm-11in) s.i.d.1897 pat.bronze incl.green marble base. 16-Jul-3 Rupert Toovey, Partridge Green #1280/R est:700-1000
£2600 $4056 €3900 Age of innocence, bust of Gracie Doncaster (37cm-15in) s. green pat bronze faux marble base lit. 9-Apr-3 Sotheby's, London #97/R est:1500-2000

DRYDEN, Helen (1887-?) American
Works on paper
£6410 $10000 €9615 Fashionable women on tennis court (41x33cm-16x13in) s. W/C ink. 9-Nov-2 Illustration House, New York #83/R est:10000-14000

DRYSDALE, Alexander John (1870-1934) American
£692 $1100 €1038 Louisiana bayou (15x51cm-6x20in) s. oil wash board painted c.1920 prov. 2-Mar-3 Toomey, Oak Park #577/R
£926 $1500 €1389 Cypress in the bayou (46x30cm-18x12in) s.d.1912 oil wash board. 24-Jan-3 New Orleans Auction, New Orleans #376/R est:1800-2500
£1026 $1600 €1539 Live oak (48x74cm-19x29in) s.d.1931 oil wash board. 12-Oct-2 Neal Auction Company, New Orleans #1359/R est:1500-2500
£1220 $2000 €1830 Bayou landscape with oak tree (28x74cm-11x29in) s. oil wash board. 8-Feb-3 Neal Auction Company, New Orleans #335 est:800-1200
£1402 $2300 €2033 Bayou landscape (23x74cm-9x29in) s. oil wash board. 7-Jun-3 Neal Auction Company, New Orleans #356/R est:2000-3000
£1447 $2300 €2171 Louisiana landscape (25x43cm-10x17in) d.1909. 2-Mar-3 Toomey, Oak Park #576/R est:2000-3000
£1481 $2400 €2222 Louisiana bayou scene (51x76cm-20x30in) s.d.1931 oil wash board. 24-Jan-3 New Orleans Auction, New Orleans #377/R est:2500-4000
£1667 $2600 €2501 Louisiana bayou scene (51x74cm-20x29in) s. oil wash board. 12-Oct-2 Neal Auction Company, New Orleans #427/R est:2500-3500
£1677 $2750 €2516 Bayou scene with live oaks (15x51cm-6x20in) s. oil wash board. 8-Feb-3 Neal Auction Company, New Orleans #337 est:1000-2000
£1677 $2750 €2432 Louisiana Bayou scene (46x74cm-18x29in) s. oil wash board. 7-Jun-3 Neal Auction Company, New Orleans #355/R est:2500-3500
£1740 $2750 €2610 Lousiana Bayou at dusk (43x58cm-17x23in) s. board. 5-Apr-3 Neal Auction Company, New Orleans #347/R est:2500-3500
£1795 $2800 €2693 Louisiana bayou with canoe (51x15cm-20x6in) s. i.verso oil wash board. 12-Oct-2 Neal Auction Company, New Orleans #1358/R est:2000-3000
£1899 $3000 €2849 Spring morning, Louisiana (25x51cm-10x20in) s. s.i.d.1922 verso oil wash board. 5-Apr-3 Neal Auction Company, New Orleans #404/R est:2000-3000
£1923 $3000 €2885 Bayou landscape with oak tree (48x74cm-19x29in) s. oil wash board. 12-Oct-2 Neal Auction Company, New Orleans #1321/R est:1500-2500
£2025 $3200 €3038 Bayou landscape (48x74cm-19x29in) s.d.1932 oil wash board. 5-Apr-3 Neal Auction Company, New Orleans #402/R est:2500-3500
£2057 $3250 €3086 Louisiana live oaks, Audubon Park, New Orleans (48x36cm-19x14in) s. i.verso oil wash board. 5-Apr-3 Neal Auction Company, New Orleans #340/R est:2500-3500
£2083 $3250 €3125 Louisiana bayou (51x74cm-20x29in) s. oil wash board prov. 12-Oct-2 Neal Auction Company, New Orleans #426/R est:3000-5000
£2096 $3250 €3144 Bayou landscape (51x74cm-20x29in) s. board. 7-Dec-2 Neal Auction Company, New Orleans #431/R est:2500-3500
£2244 $3500 €3366 Louisiana bayou (51x76cm-20x30in) s. oil wash board. 12-Oct-2 Neal Auction Company, New Orleans #660/R est:2500-3500
£2258 $3500 €3387 Louisiana cyress swamp (74x48cm-29x19in) s. board prov. 7-Dec-2 Neal Auction Company, New Orleans #427/R est:3000-5000
£2436 $3800 €3654 Brown oaks (51x76cm-20x30in) s. oil wash on board. 20-Sep-2 New Orleans Auction, New Orleans #1228/R est:4000-7000
£2564 $4000 €3846 Louisiana bayou (51x74cm-20x29in) s. oil wash board prov. 12-Oct-2 Neal Auction Company, New Orleans #643/R est:2500-3500
£2885 $4500 €4328 Early morning on Folse river (61x46cm-24x18in) s.d.1912 board. 12-Oct-2 Neal Auction Company, New Orleans #476/R est:4000-6000

£2885 $4500 €4328 Bayou landscape (25x74cm-10x29in) s.d.1916 oil wash board. 12-Oct-2 Neal Auction Company, New Orleans #659 est:1500-2500
£3049 $5000 €4421 Bayou scene with wind blown marsh grass and tree (30x46cm-12x18in) s.d.1911 board. 7-Jun-3 Neal Auction Company, New Orleans #334/R est:4000-6000
£3226 $5000 €4839 Louisiana spring scene with water hyacinths, St Martinsville (51x76cm-20x30in) s.i. i.verso oil wash paper painted c.1922. 8-Dec-2 Toomey, Oak Park #613/R est:3000-5000
£3506 $5750 €5084 Louisiana bayou (48x74cm-19x29in) s. oil wash board. 7-Jun-3 Neal Auction Company, New Orleans #335/R est:3000-5000
£3846 $6000 €5769 Cypress trees along the bayou (61x43cm-24x17in) s.d.1914 oil wash board. 12-Oct-2 Neal Auction Company, New Orleans #635/R est:4000-6000
£4808 $7500 €7212 Classical Louisiana oak tree bayou landscape (48x74cm-19x29in) s. oil wash board prov. 12-Oct-2 Neal Auction Company, New Orleans #644/R est:3000-5000

Works on paper
£1006 $1600 €1509 Louisiana scene (25x76cm-10x30in) s. W/C exec.c.1910. 2-Mar-3 Toomey, Oak Park #582/R est:1500-2500
£1125 $1800 €1631 Louisiana marsh (25x76cm-10x30in) s.d. W/C. 17-May-3 Selkirks, St. Louis #320/R est:2000-2500
£2388 $3750 €3582 Trees and still water (49x76cm-19x30in) s. W/C gouache. 19-Nov-2 Butterfields, San Francisco #8043/R est:3000-5000

DRYSDALE, Jeannie T (fl.1881-1900) British
£440 $704 €660 Gainsborough's blue boy (229x114cm-90x45in) s.d.1928. 14-Mar-3 Gardiner & Houlgate, Bath #222/R

DRYSDALE, Sir George Russell (1912-1981) Australian
£25896 $42470 €37549 Split rocks (40x51cm-16x20in) s. s.i.verso painted c.1953 prov. 4-Jun-3 Deutscher-Menzies, Melbourne #53/R est:70000-90000 (A.D 65000)
£39427 $59928 €59141 Landscape with bottle trees (30x46cm-12x18in) s. s.i.verso painted c.1952-53 prov.exhib. 28-Aug-2 Deutscher-Menzies, Melbourne #43/R est:90000-120000 (A.D 110000)
£96899 $154070 €145349 Brumby Jack Brady (51x41cm-20x16in) s.d.64 prov. 5-May-3 Sotheby's, Melbourne #139/R est:250000-350000 (A.D 250000)
£192857 $304714 €289286 Deserted out-station (86x112cm-34x44in) s. painted 1945 prov.exhib.lit. 17-Nov-2 Sotheby's, Paddington #28/R est:600000-900000 (A.D 540000)
£251572 $405031 €377358 Group of Aborigines (50x60cm-20x24in) s. painted 1953 prov.exhib.lit. 6-May-3 Christie's, Melbourne #44/R est:500000-700000 (A.D 628930)
£410853 $653256 €616280 Outstation (76x127cm-30x50in) s. i.verso painted 1965 prov.exhib.lit. 5-May-3 Sotheby's, Melbourne #10/R est:800000-1000000 (A.D 1060000)

Prints
£2326 $3698 €3489 Blacks' camp (79x56cm-31x22in) s.i. num.23/75 lithograph prov. 5-May-3 Sotheby's, Melbourne #46/R est:3000 (A.D 6000)

Works on paper
£286 $451 €429 Vincent Neylen (22x15cm-9x6in) i. pencil. 17-Nov-2 Sotheby's, Paddington #90 (A.D 800)
£286 $451 €429 Pipe smoker (23x15cm-9x6in) pencil. 17-Nov-2 Sotheby's, Paddington #94 (A.D 800)
£393 $621 €590 Outback man (23x10cm-9x4in) init. pen ink. 27-Nov-2 Deutscher-Menzies, Melbourne #215/R est:1500-2500 (A.D 1100)
£536 $846 €804 Child (22x15cm-9x6in) pencil. 17-Nov-2 Sotheby's, Paddington #33 est:2000-4000 (A.D 1500)
£571 $903 €857 Woman (22x15cm-9x6in) pencil. 17-Nov-2 Sotheby's, Paddington #34 est:2000-4000 (A.D 1600)
£698 $1109 €1047 Stockman (19x17cm-7x7in) s.i.indis.d. ink. 5-May-3 Sotheby's, Melbourne #327 (A.D 1800)
£969 $1541 €1454 Mother and child (18x12cm-7x5in) s. i.verso ink wash exhib. 5-May-3 Sotheby's, Melbourne #230 est:2500-3500 (A.D 2500)
£1286 $2031 €1929 Desert sketchbook (19x23cm-7x9in) W/C. 17-Nov-2 Sotheby's, Paddington #64 est:3000-5000 (A.D 3600)
£1500 $2370 €2250 Berrigan Sunday (22x15cm-9x6in) d.3rd December 44 i.verso pencil. 17-Nov-2 Sotheby's, Paddington #49 est:3000-5000 (A.D 4200)
£1680 $2705 €2520 Old Rosie (24x16cm-9x6in) init.d.61 ink prov.lit. 6-May-3 Christie's, Melbourne #291/R est:3000-5000 (A.D 4200)
£1786 $2821 €2679 Soldiers resting (19x22cm-7x9in) s.i.d.1944 pen ink. 27-Nov-2 Deutscher-Menzies, Melbourne #109/R est:6000-8000 (A.D 5000)
£1800 $2898 €2700 Drover resting (17x23cm-7x9in) s. ink. 6-May-3 Christie's, Melbourne #235/R est:3000-5000 (A.D 4500)
£1833 $3005 €2658 Shapes for textile designs (25x23cm-10x9in) s.i. W/C pen ink exec.c.1945. 4-Jun-3 Deutscher-Menzies, Melbourne #149/R est:5000-7000 (A.D 4600)
£1900 $3059 €2755 Old timer (20x20cm-8x8in) s. pen wash. 12-May-3 Joel, Victoria #240 est:4000-5000 (A.D 4750)
£2080 $3349 €3120 Stockman (36x27cm-14x11in) s. ink. 6-May-3 Christie's, Melbourne #259/R est:4000-6000 (A.D 5200)
£2143 $3386 €3215 No wood no dinner (47x28cm-19x11in) s. ink wash. 27-Nov-2 Deutscher-Menzies, Melbourne #132/R est:6500-9000 (A.D 6000)
£2200 $3542 €3300 Lubra (36x26cm-14x10in) s. ink W/C. 6-May-3 Christie's, Melbourne #207/R est:3000-5000 (A.D 5500)
£2429 $3837 €3644 Study for deserted out-station (13x18cm-5x7in) s. pencil. 17-Nov-2 Sotheby's, Paddington #46/R est:5000-8000 (A.D 6800)
£2590 $4247 €3756 Country town (34x57cm-13x22in) studio st. gouache ink wash. 4-Jun-3 Deutscher-Menzies, Melbourne #132/R est:7000-9000 (A.D 6500)
£2600 $4186 €3900 Study of a birder - Bass Strait (28x21cm-11x8in) s. i.verso ink. 6-May-3 Christie's, Melbourne #64/R est:7000-10000 (A.D 6500)
£2688 $4086 €4032 Portrait of Janey (47x30cm-19x12in) s.i.d.68 W/C pencil. 28-Aug-2 Deutscher-Menzies, Melbourne #66/R est:8000-12000 (A.D 7500)

D'SEVERIN, Jose Ma (fl.1930s) American
Works on paper
£305 $500 €442 Woman with melon (25x18cm-10x7in) s. W/C gouache. 1-Jun-3 Wright, Chicago #243/R

DUASSUT, C (19/20th C) British
Works on paper
£480 $749 €720 Evening landscape with shepherd and sheep (17x25cm-7x10in) s.d.96 pencil W/C. 18-Sep-2 Dreweatt Neate, Newbury #65

DUASSUT, Curtius (fl.1889-1903) British
Works on paper
£300 $477 €450 Rural landscape with figure standing beside a cottage (24x34cm-9x13in) s. W/C. 6-Mar-3 Clevedon Sale Rooms #111
£700 $1113 €1050 Riverside cottage (23x33cm-9x13in) s. W/C. 29-Apr-3 Gorringes, Lewes #2077
£750 $1193 €1125 Farm near Groombridge, Sussex (20x33cm-8x13in) s. W/C. 29-Apr-3 Gorringes, Lewes #2076

DUBASTY, Joseph (19th C) French
Miniatures
£1064 $1723 €1500 Louis XVII en buste de face (13x10cm-5x4in) s. ivory gilded brass surround prov.exhib. 21-May-3 Piasa, Paris #306/R est:1000-1500

DUBAUT, Pierre (1886-1968) French
Works on paper
£1370 $2151 €2000 Promenade en caleche a Deauville (29x42cm-11x17in) st.sig. gouache. 21-Apr-3 Rabourdin & Choppin de Janvry, Paris #59/R est:1700-1800

DUBBELS, Hendrik (1620-1676) Dutch
£15287 $23847 €24000 Moored ships in a calm, fisherfolk on a jetty nearby (39x49cm-15x19in) s. canvas on panel prov.exhib.lit. 6-Nov-2 Christie's, Amsterdam #79/R est:12000-16000

DUBIEL, Evelyn S (attrib) (c.1922-) American
Works on paper
£1156 $1850 €1734 Village by the sea. W/C. 1-Jan-3 Fallon, Copake #203

DUBLIN, Jacques (1901-1978) Swiss
Works on paper
£370 $596 €555 Ville Neu les Avignon (29x43cm-11x17in) s.i.d.1936 W/C over pencil. 7-May-3 Dobiaschofsky, Bern #468/R (S.FR 800)

DUBOIS, Charles-Edouard (1847-1885) French
£565 $882 €848 Coastal landscape with figures (38x60cm-15x24in) s. panel. 16-Sep-2 Philippe Schuler, Zurich #3466 (S.FR 1300)
£1974 $3060 €2961 Coast of Sorrento (31x46cm-12x18in) s.d.1852. 3-Oct-2 Koller, Zurich #3077/R est:3000-6000 (S.FR 4600)

DUBOIS, Ernest (1863-1931) French
Sculpture
£1361 $2163 €2000 Buste de Lebreton (79cm-31in) s.d.1904 white marble red marble socle. 23-Mar-3 Herbette, Doullens #241/R
£2884 $4529 €4500 Fauconnier a cheval (69cm-27in) s.st.f.Jollet gilt pat bronze. 10-Dec-2 Tajan, Paris #150/R est:6000

DUBOIS, Fernand (?) French?
Sculpture
£1086 $1748 €1575 Figure of a lady, nude seated on a rocky ground (39cm-15in) s. bronze marble base. 12-May-3 Joel, Victoria #415 est:3000-5000 (A.D 2715)

DUBOIS, Frederic (fl.1780-1819) French
Miniatures
£2800 $4592 €4060 Young lady in white muslin dress (5cm-2in circular) gilt metal mount. 3-Jun-3 Christie's, London #162/R est:800-1000

DUBOIS, Guillam (1620-1680) Dutch
£16547 $26475 €23000 Dune landscape with travelers, shepherds on a path (30x36cm-12x14in) s.d.1647 panel prov. 14-May-3 Christie's, Amsterdam #188/R est:10000-15000

DUBOIS, Henri Pierre Hippolyte (1837-1909) French
£1935 $3000 €2903 Aux Petites Dalles (46x38cm-18x15in) s. 2-Oct-2 Christie's, Rockefeller NY #770/R est:3000-5000

DUBOIS, Jean (attrib) (1625-1694) French
Sculpture
£21474 $33285 €33500 Projet de monument funeraire (43x28cm-17x11in) terracotta relief lit. 9-Dec-2 Rabourdin & Choppin de Janvry, Paris #1/R est:6000

DUBOIS, Jules (1864-1957) Belgian
£1224 $1947 €1800 L'etang de l'Ermite (90x100cm-35x39in) s. 18-Mar-3 Campo, Vlaamse Kaai #73 est:1500-1800
£1635 $2518 €2600 L'etang de l'Ermite (90x100cm-35x39in) s. 22-Oct-2 Campo, Vlaamse Kaai #491

DUBOIS, Louis (1830-1880) Belgian
£822 $1282 €1200 Portrait de rabbin (55x46cm-22x18in) s. panel prov. 14-Apr-3 Horta, Bruxelles #327
£1290 $2039 €2000 Riviere arbore (45x80cm-18x31in) s.d.1879. 17-Dec-2 Galerie Moderne, Brussels #658/R
£2649 $4318 €4000 Composition auc chinoiseries (136x103cm-54x41in) s.d.1866. 17-Feb-3 Horta, Bruxelles #92

DUBOIS, Louis Auguste Albert (1846-?) French
£5500 $8965 €8250 Coquette (64x43cm-25x17in) s.d.84. 29-Jan-3 Sotheby's, Olympia #335/R est:4000-5000

DUBOIS, Maria (?) French
£1103 $1754 €1600 Natures mortes aux prunes (28x34cm-11x13in) s. pair. 4-Mar-3 Livinec, Gaudcheau & Jezequel, Rennes #123

DUBOIS, P (?) ?
Sculpture
£1986 $3316 €2800 Maternite. brown pat bronze. 23-Jun-3 Amberes, Antwerp #249/R

DUBOIS, Paul (1924-) Belgian
£302 $483 €420 Nature morte (67x79cm-26x31in) s.d.48. 19-May-3 Horta, Bruxelles #257

DUBOIS, Paul (1858-1938) Belgian
Sculpture
£3311 $5165 €4900 Maternite ou la charite (78cm-31in) s. medaille pat bronze Cast F.Barbedienne. 31-Mar-3 Rossini, Paris #43/R

DUBOIS, Paul (1829-1905) French
Sculpture
£1139 $1777 €1800 Harlequin (84cm-33in) s. brown pat bronze. 21-Oct-2 Bernaerts, Antwerp #31/R est:2000-3000
£1154 $1754 €1800 Buste de jeune femme (49x24x23cm-19x9x9in) Carrare marble socle exec.c.1900. 10-Jul-2 Rabourdin & Choppin de Janvry, Paris #54/R est:1700-2000
£1325 $2159 €2000 Menestrel (48cm-19in) s.d.1865 brown pat bronze Cast Barbedienne. 17-Feb-3 Horta, Bruxelles #109
£1392 $2200 €2200 Le chanteur Florentin (62x18cm-24x7in) s.d.1865 pat bronze Cast Barbedienne. 27-Nov-2 Lemoine & Ferrando, Paris #170/R est:2200-3000
£1923 $3038 €3000 Maternite (62x25x29cm-24x10x11in) num.983 gold brown pat bronze Cast Barbedienne. 14-Nov-2 Credit Municipal, Paris #77 est:2500-3000
£2649 $4318 €4000 Joueur de mandoline (77cm-30in) s.d.1865 pat bronze Cast Barbedienne. 17-Feb-3 Horta, Bruxelles #108
£5000 $7800 €7500 Le courage militaire (82cm-32in) s.num.5992 gilt brown pat bronze wood socle st.f.F.Barbedienne. 5-Nov-2 Sotheby's, London #143/R est:4000-6000
£9500 $14915 €14250 Charite (78cm-31in) s.i. brown pat. bronze lit. 10-Dec-2 Sotheby's, London #151/R est:6000-8000
£15000 $23400 €22500 Florentine singer (116cm-46in) s.d.1865 num.71777 brown pat bronze st.f.F.Barbediene lit. 5-Nov-2 Sotheby's, London #158/R est:10000-15000

DUBOIS, Paul H (?) ?
£260 $406 €390 Between Leyden and Haay, watermeadow with cattle, cottage and boat (46x69cm-18x27in) s. 31-Jul-2 Mallams, Oxford #251/R

DUBOIS, Paul-Elie (1886-1949) French
£1132 $1743 €1800 Villa Abd-el-Tif (56x34cm-22x13in) s. canvas on cardboard. 23-Oct-2 Rabourdin & Choppin de Janvry, Paris #237
£1295 $2124 €1800 Vue d'Alger (55x65cm-22x26in) s.i. 4-Jun-3 Tajan, Paris #263/R est:2000-2300
£1447 $2228 €2300 Golfe de Tunis (24x33cm-9x13in) s. 23-Oct-2 Rabourdin & Choppin de Janvry, Paris #233/R
£1892 $2951 €2800 Cour d'amour a Hoggar (54x65cm-21x26in) s.i. s.i.verso panel. 28-Mar-3 Claude Aguttes, Neuilly #221/R

DUBOIS, Raphael (1888-?) Belgian
£253 $395 €400 Vue des toits de Bruxelles (60x51cm-24x20in) s. 10-Sep-2 Vanderkindere, Brussels #306
£278 $442 €400 Interieur (50x60cm-20x24in) s. 29-Apr-3 Campo, Vlaamse Kaai #108
£403 $648 €600 Saules pres du ruisseau (32x46cm-13x18in) s.d.1911 panel. 24-Feb-3 Bernaerts, Antwerp #776/R
£442 $703 €650 Paysage automnal (38x60cm-15x24in) s. 18-Mar-3 Vanderkindere, Brussels #158
£448 $708 €650 Vue de Montmartre (41x51cm-16x20in) s. panel. 1-Apr-3 Palais de Beaux Arts, Brussels #528
£764 $1215 €1100 Bateaux au port (35x49cm-14x19in) s. panel. 29-Apr-3 Campo & Campo, Antwerp #103/R
£800 $1328 €800 Verger en fleurs (115x100cm-45x39in) s. 16-Jun-3 Horta, Bruxelles #371
£927 $1511 €1400 Marseille harbour (49x39cm-19x15in) s. panel. 28-Jan-3 Dorotheum, Vienna #65/R
£962 $1510 €1500 La roulotte animee (75x100cm-30x39in) s.d.1915. 19-Nov-2 Vanderkindere, Brussels #120/R est:1750-2500
£1013 $1570 €1600 Mere et enfant dans un sous-bois (103x69cm-41x27in) s. 24-Sep-2 Galerie Moderne, Brussels #801/R
£1583 $2532 €2200 La Place Flagey sous en soleil d'automne (49x64cm-19x25in) s.d.18 cardboard. 13-May-3 Palais de Beaux Arts, Brussels #65/R est:2000-3000
£1699 $2736 €2600 Elegante nue a la rose (110x80cm-43x31in) s.d.1916. 20-Jan-3 Horta, Bruxelles #223/R est:3000-4000

DUBOIS, Roger Maximilien (1894-1918) ?
£538 $839 €850 L'anniversaire (27x39cm-11x15in) s. panel. 10-Sep-2 Vanderkindere, Brussels #368
£654 $1052 €1000 Les meules (22x27cm-9x11in) s.d.1917 panel. 20-Jan-3 Horta, Bruxelles #49

DUBOIS, Valborg Olsen (1860-1908) Norwegian
£679 $1046 €1019 Portrait of woman (33x26cm-13x10in) s. painted 1890. 28-Oct-2 Blomqvist, Lysaker #1031/R (N.KR 8000)

DUBOIS-PILLET, Albert (1845-1890) French
£10490 $17517 €15000 Fleurs, trois roses (41x33cm-16x13in) s. painted c.1887. 30-Jun-3 Pierre Berge, Paris #40/R est:30000-40000

DUBORD, Jean Pierre (1949-) French
£366 $600 €549 Le descente sur Rouen (76x61cm-30x24in) s. i.verso. 5-Feb-3 Doyle, New York #44/R
£513 $800 €770 La descente a la mer (33x41cm-13x16in) s. i.verso. 9-Oct-2 Doyle, New York #29
£518 $850 €777 La sortie des voiliers (51x61cm-20x24in) s. i.verso. 5-Feb-3 Doyle, New York #72/R
£566 $900 €849 Cote Normande (38x56cm-15x22in) s. s.i.verso. 5-Mar-3 Doyle, New York #19/R
£671 $1100 €973 Sur la plage (41x58cm-16x23in) s. s.i.verso. 4-Jun-3 Doyle, New York #42 est:2000-3000

£671 $1100 €973 Douarenenez (46x64cm-18x25in) s. s.i.verso. 4-Jun-3 Doyle, New York #43 est:2000-3000
£745 $1200 €1118 Pecheurs a maree basse (61x76cm-24x30in) s. s.i.verso. 19-Feb-3 Doyle, New York #76
£943 $1500 €1415 Bord de Seine en automne (25x51cm-10x20in) s. s.i.verso. 18-Mar-3 Doyle, New York #23/R est:1800-2200
£1111 $1800 €1611 La Cote Bretonne (61x76cm-24x30in) s. i.verso. 21-May-3 Doyle, New York #241/R est:3000-4000
£1210 $1900 €1815 La sortied des voiliers (20x24cm-8x9in) s. s.i.verso. 10-Dec-2 Doyle, New York #255/R est:2500-3500
£1484 $2300 €2226 Marche aux fluers a Paris (76x61cm-30x24in) s. i.verso. 25-Sep-2 Doyle, New York #24/R est:2000-3000

DUBOS, Angèle (1844-?) French
£8600 $14104 €12900 Pet bird (45x55cm-18x22in) s.d.1869. 4-Feb-3 Sworder & Son, Bishops Stortford #103/R est:6000-7000

DUBOURG, Alexandre (?) French?
£769 $1200 €1154 Fisherboy (18x13cm-7x5in) s. panel. 9-Nov-2 Sloan, North Bethesda #571/R

DUBOURG, Louis Alexandre (c.1825-1891) French
£4730 $7378 €7000 Honfleur, le Poudreux (18x34cm-7x13in) s. panel prov.exhib. 28-Mar-3 Claude Aguttes, Neuilly #41/R
£5769 $9058 €9000 Jeune berger gardant ses moutons (86x125cm-34x49in) s. 15-Dec-2 Eric Pillon, Calais #45/R

DUBOUT, Albert (1905-1978) French
Works on paper
£310 $493 €450 Il y a aussi la marche arriere, vous allex voir (19x27cm-7x11in) s. W/C. 5-Mar-3 Doutrebente, Paris #82/R

DUBOVSKOY, Nicolay Nikanorovich (1859-1918) Russian
£8000 $12560 €12000 Reaping the harvest (35x44cm-14x17in) s.i.d.1915 verso. 20-Nov-2 Sotheby's, London #69/R est:8000-12000
£35000 $54950 €52500 The south (102x132cm-40x52in) s. s.d.verso. 20-Nov-2 Sotheby's, London #73/R est:30000-40000

DUBOY, Ernest (20th C) Belgian?
Sculpture
£1986 $3316 €2800 Le Pardon. dark brown pat bronze. 23-Jun-3 Amberes, Antwerp #250/R

DUBREUIL, Cheri François (1828-1880) French
£1132 $1743 €1800 Geolette et son pilote en approche des cotes (45x65cm-18x26in) bears sig.d.1877. 27-Oct-2 Lesieur & Le Bars, Le Havre #122/R
£1179 $1839 €1769 Sailing ships on Lake Geneva (32x46cm-13x18in) s.d.1874. 6-Nov-2 Dobiaschofsky, Bern #469/R est:2200 (S.FR 2700)
£2222 $3534 €3200 Embarcations (51x74cm-20x29in) s.d.1859. 30-Apr-3 Tajan, Paris #107/R
£2516 $3874 €4000 Trois mats sous voiles (63x94cm-25x37in) s.d.i.1861. 27-Oct-2 Lesieur & Le Bars, Le Havre #79/R

DUBREUIL, Victor (19th C) French
£1506 $2500 €2184 After the rendevous (36x25cm-14x10in) s. 11-Jun-3 Butterfields, San Francisco #4033/R est:3000-5000
£45161 $70000 €67742 Barrels of money (61x51cm-24x20in) s. 5-Dec-2 Christie's, Rockefeller NY #46/R est:100000-150000

DUBUC, Jean Louis (1946-) French
£756 $1172 €1180 Chief d'orchestre (35x27cm-14x11in) s. 8-Dec-2 Feletin, Province #172

DUBUC, Roland (1924-1998) Swiss
£743 $1159 €1100 Elbeuf (46x55cm-18x22in) s. 28-Mar-3 Charbonneaux, Paris #64/R
£897 $1409 €1400 Moulin de la Galette (50x61cm-20x24in) s. 24-Nov-2 Lesieur & Le Bars, Le Havre #38/R
£986 $1587 €1400 Au fil de l'eau (50x61cm-20x24in) s. 12-May-3 Lesieur & Le Bars, Le Havre #22/R
£1208 $1945 €1800 Les clowns (60x73cm-24x29in) s. 23-Feb-3 Lesieur & Le Bars, Le Havre #37/R
£1745 $2809 €2600 Le Moulin de la Galette (60x73cm-24x29in) s. 23-Feb-3 Lesieur & Le Bars, Le Havre #38/R
£2411 $4027 €3400 Paris, le moulin de la galette a Montmartre (60x73cm-24x29in) s. lit. 18-Jun-3 Charbonneaux, Paris #108/R est:3000-3500
Works on paper
£352 $567 €500 Le moulin de la Galette (62x46cm-24x18in) s.d.83 Indian ink. 12-May-3 Lesieur & Le Bars, Le Havre #23
£379 $603 €550 Paysage vallonne (46x60cm-18x24in) s.d.1971 W/C. 7-Mar-3 Raboudin & Choppin de Janvry, Paris #45
£379 $603 €550 Au cirque (35x43cm-14x17in) s. W/C. 7-Mar-3 Raboudin & Choppin de Janvry, Paris #46
£403 $648 €600 Marins sur le quai (48x52cm-19x20in) s. gouache. 23-Feb-3 Lesieur & Le Bars, Le Havre #39
£775 $1247 €1100 Montmartre sous la neige (48x63cm-19x25in) s. gouache. 12-May-3 Lesieur & Le Bars, Le Havre #24

DUBUCAND, Alfred (1828-1894) French
Sculpture
£1146 $1789 €1800 Ane africain (18x20cm-7x8in) brown pat bronze. 10-Nov-2 Eric Pillon, Calais #30/R
£1800 $2808 €2700 Standing retriever with hare (25x36cm-10x14in) s. brown pat. bronze. 6-Nov-2 Sotheby's, Olympia #171/R est:2000-2500
£2400 $3816 €3600 Stallion (49cm-19in) s. brown pat bronze. 29-Apr-3 Sotheby's, Olympia #155/R est:2500-3500
£3000 $4890 €4350 Pheasant (70cm-28in) s. bronze. 17-Jul-3 Tennants, Leyburn #523/R est:2000-3000
£3500 $5320 €5250 Standing retriever with a pheasant (25x31cm-10x12in) s. dark brown pat. bronze. 28-Aug-2 Sotheby's, London #828/R est:2500-3500
£3600 $5472 €5400 Anier de caire - an Egyptian boy with a donkey (34x26cm-13x10in) s. brown pat. bronze. 28-Aug-2 Sotheby's, London #825/R est:4000-6000
£5500 $8580 €8250 Kaolin, a thoroughbred (51x44cm-20x17in) s.i.d.1878 brown pat bronze lit. 9-Apr-3 Sotheby's, London #158/R est:6000-8000
£14800 $22496 €22200 Le Retour de la chasse a courre - return from the hunt (41x55cm-16x22in) s.d.1870 golden brown pat. bronze. 28-Aug-2 Sotheby's, London #872/R est:12000-18000

DUBUCAND, Alfred (attrib) (1828-1894) French
Sculpture
£1420 $2300 €2130 Stag and doe (33x30cm-13x12in) s. reddish brown pat. bronze with naturalistic base. 25-Jan-3 Skinner, Boston #808/R est:700-900

DUBUFE, Claude Marie (1790-1864) French
£1200 $1944 €1800 Duc et Duchesse de Dino (51x43cm-20x17in) s.i.d.1840 prov. 23-Jan-3 Christie's, Kensington #21/R est:1500-2000
£7306 $11397 €10959 Portrait of Queen Hortense (73x79cm-29x31in) i. 28-Mar-3 Koller, Zurich #3078/R est:12000-18000 (S.FR 16000)

DUBUFE, Edouard Louis (attrib) (1820-1883) French
£338 $527 €500 Jeune femme (23x33cm-9x13in) panel. 31-Mar-3 Ribeyre & Baron, Paris #47

DUBUFE, Edouard Marie Guillaume (1853-1909) French
Works on paper
£1161 $1800 €1742 Portrait of Charles Zimmerman and Edouard Dufufe's wife (18x13cm-7x5in) init.d.1852 chl col chk htd white two. 29-Oct-2 Sotheby's, New York #14/R est:1000-1500
£5063 $8000 €7595 La flute d'ivoire (68x53cm-27x21in) s.d.1876 i.verso pencil W/C paper on canvas prov. 23-Apr-3 Christie's, Rockefeller NY #106/R est:10000-15000
£5806 $9000 €8709 Study for profane music (37x49cm-15x19in) s.i.d.30 Avril 81 pencil white black chk prov.exhib. 29-Oct-2 Sotheby's, New York #68/R est:4000-6000

DUBUFFET, Jean (1901-1985) French
£25850 $41102 €38000 Non-lieu donne H48 (67x100cm-26x39in) mono.d.1984 acrylic paper on canvas prov. 24-Mar-3 Cornette de St.Cyr, Paris #18/R est:50000
£34810 $55000 €52215 Le tragique instant (51x36cm-20x14in) s.d.79 acrylic paper collage on canvas prov.lit. 13-Nov-2 Sotheby's, New York #322/R est:50000-70000
£43750 $70000 €65625 Site avec quatre figures (68x50cm-27x20in) init.d.81 acrylic paper on canvas prov.lit. 15-May-3 Christie's, Rockefeller NY #188/R est:40000-60000
£50000 $82000 €75000 Site aletoire avec 4 personnages (68x100cm-27x39in) init.d.82 acrylic paper collage paper on canvas prov.lit. 6-Feb-3 Christie's, London #654/R est:40000-60000
£75000 $125250 €108750 Radieux matin (100x81cm-39x32in) init.d.80 i.d.Dec 80 verso acrylic prov.lit. 26-Jun-3 Sotheby's, London #181/R est:50000-70000
£81250 $130000 €121875 Illustration du lavabo (81x100cm-32x39in) s.d.65 s.i.d.verso acrylic paper on canvas prov.exhib.lit. 15-May-3 Christie's, Rockefeller NY #140/R est:100000-150000

£180000 $295200 €270000 J'accours (194x129cm-76x51in) s.d.64 s.i.d.verso vinyl on canvas prov.exhib.lit. 5-Feb-3 Christie's, London #29/R est:200000-300000
£227848 $360000 €341772 Le noctambule (116x89cm-46x35in) s.d.44 prov.exhib.lit. 13-Nov-2 Christie's, Rockefeller NY #64/R est:400000-600000
£312500 $500000 €468750 Rencontre - paysage et trois figures (89x116cm-35x46in) s.d.50 burlap prov.exhib.lit. 14-May-3 Christie's, Rockefeller NY #10/R est:650000-750000
£320000 $524800 €480000 Dingue Flibuste (100x81cm-39x32in) s.d.55 s.i.d.55 verso prov.exhib.lit. 6-Feb-3 Sotheby's, London #25/R est:400000
£341772 $540000 €512658 Barbu hirsute (47x38cm-19x15in) s.d.46 verso s. on stretcher oil sand stones rope gold foil prov. 13-Nov-2 Sotheby's, New York #211/R est:180000-220000
£350000 $584500 €525000 L'homme a sa table (129x96cm-51x38in) d.Fevrier 51 stretcher prov.exhib.lit. 25-Jun-3 Sotheby's, London #28/R est:400000-600000
£632911 $1000000 €949367 Mademoiselle Neon (91x73cm-36x29in) s.d.1948 verso prov.lit. 13-Nov-2 Christie's, Rockefeller NY #17/R est:900000-1200000

Prints

£1950 $3022 €3100 Lieux desoles (24x22cm-9x9in) s.num.11/30 col lithograph. 30-Oct-2 Artcurial Briest, Paris #530/R est:1000-1500
£2201 $3500 €3302 Jeux et travaux (66x51cm-26x20in) s.i.num.18/60 col lithograph. 29-Apr-3 Christie's, Rockefeller NY #472/R est:3500-4500
£2244 $3478 €3500 Ingenue (29x21cm-11x8in) s.i.d.1944 lithograph. 6-Dec-2 Hauswedell & Nolte, Hamburg #107/R est:4000
£2400 $3720 €3600 Organisme (67x89cm-26x35in) s.num.29/50 col screenprint. 3-Dec-2 Christie's, London #116/R est:2500-3500
£2436 $3776 €3800 Le guerrier (30x17cm-12x7in) s.i. col lithograph. 6-Dec-2 Hauswedell & Nolte, Hamburg #109/R est:5000
£2710 $4200 €4065 Site avec trois personnages (69x102cm-27x40in) init.d.1976 num.40/50 col screenprint. 25-Sep-2 Christie's, Rockefeller NY #265/R est:3500-4500
£3774 $6000 €5661 Faits memorables II (66x90cm-26x35in) init.d.num.46/70 col lithograph. 2-May-3 Sotheby's, New York #429/R est:6000-8000
£4487 $7000 €6731 Faits memorables (75x98cm-30x39in) init.d.num.58/70 col screenprint. 5-Nov-2 Christie's, Rockefeller NY #145/R est:8000-10000
£4500 $7020 €6750 L'homme au chapeau (52x38cm-20x15in) s.d.1961 num.26/50 col lithograph. 10-Oct-2 Sotheby's, London #237/R est:5000-7000
£5449 $8500 €8174 Suite de visages III (28x38cm-11x15in) s.i.d.num.2/4 col lithograph prov. 5-Nov-2 Christie's, Rockefeller NY #144/R est:6000-8000
£6918 $11000 €10377 Parcours (51x58cm-20x23in) init.d.num.51/80 col screenprint silk scroll box. 2-May-3 Sotheby's, New York #430/R est:7000-9000

Sculpture

£65000 $108550 €94250 Figure adossee (83x43x17cm-33x17x7in) init.d.68 painted polyester prov.exhib.lit. 27-Jun-3 Christie's, London #145/R est:20000-30000
£126582 $200000 €189873 Dame aux Pieds Menus (185x78cm-73x31in) init.d.71 i.num.25 verso wall relief epoxy paint polystyrene. 14-Nov-2 Christie's, Rockefeller NY #161/R est:150000-200000
£175000 $280000 €262500 Siegeant (153x50x50cm-60x20x20in) init.d.67 painted polyurethane prov.lit. 15-May-3 Christie's, Rockefeller NY #141/R est:200000-300000

Works on paper

£3000 $5010 €4350 Personnage (21x13cm-8x5in) s.i.d.Dec 1963 i.verso ball point pen lit. 24-Jun-3 Sotheby's, Olympia #79/R est:3000-4000
£5031 $7849 €8000 Big boy, portrait de Camille Renault dans son restaurant (28x28cm-11x11in) s. pen crayon cardboard prov.lit. 11-Oct-2 Binoche, Paris #134/R est:10000-15000
£5063 $8000 €7595 Porte de L'Oasis avec traces de pas dans le sable (33x25cm-13x10in) s.d.1948 col crayon. 3-Apr-3 Boos Gallery, Michigan #257/R est:9000-11000
£6500 $10660 €9750 Wall of stones with entrance blocked off by planks (26x24cm-10x9in) init.d.56 pencil prov.lit. 7-Feb-3 Sotheby's, London #222/R est:3000-4000
£6875 $11000 €10313 Situation CVI, 26 fevrier 1979 (35x25cm-14x10in) init.d.79 felt tip pen collage on paper prov.exhib.lit. 14-May-3 Sotheby's, New York #235/R est:12000-18000
£6944 $11458 €10000 Composition (50x64cm-20x25in) s.d. W/C gouache wax crayon. 1-Jul-3 Rossini, Paris #4/R
£8364 $13216 €12546 Composition M 44 (27x21cm-11x8in) init.d.66 Indian ink prov. 1-Apr-3 Rasmussen, Copenhagen #143/R est:100000-125000 (D.KR 90000)
£8387 $13000 €12581 Portrait d'homme (33x25cm-13x10in) init.d.74 col crayon felt tip marker paper collage prov.lit. 26-Sep-2 Christie's, Rockefeller NY #731/R est:12000-18000
£8491 $13160 €13500 Paulhan (20x14cm-8x6in) s.i.d.VII 45 pen Indian ink wash dr prov.lit. 30-Oct-2 Artcurial Briest, Paris #415/R est:10000-15000
£9494 $15000 €14241 Paysage avec nuage (41x25cm-16x10in) s.d.74 crayon marker collage prov.lit. 13-Nov-2 Sotheby's, New York #325/R est:15000-20000
£11000 $18040 €16500 Personnage costume - maquette for Le Mage (45x27cm-18x11in) s.init.d.71 felt tip pen paper collage prov.lit. 6-Feb-3 Christie's, London #667/R est:7000-9000
£11392 $17772 €18000 Site avec sept personnages (43x35cm-17x14in) mono.d.1981 Indian ink prov.lit. 31-Jul-2 Tajan, Paris #59/R est:20000-25000
£12903 $20000 €19355 Portrait d'Andre Dhotel (40x26cm-16x10in) s.d.46 graphite paper on rice paper prov. 26-Sep-2 Christie's, Rockefeller NY #723/R est:20000-30000
£15190 $24000 €22785 Site avec quinze personnages (51x35cm-20x14in) init.d.80 brush ink graphite felt tip prov.lit. 14-Nov-2 Christie's, Rockefeller NY #209/R est:20000-25000
£16000 $26240 €24000 Developpement horizontal (25x51cm-10x20in) init. d.2 janvier 74 verso col pen collage cardboard prov.lit. 7-Feb-3 Sotheby's, London #223/R est:10000-15000
£18065 $28542 €28000 Dans l'oasis (33x24cm-13x9in) s.d.1948 col crayon lit. 19-Dec-2 Delvaux, Paris #22/R est:35000
£22000 $36080 €33000 Palmeraie (55x44cm-22x17in) s.d.48 gouache. 6-Feb-3 Christie's, London #602/R est:20000-30000
£22436 $35224 €35000 Palmeraie avec petit soleil jaune (43x54cm-17x21in) s.d.48 peinture a la colle paper prov.lit. 11-Dec-2 Artcurial Briest, Paris #706a/R est:45000
£28000 $45920 €42000 Quatre Arabes (30x41cm-12x16in) s.d.48 gouache ink prov.lit. 6-Feb-3 Christie's, London #603/R est:25000-35000
£44872 $70449 €70000 Untitled (74x92cm-29x36in) mixed media on canvas exec.1952 prov. 11-Dec-2 Artcurial Briest, Paris #707/R est:75000
£46875 $75000 €70313 Bowery bum (47x33cm-19x13in) s.d.51 brush black ink W/C prov.exhib.lit. 14-May-3 Sotheby's, New York #158/R est:30000-40000
£52000 $85280 €78000 Deux Bedouins au desert (33x41cm-13x16in) s.d.47 gouache paper on canvas executed 1947-1948 prov.lit. 6-Feb-3 Christie's, London #604/R est:35000-45000

DUCARUGE, Léon Pierre (1843-1911) French

£793 $1261 €1150 Place dans le midi de la France (25x32cm-10x13in) s. d.1890 verso cardboard. 4-Mar-3 Livinec, Gaudcheau & Jezequel, Rennes #26

DUCASSE, Louis (1881-1939) French

£1310 $2070 €1900 Portrait de petit garcon (75x36cm-30x14in) s.d.1929 panel. 4-Apr-3 Tajan, Paris #1

DUCAYER, Jean (17th C) French

£5000 $7750 €7800 Portrait de la Comtesse de Crussol (34x27cm-13x11in) s.d.1638 panel. 4-Dec-2 Libert, Castor, Paris #45/R est:6000

DUCCIO DI BUONINSEGNA (attrib) (13/14th C) Italian

£94595 $147568 €140000 Blessing Christ (28x22cm-11x9in) tempera panel exhib.lit.prov. 27-Mar-3 Dorotheum, Vienna #42/R

DUCHAMP, Marcel (1887-1968) French

Prints

£3846 $6000 €5769 An original revolutionary faucet, mirrorical return (25x20cm-10x8in) s.d.num.81/100 black red etching. 5-Nov-2 Christie's, Rockefeller NY #146/R est:5000-8000
£6410 $10000 €9615 L H O O Q shaved (21x14cm-8x6in) s.i. col reproduction playing card on invitation edition of 100. 5-Nov-2 Christie's, Rockefeller NY #147/R est:10000-15000
£45000 $73800 €67500 Boite en valise. s. miniature replicas prov.lit. 5-Feb-3 Sotheby's, London #195/R est:35000
£164384 $256438 €240000 Obligations pour la roulette de Monte Carlo (32x20cm-13x8in) col lithograph exhib.lit. 14-Apr-3 Laurence Calmels, Paris #4044/R est:60000

Sculpture

£5063 $7899 €8000 Rotorelief (38x38x9cm-15x15x4in) s. num.85/150 mobile sculpture. 31-Jul-2 Tajan, Paris #69/R est:8000-10000

Works on paper
£47945 $75274 €70000 Mediocrite (16x20cm-6x8in) s.d.12 crayon. 15-Apr-3 Laurence Calmels, Paris #4272/R est:120000
£48000 $80160 €69600 L.H.O.O.Q. (30x23cm-12x9in) s.i. pencil gouache over colour executed 1964 prov.lit. 24-Jun-3 Sotheby's, London #240/R est:50000-70000

DUCHAMP, Suzanne (1889-1963) French
£1795 $2818 €2800 Jeux du bassin (60x81cm-24x32in) s. prov. 24-Nov-2 Laurence Calmels, Paris #106/R

DUCHARME, Rejean (?) Canadian?
Works on paper
£325 $511 €488 Ferme ton parachute (99x65cm-39x26in) s.i.d.87 verso mixed media. 12-Dec-2 Iegor de Saint Hippolyte, Montreal #26 (C.D 800)

DUCHATEAU, Hugo (1938-) Belgian
Works on paper
£468 $748 €650 Composition (105x75cm-41x30in) s.d.1976 pastel pencil. 17-May-3 De Vuyst, Lokeren #161

DUCIS, Louis (1775-1847) French
Works on paper
£297 $425 €446 View of a classical garden with a troubadour and a woman (40x32cm-16x13in) pen ink black white chk. 23-Jan-3 Swann Galleries, New York #298/R

DUCK, Jan le (1630-1676) Dutch
Works on paper
£4516 $7000 €6774 Seated man with monkey on his shoulders (25x15cm-10x6in) pen bistre prov. 7-Dec-2 South Bay, Long Island #137/R

DUCKER, Eugène Gustav (1841-1916) German
£540 $902 €783 Portrait of a mother and child, seated three quarter length turned to the right (29x23cm-11x9in) s. board. 17-Jun-3 Rosebery Fine Art, London #567/R
£570 $889 €900 Hayricks in extensive landscape (34x53cm-13x21in) s. canvas on panel lit. 14-Sep-2 Bergmann, Erlangen #777/R
£1474 $2329 €2300 Stormy sea (43x61cm-17x24in) s. 16-Nov-2 Lempertz, Koln #1455/R est:2500
£2138 $3314 €3400 Beach (62x93cm-24x37in) s. 2-Nov-2 Hans Stahl, Toestorf #28/R est:3500
Works on paper
£256 $390 €400 Ostsee coast with wooden jetty and fishing nets (17x25cm-7x10in) s. w/C. 17-Aug-2 Hans Stahl, Toestorf #38/R

DUCKER, Jack M (fl.1910-1930) British
£400 $652 €600 Lakeland landscape at sunset (50x76cm-20x30in) s. 12-Feb-3 Bonhams, Knightsbridge #272/R

DUCKETT, Charles H (fl.1905-1940) British
£600 $1002 €870 Grecian women in a temple (52x72cm-20x28in) 23-Jun-3 Bonhams, Bath #179
£800 $1336 €1160 Portrait of the artist's wife, Mrs Duckett (125x75cm-49x30in) s.d.1908. 23-Jun-3 Bonhams, Bath #171

DUCKETT, Thomas (1804-1878) British
Sculpture
£900 $1387 €1350 Bust of T Miller (97cm-38in) s.i.d.1868 white marble. 5-Sep-2 Sotheby's, Olympia #102/R est:1000-1500

DUCKWORTH, Ruth (1919-) British
£800 $1296 €1160 Nude figure (30x25cm-12x10in) init.d.1941. 29-Jul-3 Capes Dunn, Manchester #22/R

DUCLAUX, Jean Antoine (1783-1868) French
£5769 $8942 €9000 Colporteur et cheval (51x70cm-20x28in) s.d.1824 prov.exhib.lit. 6-Dec-2 Rieunier, Bailly-Pommery, Mathias, Paris #56/R est:14000
Works on paper
£476 $757 €700 Etudes d'hommes en manteau (23x35cm-9x14in) s. crayon chk. 24-Mar-3 Tajan, Paris #165

DUCLERE, Teodoro (1816-1867) Italian
£13793 $21793 €20000 Saint Peter's Bay (29x37cm-11x15in) s. 3-Apr-3 Porro, Milan #47/R est:28000
£17931 $28331 €26000 View of Naples Bay from Ischia (41x59cm-16x23in) cardboard lit. 3-Apr-3 Porro, Milan #44/R est:35000

DUCMELIC, Zdravko (1923-) Argentinian
£633 $1000 €950 Mediterranean landscape (40x55cm-16x22in) s.d.1960 canvas on board. 15-Nov-2 Naón & Cia, Buenos Aires #22/R

DUCORRON, Julien Joseph (1770-1848) French
£8000 $12480 €12000 Landscape with mill (65x95cm-26x37in) s.d.1818 panel. 17-Sep-2 Sotheby's, Olympia #216/R est:8000-12000

DUCQ, Joseph François (1762-1829) Flemish
Works on paper
£2979 $4974 €4200 Ange vu a mi corps, les mains jointes (54x42cm-21x17in) s.d.1788 col crayon. 19-Jun-3 Piasa, Paris #64/R est:3000-4000

DUCREUX, Alexandre Jules (18th C) French
Works on paper
£5068 $7905 €7500 Passage du Waal glace par les armees francaises le 9 Janvier 1795 (64x189cm-25x74in) s.i.d.1797 graphite pen ink wash prov.exhib. 27-Mar-3 Christie's, Paris #123/R est:12000

DUCREUX, Joseph (1735-1802) French
£23148 $37500 €34722 Portrait of Maximilien Francois Marie Isidore de Robespierre (48x36cm-19x14in) prov.lit. 23-Jan-3 Sotheby's, New York #101/R est:20000-30000

DUCREUX, Joseph (attrib) (1735-1802) French
£5000 $7850 €7500 Portrait of a gentleman in a salmon pink jacket (63x49cm-25x19in) 10-Dec-2 Bonhams, New Bond Street #267/R est:5000-7000

DUCROS, Abraham Louis Rodolphe (1748-1810) Swiss
Works on paper
£3000 $5010 €4350 Villa Montalto Negroni. La ville des Empereurs (32x46cm-13x18in) s. W/C engraved outlines two. 8-Jul-3 Christie's, London #85 est:4000-6000

DUCROS, Abraham Louis Rodolphe (attrib) (1748-1810) Swiss
Works on paper
£926 $1491 €1343 La vallee de Terni pres de Papigno (98x78cm-39x31in) i. verso W/C. 7-May-3 Dobiaschofsky, Bern #1122/R (S.FR 2000)

DUCROS, Abraham Louis Rodolphe and VOLPATO, Giovanni (18th C) Swiss/Italian
Works on paper
£1728 $2800 €2592 Arch of Septimus Severus (52x74cm-20x29in) s.i. W/C over engraving. 22-Jan-3 Christie's, Rockefeller NY #74/R est:5000

DUCROS, Edouard Auguste (1856-1936) French
£692 $1065 €1100 Cafe maure (33x46cm-13x18in) s.d.1927 cardboard. 23-Oct-2 Rabourdin & Choppin de Janvry, Paris #169/R

DUCROT, Victor (1852-1912) French
£15823 $24684 €25000 Pont Bonaparte a Lyon (140x223cm-55x88in) s.d.1889. 20-Oct-2 Anaf, Lyon #129/R est:30000-34000

DUDANT, Roger (1929-) Belgian
£342 $538 €500 Composition B 63 (40x50cm-16x20in) s.d.74. 15-Apr-3 Galerie Moderne, Brussels #379/R
£380 $592 €600 Paysage aux marais (66x92cm-26x36in) s.d.1961. 15-Oct-2 Vanderkindere, Brussels #87
£633 $1000 €1000 Composition (60x80cm-24x31in) s.d.64. 26-Nov-2 Palais de Beaux Arts, Brussels #238
£660 $1049 €950 Paysage abstrait (52x70cm-20x28in) s.d.1964. 29-Apr-3 Campo & Campo, Antwerp #105/R
Works on paper
£411 $650 €650 Composition (53x71cm-21x28in) s.d.64 mixed media. 26-Nov-2 Palais de Beaux Arts, Brussels #239
£629 $969 €1000 Composition (42x68cm-17x27in) s.d.1955 mixed media. 22-Oct-2 Campo & Campo, Antwerp #93

DUDFIELD, Gloria (20th C) American
£265 $425 €398 Gilroy (117x100cm-46x39in) s.d.61. 16-Mar-3 Butterfields, San Francisco #1065

DUDLEY, A (?) British?
Works on paper
£320 $496 €480 Still life of rhododendrons (53x76cm-21x30in) s.d.91 W/C. 3-Dec-2 Louis Taylor, Stoke on Trent #944

DUDLEY, Arthur (fl.1890-1907) British
Works on paper
£500 $810 €750 Still life of fruit (46x74cm-18x29in) s. W/C. 21-Jan-3 Bonhams, Knightsbridge #277/R
£550 $897 €825 Still life of fruits (27x75cm-11x30in) s.d.1893 W/C pair. 30-Jan-3 Lawrence, Crewkerne #646/R
£800 $1256 €1200 Still life with jug and fruit in a basket. Still life with fruit (26x76cm-10x30in) s.d.95 W/C pair. 10-Dec-2 Rosebery Fine Art, London #522/R
£1300 $2015 €1950 Still life of cherries in a basket and apples on a ledge (28x74cm-11x29in) s.d.1894 W/C two. 31-Oct-2 Duke & Son, Dorchester #73 est:250-450

DUDLEY, Charles (19/20th C) British
£270 $451 €392 Breaking cover (23x30cm-9x12in) s. board on panel. 24-Jun-3 Bonhams, Knowle #79
£380 $604 €570 Gillie seated with four hounds by the banks of a river (51x76cm-20x30in) s. 18-Mar-3 Capes Dunn, Manchester #569
£750 $1245 €1125 Study of a terrier seated beside a doorway (31x25cm-12x10in) s. 10-Jun-3 Bonhams, Leeds #161

DUDLEY, Frank V (1868-1957) American
£1258 $2000 €1887 Path through the dunes (46x41cm-18x16in) s. board painted c.1930. 2-Mar-3 Toomey, Oak Park #685/R est:2500-4500
£2097 $3250 €3146 Autumn in the Dunelands (51x56cm-20x22in) s. painted c.1920. 8-Dec-2 Toomey, Oak Park #685/R est:4000-6000
£4194 $6500 €6291 Forest stream (69x76cm-27x30in) s. painted c.1930. 8-Dec-2 Toomey, Oak Park #682/R est:8000-10000

DUDLEY, June (20th C) American
£2468 $3800 €3702 Cooling off (61x91cm-24x36in) acrylic. 25-Oct-2 Morris & Whiteside, Hilton Head Island #171 est:4500-5500

DUDLEY, Robert Charles (fl.1853-1891) British
£1227 $2000 €1841 Bull fight at Seville (37x55cm-15x22in) s. 16-Feb-3 Butterfields, San Francisco #2060 est:2000-3000

DUDLEY, Thomas (1857-1935) British
£500 $815 €725 Beverley Minster from the Barrack Road (31x41cm-12x16in) s.d.1879 i.verso. 17-Jul-3 Tennants, Leyburn #848
Works on paper
£320 $499 €480 Grange, Barrowdale (23x33cm-9x13in) mono.d.1881. 9-Oct-2 Andrew Hartley, Ilkley #678
£420 $655 €630 Lendal Bridge, York (20x30cm-8x12in) s.d.1886. 9-Oct-2 Andrew Hartley, Ilkley #683

DUDLEY-ROSS, J (?) ?
£1275 $2053 €1900 Vaches ecossaises (30x50cm-12x20in) s. 18-Feb-3 Galerie Moderne, Brussels #383/R est:1500-2000

DUDOVICH, Marcello (1878-1962) Italian
£1176 $1882 €1800 Sentinel (51x35cm-20x14in) s. tempera pastel. 4-Jan-3 Meeting Art, Vercelli #642/R
£1761 $2923 €2500 Alle corse (50x35cm-20x14in) s. tempera paper. 10-Jun-3 Finarte Semenzato, Milan #164/R est:800-1200

DUDREVILLE, Leonardo (1885-1974) Italian
£1088 $1731 €1600 Landscape around Pavia (18x26cm-7x10in) init.d.940 board. 18-Mar-3 Finarte, Milan #178/R
£1159 $1901 €1600 Paesaggio a Besnate sull'Adda (25x39cm-10x15in) s.d.940 s.i.verso panel. 27-May-3 Finarte, Milan #8/R est:1800-2200
£1522 $2496 €2100 Paesaggio a Borgotaro (25x39cm-10x15in) s.d.938 s.i.verso panel prov. 27-May-3 Finarte, Milan #7/R est:1800-2200
£4430 $7000 €7000 Borgotaro (24x33cm-9x13in) s.i.d.1907 verso cardboard. 30-Nov-2 Farsetti, Prato #684/R est:3000
Works on paper
£380 $592 €600 Man with mandolin (47x34cm-19x13in) chl paper on canvas. 14-Sep-2 Meeting Art, Vercelli #485

DUER, Douglas (1887-1964) American
£1346 $2100 €2019 Mounties and downed man on prairie (76x51cm-30x20in) s.d.1915 en grisaille. 9-Nov-2 Illustration House, New York #165/R est:2500-4000

DUESSEL, Henry A (19th C) American/German
£266 $425 €399 Autumn landscape with deer (74x124cm-29x49in) s. 12-Jan-3 William Jenack, New York #411

DUEZ, Ernest Ange (1846-1896) French
Works on paper
£1397 $2221 €2096 Girl on terrace with view of lake (70x52cm-28x20in) s. pastel. 5-Mar-3 Rasmussen, Copenhagen #1747/R est:25000 (D.KR 15000)

DUFAU, S (?) ?
£1392 $2200 €2200 Vue de port en Orient (21x41cm-8x16in) s. panel. 28-Nov-2 Piasa, Paris #49

DUFAUX, Frederic II (1852-1943) Swiss
£261 $404 €392 Col des planches. Courtisane assise (23x16cm-9x6in) s.i.d.juillet 1921 cardboard double-sided. 7-Dec-2 Galerie du Rhone, Sion #381/R (S.FR 600)
£617 $900 €926 Campagne (40x32cm-16x13in) s. 17-Jun-2 Philippe Schuler, Zurich #4266 (S.FR 1400)
£1087 $1696 €1631 Voiliers sur le Nil (24x36cm-9x14in) s.d.1889 exhib. 16-Sep-2 Philippe Schuler, Zurich #3365/R est:200-2400 (S.FR 2500)
£1391 $2157 €2087 Jeune femme au collier (65x49cm-26x19in) s. prov. 7-Dec-2 Galerie du Rhone, Sion #475/R est:4000-6000 (S.FR 3200)
£1391 $2157 €2087 Femme a la lecture (65x54cm-26x21in) s.d.1933 prov. 7-Dec-2 Galerie du Rhone, Sion #477/R est:4000-6000 (S.FR 3200)
£1478 $2306 €2217 Le Lido, Venise (32x40cm-13x16in) s.d.1882 canvas on board exhib. 16-Sep-2 Philippe Schuler, Zurich #3364/R est:1400-1600 (S.FR 3400)
£2009 $3134 €3014 Portrait of a young lady (46x33cm-18x13in) s.d.1924. 8-Nov-2 Dobiaschofsky, Bern #99/R est:5000 (S.FR 4600)
£4803 $7493 €7205 Female nude (59x49cm-23x19in) s.d.1906. 8-Nov-2 Dobiaschofsky, Bern #98/R est:10000 (S.FR 11000)
£6329 $9873 €10000 Toilette (102x66cm-40x26in) s. 20-Oct-2 Anaf, Lyon #130/R est:9000-10000
£23605 $37296 €35408 Peintre et femmes au bord du lac Majeur (21x33cm-8x13in) s.d.1909. 26-Nov-2 Phillips, Zurich #55/R est:3500-4000 (S.FR 55000)

DUFAUX, Henri (1878-?) French
£694 $1118 €1006 Nu debout (46x33cm-18x13in) s.i.d.44. 9-May-3 Dobiaschofsky, Bern #78/R (S.FR 1500)

DUFEU, Edouard (1840-1900) French
£818 $1267 €1300 Gondoliers a Venise (38x46cm-15x18in) s. 30-Oct-2 Coutau Begarie, Paris #159
£1500 $2505 €2250 Piazza San Marco, Venice (21x27cm-8x11in) s. panel prov. 18-Jun-3 Christie's, Kensington #137/R est:1500-2500

DUFF, Alison (1914-2000) New Zealander
Sculpture
£2431 $3792 €3647 Fantail (67x24x15cm-26x9x6in) init. steel prov. 8-Apr-3 Peter Webb, Auckland #139/R est:2500-3500 (NZ.D 7000)
£2951 $4604 €4427 Kingfisher (162x20x40cm-64x8x16in) brass copper prov. sold with base. 8-Apr-3 Peter Webb, Auckland #137/R est:4000-6000 (NZ.D 8500)
£2951 $4604 €4427 Tui (155x20x47cm-61x8x19in) init. copper brass steel prov. sold with base. 8-Apr-3 Peter Webb, Auckland #138/R est:4000-6000 (NZ.D 8500)

DUFFIELD, Mary Elizabeth (1819-1914) British
Works on paper
£280 $442 €420 Still life of fruit (18x33cm-7x13in) s.d.1887 W/C. 17-Dec-2 Gorringes, Lewes #1416
£550 $875 €825 Still life of a basket of fruit and roses on a ledge (53x42cm-21x17in) s. W/C. 25-Feb-3 Bonhams, Knightsbridge #176/R
£1400 $2002 €2100 Still life of apples and a birds nest standing on a wooden ledge (25x38cm-10x15in) s. W/C bodycol. 28-Feb-2 Greenslade Hunt, Taunton #383/R est:1200-1600

DUFFIELD, William (1816-1863) British
£270 $451 €392 Study of an old pensioner (42x34cm-17x13in) oval. 17-Jun-3 Bristol Auction Rooms #533
£500 $795 €750 Study of a pensioner (42x34cm-17x13in) i.stretcher oval. 6-Mar-3 Clevedon Sale Rooms #150/R
£1100 $1837 €1595 Still life of flowers and fruit, by a open window (61x51cm-24x20in) mono. 8-Jul-3 Bonhams, Knightsbridge #224/R est:1200-1800

£1905 $2934 €2858 Dead game, fruit in a basket, and green pot on a wooden table (51x61cm-20x24in) indis.sig. prov. 5-Sep-2 Christie's, Kensington #338/R est:2000-3000
£2065 $3200 €3098 Grapes, gourd, peach and Chinese vase on a table (25x35cm-10x14in) s.d.1841. 3-Dec-2 Christie's, Rockefeller NY #633/R est:4000-6000
£46000 $76360 €69000 Still life with peaches, pomegranate, grapes in a tazza and other fruits on draped chest (102x128cm-40x50in) s.d.1855. 10-Jun-3 Christie's, London #117/R est:25000-35000

DUFFIN, John (1965-) British
£750 $1223 €1088 Bikers jacket (128x82cm-50x32in) s.d.1988 verso. 15-Jul-3 Bonhams, Knightsbridge #186/R

DUFFY, Patrick Vincent (1836-1909) British
£801 $1170 €1250 Morning, Connemara, Co Galway (35x63cm-14x25in) s.i.verso. 10-Jun-2 Thomas Adams, Dublin #374

DUFFY, Rita (20th C) Irish?
£1370 $2151 €2000 Family affair (76x110cm-30x43in) s. board. 15-Apr-3 De Veres Art Auctions, Dublin #214/R est:2000-3000
Works on paper
£450 $698 €675 Dancer (45x15cm-18x6in) mixed media. 4-Dec-2 John Ross, Belfast #141b
£450 $698 €675 La Donna of the hair sprays (22x17cm-9x7in) s.d.88 mixed media. 4-Dec-2 John Ross, Belfast #189
£450 $698 €675 La Donna of the blue rinse I (22x17cm-9x7in) s.d.1988 mixed media. 4-Dec-2 John Ross, Belfast #190

DUFLOS, Robert Louis Raymond (1898-?) French
Works on paper
£750 $1170 €1125 Still life (38x30cm-15x12in) s.d.1956 pastel. 9-Oct-2 Andrew Hartley, Ilkley #745

DUFNER, Edward (1872-1957) American
£2201 $3500 €3302 Grandma's favourite hat (41x51cm-16x20in) s. canvas laid down painted c.1920. 4-May-3 Treadway Gallery, Cincinnati #514/R est:4000-6000

DUFOUR, Bernard (1922-) French
£322 $500 €483 Untitled, abstract composition (91x71cm-36x28in) s.d.1956. 29-Sep-2 Butterfields, Los Angeles #4419/R
£380 $589 €600 Composition (92x75cm-36x30in) s. d.verso. 28-Sep-2 Cornette de St.Cyr, Paris #295
£380 $589 €600 Composition (130x97cm-51x38in) s.d. 28-Sep-2 Cornette de St.Cyr, Paris #296/R

DUFRENE, François (1930-1992) French
£4167 $6542 €6500 Dessous d'affiche a la paysane II (81x54cm-32x21in) s.d.70 s.i.d.1970 verso torn posters. 24-Nov-2 Laurence Calmels, Paris #107/R

DUFRENOY, Georges (1870-1942) French
£500 $815 €750 Elegant figures before a French chateau (30x39cm-12x15in) s. 13-Feb-3 Christie's, Kensington #139/R
£644 $1017 €966 Mediterranean mountain village with castle (66x85cm-26x33in) s. panel. 29-Nov-2 Zofingen, Switzerland #2419/R (S.FR 1500)
£1135 $1895 €1600 Place de Vosges (81x65cm-32x26in) s.d. 23-Jun-3 Claude Boisgirard, Paris #97/R est:1000-1500

DUFRESNE, Annette (20th C) American
£252 $400 €365 Still life (61x46cm-24x18in) s.verso. 4-May-3 Treadway Gallery, Cincinnati #648/R
£377 $600 €547 Still life with pitcher and fruit (61x46cm-24x18in) s.verso painted c.1950. 4-May-3 Treadway Gallery, Cincinnati #649/R

DUFRESNE, Charles (1876-1938) French
£355 $574 €500 Paysage au pont (20x27cm-8x11in) s. oil Indian ink paper. 23-May-3 Binoche, Paris #6
£567 $919 €800 Le cheval bleu (22x24cm-9x9in) s. oil Indian ink paper. 23-May-3 Binoche, Paris #4
£567 $919 €800 Descente de croix (21x47cm-8x19in) s. paper painted c.1935. 23-May-3 Binoche, Paris #8
£641 $1006 €1000 Paul et VIrginie (17x17cm-7x7in) s. 20-Nov-2 Binoche, Paris #30
£1277 $2068 €1800 Trois femmes dans un jardin (33x38cm-13x15in) s. paper on canvas. 21-May-3 Cornette de St.Cyr, Paris #37/R est:2000-3000
£2014 $3304 €2800 Men at lion hunt (44x59cm-17x23in) s. cardboard. 3-Jun-3 Christie's, Amsterdam #33/R est:3000-5000
£4306 $6846 €6200 Les cavaliers (37x33cm-15x13in) s. oil graphite paper on canvas. 29-Apr-3 Artcurial Briest, Paris #63/R est:7000-8000
Works on paper
£355 $574 €500 Ville Orientale (14x21cm-6x8in) s. ink W/C gouache. 23-May-3 Binoche, Paris #12/R
£567 $919 €800 Scene exotique (23x18cm-9x7in) s. gouache. 23-May-3 Binoche, Paris #9/R
£1056 $1754 €1500 Leda et le cygne (33x41cm-13x16in) s. gouache paper on canvas. 15-Jun-3 Anaf, Lyon #64/R est:1500-1800

DUFRESNE, Francois (1930-1982) French
Works on paper
£4000 $6520 €6000 Untitled (85x136cm-33x54in) s.d.62 decollage. 3-Feb-3 Sotheby's, Olympia #90/R est:4000-6000

DUFY, Jean (1888-1964) French
£755 $1177 €1200 Landscape (81x45cm-32x18in) s. 8-Oct-2 Ansorena, Madrid #634/R
£3145 $5000 €4718 Nature morte aux fruits (24x35cm-9x14in) s. lit. 27-Feb-3 Christie's, Rockefeller NY #120/R est:9000
£8000 $13120 €12000 Nature morte au panier de fruits (61x50cm-24x20in) s.d.1928 paper on canvas. 4-Feb-3 Christie's, London #279/R est:15000
£8861 $14000 €13292 Circus musicians (51x61cm-20x24in) s. prov. 1-Dec-2 Susanin's, Chicago #5006/R
£9032 $14000 €13548 Paris, place pigalle (38x46cm-15x18in) s. 26-Sep-2 Christie's, Rockefeller NY #581/R est:14000-18000
£9500 $14725 €14250 Venise (46x38cm-18x15in) s.d.29. 5-Dec-2 Christie's, Kensington #139/R est:8000-12000
£9655 $15448 €14000 Concours hippique (33x46cm-13x18in) s. 12-Mar-3 Rabourdin & Choppin de Janvry, Paris #150/R est:18000
£12500 $19625 €19500 Le battage des bles (24x45cm-9x18in) s. panel. 16-Dec-2 Chochon-Barre & Allardi, Paris #43/R est:18000-20000
£12821 $19872 €20000 Paysage du Limousin (64x81cm-25x32in) s.d.24. 4-Dec-2 Lempertz, Koln #668/R est:20000-22000
£13836 $22000 €20754 Musiciens du cirque (50x61cm-20x24in) s. prov. 27-Feb-3 Christie's, Rockefeller NY #114/R est:28000
£15337 $25000 €23006 Haute ecole academique (73x60cm-29x24in) s. painted c.1925-26 prov.lit. 12-Feb-3 Sotheby's, New York #125/R est:25000-35000
£15528 $25000 €23292 Entree du port de Honfleur (27x35cm-11x14in) s. prov. 7-May-3 Sotheby's, New York #319/R est:12000-18000
£18000 $29520 €27000 Paris, la Seine vers Notre-Dame (46x55cm-18x22in) s. prov. 4-Feb-3 Christie's, London #276/R est:20000
£23006 $37500 €34509 Les pivoines (81x65cm-32x26in) s.d.22 prov. 12-Feb-3 Sotheby's, New York #124/R est:20000-30000
£24038 $37500 €36057 Paris, le moulin de la galette (46x55cm-18x22in) s. prov. 6-Nov-2 Sotheby's, New York #341/R est:25000-35000
£34839 $54000 €52259 Place de la concorde (54x73cm-21x29in) s. prov. 26-Sep-2 Christie's, Rockefeller NY #528/R est:25000-35000
£38344 $62500 €57516 Le port (60x73cm-24x29in) s. 12-Feb-3 Sotheby's, New York #108/R est:30000-40000
£39877 $65000 €59816 Caleches et cavaliers au Bois de Boulogne (50x61cm-20x24in) s. painted c.1950-52. 12-Feb-3 Sotheby's, New York #104/R est:30000-40000
£42000 $68880 €63000 Ile-de-la-Cite, Paris (50x61cm-20x24in) s. prov. 4-Feb-3 Christie's, London #275/R est:35000
£42000 $70140 €60900 La maison bleue (73x92cm-29x36in) s.d.27. 24-Jun-3 Sotheby's, London #189/R est:18000-25000
Works on paper
£282 $468 €400 Le village (28x43cm-11x17in) bears st.sig. ink dr. 11-Jun-3 Beaussant & Lefèvre, Paris #32/R
£309 $438 €500 Port de Benodet (22x28cm-9x11in) st.sig. ink dr. 16-Mar-3 Eric Pillon, Calais #232/R
£321 $456 €520 Villefranche (25x40cm-10x16in) st.sig. ink dr. 16-Mar-3 Eric Pillon, Calais #233/R
£343 $522 €515 Stockholm (25x43cm-10x17in) s. pencil W/C. 16-Aug-2 Lilla Bukowskis, Stockholm #901 (S.KR 5000)
£381 $610 €530 Le port mediterraneen (25x40cm-10x16in) st.sig. blue ink dr. 18-May-3 Eric Pillon, Calais #159/R
£443 $687 €700 Rome, place animee (30x41cm-12x16in) st.sig. ball point pen dr. 29-Sep-2 Eric Pillon, Calais #264/R
£494 $781 €741 Promenade (43x54cm-17x21in) s. Indian ink. 28-Apr-3 Bukowskis, Stockholm #301/R (S.KR 6500)
£577 $906 €900 Coquillages (13x61cm-5x24in) st.sig. gouache. 16-Dec-2 Rabourdin & Choppin de Janvry, Paris #95
£629 $1000 €944 Deux femmes (27x27cm-11x11in) st.sig. pen ink prov. 27-Feb-3 Christie's, Rockefeller NY #67/R
£629 $1000 €944 Vue de Copenhague (31x43cm-12x17in) with sig.i. pen ink. 4-Mar-3 Swann Galleries, New York #275/R est:1200-1800
£709 $1149 €1000 Paysage (45x53cm-18x21in) s. chl. 26-May-3 Joron-Derem, Paris #17/R est:1200-1800
£769 $1208 €1200 Fleurs dans un interieur (32x24cm-13x9in) s.d.1919 gouache. 10-Dec-2 Renaud, Paris #57
£800 $1272 €1200 Place Vendome (28x40cm-11x16in) st.sig. pencil. 20-Mar-3 Sotheby's, Olympia #122/R
£1026 $1600 €1539 Nature morte aux fruits (28x24cm-11x9in) s.d.1922 pastel. 14-Oct-2 Butterfields, San Francisco #2005/R est:2500-3500
£1210 $1911 €1815 Paysage ensoliel (16x20cm-6x8in) indis.sig. W/C pen ink. 18-Nov-2 Waddingtons, Toronto #217/R est:4000-6000 (C.D 3000)
£1650 $2690 €2475 Etoile with L'Arc de Triomphe, horses and carriages in the foreground (27x37cm-11x15in) s. W/C. 28-Jan-3 Bristol Auction Rooms #449/R est:500-700

£1795 $2836 €2800 Paysage du Limousin (58x44cm-23x17in) s.d.1925 W/C. 15-Nov-2 Laurence Calmels, Paris #4a/R
£1884 $3090 €2600 Ile de France mit Notre Dame (32x40cm-13x16in) s. W/C over pencil. 29-May-3 Lempertz, Koln #594/R est:2500
£1923 $3000 €2885 Canal a Venise. Etude de femme (34x27cm-13x11in) s. W/C pencil double-sided. 14-Oct-2 Butterfields, San Francisco #2007/R est:2500-3500
£2200 $3498 €3300 Fleurs sur un balcon (33x25cm-13x10in) s.d.1919 W/C over pencil. 20-Mar-3 Sotheby's, Olympia #56/R est:3000-5000
£2264 $3509 €3600 Bouquet de fleurs devant la fenetre (55x41cm-22x16in) s. W/C gouache exec.c.1935. 30-Oct-2 Artcurial Briest, Paris #204/R est:4000-5000
£3125 $5000 €4688 Place de la Concorde (46x61cm-18x24in) s. W/C. 15-Mar-3 Selkirks, St. Louis #677/R est:5000-7000
£3291 $5101 €5200 Port de l'Ile d'Yeu (48x63cm-19x25in) s.i.d.1930 pencil dr prov. 28-Sep-2 Christie's, Paris #24/R est:900-1200
£3481 $5430 €5500 Bouquet de fleurs (58x47cm-23x19in) s.d.1924 W/C prov. 20-Oct-2 Claude Boisgirard, Paris #5/R est:2000-3000
£3781 $6314 €5482 At the theatre (42x55cm-17x22in) s. gouache W/C. 24-Jun-3 Koller, Zurich #111/R est:5000-8000 (S.FR 8355)
£5044 $7515 €7566 Paris street scene (51x66cm-20x26in) s. gouache prov. 26-Jun-2 Iegor de Saint Hippolyte, Montreal #27/R (C.D 11500)
£5782 $9194 €8500 Musiciens au cirque (48x59cm-19x23in) s.d.1926 W/C. 24-Mar-3 Claude Boisgirard, Paris #76/R
£6410 $10000 €9615 Fleurs. s. gouache. 22-Sep-2 Susanin's, Chicago #5121/R est:12000-16000
£6918 $11000 €10377 Fleurs et coquillages (22x75cm-9x30in) bears sig. gouache paper on board. 27-Feb-3 Christie's, Rockefeller NY #111/R est:7000
£7500 $11625 €11250 Chateau (30x62cm-12x24in) s. W/C bodycol. 5-Dec-2 Christie's, Kensington #126/R est:5000-7000
£7895 $12790 €12000 Les ballets de Katherine Dunham (36x56cm-14x22in) s. gouache exec.c.1945 prov.lit. 22-Jan-3 Tajan, Paris #194/R est:12000-15000
£8500 $13175 €12750 Honfleur, jetee de l'est (41x59cm-16x23in) s. indis. i. W/C bodycol. 5-Dec-2 Christie's, Kensington #129/R est:4000-6000
£8940 $14573 €13500 Le carousel du Louvre (39x54cm-15x21in) s. gouache W/C. 2-Feb-3 Muizon & Le Coent, Paris #51
£9000 $14312 €13500 Le port du Havre (46x61cm-18x24in) s. gouache W/C paper on canvas. 20-Mar-3 Sotheby's, Olympia #93/R est:8000-10000
£9028 $14264 €13000 Jardins du Carrousel (43x57cm-17x22in) s. gouache. 25-Apr-3 Piasa, Paris #10/R est:12000
£9091 $15182 €13000 Au moulin, chasse a courre (48x62cm-19x24in) s. gouache prov.lit. 26-Jun-3 Tajan, Paris #114/R est:12000-15000
£10559 $17000 €15839 Paris la place de la Concorde (46x56cm-18x22in) s. W/C gouache prov. 18-Feb-3 Arthur James, Florida #409
£10692 $17000 €16038 Jardin des Tuileries (48x60cm-19x24in) s. gouache exec.c.1955-57. 27-Feb-3 Christie's, Rockefeller NY #98/R est:18000
£12000 $19080 €18000 Clowns musiciens (31x45cm-12x18in) s. W/C gouache prov. 20-Mar-3 Sotheby's, Olympia #91/R est:6000-8000
£12821 $20000 €19232 Scene du Cirque (48x63cm-19x25in) s. gouache W/C paper on canvas prov. 5-Nov-2 Phillips, New York #118/R est:15000-20000
£13889 $21944 €20000 Course a attelages (43x57cm-17x22in) s. gouache. 25-Apr-3 Piasa, Paris #9/R est:12000
£14907 $24000 €22361 Paris, Place Blanche (49x63cm-19x25in) s. gouache W/C. 7-May-3 Sotheby's, New York #374/R est:20000-30000
£32209 $52500 €48314 Caleche et cavaliers (49x65cm-19x26in) s. gouache W/C paper on canvas prov. 12-Feb-3 Sotheby's, New York #115/R est:20000-30000
£32209 $52500 €48314 Vue de Villefranche sur Mer (48x60cm-19x24in) s. W/C gouache paper on panel executedc.1925. 12-Feb-3 Sotheby's, New York #120/R est:12000-18000

DUFY, Raoul (1877-1953) French

£2051 $3221 €3200 Jete de fleurs (59x49cm-23x19in) mono. paper lit. 24-Nov-2 Lesieur & Le Bars, Le Havre #40/R
£5161 $8000 €7742 Portrait de Freddy Homburger (51x41cm-20x16in) s.i. masonite prov.exhib.lit. 26-Sep-2 Christie's, Rockefeller NY #510/R est:10000-15000
£6129 $9500 €9194 Portrait de Regina Homburger (54x46cm-21x18in) s.i.d.1952 prov.exhib.lit. 26-Sep-2 Christie's, Rockefeller NY #509/R est:12000-16000
£12500 $19625 €19500 Marseille (24x33cm-9x13in) s.d.1903 cardboard. 22-Nov-2 Millon & Associes, Paris #63/R est:20000-25000
£12821 $20128 €20000 Marseille (24x33cm-9x13in) indis.sig. cardboard. 22-Nov-2 Millon & Associes, Paris #64/R est:20000-25000
£17000 $28390 €24650 La statue aux deux vasques (16x21cm-6x8in) st.sig. masonite prov.lit. 24-Jun-3 Sotheby's, London #190/R est:14000-18000
£19000 $31160 €28500 Paysage de Bourgogne (39x46cm-15x18in) s. prov. 4-Feb-3 Christie's, London #261/R est:20000
£22436 $35224 €35000 Paysage (13x25cm-5x10in) s.i.d.1941 panel lit. 10-Dec-2 Piasa, Paris #208/R est:15000
£24359 $38244 €38000 Paysage a la tonnelle (16x51cm-6x20in) panel exhib.lit. 10-Dec-2 Piasa, Paris #206/R est:30000
£26923 $42269 €42000 Paysage a la nymphe (15x51cm-6x20in) panel lit. 10-Dec-2 Piasa, Paris #201/R est:30000
£27950 $45000 €41925 La gare Saint Lazare (53x63cm-21x25in) st.sig. painted 1902. 7-May-3 Sotheby's, New York #177/R est:50000-70000
£29487 $46295 €46000 Repos des moissonneurs (17x40cm-7x16in) s.i. painted c.1946 exhib.lit. 10-Dec-2 Piasa, Paris #200/R est:35000
£30769 $48000 €46154 Jardin a Falaise (82x65cm-32x26in) s. painted 1902 prov.exhib.lit. 7-Nov-2 Christie's, Rockefeller NY #245/R est:60000-80000
£32692 $51327 €51000 Musique de Tintoret (17x40cm-7x16in) s.i. panel prov.exhib.lit. 10-Dec-2 Piasa, Paris #209/R est:35000
£34177 $52975 €54000 L'orchestre Mexicain (41x52cm-16x20in) s. cardboard on panel painted c.1951-52 prov.exhib.lit. 28 Sep-2 Christie's, Paris #36/R est:45000-60000
£46154 $72462 €72000 Depicage jaune (33x41cm-13x16in) s. prov.exhib.lit. 10-Dec-2 Piasa, Paris #202/R est:35000
£46474 $72500 €69711 Hommage a Claude Lorrain (46x38cm-18x15in) s. prov.lit. 6-Nov-2 Sotheby's, New York #327/R est:60000-80000
£48000 $80160 €69600 Le port et le pont transbordeur, Marseille (38x46cm-15x18in) s. cardboard painted c.1942 prov. 25-Jun-3 Christie's, London #179/R est:50000-70000
£48077 $75481 €75000 Depicage a la maison blanche (38x46cm-15x18in) s. painted 1945 prov.exhib.lit. 10-Dec-2 Piasa, Paris #207/R est:40000
£49000 $81830 €71050 L'orchestre Mexicain (41x52cm-16x20in) s. cardboard on panel painted c.1951-52 prov.exhib.lit. 25-Jun-3 Christie's, London #183/R est:50000-70000
£51242 $82500 €76863 Depiquage a la machine bleue (54x66cm-21x26in) s. painted 1948 prov.exhib.lit. 7-May-3 Sotheby's, New York #369/R est:70000-90000
£55901 $90000 €83852 L'eucalyptus (55x46cm-22x18in) s. painted c.1926-27 prov.lit. 7-May-3 Sotheby's, New York #320/R est:80000-100000
£57692 $90000 €86538 Nu au coquillage (65x54cm-26x21in) s. painted 1945 prov.exhib.lit. 7-Nov-2 Christie's, Rockefeller NY #316/R est:140000-180000
£60897 $95000 €91346 Le 14 Juillet (50x41cm-20x16in) s.i.d.1950 masonite prov.exhib.lit. 7-Nov-2 Christie's, Rockefeller NY #165/R est:100000-150000
£62821 $97372 €98000 Orchestre sur la place du village (18x39cm-7x15in) s.i.d.1942 panel lit. 9-Dec-2 Piasa, Paris #6/R est:40000-50000
£70000 $114800 €105000 Fontaine de vence (81x65cm-32x26in) s. prov.exhib.lit. 5-Feb-3 Sotheby's, London #138/R est:80000
£70513 $110000 €105770 Au bois de Boulogne (54x64cm-21x25in) painted 1909 prov.lit. 7-Nov-2 Christie's, Rockefeller NY #263/R est:120000-160000
£70513 $110705 €110000 Ateliers aux trois chevalets (54x65cm-21x26in) s. painted 1946 prov.exhib.lit. 10-Dec-2 Piasa, Paris #210/R est:70000
£73718 $115000 €110577 Bateaux bleus (46x55cm-18x22in) s.i. painted c.1950 prov.exhib.lit. 7-Nov-2 Christie's, Rockefeller NY #166/R est:70000-90000
£85000 $139400 €127500 Plage de Sainte-Adresse (60x80cm-24x31in) s. painted c.1905 prov.exhib.lit. 5-Feb-3 Sotheby's, London #135/R est:200000
£87413 $145979 €125000 Le Quai, Marseille (46x55cm-18x22in) s. prov.lit. 30-Jun-3 Artcurial Briest, Paris #81e/R est:130000-150000
£95000 $158650 €137750 Le hamac (65x81cm-26x32in) s.d.13 prov.exhib.lit. 24-Jun-3 Sotheby's, London #149/R est:60000-80000
£96273 $155000 €144410 Nu a la mappemonde (54x65cm-21x26in) s. paintec 1928 prov.exhib.lit. 8-May-3 Christie's, Rockefeller NY #223/R est:80000-100000
£135000 $225450 €195750 Villerville (48x108cm-19x43in) s. painted 1935 prov. 24-Jun-3 Sotheby's, London #180/R est:140000-180000
£153846 $240000 €230769 Villerville (66x81cm-26x32in) s. painted 1927 prov.lit. 6-Nov-2 Sotheby's, New York #193/R est:250000-350000
£160000 $262400 €240000 Mozart (73x61cm-29x24in) s. painted 1915 prov.exhib.lit. 5-Feb-3 Sotheby's, London #142/R est:150000
£160839 $268601 €230000 Le pin a Golfe Juan (81x100cm-32x39in) s. lit. 30-Jun-3 Artcurial Briest, Paris #68/R est:230000-280000
£173077 $268269 €270000 Atelier au champ de ble (65x81cm-26x32in) s. painted 1942 exhib.lit. 9-Dec-2 Piasa, Paris #15/R est:150000-200000
£192308 $300000 €288462 La baie de Nice aux deux promeneurs (62x107cm-24x42in) s.i.d.1923 prov.exhib.lit. 6-Nov-2 Sotheby's, New York #184/R est:300000-400000
£253205 $392468 €395000 Concert orange (60x73cm-24x29in) s. painted 1948 exhib.lit. 9-Dec-2 Piasa, Paris #13/R est:200000-300000
£500000 $775000 €780000 Moulin de la Galette (130x162cm-51x64in) s.i. painted 1943 after Renoir exhib.lit. 9-Dec-2 Piasa, Paris #14/R est:1000000-1300000

Prints

£2759 $4386 €4000 Jeux de la mer (36x51cm-14x20in) s.num.1/25 col print htd gouache. 5-Mar-3 Doutrebente, Paris #5/R est:1200-1500
£2767 $4400 €4151 Au port (48x63cm-19x25in) s.num.71/200 col lithograph executed c.1940. 3-Mar-3 Swann Galleries, New York #80/R est:4000-6000
£4403 $7000 €6605 Le paddock (43x59cm-17x23in) col lithograph. 3-Mar-3 Swann Galleries, New York #81/R est:5000-8000

Works on paper

£345 $576 €500 Personnages chez le modiste (15x23cm-6x9in) st.init. graphite. 9-Jul-3 Cornette de St.Cyr, Paris #162
£432 $691 €600 Coquelicots et orge sur fond bleu (32x28cm-13x11in) gouache lit. 18-May-3 Eric Pillon, Calais #175/R
£464 $756 €700 Nature morte a la console (20x13cm-8x5in) mono.i.d.24-3-47 ball point pen. 31-Jan-3 Charbonneaux, Paris #79

£486 $773 €700 Tarascon (10x13cm-4x5in) pencil dr tracing paper lit. 29-Apr-3 Artcurial Briest, Paris #36
£542 $900 €786 Untitled (30x25cm-12x10in) pencil htd bodycol. 13-Jun-3 Du Mouchelle, Detroit #2077/R
£576 $921 €800 Les tulipes (30x3cm-12x1in) gouache lit. 18-May-3 Eric Pillon, Calais #173/R
£581 $900 €872 La visite de Dr Homburger (26x38cm-10x15in) s.i. pen black ink prov.exhib.lit. 3-Dec-2 Christie's, Rockefeller NY #44/R
£641 $1006 €1000 Paysage aux oiseaux (21x26cm-8x10in) graphite dr lit. 10-Dec-2 Piasa, Paris #282
£645 $1000 €968 Tucson, Arizona (21x28cm-8x11in) s.i. pen black ink board exhib. 3-Dec-2 Christie's, Rockefeller NY #42/R
£683 $1094 €950 Les fleurs rouges (54x39cm-21x15in) gouache lit. 18-May-3 Eric Pillon, Calais #174/R
£743 $1159 €1100 Fleurs (19x14cm-7x6in) st.mono. W/C gouache. 28-Mar-3 Charbonneaux, Paris #66/R
£759 $1267 €1100 Moisson (30x47cm-12x19in) bears init. pencil dr tracing paper exec.c.1930 lit. 10-Jul-3 Artcurial Briest, Paris #44
£791 $1298 €1100 Paris, Notre Dame et la Seine (51x44cm-20x17in) st.sig. conte crayon. 4-Jun-3 Marc Kohn, Paris #42 est:1500-1800
£800 $1272 €1200 Deux roses (40x26cm-16x10in) st.init. pencil exec.c.1922. 20-Mar-3 Sotheby's, Olympia #126/R
£800 $1272 €1200 Scene de chasse persane (47x31cm-19x12in) W/C gouache pencil. 20-Mar-3 Sotheby's, Olympia #129/R
£800 $1272 €1200 Bateaux a quai (21x27cm-8x11in) st.init. pencil exec.c.1924. 20-Mar-3 Sotheby's, Olympia #177/R
£903 $1435 €1300 Etude du nu (50x33cm-20x13in) st.mono. graphite dr lit. 29-Apr-3 Artcurial Briest, Paris #37 est:700-900
£962 $1510 €1500 Petite route (32x49cm-13x19in) graphite dr lit. 10-Dec-2 Piasa, Paris #287
£1007 $1612 €1400 La salle a manger (31x40cm-12x16in) st.mono. pencil dr. 18-May-3 Charbonneaux, Paris #144 est:800-1000
£1026 $1610 €1600 Cheminee fumante (25x32cm-10x13in) s. crayon lit. 10-Dec-2 Piasa, Paris #65/R
£1042 $1646 €1500 Cheval (23x34cm-9x13in) studio st. crayon stump dr. 25-Apr-3 Piasa, Paris #86/R
£1049 $1752 €1500 Paris, la Tour Eiffel (31x40cm-12x16in) s.i.d. pencil dr lit. 26-Jun-3 Tajan, Paris #59/R est:2000-2500
£1079 $1770 €1500 Moissons (50x33cm-20x13in) st.sig. exec.c.1911 ink. 4-Jun-3 Marc Kohn, Paris #41 est:1500-1800
£1118 $1812 €1700 Statue equestre sur la Place de Victoires (50x65cm-20x26in) s. dr. 22-Jan-3 Tajan, Paris #143 est:2400-3000
£1154 $1812 €1800 Paysage de Normandie et clocher (28x44cm-11x17in) crayon dr exec.1932 lit. 10-Dec-2 Piasa, Paris #75/R
£1154 $1812 €1800 Paysage a la barriere (21x27cm-8x11in) graphite dr lit. 10-Dec-2 Piasa, Paris #286
£1154 $1812 €1800 Grands arbres (20x26cm-8x10in) graphite dr lit. 10-Dec-2 Piasa, Paris #295
£1223 $1920 €1835 Fleurs (35x25cm-14x10in) gouache prov. 23-Nov-2 Burkhard, Luzern #141/R est:2800-3400 (S.FR 2800)
£1282 $2013 €2000 Chalet aux arbres (35x44cm-14x17in) s. graphite dr lit. 10-Dec-2 Piasa, Paris #66/R
£1282 $2013 €2000 Cowes (35x54cm-14x21in) s.i. graphite dr. 10-Dec-2 Piasa, Paris #283
£1282 $2013 €2000 Bles (38x56cm-15x22in) s. chl dr prov.lit. 10-Dec-2 Piasa, Paris #280
£1282 $2013 €2000 Grand champ (33x49cm-13x19in) i. graphite dr exhib.lit. 10-Dec-2 Piasa, Paris #308
£1548 $2400 €2322 Portrait de Freddy Homburger (26x40cm-10x16in) s.i.d.1951 gouache W/C. 3-Dec-2 Christie's, Rockefeller NY #43/R est:2500-3500
£1600 $2528 €2400 Marigny (33x25cm-13x10in) st.init. brush ink gouache exec.1912. 3-Apr-3 Christie's, Kensington #94/R
£1603 $2516 €2500 Route de Boulou (50x66cm-20x26in) Chinese ink dr prov.lit. 10-Dec-2 Piasa, Paris #281
£1603 $2516 €2500 Paysage aux chevaux (32x49cm-13x19in) i. graphite dr exhib. 10-Dec-2 Piasa, Paris #310
£1677 $2600 €2516 Exercise pour la recuperation (26x38cm-10x15in) s.i.d.12 mai 1950 pen black ink exhib. 3-Dec-2 Christie's, Rockefeller NY #45/R est:1500-2500
£1700 $2618 €2550 Dufy et Berthe dans l'atelier de Boston (45x55cm-18x22in) st.sig. pencil. 23-Oct-2 Sotheby's, Olympia #668/R est:2000-3000
£1923 $3019 €3000 Gerbes (49x64cm-19x25in) s. wax crayon dr prov.lit. 10-Dec-2 Piasa, Paris #301/R
£2000 $3100 €3000 Le reception (49x65cm-19x26in) s. ink. 5-Dec-2 Christie's, Kensington #102/R est:2000-3000
£2051 $3221 €3200 Coupe de bois en foret (50x66cm-20x26in) s. Chinese ink dr exhib.lit. 10-Dec-2 Piasa, Paris #76/R
£2152 $3400 €3400 Two roses (62x43cm-24x17in) pencil gouache. 27-Nov-2 Dorotheum, Vienna #17/R est:3000-5000
£2222 $3534 €3200 Voilier (17x10cm-7x4in) W/C lit. 29-Apr-3 Artcurial Briest, Paris #68/R est:3000-4000
£2244 $3522 €3500 Trouville, la grille (38x56cm-15x22in) s.i.d.1928 crayon dr lit. 10-Dec-2 Piasa, Paris #74/R
£2244 $3522 €3500 Champ de ble (34x52cm-13x20in) s. crayon dr prov.lit. 10-Dec-2 Piasa, Paris #274
£2244 $3522 €3500 Eglise et cimetiere Saint-Jean (33x49cm-13x19in) graphite dr lit. 10-Dec-2 Piasa, Paris #289
£2244 $3522 €3500 Scene de depicage (50x66cm-20x26in) s. graphite dr prov.exhib.lit. 10-Dec-2 Piasa, Paris #296/R
£2244 $3522 €3500 Centrale electrique (50x65cm-20x26in) s. Chinese ink dr lit. 10-Dec-2 Piasa, Paris #302
£2244 $3522 €3500 Clocher dans les bles (33x52cm-13x20in) s. graphite dr prov.lit. 10-Dec-2 Piasa, Paris #311
£2390 $3800 €3585 Portrait de jeune fille (65x50cm-26x20in) s. brush ink. 27-Feb-3 Christie's, Rockefeller NY #115/R est:6000
£2483 $4146 €3600 La corrida (51x36cm-20x14in) s.d.54 W/C Indian ink. 10-Jul-3 Artcurial Briest, Paris #85/R est:3800-4500
£2564 $4026 €4000 Chateau de Brissac (50x66cm-20x26in) Chinese ink dr exec.1936 exhib.lit. 10-Dec-2 Piasa, Paris #77/R
£2564 $3974 €4000 Composition aux fleurs (44x63cm-17x25in) st.sig. W/C. 4-Dec-2 Pierre Berge, Paris #9/R
£2564 $4026 €4000 Repos des moissonneurs (50x66cm-20x26in) s. Chinese ink dr exhib.lit. 10-Dec-2 Piasa, Paris #273/R
£2564 $4026 €4000 Paysage (50x65cm-20x26in) Chinese ink dr prov.lit. 10-Dec-2 Piasa, Paris #292/R
£2564 $4026 €4000 Grille (50x66cm-20x26in) s. Chinese ink dr lit. 10-Dec-2 Piasa, Paris #300
£2564 $4026 €4000 Angers (50x66cm-20x26in) s. Chinese ink dr prov.exhib.lit. 10-Dec-2 Piasa, Paris #306
£2639 $4196 €3800 Sous-bois (65x50cm-26x20in) s. W/C black pencil lit. 29-Apr-3 Artcurial Briest, Paris #35/R est:3000-4000
£2715 $4534 €3937 La fontaine (24x64cm-9x25in) st.sig. pencil Indian ink. 24-Jun-3 Koller, Zurich #132a/R est:4000-6000 (S.FR 6000)
£2759 $4607 €4000 Regate a Cowes (33x53cm-13x21in) s.i. ink sepia wash exec.c.1929 exhib.lit. 10-Jul-3 Artcurial Briest, Paris #42/R est:4500-6000
£2885 $4529 €4500 Regates a Cowes (50x66cm-20x26in) s. crayon dr exec.c.1934-35 lit. 10-Dec-2 Piasa, Paris #70/R
£3000 $4770 €4500 Paysage de Normandie (35x24cm-14x9in) W/C over pencil prov.exhib. 20-Mar-3 Sotheby's, Olympia #92/R est:3000-4000
£3077 $4831 €4800 Ramasseurs de coques (44x56cm-17x22in) s. crayon dr exec.c.1920 lit. 10-Dec-2 Piasa, Paris #71/R
£3165 $5000 €5000 Reclining nude (49x65cm-19x26in) s.d.1929 Indian ink board. 30-Nov-2 Villa Grisebach, Berlin #386/R est:3000-4000
£3205 $5032 €5000 Paysage a la voiture (22x27cm-9x11in) wax crayon dr lit. 10-Dec-2 Piasa, Paris #277
£3205 $5032 €5000 Cuirasses (44x55cm-17x22in) s. graphite dr prov.lit. 10-Dec-2 Piasa, Paris #291/R
£3291 $5101 €5200 Vase de fleurs (18x25cm-7x10in) graphite htd white gouache dr. 29-Sep-2 Eric Pillon, Calais #228/R
£3478 $5426 €5217 Paddock (51x65cm-20x26in) s. Indian ink prov. 16-Sep-2 Philippe Schuler, Zurich #3018/R est:10000-12000 (S.FR 8000)
£3500 $5530 €5250 Jardins du Val d'Esquieres (50x65cm-20x26in) s. pen ink exec.1933. 3-Apr-3 Christie's, Kensington #105/R
£3526 $5535 €5500 Langres (50x68cm-20x27in) s. Chinese ink dr. 10-Dec-2 Piasa, Paris #284/R
£3526 $5535 €5500 Fez (44x59cm-17x23in) s. graphite dr prov.exhib.lit. 10-Dec-2 Piasa, Paris #297/R
£3526 $5535 €5500 Redaction des marrges (45x56cm-18x22in) s.i. Chinese ink dr prov.lit. 10-Dec-2 Piasa, Paris #293
£3548 $5500 €5322 Nice (44x55cm-17x22in) s.i. pen India ink prov.exhib. 26-Sep-2 Christie's, Rockefeller NY #512/R est:3000-4000
£3800 $6004 €5700 Marigny (32x49cm-13x19in) st.sig. brush ink exec.1912. 3-Apr-3 Christie's, Kensington #107/R
£3846 $6038 €6000 Depicage (50x65cm-20x26in) s. crayon dr prov.exhib.lit. 10-Dec-2 Piasa, Paris #278
£3846 $6038 €6000 Bles ou la faneuse (50x65cm-20x26in) s. crayon dr. prov.lit. 10-Dec-2 Piasa, Paris #290/R
£3846 $6038 €6000 Langres II (50x66cm-20x26in) Chinese ink dr prov.lit. 10-Dec-2 Piasa, Paris #303/R
£4487 $7045 €7000 Boinville (49x64cm-19x25in) s.i. crayon exec.1918 lit. 10-Dec-2 Piasa, Paris #67/R est:5000-7000
£4487 $7045 €7000 Chanteurs de rue (50x66cm-20x26in) s. Chinese ink dr prov.lit. 10-Dec-2 Piasa, Paris #279/R
£4500 $7110 €6750 Marigny (32x25cm-13x10in) st.init. brush ink exec.1912. 3-Apr-3 Christie's, Kensington #96/R
£4808 $7452 €7500 Cowes (50x66cm-20x26in) s.i. crayon dr exec.1934-35 lit. 9-Dec-2 Piasa, Paris #9/R
£4808 $7548 €7500 Eglise de Taormina (45x56cm-18x22in) s.i. chl prov.exhib.lit. 10-Dec-2 Piasa, Paris #276/R
£4808 $7548 €7500 Sortie des six metres a Trouville (50x66cm-20x26in) prov.lit. 10-Dec-2 Piasa, Paris #275/R
£5128 $8051 €8000 Villerville (50x66cm-20x26in) s. Chinese ink htd gouache exhib.lit. 10-Dec-2 Piasa, Paris #68/R est:5000-7000
£5161 $8000 €7742 Les harvests. Vence (44x56cm-17x22in) one s. one s.i. pencil pair. 26-Sep-2 Christie's, Rockefeller NY #511/R est:5000-7000
£5500 $8470 €8250 Viaduc de Vence (43x53cm-17x21in) s. W/C pencil prov.lit. 23-Oct-2 Sotheby's, Olympia #659/R est:5500-8500
£5769 $9058 €9000 Cowes (50x66cm-20x26in) s.i. graphite dr prov.lit. 10-Dec-2 Piasa, Paris #272/R
£5769 $9058 €9000 Fenetre ouverte (50x66cm-20x26in) s. graphite dr prov.lit. 10-Dec-2 Piasa, Paris #288
£5769 $9058 €9000 Chenonceaux (50x66cm-20x26in) Chinese ink htd gouache exhib.lit. 10-Dec-2 Piasa, Paris #307/R est:4000
£5806 $9000 €8709 Paysage de provence. Regate a cowes (40x52cm-16x20in) one s. one s.i. pen India ink exhib.lit. 26-Sep-2 Christie's, Rockefeller NY #513/R est:5000-7000
£6000 $9840 €9000 Femme, pommier et lion (44x28cm-17x11in) W/C brush ink exec.c.1920. 5-Feb-3 Sotheby's, London #168/R
£6090 $9439 €9500 Baigneuse a Sainte-Adresse (14x10cm-6x4in) col crayon dr exec.1950 lit. 9-Dec-2 Piasa, Paris #1/R
£7051 $11071 €11000 Langres III (50x66cm-20x26in) s. Chinese ink dr prov.exhib.lit. 10-Dec-2 Piasa, Paris #304/R est:4000
£7194 $11511 €10000 Les anemones (40x40cm-16x16in) s. gouache prov. 13-May-3 Palais de Beaux Arts, Brussels #184/R est:10000-15000
£7500 $11925 €11250 Le paddock (45x64cm-18x25in) s. pen ink prov.exhib. 20-Mar-3 Sotheby's, Olympia #124/R est:5000-7000

£7692 $12077 €12000 Hippodrome, Ascot (50x65cm-20x26in) i. Chinese ink htd gouache lit. 10-Dec-2 Piasa, Paris #309 est:6000
£8500 $13345 €12750 Villefranche (38x52cm-15x20in) s. W/C prov. exec.c.1921-22. 16-Dec-2 Sotheby's, London #85/R est:5000-7000
£8974 $14090 €14000 Poissons (50x65cm-20x26in) s. W/C exec.1947 prov.exhib.lit. 10-Dec-2 Piasa, Paris #271/R est:15000
£9000 $14130 €13500 Les deux poissons (51x65cm-20x26in) s. W/C htd gouache prov.lit. 16-Dec-2 Sotheby's, London #84/R est:4000-6000
£9032 $14000 €13548 Le bles (48x65cm-19x26in) s. W/C brush black ink painted c.1930. 26-Sep-2 Christie's, Rockefeller NY #533/R est:12000-18000
£9615 $15096 €15000 Filets de peche a Cannes (50x66cm-20x26in) s. Chinese ink dr htd gouache prov.exhib.lit. 10-Dec-2 Piasa, Paris #305/R est:5000
£11000 $17380 €16500 Match de boxe a Londres (48x61cm-19x24in) s. W/C exec.1930. 3-Apr-3 Christie's, Kensington #101/R est:12000
£11728 $19000 €17006 Paysage en Normandie (51x66cm-20x26in) s. W/C Arches paper painted c.1928-1930. 21-May-3 Doyle, New York #44/R est:20000-30000
£12411 $20106 €17500 Paysage (49x41cm-19x16in) s. gouache. 21-May-3 Cornette de St.Cyr, Paris #54/R est:12000-15000
£13462 $20865 €21000 Hippodrome d'Epsom (50x66cm-20x26in) Chinese ink dr exec.1934 exhib.lit. 9-Dec-2 Piasa, Paris #10/R est:15000-20000
£13462 $20865 €21000 Regates a Triel (50x64cm-20x25in) s.i.d.26 Juin 1932 W/C board prov. 4-Dec-2 Lempertz, Koln #670/R est:22000
£14103 $22141 €22000 Composition, naissance de Venus (22x33cm-9x13in) i. ink W/C gouache double-sided exhib.lit. 10-Dec-2 Piasa, Paris #299/R est:9000
£15000 $25050 €22500 Les pecheurs de crevettes (50x65cm-20x26in) s. gouache W/C exec c.1924 prov.exhib.lit. 26-Jun-3 Christie's, London #384/R est:18000-25000
£16149 $26000 €24224 La Salute (50x66cm-20x26in) s. W/C executed c.1938 lit. 7-May-3 Sotheby's, New York #375/R est:25000-35000
£16667 $26000 €25001 Jardin chez les Homburger (50x66cm-20x26in) s.i.d.1950 W/C gouache prov.exhib.lit. 7-Nov-2 Christie's, Rockefeller NY #163/R est:30000-40000
£16667 $26167 €26000 Nature morte aux fruits (27x37cm-11x15in) s.i.d.1941 pastel lit. 10-Dec-2 Piasa, Paris #73/R est:8000-10000
£19231 $30192 €30000 Nu a la chaise longue (50x65cm-20x26in) st.sig. W/C exec.1942 exhib.lit. 10-Dec-2 Piasa, Paris #269/R est:45000
£19231 $30192 €30000 Venus a la coquille (30x47cm-12x19in) ink gouache W/C double-sided exhib.lit. 10-Dec-2 Piasa, Paris #298/R est:12000
£19753 $28049 €32000 Canes, la fontaine (50x39cm-20x15in) s. W/C gouache. 16-Mar-3 Eric Pillon, Calais #118/R
£20513 $32000 €30770 Anemones (50x66cm-20x26in) s.i.d.1950 W/C gouache prov.exhib.lit. 7-Nov-2 Christie's, Rockefeller NY #161/R est:40000-60000
£20513 $32205 €32000 Park (50x65cm-20x26in) s.i. W/C lit. 10-Dec-2 Piasa, Paris #270/R est:20000
£24540 $40000 €36810 Nu couche a la draperie (50x65cm-20x26in) s.d.1930 W/C gouache prov.exhib.lit. 12-Feb-3 Sotheby's, New York #57/R est:50000-70000
£25157 $39245 €40000 Venise, le quai des Esclavons (48x62cm-19x24in) s.i.d.1938 W/C gouache lit. 10-Oct-2 Ribeyre & Baron, Paris #54/R est:40000
£26923 $42269 €42000 Maisons blanches a Montsaunes (48x63cm-19x25in) s. W/C htd gouache exec.1943 exhib.lit. 10-Dec-2 Piasa, Paris #69/R est:10000-12000
£27000 $45090 €40500 La mer (50x63cm-20x25in) s. gouache W/C prov. 26-Jun-3 Christie's, London #377/R est:22000-28000
£28000 $46760 €42000 Nu a la chaise longue (50x65cm-20x26in) s. W/C exec 1942 prov.exhib.lit. 26-Jun-3 Christie's, London #380/R est:30000-40000
£29577 $42000 €44366 Bouquet a la fleur (51x64cm-20x25in) W/C. 8-Aug-1 Barridorf, Portland #110/R est:35000-45000
£29814 $48000 €44721 Philippeville (50x66cm-20x26in) s. W/C executed 1934. 8-May-3 Christie's, Rockefeller NY #120/R est:30000-40000
£35256 $55353 €55000 Grange (48x64cm-19x25in) s. W/C prov.exhib.lit. 10-Dec-2 Piasa, Paris #267/R est:30000
£37179 $58372 €58000 Moisson (50x66cm-20x26in) s.i.d.1944 W/C gouache lit. 10-Dec-2 Piasa, Paris #72/R est:18000-22000
£40000 $66800 €58000 Le repas des chasseurs (50x66cm-20x26in) s.d.1936 W/C gouache paper on canvas prov.exhib.lit. 24-Jun-3 Sotheby's, London #272/R est:40000-60000
£42000 $70140 €63000 Houses of Parliament, London (50x65cm-20x26in) s.d.1930 gouache W/C prov.lit. 26-Jun-3 Christie's, London #381/R est:30000-40000
£43590 $67564 €68000 Anemones a la fenetre (50x65cm-20x26in) s.d.1942 W/C gouache exhib.lit. 9-Dec-2 Piasa, Paris #7/R est:35000-45000
£48077 $75481 €75000 Fenetre ouverte a Cannes (65x50cm-26x20in) s.d.1942 W/C gouache lit. 10-Dec-2 Piasa, Paris #268/R est:30000
£54487 $84455 €85000 Ferme au clocher (50x65cm-20x26in) s. W/C gouache exec. 1943 lit. 9-Dec-2 Piasa, Paris #8/R est:28000-35000
£57453 $92500 €86180 Nu dans l'atelier de Vence (50x65cm-20x26in) s.d.1945 gouache W/C prov.lit. 7-May-3 Sotheby's, New York #370/R est:80000-120000
£60812 $94867 €90000 Chateau de Compiegne (50x65cm-20x26in) s. W/C prov.lit. 26-Mar-3 Tajan, Paris #4/R
£62000 $103540 €93000 Cannes, La Croisette (48x61cm-19x24in) s. gouache W/C. 26-Jun-3 Christie's, London #376/R est:50000-70000
£83333 $130000 €125000 Le champ de courses de Deauville (51x66cm-20x26in) s.i.d.1950 gouache W/C prov.exhib.lit. 7-Nov-2 Christie's, Rockefeller NY #164/R est:50000-70000
£90000 $150300 €135000 Courses a Deauville (49x65cm-19x26in) s.i. gouache W/C exec c.1940-50 prov.lit. 26-Jun-3 Christie's, London #386/R est:100000-150000
£95000 $155800 €142500 Terrasse a Nice (50x66cm-20x26in) s.i.d.1940 gouache W/C. 6-Feb-3 Christie's, London #431/R est:150000

DUGARDYN, Antoine (20th C) Belgian
Works on paper
£1034 $1634 €1500 Projets pour le salon et pour le living-room du Pavillon Royal d'Ostende (45x62cm-18x24in) s.d.nov.1954 pencil W/C gouache pair. 2-Apr-3 Vanderkindere, Brussels #213/R est:100-150

DUGDALE, John (1961-) American
Photographs
£3247 $5000 €4871 Self portrait in Roundout Creek, Rosendale, N Y (24x19cm-9x7in) s.i.d.1993 num.4/10 platinum print. 24-Oct-2 Sotheby's, New York #247/R est:4000-6000

DUGDALE, Thomas Cantrell (1880-1952) British
£300 $477 €450 Lady of the manor, portrait of Diana Heycock (75x62cm-30x24in) s. 6-Mar-3 Bonhams, Cornwall #725

DUGELAY, Anna (20th C) French
£365 $576 €548 Strawberries (38x51cm-15x20in) s. i.verso. 29-Nov-2 Zofingen, Switzerland #2804 (S.FR 850)

DUGHET, Gaspard (1615-1675) French
£5660 $8830 €9000 Mountain landscape (80x110cm-31x43in) 21-Sep-2 Berlinghof, Heidelberg #135/R est:9900

DUGHET, Gaspard (attrib) (1615-1675) French
£543 $891 €750 Paysage (54x78cm-21x31in) 27-May-3 Campo, Vlaamse Kaai #86
£1982 $2894 €2973 Wooded landscape with figures (45x62cm-18x24in) 17-Jun-2 Philippe Schuler, Zurich #4335/R (S.FR 4500)
£4800 $8016 €6960 Wooded landscape with classical figures by a river (74x99cm-29x39in) 11-Jul-3 Christie's, Kensington #239/R est:4000-6000
£8000 $12480 €12000 Capriccio view of classical buildings (36x46cm-14x18in) prov. 9-Apr-3 Christie's, London #97/R est:8000-12000

DUGMORE, Arthur Radclyffe (1870-1955) American
£700 $1120 €1050 Lough Mask, Co Mayo (23x28cm-9x11in) s.d.46 i.verso board. 15-May-3 Christie's, Kensington #180/R

DUGMORE, Edward (1915-1996) American
£1656 $2600 €2484 S-21 (22x28cm-9x11in) i.stretcher painted c.1950 prov. 19-Nov-2 Wright, Chicago #171/R est:2000-3000

DUGOURC, Jean Demosthene (1749-1825) French
Works on paper
£338 $527 €500 Mascarons (31x45cm-12x18in) mono.i.d.1776 sanguine. 31-Mar-3 Piasa, Paris #41

DUGUAY, Rodolphe (1892-1973) Canadian
£387 $604 €581 Paysage d'ete (21x25cm-8x10in) s. panel. 30-Jul-2 Iegor de Saint Hippolyte, Montreal #42 (C.D 960)
Works on paper
£1844 $2877 €2766 Le cheval blanc au clair de lune (56x75cm-22x30in) s. pastel panel. 10-Sep-2 Iegor de Saint Hippolyte, Montreal #29 (C.D 4500)

DUGUID, Henry G (fl.1831-1860) British
£8000 $12160 €12000 View of Edinburgh castle from Corstorphine Hill (70x91cm-28x36in) s.indis d.1856. 28-Aug-2 Sotheby's, London #801/R est:8000-12000

DUHEM, Marie Genevieve (1871-1918) French
£300 $489 €450 Chrysanthemums, a ewer and jug (46x61cm-18x24in) s. 13-Feb-3 Christie's, Kensington #234

Works on paper
£1000 $1550 €1500 La maison aux lauriers (38x59cm-15x23in) s. pencil chk pastel wash. 5-Dec-2 Christie's, Kensington #22/R est:800-1200

DUIFHUIZEN, Pieter Jacobsz (1608-1677) Dutch
£18000 $28080 €27000 Group of soldiers resting beside classical remains in landscape (38x50cm-15x20in) s. panel prov. 10-Apr-3 Sotheby's, London #41a/R est:15000

DUIKER, Simon (19th C) Dutch
£377 $600 €566 Shepherd with his flock (38x51cm-15x20in) s. 5-Mar-3 Doyle, New York #20/R

DUILLO, John (1928-) American
£5844 $9000 €8766 Forrest's terrible swift sword (36x61cm-14x24in) 25-Oct-2 Morris & Whiteside, Hilton Head Island #52 est:8000-12000
Works on paper
£528 $850 €792 Snowy concentration camp whipping scene (36x56cm-14x22in) s. gouache en grisaille. 20-Feb-3 Illustration House, New York #45/R

DUJARDIN, Karel (1622-1678) Dutch
£18293 $30000 €27440 Italianate landscape with travellers on horseback (65x81cm-26x32in) s. prov.lit. 29-May-3 Sotheby's, New York #17/R est:25000-35000

DUJARDIN, Karel (circle) (1622-1678) Dutch
£7006 $10930 €11000 Portrait of a gentleman, aged 27, wearing a white shirt (17x13cm-7x5in) i.d.1655 copper. 5-Nov-2 Sotheby's, Amsterdam #239/R est:7000-9000

DUJARDIN, Rene Marie (1913-) Belgian
£377 $581 €600 Paysage d'hiver (80x100cm-31x39in) s. 22-Oct-2 Campo, Vlaamse Kaai #104
£377 $581 €600 Schelde (75x95cm-30x37in) s.d.1964. 22-Oct-2 Campo & Campo, Antwerp #96
£506 $790 €800 River Scheldt (75x95cm-30x37in) s. 21-Oct-2 Bernaerts, Antwerp #771

DUJARDIN, Simone (20th C) Belgian
Works on paper
£236 $375 €354 Masked nude (51x41cm-20x16in) s.d.1954 pastel. 7-Mar-3 Jackson's, Cedar Falls #848/R

DUKE, Alfred (?-1905) British
£1262 $1994 €1893 Interior scene with two dogs (35x50cm-14x20in) s. 30-Nov-2 Goteborg Auktionsverk, Sweden #177/R est:6000 (S.KR 18000)
£2000 $3320 €2900 On the alert (35x51cm-14x20in) s. 12-Jun-3 Christie's, Kensington #237/R est:2000-3000

DUKE, Peder (1938-) Swedish
£491 $765 €737 Out from the dark (83x82cm-33x32in) s.d.1999 verso. 6-Nov-2 AB Stockholms Auktionsverk #563/R (S.KR 7000)
£734 $1181 €1101 The lens (76x83cm-30x33in) s.d.1984 verso acrylic. 7-May-3 AB Stockholms Auktionsverk #942/R (S.KR 9500)

DUKKERS, Ed (1923-1996) Dutch
£308 $483 €480 M (50x40cm-20x16in) s.verso. 25-Nov-2 Glerum, Amsterdam #250

DULAC, Edmund (1882-1953) British/French
Works on paper
£1400 $2310 €2030 Apple Barrel. Bristol. Black dog disappears (15x11cm-6x4in) s.i. pencil W/C bodycol three lit. 3-Jul-3 Christie's, Kensington #210/R est:1000-1500
£5625 $9000 €8438 Nuptial dance of Aladdin and the lady Bedir-el-Budur (31x25cm-12x10in) s. pencil W/C bodycol exhib.lit. 14-May-3 Butterfields, San Francisco #1166/R est:4000-6000

DULARY, Baudet (1782-1878) French
Works on paper
£2603 $4086 €3800 Portrait de Charles Fourier (15x11cm-6x4in) s.i.d.1831 graphite dr lit. 15-Apr-3 Laurence Calmels, Paris #4092/R

DULDIG, Karl (?) ?
Sculpture
£1286 $2006 €1929 When the big men fly (38x20x23cm-15x8x9in) s.num.2/9 bronze. 11-Nov-2 Deutscher-Menzies, Melbourne #110/R est:3000-4000 (A.D 3600)

DULERE, A (19th C) French?
Works on paper
£3228 $5100 €5100 Bord de lac italien (29x46cm-11x18in) s.d.1859 W/C. 2-Dec-2 Rieunier, Paris #20/R

DULIEU, René (20th C) French
£600 $984 €900 Street corner in Montmartre, Paris (46x56cm-18x22in) s. 4-Jun-3 Bonhams, Chester #391

DULLAH (1919-1996) Javanese
£3728 $5742 €5592 Village in Bali (50x60cm-20x24in) s.i.d.1955. 27-Oct-2 Christie's, Hong Kong #92/R est:22000-45000 (HK.D 45000)

DULMEN KRUMPELMAN, Erasmus Bernhard van (1897-1987) Dutch
£1974 $3197 €3000 Young bathers at the river Aa, near Zeegse, Drente (67x96cm-26x38in) s.d.51. 21-Jan-3 Christie's, Amsterdam #431/R est:3000-5000
£9220 $14936 €13000 Farm children from Ostend in the field (66x85cm-26x33in) s. 26-May-3 Glerum, Amsterdam #56/R est:3000-4000
Works on paper
£298 $483 €420 Round the back with a wooden cart (27x20cm-11x8in) s. W/C. 26-May-3 Glerum, Amsterdam #50
£461 $747 €650 Drentse farm behind trees (32x47cm-13x19in) s.d.40 W/C. 26-May-3 Glerum, Amsterdam #51

DUMA, William (1936-) Canadian
£221 $347 €332 Beaver Pond (23x30cm-9x12in) s.i. board. 25-Nov-2 Hodgins, Calgary #258/R (C.D 550)
£241 $378 €362 Winter vista (23x30cm-9x12in) s.i.d.1989 board. 25-Nov-2 Hodgins, Calgary #4/R (C.D 600)
£241 $378 €362 Clouds and hillside (35x45cm-14x18in) s.i. board. 25-Nov-2 Hodgins, Calgary #65/R (C.D 600)
£251 $394 €377 Foothills (23x30cm-9x12in) s.i. board. 25-Nov-2 Hodgins, Calgary #9/R (C.D 625)
£251 $394 €377 Mountains and foothills (23x30cm-9x12in) s.i. board. 25-Nov-2 Hodgins, Calgary #13/R (C.D 625)
£271 $425 €407 Sarcee Reserve (30x40cm-12x16in) s.i. board. 25-Nov-2 Hodgins, Calgary #279/R (C.D 675)
£289 $474 €419 Sarcee Reserve (30x40cm-12x16in) s.i. board. 9-Jun-3 Hodgins, Calgary #342/R (C.D 650)
£391 $610 €653 Dark water (76x102cm-30x40in) s. acrylic prov. 13-Apr-3 Levis, Calgary #28/R est:1200-1500 (C.D 900)
£445 $707 €668 Clouds over Okanagan Lake (30x40cm-12x16in) s.i.d.1980 canvasboard. 23-Mar-3 Hodgins, Calgary #20/R est:500-700 (C.D 1050)
£1144 $1819 €1716 Autumn fields (60x75cm-24x30in) s.i. acrylic prov. 23-Mar-3 Hodgins, Calgary #56/R est:800-1200 (C.D 2700)
£1205 $1904 €1808 Bend in the road (91x122cm-36x48in) acrylic. 1-Dec-2 Levis, Calgary #22/R est:1500-2000 (C.D 3000)

DUMAIGE, Étienne-Henri (1830-1888) French
Sculpture
£1083 $1689 €1700 Woman (47cm-19in) i. 6-Nov-2 Hugo Ruef, Munich #2124/R est:900
£1300 $2015 €1950 Casse Cou, country girl with putti at her feet (65cm-26in) s.i. brown pat bronze circular base. 29-Oct-2 Bonhams, New Bond Street #231/R est:900-1100
£1699 $2736 €2600 Jeune Orientale descendant les marches (96cm-38in) s. brown pat bronze marble socle. 20-Jan-3 Horta, Bruxelles #90 est:2500-3000
£1773 $2872 €2500 Figure of Lucia seated on a rocky outcrop holding a lamp (64cm-25in) s. bronze. 21-May-3 James Adam, Dublin #360/R est:2000-3000
£10323 $16000 €15485 Unveiling the princess (81cm-32in) s. brown pat. bronze. 30-Oct-2 Christie's, Rockefeller NY #105/R est:15000-20000

DUMAS, Antoine (1932-) Canadian
£2459 $3811 €3689 Tyrannie du dollar Gagner de l'argent (91x101cm-36x40in) s.d.88. 24-Sep-2 Iegor de Saint Hippolyte, Montreal #32 (C.D 6000)

DUMAS, Jack (20th C) American
Works on paper
£932 $1500 €1398 Ship in tropical cove greeted by islanders including topless women (43x61cm-17x24in) s. W/C gouache. 20-Feb-3 Illustration House, New York #46/R est:2000-3000

DUMAS, Marlene (1953-) Dutch
£26582 $42000 €39873 Candle burning (50x40cm-20x16in) s.i.d.2000 prov. 14-Nov-2 Christie's, Rockefeller NY #324/R est:25000-35000
£28000 $46760 €40600 Opposites (24x18cm-9x7in) s.i.d.1992 two prov.exhib.lit. 26-Jun-3 Sotheby's, London #298/R est:8000-12000
£160000 $267200 €240000 Feathered Stola (100x56cm-39x22in) s.i.d.2000 verso prov.exhib. 26-Jun-3 Christie's, London #41/R est:65000-85000
Works on paper
£1923 $2981 €3000 Skeleton with bust (30x24cm-12x9in) s.i.d.1990 Indian ink brush. 6-Dec-2 Hauswedell & Nolte, Hamburg #110/R est:4000
£3526 $5465 €5500 White light (24x34cm-9x13in) s.i.d.1985 mixed media. 3-Dec-2 Christie's, Amsterdam #376/R est:4000-6000
£9494 $15000 €14241 Before the nose job (48x38cm-19x15in) s.i.d.1995 W/C prov. 14-Nov-2 Christie's, Rockefeller NY #325/R est:10000-15000
£23750 $38000 €35625 How to kill your mother (44x31cm-17x12in) s.i.d.1989 ink col chk. 15-May-3 Christie's, Rockefeller NY #332/R est:12000-16000

DUMAX, Ernest Joachim (1811-?) French
£321 $503 €500 River landscape with angler (26x40cm-10x16in) s. 10-Dec-2 Dorotheum, Vienna #258/R
£437 $681 €656 Summer meadows (27x40cm-11x16in) s. 6-Nov-2 Dobiaschofsky, Bern #475 (S.FR 1000)

DUMINI, Adolfo (1863-?) Italian
£845 $1318 €1268 Woman and child by picture of a saint (88x64cm-35x25in) s.i. 23-Sep-2 Rasmussen, Vejle #130/R (D.KR 10000)

DUMINIL, Frank (1933-) French
£252 $390 €400 Composition (100x80cm-39x31in) s. 4-Oct-2 Tajan, Paris #67
£256 $403 €400 Composition (73x60cm-29x24in) s. s.d.91 verso. 16-Dec-2 Charbonneaux, Paris #247
£324 $518 €450 Kachinas XV (35x27cm-14x11in) s. 18-May-3 Neret-Minet, Paris #42
£397 $648 €600 Composition (100x81cm-39x32in) s. 31-Jan-3 Charbonneaux, Paris #80
£540 $863 €750 Empreintes XVIII (60x60cm-24x24in) s. 18-May-3 Neret-Minet, Paris #190
£561 $898 €780 Empreintes XXVIII (80x80cm-31x31in) s. 18-May-3 Neret-Minet, Paris #135

DUMITRESCO, Natalie (1915-1997) French
£326 $529 €460 Oasis (46x27cm-18x11in) s. s.i.d.1966 verso. 26-May-3 Joron-Derem, Paris #52
£700 $1112 €1050 Harmonie en bleu - Opus No.5 (46x55cm-18x22in) s. 29-Apr-3 Kunsthallen, Copenhagen #65/R (D.KR 7500)
£748 $1190 €1100 Composition (65x81cm-26x32in) s. s.d.1967 verso mixed media prov.exhib. 24-Mar-3 Claude Boisgirard, Paris #137/R
£1090 $1711 €1700 Untitled (65x54cm-26x21in) s. s.d.1965 verso. 24-Nov-2 Laurence Calmels, Paris #114/R
£1250 $1988 €1800 Composition (65x81cm-26x32in) s. 29-Apr-3 Artcurial Briest, Paris #568 est:2000-2500
£1327 $2109 €1950 Sans titre (54x65cm-21x26in) 26-Feb-3 Artcurial Briest, Paris #486 est:1500-2000
£1603 $2516 €2500 Untitled (54x65cm-21x26in) s. s.verso. 24-Nov-2 Laurence Calmels, Paris #117/R
£1667 $2617 €2600 Untitled (49x60cm-19x24in) s. s.verso. 24-Nov-2 Laurence Calmels, Paris #118/R
£1973 $3137 €2900 Planete dutu I (91x73cm-36x29in) s.d. s.i.d.verso. 26-Feb-3 Artcurial Briest, Paris #479/R est:2000-2500
£2041 $3245 €3000 Bleu (90x116cm-35x46in) s. s.i.d.1970 verso. 26-Feb-3 Artcurial Briest, Paris #489/R est:2500-3000
£2041 $3245 €3000 Lumiere dans la nuit (74x115cm-29x45in) s. s.i.d.IX-1960 verso. 26-Feb-3 Artcurial Briest, Paris #490 est:3000-3500
£2051 $3221 €3200 Untitled (60x72cm-24x28in) s. i.d.1958 verso. 24-Nov-2 Laurence Calmels, Paris #119/R
£2244 $3522 €3500 Composition 46 gris (50x61cm-20x24in) s. s.d.1962 verso prov.exhib. 24-Nov-2 Laurence Calmels, Paris #115/R
£2245 $3569 €3300 Untitled (130x162cm-51x64in) s. s.d.1976. 3-Mar-3 Marc Kohn, Paris #13/R
£2313 $3678 €3400 Composition (92x65cm-36x26in) s. 26-Feb-3 Artcurial Briest, Paris #480/R est:3500-4500
£2313 $3678 €3400 Espace (60x81cm-24x32in) s. s.i.d.1956 verso. 26-Feb-3 Artcurial Briest, Paris #477/R est:2200-2500
£2313 $3678 €3400 Untitled (65x92cm-26x36in) s. s.d.1961 verso. 3-Mar-3 Marc Kohn, Paris #12/R
£2449 $3894 €3600 C'etait ecrit (100x100cm-39x39in) s. s.i.d.XII 1968 verso prov.exhib. 26-Feb-3 Artcurial Briest, Paris #488/R est:3000-3500
£2857 $4543 €4200 Sans titre (90x116cm-35x46in) s. s.d.1959 verso. 26-Feb-3 Artcurial Briest, Paris #487 est:3000-3500
£3129 $4976 €4600 Decrivant une courbe naturelle (130x96cm-51x38in) s. s.i.d.1959 verso prov. 26-Feb-3 Artcurial Briest, Paris #483/R est:3000-3500
£3333 $5233 €5200 Jaune 62 (54x65cm-21x26in) s. s.i.d.62 verso prov.exhib. 24-Nov-2 Laurence Calmels, Paris #116/R
£4490 $7139 €6600 Sans titre (162x130cm-64x51in) s. s.d.1950 verso exhib. 26-Feb-3 Artcurial Briest, Paris #481 est:4000-4500
£6565 $10438 €9650 Composition (65x81cm-26x32in) s. s.d.1957 verso. 26-Feb-3 Artcurial Briest, Paris #478/R est:2500-3000
£6973 $11087 €10250 Essentielle a l'echelle du rythme (197x183cm-78x72in) s. s.i.d.1960 verso exhib. 26-Feb-3 Artcurial Briest, Paris #485/R est:4000-4500

Works on paper
£253 $400 €400 Avion (30x23cm-12x9in) s.i.d.1973 W/C gouache. 27-Nov-2 Blanchet, Paris #153/R
£641 $1006 €1000 Untitled (43x52cm-17x20in) s.d.64 gouache. 24-Nov-2 Laurence Calmels, Paris #110/R
£769 $1208 €1200 Untitled (41x30cm-16x12in) s. gouache. 24-Nov-2 Laurence Calmels, Paris #108/R
£845 $1403 €1200 Sans titre, fond gris (34x24cm-13x9in) s. mixed media. 15-Jun-3 Anaf, Lyon #87/R
£1154 $1812 €1800 Untitled (32x10cm-13x4in) s. gouache. 24-Nov-2 Laurence Calmels, Paris #111/R
£1410 $2214 €2200 Untitled (30x41cm-12x16in) s. gouache. 24-Nov-2 Laurence Calmels, Paris #109/R
£1701 $2704 €2500 Sans titre (100x74cm-39x29in) d.1950 ink wash W/C paper on canvas. 26-Feb-3 Artcurial Briest, Paris #484 est:3000-3500

DUMMER, Erich (1889-1929) German
£629 $975 €1000 Travemunde light house (34x40cm-13x16in) board. 2-Nov-2 Hans Stahl, Toestorf #64/R

DUMMER, H Boylston (1878-1945) American
£629 $1000 €944 Merganser and snipe (66x48cm-26x19in) s. i.verso canvasboard. 7-Mar-3 Jackson's, Cedar Falls #640/R est:1750-2000

DUMMERMUTH, Julie (1973-) American
£1585 $2600 €2298 Fall mix, September (24x183cm-9x72in) s.d.2002 verso acrylic gemstones glitter oil. 28-May-3 Sotheby's, Amsterdam #147/R est:2200-2800
£2096 $3500 €3039 It's good thing - December (244x183cm-96x72in) s.d.2002 verso acrylic gemstone oil. 25-Jun-3 Sotheby's, Moscow #198/R est:2200-2800
£2375 $3800 €3444 Arrangement of the month (183x213cm-72x84in) s.d.2002 acrylic enamel gemstones gold leaf oil glitter. 13-May-3 Sotheby's, Tel Aviv #8/R est:1800-2200

DUMONCEAU DE BERGENDAEL, Comtesse Mathilde (1877-1952) Belgian
£523 $842 €800 La terrasse animee (50x60cm-20x24in) s. panel. 14-Jan-3 Vanderkindere, Brussels #462
£588 $947 €900 Printemps a l'abbaye (76x100cm-30x39in) s. 14-Jan-3 Vanderkindere, Brussels #12

DUMOND, Frank Vincent (1865-1951) American
£380 $589 €600 Young elegant couple in 17th Century costume (46x38cm-18x15in) s. 25-Sep-2 Neumeister, Munich #565/R
£3085 $4750 €4628 Rogue River, Oregon (76x91cm-30x36in) s. 24-Oct-2 Shannon's, Milford #217/R est:5000-7000

DUMONT, Alfred (1828-1894) Swiss
£2778 $4416 €4000 Suisse, promeneurs (48x81cm-19x32in) s.d.1872. 30-Apr-3 Tajan, Paris #57

DUMONT, Augustin Alexandre (1801-1884) French
Sculpture
£1284 $2079 €1926 Gentleman (74cm-29in) s.d.1865 pat bronze. 23-Jan-3 Louis Morton, Mexico #89/R est:30000 (M.P 22000)
£1655 $2615 €2400 Hercule (72cm-28in) s. green pat bronze. 2-Apr-3 Vanderkindere, Brussels #566/R est:1250-1750

DUMONT, Cesar Alvarez (19th C) Spanish
£1195 $1864 €1900 Guardian angel (130x105cm-51x41in) s.d.1892. 23-Sep-2 Durán, Madrid #106/R

DUMONT, Claude (?) French
£690 $1097 €1000 Aubade a Venise (73x92cm-29x36in) 9-Mar-3 Feletin, Province #202

DUMONT, Edme (after) (1722-1775) French
Sculpture
£5200 $8684 €7540 Milo of Croton (160x42x37cm-63x17x15in) dk. brown pat bronze inc. yellow scagiola plinth. 8-Jul-3 Sotheby's, London #159/R est:3000-5000

DUMONT, François (1850-?) Belgian
£349 $545 €524 Standing musketeer (46x32cm-18x13in) s.d.90. 6-Nov-2 Dobiaschofsky, Bern #468/R (S.FR 800)
£690 $1103 €1000 Buveurs et fumeurs dans une auberge (55x65cm-22x26in) s.d.1904. 17-Mar-3 Horta, Bruxelles #76

DUMONT, François (1751-1831) French
Miniatures
£1844 $2987 €2600 La reine Marie Antoinette de face (3x2cm-1x1in) ivory gilded brass surround prov. 21-May-3 Piasa, Paris #277/R est:2000-3000
£4500 $7020 €6750 Gentleman wearing silver figured plum coloured coat matching waistcoat (6cm-2in circular) gilt mount. 5-Nov-2 Bonhams, New Bond Street #41/R est:4500-6500

DUMONT, François (after) (1751-1831) French
Miniatures
£1773 $2872 €2500 Jeune fille devant son pianoforte (7cm-3in circular) ivory gilded brass frame prov. 21-May-3 Piasa, Paris #316/R est:800-1200

DUMONT, Jean (1701-1781) French
£30769 $51385 €44000 Eliezer et Rebecca (65x81cm-26x32in) s.d.1736 prov.exhib. 27-Jun-3 Piasa, Paris #78/R est:15000-20000

DUMONT, Pierre (1884-1936) French
£503 $780 €800 Rue de village (70x53cm-28x21in) s. 7-Oct-2 Claude Aguttes, Neuilly #317
£764 $1260 €1100 Le chemin au portail (50x64cm-20x25in) s. 1-Jul-3 Rossini, Paris #85
£833 $1375 €1200 La cour fleurie (46x54cm-18x21in) s. 1-Jul-3 Rossini, Paris #82/R
£1389 $2292 €2000 Le pavillon sur l'eau (38x55cm-15x22in) s. 1-Jul-3 Rossini, Paris #83
£1484 $2345 €2300 Coin de jardin (65x81cm-26x32in) s. 17-Dec-2 Rossini, Paris #72/R
£3310 $5297 €4800 Pont sur la Seine (60x73cm-24x29in) s. 12-Mar-3 E & Eve, Paris #109/R est:4000-4500
£3380 $5442 €4800 Bathers (49x44cm-19x17in) s. lit. 9-May-3 Schloss Ahlden, Ahlden #1470/R est:2300
£3590 $5636 €5600 Bords de Seine (65x81cm-26x32in) s. 13-Dec-2 Piasa, Paris #135/R

DUMONT, Pierre (attrib) (1884-1936) French
£449 $704 €700 Nature morte au broc (61x50cm-24x20in) 13-Dec-2 Piasa, Paris #93

DUMONT-SMITH, Robert (20th C) British
£300 $501 €435 Still life with flowers (45x56cm-18x22in) s.d.1939. 8-Jul-3 Bonhams, Knightsbridge #116/R

DUMOULIN, Romeo (1883-1944) Belgian
£696 $1100 €1100 Les debardeurs (83x69cm-33x27in) s. 26-Nov-2 Palais de Beaux Arts, Brussels #88
£5380 $8392 €8500 Halte (66x178cm-26x70in) s.d.1917. 16-Sep-2 Horta, Bruxelles #110/R est:8000-12000
Works on paper
£417 $663 €600 La tour St Mathieu a Marlaix, Finistere (62x48cm-24x19in) mixed media. 29-Apr-3 Campo, Vlaamse Kaai #111
£1006 $1550 €1600 Adieu done, bazin, je pars (30x40cm-12x16in) s. ink dr. 22-Oct-2 Campo, Vlaamse Kaai #492
£3494 $5415 €5450 Femme a sa fenetre (60x80cm-24x31in) s. mixed media cardboard. 9-Dec-2 Horta, Bruxelles #161 est:6000-8000

DUN, Nicholas François (1764-1832) French
Miniatures
£2200 $3608 €3190 Athenal's d'Arlincourt, Comtesse de Sassenay (4cm-2xin) s. two col gold stamped flowers. 3-Jun-3 Christie's, London #200/R est:1000-1500

DUNAND, Jean (1877-1942) Swiss
£680 $1082 €1000 Portrait de Madame Rigaud (83x57cm-33x22in) s. panel painted c.1927 exhib.lit. 28-Feb-3 Tajan, Paris #72/R
£26582 $42000 €42000 Vendanges (62x57cm-24x22in) s. panel plaster lacquer prov.lit. 26-Nov-2 Tajan, Paris #25/R est:20000-25000

DUNANT, Jacques (1825-1870) Swiss
£1135 $1771 €1703 Landscape in Swiss Alps (46x66cm-18x26in) s.d.1865 prov. 9-Nov-2 Galerie Gloggner, Luzern #37/R est:1000-1200 (S.FR 2600)
£1389 $2236 €2014 Part of Lake Geneva in summer (45x55cm-18x22in) s.d.1869. 9-May-3 Dobiaschofsky, Bern #55/R est:3600 (S.FR 3000)

DUNBAR, George (20th C) American
Works on paper
£9259 $15000 €13889 Coin du lestin (155x124cm-61x49in) red gold leaf over black red clay. 24-Jan-3 New Orleans Auction, New Orleans #1042/R est:15000-25000

DUNBAR, Harold (1882-1953) American
£256 $400 €384 West Chatham landscape (28x41cm-11x16in) s.d.1952 panel. 1-Aug-2 Eldred, East Dennis #750/R
£416 $650 €624 Ocean Beach at Nauset, Cape Cod (51x66cm-20x26in) s.d.1947 s.i.verso board. 1-Aug-2 Eldred, East Dennis #465/R

DUNBAR, Sophia (fl.1860-1904) British
Works on paper
£1300 $2027 €1950 Views of Genoa, Italy (23x53cm-9x21in) one i. pencil W/C pair. 19-Sep-2 Christie's, Kensington #116/R est:700-1000

DUNCAN, Darwin (1905-) American
£290 $450 €435 Landscape (30x41cm-12x16in) s. canvasboard. 29-Oct-2 John Moran, Pasadena #789
£774 $1200 €1161 Landscape (30x41cm-12x16in) s. masonite. 29-Oct-2 John Moran, Pasadena #790

DUNCAN, Edward (1803-1882) British
£1500 $2505 €2175 Fishermen hauling in nets in a squall, with sailing boats beyond (49x73cm-19x29in) 25-Jun-3 Cheffins, Cambridge #767 est:1200-2000
£10000 $15900 €15000 Tantallon Castle, coast of Haddingtonshire (71x124cm-28x49in) s.d.1874-75 prov.exhib. 6-Mar-3 Christie's, Kensington #50/R est:10000-15000
Works on paper
£400 $632 €600 Whitby (24x34cm-9x13in) s.i.d.1866 pencil W/C. 7-Apr-3 Bonhams, Bath #12
£500 $790 €725 Coming squall (22x31cm-9x12in) W/C. 22-Jul-3 Bonhams, Knightsbridge #233/R
£960 $1526 €1440 Shipping off a jetty (24x39cm-9x15in) W/C htd white. 30-Apr-3 Hampton & Littlewood, Exeter #444/R
£1300 $2015 €1950 Fishing boat heading out to sea in a heavy swell (14x22cm-6x9in) s.d.1873 pencil W/C. 31-Oct-2 Christie's, Kensington #332/R est:600-800
£1300 $2015 €1950 Heading home (12x21cm-5x8in) s.d.1873 pencil W/C bodycol. 4-Dec-2 Christie's, Kensington #61/R est:400-600
£2400 $3936 €3600 Holy Island, Northumberland (33x50cm-13x20in) mono.i.d.1854 pencil W/C. 4-Feb-3 Bonhams, Leeds #264 est:1500-2000
£4100 $6724 €6150 Ferrying sheep across the Medway (28x57cm-11x22in) s.d.1870 pencil W/C. 4-Feb-3 Bonhams, Leeds #265 est:1000-1500
£4300 $7052 €6450 Seaweed gathering in Jersey (20x47cm-8x19in) s.i.d.1858 pencil W/C. 4-Feb-3 Bonhams, Leeds #266 est:2000-3000

DUNCAN, George Bernard (1904-1974) New Zealander
£519 $826 €779 Autumn landscape (56x76cm-22x30in) s. board. 23-Mar-3 Goodman, Sydney #115 (A.D 1380)
£821 $1273 €1232 Mending the nets (59x49cm-23x19in) s. hessian. 29-Oct-2 Lawson Menzies, Sydney #13/R est:2500-3500 (A.D 2300)
£1057 $1670 €1533 Washing day, Berrima (67x90cm-26x35in) s. hessian on board. 22-Jul-3 Lawson Menzies, Sydney #111/R est:2500-3500 (A.D 2600)
£1073 $1684 €1610 Slumbering Earth (51x60cm-20x24in) s. i.verso oil on hessian. 15-Apr-3 Lawson Menzies, Sydney #66/R est:3000-5000 (A.D 2800)
£1714 $2691 €2571 Still life with kettle (68x55cm-27x22in) s. hessian painted c.1948. 25-Nov-2 Christie's, Melbourne #395/R est:2000-4000 (A.D 4800)

DUNCAN, James D (1806-1881) Canadian
Works on paper
£1931 $3013 €2800 Pastoral landscape with figures (23x41cm-9x16in) s. W/C prov.lit. 26-Mar-3 Walker's, Ottawa #248/R est:6000-8000 (C.D 4500)
£2790 $4352 €4046 View of Ottawa from the river (25x43cm-10x17in) W/C prov.lit. 26-Mar-3 Walker's, Ottawa #249/R est:6000-8000 (C.D 6500)

DUNCAN, John (1866-1945) British
£280 $440 €420 Bulldog (11x16cm-4x6in) i.verso board. 16-Dec-2 Bonhams, Bury St Edmunds #545
£4800 $7296 €7200 Acolytes (38x46cm-15x18in) tempera on canvas. 28-Aug-2 Sotheby's, London #1016/R est:3000-5000

DUNCAN, Mary (1885-1964) British
£301 $476 €452 Residence at night (64x51cm-25x20in) d.1947 hardboard. 1-Dec-2 Levis, Calgary #23/R (C.D 750)
£333 $546 €500 Girl in yellow (62x50cm-24x20in) s.d.1943. 3-Jun-3 Joyner, Toronto #609 (C.D 750)

£435 $678 €725 Children play outside bank, cote des Neiges Road, Montreal (64x51cm-25x20in) s.d.1943 s.i.d. verso. 13-Apr-3 Levis, Calgary #29/R est:1500-1700 (C.D 1000)
£472 $736 €708 Industry no.2 (51x76cm-20x30in) s.d.1959 verso exhib. 25-Mar-3 Ritchie, Toronto #163/R est:1200-1600 (C.D 1100)
£3056 $4858 €4400 Young Irish mother (76x56cm-30x22in) s. 29-Apr-3 Whyte's, Dublin #109/R est:3000-4000

DUNCAN, Robert (1952-) American
£223 $350 €335 Interior with young girl wearing shirt with lace collar and bow-tie ribbon (46x79cm-18x31in) s. s.i.d.1976 verso egg tempera board. 19-Apr-3 James Julia, Fairfield #300/R
£8219 $12000 €12329 After lost horses (51x102cm-20x40in) 18-May-2 Altermann Galleries, Santa Fe #93/R
£12025 $19000 €17436 Girls out west (61x91cm-24x36in) s. 26-Jul-3 Coeur d'Alene, Hayden #171/R est:12000-18000

DUNCAN, Thomas (attrib) (1807-1845) British
£764 $1200 €1146 Spearing salmon (18x25cm-7x10in) panel. 22-Nov-2 Eldred, East Dennis #832/R

DUNCAN, Walter (fl.1880-c.1910) British
Works on paper
£480 $749 €720 Figure, horse and trap in a country lane in winter (13x18cm-5x7in) s. W/C. 18-Oct-2 Keys, Aylsham #634/R
£500 $760 €750 Reverie, the fisherman's daughter. Off to market (18x10cm-7x4in) s. one d.1909 W/C pair. 16-Aug-2 Keys, Aylsham #572
£1200 $1860 €1800 Picking wild flowers in spring (29x41cm-11x16in) s.d.1882 W/C. 24-Sep-2 Bonhams, Knightsbridge #171/R est:800-1200

DUNCANSON, Robert S (1821-1872) American
£20062 $32500 €30093 Summer (29x41cm-11x16in) painted c.1849 prov.lit. 21-May-3 Sotheby's, New York #105/R est:20000-30000
£27778 $45000 €41667 Landscape in Scotland (27x48cm-11x19in) s.d.1870 prov.exhib. 21-May-3 Sotheby's, New York #104/R est:40000-60000
£30864 $50000 €46296 Winter (29x41cm-11x16in) s. indis d.1849 prov.lit. 21-May-3 Sotheby's, New York #106/R est:20000-30000
£185185 $300000 €277778 Garden of Eden (83x123cm-33x48in) s.d.1852 exhib.lit. 22-May-3 Christie's, Rockefeller NY #52/R est:300000-500000

DUNDAS, Douglas Robert (1900-1981) Australian
£299 $490 €434 Untitled, Canberra landscape (54x70cm-21x28in) board. 3-Jun-3 Lawson Menzies, Sydney #824 (A.D 750)
£6452 $9806 €9678 Domain (58x66cm-23x26in) s.d.33 lit. 28-Aug-2 Deutscher-Menzies, Melbourne #169/R est:20000-30000 (A.D 18000)

DUNHAM, Carroll (1949-) American
Works on paper
£1548 $2400 €2322 Untitled no.5 (104x74cm-41x29in) s. casein acrylic dry pigment pen glue executed 1981 prov. 26-Sep-2 Christie's, Rockefeller NY #835/R est:3000-5000
£1806 $2800 €2709 Untitled (44x56cm-17x22in) i.d.3/23/89 crayon pencil prov. 26-Sep-2 Christie's, Rockefeller NY #836/R est:4000-6000
£5380 $8500 €8070 Untitled (22x28cm-9x11in) d.1995 graphite in four parts prov. 12-Nov-2 Phillips, New York #149/R est:10000-15000
£17722 $28000 €26583 Mound B (165x216cm-65x85in) mixed media on linen executed 1991-92 prov. 12-Nov-2 Phillips, New York #150/R est:30000-40000
£23750 $38000 €35625 Integrated painting no.2 (178x229cm-70x90in) mixed media on linen executed 1991-92 prov.exhib. 16-May-3 Phillips, New York #135/R est:30000-40000

DUNINGTON, A (1860-c.1928) British
£1500 $2340 €2250 Grouse shooting in North Wales (40x61cm-16x24in) s.i.d.1904 verso. 10-Oct-2 Greenslade Hunt, Taunton #588/R est:1200-1600

DUNINGTON, Albert (1860-c.1928) British
£500 $775 €750 Trial races between Shamrock I and Shamrock II off Rothesay Pier, July 1901 (36x46cm-14x18in) s. 31-Oct-2 Christie's, Kensington #414/R
£500 $815 €725 Warwick Castle (30x46cm-12x18in) s.d.1878 i.d.verso. 16-Jul-3 Sotheby's, Olympia #60/R
£750 $1178 €1125 Lancashire canal scenes (36x46cm-14x18in) s.d.1896 pair. 10-Dec-2 Capes Dunn, Manchester #720/R
£1400 $2184 €2100 See-saw, the old cottage homes, Lamlash, Arran (51x76cm-20x30in) s. i.verso. 17-Sep-2 Sotheby's, Olympia #20/R est:1200-1800

DUNKELBERGER, Ralph D (1894-1965) American
£1250 $2000 €1875 Landscape of an alley in Reading (56x66cm-22x26in) s. 17-May-3 Pook & Pook, Downington #206 est:800-1000

DUNKER, Balthasar Anton (1746-1807) German
Works on paper
£611 $954 €917 Gorge near Lucern (17cm-7in circular) s.i. W/C over pencil. 6-Nov-2 Dobiaschofsky, Bern #1321/R (S.FR 1400)
£815 $1264 €1223 Man resting in wood (15x20cm-6x8in) s.d.1776 W/C sepia pen. 3-Oct-2 Koller, Zurich #3380/R est:1500-2200 (S.FR 1900)
£858 $1330 €1287 River landscape with fishermen by grotto (17x22cm-7x9in) s.d.1794 wash W/C sepia pen. 3-Oct-2 Koller, Zurich #3379/R est:2500-3500 (S.FR 2000)

D'UNKER, Carl (1829-1866) Swedish
£377 $574 €566 On the way to church (34x27cm-13x11in) s.i.d.1855. 16-Aug-2 Lilla Bukowskis, Stockholm #493 (S.KR 5500)
£2199 $3408 €3299 Street musicians (76x52cm-30x20in) s.d.1853. 3-Dec-2 Bukowskis, Stockholm #171/R est:30000-35000 (S.KR 31000)

DUNLAP, Catherine (19th C) British
Works on paper
£769 $1100 €1154 Self portrait painting (15x14cm-6x6in) i. W/C bodycol on ivory. 23-Jan-3 Swann Galleries, New York #398/R est:700-1000

DUNLAP, Loren Edward (20th C) British?
£280 $434 €420 Floral still life. s.d.1968. 29-Sep-2 Lots Road, London #351

DUNLOP, Brian James (1938-) Australian
£2439 $3854 €3537 Paddington back yard (115x165cm-45x65in) s. board. 22-Jul-3 Lawson Menzies, Sydney #207/R est:8000-12000 (A.D 6000)
£5000 $7900 €7500 Woman in interior (122x91cm-48x36in) s. plywood. 27-Nov-2 Deutscher-Menzies, Melbourne #10/R est:18000-24000 (A.D 14000)
£5000 $7750 €7500 Interior (132x174cm-52x69in) s.d.1992 prov. 3-Dec-2 Shapiro, Sydney #94/R est:15000-20000 (A.D 13850)
£6786 $10585 €10179 Eumerella I (118x152cm-46x60in) s.d.93 prov. 11-Nov-2 Deutscher-Menzies, Melbourne #27/R est:12000-18000 (A.D 19000)
£7200 $11592 €10800 Floating world (121x91cm-48x36in) s. board prov.exhib. 6-May-3 Christie's, Melbourne #46/R est:12000-15000 (A.D 18000)
£16370 $25046 €24555 Malatesta kneeling (120x196cm-47x77in) painted c.1979 prov. 26-Aug-2 Sotheby's, Paddington #665/R est:10000-15000 (A.D 46000)

Works on paper
£571 $891 €857 Fruit vendor (26x36cm-10x14in) s.d.87 gouache. 11-Nov-2 Deutscher-Menzies, Melbourne #124/R (A.D 1600)
£728 $1143 €1092 Landscape ebeneezer 1971 (28x51cm-11x20in) s. gouache. 15-Apr-3 Lawson Menzies, Sydney #255/R est:800-1200 (A.D 1900)
£860 $1308 €1290 Portrait (40x33cm-16x13in) s. chl W/C wash prov. 28-Aug-2 Deutscher-Menzies, Melbourne #352/R (A.D 2400)
£1071 $1671 €1607 Interior (60x56cm-24x22in) s. pastel. 11-Nov-2 Deutscher-Menzies, Melbourne #5/R est:3000-5000 (A.D 3000)

DUNLOP, Ronald Ossory (1894-1973) British
£280 $440 €420 Study of a horse (42x51cm-17x20in) s. 15-Apr-3 Bonhams, Knightsbridge #172
£290 $452 €435 Portrait of Lucy Carrington Wertheim (51x40cm-20x16in) exhib. 17-Sep-2 Rosebery Fine Art, London #542
£300 $492 €450 Portrait of a lady (49x39cm-19x15in) canvas on board. 3-Jun-3 Sotheby's, Olympia #85/R
£300 $495 €435 Portrait of a lady (35x25cm-14x10in) s. canvasboard. 3-Jul-3 Christie's, Kensington #462/R
£450 $702 €675 Summer landscape (36x26cm-14x10in) s. board. 17-Sep-2 Bonhams, Knightsbridge #228/R
£493 $774 €720 Coastal view (23x28cm-9x11in) s. canvasboard. 15-Apr-3 De Veres Art Auctions, Dublin #56/R
£500 $775 €750 Ships in an estuary (20x25cm-8x10in) 4-Dec-2 Christie's, Kensington #440/R
£515 $814 €773 Critics, The Bar, Paris (25x30cm-10x12in) s. i.verso canvasboard prov. 3-Apr-3 Heffel, Vancouver #19/R (C.D 1200)
£550 $886 €825 Portrait of Mrs Topham (38x28cm-15x11in) s. board. 18-Feb-3 Bonhams, Knightsbridge #28/R
£600 $936 €900 Portrait of a lady (58x48cm-23x19in) s. 27-Mar-3 Christie's, Kensington #414/R
£650 $988 €975 Hillside with figures (28x38cm-11x15in) s.d.1944 verso. 16-Aug-2 Keys, Aylsham #488/R
£670 $1058 €1005 Wooded landscape with cottage (27x37cm-11x15in) s. canvasboard. 27-Nov-2 Sotheby's, Olympia #121/R
£700 $1169 €1015 Portrait of a man with beard and hat (62x52cm-24x20in) s. 17-Jun-3 Bonhams, Knightsbridge #57/R
£750 $1185 €1125 Farmyard (51x41cm-20x16in) prov. 27-Nov-2 Sotheby's, Olympia #107/R
£773 $1221 €1160 Haystack and wheelbarrow on the farm (41x51cm-16x20in) s. prov. 3-Apr-3 Heffel, Vancouver #20/R est:1500-2000 (C.D 1800)

£800 $1304 €1200 View in Corfu (49x59cm-19x23in) s. i.overlap. 30-Jan-3 Lawrence, Crewkerne #745
£800 $1272 €1200 Winter landscape (40x50cm-16x20in) s. 5-Mar-3 John Ross, Belfast #135
£800 $1280 €1200 Cattle grazing by a river (30x30cm-12x12in) s. board. 15-May-3 Christie's, Kensington #235/R
£800 $1312 €1200 Portrait of Ginny (61x50cm-24x20in) s.i.verso. 3-Jun-3 Sotheby's, Olympia #86/R
£800 $1312 €1200 Cotswold lane (51x40cm-20x16in) s.i.verso. 3-Jun-3 Sotheby's, Olympia #88/R
£800 $1328 €1160 Littlehampton, Sussex (36x46cm-14x18in) s. board prov. 16-Jun-3 Waddingtons, Toronto #191/R est:2000-2500 (C.D 1800)
£820 $1279 €1230 Miss Caroline Besley with her cat (64x50cm-25x20in) s.i.d.1959 verso. 10-Sep-2 David Duggleby, Scarborough #343
£850 $1386 €1233 Street in Wimbledon (25x35cm-10x14in) 15-Jul-3 Bonhams, Knightsbridge #110/R
£900 $1440 €1350 Stormy sea (45x51cm-18x20in) s. board. 15-May-3 Christie's, Kensington #207/R
£986 $1637 €1400 Village street (39x49cm-15x19in) s. 10-Jun-3 James Adam, Dublin #191 est:1500-2500
£1090 $1711 €1700 Cherry blossoms (41x51cm-16x20in) s. 19-Nov-2 Whyte's, Dublin #150/R est:1800-2200
£1100 $1716 €1650 Forest landscape with figure walking along a track (63x76cm-25x30in) s. 18-Sep-2 Dreweatt Neate, Newbury #162/R est:700-900
£1100 $1804 €1650 Street scene (41x51cm-16x20in) s. 3-Jun-3 Sotheby's, Olympia #79/R est:800-1200
£1118 $1800 €1677 Port of Martiques, Bouche du Rhone (38x49cm-15x19in) s. board prov. 12-May-3 Stephan Welz, Johannesburg #30 est:4000-6000 (SA.R 13000)
£1150 $1829 €1725 Beach scene with boats before buildings. 18-Mar-3 Lawrences, Bletchingley #1295 est:350-450
£1275 $2053 €1900 Wheatfield and farmhouse (41x51cm-16x20in) s. 18-Feb-3 Whyte's, Dublin #84/R est:1500-2000
£1275 $2053 €1900 Vase of flowers before an open window (24x29cm-9x11in) s. board. 18-Feb-3 Whyte's, Dublin #110/R est:1200-1500
£1300 $2132 €1950 River landscape (39x50cm-15x20in) s. board. 3-Jun-3 Sotheby's, Olympia #98/R est:300-500
£1458 $2319 €2100 Enniscorthy, County Wexford (41x30cm-16x12in) s. i.verso. 29-Apr-3 Whyte's, Dublin #111/R est:2000-3000
£1500 $2340 €2250 Quiet way, Surrey (64x76cm-25x30in) s. prov. 26-Mar-3 Hamptons Fine Art, Godalming #173/R est:1500-2500
£1887 $2943 €3000 Woman in a blue wrap, reading (76x61cm-30x24in) s. 17-Sep-2 Whyte's, Dublin #161/R est:3000-4000
£1944 $3092 €2800 Church and churchyard (51x61cm-20x24in) s. 29-Apr-3 Whyte's, Dublin #127/R est:2500-3500
£2000 $3200 €3000 Along the promenade, Nice (41x51cm-16x20in) s. 15-May-3 Christie's, Kensington #239/R est:2500-3500
£2148 $3458 €3200 Still life (41x30cm-16x12in) prov. 18-Feb-3 Whyte's, Dublin #108/R est:3000-4000
£2244 $3478 €3500 Fishing boats, La Ciotat (32x41cm-13x16in) s. board prov. 3-Dec-2 Bonhams & James Adam, Dublin #55/R est:3000-4000
£2372 $3724 €3700 Self portrait (42x32cm-17x13in) s. i.verso prov. 19-Nov-2 Whyte's, Dublin #217/R est:3000-4000
£2500 $4000 €3750 Moored boats, Shoreham (41x51cm-16x20in) s. prov. 15-May-3 Christie's, Kensington #237/R est:2500-3500
£2500 $4000 €3750 Boatyard (51x61cm-20x24in) s. 15-May-3 Christie's, Kensington #238/R est:3000-5000
£2564 $3974 €4000 House by loch (24x31cm-9x12in) s. 3-Dec-2 Bonhams & James Adam, Dublin #89/R est:4000-6000
£2800 $4480 €4200 Pheonix Park, Dublin (58x78cm-23x31in) s. s.i.verso. 15-May-3 Christie's, Kensington #233/R est:3000-5000
£2800 $4480 €4200 White boat in Littlehampton harbour (62x76cm-24x30in) exhib. 15-May-3 Christie's, Kensington #236/R est:3000-5000
£3000 $4680 €4500 River Arun, Pulborough (52x41cm-20x16in) s. exhib. 9-Oct-2 Woolley & Wallis, Salisbury #283/R est:500-700
£3200 $4992 €4800 White boat in Littlehampton Harbour (63x76cm-25x30in) exhib. 9-Oct-2 Woolley & Wallis, Salisbury #282/R est:800-1200
£3200 $5120 €4800 Haystack in a field (41x51cm-16x20in) s. 15-May-3 Christie's, Kensington #234/R est:1200-1800

Works on paper

£360 $598 €522 London Bridge (38x56cm-15x22in) s. W/C. 12-Jun-3 Gorringes, Lewes #1655

DUNN, Andrew (fl.1800-1820) Irish

Miniatures

£1141 $1837 €1700 Harriet, daughter of George Kiernan (9x7cm-4x3in) s.d.1807 enamel porcelain prov.lit. 18-Feb-3 Whyte's, Dublin #99/R est:1500-2000

DUNN, George (?) British?

£250 $388 €375 Circus is over (22x25cm-9x10in) s. board. 4-Dec-2 John Ross, Belfast #84
£280 $409 €420 Still life (23x25cm-9x10in) s. board. 12-Jun-2 John Ross, Belfast #61
£450 $698 €675 In the paddock (41x46cm-16x18in) s. 2-Oct-2 John Ross, Belfast #81
£650 $949 €975 Two musicians (46x41cm-18x16in) s. board. 12-Jun-2 John Ross, Belfast #36

DUNN, Harvey (1884-1952) American

£7692 $12000 €11538 Barker and assembled crowds (66x86cm-26x34in) s.d.1920. 9-Nov-2 Illustration House, New York #176/R est:12000-18000
£9317 $15000 €13976 Woman with infant visiting man in bed (91x86cm-36x34in) indis.sig. 10-May-3 Illustration House, New York #98/R est:9000-12000
£12179 $19000 €18269 Deep sea diver salvaging sunken wrecks at Pearl Harbour (61x76cm-24x30in) s.d.1945. 9-Nov-2 Illustration House, New York #183/R est:10000-15000
£32051 $50000 €48077 Couple on speeding dog sled (91x61cm-36x24in) s.d.1909. 9-Nov-2 Illustration House, New York #166/R est:30000-50000

DUNN, Joseph (1806-1860) British

£1350 $2093 €2025 Chestnut hunter in a landscape (56x66cm-22x26in) s.d.47. 3-Oct-2 Heathcote Ball, Leicester #592/R

DUNN, Madge J (20th C) British?

£3200 $5120 €4800 Travellers resting (86x112cm-34x44in) s. 16-May-3 Sotheby's, London #84/R est:3000-5000

DUNN, Patrick S (19th C) British

£520 $853 €780 Mouthwatering dish. Border terrier (25x36cm-10x14in) s.d.1887 two. 5-Jun-3 Christie's, Kensington #779

DUNNE, George (?) British?

£280 $445 €420 Pre-race tactics (22x25cm-9x10in) s. board. 5-Mar-3 John Ross, Belfast #252
£300 $465 €450 Errigal, Co Donegal (23x25cm-9x10in) s. board. 2-Oct-2 John Ross, Belfast #34
£522 $815 €820 At the races (43x37cm-17x15in) s.i. board. 6-Nov-2 James Adam, Dublin #43/R
£800 $1272 €1200 Still life, coffee pot (40x45cm-16x18in) s. board. 5-Mar-3 John Ross, Belfast #92
£900 $1314 €1350 Nude study (41x46cm-16x18in) s. 12-Jun-2 John Ross, Belfast #109
£915 $1520 €1300 Jockeys in a crowd (70x76cm-28x30in) s. 10-Jun-3 James Adam, Dublin #182/R est:800-1200

DUNNINGTON, Alfred (19th C) British

Works on paper

£400 $652 €580 Fishing sail boats in a calm sea (25x33cm-10x13in) s. W/C. 17-Jul-3 Thomson, Roddick & Medcalf, Carlisle #135/R

DUNOUY, Alexandre Hyacinthe (1757-1841) French

£1958 $3270 €2800 Paysage classique avec cheval s'abreuvant (21x27cm-8x11in) mono. 25-Jun-3 Sotheby's, Paris #62/R est:2000-3000
£4038 $6138 €6300 Les adieux du hobereau (45x58cm-18x23in) s. panel. 10-Jul-2 Rabourdin & Choppin de Janvry, Paris #91/R est:4600-4800
£4423 $6723 €6900 Cour de ferme animee (45x58cm-18x23in) s.d.1794 panel. 10-Jul-2 Rabourdin & Choppin de Janvry, Paris #90/R est:6100-6300
£7534 $11753 €11000 Paysage fluvial avec montagnes en arriere-plan (49x65cm-19x26in) s. panel. 14-Apr-3 Horta, Bruxelles #175/R est:10000-15000
£17808 $27781 €26000 Vue du chateau Saint Ange (49x65cm-19x26in) s. panel. 14-Apr-3 Horta, Bruxelles #174/R est:15000-20000
£31724 $50124 €46000 The Vesuvius erupting (46x32cm-18x13in) 3-Apr-3 Porro, Milan #43/R est:35000

Works on paper

£2138 $3399 €3100 Vues d'Italie (27x38cm-11x15in) s.i. wash pair. 4-Mar-3 Livinec, Gaudcheau & Jezequel, Rennes #36/R

DUNOUY, Alexandre Hyacinthe (attrib) (1757-1841) French

£2405 $3728 €3800 Le depart du jeune couple (29x39cm-11x15in) panel. 27-Sep-2 Rabourdin & Choppin de Janvry, Paris #121/R est:3800-4000
£3526 $5359 €5500 Paysage de riviere avec pecheur. Paysage de montagne avec lavandieres (23x31cm-9x12in) pair. 10-Jul-2 Rabourdin & Choppin de Janvry, Paris #89/R est:4600-4800

DUNOYER DE SEGONZAC, Andre (1884-1974) French

£1019 $1600 €1529 Still life with fruit and vegetables (16x25cm-6x10in) s. 10-Dec-2 Doyle, New York #248/R est:3000-5000
£3500 $5530 €5250 Village (73x91cm-29x36in) s. 3-Apr-3 Christie's, Kensington #67/R

Works on paper

£311 $485 €460 Vignes (23x30cm-9x12in) s. ink. 26-Mar-3 Millon & Associes, Paris #34
£317 $526 €450 La barque sur la riviere (25x35cm-10x14in) s. pen wash dr. 11-Jun-3 Beaussant & Lefèvre, Paris #195
£340 $541 €500 Nu allonge (17x42cm-7x17in) s. ink wash. 24-Mar-3 Claude Boisgirard, Paris #46
£428 $693 €650 Hiver, vaches au pre (33x47cm-13x19in) s. ink dr. 22-Jan-3 Tajan, Paris #120
£507 $791 €750 Cafe de Boubouroche (29x24cm-11x9in) s. i.verso ink crayon dr prov. 28-Mar-3 Charbonneaux, Paris #68/R

£560 $935 €800 Champs de Vignes en Provence (37x63cm-15x25in) s. Indian ink cardboard. 26-Jun-3 Tajan, Paris #75
£568 $886 €852 Woman dreaming (16x23cm-6x9in) s.i. col pen Indian ink chl W/C. 6-Nov-2 Dobiaschofsky, Bern #1536/R (S.FR 1300)
£600 $930 €900 Nu (30x23cm-12x9in) s. pen ink paper on card. 5-Dec-2 Christie's, Kensington #99/R
£600 $948 €900 Femme nue (16x23cm-6x9in) s.i. pencil pen ink pastel W/C. 3-Apr-3 Christie's, Kensington #68/R
£641 $1000 €962 Park scene (36x53cm-14x21in) s. pen ink. 21-Sep-2 Rachel Davis, Shaker Heights #482/R est:1000-2000
£750 $1170 €1125 Plage de la Bouillabaisse, St Tropez, France (23x30cm-9x12in) s.i. i.verso W/C prov. 17-Sep-2 Bonhams, Knightsbridge #43/R
£993 $1658 €1400 Paysage champetre (53x73cm-21x29in) s. Indian ink. 18-Jun-3 Pierre Berge, Paris #146 est:1500-1800
£1132 $1800 €1698 Paysage (48x32cm-19x13in) s. W/C pe brush ink over pencil prov. 27-Feb-3 Christie's, Rockefeller NY #65/R
£1477 $2377 €2200 Paysage aux grands arbres (32x44cm-13x17in) s. ink W/C wash. 23-Feb-3 Mercier & Cie, Lille #41
£1635 $2551 €2600 Baigneuse allongee (22x31cm-9x12in) s. W/C crayon. 8-Oct-2 Christie's, Paris #168
£1700 $2754 €2550 On the beach (30x46cm-12x18in) s. pen ink W/C prov. 23-May-3 Lyon & Turnbull, Edinburgh #14/R est:2000-3000
£1892 $2951 €2800 Sentier et arbres (55x77cm-22x30in) s. W/C. 26-Mar-3 Millon & Associes, Paris #37/R
£2244 $3500 €3254 Campagne de Seine (33x48cm-13x19in) s.d. graphite. 30-Mar-3 Simpson's, Houston #204
£5696 $9000 €8544 Still life with flowers, lemons and a basket on a table (60x80cm-24x31in) s. pen ink W/C prov. 22-Apr-3 Butterfields, San Francisco #6003/R est:10000-15000
£7000 $11480 €10500 Saint-Tropez vu de Sainte-Anne (52x103cm-20x41in) s. W/C pen ink pencil prov.exhib. 6-Feb-3 Christie's, London #428/R est:15000
£11000 $18370 €16500 Nature morte de fleur et fruits (58x79cm-23x31in) s. gouache W/C pen ink prov. 26-Jun-3 Christie's, London #389/R est:10000-15000

DUNSMORE, John Ward (1856-1945) British
£400 $636 €600 Harmony, an elegant lady pianist (14x19cm-6x7in) s.d.1886 panel. 27-Feb-3 Bonhams, Chester #373
£1098 $1800 €1592 Jester (20x28cm-8x11in) s.d.1912 panel exhib. 4-Jun-3 Doyle, New York #44 est:1500-2500

DUNSTAN, Bernard (1920-) British
£600 $948 €900 Portrait of Jo Raywid (38x25cm-15x10in) init. s.i.verso board. 27-Nov-2 Sotheby's, Olympia #133/R
£750 $1230 €1125 Joggers on deck, QEII (31x21cm-12x8in) init. canvasboard. 3-Jun-3 Sotheby's, Olympia #213/R
£900 $1423 €1350 Landing stage, Venice (31x23cm-12x9in) init.i.d.86 verso canvas on board. 27-Nov-2 Sotheby's, Olympia #119/R est:1000-1500
£900 $1467 €1350 Convalescent (30x30cm-12x12in) i.d.1984 board. 13-Feb-3 David Lay, Penzance #126/R
£950 $1473 €1425 Cyclamen (28x25cm-11x10in) init. board. 3-Dec-2 Bonhams, Knightsbridge #208/R
£1000 $1580 €1500 Portrait of the artist's wife (46x36cm-18x14in) s.d.45. 27-Nov-2 Sotheby's, Olympia #134/R est:500-700
£1000 $1610 €1500 Belgrave Square (12x22cm-5x9in) init. board. 14-Jan-3 Bonhams, Knightsbridge #51
£1000 $1620 €1500 Going to bed, san gimignano (35x27cm-14x11in) init.i.d.2.74 verso board prov. 20-May-3 Sotheby's, Olympia #141/R est:1000-2000
£1100 $1727 €1650 Campo, Siena (30x22cm-12x9in) init. board. 15-Apr-3 Bonhams, Knightsbridge #72/R est:600-800
£1100 $1826 €1595 Girl at tea (7x18cm-3x7in) board prov. 10-Jun-3 Mellors & Kirk, Nottingham #852/R est:600-800
£1200 $1872 €1800 French landscape (19x22cm-7x9in) init. s.i.verso board. 12-Sep-2 Sotheby's, Olympia #62/R est:800-1200
£1200 $1860 €1800 Welsh landscape (71x91cm-28x36in) init. 3-Dec-2 Bonhams, Knightsbridge #209/R est:800-1000
£1300 $2028 €1950 Flowers in a brown jug (26x25cm-10x10in) init. board prov. 12-Sep-2 Sotheby's, Olympia #61/R est:1000-1500
£1400 $2184 €2100 Bathroom (28x22cm-11x9in) init. board. 15-Oct-2 Bonhams, Knightsbridge #1/R est:1500-2500
£1600 $2464 €2400 Nude getting out of bed (22x26cm-9x10in) init. board prov. 5-Sep-2 Christie's, Kensington #645/R est:1500-2000
£1800 $3006 €2610 New shoes, Venice (26x28cm-10x11in) init.i.d.3.81 verso board. 24-Jun-3 Bonhams, New Bond Street #81/R est:2000-3000
£2000 $3180 €3000 Four poster and mirror (25x22cm-10x9in) init. board. 26-Feb-3 Sotheby's, Olympia #322/R est:2000-3000
£2000 $3180 €3000 At the national galley (31x25cm-12x10in) init. board. 26-Feb-3 Sotheby's, Olympia #323/R est:1000-1500
£2200 $3410 €3300 Thames at Richmond (20x39cm-8x15in) init. board prov. 3-Dec-2 Bonhams, New Bond Street #53/R est:1200-1800
£2200 $3432 €3300 Cardigan St, Oxford (46x61cm-18x24in) init. i.on stretcher prov. 25-Mar-3 Bonhams, New Bond Street #71/R est:2500-3500
£2200 $3432 €3300 Nude (39x25cm-15x10in) s.i. board. 27-Mar-3 Christie's, Kensington #434/R est:1500-2000
£2400 $3744 €3600 Rehearsal III (28x30cm-11x12in) init. i.d.2.77 verso board prov. 27-Mar-3 Christie's, Kensington #437/R est:2000-3000
£2600 $4212 €3900 Albergo Stella, night II (28x28cm-11x11in) init.i.d.10.77 verso board prov. 20-May-3 Sotheby's, Olympia #151/R est:1500-2500
£2800 $4592 €4200 Flowers in a brown jug (28x25cm-11x10in) init. board prov. 6-Jun-3 Christie's, London #132/R est:3000-5000
£2800 $4620 €4060 Nude, Malvern attic room (35x27cm-14x11in) init. board. 3-Jul-3 Christie's, Kensington #511/R est:2000-3000
£3100 $5177 €4495 Heather in the studio (55x49cm-22x19in) init. i.verso. 17-Jun-3 Bonhams, Knightsbridge #78/R est:1500-2000
£3300 $5148 €4950 Nude at a mirror (29x22cm-11x9in) init. board. 15-Oct-2 Bonhams, Knightsbridge #3/R est:1200-1800
£3800 $5928 €5700 Woman taking off nightdress (39x29cm-15x11in) init. board. 12-Sep-2 Sotheby's, Olympia #93/R est:3000-5000
£4200 $6804 €6300 Lying nude with beads (26x47cm-10x19in) s. i.d.4 76 verso prov. 20-May-3 Sotheby's, Olympia #150/R est:3000-5000
Works on paper
£300 $468 €450 Head of a lady (10x10cm-4x4in) init. pastel W/C. 15-Oct-2 Bonhams, Knightsbridge #199/R
£600 $942 €900 Reclining female nude (18x25cm-7x10in) init. pastel. 15-Apr-3 Bonhams, Knightsbridge #86/R
£720 $1166 €1080 Girl with a cat (21x15cm-8x6in) init.i.d.1981 verso pastel prov. 20-May-3 Sotheby's, Olympia #145/R
£950 $1539 €1425 Dawn, winter morning (25x31cm-10x12in) init. pastel. 20-May-3 Bonhams, Knightsbridge #129/R
£1300 $2106 €1950 Breakfast in bed (23x28cm-9x11in) init. chl pastel. 20-May-3 Sotheby's, Olympia #140/R est:600-800
£1300 $2106 €1950 Pink room, Pontaix (15x16cm-6x6in) init. i.d.1981 verso pastel prov. 20-May-3 Sotheby's, Olympia #144/R est:500-700
£2200 $3432 €3300 Nude (24x35cm-9x14in) init. col chk. 12-Sep-2 Sotheby's, Olympia #45/R est:2000-3000

DUNTON, W Herbert (1878-1936) American
£12048 $20000 €17470 July afternoon in Taos Canyon (24x20cm-9x8in) s. canvasboard prov. 11-Jun-3 Butterfields, San Francisco #4109/R est:20000-30000
£13924 $22000 €20190 Truce (74x51cm-29x20in) s. board prov.exhib.lit. 26-Jul-3 Coeur d'Alene, Hayden #126/R est:25000-35000
£71759 $116250 €104051 Buffalo runners (61x81cm-24x32in) 23-May-3 Altermann Galleries, Santa Fe #72
£81944 $132750 €118819 JT McMullin, guide (36x36cm-14x14in) board. 23-May-3 Altermann Galleries, Santa Fe #71
£108974 $170000 €163461 Orange bonnet (51x41cm-20x16in) 9-Nov-2 Altermann Galleries, Santa Fe #104

DUNTZE, Johannes Bertholomaus (1823-1895) German
£949 $1500 €1500 Norwegian fjord with small settlement in background (27x35cm-11x14in) i.d.49 panel. 30-Nov-2 Berlinghof, Heidelberg #308/R est:2000
£1410 $2214 €2200 Winter afternoon on the ice (52x76cm-20x30in) s.d.1895. 21-Nov-2 Van Ham, Cologne #1581/R est:4000
£1761 $2747 €2800 Norwegian fjord landscape (72x113cm-28x44in) s.d.1882. 21-Sep-2 Berlinghof, Heidelberg #119/R est:3900
£2014 $3223 €2800 Mountain lake with sawmill (48x62cm-19x24in) s.d.1864. 17-May-3 Lempertz, Koln #1389/R est:3000
£2025 $3139 €3200 Mountain lake (61x92cm-24x36in) s.d.1882. 28-Sep-2 Hans Stahl, Hamburg #54/R est:3800
£2692 $4227 €4200 Late Barock buildings by frozen river (59x92cm-23x36in) s.d.1841. 21-Nov-2 Van Ham, Cologne #1582/R est:7000
£3816 $5953 €5724 Man flyfishing in mountain lake (61x94cm-24x37in) s.d.1890 indis.i.stretcher. 21-Oct-2 Blomqvist, Oslo #350/R est:50000-70000 (N.KR 44000)
£9000 $14130 €13500 Skaters on a frozen lake, beside a castle (61x96cm-24x38in) s.d.1872. 19-Nov-2 Bonhams, New Bond Street #27/R est:6000-8000

DUNZENDORFER, Albrecht (1907-1980) Austrian
£641 $1013 €1000 Landscape with stream (49x39cm-19x15in) s. s.d.1977 verso panel. 18-Nov-2 Dorotheum, Linz #267/R
£897 $1418 €1400 Upper Aisttal (58x42cm-23x17in) s. s.i.d.1974 verso panel. 18-Nov-2 Dorotheum, Linz #266/R
£1439 $2302 €2000 Muhlviertel landscape with mountains (50x70cm-20x28in) s.d.1949 panel. 14-May-3 Dorotheum, Linz #399/R est:2600-2800
£1583 $2532 €2200 Muhlviertel landscape (90x100cm-35x39in) s. panel. 14-May-3 Dorotheum, Linz #391/R est:4000-4500
£1583 $2532 €2200 Curling (75x98cm-30x39in) s.d.1948 panel. 14-May-3 Dorotheum, Linz #395/R est:4400-4800
£1871 $2993 €2600 Old sawmill (70x100cm-28x39in) s.d.70 i. verso panel. 14-May-3 Dorotheum, Linz #404/R est:3200-3800
£2014 $3223 €2800 Lower Muhlviertel (59x79cm-23x31in) s. i. verso panel. 14-May-3 Dorotheum, Linz #394/R est:3200-3800
£2590 $4144 €3600 Muhlviertel landscape (60x90cm-24x35in) s. s.i.d.1974 verso panel. 14-May-3 Dorotheum, Linz #389/R est:3600-3800

DUPAGNE, Adrien (1889-1980) Belgian
£256 $403 €400 Cour de ferme, en Espagne (50x60cm-20x24in) s. 11-Dec-2 Hotel des Ventes Mosan, Brussels #243
£426 $711 €600 Nu dans un interieur (81x65cm-32x26in) s.d.1958. 18-Jun-3 Hotel des Ventes Mosan, Brussels #270
£513 $795 €800 Jeune femme nue a la mantille (93x71cm-37x28in) s.d.1948. 9-Dec-2 Horta, Bruxelles #301
£538 $839 €850 Nature morte a la casserole bleue (68x47cm-27x19in) s. panel exhib. 16-Oct-2 Hotel des Ventes Mosan, Brussels #173

£544 $865 €800 L'espagnole (80x65cm-31x26in) s. 19-Mar-3 Hotel des Ventes Mosan, Brussels #282
£641 $1006 €1000 Paysan assis (66x45cm-26x18in) s.d.1922 panel. 11-Dec-2 Hotel des Ventes Mosan, Brussels #254

DUPAGNE, Arthur (1895-1961) Belgian
Sculpture
£943 $1453 €1500 Jeune Africaine assise (44cm-17in) pat plaster. 22-Oct-2 Campo, Vlaamse Kaai #493
£3597 $5755 €5000 Nu drape (142cm-56in) s. pat plaster. 13-May-3 Palais de Beaux Arts, Brussels #68/R est:4000-6000

DUPAIN, Edmond (1847-?) French
£650 $1060 €975 Romantic couple with their faithful companion (79x52cm-31x20in) s. 12-Feb-3 Bonhams, Knightsbridge #272m/R

DUPAIN, Max Spencer (1911-1992) Australian
Photographs
£1500 $2370 €2250 Street at Central (43x37cm-17x15in) s.d.1938 silver gelatin photo. 27-Nov-2 Deutscher-Menzies, Melbourne #308/R est:2000-4000 (A.D 4200)
£1571 $2483 €2357 Mother and child (29x36cm-11x14in) s.d.1946 silver gelatin photo. 27-Nov-2 Deutscher-Menzies, Melbourne #310/R est:3000-5000 (A.D 4400)
£1705 $2712 €2558 Orchid (39x29cm-15x11in) s. silver gelatin photo. 5-May-3 Sotheby's, Melbourne #180/R est:3000-5000 (A.D 4400)
£1779 $2722 €2669 Jean with wire mesh (49x35cm-19x14in) s.d.38 silver gelatin print. 25-Aug-2 Sotheby's, Paddington #91/R est:6000-8000 (A.D 5000)
£1786 $2804 €2679 Sunbaker (50x58cm-20x23in) bears another sig.d.10.10.02 verso silver gelatin print prov. 25-Nov-2 Christie's, Melbourne #256/R est:6000-8000 (A.D 5000)
£1860 $2958 €2790 Nude in sunlight (30x22cm-12x9in) s.d.41 vintage silver gelatin photo. 5-May-3 Sotheby's, Melbourne #179/R est:4000-6000 (A.D 4800)
£2132 $3390 €3198 Flower form, solarisation (50x37cm-20x15in) s. solarised silver gelatin photo. 5-May-3 Sotheby's, Melbourne #181/R est:5000-8000 (A.D 5500)
£2132 $3390 €3198 Sunbaker (38x40cm-15x16in) s.i.d.39 silver gelatin rint prov. 5-May-3 Sotheby's, Melbourne #182/R est:5000-7000 (A.D 5500)
£2321 $3644 €3482 Rhythmic forms (33x48cm-13x19in) bears another sig.d.10.10.02 verso vintage print prov. 25-Nov-2 Christie's, Melbourne #258/R est:6000-8000 (A.D 6500)
£2321 $3644 €3482 Sun dazzle (23x29cm-9x11in) s.i.d. bears another sig.d.10.10.02 verso vintage print prov. 25-Nov-2 Christie's, Melbourne #259/R est:4500-6000 (A.D 6500)
£2321 $3644 €3482 Meat queue, Sydney (36x50cm-14x20in) s.i.d. silver gelatin print exec.c.1960 prov. 25-Nov-2 Christie's, Melbourne #260/R est:7000-10000 (A.D 6500)
£2330 $3541 €3495 Surf race start, Manly Beach (33x36cm-13x14in) s.d.40's silver gelatin photo exec.c.1940. 28-Aug-2 Deutscher-Menzies, Melbourne #284/R est:4500-6000 (A.D 6500)
£2669 $4084 €4004 Meat queue (34x49cm-13x19in) s.d.46 silver gelatin print. 25-Aug-2 Sotheby's, Paddington #83/R est:5000-7000 (A.D 7500)
£3559 $5445 €5339 At Newport (39x47cm-15x19in) s.d.52 silver gelatin print. 25-Aug-2 Sotheby's, Paddington #82/R est:7000-9000 (A.D 10000)
£6228 $9528 €9342 Sunbaker (34x41cm-13x16in) s.d.37 silver gelatin print. 25-Aug-2 Sotheby's, Paddington #81/R est:6000-9000 (A.D 17500)
£6762 $10345 €10143 Bondi (43x38cm-17x15in) s.d.39 black white photograph. 25-Aug-2 Sotheby's, Paddington #100/R est:6000-8000 (A.D 19000)

DUPAIN, Rex (20th C) ?
Photographs
£3025 $4628 €4538 Nude suit (97x97cm-38x38in) s.d.96 photograph oil on paper. 25-Aug-2 Sotheby's, Paddington #129/R est:5000-8000 (A.D 8500)

DUPARC, Amauny (20th C) ?
£300 $471 €450 Abstract (33x41cm-13x16in) s. s.verso. 16-Apr-3 Christie's, Kensington #932/R

DUPAS, Jean (1882-1964) French
£22581 $35000 €33872 Woman with flowered hat (102x62cm-40x24in) mono. board prov. 6-Dec-2 Sotheby's, New York #146/R est:35000-45000
Prints
£2177 $3461 €3200 L'enlevement d'Europe (65x80cm-26x31in) s.d.1932 black lithograph. 28-Feb-3 Tajan, Paris #2/R est:2500-3000
Works on paper
£443 $700 €700 Enfant au tambour (30x21cm-12x8in) Chinese ink. 1-Dec-2 Livinec, Gaudcheau & Jezequel, Rennes #30/R
£516 $815 €800 Le harem (25x19cm-10x7in) s.d. gouache two sheets. 17-Dec-2 Rossini, Paris #24
£3846 $6038 €6000 Cape d'hermine (41x30cm-16x12in) s.d.1929 crayon dr. 20-Nov-2 Claude Boisgirard, Paris #11/R

DUPIUS, Paul (20th C) French
Works on paper
£300 $495 €435 Comme nos Maitres (20x48cm-8x19in) s.i. pencil pen red ink W/C. 3-Jul-3 Christie's, Kensington #211

DUPLESSI-BERTAUX, Jean (1747-1819) French
Works on paper
£473 $738 €700 Bonaparte au siege de Toulon (24x42cm-9x17in) i.verso sanguine. 31-Mar-3 Paris #70

DUPLESSIS, Jean Claude (attrib) (18th C) French
Sculpture
£170139 $268819 €245000 Apollon vainqueur du serpent Python (68x34x23cm-27x13x9in) pat bronze exec.c.1700 prov. 25-Apr-3 Beaussant & Lefèvre, Paris #76/R est:50000-60000
£336806 $532153 €485000 Enlevement de Dejanire. Enlevement d'une sabine (50x38x34cm-20x15x13in) bronze after J de Bologne and F Girardon pair. 25-Apr-3 Beaussant & Lefèvre, Paris #75/R est:80000-100000

DUPLESSIS, Michel (18th C) French
£4025 $6279 €6400 Halte de cavaliers. Cavaliers a l'abreuvoir (19x26cm-7x10in) s. pair. 10-Oct-2 Ribeyre & Baron, Paris #21/R est:4500-6000
£5755 $9209 €8000 Le passage du gue (47x39cm-19x15in) s. 13-May-3 Vanderkindere, Brussels #124/R est:7000-10000
£6013 $9500 €9500 Paysans sur la place. Bohemiens sur la place (24x33cm-9x13in) s. panel pair. 27-Nov-2 Christie's, Paris #66/R est:7000-10000
£10968 $17329 €17000 Scene de campement militaire (43x58cm-17x23in) s. panel. 18-Dec-2 Tajan, Paris #49/R est:12000

DUPON, Josue (1864-1935) Belgian
Sculpture
£6329 $9873 €10000 Saint George on horseback (94x54x26cm-37x21x10in) s. brown pat bronze incl marble base. 21-Oct-2 Bernaerts, Antwerp #38/R est:10000-12000

DUPON, Josue (after) (1864-1935) Belgian
Sculpture
£5696 $8829 €9000 Boy riding a camel (45cm-18in) i. bronze. 25-Sep-2 Christie's, Amsterdam #576/R est:10000-15000

DUPONT, Emile (19th C) French
£1346 $2127 €2100 Jeune femme, des fleurs dans les cheveux (66x47cm-26x19in) s. oval. 18-Nov-2 Tajan, Paris #171/R est:2200-2400

DUPONT, François Leonard (attrib) (1756-1821) Belgian
£3654 $5773 €5700 Paysage a Tivoli (68x56cm-27x22in) painted c.1787. 14-Nov-2 Credit Municipal, Paris #19/R est:3000-5000

DUPONT, Gainsborough (1755-1797) British
£1538 $2200 €2307 Portrait of officer (76x63cm-30x25in) 22-Jan-3 Doyle, New York #154/R
£2500 $3900 €3750 Wooded landscape with a ruined tower, woodcutter, horse and sheep (41x54cm-16x21in) prov.exhib.lit. 7-Nov-2 Christie's, Kensington #72/R est:3000-5000
£3200 $5056 €4800 Portrait of Lady Baillie (90x69cm-35x27in) 28-Nov-2 Sotheby's, London #189/R est:3000-5000

DUPONT, Gainsborough (attrib) (1755-1797) British
£366 $600 €531 Portrait of Lady Gratham (51x64cm-20x25in) painted oval. 4-Jun-3 Doyle, New York #45
£1900 $3097 €2755 Gentleman with his dog in a landscape (56x41cm-22x16in) 21-Jul-3 Bonhams, Bath #47/R est:1500-2500

DUPONT, Jean (1934-) Belgian
£1389 $2208 €2000 Untitled (50x71cm-20x28in) s. 5-May-3 Bernaerts, Antwerp #404/R

DUPONT, Louis Richard François (attrib) (1734-1765) French
£1603 $2516 €2500 Portrait de la Carabillon (74x63cm-29x25in) oval. 14-Dec-2 Artcurial Briest, Paris #58/R

DUPONT, Richard John Munro (19/20th C) British
£850 $1352 €1275 Hyperion and Alcide and a stable lad in a yard (60x75cm-24x30in) s. 29-Apr-3 Rowley Fine Art, Newmarket #409/R

DUPONT, V (19/20th C) French?
£1208 $1945 €1800 Jour de marche au sablon (80x100cm-31x39in) d.1910. 18-Feb-3 Galerie Moderne, Brussels #281/R est:1000-1500

DUPRAT, Albert Ferdinand (1882-?) Italian
£946 $1476 €1400 Martigues (46x65cm-18x26in) s. 28-Mar-3 Neret-Minet, Paris #16/R
£1026 $1620 €1600 Canal a Venise (55x38cm-22x15in) s. 18-Nov-2 Tajan, Paris #148 est:2000-3000
£1410 $2228 €2200 Canal a Venise (55x38cm-22x15in) s. 18-Nov-2 Tajan, Paris #147/R est:2000-3000
£2215 $3434 €3500 Canal a Venise (54x73cm-21x29in) s. 27-Sep-2 Rabourdin & Choppin de Janvry, Paris #15/R est:4200-4500

DUPRAY, Henry-Louis (1841-1909) French
£676 $1054 €1000 La charge des militaires (23x33cm-9x13in) s. panel. 31-Mar-3 Rossini, Paris #32
£833 $1300 €1250 Cavalry soldier with horse (27x20cm-11x8in) s.d.1887. 20-Sep-2 Sloan, North Bethesda #418/R est:1000-1500
£1346 $2100 €2019 Cavalry soldiers (46x32cm-18x13in) s. oil paper on masonite. 20-Sep-2 Sloan, North Bethesda #417/R est:2000-4000
£1781 $2778 €2600 Soldiers on battlefield (41x33cm-16x13in) s. 10-Apr-3 Van Ham, Cologne #1408/R est:2800
£1800 $2808 €2700 Napoleon with his officers (39x32cm-15x13in) s.d.1891 prov. 17-Sep-2 Sotheby's, Olympia #236/R est:2000-3000

DUPRE, Georges (1807-1853) French
£709 $1184 €1000 Shipwrecked people (43x60cm-17x24in) s. canvas on cardboard. 23-Jun-3 Bernaerts, Antwerp #137/R

DUPRE, Henri (20th C) French
£361 $600 €523 Landscape with children and ducks (61x91cm-24x36in) s. 11-Jun-3 Boos Gallery, Michigan #330/R

DUPRE, Jules (1811-1889) French
£769 $1208 €1200 Paysage (12x9cm-5x4in) mono. panel. 13-Dec-2 Piasa, Paris #95
£833 $1342 €1250 Evening shoreline (15x31cm-6x12in) bears s. i. verso panel. 7-May-3 Dobiaschofsky, Bern #471/R (S.FR 1800)
£1034 $1655 €1500 Coup de lumiere sur canal (19x24cm-7x9in) s. 14-Mar-3 Libert, Castor, Paris #45
£1411 $2229 €2117 Homeward bound (72x111cm-28x44in) s. 18-Nov-2 Waddingtons, Toronto #240/R est:3500-5000 (C.D 3500)
£1667 $2633 €2600 Landscape with cows watering beneath stormy skies (39x33cm-15x13in) s. panel prov. 15-Nov-2 Reiss & Sohn, Konigstein #23/R est:4000
£2201 $3566 €3191 Paysage anime (31x22cm-12x9in) s. 26-May-3 Rasmussen, Copenhagen #1289/R est:25000 (D.KR 23000)
£2254 $3628 €3200 Farmstead in autumn landscape in the evening (32x43cm-13x17in) s. panel lit. 9-May-3 Schloss Ahlden, Ahlden #1502/R est:2800
£2658 $4200 €3987 Troupeaux s'abbrevant pres des moulins (19x26cm-7x10in) s. panel pair. 1-Apr-3 Christie's, Rockefeller NY #199/R est:4000-6000
£2793 $4524 €4050 Harvesting time (29x41cm-11x16in) s. cardboard. 26-May-3 Bukowskis, Stockholm #253a/R est:25000-30000 (S.KR 36000)
£2917 $4638 €4200 Vaches au bord de l'eau (26x32cm-10x13in) s. panel prov. 29-Apr-3 Christie's, Amsterdam #106/R est:3000-5000
£5346 $8233 €8500 Avant la tempete (55x66cm-22x26in) s. exhib. 23-Oct-2 Christie's, Amsterdam #85/R est:8000-12000
£5500 $8965 €7975 Lake landscape with figures (54x81cm-21x32in) s. 16-Jul-3 Sotheby's, Olympia #176/R est:6000-8000
£13924 $22000 €20886 Bateaux de pecheurs pres de Cayeaux (46x73cm-18x29in) s. prov.exhib. 24-Apr-3 Sotheby's, New York #110/R est:8000-12000
£22152 $35000 €33228 La lande - moorland (41x60cm-16x24in) s. panel prov.exhib. 24-Apr-3 Sotheby's, New York #109/R est:15000-20000

Works on paper
£2162 $3373 €3200 Moutons et chevaux dans un paysage (19x34cm-7x13in) s. W/C gouache. 27-Mar-3 Maigret, Paris #112

DUPRE, Jules (attrib) (1811-1889) French
£377 $581 €600 Forest clearing (11x8cm-4x3in) mono. i. verso panel. 23-Oct-2 Neumeister, Munich #630/R

DUPRE, Julien (1851-1910) French
£2244 $3522 €3500 La mare (22x32cm-9x13in) mono. panel. 16-Dec-2 Millon & Associes, Paris #150 est:3600-4000
£5479 $8603 €8000 Cow in landscape (46x55cm-18x22in) s. 15-Apr-3 Sotheby's, Amsterdam #62/R est:8000-12000
£27465 $45592 €39000 Fermiere et ses vaches (65x82cm-26x32in) s. 11-Jun-3 Beaussant & Lefèvre, Paris #26/R est:15000-20000
£145570 $230000 €218355 Au retour de la moisson (93x129cm-37x51in) s.d.1880 prov.exhib. 23-Apr-3 Christie's, Rockefeller NY #47/R est:180000-250000

DUPRE, Julien (attrib) (1851-1910) French
£480 $759 €720 Hay harvest (24x33cm-9x13in) 14-Nov-2 Stuker, Bern #183 (S.FR 1100)

DUPRE, Victor (1816-1879) French
£759 $1267 €1100 La gardienne de vaches et ses vaches a l'etang (38x45cm-15x18in) s. panel. 8-Jul-3 Gioffredo, Nice #134
£873 $1380 €1310 Small landscape (16x27cm-6x11in) s. panel. 14-Nov-2 Stuker, Bern #184/R est:2000-3000 (S.FR 2000)
£1200 $1920 €1800 River landscape at sunset (22x41cm-9x16in) s. panel. 13-May-3 Bonhams, Knightsbridge #278/R est:800-1200
£1400 $2296 €2100 Cattle watering at a lakeside cottage (26x38cm-10x15in) s. panel. 5-Jun-3 Christie's, Kensington #694/R est:800-1200
£1411 $2229 €2117 Peasants in a sunlit farm landscape (27x45cm-11x18in) s. panel. 18-Nov-2 Waddingtons, Toronto #241/R est:4000-5000 (C.D 3500)
£1646 $2600 €2600 Bergere et ses moutons pres de la mare (19x30cm-7x12in) s. panel. 1-Dec-2 Peron, Melun #20
£2109 $3353 €3100 Pecheurs au bord d'une mare (43x65cm-17x26in) s. panel. 26-Feb-3 Artcurial Briest, Paris #109/R est:3000-4000

DUPRE, Victor (attrib) (1816-1879) French
£463 $745 €695 Summer river landscape (9x18cm-4x7in) panel. 7-May-3 Dobiaschofsky, Bern #472 (S.FR 1000)

DUPUIS, Maurice (1882-1959) French
£406 $650 €609 Edwardian woman with her dog (36x28cm-14x11in) s. 12-Jan-3 William Jenack, New York #90
£1224 $1947 €1800 Le barque echouee (73x100cm-29x39in) s. 18-Mar-3 Galerie Moderne, Brussels #280 est:1500-2400

DUPUIS, Pierre (attrib) (1610-1682) French
£5674 $8794 €8511 Landscape with still life of fruit (108x108cm-43x43in) 3-Dec-2 Bukowskis, Stockholm #452/R est:100000-150000 (S.KR 80000)

DUPUY, Jean (1925-) French
£1352 $2082 €2150 Tchernobyl (24x27cm-9x11in) s.d.1986. 26-Oct-2 Cornette de St.Cyr, Paris #156/R

DUPUY, Lawrence (19th C) French
Sculpture
£1060 $1727 €1600 Daneuse aux cymbales (64cm-25in) s. pat bronze. 17-Feb-3 Horta, Bruxelles #38

DUPUY, Louis (19/20th C) French
£2535 $4082 €3600 Cargo mixte et voiliers. batiment de commerce a quai (16x22cm-6x9in) s. panel pair. 11-May-3 Thierry & Lannon, Brest #171/R est:2700-3000

DUPUY, Marthe (19/20th C) French
£276 $439 €400 Nature morte aux raisins (43x61cm-17x24in) s.d.93. 4-Mar-3 Livinec, Gaudcheau & Jezequel, Rennes #13

DUPUY, Paul Michel (1869-1949) French
£741 $1052 €1200 Femme dans le jardin (38x46cm-15x18in) init. 16-Mar-3 Eric Pillon, Calais #88/R
£3718 $5837 €5800 Enfants jouant dans le Parc Monceau (46x55cm-18x22in) s. panel. 15-Dec-2 Eric Pillon, Calais #70/R
£4400 $6996 €6600 La cueillette des fleurs (42x57cm-17x22in) s. board prov. 20-Mar-3 Sotheby's, Olympia #134/R est:4000-6000

DUQUESNOY, François (attrib) (1594-1643) Flemish
Works on paper
£850 $1420 €1233 Study of a sleeping infant (7x12cm-3x5in) i. black chk sold with another by same hand. 9-Jul-3 Bonhams, Knightsbridge #18/R

DUQUESNOY, François (studio) (1594-1643) Flemish
Sculpture
£7000 $11690 €10150 The Virgin (59cm-23in) white marble incl white marble socle. 8-Jul-3 Sotheby's, London #147/R est:6000-8000

DURA, Alberto (1888-1971) Uruguayan
£594 $950 €891 Landscape (29x34cm-11x13in) s. 5-Jan-3 Galleria Y Remates, Montevideo #82/R
£688 $1100 €1032 Flowerbed in the park (44x34cm-17x13in) s.d.1997 cardboard. 5-Jan-3 Galleria Y Remates, Montevideo #81/R

£1000 $1600 €1500 El Miguelete (42x49cm-17x19in) s. cardboard. 5-Jan-3 Galleria Y Remates, Montevideo #79/R
£2281 $3650 €3422 View of Avenida 18 Julio (61x43cm-24x17in) s.d.1931 cardboard. 5-Jan-3 Galleria Y Remates, Montevideo #80/R
£2500 $4000 €3750 Landscape in Aigua (47x78cm-19x31in) s.d.1937. 5-Jan-3 Galleria Y Remates, Montevideo #124/R

DURACK, Elizabeth (1915-2000) Australian
Works on paper
£632 $960 €948 Woman and children gathering food (43x58cm-17x23in) s. W/C. 19-Aug-2 Joel, Victoria #193 est:1200-1500 (A.D 1800)
£857 $1354 €1286 Wanderers (43x57cm-17x22in) s. W/C. 18-Nov-2 Goodman, Sydney #8/R (A.D 2400)

DURAN, Carolus (1837-1917) French
£2390 $3681 €3800 Trotteuse (55x37cm-22x15in) s.i.d.1902. 28-Oct-2 Il Ponte, Milan #245/R
£2695 $4501 €3800 Portrait de Madame Sylvain Chateau (84x62cm-33x24in) s.d.1901. 18-Jun-3 Piasa, Paris #8/R est:3200-3500
£3226 $5097 €5000 Portrait o young lady (55x46cm-22x18in) s. 18-Dec-2 Ferri, Paris #35/R
£29032 $45000 €43548 Portrait of Helena Modjeska (190x105cm-75x41in) s. prov. 30-Oct-2 Christie's, Rockefeller NY #181/R est:25000-35000
Works on paper
£329 $520 €520 Portrait d'homme (15x12cm-6x5in) s.d.68 crayon chk. 28-Nov-2 Tajan, Paris #205

DURAN, Carolus (attrib) (1837-1917) French
£1100 $1738 €1650 Back view of the artist red haired model (89x71cm-35x28in) 2-Dec-2 Gorringes, Lewes #2815/R est:1200-1500

DURAN, Rafael (1931-) Spanish
£1655 $2632 €2400 Landscape (50x65cm-20x26in) s. 4-Mar-3 Ansorena, Madrid #185/R

DURANCAMPS, Rafael (1891-1979) Spanish
£4000 $6280 €6000 Rincon del taller - corner in the artist's studio (24x33cm-9x13in) s. painted c.1933-35 prov. 19-Nov-2 Sotheby's, London #69/R est:4000-6000
£8581 $13557 €13300 Rue ensoleillee aux trois promeneurs (38x46cm-15x18in) s. 17-Dec-2 Rossini, Paris #73/R
£13793 $21931 €20000 Landscape with village (46x61cm-18x24in) s. 4-Mar-3 Ansorena, Madrid #162/R
£16000 $25120 €24000 Fantasia sobre Cadaques - capriccio view of Cadaques (54x81cm-21x32in) s. board painted c.1950-60. 19-Nov-2 Sotheby's, London #64/R est:15000-20000
£22000 $34540 €33000 El escorial en otono - escorial in autumn (73x92cm-29x36in) s. painted September 1958 prov.lit. 19-Nov-2 Sotheby's, London #63/R est:22000-28000

DURAND, A V (19/20th C) American?
Works on paper
£263 $400 €395 View of wharves at Marblehead (36x56cm-14x22in) s.d.1912 W/C. 17-Aug-2 North East Auctions, Portsmouth #88

DURAND, Asher Brown (1796-1886) American
£8917 $14000 €13376 Boating on the Fourth of July (18x28cm-7x11in) s. card. 10-Dec-2 Doyle, New York #11/R est:10000-15000

DURAND, J (19th C) American
£443 $700 €665 Lake and mountainscape with fisherman (56x91cm-22x36in) s.d.73. 26-Apr-3 Thomaston Place, Thomaston #127/R

DURAND, L (?) ?
£828 $1292 €1300 Romantic landscape with ox cart (34x47cm-13x19in) s. panel. 8-Nov-2 Auktionhaus Georg Rehm, Augsburg #8038/R

DURAND, Simon (1838-1896) Swiss
£1223 $1907 €1835 Man with copper pan in hand standing by open window (34x50cm-13x20in) st.init. paper on canvas. 20-Nov-2 Fischer, Luzern #1252/R est:3000-4000 (S.FR 2800)
£1582 $2453 €2500 Jeune fille et enfants a la pelote (34x37cm-13x15in) s. panel. 29-Sep-2 Eric Pillon, Calais #81/R

DURAND-BRAGER, Jean Baptiste Henri (1814-1879) French
£1300 $2106 €1950 Deserted harbour (25x49cm-10x19in) s. panel. 21-May-3 Christie's, Kensington #664/R est:600-800
£2200 $3432 €3300 Constantinople (31x22cm-12x9in) s. panel. 26-Mar-3 Sotheby's, Olympia #229/R est:1000-1500
£6000 $10020 €9000 Shipping outside the port (62x106cm-24x42in) s. 18-Jun-3 Christie's, Kensington #20/R est:4000-6000
£6500 $10140 €9750 View of Istanbul (47x78cm-19x31in) s.i.d.7 Mai 78 board. 15-Oct-2 Sotheby's, London #89/R est:5000-7000

DURANGEL, Leopold (1828-1898) French
£649 $987 €1000 Young girl sitting thinking before landscape with volcano (60x81cm-24x32in) s.i. 6-Jul-2 Berlinghof, Heidelberg #201/R

DURANTON, Andre (1905-) French
£764 $1192 €1200 Orange en foret (46x55cm-18x22in) s. s.i.verso. 5-Nov-2 Tajan, Paris #27/R
£955 $1490 €1500 Epicerie Crochet (38x55cm-15x22in) s. s.i.verso. 5-Nov-2 Tajan, Paris #25/R
£1241 $1961 €1800 Promenade sur e Mississippi (38x46cm-15x18in) s. i.verso. 4-Apr-3 Tajan, Paris #98/R

DURBAN, Arne (1912-1993) Norwegian
Sculpture
£1480 $2367 €2220 Seated nude (31x14x13cm-12x6x5in) s.d.1943 bronze. 17-Mar-3 Blomqvist, Oslo #396/R est:18000-22000 (N.KR 17000)
£1504 $2377 €2256 Standing nude female (47x7x11cm-19x3x4in) s. bronze. 28-Apr-3 Blomqvist, Oslo #370/R est:15000-18000 (N.KR 17000)
£2207 $3399 €3311 Girl dressing and smiling (41cm-16in) s. bronze. 28-Oct-2 Blomqvist, Lysaker #1032/R est:25000-27000 (N.KR 26000)
£9162 $14385 €13743 Girl with dove (101cm-40in) s. bronze lit. 21-Nov-2 Grev Wedels Plass, Oslo #43/R est:80000-100000 (N.KR 105000)

DURBIN, Leslie (?) British
Sculpture
£4878 $8000 €7073 Eagle spreading his wings (76cm-30in) st.f.Morris Singer silver coral base. 4-Jun-3 Christie's, Rockefeller NY #108/R est:8000-12000

DURCK, Friedrich (1809-1884) German
£2700 $4320 €4050 Man showing a picture of a saint to a young girl holding a chicken (117x92cm-46x36in) s. 11-Mar-3 Bonhams, Knightsbridge #318/R est:1500-2000

DUREAU, George (1930-) American
£949 $1500 €1424 Big Chief Wingy (81x76cm-32x30in) s.i.verso. 16-Nov-2 New Orleans Auction, New Orleans #1585/R est:1800-2500
£1069 $1700 €1604 Along the Levee (76x102cm-30x40in) s. oil wash pastel over chl. 22-Mar-3 New Orleans Auction, New Orleans #1077/R est:1200-1800
£1384 $2200 €2076 Alexander warrior with phrygian helmet (76x102cm-30x40in) s. oil wash pastel over chl. 22-Mar-3 New Orleans Auction, New Orleans #1075/R est:2000-4000
Works on paper
£220 $350 €330 Standing nude with mask (71x56cm-28x22in) s. chl. 22-Mar-3 New Orleans Auction, New Orleans #1074/R
£416 $650 €624 Centaurs (33x33cm-13x13in) s. chl. 12-Oct-2 Neal Auction Company, New Orleans #1416
£617 $1000 €926 Bust portrait (58x74cm-23x29in) s. chl dr. 24-Jan-3 New Orleans Auction, New Orleans #1046/R est:1200-1800
£617 $1000 €926 Torso of Troy (76x102cm-30x40in) s. chl dr. 24-Jan-3 New Orleans Auction, New Orleans #1047/R est:1200-1800
£2469 $4000 €3704 Mapplethorpe with horns (76x102cm-30x40in) s.d.1983 chl dr. 24-Jan-3 New Orleans Auction, New Orleans #1044/R est:4500-7000

DUREL, Auguste (1904-) French
£364 $594 €550 Les grands pins (92x55cm-36x22in) s.verso. 1-Feb-3 Claude Aguttes, Neuilly #155

DUREL, Gaston (1879-1954) French
£641 $1006 €1000 Marche a Touggourt. Portrait (45x55cm-18x22in) s. panel double-sided. 16-Dec-2 Gros & Delettrez, Paris #313

DURENCEAU, Andre (20th C) ?
£4037 $6500 €6056 Seminude woman in lush garden setting (117x117cm-46x46in) s. 10-May-3 Illustration House, New York #112/R est:5000-7000

DURENNE, Eugène Antoine (1860-1944) French
£306 $487 €450 Labours de printemps (25x40cm-10x16in) s. cardboard. 27-Feb-3 Chochon-Barre & Allardi, Paris #129/R
£306 $487 €450 Villeneuve Loubet (27x41cm-11x16in) s. paper painted 1929. 27-Feb-3 Chochon-Barre & Allardi, Paris #134
£306 $487 €450 Haut de Cagnes (24x31cm-9x12in) s. paper painted 1925. 27-Feb-3 Chochon-Barre & Allardi, Paris #139
£306 $487 €450 Bord de er a Cagnes (23x30cm-9x12in) st.sig. paper painted 1929. 27-Feb-3 Chochon-Barre & Allardi, Paris #140

£306 $487 €450 Var (21x30cm-8x12in) st.sig. paper. 27-Feb-3 Chochon-Barre & Allardi, Paris #148
£544 $865 €800 Mas et cypres (25x35cm-10x14in) s. paper painted 1930. 27-Feb-3 Chochon-Barre & Allardi, Paris #143/R
£748 $1190 €1100 Port de Rouen (34x41cm-13x16in) st.sig. paper. 27-Feb-3 Chochon-Barre & Allardi, Paris #147/R
£1042 $1656 €1500 La lecon de piano (38x46cm-15x18in) s. 29-Apr-3 Artcurial Briest, Paris #158 est:1200-1500

DURER, Albrecht (1471-1528) German
Prints
£1689 $2635 €2500 Suaire porte par deux anges (10x14cm-4x6in) engraving. 31-Mar-3 Tajan, Paris #38/R
£1887 $2943 €3000 Horse (17x12cm-7x5in) copperplate. 11-Oct-2 Winterberg, Heidelberg #229/R est:2800
£1899 $3000 €3000 Virgin Mary with two angels holding crown (15x10cm-6x4in) copperplate. 29-Nov-2 Bassenge, Berlin #5189/R est:4000
£1923 $3000 €2885 Beast with the horns like a lamb (39x28cm-15x11in) woodcut. 7-Nov-2 Swann Galleries, New York #167/R est:3000-5000
£1950 $3042 €3100 Young peasant and wife (10x7cm-4x3in) copperplate. 11-Oct-2 Winterberg, Heidelberg #228/R est:2450
£2000 $3320 €3000 Desiderius Erasmus (25x19cm-10x7in) i.verso engraving exec.c.1550. 10-Jun-3 Sworder & Son, Bishops Stortford #498/R est:2000-3000
£2027 $3162 €3000 St Christopher with birds (21x14cm-8x6in) mono. woodcut. 28-Mar-3 Dorotheum, Vienna #17/R est:1500-1700
£2100 $3276 €3150 Nativity (18x12cm-7x5in) engraving. 10-Oct-2 Sotheby's, London #183/R est:1500-2000
£2113 $3507 €3000 St Anne and Mary with Child (12x7cm-5x3in) copperplate. 12-Jun-3 Hauswedell & Nolte, Hamburg #69/R est:2000
£2152 $3400 €3400 Two angels holding shroud (10x14cm-4x6in) copperplate. 29-Nov-2 Bassenge, Berlin #5188/R est:2500
£2200 $3630 €3190 Penance of St John Chrysostom (18x12cm-7x5in) engraving exec.c.1497. 1-Jul-3 Sotheby's, London #19/R est:3000-3500
£2215 $3500 €3500 Annunciation (30x21cm-12x8in) woodcut. 29-Nov-2 Bassenge, Berlin #5170/R est:3000
£2308 $3600 €3462 St Jerome in his cell (23x16cm-9x6in) woodcut. 7-Nov-2 Swann Galleries, New York #184/R est:3000-5000
£2308 $3600 €3462 Man of sorrows with hands outstretched (12x7cm-5x3in) engraving exec.c.1500. 6-Nov-2 Swann Galleries, New York #23/R est:3000-5000
£2308 $3600 €3462 Coat of arms with a lion and cock (19x12cm-7x5in) engraving exec.c.1503. 6-Nov-2 Swann Galleries, New York #26/R est:5000-8000
£2390 $3800 €3585 Virgin and Child crowned by two angels (15x10cm-6x4in) engraving. 1-May-3 Swann Galleries, New York #147/R est:5000-8000
£2400 $3960 €3480 Christ in limbo (39x28cm-15x11in) woodcut. 1-Jul-3 Sotheby's, London #15/R est:1500-2000
£2400 $3960 €3480 Three genii (11x7cm-4x3in) engraving exec.c.1505. 1-Jul-3 Sotheby's, London #20/R est:2500-3000
£2446 $3914 €3400 The dream (18x12cm-7x5in) copperplate. 13-May-3 Hartung & Hartung, Munich #4022/R est:2400
£2568 $4006 €3800 Vierge nourissant l'Enfant (12x7cm-5x3in) engraving. 31-Mar-3 Tajan, Paris #40 est:2000
£2600 $4030 €3900 Christ before Caiaphas (12x8cm-5x3in) engraving. 3-Dec-2 Christie's, London #25/R est:1200-1800
£2600 $4030 €3900 Bagpiper (11x7cm-4x3in) engraving. 4-Dec-2 Bonhams, New Bond Street #34/R est:1200-1800
£2600 $4056 €3900 Bath house (39x28cm-15x11in) woodcut executed c.1498. 25-Mar-3 Sotheby's, London #11/R est:1000-1500
£2690 $4303 €3900 Baiser de Judas (12x7cm-5x3in) burin. 13-Mar-3 Artcurial Briest, Paris #9
£2756 $4355 €4300 La dame a cheval et le lansquenet. print. 14-Nov-2 Libert, Castor, Paris #9/R est:1250
£2800 $4340 €4200 Erasmus of Rotterdam (25x19cm-10x7in) engraving. 3-Dec-2 Christie's, London #33/R est:2500-3500
£2800 $4620 €4060 Virgin and Child seated by a tree (12x7cm-5x3in) etching. 2-Jul-3 Christie's, London #17/R est:3000-5000
£2821 $4400 €4232 Virgin and Child on a grassy bank (11x7cm-4x3in) engraving. 6-Nov-2 Swann Galleries, New York #25/R est:3000-5000
£2903 $4268 €4500 Knight, death and devil (24x19cm-9x7in) copperplate. 20-Jun-2 Dr Fritz Nagel, Stuttgart #660/R est:5000
£3000 $4950 €4350 Opening of the fifth and sixth seals (39x28cm-15x11in) woodcut. 1-Jul-3 Sotheby's, London #11/R est:2000-2500
£3205 $5000 €4808 Little fortune (12x7cm-5x3in) engraving exec.c.1497. 7-Nov-2 Swann Galleries, New York #161/R est:5000-8000
£3205 $5000 €4808 Virgin on the crescent with a sceptre and starry crown (12x7cm-5x3in) engraving. 6-Nov-2 Swann Galleries, New York #34/R est:3500-5000
£3378 $5270 €5000 Burial of Christ (38x27cm-15x11in) mono. woodcut. 28-Mar-3 Dorotheum, Vienna #18/R est:3000-3400
£3500 $5775 €5075 Saint George on foot (12x7cm-5x3in) engraving. 2-Jul-3 Christie's, London #20/R est:2000-3000
£3521 $5845 €5000 Animal with lambshorns (39x28cm-15x11in) woodcut. 12-Jun-3 Hauswedell & Nolte, Hamburg #82/R est:4500
£3526 $5147 €5500 Mary with sceptre and crown of stars. copperplate. 4-Jun-2 Karl & Faber, Munich #13/R est:6000-7000
£3716 $5797 €5500 Cuisinier et sa femme (11x8cm-4x3in) engraving. 31-Mar-3 Tajan, Paris #42/R
£3800 $5890 €5700 Virgin and child seated by a well (15x10cm-6x4in) engraving prov. 3-Dec-2 Christie's, London #27/R est:4000-6000
£3800 $5890 €5700 St. Paul (18x12cm-7x5in) engraving. 5-Dec-2 Sotheby's, London #8/R est:3000-3500
£3846 $6000 €5769 Peasant and his wife (11x8cm-4x3in) engraving exec.c.1497-98. 6-Nov-2 Swann Galleries, New York #19/R est:7000-10000
£4000 $6200 €6000 Adam and Eve (24x19cm-9x7in) engraving. 3-Dec-2 Christie's, London #24/R est:2000-3000
£4167 $6500 €6251 Interlaced cord pattern with heart shaped center (27x21cm-11x8in) mono. woodcut. 6-Nov-2 Swann Galleries, New York #29/R est:8000-12000
£4167 $6500 €6251 Bagpiper (12x8cm-5x3in) engraving. 6-Nov-2 Swann Galleries, New York #31/R est:3000-5000
£4231 $6177 €6600 Mary with Child by tree. mono.i. copperplate. 4-Jun-2 Karl & Faber, Munich #12/R est:8000-9000
£4808 $7500 €7212 Christ on the cross (13x10cm-5x4in) engraving. 7-Nov-2 Swann Galleries, New York #178/R est:5000-8000
£4808 $7500 €7212 Christ on the cross (13x10cm-5x4in) engraving. 6-Nov-2 Swann Galleries, New York #30/R est:5000-8000
£5000 $8250 €7250 Babylonian hore (39x28cm-15x11in) woodcut. 1-Jul-3 Sotheby's, London #13/R est:5000-7000
£5031 $8000 €7547 Small horse (16x11cm-6x4in) engraving. 1-May-3 Swann Galleries, New York #140/R est:4000-6000
£6090 $9500 €9135 Sea monster (25x19cm-10x7in) engraving exec.c.1500. 6-Nov-2 Swann Galleries, New York #22/R est:8000-12000
£6207 $9807 €9000 Maria with children by tree (12x7cm-5x3in) copperplate. 4-Apr-3 Venator & Hansten, Koln #1432 est:4500
£6410 $10000 €9615 Promenade (20x12cm-8x5in) i.verso engraving exec.c.1496-98. 6-Nov-2 Swann Galleries, New York #20/R est:7000-10000
£6500 $10075 €9750 Virgin and child with a monkey (18x12cm-7x5in) engraving executed c.1498. 5-Dec-2 Sotheby's, London #7/R est:6000-8000
£6500 $10725 €9425 Prodigal son (25x19cm-10x7in) engraving. 1-Jul-3 Sotheby's, London #6/R est:7000-8000
£6646 $10500 €10500 St Hubert, also known as Eutsachius (36x26cm-14x10in) copperplate. 29-Nov-2 Bassenge, Berlin #5190/R est:6000
£6731 $9827 €10500 Mary with Child by wall. copperplate. 4-Jun-2 Karl & Faber, Munich #14/R est:8000-9000
£8000 $12400 €12000 Virgin and child with a pear (16x11cm-6x4in) engraving. 3-Dec-2 Christie's, London #28/R est:7000-10000
£8000 $12400 €12000 Virgin and child on the crescent with a hairband (12x8cm-5x3in) engraving. 5-Dec-2 Sotheby's, London #6/R est:6000-8000
£12500 $19375 €18750 Adam and Eve (25x19cm-10x7in) engraving. 4-Dec-2 Bonhams, New Bond Street #32/R est:2000-3000
£14103 $22000 €21155 Four horsemen (40x29cm-16x11in) woodcut. 6-Nov-2 Swann Galleries, New York #21/R est:15000-20000
£14103 $22000 €21155 Knight, death and the devil (25x19cm-10x7in) engraving. 6-Nov-2 Swann Galleries, New York #32/R est:25000-35000
£15064 $21994 €23500 St Hieronymous. copperplate. 4-Jun-2 Karl & Faber, Munich #15/R est:10000-11000
£28000 $43400 €42000 Little passion (13x10cm-5x4in) woodcut album. 5-Dec-2 Sotheby's, London #11/R est:30000-35000
£58000 $95700 €84100 Melencolia (24x19cm-9x7in) engraving. 1-Jul-3 Sotheby's, London #8/R est:30000-35000
£120000 $186000 €180000 Saint Jerome in his study (24x19cm-9x7in) engraving prov. 3-Dec-2 Christie's, London #30/R est:120000-180000

DURER, Albrecht (style) (1471-1528) German
£14085 $23380 €20000 Christ tortured in winepress (172x121cm-68x48in) s.d.1858 stretcher prov. 11-Jun-3 Dorotheum, Vienna #164/R est:7000-9000
Works on paper
£13000 $20150 €19500 Three studies of ostrich (36x24cm-14x9in) pen ink gouache prov.exhib. 9-Dec-2 Bonhams, New Bond Street #54/R est:3000-5000

DURET, Francisque-Joseph (1804-1864) French
Sculpture
£2183 $3450 €3275 Bacchus (92cm-36in) bronze. 28-Nov-2 Louis Morton, Mexico #240/R est:60000 (M.P 35000)
£2200 $3432 €3300 Neapolitan dancer (44cm-17in) s.st.f.Delafontaine brown pat bronze. 9-Apr-3 Sotheby's, London #142/R est:1500-2000
£3797 $5924 €6000 Figure of Flora (99cm-39in) s. marble. 21-Oct-2 Bernaerts, Antwerp #552/R est:4000-5000

DURET-DUJARRIC, Isabelle (1949-) French
£1500 $2370 €2250 Deux cypres (64x49cm-25x19in) s.d.87 card. 3-Apr-3 Christie's, Kensington #267/R
£9500 $14725 €14250 Eau douce (32x25cm-13x10in) s.d.93 oil on paper. 5-Dec-2 Christie's, Kensington #267/R est:4000-6000
Works on paper
£1500 $2325 €2250 La corbeille fleurie (46x61cm-18x24in) s.i.d.96 pencil brush ink pastel bodycol. 5-Dec-2 Christie's, Kensington #269/R est:1500-2000
£7500 $11850 €11250 Printemps (56x74cm-22x29in) i.d.2000 pencil brush ink pastel bodycol. 3-Apr-3 Christie's, Kensington #265/R

DUREUIL, Michel (20th C) French
£641 $1000 €962 Monte carlo (66x81cm-26x32in) s. i.stretcher prov. 5-Nov-2 Arthur James, Florida #165

DUREY, René (1890-1959) French
£279 $444 €419 Road through Issy (54x64cm-21x25in) s. i.verso. 5-Mar-3 Rasmussen, Copenhagen #2045/R (D.KR 3000)
£471 $773 €683 Nature morte aux tomates et asperges (74x23cm-29x9in) s. 4-Jun-3 AB Stockholms Auktionsverk #2491/R (S.KR 6000)

DURHAM, J (1814-1877) British
£1795 $2800 €2693 Hunt scenes with setters (36x56cm-14x22in) s. pair. 21-Sep-2 Pook & Pook, Downington #342/R est:1000-1500

DURHAM, William Henry (19th C) British
£480 $758 €720 Four prize Ayrshire cattle at Knockdon farm (61x91cm-24x36in) s.d.1895. 7-Apr-3 Bonhams, Bath #111
£500 $790 €750 Knockdon Polly family, five pedigree Ayrshire cows in a spring landscape (61x91cm-24x36in) s.d.1895. 7-Apr-3 Bonhams, Bath #107

DURIEUX, Caroline (1896-1989) American
£270 $427 €405 Heraldic shield (89x89cm-35x35in) s.d.1962 board. 17-Nov-2 Lots Road, London #341

DURIEZ, Irene (1950-) ?
Sculpture
£1282 $2013 €2000 Un groupe d'un nu couche (116x97x35cm-46x38x14in) black pat bronze stone socle. 16-Dec-2 Bernaerts, Antwerp #626 est:2000-3000

DURIG, Rolf (1926-) Swiss
£1048 $1635 €1572 Parrots in tree (100x51cm-39x20in) s.i.d.54. 6-Nov-2 Dobiaschofsky, Bern #481/R est:3500 (S.FR 2400)
£1048 $1635 €1572 Parrots in tree (100x51cm-39x20in) s.i.d.54. 6-Nov-2 Dobiaschofsky, Bern #482/R est:3500 (S.FR 2400)

DURKIN, Tom (1928-1990) British
£350 $571 €508 Portrait of a young girl seated holding a doll (76x65cm-30x26in) s. board. 17-Jul-3 Tennants, Leyburn #807

DURNER, Hans (1896-1981) Austrian
£350 $546 €550 Huts in front of the Matterhorn (36x48cm-14x19in) mono. paper. 7-Nov-2 Allgauer, Kempten #2793/R

DURR, Louis (1896-1973) Swiss
£324 $522 €486 Jungfrau (34x44cm-13x17in) s.d.40 i. stretcher. 7-May-3 Dobiaschofsky, Bern #477/R (S.FR 700)
£393 $613 €590 Lake Thun (33x46cm-13x18in) s.d.1924. 6-Nov-2 Dobiaschofsky, Bern #485/R (S.FR 900)
£423 $693 €613 Mountain pine (60x42cm-24x17in) s.d.50. 4-Jun-3 Fischer, Luzern #2058/R (S.FR 900)
£611 $954 €917 Sunny mountain landscape with Gletscher (69x59cm-27x23in) s.d.58. 8-Nov-2 Dobiaschofsky, Bern #149/R (S.FR 1400)
£699 $1090 €1049 Spring landscape at Thun lake with Stockhorn in the background (46x46cm-18x18in) s.d.48. 8-Nov-2 Dobiaschofsky, Bern #148/R (S.FR 1600)

DURRANT, Ivan (1947-) Australian
£800 $1288 €1200 Swampy landscape (90x120cm-35x47in) s.d.72 board prov. 6-May-3 Christie's, Melbourne #326 est:2000-4000 (A.D 2000)

DURRANT, Roy Turner (1925-1998) British
£650 $1027 €975 White house (24x30cm-9x12in) s. board. 27-Nov-2 Sotheby's, Olympia #313/R
£800 $1264 €1200 Wet spring, Surrey canal, Camberwell (25x33cm-10x13in) init.d.48 canvasboard exhib. 27-Nov-2 Sotheby's, Olympia #312/R
Works on paper
£260 $411 €390 Lavenham Church in the distance (48x58cm-19x23in) s.d.1953 gouache prov.exhib. 12-Nov-2 Rosebery Fine Art, London #698
£300 $474 €450 Yellow tulips, a study (57x41cm-22x16in) initd.48 i.verso gouache prov. 12-Nov-2 Rosebery Fine Art, London #692
£300 $474 €450 Lavenham from the far fields (48x58cm-19x23in) s.d.1953 gouache prov.exhib. 12-Nov-2 Rosebery Fine Art, London #694
£380 $623 €570 Aerial form (21x28cm-8x11in) s.d.1952 W/C gouache. 3-Jun-3 Sotheby's, Olympia #277/R
£450 $738 €675 Image, July (32x20cm-13x8in) s.i.d.56 gouache. 3-Jun-3 Sotheby's, Olympia #266/R
£600 $948 €900 Plants (28x38cm-11x15in) s.d.1952 W/C crayon gouache. 27-Nov-2 Sotheby's, Olympia #311/R
£800 $1312 €1200 Flowers, Lavenham (18x25cm-7x10in) s.d.54 s.i.d.verso mixed media. 3-Jun-3 Sotheby's, Olympia #276/R

DURRBACH, Rene (1911-) French
Works on paper
£1154 $1812 €1800 Untitled (64x50cm-25x20in) bears mono. W/C prov. 24-Nov-2 Laurence Calmels, Paris #120/R

DURRIE, George Henry (1820-1863) American
£5590 $9000 €8385 Near Lyndhurst, Hampshire (71x91cm-28x36in) s.d.1862 i.stretcher. 20-Jan-3 Arthur James, Florida #79
£14384 $21000 €21576 Log cart. Cabin in winter (25x20cm-10x8in) board pair prov.lit. 3-Nov-1 North East Auctions, Portsmouth #736/R

DURY, Tony (1819-?) French
£900 $1404 €1350 Portrait of a gentleman, smoking a cigar (73x63cm-29x25in) s.d.1850. 8-Apr-3 Bonhams, Knightsbridge #140/R
£4500 $7065 €6750 Beater's rest (72x93cm-28x37in) s.i. i.on stretcher. 21-Nov-2 Tennants, Leyburn #848/R est:1000-1500

DUSA, Ferdis (1888-1958) German
£1032 $1630 €1548 From Beskydy mountains (100x110cm-39x43in) s. 30-Nov-2 Dorotheum, Prague #110/R (C.KR 50000)

DUSART, Cornelis (1660-1704) Dutch
£613 $1000 €889 Dutch figures outside a tavern (74x66cm-29x26in) 18-Jul-3 Du Mouchelle, Detroit #2136/R est:700-1200
£7194 $11511 €10000 Peasants by a doorway with a piper player, through an open arch (23x18cm-9x7in) indis sig. panel prov. 14-May-3 Christie's, Amsterdam #133/R est:7000-10000
£28302 $43868 €45000 Peasants outside an inn (60x50cm-24x20in) s.d.1683 prov.exhib.lit. 2-Oct-2 Dorotheum, Vienna #104/R est:58000-65000
Prints
£1923 $3000 €2885 Violin player seated in the inn (28x25cm-11x10in) etching roulette. 7-Nov-2 Swann Galleries, New York #198/R est:1000-1500
£2000 $3100 €3000 Large village fair (26x33cm-10x13in) etching. 3-Dec-2 Christie's, London #42/R est:1400-1800
Works on paper
£1852 $3000 €2778 Study of old man in hat (8x7cm-3x3in) pen ink wash over chk prov. 21-Jan-3 Sotheby's, New York #150/R est:4000
£10828 $16892 €17000 Corner of a kitchen with a pump and skink (18x19cm-7x7in) pen brown ink grey wash over black red chk prov.exhib. 5-Nov-2 Sotheby's, Amsterdam #69/R est:6000-8000

DUSART, Cornelis (attrib) (1660-1704) Dutch
£724 $1172 €1100 Le maitre d'ecole (40x32cm-16x13in) 21-Jan-3 Galerie Moderne, Brussels #263

DUSART, Cornelis (style) (17th C) Dutch
£9434 $14528 €15000 Scene d'interieur de taverne hollandaise (106x92cm-42x36in) 25-Oct-2 Tajan, Paris #58/R est:10000-15000

DUSART, Cornelis and OSTADE, Isaac van (17th C) Dutch
Works on paper
£2548 $3975 €4000 Boy pushing a baby in a wheelbarrow (7x7cm-3x3in) pen brown ink W/C htd white over black chk. 5-Nov-2 Sotheby's, Amsterdam #71/R est:4000-6000

DUSCH, Anton Carl (1760-1829) German
£510 $795 €765 Wooded landscape with nymphs bathing (46x39cm-18x15in) panel exhib. 5-Aug-2 Rasmussen, Vejle #149/R (D.KR 6000)

DUSHANKEVICH, Evgeny (20th C) Russian
Works on paper
£1800 $2916 €2700 Working in Filonov's forge (25x18cm-10x7in) pen col ink. 21-May-3 Sotheby's, London #215/R est:1000-1500

DUSSEAME, Marcel (1897-1932) ?
Works on paper
£260 $406 €390 Rail and air transport (51x66cm-20x26in) s. ink gouache. 13-Oct-2 Lots Road, London #336

DUTCH SCHOOL
£8000 $13040 €12000 Town scene with canal and soldiers (43x60cm-17x24in) 29-Jan-3 Dreweatt Neate, Newbury #187/R est:3000-5000
£9677 $15000 €14516 Cupid and Venus (25x20cm-10x8in) copper. 2-Nov-2 North East Auctions, Portsmouth #97/R est:3000-5000
£87097 $135000 €130646 Poseidon and bride in his chariot (30x23cm-12x9in) i.verso panel. 2-Nov-2 North East Auctions, Portsmouth #96/R est:2500-4500

DUTCH SCHOOL, 17th C
£833 $1292 €1300 Vue d'un village avec quatre villageois (45x70cm-18x28in) panel. 3-Dec-2 Campo & Campo, Antwerp #120/R
£6000 $9780 €8700 Seascape with partially dismasted vessel in stormy seas (56x92cm-22x36in) i. prov. 17-Jul-3 Tennants, Leyburn #810/R est:3000-5000
£6294 $10510 €9000 Etude de main tenant un bouquet de fleurs pres d'un coquillage (20x17cm-8x7in) copper. 27-Jun-3 Piasa, Paris #30/R est:9000-12000
£6419 $10014 €9500 Vanity (81x117cm-32x46in) 26-Mar-3 Pierre Berge, Paris #27/R
£6500 $10205 €9750 Persecution of protestants by the Duke of Alba (89x161cm-35x63in) panel. 10-Dec-2 Bonhams, New Bond Street #182/R est:5000-7000
£6731 $10433 €10500 Marine with ships (106x157cm-42x62in) 4-Dec-2 Finarte, Rome #870/R est:4500
£7556 $12542 €10956 Young prince (94x63cm-37x25in) panel. 16-Jun-3 Waddingtons, Toronto #245/R est:3000-5000 (C.D 17000)
£7643 $11924 €12000 Sea battle with men-o-war, galleons and other sailing ships (36x101cm-14x40in) mono. panel prov.exhib.lit. 5-Nov-2 Sotheby's, Amsterdam #29/R est:12000-18000
£7643 $11924 €12000 Christ and the adulterous woman (107x140cm-42x55in) prov.exhib. 5-Nov-2 Sotheby's, Amsterdam #118/R est:8000-12000
£7914 $12584 €11871 Bouquet of roses, tulips and poppies in vase on ledge (92x71cm-36x28in) 5-Mar-3 Rasmussen, Copenhagen #1641/R est:50000-75000 (D.KR 85000)
£8387 $13251 €13000 Still life with apricots and grapes (29x21cm-11x8in) s.d.1676 panel. 18-Dec-2 Tajan, Paris #26/R est:18000
£8654 $13413 €13500 Dutch boats on choppy sea (105x140cm-41x55in) 6-Dec-2 Millon & Associes, Paris #12/R est:6000
£9220 $14291 €13830 Company resting by inn (80x82cm-31x32in) 8-Dec-2 Uppsala Auktionskammare, Uppsala #25/R est:100000-125000 (S.KR 130000)
£9494 $15000 €15000 Campment scene (48x71cm-19x28in) indis.sig. panel. 2-Dec-2 Rieunier, Paris #62/R est:10000
£10072 $16115 €14000 Vanitas still life with musical instruments and score, globe, skull (107x158cm-42x62in) i. 13-May-3 Sotheby's, Amsterdam #13/R est:15000-20000
£13836 $21585 €22000 Portrait of Anne de Joigny de Pomele (117x84cm-46x33in) 20-Sep-2 Millon & Associes, Paris #740/R est:25000-40000
£14103 $22141 €22000 Portrait of young man with fur stole (65x52cm-26x20in) 21-Nov-2 Van Ham, Cologne #1402/R est:4000
£14783 $23061 €22175 Peasants drinking and making merry (49x67cm-19x26in) panel. 16-Sep-2 Philippe Schuler, Zurich #3478/R est:8000-10000 (S.FR 34000)
£17241 $27414 €25000 Coupe de fruits, fruits et verre de vin voisinant sur un entablement (50x60cm-20x24in) 7-Mar-3 Rabourdin & Choppin de Janvry, Paris #64/R est:26000-28000
£19753 $32000 €29630 Vanitas still life with a bust, seashells, books and a glass flasks (78x91cm-31x36in) prov.exhib. 24-Jan-3 Christie's, Rockefeller NY #145/R est:15000-20000
£20645 $32619 €32000 Cortege d'indigenes d'Amerique Centrale avec animeaux (50x153cm-20x60in) panel. 17-Dec-2 Palais de Beaux Arts, Brussels #423/R est:5000-7000
£30137 $47014 €44000 Portrait of young girl holding fruit (71x55cm-28x22in) panel. 10-Apr-3 Van Ham, Cologne #1219/R est:10000

DUTCH SCHOOL, 17th/18th C
£4487 $7000 €6731 Travellers crossing a stone bridge (89x114cm-35x45in) i.verso prov. 12-Apr-3 Weschler, Washington #523/R est:10000-15000
£7424 $11581 €11136 Kitchen still life (81x114cm-32x45in) 6-Nov-2 Dobiaschofsky, Bern #669/R est:5000 (S.FR 17000)

DUTCH SCHOOL, 18th C
£4545 $7000 €6818 Dutch men-o-war off the coast (34x43cm-13x17in) 4-Sep-2 Christie's, Rockefeller NY #248/R est:4000-6000
£5400 $8532 €7830 Cathedral interior (99x119cm-39x47in) panel. 22-Jul-3 Gorringes, Lewes #1732/R est:1500-2000
£6623 $10795 €10000 Dentist (57x83cm-22x33in) 11-Feb-3 Castellana, Madrid #381/R est:13000
£7692 $12077 €12000 Messenger on horseback bringing bad news to elegant figures (110x149cm-43x59in) 21-Nov-2 Van Ham, Cologne #1367/R est:10000
£8333 $13083 €13000 Halte de cavaliers (87x124cm-34x49in) 13-Dec-2 Pierre Berge, Paris #69/R
£13422 $21609 €20000 Aphrodite and Diana (136x126cm-54x50in) set of four. 18-Feb-3 Sotheby's, Amsterdam #1111/R

Miniatures
£22000 $36080 €31900 Prince Henry Casimir II of Nassau-Dietz. Princess Henrietta Amalia of Anhalt-Dessau (7x5cm-3x2in) tortoiseshell surrounds gilt metal frames pair. 3-Jun-3 Christie's, London #62/R est:2000-3000

DUTCH SCHOOL, 19th C
£7359 $11407 €11039 Still life of fruit with glasses (33x45cm-13x18in) i. verso. 24-Sep-2 Koller, Zurich #6546 est:600-900 (S.FR 17000)
£8500 $13260 €12750 Young woman seated at window plucking fowl, boy behind holding apple (36x30cm-14x12in) bears sig. panel prov. 10-Apr-3 Sotheby's, London #47/R
£8805 $13648 €14000 Landscape with ice skaters (43x57cm-17x22in) 29-Oct-2 Dorotheum, Vienna #180/R est:2000-2500
£11218 $17612 €17500 Paysage fluvial au soleil couchant (56x78cm-22x31in) panel. 19-Nov-2 Vanderkindere, Brussels #443/R est:3500-5000
£11348 $18950 €16000 Nature morte au vase de fleurs sur un entablement (78x60cm-31x24in) pair. 18-Jun-3 Tajan, Paris #106/R est:8000-10000
£18987 $29430 €30000 Flowers and fruit (82x106cm-32x42in) i. 25-Sep-2 Neumeister, Munich #684/R est:8000

DUTEIL, Jean Claude (1950-) French
£563 $907 €800 Le vainqueur (50x61cm-20x24in) s. 12-May-3 Lesieur & Le Bars, Le Havre #25

DUTEURTRE, Pierre Eugène (1911-) French
£280 $451 €420 Mother and child (60x50cm-24x20in) s. 18-Feb-3 Bonhams, Knightsbridge #172

DUTILLEUX, Constant (1807-1865) French
Works on paper
£316 $494 €500 Paysage anime (24x12cm-9x5in) mono. sanguine. 18-Oct-2 Rabourdin & Choppin de Janvry, Paris #13

DUTILLIEU, Jacques-Charles (1718-1782) French
£12195 $20000 €18293 Carnations and other flowers in urn. Parrot tulip and other flowers in urn (74x60cm-29x24in) one s.d.1741 pair. 30-May-3 Christie's, Rockefeller NY #5/R est:25000-35000

DUTILLIEU, Jef (1876-1960) Belgian
£355 $561 €550 Port de peche (53x62cm-21x24in) s. 17-Dec-2 Galerie Moderne, Brussels #818
£408 $649 €600 Peniches au bord du canal au Marly (30x45cm-12x18in) s. panel. 18-Mar-3 Vanderkindere, Brussels #16
£1800 $2988 €1800 Bords de riviere avant l'orage. Bords de riviere apres l'orage (75x100cm-30x39in) s. two. 16-Jun-3 Horta, Bruxelles #188 est:1000-1200

DUTKIEWICZ, Wladyslaw (1918-) Australian/Polish
£360 $580 €522 Holocaust (76x106cm-30x42in) init. board painted c.1958. 12-May-3 Joel, Victoria #270 est:1000-1500 (A.D 900)

DUTTON, Thomas G (c.1819-1891) British
Works on paper
£380 $593 €570 St. Michael's Mount from the Cornish Coast (24x52cm-9x20in) s.d.1877 W/C bodycol. 6-Nov-2 Bonhams, Chester #394

DUVAL, Alix (1848-?) French
£400 $632 €600 Musketeer in a courtyard (32x24cm-13x9in) s. panel. 14-Nov-2 Christie's, Kensington #41/R

DUVAL, Ambrose (18/19th C) French
Miniatures
£1524 $2500 €2286 Theodore March (8x5cm-3x2in) s.d.1817 gilt brass frame oval. 8-Feb-3 Neal Auction Company, New Orleans #324/R est:1500-2500

DUVAL, Edward J (fl.1876-1916) British
£900 $1287 €1350 Tranquil river landscape (61x91cm-24x36in) s. 28-Feb-2 Greenslade Hunt, Taunton #443/R
Works on paper
£380 $600 €570 Woodland river landscape (107x74cm-42x29in) s.d.94 W/C. 17-Dec-2 Gorringes, Lewes #1472

DUVAL, Étienne (1824-1914) Swiss
£4167 $6708 €6042 Two landscapes (50x42cm-20x17in) s. high-oval pair. 9-May-3 Dobiaschofsky, Bern #7/R est:11000 (S.FR 9000)

DUVAL, F (19/20th C) French
£948 $1554 €1450 Still life (59x45cm-23x18in) s. 7-Feb-3 Oger, Dumont, Paris #88/R

DUVAL, J (?) ?
£296 $421 €480 Priere (16x22cm-6x9in) s. panel. 17-Mar-2 Galerie de Chartres, Chartres #111

DUVAL, Pierre (19/20th C) French
Sculpture
£121795 $188782 €190000 Untitled (27x18x10cm-11x7x4in) s.d.1789 terracotta pair. 9-Dec-2 Rabourdin & Choppin de Janvry, Paris #57/R est:45000

DUVAL-GOZLAN, Léon (1853-1941) French
£1354 $2207 €1950 Chamieres pres du chemin en Bretagne (48x66cm-19x26in) s. 19-Jul-3 Thierry & Lannon, Brest #327 est:2000-3000
£2465 $3968 €3500 Pecheur en barque (50x78cm-20x31in) s. 11-May-3 Thierry & Lannon, Brest #173/R est:2000-2500

DUVAL-LECAMUS, Jules Alexandre (1814-1878) French
£3357 $5606 €4800 La visite a la grand-mere (65x54cm-26x21in) s. 25-Jun-3 Pierre Berge, Paris #34/R est:4500-5000

DUVALL, John (1816-1892) British
£320 $502 €480 Cattle resting by a pasture with a pond and cattle in the distance (20x41cm-8x16in) s. 10-Dec-2 Rosebery Fine Art, London #692/R
£1700 $2635 €2550 Pony and dogs with the day's bag (26x38cm-10x15in) s. 30-Sep-2 Bonhams, Ipswich #480/R est:1500-2000

DUVERGER, Theophile Emmanuel (1821-1886) French
£4500 $7155 €6750 First smoke (15x13cm-6x5in) s. panel prov. 20-Mar-3 Christie's, Kensington #100/R est:4000-6000
£15000 $23550 €22500 Petit dejeuner (32x40cm-13x16in) s. panel. 21-Nov-2 Christie's, Kensington #52/R est:8000-12000
£15484 $24000 €23226 Patient pet (32x24cm-13x9in) s. panel prov. 30-Oct-2 Christie's, Rockefeller NY #154/R est:10000-15000

DUVET, Jean (1485-?) French
Prints
£24359 $38487 €38000 La licorne purifie une source. etching. 14-Nov-2 Libert, Castor, Paris #10/R est:20000

DUVIEUX, Henri (?-1882) French
£944 $1492 €1416 Oriental city scene (26x20cm-10x8in) s. 29-Nov-2 Zofingen, Switzerland #2422 (S.FR 2200)
£1154 $1812 €1800 Vue du Bosphore (40x65cm-16x26in) s. 21-Nov-2 Neret-Minet, Paris #33
£1154 $1812 €1800 Sunset on the Bosphorous with ships in Istanbul harbour (21x30cm-8x12in) s. panel. 21-Nov-2 Van Ham, Cologne #1583 est:800
£1202 $1899 €1803 View of Venice (35x65cm-14x26in) s. 29-Nov-2 Zofingen, Switzerland #2421 est:1500 (S.FR 2800)
£1223 $1907 €1835 Venice at sunset (40x65cm-16x26in) s. 6-Nov-2 Dobiaschofsky, Bern #490/R est:3500 (S.FR 2800)
£1282 $2013 €2000 Gondole a Venise (22x15cm-9x6in) s. panel. 15-Dec-2 Eric Pillon, Calais #23/R
£1481 $2385 €2222 Sunset over the Lagoon, Venice (40x65cm-16x26in) s. 7-May-3 Dobiaschofsky, Bern #479/R est:3600 (S.FR 3200)
£2053 $3346 €3100 La lagune a Venise (40x65cm-16x26in) s. 16-Feb-3 Mercier & Cie, Lille #255/R est:3000-4000
£2113 $3507 €3000 Venis au soleil couchant (24x19cm-9x7in) s. panel. 11-Jun-3 Beaussant & Lefèvre, Paris #33/R est:1500-1800
£2264 $3487 €3600 Bosphore (40x65cm-16x26in) s. 23-Oct-2 Rabourdin & Choppin de Janvry, Paris #78/R
£2450 $3994 €3700 Paysage du Bosphore (65x40cm-26x16in) s. 16-Feb-3 Mercier & Cie, Lille #253/R est:3000-4000
£2518 $4130 €3500 Rassemblement aux abords de la ville (22x38cm-9x15in) s. panel. 4-Jun-3 Tajan, Paris #258/R est:3000-4000
£2581 $4077 €4000 View of Istanbul (35x65cm-14x26in) s. 19-Dec-2 Claude Aguttes, Neuilly #123/R
£3333 $5233 €5200 Crepuscule sur le Bosphore (26x41cm-10x16in) s. panel. 16-Dec-2 Gros & Delettrez, Paris #249/R est:4000-5000
£3438 $5500 €5157 View of the Grand Canal with shipping (61x81cm-24x32in) s. 14-May-3 Butterfields, San Francisco #1131/R est:4000-6000
£5443 $8600 €8600 Venise (16x24cm-6x9in) s. panel. 2-Dec-2 Rieunier, Paris #43/R
£6522 $10174 €9783 Fishing boats in the Lagoon, Venice (91x131cm-36x52in) s. prov. 16-Sep-2 Philippe Schuler, Zurich #3468/R est:15000-20000 (S.FR 15000)

DUVIEUX, Henri (attrib) (?-1882) French
£652 $1011 €978 Constantinople, barques sur le Bosphore (21x43cm-8x17in) panel prov. 7-Dec-2 Galerie du Rhone, Sion #515/R (S.FR 1500)

DUVILLIER, René (1919-2002) French
£633 $1000 €1000 Cycle aerien 54 (89x116cm-35x46in) s. s.i.d.65 verso. 26-Nov-2 Camard, Paris #139/R
£705 $1114 €1100 La naissance d'Aphrodite (80x160cm-31x63in) s.d.1960. 14-Nov-2 Credit Municipal, Paris #64/R
£1203 $1900 €1900 Vent du diable II (125x191cm-49x75in) s. s.i.d.61 verso. 26-Nov-2 Camard, Paris #131/R
£1763 $2768 €2750 Anemone sous le vent (114x146cm-45x57in) s. s.i.d.1961. 15-Dec-2 Perrin, Versailles #25/R
£3425 $5377 €5000 Cheval de mer solaire (70x70cm-28x28in) s.d.54 s.i.verso exhib.lit. 15-Apr-3 Laurence Calmels, Paris #4269/R est:1500
£3924 $6200 €6200 Mer a Gwen-Trez (59x120cm-23x47in) s. prov. 26-Nov-2 Camard, Paris #140/R

DUVIVIER, Benjamin (1730-1819) French
Works on paper
£270 $422 €400 Academie d'homme (54x36cm-21x14in) s. sanguine. 31-Mar-3 Piasa, Paris #73

DUVIVIER, Francois (?-1671) French
£769 $1208 €1200 Sacrifice de la fille de Jephte (97x237cm-38x93in) s.i.d.1653. 21-Nov-2 Neret-Minet, Paris #64

DUVIVIER, Ignaz (1758-1832) French
£1268 $2104 €1800 Peasant sleeping in stable (52x75cm-20x30in) 11-Jun-3 Dorotheum, Vienna #192/R est:1500-2500

DUVIVIER, Thomas Germain Joseph (1735-1814) French
£11613 $18348 €18000 Trompe-l'oeil a la sculpture baroque (46x49cm-18x19in) 18-Dec-2 Piasa, Paris #96/R est:15000

DUXA, Carl (1871-1937) Austrian
£477 $750 €716 Interior scene with two Dutch woman in colourful dress seated (48x38cm-19x15in) s. 19-Apr-3 James Julia, Fairfield #317/R
£612 $973 €900 Two woman sitting and working by back door (95x74cm-37x29in) s. 25-Feb-3 Dorotheum, Vienna #12/R
£1200 $1872 €1800 Blossom (50x36cm-20x14in) board. 26-Mar-3 Sotheby's, Olympia #254/R est:1000-1500

DUYCK, Francois (19/20th C) Belgian?
£486 $773 €700 Cheval blanc et son lad (58x70cm-23x28in) s. 30-Apr-3 Tajan, Paris #48
£545 $845 €850 Ane et cheval en hiver (48x60cm-19x24in) s. 9-Dec-2 Horta, Bruxelles #277

DUYCKAERTS, Eric (20th C) French?
Works on paper
£577 $906 €900 Information, insulte, grivoiserie, superstition? (50x24cm-20x9in) s.d.1993 pastel ink prov. 11-Dec-2 Artcurial Briest, Paris #771/R

DUYCKINCK, Evert III (attrib) (c.1677-1727) American
£1266 $2000 €1899 Portrait of a gentleman. Portrait of a lady (76x61cm-30x24in) pair. 24-Apr-3 Shannon's, Milford #232/R est:2500-3500

DUYK, Frans (19/20th C) Belgian
£700 $1162 €700 Chevaux au paturage (50x70cm-20x28in) s. 16-Jun-3 Horta, Bruxelles #321

DVORAK, Franz (1862-1927) Austrian
£327 $520 €491 Female nude study (80x44cm-31x17in) canvas on board. 8-Mar-3 Dorotheum, Prague #2/R est:15000-23000 (C.KR 15000)
£850 $1377 €1275 Portrait of Karla Novorna (92cm-36in circular) s.d.1912 i.verso. 23-Jan-3 Christie's, Kensington #43/R
£2000 $3340 €3000 Portrait of a young gentleman (131x80cm-52x31in) s.d.1855. 18-Jun-3 Christie's, Kensington #72/R est:2000-3000

DVORAK, Karel (1893-1950) Czechoslovakian
Sculpture
£1652 $2577 €2478 Fourteen-year-old girl (76cm-30in) s.d.1927 bronze. 12-Oct-2 Dorotheum, Prague #293/R est:80000-120000 (C.KR 80000)

DVORSKY, Bohumir (1902-1976) Czechoslovakian
£1239 $1933 €1859 Olomouc from Svaty Kopecek (73x135cm-29x53in) 12-Oct-2 Dorotheum, Prague #147/R est:50000-75000 (C.KR 60000)

DWIGHT, Mabel (1876-?) American
£377 $600 €566 Study of a nude (61x51cm-24x20in) s.d. 2-Mar-3 Toomey, Oak Park #775/R

DYBING, Sverre (1940-) Norwegian
£312 $477 €468 Beyond the paths (82x148cm-32x58in) s. painted 1974. 26-Aug-2 Blomqvist, Lysaker #1076/R (N.KR 3600)

DYCE, William (1806-1864) British
£92000 $148120 €138000 Saint John leading home his adopted mother (37x31cm-15x12in) panel prov.exhib.lit. 20-Feb-3 Christie's, London #156/R est:50000

DYCK, Abraham van (1635-1672) Dutch
£31655 $50647 €44000 Elderly woman smoking pipe (75x62cm-30x24in) panel. 13-May-3 Sotheby's, Amsterdam #70/R est:20000-30000
Works on paper
£2623 $4250 €3935 Study of seated man (19x16cm-7x6in) brush wash over chk. 21-Jan-3 Sotheby's, New York #146/R est:5000

DYCK, Albert van (1902-1951) Belgian
£2639 $4196 €3800 Jeune homme avec charrette pres de la ferme (51x67cm-20x26in) s.d.1930 panel. 29-Apr-3 Campo & Campo, Antwerp #314/R est:4000-6000
Works on paper
£314 $484 €500 Fillette debout au noeud (34x23cm-13x9in) s. dr. 22-Oct-2 Campo, Vlaamse Kaai #652

DYCK, Philip van (1680-1753) Flemish
£1401 $2186 €2200 Portrait of Maria Kiens (43x36cm-17x14in) s.i. oval prov.exhib.lit. 5-Nov-2 Sotheby's, Amsterdam #150/R est:2000-3000

DYCK, Sir Anthony van (1599-1641) Flemish
£19355 $28452 €30000 Martyrdom of St Sebastian (20x14cm-8x6in) painted with studio prov.lit. 20-Jun-2 Dr Fritz Nagel, Stuttgart #708/R
£75000 $125250 €108750 Head of a saint (42x24cm-17x9in) oil paper on canvas prov. 9-Jul-3 Christie's, London #5/R est:20000-30000
£172840 $280000 €259260 Portrait of Anne Carr, Countess of Bedford (101x82cm-40x32in) i. prov.lit. 24-Jan-3 Christie's, Rockefeller NY #141/R est:150000-250000
£200000 $316000 €300000 Portrait of Sir Francis Crane (130x98cm-51x39in) 28-Nov-2 Sotheby's, London #3/R est:200000-300000
£370370 $600000 €555555 Portrait of Mary Hill, Lady Killigrew, wearing a russet dress before a landscape (107x83cm-42x33in) i. prov.exhib.lit. 24-Jan-3 Christie's, Rockefeller NY #134/R est:400000-600000
Works on paper
£4808 $7596 €7500 Jupiter and Antiope (15x18cm-6x7in) pen wash chk prov. 16-Nov-2 Lempertz, Koln #1221/R est:6000

DYCK, Sir Anthony van (after) (1599-1641) Flemish
£7000 $10990 €10500 Madonna and Child with Mary Magdalene, King David and the Prodigal Son (116x178cm-46x70in) 10-Dec-2 Bonhams, New Bond Street #2/R est:6000-8000

DYCK, Sir Anthony van (attrib) (1599-1641) Flemish
£7792 $11377 €12000 Portrait of a young lady (45x32cm-18x13in) canvas on canvas. 15-Jun-2 Hans Stahl, Hamburg #270/R est:10000
£18868 $29245 €30000 Head of young man (21x17cm-8x7in) 2-Oct-2 Dorotheum, Vienna #138/R est:12000-16000
£70000 $109900 €105000 Madonna and Child with Saint Anne (69x55cm-27x22in) copper prov.exhib.lit. 16-Dec-2 Sotheby's, London #33/R est:80000-120000

DYCK, Sir Anthony van (circle) (1599-1641) Flemish
£5200 $8112 €7800 Head studies of two men (24x32cm-9x13in) paper on panel. 9-Apr-3 Bonhams, New Bond Street #38/R est:800-1200
£14013 $21860 €22000 St. Luke. St. Mark (38x18cm-15x7in) panel pair prov.lit. 5-Nov-2 Sotheby's, Amsterdam #55/R est:10000-15000

DYCK, Sir Anthony van (school) (1599-1641) Flemish
£8290 $13181 €12435 Portrait of nobleman (63x55cm-25x22in) panel. 8-Mar-3 Dorotheum, Prague #38/R est:260000-400000 (C.KR 380000)

DYCK, Sir Anthony van (studio) (1599-1641) Flemish
£6875 $11000 €9969 Portrait of Henrietta Maria, Queen of Charles I (127x104cm-50x41in) prov. 17-May-3 New Orleans Auction, New Orleans #1064/R est:10000-15000
£7188 $11500 €10423 Portrait of Charles I, King of England (124x102cm-49x40in) prov. 17-May-3 New Orleans Auction, New Orleans #1063/R est:12000-18000
£12000 $18960 €18000 Portrait of Thomas Wentworth, 1st Earl of Strafford (130x105cm-51x41in) indis i. prov. 28-Nov-2 Sotheby's, London #143/R est:12000-18000
£22000 $34760 €33000 Portrait of King Charles I in armour (122x92cm-48x36in) prov. 26-Nov-2 Christie's, London #2/R est:15000-25000
£23000 $36340 €34500 Portrait of Endymion Porter (68x55cm-27x22in) 28-Nov-2 Sotheby's, London #148/R est:8000-12000
£28000 $44240 €42000 Portrait of Queen Henrietta Maria in white dress white red bows (119x94cm-47x37in) prov. 26-Nov-2 Christie's, London #3/R est:20000-30000
£30864 $50000 €46296 Portrait of nobleman, said to be Henry Rich (216x128cm-85x50in) prov.exhib.lit. 23-Jan-3 Sotheby's, New York #242/R est:80000

DYCK, Sir Anthony van (style) (1599-1641) Flemish
£683 $997 €1025 Madonna with Child and two angels (110x92cm-43x36in) 17-Jun-2 Philippe Schuler, Zurich #7324 (S.FR 1550)
£5183 $8500 €7775 Portrait of a gentleman (63x56cm-25x22in) 29-May-3 Sotheby's, New York #6/R est:4000-6000
£6500 $10855 €9425 Portrait of a lady thought to be Lady Judith May, three-quarter length (127x102cm-50x40in) 9-Jul-3 Bonhams, New Bond Street #166/R est:3000-5000
£10063 $15597 €16000 Rinaldo and Armida (66x51cm-26x20in) copper 17th C. 2-Oct-2 Dorotheum, Vienna #160/R est:15000-18000
£32000 $53120 €48000 Portrait of Charles I (107x134cm-42x53in) prov.exhib. 12-Jun-3 Sotheby's, London #51/R est:15000-20000

DYCK, van (style) (16/17th C) Flemish
£3800 $6042 €5700 Portrait of Charles I (78x40cm-31x16in) 2-Mar-3 Lots Road, London #331 est:1000-2000
£3800 $6042 €5700 Portrait of Henrietta Maia (78x40cm-31x16in) oval. 2-Mar-3 Lots Road, London #332
£23500 $37365 €35250 Portrait of a young girl with a king Charles spaniel (59x51cm-23x20in) 27-Feb-3 Greenslade Hunt, Taunton #1280/R

DYCKMANS, Josephus Laurentius (1811-1888) Flemish
£638 $1034 €900 Quiet prayer - old woman and child in a church (28x23cm-11x9in) s.d.1863. 20-May-3 Mealy's, Castlecomer #948

DYE, Charlie (1906-1972) American
£9740 $15000 €14610 Stage to Redrock (61x91cm-24x36in) 25-Oct-2 Morris & Whiteside, Hilton Head Island #38b est:20000-30000
£10759 $17000 €15601 Now of never (51x76cm-20x30in) s. board lit. 26-Jul-3 Coeur d'Alene, Hayden #149/R est:15000-25000
£15924 $25000 €23886 Horse trader (51x76cm-20x30in) mono. i.verso masonite prov.lit. 19-Nov-2 Butterfields, San Francisco #8105/R est:30000-50000
£19231 $30000 €28847 Navajo trading post (61x91cm-24x36in) 9-Nov-2 Altermann Galleries, Santa Fe #85
Works on paper
£513 $800 €770 Dally roping (58x86cm-23x34in) init. graphite prov. 9-Nov-2 Santa Fe Art, Santa Fe #241/R
£769 $1200 €1154 Untitled. Laying the trip (18x58cm-7x23in) init.i. graphite set of three prov. 9-Nov-2 Santa Fe Art, Santa Fe #239/R est:4000-5000
£769 $1200 €1154 Bottled courage no.32 (48x74cm-19x29in) init.i. graphite prov. 9-Nov-2 Santa Fe Art, Santa Fe #240/R est:3000-4000
£897 $1400 €1346 Liar's hour (71x114cm-28x45in) s.i. graphite prov. 9-Nov-2 Santa Fe Art, Santa Fe #59/R est:4000-5000
£897 $1400 €1346 Battle plan (58x89cm-23x35in) s.i. graphite prov. 9-Nov-2 Santa Fe Art, Santa Fe #60/R est:3000-4000

DYER, George (19th C) British
Miniatures
£1200 $1908 €1800 Charles Evans, as a young child (10x7cm-4x3in) rectangular. 18-Mar-3 Christie's, Kensington #83 est:300-500

DYER, H Anthony (1872-1943) American
Works on paper
£897 $1400 €1346 Coastal view of Sorrento, Italy (76x56cm-30x22in) s. W/C paper on board. 14-Sep-2 Weschler, Washington #617/R est:800-1200

DYER, Ted (20th C) British
£450 $734 €675 Beneath the pine tree, St Anthony Head (15x20cm-6x8in) s. i.verso board. 13-Feb-3 David Lay, Penzance #124/R
£480 $782 €720 Campion and bluebells, St Anthony (25x30cm-10x12in) s. i.verso. 13-Feb-3 David Lay, Penzance #125
£520 $848 €780 St Ives harbour (20x23cm-8x9in) s. 13-Feb-3 David Lay, Penzance #130/R

DYER, William H (?) British
Works on paper
£250 $380 €375 Holwell, Heytor, Dartmoor (28x58cm-11x23in) s. W/C. 16-Aug-2 Keys, Aylsham #413/R

DYER, William H (attrib) (?) British
Works on paper
£400 $624 €600 Boscastle harbour inlet (23x34cm-9x13in) s. W/C. 10-Sep-2 Sworder & Son, Bishops Stortford #794/R

DYF, Marcel (1899-1985) French
£793 $1300 €1150 Satyr and nymphs (74x61cm-29x24in) s.d.30. 4-Jun-3 Doyle, New York #46 est:2000-3000
£1800 $2844 €2700 Rue principale (46x55cm-18x22in) s. prov. 3-Apr-3 Christie's, Kensington #114/R
£1859 $2900 €2789 Spanish dancers (46x38cm-18x15in) s. 20-Sep-2 Sloan, North Bethesda #413/R est:3000-5000
£1923 $2981 €3000 Modele (92x73cm-36x29in) s.d.1946. 4-Dec-2 Pierre Berge, Paris #133/R
£2000 $3180 €3000 Nature morte (46x38cm-18x15in) s. 20-Mar-3 Sotheby's, Olympia #155/R est:2000-3000
£2014 $3223 €2800 Petit mas en Provence (46x55cm-18x22in) s. 18-May-3 Eric Pillon, Calais #112/R
£2516 $4000 €3774 Bouquinistes de la Seine (38x46cm-15x18in) s. painted c.1950 prov. 27-Feb-3 Christie's, Rockefeller NY #57/R est:7000
£2518 $4029 €3500 Le campement gitan (46x54cm-18x21in) s. panel. 18-May-3 Eric Pillon, Calais #110/R
£2597 $4000 €3896 Still life floral (56x46cm-22x18in) 25-Oct-2 Morris & Whiteside, Hilton Head Island #53 est:4000-6000
£2692 $4227 €4200 Plage animee (38x46cm-15x18in) s. 15-Dec-2 Eric Pillon, Calais #165/R
£2922 $4500 €4383 River and buildings (53x64cm-21x25in) 25-Oct-2 Morris & Whiteside, Hilton Head Island #54 est:4000-6000
£2949 $4629 €4600 Danseurs de flamenco (46x38cm-18x15in) s. 15-Dec-2 Eric Pillon, Calais #168/R
£3000 $4680 €4500 Girl holding a bunch of flowers. s. 17-Sep-2 Gorringes, Bexhill #1254 est:1500-2000
£3000 $4770 €4500 En Provence (37x46cm-15x18in) s.d.1945. 20-Mar-3 Sotheby's, Olympia #140/R est:3000-4000
£3050 $5093 €4300 Les Saintes Maries de la Mer (54x55cm-21x22in) s. 23-Jun-3 Delvaux, Paris #125/R est:4200-4800
£3200 $4928 €4800 Bateaux (63x99cm-25x39in) s. 23-Oct-2 Sotheby's, Olympia #625/R est:3000-4000
£3226 $5000 €4839 Jeune gitana (65x54cm-26x21in) s. painted 1950. 26-Sep-2 Christie's, Rockefeller NY #584/R est:3000-5000
£3500 $5390 €5250 Danseuses de Flamenco (60x73cm-24x29in) s. 23-Oct-2 Sotheby's, Olympia #711/R est:4000-6000
£3600 $5832 €5400 Woman reading (55x46cm-22x18in) s. 20-May-3 Bonhams, Knightsbridge #181/R est:2000-3000
£4000 $6280 €6000 Pivoines au pot de chine (55x46cm-22x18in) s. 21-Nov-2 Tennants, Leyburn #845/R est:4000-6000
£4500 $7335 €6750 Marseilles (53x73cm-21x29in) s. board. 3-Feb-3 Bonhams, New Bond Street #29/R est:5000-7000
£4545 $7000 €6818 Still life of vase of flowers with framed picture (56x46cm-22x18in) s. i.verso. 26-Oct-2 Brunk, Ashville #893/R est:2000-4000
£4600 $7452 €6900 Woman on a balcony (73x60cm-29x24in) s. 20-May-3 Bonhams, Knightsbridge #184/R est:2000-3000
£4800 $7824 €7200 Paysage avec vignes (46x55cm-18x22in) s. 3-Feb-3 Bonhams, New Bond Street #90/R est:4000-6000
£4800 $7584 €7200 Bouquet (54x46cm-21x18in) s. painted c.1970-80 prov. 3-Apr-3 Christie's, Kensington #139/R est:6000
£4800 $7824 €6960 Lagune a Venise (46x55cm-18x22in) s. 16-Jul-3 Sotheby's, Olympia #266/R est:5000-7000
£4839 $7645 €7500 Nature morte dans un paysage champetre (80x125cm-31x49in) s. canvas on board. 19-Dec-2 Delvaux, Paris #44/R
£5128 $8000 €7692 Paris, Notre Dame (66x81cm-26x32in) s. 5-Nov-2 Arthur James, Florida #62
£5500 $8690 €8250 Jeune femme avec cerises (60x73cm-24x29in) s. 3-Apr-3 Christie's, Kensington #81/R
£5500 $8690 €8250 Vase chinois polychrome (55x46cm-22x18in) s. prov. 3-Apr-3 Christie's, Kensington #130/R
£5600 $9128 €8120 Flures (53x46cm-21x18in) s. 21-Jul-3 Bonhams, Bath #42/R est:4000-6000
£6115 $9784 €8500 Vase de fleurs des champs (73x60cm-29x24in) s. 18-May-3 Eric Pillon, Calais #108/R
£6200 $9858 €9300 Jeune fille avec corbeille de fruits (66x54cm-26x21in) s. prov. 20-Mar-3 Sotheby's, Olympia #49/R est:7000-9000
£7089 $10987 €11200 Le lever (60x73cm-24x29in) st.sig. 29-Sep-2 Eric Pillon, Calais #200/R
£7278 $11282 €11500 Jeune fille enfilant ses bas (73x60cm-29x24in) s. 29-Sep-2 Eric Pillon, Calais #208/R
£7742 $12000 €11613 Paysage de Bretagne (46x55cm-18x22in) s. prov.exhib. 26-Sep-2 Christie's, Rockefeller NY #610/R est:5000-7000
£7742 $12232 €12000 Jeune femme a la lecture (54x65cm-21x26in) s. 19-Dec-2 Claude Aguttes, Neuilly #173/R est:13000
£8392 $14014 €12000 Les bles (46x55cm-18x22in) s. 27-Jun-3 Claude Aguttes, Neuilly #73/R est:6000-8000
£8392 $14014 €12000 Jeune femme au chat (55x46cm-22x18in) s. 27-Jun-3 Claude Aguttes, Neuilly #74/R est:8000-12000
£9500 $15105 €14250 Maison a la campagne (46x55cm-18x22in) s. 20-Mar-3 Sotheby's, Olympia #139/R est:5000-7000
£11000 $16940 €16500 Le champ de coquelicots (60x73cm-24x29in) s. 22-Oct-2 Sotheby's, London #205/R est:8000-12000
Works on paper
£823 $1275 €1300 Le flamenco (23x32cm-9x13in) s. chl dr. 29-Sep-2 Eric Pillon, Calais #214/R
£1076 $1668 €1700 Le campement gitan (23x32cm-9x13in) s. chl dr. 29-Sep-2 Eric Pillon, Calais #213/R

DYKE, Samuel P (19th C) American
£1218 $1900 €1827 Delaware water Gap (56x91cm-22x36in) s.d.1891 canvas on masonite. 20-Sep-2 Sloan, North Bethesda #486/R est:2500-3500
£2611 $4100 €3917 View of Susquehanna River (51x76cm-20x30in) s. 22-Nov-2 Eldred, East Dennis #1134/R est:1000-1500

DYKHOF, Gerard van (1933-) Dutch?
£325 $511 €488 Children playing in shallow water (30x46cm-12x18in) s. board. 10-Dec-2 Pinneys, Montreal #132 (C.D 800)

DYKMAN, Henry J (1893-1972) South African
£222 $363 €333 Still life with brass and copperware (60x75cm-24x30in) s. board. 4-Feb-3 Dales, Durban #11 (SA.R 3000)
£243 $380 €365 Still life with yellow roses in a glass vase (60x49cm-24x19in) s. board. 11-Nov-2 Stephan Welz, Johannesburg #197 (SA.R 3800)
£275 $443 €413 Still life of white roses in a brass vase (75x60cm-30x24in) s. board. 12-May-3 Stephan Welz, Johannesburg #366 est:3000-4000 (SA.R 3200)
£275 $443 €413 Still life of roses in a brass vase (73x58cm-29x23in) s.d.1951 canvas on board. 12-May-3 Stephan Welz, Johannesburg #368 est:3000-5000 (SA.R 3200)
£387 $623 €581 Still life of hydrangeas in a silver vase (59x74cm-23x29in) s. board. 12-May-3 Stephan Welz, Johannesburg #371 est:3000-5000 (SA.R 4500)

DYKSTRA, Johan (1896-1978) Dutch
£11268 $18141 €16000 Reitdiep (28x37cm-11x15in) s. 7-May-3 Vendue Huis, Gravenhage #543/R est:8000-10000
Works on paper
£517 $823 €750 Female nude (54x32cm-21x13in) red chk double-sided. 10-Mar-3 Sotheby's, Amsterdam #325

D'YLEN, Jean (1866-1938) French
Prints
£2152 $3400 €3228 Bally ruby slipper (124x86cm-49x34in) s. silkscreen poster. 16-Nov-2 New Orleans Auction, New Orleans #322/R est:900-1200

DYNEVOR, Lucy (1934-) British
£1200 $1908 €1800 Dynevor Park (46x76cm-18x30in) s. board. 26-Feb-3 Sotheby's, Olympia #122/R est:500-700

DYONNET, Edmond (1859-1954) Canadian
£444 $729 €666 Sunlit summer's day (27x36cm-11x14in) s. board. 3-Jun-3 Joyner, Toronto #519 est:1500-2000 (C.D 1000)

DYRING, Moya (1908-1967) Australian
£631 $959 €947 View across Sydney Harbour to the construction of the Opera House (38x61cm-15x24in) s. s.i.d.1960 verso composition board. 28-Aug-2 Deutscher-Menzies, Melbourne #373/R (A.D 1760)
Works on paper
£264 $418 €383 Bird market Paris (30x50cm-12x20in) s.i.d.51 ink gouache. 22-Jul-3 Lawson Menzies, Sydney #150/R est:700-1000 (A.D 650)

DYS, Coran (?) French?
£966 $1536 €1420 Congre et rouget (99x122cm-39x48in) s. 24-Mar-3 Thierry & Lannon, Brest #100

DZAMA, Marcel (1974-) American
Works on paper
£2025 $3200 €3038 Untitled (32x25cm-13x10in) s. ink W/C root beer set of six prov. 12-Nov-2 Phillips, New York #223/R est:4000-6000

DZIGURSKI, Alex (1911-1995) American
£377 $600 €566 Western landscape (30x41cm-12x16in) s. 2-Mar-3 Toomey, Oak Park #623/R
£429 $670 €622 Seascape at sunset (41x51cm-16x20in) s. 26-Mar-3 Walker's, Ottawa #42/R est:700-900 (C.D 1000)
£442 $698 €663 Seascape (46x61cm-18x24in) 1-Dec-2 Levis, Calgary #216/R (C.D 1100)
£491 $800 €737 Farm landscape (36x51cm-14x20in) 14-Feb-3 Du Mouchelle, Detroit #2098/R
£577 $900 €866 Dolomites, Italy (61x91cm-24x36in) 20-Sep-2 Du Mouchelle, Detroit #2115/R
£621 $1000 €932 Rocky coastal landscape (61x91cm-24x36in) s. 15-Jan-3 Boos Gallery, Michigan #460/R
£679 $1100 €985 Crashing waves on a windy day (61x91cm-24x36in) s. 21-May-3 Doyle, New York #133/R
£688 $1100 €1032 Waves crashing on shore at sundown. 11-Jan-3 Harvey Clar, Oakland #1200

£705 $1100 €1058 Stormy Pacific. 19-Oct-2 Harvey Clar, Oakland #1433

£1026 $1600 €1539 Genova, Italy, seascape (64x76cm-25x30in) 18-Oct-2 Du Mouchelle, Detroit #2126/R est:600-1000

£1125 $1800 €1688 Storm tossed waves at sunset (61x122cm-24x48in) s. 16-Mar-3 Butterfields, San Francisco #1055 est:2000-3000

£1132 $1800 €1698 Crashing surf (61x91cm-24x36in) s. 7-Mar-3 Jackson's, Cedar Falls #638/R est:800-1200

£1132 $1800 €1698 Seascape in Carmel (61x91cm-24x36in) s. painted c.1960. 2-Mar-3 Toomey, Oak Park #618/R est:2500-4500

£1218 $1900 €1827 Breaking waves on a rocky coast (61x91cm-24x36in) s. 5-Nov-2 Arthur James, Florida #456

£1506 $2500 €2184 Coastal tranquillity (61x91cm-24x36in) s. 11-Jun-3 Butterfields, San Francisco #4292/R est:3000-5000

£3586 $5200 €5379 Gale (91x178cm-36x70in) 1-Jun-2 Russ Antiques, Waterford #42

DZUBAS, Friedel (1915-1994) American/German

£30000 $48000 €45000 Isis (244x244cm-96x96in) s. magna painted 1972 prov.exhib. 15-May-3 Christie's, Rockefeller NY #138/R est:15000-20000

EADE, Edward Douglas (1911-1984) British

Works on paper

£700 $1148 €1050 Woman with cat (37x41cm-15x16in) red ink W/C. 3-Jun-3 Sotheby's, Olympia #144/R

EADIE, Robert (1877-1954) British

Works on paper

£680 $1054 €1020 Anstruther (36x50cm-14x20in) s. W/C. 5-Dec-2 Bonhams, Edinburgh #51

£1650 $2574 €2475 Evening, West George Street (42x32cm-17x13in) s.d.1919 W/C. 14-Apr-3 Sotheby's, London #164/R est:800-1200

EADIE, William (fl.1880-1894) British

£550 $897 €825 The Penny Whistle (45x30cm-18x12in) 14-Feb-3 Lyon & Turnbull, Edinburgh #9

EAGER, Wayne (1957-) Australian

Works on paper

£338 $555 €507 Untitled, figure (67x55cm-26x22in) i.d.1985 verso synthetic polymer paint composition board. 4-Jun-3 Deutscher-Menzies, Melbourne #109/R (A.D 850)

EAKINS, Susan (1851-1938) American

£1078 $1800 €1563 Four studies (26x28cm-10x11in) board prov. 22-Jun-3 Freeman, Philadelphia #76/R est:2000-3000

£1557 $2600 €2258 Portrait of a man (29x22cm-11x9in) prov.exhib. 22-Jun-3 Freeman, Philadelphia #77/R est:1000-1500

EAKINS, Thomas (1844-1916) American

£7186 $12000 €10420 Sketch for cowboys in the Badlands (26x36cm-10x14in) painted c.1887-8 prov.exhib.lit. 22-Jun-3 Freeman, Philadelphia #74/R est:15000-20000

£54839 $85000 €82259 Ernest Lee Parker (62x51cm-24x20in) init. s.i.d.1910 verso prov.lit. 5-Dec-2 Christie's, Rockefeller NY #16/R est:60000-80000

£2962963 $4800000 €4444445 Cowboys in the Badlands (82x114cm-32x45in) s.d.88 prov.exhib.lit. 22-May-3 Christie's, Rockefeller NY #32/R est:5000000-7000000

Sculpture

£11950 $19000 €17925 Arcadia (28x60cm-11x24in) i.d.1888 dark brown pat. bronze prov.lit. 4-Mar-3 Christie's, Rockefeller NY #51/R est:8000-12000

EAKINS, Thomas (attrib) (1844-1916) American

£15924 $25000 €23886 Woman knitting (61x51cm-24x20in) panel painted c.1879-83. 13-Dec-2 Du Mouchelle, Detroit #2214/R est:30000-40000

EARDLEY, Joan (1921-1963) British

£4800 $7872 €7200 Oil lamp (38x20cm-15x8in) canvas on board prov. 3-Jun-3 Sotheby's, Olympia #140/R est:2000-3000

£5500 $8580 €8250 Watery summer landscape (36x45cm-14x18in) acrylic prov. 14-Apr-3 Sotheby's, London #168/R est:3000-5000

£5500 $9020 €8250 Land and sea II (32x44cm-13x17in) s.d.63 verso board prov. 6-Jun-3 Christie's, London #74/R est:6000-8000

£6500 $10271 €9750 Fishing nets (49x52cm-19x20in) s.d.63 verso board prov. 27-Nov-2 Sotheby's, Olympia #59/R est:4000-6000

£6800 $10336 €10200 Ginger (43x37cm-17x15in) board prov. 28-Aug-2 Sotheby's, London #1044/R est:3000-5000

£9500 $14725 €14250 Winter sea, Catterline (56x39cm-22x15in) board prov. 6-Dec-2 Lyon & Turnbull, Edinburgh #113/R est:7000-9000

£12000 $18720 €18000 Fishing nets (49x52cm-19x20in) s.d.63 board prov. 14-Apr-3 Sotheby's, London #167/R est:12000-18000

£24000 $37200 €36000 February sunset (51x51cm-20x20in) exhib. 5-Dec-2 Bonhams, Edinburgh #57/R est:7000-10000

£32000 $49600 €48000 Beehives, storm approaching (98x98cm-39x39in) board prov.exhib. 31-Oct-2 Christie's, London #181/R est:15000-20000

Works on paper

£1350 $2066 €2025 Catterline (25x27cm-10x11in) indis sig. black ink. 22-Aug-2 Bonhams, Edinburgh #973/R est:1500-2000

£1500 $2325 €2250 Stobcross Crane and Rotunda, Glasgow (22x25cm-9x10in) black ink pastel prov. 5-Dec-2 Bonhams, Edinburgh #137 est:1500-2000

£3200 $4960 €4800 Samson child (63x48cm-25x19in) s. black col chk. 31-Oct-2 Christie's, London #185/R est:2000-3000

£3200 $5088 €4800 Quayside (23x19cm-9x7in) col crayon pastel exhib. 6-Mar-3 Christie's, Kensington #231/R est:1500-2000

£4500 $6975 €6750 Jimmy (17x16cm-7x6in) s. black crayon pastel exhib. 31-Oct-2 Christie's, London #184/R est:3000-4000

£4500 $7290 €6750 Old pram (13x22cm-5x9in) pastel. 23-May-3 Lyon & Turnbull, Edinburgh #80/R est:3000-5000

EARL, George (1824-1908) British

£2468 $3800 €3702 Head of Gainer, a fox hound (41x41cm-16x16in) canvas on board. 4-Sep-2 Christie's, Rockefeller NY #378/R est:2000-3000

£4200 $6972 €6090 Return from deer stalking (71x99cm-28x39in) s.i.d.1877. 12-Jun-3 Christie's, Kensington #122/R est:1500-2500

£27607 $45000 €41411 Huddersfield Ben, Molly, Charlie, Tiger and Hylas (39x44cm-15x17in) i. five framed as one. 11-Feb-3 Bonhams & Doyles, New York #179/R est:15000-20000

EARL, George (attrib) (1824-1908) British

£675 $1100 €1013 White English terrier head study (21cm-8in circular) card. 11-Feb-3 Bonhams & Doyles, New York #256 est:800-1200

EARL, J P (18/19th C) British

£1135 $1759 €1703 Dog watching bowl with goldfish (28x38cm-11x15in) s. 8-Dec-2 Uppsala Auktionskammare, Uppsala #75/R est:8000-10000 (S.KR 16000)

EARL, Maud (1863-1943) British

£704 $1134 €1000 Five puppies with watering can (40x58cm-16x23in) mono. 7-May-3 Michael Zeller, Lindau #684/R

£986 $1587 €1400 Five puppies surrounding chick (40x58cm-16x23in) mono. 7-May-3 Michael Zeller, Lindau #683/R

£6500 $10790 €9425 Clyde Boy, a Beddington terrier (46x61cm-18x24in) s.d.99 prov.lit. 12-Jun-3 Christie's, Kensington #231/R est:3000-5000

£6600 $10428 €9900 Two dachshunds (71x91cm-28x36in) s. 2-Dec-2 Gorringes, Lewes #2620/R est:2000-3000

£6918 $11000 €10377 Play time (46x61cm-18x24in) s. 7-Mar-3 Skinner, Boston #562/R est:4000-6000

£7500 $12450 €10875 Who goes there? pass friend (102x76cm-40x30in) s. 12-Jun-3 Christie's, Kensington #226/R est:8000-12000

£8589 $14000 €12884 Tug o'war (63x76cm-25x30in) s.d.1904. 11-Feb-3 Bonhams & Doyles, New York #231/R est:12000-18000

£16352 $26000 €24528 Toy spaniels, King Charles and Rudy, the pillow is the best (46x61cm-18x24in) s. s.i.verso. 7-Mar-3 Skinner, Boston #563/R est:4000-6000

EARL, Thomas (style) (19th C) British

£7047 $10993 €10571 Anxious moments (55x71cm-22x28in) bears mono. 11-Nov-2 Stephan Welz, Johannesburg #69 est:3000-5000 (SA.R 110000)

EARL, Thomas William (1815-1885) British

£1700 $2822 €2465 Pet goldfish (28x38cm-11x15in) s. paper on canvas. 12-Jun-3 Christie's, Kensington #310/R est:1500-2500

£4063 $6175 €6095 Head of dog (41cm-16in circular) s.d.1870. 3-Jul-2 Naón & Cia, Buenos Aires #23/R est:1500-2000

£4500 $6840 €6750 Skye terrier (55x66cm-22x26in) s.d.68. 28-Aug-2 Sotheby's, London #820/R est:5000-7000

£5828 $9500 €8742 English setter (41x41cm-16x16in) s.d.1870 canvas on board. 11-Feb-3 Bonhams & Doyles, New York #178/R est:10000-15000

EARLE, John (1955-) Australian

£358 $545 €537 Landscape (90x120cm-35x47in) 27-Aug-2 Goodman, Sydney #54 (A.D 1000)

£1679 $2619 €2519 Sydney harbour from Vaucluse (71x203cm-28x80in) s. composition board. 11-Nov-2 Deutscher-Menzies, Melbourne #151/R est:2000-3000 (A.D 4700)

EARLE, Paul Barnard (1872-1955) Canadian

£889 $1458 €1334 Trees by the shoreline (62x75cm-24x30in) s.d.35. 3-Jun-3 Joyner, Toronto #439/R est:1500-2000 (C.D 2000)

£987 $1540 €1431 Farm (77x102cm-30x40in) s.i.d.1931. 26-Mar-3 Walker's, Ottawa #206/R est:2000-3000 (C.D 2300)

EARLES, Chester (19th C) British
£1607 $2539 €2411 Feather pickers, a pause in the work (33x24cm-13x9in) s.i. i.d.76 prov.exhib. 17-Nov-2 Sotheby's, Paddington #57/R est:7000-10000 (A.D 4500)

EARLOM, Richard (1743-1822) British
Prints
£3846 $6077 €6000 The book of Truth. eau forte. 13-Nov-2 Piasa, Paris #71/R

EARLOM, Richard and GREEN, Valentine (18th C) British
Prints
£19000 $29450 €28500 Houghton Gallery (52x27cm-20x11in) mezzotints two albums. 5-Dec-2 Sotheby's, London #69/R est:3000-4000

EARLY, Miles J (1886-?) American
£903 $1400 €1355 Late November (46x56cm-18x22in) s.d. 8-Dec-2 Toomey, Oak Park #643/R

EARLY, Tom (1914-1967) British
£320 $499 €480 Gypsy caravan (39x44cm-15x17in) prov. 17-Sep-2 Bonhams, Knightsbridge #29/R
£750 $1238 €1088 Gypsy (39x44cm-15x17in) s.i. canvasboard exhib. 3-Jul-3 Christie's, Kensington #694/R

EARP, Edwin (19/20th C) British
Works on paper
£600 $972 €900 Highland landscape with figures crossing a bridge over a river (71x122cm-28x48in) s. pencil W/C htd white. 23-Jan-3 Christie's, Kensington #317/R

EARP, H (snr) (1831-1914) British
£450 $707 €675 Drovers with cattle in landscape (46x46cm-18x18in) 13-Dec-2 Keys, Aylsham #702
Works on paper
£310 $487 €465 Haddon Hall from the river (25x36cm-10x14in) s. W/C. 19-Nov-2 Riddetts, Bournemouth #861/R

EARP, Henry (snr) (1831-1914) British
£460 $722 €690 Landscape with figures (19x34cm-7x13in) s. 11-Dec-2 Rupert Toovey, Partridge Green #90/R
£650 $1066 €975 Cattle pictures (23x33cm-9x13in) s. pair. 5-Feb-3 John Nicholson, Haslemere #1066
£900 $1422 €1350 Outside the Surrey Oaks - village scene with figures, horse and carts (53x81cm-21x32in) s.d.1890. 2-Dec-2 Bonhams, Bath #94/R
£2400 $3744 €3600 Beside the cottage door. First riding lesson (20x25cm-8x10in) s. pair. 18-Sep-2 Dreweatt Neate, Newbury #137/R est:1500-2500
Works on paper
£260 $411 €390 Cattle and calves in a meadow (16x43cm-6x17in) s. W/C htd white. 7-Apr-3 Bonhams, Bath #6
£360 $569 €540 River landscape with cattle and a boat (24x36cm-9x14in) s. pencil W/C htd white. 7-Apr-3 Bonhams, Bath #7
£400 $624 €600 Riverscape with cattle and sailing barge (36x53cm-14x21in) s. W/C. 15-Oct-2 Gorringes, Lewes #2116
£450 $711 €653 Droving cattle down a rural lane (46x62cm-18x24in) s. W/C. 22-Jul-3 Bonhams, Knightsbridge #164/R
£461 $719 €692 Cattle in a forest (72x51cm-28x20in) s. W/C. 15-Oct-2 Stephan Welz, Johannesburg #379/R est:5000-8000 (SA.R 7500)
£520 $848 €780 Cows resting in a meadow. Cows driven along a lane by a cowherd (22x37cm-9x15in) s. pencil W/C two. 29-Jan-3 Dreweatt Neate, Newbury #82
£700 $1078 €1050 Cattle watering, cottage beyond (58x89cm-23x35in) s. W/C. 3-Sep-2 Gorringes, Lewes #2251/R
£750 $1230 €1125 Landscapes with cattle (23x53cm-9x21in) s. W/C pair. 5-Feb-3 John Nicholson, Haslemere #1000
£1500 $2370 €2250 Cattle in a farmyard. Cattle watering (51x74cm-20x29in) s. W/C pair. 13-Nov-2 Halls, Shrewsbury #328/R est:600-800

EASLEY, Thomas (1949-) American
£1000 $1610 €1500 View of London from Westminster Bridge (78x126cm-31x50in) s.d.1988 verso board. 18-Feb-3 Bonhams, Knightsbridge #78/R est:1000-1500

EAST, Benoit (1915-) Canadian
£687 $1071 €1031 Still life (14x20cm-6x8in) s.d.44 canvas on cardboard. 25-Mar-3 Iegor de Saint Hippolyte, Montreal #44 (C.D 1600)
£1202 $1875 €1803 Still life (52x68cm-20x27in) s.d.45 cardboard. 25-Mar-3 Iegor de Saint Hippolyte, Montreal #45 (C.D 2800)

EAST, H (?) British
£1800 $2862 €2700 Betws-y-Coed and the river Lledr (30x41cm-12x16in) s. pair. 19-Mar-3 John Nicholson, Haslemere #1180/R est:1500-2000

EAST, Henry (?) British?
£750 $1193 €1125 On the Lledr, North Wales (51x71cm-20x28in) s. 30-Apr-3 Halls, Shrewsbury #288/R

EAST, Pattie (1894-?) American
£353 $550 €530 Texas spring (30x48cm-12x19in) canvasboard. 19-Oct-2 David Dike, Dallas #304/R

EAST, Sir Alfred (1849-1913) British
£356 $590 €516 Sheep in a pasture (15x24cm-6x9in) s. panel. 16-Jun-3 Waddingtons, Toronto #113/R (C.D 800)
£800 $1232 €1200 Sheep in autumn woods (46x66cm-18x26in) s. 22-Oct-2 Peter Francis, Wales #14/R
£1400 $2184 €2100 River landscape with watermill beyond (51x76cm-20x30in) s. 18-Sep-2 Dreweatt Neate, Newbury #171/R est:3000-5000
£1695 $2695 €2543 Weir near Northhampton (61x71cm-24x28in) s. 18-Mar-3 Maynards, Vancouver #5/R est:3000-4000 (C.D 4000)
£2000 $3080 €3000 Moonlight (16x24cm-6x9in) s. panel. 5-Sep-2 Christie's, Kensington #215/R est:400-600
£3000 $4650 €4500 Crail from the south west, evening (46x89cm-18x35in) s.d.1882. 5-Dec-2 Bonhams, Edinburgh #105/R est:3000-5000
£11000 $17710 €16500 Autumn ploughing (46x137cm-18x54in) prov. 20-Feb-3 Christie's, London #53/R est:7000
Works on paper
£222 $369 €322 An early autumn day (32x45cm-13x18in) init. W/C prov. 10-Jun-3 Ritchie, Toronto #26/R (C.D 500)
£320 $506 €480 Moutiers (23x36cm-9x14in) s.i. W/C. 24-Apr-3 Scarborough Perry Fine Arts, Hove #589
£400 $572 €600 Woodland nymphs (59x89cm-23x35in) s. W/C. 28-Feb-2 Greenslade Hunt, Taunton #399
£1150 $1794 €1725 Gibraltar Bay from the bullring, Algeciras (24x34cm-9x13in) s. W/C. 10-Sep-2 Sworder & Son, Bishops Stortford #775/R est:250-350
£4200 $6972 €6300 Sayonara (22x33cm-9x13in) init.i. W/C bodycol. 12-Jun-3 Bonhams, New Bond Street #849a/R est:1000-1500

EASTLAKE, Charles Herbert (fl.1889-1927) British
£1400 $2156 €2100 Riverside cottages at twilight (110x151cm-43x59in) s. 24-Oct-2 Christie's, Kensington #34/R est:1200-1800

EASTLAKE, Mary Alexandra (1864-1951) Canadian
£5333 $8747 €8000 Annunciation (63x53cm-25x21in) init. prov. 27-May-3 Sotheby's, Toronto #78/R est:8000-10000 (C.D 12000)
Works on paper
£566 $900 €849 Cottage, twilight (32x39cm-13x15in) s. pastel. 7-Mar-3 Skinner, Boston #412/R

EASTLAKE, Sidney (19th C) British
£300 $495 €435 Sand dunes with a calm sea beyond (36x56cm-14x22in) s. 3-Jul-3 Duke & Son, Dorchester #204

EASTLAKE, Sir Charles Lock (1793-1865) British
£12000 $19320 €18000 Salutation to the aged friar (94x113cm-37x44in) prov.exhib.lit. 20-Feb-3 Christie's, London #257/R est:15000
Works on paper
£900 $1423 €1350 Portrait of Napoleon (10x9cm-4x4in) pen ink oval. 28-Nov-2 Sotheby's, London #217/R est:1000-1500

EASTLAKE, Sir Charles Lock (attrib) (1793-1865) British
Works on paper
£1064 $1777 €1500 Le Theseum a Athenes, vue de l'ouest (35x54cm-14x21in) W/C pencil. 23-Jun-3 Beaussant & Lefèvre, Paris #91 est:500-800

EASTMAN, Norm (1931-) American
£559 $900 €839 Standed aviators cavorting with immodest women (25x74cm-10x29in) s. board. 20-Feb-3 Illustration House, New York #49/R

EASTMAN, Seth (1808-1875) American
Works on paper
£1242 $2000 €1863 Sioux chief (33x25cm-13x10in) gouache W/C. 9-May-3 Douglas, South Deerfield #3
£1258 $2000 €1887 Inscription Rock at esopus landing on the Hudson River (15x23cm-6x9in) W/C lit. 4-Mar-3 Christie's, Rockefeller NY #19/R est:7000-10000

EASTMAN, Seth (style) (1808-1875) American
£5938 $9500 €8907 View of West Point from garrison NY. painted c.1840. 12-Jan-3 William Jenack, New York #211

EASTMAN, William Joseph (1888-1956) American
£949 $1500 €1424 Still life of gladiolas (79x74cm-31x29in) s. 5-Apr-3 DeFina, Austinburg #1321 est:400-600
Works on paper
£237 $370 €356 Norway (74x53cm-29x21in) s.d.26 W/C. 28-Mar-3 Aspire, Cleveland #70/R
£305 $500 €442 Village in the mountains (33x38cm-13x15in) s. W/C executed 1943. 30-May-3 Aspire, Cleveland #98/R

EASTON, Reginald (1807-1893) British
Miniatures
£4500 $7020 €6750 Lady seated in chair wearing decollete white dress with frilled collar (10cm-4xin) gilt frame ormolu slip rec. 5-Nov-2 Bonhams, New Bond Street #144/R est:1500-2500
£9000 $14040 €13500 Pair of portraits of sisters Louisa Isabel Seawell and Ethelred Laura Seawell (10cm-4xin) ebonised black turned frames oval pair. 5-Nov-2 Bonhams, New Bond Street #165/R est:3000-5000

EATON, C (19th C) American
£1500 $2400 €2250 Still life of table laden with fruit, and compote with landscape background (66x102cm-26x40in) s.s. 17-May-3 Pook & Pook, Downington #220/R est:2000-3000

EATON, Charles Warren (1857-1937) American
£1948 $3000 €2922 Pines (20x25cm-8x10in) s. board prov.exhib. 24-Oct-2 Shannon's, Milford #190/R est:2000-3000
£2903 $4500 €4355 Sunlit meadow (46x61cm-18x24in) s. painted c.1910. 8-Dec-2 Toomey, Oak Park #648/R est:6000-8000
£5844 $9000 €8766 Vista, Lake Como (51x61cm-20x24in) s. s.i.verso. 24-Oct-2 Shannon's, Milford #148/R est:9000-12000
£7143 $11000 €10715 Forest interior (61x51cm-24x20in) s. 24-Oct-2 Shannon's, Milford #195/R est:6000-8000
Works on paper
£1220 $2000 €1830 River view (25x36cm-10x14in) s. W/C. 5-Feb-3 Doyle, New York #20/R est:2000-3000
£1274 $2000 €1911 Trees in winter (20x36cm-8x14in) s. W/C. 10-Dec-2 Doyle, New York #85/R est:2000-3000
£1623 $2500 €2435 Evening, Belguim (43x51cm-17x20in) s. W/C. 24-Oct-2 Shannon's, Milford #188/R est:3000-5000
£2111 $3250 €3167 Winter clouds (36x48cm-14x19in) s. W/C. 24-Oct-2 Shannon's, Milford #187/R est:3000-5000

EBATARINJA, Arnulf (1931-) Australian
Works on paper
£357 $554 €536 Central Australian landscape (50x72cm-20x28in) s. W/C. 29-Oct-2 Lawson Menzies, Sydney #134 (A.D 1000)

EBBE, Axel (1868-1941) Swedish
Sculpture
£1473 $2327 €2210 Lighter than air (49cm-19in) s. bronze incl. socle prov. 27-Nov-2 Falkkloos, Malmo #77785/R est:15000 (S.KR 21000)

EBBESEN, Torben (1945-) Danish
Works on paper
£929 $1468 €1394 Brain landscape (170x160cm-67x63in) i. s.d.1986 verso mixed media nine parts plywood prov. 1-Apr-3 Rasmussen, Copenhagen #222/R (D.KR 10000)

EBE, C (19th C) German
£2817 $4535 €4000 Visit to the harem (77x87cm-30x34in) s.d.1874. 9-May-3 Schloss Ahlden, Ahlden #1400/R est:5500

EBEL, Fritz Carl Werner (1835-1895) German
£270 $422 €400 Summer landscape (18x26cm-7x10in) s. 26-Mar-3 Hugo Ruef, Munich #93
£1362 $2070 €2043 Wooded landscape with deer (69x104cm-27x41in) s.d.1881. 27-Aug-2 Goodman, Sydney #268/R est:3000-5000 (A.D 3800)
£1818 $2800 €2727 Deer in a forest clearing (99x85cm-39x33in) s.d.186 prov. 4-Sep-2 Christie's, Rockefeller NY #326/R est:2500-3500
£2347 $3850 €3403 Wooded landscape with grazing cows (64x95cm-25x37in) s.d. 4-Jun-3 Fischer, Luzern #1148/R est:8000-12000 (S.FR 5000)
£2468 $3800 €3702 Forest clearing with figures (99x85cm-39x33in) s.d.1867 prov. 4-Sep-2 Christie's, Rockefeller NY #327/R est:4000-6000
£3022 $4835 €4200 Wooded mountain landscape (93x77cm-37x30in) s. 17-May-3 Lempertz, Koln #1390/R est:4000

EBERHARD, Heinrich (1884-1973) German
£570 $889 €900 Countryside vision (50x60cm-20x24in) s.d.1957 board. 18-Oct-2 Dr Fritz Nagel, Stuttgart #84/R
£753 $1175 €1100 Before the festivities (43x34cm-17x13in) s.d.1909. 11-Apr-3 Sigalas, Stuttgart #440

EBERL, François (1887-1962) French
£577 $906 €900 Lecture devant la mer (35x27cm-14x11in) s. 15-Dec-2 Eric Pillon, Calais #145/R
£897 $1391 €1400 Portrait de Lina (41x33cm-16x13in) s. 4-Dec-2 Pierre Berge, Paris #136/R
£1389 $2209 €2000 Nature morte aux fruits (46x55cm-18x22in) s. 29-Apr-3 Artcurial Briest, Paris #254b est:1200-1500
£1560 $2606 €2200 Modele allonge aux bras croises (73x100cm-29x39in) s. 23-Jun-3 Delvaux, Paris #130/R est:1000-1200
£3185 $4968 €5000 Grand nu assis (81x100cm-32x39in) s. 6-Nov-2 Claude Boisgirard, Paris #14 est:5000-6000

EBERL, Jean (?) French?
£456 $711 €720 Le repos du modele (27x35cm-11x14in) s. 20-Oct-2 Galerie de Chartres, Chartres #147

EBERLE, Abastenia St Leger (1878-1942) American
Sculpture
£18065 $28000 €27098 Salome - the dancer (57cm-22in) i. brown pat. bronze. 5-Dec-2 Christie's, Rockefeller NY #85/R est:40000-60000

EBERLE, Adolf (1843-1914) German
£2564 $3897 €4000 Girl writing love letter in bedroom (37x30cm-15x12in) s.d.1872 panel. 11-Jul-2 Hugo Ruef, Munich #632/R est:5500

EBERLE, Francois (20th C) French?
£1266 $2000 €2000 Clown (56x46cm-22x18in) s. 2-Dec-2 Tajan, Paris #186 est:2000-2500

EBERSBACH, Hartwig (1940-) German
Works on paper
£347 $549 €500 Brimborium 18 (73x51cm-29x20in) mono.i.d.1988 W/C board. 26-Apr-3 Dr Lehr, Berlin #17/R

EBERT, Anton (1845-1896) German
£1233 $1838 €1850 Portrait of woman (53x42cm-21x17in) s.i. oval. 25-Jun-2 Koller, Zurich #6475 est:900-1400 (S.FR 2800)
£1384 $2145 €2200 Woman with roses in hair (65x55cm-26x22in) s.d.1872 oval. 29-Oct-2 Dorotheum, Vienna #200/R est:2600-3000
£1863 $3000 €2795 Portrait of an elaborately dressed young lady (61x51cm-24x20in) s. oval. 15-Jan-3 Boos Gallery, Michigan #478/R est:4000-6000
£3425 $5342 €5000 Oriental beauties (40x31cm-16x12in) one s.i. i. verso panel two. 10-Apr-3 Dorotheum, Vienna #74/R est:4000-4500

EBERT, C (19th C) ?
£533 $885 €773 Beauty in leopard skin (52x42cm-20x17in) s. after Jean Baptiste. 16-Jun-3 Waddingtons, Toronto #356/R est:800-1000 (C.D 1200)

EBERT, Carl (1821-1885) German
£854 $1324 €1350 Children bathing in woodland pool (14x24cm-6x9in) panel. 25-Sep-2 Neumeister, Munich #569/R

EBERT, Charles H (1873-1959) American
£13924 $22000 €20886 Monhegan Island, Maine (51x64cm-20x25in) s. prov.exhib. 24-Apr-3 Shannon's, Milford #63/R est:15000-25000

EBERZ, Josef (1880-1942) German
£316 $500 €500 Beggar (31x27cm-12x11in) s.d.1915 tempera board. 27-Nov-2 Dr Fritz Nagel, Stuttgart #3207/R
£5769 $8942 €9000 Landscape with fortress (70x78cm-28x31in) s.d.20 prov.exhib.lit. 4-Dec-2 Lempertz, Koln #673/R est:14000-16000
Works on paper
£823 $1300 €1300 Frascati garden in the evening (30x37cm-12x15in) s.d.25 W/C over Indian ink. 29-Nov-2 Villa Grisebach, Berlin #583/R est:1000-1500
£1282 $1987 €2000 Woman in wood (26x20cm-10x8in) s.d.18 W/C pen. 4-Dec-2 Lempertz, Koln #674/R
£5063 $8000 €8000 Square in Taormina (71x99cm-28x39in) s.d.24 s.i.d. stretcher. 30-Nov-2 Villa Grisebach, Berlin #283/R est:8000-10000

EBICHE, Eugene (?) French?
£719 $1180 €1000 Le lievre (77x49cm-30x19in) s. 3-Jun-3 Tajan, Paris #31
£2302 $3776 €3200 Jeune fille (73x60cm-29x24in) s. 3-Jun-3 Tajan, Paris #32 est:800-1200
£4461 $7316 €6200 Nature morte (60x73cm-24x29in) s. 3-Jun-3 Tajan, Paris #33/R est:1000-1500

EBNOTHER, Josef (1937-) Swiss
£2183 $3406 €3275 Light brown, black composition (180x120cm-71x47in) s. jute. 6-Nov-2 Hans Widmer, St Gallen #122/R est:3000-7500 (S.FR 5000)
£2271 $3542 €3407 Beige, brown composition (180x120cm-71x47in) s. jute. 6-Nov-2 Hans Widmer, St Gallen #124/R est:3000-7500 (S.FR 5200)

ECCARDT, John Giles (?-1779) German
£1000 $1550 €1500 Portrait of an officer (76x64cm-30x25in) oval. 3-Dec-2 Sotheby's, Olympia #7/R est:1000-1500

ECHAURREN, Pablo (1951-) Italian
£1096 $1710 €1600 Entering from one ear, coming out from the other one (60x80cm-24x31in) s.i.d.1988 verso acrylic. 10-Apr-3 Finarte Semenzato, Rome #203/R

ECHAUZ, Francisco (1927-) Spanish
£789 $1279 €1200 Union (100x81cm-39x32in) prov.exhib. 21-Jan-3 Ansorena, Madrid #332/R
Works on paper
£258 $402 €410 Victory dove (30x42cm-12x17in) s.d.1961 gouache sand. 17-Sep-2 Segre, Madrid #302/R

ECHEVERRIA, Federico de (1911-) Spanish?
£1154 $1812 €1800 Women in a cafe (100x78cm-39x31in) s. s.i.verso. 19-Nov-2 Castellana, Madrid #65/R
£1321 $2060 €2100 Cancan (20x29cm-8x11in) s. board. 8-Oct-2 Ansorena, Madrid #468/R

ECKARDT, Christian (1832-1914) Danish
£380 $593 €570 Entrance to St Pieme (28x42cm-11x17in) init.d.1880. 23-Sep-2 Rasmussen, Vejle #116/R (D.KR 4500)
£406 $625 €609 Seascape with approaching thunder storm in Storebaelt (41x56cm-16x22in) s.d.1898. 26-Oct-2 Rasmussen, Havnen #3026/R (D.KR 4800)
£426 $660 €639 Southern harbour scene (30x48cm-12x19in) init.d.74. 4-Dec-2 AB Stockholms Auktionsverk #1918/R (S.KR 6000)
£467 $729 €701 View across a fjord (25x38cm-10x15in) init. 5-Aug-2 Rasmussen, Vejle #33/R (D.KR 5500)
£468 $740 €702 Boat space by the harbour (22x29cm-9x11in) s.d.1873. 2-Dec-2 Rasmussen, Copenhagen #1354/R (D.KR 5500)
£2153 $3273 €3230 Seascape with sailing ship and steamer at entrance to Copenhagen's Harbour (25x35cm-10x14in) s.d.1859. 27-Aug-2 Rasmussen, Copenhagen #1430/R est:25000 (D.KR 25000)
£2871 $4651 €4163 Seascape with many ship (110x180cm-43x71in) s.d.1888. 24-May-3 Rasmussen, Havnen #2040/R est:30000 (D.KR 30000)
£4255 $6723 €6383 Entrance to Korsor Harbour, morning (75x100cm-30x39in) s.d.1870 exhib. 2-Dec-2 Rasmussen, Copenhagen #1167/R est:75000-125000 (D.KR 50000)
£6518 $10363 €9777 Morning in the Bay of Corfu (80x127cm-31x50in) s.d.1875 exhib. 5-Mar-3 Rasmussen, Copenhagen #1573/R est:75000-100000 (D.KR 70000)

ECKENBRECHER, Themistocles von (1842-1921) German
£786 $1226 €1250 Fjord landscape with steamer (72x100cm-28x39in) s.d.1915 lit. 20-Sep-2 Schloss Ahlden, Ahlden #1155/R
£1702 $2689 €2553 Am Naerofjord bei Gudvangen (72x100cm-28x39in) s.d.1915. 2-Dec-2 Rasmussen, Copenhagen #1551/R est:20000 (D.KR 20000)
Works on paper
£385 $596 €600 Cairo street (13x10cm-5x4in) mono.i.d.1886 prov. 7-Dec-2 Ketterer, Hamburg #141/R
£400 $648 €600 View of Constantinople (8x13cm-3x5in) init.d.03 pencil W/C. 23-Jan-3 Christie's, Kensington #340/R
£605 $944 €950 Constantinople (15x10cm-6x4in) mono.d.04 W/C. 6-Nov-2 Hugo Ruef, Munich #1367/R
£1549 $2572 €2200 Babel-Metuale in Cairo (37x27cm-15x11in) s.d.1889 W/C ink dr. 14-Jun-3 Arnold, Frankfurt #734/R est:300

ECKENER, Alexander (1870-1944) German
£692 $1079 €1100 Flensburg Fjord in the evening (57x92cm-22x36in) s.d.32 i. stretcher. 21-Sep-2 Bolland & Marotz, Bremen #471/R
£738 $1189 €1100 Figures by fireplace in hall (52x59cm-20x23in) s. 21-Feb-3 Sigalas, Stuttgart #947/R est:1200
£1688 $2516 €2600 Bank of Ostsee (58x48cm-23x19in) s.d.1915. 28-Jun-2 Sigalas, Stuttgart #784/R
Works on paper
£962 $1462 €1500 Horse and cows (21x31cm-8x12in) s.d.03. 17-Aug-2 Hans Stahl, Toestorf #80/R

ECKENFELDER, Friedrich (1861-1938) German
£903 $1328 €1400 Goat and hen studies (33x43cm-13x17in) s.d.1882 canvas on board lit. 20-Jun-2 Dr Fritz Nagel, Stuttgart #764/R
£1677 $2381 €2700 Zollern castle in Balingen (63x59cm-25x23in) s. lit. 23-Mar-2 Geble, Radolfzell #538/R est:2500

ECKER, Franz (1943-1999) Austrian
£935 $1496 €1300 Little sister (100x110cm-39x43in) s.d.1990 i. verso. 14-May-3 Dorotheum, Linz #424/R

ECKERSBERG, C W (1783-1853) Danish
Works on paper
£429 $678 €644 From Copenhagen Harbour (12x17cm-5x7in) init.d.15 may 1826 pencil. 13-Nov-2 Kunsthallen, Copenhagen #112/R (D.KR 5000)
£468 $754 €702 Male model (18x26cm-7x10in) pencil prov. 26-Feb-3 Museumsbygningen, Copenhagen #76 (D.KR 5200)
£1021 $1614 €1532 Part of the Colonnade (31x27cm-12x11in) i. pencil study prov. 2-Dec-2 Rasmussen, Copenhagen #1848/R est:12000-15000 (D.KR 12000)
£1280 $2035 €1920 Frigates at Copenhagen's Harbour (22x39cm-9x15in) i. pencil. 26-Feb-3 Kunsthallen, Copenhagen #547/R est:12000 (D.KR 14000)

ECKERSBERG, Christoffer Wilhelm (1783-1853) Danish
£2793 $4441 €4190 Christ and Thomas (30x20cm-12x8in) prov. 5-Mar-3 Rasmussen, Copenhagen #1541/R est:40000-50000 (D.KR 30000)
£28708 $46507 €41627 Man-o-war under sail - Najaden off Helsingor with Kronborg in background (35x42cm-14x17in) painted before 1810 prov. 26-May-3 Rasmussen, Copenhagen #1176/R est:350000-450000 (D.KR 300000)
£29787 $47064 €44681 Portrait of Miss Julia Thabita Schack wearing pink dress (60x44cm-24x17in) init.d.1829 prov. 2-Dec-2 Rasmussen, Copenhagen #1173/R est:350000-400000 (D.KR 350000)
£85397 $131512 €128096 A storm - figures in street scene (32x27cm-13x11in) painted 1845. 4-Sep-2 Kunsthallen, Copenhagen #39/R est:1000000 (D.KR 1000000)
£176909 $281285 €265364 View to Sommerspiret with the Bulow family in foreground (39x45cm-15x18in) painted 1809 exhib.prov. 5-Mar-3 Rasmussen, Copenhagen #1540/R est:1200000-1800000 (D.KR 1900000)
Works on paper
£4469 $7106 €6704 Study for Scolding on the town steps (13x11cm-5x4in) pen pencil wash executed c.1841 prov. 5-Mar-3 Rasmussen, Copenhagen #1542/R est:30000 (D.KR 48000)
£6518 $10363 €9777 Frederik VI and Queen Marie Sofie and their daughters (18x13cm-7x5in) pen executed c.1820. 5-Mar-3 Rasmussen, Copenhagen #1543/R est:75000 (D.KR 70000)

ECKERSBERG, Christoffer Wilhelm (attrib) (1783-1853) Danish
£2067 $3142 €3101 Portrait of Anna Catharina Holtzer (36x29cm-14x11in) i. oval. 28-Aug-2 Museumsbygningen, Copenhagen #19/R est:25000-30000 (D.KR 24000)

ECKERSBERG, Johan Fredrik (1822-1870) Norwegian
£1298 $2050 €1947 Landscape with two figures (28x42cm-11x17in) s.d.1863 panel. 2-Dec-2 Blomqvist, Oslo #305/R est:20000-30000 (N.KR 15000)

ECKERT, Heinrich Ambros (attrib) (1807-1840) German
£952 $1514 €1400 Fishing harbour (32x41cm-13x16in) i.d.1835 panel. 19-Mar-3 Neumeister, Munich #549/R est:1500

ECKERTSPERGER, Leonhard (1899-1991) German
£294 $471 €450 Still life of daffodils (60x40cm-24x16in) s. fibreboard lit. 10-Jan-3 Allgauer, Kempten #1575/R

ECKHARDT, Oscar (19/20th C) ?
Works on paper
£280 $445 €420 Fashionable party at the ice rink (26x32cm-10x13in) s. monochrome bodycol. 29-Apr-3 Bonhams, Knightsbridge #34/R

ECKL, Vilma (1892-1982) Austrian
Works on paper
£1282 $2026 €2000 Blue horse (40x60cm-16x24in) s. pastel chk. 18-Nov-2 Dorotheum, Linz #389 est:3000-4000

ECKMAN, Nicolas (?) ?
Works on paper
£1290 $2039 €2000 Homme et enfant (53x42cm-21x17in) pen W/C. 18-Dec-2 Rieunier, Bailly-Pommery, Mathias, Paris #63/R

ECMONT, Marc (20th C) French
£1195 $1852 €1900 Le manteau de Hans Arp (65x48cm-26x19in) s.d. paper laid on panel. 4-Oct-2 Tajan, Paris #70 est:380-460

ECUADORIAN SCHOOL, 18th C
Sculpture
£7927 $13000 €11494 Mary Magdalene (51x37x15cm-20x15x6in) polychromed wood glass prov. 27-May-3 Sotheby's, New York #129

EDDELIEN, Heinrich (1802-1852) Danish
£3062 $4961 €4440 Scene from The River of Sin (130x160cm-51x63in) exhib.prov. 26-May-3 Rasmussen, Copenhagen #1285/R est:20000-30000 (D.KR 32000)
£6891 $10474 €10337 Orpheus at the grave of Euridices (110x85cm-43x33in) exhib. 27-Aug-2 Rasmussen, Copenhagen #1432/R est:80000 (D.KR 80000)

EDDINGTON, William Charles (fl.1861-1885) British
£705 $1093 €1100 Hay harvest in extensive hilly landscape (49x80cm-19x31in) s.d.1889. 5-Dec-2 Dr Fritz Nagel, Stuttgart #651/R

EDDIS, Eden Upton (1812-1901) British
£1855 $2931 €2783 Roy the terrier in a wood (61x51cm-24x20in) i. 18-Nov-2 Waddingtons, Toronto #112/R est:1000-1500 (C.D 4600)

EDE, Basil (1931-) British
Works on paper
£400 $636 €600 Blue tits and blossom (17x24cm-7x9in) s.d.1956 W/C. 4-Mar-3 Bearnes, Exeter #404/R
£700 $1134 €1050 Mistle thrush (29x19cm-11x7in) s. W/C gouache prov. 20-May-3 Sotheby's, Olympia #64/R
£1200 $1944 €1800 House martins (29x19cm-11x7in) s.d.1976 W/C gouache prov. 20-May-3 Sotheby's, Olympia #61/R est:600-800
£5696 $9000 €8544 Snowy egret with palmetto, Charleston, South Carolina (63x48cm-25x19in) s.i.d.1979 W/C gouache prov. 3-Apr-3 Christie's, Rockefeller NY #230/R est:10000-15000

EDE, Frederick Charles Vipond (1865-1907) American
£524 $828 €786 Cattle in the lane (38x56cm-15x22in) s.d.1891 prov. 14-Nov-2 Heffel, Vancouver #191 est:1300-1600 (C.D 1300)
£1228 $1830 €1842 Bergere et ses moutons (48x63cm-19x25in) s.d.92. 26-Jun-2 Iegor de Saint Hippolyte, Montreal #33 (C.D 2800)
Works on paper
£258 $402 €387 Girl picking flowers (27x43cm-11x17in) s.d.1886 W/C. 25-Mar-3 Ritchie, Toronto #135/R (C.D 600)

EDEFALK, Cecilia (1954-) Swedish?
£8059 $12572 €12089 Boy and elderberries (96x34cm-38x13in) s.d.1990 diptych. 6-Nov-2 AB Stockholms Auktionsverk #816/R est:40000-50000 (S.KR 115000)

EDEL, Bruno (1939-) French
Works on paper
£310 $499 €440 Maison cachee (45x60cm-18x24in) s. W/C gouache. 12-May-3 Lesieur & Le Bars, Le Havre #33
£317 $510 €450 Peniches sur la Seine (45x60cm-18x24in) s.d.99 W/C gouache. 12-May-3 Lesieur & Le Bars, Le Havre #34
£352 $567 €500 Falaises du Pays de Caux (45x60cm-18x24in) s. W/C gouache. 12-May-3 Lesieur & Le Bars, Le Havre #32/R

EDELBAUM, S (20th C) American
£305 $500 €442 Untitled (66x66cm-26x26in) s.d.66 board prov. 1-Jun-3 Wright, Chicago #291/R
£915 $1500 €1327 Untitled (178x127cm-70x50in) s.d.1968 oil on linen triptych. 1-Jun-3 Wright, Chicago #292/R est:3000-5000

EDELFELT, Albert (1854-1905) Finnish
£6962 $11000 €11000 Waiting - woman knitting by tree (46x35cm-18x14in) i. 1-Dec-2 Bukowskis, Helsinki #46/R est:10000-12000
£14085 $22676 €20000 Male model with sword (114x99cm-45x39in) lit. 10-May-3 Bukowskis, Helsinki #133/R est:20000-30000
£29114 $46000 €46000 The artist's villa in Haiko (60x37cm-24x15in) s. exhib.lit. 1-Dec-2 Bukowskis, Helsinki #44/R est:45000-48000
£37589 $58262 €56384 Un coin de mon atelier (39x26cm-15x10in) s.i.d.juin 1878 prov. 4-Dec-2 AB Stockholms Auktionsverk #1872/R est:300000-400000 (S.KR 530000)
£58228 $92000 €92000 By the door (117x74cm-46x29in) s.d.1901 lit. 1-Dec-2 Bukowskis, Helsinki #43/R est:42000-45000
£84507 $136056 €120000 Parisian woman (45x38cm-18x15in) s.d.1883 exhib. 10-May-3 Bukowskis, Helsinki #114/R est:120000-150000
Works on paper
£692 $1065 €1100 Hazy day (19x34cm-7x13in) W/C. 27-Oct-2 Bukowskis, Helsinki #157/R
£784 $1286 €1200 Reclining (27x44cm-11x17in) mixed media. 9-Feb-3 Bukowskis, Helsinki #220/R
£912 $1404 €1450 The soldier (48x18cm-19x7in) W/C. 27-Oct-2 Bukowskis, Helsinki #155/R
£1013 $1600 €1600 Girl (29x24cm-11x9in) i.verso pen dr. 30-Nov-2 Hagelstam, Helsinki #76/R est:1500
£12658 $20000 €20000 Lady and her dog walking in the park (47x29cm-19x11in) s.d.14 oktober 87 W/C. 1-Dec-2 Bukowskis, Helsinki #45/R est:20000-25000
£18310 $29479 €26000 Salutorget, Helsinki with figures (32x48cm-13x19in) s.d.1890 W/C exhib.lit. 10-May-3 Bukowskis, Helsinki #89/R est:25000-30000
£41772 $66000 €66000 Wounded soldier (45x61cm-18x24in) s.d.1897 gouache exhib.lit. 30-Nov-2 Hagelstam, Helsinki #94/R est:20000

EDELINE, Charles (18/19th C) French?
Works on paper
£810 $1344 €1150 Portrait d'homme (8x7cm-3x3in) s.d.1816 gouache. 16-Jun-3 Oger, Dumont, Paris #60

EDELMANN, Yrjo (1941-) Swedish
£1141 $1802 €1712 Man with arms above head (100x91cm-39x36in) s.d.75. 28-Apr-3 Bukowskis, Stockholm #904/R est:15000-20000 (S.KR 15000)
Works on paper
£280 $437 €420 Ernest Hemingway (40x26cm-16x10in) s.d.65 gouache. 6-Nov-2 AB Stockholms Auktionsverk #702/R (S.KR 4000)

EDENBERGER, J N (fl.c.1780-1800) Dutch
Miniatures
£1100 $1727 €1650 Young gentleman, called Augustin de Robespierre (5cm-2xin) silver gilt frame oval. 10-Dec-2 Christie's, London #80/R est:800-1200

EDENS, Henning (1885-1943) German
£690 $1090 €1000 Country track (30x36cm-12x14in) s.d.40 i. verso board. 5-Apr-3 Hans Stahl, Hamburg #117/R
£1154 $1788 €1800 Hamburg harbour (31x41cm-12x16in) s.d. board prov.exhib. 7-Dec-2 Ketterer, Hamburg #46/R est:2000-2500

EDER Y GATTENS, Frederico Maria (19th C) Spanish
£4200 $6552 €6300 Spanish country landscape (51x69cm-20x27in) s.d.83. 15-Oct-2 Canterbury Auctions, UK #148/R

EDER, Gyula (1875-1945) Hungarian
£300 $489 €450 Allegorical scene (34x31cm-13x12in) s. board. 12-Feb-3 Bonhams, Knightsbridge #60/R
£600 $930 €900 Putti (54x41cm-21x16in) painted c.1920. 3-Dec-2 SOGA, Bratislava #24/R (SL.K 38000)

EDERER, Carl (1875-?) German
£1282 $1987 €2000 Still life of fruit with porcelain vase and copper kettle (60x80cm-24x31in) s. i. stretcher. 4-Dec-2 Lempertz, Koln #675/R est:1500

EDES, Jonathan Welch (1750-?) American
£140741 $228000 €204074 Southwest view of Boston lighthouse and harbour (66x193cm-26x76in) s.d.1789 panel overmantel prov.exhib.lit. 22-May-3 Sotheby's, New York #748

EDHOLM, Ann (1953-) Swedish
£156 $711 €684 Untitled (60x52cm-24x20in) s.d.87 verso paper. 6-Nov-2 AB Stockholms Auktionsverk #879/R (S.KR 6500)
£927 $1492 €1391 Untitled (68x68cm-27x27in) 7-May-3 AB Stockholms Auktionsverk #996/R (S.KR 12000)

EDISS, Theodore N (20th C) American
£559 $900 €839 Pool in mountain landscape (51x61cm-20x24in) s. prov. 18-Feb-3 John Moran, Pasadena #176

EDKINS, Cathleen Elizabeth (1922-) Australian
£1143 $1806 €1715 Gathering in the hay (65x70cm-26x28in) s. 18-Nov-2 Joel, Victoria #365/R est:2500-3500 (A.D 3200)

EDLER, Eduard (20th C) German
£282 $462 €409 Ocean steamer and sailing ship in harbour (45x60cm-18x24in) s. 4-Jun-3 Fischer, Luzern #2061/R (S.FR 600)
£292 $427 €450 Portrait of the ship M/S Bilbao (50x70cm-20x28in) s. 15-Jun-2 Hans Stahl, Hamburg #233

EDLICH, Stephen (1944-) American
Works on paper
£854 $1400 €1238 Untitled (61x46cm-24x18in) mixed media collage prov. 1-Jun-3 Wright, Chicago #271/R est:2000-3000
£968 $1500 €1452 Seascape with fish form (203x102cm-80x40in) s. i.d.1984 verso acrylic gouache jute wood collage on linen prov. 26-Sep-2 Christie's, Rockefeller NY #771/R est:3000-5000

EDMONDS, Rick (?) New Zealander?
£578 $924 €838 Tranquil waters (12x29cm-5x11in) s.d.87 acrylic. 13-May-3 Watson's, Christchurch #54/R (NZ.D 1600)

EDMONSTON, Samuel (1825-?) British
£413 $657 €620 Story time (30x25cm-12x10in) s. board. 18-Mar-3 Maynards, Vancouver #46/R (C.D 975)

EDOUART, Augustin (1789-1861) French
£14194 $22000 €21291 Silhouettes of eight figures in a classical drawing room (58x74cm-23x29in) s.d.1840. 2-Nov-2 North East Auctions, Portsmouth #700/R est:8000-12000

EDRIDGE, Henry (1769-1821) British
Miniatures
£1000 $1640 €1450 Young gentleman in blue coat with gold buttons (5cm-2xin) silver gilt frame. 3-Jun-3 Christie's, London #208/R est:1000-1500
Works on paper
£280 $462 €406 Woodland path (44x30cm-17x12in) pencil blk chk. 2-Jul-3 Sotheby's, Olympia #219/R
£400 $636 €600 Street scene in Northern France (30x42cm-12x17in) W/C. 25-Feb-3 Bonhams, Knightsbridge #193/R
£400 $624 €600 Portrait of Lady Farnaby standing in garden (25x18cm-10x7in) s.d.1797 pencil grey wash dr. 25-Mar-3 Gorringes, Bexhill #1199
£800 $1304 €1160 Portrait of a lady in blue (34x26cm-13x10in) s.d.1812 pen ink W/C. 16-Jul-3 Sotheby's, Olympia #4/R
£900 $1476 €1305 Sidmouth from Salcombe Hill (26x41cm-10x16in) i.d.Aug 29 1814 pencil prov. 5-Jun-3 Christie's, London #94/R

EDSBERG, Knud (1911-) Danish
£276 $422 €414 Heifers in stable (40x50cm-16x20in) s. 24-Aug-2 Rasmussen, Havnen #2203 (D.KR 3200)
£280 $445 €420 Landscape with cows and horse (70x100cm-28x39in) s. 5-May-3 Rasmussen, Vejle #285 (D.KR 3000)

EDSON, Allan (1846-1888) Canadian
£620 $973 €930 Day's end (25x36cm-10x14in) s. 24-Jul-2 Walker's, Ottawa #244/R est:1200-1600 (C.D 1500)
£820 $1270 €1230 Mountain stream (25x20cm-10x8in) mono.d.72 panel prov. 24-Sep-2 Ritchie, Toronto #3127/R est:1000-1500 (C.D 2000)
£1244 $2041 €1866 Sunlit autumn day (35x25cm-14x10in) s.d.85 canvas on board. 3-Jun-3 Joyner, Toronto #410/R est:1000-1500 (C.D 2800)
£2263 $3508 €3395 Girl with a wheelbarrow (42x30cm-17x12in) s. canvas on board prov. 3-Dec-2 Joyner, Toronto #218/R est:2500-3000 (C.D 5500)
£6667 $10933 €10001 Children fishing by a quiet pool (47x85cm-19x33in) s. prov. 3-Jun-3 Joyner, Toronto #7/R est:8000-10000 (C.D 15000)
Works on paper
£288 $447 €432 Forest interior (24x34cm-9x13in) init. W/C. 3-Dec-2 Joyner, Toronto #439 (C.D 700)
£307 $476 €461 Faggot gatherers in a glade (34x49cm-13x19in) s.d.80 W/C prov. 24-Sep-2 Ritchie, Toronto #3099/R (C.D 750)
£652 $1017 €1088 High falls, near North Troy (44x29cm-17x11in) init.i. W/C paper board. 13-Apr-3 Levis, Calgary #30 est:2000-2500 (C.D 1500)
£984 $1525 €1476 Figures on a forest path (37x27cm-15x11in) s. W/C prov. 24-Sep-2 Ritchie, Toronto #3098a/R est:700-900 (C.D 2400)

EDWARD, Charles (19th C) British
Works on paper
£302 $475 €453 Authoress (30x20cm-12x8in) s. W/C. 22-Nov-2 Skinner, Boston #57/R

EDWARDS, Douglas (1954-) Canadian
£2556 $4191 €3706 Untitled - Southern Alberta landscape (150x270cm-59x106in) s. 9-Jun-3 Hodgins, Calgary #148/R est:3000-5000 (C.D 5750)

EDWARDS, Howard S (20th C) Canadian?
£267 $437 €387 Untitled - spring break up (53x64cm-21x25in) 1-Jun-3 Levis, Calgary #37/R (C.D 600)

EDWARDS, J W (20th C) British
£943 $1500 €1415 Fisherman (51x36cm-20x14in) s.d. 2-Mar-3 Toomey, Oak Park #579/R est:2000-4000
£1558 $2400 €2337 Man with gigging stick and bucket (51x36cm-20x14in) s.d.1886. 8-Sep-2 Treadway Gallery, Cincinnati #576/R est:3000-5000

EDWARDS, John Paul (1884-1968) American
Photographs
£3247 $5000 €4871 East side, New York (25x30cm-10x12in) s.i. chloride print prov. 22-Oct-2 Sotheby's, New York #54/R est:4000-6000

EDWARDS, Lionel (1878-1966) British
£250 $398 €375 Lanark and Renfrewshire (35x51cm-14x20in) s. 7-Mar-3 Tennants, Leyburn #16
£260 $413 €390 Goodwood Races (25x40cm-10x16in) s. 7-Mar-3 Tennants, Leyburn #9 est:260
£260 $413 €390 The kill (40x53cm-16x21in) 7-Mar-3 Tennants, Leyburn #39/R
£260 $413 €390 The Devon and Somerset staghounds, the lay-on (38x52cm-15x20in) s. 7-Mar-3 Tennants, Leyburn #59
£270 $429 €405 The Croome hounds - away from Jack's Paddock (39x51cm-15x20in) s. 7-Mar-3 Tennants, Leyburn #34
£280 $445 €420 The Bedeale, the meet at Bedale (37x51cm-15x20in) s. 7-Mar-3 Tennants, Leyburn #25
£290 $461 €435 The Middelton, Sittenton Wood (35x51cm-14x20in) s. 7-Mar-3 Tennants, Leyburn #18
£420 $668 €630 The ditch, Newmarket (29x39cm-11x15in) s. 7-Mar-3 Tennants, Leyburn #20 est:420
£1050 $1638 €1575 Gone to sea, Porlock Weir (36x54cm-14x21in) s.i.d.22 pencil col chk. 17-Oct-2 Lawrence, Crewkerne #1574/R est:600-800
£6600 $10890 €9570 Mare and a foal in a paddock with an extensive landscape beyond (51x76cm-20x30in) s.d.May 62. 3-Jul-3 Duke & Son, Dorchester #311/R est:5000-8000
£11000 $18040 €16500 Off to the meet (51x61cm-20x24in) s. 3-Jun-3 Bonhams, Knightsbridge #82/R est:12000-18000
£14000 $22120 €21000 Captain Frank Spicer with the Avon vale hounds (51x76cm-20x30in) s.d.1948. 27-Nov-2 Christie's, London #1/R est:15000-20000
Works on paper
£400 $636 €600 Drawing (20x25cm-8x10in) mono.d.1930 pencil. 7-Mar-3 Tennants, Leyburn #60
£580 $922 €870 Can Laney own a line thats cold and stale (20x28cm-8x11in) mono.d.1930 pencil. 7-Mar-3 Tennants, Leyburn #61
£720 $1123 €1080 Cottesmore near Atherstone (18x30cm-7x12in) init. i.verso pencil black ink. 10-Oct-2 Greenslade Hunt, Taunton #577/R
£1200 $1872 €1800 Work horses returning from the fields stopping for a drink (41x33cm-16x13in) s. W/C. 28-Mar-3 Dee Atkinson & Harrison, Driffield #718/R est:800-1200
£1350 $2106 €2025 Groom holding Mr Hutchinson's hunter (25x36cm-10x14in) init. gouache pencil prov. 17-Oct-2 Lawrence, Crewkerne #1575/R est:800-1200
£1500 $2340 €2250 Stag going to sea, Glenthorne (40x53cm-16x21in) s.d.24 pencil chl bodycol prov. 10-Oct-2 Greenslade Hunt, Taunton #558/R est:700-1000
£1800 $3006 €2610 Mr Pickwick arrives at Bury St. Edmunds (30x47cm-12x19in) s.d.46 W/C gouache. 25-Jun-3 Cheffins, Cambridge #731/R est:800-1200
£4500 $7290 €6750 Fox on a hillside (34x24cm-13x9in) W/C bodycol. 22-May-3 Christie's, London #3/R est:2500-3500
£5000 $8200 €7500 Autumnal hunt (44x60cm-17x24in) s.d.1904 W/C. 3-Jun-3 Bonhams, Knightsbridge #81/R est:5000-8000
£6090 $9439 €9500 Irish hunting (42x57cm-17x22in) s. W/C. 3-Dec-2 Bonhams & James Adam, Dublin #75/R est:4000-6000
£6500 $10530 €9750 Polo at Windsor (33x55cm-13x22in) s.i.d.55 black crayon W/C bodycol. 22-May-3 Christie's, London #48/R est:6000-8000

£7500 $12450 €10875 Crossing the track (42x56cm-17x22in) mono.i. W/C. 12-Jun-3 Christie's, Kensington #25/R est:8000-12000
£9000 $14580 €13500 To ground, south and west Wiltshire, the Motcombe Vale (49x74cm-19x29in) s.d.1932 W/C bodycol. 22-May-3 Christie's, London #2/R est:8000-12000
£11000 $17820 €16500 Curragh (36x55cm-14x22in) s.i.d.1965 pencil W/C paper on card. 22-May-3 Christie's, London #1/R est:7000-10000
£13500 $21870 €20250 Irish bank (37x25cm-15x10in) s. W/C bodycol. 22-May-3 Christie's, London #4/R est:3000-5000
£14000 $22120 €21000 Duke of Rutland's hounds (33x50cm-13x20in) s.i.d.1924 W/C bodycol. 27-Nov-2 Christie's, London #2/R est:10000-15000

EDWARDS, Mary A (1894-1988) Australian
£981 $1490 €1472 Sanada (52x45cm-20x18in) s. board exhib. 27-Aug-2 Goodman, Sydney #169/R est:3000-4000 (A.D 2736)

EDWARDS, McLean (1972-) Australian
£1643 $2595 €2465 Portrait (80x60cm-31x24in) i. 27-Nov-2 Deutscher-Menzies, Melbourne #166/R est:2000-3000 (A.D 4600)

EDWARDS, Simon (20th C) New Zealander?
£758 $1213 €1099 First foothills (53x72cm-21x28in) s.d.2001 canvas on board. 13-May-3 Watson's, Christchurch #28/R (NZ.D 2100)

EDY-LEGRAND, Edouard Léon Louis (1892-1970) French
£3145 $4874 €5000 Femme au grand chapeau (100x73cm-39x29in) s. cardboard painted c.1910. 30-Oct-2 Artcurial Briest, Paris #183/R est:6000-8000
£4487 $7045 €7000 Nu allonge sur un divan (54x101cm-21x40in) s. paper on canvas lit. 10-Dec-2 Tajan, Paris #160/R est:10000
£5769 $9058 €9000 Enfants du Caid (63x93cm-25x37in) s. mixed media paper on panel. 10-Dec-2 Tajan, Paris #162/R est:10000
£6090 $9561 €9500 Trois femmes a l'heure du the (63x99cm-25x39in) st.sig.d.52 masonite lit. 10-Dec-2 Tajan, Paris #163/R est:10000
£7692 $12077 €12000 Interior in Tangers (64x98cm-25x39in) s. masonite lit. 10-Dec-2 Tajan, Paris #161/R est:13000
Works on paper
£2885 $4529 €4500 Fatima et Barka (25x25cm-10x10in) Indian ink htd W/C. 16-Dec-2 Gros & Delettrez, Paris #357 est:2500-3000
£4487 $7045 €7000 Quatre femmes en bleu (64x99cm-25x39in) st.sig. mixed media masonite lit. 10-Dec-2 Tajan, Paris #164/R est:10000
£6410 $10064 €10000 Marieea Goulimine (99x63cm-39x25in) s.i.d.53 mixed media paper on masonite lit. 10-Dec-2 Tajan, Paris #159/R

EDZARD, Dietz (1893-1963) German
£667 $1107 €967 La loge (17x19cm-7x7in) s. prov. 10-Jun-3 Ritchie, Toronto #117/R est:2000-2500 (C.D 1500)
£680 $1082 €1000 Angelica chasseuse (33x22cm-13x9in) s. painted 1960. 28-Feb-3 Joron-Derem, Paris #42
£769 $1200 €1154 Tete de femme (28x20cm-11x8in) s. 9-Oct-2 Doyle, New York #31
£984 $1534 €1476 First party. Bouquet de fleurs (21x12cm-8x5in) s. panel double-sided. 10-Sep-2 Iegor de Saint Hippolyte, Montreal #44 (C.D 2400)
£987 $1470 €1481 Roses et flute (23x16cm-9x6in) s. panel. 26-Jun-2 Iegor de Saint Hippolyte, Montreal #34 (C.D 2250)
£1465 $2300 €2198 Young girl (46x38cm-18x15in) s. 22-Nov-2 Skinner, Boston #315/R est:2000-4000
£1509 $2400 €2264 Street melodies (65x53cm-26x21in) s. prov. 27-Feb-3 Christie's, Rockefeller NY #92/R
£1509 $2400 €2264 Embarcadere, Venise (22x27cm-9x11in) s. prov. 27-Feb-3 Christie's, Rockefeller NY #87/R est:3000
£2388 $3750 €3582 Barmaid (55x46cm-22x18in) s. 22-Nov-2 Skinner, Boston #313/R est:3000-5000
£3397 $5368 €5300 Young couple (65x54cm-26x21in) s. 14-Nov-2 Neumeister, Munich #554/R est:6000-8000
£8138 $13021 €11800 Renee et Gerard Albouy, le salon du modiste (100x80cm-39x31in) s. 12-Mar-3 Libert, Castor, Paris #63/R est:3000-3500

EDZARD, Kurt (1890-1972) German
Sculpture
£1739 $2852 €2400 Standing female figure with arms raised (45cm-18in) mono.d.20 stucco prov. 31-May-3 Villa Grisebach, Berlin #236/R est:3000-4000

EECKHOUDT, Jean van den (1875-1946) Belgian
£818 $1259 €1300 Arbre devant le mer a Roquebrune (61x75cm-24x30in) s.d.1916. 22-Oct-2 Campo, Vlaamse Kaai #651/R
Works on paper
£1465 $2285 €2300 Portrait d'Elisabeth Vanden Eeckhoudt (62x41cm-24x16in) pastel. 11-Nov-2 Horta, Bruxelles #58 est:2500-3500

EECKHOUT, Gerbrand van den (1621-1674) Dutch
£2083 $3312 €3000 Deposition (26x20cm-10x8in) board. 3-May-3 Finarte, Venice #142/R
Works on paper
£4054 $6324 €6000 Circumcision (9x14cm-4x6in) pen ink wash prov.lit. 27-Mar-3 Christie's, Paris #142/R

EECKHOUT, Gerbrand van den (attrib) (1621-1674) Dutch
£3871 $6116 €6000 Salomon et la reine de Saba (70x94cm-28x37in) 20-Dec-2 Tajan, Paris #40/R est:8000

EECKHOUT, Jakob Joseph (1793-1861) Flemish
£2374 $3799 €3300 Parting (84x67cm-33x26in) s.d.1836. 17-May-3 De Vuyst, Lokeren #163/R est:2000-3000
£3800 $6004 €5700 Rescued from the sea (79x70cm-31x28in) s.d.1859 panel. 14-Nov-2 Christie's, Kensington #242/R est:1000-1500

EECKHOUT, Jakob Joseph (attrib) (1793-1861) Flemish
£20000 $33400 €30000 Soldiers entering a village (97x118cm-38x46in) s.d.1832. 18-Jun-3 Christie's, Kensington #77/R est:3000-5000

EECKHOUT, Victor (1821-1879) Flemish
Works on paper
£1224 $1947 €1800 Marocain de Tanger (21x15cm-8x6in) s.i. W/C gouache. 24-Mar-3 Rabourdin & Choppin de Janvry, Paris #187/R est:2000-2500

EEGHEN, Maria Catharina van (1856-1933) Dutch
£1019 $1569 €1600 Two leaf screen containing two panels with flower still lifes (107x48cm-42x19in) init.d.1905 canvas on board prov. 3-Sep-2 Christie's, Amsterdam #227 est:1000-1500

EEKELEN, Leo Theodor van (1900-) Dutch
Works on paper
£573 $894 €900 Portrait of a lady (88x62cm-35x24in) s.d.24 pastel. 6-Nov-2 Vendue Huis, Gravenhage #105/R

EEKMAN, Nicolaas (1889-1973) Belgian
£699 $1090 €1049 Les roches bleues (27x35cm-11x14in) s.mono. i. verso panel. 6-Nov-2 Dobiaschofsky, Bern #492/R (S.FR 1600)
£784 $1263 €1200 Nu a la guirlande de fleurs (46x33cm-18x13in) s. panel. 14-Jan-3 Vanderkindere, Brussels #163
£851 $1421 €1200 La bulle (34x24cm-13x9in) s.i. d.1951 verso panel. 18-Jun-3 Hotel des Ventes Mosan, Brussels #264
£878 $1370 €1300 Couronne de lierre (35x27cm-14x11in) s. 28-Mar-3 Claude Aguttes, Neuilly #148d
£2000 $3160 €3100 La cachette, Paris (55x46cm-22x18in) s.i.d. panel. 17-Dec-2 Rossini, Paris #74/R
£2553 $4264 €3600 Demasque aux etoiles (46x38cm-18x15in) s.d. panel. 23-Jun-3 Bernaerts, Antwerp #180/R est:4000-5000
£2639 $4354 €3800 Young and the old woman (50x61cm-20x24in) s. s.i.verso board. 1-Jul-3 Christie's, Amsterdam #405/R est:3000-5000
£2837 $4738 €4000 Deux femmes regardant par la fenetre (46x61cm-18x24in) s.d. s.i.d.verso panel. 23-Jun-3 Bernaerts, Antwerp #181/R est:4000-5000
£3262 $5448 €4600 Fermiere aux poules blanches (65x50cm-26x20in) s.d. canvas on panel. 23-Jun-3 Bernaerts, Antwerp #182/R est:5000-8000
£3633 $5667 €5450 In a night-club in Berlin (27x21cm-11x8in) mixed media. 11-Apr-3 Kieselbach, Budapest #141/R est:1300000 (H.F 1300000)
Works on paper
£278 $442 €400 L'exercice (49x29cm-19x11in) s. W/C. 29-Apr-3 Campo & Campo, Antwerp #557
£345 $548 €500 Portrait de fillette (26x18cm-10x7in) s. mixed media. 4-Mar-3 Palais de Beaux Arts, Brussels #334

EELSINGH, Stien (1903-1964) Dutch
Works on paper
£5461 $8847 €7700 Two woman with young rabbit (63x48cm-25x19in) s. gouache. 26-May-3 Glerum, Amsterdam #155/R est:1000-1500

EEMANS, Marc (1907-1998) Belgian
£264 $407 €420 Arnolfini par tempete en mer (65x81cm-26x32in) s. d.1970 verso. 22-Oct-2 Campo & Campo, Antwerp #100
£823 $1300 €1300 Paysage urbain (50x70cm-20x28in) s.d.1924. 26-Nov-2 Palais de Beaux Arts, Brussels #319
£2405 $3800 €3800 Les signes (60x40cm-24x16in) s.d.1927 prov. 26-Nov-2 Palais de Beaux Arts, Brussels #90/R est:3750-5000
Works on paper
£443 $700 €700 Jeune fille dans une composition surrealiste (45x32cm-18x13in) s.d.28 col crayon prov. 26-Nov-2 Palais de Beaux Arts, Brussels #92/R

EERELMAN, Otto (1839-1926) Dutch
£3774 $5811 €6000 Watchful dog (28x22cm-11x9in) s. panel. 22-Oct-2 Sotheby's, Amsterdam #48/R est:6000-8000
£4140 $6459 €6500 Bianco (46x37cm-18x15in) s. 6 Nov-2 Vendue Huis, Gravenhage #561/R est:5000-7000
£20126 $30994 €32000 Saint-Bernard puppy (42x32cm-17x13in) s. 22-Oct-2 Sotheby's, Amsterdam #141/R est:23000-30000
£23611 $37542 €34000 Courteous greeting (60x90cm-24x35in) indis sig. prov. 29-Apr-3 Christie's, Amsterdam #186/R est:25000-35000
Works on paper
£719 $1180 €1000 A pinch of snuff (68x52cm-27x20in) s. bears i. gouache board. 4-Jun-3 Reiss & Sohn, Konigstein #137/R
£845 $1361 €1200 Figure with two horses and hound (48x58cm-19x23in) s.i.d.1856 W/C. 7-May-3 Vendue Huis, Gravenhage #407/R
£1351 $2108 €2000 Saint-Bernard (73x63cm-29x25in) s. pastel. 25-Mar-3 Campo & Campo, Antwerp #63/R est:3000-4000
£2658 $4147 €4200 Gentleman speaking near a horse-drawn carriage (35x53cm-14x21in) s. W/C. 21-Oct-2 Glerum, Amsterdam #2/R est:3000-4000

EFFRONT, Nadine (20th C) French
Sculpture
£3125 $4969 €4500 Untitled (148x192cm-58x76in) plaster. 5-May-3 Bernaerts, Antwerp #451/R

EGAN, Felim (1952-) British?
£915 $1520 €1300 Sounding 2aa (24x24cm-9x9in) s.d.2002 verso acrylic mixed media on wood prov. 10-Jun-3 James Adam, Dublin #71/R est:900-1200
£2532 $3924 €4000 Abstract - from the tree line series (60x60cm-24x24in) 25-Sep-2 James Adam, Dublin #44/R est:4000-6000
£2676 $4442 €3800 Woodnote 2n (48x48cm-19x19in) s.d.2002 verso acrylic mixed media. 10-Jun-3 James Adam, Dublin #228/R est:2500-3000
£2778 $4417 €4000 Abstract (61x41cm-24x16in) s.d.1983 verso. 29-Apr-3 Whyte's, Dublin #149/R est:2000-3000
£2911 $4513 €4600 Blue abstract (76x76cm-30x30in) s.d.99 verso. 24-Sep-2 De Veres Art Auctions, Dublin #67/R est:4500-6000
Works on paper
£2405 $3728 €3800 Untitled (36x36cm-14x14in) s.d.98 W/C set of four. 24-Sep-2 De Veres Art Auctions, Dublin #153/R est:1500-2500

EGE, Mogens (1892-1946) Danish
£266 $431 €399 Three master in high seas (87x121cm-34x48in) s. 25-Jan-3 Rasmussen, Havnen #2045 (D.KR 3000)
£507 $791 €761 Coastal landscape from Grenen, Skagen (100x139cm-39x55in) s. 11-Aug-2 Hindemae, Ullerslev #7411/R (D.KR 6000)

EGEA Y MARIN, Juan (c.1860-?) Spanish
Works on paper
£353 $557 €550 Landscape (36x51cm-14x20in) s. W/C. 19-Nov-2 Durán, Madrid #723/R
£353 $557 €550 Landscape (36x51cm-14x20in) s. W/C. 19-Nov-2 Durán, Madrid #722/R

EGERSDORFER, Konrad (1868-?) German
£382 $596 €600 Untitled (25x32cm-10x13in) s.d.37 panel. 6-Nov-2 Hugo Ruef, Munich #1063/R

EGESTORFF, Paul (20th C) ?
Works on paper
£545 $855 €850 Kinnity (25x36cm-10x14in) s. W/C prov. 19-Nov-2 Whyte's, Dublin #153/R

EGG, Augustus Leopold (1816-1863) British
£467 $765 €677 Portrait of a lady (40x35cm-16x14in) prov. 9-Jun-3 Hodgins, Calgary #357/R est:500-700 (C.D 1050)
£7000 $11270 €10500 Night on the Thames. Woman and child (17x22cm-7x9in) board double-sided prov.exhib. 20-Feb-3 Christie's, London #109/R est:7000
£10000 $16100 €15000 Contemplation (35x28cm-14x11in) s. board prov.exhib. 20-Feb-3 Christie's, London #265/R est:15000
£32000 $50560 €48000 Queen Elizabeth discovers she is no longer young (122x183cm-48x72in) s. prov.exhib. 26-Nov-2 Christie's, London #102/R est:30000-50000

EGGEN, Gene (1921-2000) Dutch
Sculpture
£1151 $1888 €1600 De luisterende - standing woman (71cm-28in) wood prov. 3-Jun-3 Christie's, Amsterdam #181/R est:800-1200
£1295 $2124 €1800 Couple (124cm-49in) mono. wood prov. 3-Jun-3 Christie's, Amsterdam #182/R est:1800-2500

EGGENA, Gustav (1850-?) German
£503 $785 €800 Girl on galloping horse (18x12cm-7x5in) s. panel. 19-Sep-2 Dr Fritz Nagel, Stuttgart #926/R

EGGENHOFER, Nick (1897-1985) American
Works on paper
£319 $500 €479 Warrior (45x30cm-18x12in) s. W/C chl. 22-Nov-2 Skinner, Boston #144/R
£574 $900 €861 Logging (27x35cm-11x14in) s. pen ink. 22-Nov-2 Skinner, Boston #149/R est:1500-2000
£1282 $2000 €1923 Putting out the fire illustration (20x23cm-8x9in) W/C. 9-Nov-2 Altermann Galleries, Santa Fe #42
£1317 $2200 €1910 Lookout (11x21cm-4x8in) s. gouache on board. 18-Jun-3 Christie's, Los Angeles #81/R est:2500-3500
£2215 $3500 €3323 Indian chiefs on horseback (36x33cm-14x13in) s. W/C gouache prov. 3-Apr-3 Christie's, Rockefeller NY #137/R est:2000-3000
£2532 $4000 €3671 Watching the herd (33x23cm-13x9in) s. gouache. 26-Jul-3 Coeur d'Alene, Hayden #180/R est:2500-3500
£2690 $4250 €3901 In turquoise land (30x23cm-12x9in) s. gouache prov. 26-Jul-3 Coeur d'Alene, Hayden #189/R est:2000-4000
£2711 $4500 €3931 Trapper with packhorses (23x18cm-9x7in) s. pencil W/C gouache. 11-Jun-3 Butterfields, San Francisco #5287/R est:5000-7000
£2922 $4500 €4383 Signal (23x33cm-9x13in) gouache. 25-Oct-2 Morris & Whiteside, Hilton Head Island #36 est:5000-6000
£3165 $5000 €4589 Bone picker (41x66cm-16x26in) s. W/C prov.exhib. 26-Jul-3 Coeur d'Alene, Hayden #80/R est:8000-12000
£3686 $5750 €5529 Last mile (46x71cm-18x28in) gouache. 9-Nov-2 Altermann Galleries, Santa Fe #43
£4046 $6555 €5867 Pony express (30x43cm-12x17in) W/C gouache. 23-May-3 Altermann Galleries, Santa Fe #93
£4747 $7500 €6883 Appaloosa scout (36x25cm-14x10in) s. gouache. 26-Jul-3 Coeur d'Alene, Hayden #179/R est:3000-5000
£8861 $14000 €12848 Out for coups (46x36cm-18x14in) s. gouache. 26-Jul-3 Coeur d'Alene, Hayden #178/R est:5000-8000

EGGER-LIENZ, Albin (1868-1926) Austrian
£43478 $71304 €60000 Farmhouse in St Martin, Passeier (49x82cm-19x32in) 27-May-3 Wiener Kunst Auktionen, Vienna #54/R est:50000-100000
£48718 $76487 €76000 Head of the peasant in 'Life' (49x44cm-19x17in) s. canvas on panel lit. 25-Nov-2 Hassfurther, Vienna #13/R est:20000-25000
£88608 $140000 €140000 Reaper (56x79cm-22x31in) s. board prov.lit. 26-Nov-2 Wiener Kunst Auktionen, Vienna #96/R est:100000-200000
£130000 $202800 €195000 Bergmaher - Mountain mower (53x43cm-21x17in) s. painted 1907 prov.lit. 9-Oct-2 Sotheby's, London #25/R est:40000-60000

EGGERS, Peter (1855-1907) Swedish
£287 $465 €431 Autumn landscape after sunset (48x100cm-19x39in) s.d.1882 exhib. 21-May-3 Museumsbygningen, Copenhagen #75 (D.KR 3000)

EGGIMANN, Hans (1872-1929) Swiss
Works on paper
£1019 $1640 €1478 Dancing in the flower glade (29x34cm-11x13in) s. W/C bodycol. 9-May-3 Dobiaschofsky, Bern #116/R (S.FR 2200)

EGGINTON, Frank (1908-1990) British
Works on paper
£340 $530 €510 Near Achsasheen (24x35cm-9x14in) s. W/C prov. 25-Mar-3 Bonhams, Leeds #511
£600 $930 €900 Near Cookstown, County Tyrone (38x53cm-15x21in) i. verso W/C. 31-Oct-2 Greenslade Hunt, Taunton #592/R
£690 $1097 €1000 Near Killarney (27x37cm-11x15in) s.d.77 W/C. 4-Mar-3 Mealy's, Castlecomer #1210/R
£720 $1174 €1080 Estuary, hills beyond (37x51cm-15x20in) s. W/C. 11-Feb-3 Bonhams, Knowle #41
£740 $1206 €1110 Melmore from Horn Head, Co. Donegal (37x53cm-15x21in) s. i.on mount W/C. 11-Feb-3 Bonhams, Knowle #20
£750 $1178 €1125 Lough Neagh (26x35cm-10x14in) indis.sig.i.verso W/C. 25-Nov-2 Bonhams, Chester #828
£800 $1240 €1200 Lake reflection, Connemara (36x53cm-14x21in) s. W/C. 2-Oct-2 John Ross, Belfast #90
£811 $1265 €1200 Cattle grazing on a hill top (37x53cm-15x21in) s. W/C. 26-Mar-3 James Adam, Dublin #101/R est:1000-1500
£897 $1418 €1400 Near Killarney (27x37cm-11x15in) s.d.77. 12-Nov-2 Mealy's, Castlecomer #1256a/R
£903 $1435 €1300 Bogland (38x53cm-15x21in) s. W/C. 29-Apr-3 Whyte's, Dublin #190/R est:1200-1500
£940 $1513 €1400 Barley Cove, West Cork (37x52cm-15x20in) s. W/C. 18-Feb-3 Whyte's, Dublin #9/R
£1000 $1600 €1500 Owenmore River, Co Mayo (26x36cm-10x14in) s. pencil W/C. 15-May-3 Christie's, Kensington #186/R est:1000-1500
£1000 $1600 €1500 Aghadoe, Killarney (25x35cm-10x14in) s. pencil W/C. 15-May-3 Christie's, Kensington #190/R est:1000-1500

£1013 $1600 €1520 Barrow Harbour, Co Kerry, Ireland (36x53cm-14x21in) s. W/C. 5-Apr-3 DeFina, Austinburg #1306 est:1200-1600
£1090 $1711 €1700 River landscape (37x53cm-15x21in) s. W/C. 19-Nov-2 Whyte's, Dublin #203/R est:2000-3000
£1090 $1711 €1700 Near Angler's Head, County Sligo (38x53cm-15x21in) s. i.verso W/C. 19-Nov-2 Whyte's, Dublin #205/R est:2000-2500
£1149 $1792 €1700 Kylemore Lough, Connemara (36x51cm-14x20in) s.d.71 W/C. 26-Mar-3 James Adam, Dublin #102/R est:1500-2000
£1149 $1792 €1700 Kylemore Lough, Connemara (36x51cm-14x20in) s.d.71 W/C. 26-Mar-3 James Adam, Dublin #103/R est:1500-2000
£1250 $1975 €1875 Crofter cottages, Ireland (36x53cm-14x21in) s. W/C. 13-Nov-2 Halls, Shrewsbury #331/R est:800-1200
£1300 $2119 €1950 Gulls on the shore, island in the distance (51x74cm-20x29in) s. W/C. 11-Feb-3 Bonhams, Knowle #44 est:500-700
£1300 $2080 €1950 Mournes near Kilkeel (26x35cm-10x14in) s. W/C. 15-May-3 Christie's, Kensington #185/R est:1000-1500
£1342 $2161 €2000 Cattle watering (37x52cm-15x20in) s. W/C. 18-Feb-3 Whyte's, Dublin #161/R est:2000-3000
£1500 $2190 €2250 Break in the clouds (36x51cm-14x20in) s. W/C. 12-Jun-2 John Ross, Belfast #37 est:1600-1800
£1550 $2527 €2325 Below Muckish, Co Donegal (36x51cm-14x20in) s. W/C. 14-Feb-3 Keys, Aylsham #497/R est:1200-1500
£1600 $2480 €2400 Belfast from Castlereagh (35x50cm-14x20in) s. W/C. 4-Dec-2 John Ross, Belfast #273 est:1500-1800
£1689 $2635 €2500 Snow scene, Co. Donegal (37x52cm-15x20in) s. W/C. 26-Mar-3 James Adam, Dublin #51/R est:2400-2800
£1800 $2682 €2700 Killary Harbour, Connemara (51x74cm-20x29in) s. bear i.verso W/C. 27-Jun-2 Greenslade Hunt, Taunton #728/R est:700-900
£1899 $2943 €3000 Lough Na Coogarrow, Connermara. Glendollagh Lough, Connemara (37x53cm-15x21in) s. W/C pair. 25-Sep-2 James Adam, Dublin #115/R est:3000-5000
£1900 $3040 €2850 Fair Head, Co. Antrim (25x35cm-10x14in) s. W/C executed c.1935 prov. 16-May-3 Sotheby's, London #49/R est:1800-2500
£2200 $3520 €3300 Carlingford Lough at Greencastle, Co. Down (26x35cm-10x14in) s. W/C executed c.1935 prov. 16-May-3 Sotheby's, London #47/R est:2000-3000
£2350 $3760 €3525 Strand, Connemara (53x75cm-21x30in) s.d.78 W/C. 15-May-3 Christie's, Kensington #187/R est:1000-1500
£2466 $3871 €3600 Coolaney, Co. Sligo (37x53cm-15x21in) s. W/C. 15-Apr-3 De Veres Art Auctions, Dublin #261/R est:2000-3000
£2600 $4160 €3900 Croagh Patrick, Co Mayo (37x52cm-15x20in) s. pencil W/C exec.c.1937. 15-May-3 Christie's, Kensington #189/R est:2000-3000
£3500 $5600 €5250 Ducks on a wet road, Co Down (37x52cm-15x20in) s. pencil W/C prov. 15-May-3 Christie's, Kensington #188/R est:1500-2500

EGGINTON, Robert (?) British?
£304 $471 €480 Extensive Donegal landscape (70x91cm-28x36in) s. 25-Sep-2 James Adam, Dublin #113/R

EGGINTON, W (1875-1951) British
Works on paper
£450 $707 €675 Landscape with a figure upon a path (26x36cm-10x14in) s. W/C. 21-Nov-2 Clevedon Sale Rooms #206
£500 $780 €750 Near Princetown, Dartmoor (36x53cm-14x21in) s. W/C. 15-Oct-2 Gorringes, Lewes #2296/R

EGGINTON, Wycliffe (1875-1951) British
£500 $820 €750 In quiet solitude, Shetland Isles (36x51cm-14x20in) s.d.1899 mono.i.verso. 29-May-3 Christie's, Kensington #87
Works on paper
£360 $587 €540 Moorland scene (35x52cm-14x20in) s. W/C. 17-Feb-3 Bonhams, Bath #141
£400 $668 €580 Flock of sheep on a moor (26x38cm-10x15in) s. W/C. 23-Jun-3 Bonhams, Bath #17
£400 $668 €580 Glen shee (36x53cm-14x21in) s. i.verso W/C. 23-Jun-3 Bonhams, Bath #223
£433 $684 €675 Bernholm beach (33x48cm-13x19in) s. W/C. 12-Nov-2 Mealy's, Castlecomer #1232
£440 $717 €660 Figures on a moor track (38x56cm-15x22in) s. 28-Jan-3 Gorringes, Lewes #1661
£440 $700 €660 Evening light, Dunster, Somerset (27x38cm-11x15in) s. W/C. 27-Feb-3 Bonhams, Chester #415
£500 $835 €725 Driving sheep (17x25cm-7x10in) W/C. 25-Jun-3 Bonhams, Bury St Edmunds #519
£560 $890 €840 Sheep resting in moorland landscape (36x52cm-14x20in) s. W/C. 4-Mar-3 Bearnes, Exeter #332/R
£600 $930 €900 Moorland scene (25x36cm-10x14in) s. W/C. 2-Oct-2 John Ross, Belfast #7
£600 $930 €900 Moorland road (25x35cm-10x14in) s. W/C. 4-Dec-2 John Ross, Belfast #77
£600 $930 €900 Cobbler, Loch Long (25x35cm-10x14in) s. W/C. 4-Dec-2 John Ross, Belfast #159
£750 $1193 €1125 Eilean Dolan Castle, near Skye (50x71cm-20x28in) s. W/C. 5-Mar-3 John Ross, Belfast #72
£750 $1163 €1125 On the coast near Morar, Scotland (35x50cm-14x20in) s. W/C. 4-Dec-2 John Ross, Belfast #184
£870 $1426 €1200 Return home (37x55cm-15x22in) s. W/C. 28-May-3 Bonhams & James Adam, Dublin #43/R est:1500-2000
£900 $1395 €1350 Wind blown trees (38x53cm-15x21in) s. W/C. 2-Oct-2 John Ross, Belfast #166
£1300 $1898 €1950 Still life (36x51cm-14x20in) s. W/C. 12-Jun-2 John Ross, Belfast #173 est:800-1200

EGGLER, Josef (1916-) Swiss
£365 $576 €548 Landscape in early spring (52x52cm-20x20in) s.d.75 panel. 26-Nov-2 Hans Widmer, St Gallen #1097 (S.FR 850)
£365 $576 €548 Late winter hilly landscape with house (50x50cm-20x20in) s.d.75 panel. 26-Nov-2 Hans Widmer, St Gallen #1098 (S.FR 850)

EGGLESTON, Benjamin (1867-1937) American
£2848 $4500 €4272 Autumn pastoral landscape (41x61cm-16x24in) s.d.1915. 5-Apr-3 Neal Auction Company, New Orleans #343/R est:5000-7000

EGGLESTON, William (1939-) American
Photographs
£1948 $3000 €2922 Untitled (49x33cm-19x13in) s.i.verso col chromogenic print 2 of 3 exec.c.1984-85 prov.lit. 25-Oct-2 Phillips, New York #139/R est:3000-5000
£2078 $3200 €3117 Memphis (49x32cm-19x13in) s.i.verso col chromogenic print 1 of 3 prov.lit. 25-Oct-2 Phillips, New York #138/R est:4000-6000
£2675 $4200 €4013 Untitled, grafitti on wall, Los Angeles, California (56x76cm-22x30in) s. num.1 of 7 iris print. 21-Apr-3 Phillips, New York #35/R est:4000-6000
£2727 $4200 €4091 Memphis, Krystal (48x32cm-19x13in) s.i.verso col chromogenic print 1 of 3 exec.c.1984-85 prov.lit. 25-Oct-2 Phillips, New York #137/R est:4000-6000
£4375 $7000 €6563 Greenwood Moose Lodge (25x38cm-10x15in) with sig. dye transfer print. 15-May-3 Swann Galleries, New York #333/R est:4000-6000
£5031 $7799 €8000 Pullen Gro. and Ser (31x44cm-12x17in) s. i. verso dye transfer print. 31-Oct-2 Van Ham, Cologne #90/R est:8500
£5063 $8000 €7595 Outskirts of Morton, Mississippi, halloween (30x45cm-12x18in) s. dye transfer print prov.lit. 23-Apr-3 Sotheby's, New York #283/R est:10000-15000
£6329 $10000 €9494 Memphis, Tennessee (33x49cm-13x19in) dye transfer print. 23-Apr-3 Sotheby's, New York #284/R est:6000-9000
£7143 $11000 €10715 Memphis (51x61cm-20x24in) s.num. verso dye transfer print 6 of 9 prov.lit. 25-Oct-2 Phillips, New York #43/R est:15000-20000
£7595 $12000 €11393 Untitled (37x56cm-15x22in) s. s.verso num.9903-064 dye transfer print prov.lit. 24-Apr-3 Phillips, New York #44/R est:15000-20000
£10127 $16000 €15191 Untitled (27x40cm-11x16in) s.d.1980 dye transfer print executed c.1978 prov.lit. 24-Apr-3 Phillips, New York #178/R est:12000-18000
£12658 $20000 €18987 St. Simons Island, Georgia (25x38cm-10x15in) s.i.d.1980 num.4/15 dye transfer print prov.lit. 24-Apr-3 Phillips, New York #45/R est:20000-30000
£14286 $22000 €21429 Jackson, Mississippi (61x51cm-24x20in) s.verso dye transfer print 5 of 6 prov.lit. 25-Oct-2 Phillips, New York #41/R est:20000-30000
£18987 $30000 €28481 Tennessee (34x27cm-13x11in) s.verso ten dye transfer prints prov. 24-Apr-3 Phillips, New York #46/R est:30000-50000
£84416 $130000 €126624 Fourteen pictures (41x51cm-16x20in) s.num.verso dye transfer print from edition of 15 fourteen prov. 25-Oct-2 Phillips, New York #42/R est:120000-150000
£101266 $160000 €151899 Seagram collection (32x47cm-13x19in) s.verso 14 dye transfer prints prov.lit. 25-Apr-3 Phillips, New York #60 est:100000-150000
Prints
£3571 $5500 €5357 Untitled (9x13cm-4x5in) st.verso col chromogenic print exec.c.1972 prov. 25-Oct-2 Phillips, New York #135/R est:5000-7000

EGGLI, Johann Jakob (1812-1880) Swiss
Works on paper
£1528 $2415 €2292 Richterswil with Zurichsee and the Alps (36x50cm-14x20in) s.i.d.1848 gouache on lithographic background. 14-Nov-2 Stuker, Bern #9104 est:4000-5000 (S.FR 3500)

EGL, Herbert (1953-) German
Works on paper
£379 $599 €550 Untitled (130x100cm 51x39in) s.d. verso mixed media. 2-Apr-3 Dr Fritz Nagel, Stuttgart #9053/R

EGLAU, Max (1825-?) American
£4908 $8000 €7362 River landscape with figures resting on a bank (30x51cm-12x20in) s. sold with a companion. 16-Feb-3 Butterfields, San Francisco #2074 est:2000-3000

EGLAU, Otto (1917-) German
Works on paper
£347 $549 €500 Mudflats (24x33cm-9x13in) s.i.d.6 April 87 W/C board. 26-Apr-3 Dr Lehr, Berlin #122/R
£486 $768 €700 Sylt landscape (42x56cm-17x22in) s.d.18/76 i. verso W/C board. 26-Apr-3 Dr Lehr, Berlin #120/R
£521 $823 €750 Red stuff (61x36cm-24x14in) s.d.1958 mixed media. 26-Apr-3 Dr Lehr, Berlin #119/R
£818 $1259 €1300 Helgoland (45x62cm-18x24in) s.d.1959 gouache. 26-Oct-2 Dr Lehr, Berlin #94/R

EGLEY, William Maw (c.1827-1916) British
£2000 $3120 €3000 Repose (45x65cm-18x26in) s.d.1883. 17-Sep-2 Sotheby's, Olympia #182/R est:2000-3000

EGMOND, Jaap (1913-) Dutch
Works on paper
£897 $1391 €1400 Cent moulin (100x100cm-39x39in) s.i.d.Dec 71 painted cardboard relief. 3-Dec-2 Christie's, Amsterdam #299/R est:1400-2000

EGMONT, Justus van (attrib) (1601-1674) Flemish
£2000 $3080 €3000 Portrait of Sir Algernon Sidney (89x71cm-35x28in) prov. 5-Sep-2 Christie's, Kensington #3/R est:2000-3000
£6500 $10140 €9750 Portrait of a lady holding springs of jasmine (129x96cm-51x38in) prov. 10-Apr-3 Christie's, Kensington #59/R est:7000-10000

EGNER, Marie (1850-1940) Austrian
£3019 $4709 €4800 Farmstead on mountain pasture (17x27cm-7x11in) s. panel lit. 20-Sep-2 Schloss Ahlden, Ahlden #1139/R est:4500
£3165 $5000 €5000 Meadow with wooden fence (23x36cm-9x14in) s. i.verso board painted 1920. 28-Nov-2 Dorotheum, Vienna #53/R est:6000-7500
£3261 $5348 €4500 Village landscape with duck pond (14x23cm-6x9in) s. 27-May-3 Hassfurther, Vienna #34/R est:4500-6000
£4000 $6520 €6000 Italian terrace garden with girl looking (36x25cm-14x10in) s. card. 28-Jan-3 Gorringes, Lewes #1777/R est:4000-6000
£6028 $9766 €8500 Rome, Palatin (23x14cm-9x6in) i.verso panel. 22-May-3 Dorotheum, Vienna #46/R est:8500-10000
£8511 $13787 €12000 On the island of Arbe (42x58cm-17x23in) s. 22-May-3 Dorotheum, Vienna #165/R est:12000-16000
£9459 $14757 €14000 Flower idyll (21x32cm-8x13in) board. 25-Mar-3 Wiener Kunst Auktionen, Vienna #130/R est:12000-20000
Works on paper
£400 $636 €600 Lady on a terrace (25x18cm-10x7in) init. W/C. 29-Apr-3 Gorringes, Lewes #2326
£692 $1072 €1100 Flowers (38x55cm-15x22in) s.d.1901 i. verso W/C. 1-Oct-2 Dorotheum, Vienna #237/R
£692 $1072 €1100 Beach on the Isle of Wight, near Shanklin (26x39cm-10x15in) s.i. verso W/C lit. 1-Oct-2 Dorotheum, Vienna #273/R
£1081 $1686 €1600 Graukogel near Hofgastein (32x29cm-13x11in) s. W/C. 28-Mar-3 Dorotheum, Vienna #266/R est:2600-3000
£3165 $5000 €5000 Boats in Italian harbour (28x22cm-11x9in) s. W/C. 26-Nov-2 Wiener Kunst Auktionen, Vienna #29/R est:4000-10000

EGRY, Jozsef (1883-1935) Hungarian
£782 $1221 €1173 In the room (55x43cm-22x17in) s. paper. 11-Apr-3 Kieselbach, Budapest #122/R est:180000-280000 (H.F 280000)
£2580 $4024 €3741 Self-portrait with painter's palette (75x55cm-30x22in) s.d.1905. 13-Sep-2 Mu Terem Galeria, Budapest #90/R est:850000 (H.F 1000000)
£3633 $5667 €5450 Painter in Badacsony landscape (31x38cm-12x15in) s. oil tempera. 11-Apr-3 Kieselbach, Budapest #130/R est:1200000-1300000 (H.F 1300000)
£4902 $7646 €7353 On the way home, 1908 (68x55cm-27x22in) s.d.1908. 11-Sep-2 Kieselbach, Budapest #133/R (H.F 1900000)
£9501 $14822 €13776 Leanyfalu (48x70cm-19x28in) s.d.915 board. 12-Apr-3 Mu Terem Galeria, Budapest #77/R est:1500000 (H.F 3400000)
£9681 $15006 €14037 Harbour in Bruges (37x45cm-15x18in) s.d.1911 card exhib. 9-Dec-2 Mu Terem Galeria, Budapest #25/R est:1500000 (H.F 3600000)
£13413 $20925 €19449 Sunny street (50x72cm-20x28in) s. board. 12-Apr-3 Mu Terem Galeria, Budapest #73/R est:1500000 (H.F 4800000)
£14791 $22926 €21447 Detail of Naples (51x62cm-20x24in) s.d.930 oil pastel paper. 9-Dec-2 Mu Terem Galeria, Budapest #83/R est:2500000 (H.F 5500000)
£16136 $25010 €24204 Rainbow over the Lake Balaton (48x58cm-19x23in) s. cardboard. 6-Dec-2 Kieselbach, Budapest #108/R (H.F 6000000)
£20169 $31263 €30254 Evening lights (90x70cm-35x28in) s. 6-Dec-2 Kieselbach, Budapest #55/R (H.F 7500000)
£30739 $47953 €46109 Lake Balaton in sunlight (70x99cm-28x39in) s.d.943 oil pastel. 11-Apr-3 Kieselbach, Budapest #52/R est:5000000-11000000 (H.F 11000000)
Works on paper
£950 $1482 €1378 Fisherman (40x30cm-16x12in) s.d.920 ink W/C. 12-Apr-3 Mu Terem Galeria, Budapest #11/R est:150000 (H.F 340000)
£4841 $7503 €7262 In the window (42x31cm-17x12in) s. mixed media. 6-Dec-2 Kieselbach, Budapest #107/R (H.F 1800000)
£14791 $22926 €22187 Wine press house (70x82cm-28x32in) s. pastel. 6-Dec-2 Kieselbach, Budapest #38/R (H.F 5500000)
£17553 $28084 €26330 Badacsony (44x43cm-17x17in) s. mixed media exec.c.1920. 16-May-3 Kieselbach, Budapest #22/R (H.F 6000000)
£26547 $41414 €39821 Evening lights on bank of the River Danube (48x66cm-19x26in) s. pastel. 11-Apr-3 Kieselbach, Budapest #21/R est:6000000-9500000 (H.F 9500000)

EGTER VAN WISSEKERKE, Anna (1872-1969) Dutch
£986 $1587 €1400 Roof tops in old part of The Hague (57x48cm-22x19in) mono.d.1907/1908. 7-May-3 Vendue Huis, Gravenhage #177/R

EGUILUZ, Miguel (?) Spanish?
£304 $445 €475 Landscape near San Juan (38x46cm-15x18in) s. i.verso. 6-Jun-2 Castellana, Madrid #271/R

EGUSQUIZA, Rogelio (1845-1913) Spanish
£16000 $25120 €24000 Bella joven - young beauty (92x68cm-36x27in) s.d.1881. 19-Nov-2 Sotheby's, London #53/R est:12000-18000
Works on paper
£430 $702 €650 Still life (30x47cm-12x19in) s.i. chl dr. 11-Feb-3 Segre, Madrid #91/R

EHLINGER, Maurice Ambrose (1896-1981) French
£1014 $1581 €1500 Jeune femme au bord de la mer (65x54cm-26x21in) s. 28-Mar-3 Delvaux, Paris #29

EHMSEN, Heinrich (1886-1964) German
£347 $549 €500 Release (41x57cm-16x22in) s. gouache board. 26-Apr-3 Dr Lehr, Berlin #124/R
£625 $987 €900 Southern bath (40x33cm-16x13in) s. s.i.d.1954 verso panel. 26-Apr-3 Dr Lehr, Berlin #123/R

EHNINGER, John W (1827-1889) American
£1852 $2981 €2778 Rendez vous (62x78cm-24x31in) s.d.1884. 7-May-3 Dobiaschofsky, Bern #483/R est:5000 (S.FR 4000)

EHRENSTRAHL, Anna Maria Klocker von (1666-1729) Swedish
£4344 $7038 €6299 Interior scene with two dogs (49x68cm-19x27in) 26-May-3 Bukowskis, Stockholm #354/R est:60000-80000 (S.KR 56000)

EHRENSTRAHL, David Klocker von (after) (1629-1698) German
Works on paper
£7447 $11543 €11171 Blackgrouse crooning (30x27cm-12x11in) gouache prov. 3-Dec-2 Bukowskis, Stockholm #534/R est:50000-60000 (S.KR 105000)

EHRENSTRAHL, David Klocker von (studio) (1629-1698) German
£9929 $15390 €14894 King Karl XI wearing Roman costume, aged 15 (147x118cm-58x46in) 3-Dec-2 Bukowskis, Stockholm #395/R est:60000-80000 (S.KR 140000)

EHRENSVARD, Carl August (1745-1800) Swedish
Works on paper
£770 $1217 €1155 Man and woman dancing. Indian ink. 16-Nov-2 Crafoord, Lund #106/R (S.KR 11000)

EHRENSVARD, Carl August (attrib) (1745-1800) Swedish
Works on paper
£282 $443 €423 Man and woman. Head of woman (18x16cm-7x6in) Indian ink double-sided prov. 16-Dec-2 Lilla Bukowskis, Stockholm #914 (S.KR 4000)

EHRENTRAUT, Julius (1841-1923) German
£488 $800 €708 Trompetir (28x20cm-11x8in) s. i.d.1880 verso. 4-Jun-3 Doyle, New York #47

EHRHARDT, Curt (1895-1972) Swiss
£552 $872 €800 Pursuit (29x39cm-11x15in) s. s.i. verso board. 2-Apr-3 Dr Fritz Nagel, Stuttgart #9054/R
£828 $1308 €1200 Figures (50x39cm-20x15in) s.d. s.i.d. verso board. 2-Apr-3 Dr Fritz Nagel, Stuttgart #9055/R
£1087 $1783 €1500 Fall out street (60x55cm-24x22in) s.d.59 i. verso. 31-May-3 Villa Grisebach, Berlin #785/R est:1300-1500
£1149 $1792 €1700 Motherhood (39x29cm-15x11in) s. s.i.d.1921 verso board prov. 28-Mar-3 Ketterer, Hamburg #296/R est:2000-2500
£1266 $2000 €2000 I would like (34x24cm-13x9in) i. s.i.d.1922 verso board on panel. 30-Nov-2 Villa Grisebach, Berlin #293/R est:3000-4000
£1282 $1987 €2000 Stroll (26x20cm-10x8in) s. s.i.d.1922 verso board prov. 7-Dec-2 Ketterer, Hamburg #274/R est:2000-2500
£1348 $2183 €1900 Abstract composition (29x36cm-11x14in) s. panel. 24-May-3 Van Ham, Cologne #160/R est:1500
£1449 $2377 €2000 Au revoir (54x73cm-21x29in) s. s.i.d.1921 verso board. 31-May-3 Villa Grisebach, Berlin #230/R est:3000-4000
£2027 $3162 €3000 Proud (57x41cm-22x16in) s. s.i.d.1921 verso board prov. 28-Mar-3 Ketterer, Hamburg #295/R est:3500-4000
£2254 $3628 €3200 Intermezzo (39x30cm-15x12in) s.i.d.25.Juni 1922 verso board lit. 9-May-3 Schloss Ahlden, Ahlden #1546/R est:3200
£4430 $6911 €7000 Last outing of Luise (79x56cm-31x22in) s. s.i.d.1920 verso masonite. 18-Oct-2 Dr Fritz Nagel, Stuttgart #477/R est:7000

EHRHARDT, Paul W (1872-?) German
£507 $791 €750 Woman seated in salon (68x51cm-27x20in) i. 31-Mar-3 Dr Fritz Nagel, Stuttgart #6933/R

EHRLER, Ludwig Max (19/20th C) German
£637 $994 €1000 Madonna with flowers (90x62cm-35x24in) s. 6-Nov-2 Hugo Ruef, Munich #1068/R

EHRLICH, Felix (1866-1931) German
£1531 $2480 €2220 Young girl wearing red dress (63x52cm-25x20in) s. 26-May-3 Rasmussen, Copenhagen #1295/R est:15000 (D.KR 16000)
£10000 $16700 €14500 Game of draughts (65x50cm-26x20in) s. i. on stretcher. 17-Jun-3 Bonhams, New Bond Street #30/R est:5000-7000

EHRSTROM, Eric O W (20th C) Finnish
Works on paper
£303 $479 €440 Rimpisuo - landscape (28x33cm-11x13in) s. d.1933 verso gouache. 3-Apr-3 Hagelstam, Helsinki #833/R

EIBISCH, Eugeniusz (1896-1987) Polish
£6122 $9735 €9000 Nature morte a l'ananas (61x73cm-24x29in) s. 3-Mar-3 Claude Boisgirard, Paris #44/R est:10000-12000

EIBL, Ludwig (1842-1918) Austrian
£1592 $2484 €2500 Still life of flowers with cherries (60x99cm-24x39in) s. 6-Nov-2 Hugo Ruef, Munich #1069/R est:2500
£1862 $2961 €2793 Still life of young goat in basket and large copper pot (82x100cm-32x39in) s.d.1878. 5-Mar-3 Rasmussen, Copenhagen #1764/R est:25000-30000 (D.KR 20000)

EIBNER, Friedrich (1825-1877) German
£4200 $6594 €6300 Doge's Palace and la Santa Maria Della Salute, Venice by moonlight (59x78cm-23x31in) indis sig. 21-Nov-2 Tennants, Leyburn #765/R est:1500-2500

EICHHOLTZ, Jacob (attrib) (1776-1842) American
£932 $1500 €1398 Portrait of a lady wearing lace bonnet, possibly Sarah Thornton Mays (76x64cm-30x25in) painted c.1825. 22-Feb-3 Pook & Pook, Downington #74/R est:800-1200
£1763 $2750 €2645 Portraits of a husband and wife (76x64cm-30x25in) pair. 21-Sep-2 Pook & Pook, Downington #282/R est:2500-3500
£5096 $8000 €7644 Seated man holding a scroll. Seated woman wearing lace bonnet (71x58cm-28x23in) pair. 23-Nov-2 Pook & Pook, Downington #431/R est:8000-10000

EICHHORN, Alfred (1909-1972) Austrian
£336 $524 €490 Strolling in southern landscape (18x24cm-7x9in) s.d. W/C over pencil. 11-Apr-3 Winterberg, Heidelberg #935

EICHINGER, Erwin (1892-1950) Austrian
£323 $510 €485 Cardinal in his study (26x32cm-10x13in) s. panel. 18-Nov-2 Waddingtons, Toronto #24/R (C.D 800)
£600 $936 €900 Portrait of an elderly man (28x21cm-11x8in) s. board. 8-Oct-2 Bonhams, Knightsbridge #266/R
£600 $936 €900 Portrait of a man holding jug in a red smock (27x21cm-11x8in) s. board. 8-Oct-2 Bonhams, Knightsbridge #278/R
£800 $1336 €1160 Cardinal (28x21cm-11x8in) s. panel. 8-Jul-3 Bonhams, Knightsbridge #87/R
£1700 $2618 €2550 Pondering the next move (41x49cm-16x19in) s.i. 24-Oct-2 Christie's, Kensington #93/R est:800-1200
£2200 $3432 €3300 Gambler. Drinker (25x19cm-10x7in) s. board pair. 26-Mar-3 Sotheby's, Olympia #281/R est:1200-1800
£2994 $5000 €4341 Card game (58x79cm-23x31in) s.i.d.46 prov. 22-Jun-3 Freeman, Philadelphia #18/R est:4000-6000
£3200 $5088 €4800 Bibliophile (25x31cm-10x12in) s. panel prov. 18-Mar-3 Bonhams, New Bond Street #25/R est:2000-3000

EICHINGER, Otto (1922-) Austrian
£242 $382 €363 Cheerful Bavarian (25x21cm-10x8in) s. masonite prov. 18-Nov-2 Waddingtons, Toronto #23/R (C.D 600)
£550 $858 €825 Card player (25x18cm-10x7in) s. board. 8-Oct-2 Bonhams, Knightsbridge #227/R
£1800 $2808 €2700 Portrait of a Rabbi (26x20cm-10x8in) s. board. 26-Mar-3 Sotheby's, Olympia #282/R est:1000-1500

EICHLER, Joseph Ignaz (1714-1763) German
£1592 $2484 €2500 Portrait of Johan van Nispen. Portrait of Petronella Susanna Cabeljau (85x67cm-33x26in) i.d.1750 verso lit. pair. 6-Nov-2 Christie's, Amsterdam #44/R est:2000-3000

EICHLER, Reinhold Max (1872-1947) German
£935 $1496 €1300 Peasant woman harvesting (60x80cm-24x31in) s. 15-May-3 Neumeister, Munich #247/R

EICHMAN, Bernard von (1899-1970) American?
Works on paper
£5414 $8500 €8121 San Francisco street scene (34x24cm-13x9in) s. W/C prov. 19-Nov-2 Butterfields, San Francisco #8245/R est:6000-8000

EICKELBERG, Willem Hendrik (1845-1920) Dutch
£955 $1490 €1500 Two anglers in a rowing boat at the waters edge (14x19cm-6x7in) s. panel. 5-Nov-2 Vendu Notarishuis, Rotterdam #195 est:1500-2000
£1300 $2080 €1950 Dutch canal scene (31x36cm-12x14in) s. 7-Jan-3 Bonhams, Knightsbridge #51/R est:1500-2000
£2300 $3750 €3450 Winter scene in Amsterdam (27x38cm-11x15in) s. i.verso panel. 16-Feb-3 Butterfields, San Francisco #2029 est:1500-2000

EICKELBERG, Willem Hendrik (attrib) (1845-1920) Dutch
£1400 $2212 €2100 Dutch street scene with figures (46x34cm-18x13in) 27-Nov-2 Hamptons Fine Art, Godalming #389 est:1000-1500

EICKEN, Elisabeth von (1862-?) German
£3896 $5688 €6000 Winter scene with farmhouse near Ahrenshoop (67x102cm-26x40in) s. 15-Jun-2 Hans Stahl, Hamburg #125/R est:4500

EICKHOFF, Gottfred (1902-) Danish
Sculpture
£1679 $2670 €2519 Guapa (46cm-18in) s.d.43 bronze. 29-Apr-3 Kunsthallen, Copenhagen #446/R est:20000 (D.KR 18000)

EIEBAKKE, August (1867-1938) Norwegian
£1471 $2324 €2207 Two children (57x66cm-22x26in) init.d.1921. 2-Dec-2 Blomqvist, Oslo #368/R est:20000-25000 (N.KR 17000)

EIELSON, Jorge (1924-) Peruvian
£2838 $4427 €4200 Qui pus A1-45 (70x70cm-28x28in) s.i.verso canvas on board. 26-Mar-3 Finarte Semenzato, Milan #133/R
Sculpture
£1013 $1600 €1600 Never-ending stairs (80x75x13cm-31x30x5in) s.d.79 verso fabric board. 29-Nov-2 Farsetti, Prato #69/R

EIJSDEN, Theo van (1900-1980) Dutch
Works on paper
£637 $994 €1000 City in the morning (51x71cm-20x28in) s. gouache exhib. 6-Nov-2 Vendue Huis, Gravenhage #209/R

EIKAAS, Ludvig (1920-) Norwegian
£752 $1226 €1128 Night time (54x61cm-21x24in) s. panel. 17-Feb-3 Blomqvist, Lysaker #1040/R (N.KR 8500)
£777 $1298 €1127 Composition (48x60cm-19x24in) s. i.verso panel. 18-Jun-3 Grev Wedels Plass, Oslo #166/R (N.KR 9000)
£1377 $2259 €1997 Seated woman (95x70cm-37x28in) s.d.78. 2-Jun-3 Blomqvist, Oslo #204/R est:18000-22000 (N.KR 15000)

£2076 $3280 €3114 Rider and lamps, possibly Frognerparken, Oslo (63x80cm-25x31in) s. 2-Dec-2 Blomqvist, Oslo #456/R est:30000-35000 (N.KR 24000)

Works on paper

£896 $1398 €1344 Self portrait as a violinist (43x30cm-17x12in) s. gouache. 23-Sep-2 Blomqvist, Lysaker #1028/R (N.KR 10500)

EIKEVIK, Arvid (1935-) Norwegian

£301 $490 €452 Mustard coloured winter (65x81cm-26x32in) s. 17-Feb-3 Blomqvist, Lysaker #1045 (N.KR 3400)

EILERS, Conrad (1845-1914) German

£634 $1020 €900 Ammersee in spring (31x26cm-12x10in) s. i. verso canvas on board. 7-May-3 Michael Zeller, Lindau #688/R

EILERSEN, Eiler Rasmussen (1827-1912) Danish

£258 $393 €387 Wooden house by water, possibly Switzerland (27x35cm-11x14in) init. 27-Aug-2 Rasmussen, Copenhagen #1675 (D.KR 3000)
£276 $419 €414 Landscape from Skanderborg Lake (41x56cm-16x22in) prov. 27-Aug-2 Rasmussen, Copenhagen #1849 (D.KR 3200)
£279 $444 €419 Lake at edge of wood, Strandmolledammen (36x65cm-14x26in) mono.d.27 juni 69. 10-Mar-3 Rasmussen, Vejle #266/R (D.KR 3000)
£422 $659 €633 Outing to the fjord (90x116cm-35x46in) 23-Sep-2 Rasmussen, Vejle #92/R (D.KR 5000)
£745 $1200 €1118 Landscape with pond (41x56cm-16x22in) s.verso. 22-Feb-3 Brunk, Ashville #175/R
£791 $1266 €1187 Summer landscape with family on Sunday outing (92x115cm-36x45in) 16-Mar-3 Hindemae, Ullerslev #377/R (D.KR 8500)
£2532 $4000 €4000 View from Torbole on lake Garda (60x81cm-24x32in) s.d.1897. 28-Nov-2 Dorotheum, Vienna #193/R est:3500-3800

EILSHEMIUS, Louis M (1864-1941) American

£239 $375 €359 Landscape with waterfall (13cm-5in circular) board prov.exhib. 14-Dec-2 Weschler, Washington #649/R
£406 $650 €589 Maine (37x53cm-15x21in) s. masonite. 16-May-3 Skinner, Boston #232/R
£938 $1500 €1407 Woman hanging out washing in country garden (13x22cm-5x9in) board. 14-Mar-3 Du Mouchelle, Detroit #2005/R est:2000-3000
£988 $1600 €1433 Passaic falls (76x102cm-30x40in) s. board prov. 21-May-3 Doyle, New York #135/R est:3000-5000
£1474 $2300 €2211 Afternoon bather (46x51cm-18x20in) s.d.1919 board prov. 20-Sep-2 Freeman, Philadelphia #43/R est:500-800

EIMER, Ernst (1881-1960) German

£385 $604 €600 The outing (50x47cm-20x19in) s.d.1923 board. 23-Nov-2 Arnold, Frankfurt #712/R

EINBECK, Georg (1870-1951) French

£613 $993 €889 Nu et fleurs (63x48cm-25x19in) s.d.32 tempera prov.lit. 24-May-3 Galerie Gloggner, Luzern #28/R (S.FR 1300)

Works on paper

£955 $1490 €1500 Paysage de Menton (46x38cm-18x15in) s.d.50 gouache. 6-Nov-2 Vendue Huis, Gravenhage #151/R est:1000-1500

EINBECK, Walter (1890-?) German

£359 $575 €550 Three female nudes on bank of wooded lake (88x105cm-35x41in) s. lit. 10-Jan-3 Allgauer, Kempten #1577/R

EINBERGER, Andreas (1878-1953) Austrian

£1583 $2596 €2200 Head of a man from Tyrol with long beard and hat (41x34cm-16x13in) s. 5-Jun-3 Dorotheum, Salzburg #554/R est:2600-3600

EINSLE, Anton (1801-1871) Austrian

£550 $869 €825 Portrait of lady (66x53cm-26x21in) 14-Nov-2 Christie's, Kensington #18/R
£943 $1462 €1500 Portrait of man in white cravat (55x42cm-22x17in) s.d.826. 29-Oct-2 Dorotheum, Vienna #230/R est:1800-2200

EISE, Ida (1894-1978) New Zealander

£251 $391 €377 Coastal scene (39x49cm-15x19in) s.d.1940 board. 7-Nov-2 International Art Centre, Auckland #149/R (NZ.D 800)
£313 $489 €470 In the Waitakare's (39x49cm-15x19in) s.d.1947 board. 7-Nov-2 International Art Centre, Auckland #147/R est:1000-2000 (NZ.D 1000)
£313 $489 €470 Manukau Harbour (40x34cm-16x13in) s.d.1947 board. 7-Nov-2 International Art Centre, Auckland #148/R est:1000-2000 (NZ.D 1000)

EISELE, Carl (?) American

Sculpture

£1500 $2505 €2175 Boxer (41cm-16in) s. greenish pat. bronze on marble plinth. 26-Jun-3 Mellors & Kirk, Nottingham #990/R est:500-700

EISEN, Charles-Dominique-Joseph (1720-1778) French

£4747 $7500 €7500 Mythological scenes (47x84cm-19x33in) pair. 2-Dec-2 Rieunier, Paris #69/R

Works on paper

£379 $622 €580 Caravane (11x7cm-4x3in) s. pen ink wash. 7-Feb-3 Piasa, Paris #36

EISEN, Charles-Dominique-Joseph (attrib) (1720-1778) French

Works on paper

£705 $1093 €1100 Venus et l'amour (14x19cm-6x7in) i. crayon chk. 4-Dec-2 Piasa, Paris #84

EISEN, Keisai (1790-1848) Japanese

Prints

£1923 $3000 €2885 Karasu river at Kuragano Station (25x38cm-10x15in) s. col print first edition. 25-Mar-3 Christie's, Rockefeller NY #161/R est:3000-3500
£2436 $3800 €3654 Melancholy type (39x26cm-15x10in) s. col print. 25-Mar-3 Christie's, Rockefeller NY #156/R est:3000-5000
£3526 $5500 €5289 Sumida river (26x38cm-10x15in) mono.i. black white border print. 25-Mar-3 Christie's, Rockefeller NY #114/R est:3500-5500
£3526 $5500 €5289 Urami Waterfall (36x25cm-14x10in) s. col print. 25-Mar-3 Christie's, Rockefeller NY #148/R est:5000-7000

EISENBERG, Yaacov (1897-1966) Israeli

£1034 $1655 €1500 Ein Karem, Jerusalem (33x46cm-13x18in) s. 12-Mar-3 Rabourdin & Choppin de Janvry, Paris #74/R

EISENDIECK, Suzanne (1908-1998) German

£679 $1100 €985 Woman with masks (41x28cm-16x11in) s. 21-May-3 Doyle, New York #222/R
£750 $1208 €1125 Portrait of a dancer (56x38cm-22x15in) s. 14-Jan-3 Bonhams, Knightsbridge #213/R
£870 $1400 €1305 A la lisiere du bois (38x53cm-15x21in) s. i.verso. 19-Feb-3 Doyle, New York #52
£926 $1500 €1343 Coiffure de sortie (46x38cm-18x15in) s. i.verso. 21-May-3 Doyle, New York #221/R est:2000-3000
£962 $1500 €1443 Lady in the park (54x74cm-21x29in) s. 9-Nov-2 Sloan, North Bethesda #561/R est:1000-1500
£962 $1500 €1443 L'aperitie (38x46cm-15x18in) s. 8-Nov-2 York Town, York #687b
£1090 $1722 €1700 Girl on beach (37x36cm-15x14in) s. i. stretcher. 14-Nov-2 Neumeister, Munich #555/R est:1500-2000
£1100 $1771 €1650 Portrait of a woman ironing (61x41cm-24x16in) s. 14-Jan-3 Bonhams, Knightsbridge #216/R
£1173 $1900 €1701 Woman by the sea (46x53cm-18x21in) s. indis.i.verso. 21-May-3 Doyle, New York #248/R est:3000-4000
£1312 $2100 €1902 At the yacht club (61x50cm-24x20in) s. 16-May-3 Skinner, Boston #183/R est:2500-3000
£1796 $3000 €2604 Plage a Santa Christian (60x74cm-24x29in) s. prov. 22-Jun-3 Freeman, Philadelphia #53/R est:3000-5000
£1946 $3250 €2822 Patrica (55x46cm-22x18in) s. prov. 22-Jun-3 Freeman, Philadelphia #56/R est:2000-3000
£2361 $3731 €3400 On the beach (57x83cm-22x33in) s. 24-Apr-3 Dorotheum, Vienna #78/R est:3000-4000

EISENHUT, Ferencz (1857-1903) Hungarian

£4110 $6411 €6000 North African Bazar (59x43cm-23x17in) s.d.1886. 10-Apr-3 Van Ham, Cologne #1410/R est:6500

EISENLOHR, Edward G (1872-1961) American

£4327 $6750 €6491 Summer field, Oak Cliff (30x46cm-12x18in) board. 19-Oct-2 David Dike, Dallas #162/R est:4000-8000
£6410 $10000 €9615 Winter mood (41x61cm-16x24in) canvasboard. 19-Oct-2 David Dike, Dallas #262/R est:10000-15000

Works on paper

£641 $1000 €962 Rinehart Road, Dallas, March 1933 (20x25cm-8x10in) pencil. 19-Oct-2 David Dike, Dallas #60/R

EISENLOHR, Friedrich (1805-1856) German

£692 $1079 €1100 Wooded hill on Perugia (27x42cm-11x17in) i.d.Settembre 26 pencil. 11-Oct-2 Winterberg, Heidelberg #510/R

Works on paper

£346 $540 €550 Italian church courtyard (36x23cm-14x9in) s. pencil. 11-Oct-2 Winterberg, Heidelberg #514/R
£629 $981 €1000 Italian house (26x21cm-10x8in) pencil. 11-Oct-2 Winterberg, Heidelberg #515
£660 $1030 €1050 Siesta (12x19cm-5x7in) i.d. pencil. 11-Oct-2 Winterberg, Heidelberg #511/R

EISENMAN, Nicole (1963-) American
£2452 $3800 €3678 Portrait of a lady (142x109cm-56x43in) s. i.d.1989 verso oil on canvas with earring prov. 26-Sep-2 Christie's, Rockefeller NY #879/R est:4000-6000

EISENMENGER, Rudolf Hermann (1902-) Austrian
£621 $993 €900 Three children in landscape (60x80cm-24x31in) s. 11-Mar-3 Dorotheum, Vienna #123/R
£972 $1546 €1400 Apocalypse (60x80cm-24x31in) s.d.952 i. verso. 29-Apr-3 Wiener Kunst Auktionen, Vienna #635/R

EISENMEYER, Johann Paul (19th C) Austrian
£2390 $3704 €3800 Family portrait with landscape beyond (94x79cm-37x31in) s.d.1845. 29-Oct-2 Dorotheum, Vienna #134/R est:2000-2400

EISENSCHITZ, Willy (1889-1974) French
£638 $1034 €900 Portrait de femme (46x33cm-18x13in) s. 23-May-3 Camard, Paris #76
£2695 $4501 €3800 Paysage (43x53cm-17x21in) s.i. 23-Jun-3 Beaussant & Lefèvre, Paris #309/R est:800-1000
£2837 $4738 €4000 Rue a Menton (65x81cm-26x32in) s.d. prov. 23-Jun-3 Beaussant & Lefèvre, Paris #307/R est:1500-2000
£3104 $4904 €4500 Toits en Provence (50x65cm-20x26in) s. 4-Apr-3 Tajan, Paris #199/R
£3481 $5500 €5500 Silo et canal gele (65x80cm-26x31in) s. lit. 27-Nov-2 Dorotheum, Vienna #200/R est:9000-13000
£9524 $15143 €14000 Paysage de Haute Provence (73x50cm-29x20in) s. 3-Mar-3 Claude Boisgirard, Paris #45/R est:6000-7000
Works on paper
£440 $682 €700 Oliviers en Provence (37x52cm-15x20in) s. W/C. 30-Oct-2 Artcurial Briest, Paris #13
£497 $775 €780 La route (36x61cm-14x24in) s. W/C. 6-Nov-2 Claude Boisgirard, Paris #15
£530 $864 €800 Coast of Marseille (22x30cm-9x12in) s. mixed media. 28-Jan-3 Dorotheum, Vienna #80/R
£535 $829 €850 Paysage de Haute-Provence (37x52cm-15x20in) s. W/C. 30-Oct-2 Artcurial Briest, Paris #14
£641 $1013 €1000 Southern landscape (38x52cm-15x20in) s. W/C. 12-Nov-2 Dorotheum, Vienna #169/R
£1111 $1756 €1600 Gard landscape (36x48cm-14x19in) s. W/C. 24-Apr-3 Dorotheum, Vienna #139/R est:1800-2400

EISENSTAEDT, Alfred (1898-1995) American
Photographs
£2147 $3500 €3221 Repairing the hull of the Graf Zeppelin during the flight over the Atlantic (39x54cm-15x21in) s.i.d.1934 num.115/250 gelatin silver print. 12-Feb-3 Christie's, Rockefeller NY #257/R est:4000-6000
£2532 $4000 €3798 Ballerinas, the Balanchine school of American ballet theatre (31x21cm-12x8in) s.verso gelatine silver print prov. 22-Apr-3 Christie's, Rockefeller NY #31/R est:5000-7000
£2750 $4400 €4125 First lesson at Truempy ballet school, Berlin (41x30cm-16x12in) s.i.d.1930 num.121/250 silver print. 15-May-3 Swann Galleries, New York #335/R est:3000-5000
£3038 $4800 €4557 Ice skating waiter, Grand Hotel Waiters' School, St. Moritz (32x24cm-13x9in) s. gelatin silver print prov.lit. 22-Apr-3 Christie's, Rockefeller NY #33/R est:3000-5000
£8228 $13000 €12342 V-J day at Times Square, New York City (34x24cm-13x9in) s.i.d.1945 verso gelatin silver print prov.lit. 22-Apr-3 Christie's, Rockefeller NY #32/R est:12000-18000

EISHIN, Kano (19th C) Japanese
Works on paper
£7547 $12000 €11321 Scenes from chapters Hatsune and Wakana part 1. Bamboo and fence (99x381cm-39x150in) s. ink col silver gold gold leaf 8-panel screen double-sided pair. 24-Mar-3 Christie's, Rockefeller NY #91/R est:10000-15000

EISLER, Georg (1928-1998) Austrian
£506 $790 €800 Small landscape (25x25cm-10x10in) s.i.d.1961 verso. 15-Oct-2 Dorotheum, Vienna #172/R
£513 $810 €800 Factory (20x30cm-8x12in) s.d.1982. 15-Nov-2 Reiss & Sohn, Konigstein #791/R
£705 $1114 €1100 Cafe Sperl (27x35cm-11x14in) canvas on board. 12-Nov-2 Dorotheum, Vienna #229/R
£2609 $4278 €3600 Paris, Metro station Tuilleries (36x45cm-14x18in) s.i.d.86. 27-May-3 Wiener Kunst Auktionen, Vienna #188/R est:3600-5500
£2754 $4516 €3800 Nude (78x58cm-31x23in) s.d.65. 27-May-3 Wiener Kunst Auktionen, Vienna #92/R est:3000-6000
£7595 $11772 €12000 Hommage to Erich Fried (127x146cm-50x57in) s.d.88. 24-Sep-2 Wiener Kunst Auktionen, Vienna #249/R est:12000-18000

EISMANN, Johann Anton (1604-1698) German
£2903 $4587 €4500 Capriccios with peasants (29x33cm-11x13in) panel pair. 18-Dec-2 Tajan, Paris #14/R

EISMANN, Johann Anton (attrib) (1604-1698) German
£10366 $17000 €15031 Capriccio of a Mediterranean port (102x148cm-40x58in) 4-Jun-3 Christie's, Rockefeller NY #183/R est:7000-10000

EISMANN, Johann Anton (circle) (1604-1698) German
£10000 $15600 €15000 Extensive landscape with a waterfall and figures shooting with dogs and horses (98x131cm-39x52in) 10-Apr-3 Christie's, Kensington #115/R est:6000-8000

EISNER, Ib (1925-) Danish
£279 $441 €419 Hilly landscape with figures (84x100cm-33x39in) s.d.88. 5-Apr-3 Rasmussen, Havnen #4129/R (D.KR 3000)
£355 $574 €533 Tivoli (80x70cm-31x28in) s. 25-Jan-3 Rasmussen, Havnen #2061 (D.KR 4000)
£443 $718 €665 Nursery in Dyrehaven (70x80cm-28x31in) s. 25-Jan-3 Rasmussen, Havnen #2037/R (D.KR 5000)

EISUKE, Miyao (19/20th C) Japanese
Sculpture
£7643 $11924 €12000 Flying tennin (30cm-12in) i. seal bronze. 9-Nov-2 Dr Fritz Nagel, Stuttgart #1771/R est:10000

EITNER, Ernst (1867-1955) German
£1603 $2484 €2500 Sunset on the Alster (27x39cm-11x15in) s. i.d.47 verso. 5-Dec-2 Schopman, Hamburg #613 est:2700
£2089 $3237 €3300 Portrait of child (39x52cm-15x20in) mono.i. verso board. 28-Sep-2 Hans Stahl, Hamburg #139/R est:2900
£2115 $3279 €3300 Sunny landscape in northern Germany (70x80cm-28x31in) s. 7-Dec-2 Ketterer, Hamburg #165/R est:4000-4500
£2564 $3974 €4000 Woodland path in autumn (53x64cm-21x25in) s. s.i. verso prov. 7-Dec-2 Ketterer, Hamburg #166/R est:4500-5000
£4710 $7725 €6500 Heath in bloom (33x41cm-13x16in) s. s.i. stretcher. 31-May-3 Villa Grisebach, Berlin #128/R est:9000-12000
Works on paper
£865 $1341 €1350 Karlsruhe - laying ashphalt (42x27cm-17x11in) s.i.d.1889 W/C prov. 7-Dec-2 Ketterer, Hamburg #163/R

EJSMOND, Franz von (1859-1931) Polish
£517 $801 €776 Model picture (70x50cm-28x20in) init.d.54. 4-Dec-2 Kunsthallen, Copenhagen #307 (D.KR 6000)

EJSTRUP, Kaj (1902-1956) Danish
£380 $586 €570 Landscape with trees in foreground (130x100cm-51x39in) init.d.51. 23-Oct-2 Kunsthallen, Copenhagen #31 (D.KR 4500)
£517 $801 €776 Self portrait (55x45cm-22x18in) init. 4-Dec-2 Kunsthallen, Copenhagen #338 (D.KR 6000)

EK, Sandor (1902-?) Hungarian
£513 $795 €800 Beach (50x60cm-20x24in) 5-Dec-2 Stadion, Trieste #181

EKELAND, Arne (1908-1995) Norwegian
£52219 $83551 €78329 From the village (144x134cm-57x53in) s.d.46 i.verso lit. 17-Mar-3 Blomqvist, Oslo #424/R est:600000-800000 (N.KR 600000)
Works on paper
£415 $692 €602 Two women wearing ballgowns (18x15cm-7x6in) init. pencil. 18-Jun-3 Grev Wedels Plass, Oslo #13/R (N.KR 4800)
£475 $793 €689 Fantasy figure (29x20cm-11x8in) init. pencil. 18-Jun-3 Grev Wedels Plass, Oslo #14 (N.KR 5500)
£734 $1226 €1064 Woman and man (29x20cm-11x8in) init. gouache. 18-Jun-3 Grev Wedels Plass, Oslo #15/R (N.KR 8500)
£742 $1164 €1113 People and animals (33x41cm-13x16in) s. gouache. 25-Nov-2 Blomqvist, Lysaker #1059/R (N.KR 8500)

EKELS, Jan (younger) (1759-1793) Dutch
£863 $1381 €1200 Tribute money (25x32cm-10x13in) indis sig.d.1776 panel prov. 14-May-3 Christie's, Amsterdam #159/R est:2000-3000

EKELUND, Poul (1920-1976) Danish
£337 $546 €506 Green archipelago (48x66cm-19x26in) s.d.1959 verso. 25-Jan-3 Rasmussen, Havnen #2142 (D.KR 3800)
£338 $521 €507 Blue landscape (50x61cm-20x24in) s. i.d.1960 verso. 26-Oct-2 Rasmussen, Havnen #2211 (D.KR 4000)
£338 $521 €507 Blue and green landscape (50x61cm-20x24in) s. 26-Oct-2 Rasmussen, Havnen #2212 (D.KR 4000)
£343 $535 €515 Standing figure (61x50cm-24x20in) s. s.d.1970 verso. 11-Nov-2 Rasmussen, Vejle #25 (D.KR 4000)
£350 $560 €525 Green landscape 1959 (56x58cm-22x23in) s. 13-Jan-3 Rasmussen, Vejle #274/R (D.KR 4000)
£379 $587 €569 Field landscape (46x66cm-18x26in) s. 4-Dec-2 Kunsthallen, Copenhagen #311 (D.KR 4400)

£388 $601 €582 Field landscape (56x79cm-22x31in) s,. 4-Dec-2 Kunsthallen, Copenhagen #358/R (D.KR 4500)
£429 $716 €622 Nobis Mill - Taagerup Mill (76x56cm-30x22in) s. prov. 17-Jun-3 Rasmussen, Copenhagen #195/R (D.KR 4500)
£466 $722 €699 Reclining figure (46x99cm-18x39in) s. s.d.1969 verso. 1-Oct-2 Rasmussen, Copenhagen #375 (D.KR 5500)
£477 $796 €692 Landscape with wagon of corn (44x59cm-17x23in) s. d.1952 stretcher. 17-Jun 3 Rasmussen, Copenhagen #178/R (D.KR 5000)
£507 $781 €761 Sea and vessels (50x62cm-20x24in) s. painted 1967 exhib. 23-Oct-2 Kunsthallen, Copenhagen #136/R (D.KR 6000)
£653 $1038 €980 Woman wearing green (31x22cm-12x9in) s. panel. 29-Apr-3 Kunsthallen, Copenhagen #219 (D.KR 7000)
£677 $1050 €1016 Landscape with fields (57x65cm-22x26in) s. 1-Oct-2 Rasmussen, Copenhagen #358/R (D.KR 8000)
£680 $1060 €1020 Yellow landscape with cattle (50x63cm-20x25in) s. 5-Aug-2 Rasmussen, Vejle #306/R (D.KR 8000)
£743 $1175 €1115 Green landscape with drifting clouds (50x73cm-20x29in) s. 1-Apr-3 Rasmussen, Copenhagen #536/R (D.KR 8000)

EKELUND, Ragnar (1892-1960) Finnish
£1069 $1647 €1700 From Borgaa skerries (54x65cm-21x26in) s. i.verso. 27-Oct-2 Bukowskis, Helsinki #160/R est:2200
£1076 $1700 €1700 Interior scene with woman (72x81cm-28x32in) s. 30-Nov-2 Hagelstam, Helsinki #143/R est:2000
£1646 $2600 €2600 Gate at Sveaborg (49x54cm-19x21in) s.d.28. 1-Dec-2 Bukowskis, Helsinki #47/R
£2152 $3400 €3400 Surroundings by mill (60x73cm-24x29in) s. exhib. 30-Nov-2 Hagelstam, Helsinki #144/R est:2500

EKENAES, Jahn (1847-1920) Norwegian
£1109 $1730 €1664 Still life of fruit (19x22cm-7x9in) s. panel. 23-Sep-2 Blomqvist, Lysaker #1030/R est:10000-14000 (N.KR 13000)
£5068 $8210 €7602 Boy feeding wagtails (41x35cm-16x14in) s.indis.d.1872. 26-May-3 Grev Wedels Plass, Oslo #2/R est:50000-70000 (N.KR 56000)
£6000 $9420 €9000 Fishing party (23x42cm-9x17in) s.d.1893 panel. 19-Nov-2 Bonhams, New Bond Street #43/R est:4000-6000
£9138 $14621 €13707 Boy with wagtails (38x30cm-15x12in) s.d.1872. 17-Mar-3 Blomqvist, Oslo #314/R est:60000-70000 (N.KR 105000)
£15666 $25065 €23499 Farewell (49x68cm-19x27in) s.i.d.1881 lit. 17-Mar-3 Blomqvist, Oslo #358/R est:200000-300000 (N.KR 180000)
£19310 $30510 €28000 Family in fjord landscape (94x74cm-37x29in) s.i.d.08. 5-Apr-3 Quittenbaum, Hamburg #21/R est:32000
£30769 $49846 €46154 Figures fishing from hole in the ice (75x120cm-30x47in) s.d.1910. 26-May-3 Grev Wedels Plass, Oslo #3/R est:300000-400000 (N.KR 340000)

EKGORST, Vasili Yefimovich (1831-1901) Russian
£1266 $2000 €2000 River landscape (22x30cm-9x12in) s. board. 1-Dec-2 Bukowskis, Helsinki #238/R

EKLUNDH, Claes (1944-) Swedish
£1141 $1802 €1712 Woman and man (242x275cm-95x108in) diptych. 28-Apr-3 Bukowskis, Stockholm #1011/R est:20000-25000 (S.KR 15000)
£1699 $2735 €2549 Head in profile (256x82cm-101x32in) init. 7-May-3 AB Stockholms Auktionsverk #1023/R est:20000-25000 (S.KR 22000)
£2453 $3826 €3680 Face (265x253cm-104x100in) init. diptych prov.exhib. 5-Nov-2 Bukowskis, Stockholm #457/R est:18000-20000 (S.KR 35000)
£3504 $5466 €5256 Nude - torso (180x107cm-71x42in) init. d.1984-86 verso paper on canvas. 6-Nov-2 AB Stockholms Auktionsverk #802/R est:30000-35000 (S.KR 50000)

EKMAN, Emil (1880-1951) Swedish
£421 $665 €632 Seascape with sailing boats in morning glow (67x130cm-26x51in) d. 30-Nov-2 Goteborg Auktionsverk, Sweden #140/R (S.KR 6000)
£926 $1444 €1389 Fishing boats in hazy sunshine (83x132cm-33x52in) s. 13-Sep-2 Lilla Bukowskis, Stockholm #270/R est:10000-12000 (S.KR 13500)

EKMAN, Robert Wilhelm (1808-1873) Finnish
£2025 $3200 €3200 Girl with basket of berries (35x26cm-14x10in) s.d.1860. 1-Dec-2 Bukowskis, Helsinki #48/R est:3300-3500
£2532 $4000 €4000 Catching crayfish (50x40cm-20x16in) board exhib.lit. 1-Dec-2 Bukowskis, Helsinki #50/R est:3000-3500
£5634 $9070 €8000 The reproachful mother (130x103cm-51x41in) s.d.1840 lit. 10-May-3 Bukowskis, Helsinki #136/R est:8000-10000

Works on paper
£1139 $1800 €1800 The steamship Noden going out into the world (30x47cm-12x19in) s.d.1867 pastel. 1-Dec-2 Bukowskis, Helsinki #49/R est:2000-2500

EKMAN, Robert Wilhelm (attrib) (1808-1873) Finnish
£1517 $2397 €2200 Virgin Mary (54x34cm-21x13in) i.verso canvas on board. 3-Apr-3 Hagelstam, Helsinki #820 est:1000

EKSTAM, Alfred (1878-1935) Danish
£309 $469 €464 View of Lake Mangene (52x80cm-20x31in) s.verso. 16-Aug-2 Lilla Bukowskis, Stockholm #708 (S.KR 4500)

EKSTROM, Per (1844-1935) Swedish
£1064 $1649 €1596 Landscape from Malmen, Segerstad, Oland (30x49cm-12x19in) s. d.c.1925 verso. 4-Dec-2 AB Stockholms Auktionsverk #1742/R est:20000-25000 (S.KR 15000)
£1190 $1891 €1785 Sunset (41x58cm-16x23in) s. 3-Mar-3 Lilla Bukowskis, Stockholm #548 est:18000-20000 (S.KR 16000)
£1235 $1926 €1853 Pine trees in evening sunshine (86x126cm-34x50in) s/ canvas on panel. 13-Sep-2 Lilla Bukowskis, Stockholm #39 est:15000-20000 (S.KR 18000)
£1277 $1979 €1916 Sunset (55x71cm-22x28in) s. canvas on panel. 8-Dec-2 Uppsala Auktionskammare, Uppsala #143/R est:20000-25000 (S.KR 18000)
£1571 $2577 €2278 Sun-gleam (38x56cm-15x22in) s. 4-Jun-3 AB Stockholms Auktionsverk #2323/R est:15000-20000 (S.KR 20000)
£1807 $2963 €2620 Landscape with farm and stone wall, Oland (40x60cm-16x24in) s. 4-Jun-3 AB Stockholms Auktionsverk #2325/R est:20000-25000 (S.KR 23000)
£1931 $3205 €2800 Flooded landscape (40x62cm-16x24in) s. 16-Jun-3 Lilla Bukowskis, Stockholm #921 est:15000-20000 (S.KR 25000)
£2017 $3268 €2925 Hazy sunshine over reeds (47x56cm-19x22in) s. 25-May-3 Uppsala Auktionskammare, Uppsala #157/R est:20000-25000 (S.KR 26000)
£2017 $3268 €2925 Silver birches in hazy sunshine (49x68cm-19x27in) s. 25-May-3 Uppsala Auktionskammare, Uppsala #161/R est:20000-25000 (S.KR 26000)
£2514 $4123 €3645 Flooded landscape at sunset (32x58cm-13x23in) s. 4-Jun-3 AB Stockholms Auktionsverk #2089/R est:20000-25000 (S.KR 32000)
£2624 $4067 €3936 Sunshine through the trees (68x104cm-27x41in) s. 4-Dec-2 AB Stockholms Auktionsverk #1663/R est:40000-45000 (S.KR 37000)
£2870 $4650 €4162 Hazy sunshine (80x117cm-31x46in) s. 26-May-3 Bukowskis, Stockholm #43/R est:40000-60000 (S.KR 37000)
£2979 $4617 €4469 Evening landscape, Oland (71x134cm-28x53in) s. 4-Dec-2 AB Stockholms Auktionsverk #1669/R est:50000-60000 (S.KR 42000)
£2979 $4617 €4469 Coastal landscape with sunset (55x78cm-22x31in) s.d.1903. 4-Dec-2 AB Stockholms Auktionsverk #1717/R est:40000-45000 (S.KR 42000)
£3142 $5153 €4556 Landscape with buildings by water, Segerstad, Oland (71x137cm-28x54in) s.i.d.1892. 4-Jun-3 AB Stockholms Auktionsverk #2131/R est:50000-60000 (S.KR 40000)
£3546 $5496 €5319 Oland in hazy sunshine (70x112cm-28x44in) s. 3-Dec-2 Bukowskis, Stockholm #31/R est:60000-80000 (S.KR 50000)
£5499 $9018 €7974 Sunny late winter landscape (150x100cm-59x39in) s.d.1898. 4-Jun-3 AB Stockholms Auktionsverk #2233/R est:100000-125000 (S.KR 70000)
£6049 $9920 €8771 Landscape at sunset (80x117cm-31x46in) s. 4-Jun-3 AB Stockholms Auktionsverk #2086/R est:50000-60000 (S.KR 77000)
£9310 $15081 €13500 French landscape (41x33cm-16x13in) s.d.1887. 26-May-3 Bukowskis, Stockholm #41/R est:60000-70000 (S.KR 120000)
£9819 $16104 €14238 Late summer landscape from Djurgarden (91x135cm-36x53in) s.d.75. 4-Jun-3 AB Stockholms Auktionsverk #2188/R est:125000-150000 (S.KR 125000)

EKSTROM, Thea (1920-1988) Swedish
£491 $765 €737 21.IX.69 (50x60cm-20x24in) s. panel exhib. 6-Nov-2 AB Stockholms Auktionsverk #918/R (S.KR 7000)

EKVALL, Emma (1838-1925) Swedish
£1454 $2254 €2181 Still life of apples, oranges and grapes (50x76cm-20x30in) s. 4-Dec-2 AB Stockholms Auktionsverk #1675/R est:12000-15000 (S.KR 20500)

EKVALL, Knut (1843-1912) Swedish
£549 $835 €824 Flirting by the woodland glade (71x54cm-28x21in) s. 16-Aug-2 Lilla Bukowskis, Stockholm #161 (S.KR 8000)
£1791 $2901 €2687 Landscape with farm by water (120x91cm-47x36in) s.d.1864. 3-Feb-3 Lilla Bukowskis, Stockholm #452 est:15000-20000 (S.KR 25000)
£3258 $5279 €4724 Fetching home the logs (75x108cm-30x43in) s. 26-May-3 Bukowskis, Stockholm #103/R est:30000-40000 (S.KR 42000)

ELAND, Leonardus Joseph (1884-1952) Dutch
£222 $369 €322 Village scene with rice fields (39x56cm-15x22in) s. prov. 16-Jun-3 Waddingtons, Toronto #229/R (C.D 500)
£267 $443 €387 Indonesian villagers on route to market (60x80cm-24x31in) s. prov. 16-Jun-3 Waddingtons, Toronto #223/R (C.D 600)
£289 $479 €419 Paddy fields, Indonesia (41x60cm-16x24in) s. prov. 16-Jun-3 Waddingtons, Toronto #224/R (C.D 650)
£318 $497 €500 Indian landscape (39x79cm-15x31in) s. 6-Nov-2 Vendue Huis, Gravenhage #275
£324 $522 €460 North African street with many people (38x59cm-15x23in) s. 6-May-3 Vendu Notarishuis, Rotterdam #180/R
£340 $538 €510 Sunset over the Mediterranean (19x24cm-7x9in) s. 2-Dec-2 Rasmussen, Copenhagen #1412/R (D.KR 4000)
£489 $812 €709 Women with baskets on a mountainous path (60x81cm-24x32in) s. prov. 16-Jun-3 Waddingtons, Toronto #225/R est:1000-1500 (C.D 1100)
£489 $812 €709 Boatman's return (60x81cm-24x32in) s. prov. 16-Jun-3 Waddingtons, Toronto #231/R est:800-1200 (C.D 1100)
£533 $885 €773 Indonesian rice harvesters (60x90cm-24x35in) s. prov. 16-Jun-3 Waddingtons, Toronto #226/R est:1000-1500 (C.D 1200)
£533 $885 €773 Moonlit Indonesian village (40x60cm-16x24in) s. prov. 16-Jun-3 Waddingtons, Toronto #230/R est:800-1200 (C.D 1200)
£711 $1180 €1031 Indonesian huts below a waterfall and distant volcano (150x100cm-59x39in) s. 16-Jun-3 Waddingtons, Toronto #221/R est:1500-1800 (C.D 1600)

ELANDER, Kristina A (1952-) Scandinavian
Works on paper
£380 $601 €570 Desperate living (33x72cm-13x28in) s.d.1988 verso mixed media triptych. 28-Apr-3 Bukowskis, Stockholm #926/R (S.KR 5000)

ELDH, Carl (1873-1955) Swedish
Sculpture
£1296 $2126 €1879 Brita - nude girl standing (27cm-11in) s. dark pat.bronze lit. 4-Jun-3 AB Stockholms Auktionsverk #2353/R est:18000-20000 (S.KR 16500)
£1414 $2319 €2050 Ariadne (25cm-10in) s.i.d.1899 dark pat.bronze lit. 4-Jun-3 AB Stockholms Auktionsverk #2352/R est:10000-12000 (S.KR 18000)
£2128 $3298 €3192 Ingalill - small girl kneeling (70cm-28in) s. pat.bronze st.f.Bergman cire perdue lit. 4-Dec-2 AB Stockholms Auktionsverk #1818/R est:15000-20000 (S.KR 30000)

ELDRED, Lemeul D (1848-1921) American
£1384 $2200 €2076 Approaching storm (25x41cm-10x16in) s.i.d.86. 7-Mar-3 Skinner, Boston #321/R est:1000-1500

ELDRIDGE, Mildred E (1909-1991) British
Works on paper
£280 $437 €420 Rosa gallica versicolor (33x25cm-13x10in) i. pencil W/C. 27-Mar-3 Christie's, Kensington #199/R

ELENBERG, Joel (1948-1980) Australian
Sculpture
£21115 $34629 €31673 Mask (104cm-41in) s.num.4/6 bronze black marble base st.f.verso prov. 4-Jun-3 Deutscher-Menzies, Melbourne #19/R est:25000-35000 (A.D 53000)
£25000 $39500 €37500 Mask 1978 (105x55x16cm-41x22x6in) black Belgian marble. 27-Nov-2 Deutscher-Menzies, Melbourne #14/R est:25000-35000 (A.D 70000)

ELESZKIEWICZ, Stanislas (1900-1963) Polish
£955 $1490 €1500 Femme a l'eventail (65x55cm-26x22in) s. cardboard. 6-Nov-2 Claude Boisgirard, Paris #18 est:2000-2500
Works on paper
£360 $580 €522 Old man with mask and female nude model (28x31cm-11x12in) s. pen blue ink. 12-Aug-3 Rosebery Fine Art, London #625

ELFFERS, Dick (1919-1991) Dutch
Works on paper
£563 $907 €800 Surrealist landscape; after the season (50x34cm-20x13in) s.d.38 gouache. 6-May-3 Vendu Notarishuis, Rotterdam #109/R

ELGOOD, George Samuel (1851-1943) British
Works on paper
£340 $541 €510 View of the Italian coastline (15x29cm-6x11in) s. W/C. 25-Feb-3 Bonhams, Knightsbridge #164/R
£600 $936 €900 Palermo, Italy (24x36cm-9x14in) s.i.d.1897 pencil W/C. 27-Mar-3 Christie's, Kensington #164/R
£1700 $2652 €2550 Pale blue iris, Florence. Peonies, Coddington (21x17cm-8x7in) one s.d.1908 pencil W/C two exhib. 27-Mar-3 Christie's, Kensington #61/R est:800-1200
£1800 $2808 €2700 Peonies and iris. Cottage garden (19x15cm-7x6in) one s.d.1902 one s.d.1908 pencil W/C two. 27-Mar-3 Christie's, Kensington #62/R est:800-1200
£2200 $3432 €3300 Foxgloves. In an allotment garden (25x17cm-10x7in) s.d.1909 one s.d.1907 pencil W/C two. 27-Mar-3 Christie's, Kensington #59/R est:800-1200
£4200 $6552 €6300 Garden pond, Melbourne (31x47cm-12x19in) s.d.1893 W/C. 8-Oct-2 Sotheby's, Olympia #423/R est:1000-1500

ELIA, F (?) ?
Sculpture
£1408 $2338 €2000 Bust, femme a la coiffe (46cm-18in) s. ivory gilt bronze st.f. 18-Jun-3 Anaf, Lyon #95/R est:3000-3500

ELIAERTS, Jean François (1761-1848) Belgian
£6452 $10000 €9678 Mixed flowers in an urn on a ledge (46x38cm-18x15in) s. prov. 2-Oct-2 Christie's, Rockefeller NY #146/R est:10000-15000

ELIAS, Alfred (19th C) British
£680 $1082 €1000 Cows in the meadow eating from trough (81x116cm-32x46in) s. 25-Feb-3 Dorotheum, Vienna #158/R

ELIAS, Étienne (1936-) Belgian
£1282 $1987 €2000 Portret van een hippie (55x45cm-22x18in) s. s.i.d.70 verso. 3-Dec-2 Christie's, Amsterdam #332/R est:2000-3000
£2051 $3179 €3200 Ik heb mijn hart op de Kemmelberg verloren (100x80cm-39x31in) s.i.d.67 prov. 3-Dec-2 Christie's, Amsterdam #338/R est:1800-2200

ELIAS, Nicolaes (1590-1656) Dutch
£15094 $23396 €24000 Group portrait of the people of the guild (130x220cm-51x87in) 4-Nov-2 Glerum, Amsterdam #8/R est:18000-25000

ELIAS, Sheila (20th C) American
Works on paper
£267 $425 €387 Down to the country (58x89cm-23x35in) mixed media exec.c.1980. 4-May-3 Treadway Gallery, Cincinnati #654/R

ELIASSON, Olafur (1967-) Danish
Photographs
£6962 $11000 €10443 Large stone series (38x58cm-15x23in) c-print in 6 parts exec.1998 prov. 13-Nov-2 Sotheby's, New York #513/R
£9494 $15000 €14241 Untitled - Iceland series (58x89cm-23x35in) s.d.1998 seven col coupler prints prov. 14-Nov-2 Christie's, Rockefeller NY #430/R est:10000-15000

ELIM, Frank (20th C) French
£1757 $2741 €2600 Portrait de Lannilis (65x81cm-26x32in) s.d.1927. 28-Mar-3 Claude Aguttes, Neuilly #75/R

ELIOT, Granville (19th C) British
£580 $945 €870 Break from the chores (23x27cm-9x11in) s. 29-Jan-3 Sotheby's, Olympia #204/R

ELIOT, Ruth (1913-2001) Canadian
£386 $603 €560 Horse grazing. Horse in field (30x41cm-12x16in) panel double-sided pair. 26-Mar-3 Walker's, Ottawa #283/R est:300-400 (C.D 900)
£601 $937 €871 Farm houses. Eliot cottage (30x41cm-12x16in) panel double-sided pair. 26-Mar-3 Walker's, Ottawa #282/R est:300-400 (C.D 1400)
£644 $1004 €934 September landscape. Farm in autumn. Summer (30x41cm-12x16in) s.i. panel set of three. 26-Mar-3 Walker's, Ottawa #284/R est:400-600 (C.D 1500)

ELIOTT, Harry (1882-1959) ?
Works on paper
£1064 $1777 €1500 Le saut de la barriere (25x34cm-10x13in) s. Indian ink W/C gouache. 20-Jun-3 Rieunier, Paris #31/R est:1000-1200

£1135 $1895 €1600 Hallali courant (26x23cm-10x9in) s.i. Indian ink W/C gouache. 20-Jun-3 Rieunier, Paris #32/R est:500-600

£1986 $3316 €2800 Partie de cartes (26x33cm-10x13in) s. Indian ink W/C gouache. 20-Jun-3 Rieunier, Paris #33/R est:1000-1200

ELISCHER (?-1935) Austrian/German

Sculpture

£1900 $3002 €2850 Nude sitting on Death's head (31cm-12in) s.d.1921 cold pat. bronze. 14-Nov-2 Christie's, Kensington #181/R est:1000-1200

ELIZAROV, Gennady (1938-) Russian

£550 $853 €825 Near the Banisters of Luxembourg Garden, Paris (50x61cm-20x24in) s. 29-Sep-2 John Nicholson, Haslemere #65/R

£650 $1007 €975 Sunday in a Parisian garden (50x61cm-20x24in) s. 29-Sep-2 John Nicholson, Haslemere #66/R

ELK, Gerard Pieter van (1941-) Dutch

Works on paper

£2778 $4416 €4000 Study for orange blanche bleu (210x102cm-83x40in) s.i.d.1985 col crayon paint prov. 29-Apr-3 Artcurial Briest, Paris #467/R est:5000-6000

ELKINS, Henry Arthur (1847-1884) American

£1138 $1900 €1650 Mountain landscape (66x109cm-26x43in) s.d.1881. 22-Jun-3 Freeman, Philadelphia #80/R est:1500-2500

ELKJAR, P M (20th C) Danish

£613 $981 €920 Branch with apples. Branch with pears (30x29cm-12x11in) s. one d.1920 pair. 13-Jan-3 Rasmussen, Vejle #46/R (D.KR 7000)

ELLE, Louis (elder) (1612-1689) French

Works on paper

£811 $1265 €1200 Femme executatnt le portrait d'une famille (24x32cm-9x13in) sanguine htd chk prov.lit. 31-Mar-3 Piasa, Paris #36/R

ELLE, Louis (elder-style) (1612-1689) French

£1761 $2712 €2800 Portrait du Duc de Longeville (144x115cm-57x45in) 25-Oct-2 Tajan, Paris #4/R est:1500-2400

ELLEGAARD, Inge (1953-) Danish

£338 $527 €507 Jungshoved (180x250cm-71x98in) s.d.1985 verso. 18-Sep-2 Kunsthallen, Copenhagen #287/R (D.KR 4000)

£380 $593 €570 Rodvig Rock (180x250cm-71x98in) s.d.85 verso. 18-Sep-2 Kunsthallen, Copenhagen #286 (D.KR 4500)

ELLENRIEDER, Maria (1791-1863) Swiss

£661 $965 €992 Guardian angel (22x15cm-9x6in) s.d.1858 verso panel. 17-Jun-2 Philippe Schuler, Zurich #4336/R (S.FR 1500)

ELLEOUET, Yves (1932-1975) French

£1233 $1936 €1800 Stele (55x46cm-22x18in) s. i.verso. 15-Apr-3 Laurence Calmels, Paris #4276/R

£3425 $5377 €5000 Untitled (100x81cm-39x32in) s. 15-Apr-3 Laurence Calmels, Paris #4278/R

£3767 $5914 €5500 Grand voyage (116x90cm-46x35in) s. i.verso. 15-Apr-3 Laurence Calmels, Paris #4277/R

ELLER, Hermann (1925-) German

£338 $527 €500 Flowers in vase (59x49cm-23x19in) s. 26-Mar-3 Hugo Ruef, Munich #292

ELLERMAN, F C (?) ?

£1500 $2505 €2175 River Nidd, Yorkshire (46x81cm-18x32in) mono. 18-Jun-3 Andrew Hartley, Ilkley #1192/R est:1500-2200

ELLIGER, Ottmar (attrib) (17/18th C) Swedish

£1087 $1696 €1631 Coronation of King Constantin (66x85cm-26x33in) 16-Sep-2 Philippe Schuler, Zurich #3469/R est:4000-6000 (S.FR 2500)

ELLIGER, Ottmar I (1633-1679) Swedish

£10000 $15700 €15000 Garland of flowers with brunches of black and white grapes and a stone niches (121x95cm-48x37in) 13-Dec-2 Christie's, Kensington #142/R est:8000-12000

£11000 $17160 €16500 Roemer of white wine with peeled lemon within a trompe l'oeil (67x85cm-26x33in) 9-Apr-3 Bonhams, New Bond Street #83/R est:3000-5000

ELLIGER, Ottmar II (attrib) (1666-1735) German

£1719 $2750 €2579 Young man playing the violin at a window (31x25cm-12x10in) panel. 14-May-3 Butterfields, San Francisco #1036/R est:3000-5000

£2908 $4507 €4362 Palace interior (42x55cm-17x22in) panel. 4-Dec-2 AB Stockholms Auktionsverk #1985/R est:40000-50000 (S.KR 41000)

ELLINGER, David (1913-2003) American

£318 $500 €477 Pineapple (30x20cm-12x8in) s. velvet. 23-Nov-2 Pook & Pook, Downington #450m/R

£955 $1500 €1433 Decorated basket of fruit surmounted by a bird (28x38cm-11x15in) s. velvet. 23-Nov-2 Pook & Pook, Downington #413/R est:1000-1500

£1125 $1800 €1688 Rooster (33x33cm-13x13in) s. 17-May-3 Pook & Pook, Downington #210b est:1400-1600

£1218 $1900 €1827 Basket of fruit and dove (25x33cm-10x13in) s. velvet theorem. 18-Sep-2 Alderfer's, Hatfield #359/R est:1000-1200

£1250 $2000 €1875 Bird sitting on a cherry trees branch (23x18cm-9x7in) s. 17-May-3 Pook & Pook, Downington #63/R est:1800-2000

£1407 $2250 €2111 Basket of fruit with bird and butterfly (46x56cm-18x22in) s. oil on velvet. 17-May-3 Pook & Pook, Downington #248/R est:2000-3000

£1563 $2500 €2345 Bird perched on top of a fruit basket (36x43cm-14x17in) s. 17-May-3 Pook & Pook, Downington #61/R est:2500-3000

£1859 $2900 €2789 Birds perched on branches (18x15cm-7x6in) s. velvet theorems pair. 21-Sep-2 Pook & Pook, Downington #483 est:700-900

£17188 $27500 €25782 Winter farm scene with stone house and barn (56x74cm-22x29in) s. board. 17-May-3 Pook & Pook, Downington #260/R est:6000-9000

Works on paper

£892 $1400 €1338 Valentine in the form of a heart (18x20cm-7x8in) s. W/C. 23-Nov-2 Pook & Pook, Downington #535/R est:800-1000

ELLIOT, Harry (1882-1939) ?

Works on paper

£256 $405 €400 La chasse (19x30cm-7x12in) s. gouache pochoir lithograph. 14-Nov-2 Credit Municipal, Paris #60

ELLIOT, John (1858-1925) American

£538 $834 €850 Hilly landscape (40x60cm-16x24in) s.d.1890 lit. 27-Sep-2 Karrenbauer, Konstanz #1623

ELLIOT, Thomas (attrib) (fl.1790-1800) British

Works on paper

£17000 $27200 €25500 Man-o-war and other shipping in the entrance to Portsmouth Harbour. HMS Woolwich (61x91cm-24x36in) bears sig two. 13-Mar-3 Duke & Son, Dorchester #220/R

ELLIOTT, Anthony (?) British

£450 $702 €675 Primitive painting of a shepherd and his flock (46x61cm-18x24in) s. panel. 9-Oct-2 Woolley & Wallis, Salisbury #192/R

ELLIOTT, Douglas Ferguson (1916-) Canadian

£870 $1357 €1450 Atlantic Harbour (40x61cm-16x24in) s. board prov. 13-Apr-3 Levis, Calgary #439/R est:300-400 (C.D 2000)

ELLIOTT, Frederic (19/20th C) Australian

Works on paper

£254 $387 €381 Ship of the line (33x48cm-13x19in) s. W/C. 27-Aug-2 Goodman, Sydney #76 (A.D 710)

£268 $415 €402 Fort Denison (12x22cm-5x9in) s. W/C. 29-Oct-2 Lawson Menzies, Sydney #235 (A.D 750)

£279 $457 €405 Last voyage of a blackbirder (28x41cm-11x16in) s. W/C. 3-Jun-3 Lawson Menzies, Sydney #730 (A.D 700)

£386 $610 €560 Schooner at sea (32x50cm-13x20in) s. W/C. 22-Jul-3 Lawson Menzies, Sydney #204/R est:1200-1800 (A.D 950)

£536 $846 €804 Square rigger leaving port with tug assistance (35x26cm-14x10in) s. W/C. 18-Nov-2 Joel, Victoria #335/R est:1000-1200 (A.D 1500)

ELLIOTT, Frederick James (1864-1949) Australian

Works on paper

£1839 $2887 €2759 Commerce centre of Sydney (46x76cm-18x30in) s.i. W/C. 15-Apr-3 Lawson Menzies, Sydney #58/R est:4000-6000 (A.D 4800)

ELLIOTT, Grace L M (fl.1900-1918) British

£1600 $2544 €2400 Cattle in a meadow with estuary beyond. Girls strolling on a coastal path (61x91cm-24x36in) s.d.1910 pair. 30-Apr-3 Halls, Shrewsbury #262/R est:800-1200

ELLIOTT, J (19th C) British

Works on paper

£1300 $2028 €1950 Pilchard boats. Lobster fishing. Herring fishing (30x52cm-12x20in) s.d.1874 pencil W/C three. 18-Sep-2 Dreweatt Neate, Newbury #88/R est:700-900

ELLIOTT, James (19th C) British

Works on paper

£600 $990 €870 Lobster fishing at the Eddystone (30x52cm-12x20in) s.d.1874 W/C. 1-Jul-3 Bearnes, Exeter #462/R

ELLIOTT, Ric (1933-1995) Australian

£299 $467 €449 Orchard at Tambo (31x56cm-12x22in) s. board. 21-Oct-2 Australian Art Auctions, Sydney #135 (A.D 850)

£496 $784 €744 Strike Talk, Lightening Ridge (50x82cm-20x32in) s. board. 1-Apr-3 Lawson Menzies, Sydney #498 (A.D 1300)

£1075 $1634 €1613 Afternoon on the street (33x46cm-13x18in) s. board. 27-Aug-2 Goodman, Sydney #246 est:1200-1800 (A.D 3000)

ELLIOTT, Robinson (1814-1894) British

£8500 $13685 €12750 Soldier's child (22x17cm-9x7in) s.d.1880 s.i.verso board prov.exhib. 20-Feb-3 Christie's, London #252/R est:8000

ELLIOTT, Russ (20th C) American

£250 $400 €375 Women on beach (76x102cm-30x40in) s. 8-Jan-3 Doyle, New York #54/R

ELLIS, Edwin (1841-1895) British

£700 $1092 €1050 Sunset landscape (91x152cm-36x60in) s.indis.d. 17-Sep-2 Sotheby's, Olympia #169/R

£1300 $2002 €1950 The day's catch (48x86cm-19x34in) s. 5-Sep-2 Christie's, Kensington #233/R est:800-1200

£1300 $2119 €1950 Seascape with figures on the shore (107x212cm-42x83in) s. 17-Feb-3 Bonhams, Bath #52 est:300-500

£1400 $2170 €2100 Bamborough castle (44x81cm-17x32in) s. 26-Sep-2 Mellors & Kirk, Nottingham #742/R est:1000-1500

£1800 $2826 €2700 Harvesting scene, with figures in the foreground and view of Robins Hood's Bay (46x64cm-18x25in) s. 21-Nov-2 Tennants, Leyburn #818/R est:1800-2500

£1900 $2926 €2850 Unloading the catch (61x107cm-24x42in) s. 5-Sep-2 Christie's, Kensington #234/R est:2000-3000

£1910 $3132 €2865 Sketching the coast (407x213cm-160x84in) s. 29-May-3 Christie's, Kensington #186/R est:2000-3000

ELLIS, Edwin John (fl.1888-1899) British

£563 $935 €800 Youngest tribunal (93x73cm-37x29in) i.verso. 14-Jun-3 Arnold, Frankfurt #736/R

ELLIS, Fremont F (1897-1985) American

£2156 $3600 €3126 Golden palomino (51x61cm-20x24in) s.d.68 i.verso. 18-Jun-3 Christie's, Los Angeles #85/R est:4000-6000

£3473 $5800 €5036 Afternoon at el Zaguan (25x20cm-10x8in) s. board. 21-Jun-3 Charlton Hall, Columbia #522/R est:3000-5000

£4259 $6900 €6176 Meadows of La Veta (28x36cm-11x14in) board. 23-May-3 Altermann Galleries, Santa Fe #163

£4487 $7000 €6731 Storm over four corners (53x66cm-21x26in) s. paperbpard prov. 9-Nov-2 Santa Fe Art, Santa Fe #110/R est:10000-20000

£4614 $7475 €6690 New Mexico landscape with Adobe house (38x51cm-15x20in) 23-May-3 Altermann Galleries, Santa Fe #162

£5422 $9000 €7862 Sun dappled tree and an adobe in a mountain landscape (56x76cm-22x30in) s. prov. 11-Jun-3 Butterfields, San Francisco #4120/R est:10000-15000

£7877 $11500 €11816 Mountain stream (51x64cm-20x25in) 18-May-2 Altermann Galleries, Santa Fe #189/R

£8333 $13000 €12500 Storm over cliffs - Arroyo Hondo, Taos (56x76cm-22x30in) s. masonite panel prov. 9-Nov-2 Santa Fe Art, Santa Fe #68/R est:12000-18000

£8361 $13050 €12542 Borderland (51x64cm-20x25in) 9-Nov-2 Altermann Galleries, Santa Fe #183

£9434 $15000 €14151 Apache country (36x43cm-14x17in) s. s.i.on stretcher prov. 5-Mar-3 Sotheby's, New York #109/R est:10000-15000

£10256 $16000 €15384 California sycamore (76x64cm-30x25in) s.d.71 prov.lit. 9-Nov-2 Santa Fe Art, Santa Fe #200/R est:20000-25000

£10577 $16500 €15866 El rancho de San Sebastian - Mora Valley (41x51cm-16x20in) 9-Nov-2 Altermann Galleries, Santa Fe #181

£10778 $18000 €15628 Old house near San Juan (51x61cm-20x24in) s.i. s.i.verso canvasboard prov. 18-Jun-3 Christie's, Los Angeles #31/R est:20000-30000

£13554 $22500 €19653 Aspen Ranch, El Rancho de San Sebastian (56x76cm-22x30in) s. i.verso canvasboard prov. 11-Jun-3 Butterfields, San Francisco #4119/R est:25000-35000

£19872 $31000 €29808 Santa Fe Canyon (56x76cm-22x30in) 9-Nov-2 Altermann Galleries, Santa Fe #182

£22754 $38000 €32993 El Cabellero (76x56cm-30x22in) s. s.i.verso canvasboard prov. 18-Jun-3 Christie's, Los Angeles #89/R est:20000-30000

ELLIS, Gordon (1920-1978) British

£900 $1404 €1350 Clearing rain River Mersey (51x81cm-20x32in) s. i.verso board. 6-Nov-2 Bonhams, Chester #350

£2000 $3100 €3000 Tankers on the Mersey off Liverpool (61x91cm-24x36in) s. 31-Oct-2 Christie's, Kensington #562/R est:2500-3000

£2400 $3888 €3600 M.V Contractor in heavy seas (59x90cm-23x35in) s. 21-Jan-3 Bonhams, New Bond Street #187/R est:400-600

ELLIS, Joseph F (1783-1848) British

£600 $930 €900 Cader Idris (39x65cm-15x26in) s.d.1876 s.i.verso. 24-Sep-2 Rowley Fine Art, Newmarket #361/R

ELLIS, Paul H (fl.1882-1908) British

£620 $1035 €899 Bedouin Arabs returning from work (92x72cm-36x28in) s. 24-Jun-3 Bonhams, Knowle #96

£26000 $40300 €39000 View of the acropolis (76x101cm-30x40in) s. prov. 2-Oct-2 Sotheby's, London #2/R est:15000-20000

ELLIS, Ralph (1885-1963) British

£580 $916 €870 Swanbourne Lake in the grounds of Arnudel Castle (46x59cm-18x23in) s.d.1950. 4-Apr-3 Moore Allen & Innocent, Cirencester #709/R

ELLIS, Richard (1938-) American

£318 $500 €477 Right whales (38x51cm-15x20in) s. tempera on board. 26-Jul-2 Eldred, East Dennis #617/R

ELLIS, Robert (1929-) New Zealander

£1242 $1950 €1863 Motorway painting (62x48cm-24x19in) s.d.1962 acrylic gouache. 10-Dec-2 Peter Webb, Auckland #19/R est:3000-4000 (NZ.D 3900)

£3647 $5690 €5471 Nga Taonga 8 Tihema (153x121cm-60x48in) s.i.d.1993 acrylic on linen canvas. 17-Sep-2 Peter Webb, Auckland #145/R est:12000-18000 (NZ.D 12000)

£9123 $14232 €13685 Self portrait as a city (122x122cm-48x48in) s.d.1965 board exhib. 27-Mar-3 International Art Centre, Auckland #41/R est:35000-55000 (NZ.D 26000)

ELLIS, Tristram (1844-1922) British

Works on paper

£320 $509 €480 Palermo (24x53cm-9x21in) s.i.d.1909 W/C. 1-May-3 Locke & England, Leamington Spa #138/R

£360 $562 €540 In a cherry orchard (42x55cm-17x22in) s.d.1876 W/C. 26-Mar-3 Sotheby's, Olympia #159/R

£1600 $2512 €2400 Overlooking the bay from the Parthenon, Athens (26x37cm-10x15in) s.i.d.1902 pencil W/C. 16-Apr-3 Christie's, Kensington #1006/R est:600-800

£4000 $6520 €6000 Jerusalem (35x72cm-14x28in) s.i.d.1899 W/C. 29-Jan-3 Sotheby's, Olympia #220/R est:1000-2000

ELLIS, William (fl.1863-1864) British

£600 $984 €900 Pandy Mill, Dolgelli, W Wales (51x76cm-20x30in) s. i.verso. 4-Jun-3 Bonhams, Chester #346

ELLIS, William E (19th C) British

£637 $1000 €956 North Wales (51x76cm-20x30in) s. 23-Nov-2 Jackson's, Cedar Falls #20/R

ELLISON, Thomas (1866-c.1942) British

Works on paper

£460 $750 €690 Wooded landscape with rocky winding stream (39x60cm-15x24in) s. W/C. 11-Feb-3 Fellows & Sons, Birmingham #72/R

£560 $874 €840 Cove with figures and fishing boats, North Wales (46x60cm-18x24in) s. W/C. 6-Nov-2 Bonhams, Chester #320

ELLMINGER, Ignaz (1843-1894) Austrian

£1300 $2132 €1950 Shoeing the horses (35x45cm-14x18in) s. panel. 5-Jun-3 Christie's, Kensington #702/R est:1500-2000

£2201 $3412 €3500 Peasants resting (31x63cm-12x25in) s. panel one of pair. 29-Oct-2 Dorotheum, Vienna #108/R est:3400-4000

£2201 $3412 €3500 Peasant with horses and cart (31x63cm-12x25in) s. panel one of pair. 29-Oct-2 Dorotheum, Vienna #109/R est:3400-4000

£12658 $20000 €20000 Preparationfor Corpus Christi (88x130cm-35x51in) s. 28-Nov-2 Dorotheum, Vienna #24/R est:22000-28000

ELLSWORTH, Clarence (1885-1961) American
£2516 $4000 €3774 Indian in canoe (46x61cm-18x24in) s.d.1934. 5-Mar-3 Sotheby's, New York #141/R est:3000-5000

ELLSWORTH, James Sanford (attrib) (1802-1874) American
Miniatures
£1585 $2600 €2378 Portrait of a lady (8x5cm-3x2in) W/C paper rec. 9-Feb-3 Caddigan, Hanover #1/R

ELMER, Stephen (1717-1796) British
£1277 $1979 €1916 Still life of fish (46x52cm-18x20in) s. 3-Dec-2 Bukowskis, Stockholm #506/R est:20000-25000 (S.KR 18000)
£5500 $8910 €8250 Fox with dead cockerel in a landscape (71x91cm-28x36in) prov. 22-May-3 Christie's, London #65/R est:5000-8000

ELMIGER, Franz Jakob (1882-1934) Swiss
£1310 $2044 €1965 Two cows in meadow (60x80cm-24x31in) s. 20-Nov-2 Fischer, Luzern #1288/R est:3000-3500 (S.FR 3000)

ELMORE, Alfred (1815-1881) British
£1000 $1560 €1500 Marie Antoinette in the prison of the temple (84x51cm-33x20in) s.d.1861. 8-Oct-2 Bonhams, Knightsbridge #161/R est:1000-1500
£2500 $3900 €3750 Final hour (122x99cm-48x39in) s.d.1870. 7-Nov-2 Christie's, Kensington #204/R est:2000-3000
£6500 $10010 €9750 Mary Queen of Scots and Christopher Norton at Bolton Castle (121x180cm-48x71in) s. canvas on board exhib. 5-Sep-2 Christie's, Kensington #326/R est:3000-4000

ELOFF, Zakkie (1925-) South African
£250 $410 €363 Migration (90x116cm-35x46in) s. 1-Jun-3 Lots Road, London #369
Works on paper
£258 $415 €387 Rhino and zebra (49x66cm-19x26in) s. ink wash. 12-May-3 Stephan Welz, Johannesburg #237 est:3000-5000 (SA.R 3000)

ELOUIS, Jean Pierre Henri (1755-1840) French
£3727 $6000 €5591 Portrait of Martha Washington (24x19cm-9x7in) i. 16-Jan-3 Christie's, Rockefeller NY #338/R est:7000-10000

ELOUT, Franchoys (1597-c.1641) Dutch
£16352 $25346 €26000 Still life with oysters, lemon on pewter plate, olives, bread (30x53cm-12x21in) panel prov.lit. 2-Oct-2 Dorotheum, Vienna #141/R est:25000-35000

ELOUT-DRABBE, Mien (1875-1956) Dutch
Works on paper
£1348 $2183 €1900 Domburg (21x22cm-8x9in) pencil pastel. 26-May-3 Glerum, Amsterdam #80 est:300-400

ELSEN, Alfred (1850-1900) Belgian
£321 $503 €500 Vue de parc (38x29cm-15x11in) wood. 10-Dec-2 Campo, Vlaamse Kaai #190
£2162 $3373 €3200 Ruisseau dans la foret (125x95cm-49x37in) s. 25-Mar-3 Campo & Campo, Antwerp #64/R est:4000-5000

ELSHEIMER, Adam (style) (1574-1620) German
£7500 $12525 €10875 Flight into Egypt (27x41cm-11x16in) prov.lit. 11-Jul-3 Christie's, Kensington #13/R est:3000-5000

ELSKEN, Ed van der (1925-1990) Dutch
Photographs
£2013 $3119 €3200 Vali (23x18cm-9x7in) s.i.d.1953 verso gelatin silver lit. 2-Nov-2 Lempertz, Koln #107/R est:3200-3500

ELSLEY, Arthur John (1861-1952) British
£12000 $18720 €18000 Lily Cocciolitti (91x70cm-36x28in) s.i.d.1884. 7-Nov-2 Christie's, Kensington #62/R est:10000-15000
£129032 $200000 €193548 Picking apples (96x68cm-38x27in) s.d.1919 prov.lit. 30-Oct-2 Christie's, Rockefeller NY #45/R est:220000-280000
£141935 $220000 €212903 Snapdragon (70x93cm-28x37in) s.d.1894 exhib.lit. 29-Oct-2 Sotheby's, New York #152/R est:250000-350000
£360000 $597600 €540000 Punch and Judy show (112x169cm-44x67in) s.d.1912 s.i.verso prov.lit. 11-Jun-3 Christie's, London #22/R est:400000-600000

ELSNER, Franz (1898-1977) Austrian
Works on paper
£288 $472 €400 Mandrill (39x31cm-15x12in) s. pastel chk. 4-Jun-3 Dorotheum, Vienna #30

ELSSNER, Jacob (?-1517) German
£86331 $138129 €120000 Portrait of a man, with a gold chain and black beret (29x24cm-11x9in) panel prov.exhib.lit. 13-May-3 Christie's, Amsterdam #27/R est:60000-80000

ELST, Jacques Vander (1925-1991) Belgian
£892 $1391 €1400 Environs de Vresse sur Semois (50x60cm-20x24in) s. pair. 11-Nov-2 Horta, Bruxelles #480

ELSTER, Toni (1862-?) German
£306 $487 €450 Harbour in winter (41x53cm-16x21in) s. 28-Mar-3 Bolland & Marotz, Bremen #330/R

ELTEN, H D Kruseman van (1829-1904) Dutch
£3481 $5500 €5222 Landscape with houses (36x53cm-14x21in) s. 24-Apr-3 Shannon's, Milford #41/R est:6000-8000

ELTEN, Hendrik Dirk Kruseman van (1829-1904) Dutch
£300 $462 €450 Barge on a Dutch waterway. Lake before a farmstead (20x25cm-8x10in) s. panel two. 24-Oct-2 Christie's, Kensington #125
£2293 $3600 €3440 Scene in Holland (32x46cm-13x18in) s. prov. 10-Dec-2 Doyle, New York #186/R est:2000-3000

ELUARD, Paul (20th C) French
Works on paper
£350 $584 €500 Dans la fraiche vallee brule le soleil fluide et fort (26x18cm-10x7in) s. W/C ink text. 26-Jun-3 Tajan, Paris #105

ELVGREN, Gil (1914-1980) American
Works on paper
£1863 $3000 €2795 Shapely young woman at ironing board (53x36cm-21x14in) s. pencil chl on glassine. 20-Feb-3 Illustration House, New York #53/R est:2500-4000

ELVGREN, Gil (attrib) (1914-1980) American
£2640 $4250 €3960 Shapely woman adjusting her garter (76x61cm-30x24in) painted c.1950. 19-Feb-3 Illustration House, New York #238/R est:3000-6000

ELWELL, Frederick William (1870-1958) British
£780 $1271 €1170 Breezy day Sandsend, Whitby (29x39cm-11x15in) s.d.1898 panel. 11-Feb-3 Dickinson, Davy & Markham, Brigg #721/R
£1300 $2106 €1885 View of lake Garda from the Hote Garden Riva (28x66cm-11x26in) board exhib. 1-Aug-3 Dee Atkinson & Harrison, Driffield #644/R est:1200-1700
£2100 $3318 €3150 Portrait of a lady with a kitten (58x48cm-23x19in) 29-Nov-2 Dee Atkinson & Harrison, Driffield #827 est:3000-5000
£4600 $7268 €6900 Stable forge (46x58cm-18x23in) 29-Nov-2 Dee Atkinson & Harrison, Driffield #831/R est:4000-6000
£5800 $9164 €8700 Family at breakfast (112x79cm-44x31in) s. 29-Nov-2 Dee Atkinson & Harrison, Driffield #832/R est:5000-7000
£7200 $11376 €10800 Maids feeding the pigeons (46x36cm-18x14in) s. board. 29-Nov-2 Dee Atkinson & Harrison, Driffield #830/R est:5000-7000

ELWELL, Mary (1874-1952) British
£1650 $2591 €2475 Quiet hour (63x76cm-25x30in) s.i.d.1942. 19-Nov-2 Bonhams, Leeds #141/R est:1500-2000

ELWELL, Robert Farrington (1874-1962) American
£1543 $2500 €2237 Roping a bear (56x86cm-22x34in) s. canvas on masonite. 21-May-3 Doyle, New York #130/R est:3000-4000
£3205 $5000 €4808 Going home (61x91cm-24x36in) s. prov. 9-Nov-2 Santa Fe Art, Santa Fe #57/R est:3000-5000
£6329 $10000 €9177 Trail drive (56x38cm-22x15in) s. board prov. 26-Jul-3 Coeur d'Alene, Hayden #18/R est:5000-10000

ELWYN, John (1916-1997) British
Works on paper
£2000 $3180 €3000 Deserted farm (48x66cm-19x26in) s.d.verso W/C lit. 29-Apr-3 Peter Francis, Wales #35/R est:600-800

ELY, Mary (?) ?
Works on paper
£828 $1275 €1300 Appeal (43x38cm-17x15in) s. W/C. 4-Sep-2 James Adam, Dublin #88/R est:800-1000

ELZEN, Staf van (1915-1987) ?
£347 $552 €500 Enfants (45x60cm-18x24in) s. 29-Apr-3 Campo & Campo, Antwerp #317
£347 $552 €500 Paysage d'hiver (75x100cm-30x39in) s. 29-Apr-3 Campo, Vlaamse Kaai #538
£486 $773 €700 Paysage d'hiver (60x80cm-24x31in) s. 29-Apr-3 Campo & Campo, Antwerp #902

ELZER, Ruud (1915-) Dutch
£1702 $2757 €2400 Still life with bottle and jug (50x40cm-20x16in) s.d.48. 26-May-3 Glerum, Amsterdam #67 est:250-350

ELZINGA, Johannes (1893-1969) Dutch
£724 $1172 €1100 House in Friesland (56x46cm-22x18in) s.d.27 Aug 32. 21-Jan-3 Christie's, Amsterdam #385 est:600-800

EMANUEL, Frank Lewis (1865-1948) British
£566 $900 €849 Bucolic landscape (64x76cm-25x30in) s.d.1893. 22-Mar-3 New Orleans Auction, New Orleans #101/R est:800-1200
£750 $1185 €1125 Oxbridge Street, Notting Hill Gate (53x38cm-21x15in) s. 27-Nov-2 Sotheby's, Olympia #80/R
Works on paper
£300 $477 €450 Houses on the hillside, Manresa (23x34cm-9x13in) s.i. W/C. 5-Mar-3 Bonhams, Bury St Edmunds #263
£320 $515 €480 Puerta de la Justitia (18x25cm-7x10in) s. W/C. 19-Feb-3 Mallams, Oxford #397

EMANUELOV, Victor (1884-1940) Russian
£300 $489 €450 Bend of the river (46x55cm-18x22in) s. 1-Feb-3 Shapes, Edinburgh #309

EMELE, Wilhelm (1830-1905) German
£5369 $8643 €8000 Military parade in North Italy with a Hussar leading a grey horse (56x69cm-22x27in) s.d.1868 prov. 18-Feb-3 Sotheby's, Amsterdam #309/R est:1800-2200

EMERSON, Charles Chase (?-1922) American
£956 $1500 €1434 Elegant lady (81x46cm-32x18in) s.d.1901. 22-Nov-2 Skinner, Boston #107/R est:1500-2200

EMERSON, Peter Henry (1856-1936) British
Photographs
£12338 $19000 €18507 Life and landscape on the Norfolk Broads. platinum prints folio prov.exhib. 22-Oct-2 Sotheby's, New York #122/R est:12000-18000

EMERSON, William C (1865-?) American
£1226 $1900 €1839 Woodland nymphs (69x89cm-27x35in) s. board painted c.1910. 8-Dec-2 Toomey, Oak Park #738/R est:2500-4500

EMETT, Rowland (1906-1990) British
Works on paper
£311 $516 €451 Classify contact us follows, fish and whale (28x37cm-11x15in) pen ink en grisaille prov. 16-Jun-3 Waddingtons, Toronto #35/R (C.D 700)
£350 $560 €508 Humorous sketch of the Lucas "B90" immediate exchange scheme (33x38cm-13x15in) s.i. pen ink sold with letter. 13-May-3 Bristol Auction Rooms #438/R
£533 $885 €773 Gallant knight to the rescue (39x56cm-15x22in) s. pen ink W/C prov. 16-Jun-3 Waddingtons, Toronto #36/R est:1500-2000 (C.D 1200)
£940 $1504 €1410 Mumbling Magna Wings for victory week (25x33cm-10x13in) s. pen ink. 11-Mar-3 Gorringes, Lewes #2495/R

EMILIAN SCHOOL (16th C) Italian
£13415 $22000 €20123 Christ carrying the cross (61x50cm-24x20in) panel. 29-May-3 Sotheby's, New York #105/R est:15000-20000

EMILIAN SCHOOL (17th C) Italian
£5500 $8525 €8250 Saint Peter (86x74cm-34x29in) 31-Oct-2 Sotheby's, Olympia #93/R est:3000-5000
£6918 $10723 €11000 Mythological scene (180x140cm-71x55in) 29-Oct-2 Finarte, Milan #440/R est:5000-6000
£8054 $12966 €12000 Madonna and Child with two angels (131x97cm-52x38in) 20-Feb-3 Christie's, Rome #39/R est:10000
£9434 $14623 €15000 Madonna with angels (75x62cm-30x24in) board. 29-Oct-2 Finarte, Milan #455/R est:5000-6000
£18868 $29057 €30000 Rinaldo and Armida (120x60cm-47x24in) 28-Oct-2 Il Ponte, Milan #67/R est:18000
£19512 $32000 €29268 Portrait of a young man (47x37cm-19x15in) 29-May-3 Sotheby's, New York #139/R est:15000-20000

EMILIAN SCHOOL (18th C) Italian
£5696 $9000 €9000 Europa's kidnapping (110x135cm-43x53in) 27-Nov-2 Finarte, Milan #97/R
£5887 $9183 €9360 Figures in landscape (66x86cm-26x34in) painted wax. 21-Sep-2 Semenzato, Venice #129/R est:6500-7500
£21000 $32970 €31500 Peasants feasting at a table, others playing musical instruments (97x67cm-38x26in) 12-Dec-2 Sotheby's, London #189/R est:15000-20000

EMIN, Tracey (1963-) British
£1800 $2808 €2700 Figure study (17x22cm-7x9in) board. 25-Mar-3 Bonhams, New Bond Street #150/R est:1200-1800
Prints
£2215 $3500 €3323 She calls herself a soul girl (41x51cm-16x20in) s.d.1998 monoprint on calico with needle thread prov. 12-Nov-2 Phillips, New York #207/R est:4000-6000
£2215 $3500 €3323 Hey Tracey you been fucked over again (36x43cm-14x17in) s.d.1998 monoprint on calico with needle thread prov. 12-Nov-2 Phillips, New York #209/R est:4000-6000
Sculpture
£9000 $14760 €13500 Fantastic to feel beautiful again (107x127x10cm-42x50x4in) neon on plexiglas one of three prov. 6-Feb-3 Christie's, London #733/R est:12000-16000
£16000 $26240 €24000 Kiss me, kiss me, cover by body in love (122x137x6cm-48x54x2in) neon plexiglas one of three prov. 6-Feb-3 Christie's, London #736/R est:15000-20000

EMIOT, Pierre Paul (1887-?) French
£1527 $2412 €2291 Untitled, coast in the evening (90x131cm-35x52in) s. 7-Apr-3 Shapiro, Sydney #516/R est:1500-2500 (A.D 4000)

EMLER, Frantisek (1912-) Czechoslovakian
£590 $956 €885 Bouquet of roses with cherries (65x53cm-26x21in) s. board. 24-May-3 Dorotheum, Prague #125/R est:10000-15000 (C.KR 26000)

EMMENEGGER, Hans (1866-1940) Swiss
£568 $886 €852 King Salomon (38x60cm-15x24in) mono. canvas on canvas prov.exhib. 9-Nov-2 Galerie Gloggner, Luzern #41/R (S.FR 1300)
£1310 $2044 €1965 View of an English garden in Munich (39x49cm-15x19in) s.d.1893 prov. 9-Nov-2 Galerie Gloggner, Luzern #40/R est:2800-3500 (S.FR 3000)
£1834 $2861 €2751 Still life with apples (30x41cm-12x16in) s.d.22 prov. 9-Nov-2 Galerie Gloggner, Luzern #42/R est:3800-4500 (S.FR 4200)

EMMERIK, Govert van (1808-1882) Dutch
£559 $906 €850 Sailing ships in stormy weather (15x21cm-6x8in) init. panel. 21-Jan-3 Christie's, Amsterdam #107/R
£1266 $1975 €2000 Ships on choppy sea near harbour mouth (61x80cm-24x31in) indis.s.d.1858. 21-Oct-2 Glerum, Amsterdam #31/R est:1800-2200
£2420 $3727 €3800 In a stiff breeze (72x97cm-28x38in) s. 3-Sep-2 Christie's, Amsterdam #284/R est:1400-1800

EMMERSON, Henry H (1831-1895) British
£6000 $9840 €9000 Calf yard (92x73cm-36x29in) s. exhib. 29-May-3 Christie's, Kensington #244/R est:6000-10000
£27000 $43740 €40500 Maid of Derwent (42x50cm-17x20in) mono. exhib.lit. 20-May-3 Sotheby's, Olympia #202/R est:15000-25000

EMMS, John (1843-1912) British
£450 $698 €675 At the farmyard (30x41cm-12x16in) bears sig.d. 3-Dec-2 Sotheby's, Olympia #85/R
£650 $1007 €975 Boy with a horse and cart on a woodland track (25x36cm-10x14in) s. 31-Oct-2 Duke & Son, Dorchester #310/R
£1700 $2652 €2550 Study of a greyhound (30x40cm-12x16in) 8-Oct-2 Bonhams, Knightsbridge #188c/R est:1000-1500
£1800 $3006 €2610 Head study of a terrier (18x18cm-7x7in) s.d.94 canvas on card. 17-Jun-3 Bonhams, New Bond Street #77/R est:2000-3000
£2301 $3750 €3452 Fox terriers (16cm-6in circular) 11-Feb-3 Bonhams & Doyles, New York #175/R est:1500-2000
£2500 $3950 €3750 Greyhound (30x41cm-12x16in) 28-Nov-2 Christie's, Kensington #315/R est:2500-3500
£2600 $4212 €3900 Punch, saddled military pony, in a landscape (48x58cm-19x23in) s.i.d.1901 with a medal. 22-May-3 Christie's, London #18/R est:2500-3500

£2600 $4238 €3770 Sheep dip. Gathering hay (35x55cm-14x22in) s. pair. 16-Jul-3 Sotheby's, Olympia #97/R est:2000-3000
£2900 $4524 €4350 Punch (48x58cm-19x23in) s.d.1904. 9-Oct-2 Woolley & Wallis, Salisbury #274/R est:800-1200
£3200 $5312 €4640 Huntsman with hounds and a terrier by a kennel door (20x23cm-8x9in) s. 12-Jun-3 Christie's, Kensington #262/R est:1000-1500
£3988 $6500 €5982 Grex (24x17cm-9x7in) s.i. 11-Feb-3 Bonhams & Doyles, New York #176/R est:2000-3000
£4200 $6972 €6090 In the stable (51x67cm-20x26in) s. 12-Jun-3 Christie's, Kensington #90/R est:3000-5000
£4500 $7110 €6750 Ponies on a riverbank (39x52cm-15x20in) s.d.94 prov. 28-Nov-2 Christie's, Kensington #146/R est:5000-7000
£4800 $7584 €7200 Rabbit (16x21cm-6x8in) s.d.74. 28-Nov-2 Christie's, Kensington #64/R est:3000-4000
£5500 $8965 €7975 Farmyard friends (51x69cm-20x27in) s. 21-Jul-3 Bonhams, Bath #81/R est:6000-8000
£6000 $9960 €9000 Saint Bernard (46x66cm-18x26in) s.d.94. 12-Jun-3 Sotheby's, London #288/R est:6000-8000
£7000 $11340 €10500 Dora, an English setter in a landscape (36x46cm-14x18in) s.i.d.1905. 22-May-3 Christie's, London #12/R est:7000-10000
£13535 $21250 €20303 Portrait of a horse in a courtyard with saddle and dogs at his feet (90x70cm-35x28in) s. 10-Dec-2 Peter Webb, Auckland #138/R est:20000-30000 (NZ.D 42500)
£14500 $23490 €21750 Ratting (30x93cm-12x37in) s. three scenes. 22-May-3 Christie's, London #11/R est:7000-10000
£21000 $32550 €31500 Keeper's boy and two setters (91x71cm-36x28in) s.d.86. 31-Oct-2 Greenslade Hunt, Taunton #626/R est:15000-25000
£22000 $34760 €33000 Hounds and a terrier (34x27cm-13x11in) s.d.1909. 28-Nov-2 Christie's, Kensington #302/R est:2000-3000
£25357 $40064 €38036 First trail (62x91cm-24x36in) s. i.on stretcher. 26-Nov-2 Sotheby's, Melbourne #222/R est:28000-35000 (A.D 71000)

Works on paper

£4000 $6240 €6000 End of the day (45x37cm-18x15in) s. 10-Oct-2 Greenslade Hunt, Taunton #568/R est:3000-5000
£5600 $9240 €8120 Figure smoking a pipe with horse and two dogs to his side (38x48cm-15x19in) s.d.1899 W/C. 3-Jul-3 Duke & Son, Dorchester #104/R est:1000-2000
£22500 $33525 €33750 Spaniels in a kennel interior (37x49cm-15x19in) s.d.81 W/C bodycol. 27-Jun-2 Greenslade Hunt, Taunton #703/R est:2000-3000

EMMS, John (attrib) (1843-1912) British

£500 $780 €750 Three puppies in a basket (15x25cm-6x10in) 11-Apr-3 Keys, Aylsham #679
£1300 $2054 €1950 Interior, a young boy trying to stroke an owl (37x29cm-15x11in) s. 18-Dec-2 John Nicholson, Haslemere #1293/R est:1000-1500

EMOD, Aurel (1897-1958) Hungarian

£774 $1207 €1161 Still life of flowers with sweetmeat Boksz (80x71cm-31x28in) s. 11-Sep-2 Kieselbach, Budapest #10/R (H.F 300000)
£1006 $1569 €1459 Italian landscape (71x81cm-28x32in) s. exhib. 12-Apr-3 Mu Terem Galeria, Budapest #79/R est:350000 (H.F 360000)
£1084 $1690 €1626 Venice (72x81cm-28x32in) s. 11-Sep-2 Kieselbach, Budapest #9/R (H.F 420000)
£1816 $2834 €2633 Colmirano (79x88cm-31x35in) s. 12-Apr-3 Mu Terem Galeria, Budapest #201/R est:350000 (H.F 650000)
£2340 $3745 €3510 Autumn in Rome (70x90cm-28x35in) s. 16-May-3 Kieselbach, Budapest #21/R (H.F 800000)

EMOND, Martin (1895-1965) Swedish

£344 $550 €499 King Lear (92x122cm-36x48in) s. panel. 18-May-3 Anders Antik, Landskrona #50 (S.KR 4400)
£359 $552 €539 Two men at an entrance (91x121cm-36x48in) s. 27-Oct-2 Anders Antik, Landskrona #506/R (S.KR 5200)
£430 $688 €624 Harbour scene (61x90cm-24x35in) s. panel. 18-May-3 Anders Antik, Landskrona #45 (S.KR 5500)

EMPI, Maurice (1932-) ?

£378 $585 €600 Notre Dame de Paris (50x65cm-20x26in) s. paper laid on canvas. 4-Oct-2 Tajan, Paris #84
£411 $642 €650 Aux courses (54x81cm-21x32in) s. 20-Oct-2 Chayette & Cheval, Paris #100
£411 $642 €650 Aux courses (46x65cm-18x26in) s. 20-Oct-2 Chayette & Cheval, Paris #101
£1014 $1581 €1500 Terrasse du Fouquet's (50x65cm-20x26in) s. s.i.verso. 25-Mar-3 Chochon-Barre & Allardi, Paris #103/R est:1500-1800

Works on paper

£423 $680 €600 Les courses (46x63cm-18x25in) s. pastel. 11-May-3 Thierry & Lannon, Brest #59
£489 $817 €700 Cafe sur la place (50x65cm-20x26in) s. gouache. 26-Jun-3 Tajan, Paris #125
£846 $1328 €1320 Auteuil (47x63cm-19x25in) s. gouache. 15-Dec-2 Thierry & Lannon, Brest #327

EMPIRE SCHOOL (19th C) French

Sculpture

£17722 $27646 €28000 Grands personnages tenant une coupe (70x71cm-28x28in) gold bronze. 16-Oct-2 Fraysse & Associes, Paris #142/R est:1200-1500

EMPRESS DOWAGER CIXI (1835-1908) Chinese

Works on paper

£3263 $5385 €4731 Peonies (16x47cm-6x19in) s.i. ink col folding fan. 7-Jul-3 Christie's, Hong Kong #510/R est:20000-30000 (HK.D 42000)

EMPRIN, Giuliano (1902-1991) Italian

£306 $487 €450 Along the Po (20x35cm-8x14in) s. s.i.verso. 1-Mar-3 Meeting Art, Vercelli #14

EMPTAGE, Arthur D (20th C) American

£360 $558 €540 Home by moonlight (51x61cm-20x24in) s. 3-Dec-2 Bonhams, Knightsbridge #72

EMSLIE, Alfred Edward (1848-1918) British

£1135 $1759 €1703 Autumn landscape with old couple and young girl (82x66cm-32x26in) s.d.1883. 8-Dec-2 Uppsala Auktionskammare, Uppsala #84/R est:20000-25000 (S.KR 16000)

Works on paper

£450 $702 €675 Cuckoo (26x19cm-10x7in) s. W/C. 17-Sep-2 Sotheby's, Olympia #49/R
£1500 $2340 €2250 Portrait of a young girl with a fan (19x11cm-7x4in) s.d.1886 W/C with scratching out. 17-Oct-2 Christie's, Kensington #4/R est:1500-2000
£1500 $2340 €2250 Portrait of a young girl with a bonnet holding a small bouquet (21x14cm-8x6in) s.d.1886 pencil W/C scratching out. 17-Oct-2 Christie's, Kensington #7/R est:1500-2000

ENARD, Colette (20th C) French

£1096 $1721 €1600 Deux coeurs a l'oiseau et a la pendule (33x41cm-13x16in) s.d.63 lit. 15-Apr-3 Laurence Calmels, Paris #4215/R est:1200

ENCKELL, Magnus (1870-1925) Finnish

£2405 $3752 €3800 Girl by rosebush (55x45cm-22x18in) s. lit. 12-Sep-2 Hagelstam, Helsinki #801/R

Works on paper

£252 $387 €400 Interior (23x27cm-9x11in) W/C exhib. 27-Oct-2 Bukowskis, Helsinki #163/R
£313 $498 €460 Tree (37x26cm-15x10in) s.d.1919 W/C. 27-Feb-3 Hagelstam, Helsinki #908
£563 $907 €800 Coastal landscape from Porto Finosta (20x30cm-8x12in) s.d.1920 W/C. 10-May-3 Bukowskis, Helsinki #176/R

ENCKELL, Rabbe (20th C) Scandinavian

£327 $536 €500 Landscape from San Gimignano (46x55cm-18x22in) s.d.67. 9-Feb-3 Bukowskis, Helsinki #223/R

ENDE, Edgar (1901-1965) German

£5769 $8942 €9000 Vanishing (75x100cm-30x39in) s.d.32. 7-Dec-2 Van Ham, Cologne #144/R est:5000

ENDE, Hans am (1864-1918) German

£5435 $8913 €7500 The moor in evening (44x64cm-17x25in) s. s.i. verso board. 31-May-3 Villa Grisebach, Berlin #131/R est:10000-12000
£12658 $20000 €20000 View from Weyerberg (123x240cm-48x94in) s. painted c.1900. 29-Nov-2 Bolland & Marotz, Bremen #497/R est:37000
£20068 $31908 €29500 Boat on the Hamme (82x66cm-32x26in) s. s. stretcher. 28-Mar-3 Bolland & Marotz, Bremen #331/R est:31000

Works on paper

£306 $487 €450 Sailing boats off Sylt (11x16cm-4x6in) mono. chk board. 28-Mar-3 Bolland & Marotz, Bremen #333
£377 $589 €600 Cupid (25x16cm-10x6in) Indian ink brush over pencil. 21-Sep-2 Bolland & Marotz, Bremen #350/R
£884 $1406 €1300 Farmstead in Worpswede (28x41cm-11x16in) s. chk. 28-Mar-3 Bolland & Marotz, Bremen #332/R

ENDER, Axel Hjalmar (1853-1920) Norwegian

£2618 $4110 €3927 Woman with horse on the way to out-farm (21x27cm-8x11in) s. paper on panel. 21-Nov-2 Grev Wedels Plass, Oslo #10/R est:30000-40000 (N.KR 30000)
£3246 $5128 €4869 Milkmaid resting (40x26cm-16x10in) s. 17-Dec-2 Grev Wedels Plass, Oslo #145/R est:40000 (N.KR 37000)
£3490 $5480 €5235 Dairy maid (65x45cm-26x18in) s. 21-Nov-2 Grev Wedels Plass, Oslo #9/R est:60000-80000 (N.KR 40000)

£5222 $8355 €7833 Mother and child in the mountains (40x33cm-16x13in) s. 17-Mar-3 Blomqvist, Oslo #354/R est:40000-50000 (N.KR 60000)
£10444 $16710 €15666 Small girl on sledge (35x26cm-14x10in) s. panel. 17-Mar-3 Blomqvist, Oslo #306/R est:50000-70000 (N.KR 120000)
£10813 $17085 €16220 Meeting on country road, two ladies in horse-carriage and man (58x84cm-23x33in) s. lit. 2-Dec-2 Blomqvist, Oslo #355/R est:80000-100000 (N.KR 125000)
£12217 $19792 €18326 Interior scene with child and dog (82x57cm-32x22in) s. 26-May-3 Grev Wedels Plass, Oslo #11/R est:150000-200000 (N.KR 135000)

ENDER, Johann Nepomuk (1793-1854) Austrian
Works on paper
£591 $922 €887 Portrait of young woman (16x13cm-6x5in) s. pen W/C prov.lit. 23-Sep-2 Rasmussen, Vejle #305/R (D.KR 7000)
£694 $1104 €1000 Four women (12x9cm-5x4in) s. s. verso W/C pencil. 29-Apr-3 Wiener Kunst Auktionen, Vienna #521/R
£705 $1093 €1100 Portrait of a young lady in white dress (13x10cm-5x4in) s.i.d.14 W/C over pencil. 4-Dec-2 Neumeister, Munich #512/R
£811 $1265 €1200 Portrait of young woman in white dress with roses (22x16cm-9x6in) s. W/C. 28-Mar-3 Dorotheum, Vienna #206/R
£1622 $2530 €2400 Portrait of young woman in white dress (22x16cm-9x6in) s. W/C. 28-Mar-3 Dorotheum, Vienna #205/R est:1200-1500
£1757 $2741 €2600 Portrait of woman wearing hat (24x19cm-9x7in) s. W/C. 28-Mar-3 Dorotheum, Vienna #207/R est:1200-1500

ENDER, Thomas (1793-1875) Austrian
£6677 $10951 €9682 Landscape with house by waterfall (110x132cm-43x52in) s. 4-Jun-3 AB Stockholms Auktionsverk #2442/R est:100000-125000 (S.KR 85000)
£8333 $13083 €13000 Prater landscape (19x30cm-7x12in) s. W/C. 25-Nov-2 Hassfurther, Vienna #35/R est:10000-15000
£44304 $70000 €70000 Sorrento grotto with view of Capp Mahea (50x60cm-20x24in) panel. 28-Nov-2 Dorotheum, Vienna #117/R est:80000-90000
Works on paper
£1130 $1752 €1695 Schloss Stixenstein (14x21cm-6x8in) s. W/C. 9-Dec-2 Philippe Schuler, Zurich #4156/R est:3500-4000 (S.FR 2600)
£1772 $2800 €2800 Landscape (22x32cm-9x13in) i.d.1873 verso W/C pencil. 26-Nov-2 Wiener Kunst Auktionen, Vienna #23/R est:1500-2500
£1923 $3019 €3000 The Thorda Spalte (31x47cm-12x19in) i. W/C bodycol. 25-Nov-2 Hassfurther, Vienna #37/R est:3000-4000
£2436 $3824 €3800 Weidenbach landscape (27x50cm-11x20in) i. W/C. 25-Nov-2 Hassfurther, Vienna #36/R est:3000-4000
£3481 $5500 €5500 Hilly landscape (25x37cm-10x15in) s. w/C. 26-Nov-2 Wiener Kunst Auktionen, Vienna #25/R est:3000-6000
£5072 $8319 €7000 Market in Gibraltar (17x24cm-7x9in) W/C exec.1817/18 prov. 27-May-3 Hassfurther, Vienna #36/R est:6000-10000
£6081 $9486 €9000 Prutz in Tyrol (27x39cm-11x15in) i. W/C. 25-Mar-3 Wiener Kunst Auktionen, Vienna #114/R est:7000-14000
£6757 $10541 €10000 Federaun in Gail valley (33x47cm-13x19in) i. W/C. 25-Mar-3 Wiener Kunst Auktionen, Vienna #113/R est:7000-14000

ENDERS, Jean Joseph (1862-?) French
£1135 $1771 €1703 Sur les quais de la Seine (65x92cm-26x36in) s. 6-Nov-2 Dobiaschofsky, Bern #493/R est:1500 (S.FR 2600)

ENDRES, Louis John (1896-1989) American
Works on paper
£374 $595 €550 Promeneur dans la campagne (19x25cm-7x10in) W/C. 24-Mar-3 Rabourdin & Choppin de Janvry, Paris #1
£884 $1406 €1300 Le fumeur joyeux (65x49cm-26x19in) s.i.d.56 pencil W/C dr. 24-Mar-3 Rabourdin & Choppin de Janvry, Paris #13/R est:1500-1800

ENEHIELM, Cris af (1954-) Finnish
£2254 $3628 €3200 Song of Praise (138x116cm-54x46in) s.d.89 acrylic. 10-May-3 Bukowskis, Helsinki #228/R est:2500-3000

ENFIELD, Henry (1849-1908) British
£260 $434 €377 Fjord entrance (51x85cm-20x33in) s. indis i.on stretcher. 17-Jun-3 Anderson & Garland, Newcastle #471
£900 $1476 €1350 Fishing boats lying on their moorings in a Norwegian fjord (108x72cm-43x28in) s. 5-Jun-3 Christie's, Kensington #739/R

ENGBERG, Gabriel Karl (1872-1953) Finnish
£314 $487 €500 After the storm (55x46cm-22x18in) s.d.1919. 6-Oct-2 Bukowskis, Helsinki #167/R
£510 $811 €750 Winter light (62x50cm-24x20in) s.d.1914. 24-Mar-3 Bukowskis, Helsinki #60/R
£516 $815 €800 Landscape (50x62cm-20x24in) s.d.1920. 19-Dec-2 Hagelstam, Helsinki #824/R

ENGBLOM, Alma (?) Finnish?
£755 $1209 €1050 Self-portrait (41x33cm-16x13in) s. mahogany panel. 17-May-3 Hagelstam, Helsinki #94/R

ENGEBRETSEN, Eivind (1890-1960) Norwegian
£265 $433 €398 Winter landscape from Soknedalen (73x91cm-29x36in) s.d.1947 panel. 17-Feb-3 Blomqvist, Lysaker #1047/R (N.KR 3000)

ENGEL, Frederick (1872-1958) Dutch
£1274 $1962 €2000 Milking time (32x42cm-13x17in) s.d.28 s.stretcher. 3-Sep-2 Christie's, Amsterdam #190 est:1000-1500
£1918 $2992 €2800 Calves feeding (40x50cm-16x20in) s.d.43. 14-Apr-3 Glerum, Amsterdam #118/R est:1200-1600
£2500 $4050 €3800 Polderlandschap - Polder landscape with cows along a ditch (49x73cm-19x29in) s.d.19 s.i.verso. 21-Jan-3 Christie's, Amsterdam #142 est:700-900

ENGEL, Johann Friedrich (1844-?) German
£1266 $1962 €2000 Bavarian peasant boy in traditional costume (24x19cm-9x7in) s.i. panel. 25-Sep-2 Neumeister, Munich #571/R est:1200

ENGEL, Werner Emil (1880-1941) Swiss
£441 $643 €662 Heiligenschwendi, above Thun (59x46cm-23x18in) s. 17-Jun-2 Philippe Schuler, Zurich #4267 (S.FR 1000)
£881 $1286 €1322 Schloss Thun (57x42cm-22x17in) s. board. 17-Jun-2 Philippe Schuler, Zurich #4268 (S.FR 2000)

ENGEL-PAK, Ernest (1885-1965) Belgian
£312 $496 €450 Composition (62x47cm-24x19in) s.d.29 paper on panel. 29-Apr-3 Artcurial Briest, Paris #291

ENGELBACH, Florence (1872-1951) British
£300 $474 €450 Still life of flowers in a pot (33x22cm-13x9in) s. board. 27-Nov-2 Hamptons Fine Art, Godalming #343

ENGELBRECHTSZ, Cornelisz (attrib) (1468-1533) Dutch
£10759 $17000 €17000 Saint Magdalene (50x30cm-20x12in) panel prov. 27-Nov-2 Christie's, Paris #1/R est:6000-8000

ENGELEN, Louis van (1856-1940) Belgian
£314 $491 €500 Fillette a la poupee (49x40cm-19x16in) panel. 14-Oct-2 Amberes, Antwerp #215
£683 $1094 €950 Village view with Maria Church (43x34cm-17x13in) s.i. panel. 17-May-3 De Vuyst, Lokeren #367

ENGELEN, Piet van (1863-1923) Belgian
£753 $1175 €1100 Perdreaux (32x40cm-13x16in) s. panel. 14-Apr-3 Horta, Bruxelles #109/R

ENGELHARD, Johann Anton (1872-1936) German
£651 $1015 €950 Bay of Naples with Sorrento (21x157cm-8x62in) s.d. 11-Apr-3 Winterberg, Heidelberg #942

ENGELHARDT, Georg (1823-1883) German
£873 $1362 €1310 Lake in summer (42x60cm-17x24in) s. 6-Nov-2 Dobiaschofsky, Bern #494/R (S.FR 2000)

ENGELHARDT, Georg-Hermann (1855-?) German
£1218 $1900 €1827 Lake of Brienz, Austrian Alps (69x97cm-27x38in) s.i. 21-Sep-2 Pook & Pook, Downington #402/R est:800-1200

ENGELHART, Josef (1864-1941) Austrian
Works on paper
£641 $1000 €962 Boulevard de Clichy (33x25cm-13x10in) s. W/C. 30-Mar-3 Susanin's, Chicago #6027/R
£1000 $1670 €1500 Salome (56x21cm-22x8in) chl W/C. 18-Jun-3 Christie's, Kensington #120/R est:1200-1800

ENGELMULLER, Ferdinand (1867-1924) Czechoslovakian
£1033 $1611 €1550 Summer landscape with a deciduous tree (42x35cm-17x14in) s. 12-Oct-2 Dorotheum, Prague #37/R (C.KR 50000)
£1960 $3097 €2940 Landscape under Rip mountain (116x150cm-46x59in) s.d.1904 lit. sold with monograph. 30-Nov-2 Dorotheum, Prague #40/R est:45000-70000 (C.KR 95000)
Works on paper
£496 $773 €744 Trees at the sunset (67x49cm-26x19in) s.d.98 pastel cardboard. 12-Oct-2 Dorotheum, Prague #188 (C.KR 24000)

ENGELS, Leo (1882-1952) Belgian
£290 $475 €400 Nature morte aux pommes (60x73cm-24x29in) s. d.1932 verso. 27-May-3 Campo, Vlaamse Kaai #93
£440 $687 €700 Chinese lady (74x75cm-29x30in) 23-Sep-2 Bernaerts, Antwerp #821

ENGELS, Robert (1866-1926) German

£308 $481 €450 Scene near Wollin (66x78cm-26x31in) 10-Apr-3 Van Ham, Cologne #1412

ENGELSEN, Hakon (1933-) Norwegian

£297 $466 €446 Moonlight over Lofoten (50x70cm-20x28in) s. exhib. 25-Nov-2 Blomqvist, Lysaker #1060/R (N.KR 3400)

ENGELSTED, Malthe (1852-1930) Danish

£1500 $2370 €2250 Afternoon frolics (64x77cm-25x30in) s.d.1885. 14-Nov-2 Christie's, Kensington #302/R est:3000-5000

ENGELUND, Svend (1908-) Danish

£527 $822 €791 Landscape with houses (28x39cm-11x15in) s. 5-Aug-2 Rasmussen, Vejle #338/R (D.KR 6200)
£630 $1009 €945 Landscape (26x36cm-10x14in) init. 13-Jan-3 Rasmussen, Vejle #275/R (D.KR 7200)
£676 $1041 €1014 Field landscape (23x43cm-9x17in) init.d.72 masonite. 23-Oct-2 Kunsthallen, Copenhagen #72/R (D.KR 8000)
£823 $1308 €1235 Landscape, Vraa (20x34cm-8x13in) init. masonite. 26-Feb-3 Kunsthallen, Copenhagen #335/R (D.KR 9000)
£1115 $1739 €1673 Landscape view (60x85cm-24x33in) init.d.43. 11-Nov-2 Rasmussen, Vejle #53/R est:10000-15000 (D.KR 13000)
£1463 $2325 €2195 Fields at Vraa, evening (28x40cm-11x16in) init. masonite. 26-Feb-3 Kunsthallen, Copenhagen #250/R est:15000 (D.KR 16000)
£1606 $2473 €2409 Field landscape (25x37cm-10x15in) init. cardboard. 23-Oct-2 Kunsthallen, Copenhagen #15/R est:12000 (D.KR 19000)
£2286 $3544 €3429 Landscape (60x81cm-24x32in) init. s.verso. 1-Oct-2 Rasmussen, Copenhagen #334/R est:20000 (D.KR 27000)
£3903 $6167 €5855 Fields in green/black (90x132cm-35x52in) init.d.62 s.verso. 1-Apr-3 Rasmussen, Copenhagen #102/R est:30000-40000 (D.KR 42000)

ENGER, Erling (1899-1990) Norwegian

£722 $1111 €1083 Landscape (38x46cm-15x18in) s. painted 1975. 28-Oct-2 Blomqvist, Lysaker #1037 (N.KR 8500)
£849 $1307 €1274 Field and wood (38x45cm-15x18in) s. panel painted 1959. 28-Oct-2 Blomqvist, Lysaker #1043/R (N.KR 10000)
£1100 $1738 €1650 Woodland landscape (81x99cm-32x39in) s.d.57. 17-Dec-2 Gorringes, Lewes #1464
£1301 $2029 €1952 Winter in the woods (78x98cm-31x39in) init.d.53 canvas on panel. 21-Oct-2 Blomqvist, Oslo #389/R est:20000-30000 (N.KR 15000)
£1858 $2936 €2787 Autumn landscape (47x56cm-19x22in) init. 28-Apr-3 Blomqvist, Oslo #367/R est:15000-20000 (N.KR 21000)
£2775 $4330 €4163 Silver birch trees against gold background (64x80cm-25x31in) s.d.69. 21-Oct-2 Blomqvist, Oslo #384/R est:40000-50000 (N.KR 32000)

Works on paper

£509 $784 €764 Mountain landscape, Vestland (42x53cm-17x21in) s. W/C executed 1964. 28-Oct-2 Blomqvist, Lysaker #1038/R (N.KR 6000)

ENGERO, G (?) ?

£270 $422 €405 Figures merrymaking at an inn (60x81cm-24x32in) s. 23-Sep-2 Rasmussen, Vejle #293/R (D.KR 3200)

ENGESTROM, Georg (1921-) Finnish

£253 $395 €400 The branded (95x103cm-37x41in) s. painted 1971-73. 15-Sep-2 Bukowskis, Helsinki #182/R
£253 $395 €400 View from Rome (93x93cm-37x37in) s. 15-Sep-2 Bukowskis, Helsinki #183/R
£264 $407 €420 Winter (31x24cm-12x9in) s. 24-Oct-2 Hagelstam, Helsinki #916

ENGILBERTS, Jon (1908-) Icelandic

£805 $1336 €1167 Vetradagur (57x43cm-22x17in) s. masonite. 12-Jun-3 Kunsthallen, Copenhagen #104/R (D.KR 8500)
£824 $1368 €1195 Composition (62x70cm-24x28in) S/ PA. 12-Jun-3 Kunsthallen, Copenhagen #106/R (D.KR 8700)

ENGL, Hugo (1852-?) Austrian

£4392 $6851 €6500 Sleeping hunter disturbed by small boy (37x51cm-15x20in) s. 26-Mar-3 Hugo Ruef, Munich #94/R est:2200

ENGLAND, E S (19/20th C) ?

£282 $443 €409 Chickens and cockerel. 15-Dec-2 Anders Antik, Landskrona #77 (S.KR 4000)

ENGLE, Alice (?) American?

£340 $550 €510 Mt Rainer (33x15cm-13x6in) board. 24-Jan-3 Douglas, South Deerfield #2

ENGLE, Harry Leon (1870-?) American

£692 $1100 €1038 Dam, probably on the Fox river (41x51cm-16x20in) s. i.d.verso. 2-Mar-3 Toomey, Oak Park #670/R

ENGLE, Nita (1925-) American

Works on paper

£236 $375 €354 New England wharf (43x74cm-17x29in) W/C. 3-May-3 Rachel Davis, Shaker Heights #689

ENGLEHART, John Joseph (1867-1915) American

£683 $1100 €1025 Lake side Indian encampment (41x51cm-16x20in) s. prov. 18-Feb-3 John Moran, Pasadena #162
£755 $1200 €1133 Mount Tamalpias with figures (46x79cm-18x31in) s. 3-May-3 Harvey Clar, Oakland #1423
£4140 $6500 €6210 Native American village in the Yosemite valley (71x122cm-28x48in) s. prov. 19-Nov-2 Butterfields, San Francisco #8156/R est:4000-6000

ENGLEHEART, Evelyn L (fl.1906-1921) British

Works on paper

£550 $869 €798 Travellers on a dusty road (52x35cm-20x14in) s. W/C. 22-Jul-3 Bonhams, Knightsbridge #225/R
£800 $1248 €1200 View of Constantinople (34x25cm-13x10in) s. W/C over pencil htd bodycol. 15-Oct-2 Sotheby's, London #94/R
£2884 $4529 €4500 Justice au campement (52x72cm-20x28in) s. W/C gouache. 10-Dec-2 Tajan, Paris #158/R est:3000

ENGLEHEART, George (1752-1829) British

Miniatures

£1700 $2618 €2550 Lady in a ruffled dress (4cm-2xin) gilt metal frame oval exec.c.1785. 24-Oct-2 Sotheby's, Olympia #8/R est:1000-1500
£1800 $2772 €2700 Lady wearing a gold trimmed dress and veil (6cm-2xin) gold frame oval exec.c.1775. 24-Oct-2 Sotheby's, Olympia #7/R est:2000-3000
£2000 $3320 €2900 Gentleman in a brown coat (5x4cm-2x2in) gem set frame gold slide oval. 10-Jun-3 Mellors & Kirk, Nottingham #529/R est:1500-2000
£2600 $4212 €3900 Gentleman wearing dark grey coat (5cm-2xin) gilt metal frame. 22-May-3 Bonhams, New Bond Street #92/R est:1500-2500
£3000 $4920 €4350 Rev Dr John Warren, Bishop of St. David and Bangor (5cm-2xin) silver gilt frame oval prov.lit. 3-Jun-3 Christie's, London #118/R est:2000-3000
£4000 $6160 €6000 Rev George Smith, Vicar of Ottery St Mary, Devon (9cm-4xin) init. mono.verso gold frame oval exec.c.1800 with case lit. 24-Oct-2 Sotheby's, Olympia #9/R est:2500-3500
£4200 $6804 €6300 Gentleman wearing green coat (5cm-2xin) gold frame plaited hair gold stars. 22-May-3 Bonhams, New Bond Street #91/R est:2000-3000
£4500 $7020 €6750 Unfinished portrait of a lady wearing decollete dress blue ribbon choker (6cm-2xin) gold frame oval. 5-Nov-2 Bonhams, New Bond Street #55/R est:2000-3000
£5500 $8635 €8250 Portrait of David Johnston of Lathrisk (8x7cm-3x3in) init. lock of hair verso oval within morocco case. 21-Nov-2 Clevedon Sale Rooms #182/R est:3500-5000
£6000 $9360 €9000 Henry Paget 1st Earl of Uxbridge wearing double-breasted dark blue coat (8cm-3xin) s. gold frame oval prov.lit. 5-Nov-2 Bonhams, New Bond Street #86/R est:3500-4500
£6500 $10335 €9750 Edward Scott, wearing a royal blue coat (5cm-2xin) ivory gold frame locks of hair prov.exhib.lit. 4-Mar-3 Bonhams, New Bond Street #166/R est:3000-5000
£6500 $10530 €9750 Officer of the Royal Regiment, wearing scarlet coat (6cm-2xin) gilt mounted rectangular papier mache frame. 22-May-3 Bonhams, New Bond Street #89/R est:5000-7000
£6500 $10530 €9750 Gentleman wearing blue coat (9cm-4xin) init. gold frame plaited hair. 22-May-3 Bonhams, New Bond Street #107/R est:4000-6000
£14500 $23490 €21750 Gentleman wearing high collared viridian green coat (6cm-2xin) gold frame with diamond border. 22-May-3 Bonhams, New Bond Street #96/R est:4000-6000
£38000 $59660 €57000 Young lady in a low cut white dress (9x7cm-4x3in) s.d.1807 gold frame rec. 10-Dec-2 Christie's, London #225/R est:6000-8000

ENGLEHEART, John Cox Dillman (1782-1862) British
Miniatures
£4800 $7536 €7200 Left eye of the artist's sister, Mary Cox Dillman Engleheart (2cm-1xin) i. gold brooch frame with lock of hair. 10-Dec-2 Christie's, London #285/R est:1000-1500

ENGLERTH, Emil (1887-?) Austrian
£440 $708 €660 Rio S Polo (40x32cm-16x13in) s.i.d.1936 i. verso panel. 7-May-3 Dobiaschofsky, Bern #485/R (S.FR 950)

ENGLISH PRIMITIVE SCHOOL, 19th C
£4500 $7155 €6525 Rural farm with numerous figures and farm animals (62x88cm-24x35in) 29-Apr-3 Henry Adams, Chichester #345 est:4000-6000

ENGLISH SCHOOL
Miniatures
£9000 $14040 €13500 General John Lambert wearing gold studded silver armour (5cm-2xin) i.d.1659 verso enamel silver frame oval. 5-Nov-2 Bonhams, New Bond Street #23/R est:2000-3000

Works on paper
£7500 $12525 €10875 Oryx gazella and strepsicerous, kudu (36x50cm-14x20in) d.22.1858 W/C. 19-Jun-3 Clevedon Sale Rooms #194

ENGLISH SCHOOL, 16th C
£8500 $14110 €12750 Portrait of Catherine of Aragon (52x37cm-20x15in) panel prov. 12-Jun-3 Sotheby's, London #50/R est:4000-6000
£16000 $26720 €23200 Portrait of Elizabeth I, bust-length in a white beaded dress and lace collar (58x44cm-23x17in) panel prov. 9-Jul-3 Bonhams, New Bond Street #45/R est:5000-7000

ENGLISH SCHOOL, 17th C
£6000 $9960 €9000 Portrait of a gentleman, aged 22 in white doublet (89x59cm-35x23in) d.1616 prov. 10-Jun-3 Christie's, London #3/R est:8000-12000
£6500 $10270 €9750 View of the Stoke Potteries (89x129cm-35x51in) painted c.1860. 26-Nov-2 Christie's, London #150/R est:6000-10000
£6500 $10400 €9750 Portrait of lady traditionally identified as Lady Elizabeth Jones (75x61cm-30x24in) painted c.1680 prov. 15-May-3 Christie's, London #8/R est:7000-10000
£6500 $10530 €9750 Group portrait of father, wife and daughter (205x222cm-81x87in) 23-May-3 Lyon & Turnbull, Edinburgh #17/R est:1500-2500
£9000 $13860 €13500 Portrait of a lady and gentleman (103x128cm-41x50in) 5-Sep-2 Christie's, Kensington #6/R est:5000-8000
£18000 $28440 €27000 Portrait of Mary, Lady Bowes and her son Thomas (195x108cm-77x43in) i.d.1630. 26-Nov-2 Christie's, London #1/R est:20000-30000

ENGLISH SCHOOL, 17th/18th C
£15000 $24900 €22500 Coastal landscape with a view of Scarborough town and castle from the south west (76x138cm-30x54in) 12-Jun-3 Sotheby's, London #104/R est:15000-20000

ENGLISH SCHOOL, 18th C
£4487 $7045 €7000 Portrait of nobleman (127x102cm-50x40in) 19-Nov-2 Castellana, Madrid #488/R
£8500 $14110 €12750 Gentlemen drinking and smoking pipes round a table in an interior (69x77cm-27x30in) 10-Jun-3 Christie's, London #12/R est:5000-8000
£12000 $19080 €18000 Portrait of a man in tri-corn hat and wearing a blue velvet coat (73x61cm-29x24in) 4-Mar-3 Bearnes, Exeter #432/R est:600-900
£16000 $25280 €24000 Prospect of the city from the north (85x117cm-33x46in) 28-Nov-2 Sotheby's, London #138/R est:12000-18000
£48000 $80160 €69600 Thames at Richmond (59x108cm-23x43in) prov. 9-Jul-3 Bonhams, New Bond Street #25/R est:25000-35000
£120000 $199200 €180000 View of Crewe Hall, Cheshire, from the South (102x127cm-40x50in) prov.exhib. 10-Jun-3 Christie's, London #46/R est:100000-150000

Sculpture
£6500 $10074 €9750 Bearded man (42cm-17in) grey marble on marble socle. 29-Oct-2 Sotheby's, London #158/R est:5000-7000
Miniatures
£8000 $13120 €11600 William IV, Prince of Orange (5cm-2xin) enamel on copper oval. 3-Jun-3 Christie's, London #35/R est:2500-3500

ENGLISH SCHOOL, 19th C
£5000 $7800 €7500 Cake shop (46x55cm-18x22in) bears sig d.1822. 7-Nov-2 Christie's, Kensington #183/R est:1500-2000
£5519 $8500 €8279 Clearing up (46x76cm-18x30in) prov. 24-Oct-2 Shannon's, Milford #61/R est:3000-5000
£6410 $10000 €9615 Returning hunter (96x140cm-38x55in) 9-Nov-2 Sloan, North Bethesda #562/R est:15000-20000
£6832 $11000 €10248 Full cry (52x61cm-20x24in) panel prov. 18-Jan-3 Sotheby's, New York #976/R est:800-1200
£7927 $13000 €11891 Towpath of the Thames with a view of Richmond Hill beyond (26x35cm-10x14in) 30-May-3 Christie's, Rockefeller NY #55/R est:6000-8000
£12195 $20000 €17683 Portrait of the Bark Mary Edson, Dover Harbour and Castle off the English coast (48x74cm-19x29in) 8-Jun-3 Skinner, Boston #122/R est:3000-5000
£12500 $20000 €18750 Lady Broughton and the three Tarleton sisters in the drawing room (51x71cm-20x28in) 14-May-3 Butterfields, San Francisco #1138/R est:3000-5000
£14000 $21840 €21000 Before the hunt (127x203cm-50x80in) painted c.1810. 26-Mar-3 Hamptons Fine Art, Godalming #258/R est:10000-15000
£24000 $38640 €36000 Portrait of prizefighter, traditionally identified as Dick Cain (76x63cm-30x25in) painted c.1830 prov.exhib. 20-Feb-3 Christie's, London #173/R est:15000
£27000 $42660 €40500 View of the Thames with the Savoy Palace and Somerset House (77x128cm-30x50in) prov. 26-Nov-2 Christie's, London #60/R est:15000-20000

Sculpture
£17037 $27600 €24704 Lady Wellington around the north foreland from the north (9x24cm-4x9in) col engraved scrimshaw sperm whale tooth. 22-May-3 Sotheby's, New York #755

Works on paper
£750 $1162 €1125 Gypsy girl (35x28cm-14x11in) bears sig.d.1868 W/C bodycol. 3-Dec-2 Sotheby's, Olympia #95/R

ENGLISH SCHOOL, 20th C
Sculpture
£2800 $4508 €4200 Sailors (41cm-16in) i. bronze two prov. 20-Feb-3 Christie's, London #61/R
Works on paper
£20000 $32200 €30000 Orchids (26x18cm-10x7in) W/C 67 folio. 7-May-3 Sotheby's, London #30/R est:20000-30000

ENGLISH, Frank F (1854-1922) American
£13376 $21000 €20064 Country landscape with figures conversing beside a horse drawn cart (61x91cm-24x36in) s. prov. 14-Dec-2 Weschler, Washington #658/R est:2000-4000

Works on paper
£1090 $1700 €1635 Gentleman and a lady conversing beside a stone house (46x68cm-18x27in) s. gouache W/C. 12-Apr-3 Weschler, Washington #561/R est:2500-3500
£1146 $1800 €1719 Figure on a country road (25x36cm-10x14in) s.i. W/C. 23-Nov-2 Jackson's, Cedar Falls #73/R est:1400-1600
£1304 $2100 €1956 Haying scene with horse and figures (41x81cm-16x32in) s. W/C. 22-Feb-3 Brunk, Ashville #789/R
£1806 $2800 €2709 Horsecart in the fields (75x49cm-30x19in) s. W/C. 8-Dec-2 Freeman, Philadelphia #108/R est:2500-4000
£2083 $3250 €3125 Boy with horse and pony outside a blacksmith shop (43x58cm-17x23in) s. W/C. 18-Sep-2 Alderfer's, Hatfield #325/R est:3500-4500

ENGLISH, James (1916-1988) British
£317 $526 €450 Beach water, Co. Sligo (27x12cm-11x5in) s. canvasboard. 10-Jun-3 James Adam, Dublin #255/R
£1301 $2043 €1900 Still life with pigeon's feathers (31x25cm-12x10in) s.i.d.01 verso canvasboard. 15-Apr-3 De Veres Art Auctions, Dublin #100x est:1000-1500
£1319 $2098 €1900 Checking the girths (46x61cm-18x24in) s. i.d.1981 verso. 29-Apr-3 Whyte's, Dublin #122/R est:2000-2500
£1384 $2158 €2200 Canal, Venice (41x30cm-16x12in) s. 17-Sep-2 Whyte's, Dublin #220/R est:2000-2500

ENGLISH, Kim (1957-) American
£1948 $3000 €2922 Breakfast (46x56cm-18x22in) 25-Oct-2 Morris & Whiteside, Hilton Head Island #117 est:3000-4000
£2922 $4500 €4383 Valencia, Spain (69x61cm-27x24in) 25-Oct-2 Morris & Whiteside, Hilton Head Island #105 est:4500-5000

ENGLISH, Simon (1959-) British

£1500 $2310 €2250 Box 2. Box deep 3. Box deep 4. Wall 2. s.d.92 oil on PVC rigid variable sizes prov. 23-Oct-2 Christie's, London #230/R est:1500 2500

ENGLUND, Lars (1933-) Swedish

Works on paper

£1313 $2114 €1970 Untitled (30x49cm-12x19in) mixed media black plastic prov. 7-May-3 AB Stockholms Auktionsverk #1079/R est:6000-7000 (S.KR 17000)

ENGMAN, Harald (1903-1968) Danish

£313 $498 €460 Street at night (51x41cm-20x16in) s.d.1941. 27-Feb-3 Hagelstam, Helsinki #958
£339 $525 €509 Self portrait in front of bookcase (40x30cm-16x12in) s.d.31. 1-Oct-2 Rasmussen, Copenhagen #278/R (D.KR 4000)
£360 $562 €540 Villebille and Hordis (34x48cm-13x19in) s. i.stretcher. 11-Nov-2 Rasmussen, Vejle #34/R (D.KR 4200)
£423 $651 €635 Interior scene with figures at cafe (30x42cm-12x17in) s/. 23-Oct-2 Kunsthallen, Copenhagen #28/R (D.KR 5000)
£677 $1050 €1016 Man and woman at a cafe (44x36cm-17x14in) s. 1-Oct-2 Rasmussen, Copenhagen #281/R (D.KR 8000)
£930 $1432 €1395 Street fight (40x35cm-16x14in) s.d.1933 panel. 23-Oct-2 Kunsthallen, Copenhagen #29/R (D.KR 11000)
£933 $1483 €1400 A clown - Buster Larsen (27x36cm-11x14in) s.d.1963 masonite. 29-Apr-3 Kunsthallen, Copenhagen #297/R (D.KR 10000)
£957 $1550 €1388 Figures in shine of street lamps, Nyboder (37x47cm-15x19in) s. 24-May-3 Rasmussen, Havnen #4001/R (D.KR 10000)
£972 $1497 €1458 Evening street scene from the corner of Gothersgade (40x55cm-16x22in) s.d.1934 panel. 23-Oct-2 Kunsthallen, Copenhagen #144/R est:8000 (D.KR 11500)
£1586 $2521 €2379 Evening in Norre Voldgate with musician (30x40cm-12x16in) s. masonite. 29-Apr-3 Kunsthallen, Copenhagen #284/R est:10000 (D.KR 17000)
£1691 $2604 €2537 The disgrace tombstone (40x30cm-16x12in) s.i.d.1941 lit. 23-Oct-2 Kunsthallen, Copenhagen #121/R est:20000 (D.KR 20000)
£1775 $2734 €2663 Big expectation - a mother's dream (40x30cm-16x12in) s.i.d.1941 lit. 23-Oct-2 Kunsthallen, Copenhagen #150/R est:20000 (D.KR 21000)
£2425 $3856 €3638 Evening at Nyboder (30x40cm-12x16in) s. masonite. 29-Apr-3 Kunsthallen, Copenhagen #290/R est:10000 (D.KR 26000)
£3043 $4686 €4565 Water from the trenches (73x60cm-29x24in) s. exhib.lit. 23-Oct-2 Kunsthallen, Copenhagen #35/R est:35000 (D.KR 36000)
£3291 $5232 €4937 People's friend (65x50cm-26x20in) s.d.39 exhib. 26-Feb-3 Kunsthallen, Copenhagen #323/R est:35000 (D.KR 36000)

Works on paper

£279 $441 €419 The beggar (70x36cm-28x14in) W/C Indian ink pencil. 1-Apr-3 Rasmussen, Copenhagen #621 (D.KR 3000)
£465 $734 €698 Nude couple dancing (65x49cm-26x19in) s. W/C Indian ink pencil. 1-Apr-3 Rasmussen, Copenhagen #594/R (D.KR 5000)
£604 $954 €906 Female model standing, man in foreground (74x54cm-29x21in) s.d.1923 W/C pencil. 1-Apr-3 Rasmussen, Copenhagen #596/R (D.KR 6500)
£929 $1468 €1394 Night-mare, battle with death (64x41cm-25x16in) s.d.1923 W/C Indian ink pencil. 1-Apr-3 Rasmussen, Copenhagen #39/R (D.KR 10000)

ENGONOPOULOS, Nikos (1910-1985) Greek

£55000 $85250 €82500 Poet in Piraeus (60x50cm-24x20in) s.d.51 prov.exhib.lit. 2-Oct-2 Sotheby's, London #59/R est:30000-50000

ENGSTROM, Albert (1869-1940) Swedish

£1074 $1741 €1611 Archipelago, early spring (73x98cm-29x39in) s. 3-Feb-3 Lilla Bukowskis, Stockholm #197 est:20000 (S.KR 15000)

Works on paper

£260 $414 €390 Old man with rake (35x25cm-14x10in) s. i.verso chl Indian ink. 2-Mar-3 Uppsala Auktionskammare, Uppsala #85 (S.KR 3500)
£297 $473 €446 Visit from the Bishop (25x36cm-10x14in) s. i.verso Indian ink. 2-Mar-3 Uppsala Auktionskammare, Uppsala #87 (S.KR 4000)

ENGSTROM, Leander (1886-1927) Swedish

£461 $715 €692 Mountain landscape in hazy sunshine (32x41cm-13x16in) s. panel. 8-Dec-2 Uppsala Auktionskammare, Uppsala #200/R (S.KR 6500)
£1467 $2362 €2201 Mountain rapids (53x63cm-21x25in) s. panel. 7-May-3 AB Stockholms Auktionsverk #838/R est:20000-25000 (S.KR 19000)
£3089 $4973 €4634 Norrforsen - waterfall, midsummer evening (40x52cm-16x20in) s.d.1924 panel exhib.lit. 7-May-3 AB Stockholms Auktionsverk #912/R est:50000-60000 (S.KR 40000)
£7336 $11811 €11004 Mountain landscape (40x52cm-16x20in) s.d.1925 panel. 7-May-3 AB Stockholms Auktionsverk #703/R est:50000-60000 (S.KR 95000)
£10161 $15851 €15242 Still life of roses (50x37cm-20x15in) s. 6-Nov-2 AB Stockholms Auktionsverk #546/R est:125000-150000 (S.KR 145000)
£17490 $27635 €26235 The artist's wife Maria (61x43cm-24x17in) s.d.1915 exhib. 28-Apr-3 Bukowskis, Stockholm #160/R est:175000-200000 (S.KR 230000)
£23234 $36710 €34851 Fjord landscape from Lofoten, summer (96x80cm-38x31in) s.d.1916 panel. 1-Apr-3 Rasmussen, Copenhagen #46/R est:75000-125000 (D.KR 250000)
£32936 $51381 €49404 Woman embroidering (83x68cm-33x27in) s.d.1918. 5-Nov-2 Bukowskis, Stockholm #57/R est:300000-400000 (S.KR 470000)

Works on paper

£631 $984 €947 Man with dark skin wearing a bathing cap (20x15cm-8x6in) s.i.d.25/8 22 W/C. 5-Nov-2 Bukowskis, Stockholm #56/R (S.KR 9000)
£3924 $6122 €5886 Sketch for The park (123x87cm-48x34in) gouache lit. 5-Nov-2 Bukowskis, Stockholm #67/R est:40000-50000 (S.KR 56000)
£57795 $91316 €86693 Ode to Norrland I-III - or - Anthem to the wilderness (65x77cm-26x30in) gouache htd. tempera triptych executed 1921 prov.exhib.lit. 28-Apr-3 Bukowskis, Stockholm #154/R est:800000-1000000 (S.KR 760000)

ENJOLRAS, Delphin (1857-1945) French

£1268 $2041 €1800 Portrait d'elegante. s.d.1890. 11-May-3 Thierry & Lannon, Brest #355 est:800-1000
£2628 $4126 €4100 Le temps qui passe (73x50cm-29x20in) s. 22-Nov-2 Millon & Associes, Paris #55/R
£4397 $6816 €6596 Le boudoir (54x37cm-21x15in) s. paper on cardboard. 3-Dec-2 Bukowskis, Stockholm #333/R est:25000-30000 (S.KR 62000)
£6081 $9486 €9000 Reading (37x54cm-15x21in) s. 26-Mar-3 Millon & Associes, Paris #64/R
£10256 $16103 €16000 The (60x73cm-24x29in) s. 16-Dec-2 Rabourdin & Choppin de Janvry, Paris #77/R est:24000
£10897 $17109 €17000 Seance de lecture (46x55cm-18x22in) s. 22-Nov-2 Millon & Associes, Paris #57/R est:3000-3500
£11200 $17584 €16800 Le boudoir (35x26cm-14x10in) s. panel. 16-Dec-2 Bonhams, Bury St Edmunds #486 est:4000-6000
£13462 $21135 €21000 Soir sur la terrasse (46x55cm-18x22in) s. 22-Nov-2 Millon & Associes, Paris #56/R est:3000-3500
£16026 $25160 €25000 Soiree au bord de lac (60x80cm-24x31in) s. oval. 15-Dec-2 Lombrail & Teucquam, Paris #8/R

Works on paper

£2590 $4144 €3600 Elegante devant sa coiffeuse (59x42cm-23x17in) s. pastel. 13-May-3 Vanderkindere, Brussels #73 est:1000-1500
£3000 $4680 €4500 Seductive scent (71x51cm-28x20in) s. pastel. 5-Nov-2 Bonhams, New Bond Street #111/R est:2000-3000
£7183 $11565 €10200 Nu a sa toilette (71x57cm-28x22in) s. pastel. 11-May-3 Thierry & Lannon, Brest #60/R est:8000-10000
£7319 $12003 €10100 Jeune femme aux chrysanthemes (72x54cm-28x21in) s. pastel exec.c.1909. 27-May-3 Artcurial Briest, Paris #104/R est:10000-12000
£8000 $13120 €12000 Le bouquet (44cm-17in circular) s. pastel. 3-Jun-3 Sotheby's, London #175/R est:6000-8000
£13000 $21320 €19500 Un monent de reflexion (71x52cm-28x20in) s. pastel. 3-Jun-3 Sotheby's, London #177/R est:12000-18000
£13406 $21986 €18500 Jeune femme au tulle vert (72x53cm-28x21in) s. pastel exec.c.1908. 27-May-3 Artcurial Briest, Paris #102/R est:10000-12000
£14865 $23189 €22000 Jeune femme a sa coiffeuse (71x52cm-28x20in) s. pastel. 30-Mar-3 Anaf, Lyon #97 est:25000
£16000 $26240 €24000 La lettre (71x52cm-28x20in) s. pastel. 3-Jun-3 Sotheby's, London #178/R est:12000-18000

ENNEKING, John J (1841-1916) American

£477 $750 €716 Landscape (8x13cm-3x5in) board prov. 23-Nov-2 Pook & Pook, Downington #290b/R
£541 $850 €812 Landscape (15x13cm-6x5in) board prov. 23-Nov-2 Pook & Pook, Downington #290e/R
£828 $1300 €1242 Two ladies picnicking along a river (10x23cm-4x9in) board prov. 23-Nov-2 Pook & Pook, Downington #290a/R
£828 $1300 €1242 Landscape with two figures walking (23x13cm-9x5in) board. 23-Nov-2 Pook & Pook, Downington #290d/R
£892 $1400 €1338 Fisherman with house and sailboats in the background (8x13cm-3x5in) s. board with sketch of sailboats two prov. 23-Nov-2 Pook & Pook, Downington #290/R est:800-1000
£1314 $2050 €1971 Twilight landscape with a flock of sheep grazing (18x23cm-7x9in) s.d.81 board. 28-Mar-3 Aspire, Cleveland #1/R est:2000-4000
£1875 $3000 €2719 In the clearing, twilight (20x25cm-8x10in) s. 16-May-3 Skinner, Boston #72/R est:3000-5000
£2692 $4200 €4038 Mountain landscape with waterfall (67x102cm-26x40in) s. canvas on aluminum. 14-Sep-2 Weschler, Washington #618/R est:6000-8000
£2848 $4500 €4272 Spring landscape (20x30cm-8x12in) s.i.d.1903 board prov. 24-Apr-3 Shannon's, Milford #6/R est:2500-3500

£3437 $5500 €4984 Autumn twilight (46x56cm-18x22in) s. 16-May-3 Skinner, Boston #252/R est:3000-5000
£3571 $5500 €5357 Sunset (25x41cm-10x16in) s. panel. 24-Oct-2 Shannon's, Milford #156/R est:3000-5000
£3899 $6200 €5849 Autumn (51x61cm-20x24in) s.d.98 s.i.verso prov. 1-Mar-3 North East Auctions, Portsmouth #732/R est:5000-8000
£5806 $9000 €8709 Sunset river landscape, old bridge (46x61cm-18x24in) indis.sig. prov. 29-Oct-2 John Moran, Pasadena #762 est:5000-8000
£8805 $14000 €13208 Mountain vista with pines (64x76cm-25x30in) s. 1-Mar-3 North East Auctions, Portsmouth #733/R est:5000-8000
£13376 $21000 €20064 Landscape, late summer (64x76cm-25x30in) s. 22-Nov-2 Skinner, Boston #229/R est:18000-22000

ENNEKING, Joseph Elliot (1881-1942) American
£710 $1100 €1065 Breezy day (20x25cm-8x10in) s. canvasboard. 7-Dec-2 South Bay, Long Island #153a/R
£1350 $2200 €2025 Old apple orchard (28x36cm-11x14in) s.d.1914 board. 2-Feb-3 Grogan, Boston #25 est:800-1200
£8280 $13000 €12420 Hollyhocks garden, Mystic, Connecticut (64x76cm-25x30in) s. 10-Dec-2 Doyle, New York #67/R est:12000-18000

ENNEKING, Joseph Elliot (attrib) (1881-1942) American
£1108 $1750 €1662 Winter landscape with church steeple at center (33x48cm-13x19in) board. 26-Apr-3 Thomaston Place, Thomaston #122

ENNESS, Augustus William (1876-1948) British
£250 $385 €375 North African street scene (23x33cm-9x13in) s. board. 24-Oct-2 Richardson & Smith, Whitby #485
£280 $417 €420 Bathers on rocks, cove beyond (30x40cm-12x16in) s. 27-Jun-2 Greenslade Hunt, Taunton #765
£560 $874 €840 Early morning view with fishing boats (24x35cm-9x14in) indis.sig.d. 10-Sep-2 David Duggleby, Scarborough #351/R
£600 $936 €900 River Dwryd (41x51cm-16x20in) s. 26-Mar-3 Sotheby's, Olympia #163/R
£650 $1034 €975 Whitby Harbour (25x36cm-10x14in) s. 6-Mar-3 Christie's, Kensington #493/R
£1300 $2041 €1950 Gypsy camp (26x36cm-10x14in) s.d.1912. 21-Nov-2 Tennants, Leyburn #821 est:300-400
£1500 $2355 €2250 Arab town scene, with figures by a pool (51x61cm-20x24in) s.d.1911. 21-Nov-2 Tennants, Leyburn #820 est:500-700

ENNESS, Augustus William (attrib) (1876-1948) British
£300 $462 €450 Bathers (40x52cm-16x20in) 22-Oct-2 Bonhams, Ipswich #284

ENNION, Eric (1900-1981) British
Works on paper
£250 $415 €363 White-spotted bluethroat, Northumberland (15x18cm-6x7in) s. pencil W/C prov. 12-Jun-3 Christie's, Kensington #154

ENNIS, George Pearse (1884-1936) American
£4112 $6250 €6168 New England fishing village (64x76cm-25x30in) s. board. 17-Aug-2 North East Auctions, Portsmouth #1096/R est:3000-5000

ENOCK, Arthur Henry (fl.1869-1910) British
Works on paper
£300 $492 €450 Off Dartmouth, a three-master entering harbour under tow (34x51cm-13x20in) s. W/C. 3-Jun-3 Bearnes, Exeter #417
£364 $560 €546 Dartmouth (41x62cm-16x24in) s. W/C. 4-Sep-2 Dunbar Sloane, Wellington #80 est:500-1000 (NZ.D 1200)
£420 $668 €630 Peep at the Channel, Torquay (35x51cm-14x20in) s. W/C. 30-Apr-3 Hampton & Littlewood, Exeter #460/R
£480 $792 €696 Beach scene with children to the foreground (33x51cm-13x20in) s.d.1887 W/C bodycol. 3-Jul-3 Duke & Son, Dorchester #136/R
£650 $1073 €943 Cattle by a river landscape (33x53cm-13x21in) s.d.1888 W/C. 3-Jul-3 Duke & Son, Dorchester #55

ENOTRIO (1920-1989) Argentinian
£685 $1068 €1000 Landscape in Calabria (60x80cm-24x31in) s. board. 10-Apr-3 Finarte Semenzato, Rome #132/R
£685 $1068 €1000 Dead train line (50x70cm-20x28in) s. s.i.verso board. 10-Apr-3 Finarte Semenzato, Rome #158/R
£769 $1208 €1200 Marine (40x60cm-16x24in) s. s.i.verso. 21-Nov-2 Finarte, Rome #215
£1218 $1912 €1900 Landscape in Calabria (80x100cm-31x39in) s. s.i.d.1964 verso prov.exhib. 21-Nov-2 Finarte, Rome #220/R

ENROTH, Erik (1917-1975) Finnish
£458 $750 €700 Element (80x69cm-31x27in) i. 9-Feb-3 Bukowskis, Helsinki #225/R
£570 $900 €900 Composition (36x71cm-14x28in) s.d.1963. 30-Nov-2 Hagelstam, Helsinki #167/R
£1197 $1927 €1700 Composition with guitar and sword (91x129cm-36x51in) board. 10-May-3 Bukowskis, Helsinki #208/R est:2000-3000

ENSLIN, George (1919-1972) South African
£257 $406 €386 Shacks scattered along a dirt road (39x49cm-15x19in) s.d.57 board. 1-Apr-3 Stephan Welz, Johannesburg #214 est:800-1200 (SA.R 3200)

ENSOR, James (1860-1949) Belgian
£1528 $2429 €2200 Moulin a Slykens. lit. 29-Apr-3 Campo & Campo, Antwerp #110/R est:2500-3000
£12000 $18480 €18000 Nature morte a la raie (16x21cm-6x8in) panel painted c.1890-95 prov. 22-Oct-2 Sotheby's, London #173/R est:14000-18000
£43478 $70000 €65217 Une symphonie musicale - vision Claire (37x41cm-15x16in) s. prov.exhib.lit. 7-May-3 Sotheby's, New York #141/R est:40000-60000
£100000 $164000 €150000 Masques regardant une tortue (22x37cm-9x15in) s. canvas on panel prov.exhib.lit. 4-Feb-3 Christie's, London #251/R est:80000
Prints
£1887 $3000 €2831 Bad doctors (18x25cm-7x10in) s.i.d.95 etching. 2-May-3 Sotheby's, New York #144/R est:3000-5000
£2000 $3120 €3000 Les mauvais medecins (17x25cm-7x10in) etching. 10-Oct-2 Sotheby's, London #33/R est:2500-3500
£2113 $3507 €3000 Diables rossant anges et arcanges - le combat des demons (26x31cm-10x12in) s.i.d. etching. 14-Jun-3 Hauswedell & Nolte, Hamburg #1140/R est:4000
£2138 $3336 €3400 La mort poursuivant le truopeau des humains (24x18cm-9x7in) etching. 11-Oct-2 Winterberg, Heidelberg #1055/R est:2200
£2358 $3750 €3537 Scoundrels (12x8cm-5x3in) s.i.d. hand col etching. 2-May-3 Sotheby's, New York #148 est:2500-3500
£2516 $4000 €3774 Cathedral (24x19cm-9x7in) s.d. etching. 2-May-3 Sotheby's, New York #147/R est:4000-6000
£2800 $4368 €4200 Les patineurs (17x24cm-7x9in) s.i.d.1889 etching. 10-Oct-2 Sotheby's, London #34/R est:1500-2000
£2817 $4676 €4000 Grande vue de Mariakerke (22x27cm-9x11in) s.i.d. s.i. verso etching. 14-Jun-3 Hauswedell & Nolte, Hamburg #1139/R est:3500
£3459 $5362 €5500 Mon portrait Squelettise (12x8cm-5x3in) s.i. etching lit. 5-Oct-2 De Vuyst, Lokeren #132/R est:3500-4500
£3459 $5500 €5189 Death chasing the flock of mortals (24x18cm-9x7in) etching. 2-May-3 Sotheby's, New York #146/R est:4000-6000
£3662 $6079 €5200 Les patineurs (18x24cm-7x9in) s.d. i. verso etching. 14-Jun-3 Hauswedell & Nolte, Hamburg #1141/R est:7000
£3800 $5890 €5700 Le bal fantastique (22x28cm-9x11in) s.i.d.1889 hand col etching W/C. 3-Dec-2 Christie's, London #117a/R est:4000-6000
£3873 $6430 €5500 Cortege infrenal - diables se rendant au Sabbat (22x27cm-9x11in) s.i.d.1887 s.i.d. verso etching. 14-Jun-3 Hauswedell & Nolte, Hamburg #1138/R est:3500
£4088 $6500 €6132 Devils thrashing angels and archangels (26x31cm-10x12in) s.d. etching. 2-May-3 Sotheby's, New York #134/R est:3000-5000
£5205 $8121 €7600 Peste dessous, peste dessus, peste partout (19x29cm-7x11in) s.d.1904 estampe etching. 14-Apr-3 Horta, Bruxelles #147/R est:2500-3500
£7547 $12000 €11321 Avarice (10x15cm-4x6in) s.i.d.1904 hand col etching. 2-May-3 Sotheby's, New York #152/R est:6000-8000
£8333 $13250 €12000 Les bons juges. s. d.1894 num.3 verso etching lit. 29-Apr-3 Campo & Campo, Antwerp #113/R est:4000-5000
£10417 $16563 €15000 L'entree du Christ a Bruxelles. s.d.1898 etching lit. 29-Apr-3 Campo & Campo, Antwerp #114/R est:3000-4000
£10692 $17000 €16038 Entry of Christ into Brussels (25x36cm-10x14in) s.i. etching. 2-May-3 Sotheby's, New York #151/R est:6000-8000
£11511 $18417 €16000 Assemblee dans un parc (9x14cm-4x6in) s.d.1891 etching prov.lit. 17-May-3 De Vuyst, Lokeren #171/R est:15000-17000
£16352 $26000 €24528 Hop-frog's revenge (36x26cm-14x10in) s.i. hand col etching. 2-May-3 Sotheby's, New York #150/R est:8000-10000
Works on paper
£818 $1275 €1300 Etude (22x17cm-9x7in) s. graphite dr prov.exhib.lit. 11-Oct-2 Binoche, Paris #118
£1548 $2400 €2322 Figure studies (22x17cm-9x7in) s. brush black ink on board. 26-Sep-2 Christie's, Rockefeller NY #517/R est:3000-4000
£1761 $2747 €2800 Etude (22x17cm-9x7in) s.d.1883 graphite dr prov.exhib.lit. 11-Oct-2 Binoche, Paris #117/R
£4575 $7366 €7000 L'artiste a son chevalet. Augusta Boogaerts, son amie (33x24cm-13x9in) s. sanguine col crayon double-sided. 14-Jan-3 Vanderkindere, Brussels #475 est:2000-3000
£13103 $20966 €19000 Une reine, une tour et un pion (19x27cm-7x11in) s.i. W/C col pencil exec.c.1902-1903 prov.exhib.lit. 15-Mar-3 De Vuyst, Lokeren #435/R
£16667 $25833 €26000 Le pecheur - fisherman (74x60cm-29x24in) s. init. pastel executed c.1881-1900 prov.exhib.lit. 3-Dec-2 Christie's, Amsterdam #227/R est:15000-20000

ENTWISTLE, W John (20th C) British
Works on paper
£550 $880 €825 The Rock, self portraits (38x94cm-15x37in) s. black ink felt pen dr. 13-May-3 Sotheby's, Olympia #187/R
£650 $1040 €975 Hear evil-see evil-speak evil (27x109cm-11x43in) black ink dr. 13-May-3 Sotheby's, Olympia #343/R

£800 $1280 €1200 Eric Clapton (55x76cm-22x30in) s.d.2000 ink felt pens dr. 13-May-3 Sotheby's, Olympia #15/R
£800 $1280 €1200 Self portrait and portrait of Roger Daltrey (41x50cm-16x20in) s. black ink dr. 13-May-3 Sotheby's, Olympia #267/R
£800 $1280 €1200 Sir Henry Entwistle, the silent knight (53x71cm-21x28in) s. ink felt pen dr. 13-May-3 Sotheby's, Olympia #351/R
£850 $1360 €1275 Ahab Entwistle (54x75cm-21x30in) s. ink felt pen dr. 13-May-3 Sotheby's, Olympia #92/R est:600-800
£900 $1440 €1350 Wild Bill Daltrey (53x71cm-21x28in) s. ink felt pen dr. 13-May-3 Sotheby's, Olympia #91/R est:600-800
£1200 $1920 €1800 Jimi Hendrix (40x29cm-16x11in) black ink. 13-May-3 Sotheby's, Olympia #95/R est:500-600
£1200 $1920 €1800 Sherlock Townshend (53x71cm-21x28in) s. ink felt pen dr. 13-May-3 Sotheby's, Olympia #352/R est:600-800
£1300 $2080 €1950 Jimmy Page (55x76cm-22x30in) s.d.2000 ink felt pen dr. 13-May-3 Sotheby's, Olympia #16/R est:600-800
£1400 $2240 €2100 Bill (53x71cm-21x28in) s. ink felt pen dr. 13-May-3 Sotheby's, Olympia #188/R est:600-800
£1600 $2560 €2400 Jimi Hendrix (43x58cm-17x23in) s.d.2000 ink felt pen dr. 13-May-3 Sotheby's, Olympia #17/R est:600-800
£1600 $2560 €2400 Long John Moon (53x71cm-21x28in) s. ink felt pen dr. 13-May-3 Sotheby's, Olympia #93/R est:600-800
£2000 $3200 €3000 Sir Pierre Le Conk Townshend (55x75cm-22x30in) s. ink felt pen dr. 13-May-3 Sotheby's, Olympia #90/R est:600-800
£3600 $5760 €5400 Vindaloo Who (58x78cm-23x31in) s.i. ink felt pen ballpoint dr. 13-May-3 Sotheby's, Olympia #45/R est:1500-2000

ENWRIGHT, J J (?) ?
£962 $1500 €1443 Coastal harbour (61x76cm-24x30in) s. 20-Sep-2 Freeman, Philadelphia #71/R est:700-1000
£1731 $2700 €2597 New England dock scene (70x96cm-28x38in) s. 20-Sep-2 Sloan, North Bethesda #467/R est:1500-2500

ENZINGER, Hans (1889-1972) Austrian
£621 $993 €900 Dahlias and Asters in jug (68x50cm-27x20in) s.d.1957 board. 11-Mar-3 Dorotheum, Vienna #118/R

ENZLER, Albert (1882-1974) Swiss
£300 $475 €450 Alpine journey in front of mountain landscape (18x50cm-7x20in) s. gouache board on panel. 26-Nov-2 Hans Widmer, St Gallen #1449 (S.FR 700)

Works on paper
£300 $475 €450 Landscape with farm buildings and alpine journey (19x57cm-7x22in) s. gouache board on panel. 26-Nov-2 Hans Widmer, St Gallen #1448 (S.FR 700)
£755 $1223 €1095 Alpine scene (24x69cm-9x27in) s.i. W/C bodycol board prov. 24-May-3 Galerie Gloggner, Luzern #29/R (S.FR 1600)

EPINAT, Fleury (1764-1830) French

Works on paper
£1081 $1686 €1600 Paysage montagneux (31x46cm-12x18in) s. W/C. 30-Mar-3 Anaf, Lyon #369
£3086 $5000 €4629 Coastal landscape (77x56cm-30x22in) s. chk pen ink wash prov. 22-Jan-3 Christie's, Rockefeller NY #101a/R est:6000

EPP, R (1834-1910) German
£450 $698 €675 Tea time, mother and two children saying grace (25x19cm-10x7in) 25-Sep-2 Wintertons, Lichfield #575/R

EPP, Rudolf (1834-1910) German
£1100 $1793 €1650 First lesson (20x23cm-8x9in) s. panel. 13-Feb-3 Christie's, Kensington #202/R est:800-1200
£1703 $2657 €2555 Mother love (34x42cm-13x17in) s. 6-Nov-2 Dobiaschofsky, Bern #498/R est:6000 (S.FR 3900)
£2013 $3200 €3020 Breakfast with the cat (57x45cm-22x18in) s. prov. 5-Mar-3 Christie's, Rockefeller NY #64/R est:4000-6000
£3831 $5709 €5747 Mother love (108x88cm-43x35in) s.d.69 prov. 27-Aug-2 Christie's, Melbourne #106/R est:10000-15000 (A.D 10000)
£5031 $8000 €7547 Father arriving home (66x56cm-26x22in) s.d. 4-May-3 Treadway Gallery, Cincinnati #478/R est:8000-12000
£7500 $11775 €11250 Young girl feeding a lamb (96x66cm-38x26in) s. 19-Nov-2 Bonhams, New Bond Street #38/R est:7000-10000

EPPENS, Francisco (20th C) Mexican?
£989 $1583 €1434 Caravelas (70x50cm-28x20in) s. 15-May-3 Louis Morton, Mexico #11/R est:14000-16000 (M.P 16000)

EPPENS, William H (1885-?) American
£552 $850 €828 Dunes (41x51cm-16x20in) s. painted c.1930. 8-Sep-2 Treadway Gallery, Cincinnati #624/R
£1935 $3000 €2903 Purple shadows (36x46cm-14x18in) s. painted c.1930. 8-Dec-2 Toomey, Oak Park #731/R est:1000-2000

EPPER, Ignaz (1892-1969) Swiss
£1179 $1910 €2088 Lily (46x38cm-18x15in) mono.d.1950 prov. 26-May-3 Sotheby's, Zurich #118/R est:2500-3500 (S.FR 2500)
£7424 $11655 €11136 River (52x44cm-20x17in) mono. 25-Nov-2 Sotheby's, Zurich #58/R est:20000-30000 (S.FR 17000)
£20601 $32549 €30902 Industrial landscape with train track. (61x50cm-24x20in) mono. painted c.1919 double-sided prov. 26-Nov-2 Phillips, Zurich #61/R est:30000-40000 (S.FR 48000)

Works on paper
£262 $409 €393 Tessin landscape (28x40cm-11x16in) W/C. 6-Nov-2 Dobiaschofsky, Bern #499/R (S.FR 600)
£292 $461 €438 River estuary with boat harbour (25x40cm-10x16in) s.d.36 pen W/C. 26-Nov-2 Hans Widmer, St Gallen #1101 (S.FR 680)
£343 $542 €515 Female healer (75x45cm-30x18in) chl. 29-Nov-2 Zofingen, Switzerland #2863 (S.FR 800)
£370 $577 €555 Gypsy caravan (19x27cm-7x11in) mixed media. 16-Sep-2 Philippe Schuler, Zurich #3191/R (S.FR 850)
£652 $1011 €978 Untitled man's portrait (43x38cm-17x15in) s. chl. 9-Dec-2 Philippe Schuler, Zurich #3535 (S.FR 1500)
£696 $1078 €1044 Untitled fisherman with nets on boat (26x34cm-10x13in) s. col chk chl. 9-Dec-2 Philippe Schuler, Zurich #3540 (S.FR 1600)
£802 $1283 €1203 Portrait of man with pince-nez (45x40cm-18x16in) s. chl. 17-Mar-3 Philippe Schuler, Zurich #4306 est:2000-3000 (S.FR 1700)
£870 $1348 €1305 Untitled seated female nude (51x32cm-20x13in) i. verso chl. 9-Dec-2 Philippe Schuler, Zurich #3538 est:2000-3000 (S.FR 2000)
£1217 $1887 €1826 Untitled parakeet and standing nude in tent (49x40cm-19x16in) bears mono. i. verso chl. 9-Dec-2 Philippe Schuler, Zurich #3537 est:2000-3000 (S.FR 2800)
£1226 $1962 €1839 Figures in boat (24x19cm-9x7in) s. Indian ink wash chl wax. 17-Mar-3 Philippe Schuler, Zurich #4312 est:400-600 (S.FR 2600)
£1321 $2113 €1982 Man walking and man reclining in lake landscape (39x56cm-15x22in) s. i. verso chl. 17-Mar-3 Philippe Schuler, Zurich #4309/R est:2000-3000 (S.FR 2800)
£1435 $2224 €2153 Untitled couple in landscape (47x42cm-19x17in) i. chl. 9-Dec-2 Philippe Schuler, Zurich #3539/R est:2000-3000 (S.FR 3300)
£1651 $2642 €2477 Woman wearing head scarf (46x31cm-18x12in) s. chl. 17-Mar-3 Philippe Schuler, Zurich #4310 est:2000-3000 (S.FR 3500)
£2123 $3396 €3185 Figure composition (45x47cm-18x19in) s. chl. 17-Mar-3 Philippe Schuler, Zurich #4305/R est:2000-3000 (S.FR 4500)
£2264 $3623 €3396 Reclining man in landscape (43x49cm-17x19in) s. chl. 17-Mar-3 Philippe Schuler, Zurich #4307/R est:2000-3000 (S.FR 4800)
£2594 $4151 €3891 Couple in landscape (49x40cm-19x16in) s. i. verso chl. 17-Mar-3 Philippe Schuler, Zurich #4308/R est:2000-3000 (S.FR 5500)

EPSTEIN, Henri (1892-1944) Polish/French
£1258 $1950 €2000 Bateaux a quai (54x73cm-21x29in) s. 30-Oct-2 Artcurial Briest, Paris #17 est:2200-2700
£1773 $2961 €2500 Baigneuses au bord de mer (45x82cm-18x32in) prov. 17-Jun-3 Claude Boisgirard, Paris #52/R est:3000-3500
£1931 $3051 €2800 Silhouette pres d'une grotte (50x65cm-20x26in) s. 4-Apr-3 Tajan, Paris #198
£2308 $3623 €3600 Vase de fleurs des champs (41x33cm-16x13in) s. panel. 12-Dec-2 Rabourdin & Choppin de Janvry, Paris #48/R
£2885 $4529 €4500 Femme assise (73x50cm-29x20in) s. painted c.1920. 12-Dec-2 Rabourdin & Choppin de Janvry, Paris #73/R
£3819 $6073 €5500 Maisons au bord d'un canal (54x65cm-21x26in) s. 29-Apr-3 Artcurial Briest, Paris #233/R est:6000-7000
£4403 $6824 €7000 Carriere pres d'epernon (60x73cm-24x29in) s. painted c.1937. 30-Oct-2 Artcurial Briest, Paris #16/R est:5000-6000
£5414 $8446 €8500 Nature morte au gibier (81x101cm-32x40in) s. 6-Nov-2 Claude Boisgirard, Paris #20 est:9000-10000
£6289 $9748 €10000 Les couturieres (72x90cm-28x35in) s.d.1923 s.verso. 30-Oct-2 Artcurial Briest, Paris #15/R est:10000-15000
£9929 $16582 €14000 Village (73x54cm-29x21in) s. 17-Jun-3 Claude Boisgirard, Paris #51/R est:9000-11000

Works on paper
£823 $1300 €1300 Palais Belle-Ile (40x56cm-16x22in) s.i. W/C. 27-Nov-2 Blanchet, Paris #103/R
£943 $1462 €1500 Scene de marche en Provence (22x28cm-9x11in) s. gouache. 30-Oct-2 Coutau Begarie, Paris #106/R
£1019 $1590 €1600 Village dans la Montagne (38x45cm-15x18in) s. W/C. 6-Nov-2 Claude Boisgirard, Paris #19 est:1500-1800

EPSTEIN, Sir Jacob (1880-1959) British/American

Sculpture
£1700 $2703 €2550 Merton Francis Frankenberg (63cm-25in) s.d. brown pat. bronze executed c.1942-43. 26-Feb-3 Sotheby's, Olympia #267/R est:1000-1500
£2200 $3432 €3300 Lovers on an eagle's back (20cm-8in) s. light brown pat. bronze lit. 27-Mar-3 Christie's, Kensington #452/R est:2500-3500
£2200 $3476 €3190 9th Portrait of Peggy Jean laughing (29cm-11in) dark gold pat bronze incl stand lit. 22-Jul-3 Sotheby's, Olympia #271/R est:2000-3000
£2600 $4108 €3770 Ian (30cm-12in) dark gold pat bronze incl stand lit. 22-Jul-3 Sotheby's, Olympia #270/R est:2000-3000
£2800 $4368 €4200 Third portrait of Kitty (49cm-19in) brown pat. bronze lit. 25-Mar-3 Bonhams, New Bond Street #61/R est:3000-5000
£3000 $4650 €4500 Portrait of Rabindranath Tagore (51cm-20in) s. green pat. bronze lit. 4-Dec-2 Christie's, Kensington #413/R est:2500-3500

£3400 $5304 €5100 Fourth portrait of Peggy Jean (26cm-10in) Bronze brown patina executed c.1920 lit. 12-Sep-2 Sotheby's, Olympia #135/R est:2000-3000
£4194 $6500 €6291 Rani Rama (57cm-22in) green pat. bronze prov.lit. 26-Sep-2 Christie's, Rockefeller NY #603/R est:7000-9000
£4400 $7216 €6600 Mask of Mrs Epstein (27cm-11in) green pat bronze black marble base prov.lit. 3-Jun-3 Sotheby's, Olympia #104/R est:1000-1500
£4500 $7020 €6750 Eighth portrait of Peggy Jean at 2 years and 4 months (27cm-11in) s. dark brown pat. bronze conceived 1921 lit. 27-Mar-3 Christie's, Kensington #449/R est:1500-2500
£7000 $11410 €10500 Eve Deruich (46cm-18in) bronze prov. 28-Jan-3 Henry Adams, Chichester #485/R est:3000-5000
£7362 $12000 €11043 First portrait of Kathleen (47cm-19in) i. green pat. bronze lit. 12-Feb-3 Sotheby's, New York #113/R est:8000-10000
£7500 $11925 €11250 Piccaninny (29cm-11in) s. pale green pat. bronze on plinth lith. 26-Feb-3 Sotheby's, Olympia #269/R est:3000-5000
£7500 $11700 €11250 Albert Einstein (44cm-17in) s. green pat. bronze lit. 25-Mar-3 Bonhams, New Bond Street #59/R est:6000-8000
£8200 $12710 €12300 Nan seated (50cm-20in) green pat. bronze lit. 3-Dec-2 Bonhams, New Bond Street #59/R est:3000-5000
£8500 $13176 €12750 Picanniny (22cm-9in) s. pale green pat. bronze lit. 4-Dec-2 Sotheby's, London #55/R est:2000-3000
£10000 $15600 €15000 Jacob Kramer (64cm-25in) brown pat. bronze lit. 25-Mar-3 Bonhams, New Bond Street #60/R est:10000-15000
£10500 $16275 €15750 Maquette for night (36cm-14in) green brown pat. bronze lit. 3-Dec-2 Bonhams, New Bond Street #65/R est:3000-5000

Works on paper

£400 $624 €600 Landscape with conifer tree (42x56cm-17x22in) s. W/C. 15-Oct-2 Bonhams, Knightsbridge #12/R
£450 $698 €675 Epping forest (35x56cm-14x22in) s. W/C. 25-Sep-2 John Nicholson, Haslemere #888
£597 $950 €896 Reclining nude (45x59cm-18x23in) s. pencil dr. 4-Mar-3 Swann Galleries, New York #282a/R
£608 $948 €912 Portrait of Jackie as a baby (38x43cm-15x17in) s. pencil dr. 17-Sep-2 Peter Webb, Auckland #190/R est:1000-2500 (NZ.D 2000)
£700 $1078 €1050 Reclining female nude (38x56cm-15x22in) s. pencil. 5-Sep-2 Christie's, Kensington #519/R
£800 $1232 €1200 Old Testament figure (56x43cm-22x17in) i.verso pencil W/C. 5-Sep-2 Christie's, Kensington #517/R
£800 $1320 €1160 Irises (56x43cm-22x17in) s. W/C bodycol. 3-Jul-3 Christie's, Kensington #308/R
£1500 $2385 €2250 Reclining nude (36x54cm-14x21in) s. pencil prov. 26-Feb-3 Sotheby's, Olympia #166/R est:800-1200
£1500 $2460 €2250 Epping Forest (55x43cm-22x17in) s. gouache. 3-Jun-3 Sotheby's, Olympia #103/R est:1500-2500
£1600 $2464 €2400 David and Abishag (43x56cm-17x22in) s. pencil W/C. 5-Sep-2 Christie's, Kensington #516/R est:1200-1800
£2000 $3300 €2900 Roses (56x43cm-22x17in) s. W/C bodycol prov. 3-Jul-3 Christie's, Kensington #310/R est:1000-1500
£2200 $3498 €3300 Study of flowers (56x43cm-22x17in) s. W/C gouache. 26-Feb-3 Sotheby's, Olympia #265/R est:2000-3000
£2200 $3674 €3190 Portrait of Jackie, the artist's son (55x43cm-22x17in) s. 24-Jun-3 Bonhams, New Bond Street #33/R est:1500-2000
£2400 $3936 €3600 Portrait of a child (56x43cm-22x17in) s. pencil. 3-Jun-3 Sotheby's, Olympia #105/R est:600-800
£2600 $4108 €3900 Les fleurs du mal (56x43cm-22x17in) s. pencil prov. 27-Nov-2 Sotheby's, Olympia #2/R est:1200-1800
£2800 $4368 €4200 Reclining nude (43x56cm-17x22in) s. pencil exhib. 10-Apr-3 Tennants, Leyburn #916/R est:800-1200

EQUIPO CRONICA (20th C) Spanish

£487 $711 €750 Homage to Picasso (48x63cm-19x25in) s. serigraph. 17-Jun-2 Ansorena, Madrid #255/R

ERBE, Julius (18th C) German

£676 $1054 €1014 Mountain landscape with cattle and geese by house (63x84cm-25x33in) s.d.69. 23-Sep-2 Rasmussen, Vejle #237/R (D.KR 8000)
£1384 $2145 €2200 Upper Inn valley (42x58cm-17x23in) mono. 29-Oct-2 Dorotheum, Vienna #120/R est:2200-2500

ERBEN, Ulrich (1940-) German

£481 $745 €750 Untitled (61x86cm-24x34in) s.d.1972 verso oil over pencil. 3-Dec-2 Lempertz, Koln #120/R
£2174 $3565 €3000 Untitled (130x100cm-51x39in) s.d.1975 verso prov. 28-May-3 Lempertz, Koln #125/R est:3000
£2244 $3478 €3500 Untitled (170x190cm-67x75in) s.d.1989 verso acrylic pigment. 7-Dec-2 Ketterer, Hamburg #701/R est:4000-5000

ERDELY, Francis de (1904-1959) American/Hungarian

£2014 $3223 €2800 Les joueurs de cartes (100x110cm-39x43in) s.d.1926. 13-May-3 Palais de Beaux Arts, Brussels #187/R est:2000-3000
£2207 $3509 €3200 Jeune femme au bain (110x115cm-43x45in) s.d.1928. 4-Mar-3 Palais de Beaux Arts, Brussels #335 est:1250-1750
£22455 $37500 €32560 Figures at a table, lunch time (102x127cm-40x50in) i.verso prov. 17-Jun-3 John Moran, Pasadena #125 est:15000-20000

ERDELYI, Bela (20th C) Hungarian?

£2655 $4141 €3850 River bend (119x100cm-47x39in) s. 12-Apr-3 Mu Terem Galeria, Budapest #203/R est:550000 (H.F 950000)

ERDELYI, Vojtech (1891-1955) Czechoslovakian

£473 $732 €710 Overflowing river (27x46cm-11x18in) tempera painted c.1940. 1-Oct-2 SOGA, Bratislava #40/R est:12000 (SL.K 30000)
£551 $783 €827 Village below mountains (32x40cm-13x16in) painted c.1950. 26-Mar-2 SOGA, Bratislava #73/R (SL.K 35000)

ERDMANN, Axel (1873-1954) Swedish

£340 $564 €493 View from Gothenburg (69x58cm-27x23in) s.d.1915. 16-Jun-3 Lilla Bukowskis, Stockholm #666 (S.KR 4400)
£342 $544 €513 Town scene (57x59cm-22x23in) s.d.1916. 3-Mar-3 Lilla Bukowskis, Stockholm #503 (S.KR 4600)

ERDMANN, Moritz (1845-1919) German

£327 $519 €480 Mountain valley beneath full moon (42x59cm-17x23in) s. 20-Mar-3 Neumeister, Munich #2610

Works on paper

£318 $497 €500 Eastern town with figures by a gateway (38x28cm-15x11in) s. W/C. 6-Nov-2 Vendue Huis, Gravenhage #522/R

ERDMANN, Otto (1834-1905) German

£15000 $24600 €22500 Das rezitativ - recitation (89x110cm-35x43in) s.d.88. 3-Jun-3 Sotheby's, London #34/R est:15000-20000

ERDTMANN, Elias (1862-1945) Swedish

£294 $482 €450 Stooks (50x72cm-20x28in) s. 9-Feb-3 Bukowskis, Helsinki #406/R

ERENTXUN, Eloy (20th C) Spanish

£559 $906 €850 Basque landscape (61x79cm-24x31in) s.d.49 s.d.verso. 21-Jan-3 Ansorena, Madrid #248/R

ERFMANN, Ferdinand (1901-1968) Dutch

£11511 $18878 €16000 De walletjes II (60x40cm-24x16in) init.d.1966 prov.exhib. 3-Jun-3 Christie's, Amsterdam #382/R est:8000-12000
£11511 $18878 €16000 Scootermeisje - scooter girl (60x50cm-24x20in) init.d.1965 prov.exhib.lit. 3-Jun-3 Christie's, Amsterdam #383/R est:8000-12000
£12230 $20058 €17000 Floorshow in the new karseboom (80x40cm-31x16in) init.d.1965 prov.exhib.lit. 3-Jun-3 Christie's, Amsterdam #384/R est:7000-9000
£14388 $23597 €20000 De Glabrio's (70x40cm-28x16in) init.d.1964 prov.exhib.lit. 3-Jun-3 Christie's, Amsterdam #385/R est:10000-15000

Works on paper

£313 $516 €450 Amsterdam city view (29x44cm-11x17in) s.d.8/5/28 black chk col crayon. 1-Jul-3 Christie's, Amsterdam #354
£1135 $1838 €1600 Tribune with onlookers (20x26cm-8x10in) s.d.1928 chk. 26-May-3 Glerum, Amsterdam #79 est:800-1200

ERHARDT, Johann Christoph (1795-1822) German

Works on paper

£1923 $3038 €3000 Tower of the former Pillenreuth monastery near Nurnberg (16x18cm-6x7in) s.i.d.Juni 1812 pen wash prov. 16-Nov-2 Lempertz, Koln #1318/R est:3000
£2436 $3849 €3800 Erhard's travelling companions Klein and Welker (25x20cm-10x8in) s.i. Indian ink brush wash over pencil prov. 16-Nov-2 Lempertz, Koln #1319/R est:4000
£3472 $5521 €5000 Rome, near Torre quinto on the Tiber (18x23cm-7x9in) s.i.d.1820 pencil prov. 5-May-3 Ketterer, Munich #292/R est:1000-1200

ERHARDT, Wilhelm (1815-1890) Czechoslovakian

£500 $785 €750 On the river at dusk (42x69cm-17x27in) s. 16-Apr-3 Christie's, Kensington #728/R

ERIC, Dominique (20th C) American?

Works on paper

£2658 $4200 €3987 Portrait of Clare Booth Luce (41x38cm-16x15in) s. W/C board prov. 3-Apr-3 Christie's, Rockefeller NY #166/R est:1000-1500

ERICHSEN, Thorvald (1868-1939) Norwegian

£1053 $1663 €1580 From Lillehammer (32x41cm-13x16in) init. s.verso panel. 17-Dec-2 Grev Wedels Plass, Oslo #214/R (N.KR 12000)

£1567	$2507	€2351	Landscape (32x40cm-13x16in) init. panel. 17-Mar-3 Blomqvist, Oslo #387/R est:20000-25000 (N.KR 18000)
£8651	$13668	€12977	The church in Lillehammer (73x60cm-29x24in) s. exhib.lit. 2-Dec-2 Blomqvist, Oslo #384/R est:80000-100000 (N.KR 100000)
£8651	$13668	€12977	Mountain landscape, Knivsfjellet with the pier in Holmsbu (73x90cm-29x35in) s.d.21 i.stretcher. 2-Dec-2 Blomqvist, Oslo #388/R est:125000 (N.KR 100000)
£23560	$36990	€35340	Landscape from Holmsbu (73x92cm-29x36in) s.d.31. 21-Nov-2 Grev Wedels Plass, Oslo #46/R est:300000-350000 (N.KR 270000)

ERICHSEN, Wilhelm (?) ?

£390	$617	€585	The steam schooner Fox, Greenland (45x61cm-18x24in) s. panel. 5-Apr-3 Rasmussen, Havnen #2190 (D.KR 4200)

ERICKSON, Oscar B (1883-1968) American

£484	$750	€726	October willows (36x38cm-14x15in) s. canvas laid down painted c.1920. 8-Dec-2 Toomey, Oak Park #726/R

ERICSON, David (1869-1946) American

£3247	$5000	€4871	Life magazine cover, woman amongst flowers (48x41cm-19x16in) s. board prov. 24-Oct-2 Shannon's, Milford #124/R est:5000-7000

ERICSON, Johan (1849-1925) Swedish

£633	$1051	€918	West coast landscape (35x55cm-14x22in) s.d.1897. 16-Jun-3 Lilla Bukowskis, Stockholm #600 (S.KR 8200)
£669	$1064	€1004	Glittering sun (39x60cm-15x24in) s.d.1919. 3-Mar-3 Lilla Bukowskis, Stockholm #35 (S.KR 9000)
£1418	$2199	€2127	Entrance to Marstrand (55x81cm-22x32in) s.d.1916. 3-Dec-2 Bukowskis, Stockholm #140/R est:25000-30000 (S.KR 20000)
£1571	$2577	€2278	Farm with flowering summer meadow, Skaane (30x47cm-12x19in) indis sig.d. panel. 4-Jun-3 AB Stockholms Auktionsverk #2183/R est:20000-25000 (S.KR 20000)
£1631	$2528	€2447	Landscape with woman (38x52cm-15x20in) s. 4-Dec-2 AB Stockholms Auktionsverk #1561/R est:25000-30000 (S.KR 23000)
£1844	$2858	€2766	Summer meadow by the sea (50x61cm-20x24in) s. 3-Dec-2 Bukowskis, Stockholm #138/R est:35000-40000 (S.KR 26000)
£2979	$4617	€4469	Gathering seaweed on moonlit beach (110x164cm-43x65in) s. exhib. 3-Dec-2 Bukowskis, Stockholm #286/R est:40000-50000 (S.KR 42000)
£3103	$5027	€4499	Field of poppies (75x100cm-30x39in) s.d.1920. 26-May-3 Bukowskis, Stockholm #80/R est:50000-70000 (S.KR 40000)
£3142	$5153	€4556	House by meadow of flowering poppies (62x92cm-24x36in) s.d.1920. 4-Jun-3 AB Stockholms Auktionsverk #2157/R est:50000-60000 (S.KR 40000)
£3258	$5279	€4724	On the jetty, Smogen (75x120cm-30x47in) s.d.1918. 26-May-3 Bukowskis, Stockholm #81/R est:30000-35000 (S.KR 42000)
£4752	$7365	€7128	Summer landscape with houses (73x100cm-29x39in) s.d.1920. 4-Dec-2 AB Stockholms Auktionsverk #1718/R est:70000-80000 (S.KR 67000)

ERICSON, Kate and ZIEGLER, Mel (20th C) American

£602	$1000	€903	Old glory red bleached white national flag blue (40x103cm-16x41in) oil paper etched glass prov. 11-Jun-3 Phillips, New York #544/R
£1325	$2200	€1988	Old glory (39x81cm-15x32in) oil paper etched glass three parts prov. 11-Jun-3 Phillips, New York #542/R est:2000-3000

ERIKSEN, Bjarne (1882-1970) Norwegian

£255	$392	€383	Landscape with farm (68x71cm-27x28in) s,. 28-Oct-2 Blomqvist, Lysaker #1046/R (N.KR 3000)

ERIKSEN, Gorm (20th C) Danish

£411	$654	€617	Life of women II (100x100cm-39x39in) init. acrylic. 26-Feb-3 Kunsthallen, Copenhagen #96 (D.KR 4500)

ERIKSEN, Sigurd (1884-1976) Norwegian

£439	$693	€659	Rocky landscape with man and boat (56x68cm-22x27in) s.d.1921. 17-Dec-2 Grev Wedels Plass, Oslo #215 (N.KR 5000)

ERIKSSON, Christian (1858-1935) Swedish

Sculpture

£1241	$2011	€1799	Elof - small boy standing (20cm-8in) s.d.1901 dark pat.bronze Cast H Bergman lit. 25-May-3 Uppsala Auktionskammare, Uppsala #374/R est:10000-15000 (S.KR 16000)
£1844	$2858	€2766	Elof - small boy standing (19cm-7in) s.i.d.1901 dark pat.bronze st.f.Bergman lit. 4-Dec-2 AB Stockholms Auktionsverk #1820/R est:12000-15000 (S.KR 26000)

ERIKSSON, Ernst Elis (1906-) Swedish

Works on paper

£280	$437	€420	Untitled (35x29cm-14x11in) s.d.65 collage silver paper. 6-Nov-2 AB Stockholms Auktionsverk #886/R (S.KR 4000)
£420	$656	€630	Untitled (47x60cm-19x24in) collage silver paper. 6-Nov-2 AB Stockholms Auktionsverk #887/R (S.KR 6000)

ERIKSSON, Liss (1919-2000) Swedish

Sculpture

£1542	$2405	€2313	Balancing (44cm-17in) s/num.1/5 dark gold pat.bronze prov. 5-Nov-2 Bukowskis, Stockholm #72/R est:5000-6000 (S.KR 22000)

ERINQUE, G (after) (?) French

Sculpture

£5063	$7848	€8000	Eglantine (70cm-28in) i. bronze. 25-Sep-2 Christie's, Amsterdam #569/R est:2500-3500

ERIXSON, Sven (1899-1970) Swedish

£372	$603	€539	Barbedwired fence (45x37cm-18x15in) s.d.68 panel. 25-May-3 Uppsala Auktionskammare, Uppsala #295 (S.KR 4800)
£423	$665	€613	Untitled. 15-Dec-2 Anders Antik, Landskrona #1207 (S.KR 6000)
£603	$934	€905	Coronation scene from Shakespeare's Richard III (55x50cm-22x20in) s. lit. 8-Dec-2 Uppsala Auktionskammare, Uppsala #266/R (S.KR 8500)
£659	$1068	€956	Midsummer celebration (34x41cm-13x16in) s. 25-May-3 Uppsala Auktionskammare, Uppsala #294/R (S.KR 8500)
£690	$1062	€1035	The story of King Georg (41x49cm-16x19in) s.d.1947 panel. 27-Oct-2 Anders Antik, Landskrona #505/R (S.KR 10000)
£736	$1148	€1104	Floating islands (33x41cm-13x16in) s. panel. 6-Nov-2 AB Stockholms Auktionsverk #664/R (S.KR 10500)
£888	$1474	€1288	Expressionistic landscape (63x87cm-25x34in) s.d.62. 16-Jun-3 Lilla Bukowskis, Stockholm #536 (S.KR 11500)
£989	$1562	€1484	The arrest (66x50cm-26x20in) s.d.32 panel cardboard. 28-Apr-3 Bukowskis, Stockholm #8/R est:15000-20000 (S.KR 13000)
£1191	$1858	€1787	Gun - girl in garden (46x38cm-18x15in) s.d.40 panel prov.exhib.lit. 5-Nov-2 Bukowskis, Stockholm #81/R est:20000-25000 (S.KR 17000)
£1413	$2246	€2120	Unloading in Lisbon (51x65cm-20x26in) s.d.35 lit. 3-Mar-3 Lilla Bukowskis, Stockholm #14 est:15000-18000 (S.KR 19000)
£1612	$2514	€2418	Blue coast (48x61cm-19x24in) s.d.52. 5-Nov-2 Bukowskis, Stockholm #80/R est:20000-25000 (S.KR 23000)
£1612	$2514	€2418	Southern street scene with figures (53x65cm-21x26in) s. exhib. 5-Nov-2 Bukowskis, Stockholm #160/R est:30000-40000 (S.KR 23000)
£1699	$2735	€2549	View from Majorca (46x54cm-18x21in) s. 7-May-3 AB Stockholms Auktionsverk #679/R est:12000-15000 (S.KR 22000)
£1752	$2733	€2628	Man by farm in Skaane (54x66cm-21x26in) s. 6-Nov-2 AB Stockholms Auktionsverk #676/R est:12000-15000 (S.KR 25000)
£1931	$3108	€2897	Park landscape at dusk (46x55cm-18x22in) s. 7-May-3 AB Stockholms Auktionsverk #700/R est:30000-35000 (S.KR 25000)
£2242	$3498	€3363	Man on beach in Sondrum (56x70cm-22x28in) s,. 5-Nov-2 Bukowskis, Stockholm #163/R est:35000-40000 (S.KR 32000)
£2313	$3608	€3470	Fountain in garden (54x44cm-21x17in) st.sig. i.verso panel. 5-Nov-2 Bukowskis, Stockholm #162/R est:25000-28000 (S.KR 33000)
£2593	$4045	€3890	Picking fruit (48x33cm-19x13in) panel exhib. 6-Nov-2 AB Stockholms Auktionsverk #642/R est:25000-30000 (S.KR 37000)
£2593	$4045	€3890	Vineyard workers (56x66cm-22x26in) s. 5-Nov-2 Bukowskis, Stockholm #159/R est:35000-40000 (S.KR 37000)
£2663	$4154	€3995	Family by house (37x46cm-15x18in) s. panel. 6-Nov-2 AB Stockholms Auktionsverk #645/R est:50000-60000 (S.KR 38000)
£2663	$4154	€3995	Outdoor cafe (54x66cm-21x26in) s. 6-Nov-2 AB Stockholms Auktionsverk #658/R est:20000-25000 (S.KR 38000)
£3243	$5222	€4865	Vikings (93x143cm-37x56in) s. lit. 7-May-3 AB Stockholms Auktionsverk #708/R est:45000-50000 (S.KR 42000)
£3364	$5247	€5046	Ekharads Bridge (49x55cm-19x22in) s.d.42. 6-Nov-2 AB Stockholms Auktionsverk #660/R est:30000-35000 (S.KR 48000)
£3498	$5527	€5247	View over Florence (49x71cm-19x28in) s.d.24. 28-Apr-3 Bukowskis, Stockholm #7/R est:60000-80000 (S.KR 46000)
£3861	$6216	€5792	The black horse - or horse on beach (39x51cm-15x20in) s.d.24 panel lit. 7-May-3 AB Stockholms Auktionsverk #750/R est:80000-100000 (S.KR 50000)
£4625	$7215	€6938	Sylvie - model resting (64x80cm-25x31in) s.d.29 exhib. 5-Nov-2 Bukowskis, Stockholm #31/R est:60000-80000 (S.KR 66000)
£4765	$7434	€7148	Palms and lilies (54x65cm-21x26in) s.d.juni 29 exhib. 6-Nov-2 AB Stockholms Auktionsverk #637/R est:30000-40000 (S.KR 68000)

£6307 $9839 €9461 Women in Portugal (109x126cm-43x50in) s.d.37-41 lit. 6-Nov-2 AB Stockholms Auktionsverk #678/R est:125000-150000 (S.KR 90000)
£12741 $20514 €19112 My wife among autumn flowers (70x55cm-28x22in) s.d.28 exhib.prov. 7-May-3 AB Stockholms Auktionsverk #889/R est:70000-80000 (S.KR 165000)
£13127 $21135 €19691 From my studio in Paris (100x80cm-39x31in) s.d.1931. 7-May-3 AB Stockholms Auktionsverk #687/R est:180000-200000 (S.KR 170000)
£13665 $21317 €20498 Grape harvest (60x73cm-24x29in) s.i.d.27. 6-Nov-2 AB Stockholms Auktionsverk #644/R est:50000-60000 (S.KR 195000)

Works on paper

£302 $471 €453 Stone quarry (64x36cm-25x14in) s.d.62 mixed media. 13-Sep-2 Lilla Bukowskis, Stockholm #506 (S.KR 4400)
£387 $615 €581 Landscape from Canary Islands (27x34cm-11x13in) s.d.1968 W/C. 3-Mar-3 Lilla Bukowskis, Stockholm #689 (S.KR 5200)
£420 $656 €630 Janne on her way to the sauna (34x24cm-13x9in) s. W/C. 6-Nov-2 AB Stockholms Auktionsverk #672/R (S.KR 6000)
£618 $995 €927 Composition (43x61cm-17x24in) s.d.61 mixed media. 7-May-3 AB Stockholms Auktionsverk #730/R (S.KR 8000)
£981 $1530 €1472 Girl in forest (37x24cm-15x9in) s.i.d.maj 48 W/C. 5-Nov-2 Bukowskis, Stockholm #25/R est:18000-20000 (S.KR 14000)
£1261 $1968 €1892 Flower (43x33cm-17x13in) s. W/C. 5-Nov-2 Bukowskis, Stockholm #24/R est:18000-20000 (S.KR 18000)
£1915 $2968 €2873 Bon Marche - street scene in Paris (31x37cm-12x15in) s.d.26 gouache prov. 8-Dec-2 Uppsala Auktionskammare, Uppsala #255/R est:8000-10000 (S.KR 27000)

ERLER, Fritz (1868-1940) German

Works on paper

£962 $1490 €1500 Sketch for 'Youth' (57x43cm-22x17in) s.i. W/C Indian ink chl bodycol. 7-Dec-2 Ketterer, Hamburg #136/R est:1400-1600

ERLER-SAMADEN, Erich (1870-1946) German

£641 $1006 €1000 High mountain lake in summer (70x80cm-28x31in) s. 21-Nov-2 Van Ham, Cologne #1590/R
£1295 $2072 €1800 Preaching to the herdsmen (100x130cm-39x51in) s. i. stretcher. 15-May-3 Neumeister, Munich #248/R est:1800-2000
£1603 $2484 €2500 Figures harvesting in landscape (92x95cm-36x37in) s.d.13 bears i. verso. 7-Dec-2 Ketterer, Hamburg #160/R est:2800-3200

ERMELS, Johann Franciscus (1641-1693) German

£3930 $6131 €5895 Landscapes with figures (17x23cm-7x9in) panel pair prov. 20-Nov-2 Fischer, Luzern #1049/R est:10000-12000 (S.FR 9000)
£7500 $11775 €11250 Coastal landscape with figures by classical ruins, port beyond (43x36cm-17x14in) s.d.1691. 13-Dec-2 Christie's, Kensington #149/R est:8000-12000

ERMINI, Pietro (18/19th C) Italian

Works on paper

£327 $519 €480 Maternite (32x32cm-13x13in) s.d.1792. 19-Mar-3 Hotel des Ventes Mosan, Brussels #146

ERNI, Hans (1909-) Swiss

£568 $886 €852 Goat shepherd (28x21cm-11x8in) s.d.42 tempera ink paper prov. 9-Nov-2 Galerie Gloggner, Luzern #43/R (S.FR 1300)
£613 $981 €920 Girl with grapes (32x25cm-13x10in) s.d. i. stretcher. 17-Mar-3 Philippe Schuler, Zurich #4313 est:1400-1800 (S.FR 1300)
£873 $1380 €1310 Portrait of woman (19x20cm-7x8in) s.d.12.9.83 pencil. 14-Nov-2 Stuker, Bern #198 est:1200-1400 (S.FR 2000)
£1179 $1863 €1769 Lovers (48x17cm-19x7in) s.d. 17 8 68 W/C. 14-Nov-2 Stuker, Bern #196 est:2500-3000 (S.FR 2700)
£1310 $2057 €1965 Still life (63x48cm-25x19in) s.d.1974 pavatex. 25-Nov-2 Germann, Zurich #41/R est:3000-5000 (S.FR 3000)
£1397 $2180 €2096 Doves (27x37cm-11x15in) s.d.65 tempera paper. 20-Nov-2 Fischer, Luzern #2607/R est:3000-4000 (S.FR 3200)
£1572 $2452 €2358 Child sat on ground with stick (47x45cm-19x18in) s.d.52-1.4.67 tempera. 20-Nov-2 Fischer, Luzern #1294/R est:4000-6000 (S.FR 3600)
£2402 $3747 €3603 Sleeping figure (64x55cm-25x22in) s.d.61 tempera. 20-Nov-2 Fischer, Luzern #1296/R est:6000-8000 (S.FR 5500)
£3241 $5218 €4699 Violinist (98x53cm-39x21in) s.d.60 i.verso. 9-May-3 Dobiaschofsky, Bern #220/R est:9500 (S.FR 7000)
£3275 $5109 €4913 Horse with foal (55x64cm-22x25in) s.d.11.12.71 tempera. 20-Nov-2 Fischer, Luzern #1297/R est:8000-12000 (S.FR 7500)
£3712 $5790 €5568 Bull and cow lying down (75x90cm-30x35in) s.d.27.61 spray technique tempera pavatex exhib. 20-Nov-2 Fischer, Luzern #1295/R est:8000-12000 (S.FR 8500)

Works on paper

£354 $573 €513 Reclining male nude (37x28cm-15x11in) s.d.49 Indian ink prov. 24-May-3 Galerie Gloggner, Luzern #30/R (S.FR 750)
£415 $647 €623 Charon (33x27cm-13x11in) s.d.41 pen dr prov. 9-Nov-2 Galerie Gloggner, Luzern #44/R (S.FR 950)
£463 $745 €695 Young couple (36x27cm-14x11in) s. Indian ink. 7-May-3 Dobiaschofsky, Bern #1562/R (S.FR 1000)
£524 $817 €786 Weaver (37x55cm-15x22in) s.i.d.56 Indian ink wash. 20-Nov-2 Fischer, Luzern #2606/R (S.FR 1200)
£568 $886 €852 Ouvrier pensif (63x49cm-25x19in) s.d.71 htd chk. 20-Nov-2 Fischer, Luzern #2604/R (S.FR 1300)
£611 $954 €917 Youth playing harp (49x64cm-19x25in) s.d.22.12.62 Indian ink brush. 6-Nov-2 Dobiaschofsky, Bern #1545/R (S.FR 1400)
£699 $1090 €1049 Loving couple in bath (30x21cm-12x8in) s.d.42 pen dr prov. 9-Nov-2 Galerie Gloggner, Luzern #46/R est:1200-1400 (S.FR 1600)
£699 $1090 €1049 Bacchantal scene with young girl (31x40cm-12x16in) s.d.66 Indian ink. 20-Nov-2 Fischer, Luzern #2608/R est:1600-1800 (S.FR 1600)
£787 $1267 €1141 Loving couple (34x24cm-13x9in) s. pen ink dr. 9-May-3 Dobiaschofsky, Bern #222/R (S.FR 1700)
£852 $1345 €1278 Two boys with fishing net (27x19cm-11x7in) s.d.11.10.42 Indian ink. 14-Nov-2 Stuker, Bern #199/R est:800-1200 (S.FR 1950)
£873 $1362 €1310 Cavaliere mystique (37x27cm-15x11in) s.d.1983 chl. 6-Nov-2 Dobiaschofsky, Bern #1546/R (S.FR 2000)
£927 $1511 €1400 Couple enlace (42x28cm-17x11in) s.i. red ballpoint pen exec.1959. 28-Jan-3 Dorotheum, Vienna #136/R
£1004 $1567 €1506 Two ducks (23x30cm-9x12in) i.d.96 W/C bodycol. 8-Nov-2 Dobiaschofsky, Bern #246/R (S.FR 2300)
£1397 $2180 €2096 Socrates (66x92cm-26x36in) s.d.66 Indian ink wash. 20-Nov-2 Fischer, Luzern #2605/R est:2500-3000 (S.FR 3200)
£1485 $2168 €2228 Two faces (26x48cm-10x19in) s.d.1974 gouache pencil. 4-Jun-2 Germann, Zurich #58/R est:3000-3500 (S.FR 3400)
£1703 $2657 €2555 Scene in artist's studio (37x23cm-15x9in) s.d.92 pen ink dr. 8-Nov-2 Dobiaschofsky, Bern #228/R est:2400 (S.FR 3900)
£2445 $3815 €3668 Young couple (98x67cm-39x26in) s.d.93 pastel chk. 20-Nov-2 Fischer, Luzern #2603/R est:2500-3000 (S.FR 5600)

ERNST, Helge (1916-1990) Danish

£299 $475 €449 Around sunset (19x55cm-7x22in) init. 29-Apr-3 Kunsthallen, Copenhagen #18 (D.KR 3200)
£304 $474 €456 Yellow picture (27x46cm-11x18in) init. 18-Sep-2 Kunsthallen, Copenhagen #78 (D.KR 3600)
£337 $546 €506 Composition (50x71cm-20x28in) init. 25-Jan-3 Rasmussen, Havnen #2001/R (D.KR 3800)
£372 $580 €558 Etude V (90x37cm-35x15in) init. painted 1958 exhib. 18-Sep-2 Kunsthallen, Copenhagen #70 (D.KR 4400)
£381 $637 €552 Fruit in yellow room (38x55cm-15x22in) init. s.d.1980 verso. 17-Jun-3 Rasmussen, Copenhagen #138/R (D.KR 4000)
£419 $666 €629 Composition in blue and black (81x54cm-32x21in) mono. d.april 59 verso. 10-Mar-3 Rasmussen, Vejle #638/R (D.KR 4500)
£560 $890 €840 Figure (38x90cm-15x35in) init. masonite. 29-Apr-3 Kunsthallen, Copenhagen #62 (D.KR 6000)
£762 $1181 €1143 Composition in yellow and blue (65x100cm-26x39in) init. 1-Oct-2 Rasmussen, Copenhagen #224/R (D.KR 9000)
£1228 $1903 €1842 Ting - still life (33x46cm-13x18in) init. s.d.1986 verso. 1-Oct-2 Rasmussen, Copenhagen #244a est:8000-10000 (D.KR 14500)
£1463 $2325 €2195 Table in summer (65x81cm-26x32in) init. 26-Feb-3 Kunsthallen, Copenhagen #103/R est:10000 (D.KR 16000)
£1809 $2804 €2714 The red flowers (73x100cm-29x39in) s. painted 1987-88. 4-Dec-2 Kunsthallen, Copenhagen #59/R est:20000 (D.KR 21000)

ERNST, Jimmy (1920-1984) American/German

£732 $1200 €1061 Untitled (7x10cm-3x4in) s. oil W/C pen ink board pair. 5-Jun-3 Swann Galleries, New York #87/R
£7534 $11829 €11000 Aeroflower (46x25cm-18x10in) s.d.42 s.i.d.verso. 15-Apr-3 Laurence Calmels, Paris #4213/R

Works on paper

£449 $700 €674 Skylight (53x41cm-21x16in) s.d.71 gouache prov. 5-Nov-2 Doyle, New York #32/R
£579 $950 €840 Abstract composition (30x22cm-12x9in) s.d. W/C brush ink. 5-Jun-3 Swann Galleries, New York #86/R

ERNST, Max (1891-1976) German

£17483 $29196 €25000 Les canards (40x29cm-16x11in) s. s.d.1954 verso paper on canvas prov.exhib.lit. 30-Jun-3 Artcurial Briest, Paris #81/R est:30000-40000
£64000 $106880 €92800 Nu allonge et personnage (20x25cm-8x10in) s. painted 1934 prov. 24-Jun-3 Sotheby's, London #167/R est:70000-90000
£73394 $122569 €106421 La terre vue de Uranus (22x27cm-9x11in) s.i. bears i. verso panel prov. 20-Jun-3 Kornfeld, Bern #28/R est:175000 (S.FR 160000)
£75000 $122250 €112500 Untitled (41x33cm-16x13in) s. s.d.1926 verso prov.lit. 3-Feb-3 Christie's, London #165/R est:80000
£109589 $170959 €160000 Portrait of Andre Breton (60x73cm-24x29in) s. exhib.lit. 14-Apr-3 Laurence Calmels, Paris #4076/R est:90000
£131004 $205677 €196506 Trois jeunes filles en de belles poses (41x33cm-16x13in) prov.lit. 25-Nov-2 Germann, Zurich #22/R est:320000-350000 (S.FR 300000)

£290000 $472700 €435000 Colombes s'enfermant das leurs ailes (55x46cm-22x18in) s.d.25 s.i.d.verso prov.exhib.lit. 3-Feb-3 Christie's, London #159/R est:300000
£320000 $524800 €480000 Messaline enfant (122x91cm-48x36in) s.d.1957 s.i.d.verso prov.exhib.lit. 4-Feb-3 Sotheby's, London #42/R est:350000
£320000 $534400 €464000 Tete d'homme (73x60cm-29x24in) s.d.34 s.i.d.34 verso prov.exhib.lit. 24-Jun-3 Christie's, London #46/R est:320000-380000
£660000 $1075800 €990000 Convolvulus! Convolvulus (33x41cm-13x16in) s. painted 1941 prov.exhib.lit. 3-Feb-3 Christie's, London #155/R est:600000
£900000 $1467000 €1350000 Epiphanie - Dream landscape (54x65cm-21x26in) s.d.1940 prov.exhib.lit. 3-Feb-3 Christie's, London #191/R est:1200000

Prints
£1646 $2600 €2600 To: Robert Lebel, l'oiseau caramel (34x24cm-13x9in) s. photo lithograph. 29-Nov-2 Villa Grisebach, Berlin #599/R est:1500-1600
£1875 $2981 €2700 Untitled (24x18cm-9x7in) s.i. num.29/33 etching aquatint. 5-May-3 Ketterer, Munich #20/R est:1600-1800
£1944 $3092 €2800 Masques (33x50cm-13x20in) s.i. col lithograph. 5-May-3 Ketterer, Munich #18/R est:1800-2000
£2564 $4000 €3846 La loterie du jardin zoologique (12x9cm-5x4in) s.i. etching. 7-Nov-2 Swann Galleries, New York #631/R est:3000-5000
£3681 $5852 €5300 Correspondences dangereuses (30x22cm-12x9in) s.i. drypoint. 5-May-3 Ketterer, Munich #19/R est:2500-3500

Sculpture
£2464 $4041 €3400 Chess figure - Queen (12cm-5in) s. bronze Cast.Barth Elmenhorst. 29-May-3 Lempertz, Koln #597/R est:3000
£2885 $4471 €4500 Petit totue (31cm-12in) s.verso num.123/150 black marble exec.1967/75. 7-Dec-2 Van Ham, Cologne #147/R est:8400
£3077 $4831 €4800 Petit ovale (4cm-2in) st.sig. gold lit. 11-Dec-2 Artcurial Briest, Paris #598/R
£3104 $5183 €4500 Le roi, la reine, le fou (14x29x9cm-6x11x4in) s.num. black pat bronze st.f.Valsuani lit. 10-Jul-3 Artcurial Briest, Paris #242/R est:3000-4000
£3205 $4968 €5000 Cheri bibi (34x18x17cm-13x7x7in) i. num.154/175 black pat bronze exec.1964/1973. 7-Dec-2 Van Ham, Cologne #146/R est:9500
£3846 $6038 €6000 Petite tete ronde (5x5x5cm-2x2x2in) st.sig. gold lit. 11-Dec-2 Artcurial Briest, Paris #599/R
£4299 $7179 €6234 Petite tortue sur socle (32cm-13in) s. black marble. 24-Jun-3 Koller, Zurich #368/R est:8000-12000 (S.FR 9500)
£4615 $7246 €7200 Masque (7x7x7cm-3x3x3in) st.sig. gold lit. 11-Dec-2 Artcurial Briest, Paris #591/R
£5000 $7850 €7800 Tete (7cm-3in) st.sig. gold lit. 11-Dec-2 Artcurial Briest, Paris #590/R
£5769 $9058 €9000 Tete ovale (5cm-2in) st.sig. gold lit. 11-Dec-2 Artcurial Briest, Paris #605/R
£6690 $11106 €9500 Cher Bibi (34x18x17cm-13x7x7in) bronze. 14-Jun-3 Hauswedell & Nolte, Hamburg #1145/R est:10000
£7692 $12077 €12000 Cheri bibi (34cm-13in) s.st.f.Valsuani num.78/175 green pat bronze. 11-Dec-2 Artcurial Briest, Paris #547/R est:6000
£9231 $14492 €14400 Nez de cone (7x7x7cm-3x3x3in) st.sig. gold lit. 11-Dec-2 Artcurial Briest, Paris #579/R
£9317 $15000 €13976 Cheri Bibi (34cm-13in) i.num.78/175 brown pat. bronze st.f.Valsuani prov.lit. 7-May-3 Sotheby's, New York #328a/R est:7000-9000
£11583 $18649 €17375 Tete carree - relief mask (30x30cm-12x12in) stamped sig. gold weight 817 grams prov.lit. 7-May-3 AB Stockholms Auktionsverk #805/R est:150000-175000 (S.KR 150000)
£12340 $19373 €19250 Grande tete (14cm-6in) st.sig. gold lit. 11-Dec-2 Artcurial Briest, Paris #607/R
£19231 $30000 €28847 Tete a cornes (20cm-8in) st.5/8 cast gold conceived 1959 lit. 6-Nov-2 Sotheby's, New York #300/R est:30000-40000
£31056 $50000 €46584 La tourangelle (28cm-11in) i.num.VII/VIII black pat. bronze st.f.Susse conceived 1960 prov. 7-May-3 Sotheby's, New York #329/R est:60000-80000
£1410257 $2200000 €2115386 Le roi jouant avec le reine (101cm-40in) green brown pat. bronze conceived 1944 prov.exhib.lit. 5-Nov-2 Sotheby's, New York #32/R est:2500000-3500000

Works on paper
£1090 $1722 €1700 Three figures (23x13cm-9x5in) mono. Indian ink. 15-Nov-2 Reiss & Sohn, Konigstein #491/R est:2000
£5449 $8500 €8174 Zoology lesson (9x10cm-4x4in) s. collage executed c.1968 prov. 5-Nov-2 Doyle, New York #29/R est:9000-12000
£5556 $9167 €8000 La science des Reves (7x10cm-3x4in) s. ink collage prov.lit. 2-Jul-3 Artcurial Briest, Paris #699/R est:6000-8000
£7801 $13028 €11000 Composition (18x21cm-7x8in) s.i. rubbing. 18-Jun-3 Charbonneaux, Paris #47/R est:10000-12000
£8500 $14195 €12750 Paysage alpin (10x7cm-4x3in) s.i. gouache paper on mount exec 1959 prov.exhib.lit. 26-Jun-3 Christie's, London #399/R est:7000-10000
£15000 $25050 €22500 Sans souffler mot et par n'importe quel temps, lumiere magique (8x6cm-3x2in) s. collage paper on mount exec.1929 prov.exhib.lit. 26-Jun-3 Christie's, London #398/R est:10000-15000
£17949 $28179 €28000 Diamants conjugaux (25x17cm-10x7in) s. pencil frottage paper on cardboard exec.1925 exhib.lit. 19-Nov-2 Finarte, Milan #196/R
£40000 $65600 €60000 Untitled (48x65cm-19x26in) s.i.d.1931 collage gouache pencil card prov.lit. 5-Feb-3 Sotheby's, London #186/R est:60000
£41935 $66258 €65000 Made in France (14x19cm-6x7in) s.i.d.1941 verso gouache paper on panel prov.exhib.lit. 18-Dec-2 Tajan, Paris #51/R

ERNST, Otto (1884-1967) Swiss
£300 $475 €450 Coastal landscape (50x60cm-20x24in) s. board. 29-Nov-2 Zofingen, Switzerland #2866 (S.FR 700)
£343 $542 €515 Autumn in Val Suvretta (47x59cm-19x23in) s.i.d.1925 verso board. 29-Nov-2 Zofingen, Switzerland #2865 (S.FR 800)

ERNST, Rita (1956-) Swiss
£1747 $2742 €2621 Untitled (94x94cm-37x37in) s.d.1990 verso acrylic. 23-Nov-2 Burkhard, Luzern #31/R est:4000-5000 (S.FR 4000)

ERNST, Rudolph (1854-1932) Austrian
£276 $441 €400 Barque amarree a la grotte (32x36cm-13x14in) s. cardboard. 12-Mar-3 E & Eve, Paris #82
£19000 $30210 €28500 Chinese family at worship (55x45cm-22x18in) s. panel. 29-Apr-3 Bonhams, New Bond Street #33a/R est:15000-20000
£20645 $32000 €30968 An afternoon show (82x61cm-32x24in) s.i. panel. 30-Oct-2 Christie's, Rockefeller NY #85/R est:40000-60000
£38710 $60000 €58065 Return from the tiger hunt (81x100cm-32x39in) s. panel. 30-Oct-2 Christie's, Rockefeller NY #89/R est:70000-90000
£40000 $62800 €60000 Smoker (47x37cm-19x15in) s. panel. 19-Nov-2 Bonhams, New Bond Street #36/R est:40000-60000
£58065 $90000 €87098 Smoking the hookah (60x41cm-24x16in) s. panel. 29-Oct-2 Sotheby's, New York #51/R est:100000-150000
£60000 $93600 €90000 Evening prayer (81x64cm-32x25in) s. panel painted c.1910 prov. 15-Oct-2 Sotheby's, London #138/R est:60000-80000
£80645 $127419 €125000 Halte au kiosque (63x48cm-25x19in) s. panel. 19-Dec-2 Claude Aguttes, Neuilly #115/R est:120000

ERNSTBERGER (19th C) German
£1206 $1833 €1809 Small boy with sable (37x23cm-15x9in) s.i.d.1846 verso. 27-Aug-2 Rasmussen, Copenhagen #1973/R est:20000-25000 (D.KR 14000)

EROLI, Erulo (attrib) (1854-1916) Italian
£633 $1000 €950 Still life of pears and grapes (28x20cm-11x8in) s.d. panel. 16-Nov-2 New Orleans Auction, New Orleans #1093/R

ERRO, Gudmundur (1932-) Icelandic
£949 $1472 €1500 Le magicien (56x76cm-22x30in) s.verso acrylic. 28-Sep-2 Cornette de St.Cyr, Paris #301 est:2200-2500
£1042 $1719 €1500 Le tableaux des arrivees (77x58cm-30x23in) s.d.1996 verso acrylic prov.lit. 1-Jul-3 Artcurial Briest, Paris #859a/R est:1500-2000
£1944 $3091 €2800 Serie Matisse-Picasso (46x33cm-18x13in) s.d.verso acrylic lit. 29-Apr-3 Artcurial Briest, Paris #401 est:2000-2500
£2138 $3293 €3400 Sonja (96x68cm-38x27in) s. d.1989 verso acrylic. 22-Oct-2 Campo & Campo, Antwerp #103/R est:4250
£2917 $4638 €4200 BD leger (46x33cm-18x13in) s.d.verso acrylic prov. 29-Apr-3 Artcurial Briest, Paris #400/R est:2000-3000
£3401 $5408 €5000 Miss Suisse (128x66cm-50x26in) s.d.1967-68 verso lit. 24-Mar-3 Cornette de St.Cyr, Paris #54/R
£3462 $5435 €5400 Korean leftover, de la serie, Mind Games (100x73cm-39x29in) s.d.verso acrylic. 16-Dec-2 Chochon-Barre & Allardi, Paris #47/R est:5000-5500
£4808 $7548 €7500 Agression (128x66cm-50x26in) s.i.d.1967 lit. 20-Nov-2 Binoche, Paris #40/R est:7000-7500
£4937 $7800 €7800 Notre Georges (66x102cm-26x40in) s. d.1962 verso. 2-Dec-2 Tajan, Paris #203/R
£5208 $8229 €7500 Manga (150x20cm-59x8in) s.d.verso acrylic. 28-Apr-3 Cornette de St.Cyr, Paris #389 est:8000-10000
£8503 $13520 €12500 Saloon (195x97cm-77x38in) s.d.1982 acrylic lit. 24-Mar-3 Claude Boisgirard, Paris #126/R est:15000

Works on paper
£312 $496 €450 Serie chinoise (17x22cm-7x9in) s.d.79 collage cardboard. 29-Apr-3 Artcurial Briest, Paris #397
£344 $561 €520 Scene erotique (20x13cm-8x5in) s.d.1990 collage. 3-Feb-3 Cornette de St.Cyr, Paris #417
£397 $648 €600 Mao (10x14cm-4x6in) s.d.1978 collage. 3-Feb-3 Cornette de St.Cyr, Paris #415
£417 $688 €600 Isaac Albeniz (32x32cm-13x13in) s.d.1981 verso collage prov.lit. 1-Jul-3 Artcurial Briest, Paris #843/R
£451 $713 €650 Lenine et buste d'homme en marbre (42x33cm-17x13in) s.d. collage. 28-Apr-3 Cornette de St.Cyr, Paris #387/R
£451 $713 €650 Lenine et sculpture en bronze (42x33cm-17x13in) collage. 28-Apr-3 Cornette de St.Cyr, Paris #388
£486 $768 €700 Lenine et sculpture de femme en marbre (42x33cm-17x13in) s.d. collage. 28-Apr-3 Cornette de St.Cyr, Paris #386/R
£497 $810 €750 Jeune chinoise a l'arrosoir (20x20cm-8x8in) s.d. collage. 3-Feb-3 Cornette de St.Cyr, Paris #416
£510 $811 €750 Les Chinois a Pairs (30x23cm-12x9in) s.d.77 collage cardboard. 26-Feb-3 Artcurial Briest, Paris #398/R

£705 $1107 €1100 Dingo (25x41cm-10x16in) s.d.1963 collage. 15-Dec-2 Perrin, Versailles #107/R
£1013 $1570 €1600 Superart (78x57cm-31x22in) s.d.verso W/C. 28-Sep-2 Cornette de St.Cyr, Paris #302 est:2200-2500
£1103 $1843 €1600 But I am afraid of nothing (55x75cm-22x30in) s.d.verso W/C. 9-Jul-3 Cornette de St.Cyr, Paris #279/R est:1800-2000
£1483 $2476 €2150 Gifts (75x56cm-30x22in) s.d.verso W/C. 9-Jul-3 Cornette de St.Cyr, Paris #278/R est:2300-2500
£1731 $2683 €2700 Untitled (89x70cm-35x28in) s.d.1990 verso W/C. 7-Dec-2 Cornette de St.Cyr, Paris #128/R
£2222 $3534 €3200 Sans titre (75x54cm-30x21in) s.d.1955 verso W/C gouache. 29-Apr-3 Artcurial Briest, Paris #433/R est:2000-2500
£4500 $6975 €6750 Preliminary study for Carscape (157x255cm-62x100in) collage on three joined boards. 5-Dec-2 Christie's, Kensington #249/R est:3000-4000

ERTE, Romain de Tirtoff (1892-1990) Russian
£400 $640 €600 Fireflies - design for Harper's Bazaar (21x18cm-8x7in) s.verso tempera on paper. 15-May-3 Christie's, Kensington #229/R
£1923 $2981 €3000 Costumes (37x27cm-15x11in) s. tempera paper set of 3. 4-Dec-2 Finarte, Milan #188/R
Sculpture
£1063 $1700 €1541 Les bijoux de pearls (46cm-18in) i. gold pat bronze edition 460/500. 17-May-3 Selkirks, St. Louis #246/R est:1800-2000
£1063 $1700 €1541 Fedora (48cm-19in) i. gold pat bronze edition 159/500. 17-May-3 Selkirks, St. Louis #247/R est:1800-2000
£1603 $2340 €2500 Daydreams (35x45x14cm-14x18x6in) s. col bronze. 4-Jun-2 Karl & Faber, Munich #231/R est:5000
Works on paper
£380 $627 €551 Theatre costume design for a woman (24x17cm-9x7in) s. studio st. pencil bodycol. 3-Jul-3 Christie's, Kensington #215
£440 $682 €700 Etude de robe (30x23cm-12x9in) s. W/C pencil prov. 30-Oct-2 Artcurial Briest, Paris #106
£566 $877 €900 Etude de manteau du soir (31x23cm-12x9in) s. W/C pencil exec.c.1913 prov. 30-Oct-2 Artcurial Briest, Paris #104/R
£566 $877 €900 Etude de robe du soir (31x23cm-12x9in) s. W/C pencil prov. 30-Oct-2 Artcurial Briest, Paris #105
£629 $975 €1000 La nouvelle caledonie, les nouvelles (30x21cm-12x8in) st.sig. i.verso gouache. 30-Oct-2 Artcurial Briest, Paris #111
£633 $1000 €1000 Souvenir (16x11cm-6x4in) s. gouache. 26-Nov-2 Camard, Paris #84
£692 $1072 €1100 Etude de rideau de scene (24x26cm-9x10in) s. gouache htd gold paint prov. 30-Oct-2 Artcurial Briest, Paris #103/R
£748 $1190 €1100 La dinde (35x23cm-14x9in) s. gouache htd gold. 28-Feb-3 Tajan, Paris #5
£755 $1170 €1200 La nouvelle caledonie, premiere danseuse (30x21cm-12x8in) st.sig. i.verso gouache. 30-Oct-2 Artcurial Briest, Paris #110
£1006 $1560 €1600 Costume de danseur pour castor et pollux (44x37cm-17x15in) s. gouache. 30-Oct-2 Artcurial Briest, Paris #108 est:1500-1800
£1132 $1755 €1800 Costume de danseuse pour castor et pollux (44x38cm-17x15in) s. i.verso gouache. 30-Oct-2 Artcurial Briest, Paris #107/R est:1500-1800
£1132 $1755 €1800 La canasta (37x26cm-15x10in) s. i.verso gouache ink. 30-Oct-2 Artcurial Briest, Paris #109/R est:1200-1500
£1270 $2108 €2163 Untitled - Beatrice (29x15cm-11x6in) s. i.verso gouache. 10-Jun-3 Shapiro, Sydney #101/R est:3000-5000 (A.D 3200)
£1384 $2145 €2200 Femmes des annees (27x17cm-11x7in) s. W/C ink pair. 4-Oct-2 Tajan, Paris #85 est:1200-1500
£1400 $2282 €2100 Costume design for the bal tabarin, Paris 1936 (36x26cm-14x10in) s. pencil gouache gold paint. 3-Feb-3 Bonhams, New Bond Street #45/R est:700-1000
£1700 $2703 €2550 Lady in red. Red caperchous (32x24cm-13x9in) s.d.1957 gouache over pencil pair. 27-Feb-3 Sotheby's, Olympia #145/R est:1800-2200
£1923 $2981 €3000 Costumes (37x27cm-15x11in) s. one Chinese ink one tempera paper two. 4-Dec-2 Finarte, Milan #186/R
£2761 $4500 €4142 Courtesan (20x30cm-8x12in) s. gouache card. 2-Feb-3 Simpson's, Houston #283
£4200 $6678 €6300 Cover of Harper's Bazaar magazine, May 1928 (37x28cm-15x11in) s. gouache. 27-Feb-3 Sotheby's, Olympia #146/R est:4000-6000

ERTZ, Bruno (1873-1956) American
Works on paper
£299 $475 €449 Red-wing blackbird (23x33cm-9x13in) s.d. W/C. 2-Mar-3 Toomey, Oak Park #671/R

ERWIN, Jack (1920-) American
£833 $1300 €1250 RR depot, Cleburne (30x41cm-12x16in) masonite. 19-Oct-2 David Dike, Dallas #306/R

ERWITT, Elliott (1928-) American
Photographs
£2128 $3447 €3000 Paris (34x25cm-13x10in) gelatin silver s.i.d. verso lit. 23-May-3 Van Ham, Cologne #69/R est:3000

ES, Jacob van (1596-1666) Flemish
£10072 $16115 €14000 Still life with oysters, chestnuts and roll with fork on pewter plates (52x73cm-20x29in) panel. 13-May-3 Sotheby's, Amsterdam #19/R est:15000-20000
£11465 $17885 €18000 Still life with a carp on an earthware colander, oysters (61x93cm-24x37in) prov.exhib. 5-Nov-2 Sotheby's, Amsterdam #261/R est:20000-30000
£20000 $31400 €30000 Still life of green olives in a bowl, shrimps, oyster, roemer and lemon (25x35cm-10x14in) s. panel. 12-Dec-2 Sotheby's, London #159/R est:20000-30000

ESBENS, Emile Étienne (1821-?) French
£1807 $3000 €2620 Continental street scene with young man (38x28cm-15x11in) panel. 11-Jun-3 Boos Gallery, Michigan #549/R est:5000-7000

ESCALERA, Pio (19th C) Spanish
£4258 $6728 €6600 Harbour (60x100cm-24x39in) s.d.88. 18-Dec-2 Ansorena, Madrid #70/R est:6100

ESCHARD, Charles (attrib) (1748-1810) French
£2162 $3373 €3200 Paysage au lac avec berger se reposant (38x50cm-15x20in) 26-Mar-3 Tajan, Paris #87
Works on paper
£304 $474 €450 Porte de jardin (17x15cm-7x6in) pierre noire. 27-Mar-3 Maigret, Paris #62

ESCHBACH, Paul Andre Jean (1881-1961) French
£289 $480 €419 Figure nearing mill in winter (46x55cm-18x22in) s.i. 10-Jun-3 Ritchie, Toronto #121/R (C.D 650)
£451 $745 €650 Barques devant les maisons, les Martigues (33x24cm-13x9in) s. panel. 1-Jul-3 Rossini, Paris #88
£608 $949 €900 Paysage enneige (50x61cm-20x24in) s. 28-Mar-3 Claude Aguttes, Neuilly #78/R
£1042 $1698 €1500 Effet marin a Douarnenez (55x65cm-22x26in) s. 19-Jul-3 Thierry & Lannon, Brest #125 est:1500-2000
£1197 $1927 €1700 Retour de peche (50x65cm-20x26in) s. 11-May-3 Thierry & Lannon, Brest #174 est:1500-2000
£2817 $4535 €4000 Barques de peche sous voiles pres de la cale (55x110cm-22x43in) s. 11-May-3 Thierry & Lannon, Brest #175/R est:2400-2800

ESCHE, Emil (1896-1948) German
£544 $865 €800 Grunten (64x92cm-25x36in) s. 21-Mar-3 Auktionhaus Georg Rehm, Augsburg #8025/R
£544 $865 €800 Romelsried (78x112cm-31x44in) s. 21-Mar-3 Auktionhaus Georg Rehm, Augsburg #8024/R
Works on paper
£272 $433 €400 Still life of geraniums and jugs (60x47cm-24x19in) s.d.43 W/C. 21-Mar-3 Auktionhaus Georg Rehm, Augsburg #8027/R

ESCHENBURG, Marianne von (1883-1942) Austrian
£1141 $1836 €1700 Portrait of a young girl (21x16cm-8x6in) s.d.1887 panel. 18-Feb-3 Sotheby's, Amsterdam #323/R est:900-1200

ESCHER, Albert von (1833-1905) Swiss
Works on paper
£786 $1226 €1179 Swiss Army manoeuvre around 1865 (25x34cm-10x13in) s. W/C. 20-Nov-2 Fischer, Luzern #2715/R est:1800-2000 (S.FR 1800)

ESCHER, Hans (1918-) Austrian
Works on paper
£321 $506 €500 Lawyers (29x21cm-11x8in) s.i.d.10.49 pen brush Indian ink W/C. 12-Nov-2 Dorotheum, Vienna #154/R

ESCHER, Maurits Cornelis (1898-1972) Dutch
Prints
£2518 $4129 €3500 Order and chaos (28x28cm-11x11in) s. num.22/29 lithograph. 3-Jun-3 Christie's, Amsterdam #408/R est:4000-6000
£2518 $4129 €3500 Saint Franciscus (51x31cm-20x12in) woodcut. 3-Jun-3 Christie's, Amsterdam #425/R est:2000-3000
£2813 $4500 €4220 Dragon (33x25cm-13x10in) s. wood engraving. 18-May-3 Jeffery Burchard, Florida #18/R est:2500-3500
£2878 $4719 €4000 Dragon (32x24cm-13x9in) s.i. wood engraving. 3-Jun-3 Christie's, Amsterdam #405/R est:5000-7000
£3165 $5000 €5000 Tegenstelling (28x28cm-11x11in) s. lithograph. 26-Nov-2 Sotheby's, Amsterdam #349/R est:5000-7000
£3453 $5663 €4800 Three spheres (28x17cm-11x7in) s.i. wood engraving. 3-Jun-3 Christie's, Amsterdam #424/R est:4000-6000

£3597 $5899 €5000 Rippling (26x32cm-10x13in) s.i. linocut. 3-Jun-3 Christie's, Amsterdam #409/R est:3000-5000
£4317 $7079 €6000 Flatworms (34x41cm-13x16in) s.num.43/45 lithograph. 3-Jun-3 Christie's, Amsterdam #419/R est:4000-6000
£4317 $7079 €6000 Three worlds (36x25cm-14x10in) s.i. lithograph. 3-Jun-3 Christie's, Amsterdam #421/R est:2500-3500
£4487 $7000 €6731 Other world (38x32cm-15x13in) s.i. col woodcut engraving. 5-Nov-2 Christie's, Rockefeller NY #153/R est:5000-7000
£4676 $7669 €6500 Swans (20x32cm-8x13in) s.i. wood engraving. 3-Jun-3 Christie's, Amsterdam #412/R est:7000-9000
£4717 $7500 €7076 Up and down (50x20cm-20x8in) s. lithograph. 1-May-3 Swann Galleries, New York #449/R est:7000-10000
£5036 $8259 €7000 Puddle (24x32cm-9x13in) s.i. woodcut. 3-Jun-3 Christie's, Amsterdam #422/R est:7000-9000
£5063 $8000 €7595 Print gallery (32x32cm-13x13in) s.num.49/5511 lithograph. 22-Apr-3 Butterfields, San Francisco #2136/R est:6000-8000
£5128 $8000 €7692 Print gallery (41x40cm-16x16in) s.num.49/55II lithograph. 14-Oct-2 Butterfields, San Francisco #1122/R est:6000-8000
£5396 $8849 €7500 Planefilling II (32x37cm-13x15in) s.num.27/53 lithograph. 3-Jun-3 Christie's, Amsterdam #415/R est:5000-7000
£5449 $8500 €8174 Belvedere (58x40cm-23x16in) s.i. lithograph. 5-Nov-2 Christie's, Rockefeller NY #157/R est:10000-15000
£6115 $10029 €8500 Bond of union (25x34cm-10x13in) s.num.16/52 lithograph. 3-Jun-3 Christie's, Amsterdam #414/R est:7000-9000
£6329 $10000 €9494 Double planetoid (38cm-15in circular) s. wood engraving. 22-Apr-3 Butterfields, San Francisco #2135/R est:10000-15000
£6410 $10000 €9615 Print gallery (41x41cm-16x16in) s.num.27/43 lithograph. 5-Nov-2 Christie's, Rockefeller NY #156/R est:8000-12000
£6410 $10000 €9615 Ascending and descending (47x39cm-19x15in) s.num.36/108 lithograph. 5-Nov-2 Christie's, Rockefeller NY #158/R est:4000-6000
£6475 $10619 €9000 Convex and concave (27x35cm-11x14in) s.num.50/56 lithograph. 3-Jun-3 Christie's, Amsterdam #411/R est:8000-12000
£6475 $10619 €9000 Sky and water II (62x41cm-24x16in) s.i. woodcut. 3-Jun-3 Christie's, Amsterdam #423/R est:9000-11000
£6835 $11209 €9500 Knots (43x32cm-17x13in) s.i. wood engraving. 3-Jun-3 Christie's, Amsterdam #410/R est:6000-8000
£6835 $11209 €9500 Belvedere (46x29cm-18x11in) s.i.num.8/107 lithograph. 3-Jun-3 Christie's, Amsterdam #418/R est:9000-11000
£7051 $11000 €10577 Day and night (51x80cm-20x31in) s.i. col woodcut. 14-Oct-2 Butterfields, San Francisco #1121 est:12000-18000
£7051 $11000 €10577 Rind (42x29cm-17x11in) s.i. col woodcut. 5-Nov-2 Christie's, Rockefeller NY #155/R est:8000-12000
£7051 $10929 €11000 Goriano Sicoli, Abruzzi (24x29cm-9x11in) s.num.23/30 lithograph. 3-Dec-2 Christie's, Amsterdam #467/R est:1500-2000
£7500 $11850 €11250 Sky and water I (53x53cm-21x21in) s.i. woodblack print prov. 26-Nov-2 Sotheby's, Melbourne #251/R est:18000-22000 (A.D 21000)
£7692 $12000 €11538 Day and night (47x76cm-19x30in) s.i. black grey woodcut. 5-Nov-2 Christie's, Rockefeller NY #152/R est:15000-20000
£7914 $12978 €11000 Ascending and descending (35x28cm-14x11in) s.num.11/108 lithograph. 3-Jun-3 Christie's, Amsterdam #420/R est:9000-11000
£8861 $14000 €14000 Prententenoon stelling (32x32cm-13x13in) s.num.27/47 lithograph. 26-Nov-2 Sotheby's, Amsterdam #348/R est:8000-12000
£9000 $14040 €13500 Other World (40x30cm-16x12in) s.i. col woodcut. 10-Oct-2 Sotheby's, London #38/R est:4000-6000
£9353 $15338 €13000 Gallery of prints (32x32cm-13x13in) s.i.num.18/55 lithograph. 3-Jun-3 Christie's, Amsterdam #413/R est:12000-16000
£9353 $15338 €13000 Path of life III (36x37cm-14x15in) i. woodcut. 3-Jun-3 Christie's, Amsterdam #417/R est:9000-11000
£9615 $14904 €15000 Ascending and descending (35x28cm-14x11in) s.num.13/5011 lithograph prov. 3-Dec-2 Christie's, Amsterdam #469/R est:8000-10000
£10072 $16518 €14000 Still life with mirror (39x29cm-15x11in) s.num.9/24 lithograph. 3-Jun-3 Christie's, Amsterdam #404/R est:9000-11000
£10072 $16518 €14000 Day and night (39x68cm-15x27in) s.i. wood engraving. 3-Jun-3 Christie's, Amsterdam #407/R est:10000-15000
£10072 $16518 €14000 Square limit (34x34cm-13x13in) s.i. wood engraving. 3-Jun-3 Christie's, Amsterdam #416/R est:9000-11000
£10256 $16000 €15384 Drawing hands (33x40cm-13x16in) s.num.5/17 lithograph. 5-Nov-2 Christie's, Rockefeller NY #154/R est:20000-30000
£11511 $18878 €16000 Day and night (39x68cm-15x27in) s.i. wood engraving. 3-Jun-3 Christie's, Amsterdam #406 est:10000-15000
£15385 $24000 €23078 Snakes (56x47cm-22x19in) s.i. col woodcut. 5-Nov-2 Christie's, Rockefeller NY #159/R est:15000-20000

ESCHER, Rolf (1936-) German?
Works on paper
£506 $785 €800 Intruder (28x18cm-11x7in) s.d.1974 pencil. 28-Sep-2 Ketterer, Hamburg #728/R

ESCHKE, Hermann (1823-1900) German
£897 $1409 €1400 Fishermen on Brittany coast (57x46cm-22x18in) s. 21-Nov-2 Van Ham, Cologne #1592
£2222 $3644 €3400 Rugen coast (38x67cm-15x26in) s.d.1872 i.d.1872 verso. 8-Feb-3 Hans Stahl, Hamburg #92/R est:3600

ESCHKE, Richard-Hermann (1859-1944) German
£641 $1006 €1000 Landscape on the Azores (50x80cm-20x31in) s.d.25.10.89. 21-Nov-2 Van Ham, Cologne #1594/R
£1901 $3061 €2700 Ostend harbour entrance (63x89cm-25x35in) s. lit. 9-May-3 Schloss Ahlden, Ahlden #1409/R est:2400

ESCOBEDO, Helen (1936-) South American?
Sculpture
£38217 $60000 €57326 Dialogue (183x89x52cm-72x35x20in) green pat bronze exec.c.1965 prov. 19-Nov-2 Sotheby's, New York #89/R est:20000

ESCONDEUR, Marta (1957-) Uruguayan
£269 $420 €404 Dance (80x60cm-31x24in) s.d.2002 tempera panel. 10-Oct-2 Galleria Y Remates, Montevideo #92/R

ESCOULA, Jean (1851-1911) French
Sculpture
£1026 $1621 €1600 Buste de jeune fille (55cm-22in) s. white narblwe sold with socle lit. 18-Nov-2 Sotheby's, Paris #423/R est:3000-4500

ESCUDIE, Roger (1920-) French
£321 $503 €500 Port de Noirmoutier (54x73cm-21x29in) s. 15-Dec-2 Eric Pillon, Calais #268/R

ESHUYS, Hendrikus Jacobus (1888-1967) Dutch
£269 $423 €420 Dying horse (89x114cm-35x45in) s.d.62. 25-Nov-2 Glerum, Amsterdam #84
£269 $423 €420 Abstract landscape (104x90cm-41x35in) s.d.64. 25-Nov-2 Glerum, Amsterdam #85
£321 $503 €500 Unexpected kiss (61x51cm-24x20in) s. 25-Nov-2 Glerum, Amsterdam #93
£385 $604 €600 Man and woman (90x90cm-35x35in) s. 25-Nov-2 Glerum, Amsterdam #87
£449 $704 €700 Harbour cafe (53x79cm-21x31in) s. 25-Nov-2 Glerum, Amsterdam #83/R
£577 $906 €900 Artist in his studio (64x54cm-25x21in) s. 25-Nov-2 Glerum, Amsterdam #89/R
£833 $1308 €1300 In the studio (80x60cm-31x24in) s. 25-Nov-2 Glerum, Amsterdam #92/R
£1410 $2214 €2200 Bread meal (100x125cm-39x49in) s. 25-Nov-2 Glerum, Amsterdam #90/R est:300-500

ESINGER, Adele (1846-?) Austrian
£962 $1510 €1500 At the well (39x30cm-15x12in) s. 21-Nov-2 Dorotheum, Vienna #167/R est:1300-1800

ESKILSON, Per (1820-1872) Swedish
£421 $665 €632 Girl peeling vegetables at kitchen table (21x18cm-8x7in) s.d.59 panel. 30-Nov-2 Goteborg Auktionsverk, Sweden #141/R (S.KR 6000)

ESKOLA, Kalle (1912-) Finnish
£367 $573 €580 Green park (70x60cm-28x24in) s.d.55. 15-Sep-2 Bukowskis, Helsinki #184/R
£504 $826 €700 Towards the light (122x73cm-48x29in) s.d.1945-49. 4-Jun-3 Bukowskis, Helsinki #274/R
£2759 $4359 €4000 Sailors' cafe (54x63cm-21x25in) s.d.1939. 3-Apr-3 Hagelstam, Helsinki #1021 est:500

ESLING, Gordon (1897-?) Australian
£249 $381 €374 Looking down to fox ground (61x91cm-24x36in) s. painted c.1950 prov. 26-Aug-2 Sotheby's, Paddington #781 (A.D 700)

ESMONDE-WHITE, Eleanore (1914-) South African
£1720 $2769 €2580 Mother and child on the beach (33x28cm-13x11in) s. 12-May-3 Stephan Welz, Johannesburg #70/R est:5000-8000 (SA.R 20000)

ESPALIU, Pepe (1955-1993) Spanish
Works on paper
£1103 $1743 €1600 Carrying (23x17cm-9x7in) s.d.1992 ink col pencil dr. 1-Apr-3 Segre, Madrid #211/R
£2800 $4564 €4200 Octubre, Octubre (152x165cm-60x65in) s.i.d.87 verso mixed media on canvas in two parts prov.exhib. 3-Feb-3 Sotheby's, Olympia #108/R est:500-700

ESPINA Y CAPO, Juan (1848-1933) Spanish
£323 $510 €500 Rocky coast (35x64cm-14x25in) s.d.96. 18-Dec-2 Ansorena, Madrid #24/R

ESPINOS, Benito (attrib) (1748-1818) Spanish
£4437 $7365 €6300 Bouquets de fleurs sur un entablement (29x20cm-11x8in) pair. 16-Jun-3 Claude Aguttes, Neuilly #27/R est:6000-8000

ESPINOSA, Jose Maria (1796-1883) South American
Miniatures
£6369 $10000 €9554 Portrait of Simon Bolivar (6x4cm-2x2in) W/C exec.c.1828 prov.lit. 19-Nov-2 Sotheby's, New York #60/R est:18000

ESPINOUZE (1915-1982) French
Works on paper
£1027 $1613 €1500 Jumeaux (13x10cm-5x4in) mono. ink cardboard lit. 15-Apr-3 Laurence Calmels, Paris #4217/R

ESPLIN, Clarke (20th C) New Zealander?
£282 $440 €423 Mediterranean town scene (29x40cm-11x16in) s. 5-Nov-2 Peter Webb, Auckland #51/R (NZ.D 900)

ESPLIN, Tom (?) New Zealander?
£721 $1125 €1082 Convent (23x31cm-9x12in) s. board. 7-Nov-2 International Art Centre, Auckland #127/R est:2500-3500 (NZ.D 2300)
Works on paper
£523 $838 €758 Elgan cathedral (25x34cm-10x13in) s. W/C exec.c.1960. 13-May-3 Watson's, Christchurch #61/R (NZ.D 1450)

ESPOSITO, Dino Salvatore (1937-) Italian
Works on paper
£458 $732 €700 Extensive Italian landscape (60x100cm-24x39in) s.i.d.1968 verso mixed media canvas. 10-Jan-3 Allgauer, Kempten #1581/R
£458 $732 €700 Composition in blue with young woman (80x101cm-31x40in) s.indis.i.d.1967 mixed media canvas. 10-Jan-3 Allgauer, Kempten #1583/R

ESPOSITO, Enzo (1946-) Spanish
£780 $1264 €1100 Composition (100x150cm-39x59in) s.verso oil mixed media. 22-May-3 Stadion, Trieste #268/R
Sculpture
£1310 $1913 €1965 Composition (117x204x6cm-46x80x2in) s.d.1988 verso panel acrylic canvas. 4-Jun-2 Germann, Zurich #22/R est:4000-6000 (S.FR 3000)
Works on paper
£780 $1264 €1100 Untitled (51x46cm-20x18in) s.d.87 mixed media collage paper on canvas. 26-May-3 Christie's, Milan #74

ESPOSITO, G (1858-1911) Italian
Works on paper
£650 $1027 €975 Sailing boat with sails down (31x48cm-12x19in) s. W/C. 18-Dec-2 John Nicholson, Haslemere #1130

ESPOSITO, Gaetano (1858-1911) Italian
£262 $409 €393 Faraglioni cliffs (27x37cm-11x15in) s. panel. 6-Nov-2 Dobiaschofsky, Bern #3317/R (S.FR 600)
£318 $500 €477 Sorrento, Italy with rock wall high above water and figures (56x69cm-22x27in) s. 19-Apr-3 James Julia, Fairfield #168/R
£900 $1413 €1350 Continental harbour scene in evening sunlight (40x39cm-16x15in) s. board. 16-Dec-2 Bonhams, Bury St Edmunds #511/R
Works on paper
£244 $383 €380 Repairing boats (17x19cm-7x7in) s. pastel paper on card. 16-Dec-2 Pandolfini, Florence #51

ESPOSITO, Vincenzo (fl.1890-1920) Maltese
Works on paper
£550 $858 €825 Valetta harbour, Malta. Maltese harbour (20x34cm-8x13in) s. W/C bodycol pair. 19-Sep-2 Christie's, Kensington #118/R

ESPOY, Angel (1879-1963) American
£778 $1300 €1128 Sail ship in moderate seas (61x76cm-24x30in) s. prov. 17-Jun-3 John Moran, Pasadena #142 est:2000-3000
£903 $1400 €1355 Crashing waves (36x46cm-14x18in) s. painted c.1920. 8-Dec-2 Toomey, Oak Park #616/R
£1625 $2600 €2356 Sunset sail (23x30cm-9x12in) s. 16-May-3 Skinner, Boston #102/R est:2500-3500
£2548 $4000 €3822 Rolling surf under the Pacific sunset (71x96cm-28x38in) s. prov. 19-Nov-2 Butterfields, San Francisco #8208/R est:5000-7000
£4491 $7500 €6512 Wild flowers in rolling California landscape (76x64cm-30x25in) s. prov. 17-Jun-3 John Moran, Pasadena #138 est:8000-12000
£5280 $8500 €7920 Eucalyptus landscape with flower field (46x51cm-18x20in) s. 18-Feb-3 John Moran, Pasadena #51a est:5500-7500
£6211 $10000 €9317 Eucalyptus landscape with flower field (76x91cm-30x36in) s. 18-Feb-3 John Moran, Pasadena #92 est:6000-9000
£7229 $12000 €10482 Along the Pacific (76x102cm-30x40in) s. prov. 11-Jun-3 Butterfields, San Francisco #4290/R est:3000-5000

ESQUIVEL, Antonio Maria de (1806-1857) Spanish
£1698 $2649 €2700 Portrait of Sir Manuel Rodriguez (73x57cm-29x22in) s.d.1841. 17-Sep-2 Segre, Madrid #78/R
£1887 $2943 €3000 Portrait of Lady Josefa Feito (73x56cm-29x22in) s. 17-Sep-2 Segre, Madrid #77/R
£4487 $7090 €7000 Portrait of Antonio Gutierrez Solana (112x90cm-44x35in) s.d.1834. 14-Nov-2 Arte, Seville #267/R
£7586 $12138 €11000 Portrait of Isabel II (120x87cm-47x34in) 11-Mar-3 Castellana, Madrid #336/R est:14000
£8000 $12560 €12000 Studio chess game (55x61cm-22x24in) 19-Nov-2 Sotheby's, London #199/R est:6000-8000

ESSCHE, Maurice van (1906-1977) South African
£480 $750 €720 Boats and seagulls in the harbour (30x40cm-12x16in) s. board. 11-Nov-2 Stephan Welz, Johannesburg #494/R (SA.R 7500)
£522 $814 €783 Portrait of a boy (34x24cm-13x9in) s.d.69 board. 15-Oct-2 Stephan Welz, Johannesburg #448/R est:4000-6000 (SA.R 8500)
£731 $1177 €1097 Extensive landscape with farmhouses (29x40cm-11x16in) s. board. 12-May-3 Stephan Welz, Johannesburg #488/R est:7000-10000 (SA.R 8500)
£884 $1397 €1326 Reclining harlequin (26x48cm-10x19in) s. board. 1-Apr-3 Stephan Welz, Johannesburg #458/R est:7000-10000 (SA.R 11000)
£1025 $1599 €1538 Portrait of a young girl (43x28cm-17x11in) s. canvas on board prov. 11-Nov-2 Stephan Welz, Johannesburg #500/R est:7000-10000 (SA.R 16000)
£1044 $1629 €1566 Karoo landscape (34x58cm-13x23in) s. board. 15-Oct-2 Stephan Welz, Johannesburg #451/R est:9000-12000 (SA.R 17000)
£1118 $1800 €1677 Head of a boy (29x18cm-11x7in) s. board. 12-May-3 Stephan Welz, Johannesburg #71/R est:4000-6000 (SA.R 13000)
£1153 $1799 €1730 Two figures walking in front of houses (35x52cm-14x20in) s. board. 11-Nov-2 Stephan Welz, Johannesburg #538/R est:10000-15000 (SA.R 18000)
£1720 $2683 €2580 Still life with white vase and grapes on a table (68x51cm-27x20in) s. canvas on board. 15-Oct-2 Stephan Welz, Johannesburg #450/R est:30000-40000 (SA.R 28000)
£2408 $3876 €3612 Seated Malay woman (52x36cm-20x14in) s. panel. 12-May-3 Stephan Welz, Johannesburg #521/R est:20000-30000 (SA.R 28000)
£2691 $4197 €4037 Couple (52x62cm-20x24in) s. i.verso prov. 11-Nov-2 Stephan Welz, Johannesburg #501/R est:30000-40000 (SA.R 42000)
£2923 $4707 €4385 Woman in a blue shirt (60x44cm-24x17in) s.d.66 board. 12-May-3 Stephan Welz, Johannesburg #454/R est:12000-18000 (SA.R 34000)
Works on paper
£215 $335 €323 Seated nude (49x37cm-19x15in) s.d.48 chl. 15-Oct-2 Stephan Welz, Johannesburg #184 est:1800-2400 (SA.R 3500)

ESSELENS, Jacob (circle) (1626-1687) Dutch
£6000 $9360 €9000 Dutch shipping by a shore with figure unloading a wagon (34x46cm-13x18in) init. panel. 9-Apr-3 Christie's, London #36/R est:6000-8000

ESSEN, Cornelis van (17/18th C) Dutch
£10063 $15597 €16000 Resting horsemen outside an inn (45x61cm-18x24in) mono. 2-Oct-2 Dorotheum, Vienna #188/R est:8000-12000

ESSEN, Cornelis van (attrib) (17/18th C) Dutch
£5479 $8548 €8000 Rider in Dutch village (59x84cm-23x33in) mono. 10-Apr-3 Van Ham, Cologne #1192/R est:12000

ESSEN, Didrik von (19th C) Swedish
£511 $837 €741 Summer landscape with hay stooks near farm (32x62cm-13x24in) init.d.79. 4-Jun-3 AB Stockholms Auktionsverk #2191/R (S.KR 6500)

ESSEN, Ebba von (20th C) Irish?
£1096 $1721 €1600 Female portrait (56x41cm-22x16in) s.d.49. 15-Apr-3 De Veres Art Auctions, Dublin #99a est:1000-1500

ESSEN, Johannes Cornelis (1854-1936) Dutch
£472 $746 €708 Garden in autumn (66x52cm-26x20in) s.d.1879. 29-Nov-2 Zofingen, Switzerland #2426 (S.FR 1100)
Works on paper
£215 $335 €312 Animals in a Dutch farmyard (36x51cm-14x20in) s. gouache W/C lit. 26-Mar-3 Walker's, Ottawa #2/R (C.D 500)
£386 $606 €579 Returning home (35x53cm-14x21in) s. W/C. 10-Dec-2 Pinneys, Montreal #85 (C.D 950)

ESSENHIGH, Inka (1969-) American
£2532 $4000 €3798 Light purple (51x72cm-20x28in) oil ink paper painted 2000 prov. 13-Nov-2 Sotheby's, New York #406/R
£6329 $10000 €9494 Hurricane Mary (122x122cm-48x48in) s.i.d.1998 verso oil enamel prov. 14-Nov-2 Christie's, Rockefeller NY #339/R est:15000-20000
£7500 $12000 €11250 Untitled (61x27cm-24x11in) painted 2000 prov.lit. 14-May-3 Sotheby's, New York #315/R est:8000-12000
£34810 $55000 €52215 Ozone hole (183x183cm-72x72in) oil enamel painted 1998 prov. 14-Nov-2 Christie's, Rockefeller NY #338/R est:35000-45000

ESSER, Elgar (1967-) German
Photographs
£8000 $12320 €12000 Chattresac I Frankreich. Chattresac II Frankreich (119x156cm-47x61in) s. two chromagenic prints mounted on plexiglas prov. 23-Oct-2 Christie's, London #212/R est:10000-15000
£8861 $14000 €13292 Canal des Allemands, France (124x162cm-49x64in) s.d.1997 verso num.3 chromogenic col print prov. 24-Apr-3 Phillips, New York #69/R est:12000-15000

ESSEX, William (1784-1869) British
Miniatures
£1500 $2355 €2250 King William IV, when Duke of Clarence (8x6cm-3x2in) s.d.1828 enamel on copper rectangular. 10-Dec-2 Christie's, London #28/R est:600-800
£4000 $6240 €6000 Sir David Wilkie seated in an interior wearing black cloak (13cm-5xin) i. enamel ormolu frame octagonal exhib.lit. 5-Nov-2 Bonhams, New Bond Street #161/R est:4000-6000
£4500 $7380 €6525 Charlotte, Duchess of Northumberland (4x4cm-2x2in) s.d.1834 enamel on gold octagonal prov. 3-Jun-3 Christie's, London #40/R est:2500-3500

ESSFELD, Alexander (20th C) German
£308 $481 €450 Harbour with sailing ships and steam ship (80x100cm-31x39in) s.i.d.04. 10-Apr-3 Allgauer, Kempten #2765/R

ESSIG, George E (1838-?) American
Works on paper
£481 $750 €722 Fishing boat at sunset (41x66cm-16x26in) s. W/C. 20-Sep-2 Freeman, Philadelphia #16/R

ESTALELLA PUJOLA, Ramon (1895-1986) Spanish
£428 $693 €650 Playing (100x129cm-39x51in) after Goya. 21-Jan-3 Durán, Madrid #662/R
£993 $1619 €1500 Toledo (39x31cm-15x12in) s.d.1963 board prov. 11-Feb-3 Segre, Madrid #188/R

ESTERL, Felix (1904-1941) German
£523 $858 €800 Highway in the mountains (71x57cm-28x22in) s.d.31. 5-Feb-3 Neumeister, Munich #702

ESTES, Richard (1932-) American
£31646 $50000 €47469 Deck of Staten Island Ferry with view of Manhattan (60x32cm-24x13in) s.d.95 prov.exhib. 13-Nov-2 Sotheby's, New York #259/R est:60000-80000
£190000 $317300 €285000 Paris Opera House (100x202cm-39x80in) s.d.00 prov.exhib. 26-Jun-3 Christie's, London #22/R est:200000-300000
Prints
£4403 $7000 €6605 Holland hotel (122x183cm-48x72in) s.i. col screenprint. 2-May-3 Sotheby's, New York #431/R est:8000-10000
£9615 $15000 €14423 D-train. Chock full o'nuts (106x212cm-42x83in) s. one num.100/125 board one num.44/100 col screenprint pair. 5-Nov-2 Christie's, Rockefeller NY #369/R est:16000-22000
Works on paper
£769 $1192 €1200 Wake (11x9cm-4x4in) s.i. gouache. 3-Dec-2 Lempertz, Koln #122/R

ESTEVA, Isabel (1958-) Spanish
£597 $920 €950 Egyptian series IV (140x132cm-55x52in) s.d.1983 acrylic paper prov. 28-Oct-2 Segre, Madrid #153/R

ESTEVAN, Enrique (1849-1927) Spanish
£362 $586 €550 Fight (28x23cm-11x9in) s. paper. 21-Jan-3 Durán, Madrid #18/R
£395 $639 €600 Soldiers (26x23cm-10x9in) s. paper. 21-Jan-3 Durán, Madrid #17/R

ESTEVAN, Hermengildo (1851-1945) Spanish
£1763 $2785 €2750 View of Venice (73x43cm-29x17in) s. 14-Nov-2 Arte, Seville #376/R

ESTEVE Y BOTTEY, Francisco (1884-1959) Spanish
Works on paper
£310 $489 €480 Apolo Fountain, Madrid (35x24cm-14x9in) s. pencil dr. 17-Dec-2 Segre, Madrid #9/R
£355 $561 €550 Alcantara bridge in Toledo (22x29cm-9x11in) s. W/C. 17-Dec-2 Segre, Madrid #11/R

ESTEVE, Agustin (1753-1809) Spanish
£96552 $154483 €140000 Portrait de la Duchesse d'Albe (206x121cm-81x48in) prov.exhib.lit. after Goya. 11-Mar-3 Christie's, Paris #425/R est:60000

ESTEVE, Agustin (attrib) (1753-1809) Spanish
£1892 $2951 €2800 Portrait de jeune femme en robe blanche (159x82cm-63x32in) 26-Mar-3 Tajan, Paris #81/R

ESTEVE, Maurice (1904-2001) French
£694 $1104 €1000 Le lecteur (27x43cm-11x17in) s.i. graphite estompe dr. 29-Apr-3 Artcurial Briest, Paris #66
£2239 $3560 €3359 Composition (46x33cm-18x13in) s. chl. 29-Apr-3 Kunsthallen, Copenhagen #120/R est:30000 (D.KR 24000)
£9434 $14623 €15000 Composition (22x27cm-9x11in) s.d.57 lit. 30-Oct-2 Artcurial Briest, Paris #426/R est:15000-18000
£16026 $25160 €25000 Cour de ferme (54x65cm-21x26in) s. s.i.d.43 verso prov.exhib.lit. 10-Dec-2 Piasa, Paris #239/R est:20000
£17785 $28634 €26500 Scaphandriers (50x64cm-20x25in) s.d.1947 prov.lit. 23-Feb-3 Mercier & Cie, Lille #123/R est:38000
£17949 $28179 €28000 Cafetiere et tapis rouge (61x46cm-24x18in) s.d.42 s.i.d.verso prov.lit. 10-Dec-2 Piasa, Paris #238/R est:20000
£25641 $39744 €40000 Vieille chaise devant une table (120x80cm-47x31in) s.d.41 s.i.d.verso exhib.lit. 9-Dec-2 Piasa, Paris #30/R est:45000-60000
£27338 $43741 €38000 Ouche a Trenay (50x73cm-20x29in) s.d.45 prov.exhib.lit. 14-May-3 Blanchet, Paris #183/R est:40000-50000
£27376 $43255 €41064 Le sabotier (65x54cm-26x21in) s.d.49. 28-Apr-3 Bukowskis, Stockholm #320/R est:400000-500000 (S.KR 360000)
£33333 $52333 €52000 Buffet a la lampe (54x65cm-21x26in) s.d.43 s.i.d.verso exhib.lit. 10-Dec-2 Piasa, Paris #107/R est:30000-40000
£44872 $70449 €70000 Canape bleu (90x116cm-35x46in) s.d.35 s.i.d.verso prov.exhib.lit. 10-Dec-2 Piasa, Paris #237/R est:60000
£45390 $73532 €64000 Les barrieres dans la cour (65x92cm-26x36in) s.d.45 s.i.d. verso prov. 24-May-3 Van Ham, Cologne #170/R est:40000
£48077 $74519 €75000 Fobora (73x92cm-29x36in) s.d.82 s.i.d.verso exhib.lit. 9-Dec-2 Piasa, Paris #52/R est:45000-60000
£48966 $77366 €71000 Loxos (100x73cm-39x29in) s.d.78 s.i.d.verso prov.lit. 2-Apr-3 Christie's, Paris #20/R est:55000-70000
£51724 $81724 €75000 Bourriot (65cm-26in circular) s.d.73 s.i.d.verso prov.lit. 2-Apr-3 Christie's, Paris #33/R est:45000
£60897 $94391 €95000 Jeune fille au pichet (100x81cm-39x32in) s. s.i.d.1942 verso exhib.lit. 9-Dec-2 Piasa, Paris #29/R est:100000-130000
£70513 $110705 €110000 Nappe ecossaise (146x97cm-57x38in) s.d.38 prov.exhib.lit. 10-Dec-2 Piasa, Paris #236/R est:60000
£84615 $131154 €132000 Souffleur de verre (81x65cm-32x26in) s.d.48 s.i.d.48 verso prov.exhib.lit. 9-Dec-2 Piasa, Paris #42/R est:70000-90000
£128205 $201282 €200000 Mitoi (38x55cm-15x22in) s.d.64 s.i.d.verso lit. 10-Dec-2 Piasa, Paris #108/R est:30000-45000
Works on paper
£769 $1208 €1200 Femme au jardin (24x32cm-9x13in) s.d.43 chl. 10-Dec-2 Piasa, Paris #331
£833 $1308 €1300 Figure penchee (31x24cm-12x9in) s.d.44 i.verso chl dr. 10-Dec-2 Piasa, Paris #114
£833 $1308 €1300 Homme au lapin (24x29cm-9x11in) s.d.44 crayon. 10-Dec-2 Piasa, Paris #113/R
£962 $1510 €1500 Nu sombre (39x31cm-15x12in) s.d.43 chl dr. 10-Dec-2 Piasa, Paris #111
£1151 $1842 €1600 Compositions (15x14cm-6x6in) s. W/C collage prov. two. 17-May-3 De Vuyst, Lokeren #173/R est:1600-1800
£1410 $2214 €2200 Femme lisant (41x50cm-16x20in) s.d.45 chl dr. 10-Dec-2 Piasa, Paris #116
£1410 $2214 €2200 Toilette (36x32cm-14x13in) s.d.43 chl dr. 10-Dec-2 Piasa, Paris #110
£1410 $2214 €2200 Servante (24x31cm-9x12in) s.d.43 crayon col crayon. 10-Dec-2 Piasa, Paris #109/R
£1603 $2516 €2500 Femme assoupie (40x31cm-16x12in) s.d.43 chl prov. 10-Dec-2 Piasa, Paris #329
£1667 $2617 €2600 Peintre au chevalet (24x31cm-9x12in) s.d.43 chl prov. 10-Dec-2 Piasa, Paris #338
£1923 $3019 €3000 Matin dans l'embrasure (31x23cm-12x9in) s.d.43 chl prov. 10-Dec-2 Piasa, Paris #333
£1923 $3019 €3000 Lecture sous la lampe (29x24cm-11x9in) s.d.43 chl prov. 10-Dec-2 Piasa, Paris #332
£1923 $3019 €3000 Nature morte (24x29cm-9x11in) s.d.43 chl col crayon prov. 10-Dec-2 Piasa, Paris #340
£1923 $3019 €3000 Trois tables (22x27cm-9x11in) s.d.43 chl. 10-Dec-2 Piasa, Paris #335
£1987 $3120 €3100 Plaisant (24x32cm-9x13in) s.d.44 chl prov. 10-Dec-2 Piasa, Paris #336

£2436 $3824 €3800 Sculpteur (32x45cm-13x18in) s.d.44 chl dr. 10-Dec-2 Piasa, Paris #112
£2564 $4026 €4000 Ombre de l'aquarium (31x24cm-12x9in) s.d.43 chl prov. 10-Dec-2 Piasa, Paris #328
£2564 $4026 €4000 Femme au piano (31x39cm-12x15in) s.d.44 chl prov. 10-Dec-2 Piasa, Paris #327
£3205 $5032 €5000 Habitude du silence (24x31cm-9x12in) s.d.43 chl col crayon prov. 10-Dec-2 Piasa, Paris #334/R
£3205 $5032 €5000 Peintre (31x38cm-12x15in) s.d.44 chl prov. 10-Dec-2 Piasa, Paris #325 est:700
£3526 $5535 €5500 Voyante (24x29cm-9x11in) s.d.43 chl prov. 10-Dec-2 Piasa, Paris #337
£3846 $6038 €6000 Oisellerie (32x39cm-13x15in) s.d.44 chl prov. 10-Dec-2 Piasa, Paris #326/R
£4138 $6538 €6000 Untitled (35x27cm-14x11in) s.d.71 chl col crayon prov. 2-Apr-3 Christie's, Paris #24/R
£4138 $6538 €6000 Composition (29x25cm-11x10in) s.d.67 chl col crayon prov. 2-Apr-3 Christie's, Paris #31/R
£4167 $6542 €6500 Clarinettiste (25x31cm-10x12in) s.d.44 chl prov. 10-Dec-2 Piasa, Paris #339/R
£4487 $7045 €7000 Envol des oiseaux (54x43cm-21x17in) s.d.45 chl dr. 10-Dec-2 Piasa, Paris #115/R
£4828 $7628 €7000 Composition (24x32cm-9x13in) s.d.69 chl col crayon prov. 2-Apr-3 Christie's, Paris #35/R est:9000
£5128 $8051 €8000 Ombre des persiennes (39x32cm-15x13in) s.d.44 prov. 10-Dec-2 Piasa, Paris #330/R est:1500
£5172 $8172 €7500 Untitled (50x38cm-20x15in) s. W/C exec.1953 prov. 2-Apr-3 Christie's, Paris #41/R
£6250 $10313 €9000 Composition (30x42cm-12x17in) s. exhib. 1-Jul-3 Artcurial Briest, Paris #509/R est:10000-15000
£7092 $11844 €10000 Composition (60x46cm-24x18in) s.d. W/C prov.lit. 23-Jun-3 Claude Boisgirard, Paris #150/R est:12000-15000
£7500 $12525 €10875 Composition (48x36cm-19x14in) s. W/C prov. 26-Jun-3 Sotheby's, London #185/R est:7000-9000
£8276 $13076 €12000 Untitled (52x40cm-20x16in) s. W/C exec.1972 prov. 2-Apr-3 Christie's, Paris #29/R est:18000
£11458 $18104 €16500 Composition (49x40cm-19x16in) s.d. W/C prov. 27-Apr-3 Perrin, Versailles #38/R est:20000-25000
£13103 $20703 €19000 Untitled (49x49cm-19x19in) s. W/C exec.1972 prov. 2-Apr-3 Christie's, Paris #30/R est:18000
£13542 $22344 €19500 Composition (50x65cm-20x26in) s.d.93 W/C prov. 1-Jul-3 Artcurial Briest, Paris #792/R est:12000-15000

ESTLER, Georg Gustav (1860-1954) German
£440 $687 €700 Spreewald (96x72cm-38x28in) s.i. 21-Sep-2 Dannenberg, Berlin #551/R

ESTOPPEY, David (1862-1952) Swiss
£701 $1093 €1100 Pre alpine landscape with lake (69x53cm-27x21in) s. lit. 8-Nov-2 Auktionhaus Georg Rehm, Augsburg #8041/R

ESTRUCH, Antonio Jose (1838-1907) Spanish
£303 $482 €440 Saint Joaquin (29x20cm-11x8in) s. i.verso board. 4-Mar-3 Ansorena, Madrid #29/R
£516 $815 €800 Saint Joaquin (29x20cm-11x8in) s. i.d.1890 verso board. 18-Dec-2 Ansorena, Madrid #131/R

ESTRUGA, Oscar (1933-) Spanish
Works on paper
£377 $589 €600 Resting (36x50cm-14x20in) s. wash lit. 23-Sep-2 Durán, Madrid #43/R

ETCHEVERRY, Denis (1867-1950) French
£1090 $1689 €1700 Portrait de femme de profil (64x55cm-25x22in) s.d.1886. 6-Dec-2 Maigret, Paris #112/R
£1218 $1888 €1900 Vanity (55x72cm-22x28in) s.d.1886. 9-Dec-2 Beaussant & Lefèvre, Paris #43/R

ETERNOD, Marcel Victor (1891-1971) Swiss
£519 $830 €779 Les Iles Baleares (45x61cm-18x24in) s.d. i. verso. 17-Mar-3 Philippe Schuler, Zurich #4522 (S.FR 1100)

ETEVE, Felix Raoul (20th C) French
£267 $443 €387 Paysage vec pont (37x46cm-15x18in) s. 16-Jun-3 Waddingtons, Toronto #270/R (C.D 600)

ETGENS, Johann Georg (1693-1757) Czechoslovakian
Works on paper
£556 $883 €800 Apotheose (13cm-5in circular) pen wash. 5-May-3 Ketterer, Munich #247/R

ETHOFER, Theodor J (1849-1915) Austrian
£354 $564 €531 Portrait of Dr Max Strauss (62x49cm-24x19in) s.i.d.MDCCCLXX. 5-May-3 Rasmussen, Vejle #411/R (D.KR 3800)

ETIENNE-MARTIN (1913-1995) French
Sculpture
£3205 $5032 €5000 Petit couple (30x13cm-12x5in) s. num.3/9 brown pat bronze Cast Busato lit. 24-Nov-2 Laurence Calmels, Paris #295/R
£19231 $30385 €30000 Nuit Nina (136cm-54in) s.stf.Bonvicini num.7/9 bronze exec.1951 prov.exhib.lit. 15-Nov-2 Laurence Calmels, Paris #28a/R est:40000

ETNIER, Stephen (1903-1984) American
£881 $1400 €1322 View from the New Windsor Hotel, Hamilton, Bermuda. s. 22-Mar 3 Nadeau, Windsor #389 est:600-900
£1863 $3000 €2795 Beach shack, Jamaica; shoreline scene with rowing boats on the beach (30x61cm-12x24in) s. i.verso painted 1971. 21-Feb-3 York Town, York #1069a
£3750 $6000 €5625 From Hollywood (48x58cm-19x23in) s.d.45. 16-May-3 York Town, York #945 est:5000-7000
£4063 $6500 €6095 Beach at Ogunquit (20x33cm-8x13in) s. 11-Jan-3 James Julia, Fairfield #50 est:6000-8000
£4969 $8000 €7454 Shore scene at Nassau with docked fishing boat (33x61cm-13x24in) s.d.69 i.verso. 21-Feb-3 York Town, York #1066
£6250 $10000 €9375 Lower Battery Nasau (36x61cm-14x24in) s.d.69 panel. 16-May-3 York Town, York #967 est:6000-8000
£6891 $10750 €10337 Dolphin marina, S Harpswell ME (61x41cm-24x16in) s.d.1969 acrylic board. 8-Nov-2 York Town, York #687
£7372 $11500 €11058 River at Phippsburg, Kennebec River (61x36cm-24x14in) s.d.1965 acrylic. 8-Nov-2 York Town, York #686
£10313 $16500 €15470 Maine sunrise over the water with man in his boat (41x91cm-16x36in) s.d.66. 16-May-3 York Town, York #936 est:7000-9000
£10625 $17000 €15938 In the hanger (89x124cm-35x49in) s.d.41. 16-May-3 York Town, York #918 est:25000-35000
£26056 $37000 €39084 Monhegan Harbour (56x91cm-22x36in) 8-Aug-1 Barridorf, Portland #6/R est:20000-30000

ETROG, Sorel (1933-) Canadian/Rumanian
Sculpture
£800 $1312 €1200 Abstract composition (16cm-6in) num.2/5 bronze. 3-Jun-3 Joyner, Toronto #298/R est:1000-1500 (C.D 1800)
£823 $1276 €1235 Figure (33cm-13in) s.num.3/10 bronze. 3-Dec-2 Joyner, Toronto #392 est:1000-1500 (C.D 2000)
£1311 $2071 €1967 Horse's armour (48cm-19in) bronze prov. 18-Nov-2 Sotheby's, Toronto #40/R est:4000-6000 (C.D 3250)
£1422 $2332 €2133 Untitled (12cm-5in) s.num.1/10 bronze lit. 3-Jun-3 Joyner, Toronto #282/R est:1000-1500 (C.D 3200)
£1778 $2916 €2667 Little ballerina (24cm-9in) s.num.7/10 bronze. 3-Jun-3 Joyner, Toronto #203/R est:2000-3000 (C.D 4000)
£3556 $5831 €5334 Abstract figure (77cm-30in) s.i. bronze. 3-Jun-3 Joyner, Toronto #92/R est:6000-8000 (C.D 8000)
£3778 $6196 €5667 Untitled (55cm-22in) s.i.num.6/7 bronze lit. 3-Jun-3 Joyner, Toronto #119/R est:5000-7000 (C.D 8500)
£5242 $8282 €7863 Quartet (139cm-55in) s. num.3/7 bronze prov.exhib. 18-Nov-2 Sotheby's, Toronto #42/R est:16000-19000 (C.D 13000)
£8805 $14000 €13208 Queen III (126cm-50in) st.sig.num.6/6 gold pat bronze. 27-Feb-3 Christie's, Rockefeller NY #40/R est:9000

ETTY, William (1787-1849) British
£400 $640 €600 Study of a semi draped female nude seated on a chair (31x23cm-12x9in) millboard. 13-May-3 Bonhams, Knightsbridge #92/R
£750 $1170 €1125 Seated female nude (47x37cm-19x15in) millboard. 8-Apr-3 Bonhams, Knightsbridge #314/R
£817 $1259 €1300 Diane (40x28cm-16x11in) panel. 25-Oct-2 Tajan, Paris #150 est:1200-1500
£1500 $2415 €2250 Male nude (61x47cm-24x19in) panelprov. 20-Feb-3 Christie's, London #329/R
£1600 $2464 €2400 Female nude (37x30cm-15x12in) 5-Sep-2 Christie's, Kensington #248/R est:1000-1500
£1800 $2808 €2700 Female nude in an interior (41x50cm-16x20in) board. 7-Nov-2 Christie's, Kensington #238/R est:1200-1800
£1900 $2964 €2850 Study of a standing female nude (65x49cm-26x19in) board. 10-Sep-2 Bonhams, Knightsbridge #208/R est:1000-2000
£2000 $3200 €3000 Andromeda (90x57cm-35x22in) 11-Mar-3 Bonhams, Knightsbridge #135/R est:1000-1500
£2200 $3542 €3300 Male nude (50x62cm-20x24in) prov. 20-Feb-3 Christie's, London #330/R
£2200 $3498 €3300 Bather (61x46cm-24x18in) board prov. 6-Mar-3 Christie's, Kensington #557/R est:2000-4000
£2400 $3696 €3600 Male nude (44x31cm-17x12in) board on panel prov. 5-Sep-2 Christie's, Kensington #246/R est:700-1200
£2800 $4508 €4200 Female nude in landscape (44x56cm-17x22in) 20-Feb-3 Christie's, London #312/R
£2923 $4619 €4385 Seated male nude (45x36cm-18x14in) indis.sig. board prov. 18-Nov-2 Waddingtons, Toronto #132/R est:3000-4000 (C.D 7250)
£3000 $4830 €4500 Male nude from behind (61x46cm-24x18in) prov. 20-Feb-3 Christie's, London #183/R
£3200 $5152 €4800 Study for Phaedria and Cymochles (33cm-13in circular) board prov. 20-Feb-3 Christie's, London #175/R
£3200 $5152 €4800 Female nude on balcony (62x48cm-24x19in) board on canvas prov. 20-Feb-3 Christie's, London #181/R
£3200 $5152 €4800 Female nude (59x42cm-23x17in) board on panel prov.exhib. 20-Feb-3 Christie's, London #308/R
£3200 $5152 €4800 Wrestlers. Study of man with staff (49x40cm-19x16in) mono. board double-sided prov. 20-Feb-3 Christie's, London #309/R

£3500 $5635 €5250 Male nude (59x49cm-23x19in) boardprov. 20-Feb-3 Christie's, London #184/R

£4032 $6371 €6048 Musidora, the bather at the doubtful breeze alarmed (30x23cm-12x9in) board prov.lit. 18-Nov-2 Waddingtons, Toronto #131/R est:3000-4000 (C.D 10000)

£4200 $6762 €6300 Bacchus (42x49cm-17x19in) board on panel prov.exhib.lit. 20-Feb-3 Christie's, London #313/R

£5000 $8050 €7500 Guardsman Higgins (66x51cm-26x20in) i. board prov.exhib. 20-Feb-3 Christie's, London #326/R

£5500 $8855 €8250 Female nude (67x51cm-26x20in) board on panel. 20-Feb-3 Christie's, London #182/R

£5500 $8855 €8250 Study of girl at toilet. Study of king seated (28x24cm-11x9in) s. board double-sided prov. 20-Feb-3 Christie's, London #332/R

£6000 $9660 €9000 Female nude (61x44cm-24x17in) exhib. 20-Feb-3 Christie's, London #307/R

£8000 $12880 €12000 Reclining female nude (42x50cm-17x20in) board prov. 20-Feb-3 Christie's, London #178/R est:8000

£8000 $12880 €12000 Manlius hurled from the rock (76x67cm-30x26in) 20-Feb-3 Christie's, London #314/R

£9000 $14490 €13500 Study of girl reading book (46x65cm-18x26in) board. 20-Feb-3 Christie's, London #311/R est:5000

£10000 $16100 €15000 Despair. Nude study (48x67cm-19x26in) board arched top double-sided prov. 20-Feb-3 Christie's, London #179/R est:12000

£17000 $27370 €25500 Phaedria and Cymochles on the Idle lake (58x79cm-23x31in) arched top prov.exhib.lit. 20-Feb-3 Christie's, London #174/R est:30000

ETTY, William (attrib) (1787-1849) British

£528 $850 €792 Study of a female nude (39x36cm-15x14in) board. 23-Feb-3 Butterfields, Los Angeles #7006

£843 $1400 €1222 Centaur and draped female figure (53x64cm-21x25in) 11-Jun-3 Boos Gallery, Michigan #489/R est:1500-2500

£3448 $5310 €5172 Diana resting, dog in foreground (56x82cm-22x32in) panel. 27-Oct-2 Anders Antik, Landskrona #228/R est:15000-20000 (S.KR 50000)

EUBANKS, Tony (1939-) American

£7534 $11000 €11301 From where the sun now stands (76x127cm-30x50in) 18-May-2 Altermann Galleries, Santa Fe #19/R

EUFEMIANO (1921-1955) Spanish

£755 $1177 €1200 Pomegranates (23x48cm-9x19in) s. board. 8-Oct-2 Ansorena, Madrid #311/R

£3019 $4679 €4800 Apples (60x73cm-24x29in) 7-Oct-2 Ansorena, Madrid #92/R est:4800

EUGEN (1865-1947) Swedish

£3569 $5781 €5175 Study for - Hoare-frost (29x48cm-11x19in) s.d.1908 verso canvas on panel. 26-May-3 Bukowskis, Stockholm #45/R est:25000-30000 (S.KR 46000)

£3692 $6055 €5353 Oak trees II (38x46cm-15x18in) s.d.1940 panel. 4-Jun-3 AB Stockholms Auktionsverk #2259/R est:30000-35000 (S.KR 47000)

£3879 $6284 €5625 Harvesting landscape (34x75cm-13x30in) s. panel. 25-May-3 Uppsala Auktionskammare, Uppsala #154/R est:50000-60000 (S.KR 50000)

£3901 $6046 €5852 The bay - summer landscape with water (29x41cm-11x16in) s. i.d.c.1910 verso panel. 4-Dec-2 AB Stockholms Auktionsverk #1752/R est:50000-60000 (S.KR 55000)

£4321 $7086 €6265 Green house in snow, W.udden 1910 (58x75cm-23x30in) s. prov. 4-Jun-3 AB Stockholms Auktionsverk #2324/R est:60000-80000 (S.KR 55000)

£4713 $7730 €6834 Autumn colours at Waldemarsudde (39x49cm-15x19in) s. d.1923 verso panel. 4-Jun-3 AB Stockholms Auktionsverk #2219/R est:60000-70000 (S.KR 60000)

£6738 $10443 €10107 Strandvagen, Stockholm - boats at quay (33x46cm-13x18in) s.d. panel. 4-Dec-2 AB Stockholms Auktionsverk #1705/R est:60000-80000 (S.KR 95000)

£8641 $14171 €12529 Fenris at Finnboda, view from Waldemarsudde (38x55cm-15x22in) s.d.1940. 4-Jun-3 AB Stockholms Auktionsverk #2091/R est:60000-80000 (S.KR 110000)

Works on paper

£1021 $1675 €1480 Summer landscape from Vattern areas (20x23cm-8x9in) mono.d.1927 mixed media. 4-Jun-3 AB Stockholms Auktionsverk #2107/R (S.KR 13000)

EURICH, Richard (1903-1992) British

£1200 $1860 €1800 Landscape with chestnut trees (18x46cm-7x18in) s.d.68 s.i.verso board prov. 4-Dec-2 Christie's, Kensington #571/R est:1500-2000

£1400 $2310 €2030 Portland Bill Pulpit Rock, Dorest (41x51cm-16x20in) s.d.1957. 3-Jul-3 Christie's, Kensington #444/R est:800-1200

£1900 $2945 €2850 Sebastian (20x51cm-8x20in) s.d.77 canvasboard. 4-Dec-2 Christie's, Kensington #568/R est:1000-1500

£2200 $3674 €3190 Old Yorkshire quarry, Wharfedale (40x51cm-16x20in) s.d.1961 s.i.verso prov. 24-Jun-3 Bonhams, New Bond Street #26/R est:2000-3000

£2400 $3960 €3480 Southampton (41x51cm-16x20in) s.d.57 prov. 3-Jul-3 Christie's, Kensington #442/R est:800-1200

£4800 $7488 €7200 Seaweed beach (48x68cm-19x27in) s.d.85 i.verso board prov. 27-Mar-3 Christie's, Kensington #566/R est:3000-5000

Works on paper

£2200 $3630 €3190 Young woman with child (31x20cm-12x8in) s.d.1929 pencil. 3-Jul-3 Christie's, Kensington #269/R est:800-1200

EUROPEAN SCHOOL

Sculpture

£5500 $8524 €8250 Bust of Marcus Aurelius Roman (74cm-29in) white marble 5th Century with 18th C additions. 29-Oct-2 Sotheby's, London #204/R est:5000-7000

£7449 $11844 €11174 Classic torso (155cm-61in) white marble incl. black marble socle. 10-Mar-3 Rasmussen, Vejle #1168/R est:100000 (D.KR 80000)

£10377 $16189 €16500 Male figures (190cm-75in) bronze two. 23-Sep-2 Wiener Kunst Auktionen, Vienna #83/R est:11000-22000

Miniatures

£15141 $25134 €21500 Les places et colonnes Trajane et Antonine, a Rome (8x10cm-3x4in) gouache pair rec. 16-Jun-3 Claude Aguttes, Neuilly #239/R est:1500-2000

EUROPEAN SCHOOL, 16th C

Sculpture

£19497 $30415 €31000 Adam and Eve (46cm-18in) boxwood. 19-Sep-2 Dr Fritz Nagel, Stuttgart #1113/R est:9500

EUROPEAN SCHOOL, 17th C

£4839 $7887 €7259 Concert in front of palace (99x111cm-39x44in) 12-Feb-3 Iegor de Saint Hippolyte, Montreal #67 (C.D 12000)

£5106 $8068 €7659 The Holy Family (84x115cm-33x45in) prov. 2-Dec-2 Rasmussen, Copenhagen #1630/R est:25000 (D.KR 60000)

£5128 $8051 €8000 Adoration des Mages (163x134cm-64x53in) 16-Dec-2 Marc Kohn, Paris #7/R

£5168 $7855 €7752 Vegetables being unloaded from a horse cart in village by the coast (84x117cm-33x46in) 27-Aug-2 Rasmussen, Copenhagen #1535/R est:60000-80000 (D.KR 60000)

£11538 $18115 €18000 La decapitation de Saint Jean Baptiste (136x205cm-54x81in) 16-Dec-2 Amberes, Antwerp #286

£11950 $18642 €19000 Vase with flowers on a ledge (107x128cm-42x50in) 20-Sep-2 Millon & Associes, Paris #267/R est:20000-30000

Sculpture

£6289 $9811 €10000 God the Father (76cm-30in) wood. 19-Sep-2 Dr Fritz Nagel, Stuttgart #1127/R est:8000

EUROPEAN SCHOOL, 17th/18th C

£7222 $11266 €10833 Landscape with many cupids, angels and figures (97x115cm-38x45in) 5-Aug-2 Rasmussen, Vejle #144/R est:100000-125000 (D.KR 85000)

EUROPEAN SCHOOL, 18th C

£5405 $8432 €8000 Jason enchanting the dragon (160x114cm-63x45in) 25-Mar-3 Finarte Semenzato, Rome #111/R est:5000

£5517 $8828 €8000 Scene historique (100x140cm-39x55in) 17-Mar-3 Amberes, Antwerp #248

£6090 $9439 €9500 Landscape with ancient ruins and figures (135x179cm-53x70in) canvas on canvas. 4-Dec-2 Neumeister, Munich #648/R est:7000

£10316 $16299 €15474 Battle scene (142x214cm-56x84in) canvas on canvas. 30-Nov-2 Dorotheum, Prague #34/R est:160000-250000 (C.KR 500000)

Sculpture

£5806 $9174 €9000 Nobleman (120x150cm-47x59in) stone. 28-Dec-2 Marc Kohn, Paris #3/R

£6000 $9480 €9000 Crucifixion (16x10cm-6x4in) ivory relief. 14-Nov-2 Christie's, London #63/R est:4000-6000

Works on paper

£5976 $9801 €8964 Hagar and Ishmael being cast out by Abraham (160x196cm-63x77in) 4-Jun-3 Deutscher-Menzies, Melbourne #426/R est:20000-30000 (A.D 15000)

EUROPEAN SCHOOL, 18th/19th C
Sculpture
£5578 $8869 €8200 Washerwoman (91x70cm-36x28in) terracotta. 23-Mar-3 Herbette, Doullens #250/R

EUROPEAN SCHOOL, 19th C
£6897 $11034 €10000 European landscape by river (248x276cm-98x109in) 11-Mar-3 Christie's, Paris #252/R
£7241 $11586 €10500 Chines landscape (248x276cm-98x109in) 11-Mar-3 Christie's, Paris #251/R
£14013 $21580 €22000 Dachstein with farmstead and figures (55x70cm-22x28in) panel. 5-Sep-2 Arnold, Frankfurt #866/R est:2000
Sculpture
£10897 $17109 €17000 Putti in concert (63x90cm-25x35in) white marble. 10-Dec-2 Della Rocca, Turin #328/R est:15000
Works on paper
£10504 $16597 €15756 View from Rome (42x33cm-17x13in) indis.sig.d.1855. 16-Nov-2 Crafoord, Lund #48/R est:1500 (S.KR 150000)

EUROPEAN SCHOOL, 19th/20th C
£9311 $14804 €13967 Life's perishables (98x97cm-39x38in) 10-Mar-3 Rasmussen, Vejle #519/R est:100000 (D.KR 100000)

EUROPEAN SCHOOL, 20th C
Works on paper
£448 $717 €650 Portrait du Baron Fould-Springer (30x24cm-12x9in) crayon. 11-Mar-3 Christie's, Paris #258/R

EVANGELISTA, Francesco Paolo (attrib) (1837-?) Italian
Sculpture
£15493 $24944 €22000 Leda and the swan (134x143x49cm-53x56x19in) s.d.1897 white marble. 11-May-3 Finarte, Venice #30/R est:25000-30000

EVANS OF BRISTOL, William (1809-1858) British
Works on paper
£350 $557 €525 View of Snowdon (42x63cm-17x25in) s.d.1848 W/C. 29-Apr-3 Bonhams, Knightsbridge #152/R

EVANS OF ETON, William (1798-1877) British
Works on paper
£280 $434 €420 Lock Crick, bathers in a landscape (36x51cm-14x20in) s.i. W/C htd white. 18-Jul-2 Neales, Nottingham #640
£2000 $3320 €3000 Windsor from the locks (35x44cm-14x17in) W/C prov. 12-Jun-3 Bonhams, New Bond Street #627/R est:1500-2000
£8000 $13120 €11600 Shooting party outside Haddon Hallon Hall, Derbyshire (56x77cm-22x30in) init.d.1873 pencil W/C gum arabic htd bodycol prov.exhib. 5-Jun-3 Christie's, London #73/R est:4000-6000

EVANS, Bernard (1848-1922) British
Works on paper
£400 $660 €580 Whittington Common, Worcester (36x51cm-14x20in) s. W/C. 3-Jul-3 Ewbank, Send #297

EVANS, Bruce (20th C) American?
£481 $750 €722 Trouble on 34th Street (51x71cm-20x28in) s.d.83 s.i.verso acrylic. 9-Nov-2 Sloan, North Bethesda #596/R

EVANS, Cerith Wyn (1959-) British
Sculpture
£8000 $12320 €12000 Inverse reverse perverse (73cm-29in) surface mirrored acrylic executed 1996 prov. 23-Oct-2 Christie's, London #161/R est:10000-15000

EVANS, David (1942-) British
£320 $515 €480 Still life with bowl of fruit (45x55cm-18x22in) 18-Feb-3 Bonhams, Knightsbridge #190/R
£460 $741 €690 Still life of a plate and cutlery (40x50cm-16x20in) 18-Feb-3 Bonhams, Knightsbridge #187/R

EVANS, De Scott (1847-1898) American
£368 $600 €534 Portrait of Prof Edward Moyerhofer (41x30cm-16x12in) 18-Jul-3 Du Mouchelle, Detroit #2009/R
£2108 $3500 €3057 Brass pot (109x62cm-43x24in) s.d.1885. 11-Jun-3 Butterfields, San Francisco #4022/R est:4000-6000
£10063 $16000 €15095 Hanging apples (30x25cm-12x10in) s. prov. 4-Mar-3 Christie's, Rockefeller NY #28/R est:15000-25000
£17610 $28000 €26415 Free sample, try one (30x25cm-12x10in) s. prov. 4-Mar-3 Christie's, Rockefeller NY #18/R est:15000-25000

EVANS, Donald (1945-1977) American
Works on paper
£1410 $2186 €2200 Domino - 12 stamps in one frame (30x21cm-12x8in) pen ink W/C executed 1973 prov.exhib.lit. 3-Dec-2 Christie's, Amsterdam #298/R est:2200-2600

EVANS, Frederick Henry (1853-1943) British
Photographs
£5195 $8000 €7793 Step at Avignon, Le Palais des Papes (25x19cm-10x7in) s.i.d.1907 platinum print. 24-Oct-2 Sotheby's, New York #65/R est:8000-12000
£6329 $10000 €9494 Alvin Langdon Coburn in Eastern clothing (23x19cm-9x7in) d.1901 verso platinum print prov. 23-Apr-3 Sotheby's, New York #112/R est:10000-15000
£9740 $15000 €14610 Font at Bonham Priory, Norfolk (27x22cm-11x9in) s.i.d.1924 platinum print. 24-Oct-2 Sotheby's, New York #59/R est:15000-25000

EVANS, Frederick M (1859-1929) British
Works on paper
£510 $791 €765 Portrait of a bearded fisherman (43x28cm-17x11in) s. W/C. 26-Sep-2 Lane, Penzance #191
£580 $940 €870 Cornish fisherman (28x23cm-11x9in) s. W/C. 21-May-3 Bonhams, Knightsbridge #41/R
£1200 $1860 €1800 Fisherman lighting his pipe (99x74cm-39x29in) s. W/C. 26-Sep-2 Lane, Penzance #55/R est:1200-1500
£3200 $5312 €4800 Spellbound with tales from the past (64x85cm-25x33in) s. W/C. 12-Jun-3 Bonhams, New Bond Street #657/R est:1500-2500

EVANS, Jane (1946-) Australian
Works on paper
£880 $1452 €1276 Dressed up (76x56cm-30x22in) s.d.1985 gouache. 1-Jul-3 Peter Webb, Auckland #90/R est:2500-3500 (NZ.D 2500)
£880 $1452 €1276 In the garden (42x49cm-17x19in) s.i.d.1978 gouache. 1-Jul-3 Peter Webb, Auckland #91/R est:3000-4000 (NZ.D 2500)
£1724 $2690 €2586 Mostly cosmos black eyed Susans (105x74cm-41x29in) s.d.1990 gouache arches of paper. 7-Nov-2 International Art Centre, Auckland #44/R est:5000-8000 (NZ.D 5500)
£1736 $2708 €2604 Floral still life (57x76cm-22x30in) s.d.1990 gouache. 8-Apr-3 Peter Webb, Auckland #148/R est:3500-4500 (NZ.D 5000)
£2351 $3668 €3527 Mixed poppies I (56x76cm-22x30in) s.d.1984 gouache. 7-Nov-2 International Art Centre, Auckland #80/R est:4500-6500 (NZ.D 7500)

EVANS, Jessie Benton (1866-1954) American
£736 $1200 €1104 Venetian canal scene (48x36cm-19x14in) board. 16-Feb-3 Jeffery Burchard, Florida #47
£920 $1500 €1380 Southwestern desert landscape (38x41cm-15x16in) s. board. 16-Feb-3 Jeffery Burchard, Florida #46a
£1074 $1750 €1611 Arizona desert landscape. Self portrait (64x51cm-25x20in) s. double-sided. 16-Feb-3 Jeffery Burchard, Florida #46

EVANS, Leonard (1926-1990) British
£720 $1123 €1080 Cottages in North Pembrokeshire, Dyfed (22x49cm-9x19in) s.d.verso board. 11-Sep-2 Bonhams, Newport #310

EVANS, Merlyn (1910-1973) British
£9000 $14760 €13050 Interior with red and green (101x76cm-40x30in) s.d.52 prov.exhib.lit. 4-Jun-3 Sotheby's, London #31/R est:5000-7000

EVANS, Minnie (1892-1987) American
Works on paper
£926 $1500 €1389 Untitled - face design with ribbon and flowers (30x22cm-12x9in) s. crayon ink collage executed c.1945 prov. 27-Jan-3 Christie's, Rockefeller NY #17/R est:2000-3000
£3086 $5000 €4629 Untitled - design with angels and sunset (27x34cm-11x13in) s.d.June 1972 graphite col pencil paint prov. 27-Jan-3 Christie's, Rockefeller NY #18/R est:6000-8000

EVANS, Ray (1920-) British
Works on paper
£460 $736 €690 Hillside with cottages (38x53cm-15x21in) s.d.12/63 gouache. 14-Mar-3 Gardiner & Houlgate, Bath #43/R

EVANS, Walker (1903-1975) American
Photographs
£1951 $3200 €2927 House in Negro quarter, Mississippi (18x23cm-7x9in) s.num.111/142 st.verso silver print. 10-Feb-3 Swann Galleries, New York #54/R est:4000-5000
£2110 $3250 €3165 Window study (26x15cm-10x6in) photograph prov. 22-Oct-2 Sotheby's, New York #192/R est:5000-8000
£2373 $3750 €3560 Roadside houses for Birmingham, Alabama (19x24cm-7x9in) i.d.1936 num.1/124 photograph. 23-Apr-3 Sotheby's, New York #197/R est:3000-5000
£2760 $4250 €4140 State and Randolph Street, Chicago (16x16cm-6x6in) photograph prov.lit. 22-Oct-2 Sotheby's, New York #188/R est:7000-10000
£3038 $4800 €4557 Show Bill, Demopolis, Alabama (18x23cm-7x9in) i. gelatin silver print prov.lit. 25-Apr-3 Phillips, New York #84/R est:3000-5000
£3165 $5000 €4748 Corrugated tin facade (17x23cm-7x9in) s.d.1974 photograph. 23-Apr-3 Sotheby's, New York #193/R est:3000-5000
£3205 $5000 €4808 Hart Crane, Brooklyn (12x9cm-5x4in) s.d. i.d. verso silver. 21-Oct-2 Swann Galleries, New York #133/R est:4000-6000
£4545 $7000 €6818 Two members of a prison work gang (12x9cm-5x4in) i.d.1936 verso photograph prov.lit. 22-Oct-2 Sotheby's, New York #190/R est:3000-5000
£4870 $7500 €7305 Paul's restaurant New York City (18x15cm-7x6in) s. photograph. 24-Oct-2 Sotheby's, New York #108/R est:4000-6000
£4870 $7500 €7305 Corner of Felicity and Orange Street, New Orleans, Louisiana (18x21cm-7x8in) photograph prov.lit. 22-Oct-2 Sotheby's, New York #65/R est:10000-15000
£4870 $7500 €7305 State Street Theatre, Chicago (16x19cm-6x7in) photograph prov.lit. 22-Oct-2 Sotheby's, New York #187/R est:7000-10000
£4870 $7500 €7305 Tuscaloosa wrecking company, Alabama (19x24cm-7x9in) photograph prov.lit. 22-Oct-2 Sotheby's, New York #191/R est:7000-10000
£5195 $8000 €7793 Breakfast room at Belle Grove Plantation, White Chapel, Louisiana (26x33cm-10x13in) s.num.52/75 photograph. 24-Oct-2 Sotheby's, New York #105/R est:5000-8000
£5844 $9000 €8766 Grocery store, Greensboro, Alabama (19x24cm-7x9in) photograph prov.lit. 22-Oct-2 Sotheby's, New York #61/R est:7000-10000
£6329 $10000 €9494 Traffic, New York City (13x22cm-5x9in) i.verso gelatin silver print prov.lit. 25-Apr-3 Phillips, New York #9/R est:8000-12000
£6962 $11000 €10443 Untitled - New York subway portrait (12x20cm-5x8in) gelatin silver print prov.lit. 24-Apr-3 Phillips, New York #118/R est:12000-15000
£6962 $11000 €10443 Roadside gas station (12x17cm-5x7in) i.verso gelatin silver print prov.lit. 25-Apr-3 Phillips, New York #12/R est:15000-20000
£7792 $12000 €11688 Traffic, NYC (13x20cm-5x8in) i.verso gelatin silver print prov.lit. 25-Oct-2 Phillips, New York #15/R est:12000-15000
£8228 $13000 €12342 Sidewalk in Vicksburg, Mississippi (32x36cm-13x14in) s.d.1936 gelatin silver print on board lit. 25-Apr-3 Phillips, New York #10/R est:15000-20000
£8228 $13000 €12342 Signs, Charleston, South Carolina (19x24cm-7x9in) s.d.1935 s.i.d.verso gelatin silver print on board prov.lit. 25-Apr-3 Phillips, New York #11/R est:10000-15000
£8861 $14000 €13292 Selma, Alabama storefronts (16x13cm-6x5in) s. s.i.d.1935 verso gelatin silver print prov.lit. 25-Apr-3 Phillips, New York #13/R est:20000-30000
£10759 $17000 €16139 Untitled - New York subway portrait (12x19cm-5x7in) gelatin silver print prov.exhib.lit. 25-Apr-3 Phillips, New York #16/R est:10000-15000
£13924 $22000 €20886 Lever building (23x34cm-9x13in) i.verso gelatin silver print prov. 25-Apr-3 Phillips, New York #47/R est:3000-5000
£18987 $30000 €28481 Penny picture display, Savannah, Georgia (22x18cm-9x7in) s. gelatin silver print prov.lit. 25-Apr-3 Phillips, New York #14/R est:100000-150000
£33766 $52000 €50649 Alabama cotton tenants farmer family - Fields Family (18x23cm-7x9in) photograph prov.exhib.lit. 22-Oct-2 Sotheby's, New York #62/R est:30000-50000
£35065 $54000 €52598 Country store and gas station, Alabama (17x24cm-7x9in) i. photograph prov.exhib.lit. 22-Oct-2 Sotheby's, New York #66/R est:50000-80000
£51948 $80000 €77922 Negro barbershop interior Atlanta (19x24cm-7x9in) i.d.1936 photograph prov.exhib.lit. 22-Oct-2 Sotheby's, New York #63/R est:70000-100000
£53797 $85000 €80696 Main Street, Saratoga Springs, New York (18x13cm-7x5in) s.d.1933 i.verso gelatin silver print prov.exhib.lit. 25-Apr-3 Phillips, New York #15/R est:40000-60000
£77922 $120000 €116883 Breakfast room, Belle Grove Plantation, White Chapel, Louisiana (18x22cm-7x9in) photograph prov.lit. 22-Oct-2 Sotheby's, New York #64/R est:150000-250000

EVANS, William E (fl.1889-1897) British
Works on paper
£700 $1092 €1050 Portrait of a young lady carrying a basket of roses (53x33cm-21x13in) s. W/C htd white. 18-Sep-2 Dreweatt Neate, Newbury #59

EVE, Harwood (20th C) British
£275 $429 €413 Beach scene, Corfu (46x51cm-18x20in) s. 17-Sep-2 Bonhams, Knightsbridge #125/R

EVE, Jean (1900-1968) French
£719 $1151 €1000 Anemones dans un vase (33x24cm-13x9in) s.d. s.i.d. verso. 15-May-3 Neumeister, Munich #249/R
£839 $1300 €1259 Village sous la neige (33x46cm-13x18in) s. s.i.d.1965 verso prov. 1-Oct-2 Arthur James, Florida #332
£2166 $3378 €3400 Petit village (54x73cm-21x29in) s. 10-Nov-2 Eric Pillon, Calais #179/R
£2245 $3569 €3300 Vue du vieux pont a Pont-sur-Yonne (50x60cm-20x24in) s.d.1957. 28-Feb-3 Joron-Derem, Paris #47
£6051 $9439 €9500 Printemps dans la vallee de Chevreuse (55x73cm-22x29in) s. painted 1945 prov. 5-Nov-2 Tajan, Paris #49/R est:10000-15000

EVELEIGH, John (20th C) British
£480 $778 €696 The City (90x120cm-35x47in) s. 10-Aug-3 Lots Road, London #333

EVEN, Andre (1918-) French
£324 $518 €450 Hameau a flancs de coteaux (46x61cm-18x24in) s. paper on canvas. 14-May-3 Blanchet, Paris #140
£576 $921 €800 Paysage (54x73cm-21x29in) s. paper on canvas. 14-May-3 Blanchet, Paris #139/R
£641 $1006 €1000 Paysage (50x65cm-20x26in) s. 24-Nov-2 Lesieur & Le Bars, Le Havre #43

EVENEPOEL, Henri (1872-1899) Belgian
£10791 $17266 €15000 Les jardins, rue Dupont en ete (55x65cm-22x26in) painted c.1891-92 prov.lit. 13-May-3 Palais de Beaux Arts, Brussels #77/R est:15000-20000
£14103 $21859 €22000 Pier of the port of Algiers (24x33cm-9x13in) mono. panel painted 1897 prov.exhib.lit. 7-Dec-2 De Vuyst, Lokeren #436/R est:16000-20000
Works on paper
£409 $630 €650 Petit enfant a la poupee (30x24cm-12x9in) mono. dr. 22-Oct-2 Campo & Campo, Antwerp #104
£517 $828 €750 Tete d'homme (16x12cm-6x5in) Indian ink dr. 15-Mar-3 De Vuyst, Lokeren #114
£764 $1215 €1100 Petites figures (19x12cm-7x5in) dr. 29-Apr-3 Campo & Campo, Antwerp #117/R

EVERBROECK, Frans van (17th C) Flemish
£6944 $11181 €10416 Still life of flowers and fruit (75x64cm-30x25in) 7-May-3 Dobiaschofsky, Bern #489/R est:17000 (S.FR 15000)

EVERBROECK, Frans van (attrib) (17th C) Flemish
£7927 $13000 €11494 Fruit in a bowl and on a partially covered table (42x56cm-17x22in) bears sig. 4-Jun-3 Christie's, Rockefeller NY #179/R est:6000-8000

EVERDINGEN, Adriaen van (1832-1912) Dutch
£962 $1510 €1500 Dutch coastal landscape with reedy shore (46x85cm-18x33in) s. 21-Nov-2 Van Ham, Cologne #1595/R

EVERDINGEN, Allart (1621-1675) Dutch
£6475 $10360 €9000 Wooded river landscape with peasants loading a boat (48x61cm-19x24in) 14-May-3 Christie's, Amsterdam #187/R est:7000-10000
Works on paper
£355 $592 €500 Chaumiere dans un paysage (11x14cm-4x6in) pen brown ink black crayon. 19-Jun-3 Piasa, Paris #47

EVERDINGEN, Allart (attrib) (1621-1675) Dutch
Works on paper
£674 $1044 €1011 Landscape with building and figures (18x30cm-7x12in) pencil. 3-Dec-2 Bukowskis, Stockholm #539/R (S.KR 9500)
£1329 $2100 €2100 Ships off island (5x8cm-2x3in) pen wash. 29-Nov-2 Bassenge, Berlin #5253/R est:2000
£1456 $2300 €2300 Golfers by building (5x8cm-2x3in) pen wash. 29-Nov-2 Bassenge, Berlin #5254/R est:2500

EVERGOOD, Phillip (1901-1973) American
£915 $1500 €1327 Landscape with horses (35x47cm-14x19in) s. canvas on board painted c.1930. 5-Jun-3 Swann Galleries, New York #88/R est:1000-1500
Works on paper
£256 $400 €384 Portrait of an artist (48x36cm-19x14in) s. pastel prov. 20-Sep-2 Freeman, Philadelphia #20/R
£417 $650 €626 Amazons (26x51cm-10x20in) s. W/C gouache over pencil exec.c.1955. 19-Sep-2 Swann Galleries, New York #335
£478 $750 €717 Untitled (64x53cm-25x21in) black ink dr. 13-Dec-2 Du Mouchelle, Detroit #2184/R
£833 $1300 €1250 Femme a la pipe (81x66cm-32x26in) s.i. chl wash. 19-Sep-2 Swann Galleries, New York #336/R est:1000-1500

EVERITT, Allen Edward (1824-1882) British
Works on paper
£5200 $8268 €7800 Aston Hall Warwickshire - the east front (35x57cm-14x22in) W/C over pencil bodycol prov. 20-Mar-3 Sotheby's, London #329/R est:4000-6000
£9000 $14310 €13500 Heathfield House, Handsworth, Birmingham (33x56cm-13x22in) W/C over pencil htd white prov. 20-Mar-3 Sotheby's, London #48/R est:4000-6000

EVERS, John (1797-1884) American
£3481 $5500 €5222 Hempstead L Island (28x38cm-11x15in) s. i.d.1864 verso prov. 24-Apr-3 Shannon's, Milford #125/R est:2500-3500

EVERSDYCK, Cornelis Willemsz (attrib) (1590-1644) Dutch
£4800 $8016 €6960 Still life with vegetables and fruits with a body holding a bunch of grapes (61x74cm-24x29in) 8-Jul-3 Sotheby's, Olympia #466/R est:3000-5000

EVERSE, Theodorus (1910-) Dutch
£255 $397 €400 Decent from the cross (229x115cm-90x45in) s. 5-Nov-2 Vendu Notarishuis, Rotterdam #271

EVERSEN, Adrianus (1818-1897) Dutch
£3082 $4839 €4500 Town view with a moored boat (12x10cm-5x4in) mono. panel. 15-Apr-3 Sotheby's, Amsterdam #69/R est:3000-5000
£4088 $6296 €6500 Villagers in the streets of a Dutch town (19x24cm-7x9in) mono. panel. 22-Oct-2 Sotheby's, Amsterdam #4/R est:5000-7000
£4167 $6542 €6500 Dutch city (15x19cm-6x7in) mono. panel. 21-Nov-2 Van Ham, Cologne #1596/R est:8000
£4795 $7527 €7000 Villagers in a Dutch town (41x33cm-16x13in) mono. 15-Apr-3 Sotheby's, Amsterdam #30/R est:7000-9000
£5479 $8603 €8000 Town view in summer (23x30cm-9x12in) s. panel. 15-Apr-3 Sotheby's, Amsterdam #10/R est:4000-6000
£7000 $11130 €10500 Town in summer (17x26cm-7x10in) init. panel. 20-Mar-3 Christie's, Kensington #147/R est:4000-6000
£7639 $12146 €11000 Elegant figures in a sunlit street (13x10cm-5x4in) mono. panel. 29-Apr-3 Christie's, Amsterdam #11/R est:8000-12000
£8280 $12917 €13000 City view in the summer (18x14cm-7x6in) s. panel. 6-Nov-2 Vendue Huis, Gravenhage #425/R est:10000-15000
£8280 $12917 €13000 City view in the winter (18x14cm-7x6in) s. panel. 6-Nov-2 Vendue Huis, Gravenhage #426/R est:10000-15000
£9211 $14921 €14000 Town scene with elegant people strolling (19x15cm-7x6in) s.d.59 panel. 21-Jan-3 Christie's, Amsterdam #54/R est:8000-12000
£9748 $15013 €15500 Wintry view of the Dijkpoort in the Hattem (24x18cm-9x7in) s. panel. 22-Oct-2 Sotheby's, Amsterdam #166/R est:12000-15000
£10274 $16130 €15000 Figures in a wintry town (24x21cm-9x8in) s. panel. 15-Apr-3 Sotheby's, Amsterdam #7/R est:7000-9000
£11006 $16950 €17500 Townsfolk conversing on a sunlit square (27x21cm-11x8in) s. panel. 23-Oct-2 Christie's, Amsterdam #135/R est:18000-25000
£12500 $19875 €18000 Townsfolk on a square, Ransdorp (42x53cm-17x21in) s. prov. 29-Apr-3 Christie's, Amsterdam #185/R est:20000-30000
£16352 $25182 €26000 Villagers in the streets of a Dutch town (29x37cm-11x15in) s. 22-Oct-2 Sotheby's, Amsterdam #172/R est:14000-18000
£17123 $26884 €25000 Figures near a church entrance (28x22cm-11x9in) s. panel. 15-Apr-3 Sotheby's, Amsterdam #197/R est:20000-25000
£27397 $43014 €40000 Townspeople on a square (33x43cm-13x17in) s. 15-Apr-3 Sotheby's, Amsterdam #170/R est:40000-60000
£32877 $51616 €48000 Townsfolk in a sunlit street (36x44cm-14x17in) s. panel prov. 15-Apr-3 Sotheby's, Amsterdam #192a/R est:30000-50000
£33766 $49299 €52000 Town scene with various figures in front of sunlit ruin (40x48cm-16x19in) s. 15-Jun-2 Hans Stahl, Hamburg #79 est:4000
£50000 $79500 €72000 Bustling street by a church in a Dutch town (71x61cm-28x24in) s.d.56 prov.exhib. 29-Apr-3 Christie's, Amsterdam #200/R est:40000-60000

EVERSEN, Johannes Hendrik (1906-1995) Dutch
£13000 $20410 €19500 Lobster, partly peeled lemon, pewter jug on a pewter plate on a wooded table (51x71cm-20x28in) s.d.1954. 21-Nov-2 Christie's, Kensington #91/R est:7000-10000

EVES, Reginald Grenville (1876-1941) British
£280 $437 €420 Portrait of an Indian (40x34cm-16x13in) s.d.1938. 9-Oct-2 Woolley & Wallis, Salisbury #324/R

EVES, Reginald Grenville (attrib) (1876-1941) British
£650 $1021 €975 Portrait of a lady in a mauve wrap (61x51cm-24x20in) 21-Nov-2 Tennants, Leyburn #744

EVOLA, Giulio (1898-1974) Italian
£12766 $20681 €18000 Composition Dada (115x50cm-45x20in) tempera canvas on canvas painted 1919-20 prov.exhib. 26-May-3 Christie's, Milan #206/R est:18000-24000

EVRARD, Andre (1936-) Swiss
£786 $1234 €1179 Hommage au carre IV-27/84 - 821 (119x116cm-47x46in) s.i.d.1984 verso acrylic. 25-Nov-2 Germann, Zurich #104/R est:2000-4000 (S.FR 1800)

EWALD, Reinhold (1890-1974) German
£612 $978 €850 Strolling figures (49x43cm-19x17in) s.d. panel. 15-May-3 Neumeister, Munich #250/R

EWART, David Shanks (1901-1965) British
£2200 $3432 €3300 Eve (46x35cm-18x14in) s. 14-Apr-3 Sotheby's, London #165/R est:1000-1500

EWART, Peter (1918-2001) Canadian
£244 $401 €354 Near Spences bridge (30x25cm-12x10in) s.i. board prov. 9-Jun-3 Hodgins, Calgary #424/R (C.D 550)
£254 $394 €381 Fishing boats at rest (51x61cm-20x24in) s. board. 24-Sep-2 Maynards, Vancouver #394 (C.D 620)
£258 $402 €387 October dawn (49x63cm-19x25in) s. canvasboard prov. 25-Mar-3 Ritchie, Toronto #106/R (C.D 600)
£258 $402 €374 Spide Island, B.C (41x51cm-16x20in) s.i. 26-Mar-3 Walker's, Ottawa #449/R (C.D 600)
£341 $536 €512 William's Lake stampede (25x30cm-10x12in) s.i.d.1956 board. 25-Nov-2 Hodgins, Calgary #17/R (C.D 850)
£975 $1550 €1463 Moonlight solitude, Gang Ranch, BC interior (60x75cm-24x30in) s.i. board. 23-Mar-3 Hodgins, Calgary #11/R est:1000-1500 (C.D 2300)
£1102 $1752 €1653 Three Sisters (60x75cm-24x30in) s.i. canvasboard. 23-Mar-3 Hodgins, Calgary #31/R est:1000-1500 (C.D 2600)

EWBANK, John Wilson (1799-1847) British
£400 $624 €600 Bridge near Ambleside (22x32cm-9x13in) board. 10-Apr-3 Tennants, Leyburn #971
£900 $1431 €1350 On the moors, Dumfriesshire (30x46cm-12x18in) board. 6-Mar-3 Christie's, Kensington #39/R
£1300 $1989 €1950 Ardarden Old Watch Tower, Firth of Clyde, morning calm (24x34cm-9x13in) s.i.verso sold with three similar. 22-Aug-2 Bonhams, Edinburgh #1005 est:1000-1500
£35000 $54250 €52500 Shipping in the harbour, South Shields (102x157cm-40x62in) prov.exhib. 31-Oct-2 Christie's, London #11/R est:10000-15000

EWEN, William Paterson (1925-2002) Canadian
£5778 $9476 €8667 Life stream with time intervals B (124x127cm-49x50in) s.d.1968 verso acrylic prov. 27-May-3 Sotheby's, Toronto #138/R est:7000-9000 (C.D 13000)

EWING, Raymond A (1891-1975) American
£687 $1100 €996 Sterling Spring (63x76cm-25x30in) s. 16-May-3 Skinner, Boston #217/R

EXNER, Antoine (1922-) ?
£316 $500 €500 Fishing boats on the open seas (24x30cm-9x12in) s. panel. 29-Nov-2 Schloss Ahlden, Ahlden #1313/R

EXNER, Julius (1825-1910) Danish
£559 $888 €839 Farmyard with woman feeding chickens (23x28cm-9x11in) sold with photo. 5-Mar-3 Rasmussen, Copenhagen #1876/R (D.KR 6000)
£793 $1261 €1190 Cottage interior (26x37cm-10x15in) s. 5-May-3 Rasmussen, Vejle #474/R (D.KR 8500)
£851 $1345 €1277 Mother and two children on jetty (16x13cm-6x5in) panel prov. 2-Dec-2 Rasmussen, Copenhagen #1315/R (D.KR 10000)
£1490 $2369 €2235 Portrait of girl wearing grey dress (47x49cm-19x19in) prov. 10-Mar-3 Rasmussen, Vejle #417/R est:20000 (D.KR 16000)
£2985 $4746 €4478 Interior scene with woman sewing, white cat on window ledge (40x32cm-16x13in) s.d.1877 prov. 5-May-3 Rasmussen, Vejle #473/R est:25000 (D.KR 32000)
£3828 $6201 €5551 Disturbed during dinner rest - two girls tickling sleeping farmer with feather (53x63cm-21x25in) s.d.1880. 26-May-3 Rasmussen, Copenhagen #112/R est:40000-60000 (D.KR 40000)
£10048 $16278 €14570 Small Fano girl learning to read (53x60cm-21x24in) s.d.1908. 26-May-3 Rasmussen, Copenhagen #1105/R est:50000-75000 (D.KR 105000)
£38298 $60511 €57447 Bride and groom returning from church, Dragor, Amager (104x147cm-41x58in) s.d.1863 exhib. 2-Dec-2 Rasmussen, Copenhagen #1159/R est:300000-400000 (D.KR 450000)
Works on paper
£355 $574 €533 Woman by window (16x14cm-6x6in) s.d.81 pen W/C. 25-Jan-3 Rasmussen, Havnen #2258 (D.KR 4000)

EXNER, Julius (attrib) (1825-1910) Danish
£3518 $5629 €5101 The vicar is visiting (103x124cm-41x49in) 18-May-3 Anders Antik, Landskrona #109 est:50000 (S.KR 45000)

EXTER, Alexandra (1882-1949) Russian
Works on paper
£28000 $45360 €42000 Costume desing for a dancer (50x34cm-20x13in) gouache prov. 21-May-3 Sotheby's, London #189/R est:20000-25000

EXTER, Julius (1863-1939) German
£633 $981 €1000 Bavarian alpine landscape (29x40cm-11x16in) s. board. 27-Sep-2 Karrenbauer, Konstanz #1624
£1806 $2817 €2709 In a cafe (45x60cm-18x24in) cardboard. 11-Sep-2 Kieselbach, Budapest #6/R (H.F 700000)

EYBEN, Antonius Cornelis Ninaber van (1896-1977) Dutch
£481 $755 €750 Still life with flowers (52x43cm-20x17in) s. prov. 25-Nov-2 Glerum, Amsterdam #170

EYCK, Caspar van (circle) (1613-1673) Flemish
£13000 $20280 €19500 English gallery frigate flanked by Ottoman state barges and other vessels (56x109cm-22x43in) pair. 9-Apr-3 Bonhams, New Bond Street #49/R est:5000-8000

EYCK, Charles (1897-1983) Dutch
£414 $638 €650 Flying Dutchman (160x200cm-63x79in) s.i.d.68. 3-Sep-2 Christie's, Amsterdam #388

EYCK, Robert van (20th C) British?
£290 $441 €435 Etruscan (33x41cm-13x16in) s.1962 verso tempera prov. 16-Aug-2 Keys, Aylsham #468

EYCKELBOSCH, Jean (?) Belgian?
£962 $1510 €1500 L'Egyptienne devant las pyramides (64x89cm-25x35in) s. 10-Dec-2 Vanderkindere, Brussels #40/R est:750-1250

EYCKEN, Charles van den (19th C) Belgian
£545 $845 €850 Le chien de famille (24x19cm-9x7in) s.d.1880. 9-Dec-2 Horta, Bruxelles #420
£1184 $1918 €1800 Les chiens se reosent (21x28cm-8x11in) s.d.1880 s.d.verso panel. 21-Jan-3 Christie's, Amsterdam #47/R est:2000-3000
£1410 $2214 €2200 Dogs with cart drinking from spring (21x28cm-8x11in) s. panel. 21-Nov-2 Van Ham, Cologne #1597/R est:2000
£1895 $3052 €2900 Wulf (51x41cm-20x16in) s.d.16. 14-Jan-3 Vanderkindere, Brussels #39/R est:2500-3500
£13836 $21308 €22000 La mere bien veillante (69x97cm-27x38in) s.d.1907. 23-Oct-2 Christie's, Amsterdam #127/R est:20000-30000

EYCKEN, Charles van den (jnr) (1859-1923) Belgian
£1871 $2993 €2600 Interior with two dogs (24x17cm-9x7in) s. panel. 17-May-3 De Vuyst, Lokeren #360/R est:2800-3300
£18868 $29057 €30000 In the boudoir (80x61cm-31x24in) s.i. prov. 23-Oct-2 Christie's, Amsterdam #140/R est:15000-20000

EYCKEN, Charles van den (snr) (1809-1891) Belgian
£3472 $5521 €5000 Winterfun in a hilly forest landscape (41x48cm-16x19in) s.d.40. 29-Apr-3 Christie's, Amsterdam #26/R est:4000-6000

EYCKEN, Felix van den (19th C) Belgian
£1088 $1731 €1600 Farm interior with woman at work (47x64cm-19x25in) s. panel. 24-Mar-3 Bernaerts, Antwerp #125 est:1250-1500

EYDEN, William A (1893-1982) American
£218 $350 €327 Fall landscape (46x61cm-18x24in) s. masonite. 15-Mar-3 Eldred, East Dennis #126/R

EYERS, J J (19th C) ?
£3034 $4855 €4400 Nature morte aux fruits et aux fleurs (42x35cm-17x14in) s.d.1871. 17-Mar-3 Horta, Bruxelles #73 est:1800-2200

EYKEN, Moritz van (1865-?) German
£950 $1492 €1425 Allegory of summer (164x80cm-65x31in) s.d.07 prov. 16-Apr-3 Christie's, Kensington #798/R

EYMER, Arnoldus Johannes (1803-1863) Dutch
£759 $1200 €1139 Lady painting in a river landscape (25x36cm-10x14in) s. panel. 16-Nov-2 New Orleans Auction, New Orleans #306/R
£1923 $2981 €3000 View of a canal with train bridge (26x33cm-10x13in) s. panel. 4-Dec-2 Neumeister, Munich #728/R est:1800

EYRE, Gladstone (1863-1933) Australian
Works on paper
£250 $398 €375 Breaking surf at Bondi Beach (18x44cm-7x17in) s. W/C. 20-Mar-3 Martel Maides, Guernsey #156/R

EYRE, Ivan Kenneth (1935-) Canadian
£10222 $16764 €15333 Celestial meadow (94x116cm-37x46in) s. acrylic prov. 3-Jun-3 Joyner, Toronto #68/R est:20000-30000 (C.D 23000)
£11752 $18686 €17628 Hill mist (142x152cm-56x60in) s. s.i.verso acrylic painted 1986 prov. 6-Mar-3 Heffel, Vancouver #14/R est:27500-32500 (C.D 27500)

EYRES, John W (fl.1877-1904) British
£320 $515 €464 River landscape (48x73cm-19x29in) s. board. 12-May-3 Joel, Victoria #350 (A.D 800)
£360 $565 €540 Coastal landscape (51x76cm-20x30in) s.d.1886. 16-Dec-2 Bonhams, Bury St Edmunds #536
£1150 $1817 €1725 Children playing with a wooden cart in a yard (63x75cm-25x30in) s. 15-Nov-2 Rowley Fine Art, Newmarket #398/R

EYSKENS, Felix (1882-1968) Belgian
£314 $484 €500 Devant la ferme (70x80cm-28x31in) s. panel. 22-Oct-2 Campo, Vlaamse Kaai #112
£316 $494 €500 Kruithakker (30x45cm-12x18in) s. i.verso. 21-Oct-2 Glerum, Amsterdam #123

EYSKENS, Felix (attrib) (1882-1968) Belgian
£704 $1126 €1021 Pulling the barges (80x126cm-31x50in) 18-May-3 Anders Antik, Landskrona #150i (S.KR 9000)

EYTON, Anthony (1923-) British
£300 $489 €450 Children playing (120x106cm-47x42in) s. 28-Jan-3 Bristol Auction Rooms #489
£600 $942 €900 Japanese iris (48x30cm-19x12in) s. board prov. 15-Apr-3 Bonhams, Knightsbridge #156/R
£1300 $2132 €1950 Chrys (119x110cm-47x43in) s. s.i.d.1995 verso board. 3-Jun-3 Sotheby's, Olympia #187/R est:1500-2000
Works on paper
£400 $636 €600 Seated nude (46x38cm-18x15in) s.d.1990 W/C. 26-Feb-3 Sotheby's, Olympia #318/R

EZCURRA, Agustin (1880-1958) South American
£1156 $1850 €1734 Washerwomen (99x99cm-39x39in) s. 5-Jan-3 Galleria Y Remates, Montevideo #84/R

EZDORF, Christian (1801-1851) German
£1282 $1987 €2000 Rocky mountain valley with sawmill in foreground (68x89cm-27x35in) s.d.1839 canvas on canvas. 4-Dec-2 Neumeister, Munich #729/R est:1500
£1795 $2782 €2800 Storm over the North Cape (30x42cm-12x17in) s.i.d.1823 verso. 5-Dec-2 Schopman, Hamburg #652 est:2200

EZDORF, Christian Friedrich (1807-1858) German
£2500 $4000 €3750 Seabirds off a rocky coastline with stormy skies (60x72cm-24x28in) s.d.1833. 14-May-3 Butterfields, San Francisco #1076/R est:4000-6000

EZEKIEL, Moses (1844-1917) American
Sculpture
£1090 $1700 €1635 Robert E Lee (20x10x10cm-8x4x4in) s.i. pat bronze socle square plinth. 12-Oct-2 Neal Auction Company, New Orleans #466/R est:1500-2500

FABBI, Alberto (1858-1906) Italian
£2817 $4676 €4000 Le rocking-chair (69x103cm-27x41in) s.i.d.1880. 16-Jun-3 Oger, Dumont, Paris #43/R est:4500-6000
£11613 $18000 €17420 Musical interlude in the harem (102x68cm-40x27in) s. 30-Oct-2 Christie's, Rockefeller NY #96/R est:20000-30000

FABBI, Fabio (1861-1946) Italian
£943 $1453 €1500 Landscape (15x8cm-6x3in) s. board. 23-Oct-2 Finarte, Milan #196/R
£962 $1510 €1500 Portrait (64x46cm-25x18in) s. 16-Dec-2 Pandolfini, Florence #74
£5031 $7748 €8000 View of Florence, the Duomo (15x9cm-6x4in) s. board. 23-Oct-2 Finarte, Milan #128/R est:8000-9000
£7500 $12525 €11250 Snake charmer (71x41cm-28x16in) s. 18-Jun-3 Christie's, Kensington #197/R est:8000-12000
£11348 $18383 €16000 Flight from the harem (70x40cm-28x16in) s. i.verso. 22-May-3 Dorotheum, Vienna #128/R est:16000-18000
£20000 $31800 €30000 Slave market (76x59cm-30x23in) s. 18-Mar-3 Bonhams, New Bond Street #81/R est:20000-30000
£24000 $40080 €36000 Difficult decision (70x53cm-28x21in) s. 19-Jun-3 Christie's, London #6/R est:15000-20000
£25806 $40000 €38709 Wedding procession (97x140cm-38x55in) s. 30-Oct-2 Christie's, Rockefeller NY #86/R est:50000-70000
£100000 $167000 €150000 Lazy afternoon on the terrace (90x150cm-35x59in) s. 19-Jun-3 Christie's, London #4/R est:100000-150000
Works on paper
£321 $500 €482 Two dancing harem girls (30x43cm-12x17in) s. 8-Nov-2 York Town, York #694
£961 $1499 €1442 Two harem women (28x43cm-11x17in) s. W/C. 20-Nov-2 Fischer, Luzern #2459/R est:1400-1500 (S.FR 2200)
£1667 $2733 €2300 Odalische (30x45cm-12x18in) s. W/C board. 27-May-3 Finarte, Milan #38/R est:2500-2800
£7500 $12525 €11250 Harem dancer (59x35cm-23x14in) s. pencil W/C. 18-Jun-3 Christie's, Kensington #196/R est:4000-5000

FABBRI, Agenore (1911-1998) Italian
Sculpture
£1622 $2530 €2400 Crucifixion (44cm-17in) s. bronze. 26-Mar-3 Finarte Semenzato, Milan #232/R
£1667 $2650 €2400 Dominant bull (13x15x6cm-5x6x2in) s. terracotta. 1-May-3 Meeting Art, Vercelli #144
£1871 $2956 €2900 Figure (63cm-25in) s. bronze. 18-Dec-2 Christie's, Rome #196/R
£3716 $5797 €5500 Horse (22x40x40cm-9x16x16in) s. terracotta. 26-Mar-3 Finarte Semenzato, Milan #357/R

FABBRI, Alfredo (1926-) Italian
£316 $494 €500 Nice harbour at night (55x75cm-22x30in) s.d.1968 s.i.d.verso. 19-Oct-2 Semenzato, Venice #35/R

FABBRICOTTI, Gabriella (1878-?) Italian
£460 $718 €690 Berceau (33x40cm-13x16in) s.i.verso. 17-Sep-2 Bonhams, Oxford #43/R

FABER, Jules (?) Belgian?
£6101 $9395 €9700 Cavaliers arabes. Caid a cheval (109x75cm-43x30in) s.d.97 pair. 23-Oct-2 Rabourdin & Choppin de Janvry, Paris #189/R

FABER, Will (1901-1987) German/Spanish
£464 $756 €700 Untitled (56x46cm-22x18in) s.d.1986. 11-Feb-3 Segre, Madrid #299/R
£1132 $1766 €1800 Composition (33x47cm-13x19in) s. 8-Oct-2 Ansorena, Madrid #633/R
£3020 $4862 €4500 Composition (65x81cm-26x32in) s.d.72. 18-Feb-3 Durán, Madrid #196/R

FABIAN, Lydia Dunham (1857-?) American
£962 $1500 €1443 Pueblo of Taos, New Mexico (56x71cm-22x28in) s. prov. 9-Nov-2 Santa Fe Art, Santa Fe #192/R est:2000-4000

FABIEN, Henri (19/20th C) Canadian
£429 $670 €644 Dead duck (38x30cm-15x12in) s. panel. 25-Mar-3 Iegor de Saint Hippolyte, Montreal #49 (C.D 1000)

FABINI, Jozef (1908-1984) Czechoslovakian?
£378 $552 €567 Autumn landscape (27x80cm-11x31in) oil tempera board. 4-Jun-2 SOGA, Bratislava #236/R est:30000 (SL.K 24000)
£378 $552 €567 On the bridge (33x50cm-13x20in) cardboard painted c.1960. 4-Jun-2 SOGA, Bratislava #237/R est:30000 (SL.K 24000)

FABRE, François-Xavier (1766-1837) French
£7763 $12110 €11645 Portrait of William Fitzgerald (31x27cm-13x11in) mono.d.1815. 28-Mar-3 Koller, Zurich #3123/R est:16000-20000 (S.FR 17000)

FABRE, François-Xavier (attrib) (1766-1837) French
£1769 $2812 €2600 Etude d'homme (68x55cm-27x22in) 19-Mar-3 Hotel des Ventes Mosan, Brussels #207/R est:2500-3000

FABRE, Louis Andre (1750-1814) Swiss
Miniatures
£3000 $4680 €4500 Young gentleman wearing double-breasted blue coat white lace cravat (5cm-2xin) gold frame oval. 5-Nov-2 Bonhams, New Bond Street #38/R est:3000-5000

FABRIS, Jacobo (1689-1761) Italian
£10000 $16600 €15000 View of St. Paul's Cathedral (63x108cm-25x43in) s. prov. 12-Jun-3 Sotheby's, London #108/R est:12000-18000

FABRIS, Jacobo (attrib) (1689-1761) Italian
£40000 $62800 €60000 Piazza Navona, Rome (55x90cm-22x35in) prov. 11-Dec-2 Christie's, London #105/R est:20000-30000

FABRIS, Pietro (18th C) Italian
£17931 $28331 €26000 Posillipo grotto (42x58cm-17x23in) s. tempera paper prov. 3-Apr-3 Porro, Milan #35/R est:35000
£86207 $136207 €125000 View of Naples from Santa Lucia (42x76cm-17x30in) s. prov.lit. 3-Apr-3 Porro, Milan #40/R est:180000
£432099 $700000 €648149 Festival of the Madonna dell'Arco Naples (103x154cm-41x61in) s.d.1777. 23-Jan-3 Sotheby's, New York #112/R est:700000-900000
Works on paper
£9000 $14400 €13500 Bay of Naples with children dancing (18x43cm-7x17in) s. gouache. 11-Mar-3 Bonhams, New Bond Street #1/R est:1200-1800
£14557 $23000 €23000 Les mangeurs de spaghettis sur la baie de Naples, le Vesuve au fond (42x56cm-17x22in) gouache. 27-Nov-2 Christie's, Paris #114/R est:8000-12000

FABRO, Luciano (1936-) Italian
Sculpture
£8000 $13120 €12000 Hole 8 mm (194x99cm-76x39in) stainless steel exec.1967 prov.exhib.lit. 6-Feb-3 Sotheby's, London #35/R est:40000
£70000 $109200 €105000 L'Italia de pelo (168cm-66in) s. verso executed 1969 prov.exhib.lit. 21-Oct-2 Sotheby's, London #33/R est:80000-120000
£145000 $223300 €217500 Italia d'oro (91cm-36in) gilt bronze steel cable prov.lit. 22-Oct-2 Christie's, London #45/R est:70000-100000

FABRON, Luigi (1855-1905) Italian
£1319 $2098 €1900 Spanish herdsmen conversing (34x20cm-13x8in) s. panel prov. 29-Apr-3 Christie's, Amsterdam #101/R est:1500-2000

FABRY, Émile (1865-1966) Belgian
£1589 $2591 €2400 Regard (60x47cm-24x19in) s.d.1953 panel. 17-Feb-3 Horta, Bruxelles #26
£7547 $11698 €12000 Petite vierge (46x40cm-18x16in) s.d.1913 panel exhib. 5-Oct-2 De Vuyst, Lokeren #447/R est:8500-10000
Works on paper
£360 $576 €500 Profil de femme (31x39cm-12x15in) s. chl. 13-May-3 Vanderkindere, Brussels #41
£728 $1187 €1100 Hiver (40x50cm-16x20in) col crayon dr. 17-Feb-3 Horta, Bruxelles #25

FACCINCANI, Athos (1951-) Italian
£321 $503 €500 Tale about a lake (25x35cm-10x14in) s. s.i.verso gouache oil paper on canvas. 23-Nov-2 Meeting Art, Vercelli #430
£347 $552 €500 On the lake (50x30cm-20x12in) s. paper on canvas. 1-May-3 Meeting Art, Vercelli #247
£348 $543 €550 Fruit basket (25x35cm-10x14in) s. 14-Sep-2 Meeting Art, Vercelli #879/R
£374 $595 €550 Roses (45x25cm-18x10in) s. card on canvas. 1-Mar-3 Meeting Art, Vercelli #699
£475 $741 €750 Garda lake (30x50cm-12x20in) s. 14-Sep-2 Meeting Art, Vercelli #914/R

£481 $755 €750 View on the sea (35x45cm-14x18in) s. 23-Nov-2 Meeting Art, Vercelli #401/R
£510 $811 €750 Flowrrs in the garden (50x50cm-20x20in) s. 1-Mar-3 Meeting Art, Vercelli #530
£556 $883 €800 Roses in Capri (35x45cm-14x18in) s. painted 1997. 1-May-3 Meeting Art, Vercelli #68
£590 $939 €850 Vase of flowers (35x45cm-14x18in) s. 1-May-3 Meeting Art, Vercelli #294
£609 $956 €950 Hydrangeas at Santorini (45x35cm-18x14in) s. 23-Nov-2 Meeting Art, Vercelli #142/R
£609 $956 €950 Portofino in bloom (25x35cm-10x14in) s. painted 1999. 23-Nov-2 Meeting Art, Vercelli #392/R
£833 $1325 €1200 Pink house in Positano (40x70cm-16x28in) s. painted 1997. 1-May-3 Meeting Art, Vercelli #579
£962 $1510 €1500 Garden by the lake (50x80cm-20x31in) s. painted 1999. 23-Nov-2 Meeting Art, Vercelli #198/R
£1156 $1839 €1700 Positano (50x80cm-20x31in) s. painted 1996. 1-Mar-3 Meeting Art, Vercelli #539
£1389 $2208 €2000 Portofino (90x100cm-35x39in) s. 1-May-3 Meeting Art, Vercelli #355
£1961 $3137 €3000 Vases of flowers (120x140cm-47x55in) s. 4-Jan-3 Meeting Art, Vercelli #503

Works on paper

£272 $433 €400 Lake (25x35cm-10x14in) s. gouache paper on canvas. 1-Mar-3 Meeting Art, Vercelli #674
£327 $523 €500 Path towards the sea (50x35cm-20x14in) s. gouache oil paper on canvas. 4-Jan-3 Meeting Art, Vercelli #116
£340 $541 €500 Colours taking you to the hill (25x35cm-10x14in) s. gouache paper on canvas. 1-Mar-3 Meeting Art, Vercelli #666
£347 $552 €500 Spring at the seaside (35x25cm-14x10in) s.i. gouache paper on canvas. 1-May-3 Meeting Art, Vercelli #5
£347 $552 €500 Roses on the balcony (35x50cm-14x20in) s. gouache oil paper on canvas. 1-May-3 Meeting Art, Vercelli #492
£381 $606 €560 Street in Portofino (25x35cm-10x14in) s. s.i.verso gouache card on canvas. 1-Mar-3 Meeting Art, Vercelli #510

FACCINI, Pietro (1560-1602) Italian

Works on paper

£759 $1200 €1200 Tete de moine (19x18cm-7x7in) col chk. 27-Nov-2 Christie's, Paris #43/R
£18519 $30000 €27779 Two elders conversing (31x22cm-12x9in) pen ink wash. 22-Jan-3 Christie's, Rockefeller NY #23/R est:15000

FACEY, Florence (20th C) Australian

£1214 $1919 €1760 Cradle Mountain Tasmania (28x44cm-11x17in) board. 18-Nov-2 Goodman, Sydney #212/R (A.D 3400)

FACKERE, Jef van de (1879-1946) Belgian

Works on paper

£870 $1348 €1305 Reclining female nude (81x105cm-32x41in) s.d.1930 pastel chk. 9-Dec-2 Philippe Schuler, Zurich #3428/R est:2000-3000 (S.FR 2000)
£2055 $3205 €3000 Promenade du couple dans la campagne (82x62cm-32x24in) s.d.1916 pastel paper on canvas. 14-Apr-3 Horta, Bruxelles #105/R est:3500-4500

FAED, James (jnr) (1856-1920) British

£680 $1108 €1020 Moors on the road to Loch Dee, Galloway (11x17cm-4x7in) i.verso board. 17-Feb-3 Bonhams, Bath #12
£2200 $3564 €3300 Heather in bloom, Galloway (50x40cm-20x16in) s.d.1905. 23-May-3 Lyon & Turnbull, Edinburgh #5/R est:1000-1500

FAED, James (jnr-attrib) (1856-1920) British

£510 $796 €765 Heathery moor and burn (36x29cm-14x11in) card. 17-Oct-2 Bonhams, Edinburgh #248

FAED, James (snr) (1821-1911) British

£750 $1148 €1125 Pet (50x40cm-20x16in) mono.d.1870. 22-Aug-2 Bonhams, Edinburgh #1173

FAED, John (1820-1902) British

£480 $782 €720 The letter (12x15cm-5x6in) 14-Feb-3 Lyon & Turnbull, Edinburgh #43
£700 $1113 €1050 Pitcher girl (60x47cm-24x19in) s.verso panel. 2-Mar-3 Lots Road, London #350
£2100 $3318 €3150 Seated gentleman reading a document in his study (28x24cm-11x9in) s. board. 28-Nov-2 Martel Maides, Guernsey #35/R est:500-700
£6500 $10075 €9750 What will happen next (46x54cm-18x21in) s.d.68 panel prov. 31-Oct-2 Christie's, London #60/R est:3000-4000
£9000 $13680 €13500 Cotter's Saturday night (20x27cm-8x11in) board prov.exhib. 28-Aug-2 Sotheby's, London #898/R est:8000-12000
£22000 $36520 €33000 Spring flowers (61x45cm-24x18in) s.d.64 board prov. 10-Jun-3 Christie's, London #102/R est:25000-35000
£210000 $338100 €315000 Boyhood (102x86cm-40x34in) prov.exhib.lit. 19-Feb-3 Christie's, London #7/R est:200000-300000

FAED, Thomas (1826-1900) British

£380 $631 €551 Friar tuck (10x18cm-4x7in) mono. grisaille prov. 13-Jun-3 Lyon & Turnbull, Edinburgh #24
£763 $1213 €1145 Preparing dinner (30x25cm-12x10in) s. 18-Mar-3 Maynards, Vancouver #4/R (C.D 1800)
£900 $1404 €1350 Crofter (15x14cm-6x6in) s. board. 7-Nov-2 Christie's, Kensington #227/R
£1300 $2028 €1950 Family group seated in a landscape (53x70cm-21x28in) 8-Apr-3 Bonhams, Knightsbridge #149/R est:1000-1500
£1994 $3250 €2991 Waiting (14x19cm-6x7in) s. board. 11-Feb-3 Bonhams & Doyles, New York #126/R est:1200-1800
£2000 $3100 €3000 Highland Mary (53x35cm-21x14in) s.d.1864. 6-Dec-2 Lyon & Turnbull, Edinburgh #76/R est:2000-3000
£2805 $4432 €4208 The fishergirl (52x38cm-20x15in) s.d.1869. 30-Nov-2 Goteborg Auktionsverk, Sweden #178/R est:40000 (S.KR 40000)
£4292 $6652 €6438 Returning home from the hunt (66x89cm-26x35in) s.d.1856 prov. 3-Oct-2 Koller, Zurich #3098/R est:12000-18000 (S.FR 10000)
£10000 $15300 €15000 Lucy's flittin (57x35cm-22x14in) s.d.1864 lit. 22-Aug-2 Bonhams, Edinburgh #994/R est:10000-15000
£230000 $370300 €345000 Worn out (106x145cm-42x57in) s.d.1868 prov.exhib.lit. 19-Feb-3 Christie's, London #15/R est:150000-200000

Works on paper

£780 $1217 €1170 Cottage interior (17x25cm-7x10in) s. W/C htd white. 10-Apr-3 Bonhams, Edinburgh #106/R

FAERGEMANN, Knud Erik (1925-) Danish

£729 $1137 €1094 Circus in Lilleby (66x75cm-26x30in) init. 11-Nov-2 Rasmussen, Vejle #71/R (D.KR 8500)

FAES, Pieter (1750-1814) Belgian

£14000 $21700 €21000 Tulips, roses and other flowers with butterfly in urn on a marble ledge (79x65cm-31x26in) with sig. 30-Oct-2 Christie's, Kensington #69/R est:15000-20000

FAFARD, Joseph (1942-) Canadian

Sculpture

£5242 $8282 €7863 Taureau (46cm-18in) s. ceramic prov. 18-Nov-2 Sotheby's, Toronto #116/R est:6000-8000 (C.D 13000)

FAGAN, Betty Maud Christian (?-1932) British

£2000 $3260 €3000 Portrait of a beautiful lady (59x49cm-23x19in) s. 12-Feb-3 Bonhams, Knightsbridge #289/R est:2000-3000

FAGERLIN, Ferdinand (1825-1907) Swedish

£310 $503 €450 Palmtree (40x29cm-16x11in) s.d.1856. 25-May-3 Uppsala Auktionskammare, Uppsala #149 (S.KR 4000)

FAGES, Arthur R (1902-) French

£417 $654 €650 Les toits (46x55cm-18x22in) s.d.30. 11-Dec-2 Maigret, Paris #173/R

FAGUAYS, Pierre le (1892-1935) French

Sculpture

£952 $1514 €1400 Le penseur (27cm-11in) s. green pat bronze. 28-Feb-3 Tajan, Paris #34 est:1500-2000
£1600 $2560 €2400 Female warrior (29cm-11in) s. cold pat. bronze. 15-May-3 Christie's, Kensington #409/R est:1500-2000
£1761 $2800 €2642 Satyr (12x9x3cm-5x4x1in) s. silver bronze exec.c.1920. 4-May-3 Treadway Gallery, Cincinnati #571/R est:3000-5000
£1793 $2869 €2600 Lanceur de javelot (35x52cm-14x20in) s. 17-Mar-3 Horta, Bruxelles #134 est:2500-3500
£2000 $3180 €3000 Message of love (45cm-18in) s. bronze. 27-Feb-3 Sotheby's, Olympia #192/R est:2000-3000
£8500 $13430 €12750 Figural group of a nymph and faun (73cm-29in) silvered bronze. 14-Nov-2 Christie's, Kensington #245/R est:4000-6000
£10000 $15900 €15000 Leaving for the crusade (92cm-36in) bronze ivory on onyx base. 27-Feb-3 Sotheby's, Olympia #193/R est:12000-18000

FAGUAYS, le (20th C) French

Sculpture

£2800 $4480 €4200 Female dancer (24cm-9in) i. silvered bronze ivory. 15-May-3 Christie's, Kensington #451/R est:2500-3000

FAHEY, Edward Henry (1844-1907) British

Works on paper

£350 $543 €525 Coastal landscape (25x41cm-10x16in) s.d.1890 W/C. 4-Dec-2 Christie's, Kensington #63
£400 $624 €600 Norfolk Broads (17x32cm-7x13in) s. W/C. 25-Mar-3 Bonhams, Knightsbridge #171/R

£490 $769 €735 Entrance to Wroxham Broad (31x53cm-12x21in) s.i.d.1886 W/C over pencil. 15-Apr-3 Bonhams, Knowle #102

FAHEY, Jacqueline (1929-) New Zealander
£702 $1116 €1053 Portrait of a poet (60x89cm-24x35in) s.i.d.1978 verso board. 25-Feb-3 Peter Webb, Auckland #151/R est:2000-3000 (NZ.D 2000)

FAHEY, Terry (20th C) New Zealander
£643 $997 €965 Fete champetre (110x66cm-43x26in) s. i.verso board. 4-Dec-2 Dunbar Sloane, Auckland #32/R (NZ.D 2000)

FAHLBERG, Samuel (1758-1804) Swedish
Works on paper
£26377 $42731 €38247 View over the harbour in Gustavia, Saint Barthelmy (75x95cm-30x37in) i. W/C. 25-May-3 Uppsala Auktionskammare, Uppsala #27/R est:6600-8800 (S.KR 340000)

FAHLCRANTZ, Axel-Erik-Valerius (1851-1925) Swedish
£412 $642 €618 Autumn evening (85x130cm-33x51in) s.d.1919 panel. 13-Sep-2 Lilla Bukowskis, Stockholm #266 (S.KR 6000)

FAHLCRANTZ, Carl Johan (1774-1861) Swedish
£993 $1539 €1490 Thorsten Wikingson's burial mount, Framnas (35x45cm-14x18in) s.d.1827. 3-Dec-2 Bukowskis, Stockholm #417/R est:12000-15000 (S.KR 14000)
£1086 $1760 €1575 Park landscape with manor house (48x67cm-19x26in) s. 26-May-3 Bukowskis, Stockholm #367/R (S.KR 14000)

FAHLCRANTZ, Carl Johan (attrib) (1774-1861) Swedish
£305 $473 €458 Landscape with figures on country road (25x37cm-10x15in) mono. 8-Dec-2 Uppsala Auktionskammare, Uppsala #67 (S.KR 4300)

FAHLSTROM, Oyvind (1928-1976) Swedish
£5396 $8418 €8094 Study for life - span no.3 - Marilyn Monroe (25x35cm-10x14in) s.d.68 tempera Indian ink prov. 6-Nov-2 AB Stockholms Auktionsverk #560/R est:40000-45000 (S.KR 77000)
£12263 $19131 €18395 Steps (33x42cm-13x17in) s.d.1960 tempera varnish Indian ink prov. 5-Nov-2 Bukowskis, Stockholm #352/R est:175000-200000 (S.KR 175000)
Prints
£2803 $4373 €4205 Sitting - Dominoes - Movable modular painting (70x100cm-28x39in) s.num.30/50 verso silkscreen on plexiglas magnets prov. 6-Nov-2 AB Stockholms Auktionsverk #556/R est:35000-40000 (S.KR 40000)
Works on paper
£261 $396 €392 Untitled (27x16cm-11x6in) indis.sig.d. pencil. 16-Aug-2 Lilla Bukowskis, Stockholm #617 (S.KR 3800)
£316 $480 €474 Untitled (22x26cm-9x10in) Indian ink. 16-Aug-2 Lilla Bukowskis, Stockholm #618 (S.KR 4600)
£981 $1530 €1472 Untitled (34x26cm-13x10in) pastel prov. 6-Nov-2 AB Stockholms Auktionsverk #559/R est:5000-6000 (S.KR 14000)
£1016 $1585 €1524 Untitled (13x17cm-5x7in) W/C prov. 6-Nov-2 AB Stockholms Auktionsverk #558/R est:5000-6000 (S.KR 14500)
£1191 $1858 €1787 Untitled (20x14cm-8x6in) W/C prov. 6-Nov-2 AB Stockholms Auktionsverk #557/R est:5000-6000 (S.KR 17000)
£1699 $2735 €2549 Composition (46x19cm-18x7in) S. MM. 7-May-3 AB Stockholms Auktionsverk #808/R est:12000-15000 (S.KR 22000)
£1822 $2842 €2733 20 mouches mortes - 20 dead flies (27x37cm-11x15in) s.d.59 Indian ink varnish mixed media prov.exhib. 5-Nov-2 Bukowskis, Stockholm #353/R est:30000-35000 (S.KR 26000)
£2162 $3481 €3243 Untitled (26x34cm-10x13in) pastel prov. 7-May-3 AB Stockholms Auktionsverk #692/R est:10000-15000 (S.KR 28000)
£2239 $3605 €3359 Untitled (26x33cm-10x13in) pastel prov. 7-May-3 AB Stockholms Auktionsverk #693/R est:10000-15000 (S.KR 29000)
£2857 $4600 €4286 Untitled (29x20cm-11x8in) pastel prov. 7-May-3 AB Stockholms Auktionsverk #694/R est:15000-18000 (S.KR 37000)
£2934 $4724 €4401 You believed that (27x35cm-11x14in) s. mixed media. 7-May-3 AB Stockholms Auktionsverk #809/R est:20000-25000 (S.KR 38000)
£4695 $7324 €7043 Anonymous (43x61cm-17x24in) init.d.1957 gouache prov.exhib. 6-Nov-2 AB Stockholms Auktionsverk #561/R est:50000-60000 (S.KR 67000)

FAHN, A (?) Belgian?
Sculpture
£1224 $1947 €1800 Art Deco figure of Othello (56cm-22in) s. marble. 24-Mar-3 Bernaerts, Antwerp #142/R est:1600-2000

FAHNESTOCK, Wallace Weir (1877-?) American
£290 $450 €435 Evening light, Dorset (20x25cm-8x10in) s. i.verso board. 2-Nov-2 Thomaston Place, Thomaston #167
£3281 $5250 €4757 Mountain landscape with birch (64x76cm-25x30in) s.d.1919. 17-May-3 CRN Auctions, Cambridge #33

FAHRBACH, Carl Ludwig (1835-1902) German
£417 $633 €650 Forest clearing (75x100cm-30x39in) s. lit. 31-Aug-2 Geble, Radolfzell #626/R
£1127 $1814 €1600 Wooded landscape with stream (27x22cm-11x9in) s. 10-May-3 Berlinghof, Heidelberg #230/R est:1000

FAHRI, Jean Claude (1940-) ?
Sculpture
£1584 $2645 €2297 Sugar blues (88x64cm-35x25in) s. acrylic glass lit. 24-Jun-3 Koller, Zurich #186/R est:3000-5000 (S.FR 3500)

FAHRINGER, Carl (1874-1952) Austrian
£696 $1086 €1100 Delft cattle market (43x36cm-17x14in) s. 21-Oct-2 Glerum, Amsterdam #8/R
£1013 $1580 €1600 View of Rotterdam harbour (24x44cm-9x17in) s. board painted c.1920. 21-Oct-2 Glerum, Amsterdam #170/R est:800-1200
£1146 $1789 €1800 Balinese village (42x54cm-17x21in) mono. board. 6-Nov-2 Hugo Ruef, Munich #1081/R est:300
£1592 $2484 €2500 Parrot (50x37cm-20x15in) s. board. 6-Nov-2 Hugo Ruef, Munich #1080/R est:800
£1603 $2516 €2500 Resting (38x58cm-15x23in) s. board. 25-Nov-2 Hassfurther, Vienna #38/R est:2900-4100
£1731 $2717 €2700 Peasant market (56x79cm-22x31in) s. 25-Nov-2 Hassfurther, Vienna #39/R est:2900-4100
£2308 $3646 €3600 Canal in Holland (26x36cm-10x14in) s.i. canvas on board. 12-Nov-2 Dorotheum, Vienna #35/R est:2600-3600
£4255 $6894 €6000 Lustenau (39x53cm-15x21in) s.d.47 board. 20-May-3 Dorotheum, Vienna #170/R est:4500-6000
£4747 $7500 €7500 Leopard (45x65cm-18x26in) s. canvas on masonite. 27-Nov-2 Dorotheum, Vienna #136/R est:4000-6000
£5696 $9000 €9000 Cattle market in Holland (45x55cm-18x22in) s. canvas on panel. 27-Nov-2 Dorotheum, Vienna #158/R est:9000-11000
£6757 $10541 €10000 Cattle market (33x44cm-13x17in) s. 25-Mar-3 Wiener Kunst Auktionen, Vienna #138/R est:8000-14000
£8276 $13241 €12000 Bison (83x85cm-33x33in) mono. lit.prov. 11-Mar-3 Dorotheum, Vienna #1/R est:10000-13000
Works on paper
£288 $453 €450 Soldiers' camp (47x35cm-19x14in) s.indis.i.d.17 gouache. 21-Nov-2 Dorotheum, Vienna #471/R
£379 $607 €550 Wallenstein (12x14cm-5x6in) mono.i. gouache. 11-Mar-3 Dorotheum, Vienna #51/R
£897 $1434 €1300 Unloading freight (38x29cm-15x11in) mono. W/C gouache. 11-Mar-3 Dorotheum, Vienna #50/R
£1013 $1580 €1600 View of cattle market in Delft (44x65cm-17x26in) s.d.20 gouache. 21-Oct-2 Glerum, Amsterdam #4/R est:1500-2000
£1076 $1678 €1700 Delft cattle market with many figures (46x70cm-18x28in) s. gouache. 21-Oct-2 Glerum, Amsterdam #1/R est:1200-1800

FAIG, Frances Wiley (20th C) American?
£260 $400 €377 Burnt wood lake (36x43cm-14x17in) s. 8-Sep-2 DeFina, Austinburg #349

FAIRBAIRN (20th C) British
£1700 $2754 €2550 M.V Factor in the Mersey (50x75cm-20x30in) s. 21-Jan-3 Bonhams, New Bond Street #190/R est:200-300

FAIRBAIRN, H (fl.1893) British
£950 $1463 €1425 Young boy fishing besides a stream (51x33cm-20x13in) s.d.1897. 6-Sep-2 Biddle & Webb, Birmingham #125

FAIRBAIRN, Thomas (1820-1884) British
Works on paper
£380 $600 €570 Highland crofting scene with figure and hens (33x50cm-13x20in) s. W/C htd white. 7-Apr-3 Bonhams, Bath #16
£380 $635 €551 Gamekeeper (44x60cm-17x24in) W/C. 25-Jun-3 Bonhams, Bury St Edmunds #490

FAIRFAX-LUCY, Edmund (1945-) British
£300 $501 €435 Avon - very cold evening winter 1986 (20x25cm-8x10in) i.verso board. 23-Jun-3 Bonhams, Bath #69
£1800 $2808 €2700 Lake, early morning (45x56cm-18x22in) prov. 25-Mar-3 Bonhams, New Bond Street #67/R est:1200-1800

FAIRHOLME, Adele (fl.1899-1936) British
£1418 $2298 €2000 Two young girls in a nursery playing with toys (84x71cm-33x28in) 20-May-3 Mealy's, Castlecomer #1255/R est:2500-3500

FAIRHURST, Angus (1966-) British
£2500 $4000 €3750 Underdone/overdone painting no.7 (90x60cm-35x24in) acrylic silkscreen on panel prov.exhib. 16-May-3 Phillips, New York #123/R est:4500-5500

FAIRLEY, Barker (1887-1986) Canadian
£741 $1148 €1112 Portrait of Brenda Sproule (35x28cm-14x11in) s. board prov. 3-Dec-2 Joyner, Toronto #280/R est:1500-2000 (C.D 1800)
£1481 $2296 €2222 Rainy day, Palgrave (28x35cm-11x14in) s. board painted September 1962. 3-Dec-2 Joyner, Toronto #208/R est:2000-3000 (C.D 3600)
Works on paper
£667 $1093 €1001 Landscape with farm building (21x28cm-8x11in) s. W/C. 3-Jun-3 Joyner, Toronto #570/R est:600-900 (C.D 1500)

FAIRMAN, James (1826-1904) American
£4500 $7065 €6750 Camel trail in evening sunlight (81x114cm-32x45in) s. 21-Nov-2 Christie's, Kensington #191/R est:4000-6000

FAIRWEATHER, Ian (1891-1974) Australian
£10728 $16843 €16092 Family (50x35cm-20x14in) init. board. 15-Apr-3 Lawson Menzies, Sydney #29/R est:30000-40000 (A.D 28000)
£13953 $22186 €20930 Yangtse River (39x53cm-15x21in) init. exhib. 5-May-3 Sotheby's, Melbourne #115/R est:18000-25000 (A.D 36000)
Works on paper
£24904 $37107 €37356 Alpha (75x50cm-30x20in) s.i. gouache executed c.1951 prov. 27-Aug-2 Christie's, Melbourne #20/R est:55000-70000 (A.D 65000)
£29570 $44945 €44355 Birdcage (53x38cm-21x15in) init. gouache prov.exhib.lit. 28-Aug-2 Deutscher-Menzies, Melbourne #33/R est:55000-65000 (A.D 82500)
£64800 $104328 €97200 Queen of diamonds (95x71cm-37x28in) init. synthetic polymer on composition board prov.exhib.lit. 6-May-3 Christie's, Melbourne #22/R est:120000-150000 (A.D 162000)

FAIS, Eunice (20th C) American
£250 $400 €375 Huddled herd (41x51cm-16x20in) s. board. 11-Jan-3 James Julia, Fairfield #624

FAISTAUER, Anton (1887-1930) Austrian
£35000 $57400 €52500 Doppelakt - two nudes (203x168cm-80x66in) s.d.13 prov. 3-Jun-3 Sotheby's, London #97/R est:30000-50000
£38462 $59615 €60000 Reclining female nude (74x103cm-29x41in) s.d.1919 prov. 4-Dec-2 Lempertz, Koln #12/R est:60000-80000
Works on paper
£977 $1387 €1466 Head of a woman (41x33cm-16x13in) chl exec.1929. 26-Mar-2 SOGA, Bratislava #190/R est:28000 (SL.K 62000)
£1087 $1783 €1500 Reclining male nude (32x45cm-13x18in) s.i.d.12 chk W/C over pencil. 29-May-3 Lempertz, Koln #601/R est:750
£1282 $1987 €2000 Sketch for fresco (52x40cm-20x16in) s.i.d.1926 Indian ink chl pastel chk prov.lit. 4-Dec-2 Lempertz, Koln #701/R est:2000
£1795 $2782 €2800 Max Reinhardt (65x49cm-26x19in) i. pastel chk wash Indian ink prov. 4-Dec-2 Lempertz, Koln #702/R est:3000
£1923 $2981 €3000 Diana's return from the hunt (43x60cm-17x24in) i. verso mixed media prov.lit. 4-Dec-2 Lempertz, Koln #703/R est:3000
£2174 $3565 €3000 Standing female nude (61x38cm-24x15in) s.i.d.1926 pastel chk Indian ink. 29-May-3 Lempertz, Koln #603/R est:1000
£2899 $4754 €4000 Flight to Egypt (21x31cm-8x12in) W/C pencil exec.1923 lit. 27-May-3 Hassfurther, Vienna #39/R est:3000-4000
£3481 $5500 €5500 Lakeside town (13x21cm-5x8in) s. WC. 26-Nov-2 Wiener Kunst Auktionen, Vienna #153/R est:600-2500
£3696 $6061 €5100 Home-coming of Diana (60x44cm-24x17in) chl ink chl exec.1929 prov.lit. 27-May-3 Hassfurther, Vienna #37/R est:5000-6000
£5072 $8319 €7000 Holy Family (25x18cm-10x7in) W/C exec.1923 lit. 27-May-3 Hassfurther, Vienna #38/R est:3000-4000

FAISTENBERGER, Anton (style) (1663-1708) Austrian
£5000 $7750 €7500 Mountain landscape with herders and animals (97x145cm-38x57in) prov. 31-Oct-2 Sotheby's, Olympia #136/R est:5000-7000

FAIVRE, Jules-Abel (1867-1945) French
£650 $1060 €943 Portrait of a female nude. Portrait of a young woman (26x22cm-10x9in) s. pair. 15-Jul-3 Bonhams, Knightsbridge #58/R
£2065 $3262 €3200 Baigneuse aux cerises (46x38cm-18x15in) s. 17-Dec-2 Rossini, Paris #76/R
Works on paper
£1189 $1986 €1700 Femme (81x65cm-32x26in) s. pastel. 26-Jun-3 Tajan, Paris #21/R est:1000-1200

FAIVRE, Justin (1902-) American
Works on paper
£389 $650 €564 Bathers on the beach (30x41cm-12x16in) s.d.52 W/C gouache. 17-Jun-3 John Moran, Pasadena #90

FALCHETTI, Giuseppe (1843-1918) Italian
£429 $678 €644 Village in mountains with cow and calf (39x51cm-15x20in) s.d.1887. 29-Nov-2 Zofingen, Switzerland #2428 (S.FR 1000)
£1667 $2617 €2600 Landscape (44x58cm-17x23in) s. 10-Dec-2 Della Rocca, Turin #302/R
£1795 $2818 €2800 Landscape (44x58cm-17x23in) s. 10-Dec-2 Della Rocca, Turin #303/R
£5797 $9507 €8000 Veduta del lago di Como (65x88cm-26x35in) s.d.1887. 27-May-3 Finarte, Milan #89/R est:8000-12000

FALCO PUJOL, Joaquim (1958-) Spanish
£273 $398 €420 Coca Cola (130x97cm-51x38in) s.d.00 s.i.d.verso acrylic. 17-Jun-2 Ansorena, Madrid #86/R
£479 $748 €700 King and black prisoner (130x98cm-51x39in) s.d.2001 s.i.d.2001. 8-Apr-3 Ansorena, Madrid #276/R
£487 $711 €750 Olimpia cinema (90x120cm-35x47in) s.d.92 s.i.d.verso acrylic. 17-Jun-2 Ansorena, Madrid #87/R
£617 $901 €950 Shoe (60x91cm-24x36in) s.d.90 s.i.d.verso acrylic. 17-Jun-2 Ansorena, Madrid #85/R
Works on paper
£274 $427 €400 King (85x65cm-33x26in) s. mixed media. 8-Apr-3 Ansorena, Madrid #297/R
£284 $449 €440 King and queen (82x100cm-32x39in) s.d.2001 mixed media on canvas. 18-Dec-2 Ansorena, Madrid #209
£329 $513 €480 Tennis racket (100x80cm-39x31in) s. mixed media on canvas. 8-Apr-3 Ansorena, Madrid #287/R
£414 $658 €600 Bull scenes (33x41cm-13x16in) s.i. mixed media on canvas pair. 4-Mar-3 Ansorena, Madrid #251/R
£422 $616 €650 Bull scene (140x20cm-55x8in) s.i.d.1998 verso mixed media on canvas. 17-Jun-2 Ansorena, Madrid #42/R

FALCO, Joaquim (1958-) Spanish
Works on paper
£694 $1104 €1000 Tampax (81x100cm-32x39in) s.d.2000 mixed media on canvas. 1-May-3 Meeting Art, Vercelli #186

FALCONBRIDGE, Joseph (19th C) British
£284 $460 €426 Allegorical scene (94x127cm-37x50in) 23-Jan-3 Aspire, Cleveland #8

FALCONE, Aniello (1607-1656) Italian
Works on paper
£420 $600 €630 Standing Oriental salesman (21x11cm-8x4in) red chk. 23-Jan-3 Swann Galleries, New York #68/R

FALCONE, Aniello (attrib) (1607-1656) Italian
£774 $1223 €1200 Cavalry charging (28x40cm-11x16in) octagonal. 18-Dec-2 Piasa, Paris #8

FALCONE, Aniello (circle) (1607-1656) Italian
£11585 $19000 €17378 Cavalry skirmish (95x145cm-37x57in) 29-May-3 Sotheby's, New York #91/R est:5000-7000

FALENS, Carel van (1683-1733) Dutch
£7547 $11698 €12000 Elegantly dressed falconers on horseback (50x54cm-20x21in) 2-Oct-2 Dorotheum, Vienna #76/R est:12000-15000
£9434 $14623 €15000 Elegant hunting party outside chateau (49x67cm-19x26in) panel. 2-Oct-2 Dorotheum, Vienna #82/R est:15000-20000
£13100 $20699 €19650 Fauconnier a cheval (36x32cm-14x13in) panel prov. 17-Nov-2 Koller, Geneva #1325/R (S.FR 30000)

FALENS, Carel van (attrib) (1683-1733) Dutch
£4000 $6440 €6000 Figures and horse in a landscape (28x33cm-11x13in) init. copper. 20-Feb-3 Christie's, Kensington #67/R est:1200-1800

FALERO, Luis Riccardo (1851-1896) Spanish
£18065 $28000 €27098 An oriental beauty (74x41cm-29x16in) s. 30-Oct-2 Christie's, Rockefeller NY #97/R est:20000-30000

FALGUIERE, Alexandre (1831-1900) French
Sculpture
£2158 $3453 €3000 Diane a l'arc (78x31cm-31x12in) s. green pat bronze Cast Thiebaut Freres. 18-May-3 Rabourdin & Choppin de Janvry, Paris #73/R est:3000-3500
£2800 $4368 €4200 Diana the huntress (42cm-17in) s. green pat bronze st.f.Thiebaut. 9-Apr-3 Sotheby's, London #127/R est:1500-2500

£2800 $4676 €4060 Nude with peacock (60cm-24in) s. dk brown pat bronze incl red marble socle st.f.Theibaut. 8-Jul-3 Sotheby's, London #210/R est:2500-3500
£3000 $4800 €4500 Standing female nude (64cm-25in) gilt bronze. 15-May-3 Christie's, Kensington #378/R est:2500-3500
£3064 $4750 €4596 Diana (27cm-11in) s.i. brown pat. bronze on red marble base. 29-Oct-2 Sotheby's, New York #237/R est:4000-6000
£3200 $4992 €4800 Guitar player (38cm-15in) i.num.46 silvered bronze. 5-Nov-2 Sotheby's, London #149/R est:2000-3000
£3503 $5500 €5255 Bust of Diana, goddess of the hunt (17cm-7in) s.i. green brown pat. bronze on marble base. 10-Dec-2 Doyle, New York #201/R est:7000-9000
£10072 $16115 €14000 Suzanne surprise (66x46cm-26x18in) s. marble. 18-May-3 Rabourdin & Choppin de Janvry, Paris #72/R est:13500-15000
£17000 $27030 €25500 Victory in the cockfight (174cm-69in) bronze st.f.Artisique. 27-Feb-3 Bonhams, Chester #867/R est:3000-5000
£45000 $75150 €65250 Etude for the monument to Balzac (72x42x37cm-28x17x15in) terracotta on shaped wood modelling board prov. 8-Jul-3 Sotheby's, London #216/R est:20000-30000

FALK, Hans (1918-2002) Swiss
£1180 $1865 €1770 Couple in interior (33x55cm-13x22in) s. 29-Nov-2 Zofingen, Switzerland #2869/R est:3000 (S.FR 2750)
£3275 $5142 €4913 Untitled (51x67cm-20x26in) s. panel. 25-Nov-2 Germann, Zurich #2/R est:5000-7000 (S.FR 7500)
Works on paper
£524 $823 €786 Stromboli (63x83cm-25x33in) s. mixed media. 25-Nov-2 Germann, Zurich #717 (S.FR 1200)
£655 $1028 €983 Container (38x42cm-15x17in) s. num.4/100 gouache collage on lithograph. 25-Nov-2 Germann, Zurich #335 est:1000-1200 (S.FR 1500)
£1135 $1783 €1703 Stromboli (100x70cm-39x28in) s.i. mixed media collage. 25-Nov-2 Germann, Zurich #125/R est:3000-4000 (S.FR 2600)
£2096 $3060 €3144 Work year (74x98cm-29x39in) s. mixed media over lithograph. 4-Jun-2 Germann, Zurich #40/R est:4800-5200 (S.FR 4800)

FALK, Hjalmar (1856-1938) Swedish
£618 $1025 €896 Fishermen on road (35x53cm-14x21in) s. 16-Jun-3 Lilla Bukowskis, Stockholm #72 (S.KR 8000)

FALK, Lars-Erik (1922-) Swedish
Sculpture
£1141 $1802 €1712 Module relief in colour 86 (27x198x150cm-11x78x59in) s.d.1982 painted aluminium. 28-Apr-3 Bukowskis, Stockholm #242a/R est:20000-25000 (S.KR 15000)
£1390 $2238 €2085 Module sculpture in colour 35 (73cm-29in) s.d.1986 varnished aluminium profiles on black wood socle. 7-May-3 AB Stockholms Auktionsverk #941/R est:20000-25000 (S.KR 18000)

FALK, Ragnar (1903-1977) Swedish
£372 $587 €558 Still life of flowers and fruit (49x62cm-19x24in) s. 30-Nov-2 Goteborg Auktionsverk, Sweden #528/R (S.KR 5300)

FALK, Robert Rafailovich (1886-1958) Russian
£60000 $97200 €90000 Portrait of an Indian boy (99x71cm-39x28in) s. prov.lit. 21-May-3 Sotheby's, London #191/R est:40000-60000
Works on paper
£880 $1417 €1250 Parisian Boulevard (26x31cm-10x12in) s.i.d.1937 gouache. 10-May-3 Bukowskis, Helsinki #395/R

FALKENBERG, Georg Richard (1850-?) German
£318 $497 €500 Girl wearing shawl (44x37cm-17x15in) s. 6-Nov-2 Hugo Ruef, Munich #1092

FALKENBERG, Richard (1875-?) German
£306 $487 €450 Lower Rhineland fields (60x80cm-24x31in) s. 28-Mar-3 Bolland & Marotz, Bremen #442/R
£314 $491 €500 Sunny forest track (50x60cm-20x24in) s. panel. 21-Sep-2 Bolland & Marotz, Bremen #474
£541 $845 €850 Stream in lower Rhine landscape (130x119cm-51x47in) s. 6-Nov-2 Hugo Ruef, Munich #1083/R

FALKENSTEIN, Claire (1908-1997) American
Sculpture
£961 $1500 €1442 Untitled, reclining female nude (12x25cm-5x10in) init.i. green pat bronze exec.c.1960-65 Cast Alfred Petersen. 14-Oct-2 Butterfields, San Francisco #2083/R est:2500-3500

FALL, George (c.1848-1925) British
Works on paper
£250 $393 €375 York Minster from across the Ouse (17x11cm-7x4in) s.d.d.1884 W/C. 21-Nov-2 Tennants, Leyburn #644
£350 $546 €525 Barges on the river Ouse at York (17cm-7in circular) s. W/C htd white. 25-Mar-3 Bonhams, Leeds #509
£360 $565 €540 Water tower, Minster York (27x21cm-11x8in) s.i. pencil W/C. 19-Nov-2 Bonhams, Leeds #82
£400 $624 €600 Old Guildhall, York (20x29cm-8x11in) s.i. W/C. 10-Apr-3 Tennants, Leyburn #829
£420 $685 €609 Clifford's Tower, York (20x29cm-8x11in) s.i. W/C. 17-Jul-3 Tennants, Leyburn #715
£420 $685 €609 Barges on the river, York (30x22cm-12x9in) s.d.1890 W/C. 17-Jul-3 Tennants, Leyburn #716

FALLER, Louis-Clement (1819-1901) French
£365 $576 €548 Portrait study of Arlesienne (24x19cm-9x7in) mono.d.87. 29-Nov-2 Zofingen, Switzerland #2429 (S.FR 850)

FALLS, Rolfe (fl.1893-1899) British
£300 $498 €435 Les Autelets, and west coast of Sark (18x39cm-7x15in) s.d.02. 12-Jun-3 Martel Maides, Guernsey #26

FALTER, Marcel (1866-?) French
£3262 $5285 €4600 Exaltation du travail (114x145cm-45x57in) s. d.1914 verso. 23-May-3 Camard, Paris #71/R est:3000-4000

FALZONI, Giulio (1900-1978) Italian
Works on paper
£654 $1046 €1000 Landscape by Chioggia (70x50cm-28x20in) s.i. W/C cardboard. 4-Jan-3 Meeting Art, Vercelli #426
£719 $1150 €1100 Paris, Sacre-Coeur (50x70cm-20x28in) s. W/C cardboard. 4-Jan-3 Meeting Art, Vercelli #149

FAN ZENG (1938-) Chinese
Works on paper
£1739 $2852 €2400 Portrait of the poet Li Taibo (94x61cm-37x24in) i. seals Indian ink col hanging scroll. 30-May-3 Dr Fritz Nagel, Stuttgart #1242/R est:1200-1800

FANE, General Walter (18th C) British
£500 $780 €750 Country house in a landscape (61x102cm-24x40in) 8-Oct-2 Sotheby's, Olympia #415/R
£1900 $2964 €2850 Grand Chartreuse Monastery. Grand St Bernard Monastery (92x137cm-36x54in) pair. 8-Oct-2 Sotheby's, Olympia #416/R est:1000-1500

FANELLI, Francesco (c.1590-c.1661) Italian
Sculpture
£12000 $18840 €18000 Group of Venus and Cupid (19cm-7in) brown pat. bronze after Giambologna lit. 10-Dec-2 Sotheby's, London #98/R est:8000-12000
£32000 $50240 €48000 Nessus and Deianara (19x14cm-7x6in) bronze prov.lit. 10-Dec-2 Sotheby's, London #99/R est:15000-20000

FANELLI, Francesco (1863-1924) Italian
£3265 $5192 €4800 My garen (55x55cm-22x22in) s. cardboard. 18-Mar-3 Finarte, Milan #67/R

FANFANI, Enrico (19th C) Italian
£900 $1467 €1350 Mother and son in the desert (82x65cm-32x26in) s. 29-Jan-3 Sotheby's, Olympia #270/R est:1000-1500

FANG CONG (17/18th C) Chinese
Works on paper
£4507 $7436 €6535 Landscape (95x47cm-37x19in) s. ink hanging scroll. 7-Jul-3 Christie's, Hong Kong #516/R est:50000-60000 (HK.D 58000)

FANG RENDING (1901-1975) Chinese
Works on paper
£4065 $6423 €6098 Lake Xuanwu (173x94cm-68x37in) s.d.1947 ink col hanging scroll exhib. 28-Apr-3 Sotheby's, Hong Kong #614/R est:25000-30000 (HK.D 50000)

FANGE, Jens (1965-) Swedish
£888 $1430 €1332 Untitled (24x33cm-9x13in) s.verso. 7-May-3 AB Stockholms Auktionsverk #952/R (S.KR 11500)

FANGOR, Wojciech (1922-) Polish
£1667 $2600 €2501 Square 16 (90x89cm-35x35in) i.d.1962 i.verso acrylic. 14-Sep-2 Weschler, Washington #649/R est:800-1200
£3333 $5467 €4600 B 115 (71x71cm-28x28in) s.i.d.1966 verso prov. 28-May-3 Lempertz, Koln #128/R est:1400-1600

FANNEN, J (fl.1890-1900) British
£920 $1463 €1380 Brigantine Henry of Guernsey (49x62cm-19x24in) s.d.1886 canvas on board. 20-Mar-3 Martel Maides, Guernsey #62/R
£2500 $3875 €3750 Steamer Seaham Harbour towing a Royal Navy barquentine (66x102cm-26x40in) s.d.1887 prov. 31-Oct-2 Christie's, Kensington #499/R est:3000-5000

FANNER, Alice (1865-1930) British
£949 $1500 €1424 Heading for the Channel. s. 16-Nov-2 Harvey Clar, Oakland #1254

FANSHAW, Hubert Valentine (20th C) Canadian?
£221 $349 €332 Harvest time, Manitoba (36x46cm-14x18in) d.1938. 1-Dec-2 Levis, Calgary #26/R (C.D 550)
£241 $381 €362 Autumn (36x46cm-14x18in) 1-Dec-2 Levis, Calgary #25/R (C.D 600)
£482 $761 €723 Birch on riding mountain (61x76cm-24x30in) 1-Dec-2 Levis, Calgary #24/R (C.D 1200)

FANTACCHIOTTI, Cesare (1844-1922) Italian
Sculpture
£2721 $4327 €4000 David (100x40x40cm-39x16x16in) s. white marble sold with base. 24-Mar-3 Finarte Semenzato, Rome #398/R est:7000

FANTIN-LATOUR, Henri (1836-1904) French
£1500 $2324 €2250 Toilette (14x11cm-6x4in) i.verso panel prov. 3-Dec-2 Sotheby's, Olympia #229/R est:700-1000
£2744 $4500 €3979 La verite sortant du puit (29x14cm-11x6in) prov.lit. 4-Jun-3 Christie's, Rockefeller NY #223/R est:5000-7000
£2817 $4676 €4000 L'ange de Tobie (31x27cm-12x11in) s. painted c.1855 after Rembrandt. 11-Jun-3 Beaussant & Lefèvre, Paris #48 est:5000-6000
£5484 $8500 €8226 Odalisque (52x63cm-20x25in) s. prov.exhib.lit. 2-Oct-2 Christie's, Rockefeller NY #777/R est:8000-12000
£6129 $9500 €9194 La source dans le bois (34x51cm-13x20in) s. paper on canvas painted 1897. 30-Oct-2 Christie's, Rockefeller NY #197/R est:12000-18000
£6129 $9500 €9194 Danae (27x35cm-11x14in) s. painted 1898 prov.exhib.lit. 30-Oct-2 Christie's, Rockefeller NY #198/R est:8000-12000
£9032 $14000 €13548 Odalisque (50x61cm-20x24in) s. painted c.1904 prov.exhib.lit. 30-Oct-2 Christie's, Rockefeller NY #199/R est:15000-20000
£10000 $16400 €15000 Tannhauser (33x44cm-13x17in) s. panel painted c.1895 prov. 4-Feb-3 Christie's, London #206/R
£10968 $17000 €16452 Vision (32x24cm-13x9in) s. oil paper on canvas painted 1869 prov.exhib.lit. 30-Oct-2 Christie's, Rockefeller NY #202/R est:10000-15000
£15035 $25108 €21500 La toilette (32x40cm-13x16in) s. 27-Jun-3 Claude Aguttes, Neuilly #77/R est:20000-25000
£16774 $26000 €25161 Sortie de bain (57x47cm-22x19in) s. painted 1898 prov.exhib.lit. 30-Oct-2 Christie's, Rockefeller NY #201/R est:15000-20000
£30769 $48000 €46154 Fleurs, roses (20x26cm-8x10in) s.d.83 prov.exhib. 7-Nov-2 Christie's, Rockefeller NY #233/R est:25000-35000
£55000 $90200 €82500 Fruits (39x54cm-15x21in) s. painted 1886 prov.exhib.lit. 5-Feb-3 Sotheby's, London #105/R est:80000
£75000 $123000 €112500 Damnation de Faust (96x63cm-38x25in) s.d.88 prov.exhib.lit. 4-Feb-3 Christie's, London #207/R est:80000
£92000 $150880 €138000 Peches (26x40cm-10x16in) s.d.66 prov.exhib. 5-Feb-3 Sotheby's, London #106/R est:90000
£140000 $233800 €210000 Roses (41x37cm-16x15in) s.d.86 prov.exhib.lit. 23-Jun-3 Sotheby's, London #4/R est:150000-200000
£180000 $300600 €270000 Roses blanches et cerises (48x39cm-19x15in) s.d.1865 prov. 23-Jun-3 Sotheby's, London #1/R est:150000-200000
£248447 $400000 €372671 Pavots (56x63cm-22x25in) s.d.83 prov.exhib.lit. 7-May-3 Christie's, Rockefeller NY #1/R est:400000-600000
£400000 $656000 €600000 Pommes dans un panier (44x56cm-17x22in) s.d.88 prov.exhib.lit. 4-Feb-3 Sotheby's, London #5/R est:600000
£420000 $688800 €630000 Oeillets (46x51cm-18x20in) s.d.90 prov.exhib. 4-Feb-3 Sotheby's, London #7/R est:600000
£500000 $780000 €750000 Nature morte, dahlias, raisins et peches (51x49cm-20x19in) s.d.1868 prov.exhib.lit. 6-Nov-2 Christie's, Rockefeller NY #5/R est:600000-800000

Works on paper
£264 $412 €420 Etudes de nus (17x12cm-7x5in) dr tracing paper. 14-Oct-2 Blache, Grenoble #71
£1456 $2300 €2300 Nuque et chevelure (14x13cm-6x5in) st.sig. chl dr. 29-Nov-2 Drouot Estimations, Paris #37/R
£1800 $2862 €2700 Study of nudes (18x26cm-7x10in) s. pencil on tracing paper exhib. 20-Mar-3 Christie's, Kensington #20/R est:2000-3000
£2548 $4000 €3822 Study of nudes (10x6cm-4x2in) pencil set of six prov. 10-Dec-2 Doyle, New York #205/R est:3000-4000
£5556 $9000 €8334 Head of bearded man (42x34cm-17x13in) s.i.d.1859 crayon prov.lit. 22-Jan-3 Christie's, Rockefeller NY #117/R est:6000

FANTIN-LATOUR, Henri (attrib) (1836-1904) French
Works on paper
£1050 $1660 €1575 Portrait of Edouard Manet (37x26cm-15x10in) bears sig.d.1867 W/C prov. 16-Nov-2 Crafoord, Lund #43/R est:5000 (S.KR 15000)

FANTIN-LATOUR, Theodore (1805-1872) French
Works on paper
£4500 $7155 €6750 Pensive moment. Passage of time (41x33cm-16x13in) pastel oval pair. 20-Mar-3 Christie's, Kensington #120/R est:5000-7000

FANTIN-LATOUR, Victoria (1840-1926) French
£7097 $11213 €11000 Bouquet printanier (22x27cm-9x11in) mono. 19-Dec-2 Claude Aguttes, Neuilly #54/R est:15000
£10063 $15497 €16000 White roses in a vase with peaches and grapes on a table (49x60cm-19x24in) s. 23-Oct-2 Christie's, Amsterdam #80/R est:8000-12000

Works on paper
£12000 $19680 €18000 Vase de fleurs (47x40cm-19x16in) s. W/C htd gouache. 3-Jun-3 Sotheby's, London #164/R est:4000-6000

FANTON-LEKEU, Henri Ferdinand (1791-1858) Belgian
£962 $1510 €1500 Halte du cavalier a un relais (26x22cm-10x9in) s.d.1835. 11-Dec-2 Hotel des Ventes Mosan, Brussels #231 est:1800-2200

FANTONI, Marcello (20th C) ?
Sculpture
£903 $1400 €1355 Untitled (69x71x23cm-27x28x9in) s. exec.c.1957. 29-Sep-2 Butterfields, Los Angeles #4355/R est:1200-1500

FANTUZZI, Antonio (16th C) Italian
Prints
£6329 $10000 €10000 The sacrifice (27x39cm-11x15in) etching after Rosso Fiorentino. 29-Nov-2 Bassenge, Berlin #5214/R est:12000

FANTUZZI, Eliano (1909-1987) Italian
£321 $497 €500 Girl (70x50cm-28x20in) s. s.i.d.67 verso. 4-Dec-2 Finarte, Milan #278
£411 $641 €600 Women (36x28cm-14x11in) s. s.verso board. 10-Apr-3 Finarte Semenzato, Rome #154
£545 $855 €850 Little harbour (40x50cm-16x20in) s.s.d.1955 verso. 21-Nov-2 Finarte, Rome #56/R
£581 $917 €900 Women at the bar (60x50cm-24x20in) s. s.verso. 18-Dec-2 Christie's, Rome #222
£769 $1215 €1200 Concert (50x40cm-20x16in) s. painted 1986. 15-Nov-2 Farsetti, Prato #3/R
£833 $1308 €1300 At the bar (60x80cm-24x31in) s. s.verso painted 1986. 21-Nov-2 Finarte, Rome #208
£1090 $1711 €1700 Roman night scene (50x40cm-20x16in) s. s.d.1953 verso. 21-Nov-2 Finarte, Rome #219/R
£1538 $2415 €2400 In the tailor's shop (80x120cm-31x47in) s. s.verso. 21-Nov-2 Finarte, Rome #195/R

FARAGO, Geza (1877-1928) Hungarian
£2958 $4585 €4289 Rendezvous by night (30x30cm-12x12in) s. 9-Dec-2 Mu Terem Galeria, Budapest #47/R est:250000 (H.F 1100000)
£10000 $16400 €15000 Mephisto and Gretchen (145x110cm-57x43in) s. painted c.1900-91. 3-Jun-3 Sotheby's, London #71/R est:10000-15000
Works on paper
£7530 $11671 €10919 Lady at the bar counter (77x57cm-30x22in) mixed media. 9-Dec-2 Mu Terem Galeria, Budapest #51/R est:850000 (H.F 2800000)

FARALLI, Gianpaolo (1955-) Italian
£347 $552 €500 Italian square (70x70cm-28x28in) s. s.i.verso. 1-May-3 Meeting Art, Vercelli #35

FARAND, Mark (20th C) Canadian
Works on paper
£466 $741 €699 Melvin St. RY (45x69cm-18x27in) s. W/C. 23-Mar-3 Hodgins, Calgary #4/R est:500-800 (C.D 1100)

FARASYN, Edgard (1858-1938) Belgian
£284 $460 €400 Berger de moutons au coucher du soleil (31x45cm-12x18in) 26-May-3 Amberes, Antwerp #33

£284 $460 €400 Porteuse d'eau (40x28cm-16x11in) 26-May-3 Amberes, Antwerp #34
£380 $592 €600 Back from fishing (27x35cm-11x14in) s. oil gouache paper. 21-Oct-2 Bernaerts, Antwerp #10/R
£496 $829 €700 Yachts at the quay (57x46cm-22x18in) s. 23-Jun-3 Bernaerts, Antwerp #36/R
£1154 $1812 €1800 Pecheur de crevettes et barque de peche dans une mer agitee (85x77cm-33x30in) 25-Nov-2 Amberes, Antwerp #158
£2390 $3681 €3800 Jeune fille se promenant avec chevre (60x80cm-24x31in) s. 22-Oct-2 Campo & Campo, Antwerp #105/R
£3103 $4966 €4500 Pecheurs de crevettes (85x133cm-33x52in) 17-Mar-3 Amberes, Antwerp #212/R
Works on paper
£256 $403 €400 Marine (33x52cm-13x20in) W/C. 25-Nov-2 Amberes, Antwerp #159

FARASYN, L (1822-1899) Belgian
£1400 $2282 €2030 Descent from the Cross (145x110cm-57x43in) s.d.1855. 21-Jul-3 Bonhams, Bath #51/R est:800-1200

FARE, Arthur Cecil (?) British
Works on paper
£250 $395 €363 Matterhorn from the south (77x52cm-30x20in) s.i. W/C over pencil. 22-Jul-3 Bristol Auction Rooms #298/R
£330 $551 €479 Corn St, Bristol (36x26cm-14x10in) s.i. W/C over pencil. 17-Jun-3 Bristol Auction Rooms #456/R
£350 $557 €525 Redland Chapel, Bristol (25x42cm-10x17in) s.i. W/C over pencil. 4-Mar-3 Bristol Auction Rooms #279/R

FARE, Arthur Charles (1876-1958) British
Works on paper
£400 $616 €600 Hetling House, Bath (30x44cm-12x17in) s.d.1942 W/C over pencil. 22-Oct-2 Bonhams, Bath #166

FAREY, Cyril A (1888-?) British
Works on paper
£500 $825 €725 New rectory, St. James's Church (23x30cm-9x12in) s. W/C bodycol. 3-Jul-3 Duke & Son, Dorchester #69/R

FARGUE, Paulus Constantin la (1732-1782) Dutch
£1892 $2951 €2800 Elegant figures in garden (25x32cm-10x13in) panel. 26-Mar-3 Tajan, Paris #154/R est:3000
£19108 $29809 €30000 Hague, the grote market seen from the Prinsergrach (41x58cm-16x23in) s. panel prov. 5-Nov-2 Sotheby's, Amsterdam #244/R est:12000-18000

FARHI, Jean Claude (1940-) French
Sculpture
£962 $1490 €1500 Precious dream vision, version I (150x70x52cm-59x28x20in) polymethacrylate executed 1995 lit. 3-Dec-2 Christie's, Amsterdam #62/R est:1500-2200

FARINATI, Orazio (1559-c.1616) Italian
Works on paper
£845 $1361 €1200 Cristo che risana un cieco (42x59cm-17x23in) pen brown ink W/C blk pencil. 12-May-3 Sotheby's, Milan #26/R est:1200-1500

FARINATI, Paolo (1524-1606) Italian
£8025 $13000 €12038 Lamentation over the dead Christ (30x24cm-12x9in) oil on slate. 23-Jan-3 Sotheby's, New York #64/R est:10000-15000
Works on paper
£9877 $16000 €14816 Saint Barbara with Saint Anthony (43x25cm-17x10in) chk pen ink wash htd white. 22-Jan-3 Christie's, Rockefeller NY #5/R est:20000

FARINGTON, Joseph (1747-1821) British
Works on paper
£260 $413 €390 East view Dartmouth (21x36cm-8x14in) i.d.Oct 11 1809 pencil. 4-Mar-3 Bearnes, Exeter #368
£300 $495 €435 On the banks of the Tavey (15x30cm-6x12in) i.d.1809 pencil. 3-Jul-3 Christie's, Kensington #137
£800 $1272 €1200 Buildings above a cliff near a river (31x43cm-12x17in) i. pen sepia ink wash over pencil squared for transfer. 19-Mar-3 Sotheby's, London #194/R
£1000 $1590 €1500 Figures by a cottage in a wooded landscape (56x45cm-22x18in) s. pen ink grey brown wash over pencil exhib. 19-Mar-3 Sotheby's, London #170/R est:1200-1800

FARJON, Jean Francois (fl.1864-1882) French
£391 $607 €587 Peasant woman and cows by pond (38x56cm-15x22in) s. panel. 9-Dec-2 Philippe Schuler, Zurich #8635 (S.FR 900)

FARKAS, Istvan (1887-1947) Hungarian
£16136 $25010 €24204 Hungarian landscape (65x81cm-26x32in) s. tempera board. 6-Dec-2 Kieselbach, Budapest #142/R (H.F 6000000)
£20169 $31263 €30254 Woman by the window (100x100cm-39x39in) tempera cardboard on canvas. 6-Dec-2 Kieselbach, Budapest #83/R (H.F 7500000)
£20478 $32765 €30717 By a garden table (45x54cm-18x21in) s.d.1930. 16-May-3 Kieselbach, Budapest #59/R (H.F 7000000)
£67074 $104636 €100611 At the level crossing, 1934 (81x100cm-32x39in) s. board. 11-Sep-2 Kieselbach, Budapest #117/R (H.F 26000000)
Works on paper
£568 $885 €852 Girl in National costume, 1917 (49x36cm-19x14in) s.d.1917 pastel. 11-Sep-2 Kieselbach, Budapest #214/R (H.F 220000)

FARKASHAZY, Nicolas (1895-1964) Hungarian
£7266 $11334 €10536 Still life of flowers (98x71cm-39x28in) s. tempera paperboard. 12-Apr-3 Mu Terem Galeria, Budapest #163/R est:2500000 (H.F 2600000)
Works on paper
£774 $1207 €1161 Venice (52x72cm-20x28in) s. pastel cardboard. 11-Sep-2 Kieselbach, Budapest #7/R (H.F 300000)

FARLOW, Harry (1882-?) American
£481 $750 €722 Portrait of a man with cane seated on a green wicker bench (76x61cm-30x24in) s. 15-Oct-2 Winter Associates, Plainville #221

FARMER, Edward G (19/20th C) American
£701 $1100 €1052 Sunshine in the glen (41x66cm-16x26in) s.d.25. 23-Nov-2 Jackson's, Cedar Falls #90/R

FARNDON, Walter (1876-1964) American
£1625 $2600 €2356 Harbour inlet (31x41cm-12x16in) s. board. 16-May-3 Skinner, Boston #275/R est:1500-2500
£3459 $5500 €5189 Harbour view (66x81cm-26x32in) s. 7-Mar-3 Skinner, Boston #471a/R est:6000-8000

FARNSWORTH, Alfred Villiers (1858-1908) American
Works on paper
£1198 $2000 €1737 Cattle watering in marin landscape (33x48cm-13x19in) s.d.1904 W/C. 17-Jun-3 John Moran, Pasadena #166 est:1500-2500

FARNY, Henry F (1847-1916) American
£45161 $70000 €67742 Indian head (24x16cm-9x6in) s.i.d.1908 board prov.exhib.lit. 3-Dec-2 Phillips, New York #42/R est:60000-80000
£516129 $800000 €774194 Moment of suspense (61x41cm-24x16in) s.d.1911 prov.exhib.lit. 3-Dec-2 Phillips, New York #43/R est:500000-700000
Sculpture
£1266 $2000 €1899 Head of a Native American (13cm-5in) s.d.99 brown pat. bronze. 24-Apr-3 Shannon's, Milford #177/R est:1000-1500
Works on paper
£2343 $3750 €3515 Indian portrait (15x10cm-6x4in) s. W/C. 11-Jan-3 James Julia, Fairfield #214a est:4000-6000
£9589 $14000 €14384 Cornered (33x20cm-13x8in) s.d.98 pen ink. 3-Nov-1 North East Auctions, Portsmouth #729/R
£45513 $71000 €68270 Red horse Nez perce scout (20x13cm-8x5in) W/C. 9-Nov-2 Altermann Galleries, Santa Fe #103
£54839 $85000 €82259 Hunter (20x14cm-8x6in) s.d.99 gouache prov.exhib.lit. 5-Dec-2 Christie's, Rockefeller NY #172/R est:100000-150000

FARQUHARSON, David (1839-1907) British
£343 $535 €515 Milking time (36x54cm-14x21in) s.d.1878. 13-Sep-2 Lilla Bukowskis, Stockholm #368 (S.KR 5000)
£420 $651 €630 Ploughing (13x23cm-5x9in) board. 5-Dec-2 Bonhams, Edinburgh #93
£1150 $1863 €1725 Dredging (20x31cm-8x12in) init.d.1876 panel. 23-Jan-3 Bonhams, Edinburgh #334 est:600-800
£1200 $1968 €1800 Inverness under moonlight (20x36cm-8x14in) init.i.verso. 5-Jun-3 Christie's, Kensington #729/R est:500-700
£1300 $2028 €1950 Cattle in winter (20x30cm-8x12in) with sig. board. 26-Mar-3 Sotheby's, Olympia #119/R est:1000-1500
£1500 $2340 €2250 Path to Ben Lomond (30x51cm-12x20in) s.d.84 indis i.verso. 14-Apr-3 Sotheby's, London #32/R est:1500-2000
£1650 $2525 €2475 Loch Coruisk, Isle of Skye (22x32cm-9x13in) s. 22-Aug-2 Bonhams, Edinburgh #999/R est:800-1200
£3200 $4864 €4800 Lily pond in the park, Castle Kennedy, Stranraer (30x51cm-12x20in) s.d.1901. 28-Aug-2 Sotheby's, London #923/R est:3000-4000

£3800 $6194 €5510 Seed time (23x33cm-9x13in) s.d.1877 i.verso. 17-Jul-3 Tennants, Leyburn #846/R est:3800-4000
£5000 $7800 €7500 At Loch Maree-Side (41x56cm-16x22in) s. 14-Apr-3 Sotheby's, London #35/R est:5000-7000

Works on paper
£550 $869 €825 Sheep crossing a stream (25x34cm-10x13in) s.d.1879 W/C. 26-Nov-2 Bonhams, Knightsbridge #241/R

FARQUHARSON, John (1865-1931) British

Works on paper
£750 $1163 €1125 Cattle grazing beside a stream with a cottage beyond (36x51cm-14x20in) s.d.1904 W/C. 31-Oct-2 Duke & Son, Dorchester #145/R

FARQUHARSON, Joseph (1846-1935) British
£892 $1400 €1338 In the valley (51x77cm-20x30in) s. verso. 22-Nov-2 Skinner, Boston #222/R est:800-1200
£2600 $4056 €3900 Clachans at Loch Duich (26x40cm-10x16in) s. 14-Apr-3 Sotheby's, London #34/R est:2500-3000
£5500 $8525 €8250 Scene in Arran (36x56cm-14x22in) init. prov. 31-Oct-2 Christie's, London #89/R est:5000-8000
£32000 $51520 €48000 Winter evening (52x70cm-20x28in) s. s.i.verso prov.exhib.lit. 20-Feb-3 Christie's, London #359/R est:15000
£36000 $55800 €54000 Sheep in the moonlit snow (30x76cm-12x30in) s. 31-Oct-2 Christie's, London #86/R est:25000-35000
£36000 $58320 €54000 Sheep in a snowy landscape by moonlight (60x50cm-24x20in) s. 23-May-3 Lyon & Turnbull, Edinburgh #67/R est:6000-8000
£76000 $115520 €114000 Herding sheep in a winter landscape at sunset (81x122cm-32x48in) s. prov. 28-Aug-2 Sotheby's, London #1047/R est:70000-100000

FARR, Ellen B (1840-1907) American
£323 $500 €485 Trompe l'oeil image of trout hung in front of nets (66x41cm-26x16in) s. 28-Sep-2 Thomaston Place, Thomaston #23
£1452 $2250 €2178 Pepper tree (30x20cm-12x8in) s.d.89 prov. 29-Oct-2 John Moran, Pasadena #611 est:1500-2000
£2329 $3750 €3494 California poppies in an Indian basket (48x64cm-19x25in) s. prov. 18-Feb-3 John Moran, Pasadena #53 est:4000-6000

FARRAR, Frances (1855-?) American
£304 $475 €456 Portrait of a woman seated in a forest green (135x64cm-53x25in) s. 15-Oct-2 Winter Associates, Plainville #84

FARRER, Henry (1843-1903) American/British

Works on paper
£510 $800 €765 Reflecting pond at sunset (41x33cm-16x13in) s. W/C htd white paper on card. 10-Dec-2 Doyle, New York #39/R
£1887 $3000 €2831 Sunlit landscape (23x38cm-9x15in) s.d.1894 W/C. 5-Mar-3 Christie's, Rockefeller NY #95/R est:2500-3500
£3185 $5000 €4778 Autumn (51x81cm-20x32in) s.d.1881 W/C prov. 10-Dec-2 Doyle, New York #38/R est:3000-5000

FARRERAS, Francisco (1927-) Spanish
£1457 $2375 €2200 Small format (42x34cm-17x13in) s.d.1987 oil collage cardboard. 11-Feb-3 Segre, Madrid #221/R
£2564 $4051 €4000 Composition 62 (81x65cm-32x26in) s. board lit. 19-Nov-2 Durán, Madrid #217/R

Sculpture
£2516 $3925 €4000 227A (50x50x8cm-20x20x3in) s.i.d.1988 wood relief. 17-Sep-2 Segre, Madrid #166/R

Works on paper
£1064 $1723 €1500 Collage (41x57cm-16x22in) s.d.1981 collage wash prov. 20-May-3 Segre, Madrid #182/R est:1400
£2000 $3160 €3100 Collage 278 (50x61cm-20x24in) collage wood panel lit. 17-Dec-2 Segre, Madrid #145/R
£3484 $5505 €5400 Collage 254 (91x73cm-36x29in) s.i.d.1965 collage panel exhib.lit. 17-Dec-2 Segre, Madrid #147/R est:5400

FARRINGTON, John (20th C) British
£500 $791 €750 Autumn day (152x183cm-60x72in) s.d.83. 27-Nov-2 Sotheby's, Olympia #250/R

FARRIS, H G (?) American?
£1053 $1600 €1580 Salem witch hunt (64x91cm-25x36in) s. 17-Aug-2 North East Auctions, Portsmouth #570/R

FARSKY, Otto (19/20th C) American
£471 $750 €707 Returning from the garden (66x41cm-26x16in) s. 7-Mar-3 Jackson's, Cedar Falls #641/R

FASCINI, C van (19th C) ?
£255 $400 €383 Sunrise landscape with shepherd leading a herd (51x76cm-20x30in) s. 23-Nov-2 Pook & Pook, Downington #488

FASCIOTTI, Titta (1927-1993) South African
£333 $520 €500 Woman from the rear wearing a black head scarf (34x29cm-13x11in) s. board. 11-Nov-2 Stephan Welz, Johannesburg #234 (SA.R 5200)
£447 $720 €671 Extensive landscape (60x90cm-24x35in) s.d.79. 12-May-3 Stephan Welz, Johannesburg #134 est:3000-5000 (SA.R 5200)
£688 $1107 €1032 Red landscape, Calitzdorp, Cape (34x50cm-13x20in) s. i.verso board. 12-May-3 Stephan Welz, Johannesburg #211 est:3000-5000 (SA.R 8000)

FASSBENDER, Adolf (20th C) American?

Photographs
£7200 $11664 €10800 White night (38x26cm-15x10in) i.verso blue toned silver print card lit. 22-May-3 Sotheby's, London #124/R est:4000-6000

FASSBENDER, Josef (1903-1974) German
£2564 $3974 €4000 Composition II (90x135cm-35x53in) s.d.49 prov.exhib. 3-Dec-2 Lempertz, Koln #123/R est:5500-6000

Works on paper
£538 $850 €850 Composition in violet tones with blue and grey (88x67cm-35x26in) s.d.1953 gouache. 30-Nov-2 Arnold, Frankfurt #151/R

FASSETT, Kaffe (1937-) American
£1300 $2028 €1950 Still life (92x122cm-36x48in) prov. 12-Sep-2 Sotheby's, Olympia #89/R est:1500-2000

FASSETT, Samuel M (19th C) American

Photographs
£4430 $7000 €6645 Abraham Lincoln (19x13cm-7x5in) oval albumen print. 23-Apr-3 Sotheby's, New York #49/R est:3000-5000

FASSIANOS, Alecos (1935-) Greek
£645 $1019 €1000 Composition (51x37cm-20x15in) s. acrylic paper. 18-Dec-2 Digard, Paris #156
£1486 $2319 €2200 Le crepuscule (36x49cm-14x19in) s.i.d. paint. 31-Mar-3 Rossini, Paris #108/R
£2700 $4266 €4050 La fumeur rouge (46x33cm-18x13in) 1-Apr-3 Bonhams, New Bond Street #90 est:2000-3000
£3500 $5425 €5250 Apostles (36x58cm-14x23in) s.i.d.1970 panel prov. 2-Oct-2 Sotheby's, London #118/R
£3600 $5688 €5400 Jeune grec au chapeau (30x36cm-12x14in) 1-Apr-3 Bonhams, New Bond Street #104 est:2400-3400
£3784 $5903 €5676 Untitled (64x46cm-25x18in) s. 5-Nov-2 Bukowskis, Stockholm #294/R est:30000-40000 (S.KR 54000)
£7000 $10850 €10500 Epmio (92x73cm-36x29in) s. oil silver leaf. 2-Oct-2 Sotheby's, London #114/R est:7000-9000
£8280 $12917 €13000 Figure bleue a la cravatte a pois rouges (157x84cm-62x33in) s. 7-Nov-2 Chochon-Barre & Allardi, Paris #142/R
£11458 $18104 €16500 Sans titre (161x128cm-63x50in) s.d. acrylic prov. 27-Apr-3 Perrin, Versailles #98/R est:15000-20000
£12355 $19892 €18533 Woman with bicycle (195x130cm-77x51in) s. lit. 7-May-3 AB Stockholms Auktionsverk #1117/R est:200000-250000 (S.KR 160000)

Works on paper
£390 $608 €620 Reclining man (17x25cm-7x10in) s.i. pen dr. 11-Oct-2 Binoche, Paris #169
£561 $875 €842 At the cafe (36x28cm-14x11in) s. pencil. 5-Nov-2 Bukowskis, Stockholm #293/R (S.KR 8000)
£2500 $3875 €3750 Acropolis (74x71cm-29x28in) s. pastel. 2-Oct-2 Sotheby's, London #106/R
£2500 $3875 €3750 Man on bicycle (67x46cm-26x18in) s. gouache paper on canvas. 2-Oct-2 Sotheby's, London #110/R
£2537 $4160 €3500 L'homme bleu (37x30cm-15x12in) s. gouache. 27-May-3 Tajan, Paris #66/R est:4000-5000
£3000 $4650 €4500 Moi (32x28cm-13x11in) s. gouache. 2-Oct-2 Sotheby's, London #3112/R est:4000
£3800 $6004 €5700 Trois personnages (34x53cm-13x21in) blue gouache paper on canvas. 1-Apr-3 Bonhams, New Bond Street #105 est:2200-3200

FASSIN, Nicholas de (1728-1811) Flemish
£5000 $7750 €7500 Shepherd and his family resting amongst their livestock (88x116cm-35x46in) s. 30-Oct-2 Bonhams, New Bond Street #164/R est:6000-8000

FATTORI, Giovanni (1825-1908) Italian
£1064 $1723 €1500 Cipressi. Paesaggio (16x22cm-6x9in) one panel one board two. 22-May-3 Stadion, Trieste #258/R est:500-700
£1438 $2301 €2200 Study of a stall interior with cows (19x25cm-7x10in) s. paper lit. 10-Jan-3 Allgauer, Kempten #1585/R est:1500
£4516 $7000 €6774 Shady path (21x11cm-8x4in) s. panel. 30-Oct-2 Christie's, Rockefeller NY #122/R est:10000-15000

£14839 $23445 €23000 Olive grove (23x13cm-9x5in) init. board prov.lit. 18-Dec-2 Finarte, Milan #95/R est:35000

FATTORINI, Eliseo Tuderte (1830-1887) Italian
Works on paper
£380 $589 €570 Bathing (34x60cm-13x24in) s.d.1877 W/C. 24-Sep-2 Bonhams, Knightsbridge #205/R

FAUBERT, Christelle (20th C) French
Works on paper
£288 $460 €400 J'ai soif d'infini (40x60cm-16x24in) mono. mixed media collage. 18-May-3 Neret-Minet, Paris #67/R

FAUBERT, Jean (1946-) French
£288 $460 €400 Personnage au chat (25x20cm-10x8in) s. canvasboard. 18-May-3 Charbonneaux, Paris #151
£321 $503 €500 Contrebassiste (35x27cm-14x11in) s. isorel. 16-Dec-2 Charbonneaux, Paris #250
£472 $731 €750 Guibre et la bouteille (46x38cm-18x15in) s. panel. 7-Oct-2 Claude Aguttes, Neuilly #285
£491 $760 €780 Guibriste fumeur (44x30cm-17x12in) s. panel. 7-Oct-2 Claude Aguttes, Neuilly #134
Works on paper
£308 $483 €480 Musicien assis (51x43cm-20x17in) s. gouache cardboard. 16-Dec-2 Charbonneaux, Paris #139

FAUCONNIER, Emile Eugène (1857-1920) French
£385 $604 €600 Bouquet au chaudron de cuivre (92x73cm-36x29in) s.d.1883. 24-Nov-2 Lesieur & Le Bars, Le Havre #44

FAUCONNIER, Henri le (1881-1946) French
£1171 $1850 €1850 Paysage nocturne (60x73cm-24x29in) mono. 27-Nov-2 Lemoine & Ferrando, Paris #100/R est:1300-1800
£1702 $2757 €2400 Chaumiere, ciel bleu (65x64cm-26x25in) s. 23-May-3 Camard, Paris #129/R est:2000-3000
£2405 $3800 €3800 View from the window of the artist studio of the artist (114x81cm-45x32in) s. 26-Nov-2 Sotheby's, Amsterdam #22/R est:3000-5000

FAUERHOLDT, Viggo (1832-1883) Danish
£553 $874 €830 Sailing vessel off the coast (27x38cm-11x15in) init.d.1869. 2-Dec-2 Rasmussen, Copenhagen #1351/R (D.KR 6500)
£596 $941 €894 Seascape with vessels in a calm (22x30cm-9x12in) init.d.1855. 2-Dec-2 Rasmussen, Copenhagen #1347/R (D.KR 7000)
£794 $1287 €1151 Seascape with steamship by jetty (27x38cm-11x15in) s.d.1872. 24-May-3 Rasmussen, Havnen #2204/R (D.KR 8300)
£933 $1483 €1400 Seascape with Swedish and Danish sailing vessels (42x68cm-17x27in) s.d.1852. 5-May-3 Rasmussen, Vejle #279/R (D.KR 10000)
£2365 $3689 €3548 Landscape from Mosel river near Gondorff (60x93cm-24x37in) s.d.1866 exhib. 23-Sep-2 Rasmussen, Vejle #274/R est:12000-15000 (D.KR 28000)
£2553 $4034 €3830 Coastal landscape with boats at edge of water, possibly Fano (38x50cm-15x20in) s.d.1884. 2-Dec-2 Rasmussen, Copenhagen #1402/R est:30000 (D.KR 30000)
£10336 $15711 €15504 Entrance by Copenhagen's Customs House (47x63cm-19x25in) s.d.1855. 27-Aug-2 Rasmussen, Copenhagen #1429/R est:150000 (D.KR 120000)

FAULCONER, Mary (1912-) American
Works on paper
£396 $650 €574 Natural history (17x24cm-7x9in) s. gouache W/C card stock. 5-Jun-3 Swann Galleries, New York #89/R

FAULDS, James (fl.1896-1938) British
£550 $875 €825 Children and nursemaid on grassy knoll, sea beyond (23x36cm-9x14in) s. 30-Apr-3 Goldings, Lincolnshire #159
Works on paper
£400 $636 €600 Study of two children by the sea with seagulls (25x36cm-10x14in) s. W/C. 30-Apr-3 Goldings, Lincolnshire #155
£400 $636 €600 Mussel collectors (25x36cm-10x14in) s. W/C. 30-Apr-3 Goldings, Lincolnshire #156
£500 $795 €750 Children and nursemaid paddling on a beach with toy yachts (25x36cm-10x14in) s. W/C. 30-Apr-3 Goldings, Lincolnshire #158
£560 $890 €840 Children swinging from the prow of a fishing boat (25x36cm-10x14in) s. W/C. 30-Apr-3 Goldings, Lincolnshire #160
£580 $922 €870 Children playing on a beach wuth fishing nets (25x36cm-10x14in) s. W/C. 30-Apr-3 Goldings, Lincolnshire #157/R

FAULKNER, John (c.1830-1888) British
Works on paper
£371 $615 €538 Road ride, Bagington, Warwickshire (40x64cm-16x25in) s. W/C. 16-Jun-3 Lilla Bukowskis, Stockholm #489 (S.KR 4800)
£600 $930 €900 Near Birmingham (46x71cm-18x28in) s.i. W/C. 3-Dec-2 Sotheby's, Olympia #49/R
£764 $1260 €1100 Fishing smacks and other shipping in a breeze (64x100cm-25x39in) s. W/C. 7-Jul-3 Hamilton Osborne King, Dublin #158/R est:1200-1500
£1014 $1581 €1500 View at Gougane Barra, Co. Cork (33x51cm-13x20in) s.d.1876 W/C. 26-Mar-3 James Adam, Dublin #6/R est:1500-2500
£1014 $1581 €1500 Cliffs of Meenaun, Achill Island (46x59cm-18x23in) s.i. W/C. 26-Mar-3 James Adam, Dublin #8/R est:1500-2500
£1258 $1962 €2000 Mill on the plains (44x75cm-17x30in) s.i. W/C htd white. 17-Sep-2 Whyte's, Dublin #124/R est:2000-3000
£1622 $2530 €2400 Landscape with cottages and figures on a path, Dorking (46x75cm-18x30in) s. indis i. W/C. 26-Mar-3 James Adam, Dublin #24/R est:1500-2500
£2516 $3925 €4000 Horseman at bridge (71x44cm-28x17in) s. W/C. 17-Sep-2 Whyte's, Dublin #113/R est:3000-4000
£3500 $5600 €5250 Cottage near Roundwood, County Wicklow (42x71cm-17x28in) s.i. W/C. 16-May-3 Sotheby's, London #29/R est:4000-6000
£3846 $5962 €6000 Valley of the Chess, Herts (48x99cm-19x39in) s.i. W/C. 3-Dec-2 Bonhams & James Adam, Dublin #10/R est:3000-5000

FAULKNER, Richard (1917-1988) British
Works on paper
£250 $390 €375 Rough sea, Ballintoy, Co Antrim. s. W/C. 17-Sep-2 Goldings, Lincolnshire #625/R

FAULKNER, Sarah (1959-) Australian
£597 $980 €896 Lorne (38x58cm-15x23in) s.d.91 composition board. 4-Jun-3 Deutscher-Menzies, Melbourne #110/R (A.D 1500)
Works on paper
£573 $872 €860 Kangaroo (43x66cm-17x26in) s.verso synthetic polymer paint ply board exec.c.1985. 28-Aug-2 Deutscher-Menzies, Melbourne #397/R (A.D 1600)

FAURE DE BROUSSE, Vincent Desire (19th C) French
Sculpture
£1871 $3068 €2600 La musicienne (58cm-23in) i. gold brown pat bronze lit. 4-Jun-3 Tajan, Paris #282/R est:1500-2000

FAURE, Amandus (1874-1931) German
£411 $650 €650 Spring still life with wood-anemones, snowdrops and catkins (34x24cm-13x9in) s.d.17 board. 29-Nov-2 Bolland & Marotz, Bremen #685/R
£1747 $2725 €2621 Odaliske (130x201cm-51x79in) s.d.23 prov. 9-Nov-2 Galerie Gloggner, Luzern #53/R est:2000-2500 (S.FR 4000)

FAURE, Victor Amedee (1801-1878) French
£3205 $5064 €5000 Nobles rentrant au Palais Royal (31x30cm-12x12in) cardboard. 18-Nov-2 Sotheby's, Paris #46/R est:4000

FAURER, Louis (1916-) American
Photographs
£2215 $3500 €3323 New York, N.Y (25x34cm-10x13in) s.i.d.1945 gelatin silver print mounted on board prov. 24-Apr-3 Phillips, New York #158/R est:4000-6000
£3291 $5200 €4937 Pennsylvia station, New York (33x22cm-13x9in) s.i.d.1949 verso gelatin silver print prov.exhib. 25-Apr-3 Phillips, New York #102/R est:5000-7000
£4430 $7000 €6645 New York City (34x27cm-13x11in) s.i.d.1948 verso gelatin silver print mounted on board prov.lit. 24-Apr-3 Phillips, New York #157/R est:4000-6000
£6494 $10000 €9741 Freudian handclasp (34x23cm-13x9in) photograph prov.lit. 22-Oct-2 Sotheby's, New York #59/R est:15000-25000
£7595 $12000 €11393 New York, New York (23x34cm-9x13in) s.d.1949 verso gelatin silver print prov.lit. 25-Apr-3 Phillips, New York #30/R est:6000-8000
£8228 $13000 €12342 Philadelphia (34x22cm-13x9in) s.d.1937 verso gelatin silver print prov.exhib.lit. 25-Apr-3 Phillips, New York #31/R est:10000-15000
£12658 $20000 €18987 Times Square, New York (34x23cm-13x9in) s.d.1950 gelatin silver print prov.exhib. 25-Apr-3 Phillips, New York #28/R est:10000-15000

£22785 $36000 €34178 Times Square convertible, New York (22x33cm-9x13in) s.d.1949 gelatin silver print prov.exhib.lit. 25-Apr-3 Phillips, New York #29/R est:10000-15000

FAURET, Léon (1863-1955) French
£496 $770 €744 Gentlemen and a soldier (27x19cm-11x7in) s. panel. 3-Dec-2 Bukowskis, Stockholm #327/R (S.KR 7000)

FAUSETT, Lynn (1894-1977) American
£1899 $3000 €2849 Day in June (61x91cm-24x36in) s. masonite painted c.1961 prov. 24-Apr-3 Shannon's, Milford #131/R est:4000-6000
£2532 $4000 €3798 Dugout Ranch (61x102cm-24x40in) s.d.1961 board. 24-Apr-3 Shannon's, Milford #130/R est:5000-7000
£3151 $4980 €4727 Muddy river canyon (61x102cm-24x40in) s.d.1961 board. 24-Apr-3 Shannon's, Milford #129/R est:6000-8000

FAUSTO, Biggi (19th C) Italian
Sculpture
£4800 $7440 €7200 Young maiden standing by a reedy outcrop (113cm-44in) white marble. 29-Oct-2 Bonhams, New Bond Street #220/R est:5000-6000

FAUTRIER, Jean (1898-1964) French
£1079 $1727 €1500 Composition (27x22cm-11x9in) s.d.63 double-sided. 14-May-3 Blanchet, Paris #168/R est:1500-1800
£3000 $4620 €4500 Composition (50x65cm-20x26in) indis sig tempera oil on paper painted 1952 prov. 22-Oct-2 Sotheby's, London #430/R est:5000-7000
£3425 $5377 €5000 Visages (22x27cm-9x11in) oil over lithograph lit. 15-Apr-3 Laurence Calmels, Paris #4216/R
£3774 $6000 €5661 Untitled (50x65cm-20x26in) s.d.57 oil pen brush ink. 27-Feb-3 Christie's, Rockefeller NY #45/R est:6000
£9615 $15096 €15000 Portrait de Compin (46x38cm-18x15in) s.d.25 exhib.lit. 24-Nov-2 Laurence Calmels, Paris #122/R est:15000
£19355 $30000 €29033 Nature morte (85x116cm-33x46in) s.d.25 prov. 26-Sep-2 Christie's, Rockefeller NY #519/R est:12000-16000
£26000 $42640 €39000 Les pommes (38x46cm-15x18in) s. prov.lit. 7-Feb-3 Sotheby's, London #234/R est:25000-35000
£40000 $66800 €58000 Petit objet precieux (27x35cm-11x14in) init.d.57 oil pigment paper on canvas prov. 26-Jun-3 Sotheby's, London #193/R est:40000-60000
£44000 $73480 €63800 Bouquet (73x92cm-29x36in) s. painted 1928 prov.exhib.lit. 27-Jun-3 Christie's, London #113/R est:35000-45000
£55000 $84700 €82500 Herbages (50x65cm-20x26in) s.d.58 oil composition paper on canvas prov.lit. 22-Oct-2 Sotheby's, London #366/R est:60000-80000
£67308 $105000 €100962 Tete de Partisan, Budapest (27x22cm-11x9in) init.d.57 oil paper on canvas. 11-Nov-2 Phillips, New York #20/R est:150000-200000
£80000 $133600 €120000 Composition (73x116cm-29x46in) s. oil composition paper on canvas exc.1961 prov.exhib. 25-Jun-3 Sotheby's, London #29/R est:90000-120000
£82759 $130759 €120000 Fruit (27x35cm-11x14in) s.d.43 oil pigment paper on canvas prov. 2-Apr-3 Christie's, Paris #8/R est:150000
Works on paper
£789 $1279 €1200 Sans titre (31x50cm-12x20in) chl dr. 22-Jan-3 Tajan, Paris #235
£1418 $2298 €2000 Untitled (33x50cm-13x20in) s.d.54 W/C. 26-May-3 Christie's, Milan #68/R est:2500-3000
£1582 $2453 €2500 Griffures (16x25cm-6x10in) s. graphite red ink exec.c.1950. 28-Sep-2 Cornette de St.Cyr, Paris #306 est:2800-3000
£3205 $5032 €5000 Untitled (30x47cm-12x19in) st.sig. Chinese ink prov. 24-Nov-2 Laurence Calmels, Paris #121/R
£4038 $6340 €6300 Composition (50x65cm-20x26in) W/C gouache ink exec.1960 exhib. 11-Dec-2 Artcurial Briest, Paris #701/R

FAUVEL, Georges (1890-?) French
£350 $553 €525 Trouble in store (65x92cm-26x36in) s. indis i. 28-Nov-2 Christie's, Kensington #321

FAUX-FROIDURE, Eugenie-Juliette (1886-?) French
Works on paper
£300 $465 €450 Still life with red roses in a vase on a ledge (38cm-15in circular) s. W/C oval. 25-Sep-2 Hamptons Fine Art, Godalming #132
£400 $656 €600 Roses (34cm-13in circular) s. pencil W/C htd gum arabic. 5-Jun-3 Christie's, Kensington #896/R
£2222 $3578 €3400 Elegante souriante a la gerbe de roses (128x68cm-50x27in) s. W/C. 20-Jan-3 Horta, Bruxelles #94/R est:3500-4500

FAVAI, Gennaro (1882-?) Italian?
£3038 $4800 €4800 Redemptor's celebrations (110x152cm-43x60in) s.i.d.1909. 26-Nov-2 Christie's, Rome #215/R est:6000

FAVELLE, Robert (19th C) ?
£600 $912 €900 Harvest time (23x34cm-9x13in) s.d.1865 panel. 4-Jul-2 Mellors & Kirk, Nottingham #832

FAVEN, Antti (1882-1948) Finnish
£538 $839 €850 Portrait of man (55x48cm-22x19in) s.d.1916. 12-Sep-2 Hagelstam, Helsinki #822/R
£619 $979 €960 Outer skerries (49x42cm-19x17in) s.d.1931. 19-Dec-2 Hagelstam, Helsinki #830/R
£1583 $2532 €2200 View towards town (24x42cm-9x17in) s.i.d.1903. 17-May-3 Hagelstam, Helsinki #127/R est:2500
£1844 $2858 €2766 Landscape in evening light (19x24cm-7x9in) s.d.1911 panel. 8-Dec-2 Uppsala Auktionskammare, Uppsala #130/R est:10000-12000 (S.KR 26000)
£2041 $3245 €3000 Helsinki (63x51cm-25x20in) s.d.1919. 27-Feb-3 Hagelstam, Helsinki #805/R est:3000
£3521 $5669 €5000 After the rain (70x53cm-28x21in) s.d.1901. 10-May-3 Bukowskis, Helsinki #194/R est:3000-4000
Works on paper
£453 $697 €720 Tosca (34x35cm-13x14in) s.i.d.1905 mixed media. 24-Oct-2 Hagelstam, Helsinki #808/R

FAVERO, Andrea (attrib) (1837-1914) Italian
£478 $775 €693 Young girl having caught a small fish (50x37cm-20x15in) with sig. 26-May-3 Rasmussen, Copenhagen #1326/R (D.KR 5000)

FAVEROT, Joseph (1862-?) French
£1004 $1567 €1506 Poultry yard (33x41cm-13x16in) s. 6-Nov-2 Dobiaschofsky, Bern #503/R est:3500 (S.FR 2300)

FAVIER, Philippe (1957-) French
£2721 $4327 €4000 Citron (12x17cm-5x7in) s.i.d.87 on glass. 24-Mar-3 Cornette de St.Cyr, Paris #122/R
£2925 $4651 €4300 Nappe violette (16x14cm-6x6in) on glass prov. 24-Mar-3 Cornette de St.Cyr, Paris #124/R
£3061 $4867 €4500 Nature morte aux poires (13x15cm-5x6in) on glass prov. 24-Mar-3 Cornette de St.Cyr, Paris #123/R
Works on paper
£861 $1403 €1300 Lieu dit (24x24cm-9x9in) W/C crayon. 3-Feb-3 Cornette de St.Cyr, Paris #418/R
£2585 $4110 €3800 Tabarin (63x49cm-25x19in) s.i.d.1981 verso collage prov. 24-Mar-3 Cornette de St.Cyr, Paris #125/R

FAVORIN, Ellen (1853-1919) Finnish
£654 $1072 €1000 Lake landscape (9x14cm-4x6in) 9-Feb-3 Bukowskis, Helsinki #227/R
£1197 $1927 €1700 The well (26x26cm-10x10in) s. board. 10-May-3 Bukowskis, Helsinki #116/R est:1700-2000
£1329 $2073 €2100 Woodland tarn (22x30cm-9x12in) s. 12-Sep-2 Hagelstam, Helsinki #1012 est:1500
£2590 $4144 €3600 Cottage interior with figures (28x42cm-11x17in) s.d.1880. 17-May-3 Hagelstam, Helsinki #84/R est:3500
£2911 $4600 €4600 The Sunday outing (64x94cm-25x37in) s. 1-Dec-2 Bukowskis, Helsinki #52/R est:5000-5500

FAVORY, Andre (1888-1937) French
£278 $442 €400 Nu allonge (22x27cm-9x11in) s. d.1946 verso. 29-Apr-3 Campo, Vlaamse Kaai #118
£486 $773 €700 Nature morte ou l'abat jour rose (63x64cm-25x25in) s. s.i.verso. 29-Apr-3 Artcurial Briest, Paris #179
Works on paper
£442 $703 €650 Le pique-nique (26x20cm-10x8in) W/C gold paint sold with a dr. 26-Feb-3 Fraysse & Associes, Paris #18

FAVRAY, Antoine de (style) (1706-1791) French
£21000 $35070 €30450 Interior of a church at carnival time (70x86cm-28x34in) 10-Jul-3 Sotheby's, London #207/R est:18000-25000

FAVRE DE THIERRENS, Jacques (1895-1973) French
£577 $906 €900 Femme au collier (60x73cm-24x29in) s.d. panel. 21-Nov-2 Neret-Minet, Paris #38
£1923 $3000 €2885 Place de Theime (58x74cm-23x29in) s. board. 30-Mar-3 Susanin's, Chicago #6064/R est:1500-2000

FAVRETTO, Giacomo (1849-1887) Italian
£6522 $10174 €9783 Bozzetto di Bollettino del Lotto (41x30cm-16x12in) prov. 16-Sep-2 Philippe Schuler, Zurich #3470/R est:6000-8000 (S.FR 15000)
Works on paper
£774 $1200 €1161 Standing male nude (47x31cm-19x12in) s. pencil htd white exhib. 29-Oct-2 Sotheby's, New York #118/R est:2000-3000

£1156 $1839 €1700 Artist's father (19x11cm-7x4in) s. Chinese ink. 18-Mar-3 Finarte, Milan #172/R
£1156 $1839 €1700 Study for 'The mouse' (19x10cm-7x4in) s. Chinese ink. 18-Mar-3 Finarte, Milan #173/R
£3378 $5270 €5000 Young girl with bird cage (28x19cm-11x7in) s. sketch verso. 28-Mar-3 Dorotheum, Vienna #136/R est:600-900

FAVRETTO, Giacomo (attrib) (1849-1887) Italian
£566 $872 €900 Head of elderly man (21x14cm-8x6in) s. board. 28-Oct-2 Il Ponte, Milan #265
£943 $1453 €1500 Nude (23x15cm-9x6in) card. 28-Oct-2 Il Ponte, Milan #246/R
£4430 $7000 €7000 Portrait in the study (25x15cm-10x6in) s.i.d.1881 board. 26-Nov-2 Christie's, Rome #74/R est:7000-10000

FAVRO, Murray (1940-) Canadian
Sculpture
£2444 $4009 €3666 Guitar no.2 (93cm-37in) s.i.d.1983 cherry wood string guitar hardware steel prov.exhib.lit. 27-May-3 Sotheby's, Toronto #139/R est:3000-5000 (C.D 5500)
£2444 $4009 €3666 Guitar no.3 (92cm-36in) s.i.d.1983 cherry wood string guitar hardware steel prov. 27-May-3 Sotheby's, Toronto #140/R est:3000-5000 (C.D 5500)

FAWCETT, John (1952-) American
£2436 $3800 €3654 Cool water (46x61cm-18x24in) 9-Nov-2 Altermann Galleries, Santa Fe #66
Works on paper
£3630 $5300 €5445 Sagebrush stories (51x71cm-20x28in) W/C. 18-May-2 Altermann Galleries, Santa Fe #112/R

FAWCETT, Robert (1903-1967) American
Works on paper
£2174 $3500 €3261 Policeman pulling man along sidewalk and woman swinging wrench (46x48cm-18x19in) mono. brush ink W/C gouache. 10-May-3 Illustration House, New York #104/R est:4000-6000

FAWKES, Madeline C (fl.1909-1931) British
£950 $1501 €1425 Chinese vase (91x71cm-36x28in) s.i.d.1928 exhib. 14-Nov-2 Christie's, Kensington #309/R

FAXOE, Peder (attrib) (1761-1840) Danish
£298 $471 €447 Profile portrait of the young Dorothea Melchior (32x26cm-13x10in) indis.i. stretcher painted c.1820. 27-Nov-2 Museumsbygningen, Copenhagen #45/R (D.KR 3500)

FAXON, Richard (19th C) French
£2535 $4082 €3600 Marines (18x23cm-7x9in) one on paper two. 11-May-3 Thierry & Lannon, Brest #357 est:2000-2500

FAY, Albert (19th C) ?
£652 $1016 €978 Oriental scene (71x56cm-28x22in) s.d.1865. 13-Sep-2 Lilla Bukowskis, Stockholm #305 (S.KR 9500)

FAY, Heman (jnr) (20th C) American
£745 $1200 €1118 Bear prepares to protect two cubs (71x56cm-28x22in) s. 20-Feb-3 Illustration House, New York #58/R est:1500-2500

FAY, Joseph (1813-1875) German
£915 $1474 €1300 Neapolitan fishermen and wives on beach (47x65cm-19x26in) s. lit. 9-May-3 Schloss Ahlden, Ahlden #1377/R

FAY, Ludwig Benno (1859-1906) German
£3228 $5100 €5100 Hunting dog in the snow with slain hare (57x70cm-22x28in) s. 29-Nov-2 Bolland & Marotz, Bremen #686/R est:2200

FAYE, Alice (?) British
£820 $1271 €1230 Garden party (41x33cm-16x13in) s. 7-Dec-2 Shapes, Edinburgh #361/R

FAYOD, Charles (1857-?) Swiss
Works on paper
£288 $450 €432 Roses (33x51cm-13x20in) s.i.d.15 Nov 1913 W/C. 20-Sep-2 Sloan, North Bethesda #324/R

FAZZINI, Pericle (1913-1987) Italian
Sculpture
£4516 $7000 €6774 Buste de femme (71cm-28in) brown black pat. bronze prov. 26-Sep-2 Christie's, Rockefeller NY #548/R est:4000-6000
£5484 $8500 €8226 Homme assise (99cm-39in) s.d.1956 gray pat. bronze prov. 26-Sep-2 Christie's, Rockefeller NY #550/R est:5000-7000
Works on paper
£327 $523 €500 Figure (37x24cm-15x9in) s.i.d.1933 ink paper on canvas. 4-Jan-3 Meeting Art, Vercelli #682

FEARNLEY, Alan (20th C) British
£2500 $3850 €3750 Grand Epreuve, Baron Emanuel, Toulo de Graffenried (91x61cm-36x24in) s. by the artist and driver d.1995 verso. 6-Sep-2 Bonhams, Knightsbridge #45a/R est:3000-4000

FEARNLEY, Thomas (1802-1842) Norwegian
£9599 $15070 €14399 View of Procida and Ischia with Epomeo Mountain (26x39cm-10x15in) paper on panel painted c.1833. 21-Nov-2 Grev Wedels Plass, Oslo #17/R est:80000-100000 (N.KR 110000)
£17406 $27850 €26109 Fisherman near Sorrento (27x39cm-11x15in) s.i.d.30 aug.34 lit. paper on canvas. 17-Mar-3 Blomqvist, Oslo #320/R est:80000-100000 (N.KR 200000)
£18100 $29321 €27150 Landscape from Sorrento (39x55cm-15x22in) s.d.1840 i.verso exhib.lit. 26-May-3 Grev Wedels Plass, Oslo #28/R est:200000-300000 (N.KR 200000)

FEARON, Hilda (1878-1917) British
£280 $437 €420 Evening time, Newlyn Harbour (41x61cm-16x24in) s. 17-Oct-2 David Lay, Penzance #1095/R

FEBVRE FOINEL, Lucien le (20th C) American
£443 $700 €665 Dory on shore with lighthouse in distance (51x61cm-20x24in) s.verso. 26-Apr-3 Thomaston Place, Thomaston #216

FEBVRE, Edouard (20th C) French
Works on paper
£278 $439 €400 Passant devant un cafe (32x26cm-13x10in) s. W/C. 25-Apr-3 Piasa, Paris #101

FEBVRE, Eugene (19/20th C) French
£795 $1295 €1200 Au cirque (54x65cm-21x26in) s. 31-Jan-3 Rabourdin & Choppin de Janvry, Paris #125

FECHIN, Nicolai (1881-1955) American/Russian
£1266 $2000 €2000 Summer landscape (27x38cm-11x15in) 1-Dec-2 Bukowskis, Helsinki #241/R est:2500-3000
£7372 $11500 €11058 Horses hitched to a wagon (25x53cm-10x21in) 9-Nov-2 Altermann Galleries, Santa Fe #113
£10191 $16000 €15287 Balinese girl (46x33cm-18x13in) s. prov.exhib. 20-Nov-2 Christie's, Los Angeles #113/R est:20000-30000
£16975 $27500 €25463 Bend in the river (76x91cm-30x36in) s. prov. 21-May-3 Sotheby's, New York #224/R est:30000-50000
£35256 $55000 €52884 Nude (61x51cm-24x20in) s. prov.lit. 9-Nov-2 Santa Fe Art, Santa Fe #145/R est:110000-150000
£95525 $154750 €138511 Mandolin (41x36cm-16x14in) 23-May-3 Altermann Galleries, Santa Fe #77
£261146 $410000 €391719 Drum player (82x49cm-32x19in) s. prov. 20-Nov-2 Christie's, Los Angeles #25/R est:200000-300000
Works on paper
£818 $1300 €1227 Portrait of a man (38x25cm-15x10in) s. chl dr exec.c.1920. 2-Mar-3 Toomey, Oak Park #608/R
£3846 $6000 €5769 Girl with long hair (30x41cm-12x16in) init. chl prov.lit. 9-Nov-2 Santa Fe Art, Santa Fe #93/R est:6000-8000
£5679 $9200 €8235 Portrait of a woman (41x30cm-16x12in) chl. 23-May-3 Altermann Galleries, Santa Fe #75

FECHTER, Emerich (1854-1912) Austrian
£738 $1188 €1100 Field of flowers (77x93cm-30x37in) s.d.1913 exhib. 18-Feb-3 Sotheby's, Amsterdam #329/R est:1200-1800

FECTEAU, Marcel (1927-) Canadian
£192 $303 €288 Pot de fleurs et oranges (51x41cm-20x16in) s.d.1985 s.i.verso. 14-Nov-2 Heffel, Vancouver #253 (C.D 475)
£297 $461 €446 Inspirer de Charlevoix (40x51cm-16x20in) s.d.88 s.i.verso prov. 24-Sep-2 Ritchie, Toronto #3181c (C.D 725)

FEDDEN, A Romilly (1875-1939) British
Works on paper
£330 $515 €495 Salute, Venice (36x46cm-14x18in) s.d.1926. 9-Oct-2 Andrew Hartley, Ilkley #624
£540 $859 €810 Woman wearing green dress earrings and a feathered hat (22x14cm-9x6in) s. W/C. 27-Feb-3 Bonhams, Chester #372

FEDDEN, Mary (1915-) British

£1532 $2421 €2298 Tuscan spring (61x51cm-24x20in) s.d.1967 masonite. 18-Nov-2 Waddingtons, Toronto #140/R est:4000-6000 (C.D 3800)
£2000 $3340 €2900 Still life of summer flowers (50x40cm-20x16in) s.d.1946. 24-Jun-3 Bonhams, New Bond Street #91/R est:2000-3000
£2400 $3744 €3600 Pussy-cat (20x13cm-8x5in) s.d.1987 panel. 25-Mar-3 Bonhams, New Bond Street #85/R est:1200-1800
£2600 $4264 €3900 Tuscan spring (61x51cm-24x20in) s.d.1967 board. 6-Jun-3 Christie's, London #213/R est:4000-6000
£2800 $4340 €4200 Cottage in Portugal (30x41cm-12x16in) i. canvas on board exhib. 4-Dec-2 Christie's, Kensington #564/R est:3000-5000
£2800 $4676 €4060 Yorkshire farm (61x51cm-24x20in) s.d.1990 board. 24-Jun-3 Bonhams, New Bond Street #95/R est:2500-3500
£2800 $4620 €4060 Cat on a beach (17x20cm-7x8in) s.d.1991 board prov. 3-Jul-3 Christie's, Kensington #626/R est:1500-2000
£3000 $4950 €4350 Dressing 1 (51x41cm-20x16in) s.d.1988 prov. 3-Jul-3 Christie's, Kensington #562/R est:3000-5000
£3200 $5280 €4640 Red dress (16x21cm-6x8in) s.d.1991 prov. 3-Jul-3 Christie's, Kensington #622/R est:1500-2000
£3500 $5425 €5250 Still life with yellow irises (30x41cm-12x16in) s.d.1980. 4-Dec-2 Christie's, Kensington #589/R est:3000-5000
£3800 $6346 €5510 Still life of flowers in a vase (55x55cm-22x22in) s.d.1977 board. 24-Jun-3 Bonhams, New Bond Street #90/R est:3500-4500
£4000 $6200 €6000 Milk jug (76x61cm-30x24in) s.d.1975. 3-Dec-2 Bonhams, New Bond Street #92/R est:4000-6000
£4000 $6200 €6000 Sleeping poet (40x51cm-16x20in) s.d.1999 prov. 3-Dec-2 Bonhams, New Bond Street #93/R est:3000-5000
£4000 $6240 €6000 Lemon and grapes (40x30cm-16x12in) s.d.1977 board. 25-Mar-3 Bonhams, New Bond Street #83/R est:2000-3000
£4800 $7392 €7200 Washstand (35x30cm-14x12in) s.d.1952 exhib. 5-Sep-2 Christie's, Kensington #734/R est:3000-5000
£4900 $7595 €7350 White horse (34x41cm-13x16in) s.d.1961 s.i.verso board prov. 30-Sep-2 Bonhams, Ipswich #362/R est:5000-7000
£5400 $8370 €8100 Still life with jug and fruit on a table cloth (48x58cm-19x23in) s.d.64. 4-Oct-2 Mallams, Oxford #537/R est:1500-2000
£5500 $8635 €8250 Lost sheep (51x61cm-20x24in) s.d.02. 22-Nov-2 Christie's, London #115/R est:6000-8000
£5500 $8689 €8250 Still life with table and fruit (51x61cm-20x24in) s.d.1990. 27-Nov-2 Sotheby's, Olympia #285/R est:4000-6000
£5500 $8580 €8250 Red tablecloth (40x76cm-16x30in) s.d.1995. 25-Mar-3 Bonhams, New Bond Street #81/R est:4000-6000
£5500 $9020 €8250 Village in Portugal (63x76cm-25x30in) s.d.1961 prov. 6-Jun-3 Christie's, London #75/R est:5000-8000
£6000 $9840 €9000 Few violets (51x61cm-20x24in) s.d.1977 exhib. 6-Jun-3 Christie's, London #214/R est:6000-8000
£6500 $10205 €9750 Stalker (42x22cm-17x9in) s.d.02 canvas on board. 22-Nov-2 Christie's, London #116/R est:5000-7000
£7000 $10920 €10500 Still life with artichokes (51x60cm-20x24in) s.d.1962. 25-Mar-3 Bonhams, New Bond Street #82/R est:5000-7000
£7500 $11775 €11250 Purple table (61x51cm-24x20in) s.d.1986 board prov. 22-Nov-2 Christie's, London #110/R est:8000-12000
£8000 $12400 €12000 Yellow butterfly (76x91cm-30x36in) s.d.1973 s.i.on stretcher exhib. 4-Dec-2 Sotheby's, London #77/R est:8000-12000
£8500 $13940 €12750 Orange and green still life (61x76cm-24x30in) s.d.1957. 6-Jun-3 Christie's, London #212/R est:7000-10000
£11000 $18040 €16500 Gull's eggs (76x101cm-30x40in) s.d.01 exhib. 6-Jun-3 Christie's, London #211/R est:10000-15000
£12000 $18600 €18000 Red still life (91x76cm-36x30in) s.d.1970 s.i.d.verso prov. 4-Dec-2 Christie's, Kensington #587/R est:8000-12000
£12000 $18960 €18000 Whitby shells (76x92cm-30x36in) s.d.1991 exhib.lit. 27-Nov-2 Sotheby's, Olympia #287/R est:6000-8000
£25000 $39500 €37500 Still life of flowers and fruit (91x77cm-36x30in) s.d.1989 board. 27-Nov-2 Sotheby's, Olympia #286/R est:12000-18000

Works on paper

£950 $1482 €1425 Sunset (18x13cm-7x5in) s.d.1969 W/C. 25-Mar-3 Bonhams, New Bond Street #84/R
£1000 $1560 €1500 Cat (12x18cm-5x7in) s.d.1992 gouache. 27-Mar-3 Christie's, Kensington #352/R est:700-1000
£1000 $1650 €1450 Bird (17x20cm-7x8in) s.d.1987 pen ink W/C bodycol prov. 3-Jul-3 Christie's, Kensington #625/R est:700-1000
£1100 $1815 €1595 Thrush (10x13cm-4x5in) s.d.1991 W/C bodycol. 3-Jul-3 Christie's, Kensington #623/R est:400-600
£1200 $1872 €1800 Grey horse (18x19cm-7x7in) s.d.1984 W/C. 25-Mar-3 Bonhams, Leeds #561/R est:600-900
£1200 $2004 €1740 Still life with pears (18x25cm-7x10in) s.d.1987 W/C bodycol. 25-Jun-3 Bonhams, Bury St Edmunds #526 est:1200-1600
£1200 $1980 €1740 Girl with horse and clown (14x20cm-6x8in) s.d.1987 W/C bodycol. 3-Jul-3 Christie's, Kensington #560/R est:800-1200
£1300 $2132 €1950 Cat and mouse (15x12cm-6x5in) s.d.1991 W/C gouache ink. 3-Jun-3 Sotheby's, Olympia #168/R est:800-1200
£1300 $2145 €1885 Two ladies strolling on a beach (16x18cm-6x7in) s.d.1975 pencil W/C col crayons. 3-Jul-3 Christie's, Kensington #564/R est:800-1200
£1400 $2310 €2030 Robin (11x15cm-4x6in) s.d.1982 W/C bodycol. 3-Jul-3 Christie's, Kensington #624/R est:400-600
£1500 $2325 €2250 Oyster mushroom (21x25cm-8x10in) s.d.1998 W/C gouache. 3-Dec-2 Bonhams, New Bond Street #96/R est:800-1200
£1500 $2325 €2250 Still life with setting sun (12x20cm-5x8in) s.d.1987 W/C bodycol prov. 4-Dec-2 Christie's, Kensington #324/R est:1000-1500
£1500 $2415 €2250 Hellebore (42x28cm-17x11in) s.d.1999 W/C. 14-Jan-3 Bonhams, Knightsbridge #1/R est:800-1200
£1500 $2475 €2175 Looking out to sea (15x16cm-6x6in) s.d.1975 pastel W/C bodycol. 3-Jul-3 Christie's, Kensington #559/R est:700-1000
£1700 $2788 €2550 Sheep (15x11cm-6x4in) s.d.1991 W/C ink. 3-Jun-3 Sotheby's, Olympia #169/R est:800-1200
£1700 $2839 €2465 Still life with avocados and flowers on a table (20x24cm-8x9in) s.d.1992 W/C bodycol. 25-Jun-3 Bonhams, Bury St Edmunds #523 est:1400-1800
£1800 $2970 €2610 Sleeping cat (13x18cm-5x7in) s.d.1991 pastel W/C. 3-Jul-3 Christie's, Kensington #629/R est:600-800
£1900 $3116 €2850 Green apple (56x75cm-22x30in) s.d.1979 pencil W/C collage exhib. 6-Jun-3 Christie's, London #117/R est:2000-3000
£2000 $3100 €3000 Julian shepherding goats (15x21cm-6x8in) s.d.1987 W/C bodycol prov. 4-Dec-2 Christie's, Kensington #321/R est:1200-1800
£2000 $3340 €2900 Still life with bowl of fruit and wine bottle on a table (21x28cm-8x11in) s.d.1990 W/C bodycol. 25-Jun-3 Bonhams, Bury St Edmunds #525 est:1500-2500
£2200 $3674 €3190 Black cat (16x22cm-6x9in) s.d.1982 W/C. 24-Jun-3 Bonhams, New Bond Street #92/R est:800-1200
£2200 $3674 €3190 Tabby and pineapple (76x56cm-30x22in) s.d.1981 pencil W/C. 24-Jun-3 Bonhams, New Bond Street #93/R est:1000-1500
£2400 $3720 €3600 Bird - black eared wheatear (24x29cm-9x11in) s.d.1999 W/C gouache. 3-Dec-2 Bonhams, New Bond Street #95/R est:1000-1500
£2800 $4676 €4060 Cat and apple (16x22cm-6x9in) s.d.1982 W/C. 24-Jun-3 Bonhams, New Bond Street #96/R est:1000-1500
£3800 $6042 €5700 Breakfast at bamber's (18x21cm-7x8in) s.d.01 ink W/C. 26-Feb-3 Sotheby's, Olympia #344/R est:2000-3000
£4000 $6600 €5800 Cat with still life (29x21cm-11x8in) s.d.00 pencil W/C bodycol. 3-Jul-3 Christie's, Kensington #628/R est:2000-3000

FEDDER, Otto (1873-1919) German

£255 $397 €400 Riders by moonlight (21x30cm-8x12in) board. 6-Nov-2 Hugo Ruef, Munich #1086
£380 $600 €600 Gossau See (45x63cm-18x25in) s.i.d.95 lit. 29-Nov-2 Schloss Ahlden, Ahlden #1210/R
£411 $641 €600 Morning on the moor (25x47cm-10x19in) s. canvas on board. 9-Apr-3 Neumeister, Munich #663
£519 $774 €800 Farmstead in snowy landscape (18x41cm-7x16in) s.d.98 pair. 26-Jun-2 Neumeister, Munich #731
£844 $1258 €1300 Winter pleasures (18x41cm-7x16in) s. one of pair. 26-Jun-2 Neumeister, Munich #730/R
£2086 $3338 €2900 L'arrivee dans le village (13x19cm-5x7in) s. panel. 14-May-3 Rabourdin & Choppin de Janvry, Paris #8/R est:3500-4000

FEDDERSEN, Hans Peter (younger) (1848-1941) Danish

£755 $1170 €1200 Sleeping hunting dog (11x19cm-4x7in) mono. study board. 2-Nov-2 Hans Stahl, Toestorf #69/R
£1887 $2925 €3000 Fishing boats on the beach - Capri I (16x37cm-6x15in) mono.i.d.Juli 77 canvas on board. 2-Nov-2 Hans Stahl, Toestorf #68/R est:3000

Works on paper

£253 $400 €400 Landscape with children's carriages at dusk (25x37cm-10x15in) mono. W/C. 29-Nov-2 Bolland & Marotz, Bremen #688/R

FEDDES, Pieter van Harlingen (attrib) (1586-1634) Dutch

£1560 $2606 €2200 Saint benissant deux moines avec sur l'arriere-plan une scene de naufrage (49x65cm-19x26in) mono.d. panel. 17-Jun-3 Palais de Beaux Arts, Brussels #477/R est:4500-6400

FEDELER, Carl (1837-1897) German

£2324 $3742 €3300 Winter wood with ruins, frozen water, hunter and dog (81x107cm-32x42in) s.d.1859. 10-May-3 Hans Stahl, Toestorf #69/R est:2200

FEDELER, Carl Justus Harmen (1799-1858) German

£7237 $11000 €10856 Clipper ship, Panama (61x89cm-24x35in) s.d.1855 prov. 17-Aug-2 North East Auctions, Portsmouth #606/R est:10000-15000

FEDER, Adolphe (1886-1940) French

£641 $1006 €1000 Vue du Lac de Tiberiade (43x56cm-17x22in) s.verso. 12-Dec-2 Rabourdin & Choppin de Janvry, Paris #29
£903 $1435 €1300 L'acrobate (82x51cm-32x20in) s. 29-Apr-3 Artcurial Briest, Paris #234 est:1300-1800
£962 $1510 €1500 Femme a sa couture (60x73cm-24x29in) s. 12-Dec-2 Rabourdin & Choppin de Janvry, Paris #28
£1282 $2013 €2000 Vase de fleurs (55x46cm-22x18in) s. 12-Dec-2 Rabourdin & Choppin de Janvry, Paris #40/R
£2436 $3824 €3800 Still life of flowers and fruit (71x55cm-28x22in) s. s.i.verso. 12-Dec-2 Rabourdin & Choppin de Janvry, Paris #27/R

Works on paper

£327 $519 €480 Port Mediterraneen (25x33cm-10x13in) s. W/C ink. 26-Feb-3 Artcurial Briest, Paris #191
£436 $684 €680 Famille a Jerusalem (30x25cm-12x10in) s.i.d.1924 gouache. 12-Dec-2 Rabourdin & Choppin de Janvry, Paris #125/R
£816 $1298 €1200 Couple de Jerusalem (41x21cm-16x8in) s. W/C ink drs two. 26-Feb-3 Artcurial Briest, Paris #192

FEDERICI, Enzo (1953-) Italian
£353 $554 €550 Light island (50x50cm-20x20in) s.i.d.2000 verso silicon. 23-Nov-2 Meeting Art, Vercelli #51/R
£359 $575 €550 Village in spring (50x50cm-20x20in) s.i.verso silicon. 4-Jan-3 Meeting Art, Vercelli #559

FEDERICO, Cavalier Michele (1884-1966) Italian
£300 $475 €450 Arcata in Capri (18x28cm-7x11in) s.i.verso. 29-Nov-2 Zofingen, Switzerland #2431 (S.FR 700)
£387 $612 €600 Marina in capri (50x74cm-20x29in) s. 18-Dec-2 Finarte, Milan #206
£483 $764 €725 Crashing surf, stormy coast (55x71cm-22x28in) s.i. 18-Nov-2 Waddingtons, Toronto #278/R (C.D 1200)
£578 $959 €838 Monacone Rock, Capri (25x33cm-10x13in) s. s.i.verso. 16-Jun-3 Waddingtons, Toronto #331/R est:500-700 (C.D 1300)
£711 $1180 €1031 Sunset afternoon, Capri (47x61cm-19x24in) s. 16-Jun-3 Waddingtons, Toronto #330/R est:800-1200 (C.D 1600)
£785 $1233 €1178 Capri (66x86cm-26x34in) s.i. 24-Jul-2 Walker's, Ottawa #38/R est:900-1200 (C.D 1900)
£1140 $1699 €1710 Capri (68x89cm-27x35in) s.i. 26-Jun-2 Iegor de Saint Hippolyte, Montreal #35/R (C.D 2600)
£1200 $1908 €1800 Capri coastline at dusk (51x71cm-20x28in) s. 20-Mar-3 Christie's, Kensington #74/R est:1500-2000
£1600 $2608 €2400 Waves crashing on the coast at Capri (69x98cm-27x39in) s.i. 13-Feb-3 Christie's, Kensington #108/R est:1200-1800

FEDERLE, Helmut (1944-) Swiss
Works on paper
£522 $809 €783 Reclining H (19x19cm-7x7in) mono.i.d.1983 Indian ink brush. 9-Dec-2 Philippe Schuler, Zurich #3430 (S.FR 1200)
£786 $1234 €1179 Wind, Paris. s.d.1972 verso pencil w/C gouache prov. 25-Nov-2 Germann, Zurich #721/R est:1500-2000 (S.FR 1800)
£897 $1391 €1400 Compasses of the day (28x21cm-11x8in) mono.d.82 verso felt pen. 3-Dec-2 Lempertz, Koln #125/R

FEDERLEY, Alexander Thiodolf (1864-1932) Finnish
Works on paper
£360 $576 €500 Goldcrests (25x32cm-10x13in) s.d.1903 W/C. 17-May-3 Hagelstam, Helsinki #61/R

FEDI, Pio (1816-1892) Italian
Sculpture
£46000 $71760 €69000 Supreme fisher boy (135cm-53in) s.d.1864 white marble lit. 9-Apr-3 Sotheby's, London #89/R est:20000-30000

FEDIER, Franz (1922-) Swiss
Works on paper
£282 $462 €409 Pont Marcadet (38x57cm-15x22in) s.d.49 mixed media. 4-Jun-3 Fischer, Luzern #2624/R (S.FR 600)

FEDNARSKI, J (19/20th C) ?
£617 $938 €950 Horse drawn sleigh in winter. Horse drawn cart in summer (15x12cm-6x5in) s.i. panel. 6-Jul-2 Berlinghof, Heidelberg #202/R

FEDOROV, Simeon Fedorovich (1867-1910) Russian
£8273 $13237 €11500 Winter's day in the forest (90x58cm-35x23in) s. 17-May-3 Hagelstam, Helsinki #32/R est:8000
£10211 $16440 €14500 Evening sun by the swamp (49x85cm-19x33in) s. 10-May-3 Bukowskis, Helsinki #401/R est:4000-6000

FEDOROVA, Maria (1859-1934) Russian
£317 $501 €460 Landscape (22x28cm-9x11in) s. 3-Apr-3 Hagelstam, Helsinki #869/R

FEELEY, Paul (1913-1966) American
£10000 $16000 €15000 Apyu (152x122cm-60x48in) i.on stretcher painted 1963 prov.exhib.lit. 15-May-3 Christie's, Rockefeller NY #137/R est:18000-22000

FEGA, Luis (1952-) Spanish
£851 $1379 €1200 Fornelo (100x81cm-39x32in) s.i.d.2001 verso acrylic. 20-May-3 Segre, Madrid #176/R
£1064 $1723 €1500 Maizan (100x100cm-39x39in) s.i.d.2001. 20-May-3 Segre, Madrid #183/R est:1400

FEHDMER, Eugène (19/20th C) Belgian
£417 $654 €650 Winter evening (63x81cm-25x32in) 23-Nov-2 Arnold, Frankfurt #715
£986 $1587 €1400 Winter water landscape with people at work, Antwerp in the background (56x77cm-22x30in) s.d.1890. 12-May-3 Bernaerts, Antwerp #30/R

FEHR, Friedrich (1862-1927) German
£884 $1406 €1300 Shepherd with flock by farmstead (76x101cm-30x40in) s.i.d.1924. 19-Mar-3 Neumeister, Munich #551/R est:1300

FEHR, H P (19th C) Swiss?
Works on paper
£1747 $2760 €2621 School fete in Langental (33x46cm-13x18in) W/C pen. 14-Nov-2 Stuker, Bern #9111 est:1800-2200 (S.FR 4000)

FEHR, Henri (1888-1974) Swiss
£1135 $1771 €1703 Young ballerina at her make-up (91x72cm-36x28in) s. 8-Nov-2 Dobiaschofsky, Bern #124/R est:3600 (S.FR 2600)
Works on paper
£610 $1001 €885 Seated girl with shoe off (62x47cm-24x19in) i. verso pastel chk. 4-Jun-3 Fischer, Luzern #2077/R (S.FR 1300)

FEHRER, Oscar (1872-1958) American
£379 $550 €569 Woman with parasol (76x61cm-30x24in) 1-Jun-2 Russ Antiques, Waterford #154
£1125 $1800 €1631 Portrait of a woman (51x41cm-20x16in) s. 16-May-3 Skinner, Boston #144/R est:1800-2200

FEHRER, Walter (1899-1981) Austrian
£791 $1266 €1100 Altmunster (100x80cm-39x31in) s.d.1941. 14-May-3 Dorotheum, Linz #403/R

FEHRINGER, Oskar (1875-?) German
£411 $650 €596 Seascape with clipper ships and small fishing vessel (48x69cm-19x27in) s. 26-Apr-3 Jeffery Burchard, Florida #124

FEHRLE, Jakob Wilhelm (1884-1974) German
Sculpture
£1026 $1590 €1600 Standing female figure (47cm-19in) mono. bronze. 6-Dec-2 Michael Zeller, Lindau #1815/R
£2215 $3456 €3500 Female nude wearing cape (73cm-29in) mono. brown green pat.bronze. 18-Oct-2 Dr Fritz Nagel, Stuttgart #492/R est:3500
Works on paper
£528 $850 €750 Female nude (49x32cm-19x13in) mono.d.39 chl lit. 9-May-3 Schloss Ahlden, Ahlden #1572/R

FEIBUSCH, Hans (1898-1998) German
£900 $1395 €1350 Head (25x41cm-10x16in) init.d.38. 4-Dec-2 Christie's, Kensington #525/R est:1000-1500

FEID, Josef (1806-1870) Austrian
£3165 $5000 €5000 Landscape with deer on the ford (76x94cm-30x37in) s.d.1832. 28-Nov-2 Dorotheum, Vienna #164/R est:6000-8000
Works on paper
£692 $1072 €1100 Hallstadt (14x22cm-6x9in) s.d.1835 W/C. 1-Oct-2 Dorotheum, Vienna #354/R est:1800-2000

FEILER, Paul (1918-) British
£4800 $7440 €7200 Brown and black oval (25x25cm-10x10in) s.d.63. 4-Dec-2 Christie's, Kensington #618/R est:1500-2000
£5000 $7750 €7500 Boboli Gardens, Florence (41x56cm-16x22in) s.d.53 s.i.d.verso board. 4-Dec-2 Christie's, Kensington #575/R est:2500-3500
£7500 $11625 €11250 Landing stage with masts (63x76cm-25x30in) s. i.d.64 verso board. 4-Dec-2 Christie's, Kensington #617/R est:3000-5000
£9000 $13950 €13500 Seawall (43x53cm-17x21in) s.d.51 prov. 4-Dec-2 Christie's, Kensington #572/R est:2000-3000
£12000 $18840 €18000 Winter coast, Cornwall (50x84cm-20x33in) s.d.55 s.i.verso board exhib. 16-Dec-2 Sotheby's, London #93/R est:8000-12000
£17000 $27880 €24650 Lamorna Harbour (66x76cm-26x30in) s.d.52 board prov.exhib.lit. 4-Jun-3 Sotheby's, London #34/R est:5000-7000
£20000 $33200 €29000 Morning harbour, Mousehole (66x97cm-26x38in) s.i.d.1954 verso board. 10-Jun-3 David Lay, Penzance #494/R est:8000-10000
Works on paper
£400 $644 €600 Gwavas vertical (25x25cm-10x10in) chl pastel. 14-Jan-3 Bonhams, Knightsbridge #211/R
£580 $911 €870 Ambit G IV (49x39cm-19x15in) s.d.1976 gouache. 10-Dec-2 Lane, Penzance #102
£1700 $2805 €2465 Gwithian sketch (25x35cm-10x14in) s.d.63 chl bodycol col chks prov. 3-Jul-3 Christie's, Kensington #744/R est:1500-2500

FEIN, Nat (20th C) American
Photographs
£2577 $4200 €3866 Babe Ruth bows out (27x54cm-11x21in) s.i.d.1957 gelatin silver print. 12-Feb-3 Christie's, Rockefeller NY #38/R est:5000-7000

FEINGERSH, Oded (1938-) Israeli

£1646	$2600	€2469	Landscape of the carmel (114x74cm-45x29in) s.d.98. 27-Apr-3 Sotheby's, Tel Aviv #97/R est:2500-3500

FEININGER, Andreas (1906-) French

Photographs

£2073	$3400	€3110	Opera house (24x19cm-9x7in) s. st.verso silver print exec.c.1940. 10-Feb-3 Swann Galleries, New York #61/R est:3000-4000
£2215	$3500	€3323	Brooklyn Bridge (26x34cm-10x13in) s.d.1954 photograph. 23-Apr-3 Sotheby's, New York #91/R est:3000-5000
£2405	$3800	€3608	George Washington Bridge, New York (34x27cm-13x11in) s.i.d.1949 gelatin silver print prov.lit. 22-Apr-3 Christie's, Rockefeller NY #142/R est:3000-5000
£2692	$4200	€4038	Woolworth Building, New York (22x16cm-9x6in) silver. 21-Oct-2 Swann Galleries, New York #140/R est:5000-7000
£3084	$4750	€4626	View of Midtown Manhattan (48x39cm-19x15in) s. ferrotyped photograph. 24-Oct-2 Sotheby's, New York #117/R est:4000-6000
£3648	$5654	€5800	Brooklyn Bridge in fog, New York (37x51cm-15x20in) i. s.i.d.1948 verso silver gelatine. 31-Oct-2 Van Ham, Cologne #100/R est:5000
£3797	$6000	€5696	Fifth Avenue at lunch time (49x40cm-19x16in) s. oversized ferrotyped. 23-Apr-3 Sotheby's, New York #90/R est:5000-7000
£4294	$7000	€6441	Photojournalist (34x26cm-13x10in) s.i.d.1955/1992 num.33/50 gelatin silver print. 12-Feb-3 Christie's, Rockefeller NY #171/R est:8000-10000
£4747	$7500	€7121	The photojournalist (35x27cm-14x11in) s.i. photograph. 23-Apr-3 Sotheby's, New York #204/R est:8000-12000
£4747	$7500	€7121	Brooklyn Bridge (36x28cm-14x11in) s.i.d.1941 verso gelatin silver print prov. 25-Apr-3 Phillips, New York #90/R est:4000-6000
£5063	$8000	€7595	42 Street as viewed from Weehawken (35x48cm-14x19in) s. photograph. 23-Apr-3 Sotheby's, New York #89/R est:5000-7000
£9091	$14000	€13637	42nd Street as viewed from Weehawken (38x48cm-15x19in) num.76 ferrotyed photo prov.exhib. 22-Oct-2 Sotheby's, New York #70/R est:7000-10000

FEININGER, Lyonel (1871-1956) American/German

£2464	$4041	€3400	Gelmeroda (20x16cm-8x6in) d.20 IV 15 oil chk prov. 29-May-3 Lempertz, Koln #605/R est:3000
£1290323	$2000000	€1935485	Die zeitungsleser - Newspaper readers (50x63cm-20x25in) s.d.09 prov.exhib.lit. 4-Nov-2 Phillips, New York #16/R est:1700000-2000000

Prints

£1923	$3000	€2885	Windmuhle im regen (12x16cm-5x6in) s. woodcut. 7-Nov-2 Swann Galleries, New York #634/R est:3500-5000
£2000	$3120	€3000	Mellingen (30x25cm-12x10in) s. woodcut. 10-Oct-2 Sotheby's, London #109/R est:2000-2500
£2083	$3312	€3000	Yellow village church 3 (19x23cm-7x9in) s. woodcut. 5-May-3 Ketterer, Munich #846/R est:1000-1500
£2113	$3507	€3000	Off the coast (23x37cm-9x15in) s. lithograph. 14-Jun-3 Hauswedell & Nolte, Hamburg #1175/R est:2500
£2200	$3432	€3300	Topsail ketches (17x24cm-7x9in) s.i.num.3103 woodcut. 10-Oct-2 Sotheby's, London #111/R est:2000-2500
£2201	$3434	€3500	Ships at sea (18x18cm-7x7in) s. woodcut. 11-Oct-2 Winterberg, Heidelberg #1074/R est:4300
£2431	$3865	€3500	Harbour - warship in harbour entrance (16x22cm-6x9in) s. woodcut. 5-May-3 Ketterer, Munich #847/R est:1000-1500
£2468	$3900	€3900	Marine 2 (16x26cm-6x10in) s.i. woodcut. 30-Nov-2 Villa Grisebach, Berlin #263/R est:3500-4500
£2848	$4500	€4500	Marine (28x38cm-11x15in) s. woodcut. 30-Nov-2 Villa Grisebach, Berlin #262/R est:5000-6000
£2885	$4471	€4500	Ready to put to sea - in the offering (23x31cm-9x12in) s. woodcut exec.1919. 6-Dec-2 Ketterer, Munich #63/R est:4000-4500
£3038	$4800	€4800	Zottelstedt town hall 2 (22x28cm-9x11in) s.i. woodcut. 30-Nov-2 Villa Grisebach, Berlin #266/R est:3000-4000
£3145	$4906	€5000	Pariser hauser (37x27cm-15x11in) s.i.num.2006 woodcut. 9-Oct-2 Sotheby's, London #440/R est:3000-5000
£3239	$5377	€4600	Sunrise (15x23cm-6x9in) s.i.d. etching. 14-Jun-3 Hauswedell & Nolte, Hamburg #1172/R est:4000
£3333	$5300	€4800	Marine (28x38cm-11x15in) s. woodcut. 5-May-3 Ketterer, Munich #848/R est:2000-3000
£3380	$5611	€4800	Troistedt - village with rays of sunshine (17x22cm-7x9in) s. woodcut. 14-Jun-3 Hauswedell & Nolte, Hamburg #1183/R est:4000
£3797	$6000	€6000	Sunset - small town (15x23cm-6x9in) s.i. drypoint prov. 30-Nov-2 Villa Grisebach, Berlin #153/R est:4000-5000
£5072	$8319	€7000	Vollersroda (25x30cm-10x12in) s. woodcut. 31-May-3 Villa Grisebach, Berlin #202/R est:6000-8000
£5128	$7949	€8000	Gelmeroda (33x24cm-13x9in) s.i. woodcut. 7-Dec-2 Hauswedell & Nolte, Hamburg #653/R est:6000
£5256	$8147	€8200	Sailing ships I (17x24cm-7x9in) s.i. woodcut. 7-Dec-2 Hauswedell & Nolte, Hamburg #654/R est:5500
£6056	$10054	€8600	The gate (27x20cm-11x8in) s.i.d. etching drypoint. 14-Jun-3 Hauswedell & Nolte, Hamburg #1173/R est:7000
£8974	$13910	€14000	Vollersroda (25x30cm-10x12in) s. woodcut. 7-Dec-2 Hauswedell & Nolte, Hamburg #650/R est:15000
£12319	$20203	€17000	The green bridge (27x20cm-11x8in) s.i.d.1911 etching W/C. 29-May-3 Lempertz, Koln #610/R est:18000-20000

Works on paper

£737	$1077	€1150	Portrait of Schelfhout (13x10cm-5x4in) i.d.08 pencil. 4-Jun-2 Karl & Faber, Munich #233
£818	$1259	€1300	Ostsee coast (14x22cm-6x9in) d.8.8.25 pencil. 26-Oct-2 Dr Lehr, Berlin #99/R
£1111	$1756	€1600	Steamer and boats (14x22cm-6x9in) d.2.7.29 pencil. 26-Apr-3 Dr Lehr, Berlin #128/R est:1400
£1127	$1870	€1600	Sailing ship and steamer (9x15cm-4x6in) i. pencil. 14-Jun-3 Hauswedell & Nolte, Hamburg #1162/R est:2000
£1159	$1901	€1600	Male figure from behind (11x7cm-4x3in) d.11 VI 12 pencil prov. 29-May-3 Lempertz, Koln #604/R est:1200
£1268	$2104	€1800	Man running (10x10cm-4x4in) d.24V09 col pen. 14-Jun-3 Hauswedell & Nolte, Hamburg #1163/R est:2000
£1410	$2059	€2200	Sailboats (16x20cm-6x8in) pen. 4-Jun-2 Karl & Faber, Munich #236 est:2000
£1456	$2300	€2300	Steamer at sea (14x22cm-6x9in) i. 29-Nov-2 Villa Grisebach, Berlin #605/R est:1500-1800
£1603	$2532	€2500	Our vis a vis in Zehlendorf (14x22cm-6x9in) s.i.d.1910 chk. 14-Nov-2 Neumeister, Munich #559/R est:2000-2500
£1812	$2971	€2500	Old houses (22x14cm-9x6in) d.14 7 33 pencil col chk. 31-May-3 Villa Grisebach, Berlin #545/R est:2500-3000
£2464	$4041	€3400	Gelmeroda church (21x16cm-8x6in) d.17 6 19 graphite prov. 29-May-3 Lempertz, Koln #606/R est:2500
£2564	$3744	€4000	Strollers on the beach and side wheeler (20x24cm-8x9in) d.11 Indian ink brush pen. 4-Jun-2 Karl & Faber, Munich #234/R est:3500
£2821	$4372	€4400	Sailing ships (11x20cm-4x8in) pen. 7-Dec-2 Hauswedell & Nolte, Hamburg #646/R est:4000
£3191	$5170	€4500	Marina (24x31cm-9x12in) s.d.21.X.54 blk.ink pen pencil. 26-May-3 Christie's, Milan #66/R est:5000-7000
£3774	$6000	€5661	Harbour sketch (19x28cm-7x11in) s.d.1946 pen ink W/C. 7-Mar-3 Skinner, Boston #510/R est:6000-8000
£4717	$7500	€7076	Four figures (9x15cm-4x6in) s.d.1953 W/C pen ink. 27-Feb-3 Christie's, Rockefeller NY #4/R est:8000
£4930	$8183	€7000	Running and shortening sail (13x19cm-5x7in) i.d.15 aug 1911 col pen. 14-Jun-3 Hauswedell & Nolte, Hamburg #1164/R est:8000
£5500	$8470	€8250	Traveller (21x17cm-8x7in) d.Sep 11 09 col crayon prov. 23-Oct-2 Sotheby's, Olympia #767/R est:4000-6000
£5828	$9500	€8742	Waterway mists (31x48cm-12x19in) s.d.1950 W/C ink chk prov. 12-Feb-3 Sotheby's, New York #85/R est:10000-15000
£7042	$11690	€10000	Lubeck (28x21cm-11x8in) s.i.d. W/C Indian ink. 14-Jun-3 Hauswedell & Nolte, Hamburg #1171/R est:15000
£7453	$12000	€11180	Houses in Hildesheim (52x39cm-20x15in) s.d.1950 W/C pen ink prov.exhib. 7-May-3 Sotheby's, New York #202/R est:15000-20000
£7595	$12000	€12000	Sunrise over sea (24x31cm-9x12in) s.d.I.X.53 Indian ink pencil W/C exhib. 30-Nov-2 Villa Grisebach, Berlin #264/R est:12000-15000
£7595	$12000	€12000	Ghosties (7x16cm-3x6in) s.d.1953 Indian ink W/C prov. 30-Nov-2 Villa Grisebach, Berlin #265/R est:7000-8000
£7975	$13000	€11963	Coast of Faraway (17x35cm-7x14in) s.i.d.1939 W/C pen ink. 12-Feb-3 Sotheby's, New York #83/R est:10000-12000
£7975	$13000	€11963	Composition (15x23cm-6x9in) s.d.14.11.53 W/C India ink prov. 12-Feb-3 Sotheby's, New York #84/R est:8000-12000
£8696	$14000	€13044	One world (32x48cm-13x19in) s.i.d.1953 W/C pen India ink prov. 7-May-3 Sotheby's, New York #218/R est:8000-12000
£9317	$15000	€13976	Gaberndorf III (24x30cm-9x12in) s.i.d.May 7 1914 chl prov.exhib. 7-May-3 Sotheby's, New York #201/R est:10000-15000
£10559	$17000	€15839	Brigantine und kutter (25x40cm-10x16in) s.i.d.Sept 30 1931 W/C oen ink chl prov.exhib. 7-May-3 Sotheby's, New York #217/R est:15000-20000
£10559	$17000	€15839	Beleuchtete Hauser II (23x29cm-9x11in) s.i.d.17 vi 23 W/C pen India ink prov.exhib. 8-May-3 Christie's, Rockefeller NY #122/R est:15000-20000
£11180	$18000	€16770	Buttelstedt (35x28cm-14x11in) s.i.d.24-8-27 chl pen ink prov.exhib. 8-May-3 Christie's, Rockefeller NY #105/R est:20000-25000
£11218	$17388	€17500	Three mannequins - ghosties (28x21cm-11x8in) s.d.1955 W/C Indian ink. 7-Dec-2 Hauswedell & Nolte, Hamburg #649/R est:20000
£12368	$20037	€18800	Figures (30x46cm-12x18in) s.d.1952 Chinese ink W/C. 24-Jan-3 Chayette & Cheval, Paris #16/R est:18000
£12422	$20000	€18633	Regatta (19x28cm-7x11in) s.d.6 vii 46 W/C pen India ink prov.exhib. 8-May-3 Christie's, Rockefeller NY #101/R est:15000-20000
£13043	$21391	€18000	Marine (32x48cm-13x19in) s.d.July 16 1953 W/C chl Indian ink prov. 29-May-3 Lempertz, Koln #609/R est:20000-25000

£13665 $22000 €20498 Stranded (24x32cm-9x13in) s.i.d.1941 W/C pen India ink gouache prov. 7-May-3 Sotheby's, New York #216/R est:12000-18000
£13665 $22000 €20498 Thunderstorm passes through a mountainside hamlet (25x30cm-10x12in) s.d. pen ink pair prov. 10-May-3 Illustration House, New York #31/R est:25000-35000
£14493 $23768 €20000 Desert coast (21x29cm-8x11in) s.i.d.13.IX.46 W/C pen prov. 29-May-3 Lempertz, Koln #607/R est:20000
£15823 $25000 €25000 Windclouds at sundown (31x48cm-12x19in) s.d.48 W/C brush over chl prov. 29-Nov-2 Villa Grisebach, Berlin #74/R est:25000-30000
£16026 $24840 €25000 Seascape with clear cloud (30x48cm-12x19in) s.i.d.1950 X W/C Indian ink. 4-Dec-2 Lempertz, Koln #708/R est:25000-30000
£16197 $26887 €23000 Old gables (31x47cm-12x19in) s.d. W/C Indian ink chk. 14-Jun-3 Hauswedell & Nolte, Hamburg #1169/R est:22000
£16667 $25833 €26000 High houses I (31x24cm-12x9in) s.i.d.Dec.18.1912 chl. 4-Dec-2 Lempertz, Koln #704/R est:20000-25000

FEINT, Adrian (1894-1971) Australian
£253 $392 €380 Hibiscus (15x13cm-6x5in) s. board. 3-Dec-2 Shapiro, Sydney #20/R (A.D 700)
£894 $1413 €1296 Still life and figure (18x14cm-7x6in) s.d.57 board. 22-Jul-3 Lawson Menzies, Sydney #12/R est:2500-4000 (A.D 2200)
£1149 $1713 €1724 Boat man at Lion Island (29x24cm-11x9in) s.d.39 board. 27-Aug-2 Christie's, Melbourne #337/R est:3000-5000 (A.D 3000)
£1298 $2050 €1947 Camelias in a jug (46x25cm-18x10in) s.d. prov. 7-Apr-3 Shapiro, Sydney #414/R est:3000-5000 (A.D 3400)
£1514 $2483 €2195 White roses, Pittwater scene (49x39cm-19x15in) s. 3-Jun-3 Lawson Menzies, Sydney #879 est:4500-5000 (A.D 3800)
£1846 $2935 €2769 Still life with flowers in vase (44x40cm-17x16in) s.d.1939. 4-Mar-3 Deutscher-Menzies, Melbourne #198/R est:5500-7500 (A.D 4800)

FEITELSON, Lorser (1898-1978) American
£1592 $2500 €2388 Seated female nude. Reclining female nude (75x60cm-30x24in) one s. board on board pair prov. 19-Nov-2 Butterfields, San Francisco #8336/R est:3000-5000
Works on paper
£6962 $11000 €10443 Untitled (152x102cm-60x40in) s.d.1964 i.verso enamel oil. 22-Apr-3 Butterfields, San Francisco #6069/R est:15000-20000

FEITH, Gustav (1875-1951) Austrian
Works on paper
£405 $632 €600 Schwallenbach in the Wachau (31x22cm-12x9in) s.d.1908 W/C. 28-Mar-3 Dorotheum, Vienna #298/R
£755 $1170 €1200 Spring flowers in vase (34x24cm-13x9in) s.d.1942 W/C paper on board. 1-Oct-2 Dorotheum, Vienna #300/R
£755 $1170 €1200 Autumn flowers in vase (34x24cm-13x9in) s.d.1942 W/C paper on board. 1-Oct-2 Dorotheum, Vienna #321/R
£1384 $2145 €2200 Violets (16x13cm-6x5in) s.d.1931 W/C. 1-Oct-2 Dorotheum, Vienna #298/R est:2200-2500
£1509 $2340 €2400 Spring flowers (30x23cm-12x9in) s.d.Marz 1923 W/C. 1-Oct-2 Dorotheum, Vienna #301/R est:2000-2500
£1622 $2530 €2400 Perchtoldsdorf (30x36cm-12x14in) s.i. W/C board. 28-Mar-3 Dorotheum, Vienna #282/R est:2000-2500
£1899 $3000 €3000 Summer flowers (41x30cm-16x12in) s.d.1943 W/C. 28-Nov-2 Dorotheum, Vienna #187/R est:3000-5000
£2297 $3584 €3400 Violet plant (16x13cm-6x5in) s.d.April 1929 W/C. 28-Mar-3 Dorotheum, Vienna #299/R est:2200-2500

FEITO, Luis (1929-) Spanish
£1923 $2981 €3000 Composition (50x80cm-20x31in) s.d.1979 verso panel. 7-Dec-2 Cornette de St.Cyr, Paris #96/R
£2025 $3200 €3200 Untitled (62x50cm-24x20in) s.d.70 acrylic card. 29-Nov-2 Farsetti, Prato #105/R est:3000
£2179 $3422 €3400 Luna (60x84cm-24x33in) s.i.d.65 oil collage canvas on panel. 16-Dec-2 Charbonneaux, Paris #251/R est:2500-3000
£8000 $12400 €12000 Peinture 847 (97x130cm-38x51in) s.d.1971 verso acrylic prov. 5-Dec-2 Christie's, Kensington #217/R est:6000-8000
£8000 $12400 €12000 Peinture 488 (89x116cm-35x46in) s.d.1965 verso oil sand prov. 5-Dec-2 Christie's, Kensington #218/R est:6000-8000
£14894 $24128 €21000 Pintura 701 (92x147cm-36x58in) s.i.d.1969 verso diptych. 20-May-3 Segre, Madrid #151/R est:21000
£30000 $50100 €43500 Pintura 139 (114x145cm-45x57in) s. s.i.d.1959 verso oil mixed media prov.exhib. 26-Jun-3 Sotheby's, London #197/R est:8000-12000
Works on paper
£2338 $3413 €3600 Untitled (35x46cm-14x18in) s. gouache mixed media painted 1953. 17-Jun-2 Ansorena, Madrid #57/R

FEJES, Emerik (1904-1969) Yugoslavian
£425 $679 €638 Beograd 1642 C (58x74cm-23x29in) s.i. tempera. 17-Mar-3 Philippe Schuler, Zurich #4023 (S.FR 900)

FEKETE, Esteban (1924-) Hungarian
£491 $765 €780 Reclining female nude with watering can beneath trees (36x60cm-14x24in) s.d.1968 panel. 11-Oct-2 Winterberg, Heidelberg #1084/R

FELBER, Carl (1880-1932) Swiss
£694 $1118 €1041 Mountain pasture (90x120cm-35x47in) s.i. i.d.1918 verso. 7-May-3 Dobiaschofsky, Bern #499/R est:1600 (S.FR 1500)

FELD, Otto (1860-1911) German
£324 $518 €450 In conversation (68x54cm-27x21in) s. 14-May-3 Dorotheum, Linz #341/R

FELDER, Franz Anton (attrib) (?-1782) German
Works on paper
£566 $877 €900 St Andreas (30x18cm-12x7in) i.d.1775 ochre chk htd white. 1-Oct-2 Dorotheum, Vienna #51/R

FELDHUTTER, Ferdinand (1842-1898) German
£850 $1393 €1300 Alpine valley with peasants and farmstead on sunny evening (53x73cm-21x29in) s.d.1881. 8-Feb-3 Hans Stahl, Hamburg #14/R
£1026 $1610 €1600 Waterfall near Bad Gastein, Tyrol (48x41cm-19x16in) s. 21-Nov-2 Van Ham, Cologne #1599/R
£1765 $2894 €2700 Konigssee with figures (69x98cm-27x39in) s.i.d.1892. 6-Feb-3 Weidler, Nurnberg #317/R est:2700

FELDHUTTER, Ferdinand (attrib) (1842-1898) German
£360 $587 €540 Moonlit lake view with figures in the foreground (54x74cm-21x29in) 12-Feb-3 Bonhams, Knightsbridge #38/R

FELDMANN, Wilhelm (1859-1932) German
£272 $433 €400 Spring (40x47cm-16x19in) s.i. verso. 28-Mar-3 Bolland & Marotz, Bremen #444
£1266 $2000 €2000 After the storm (100x130cm-39x51in) s.d.1916 i.verso. 29-Nov-2 Bolland & Marotz, Bremen #689/R est:3000

FELGENTREFF, Paul (1854-1933) German
£1274 $1987 €2000 Boy with beer tankard and radishes (51x31cm-20x12in) s. 6-Nov-2 Hugo Ruef, Munich #1088/R est:2000
£10323 $16000 €15485 Rest after the hunt at an Alpine tavern (80x69cm-31x27in) s.i. 2-Oct-2 Christie's, Rockefeller NY #784/R est:8000-12000

FELGENTREFF, Paul (attrib) (1854-1933) German
£748 $1190 €1100 In the snow (14x17cm-6x7in) i.d.1916 panel. 19-Mar-3 Neumeister, Munich #552/R est:750

FELISARI, Enrico (1897-1981) Italian
£348 $543 €550 At the mirror (70x65cm-28x26in) s. s.verso. 14-Sep-2 Meeting Art, Vercelli #410/R
Works on paper
£338 $527 €500 Portrait of woman (59x42cm-23x17in) s.d.942 col chk. 26-Mar-3 Finarte Semenzato, Milan #44

FELIX, Auguste (1860-1936) French
£811 $1265 €1200 A la fontaine. Maison dans un sous-bois (38x46cm-15x18in) pair. 30-Mar-3 Anaf, Lyon #99

FELIX, Eugen (1837-1906) Austrian
£285 $450 €428 New England autumn landscape (53x91cm-21x36in) s. 17-Nov-2 CRN Auctions, Cambridge #3/R

FELIX, Léon Pierre (1869-1940) French
£18705 $30676 €26000 L'idylle champetre (116x186cm-46x73in) s.i.d. 4-Jun-3 Marc Kohn, Paris #31/R est:25000-30000

FELIXMULLER, Conrad (1897-1977) German
£2830 $4358 €4500 Docks (41x65cm-16x26in) s.d.1951. 26-Oct-2 Dr Lehr, Berlin #102/R est:5000
£24000 $39360 €36000 Portrait of Sofie Isakowitz (58x67cm-23x26in) s.i. prov.exhib.lit. 4-Feb-3 Christie's, London #336/R est:35000
£160000 $260800 €240000 Liegende frau (68x97cm-27x38in) s. painted 1923 prov.exhib.lit. 3-Feb-3 Christie's, London #20/R est:120000-160000
£510000 $831300 €765000 Heimweg (95x95cm-37x37in) s. s.d.1921 verso prov.exhib.lit. 3-Feb-3 Christie's, London #16/R est:400000-600000
Prints
£1923 $3000 €2885 Selbstbildnis (26x18cm-10x7in) s.i.d.1913 etching. 7-Nov-2 Swann Galleries, New York #640/R est:4000-6000
£2113 $3507 €3000 Winter (47x40cm-19x16in) s.mono.i.d. woodcut. 14-Jun-3 Hauswedell & Nolte, Hamburg #1189/R est:2600
£2949 $4571 €4600 Loving woman (52x37cm-20x15in) s.i.d. col lithograph prov. 4-Dec-2 Lempertz, Koln #712/R est:5000

£3425 $5342 €5000 Winter (47x40cm-19x16in) s.i.d. woodcut. 11-Apr-3 Winterberg, Heidelberg #975/R est:6800

Works on paper

£755 $1177 €1200 Female nude seated on floor (25x32cm-10x13in) s.d.19.8.70 pencil. 11-Oct-2 Winterberg, Heidelberg #1089/R
£1594 $2614 €2200 Herr Deutsch (35x25cm-14x10in) s.i. i. verso Indian ink. 31-May-3 Villa Grisebach, Berlin #548/R est:2200-2600
£3797 $6000 €6000 Uttwil - Bodensee landscape with fishing nets (32x43cm-13x17in) s.i.d.19/9/25 W/C gouache board exhib. 30-Nov-2 Villa Grisebach, Berlin #297/R est:6000-7000
£4747 $7500 €7500 Uttwil - Bodensee landscape with lakeshore (32x42cm-13x17in) s.i.d.1925 W/C gouache board exhib. 30-Nov-2 Villa Grisebach, Berlin #298/R est:6000-7000
£5072 $8319 €7000 Landscape with wood (43x33cm-17x13in) s.d.24 s.i.d.6/Sept 1924 verso gouache board prov. 29-May-3 Lempertz, Koln #614/R est:7000
£5769 $8942 €9000 Studie no 214 (59x46cm-23x18in) s.i.d.20 W/C gouache lit. 7-Dec-2 Van Ham, Cologne #156/R est:12000
£14493 $23768 €20000 The kiss (61x48cm-24x19in) s.d.1924 gouache prov. 29-May-3 Lempertz, Koln #615/R est:25000
£150000 $244500 €225000 Selbstbildnis mit meiner frau Londa und meinen sohn Titus (54x50cm-21x20in) s.d.1923 gouache W/C pencil. 3-Feb-3 Christie's, London #14/R est:150000-250000

FELKEL, Carl (1896-1973) Austrian

£440 $717 €660 Mediterranean harbour scene (41x54cm-16x21in) s. 17-Feb-3 Bonhams, Bath #115

FELL, Sheila (1931-1979) British

£600 $954 €900 Moorland landscape with approaching storm. s. 7-Mar-3 Biddle & Webb, Birmingham #99
£2200 $3608 €3300 Planting potatoes II (25x30cm-10x12in) s. 3-Jun-3 Sotheby's, Olympia #253/R est:2000-3000
£4000 $6600 €5800 Snowscape, Cumbria (25x30cm-10x12in) s. prov.exhib. 3-Jul-3 Christie's, Kensington #711/R est:1500-2000
£4500 $7425 €6525 Boats near Maryport, Cumbria (25x30cm-10x12in) s. s.on overlap prov.exhib. 3-Jul-3 Christie's, Kensington #714/R est:1200-1800
£5500 $9020 €8250 Cumberland landscape (65x82cm-26x32in) s. board painted c.1965. 3-Jun-3 Sotheby's, Olympia #252/R est:4000-6000
£11000 $16940 €16500 Farm in a field (76x101cm-30x40in) s. prov. 5-Sep-2 Christie's, Kensington #691/R est:2000-3000
£11000 $16940 €16500 Cumberland landscape I (101x127cm-40x50in) s. s.i.d.1967 stretcher. 5-Sep-2 Christie's, Kensington #692/R est:2000-3000
£11000 $17490 €16500 Men gathering corn 1 (51x61cm-20x24in) s. 6-Mar-3 Mitchells, Cockermouth #809/R est:4000-6000
£13000 $20670 €19500 Potato picking at Aigle Ghyll 1 (74x100cm-29x39in) s. exhib. 26-Feb-3 Sotheby's, Olympia #242/R est:4000-6000

FELLER, Frank (1848-1908) Swiss

Works on paper

£400 $660 €580 Russian outposts (31x46cm-12x18in) init. W/C. 1-Jul-3 Bearnes, Exeter #434/R

FELLER-BRAND, Walter (1917-) Swiss

£306 $477 €459 Standing female nude (32x16cm-13x6in) s. panel. 6-Nov-2 Dobiaschofsky, Bern #3322 (S.FR 700)
£371 $586 €557 Small river landscape (8x13cm-3x5in) s. panel. 14-Nov-2 Stuker, Bern #204 (S.FR 850)

FELLINGER, Leo (1884-1975) Austrian

£1282 $1987 €2000 Roses in blue vase (56x48cm-22x19in) mono. juste. 5-Dec-2 Dorotheum, Graz #11/R est:1300

FELLINI, Federico (1920-1993) Italian

Works on paper

£1522 $2374 €2283 I clowns (31x24cm-12x9in) i. mixed media prov. 16-Sep-2 Philippe Schuler, Zurich #3021/R est:4000-6000 (S.FR 3500)

FELLOWES, James (18th C) British

£833 $1299 €1250 Portrait of Mr Joseph Fluit (122x99cm-48x39in) i.indis.d.1747 verso. 11-Nov-2 Stephan Welz, Johannesburg #48 (SA.R 13000)

FELLOWS, Byron W (20th C) American

£514 $750 €771 October (51x60cm-20x24in) s.d.09. 10-May-2 Skinner, Boston #183/R

FELLOWS, Fred (1934-) American

£962 $1500 €1443 Winter reflections (51x76cm-20x30in) s. masonite panel prov. 9-Nov-2 Santa Fe Art, Santa Fe #62/R est:2000-4000
£2754 $4600 €3993 Away from prairie winds (81x122cm-32x48in) s.d.1979 masonite. 21-Jun-3 Selkirks, St. Louis #189/R est:6000-8000

Sculpture

£16026 $25000 €24039 No easy way out (107x107x64cm-42x42x25in) bronze. 9-Nov-2 Altermann Galleries, Santa Fe #172

FELON, Joseph (1818-1896) French

£1268 $2041 €1800 City on canal (23x33cm-9x13in) s.d.1838 panel lit. 9-May-3 Schloss Ahlden, Ahlden #1343/R est:1800

FELYN, Ithel (17th C) British?

£3600 $5688 €5400 Seventeenth century portrait (76x58cm-30x23in) i. on stretcher painted c.1620 exhib. 5-Apr-3 Finan Watkins & Co, Mere #196/R

FENDEL, Allan (?) American?

Works on paper

£305 $500 €442 Autumn landscape (43x69cm-17x27in) s. W/C. 4-Jun-3 Doyle, New York #49

FENDI, Peter (1796-1842) Austrian

£12658 $20000 €20000 Interior of apartment at Alserstrasse 19, Vienna IX (23x32cm-9x13in) s.d.831 panel. 26-Nov-2 Wiener Kunst Auktionen, Vienna #15/R est:20000-35000

Works on paper

£1258 $1950 €2000 Portrait of young woman wearing drop earrings (11x9cm-4x4in) s.d.823 i. verso W/C. 1-Oct-2 Dorotheum, Vienna #369/R est:1400-1800

FENETTY, Frederick M (1854-1915) American/Italian

£1282 $2000 €1923 Floral still life of roses (23x33cm-9x13in) s. 22-Sep-2 Jeffery Burchard, Florida #28
£2044 $3250 €3066 Still life with roses and peaches (51x76cm-20x30in) s. 7-Mar-3 Skinner, Boston #303/R est:3000-5000
£6329 $10000 €9494 Nasturtiums (46x56cm-18x22in) s. 24-Apr-3 Shannon's, Milford #170/R est:8000-12000

FENG CHANGJIANG (1943-) Chinese

Works on paper

£12432 $20513 €18026 Golden wish (91x84cm-36x33in) s. ink scroll. 6-Jul-3 Christie's, Hong Kong #275/R est:100000-120000 (HK.D 160000)

FENG LINZHANG (1943-) Chinese

Works on paper

£9324 $15385 €13520 Spring (129x64cm-51x25in) s. ink scroll. 6-Jul-3 Christie's, Hong Kong #274/R est:100000-120000 (HK.D 120000)

FENG ZIKAI (1898-1975) Chinese

Works on paper

£2020 $3333 €2929 Planting melon (32x27cm-13x11in) s.i. col ink scroll. 6-Jul-3 Christie's, Hong Kong #225/R est:20000-30000 (HK.D 26000)
£2953 $4872 €4282 Returning home with flowers (34x27cm-13x11in) s.i. ink scroll. 6-Jul-3 Christie's, Hong Kong #353/R est:18000-22000 (HK.D 38000)
£3730 $6154 €5409 Destroy and construct (32x36cm-13x14in) s.i. ink scroll. 6-Jul-3 Christie's, Hong Kong #350/R est:15000-20000 (HK.D 48000)
£3885 $6410 €5633 Eating cake (33x35cm-13x14in) s.i. ink scroll. 6-Jul-3 Christie's, Hong Kong #351/R est:20000-25000 (HK.D 50000)
£5041 $7964 €7562 Celebrating the National Day (33x26cm-13x10in) s.i. ink col exec.c.1959. 28-Apr-3 Sotheby's, Hong Kong #562/R est:20000-30000 (HK.D 62000)
£5828 $9615 €8451 Away from the war (74x40cm-29x16in) s.i. ink scroll. 6-Jul-3 Christie's, Hong Kong #355/R est:25000-30000 (HK.D 75000)
£6098 $9634 €9147 Various (26x36cm-10x14in) s. one i.d.1965 ink col four. 28-Apr-3 Sotheby's, Hong Kong #563/R est:40000-60000 (HK.D 75000)
£6216 $10256 €9013 Drunken revelers. Mountain stream (23x39cm-9x15in) s.i. ink scroll pair. 6-Jul-3 Christie's, Hong Kong #352/R est:20000-30000 (HK.D 80000)
£12432 $20513 €18026 Chines new year (68x34cm-27x13in) s.i. ink scroll. 6-Jul-3 Christie's, Hong Kong #354/R est:30000-40000 (HK.D 160000)

FENN, Harry (1845-1911) American

Works on paper

£472 $750 €708 Brantwood (22x21cm-9x8in) s. pen ink gouache W/C. 7-Mar-3 Skinner, Boston #571/R

FENN, Werner (1932-) German
Sculpture
£1690 $2806 €2400 Shepherd with flock (23x40x15cm-9x16x6in) bronze. 14-Jun-3 Hauswedell & Nolte, Hamburg #1191/R est:1000

FENNEKER, Josef (1890-1956) German
Works on paper
£1268 $2104 €1800 Composition (44x29cm-17x11in) s. bears i.d. chk W/C bodycol. 14-Jun-3 Hauswedell & Nolte, Hamburg #1192/R est:2500

FENNELL, John Greville (1807-1885) British
£675 $1100 €1013 Village incident (30x36cm-12x14in) s.d. 16-Feb-3 Butterfields, San Francisco #2051

FENNELL, Peter (20th C) Australian
£358 $545 €537 By the lagoon (49x39cm-19x15in) s. canvas on board. 27-Aug-2 Goodman, Sydney #193 (A.D 1000)

FENNER-BEHMER, Herman (1866-1913) German
£276 $439 €400 Riverside farmstead (31x28cm-12x11in) s. 8-Mar-3 Arnold, Frankfurt #582

FENOSA, Apelles (1899-1989) Spanish
Sculpture
£3481 $5430 €5500 Buste de jeune fille (35cm-14in) s.num. 1 sur 5 brown pat bronze green marble socle exhib. 20-Oct-2 Mercier & Cie, Lille #135/R est:5000-6000

FENSON, Robert (19/20th C) British
£504 $817 €731 Haslemere, Surrey - farm in evening sunshine (50x75cm-20x30in) s.d.1906. 25-May-3 Uppsala Auktionskammare, Uppsala #158 (S.KR 6500)
£720 $1109 €1080 Sweet summertime, rural river landscape (50x75cm-20x30in) s.d.98. 22-Oct-2 Bonhams, Bath #270
£950 $1558 €1425 Returning home at sunset (30x39cm-12x15in) s. 29-May-3 Christie's, Kensington #179/R

FENTON, Roger (1819-1869) British
Photographs
£4808 $7596 €7500 Trafalgar Square (29x42cm-11x17in) i.num.20 albumin print exec.c.1856-59 prov. 16-Nov-2 Christie's, Paris #76/R est:7000-9000
£32000 $51840 €48000 Orientalist study, water carrier (27x25cm-11x10in) albumen print prov.lit. 21-May-3 Christie's, London #36/R est:12000-18000
£50000 $81000 €75000 Historical portrait gallery, incidents of camp life (58x43cm-23x17in) i. salt albumen prints 86 album prov.lit. 21-May-3 Christie's, London #33/R est:20000-30000

FENTON, Roger and ROBERTSON, James (19th C) British
Photographs
£135000 $218700 €202500 Scenery views of the camp (58x43cm-23x17in) i. salt albumen prints 100 album prov.lit. 21-May-3 Christie's, London #32/R est:20000-30000

FENWICK, Thomas (?-1850) British
£2000 $3120 €3000 On the Dutch coast (50x63cm-20x25in) s. 17-Oct-2 Bonhams, Edinburgh #179 est:1000-1500

FENYES, Adolphe (1867-1945) Hungarian
£774 $1207 €1122 Landscape of the plain (27x40cm-11x16in) s. panel. 13-Sep-2 Mu Terem Galeria, Budapest #87/R est:280000 (H.F 300000)
£877 $1368 €1316 Hilly landscape (38x28cm-15x11in) 11-Sep-2 Kieselbach, Budapest #14/R (H.F 340000)
£968 $1501 €1452 Rococo scene in the open air (29x37cm-11x15in) s. 6-Dec-2 Kieselbach, Budapest #9/R (H.F 360000)
£978 $1526 €1467 Boy (42x34cm-17x13in) 11-Apr-3 Kieselbach, Budapest #195/R est:350000 (H.F 350000)
£1614 $2501 €2421 Hillside in spring (15x22cm-6x9in) s. board. 6-Dec-2 Kieselbach, Budapest #4/R (H.F 600000)
£1689 $2804 €2449 Horse and carriage in stormy country side (27x36cm-11x14in) s. panel. 16-Jun-3 Waddingtons, Toronto #304/R est:300-500 (C.D 3800)
£1806 $2817 €2709 Landscape behind Szolnok (45x60cm-18x24in) s. 11-Sep-2 Kieselbach, Budapest #13/R (H.F 700000)
£4128 $6439 €5986 In the garden (31x41cm-12x16in) s. 13-Sep-2 Mu Terem Galeria, Budapest #28/R est:950000 (H.F 1600000)
£7223 $11268 €10835 Spring by the river Zagyva (77x97cm-30x38in) s. 11-Sep-2 Kieselbach, Budapest #215/R (H.F 2800000)
£11333 $18813 €16433 Gathering in a pastoral landscape outside a town (66x96cm-26x38in) s. 16-Jun-3 Waddingtons, Toronto #307/R est:1500-2000 (C.D 25500)
£27945 $43594 €41918 Woman in hat, sitting in shadowy courtyard (43x61cm-17x24in) s. 11-Apr-3 Kieselbach, Budapest #20/R est:5000000-10000000 (H.F 10000000)

FENZONI, Ferrau (1562-1645) Italian
£26000 $43420 €37700 The Holy Family (82x65cm-32x26in) 9-Jul-3 Bonhams, New Bond Street #5/R est:8000-12000

FEODOROVA, Maria Alekseevna (1859-1916) Russian
£577 $930 €820 Boat by the shore (36x50cm-14x20in) s. 10-May-3 Bukowskis, Helsinki #410/R

FERAT, Serge (1881-1958) Russian
£1935 $3058 €3000 Partie de peche (81x60cm-32x24in) s. painted c.1940. 19-Dec-2 Delvaux, Paris #45/R
£9091 $13273 €14000 Composition (43x50cm-17x20in) s. 12-Jun-2 Castellana, Madrid #100/R est:12000

FERAUD, Albert (1921-) French
Sculpture
£962 $1510 €1500 Untitled (31x47cm-12x19in) s. stainless steel. 24-Nov-2 Laurence Calmels, Paris #296/R
£1923 $3019 €3000 Untitled (105x80cm-41x31in) s. welded metal. 24-Nov-2 Laurence Calmels, Paris #297/R

FERBER, Herbert (1906-1991) American
Sculpture
£5161 $8000 €7742 Homage to Piranesi II a2 (95x46x44cm-37x18x17in) s. copper executed 1962 prov. 26-Sep-2 Christie's, Rockefeller NY #720/R est:10000-15000

FERBUS, Rudolf (1929-) Austrian?
£612 $1003 €850 Flying swans (58x78cm-23x31in) s,. 5-Jun-3 Dorotheum, Salzburg #642/R

FERENCZ, Ingomar (?) ?
£629 $1000 €944 Untitled, woman with cherries in her hair (51x46cm-20x18in) 28-Feb-3 Douglas, South Deerfield #9

FERENCZY, Karoly (1862-1917) Hungarian
£352 $550 €528 Connoisseur amongst his treasures (38x28cm-15x11in) s. 11-Nov-2 Stephan Welz, Johannesburg #420 (SA.R 5500)
£13972 $21797 €20958 Venus still life (57x34cm-22x13in) s. 11-Apr-3 Kieselbach, Budapest #182/R est:3500000-5000000 (H.F 5000000)

FERENCZY, Noemi (1890-1957) Hungarian
£25798 $40245 €38697 Sleeping shepherd, 1937 (80x173cm-31x68in) 11-Sep-2 Kieselbach, Budapest #72/R (H.F 10000000)
Works on paper
£1548 $2415 €2245 Forest (35x35cm-14x14in) W/C lit. 13-Sep-2 Mu Terem Galeria, Budapest #63/R est:440000 (H.F 600000)
£2580 $4024 €3741 Abundance (221x123cm-87x48in) W/C prov.lit. 13-Sep-2 Mu Terem Galeria, Budapest #71/R est:750000 (H.F 1000000)

FERENCZY, Valer (1885-1954) Hungarian
£1677 $2616 €2432 Reformed church in Nagibanya (79x96cm-31x38in) s. 12-Apr-3 Mu Terem Galeria, Budapest #35/R est:450000 (H.F 600000)
£1935 $3018 €2806 Rest under the trees (77x91cm-30x36in) s.d.1927. 13-Sep-2 Mu Terem Galeria, Budapest #43/R est:550000 (H.F 750000)
£2017 $3126 €3026 Courtyard in Nagybanya (68x62cm-27x24in) s.verso. 6-Dec-2 Kieselbach, Budapest #102/R (H.F 750000)
£3511 $5617 €5267 Nude in the studio (43x56cm-17x22in) s. 16-May-3 Kieselbach, Budapest #72/R (H.F 1200000)
£4303 $6669 €6239 Sunlit street in Munich (60x76cm-24x30in) s.d.1910. 9-Dec-2 Mu Terem Galeria, Budapest #81/R est:1000000 (H.F 1600000)
Works on paper
£645 $1000 €968 Model (50x70cm-20x28in) s. pastel. 6-Dec-2 Kieselbach, Budapest #138/R (H.F 240000)

FEREY, E (19/20th C) French
£1541 $2434 €2312 Winter landscape with skaters and women in sleigh (64x52cm-25x20in) s. 16-Nov-2 Crafoord, Lund #30/R est:3000 (S.KR 22000)

FEREY, Edouard (19/20th C) French
£2000 $3340 €3000 Skating party (65x54cm-26x21in) s. 18-Jun-3 Christie's, Kensington #62/R est:2000-3000

FERG, Franz de Paula (1689-1740) Austrian
£2027 $3162 €3000 Boats and figures in seaport (14x11cm-6x4in) copper prov. 27-Mar-3 Dorotheum, Vienna #234/R est:1800-2500
£4839 $7646 €7500 Wooded landscape (18x23cm-7x9in) mono. copper prov. 18-Dec-2 Tajan, Paris #18/R
£5031 $7799 €8000 Bustling market square (40x46cm-16x18in) s. 2-Oct-2 Dorotheum, Vienna #209/R est:8000-12000

FERGOLA, Francesco (19th C) Italian
£750 $1193 €1125 View of the Bay of Naples (33x51cm-13x20in) i.d.1869 stretcher. 5-Mar-3 Bonhams, Bury St Edmunds #411
Works on paper
£2152 $3400 €3400 Panoramic view over the coast of Naples (37x56cm-15x22in) s.d.1838 gouache. 28-Nov-2 Dorotheum, Vienna #43/R est:3600-3800

FERGOLA, Salvatore (1799-1877) Italian
£6207 $9807 €9000 Capri (27x33cm-11x13in) 3-Apr-3 Porro, Milan #56/R est:12000

FERGOLA, Salvatore (attrib) (1799-1877) Italian
£9434 $14528 €15000 Vue de la Baie de Naples. Vue de la Cote Amalfitaine (55x88cm-22x35in) 25-Oct-2 Tajan, Paris #45/R est:15000-20000
Works on paper
£1300 $2119 €1950 Ischia e procida da miseno (28x40cm-11x16in) bears sigd.1821 gouache. 29-Jan-3 Sotheby's, Olympia #283/R est:800-1200

FERGUSON, Andrew (1959-) Australian
£1514 $2483 €2195 Cityscape (101x122cm-40x48in) s.i.d.85 verso. 4-Jun-3 Deutscher-Menzies, Melbourne #108/R est:1800-2400 (A.D 3800)

FERGUSON, Henry Augustus (1842-1911) American
£1424 $2250 €2136 In the Andes of Chile, South America (23x48cm-9x19in) s.i.verso canvas on board prov. 24-Apr-3 Shannon's, Milford #101/R est:2500-3500
£1923 $3000 €2885 Country landscape (38x69cm-15x27in) init.d.63. 30-Mar-3 Susanin's, Chicago #6125/R est:3000-4000

FERGUSON, James W (fl.1915-1940) British
Works on paper
£199 $322 €280 Figure and cattle watering in a mountain river landscape (22x34cm-9x13in) s. W/C. 21-May-3 James Adam, Dublin #57

FERGUSON, John Knox (fl.1880-1891) British
£360 $547 €540 Logger with horses in a wooded clearing (28x38cm-11x15in) mono. 16-Aug-2 Keys, Aylsham #727
£8228 $13000 €12342 Last interview (183x133cm-72x52in) s.d.1885. 23-Apr-3 Christie's, Rockefeller NY #89/R est:15000-20000

FERGUSON, Nancy Maybin (1872-1967) American
£1317 $2200 €1910 Landscape with houses (30x36cm-12x14in) board. 22-Jun-3 Freeman, Philadelphia #159/R est:1500-2500
£3548 $5500 €5322 Church, Provincetown (34x34cm-13x13in) mono. board prov. 8-Dec-2 Freeman, Philadelphia #174/R est:2000-3000

FERGUSON, Roy Young (1907-) British
Works on paper
£750 $1163 €1125 Valetta Harbour, Malta (38x73cm-15x29in) W/C htd white. 4-Dec-2 Christie's, Kensington #269

FERGUSON, Vivienne (1962-) Australian
£830 $1287 €1245 Dwelt (121x121cm-48x48in) s.verso acrylic prov. 3-Dec-2 Shapiro, Sydney #49/R (A.D 2300)

FERGUSON, W J (fl.1848-1886) British
£310 $496 €465 River scene with figure of fisherman in boat (51x51cm-20x20in) s. 10-Jan-3 Biddle & Webb, Birmingham #231

FERGUSON, William Gowe (1632-1695) British
£3041 $4743 €4500 Hunting still life (64x51cm-25x20in) 27-Mar-3 Dorotheum, Vienna #323/R est:5000-9000
£3145 $5000 €4718 Still life of birds on a marble ledge (63x76cm-25x30in) s.d.1661. 30-Apr-3 Sotheby's, New York #550/R est:4000-6000
£3503 $5465 €5500 Hunting still life of partridge, woodcock and other birds on a marble ledge (73x60cm-29x24in) 5-Nov-2 Sotheby's, Amsterdam #317/R est:6000-8000

FERGUSON, van Hood (1903-) ?
£1586 $2521 €2379 Figure composition (51x40cm-20x16in) s.d.41. 29-Apr-3 Kunsthallen, Copenhagen #199/R est:20000 (D.KR 17000)

FERGUSSON, John Duncan (1874-1961) British
£2200 $3344 €3300 Antibes (15x12cm-6x5in) board. 28-Aug-2 Sotheby's, London #1089/R est:1500-2000
£2700 $4185 €4050 Landscape study with cloud (10x12cm-4x5in) board. 6-Dec-2 Lyon & Turnbull, Edinburgh #43/R est:1000-1500
£3200 $4960 €4800 Forth near Edinburgh, Evening (14x12cm-6x5in) board exhib. 6-Dec-2 Lyon & Turnbull, Edinburgh #42/R est:2000-3000
£8800 $13464 €13200 Flower market (36x25cm-14x10in) prov. 22-Aug-2 Bonhams, Edinburgh #1116/R est:6000-8000
£15000 $23250 €22500 Le phare et la tour, near St Estephe (24x19cm-9x7in) panel painted c.1913-14 prov. 31-Oct-2 Christie's, London #134/R est:10000-15000
£15000 $23400 €22500 Near la canche, Piccardy (18x23cm-7x9in) panel. 14-Apr-3 Sotheby's, London #100/R est:7000-10000
£62000 $94240 €93000 Cassis through the trees (66x76cm-26x30in) s. prov. 28-Aug-2 Sotheby's, London #1087/R est:50000-70000
Works on paper
£300 $459 €450 Head of a negro (17x11cm-7x4in) conte. 22-Aug-2 Bonhams, Edinburgh #1021/R
£850 $1301 €1275 Waxed moustache (17x11cm-7x4in) conte. 22-Aug-2 Bonhams, Edinburgh #1018/R
£880 $1373 €1320 Study of a woman's head (24x19cm-9x7in) pencil. 10-Apr-3 Bonhams, Edinburgh #148
£1000 $1530 €1500 Head study of a girl (22x17cm-9x7in) pencil. 22-Aug-2 Bonhams, Edinburgh #1017/R est:1200-1800
£1000 $1530 €1500 Self portrait (14x8cm-6x3in) pencil. 22-Aug-2 Bonhams, Edinburgh #1023/R est:600-800
£1000 $1530 €1500 Head of a girl (19x15cm-7x6in) conte. 22-Aug-2 Bonhams, Edinburgh #1024/R est:1200-1800
£1200 $1836 €1800 Head, possibly Meg (19x15cm-7x6in) conte. 22-Aug-2 Bonhams, Edinburgh #1022/R est:1000-1500
£1200 $1872 €1800 Portrait of a lady (22x18cm-9x7in) pencil. 17-Sep-2 Sotheby's, Olympia #77/R est:1200-1500
£1400 $2142 €2100 Michelle (19x6cm-7x2in) conte W/C. 22-Aug-2 Bonhams, Edinburgh #1020/R est:1200-1800
£1400 $2128 €2100 Margaret Peploe and son Willie, Cassis 1913. Willie Peploe, aged 2, Cassis (20x15cm-8x6in) one pencil one pen ink prov. 28-Aug-2 Sotheby's, London #1084/R est:1000-1500
£1400 $2170 €2100 Nude lying on a balcony (34x26cm-13x10in) black crayon prov. 31-Oct-2 Christie's, London #140/R est:1500-2000
£1500 $2325 €2250 Nude seated on a balcony (34x26cm-13x10in) black crayon prov. 31-Oct-2 Christie's, London #141/R est:1500-2000
£1500 $2460 €2250 Head studies (17x22cm-7x9in) pencil. 3-Jun-3 Sotheby's, Olympia #6/R est:1500-2000
£1600 $2448 €2400 Miss B in profile (16x20cm-6x8in) conte. 22-Aug-2 Bonhams, Edinburgh #1019/R est:800-1200
£1600 $2480 €2400 Anne Estelle Rice on a balcony, Paris (34x26cm-13x10in) black crayon prov. 31-Oct-2 Christie's, London #143/R est:1500-2000
£1700 $2601 €2550 Head study of Margaret Morris (22x16cm-9x6in) pencil. 22-Aug-2 Bonhams, Edinburgh #1025/R est:1500-2000
£1900 $2945 €2850 Evening dress (34x26cm-13x10in) black crayon prov. 31-Oct-2 Christie's, London #136/R est:1500-2000
£2200 $3410 €3300 Engine room. Loading cannon (16x21cm-6x8in) black crayon two in one frame prov. 31-Oct-2 Christie's, London #146/R est:1500-2000
£2400 $3744 €3600 Parisian faces. Salle d'attente, gare du nord. Porteurs a la gare du nord (8x6cm-3x2in) pencil set of three. 14-Apr-3 Sotheby's, London #103/R est:2000-3000
£2600 $3952 €3900 Cassis from the west, 1913. Le jardin du Luxembourg, Paris (19x15cm-7x6in) pencil two prov. 28-Aug-2 Sotheby's, London #1085/R est:1000-1500
£3000 $4650 €4500 Margaret Morris (25x20cm-10x8in) pencil prov. 31-Oct-2 Christie's, London #139/R est:2000-3000
£3000 $4650 €4500 Nudes embracing (26x16cm-10x6in) black crayon sold with brass maquette prov. 31-Oct-2 Christie's, London #147/R est:3000-5000
£3000 $4680 €4500 Waiting. City or country. Waiting (21x16cm-8x6in) pencil set of three. 14-Apr-3 Sotheby's, London #104/R est:1000-1500
£3200 $4960 €4800 Submarines (16x21cm-6x8in) pastel prov. 31-Oct-2 Christie's, London #144/R est:2000-3000
£3200 $4960 €4800 Submarines. Monitor class (16x22cm-6x9in) black crayon two in one frame prov. 31-Oct-2 Christie's, London #145/R est:1500-2000
£3500 $5320 €5250 Samuel and Margaret Peploe, Paris. Mrs Margaret Peploe Cassis (20x15cm-8x6in) one chl one pencil pair prov. 28-Aug-2 Sotheby's, London #1082/R est:1500-2000

£3800 $5776 €5700 Dans les jardins du Luxembourg, Paris. Nurse, dan le jardin du Luxembourg (20x11cm-8x4in) chl pencil set of four prov. 28-Aug-2 Sotheby's, London #1086/R est:2000-3000
£3800 $5928 €5700 Two men about town. Playing diabalo in the Luxembourg gardens. Three midinettes (21x16cm-8x6in) pencil set of three. 14-Apr-3 Sotheby's, London #105/R est:1500-2000
£4000 $6240 €6000 Keeping up with the news. Two suitors. Chaperone (21x16cm-8x6in) pencil set of three. 14-Apr-3 Sotheby's, London #101/R est:2000-3000
£4000 $6240 €6000 Rendez-vous on the boulevard. Corner of Boulevard Edgar Quinet, Montparnasse (21x16cm-8x6in) pencil set of three. 14-Apr-3 Sotheby's, London #102/R est:1500-2000
£4200 $6384 €6300 Tennis game, Royan. Une partie de tennis Royan (11x14cm-4x6in) chl two prov. 28-Aug-2 Sotheby's, London #1088/R est:1000-1500
£4200 $6384 €6300 Ann Estelle Rice, the artist great friend, Paris. Portrait of the artist sketching, Paris (19x12cm-7x5in) chl two prov. 28-Aug-2 Sotheby's, London #1083/R est:1200-1800
£4200 $6510 €6300 Three bathers (25x21cm-10x8in) W/C exhib. 6-Dec-2 Lyon & Turnbull, Edinburgh #84/R est:1200-1500
£4500 $6975 €6750 Nude (27x12cm-11x5in) black crayon W/C exhib. 31-Oct-2 Christie's, London #135/R est:4000-6000
£5500 $8525 €8250 Seated nude (34x26cm-13x10in) black crayon prov. 31-Oct-2 Christie's, London #142/R est:1500-2000

FERMARIELLO, Sergio (1961-) Italian
£2027 $3162 €3000 Warriors (60x60cm-24x24in) s.i.verso. 26-Mar-3 Finarte Semenzato, Milan #170
£2405 $3800 €3800 Warriors (100x100cm-39x39in) s.d.2001 verso acrylic. 29-Nov-2 Farsetti, Prato #255/R

FERMEUS, Victor (1894-1963) Belgian
£540 $863 €750 La sauleraie (40x50cm-16x20in) s.d.1933. 19-May-3 Horta, Bruxelles #459
£612 $978 €850 Les ramasseurs de coquillages (50x60cm-20x24in) s. 13-May-3 Galerie Moderne, Brussels #346

FERMIER, Jacques (?) ?
£382 $600 €573 American full-rigged ship (61x91cm-24x36in) s. 26-Jul-2 Eldred, East Dennis #375/R

FERN, Harry (19/20th C) British?
Works on paper
£340 $538 €510 The Temple of Karnak (29x47cm-11x19in) mono. W/C. 2-Dec-2 Rasmussen, Copenhagen #1842/R (D.KR 4000)

FERNAND-RENAULT, Albert (20th C) French
£1250 $2037 €1800 Rue du port a Douarnenez (65x81cm-26x32in) s. 19-Jul-3 Thierry & Lannon, Brest #126/R est:1800-2000

FERNAND-TROCHAIN, Jean (1879-1969) French
£446 $696 €700 Eglise sous la neige (42x31cm-17x12in) s. cardboard. 7-Nov-2 Chochon-Barre & Allardi, Paris #144
£833 $1358 €1200 Doelan (46x54cm-18x21in) s. 19-Jul-3 Thierry & Lannon, Brest #127/R

FERNANDEZ GONZALEZ, Armando (1912-) Spanish
£274 $433 €425 Galaxy (25x20cm-10x8in) s. 17-Dec-2 Durán, Madrid #13/R

FERNANDEZ GRANELL, Eugenio (20th C) Spanish
Works on paper
£881 $1374 €1400 Two figures (35x25cm-14x10in) s.d.1991 W/C. 17-Sep-2 Segre, Madrid #193/R

FERNANDEZ LACOMBA, Juan (1954-) Spanish
£962 $1519 €1500 Confusion (26x35cm-10x14in) s.i.d.1994 verso oil encaustic board. 14-Nov-2 Arte, Seville #438/R

FERNANDEZ LOPEZ, R (?) Spanish
£755 $1177 €1200 Painter's study (35x45cm-14x18in) s. 23-Sep-2 Durán, Madrid #167/R

FERNANDEZ MARTIN, Trinidad (1937-) Spanish
£609 $962 €950 Landscape with houses (33x41cm-13x16in) s. s.d.1961 verso. 13-Nov-2 Ansorena, Madrid #271
£641 $1013 €1000 Landscape (60x73cm-24x29in) s.d.1960 verso. 13-Nov-2 Ansorena, Madrid #272/R
£753 $1175 €1100 Asturian landscape (61x85cm-24x33in) s. s.i.d.1991 verso. 8-Apr-3 Ansorena, Madrid #31/R
£1351 $2108 €2000 View of Luarca (73x92cm-29x36in) s. s.i.d.1961 verso. 25-Mar-3 Durán, Madrid #174

FERNANDEZ SANCHEZ, Jose (1913-) Spanish
£4054 $6324 €6000 Extravagance (131x197cm-52x78in) s. exhib. 25-Mar-3 Durán, Madrid #194/R est:5000

FERNANDEZ Y GONZALEZ, Domingo (1862-c.1918) Spanish
£818 $1275 €1300 Cathedral interior (27x16cm-11x6in) s. board. 23-Sep-2 Durán, Madrid #133/R
Works on paper
£369 $594 €550 Building (48x34cm-19x13in) s. wash. 18-Feb-3 Durán, Madrid #119/R

FERNANDEZ, Amneris (1950-) Canadian
£391 $610 €653 Untitled - timber wolves (41x51cm-16x20in) s. 13-Apr-3 Levis, Calgary #33/R est:1200-1500 (C.D 900)
£703 $1110 €1055 Almost home (76x102cm-30x40in) acrylic. 1-Dec-2 Levis, Calgary #27/R est:2000-2500 (C.D 1750)

FERNANDEZ, Augustin (1928-) Cuban
£4140 $6500 €6210 Still life of fruit (96x122cm-38x48in) s. prov. 20-Nov-2 Christie's, Rockefeller NY #112/R
£8280 $13000 €12420 Seated woman (10x95cm-4x37in) s. painted c.1950. 20-Nov-2 Christie's, Rockefeller NY #110/R est:8000-10000

FERNANDEZ, Guillermo (1928-) Uruguayan
£406 $650 €609 Building (101x84cm-40x33in) s, d.66 verso cardboard. 5-Jan-3 Galleria Y Remates, Montevideo #105/R

FERNANDEZ, Jose (18/19th C) ?
£13000 $20410 €19500 Mercado - market place (60x100cm-24x39in) s. 19-Nov-2 Sotheby's, London #75/R est:6000-8000

FERNANDEZ, Louis (1900-1973) French
£44521 $69897 €65000 Paysage (12x22cm-5x9in) s. i.verso panel prov.exhib.lit. 15-Apr-3 Laurence Calmels, Paris #4279/R est:15000

FERNANDEZ, Mariusa (20th C) Brazilian
£400 $648 €600 Composition with religious figure (30x37cm-12x15in) s. s.d.1943 verso tempera exhib. 20-May-3 Bonhams, Knightsbridge #130/R

FERNANDEZ, Trinidad (1937-) Spanish
£779 $1138 €1200 Landscape (80x100cm-31x39in) s. s.i.d.1960 verso. 17-Jun-2 Ansorena, Madrid #145/R

FERNELEY, John (jnr) (1815-1862) British
£5800 $9628 €8700 Soldiers and officers of the 1st Dragoon Guards (24x29cm-9x11in) pair. 12-Jun-3 Sotheby's, London #101/R est:5000-7000

FERNELEY, John (jnr-attrib) (1815-1862) British
£1050 $1670 €1575 Bay hunter in an open landscape (40x57cm-16x22in) indis sig.d.1877. 29-Apr-3 Sworder & Son, Bishops Stortford #343/R est:400-600

FERNELEY, John (snr) (1781-1860) British
£2200 $3476 €3300 Portrait of a gentleman (37x29cm-15x11in) s. 28-Nov-2 Sotheby's, London #196/R est:1500-2000
£6000 $9960 €8700 Bay hunter and a dog outside a stable (70x90cm-28x35in) with sig.d.1814 prov. 12-Jun-3 Christie's, Kensington #37/R est:7000-10000
£6329 $10000 €9494 Horse in a landscape (51x69cm-20x27in) 15-Nov-2 Du Mouchelle, Detroit #2053/R est:10000-15000
£18000 $28440 €27000 Gentleman with bay hunter outside stable (70x91cm-28x36in) s.d.1807 prov. 27-Nov-2 Christie's, London #17/R est:20000-30000

FERNELEY, John (snr-attrib) (1781-1860) British
£2778 $4000 €4167 Bay hunter (61x75cm-24x30in) 15-Jan-3 Christie's, Rockefeller NY #155/R est:8000

FERNHOUT, Edgar (1912-1976) Dutch
£3205 $4968 €5000 Bloemen - still life with flowers (40x31cm-16x12in) s.d.46 panel prov.lit. 3-Dec-2 Christie's, Amsterdam #5/R est:4000-6000
£4430 $7000 €7000 Bloemen (40x45cm-16x18in) s.d.48 s.i.d.verso panel lit. 26-Nov-2 Sotheby's, Amsterdam #126/R est:4500-5500

FERNIER, Robert (1895-1977) French
£306 $477 €459 Le Doubs a la Fouconniere pres Pontarlier (11x18cm-4x7in) s.d.1921 i. verso board. 6-Nov-2 Dobiaschofsky, Bern #508/R (S.FR 700)
£786 $1242 €1179 Fermes jurassiens (38x55cm-15x22in) s. i.verso. 17-Nov-2 Koller, Geneva #1304 (S.FR 1800)
£1169 $1906 €1754 Maree descendante, Moroni, mai 1954 (50x61cm-20x24in) s. panel. 12-Feb-3 Iegor de Saint Hippolyte, Montreal #73 (C.D 2900)
£1204 $1938 €1806 Paysage a Betafo (33x41cm-13x16in) s. i.d.1953 verso panel. 7-May-3 Dobiaschofsky, Bern #504/R est:2600 (S.FR 2600)

FEROGIO, F (19th C) French
Works on paper
£2264 $3532 €3600 Projet de sarcophage (48x64cm-19x25in) i. pe ink wash. 8-Oct-2 Christie's, Paris #11/R
£2642 $4121 €4200 Projet de citadelle (48x62cm-19x24in) s.i. pen ink wash. 8-Oct-2 Christie's, Paris #8/R
£2893 $4513 €4600 Projet (50x73cm-20x29in) pen ink wash. 8-Oct-2 Christie's, Paris #10/R
£3145 $4906 €5000 Projet (52x70cm-20x28in) s. pen ink wash. 8-Oct-2 Christie's, Paris #9/R

FERON, William (1858-1894) Swedish
£3546 $5496 €5319 At the garden plot (57x81cm-22x32in) s. 3-Dec-2 Bukowskis, Stockholm #36/R est:40000-50000 (S.KR 50000)

FERRAGUTI, Arnaldo (1862-1925) Italian
Works on paper
£503 $775 €800 Olive tree by the sea (23x34cm-9x13in) s. mixed media. 28-Oct-2 Il Ponte, Milan #290
£503 $775 €800 Cherry trees in bloom (24x34cm-9x13in) s. mixed media. 28-Oct-2 Il Ponte, Milan #292
£2516 $3874 €4000 Bather (47x35cm-19x14in) mixed media. 28-Oct-2 Il Ponte, Milan #283/R

FERRAN, Brian (1940-) British
£962 $1510 €1500 Mad Sweeney II (61x41cm-24x16in) s.d.1967 i.verso acrylic board. 19-Nov-2 Whyte's, Dublin #46/R est:1500-2500
£2148 $3458 €3200 Tain painting 30 (61x61cm-24x24in) s.d.1998 acrylic gold leaf. 18-Feb-3 Whyte's, Dublin #35/R est:2000-3000

FERRAND, Ernest Justin (1846-?) French
Sculpture
£1300 $2015 €1950 Fisher boy with spear (75cm-30in) s. golden brown pat bronze circular base. 29-Oct-2 Bonhams, New Bond Street #168/R est:1200-1800

FERRAND, Jean Pierre (1902-1983) French
£307 $476 €461 River landscape (33x41cm-13x16in) s. board. 24-Sep-2 Maynards, Vancouver #374 (C.D 750)

FERRANT Y FISCHERMANS, Alejandro (1843-1917) Spanish
Works on paper
£1538 $2431 €2400 Afternoon nap (21x27cm-8x11in) s.d.1888 W/C. 13-Nov-2 Ansorena, Madrid #189/R

FERRANT Y LLAUSAS, Luis (1806-1868) Spanish
£1800 $2898 €2700 Christ's charge to Peter (67x84cm-26x33in) i. after Poussin. 20-Feb-3 Christie's, Kensington #308/R est:2000-3000

FERRANT, Angel (1891-1961) Spanish
Works on paper
£1039 $1517 €1600 Study for sculpture (21x17cm-8x7in) s.d.55 ink dr. 17-Jun-2 Ansorena, Madrid #20/R

FERRANTE, Mario de (1898-1992) Italian
£472 $750 €708 Abstraction (51x61cm-20x24in) s. painted c.1960. 4-May-3 Treadway Gallery, Cincinnati #637/R
£472 $750 €708 Abstraction (76x102cm-30x40in) s. painted c.1960. 4-May-3 Treadway Gallery, Cincinnati #639/R
£566 $900 €849 Abstraction (102x76cm-40x30in) s. painted c.1960. 4-May-3 Treadway Gallery, Cincinnati #636/R
£943 $1500 €1415 Abstract (71x56cm-28x22in) s. painted c.1960. 4-May-3 Treadway Gallery, Cincinnati #635/R est:1000-2000
£1039 $1600 €1559 Abstracted figures (56x71cm-22x28in) s. painted c.1940. 8-Sep-2 Treadway Gallery, Cincinnati #737/R est:1500-2000
£1097 $1700 €1646 Abstract composition (76x102cm-30x40in) s. painted c.1960. 8-Dec-2 Toomey, Oak Park #838/R est:2000-3000
£1097 $1700 €1646 Abstract composition (76x102cm-30x40in) s. painted c.1960. 8-Dec-2 Toomey, Oak Park #840/R est:2000-3000
£1161 $1800 €1742 Abstract composition (76x102cm-30x40in) s. painted c.1960. 8-Dec-2 Toomey, Oak Park #839/R est:2000-3000

FERRANTI, Carlo (19th C) Italian
£2656 $4250 €3984 Venetian scene with elegant figures boarding a gondola (56x41cm-22x16in) s.i. 14-May-3 Butterfields, San Francisco #1048/R est:4000-6000

FERRARA (?) Italian
£6438 $9979 €9657 Madonna with child (58x39cm-23x15in) panel prov.exhib. 3-Oct-2 Koller, Zurich #3007/R est:15000-22000 (S.FR 15000)
£14163 $21953 €21245 Peter on a throne (160x91cm-63x36in) panel. 3-Oct-2 Koller, Zurich #3012/R est:15000-20000 (S.FR 33000)

FERRARA, Joe (20th C) American
£2848 $4500 €4130 Time out cowboys (56x79cm-22x31in) s. sold with Marie Conway, wood duck. 26-Jul-3 Coeur d'Alene, Hayden #12/R est:4000-6000

FERRARESE SCHOOL (16th C) Italian
£8966 $14166 €13000 Nativity (72x56cm-28x22in) board. 5-Apr-3 Finarte Semenzato, Milan #9/R est:9000

FERRARI, Antoine (1910-1996) French
£440 $682 €700 Paysage du Midi (60x80cm-24x31in) s. 30-Oct-2 Coutau Begarie, Paris #161
£566 $877 €900 Nature morte au compotier (54x64cm-21x25in) s. masonite. 30-Oct-2 Coutau Begarie, Paris #162/R

FERRARI, Arturo (1861-1932) Italian
£506 $790 €800 Tuscan landscape with bridge (30x20cm-12x8in) s. board. 20-Oct-2 Semenzato, Venice #778/R
Works on paper
£321 $503 €500 View of chapel (52x35cm-20x14in) s. W/C. 16-Dec-2 Pandolfini, Florence #12

FERRARI, Berto (1887-1965) Italian
£609 $944 €950 Landscape (50x35cm-20x14in) s.d.16. 5-Dec-2 Stadion, Trieste #859/R
£699 $1090 €1049 Southern Italian coast (29x39cm-11x15in) s.d.23.II.950 board. 6-Nov-2 Dobiaschofsky, Bern #3323 (S.FR 1600)

FERRARI, Ettore (1849-1929) Italian
Sculpture
£3839 $5643 €5950 Gypsum (72cm-28in) s.d. bronze. 24-Jun-2 Babuino, Rome #338 est:2000-3000

FERRARI, Giovanni Andrea de (1598-1669) Italian
£13605 $21633 €20000 Joseph and the lady from Putiphar (107x144cm-42x57in) 28-Feb-3 Joron-Derem, Paris #18/R
Works on paper
£1892 $2951 €2800 Bapteme du CHrist (31x21cm-12x8in) chk. 27-Mar-3 Christie's, Paris #15/R

FERRARI, Giovanni Battista (1829-1906) Italian
£510 $811 €750 Fermiere et sa vache a l'abreuvoir (34x48cm-13x19in) s.d.1903. 18-Mar-3 Vanderkindere, Brussels #32
£2448 $4087 €3500 Vue d'Isola Bella (17x33cm-7x13in) s.d.1880 panel. 25-Jun-3 Artcurial Briest, Paris #543 est:1500-2000
£5417 $8558 €7800 Cueillette du mais et porteur de fagots (56x86cm-22x34in) s. 25-Apr-3 Piasa, Paris #92/R est:3000

FERRARI, Lorenzo de (1680-1744) Italian
Works on paper
£5405 $8432 €8000 Reclining man (41x55cm-16x22in) chk prov. 27-Mar-3 Christie's, Paris #17/R
£8108 $12649 €12000 Young man (61x33cm-24x13in) chk prov. 27-Mar-3 Christie's, Paris #18/R

FERRARI, Luca (1605-1654) Italian
£90000 $141300 €135000 Agamemnon refusing to allow Chryses to ransom his daughter Chryseis (130x141cm-51x56in) s. prov.exhib.lit. 11-Dec-2 Christie's, London #113/R est:100000-150000

FERRARI, Orazio de (circle) (1605-1657) Italian
£13174 $22000 €19102 Supper at Emmaus (63x86cm-25x34in) 22-Jun-3 Freeman, Philadelphia #3/R est:2000-3000

FERRARI, Teodoro Wolf (1876-1945) Italian
£1361 $2163 €2000 Wood (25x42cm-10x17in) s.d.1906 board. 18-Mar-3 Finarte, Milan #7/R
£1905 $3029 €2800 Mountainous landscape with houses (24x41cm-9x16in) s.d.1906 board. 18-Mar-3 Finarte, Milan #8/R

FERRARIO, Carlo (1833-1907) Italian
£680 $1082 €1000 Sunset at the seaside (29x40cm-11x16in) init. cardboard. 1-Mar-3 Meeting Art, Vercelli #161

FERRAT, H (19th C) French
Sculpture
£2431 $3500 €3647 Water carriers (57cm-22in) bronze pair. 15-Jan-3 Christie's, Rockefeller NY #251/R

FERRATO, Georges (20th C) ?
£517 $864 €750 Les anges inconnus II (130x162cm-51x64in) s.i.verso prov. 9-Jul-3 Cornette de St.Cyr, Paris #281

FERRAZZI, Benvenuto (1892-1969) Italian
£1795 $2818 €2800 First lights on the bridge (85x84cm-33x33in) s. painted c.1930. 21-Nov-2 Finarte, Rome #254/R

FERREN, John (1905-1970) American
£705 $1100 €1058 Untitled (67x76cm-26x30in) s.d.1950 prov. 5-Nov-2 Doyle, New York #38/R
£1146 $1800 €1719 Untitled (31x36cm-12x14in) s.d. 19-Nov-2 Wright, Chicago #201/R est:2500-3500

FERRER, J (20th C) ?
£613 $968 €950 Figures on the beach (31x47cm-12x19in) s. cardboard. 18-Dec-2 Ansorena, Madrid #42

FERRERS, Benjamin (?-1732) British
£4000 $6520 €5800 Portrait of a Lady (127x101cm-50x40in) s. 21-Jul-3 Sotheby's, London #3/R est:3000-5000

FERRERS, Benjamin (attrib) (?-1732) British
£9500 $15485 €13775 Portrait of Richard Clarke of Hill Court, Herefordshire (236x150cm-93x59in) prov. 21-Jul-3 Sotheby's, London #169/R est:6000-8000

FERRETTI, Gian Domenico (attrib) (1692-1766) Italian
£1703 $2844 €2400 Jeune femme tenant un masque (89x72cm-35x28in) 18-Jun-3 Tajan, Paris #11/R est:3000-4000

FERRETTINI ROSSOTTI, Emilia (1866-1951) Italian
£323 $510 €500 Landscape (31x44cm-12x17in) s. board. 18-Dec-2 Finarte, Milan #225
£645 $1019 €1000 Landscape with figures (30x44cm-12x17in) s. board. 18-Dec-2 Finarte, Milan #230

FERRI, Ciro (1634-1689) Italian
£9459 $14757 €14000 The Guardian Angel (76x49cm-30x19in) prov. 27-Mar-3 Dorotheum, Vienna #55/R est:7000-9000
£23490 $37819 €35000 Cleopatra (80x67cm-31x26in) 19-Feb-3 Semenzato, Venice #33/R est:40000
Works on paper
£769 $1100 €1154 Apollo and two mythological figures seated in the clouds (20x36cm-8x14in) pencil htd white. 23-Jan-3 Swann Galleries, New York #87/R est:2000-3000

FERRIER, Dick (1929-) Canadian
£1229 $1954 €1844 Near Golden, BC (45x60cm-18x24in) s.d.1982 acrylic on board. 23-Mar-3 Hodgins, Calgary #64/R est:500-800 (C.D 2900)
£1378 $2260 €1998 Grain elevators, Alberta (100x148cm-39x58in) s.i. acrylic. 9-Jun-3 Hodgins, Calgary #12/R est:2000-3000 (C.D 3100)

FERRIER, James (fl.1843-1883) British
Works on paper
£300 $462 €450 Scottish highland landscape with mountains and a lake (33x48cm-13x19in) W/C. 24-Oct-2 Grant, Worcester #283

FERRIERE, Francis (1752-1839) Swiss
Miniatures
£1250 $1938 €1875 Thomas Sandy R A (8cm-3xin) init.d.1794 i.verso gilt mount rec. papier mache frame oval prov. 1-Oct-2 Bonhams, New Bond Street #284/R est:800-1200
£1500 $2400 €2175 Portrait of a blond lady (5x3cm-2x1in) s. 17-May-3 New Orleans Auction, New Orleans #26/R est:2500-4000
£2000 $3100 €3000 Lady Elizabeth and Lady Caroline Montagu Scott (7cm-3xin) one s.d.1794 gilt metal mount oval pair prov.exhib. 1-Oct-2 Bonhams, New Bond Street #112/R est:800-1200

FERRINI, Alberto (?) Italian
£2200 $3432 €3300 Palazzo Ducale e Campanile Venezia (50x76cm-20x30in) s. s.i.verso. 10-Sep-2 Bonhams, Knightsbridge #62/R est:1200-1800

FERRIS, C W (20th C) British
£1731 $2735 €2700 Fishing boats in rough seas (28x45cm-11x18in) s. pair. 12-Nov-2 Mealy's, Castlecomer #1039/R

FERRO, Sergio (20th C) ?
£377 $585 €600 Variation sur theme divin (60x45cm-24x18in) s. paper. 7-Oct-2 Claude Aguttes, Neuilly #281

FERRO-LA-GREE, Georges (1941-) French
£764 $1192 €1200 Verger pres du village (46x55cm-18x22in) s. 10-Nov-2 Eric Pillon, Calais #5/R

FERRON, Marcelle (1924-2001) Canadian
£574 $895 €861 Toujours toujours (20x25cm-8x10in) s. acrylic panel. 10-Sep-2 Iegor de Saint Hippolyte, Montreal #46 (C.D 1400)
£2263 $3508 €3395 Painting (49x60cm-19x24in) s.d.61 canvas on board prov. 3-Dec-2 Joyner, Toronto #299/R est:1500-2000 (C.D 5500)
Works on paper
£386 $603 €579 Untitled (46x29cm-18x11in) s. gouache. 25-Mar-3 Iegor de Saint Hippolyte, Montreal #50 (C.D 900)
£614 $915 €921 L'inconnue no 5 (47x38cm-19x15in) s.d.78 i.verso mixed media panel. 26-Jun-2 Iegor de Saint Hippolyte, Montreal #36/R (C.D 1400)

FERRONI, Egisto (1835-1912) Italian
£600 $948 €900 Girl with a guitar (81x33cm-32x13in) s. 7-Apr-3 Bonhams, Bath #131/R
£1100 $1694 €1650 Poetry of the love by the fountain (81x50cm-32x20in) s. 24-Oct-2 Christie's, Kensington #171/R est:1000-1500
£1852 $2981 €2778 Florentine woman (92x47cm-36x19in) s. 7-May-3 Dobiaschofsky, Bern #505/R est:6000 (S.FR 4000)
£1900 $3097 €2755 Girl with guitar (82x35cm-32x14in) s. 16-Jul-3 Sotheby's, Olympia #200/R est:800-1200
£11392 $18000 €18000 Here is dad! (181x90cm-71x35in) s. 26-Nov-2 Christie's, Rome #176/R est:20000-25000

FERRONI, Gianfranco (1927-2001) Italian
£1835 $2863 €2900 Marcinelle (100x65cm-39x26in) s.d.1965. 14-Sep-2 Meeting Art, Vercelli #919
£2308 $3623 €3600 Self-portrait (40x29cm-16x11in) s.d.1956. 19-Nov-2 Finarte, Milan #144/R
£3378 $5270 €5000 Still life (60x92cm-24x36in) s. 26-Mar-3 Finarte Semenzato, Milan #338/R
£5068 $7905 €7500 Landscape with fire (38x38cm-15x15in) s.d.65. 26-Mar-3 Finarte Semenzato, Milan #344/R
£8013 $12580 €12500 Vegetation in landscape (110x110cm-43x43in) s.d.66 exhib. 19-Nov-2 Finarte, Milan #172/R est:20000-26000
£8974 $14090 €14000 Objects and skull (56x84cm-22x33in) s.d.1966. 19-Nov-2 Finarte, Milan #232/R est:18000-24000
Works on paper
£1282 $1872 €2000 Childhood (33x48cm-13x19in) s.d.49 Chinese ink. 5-Jun-2 Il Ponte, Milan #47/R
£1351 $2108 €2000 Table with objects at night (17x25cm-7x10in) s.d.61 mixed media. 26-Mar-3 Finarte Semenzato, Milan #390/R
£1538 $2415 €2400 Lake landscape (19x23cm-7x9in) s.d.63 mixed media. 19-Nov-2 Finarte, Milan #166/R
£1689 $2635 €2500 Study of objects (36x48cm-14x19in) s.d.64 Chinese ink. 26-Mar-3 Finarte Semenzato, Milan #273/R
£1757 $2741 €2600 Spring in the lab (18x27cm-7x11in) s.d.62 mixed media. 26-Mar-3 Finarte Semenzato, Milan #274/R

FERRONI, Guido (1888-1979) Italian
£473 $738 €700 Red wall (49x35cm-19x14in) s. cardboard. 28-Mar-3 Farsetti, Prato #766/R

FERRUCCI, Romolo (?-1621) Italian
Sculpture
£10323 $16310 €16000 Dog (102x60x34cm-40x24x13in) stone. 19-Dec-2 Semenzato, Venice #11/R est:25000

FERY, A (19th C) French
Sculpture
£1400 $2240 €2100 Maiden semi nude (35cm-14in) s. bronze. 15-May-3 Christie's, Kensington #381/R est:600-800

FERY, John (1859-1934) American/Hungarian

£4167 $6500 €6251 Moose in a winter landscape (30x46cm-12x18in) s. 19-Oct-2 Harvey Clar, Oakland #1598
£4808 $7500 €7212 Moose by a mountain (107x84cm-42x33in) s. 19-Oct-2 Harvey Clar, Oakland #1597
£5380 $8500 €7801 St. Mary lake (25x41cm-10x16in) s. 26-Jul-3 Coeur d'Alene, Hayden #232/R est:3000-5000
£6410 $10000 €9615 Mountain Lake. 21-Sep-2 Harvey Clar, Oakland #1503
£8974 $14000 €13461 Lake Tahoe. 21-Sep-2 Harvey Clar, Oakland #1502

FESCH, Jean Louis (1738-1773) French
Works on paper
£2452 $3874 €3800 Mithridate (8x6cm-3x2in) gouache. 18-Dec-2 Beaussant & Lefèvre, Paris #31

FESEL, Christoph (attrib) (1737-1805) German
£345 $548 €500 Holy Family (64x48cm-25x19in) panel. 8-Mar-3 Arnold, Frankfurt #583/R

FESER, Albert (1901-1993) German
£617 $901 €950 Boat jetty on the Elbe (20x37cm-8x15in) s. board. 15-Jun-2 Hans Stahl, Hamburg #170/R
£769 $1192 €1200 Blankensee (35x50cm-14x20in) s. 7-Dec-2 Ketterer, Hamburg #349/R
£769 $1192 €1200 The Elbe (34x46cm-13x18in) d.57 bears i. 7-Dec-2 Ketterer, Hamburg #350/R

FESSLER, Albert (1908-) German
£270 $422 €400 Summer flowers (76x66cm-30x26in) s. 26-Mar-3 Hugo Ruef, Munich #295

FESTA, Bianca (19th C) Italian
Miniatures
£1300 $2002 €1950 Princess Chigi, nee Aldobrandini (13cm-5xin) s.d.1831 gilt metal frame rec. 24-Oct-2 Sotheby's, Olympia #94/R est:1000-1500

FESTA, Tano (1938-1988) Italian
£1176 $1882 €1800 Confetti (60x60cm-24x24in) s.d.1982 acrylic confetti. 4-Jan-3 Meeting Art, Vercelli #400
£1233 $1838 €1850 Figure (60x60cm-24x24in) s.d.81 verso acrylic. 25-Jun-2 Koller, Zurich #6048/R est:3000-5000 (S.FR 2800)
£1277 $2068 €1800 Natura morta (54x65cm-21x26in) s.d.86 verso acrylic prov. 26-May-3 Christie's, Milan #86 est:2000-2500
£1389 $2208 €2000 For J Pollock (60x80cm-24x31in) s.i.verso acrylic. 1-May-3 Meeting Art, Vercelli #168
£1438 $2301 €2200 Renoir (100x80cm-39x31in) s.d.1981 acrylic. 4-Jan-3 Meeting Art, Vercelli #374
£1479 $2455 €2100 Persiana e still ife (80x60cm-31x24in) s.verso acrylic painted 1985/86. 10-Jun-3 Finarte Semenzato, Milan #268/R est:3000-3500
£1486 $2319 €2200 After Michelangelo (46x39cm-18x15in) s.d.78 verso acrylic. 28-Mar-3 Farsetti, Prato #50/R
£1633 $2596 €2400 Untitled (70x90cm-28x35in) s.verso acrylic lit. 1-Mar-3 Meeting Art, Vercelli #601
£1644 $2564 €2400 Angels series (70x50cm-28x20in) s.d.1981 verso. 10-Apr-3 Finarte Semenzato, Rome #231/R
£1709 $2666 €2700 Blind (100x80cm-39x31in) s.verso enamel. 14-Sep-2 Meeting Art, Vercelli #804/R
£1736 $2760 €2500 Untitled (70x50cm-28x20in) s.verso acrylic painted 1986. 1-May-3 Meeting Art, Vercelli #43
£1757 $2741 €2600 After Michelangelo (55x35cm-22x14in) s.verso acrylic. 26-Mar-3 Finarte Semenzato, Milan #401/R
£1795 $2818 €2800 After Michelangelo (59x40cm-23x16in) s.d.1978 acrylic. 19-Nov-2 Finarte, Milan #85/R
£1830 $2928 €2800 Untitled (45x55cm-18x22in) s.verso acrylic. 4-Jan-3 Meeting Art, Vercelli #664
£1918 $2992 €2800 Confetti (120x70cm-47x28in) s.verso acrylic confetti. 10-Apr-3 Finarte Semenzato, Rome #296/R
£1923 $3019 €3000 Untitled (80x100cm-31x39in) s.verso acrylic. 19-Nov-2 Finarte, Milan #125/R
£2014 $3202 €2900 Untitled (70x50cm-28x20in) s.d.1981 acrylic. 1-May-3 Meeting Art, Vercelli #179
£2025 $3159 €3200 Landscape (70x90cm-28x35in) s.verso acrylic painted 1985. 14-Sep-2 Meeting Art, Vercelli #370/R
£2115 $3321 €3300 Confetti (120x70cm-47x28in) s. acrylic. 19-Nov-2 Finarte, Milan #280/R
£2215 $3500 €3500 Confetti (100x70cm-39x28in) s.i.verso acrylic confetti painted 1981. 29-Nov-2 Farsetti, Prato #277/R
£2260 $3526 €3300 Piazza del Popolo (60x80cm-24x31in) s.d.86 verso acrylic. 10-Apr-3 Finarte Semenzato, Rome #181/R
£2329 $3633 €3400 Teams and clouds (80x60cm-31x24in) s.verso acrylic. 10-Apr-3 Finarte Semenzato, Rome #196/R
£2329 $3633 €3400 Duke of Wellington (100x90cm-39x35in) s.verso. 10-Apr-3 Finarte Semenzato, Rome #229/R
£2500 $3975 €3600 Untitled (70x90cm-28x35in) s.verso acrylic. 1-May-3 Meeting Art, Vercelli #465
£2517 $4002 €3700 Don Quixote (70x100cm-28x39in) s.verso acrylic. 1-Mar-3 Meeting Art, Vercelli #634
£2564 $4026 €4000 Man creation (60x80cm-24x31in) s.d.78 acrylic. 21-Nov-2 Finarte, Rome #305 est:5000
£2671 $4167 €3900 Trip to Mexico (80x190cm-31x75in) s.d.1986 verso. 10-Apr-3 Finarte Semenzato, Rome #230/R
£2756 $4328 €4300 After Michelangelo (100x80cm-39x31in) s.d.1976 acrylic. 23-Nov-2 Meeting Art, Vercelli #75/R
£3283 $5252 €4760 Confetti (160x130cm-63x51in) s.d.1987 verso acrylic confetti. 11-Mar-3 Babuino, Rome #347/R
£3526 $5535 €5500 Landscape (92x73cm-36x29in) s.i.d.1969 on stretcher enamel. 19-Nov-2 Finarte, Milan #264/R
£3797 $5924 €6000 Mirages (100x80cm-39x31in) s.i.d.1981 acrylic lit. 14-Sep-2 Meeting Art, Vercelli #812/R
£3846 $6038 €6000 After Michelangelo (80x60cm-31x24in) s.d.78 verso acrylic. 21-Nov-2 Finarte, Rome #337/R est:5000-6000
£4487 $7045 €7000 After Michelangelo (80x60cm-31x24in) s.d.1976 acrylic. 19-Nov-2 Finarte, Milan #46/R
£8861 $14000 €14000 Interior (116x81cm-46x32in) s.i.d.1962 verso acrylic panel. 29-Nov-2 Farsetti, Prato #546/R est:15000
£14184 $22979 €20000 Bicromia del cielo (140x99cm-55x39in) s.i.d.1964 enamel wood prov.exhib. 26-May-3 Christie's, Milan #262/R est:20000-25000
Works on paper
£321 $503 €500 Untitled (70x50cm-28x20in) s.d.1987 mixed media. 23-Nov-2 Meeting Art, Vercelli #300/R
£897 $1434 €1300 Portrait of Silvia with wings (70x100cm-28x39in) s.d.1977 mixed media. 11-Mar-3 Babuino, Rome #412/R
£1806 $2854 €2800 Italian square (70x100cm-28x39in) s.d.87 verso pencil photograph. 18-Dec-2 Christie's, Rome #20/R
£2215 $3500 €3500 Blinds (70x100cm-28x39in) s.d.62 mixed media card. 29-Nov-2 Farsetti, Prato #104/R est:4000
£2278 $3600 €3600 Untitled (70x100cm-28x39in) s.d.1962 mixed media. 29-Nov-2 Farsetti, Prato #419/R

FETI, Domenico (1589-1624) Italian
£27778 $45000 €41667 Parable of the treasure hidden in the field (61x45cm-24x18in) panel prov.exhib.lit. 24-Jan-3 Christie's, Rockefeller NY #153/R est:25000-35000

FETI, Domenico (attrib) (1589-1624) Italian
£12821 $20256 €20000 Saint Francis (140x109cm-55x43in) 16-Nov-2 Farsetti, Prato #303/R est:20000-24000
£31646 $50000 €50000 Aristarco of Samo (93x71cm-37x28in) 2-Dec-2 Finarte, Milan #141/R est:70000

FETI, Domenico (studio) (1589-1624) Italian
£12258 $19368 €19000 Saint Francis' ecstasy (167x116cm-66x46in) 18-Dec-2 Piasa, Paris #6 est:7000

FETRIS, Alison (20th C) British?
£550 $847 €825 Tulips, narcissi, pansies and other flowers in a vase (66x57cm-26x22in) s. 24-Oct-2 Christie's, Kensington #81/R

FETT, William (1918-) American
£438 $700 €635 Concert (97x114cm-38x45in) s.d. 17-May-3 Selkirks, St. Louis #324
Works on paper
£417 $650 €626 Earth and sky (48x66cm-19x26in) s.i.d.1943 W/C. 10-Nov-2 Selkirks, St. Louis #802/R

FETTING, Rainer (1949-) German
£1538 $2431 €2400 Olana - Hudson River Valley (46x61cm-18x24in) s.i.d.1986 verso. 14-Nov-2 Neumeister, Munich #768/R est:4000-4500
£3481 $5500 €5500 Woman with hen (65x90cm-26x35in) s.d.82 verso. 30-Nov-2 Villa Grisebach, Berlin #470/R est:6000-8000
£4000 $6680 €5800 Nicolai turm Copenhagen (150x95cm-59x37in) s.i.d.96 verso prov. 26-Jun-3 Sotheby's, London #249/R est:5000-7000
£5019 $8081 €7529 Selbst (175x120cm-69x47in) s.d.80/83 verso. 7-May-3 AB Stockholms Auktionsverk #1132/R est:60000-80000 (S.KR 65000)
£7246 $11884 €10000 Mike Hill (203x147cm-80x58in) s.i.d.86 verso. 31-May-3 Villa Grisebach, Berlin #396/R est:12000-15000
£7500 $12525 €10875 Grapes (127x127cm-50x50in) s.i.d.93 verso prov. 26-Jun-3 Sotheby's, London #248/R est:4000-6000
£8544 $13500 €13500 S.O.36 (179x160cm-70x63in) s.i.d.1977 verso prov. 30-Nov-2 Villa Grisebach, Berlin #468/R est:10000-12000
£9177 $14500 €14500 CBGB (200x150cm-79x59in) mono.i.d. acrylic cotton. 30-Nov-2 Villa Grisebach, Berlin #469/R est:14000-18000
£15000 $23100 €22500 Katja Lesend (190x140cm-75x55in) s. i.d.88 verso dispersion on linen prov. 22-Oct-2 Sotheby's, London #451/R est:10000-15000
Works on paper
£1923 $2981 €3000 Ruckenakt (143x108cm-56x43in) s.d.83 s.i.d.verso wax crayon prov. 3-Dec-2 Christie's, Amsterdam #302/R est:3000-5000

FETTOLINI, Armando (1960-) Italian
Works on paper
£347 $552 €500 Memory fragment (62x62cm-24x24in) s. s.i.verso polymer board exec.2000. 1-May-3 Meeting Art, Vercelli #429

FEUBURE, Ferdinand le (1815-1898) German
Works on paper
£1130 $1763 €1650 Gralstempel (16x13cm-6x5in) s.d. verso W/C htd gold. 11-Apr-3 Winterberg, Heidelberg #465/R est:880

FEUCHERE, Jean-Jacques (1807-1852) French
Sculpture
£6250 $9938 €9000 Satan, ange dechu (34cm-13in) pat bronze lit. 30-Apr-3 Tajan, Paris #122/R est:9000

FEUCHT, Theodore (1867-1944) German
£503 $785 €800 Old street in Latin Quarter, Paris (55x48cm-22x19in) s. 9-Oct-2 Michael Zeller, Lindau #673/R
£1090 $1722 €1700 Parisian courtyard (36x45cm-14x18in) s. board. 15-Nov-2 Reiss & Sohn, Konigstein #26/R est:2000

FEUERBACH, Anselm (1829-1880) German
£1883 $2806 €2900 Young woman dressed in mourning (53x42cm-21x17in) s. lit. 26-Jun-2 Neumeister, Munich #731sa/R est:2900
£2115 $3279 €3300 Study of head in profile of an old man with cap (40x35cm-16x14in) mono. paper on board lit. 4-Dec-2 Neumeister, Munich #730/R est:1900
Works on paper
£884 $1406 €1300 Study of young man's head (14x11cm-6x4in) s. i. verso chk pencil htd white. 19-Mar-3 Neumeister, Munich #353/R est:1000
£10323 $16000 €15485 Portrait of a young man (21x15cm-8x6in) mono. pencil black white chk prov.exhib. 29-Oct-2 Sotheby's, New York #103/R est:2000-3000

FEUERLEIN, Johann Peter (attrib) (1668-1728) German
£2000 $3120 €3000 Portrait of a gentleman, wearing oriental dress (67x58cm-26x23in) painted oval. 9-Apr-3 Bonhams, New Bond Street #97/R est:2000-3000

FEUERRING, Maximilian (1896-1985) Polish
£717 $1176 €1076 Standing nude (61x51cm-24x20in) s. board. 4-Jun-3 Deutscher-Menzies, Melbourne #291/R (A.D 1800)

FEUERSTEIN, Martin (1856-1931) French
£429 $678 €644 Christ standing with goblet and consecrated wafer (153x85cm-60x33in) mono.prov. 29-Nov-2 Zofingen, Switzerland #2434 (S.FR 1000)
£1307 $2144 €2000 Concert sur la terrasse (77x56cm-30x22in) s. 7-Feb-3 Oger, Dumont, Paris #92/R

FEUILLAS-CREUSY, Caroline (1861-?) French
Miniatures
£1081 $1686 €1600 Jeune fille au bouquet de fleurs a la robe jaune (13x10cm-5x4in) s. oval. 28-Mar-3 Piasa, Paris #73/R

FEURE, Georges de (1868-1943) French
Works on paper
£1633 $2596 €2400 Les deux amies (44x37cm-17x15in) s. gouache lit. 28-Feb-3 Tajan, Paris #9/R est:2500-3000

FEUZ, Werner (1882-1956) Swiss
£696 $1078 €1044 Valaisanne a la hotte (92x79cm-36x31in) s.d.07. 7-Dec-2 Galerie du Rhone, Sion #384/R (S.FR 1600)

FEVRET DE ST MEMIN, Charles (1770-1852) American
Works on paper
£4063 $6500 €6095 Brigadier General Federal. pastel chk. 16-May-3 Du Mouchelle, Detroit #2434/R est:400-500

FEYEN, Eugène (1826-1895) French
£1218 $1888 €1900 Porteuse de fruits (68x52cm-27x20in) d.1845. 8-Dec-2 Teitgen, Nancy #63/R
£2115 $3321 €3300 Oyster collectors on Britanny beach (31x50cm-12x20in) s. panel. 21-Nov-2 Van Ham, Cologne #1602/R est:2200
£2885 $4529 €4500 Panier renverse (17x13cm-7x5in) s. panel. 13-Dec-2 Piasa, Paris #122/R
£8974 $13910 €14000 Travails aux champs (65x95cm-26x37in) 8-Dec-2 Teitgen, Nancy #64
£45513 $70545 €71000 Les regates de Cancale (54x102cm-21x40in) exhib. 8-Dec-2 Teitgen, Nancy #62/R

FEYEN, Jacques Eugène (1815-1908) French
£69620 $110000 €104430 Regates a Cancale, Bretagne (60x105cm-24x41in) s. prov.exhib.lit. 24-Apr-3 Sotheby's, New York #81/R est:100000-150000

FEYEN-PERRIN, François Nicolas Augustin (1826-1888) French
£641 $994 €1000 La bouquetiere (65x52cm-26x20in) 8-Dec-2 Teitgen, Nancy #60
£2628 $4126 €4100 Retour des pecheuses (32x42cm-13x17in) s. panel. 15-Dec-2 Eric Pillon, Calais #112/R

FEYERABEND, Johann Rudolf (1779-1814) Swiss
Works on paper
£2194 $3466 €3400 Still lives (17x22cm-7x9in) gouache pair. 19-Dec-2 Delvaux, Paris #251/R est:1500
£2390 $3728 €3800 Still lives (15x20cm-6x8in) gouache pair. 11-Oct-2 Pierre Berge, Paris #14/R

FIALA, Josef (?) ?
£583 $903 €875 In Clade (35x46cm-14x18in) 1-Oct-2 SOGA, Bratislava #213/R est:35000 (SL.K 37000)

FIAMMINGO, Paolo (1540-1596) Flemish
£20000 $31400 €30000 Allegory of water (155x217cm-61x85in) prov. 12-Dec-2 Sotheby's, London #120/R est:20000-30000

FIAMMINGO, Paolo (attrib) (1540-1596) Flemish
£7000 $11690 €10150 Andromeda (118x99cm-46x39in) 11-Jul-3 Christie's, Kensington #196/R est:7000-10000

FIASCHI, E (19th C) Italian
Sculpture
£1400 $2282 €2100 Young man seated on a wall, holding the hand of a maiden (84cm-33in) s. alabaster. 11-Feb-3 Gorringes, Lewes #74/R est:1500-2000

FIASELLA, Domenico (1589-1669) Italian
£8000 $12400 €12000 Queen Artemisia (101x76cm-40x30in) lit. 30-Oct-2 Christie's, Kensington #131/R est:8000-12000
£45000 $75150 €65250 Madonna and Child with Saints Dominic, Catherine and John the Baptist (141x166cm-56x65in) init. prov. 9-Jul-3 Bonhams, New Bond Street #49/R est:30000-40000

FIAUX, Lelo (1909-1963) Swiss
£217 $337 €326 Le bouquet (61x50cm-24x20in) s. 7-Dec-2 Galerie du Rhone, Sion #387/R (S.FR 500)

FICARA, Franz (1926-1994) Italian
£385 $604 €600 Faces (50x60cm-20x24in) s. card painted1984. 23-Nov-2 Meeting Art, Vercelli #407
Works on paper
£545 $855 €850 Landscape (50x70cm-20x28in) s. painted 1985. 23-Nov-2 Meeting Art, Vercelli #439

FICHEL, Benjamin Eugène (1826-1895) French
£793 $1158 €1190 Foot soldier with musket resting (21x16cm-8x6in) s.d.1866 panel. 17-Jun-2 Philippe Schuler, Zurich #7326/R (S.FR 1800)
£1622 $2530 €2400 Interior with young woman at tapestry and kitten playing (32x24cm-13x9in) s. panel. 27-Mar-3 Dr Fritz Nagel, Stuttgart #811/R est:4000
£3800 $5928 €5700 Reading the newspaper (22x16cm-9x6in) s.d.1871 panel. 17-Sep-2 Sotheby's, Olympia #241/R est:2000-3000
£4200 $6552 €6300 Card players (22x16cm-9x6in) s.d.1871 panel. 17-Sep-2 Sotheby's, Olympia #240/R est:2000-3000
£7000 $11130 €10500 Game of chess (24x34cm-9x13in) s.d.1881 panel prov. 18-Mar-3 Bonhams, New Bond Street #119/R est:7000-10000

FICKE, Nicolaes (?-1702) Flemish
£7172 $11117 €10758 Travellers before tavern (55x67cm-22x26in) mono. panel prov. 3-Oct-2 Koller, Zurich #3037/R est:20000-30000 (S.FR 16710)

FICKLIN, Herb (1911-1980) American
£256 $400 €384 South Padre Dunes (28x61cm-11x24in) 19-Oct-2 David Dike, Dallas #278/R

FICUS, Andre Hans (1919-2000) German
£321 $497 €500 Lost area (54x71cm-21x28in) s. panel lit. 6-Dec-2 Karlheinz Kaupp, Staufen #2147/R

FIDANI, Orazio (1610-1656) Italian
£28000 $43960 €42000 Entombment (179x142cm-70x56in) 12-Dec-2 Sotheby's, London #186/R est:8000-12000

FIDANZA, Francesco (attrib) (1747-1819) Italian
£2113 $3507 €3000 Paysage de cascade (48x74cm-19x29in) copper. 16-Jun-3 Claude Aguttes, Neuilly #28/R est:3000-4000
£3800 $5928 €5700 View of Posillipo, near Naples (35x52cm-14x20in) 8-Apr-3 Sotheby's, Olympia #247/R est:3500-4500

FIDLER, Anton (fl.1825-1855) Austrian
£1519 $2400 €2400 Still life of fruit with a small bird (42x53cm-17x21in) s.i.d.1831. 28-Nov-2 Dorotheum, Vienna #148/R est:2800-3200
£1931 $3052 €2897 Roses in a glass vase and cherries on a marble table (28x24cm-11x9in) s.d.1846 lit. 29-Nov-2 Zofingen, Switzerland #2332/R est:5500 (S.FR 4500)
£1931 $3052 €2897 Yellow and white roses in a glass vase on a marble table (29x24cm-11x9in) s.d.1864 lit. 29-Nov-2 Zofingen, Switzerland #2333/R est:5500 (S.FR 4500)

FIDLER, Harry (1856-1935) British
£300 $480 €450 Cows and calves in a meadow (30x36cm-12x14in) 8-Jan-3 Brightwells, Leominster #1009
£800 $1240 €1200 Leading the flock home (58x47cm-23x19in) s. 25-Sep-2 Hamptons Fine Art, Godalming #358/R
£895 $1459 €1343 End of the day (56x46cm-22x18in) s. 30-Jan-3 Lawrence, Crewkerne #741/R
£1376 $2215 €2064 Cows grazing in a pasture (36x49cm-14x19in) init. board. 12-May-3 Stephan Welz, Johannesburg #423/R est:12000-18000 (SA.R 16000)
£1450 $2248 €2175 Horse and cart (20x28cm-8x11in) 3-Dec-2 Louis Taylor, Stoke on Trent #936
£1750 $2730 €2625 Horse and trap with driver leading a cow (50x61cm-20x24in) init. 18-Sep-2 Dreweatt Neate, Newbury #123/R est:2000-3000
£2111 $3505 €3061 Down the Nadder, Wiltshire (38x41cm-15x16in) s.i.d.July 25. 10-Jun-3 Ritchie, Toronto #75/R est:3000-5000 (C.D 4750)
£2300 $3565 €3450 Shepherd with sheep (25x28cm-10x11in) 3-Dec-2 Louis Taylor, Stoke on Trent #935
£3000 $4650 €4500 Ploughing scene (20x25cm-8x10in) 3-Dec-2 Louis Taylor, Stoke on Trent #934
£3024 $4778 €4536 Binder (38x41cm-15x16in) i.stretcher. 18-Nov-2 Waddingtons, Toronto #135/R est:4000-6000 (C.D 7500)
£3512 $5514 €5268 First furrow (46x56cm-18x22in) s.i. s.i.verso. 24-Jul-2 Walker's, Ottawa #21/R est:5000-6000 (C.D 8500)
£4400 $6820 €6600 Horse and haywagon with figure (33x38cm-13x15in) indis sig. 3-Dec-2 Louis Taylor, Stoke on Trent #933

FIDRIT, Louis (20th C) French
£641 $1006 €1000 La victoire (117x89cm-46x35in) s. 16-Dec-2 Millon & Associes, Paris #163/R

FIDUS (1868-1948) German
£1583 $2517 €2375 Morgenstimmung (80x119cm-31x47in) s. d.Marz 1895 verso. 5-Mar-3 Rasmussen, Copenhagen #2020/R est:18000-20000 (D.KR 17000)

Works on paper
£949 $1500 €1500 Fulfilment (40x47cm-16x19in) s.d.1912 i. verso pencil chl W/C prov. 27-Nov-2 Dorotheum, Vienna #122/R est:1500-2000

FIEBIG, Carl Rudolph (1812-1874) Danish
£7531 $12049 €11297 Portrait of young girl wearing blue dress, dog at her side (74x56cm-29x22in) s.d.1856. 13-Jan-3 Rasmussen, Vejle #12/R est:20000-30000 (D.KR 86000)

FIEDLER, Franz (1885-1956) German
Photographs
£2025 $3200 €3200 Otto Dix (21x16cm-8x6in) i. verso silver gelatin. 28-Nov-2 Villa Grisebach, Berlin #1179/R est:800-1200

FIEDLER, Herbert (1891-1962) Dutch
Works on paper
£764 $1260 €1100 Sensation at the fair (28x20cm-11x8in) s.d.29 pencil W/C prov. 1-Jul-3 Christie's, Amsterdam #492/R
£1295 $2124 €1800 Putting on make up (63x37cm-25x15in) s. gouache prov. 3-Jun-3 Christie's, Amsterdam #43/R est:2000-3000

FIEDLER, Johann Christian (attrib) (1697-1765) German
£4362 $7023 €6500 Hilly riverland with a stag hunt (60x76cm-24x30in) i.verso. 18-Feb-3 Sotheby's, Amsterdam #646/R est:2500-3000

FIELD, E Loyal (1856-1914) American
£429 $678 €644 Landscape with stream (59x69cm-23x27in) canvas laid down masonite. 3-Apr-3 Heffel, Vancouver #24/R (C.D 1000)
£1592 $2500 €2388 Extensive river landscape with farm (51x76cm-20x30in) s. 19-Nov-2 Butterfields, San Francisco #8032/R est:3000-5000

Works on paper
£211 $350 €306 Atmospheric landscape (36x48cm-14x19in) s. W/C. 14-Jun-3 Jackson's, Cedar Falls #419/R

FIELD, Robert (1948-) Canadian
Works on paper
£267 $437 €387 Jumping salmon (31x48cm-12x19in) s.d.2001 pastel. 9-Jun-3 Hodgins, Calgary #179/R (C.D 600)

FIELDING, A V C (1787-1855) British
Works on paper
£1100 $1705 €1650 Wrecking Lady Elizabeth, coastal landscape (38x56cm-15x22in) s.i.d.1825 W/C. 1-Nov-2 Moore Allen & Innocent, Cirencester #162/R est:800-1200

FIELDING, Anthony Vandyke Copley (1787-1855) British
£320 $522 €480 Lakeland scene with cattle and drover in foreground (5x7cm-2x3in) i.verso. 12-Feb-3 Andrew Hartley, Ilkley #863
£1500 $2475 €2175 Cows watering (30x43cm-12x17in) s. 2-Jul-3 Sotheby's, Olympia #131/R est:1500-2000

Works on paper
£500 $770 €750 Newhaven, with boats in the bay (14x19cm-6x7in) s. W/C. 7-Sep-2 Shapes, Edinburgh #521
£600 $930 €900 In Perthshire (20x15cm-8x6in) s.i.d.1837 W/C. 3-Dec-2 Sotheby's, Olympia #30/R
£1000 $1640 €1500 Benares (15x25cm-6x10in) s. indis d. pencil W/C. 4-Feb-3 Bonhams, Leeds #239 est:600-800
£1000 $1640 €1500 Fisherwoman inspecting the catch (17x25cm-7x10in) init. W/C. 4-Feb-3 Bonhams, Leeds #278 est:400-600
£1100 $1705 €1650 Boats by the harbour entrance (25x46cm-10x18in) s. W/C. 6-Dec-2 Chrystals Auctions, Isle of Man #258 est:800-1200
£1100 $1804 €1650 Vessels in a squall off a promontory (26x47cm-10x19in) bears sig.i.d.1810 W/C scratching out. 4-Feb-3 Bonhams, Leeds #241 est:700-900
£1150 $1898 €1668 Shipping in a bay at sunset (35x52cm-14x20in) s.d.1844 W/C. 2-Jul-3 Sotheby's, Olympia #301/R est:1000-1500
£1300 $2106 €1950 Fishing vessel heading out to sea in a squall (13x23cm-5x9in) s. W/C. 21-May-3 Christie's, Kensington #485/R est:1500-2000
£1500 $2385 €2250 Harlech Castle from the north, Merionethshire (18x25cm-7x10in) W/C over pencil htd gum arabic. 19-Mar-3 Sotheby's, London #193/R est:1500-2000
£1550 $2542 €2325 Conway Castle (28x39cm-11x15in) i.d. W/C. 4-Feb-3 Bonhams, Leeds #240 est:700-1000
£1650 $2574 €2475 Extensive river landscape with cattle grazing (18x26cm-7x10in) s. pencil W/C scratching out. 25-Mar-3 Bonhams, Leeds #530/R est:1200-1500
£2000 $3320 €3000 Fishing fleet at dusk (18x25cm-7x10in) s. W/C. 12-Jun-3 Bonhams, New Bond Street #631/R est:2500-3500
£2100 $3339 €3150 Shepherd and his flock on a country track (25x36cm-10x14in) s. W/C over pencil htd bodycol. 19-Mar-3 Sotheby's, London #192/R est:1500-2000
£2500 $3925 €3750 Fishing boats in a stiff breeze, off shore (53x76cm-21x30in) s.d.1882 prov. 21-Nov-2 Christie's, London #54/R est:3000-5000
£3200 $5056 €4800 Loch Tay, Perthshire (17x25cm-7x10in) s. W/C over pencil htd bodycol scratching out. 28-Nov-2 Sotheby's, London #298/R est:2000-3000
£4000 $6560 €5800 Nanette Rocks (15x21cm-6x8in) pencil W/C scratching out. 5-Jun-3 Christie's, London #67/R est:3000-5000
£6000 $9540 €9000 Fisherboy on the shore at sunset (42x52cm-17x20in) s. W/C over pencil htd bodycol. 19-Mar-3 Sotheby's, London #184/R est:4000-6000
£7700 $12782 €11550 Mull of Galloway (64x91cm-25x36in) s. W/C over pencil htd bodycol gum arabic scratching out prov.exhib. 12-Jun-3 Sotheby's, London #133/R est:6000-8000
£8000 $13120 €12000 Folkestone, Kent (41x58cm-16x23in) i. W/C. 4-Feb-3 Bonhams, Leeds #242 est:3000-5000
£21000 $34440 €30450 Extensive view of Greenwich, London (56x110cm-22x43in) with sig.d.1821 pencil pen ink W/C arabic scratching out exhib. 5-Jun-3 Christie's, London #70/R est:5000-8000

FIELDING, Anthony Vandyke Copley (attrib) (1787-1855) British
Works on paper
£400 $652 €600 Beached fishing vessels (18x26cm-7x10in) W/C. 29-Jan-3 Dreweatt Neate, Newbury #29
£750 $1162 €1125 Stormy effect, head of Glen Coe (12x19cm-5x7in) i. W/C pair. 3-Dec-2 Sotheby's, Olympia #38/R

FIELDING, Nathan Theodore (1747-1815) British
£2100 $3256 €3150 Extensive landscape with figures crossing a bridge (52x65cm-20x26in) mono.d.1796. 3-Dec-2 Sotheby's, Olympia #13/R est:1200-1800

FIELDING, Newton Limbird Smith (1799-1856) British
Works on paper
£600 $936 €900 Vessel in a squall (28x20cm-11x8in) s.d.35 W/C htd gum arabic. 5-Nov-2 Bonhams, New Bond Street #83/R

FIELDS, Duggie (20th C) ?
£1200 $1908 €1800 Three women (163x183cm-64x72in) s.i.d.12 June 74 verso. 26-Feb-3 Sotheby's, Olympia #384/R est:1200-1800

FIELDS, George (19/20th C) American
£337 $550 €506 Spring on the river (61x91cm-24x36in) s. 1-Feb-3 Van Blarcom, South Natick #128

FIENE, Ernest (1894-1965) American/German
£625 $1000 €938 Kids off to a picnic (30x43cm-12x17in) exhib. 11-Jan-3 James Julia, Fairfield #151 est:1500-2000
£2813 $4500 €4220 White rose in blue vase (51x33cm-20x13in) s. 11-Jan-3 James Julia, Fairfield #150a est:3000-4000
£8537 $14000 €12379 Cityscape (91x76cm-36x30in) s.d.1930 prov.exhib. 1-Jun-3 Wright, Chicago #184/R est:6000-8000
Works on paper
£259 $425 €376 Gloucester harbour (56x76cm-22x30in) s. gouache W/C illustration board. 5-Jun-3 Swann Galleries, New York #93/R
£366 $600 €531 Reclining nude (25x32cm-10x13in) s.d. pen ink sold with a dr by John Carroll. 5-Jun-3 Swann Galleries, New York #91/R
£3659 $6000 €5306 Manhattan construction (54x35cm-21x14in) pencil exec.c.1932. 5-Jun-3 Swann Galleries, New York #92/R est:3000-5000

FIERAVINO, Francesco (attrib) (17th C) Italian
£11000 $17270 €16500 Two spaniels on a gold trimmed red cushions, parrot, grapes on a table with a carpet (77x95cm-30x37in) 13-Dec-2 Christie's, Kensington #227/R est:12000-16000

FIERAVINO, Francesco (style) (17th C) Italian
£6000 $9360 €9000 Still life with armour and embroidered carped on marble table (74x99cm-29x39in) 10-Apr-3 Sotheby's, London #74/R est:8000

FIERROS, Dionisio (1827-1894) Spanish
£909 $1327 €1400 Shepherd (23x18cm-9x7in) s. 17-Jun-2 Ansorena, Madrid #311/R
Works on paper
£289 $469 €440 Figures (11x15cm-4x6in) i.verso pencil dr. 21-Jan-3 Ansorena, Madrid #812

FIERZ, Albert (1861-?) German
£696 $1078 €1044 Two girls in rowing boat (42x58cm-17x23in) s.i.d.91. 9-Dec-2 Philippe Schuler, Zurich #3900 est:1500-2000 (S.FR 1600)
£1435 $2224 €2153 Boats by shore (75x60cm-30x24in) s.i.d.1889. 9-Dec-2 Philippe Schuler, Zurich #3899/R est:3000-3500 (S.FR 3300)

FIETZ, Gerhard (1910-1997) German
£1582 $2453 €2500 Picture 1952/90 (40x64cm-16x25in) s.d.1952 s.i.d. verso egg tempera masonite. 28-Sep-2 Ketterer, Hamburg #366/R est:2500-3500

FIEVRE, Yolande (1907-) French
Sculpture
£1944 $3208 €2800 Composition (12x12cm-5x5in) s. mixed media box. 1-Jul-3 Artcurial Briest, Paris #810/R est:1000-1200
£2222 $3667 €3200 Composition (24x24x7cm-9x9x3in) s. s.d.Aout 1962 verso mixed media box. 1-Jul-3 Artcurial Briest, Paris #811/R est:1500-2000
£4028 $6646 €5800 Miserere du reve (36x35x11cm-14x14x4in) s. s.i.d.Fevrier/Mars 1965 verso mixed media box. 1-Jul-3 Artcurial Briest, Paris #809/R est:3000-4000
£4375 $7219 €6300 Anges et demons d'ocean (65x20x8cm-26x8x3in) s. s.i.d.Juin 1966 verso mixed media box. 1-Jul-3 Artcurial Briest, Paris #808/R est:3000-4000

FIFE, Ivy Grace (1905-1976) New Zealander
£727 $1120 €1091 Low tide (45x54cm-18x21in) s. canvas on board. 4-Sep-2 Dunbar Sloane, Wellington #115 est:800-1200 (NZ.D 2400)
Works on paper
£776 $1133 €1164 Oxford foothills, Canterbury (15x19cm-6x7in) s. W/C. 12-Sep-1 Watson's, Christchurch #11 est:3000-5000 (NZ.D 2600)

FIGARI, Juan Carlos (1894-1927) South American
£1500 $2400 €2250 Trip (40x60cm-16x24in) cardboard lit. 5-Jan-3 Galleria Y Remates, Montevideo #115/R
£1750 $2800 €2625 Patio (40x49cm-16x19in) s. cardboard lit. 5-Jan-3 Galleria Y Remates, Montevideo #114/R

FIGARI, Pedro (1861-1938) Uruguayan
£3188 $5100 €4782 Friends (28x43cm-11x17in) panel. 5-Jan-3 Galleria Y Remates, Montevideo #113/R
£4088 $6500 €6132 Animals (33x40cm-13x16in) i.verso cardboard. 2-Mar-3 Galleria Y Remates, Montevideo #66/R
£7051 $11000 €10577 Intimity (33x40cm-13x16in) s. i.verso cardboard. 10-Oct-2 Galleria Y Remates, Montevideo #52/R est:12000-18000
£7673 $12200 €11510 Patio (27x35cm-11x14in) i.verso cardboard. 2-Mar-3 Galleria Y Remates, Montevideo #67/R
£9182 $14600 €13773 Pasture (35x50cm-14x20in) s. cardboard. 2-Mar-3 Galleria Y Remates, Montevideo #64/R est:22000
£11218 $17500 €16827 Troperos de paso (31x49cm-12x19in) s.d.1933 cardboard prov. 30-Jul-2 Galleria Y Remates, Montevideo #65/R est:18000-23000
£14013 $22000 €21020 Coloured people (35x49cm-14x19in) s. board painted c.1930 prov.lit. 19-Nov-2 Sotheby's, New York #28/R est:30000
Works on paper
£333 $520 €500 THree coloured women (10x20cm-4x8in) d.22 pencil dr. 10-Oct-2 Galleria Y Remates, Montevideo #18/R
£641 $1000 €962 Dance (14x16cm-6x6in) pencil dr. 10-Oct-2 Galleria Y Remates, Montevideo #17/R

FIGARO, Charles (20th C) American?
£828 $1300 €1242 Scouting party (48x61cm-19x24in) s. 10-Dec-2 Doyle, New York #121/R est:2500-3500

FIGGE VON GRABOW, Hugo (19/20th C) German
Works on paper
£969 $1415 €1454 Elegant woman in chair (112x77cm-44x30in) s. bars i.d.1907 pastel chk. 17-Jun-2 Philippe Schuler, Zurich #4023/R (S.FR 2200)

FIGGE, Eddie (1904-) Swedish
Works on paper
£268 $426 €402 Skylab - Space (44x54cm-17x21in) s.d.1973 chk pencil. 3-Mar-3 Lilla Bukowskis, Stockholm #85 (S.KR 3600)
£426 $660 €639 Renew life (69x49cm-27x19in) s.d.1995 collage chk. 8-Dec-2 Uppsala Auktionskammare, Uppsala #283/R (S.KR 6000)

FIGUEIRA, Balthazar Gomes (attrib) (1604-1674) Portuguese
£20062 $32500 €30093 Still life of cherries, plums and figs in a basket, parrot looking on (41x53cm-16x21in) 23-Jan-3 Sotheby's, New York #155/R est:15000

FIKENTSCHER, Otto Clemens (1831-1880) German
£1210 $1888 €1900 Forest clearing with deer (130x132cm-51x52in) s. lit. 7-Nov-2 Allgauer, Kempten #2803/R est:1900

FIKS, Albert (20th C) ?
£255 $392 €400 Apple trees (39x30cm-15x12in) s.d.1930. 3-Sep-2 Christie's, Amsterdam #363

FILA, Rudolf (1932-) ?
£756 $1172 €1134 Sign (84x65cm-33x26in) 1-Oct-2 SOGA, Bratislava #289/R est:60000 (SL.K 48000)

FILARSKI, Dirk Herman Willem (1885-1964) Flemish
£2014 $3304 €2800 De Roode stier (100x80cm-39x31in).d.1939. 3-Jun-3 Christie's, Amsterdam #10/R est:3000-5000
£2532 $4000 €4000 Stilleven met bloemen (100x80cm-39x31in) s. prov. 26-Nov-2 Sotheby's, Amsterdam #20/R est:4000-5000
£2848 $4500 €4500 Stilleven met bloemen (100x90cm-39x35in) s. prov. 26-Nov-2 Sotheby's, Amsterdam #88/R est:4500-5500

£3453 $5663 €4800 Herfst in Staphorst - autumn in Staphorst (38x48cm-15x19in) s.d.40 s.i.on stretcher lit. 3-Jun-3 Christie's, Amsterdam #232/R est:6000-8000
£3526 $5535 €5500 Paris - battle advance (54x65cm-21x26in) s. i.verso. 25-Nov-2 Glerum, Amsterdam #109/R est:3200-3600
£3793 $6031 €5500 Still life with flowers in a vase and flowers in a bottle (98x87cm-39x34in) s. 10-Mar-3 Sotheby's, Amsterdam #264/R est:4500-6500
£3797 $6000 €6000 Stilleven met velboeket (120x100cm-47x39in) s.d.1947 prov. 26-Nov-2 Sotheby's, Amsterdam #21/R est:6000-8000
£4808 $7548 €7500 Autumn in Switzerland (41x57cm-16x22in) s.d.12. 25-Nov-2 Glerum, Amsterdam #79/R est:5000-7000
£6410 $10064 €10000 View of a North African landscape (65x83cm-26x33in) s. 25-Nov-2 Glerum, Amsterdam #95/R est:6000-8000
£9615 $14904 €15000 Shipyard in Spain (75x100cm-30x39in) s. 3-Dec-2 Christie's, Amsterdam #16/R est:5000-7000

Works on paper

£1206 $1953 €1700 View of a church and a square (44x53cm-17x21in) s.d.58 gouache. 26-May-3 Glerum, Amsterdam #22 est:2000-2500

FILATOV, Alexei (1972-) Russian

£650 $1007 €975 Native melody (40x60cm-16x24in) s. 8-Dec-2 John Nicholson, Haslemere #207/R

FILDES, Sir Luke (1843-1927) British

£2000 $3200 €3000 Portrait of a young girl with a pink dress and a white vale (36x30cm-14x12in) i.verso. 11-Mar-3 Bonhams, Knightsbridge #315/R est:2000-3000

Works on paper

£2188 $3500 €3282 Sophia (38x26cm-15x10in) init.d.1875 pencil W/C board. 14-May-3 Butterfields, San Francisco #1170/R est:3000-5000
£8500 $13685 €12750 Homeless and hungry (17x25cm-7x10in) pencil W/C bodycol gum arabic prov.exhib. 20-Feb-3 Christie's, London #113/R est:10000

FILER, Franz Xavier (?) ?

£800 $1320 €1160 Still life of flowers in a stone niche with a carved frieze (64x48cm-25x19in) s. 3-Jul-3 Duke & Son, Dorchester #225/R

FILIGER, Charles (1863-1928) French

Works on paper

£2937 $4905 €4200 L'Ile de Sein (16x29cm-6x11in) s.i.d.25 W/C prov. 26-Jun-3 Tajan, Paris #42/R est:4500-5000
£6604 $10302 €10500 Homme nu (36x23cm-14x9in) s.d.1890 gouache cardboard exhib. 11-Oct-2 Binoche, Paris #122/R est:10000-12000
£8219 $12904 €12000 Prototype de J d'Arc (24x24cm-9x9in) i. W/C lit. 15-Apr-3 Laurence Calmels, Paris #4282/R est:10000
£9589 $15055 €14000 Portrait d'Emile Bernard (15x11cm-6x4in) i.verso ink col crayon htd gouache lit. 15-Apr-3 Laurence Calmels, Paris #4280/R
£10274 $16130 €15000 Chardons (18x13cm-7x5in) s.i. gouache cardboard lit. 15-Apr-3 Laurence Calmels, Paris #4286/R est:3000
£12329 $19233 €18000 Salomon I, roi de Bretagne (25x30cm-10x12in) i.verso gouache W/C collage exec.1903 exhib.lit. 14-Apr-3 Laurence Calmels, Paris #4042/R est:7000
£12329 $19356 €18000 Architecture symboliste (26x21cm-10x8in) s. gouache prov.exhib.lit. 15-Apr-3 Laurence Calmels, Paris #4285/R est:12000
£12838 $20027 €19000 Enfant en priere (13x8cm-5x3in) s. gouache paper on cardboard prov. 26-Mar-3 Tajan, Paris #15/R
£14384 $22582 €21000 A la memoire de Franz Hals (15x22cm-6x9in) i. gouache ink paint lit. 15-Apr-3 Laurence Calmels, Paris #4281/R est:10000
£27397 $43014 €40000 Notation chromatique (24x29cm-9x11in) gouache crayon double-sided prov.exhib.lit. 15-Apr-3 Laurence Calmels, Paris #4284/R est:12000
£37671 $59144 €55000 Christ en Croix (34x23cm-13x9in) s. i.verso gouache prov.lit. 15-Apr-3 Laurence Calmels, Paris #4283/R est:12000
£50001 $78002 €74000 Paysage pointilliste (17x29cm-7x11in) s. gouache paper on panel prov. 26-Mar-3 Tajan, Paris #16/R
£116438 $181644 €170000 Vierge et deux anges (23x29cm-9x11in) s. gouache exhib.lit. 14-Apr-3 Laurence Calmels, Paris #4043/R est:40000

FILION, Gabriel (1920-) Canadian

£702 $1046 €1053 Abstraction (102x127cm-40x50in) s.d.60 prov.exhib. 26-Jun-2 Iegor de Saint Hippolyte, Montreal #37/R (C.D 1600)

FILIPKIEWICZ, Stefan (1879-1944) Polish

Works on paper

£903 $1400 €1355 Orchard in bloom (48x66cm-19x26in) W/C. 7-Dec-2 South Bay, Long Island #56/R

FILIPPELLI, Cafiero (1889-1973) Italian

£705 $1107 €1100 Bedroom (11x11cm-4x4in) s. board. 16-Dec-2 Pandolfini, Florence #299/R
£769 $1208 €1200 Rural kitchen. Shoe repairer (10x8cm-4x3in) card pair. 16-Dec-2 Pandolfini, Florence #297/R
£886 $1382 €1400 Femme et enfant (30x37cm-12x15in) s. 15-Sep-2 Feletin, Province #67
£946 $1476 €1400 Bocca d'Arno (20x30cm-8x12in) s. board. 28-Mar-3 Farsetti, Prato #428/R
£1282 $2026 €2000 Interior in the evening (24x28cm-9x11in) s. board. 15-Nov-2 Farsetti, Prato #587/R
£2635 $4111 €3900 Evening homework (27x26cm-11x10in) s.d.22 board. 28-Mar-3 Farsetti, Prato #650/R

FILIPPI, Fernando de (1940-) Italian

£641 $936 €1000 Imagination (70x100cm-28x39in) s.d.65. 5-Jun-2 Il Ponte, Milan #35

Works on paper

£253 $395 €400 Eden (73x51cm-29x20in) s. mixed media cardboard. 14-Sep-2 Meeting Art, Vercelli #733

FILIPPI, Leonida de (1969-) Italian

£2270 $3677 €3200 Magma (160x120cm-63x47in) s.i.d.2003 verso acrylic. 20-May-3 Porro, Milan #11/R est:3800-4000

FILIPPINI, Felice (1917-1988) Italian

£787 $1267 €1141 Four figures at bar (79x60cm-31x24in) s. acrylic. 7-May-3 Dobiaschofsky, Bern #509/R (S.FR 1700)
£1064 $1723 €1500 Danza in bianco e oro (83x125cm-33x49in) s.d.66 prov.lit. 26-May-3 Christie's, Milan #297 est:400-600

FILKINS, George (?) British?

£600 $936 €900 Carting hay near Alton, Hampshire (26x36cm-10x14in) mono. s.i.verso. 10-Apr-3 Tennants, Leyburn #1003

FILKO, Stanislav (1937-) Czechoslovakian

£426 $661 €639 Process (45x33cm-18x13in) painted 1962-63. 3-Dec-2 SOGA, Bratislava #295/R (SL.K 27000)
£583 $851 €875 Faces (45x37cm-18x15in) 4-Jun-2 SOGA, Bratislava #275/R est:15000 (SL.K 37000)
£772 $1127 €1158 Drinker (45x37cm-18x15in) 4-Jun-2 SOGA, Bratislava #276/R est:49000 (SL.K 49000)
£977 $1387 €1466 Nude seated (100x70cm-39x28in) painted 1957. 26-Mar-2 SOGA, Bratislava #274/R est:30000 (SL.K 62000)

FILKUKA, Anton (1888-1957) Austrian

£414 $662 €600 Evening (70x100cm-28x39in) s. 11-Mar-3 Dorotheum, Vienna #71/R
£1139 $1800 €1800 Rosegger's wooded homeland (74x100cm-29x39in) s. i. verso. 26-Nov-2 Wiener Kunst Auktionen, Vienna #69/R est:1200-1500
£1795 $2836 €2800 Sledge ride (100x130cm-39x51in) s. 12-Nov-2 Dorotheum, Vienna #72/R est:2000-2800

Works on paper

£1060 $1727 €1600 Landscape with birch trees (74x104cm-29x41in) mixed media board. 28-Jan-3 Dorotheum, Vienna #43/R est:1100-1500

FILLA, Emil (1882-1953) Czechoslovakian

£5435 $8913 €7500 Untitled (38x47cm-15x19in) tempera chk collage prov. 31-May-3 Villa Grisebach, Berlin #209/R est:5000-7000

FILLEAU, Emery A (fl.1890-1910) American

£1603 $2500 €2405 Wagon trail (56x69cm-22x27in) 19-Oct-2 David Dike, Dallas #254/R est:2000-4000

FILLERUP, Mel (1924-) American

£1006 $1600 €1509 New star (15x13cm-6x5in) s. i.verso board prov. 4-Mar-3 Christie's, Rockefeller NY #93/R est:2000-3000

FILLIA (1904-1936) Italian

£4452 $6945 €6500 Drum player (25x18cm-10x7in) s. tempera card exhib. 10-Apr-3 Finarte Semenzato, Rome #288/R

FILLIARD, Ernest (1868-1933) French

£285 $450 €450 Jetee de roses (24x33cm-9x13in) s. panel. 1-Dec-2 Peron, Melun #22

Works on paper

£1014 $1581 €1500 Bouquet de fleurs dans un pot vert (46x48cm-18x19in) s. W/C. 28-Mar-3 Claude Aguttes, Neuilly #100/R

FILLIOU, Robert (1926-1987) French

Sculpture

£1389 $2194 €2000 New card game (32x37x6cm-13x15x2in) s.num.37/100 various objects wood suitcase photo. 28-Apr-3 Cornette de St.Cyr, Paris #384/R est:2000-2500

FILLOL GRANER, Antonio (1870-1930) Spanish
£484 $765 €750 Nymphs (42x62cm-17x24in) s. 17-Dec-2 Durán, Madrid #85/R

FILLON, Arthur (1900-1974) French
£1146 $1789 €1800 Paris, la Seine vue de la colline de Chaillot (60x73cm-24x29in) s. 10-Nov-2 Eric Pillon, Calais #46/R
£1923 $3000 €2885 Les bouquinistes (81x64cm-32x25in) 18-Oct-2 Du Mouchelle, Detroit #2073/R est:3000-5000

FILMUS, Tully (1903-) American
£449 $750 €651 Three rabbis in a discussion (51x41cm-20x16in) s. sold with six others. 29-Jun-3 Butterfields, Los Angeles #7062/R

FILOCAMO, Luigi (1906-1988) Italian
£2041 $3245 €3000 Mussolini entering Adis Abeba in triumph (70x100cm-28x39in) s. board. 18-Mar-3 Finarte, Milan #46/R

FILOSA, Giovanni B (1850-1935) Italian
Works on paper
£243 $375 €365 Seated woman (25x18cm-10x7in) s.d.1884 W/C. 27-Oct-2 Grogan, Boston #44
£949 $1500 €1500 On the terrace (60x45cm-24x18in) s. W/C card. 26-Nov-2 Christie's, Rome #28/R
£949 $1500 €1500 Waitig (60x45cm-24x18in) s.d.1885 W/C card. 26-Nov-2 Christie's, Rome #30
£1400 $2184 €2100 Costume ball (45x72cm-18x28in) s. W/C. 26-Mar-3 Sotheby's, Olympia #250/R est:1500-2000
£7000 $10990 €10500 Visito al palazzo pitti (98x71cm-39x28in) s. W/C. 19-Nov-2 Sotheby's, London #112/R est:5000-7000

FILZMOSER, Anton (1897-1969) Austrian
£324 $531 €450 Mountain landscape (24x31cm-9x12in) s. panel. 5-Jun-3 Dorotheum, Salzburg #630/R

FINART, Noel Dieudonne (attrib) (1797-1852) French
£1689 $2635 €2500 La deportation du peuple juif a Babylone (48x81cm-19x32in) 25-Mar-3 Chochon-Barre & Allardi, Paris #25/R est:2500-3000

FINCH, Alfred William (1854-1930) Belgian
£2014 $3223 €2800 Sand dunes (31x41cm-12x16in) s. canvas on board. 17-May-3 Hagelstam, Helsinki #143/R est:3000
£2658 $4200 €4200 The gate (27x35cm-11x14in) s. board. 1-Dec-2 Bukowskis, Helsinki #54/R est:4000-5000
£3239 $5215 €4600 Boat shelter by the shore (27x34cm-11x13in) s. board. 10-May-3 Bukowskis, Helsinki #98/R est:3500-4000
£6646 $10500 €10500 Rosehearty Pier in storm (31x41cm-12x16in) s. board exhib. 1-Dec-2 Bukowskis, Helsinki #53/R est:5000-6000
£9494 $15000 €15000 Red cottages (61x73cm-24x29in) s. exhib. 1-Dec-2 Bukowskis, Helsinki #55/R est:15000-20000

FINCH, Francis Oliver (1802-1862) British
Works on paper
£320 $509 €480 Waterfall under moonlight (16x21cm-6x8in) W/C. 25-Feb-3 Bonhams, Knightsbridge #163/R
£650 $1027 €975 Figures in a landscape (8x13cm-3x5in) W/C. 18-Dec-2 Mallams, Oxford #568
£2800 $4340 €4200 Dell of Comus (29x34cm-11x13in) W/C bodycol. 4-Dec-2 Christie's, Kensington #75/R est:1500-2000

FINCH, Spencer (1962-) American
Works on paper
£319 $505 €479 Blind spot - Dealy Plaza - Grassy knoll from the triple underpass (22x61cm-9x24in) d.12/5/96 W/C prov. 28-Apr-3 Bukowskis, Stockholm #953/R (S.KR 4200)
£335 $529 €503 Trying to remember the colour of Jackie Kennedy's pillbox hat 65 (28x22cm-11x9in) pastel prov. 28-Apr-3 Bukowskis, Stockholm #951/R (S.KR 4400)
£380 $601 €570 Trying to remember the colour of Jackie Kennedy's pillbox hat 66 (28x22cm-11x9in) pastel prov. 28-Apr-3 Bukowskis, Stockholm #952/R (S.KR 5000)

FINCHETT, Thomas (?) British
£410 $640 €615 Llyn Grafnand, near Llanwst (38x50cm-15x20in) s. s.i.on stretcher. 11-Sep-2 Bonhams, Newport #246

FINCK, Ludwig (1857-?) German
£1006 $1570 €1600 Taunus on autumn day (72x97cm-28x38in) s.d.1907 i. verso. 19-Sep-2 Dr Fritz Nagel, Stuttgart #928/R

FIND, Ludvig (1869-1945) Danish
£405 $653 €608 Young woman fixing her hat with flowers (37x32cm-15x13in) s.d.07 prov. 26-Feb-3 Muscumsbygningen, Copenhagen #60 (D.KR 4500)

FINDENIGG, Franz Paul (1726-1771) Austrian
£8784 $13703 €13000 Battle scenes from Wars of Prince Eugene of Saoy (37x50cm-15x20in) two. 27-Mar-3 Dorotheum, Vienna #309/R est:7000-10000

FINDORFF, Dietrich (1722-1792) German
£3205 $5032 €5000 Europa comes before her maid and sitting bull (40x49cm-16x19in) panel. 21-Nov-2 Dorotheum, Vienna #57/R est:7500-10000

FINELLI, Giuliano (style) (1601-1657) Italian
Sculpture
£10000 $16700 €14500 Bust of a gentleman (63cm-25in) white marble blk painted limestone base. 8-Jul-3 Sotheby's, London #132/R est:10000-15000

FINES, Eugène Francois (1826-1882) French
£670 $1085 €972 Figures at Rue de Lannion in Brittany (48x40cm-19x16in) s/. 26-May-3 Rasmussen, Copenhagen #1339/R (D.KR 7000)

FINETTI, Frank (19/20th C) Italian
£1258 $2000 €1887 Still life (46x38cm-18x15in) s. painted c.1900. 2-Mar-3 Toomey, Oak Park #592/R est:800-1200

FINEY, George Edmund (1895-1987) New Zealander
£299 $467 €449 Burnt log (25x35cm-10x14in) s. board. 21-Oct-2 Australian Art Auctions, Sydney #152 (A.D 850)

FINGESTEN, Michel (1884-1943) German?
Works on paper
£519 $758 €800 Hilly landscape with Spanish village (47x65cm-19x26in) s. W/C gouache pastel mixed media. 15-Jun-2 Hans Stahl, Hamburg #579/R

FINI, Leonor (1908-1996) Italian
£2500 $3975 €3750 Portrait de femme (24x19cm-9x7in) indis.sig. painted c.1946-50. 20-Mar-3 Sotheby's, Olympia #200/R est:3000-4000
£3600 $5544 €5400 Portrait de Raffaeli Carrieri (22x18cm-9x7in) s.d.1938 i.verso panel prov. 23-Oct-2 Sotheby's, Olympia #774/R est:4000-6000
£4690 $7503 €6800 Portrait de Madame Albouy (24x24cm-9x9in) s. 12-Mar-3 Libert, Castor, Paris #81 est:2000-2500
£10000 $16700 €14500 L'homme aux masques (61x38cm-24x15in) s. painted 1949 exhib. 25-Jun-3 Christie's, London #210/R est:10000-15000
£15000 $25050 €21750 L'eau endormie (60x92cm-24x36in) s. painted 1962 prov.lit. 25-Jun-3 Christie's, London #211/R est:15000-20000
£21583 $35396 €30000 Les enfants justiciers (101x81cm-40x32in) s. s.i.d.1976 on stretcher prov.exhib.lit. 3-Jun-3 Christie's, Amsterdam #223/R est:30000-50000
£24828 $39724 €36000 Gerard Albouy et sa soeur (46x38cm-18x15in) s. 12-Mar-3 Libert, Castor, Paris #82/R est:3000-4000
Sculpture
£306 $477 €459 Composition (26x16x700cm-10x6x276in) s. W/C. 6-Nov-2 Dobiaschofsky, Bern #1572 (S.FR 700)
Works on paper
£284 $414 €426 Il bacio (25x29cm-10x11in) s. ink. 4-Jun-2 Germann, Zurich #765 (S.FR 650)
£380 $600 €600 Danseuses (32x24cm-13x9in) s. W/C. 26-Nov-2 Palais de Beaux Arts, Brussels #93/R
£417 $658 €600 Scene erotique (28x19cm-11x7in) s. ink. 28-Apr-3 Cornette de St.Cyr, Paris #257/R
£420 $701 €600 Antonio (26x19cm-10x7in) s. ink dr. 26-Jun-3 Tajan, Paris #175
£451 $713 €650 Scene erotique (28x19cm-11x7in) s. ink. 28-Apr-3 Cornette de St.Cyr, Paris #255/R
£451 $713 €650 Scene erotique, deux personnages (28x19cm-11x7in) s. sanguine. 28-Apr-3 Cornette de St.Cyr, Paris #256/R
£451 $713 €650 Scene erotique (28x19cm-11x7in) s. ink. 28-Apr-3 Cornette de St.Cyr, Paris #258/R
£552 $883 €800 Four dancing figures (39x32cm-15x13in) s. pen ink dr. 15-Mar-3 De Vuyst, Lokeren #118
£574 $896 €850 Figures (42x33cm-17x13in) s. Chinese ink dr. 28-Mar-3 Farsetti, Prato #36
£611 $954 €917 Reclining woman with bare chest (43x40cm-17x16in) s. chl wash. 6-Nov-2 Dobiaschofsky, Bern #1573/R (S.FR 1400)
£633 $987 €1000 Femmes fleur (42x30cm-17x12in) dr htd chk. 20-Oct-2 Mercier & Cie, Lille #332a
£655 $1048 €950 Nude with hat (38x16cm-15x6in) s.pen ink dr. 15-Mar-3 De Vuyst, Lokeren #117
£699 $1168 €1000 Couple de femme (30x50cm-12x20in) s. W/C. 26-Jun-3 Tajan, Paris #174

£700 $1078 €1050 Personnages enturbannes (31x22cm-12x9in) s. pen ink htd gouache prov. 23-Oct-2 Sotheby's, Olympia #773/R
£750 $1155 €1125 Deux figures (36x23cm-14x9in) s. pen ink prov. 23-Oct-2 Sotheby's, Olympia #771/R
£800 $1232 €1200 Figures au jardin (38x29cm-15x11in) s. W/C pen ink htd gouache prov. 23-Oct-2 Sotheby's, Olympia #770/R
£897 $1391 €1400 Couple (39x29cm-15x11in) s. pen dr W/C pastel gouache. 7-Dec-2 De Vuyst, Lokeren #119
£1377 $2300 €1997 Fashion illustration (31x23cm-12x9in) s. ink wash two. 22-Jun-3 Freeman, Philadelphia #68/R est:1000-1500
£1799 $2878 €2500 Scene erotique (30x23cm-12x9in) s. Indian ink dr. 18-May-3 Eric Pillon, Calais #164/R
£1862 $2979 €2700 Le sphinx (32x23cm-13x9in) s. ink. 12-Mar-3 Libert, Castor, Paris #86 est:1000-1200
£2128 $3553 €3000 Sans titre (22x33cm-9x13in) s. mixed media cardboard exec.c.1960. 23-Jun-3 Claude Boisgirard, Paris #116/R est:3000-3500
£2414 $3862 €3500 Portrait de femme (33x23cm-13x9in) s. W/C. 12-Mar-3 Libert, Castor, Paris #85 est:800-1000
£2621 $4193 €3800 Femme de cirque (60x39cm-24x15in) s. gouache. 12-Mar-3 Libert, Castor, Paris #83 est:1200-1500
£2878 $4604 €4000 Face a face erotique (46x32cm-18x13in) s. mixed media lit. 18-May-3 Eric Pillon, Calais #162/R
£3205 $5032 €5000 Deux amies (68x51cm-27x20in) s.d.1935 gouache. 15-Dec-2 Eric Pillon, Calais #140/R
£4483 $7172 €6500 Autoportrait (57x53cm-22x21in) s. wax pastel. 12-Mar-3 Libert, Castor, Paris #84 est:1500-1800

FINK, Aaron (1955-) American
£892 $1400 €1338 Steaming cup (200x137cm-79x54in) s.d.1987 paper. 21-Nov-2 Swann Galleries, New York #46/R

FINK, Don (1923-) American
£795 $1295 €1200 Composition (81x100cm-32x39in) s.d.1960 oil acrylic prov.lit. 11-Feb-3 Segre, Madrid #282/R

FINK, Tone (1944-) Austrian
Works on paper
£314 $487 €500 Green grass (29x21cm-11x8in) s.i.d.79 mixed media. 30-Oct-2 Dorotheum, Vienna #44
£379 $607 €550 Composition (21x29cm-8x11in) s.i.d.1983 mixed media. 11-Mar-3 Dorotheum, Vienna #266/R
£483 $772 €700 Pointed hat (30x21cm-12x8in) s.i.d.80 mixed media. 11-Mar-3 Dorotheum, Vienna #260/R

FINK, Waldemar (1893-1948) Swiss
£278 $447 €417 Late summer evening near Adelboden (53x65cm-21x26in) s.d.1942 i. verso. 7-May-3 Dobiaschofsky, Bern #3231 (S.FR 600)
Works on paper
£307 $497 €445 Landscape near Adelboden (45x60cm-18x24in) s.i.d.1915-16 gouache prov. 24-May-3 Galerie Gloggner, Luzern #32 (S.FR 650)

FINKE, Auguste (19th C) Austrian
£4000 $6680 €6000 Hagia Sophia, Istanbul (57x75cm-22x30in) s. 18-Jun-3 Christie's, Kensington #185/R est:4000-6000

FINLAY, Virgil (1914-1971) American
£4348 $7000 €6522 Man hoisting himself out of water onto dock of golden city (36x25cm-14x10in) s. board. 10-May-3 Illustration House, New York #165/R est:4000-6000
£7051 $11000 €10577 Woman fleeing apocalyptic wave (51x36cm-20x14in) s. board. 9-Nov-2 Illustration House, New York #59/R est:5000-8000

FINLAYSON, Alfred (19th C) British
Works on paper
£380 $600 €551 Lilies in an Oriental vase (34x24cm-13x9in) s.d.1873 W/C bodycol. 22-Jul-3 Bonhams, Knightsbridge #173/R

FINN, Herbert John (1861-?) British
Works on paper
£300 $474 €450 On the Thames (56x76cm-22x30in) s. W/C. 27-Nov-2 Hamptons Fine Art, Godalming #242
£800 $1336 €1160 View of St Pauls from the Thames (55x73cm-22x29in) s.d.1916 W/C. 24-Jun-3 Bonhams, Knowle #17/R

FINNE, Ferdinand (1910-1999) Norwegian
£518 $865 €751 Almunecar, Spain (63x77cm-25x30in) s. i.d.April 1959 verso. 18-Jun-3 Grev Wedels Plass, Oslo #169/R (N.KR 6000)
£1301 $2029 €1952 Landscape from Langoya (84x91cm-33x36in) s.d.52. 21-Oct-2 Blomqvist, Oslo #397/R est:20000-30000 (N.KR 15000)
£1357 $2199 €2036 Landscape from Narestoe (70x90cm-28x35in) s. i.d.1963 verso. 26-May-3 Grev Wedels Plass, Oslo #67/R est:20000-30000 (N.KR 15000)

FINNE, Gunnar (1886-1952) Finnish
Sculpture
£1408 $2268 €2000 Cosmos (42x89cm-17x35in) s. bronze exhib. 10-May-3 Bukowskis, Helsinki #5/R est:3500-4000

FINOT, Jules Baron (1826-1906) French
Works on paper
£769 $1177 €1200 Chevaux au galop (10x12cm-4x5in) s. gouache. 23-Aug-2 Deauville, France #112

FINOTTI, Novello (1939-) Italian
Sculpture
£2436 $3824 €3800 Metamorphosis (47x21cm-19x8in) s. bronze. 19-Nov-2 Finarte, Milan #41/R est:3000-4000

FINSON, Louis (attrib) (1580-1617) Flemish
£2293 $3577 €3600 Maria Magdalena (111x91cm-44x36in) 6-Nov-2 Vendue Huis, Gravenhage #364/R est:3000-4000
£5063 $8000 €8000 JUdith with Olopherne's head (115x90cm-45x35in) 2-Dec-2 Finarte, Milan #184/R est:12000
£8000 $12560 €12000 Man in a fir-lined cap holding a glass of wine with a gold chain (54x46cm-21x18in) 13-Dec-2 Christie's, Kensington #8/R est:8000-12000

FINSON, Louis (circle) (1580-1617) Flemish
£12000 $18840 €18000 Portrait of a cavalier (57x46cm-22x18in) 10-Dec-2 Sotheby's, Olympia #343/R est:6000-8000

FINSTER, Howard (1916-) American
£1481 $2400 €2222 Highway to heaven (61x48cm-24x19in) s. enamel on wood painted c.1986 prov.lit. 27-Jan-3 Christie's, Rockefeller NY #99/R est:2500-3500

FINZI, Ennio (1931-) Italian
£590 $939 €850 Untitled (70x100cm-28x39in) s.d.1987 tempera paper. 1-May-3 Meeting Art, Vercelli #32
£612 $973 €900 Untitled (70x100cm-28x39in) s.d.1987 tempera paper. 1-Mar-3 Meeting Art, Vercelli #341
£759 $1200 €1200 Untitled (70x100cm-28x39in) s. card on canvas. 29-Nov-2 Farsetti, Prato #225/R
£833 $1292 €1300 Towards light (50x50cm-20x20in) s. painted 2000. 5-Dec-2 Stadion, Trieste #802/R
£833 $1325 €1200 Towards pink (50x70cm-20x28in) s.i.d.1988 verso. 1-May-3 Meeting Art, Vercelli #150
£980 $1569 €1500 Black light (50x70cm-20x28in) s. cardboard on canvas lit. 4-Jan-3 Meeting Art, Vercelli #693
Works on paper
£374 $595 €550 Plan or tablecloth (70x50cm-28x20in) s.d.1984 mixed media paper on canvas. 1-Mar-3 Meeting Art, Vercelli #579
£544 $865 €800 Plan for tablecloth (50x50cm-20x20in) s.d.1984 mixed media paper on canvas. 1-Mar-3 Meeting Art, Vercelli #580
£612 $973 €900 Composition (70x100cm-28x39in) s. mixed media paper on canvas. 1-Mar-3 Meeting Art, Vercelli #334
£633 $987 €1000 Untitled (70x100cm-28x39in) s.d.1985 mixed media cardboard on canvas. 14-Sep-2 Meeting Art, Vercelli #736/R
£633 $987 €1000 Untitled (70x100cm-28x39in) s.d.1987 mixed media cardboard on canvas. 14-Sep-2 Meeting Art, Vercelli #759/R
£680 $1082 €1000 Untitled (70x100cm-28x39in) s. mixed media card on canvas. 1-Mar-3 Meeting Art, Vercelli #592
£680 $1082 €1000 Untitled (70x100cm-28x39in) s. mixed media card on canvas. 1-Mar-3 Meeting Art, Vercelli #614
£694 $1104 €1000 Composition (100x70cm-39x28in) s.d.1994 mixed media card on canvas. 1-May-3 Meeting Art, Vercelli #232

FIOL, Gabriel (1905-) Spanish
£987 $1599 €1500 View of San Vicente (38x46cm-15x18in) s. board. 21-Jan-3 Ansorena, Madrid #60/R
£987 $1599 €1500 Coastal landscape (34x41cm-13x16in) s. 21-Jan-3 Ansorena, Madrid #59/R

FIORAVANTI, Ugo (19/20th C) Italian
£226 $375 €328 Spanish Steps, Rome (28x38cm-11x15in) s. canvas on board. 14-Jun-3 Jackson's, Cedar Falls #206/R

FIORESI, Garcia (1888-1968) Italian
£1384 $2131 €2200 Virginia (58x66cm-23x26in) s. cardboard. 28-Oct-2 Il Ponte, Milan #332

FIORI, Ernesto di (1884-1945) German
Works on paper
£652 $1070 €900 Seated woman. Nude sketch (41x25cm-16x10in) s. pencil two. 29-May-3 Lempertz, Koln #619/R

FIORINI, Ilio (1912-) Italian
£372 $580 €550 Harbour (50x79cm-20x31in) s. board. 28-Mar-3 Farsetti, Prato #444/R

FIORONI, Giosetta (1932-) Italian
£490 $784 €750 Mundial (40x40cm-16x16in) s.i.tempera oil card. 4-Jan-3 Meeting Art, Vercelli #473

Works on paper
£385 $604 €600 Acrobat on the table (70x50cm-28x20in) s. mixed media card. 23-Nov-2 Meeting Art, Vercelli #62
£641 $1026 €930 Untitled (70x48cm-28x19in) s. mixed media cardboard. 11-Mar-3 Babuino, Rome #344/R

FIOT, Maximilien Louis (1886-1953) French
Sculpture
£2800 $4676 €4060 Two panthers grooming (42x64cm-17x25in) s.i. green pat bronze f.Susse. 8-Jul-3 Sotheby's, London #193/R est:3000-5000
£3800 $6156 €5700 Pair of lionesses (43cm-17in) s. green pat. bronze. 20-May-3 Sotheby's, Olympia #118/R est:2000-3000

FIRFIRES, Nicholas S (1917-1990) American
Works on paper
£1122 $1750 €1683 Bucking bronco (28x23cm-11x9in) s. W/C prov. 9-Nov-2 Santa Fe Art, Santa Fe #17/R est:500-1500

FIRLE, Walter (1859-1929) German
£779 $1161 €1200 Two small girls looking at a picture book (62x54cm-24x21in) s. 28-Jun-2 Sigalas, Stuttgart #788/R

FIRTH, Margaret (1898-1991) British
£360 $558 €540 Soft brown flower (45x55cm-18x22in) s. board. 1-Oct-2 Bonhams, Leeds #347/R

FIRTH-SMITH, John (1943-) Australian
£1286 $2006 €1929 Ham at sea (61x90cm-24x35in) s.i.d.97 verso prov. 11-Nov-2 Deutscher-Menzies, Melbourne #72/R est:4000-6000 (A.D 3600)
£2129 $3364 €3194 Yacht in slip III (79x119cm-31x47in) s.i.d.77 oil collage synthetic polymer on paper prov. 27-Nov-2 Deutscher-Menzies, Melbourne #160/R est:2500-3500 (A.D 5960)
£2829 $4413 €4902 Untitled (151x57cm-59x22in) oil rag paper prov. 31-Mar-3 Goodman, Sydney #162 (A.D 7500)
£3036 $4736 €4554 Time at Jim Jim (92x92cm-36x36in) s.i.d.1981 verso linen. 11-Nov-2 Deutscher-Menzies, Melbourne #12/R est:6000-9000 (A.D 8500)
£5357 $8464 €8036 Out there, first on the harbour (101x200cm-40x79in) s. i.d.1977 verso prov. 17-Nov-2 Sotheby's, Paddington #5/R est:18000-28000 (A.D 15000)
£6400 $10304 €9600 Time being (91x91cm-36x36in) s.i.d.81 oil on linen prov. 6-May-3 Christie's, Melbourne #12/R est:16000-20000 (A.D 16000)
£7692 $12231 €11538 Storm light (91x91cm-36x36in) s.i. s.i.d.99 verso. 4-Mar-3 Deutscher-Menzies, Melbourne #6/R est:12000-16000 (A.D 20000)
£9195 $13701 €13793 Heatwave (91x91cm-36x36in) s.i. prov. 27-Aug-2 Christie's, Melbourne #13/R est:15000-20000 (A.D 24000)
£10676 $16335 €16014 Altered time (94x367cm-37x144in) s.d.81 verso. 25-Aug-2 Sotheby's, Paddington #28/R est:30000-50000 (A.D 30000)
£10769 $17123 €16154 Ding-a-ding day (137x198cm-54x78in) s. s.i.d.1963 verso composition board exhib. 4-Mar-3 Deutscher-Menzies, Melbourne #88/R est:25000-35000 (A.D 28000)
£14286 $22286 €21429 Eye of the storm (122x244cm-48x96in) s.i.d.85 verso linen lit. 11-Nov-2 Deutscher-Menzies, Melbourne #34/R est:30000-50000 (A.D 40000)

Works on paper
£1357 $2117 €2036 Rock, turkey at sea (61x90cm-24x35in) s.i.d.1997 verso. 11-Nov-2 Deutscher-Menzies, Melbourne #73/R est:4000-6000 (A.D 3800)
£1357 $2157 €2036 Untitled (56x76cm-22x30in) s.d.69 synthetic polymer paint. 5-May-3 Sotheby's, Melbourne #229 est:2000-4000 (A.D 3500)
£1731 $2752 €2597 Abstract, New York City (75x37cm-30x15in) s.i.d.82 W/C gouache pastel. 4-Mar-3 Deutscher-Menzies, Melbourne #171/R est:3200-3800 (A.D 4500)
£1833 $3005 €2750 Fighting flag, straight left to the Americans (77x115cm-30x45in) s.i.d.84 W/C. 4-Jun-3 Deutscher-Menzies, Melbourne #323/R est:3000-5000 (A.D 4600)
£2390 $3920 €3585 Flying time (57x93cm-22x37in) s.i.d.81 synthetic polymer paint prov. 4-Jun-3 Deutscher-Menzies, Melbourne #155/R est:6500-8500 (A.D 6000)
£5658 $8827 €9803 Tide (300x92cm-118x36in) s.d.92 mixed media paper on canvas prov. 31-Mar-3 Goodman, Sydney #167/R (A.D 15000)
£11240 $17872 €16860 Sweedee dee no 2; thinking of sayonora (153x460cm-60x181in) s.d.1973 i.verso synthetic polymer canvas exhib. 5-May-3 Sotheby's, Melbourne #154/R est:25000-35000 (A.D 29000)

FISCHBACH, Johann (1797-1871) German
£4114 $6500 €6500 Smuggler (87x70cm-34x28in) s.d.1850. 28-Nov-2 Dorotheum, Vienna #122/R est:6000-8500

FISCHBECK, Ludwig (1866-?) German
£374 $595 €550 Hasbruch in autumn (70x100cm-28x39in) s. 28-Mar-3 Bolland & Marotz, Bremen #337

FISCHER, Adam (1888-1968) Danish
Sculpture
£2032 $3150 €3048 Head (64cm-25in) stone executed 1922 lot. 1-Oct-2 Rasmussen, Copenhagen #297/R est:25000-30000 (D.KR 24000)

FISCHER, Anton Otto (1882-1962) American
£573 $900 €860 Still life of a large potted violet with lush foliage (46x61cm-18x24in) s. 23-Nov-2 Pook & Pook, Downington #141/R
£932 $1500 €1398 Expedition trekking though hilly landscape (33x76cm-13x30in) s.d. 20-Feb-3 Illustration House, New York #60/R est:2000-3000
£1019 $1600 €1529 Eight gentlemen celebrating around a table (56x71cm-22x28in) s. 23-Nov-2 Pook & Pook, Downington #160/R est:800-1200
£1667 $2700 €2501 Battle royal (41x76cm-16x30in) s.d.15 i.verso. 24-Jan-3 Freeman, Philadelphia #169/R est:2000-3000
£1923 $3000 €2885 Interior scene with men smoking pipes (61x56cm-24x22in) s.d.1935. 22-Sep-2 Jeffery Burchard, Florida #90a
£1923 $3000 €2885 Urban street with police officer and postal worker (71x56cm-28x22in) s.d.1938. 22-Sep-2 Jeffery Burchard, Florida #90b
£2019 $3250 €3029 Ship burning at sea (51x122cm-20x48in) s. painted c.1940. 10-May-3 Illustration House, New York #52/R est:4000-6000

FISCHER, August (1854-1921) Danish
£272 $430 €408 Coastal landscape with figures, Italy (18x34cm-7x13in) s.i.d.1905. 30-Nov-2 Rasmussen, Havnen #2240 (D.KR 3200)
£359 $574 €539 View from Nuremberg (37x29cm-15x11in) s. 13-Jan-3 Rasmussen, Vejle #221/R (D.KR 4100)
£399 $646 €599 Canal view from Brugge (43x30cm-17x12in) s. 25-Jan-3 Rasmussen, Havnen #2010/R (D.KR 4500)
£517 $786 €776 Young woman by village house (43x30cm-17x12in) s. 27-Aug-2 Rasmussen, Copenhagen #1706/R (D.KR 6000)
£541 $870 €812 Rakkernes Tower, Nuremberg (58x43cm-23x17in) s.d.1902. 22-Feb-3 Rasmussen, Havnen #2001/R (D.KR 6000)
£553 $874 €830 Town scene, possibly Hamburg (43x56cm-17x22in) s. 2-Dec-2 Rasmussen, Copenhagen #1215/R (D.KR 6500)
£559 $888 €839 Figures at market in Verona (38x28cm-15x11in) s.i. 5-Mar-3 Rasmussen, Copenhagen #1785/R (D.KR 6000)
£574 $930 €832 Am Pferdebom im Hamborg (28x38cm-11x15in) s. 26-May-3 Rasmussen, Copenhagen #1570/R (D.KR 6000)
£641 $994 €1000 Nurnberg (26x37cm-10x15in) s. 7-Dec-2 Hans Stahl, Hamburg #12/R
£811 $1305 €1217 Street scene with figures, Koge (46x57cm-18x22in) s.i.d.1916. 22-Feb-3 Rasmussen, Havnen #2016/R (D.KR 9000)
£840 $1311 €1260 Fishing trip, Ribe river (40x30cm-16x12in) s.i.d.1916. 11-Nov-2 Rasmussen, Vejle #690/R (D.KR 9800)
£1138 $1821 €1707 View of the harbour in Palermo (26x39cm-10x15in) s.d.Feb.84. 13-Jan-3 Rasmussen, Vejle #64/R est:15000-18000 (D.KR 13000)

FISCHER, Benno Joachim Theodor (1828-1865) German
£458 $750 €700 Portraits of elegant man and woman (84x68cm-33x27in) s.d.848 pair. 29-Mar-3 Dannenberg, Berlin #567/R

FISCHER, C (?) ?
£988 $1531 €1482 Mother minding sleeping child (85x70cm-33x28in) s.d.1886. 3-Dec-2 Ritchie, Toronto #3091/R est:2000-3000 (C.D 2400)

FISCHER, Carl (1887-1962) Danish
£279 $441 €419 Still life (61x52cm-24x20in) 1-Apr-3 Rasmussen, Copenhagen #544 (D.KR 3000)
£419 $700 €608 Landscape from Haervejen, Viborg (66x75cm-26x30in) s. prov. 17-Jun-3 Rasmussen, Copenhagen #183/R (D.KR 4400)
£450 $725 €675 Girl wearing white dress seen from behind (40x32cm-16x13in) s.d.14 panel. 22-Feb-3 Rasmussen, Havnen #2040/R (D.KR 5000)
£467 $729 €701 Woman seated on chair with straw hat next to her (52x42cm-20x17in) s.d.24 exhib. 5-Aug-2 Rasmussen, Vejle #78/R (D.KR 5500)
£548 $872 €822 Portrait of the artist's wife (80x60cm-31x24in) s. 26-Feb-3 Kunsthallen, Copenhagen #358/R (D.KR 6000)

FISCHER, Carl H (1885-1955) Danish
£287 $443 €431 Still life of fruit and lobster (69x99cm-27x39in) s. 26-Oct-2 Rasmussen, Havnen #2033 (D.KR 3400)
£338 $527 €507 Picnic in the field (46x62cm-18x24in) s. 23-Sep-2 Rasmussen, Vejle #197/R (D.KR 4000)
£350 $532 €525 Poppies, daisies and wild flowers in a vase (70x100cm-28x39in) s. 29-Aug-2 Christie's, Kensington #74

FISCHER, Clara (1856-?) German
£1905 $3029 €2800 Bunch of roses in vase (46x38cm-18x15in) s. 25-Feb-3 Dorotheum, Vienna #203/R est:2800-3200

FISCHER, Eduard (1852-1905) German
£1020 $1622 €1500 Lake in the evening (53x91cm-21x36in) s.d.89. 19-Mar-3 Neumeister, Munich #554 est:1300

FISCHER, Eugen (20th C) American
Works on paper
£683 $1100 €1025 Theorem of George Washington in uniform astride his white steed (56x43cm-22x17in) ink W/C fabric. 22-Feb-3 Pook & Pook, Downington #267/R

FISCHER, Fritz (1925-1986) Austrian
£282 $468 €400 Hilly landscape in summer with sluice and houses (43x58cm-17x23in) s. 14-Jun-3 Arnold, Frankfurt #740

FISCHER, Georges Alexandre (1820-?) French
£2885 $4529 €4500 Famille paysanne devant la chaumiere (64x83cm-25x33in) s. 15-Dec-2 Thierry & Lannon, Brest #137

FISCHER, Hans Christian (1849-1886) Danish
£2239 $3560 €3359 Summer landscape with woodland lake, harvesters in background (125x86cm-49x34in) s.d.1882-83 exhib. 5-May-3 Rasmussen, Vejle #432/R est:20000-25000 (D.KR 24000)

FISCHER, Heinrich (1820-1886) Swiss
£510 $811 €750 Goats in the hight mountains (27x37cm-11x15in) s.i. board. 20-Mar-3 Neumeister, Munich #2616/R
£2096 $3270 €3144 View from Pilatus to Vierwaldstat lake (41x55cm-16x22in) s.i. paper on board. 8-Nov-2 Dobiaschofsky, Bern #28/R est:6000 (S.FR 4800)

FISCHER, Hermann (1905-1991) German
Works on paper
£317 $510 €450 Cote d'Azur (19x31cm-7x12in) s. W/C. 7-May-3 Michael Zeller, Lindau #697/R
£352 $567 €500 Vierwaldstatter See (31x46cm-12x18in) s.d.71 W/C. 7-May-3 Michael Zeller, Lindau #699/R

FISCHER, Joel (1947-) American
Sculpture
£2800 $4564 €4200 Untitled (64x116cm-25x46in) s.d.1994 bronze prov. 3-Feb-3 Sotheby's, Olympia #100/R est:3000-4000

FISCHER, Johann (1919-) Austrian
Works on paper
£741 $1200 €1112 Untitled - cow. Untitled- dog (30x40cm-12x16in) init.d.1985 col pencil pair. 27-Jan-3 Christie's, Rockefeller NY #118/R est:800-1200

FISCHER, Johann Georg Paul (1786-1875) German
Miniatures
£1700 $2839 €2465 Possibly Augustus, 1st Duke of Cambridge, in uniform (8cm-3xin) init.d.18 gilt metal mount rec. frame oval. 25-Jun-3 Sotheby's, Olympia #10/R est:1000-1500

FISCHER, L (?) ?
£1026 $1600 €1539 Mountain landscape (41x51cm-16x20in) 11-Apr-3 Du Mouchelle, Detroit #2156/R est:300-500

FISCHER, Leopold (1813-1864) Austrian
Works on paper
£1081 $1686 €1600 Portrait of woman in black velvet dress (20x15cm-8x6in) s.d.839 W/C. 28-Mar-3 Dorotheum, Vienna #208/R est:800-1000

FISCHER, Ludwig Hans (1848-1915) German
£262 $414 €393 Middle sea bay with fishing boat (14x27cm-6x11in) s.d.1879 panel. 26-Nov-2 Hans Widmer, St Gallen #1105 (S.FR 610)
Works on paper
£393 $624 €590 From Sorrento (38x23cm-15x9in) s.i. w/C. 8-Mar-3 Dorotheum, Prague #164/R est:18000-27000 (C.KR 18000)
£946 $1476 €1400 View from Liliengasse of Stefansdom (41x25cm-16x10in) s.d.1911 W/C. 28-Mar-3 Dorotheum, Vienna #356/R

FISCHER, Paul (1860-1934) Danish
£273 $422 €410 Young woman with basket, Copenhagen (9x13cm-4x5in) mono. sketch. 28-Sep-2 Rasmussen, Havnen #2012 (D.KR 3200)
£431 $655 €647 View towards Frederiksborg Palace (28x18cm-11x7in) prov. 27-Aug-2 Rasmussen, Copenhagen #1832/R (D.KR 5000)
£441 $710 €662 Four horses with nosebags and two carts waiting (17x28cm-7x11in) s.verso panel. 19-Jan-3 Hindemae, Ullerslev #7294/R (D.KR 5000)
£700 $1112 €1050 Feeding the horses (17x28cm-7x11in) with sig. verso. 5-May-3 Rasmussen, Vejle #600/R (D.KR 7500)
£1053 $1705 €1527 The artist Peder Monsted and his wife Elna Mathilde (40x30cm-16x12in) s. one d.9-8-95 one d.13-9-94 pair prov. 26-May-3 Rasmussen, Copenhagen #1550/R (D.KR 11000)
£1206 $1833 €1809 Street scene in Naples with figures (38x29cm-15x11in) s.i.d.1922. 28-Aug-2 Museumsbygningen, Copenhagen #26/R est:10000-12000 (D.KR 14000)
£1532 $2420 €2298 Pink flowers in vase (38x26cm-15x10in) s. 2-Dec-2 Rasmussen, Copenhagen #1462/R est:20000-25000 (D.KR 18000)
£1550 $2357 €2325 Lady's leg with black stiletto shoe (7x9cm-3x4in) s. grisaille. 27-Aug-2 Rasmussen, Copenhagen #1955/R est:12000-15000 (D.KR 18000)
£1715 $2676 €2573 Portrait of the artist's wife (41x25cm-16x10in) mono. 11-Nov-2 Rasmussen, Vejle #520/R est:20000 (D.KR 20000)
£1802 $2901 €2703 Grey day with figures at Town Hall Square (20x25cm-8x10in) s. panel. 22-Feb-3 Rasmussen, Havnen #2262/R est:20000 (D.KR 20000)
£1872 $2958 €2808 Italian woman with water jug (42x56cm-17x22in) s.i.d.Dec 94. 2-Dec-2 Rasmussen, Copenhagen #1185/R est:30000 (D.KR 22000)
£1872 $2958 €2808 Portrait of lady in profile wearing hat (25x21cm-10x8in) s.d.feb.1890 panel. 30-Nov-2 Rasmussen, Havnen #2173/R est:10000 (D.KR 22000)
£2067 $3142 €3101 View of Kongen's Nytorv with the Royal Theatre (17x22cm-7x9in) study prov. 27-Aug-2 Rasmussen, Copenhagen #1501/R est:12000-15000 (D.KR 24000)
£2270 $3518 €3405 Town gate with guard, Copenhagen (40x56cm-16x22in) s. 4-Dec-2 AB Stockholms Auktionsverk #1884/R est:40000-50000 (S.KR 32000)
£2534 $3953 €3801 Interior scene with young woman writing letter by lamp-light (29x23cm-11x9in) s. panel. 23-Sep-2 Rasmussen, Vejle #33/R est:20000-25000 (D.KR 30000)
£2756 $4189 €4134 Square in Naples with figures, horses and carts (38x28cm-15x11in) s.i.d.1922. 28-Aug-2 Museumsbygningen, Copenhagen #28/R est:15000-20000 (D.KR 32000)
£3078 $4895 €4617 From Magstraede, Copenhagen - street scene (25x20cm-10x8in) s. 5-May-3 Rasmussen, Vejle #317/R est:25000-30000 (D.KR 33000)
£3103 $5027 €4499 Coastal landscape (43x63cm-17x25in) s. 26-May-3 Bukowskis, Stockholm #286/R est:30000-40000 (S.KR 40000)
£3445 $5237 €5168 Southern terrace with pots (36x35cm-14x14in) s.i. 27-Aug-2 Rasmussen, Copenhagen #1438/R est:40000-50000 (D.KR 40000)
£3445 $5237 €5168 Selling fish at Gammel Strand on a rainy day (24x18cm-9x7in) s. panel. 27-Aug-2 Rasmussen, Copenhagen #1446/R est:12000-18000 (D.KR 40000)
£3731 $5933 €5597 From Town Hall Square, Copenhagen (25x209cm-10x82in) s. 5-May-3 Rasmussen, Vejle #316/R est:25000-30000 (D.KR 40000)
£3797 $6000 €6000 Summer landscape (57x75cm-22x30in) s.i.d.1913. 1-Dec-2 Bukowskis, Helsinki #243/R est:7000-10000
£4306 $6976 €6244 Girl by well outside a red wooden Swedish house (37x53cm-15x21in) s.i. 26-May-3 Rasmussen, Copenhagen #1161/R est:50000 (D.KR 45000)
£4307 $6546 €6461 Italian street scene, possibly Naples with church in background (47x33cm-19x13in) s. 28-Aug-2 Museumsbygningen, Copenhagen #30/R est:40000 (D.KR 50000)
£4307 $6546 €6461 Coastal landscape with girl looking out at water, possibly Hvidsten (44x31cm-17x12in) 27-Aug-2 Rasmussen, Copenhagen #1487/R est:50000 (D.KR 50000)

£4307 $6546 €6461 Elegant couple walking by church in winter (32x35cm-13x14in) indis.sig. painted c.1890. 27-Aug-2 Rasmussen, Copenhagen #1837/R est:25000-30000 (D.KR 50000)

£4737 $7201 €7106 Small girl by farmhouse in Baastad (33x48cm-13x19in) s.d.1915. 27-Aug-2 Rasmussen, Copenhagen #1459/R est:40000-50000 (D.KR 55000)

£4842 $7698 €7263 Figures walking in town in autumn (31x38cm-12x15in) s. panel. 5-Mar-3 Rasmussen, Copenhagen #1524/R est:50000 (D.KR 52000)

£5028 $7994 €7542 Fisherwomen at Gammel Strand (33x42cm-13x17in) s.i. 5-Mar-3 Rasmussen, Copenhagen #1565/R est:60000 (D.KR 54000)

£5161 $8000 €7742 Female bathers on a beach (39x55cm-15x22in) s. 30-Oct-2 Christie's, Rockefeller NY #174/R est:10000-15000

£5214 $8291 €7821 Prince Georg and Prince Valdemar toasting with champagne (26x22cm-10x9in) mono. 5-Mar-3 Rasmussen, Copenhagen #1533/R est:30000-40000 (D.KR 56000)

£5319 $8245 €7979 Copenhagen station (19x25cm-7x10in) s. panel. 4-Dec-2 AB Stockholms Auktionsverk #1855/R est:80000-100000 (S.KR 75000)

£6517 $10557 €9450 In the lamp-light, evening (29x22cm-11x9in) s. panel. 26-May-3 Bukowskis, Stockholm #283/R est:70000-80000 (S.KR 84000)

£6517 $10557 €9450 Street scene in winter, Copenhagen (25x20cm-10x8in) s. panel. 26-May-3 Bukowskis, Stockholm #287/R est:60000-70000 (S.KR 84000)

£6518 $10363 €9777 The artist's wife Martha Vilhelmine reading on a terrace (56x40cm-22x16in) s. painted c.1912. 5-Mar-3 Rasmussen, Copenhagen #1530/R est:75000 (D.KR 70000)

£6699 $10852 €9714 Summer's day with girl cyclist in front of Nyboder (32x38cm-13x15in) s. panel. 26-May-3 Rasmussen, Copenhagen #1214/R est:75000 (D.KR 70000)

£6699 $10852 €9714 Education - Why have they cut her arms off? Because she sucked her fingers (29x22cm-11x9in) mono. grisaille. 26-May-3 Rasmussen, Copenhagen #1218/R est:80000 (D.KR 70000)

£6699 $10852 €9714 Mother and child feeding swans near Soepavillion (20x25cm-8x10in) s. grisaille panel. 26-May-3 Rasmussen, Copenhagen #1219/R est:80000 (D.KR 70000)

£6797 $10603 €10196 Street scene with figures, Naples (50x58cm-20x23in) s.i.d.1922. 5-Aug-2 Rasmussen, Vejle #125/R est:75000-100000 (D.KR 80000)

£6891 $10474 €10337 Autumn day at Town Hall Square (32x39cm-13x15in) s. 27-Aug-2 Rasmussen, Copenhagen #1449/R est:40000-60000 (D.KR 80000)

£6891 $10474 €10337 Young female student with cap (33x41cm-13x16in) s. 27-Aug-2 Rasmussen, Copenhagen #1838/R est:80000 (D.KR 80000)

£7234 $11430 €10851 Guards at Amalienborg Palace (32x39cm-13x15in) s. panel. 2-Dec-2 Rasmussen, Copenhagen #1179/R est:60000-80000 (D.KR 85000)

£8134 $13177 €11794 After the concert - many figures by Odd Fellows Palace in Bredgade (20x25cm-8x10in) s. grisaille. 26-May-3 Rasmussen, Copenhagen #1217/R est:100000 (D.KR 85000)

£9311 $14804 €13967 Walking underneath the palm trees, San Remo (39x54cm-15x21in) s.i.d.1913. 5-Mar-3 Rasmussen, Copenhagen #1570/R est:100000 (D.KR 100000)

£9427 $15460 €13669 Winter's day in Copenhagen (32x39cm-13x15in) s. 4-Jun-3 AB Stockholms Auktionsverk #2437/R est:150000-200000 (S.KR 120000)

£10000 $16700 €14500 Figures in a town square in winter (39x55cm-15x22in) s.d.1918. 17-Jun-3 Bonhams, New Bond Street #31/R est:10000-15000

£10213 $16136 €15320 View of Holmen Canal with buildings (73x102cm-29x40in) s.d.1929. 2-Dec-2 Rasmussen, Copenhagen #1216/R est:75000-125000 (D.KR 120000)

£11483 $18603 €16650 In front of Domhuset, Nytorv in winter (39x56cm-15x22in) s. painted c.1930. 26-May-3 Rasmussen, Copenhagen #1216/R est:125000-150000 (D.KR 120000)

£11915 $18826 €17873 Where is my partner for tennis? (40x32cm-16x13in) s. 2-Dec-2 Rasmussen, Copenhagen #1119/R est:75000-125000 (D.KR 140000)

£12766 $20170 €19149 The garden at Hvidsten with artist's son Sigurd and friend picking flowers (47x37cm-19x15in) s.d.94 panel. 2-Dec-2 Rasmussen, Copenhagen #1101/R est:150000-200000 (D.KR 150000)

£15319 $24204 €22979 View of Kongen's Nytorv with figures (39x55cm-15x22in) s.d.1905. 2-Dec-2 Rasmussen, Copenhagen #1180/R est:225000 (D.KR 180000)

£15319 $24204 €22979 Girls bathing (50x60cm-20x24in) s. 2-Dec-2 Rasmussen, Copenhagen #1191/R est:175000-200000 (D.KR 180000)

£15711 $25766 €22781 Evening on the water - figures on board a passenger ship (18x27cm-7x11in) mono. panel. 4-Jun-3 AB Stockholms Auktionsverk #2438/R est:200000-225000 (S.KR 200000)

£16596 $26221 €24894 Street scene with two friends (34x42cm-13x17in) mono. 2-Dec-2 Rasmussen, Copenhagen #1205/R est:75000-100000 (D.KR 195000)

£17021 $26894 €25532 Three bathing girls by beach (42x63cm-17x25in) s. 2-Dec-2 Rasmussen, Copenhagen #1192/R est:200000-250000 (D.KR 200000)

£17691 $28128 €26537 Copenhagen scene with ladies bying flowers at Hojbro Plads (39x54cm-15x21in) s. 5-Mar-3 Rasmussen, Copenhagen #1534/R est:200000-300000 (D.KR 190000)

£20672 $31421 €31008 Elegant gentleman buying flowers at Hojbro Plads (27x41cm-11x16in) s. prov. 27-Aug-2 Rasmussen, Copenhagen #1453/R est:200000-250000 (D.KR 240000)

£22000 $36080 €33000 Ved gammel strand - Gammel Strand (58x74cm-23x29in) s. prov.lit. 3-Jun-3 Sotheby's, London #229/R est:30000-50000

£22695 $35177 €34043 Flower market at Hojebro Square, Copenhagen (39x32cm-15x13in) s. panel. 4-Dec-2 AB Stockholms Auktionsverk #1907/R est:200000-250000 (S.KR 320000)

£25532 $39574 €38298 Fishwives at Gammel Strand (58x75cm-23x30in) s.d.1924. 3-Dec-2 Bukowskis, Stockholm #313/R est:350000-400000 (S.KR 360000)

£25840 $39276 €38760 Street scene from Vesterbrogade with Liberty Statue in background (57x75cm-22x30in) s. 27-Aug-2 Rasmussen, Copenhagen #1448/R est:300000 (D.KR 300000)

£33493 $54258 €48565 Evening at Stroget in Ostergade near Illum (51x37cm-20x15in) s. 26-May-3 Rasmussen, Copenhagen #1221/R est:400000 (D.KR 350000)

£43062 $69761 €62440 Interior scene with the artist's brother Erik and his wife Anna and children (54x72cm-21x28in) s.d.April 1912 sold with two oval portraits. 26-May-3 Rasmussen, Copenhagen #1139/R est:450000-500000 (D.KR 450000)

£43062 $69761 €62440 The artist's wife Musse reading at home, Sofievej (57x40cm-22x16in) s.d.1917. 26-May-3 Rasmussen, Copenhagen #1143/R est:500000 (D.KR 450000)

£48234 $73316 €72351 Summer evening at Tivoli with many figures (42x53cm-17x21in) s.d.1888. 27-Aug-2 Rasmussen, Copenhagen #1450/R est:500000 (D.KR 560000)

£55319 $87404 €82979 Girl with bicycle buying summer flowers at Hojbro Plads (50x58cm-20x23in) s. 2-Dec-2 Rasmussen, Copenhagen #1186/R est:600000-700000 (D.KR 650000)

£55866 $88827 €83799 Red tulips - scene from Amagertorv (58x76cm-23x30in) s. 5-Mar-3 Rasmussen, Copenhagen #1523/R est:600000-800000 (D.KR 600000)

£59574 $94128 €89361 Winter's day in town - figures by Hellingands Church (84x65cm-33x26in) S.I.D.1912. 2-Dec-2 Rasmussen, Copenhagen #1181/R est:700000-1000000 (D.KR 700000)

£86133 $130922 €129200 Many figures at Kongen's Nytorv - among them the artist's second wife Musse (58x79cm-23x31in) s. exhib. 27-Aug-2 Rasmussen, Copenhagen #1458/R est:1200000 (D.KR 1000000)

£102128 $161362 €153192 Afternoon tea at the artist's home at Sofievej (62x74cm-24x29in) s. 2-Dec-2 Rasmussen, Copenhagen #1187/R est:1000000 (D.KR 1200000)

Prints

£105263 $170526 €152631 Artist's wife Musse and daughter Grethe in front of Palace Hotel with elegant cyclists (76x58cm-30x23in) s. 26-May-3 Rasmussen, Copenhagen #1137/R est:1200000 (D.KR 1100000)

Works on paper

£791 $1258 €1187 From Holmen's canal with figures in front of Niels Juel's statue (12x17cm-5x7in) mono. pen. 5-Mar-3 Rasmussen, Copenhagen #2108/R (D.KR 8500)

£1257 $1999 €1886 Street scene, Copenhagen (20x14cm-8x6in) mono. W/C. 5-Mar-3 Rasmussen, Copenhagen #2093/R est:5000 (D.KR 13500)

FISCHER, Rita (1972-) Uruguayan

Works on paper

£541 $850 €812 Figure (90x80cm-35x31in) mixed media. 20-Nov-2 Galleria Y Remates, Montevideo #68

£962 $1500 €1443 Cara (50x80cm-20x31in) mixed media. 30-Jul-2 Galleria Y Remates, Montevideo #101 est:450-550

FISCHER, T (20th C) British?
£250 $395 €363 Taking tea (60x50cm-24x20in) s. 27-Apr-3 Lots Road, London #335

FISCHER, V T (1857-1928) Danish
£483 $764 €725 Parrot with strawberry in his beak (47x37cm-19x15in) s.d.1878. 5-Apr-3 Rasmussen, Havnen #2131 (D.KR 5200)

FISCHER, Vilhelm Theodor (1857-1928) Danish
£272 $424 €408 Coastal landscape from Rorvig with large stones and seagulls (39x54cm-15x21in) s.d.1901. 5-Aug-2 Rasmussen, Vejle #269/R (D.KR 3200)
£279 $444 €419 Coastal landscape with children playing (41x52cm-16x20in) s.d.1908. 10-Mar-3 Rasmussen, Vejle #320/R (D.KR 3000)
£680 $1060 €1020 Guinea pigs (35x48cm-14x19in) s. 5-Aug-2 Rasmussen, Vejle #116/R (D.KR 8000)
£1981 $3011 €2972 Coastal landscape with sheep by shore (79x111cm-31x44in) s. exhib. 27-Aug-2 Rasmussen, Copenhagen #1896/R est:25000 (D.KR 23000)

FISCHER, Wilhelm (1912-1970) German
£552 $872 €800 Figural composition II. s.d. masonite. 2-Apr-3 Dr Fritz Nagel, Stuttgart #9074/R

FISCHER-ELPONS, Georg (1866-?) German
£2848 $4500 €4500 Still life with lobster on a silver plate (68x116cm-27x46in) s. 28-Nov-2 Dorotheum, Vienna #194/R est:3000-4000

FISCHER-HANSEN, Else (1905-) Danish
£276 $427 €414 Cloudy weather (81x65cm-32x26in) s.d.1962 verso. 4-Dec-2 Kunsthallen, Copenhagen #110 (D.KR 3200)
£700 $1112 €1050 The sea (60x50cm-24x20in) init.d.1950 verso. 29-Apr-3 Kunsthallen, Copenhagen #93/R (D.KR 7500)
£947 $1469 €1421 Composition in blue (81x66cm-32x26in) s.d.1949 verso. 4-Dec-2 Kunsthallen, Copenhagen #230/R (D.KR 11000)

FISCHER-LAUTERBACH, Wolfgang (1939-) German
£327 $523 €500 Flower still life with peonies (60x70cm-24x28in) s. 10-Jan-3 Allgauer, Kempten #1589/R
£458 $732 €700 Still life of wild flowers in glass vase (60x50cm-24x20in) s. 10-Jan-3 Allgauer, Kempten #1588/R

FISCHETTI, Fedele (1734-1789) Italian
£3797 $6000 €6000 Saint Anthony and the Infant (76x62cm-30x24in) 27-Nov-2 Finarte, Milan #93/R

Works on paper
£1218 $1888 €1900 Portrait of lady with putto (25x19cm-10x7in) pencil pen ink W/C prov. 4-Dec-2 Christie's, Rome #404
£3103 $4934 €4500 Redition royale au cours d'une bataille (48x74cm-19x29in) mono. pen wash. 7-Mar-3 Rabourdin & Choppin de Janvry, Paris #53/R est:5000-6000

FISCHHOF, Georg (1859-1914) Austrian
£552 $839 €850 Fishing boats in harbour of coastal town (73x100cm-29x39in) s. 6-Jul-2 Berlinghof, Heidelberg #203/R
£568 $885 €852 Cattle at the edge of the woods, 1909 (68x55cm-27x22in) s. 11-Sep-2 Kieselbach, Budapest #193/R (H.F 220000)
£641 $1006 €1000 Cow herd at the waters edge (51x40cm-20x16in) s.d.896 panel. 21-Nov-2 Dorotheum, Vienna #186/R
£692 $1072 €1100 Sailing ships in harbour (50x82cm-20x32in) s.pseudonym. 29-Oct-2 Dorotheum, Vienna #100/R

FISCHINGER, August (1887-1958) Austrian
£385 $604 €600 Landscape with pond (35x43cm-14x17in) s.d.1918. 21-Nov-2 Dorotheum, Vienna #251/R
£385 $604 €600 Extensive landscape with birch trees (45x35cm-18x14in) s.d.1918 canvas on board. 21-Nov-2 Dorotheum, Vienna #250/R

FISCHINGER, Georg (1859-1944) Austrian
£481 $755 €750 View above Salzburger moor in the direction of Untersberg (23x37cm-9x15in) s.d.1923 canvas on board. 21-Nov-2 Dorotheum, Vienna #184/R

FISCHL, Eric (1948-) American
£6000 $9240 €9000 Untitled (117x89cm-46x35in) s. i.d.1984 verso oil on paper prov. 22-Oct-2 Sotheby's, London #331/R est:6000-8000
£7595 $12000 €11393 Untitled (45x38cm-18x15in) s.d.96 oil on paper prov. 13-Nov-2 Sotheby's, New York #143/R est:15000-20000
£13750 $22000 €20625 Untitled (41x30cm-16x12in) s.d.85 oil on paper prov. 14-May-3 Sotheby's, New York #452/R est:8000-12000
£14557 $23000 €21836 Untitled (61x61cm-24x24in) s.d.90 verso prov. 13-Nov-2 Sotheby's, New York #578/R est:20000-30000
£16250 $26000 €24375 Untitled (89x107cm-35x42in) s.i.d.86 oil on two attached sheets of chromecoat paper prov. 15-May-3 Christie's, Rockefeller NY #376/R est:18000-22000
£20000 $32000 €30000 Artist (70x100cm-28x39in) s.d.93 oil on chromecoat paper prov. 15-May-3 Christie's, Rockefeller NY #377/R est:20000-30000
£240506 $380000 €360759 What there is between you and me (249x188cm-98x74in) s. i.d.1992 verso oil on linen prov.exhib.lit. 12-Nov-2 Sotheby's, New York #24/R est:400000-600000

Prints
£2201 $3500 €3302 Untitled (38x57cm-15x22in) s.i.d.3.19.86 col monotype exhib.lit. 2-May-3 Sotheby's, New York #435/R est:4000-6000
£3019 $4800 €4529 Digging kids (137x98cm-54x39in) s.d.num.23/40 col soft ground etching aquatint. 2-May-3 Sotheby's, New York #432/R est:2500-3500
£3145 $5000 €4718 Untitled (57x49cm-22x19in) s.i.d.3.19.86 col monotype exhib.lit. 2-May-3 Sotheby's, New York #434/R est:4000-6000
£3774 $6000 €5661 Untitled (36x56cm-14x22in) s.i.d.3.21.86 col monotype exhib.lit. 2-May-3 Sotheby's, New York #433/R est:4000-6000

FISCHLI, Peter and WEISS, David (20th C) Swiss

Photographs
£4000 $6680 €5800 Untitled - pilze (74x107cm-29x42in) s.d.1998 num.9/9 inkjet print behind plexiglas prov. 27-Jun-3 Christie's, London #257/R est:4000-6000
£4500 $7515 €6525 Untitled (65x98cm-26x39in) s.d.98 num.7/9 verso inkjet print prov. 26-Jun-3 Sotheby's, London #105/R est:2500-3500
£6250 $10000 €9375 Untitled (74x107cm-29x42in) s.d.1998 num.7/9 inkjet print prov. 14-May-3 Sotheby's, New York #357/R est:5000-7000
£6250 $10000 €9375 Untitled (74x107cm-29x42in) s.d.1998 num.7/9 inkjet print prov. 14-May-3 Sotheby's, New York #358/R est:5000-7000
£7500 $12000 €11250 Airport - Frankfurt, Delta (119x180cm-47x71in) cibachrome print on board executed 1989 prov.exhib. 15-May-3 Christie's, Rockefeller NY #403/R est:15000-20000
£7595 $12000 €11393 Lugano (162x220cm-64x87in) col coupler print executed 1989 prov. 14-Nov-2 Christie's, Rockefeller NY #440/R est:15000-20000
£7595 $12000 €11393 Airport - Rio de Janeiro (161x220cm-63x87in) s.d.1990 num.3/6 col coupler print prov.lit. 14-Nov-2 Christie's, Rockefeller NY #442/R est:15000-20000
£8228 $13000 €12342 Woods (160x220cm-63x87in) col coupler print executed 1989 prov. 14-Nov-2 Christie's, Rockefeller NY #443/R est:15000-20000
£13750 $22000 €20625 Airport - Los Angeles, Lufthansa cargo (160x221cm-63x87in) cibachrome print on board executed 1989 prov.exhib. 15-May-3 Christie's, Rockefeller NY #402/R est:15000-20000
£15000 $24600 €22500 Untitled (119x180cm-47x71in) cibachrome print edition of six prov.exhib. 7-Feb-3 Sotheby's, London #148/R est:10000-15000
£17000 $26180 €25500 Eiffelturm (180x120cm-71x47in) cibachrome print executed 1988-89 prov. 22-Oct-2 Sotheby's, London #303/R est:10000-15000
£22000 $36080 €33000 Scandanavian, NY (119x180cm-47x71in) cibachrome print edition of six prov.exhib. 7-Feb-3 Sotheby's, London #149/R est:10000-15000

Sculpture
£48000 $78720 €72000 Four stewardesses (56x16x18cm-22x6x7in) plaster cast over polyester resin four parts prov.exhib.lit. 7-Feb-3 Sotheby's, London #147/R est:20000-30000

FISH, Anne Harriet (?-1964) British

Works on paper
£420 $701 €609 Cats in the garden (34x46cm-13x18in) s. i.verso W/C pencil. 19-Jun-3 Lane, Penzance #284

FISH, George Drummond (1876-1938) Irish

Works on paper
£411 $645 €600 Ireland's eye (28x41cm-11x16in) s. W/C. 15-Apr-3 De Veres Art Auctions, Dublin #10/R
£700 $1092 €1050 Irish river landscapes (23x33cm-9x13in) s. W/C pair. 11-Apr-3 Keys, Aylsham #470
£743 $1159 €1100 Mountainous landscape with sheep in heather (37x58cm-15x23in) s. W/C. 26-Mar-3 James Adam, Dublin #25/R est:800-1200

FISHBEIN, Jason B (20th C) American
£513 $800 €770 Hillside town, trees in the foreground (147x97cm-58x38in) s. 20-Sep-2 Freeman, Philadelphia #61/R

FISHER, A (19th C) ?
£786 $1241 €1179 Rural scenes, Horse and cart and picking flowers (20x40cm-8x16in) s. enamel on porcelain pair. 27-Nov-2 Deutscher-Menzies, Melbourne #266/R est:2500-3500 (A.D 2200)

FISHER, Alfred Hugh (1867-1945) British
£460 $727 €690 Harvesters building a haystack (18x36cm-7x14in) s. board. 2-Dec-2 Gorringes, Lewes #2610

FISHER, Alvan (1792-1863) American
£6289 $10000 €9434 Indians at sunset (36x51cm-14x20in) init. prov. 5-Mar-3 Sotheby's, New York #113/R est:8000-12000

FISHER, Anna S (1873-1942) American
£406 $650 €609 Sugar house (23x30cm-9x12in) s. 11-Jan-3 James Julia, Fairfield #513
£563 $900 €816 Still life (91x66cm-36x26in) s. 17-May-3 CRN Auctions, Cambridge #15
£3571 $5500 €5357 Path to the harbour. Low tide (38x28cm-15x11in) one s. pair prov. 24-Oct-2 Shannon's, Milford #191/R est:3000-5000

FISHER, Arthur (20th C) British
£650 $1079 €943 Parasol (76x64cm-30x25in) s.d.1936 verso. 10-Jun-3 David Lay, Penzance #153

FISHER, Charles (19/20th C) ?
£295 $466 €460 Coastal scene with fishing vessels and haarbour beyond (30x45cm-12x18in) 12-Nov-2 Mealy's, Castlecomer #1053

FISHER, Harrison (1875-1934) American
Works on paper
£396 $650 €574 Portrait of a lady (27x14cm-11x6in) s.d. W/C gouache card stock. 5-Jun-3 Swann Galleries, New York #94/R
£1032 $1600 €1548 Portrait of a woman (36x25cm-14x10in) s.i.d.1904 pencil wash. 25-Sep-2 Doyle, New York #28/R est:1500-2000
£1656 $2750 €2401 Portrait of a young woman in profile (44x30cm-17x12in) s. pastel prov. 11-Jun-3 Butterfields, San Francisco #4103/R est:3000-5000
£4777 $7500 €7166 Portrait of a lady in an evening gown (60x38cm-24x15in) s.d.1909 pencil W/C prov. 19-Nov-2 Butterfields, San Francisco #8057/R est:3000-5000

FISHER, Hugo Antoine (1854-1916) American
Works on paper
£316 $500 €474 Walking down a snowy path. s. gouache. 16-Nov-2 Harvey Clar, Oakland #1256
£323 $500 €485 Redwood sunset (46x36cm-18x14in) s. W/C. 7-Dec-2 Harvey Clar, Oakland #1315
£659 $1100 €956 Cows in landscape (25x38cm-10x15in) s. W/C. 17-Jun-3 John Moran, Pasadena #120a est:800-1200
£3313 $5500 €4804 View of Port Point, San Francisco (20x46cm-8x18in) s.d.1894 pencil W/C gouache prov. 11-Jun-3 Butterfields, San Francisco #4183/R est:3000-5000

FISHER, Hugo Melville (1876-1946) American
£353 $550 €530 Winter cold. 21-Sep-2 Harvey Clar, Oakland #1511
£389 $650 €564 Landscape with boats by a dock (66x71cm-26x28in) s. 21-Jun-3 Charlton Hall, Columbia #523/R
£605 $950 €908 Landscape building by a lake (66x74cm-26x29in) s. 14-Dec-2 Charlton Hall, Columbia #456/R
£637 $1000 €956 Landscape with boats by a dock (66x71cm-26x28in) s. 14-Dec-2 Charlton Hall, Columbia #494/R est:1000-1500

FISHER, Joshua (1859-?) British
Works on paper
£2200 $3278 €3300 Old Sulby village. Old cottage in Sulby glen (28x46cm-11x18in) s. W/C two. 28-Jun-2 Chrystals Auctions, Isle of Man #171a est:2000-2800

FISHER, Melton (?) British
£750 $1200 €1125 Portrait of Marion Dorothy Webb. Portrait of Sir Luke Fildes Of Phil (76x64cm-30x25in) s.i.d.1919 pair. 13-Mar-3 Duke & Son, Dorchester #201

FISHER, Orville Norman (1911-1999) Canadian
£448 $717 €672 Sunrise - first narrows, Vancouver, BC (80x95cm-31x37in) s. s.i.d.1970 acrylic. 15-May-3 Heffel, Vancouver #179 est:1200-1700 (C.D 1000)

FISHER, Percy Harland (1867-1944) British
£9000 $14940 €13500 Charity (52x36cm-20x14in) s.d.1892 exhib. 10-Jun-3 Christie's, London #96/R est:8000-12000

FISHER, Roland (1958-) Dutch
Photographs
£2051 $3179 €3200 O.T - Tamlyn (140x160cm-55x63in) s.d.1992 num.1/5 c-print prov. 3-Dec-2 Christie's, Amsterdam #385/R est:1500-2000

FISHER, Rowland (1885-1969) British
£380 $619 €551 Busy street scene (31x38cm-12x15in) s. board. 15-Jul-3 Bonhams, Knightsbridge #46
£800 $1336 €1160 St Ives (32x38cm-13x15in) s. board. 17-Jun-3 Bonhams, Knightsbridge #121/R
£1350 $2093 €2025 Pulling in the lobster pots (63x102cm-25x40in) s. board. 30-Sep-2 Bonhams, Ipswich #375/R est:1500-2000

FISHER, W C (19th C) British
£3400 $5168 €5100 Scene in the Grampians - the drovers departure (99x149cm-39x59in) s.d.1879 after Sir Edwin Landseer. 28-Aug-2 Sotheby's, London #911/R est:2000-3000

FISHER, William (1817-1895) British
£258 $400 €387 Spring landscape (41x51cm-16x20in) s. canvasboard. 3-Dec-2 Christie's, Rockefeller NY #594/R
£755 $1200 €1133 Gaspe, Perce Rock, Quebec (63x76cm-25x30in) s. i.d.1930 verso. 7-Mar-3 Skinner, Boston #432/R

FISHER, William Mark (1841-1923) British/American
£550 $853 €825 Flowers in a gold jardiniere (35x53cm-14x21in) s. prov. 4-Dec-2 Christie's, Kensington #463/R
£550 $853 €825 Flowers in a blue jardiniere (30x46cm-12x18in) s. 4-Dec-2 Christie's, Kensington #467/R
£2200 $3432 €3300 Cattle in a meadow (46x60cm-18x24in) s. 26-Mar-3 Sotheby's, Olympia #118/R est:1500-2500
£3400 $5304 €5100 Sheep and cattle in a pasture landscape (46x66cm-18x26in) s.d.84. 26-Mar-3 Sotheby's, Olympia #214/R est:1000-2000

FISHER, William Mark (attrib) (1841-1923) British/American
£300 $501 €435 Hayrick on a country track (32x37cm-13x15in) s. 25-Jun-3 Cheffins, Cambridge #818
£1093 $1750 €1640 Summer landscape with cows (51x61cm-20x24in) s. 11-Jan-3 James Julia, Fairfield #171 est:2000-3000
£2000 $3340 €2900 Plough team at work, extensive landscape (48x74cm-19x29in) bears sig. 20-Jun-3 Keys, Aylsham #675 est:450-550

FISHWICK, Clifford (1923-1997) British
Works on paper
£250 $390 €375 Rain Island (36x53cm-14x21in) s.d.1963 W/C. 16-Oct-2 David Lay, Penzance #268/R

FISK, Harry T (1887-1974) American
£219 $350 €318 Train yard (20x25cm-8x10in) s. canvasboard. 16-May-3 Skinner, Boston #322/R

FISSETTE, Leopold (1814-1889) German
£680 $1082 €1000 Preparation (30x23cm-12x9in) s. panel. 24-Mar-3 Bernaerts, Antwerp #2/R est:1000-1500
£884 $1406 €1300 Lonely in the garret (30x23cm-12x9in) s. panel. 24-Mar-3 Bernaerts, Antwerp #1/R est:1000-1500
£1342 $2161 €2000 Narration interessante (38x50cm-15x20in) s. panel exhib. 24-Feb-3 Bernaerts, Antwerp #165/R

FISSORE, Daniele (1947-) Italian
£316 $494 €500 Sea and green (20x30cm-8x12in) s. 14-Sep-2 Meeting Art, Vercelli #282
£340 $541 €500 Sea and green (25x25cm-10x10in) s. 1-Mar-3 Meeting Art, Vercelli #533
£348 $543 €550 Sea and green (25x25cm-10x10in) s. 14-Sep-2 Meeting Art, Vercelli #175
£359 $575 €550 Sea and green (25x25cm-10x10in) s. 4-Jan-3 Meeting Art, Vercelli #38
£392 $627 €600 Sea and green (20x30cm-8x12in) s. 4-Jan-3 Meeting Art, Vercelli #480
£486 $773 €700 Seascape (40x30cm-16x12in) s. 1-May-3 Meeting Art, Vercelli #76
£521 $828 €750 Sea (40x50cm-16x20in) s. s.verso. 1-May-3 Meeting Art, Vercelli #507
£544 $865 €800 Sea and green (40x50cm-16x20in) s. 1-Mar-3 Meeting Art, Vercelli #504
£590 $939 €850 Sea and green (40x50cm-16x20in) s. 1-May-3 Meeting Art, Vercelli #67

£633 $987 €1000 Sea (50x60cm-20x24in) s. 14-Sep-2 Meeting Art, Vercelli #362
£633 $987 €1000 Sea and green (40x50cm-16x20in) s. 14-Sep-2 Meeting Art, Vercelli #420/R
£850 $1359 €1300 Sea (70x100cm-28x39in) s. 4-Jan-3 Meeting Art, Vercelli #735
£929 $1459 €1450 Sea and green (70x120cm-28x47in) s. painted 1987. 23-Nov-2 Meeting Art, Vercelli #409/R

FITCH, John Lee (1836-1895) American
£9155 $13000 €13733 Brook in autumn (61x86cm-24x34in) 8-Aug-1 Barridorf, Portland #25/R est:9000-12000

FITCHEW, Edward H (1851-1934) British
Works on paper
£800 $1248 €1200 View of Jaffa (17x27cm-7x11in) s. W/C over pencil htd bodycol. 15-Oct-2 Sotheby's, London #125/R

FITGER, Arthur (1840-1909) German
£3741 $5949 €5500 Bacchantal party (95x151cm-37x59in) s. 28-Mar-3 Bolland & Marotz, Bremen #445/R est:4900
£4747 $7500 €7500 Joseph and Potiphars in the nude (158x166cm-62x65in) s. 29-Nov-2 Bolland & Marotz, Bremen #693/R est:7500

FITLER, William Crothers (1857-1915) American
Works on paper
£1013 $1600 €1520 Winter sunset on the farm (30x43cm-12x17in) s. gouache. 17-Nov-2 CRN Auctions, Cambridge #66/R

FITO, Ettore (attrib) (?) Italian
£2700 $4212 €4050 Untitled. indis.s. 25-Mar-3 Tayler & Fletcher, Cheltenham #1/R

FITTKE, Arturo (1873-1910) Spanish
£1418 $2298 €2000 Ritratto della madre (65x45cm-26x18in) s. 22-May-3 Stadion, Trieste #356/R est:500-700

FITZGERALD, Edward J (20th C) American
£577 $900 €866 Nubble light (30x41cm-12x16in) s. canvasboard exhib. 18-Sep-2 Alderfer's, Hatfield #300/R

FITZGERALD, Florence (?-1927) British
£610 $964 €1058 Flowers that bloom in spring (60x45cm-24x18in) s. i.verso. 1-Apr-3 Goodman, Sydney #46/R (A.D 1600)

FITZGERALD, Gerald (1873-1935) Australian
Works on paper
£1071 $1682 €1607 Paris nocturne (22x28cm-9x11in) s.i.d.13.11.99 W/C. 25-Nov-2 Christie's, Melbourne #416/R est:1800-2200 (A.D 3000)

FITZGERALD, James (1899-?) American
£19737 $30000 €29606 Men hauling nets (81x81cm-32x32in) s. 30-Aug-2 Thomaston Place, Thomaston #50

FITZGERALD, John (?) Irish?
Works on paper
£334 $485 €525 Old Blackrock Castle and Admiralty Court 1800 (26x39cm-10x15in) W/C. 29-May-2 Woodwards, Cork #202

FITZGERALD, John Austen (1832-1906) British
£5500 $8855 €8250 Tempting present (41x30cm-16x12in) prov.exhib. 20-Feb-3 Christie's, London #49/R
Works on paper
£50000 $78500 €75000 Fairies and bird's nest (26x20cm-10x8in) init. pencil W/C bodycol gum arabic arched prov.lit. 21-Nov-2 Christie's, London #95/R est:50000-80000

FITZGERALD, Lady Edward (19th C) British
Works on paper
£450 $702 €675 Tulip (25x15cm-10x6in) s.i. pencil W/C on vellum. 27-Mar-3 Christie's, Kensington #198/R

FITZGERALD, Lionel Lemoine (1890-1956) Canadian
£1317 $2041 €1976 Summer landscape, Manitoba (19x23cm-7x9in) d.July 19 board. 3-Dec-2 Joyner, Toronto #319/R est:1500-2000 (C.D 3200)
£3139 $5022 €4709 Early morning, autumn (33x41cm-13x16in) init.d.1953 board. 15-May-3 Heffel, Vancouver #184/R est:4000-5000 (C.D 7000)
£5778 $9476 €8667 In the marsh (28x33cm-11x13in) s.d.1912 prov.exhib. 27-May-3 Sotheby's, Toronto #23/R est:5000-7000 (C.D 13000)
Works on paper
£317 $521 €476 Trees (24x30cm-9x12in) estate s. conte. 6-Feb-3 Heffel, Vancouver #013/R (C.D 800)
£323 $510 €485 Abstract (30x47cm-12x19in) ink executed c.1953 prov. 14-Nov-2 Heffel, Vancouver #122 (C.D 800)
£341 $536 €512 Untitled - landscape (27x35cm-11x14in) init.d.1954 ink. 25-Nov-2 Hodgins, Calgary #21/R (C.D 850)
£363 $573 €545 Poppies (57x40cm-22x16in) s. July.1.1947 i.verso graphite prov. 14-Nov-2 Heffel, Vancouver #120 est:1000-1500 (C.D 900)
£444 $729 €644 Untitled - mountain top (59x44cm-23x17in) col pencil prov. 9-Jun-3 Hodgins, Calgary #126/R est:800-1200 (C.D 1000)
£484 $765 €726 Autumn leaves (35x47cm-14x19in) init.d.1953 col chk prov.exhib. 14-Nov-2 Heffel, Vancouver #201 est:600-800 (C.D 1200)
£658 $1021 €987 Rocks and ripples, Hows Sound, B.C (60x45cm-24x18in) init.d.42 col pencil. 3-Dec-2 Joyner, Toronto #367 est:1500-2000 (C.D 1600)
£1067 $1749 €1601 Entwined trees (36x19cm-14x7in) W/C prov. 3-Jun-3 Joyner, Toronto #227/R est:4000-6000 (C.D 2400)
£1310 $2071 €1965 Harvest (23x30cm-9x12in) s.d.1928 i.verso W/C prov. 14-Nov-2 Heffel, Vancouver #184/R est:3000-4000 (C.D 3250)
£1345 $2152 €2018 Tree apples (58x46cm-23x18in) init. col pencil executed c.1948 prov. 15-May-3 Heffel, Vancouver #21 est:4000-5000 (C.D 3000)
£3812 $6099 €5718 Winter (42x33cm-17x13in) s.d.1910 W/C prov. 15-May-3 Heffel, Vancouver #152/R est:6000-8000 (C.D 8500)

FITZGERALD, Lloyd (1941-) Canadian
£302 $478 €453 Hunter and sunrise (30x41cm-12x16in) s.d.1981 s.d.verso ca. on board. 14-Nov-2 Heffel, Vancouver #251 (C.D 750)
£359 $574 €539 Interlude (38x61cm-15x24in) s.d.1981 acrylic polymer emulsion board prov. 15-May-3 Heffel, Vancouver #153 (C.D 800)
£378 $619 €567 Black duck (62x80cm-24x31in) s.d.1980 acrylic board. 3-Jun-3 Joyner, Toronto #384/R (C.D 850)
£806 $1274 €1209 Snowing at Moore's (33x76cm-13x30in) s.d.1989 s.i.d.verso acrylic prov. 18-Nov-2 Sotheby's, Toronto #132/R est:2500-3000 (C.D 2000)
£1008 $1593 €1512 New snow - the next day (51x76cm-20x30in) s.d.1989 s.i.d.verso ca. on board prov. 18-Nov-2 Sotheby's, Toronto #34/R est:3000-4000 (C.D 2500)
£1532 $2421 €2298 First light (76x102cm-30x40in) s.d.1988 init.i.d.on stretcher prov. 18-Nov-2 Sotheby's, Toronto #185/R est:3500-4500 (C.D 3800)
£2000 $3280 €3000 North point (96x76cm-38x30in) s.d.1988 acrylic prov. 27-May-3 Sotheby's, Toronto #49/R est:3500-4500 (C.D 4500)
Works on paper
£402 $635 €603 Farm buildings, Manitoba, Sept 1930 (23x38cm-9x15in) d.1930 graphite. 1-Dec-2 Levis, Calgary #28/R (C.D 1000)

FITZHARRIS, Mike (20th C) Irish
£1258 $1962 €2000 Orange abstract (36x46cm-14x18in) s.d.1989. 17-Sep-2 Whyte's, Dublin #90/R est:1500-1800
Works on paper
£897 $1391 €1400 Abstract - from Berlin series (37x52cm-15x20in) s. mixed media. 3-Dec-2 Bonhams & James Adam, Dublin #129/R
£1154 $1812 €1800 Aerial view (51x64cm-20x25in) s.d.1989 mixed media board. 19-Nov-2 Whyte's, Dublin #173/R est:2000-2500

FITZPATRICK, Arthur and KAUFMAN, van (20th C) American
Works on paper
£1218 $1900 €1827 Young couple and Pontiac Bonnenville on the beach (33x33cm-13x13in) init. gouache. 9-Nov-2 Illustration House, New York #126/R est:2000-3000

FIUME, Salvatore (1915-1997) Italian
£3262 $5285 €4600 Isola di statue n.26 (23x36cm-9x14in) canvas on masonite prov. 26-May-3 Christie's, Milan #335/R est:3000-3500
£3401 $5408 €5000 Toreador (49x38cm-19x15in) s. board. 1-Mar-3 Meeting Art, Vercelli #727
£3797 $5924 €6000 Hararine in the wind (27x36cm-11x14in) s. fabric on masonite. 14-Sep-2 Meeting Art, Vercelli #966/R
£4539 $7353 €6400 Statue sul mare n.24 (36x53cm-14x21in) s. faesite. 26-May-3 Christie's, Milan #352/R est:3500-5000
£4823 $7813 €6800 Scogliera no.30 (44x57cm-17x22in) s. canvas on masonite prov.exhib. 26-May-3 Christie's, Milan #351/R est:5000-7000
£5128 $8051 €8000 Islands (39x58cm-15x23in) s. cardboard prov. 19-Nov-2 Finarte, Milan #176/R est:6000-8000
£5128 $8051 €8000 Sultan and odalisk (35x53cm-14x21in) s. masonite. 20-Nov-2 Pandolfini, Florence #81/R
£5479 $8548 €8000 Forbidden games (34x41cm-13x16in) s. board. 10-Apr-3 Finarte Semenzato, Rome #269/R est:18000
£6090 $9561 €9500 Mexican woman (54x36cm-21x14in) s. masonite. 23-Nov-2 Meeting Art, Vercelli #238/R
£7051 $11071 €11000 Odalisk (35x53cm-14x21in) s. board. 21-Nov-2 Finarte, Rome #297/R est:8000

£7692 $12077 €12000 Jesus by Pilate (89x156cm-35x61in) s. masonite. 19-Nov-2 Finarte, Milan #250/R est:11000-14000
£9494 $15000 €15000 Odalisk (54x72cm-21x28in) s. board. 30-Nov-2 Farsetti, Prato #672/R est:16000
£9494 $14810 €15000 Girls from Ridawa (71x53cm-28x21in) s. masonite. 14-Sep-2 Meeting Art, Vercelli #985/R
£15385 $24154 €24000 Woman from Somalia (160x85cm-63x33in) s. masonite prov. 20-Nov-2 Pandolfini, Florence #82/R est:26000
£18056 $28708 €26000 Island lover (80x110cm-31x43in) s. masonite lit. 1-May-3 Meeting Art, Vercelli #587 est:25000

Works on paper

£897 $1409 €1400 Figures (34x50cm-13x20in) s.d.1954 Chinese ink. 21-Nov-2 Finarte, Rome #112/R
£1154 $1812 €1800 Gargantua and Pantagruel (17x11cm-7x4in) s. Chinese ink pair. 21-Nov-2 Finarte, Rome #130
£2695 $4366 €3800 Nudo sdraiato (40x50cm-16x20in) s. felt pen paper on faesite. 26-May-3 Christie's, Milan #43/R est:2500-3000

FIZELLE, Rah (1891-1964) Australian

Works on paper

£386 $610 €560 Positano (32x42cm-13x17in) s. i.verso W/C prov. 22-Jul-3 Lawson Menzies, Sydney #165/R est:1500-2500 (A.D 950)
£491 $747 €737 Washing day (32x43cm-13x17in) s. W/C. 19-Aug-2 Joel, Victoria #187 est:1400-1600 (A.D 1400)
£714 $1121 €1071 Southern France (33x43cm-13x17in) s. W/C. 25-Nov-2 Christie's, Melbourne #293/R (A.D 2000)
£1210 $1851 €1815 View of Macquarie Place, Sydney (31x43cm-12x17in) s.d.24 W/C gouache paper on board prov. 25-Aug-2 Sotheby's, Paddington #133 est:4000-6000 (A.D 3400)
£3200 $5152 €4800 Seated nude (74x54cm-29x21in) s. W/C. 6-May-3 Christie's, Melbourne #216/R est:7000-9000 (A.D 8000)

FJAESTAD, Gustaf (1868-1948) Swedish

£1372 $2140 €2058 Underneath snow covered pine trees. Landscape study (58x74cm-23x29in) with sig. double-sided. 13-Sep-2 Lilla Bukowskis, Stockholm #44 est:15000-18000 (S.KR 20000)
£1414 $2319 €2050 Winter landscape with marks in snow (35x50cm-14x20in) s.i.d.1909 panel. 4-Jun-3 AB Stockholms Auktionsverk #2318/R est:20000-25000 (S.KR 18000)
£3127 $5004 €4534 Summer landscape (54x103cm-21x41in) s.d.99 oil pastel cardboard on canvas. 18-May-3 Anders Antik, Landskrona #74 est:40000 (S.KR 40000)
£5750 $9086 €8625 Early morning (88x95cm-35x37in) s.i.indis.d.87 exhib.prov. 27-Nov-2 Falkkloos, Malmo #77540/R est:80000 (S.KR 82000)
£6738 $10443 €10107 The first snow (84x109cm-33x43in) s.d.1913 exhib.lit. 3-Dec-2 Bukowskis, Stockholm #241/R est:125000-150000 (S.KR 95000)
£6738 $10443 €10107 Tracks in the snow (91x121cm-36x48in) s.d.45 panel. 4-Dec-2 AB Stockholms Auktionsverk #1724/R est:60000-80000 (S.KR 95000)
£7801 $12092 €11702 Bay in winter (105x128cm-41x50in) s.i.d.19. 3-Dec-2 Bukowskis, Stockholm #254/R est:150000-175000 (S.KR 110000)
£7801 $12092 €11702 Lake in winter (115x157cm-45x62in) s.d.1913. 4-Dec-2 AB Stockholms Auktionsverk #1664/R est:150000-175000 (S.KR 110000)
£9220 $14291 €13830 Snow crystals on frozen lake (81x100cm-32x39in) s. panel. 3-Dec-2 Bukowskis, Stockholm #242/R est:60000-70000 (S.KR 130000)
£9220 $14291 €13830 Norwegian spruce in sunshine (138x114cm-54x45in) s.d.31 panel. 3-Dec-2 Bukowskis, Stockholm #253/R est:100000-125000 (S.KR 130000)
£10993 $17039 €16490 Sunny winter landscape (101x132cm-40x52in) s.d.05. 4-Dec-2 AB Stockholms Auktionsverk #1624/R est:100000-125000 (S.KR 155000)
£11249 $18223 €16311 Winter landscape with pine trees in sunshine (95x122cm-37x48in) s. panel prov. 26-May-3 Bukowskis, Stockholm #106/R est:100000-125000 (S.KR 145000)
£13576 $21994 €19685 Winter landscape at sunset (103x119cm-41x47in) s.d.21. 26-May-3 Bukowskis, Stockholm #188/R est:175000-200000 (S.KR 175000)
£15957 $24734 €23936 Twilight at Racken (120x147cm-47x58in) s.d.1905 lit. 3-Dec-2 Bukowskis, Stockholm #78/R est:250000-300000 (S.KR 225000)

FJAESTAD, Maja (1873-1961) Swedish

Works on paper

£1135 $1759 €1703 Coastal landscape from Racken (37x47cm-15x19in) s.d.1918 W/C. 4-Dec-2 AB Stockholms Auktionsverk #1723/R est:15000-18000 (S.KR 16000)

FJEDERHOLT, Preben (20th C) Danish

£746 $1187 €1119 Composition (100x100cm-39x39in) s.d.1994 verso. 29-Apr-3 Kunsthallen, Copenhagen #63 (D.KR 8000)

FJELL, Kai (1907-1989) Norwegian

£5236 $8220 €7854 Fiddler on the roof (70x60cm-28x24in) s.d.57 lit. 21-Nov-2 Grev Wedels Plass, Oslo #81/R est:80000-100000 (N.KR 60000)
£6981 $10960 €10472 Reclining nude on bed (50x45cm-20x18in) s.d.58. 21-Nov-2 Grev Wedels Plass, Oslo #80/R est:100000 (N.KR 80000)

Works on paper

£311 $472 €467 Valley landscape with woman (20x27cm-8x11in) s.d.79 i.verso exhib. 31-Aug-2 Grev Wedels Plass, Oslo #7/R (N.KR 3600)
£431 $656 €647 The cycle trip (20x29cm-8x11in) init.i.d.83 W/C. 31-Aug-2 Grev Wedels Plass, Oslo #47 (N.KR 5000)
£604 $918 €906 Girl 's room (26x32cm-10x13in) s.i.d.69 Indian ink W/C. 31-Aug-2 Grev Wedels Plass, Oslo #46 (N.KR 7000)
£1041 $1624 €1562 Lyarslaat (36x44cm-14x17in) s.i.d.74 W/C Indian ink. 21-Oct-2 Blomqvist, Oslo #455/R (N.KR 12000)
£1294 $1967 €1941 Head of girl (48x50cm-19x20in) s.i. pastel silkscreen. 31-Aug-2 Grev Wedels Plass, Oslo #9/R est:20000-25000 (N.KR 15000)
£5759 $9042 €8639 Two women and child (41x55cm-16x22in) s.d.42 pastel. 21-Nov-2 Grev Wedels Plass, Oslo #12/R est:50000-70000 (N.KR 66000)

FJELLMAN, Carl (?) Swedish?

£282 $443 €423 Landscape from the skerries with fishermen (35x54cm-14x21in) s. 16-Dec-2 Lilla Bukowskis, Stockholm #407 (S.KR 4000)

FLACH, Charles (1863-1933) ?

£279 $441 €419 Canton village in Puschlav (48x60cm-19x24in) s.i.d.1925 verso. 29-Nov-2 Zofingen, Switzerland #2435 (S.FR 650)

Works on paper

£300 $475 €450 Young girl with blossom branch (38x29cm-15x11in) s.d.1910 pastel. 29-Nov-2 Zofingen, Switzerland #2437 (S.FR 700)
£1030 $1627 €1545 Portrait of Mlle P de L (52x36cm-20x14in) mono.d.1898 pastel. 29-Nov-2 Zofingen, Switzerland #2436/R (S.FR 2400)

FLACHE, Julius (1892-1967) Czechoslovakian

£299 $464 €449 Bunch of flowers (62x52cm-24x20in) painted c.1955. 1-Oct-2 SOGA, Bratislava #229/R est:24000 (SL.K 19000)

FLACHENECKER, Ferdinand Wolfgang (1792-?) German

£255 $403 €383 Portrait of the architect Frederik Ferdinand Friis (41x33cm-16x13in) prov. 2-Dec-2 Rasmussen, Copenhagen #1274/R (D.KR 3000)

FLACHERON, Frederic (1813-1883) French

Photographs

£115000 $186300 €172500 Vues d'Italie, tableaux. salt prints 219 folio photographed with his circle lit. 22-May-3 Sotheby's, London #36/R est:12000-18000

FLAGG, H Peabody (1859-1937) American

£236 $375 €354 Old bridge at Quimperle, Brittany (23x30cm-9x12in) s.d.34 canvasboard. 7-Mar-3 Jackson's, Cedar Falls #735/R
£316 $500 €474 Autumn (23x28cm-9x11in) s.d.1915 canvasboard. 17-Nov-2 Jeffery Burchard, Florida #16/R

FLAGG, James Montgomery (1877-1960) American

Works on paper

£621 $1000 €932 Older couple reminiscing about younger days (56x51cm-22x20in) s. W/C pencil en grisaille. 20-Feb-3 Illustration House, New York #62/R est:1500-2400
£1118 $1800 €1677 Couple at breakfast table, man upset by newspaper (46x66cm-18x26in) s. W/C oil exec.c.1920. 10-May-3 Illustration House, New York #100/R est:2000-3000
£1282 $2000 €1923 Woman ascending stairs to brownstone (53x25cm-21x10in) s. pen ink lit. 9-Nov-2 Illustration House, New York #99/R est:2500-3500
£2192 $3200 €3288 Cowboys round the political campfire (53x84cm-21x33in) s. gouache board. 3-Nov-1 North East Auctions, Portsmouth #273/R
£2244 $3500 €3366 Young woman escorted by dapper man, surprised dejected suitor (48x69cm-19x27in) s. pen ink. 9-Nov-2 Illustration House, New York #94/R est:2000-3000

FLAIG, Waldemar (1892-1932) German
£348 $540 €550 Meersburg in late evening (42x69cm-17x27in) s. panel lit. 27-Sep-2 Karrenbauer, Konstanz #1625

FLAMAND, Georges (19/20th C) French?
Sculpture
£1538 $2569 €2200 Femme nue debout (34cm-13in) s. gilt pat bronze col marble socle. 25-Jun-3 Tajan, Paris #19/R est:2000-2500

FLAMENG, François (1856-1923) French
£15190 $24000 €24000 Joueurs d'echecs (38x46cm-15x18in) s. i.verso panel. 29-Nov-2 Drouot Estimations, Paris #71/R est:18000
£25316 $40000 €37974 Next move (37x47cm-15x19in) s. panel. 24-Apr-3 Sotheby's, New York #76/R est:30000-40000

FLAMENG, François (attrib) (1856-1923) French
£2100 $3423 €3045 Portrait of a young lady seat, in a window holding a fan (116x88cm-46x35in) with sig. 17-Jul-3 Tennants, Leyburn #922/R est:1000-1500

FLAMM, Albert (1823-1906) German
£1410 $2186 €2200 Southern Italian town in the evening (19x15cm-7x6in) s. panel prov. 7-Dec-2 Ketterer, Hamburg #100/R est:2500-3000

FLAMM, Albert (attrib) (1823-1906) German
£2436 $3824 €3800 Castellamare and Vesuvius on Gulf of Naples (68x96cm-27x38in) o,. 21-Nov-2 Van Ham, Cologne #1605/R est:5000

FLANAGAN, Barry (1941-) British
Sculpture
£3000 $5010 €4350 Woman and bird (28x21x21cm-11x8x8in) init.num.7/7 bronze st.f.Susse prov.exhib.lit. 26-Jun-3 Sotheby's, London #226/R est:3000-4000
£56962 $90000 €85443 Left and right handed nijinsky on anvil (165x140x66cm-65x55x26in) mono.st.f. num.4/8 cast brown pat bronze prov. 13-Nov-2 Sotheby's, New York #537/R est:100000-150000
£60127 $95000 €90191 Thinker on rock plus X (114x64x57cm-45x25x22in) brown pat bronze exec.1997 prov. 13-Nov-2 Sotheby's, New York #552/R est:70000-90000
£80000 $133600 €120000 Hare and Bell (131x95x61cm-52x37x24in) mono.num.3/7 hare brown pat.bronze exc.1981 prov. 26-Jun-3 Christie's, London #20/R est:80000-120000
£260000 $426400 €390000 Boxing hare on anvil (304x180x77cm-120x71x30in) mono. num.4/5 bronze exec.1989 prov.lit. 6-Feb-3 Sotheby's, London #17/R est:250000
Works on paper
£1500 $2505 €2175 Diagram (26x19cm-10x7in) i. col markers prov. 24-Jun-3 Sotheby's, Olympia #22/R est:1500-2000

FLANAGAN, Francis (fl.1897-1927) American
£443 $700 €665 In the White Mountains (64x74cm-25x29in) s. 17-Nov-2 CRN Auctions, Cambridge #68/R
£472 $750 €708 Marblehead rocks (64x82cm-25x32in) s. i.verso. 7-Mar-3 Skinner, Boston #473/R

FLANAGAN, John Richard (1895-1964) American
Works on paper
£248 $400 €372 Pitched battle scene with black soldiers (28x28cm-11x11in) s. pen ink. 20-Feb-3 Illustration House, New York #63/R

FLANAGAN, Terence P (1929-) British
£1319 $2098 €1900 Winter dawn (25x30cm-10x12in) s. i.verso board prov. 29-Apr-3 Whyte's, Dublin #14/R est:2000-2500
£1900 $2945 €2850 Bangor (50x61cm-20x24in) s.d.60. 4-Dec-2 John Ross, Belfast #43 est:1000-1200
£2564 $3974 €4000 Spring lough (51x61cm-20x24in) 3-Dec-2 Bonhams & James Adam, Dublin #68/R est:4000-5000
£3333 $5167 €5200 Lough Erne at Castle Archdale (64x76cm-25x30in) s.d.99. 3-Dec-2 Bonhams & James Adam, Dublin #69/R est:5000-8000
£3851 $6008 €5700 Roughra Sequence (30x30cm-12x12in) s.i.verso acrylic pair prov. 26-Mar-3 James Adam, Dublin #54/R est:4000-6000
£14744 $22853 €23000 Winter sequence (39x39cm-15x15in) s.d.76 board six. 3-Dec-2 Bonhams & James Adam, Dublin #70/R est:10000-15000

FLANDIN, Eugène Napoleon (1803-1876) French
Works on paper
£1384 $2131 €2200 Scene de rue en Orient (36x25cm-14x10in) s. W/C. 23-Oct-2 Rabourdin & Choppin de Janvry, Paris #113/R

FLANDRIN, Jean Hippolyte (1809-1864) French
£14103 $22282 €22000 David. Jeremie (32x12cm-13x5in) mono. cardboardpair prov.exhib. 18-Nov-2 Sotheby's, Paris #47/R est:6500
Works on paper
£946 $1476 €1400 Homme debout de profil tenant une epee (29x19cm-11x7in) crayon. 28-Mar-3 Delvaux, Paris #114

FLANDRIN, Jules (1871-1947) French
£7564 $11724 €11800 Paris, pont Saint-Michel (60x92cm-24x36in) s. prov. 9-Dec-2 Beaussant & Lefèvre, Paris #47/R

FLANDRIN, Paul Jean (1811-1902) French
£2500 $3925 €3900 Vue de Montredon, pres de Marseille (22x27cm-9x11in) cardboard prov. 16-Dec-2 Millon & Associes, Paris #143/R est:3000-4000
£26129 $41284 €40500 Paysage, lutte de bergers (74x99cm-29x39in) s.d.1847. 18-Dec-2 Beaussant & Lefèvre, Paris #37/R est:20000

FLANNAGAN, John B (1895-1942) American
Sculpture
£11728 $19000 €17592 Figure (89cm-35in) stone executed 1942 prov.exhib.lit. 21-May-3 Sotheby's, New York #45/R est:30000-50000
£23148 $37500 €34722 Standing child (41cm-16in) brown stone on wood base executed c.1928 prov.lit. 21-May-3 Sotheby's, New York #46/R est:25000-35000

FLANNAGAN, John B (attrib) (1895-1942) American
Sculpture
£3800 $6194 €5700 Sleeping fawn (9x13x12cm-4x5x5in) stone prov. 3-Feb-3 Bonhams, New Bond Street #52/R est:1500-2000

FLASSCHOEN, Gustave (1868-1940) Belgian
£283 $436 €450 Famille de pecheurs, Volendam (16x22cm-6x9in) s. panel. 22-Oct-2 Campo, Vlaamse Kaai #498
£342 $533 €540 Zelandaises conversant (35x27cm-14x11in) s. 16-Sep-2 Horta, Bruxelles #171
£411 $642 €650 Depart des cavaliers (18x24cm-7x9in) s. panel. 16-Sep-2 Horta, Bruxelles #170
£468 $748 €650 Fermette a la cote beige (29x39cm-11x15in) s. panel. 13-May-3 Vanderkindere, Brussels #219
£490 $789 €750 Conversation dans la cour, Orientalist (25x20cm-10x8in) s. cardboard. 20-Jan-3 Horta, Bruxelles #257
£769 $1207 €1200 Kasbah d'Alger (33x24cm-13x9in) s. panel. 10-Dec-2 Tajan, Paris #180
£823 $1284 €1300 Marche a Fez (24x30cm-9x12in) s. panel. 15-Oct-2 Horta, Bruxelles #308
£886 $1382 €1400 Traversee du pont-levis (65x53cm-26x21in) s. 16-Sep-2 Horta, Bruxelles #169
£903 $1427 €1400 Fantasia (39x50cm-15x20in) s. 17-Dec-2 Rossini, Paris #77
£3125 $5156 €4500 Vieux port (40x50cm-16x20in) s. 1-Jul-3 Christie's, Amsterdam #127/R est:2000-3000
£4403 $6824 €7000 Au bal (29x37cm-11x15in) s. 5-Oct-2 De Vuyst, Lokeren #543/R est:5500-6500

FLATHER, Donald M (1903-1990) Canadian
£866 $1377 €1256 Black Tusk Peak, summer from southwest (114x84cm-45x33in) i.verso board prov. 1-May-3 Heffel, Vancouver #21/R est:3000-4000 (C.D 2000)
£1299 $2065 €1884 Mt Breidablik, Pangnirtung Pass, Baffin Island (91x122cm-36x48in) i.verso canvas on board prov. 1-May-3 Heffel, Vancouver #22/R est:3000-4000 (C.D 3000)
£1411 $2230 €2117 Icebergs II (69x91cm-27x36in) i.verso board. 14-Nov-2 Heffel, Vancouver #158/R est:6000-8000 (C.D 3500)
£1778 $2916 €2667 Mt. Louis (60x105cm-24x41in) s. board. 3-Jun-3 Joyner, Toronto #296/R est:6000-8000 (C.D 4000)
£1778 $2916 €2667 Autumn larches (90x60cm-35x24in) s. board. 3-Jun-3 Joyner, Toronto #352/R est:5000-7000 (C.D 4000)
£1794 $2870 €2691 Howe Sound lookout (69x109cm-27x43in) board prov. 15-May-3 Heffel, Vancouver #216/R est:6000-8000 (C.D 4000)
£2419 $3823 €3629 Prairie storm (61x74cm-24x29in) s. board prov. 14-Nov-2 Heffel, Vancouver #192/R est:5000-6000 (C.D 6000)
£2621 $4141 €3932 Seven spruce marsh (69x91cm-27x36in) s.i.d.1971 board prov. 14-Nov-2 Heffel, Vancouver #161/R est:5000-7000 (C.D 6500)
£3024 $4778 €4536 Mt. Sir Donald (91x112cm-36x44in) s. painted 1978 canvas on board prov. 14-Nov-2 Heffel, Vancouver #159/R est:12000-15000 (C.D 7500)

FLATTELY, Alistair (1922-) British
£420 $685 €630 Concert at the Usher Hall (33x53cm-13x21in) 14-Feb-3 Lyon & Turnbull, Edinburgh #8

FLAUBERT, Paul (1928-) French
£348 $540 €550 Canotage sur la riviere (19x24cm-7x9in) s. panel. 29-Sep-2 Eric Pillon, Calais #276/R

FLAVIN, Dan (1933-1996) American
Sculpture
£15625 $25000 €23438 Barbara roses (22cm-9in) s.d.1962-64 num.7 terracotta flower pot flowerlite light blub. 14-May-3 Sotheby's, New York #221/R est:25000-35000
£16000 $26720 €23200 Roses (22x13x13cm-9x5x5in) s.i.d.1962 flowerlite bulb plastic pot porcelain chain prov. 27-Jun-3 Christie's, London #210/R est:20000-30000
£17500 $28000 €26250 East New York shrine (29x11cm-11x4in) s.d.1962-65 num4 tin can porcelain pull chain glass beads. 15-May-3 Christie's, Rockefeller NY #308/R est:25000-35000
£18987 $30000 €28481 Barabara roses (23x13x13cm-9x5x5in) i.d.1962-71 num.3 aerolux flowerlight. 14-Nov-2 Christie's, Rockefeller NY #372/R est:25000-35000
£20000 $32800 €30000 Untitled - For Otto Freunlich (125x35x63cm-49x14x25in) one of five pink yellow red florescent light. 6-Feb-3 Christie's, London #700/R est:25000-35000
£31250 $50000 €46875 Untitled - to Lucie Rie mmaster Potter (183x43x61cm-72x17x24in) yellow blue red green fluorescent light executed 1990 prov.exhib. 16-May-3 Phillips, New York #131/R est:50000-70000
£33548 $52000 €50322 Untitled (124x170x10cm-49x67x4in) pink blue green fluorescent lights executed 1987 prov.exhib. 26-Sep-2 Christie's, Rockefeller NY #804/R est:25000-35000
£43750 $70000 €65625 Untitled - for Hans Coper, master potter (254x61x13cm-100x24x5in) five daylight cool white fluorescent lights executed 1990. 15-May-3 Christie's, Rockefeller NY #317/R est:30000-40000
£49367 $78000 €74051 Untitled (183cm-72in) red fluorescent light executed 1987 prov.exhib.lit. 12-Nov-2 Phillips, New York #104/R est:40000-60000
£50633 $80000 €75950 Untitled - to Mr.Mrs Thomas Inch (122cm-48in) fluorescent light pink daylight white executed 1964 prov. 13-Nov-2 Sotheby's, New York #316/R est:60000-80000
£56962 $90000 €85443 Untitled - to Don Judd, colorist (132x36x15cm-52x14x6in) four red two pink fluorescent lights executed 1987 prov.exhib. 14-Nov-2 Christie's, Rockefeller NY #365/R est:35000-45000
£64103 $100000 €96155 Red green alternatives - to Sonja (122cm-48in) red green fluorescent light executed 1964 prov. 11-Nov-2 Phillips, New York #36/R est:100000-150000
£75000 $120000 €112500 Untitled (244x61cm-96x24in) fluorescent lights exec.1969 prov.exhib.lit. 13-May-3 Sotheby's, New York #33/R est:120000-180000
£93750 $150000 €140625 Untitled - for Charlotte and Jim Brooks (18x244x13cm-7x96x5in) blue red fluorescent lights executed 1964 prov.exhib.lit. 15-May-3 Christie's, Rockefeller NY #307/R est:100000-150000
£96875 $155000 €145313 Untitled (244cm-96in) blue green yellow fluorescent light executed 1976 prov.exhib. 15-May-3 Phillips, New York #8/R est:80000-120000
£200000 $320000 €300000 Untitled - monument to V Tatlin (244x49x11cm-96x19x4in) fluorescent light exec.1967 prov.exhib. 14-May-3 Christie's, Rockefeller NY #29/R est:300000-400000
£227848 $360000 €341772 Alternate diagonals of March 2, 1964 (360cm-142in) daylight fluorescent light executed 1964 prov.exhib.lit. 13-Nov-2 Christie's, Rockefeller NY #42/R est:300000-400000
Works on paper
£13924 $22000 €20886 Untitled (35x25cm-14x10in) s.i.d.5 June 1964 col pencil prov. 14-Nov-2 Christie's, Rockefeller NY #373/R est:18000-22000
£19000 $31730 €27550 Iconostasis for icons III and IV (28x35cm-11x14in) s.i.d.12.3.62 graphite col crayon prov. 27-Jun-3 Christie's, London #223/R est:10000-12000

FLAXMAN, John (1755-1826) British
Works on paper
£1300 $2132 €1885 Study for Pandora brought to Epimetheus (29x40cm-11x16in) s.i. pencil prov.lit. 5-Jun-3 Christie's, London #10/R est:1500-2000

FLECK, Joseph (1850-1921) American
£2568 $3750 €3852 Summer idyll, Taos (43x46cm-17x18in) s. 10-May-2 Skinner, Boston #127/R est:2800-3200

FLECK, Karl Anton (1928-1983) Austrian
£1519 $2354 €2400 Malli (88x62cm-35x24in) mono.i.d.1976 graphite. 24-Sep-2 Wiener Kunst Auktionen, Vienna #301/R est:1500-3000
Works on paper
£252 $390 €400 Landscape (22x26cm-9x10in) i.d.22.7.1982 pencil. 30-Oct-2 Dorotheum, Vienna #46
£409 $634 €650 Landscape (23x18cm-9x7in) mono.d.1980 w/C. 30-Oct-2 Dorotheum, Vienna #45
£409 $634 €650 Wine country (23x30cm-9x12in) mono.i.d.1982 W/C. 30-Oct-2 Dorotheum, Vienna #47
£705 $1114 €1100 Amaryllis (62x44cm-24x17in) mono.i.d.1982 graphite col pen board. 12-Nov-2 Dorotheum, Vienna #271/R
£759 $1177 €1200 F Zadrazil (62x90cm-24x35in) mono.i.d.1976 graphite. 24-Sep-2 Wiener Kunst Auktionen, Vienna #303/R
£861 $1403 €1300 Landscape (24x32cm-9x13in) mono.d.1975 W/C. 28-Jan-3 Dorotheum, Vienna #235/R
£1126 $1835 €1700 Wine garden near Thallern (30x44cm-12x17in) mono.i.d.1981 pencil. 28-Jan-3 Dorotheum, Vienna #234/R est:1100-1500
£1218 $1924 €1900 Kurfurst Fleck (90x62cm-35x24in) mono.i.d.1974 pencil oil chk. 12-Nov-2 Dorotheum, Vienna #238/R est:1300-2000

FLEGEL, Georg (1563-1638) German
£294872 $465897 €460000 Still life with fruit, mouse and bird (28x42cm-11x17in) mono. exhib.prov.lit. 16-Nov-2 Lempertz, Koln #1028/R est:300000-500000

FLEGEL, Georg (circle) (1563-1638) German
£30000 $46800 €45000 Grapes in a pewter bowl, roemer of white wine, hazelnuts and slices of butter in a dish on a ledge (39x49cm-15x19in) panel. 9-Apr-3 Christie's, London #68/R est:8000-12000

FLEGEL, Georg and VALKENBORCH, Lucas van (style) (16th C) German/Flemish
£7000 $10850 €10500 Kitchen maid holding a pewter platter of fruit before a partially draped table (78x69cm-31x27in) 30-Oct-2 Christie's, Kensington #19/R est:4000-6000

FLEGIER, M (20th C) French?
£1282 $2013 €2000 Marocaines devant la casbah de l'Atlas (40x60cm-16x24in) s. panel. 16-Dec-2 Gros & Delettrez, Paris #81/R est:1500-2000

FLEISCHMANN, Adolf (1892-1969) German
Works on paper
£2532 $3949 €4000 Composition in red, brown and blue (62x48cm-24x19in) s. gouache prov. 18-Oct-2 Dr Fritz Nagel, Stuttgart #498/R est:5200
£2949 $4571 €4600 Composition on blue (49x32cm-19x13in) mono. gouache prov. 7-Dec-2 Ketterer, Hamburg #377/R est:4800-5300
£3623 $5942 €5000 Untitled (45x31cm-18x12in) s.d.54 gouache over pencil. 29-May-3 Lempertz, Koln #620/R est:6000-8000

FLEMING, Ian (1906-1994) British
£850 $1386 €1275 Rain Ferryden (61x91cm-24x36in) 14-Feb-3 Lyon & Turnbull, Edinburgh #139
£1050 $1638 €1575 Sunset, St Monance (44x64cm-17x25in) s. i.verso board exhib. 17-Oct-2 Bonhams, Edinburgh #51/R

FLEMING, John (1792-1845) British
£950 $1454 €1425 New recruit for the Black Watch (25x20cm-10x8in) s.d.1821 board. 22-Aug-2 Bonhams, Edinburgh #953/R

FLEMING, John (attrib) (1792-1845) British
£600 $918 €900 Loch Lomond (38x53cm-15x21in) board. 22-Aug-2 Bonhams, Edinburgh #1138

FLEMING, Rona (1901-1976) New Zealander
£411 $599 €617 Sunset Lyttelton Harbour (42x57cm-17x22in) s. board. 12-Sep-1 Watson's, Christchurch #23 est:600-1600 (NZ.D 1375)

FLEMISH SCHOOL, 15th C
£8333 $13167 €13000 Vierge a l'enfant (26x23cm-10x9in) panel prov. 15-Nov-2 Drouot Estimations, Paris #85/R est:5000
£10759 $17000 €17000 Saint barbara. Saint Agnes (68x28cm-27x11in) tempera board pair. 2-Dec-2 Finarte, Milan #168/R

FLEMISH SCHOOL, 16th C
£4430 $6867 €7000 Diable semant l'ivraie (55x65cm-22x26in) d.1575 panel. 24-Sep-2 Galerie Moderne, Brussels #815/R
£5422 $9000 €7862 Madonna and Child (28x23cm-11x9in) panel. 11-Jun-3 Boos Gallery, Michigan #411/R est:4000-6000
£7500 $11775 €11250 Portrait of a lady holding a gold chain (107x79cm-42x31in) i.d.1566 coat of arms panel. 12-Dec-2 Sotheby's, London #144/R est:8000-12000

£8844	$14061	€13000	Arch Angel Michael (155x132cm-61x52in) 19-Mar-3 Neumeister, Munich #430/R est:12000
£11268	$18704	€16000	Les rejouissances dans le parc du chateau (86x100cm-34x39in) paper. 15-Jun-3 Anaf, Lyon #244/R est:16000-18000
£11538	$17885	€18000	Holy family - Mary and Joseph offering apples to the Christ child (74x48cm-29x19in) i.verso panel. 4-Dec-2 Neumeister, Munich #591/R est:3500
£12025	$19000	€19000	Harvest. Back from hunting (13x20cm-5x8in) copper pair. 2-Dec-2 Rieunier, Paris #59/R est:10000
£13456	$21260	€20184	Madonna and Child (70x53cm-28x21in) board. 15-Nov-2 Naón & Cia, Buenos Aires #103/R
£17000	$26520	€25500	Rest on the flight into Egypt (66x82cm-26x32in) mono. canvas transferred from panel prov. 9-Apr-3 Christie's, London #5/R est:15000-25000
£18354	$29000	€29000	Holy Family (131x100cm-52x39in) panel painted c.1560. 2-Dec-2 Cornette de St.Cyr, Paris #10/R est:9000
£19512	$32000	€29268	Fortune (190x119cm-75x47in) prov.exhib.lit. 30-May-3 Christie's, Rockefeller NY #10/R est:15000-20000
£30000	$50100	€43500	Virgin and child. Saint Lucy. Saint Beatrice. Saints Francis and Clare (30x50cm-12x20in) d.1555 panel wings en grisaille wings double-sided triptych prov. 10-Jul-3 Sotheby's, London #107/R est:10000-15000
£54487	$85545	€85000	Saint Jerome meditating (38x47cm-15x19in) panel painted c.1560. 14-Dec-2 Artcurial Briest, Paris #31 est:8000

Prints

£6329	$10000	€10000	Village fair (20x26cm-8x10in) etching. 29-Nov-2 Bassenge, Berlin #5215/R est:6000

FLEMISH SCHOOL, 16th/17th C

£5500	$8470	€8250	Blacksmith by cave (20x25cm-8x10in) 25-Oct-2 Gorringes, Lewes #908
£6383	$9894	€9575	Landscape with figures and vanitas symbols (39x63cm-15x25in) panel. 8-Dec-2 Uppsala Auktionskammare, Uppsala #26/R est:50000-60000 (S.KR 90000)

FLEMISH SCHOOL, 17th C

£3712	$5790	€5568	Rest on the Flight (113x85cm-44x33in) panel. 20-Nov-2 Fischer, Luzern #1032/R est:9000-12000 (S.FR 8500)
£5128	$7949	€8000	Nativity (91x88cm-36x35in) 4-Dec-2 Finarte, Rome #838/R est:6000
£5769	$9000	€8654	Village scene with horses and figures. board. 21-Sep-2 Harvey Clar, Oakland #1407
£6164	$9678	€9000	Kermesse flamande (45x60cm-18x24in) mono. 15-Apr-3 Galerie Moderne, Brussels #340/R est:8000-10000
£6621	$10329	€9932	King Constantin's victory over Licinius (206x125cm-81x49in) panel. 28-Mar-3 Koller, Zurich #3021/R est:8000-12000 (S.FR 14500)
£6731	$10567	€10500	Harbour scene (66x88cm-26x35in) 13-Dec-2 Pierre Berge, Paris #65/R
£6849	$10685	€10274	Allegory of summer - peasants and sheep in landscape (77x93cm-30x37in) 28-Mar-3 Koller, Zurich #3039/R est:15000-25000 (S.FR 15000)
£7500	$12525	€10875	God creating the animals and birds (38x48cm-15x19in) i. copper. 9-Jul-3 Bonhams, New Bond Street #161/R est:8000-12000
£8000	$12400	€12000	Still life of flowers in wicker basket, blooms and leaves scattered (26x33cm-10x13in) panel. 31-Oct-2 Sotheby's, Olympia #41/R est:6000-8000
£8228	$13000	€13000	Naan and Eliseo (101x126cm-40x50in) 2-Dec-2 Finarte, Milan #178/R est:8000
£8333	$12917	€13000	Wooded. (106x165cm-42x65in) 6-Dec-2 Maigret, Paris #90/R est:5500
£9000	$13950	€13500	Marriage feast at Cana (138x199cm-54x78in) 31-Oct-2 Sotheby's, Olympia #31/R est:5000-7000
£9000	$15030	€13050	Mater Dolorosa (60x44cm-24x17in) panel prov. 10-Jul-3 Sotheby's, London #157/R est:6000-8000
£10345	$16448	€15000	Neptune. Dido and Eneas (64x58cm-25x23in) board pair. 4-Mar-3 Ansorena, Madrid #75/R est:6000
£10959	$17096	€16000	Kermesse Flamande (103x143cm-41x56in) 14-Apr-3 Horta, Bruxelles #195/R est:20000-25000
£12838	$20027	€19000	Landscape with under-growth (12x18cm-5x7in) panel painted c.1600. 26-Mar-3 Tajan, Paris #122/R est:12000
£12987	$19351	€20000	Holy Family with four putti (127x98cm-50x39in) panel. 26-Jun-2 Neumeister, Munich #627/R est:4500
£21622	$33730	€32000	Bouquet (65x53cm-26x21in) panel. 26-Mar-3 Pierre Berge, Paris #20/R est:5000
£23973	$37637	€35000	Triomphe de la Mort (87x116cm-34x46in) 15-Apr-3 Laurence Calmels, Paris #4103/R est:4000
£26000	$40560	€39000	Extensive landscape with a cavalry battle, church beyond (104x185cm-41x73in) s. indis d.1675 prov.exhib. 10-Apr-3 Christie's, Kensington #65/R est:10000-15000
£30000	$47100	€45000	Roman battle before a classic city (25x41cm-10x16in) s.i.d.1643 copper. 10-Dec-2 Bonhams, New Bond Street #286/R est:7000-10000
£33121	$51669	€52000	Siege of Gravelines possibly that of 28 July 1644 (144x254cm-57x100in) prov. 5-Nov-2 Sotheby's, Amsterdam #283/R est:30000-50000

FLEMISH SCHOOL, 17th/18th C

£7692	$12077	€12000	Ship battle (108x177cm-43x70in) 19-Nov-2 Servarts Themis, Bruxelles #276/R est:8000
£7843	$12627	€12000	Scene de l'ancien testament (122x170cm-48x67in) indis.sig. 20-Jan-3 Horta, Bruxelles #115/R est:15000-20000

FLEMISH SCHOOL, 18th C

£4375	$7000	€6563	Celebration of the cherubs (48x64cm-19x25in) prov. 14-May-3 Butterfields, San Francisco #1030/R est:4000-6000
£4906	$7555	€7800	River landscape with hunters (50x72cm-20x28in) board. 23-Oct-2 Finarte, Rome #431/R
£5031	$7799	€8000	Shepherd playing the shawm in landscape. Herdsman and flock by ford (14x16cm-6x6in) panel two. 2-Oct-2 Dorotheum, Vienna #334/R est:8000-10000
£6090	$9561	€9500	Still life of fruit and oysters (61x76cm-24x30in) i. 21-Nov-2 Van Ham, Cologne #1353/R est:8000
£7000	$10850	€10500	River landscape with boors carousing before tavern (94x113cm-37x44in) 31-Oct-2 Sotheby's, Olympia #48/R est:4000-6000
£9032	$14271	€14000	Farm interior (55x74cm-22x29in) painted c.1700. 19-Dec-2 Delvaux, Paris #104/R est:12000
£9395	$15127	€14000	Wooded landscape with a herd, and shepherds playing cards (84x117cm-33x46in) bears d.1644 prov.lit. 18-Feb-3 Sotheby's, Amsterdam #258/R est:3000-5000
£11321	$17434	€18000	Bacchus and Arianna (152x225cm-60x89in) 23-Oct-2 Finarte, Rome #465/R est:7500-8500
£11332	$17905	€16998	Untitled (87x68cm-34x27in) 15-Nov-2 Naón & Cia, Buenos Aires #83/R
£14000	$21980	€21000	Huntsman seated, holding a rifle and his two spaniels by his side (229x164cm-90x65in) 10-Dec-2 Bonhams, New Bond Street #291/R est:15000-20000
£15385	$23846	€24000	Village covered in snoww (66x81cm-26x32in) panel. 6-Dec-2 Maigret, Paris #93/R est:6000

FLEMISH SCHOOL, 19th C

£5128	$8000	€7692	Christ and the woman at the well (87x70cm-34x28in) copper prov. 14-Sep-2 Weschler, Washington #570/R est:5000-7000
£5449	$8500	€8174	Return from Egypt (88x70cm-35x28in) copper prov. 14-Sep-2 Weschler, Washington #569/R est:5000-7000
£8500	$13345	€12750	Still life of flowers in an urn in a landscape (98x75cm-39x30in) 21-Nov-2 Tennants, Leyburn #841/R est:1500-2000

FLEMISH SCHOOL, 19th/20th C

£4321	$7000	€6482	Portrait of lady presumed to be Jeanne-la-Folle (36x24cm-14x9in) panel. 23-Jan-3 Sotheby's, New York #161/R

FLEMISH-SPANISH SCHOOL

£5031	$7849	€8000	Crucifixion (90x58cm-35x23in) triptych. 23-Sep-2 Durán, Madrid #260/R

FLEPS, Peter (20th C) American

£271	$425	€407	Lake (74x91cm-29x36in) acrylic on metal prov. 14-Dec-2 Charlton Hall, Columbia #502/R

FLERS, Camille (1802-1868) French

£2244	$3522	€3500	Bouquet de fleurs sur fond dore (150x100cm-59x39in) s.indis.d. 15-Dec-2 Mercier & Cie, Lille #376/R
£3861	$6100	€6100	Voiliers au fild de l'eau (45x67cm-18x26in) s. 1-Dec-2 Peron, Melun #81

Works on paper

£306	$477	€459	Rider in hilly landscape beneath cloudy skies (31x48cm-12x19in) s.d.1846 pastel. 6-Nov-2 Dobiaschofsky, Bern #514/R (S.FR 700)

FLETCHER, Aaron Dean (attrib) (1817-1902) American

£2592	$4250	€3758	Portrait of a man with red hair (61x0cm-24x0in) 8-Jun-3 Skinner, Boston #289/R est:1500-2500

FLETCHER, Blythe (1890-1949) New Zealander

Works on paper

£245	$348	€368	Cattle resting at dusk (38x48cm-15x19in) s. W/C. 20-Mar-2 Watson's, Christchurch #53/R (NZ.D 800)
£299	$436	€449	Hay making (34x43cm-13x17in) s. W/C. 12-Sep-1 Watson's, Christchurch #3 est:700-1700 (NZ.D 1000)
£361	$578	€523	Pastoral scene with donkey (25x35cm-10x14in) s. W/C. 13-May-3 Watson's, Christchurch #36/R (NZ.D 1000)
£361	$578	€523	Grand Canal, Venice (34x45cm-13x18in) s. gouache. 13-May-3 Watson's, Christchurch #17/R (NZ.D 1000)
£491	$721	€737	Clam gatherers at low tide (49x63cm-19x25in) s.d.34 W/C. 19-Jun-2 Watson's, Christchurch #48/R est:1500-2500 (NZ.D 1500)
£508	$722	€762	English rural scene (54x56cm-21x22in) s. gouache prov. 21-Nov-1 Watson's, Christchurch #29/R (NZ.D 1750)

£627 $915 €941 Clam gathers at low tide (34x47cm-13x19in) s. W/C. 12-Sep-1 Watson's, Christchurch #1 est:1600-2600 (NZ.D 2100)
£697 $1073 €1046 Gathering firewood (54x79cm-21x31in) s. W/C. 4-Sep-2 Dunbar Sloane, Wellington #119/R est:2000-3000 (NZ.D 2300)
£722 $1155 €1047 Moroccan market scene (35x65cm-14x26in) s.d.1926 gouache. 13-May-3 Watson's, Christchurch #1/R (NZ.D 2000)
£965 $1505 €1448 Remarkables, Queenstown (55x83cm-22x33in) s. gouache. 27-Mar-3 International Art Centre, Auckland #121/R (NZ.D 2750)

FLETCHER, Edwin (1857-1945) British
£338 $527 €507 Shipping in a harbour (49x75cm-19x30in) s. 15-Oct-2 Stephan Welz, Johannesburg #388 est:6000-9000 (SA.R 5500)
£420 $668 €630 Thames with sailing barges and other vessels (51x66cm-20x26in) 20-Mar-3 Ewbank, Send #384/R
£450 $707 €675 Shipping on the Thames in London (36x55cm-14x22in) s.i.d.1856 verso. 16-Dec-2 Sotheby's, Olympia #143/R
£550 $891 €825 Setting out to sea (41x61cm-16x24in) s. 23-Jan-3 Christie's, Kensington #75/R
£650 $1053 €975 Shipping on the lower Thames (18x23cm-7x9in) s. pair. 21-May-3 Christie's, Kensington #674/R
£1250 $2038 €1875 Thames barges at sunset (40x60cm-16x24in) sold with a companion. 14-Feb-3 Lyon & Turnbull, Edinburgh #110
£1500 $2325 €2250 H.M.S Victory at her permanent moorings in Portsmouth Harbour (91x71cm-36x28in) init. 31-Oct-2 Christie's, Kensington #553/R est:1500-2500
£1700 $2618 €2550 Thames at Tower Bridge (38x76cm-15x30in) s. 5-Sep-2 Christie's, Kensington #222/R est:2000-3000

FLETCHER, William Blandford (1858-1936) British
£4100 $6847 €5945 Vegetable seller (36x23cm-14x9in) s. panel. 19-Jun-3 Lane, Penzance #125/R est:3000-4000

FLETTRICH, Leonard T (1916-1970) American
£641 $1000 €962 Portrait of an Uptown lady (122x91cm-48x36in) s. 20-Sep-2 New Orleans Auction, New Orleans #1246/R est:1200-1800

FLEUR, Johan Willem (1888-1967) Dutch
£605 $932 €950 Flowering plants in a basket (50x60cm-20x24in) s. 3-Sep-2 Christie's, Amsterdam #370
£1529 $2354 €2400 Still life with flowers in a vase (100x81cm-39x32in) s.d.39. 3-Sep-2 Christie's, Amsterdam #401 est:1500-2000

FLEURY, François-Antoine (1804-1858) French
£4268 $7000 €6402 Young woman and a girl in front of a house (59x69cm-23x27in) s.d.1834. 29-May-3 Sotheby's, New York #45/R est:8000-12000

FLEURY, J Vivien de (19th C) British
£3000 $4710 €4500 Lago di Bolsena (61x109cm-24x43in) s.d.1870. 19-Nov-2 Bonhams, New Bond Street #112/R est:3000-5000

FLEURY, Mme Fanny (1848-?) French
£256 $403 €400 Portrait d'un enfant en uniforme (32x25cm-13x10in) s. 10-Dec-2 Renaud, Paris #13
£1019 $1590 €1600 Portrait de jeune fille (27x22cm-11x9in) s. panel. 7-Nov-2 Chochon-Barre & Allardi, Paris #145/R

FLEURY, Pierre (1900-1985) French
£994 $1560 €1550 Paysage cotier (65x81cm-26x32in) s. 22-Nov-2 Millon & Associes, Paris #80

FLEXOR, Samson (1907-) French
£5319 $8617 €7500 Croisillion (73x92cm-29x36in) s.d. 23-May-3 Binoche, Paris #82/R est:7500-8500

FLICKEL, Paul Franz (1852-1903) German
£600 $936 €900 Villa Borghese a Roma (14x18cm-6x7in) s. i.verso panel. 17-Sep-2 Rosebery Fine Art, London #514/R
£1972 $3175 €2800 Wild garden at dusk (53x37cm-21x15in) s.d.8.9.89 board lit. 10-May-3 Hans Stahl, Toestorf #34/R est:2000
£3750 $6000 €5438 Working a plein air (58x84cm-23x33in) 16-May-3 Skinner, Boston #344/R est:1500-2000

FLIEHER, Karl (1881-1958) Austrian
£382 $603 €550 Moserboden in Kaprun valley (25x33cm-10x13in) s.d.1929 i. verso. 24-Apr-3 Dorotheum, Vienna #46/R
£764 $1207 €1100 Zell am See with Kitzsteinhorn (24x32cm-9x13in) s.d.1930 i. stretcher. 24-Apr-3 Dorotheum, Vienna #86/R

Works on paper
£878 $1370 €1300 Old house in Lotz with Thialspitze, Tyrol (20x26cm-8x10in) s.i. gouache. 28-Mar-3 Dorotheum, Vienna #285/R
£1538 $2415 €2400 Johann-Strauss house near Vienna (22x28cm-9x11in) s.i.d.1929 gouache. 21-Nov-2 Dorotheum, Vienna #446/R est:1800-2600
£1538 $2415 €2400 Old village street in Schwalbenbach on the Donau/Wachau (21x27cm-8x11in) s.i.d.1931 gouache. 21-Nov-2 Dorotheum, Vienna #447/R est:1800-2600

FLIER, Helmert Richard van der (1827-1899) Dutch
£1206 $2013 €1700 Vaches et moutons dans un paysage (32x43cm-13x17in) s.d.1853 panel. 23-Jun-3 Beaussant & Lefèvre, Paris #281/R est:1500-2000

FLIGHT, Claude (1881-1955) British

Prints
£8000 $13200 €11600 Dirt track (26x30cm-10x12in) s.i.num.3/50 col linocut exec.c.1928. 1-Jul-3 Sotheby's, London #162/R est:3500-4500
£8500 $14025 €12325 Paris omnibus (22x28cm-9x11in) s.i. col linocut. 1-Jul-3 Sotheby's, London #163/R est:5000-6000

FLINCK, Govaert (1615-1660) Dutch
£72327 $112107 €115000 Portrait of Saskia, wife of Rembrandt (69x49cm-27x19in) panel lit. 2-Oct-2 Dorotheum, Vienna #167/R est:40000-60000

Works on paper
£6500 $10855 €9425 Portrait of a gentleman, half length (17x13cm-7x5in) s.d.1646 blk chk point of brush wash htd white prov.exhib.lit. 9-Jul-3 Sotheby's, London #94/R est:5000-7000

FLINCK, Govaert (circle) (1615-1660) Dutch
£6000 $10020 €8700 Portrait of a bearded man in a fur trimmed black coat and velvet cap (63x50cm-25x20in) 11-Jul-3 Christie's, Kensington #31/R est:3000-5000

FLINCK, Govaert (style) (1615-1660) Dutch
£21000 $32760 €31500 Bearded old man, seated at a ledge in fur and brocade lined cloack (71x60cm-28x24in) prov. 9-Apr-3 Christie's, London #32/R est:15000-20000

FLINN, John (20th C) Irish?
£306 $477 €480 Boats in the harbour (38x50cm-15x20in) s. 6-Nov-2 James Adam, Dublin #38/R

FLINT, Francis Russell (1915-1977) British
£300 $468 €450 Ambush (51x76cm-20x30in) s. 12-Sep-2 Sotheby's, Olympia #117/R
£500 $775 €750 Gossiping flowers seller (51x61cm-20x24in) s. 1-Oct-2 Bonhams, Leeds #282
£1500 $2430 €2250 M.V Herdsman off Dover (48x58cm-19x23in) s. board. 21-Jan-3 Bonhams, New Bond Street #206/R est:600-800
£2200 $3564 €3300 M.V Factor at Castries (59x60cm-23x24in) s. 21-Jan-3 Bonhams, New Bond Street #205/R est:300-500

Works on paper
£246 $383 €369 White horses in the Sound of Sleat (37x55cm-15x22in) s. W/C. 15-Oct-2 Stephan Welz, Johannesburg #410 est:3000-5000 (SA.R 4000)
£400 $656 €600 Busy shipyard (36x54cm-14x21in) s. W/C. 7-Feb-3 Honiton Galleries, Honiton #298/R
£550 $897 €825 Squalls and sails, Clyde (25x38cm-10x15in) W/C. 28-Jan-3 Gorringes, Lewes #1582/R
£850 $1318 €1275 Spanish market (49x75cm-19x30in) s. W/C. 26-Sep-2 Mellors & Kirk, Nottingham #629/R

FLINT, Leroy (1909-1991) American
£256 $400 €384 Space probe (69x53cm-27x21in) s. i.verso. 28-Mar-3 Aspire, Cleveland #28/R
£272 $425 €408 Crazy horse (43x28cm-17x11in) s. paperboard. 28-Mar-3 Aspire, Cleveland #59/R
£721 $1125 €1082 Untitled (61x46cm-24x18in) s. board sold with original sketch. 28-Mar-3 Aspire, Cleveland #57/R

FLINT, Sir William Russell (1880-1969) British
£4500 $6975 €6750 Pink feather (37x30cm-15x12in) s. s.i.verso tempera prov.lit. 31-Oct-2 Christie's, London #150/R est:5000-7000
£7000 $11690 €10150 Carmelito's pink comb (60x49cm-24x19in) s. prov. 17-Jun-3 Bristol Auction Rooms #546 est:5000-7000
£24000 $39360 €34800 Casilda (52x68cm-20x27in) s. s.i.verso tempera prov.exhib. 5-Jun-3 Christie's, London #183/R est:20000-30000
£40000 $65600 €60000 Dice players (51x76cm-20x30in) s.i. prov.exhib. 6-Jun-3 Christie's, London #142/R est:40000-60000

Works on paper
£600 $924 €900 Consolito Carmen (18x25cm-7x10in) s.i. pencil. 5-Sep-2 Christie's, Kensington #535/R
£619 $997 €929 Pretty Gitana (23x17cm-9x7in) init.i. red chk. 12-May-3 Stephan Welz, Johannesburg #18 est:2000-3000 (SA.R 7200)
£940 $1495 €1410 Study for the campers and Dryad (35x25cm-14x10in) s.i. W/C. 4-Mar-3 Bearnes, Exeter #395/R

£	$	€	Description
£1071	$1693	€1607	Helen (19x15cm-7x6in) s. i.verso chl pastel prov. 26-Nov-2 Sotheby's, Melbourne #243/R est:3000-5000 (A.D 3000)
£1100	$1749	€1650	Storm over Morven (13x26cm-5x10in) s.i. verso W/C. 6-Mar-3 Christie's, Kensington #195/R est:1000-1500
£1300	$2028	€1950	Two girls in ballgowns (23x33cm-9x13in) init. sanguine. 10-Apr-3 Bonhams, Edinburgh #151/R est:1000-1500
£1500	$2310	€2250	Old castle (24x37cm-9x15in) s.d.4.2.55 red chk. 5-Sep-2 Christie's, Kensington #569/R est:1500-2000
£1502	$2343	€2178	Audrey as Amanda (30x22cm-12x9in) s.i.d. March 1948 blue chk prov. 26-Mar-3 Walker's, Ottawa #60/R est:1500-2000 (C.D 3500)
£1700	$2839	€2465	Moonset at morning (32x48cm-13x19in) s. i.verso prov. 24-Jun-3 Bonhams, New Bond Street #39/R est:1500-2500
£1719	$2750	€2579	View of a rolling landscape near Dartmoor, Devon (28x39cm-11x15in) s. s.i.verso W/C board. 14-May-3 Butterfields, San Francisco #1174/R est:2000-3000
£2000	$3140	€3000	St. Fillan's Hill (26x37cm-10x15in) s.d.1913 W/C prov. 21-Nov-2 Christie's, London #111/R est:2000-3000
£2000	$3180	€3000	Figure on the shore (25x17cm-10x7in) s.d.1909 W/C. 26-Feb-3 Sotheby's, Olympia #167/R est:1000-1500
£2000	$3120	€3000	On the Arun, near Arundel (19x26cm-7x10in) s. W/C prov. 25-Mar-3 Bonhams, New Bond Street #56/R est:1000-1500
£2200	$3388	€3300	Bacchand (23x13cm-9x5in) s. chk. 5-Sep-2 Christie's, Kensington #533/R est:1000-1500
£2200	$3608	€3300	Elegant lady (22x16cm-9x6in) s. pastel. 3-Jun-3 Sotheby's, Olympia #4/R est:1000-1500
£2200	$3608	€3300	Carlotta (33x17cm-13x7in) s. pencil pastel. 3-Jun-3 Sotheby's, Olympia #5/R est:1500-2000
£2500	$3900	€3750	Dell quay (26x34cm-10x13in) s. W/C. 25-Mar-3 Bonhams, New Bond Street #54/R est:2000-3000
£2800	$4340	€4200	Rosneath from above Shandon, Argyll, blue morning (25x33cm-10x13in) s. W/C prov. 31-Oct-2 Christie's, London #149/R est:2000-3000
£3000	$4680	€4500	Halnaker Mill, near Goodwood (38x54cm-15x21in) s. W/C prov. 25-Mar-3 Bonhams, New Bond Street #55/R est:3000-5000
£3000	$4740	€4500	Gypsy girl in the stocks (30x19cm-12x7in) s. red wax crayon dr. 7-Apr-3 Bonhams, Bath #46/R est:3000-5000
£3200	$5024	€4800	Evangeline (30x18cm-12x7in) s. red crayon. 21-Nov-2 Christie's, London #114/R est:3000-4000
£3500	$5460	€5250	Saraband (33x26cm-13x10in) s. red chk. 27-Mar-3 Christie's, Kensington #272/R est:4000-6000
£3800	$5890	€5700	Standing nude (25x12cm-10x5in) s. black red chk. 31-Oct-2 Christie's, London #152/R est:3000-5000
£4000	$6560	€5800	Fiametta (24x16cm-9x6in) s. red crayon prov. 5-Jun-3 Christie's, London #181/R est:2000-3000
£4200	$6510	€6300	Reclining nude (17x33cm-7x13in) s. red chk. 31-Oct-2 Christie's, London #151/R est:4000-6000
£4800	$7872	€6960	Stiffened petticoat (30x20cm-12x8in) s. red crayon prov. 5-Jun-3 Christie's, London #180/R est:3000-5000
£5000	$7800	€7500	Minx (20x33cm-8x13in) s. pastel. 25-Mar-3 Bonhams, New Bond Street #57/R est:4000-6000
£5000	$8200	€7250	Homer's odyssey, no6 (24x29cm-9x11in) s.i.d. W/C sold print. 5-Jun-3 Christie's, London #188/R est:5000-7000
£5000	$8200	€7250	Five ages of gossips (46x56cm-18x22in) s.d.1906 s.i.verso W/C bodycol. 5-Jun-3 Christie's, London #189/R est:5000-8000
£5364	$7992	€8046	Bathers (45x37cm-18x15in) s. W/C prov. 27-Aug-2 Christie's, Melbourne #103/R est:15000-20000 (A.D 14000)
£7500	$11625	€11250	Study of reclining nude (29x40cm-11x16in) s. col chk. 24-Sep-2 Rowley Fine Art, Newmarket #371/R est:3500
£7500	$12300	€10875	Nude reclining (28x44cm-11x17in) s. black crayon prov. 5-Jun-3 Christie's, London #182/R est:3000-5000
£9500	$14915	€14250	Ray (37x45cm-15x18in) s. red crayon. 21-Nov-2 Christie's, London #113/R est:5000-7000
£10000	$16700	€14500	Vineyard workers resting (38x55cm-15x22in) s. 24-Jun-3 Bonhams, New Bond Street #41/R est:12000-15000
£12000	$18720	€18000	Lilette and Lucille (37x55cm-15x22in) s. W/C prov. 25-Mar-3 Bonhams, New Bond Street #47/R est:12000-18000
£12000	$18720	€18000	Barbican, cordes (49x68cm-19x27in) s. s.i.verso W/C. 25-Mar-3 Bonhams, New Bond Street #52/R est:12000-18000
£14000	$21980	€21000	Bamburgh Beach and Holy Island (48x66cm-19x26in) s. s.i.d.1921 verso W/C bodycol prov. 21-Nov-2 Christie's, London #108/R est:15000-20000
£14000	$22960	€20300	Dancing lesson, ladies of old Castile receiving instruction from gypsies (51x68cm-20x27in) s.i.d.1921 W/C. 5-Jun-3 Christie's, London #185/R est:15000-20000
£15000	$23250	€22500	Flickers - sun, sand and fir trees (49x66cm-19x26in) s. W/C exhib. 3-Dec-2 Bonhams, New Bond Street #46/R est:15000-20000
£16500	$25575	€24750	Studies of Cecilia (51x36cm-20x14in) s. s.i. conte prov.exhib. 3-Dec-2 Bonhams, New Bond Street #45/R est:10000-15000
£17000	$26520	€25500	Amanda in the shallows (48x66cm-19x26in) s. s.i.verso W/C. 25-Mar-3 Bonhams, New Bond Street #46/R est:12000-18000
£20000	$32800	€29000	Rococo Aphrodite (41x67cm-16x26in) s. s.i.verso W/C bodycol lit. 5-Jun-3 Christie's, London #184/R est:20000-30000
£22000	$34540	€33000	Veiled silver (51x67cm-20x26in) s. s.i.d.1920 verso W/C bodycol prov.exhib. 21-Nov-2 Christie's, London #109/R est:15000-20000
£30000	$46500	€45000	Gift of gladioli (30x40cm-12x16in) s. s.i. pencil W/C. 3-Dec-2 Bonhams, New Bond Street #42/R est:30000-50000
£35065	$54000	€52598	Venetian canal scene with many figures and boats (51x69cm-20x27in) s. i.verso W/C. 26-Oct-2 Brunk, Ashville #889/R est:15000-25000

FLOCH, Josef (1895-1977) American/Austrian

£	$	€	Description
£4012	$6500	€5817	California landscape (41x61cm-16x24in) s. prov. 21-May-3 Doyle, New York #228/R est:5000-7000
£4459	$7000	€6689	Woman in interior (15x18cm-6x7in) s. prov. 10-Dec-2 Doyle, New York #232/R est:4000-6000
£4777	$7500	€7166	Mother and child, 1927 (29x20cm-11x8in) lit. 10-Dec-2 Doyle, New York #231/R est:5000-7000
£5093	$8199	€7385	City on the sea (40x66cm-16x26in) s. 7-May-3 Dobiaschofsky, Bern #514/R est:7500 (S.FR 11000)
£5732	$9000	€8598	Day dreamer, 1969 (32x40cm-13x16in) s. lit. 10-Dec-2 Doyle, New York #233/R est:8000-12000
£13043	$21391	€18000	On the terrace (75x55cm-30x22in) s. painted 1952 lit. 27-May-3 Hassfurther, Vienna #40/R est:18000-25000

Works on paper

£	$	€	Description
£481	$745	€750	Sketch (50x36cm-20x14in) col chk. 5-Dec-2 Dorotheum, Graz #145/R

FLOCH, Lionel (20th C) French

£	$	€	Description
£333	$543	€480	Portrait de marin (32x24cm-13x9in) s.d.1916 panel. 19-Jul-3 Thierry & Lannon, Brest #331
£437	$703	€620	Cote rocheuse en Bretagne (24x33cm-9x13in) s. board. 11-May-3 Thierry & Lannon, Brest #358
£1013	$1590	€1580	Brulage (24x32cm-9x13in) s. 15-Dec-2 Thierry & Lannon, Brest #383
£1268	$2041	€1800	Port en Bretagne (24x32cm-9x13in) s. board. 11-May-3 Thierry & Lannon, Brest #178 est:800-1000

FLOCKENHAUS, Heinz (1856-1919) German

£	$	€	Description
£601	$950	€950	Moonlit lower Rhine (36x59cm-14x23in) s.i. panel. 29-Nov-2 Schloss Ahlden, Ahlden #1227/R
£2308	$3623	€3600	Winter landscape. Autumn landscape (24x16cm-9x6in) s. panel two. 21-Nov-2 Van Ham, Cologne #1606/R est:2500

FLODBERG, Gilbert (1938-) Canadian

£	$	€	Description
£221	$347	€332	Autumn's end (30x40cm-12x16in) s.i.d.1971 board. 25-Nov-2 Hodgins, Calgary #142/R (C.D 550)
£657	$1044	€986	Autumn Calgary Parkland (30x40cm-12x16in) s.i.d.1979 board. 23-Mar-3 Hodgins, Calgary #105/R est:400-600 (C.D 1550)
£1956	$3207	€2836	Autumn's soft whisper (120x180cm-47x71in) s.i. 9-Jun-3 Hodgins, Calgary #40/R est:4000-5000 (C.D 4400)

FLORA, Paul (1922-) Austrian

Works on paper

£	$	€	Description
£403	$648	€600	Well wisher (9x7cm-4x3in) s.d. s.i.d. pencil pen Indian ink. 18-Feb-3 Dorotheum, Vienna #22
£463	$745	€695	Figure (30x50cm-12x20in) s. Indian ink. 7-May-3 Dobiaschofsky, Bern #1586 (S.FR 1000)
£577	$906	€900	Prophets of evil (23x31cm-9x12in) s.i. pen ink. 21-Nov-2 Dorotheum, Vienna #454/R
£629	$981	€1000	Winter in the Rocky Mountains (27x37cm-11x15in) s.i.d.87 Indian ink. 23-Sep-2 Wiener Kunst Auktionen, Vienna #86
£629	$981	€1000	Composition (27x37cm-11x15in) s.i.d.87 Indian ink. 23-Sep-2 Wiener Kunst Auktionen, Vienna #90
£629	$981	€1000	Night train (27x37cm-11x15in) s.i.d.87 Indian ink. 23-Sep-2 Wiener Kunst Auktionen, Vienna #94
£755	$1177	€1200	Still life with cat and locomotive (27x37cm-11x15in) s.i.d.87 Indian ink col pen. 23-Sep-2 Wiener Kunst Auktionen, Vienna #93
£759	$1185	€1200	Owls meeting in classical ruins (12x16cm-5x6in) s.i.d.78 Indian ink. 15-Oct-2 Dorotheum, Vienna #197
£1006	$1570	€1600	Royal train (27x37cm-11x15in) s.i.d.87 Indian ink col pen. 23-Sep-2 Wiener Kunst Auktionen, Vienna #91/R est:1000-2000
£1006	$1570	€1600	Wild West (27x37cm-11x15in) s.i.d.87 Indian ink col pen. 23-Sep-2 Wiener Kunst Auktionen, Vienna #96 est:1000-2000
£1006	$1570	€1600	Pioneers (27x37cm-11x15in) s.i.d.87 Indian ink. 23-Sep-2 Wiener Kunst Auktionen, Vienna #97 est:1000-2000
£1030	$1627	€1545	Venetian carnival (20x25cm-8x10in) s.i.d.90 pen ink col pencil. 26-Nov-2 Hans Widmer, St Gallen #1107 est:1800-2800 (S.FR 2400)
£1111	$1756	€1600	Seated female nude (24x15cm-9x6in) s.d.42 Indian ink. 24-Apr-3 Dorotheum, Vienna #107/R est:1000-1400
£1132	$1766	€1800	Train in tunnel (27x37cm-11x15in) s.i.d.87 Indian ink. 23-Sep-2 Wiener Kunst Auktionen, Vienna #85/R est:1000-2000
£1132	$1766	€1800	A reminder (27x37cm-11x15in) s.i.d.87 Indian ink col pen. 23-Sep-2 Wiener Kunst Auktionen, Vienna #88
£1195	$1864	€1900	Composition (27x37cm-11x15in) s.i.d.87 Indian ink col pen. 23-Sep-2 Wiener Kunst Auktionen, Vienna #95 est:1000-2000
£1258	$1962	€2000	Stream train pulling cannon (27x37cm-11x15in) s.i.d.87 Indian ink. 23-Sep-2 Wiener Kunst Auktionen, Vienna #84/R est:1000-2000
£1258	$1962	€2000	Orient Express (27x37cm-11x15in) s.i.d.87 Indian ink col pen. 23-Sep-2 Wiener Kunst Auktionen, Vienna #87 est:1000-2000

£1258 $1962 €2000 Harem boarding Orient Express (27x37cm-11x15in) s.i.d.87 Indian ink col pen. 23-Sep-2 Wiener Kunst Auktionen, Vienna #92/R est:1000-2000
£1519 $2400 €2400 Cycling club (35x50cm-14x20in) s.i. pen Indian ink. 27-Nov-2 Dorotheum, Vienna #273/R est:1800-2600
£1519 $2400 €2400 Pioneer landing (35x50cm-14x20in) s.i. pen Indian ink. 27-Nov-2 Dorotheum, Vienna #274/R est:1600-2200
£1667 $2633 €2600 Night time messenger (25x33cm-10x13in) s.i.d.79 pen Indian ink. 12-Nov-2 Dorotheum, Vienna #235/R est:1300-1900
£1806 $2853 €2600 Cat (28x18cm-11x7in) s.d.45 Indian ink. 24-Apr-3 Dorotheum, Vienna #106/R est:1400-2000

FLOREN, Lars (1889-1979) Swedish
£456 $711 €684 View from Skinnarviksberget, Stockholm (50x73cm-20x29in) s. painted 1960s. 6-Nov-2 AB Stockholms Auktionsverk #670/R (S.KR 6500)

FLORENTINE SCHOOL (14th C) Italian
£5449 $8609 €8500 Madonna with child (41x27cm-16x11in) oil tempera panel prov. 16-Nov-2 Lempertz, Koln #1029/R est:10000
£75000 $125250 €108750 Saint Agnes receiving a cloak from an angel (49x41cm-19x16in) tempera triptych prov.lit. 10-Jul-3 Sotheby's, London #30/R est:60000-80000

FLORENTINE SCHOOL (15th C) Italian
£8333 $12917 €13000 Madonna and Child (38x27cm-15x11in) panel painted c.1420. 4-Dec-2 Libert, Castor, Paris #44/R est:15000
£8387 $13252 €13000 Bishop and monk (132x51cm-52x20in) fresco canvas on board pair. 19-Dec-2 Semenzato, Venice #118/R est:12000
£19355 $30581 €30000 Allegory of the Virgin's Intercession (55x30cm-22x12in) tempera board. 19-Dec-2 Semenzato, Venice #22/R est:40000
£21000 $32970 €31500 Madonna and Child (42x30cm-17x12in) tempera gold ground panel prov. 12-Dec-2 Sotheby's, London #102/R est:15000-20000

FLORENTINE SCHOOL (16th C) Italian
£5500 $8635 €8250 Saint Sebastian (36x13cm-14x5in) panel. 10-Dec-2 Sotheby's, Olympia #302/R est:4000-6000
£21000 $32970 €31500 Madonna and Child with infant Saint John the Baptist (70x55cm-28x22in) panel. 13-Dec-2 Christie's, Kensington #202/R est:7000-10000

Works on paper
£4630 $7500 €6945 Study of kneeling female figure (19x13cm-7x5in) chk pen ink. 21-Jan-3 Sotheby's, New York #59/R est:5000

FLORENTINE SCHOOL (17th C) Italian
£6289 $9686 €10000 Le mariage mystique de Sainte Catherine (35x27cm-14x11in) marble. 25-Oct-2 Tajan, Paris #18/R est:10000-12000
£6962 $11000 €11000 Milvio Bridge battle (96x148cm-38x58in) 27-Nov-2 Finarte, Milan #103/R est:12000-15000
£13176 $20554 €19500 Rosalie (42x39cm-17x15in) painted c.1640. 28-Mar-3 Piasa, Paris #6/R
£16552 $26483 €24000 Still life with dead game and page (115x150cm-45x59in) 17-Mar-3 Pandolfini, Florence #714/R
£26000 $40560 €39000 Noli me tangere (200x145cm-79x57in) 9-Apr-3 Bonhams, New Bond Street #89/R est:5000-7000
£73718 $114263 €115000 Portrait of lady as Cleopatra (63x47cm-25x19in) 6-Dec-2 Rieunier, Bailly-Pommery, Mathias, Paris #11/R est:15000

FLORES KAPEROTXIPI, Mauricio (1901-1997) Argentinian
£3846 $6077 €6000 Snack (60x73cm-24x29in) s. 19-Nov-2 Durán, Madrid #210/R

FLORES, Francisco (?) Mexican
Works on paper
£703 $1111 €1055 Manuel Capetillo (43x53cm-17x21in) gouache. 14-Nov-2 Louis Morton, Mexico #61 (M.P 11500)

FLORES, Pedro (1897-1967) Spanish
Works on paper
£256 $374 €400 Untitled (32x25cm-13x10in) gouache. 6-Jun-2 Castellana, Madrid #549/R
£390 $632 €550 Parque con iglesia (15x23cm-6x9in) s. W/C pen. 20-May-3 Segre, Madrid #272/R
£516 $815 €800 French village (17x25cm-7x10in) W/C. 17-Dec-2 Segre, Madrid #126/R
£548 $866 €850 Landscape with house (23x30cm-9x12in) W/C. 17-Dec-2 Segre, Madrid #127/R
£613 $968 €950 Don Quixote (31x23cm-12x9in) s.d.45 W/C gouache. 18-Dec-2 Ansorena, Madrid #245/R

FLORIAN, Henrietta (1938-) Austrian
£385 $608 €600 Portrait of girl (72x55cm-28x22in) mono.d.1962. 12-Nov-2 Dorotheum, Vienna #187/R
£692 $1079 €1100 Sphinx (70x150cm-28x59in) s.d.1986. 23-Sep-2 Wiener Kunst Auktionen, Vienna #68/R
£692 $1079 €1100 Flowers in vase and oil lamp (84x94cm-33x37in) s.d.1987. 23-Sep-2 Wiener Kunst Auktionen, Vienna #55/R

FLORIAN, Maximilian (1901-1982) Austrian
£14493 $23768 €20000 Still life of flowers (92x70cm-36x28in) s.d.1947. 27-May-3 Hassfurther, Vienna #41/R est:15000-18000
Works on paper
£432 $708 €600 Landscape (42x55cm-17x22in) s.d.72 W/C. 5-Jun-3 Dorotheum, Salzburg #777/R

FLORIDO, Enrique (19th C) Spanish
£452 $714 €700 Houses by the river (32x18cm-13x7in) s. board. 17-Dec-2 Durán, Madrid #135/R

FLORIS, Frans (16/17th C) Flemish
£5660 $8830 €9000 Bathseba and David (11x140cm-4x55in) panel. 23-Sep-2 Wiener Kunst Auktionen, Vienna #6/R est:12000-25000

FLORIS, Frans (elder) (1516-1570) Flemish
Prints
£3797 $6000 €6000 Victory surrounded by prisoners and trophies (31x43cm-12x17in) etching. 29-Nov-2 Bassenge, Berlin #5216/R est:6000

FLORIT, Josep Lluis (1909-) Spanish
£577 $912 €900 Urban landscape (61x76cm-24x30in) s. 13-Nov-2 Ansorena, Madrid #270/R

FLORSHEIM, Richard Aberle (1916-1979) American
£340 $500 €510 Overflight (102x76cm-40x30in) s. acrylic painted c.1970. 23-Jun-2 Susanin's, Chicago #5047/R

FLOURENS, Renée (20th C) French
£2000 $3160 €3000 Reclining female nude from behind (75x150cm-30x59in) 12-Nov-2 Bonhams, Knightsbridge #299/R est:2000-3000

FLOUTIER, Louis (20th C) French
£260 $419 €390 La Terrasse Jardin, St Tropez (38x32cm-15x13in) s.i.verso board. 14-Jan-3 Bonhams, Ipswich #382

FLOUTIER, Louis (attrib) (20th C) French
£1667 $2617 €2600 Le retour a la ferme (60x50cm-24x20in) s. panel. 10-Dec-2 Vanderkindere, Brussels #97 est:800-1200

FLOWER, Cedric (1920-) Australian
£323 $490 €485 Coastal scene with pelican (36x44cm-14x17in) s.indis.d.88 board. 27-Aug-2 Goodman, Sydney #81 (A.D 900)

FLOYD, Donald H (1892-1965) British
£330 $515 €495 On the wharfe, near Ilkely (23x33cm-9x13in) s. 18-Oct-2 Keys, Aylsham #670/R
£460 $718 €690 In the heart of Connemara (50x60cm-20x24in) s. i.verso. 6-Nov-2 Bonhams, Chester #492
£520 $868 €754 Wye Valley (101x126cm-40x50in) s.d. 23-Jun-3 Bonhams, Bath #167/R
£980 $1529 €1470 Bridge over the River Wye at Tintern (70x90cm-28x35in) s. 11-Sep-2 Bonhams, Newport #335/R
£1250 $1950 €1875 Coastal hamlet (67x98cm-26x39in) s. 11-Sep-2 Bonhams, Newport #338 est:1000-1500
£1550 $2418 €2325 Autumn glitter, Tintern (61x92cm-24x36in) s. 11-Sep-2 Bonhams, Newport #337 est:1000-1500

FLUBERT, D (19th C) Belgian?
£570 $889 €900 Barques depeche dans un paysage fluvial avec un moulin (74x105cm-29x41in) panel. 16-Sep-2 Amberes, Antwerp #199

FLUCK, Martin Peter (1935-) Swiss
£324 $522 €486 Gypsy woman (80x64cm-31x25in) s. i.d.1966 verso. 7-May-3 Dobiaschofsky, Bern #517/R (S.FR 700)
£873 $1362 €1310 Colourful forest landscape (101x122cm-40x48in) s. panel. 8-Nov-2 Dobiaschofsky, Bern #170/R (S.FR 2000)

FLUCK, Roland (1957-) Swiss
£2870 $4621 €4162 House facade in sunshine (170x240cm-67x94in) s.d.91. 9-May-3 Dobiaschofsky, Bern #209/R est:6000 (S.FR 6200)

FLUMIANI, Ugo (1876-1938) Italian
£833 $1317 €1300 Church square (20x28cm-8x11in) s. board. 14-Nov-2 Neumeister, Munich #565/R
£3546 $5745 €5000 Pomeriggio in giardino (46x34cm-18x13in) s.i. board. 22-May-3 Stadion, Trieste #383/R est:2500-3500

FLURI, August (19th C) Swiss
Works on paper
£393 $621 €590 St Ursen Cathedral in Solothurn (74x65cm-29x26in) pastel. 14-Nov-2 Stuker, Bern #9114 (S.FR 900)

FLURY, Burckhardt (1862-1928) Swiss
Works on paper
£787 $1267 €1181 Two cats' heads (11x15cm-4x6in) s. pastel. 7-May-3 Dobiaschofsky, Bern #519/R est:1400 (S.FR 1700)

FLURY, Karl (1898-1971) Swiss
£264 $394 €396 Zurich (61x85cm-24x33in) s.d.46. 25-Jun-2 Koller, Zurich #6617 (S.FR 600)

FLY, Camillus S (1849-1901) American
Photographs
£2692 $4200 €4038 Portrait of Geronimo, Apache Chief (19x13cm-7x5in) promenade card. 21-Oct-2 Swann Galleries, New York #29/R est:3500-4500

FOCARDI, Ruggero (1864-1934) Italian
£4717 $7264 €7500 Waiting (19x13cm-7x5in) s. cardboard. 23-Oct-2 Finarte, Milan #138/R est:11000-12000

FOG, Rose (19th C) Danish
Works on paper
£478 $775 €693 Lundbygaard (16x24cm-6x9in) s.i.d.20 Martz 1846 gouache. 26-May-3 Rasmussen, Copenhagen #1589/R (D.KR 5000)
£766 $1240 €1111 Cobble stone street scene with figures, Koeng, Sjaelland (18x31cm-7x12in) s.d.6 October 1848 gouache. 26-May-3 Rasmussen, Copenhagen #1587/R (D.KR 8000)

FOGG, Sarah Anne (attrib) (1829-1922) Australian
Works on paper
£2789 $4573 €4044 View of Mount Wellington, Hobart (25x35cm-10x14in) W/C prov. 4-Jun-3 Deutscher-Menzies, Melbourne #145/R est:5000-10000 (A.D 7000)

FOGG, Silas (19th C) British
£330 $551 €479 Portrait of this eccentric character, clay pipe in his hat band (38x25cm-15x10in) i.verso. 12-Jul-3 Finan Watkins & Co, Mere #148

FOGGIA, Mario Moretti (1882-1954) Italian
£1935 $3058 €3000 Milk pans (39x50cm-15x20in) s. i.verso board. 18-Dec-2 Finarte, Milan #50/R

FOGGIE, David (1878-1948) British
Works on paper
£460 $754 €690 Wet stooks (28x39cm-11x15in) s. W/C. 7-Jun-3 Shapes, Edinburgh #366/R

FOHN, Emanuel (1881-1966) German
£2532 $4000 €4000 Still life of flowers (44x31cm-17x12in) i. verso board. 30-Nov-2 Villa Grisebach, Berlin #317/R est:3000-4000
£2837 $4596 €4000 Over the tree line - southern Tyrol (68x87cm-27x34in) s. masonite. 20-May-3 Dorotheum, Vienna #171/R est:4000-6000
£3311 $5397 €5000 Church (45x54cm-18x21in) s. painted c.1935. 28-Jan-3 Dorotheum, Vienna #86/R est:5000-7000

FOHR, Daniel (1801-1862) German
£2308 $3623 €3600 Coastal landscape in the evening with figure (81x112cm-32x44in) s. 23-Nov-2 Arnold, Frankfurt #720/R est:5000

FOIRIE, Albert Auguste (1854-1896) French
£3226 $5000 €4839 Elegant lady by the shore with a pink parasol (22x15cm-9x6in) s.d.79 panel. 3-Dec-2 Christie's, Rockefeller NY #621/R est:6000-8000

FOISIL, Edith (20th C) French
£694 $1132 €1000 A bord du Blue Bird (73x54cm-29x21in) s. 19-Jul-3 Thierry & Lannon, Brest #198

FOLDES, Peter (1924-) Hungarian
£321 $503 €500 Untitled (61x38cm-24x15in) s.d.61. 24-Nov-2 Laurence Calmels, Paris #126/R
£513 $805 €800 Untitled (133x178cm-52x70in) s.d.60 oil collage. 24-Nov-2 Laurence Calmels, Paris #124/R
£769 $1208 €1200 Untitled (54x72cm-21x28in) s.d.61 oil collage. 24-Nov-2 Laurence Calmels, Paris #127/R
£1410 $2214 €2200 Start (139x100cm-55x39in) s.d.58 s.i.d.verso. 24-Nov-2 Laurence Calmels, Paris #125/R
£1795 $2818 €2800 Untitled (108x162cm-43x64in) s.d.58. 24-Nov-2 Laurence Calmels, Paris #123/R

FOLDI, Peter (1949-) Hungarian
Works on paper
£826 $1288 €1198 Beginning of life (66x96cm-26x38in) s.d.93 pastel cardboard. 13-Sep-2 Mu Terem Galeria, Budapest #133/R est:300000 (H.F 320000)

FOLDSONE, John (fl.1769-1784) British
£1071 $1703 €1607 Lucretia (91x70cm-36x28in) i. 5-Mar-3 Rasmussen, Copenhagen #1661/R (D.KR 11500)

FOLEY, H (19th C) British
£313 $500 €470 Mediterranean coastal view (33x25cm-13x10in) s. 15-Mar-3 Selkirks, St. Louis #73
£500 $800 €750 Study of a coastal scene with figures (48cm-19in circular) s.i. 10-Jan-3 Biddle & Webb, Birmingham #295

FOLEY, Herb (20th C) New Zealander
Works on paper
£1176 $1834 €1764 Riga Quod Est Aridum (125x122cm-49x48in) s.d.1999 mixed media. 7-Nov-2 International Art Centre, Auckland #7/R est:2500-4000 (NZ.D 3750)

FOLEY, J H (1818-1874) British
Sculpture
£2000 $3160 €3000 Figure of Edmund Burke (51cm-20in) i. dark brown pat. bronze with base executed c.1865. 27-Nov-2 Wintertons, Lichfield #859/R est:2000-3000

FOLEY, John Henry (1818-1874) British
Sculpture
£3500 $5705 €5075 John Julius (66cm-26in) s.d.1862 verso white marble moulded socle prov. 21-Jul-3 Sotheby's, London #481/R est:1000-1500

FOLINSBEE, John F (1892-1972) American
£705 $1100 €1058 Portrait of Henry Chapin (61x51cm-24x20in) s. i.verso. 20-Sep-2 Freeman, Philadelphia #47/R est:400-600
£978 $1565 €1467 Impressionistic landscape (20x25cm-8x10in) s. masonite. 11-Jan-3 James Julia, Fairfield #322 est:2500-3000
£2156 $3450 €3234 New Hope Street scene (30x25cm-12x10in) s. 11-Jan-3 James Julia, Fairfield #323 est:3000-5000
£8861 $14000 €13292 Grey buildings (41x51cm-16x20in) canvasboard prov. 24-Apr-3 Shannon's, Milford #35/R est:12000-18000

FOLK ART SCHOOL, American
Works on paper
£5660 $9000 €8490 Liberty holding an American flag in a sea chariot drawn by horses (25x43cm-10x17in) ink W/C. 1-Mar-3 North East Auctions, Portsmouth #3/R est:3000-5000

FOLKERTS, Poppe (1875-1943) German
£3896 $5688 €6000 Two men in a large fishing boat (56x58cm-22x23in) s. i.verso panel. 15-Jun-2 Hans Stahl, Hamburg #234/R est:6000

FOLKESTAD, Bernhard (1879-1933) Norwegian
£7240 $11729 €10860 Woman with hat and a stuffed jay (75x80cm-30x31in) s. 26-May-3 Grev Wedels Plass, Oslo #43/R est:60000-80000 (N.KR 80000)

FOLLENFANT, Henry (19/20th C) French
£340 $530 €510 Tending to the farm (45x36cm-18x14in) s. 8-Oct-2 Bonhams, Knightsbridge #192

FOLLER, L (19th C) French?
£1290 $2000 €1935 Portrait of a boy (161x67cm-63x26in) s.d.8.95. 3-Dec-2 Christie's, Rockefeller NY #592/R est:3000-5000

FOLLI, E (?) ?
£700 $1085 €1050 Young woman in Continental dress. Lady beside a lake (51x24cm-20x9in) s. two. 25-Sep-2 Wintertons, Lichfield #584

FOLLINI, Carlo (1848-1938) Italian
£1081 $1686 €1600 La falaise (15x24cm-6x9in) s.d.30.1.28 panel. 25-Mar-3 Chochon-Barre & Allardi, Paris #109/R est:1300-1500
£1635 $2518 €2600 Sea storm in Pegli (26x43cm-10x17in) s. cardboard. 28-Oct-2 Il Ponte, Milan #334
£2449 $3894 €3600 Figures on the quay (22x30cm-9x12in) s. cardboard. 1-Mar-3 Meeting Art, Vercelli #210
£3019 $4649 €4800 Fishing (27x44cm-11x17in) s.d.33 board prov. 23-Oct-2 Finarte, Milan #28/R
£3741 $5949 €5500 Back from the fields (23x36cm-9x14in) s.d.1914 paper on cardboard. 1-Mar-3 Meeting Art, Vercelli #263
£5449 $8554 €8500 Countryside around Cavour (26x44cm-10x17in) s.d.11 board prov. 10-Dec-2 Della Rocca, Turin #307/R est:8000

FOLON, Jean Michel (1934-) Belgian
Works on paper
£1458 $2304 €2100 L'homme volant (55x75cm-22x30in) s. i.verso W/C. 28-Apr-3 Cornette de St.Cyr, Paris #393 est:1500-2000
£1772 $2800 €2800 L'homme et la machine (36x47cm-14x19in) s. W/C. 26-Nov-2 Palais de Beaux Arts, Brussels #320/R est:2000-3000
£1806 $2853 €2600 Fenetre (78x58cm-31x23in) i.d.verso W/C. 28-Apr-3 Cornette de St.Cyr, Paris #392 est:2000-3000
£1921 $3130 €2900 Le mathematicien poete (45x30cm-18x12in) s. W/C. 1-Feb-3 Claude Aguttes, Neuilly #242/R est:1220-1525

FOLTYN, Frantisek (1891-1976) ?
£3405 $5516 €5108 Village at fish pond (49x66cm-19x26in) double-sided. 24-May-3 Dorotheum, Prague #120/R est:80000-120000 (C.KR 150000)
£10000 $15700 €15600 Composition (73x92cm-29x36in) s. double-sided. 11-Dec-2 Artcurial Briest, Paris #541/R est:8000
£14000 $21560 €21000 Composition (92x60cm-36x24in) s.d.1926 prov. 23-Oct-2 Sotheby's, Olympia #699/R est:8000-12000
£24783 $38662 €37175 Non-depicting composition (100x80cm-39x31in) s. indis.d.1928. 12-Oct-2 Dorotheum, Prague #112/R est:800000-1200000 (C.KR 1200000)
Works on paper
£590 $956 €885 Non-representational composition (34x44cm-13x17in) s. ink W/C. 24-May-3 Dorotheum, Prague #174/R est:26000-40000 (C.KR 26000)

FOMISON, Tony (1939-1990) New Zealander
£3376 $5233 €5064 Portrait of Julia Fomison (120x151cm-47x59in) i. board painted c.1962 prov. 4-Dec-2 Dunbar Sloane, Auckland #35/R est:12000-16000 (NZ.D 10500)
£9554 $15000 €14331 White faced lady no.151 (40x53cm-16x21in) i.verso canvas on board prov.exhib. 10-Dec-2 Peter Webb, Auckland #39/R est:30000-40000 (NZ.D 30000)
£17958 $29630 €26039 Study window (29x42cm-11x17in) i. s.d.1979-80 verso oil hessian on board prov. 1-Jul-3 Peter Webb, Auckland #33/R est:30000-40000 (NZ.D 51000)
£22887 $37764 €33186 Question No 118 (41x62cm-16x24in) s.d.1976 canvas on board. 1-Jul-3 Peter Webb, Auckland #31/R est:75000-100000 (NZ.D 65000)

FONDA, Attilio (1880-?) Italian
£408 $649 €600 Seamstress (16x11cm-6x4in) s. 18-Mar-3 Finarte, Milan #203/R
£599 $952 €880 Pirano hills from Strugnano (30x40cm-12x16in) s. i.verso board. 1-Mar-3 Stadion, Trieste #328b

FONECHE, Andre (20th C) French
£1050 $1638 €1575 Calm Sunday evening (17x35cm-7x14in) s. panel sold with a companion. 10-Sep-2 David Duggleby, Scarborough #368 est:1000-1500

FONG, Luise (1912-) New Zealander
£1736 $2708 €2604 Untitled (40x50cm-16x20in) s.d.1994 verso acrylic felt. 8-Apr-3 Peter Webb, Auckland #142/R est:6000-8000 (NZ.D 5000)
£4401 $7262 €6381 Cluster diptych (122x62cm-48x24in) s.i.d.1996 verso acrylic Chinese silk gouache on linen exhib. 1-Jul-3 Peter Webb, Auckland #12/R est:6000-8000 (NZ.D 12500)
Works on paper
£1458 $2275 €2187 Feed (66x30cm-26x12in) s.i.d.1998 mixed media canvas. 8-Apr-3 Peter Webb, Auckland #143/R est:3000-5000 (NZ.D 4200)

FONGUEUSE, Maurice (20th C) French
£548 $850 €822 Englise St. Medard (46x56cm-18x22in) s.d.1950 masonite. 16-Jul-2 Arthur James, Florida #53

FONSECA, Antonio Manuel da (1796-1890) Portuguese
£1690 $2721 €2400 King Pedro V of Portugal (70x51cm-28x20in) s. 7-May-3 Dorotheum, Vienna #351/R est:2000-3000

FONSECA, Gonzalo (1922-1997) Uruguayan
£2390 $3800 €3585 Coastal landscape (45x68cm-18x27in) s. 2-Mar-3 Galleria Y Remates, Montevideo #84/R
£6410 $10000 €9615 Puerto del Mediterraneo (50x60cm-20x24in) s. 30-Jul-2 Galleria Y Remates, Montevideo #84/R est:13000-15000
Works on paper
£440 $700 €660 Constructive bar (26x30cm-10x12in) ink exec.c.1947. 2-Mar-3 Galleria Y Remates, Montevideo #27/R
£641 $1000 €962 Still life with basket (11x20cm-4x8in) s. ink W/C. 10-Oct-2 Galleria Y Remates, Montevideo #20/R

FONT Y VIDAL, Juan (fl.1852-1874) Spanish
£3000 $4980 €4350 Spanish three masted barque Juanita Clar running into Port Mahon, Minorca (60x86cm-24x34in) 12-Jun-3 Christie's, London #508/R est:1500-2500
£3200 $5312 €4640 British Royal Naval corvette at anchor and drying her sails in Port Mahon, Minorca (45x65cm-18x26in) s.i.d.1874 canvas on board. 12-Jun-3 Christie's, London #510/R est:1500-2500
£4000 $6640 €5800 Juanita Clar in the harbour at Port Mahon, Minorca (41x69cm-16x27in) s.i. 12-Jun-3 Christie's, London #507/R est:1500-2500
£14000 $23240 €20300 Le Duque de Montpensier coming ashore from a Spanish ship lying in Port Mahon (39x63cm-15x25in) s.i. 12-Jun-3 Christie's, London #506/R est:1500-2500

FONT, Constantin (1890-1954) French
£537 $864 €800 Marine soleil couchant (46x55cm-18x22in) s. 23-Feb-3 Lesieur & Le Bars, Le Havre #50

FONTAINE, Allen (20th C) American
Works on paper
£732 $1200 €1061 Seascape with waves (51x102cm-20x40in) W/C. 31-May-3 Van Blarcom, South Natick #12/R est:150-250

FONTAINE, Gustave (19th C) French
£1644 $2581 €2400 Dans la cuisine (115x180cm-45x71in) s. 15-Apr-3 Galerie Moderne, Brussels #333 est:1500-2000

FONTAINE, Jenny Maria (1862-1938) French
£5800 $8990 €8700 Portrait of a young lady (118x90cm-46x35in) s.d.1906 oval. 3-Dec-2 Sotheby's, Olympia #297/R est:3000-5000

FONTAINE, Pierre François Leonard (1762-1853) French
Works on paper
£2381 $3786 €3500 Recueil d'ornements (24x19cm-9x7in) pen ink wash. 24-Mar-3 Tajan, Paris #127/R

FONTAINE, Pierre François Leonard (attrib) (1762-1853) French
Works on paper
£2041 $3245 €3000 Galerie d'antiques (50x37cm-20x15in) W/C pen ink. 24-Mar-3 Tajan, Paris #45/R

FONTAINE, Thomas Sherwood la (1915-) British
£1900 $3097 €2850 Impromptu (85x131cm-33x52in) s. 28-Jan-3 Bristol Auction Rooms #491/R est:600-800

FONTAINE, Victor (1837-1884) Belgian
£399 $654 €550 Le galant (57x42cm-22x17in) s.d.1859. 27-May-3 Campo & Campo, Antwerp #90
£637 $994 €1000 Le chasseur faisant ses avances (56x42cm-22x17in) s.d.1859. 11-Nov-2 Horta, Bruxelles #63
£949 $1500 €1424 Distant thoughts (102x84cm-40x33in) s. 16-Nov-2 New Orleans Auction, New Orleans #1108/R est:2000-4000

FONTAINEBLEAU SCHOOL (16th C) French
£6644 $11095 €9500 Portrait de Gabrielle d'Estree (36x27cm-14x11in) i. panel. 25-Jun-3 Tajan, Paris #43/R est:8000-12000
£15094 $23396 €24000 Bathseba at Bath in French palace garden (119x146cm-47x57in) 2-Oct-2 Dorotheum, Vienna #288/R est:15000-20000
£37000 $57720 €55500 Contest of Apollo and Pan (100x127cm-39x50in) panel exhib.lit. 9-Apr-3 Christie's, London #369/R est:20000-30000

FONTAINEBLEAU SCHOOL (17th C) French

£11159 $17296 €16739 Henri IV conquering France, protector of art (121x188cm-48x74in) prov. 3-Oct-2 Koller, Zurich #3001/R est:20000-30000 (S.FR 26000)

£97902 $163497 €140000 La nymphe de Fontainebleau (70x108cm-28x43in) panel painted c.1600. 27-Jun-3 Piasa, Paris #63/R est:40000-45000

FONTAINES, Andre des (1869-?) French

Works on paper

£946 $1476 €1400 Bord de riviere anime de figures. Lavandieres (15x20cm-6x8in) s. wax crayon paper on cardboard pair. 28-Mar-3 Delvaux, Paris #24

FONTALLARD, Jean François Gerard (1877-1858) French

Miniatures

£2200 $3454 €3300 Young lady in a maroon dress (6cm-2xin) mono.d.1818 gilt metal frame oval. 10-Dec-2 Christie's, London #154/R est:2000-3000

£2900 $4524 €4350 Lady Susan Reeve (10cm-4in circular) s.d.1821 prov. 8-Oct-2 Sotheby's, Olympia #442/R est:1000-1500

FONTANA, Aristida (19th C) Italian

Sculpture

£82278 $130000 €123417 Figures of Ruth and Rebecca (107cm-42in) i. marble on pedestals pair. 24-Apr-3 Christie's, Rockefeller NY #342/R est:60000-80000

FONTANA, Fortunato (20th C) Italian

£750 $1230 €1125 Fishing vessels on the Neapolitan coast. Fishing vessels at night (30x40cm-12x16in) s. board pair. 5-Jun-3 Christie's, Kensington #830/R

FONTANA, Franco (1933-) Italian

Photographs

£2215 $3500 €3500 Urban landscape, Prague (100x70cm-39x28in) s.i.d.1967 verso num.4/5 col photograph. 29-Nov-2 Farsetti, Prato #519/R

FONTANA, Lucio (1899-1968) Italian

£1090 $1711 €1700 Project for neon lights (27x20cm-11x8in) s.i.d.1951 tempera pen paper. 23-Nov-2 Meeting Art, Vercelli #276/R

£1991 $3325 €2887 From Teatrino (72x72cm-28x28in) s.i. relief cut. 24-Jun-3 Koller, Zurich #376/R est:2800-3800 (S.FR 4400)

£60000 $92400 €90000 Concetto spaziale, I Muri (100x70cm-39x28in) s. s.i.d.1957 verso oil pastel chk on canvas prov. 22-Oct-2 Sotheby's, London #387/R est:60000-80000

£68000 $106080 €102000 Concetto spaziale (76x60cm-30x24in) s.d.58 aniline collage pastel on canvas prov.exhib.lit. 21-Oct-2 Sotheby's, London #61/R est:80000-120000

£70000 $114800 €105000 Concetto spaziale (89x116cm-35x46in) s. s.i.verso prov.exhib.lit. 7-Feb-3 Sotheby's, London #204/R est:70000-90000

£76000 $126920 €110200 Concetto spaziale (40x25cm-16x10in) s. s.i.verso prov.lit. 26-Jun-3 Sotheby's, London #214/R est:25000-35000

£700000 $1148000 €1050000 Spacial concept, God's end (178x123cm-70x48in) s.i.verso oil glitter painted 1963 oval prov.exhib.lit. 6-Feb-3 Sotheby's, London #4/R est:700000

£1225000 $2045750 €1837500 Concetto Spaziale, La fine de dio (178x123cm-70x48in) s. s.verso exc.1964 prov.lit. 25-Jun-3 Sotheby's, London #15/R est:650000-850000

Prints

£2586 $4085 €3879 Untitled (64x50cm-25x20in) s.num.48/50 etching with puncturing. 28-Apr-3 Bukowskis, Stockholm #420/R est:20000-22000 (S.KR 34000)

Sculpture

£2129 $3364 €3194 Concetto Spaziale (12x9cm-5x4in) s.indis.d. metal foil. 28-Apr-3 Bukowskis, Stockholm #908/R est:6000-8000 (S.KR 28000)

£5886 $9183 €8829 Concetto spaziale (25cm-10in) s.num.172/500 bronze pair. 5-Nov-2 Bukowskis, Stockholm #446/R est:60000-70000 (S.KR 84000)

£8880 $14297 €13320 Concetto Spaziale (26cm-10in) s.num.250/500 polished bronze pair. 7-May-3 AB Stockholms Auktionsverk #798/R est:100000-150000 (S.KR 115000)

£13548 $21406 €21000 Table base (64cm-25in) s. polychrome ceramic. 18-Dec-2 Christie's, Rome #242/R est:18000

£19000 $31730 €27550 Concetto spaziale (30x25cm-12x10in) incised sig. painted terracotta executed 1950-57 prov. 27-Jun-3 Christie's, London #148/R est:12000-15000

£22000 $36740 €31900 Concetto spaziale (20x28x22cm-8x11x9in) s.num.108/500 polished bronze two parts prov. 26-Jun-3 Sotheby's, London #213/R est:8000-12000

£23404 $37915 €33000 Corrida (36x72x11cm-14x28x4in) s. enamelled ceramic polychrome executed 1950-55. 26-May-3 Christie's, Milan #258/R est:30000-40000

£29487 $43051 €46000 Spacial concept (78cm-31in) s.d.52 terracotta. 5-Jun-2 Il Ponte, Milan #130/R est:40000-50000

£32319 $51065 €48479 Concetto Spaziale, Natura (47x35x7cm-19x14x3in) st.init.num.2/2 bronze prov.lit. 28-Apr-3 Bukowskis, Stockholm #1020/R est:300000-325000 (S.KR 425000)

£75000 $115500 €112500 Mujer desnudandose - viento en catamarca (79cm-31in) s.d.47 painted plaster prov.exhib.lit. 22-Oct-2 Christie's, London #15/R est:40000-60000

£560000 $873600 €840000 Concetto spaziale (172x130cm-68x51in) glazed iron executed 1957 prov.exhib.lit. 21-Oct-2 Sotheby's, London #30/R est:400000-600000

Works on paper

£742 $1084 €1113 Composition (64x47cm-25x19in) s. mixed media. 4-Jun-2 Germann, Zurich #298 (S.FR 1700)

£915 $1520 €1300 Untitled (33x24cm-13x9in) s.d.48 mixed media. 10-Jun-3 Finarte Semenzato, Milan #228/R est:8000-10000

£1603 $2516 €2500 Composition (50x35cm-20x14in) s.d.1963 pen dr. 23-Nov-2 Meeting Art, Vercelli #22/R

£1603 $2484 €2500 Concetto spaziale (12x9cm-5x4in) s.d.57 biro perforations silver foil. 3-Dec-2 Lempertz, Koln #139/R est:2500

£1761 $2923 €2500 Studi di nudi (21x31cm-8x12in) ink. 10-Jun-3 Finarte Semenzato, Milan #227/R est:2500-3500

£1986 $3217 €2800 Primo progetto di taglio di Lucio Fontana (31x21cm-12x8in) s.d.53 biro double-sided. 26-May-3 Christie's, Milan #79/R est:2000-3000

£3191 $5170 €4500 Concetto spaziale (50x50cm-20x20in) s. aluminium board aluminium foil. 20-May-3 Dorotheum, Vienna #181/R est:4500-5000

£3481 $5396 €5500 Untitled (47x34cm-19x13in) s.d.1963 biro board prov.exhib.lit. 28-Sep-2 Ketterer, Hamburg #507/R est:6000-7000

£4965 $8043 €7000 Untitled (37x32cm-15x13in) s.d.58 aniline collage canvas. 26-May-3 Christie's, Milan #163/R est:7000-10000

£5600 $9128 €8400 Concetto spaziale (25x20cm-10x8in) i. pencil paper on card executed 1958-60. 3-Feb-3 Bonhams, New Bond Street #87/R est:5000-8000

£8156 $13213 €11500 Concetto spaziale (16x11cm-6x4in) s. s.i.verso col.pencil executed 1961-63. 26-May-3 Christie's, Milan #219/R est:4000-6000

£12761 $19652 €20290 Spacial concept (10x8cm-4x3in) s.i.d.1959 water paint. 26-Oct-2 Cornette de St.Cyr, Paris #80/R est:15000

£13542 $21396 €19500 Concetto spaziale (58x45cm-23x18in) s. perforations blotting paper exec.c.1960 prov. 27-Apr-3 Perrin, Versailles #58/R est:20000-25000

£22000 $34320 €33000 Concetto spaziale (64x44cm-25x17in) s. W/C executed 1966-67 prov.exhib. 21-Oct-2 Sotheby's, London #20/R est:18000-25000

£68000 $111520 €102000 Concetto spaziale, Attesa (80x81cm-31x32in) s.i.verso waterpaint canvas prov.lit. 6-Feb-3 Christie's, London #640/R est:50000-70000

£70000 $109200 €105000 Concetto spaziale, teatrino (90x100cm-35x39in) s.i.verso waterpaint on canvas lacquered executed 1965 prov.lit. 21-Oct-2 Sotheby's, London #41/R est:70000-90000

£73718 $115737 €115000 Spacial concept (65x45cm-26x18in) s. s.i.verso waterpaint on canvas prov.exhib.lit. 20-Nov-2 Pandolfini, Florence #120/R est:120000

£80000 $131200 €120000 Concetto spaziale, attese (61x50cm-24x20in) s.i. verso waterpaint canvas prov.lit. 7-Feb-3 Sotheby's, London #230/R est:80000-120000

£95745 $155106 €135000 Concetto spaziale, Attese (33x46cm-13x18in) i.verso water paint canvas. 26-May-3 Christie's, Milan #330/R est:60000-80000

£96774 $152903 €150000 Spacial concept (55x46cm-22x18in) s.i.verso waterpaint on canvas lit. 18-Dec-2 Christie's, Rome #293/R est:200000

£100000 $154000 €150000 Concetto spaziale, attese (54x73cm-21x29in) s.i.verso waterpaint on canvas executed 1961 prov.exhib.lit. 22-Oct-2 Christie's, London #40/R est:100000-150000

£156250 $250000 €234375 Concetto spaziale, attese (93x73cm-37x29in) s.i.verso waterpaint on canvas executed 1965 prov.exhib.lit. 15-May-3 Phillips, New York #20/R est:300000-400000

£220000 $343200 €330000 Concetto spaziale, attese (76x60cm-30x24in) s.i. waterpaint on canvas executed 1966 prov.lit. 21-Oct-2 Sotheby's, London #21/R est:180000-250000

£280000 $431200 €420000 Concetto spaziale, teatrino (150x150cm-59x59in) s.i.verso neon waterpaint on canvas with lacquered wood. 22-Oct-2 Christie's, London #26/R est:250000-350000
£350000 $539000 €525000 Concetto spaziale, attese (100x81cm-39x32in) s.i.verso waterpaint on canvas executed 1968 prov.lit. 22-Oct-2 Christie's, London #38/R est:360000-420000

FONTANALS Y ROVIROSA, Francisco (1777-1827) Spanish
Works on paper
£2500 $4175 €3625 Barcelona, seen from the water (12x38cm-5x15in) gouache vellum on card. 9-Jul-3 Sotheby's, London #70/R est:2500-3500

FONTANAROSA, Lucien (1912-1975) French
£1605 $2279 €2600 Reussite (29x64cm-11x25in) s. i.verso. 17-Mar-2 Galerie de Chartres, Chartres #141

FONTANESI, Antonio (attrib) (1818-1882) Italian
£755 $1162 €1200 Under-growth (36x29cm-14x11in) s. cardboard. 28-Oct-2 Il Ponte, Milan #266
£1761 $2712 €2800 Lights (24x29cm-9x11in) s. i.verso. 28-Oct-2 Il Ponte, Milan #220/R

FONTEBASSO, Francesco (1709-1769) Italian
Works on paper
£1761 $2923 €2500 Head of bearded man (19x16cm-7x6in) chk htd white. 12-Jun-3 Hauswedell & Nolte, Hamburg #272/R est:3000
£2500 $3900 €3700 Disciples d'Emmaus (21x20cm-8x8in) pen ink wash. 27-Mar-3 Maigret, Paris #8/R
£3800 $6346 €5510 Saint Jerome seated in profile (38x25cm-15x10in) black chk pen brown ink. 8-Jul-3 Christie's, London #54/R est:3000-5000

FONTEBASSO, Francesco (attrib) (1709-1769) Italian
Works on paper
£1266 $2000 €2000 Alexander's charity (22x27cm-9x11in) W/C pen. 2-Dec-2 Finarte, Milan #97/R
£1622 $2530 €2400 Saint Jerome in meditation (37x25cm-15x10in) pen ink pierre noire. 26-Mar-3 Rossini, Paris #90/R

FONTEBASSO, Francesco (style) (1709-1769) Italian
£5200 $8164 €7800 King presenting his crown to a general (94x113cm-37x44in) 10-Dec-2 Bonhams, New Bond Street #207/R est:5000-8000

FONTENAY, Andre (1913-) French
£350 $547 €550 Moulin de la Galette (45x37cm-18x15in) s.d.1960. 5-Nov-2 Tajan, Paris #133

FONTENE, Robert (1892-1980) French
£506 $800 €800 Composition abstraite (70x92cm-28x36in) s. 27-Nov-2 Lemoine & Ferrando, Paris #93/R

FONTEYN, Carel (17th C) Dutch
£4255 $6596 €6383 Vanitas still life with playing cards (34x47cm-13x19in) s. 4-Dec-2 AB Stockholms Auktionsverk #1933/R est:40000-50000 (S.KR 60000)

FONTIROSSI, Roberto (1940-) Italian
£316 $494 €500 Looking for mushrooms (25x15cm-10x6in) s. cardboard on canvas painted 1998. 14-Sep-2 Meeting Art, Vercelli #386

FONVILLE, Horace-Antoine (1832-1910) French
£516 $815 €800 Personnage embarquant sur lac de montagne (33x50cm-13x20in) s.d.1867. 18-Dec-2 Ferri, Paris #51

FOO FAT, Dulcie (1946-) Canadian?
Works on paper
£382 $599 €573 Heart Mountain groundscape (48x93cm-19x37in) s.i. mixed media board. 25-Nov-2 Hodgins, Calgary #160/R (C.D 950)

FOOTTIT, Frederick Francis (1850-1935) British
Works on paper
£450 $702 €675 Sospel, Alpes Maritimes (51x60cm-20x24in) s. pencil W/C. 27-Mar-3 Christie's, Kensington #309/R

FORAIN, Henri (1917-) French
Works on paper
£400 $624 €600 Female nude reading (20x22cm-8x9in) s. gouache pencil prov. 12-Sep-2 Sotheby's, Olympia #49/R

FORAIN, J L (1852-1931) French
Works on paper
£3226 $5000 €4839 Standing nude (46x38cm-18x15in) prov. 29-Oct-2 Sotheby's, New York #85/R est:2000-3000

FORAIN, Jean Louis (1852-1931) French
£2658 $4200 €4200 Lever (33x41cm-13x16in) s. panel. 2-Dec-2 Tajan, Paris #19/R est:4000-6000
£6897 $11034 €10000 La dessinatrice (73x60cm-29x24in) 12-Mar-3 Libert, Castor, Paris #87/R est:4500-6000
£11111 $17667 €16000 Chez le modiste (45x29cm-18x11in) init. painted c.1889 prov. 29-Apr-3 Christie's, Amsterdam #112/R est:12000-16000
£22152 $35000 €33228 Scene de ballet (66x81cm-26x32in) s.d.1906 prov. 24-Apr-3 Sotheby's, New York #143/R est:30000-50000
£65217 $105000 €97826 Le dialogue (70x55cm-28x22in) s. prov.exhib.lit. 8-May-3 Christie's, Rockefeller NY #159/R est:70000-90000
Sculpture
£943 $1500 €1415 Republique joive (51x15x16cm-20x6x6in) s.num.XXS black pat bronze. 27-Feb-3 Christie's, Rockefeller NY #47/R
Works on paper
£288 $453 €450 Le jour des morts (31x24cm-12x9in) s. W/C. 16-Dec-2 Millon & Associes, Paris #51/R
£346 $540 €550 Modele (34x27cm-13x11in) mono. chl chk sanguine. 10-Oct-2 Ribeyre & Baron, Paris #44
£350 $571 €525 Les Deux Juges (33x26cm-13x10in) s. W/C. 3-Feb-3 Bonhams, New Bond Street #18/R
£377 $589 €600 Danseuse au vestiaire (29x24cm-11x9in) s. 10-Oct-2 Ribeyre & Baron, Paris #43
£379 $603 €550 Femme de profil (26x19cm-10x7in) s. W/C. 5-Mar-3 Doutrebente, Paris #32
£409 $638 €650 Jeune femme reveuse et amour (17x26cm-7x10in) mono. wash. 10-Oct-2 Ribeyre & Baron, Paris #38
£414 $646 €650 Ce n'est pas mal, mais vous n'etes pas flattee (22x20cm-9x8in) s. Indian ink dr. 11-Nov-2 Horta, Bruxelles #720
£490 $817 €700 Le chagrin (29x34cm-11x13in) bears sig. mixed media. 27-Jun-3 Claude Aguttes, Neuilly #79
£676 $1054 €1000 Jeune fille attristee (34x25cm-13x10in) mono. Indian ink. 25-Mar-3 Chochon-Barre & Allardi, Paris #110
£676 $1054 €1000 La lecon de chant (37x27cm-15x11in) s. sanguine gouache. 25-Mar-3 Chochon-Barre & Allardi, Paris #111
£700 $1091 €1050 Le repli Allemand (38x53cm-15x21in) s.i.d.1917 black chk htd white. 19-Sep-2 Christie's, Kensington #22/R
£1139 $1777 €1800 Assassinat de jaures (34x48cm-13x19in) s. wax crayon. 18-Oct-2 Rabourdin & Choppin de Janvry, Paris #14/R
£1538 $2338 €2400 Ballerine sur chaise de profil (28x20cm-11x8in) s. crayon dr htd chk. 16-Aug-2 Deauville, France #44/R
£2201 $3500 €3302 Coin des coulisses de l'opera (33x20cm-13x8in) gouache W/C pen ink paper on board. 27-Feb-3 Christie's, Rockefeller NY #49/R est:2000
£26573 $44378 €38000 Dans les coulisses (38x30cm-15x12in) s. pastel. 27-Jun-3 Claude Aguttes, Neuilly #78/R est:15000-20000

FORAIN, Jean Louis (attrib) (1852-1931) French
£503 $775 €800 Dame dans un interieur (55x45cm-22x18in) 22-Oct-2 Campo, Vlaamse Kaai #501

FORBES, Alexander (1802-1839) British
£1500 $2280 €2250 Terriers ratting (58x74cm-23x29in) s.d.1839. 14-Aug-2 Andrew Hartley, Ilkley #662/R est:1500-2200

FORBES, Elizabeth Adela (1859-1912) British
£9500 $14820 €14250 Portrait of a young girl (26x31cm-10x12in) mono. panel. 25-Mar-3 Bonhams, New Bond Street #1/R est:8000-12000
£20000 $31400 €30000 Picking blossom (35x26cm-14x10in) s. panel. 22-Nov-2 Christie's, London #27/R est:20000-30000
Works on paper
£5000 $8350 €7250 Gathering flowers, woman and a cat on a driveway at Trewinnard Manor (44x30cm-17x12in) s. W/C gouache. 19-Jun-3 Lane, Penzance #165/R est:5000-6000

FORBES, John Colin (1846-1925) Canadian
£661 $1038 €992 Lily pads in the afternoon (30x46cm-12x18in) s. board. 24-Jul-2 Walker's, Ottawa #247/R est:1000-1500 (C.D 1600)
£711 $1166 €1067 Fishermen, Hanlon's Point (32x51cm-13x20in) s. prov. 3-Jun-3 Joyner, Toronto #263/R est:2000-3000 (C.D 1600)
£741 $1148 €1112 View of Toronto at sunset (32x51cm-13x20in) s. prov. 3-Dec-2 Joyner, Toronto #200/R est:2500-3000 (C.D 1800)
£978 $1604 €1467 Coastal scene with cattle (30x44cm-12x17in) s. canvas on board prov. 3-Jun-3 Joyner, Toronto #414/R est:1200-1500 (C.D 2200)
£988 $1531 €1482 Path through the willows (32x49cm-13x19in) s. board exhib. 3-Dec-2 Joyner, Toronto #302/R est:2000-2500 (C.D 2400)

FORBES, Kenneth (1892-1980) Canadian
£328 $508 €492 Self portrait (46x33cm-18x13in) s.i. 24-Sep-2 Ritchie, Toronto #3129/R (C.D 800)
£369 $572 €554 Pond fishing. Flying ducks (34x45cm-13x18in) plywood panel double-sided prov. 24-Sep-2 Ritchie, Toronto #3152/R (C.D 900)
£1156 $1895 €1734 At the turn (50x90cm-20x35in) s.d.1976 canvas on board. 3-Jun-3 Joyner, Toronto #131/R est:2500-3500 (C.D 2600)
£1244 $2041 €1866 Horse race (45x67cm-18x26in) s.d.1978. 3-Jun-3 Joyner, Toronto #159/R est:2000-2500 (C.D 2800)
£1310 $2071 €1965 Portrait of a Lady Skier (69x58cm-27x23in) s. prov. 14-Nov-2 Heffel, Vancouver #190/R est:3500-4000 (C.D 3250)

FORBES, Leyton (fl.1900-1925) British
Works on paper
£260 $411 €390 By the cottage (14x22cm-6x9in) s. W/C. 14-Nov-2 Bonhams, Edinburgh #312
£340 $527 €510 Rural cottage scene (15x23cm-6x9in) W/C. 6-Dec-2 Biddle & Webb, Birmingham #445
£650 $1027 €975 By a cottage. On a track by a farmhouse (16x23cm-6x9in) s.d.08 W/C htd gouache pair. 27-Nov-2 Hamptons Fine Art, Godalming #271

FORBES, Pieter (1637-?) Dutch
£26000 $40820 €39000 Still life of fruit in a bowl, gilt cup, and glass on a carpet (127x104cm-50x41in) s.d.1663 prov.lit. 12-Dec-2 Sotheby's, London #162/R est:20000-30000

FORBES, Stanhope Alexander (1857-1947) British
£3648 $5764 €5472 Old fisherman (38x29cm-15x11in) s. prov. 3-Apr-3 Heffel, Vancouver #29/R est:4000-5000 (C.D 8500)
£5500 $8580 €8250 Dutch river landscape (20x29cm-8x11in) s. s.i.verso board. 27-Mar-3 Christie's, Kensington #465/R est:6000-8000
£8000 $13360 €11600 Cornish harbour at dusk (44x57cm-17x22in) s. 19-Jun-3 Lane, Penzance #100/R est:8000-12000
£10000 $16700 €14500 Girls at the quayside, Newlyn (51x41cm-20x16in) prov. 24-Jun-3 Bonhams, New Bond Street #1/R est:10000-15000
£24000 $37200 €36000 Study for Lighting up time (157x127cm-62x50in) s.d.1911 lit. 26-Sep-2 Lane, Penzance #100/R est:30000-40000
£24000 $39360 €36000 Old bridge of Relebbus (61x76cm-24x30in) s.d.1927 exhib. 6-Jun-3 Christie's, London #10/R est:12000-18000
£38000 $58900 €57000 Village cobbler (155x117cm-61x46in) s. 26-Sep-2 Lane, Penzance #140/R est:40000-50000
£53797 $85000 €80696 Lighting up time (115x176cm-45x69in) s.d.1902 prov.exhib.lit. 24-Apr-3 Sotheby's, New York #34/R est:70000-100000
£145000 $226200 €217500 Short cut across the fields (100x127cm-39x50in) s.d.1921 prov. 25-Mar-3 Bonhams, New Bond Street #48/R est:100000-150000

FORD, Dale (1934-) American
Works on paper
£1859 $2900 €2789 Hearse (41x61cm-16x24in) mixed media. 9-Nov-2 Altermann Galleries, Santa Fe #40
£3151 $4600 €4727 Stagecoach (41x58cm-16x23in) mixed media. 18-May-2 Altermann Galleries, Santa Fe #117/R
£3288 $4800 €4932 Wells Fargo Express (43x58cm-17x23in) mixed media. 18-May-2 Altermann Galleries, Santa Fe #118/R
£3288 $4800 €4932 Overland freight wagon (46x61cm-18x24in) mixed media. 18-May-2 Altermann Galleries, Santa Fe #119/R
£3288 $4800 €4932 Hearse (41x61cm-16x24in) mixed media. 18-May-2 Altermann Galleries, Santa Fe #120/R

FORD, Henry Chapman (1828-1894) American
£6051 $9500 €9077 Water lilies and Spanish moss (76x122cm-30x48in) s.d.1874. 20-Nov-2 Christie's, Los Angeles #74/R est:12000-18000

FORD, Henry Justice (1860-1941) British
Works on paper
£1600 $2640 €2320 Perseus (25x20cm-10x8in) s. pencil pen black ink htd white prov.lit. 3-Jul-3 Christie's, Kensington #229/R est:1500-2000
£3200 $5248 €4640 Princes and the wolves in the forest (22x37cm-9x15in) s.i. pencil W/C htd bodycol lit. 5-Jun-3 Christie's, London #143/R est:3500-4500

FORD, Marcus (20th C) British
£320 $518 €480 Friston, Sussex (41x61cm-16x24in) s. 20-May-3 Sotheby's, Olympia #167/R
£350 $585 €508 River estuary and harbour scene, possibly at Aldeburgh, Suffolk (25x38cm-10x15in) s. 20-Jun-3 Keys, Aylsham #975/R
£500 $810 €750 Brancaster (46x61cm-18x24in) s. 20-May-3 Sotheby's, Olympia #168/R
£620 $1004 €930 Happisburgh, Norfolk (46x84cm-18x33in) s. 20-May-3 Sotheby's, Olympia #166/R

FORD, Walton (20th C) American
£1220 $2000 €1769 Please forgive me (86x91cm-34x36in) s.d.1986 i.verso board exhib. 1-Jun-3 Wright, Chicago #321/R est:2000-3000

FOREAU, Louis Henri (1866-1938) French
£267 $422 €462 Street scene (50x60cm-20x24in) s. board. 1-Apr-3 Goodman, Sydney #60 (A.D 700)

FOREST, Henry J de (1860-1924) Canadian
£533 $875 €773 Harrison Lake, BC (35x50cm-14x20in) s.i.d.1894. 9-Jun-3 Hodgins, Calgary #310/R est:1000-1400 (C.D 1200)

FOREST, Pierre (1881-1971) French
£284 $474 €400 Le port de Saint Tropez (46x55cm-18x22in) s. 23-Jun-3 Delvaux, Paris #194
£328 $511 €492 Journey in the snow (59x73cm-23x29in) s. panel. 6-Nov-2 Dobiaschofsky, Bern #3333 (S.FR 750)

FOREST, Roy de (1930-) American
Prints
£1740 $2750 €2610 Dog's view of Egypt (94x145cm-37x57in) s.d.1995 num.20/20 col lithograph. 22-Apr-3 Butterfields, San Francisco #2260/R est:3000-5000

FORESTIER, René le (20th C) ?
Works on paper
£347 $566 €500 Jour de marche a Concarneau (16x20cm-6x8in) s. gouache. 19-Jul-3 Thierry & Lannon, Brest #276

FORG, Gunther (1952-) German
£1135 $1838 €1600 Untitled (100x70cm-39x28in) s.d.97 acrylic. 24-May-3 Van Ham, Cologne #182/R est:3200
£2069 $3269 €3000 Composition in red and black (99x69cm-39x27in) s.d.1992 tempera. 2-Apr-3 Dr Fritz Nagel, Stuttgart #9335/R est:4000
£3846 $6000 €5769 IV (259x152cm-102x60in) s.d.14/7/89 acrylic paper prov. 14-Oct-2 Butterfields, San Francisco #2117/R est:7000-9000
£10145 $16638 €14000 Window I (160x140cm-63x55in) s.i.d.27/12/89 acrylic panel prov. 31-May-3 Villa Grisebach, Berlin #399/R est:14000-18000
£11538 $17885 €18000 Untitled (90x250cm-35x98in) s.d.87 verso acrylic lead on panel two. 3-Dec-2 Lempertz, Koln #132/R est:25000
Sculpture
£3043 $4991 €4200 Mask (23cm-9in) st.sig. gold brown pat.bronze exhib. 28-May-3 Lempertz, Koln #132/R est:4000
Works on paper
£769 $1192 €1200 Abstract composition (55x76cm-22x30in) s.d.1998 i. verso gouache. 7-Dec-2 Ketterer, Hamburg #765/R
£1232 $2020 €1700 Composition in green and black (56x38cm-22x15in) s.i.d.92/4 i. verso gouache. 31-May-3 Villa Grisebach, Berlin #800/R est:2000-2200
£1410 $2186 €2200 Abstract compositions (56x38cm-22x15in) s.i.d.92/2 92/4 gouache two. 7-Dec-2 Ketterer, Hamburg #763/R est:3000-4000
£2800 $4424 €4200 Untitled (64x48cm-25x19in) s.d.88 wax crayon pair. 3-Apr-3 Christie's, Kensington #249/R

FORGIOLI, Attilio (1933-) Italian
£449 $704 €700 Landscape (70x81cm-28x32in) s. 23-Nov-2 Meeting Art, Vercelli #399/R
£609 $956 €950 Island (50x65cm-20x26in) s.d.1972 tempera paper. 19-Nov-2 Finarte, Milan #38
£676 $1054 €1000 Hawk (56x56cm-22x22in) s. 26-Mar-3 Finarte Semenzato, Milan #109/R

FORNARA, Carlo (1871-1968) Italian
£12821 $20128 €20000 April (6x25cm-2x10in) s. board exhib.lit. 10-Dec-2 Della Rocca, Turin #397/R est:30000

FORNEROD, Rodolphe (1877-1953) Swiss
£625 $1019 €900 Nature morte a la poire (36x50cm-14x20in) s. cardboard. 19-Jul-3 Thierry & Lannon, Brest #128
£858 $1356 €1287 Still life with bowl, grapes and apples (32x40cm-13x16in) s. board on panel. 29-Nov-2 Zofingen, Switzerland #2871/R est:2500 (S.FR 2000)

FORNES ISERN, Pablo (1930-) Spanish
£506 $800 €800 Portrait of Spanish woman in garden (70x80cm-28x31in) s.d.1972. 30-Nov-2 Arnold, Frankfurt #164/R

FORREST, Captain J Haughton (1826-1925) Australian
£996 $1525 €1494 Tasmanian Lake scene (11x21cm-4x8in) init. board. 25-Aug-2 Sotheby's, Paddington #191/R est:3000-4000 (A.D 2800)
£1000 $1580 €1500 Seascape (30x45cm-12x18in) s. board. 27-Nov-2 Deutscher-Menzies, Melbourne #100/R est:3000-5000 (A.D 2800)
£1281 $1960 €1922 Ships in rough seas (14x29cm-6x11in) s. board. 25-Aug-2 Sotheby's, Paddington #138 est:4000-5000 (A.D 3600)
£1281 $1960 €1922 Approaching storm (15x29cm-6x11in) init. board. 25-Aug-2 Sotheby's, Paddington #192/R est:4000-5000 (A.D 3600)
£1429 $2257 €2144 Organ pipes, Southern Tasmania (31x47cm-12x19in) board. 27-Nov-2 Deutscher-Menzies, Melbourne #99/R est:4000-6000 (A.D 4000)
£1473 $2342 €2210 Lake St Clair, Tasmania (29x46cm-11x18in) s. board. 5-May-3 Sotheby's, Melbourne #284/R est:2500-4500 (A.D 3800)
£1500 $2430 €2250 Paddle steamer in heavy swell off a fortified rocky outcrop (44x60cm-17x24in) s.d.1856. 21-May-3 Christie's, Kensington #595/R est:1500-2000
£3920 $6311 €5880 Stormy seas (31x45cm-12x18in) s. board. 6-May-3 Christie's, Melbourne #390/R est:6000-8000 (A.D 9800)
£3929 $6207 €5894 Lake scene (31x47cm-12x19in) board. 26-Nov-2 Sotheby's, Melbourne #63/R est:12000-18000 (A.D 11000)
£4598 $6851 €6897 Moored boat at low tide (30x45cm-12x18in) s. board. 27-Aug-2 Christie's, Melbourne #101/R est:12000-16000 (A.D 12000)
£4800 $7728 €7200 Tasmanian view (30x22cm-12x9in) mono. cardboard. 6-May-3 Christie's, Melbourne #109/R est:9000-12000 (A.D 12000)
£4962 $7840 €7443 Last unit of the fleet, Helen (42x57cm-17x22in) init. cardboard prov.lit. 2-Apr-3 Christie's, Melbourne #24/R est:9000-12000 (A.D 13000)
£5000 $8100 €7500 Racing cutter tacking across the mouth of the Dart (35x57cm-14x22in) s. 21-May-3 Christie's, Kensington #563/R est:4000-6000
£6000 $9720 €9000 HMS Nassau passing a steamer. HSM Nassau at Hong Kong in a typhoon (46x76cm-18x30in) one s.d.1870 one s.i. pair. 21-May-3 Christie's, Kensington #380/R est:10000-15000
£6071 $9593 €9107 Mount Wellington from Huon Road (47x62cm-19x24in) s. board. 27-Nov-2 Deutscher-Menzies, Melbourne #101/R est:15000-20000 (A.D 17000)
£28000 $45360 €42000 Royal yacht squadron's famous cutter Arrow under full sail (41x69cm-16x27in) s.i. prov. 22-Jan-3 Bonhams, New Bond Street #319/R est:15000-20000

FORREST, Lee (20th C) American
£705 $1100 €1058 Abstract landscape with bobbies at the bottom (196x165cm-77x65in) 20-Sep-2 Du Mouchelle, Detroit #2118/R est:1000-1500

FORRESTALL, Thomas de Vany (1936-) Canadian
£2444 $4009 €3666 Midsummer (46x102cm-18x40in) s.d.1964 i.verso masonite prov. 27-May-3 Sotheby's, Toronto #5/R est:3000-5000 (C.D 5500)
£3111 $5102 €4667 Culvert (58x112cm-23x44in) s.d.1965 s.i.d.verso acrylic gesso on masonite prov. 27-May-3 Sotheby's, Toronto #125/R est:3000-5000 (C.D 7000)
Works on paper
£244 $401 €366 Fall ploughing (37x48cm-15x19in) s. W/C prov. 3-Jun-3 Joyner, Toronto #462 (C.D 550)

FORRESTER, John (1922-) New Zealander
£700 $1092 €1050 EG mark (99x81cm-39x32in) s.i.d.1961 verso. 27-Mar-3 Christie's, Kensington #660/R

FORRESTER, Patricia Tobacco (20th C) American
Works on paper
£1647 $2750 €2388 California maple, winter light (208x132cm-82x52in) s. W/C on four sheets. 29-Jun-3 Butterfields, Los Angeles #7083/R est:400-600

FORSBERG, Carl Johan (1868-1938) Swedish
Works on paper
£510 $795 €765 Coastal landscape from Fano with beached boat in foreground (49x60cm-19x24in) s.i. 5-Aug-2 Rasmussen, Vejle #30/R (D.KR 6000)

FORSSELL, Victor (1846-1931) Swedish
£465 $754 €674 Still life of fruit and hock-glass (35x35cm-14x14in) s.d.97. 25-May-3 Uppsala Auktionskammare, Uppsala #112/R (S.KR 6000)
£1064 $1649 €1596 Old saltmill (30x26cm-12x10in) s. panel. 4-Dec-2 AB Stockholms Auktionsverk #1779/R est:12000-15000 (S.KR 15000)
£1086 $1760 €1575 From the outskirts of Stockholm (20x28cm-8x11in) s. panel. 26-May-3 Bukowskis, Stockholm #10/R (S.KR 14000)

FORSSLUND, Jonas (1754-1809) Swedish
Works on paper
£824 $1252 €1236 Portrait of lady (56x44cm-22x17in) pastel oval. 16-Aug-2 Lilla Bukowskis, Stockholm #452 (S.KR 12000)
£1335 $2190 €1936 Portraits of Pehr Alexander Rudbeck and his wife Anna Elisabeth (56x46cm-22x18in) one s.d.1789 pastel oval pair. 4-Jun-3 AB Stockholms Auktionsverk #2249/R est:12000-15000 (S.KR 17000)
£1899 $3000 €3000 Young woman (60x40cm-24x16in) pastel oval. 1-Dec-2 Bukowskis, Helsinki #244/R est:1500-1600

FORSSLUND, Jonas (attrib) (1754-1809) Swedish
Works on paper
£851 $1319 €1277 Portrait of lady (67x58cm-26x23in) pastel oval. 4-Dec-2 AB Stockholms Auktionsverk #1609/R (S.KR 12000)

FORSTEN, Lennart (1817-1886) Finnish
£1020 $1622 €1500 Foaming rapids (45x62cm-18x24in) s.d.1847. 24-Mar-3 Bukowskis, Helsinki #68/R est:1200
£2092 $3430 €3200 Winter landscape with figures on the way home (57x45cm-22x18in) s.d.1879. 9-Feb-3 Bukowskis, Helsinki #231/R est:2500

FORSTER, George (1817-1896) American
£10191 $16000 €15287 Still life of grapes and plums in a bowl (20x25cm-8x10in) s.d.1866. 22-Nov-2 Eldred, East Dennis #843/R est:500-10000

FORSTER, George (attrib) (1817-1896) American
£12000 $18840 €18000 Peaches, cherries and grapes in a wicker basket (37x48cm-15x19in) s.d.1861. 16-Apr-3 Christie's, Kensington #882/R est:3000-5000

FORSTER, George E (19th C) American
£27097 $42000 €40646 Plums and gooseberries (20x25cm-8x10in) s.d.1869 prov. 5-Dec-2 Christie's, Rockefeller NY #17/R est:20000-30000

FORSTER, Hans (1917-) Swiss
£283 $453 €425 Light form (80x100cm-31x39in) s.d. 17-Mar-3 Philippe Schuler, Zurich #8429 (S.FR 600)
£377 $604 €566 Light (76x50cm-30x20in) s.d. panel. 17-Mar-3 Philippe Schuler, Zurich #8431 (S.FR 800)

FORSTER, John Wycliffe Lowes (1850-1938) Canadian
£258 $402 €387 Portrait of a woman (45x35cm-18x14in) s. 25-Mar-3 Ritchie, Toronto #85/R (C.D 600)

FORSTERLING, Otto (1843-?) German
Works on paper
£503 $785 €800 Idyllic compositions (11x18cm-4x7in) i. verso W/C pen pencil two. 11-Oct-2 Winterberg, Heidelberg #525/R

FORSTMOSER, Alois (1866-1905) Austrian
£748 $1190 €1100 Mountain landscape with lake (47x65cm-19x26in) i. pair. 21-Mar-3 Auktionhaus Georg Rehm, Augsburg #8029

FORSYTH, Gordon Mitchell (1879-1952) British
Works on paper
£380 $600 €570 Cauld blast (36x53cm-14x21in) init.d.1947 W/C. 13-Nov-2 Halls, Shrewsbury #365/R

FORSYTH, William (1854-1935) American
£1220 $2000 €1769 Spring landscape (43x56cm-17x22in) s. egg tempera prov. 7-Jun-3 Neal Auction Company, New Orleans #348/R est:2500-4000
£3774 $6000 €5661 Floral still life (41x30cm-16x12in) s. board painted c.1920. 2-Mar-3 Toomey, Oak Park #661/R est:4000-6000
£6832 $11000 €10248 Children in summer landscape (46x61cm-18x24in) s. prov. 18-Feb-3 John Moran, Pasadena #36 est:6000-8000
Works on paper
£854 $1400 €1281 Country road, Southern Indiana (38x51cm-15x20in) s. W/C card stock prov. 8-Feb-3 Neal Auction Company, New Orleans #387/R est:1800-2400
£881 $1400 €1322 Indiana landscape (33x51cm-13x20in) s. W/C exec.c.1920. 4-May-3 Treadway Gallery, Cincinnati #522/R
£915 $1500 €1327 Mid October, Cedar Farm (38x56cm-15x22in) W/C prov. 7-Jun-3 Neal Auction Company, New Orleans #351/R est:1800-2400
£1159 $1900 €1739 Logan's Point, Ohio river (38x53cm-15x21in) s.d.93 W/C paper on card stock prov. 8-Feb-3 Neal Auction Company, New Orleans #388/R est:1800-2400

FORSYTHE, Victor Clyde (1885-1962) American
£1138 $1900 €1650 Atmospheric landscape (30x41cm-12x16in) s. board prov. 17-Jun-3 John Moran, Pasadena #194 est:2000-3000

FORT, Paul (20th C) French
£1000 $1580 €1500 Folie Bergere (41x34cm-16x13in) s.i. board. 3-Apr-3 Christie's, Kensington #19/R

FORT, Theodore (19th C) French
Works on paper
£288 $453 €450 Le depart des chasseurs. s. W/C. 19-Nov-2 Galerie Moderne, Brussels #198

FORTE, Luca (attrib) (fl.1625-c.1670) Italian
£6452 $10194 €10000 Bouquet in bronze vase (35x25cm-14x10in) panel. 18-Dec-2 Tajan, Paris #5/R est:8000

FORTE, Luca (circle) (fl.1625-c.1670) Italian
£8000 $12480 €12000 Pears, apples, oranges and nuts on a ledge (44x53cm-17x21in) 10-Apr-3 Christie's, Kensington #242/R est:5000-8000
£22000 $34100 €33000 Pear, apples and plum in a woven basket, with figs, jasmine (47x59cm-19x23in) 30-Oct-2 Christie's, Kensington #133/R est:7000-10000

FORTESCUE, William B (1850-1924) British
£2300 $3657 €3450 Portrait of a girl wearing a red shawl bonnet, bust length (28x20cm-11x8in) s. 30-Apr-3 Halls, Shrewsbury #289/R est:2500-3000
£7819 $12119 €11729 Young angler (21x30cm-8x12in) s. prov. 3-Dec-2 Ritchie, Toronto #3029/R est:2500-4000 (C.D 19000)
£8200 $13694 €11890 Fetching water, back lane Newlyn. s. 19-Jun-3 Lane, Penzance #190/R est:6000-8000
£9500 $14725 €14250 Cornish pasty (91x117cm-36x46in) s. 26-Sep-2 Lane, Penzance #125/R est:9000-12000

FORTEZA FORTEZA, Miguel (1881-?) Spanish
£552 $877 €800 Seascape (21x35cm-8x14in) s. 4-Mar-3 Ansorena, Madrid #122/R

FORTEZA, Nicolas (1918-) Spanish
£927 $1511 €1400 Bay in Majorca (56x66cm-22x26in) s. 11-Feb-3 Segre, Madrid #338/R

FORTHUN, Louise (1959-) Australian
Works on paper
£536 $825 €804 Spiraling (203x202cm-80x80in) synthetic polymer on canvas. 8-Sep-2 Sotheby's, Melbourne #26 est:1200-1800 (A.D 1500)

FORTI, Ettore (19th C) Italian
£3871 $6000 €5807 Pompeiian garden (47x100cm-19x39in) s.i. 3-Dec-2 Christie's, Rockefeller NY #649/R est:7000-9000
£8861 $14000 €13292 New friend (65x30cm-26x12in) s.i. prov. 23-Apr-3 Christie's, Rockefeller NY #123/R est:10000-15000
£14650 $23000 €21975 Pottery seller (49x78cm-19x31in) s.i. prov. 21-Nov-2 Sotheby's, New York #180/R est:25000-35000
£19868 $32384 €30000 Femmes a la toilette (95x54cm-37x21in) s.i. 31-Jan-3 Rabourdin & Choppin de Janvry, Paris #146/R est:35000-40000
£25000 $39250 €37500 Merchant of Pompei (54x85cm-21x33in) s.i. prov. 19-Nov-2 Sotheby's, London #128/R est:15000-20000

FORTIN, Edmond (1881-1955) French
£483 $762 €700 Lavandieres (50x101cm-20x40in) s. 4-Apr-3 Tajan, Paris #60/R

FORTIN, Marc-Aurele (1888-1970) Canadian
£617 $957 €926 Landscape (15x20cm-6x8in) s. 3-Dec-2 Joyner, Toronto #378 est:1500-1800 (C.D 1500)
£3556 $5831 €5334 French Canadian house (24x27cm-9x11in) s. board prov. 3-Jun-3 Joyner, Toronto #29/R est:8000-12000 (C.D 8000)
£3863 $6026 €5795 Montreal port (23x24cm-9x9in) s. cardboard. 25-Mar-3 Iegor de Saint Hippolyte, Montreal #53/R (C.D 9000)
£3871 $6039 €5807 Maison a Ste Rose (19x25cm-7x10in) s. i.verso panel. 30-Jul-2 Iegor de Saint Hippolyte, Montreal #54 (C.D 9600)
£4000 $6560 €6000 Vue de l'Ile ste-Helene (25x34cm-10x13in) s. board painted c.1918-19. 3-Jun-3 Joyner, Toronto #160/R est:10000-12000 (C.D 9000)
£4839 $7645 €7259 Neige a Ste-Rose (25x33cm-10x13in) s.i.verso board. 14-Nov-2 Heffel, Vancouver #146/R est:9000-12000 (C.D 12000)
£5333 $8747 €8000 Hochelaga (30x30cm-12x12in) s. board prov. 3-Jun-3 Joyner, Toronto #11/R est:12000-15000 (C.D 12000)
£6579 $9803 €9869 Village (30x42cm-12x17in) s. cardboard. 26-Jun-2 Iegor de Saint Hippolyte, Montreal #39/R (C.D 15000)
£9333 $15307 €14000 Street scene with figure (35x31cm-14x12in) bears sig textured board on panel prov. 27-May-3 Sotheby's, Toronto #79/R est:12000-15000 (C.D 21000)
£9778 $16036 €14667 Homestead in winter (20x22cm-8x9in) s. board painted c.1919-20 prov. 3-Jun-3 Joyner, Toronto #60/R est:4000-6000 (C.D 22000)
£13333 $21867 €20000 Paysage d'automne (56x71cm-22x28in) s. s.i.verso board prov. 27-May-3 Sotheby's, Toronto #146/R est:20000-30000 (C.D 30000)

Works on paper
£1411 $2230 €2117 Ships in the harbour (72x57cm-28x22in) s.. chl paper on board prov. 14-Nov-2 Heffel, Vancouver #185/R est:4000-4500 (C.D 3500)
£1842 $2745 €2763 Voilier (51x32cm-20x13in) s. W/C chl. 26-Jun-2 Iegor de Saint Hippolyte, Montreal #38/R (C.D 4200)
£2667 $4373 €4001 Untitled cityscape (40x50cm-16x20in) s. W/C prov. 3-Jun-3 Joyner, Toronto #100/R est:8000-10000 (C.D 6000)
£3427 $5415 €5141 Petite cote - Ste Rose (58x72cm-23x28in) s. mixed media prov. 18-Nov-2 Sotheby's, Toronto #67/R est:4000-6000 (C.D 8500)
£4484 $7175 €6726 Country landscape (70x112cm-28x44in) s. W/C prov.lit. 15-May-3 Heffel, Vancouver #6/R est:12000-15000 (C.D 10000)
£6584 $10206 €9876 Chute d'eau, Gaspesie (54x75cm-21x30in) s. W/C crayon. 3-Dec-2 Joyner, Toronto #127/R est:20000-25000 (C.D 16000)

FORTINI, A (19th C) Italian
£450 $716 €675 Pergola (62x75cm-24x30in) s. 2-Mar-3 Lots Road, London #340

FORTSCH, Marie Anne (18/19th C) ?
Works on paper
£385 $550 €578 Interior view of the Roman coliseum (30x41cm-12x16in) s.d.1800 pen ink. 23-Jan-3 Swann Galleries, New York #370/R

FORTUNATO, Franco (1946-) Italian
£321 $503 €500 Thorns king (50x40cm-20x16in) s.d.1985. 23-Nov-2 Meeting Art, Vercelli #148/R
£588 $941 €900 Ville qui aime la nuit (50x60cm-20x24in) s. s.i.verso. 4-Jan-3 Meeting Art, Vercelli #76
£952 $1514 €1400 Season (50x60cm-20x24in) s. 1-Mar-3 Meeting Art, Vercelli #770

FORTUNEY (1878-1950) French
£1172 $1876 €1700 Barque (41x32cm-16x13in) s.d.1906. 12-Mar-3 Libert, Castor, Paris #89/R est:1000-1200
Works on paper
£452 $714 €700 Gitane en pied (30x23cm-12x9in) s.pastel. 19-Dec-2 Delvaux, Paris #27
£517 $828 €750 Elegante au marche aux fleurs (48x31cm-19x12in) s. pastel. 12-Mar-3 Libert, Castor, Paris #90
£552 $883 €800 Joueuse de tennis (39x32cm-15x13in) s. pastel. 12-Mar-3 Libert, Castor, Paris #91
£828 $1324 €1200 Elegante sure un voilier (50x32cm-20x13in) bears sig. pastel. 12-Mar-3 Libert, Castor, Paris #88
£1000 $1600 €1450 Deux femmes et un homme dans une loge (48x31cm-19x12in) s. pastel. 12-Mar-3 Libert, Castor, Paris #92

FORTUNEY, Louis (1878-1950) French
Works on paper
£356 $590 €516 Elegante au bord du lac (49x32cm-19x13in) s. pastel. 16-Jun-3 Waddingtons, Toronto #261/R (C.D 800)
£356 $590 €516 Elegante au salon (53x35cm-21x14in) s. pastel. 16-Jun-3 Waddingtons, Toronto #261a/R (C.D 800)
£556 $789 €900 Danseuse a la cigarette (53x44cm-21x17in) s.i.d.1923 verso pastel. 17-Mar-2 Galerie de Chartres, Chartres #142

FORTUNY Y CARBO, Mariano (1838-1874) Spanish
£154839 $240000 €232259 Council house, Granada (35x48cm-14x19in) s.d.73 panel prov.exhib.lit. 30-Oct-2 Christie's, Rockefeller NY #66/R est:200000-300000

Prints
£1452 $2294 €2250 Arab mourning (61x75cm-24x30in) eau forte aquatint exec.1866. 17-Dec-2 Durán, Madrid #565/R
£2097 $3313 €3250 Lunch at the Alhambra (17x23cm-7x9in) engraving. 17-Dec-2 Durán, Madrid #1252
Works on paper
£4516 $7135 €7000 Bust of woman (19x14cm-7x6in) pencil htd white. 17-Dec-2 Segre, Madrid #25/R est:1700
£5484 $8500 €8226 Portrait of a seated lady (40x31cm-16x12in) pencil W/C htd white prov.exhib. 29-Oct-2 Sotheby's, New York #114/R est:10000-15000

£11724 $18641 €17000 Tanger street (23x17cm-9x7in) pen ink wash. 4-Mar-3 Ansorena, Madrid #163/R

£24194 $38226 €37500 Avant-poste arabe (28x44cm-11x17in) s.i. W/C exec.c.1860 lit. 17-Dec-2 Durán, Madrid #229/R est:2000

FORUP, Carl Christian (1883-1939) Danish

£297 $481 €431 Landscape with children at Vejrhoj (50x59cm-20x23in) s. 24-May-3 Rasmussen, Havnen #2018 (D.KR 3100)

£333 $532 €500 Southern market place with figures (56x65cm-22x26in) s. 13-Jan-3 Rasmussen, Vejle #196/R (D.KR 3800)

£422 $659 €633 Garden scene with two nude women (50x52cm-20x20in) s. 23-Sep-2 Rasmussen, Vejle #200/R (D.KR 5000)

£553 $874 €830 From a fruit stall in Capri, Italy (42x51cm-17x20in) s.d.20. 2-Dec-2 Rasmussen, Copenhagen #1598/R (D.KR 6500)

FOSCHI, Pier Francesco (1502-1567) Italian

£48780 $80000 €73170 Madonna and Child with the infant Saint John the Baptist (104x84cm-41x33in) panel. 30-May-3 Christie's, Rockefeller NY #25/R est:80000-120000

Works on paper

£32407 $52500 €48611 Madonna and Child and St. john the Baptist (23x11cm-9x4in) red chk htd white black chk prov.exhib.lit. 21-Jan-3 Sotheby's, New York #3/R est:40000-60000

FOSS, Harald (1843-1922) Danish

£279 $444 €419 View of Silkeborg Islands (28x43cm-11x17in) 10-Mar-3 Rasmussen, Vejle #336/R (D.KR 3000)

£301 $458 €452 Heath landscape, Jylland (24x41cm-9x16in) s. 27-Aug-2 Rasmussen, Copenhagen #1900/R (D.KR 3500)

£947 $1440 €1421 Woman on bridge at sunset (40x32cm-16x13in) with sig.d.1894. 27-Aug-2 Rasmussen, Copenhagen #1864/R (D.KR 11000)

£1806 $2800 €2709 View from the dunes (37x61cm-15x24in) s.i.d.1915. 2-Oct-2 Christie's, Rockefeller NY #797/R est:2000-3000

FOSS, Olivier (1920-) French/American

£290 $467 €435 Rainy Paris street scene at dusk (46x55cm-18x22in) s. 18-Feb-3 Rosebery Fine Art, London #620

£390 $632 €550 Peniches a quai a la Bastille (55x46cm-22x18in) s. 26-May-3 Joron-Derem, Paris #55

£414 $646 €650 Paris, port de la Bastille (61x50cm-24x20in) s. 10-Nov-2 Eric Pillon, Calais #240/R

£550 $864 €825 Rainy Paris street scene at dusk (46x55cm-18x22in) s. prov. 10-Dec-2 Rosebery Fine Art, London #635/R

FOSS, T (19th C) Danish?

£1500 $2280 €2250 Danish coastal view with three sea nymphs (43x51cm-17x20in) i. s.d.1862 verso. 16-Aug-2 Keys, Aylsham #651

FOSSAT, V (19th C) Italian

Works on paper

£993 $1609 €1400 Harbour scene with steamer ship and vessels. Harbour scene with steamer ship arriving and figures (18x30cm-7x12in) s. gouache board two. 20-May-3 Mealy's, Castlecomer #962/R est:700-1100

FOSSATI, Domenico (1743-1784) Italian

Works on paper

£633 $1000 €1000 Fountain with personification of Africa riding on elephant (39x25cm-15x10in) s.i. pen wash. 29-Nov-2 Bassenge, Berlin #5628/R

FOSSOUX, Claude (1946-) French

£323 $510 €500 Le bassin aux Tuileries (46x55cm-18x22in) s. 17-Dec-2 Rossini, Paris #78

FOSTER, Ben (1852-1926) American

£622 $1033 €902 Summer landscape (38x51cm-15x20in) s. 16-Jun-3 Waddingtons, Toronto #8/R est:1500-2000 (C.D 1400)

£1656 $2600 €2484 Congregational church, North Cornwall, Connecticut (92x106cm-36x42in) s. 22-Nov-2 Skinner, Boston #256/R est:3000-5000

FOSTER, Bernard (?) ?

Works on paper

£450 $752 €653 Summer evening (178x25cm-70x10in) s. 18-Jun-3 Andrew Hartley, Ilkley #1074

FOSTER, H (?) ?

Works on paper

£360 $554 €540 Study of country cottage with mother and child on path with sheep (28x38cm-11x15in) s. W/C. 6-Sep-2 Biddle & Webb, Birmingham #150a

FOSTER, John (1648-1681) American

£1442 $2250 €2163 Landscape with buildings and blossoming tree (51x76cm-20x30in) s. 18-Sep-2 Alderfer's, Hatfield #393/R est:700-900

Works on paper

£1603 $2500 €2405 Winter landscape with country road and yellow house (43x56cm-17x22in) s. gouache. 18-Sep-2 Alderfer's, Hatfield #392/R est:800-1200

FOSTER, John Ernest (1877-?) British

£900 $1404 €1350 Tithe barn at Rectory Farm, Easington, East Yorkshire (76x63cm-30x25in) s. 10-Apr-3 Tennants, Leyburn #1122/R

FOSTER, Leroy (20th C) American

£2083 $3250 €3125 Untitled (91x104cm-36x41in) 18-Oct-2 Du Mouchelle, Detroit #2295/R est:300-400

FOSTER, Myles Birket (1825-1899) British

£5000 $7900 €7500 Rochester from the river (3x5cm-1x2in) mono. W/C htd bodycol. 2-Dec-2 Sotheby's, London #50/R est:5000-7000

Works on paper

£280 $426 €420 Family group resting by a stile (23cm-9in circular) bears mono. W/C circular. 16-Aug-2 Keys, Aylsham #452/R

£280 $437 €420 Children playing at a rivers edge (13x10cm-5x4in) init. W/C. 7-Nov-2 Mallams, Cheltenham #341/R

£280 $437 €420 Children blackberrying in landscape (23x28cm-9x11in) bears mono. W/C. 11-Apr-3 Keys, Aylsham #443

£300 $489 €450 Mother and child at the door of a country cottage (20x13cm-8x5in) bears mono. W/C. 14-Feb-3 Keys, Aylsham #464

£340 $554 €510 Children bird nesting (20x30cm-8x12in) mono. W/C. 14-Feb-3 Keys, Aylsham #383/R

£380 $619 €570 Children with cat before a thatched cottage (10x8cm-4x3in) mono. W/C. 14-Feb-3 Keys, Aylsham #488

£380 $631 €570 River view with ruins beyond (8x13cm-3x5in) mono. W/C. 10-Jun-3 Sworder & Son, Bishops Stortford #470/R

£400 $624 €600 Children outside a cottage (12x10cm-5x4in) mono. W/C. 10-Sep-2 David Duggleby, Scarborough #146

£420 $701 €609 Young harvesters by a stile (25x18cm-10x7in) bear mono. W/C. 20-Jun-3 Keys, Aylsham #502

£766 $1142 €1149 Carriage (12x20cm-5x8in) mono. W/C gouache. 27-Aug-2 Christie's, Melbourne #205/R est:2000-3000 (A.D 2000)

£800 $1312 €1200 Mumbles head, figure on the cliff top path above Mumbles Lighthouse (15x38cm-6x15in) mono. W/C. 5-Feb-3 Goldings, Lincolnshire #293

£950 $1482 €1425 View of a continental lakeside town (12x20cm-5x8in) studio st. pencil W/C htd white. 19-Sep-2 Christie's, Kensington #119/R est:700-1000

£1200 $1884 €1800 Family group by a stile picking wild flowers (23x36cm-9x14in) bears mono. W. 13-Dec-2 Keys, Aylsham #612 est:1000-1500

£1200 $1872 €1800 Children gathering wild flowers in landscape (25x36cm-10x14in) mono. W/C. 11-Apr-3 Keys, Aylsham #431/R est:1200-1600

£1400 $2226 €2100 Near Loch Awe (21x26cm-8x10in) mono.i. W/C. 4-Mar-3 Bearnes, Exeter #382/R est:500-700

£1500 $2340 €2250 Kew Bridge (11x16cm-4x6in) mono.i. W/C prov. 9-Oct-2 Woolley & Wallis, Salisbury #103/R est:500-700

£2200 $3432 €3300 Boating on the lake (9x22cm-4x9in) mono. W/C htd white. 27-Mar-3 Christie's, Kensington #168/R est:1000-2000

£2500 $4050 €3750 Cattle watering (15x20cm-6x8in) mono. W/C. 20-May-3 Sotheby's, Olympia #189/R est:1500-2000

£2500 $4050 €3625 Landscape with cottage, figures and poultry (3x5cm-1x2in) s. W/C. 29-Jul-3 Capes Dunn, Manchester #25/R

£2800 $4480 €4200 On the Italian lakes (9x13cm-4x5in) mono. W/C prov. 11-Mar-3 Bonhams, New Bond Street #63/R est:3000-5000

£2800 $4480 €4200 Bridge over the Mosel at Coblenz (12x16cm-5x6in) mono.i. W/C. 11-Mar-3 Bonhams, New Bond Street #64/R est:3000-5000

£3400 $5440 €5100 San Giorgio Maggiore, Venice (13x18cm-5x7in) mono. W/C htd white. 11-Mar-3 Bonhams, New Bond Street #62/R est:3000-5000

£3800 $6080 €5700 Flower seller (14x10cm-6x4in) mono. W/C htd white. 11-Mar-3 Bonhams, New Bond Street #60/R est:4000-6000

£4000 $6200 €6000 Council Hall, Constance (21x32cm-8x13in) mono. W/C. 24-Sep-2 Anderson & Garland, Newcastle #391/R est:4000-6000

£4200 $6846 €6090 Two girls paddling in the sea (17x14cm-7x6in) mono. W/C over pencil htd white. 21-Jul-3 Bonhams, Bath #11 est:3000-5000

£4800 $7488 €7200 Loch Etive (15x20cm-6x8in) mono. W/C prov. 6-Nov-2 Bonhams, Chester #408/R est:2500-3500

£5200 $8320 €7800 Washing day (41x34cm-16x13in) bears studio st. W/C bodycol prov. 11-Mar-3 Bonhams, New Bond Street #59/R est:4000-6000

£5500 $8580 €8250 Cattle watering at the riverbank. Sheep grazing in a rural landscape (10x15cm-4x6in) mono. pencil W/C htd white pair. 17-Oct-2 Christie's, Kensington #60/R est:4000-6000

£5500 $8580 €8250 Statue of Erasmus, Rotterdam, Netherlands (15x9cm-6x4in) mono. W/C. 5-Nov-2 Bonhams, New Bond Street #112/R est:4000-6000
£5500 $8800 €8250 Cooling drink (10x15cm-4x6in) mono W/C. 11-Mar-3 Bonhams, New Bond Street #58/R est:6000-9000
£5500 $9020 €7975 San Georgio and San Salute, Venice (17x22cm-7x9in) mono. i.verso pencil W/C bodycol. 5-Jun-3 Christie's, London #167/R est:3000-5000
£6200 $9920 €9300 Isola Pescatori, Lago Maggiore (14x18cm-6x7in) mono. W/C htd white. 11-Mar-3 Bonhams, New Bond Street #61/R est:3500-5000
£7500 $12000 €11250 Alhambra, Granada, Spain (17x25cm-7x10in) mono. W/C htd bodycol. 11-Mar-3 Bonhams, New Bond Street #56/R est:6000-9000
£8500 $13260 €12750 Girls gathering firewood near Dorking, Surrey (18x28cm-7x11in) mono. W/C bodycol. 5-Nov-2 Bonhams, New Bond Street #115/R est:5000-8000
£9000 $14040 €13500 Feeding the duckings (20x28cm-8x11in) mono. W/C bodycol. 5-Nov-2 Bonhams, New Bond Street #113/R est:8000-12000
£9000 $14040 €13500 Venice from the Lido. Lagoon, Venice (10x14cm-4x6in) mono. W/C pair. 5-Nov-2 Bonhams, New Bond Street #114/R est:6000-9000
£10500 $16695 €15750 Streatley on Thames, Berkshire (20x32cm-8x13in) mono. W/C over pencil htd bodycol prov.exhib. 19-Mar-3 Sotheby's, London #166/R est:8000-12000
£10500 $16800 €15750 Fording the stream (16x13cm-6x5in) mono. W/C. 11-Mar-3 Bonhams, New Bond Street #57/R est:7000-10000
£12000 $19200 €18000 Gathering berries. Birds nest (10x15cm-4x6in) mono. W/C htd white pair. 11-Mar-3 Bonhams, New Bond Street #55/R est:10000-15000
£17000 $26860 €25500 Stile (17x23cm-7x9in) mono. W/C htd bodycol prov.exhib. 2-Dec-2 Sotheby's, London #49/R est:10000-15000
£22500 $35325 €33750 Picking blackberries (36x61cm-14x24in) mono. pencil W/C bodycol prov. 21-Nov-2 Christie's, London #96/R est:25000-35000

FOSTER, Myles Birket (attrib) (1825-1899) British
£420 $647 €630 Children playing in a harvest field (28x43cm-11x17in) mono. 6-Sep-2 Richardson & Smith, Whitby #400/R
Works on paper
£650 $1007 €975 Warkworth Castle, Northumberland (29x44cm-11x17in) init.i.d. pencil W/C prov. 4-Dec-2 Christie's, Kensington #90/R

FOSTER, Walter H W (fl.1861-1888) British
£320 $499 €480 Barnard Castle (36x61cm-14x24in) mono.d.74 i.verso. 7-Nov-2 Christie's, Kensington #156/R
£450 $729 €653 Heron and kingfisher beside a riverbank (50x61cm-20x24in) 22-May-3 Wintertons, Lichfield #658/R

FOSTER, Walter and NOBLE, John Sargeant (19th C) British
£2200 $3630 €3190 Edge of a wood, figure standing with a pony and two dogs by tree trunk (76x61cm-30x24in) s.verso. 3-Jul-3 Ewbank, Send #339/R est:1000-1500
£7975 $13000 €11963 Waiting for the guns (76x61cm-30x24in) i.verso. 11-Feb-3 Bonhams & Doyles, New York #261/R est:15000-20000

FOSTER, William (1853-1924) British
£385 $600 €578 Seated female nude. board. 19-Oct-2 Harvey Clar, Oakland #1415
Works on paper
£280 $434 €420 Herons on the Llugwy (36x52cm-14x20in) s.d.1882 W/C. 24-Sep-2 Bonhams, Knightsbridge #7/R

FOSTER, William Gilbert (1855-1906) British
£360 $562 €540 In the Dingle, County Wicklow, Ireland (91x71cm-36x28in) s.d. i.stretcher. 23-Sep-2 Bonhams, Chester #954
£360 $576 €540 Mother and child outside a cottage (41x61cm-16x24in) s.d.1878. 7-Jan-3 Bonhams, Knightsbridge #285p/R
£1400 $2282 €2030 Watermill in tranquil wooded landscape (56x91cm-22x36in) s. indis d. 17-Jul-3 Tennants, Leyburn #840 est:800-1000
£1497 $2380 €2200 Young girl carrying pail of water along field path (91x56cm-36x22in) s. 19-Mar-3 Neumeister, Munich #555/R est:2500

FOTINSKY, Serge (1897-1971) Russian
£385 $604 €600 Vase de fleurs (61x46cm-24x18in) s. 24-Nov-2 Chayette & Cheval, Paris #308a

FOUACE, Guillaume Romain (1827-1895) French
£6507 $10216 €9500 Still life with a lobster (65x94cm-26x37in) s.d.1885 prov. 15-Apr-3 Sotheby's, Amsterdam #63/R est:4000-6000

FOUBERT, Émile (1840-1910) French
£1441 $2248 €2162 La balance (55x46cm-22x18in) s.d.1906. 6-Nov-2 Dobiaschofsky, Bern #517/R est:4800 (S.FR 3300)
£1600 $2608 €2400 Nude in a summer landscape (44x54cm-17x21in) s. 29-Jan-3 Sotheby's, Olympia #343/R est:1500-2000
£5000 $8150 €7500 La peche a bougival (26x22cm-10x9in) s. board prov. 29-Jan-3 Sotheby's, Olympia #264/R est:800-1200

FOUCART, A (?) ?
£1635 $2518 €2600 Lavandieres au bord de l'Oued (43x61cm-17x24in) s. 23-Oct-2 Raboordin & Choppin de Janvry, Paris #127/R

FOUET, Louise Berthe (19th C) French
£382 $600 €573 Bouquet of field flowers (61x43cm-24x17in) s. 23-Nov-2 Jackson's, Cedar Falls #57/R

FOUGERON, Andre (1913-) French
£573 $894 €900 Nature morte (46x61cm-18x24in) s.d.45. 7-Nov-2 Claude Aguttes, Neuilly #44
£669 $1043 €1050 Fleurs et fruits (55x38cm-22x15in) s.d.46 s.d. verso. 7-Nov-2 Claude Aguttes, Neuilly #43

FOUGSTEDT, Arvid (1888-1949) Swedish
£6307 $9839 €9461 Spanish street musicians (54x65cm-21x26in) s. painted 1918 exhib. 6-Nov-2 AB Stockholms Auktionsverk #576/R est:80000-100000 (S.KR 90000)

FOUJITA, Tsuguharu (1886-1968) French/Japanese
£9494 $15000 €15000 Chat noir (37x53cm-15x21in) mono. panel exhib.lit. 26-Nov-2 Tajan, Paris #103/R est:16000-18000
£9494 $15000 €15000 Chat blanc (36x56cm-14x22in) mono. panel exhib.lit. 26-Nov-2 Tajan, Paris #102/R est:16000-18000
£10417 $16458 €15000 Rue de banlieue (32x40cm-13x16in) s. 25-Apr-3 Piasa, Paris #11/R est:10000
£13462 $21135 €21000 Marche aux puces a Paris (27x35cm-11x14in) s. painted 1918 lit. 13-Dec-2 Piasa, Paris #19/R est:30000
£14000 $22260 €21000 Portrait de femme (41x33cm-16x13in) s.d.1926 oil pen ink prov. 20-Mar-3 Sotheby's, Olympia #84/R est:15000-20000
£21000 $35070 €30450 Portrait de femme (35x27cm-14x11in) s.d.1927 s.d.on stretcher oil brush ink prov. 24-Jun-3 Sotheby's, London #182/R est:18000-25000
£28846 $45000 €43269 Untitled, young girl with doll (33x24cm-13x9in) s.i.d.1950 stretcher tempera prov. 14-Oct-2 Butterfields, San Francisco #2015/R est:40000-60000
£65217 $105000 €97826 Petite fille au noeud rouge devant la cheminee (33x24cm-13x9in) s.i.d.1950. 7-May-3 Sotheby's, New York #387/R est:100000-150000
£118012 $190000 €177018 Maternite au chat (55x33cm-22x13in) s. s.d.59 verso prov. 7-May-3 Sotheby's, New York #378/R est:140000-180000
£124224 $200000 €186336 Fillettes aux masques (55x31cm-22x12in) s. painted 1959 prov. 7-May-3 Sotheby's, New York #183/R est:180000-250000
£150000 $250500 €217500 Youki au chat (50x65cm-20x26in) s.d.1923 s.i.d.on stretcher prov. 24-Jun-3 Sotheby's, London #157/R est:120000-150000
Prints
£2800 $4368 €4200 Les deux amies (40x60cm-16x24in) s.num.75/100 etching aquatint executed c.1930. 10-Oct-2 Sotheby's, London #42/R est:3000-4000
£3782 $5976 €5900 Chat endormi. s. etching. 14-Nov-2 Credit Municipal, Paris #27/R est:1200-1500
£4114 $6418 €6500 Reclining female nude (52x67cm-20x26in) s.i. col etching. 18-Oct-2 Dr Fritz Nagel, Stuttgart #511/R est:8500
£4167 $6500 €6251 Chaton avec une balle (32x38cm-13x15in) s.i. col etching aquatint roulette. 7-Nov-2 Swann Galleries, New York #643/R est:5000-8000
£5031 $8000 €7547 Chat couchee sur le dos (31x38cm-12x15in) s.num.72/100 col etching aquatint. 1-May-3 Swann Galleries, New York #453/R est:6000-9000
Works on paper
£1241 $1974 €1800 Tete de chat (13x8cm-5x3in) s. dr. 5-Mar-3 Doutrebente, Paris #34 est:500
£1384 $2200 €2076 Poppy and bee (138x34cm-54x13in) s. hand emblem ink col hanging scroll. 24-Mar-3 Christie's, Rockefeller NY #209/R est:2000-3000
£1923 $2981 €3000 Scene d'interieur (26x19cm-10x7in) s. Chinese ink. 7-Dec-2 Cornette de St.Cyr, Paris #32/R est:4000
£2105 $3410 €3200 Etude de pieds (17x22cm-7x9in) s.d.1924 Indian ink estompe. 22-Jan-3 Tajan, Paris #203 est:460-600
£2372 $3605 €3700 Chat (18x12cm-7x5in) s. Chinese ink dr. 16-Aug-2 Deauville, France #40/R

£3688 $5974 €5200 Madeleine (37x14cm-15x6in) s. ink brush tracing paper exec.c.1932. 21-May-3 Cornette de St.Cyr, Paris #59/R est:5000-6000
£4800 $7584 €7200 Paysage de Paris (35x25cm-14x10in) s.i. pen brush ink W/C exec.1951. 3-Apr-3 Christie's, Kensington #112/R est:6000
£5000 $7800 €7400 Nus combattant (128x123cm-50x48in) s.d.1928 crayon chl dr exhib. 30-Mar-3 Anaf, Lyon #100/R
£6000 $10020 €9000 Youki, the artist's wife (21x17cm-8x7in) s.d.1924 pen ink wash pencil. 26-Jun-3 Christie's, London #378/R est:8000-12000
£6081 $9486 €9000 Boy with pomegranate (22x17cm-9x7in) s.d.1924 W/C Indian ink. 28-Mar-3 Ketterer, Hamburg #308/R est:8000-12000
£7000 $11690 €10150 Two studies of Cats, Showa Period (23x9cm-9x4in) s.d.1929 ink colours two in silk covered mount and painting. 18-Jun-3 Christie's, London #404/R est:5000-7000
£8000 $13120 €12000 Madeleine (27x32cm-11x13in) s.i.d.1932 W/C pen ink wash prov. 5-Feb-3 Sotheby's, London #260/R
£9500 $15010 €14250 Portrait de femme (24x17cm-9x7in) s.d.1952 pen brush ink paper on card prov. 3-Apr-3 Christie's, Kensington #136/R est:15000
£9615 $15096 €15000 Chat couche (22x30cm-9x12in) s.i.d.1950 Chinese ink dr. 15-Dec-2 Lombrail & Teucquam, Paris #16/R
£10577 $16606 €16500 Portrait d'enfant (37x26cm-15x10in) s. pen wash dr. 13-Dec-2 Piasa, Paris #152/R est:7000
£11000 $18040 €16500 Femme endormie (17x23cm-7x9in) s.i.d.1951 pen brush ink. 5-Feb-3 Sotheby's, London #265/R est:15000
£12422 $20000 €18633 Otilia (38x28cm-15x11in) s.i.d.1952 W/C pen ink. 7-May-3 Sotheby's, New York #389/R est:25000-35000
£12500 $20500 €18750 Tete de femme (25x19cm-10x7in) s.d.1933 W/C pen ink wash. 5-Feb-3 Sotheby's, London #266/R
£12821 $20000 €19232 Autoportrait - Charite (26x21cm-10x8in) s.d.1924 pen black ink wash lit. 7-Nov-2 Christie's, Rockefeller NY #124/R est:20000-30000
£13000 $20150 €19500 Portrait de femme (24x17cm-9x7in) s.d.1952 pen brush ink paper on card. 5-Dec-2 Christie's, Kensington #100/R est:15000-20000
£13462 $21135 €21000 Jeune fille (38x28cm-15x11in) s.i.d.1952 Chinese ink dr htd W/C. 13-Dec-2 Piasa, Paris #18/R est:15000
£14000 $22120 €21000 Confidences (25x26cm-10x10in) s.i. pencil W/C gouache prov.lit. 3-Apr-3 Christie's, Kensington #77/R est:10000
£15544 $24715 €22850 Maternite (23x16cm-9x6in) s.i.d.1951 Indian ink brush dr. 26-Feb-3 Artcurial Briest, Paris #55/R est:15000-18000
£16000 $26240 €24000 Deux amies (36x31cm-14x12in) s. pen Chinese ink lit. 6-Feb-3 Christie's, London #430/R est:18000
£16667 $25833 €26000 Jeune fille a la robe bleue (23x17cm-9x7in) s.i. W/C gouache ink exhib.lit. 6-Dec-2 Rieunier, Bailly-Pommery, Mathias, Paris #93/R est:30000
£16776 $27178 €25500 La lecture (16x24cm-6x9in) s.i.d. Indian ink prov.lit. 22-Jan-3 Tajan, Paris #204/R est:13000-15000
£17177 $27311 €25250 Portrait de fillette (21x16cm-8x6in) s.d.59 Indian ink brush. 26-Feb-3 Artcurial Briest, Paris #54/R est:18000-22000
£17949 $28359 €28000 Mother and child (35x29cm-14x11in) s.i.d.1932 W/C. 13-Nov-2 Ansorena, Madrid #42/R est:28000
£20833 $32500 €31250 Mere et enfant (39x28cm-15x11in) s.d.1917 W/C. 6-Nov-2 Sotheby's, New York #349/R est:20000-30000
£21000 $35070 €30450 Famille a l'ane (35x30cm-14x12in) s.i.d.1917 gouache W/C brush ink prov. 24-Jun-3 Sotheby's, London #288/R est:18000-25000
£23684 $38368 €36000 Mother and child (35x29cm-14x11in) s.i.d.1932 W/C lit. 21-Jan-3 Ansorena, Madrid #293/R est:18000
£28846 $45000 €43269 Jeanette (27x22cm-11x9in) s.d.1928 pen ink wash prov.exhib. 6-Nov-2 Sotheby's, New York #329/R est:35000-45000

FOULLON-VACHOT, Lucille (1775-1865) French
£1829 $3000 €2744 Portrait of a woman in white with a paisley shawl holding a fan (81x64cm-32x25in) s.d.1811 exhib. 29-May-3 Sotheby's, New York #24/R est:3000-4000

FOUQUERAY, Charles (1872-1956) French
£9677 $15290 €15000 A bord du paquebot 'La Couronne' (64x65cm-25x26in) s.i.d.1895. 19-Dec-2 Claude Aguttes, Neuilly #85a/R est:15000
£9677 $15290 €15000 A bord du paquebot 'La Couronne' (64x65cm-25x26in) s. painted 1895. 19-Dec-2 Claude Aguttes, Neuilly #85/R est:15000
Works on paper
£2564 $4026 €4000 Pelerins de la Mecque debarquant a Djed-dah, Arabie Saoudite (73x60cm-29x24in) s.i. gouache W/C chl lit. 16-Dec-2 Gros & Delettrez, Paris #315/R est:4000-5000

FOUQUET, Louis Socrate (1795-1831) French
Works on paper
£709 $1100 €1064 Portrait of a young man (32x24cm-13x9in) s. pencil prov. 29-Oct-2 Sotheby's, New York #10/R est:500-700

FOUQUET, Louis Vincent (1803-1869) French
Works on paper
£833 $1308 €1300 Marchand d'eau au bord du Nil (16x11cm-6x4in) s. gouache pair. 16-Dec-2 Gros & Delettrez, Paris #304/R

FOUQUIER, Jacques (1580-1659) French
£26282 $41526 €41000 Winter landscape with skaters (18x25cm-7x10in) copper. 13-Nov-2 Marc Kohn, Paris #21/R est:45000-50000

FOUQUIER, Jacques (attrib) (1580-1659) French
£33333 $52333 €52000 Place de village rn hiver (25x33cm-10x13in) copper. 14-Dec-2 Artcurial Briest, Paris #40/R est:12000

FOURDRIN, Adrien (19th C) French
Sculpture
£1282 $2026 €2000 Mid 19th century group depicting girl with putto and young Bacchus figure (52cm-20in) s.d.1854 st.f.Gautier Editeur green pat bronze marble base. 18-Nov-2 Bernaerts, Antwerp #346/R est:2000-2500

FOURMOIS, F (?) ?
£260 $406 €390 Shepherd with his flock on a country lane (32x38cm-13x15in) s. 10-Sep-2 Bonhams, Knightsbridge #111

FOURMOIS, Theodore (1814-1871) Belgian
£285 $450 €450 Ardennes (33x48cm-13x19in) s.d.1866. 29-Nov-2 Bolland & Marotz, Bremen #694
£470 $756 €700 Paysage a la ferme (28x40cm-11x16in) s. 18-Feb-3 Vanderkindere, Brussels #224
£737 $1157 €1150 Paysage (38x31cm-15x12in) studio st. 10-Dec-2 Vanderkindere, Brussels #33
£1549 $2447 €2400 Etude d'arbre abattu (18x36cm-7x14in) s. 20-Dec-2 Tajan, Paris #105/R est:4000
£4684 $7400 €7400 Paysage anime de voyageurs (98x145cm-39x57in) s.d.1867 prov. 26-Nov-2 Palais de Beaux Arts, Brussels #95/R est:7500-10000

FOURNIALS, J Marguerite (20th C) French
£608 $949 €900 Village au bord du nil (53x65cm-21x26in) s. 25-Mar-3 Chochon-Barre & Allardi, Paris #113/R

FOURNIER, Jean Simon (18th C) French?
Works on paper
£3243 $5059 €4800 Trois jeunes filles dans un interieur (51x41cm-20x16in) graphite chk. 27-Mar-3 Christie's, Paris #116/R

FOURNIER, Max (?) French
£276 $441 €400 Une pensee pour Eugene Boudin (35x27cm-14x11in) s. s.i.d.1995 verso. 12-Mar-3 Libert, Castor, Paris #99
£483 $772 €700 Port Levant (38x46cm-15x18in) s. i.verso. 12-Mar-3 Libert, Castor, Paris #93/R

FOURNIER, Paul (1939-) Canadian
£389 $603 €584 Cape Cod orange no 2 (91x61cm-36x24in) s.i.d.76 paper. 24-Sep-2 Ritchie, Toronto #3199/R (C.D 950)
Works on paper
£343 $536 €515 Rats no.4 (72x88cm-28x35in) s.i.d.67 verso sold with poster. 25-Mar-3 Ritchie, Toronto #143/R (C.D 800)

FOURNIER, Victor Alfred (1872-1924) French
£380 $619 €551 Lady at the loom (44x56cm-17x22in) s.d.1900 board. 16-Jul-3 Sotheby's, Olympia #258/R
£865 $1367 €1350 Coin de marche a Concarneau (24x35cm-9x14in) i.verso panel prov. 12-Nov-2 Thierry & Lannon, Brest #93/R
£2958 $4762 €4200 Jeunes Bretonnes devant Concarneau (50x72cm-20x28in) s. 11-May-3 Thierry & Lannon, Brest #179 est:4000-4500

FOUS, Jean (1901-1971) French
£446 $696 €700 Bouquinistes (29x53cm-11x21in) s. s.i.verso panel. 5-Nov-2 Tajan, Paris #31/R
£483 $762 €700 Chasse aux lions (38x54cm-15x21in) s. s.i.d.1950 verso. 4-Apr-3 Tajan, Paris #19/R
£510 $795 €800 Noce (38x55cm-15x22in) s. s.i.d.1957. 5-Nov-2 Tajan, Paris #30
£510 $795 €800 Patineurs (18x23cm-7x9in) s. s.i.verso panel. 5-Nov-2 Tajan, Paris #32

FOWERAKER, A M (1873-1942) British
Works on paper
£700 $1141 €1050 Evening Almoraima; rural landscape with tall trees, white cottages and figure (27x22cm-11x9in) s. W/C. 11-Feb-3 Fellows & Sons, Birmingham #113/R

£1300 $2119 €1950 Continental townscape with entrance arch and lone figure to the foreground (28x23cm-11x9in) s. i.verso W/C. 11-Feb-3 Fellows & Sons, Birmingham #111/R est:300-500
£1500 $2445 €2250 Old convent, Antiquera, Spain, viewed from a distance with figures in foreground (27x18cm-11x7in) s. i.verso W/C. 11-Feb-3 Fellows & Sons, Birmingham #112/R est:400-600

FOWERAKER, A Moulton (1873-1942) British
£500 $815 €750 Sheep grazing before the church (23x33cm-9x13in) s. panel. 13-Feb-3 David Lay, Penzance #465
Works on paper
£520 $842 €780 Evening twilight (34x53cm-13x21in) s. W/C. 21-May-3 Bonhams, Knightsbridge #209/R
£600 $936 €900 Lower Trevorgus, Cornwall (22x27cm-9x11in) s. pencil pen ink W/C. 19-Sep-2 Christie's, Kensington #64/R
£720 $1152 €1080 Mill, Cordes, France (23x28cm-9x11in) s. W/C. 13-May-3 Bonhams, Sevenoaks #381
£800 $1216 €1200 Figure before a moonlit thatched cottage (28x23cm-11x9in) s. W/C. 14-Aug-2 Andrew Hartley, Ilkley #617
£800 $1240 €1200 Figures by processional gate (34x47cm-13x19in) s. W/C. 2-Oct-2 Bonhams, Knowle #35/R
£850 $1318 €1275 The Papal Palace, Avignon, by moonlight (34x50cm-13x20in) s. i. verso w/C over pencil htd white. 2-Oct-2 Bonhams, Knowle #28/R
£850 $1352 €1275 Devonshire lane (25x35cm-10x14in) s. W/C. 18-Mar-3 Bonhams, Sevenoaks #223
£850 $1377 €1275 Gibralter from Algeciras (24x34cm-9x13in) s. bodycol. 21-May-3 Bonhams, Knightsbridge #22/R
£900 $1404 €1350 Farmstead by trees (23x28cm-9x11in) s. W/C htd white. 26-Mar-3 Hamptons Fine Art, Godalming #110
£1000 $1590 €1500 Figures in a Spanish village (25x35cm-10x14in) s. W/C. 4-Mar-3 Bearnes, Exeter #406/R est:300-500
£1200 $1896 €1800 Night watchman by the city wall (21x27cm-8x11in) s. W/C. 27-Nov-2 Peter Wilson, Nantwich #127
£1451 $2250 €2177 Moonlit, Norway Square (24x29cm-9x11in) s.i.verso W/C prov. 29-Oct-2 Sotheby's, New York #148/R est:1500-2500
£1700 $2822 €2550 Sloop Inn, St Ives, Cornwall (22x28cm-9x11in) s. W/C. 12-Jun-3 Bonhams, New Bond Street #659/R est:1500-2000
£1900 $3040 €2850 Devon village (23x28cm-9x11in) s.d.30 W/C. 11-Mar-3 Bonhams, New Bond Street #102/R est:1500-2000

FOWLER, Graham (1952-) Canadian
£1068 $1699 €1602 Secret stream (112x149cm-44x59in) s.i. d.1987 verso. 6-Mar-3 Heffel, Vancouver #16/R est:3500-4000 (C.D 2500)

FOWLER, Robert (1853-1926) British
£250 $408 €375 Scene on the north Wales coast (39x54cm-15x21in) s. 30-Jan-3 Lawrence, Crewkerne #748a
£350 $553 €525 Bay with boats moored, small village and castle (33x55cm-13x22in) s. 18-Dec-2 John Nicholson, Haslemere #1275/R
£410 $652 €615 Figures by a river in a wooded landscape (41x61cm-16x24in) s. 6-Mar-3 Christie's, Kensington #478/R
£524 $828 €786 Pathway to village (32x42cm-13x17in) s. canvasboard. 18-Nov-2 Waddingtons, Toronto #174/R (C.D 1300)
£549 $856 €824 Landscape with shepherd and sheep (76x127cm-30x50in) s. 13-Sep-2 Lilla Bukowskis, Stockholm #426 (S.KR 8000)
£2143 $3300 €3215 Untitled - seated woman (62x46cm-24x18in) s. 3-Sep-2 Shapiro, Sydney #361/R est:6000-8000 (A.D 6000)

FOWLES, A W (c.1815-1878) British
£1266 $1987 €1899 Yachts racing in the Solent (29x48cm-11x19in) panel. 25-Nov-2 Peter Webb, Auckland #20/R est:5000-8000 (NZ.D 4000)

FOWLES, Arthur W (c.1815-1878) British
£5500 $8910 €8250 Vying for the start, a melee of big cutters in Osborn Bay (66x102cm-26x40in) s.i.d.1862. 21-May-3 Christie's, Kensington #561/R est:8000-12000
£12000 $19440 €18000 Racing schooners rounding the turning mark in Osborne Bay (51x81cm-20x32in) s.i.d.1878. 21-May-3 Christie's, Kensington #559/R est:12000-18000
£30000 $48600 €45000 Cambria winning at Cowes, 1868 (71x99cm-28x39in) s.i.d.1869 arched top prov. 22-Jan-3 Bonhams, New Bond Street #315/R est:30000-50000
£30000 $48600 €45000 Cambria winning the international race, Cowes (71x99cm-28x39in) s.i.1859 prov. 22-Jan-3 Bonhams, New Bond Street #313/R est:30000-50000

FOWLES, Arthur W (attrib) (c.1815-1878) British
£2000 $3240 €3000 Yachts racing for the mark at Cowes Regatta (30x51cm-12x20in) prov. 22-Jan-3 Bonhams, New Bond Street #308/R est:2000-3000

FOX, Charles James (1860-?) British
£420 $651 €630 Cumberland beck (29x44cm-11x17in) s.d.1895. 24-Sep-2 Anderson & Garland, Newcastle #521
£700 $1092 €1050 Cotswold village (43x65cm-17x26in) s. 8-Apr-3 Bonhams, Knightsbridge #239/R

FOX, Edwin M (19th C) British
£5380 $8392 €8500 Gentleman on black hunter with two greyhounds (64x76cm-25x30in) 15-Oct-2 Mealy's, Castlecomer #271/R est:4000-6000

FOX, Emanuel Phillips (1865-1915) Australian
£1040 $1674 €1508 Ladies in an outdoor setting (28x22cm-11x9in) board. 12-May-3 Joel, Victoria #339 est:3000-5000 (A.D 2600)
£1964 $3045 €2946 Glade (40x23cm-16x9in) panel. 29-Oct-2 Lawson Menzies, Sydney #6/R est:6000-8000 (A.D 5500)
£2988 $4900 €4482 Evening, Shoreham (45x76cm-18x30in) s. painted c.1890 lit. 4-Jun-3 Deutscher-Menzies, Melbourne #140/R est:7000-10000 (A.D 7500)
£3559 $5445 €5339 Wooded landscape (46x38cm-18x15in) s. painted c.1900-04 prov. 26-Aug-2 Sotheby's, Paddington #541/R est:12000-18000 (A.D 10000)
£3943 $5993 €5915 Seascape at dusk (38x46cm-15x18in) s. 28-Aug-2 Deutscher-Menzies, Melbourne #234/R est:9000-12000 (A.D 11000)
£28674 $43585 €43011 Cremorne Point (38x46cm-15x18in) s. painted c.1913-14 prov.exhib.lit. 28-Aug-2 Deutscher-Menzies, Melbourne #50/R est:95000-120000 (A.D 80000)

FOX, Ethel Carrick (1872-1952) Australian
£1600 $2576 €2400 Glass house mountains, Queensland (23x33cm-9x13in) s. canvas on board. 6-May-3 Christie's, Melbourne #368/R est:6000-8000 (A.D 4000)
£1628 $2588 €2442 River scene (26x36cm-10x14in) s. canvasboard. 5-May-3 Sotheby's, Melbourne #268/R est:3000-4000 (A.D 4200)
£2400 $3864 €3600 Autumn Canberra (25x34cm-10x13in) s. canvasboard. 6-May-3 Christie's, Melbourne #282/R est:4000-6000 (A.D 6000)
£5179 $8494 €7769 Crimson and gold, autumn, Canberra (25x37cm-10x15in) s. canvas on board prov. 4-Jun-3 Deutscher-Menzies, Melbourne #139/R est:8000-12000 (A.D 13000)
£6538 $10396 €9807 Workers (13x21cm-5x8in) s. panel prov. 4-Mar-3 Deutscher-Menzies, Melbourne #140/R est:4000-6000 (A.D 17000)
£7829 $11979 €11744 Flower stall, Nice (38x46cm-15x18in) s.i. painted c.1925 prov.exhib. 26-Aug-2 Sotheby's, Paddington #525/R est:22000-28000 (A.D 22000)
£8571 $13457 €12857 Autumn in Paris (26x34cm-10x13in) board prov., 25-Nov-2 Christie's, Melbourne #24/R est:20000-30000 (A.D 24000)
Works on paper
£714 $1107 €1071 Countryside (19x31cm-7x12in) s. W/C. 29-Oct-2 Lawson Menzies, Sydney #374 (A.D 2000)

FOX, George (19th C) British
£311 $516 €451 Gentlemen enjoying a meal (26x36cm-10x14in) s. 10-Jun-3 Ritchie, Toronto #47/R (C.D 700)
£382 $600 €573 Reading a brief (66x53cm-26x21in) s. canvas laid down. 23-Nov-2 Jackson's, Cedar Falls #7/R
£513 $795 €800 Three 18th C lawyers drinking sherry and smoking pipes (24x31cm-9x12in) s. lit. 6-Dec-2 Karlheinz Kaupp, Staufen #2384/R
£750 $1170 €1125 Prize cauliflower (31x23cm-12x9in) s. 10-Apr-3 Tennants, Leyburn #1111
£1900 $3097 €2755 Good vintage. Good tale (25x34cm-10x13in) s. pair. 21-Jul-3 Bonhams, Bath #92/R est:800-1200

FOX, H C (1860-?) British
Works on paper
£450 $738 €675 Huntsman and hounds on a lane lined with trees (51x74cm-20x29in) d.1907 W/C. 7-Feb-3 Biddle & Webb, Birmingham #359

FOX, Henry Charles (1860-1929) British
£500 $815 €750 On the Thames, Windsor Castle in the distance (36x55cm-14x22in) 14-Feb-3 Lyon & Turnbull, Edinburgh #64
Works on paper
£250 $390 €375 Changing pasture (51x35cm-20x14in) s.d.1900 pencil W/C htd white. 27-Mar-3 Christie's, Kensington #98
£281 $446 €422 Cattle on riverbank (38x71cm-15x28in) s.d.1899 W/C. 25-Feb-3 Peter Webb, Auckland #218 (NZ.D 800)
£295 $460 €443 River scene with boat and cattle (35x52cm-14x20in) s.d.1902 W/C. 6-Aug-2 Peter Webb, Auckland #9/R est:1200-2000 (NZ.D 1000)
£300 $471 €450 Figures fishing from a boat in river landscape (30x51cm-12x20in) s.d.99 W/C. 13-Dec-2 Keys, Aylsham #628/R
£300 $483 €450 Farmer and cattle on a country road (35x52cm-14x20in) s.d.1905 W/C. 15-Jan-3 James Thompson, Kirby Lonsdale #87

£300 $477 €450 South country lane, with driver, horse and cart crossing a stream (54x36cm-21x14in) s.indis d. W/C. 27-Feb-3 Bonhams, Chester #413
£300 $477 €450 Returning home (38x53cm-15x21in) s.d.1916 W/C htd bodycol. 30-Apr-3 Halls, Shrewsbury #223
£340 $530 €510 Gomshall Mill (38x53cm-15x21in) s.i.d.1906 W/C. 6-Nov-2 Bonhams, Chester #423
£360 $558 €540 Shepherding the flock along a road (36x55cm-14x22in) s.d.1920 W/C bodycol. 24-Sep-2 Bonhams, Knightsbridge #1/R
£370 $607 €555 Crossing the ford, farm worker with horse and cart in an autumn landscape (54x36cm-21x14in) s. indis d. W/C. 3-Jun-3 Bonhams, Oxford #19
£480 $744 €720 Droving cattle on a rural lane (53x74cm-21x29in) s.d.1912 W/C. 24-Sep-2 Bonhams, Knightsbridge #2/R
£480 $754 €720 Christchurch view (35x52cm-14x20in) s. pencil W/C. 16-Apr-3 Christie's, Kensington #1045/R
£500 $790 €725 By the Thames (37x54cm-15x21in) s.d.92 W/C bodycol. 22-Jul-3 Bonhams, Knightsbridge #154/R
£520 $806 €780 Rural landscape with windmill and farm worker with horses (33x51cm-13x20in) s. W/C. 6-Dec-2 Biddle & Webb, Birmingham #246
£520 $863 €754 At the ford (36x51cm-14x20in) s.d.1903 W/C. 10-Jun-3 David Lay, Penzance #190
£600 $936 €900 Horses watering (55x38cm-22x15in) s.d.07 pencil W/C. 19-Sep-2 Christie's, Kensington #61
£600 $948 €900 In the New Forest (36x53cm-14x21in) s.d.1907 W/C. 13-Nov-2 Halls, Shrewsbury #347/R
£600 $990 €870 Cart by farm buildings in a rural landscape (36x53cm-14x21in) s.d.1917. 3-Jul-3 Duke & Son, Dorchester #97/R
£620 $973 €930 Shepherd with sheep in a country lane (36x51cm-14x20in) s.d.1920 W/C. 13-Dec-2 Keys, Aylsham #626/R
£650 $1021 €975 Suffolk Lane (36x51cm-14x20in) s.d.1918 W/C prov. 13-Dec-2 Keys, Aylsham #625/R
£650 $1053 €975 Near Marlow on the Thames (38x54cm-15x21in) s.d.1898 W/C. 20-May-3 Sotheby's, Olympia #248/R
£720 $1145 €1080 Cattle on a country track, buildings beyond (35x52cm-14x20in) s.d.1904 W/C. 27-Feb-3 Greenslade Hunt, Taunton #1264/R
£750 $1155 €1125 Droving sheep along a rural lane. Shepherd and his flock (37x27cm-15x11in) s.d.1914 W/C pair. 22-Oct-2 Bonhams, Knightsbridge #57/R
£750 $1170 €1125 Horses pulling cart watering in a river by a rural village (61x96cm-24x38in) s.d.1900 pencil W/C htd bodycol. 17-Oct-2 Christie's, Kensington #65/R
£750 $1238 €1088 Shepherd on a country lane. Horseman on a wooded lane (56x38cm-22x15in) s.d.1910 W/C pair. 1-Jul-3 Bearnes, Exeter #431/R
£760 $1246 €1140 Drover and cattle on a country lane (56x74cm-22x29in) s. W/C. 7-Feb-3 Honiton Galleries, Honiton #329
£780 $1209 €1170 Herdsmen and cattle in an autumnal lane (38x55cm-15x22in) s.d.1913 W/C bodycol. 30-Sep-2 Bonhams, Ipswich #360/R
£780 $1295 €1170 Near Haselmere, Surrey, with horses and figures before a barn. s.d.1900 W/C. 10-Jun-3 Lawrences, Bletchingley #1426
£850 $1326 €1275 Driving sheep. Driving cattle (55x38cm-22x15in) s. W/C card pair. 17-Sep-2 Sotheby's, Olympia #113/R
£850 $1386 €1275 Canal and lock scene with barge and man and horse on towpath (36x53cm-14x21in) s.d.1913 W/C. 28-Jan-3 Rogers Jones, Clwyd #124
£960 $1526 €1440 Shepherd, flock on a country lane. Farmer horse and cart on a village lane (56x37cm-22x15in) s. W/C pair. 27-Feb-3 Bonhams, Chester #408
£1300 $2028 €1950 Homewards. Watering horses (37x55cm-15x22in) s.d.1917 W/C bodycol pair. 10-Apr-3 Tennants, Leyburn #859/R est:1000-1500
£1400 $2184 €2100 Drinking pool. Homewards (37x27cm-15x11in) s.d.1924 W/C pair. 21-Sep-2 Lacy Scott, Bury St.Edmunds #409/R
£1400 $2198 €2100 Herdsman with cattle on a lane with cottages. Farmhands with shire horse (37x53cm-15x21in) s.d.1908/09 W/C framed as a pair. 14-Dec-2 Lacy Scott, Bury St.Edmunds #441/R

FOX, John R (1927-) Canadian
£823 $1276 €1235 Still life (50x60cm-20x24in) s. prov. 3-Dec-2 Joyner, Toronto #353 est:2000-3000 (C.D 2000)
£1244 $2041 €1866 Boats at mooring (80x55cm-31x22in) s. prov. 3-Jun-3 Joyner, Toronto #315/R est:1500-2000 (C.D 2800)

FOX, Kathleen (1880-1963) British
£2027 $3162 €3000 June (63x74cm-25x29in) s. 26-Mar-3 James Adam, Dublin #43/R est:3000-4000
£9494 $14715 €15000 Fishmarket, Bruges (81x112cm-32x44in) s. prov. 24-Sep-2 De Veres Art Auctions, Dublin #40/R est:15000-20000

FOX, Minnie (fl.1912-1935) British
£520 $827 €780 English terrier (25x20cm-10x8in) init. board sold with another by the same hand. 5-Mar-3 Bonhams, Bury St Edmunds #341

FOX, R A (?) ?
£1563 $2500 €2345 Horse in a stable (64x76cm-25x30in) s.d. 15-Mar-3 Selkirks, St. Louis #87/R est:2000-3000

FOX, R Atkinson (1860-1935) Canadian
£813 $1300 €1220 Interior scene of a woman peeling apples (36x28cm-14x11in) s. 17-May-3 Pook & Pook, Downington #289/R est:800-1200

FOXHILL, George (1921-) Australian
£321 $501 €482 Meditation (88x68cm-35x27in) init. s.i.d.1988 verso. 11-Nov-2 Deutscher-Menzies, Melbourne #189 (A.D 900)

FRAASS, Erich (1893-1974) German
Works on paper
£347 $549 €500 Arable land (53x74cm-21x29in) s. i. verso W/C. 26-Apr-3 Dr Lehr, Berlin #135/R

FRACANZANO, Francesco (1612-1656) Italian
£10000 $15700 €15000 Executioner with head of Saint John the Baptist (63x50cm-25x20in) painted c.1630. 12-Dec-2 Sotheby's, London #183/R est:10000-15000

FRACANZANO, Francesco (circle) (1612-1656) Italian
£13415 $22000 €20123 Head of a bearded man, possibly St Peter (79x69cm-31x27in) 5-Feb-3 Christie's, Rockefeller NY #281/R est:4000-6000

FRADEL, Henri Joseph (1778-1865) French
£2911 $4600 €4367 Interior scene depicting a Shakespearean man reciting poetry to a lady (64x53cm-25x21in) s.d.1810. 16-Nov-2 New Orleans Auction, New Orleans #554/R est:5000-8000

FRAGIACOMO, Pietro (1856-1922) Italian
£1258 $1937 €2000 Landscape (16x25cm-6x10in) s. cardboard. 23-Oct-2 Finarte, Milan #134/R
£1899 $3000 €3000 Hut and boats (17x24cm-7x9in) s. cardboard. 26-Nov-2 Christie's, Rome #204/R
£3165 $5000 €5000 Venice, boats in the Lagoon (14x29cm-6x11in) s. board. 26-Nov-2 Christie's, Rome #203/R est:6000
£4430 $7000 €7000 Sailing in the Lagoon (24x30cm-9x12in) s. cardboard. 26-Nov-2 Christie's, Rome #210/R est:9000
£35507 $58232 €49000 Venezia, il Gamalo di S. Marco (65x103cm-26x41in) s. 27-May-3 Finarte, Milan #86/R est:45000-55000

FRAGIACOMO, Pietro (attrib) (1856-1922) Italian
£327 $536 €500 Pond in the park (16x21cm-6x8in) s. card. 5-Feb-3 Il Ponte, Milan #287

FRAGONARD, Alexandre Evariste (1780-1850) French
£8621 $13621 €12500 Virginie pendant la tempete (32x24cm-13x9in) 2-Apr-3 Marc Kohn, Paris #46b
£18881 $31531 €27000 Francois 1er recevant les oeuvres rapportees d'Italie (65x82cm-26x32in) 25-Jun-3 Sotheby's, Paris #68/R est:30000-40000
Works on paper
£390 $608 €620 Elegant scene with women listening to lute player (22x27cm-9x11in) mono.d.1803 W//c pen board. 11-Oct-2 Winterberg, Heidelberg #526
£1259 $2102 €1800 Entree des Francais dans un ville en Flammes (20x78cm-8x31in) s. pen sepia wash graphite prov. 25-Jun-3 Sotheby's, Paris #54/R est:600-900
£1329 $2219 €1900 Rencontre d'avant-garde a Saalfeld (20x79cm-8x31in) s.i. pen sepia wash graphite prov. 25-Jun-3 Sotheby's, Paris #51/R est:600-900
£1329 $2219 €1900 Fantassins fuyant devant l'avant-garde Francaise a cheval (20x79cm-8x31in) s. pen sepia wash graphite prov. 25-Jun-3 Sotheby's, Paris #52/R est:600-900
£1329 $2219 €1900 Episode de la Bataille d'Iena (19x77cm-7x30in) s. pen sepia wash graphite prov. 25-Jun-3 Sotheby's, Paris #53/R est:600-900
£1329 $2219 €1900 Mort au combat du Prince de Prusse Louis-Ferdinand (20x81cm-8x32in) s. pen sepia wash graphite prov. 25-Jun-3 Sotheby's, Paris #55/R est:600-900
£2128 $3553 €3000 Episode de la bataille d'Iena, la prise de Weimar (19x80cm-7x31in) s. brown wash black crayon gouache prov. 19-Jun-3 Piasa, Paris #151/R est:3000-4000

FRAGONARD, Alexandre Evariste (attrib) (1780-1850) French
Works on paper
£705 $1093 €1100 Oreste et l'une des Erynnies (24x30cm-9x12in) crayon W/C. 4-Dec-2 Piasa, Paris #159/R

FRAGONARD, Jean Honore (1732-1806) French
£148148 $240000 €222222 Venus crowning love, or Le Jour (73x127cm-29x50in) prov.exhib.lit. 24-Jan-3 Christie's, Rockefeller NY #108/R est:200000-300000
Prints
£3846 $6077 €6000 Le petit parc. etching. 14-Nov-2 Libert, Castor, Paris #12 est:1200
Works on paper
£633 $1000 €1000 Scene de caravane, d'apres Francesco Castiglione (19x25cm-7x10in) i. black chk prov. 27-Nov-2 Christie's, Paris #197/R
£750 $1178 €1125 Adoration of the shepherds, after Castiglione (28x18cm-11x7in) i. black chk. 13-Dec-2 Christie's, Kensington #317
£2937 $4905 €4200 La mort de Seneque (20x25cm-8x10in) i. bistre wash prov.lit. 25-Jun-3 Sotheby's, Paris #32/R est:3000-4000
£4430 $7000 €7000 Jeune paysan italien debout (15x9cm-6x4in) i.d.1774 crayon wash. 28-Nov-2 Tajan, Paris #49/R est:5000
£5063 $8000 €8000 Trois etudes des chats (16x15cm-6x6in) red chk prov. 27-Nov-2 Christie's, Paris #189/R est:10000-15000
£7595 $11848 €12000 Eruption de Montenuovo (31x23cm-12x9in) i. pierre noire Chinese ink htd white prov.lit. 18-Oct-2 Rabourdin & Choppin de Janvry, Paris #90/R est:3000
£8500 $14195 €12325 Garden with sculpture among Roman pines, steps mounting a high wall (16x21cm-6x8in) black chk prov. 8-Jul-3 Christie's, London #80/R est:6000-8000
£25850 $41102 €38000 Lavandieres et figures dans un parc italien (27x38cm-11x15in) pierre noire W/C. 24-Mar-3 Tajan, Paris #41/R est:60000

FRAGONARD, Jean Honore (attrib) (1732-1806) French
£1688 $2616 €2532 Portrait of boy (39x33cm-15x13in) 3-Oct-2 Koller, Zurich #3064/R est:5000-8000 (S.FR 3930)
Works on paper
£321 $497 €500 Trois etudes d'ecoincons (27x20cm-11x8in) i. crayon. 4-Dec-2 Piasa, Paris #68
£385 $596 €600 Etude d'amour (15x10cm-6x4in) crayon. 4-Dec-2 Piasa, Paris #67/R
£961 $1499 €1442 Female half-nude (42x51cm-17x20in) chl red ochre prov. 9-Nov-2 Galerie Gloggner, Luzern #54/R est:500-600 (S.FR 2200)

FRAGONARD, Jean Honore (circle) (1732-1806) French
£4573 $7500 €6860 Head of a young boy (39x33cm-15x13in) painted oval. 29-May-3 Sotheby's, New York #134/R est:8000-12000

FRAHM, Hans (?) German
£517 $786 €776 In Klausen a.d. Bergstrasse, Tirol (43x34cm-17x13in) s.i. 27-Aug-2 Rasmussen, Copenhagen #1645/R (D.KR 6000)
£1027 $1603 €1500 Snowy mountain town (87x127cm-34x50in) s.i. 9-Apr-3 Neumeister, Munich #665/R est:600

FRAI, Felicita (1914-) Czechoslovakian
£816 $1298 €1200 Flower in the hair (40x50cm-16x20in) s. 1-Mar-3 Meeting Art, Vercelli #505

FRAILE, Alfonso (1930-1988) Spanish
£5346 $8340 €8500 Boy with bird (82x60cm-32x24in) s. 23-Sep-2 Durán, Madrid #204/R
Works on paper
£2581 $4077 €4000 Woman and dove (70x50cm-28x20in) s.d.1959 gouache. 17-Dec-2 Segre, Madrid #213/R
£6452 $10194 €10000 Pinta Punto (152x130cm-60x51in) s.d.1980 mixed media paper on board exhib.lit. 17-Dec-2 Segre, Madrid #170/R est:9000

FRAILONG, Pierre Jean Charles (20th C) French
£2065 $3262 €3200 Orientales au patio (73x60cm-29x24in) s. 19-Dec-2 Claude Aguttes, Neuilly #135/R

FRAME, Robert Aaron (1924-) American
£599 $1000 €869 Monuments (56x76cm-22x30in) s. 17-Jun-3 John Moran, Pasadena #24 est:2000-3000

FRAMPTON, Edward Reginald (1872-1923) British
£350 $543 €525 Across the Lagoon, Venice (20x25cm-8x10in) s.d.1902 board. 4-Dec-2 Christie's, Kensington #443/R
£16000 $25760 €24000 Maiden holding book and flowers (58x21cm-23x8in) s.d.1901 prov. 20-Feb-3 Christie's, London #237/R est:12000

FRAMPTON, Sir George James (1860-1928) British
Sculpture
£2100 $3276 €3150 Madonna (28cm-11in) init.d.1915 bronze. 5-Nov-2 Woolley & Wallis, Salisbury #118/R est:1000-1500
£3700 $5883 €5550 Bust of a girl (53cm-21in) s.i.d.1907 dark brown pat. bronze. 30-Apr-3 Mallams, Oxford #100/R est:2000-3000
£30000 $47400 €45000 Peter Pan (52cm-20in) mono.i.d.1918 brown pat.bronze. 26-Nov-2 Christie's, London #157/R est:30000-50000

FRAN-BARO (1926-2000) French
£1007 $1621 €1500 Paddock (47x55cm-19x22in) s. s.i.verso. 18-Feb-3 Durán, Madrid #212/R
£1655 $2647 €2300 Honfleur, le port et la Lieutenance (52x71cm-20x28in) s. 18-May-3 Eric Pillon, Calais #237/R
£1678 $2701 €2500 Pont Saint-Michel, Paris (54x65cm-21x26in) s. s.i.verso. 18-Feb-3 Durán, Madrid #213/R

FRANC, François (1926-) French
£321 $503 €500 Le Havre (54x65cm-21x26in) s. 24-Nov-2 Lesieur & Le Bars, Le Havre #48
£417 $654 €650 Canal (55x33cm-22x13in) s. 24-Nov-2 Lesieur & Le Bars, Le Havre #47

FRANC-LAMY, Pierre (1855-1919) French
£845 $1318 €1268 Seated woman wearing shawl in garden (176x107cm-69x42in) s.i.d.1910 prov. 23-Sep-2 Rasmussen, Vejle #132/R (D.KR 10000)

FRANCAIS, Anne (1909-1995) French
£1218 $1912 €1900 Cannes (65x50cm-26x20in) s. 24-Nov-2 Lesieur & Le Bars, Le Havre #49/R
£1549 $2494 €2200 Route et facade du Palm beach (65x81cm-26x32in) s. 12-May-3 Lesieur & Le Bars, Le Havre #36/R
£1812 $2917 €2700 Le Triomphe au cafe des Champs Elysees (54x65cm-21x26in) s. exhib. 23-Feb-3 Lesieur & Le Bars, Le Havre #51

FRANCAIS, François Louis (1814-1897) French
£694 $1118 €1041 Evening landscape (46x38cm-18x15in) s.d.78. 7-May-3 Dobiaschofsky, Bern #522/R est:2600 (S.FR 1500)
Works on paper
£862 $1371 €1250 Paysage (20x28cm-8x11in) s. W/C. 7-Mar-3 Rabourdin & Choppin de Janvry, Paris #17
£1795 $2782 €2800 Bucheron (26x21cm-10x8in) s. W/C gouache. 4-Dec-2 Piasa, Paris #156/R

FRANCALANCIA, Riccardo (1886-1965) Italian
£3151 $4915 €4600 Jug and shell (65x50cm-26x20in) s. 10-Apr-3 Finarte Semenzato, Rome #254/R

FRANCE, Charles (19th C) British
£1300 $2093 €1950 Yorkshire landscape with cattle on a meandering path (74x112cm-29x44in) s.d.1883. 19-Feb-3 Rupert Toovey, Partridge Green #60/R est:1200-1800
£2013 $3119 €3200 Sheep grazing in English landscape (57x92cm-22x36in) s.d.1893. 29-Oct-2 Dorotheum, Vienna #16/R est:2800-3000
Works on paper
£266 $420 €399 Summer landscape with cows in waterway (30x44cm-12x17in) pastel. 16-Nov-2 Crafoord, Lund #56/R (S.KR 3800)

FRANCE, Patricia (1911-1995) New Zealander
£821 $1280 €1232 Between friends (18x27cm-7x11in) s. acrylic on board. 17-Sep-2 Peter Webb, Auckland #161/R est:2500-3500 (NZ.D 2700)
£1042 $1625 €1563 Still life (28x36cm-11x14in) s. acrylic board. 8-Apr-3 Peter Webb, Auckland #100/R est:2000-3000 (NZ.D 3000)
£1380 $1960 €2070 Tuataha (45x38cm-18x15in) s.d.1988 board. 20-Mar-2 Watson's, Christchurch #39/R est:4500-6000 (NZ.D 4500)
Works on paper
£364 $560 €546 Man and a woman (31x39cm-12x15in) s. W/C. 4-Sep-2 Dunbar Sloane, Wellington #125 est:800-1500 (NZ.D 1200)
£636 $980 €954 Open window (38x42cm-15x17in) s. W/C. 4-Sep-2 Dunbar Sloane, Wellington #126 est:1500-2500 (NZ.D 2100)

FRANCESCHI, Louis Julien (1825-1893) French
Sculpture
£4012 $6500 €5817 Belle Egyptienne (97x46cm-38x18in) s.i. brown pat bronze. 21-May-3 Doyle, New York #191/R est:8000-10000

FRANCESCHI, Mariano de (1849-1896) Italian
£1500 $2445 €2175 Ragazzina di Capri. Lavanderie de Capri (16x10cm-6x4in) s.i. panel pair. 21-Jul-3 Sotheby's, London #613 est:1000-1500

Works on paper
£357 $564 €536 Gypsy girl (53x36cm-21x14in) s. W/C. 18-Nov-2 Joel, Victoria #329 est:1250-1750 (A.D 1000)
£700 $1134 €1050 Sunlight street (50x33cm-20x13in) s.i.d.77 pencil W/C. 23-Jan-3 Christie's, Kensington #300/R
£1032 $1600 €1548 Peasant woman and boy watching baby near archway (74x53cm-29x21in) s.i. W/C. 16-Jul-2 Arthur James, Florida #340

FRANCESCHINI, Baldassare (1611-1689) Italian
Works on paper
£1197 $1927 €1700 Due studi di mano (26x16cm-10x6in) sanguine htd white. 12-May-3 Sotheby's, Milan #33/R est:600-800
£2098 $3000 €3147 Study of a left hand (18x15cm-7x6in) red chk htd white. 23-Jan-3 Swann Galleries, New York #77/R est:3000-5000
£4054 $6324 €6000 Studies of hands (27x38cm-11x15in) chk prov. 27-Mar-3 Christie's, Paris #70/R

FRANCESCHINI, Baldassare (attrib) (1611-1689) Italian
Works on paper
£1701 $2704 €2500 Plan for ceiling (12x8cm-5x3in) sanguine pen ink. 24-Mar-3 Tajan, Paris #6/R

FRANCESCHINI, Edoardo (1928-) Italian
£347 $552 €500 Landscape (70x100cm-28x39in) s.d.1993 mixed media card on canvas. 1-May-3 Meeting Art, Vercelli #390
£949 $1481 €1500 Landscape in my tale (160x130cm-63x51in) s. acrylic painted 1992. 14-Sep-2 Meeting Art, Vercelli #719/R
Works on paper
£449 $704 €700 Composition (66x92cm-26x36in) s.d.1957 mixed media card on masonite. 23-Nov-2 Meeting Art, Vercelli #271/R

FRANCESCHINI, Marco Antonio (style) (1648-1729) Italian
£10000 $15700 €15000 Bacchanal (112x154cm-44x61in) 12-Dec-2 Sotheby's, London #193/R est:12000-18000

FRANCESE, Franco (1920-1996) Italian
£1389 $2208 €2000 Starry night (58x34cm-23x13in) s.i.d.1973 verso. 1-May-3 Meeting Art, Vercelli #222
Works on paper
£641 $1006 €1000 The beast on you (58x48cm-23x19in) s.i.d.1961 pastel. 19-Nov-2 Finarte, Milan #1
£1268 $2104 €1800 Gallo (120x80cm-47x31in) s.d.11.IV.54 mixed media. 10-Jun-3 Finarte Semenzato, Milan #184/R est:1800-2200

FRANCHERE, Joseph-Charles (1866-1921) Canadian
£533 $831 €800 Voilier pres du rivage (24x34cm-9x13in) s. cardboard. 10-Sep-2 Iegor de Saint Hippolyte, Montreal #48 (C.D 1300)
£1016 $1596 €1524 Jeune fille au drape vert (39x30cm-15x12in) s. 12-Dec-2 Iegor de Saint Hippolyte, Montreal #32 (C.D 2500)
£1778 $2916 €2667 Country house (46x60cm-18x24in) s. 27-May-3 Sotheby's, Toronto #100/R est:5000-7000 (C.D 4000)
£2133 $3499 €3200 Landscape with house by a river (25x30cm-10x12in) s. canvasboard. 3-Jun-3 Joyner, Toronto #234/R est:5000-6000 (C.D 4800)
£5044 $7515 €7566 La nonchalante (87x65cm-34x26in) s. 26-Jun-2 Iegor de Saint Hippolyte, Montreal #40/R (C.D 11500)
£11694 $19060 €17541 Campement (59x80cm-23x31in) s. canvas on board. 12-Feb-3 Iegor de Saint Hippolyte, Montreal #78b (C.D 29000)
£28807 $44650 €43211 La rue de Lagauchetiere (61x90cm-24x35in) s. prov.exhib. 3-Dec-2 Joyner, Toronto #105/R est:80000-100000 (C.D 70000)

FRANCHI, Pietro (19th C) Italian
Sculpture
£10135 $15811 €15000 Venus at bath (99cm-39in) s.d.1869 Carrara marble green marble base lit. 31-Mar-3 Finarte Semenzato, Milan #292/R

FRANCHINA, Nino (1912-1988) Italian
Sculpture
£1290 $2039 €2000 Untitled (60cm-24in) s. painted steel. 18-Dec-2 Christie's, Rome #43/R

FRANCHOYS, Lucas II (1616-1681) Flemish
£9459 $14757 €14000 Portrait of gentleman in black costume with lace collar (101x79cm-40x31in) prov. 27-Mar-3 Dorotheum, Vienna #205/R est:9000-14000

FRANCIA, Alexandre T (1820-1884) French
£4000 $6080 €6000 Congested shipping lanes offshore (100x160cm-39x63in) s. 15-Aug-2 Bonhams, New Bond Street #300/R est:4000-6000
Works on paper
£1300 $2145 €1885 River scene with burning city to the far bank (46x69cm-18x27in) W/C bodycol. 3-Jul-3 Duke & Son, Dorchester #144/R est:800-1500
£1456 $2256 €2300 Venise, vue de l'eglise San Giorgio (26x42cm-10x17in) s. W/C. 29-Sep-2 Eric Pillon, Calais #4/R

FRANCIA, Camillo (1955-) Italian
£382 $607 €550 Butterfly (50x50cm-20x20in) s. painted 2002. 1-May-3 Meeting Art, Vercelli #41
£521 $828 €750 Landscape of souveniers (80x100cm-31x39in) s.i.d.2002 lit. 1-May-3 Meeting Art, Vercelli #205
£694 $1104 €1000 Light blade (100x100cm-39x39in) s.d.2002 s.i.verso. 1-May-3 Meeting Art, Vercelli #50
£1042 $1656 €1500 Night scene (100x150cm-39x59in) s.d.2001 lit. 1-May-3 Meeting Art, Vercelli #438

FRANCIA, François Louis Thomas (1772-1839) French
Works on paper
£450 $702 €675 Hulks moored at the mouth of an estuary (10x18cm-4x7in) grey wash. 10-Apr-3 Tennants, Leyburn #814
£1150 $1817 €1725 Fresh breeze - French man-o'war (18x23cm-7x9in) i.d.1814 verso W/C. 26-Nov-2 Bonhams, Oxford #25 est:300-400
£7000 $10010 €10500 Chasse-maree (9x15cm-4x6in) pencil pen ink W/C scratching out prov.exhib.lit. 22-Jan-3 Christie's, London #63/R

FRANCIA, Giulio (studio) (1487-1545) Italian
£4730 $7378 €7000 Madonna and Child (53x42cm-21x17in) board. 31-Mar-3 Finarte Semenzato, Milan #481/R

FRANCIABIGIO (1482-1525) Italian
£6098 $10000 €9147 Portrait of a gentleman, in a black coat and hat (57x49cm-22x19in) panel prov.lit. 5-Feb-3 Christie's, Rockefeller NY #305/R est:10000-15000

FRANCIABIGIO (attrib) (1482-1525) Italian
Works on paper
£1392 $2158 €2200 Standing female nude with doves (52x25cm-20x10in) chk paper on board. 27-Sep-2 Venator & Hansten, Koln #944/R est:900

FRANCIS, Dorothea (?) ?
£239 $392 €359 Figure and boats on the beach (22x30cm-9x12in) s. canvas on board exhib. 4-Jun-3 Deutscher-Menzies, Melbourne #407/R (A.D 600)
Works on paper
£430 $654 €645 Village from the hillside (16x27cm-6x11in) s. W/C. 28-Aug-2 Deutscher-Menzies, Melbourne #384/R (A.D 1200)

FRANCIS, John (1780-1861) British
Sculpture
£3200 $5024 €4800 Busts of George IV and Queen Caroline (33cm-13in) s.d.1823 marble socle siena stand pair. 16-Dec-2 Sotheby's, London #68/R est:2000-3000

FRANCIS, John F (1808-1886) American
£4487 $7000 €6731 Portrait of a young girl dressed in white (76x64cm-30x25in) s.d.July 1836. 12-Oct-2 Neal Auction Company, New Orleans #462/R est:4000-6000
£23438 $37500 €35157 Still life with bottles of cognac and wine surrounded by goblets and glasses, cheese and biscuits (48x58cm-19x23in) 17-May-3 Pook & Pook, Downington #305/R est:50000-60000
£25806 $40000 €38709 Red and yellow apples in a basket (37x48cm-15x19in) s.d.1862 panel prov.exhib. 4-Dec-2 Sotheby's, New York #102/R est:40000-60000

FRANCIS, Mark (1962-) British
£2848 $4500 €4272 Small study painting (61x61cm-24x24in) s.i.d.95 verso prov. 12-Nov-2 Phillips, New York #231/R est:4000-6000
£3600 $6012 €5220 Untitled (380x65cm-150x26in) s.d.1999 verso paper prov. 24-Jun-3 Sotheby's, Olympia #19/R est:3500-4500
£3800 $6232 €5700 Ovum - small (64x64cm-25x25in) prov. 6-Feb-3 Christie's, London #757/R est:2000-3000
£4062 $6500 €6093 Fuse (244x183cm-96x72in) s.i.d.1991 prov.exhib. 16-May-3 Phillips, New York #230/R est:6000-8000
£6500 $10660 €9750 Black Ovum (244x153cm-96x60in) i.d.1991 verso prov.exhib. 6-Feb-3 Christie's, London #756/R est:6000-8000
£6500 $10855 €9425 Colonise (305x274cm-120x108in) s.i.d.1996 verso prov. 24-Jun-3 Sotheby's, Olympia #21/R est:7000-9000
£6800 $11356 €9860 Untitled - compression (213x183cm-84x72in) s.i.d.95 prov. 27-Jun-3 Christie's, London #272/R est:7000-9000

£8500 $13940 €12750 Strata (102x86cm-40x34in) s.overlap s.i.verso acrylic canvas on aluminium prov. 7-Feb-3 Sotheby's, London #117/R est:6000-8000

£8861 $14000 €13292 Embyonic (244x183cm-96x72in) s.i.d.1992 verso prov. 12-Nov-2 Phillips, New York #189/R est:10000-15000

£9494 $15000 €14241 Generation (213x183cm-84x72in) s.i.d.1996 verso prov. 13-Nov-2 Sotheby's, New York #412/R est:15000-20000

£19000 $31730 €27550 Spread (213x183cm-84x72in) s.i.d.1996 verso prov. 26-Jun-3 Sotheby's, London #293/R est:8000-12000

£45000 $72000 €67500 Positive clones (245x213cm-96x84in) painted 1996 prov. 16-May-3 Phillips, New York #227/R est:6000-8000

FRANCIS, Mike (1938-) British

£1600 $2640 €2320 Hide and sneak (48x60cm-19x24in) s.i. acrylic collage. 3-Jul-3 Christie's, Kensington #582/R est:1000-1500

FRANCIS, Sam (1923-1994) American

£1000 $1550 €1500 Untitled (9x5cm-4x2in) estate st. verso acrylic painted 1986. 5-Dec-2 Christie's, Kensington #241/R est:1200-1500

£2800 $4340 €4200 Untitled - Tokyo (28x29cm-11x11in) s.i.d.1960 verso acrylic on paper. 5-Dec-2 Christie's, Kensington #194/R est:3000-4000

£4500 $6930 €6750 Untitled (41x26cm-16x10in) estate st. acrylic executed 1991 prov. 23-Oct-2 Christie's, London #130/R est:5000-6000

£4585 $7199 €6878 Untitled (36x43cm-14x17in) s.d.1976 acrylic prov. 23-Nov-2 Burkhard, Luzern #117/R est:12000-16000 (S.FR 10500)

£4906 $7555 €7800 Composition SF90 (46x38cm-18x15in) acrylic paper on cardboard prov. 26-Oct-2 Cornette de St.Cyr, Paris #88/R

£5000 $7900 €7500 Untitled (150x20cm-59x8in) acrylic paper painted 1986 exhib. 3-Apr-3 Christie's, Kensington #256/R

£5161 $8000 €7742 Untitled (58x74cm-23x29in) s.d.1974 verso acrylic on paper prov. 26-Sep-2 Christie's, Rockefeller NY #719/R est:10000-15000

£5484 $8500 €8226 Untitled (46x31cm-18x12in) estate st. acrylic on paper painted 1989 prov. 26-Sep-2 Christie's, Rockefeller NY #718/R est:8000-10000

£6000 $9480 €9000 Untitled (152x22cm-60x9in) acrylic paper on board painted 1986 exhib. 3-Apr-3 Christie's, Kensington #257/R

£6200 $9610 €9300 Untitled (62x47cm-24x19in) estate st. acrylic painted 1974. 5-Dec-2 Christie's, Kensington #221/R est:5000-7000

£6500 $10010 €9750 Untitled (44x31cm-17x12in) estate st. acrylic on board executed 1973 prov.exhib. 23-Oct-2 Christie's, London #129/R est:6000-8000

£6939 $11033 €10200 Composition (46x38cm-18x15in) acrylic paper on cardboard prov. 3-Mar-3 Marc Kohn, Paris #11/R

£6962 $11000 €11000 Untitled (25x30cm-10x12in) s. acrylic paper painted 1977. 29-Nov-2 Farsetti, Prato #268/R est:12000

£7000 $11480 €10500 Untitled (35x49cm-14x19in) s.d.1980 verso acrylic prov. 7-Feb-3 Sotheby's, London #164/R est:5000-7000

£7642 $11998 €11463 Untitled (30x23cm-12x9in) s. verso acrylic prov. 23-Nov-2 Burkhard, Luzern #118/R est:18000-24000 (S.FR 17500)

£8000 $12640 €12000 Untitled (152x21cm-60x8in) acrylic paper painted 1986 exhib. 3-Apr-3 Christie's, Kensington #258/R est:6000

£8023 $12675 €12675 Fiac (87x61cm-34x24in) acrylic paper painted 1985 prov. 27-Nov-2 Tajan, Paris #54/R est:18000-22000

£9494 $15000 €15000 Upper yellow and orange (76x57cm-30x22in) acrylic prov. 30-Nov-2 Villa Grisebach, Berlin #396/R est:15000-18000

£12761 $19652 €20290 SF73-75 (47x62cm-19x24in) s.i.d.1973 verso acrylic paper. 26-Oct-2 Cornette de St.Cyr, Paris #82/R est:30000

£13000 $21320 €19500 Untitled (91x61cm-36x24in) s.indis.i.d.1986 acrylic paper. 6-Feb-3 Christie's, London #683/R est:10000-15000

£14063 $22500 €21095 Coral made (76x57cm-30x22in) s. i.d.1973 verso acrylic on paper prov. 14-May-3 Sotheby's, New York #150/R est:15000-20000

£15190 $24000 €22785 Untitled - composition (76x56cm-30x22in) s. i.d.1976 acrylic prov. 14-Nov-2 Christie's, Rockefeller NY #156/R est:12000-18000

£15625 $25000 €23438 Untitled (81x60cm-32x24in) s.d.1965 verso acrylic on masonite prov. 14-May-3 Sotheby's, New York #135/R est:30000-40000

£18750 $30000 €28125 Untitled (75x105cm-30x41in) s.d.1978 verso acrylic on paper prov. 14-May-3 Sotheby's, New York #151/R est:30000-40000

£26563 $42500 €39845 Untitled (101x69cm-40x27in) s.d.1973 verso acrylic on paper prov. 14-May-3 Sotheby's, New York #167/R est:20000-30000

£30000 $49200 €45000 Out of coral struck (70x80cm-28x31in) prov.exhib. 7-Feb-3 Sotheby's, London #262/R est:45000-65000

£32000 $52480 €48000 Your only chance (181x94cm-71x37in) acrylic Japanese paper prov.exhib. 6-Feb-3 Christie's, London #682/R est:25000-35000

£37975 $60000 €56963 Untitled (182x92cm-72x36in) acrylic on paper painted 1983 prov. 13-Nov-2 Sotheby's, New York #294/R est:40000-50000

£40625 $65000 €60938 Untitled (91x183cm-36x72in) s.verso acrylic paper prov. 15-May-3 Christie's, Rockefeller NY #190/R est:35000-45000

£47468 $75000 €71202 Untitled (57x81cm-22x32in) s.verso tempera on paper painted c.1960-61 prov.exhib. 13-Nov-2 Sotheby's, New York #223/R est:80000-120000

£58974 $86103 €92000 Untitled (121x161cm-48x63in) acrylic paper on canvas painted c.1970 prov. 5-Jun-2 Il Ponte, Milan #144/R est:80000-100000

£60000 $98400 €90000 Untitled (96x51cm-38x20in) s.d.1964 verso prov.exhib. 7-Feb-3 Sotheby's, London #258/R est:60000-80000

£1500000 $2400000 €2250000 Big orange (300x193cm-118x76in) painted 1954-55 prov.exhib.lit. 14-May-3 Christie's, Rockefeller NY #18/R est:2000000-3000000

Prints

£1923 $3000 €2885 Untitled, SF-18s (79x63cm-31x25in) i. mixed media monoprint col screenprint. 5-Nov-2 Christie's, Rockefeller NY #375/R est:4000-5000

£1963 $3200 €2945 Web (108x138cm-43x54in) s. num.31/50 col screenprint. 13-Feb-3 Christie's, Rockefeller NY #251/R

£1963 $3200 €2945 Spun for James Kirsch (75x56cm-30x22in) s. num.31/100 col screenprint exec.1972. 13-Feb-3 Christie's, Rockefeller NY #250/R

£2044 $3250 €3066 Untitled (78x63cm-31x25in) st.i.verso col screenprint mixed media monoprint exec.c.1973. 2-May-3 Sotheby's, New York #438/R est:3500-4500

£2051 $3200 €3077 Blue green, L L56 (63x91cm-25x36in) s.num.25/40 col lithograph. 5-Nov-2 Christie's, Rockefeller NY #373/R est:4000-6000

£2258 $3500 €3387 An other set-X, from Pasadena Box (132x48cm-52x19in) s.num.34/100 col lithograph. 25-Sep-2 Christie's, Rockefeller NY #269/R est:4000-6000

£2405 $3800 €3800 Bright Jade Ghost (63x90cm-25x35in) s. col lithograph. 30-Nov-2 Villa Grisebach, Berlin #394/R est:3500-4500

£2436 $3800 €3654 Untitled (66x91cm-26x36in) s.num.15/40 col lithograph. 5-Nov-2 Christie's, Rockefeller NY #371/R est:5000-7000

£2516 $4000 €3774 Untitled (91x60cm-36x24in) s.num.8/20 col etching. 2-May-3 Sotheby's, New York #439/R est:3000-4000

£2943 $4591 €4415 Blue-Green (63x90cm-25x35in) s.num.22/40 col lithograph 1963 lit. 6-Nov-2 AB Stockholms Auktionsverk #1005/R est:40000-50000 (S.KR 42000)

£4088 $6500 €6132 First stone (36x90cm-14x35in) s.num.20/65 col lithograph. 2-May-3 Sotheby's, New York #436/R est:10000-15000

£6000 $9900 €8700 Untitled (42x149cm-17x59in) s.i. col monotype. 2-Jul-3 Christie's, London #80/R est:7000-10000

£8333 $13167 €12000 SFS 291 (213x153cm-84x60in) s.i. col serigraph edition of 56 lit. 26-Apr-3 Cornette de St.Cyr, Paris #95/R est:12000-15000

£11538 $18000 €17307 Pasadena box. s.num.8/100 col lithograph 8 scroll screen gouache plexiglas. 14-Oct-2 Butterfields, San Francisco #1249/R est:20000-30000

£12009 $18854 €18014 Poemes dans le ciel. s. num.81/100 col lithograph six. 23-Nov-2 Burkhard, Luzern #123/R est:25000-28000 (S.FR 27500)

£13836 $22000 €20754 White line (90x63cm-35x25in) s.num.17/75 col lithograph. 2-May-3 Sotheby's, New York #437/R est:25000-35000

£16556 $26987 €25000 SFM82-051 (108x198cm-43x78in) monotype pigment ink oil. 3-Feb-3 Cornette de St.Cyr, Paris #423/R est:25000

Works on paper

£2448 $4088 €3500 Composition (34x24cm-13x9in) W/C prov. 26-Jun-3 Tajan, Paris #180/R est:4000-5000

£4200 $6468 €6300 Tokyo (25x33cm-10x13in) s.i.d.1964 gouache prov. 22-Oct-2 Sotheby's, London #462/R est:4000-6000

£4514 $7177 €6500 Monica, California (16x23cm-6x9in) s.d.1973 verso mixed media. 1-May-3 Meeting Art, Vercelli #210

£5696 $9000 €8544 Untitled (14x10cm-6x4in) s.d.1960 verso gouache prov. 13-Nov-2 Sotheby's, New York #292/R est:8000-12000

£5869 $9449 €8804 Sketch (33x55cm-13x22in) s.i.d.1976 gouache. 7-May-3 AB Stockholms Auktionsverk #1134/R est:80000-100000 (S.KR 76000)

£10191 $16000 €15287 Running colour (36x28cm-14x11in) estate st. W/C. 21-Nov-2 Swann Galleries, New York #54/R est:18000-22000

£16000 $26720 €23200 Untitled, blue and yellow (24x20cm-9x8in) s.verso gouache prov. 26-Jun-3 Sotheby's, London #177/R est:10000-15000

£37500 $60000 €56250 Untitled (67x102cm-26x40in) init. W/C gouache paper on board prov. 15-May-3 Christie's, Rockefeller NY #110/R est:70000-90000

£55000 $90200 €82500 White Line No.5 (67x101cm-26x40in) s.i.verso gouache prov. 6-Feb-3 Christie's, London #675/R est:25000-35000

£59375 $95000 €89063 Yellow surroundings (44x36cm-17x14in) W/C gouache exec.1954. 15-May-3 Christie's, Rockefeller NY #105/R est:30000-40000

£82569 $137890 €119725 Moby Dick (49x61cm-19x24in) s.d.58 verso WC prov. 20-Jun-3 Kornfeld, Bern #31/R est:200000 (S.FR 180000)

£91743 $153211 €133027 Yellow green (102x69cm-40x27in) s.i.d.1955 verso gouache W/C prov. 20-Jun-3 Kornfeld, Bern #30/R est:200000 (S.FR 200000)

FRANCIS, Thomas E (fl.1899-1912) British

Works on paper

£260 $416 €390 View of the market place, Bruges (38x28cm-15x11in) s. W/C. 8-Jan-3 Brightwells, Leominster #1076/R

FRANCISCO, Carlos Villaluz (1913-1968) Philippino

Works on paper

£9942 $15311 €14913 Untitled - fiesta with higantes, Angono in Rizal Philippines (46x41cm-18x16in) s.i.d.June 58 W/C. 27-Oct-2 Christie's, Hong Kong #71/R est:95000-125000 (HK.D 120000)

FRANCISCO, J Bond (1863-1931) American
£1708 $2750 €2562 Mountain river landscape (71x81cm-28x32in) s. 18-Feb-3 John Moran, Pasadena #46 est:3000-5000

FRANCK, Albert Jacques (1899-1973) Canadian
£222 $364 €333 Rural street scene (44x34cm-17x13in) s.d.46 oil monotype. 3-Jun-3 Joyner, Toronto #412/R (C.D 500)
£378 $619 €567 Ships at dock (12x15cm-5x6in) s. board. 3-Jun-3 Joyner, Toronto #522 (C.D 850)
£711 $1166 €1067 Elm and Simcoe St. (25x16cm-10x6in) s. indis d. canvasboard prov. 3-Jun-3 Joyner, Toronto #279/R est:1000-1500 (C.D 1600)
£772 $1213 €1158 Nature morte (61x76cm-24x30in) s.d.44 board exhib. 10-Dec-2 Pinneys, Montreal #192 (C.D 1900)
£3086 $4784 €4629 Bellair street (40x50cm-16x20in) s.d.56 canvas on board prov. 3-Dec-2 Joyner, Toronto #169/R est:5000-7000 (C.D 7500)
£3333 $5467 €5000 Behind Glasgow Street (50x40cm-20x16in) s.d.66 board prov. 3-Jun-3 Joyner, Toronto #99/R est:10000-15000 (C.D 7500)
£5333 $8747 €8000 Lane on Rose Ave (72x65cm-28x26in) s.d.62 board. 3-Jun-3 Joyner, Toronto #81/R est:15000-20000 (C.D 12000)
£5778 $9476 €8667 Behind Euclid Avenue (76x61cm-30x24in) s.d.68 masonite. 27-May-3 Sotheby's, Toronto #114/R est:5000-7000 (C.D 13000)
£6667 $10933 €10001 House on Isabella Street (75x60cm-30x24in) s.d.62 board prov.exhib.lit. 3-Jun-3 Joyner, Toronto #66/R est:15000-20000 (C.D 15000)
£10700 $16584 €16050 Back of Berkeley St (30x25cm-12x10in) s.d.65 board prov.exhib.lit. 3-Dec-2 Joyner, Toronto #101/R est:6000-8000 (C.D 26000)

Works on paper
£244 $401 €366 St. Nicolas St. (12x13cm-5x5in) s.i. ink. 3-Jun-3 Joyner, Toronto #584 (C.D 550)
£489 $802 €734 Behind Scollard St. (12x19cm-5x7in) s.d.66 W/C. 3-Jun-3 Joyner, Toronto #494 est:800-1200 (C.D 1100)
£667 $1093 €1001 Behind Huron street (18x13cm-7x5in) s.d.66 W/C. 3-Jun-3 Joyner, Toronto #287/R est:1800-2200 (C.D 1500)
£667 $1093 €1001 Back of Sumach St. (19x14cm-7x6in) s.d.70 W/C. 3-Jun-3 Joyner, Toronto #295/R est:1800-2200 (C.D 1500)
£1000 $1560 €1668 Behind Sackville Street (16x14cm-6x6in) s. W/C prov. 13-Apr-3 Levis, Calgary #34/R est:2500-3000 (C.D 2300)
£1152 $1786 €1728 Backyard at Carlton Street (15x12cm-6x5in) s.d.65 W/C ink prov.lit. 3-Dec-2 Joyner, Toronto #251/R est:1800-2200 (C.D 2800)

FRANCKE-NAUTSCHUTZ, Rudolf (1860-?) German
Sculpture
£1064 $1649 €1596 Snake charmer (32cm-13in) bronze marble. 8-Dec-2 Uppsala Auktionskammare, Uppsala #342/R est:15000-20000 (S.KR 15000)

FRANCKEN, Ambrosius (16/17th C) Flemish
£1887 $2905 €3000 La descente de crois (22x17cm-9x7in) copper htd gold. 25-Oct-2 Tajan, Paris #47/R est:3000-4000

FRANCKEN, Ambrosius I (attrib) (1544-1618) Flemish
£3830 $5936 €5745 Judas' kiss (41x30cm-16x12in) copper. 3-Dec-2 Bukowskis, Stockholm #433/R est:30000-35000 (S.KR 54000)

FRANCKEN, Ambrosius II (?-1632) Flemish
£22603 $35260 €33000 Scenes (65x86cm-26x34in) board. 8-Apr-3 Ansorena, Madrid #109a/R est:33000

FRANCKEN, Frans I (1542-1616) Flemish
£5660 $8774 €9000 Ecce Homo (35x28cm-14x11in) copper. 7-Oct-2 Ansorena, Madrid #4/R est:9000
£15094 $23396 €24000 The visitation. The annunciation (69x55cm-27x22in) s. copper two. 2-Oct-2 Dorotheum, Vienna #114/R est:22000-26000

FRANCKEN, Frans II (1581-1642) Flemish
£3896 $6000 €5844 Crucifixion (53x73cm-21x29in) panel. 4-Sep-2 Christie's, Rockefeller NY #237/R est:3000-5000
£4000 $6680 €5800 Mocking of Christ, in grisaille surround depicting God the Father, Evangelist, Crucifixion (36x28cm-14x11in) copper. 11-Jul-3 Christie's, Kensington #7/R est:4000-6000
£5500 $8525 €8250 Christ in the house of Mary and Martha (36x48cm-14x19in) panel. 30-Oct-2 Christie's, Kensington #5/R est:6000-8000
£6173 $10000 €9260 Feast of Perseus and Andromeda (46x57cm-18x22in) panel painted with studio prov. 24-Jan-3 Christie's, Rockefeller NY #12/R est:10000-15000
£6849 $10685 €10000 Apollo with muses (31x63cm-12x25in) panel. 10-Apr-3 Van Ham, Cologne #1201/R est:11000
£8584 $13305 €12876 Maria with Child and Infant St John (30x24cm-12x9in) copper prov. 3-Oct-2 Koller, Zurich #3015/R est:20000-30000 (S.FR 20000)
£10063 $15597 €16000 Adoration of the Mgi (35x28cm-14x11in) copper. 7-Oct-2 Ansorena, Madrid #9/R
£10063 $15597 €16000 Jesus in front of Pilatus (111x178cm-44x70in) s. 7-Oct-2 Ansorena, Madrid #15/R est:15000
£11538 $18231 €18000 Worship of the golden calf (71x95cm-28x37in) mono. panel. 18-Nov-2 Bernaerts, Antwerp #175/R est:18000-20000
£12025 $19000 €19000 Bacchanal (49x64cm-19x25in) copper on board. 2-Dec-2 Finarte, Milan #144/R est:15000
£12676 $20408 €18000 Apelles painting Pankaspe (35x28cm-14x11in) copper. 10-May-3 Hans Stahl, Toestorf #91/R est:18000
£13000 $20280 €19500 Death and the mister (23x32cm-9x13in) panel prov.lit. 9-Apr-3 Christie's, London #22/R est:7000-10000
£13836 $21447 €22000 Moses at the Red Sea (51x41cm-20x16in) copper. 7-Oct-2 Ansorena, Madrid #11/R est:20000
£15068 $23507 €22000 Moses at the Red Sea (51x41cm-20x16in) copper. 8-Apr-3 Ansorena, Madrid #111/R est:22000
£19481 $28442 €30000 Jesus and the adulterer (71x88cm-28x35in) copper. 17-Jun-2 Ansorena, Madrid #182/R est:30000
£20690 $32897 €30000 Salomon's judgement (40x57cm-16x22in) s. board. 4-Mar-3 Ansorena, Madrid #51/R est:30000
£26415 $40943 €42000 Charity (115x112cm-45x44in) 7-Oct-2 Ansorena, Madrid #13/R est:42000
£30323 $47910 €47000 Adoration des Mages (52x78cm-20x31in) bears sig. panel. 18-Dec-2 Piasa, Paris #33/R est:30000
£40000 $62800 €60000 Belshazzar's feast (150x227cm-59x89in) s.d.1614. 12-Dec-2 Sotheby's, London #4/R est:40000-60000
£43312 $67567 €68000 Parable of the Royal wedding feast (49x46cm-19x18in) s. i.verso panel. 5-Nov-2 Sotheby's, Amsterdam #263/R est:25000-35000

FRANCKEN, Frans II (attrib) (1581-1642) Flemish
£2179 $3444 €3400 Calvary (21x27cm-8x11in) copper. 17-Nov-2 Herbette, Doullens #32/R
£4430 $6867 €7000 Mocking of Christ (37x30cm-15x12in) i. verso copper. 25-Sep-2 Neumeister, Munich #479/R est:6000
£5405 $8432 €8000 Triumph of David (25x38cm-10x15in) copper prov. 27-Mar-3 Dorotheum, Vienna #385/R est:8000-12000

FRANCKEN, Frans II (studio) (1581-1642) Flemish
£7000 $11690 €10150 The Triumph of Neptune and Aphitrite (48x62cm-19x24in) i.verso panel prov. 8-Jul-3 Sotheby's, Olympia #357/R est:4000-6000
£9000 $14130 €13500 Prodigal Son feasting bordered by scenes from the parable (64x86cm-25x34in) panel en brunaille en grisaille prov.exhib. 12-Dec-2 Sotheby's, London #137/R est:10000-15000
£10000 $15700 €15000 Croesus and Solon (92x122cm-36x48in) panel. 13-Dec-2 Christie's, Kensington #5/R est:10000-12000

FRANCKEN, Frans II and UDEN, Lucas van (17th C) Flemish
£42759 $67986 €62000 Apollo, muses and Pegasus (118x75cm-46x30in) s. board. 4-Mar-3 Ansorena, Madrid #53/R est:57000
£44872 $70897 €70000 Gods and muses (118x75cm-46x30in) s. board. 13-Nov-2 Ansorena, Madrid #132/R est:70000

FRANCKEN, Frans III (1607-1667) Flemish
£5000 $8350 €7250 Sense of Sight (19x16cm-7x6in) panel. 9-Jul-3 Bonhams, New Bond Street #116/R est:5000-7000

FRANCKEN, Hieronymus (studio) (16/17th C) Flemish
£8099 $13444 €11500 Peintre dans un cabinet d'amateur ou allegorie de la peinture (57x110cm-22x43in) 16-Jun-3 Claude Aguttes, Neuilly #8/R est:12000-15000

FRANCKEN, Hieronymus I (attrib) (1540-1610) Flemish
£1419 $2243 €2200 Lazare et le mauvais riche (74x104cm-29x41in) panel. 19-Dec-2 Bondu, Paris #1/R

FRANCKEN, Hieronymus II (1578-1623) Flemish
£7237 $11724 €11000 Jesus in front of Pilatus (56x72cm-22x28in) mono. copper. 21-Jan-3 Ansorena, Madrid #94/R est:11000
£8176 $12673 €13000 Jesus i front of Pilatus (56x72cm-22x28in) copper. 7-Oct-2 Ansorena, Madrid #8/R est:13000

FRANCKEN, Hieronymus III (1611-?) Flemish
£17500 $29225 €25375 Israelites after the crossing of the Red Sea (56x83cm-22x33in) mono. panel prov. 9-Jul-3 Christie's, London #7/R est:15000-20000

FRANCKEN, Isabella (attrib) (?) ?
£3145 $4874 €5000 Witch scene (23x31cm-9x12in) copper lit. 2-Oct-2 Dorotheum, Vienna #360/R est:5000-7000

FRANCO Y CORDERO, Jose (19th C) Spanish
£1258 $1962 €2000 Landscape (40x75cm-16x30in) s. 23-Sep-2 Durán, Madrid #215/R
£3846 $6077 €6000 Landscape (36x52cm-14x20in) s. 14-Nov-2 Arte, Seville #350/R

FRANCO Y SALINAS, Luis (1850-1899) Spanish
£1800 $2772 €2700 Spanish beauty (46x30cm-18x12in) s. 24-Oct-2 Christie's, Kensington #186/R est:700-1000
£5449 $8609 €8500 Looking at the sea (60x44cm-24x17in) s. 19-Nov-2 Durán, Madrid #243/R

FRANCO, Giacomo (1550-1620) Italian
Works on paper
£943 $1472 €1500 Venice (39x53cm-15x21in) s.d.1597 W/C over engraving. 20-Sep-2 Semenzato, Venice #699

FRANCO, Giovanni Battista (c.1498-1580) Italian
Works on paper
£6173 $10000 €9260 Studies (24x35cm-9x14in) chk pen ink prov. 22-Jan-3 Christie's, Rockefeller NY #11/R est:30000
£17284 $28000 €25926 Ideal female head (36x25cm-14x10in) i. pen chk ink prov. 22-Jan-3 Christie's, Rockefeller NY #10/R

FRANCO, Giovanni Battista (attrib) (c.1498-1580) Italian
Works on paper
£1923 $3019 €3000 Meeting (25x20cm-10x8in) pen ink wash. 14-Dec-2 Artcurial Briest, Paris #1/R

FRANCO-DUTCH SCHOOL, 17th C
£10976 $18000 €16464 Portrait of a gentleman in black costume, holding a letter (128x92cm-50x36in) i. 29-May-3 Sotheby's, New York #36/R est:20000-30000

FRANCO-FLEMISH SCHOOL, 17th C
£7200 $11304 €10800 Five senses (72x90cm-28x35in) bears sig.d.1645 prov. 10-Dec-2 Sotheby's, Olympia #335/R est:4000-6000

FRANCO-FLEMISH SCHOOL, 18th C
£32000 $53440 €46400 Mars and Venus in the garden of love (163x227cm-64x89in) prov. 10-Jul-3 Sotheby's, London #1/R est:12000-18000

FRANCOIS, Ange (1800-?) Flemish
£3401 $5408 €5000 Femme a la grappe de raisins (41x32cm-16x13in) s. panel. 18-Mar-3 Campo, Vlaamse Kaai #85 est:5000-7000

FRANCOIS, Joseph Charles (1851-1940) Belgian
£288 $447 €450 Chemin forestier (40x65cm-16x26in) s. 9-Dec-2 Horta, Bruxelles #280
£316 $500 €500 Le depart des pecheurs (49x75cm-19x30in) 26-Nov-2 Palais de Beaux Arts, Brussels #96
£327 $526 €500 L'entree du manoir anime (41x60cm-16x24in) s. 14-Jan-3 Vanderkindere, Brussels #161
£360 $576 €500 Brume hivernale sur le village (65x80cm-26x31in) studio st.verso. 13-May-3 Palais de Beaux Arts, Brussels #253
£448 $717 €650 Hens in the yard (40x52cm-16x20in) s. 15-Mar-3 De Vuyst, Lokeren #121
£475 $750 €750 Eclaircies en campines (50x75cm-20x30in) s. 26-Nov-2 Palais de Beaux Arts, Brussels #98
£506 $790 €800 Vue de village anime en Ardennes (65x80cm-26x31in) s. 15-Oct-2 Vanderkindere, Brussels #100
£690 $1103 €1000 Paysage de Fagnes avant l'orage (55x75cm-22x30in) s. 17-Mar-3 Horta, Bruxelles #228
£759 $1200 €1200 Mer du Nord au coucher du soleil (45x65cm-18x26in) s. 26-Nov-2 Palais de Beaux Arts, Brussels #97
£863 $1381 €1200 Ramasseuses de bois mort dans la foret (72x58cm-28x23in) s. 13-May-3 Palais de Beaux Arts, Brussels #252
£1083 $1689 €1700 La maison dans les bruyeres (100x124cm-39x49in) s. 11-Nov-2 Horta, Bruxelles #62 est:1750-2200
£1389 $2208 €2000 Paysage d'hiver (83x130cm-33x51in) s. panel. 29-Apr-3 Campo, Vlaamse Kaai #121/R est:2000-2500
£2158 $3453 €3000 Paysage Ardennais sous une brume d'automne (168x233cm-66x92in) s. 13-May-3 Palais de Beaux Arts, Brussels #73/R est:3000-4000
£6475 $10360 €9000 On the beach (42x75cm-17x30in) s. 17-May-3 De Vuyst, Lokeren #450/R est:8500-9500

FRANCOIS, Pierre Joseph C (1759-1851) Flemish
£288 $453 €450 Foret de Soignes en automne (65x80cm-26x31in) s. 10-Dec-2 Campo, Vlaamse Kaai #202
£321 $503 €500 Les fagotteuses (64x88cm-25x35in) s. 10-Dec-2 Campo, Vlaamse Kaai #201

FRANCOLINI, C (?) Italian
£1500 $2310 €2250 Fortune teller (51x41cm-20x16in) s. 24-Oct-2 Christie's, Kensington #98 est:1500-2000

FRANCOLINI, G (19th C) Italian
£4000 $6280 €6000 Refreshing cup (48x31cm-19x12in) s. 21-Nov-2 Christie's, Kensington #148/R est:4000-6000

FRANCUCCI, Innocenzo (style) (1494-1550) Italian
£6173 $10000 €9260 Saint Paul. Saint Peter (45x14cm-18x6in) d.1554 panel pair prov. 23-Jan-3 Sotheby's, New York #191/R est:15000

FRANDSEN, Erik A (1957-) Danish
£280 $445 €420 Composition (64x48cm-25x19in) init.d.14-11-84 paper. 29-Apr-3 Kunsthallen, Copenhagen #68 (D.KR 3000)
£1778 $2756 €2667 Bouquet in brass vase (151x121cm-59x48in) s.d.2001 verso steel panel exhib. 1-Oct-2 Rasmussen, Copenhagen #197/R est:25000 (D.KR 21000)
Works on paper
£426 $672 €639 Collage composition (138x100cm-54x39in) s.d.86 mixed media. 30-Nov-2 Rasmussen, Havnen #2170 (D.KR 5000)

FRANDZEN, Eugene M (1893-1972) American
£389 $650 €564 Seascape crashing waves and rocks (46x61cm-18x24in) s. prov. 17-Jun-3 John Moran, Pasadena #206
£599 $1000 €869 Barn and sheep in landscape (56x76cm-22x30in) s. i.verso prov. 17-Jun-3 John Moran, Pasadena #205 est:2500-3500
£1774 $2750 €2661 Stream in winter landscape (46x61cm-18x24in) s. prov. 29-Oct-2 John Moran, Pasadena #773 est:2500-3500

FRANG, Felix (1862-1932) Finnish
£975 $1501 €1550 Frosty day (36x61cm-14x24in) s.d.1918. 27-Oct-2 Bukowskis, Helsinki #168/R est:1300

FRANG, Thomas (1889-1968) Norwegian
£397 $663 €576 Archipelago (50x61cm-20x24in) s. 18-Jun-3 Grev Wedels Plass, Oslo #172/R (N.KR 4600)

FRANGI, Giovanni (1959-) Italian
£2353 $3765 €3600 Always pink (40x50cm-16x20in) painted 2001. 4-Jan-3 Meeting Art, Vercelli #346
£2532 $4000 €4000 Untitled (55x46cm-22x18in) s.d.2001 verso. 29-Nov-2 Farsetti, Prato #32 est:2600
£13380 $22211 €19000 Bosco (182x125cm-72x49in) s.verso prov. 10-Jun-3 Finarte Semenzato, Milan #299/R est:8000-10000
Works on paper
£1418 $2298 €2000 Happy together (42x35cm-17x14in) s. pastel oil W/C. 20-May-3 Porro, Milan #20/R est:1500-1800
£1429 $2271 €2100 Alessandra (70x50cm-28x20in) s. mixed media card. 1-Mar-3 Meeting Art, Vercelli #762

FRANK (?) ?
Works on paper
£448 $717 €650 Palais abbatial (42x58cm-17x23in) s.d.66 ink wash. 11-Mar-3 Christie's, Paris #255/R

FRANK WILL (1900-1951) French
£955 $1490 €1500 Pont-Neuf (46x60cm-18x24in) s. 7-Nov-2 Chochon-Barre & Allardi, Paris #150
Works on paper
£263 $427 €400 Marche sur la Place de l'Eglise (34x24cm-13x9in) s. W/C. 22-Jan-3 Tajan, Paris #17
£345 $552 €500 Steamer au Treport (19x27cm-7x11in) s.i. W/C. 14-Mar-3 Libert, Castor, Paris #24
£486 $768 €700 Conciergerie (30x40cm-12x16in) s. W/C. 25-Apr-3 Piasa, Paris #104
£506 $800 €800 Treport (26x19cm-10x7in) s. Chinese ink wash. 1-Dec-2 Anaf, Lyon #88
£595 $993 €850 Paris, Place de la Concorde (23x31cm-9x12in) s.i. W/C gouache. 26-Jun-3 Tajan, Paris #72
£629 $975 €1000 Le beffroi de bethune (30x22cm-12x9in) s.i. pencil htd W/C gouache prov. 4-Oct-2 Tajan, Paris #91
£629 $1051 €900 Paris, la Seine au Pont Alexandre III (23x31cm-9x12in) s.i. W/C gouache. 26-Jun-3 Tajan, Paris #73
£793 $1261 €1150 La Cathedrale de Chartres (62x47cm-24x19in) s.i. W/C black pencil. 5-Mar-3 Doutrebente, Paris #39
£811 $1265 €1200 Moulin de la Galette (30x44cm-12x17in) s. W/C. 28-Mar-3 Delvaux, Paris #33
£833 $1308 €1300 Vapeur a Paris (31x22cm-12x9in) s.i. W/C. 15-Dec-2 Lombrail & Teucquam, Paris #6/R
£837 $1356 €1270 Le treport (40x55cm-16x22in) s.i. W/C. 22-Jan-3 Tajan, Paris #16 est:1800-2400
£839 $1325 €1300 Le marche devant l'eglise a Paris (43x28cm-17x11in) s.i. W/C. 17-Dec-2 Rossini, Paris #25

£897	$1426	€1300	Port en Bessin, retour de peche (4x62cm-2x24in) s.i. W/C gouache. 5-Mar-3 Doutrebente, Paris #38/R
£988	$1402	€1600	Peniches a quai (40x62cm-16x24in) s.i.d.1923 W/C dr. 17-Mar-2 Galerie de Chartres, Chartres #143
£1111	$1789	€1667	Sailing boats off Honfleur (48x64cm-19x25in) s.i.d.1927 W/C over pencil. 7-May-3 Dobiaschofsky, Bern #524/R est:2000 (S.FR 2400)
£1195	$1852	€1900	Vue de Rouen (35x27cm-14x11in) s. W/C. 6-Oct-2 Feletin, Province #115b/R
£1204	$1938	€1806	Honfleur harbour (49x64cm-19x25in) s.i. W/C over pencil. 7-May-3 Dobiaschofsky, Bern #525/R est:2000 (S.FR 2600)
£1329	$2073	€2100	Paris, Ile St Louis (35x27cm-14x11in) s. W/C. 15-Sep-2 Feletin, Province #73
£1351	$2108	€2000	Moulin de la Galette a Montmartre (23x31cm-9x12in) s.i. W/C. 30-Mar-3 Anaf, Lyon #101/R
£1379	$2193	€2000	Honfleur (44x62cm-17x24in) s.i.d. W/C black pencil. 5-Mar-3 Doutrebente, Paris #37/R est:1200-1500
£1592	$2484	€2500	Paris, Notre-Dame (36x54cm-14x21in) s. W/C. 10-Nov-2 Eric Pillon, Calais #2/R
£1633	$2596	€2400	Le pont d'Avignon et le Palais des Papes (29x37cm-11x15in) s.i. W/C gouache. 26-Feb-3 Artcurial Briest, Paris #52/R est:2000-2500
£1731	$2717	€2700	Pont Neuf, Paris (45x60cm-18x24in) s.i. W/C. 22-Nov-2 Millon & Associes, Paris #23/R
£1905	$3029	€2800	Paris, la Conciergerie (38x55cm-15x22in) s.i. W/C. 24-Mar-3 Coutau Begarie, Paris #185/R
£1975	$2805	€3200	Paris, bouquinistes et Notre-Dame (44x55cm-17x22in) s. W/C. 16-Mar-3 Eric Pillon, Calais #137/R
£1986	$3217	€2800	Paris les quais (63x39cm-25x15in) s. W/C. 23-May-3 Camard, Paris #141/R est:1500-2500
£2179	$3422	€3400	Port de Dunkerque (48x60cm-19x24in) s.i. W/C gouache. 15-Dec-2 Eric Pillon, Calais #97/R
£2324	$3742	€3300	Peniches devant Notre Dame (49x65cm-19x26in) s. W/C. 11-May-3 Lombrail & Teucquam, Paris #194/R
£2568	$4005	€3800	Place d l'Opera (51x60cm-20x24in) s.i. chl W/C. 25-Mar-3 Chochon-Barre & Allardi, Paris #116/R est:4000-4500
£2662	$4259	€3700	Paris, le Pont-Neuf et la cite (44x59cm-17x23in) s. W/C. 18-May-3 Eric Pillon, Calais #101/R
£2710	$4281	€4200	Port de Marseille (63x80cm-25x31in) s.i. W/C. 18-Dec-2 Digard, Paris #130/R
£2885	$4529	€4500	Montmartre sous la neige (30x39cm-12x15in) s.i. W/C. 16-Dec-2 Eric Coutrier, Paris #59/R
£3041	$4743	€4500	Combat naval (31x46cm-12x18in) s. W/C. 28-Mar-3 Claude Aguttes, Neuilly #27/R
£4231	$6642	€6600	Paris, Place de l'Opera (48x60cm-19x24in) s.i. W/C. 16-Dec-2 Eric Coutrier, Paris #60/R
£4730	$7378	€7000	Port de Fecamps (93x52cm-37x20in) s.i. W/C over crayon. 28-Mar-3 Claude Aguttes, Neuilly #26/R

FRANK, Dale (1958-) Australian

£3036	$4766	€4554	Tyson stable 3 (140x120cm-55x47in) s.d.2000 verso acrylic varnish linen prov. 25-Nov-2 Christie's, Melbourne #48/R est:9000-12000 (A.D 8500)

Works on paper

£245	$382	€425	Untitled (53x37cm-21x15in) inid.d.84 collage pencil prov. 31-Mar-3 Goodman, Sydney #78/R (A.D 650)
£1423	$2178	€2135	What is this marvellous thing called art and the blue butterfly (200x180cm-79x71in) i.verso synthetic polymer mixed media on canvas prov. 25-Aug-2 Sotheby's, Paddington #111/R est:4000-6000 (A.D 4000)
£1429	$2243	€2144	I (181x242cm-71x95in) init.i.d.85 W/C pencil. 25-Nov-2 Christie's, Melbourne #220/R est:4000-6000 (A.D 4000)
£1938	$3081	€2907	Untitled (230x180cm-91x71in) s.d.89 synthetic polymer. 5-May-3 Sotheby's, Melbourne #249/R est:4000-6000 (A.D 5000)
£3559	$5445	€5339	Thomas Howell (200x200cm-79x79in) s.d.2000 synthetic polymer on canvas prov. 25-Aug-2 Sotheby's, Paddington #23/R est:12000-18000 (A.D 10000)
£3571	$5500	€5357	Two paintings out for a midnight swim (201x179cm-79x70in) synthetic polymer on linen executed c.1985. 8-Sep-2 Sotheby's, Melbourne #88/R est:3000-5000 (A.D 10000)

FRANK, Eugene C (1844-1914) American

£16026	$25000	€24039	Buffalo at sunset (61x91cm-24x36in) 9-Nov-2 Altermann Galleries, Santa Fe #94

FRANK, Franz (1897-1986) German

£3793	$5993	€5500	Still life of flowers and fruit before winter landscape (90x60cm-35x24in) mono.d.1956. 2-Apr-3 Dr Fritz Nagel, Stuttgart #9333/R est:6000

FRANK, Friedrich (1871-1945) Austrian

Works on paper

£629	$975	€1000	Busy Cairo street (29x49cm-11x19in) s.d.1931 W/C. 1-Oct-2 Dorotheum, Vienna #272/R
£1069	$1657	€1700	Soldiers on Gleinalm (24x32cm-9x13in) i.d.1917 gouache. 1-Oct-2 Dorotheum, Vienna #351/R est:1400-1600
£1389	$2208	€2000	Vienna I. Habsburgergasse (32x25cm-13x10in) s. W/C. 29-Apr-3 Wiener Kunst Auktionen, Vienna #561/R est:2000-4000
£1439	$2302	€2000	Michaelerkirche (31x23cm-12x9in) s. W/C. 14-May-3 Dorotheum, Linz #452/R est:1000-1500

FRANK, Frigyes (1890-1976) Hungarian

£1084	$1690	€1572	Peonies in dotted vase (75x60cm-30x24in) s. 13-Sep-2 Mu Terem Galeria, Budapest #81/R est:380000 (H.F 420000)
£1677	$2616	€2516	Lady in evening dress (35x54cm-14x21in) s. 11-Sep-2 Kieselbach, Budapest #39/R (H.F 650000)
£2487	$3979	€3731	Taban in Gellerthegyi (38x55cm-15x22in) s. 16-May-3 Kieselbach, Budapest #7/R (H.F 850000)
£8255	$12878	€11970	Mimi in a yellow armchair (131x90cm-52x35in) s.d.1938 panel exhib. 13-Sep-2 Mu Terem Galeria, Budapest #64/R est:1200000 (H.F 3200000)
£10500	$17220	€15750	Zuska (92x58cm-36x23in) s. prov. 3-Jun-3 Sotheby's, London #95/R est:8000-12000
£42000	$68880	€63000	Mini embroidering (92x65cm-36x26in) s.d.1929. 3-Jun-3 Sotheby's, London #107/R est:25000-35000

Works on paper

£2340	$3745	€3510	Self portrait (47x42cm-19x17in) s.d.963 mixed media. 16-May-3 Kieselbach, Budapest #46a/R (H.F 800000)

FRANK, Gwen (1960-) Canadian

Works on paper

£424	$674	€636	Thone cannie (45x46cm-18x18in) s. col chk. 23-Mar-3 Hodgins, Calgary #3/R est:400-600 (C.D 1000)

FRANK, Hans (1884-1948) Austrian

£397	$648	€600	Evening landscape (35x50cm-14x20in) s.i.d.27 board. 28-Jan-3 Dorotheum, Vienna #37/R

FRANK, Leo (attrib) (1884-1959) Austrian

£258	$400	€387	Floral still life (61x43cm-24x17in) s.d.1904. 25-Sep-2 Doyle, New York #31/R

FRANK, Louis (19th C) Australian

£4270	$6534	€6405	Coogee (36x62cm-14x24in) s. board painted 1880 prov. 26-Aug-2 Sotheby's, Paddington #567/R est:10000-12000 (A.D 12000)

FRANK, Lucien (1857-1920) Belgian

£654	$1052	€1000	Sous-bois (16x23cm-6x9in) s. panel. 14-Jan-3 Vanderkindere, Brussels #59
£662	$1079	€1000	Chaumiere animee (30x43cm-12x17in) s. 17-Feb-3 Horta, Bruxelles #50
£719	$1151	€1000	Paysage anime (31x40cm-12x16in) s. 13-May-3 Vanderkindere, Brussels #86
£728	$1187	€1100	Avan l'orage. Apres l'orage (22x29cm-9x11in) s. canvas on panel pair. 17-Feb-3 Horta, Bruxelles #51
£833	$1292	€1300	Travaux de sarclage (30x43cm-12x17in) s. 9-Dec-2 Horta, Bruxelles #71/R
£1096	$1710	€1600	Promeneur en sous-bois (61x85cm-24x33in) s. 14-Apr-3 Horta, Bruxelles #77 est:1200-1800
£1242	$1999	€1900	Coucher de soleil sur l'etang (27x36cm-11x14in) s. panel. 20-Jan-3 Horta, Bruxelles #176 est:1500-2000
£1438	$2315	€2200	Elegante et sa fille au bord du canal (32x49cm-13x19in) s. panel. 20-Jan-3 Horta, Bruxelles #175/R est:2500-3500
£2025	$3159	€3200	Promeneurs au crepuscule en Hollande (30x38cm-12x15in) s. panel. 16-Sep-2 Horta, Bruxelles #130
£2466	$3847	€3600	Coucher de soleil sur le moulin (47x38cm-19x15in) s. panel. 14-Apr-3 Horta, Bruxelles #76 est:3000-5000
£2658	$4147	€4200	Charrette en automne au bord de l'etang (75x103cm-30x41in) s. 16-Sep-2 Horta, Bruxelles #129/R est:5000-7500
£3459	$5362	€5500	Landscape with pond (60x84cm-24x33in) s. 5-Oct-2 De Vuyst, Lokeren #542/R est:5000-6000
£3459	$5327	€5500	Bar de Voyage, Paris (47x64cm-19x25in) s. exhib. 22-Oct-2 Campo & Campo, Antwerp #108/R
£6207	$9931	€9000	Pecheur dans un paysage fluvial devant un village (60x84cm-24x33in) 17-Mar-3 Amberes, Antwerp #231/R
£7586	$12138	€11000	Lisiere a Vossem (75x105cm-30x41in) s. 15-Mar-3 De Vuyst, Lokeren #426/R est:12000-16000

Works on paper

£2621	$4193	€3800	Evening (55x77cm-22x30in) s. pastel. 15-Mar-3 De Vuyst, Lokeren #122/R est:4000-5000
£2949	$4571	€4600	Barque au crepuscule, dans la Venise du Nord (88x68cm-35x27in) s. mixed media cardboard. 9-Dec-2 Horta, Bruxelles #68/R est:5500-7500

FRANK, Lucien (attrib) (1857-1920) Belgian

£1384	$2158	€2200	Sun dappled woodland path (63x73cm-25x29in) bears sig. 19-Sep-2 Dr Fritz Nagel, Stuttgart #929/R est:2700

FRANK, Mary (1933-) American
Works on paper
£513 $800 €770 Untitled (61x46cm-24x18in) s.d.1969 ink wash. 30-Mar-3 Susanin's, Chicago #6121/R

FRANK, Robert (1924-) American/Swiss
Photographs
£2575 $4069 €3863 Mary and Pablo, Paris (27x35cm-11x14in) s.i.d.1950 gelatin silver print. 26-Nov-2 Phillips, Zurich #48/R est:6000-8000 (S.FR 6000)
£2761 $4500 €4142 New York (25x17cm-10x7in) init. gelatin silver print. 12-Feb-3 Christie's, Rockefeller NY #239/R est:5000-7000
£2922 $4500 €4383 Parade in Hoboken, N.J. s.d.c.1960 photograph. 24-Oct-2 Sotheby's, New York #192/R est:6000-8000
£2922 $4500 €4383 Rooming house (31x21cm-12x8in) s.d.1955 photograph. 24-Oct-2 Sotheby's, New York #193/R est:7000-10000
£2922 $4500 €4383 Chicago (21x34cm-8x13in) s.i.d.1956 photograph. 24-Oct-2 Sotheby's, New York #195/R est:6000-8000
£3171 $5200 €4757 San Francisco convention (33x43cm-13x17in) s.i.d. silver print. 10-Feb-3 Swann Galleries, New York #95/R est:6000-9000
£3291 $5200 €4937 Salt Lake City, Utah (25x16cm-10x6in) s.d.1955-1973 verso gelatin silver print prov.lit. 25-Apr-3 Phillips, New York #130/R est:5000-7000
£4292 $6781 €6438 Boulevard Quinet, Paris (33x22cm-13x9in) s.i.d.1947 gelatin silver print. 26-Nov-2 Phillips, Zurich #49/R est:7000-9000 (S.FR 10000)
£4430 $7000 €6645 Rodeo, Detroit (20x30cm-8x12in) s.i.d.1955 photograph prov. 23-Apr-3 Sotheby's, New York #220/R est:7000-10000
£5063 $8000 €7595 Rodeo cowboy, Madison Square Garden (31x20cm-12x8in) s.i.d.1955/1970 gelatin silver print prov.lit. 22-Apr-3 Christie's, Rockefeller NY #70/R est:9000-12000
£5063 $8000 €7595 Coney Island, 4th of July - lovers on sand (28x19cm-11x7in) s.i.d.1958 photograph. 23-Apr-3 Sotheby's, New York #218/R est:10000-15000
£6000 $9720 €9000 Coney Island (27x18cm-11x7in) s.i. i.verso gelatin silver print. 21-May-3 Christie's, London #197/R est:2000-3000
£6329 $10000 €9494 23rd St., NYC (32x21cm-13x8in) s.i.d.1955 photograph prov. 23-Apr-3 Sotheby's, New York #215/R est:7000-10000
£6369 $10000 €9554 London (36x28cm-14x11in) s.i.d. gelatin silver print. 21-Apr-3 Phillips, New York #12/R est:10000-15000
£8228 $13000 €12342 Metropolitan life Insurance Building, New York City (34x23cm-13x9in) s.d.1954-1973 verso gelatin silver print prov.exhib.lit. 25-Apr-3 Phillips, New York #131/R est:5000-7000
£9442 $14918 €14163 Pair on garden bench, Paris (19x31cm-7x12in) s.d.1952 verso gelatin silver print. 26-Nov-2 Phillips, Zurich #50/R est:10000-12000 (S.FR 22000)
£9494 $15000 €14241 Rooming house, Bunker Hill, Los Angeles (32x20cm-13x8in) gelatin silver print prov. 25-Apr-3 Phillips, New York #133/R est:5000-7000
£12658 $20000 €18987 Platte River, Tennessee (43x32cm-17x13in) s.i.d.1962 verso gelatin silver print prov. 22-Apr-3 Christie's, Rockefeller NY #127/R est:25000-35000
£12658 $20000 €18987 Coffee shop, railway station, Indianapolis (18x27cm-7x11in) s.i.d.1955 verso photograph prov.lit. 25-Apr-3 Phillips, New York #134/R est:5000-7000
£12987 $20000 €19481 Long Island (21x31cm-8x12in) s.i.d.1954 i.d.verso gelatin silver print prov.lit. 25-Oct-2 Phillips, New York #30/R est:22000-28000
£13291 $21000 €19937 View from hotel window - Butte Montana (21x32cm-8x13in) s.i.d.1973 verso gelatin silver print prov.exhib.lit. 25-Apr-3 Phillips, New York #39/R est:5000-7000
£16456 $26000 €24684 Santa Fe, New Mexico (23x34cm-9x13in) s.i.d.1955 photograph. 23-Apr-3 Sotheby's, New York #214/R est:8000-12000
£16456 $26000 €24684 Barber shop through screen door, McClellanville, South Carolina (22x33cm-9x13in) s.d.1973 gelatin silver print prov.exhib. 25-Apr-3 Phillips, New York #132/R est:5000-7000
£17722 $28000 €26583 Los Angeles (24x22cm-9x9in) s.d.1954-1973 gelatin silver print prov.lit. 25-Apr-3 Phillips, New York #129/R est:5000-7000
£25316 $40000 €37974 London (23x31cm-9x12in) s.i.d.verso gelatin silver print prov. 24-Apr-3 Phillips, New York #38/R est:40000-60000
£28481 $45000 €42722 Charleston, South Carolina (30x42cm-12x17in) s.i.d.1956/1970 gelatin silver print prov.lit. 22-Apr-3 Christie's, Rockefeller NY #128/R est:40000-60000
£29114 $46000 €43671 Covered car - Long Beach, California (23x34cm-9x13in) s.d.1954-1973 verso gelatin silver print prov.lit. 25-Apr-3 Phillips, New York #40/R est:5000-7000

FRANK-COLON, Eugen (?) ?
£528 $850 €750 Cock fight (34x47cm-13x19in) s.d.07 i. verso. 9-May-3 Schloss Ahlden, Ahlden #1497/R

FRANK-KRAUSS, Robert (1893-1950) German
£475 $736 €750 Young woman from Dachau in traditional costume (21x16cm-8x6in) s. panel. 25-Sep-2 Neumeister, Munich #574
£764 $1192 €1200 Dachau girls (30x24cm-12x9in) s. panel. 6-Nov-2 Hugo Ruef, Munich #1093
£915 $1501 €1400 Market in Frank town (41x29cm-16x11in) s. i. verso panel lit. 8-Feb-3 Hans Stahl, Hamburg #15/R
£1026 $1590 €1600 Young couple in Dachau costume (81x72cm-32x28in) s. 5-Dec-2 Dr Fritz Nagel, Stuttgart #652/R est:1500
£1507 $2351 €2200 Dachau couple (80x70cm-31x28in) s. 9-Apr-3 Neumeister, Munich #666/R est:1200

FRANKE, Albert (1860-1924) German
£1689 $2635 €2500 In the art room (18x22cm-7x9in) s. panel. 26-Mar-3 Hugo Ruef, Munich #100/R est:2500
£3659 $6000 €5306 Admiring Giambologna's Rape of the Sabine Woman (31x40cm-12x16in) s. panel prov. 4-Jun-3 Christie's, Rockefeller NY #220/R est:7000-9000

FRANKE, Hanny (1890-1973) German
£318 $490 €500 Taunus (40x55cm-16x22in) 5-Sep-2 Arnold, Frankfurt #766/R
£332 $550 €481 Summer landscape with distant vista (46x61cm-18x24in) s. 14-Jun-3 Jackson's, Cedar Falls #367/R
£833 $1308 €1300 Field path in early spring (23x32cm-9x13in) bears sig.d.44. 23-Nov-2 Arnold, Frankfurt #721/R
£1761 $2747 €2800 Early spring on the Urselbach (33x43cm-13x17in) s. s.i. verso board. 11-Oct-2 Winterberg, Heidelberg #1107/R est:1380
Works on paper
£310 $490 €450 Wooded landscape. Fjord landscape (25x38cm-10x15in) s. W/C board htd egg white two. 5-Apr-3 Quittenbaum, Hamburg #24/R

FRANKE, Johann Andreas Joseph (attrib) (19/20th C) German
£1146 $1800 €1719 Foothills of the Alps (65x86cm-26x34in) s. 14-Dec-2 Weschler, Washington #629/R est:1000-1500

FRANKEN, Paul von (1818-1884) German
£16000 $25920 €24000 Ibex in the Caucasus (76x114cm-30x45in) s.d.1868. 21-May-3 Sotheby's, London #25/R est:6000-8000
£16340 $26797 €25000 Tiflis (72x118cm-28x46in) s.d.1866. 8-Feb-3 Hans Stahl, Hamburg #51/R est:4800

FRANKENBERG, Desiree Oscar Leopold van (1822-1907) Belgian
Works on paper
£317 $510 €450 Letter (37x27cm-15x11in) s. W/C. 7-May-3 Vendue Huis, Gravenhage #410/R

FRANKENTHAL SCHOOL (17th C) German
£6393 $9973 €9590 Wooded landscape with castle and robbers (43x64cm-17x25in) panel. 28-Mar-3 Koller, Zurich #3014/R est:20000-30000 (S.FR 14000)
£8000 $12560 €12000 Wooded river landscape with a hunting scene beside a bridge (34x48cm-13x19in) panel. 10-Dec-2 Sotheby's, Olympia #361/R est:6000-8000

FRANKENTHALER, Helen (1928-) American
£2675 $4200 €4013 Untitled (28x29cm-11x11in) s. acrylic linen binding plexiglas case. 21-Nov-2 Swann Galleries, New York #56/R est:4000-6000
£4430 $7000 €6645 Emerson series III (46x61cm-18x24in) s. acrylic prov. 3-Apr-3 Boos Gallery, Michigan #258/R est:8000-10000
£5660 $9000 €8490 Untitled (20x18cm-8x7in) s. s.i.d.78 verso canvasboard. 5-Mar-3 Doyle, New York #102/R est:3000-5000
£7097 $11000 €10646 Untitled (30x41cm-12x16in) masonite painted c.1961. 26-Sep-2 Christie's, Rockefeller NY #713/R est:12000-16000
£19231 $30000 €28847 Holidays no 3 (76x51cm-30x20in) s.d.75 acrylic paper board prov. 14-Oct-2 Butterfields, San Francisco #2056/R est:11000-18000
£36232 $59420 €50000 Thicket (212x175cm-83x69in) s.i.d.1977 acrylic prov. 30-May-3 Villa Grisebach, Berlin #82/R est:50000-70000
£81250 $130000 €121875 Herald (274x206cm-108x81in) s.d.70 i.d.on stretcher acrylic prov.exhib. 15-May-3 Christie's, Rockefeller NY #136/R est:120000-180000
£87500 $140000 €131250 Point lookout (175x71cm-69x28in) s. i.d.1966 on stretcher acrylic prov. 15-May-3 Christie's, Rockefeller NY #133/R est:60000-80000
£88608 $140000 €132912 Devil's mist (201x192cm-79x76in) s.d.67 s.d.on stretcher acrylic. 14-Nov-2 Christie's, Rockefeller NY #150/R est:80000-120000

Prints
£1840 $3000 €2760 Yellow Jack (76x96cm-30x38in) s.d.85-87 col lithograph. 13-Feb-3 Christie's, Rockefeller NY #260/R
£1887 $3000 €2831 Bridges (10x45cm-4x18in) s.d.num.1/30 col etching. 2-May-3 Sotheby's, New York #447/R est:1500-2000
£1923 $3000 €2885 Plaza real, H 139 (72x89cm-28x35in) s.d.num.17/60 col softground etching aquatint. 5-Nov-2 Christie's, Rockefeller NY #379/R est:2500-3500
£2013 $3200 €3020 I need yellow (43x29cm-17x11in) s.d.num.27/29 col lithograph. 29-Apr-3 Christie's, Rockefeller NY #611/R est:3000-4000
£2083 $3250 €3125 Westwind (107x92cm-42x36in) s.num.41/110 col silkscreen. 14-Oct-2 Butterfields, San Francisco #1259/R est:2000-3000
£2452 $3800 €3678 Yellow Jack (74x94cm-29x37in) s.d.1987 num.10/54 col lithograph stencil. 25-Sep-2 Christie's, Rockefeller NY #276/R est:2500-3500
£2516 $4000 €3774 Madame de Pompadour (110x75cm-43x30in) s.i.d.num.AP 10/14 col lithograph. 2-May-3 Sotheby's, New York #442/R est:4000-5000
£2710 $4200 €4065 Madame de Pompadour (110x74cm-43x29in) s.d.1985-90 num.11/14 col lithograph. 25-Sep-2 Christie's, Rockefeller NY #277/R est:4000-6000
£3226 $5000 €4839 Corot's Mark (69x80cm-27x31in) s.d.1987 num.49/52 col aquatint soft ground. 25-Sep-2 Christie's, Rockefeller NY #275/R est:3500-4500
£3459 $5500 €5189 All about blue (123x73cm-48x29in) s.d.num.AP 7/12 col lithograph woodcut. 2-May-3 Sotheby's, New York #444/R est:3500-4500
£3681 $6000 €5522 Harvest (66x55cm-26x22in) s.d.1976 col lithograph. 13-Feb-3 Christie's, Rockefeller NY #258/R
£3774 $6000 €5661 First stone (56x76cm-22x30in) s.d.num.10/12 col lithograph. 2-May-3 Sotheby's, New York #440/R est:6000-8000
£3774 $6000 €5661 Radius (71x71cm-28x28in) s.d.93 num.AP 6/8 col woodcut. 2-May-3 Sotheby's, New York #443/R est:4000-6000
£4088 $6500 €6132 Barcelona (104x81cm-41x32in) s.d.num.8/30 col lithograph. 2-May-3 Sotheby's, New York #441/R est:7000-9000
£5660 $9000 €8490 Tahiti (81x137cm-32x54in) s.d.num.27/45 col mixograph. 29-Apr-3 Christie's, Rockefeller NY #612/R est:8000-10000
£7051 $11000 €10577 Guadalupe (176x115cm-69x45in) s.d.num.29/74 col mixographia. 14-Oct-2 Butterfields, San Francisco #1257/R est:12000-15000
£16352 $26000 €24528 Tales of Genji V (107x119cm-42x47in) s.num.AP 10/14 col woodcut. 2-May-3 Sotheby's, New York #449/R est:15000-20000

Works on paper
£2358 $3750 €3537 Untitled (36x25cm-14x10in) s.d.67 s.i.d.67 verso gouache paper on board prov. 5-Mar-3 Doyle, New York #115/R est:3000-5000

FRANKFORT, Ed (1864-1920) Dutch
£552 $877 €800 Mother and children in an interior (46x44cm-18x17in) s. canvas on panel. 10-Mar-3 Sotheby's, Amsterdam #139

FRANKL, Gerhart (1901-1965) Austrian
£1319 $2098 €1900 Portrait of a man (77x63cm-30x25in) 29-Apr-3 Wiener Kunst Auktionen, Vienna #634/R est:2500-4000
£17722 $28000 €28000 Flowers with roses (71x51cm-28x20in) 27-Nov-2 Dorotheum, Vienna #198/R est:28000-34000

Works on paper
£2152 $3357 €3400 Rose study (51x37cm-20x15in) s.i. pencil W/C. 15-Oct-2 Dorotheum, Vienna #111/R est:1700-2500
£2278 $3554 €3600 Flower study (52x36cm-20x14in) s.i. pencil W/C. 15-Oct-2 Dorotheum, Vienna #112/R est:1700-2500
£4054 $6324 €6000 Vienna from belvedere (37x55cm-15x22in) W/C. 25-Mar-3 Wiener Kunst Auktionen, Vienna #135/R est:6000-12000

FRANQUELIN, Jean Augustin (1798-1839) French
£2000 $3340 €2900 At the milliners (18x24cm-7x9in) s.d.1829. 8-Jul-3 Bonhams, Knightsbridge #208/R est:800-1200

FRANQUIN, Andre (20th C) Belgian?
Works on paper
£1379 $2179 €2000 Gaston (10x21cm-4x8in) s. Chinese ink. 7-Apr-3 Claude Aguttes, Neuilly #130/R
£1379 $2179 €2000 Gaston (10x21cm-4x8in) Chinese ink. 7-Apr-3 Claude Aguttes, Neuilly #129/R

FRANQUINET, Eugene Pierre (1875-1940) American
£1032 $1600 €1548 Shack by the sea (30x41cm-12x16in) s. i.verso masonite. 29-Oct-2 John Moran, Pasadena #615 est:1000-2000

FRANS, George (1821-1898) British?
£1400 $2226 €2030 Still life of poppies, lilies and birds (84x76cm-33x30in) s.d.1862 panel pair. 29-Apr-3 Gorringes, Lewes #2341

FRANS, Paul (20th C) French
£364 $594 €550 Maison (78x70cm-31x28in) s. 17-Feb-3 Horta, Bruxelles #430

FRANSE, Cornelis (1924-1982) Dutch
£605 $944 €950 Still life with flowers on a drawing-room table (75x85cm-30x33in) i.verso prov. 5-Nov-2 Vendu Notarishuis, Rotterdam #139/R

FRANSZ, Jan (?) Czechoslovakian?
£309 $489 €464 Girl with tambourine (25x20cm-10x8in) bears sig. wood. 30-Nov-2 Dorotheum, Prague #78 (C.KR 15000)

FRANTA, Anyz (1879-1934) Czechoslovakian
Sculpture
£2038 $3200 €3057 St George slaying the dragon (58x43cm-23x17in) s. brown pat bronze. 23-Nov-2 Jackson's, Cedar Falls #243/R est:2000-3000

FRANTA, Hans (1893-?) Austrian
£417 $658 €650 Mountain landscape (52x44cm-20x17in) s. panel study verso. 18-Nov-2 Dorotheum, Linz #270/R

FRANZ, Ettore Roesler (1845-1907) Italian
Works on paper
£2600 $4134 €3900 Villa D'Este, Tivoli (75x53cm-30x21in) s.i. W/C. 18-Mar-3 Rosebery Fine Art, London #708 est:250-350

FRANZ, Heinrich (1871-1942) German
£506 $790 €800 Roses and anemones (67x81cm-26x32in) s.i.d.1914 verso. 15-Oct-2 Dorotheum, Vienna #12/R

FRAPPA, Jose (1854-1904) French
£2500 $4175 €3750 Recital (46x37cm-18x15in) s. panel. 18-Jun-3 Christie's, Kensington #155/R est:3000-5000

FRARY, Michael (1918-) American
£337 $550 €506 Crashing waves (61x127cm-24x50in) s. panel. 2-Feb-3 Simpson's, Houston #229

FRASCONI, Antonio (1919-) Uruguayan
Prints
£2065 $3200 €3098 Fulton fish market - sunrise (48x66cm-19x26in) s.i. col woodcut. 25-Sep-2 Christie's, Rockefeller NY #18/R est:2000-3000

FRASER, Alec (fl.1902-1912) British
£1440 $2218 €2160 Riviere en automne (119x150cm-47x59in) s. 22-Oct-2 Iegor de Saint Hippolyte, Montreal #40/R (C.D 3500)

FRASER, Alexander (jnr) (1828-1899) British
£320 $531 €464 Cottage near Calais (15x20cm-6x8in) s.i.verso board. 10-Jun-3 David Lay, Penzance #75
£400 $632 €600 Waiting for the tide (22x32cm-9x13in) s. panel. 14-Nov-2 Christie's, Kensington #263
£503 $775 €800 River landscape (28x42cm-11x17in) 26-Oct-2 Quittenbaum, Hamburg #8/R
£503 $775 €800 Woodland mill (84x66cm-33x26in) 26-Oct-2 Quittenbaum, Hamburg #9/R
£644 $1004 €934 Haymaking (66x102cm-26x40in) s. prov. 26-Mar-3 Walker's, Ottawa #71/R est:1500-2000 (C.D 1500)
£675 $1033 €1013 Gathering sticks in a river landscape, ruined castle behind (41x60cm-16x24in) s. 22-Aug-2 Bonhams, Edinburgh #1185
£1300 $2067 €1950 Haymaking (9x14cm-4x6in) indis sig. board. 6-Mar-3 Christie's, Kensington #80/R est:400-600
£1500 $2340 €2250 Fishing boats on a loch (17x42cm-7x17in) s. 14-Apr-3 Sotheby's, London #48/R est:1500-2000
£2000 $3120 €3000 An old watermill, North Wales (85x67cm-33x26in) s. 14-Apr-3 Sotheby's, London #55/R est:2000-3000

FRASER, Alexander (jnr-attrib) (1828-1899) British
£700 $1092 €1050 Scottish landscape with mansion house (70x86cm-28x34in) 28-Mar-3 Bonhams, Edinburgh #139

FRASER, Alexander (snr) (1786-1865) British
£950 $1482 €1425 New suitor (17x20cm-7x8in) s. panel. 13-Sep-2 Lyon & Turnbull, Edinburgh #30/R

FRASER, Alexander (snr-attrib) (1786-1865) British
£1400 $2184 €2100 Courting in the kitchen (63x80cm-25x31in) bears sig. 28-Mar-3 Bonhams, Edinburgh #136/R est:2000-3000

£17000 $26520 €25500 First of the oysters (91x126cm-36x50in) 28-Mar-3 Bonhams, Edinburgh #146/R est:10000-15000

FRASER, Arthur Anderson (1861-1904) British
Works on paper
£260 $406 €390 Bromham Bridge, Bedfordshire (13x33cm-5x13in) init.d.84 W/C. 9-Apr-3 Cheffins Grain & Comins, Cambridge #628/R
£400 $660 €580 Vessel on the Ouse before Ely Cathedral (28x43cm-11x17in) mono.d.1890 W/C bodycol. 1-Jul-3 Bonhams, Norwich #119/R
£420 $701 €609 View along a river (21x29cm-8x11in) init.d.1884 W/C. 24-Jun-3 Bonhams, Knightsbridge #162/R
£720 $1116 €1080 Flooded meadows (44x72cm-17x28in) s.d.1883 W/C. 30-Sep-2 Bonhams, Ipswich #294
£720 $1181 €1080 Hemmingford grey, St. Ives (36x55cm-14x22in) mono.d.1895 W/C. 3-Jun-3 Bonhams, Oxford #37/R

FRASER, Charles (attrib) (1782-1860) American
Works on paper
£3106 $5000 €4659 Portrait of George Norton Miller (8x8cm-3x3in) i.verso W/C ivory oval prov. 23-Feb-3 Skinner, Boston #21/R

FRASER, Claude Lovat (1890-1921) British
Works on paper
£258 $400 €387 Design for perfume bottle (13x15cm-5x6in) s.d. W/C gold silver leaf. 8-Dec-2 Toomey, Oak Park #615/R
£600 $930 €900 Female nude (27x23cm-11x9in) d.Nov 1919 pen ink W/C. 24-Sep-2 Bonhams, Knightsbridge #224/R

FRASER, Donald (?) ?
£2581 $4000 €3872 Still life flowers (91x71cm-36x28in) s. s.i.stretcher prov. 2-Oct-2 Christie's, Rockefeller NY #86/R est:2000-3000
£4516 $7000 €6774 Still life red and violet (71x92cm-28x36in) s. s.i.d.1966 stretcher prov. 2-Oct-2 Christie's, Rockefeller NY #84/R est:2000-3000

FRASER, Donald Hamilton (1929-) British
£900 $1395 €1350 Abstract landscape (16x24cm-6x9in) paper. 4-Dec-2 Christie's, Kensington #359/R
£1100 $1782 €1650 Landscape study, storm (12x19cm-5x7in) oil on paper. 20-May-3 Bonhams, Knightsbridge #13/R est:400-600
£2200 $3674 €3190 Irises (51x41cm-20x16in) s. i.d.1975 verso paper. 25-Jun-3 Bonhams, Bury St Edmunds #585/R est:800-1200
£2800 $4396 €4200 Still life with bowl, opus 268 (35x46cm-14x18in) painted 1958 prov. 22-Nov-2 Christie's, London #107/R est:2500-3500
£3000 $4680 €4500 Vertical landscape with Eiffel Tower, Oct 53 (37x29cm-15x11in) init. oil on paper prov. 25-Mar-3 Bonhams, New Bond Street #140/R est:2500-4000
£3400 $5304 €5100 Painting towards childhood (38x32cm-15x13in) s. panel exhib. 14-Apr-3 Sotheby's, London #183/R est:2000-3000
£3600 $5616 €5400 Coastal fortress (50x40cm-20x16in) s. prov. 12-Sep-2 Sotheby's, Olympia #143/R est:2000-3000
£5000 $7750 €7500 Horizontal composition - blue (42x54cm-17x21in) init. prov. 3-Dec-2 Bonhams, New Bond Street #117/R est:1000-1500
£5200 $8060 €7800 Blue seascape (72x92cm-28x36in) s.d.57. 1-Nov-2 Moore Allen & Innocent, Cirencester #494/R est:3000-5000
Works on paper
£900 $1395 €1350 Petronchka, blue and green (56x46cm-22x18in) s. s.i.verso pencil W/C oil. 4-Dec-2 Christie's, Kensington #317/R
£2800 $4340 €4200 Headland with tower (38x30cm-15x12in) s. s.i.d.1971 verso W/C bodycol oil. 4-Dec-2 Christie's, Kensington #323/R est:800-1200

FRASER, Hamilton (20th C) ?
£2439 $4000 €3537 Seascape with cliffs (122x91cm-48x36in) si.d.1966 prov. 1-Jun-3 Wright, Chicago #314/R est:2000-3000

FRASER, James Earle (1876-1953) American
Sculpture
£2130 $3450 €3089 Roosevelt bas relief (33x25cm-13x10in) bronze. 23-May-3 Altermann Galleries, Santa Fe #96
£3288 $4800 €4932 The Roosevelt Bas-relief (33x25cm-13x10in) bronze plaque. 18-May-2 Altermann Galleries, Santa Fe #60/R

FRASER, James Earle (after) (1876-1953) American
Sculpture
£3459 $5500 €5189 End of the trail (72cm-28in) i.num.17 dark reddish brown pat. large base. 5-Mar-3 Sotheby's, New York #161/R est:1500-2500

FRASER, John (20th C) ?
Works on paper
£480 $758 €720 Fisherfolk on a shore (18x25cm-7x10in) s.d.1910 W/C. 27-Nov-2 Hamptons Fine Art, Godalming #241
£1500 $2325 €2250 Leigh, near Southend. Holehaven, Canvey Island (37x55cm-15x22in) s. W/C pair. 31-Oct-2 Christie's, Kensington #347/R est:1500-2000

FRASER, John (1858-1927) British
Works on paper
£289 $454 €434 Strolling on the beach (30x46cm-12x18in) s.d.79 W/C. 24-Jul-2 Walker's, Ottawa #33 (C.D 700)

FRASER, John Arthur (1839-1898) Canadian/British
£3333 $5467 €5000 Hermit Range at the summit of the Selkirks on line of CPR (56x76cm-22x30in) s. s.i.d.1886 verso prov. 27-May-3 Sotheby's, Toronto #212/R est:3000-4000 (C.D 7500)
Works on paper
£766 $1210 €1149 Mount Assiniboine, Rocky Mountains (34x23cm-13x9in) s. i.verso W/C prov. 14-Nov-2 Heffel, Vancouver #25/R est:1200-1500 (C.D 1900)

FRASER, John S (fl.188Os) British
Works on paper
£572 $910 €858 Fetching water (76x51cm-30x20in) s.d.92 W/C. 18-Mar-3 Maynards, Vancouver #2/R (C.D 1350)

FRASER, Robert Winchester (1848-1906) British
Works on paper
£260 $424 €390 On the Ouse, Beds (26x42cm-10x17in) s.i. W/C bodycol. 17-Feb-3 Bonhams, Bath #17
£320 $496 €480 Near Wroxham, Norfolk (28x42cm-11x17in) s.d.89 W/C. 30-Sep-2 Bonhams, Ipswich #283
£320 $509 €464 Near Potter Heigham, Norfolk (17x34cm-7x13in) s. W/C. 26-Feb-3 John Bellman, Billingshurst #1742/R
£440 $717 €660 Rollesby Broad (25x53cm-10x21in) s.i. W/C dr. 14-Feb-3 Bracketts, Tunbridge Wells #948/R
£450 $752 €653 Children fishing in the fens (1x36cm-0x14in) s.d.94 pencil W/C htd white. 26-Jun-3 Mellors & Kirk, Nottingham #817/R
£700 $1099 €1050 River at Kempton, Bedfordshire (39x64cm-15x25in) s. W/C. 16-Dec-2 Bonhams, Bury St Edmunds #433/R
£5000 $8200 €7250 In the Isle of Ely (20x56cm-8x22in) s.i.d.90 W/C htd white. 5-Jun-3 Christie's, London #148/R est:2500-3500

FRASER, Robert Winter (1872-1930) British
Works on paper
£260 $403 €390 Tranquil river landscape with houses near trees (18x37cm-7x15in) s.d.98 W/C. 25-Sep-2 Hamptons Fine Art, Godalming #284
£400 $620 €600 Two children by a brook a farmyard beyond (20x38cm-8x15in) s.i.d.98 W/C. 25-Sep-2 Hamptons Fine Art, Godalming #101
£920 $1518 €1334 River landscape with school house and ferry (37x54cm-15x21in) s. W/C. 1-Jul-3 Bearnes, Exeter #475/R

FRASNEDI, Alfonso (1934-) Italian
£380 $592 €600 Composition (55x65cm-22x26in) painted 1958. 19-Oct-2 Semenzato, Venice #135/R

FRATER, William (1890-1974) Australian/British
£250 $395 €375 Castlemaine district (71x81cm-28x32in) s.d.72 board. 18-Nov-2 Joel, Victoria #162 (A.D 700)
£299 $490 €449 Trees (42x51cm-17x20in) s. composition board. 4-Jun-3 Deutscher-Menzies, Melbourne #413/R (A.D 750)
£543 $863 €815 Strath Creek (64x74cm-25x29in) board. 5-May-3 Sotheby's, Melbourne #319 (A.D 1400)
£571 $903 €857 Landscape (40x45cm-16x18in) s.verso board. 27-Nov-2 Deutscher-Menzies, Melbourne #205/R est:1800-2400 (A.D 1600)
£571 $903 €857 Still life, quinces (50x61cm-20x24in) s. i.verso board. 27-Nov-2 Deutscher-Menzies, Melbourne #222/R est:2000-3000 (A.D 1600)
£676 $1035 €1014 Beach track (45x39cm-18x15in) s. board prov. 26-Aug-2 Sotheby's, Paddington #730/R est:3000-5000 (A.D 1900)
£1000 $1580 €1500 Farm house (44x54cm-17x21in) s. canvasboard prov. 17-Nov-2 Sotheby's, Paddington #65 est:2000-3000 (A.D 2800)
£1280 $2061 €1920 Self portrait (59x49cm-23x19in) s.d.74 board. 6-May-3 Christie's, Melbourne #389 est:1000-2000 (A.D 3200)
Works on paper
£239 $392 €359 Landscape (38x56cm-15x22in) s. W/C. 4-Jun-3 Deutscher-Menzies, Melbourne #414/R (A.D 600)

FRATIN, Christopher (1800-1864) French
Sculpture
£500 $800 €750 Stallion (61x79cm-24x31in) s. bronze marble plinth. 18-May-3 Jeffery Burchard, Florida #90/R

£1410 $2200 €2115 Balancing bears. s. gilt bronze candelabra onyx base pair. 14-Sep-2 Selkirks, St. Louis #928/R est:1200-1600
£1871 $2993 €2600 Lion haletant tenant ungnou (19x41cm-7x16in) s. brown pat bronze. 18-May-3 Rabourdin & Choppin de Janvry, Paris #120/R est:2800-3000
£1923 $3038 €3000 Cheval attaque par un felin (22x23x11cm-9x9x4in) s.i. green pat bronze. 18-Nov-2 Tajan, Paris #68/R est:2400-3000
£2500 $3900 €3750 Rainbow, a standing stallion (31x37cm-12x15in) s.num.R brown pat bronze st.Raimbow. 9-Apr-3 Sotheby's, London #123/R est:2500-3500
£5000 $8350 €7250 Huntsman in full chase (41x37cm-16x15in) s. dk brown pat bronze. 8-Jul-3 Sotheby's, London #189/R est:5000-7000

FRATTA, Domenico Maria (1696-1763) Italian
Works on paper
£811 $1265 €1200 Mountainous landscape (26x30cm-10x12in) i. pen ink. 27-Mar-3 Christie's, Paris #77/R
£1081 $1686 €1600 River landscape (26x18cm-10x7in) pen ink. 27-Mar-3 Christie's, Paris #75/R

FRAU, Jose (1898-1976) Spanish
£566 $883 €900 Landscape (22x20cm-9x8in) s. board. 23-Sep-2 Durán, Madrid #63/R

FRAZER, Hugh (fl.1813-1861) Irish
£250 $365 €375 View on the water of Lelth (36x51cm-14x20in) s. board. 12-Jun-2 John Ross, Belfast #189
£260 $380 €390 House by the river (30x41cm-12x16in) s.verso board. 12-Jun-2 John Ross, Belfast #4

FRAZER, Jacqueline (20th C) ?
Works on paper
£353 $569 €530 Who whacked that bobbing head! (50x36cm-20x14in) s.d.22-7-2000 mixed media. 7-May-3 Dunbar Sloane, Auckland #79 (NZ.D 1000)

FRAZER, Oliver (attrib) (1808-1864) American
£1603 $2500 €2405 Portrait of George Washington (96x90cm-38x35in) after Lansdowne prov. 12-Apr-3 Freeman, Philadelphia #199/R est:2000-3000

FRAZER, William Miller (1864-1961) British
£280 $437 €420 River scene with steamer (10x13cm-4x5in) indis.sig. paper. 10-Apr-3 Bonhams, Edinburgh #92
£310 $518 €450 In Northern Tuscany (34x44cm-13x17in) board. 11-Jul-3 Bracketts, Tunbridge Wells #840/R
£480 $782 €720 Rural landscape (40x50cm-16x20in) s. 17-Feb-3 Bonhams, Bath #13
£600 $936 €900 Moorland, Machrie, Arran (22x28cm-9x11in) s. board. 10-Apr-3 Bonhams, Edinburgh #137
£750 $1170 €1125 Pastoral (25x30cm-10x12in) s. canvasboard. 17-Oct-2 Bonhams, Edinburgh #256
£800 $1240 €1200 Near Elton, Northants (27x37cm-11x15in) s. canvas on board. 3-Dec-2 Sotheby's, Olympia #193/R
£800 $1240 €1200 Windmill, Cambridgeshire (27x34cm-11x13in) s. canvasboard. 5-Dec-2 Bonhams, Edinburgh #94
£820 $1312 €1189 At Struan, Athole (36x45cm-14x18in) s. canvasboard. 17-May-3 Thomson Roddick & Medcalf, Edinburgh #696
£850 $1318 €1275 Bondagers (23x32cm-9x13in) s.d.97 panel. 5-Dec-2 Bonhams, Edinburgh #73/R
£900 $1458 €1350 Evening (20x30cm-8x12in) s. indis d. board. 23-May-3 Lyon & Turnbull, Edinburgh #48
£950 $1473 €1425 Fishing boats moored, Arran (24x34cm-9x13in) s. canvas on board. 5-Dec-2 Bonhams, Edinburgh #14/R
£1000 $1550 €1500 Farm buildings at sunset (45x61cm-18x24in) s. 6-Dec-2 Lyon & Turnbull, Edinburgh #96 est:1000-1500
£1000 $1560 €1500 In Norfolk (26x34cm-10x13in) s. 26-Mar-3 Hamptons Fine Art, Godalming #131 est:300-400
£1150 $1840 €1668 Overferry, Cambridgeshire (25x35cm-10x14in) s. canvasboard. 17-May-3 Thomson Roddick & Medcalf, Edinburgh #697/R
£1277 $1979 €1916 Farmer with wheelbarrow on road (47x60cm-19x24in) s.d.1889. 8-Dec-2 Uppsala Auktionskammare, Uppsala #45/R est:18000-20000 (S.KR 18000)
£1400 $2226 €2100 East Linton, East Lothian (35x46cm-14x18in) s. s.i.on stretcher. 6-Mar-3 Christie's, Kensington #165/R est:1000-1500
£1400 $2240 €2030 Holywell, Huntingshire (25x35cm-10x14in) s. canvasboard. 17-May-3 Thomson Roddick & Medcalf, Edinburgh #699/R
£1450 $2364 €2175 At Potter Heigham, Norfolk (24x34cm-9x13in) s. s.i.verso board. 17-Feb-3 Bonhams, Bath #8 est:400-600
£1450 $2320 €2103 Nussington, Northamptonshire (31x46cm-12x18in) s. 17-May-3 Thomson Roddick & Medcalf, Edinburgh #698/R
£1600 $2544 €2400 On the beach (30x51cm-12x20in) s. 6-Mar-3 Christie's, Kensington #166/R est:1000-1500
£1667 $2633 €2600 Landscape with farm buildings and cottages (51x76cm-20x30in) s. 12-Nov-2 Mealy's, Castlecomer #1032/R
£1700 $2636 €2550 Duddingston Mill, Northants. Duddingston, Northants (24x34cm-9x13in) s. canvasboard pair. 3-Dec-2 Sotheby's, Olympia #194/R est:1000-1500
£1750 $2800 €2538 Mallard rising (40x61cm-16x24in) s. 17-May-3 Thomson Roddick & Medcalf, Edinburgh #700/R
£1900 $2964 €2850 Cattle watering in summer pasture (25x35cm-10x14in) s. canvasboard. 17-Oct-2 Bonhams, Edinburgh #161 est:1000-1500
£2100 $3276 €3150 Ploughing, possibly near Kinross (39x59cm-15x23in) s. 10-Apr-3 Bonhams, Edinburgh #166 est:1500-2000
£4200 $6384 €6300 Blackwaterfoot, Arran (46x61cm-18x24in) s. 28-Aug-2 Sotheby's, London #1003/R est:4000-6000

FRAZETTA, Frank (1928-) American
Works on paper
£1677 $2700 €2516 Barbarians in pitched combat (13x13cm-5x5in) s. pen ink. 20-Feb-3 Illustration House, New York #65/R est:1200-1800

FRAZIER, C James (1946-) American
£2945 $4300 €4418 Duck pond (91x122cm-36x48in) 18-May-2 Altermann Galleries, Santa Fe #263/R

FRAZIER, Kenneth (1867-1949) American
£1538 $2400 €2307 West Point from Garrison-on-Hudson. 9-Aug-2 Skinner, Bolton #449

FRAZIER, Luke (20th C) American
£2564 $4000 €3846 Entourage (36x46cm-14x18in) 9-Nov-2 Altermann Galleries, Santa Fe #239
£5222 $8250 €7572 Big fish on a log jam (51x102cm-20x40in) s. board. 26-Jul-3 Coeur d'Alene, Hayden #73/R est:8000-12000

FREAR, Tom (?) British?
£280 $442 €420 Moored vessels and figures on a quayside (23x30cm-9x12in) s. board. 24-Apr-3 Richardson & Smith, Whitby #139/R

FRECHKOP, Leonid (1897-1982) Belgian
£379 $607 €550 Nude sitting (76x55cm-30x22in) s. 15-Mar-3 De Vuyst, Lokeren #124
£510 $795 €800 Jeune femme au cheval de bois (140x100cm-55x39in) s.d.66. 11-Nov-2 Horta, Bruxelles #42

FRECKLETON, Harold (1890-1979) British
£680 $1074 €1020 Three girls playing in a farmyard (61x75cm-24x30in) s.d.48. 5-Apr-3 Shapes, Edinburgh #314

FRECSKAY, Laszlo von (1844-1916) Austrian
£9028 $14354 €13000 Hitting the high note (42x60cm-17x24in) s.d.1908 prov. 29-Apr-3 Christie's, Amsterdam #90/R est:2500-3500

FREDDIE, Wilhelm (1909-1995) Danish
£1580 $2496 €2370 Surrealistic composition (33x41cm-13x16in) s.d.juni 46 prov. 1-Apr-3 Rasmussen, Copenhagen #277/R est:20000-25000 (D.KR 17000)
£2032 $3150 €3048 Lady in white chair (81x65cm-32x26in) s.d.66 prov. 1-Oct-2 Rasmussen, Copenhagen #54/R est:20000 (D.KR 24000)
£2710 $4200 €4065 Le petit dejeuner (81x65cm-32x26in) s.d.67 s.d.1967 verso exhib. 1-Oct-2 Rasmussen, Copenhagen #53/R est:25000-30000 (D.KR 32000)
£4996 $7743 €7494 Sakral magi (55x46cm-22x18in) s.d.1948 verso masonite prov.exhib.lit. 4-Dec-2 Kunsthallen, Copenhagen #134/R est:75000 (D.KR 58000)
£5112 $8076 €7668 Dying for your country (45x55cm-18x22in) s.d.36 prov.lit. 1-Apr-3 Rasmussen, Copenhagen #158/R est:60000-80000 (D.KR 55000)
£6307 $9839 €9461 Surrealistic composition (38x46cm-15x18in) s.d.April 42. 5-Nov-2 Bukowskis, Stockholm #246/R est:25000-30000 (S.KR 90000)
£6950 $11189 €10425 Symphonic catastrophe (73x92cm-29x36in) s.d.1946 prov. 7-May-3 AB Stockholms Auktionsverk #1110/R est:100000-125000 (S.KR 90000)
£9056 $15124 €13131 The lion's very nice present - lion foot (60x73cm-24x29in) s.d.maj 1950 s.d.verso prov.exhib.lit. 17-Jun-3 Rasmussen, Copenhagen #17/R est:80000-100000 (D.KR 95000)
£10688 $16887 €16032 Progress, dreams and awakening terror - composition (90x152cm-35x60in) s.d.1947-48 exhib.lit. 1-Apr-3 Rasmussen, Copenhagen #160/R est:125000-150000 (D.KR 115000)
£13011 $20558 €19517 Front promenade - surrealistic composition (100x89cm-39x35in) s.d.1943-46 exhib.lit. 1-Apr-3 Rasmussen, Copenhagen #148/R est:150000 (D.KR 140000)

Sculpture

£3716 $5797 €5574 Sphinx (28x56x31cm-11x22x12in) s.d.47 brass lit. 18-Sep-2 Kunsthallen, Copenhagen #152/R est:40000 (D.KR 44000)

Works on paper

£718 $1120 €1077 Wilhelm Freddie (58x42cm-23x17in) crayon collage sketch. 18-Sep-2 Kunsthallen, Copenhagen #172/R (D.KR 8500)
£1487 $2349 €2231 Olympia (62x49cm-24x19in) s.d.81 collage crayon chl. 1-Apr-3 Rasmussen, Copenhagen #221/R est:20000-25000 (D.KR 16000)

FREDENTHAL, David (1914-1958) American

Works on paper

£783 $1300 €1135 Landscape with houses (30x36cm-12x14in) W/C. 13-Jun-3 Du Mouchelle, Detroit #2108/R

FREDERIC, Georges (1900-1981) Belgian

£296 $480 €450 Nature morte a la Maquette de Bateau (60x80cm-24x31in) s. 21-Jan-3 Galerie Moderne, Brussels #209/R
£318 $497 €500 Composition aux objets de la marine (60x80cm-24x31in) s.d.1963. 11-Nov-2 Horta, Bruxelles #694
£755 $1209 €1050 Le Port d'Ostende anime (65x80cm-26x31in) s.d.1929. 13-May-3 Vanderkindere, Brussels #82

FREDERIC, Léon (1856-1940) Belgian

£323 $510 €500 Paysanne assise (18x15cm-7x6in) studio st.verso canvas laid down exhib. 17-Dec-2 Palais de Beaux Arts, Brussels #532
£417 $646 €650 Canal (28x42cm-11x17in) st.sig. panel. 7-Dec-2 De Vuyst, Lokeren #130
£638 $1066 €900 Vue sur Nafraiture (37x58cm-15x23in) 23-Jun-3 Amberes, Antwerp #93
£719 $1151 €1000 Parodie du Sphynx Parisien d'Alfred Stevens (66x51cm-26x20in) s.d.1887 exhib. 13-May-3 Palais de Beaux Arts, Brussels #72
£753 $1175 €1100 Fenaison (30x29cm-12x11in) s. canvas on panel. 14-Apr-3 Horta, Bruxelles #345
£759 $1185 €1200 Moine de dos au bord de riviere (110x44cm-43x17in) s.d.1903. 16-Sep-2 Horta, Bruxelles #390

Works on paper

£490 $789 €750 Vieille femme et fillettes a l'ouvrage (89x68cm-35x27in) s. chl dr. 14-Jan-3 Vanderkindere, Brussels #75
£1795 $2782 €2800 Three children praying (33x62cm-13x24in) s.d.1888 chl dr. 7-Dec-2 De Vuyst, Lokeren #128/R est:2600-3000

FREDERICK, Rod (20th C) American

£2008 $3153 €3012 Winters warming (60x100cm-24x39in) s.d.1983 prov. 25-Nov-2 Hodgins, Calgary #372/R est:10000-12500 (C.D 5000)
£4747 $7500 €6883 Winter's warming (61x102cm-24x40in) s. 26-Jul-3 Coeur d'Alene, Hayden #209a/R est:10000-15000

FREDERICKS, Ernest (1877-1927) American

£302 $475 €453 Autumn landscape (41x51cm-16x20in) s. painted c.1929 exhib. 23-Nov-2 Jackson's, Cedar Falls #79/R
£355 $550 €533 Winter glory, Woodstock New York (66x86cm-26x34in) s. painted c.1930. 8-Dec-2 Toomey, Oak Park #734/R
£373 $600 €560 Autumn wooded river landscape (71x97cm-28x38in) s. 20-Jan-3 Arthur James, Florida #82
£449 $700 €674 Woodland forest scene (41x51cm-16x20in) s. 12-Apr-3 Susanin's, Chicago #5029
£613 $950 €920 Winter river landscape (41x51cm-16x20in) s. prov. 29-Oct-2 John Moran, Pasadena #607a
£774 $1200 €1161 Autumn landscape (56x71cm-22x28in) s. painted c.1925. 8-Dec-2 Toomey, Oak Park #724/R

FREDERICKS, Marshall Maynard (1908-1998) American

Sculpture

£932 $1500 €1398 Flying geese (36cm-14in) s. pat bronze black marble plinth. 15-Jan-3 Boos Gallery, Michigan #537/R est:3000-5000
£1519 $2400 €2279 Hock shot (24cm-9in) i. brown pat. bronze prov. 3-Apr-3 Christie's, Rockefeller NY #161/R est:7000-10000
£2866 $4500 €4299 Frog (25cm-10in) pat. bronze. 20-Nov-2 Boos Gallery, Michigan #440/R est:5000-7000
£5063 $8000 €7595 Black bear and cub (39cm-15in) i. dark brown pat. bronze prov. 3-Apr-3 Christie's, Rockefeller NY #157/R est:5000-7000

FREDERIKSEN, C (20th C) ?

£318 $490 €500 Sailing vessels near Dordrecht (32x41cm-13x16in) s. 3-Sep-2 Christie's, Amsterdam #328a

FREDERIKSEN, Lauritz (20th C) Danish

£263 $420 €395 Garden with trees and hut (33x44cm-13x17in) s.d.5 maj 14. 13-Jan-3 Rasmussen, Vejle #181/R (D.KR 3000)

FREDOU, Jean Martial (1711-1795) French

Works on paper

£5068 $7905 €7500 Portrait de jeune dessinateur (36x27cm-14x11in) i. chk wash prov. 27-Mar-3 Christie's, Paris #98/R

FREDOU, Jean Martial (attrib) (1711-1795) French

Works on paper

£425 $697 €650 Portrait presume de Louis XVII (33x24cm-13x9in) sanguine. 7-Feb-3 Piasa, Paris #39

FREE, J A (19/20th C) ?

£1550 $2387 €2325 Sleeping Arab guard (36x28cm-14x11in) s.d.1862. 24-Oct-2 Thomson, Roddick & Medcalf, Carlisle #315/R

FREED, Leonard (20th C) American

Photographs

£4601 $7500 €6902 Harlem, New York (36x23cm-14x9in) s.i.d.1963/1980 verso gelatin silver print two. 12-Feb-3 Christie's, Rockefeller NY #177/R est:3000-5000

FREED, William (1904-1984) American

Works on paper

£1341 $2200 €1944 Abstract collage. Abstract composition. Abstract shapes. two s. 1 mixed media board 1 oil 1 oil on plywood double-sided 3. 5-Jun-3 Swann Galleries, New York #95/R est:1000-1500

FREEMAN, Dick (1932-1991) Canadian

£211 $347 €306 Stormy weather (25x30cm-10x12in) s.i. board. 9-Jun-3 Hodgins, Calgary #339/R est:600-800 (C.D 475)
£1059 $1684 €1589 Shooting the breeze (45x60cm-18x24in) a.i.d.1980 board. 23-Mar-3 Hodgins, Calgary #14/R est:2000-2500 (C.D 2500)
£2860 $4548 €4290 Alberta scene (60x90cm-24x35in) s.i.d.1980 board. 23-Mar-3 Hodgins, Calgary #30/R est:2750-3250 (C.D 6750)

FREEMAN, Don (1908-1978) American

Works on paper

£419 $650 €629 Studio (33x51cm-13x20in) estate st. W/C gouache pencil exec.c.1948. 8-Dec-2 Toomey, Oak Park #779/R
£452 $700 €678 Box office boredom (39x34cm-15x13in) s. W/C board. 3-Dec-2 Christie's, Rockefeller NY #617/R

FREEMAN, Eric (1970-) American

£662 $1100 €960 Unvisited (30x30cm-12x12in) s.i.d.2001 verso linen prov. 11-Jun-3 Phillips, New York #339

FREEMAN, William Philip Barnes (1813-1897) British

£2600 $4056 €3900 Reed wherry and other boats on the Norfolk Broads (23x30cm-9x12in) 18-Oct-2 Keys, Aylsham #688/R est:1750-2500

Works on paper

£980 $1617 €1421 Fishmarket, Norwich (33x55cm-13x22in) s.d.1877 W/C. 1-Jul-3 Bonhams, Norwich #69/R

FREENEY, John J (20th C) Irish

£336 $524 €490 Connemara, Co Galway (50x60cm-20x24in) s. board. 8-Apr-3 James Adam, Dublin #121/R

Works on paper

£329 $513 €480 Sorrento, Italy (35x52cm-14x20in) s. W/C. 8-Apr-3 James Adam, Dublin #122/R

FREER, Frederick W (1849-1908) American

£3097 $4800 €4646 Last look (36x25cm-14x10in) panel. 2-Nov-2 North East Auctions, Portsmouth #25/R

FREEZOR, George Augustus (fl.1861-1879) British

£320 $512 €480 Young girl seated on a coastal hillside (21x25cm-8x10in) s. panel. 13-May-3 Bonhams, Knightsbridge #9
£400 $628 €600 Flower girl (25x20cm-10x8in) s. indis d. 19-Nov-2 Bonhams, Leeds #199/R

FREGEVIZE, Frederic (1770-1849) Swiss

£2516 $3925 €4000 Fredericke A Frick with son (79x62cm-31x24in) s.d.1812 lit. 20-Sep-2 Schloss Ahlden, Ahlden #1075/R est:2800

FREIDHEIM, Leon J (1871-1936) American

£313 $500 €454 Shelter house in Forest Park (25x36cm-10x14in) s.d. 17-May-3 Selkirks, St. Louis #332/R
£516 $825 €748 Boat dock in Forest Park lagoon, St Louis (41x51cm-16x20in) s. 17-May-3 Selkirks, St. Louis #331/R

FREIFELD, Eric (1919-1984) Canadian
Works on paper
£700 $1084 €1050 Toronto nocturne (54x72cm-21x28in) s.d.1975 W/C lit. 3-Dec-2 Joyner, Toronto #118/R est:1000-1500 (C.D 1700)

FREIMAN, Lillian (1908-1986) Canadian
Works on paper
£413 $649 €620 Dutch festival (122x41cm-48x16in) s. mixed media. 24-Jul-2 Walker's, Ottawa #416/R est:1000-1500 (C.D 1000)

FREINIK, William (1905-) American/German
£274 $425 €411 Untitled (51x61cm-20x24in) d.1960 board. 8-Dec-2 Toomey, Oak Park #837/R

FREITAG, Clemens (1883-?) German
£256 $397 €400 Autumn landscape (80x100cm-31x39in) i. 9-Dec-2 Dr Fritz Nagel, Stuttgart #6960/R

FREITAG, Conrad (attrib) (?-1894) American
Works on paper
£300 $486 €450 New York pilot cutter Edward E Barret off the approaches to the harbour (29x41cm-11x16in) s.i. pencil W/C. 21-May-3 Christie's, Kensington #471/R

FREIXAS CORTES, Jordi (1917-1984) Spanish
£374 $595 €550 Barques de pecheurs (55x74cm-22x29in) s. 21-Mar-3 Rieunier, Bailly-Pommery, Mathias, Paris #130
£637 $994 €1000 Port (33x46cm-13x18in) s. 10-Nov-2 Eric Pillon, Calais #114/R
£899 $1439 €1250 Barques a maree basse (54x73cm-21x29in) s. 18-May-3 Eric Pillon, Calais #120/R

FREJO GUTIERREZ, Emilio (1956-) Spanish
£872 $1405 €1300 Fisherwomen (50x57cm-20x22in) s. 18-Feb-3 Durán, Madrid #143/R

FRELAUT, Jean (1879-1954) French?
£750 $1163 €1125 French town, boats on a river and church in the distance (49x59cm-19x23in) s.d.1919. 24-Sep-2 Anderson & Garland, Newcastle #460/R

FREMIET, E (1824-1910) French
Sculpture
£2000 $3120 €3000 Joan of Arc on horseback (74x43cm-29x17in) s.num.136 brown pat bronze lit. 9-Apr-3 Sotheby's, London #197/R est:2500-3500

FREMIET, Emmanuel (1824-1910) French
Sculpture
£920 $1500 €1380 Ravageot and Ravageole (15cm-6in) brown pat. bronze. 11-Feb-3 Bonhams & Doyles, New York #15/R est:1500-2000
£1020 $1622 €1500 Attelage (25x32cm-10x13in) s. plaster. 23-Mar-3 Herbette, Doullens #160/R
£1049 $1752 €1500 Ravageot - ravageole (16x17cm-6x7in) s.num.749 medaille pat bronze. 30-Jun-3 Pierre Berge, Paris #35/R est:1000-1200
£1338 $2221 €1900 Chat devorant un poulet (25cm-10in) num.2 brown pat bronze prov. 16-Jun-3 Oger, Dumont, Paris #102/R est:1000
£1400 $2184 €2100 Saint Michael (29cm-11in) s.st.f.F Barbedienne gilt bronze lit. 9-Apr-3 Sotheby's, London #132/R est:1500-2000
£1500 $2340 €2250 Gallic chieftain (40x26x150cm-16x10x59in) s.num.356 brown pat bronze lit. 5-Nov-2 Sotheby's, London #136/R est:1500-2000
£1728 $2454 €2800 Vercingetorix a cheval (42x26cm-17x10in) s. gilt pat bronze Cast Barbedienne. 16-Mar-3 Eric Pillon, Calais #10/R
£2318 $3778 €3500 Louis XIII enfant (45x11x17cm-18x4x7in) s. pat bronze Cast Barbedienne. 31-Jan-3 Rabourdin & Choppin de Janvry, Paris #164/R
£2500 $3925 €3750 Ours blesse - wounded bear attacking a gladiator (30cm-12in) s. brown pat. bronze lit. 10-Dec-2 Sotheby's, London #168/R est:3000-5000
£2866 $4500 €4299 Mounted knight, Louis d'Orleans (46x41cm-18x16in) s. brown pat bronze. 23-Nov-2 Jackson's, Cedar Falls #245/R est:4500-6500
£3000 $4680 €4500 Roman charioteer (40cm-16in) s.num.17 brown pat bronze exhib. lit. 5-Nov-2 Sotheby's, London #132/R est:3000-5000
£3205 $5032 €5000 Saint-Hubert (69x36x19cm-27x14x7in) brown pat bronze Cast Barbedienne. 24-Nov-2 Lesieur & Le Bars, Le Havre #51/R
£3311 $5397 €5000 Etienne Marcel (50x38x22cm-20x15x9in) s. num.1 bronze. 31-Jan-3 Rabourdin & Choppin de Janvry, Paris #163/R
£3400 $5406 €5100 Credo (38cm-15in) s. brown pat bronze. 29-Apr-3 Sotheby's, Olympia #169/R est:1500-2500
£3600 $5616 €5400 Napoleon on horseback (33x26cm-13x10in) s.num.2 brown pat bronze lit. 9-Apr-3 Sotheby's, London #200/R est:4000-6000
£3741 $5949 €5500 Grand Conde (55x39x15cm-22x15x6in) s. pat bronze green marble base. 23-Mar-3 Herbette, Doullens #158/R
£3800 $6346 €5510 Napoleon III on horseback (37x28cm-15x11in) s. dk brown pat bronze. 8-Jul-3 Sotheby's, London #188/R est:4000-6000
£3811 $6250 €5526 Le char de minerve (64x53x30cm-25x21x12in) gilt bronze i.f.F Barbedienne. 7-Jun-3 Neal Auction Company, New Orleans #69/R est:4000-6000
£4000 $6240 €6000 St Michael (55cm-22in) s.indis.d.1876 num.522 gilt bronze lit. 5-Nov-2 Sotheby's, London #141/R est:3000-5000
£5500 $9185 €7975 Cheval prime (43x36cm-17x14in) s. num.35 dk brown pat bronze incl green marble base. 8-Jul-3 Sotheby's, London #185/R est:6000-8000

FREMIET, Emmanuel (after) (1824-1910) French
Sculpture
£4800 $7584 €7200 Stallion (37cm-15in) st.f. Barbedienne bronze. 27-Nov-2 Christie's, London #51/R est:3000-5000

FREMINET, Martin (1567-1619) French
Works on paper
£17000 $28390 €24650 Penitent attended by an angel and another figure (44x32cm-17x13in) bears i.verso pen brown ink wash. 9-Jul-3 Sotheby's, London #26/R est:8000-12000

FREMOND, Andre (20th C) French
£329 $520 €520 Chasse au faucon (46x55cm-18x22in) s. panel. 27-Nov-2 Lemoine & Ferrando, Paris #94
Works on paper
£395 $640 €600 Les etalons (41x55cm-16x22in) s.i.d. mixed media. 22-Jan-3 Tajan, Paris #64

FREMONT, L Charles (19th C) French
Sculpture
£1701 $2704 €2500 Elephant (34x46cm-13x18in) s.i. plaster prov. 23-Mar-3 Herbette, Doullens #161/R

FREMONT, Suzanne Camille Desiree (1876-1962) French
£3404 $5379 €5106 Reclining model (54x81cm-21x32in) s.d.14. 2-Dec-2 Rasmussen, Copenhagen #1193/R est:40000 (D.KR 40000)

FRENCH SCHOOL, 14th C
Sculpture
£14388 $23022 €20000 Vierge et l'enfant (33cm-13in) marble. 15-May-3 Christie's, Paris #23/R est:15000-20000

FRENCH SCHOOL, 15th C
Works on paper
£4721 $7318 €7082 Book miniature (22x22cm-9x9in) gouache htd gold parchment. 3-Oct-2 Koller, Zurich #3369/R est:2400-3800 (S.FR 11000)

FRENCH SCHOOL, 16th C
£5063 $8000 €8000 Christ Salvator Mundi et la Vierge Mater Dolorosa (78x67cm-31x26in) panel. 27-Nov-2 Christie's, Paris #29/R est:8000-12000

FRENCH SCHOOL, 17th C
£4839 $7645 €7500 Portrait de la Duchesse de Luynes (66x54cm-26x21in) i. 20-Dec-2 Ribeyre & Baron, Paris #18/R
£4895 $8175 €7000 La Sainte famille (68x51cm-27x20in) 25-Jun-3 Sotheby's, Paris #3/R est:8000-12000
£5032 $7951 €7800 Portrait presume de William Shakespeare (60x44cm-24x17in) i. 20-Dec-2 Ribeyre & Baron, Paris #16
£5141 $8277 €7300 Let the children come to me (76x102cm-30x40in) 11-May-3 Finarte, Venice #20/R est:7000-8000
£6090 $9561 €9500 Angelique et Medor (102x164cm-40x65in) 19-Nov-2 Servarts Themis, Bruxelles #249/R est:4000
£6389 $10158 €9200 Magdalene (138x100cm-54x39in) 3-May-3 Finarte, Venice #138/R
£6410 $10064 €10000 Portrait de jeune femme en Diane (121x91cm-48x36in) 20-Nov-2 Libert, Castor, Paris #85/R est:15000-18000
£6410 $9936 €10000 Allegory of art of sculpture (109x85cm-43x33in) canvas on canvas. 4-Dec-2 Neumeister, Munich #595/R est:8500
£6410 $9936 €10000 Allegory of poetry (109x85cm-43x33in) canvas on canvas. 4-Dec-2 Neumeister, Munich #596/R est:8500
£6410 $9936 €10000 Allegory of architecture (109x85cm-43x33in) canvas on canvas. 4-Dec-2 Neumeister, Munich #597/R est:8500

£6410	$9936	€10000	Allegory of painting (109x85cm-43x33in) canvas on canvas. 4-Dec-2 Neumeister, Munich #598/R est:8500
£6849	$10685	€10000	School of Bacchus (104x81cm-41x32in) 10-Apr-3 Van Ham, Cologne #1204/R est:11000
£6962	$11000	€11000	Martyr refusing to worship idols (98x125cm-39x49in) i.verso. 29-Nov-2 Semenzato, Venice #469/R est:12000-15000
£86538	$135865	€135000	Portrait de femme au manteau bleu et collier de perles (73x60cm-29x24in) 13-Dec-2 Rossini, Paris #154/R

Miniatures

£12000	$18840	€18000	Diana and Actaeon (6x7cm-2x3in) enamel gold. 10-Dec-2 Christie's, London #2/R est:1000-1500

Works on paper

£5000	$7850	€7500	Ecclesiastical interior, with two cardinals receiving a document. Male nude (49x34cm-19x13in) i. pen ink black chk wash squared for transfer two prov. 11-Dec-2 Sotheby's, Olympia #248/R est:600-800

FRENCH SCHOOL, 17th/18th C

Sculpture

£32168	$53720	€46000	Statue de Flore ou l'allegorie du printemps (190cm-75in) stone lit. 25-Jun-3 Sotheby's, Paris #30/R est:12000-18000

FRENCH SCHOOL, 18th C

£4516	$7135	€7000	Boutique du barbier (32x46cm-13x18in) paper on canvas prov.lit. 20-Dec-2 Ribeyre & Baron, Paris #36/R est:6000
£4808	$7596	€7500	Portrait of young girl reading music (67x50cm-26x20in) 16-Nov-2 Farsetti, Prato #324/R est:8500
£5000	$8150	€7500	The muse (75x94cm-30x37in) 2-Feb-3 Lots Road, London #331/R est:3000-5000
£5128	$7487	€8000	Lady and gentleman (102x84cm-40x33in) 5-Jun-2 Il Ponte, Milan #280/R est:6000-7000
£5128	$8051	€8000	Portrait de Philippe Fabre d'Eglantine (69x56cm-27x22in) oval. 13-Dec-2 Pierre Berge, Paris #60/R
£5128	$7949	€8000	Leda and the swan (22x29cm-9x11in) bears i. verso panel. 5-Dec-2 Dr Fritz Nagel, Stuttgart #605/R est:2000
£5449	$8554	€8500	Portrait d'un enfant jouant avec une pomme (100x82cm-39x32in) s.d.1797. 21-Nov-2 Neret-Minet, Paris #72/R est:10000-12000
£5806	$9174	€9000	Lorgneur (57x71cm-22x28in) after Antoine Watteau prov. 18-Dec-2 Beaussant & Lefèvre, Paris #24/R
£5944	$9927	€8500	Moise sauve des eaux (88x109cm-35x43in) 25-Jun-3 Artcurial Briest, Paris #492/R est:6000-8000
£6000	$9240	€9000	Storming of the Bastille (36x46cm-14x18in) painted c.1790. 25-Oct-2 Gorringes, Lewes #909
£6173	$10000	€9260	Portrait of young girl weraing bonnet (32x26cm-13x10in) 23-Jan-3 Sotheby's, New York #216/R est:15000
£6646	$10500	€10500	Historical scene (75x160cm-30x63in) 27-Nov-2 Finarte, Milan #16 est:5000-6000
£6757	$10541	€10000	Vases de fleurs sur entablement (66x135cm-26x53in) 26-Mar-3 Pierre Berge, Paris #25/R
£6863	$11255	€10500	Two little children sleeping (52x67cm-20x26in) paper on canvas. 29-Mar-3 Dannenberg, Berlin #571/R est:800
£6993	$11678	€10000	Les adieux d'un aristocrate. Le proces de Marie-Antoinette (54x65cm-21x26in) pair. 25-Jun-3 Sotheby's, Paris #40/R est:10000-15000
£7449	$11844	€11174	Mythological scene with Mercury watching a small child (84x125cm-33x49in) 5-Mar-3 Rasmussen, Copenhagen #1664/R est:100000 (D.KR 80000)
£8392	$14014	€12000	Portrait d'un notable du sud-ouest dans sa bibliotheque (169x121cm-67x48in) prov. 25-Jun-3 Sotheby's, Paris #39/R est:12000-15000
£8861	$13823	€14000	Still life with monkey. Still life with parrot (184x63cm-72x25in) pair. 19-Oct-2 Semenzato, Venice #173/R est:12000-16000
£9500	$14915	€14250	Still life with roses, daisies and other flowers in a vase on a stone pedestal (73x60cm-29x24in) 10-Dec-2 Sotheby's, Olympia #382/R est:4000-6000
£13000	$20410	€19500	Christ before Caiaphas. Soldiers stripping the robe of Christ (43x36cm-17x14in) copper pair prov.exhib. 16-Dec-2 Sotheby's, London #48/R est:3000-4000
£13580	$22000	€20370	Onions and a truffle (24x31cm-9x12in) panel prov.exhib.lit. 24-Jan-3 Christie's, Rockefeller NY #101/R est:15000-20000
£14000	$22680	€21000	Portrait of Charles Edward Stuart in armour (75x63cm-30x25in) exhib. 23-May-3 Lyon & Turnbull, Edinburgh #18/R est:2000-3000
£16901	$27211	€24000	Venus and Love (76x102cm-30x40in) i.verso. 11-May-3 Finarte, Venice #29/R est:22000
£22152	$34557	€35000	Jetes de fleurs sur des buirlandes (37x73cm-15x29in) canvas on panel painted c.1710 set of four. 16-Oct-2 Fraysse & Associes, Paris #32/R est:12000-15000
£22222	$36000	€33333	Lady reclining on a canape (54x69cm-21x27in) prov.exhib.lit. 24-Jan-3 Christie's, Rockefeller NY #112/R est:40000-60000

Sculpture

£5769	$8942	€9000	Portrait d'homme (36x21x15cm-14x8x6in) terracotta. 9-Dec-2 Rabourdin & Choppin de Janvry, Paris #108/R est:3000
£5782	$9194	€8500	Homme (64x55cm-25x22in) marble medallion. 28-Feb-3 Joron-Derem, Paris #51/R
£11935	$18858	€18500	Figures (46x49x30cm-18x19x12in) ceramic. 20-Dec-2 Piasa, Paris #36/R est:4500-6000
£12581	$19877	€19500	Woman's head (60x30cm-24x12in) marble prov. 20-Dec-2 Piasa, Paris #51/R est:20000-30000
£12821	$19872	€20000	Portrait de femme en Diane (48x24x35cm-19x9x14in) white marble painted wood base prov. 9-Dec-2 Rabourdin & Choppin de Janvry, Paris #7/R est:30000
£25641	$39744	€40000	Fleuve couche (34x56cm-13x22in) pat. terracotta. 9-Dec-2 Rabourdin & Choppin de Janvry, Paris #21/R est:9000
£32258	$50968	€50000	Candlesticks (106x37cm-42x15in) gilded pat.bronze lit. 20-Dec-2 Piasa, Paris #52/R est:70000-80000
£43590	$67564	€68000	Portrait (65x40x23cm-26x16x9in) terracotta prov.exhib. 9-Dec-2 Rabourdin & Choppin de Janvry, Paris #87/R est:15000
£45139	$71319	€65000	Venus de Medicis. Antinous du Belvedere (39cm-15in) pat bronze pair prov. 25-Apr-3 Beaussant & Lefèvre, Paris #77/R est:20000-30000
£82051	$128821	€128000	Neptune (170x125x67cm-67x49x26in) stone fountain. 16-Dec-2 Marc Kohn, Paris #94/R

Works on paper

£7407	$12000	€11111	View of Sully Castle. View of the gardens at Sully Castle (94x46cm-37x18in) i. W/C bodycol htd white pair prov. 22-Jan-3 Christie's, Rockefeller NY #71/R est:30000
£24691	$40000	€37037	Untitled (57x148cm-22x58in) chk pen ink wash W/C bodycol pair. 22-Jan-3 Christie's, Rockefeller NY #72/R est:60000

FRENCH SCHOOL, 18th/19th C

Sculpture

£7051	$10929	€11000	Scene de sacrifice (34x33x17cm-13x13x7in) terracotta. 9-Dec-2 Rabourdin & Choppin de Janvry, Paris #118/R est:3700
£8387	$13252	€13000	Chinese scene (40x49cm-16x19in) terracotta lit. 17-Dec-2 Sotheby's, Paris #75/R est:20000

FRENCH SCHOOL, 19th C

£3642	$5937	€5500	Vase de fleurs (79x64cm-31x25in) painted c.1840. 31-Jan-3 Rabourdin & Choppin de Janvry, Paris #173/R
£3750	$6000	€5625	Lion hunt (46x56cm-18x22in) sold with another possibly by a different hand. 14-May-3 Butterfields, San Francisco #1126/R est:4000-6000
£4620	$7208	€7300	La mort de Demosthene (114x148cm-45x58in) 16-Oct-2 Fraysse & Associes, Paris #35/R est:5000-6000
£5208	$7500	€7812	Cattle and other farm animals in country landscape (85x111cm-33x44in) 15-Jan-3 Christie's, Rockefeller NY #146/R est:12000
£5449	$8446	€8500	Minerve et la Renommee (336x278cm-132x109in) 6-Dec-2 Maigret, Paris #106/R est:6000
£5634	$9352	€8000	Cavalier et berger sous une arche (127x104cm-50x41in) painted c.1810. 16-Jun-3 Claude Aguttes, Neuilly #31/R est:8500-9000
£6207	$9931	€9000	La valse (38x46cm-15x18in) bears sig. 12-Mar-3 Libert, Castor, Paris #66 est:600-800
£6757	$10541	€10000	Pastorale et pastoreaux (242x415cm-95x163in) 30-Mar-3 Anaf, Lyon #262/R est:12000
£7448	$11843	€10800	Nature morte aux fruits et au gibier (79x117cm-31x46in) 4-Mar-3 Livinec, Gaudcheau & Jezequel, Rennes #40/R
£7483	$11898	€11000	Cueillette des cerises (151x200cm-59x79in) mono.d.1839. 26-Feb-3 Marc Kohn, Paris #30/R est:12000
£7975	$13000	€11963	Favourite dachshund (56x45cm-22x18in) init.d.1884. 11-Feb-3 Bonhams & Doyles, New York #260/R est:12000-18000
£8013	$12420	€12500	Portrait de Francois Victor (146x94cm-57x37in) 4-Dec-2 Libert, Castor, Paris #55/R est:9000
£8387	$13252	€13000	Arrivee a Fort-de-France (54x84cm-21x33in) panel. 19-Dec-2 Claude Aguttes, Neuilly #36/R est:6000
£9259	$15000	€13889	View of Taormina, Sicily (43x60cm-17x24in) 24-Jan-3 Christie's, Rockefeller NY #127/R est:15000-20000
£12338	$18383	€19000	Man preaching to gathering, possibly St John the Baptist (130x182cm-51x72in) i. 26-Jun-2 Neumeister, Munich #735/R est:14000
£14286	$22714	€21000	Romulus offre a Jupiter les depouilles opimes d'Acron (114x129cm-45x51in) painted c.1810. 21-Mar-3 Millon & Associes, Paris #29/R est:20000
£17241	$27586	€25000	Tete d'homme au chapeau (63x52cm-25x20in) after Roybet. 13-Mar-3 Artcurial Briest, Paris #50
£33566	$56056	€48000	Portrait d'Ali (46x38cm-18x15in) i.verso. 27-Jun-3 Piasa, Paris #94/R est:6000-8000

Sculpture

£5000	$8150	€7250	Susini boar. Dog (17cm-7in) bronze Sienna marble bases two prov. 21-Jul-3 Sotheby's, London #21/R est:2000-3000
£5253	$8300	€8300	Napoleon (47cm-19in) white marble. 2-Dec-2 Cornette de St.Cyr, Paris #136/R
£6329	$9873	€10000	Tete d'homme barbu (49cm-19in) bronze exec.1875. 18-Oct-2 Rabourdin & Choppin de Janvry, Paris #55
£6500	$10595	€9750	Allegory of the element water with figure of a child (75cm-30in) white marble exec.c.1860. 11-Feb-3 Sotheby's, Olympia #311/R est:6000-8000

£7343 $12262 €10500 Hermaphrodite (20x40cm-8x16in) brown pat bronze wood socle lit. 25-Jun-3 Sotheby's, Paris #122/R est:3000-4000
£7742 $12232 €12000 Laocoon and his children (63x47cm-25x19in) brown pat bronze sold with base lit. 17-Dec-2 Sotheby's, Paris #15/R est:18000
£8861 $14000 €13292 Figure of an Arab serving girl (140cm-55in) painted polychrome on velvet base prov. 24-Apr-3 Christie's, Rockefeller NY #240/R est:8000-12000
£10127 $15797 €16000 Goddesses (92cm-36in) gilt pat bronze pair. 19-Oct-2 Semenzato, Venice #65/R est:14000-16000
£10759 $16785 €17000 Belissaire assis (53x40x40cm-21x16x16in) brown pat bronze. 18-Oct-2 Raboudin & Choppin de Janvry, Paris #47/R

Works on paper

£5128 $8103 €8000 Empereur Napoleon et son Etat-Major (36x47cm-14x19in) W/C gouache. 17-Nov-2 Osenat, Fontainebleau #221
£5346 $8340 €8500 Reconstitution de la villa de Pline (52x181cm-20x71in) graphite wash W/C exec.c.1840. 8-Oct-2 Christie's, Paris #6/R est:15000

FRENCH SCHOOL, 19th/20th C

Sculpture

£26000 $40560 €39000 Cupid and Psyche (201cm-79in) white marble purple marble socle grey marble column lit. 5-Nov-2 Sotheby's, London #165/R est:20000-25000

FRENCH SCHOOL, 20th C

£6962 $10861 €11000 Jeune femme a l'ombrelle et son enfant (60x44cm-24x17in) bears sig. canvas on board. 18-Oct-2 Raboudin & Choppin de Janvry, Paris #23/R est:1200

Sculpture

£5479 $8548 €8000 Untitled (44x15cm-17x6in) wood prov.exhib.lit. 14-Apr-3 Laurence Calmels, Paris #4028/R
£6500 $10140 €9750 Woman reading seated on a bench (50cm-20in) bears i. white marble. 5-Nov-2 Sotheby's, London #177/R est:4000-5000
£7051 $11141 €11000 Mercury (187cm-74in) pat.bronze lit. 16-Nov-2 Lempertz, Koln #1193/R est:7500
£8633 $13813 €12000 L'oiseleur (157x29x33cm-62x11x13in) plaster prov.lit. 19-May-3 Tajan, Paris #165/R est:6000-8000
£15753 $24575 €23000 Masque d'Andre Breton (30cm-12in) plaster. 14-Apr-3 Laurence Calmels, Paris #4080/R est:15000
£17808 $27781 €26000 Untitled (42x15cm-17x6in) wood prov.exhib.lit. 14-Apr-3 Laurence Calmels, Paris #4027/R

Works on paper

£8904 $13979 €13000 Cadavre exquis (32x25cm-13x10in) col crayon. 15-Apr-3 Laurence Calmels, Paris #4255/R est:8000
£9589 $15055 €14000 Cadavre exquis (30x23cm-12x9in) i.verso ink col crayon. 15-Apr-3 Laurence Calmels, Paris #4254/R est:8000
£12329 $19356 €18000 Dessin (28x22cm-11x9in) i.verso ink exhib. 15-Apr-3 Laurence Calmels, Paris #4262/R est:8000
£24138 $38621 €35000 Femme au chapeau (46x28cm-18x11in) gouache. 12-Mar-3 Libert, Castor, Paris #69 est:200-300

FRENCH, Alice Helm (1864-1934) Austrian

Works on paper

£1647 $2750 €2388 Winter landscape - path through the drifts (51x74cm-20x29in) s.d.1908 pastel. 17-Jun-3 John Moran, Pasadena #99 est:2000-3000

FRENCH, Annie (1872-1965) British

Works on paper

£250 $388 €375 In the silence deep (21x13cm-8x5in) pen ink. 7-Dec-2 Shapes, Edinburgh #339
£440 $682 €660 Floral dress (13x10cm-5x4in) ink W/C. 5-Dec-2 Bonhams, Edinburgh #136
£900 $1485 €1305 Led away by fairies (13x21cm-5x8in) i.verso pen brown ink brown wash prov.lit. 3-Jul-3 Christie's, Kensington #232/R

FRENCH, E O (20th C) British

Works on paper

£500 $760 €750 Yacht Cambria (54x42cm-21x17in) s.i. W/C. 15-Aug-2 Bonhams, New Bond Street #238

FRENCH, Jared (1905-1987) American

£35484 $55000 €53226 Three women and a lifeguard (62x71cm-24x28in) s. exhib. 4-Dec-2 Sotheby's, New York #85/R est:125000-175000

FRENCH, Leonard (1928-) Australian

£4406 $6565 €6609 Flight (67x59cm-26x23in) s. enamel on board. 27-Aug-2 Christie's, Melbourne #224/R est:8000-12000 (A.D 11500)
£10000 $15900 €15000 Scroll of the turtle (91x76cm-36x30in) s. enamel composition board. 4-Mar-3 Deutscher-Menzies, Melbourne #89/R est:20000-25000 (A.D 26000)
£13178 $20953 €19767 Night fisherman (152x183cm-60x72in) s. enamel gold leaf hessian. 5-May-3 Sotheby's, Melbourne #176/R est:40000-50000 (A.D 34000)

Works on paper

£464 $720 €696 Pattern of warriors no 1 (19x29cm-7x11in) s.d.1963 verso mixed media. 29-Oct-2 Lawson Menzies, Sydney #29/R (A.D 1300)
£521 $812 €782 Blue cruiciform (25x18cm-10x7in) s. ink W/C board prov. 8-Apr-3 Peter Webb, Auckland #110/R est:2500-3500 (NZ.D 1500)
£4270 $6534 €6405 Song for morning (59x65cm-23x26in) s. mixed media executed c.1980 prov. 26-Aug-2 Sotheby's, Paddington #693/R est:6000-8000 (A.D 12000)

FRENCH, Percy (1854-1920) Irish

Works on paper

£640 $1024 €960 Moorland stream (9x19cm-4x7in) s. W/C. 11-Mar-3 David Duggleby, Scarborough #150
£976 $1376 €1600 Country landscape (15x23cm-6x9in) s. W/C. 7-Feb-2 Woodwards, Cork #239
£1000 $1560 €1500 Moorland landscape (8x18cm-3x7in) s. W/C. 11-Apr-3 Keys, Aylsham #469/R est:350-450
£1100 $1727 €1650 Mountains, county Wicklow (28x39cm-11x15in) s. W/C. 21-Nov-2 Tennants, Leyburn #620 est:300-400
£1220 $1720 €2000 Bogland landscape (10x18cm-4x7in) s. W/C. 7-Feb-2 Woodwards, Cork #240
£1351 $2108 €2000 View across an estuary to distant headland (13x21cm-5x8in) s. W/C. 26-Mar-3 James Adam, Dublin #4/R est:2000-3000
£1410 $2214 €2200 View of a round tower and monastery in the west (24x35cm-9x14in) s. W/C. 19-Nov-2 Hamilton Osborne King, Dublin #415/R est:800-1200
£1463 $2063 €2400 Country landscape (18x25cm-7x10in) s. W/C. 7-Feb-2 Woodwards, Cork #241
£1622 $2530 €2400 Beach scene with sand dunes (14x21cm-6x8in) s. W/C. 26-Mar-3 James Adam, Dublin #5/R est:2000-3000
£1689 $2635 €2500 Sailing boats at sunset (16x21cm-6x8in) W/C. 26-Mar-3 James Adam, Dublin #16/R est:2500-3500
£1731 $2683 €2700 Bog landscape, sunrise (11x17cm-4x7in) s.d.1909 W/C. 3-Dec-2 Bonhams & James Adam, Dublin #1/R est:2000-3000
£1739 $2852 €2400 Snowy woodland clearing (15x22cm-6x9in) s.d.1914 W/C. 28-May-3 Bonhams & James Adam, Dublin #33/R est:2500-3500
£1772 $2747 €2800 Near Brighton (19x26cm-7x10in) s. W/C. 25-Sep-2 James Adam, Dublin #7/R est:2500-4000
£1923 $2981 €3000 South Sligo Bay (17x25cm-7x10in) s. W/C. 3-Dec-2 Bonhams & James Adam, Dublin #2/R est:1200-1800
£1923 $2981 €3000 Irish lough (12x17cm-5x7in) W/C. 3-Dec-2 Bonhams & James Adam, Dublin #5/R est:2500-3500
£1923 $3019 €3000 Lake landscape (13x17cm-5x7in) s. W/C. 19-Nov-2 Hamilton Osborne King, Dublin #449/R est:1000-1500
£1923 $3019 €3000 In the west (17x25cm-7x10in) s.indis.d.19. 19-Nov-2 Hamilton Osborne King, Dublin #450/R est:2000-3000
£2000 $3180 €3000 Summer, boglands, Connemara (17x22cm-7x9in) s.d.1907 W/C. 5-Mar-3 John Ross, Belfast #148 est:2000-2500
£2300 $3565 €3450 Morning Boglans, Connemara (15x23cm-6x9in) s. W/C. 2-Oct-2 John Ross, Belfast #155a est:2500-3000
£2391 $3922 €3300 Cottage in bogland landscape with goose (16x26cm-6x10in) s. W/C. 28-May-3 Bonhams & James Adam, Dublin #37a
£2439 $3439 €4000 Riverside study (10x18cm-4x7in) s. W/C. 7-Feb-2 Woodwards, Cork #242
£2464 $4041 €3400 Bog landscape with mountains beyond (17x24cm-7x9in) s. W/C. 28-May-3 Bonhams & James Adam, Dublin #37/R est:2000-2800
£2550 $4106 €3800 Bog landscape (18x25cm-7x10in) init. W/C. 18-Feb-3 Whyte's, Dublin #19/R est:3000-4000
£2550 $3953 €3825 Convent at Portstewart (15x21cm-6x8in) s. W/C. 4-Dec-2 John Ross, Belfast #164 est:3250-3500
£2564 $3974 €4000 An Irish bog land, sunset (17x25cm-7x10in) s. W/C. 3-Dec-2 Bonhams & James Adam, Dublin #3/R est:3000-4000
£2600 $4056 €3900 Castle on a lough at dusk (25x35cm-10x14in) init. W/C. 10-Apr-3 Tennants, Leyburn #871/R est:600-800
£2600 $4056 €3900 Sailing boat passing a town at dusk (17x24cm-7x9in) init.d.1919 W/C. 10-Apr-3 Tennants, Leyburn #873/R est:400-600
£3000 $4380 €4500 River and boglands, Connemara (15x23cm-6x9in) s.d.1915 W/C. 12-Jun-2 John Ross, Belfast #178 est:3500-4000
£3019 $4709 €4800 Falcarragh, County Donegal (13x19cm-5x7in) s.d.1916 i.verso W/C prov. 17-Sep-2 Whyte's, Dublin #110/R est:3000-5000
£3243 $5059 €4800 Western bogland river (17x25cm-7x10in) s.d.1905 W/C. 26-Mar-3 James Adam, Dublin #12 est:3000-5000
£3333 $5167 €5200 Garden path (25x18cm-10x7in) s.d.1906 W/C. 3-Dec-2 Bonhams & James Adam, Dublin #6/R est:2000-3000
£3500 $5460 €5250 Bogland at sunset (25x41cm-10x16in) s. W/C. 10-Apr-3 Tennants, Leyburn #872 est:600-800
£3500 $5600 €5250 Achill Island, Co. Mayo (17x23cm-7x9in) init.i.d.1911 W/C prov. 15-May-3 Christie's, London #34/R
£3500 $5600 €5250 Turf stacks and pine trees (17x24cm-7x9in) s. W/C. 15-May-3 Christie's, London #33/R est:3500
£3590 $5564 €5600 River through bog land landscape (16x24cm-6x9in) s. W/C. 3-Dec-2 Bonhams & James Adam, Dublin #4/R est:3000-4000
£4800 $7632 €7200 Dusk boglands, Connemara (22x33cm-9x13in) s. W/C. 5-Mar-3 John Ross, Belfast #117 est:3000-3500

£5660 $8830 €9000 Limerick (27x36cm-11x14in) s. W/C. 17-Sep-2 Whyte's, Dublin #58/R est:8000-10000
£8974 $14090 €14000 Garden that I love (29x44cm-11x17in) init.d.1896 W/C exhib. 19-Nov-2 Whyte's, Dublin #62/R est:8000-10000

FRENCH, Percy (attrib) (1854-1920) Irish
£962 $1510 €1500 Donkey and cart in the west (16x24cm-6x9in) board. 19-Nov-2 Hamilton Osborne King, Dublin #459 est:500-1000

FRENCH, Thomas (19th C) British
£350 $571 €525 Off to work (98x67cm-39x26in) s. 29-Jan-3 Sotheby's, Olympia #61/R

FRENDER, Helge (1906-1976) Swedish
£295 $465 €443 Landscape with waterway (51x54cm-20x21in) s.d.32 panel. 30-Nov-2 Goteborg Auktionsverk, Sweden #532/R (S.KR 4200)

FRENET, Jean Baptiste (1814-1889) French
Photographs
£2179 $3444 €3400 Trois femmes (23x17cm-9x7in) salt print prov. 16-Nov-2 Christie's, Paris #225/R est:4000-6000

FRENKEL, Boris Borvine (1900-1984) Polish
£449 $714 €660 La place animee (50x55cm-20x22in) s. isorel panel. 26-Feb-3 Artcurial Briest, Paris #185
£993 $1658 €1400 Jeune homme avec le coq (44x27cm-17x11in) s. cardboard. 17-Jun-3 Claude Boisgirard, Paris #30

FRENKEL, Itzhak (1900-1981) Israeli
£420 $655 €630 Marriage ceremony in a nocturnal village setting (29x45cm-11x18in) s. board. 17-Sep-2 Rosebery Fine Art, London #695/R

FRENKIEL, H (?) French?
£252 $413 €350 L'etudiant (35x27cm-14x11in) s. 3-Jun-3 Tajan, Paris #35

FRENNET, L (19th C) Belgian
£316 $494 €500 Cheval et charrette (48x58cm-19x23in) 16-Sep-2 Amberes, Antwerp #202

FRENTZ, Rudolf (1831-1888) German
Works on paper
£1013 $1570 €1600 Hunters with dogs and dead stag (34x50cm-13x20in) s.cyrillic brush over pencil. 25-Sep-2 Neumeister, Munich #398/R

FRERE, C (?) French?
£1100 $1826 €1650 Horses in a stable (54x68cm-21x27in) s. 10-Jun-3 Bonhams, Knightsbridge #62/R est:800-1200

FRERE, Charles Theodore (1814-1888) French
£600 $936 €900 Le Vieux Maronnier (22x33cm-9x13in) s. panel. 26-Mar-3 Sotheby's, Olympia #200/R
£1216 $1897 €1800 Elegante pres du Caire (40x28cm-16x11in) s.d.1875 panel. 25-Mar-3 Chochon-Barre & Allardi, Paris #117/R est:2800-3000
£2349 $3782 €3500 Le campement des Bedouins (26x34cm-10x13in) s. panel. 23-Feb-3 Lesieur & Le Bars, Le Havre #54/R
£3526 $5500 €5289 Les pyramid de Gyzah (13x23cm-5x9in) s. panel. 29-Mar-3 Charlton Hall, Columbia #149/R est:3000-4000
£4200 $6552 €6300 Arrival of a caravan at the Nile (17x28cm-7x11in) s. panel. 15-Oct-2 Sotheby's, London #141/R est:3000-4000
£5000 $7850 €7800 Vue de l'Acropole, Athenes (19x27cm-7x11in) s.i.d.1851. 16-Dec-2 Gros & Delettrez, Paris #299/R est:3000-3800
£5756 $9439 €8000 Chameliers aux abords du village (24x40cm-9x16in) s. panel. 4-Jun-3 Tajan, Paris #264/R est:3000-4000
£6410 $10064 €10000 Caravane dans le desert (41x63cm-16x25in) s. 15-Dec-2 Lombrail & Teucquam, Paris #1/R
£7051 $11071 €11000 Le chateau d'Europe, Humail-Hissar (21x37cm-8x15in) s.i.d.1852 prov. 16-Dec-2 Gros & Delettrez, Paris #280/R est:8000-10000
£8387 $13000 €12581 Sunset on the Nile (46x65cm-18x26in) s.i. prov. 29-Oct-2 Sotheby's, New York #50/R est:15000-20000
£8974 $14090 €14000 La halte sur les bords du Nil (21x37cm-8x15in) s. s.i.verso panel. 16-Dec-2 Gros & Delettrez, Paris #281/R est:12000-15000
£9930 $16583 €14200 L'arrivee de la caravane a Gizeh (21x37cm-8x15in) s. panel. 27-Jun-3 Claude Aguttes, Neuilly #136/R est:14000-16000
Works on paper
£1761 $2712 €2800 Coucher de soleil sur le Nil (13x21cm-5x8in) s. W/C. 23-Oct-2 Rabourdin & Choppin de Janvry, Paris #90/R
£1986 $3316 €2800 Vue du Caire (39x26cm-15x10in) s.d.1886 pencil W/C. 23-Jun-3 Beaussant & Lefèvre, Paris #103/R est:500-600

FRERE, Edouard (1819-1886) French
£417 $654 €650 Les lavandieres (21x28cm-8x11in) s. 16-Dec-2 Chochon-Barre & Allardi, Paris #50
£800 $1248 €1200 Young artist (33x25cm-13x10in) s.d.55 panel. 17-Sep-2 Sotheby's, Olympia #245/R
£974 $1500 €1461 Children returning from church (33x23cm-13x9in) s. panel. 27-Oct-2 Grogan, Boston #47 est:2000-2500
£1317 $2041 €1976 Tending the pot (25x20cm-10x8in) s.d.66 panel. 3-Dec-2 Ritchie, Toronto #3073/R est:2000-3000 (C.D 3200)
£1778 $2951 €2578 Faggott gatherers in the snow (46x37cm-18x15in) s.d.1868 panel prov. 16-Jun-3 Waddingtons, Toronto #281/R est:8000-12000 (C.D 4000)
£1875 $3000 €2719 In the courtyard (46x38cm-18x15in) s.d.59. 16-May-3 Skinner, Boston #20/R est:5000-7000
£3600 $5868 €5400 Children by a pool (34x25cm-13x10in) s.d.1876 board. 12-Feb-3 Bonhams, Knightsbridge #69/R est:4000-6000
£4200 $6510 €6300 Gathering faggots (33x24cm-13x9in) s.d.83 panel. 3-Dec-2 Sotheby's, Olympia #251/R est:3000-4000
£5500 $8745 €8250 Special bathe (25x19cm-10x7in) s. panel prov. 20-Mar-3 Christie's, Kensington #98/R est:6000-8000
Works on paper
£256 $425 €371 Motherly care (25x20cm-10x8in) s. pencil W/C. 14-Jun-3 Jackson's, Cedar Falls #363/R

FRERICHS, William C A (1829-1905) American
£1355 $2250 €1965 Wooded landscape with fishermen (36x56cm-14x22in) s. 11-Jun-3 Boos Gallery, Michigan #555/R est:3500-4500
£3521 $5000 €5282 Outing at Stairway Falls, North Carolina (58x76cm-23x30in) 8-Aug-1 Barridorf, Portland #3/R est:6000-9000
Works on paper
£2903 $4500 €4355 Figures in a mountainous landscape (51x41cm-20x16in) init. 29-Oct-2 Doyle, New York #50 est:1500-2500

FRESCO, Abraham (1903-1942) Dutch
Works on paper
£655 $1042 €950 View of the Nieuwmart, Amsterdam (33x46cm-13x18in) s.d.1934 W/C. 10-Mar-3 Sotheby's, Amsterdam #334/R est:400-600

FRESENIUS, Hermann Julius Richard (1844-1903) German
£350 $539 €550 Summer mountain landscape with figures (36x58cm-14x23in) board. 5-Sep-2 Arnold, Frankfurt #768
£379 $603 €550 Deer on snowy woodland track in the evening (31x21cm-12x8in) s. panel. 8-Mar-3 Arnold, Frankfurt #587/R

FRESNAYE, Roger de la (1885-1925) French
£37762 $63063 €54000 Nu debout a la cheminee (107x67cm-42x26in) c.1910-1911 prov.exhib.lit. 30-Jun-3 Artcurial Briest, Paris #51/R
£57692 $90577 €90000 Nature morte a l'encrier (54x65cm-21x26in) s.d.13 lit. 10-Dec-2 Artcurial Briest, Paris #494/R est:60000-80000
£105000 $172200 €157500 Bouteille de Porto Sandeman (73x92cm-29x36in) s.d.1914 prov.exhib.lit. 5-Feb-3 Sotheby's, London #163/R est:150000
Works on paper
£380 $600 €600 Cubist composition (20x12cm-8x5in) s. pencil. 29-Nov-2 Villa Grisebach, Berlin #614/R
£1090 $1689 €1700 Etudes (25x19cm-10x7in) studio st. crayon prov.lit. 4-Dec-2 Piasa, Paris #206
£1346 $2113 €2100 Etude (26x20cm-10x8in) s.i.d.21 wash dr. 13-Dec-2 Piasa, Paris #65/R
£1899 $3000 €3000 Jeune homme aux ains levees (20x16cm-8x6in) s.d.1920 crayon dr prov.lit. 27-Nov-2 Blanchet, Paris #61
£2564 $4026 €4000 Soldats dont un fumant la pipe (30x20cm-12x8in) W/C pen paper on cardboard. 22-Nov-2 Millon & Associes, Paris #22
£6000 $10020 €8700 La madelon (30x20cm-12x8in) W/C over brush ink executed c.1917. 24-Jun-3 Sotheby's, London #231/R est:8000-12000

FREUD, Lucian (1922-) British/German
£115000 $177100 €172500 Rose and sweet pea (31x20cm-12x8in) s.i.verso painted c.1974 prov.exhib. 23-Oct-2 Christie's, London #103/R est:55000-75000
£300000 $492000 €450000 Head of a child (25x17cm-10x7in) painted c.1954 prov. 5-Feb-3 Christie's, London #2/R est:250000-350000
Prints
£2051 $3200 €3077 Lawrence Gowing (33x28cm-13x11in) init.i. etching. 5-Nov-2 Christie's, Rockefeller NY #380/R est:3000-5000
£2642 $4200 €3963 Head on a pillow (10x13cm-4x5in) init.i. etching. 2-May-3 Sotheby's, New York #451/R est:3500-4500
£2830 $4500 €4245 Head of girl II (16x13cm-6x5in) init.num.16/16 etching. 2-May-3 Sotheby's, New York #450/R est:4000-6000
£3000 $4650 €4500 Naked man on a bed (58x57cm-23x22in) init.num.6/40 etching. 3-Dec-2 Christie's, London #125/R est:3500-4500
£3205 $5000 €4808 Two men in the studio (40x37cm-16x15in) init.num.3/25 etching. 5-Nov-2 Christie's, Rockefeller NY #382/R est:6000-8000
£3800 $6270 €5510 Naked man on a bed (30x30cm-12x12in) init.num.21/40 etching. 1-Jul-3 Sotheby's, London #173/R est:2500-3500
£4717 $7500 €7076 Head and shoulders (24x29cm-9x11in) init.num.18/20 etching. 2-May-3 Sotheby's, New York #452/R est:8000-10000
£4808 $7500 €7212 Woman on a bed (45x39cm-18x15in) init.num.3/30 etching. 5-Nov-2 Christie's, Rockefeller NY #383/R est:8000-10000

£5031 $8000 €7547 Bella (42x35cm-17x14in) init.num.14/50 etching. 2-May-3 Sotheby's, New York #453/R est:5000-7000

£5500 $8580 €8250 Head of Ib (21x15cm-8x6in) init.num.5/40 etching. 25-Mar-3 Sotheby's, London #166/R est:4000-6000

£7500 $11625 €11250 Girl sitting (60x77cm-24x30in) init.num.28/50 etching. 3-Dec-2 Christie's, London #124/R est:5000-7000

£19231 $30000 €28847 Pluto (42x69cm-17x27in) init.num.3/40 etching drypoint W/C. 5-Nov-2 Christie's, Rockefeller NY #381/R est:28000-32000

£20000 $33000 €29000 Garden in winter (77x60cm-30x24in) inid.d.num.40/46 etching. 1-Jul-3 Sotheby's, London #176/R est:20000-30000

£24000 $37440 €36000 Woman sleeping (73x60cm-29x24in) etching. 10-Oct-2 Sotheby's, London #239/R est:10000-15000

£27000 $42120 €40500 Pluto (32x60cm-13x24in) init.d.1988 etching drypoint grey W/C. 25-Mar-3 Sotheby's, London #167/R est:25000-30000

£47170 $75000 €70755 Ill in Paris (13x18cm-5x7in) s.num.1/10 etching. 29-Apr-3 Christie's, Rockefeller NY #613/R est:35000-45000

Works on paper

£2000 $3340 €2900 Potato men (20x14cm-8x6in) pencil exec.c.1940 sold with a letter and postcard prov. 24-Jun-3 Sotheby's, Olympia #54/R est:2000-3000

£15000 $25050 €21750 Clarendon Crescent, Paddington (34x25cm-13x10in) i. pencil col crayon pen ink executed 1953 prov. 27-Jun-3 Christie's, London #187/R est:15000-20000

£35000 $57400 €52500 Untitled, quince (13x22cm-5x9in) s.d.7 Oct 1947 conte col pencil pencil ink prov. 7-Feb-3 Sotheby's, London #248/R est:20000-30000

£38000 $62320 €57000 Child reading II (34x23cm-13x9in) pencil W/C bodycol executed 1961 prov. 6-Jun-3 Christie's, London #190/R est:20000-30000

£38000 $63460 €55100 Drawing for poster I (56x45cm-22x18in) ink executed 1973 prov. 27-Jun-3 Christie's, London #193/R est:40000-60000

FREUDENBERGER, S (1745-1801) Swiss

£1700 $2720 €2550 Couple standing by a well (61x46cm-24x18in) s. 11-Mar-3 Bonhams, Knightsbridge #318b/R est:1000-2000

FREUDENBERGER, Sigmund (1745-1801) Swiss

Works on paper

£256 $405 €400 Little Swiss girl (11x10cm-4x4in) pencil. 15-Nov-2 Reiss & Sohn, Konigstein #137/R

£1103 $1766 €1600 La lecon de physique (14x10cm-6x4in) pen black ink grey wish. 12-Mar-3 E & Eve, Paris #40 est:800-1000

FREUDENBERGER, Sigmund (attrib) (1745-1801) Swiss

Works on paper

£380 $589 €600 Momento mori (14x17cm-6x7in) i. pen Indian ink brush sepia. 27-Sep-2 Venator & Hansten, Koln #950/R

£699 $1104 €1049 Guggisberg egg seller on bench (19x14cm-7x6in) s. W/C. 14-Nov-2 Stuker, Bern #9119 est:800-1200 (S.FR 1600)

FREUDENTHAL, Peter (1938-) Swedish

£561 $875 €842 Besuch in Tann - der verklarte Friedhof (100x110cm-39x43in) s.d.1987 verso acrylic prov. 6-Nov-2 AB Stockholms Auktionsverk #562/R (S.KR 8000)

Works on paper

£1542 $2405 €2313 Untitled composition (200x36cm-79x14in) mixed media. 5-Nov-2 Bukowskis, Stockholm #282/R est:15000-20000 (S.KR 22000)

FREUND, Gisele (1908-2000) French

Photographs

£1923 $2981 €3000 The painter Frida Kahlo and her doctor, Mexico City (29x25cm-11x10in) i. verso gelatin silver lit. 6-Dec-2 Bassenge, Berlin #4688/R est:1500

FREUNDLICH, Jeanne (1892-1966) Austrian?

£574 $896 €850 Composition (22x15cm-9x6in) init. panel. 28-Mar-3 Charbonneaux, Paris #74

FREUNDLICH, Otto (1878-1943) German

£1282 $1987 €2000 Untitled (16x18cm-6x7in) painted c.1928 prov.exhib. 3-Dec-2 Christie's, Amsterdam #38/R est:3000-5000

£2941 $4912 €4264 Composition, unfinished (32x25cm-13x10in) pastel chamois. 24-Jun-3 Koller, Zurich #128/R est:2000-3000 (S.FR 6500)

Works on paper

£986 $1637 €1400 Composition (17x16cm-7x6in) mono. pencil two. 14-Jun-3 Hauswedell & Nolte, Hamburg #1194/R

£3333 $5300 €4800 Composition (19x14cm-7x6in) mono. gouache. 29-Apr-3 Artcurial Briest, Paris #123/R est:4000-5000

£3459 $5362 €5500 Composition (23x17cm-9x7in) mono. Indian ink dr. 30-Oct-2 Artcurial Briest, Paris #214/R est:6000-7000

£3462 $5435 €5400 Composition (19x14cm-7x6in) mono. Chinese ink dr. 11-Dec-2 Artcurial Briest, Paris #538/R

£3611 $5742 €5200 Composition (19x13cm-7x5in) mono. gouache. 29-Apr-3 Artcurial Briest, Paris #124/R est:4000-5000

FREW, Alexander (?-1908) British

£2400 $3720 €3600 North End, Iona (91x152cm-36x60in) s.d.1899. 6-Dec-2 Lyon & Turnbull, Edinburgh #44/R est:2000-3000

FREWIN, Moira (20th C) British

£280 $437 €420 Autumn afternoon (90x121cm-35x48in) s. board. 10-Apr-3 Bonhams, Edinburgh #51

FREY, Alice (1895-1981) Belgian

£513 $795 €800 Interior with kitchen (24x19cm-9x7in) s. board. 7-Dec-2 De Vuyst, Lokeren #132

£897 $1434 €1300 Fantaisie carnavalesque (80x66cm-31x26in) s. exhib. 15-Mar-3 De Vuyst, Lokeren #126/R

£1006 $1570 €1600 Gypsies on the beach (38x47cm-15x19in) s. 23-Sep-2 Bernaerts, Antwerp #822/R est:1250-1500

£1079 $1770 €1500 Three ladies bathing (32x40cm-13x16in) s. 3-Jun-3 Christie's, Amsterdam #290/R est:800-1200

£1389 $2208 €2000 Femme nue et satyre (61x50cm-24x20in) s. 29-Apr-3 Campo & Campo, Antwerp #124/R est:2500-3000

FREY, August (1912-) Swiss

£330 $535 €479 Winter in Boschenroth (70x50cm-28x20in) s.d.83 i. stretcher prov. 24-May-3 Galerie Gloggner, Luzern #38/R (S.FR 700)

FREY, Eugène (1864-1930) French

£1583 $2595 €2200 Campement au soleil couchant (38x55cm-15x22in) s. 4-Jun-3 Tajan, Paris #260/R est:1800-2200

FREY, Johann Jakob (1813-1865) Swiss

£1761 $2747 €2800 Italian landscape with cattle by stream (44x58cm-17x23in) paper on canvas. 11-Oct-2 Winterberg, Heidelberg #528/R est:1850

£4077 $6320 €6116 Southern landscape with goatherder (33x44cm-13x17in) s.i.d.1854. 3-Oct-2 Koller, Zurich #3076/R est:5000-8000 (S.FR 9500)

£9500 $15865 €14250 Ruins at Philae, Egypt (76x113cm-30x44in) prov. 18-Jun-3 Christie's, Kensington #179/R est:10000-15000

FREY, Johann Wilhelm (1830-1909) Austrian

Works on paper

£345 $545 €500 Karntnertor, Vienna (26x21cm-10x8in) s. pen W/C gouache over pencil. 4-Apr-3 Venator & Hansten, Koln #1785

£345 $545 €500 Karntnertor, Vienna (27x21cm-11x8in) s. pen W/C gouache over pencil. 4-Apr-3 Venator & Hansten, Koln #1786

FREY, Joseph F (1892-1977) American

£613 $950 €920 River landscape (61x76cm-24x30in) s. prov. 29-Oct-2 John Moran, Pasadena #779

£745 $1200 €1118 Mountain landscape (41x51cm-16x20in) s. masonite. 18-Feb-3 John Moran, Pasadena #167a

£839 $1300 €1259 Landscape, verbena (51x61cm-20x24in) s. prov. 29-Oct-2 John Moran, Pasadena #780

FREY, Louis (19th C) German

£288 $438 €450 Figures on lake edge (20x25cm-8x10in) s. panel. 11-Jul-2 Allgauer, Kempten #2481/R

FREY, Oskar (1883-1966) German

£563 $907 €800 Bodensee landscape (76x101cm-30x40in) s. 7-May-3 Michael Zeller, Lindau #708/R

FREY, Wilhelm (1826-1911) German

£1006 $1570 €1600 Northern German landscape with lake and ducks (43x61cm-17x24in) s.d.1902 lit. 20-Sep-2 Karlheinz Kaupp, Staufen #1907/R est:1600

£1410 $2144 €2200 Resting cows with shepherdess on forest edge (68x58cm-27x23in) s.i.d.1882 lit. 11-Jul-2 Allgauer, Kempten #2483/R

£3000 $4800 €4500 Cattle and sheep in a coastal landscape (95x154cm-37x61in) s.indis.i. 7-Jan-3 Bonhams, Knightsbridge #178/R est:4000-6000

FREY-MOOCK, Adolf (1881-1954) German

£300 $475 €450 Satyr and Nymph (32x45cm-13x18in) s. panel. 29-Nov-2 Zofingen, Switzerland #2875 (S.FR 700)

£300 $475 €450 Penelope (34x27cm-13x11in) s.i.verso panel. 29-Nov-2 Zofingen, Switzerland #2876 (S.FR 700)

£342 $534 €500 Flora in Arcadian landscape (46x35cm-18x14in) s. 10-Apr-3 Schopman, Hamburg #624/R

£528 $850 €750 Salome (45x45cm-18x18in) s. 7-May-3 Michael Zeller, Lindau #709/R

£764 $1192 €1200 Gloom - Christ with halo (45x35cm-18x14in) s. i.verso panel lit. 7-Nov-2 Allgauer, Kempten #2816/R

£828 $1292 €1300 Figures (42x32cm-17x13in) s.i. panel. 6-Nov-2 Hugo Ruef, Munich #1096/R

£897 $1364 €1400 Mythological scene - Chiron with figures (33x43cm-13x17in) s. board lit. 11-Jul-2 Allgauer, Kempten #2484/R

£1013 $1600 €1600 Fawn and nymphs (28x35cm-11x14in) s. board lit. 29-Nov-2 Schloss Ahlden, Ahlden #1403/R est:1800

£1592 $2484 €2500 Bacchanal scene with fawn, Pan and young couple (57x47cm-22x19in) s. panel. 6-Nov-2 Hugo Ruef, Munich #1095/R est:1500

FREY-SURBECK, Marguerite (1886-1981) Swiss

£370 $596 €555 East River from Beckmann Town Hotel (61x46cm-24x18in) s. i. verso i. stretcher. 7-May-3 Dobiaschofsky, Bern #558/R (S.FR 800)

£556 $894 €834 Interior with birdcage on window ledge (100x65cm-39x26in) s. i. verso. 7-May-3 Dobiaschofsky, Bern #557/R est:1600 (S.FR 1200)

£655 $1022 €983 Pommiers en fleurs pres de Paris (33x40cm-13x16in) s.i.d.1911 board. 6-Nov-2 Dobiaschofsky, Bern #3358/R (S.FR 1500)

£1528 $2384 €2292 Bunch of mallows (145x95cm-57x37in) s. 8-Nov-2 Dobiaschofsky, Bern #111/R est:3600 (S.FR 3500)

FREYBERG, Conrad (1842-?) German

£949 $1500 €1500 Bust portrait of a young woman (53x48cm-21x19in) s. oval. 29-Nov-2 Bolland & Marotz, Bremen #697/R est:1700

£12987 $20000 €19481 Ubergabe von Metz (123x265cm-48x104in) s.d.1876 prov.exhib.lit. 4-Sep-2 Christie's, Rockefeller NY #324/R est:8000-12000

FREYMUTH, Alphons (1940-) Dutch

£2564 $3974 €4000 De rode tafel - red table (115x95cm-45x37in) s.d.67 verso acrylic. 3-Dec-2 Christie's, Amsterdam #333/R est:4000-6000

FREYTAG, Albert (1851-?) German

£652 $1017 €978 Desperation (66x27cm-26x11in) s.d.1917 panel. 16-Sep-2 Philippe Schuler, Zurich #6446 (S.FR 1500)

FRIANT, Émile (1863-1932) French

£980 $1569 €1500 Reclining female nude (30x44cm-12x17in) s. board lit. 10-Jan-3 Allgauer, Kempten #1596/R est:1500

FRIBERG, Roj (1934-) Swedish

Works on paper

£570 $901 €855 Field of death (92x122cm-36x48in) mono.d.73 pencil. 28-Apr-3 Bukowskis, Stockholm #998/R (S.KR 7500)

£722 $1141 €1083 Giant's head (118x144cm-46x57in) init.d.78 pencil exhib. 28-Apr-3 Bukowskis, Stockholm #925/R (S.KR 9500)

£927 $1492 €1391 Olskroken (118x134cm-46x53in) init.d.77 pencil. 7-May-3 AB Stockholms Auktionsverk #1000/R (S.KR 12000)

FRIBOULET, Jef (1919-) French

£387 $612 €600 Femme en rouge (46x38cm-18x15in) s. 17-Dec-2 Rossini, Paris #80

£403 $648 €600 La lampe a petrole (83x25cm-33x10in) s. panel. 23-Feb-3 Lesieur & Le Bars, Le Havre #56

£417 $654 €650 Lampe a petrole (83x25cm-33x10in) s.d.59 panel. 24-Nov-2 Lesieur & Le Bars, Le Havre #54

£513 $805 €800 Coucher de soleil en Camargue (73x92cm-29x36in) s.d.58 verso. 24-Nov-2 Lesieur & Le Bars, Le Havre #53

£962 $1510 €1500 Detente (65x46cm-26x18in) s. 24-Nov-2 Lesieur & Le Bars, Le Havre #55

£1342 $2161 €2000 Les harengs (81x38cm-32x15in) s. 23-Feb-3 Lesieur & Le Bars, Le Havre #58

£1408 $2268 €2000 Bouquet de fleurs (56x46cm-22x18in) s. 12-May-3 Lesieur & Le Bars, Le Havre #39/R

£1418 $2369 €2000 Nature morte a la chaise (116x89cm-46x35in) s. 18-Jun-3 Charbonneaux, Paris #90/R est:2000-2500

£2013 $3242 €3000 La table devant la fenetre (80x60cm-31x24in) s. 23-Feb-3 Lesieur & Le Bars, Le Havre #55/R

FRICK, Paul de (1864-1935) French

£294 $471 €450 Breton coastal landscape near Ebbe with fishing boat and wealthy figures (16x32cm-6x13in) s. lit. 10-Jan-3 Allgauer, Kempten #1597/R

FRICKE, August (1829-1894) German

£786 $1219 €1250 Sailing regatta on the Weser (51x80cm-20x31in) s. 2-Nov-2 Hans Stahl, Toestorf #70/R

FRIDELL, Axel (1894-1935) Swedish

Prints

£5186 $8090 €7779 Mr Simmons reading the newspaper (30x24cm-12x9in) s. drypoint lit. 5-Nov-2 Bukowskis, Stockholm #563/R est:50000-60000 (S.KR 74000)

Works on paper

£543 $880 €787 In the shade of the tree (12x14cm-5x6in) s.d.13 Indian ink lit. 26-May-3 Bukowskis, Stockholm #173/R (S.KR 7000)

FRIE, Peter (1947-) Swedish

£849 $1368 €1274 Landscape from Bornholm (30x25cm-12x10in) s. 7-May-3 AB Stockholms Auktionsverk #978/R (S.KR 11000)

£927 $1492 €1391 Landscape (13x24cm-5x9in) s. panel. 7-May-3 AB Stockholms Auktionsverk #1069/R (S.KR 12000)

£1217 $1922 €1826 Landscape (37x44cm-15x17in) s.d.91 verso panel. 28-Apr-3 Bukowskis, Stockholm #889/R est:20000-25000 (S.KR 16000)

£1402 $2186 €2103 Landscape (50x61cm-20x24in) s. 5-Nov-2 Bukowskis, Stockholm #409/R est:15000-20000 (S.KR 20000)

£1544 $2486 €2316 Yellow landscape (37x41cm-15x16in) s.d.90 verso panel exhib. 7-May-3 AB Stockholms Auktionsverk #1022/R est:25000-30000 (S.KR 20000)

£1597 $2523 €2396 The wave (90x100cm-35x39in) s. 28-Apr-3 Bukowskis, Stockholm #903/R est:10000-12000 (S.KR 21000)

£1977 $3124 €2966 Wooded landscape (36x41cm-14x16in) s.verso panel. 28-Apr-3 Bukowskis, Stockholm #888/R est:20000-25000 (S.KR 26000)

£2317 $3730 €3476 Seascape (50x69cm-20x27in) s.d.92 verso panel exhib. 7-May-3 AB Stockholms Auktionsverk #1060/R est:30000-40000 (S.KR 30000)

£2383 $3717 €3575 Beech wood (140x200cm-55x79in) s.d.87 verso. 5-Nov-2 Bukowskis, Stockholm #408/R est:35000-40000 (S.KR 34000)

£2873 $4482 €4310 Landscape (70x93cm-28x37in) s. 5-Nov-2 Bukowskis, Stockholm #426/R est:25000-30000 (S.KR 41000)

£4695 $7324 €7043 Listening (152x99cm-60x39in) s.d.99 verso panel exhib. 6-Nov-2 AB Stockholms Auktionsverk #897/R est:60000-80000 (S.KR 67000)

Works on paper

£1331 $2077 €1997 Landscape (10x16cm-4x6in) s.d.1998 mixed media exhib. 6-Nov-2 AB Stockholms Auktionsverk #919/R est:10000-12000 (S.KR 19000)

£1472 $2296 €2208 Landscape (10x15cm-4x6in) s. s.d.95 verso mixed media prov. 5-Nov-2 Bukowskis, Stockholm #427/R est:10000-12000 (S.KR 21000)

FRIEBERGER, Padhi (1929-) Austrian

Sculpture

£2278 $3600 €3600 Anniversary of the liberation of Europe (86x57x9cm-34x22x4in) s.i. newspaper paper gouache W/C gold cloth metal board prov. 27-Nov-2 Dorotheum, Vienna #226/R est:5000-7000

FRIED, Pal (1893-1976) Hungarian/American

£385 $600 €578 Flamenco dancers (76x61cm-30x24in) s. prov. 18-Sep-2 Boos Gallery, Michigan #302/R

£513 $800 €770 Horse race (61x76cm-24x30in) painted c.1950. 18-Oct-2 Du Mouchelle, Detroit #2070/R

£538 $850 €850 Ballet dancer (80x60cm-31x24in) s. lit. 29-Nov-2 Schloss Ahlden, Ahlden #1419/R

£737 $1143 €1150 Ballet dancer tying ribbons (80x60cm-31x24in) s. 6-Dec-2 Michael Zeller, Lindau #760/R

£803 $1269 €1205 L'ouverture (61x76cm-24x30in) 1-Dec-2 Levis, Calgary #218/R (C.D 2000)

£978 $1623 €1418 Violetta (73x61cm-29x24in) s. i.verso. 16-Jun-3 Waddingtons, Toronto #308/R est:1500-2500 (C.D 2200)

£1024 $1495 €1536 Laying nude (70x96cm-28x38in) board painted c.1920. 4-Jun-2 SOGA, Bratislava #121/R est:48000 (SL.K 65000)

£1325 $2094 €1988 Riders near Gleichen (61x76cm-24x30in) 1-Dec-2 Levis, Calgary #218a/R (C.D 3300)

£1333 $2213 €1933 Maxine (61x76cm-24x30in) s. i.verso. 16-Jun-3 Waddingtons, Toronto #309/R est:1800-2200 (C.D 3000)

£1357 $2225 €1968 Seated ballerina (79x58cm-31x23in) s. 30-May-3 Aspire, Cleveland #41/R est:800-1200

£1452 $2251 €2178 Lady with bonnet (64x18cm-25x7in) painted c.1935. 3-Dec-2 SOGA, Bratislava #118/R est:35000 (SL.K 92000)

£1511 $2508 €2191 Eve (61x76cm-24x30in) s. i.verso prov. 16-Jun-3 Waddingtons, Toronto #310/R est:1800-2200 (C.D 3400)

£1548 $2400 €2322 Parisian street scene (66x81cm-26x32in) s. 1-Oct-2 Arthur James, Florida #60

£1751 $2750 €2627 Ballerina dressing (76x61cm-30x24in) s. 24-Nov-2 Butterfields, San Francisco #2688/R est:1000-1500

£2008 $3173 €3012 Audrey (61x76cm-24x30in) 1-Dec-2 Levis, Calgary #217/R (C.D 5000)

Works on paper

£323 $500 €485 Young Hispanic girl and burro (38x48cm-15x19in) s. W/C. 21-Jul-2 Jeffery Burchard, Florida #26a/R

£441 $656 €662 Spanish dancer (78x58cm-31x23in) s. pastel. 25-Jun-2 Koller, Zurich #6685 (S.FR 1000)

£573 $872 €860 Portrait of a nude woman (67x48cm-26x19in) s. pastel. 28-Aug-2 Deutscher-Menzies, Melbourne #443/R (A.D 1600)

£962 $1462 €1500 Two ballerinas lacing their shoes (98x69cm-39x27in) s. pastel lit. 11-Jul-2 Allgauer, Kempten #2281/R

FRIEDEBERG, Pedro (1937-) Italian
£1113 $1781 €1614 Eibulo del divino inefable (39x39cm-15x15in) s.d.1996 acrylic paper. 15-May-3 Louis Morton, Mexico #29/R est:20000-24000 (M.P 18000)

FRIEDENSON, Arthur (1872-1955) British
£520 $863 €754 Road to Steeperton Tor, Belstone (33x41cm-13x16in) s.d.1926 s.i.verso panel. 10-Jun-3 David Lay, Penzance #165
£769 $1215 €1200 Gypsies and caravan in landscape (30x41cm-12x16in) s. board. 12-Nov-2 Mealy's, Castlecomer #1057/R
£1950 $3042 €2925 River landscape with bridge and figures (33x40cm-13x16in) s.d.1910 panel. 18-Sep-2 Dreweatt Neate, Newbury #118 est:400-600

Works on paper
£1600 $2496 €2400 Cattle grazing, Ridge Lane near Staithes (25x41cm-10x16in) s. i.verso. 20-Sep-2 Richardson & Smith, Whitby #108/R est:1300-1500

FRIEDLANDER, Alfred (1860-1927) Austrian
£405 $632 €600 Military field camp (19x31cm-7x12in) s. lit. 28-Mar-3 Karrenbauer, Konstanz #1732/R
£443 $700 €700 The arrest (21x31cm-8x12in) s. panel lit. 29-Nov-2 Schloss Ahlden, Ahlden #1153/R
£705 $1093 €1100 Ambush of a seller's wagon by three riders in armour (26x39cm-10x15in) s. panel. 4-Dec-2 Neumeister, Munich #733/R est:1000
£3077 $4831 €4800 Filling the pipe. Enjoying the pipe (24x15cm-9x6in) s. panel two. 21-Nov-2 Van Ham, Cologne #1628/R est:3200

FRIEDLANDER, Alfred (attrib) (1860-1927) Austrian
Works on paper
£441 $675 €662 Portrait of a military officer (53x43cm-21x17in) s. W/C. 23-Aug-2 York Town, York #522

FRIEDLANDER, Camilla (1856-1928) Austrian
£1972 $3273 €2800 Still life with porcelain vase, trophy, and glass centre-piece with fruits (23x17cm-9x7in) s. panel. 14-Jun-3 Arnold, Frankfurt #743/R est:1800
£2800 $4452 €4200 Arabic still life (30x22cm-12x9in) s. panel. 20-Mar-3 Christie's, Kensington #185/R est:3000-5000

FRIEDLANDER, Friedrich (1825-1901) Austrian
£432 $691 €600 A pleasant chat (22x17cm-9x7in) s. panel. 14-May-3 Dorotheum, Linz #344/R
£897 $1400 €1346 Untitled (56x79cm-22x31in) 20-Sep-2 Du Mouchelle, Detroit #2220/R est:800-1200
£1887 $2906 €3000 Quiet pleasure (24x15cm-9x6in) s. panel. 22-Oct-2 Wiener Kunst Auktionen, Vienna #1079/R est:1200-4000
£2270 $3677 €3200 Two veterans in friendly chat (26x20cm-10x8in) s. panel. 22-May-3 Dorotheum, Vienna #170/R est:3000-3600
£2848 $4500 €4500 Two veterans with snuff (40x31cm-16x12in) s. panel. 28-Nov-2 Dorotheum, Vienna #76/R est:4500-5500
£3095 $4890 €4643 Dialog (42x31cm-17x12in) s. board. 30-Nov-2 Dorotheum, Prague #6 est:150000-230000 (C.KR 150000)
£4088 $6296 €6500 Two invalids (53x41cm-21x16in) s. panel lit. 22-Oct-2 Wiener Kunst Auktionen, Vienna #1080/R est:3000-7000

FRIEDLANDER, Julius (1810-1861) Danish
£255 $403 €383 Portrait of gentleman wearing glasses and black jacket (63x51cm-25x20in) 2-Dec-2 Rasmussen, Copenhagen #1789/R (D.KR 3000)
£1378 $2095 €2067 Fishermen and families by fishing place (23x27cm-9x11in) 27-Aug-2 Rasmussen, Copenhagen #1862/R est:12000-15000 (D.KR 16000)

FRIEDLANDER, Lee (1934-) American
Photographs
£2025 $3200 €3038 Cleveland (19x29cm-7x11in) s.i.d.1980 verso gelatin silver print prov.lit. 25-Apr-3 Phillips, New York #188/R est:3000-5000
£2848 $4500 €4272 Paris (16x25cm-6x10in) i.d.1964 verso gelatin silver print prov. 25-Apr-3 Phillips, New York #148/R est:4000-6000
£3291 $5200 €4937 Hollywood, California (17x24cm-7x9in) s. verso gelatin silver print prov.lit. 25-Apr-3 Phillips, New York #295/R est:2000-3000
£4114 $6500 €6171 Cincinnati (25x28cm-10x11in) s.verso gelatin silver print. 25-Apr-3 Phillips, New York #149/R est:4000-6000
£5696 $9000 €8544 Mobile, Alabama (17x26cm-7x10in) s.verso gelatin silver print prov.lit. 25-Apr-3 Phillips, New York #56/R est:5000-7000
£6329 $10000 €9494 New York City (16x25cm-6x10in) s. verso gelatin silver print prov.lit. 25-Apr-3 Phillips, New York #294/R est:2000-3000
£6748 $11000 €10122 Basie band on the road (20x30cm-8x12in) s.i.d.1956 gelatin silver print. 12-Feb-3 Christie's, Rockefeller NY #176/R est:3000-5000
£6962 $11000 €10443 New York City (15x23cm-6x9in) s. verso gelatin silver print prov.lit. 25-Apr-3 Phillips, New York #275/R est:2000-3000
£8442 $13000 €12663 Hillcrest, New York (16x25cm-6x10in) s.i.d.1970 verso gelatin silver print prov.lit. 25-Oct-2 Phillips, New York #35/R est:7000-10000
£11392 $18000 €17088 Fifteen photographs (17x25cm-7x10in) s. num.48/75 15 gelatin silver print prov.lit. 25-Apr-3 Phillips, New York #57/R est:20000-30000

FRIEDLINGER, J (20th C) ?
£646 $1060 €937 Still life (79x99cm-31x39in) s. 30-May-3 Aspire, Cleveland #52/R est:400-800

FRIEDMAN, Tom (1965-) American
Prints
£2885 $4500 €4328 Untitled (55x105cm-22x41in) s.num.99/100 inkjet print. 5-Nov-2 Christie's, Rockefeller NY #384/R est:5000-7000
Sculpture
£25000 $40000 €37500 Untitled - polystyrene tower (77cm-30in) styrofoam executed 1996 prov.exhib.lit. 15-May-3 Christie's, Rockefeller NY #326/R est:40000-50000
Works on paper
£7595 $12000 €11393 Untitled (7x1cm-3x0in) caterpillar made with artist hair glue stick pin executed 1999. 12-Nov-2 Phillips, New York #165/R est:15000-20000

FRIEDRICH, A C (1815-1855) German
£4303 $6669 €6455 Horses. s. painted 1853. 6-Dec-2 Kieselbach, Budapest #87/R (H.F 1600000)

FRIEDRICH, Alexander (1895-1968) German
£379 $599 €550 Village spring (49x61cm-19x24in) s. 5-Apr-3 Quittenbaum, Hamburg #25/R

FRIEDRICH, Caroline (1828-1914) German
£2158 $3453 €3000 Flower still life with hyacinths (31x25cm-12x10in) s.d.1868 board. 17-May-3 Lempertz, Koln #1395/R est:3000

FRIEDRICH, Caspar David (1774-1840) German
Works on paper
£25641 $40513 €40000 Studies of young man (26x21cm-10x8in) i.d.5 t Mei 1798 pencil prov.lit. 16-Nov-2 Lempertz, Koln #1325/R est:30000-40000

FRIEDRICH, Clara (1894-1969) Swiss?
£3231 $5073 €4847 Composition (60x50cm-24x20in) s.d.1933 verso. 23-Nov-2 Burkhard, Luzern #171/R est:3000-4000 (S.FR 7400)

FRIEDRICH, Ernst (1951-) Austrian?
Works on paper
£629 $1025 €950 1891 (140x85cm-55x33in) s.i.verso mixed media. 28-Jan-3 Dorotheum, Vienna #301/R

FRIEDRICH, Gustav-Adolf (1824-1889) German
£8219 $12822 €12329 Winter market (74x100cm-29x39in) s.d.1871. 28-Mar-3 Koller, Zurich #3174/R est:18000-22000 (S.FR 18000)

FRIEDRICH, Nicolaus (1865-?) German
Sculpture
£1007 $1621 €1500 Athlete (53cm-21in) s.d.1903 dark pat bronze sold with base. 18-Feb-3 Durán, Madrid #1375/R

FRIEND, Donald Stuart Leslie (1915-1989) Australian
£657 $1038 €1139 Sofala (16x21cm-6x8in) s.d.44 board. 1-Apr-3 Goodman, Sydney #72 (A.D 1720)
£1720 $2615 €2580 Boy with guitar (34x25cm-13x10in) s. acrylic masonite. 27-Aug-2 Goodman, Sydney #153/R est:3000-5000 (A.D 4800)
£5018 $7627 €7527 Still life with fish (36x45cm-14x18in) s.d.45 board. 28-Aug-2 Deutscher-Menzies, Melbourne #134/R est:15000-20000 (A.D 14000)

£7663 $11418 €11495 Fishermen (27x37cm-11x15in) s. oil gold leaf on board prov. 27-Aug-2 Christie's, Melbourne #38/R est:20000-30000 (A.D 20000)
£8429 $12559 €12644 Kebele kurali Dau (40x30cm-16x12in) s.d.48 s.i.d.verso board. 27-Aug-2 Christie's, Melbourne #1/R est:10000-15000 (A.D 22000)
£8915 $14174 €13373 Procession (27x37cm-11x15in) s. oil gold-leaf board. 5-May-3 Sotheby's, Melbourne #127/R est:18000-28000 (A.D 23000)
£11628 $18488 €17442 Boy playing guitar (60x44cm-24x17in) s.d.48. 5-May-3 Sotheby's, Melbourne #110/R est:22000-28000 (A.D 30000)
£15200 $24472 €22800 Untitled (76x101cm-30x40in) s. painted c.1956 exhib. 6-May-3 Christie's, Melbourne #38/R est:20000-25000 (A.D 38000)

Sculpture

£2679 $4232 €4019 Fishermen (54x43x40cm-21x17x16in) aluminium executed c.1960. 27-Nov-2 Deutscher-Menzies, Melbourne #131/R est:9000-12000 (A.D 7500)
£2682 $3996 €4023 Boat man (27cm-11in) s. aluminum prov. 27-Aug-2 Christie's, Melbourne #262/R est:7000-9000 (A.D 7000)

Works on paper

£269 $428 €404 Milk bottle hopscotch (24x34cm-9x13in) s.i. pen ink. 4-Mar-3 Deutscher-Menzies, Melbourne #269/R (A.D 700)
£281 $427 €422 Quinalow, Queensland (38x50cm-15x20in) s.i. pen ink. 19-Aug-2 Joel, Victoria #165 (A.D 800)
£305 $463 €458 Southwalk Cathedral (29x47cm-11x19in) s.i. pastel ink. 27-Aug-2 Goodman, Sydney #70 (A.D 850)
£320 $499 €480 Sketch of two boys (23x21cm-9x8in) s.d.1953 black pen ink. 26-Mar-3 Hamptons Fine Art, Godalming #62
£480 $773 €720 Mother and child (31x24cm-12x9in) W/C ink. 6-May-3 Christie's, Melbourne #384/R est:800-1200 (A.D 1200)
£538 $856 €807 Portrait of a boy (46x32cm-18x13in) s. pen ink prov. 4-Mar-3 Deutscher-Menzies, Melbourne #222/R (A.D 1400)
£880 $1417 €1320 Eva on the stairs (46x28cm-18x11in) s.i.d.51 W/C ink pastel. 6-May-3 Christie's, Melbourne #301 est:2000-3000 (A.D 2200)
£1032 $1713 €1757 Studies of Ono (31x47cm-12x19in) s.i.d.1952 pen ink wash crayon. 10-Jun-3 Shapiro, Sydney #56b est:2000-4000 (A.D 2600)
£1068 $1633 €1602 Leopard amongst boulders (33x49cm-13x19in) s.i. W/C ink executed c.1963 prov. 26-Aug-2 Sotheby's, Paddington #596/R est:4000-6000 (A.D 3000)
£1116 $1829 €1674 Double Bay (49x36cm-19x14in) s.i. gouache pen ink paper on board prov. 4-Jun-3 Deutscher-Menzies, Melbourne #352/R est:3000-4000 (A.D 2800)
£1157 $1770 €1736 Pool (56x76cm-22x30in) s.i. W/C ink paper on board executed c.1973 prov. 26-Aug-2 Sotheby's, Paddington #631/R est:7000-10000 (A.D 3250)
£1280 $2061 €1920 Fisherman (30x40cm-12x16in) s. gouache acrylic on board. 6-May-3 Christie's, Melbourne #234/R est:4000-6000 (A.D 3200)
£1357 $2144 €2036 Nude with chair and still life (61x45cm-24x18in) s.i. W/C pastel ink wash prov. 27-Nov-2 Deutscher-Menzies, Melbourne #133/R est:4000-6000 (A.D 3800)
£1423 $2178 €2135 New Ponte Alla Carraia, Firenze (31x47cm-12x19in) s.i.d.52 ink pastel. 25-Aug-2 Sotheby's, Paddington #122/R est:4000-6000 (A.D 4000)
£1473 $2342 €2210 Seated woman (34x24cm-13x9in) s.d.47 ink wash prov. 5-May-3 Sotheby's, Melbourne #53/R est:6000 (A.D 3800)
£1538 $2446 €2307 Standing man (75x41cm-30x16in) s.indis.d.89 pen ink W/C pastel prov. 4-Mar-3 Deutscher-Menzies, Melbourne #129/R est:4500-6500 (A.D 4000)
£1609 $2398 €2414 Rosario in Assisi (30x48cm-12x19in) s.i.d.52 ink pastel. 27-Aug-2 Christie's, Melbourne #157/R est:4000-6000 (A.D 4200)
£1769 $2813 €2654 Queen of the night (30x40cm-12x16in) s. gouache board. 4-Mar-3 Deutscher-Menzies, Melbourne #123/R est:6000-9000 (A.D 4600)
£1786 $2804 €2679 God figure in the cave at Bratan (57x75cm-22x30in) s.i. W/C ink gouache paper on board. 25-Nov-2 Christie's, Melbourne #376/R est:5000-8000 (A.D 5000)
£1938 $3081 €2907 Monsoon weather, Ceylon (34x49cm-13x19in) s.i.d.1957 ink W/C. 5-May-3 Sotheby's, Melbourne #344/R est:5000-8000 (A.D 5000)
£2143 $3321 €3215 Balinese boy (62x47cm-24x19in) s.i. ink pastel W/C. 29-Oct-2 Lawson Menzies, Sydney #57/R est:5000-7000 (A.D 6000)
£2500 $3925 €3750 Guitar players (51x69cm-20x27in) s. W/C ink paper on board prov. 25-Nov-2 Christie's, Melbourne #294/R est:7000-10000 (A.D 7000)
£2600 $4186 €3900 Athlete (79x56cm-31x22in) s.i. W/C ink paper on board. 6-May-3 Christie's, Melbourne #353 est:5000-7000 (A.D 6500)
£2847 $4356 €4271 Bastian's Balia band, Ceylon (50x68cm-20x27in) s.i. ink W/C prov. 25-Aug-2 Sotheby's, Paddington #181/R est:5000-7000 (A.D 8000)
£2857 $4514 €4286 Three shy nudes (74x54cm-29x21in) s. W/C. 18-Nov-2 Goodman, Sydney #57/R est:6000-10000 (A.D 8000)
£3566 $5670 €5349 Sofala (30x46cm-12x18in) s. mixed media. 5-May-3 Sotheby's, Melbourne #320/R est:8000-12000 (A.D 9200)
£3584 $5448 €5376 In the temple (50x69cm-20x27in) s.i. W/C gouache ink pencil composition board exec.c.1961. 28-Aug-2 Deutscher-Menzies, Melbourne #103/R est:12000-15000 (A.D 10000)
£4270 $6534 €6405 Boy, Ceylon (51x31cm-20x12in) s.i. mixed media paper on board prov. 25-Aug-2 Sotheby's, Paddington #167/R est:12000-18000 (A.D 12000)
£4270 $6534 €6405 Untroubled by worldly distraction the guru in the wisdom tree (47x63cm-19x25in) s. W/C gold leaf prov. 25-Aug-2 Sotheby's, Paddington #234/R est:10000-12000 (A.D 12000)
£4651 $7395 €6977 Boys with masks and monkey, Bali (54x76cm-21x30in) s.i. ink W/C gouache prov. 5-May-3 Sotheby's, Melbourne #19/R est:20000 (A.D 12000)
£7527 $11441 €11291 Cocos Islands, the visit of Miss Universe and Mr World (46x59cm-18x23in) s. mixed media prov. 27-Aug-2 Goodman, Sydney #140/R est:15000-20000 (A.D 21000)

FRIEND, Washington F (1820-1886) British

Works on paper

£578 $948 €867 Lumber raft (17x37cm-7x15in) W/C. 3-Jun-3 Joyner, Toronto #254/R est:1000-1500 (C.D 1300)
£1955 $3030 €2933 Niagara Falls (68x85cm-27x33in) W/C prov. 3-Dec-2 Ritchie, Toronto #3108/R est:2000-3000 (C.D 4750)

FRIER, Harry (c.1849-1919) British

Works on paper

£300 $468 €450 Bee Sands (26x52cm-10x20in) s.d.1907 W/C. 26-Mar-3 Woolley & Wallis, Salisbury #74/R

FRIER, Wilfred M (?) British?

Works on paper

£300 $471 €450 At a landing point (26x36cm-10x14in) s. W/C htd gouache. 24-Jul-2 Hamptons Fine Art, Godalming #105/R

FRIERS, Rowel (?) ?

Works on paper

£250 $398 €375 Old guard (40x30cm-16x12in) s. pen ink W/C wash. 5-Mar-3 John Ross, Belfast #140

FRIES, Charles Arthur (1854-1940) American

£1935 $3000 €2903 Earl Morn Mesa Grande (20x30cm-8x12in) s. i.d.1918 verso canvasboard. 29-Oct-2 John Moran, Pasadena #612 est:1000-2000
£2742 $4250 €4113 When the morning stars sang together (36x61cm-14x24in) s. i.verso prov. 29-Oct-2 John Moran, Pasadena #619 est:2500-3500
£3593 $6000 €5210 Landscape, Rocky Arroyo (46x61cm-18x24in) s. i.verso. 17-Jun-3 John Moran, Pasadena #62 est:4000-6000
£4839 $7500 €7259 California landscape (61x91cm-24x36in) s. painted c.1910. 8-Dec-2 Toomey, Oak Park #667/R est:8000-12000
£5161 $8000 €7742 Ocean front (30x46cm-12x18in) s. i.verso prov. 29-Oct-2 John Moran, Pasadena #618 est:2500-3500
£9639 $16000 €13977 View of San Diego from Point Loma (36x71cm-14x28in) s.d.1898 i.verso prov.lit. 11-Jun-3 Butterfields, San Francisco #4235/R est:3000-5000

Works on paper

£304 $475 €456 Road in spring (34x25cm-13x10in) s. i.verso W/C. 13-Apr-3 Butterfields, Los Angeles #7007

FRIES, Emmanuel (1801-1833) German

£12658 $20000 €18987 Grapes, peaches and a classically inspired pitcher on a marble relief depicting classical figures (146x113cm-57x44in) s.d.1839 prov. 23-Apr-3 Christie's, Rockefeller NY #99/R est:25000-35000

FRIES, Ernst (1801-1833) German

£5727 $8361 €8591 Italian study (26x37cm-10x15in) paper on board. 17-Jun-2 Philippe Schuler, Zurich #4340/R est:1000-1400 (S.FR 13000)

Works on paper

£478 $745 €750 Italian coastal landscape (24x38cm-9x15in) d.6. Dec. 1824 W/C over pencil. 5-Nov-2 Hartung & Hartung, Munich #5060/R

FRIES, Willy (1881-1965) Swiss

£1310 $2044 €1965 Village in the dunes (43x54cm-17x21in) s. i.d.30 verso. 8-Nov-2 Dobiaschofsky, Bern #138/R est:3500 (S.FR 3000)

FRIESE, Richard (1854-1918) German

£25751 $40687 €38627 Moose in fall (89x71cm-35x28in) s.d.1894 s.verso prov. 3-Apr-3 Heffel, Vancouver #30/R est:16000-20000 (C.D 60000)

£25751 $40687 €38627 Moose in winter (89x71cm-35x28in) s.d.1893 prov. 3-Apr-3 Heffel, Vancouver #31/R est:16000-20000 (C.D 60000)

Works on paper

£1972 $3175 €2800 Stag in the snow (6x27cm-2x11in) s.d.1913 gouache lit. 9-May-3 Schloss Ahlden, Ahlden #1415/R est:1400

FRIESEKE, Frederick Carl (1874-1939) American

£6250 $10000 €9375 Still life flower in a vase (69x58cm-27x23in) s.d.31 prov. 11-Jan-3 James Julia, Fairfield #88 est:10000-15000
£15060 $25000 €21837 Blue gown (91x91cm-36x36in) 13-Jun-3 Du Mouchelle, Detroit #2135/R est:25000-30000
£52469 $85000 €78704 On the river, Giverny (65x81cm-26x32in) s. prov. 22-May-3 Christie's, Rockefeller NY #46/R est:50000-70000
£55556 $90000 €83334 Silhouette (92x74cm-36x29in) s.d.33 prov.exhib.lit. 21-May-3 Sotheby's, New York #151/R est:80000-120000
£503226 $780000 €754839 Garden path (65x81cm-26x32in) s. prov.exhib. 5-Dec-2 Christie's, Rockefeller NY #83/R est:600000-800000

FRIESEN, Ludwig (fl.1800) German

£1026 $1590 €1600 River landscape with village and mountains by the bank (57x74cm-22x29in) s. 4-Dec-2 Neumeister, Munich #734/R est:1000

FRIESZ, Émile Othon (1879-1949) French

£826 $1280 €1239 Nu assis (32x17cm-13x7in) s. painted c.1924-25. 7-Dec-2 Galerie du Rhone, Sion #132 (S.FR 1900)
£1384 $2145 €2200 Portrait de femme (22x16cm-9x6in) s. panel. 4-Oct-2 Tajan, Paris #94/R est:2500-3000
£1810 $3023 €2625 Woodland path (21x16cm-8x6in) s. panel. 24-Jun-3 Koller, Zurich #112/R est:4000-6000 (S.FR 4000)
£2000 $3180 €3000 Jeune femme (65x54cm-26x21in) s.d.35 prov. 20-Mar-3 Sotheby's, Olympia #158/R est:2500-3500
£2089 $3258 €3300 Femme nue assise (63x48cm-25x19in) s. 18-Oct-2 Rabourdin & Choppin de Janvry, Paris #27/R
£2128 $3447 €3000 Nu assis (80x60cm-31x24in) s. 26-May-3 Joron-Derem, Paris #70b
£2183 $3406 €3275 Still life with cyclamen (46x38cm-18x15in) s. prov. 9-Nov-2 Galerie Gloggner, Luzern #56/R est:4800-5500 (S.FR 5000)
£2200 $3498 €3300 Paysage (34x44cm-13x17in) s. panel prov. 20-Mar-3 Sotheby's, Olympia #64/R est:2000-3000
£2229 $3478 €3500 Baigneuses (36x43cm-14x17in) mono. panel. 10-Nov-2 Eric Pillon, Calais #224/R
£2384 $3886 €3600 Paysage a la maison (40x32cm-16x13in) s. 2-Feb-3 Muizon & Le Coent, Paris #53
£2759 $4414 €4000 Le jardin des Jarres a Toulon (60x73cm-24x29in) s.d.1930 prov. 12-Mar-3 Libert, Castor, Paris #105/R est:6000-8000
£2778 $3944 €4500 Port de Toulon (19x24cm-7x9in) s. 16-Mar-3 Eric Pillon, Calais #162/R
£3000 $4740 €4500 Paysage (50x61cm-20x24in) s. 3-Apr-3 Christie's, Kensington #29/R
£3114 $4920 €4671 Landscape (38x46cm-15x18in) s.d.10. 2-Dec-2 Blomqvist, Oslo #383/R est:40000-50000 (N.KR 36000)
£3165 $5000 €5000 Toulon, chemin dans la foret (38x46cm-15x18in) s.i.d.1918 cardboard. 27-Nov-2 Marc Kohn, Paris #14/R est:8000
£3774 $6113 €5472 Port de la Rochelle (54x65cm-21x26in) s.d.47 prov.lit. 24-May-3 Galerie Gloggner, Luzern #40/R est:10000-12000 (S.FR 8000)
£3797 $5924 €6000 L'ecuyere de cirque (38x46cm-15x18in) s. panel prov. 31-Jul-2 Tajan, Paris #40/R est:6000-7500
£3901 $6319 €5500 Maison dans la campagne Normande (54x65cm-21x26in) s. 21-May-3 Cornette de St.Cyr, Paris #52/R est:4000-5000
£3974 $6160 €6200 Nature morte a la cafetiere (60x73cm-24x29in) s. prov.lit. 4-Dec-2 Pierre Berge, Paris #139/R
£4114 $6377 €6500 L'arbre en fleurs (38x61cm-15x24in) s. 29-Sep-2 Eric Pillon, Calais #201/R
£4138 $6621 €6000 Sentier dans le bois (73x60cm-29x24in) s. painted c.1924. 12-Mar-3 Libert, Castor, Paris #106/R est:6000-8000
£4138 $6911 €6000 Le Chateau Fort de Falaise (73x54cm-29x21in) s.d.19. 10-Jul-3 Artcurial Briest, Paris #161/R est:8000-10000
£4522 $7055 €7100 Bord de mer (33x41cm-13x16in) s. 10-Nov-2 Eric Pillon, Calais #91/R
£4551 $7146 €7100 Bateaux a Saint-Malo (55x65cm-22x26in) s.d.1935. 15-Dec-2 Eric Pillon, Calais #154/R
£4777 $7452 €7500 Sous-bois (73x60cm-29x24in) s. 10-Nov-2 Eric Pillon, Calais #83/R
£4931 $7840 €7100 Baigneuse (65x54cm-26x21in) s. 29-Apr-3 Artcurial Briest, Paris #180/R est:6000-8000
£4968 $7750 €7800 Maisons roses (46x38cm-18x15in) s. 7-Nov-2 Chochon-Barre & Allardi, Paris #151/R
£5063 $8000 €8000 Nature morte a l'anemone (65x54cm-26x21in) s. s.i.verso. 26-Nov-2 Sotheby's, Amsterdam #89/R est:8000-10000
£5380 $8500 €8500 Paysage, bord de riviere (54x65cm-21x26in) s.d.1935. 27-Nov-2 Marc Kohn, Paris #23/R est:7000-8000
£5696 $8829 €9000 Bretonnes au pardon de Sainte Anne la Palud (46x55cm-18x22in) s.d.1899. 29-Sep-2 Eric Pillon, Calais #192/R
£6000 $9240 €9000 Nu couche (64x81cm-25x32in) s.d.1938 prov.exhib.lit. 23-Oct-2 Sotheby's, Olympia #708/R est:6000-8000
£6122 $9735 €9000 Baigneuses a Saint-Leonard, Sarthe (65x81cm-26x32in) s. painted c.1940. 26-Feb-3 Artcurial Briest, Paris #264/R est:7500-10500
£6329 $9873 €10000 Le Port d'Honfleur (65x81cm-26x32in) s.d.45 prov. 31-Jul-2 Tajan, Paris #44/R est:9000-12000
£6410 $10064 €10000 Nu assis (54x85cm-21x33in) s.d.1938. 16-Dec-2 Chochon-Barre & Allardi, Paris #51 est:10000-12000
£6944 $11181 €10069 Track in southern wooded landscape (92x73cm-36x29in) s. 7-May-3 Dobiaschofsky, Bern #560/R est:17000 (S.FR 15000)
£7500 $12299 €11250 Rade de Toulon (81x100cm-32x39in) s.prov.exhib.lit. 4-Feb-3 Christie's, London #262/R
£7500 $12299 €11250 Port de Toulon (65x81cm-26x32in) s. exhib.lit. 4-Feb-3 Christie's, London #281/R
£7500 $11850 €11250 Sieste (34x92cm-13x36in) s. prov.exhib.lit. 3-Apr-3 Christie's, Kensington #63/R est:10000
£7801 $12638 €11000 Paysage - foret (74x60cm-29x24in) s.d.14. 26-May-3 Joron-Derem, Paris #70/R est:10000-12000
£10000 $16300 €15000 Les yachts, Toulon (65x81cm-26x32in) s.d.1929 s.i.d.verso prov. 3-Feb-3 Bonhams, New Bond Street #11/R est:10000-15000
£10646 $16928 €15650 Jardin au Cap Brun (50x61cm-20x24in) s.i.d.1933 mono.verso. 26-Feb-3 Artcurial Briest, Paris #265/R est:12000-15000
£10897 $17000 €16346 Port de Toulon (65x81cm-26x32in) s.i. prov. 7-Nov-2 Christie's, Rockefeller NY #262/R est:18000-22000
£10897 $17109 €17000 Port de Honfleur (54x65cm-21x26in) s. 15-Dec-2 Eric Pillon, Calais #149/R
£11321 $17660 €18000 Le port de Toulon (54x65cm-21x26in) s. s.i. verso prov.exhib.lit. 10-Oct-2 Ribeyre & Baron, Paris #63/R est:10000-12000
£12057 $19532 €17000 Paysage (65x81cm-26x32in) s.d.24. 26-May-3 Joron-Derem, Paris #65/R est:15000-25000
£12227 $19074 €18341 Adam and Eve (95x90cm-37x35in) s.d.09 i. stretcher. 6-Nov-2 Dobiaschofsky, Bern #547/R est:29000 (S.FR 28000)
£18012 $29000 €27018 La petite ville derriere les arbres (54x74cm-21x29in) s. painted 1904. 8-May-3 Christie's, Rockefeller NY #169/R est:30000-40000
£18987 $29620 €30000 Les collines de Cassis (54x65cm-21x26in) s.d.09 prov. 31-Jul-2 Tajan, Paris #41/R est:27000-33000
£211180 $340000 €316770 L'Estaque (55x65cm-22x26in) s. painted 1907 prov. 8-May-3 Christie's, Rockefeller NY #167/R est:220000-280000

Works on paper

£285 $450 €450 Femme assise (50x39cm-20x15in) st. pierre noire dr. 27-Nov-2 Lemoine & Ferrando, Paris #95
£288 $453 €450 Nu couche (30x40cm-12x16in) s. chl. 24-Nov-2 Lesieur & Le Bars, Le Havre #57
£310 $493 €450 Nu assis (43x32cm-17x13in) s. chl dr. 5-Mar-3 Doutrebente, Paris #35
£318 $497 €500 Femme nue (21x11cm-8x4in) st.sig. dr. double-sided. 7-Nov-2 Chochon-Barre & Allardi, Paris #152
£400 $652 €600 Landscape, Piedmont (30x24cm-12x9in) init. col chk prov. 3-Feb-3 Bonhams, New Bond Street #16/R
£420 $701 €600 Pres de la Fontaine en Provence (26x22cm-10x9in) bears st.mono. pencil dr. 26-Jun-3 Tajan, Paris #141
£475 $736 €750 Le petit village de pecheur (18x26cm-7x10in) mono. graphite dr. 29-Sep-2 Eric Pillon, Calais #230/R
£506 $785 €800 Nu debout (40x26cm-16x10in) s. chl dr. 29-Sep-2 Eric Pillon, Calais #227/R
£538 $834 €850 Bateau dans le port (18x26cm-7x10in) mono. graphite dr. 29-Sep-2 Eric Pillon, Calais #229/R
£853 $1425 €1220 Femme nue (38x21cm-15x8in) st.sig. crayon dr. 27-Jun-3 Claude Aguttes, Neuilly #89/R
£1233 $1936 €1800 Nu debout (31x22cm-12x9in) mono. W/C. 21-Apr-3 Rabourdin & Choppin de Janvry, Paris #88/R est:1500-2000
£2500 $3975 €3750 Paysage (45x59cm-18x23in) s. gouache W/C. 20-Mar-3 Sotheby's, Olympia #55/R est:3000-4000
£23741 $38935 €33000 Paysage du Midi (43x31cm-17x12in) st.mono. W/C gouache. 4-Jun-3 Marc Kohn, Paris #70/R est:25000-30000

FRIGERIO, R (19/20th C) ?

£1192 $1943 €1800 Neapolitans (40x30cm-16x12in) s. pair. 31-Jan-3 Rabourdin & Choppin de Janvry, Paris #116

FRIGERIO, Raffaele (19th C) Italian

£500 $815 €750 Good smoke (46x30cm-18x12in) s. 13-Feb-3 David Lay, Penzance #261
£700 $1134 €1050 Sharing a joke. Up to mischief (30x40cm-12x16in) s. pair. 23-Jan-3 Christie's, Kensington #120/R
£800 $1240 €1200 Portraits of Italian fisherfolk (39x29cm-15x11in) s. pair. 24-Sep-2 Anderson & Garland, Newcastle #502/R

FRIIO, Rino (20th C) Canadian

£244 $401 €354 Sunnyside tress (50x60cm-20x24in) s.i. 9-Jun-3 Hodgins, Calgary #52/R (C.D 550)
£244 $401 €354 Sidewalk cafe (49x39cm-19x15in) s.d.2001. 9-Jun-3 Hodgins, Calgary #171/R (C.D 550)
£341 $536 €512 Inglewood (60x50cm-24x20in) s.i.d.2002. 25-Nov-2 Hodgins, Calgary #154/R (C.D 850)

FRIIS, Hans Gabriel (1838-1892) Danish

£957 $1550 €1388 Landscape with shepherd and flock on hillside, Paarup (49x76cm-19x30in) s.d.1870. 26-May-3 Rasmussen, Copenhagen #1524/R (D.KR 10000)
£1702 $2689 €2553 Landscape from Handeck, Switzerland (67x100cm-26x39in) s.d.1873 exhib. 2-Dec-2 Rasmussen, Copenhagen #1550/R est:20000-25000 (D.KR 20000)
£4283 $6810 €6425 Twilight in winter (79x126cm-31x50in) s.d.1891 exhib. 10-Mar-3 Rasmussen, Vejle #229/R est:40000 (D.KR 46000)

FRIIS, T (19/20th C) Danish
£681 $1076 €1022 Young girl on beach by bathing house (45x65cm-18x26in) s,. 2-Dec-2 Rasmussen, Copenhagen #1345/R (D.KR 8000)

FRIIS, Tove (1898-1977) Danish
£701 $1093 €1052 Model in the dance studio (35x27cm-14x11in) init. s.d.1927 verso panel. 5-Nov-2 Bukowskis, Stockholm #77/R (S.KR 10000)

FRILLI, A (19th C) Italian
Sculpture
£1174 $1925 €1702 Bust of a woman (57cm-22in) s.i. alabaster. 4-Jun-3 Fischer, Luzern #1367/R est:3000-4000 (S.FR 2500)

FRILLI, Antonio (19/20th C) Italian
Sculpture
£1311 $2033 €1967 Femme aux paons (45x92x24cm-18x36x9in) s. bronze white marble. 24-Sep-2 Iegor de Saint Hippolyte, Montreal #179 (C.D 3200)
£1935 $3000 €2903 Bust of a woman (54cm-21in) s. white marble circular socle. 2-Oct-2 Christie's, Rockefeller NY #736/R est:3000-5000
£2216 $3700 €3213 Bust of a woman in lace hat, flowers on her breast (104cm-41in) i. white marble with green marble pedestal. 21-Jun-3 Selkirks, St. Louis #1000 est:1200-1600
£2710 $4200 €4065 Figure of a woman (87cm-34in) s. alabaster rockwork base. 2-Oct-2 Christie's, Rockefeller NY #737/R est:3000-4000

FRINK, Elizabeth (1930-1993) British
Prints
£2200 $3388 €3300 Strawberry roan (68x91cm-27x36in) s.num.39/75 etching aquatint. 24-Oct-2 Christie's, Kensington #57/R est:1200-1600
£2200 $3388 €3300 Rolling over horse (54x69cm-21x27in) s.num.49/75 aquatint. 24-Oct-2 Christie's, Kensington #58/R est:1200-1800
Sculpture
£5000 $8200 €7500 Dead hen (38cm-15in) s. dark brown pat. bronze conceived 1956 lit. 6-Jun-3 Christie's, London #182/R est:4000-6000
£6500 $10855 €9425 Warrior (37cm-15in) s. brown pat bronze edition of 10 lit. 24-Jun-3 Bonhams, New Bond Street #115/R est:5000-7000
£7000 $10850 €10500 Warrior (37cm-15in) s. brown pat. bronze lit. 4-Dec-2 Sotheby's, London #81/R est:6000-8000
£12000 $19680 €18000 Harbinger bird IV (51cm-20in) s.num.8/9 mid brown pat. bronze conceived 1961 lit. 6-Jun-3 Christie's, London #181/R est:8000-12000
£13000 $21320 €18850 Falling man (68cm-27in) s.num.3/6 dark brown pat. bronze one of six exec.1961 lit. 4-Jun-3 Sotheby's, London #82/R est:8000-12000
£15000 $24600 €21750 Bird (50cm-20in) s. dark brown pat bronze one of ten exec.1958 prov.exhib.lit. 4-Jun-3 Sotheby's, London #81/R est:12000-16000
£16000 $24800 €24000 Horse (32cm-13in) s.num.1/8 brown pat. bronze lit. 3-Dec-2 Bonhams, New Bond Street #100/R est:14000-18000
£17284 $28000 €25062 Rolling over horse (13cm-5in) s. num.12/12 yellow gold blk marble base st.f.M Singer lit. 21-May-3 Doyle, New York #36/R est:15000-25000
£19000 $31160 €28500 Assassins II (52cm-20in) s.num.4/8 dark brown pat. bronze lit. 6-Jun-3 Christie's, London #76/R est:10000-15000
£28000 $45920 €42000 Soldier's head II (38cm-15in) s.num.1/6 brown pat. bronze conceived 1965 prov.lit. 6-Jun-3 Christie's, London #178/R est:20000-30000
£33000 $51810 €49500 Rolling over horse (13cm-5in) s.num.7/12 18 caret yellow gold cast 1974 prov.lit. 22-Nov-2 Christie's, London #45/R est:25000-35000
£37000 $58090 €55500 Riace IV (218cm-86in) s. brown pat. bronze conceived 1989 lit. 22-Nov-2 Christie's, London #103/R est:25000-35000
£39000 $61230 €58500 Riace II (206cm-81in) s.num.2/4 brown pat. bronze conceived 1986 lit. 22-Nov-2 Christie's, London #104/R est:25000-35000
£40000 $62800 €60000 Riace III (206cm-81in) s.num.2/4 brown pat. bronze cast 1986 lit. 22-Nov-2 Christie's, London #102/R est:25000-35000
£48000 $78720 €72000 Small rolling horse (33cm-13in) s.num.7/10 dark brown pat. bronze conceived 1986 lit. 6-Jun-3 Christie's, London #180/R est:20000-30000
£50000 $83500 €72500 Resting horseman (82cm-32in) s.num.6/6 brown pat bronze lit. 24-Jun-3 Bonhams, New Bond Street #114/R est:50000-70000
Works on paper
£450 $698 €675 Self portrait (10x9cm-4x4in) s.i.d.July 6 1956 pen black ink. 4-Dec-2 Christie's, Kensington #287
£1000 $1550 €1500 Knight's tale (65x91cm-26x36in) s.d.80 pencil. 4-Dec-2 Christie's, Kensington #289/R est:1000-1500
£1500 $2325 €2250 Carapace (76x56cm-30x22in) s.d.63 chl prov. 3-Dec-2 Bonhams, New Bond Street #101/R est:1000-1500
£2600 $4056 €3900 Study for the Dying King (76x65cm-30x26in) s.d.Dec.62 chl dr prov. 17-Sep-2 Bonhams, Knightsbridge #289/R est:2500-3500
£2800 $4340 €4200 Recumbent horse (54x74cm-21x29in) s.d.87 chl W/C prov. 4-Dec-2 Christie's, Kensington #325/R est:3000-5000
£3000 $4680 €4500 Head (75x55cm-30x22in) s. pencil W/C. 25-Mar-3 Bonhams, New Bond Street #132/R est:3000-5000
£3000 $4920 €4500 Stoat (62x45cm-24x18in) s. collage pencil W/C. 3-Jun-3 Sotheby's, Olympia #154/R est:2000-3000
£3200 $5344 €4640 Resting horse (39x57cm-15x22in) s.d.82 pencil. 24-Jun-3 Bonhams, New Bond Street #116/R est:1500-2000
£4000 $6200 €6000 Moorhen (49x66cm-19x26in) s.d.68 pencil W/C prov. 4-Dec-2 Christie's, Kensington #329/R est:3000-5000
£4200 $6888 €6300 Swimming duck (56x77cm-22x30in) s.d.67 ink W/C wash. 3-Jun-3 Sotheby's, Olympia #155/R est:1000-1500
£5400 $8910 €7830 Resting horse (28x39cm-11x15in) s.d.75 pencil col wash. 1-Jul-3 Bonhams, Norwich #141/R est:2000-3000
£5500 $8525 €8250 Man and baboon (101x104cm-40x41in) s.d.88 chl W/C bodycol. 4-Dec-2 Christie's, Kensington #314/R est:6000-8000

FRINK, Elizabeth (attrib) (1930-1993) British
Works on paper
£500 $835 €725 Horse lying down (23x33cm-9x13in) bears sig.d.56 pencil. 20-Jun-3 Keys, Aylsham #247

FRIPP, Alfred Downing (1822-1895) British
Works on paper
£372 $603 €539 Waiting (60x50cm-24x20in) mono. verso W/C. 25-May-3 Uppsala Auktionskammare, Uppsala #107 (S.KR 4800)
£774 $1200 €1161 Italian peasant family by the cottage door (53x61cm-21x24in) s.i. W/C gouache prov. 29-Oct-2 Sotheby's, New York #132/R est:1000-1500
£1600 $2496 €2400 Traghetto, ferry on the Grand Canal, Venice (33x60cm-13x24in) s.i.indis d.185 exhib. 5-Nov-2 Bonhams, New Bond Street #85/R est:2000-3000
£3000 $4560 €4500 Leaving Arran (54x69cm-21x27in) s. W/C htd bodycol exhib. 28-Aug-2 Sotheby's, London #870/R est:3000-4000

FRIPP, George Arthur (1813-1896) British
£1500 $2445 €2175 Figures beside a stone bridge with a cottage nearby (34x44cm-13x17in) init.d.1840. 17-Jul-3 Tennants, Leyburn #835/R est:1000-1500
Works on paper
£400 $652 €580 Evening near Trawsfynydd, North Wales (17x22cm-7x9in) s. W/C. 16-Jul-3 Sotheby's, Olympia #31/R
£500 $775 €750 Caversham, Reading (24x37cm-9x15in) W/C. 25-Sep-2 Hamptons Fine Art, Godalming #100/R
£650 $1014 €975 Cattle by a stream (21x29cm-8x11in) s.d.1831 W/C. 26-Mar-3 Sotheby's, Olympia #87/R
£980 $1529 €1470 Continental street scene (51x35cm-20x14in) s. W/C. 5-Nov-2 Bristol Auction Rooms #944/R
£1200 $1968 €1740 Vale of Neath, Wales (33x27cm-13x11in) s.d.1837 pencil W/C gum arabic bodycol prov. 5-Jun-3 Christie's, London #95/R est:1000-1500
£1800 $2844 €2700 Easby Abbey, Yorkshire (36x48cm-14x19in) s. W/C over pencil htd bodycol scratching out. 28-Nov-2 Sotheby's, London #302/R est:2000-3000
£1800 $2934 €2610 View from Balmoral looking up the valley of the Dee (36x66cm-14x26in) s.d.1887 W/C. 16-Jul-3 Sotheby's, Olympia #52/R est:1200-1800
£4200 $6006 €6300 Trees on the banks of a lake at dusk (29x21cm-11x8in) s.d.1837 pencil W/C scratching out prov.exhib.lit. 22-Jan-3 Christie's, London #49/R est:5000

FRIPP, Thomas William (1864-1931) Canadian/British
Works on paper
£198 $325 €297 Along the shore, Canmore (15x24cm-6x9in) s.i.d.1925 W/C. 6-Feb-3 Heffel, Vancouver #016/R (C.D 500)
£238 $390 €357 Chekamus River (39x55cm-15x22in) init. W/C. 6-Feb-3 Heffel, Vancouver #020/R (C.D 600)
£260 $413 €377 Howe Sound (36x25cm-14x10in) s.i.verso W/C prov. 1-May-3 Heffel, Vancouver #24/R (C.D 600)
£321 $504 €482 Mountain river (29x21cm-11x8in) s. W/C. 25-Nov-2 Hodgins, Calgary #309/R (C.D 800)
£357 $586 €536 Anderson Lake, BC (23x32cm-9x13in) s. W/C. 6-Feb-3 Heffel, Vancouver #018/R (C.D 900)
£378 $620 €548 Coast range (19x16cm-7x6in) s.i.d.1923 W/C prov. 9-Jun-3 Hodgins, Calgary #414/R (C.D 850)
£482 $757 €723 Birken, summit of Goat Mountain (35x24cm-14x9in) s.i.d.1929 W/C. 25-Nov-2 Hodgins, Calgary #52/R (C.D 1200)
£502 $788 €753 Lions, from North Vancouver, BC (16x24cm-6x9in) s. W/C prov. 25-Nov-2 Hodgins, Calgary #30/R (C.D 1250)

£516 $846 €774 Deadman's Island (11x19cm-4x7in) s.d.1920 W/C. 6-Feb-3 Heffel, Vancouver #021/R (C.D 1300)
£556 $911 €834 Old Indian shacks, Stanley Park (14x19cm-6x7in) s. W/C. 6-Feb-3 Heffel, Vancouver #023/R (C.D 1400)
£635 $1041 €953 Pitt River (33x48cm-13x19in) init. W/C. 6-Feb-3 Heffel, Vancouver #024/R (C.D 1600)

FRISCH, Friedrich (1813-1886) German
£1027 $1603 €1500 Hunter admonishing disobedient dog (27x22cm-11x9in) s.d. verso. 11-Apr-3 Winterberg, Heidelberg #380/R est:1850

FRISCHKNECHT, F (20th C) ?
Works on paper
£1073 $1695 €1610 Alpine journey (24x37cm-9x15in) s.d.1974 mixed media. 29-Nov-2 Zofingen, Switzerland #2877 est:3000 (S.FR 2500)

FRISHMUTH, Harriet Whitney (1880-1980) American
Sculpture
£3822 $6000 €5733 Star (48cm-19in) s.d.1918 no.74 brown pat bronze. 10-Dec-2 Doyle, New York #95/R est:7000-9000
£4403 $7000 €6605 Vine (30cm-12in) s.d.1921 bronze st.f.Gorham Co. 7-Mar-3 Skinner, Boston #576/R est:3500-5500
£4717 $7500 €7076 Mrs Wagner (50cm-20in) i. black pat. bronze prov. 4-Mar-3 Christie's, Rockefeller NY #40/R est:5000-7000
£10494 $17000 €15741 Vine (30cm-12in) i. brown pat. bronze on marble base lit. 21-May-3 Sotheby's, New York #188/R est:15000-25000
£19355 $30000 €29033 Vine (29cm-11in) i. reddish brown pat. bronze lit. 5-Dec-2 Christie's, Rockefeller NY #52/R est:15000-25000
£22013 $35000 €33020 Playdays (57cm-22in) i. greenish brown pat. bronze i.f.Gorham prov.lit. 5-Mar-3 Sotheby's, New York #63/R est:15000-25000
£23457 $38000 €35186 Leaf (69cm-27in) i. green brown pat. bronze. 22-May-3 Christie's, Rockefeller NY #43/R est:20000-30000
£80247 $130000 €120371 Reflections (146cm-57in) i. greenish brown pat. bronze prov.lit. 21-May-3 Sotheby's, New York #186/R est:50000-70000
£92593 $150000 €138890 Joy of the waters (156cm-61in) i. verdigris pat. bronze i.f.Roman prov.lit. 22-May-3 Christie's, Rockefeller NY #49/R est:100000-150000

FRISON, Gustave (1850-?) French
Works on paper
£570 $918 €850 Cabinet de l'amateur (22x15cm-9x6in) s. gouache. 18-Feb-3 Vanderkindere, Brussels #137

FRISON, Jehan (1882-1961) Belgian
£374 $595 €550 Nature morte au vase de fleurs et a la cruche (49x62cm-19x24in) s. panel. 18-Mar-3 Campo, Vlaamse Kaai #90
£475 $741 €750 Composition aux myosotis et masque japonais (46x38cm-18x15in) s.d.32. 16-Sep-2 Horta, Bruxelles #357
£481 $755 €750 Nature morte au homard (55x59cm-22x23in) s. 19-Nov-2 Vanderkindere, Brussels #431
£503 $775 €800 Maison cote jardin (40x55cm-16x22in) s. 22-Oct-2 Galerie Moderne, Brussels #1661
£629 $969 €1000 Mauresques a Alger le soir (31x40cm-12x16in) s. cardboard. 22-Oct-2 Galerie Moderne, Brussels #739
£719 $1151 €1000 Vieux chalutier a Zeebruges (50x60cm-20x24in) s. 19-May-3 Horta, Bruxelles #419
£2436 $3776 €3800 La porte jaune (70x60cm-28x24in) s.d.1943. 9-Dec-2 Horta, Bruxelles #162/R est:4000-6000
£2564 $3974 €4000 Femme a la glace (58x42cm-23x17in) s.d.1913 mono.verso exhib. 7-Dec-2 De Vuyst, Lokeren #549/R est:4500-5000

FRISTROM, Claus Eduard (1864-1942) Swedish
£1254 $1956 €1881 Under the pines, Botanical gardens, Wellington (22x31cm-9x12in) s. board. 7-Nov-2 International Art Centre, Auckland #65/R est:4000-7000 (NZ.D 4000)
£1881 $2934 €2822 Fruit seller (32x20cm-13x8in) s. panel. 7-Nov-2 International Art Centre, Auckland #66/R est:6000-10000 (NZ.D 6000)
£2604 $4062 €3906 Homestead, Queenstown (24x34cm-9x13in) s. i. on stretcher. 8-Apr-3 Peter Webb, Auckland #170/R est:7000-9000 (NZ.D 7500)

FRISTRUP, Niels (1837-1909) Danish
£3745 $5917 €5618 La Piazetta, Venice with figures at sunset (108x80cm-43x31in) s.d.1878 exhib. 2-Dec-2 Rasmussen, Copenhagen #1490/R est:50000 (D.KR 44000)

FRISWELL, Harry P (fl.1881-1906) British
£1000 $1600 €1500 Awaiting the ferry (42x55cm-17x22in) s. 15-May-3 Lawrence, Crewkerne #1003/R est:1000-1200

FRITH, Clifford (1924-) British
£300 $483 €450 Portrait of a girl (30x26cm-12x10in) s. board. 18-Feb-3 Bonhams, Knightsbridge #195/R

FRITH, Francis (1822-1898) American?
Photographs
£65000 $105300 €97500 Egypt, Sinai and Jerusalem (38x48cm-15x19in) eight s.d.1858 albumen prints 20 elephant folio lit. 22-May-3 Sotheby's, London #7/R est:30000-50000

FRITH, William Powell (1819-1909) British
£400 $608 €600 Sketch for Dolly Varden (15x13cm-6x5in) s.d.1852. 16-Aug-2 Keys, Aylsham #643
£1154 $1800 €1731 Eavesdropping (56x46cm-22x18in) s.i. prov. 12-Apr-3 Weschler, Washington #508/R est:2000-3000
£4000 $6320 €6000 Christmas choristers (61x51cm-24x20in) s.d.1889. 2-Dec-2 Sotheby's, London #16/R est:3000-5000
£10500 $16905 €15750 After the bath (54x70cm-21x28in) s.d.1897 prov.exhib. 20-Feb-3 Christie's, London #285/R est:8000
£18000 $28980 €27000 Study for 'For better, for worse' (62x48cm-24x19in) s.d.1881 prov.exhib.lit. 20-Feb-3 Christie's, London #335/R est:30000
£28000 $45080 €42000 Hope. Fear (39x35cm-15x14in) s.d.1869 i.verso pair prov.exhib. 20-Feb-3 Christie's, London #99/R est:35000
£34000 $56440 €51000 Crossing sweeper (43x35cm-17x14in) s.d.1858. 12-Jun-3 Sotheby's, London #247/R est:15000-20000
£230000 $370300 €345000 For better, for worse (155x126cm-61x50in) s.d.1881 prov.exhib.lit. 19-Feb-3 Christie's, London #10/R est:250000-350000

FRITH, William Powell (attrib) (1819-1909) British
£900 $1467 €1350 Supplication (33x28cm-13x11in) s.i.on stretcher. 29-Jan-3 Sotheby's, Olympia #71/R est:600-800
Works on paper
£350 $546 €525 Gathering (12x18cm-5x7in) W/C pencil. 17-Sep-2 Sotheby's, Olympia #104/R

FRITSCH, Katarina (1956-) American?
Sculpture
£3237 $5309 €4500 Poodle (42x15x42cm-17x6x17in) s.i.d. plaster black pigment. 6-Jun-3 Ketterer, Munich #164/R est:4000-5000
£28481 $45000 €42722 Display stand with vases (269x112x112cm-106x44x44in) plastic aluminium assemblage prov.exhib. 13-Nov-2 Sotheby's, New York #511/R est:50000-70000

FRITSCH, Melchior (1825-1889) Austrian
£4795 $7527 €7000 Mountain landscape with view of Dachstein (110x152cm-43x60in) s.d.871. 16-Apr-3 Dorotheum, Salzburg #68/R est:8000-10000

FRITZ, Andreas (1828-1906) Danish
£986 $1539 €1479 Landscape view from Orneredet towards Aarhus (58x92cm-23x36in) s.d.1885. 11-Nov-2 Rasmussen, Vejle #642/R (D.KR 11500)

FRITZ, Charles (20th C) American
£10191 $16000 €15287 Autumn landscape (81x123cm-32x48in) s. 19-Nov-2 Butterfields, San Francisco #8106/R est:25000-35000

FRITZ, Max (1849-?) German
£1132 $1766 €1800 Lower Rhine landscape (63x99cm-25x39in) s. 19-Sep-2 Dr Fritz Nagel, Stuttgart #930 est:1800

FRITZ, Max Daniel Hermann (1873-1948) German
Sculpture
£1020 $1622 €1500 Otter (20x44cm-8x17in) i.pat.bronze stone socle. 28-Mar-3 Bolland & Marotz, Bremen #862/R est:2000

FRITZEL, Wilhelm (1870-1943) German
£449 $704 €700 Harvesting on lower Rhine (60x80cm-24x31in) s. 21-Nov-2 Van Ham, Cologne #1629

FRITZLER, Gerald J (1953-) American
Works on paper
£513 $800 €770 Bringing em home (33x53cm-13x21in) s. W/C prov. 9-Nov-2 Santa Fe Art, Santa Fe #18/R

FRITZSCHING, Alfred (1935-) German
£411 $641 €600 Cows grazing in extensive pre-alpine landscape (10x20cm-4x8in) s. panel. 10-Apr-3 Van Ham, Cologne #1434

FRITZVOLD, Reidar (1920-1998) Norwegian
£290 $453 €435 Winter in Slottsparken (47x28cm-19x11in) s. painted 1949. 23-Sep-2 Blomqvist, Lysaker #1044/R (N.KR 3400)
£297 $466 €446 Winter in the Royal Park (47x28cm-19x11in) s. 25-Nov-2 Blomqvist, Lysaker #1070 (N.KR 3400)
£442 $721 €663 Landscape from Bossvatn, Bykle (60x73cm-24x29in) s.d.1964 panel. 17-Feb-3 Blomqvist, Lysaker #1062/R (N.KR 5000)
£467 $719 €701 Mountain farm, evening, Telemark (38x46cm-15x18in) s. painted 1967. 28-Oct-2 Blomqvist, Lysaker #1053/R (N.KR 5500)
£541 $849 €812 Midsummer Night's evening (45x54cm-18x21in) s. 25-Nov-2 Blomqvist, Lysaker #1071 (N.KR 6200)
£594 $915 €891 Summer night, Vinje (57x46cm-22x18in) s. painted 1981. 28-Oct-2 Blomqvist, Lysaker #1052 (N.KR 7000)
£811 $1265 €1217 Calm day in autumn (50x62cm-20x24in) s. painted 1980. 23-Sep-2 Blomqvist, Lysaker #1045 (N.KR 9500)
£952 $1503 €1428 Digging for sand (60x73cm-24x29in) s.d.47 i.verso. 2-Dec-2 Blomqvist, Oslo #427/R est:15000-18000 (N.KR 11000)
£1298 $2050 €1947 Street market in Barcelona (73x92cm-29x36in) s.d.54 s.i.d.1953 verso panel. 2-Dec-2 Blomqvist, Oslo #430/R est:18000-22000 (N.KR 15000)

FRIZE, Bernard (1949-) French
Works on paper
£818 $1259 €1300 Partage des sentiments (75x55cm-30x22in) s.i.d.1982 collage W/C. 26-Oct-2 Cornette de St.Cyr, Paris #153/R

FRIZZELL, Dick (1943-) New Zealander
£3819 $5958 €5729 Self portrait with camera detail from 'Good Value' (43x39cm-17x15in) s.i.d.81 enamel board. 8-Apr-3 Peter Webb, Auckland #38/R est:8000-15000 (NZ.D 11000)
£4340 $6771 €6510 Still life with daffodils (49x36cm-19x14in) s.i.d.83 board. 8-Apr-3 Peter Webb, Auckland #39/R est:7000-9000 (NZ.D 12500)
£7295 $11380 €10943 Halley's Comet over Taupiri Mountain (119x90cm-47x35in) s.i.d.24/1/86. 17-Sep-2 Peter Webb, Auckland #117/R est:25000-30000 (NZ.D 24000)
£7746 $12782 €11232 Old Synagogue (100x120cm-39x47in) s.i.d.17/8/87 board prov. 1-Jul-3 Peter Webb, Auckland #23/R est:15000-25000 (NZ.D 22000)
£9155 $15106 €13275 Man rowing a boat (239x182cm-94x72in) s.i.d.16.7.85. 1-Jul-3 Peter Webb, Auckland #63/R est:15000-20000 (NZ.D 26000)
Works on paper
£627 $978 €941 Getting through the desert (22x29cm-9x11in) s.d.1.11.79 pastel ink. 5-Nov-2 Peter Webb, Auckland #168/R est:1000-1500 (NZ.D 2000)
£634 $1046 €919 Cubist tiki (30x15cm-12x6in) s.i.d.30/1/92 pencil W/C. 1-Jul-3 Peter Webb, Auckland #8/R est:1500-2500 (NZ.D 1800)
£702 $1116 €1053 Milkshake at HJ's (27x23cm-11x9in) s.i.d.25/9/79 ink pastel. 25-Feb-3 Peter Webb, Auckland #243 est:1500-2500 (NZ.D 2000)
£4777 $7500 €7166 Cubist still life with hulk comic/lemon and jug (61x61cm-24x24in) s.i.d.9/76 mixed media on canvas exhib. 10-Dec-2 Peter Webb, Auckland #33/R est:15000-20000 (NZ.D 15000)

FROBERG, Bror Ingemar (1921-) Swedish
£543 $880 €787 The car (126x156cm-50x61in) s.d.64. 25-May-3 Uppsala Auktionskammare, Uppsala #331 (S.KR 7000)

FROHLICH, Bernard (1823-1885) Austrian
£696 $1079 €1100 Fisherman mending nets outside house (30x36cm-12x14in) s.i. 25-Sep-2 Neumeister, Munich #578/R

FROHLICH, Fritz (1910-) Austrian
£1583 $2532 €2200 At night (40x78cm-16x31in) s.i.d.1978 acrylic. 14-May-3 Dorotheum, Linz #390/R est:4400-5500
£1795 $2836 €2800 Yes, what are you looking for then? (37x49cm-15x19in) s.d.97. 18-Nov-2 Dorotheum, Linz #272/R est:5600-6000
Works on paper
£256 $405 €400 Figure composition (15x17cm-6x7in) mono.d.99 mixed media. 18-Nov-2 Dorotheum, Linz #421/R
£288 $456 €450 Figure composition (14x16cm-6x6in) mono.d.99 mixed media. 18-Nov-2 Dorotheum, Linz #423/R
£288 $456 €450 Figure composition (17x15cm-7x6in) mono.d.99 mixed media. 18-Nov-2 Dorotheum, Linz #424/R
£321 $506 €500 Figure composition (15x15cm-6x6in) mono.d.99 mixed media. 18-Nov-2 Dorotheum, Linz #408/R
£353 $557 €550 Figure composition (15x21cm-6x8in) mono.d.99 mixed media. 18-Nov-2 Dorotheum, Linz #398/R
£353 $557 €550 Figure composition (15x23cm-6x9in) mono.d.99 mixed media. 18-Nov-2 Dorotheum, Linz #399/R
£353 $557 €550 Figure composition (15x20cm-6x8in) s.d.99 mixed media. 18-Nov-2 Dorotheum, Linz #401/R
£360 $576 €500 Figure composition (24x24cm-9x9in) mono.d.99 mixed media. 14-May-3 Dorotheum, Linz #489
£385 $608 €600 Figure composition (17x21cm-7x8in) s.d.99 mixed media. 18-Nov-2 Dorotheum, Linz #400/R
£385 $608 €600 Figure composition (24x25cm-9x10in) s.d.1999 mixed media. 18-Nov-2 Dorotheum, Linz #402/R
£385 $608 €600 Figure composition (23x26cm-9x10in) mono.d.2000 mixed media. 18-Nov-2 Dorotheum, Linz #406/R
£385 $608 €600 Figure composition (16x24cm-6x9in) mono.d.99 mixed media. 18-Nov-2 Dorotheum, Linz #410/R
£385 $608 €600 Figure composition (15x24cm-6x9in) mono.d.99 mixed media. 18-Nov-2 Dorotheum, Linz #411/R
£417 $658 €650 Figure composition (23x22cm-9x9in) mono.d.2000 mixed media. 18-Nov-2 Dorotheum, Linz #407/R
£432 $691 €600 Figure composition (29x21cm-11x8in) s.d.93 collage. 14-May-3 Dorotheum, Linz #486/R
£432 $691 €600 Figure composition (29x27cm-11x11in) s.d.90 mixed media. 14-May-3 Dorotheum, Linz #487/R

FROHNER, Adolf (1934-) German
£17722 $27468 €28000 Man showing his wounds (192x76cm-76x30in) s.d.79 tempera graphite paper on panel exhib.lit. 24-Sep-2 Wiener Kunst Auktionen, Vienna #245/R est:12000-20000
Works on paper
£321 $506 €500 Skull (69x50cm-27x20in) s.d.86 mixed media. 12-Nov-2 Dorotheum, Vienna #269/R
£449 $709 €700 Head (65x47cm-26x19in) s.d.86 mixed media. 12-Nov-2 Dorotheum, Vienna #279/R
£769 $1215 €1200 Seated figure (98x69cm-39x27in) s.d.72 graphite. 12-Nov-2 Dorotheum, Vienna #237/R
£795 $1295 €1200 Mitzi stands in front of the gate in mini-skirt (65x50cm-26x20in) s. i.verso pencil. 28-Jan-3 Dorotheum, Vienna #255/R
£811 $1265 €1200 Testa di donna (50x38cm-20x15in) s.d.1973 Indian ink. 28-Mar-3 Ketterer, Hamburg #314/R
£1034 $1655 €1500 Seated figure (65x50cm-26x20in) s.d.73 graphie htd white. 11-Mar-3 Dorotheum, Vienna #205/R est:1800-2500
£1216 $1897 €1800 Bindings 26 (104x68cm-41x27in) s.d.1971 pencil. 28-Mar-3 Ketterer, Hamburg #312/R est:2200-2400
£1486 $2319 €2200 Contortions (70x104cm-28x41in) s.d.1972 chl chk. 28-Mar-3 Ketterer, Hamburg #313/R est:2400-2800

FROLICH, Lorenz (1820-1908) Danish
£605 $962 €908 Staerkodder and Hother (47x33cm-19x13in) mono.d.1852 lit. 5-Mar-3 Rasmussen, Copenhagen #1927/R (D.KR 6500)
£775 $1178 €1163 Deer under large tree (38x45cm-15x18in) prov. 28-Aug-2 Museumsbygningen, Copenhagen #20/R (D.KR 9000)
Works on paper
£266 $431 €399 Agnete and Neptune (58x43cm-23x17in) mono.d.1903 gouache. 25-Jan-3 Rasmussen, Havnen #2091/R (D.KR 3000)

FROLICH, Lorenz (attrib) (1820-1908) Danish
£370 $596 €555 Portrait of gentleman (17x14cm-7x6in) panel. 19-Jan-3 Hindemae, Ullerslev #7335 (D.KR 4200)

FROLICHER, Otto (1840-1890) Swiss
£1660 $2323 €2490 Landscape with pond and village (25x31cm-10x12in) mono.d.77. 29-Nov-1 Falk & Falk, Zurich #679/R est:2800 (S.FR 3900)
£21226 $34387 €37571 Riverside mill (74x110cm-29x43in) s. 26-May-3 Sotheby's, Zurich #24/R est:45000-60000 (S.FR 45000)

FROM, Einar (1872-1972) Norwegian
£340 $523 €510 Northern landscape (50x60cm-20x24in) s. panel. 28-Oct-2 Blomqvist, Lysaker #1058/R (N.KR 4000)
£950 $1586 €1378 Steam ship in high seas (60x96cm-24x38in) s.d.1904. 18-Jun-3 Grev Wedels Plass, Oslo #173/R (N.KR 11000)

FROM, K C (19th C) Danish
£574 $930 €832 Landscape from Silkeborgs Islands (27x35cm-11x14in) s. 26-May-3 Rasmussen, Copenhagen #1533/R (D.KR 6000)

FROMANGER, Gerard (1939-) French
£818 $1267 €1300 Passages (73x60cm-29x24in) s.i.d.juillet-aout 1978 verso exhib.lit. 30-Oct-2 Artcurial Briest, Paris #672/R
£1266 $1962 €2000 Le sang (130x97cm-51x38in) s.i.verso. 28-Sep-2 Cornette de St.Cyr, Paris #309/R est:2000-3000
£7547 $11623 €12000 Adriana (130x97cm-51x38in) s.i.d.1976 verso exhib.lit. 26-Oct-2 Cornette de St.Cyr, Paris #69/R est:12000
£8013 $12580 €12500 Rue de la danse (73x60cm-29x24in) s.i.verso prov.exhib. 24-Nov-2 Laurence Calmels, Paris #128/R est:6000
£8333 $13083 €13000 Rue du fleuve (73x60cm-29x24in) s.i.verso prov.exhib. 24-Nov-2 Laurence Calmels, Paris #129/R est:6000
£16346 $25663 €25500 Circule (130x195cm-51x77in) s.i.d.1977 verso exhib.lit. 11-Dec-2 Artcurial Briest, Paris #733/R est:20000
Works on paper
£348 $540 €550 Belle Ile en Mer (23x30cm-9x12in) collage prov.exhib. 28-Sep-2 Cornette de St.Cyr, Paris #310

FROMANTIOU, Hendrik de (1633-c.1700) German
£80000 $125600 €120000 Still life of flowers in a glass vase on a marble ledge (93x68cm-37x27in) prov.lit. 12-Dec-2 Sotheby's, London #41/R est:50000-70000

FROMENTIN, Eugène (1820-1876) French
£16774 $26000 €25161 Horses watering in a river (41x30cm-16x12in) s.d.72 panel. 30-Oct-2 Christie's, Rockefeller NY #92/R est:15000-20000
£17419 $27523 €27000 Cavaliers (31x52cm-12x20in) s. 19-Dec-2 Claude Aguttes, Neuilly #130/R est:20000
£23718 $37237 €37000 Cavaliers et chevaux s'abreuvant a la riviere (72x109cm-28x43in) prov. 16-Dec-2 Gros & Delettrez, Paris #321/R est:23000-30000
Works on paper
£417 $658 €650 Campement arabe (15x25cm-6x10in) s.d. W/C. 14-Nov-2 Credit Municipal, Paris #38
£566 $872 €900 Etude d'hommes etd'arbres (22x14cm-9x6in) crayon ink dr. 23-Oct-2 Rabourdin & Choppin de Janvry, Paris #210
£6950 $11607 €9800 Autoportrait (28x21cm-11x8in) mono.d.1843 black crayon gouache prov.exhib.lit. 19-Jun-3 Piasa, Paris #155/R est:10000-12000

FROMKES, Maurice (1872-?) American
£1603 $2500 €2405 Vegetable seller (51x36cm-20x14in) s.d.1914 board. 12-Oct-2 Neal Auction Company, New Orleans #650 est:2000-3000
£1656 $2600 €2484 La Madrilena (91x81cm-36x32in) s. exhib. 14-Dec-2 Weschler, Washington #657/R est:1500-2500

FROMMEL, Carl Ludwig (1789-1863) German
Works on paper
£854 $1350 €1350 View from a villa terrace of Baden Baden (26x35cm-10x14in) s.d.1844 W/C. 29-Nov-2 Bassenge, Berlin #5892/R

FROMUTH, Charles Henry (1861-1937) American
Works on paper
£1042 $1698 €1500 Effet de vagues (21x31cm-8x12in) s. pastel. 19-Jul-3 Thierry & Lannon, Brest #264 est:1500-1800

FRONIUS, Hans (1903-1988) Austrian
£2621 $4141 €3800 Still life with bottle, fruit and flowers (45x60cm-18x24in) mono.d.1975 board. 2-Apr-3 Dr Fritz Nagel, Stuttgart #9332/R est:4000
£4430 $7000 €7000 Poor Lazarus (46x60cm-18x24in) mono.d.79 panel. 27-Nov-2 Dorotheum, Vienna #214/R est:7000-9000
£5674 $9191 €8000 Still life of flowers (69x49cm-27x19in) mono.d.72 masonite. 24-May-3 Van Ham, Cologne #190/R est:5000
£6757 $10541 €10000 Evening landscape (55x68cm-22x27in) mono.d.83 i.stretcher panel lit. 25-Mar-3 Wiener Kunst Auktionen, Vienna #1/R est:10000-16000

FRONTH, Per (1963-) Norwegian
Works on paper
£908 $1435 €1362 Movement I - study II - 2000 (42x53cm-17x21in) s.i. mixed media exhib. 2-Dec-2 Blomqvist, Oslo #492/R (N.KR 10500)
£1211 $1913 €1817 Generation I - Version II - 2000 (41x51cm-16x20in) s. mixed media canvas exhib. 2-Dec-2 Blomqvist, Oslo #493/R est:12000-15000 (N.KR 14000)

FRORSAN, Knut (20th C) Swedish
£417 $650 €605 Aftensol over lista (53x122cm-21x48in) s.d.1969. 30-Mar-3 Simpson's, Houston #473

FROSCHL, Carl (1848-1934) Austrian
Works on paper
£346 $536 €550 Portrait of girl (63x60cm-25x24in) s.d.1905 pastel canvas. 1-Oct-2 Dorotheum, Vienna #146/R
£1154 $1788 €1800 Girl with bunch of white flowers (89x56cm-35x22in) s. pastel. 4-Dec-2 Neumeister, Munich #513/R est:2000

FROSCHLE, Pius (19th C) German?
£654 $1072 €1000 Portraits of woman with dog and man with book (74x59cm-29x23in) i.d. verso pair. 29-Mar-3 Dannenberg, Berlin #575/R

FROST, A B (1851-1928) American
Works on paper
£906 $1450 €1359 He was Buck Harlow and Captain Briggs scene with witness and reporter in a courtyard. s. ink wash en grisaille. 1-Jan-3 Nadeau, Windsor #46/R est:2500-4000

FROST, Anna S R (1873-1955) American
£250 $400 €375 Moving shadows (60x74cm-24x29in) s. 18-May-3 Butterfields, Los Angeles #7027

FROST, Arthur Burdett (1851-1928) American
£637 $1000 €956 Brook trout with head arched up with artificial fly in upper lip (18x33cm-7x13in) s.d.03 board. 19-Apr-3 James Julia, Fairfield #88a/R
Works on paper
£3205 $5000 €4808 Two older couples racing sleighs (53x48cm-21x19in) s. gouache en grisaille. 9-Nov-2 Illustration House, New York #22/R est:6000-9000
£6211 $10000 €9317 Twelve views of baseball players (36x23cm-14x9in) s. pen ink. 10-May-3 Illustration House, New York #24/R est:6000-9000
£20513 $32000 €30770 Br'er Fox confronts Terrapin. Terrapin speaking to Br'er Rabbit (20x25cm-8x10in) s. pen ink two. 9-Nov-2 Illustration House, New York #56/R est:7000-9000

FROST, George Albert (1843-?) American
Works on paper
£1250 $2000 €1813 Home stretch, a dog sledding scene (32x44cm-13x17in) s.d.1896 W/C graphite. 16-May-3 Skinner, Boston #125/R

FROST, J O J (19th C) American
£3148 $5100 €4565 Rolling waves with fishing vessels and men in rowboats hauling fish (14x94cm-6x37in) panel. 22-May-3 Sotheby's, New York #750

FROST, John (1890-1937) American
£13975 $22500 €20963 Desert landscape (46x51cm-18x20in) s.d.1921 canvasboard. 18-Feb-3 John Moran, Pasadena #51 est:8000-11000
£44586 $70000 €66879 Sunlight study, California scene (61x71cm-24x28in) s.d.23 i.on stretcher. 22-Nov-2 Skinner, Boston #238/R est:5000-7000

FROST, Joseph Ambrose (1953-) Australian
£305 $482 €458 Ship on the seas (44x59cm-17x23in) s. 1-Apr-3 Lawson Menzies, Sydney #488 (A.D 800)
£324 $513 €470 Stanwell Park reflections (20x20cm-8x8in) s. board. 7-Apr-3 Australian Art Auctions, Sydney #98 (A.D 850)
£538 $882 €780 Clipper (55x70cm-22x28in) s. 3-Jun-3 Lawson Menzies, Sydney #727 (A.D 1350)
£902 $1435 €1353 Cooma farmstead (60x75cm-24x30in) s. board. 3-Mar-3 Lawson Menzies, Sydney #451 est:1500-3000 (A.D 2400)

FROST, Sergius (1900-1994) Danish
£298 $471 €447 Torpedo boat flotilla in Copenhagen Bay (79x128cm-31x50in) s.d.1934-35. 2-Dec-2 Rasmussen, Copenhagen #1416/R (D.KR 3500)
£304 $474 €456 Seascape with torpedo boat (88x107cm-35x42in) s.d.1938. 22-Sep-2 Hindemae, Ullerslev #7190/R (D.KR 3600)
£364 $589 €528 The training ship Danmark with Kronborg on the side (70x101cm-28x40in) s.d.1936. 24-May-3 Rasmussen, Havnen #2051/R (D.KR 3800)

FROST, Terry (1915-) British
£400 $624 €600 Olympic motif (21x42cm-8x17in) s.d.96 i. monotype on paper. 27-Mar-3 Christie's, Kensington #667
£650 $1014 €975 Swirl (20x20cm-8x8in) s.d.1995 acrylic card prov. 17-Sep-2 Bonhams, Knightsbridge #153/R
£1500 $2475 €2175 Blue spiral (29x28cm-11x11in) s. oil monotype. 3-Jul-3 Christie's, Kensington #743/R est:600-800
£2200 $3432 €3300 Five spirals (51x75cm-20x30in) s. acrylic. 27-Mar-3 Christie's, Kensington #665/R est:800-1200
£2405 $3800 €3800 Ochre and black (76x64cm-30x25in) s.d.June 1965 verso. 1-Dec-2 Bukowskis, Helsinki #384/R est:3000-3500
£2900 $4524 €4205 Abstract in black and white (241x183cm-95x72in) s.i.verso. 27-Mar-3 Lane, Penzance #373 est:3000-4000
£3100 $4836 €4650 Up red and yellow on blue (58x41cm-23x16in) s.d.1988 i.verso acrylic collage. 17-Oct-2 David Lay, Penzance #1412/R est:1500-2000
£4000 $6600 €5800 Blue grey (35x53cm-14x21in) 3-Jul-3 Christie's, Kensington #741/R est:3000-5000
£4200 $6510 €6300 Black, white and red spirals, Lorca (51x61cm-20x24in) s. i.d.92 verso. 4-Dec-2 Christie's, Kensington #616/R est:3000-5000
£4500 $7380 €6750 Diamonds for Aphrodite (55x55cm-22x22in) s. i.d.1995 verso. 3-Jun-3 Sotheby's, Olympia #300/R est:2000-3000

£6500 $10140 €9750 Green, black and white alone (152x122cm-60x48in) s.i.d.98 verso acrylic collage on canvas. 27-Mar-3 Christie's, Kensington #666/R est:4000-6000
£8000 $12480 €12000 Blue, black and white (152x91cm-60x36in) s.i.d.May 59 verso prov. 25-Mar-3 Bonhams, New Bond Street #126/R est:6000-8000
£8000 $13120 €12000 Lemon, black and white vertical (76x40cm-30x16in) s.i.d.1959 verso oil collage on canvas prov.exhib. 6-Jun-3 Christie's, London #200/R est:5000-8000
£17000 $27880 €24650 Yellow chevron for blue (122x74cm-48x29in) painted 1956. 4-Jun-3 Sotheby's, London #75/R est:10000-15000

Works on paper

£320 $496 €480 Black abstract (25x20cm-10x8in) s. s.i.d.1969 verso brush col ink oil. 4-Dec-2 Christie's, Kensington #366
£400 $660 €580 Study of a nude kneeling on a chair (18x13cm-7x5in) s. pencil. 3-Jul-3 Christie's, Kensington #738
£450 $738 €675 Lorry front abstract (23x30cm-9x12in) s. col chk exec.c.1965. 3-Jun-3 Sotheby's, Olympia #278/R
£480 $744 €720 Red and yellow semi circles (22x27cm-9x11in) s. W/C. 4-Dec-2 Christie's, Kensington #367/R
£550 $858 €825 Abstract (23x8cm-9x3in) mixed media. 17-Oct-2 David Lay, Penzance #1129
£650 $1073 €943 Pink, black and grey abstract (51x38cm-20x15in) s.d.64 s.d.verso col crayon. 3-Jul-3 Christie's, Kensington #740/R
£900 $1395 €1350 Sun journey, Cyprus (56x38cm-22x15in) s.d.75 pen brush black ink bodycol exhib. 4-Dec-2 Christie's, Kensington #357/R
£1200 $1968 €1800 Three graces, red, black and white (30x30cm-12x12in) s.d.86 gouache. 3-Jun-3 Sotheby's, Olympia #301/R est:600-800
£1800 $2808 €2700 Abstract compositions (15x10cm-6x4in) mixed media collage pair. 12-Sep-2 Sotheby's, Olympia #148/R est:1500-2500
£1900 $3135 €2755 Composition - blue and red (51x76cm-20x30in) s.d.69 W/C bodycol prov. 3-Jul-3 Christie's, Kensington #736/R est:1500-2000

FROST, William Edward (1810-1877) British

£500 $795 €750 Portrait of a lady, head and shoulders from behind and turned to the right (12cm-5in circular) board. 18-Mar-3 Rosebery Fine Art, London #944/R
£8500 $13685 €12750 Venus and Cupid (32x46cm-13x18in) s. prov. 20-Feb-3 Christie's, London #172/R
£32000 $51520 €48000 Venus disarming Cupid (90x78cm-35x31in) s.d.1852 arched top prov. 20-Feb-3 Christie's, London #171/R est:15000

Works on paper

£650 $1047 €975 Self-portrait (18x11cm-7x4in) pencil prov.exhib. 20-Feb-3 Christie's, London #170/R
£750 $1245 €1125 Sirens (15x24cm-6x9in) W/C htd bodycol prov. 12-Jun-3 Bonhams, New Bond Street #646/R

FROST, William Edward (attrib) (1810-1877) British

£385 $604 €600 Portrait of an Oriental man (20x15cm-8x6in) 16-Dec-2 Bernaerts, Antwerp #43/R

FROSTERUS-SALTIN, Alexandra (1837-1916) Finnish

£1268 $2041 €1800 Father's mother (48x38cm-19x15in) 10-May-3 Bukowskis, Helsinki #150/R est:1500-2000

FROULA, Josef (20th C) American

£590 $950 €885 Winter landscape (36x46cm-14x18in) s. 18-Feb-3 John Moran, Pasadena #47

FRUHTRUNK, Gunther (1923-1983) German

£3038 $4709 €4800 Falling diagonals in black red and blue - Paris (42x35cm-17x14in) mono.i.d.1965/66 oil casein panel. 28-Sep-2 Ketterer, Hamburg #482/R est:3500-4500
£13000 $21190 €19500 Strahling/exemple (126x131cm-50x52in) s. i.d.1959 verso board. 3-Feb-3 Sotheby's, Olympia #194/R est:4000-6000
£14000 $22820 €21000 Unbedingtes und blau-violetter widerhall (125x162cm-49x64in) s.i.d.59 verso board prov. 3-Feb-3 Sotheby's, Olympia #195/R est:4000-6000

FRUMERIE, Agnes de (1869-1937) Swedish

Sculpture

£1489 $2309 €2234 Smooth gathering - figures in sofa (33x62cm-13x24in) s.i.d.1906 green pat.bronze sold with wooden pedestal. 4-Dec-2 AB Stockholms Auktionsverk #1806/R est:15000-20000 (S.KR 21000)

FRUNZO, Vincenzo (1910-) Italian

£253 $395 €400 First sun (70x100cm-28x39in) s. s.i.d.1961 verso. 19-Oct-2 Semenzato, Venice #9/R

FRY, Roger (1866-1934) British

Works on paper

£1550 $2465 €2325 In the Pyrenees (21x27cm-8x11in) W/C over pencil. 5-Mar-3 Bonhams, Bury St Edmunds #329/R est:400-600
£2600 $4134 €3900 Adam and Eve (18x11cm-7x4in) i.verso gouache. 26-Feb-3 Sotheby's, Olympia #83/R est:400-600

FRY, William Henry (fl.1937-1938) British

£300 $477 €450 Poets corner (61x50cm-24x20in) s. board. 5-Mar-3 John Ross, Belfast #108

FRY, Windsor Arthur (20th C) Irish

Works on paper

£213 $345 €300 Cliffside village (34x46cm-13x18in) s.d.97 W/C. 21-May-3 James Adam, Dublin #58

FRYDENSBERG, Carl (1872-1944) Danish?

£766 $1233 €1149 Interior scene with lilacs in an Italian vase (72x65cm-28x26in) init.d.09 exhib.prov. 26-Feb-3 Museumsbygningen, Copenhagen #117/R (D.KR 8500)

FRYE, Thomas (attrib) (1710-1762) British

£1543 $2500 €2315 Red coat (107x91cm-42x36in) canvas on masonite. 25-Jan-3 Skinner, Boston #210/R est:4000-5000

FRYER, George G (fl.1882) British

£750 $1178 €1125 Crowded barges at dusk (51x76cm-20x30in) s.d.1882. 16-Apr-3 Christie's, Kensington #902/R

FRYER, Katherine Mary (1910-) British

£700 $1162 €1050 Still life of flowers in a jug with a cut melon, basket of fruit (66x86cm-26x34in) s. 10-Jun-3 Bonhams, Leeds #114/R

FRYXELL, Louise (19th C) ?

£465 $754 €674 Aristocrat in hunting gear (36x31cm-14x12in) 25-May-3 Uppsala Auktionskammare, Uppsala #135 (S.KR 6000)

FU BAOSHI (1904-1965) Chinese

Works on paper

£5439 $8974 €7887 Strolling in a winter forest (27x24cm-11x9in) s.i. ink scroll. 6-Jul-3 Christie's, Hong Kong #217/R est:40000-50000 (HK.D 70000)
£28455 $44959 €42683 Pathway in the woods (41x64cm-16x25in) s.i.d.December 1964 ink col. 28-Apr-3 Sotheby's, Hong Kong #590/R est:35000-50000 (HK.D 350000)
£28455 $44959 €42683 Viewing the waterfall (56x39cm-22x15in) s.i.d.1965 ink col. 28-Apr-3 Sotheby's, Hong Kong #597/R est:150000-200000 (HK.D 350000)
£97561 $154146 €146342 Two ladies (90x61cm-35x24in) s.i.d.1950 ink col hanging scroll exhib. 28-Apr-3 Sotheby's, Hong Kong #568/R est:1200000-1800000 (HK.D 1200000)

FU XILING (20th C) Chinese

Works on paper

£1594 $2614 €2200 Four seasons - cranes in landscapes. s. seal Indian ink col four. 30-May-3 Dr Fritz Nagel, Stuttgart #1179/R est:1200-1800

FUCHS, Bernard (1932-) American

£2244 $3500 €3366 Frigate with lightning in background (71x48cm-28x19in) s. 9-Nov-2 Illustration House, New York #33/R est:5000-7000
£3045 $4750 €4568 Wolf howling at moon in snowy landscape (61x91cm-24x36in) s. 9-Nov-2 Illustration House, New York #41/R est:4000-6000

FUCHS, Ernst (1930-2000) Austrian

£2450 $3994 €3700 Nude (50x60cm-20x24in) s.d.1968. 3-Feb-3 Cornette de St.Cyr, Paris #299/R

Prints

£1899 $3000 €3000 Triumph of the unicorn (69x32cm-27x13in) s.i. etching. 27-Nov-2 Dorotheum, Vienna #220/R est:3000-3200

Sculpture

£1348 $2183 €1900 Sphinx (19x35x16cm-7x14x6in) i. brown pat.bronze marble socle. 24-May-3 Van Ham, Cologne #193/R est:1600

Works on paper

£320 $534 €464 Portrait of a lady, head and shoulders wearing spectacles (54x43cm-21x17in) s.d.1984 i.verso col chk. 17-Jun-3 Rosebery Fine Art, London #485

£897 $1434 €1300 Female nude (38x27cm-15x11in) s.d.1987 pencil. 11-Mar-3 Dorotheum, Vienna #274/R
£1126 $1835 €1700 Hypnosis (162x72cm-64x28in) pencil paper on canvas. 28-Jan-3 Dorotheum, Vienna #177/R est:2800-4000
£2069 $3310 €3000 Verso of the sacrifice of Samson (40x27cm-16x11in) s.i.d.1966 pen Indian ink transparent paper. 11-Mar-3 Dorotheum, Vienna #163/R est:4000-6000
£2365 $3689 €3500 Rearview nude (73x46cm-29x18in) s.d.1981 col chk over gouache. 28-Mar-3 Ketterer, Hamburg #317/R est:3000-4000
£2837 $4596 €4000 Regina - head (54x37cm-21x15in) s.d.marz 1970 spray pastel. 20-May-3 Dorotheum, Vienna #215/R est:5000-9000
£6013 $9500 €9500 In spring (50x37cm-20x15in) s.d.89 mixed media. 27-Nov-2 Dorotheum, Vienna #317/R est:7000-9500
£7092 $11489 €10000 Sphynx in Eva (53x38cm-21x15in) s.d.Nov.1965 gouache col pen chl prov. 20-May-3 Dorotheum, Vienna #212/R est:10000-16000

FUCHS, Georg (1835-1885) German
Works on paper
£500 $779 €750 Virgin and Child in a rose arbour (24x19cm-9x7in) s.i.d.1870 bodycol gold ground vellum after Stefan Lochner. 19-Sep-2 Christie's, Kensington #12

FUCHS, Karl (1872-1968) German
£463 $745 €695 Winter skating (41x51cm-16x20in) s.i.d.Januar 1871 board. 7-May-3 Dobiaschofsky, Bern #562/R (S.FR 1000)

FUCHS, Richard (1852-?) German
£1197 $1927 €1700 Nile near Cairo in the evening (29x47cm-11x19in) s. i. verso board lit. 9-May-3 Schloss Ahlden, Ahlden #1397/R est:1500
£2500 $3900 €3750 Birds on a lake by sunset (79x54cm-31x21in) s. 26-Mar-3 Sotheby's, Olympia #230/R est:2500-3500
£3500 $5460 €5250 An Arab camp at sunset (60x100cm-24x39in) s. 26-Mar-3 Sotheby's, Olympia #231/R est:3000-5000

FUCHS, Therese (1849-?) German
£559 $888 €839 Sailing boat and houses in Hardanger Fjord (62x106cm-24x42in) s.i.d.1897. 10-Mar-3 Rasmussen, Vejle #520/R (D.KR 6000)

FUCIGNAS, V A (20th C) American
Sculpture
£2065 $3200 €3098 Wealthy planter (74x36x25cm-29x14x10in) s.i. white marble. 7-Dec-2 Neal Auction Company, New Orleans #521/R est:1500-2500

FUEGER, Friedrich Heinrich (1751-1818) German
Works on paper
£1258 $1950 €2000 Mother with two children (33x23cm-13x9in) s. Indian ink. 1-Oct-2 Dorotheum, Vienna #115/R est:550-750

FUEGER, Friedrich Heinrich (attrib) (1751-1818) German
Works on paper
£2568 $4005 €3800 Portrait of Kaiser Josef II in blue uniform (7x5cm-3x2in) W/C ivory oval. 28-Mar-3 Dorotheum, Vienna #367/R est:4000-4500

FUEGER, Friedrich Heinrich (circle) (1751-1818) German
£6757 $10541 €10000 Judgement of Midas (71x91cm-28x36in) 27-Mar-3 Dorotheum, Vienna #243/R est:10000-16000

FUERTES, Louis Agassiz (1874-1927) American
Works on paper
£500 $770 €750 Study of a tiger (17x31cm-7x12in) s.d.97 pencil. 22-Oct-2 Bonhams, Knightsbridge #67/R
£1401 $2200 €2102 Two colourful birds on a branch with landscape behind (25x23cm-10x9in) s.i. W/C gouache. 19-Apr-3 James Julia, Fairfield #338/R est:2000-3000
£2215 $3500 €3323 Upland plover (30x23cm-12x9in) mono. W/C ink prov. 3-Apr-3 Christie's, Rockefeller NY #215/R est:800-1200
£2532 $4000 €3798 Two pygmy geese (23x30cm-9x12in) s. W/C gouache on board. 3-Apr-3 Christie's, Rockefeller NY #202/R est:6000-8000
£3165 $5000 €4748 Two pintails flying over a marsh (29x20cm-11x8in) s. W/C gouache on board. 3-Apr-3 Christie's, Rockefeller NY #194/R est:4000-6000
£3165 $5000 €4748 Bufflehead flying (36x28cm-14x11in) s.d.1913 W/C gouache on board prov. 3-Apr-3 Christie's, Rockefeller NY #207/R est:4000-6000

FUGAI, Ekun (attrib) (1568-1650) Japanese
Works on paper
£1139 $1800 €1800 Daruma en buste (65x31cm-26x12in) ink paper on kakemono. 29-Nov-2 Tajan, Paris #81 est:2000-3000

FUGE, W H (?) British?
£300 $477 €435 Portrait of a seated lady (44x34cm-17x13in) 29-Apr-3 Henry Adams, Chichester #279

FUGER, Heinrich Friedrich (1751-1818) German
£1026 $1610 €1600 Light entertainment with advent of Apollo (12x20cm-5x8in) mono. paper. 21-Nov-2 Dorotheum, Vienna #61/R est:1800-2600
Miniatures
£1600 $2512 €2400 Joseph Gabriel Fuger, the artist father (5cm-2xin) gilt metal frame oval. 10-Dec-2 Christie's, London #153/R est:1500-2500

FUGER, Heinrich Friedrich (attrib) (1751-1818) German
Miniatures
£1700 $2669 €2550 Madame Royale, Princess Marie Therese of France (7cm-3xin) oval. 10-Dec-2 Christie's, London #104/R est:1000-1500
Works on paper
£408 $649 €600 Taking Jesus prisoner (75x41cm-30x16in) i. i. verso pen chk. 19-Mar-3 Neumeister, Munich #332/R

FUHR, Franz Xaver (1898-1973) German
£11538 $17885 €18000 Bay (70x110cm-28x43in) s. 7-Dec-2 Hauswedell & Nolte, Hamburg #663/R est:15000
Works on paper
£526 $784 €810 Woodland (63x35cm-25x14in) s.i. w/C htd white. 26-Jun-2 Neumeister, Munich #579/R
£577 $912 €900 Bridge over the Elbe near Dresden (46x59cm-18x23in) i. verso W/C. 14-Nov-2 Neumeister, Munich #566/R
£797 $1307 €1100 At the edge of the desert (60x50cm-24x20in) i. verso W/C gouache board. 31-May-3 Villa Grisebach, Berlin #560/R
£1026 $1590 €1600 Houses and car (36x47cm-14x19in) s. W/C bodycol exhib. 7-Dec-2 Ketterer, Hamburg #406/R est:1600-1800
£1218 $1888 €1900 Postman (55x39cm-22x15in) W/C bodycol over pencil. 7-Dec-2 Ketterer, Hamburg #405/R est:1900-2200

FUHRICH, Josef von (1800-1876) Austrian
Works on paper
£346 $536 €550 Gregory I (51x37cm-20x15in) s. bears i. pencil. 1-Oct-2 Dorotheum, Vienna #114/R

FUHRICH, Josef von (attrib) (1800-1876) Austrian
£723 $1172 €1085 Huus before his death sentence (78x117cm-31x46in) init. 27-Jan-3 Blomqvist, Lysaker #1067/R (N.KR 8000)

FUHRMANN, Arend (20th C) Swiss?
£2838 $4456 €4257 Composition with coloured lines (110x55cm-43x22in) s. exhib.prov. 23-Nov-2 Burkhard, Luzern #45/R est:6000-8000 (S.FR 6500)

FUJIWARA SUKENOBU (1671-1751) Oriental
Works on paper
£5031 $7748 €8000 Three boats leaving an island (127x99cm-50x39in) ink. 23-Oct-2 Piasa, Paris #335/R

FUKA, Vladimir (1926-1977) Czechoslovakian
£3054 $4856 €4581 Rope walkers on Letna (64x54cm-25x21in) s. i.d. verso board. 8-Mar-3 Dorotheum, Prague #127/R est:100000-150000 (C.KR 140000)

FUKUI, Ryonosuke (1924-1986) Japanese
Works on paper
£577 $900 €866 Landscapes (25x18cm-10x7in) s. W/C dr pair. 10-Nov-2 Selkirks, St. Louis #612/R

FUKUSHIMA, Tikashi (1920-) Brazilian/Japanese
£1424 $2250 €2136 Abstract (76x102cm-30x40in) d.1965. 15-Nov-2 Du Mouchelle, Detroit #1221/R est:3000-5000

FULLA, Ludovit (1902-1980) Czechoslovakian
£6930 $10118 €10395 Suburb of Ruzomberok town (45x53cm-18x21in) board painted c.1928. 4-Jun-2 SOGA, Bratislava #69/R est:190000 (SL.K 440000)
£14998 $23248 €22497 Ascension (71x45cm-28x18in) painted c.1941. 3-Dec-2 SOGA, Bratislava #51/R est:950000 (SL.K 950000)
£15751 $22996 €23627 Foxes in an orchard (54x70cm-21x28in) 4-Jun-2 SOGA, Bratislava #68/R est:650000 (SL.K 1000000)

FULLARTON, James (1946-) British
£520 $811 €780 Ponies at Glenfoot (64x75cm-25x30in) 28-Mar-3 Bonhams, Edinburgh #172
Works on paper
£620 $967 €930 Jard sur Mar (28x28cm-11x11in) s. gouache sold with another similar. 10-Apr-3 Bonhams, Edinburgh #49
£700 $1092 €1050 Lochgoilhead. French street scene (21x26cm-8x10in) s. gouache pair. 10-Apr-3 Bonhams, Edinburgh #43

FULLBROOK, Samuel Sydney (1922-) Australian
£1992 $3267 €2888 Wheat fields, Pilbara (16x17cm-6x7in) init. i.verso canvas on board prov. 4-Jun-3 Deutscher-Menzies, Melbourne #289/R est:3800-4600 (A.D 5000)
£2135 $3267 €3203 Pool on the Coliban (60x66cm-24x26in) init. painted 2002. 25-Aug-2 Sotheby's, Paddington #156/R est:6000-9000 (A.D 6000)
£3200 $5152 €4800 Bird sleeping (47x50cm-19x20in) init. 6-May-3 Christie's, Melbourne #30/R est:8000-12000 (A.D 8000)
£3381 $5173 €5072 Young bear (40x38cm-16x15in) init. painted 1982. 25-Aug-2 Sotheby's, Paddington #114/R est:5000-8000 (A.D 9500)
£3831 $5709 €5747 Boy with watermelon (48x29cm-19x11in) canvas on board exhib.lit. 27-Aug-2 Christie's, Melbourne #91/R est:10000-15000 (A.D 10000)
£5000 $7950 €7500 Koala (30x50cm-12x20in) init. i.verso. 4-Mar-3 Deutscher-Menzies, Melbourne #159/R est:7000-10000 (A.D 13000)
£7681 $11906 €11522 Young drover (55x35cm-22x14in) s. panel painted c.1955 prov. 3-Dec-2 Shapiro, Sydney #29/R est:25000-30000 (A.D 21300)
£7885 $11986 €11828 Landscape (75x78cm-30x31in) init. 28-Aug-2 Deutscher-Menzies, Melbourne #126/R est:14000-18000 (A.D 22000)
£9253 $14157 €13880 Tulips (72x72cm-28x28in) init. 25-Aug-2 Sotheby's, Paddington #49/R est:25000-35000 (A.D 26000)
£14000 $22540 €21000 Visitation (83x74cm-33x29in) init. painted 1981 prov.exhib.lit. 6-May-3 Christie's, Melbourne #67/R est:40000-50000 (A.D 35000)
Works on paper
£285 $436 €428 Lady Macquarie's chair (21x29cm-8x11in) s. pastel executed 1974 prov. 26-Aug-2 Sotheby's, Paddington #597/R (A.D 800)
£763 $1206 €1322 Landscape (25x38cm-10x15in) s. pastel. 1-Apr-3 Goodman, Sydney #104 (A.D 2000)

FULLER, Alfred (1899-?) American
£658 $1000 €987 Storm coming ashore (84x97cm-33x38in) s. board. 30-Aug-2 Thomaston Place, Thomaston #52a

FULLER, Arthur Davenport (1889-1967) American
£3819 $5500 €5729 Fly fishing (64x56cm-25x22in) s. i.verso. 15-Jan-3 Christie's, Rockefeller NY #171/R

FULLER, Edmund G (fl.1900-1920) British
£1800 $2790 €2700 Gentle swell and sparkling seas breaking on the Cornish coast (193x323cm-76x127in) s. 26-Sep-2 Lane, Penzance #373 est:1500-1750
Works on paper
£500 $815 €750 Sloop, St Ives (18x23cm-7x9in) s. W/C. 13-Feb-3 David Lay, Penzance #164

FULLER, F (?) ?
£549 $856 €824 Landscape with figures and cattle by river (26x53cm-10x21in) s. sold with another. 23-Sep-2 Rasmussen, Vejle #276/R (D.KR 6500)

FULLER, Florence Ada (1867-1946) Australian
£5200 $8008 €7800 Portrait of Mrs J W Hackett, seated in a wicker chair (81x64cm-32x25in) s. 3-Sep-2 Gorringes, Lewes #2100/R est:5000-7000

FULLEYLOVE, John (1845-1908) British
£1300 $2002 €1950 University church of Saint Mary's, Oxford (24x14cm-9x6in) s. panel prov. 5-Sep-2 Christie's, Kensington #223/R est:600-800
Works on paper
£300 $468 €450 Nice (22x34cm-9x13in) s. W/C. 25-Mar-3 Bonhams, Knightsbridge #222/R
£650 $1013 €975 Eleanor Cross, Hardingstone, Northamptonshire (25x18cm-10x7in) s. pencil W/C htd white. 19-Sep-2 Christie's, Kensington #150/R
£1000 $1630 €1500 Clare Cottage, Cambridge (12x17cm-5x7in) s.d.1889 pencil W/C. 13-Feb-3 Mellors & Kirk, Nottingham #779/R est:200-400
£1200 $1872 €1800 Temple of Apollo at Bassae (12x18cm-5x7in) s. W/C over pencil bodycol. 15-Oct-2 Sotheby's, London #35/R est:600-800
£1200 $1956 €1800 Paris viewed from the Seine (13x18cm-5x7in) s. W/C pair. 28-Jan-3 Gorringes, Lewes #1739 est:600-800
£3000 $4620 €4500 Acropolis from the Temple of Jupiter, Olympus, Athens (26x38cm-10x15in) s.d.1895 W/C. 22-Oct-2 Bonhams, Knightsbridge #210/R est:500-700
£3500 $5460 €5250 Jerusalem from the Mount of Olives (59x100cm-23x39in) s. W/C. 26-Mar-3 Sotheby's, Olympia #34/R est:3000-5000

FULLWOOD, Albert Henry (1863-1930) British
£714 $1107 €1071 Chalk cliffs, Sussex, England (43x53cm-17x21in) s.d.18 canvasboard. 29-Oct-2 Lawson Menzies, Sydney #272 (A.D 2000)
£916 $1447 €1374 Home sweet home (14x17cm-6x7in) s. board sold with and etching by another artist. 7-Apr-3 Shapiro, Sydney #426/R (A.D 2400)
£2099 $3317 €3149 Tweed River (16x17cm-6x7in) init. board. 2-Apr-3 Christie's, Melbourne #31/R est:3000-5000 (A.D 5500)
£8397 $13267 €12596 Mosman (15x24cm-6x9in) s.i. panel exhib.lit. 2-Apr-3 Christie's, Melbourne #5/R est:8000-12000 (A.D 22000)
£9160 $14473 €13740 Haymaking (14x24cm-6x9in) s.i. board. 2-Apr-3 Christie's, Melbourne #39/R est:5000-8000 (A.D 24000)
£9542 $15076 €14313 Sirius Cove (20x24cm-8x9in) s. panel painted c.1894 exhib.lit. 2-Apr-3 Christie's, Melbourne #18/R est:8000-12000 (A.D 25000)

FULLWOOD, Charles (fl.1888-1889) British
£650 $1001 €975 Heavy horses (76x96cm-30x38in) s. after Rosa Bonheur. 5-Sep-2 Christie's, Kensington #147/R

FULLWOOD, John (1854-1931) British
Works on paper
£750 $1178 €1125 Corn stooks in a coastal landscape (33x50cm-13x20in) s.i. W/C. 16-Dec-2 Bonhams, Bury St Edmunds #386/R

FULOP, Karoly (1893-1963) American
Sculpture
£5901 $9500 €8852 Modernist figures (26x21cm-10x8in) s. porcelain wood panel prov. 18-Feb-3 John Moran, Pasadena #79 est:10000-15000

FULTON, David (1848-1930) British
£280 $442 €420 West coast scene with sailing boats (29x44cm-11x17in) 1-Apr-3 Patersons, Paisley #544
£700 $1141 €1050 Cobbler (46x41cm-18x16in) 14-Feb-3 Lyon & Turnbull, Edinburgh #3
£1600 $2496 €2400 Village shoemaker (46x61cm-18x24in) s. prov. 14-Apr-3 Sotheby's, London #63/R est:1500-2000

FULTON, David (attrib) (1848-1930) British
£1100 $1716 €1650 Eating her porridge (40x28cm-16x11in) indis sig. 28-Mar-3 Bonhams, Edinburgh #181 est:600-800
£1200 $1872 €1800 Stitch in time (51x41cm-20x16in) bears sig. 17-Sep-2 Sotheby's, Olympia #15/R est:1000-1500

FULTON, Fitch Burt (1879-1955) American
£2707 $4250 €4061 High Sierra lake (61x76cm-24x30in) s. 19-Nov-2 Butterfields, San Francisco #8276/R est:4000-6000
£3548 $5500 €5322 Mountain landscape (61x71cm-24x28in) s.d.34. 29-Oct-2 John Moran, Pasadena #708 est:5000-7000

FULTON, Hamish (1946-) British
Photographs
£5063 $8000 €7595 Black smoke caves (95x245cm-37x96in) s.i.d.1987 black/white photograph prov. 13-Nov-2 Sotheby's, New York #504/R

FULTON, Samuel (1855-1941) British
£1500 $2430 €2250 Study of a Scots terrier (45x35cm-18x14in) s. 23-May-3 Lyon & Turnbull, Edinburgh #77/R est:1500-2000
£1850 $3071 €2683 Study of a dandy dinmont champion Netherby II (51x61cm-20x24in) i. 13-Jun-3 Lyon & Turnbull, Edinburgh #52 est:1000-1500
£1994 $3250 €2991 Pug (46x35cm-18x14in) s. 11-Feb-3 Bonhams & Doyles, New York #211/R est:1500-2000
£2000 $3160 €3000 Cocker spaniel (51x41cm-20x16in) s. 28-Nov-2 Christie's, Kensington #353/R est:2000-3000
£2200 $3498 €3300 Cocker spaniel (51x41cm-20x16in) s. exhib. 6-Mar-3 Christie's, Kensington #122/R est:1000-1500

£3600 $5508 €5400 Scottie dog seated in a stable (61x51cm-24x20in) s. 22-Aug-2 Bonhams, Edinburgh #1073/R est:2000-3000
£3681 $6000 €5522 Jack Russell puppy in a barn (46x35cm-18x14in) s. 11-Feb-3 Bonhams & Doyles, New York #156/R est:6000-8000
£5521 $9000 €8282 Cosy place (63x76cm-25x30in) s. 11-Feb-3 Bonhams & Doyles, New York #259/R est:10000-15000

FUNCK, Theodor (1867-1919) German
£252 $390 €400 Le fagotier (40x27cm-16x11in) s. 4-Oct-2 Tajan, Paris #95

FUNCKEL, Karl Albert (19/20th C) ?
£1081 $1686 €1600 Old lady sewing in interior (37x31cm-15x12in) s. board. 25-Mar-3 Durán, Madrid #154/R

FUNGAI, Bernardino (1460-1516) Italian
£50000 $83500 €72500 Scipio proclaims his candidature for command of the Roman forces in Spain (61x106cm-24x42in) i. panel prov.lit. 10-Jul-3 Sotheby's, London #32/R est:50000-70000

FUNGAI, Bernardino (attrib) (1460-1516) Italian
£21379 $34207 €31000 Madonna and Child with Saints (102x60cm-40x24in) tempera board. 17-Mar-3 Pandolfini, Florence #680/R est:40000

FUNGE, Paul (1944-) Irish
£352 $585 €500 Galway football player (59x45cm-23x18in) s. board. 10-Jun-3 James Adam, Dublin #27/R

FUNI, Achille (1890-1972) Italian
Works on paper
£943 $1453 €1500 Study of head of angel (41x49cm-16x19in) s. pastel pencil. 28-Oct-2 Il Ponte, Milan #164/R
£3846 $6038 €6000 Comic muse (220x135cm-87x53in) init. cardboard painted c.1946. 21-Nov-2 Finarte, Rome #249/R est:7000
£4808 $7452 €7500 Allegorical figure (209x75cm-82x30in) s. pastel paper on canvas exec.c.1935 exhib.lit. 4-Dec-2 Finarte, Milan #325/R est:8000

FUNK, J (fl.1835-1840) German
£2568 $4005 €3800 Schussental (56x75cm-22x30in) s. 27-Mar-3 Dr Fritz Nagel, Stuttgart #808/R est:7000

FUNKE, Anton (1869-1955) Dutch
£326 $519 €489 Still life of pink roses with blue and green grapes (46x35cm-18x14in) s. panel. 5-May-3 Rasmussen, Vejle #587/R (D.KR 3500)
£437 $703 €620 Still life of fruit (29x39cm-11x15in) s. 6-May-3 Vendu Notarishuis, Rotterdam #111
£1911 $2981 €3000 Hunting still life (119x95cm-47x37in) s. 5-Nov-2 Vendu Notarishuis, Rotterdam #293/R est:2500-3000

FUNKE, Helene (1869-1957) Austrian
£513 $805 €800 Summer landscape (46x60cm-18x24in) s. 23-Nov-2 Arnold, Frankfurt #723/R
£3481 $5500 €5500 Landscape with waterfall and horses (79x48cm-31x19in) s. prov. 27-Nov-2 Dorotheum, Vienna #151/R est:5000-7000
£6013 $9500 €9500 Still life with fruit and jugs (58x70cm-23x28in) s. prov. 27-Nov-2 Dorotheum, Vienna #150/R est:9000-12000

FUNKE, Jaromir (1896-1945) Czechoslovakian
Photographs
£5063 $8000 €7595 Photographic composition, loneliness I (11x14cm-4x6in) gelatin silver print lit. 22-Apr-3 Christie's, Rockefeller NY #85/R est:7000-9000

FUNNO, Michele (19th C) ?
Works on paper
£1400 $2268 €2100 Helen of Montrose in Neapolitan waters (51x76cm-20x30in) s.i. bodycol. 21-May-3 Christie's, Kensington #425/R est:1000-1500

FURCY DE LAVAULT, Albert Tibule (19th C) French
£1804 $2796 €2850 Jardiniere de lilas et fleurs des champs (60x73cm-24x29in) s. 29-Sep-2 Eric Pillon, Calais #27/R

FURET, François (1842-1909) Swiss
£1415 $2264 €2123 Wooded river landscape with girl and sheep (69x101cm-27x40in) s. 17-Mar-3 Philippe Schuler, Zurich #4523/R est:3000-5000 (S.FR 3000)
Works on paper
£1019 $1640 €1478 Young goat herder by a stream (45x70cm-18x28in) s. pastel. 9-May-3 Dobiaschofsky, Bern #53/R (S.FR 2200)

FURINI, Francesco (1604-1646) Italian
£3448 $5517 €5000 Allegory of Temperance (64x52cm-25x20in) 17-Mar-3 Pandolfini, Florence #699/R est:11000

FURINI, Francesco (attrib) (1604-1646) Italian
£1773 $2748 €2660 Female saint (65x50cm-26x20in) oval prov. 3-Dec-2 Bukowskis, Stockholm #521/R est:30000-35000 (S.KR 25000)

FURLONGER, Joseph (1952-) Australian
£452 $706 €785 New Guinea woman (60x49cm-24x19in) prov. 31-Mar-3 Goodman, Sydney #154/R (A.D 1200)
£3018 $4708 €5228 Circus royale (133x264cm-52x104in) s. three panels prov. 31-Mar-3 Goodman, Sydney #150/R (A.D 8000)
Works on paper
£340 $530 €588 Beach scene (45x49cm-18x19in) s.d.88 pastel three panels. 31-Mar-3 Goodman, Sydney #36 (A.D 900)
£415 $648 €719 Two people on a beach (19x56cm-7x22in) s.d.87 pastel prov. 31-Mar-3 Goodman, Sydney #35 (A.D 1100)
£698 $1088 €1209 People doing cartwheels (56x75cm-22x30in) s.d.88 W/C ink prov. 31-Mar-3 Goodman, Sydney #4/R (A.D 1850)
£1207 $1883 €2091 Deposition (118x122cm-46x48in) init.d.90 mixed media. 31-Mar-3 Goodman, Sydney #249/R (A.D 3200)

FURNEAUX, Charles (1835-1913) American
£679 $1100 €985 Landscape study, Melrose, Massachusetts (41x61cm-16x24in) s. panel prov.exhib. 21-May-3 Doyle, New York #64/R

FURNESS, Robin (1933-) British
Works on paper
£320 $509 €480 The Belvoir (35x53cm-14x21in) s. gouache. 7-Mar-3 Tennants, Leyburn #150

FURST, M (?) ?
£480 $753 €720 Bouquet of autumn flowers in vase (100x61cm-39x24in) s. 25-Nov-2 Blomqvist, Lysaker #1077/R (N.KR 5500)

FURT, Leonce (19/20th C) French
£800 $1232 €1200 Figures promenading in El Retiro, Madrid (14x22cm-6x9in) s.i.d1903 panel. 24-Oct-2 Christie's, Kensington #102/R
£1923 $2923 €3000 Port de Cherbourg (16x24cm-6x9in) s.i. panel. 16-Aug-2 Deauville, France #99/R

FURUNES, Anne Karin (1961-) Norwegian
Works on paper
£2490 $3910 €3735 Charlotte 2002 (100x100cm-39x39in) s.verso dyed perforated canvas. 15-Apr-3 Lawson Menzies, Sydney #81/R est:5500-7500 (A.D 6500)

FUSARO, Jean (1925-) French
£2838 $4427 €4200 Dans le port (33x46cm-13x18in) s. 28-Mar-3 Delvaux, Paris #57/R est:2500
£4167 $6625 €6000 L'embarquement de St Pauline a ostie d'apres Claude le Lorrain (46x55cm-18x22in) s. s.i.d.1957 verso. 29-Apr-3 Artcurial Briest, Paris #289/R est:2000-3000
£5882 $9647 €9000 Canal de Sete (59x72cm-23x28in) s.d.1951 prov. 9-Feb-3 Anaf, Lyon #106/R

FUSI, Walter (1924-) Italian
£321 $503 €500 Untitled (50x70cm-20x28in) s. painted 1991. 23-Nov-2 Meeting Art, Vercelli #279/R
£359 $575 €550 Untitled (50x70cm-20x28in) s. s.verso mixed media on canvas exec.1991. 4-Jan-3 Meeting Art, Vercelli #470
Works on paper
£306 $487 €450 Composition (50x70cm-20x28in) s.d.1994 mixed media card. 1-Mar-3 Meeting Art, Vercelli #345

FUSS, Adam (1961-) American
Photographs
£1899 $3000 €2849 Untitled (66x74cm-26x29in) s.d.1995 num.342-2 cibachrome photogram. 23-Apr-3 Sotheby's, New York #290/R est:5000-7000
£3571 $5500 €5357 Untitled (112x51cm-44x20in) s.d.num.verso cibachrome photogram prov.lit. 25-Oct-2 Phillips, New York #186/R est:6000-8000
£3797 $6000 €5696 Snake powder (102x76cm-40x30in) s.d.1991 verso cibachrome photogram prov. 24-Apr-3 Phillips, New York #226/R est:6000-8000
£4114 $6500 €6171 Untitled - spiral (102x76cm-40x30in) cibachrome photogram prov. 24-Apr-3 Phillips, New York #225/R est:4000-6000

£5065 $7800 €7598 Untitled (38x30cm-15x12in) s.d.num.257.2 verso cibachrome photogram board prov.lit. 25-Oct-2 Phillips, New York #65/R est:6000-8000

£6329 $10000 €9494 Small smoke - my ghost series (51x61cm-20x24in) silver gelatin print board executed 1999 prov. 12-Nov-2 Phillips, New York #168/R est:10000-15000

£6329 $10000 €9494 Untitled - sunflower (35x28cm-14x11in) dye destruction photogram. 22-Apr-3 Christie's, Rockefeller NY #114/R est:6000-8000

£12658 $20000 €18987 Large flowers, Plants (101x76cm-40x30in) s.d.1994 cibachrome. 14-Nov-2 Christie's, Rockefeller NY #488/R est:12000-18000

£14375 $23000 €21563 Untitled (109x83cm-43x33in) s.d.1994 num.312.2 verso cibachrome print. 14-May-3 Sotheby's, New York #408/R est:12000-15000

£16250 $26000 €24375 Untitled - double sunflowers (102x76cm-40x30in) s.d.1994 verso cibachrome print prov. 14-May-3 Sotheby's, New York #359/R est:15000-20000

£16883 $26000 €25325 Untitled (102x76cm-40x30in) init.d.1992 verso cibachrome photogram prov. 25-Oct-2 Phillips, New York #64/R est:15000-20000

£22727 $35000 €34091 Untitled (326x142cm-128x56in) gelatin silver print photogram linen over board prov.exhib. 25-Oct-2 Phillips, New York #54/R est:20000-30000

Prints

£5500 $9020 €8250 Untitled (60x50cm-24x20in) silver print photogram prov. 7-Feb-3 Sotheby's, London #104/R est:4000-6000

£8917 $14000 €13376 From the series, My Ghost (152x229cm-60x90in) num.3 of 11 pigment print. 21-Apr-3 Phillips, New York #37 est:15000-20000

FUSSLI, Johann Heinrich (1741-1825) Swiss

£85000 $136850 €127500 Vision of the Deluge (254x210cm-100x83in) prov.exhib.lit. 20-Feb-3 Christie's, London #216/R est:150000

£197531 $320000 €296297 Three witches, or the weird sisters (63x77cm-25x30in) i. prov. 24-Jan-3 Christie's, Rockefeller NY #135/R est:250000-350000

Works on paper

£15000 $24900 €22500 Sin and Death bridging chaos meet Satan on his return from Earth (31x38cm-12x15in) i. wash over pencil prov. 12-Jun-3 Sotheby's, London #120/R est:15000-20000

FUSSMANN, Klaus (1938-) German

£692 $1065 €1100 Still life of flowers (24x32cm-9x13in) s.i.d.21.8.78 W/C. 26-Oct-2 Dr Lehr, Berlin #115

£886 $1400 €1400 Cloud study (10x17cm-4x7in) board. 29-Nov-2 Villa Grisebach, Berlin #622/R est:1400-1800

£1026 $1590 €1600 Lilac (41x54cm-16x21in) s.d.91 oil W/C paper. 7-Dec-2 Van Ham, Cologne #177/R est:2800

£1392 $2200 €2200 Landscape study (19x18cm-7x7in) 29-Nov-2 Villa Grisebach, Berlin #623/R est:2200-3000

£2778 $4389 €4000 Coats hanging on hooks (62x70cm-24x28in) s.i.d.18.VI.1974 board. 26-Apr-3 Dr Lehr, Berlin #145/R est:5000

£2899 $4754 €4000 Clouds (90x105cm-35x41in) s.i.d.I.VI.78. 31-May-3 Villa Grisebach, Berlin #379/R est:4000-6000

£3205 $4968 €5000 Lilac (50x50cm-20x20in) s.d.95. 3-Dec-2 Lempertz, Koln #144/R est:5000

£3986 $6536 €5500 Still life (53x56cm-21x22in) s.i.d.17.6.1977. 31-May-3 Villa Grisebach, Berlin #378/R est:3000-4000

£4167 $6583 €6000 Interior - bed by mirror (70x71cm-28x28in) s.d.27.VI.1977 paper. 26-Apr-3 Dr Lehr, Berlin #146/R est:7000

£5556 $8778 €8000 Still life with cups (69x74cm-27x29in) s.d.1973. 26-Apr-3 Dr Lehr, Berlin #144/R est:9000

£5797 $9507 €8000 Dahlias (75x76cm-30x30in) s.d.92 paper on board. 31-May-3 Villa Grisebach, Berlin #384/R est:8000-10000

£7246 $11884 €10000 Still life (95x113cm-37x44in) s.d.1971. 31-May-3 Villa Grisebach, Berlin #380/R est:12000-15000

£7692 $11923 €12000 Untitled - Hardenbergstrasse studio (130x140cm-51x55in) s.d.19.11.1977. 3-Dec-2 Lempertz, Koln #143/R est:12000-15000

£8228 $13000 €13000 Still life (100x85cm-39x33in) s.i.d.10.II.73. 30-Nov-2 Villa Grisebach, Berlin #450/R est:8000-10000

Works on paper

£570 $900 €900 Flower sketch (11x13cm-4x5in) mono.d.97 s.i.d. verso gouache W/C. 29-Nov-2 Villa Grisebach, Berlin #621/R

£759 $1200 €1200 Landscape (42x55cm-17x22in) s.d.9.8.85 W/C sold with another. 29-Nov-2 Villa Grisebach, Berlin #620/R

£761 $1248 €1050 Pansies (24x32cm-9x13in) mono.i.d.2.4.85 W/C. 31-May-3 Villa Grisebach, Berlin #810/R

£870 $1426 €1200 Landscape with houses (30x40cm-12x16in) s.d.1977 bears i. W/C. 31-May-3 Villa Grisebach, Berlin #807/R

£942 $1545 €1300 Marguerites (15x22cm-6x9in) mono.d.88 W/C gouache. 31-May-3 Villa Grisebach, Berlin #811/R est:700-900

£1154 $1823 €1800 Still life with poppies (29x40cm-11x16in) s.d.1986 W/C gouache. 15-Nov-2 Reiss & Sohn, Konigstein #808/R est:1800

£1154 $1788 €1800 Landscape - Gelting (22x31cm-9x12in) s.d.9.8.82 W/c. 3-Dec-2 Lempertz, Koln #146/R est:2000

£1159 $1901 €1600 Landscape (64x76cm-25x30in) s.i.d.21.X.79 W/C. 31-May-3 Villa Grisebach, Berlin #808/R est:1800-2400

£1266 $2000 €2000 Foxgloves (29x41cm-11x16in) mono.d.83 W/C Indian ink brush. 29-Nov-2 Villa Grisebach, Berlin #619/R est:2000-2500

£1282 $1987 €2000 Untitled - landscape with clouds, Gelting (29x41cm-11x16in) s.i.d.2.9.78 W/C bodycol. 3-Dec-2 Lempertz, Koln #145/R est:2000

£1346 $2127 €2100 Landscape near Gelting (41x55cm-16x22in) s.d.1994 gouache bodycol. 14-Nov-2 Neumeister, Munich #771/R est:2800-3500

£1667 $2633 €2600 Dahlias (28x38cm-11x15in) s. W/C Indian ink bodycol. 14-Nov-2 Neumeister, Munich #773/R est:2000-2500

£1772 $2800 €2800 Wannsee (62x68cm-24x27in) s.i.d.27.1.74 gouache oil board. 30-Nov-2 Villa Grisebach, Berlin #445/R est:3000-4000

£1773 $2872 €2500 Still life of flowers (41x55cm-16x22in) mono.d.89 pastel gouache W/C. 24-May-3 Van Ham, Cologne #194/R est:5000

£1812 $2971 €2500 Still life of flowers (29x40cm-11x16in) mono. pastel bodycol. 31-May-3 Villa Grisebach, Berlin #381/R est:2500-3500

£1812 $2971 €2500 Still life of flowers (43x53cm-17x21in) mono.i.d.90 pastel bodycol. 31-May-3 Villa Grisebach, Berlin #382/R est:2500-3500

£1859 $2881 €2900 Landscape near Pommerby (42x56cm-17x22in) s.d.97 pastel chk. 3-Dec-2 Lempertz, Koln #149/R est:3000

£1957 $3209 €2700 Roses (23x30cm-9x12in) s.d.96 w/C. 28-May-3 Lempertz, Koln #144/R est:2500

£2014 $3223 €2800 Red poppy (20x30cm-8x12in) s.d.2002 W/C. 15-May-3 Neumeister, Munich #437/R est:2000-2500

£2174 $3565 €3000 Larkspur (66x51cm-26x20in) s.d.1.96 W/C. 28-May-3 Lempertz, Koln #143/R est:4000-5000

£2174 $3565 €3000 Still life of flowers (24x30cm-9x12in) mono.i.d.89 pastel bodycol. 31-May-3 Villa Grisebach, Berlin #812/R est:2500-3000

£2532 $4000 €4000 Still life of flowers (29x41cm-11x16in) mono.d.80 pastel W/C. 30-Nov-2 Villa Grisebach, Berlin #449/R est:3200-3500

£2949 $4571 €4600 Untitled - Roses (48x65cm-19x26in) s.d.96 W/C tempera. 3-Dec-2 Lempertz, Koln #148/R est:5000

£3205 $4968 €5000 Narcissus and crown imperials (42x56cm-17x22in) s.d.92 pastel lit. 7-Dec-2 Van Ham, Cologne #175/R est:6200

£3526 $5465 €5500 Interior (62x73cm-24x29in) s.d.1970 mixed media. 7-Dec-2 Van Ham, Cologne #174/R est:8000

£3623 $5942 €5000 Red gladioli (90x77cm-35x30in) s.i.d.8.8.90 W/C bodycol. 28-May-3 Lempertz, Koln #142/R est:6000-8000

£3623 $5942 €5000 Portrait of H K Hardenberg-Strasse (70x71cm-28x28in) s.i.d.26.VI.1976 gouache graphite. 28-May-3 Lempertz, Koln #141/R est:6000-8000

£3846 $5962 €6000 Still life of flowers with tulips and hyacinths (40x50cm-16x20in) s.d.1995 W/C. 6-Dec-2 Ketterer, Munich #209/R est:5000-6000

£4114 $6500 €6500 In the studio (76x84cm-30x33in) s.i.d.29.V.81 gouache. 30-Nov-2 Villa Grisebach, Berlin #448/R est:6500-8500

FUSTER, Juan (1870-1934) Spanish

£818 $1275 €1300 Landscape (22x30cm-9x12in) s. cardboard. 8-Oct-2 Ansorena, Madrid #656/R

FUTTERER, Joseph (1871-1930) German

£513 $795 €800 Peasant woman and boy peeling potatoes (40x33cm-16x13in) s.d.08 panel. 5-Dec-2 Neumeister, Munich #2792

FUX, Hans Georg (attrib) (1661-1706) German

Sculpture

£5493 $9118 €7800 Saint Sebastian represente adosse a un tronc d'arbre (21cm-8in) ivory socle exec.c.1700. 16-Jun-3 Anaf, Lyon #62/R est:4000-5000

FUZESI, Lajos (1931-) Hungarian

£448 $713 €650 Thoughtful woman (80x60cm-31x24in) s. 4-Mar-3 Ansorena, Madrid #315/R

FYFE, William (1836-1882) British

£1100 $1793 €1595 Young flower seller (33x24cm-13x9in) s. 17-Jul-3 Tennants, Leyburn #913/R est:600-800

£1250 $1938 €1875 Shore scene with figures on pebbly beach (33x46cm-13x18in) s.d.1871. 25-Sep-2 Brightwells, Leominster #951 est:800-1200

£2800 $4452 €4200 Orange girl (39x26cm-15x10in) s.d.1879 exhib. 6-Mar-3 Christie's, Kensington #111/R est:2000-3000

£6000 $9240 €9000 Bide a see (91x66cm-36x26in) s.d.1873 exhib. 5-Sep-2 Christie's, Kensington #286/R est:3000-5000

GAAL, Ferenc (1891-1956) Hungarian

£756 $1254 €1096 Fieldworkers (35x44cm-14x17in) s. board. 16-Jun-3 Waddingtons, Toronto #305/R est:800-1200 (C.D 1700)

£1419 $2213 €2058 Campiello del Terchio (60x80cm-24x31in) s. 13-Sep-2 Mu Terem Galeria, Budapest #17/R est:350000 (H.F 550000)

£3353 $5231 €4862 Pont des Arts (68x88cm-27x35in) s.i.d.1931. 12-Apr-3 Mu Terem Galeria, Budapest #83/R est:300000 (H.F 1200000)

GAAL, Pieter (1785-1819) Dutch
£6369 $9936 €10000 Italianate river landscape with peasant woman returning from a market (28x21cm-11x8in) s. panel. 6-Nov-2 Christie's, Amsterdam #40/R est:6000-8000

GABAIN, Ethel (1883-1950) British
£680 $1074 €1020 Spring flowers (40x51cm-16x20in) s. 27-Nov-2 Sotheby's, Olympia #123/R
£700 $1092 €1050 Tulips and acacia (51x40cm-20x16in) 27-Mar-3 Christie's, Kensington #532/R
£750 $1178 €1125 Bridge (51x41cm-20x16in) s. 15-Apr-3 Bonhams, Knightsbridge #74/R
Works on paper
£600 $960 €900 Rain on the moors. W/C. 8-Jan-3 Brightwells, Leominster #1090

GABALI, Alfred (c.1870-1940) German
£256 $400 €384 Four masted clipper ship in rough seas (61x91cm-24x36in) s. 28-Mar-3 Eldred, East Dennis #645

GABBIANI, Antonio Domenico (1652-1726) Italian
Works on paper
£1100 $1727 €1650 Rape of the Sabines (7x24cm-3x9in) pen ink wash over black chk. 11-Dec-2 Sotheby's, Olympia #118/R est:600-800
£3704 $6000 €5556 Invention of the cross (33x45cm-13x18in) pen ink wash partly squared prov.exhib. 21-Jan-3 Sotheby's, New York #19/R est:8000-12000

GABBIANI, Antonio Domenico (attrib) (1652-1726) Italian
Works on paper
£1348 $2250 €1900 Scene allegorique (28x27cm-11x11in) pen htd white gouache. 17-Jun-3 Palais de Beaux Arts, Brussels #484 est:1500-2000

GABBRIELLI, Donatello (20th C) Italian
Sculpture
£45000 $69750 €67500 Dante. Machiavelli. Ghiberti. De Medici. Possibly Niccolo da Uzzano (66cm-26in) s. four i. sold with circular socle five. 1-Oct-2 Christie's, London #308/R est:25000-35000

GABE, Nicolas Edward (1814-1865) French
£2344 $3750 €3516 Ships beached by a jetty with numerous figures (45x60cm-18x24in) s. 14-May-3 Butterfields, San Francisco #1155/R est:3000-5000
£3205 $5032 €5000 Barques de peche a la cote (39x61cm-15x24in) s. 16-Dec-2 Eric Coutrier, Paris #33/R

GABELLIERI, Alessandro G (attrib) (1882-1961) American
Sculpture
£994 $1600 €1491 Young woman (48cm-19in) s. marble. 19-Jan-3 Jeffery Burchard, Florida #90a/R

GABELLONE, Giuseppe (1973-) British?
Photographs
£5000 $7700 €7500 Tank (150x190cm-59x75in) s.d.1996 num.1/3 verso c-print mounted on aluminium prov. 23-Oct-2 Christie's, London #252/R est:2000-3000

GABO, Naum (1890-1977) American/Russian
Works on paper
£2564 $3974 €4000 Etude pour une construction (24x21cm-9x8in) s.d.34 pencil exhib. 4-Dec-2 Lempertz, Koln #721/R est:4000

GABOR, Jeno (1893-1971) Hungarian
£753 $1167 €1092 Geometrical forms (70x50cm-28x20in) s.d.67 tempera paper. 9-Dec-2 Mu Terem Galeria, Budapest #97/R est:220000 (H.F 280000)
£2689 $4168 €3899 Woman with fish (62x57cm-24x22in) s.d.42 canvas on card. 9-Dec-2 Mu Terem Galeria, Budapest #207/R est:650000 (H.F 1000000)
£8606 $13339 €12479 Muse making music, portrait of his wife (90x70cm-35x28in) s.d.1932 exhib. 9-Dec-2 Mu Terem Galeria, Budapest #180/R est:1600000 (H.F 3200000)
£13972 $21797 €20958 Market acrobats (130x221cm-51x87in) s.d.1940. 11-Apr-3 Kieselbach, Budapest #129/R est:500000-5000000 (H.F 5000000)

GABRIEL, François (?-1993) French
£1911 $3000 €2867 Still life with fruit and flowers (122x91cm-48x36in) s. 22-Nov-2 Skinner, Boston #44/R est:2000-4000
£1951 $3200 €2829 Flowers in an urn on a stone ledge (127x11cm-50x4in) s. 4-Jun-3 Christie's, Rockefeller NY #257/R est:3000-5000

GABRIEL, G D (?) ?
£2532 $4000 €4000 Envol de canards (105x130cm-41x51in) s. lacquer panel. 26-Nov-2 Tajan, Paris #42/R

GABRIEL, G L (1958-) German
Works on paper
£461 $747 €650 Dagmar (106x78cm-42x31in) s.d.83 mixed media. 24-May-3 Van Ham, Cologne #195/R

GABRIEL, Josef (20th C) Austrian?
Works on paper
£738 $1188 €1100 Cross Ullersdorf Castle, Czech Republic (55x75cm-22x30in) s.d.1936 exhib. 18-Feb-3 Sotheby's, Amsterdam #285/R est:700-900

GABRIEL, Justin J (1838-?) French
£280 $468 €406 Milking cattle by a lowland canal with windmills (81x140cm-32x55in) s. 17-Jun-3 Rosebery Fine Art, London #551/R

GABRIEL, P (?) ?
£1050 $1712 €1575 Roses, tulips, hyacinths and other flowers in a classical urn (101x76cm-40x30in) s. 11-Feb-3 Bonhams, Knowle #97 est:700-1000

GABRIEL, Paul Joseph Constantin (1828-1903) Dutch
£1572 $2421 €2500 Houses in a landscape (32x42cm-13x17in) s. canvas on panel. 22-Oct-2 Sotheby's, Amsterdam #101/R est:2500-3500
£1690 $2721 €2400 House by the water (30x42cm-12x17in) s. 7-May-3 Vendue Huis, Gravenhage #435/R est:2000-3000
£2250 $3645 €3263 Canal landscape (19x29cm-7x11in) s.indis.d.60 panel. 26-May-3 Bukowskis, Stockholm #254/R est:12000-15000 (S.KR 29000)
£2431 $4010 €3500 In het Gein bij Abcoude (31x52cm-12x20in) s. canvas on panel prov. 1-Jul-3 Christie's, Amsterdam #198 est:4000-6000
£3125 $4969 €4500 Elegant company promenading in the garden of a country house (32x43cm-13x17in) s.d.1851 panel. 29-Apr-3 Christie's, Amsterdam #120/R est:5000-7000
£3425 $5377 €5000 Bij elspeet (16x40cm-6x16in) s.d.92 canvas on panel prov. 15-Apr-3 Sotheby's, Amsterdam #151/R est:5000-7000
£3472 $5521 €5000 Farm in a polder landscape (39x63cm-15x25in) s. canvas on panel. 29-Apr-3 Christie's, Amsterdam #115/R est:5000-7000
£3774 $5811 €6000 An angler in a polder landscape (30x41cm-12x16in) s. canvas on panel. 23-Oct-2 Christie's, Amsterdam #197/R est:5000-7000
£5499 $9018 €7974 Summer landscape (32x56cm-13x22in) s.d.1872 prov. 4-Jun-3 AB Stockholms Auktionsverk #2454/R est:75000-100000 (S.KR 70000)
£11500 $18745 €17250 Landscape with windmill (28x45cm-11x18in) bears sig. 29-Jan-3 Sotheby's, Olympia #326/R est:3000-5000
£16352 $25182 €26000 Windmills in a landscape near Abcoude (29x46cm-11x18in) s. prov. 22-Oct-2 Sotheby's, Amsterdam #197/R est:20000-30000
Works on paper
£263 $426 €400 Molen aan de Kinderijk (32x56cm-13x22in) init.i.d.86 black chk prov. 21-Jan-3 Christie's, Amsterdam #236
£274 $425 €411 Windmill (48x33cm-19x13in) s. W/C exec.c.1880 prov. 8-Dec-2 Toomey, Oak Park #742/R
£2300 $3726 €3450 Fisherman (30x45cm-12x18in) s. W/C. 23-May-3 Lyon & Turnbull, Edinburgh #50/R est:2000-3000

GABRIEL-ROUSSEAU (20th C) French
Works on paper
£272 $433 €400 Venise la nuit (12x20cm-5x8in) s. W/C. 24-Mar-3 Coutau Begarie, Paris #169/R

GABRINI, Pietro (1865-1926) Italian
£800 $1328 €1160 Fisherman with young woman on shore (80x50cm-31x20in) s.i. 10-Jun-3 Ritchie, Toronto #126/R est:2500-4000 (C.D 1800)
Works on paper
£1497 $2500 €2171 Day's catch (64x98cm-25x39in) s.i. W/C. 22-Jun-3 Freeman, Philadelphia #37/R est:2500-3500

GABRON, Guilliam (attrib) (1619-1678) Belgian
£2177 $3461 €3200 Nature morte au lievre (76x60cm-30x24in) bears sig. canvas on panel. 28-Feb-3 Joron-Derem, Paris #17/R

£5120 $8295 €7424 Still life with earthenware (49x39cm-19x15in) panel prov. 26-May-3 Bukowskis, Stockholm #399/R est:50000-60000 (S.KR 66000)

GAC, Jean le (c.1936-) French
Works on paper
£1258 $1950 €2000 Le delassement d'un peintre Parisien (79x102cm-31x40in) dr photo text diptych prov. 30-Oct-2 Artcurial Briest, Paris #603/R est:2300-3000

GACHET, Jules (1859-1914) Swiss
£522 $809 €783 Voiles au Bouveret (43x71cm-17x28in) s. 7-Dec-2 Galerie du Rhone, Sion #317/R (S.FR 1200)

GACHET, Mario (1879- 1981) Italian
£578 $919 €850 Castiglione Torinese (35x45cm-14x18in) s. cardboard. 1-Mar-3 Meeting Art, Vercelli #102
£680 $1082 €1000 Winter (34x44cm-13x17in) s. s.i.verso cardboard. 1-Mar-3 Meeting Art, Vercelli #22

GACHET, Paul (c.1828-1909) French
£1592 $2484 €2500 Paysage des environs de Lille (27x35cm-11x14in) painted c.1855 prov.exhib. 7-Nov-2 Chochon-Barre & Allardi, Paris #155/R

GAD, Mogens (1887-1931) Danish
£280 $445 €420 Interior scene with woman at table (73x93cm-29x37in) s. 5-May-3 Rasmussen, Vejle #102/R (D.KR 3000)
£760 $1186 €1140 Interior scene with woman washing herself (47x34cm-19x13in) s.i.d.1912. 23-Sep-2 Rasmussen, Vejle #204/R (D.KR 9000)

GADANYI, Jeno (1896-1960) Hungarian
£2925 $4681 €4388 Hilly landscape with sundisc (31x43cm-12x17in) s. cardboard. 16-May-3 Kieselbach, Budapest #53/R (H.F 1000000)

GADBOIS, L (?-1826) French
Works on paper
£2238 $3737 €3200 Vue de l'entree d'une ville fortifiee pres d'une riviere (39x47cm-15x19in) s. gouache. 25-Jun-3 Tajan, Paris #84/R est:2500-3000
£3846 $6423 €5500 Une halte de cavaliers (39x52cm-15x20in) gouache. 25-Jun-3 Tajan, Paris #83/R est:3000-4000

GADDER, L (19th C) ?
£1100 $1738 €1650 Meditation (56x46cm-22x18in) s.d.1874. 28-Nov-2 Morphets, Harrogate #565/R est:300-400

GADDI, Angelo di Taddeo (c.1345-1396) Italian
£197531 $320000 €296297 Madonna and Child with Saint Catherine of Alexandria, John the Baptist (90x53cm-35x21in) t, gold ground panel prov.lit. 24-Jan-3 Christie's, Rockefeller NY #22/R est:80000-120000

GADDI, Taddeo (?-1366) Italian
£444444 $720000 €666666 Saint Matthew Pinnacle to the San Giovanno Fuorcivitas Polyptych (61x24cm-24x9in) tempera on panel gold ground shaped top. 23-Jan-3 Sotheby's, New York #61/R est:400000-600000

GADEGAARD, Paul (1920-1996) Danish
£423 $656 €635 Concrete composition in blue and red (92x73cm-36x29in) 1-Oct-2 Rasmussen, Copenhagen #22a (D.KR 5000)
£947 $1469 €1421 Composition (72x92cm-28x36in) s.d.49. 4-Dec-2 Kunsthallen, Copenhagen #22/R (D.KR 11000)
£1115 $1762 €1673 Composition in oragne (92x73cm-36x29in) 1-Apr-3 Rasmussen, Copenhagen #299/R est:12000-15000 (D.KR 12000)
£1371 $2180 €2057 Composition (92x73cm-36x29in) s.d.53 exhib.prov. 26-Feb-3 Kunsthallen, Copenhagen #5/R est:12000 (D.KR 15000)
£1371 $2180 €2057 Composition (46x55cm-18x22in) s.d.53 exhib. 26-Feb-3 Kunsthallen, Copenhagen #8/R est:8000 (D.KR 15000)
Works on paper
£253 $395 €380 Composition (45x90cm-18x35in) gouache executed c.1950. 18-Sep-2 Kunsthallen, Copenhagen #55 (D.KR 3000)
£253 $395 €380 Composition (45x90cm-18x35in) gouache executed c.1950. 18-Sep-2 Kunsthallen, Copenhagen #74 (D.KR 3000)
£258 $401 €387 Composition (44x89cm-17x35in) gouache painted c.1950. 4-Dec-2 Kunsthallen, Copenhagen #77/R (D.KR 3000)
£270 $422 €405 Composition (45x90cm-18x35in) gouache executed c.1950. 18-Sep-2 Kunsthallen, Copenhagen #56 (D.KR 3200)
£396 $614 €594 Composition (44x89cm-17x35in) gouache painted c.1950. 4-Dec-2 Kunsthallen, Copenhagen #78/R (D.KR 4600)
£491 $761 €737 Composition (44x89cm-17x35in) gouache painted c.1950. 4-Dec-2 Kunsthallen, Copenhagen #76/R (D.KR 5700)

GADEYNE, Jules (1857-1936) Belgian?
£510 $811 €750 Fishing boats at the beach (24x50cm-9x20in) s. panel. 24-Mar-3 Bernaerts, Antwerp #113/R

GAEL, Barent (c.1620-1703) Dutch
£1103 $1754 €1600 Hunting party resting near tress (54x66cm-21x26in) 10-Mar-3 Sotheby's, Amsterdam #15 est:1200-1500
£3597 $5755 €5000 Travelers resting and watering their horses at a tavern (30x35cm-12x14in) s. panel. 14-May-3 Christie's, Amsterdam #125/R est:6000-8000
£3742 $5912 €5800 Halte de cavaliers (37x31cm-15x12in) s. 18-Dec-2 Piasa, Paris #54/R

GAEL, Barent (attrib) (c.1620-1703) Dutch
£2327 $3770 €3374 Figures and horses outside an inn (42x57cm-17x22in) 26-May-3 Bukowskis, Stockholm #441/R est:40000-50000 (S.KR 30000)

GAERTNER, Georg (attrib) (17th C) German
£791 $1266 €1100 La morte della Vergine (14x11cm-6x4in) tempera paper on panel. 17-May-3 Meeting Art, Vercelli #375/R

GAERTNER, Johann Philipp Eduard (1801-1877) German
£40000 $66800 €60000 Thorn von der Bazer-Kampe aus gesehen (33x52cm-13x20in) s.d.1849 prov.exhib.lit. 19-Jun-3 Christie's, London #65/R est:40000-60000

GAGEN, Robert Ford (1847-1926) Canadian
Works on paper
£783 $1221 €1305 Storm on the Great Glacier, B.C (44x29cm-17x11in) s.d.1901 i.verso W/C. 13-Apr-3 Levis, Calgary #36/R est:2400-2600 (C.D 1800)

GAGEY, Auguste (19th C) French
Works on paper
£513 $795 €800 Vue du temple de Paestum (11x18cm-4x7in) W/C. 4-Dec-2 Libert, Castor, Paris #40

GAGG, Gebhard (1838-1921) Swiss
£601 $932 €950 Landscape in evening (15x29cm-6x11in) s.i. panel. 27-Sep-2 Karrenbauer, Konstanz #1627
Works on paper
£256 $403 €400 Constance harbour (24x38cm-9x15in) 22-Nov-2 Karrenbauer, Konstanz #1819
£256 $403 €400 Kornhaus (23x33cm-9x13in) W/C board. 22-Nov-2 Karrenbauer, Konstanz #1821
£256 $403 €400 Constance (27x41cm-11x16in) W/C board. 22-Nov-2 Karrenbauer, Konstanz #1824
£282 $443 €440 Swiss landscape (24x36cm-9x14in) W/C board. 22-Nov-2 Karrenbauer, Konstanz #1820
£288 $453 €450 Untitled (25x41cm-10x16in) W/C board. 22-Nov-2 Karrenbauer, Konstanz #1823/R
£321 $503 €500 Constance in 1808 (31x44cm-12x17in) W/C board. 22-Nov-2 Karrenbauer, Konstanz #1822/R

GAGLIARDINI, Julien Gustave (1846-1927) French
£485 $707 €728 Coastal landscape with boats, horse and cart and figures (16x27cm-6x11in) s. panel. 17-Jun-2 Philippe Schuler, Zurich #4341/R (S.FR 1100)
£759 $1185 €1200 Maison pres de la plage en Camargue (32x46cm-13x18in) s. 20-Oct-2 Anaf, Lyon #136/R
£1503 $2465 €2300 Village au bord de la Mediterranee (27x143cm-11x56in) s. panel. 9-Feb-3 Anaf, Lyon #108/R
£1935 $3058 €3000 Arrivage de poisoons, Cayeux (27x46cm-11x18in) s. i.verso. 19-Dec-2 Claude Aguttes, Neuilly #214/R
£2658 $4147 €4200 Ramasseurs e coquillages (54x74cm-21x29in) s. 20-Oct-2 Anaf, Lyon #135/R

GAGNEAU, Paul Léon (?-c.1910) French
£3418 $5400 €5400 Paysanne revenant de la moisson (81x60cm-32x24in) s. 1-Dec-2 Peron, Melun #117

GAGNEREAUX, Benigne (1756-1795) French
£6962 $11000 €11000 Oedipe aveugle recommande sa famille aux dieux (59x82cm-23x32in) s.d.1783 paper on canvas prov. 27-Nov-2 Christie's, Paris #56/R est:15000-20000

GAGNEUX, Paul (?-1892) French
£1014 $1581 €1500 Pecheur (65x48cm-26x19in) s.d.85. 28-Mar-3 Claude Aguttes, Neuilly #80/R
£5245 $8759 €7500 Bord de mer a Royan (18x24cm-7x9in) s.i.d.88 panel. 27-Jun-3 Claude Aguttes, Neuilly #36/R est:6000-8000

GAGNON, Charles (20th C) Canadian
Works on paper
£1754 $2614 €2631 Composition (50x40cm-20x16in) s. gouache oil. 26-Jun-2 Iegor de Saint Hippolyte, Montreal #43/R (C.D 4000)

GAGNON, Clarence A (1881-1942) Canadian
£1512 $2389 €2268 In Norway (15x22cm-6x9in) i.d.1934 verso panel prov. 18-Nov-2 Sotheby's, Toronto #4/R est:4000-6000 (C.D 3750)
£3556 $5831 €5334 Autumn in the Laurentians, Charlevoix (15x22cm-6x9in) panel prov. 3-Jun-3 Joyner, Toronto #110/R est:8000-10000 (C.D 8000)
£5761 $8930 €8642 Dent du midim vue au chamossaire, Chesieres Suisse (15x22cm-6x9in) s. panel prov. 3-Dec-2 Joyner, Toronto #172/R est:8000-12000 (C.D 14000)
£6774 $10568 €10161 Reflets dans la riviere (38x55cm-15x22in) s. panel. 30-Jul-2 Iegor de Saint Hippolyte, Montreal #62 (C.D 16800)
£8072 $12915 €12108 Granges en automne dans charlevoix (12x18cm-5x7in) d.1922 verso panel prov. 15-May-3 Heffel, Vancouver #227/R est:18000-22000 (C.D 18000)
£8889 $14578 €13334 Baie St. Paul (16x23cm-6x9in) panel. 3-Jun-3 Joyner, Toronto #117/R est:20000-25000 (C.D 20000)
£14815 $22963 €22223 After a snowfall (12x18cm-5x7in) s. panel prov. 3-Dec-2 Joyner, Toronto #7/R est:35000-40000 (C.D 36000)
Works on paper
£328 $511 €492 Tricoteuse (25x20cm-10x8in) s. pencil. 10-Sep-2 Iegor de Saint Hippolyte, Montreal #50 (C.D 800)
£444 $729 €666 Studies of peasants (12x18cm-5x7in) pencil. 3-Jun-3 Joyner, Toronto #591 est:500-700 (C.D 1000)
£658 $1021 €987 Farm house, Bail St. Paul (10x17cm-4x7in) col crayon chk prov. 3-Dec-2 Joyner, Toronto #418 est:1000-1500 (C.D 1600)
£700 $1084 €1050 Maison a L'Lile d'Orleans (10x14cm-4x6in) studio st.verso col crayon chk prov. 3-Dec-2 Joyner, Toronto #419 est:800-1000 (C.D 1700)
£1728 $2679 €2592 Christmas 1919. Christmas toast (12x14cm-5x6in) s.i. col pencil two. 3-Dec-2 Joyner, Toronto #441 est:1000-1200 (C.D 4200)
£1728 $2679 €2592 Hard pull (11x11cm-4x4in) studio st. pencil gouache prov.lit. 3-Dec-2 Joyner, Toronto #70/R est:4000-5000 (C.D 4200)
£2410 $3783 €3615 St Simeon Co, Charlevoix (12x18cm-5x7in) st. W/C gouache prov. 25-Nov-2 Hodgins, Calgary #108/R est:8000-10000 (C.D 6000)

GAIDAN, Louis (1847-1925) French
£2449 $3894 €3600 Ruines romaines de Saint-Remy de Provence (50x73cm-20x29in) s. panel. 21-Mar-3 Rieunier, Bailly-Pommery, Mathias, Paris #124/R
£2903 $4587 €4500 Paysage du Var (54x74cm-21x29in) 19-Dec-2 Claude Aguttes, Neuilly #215/R
£5000 $7700 €7500 Villa a Saint Tropez (54x73cm-21x29in) s. oil over pencil paper on canvas. 23-Oct-2 Sotheby's, Olympia #649/R est:6000-8000

GAIDANO, Paolo (1861-1916) Italian
£724 $1151 €1050 Madonna (39x36cm-15x14in) s.d.1887 board. 7-Mar-3 Semenzato, Venice #149/R

GAIGER, Miklos Jobbagyi (1892-1959) Hungarian
£929 $1449 €1394 Paris with the Bank of the Seine, 1937 (81x100cm-32x39in) s.d.1937. 11-Sep-2 Kieselbach, Budapest #90/R (H.F 360000)
£1032 $1610 €1496 Hansom cab (54x71cm-21x28in) s.i.d.1931. 13-Sep-2 Mu Terem Galeria, Budapest #24/R est:320000 (H.F 400000)

GAIGHER, Horazio (1870-1938) ?
£2013 $3119 €3200 Mountain valley in spring (60x73cm-24x29in) s. board. 29-Oct-2 Dorotheum, Vienna #4/R est:1800-2000

GAIGNEAU, P (20th C) French
£1795 $2818 €2800 Berger (32x40cm-13x16in) s. 11-Dec-2 Fraysse & Associes, Paris #12 est:500
£3077 $4831 €4800 Jeune saltimbanque (131x81cm-52x32in) s.d.1895. 11-Dec-2 Fraysse & Associes, Paris #13 est:1200

GAILLARD, Arthur (19th C) French
£5634 $9239 €8169 Hommage to the Queen of the Fairies (80x124cm-31x49in) s. 4-Jun-3 Fischer, Luzern #1072/R est:12000-15000 (S.FR 12000)

GAILLARD, Pierre Arthur (fl.1878-1895) French
£3548 $5500 €5322 Country villa (46x64cm-18x25in) s.d.1895. 3-Dec-2 Christie's, Rockefeller NY #645/R est:7000-9000

GAILLARDOT, Pierre (1910-2002) French
£470 $756 €700 Canters du matin (30x60cm-12x24in) s. 23-Feb-3 Lesieur & Le Bars, Le Havre #59
£641 $1006 €1000 Jumping (54x65cm-21x26in) s. 24-Nov-2 Lesieur & Le Bars, Le Havre #59
£705 $1107 €1100 Bar de la mer (46x56cm-18x22in) s. 24-Nov-2 Lesieur & Le Bars, Le Havre #58/R
£775 $1247 €1100 Retour de peche (45x54cm-18x21in) s. 12-May-3 Lesieur & Le Bars, Le Havre #41/R
£890 $1398 €1300 Concours hippique (50x45cm-20x18in) s. 21-Apr-3 Raboudin & Choppin de Janvry, Paris #113/R
£1027 $1613 €1500 Le bassin (54x75cm-21x30in) s. 21-Apr-3 Rabourdin & Choppin de Janvry, Paris #112/R est:1600-1800
£1410 $2158 €2200 Route des sulkys (53x63cm-21x25in) s.d.1989. 23-Aug-2 Deauville, France #181/R
Works on paper
£282 $454 €400 Le port de plaisance (28x33cm-11x13in) s. W/C. 12-May-3 Lesieur & Le Bars, Le Havre #400

GAILLIARD, Franz (1861-1932) Belgian
£1266 $2000 €2000 Rue a Athenes (68x55cm-27x22in) s. panel. 26-Nov-2 Palais de Beaux Arts, Brussels #100/R est:2000-3000
Works on paper
£4902 $7892 €7500 Le Parc de Bruxelles anime (88x68cm-35x27in) s. mixed media cardboard. 20-Jan-3 Horta, Bruxelles #177/R est:8000-12000

GAILLIARD, Jean Jacques (1890-1976) Belgian
£315 $492 €460 Lumiere odoriferante (22x29cm-9x11in) s. panel. 14-Apr-3 Horta, Bruxelles #274
£452 $714 €700 Pont de bois au ravin du Bois de la Cambre (27x34cm-11x13in) s. panel. 17-Dec-2 Palais de Beaux Arts, Brussels #533
£863 $1381 €1200 La balancoire (40x40cm-16x16in) s. cardboard. 13-May-3 Palais de Beaux Arts, Brussels #256/R
£1274 $1987 €2000 Entree au domaine (70x50cm-28x20in) s. 10-Nov-2 Eric Pillon, Calais #190/R
Works on paper
£313 $497 €450 La place de Scridno, Italie (40x28cm-16x11in) s.d.1968 ink dr. 29-Apr-3 Campo, Vlaamse Kaai #124

GAINES, John R (20th C) American
£516 $800 €774 Discarded (33x46cm-13x18in) s. tempera board painted c.1950. 8-Dec-2 Toomey, Oak Park #780/R

GAINON, Jacqueline (attrib) (1951-) French
£411 $650 €650 Chair (190x170cm-75x67in) d.1990. 30-Nov-2 Arnold, Frankfurt #185/R

GAINSBOROUGH, Thomas (1727-1788) British
£18293 $30000 €27440 Lodge in a park, with children descending steps (152x183cm-60x72in) prov.exhib.lit. 30-May-3 Christie's, Rockefeller NY #54/R est:30000-50000
£24691 $40000 €37037 Sheep and lambs by a fence in a landscape (23x27cm-9x11in) prov.exhib.lit. 24-Jan-3 Christie's, Rockefeller NY #139/R est:20000-30000
£40000 $66400 €60000 Portrait of George Charles Garnier of Rookesbury Park, Hampshire (108x88cm-43x35in) prov.lit. 12-Jun-3 Sotheby's, London #71/R est:40000-60000
£50000 $79500 €75000 Portrait of Lady Alston (74x61cm-29x24in) 19-Mar-3 Sotheby's, London #40/R est:20000-30000
£215000 $339700 €322500 Greyhound in landscape (88x69cm-35x27in) prov.lit. 26-Nov-2 Christie's, London #29/R est:30000-50000
Works on paper
£14000 $23240 €21000 Wooded landscape with a figure and a dog (27x34cm-11x13in) pen ink white chk wash prov. 12-Jun-3 Sotheby's, London #126/R est:15000-20000
£28000 $40040 €42000 Wooded landscape with flock (18x22cm-7x9in) i. chk stump prov.exhib.lit. 22-Jan-3 Christie's, London #3/R est:20000

GAINSBOROUGH, Thomas (attrib) (1727-1788) British
£890 $1415 €1335 Portrait of a woman in period dress (20x15cm-8x6in) panel. 18-Mar-3 Maynards, Vancouver #40/R est:1000-1500 (C.D 2100)
£1314 $2089 €1971 Portrait of a woman wearing a cream dress (20x15cm-8x6in) panel. 18-Mar-3 Maynards, Vancouver #41/R est:1000-1500 (C.D 3100)

GAINSBOROUGH, Thomas (circle) (1727-1788) British
£5793 $9500 €8400 Portrait of Frederick Howard, 5th Earl of Carlisle (91x67cm-36x26in) i.verso oval. 4-Jun-3 Christie's, Rockefeller NY #170/R est:8000-12000

GAISSER, Jakob Emmanuel (1825-1899) German
£1092 $1703 €1638 Chess game (35x30cm-14x12in) s.d.1864. 6-Nov-2 Dobiaschofsky, Bern #554/R est:5000 (S.FR 2500)

£1795 $2800 €2693 Trumped. Cheaters (23x30cm-9x12in) s. panel pair. 9-Oct-2 Doyle, New York #35 est:2500-3500
£2041 $3245 €3000 Rococo figures making merry at table (29x38cm-11x15in) s. panel. 19-Mar-3 Neumeister, Munich #558/R est:3000
£3125 $4969 €4500 Zecherrunde im klosterkeller (30x40cm-12x16in) s. panel. 29-Apr-3 Christie's, Amsterdam #59/R est:4000-6000
£3526 $5465 €5500 Figures in historical costume (113x86cm-44x34in) s. 5-Dec-2 Dr Fritz Nagel, Stuttgart #653/R est:3000

GAISSER, Jakob Emmanuel (attrib) (1825-1899) German
£377 $589 €600 Man's portrait (20x17cm-8x7in) s. board. 19-Sep-2 Dr Fritz Nagel, Stuttgart #931/R

GAISSER, Max (1857-1922) German
£1000 $1520 €1500 Le scribe (19x15cm-7x6in) s. board. 3-Jul-2 Naón & Cia, Buenos Aires #69/R est:1300-1600
£1389 $2208 €2000 Gelechrter am Schreibtisch (36x30cm-14x12in) s. panel. 29-Apr-3 Christie's, Amsterdam #57/R est:2000-3000
£5163 $8468 €7900 Men in Dutch interior (43x51cm-17x20in) s. panel. 6-Feb-3 Weidler, Nurnberg #316/R est:7900

GAITIS, Yannis (1923-1984) Greek
£1727 $2832 €2400 Untitled (46x54cm-18x21in) s. 3-Jun-3 Christie's, Amsterdam #91/R est:2000-3000
£2564 $4026 €4000 Untitled (33x46cm-13x18in) s. 24-Nov-2 Laurence Calmels, Paris #131/R
£2721 $4327 €4000 Untitled (46x54cm-18x21in) s.d.1966 verso. 24-Mar-3 Claude Boisgirard, Paris #175/R
£3526 $5535 €5500 Profils d'hommes sur fond jaune (41x55cm-16x22in) s.d.1971 apint on metal. 24-Nov-2 Laurence Calmels, Paris #130/R est:1500
£4000 $6320 €6000 Foliage (54x38cm-21x15in) 1-Apr-3 Bonhams, New Bond Street #101 est:4000-6000
£4200 $6636 €6300 Untitled (54x64cm-21x25in) 1-Apr-3 Bonhams, New Bond Street #81 est:3500-4500
£22000 $34100 €33000 Petits chevaux (160x200cm-63x79in) s.d.67 exhib. 2-Oct-2 Sotheby's, London #74/R est:35000

GAITONDE, Vasudeo S (1924-) Indian
£5828 $9615 €8451 Untitled (19x20cm-7x8in) s.d. board prov. 6-Jul-3 Christie's, Hong Kong #78/R est:42000-48000 (HK.D 75000)
£13986 $23077 €20280 Untitled (51x61cm-20x24in) s.d. 6-Jul-3 Christie's, Hong Kong #77/R est:140000-180000 (HK.D 180000)

GAJDOS, Janos (1912-1950) Hungarian
£3803 $6085 €5705 Dance (110x80cm-43x31in) s.d.1942 board. 16-May-3 Kieselbach, Budapest #83/R (H.F 1300000)

GAKUO (attrib) (16th C) Oriental
Works on paper
£1266 $2000 €2000 Personnage et serviteur traversant un pont (27x37cm-11x15in) ink paper on kakemono. 29-Nov-2 Tajan, Paris #80 est:1500-1800

GAL, Menchu (1923-) Spanish
£11538 $18231 €18000 Beach (50x73cm-20x29in) s. board. 13-Nov-2 Ansorena, Madrid #40/R est:8000
Works on paper
£2453 $3777 €3900 Landscape with trees (35x50cm-14x20in) s. W/C. 28-Oct-2 Segre, Madrid #124/R
£3546 $5745 €5000 Costa Vasca (32x48cm-13x19in) s. W/C. 20-May-3 Segre, Madrid #129/R est:4500

GALAIS, L (?) ?
£881 $1356 €1400 Couple galant dans un jardin (100x80cm-39x31in) s. 22-Oct-2 Galerie Moderne, Brussels #746/R

GALAN, Julio (1958-) Mexican
£7643 $12000 €11465 Argentina (99x100cm-39x39in) s.d.80 oil mixed media collage prov.lit. 19-Nov-2 Sotheby's, New York #129/R est:20000
£30573 $48000 €45860 Like a garden (210x160cm-83x63in) s. oil paper collage painted 1990 prov.exhib.lit. 20-Nov-2 Christie's, Rockefeller NY #37/R est:50000-60000

GALAND, Léon (1872-1960) French
£506 $800 €800 View of Bagatelle (46x61cm-18x24in) s. 1-Dec-2 Livinec, Gaudcheau & Jezequel, Rennes #62
£650 $1007 €975 Woman on a river bank (51x61cm-20x24in) s.d.1904. 30-Sep-2 Bonhams, Ipswich #432/R
£2893 $4484 €4600 Jeune femme lisant au jardin (50x61cm-20x24in) s. 1-Oct-2 Palais de Beaux Arts, Brussels #470/R est:2000-3000

GALANDA, Miguel (1951-) Spanish
Works on paper
£379 $603 €550 Walker (190x90cm-75x35in) s.i.d.verso collage on canvas. 4-Mar-3 Ansorena, Madrid #204/R
£645 $1019 €1000 Walker (190x90cm-75x35in) s.i.d.87 collage on canvas. 18-Dec-2 Ansorena, Madrid #195/R

GALANDA, Mikulas (1895-1938) Czechoslovakian
Works on paper
£347 $492 €521 Icarus (16x21cm-6x8in) pencil exec.c.1929. 26-Mar-2 SOGA, Bratislava #51/R (SL.K 22000)
£378 $552 €567 Combing woman (26x18cm-10x7in) pencil exec.c.1930-32. 4-Jun-2 SOGA, Bratislava #73/R est:25000 (SL.K 24000)
£394 $559 €591 Lunch for the poor (21x30cm-8x12in) pencil exec.c.1932. 26-Mar-2 SOGA, Bratislava #50/R (SL.K 25000)

GALANIS, Demetrius (1882-1966) French
£3600 $5688 €5400 Lady lying on a couch (48x67cm-19x26in) 1-Apr-3 Bonhams, New Bond Street #47 est:1800-2200
£16000 $25280 €24000 Provencal landscape with figure (60x77cm-24x30in) 1-Apr-3 Bonhams, New Bond Street #44 est:12000-18000

GALANTE, Nicola (1883-1969) Italian
£3333 $5233 €5200 Still life (43x54cm-17x21in) s.d.1923 cardboard. 10-Dec-2 Della Rocca, Turin #364/R
£3333 $5233 €5200 Still life (43x54cm-17x21in) s. s.d.1924 verso cardboard. 10-Dec-2 Della Rocca, Turin #363/R

GALBALLY, Cecil (20th C) Irish
£1410 $2214 €2200 Autumn (45x39cm-18x15in) board exhib. 19-Nov-2 Hamilton Osborne King, Dublin #476 est:1500-2000
£2051 $3221 €3200 Crimson Door, Inishmore (45x34cm-18x13in) board exhib. 19-Nov-2 Hamilton Osborne King, Dublin #475/R est:2000-3000

GALBUSERA, Giovacchino (1871-1944) Italian
£400 $664 €600 Houses by an Italian lake (23x32cm-9x13in) s. 10-Jun-3 Bonhams, Knightsbridge #54/R
£699 $1090 €1049 Forest landscape in autumn (51x71cm-20x28in) s. 8-Nov-2 Dobiaschofsky, Bern #174/R (S.FR 1600)
£1834 $2861 €2751 Piz Uccello, San Bernardino (46x54cm-18x21in) s. i.verso masonite. 8-Nov-2 Dobiaschofsky, Bern #176/R est:4500 (S.FR 4200)
£2009 $3134 €3014 Chapel in Tessin (63x84cm-25x33in) s. 8-Nov-2 Dobiaschofsky, Bern #175/R est:7500 (S.FR 4600)
£2778 $4472 €4028 San Bernardino with view of the Moesolasee (35x49cm-14x19in) s. masonite. 9-May-3 Dobiaschofsky, Bern #162/R est:3800 (S.FR 6000)

GALDEANO, Andres (20th C) Spanish
£1006 $1570 €1600 Experiments abour Sisyph (110x162cm-43x64in) s.d.85. 8-Oct-2 Ansorena, Madrid #638/R

GALE, Martin (1949-) British
£1139 $1766 €1800 River at Belderg (21x36cm-8x14in) s.d.99 panel. 24-Sep-2 De Veres Art Auctions, Dublin #62/R est:1500-2000
£1923 $2981 €3000 Between the showers, Ballycastle (30x77cm-12x30in) s. board triptych. 3-Dec-2 Bonhams & James Adam, Dublin #43/R est:1800-2500
£5903 $9385 €8500 Lie of the land (71x86cm-28x34in) s.d.2002 verso prov. 29-Apr-3 Whyte's, Dublin #20/R est:4000-6000

GALEA, Luigi M (1847-1917) Maltese
£650 $1034 €975 Grand harbour by night (10x27cm-4x11in) s. board. 29-Apr-3 Bonhams, New Bond Street #152
£1100 $1716 €1650 Harbour, probably Valletta (15x34cm-6x13in) s. board. 17-Oct-2 Bonhams, Edinburgh #201 est:200-300
£1400 $2268 €2100 Sunset over Grand Harbour, Valetta (15x34cm-6x13in) s. board. 21-May-3 Christie's, Kensington #650/R est:1200-1800
£1550 $2542 €2325 Fishing boats in Grand Harbour, Valetta (10x26cm-4x10in) s. pair. 10-Feb-3 Robin Fenner, Tavistock #680 est:800-1000
£1650 $2706 €2475 Fishermen on the seafront watching a storm approaching the Maltese coast (21x54cm-8x21in) s. board. 3-Jun-3 Bonhams, Oxford #53/R est:1000-1500
£2000 $3340 €2900 Grand Harbour, Valetta, Malta (20x51cm-8x20in) s. 20-Jun-3 Keys, Aylsham #668/R est:800-1000
£2400 $3888 €3600 Grand Harbour, Valetta, early morning and at dusk (17x35cm-7x14in) s. one i.d.1911 board pair. 21-May-3 Christie's, Kensington #652/R est:2000-3000
£2600 $4342 €3770 Steam entering the Grand Harbour, Valetta (15x35cm-6x14in) s. board sold with a companion. 25-Jun-3 Bonhams, Bury St Edmunds #576/R est:2500-4000

£3000 $4860 €4500 Crowded small craft running out of Grand Harbour, Valetta, moonlight (27x75cm-11x30in) s. board. 21-May-3 Christie's, Kensington #649/R est:3000-4000

£3900 $6396 €5850 Shipping and fishing boats in Grand Harbour, Valletta (23x54cm-9x21in) s.d.1913 two. 10-Feb-3 Robin Fenner, Tavistock #679 est:3000-4000

Works on paper

£600 $936 €900 Grand Harbour, Valetta, Malta (10x26cm-4x10in) s. bodycol. 10-Apr-3 Tennants, Leyburn #827/R

£1450 $2378 €2103 Harbour at Valetta, small boat, ferry boat and small sailing ship (20x53cm-8x21in) s. W/C. 5-Feb-3 John Nicholson, Haslemere #982 est:1000-1500

GALEOTTI, Sebastiano (1676-1746) Italian

Works on paper

£1549 $2494 €2200 Decorazione per parte di soffitto con satiro e figure femminili (46x39cm-18x15in) pen blk ink grey W/C. 12-May-3 Sotheby's, Milan #55/R est:2000-3000

£1892 $2951 €2800 Seated faun (23x23cm-9x9in) i. pe ink wash prov. 27-Mar-3 Christie's, Paris #78/R

GALERNE, Prosper (1836-?) French

£1700 $2839 €2550 Aux bords de le Seine a Meudon (40x60cm-16x24in) s.d.1881. 18-Jun-3 Christie's, Kensington #3/R est:1500-2000

GALEY, Gaston-Pierre (1880-1959) French

£5800 $9164 €8700 Venetian fruit seller (54x44cm-21x17in) board. 3-Apr-3 Christie's, Kensington #56/R

Works on paper

£1100 $1738 €1650 Figure below tree (36x26cm-14x10in) s. pencil W/C. 3-Apr-3 Christie's, Kensington #57/R

GALEY, Jean Fabien (1877-?) French

£1007 $1652 €1400 Jeune Bedouine devant la mosquee (65x50cm-26x20in) s. cardboard. 4-Jun-3 Tajan, Paris #272/R est:2000-3000

GALIEN-LALOUE, E (1854-1941) French

£1655 $2549 €2483 Village street (51x65cm-20x26in) s. 28-Oct-2 Blomqvist, Lysaker #1061/R est:12000-15000 (N.KR 19500)

GALIEN-LALOUE, Eugène (1854-1941) French

£335 $530 €530 Cour de ferme (29x239cm-11x94in) s. prov. 27-Nov-2 Blanchet, Paris #31/R

£889 $1476 €1289 Figure by a village stream. Village on a river (16x22cm-6x9in) s. panel pair. 16-Jun-3 Waddingtons, Toronto #276/R est:3000-4000 (C.D 2000)

£1282 $2013 €2000 Fermieres pres d'un village (22x31cm-9x12in) s. panel. 16-Dec-2 Chochon-Barre & Allardi, Paris #53 est:1200-1400

£1314 $2063 €2050 Paysanne pres d'une eglise (22x31cm-9x12in) s. panel. 16-Dec-2 Chochon-Barre & Allardi, Paris #54 est:1200-1400

£1474 $2285 €2300 Femmes aux puits (22x16cm-9x6in) s. panel. 7-Dec-2 Martinot & Savignat, Pontoise #154

£1698 $2632 €2700 Moulin (50x65cm-20x26in) s. 30-Oct-2 Coutau Begarie, Paris #92/R est:2300-2800

£1899 $3000 €3000 Le hameau au bord de l'eau, ete (50x65cm-20x26in) s.pseudonym Louis Dupuy. 1-Dec-2 Peron, Melun #158

£1911 $2981 €3000 Paysage d'Ile de France (41x65cm-16x26in) s. 7-Nov-2 Chochon-Barre & Allardi, Paris #158/R

£2152 $3400 €3228 Riverbend path (25x41cm-10x16in) s. 16-Nov-2 New Orleans Auction, New Orleans #309/R est:3000-5000

£2157 $3537 €3300 French village in the evening (48x65cm-19x26in) s. 8-Feb-3 Hans Stahl, Hamburg #67/R est:1000

£2767 $4400 €4151 Harbor scene (20x23cm-8x9in) s. 22-Mar-3 New Orleans Auction, New Orleans #413/R est:5000-8000

£3526 $5500 €5289 Country landscape (48x64cm-19x25in) s. 12-Oct-2 Neal Auction Company, New Orleans #186/R est:7000-10000

£4392 $6851 €6500 Trois mats a quai (65x54cm-26x21in) s.pseudonyme A. Michel. 25-Mar-3 Chochon-Barre & Allardi, Paris #122/R est:6000-7000

£4610 $7468 €6500 Sun setting over a harbour (46x61cm-18x24in) s. 22-May-3 Dorotheum, Vienna #93/R est:4000-5000

£6013 $9380 €9500 La Seine, Quai Henri IV (61x80cm-24x31in) s. painted 1885. 18-Oct-2 Rabourdin & Choppin de Janvry, Paris #28/R est:7000

£34810 $55000 €52215 Les Grands Boulevards de Paris, crepuscule (63x114cm-25x45in) s. prov. 23-Apr-3 Christie's, Rockefeller NY #22/R est:70000-90000

£51000 $83640 €76500 Animation pres de la porte Saint Denis, le Soir (46x65cm-18x26in) s. 3-Jun-3 Sotheby's, London #180/R est:20000-30000

Works on paper

£705 $1107 €1100 La cour de ferme (15x25cm-6x10in) s. graphite exec.c.1890 prov. 16-Dec-2 Chochon-Barre & Allardi, Paris #57

£743 $1159 €1100 Le marche aux fleurs et la Conciergerie (11x14cm-4x6in) st.sig. graphite prov. 25-Mar-3 Chochon-Barre & Allardi, Paris #126

£946 $1476 €1400 Les arbres couches a Sannois (21x25cm-8x10in) s.i. graphite. 25-Mar-3 Chochon-Barre & Allardi, Paris #125

£1090 $1711 €1700 Fermette a Egly (21x28cm-8x11in) s. graphite exec.c.1890 prov. 16-Dec-2 Chochon-Barre & Allardi, Paris #55 est:900-1000

£1689 $2635 €2500 Etude pour Animations devant les magasins (10x17cm-4x7in) s. graphite W/C double sided. 25-Mar-3 Chochon-Barre & Allardi, Paris #124/R est:3300-4000

£1923 $3019 €3000 Village imaginaire (10x15cm-4x6in) s.d.1874 gouache. 16-Dec-2 Chochon-Barre & Allardi, Paris #52/R est:3000-3200

£2067 $3142 €3101 Cool winter's day in Paris by Notre Dame (18x30cm-7x12in) s.d.97 gouache. 27-Aug-2 Rasmussen, Copenhagen #1699/R est:25000 (D.KR 24000)

£3671 $5800 €5800 Une vue du Boulevard de la Villette, pres du metro Stalingrad, Paris (19x31cm-7x12in) s.i. i.verso graphite gouache. 27-Nov-2 Christie's, Paris #293/R est:6000-8000

£5063 $8000 €8000 Une vue du Chatelet pris depuis le Pont au Change, Paris (20x31cm-8x12in) s.i. i.verso graphite gouache. 27-Nov-2 Christie's, Paris #294/R est:6000-8000

£6250 $10313 €9000 Rue animee devant la cathedrale (23x28cm-9x11in) s. gouache. 1-Jul-3 Rossini, Paris #8/R

£6290 $9750 €9435 Paris street scene (20x30cm-8x12in) s. gouache. 7-Dec-2 Selkirks, St. Louis #768 est:10000-13000

£6389 $10542 €9200 Le parvis anime (24x29cm-9x11in) s. gouache. 1-Jul-3 Rossini, Paris #7/R

£6500 $10205 €9750 La porte saint Denie sous la neige (23x32cm-9x13in) s. W/C bodycol. 19-Nov-2 Bonhams, New Bond Street #175/R est:7000-10000

£7534 $11753 €11000 Porte St Martin (27x26cm-11x10in) s. W/C. 14-Apr-3 Glerum, Amsterdam #93/R est:6000-8000

£7643 $11924 €12000 Berges du Pont-Neuf (18x30cm-7x12in) s. gouache lit. 7-Nov-2 Chochon-Barre & Allardi, Paris #157/R

£7643 $11924 €12000 Animations Porte de Chatillon (18x30cm-7x12in) s. gouache lit. 7-Nov-2 Chochon-Barre & Allardi, Paris #156/R

£8280 $12917 €13000 Place de la Nation (18x30cm-7x12in) s. gouache lit. 7-Nov-2 Chochon-Barre & Allardi, Paris #159

£8500 $13515 €12750 La Place du chatelet, Paris (20x31cm-8x12in) s. gouache. 18-Mar-3 Bonhams, New Bond Street #130/R est:6000-8000

£9615 $15192 €15000 Place de la Republique (19x31cm-7x12in) s. gouache. 14-Nov-2 Arte, Seville #384/R est:12000

£9677 $15290 €15000 Elegantes au marche aux fleurs, Place de la Madeleine (19x31cm-7x12in) s. W/C. 19-Dec-2 Claude Aguttes, Neuilly #81/R est:20000

£9934 $16192 €15000 Notre Dame vue es quais (18x30cm-7x12in) s. gouache. 16-Feb-3 Mercier & Cie, Lille #236/R est:15000-18000

£10256 $16103 €16000 Boulevard des Italiens (19x31cm-7x12in) s. gouache. 21-Nov-2 Neret-Minet, Paris #26/R est:10000-12000

£10256 $16205 €16000 Quais (19x31cm-7x12in) s. gouache. 14-Nov-2 Arte, Seville #386/R est:12000

£12766 $19787 €19149 Le Theatre du Chatelet, Paris (18x30cm-7x12in) s. gouache. 4-Dec-2 AB Stockholms Auktionsverk #1838/R est:40000-50000 (S.KR 180000)

£15190 $24000 €22785 Paris, Place de la Republique (30x46cm-12x18in) s. gouache ink. 24-Apr-3 Sotheby's, New York #149/R est:10000-15000

£15484 $24000 €23226 L'ancien trocadero et la place de la Bastille (19x31cm-7x12in) s. W/C gouache pair. 29-Oct-2 Sotheby's, New York #96/R est:18000-25000

£16129 $25000 €24194 Paris, Place de la Republique, the flower market (22x39cm-9x15in) s. gouache. 29-Oct-2 Sotheby's, New York #95/R est:18000-25000

£19355 $30581 €30000 Paris: promeneurs sur les Quais de la Megisserie. s. gouache pair. 17-Dec-2 Galerie Moderne, Brussels #761/R est:40000

£44206 $68961 €66309 Chatelet Place (19x32cm-7x13in) s. gouache. 25-Mar-3 Iegor de Saint Hippolyte, Montreal #55/R (C.D 103000)

GALIEN-LALOUE, Eugène (attrib) (1854-1941) French

£1090 $1711 €1700 View of Normandy (24x33cm-9x13in) s. panel. 10-Dec-2 Dorotheum, Vienna #18/R est:1700-1900

£1090 $1711 €1700 View of Normandy (24x33cm-9x13in) s. panel i.verso. 10-Dec-2 Dorotheum, Vienna #20/R est:1700-1900

GALIMBERTI, Maurizio (1956-) Italian

Prints

£3546 $5745 €5000 La Vucciria (98x183cm-39x72in) s.i.d.2003 verso ed.1/3 digital print. 20-May-3 Porro, Milan #22/R est:8000-8500

GALINDO, Jorge (1965-) Spanish

£2710 $4281 €4200 Untitled (159x120cm-63x47in) s.d.1992 verso oil mixed media. 17-Dec-2 Segre, Madrid #178/R est:3900

GALIZIA, Fede (attrib) (1578-1630) Italian

£5500 $8580 €8250 Strawberries and a glass of wine on a wood ledge (25x33cm-10x13in) 10-Apr-3 Christie's, Kensington #237/R est:4000-6000

GALL, Ferenc (20th C) ?
£950 $1482 €1378 Sunshine (61x51cm-24x20in) s. 12-Apr-3 Mu Terem Galeria, Budapest #33/R est:250000 (H.F 340000)

GALL, François (1912-1987) French
£522 $820 €783 Eglise le Murel (50x61cm-20x24in) s. 16-Dec-2 Lilla Bukowskis, Stockholm #148 (S.KR 7400)
£545 $796 €850 Promenade sur les quais, ciel nuageux (30x40cm-12x16in) s.i. board. 4-Jun-2 Karl & Faber, Munich #249/R
£603 $934 €905 Bridge over the river Seine (27x41cm-11x16in) s.i.d.44 prov. 8-Dec-2 Uppsala Auktionskammare, Uppsala #199/R (S.KR 8500)
£649 $1000 €974 Going to the gate (23x28cm-9x11in) s. prov. 24-Oct-2 Shannon's, Milford #220/R
£655 $1022 €983 Afternoon in the Jardin du Luxembourg (22x27cm-9x11in) s.i. board. 6-Nov-2 Dobiaschofsky, Bern #563/R (S.FR 1500)
£700 $1085 €1050 Promenade, Quai de la Seine a Paris (19x24cm-7x9in) s.d.46 board. 5-Dec-2 Christie's, Kensington #123/R
£736 $1200 €1104 Paris street scene (30x43cm-12x17in) 14-Feb-3 Du Mouchelle, Detroit #24/R
£743 $1159 €1100 View of Montmartre (19x27cm-7x11in) s. panel. 28-Mar-3 Delvaux, Paris #47/R
£828 $1382 €1200 Plage a Arcachon (22x27cm-9x11in) s.i. 10-Jul-3 Artcurial Briest, Paris #271
£1065 $1682 €1598 Treport (38x46cm-15x18in) s. 28-Apr-3 Bukowskis, Stockholm #318/R est:20000-25000 (S.KR 14000)
£1132 $1755 €1800 Avant la messe (27x22cm-11x9in) s. 4-Oct-2 Tajan, Paris #97 est:1800-2400
£1223 $1907 €1835 Young woman (27x22cm-11x9in) s.d.1944 i. verso panel. 6-Nov-2 Dobiaschofsky, Bern #564/R est:5000 (S.FR 2800)
£1241 $1912 €1862 Harbour scene with figures and boats at anchor (37x45cm-15x18in) s. 27-Oct-2 Anders Antik, Landskrona #588/R est:20000-25000 (S.KR 18000)
£1361 $2205 €2042 Men about town near Notre-Dame (60x83cm-24x33in) s.i.d.56. 3-Feb-3 Lilla Bukowskis, Stockholm #473 est:18000-20000 (S.KR 19000)
£1446 $2271 €2169 La plage (23x28cm-9x11in) i. s.verso prov. 24-Jul-2 Walker's, Ottawa #45/R est:3500-4500 (C.D 3500)
£1472 $2296 €2208 Still life of flowers (61x50cm-24x20in) s.i. 6-Nov-2 AB Stockholms Auktionsverk #942/R est:12000-15000 (S.KR 21000)
£1545 $2441 €2318 Mother with small child. s. 29-Nov-2 Zofingen, Switzerland #2445/R est:4000 (S.FR 3600)
£1563 $2500 €2345 Two ladies in an outdoor cafe (41x28cm-16x11in) 10-Jan-3 Du Mouchelle, Detroit #2164/R est:2000-3000
£1615 $2600 €2423 Sur les quais (36x28cm-14x11in) s. s.i.verso prov. 18-Feb-3 Arthur James, Florida #410
£1656 $2583 €2600 Paris, le Pont Neuf (47x65cm-19x26in) s.d.1948. 10-Nov-2 Eric Pillon, Calais #103/R
£1698 $2632 €2700 Sur les berges (21x27cm-8x11in) s. 4-Oct-2 Tajan, Paris #98 est:2400-3000
£1747 $2725 €2621 Montmartre (24x32cm-9x13in) s.i. board prov. 6-Nov-2 Dobiaschofsky, Bern #560/R est:6000 (S.FR 4000)
£1911 $2981 €3000 Paris, cafe de Flore (22x33cm-9x13in) s. panel. 10-Nov-2 Eric Pillon, Calais #101/R
£1931 $3013 €2800 Activity on the beach (22x27cm-9x11in) s. prov. 26-Mar-3 Walker's, Ottawa #23/R est:4500-5500 (C.D 4500)
£2070 $3250 €3105 Day at the races (10x18cm-4x7in) s. 10-Dec-2 Doyle, New York #239/R est:5000-7000
£2183 $3406 €3275 Young Parisian near Saint-Michel bridge and Notre-Dame (33x41cm-13x16in) s.i. prov. 9-Nov-2 Galerie Gloggner, Luzern #58/R est:2500-2800 (S.FR 5000)
£2183 $3515 €3100 Danseuse au chausson (27x22cm-11x9in) s. 11-May-3 Lombrail & Teucquam, Paris #221/R
£2373 $3750 €3560 Young lady walking near the Seine (23x28cm-9x11in) s.i. 22-Apr-3 Arthur James, Florida #56
£2533 $3951 €3800 Young ballet dance warming up (22x27cm-9x11in) s. 6-Nov-2 Dobiaschofsky, Bern #561/R est:6000 (S.FR 5800)
£2548 $4000 €3822 Young French girl seated in front of dressing mirror (25x23cm-10x9in) s. 19-Apr-3 James Julia, Fairfield #166/R est:6000-9000
£2639 $4249 €3959 Eugenie a Argenteuil (27x22cm-11x9in) s.i. 7-May-3 Dobiaschofsky, Bern #564/R est:7500 (S.FR 5700)
£2724 $4250 €4086 Waiting at the gate (23x28cm-9x11in) s.i. 9-Oct-2 Doyle, New York #37 est:1500-2500
£2778 $4500 €4028 Women at an outdoor cafe (23x28cm-9x11in) s. 21-May-3 Doyle, New York #232/R est:2000-3000
£2778 $4500 €4028 Day at the beach (23x41cm-9x16in) s. 21-May-3 Doyle, New York #250/R est:4000-6000
£2932 $4750 €4251 Woman on a park bench (61x51cm-24x20in) s. 21-May-3 Doyle, New York #247/R est:4000-6000
£3165 $4937 €5000 Dans les coulisses (61x50cm-24x20in) s. 16-Oct-2 Fraysse & Associes, Paris #47/R est:4500-6000
£3493 $5450 €5240 Place du Tertre (38x46cm-15x18in) s. 6-Nov-2 Dobiaschofsky, Bern #559/R est:12000 (S.FR 8000)
£4012 $6500 €5817 Beach at Trouville (25x46cm-10x18in) s.i. 21-May-3 Doyle, New York #249/R est:8000-10000
£4037 $6500 €6056 La plage a cabourg (61x81cm-24x32in) s. i.on stretcher prov. 18-Feb-3 Arthur James, Florida #411
£4366 $7030 €6200 Ballet performance (27x22cm-11x9in) s. lit. 9-May-3 Schloss Ahlden, Ahlden #1511/R est:5800
£4459 $7000 €6689 Girl at dressing table (18x11cm-7x4in) s. 10-Dec-2 Doyle, New York #244/R est:5000-7000
£4487 $7000 €6731 Jeune femme devant la coiffeuse (81x65cm-32x26in) s. i.verso. 20-Sep-2 Sloan, North Bethesda #369/R est:6000-8000
£4647 $7250 €6971 La terrace du cafe (61x50cm-24x20in) s.verso. 20-Sep-2 Sloan, North Bethesda #375/R est:5000-6000
£8000 $12640 €12000 Plage a Trouville (64x76cm-25x30in) s. 3-Apr-3 Christie's, Kensington #17/R
Works on paper
£404 $638 €606 Bois de Bologne (18x23cm-7x9in) s. W/C htd oil. 18-Nov-2 Waddingtons, Toronto #216/R (C.D 1000)

GALLAGHER, Ellen (1967-) American
£53797 $85000 €80696 Untitled (305x244cm-120x96in) oil ink paper on canvas exec.1999 prov.exhib. 13-Nov-2 Sotheby's, New York #467/R est:80000-120000
Works on paper
£2625 $4200 €3938 Untitled (71x69cm-28x27in) ink executed 1996 prov. 15-May-3 Christie's, Rockefeller NY #322/R est:8000-12000

GALLAGHER, Frederick O'Neill (fl.1910) British
£250 $405 €375 Suspension bridge, Eveypetit Bourig (38x55cm-15x22in) s.i.d.1914. 23-Jan-3 Christie's, Kensington #272
£380 $616 €570 River path (33x46cm-13x18in) s.d.1911. 23-Jan-3 Christie's, Kensington #271

GALLAGHER, Sears (1869-1955) American
Works on paper
£688 $1100 €1032 Summer landscape (28x43cm-11x17in) s. pastel. 11-Jan-3 James Julia, Fairfield #470 est:1000-1500
£750 $1200 €1125 Landscape with haystacks and buildings (28x43cm-11x17in) s. pastel. 11-Jan-3 James Julia, Fairfield #471 est:1500-2500

GALLAIT, Louis (1810-1887) Belgian
£342 $534 €500 Meditation (76x64cm-30x25in) bears sig. 14-Apr-3 Horta, Bruxelles #392

GALLAIT, Louis (attrib) (1810-1887) Belgian
£616 $968 €900 La Bataille de Bouillon (77x105cm-30x41in) 15-Apr-3 Galerie Moderne, Brussels #332

GALLAND, Gilbert (1870-?) French
Works on paper
£863 $1381 €1200 Le port de Marseille (37x54cm-15x21in) s. W/C. 14-May-3 Blanchet, Paris #61 est:1200-1500

GALLAND, Pierre Victor (1822-1892) French
£845 $1403 €1200 Jeune femme drapee s'elevant dans les airs (101x81cm-40x32in) 16-Jun-3 Oger, Dumont, Paris #44i/R
£1127 $1870 €1600 Etude pour un violon pose sur une tablette (35x44cm-14x17in) 16-Jun-3 Oger, Dumont, Paris #44d/R est:900-1200
£1268 $2104 €1800 Projet de fronton de porte pour Fontainebleau (39x39cm-15x15in) studio st. cardboard. 16-Jun-3 Oger, Dumont, Paris #44h/R est:1500-1800
Works on paper
£282 $468 €400 Etude pour un palais a l'Italienne (24x21cm-9x8in) s. pierre noire W/C. 16-Jun-3 Oger, Dumont, Paris #44b/R
£282 $468 €400 Nus au bord d'une riviere (15x41cm-6x16in) studio st. chl W/C. 16-Jun-3 Oger, Dumont, Paris #44g/R
£296 $491 €420 Etude plafonnante a l'ange (36x34cm-14x13in) i.d.1874 chl crayon. 16-Jun-3 Oger, Dumont, Paris #44c/R
£437 $725 €620 Etude pour des vases a l'Antique (30x20cm-12x8in) studio st.verso chl crayon htd gold. 16-Jun-3 Oger, Dumont, Paris #44a

GALLARD, Michel de (1921-) French
£1103 $1754 €1600 Hiver, toits rouges (55x38cm-22x15in) s.d.56 panel. 5-Mar-3 Doutrebente, Paris #60 est:1000
£2517 $4002 €3650 Poires et bouteilles (92x73cm-36x29in) s. 5-Mar-3 Doutrebente, Paris #61/R est:1500-2000

GALLARD-LEPINAY, Paul Charles Emmanuel (1842-1885) French
£1656 $2699 €2500 Entree du port (26x40cm-10x16in) s. panel. 31-Jan-3 Rabourdin & Choppin de Janvry, Paris #72/R
£3750 $6000 €5625 View of Istanbul with ships in the foreground (55x96cm-22x38in) s. 14-May-3 Butterfields, San Francisco #1130/R est:6000-8000

GALLARDO, Mario (1937-) Mexican
£705 $1107 €1100 Homme puzzle (73x60cm-29x24in) s. panel. 16-Dec-2 Eric Coutrier, Paris #92

GALLATIN, Albert E (1881-1952) American
£3247 $5000 €4871 Abstraction (41x30cm-16x12in) s.d.1939 verso panel prov. 24-Oct-2 Shannon's, Milford #39/R est:5000-7000

GALLE, Hieronymus (17/18th C) Flemish
£10366 $17000 €15549 Tulips, peonies, morning glory and other flowers in a vase on a ledge (56x44cm-22x17in) 30-May-3 Christie's, Rockefeller NY #3/R est:10000-15000

GALLE, Pierre Vincent (1883-1960) French
Works on paper
£310 $493 €450 Vue du marche de St-Anne le Palud (25x35cm-10x14in) s.i.d.septembre 1928 W/C. 4-Mar-3 Livinec, Gaudcheau & Jezequel, Rennes #66

GALLEBAERT, Maria van (?) Belgian?
£327 $526 €500 Nature morte aux fruits et legumes (70x80cm-28x31in) s. 14-Jan-3 Vanderkindere, Brussels #115

GALLEGO CANAMERO, Antonio (1936-) Spanish
£260 $379 €400 Landscape (38x47cm-15x19in) s. 17-Jun-2 Ansorena, Madrid #224/R

GALLEGO MARQUINA, Jesus (1900-1987) Spanish
£881 $1356 €1400 View of Toro (64x80cm-25x31in) s. 22-Oct-2 Durán, Madrid #157/R
£41000 $64370 €61500 Despues de la cena - after dinner (25x35cm-10x14in) s. board. 19-Nov-2 Sotheby's, London #58a/R est:15000-20000

GALLEGOS Y ARNOSA, Jose (1859-1917) Spanish
£12258 $19368 €19000 Praying in the chapel (23x17cm-9x7in) s.d.1894 board. 18-Dec-2 Ansorena, Madrid #167/R est:16000
£37037 $52593 €60000 Petite chorale d'enfants de coeur (46x66cm-18x26in) s.i. panel. 17-Mar-2 Galerie de Chartres, Chartres #113
£44000 $68200 €66000 Midday feast (25x37cm-10x15in) s.d.1900 panel prov. 4-Dec-2 Christie's, London #3/R est:40000-60000
£46548 $75407 €67495 Church interior with figures praying (33x43cm-13x17in) s.i.d.1899 panel prov. 25-May-3 Uppsala Auktionskammare, Uppsala #69/R est:80000-100000 (S.KR 600000)

Works on paper
£5355 $8461 €8300 Reclining odalisk (55x38cm-22x15in) s.i.d.1906 W/C. 18-Dec-2 Ansorena, Madrid #236/R

GALLELLI, Massimiliano (1863-1956) Italian
£1266 $2000 €2000 Lady with pearl necklace (78x58cm-31x23in) s. 26-Nov-2 Christie's, Rome #89

GALLEN-KALLELA, Akseli Valdemar (1865-1931) Finnish
£7595 $12000 €12000 Reflection between the trees (36x38cm-14x15in) board painted 1920s. 1-Dec-2 Bukowskis, Helsinki #58/R est:12000-13000
£8099 $13039 €11500 Stones on the beach (43x51cm-17x20in) s.d.1904. 10-May-3 Bukowskis, Helsinki #180/R est:8000-10000
£18354 $29000 €29000 Lake landscape (56x71cm-22x28in) s.d.1900. 30-Nov-2 Hagelstam, Helsinki #121/R est:18000
£23944 $38549 €34000 Winter landscape with skiers (36x28cm-14x11in) s.d.1908. 10-May-3 Bukowskis, Helsinki #108/R est:15000-20000
£24684 $39000 €39000 Summer morning at Ruovesi (35x25cm-14x10in) s.i.d.89 board. 1-Dec-2 Bukowskis, Helsinki #57/R est:15000-18000
£26761 $43085 €38000 Coastal landscape, windy day - Ruovesi (58x42cm-23x17in) s. 10-May-3 Bukowskis, Helsinki #99/R est:25000-30000
£27338 $43741 €38000 Late winter landscape, Konginkangas (22x57cm-9x22in) s.d.1906. 17-May-3 Hagelstam, Helsinki #132/R est:20000
£31646 $50000 €50000 Lady dressed in white party dress (20x15cm-8x6in) s.d.1887 panel exhib.lit. 30-Nov-2 Hagelstam, Helsinki #122/R est:60000
£107914 $172662 €150000 Summer night (68x42cm-27x17in) s.d.1898. 17-May-3 Hagelstam, Helsinki #133/R est:150000
Works on paper
£1408 $2268 €2000 By the bonfire (27x20cm-11x8in) s.i.d.1928 crayon pencil. 10-May-3 Bukowskis, Helsinki #141/R est:2000-2500
£3291 $5200 €5200 View from Paanajarvi (19x39cm-7x15in) s.d.1892 mixed media. 1-Dec-2 Bukowskis, Helsinki #59/R est:1700-2000
£3521 $5669 €5000 Kullervo Enekel (20x13cm-8x5in) s.d.1908 mixed media illustration to Vikar Belas book. 10-May-3 Bukowskis, Helsinki #188/R est:5000-6000

GALLI, Giovanni Antonio (attrib) (17th C) Italian
£3931 $6211 €5700 Heads of angels (39x45cm-15x18in) 5-Apr-3 Finarte Semenzato, Milan #144/R

GALLI, Giuseppe (1866-1953) Italian
£1020 $1622 €1500 Interior with vase of roses (70x50cm-28x20in) s. tempera W/C cardboard. 1-Mar-3 Meeting Art, Vercelli #116

GALLI, Luigi (1820-1906) Italian
£629 $969 €1000 Lion and lioness (17x28cm-7x11in) s.i. cardboard. 28-Oct-2 Il Ponte, Milan #209

GALLI, Sergio (20th C) ?
£957 $1483 €1436 Tropical fish (91x122cm-36x48in) s. acrylic. 4-Dec-2 Koller, Zurich #201/R est:1400-2200 (S.FR 2200)

GALLI, Stefano (1950-) Italian
£253 $395 €400 Family fragments (40x30cm-16x12in) ss. s.i.d.1994 verso acrylic. 14-Sep-2 Meeting Art, Vercelli #225
£316 $494 €500 Group photo with curate (70x100cm-28x39in) s. s.i.d.1993 verso acrylic. 14-Sep-2 Meeting Art, Vercelli #935/R
£327 $523 €500 Harvest (60x60cm-24x24in) s. s.i.d.1999 verso. 4-Jan-3 Meeting Art, Vercelli #37
£327 $523 €500 Class (70x70cm-28x28in) s. acrylic painted 1998. 4-Jan-3 Meeting Art, Vercelli #143
£347 $552 €500 Little wave (80x80cm-31x31in) s.s id.1997 verso acrylic. 1-May-3 Meeting Art, Vercelli #284
£353 $554 €550 Three women in red (80x80cm-31x31in) s. s.i.d.1997 verso acrylic. 23-Nov-2 Meeting Art, Vercelli #155/R
£353 $554 €550 Afternoon at the club (60x50cm-24x20in) s. s.i.d.1996 verso acrylic. 23-Nov-2 Meeting Art, Vercelli #403/R
£359 $575 €550 Family fragments (40x60cm-16x24in) s. s.i.d.1994 verso acrylic lit. 4-Jan-3 Meeting Art, Vercelli #546
£451 $718 €650 Little hotel (80x80cm-31x31in) s. acrylic painted 1997 lit. 1-May-3 Meeting Art, Vercelli #512
£633 $987 €1000 Philarmonic (75x120cm-30x47in) s. s.i.d.1993 acrylic. 14-Sep-2 Meeting Art, Vercelli #906/R
£714 $1136 €1050 Beach (30x40cm-12x16in) s. acrylic painted 1990. 1-Mar-3 Meeting Art, Vercelli #549

GALLIANI, Omar (1954-) Italian
£1538 $2415 €2400 Face (71x71cm-28x28in) s.i.verso. 23-Nov-2 Meeting Art, Vercelli #90/R
£4487 $6955 €7000 Shipwreck (205x238cm-81x94in) s.d.1982 verso exhib. 4-Dec-2 Finarte, Milan #535/R est:5000
Works on paper
£1408 $2338 €2000 Vaso (72x100cm-28x39in) chl. 10-Jun-3 Finarte Semenzato, Milan #295/R est:1400-1800
£4422 $7031 €6500 Traces (100x100cm-39x39in) s.i.verso graphite board. 1-Mar-3 Meeting Art, Vercelli #641

GALLIANO, Daniele (1961-) Italian
£1689 $2635 €2500 Untitled (40x50cm-16x20in) s.d.1996 verso prov. 26-Mar-3 Finarte Semenzato, Milan #174/R
£4539 $7353 €6400 Untitled (108x150cm-43x59in) s.d.2002 verso. 20-May-3 Porro, Milan #23/R est:6400-6600

GALLIARI, Gaspare (1761-1823) Italian
Works on paper
£385 $550 €578 View of a town (22x27cm-9x11in) pen brown ink wash. 23-Jan-3 Swann Galleries, New York #163/R

GALLIEN, Pierre Antoine (1896-1963) French
£1081 $1686 €1600 Synthese du dancing (24x17cm-9x7in) init. i.verso tempera card exhib. 26-Mar-3 Finarte Semenzato, Milan #92/R

GALLIER, Gratien Achille (attrib) (1814-1871) French
£440 $678 €700 Jeunes femmes puisant de l'eau a la fontaine (22x30cm-9x12in) 27-Oct-2 Muizon & Le Coent, Paris #26/R

GALLIERA, L (19/20th C) ?
£750 $1185 €1125 Figures at the edge of a mountainous lake (55x69cm-22x27in) s. 14-Nov-2 Christie's, Kensington #121/R

GALLIS, Pieter (1633-1697) Dutch
£18705 $29928 €26000 Swag of mixed flowers in a niche (36x44cm-14x17in) indis sig. panel prov. 14-May-3 Christie's, Amsterdam #186/R est:20000-30000

GALLIZIO, Pinot (1902-1964) Italian
£697 $1101 €1046 Valhalla (55x46cm-22x18in) s.d.61 verso prov. 5-Apr-3 Rasmussen, Havnen #4160 (D.KR 7500)
£2235 $3553 €3353 Composition (72x60cm-28x24in) s.d.61 verso. 10-Mar-3 Rasmussen, Vejle #711/R est:6000-8000 (D.KR 24000)
£3526 $5465 €5500 Untitled (81x65cm-32x26in) s.d.61 verso prov. 3-Dec-2 Christie's, Amsterdam #113/R est:900-1200

GALLO, Beppe (1942-) Italian
£316 $494 €500 Poppies in the Bassa Langa (50x60cm-20x24in) s. painted 1994. 14-Sep-2 Meeting Art, Vercelli #435
£321 $503 €500 Still life (60x50cm-24x20in) s. s.verso. 23-Nov-2 Meeting Art, Vercelli #218
£340 $541 €500 Basket (70x50cm-28x20in) s. s.i.d.1992 verso. 1-Mar-3 Meeting Art, Vercelli #464
£359 $575 €550 White fishing boats (50x60cm-20x24in) s. s.verso. 4-Jan-3 Meeting Art, Vercelli #646

£408 $649 €600 Winter stroll (80x70cm-31x28in) s. 1-Mar-3 Meeting Art, Vercelli #438
£411 $642 €650 Cottages in Amai Col de Joux (50x60cm-20x24in) s. s.i.d.1996 verso. 14-Sep-2 Meeting Art, Vercelli #220/R
£443 $691 €700 Vineyards (50x60cm-20x24in) s. s.i.d.1999 verso. 14-Sep-2 Meeting Art, Vercelli #310
£481 $755 €750 Gran Madre seen from the convent (70x70cm-28x28in) s. s.i.d.1999 verso. 23-Nov-2 Meeting Art, Vercelli #157/R
£510 $811 €750 Snow cart at Porta Palazzo (80x80cm-31x31in) s. s.i.d.1997 verso. 1-Mar-3 Meeting Art, Vercelli #496
£510 $811 €750 Gran Madre seen from the Cappuccini (70x70cm-28x28in) s. painted 1999. 1-Mar-3 Meeting Art, Vercelli #742
£521 $828 €750 San Bovo's woods (70x70cm-28x28in) s. painted 1998. 1-May-3 Meeting Art, Vercelli #287
£625 $994 €900 October on the hill (60x70cm-24x28in) s. s.i.d.1998 verso. 1-May-3 Meeting Art, Vercelli #93
£633 $987 €1000 Market closing at Porta Palazzo (90x100cm-35x39in) s. s.i.d.1997 verso. 14-Sep-2 Meeting Art, Vercelli #909/R
£705 $1107 €1100 Portofino from the hills (100x100cm-39x39in) s. painted 1996 lit. 23-Nov-2 Meeting Art, Vercelli #427/R
£719 $1150 €1100 After the storm (80x100cm-31x39in) s.i.d.1997 verso lit. 4-Jan-3 Meeting Art, Vercelli #198
£764 $1215 €1100 Sunset on the lagoon (100x120cm-39x47in) s. s.i.d.1998 verso lit. 1-May-3 Meeting Art, Vercelli #560

GALLO, Giuseppe (1954-) Italian
£1026 $1610 €1600 Untitled (47x75cm-19x30in) s.i.verso paper. 20-Nov-2 Pandolfini, Florence #160/R
£1923 $3019 €3000 Hyena (97x52cm-38x20in) s.i.d.2000 verso. 23-Nov-2 Meeting Art, Vercelli #361/R

GALLOIS, Émile (1882-1965) French
Works on paper
£6207 $9869 €9000 Etude de perdrix et cailles (31x45cm-12x18in) W/C pencil htd gouache. 10-Mar-3 Coutau Begarie, Paris #133

GALLOIS, V (?) French
£976 $1600 €1464 Still life with copper kettle and grapes (56x46cm-22x18in) s. 8-Feb-3 Neal Auction Company, New Orleans #121/R est:2000-3000

GALLON, Robert (1845-1925) British
£280 $437 €420 On the old road Bettws-y-Coed (18x30cm-7x12in) i.verso board. 26-Mar-3 Woolley & Wallis, Salisbury #268/R
£360 $562 €540 Old mill, Hughtown, Scilly Isles (18x30cm-7x12in) i.verso board. 26-Mar-3 Woolley & Wallis, Salisbury #270/R
£410 $644 €615 Open seas (48x76cm-19x30in) s. 15-Apr-3 Bonhams, Knowle #112
£420 $655 €630 Burra Fort, Uist, Shetland (18x30cm-7x12in) i.verso board. 26-Mar-3 Woolley & Wallis, Salisbury #269/R
£974 $1500 €1461 Figures in a coastal village (28x41cm-11x16in) s. panel painted c.1880. 8-Sep-2 Treadway Gallery, Cincinnati #537/R est:1500-2500
£1740 $2750 €2610 Farm by the mountainside (51x76cm-20x30in) s. prov. 24-Apr-3 Shannon's, Milford #108/R est:3000-5000
£2800 $4480 €4200 Boy with horses in a stream, with a bridge beyond (61x101cm-24x40in) s.d.1882. 7-Jan-3 Bonhams, Knightsbridge #245/R est:3000-5000
£3200 $5248 €4800 On the Lledr (41x56cm-16x22in) s.d.1874. 29-May-3 Christie's, Kensington #100/R est:1500-2500
£4839 $7500 €7259 Landscape with figures at Colwyn Bay (61x102cm-24x40in) s. 7-Dec-2 Neal Auction Company, New Orleans #284/R est:6000-9000
Works on paper
£1700 $2771 €2550 Fishing vessels in Whitby harbour at night (60x40cm-24x16in) s.i. W/C htd bodycol. 11-Feb-3 Fellows & Sons, Birmingham #132/R est:400-600

GALOFRE Y GIMENEZ, Baldomero (1849-1902) Spanish
£1875 $2850 €2813 Paisaje montanoso con cienaga (60x100cm-24x39in) s.d. 3-Jul-2 Naón & Cia, Buenos Aires #19/R est:3000-3500
£5161 $8000 €7742 Gypsy camp (19x32cm-7x13in) s.i.d. panel. 30-Oct-2 Christie's, Rockefeller NY #118/R est:12000-16000
£18293 $30000 €27440 Fishing boats on the shore (25x43cm-10x17in) s. 5-Feb-3 Christie's, Rockefeller NY #209/R est:7000-9000
Works on paper
£1081 $1686 €1600 Naples marine (24x16cm-9x6in) s. W/C. 25-Mar-3 Durán, Madrid #700/R
£1355 $2141 €2100 Seascape (52x36cm-20x14in) s.d.1887 W/C. 17-Dec-2 Durán, Madrid #75/R
£2097 $3313 €3250 Seascape (52x36cm-20x14in) s. W/C. 17-Dec-2 Durán, Madrid #76/R

GALOYER, Francois (1944-) French
Sculpture
£1290 $2039 €2000 Rouge gorge (28cm-11in) s. brown green pat.bronze. 17-Dec-2 Claude Aguttes, Neuilly #65/R est:1000-1300
£1613 $2548 €2500 Moyen Duc (40cm-16in) s. green brown pat.bronze marble socle. 17-Dec-2 Claude Aguttes, Neuilly #63/R est:2000-2500
£1731 $2683 €2700 Rouge-gorge sur un branchage (16x12x8cm-6x5x3in) s. num.4/8 pat bronze. 7-Dec-2 Martinot & Savignat, Pontoise #127/R

GALOYER, Raymond (1896-?) French
Works on paper
£2975 $4700 €4700 Danseurs bretons. Joueur de biniou (190x70cm-75x28in) s. gouache pair. 1-Dec-2 Livinec, Gaudcheau & Jezequel, Rennes #38/R

GALT, Cameron (1964-) British?
Works on paper
£380 $619 €570 Portrait of Eileen (69x35cm-27x14in) mono.d.1990 compressed chl white chk. 3-Feb-3 Sotheby's, Olympia #143/R

GALVANO, Albino (1907-1991) Italian
£374 $595 €550 Figure with hat (60x50cm-24x20in) s. 1-Mar-3 Meeting Art, Vercelli #710
£475 $741 €750 Composition (63x47cm-25x19in) s. board. 14-Sep-2 Meeting Art, Vercelli #939/R
£490 $784 €750 Composition with book (50x69cm-20x27in) s. cardboard. 4-Jan-3 Meeting Art, Vercelli #189
£1275 $2039 €1950 Abstraction moving (50x40cm-20x16in) s. cardboard. 4-Jan-3 Meeting Art, Vercelli #649
£1389 $2208 €2000 Abstract composition (60x70cm-24x28in) s.d.1952. 1-May-3 Meeting Art, Vercelli #464
Works on paper
£347 $552 €500 Composition (50x35cm-20x14in) s.verso mixed media card. 1-May-3 Meeting Art, Vercelli #433

GALVEZ, Byron (1941-) Mexican
£742 $1187 €1076 Personaje (36x31cm-14x12in) s.d.1990 acrylic. 15-May-3 Louis Morton, Mexico #141 (M.P 12000)
£1484 $2375 €2152 Personaje en morado (60x50cm-24x20in) s. acrylic. 15-May-3 Louis Morton, Mexico #135/R est:26000-30000 (M.P 24000)

GALWEY Y GARCIA, Enrique (1864-1931) Spanish
£1645 $2664 €2500 Landscape (120x80cm-47x31in) s. 21-Jan-3 Durán, Madrid #133/R

GAMAGE, Parker (20th C) American
£696 $1100 €1044 At the head of the harbor (43x5cm-17x2in) s.verso board. 30-Nov-2 Thomaston Place, Thomaston #204

GAMARRA, Jose (1934-) Uruguayan
£3819 $6302 €5500 Pervivencias (78x106cm-31x42in) s. s.i.d.1981 verso prov. 1-Jul-3 Artcurial Briest, Paris #799/R est:5000-7000

GAMBARA, Lattanzio (1530-1574) Italian
Works on paper
£6790 $11000 €10185 Design for the decoration of a spandrel (43x26cm-17x10in) red chk. 21-Jan-3 Sotheby's, New York #34/R est:9000

GAMBARA, Lattanzio (attrib) (1530-1574) Italian
Works on paper
£1358 $2200 €2037 Corner of classical altar (13x20cm-5x8in) chk pen ink wash prov. 22-Jan-3 Christie's, Rockefeller NY #7/R

GAMBERT (19th C) French
£1135 $1759 €1703 Drawing room interior with couples conversing (37x46cm-15x18in) s. panel. 4-Dec-2 AB Stockholms Auktionsverk #1901/R est:20000-25000 (S.KR 16000)

GAMBERT, O (?) German?
£323 $474 €500 Lower Alps landscape with lake (70x99cm-28x39in) s. 24-Jun-2 Dr Fritz Nagel, Stuttgart #6088/R

GAMBINO, Giuseppe (1928-) Italian
£1032 $1600 €1548 Paesaggio a Cordoba (71x91cm-28x36in) s.i.d. 8-Dec-2 Toomey, Oak Park #825/R est:1000-2000
£1139 $1777 €1800 Still life with violin (70x100cm-28x39in) s.d.1958 s.i.d.verso. 19-Oct-2 Semenzato, Venice #39/R
£1203 $1876 €1900 Landscape in Venice (70x50cm-28x20in) s.d.1957. 19-Oct-2 Semenzato, Venice #38/R

GAMBLE, John M (1863-1957) American
£964 $1600 €1398 View of a California ranch (41x61cm-16x24in) s. 11-Jun-3 Butterfields, San Francisco #4200/R est:3000-5000
£9554 $15000 €14331 Landscape with mission ruins and ocean in the distance (32x42cm-13x17in) s. prov. 19-Nov-2 Butterfields, San Francisco #8266/R est:20000-30000
£10828 $17000 €16242 Mustard and lupine near Litton springs (30x41cm-12x16in) s.d.1904 prov. 19-Nov-2 Butterfields, San Francisco #8191/R est:12000-16000
£19355 $30000 €29033 Poppies and wild flowers in a coastal landscape (23x30cm-9x12in) s. prov. 29-Oct-2 John Moran, Pasadena #608a est:20000-30000
£20482 $34000 €29699 Poppies and lupine on a hillside with the ocean in the distance (30x46cm-12x18in) s. prov. 11-Jun-3 Butterfields, San Francisco #4233/R est:30000-50000
£23885 $37500 €35828 California landscape with poppies and lupine (30x41cm-12x16in) s. prov. 19-Nov-2 Butterfields, San Francisco #8216/R est:25000-35000
£25602 $42500 €37123 California landscape with poppies and lupine with mountains in distance (46x61cm-18x24in) s. prov. 11-Jun-3 Butterfields, San Francisco #4232/R est:40000-60000
£34161 $55000 €51242 Poppies and lupine in rolling California landscape (36x51cm-14x20in) s. prov. 18-Feb-3 John Moran, Pasadena #33 est:50000-70000
£35928 $60000 €52096 Blooming fields (30x41cm-12x16in) s.d.1903. 18-Jun-3 Christie's, Los Angeles #50/R est:30000-50000
£57325 $90000 €85988 Rising moon (76x63cm-30x25in) s. i.verso board. 20-Nov-2 Christie's, Los Angeles #89/R est:100000-150000

GAMBOGI, Fanny (19th C) French
£1200 $1908 €1800 Rest on the journey (49x65cm-19x26in) s.d.1882. 20-Mar-3 Christie's, Kensington #106/R est:1500-2000

GAMBOGI, G (19th C) Italian
Sculpture
£2051 $3221 €3200 Kids' cuddles (41cm-16in) s. marble. 16-Dec-2 Pandolfini, Florence #197/R

GAMBUGI, G (?) ?
Sculpture
£1170 $1954 €1650 La femme a la lecture (48cm-19in) s. bronze Carrare marble alabaster. 21-Jun-3 Bretagne Encheres, St Malo #185

GAMELIN, Jacques (1738-1803) French
Works on paper
£676 $1054 €1000 Deux canons tirant durant une bataille (19x25cm-7x10in) pen ink wash. 27-Mar-3 Christie's, Paris #109/R
£3924 $6122 €6200 Martyre de Vitellius (40x54cm-16x21in) s.i.d. Chinese ink wash pen htd white. 18-Oct-2 Rabourdin & Choppin de Janvry, Paris #113/R

GAMLEY, Andrew (?-1949) British
Works on paper
£280 $437 €420 Harbour of Pittenweem (33x43cm-13x17in) s. pencil W/C. 19-Sep-2 Christie's, Kensington #155
£360 $562 €540 Port, possibly Leith (25x35cm-10x14in) s.d.1917 W/C. 17-Oct-2 Bonhams, Edinburgh #228

GAMMON, Reg (1894-1997) British
£290 $464 €435 Wine, woman and ? (41x56cm-16x22in) s. board. 15-May-3 Lawrence, Crewkerne #1007/R
£300 $480 €450 Goose fair, Castelnaudry, Toulouse (29x39cm-11x15in) oil pencil board. 15-May-3 Lawrence, Crewkerne #1006
Works on paper
£520 $822 €780 Galway (35x47cm-14x19in) s.i. W/C. 2-Dec-2 Bonhams, Bath #34/R

GAMOTIS, Alphonse J (1842-1919) American
£806 $1250 €1209 Western landscape (18x28cm-7x11in) s.d.98 board. 7-Dec-2 Neal Auction Company, New Orleans #429/R est:1500-2500
£2903 $4500 €4355 Louisiana bayou with cabin and pirogue (18x28cm-7x11in) s.d.91 board. 7-Dec-2 Neal Auction Company, New Orleans #428/R est:3000-5000
Works on paper
£710 $1100 €1065 Cyprus landscapes (8x8cm-3x3in) s.d.06 gouache pair framed together. 7-Dec-2 Neal Auction Company, New Orleans #432/R est:1000-1500

GAMP, Botho von (1894-1977) German
£1056 $1701 €1500 Forio church on Ischia (46x70cm-18x28in) s. 7-May-3 Michael Zeller, Lindau #714/R est:1500

GAMPENRIEDER, Karl (1860-1930) German
£286 $426 €440 Still life with geisha, fan and other items (55x55cm-22x22in) s. 27-Jun-2 Neumeister, Munich #2715/R

GAMPERT, Otto (1842-1924) Swiss
£302 $471 €480 Lake (61x4cm-24x2in) s. 21-Sep-2 Berlinghof, Heidelberg #120
£652 $1017 €978 Morning mist on the Bodensee near Hard (54x77cm-21x30in) s. 16-Sep-2 Philippe Schuler, Zurich #3367 (S.FR 1500)
£694 $1118 €1041 Duck hunt (37x55cm-15x22in) s. 7-May-3 Dobiaschofsky, Bern #567/R (S.FR 1500)

GANAY, Isabelle de (20th C) French?
£5414 $8500 €8121 Figures resting on a hillside along the coast of Menton (137x195cm-54x77in) s.d.1932. 14-Dec-2 Weschler, Washington #608/R est:3000-5000

GANDARA, Antonio de la (1862-1917) French
£2848 $4500 €4500 Don Quichotte et Sancho Pancha (81x60cm-32x24in) s. 2-Dec-2 Tajan, Paris #3
Works on paper
£260 $406 €390 Portrait of Jean Pierre Dubost (43x36cm-17x14in) s. col chks oval. 26-Mar-3 Sotheby's, Olympia #239/R
£1042 $1646 €1500 Fillette a la robe bleue (58x45cm-23x18in) s. pastel. 25-Apr-3 Piasa, Paris #120/R
£1111 $1756 €1600 Mere et enfant (58x45cm-23x18in) s. pastel. 25-Apr-3 Piasa, Paris #122/R

GANDOLFI, Gaetano (1734-1802) Italian
£10180 $17000 €14761 Sleeping Endymion (33x38cm-13x15in) 21-Jun-3 Selkirks, St. Louis #1051/R est:20000-25000
Works on paper
£475 $750 €750 L'education de la Vierge (16x11cm-6x4in) pen brown ink brown wash. 27-Nov-2 Christie's, Paris #103/R
£1127 $1814 €1600 Studio di Sacra Famigilia con san Giovannino (18x14cm-7x6in) blk pencil. 12-May-3 Sotheby's, Milan #45/R est:1800-2200
£2600 $4082 €3900 St. Martin and the beggar (18x14cm-7x6in) pen ink wash oval prov. 11-Dec-2 Sotheby's, Olympia #37/R est:1000-1500
£4938 $8000 €7407 Head of Christ (44x32cm-17x13in) i. chk ink. 22-Jan-3 Christie's, Rockefeller NY #55/R est:20000
£5200 $8684 €7540 Pan embracing a putto (14x10cm-6x4in) pen ink wash over black chk. 9-Jul-3 Bonhams, Knightsbridge #64/R est:1000-1500
£10135 $15811 €15000 Studies of heads (14x19cm-6x7in) pen ink. 27-Mar-3 Christie's, Paris #36/R

GANDOLFI, Gaetano (attrib) (1734-1802) Italian
Works on paper
£1029 $1595 €1544 Study of a seated man (52x41cm-20x16in) red chk dr. 3-Dec-2 Ritchie, Toronto #3121/R est:2500-3500 (C.D 2500)

GANDOLFI, Mauro (attrib) (1764-1834) Italian
Works on paper
£455 $650 €683 Study of a reclining young man (20x31cm-8x12in) red chk htd white. 23-Jan-3 Swann Galleries, New York #142/R

GANDOLFI, Paola (1949-) Italian
£612 $973 €900 Road to the sea (30x30cm-12x12in) s.i.d.1993 verso board. 1-Mar-3 Meeting Art, Vercelli #403
£1757 $2741 €2600 Untitled (60x60cm-24x24in) s.d.1999 verso acrylic. 26-Mar-3 Finarte Semenzato, Milan #163/R

GANDOLFI, Ubaldo (1728-1781) Italian
Works on paper
£420 $600 €630 Crucifixion (18x19cm-7x7in) ink wash. 22-Jan-3 Doyle, New York #3
£4630 $7500 €6945 Seated nude (39x27cm-15x11in) chk prov. 22-Jan-3 Christie's, Rockefeller NY #56/R est:10000
£11486 $17919 €17000 Allegory of Wealth (21x17cm-8x7in) chk pen ink wash oval. 27-Mar-3 Christie's, Paris #35/R est:12000

GANDOLFI, Ubaldo (attrib) (1728-1781) Italian
Works on paper
£2160 $3500 €3240 Male academy (45x29cm-18x11in) chk wash htd white. 21-Jan-3 Sotheby's, New York #83/R

GANDON, Adolphe (1828-1889) French
£1087 $1685 €1631 Artillerie de campagne (32x48cm-13x19in) s.d.53. 7-Dec-2 Galerie du Rhone, Sion #104/R est:2500-3500 (S.FR 2500)

GANG, Fabien (1972-) Swiss
£1065 $1714 €1544 Arlequin et la tentation (100x80cm-39x31in) s. i.d.nov. 2002 verso. 7-May-3 Dobiaschofsky, Bern #490/R est:2400 (S.FR 2300)

GANGOLF, Paul (1879-1945) German
Works on paper
£493 $808 €680 Leopard (15x24cm-6x9in) s. W/C sketch verso. 31-May-3 Villa Grisebach, Berlin #561/R

GANGOOLY, Jamini Prakash (1876-1953) Indian
£1000 $1590 €1500 Sunrise over the Himalayas (23x31cm-9x12in) s. board. 29-Apr-3 Bonhams, New Bond Street #67 est:400-600

GANLY, Rose Brigid (1934-) Irish?
£833 $1292 €1300 Blue eyed plant (50x39cm-20x15in) init. board. 3-Dec-2 Bonhams & James Adam, Dublin #87/R
Works on paper
£269 $417 €420 Copper Beech, Corrig Ave (28x37cm-11x15in) init. i.verso pastel prov. 3-Dec-2 Bonhams & James Adam, Dublin #85/R
£417 $646 €650 Street cafe (23x35cm-9x14in) gouache. 3-Dec-2 Bonhams & James Adam, Dublin #84/R

GANNAM, John (1907-1965) American
Works on paper
£932 $1500 €1398 Counterfeiter inspects the goods while another looks on (48x51cm-19x20in) gouache board. 10-May-3 Illustration House, New York #106/R est:2000-4000
£962 $1500 €1443 Western couple in interior, she seated on bed (33x51cm-13x20in) W/C gouache en grisaille. 9-Nov-2 Illustration House, New York #169/R est:2500-3500
£2083 $3250 €3125 Mother and dozing baby lying on bed (33x28cm-13x11in) s. W/C. 9-Nov-2 Illustration House, New York #112/R est:3000-5000

GANPAZANN, C (?) ?
£875 $1418 €1313 Portrait of soldier with medal (77x62cm-30x24in) 23-Jan-3 Louis Morton, Mexico #137/R est:18000-25000 (M.P 15000)

GANSO, Emil (1895-1941) American
£318 $500 €477 Country lane with view of a house (46x37cm-18x15in) s.o.d.32 prov. 14-Dec-2 Weschler, Washington #695/R
£556 $900 €834 New York State landscape, possibly Woodstock (58x76cm-23x30in) s. s.i.verso tempera on board. 24-Jan-3 Freeman, Philadelphia #94/R
£8280 $13000 €12420 Still life of peaches (31x41cm-12x16in) s. masonite prov. 14-Dec-2 Weschler, Washington #698/R est:1000-1500
Works on paper
£335 $550 €486 Female nude from behind with reflection in mirror (37x31cm-15x12in) s. col chk. 5-Jun-3 Swann Galleries, New York #98/R
£427 $700 €619 Reclining nude (45x55cm-18x22in) s. col crayon. 5-Jun-3 Swann Galleries, New York #100/R
£457 $750 €663 Reclining nude (36x54cm-14x21in) s.d. chl pastel. 5-Jun-3 Swann Galleries, New York #99/R

GANT, James (fl.1827-1841) British
£850 $1343 €1275 Timber felling beside a river, castle beyond. Ancient stone bridge with cattle (25x33cm-10x13in) s. pair. 7-Apr-3 Bonhams, Bath #98/R

GANTNER, Bernard (1928-) French
£283 $439 €450 Peniche (19x24cm-7x9in) s. panel painted 1977. 7-Oct-2 Claude Aguttes, Neuilly #287
£780 $1264 €1100 Les forains (38x61cm-15x24in) s. 23-May-3 Camard, Paris #171/R
£881 $1365 €1400 Vue d'un port (50x73cm-20x29in) s.d.61. 30-Oct-2 Artcurial Briest, Paris #388
£943 $1462 €1500 Paysages des Vosges sous la neige (116x89cm-46x35in) s.d.61. 30-Oct-2 Artcurial Briest, Paris #386/R est:2500-3000
£943 $1462 €1500 La gare (81x65cm-32x26in) s.d.61. 30-Oct-2 Artcurial Briest, Paris #387 est:2000-2500
£1195 $1852 €1900 Village enneige (89x129cm-35x51in) s. 30-Oct-2 Artcurial Briest, Paris #389/R est:2500-3000
£1200 $1860 €1800 Neige fondante (61x50cm-24x20in) s.d.69 s.i.d.verso prov. 5-Dec-2 Christie's, Kensington #196/R est:1500-2000
Works on paper
£269 $417 €420 Paysage. s. gouache. 8-Dec-2 Feletin, Province #220
£360 $576 €500 Le verger (52x40cm-20x16in) s. W/C gouache. 18-May-3 Eric Pillon, Calais #157/R
£360 $576 €500 L'etang (40x51cm-16x20in) s.d. pastel gouache. 18-May-3 Eric Pillon, Calais #160/R

GANTZ, Ann Cushing (1935-) American
£641 $1000 €962 Caddo Lake (61x91cm-24x36in) 19-Oct-2 David Dike, Dallas #238/R

GANZ, Edwin (1871-1948) Swiss
£728 $1187 €1100 Charrette attelee (37x56cm-15x22in) s. canvas on panel. 17-Feb-3 Horta, Bruxelles #29

GANZ, Julian Johann (1844-1892) Swiss
£513 $805 €800 View of Venice at moonlight (16x22cm-6x9in) s. 19-Nov-2 Servarts Themis, Bruxelles #102

GANZ, Valerie (1936-) British
£2050 $3198 €3075 End of the shift - returning from the coalface (61x75cm-24x30in) s. 11-Sep-2 Bonhams, Newport #301/R est:2000-2500
Works on paper
£280 $465 €406 The Black Mountain (56x69cm-22x27in) s. 10-Jun-3 Peter Francis, Wales #48
£700 $1098 €1050 Preparing for blasting (48x39cm-19x15in) s.d.90 W/C black chk. 20-Nov-2 Sotheby's, Olympia #91/R
£900 $1414 €1350 Seated miner (51x36cm-20x14in) s. black chk. 20-Nov-2 Sotheby's, Olympia #92/R est:1000-1500
£920 $1435 €1380 Swansea docks (81x137cm-32x54in) s.d.75 W/C. 10-Sep-2 Peter Francis, Wales #1
£1000 $1570 €1500 Three miners resting (35x56cm-14x22in) s. chk W/C. 20-Nov-2 Sotheby's, Olympia #90/R est:1000-1500

GANZER, Jim and RUSCHA, Edward (20th C) American
Prints
£2358 $3750 €3537 Sea of desire (25x50cm-10x20in) s.d.num.29/40 col etching aquatint. 2-May-3 Sotheby's, New York #587/R est:4000-6000

GAO QIPEI (?-1734) Chinese
Works on paper
£5051 $8333 €7324 Fish (111x53cm-44x21in) s. ink hanging scroll. 6-Jul-3 Christie's, Hong Kong #454/R est:50000-60000 (HK.D 65000)

GAO YEHOU (1878-1952) Chinese
Works on paper
£813 $1285 €1220 Plum blossom (16x55cm-6x22in) s.i. one d.1938 one d.1929 i.verso ink folding fan two. 28-Apr-3 Sotheby's, Hong Kong #555/R est:7000-9000 (HK.D 10000)
£2602 $4111 €3903 Green plum blossom (19x52cm-7x20in) s.i.d.1927 i.verso ink col folding fan. 28-Apr-3 Sotheby's, Hong Kong #531/R est:8000-12000 (HK.D 32000)

GARABEDIAN, Giragos der (1893-?) American
£307 $500 €461 Three fishermen (46x61cm-18x24in) s. 2-Feb-3 Grogan, Boston #61
£437 $700 €634 Rockport fisherman (28x36cm-11x14in) s. i.verso board. 16-May-3 Skinner, Boston #273/R

GARAT, Francis (19th C) French
£1139 $1766 €1800 Animations sur les grands boulevards (33x24cm-13x9in) s.d.1910 panel. 27-Sep-2 Rabourdin & Choppin de Janvry, Paris #53/R est:2000-2200
Works on paper
£308 $483 €480 Treport (25x34cm-10x13in) s. chl W/C. 24-Nov-2 Lesieur & Le Bars, Le Havre #61
£345 $552 €500 Le Carrefour (23x17cm-9x7in) s. crayon W/C. 12-Mar-3 Libert, Castor, Paris #108/R
£690 $1103 €1000 La Place de la Concorde (21x29cm-8x11in) s. W/C. 12-Mar-3 Libert, Castor, Paris #109/R
£897 $1409 €1400 Place de la Concorde (48x59cm-19x23in) s. W/C. 24-Nov-2 Lesieur & Le Bars, Le Havre #60/R

GARATE Y CLAVERO, Juan Jose (1870-1939) Spanish
£1004 $1567 €1506 Female nude outdoors (17x27cm-7x11in) s. panel. 6-Nov-2 Dobiaschofsky, Bern #570/R est:1400 (S.FR 2300)
£1572 $2453 €2500 Venice (70x100cm-28x39in) s.i. 17-Sep-2 Segre, Madrid #104/R
£2581 $4077 €4000 Party (14x21cm-6x8in) s. board. 17-Dec-2 Durán, Madrid #222/R

£4054 $6324 €6000 Village (67x100cm-26x39in) s. 25-Mar-3 Durán, Madrid #197/R

GARAY Y AREVALO, Manuel (19th C) Spanish
£4362 $7023 €6500 Unravelling the plot (43x53cm-17x21in) s. board. 18-Feb-3 Durán, Madrid #218/R

GARBELL, Alexandre (1903-1970) Latvian
£220 $341 €350 Dans Baker Street (55x46cm-22x18in) s. 4-Oct-2 Tajan, Paris #101
£281 $450 €407 Street in Naples (157x79cm-62x31in) s.d. 17-May-3 Selkirks, St. Louis #248
£327 $519 €480 Scene du rue a Paris (50x61cm-20x24in) s. 26-Feb-3 Artcurial Briest, Paris #194/R
£353 $554 €550 Plage cristaline, Etretat (53x67cm-21x26in) painted c.1950. 24-Nov-2 Chayette & Cheval, Paris #260
£353 $554 €550 Plage du Treport (73x90cm-29x35in) painted c.1962. 24-Nov-2 Chayette & Cheval, Paris #265
£385 $604 €600 Copenhague (27x46cm-11x18in) painted c.1952. 24-Nov-2 Chayette & Cheval, Paris #259
£409 $650 €614 Harbour scene (51x74cm-20x29in) painted c.1955 prov. 2-Mar-3 Toomey, Oak Park #829/R
£417 $654 €650 Baigneuses (50x74cm-20x29in) painted c.1936. 24-Nov-2 Chayette & Cheval, Paris #255
£426 $711 €600 La passerelle (65x81cm-26x32in) s. painted c.1940. 23-Jun-3 Delvaux, Paris #131/R
£641 $1006 €1000 Treport sur la plage (65x100cm-26x39in) s. painted c.1935. 24-Nov-2 Chayette & Cheval, Paris #257
£705 $1107 €1100 Garage azur (60x92cm-24x36in) s. painted c.1947. 24-Nov-2 Chayette & Cheval, Paris #256
£755 $1170 €1200 Une gare (80x65cm-31x26in) s. 4-Oct-2 Tajan, Paris #99
£833 $1308 €1300 Odette a la mandoline (65x80cm-26x31in) painted c.1944. 24-Nov-2 Chayette & Cheval, Paris #254/R
£1000 $1630 €1500 Composition (64x54cm-25x21in) s.d.55. 3-Feb-3 Sotheby's, Olympia #196/R est:1000-1500

GARBER, Daniel (1880-1958) American
£5484 $8500 €8226 Portrait of Roy Lynde (76x63cm-30x25in) prov. 8-Dec-2 Freeman, Philadelphia #145/R est:10000-15000
£32468 $50000 €48702 Winter landscape (71x91cm-28x36in) prov. 24-Oct-2 Shannon's, Milford #69/R est:50000-75000
£96774 $150000 €145161 Frog hollow (45x49cm-18x19in) s. prov. 8-Dec-2 Freeman, Philadelphia #138/R est:75000-100000

GARBIERI, Lorenzo (attrib) (1580-1654) Italian
£1800 $3006 €2610 Saint Irene nursing Saint Sebastian (32x34cm-13x13in) slate arched top. 9-Jul-3 Bonhams, New Bond Street #162/R est:2000-3000

GARBO, Raffaellino del (c.1476-1524) Italian
£80000 $125600 €120000 Annunciation (58x91cm-23x36in) panel prov.exhib.lit. 11-Dec-2 Christie's, London #90/R est:30000-40000

GARBUZ, Yair (1945-) Israeli
Works on paper
£2532 $4000 €3798 Untitled (130x88cm-51x35in) mixed media on canvas painted 1971-72. 27-Apr-3 Sotheby's, Tel Aviv #76/R est:5000-7000

GARCIA ASARTA, Inocencio (1862-1921) Spanish
£641 $1013 €1000 Portrait of a friend (19x15cm-7x6in) lit. 19-Nov-2 Durán, Madrid #64/R

GARCIA BARRENA, Carmelo (1926-) Spanish
£2123 $3312 €3100 Yellow huts (50x58cm-20x23in) s. s.i.verso. 8-Apr-3 Ansorena, Madrid #205/R

GARCIA ERGUIN, Ignacio (1934-) Spanish
£507 $791 €750 Hat with flowers (18x20cm-7x8in) s. paper. 25-Mar-3 Durán, Madrid #109/R

GARCIA ESCARRE, Francesc (1871-?) Spanish
£334 $532 €485 Still life of fruit (37x45cm-15x18in) s. board. 4-Mar-3 Ansorena, Madrid #5/R
£345 $548 €500 Still life of fruit (37x45cm-15x18in) s. board. 4-Mar-3 Ansorena, Madrid #6/R

GARCIA MARTINEZ, Emilio (1875-1950) Spanish
£411 $641 €600 Woman with mask (15x30cm-6x12in) s.i.d.1901 paper. 8-Apr-3 Ansorena, Madrid #137/R

GARCIA MORALES, Antonio (1910-) Spanish
Works on paper
£448 $713 €650 Portrait of woman (65x54cm-26x21in) s. 4-Mar-3 Ansorena, Madrid #318/R

GARCIA OCHOA, Luis (1920-) Spanish
Works on paper
£252 $392 €400 Nude mad woman (36x27cm-14x11in) s. dr. 8-Oct-2 Ansorena, Madrid #487/R
£293 $474 €445 Card game (30x43cm-12x17in) ink dr. 21-Jan-3 Ansorena, Madrid #805/R
£479 $748 €700 Landscape (32x48cm-13x19in) s. felt-tip pen dr. 8-Apr-3 Ansorena, Madrid #675/R
£789 $1279 €1200 Rocky landscape (47x33cm-19x13in) s. W/C. 21-Jan-3 Ansorena, Madrid #6/R

GARCIA PANADERO, Manuel (1899-1978) Spanish
£252 $392 €400 Seascape at Cabo de Palos (73x100cm-29x39in) s. 8-Oct-2 Ansorena, Madrid #405/R

GARCIA PATINO, Antonio (1932-) Spanish
Works on paper
£414 $658 €600 Urban landscape (33x24cm-13x9in) s. s.i.verso mixed media. 4-Mar-3 Ansorena, Madrid #252/R

GARCIA REINO, Oscar (1910-1993) Uruguayan
£446 $700 €669 Boats (50x61cm-20x24in) s. 20-Nov-2 Galleria Y Remates, Montevideo #52/R
£462 $720 €693 Julita (46x36cm-18x14in) s. fabric prov. 30-Jul-2 Galleria Y Remates, Montevideo #36/R
£510 $800 €765 Lady in orange (45x36cm-18x14in) s. 20-Nov-2 Galleria Y Remates, Montevideo #51/R
£513 $800 €770 Joven (65x50cm-26x20in) s. acrillio paper. 30-Jul-2 Galleria Y Remates, Montevideo #110/R
£513 $800 €770 Profile (45x37cm-18x15in) s. acrylic. 10-Oct-2 Galleria Y Remates, Montevideo #82/R
£629 $1000 €944 Boats (44x64cm-17x25in) s. paper. 2-Mar-3 Galleria Y Remates, Montevideo #95/R

GARCIA SAUCO, Guillermo (?) Spanish
£428 $693 €650 Landscape (150x40cm-59x16in) enamel panel. 21-Jan-3 Durán, Madrid #682

GARCIA VILELLA, Francisco (1922-) Spanish
£331 $540 €500 Untitled (62x90cm-24x35in) s.d.1967. 11-Feb-3 Segre, Madrid #204/R

GARCIA Y HISPALETO, Manuel (1836-1898) Spanish
£1006 $1570 €1600 Monk (39x26cm-15x10in) s. 23-Sep-2 Durán, Madrid #145/R
Works on paper
£1689 $2635 €2500 Lady and toreador (66x46cm-26x18in) s. W/C cardboard. 25-Mar-3 Durán, Madrid #189/R est:1700

GARCIA Y RAMOS, F (19th C) ?
£774 $1200 €1161 Portrait of a woman seated in a landscape (74x53cm-29x21in) s. 7-Dec-2 Selkirks, St. Louis #741 est:500-600

GARCIA Y RAMOS, Jose (1852-1912) Spanish
£9875 $15010 €14813 Retrato de dama Espanola con mantilla (68x50cm-27x20in) s. 3-Jul-2 Naón & Cia, Buenos Aires #21/R est:13000-15000
£11321 $17660 €18000 Spanish children playing in the street (28x18cm-11x7in) s. board. 23-Sep-2 Durán, Madrid #229/R est:15000
£15000 $23550 €22500 La corrida de toros (122x94cm-48x37in) s. 19-Nov-2 Bonhams, New Bond Street #108/R est:15000-20000
Works on paper
£1711 $2771 €2600 Blade sharpener (29x49cm-11x19in) s.i. wash. 21-Jan-3 Ansorena, Madrid #48/R
£1923 $3038 €3000 Fruit seller (18x28cm-7x11in) s. gouache. 14-Nov-2 Arte, Seville #324/R

GARCIA Y RODRIGUEZ, Manuel (1863-1925) Spanish
£873 $1275 €1310 Paseo, Sevilla (19x8cm-7x3in) s.d.1899 canvas on board. 4-Jun-2 Germann, Zurich #766 est:1000-1500 (S.FR 2000)
£1800 $2826 €2700 Quiet stroll (9x19cm-4x7in) s.d.99 board. 19-Nov-2 Sotheby's, London #192/R est:2000-3000
£2260 $3526 €3300 Landscape (34x42cm-13x17in) s.d.1901 cardboard. 8-Apr-3 Ansorena, Madrid #246/R
£2564 $4051 €4000 Sevillan garden (26x34cm-10x13in) s.i.d.1917 board. 13-Nov-2 Ansorena, Madrid #173/R
£3448 $5448 €5000 Bread seller with donkey (35x25cm-14x10in) s.d.1904. 1-Apr-3 Segre, Madrid #109/R est:5000
£3548 $5606 €5500 Just outside the village (23x33cm-9x13in) s.d.97 board. 17-Dec-2 Durán, Madrid #186/R
£4483 $7083 €6500 View of beach in Sanlucar de Barrameda (29x45cm-11x18in) s.d.1913 board. 7-Apr-3 Castellana, Madrid #67/R est:3000
£10063 $15698 €16000 Patio in Seville (52x62cm-20x24in) s.i.d.1924. 23-Sep-2 Durán, Madrid #256/R

£11637 $18852 €16874 On the patio (39x28cm-15x11in) s.i.d.1905. 26-May-3 Bukowskis, Stockholm #259/R est:20000-25000 (S.KR 150000)
£15000 $23550 €22500 Un patio Sevillno - Sevillian courtyard (56x70cm-22x28in) s.d.1925. 19-Nov-2 Sotheby's, London #60/R est:15000-20000
£28000 $43960 €42000 Jardines de Sevilla - gardens in Seville (39x31cm-15x12in) s.d.1905 board. 19-Nov-2 Sotheby's, London #61/R est:25000-35000

Works on paper

£9000 $14130 €13500 Paisaje junto al rio - river landscape (64x62cm-25x24in) s.i. W/C gouache paper on board. 19-Nov-2 Sotheby's, London #78/R est:8000-12000

GARCIA, Daniel (1958-) Argentinian

£2229 $3500 €3344 Red Hood (150x150cm-59x59in) s.verso acrylic painted 1997 prov.exhib. 20-Nov-2 Christie's, Rockefeller NY #161/R

GARCIA, Juan Gil (1879-1931) Cuban

£346 $540 €550 Still life of fruit and roses (59x97cm-23x38in) s. 17-Sep-2 Segre, Madrid #55/R

GARCIA, Mario (1927-) American

£252 $390 €400 Composition (50x61cm-20x24in) s.d.60 verso. 5-Oct-2 De Vuyst, Lokeren #152

GARCIA-SEVILLA, Ferran (1949-) Spanish

£10993 $17809 €15500 Cima 2 (195x195cm-77x77in) s.verso exhib. 20-May-3 Segre, Madrid #171/R est:14500
£11724 $18524 €17000 Letter G, black tree (150x150cm-59x59in) s.verso oil mixed media prov.exhib.lit. 1-Apr-3 Segre, Madrid #201/R est:13000

GARCIN, Louis Marius (1821-1898) French

£4054 $6324 €6000 Promenade en gondole a Venise (81x126cm-32x50in) s.d.1853. 28-Mar-3 Claude Aguttes, Neuilly #54/R

GARDELL-ERICSON, Anna (1853-1939) Swedish

Works on paper

£309 $513 €448 Fishing huts at sunset (24x17cm-9x7in) s. W/C. 16-Jun-3 Lilla Bukowskis, Stockholm #1061 (S.KR 4000)
£339 $532 €509 Water carrier (30x22cm-12x9in) s. W/C. 16-Dec-2 Lilla Bukowskis, Stockholm #93 (S.KR 4800)
£371 $615 €538 Landscape with watercourse (21x28cm-8x11in) s. W/C. 16-Jun-3 Lilla Bukowskis, Stockholm #78 (S.KR 4800)
£423 $665 €635 Lake landscape with woman in rowing boat (50x34cm-20x13in) s. W/C. 16-Dec-2 Lilla Bukowskis, Stockholm #437 (S.KR 6000)
£550 $902 €798 Sailing boats at Marstrand Bay, twilight (24x18cm-9x7in) s. W/C. 4-Jun-3 AB Stockholms Auktionsverk #2273/R (S.KR 7000)
£707 $1159 €1025 Breakers and rocky coast, evening light (35x26cm-14x10in) s. W/C. 4-Jun-3 AB Stockholms Auktionsverk #2272/R (S.KR 9000)
£776 $1257 €1125 Girls by waterway (34x49cm-13x19in) s. W/C. 25-May-3 Uppsala Auktionskammare, Uppsala #211/R (S.KR 10000)
£780 $1209 €1170 Coastal landscape, Marstrand (20x37cm-8x15in) s.i.d.24 aug.95 W/C. 3-Dec-2 Bukowskis, Stockholm #143/R (S.KR 11000)
£842 $1330 €1263 Garden scene with grinder (30x42cm-12x17in) s. W/C htd white. 30-Nov-2 Goteborg Auktionsverk, Sweden #212/R (S.KR 12000)
£917 $1440 €1376 Landscape, Klockareangen, Koon (30x44cm-12x17in) s. W/C. 16-Dec-2 Lilla Bukowskis, Stockholm #412 (S.KR 13000)
£1135 $1759 €1703 Wooded landscape with young girl (46x29cm-18x11in) s. W/C. 8-Dec-2 Uppsala Auktionskammare, Uppsala #145/R est:15000-20000 (S.KR 16000)
£1474 $2388 €2137 On the quay, Marstrand (34x49cm-13x19in) s. W/C. 26-May-3 Bukowskis, Stockholm #82/R est:25000-30000 (S.KR 19000)
£1699 $2820 €2464 Woman on green steps (50x35cm-20x14in) s. W/C. 16-Jun-3 Lilla Bukowskis, Stockholm #812 est:15000-18000 (S.KR 22000)
£2128 $3298 €3192 Summer's day, Marstrand (35x49cm-14x19in) s. W/C. 8-Dec-2 Uppsala Auktionskammare, Uppsala #144/R est:35000-40000 (S.KR 30000)
£4112 $6661 €5962 Summer landscape from Bohuslan's skerries (50x98cm-20x39in) s. W/C. 25-May-3 Uppsala Auktionskammare, Uppsala #209/R est:40000-50000 (S.KR 53000)

GARDEN, William Fraser (1856-1921) British

Works on paper

£600 $978 €900 Children playing on a riverside meadow (18x25cm-7x10in) s. W/C. 14-Feb-3 Keys, Aylsham #634/R
£820 $1304 €1230 Tranquil river landscape with distant church spire (15x27cm-6x11in) s.d.1894 W/C. 30-Apr-3 Hampton & Littlewood, Exeter #448/R
£960 $1517 €1392 Raven Toll, Asburnham (26x37cm-10x15in) s.d.1883 W/C. 22-Jul-3 Bristol Auction Rooms #321/R
£1000 $1600 €1500 Pike and Eel Inn near Needingworth, Huntingdonshire (19x28cm-7x11in) s.d.1910 W/C. 11-Mar-3 Bonhams, New Bond Street #123/R est:1000-1500
£1000 $1630 €1450 Fenland Lane with pollarded willows and other trees (26x37cm-10x15in) W/C htd white. 17-Jul-3 Tennants, Leyburn #730/R est:600-800
£1320 $2059 €1980 Calm mill pool (18x27cm-7x11in) s.d.92 W/C. 15-Oct-2 Bearnes, Exeter #367/R est:800-1200
£4100 $6396 €6150 Trees reflected in the river (28x18cm-11x7in) s. W/C pair. 11-Apr-3 Keys, Aylsham #601/R est:2500-3500

GARDENIER, Jean Jacques (1930-) Dutch

£276 $448 €420 Harbour of L'Estagne (65x92cm-26x36in) s.d.68. 21-Jan-3 Christie's, Amsterdam #420
£390 $632 €550 Autumn still life (64x84cm-25x33in) panel exhib. 26-May-3 Glerum, Amsterdam #48

GARDET, Georges (1863-1939) French

Sculpture

£1164 $1816 €1700 Lione et tortue (20x46cm-8x18in) s.st.f.Siot green pat bronze. 14-Apr-3 Horta, Bruxelles #119 est:1300-1800
£2000 $3120 €3000 Standing lamb (47x33cm-19x13in) s.st.f.Siot brown pat bronze. 9-Apr-3 Sotheby's, London #189/R est:2000-3000

GARDIER, Raoul du (1871-1952) French

£6962 $11000 €11000 Enfants jouant dans la mer (65x10cm-26x4in) s. 26-Nov-2 Camard, Paris #70/R est:7600
£32432 $50595 €48000 Elegante sur la plage (50x52cm-20x20in) s. panel. 28-Mar-3 Delvaux, Paris #22/R est:12000-15000

Works on paper

£11724 $18641 €17000 Dechargement du bateau au Maroc (99x80cm-39x31in) s. gouache W/C paper on canvas. 8-Mar-3 Peron, Melun #18

GARDINER, Frank Joseph Henry (1942-) British

Works on paper

£988 $1600 €1433 American clipper Abner Coburn (38x56cm-15x22in) s. W/C gouache. 29-Jul-3 Christie's, Rockefeller NY #114/R est:800-1200

GARDINER, Gerald (1902-) British

£450 $702 €675 Coastal scene, possibly at Lulworth Cove, Dorset (59x48cm-23x19in) init.d.1949 prov. 25-Mar-3 Bonhams, Leeds #573/R

Works on paper

£340 $541 €510 Winter stacks (20x35cm-8x14in) init.d.1947 gouache. 26-Feb-3 Sotheby's, Olympia #208/R

GARDINER, Stanley (1888-1952) British

£300 $468 €450 Pool in the rocks near Lamorna (31x39cm-12x15in) s. i.verso panel. 17-Sep-2 Bonhams, Sevenoaks #193
£560 $874 €840 Still life (61x51cm-24x20in) s. 15-Oct-2 Canterbury Auctions, UK #133
£600 $930 €900 Pool in the Rocks in Lamorna (31x39cm-12x15in) s. board. 4-Dec-2 Christie's, Kensington #448/R
£700 $1085 €1050 Expansive sunlit valley (157x191cm-62x75in) s. 26-Sep-2 Lane, Penzance #319
£700 $1127 €1050 In a Cornish valley (86x100cm-34x39in) s. board. 15-Jan-3 Cheffins Grain & Comins, Cambridge #450/R
£2700 $4509 €3915 In a Cornish valley (86x102cm-34x40in) s. board. 19-Jun-3 Lane, Penzance #70/R est:1800-2500

GARDNER, Alexander (1821-1882) American

Photographs

£13462 $21000 €20193 Abraham Lincoln and his son Tad (43x33cm-17x13in) st.sig. albumen print. 14-Oct-2 Butterfields, San Francisco #1392/R est:2000-3000

GARDNER, Daniel (1750-1805) British

£4500 $7470 €6750 Portrait of a gentleman in a brown coat, holding a hat, in a wooded landscape (53x46cm-21x18in) feigned oval prov. 10-Jun-3 Christie's, London #37/R est:3000-5000

Works on paper

£300 $486 €450 Portrait of John Corbet, half length (22x18cm-9x7in) pencil pastel bodycol oval. 23-Jan-3 Christie's, Kensington #289/R

GARDNER, Daniel (attrib) (1750-1805) British

Works on paper

£1000 $1560 €1500 Two children and their pet dog in a wood (42x52cm-17x20in) pastel. 10-Apr-3 Tennants, Leyburn #813/R est:1000-1500

GARDNER, Derek George Montague (1914-) British
Works on paper
£350 $546 €525 His Britannic Majesty' frigate Castor (15x23cm-6x9in) s.i.d.1991 W/C. 23-Apr-3 Rupert Toovey, Partridge Green #19

GARDNER, Sandi (20th C) British?
£300 $468 €450 Black and gold (155x155cm-61x61in) s. 13-Sep-2 Lyon & Turnbull, Edinburgh #82/R

GARDNER, Sandy (20th C) British?
Works on paper
£900 $1395 €1350 Portrait of a woman (38x28cm-15x11in) s. chl. 4-Dec-2 Christie's, Kensington #8

GARDNER, William Biscombe (c.1847-1919) British
Works on paper
£1100 $1782 €1650 Mowers near Tunbridge Wells (26x17cm-10x7in) s. W/C. 20-May-3 Sotheby's, Olympia #11/R est:800-1200

GARDUNO, Alberto (1885-1948) Uruguayan
£755 $1200 €1133 Valley of the volcanoes (21x26cm-8x10in) s. board. 7-Mar-3 Skinner, Boston #358/R

GARDUNO, Flor (1957-) South American
Photographs
£6051 $9500 €9077 Untitled. s.i.d. silver gelatin print set of 4 prov. 19-Nov-2 Sotheby's, New York #49/R est:15000

GAREL, Philippe (1945-) French
Sculpture
£1026 $1610 €1600 Homage to Rembrandt (62x28x17cm-24x11x7in) s.d.1989 num.2/12 green pat bronze. 15-Dec-2 Perrin, Versailles #128/R

GARELICK, Harry (20th C) American
£875 $1400 €1313 Blue harlequin (30x25cm-12x10in) 14-Mar-3 Du Mouchelle, Detroit #2136/R

GAREMYN, Jan Anton (1712-1799) Flemish
Works on paper
£850 $1335 €1275 Four studies of hands. Head of a man (25x18cm-10x7in) d.April 1732 red chk double-sided. 11-Dec-2 Sotheby's, Olympia #229/R

GAREMYN, Jan Anton (attrib) (1712-1799) Flemish
£5634 $9352 €8000 Le marche aux legumes (99x160cm-39x63in) 15-Jun-3 Anaf, Lyon #93/R est:8000-10000

GARF, Salomon (1879-?) Dutch
£290 $461 €420 Sleeping bird (8x22cm-3x9in) s. panel. 10-Mar-3 Sotheby's, Amsterdam #195

GARFINKIEL, David (1902-1970) Polish
£476 $757 €700 L'ours et la poupee (65x53cm-26x21in) s.d.50 prov. 26-Feb-3 Artcurial Briest, Paris #195/R

GARGALLO, Pablo (1881-1934) Spanish
Sculpture
£1026 $1621 €1600 Head of D Rafael Lapesa (40x33cm-16x13in) s. stone relief. 13-Nov-2 Ansorena, Madrid #869/R
£21519 $34000 €34000 Bain de soleil (25x29x47cm-10x11x19in) s. num.EA3/3 brown pat bronze exec.1932 lit. 27-Nov-2 Marc Kohn, Paris #34/R est:45000-55000
£27848 $44000 €44000 Jeune fille espagnole (37x30x25cm-15x12x10in) s. num.EA1/3 black pat bronze Cast Godard lit. 27-Nov-2 Marc Kohn, Paris #32/R est:45000-60000

GARIBALDI, Joseph (1863-?) French
£4610 $7468 €6500 La halte au riad (43x56cm-17x22in) s. 23-May-3 Camard, Paris #64/R est:6500-7500
£8500 $13515 €12750 Le port de Marseille (54x65cm-21x26in) s. 20-Mar-3 Christie's, Kensington #81/R est:8000-12000

GARIBBO, Alberte (20th C) American?
Works on paper
£272 $400 €408 Sutra (91x66cm-36x26in) s.i.d.1989 verso mixed media. 23-Jun-2 Susanin's, Chicago #5084/R

GARIN, Louis (1888-1959) French
£2958 $4762 €4200 Thoniers a l'ancre (120x60cm-47x24in) s. 11-May-3 Thierry & Lannon, Brest #180 est:4000-4500
Works on paper
£767 $1189 €1220 Coin de marche (26x28cm-10x11in) s.i.d.1921 W/C. 6-Oct-2 Livinec, Gaudcheau & Jezequel, Rennes #19a/R

GARINOZ, A (19/20th C) ?
£1154 $1823 €1800 Femme tenant un chien (75x38cm-30x15in) s.d.1900. 18-Nov-2 Tajan, Paris #164 est:1500-1800

GARLAND, A (19th C) British
£1277 $2068 €1800 Mountainous lake scene with sheep in foreground (75x126cm-30x50in) 20-May-3 Mealy's, Castlecomer #968/R est:1200-1800

GARLAND, H (19th C) British
£1509 $2340 €2400 Boys playing in the street (35x46cm-14x18in) s. 29-Oct-2 Dorotheum, Vienna #265/R est:2400-2600

GARLAND, Henry (fl.1854-1900) British
£300 $471 €450 Swan in river landscape (23x38cm-9x15in) prov. 21-Nov-2 Tennants, Leyburn #805
£580 $899 €870 Highland drove (94x171cm-37x67in) s.d.1872 en grisaille. 30-Sep-2 Bonhams, Ipswich #496/R
£3103 $5027 €4499 Resting under the parasol (57x76cm-22x30in) s.d.1867. 26-May-3 Bukowskis, Stockholm #232/R est:20000-25000 (S.KR 40000)
£3900 $6474 €5850 Driving the cattle home (91x71cm-36x28in) s.d.1895 s.i.d.verso. 10-Jun-3 Bonhams, Leeds #180/R est:1800-2500

GARLAND, Henry (attrib) (fl.1854-1900) British
£800 $1232 €1200 Cattle watering in a Highland river (32x47cm-13x19in) bears another sig. indis.i.verso canvasboard. 22-Oct-2 Bonhams, Bath #116

GARLAND, Valentine Thomas (1868-1914) British
£1250 $2038 €1875 Winter sketch at Winnall Moor (21x17cm-8x7in) s. panel. 29-Jan-3 Dreweatt Neate, Newbury #152/R est:1500-2000
£2200 $3432 €3300 Favourite book (33x22cm-13x9in) s. board. 6-Nov-2 Sotheby's, Olympia #161/R est:1500-2000
£8966 $14345 €13000 Puppies at a bowl (39x29cm-15x11in) s. board. 12-Mar-3 James Adam, Dublin #128/R est:1500-2000

GARLIEB, Louise (19th C) Danish
£11392 $18000 €17088 Orange tree, streptocarpus, oleader, a calla lily and cactus flower (120x94cm-47x37in) prov. 23-Apr-3 Christie's, Rockefeller NY #100/R est:20000-30000

GARLING, Frederick (1806-1873) Australian
Works on paper
£358 $545 €537 Waterfall (37x26cm-15x10in) W/C. 27-Aug-2 Goodman, Sydney #233 (A.D 1000)
£920 $1444 €1380 Brig, Christina Captain Saunders leaving Sydney Heads, 1845 (29x43cm-11x17in) W/C. 15-Apr-3 Lawson Menzies, Sydney #138/R est:2000-3000 (A.D 2400)

GARNEAU, Marc (20th C) Canadian
£687 $1071 €1031 Blitz (122x101cm-48x40in) s.i.d.92 verso. 25-Mar-3 Iegor de Saint Hippolyte, Montreal #56 (C.D 1600)

GARNER, Alex John (1897-1995) Canadian
£301 $473 €452 Cottonwood trunks by Kootenay Lake, BC (35x45cm-14x18in) s.i.d.1959 board. 25-Nov-2 Hodgins, Calgary #406/R (C.D 750)

GARNERAY, Ambroise Louis (1783-1857) French
£2102 $3279 €3300 Vue de l'Escaut (38x46cm-15x18in) s. 7-Nov-2 Chochon-Barre & Allardi, Paris #161
£2420 $3776 €3800 Phare dans la tempete (38x46cm-15x18in) s. cardboard. 7-Nov-2 Chochon-Barre & Allardi, Paris #160/R
£5000 $8100 €7500 Battle of Lake Erie, 10th September 1813 (23x46cm-9x18in) panel prov. 22-Jan-3 Bonhams, New Bond Street #317/R est:5000-8000
£5921 $9000 €8882 Sir John Thomas Duckworth's action off Santo Domingo (48x76cm-19x30in) s. 17-Aug-2 North East Auctions, Portsmouth #839/R est:9000-15000
£6000 $9480 €9000 Figures pulling a boat to sea whilst under attack (38x47cm-15x19in) s. 15-Nov-2 Sotheby's, London #54/R est:6000-8000
£6452 $10194 €10000 Vue de Batavia (24x29cm-9x11in) s.d.1817 panel. 18-Dec-2 Piasa, Paris #94/R est:9000

£6500 $10530 €9750 Panorama of Portsmouth harbour (50x99cm-20x39in) 21-May-3 Christie's, Kensington #379/R est:8000-12000
£7000 $11340 €10500 Capture of H.M.S Macedonian by the American frigate United States, 25th October 1812 (23x35cm-9x14in) s. panel prov. 22-Jan-3 Bonhams, New Bond Street #318/R est:5000-8000
£12805 $21000 €19208 View of a tropical port (49x29cm-19x11in) s.d.1817 panel. 29-May-3 Sotheby's, New York #41/R est:8000-12000

GARNEREY, Hippolyte Jean-Baptiste (1787-1858) French
Works on paper
£633 $981 €1000 Voiliers par gros temps (20x36cm-8x14in) s.d.1836 W/C. 27-Sep-2 Rabourdin & Choppin de Janvry, Paris #86

GARNETT, Angelica (1918-) British
£700 $1113 €1050 Still life (46x31cm-18x12in) s. two. 26-Feb-3 Sotheby's, Olympia #252/R

GARNIER, Étienne (1759-1849) French
£2817 $4676 €4000 Portrait du Cardinal Jean Sifrein Maury (133x98cm-52x39in) s.d.1836 sold with an engraving. 16-Jun-3 Claude Aguttes, Neuilly #35/R est:4500

GARNIER, F (?) French
Works on paper
£3500 $5425 €5250 Vue d'un chantier de construction, a coupang sur ile, Timor (27x35cm-11x14in) s.i. pencil brown wash three. 26-Sep-2 Christie's, London #52/R est:3000-5000

GARNIER, François (?-1672) French
£27973 $46714 €40000 Nature morte aux raisins et peches sur un entablement (44x63cm-17x25in) 25-Jun-3 Tajan, Paris #48/R est:40000-50000
£38462 $64231 €55000 Nature morte au panier de cerises et a la coupe de fraises (31x43cm-12x17in) panel lit. 27-Jun-3 Piasa, Paris #22/R est:60000-75000
£80420 $134301 €115000 Nature morte au plat de cerises (31x43cm-12x17in) panel lit. 27-Jun-3 Piasa, Paris #21/R est:120000-150000

GARNIER, Jules Arsene (1847-1889) French
£283 $439 €450 Soldats sur un cheval (41x47cm-16x19in) s. 4-Oct-2 Tajan, Paris #102
£1571 $2577 €2278 Le trio (20x32cm-8x13in) s. panel. 4-Jun-3 AB Stockholms Auktionsverk #2455/R est:22000-25000 (S.KR 20000)
£2975 $4700 €4700 Badinage au bord de l'eau (47x32cm-19x13in) 1-Dec-2 Peron, Melun #24

GARNIER, Pierre (1847-1937) French
Works on paper
£2817 $4676 €4000 Vase de fleurs sur un entablement (78x55cm-31x22in) s. gouache. 15-Jun-3 Anaf, Lyon #94/R est:4000-5000

GAROLERA, Carmen (1955-) Spanish
£419 $663 €650 Red rose (150x150cm-59x59in) s.i.d.97 verso. 17-Dec-2 Durán, Madrid #648/R

GAROUSTE, Gerard (1946-) French
£15646 $24878 €23000 Jeremie et Hananaya (200x160cm-79x63in) s.i.d.1991 exhib.lit. 24-Mar-3 Cornette de St.Cyr, Paris #135/R est:30000
£15646 $24878 €23000 Untitled (162x130cm-64x51in) s.d.1990-91 exhib.lit. 24-Mar-3 Cornette de St.Cyr, Paris #140/R est:25000
£19149 $31979 €27000 Le Qohelet, Salomon (200x180cm-79x71in) s. prov. 18-Jun-3 Pierre Berge, Paris #106/R est:30000-40000
Works on paper
£612 $973 €900 Les choses vont seulement autrement (27x20cm-11x8in) s. ink prov. 24-Mar-3 Cornette de St.Cyr, Paris #137/R
£1944 $3208 €2800 Untitled (31x62cm-12x24in) s. gouache pastel chl exhib.lit. 3-Jul-3 Christie's, Paris #48/R est:2500-3500
£2482 $4145 €3500 Composition (25x32cm-10x13in) s.d.3.6.89 gouache prov. 18-Jun-3 Pierre Berge, Paris #105/R est:4000-5000

GARRALDA, Elias (1926-) Spanish
£1935 $3058 €3000 San Servan Sierra (45x55cm-18x22in) s. s.i.verso. 17-Dec-2 Durán, Madrid #99/R
£1935 $3058 €3000 Landscape in Cerdena (49x61cm-19x24in) s. s.i.verso. 17-Dec-2 Durán, Madrid #98/R

GARRARD, George (1760-1826) British
£3800 $6042 €5700 Earl of Orfords elk from Norway (27x43cm-11x17in) squared for transfer copper. 19-Mar-3 Sotheby's, London #106/R est:2500-3500

GARRAUD, Gabriel Joseph (1807-1880) French
Works on paper
£1565 $2488 €2300 Projet pour plaque a schakos (24x20cm-9x8in) s.i. crayon pen Chinese ink exec.c.1848. 26-Feb-3 Coutau Begarie, Paris #147/R

GARRETT, E Alan (20th C) Canadian
£244 $401 €354 High water mark (40x50cm-16x20in) s.i. acrylic board. 9-Jun-3 Hodgins, Calgary #324/R (C.D 550)

GARRETT, Edmund (1853-1929) American
£538 $850 €807 Landscape with pond (41x51cm-16x20in) s. 17-Nov-2 CRN Auctions, Cambridge #53/R

GARRETT, Thomas Balfour (1879-1952) Australian
Works on paper
£344 $543 €516 Pottery works (24x37cm-9x15in) W/C. 7-Apr-3 Shapiro, Sydney #423/R (A.D 900)
£536 $846 €804 Pink blossom (27x38cm-11x15in) W/C gouache. 18-Nov-2 Joel, Victoria #387 est:1500-2000 (A.D 1500)
£643 $996 €965 Bush shed (21x36cm-8x14in) s. W/C. 29-Oct-2 Lawson Menzies, Sydney #152 (A.D 1800)
£681 $1035 €1022 Bush camp (26x30cm-10x12in) s. W/C prov.exhib. 28-Aug-2 Deutscher-Menzies, Melbourne #312/R (A.D 1900)
£1069 $1689 €1604 Figure approaching a house (23x30cm-9x12in) s. W/C. 2-Apr-3 Christie's, Melbourne #42/R est:2000-3000 (A.D 2800)

GARRIDO, Eduardo Léon (1856-1949) Spanish
£696 $1086 €1100 Le pot de fleurs (22x16cm-9x6in) s. cardboard. 15-Sep-2 Etude Bailleul, Bayeux #56/R
£1300 $2119 €1885 Portrait of a young boy (35x24cm-14x9in) s.d.1889. 16-Jul-3 Sotheby's, Olympia #245/R est:1500-2000
£3019 $4709 €4800 Elegante au bouquet de fleurs rouges (32x23cm-13x9in) s. panel. 9-Oct-2 Lombrail & Teucquam, Paris #1/R
£5200 $8112 €7800 Walk in the country (24x19cm-9x7in) s. panel. 17-Sep-2 Sotheby's, Olympia #266/R est:2500-3500
£8861 $13734 €14000 Mere et enfant devant la plage (60x46cm-24x18in) s. 29-Sep-2 Eric Pillon, Calais #99/R
£9677 $15000 €14516 Leisurely promenade (46x37cm-18x15in) s. panel. 30-Oct-2 Christie's, Rockefeller NY #188/R est:15000-20000
£18065 $28542 €28000 Dance (59x75cm-23x30in) s. board. 18-Dec-2 Ansorena, Madrid #164/R est:24000
Works on paper
£759 $1200 €1200 Pantin et Colombine (33x22cm-13x9in) s. W/C gouache. 26-Nov-2 Palais de Beaux Arts, Brussels #405

GARRIDO, Fernando (19th C) Spanish
£862 $1379 €1250 Untitled (30x21cm-12x8in) s. 11-Mar-3 Castellana, Madrid #26/R

GARRIDO, Louis Edouard (1893-1982) French
£759 $1185 €1200 Pecheur au bord de l'Orne a Thury-Harcourt (61x81cm-24x32in) s. isorel. 15-Sep-2 Etude Bailleul, Bayeux #88/R
£1013 $1580 €1600 Repos apres la moisson (47x61cm-19x24in) s. panel. 15-Sep-2 Etude Bailleul, Bayeux #87/R
£1266 $1975 €2000 Courseulles-sur-Mer, l'avant-port (21x27cm-8x11in) s. isorel. 15-Sep-2 Etude Bailleul, Bayeux #85/R
£1489 $2487 €2100 Le port de Crouseulles sur mer (60x81cm-24x32in) s. panel. 23-Jun-3 Delvaux, Paris #126/R est:2200-2400
£1772 $2765 €2800 Pommiers en fleur (34x40cm-13x16in) s. panel. 15-Sep-2 Etude Bailleul, Bayeux #92/R
£2025 $3159 €3200 St Vaast La Hougue (38x55cm-15x22in) s. i.verso isorel. 15-Sep-2 Etude Bailleul, Bayeux #89/R
£4304 $6714 €6800 Port de St-Vaast-la-Hougue (46x61cm-18x24in) s. isorel. 15-Sep-2 Etude Bailleul, Bayeux #90/R

GARROS, Catherine (1954-) French
£719 $1151 €1000 Plage animee pres de la digue (39x46cm-15x18in) s. 18-May-3 Eric Pillon, Calais #248/R
£759 $1177 €1200 Marche en Provence (46x55cm-18x22in) s. 29-Sep-2 Eric Pillon, Calais #240/R
£1007 $1612 €1400 Le port de Sanary (55x46cm-22x18in) s. 18-May-3 Eric Pillon, Calais #243/R

GARSIDE, Oswald (1879-1942) British
Works on paper
£360 $572 €540 Figures on a riverside path at moonrise (23x61cm-9x24in) s. W/C. 27-Feb-3 Bonhams, Chester #328
£540 $859 €810 Low tide (36x49cm-14x19in) s. W/C. 4-Mar-3 Bearnes, Exeter #336/R
£640 $1018 €960 On the Thames, Barnes - with moored barges (50x37cm-20x15in) s. W/C. 27-Feb-3 Bonhams, Chester #329
£720 $1145 €1080 Fishing boats on the Venetian lagoon (28x47cm-11x19in) s. W/C. 27-Feb-3 Bonhams, Chester #327

GARSIDE, Thomas H (1906-1980) Canadian

£444 $729 €666 Early spring, Laurentians (30x40cm-12x16in) s. 3-Jun-3 Joyner, Toronto #521 est:800-1000 (C.D 1000)

£711 $1166 €1067 Winter landscape with horses and sleighs (21x26cm-8x10in) s. prov. 3-Jun-3 Joyner, Toronto #194/R est:1000-1500 (C.D 1600)

Works on paper

£181 $296 €272 Laurentians (21x26cm-8x10in) s. i. verso pastel. 12-Feb-3 Iegor de Saint Hippolyte, Montreal #83b (C.D 450)

£535 $829 €803 Autumn, riverscape with hillside trees (30x40cm-12x16in) s. pastel prov. 3-Dec-2 Joyner, Toronto #397 est:1200-1500 (C.D 1300)

GARSTIN, Alethea (1894-1978) British

£600 $1002 €870 Mrs Edwin Lascelles with her dog (74x61cm-29x24in) i.verso exhib. 19-Jun-3 Lane, Penzance #80/R

£1600 $2544 €2400 Harbour and shipyard (33x40cm-13x16in) board. 26-Feb-3 Sotheby's, Olympia #244/R est:400-600

Works on paper

£320 $499 €464 Low tide - ducks on an estuary (20x24cm-8x9in) s. W/C. 27-Mar-3 Lane, Penzance #275/R

GARSTIN, Norman (1847-1926) British/Irish

£550 $875 €825 Blacksmiths workshop (25x35cm-10x14in) s.d.1910 board. 5-Mar-3 John Ross, Belfast #60

£750 $1170 €1125 Night scene with bonfire (22x30cm-9x12in) s.d.Aug 8 '87 canvas on board. 17-Sep-2 Bonhams, Knightsbridge #263/R

£950 $1482 €1425 Market, Caudebec (17x12cm-7x5in) s. 7-Nov-2 Bonhams, Cornwall #797

£1100 $1760 €1650 Artist's home Caherconlish, Co Limerick (21x27cm-8x11in) panel. 15-May-3 Christie's, Kensington #184/R est:1200-1800

£4500 $7200 €6750 Breton parade (60x71cm-24x28in) 15-May-3 Christie's, London #39/R est:8000

Works on paper

£280 $437 €406 Breton cottage and garden (236x27cm-93x11in) s. W/C. 27-Mar-3 Lane, Penzance #288

£310 $484 €465 Corner by the church (26x18cm-10x7in) s. W/C. 8-Apr-3 Bearnes, Exeter #537

£600 $936 €900 Landscape with pools (24x29cm-9x11in) s.d.1922 W/C. 10-Oct-2 Rupert Toovey, Partridge Green #1405

£620 $1011 €930 Hayle Estuary (23x28cm-9x11in) s. W/C. 13-Feb-3 David Lay, Penzance #405

£850 $1420 €1233 Street leading to the harbour par Cornwall (27x19cm-11x7in) s. W/C. 19-Jun-3 Lane, Penzance #260/R

£897 $1409 €1400 French town landscape viewed from across river (39x32cm-15x13in) s. W/C over pencil. 19-Nov-2 Whyte's, Dublin #146/R

£3200 $5312 €4640 Washerwomen by a canal (28x23cm-11x9in) s. W/C. 10-Jun-3 David Lay, Penzance #53/R est:1200-1800

GARTHE, William Edward de (?) ?

£207 $322 €344 Untitled - Dock scene (18x23cm-7x9in) s. canvasboard. 13-Apr-3 Levis, Calgary #432/R (C.D 475)

£304 $475 €508 Stormy Atlantic (55x76cm-22x30in) s. s.i.verso canvasboard. 13-Apr-3 Levis, Calgary #431/R (C.D 700)

GARTMANN, A (1876-?) German

£260 $387 €400 Courtyard entrance (50x60cm-20x24in) s.d.1917. 27-Jun-2 Neumeister, Munich #2716/R

GARTMEIER, Hans (1910-1986) Swiss

£472 $746 €708 Tobacco pipe (39x30cm-15x12in) s. masonite. 29-Nov-2 Zofingen, Switzerland #2833 (S.FR 1100)

£602 $969 €873 Old farmer smoking his pipe (59x49cm-23x19in) s. panel. 9-May-3 Dobiaschofsky, Bern #180/R (S.FR 1300)

£648 $1044 €940 Old farmer lighting his pipe (34x26cm-13x10in) s. panel. 9-May-3 Dobiaschofsky, Bern #181/R (S.FR 1400)

£833 $1300 €1250 Pause in the day (49x69cm-19x27in) s. board. 20-Sep-2 Sloan, North Bethesda #367/R est:1000-1500

GARTNER DE LA PENA, Jose (1866-1918) Spanish

£2703 $4216 €4000 Seascape (26x41cm-10x16in) s. 25-Mar-3 Durán, Madrid #706/R est:2750

£5031 $7849 €8000 Malaga harbour (53x82cm-21x32in) s.d.1889. 23-Sep-2 Durán, Madrid #166/R

GARTNER, Adolf (1889-1937) Czechoslovakian

£10326 $16109 €15489 Melancholy (95x70cm-37x28in) 12-Oct-2 Dorotheum, Prague #148/R est:260000-400000 (C.KR 500000)

GARTNER, L (19/20th C) ?

£850 $1343 €1275 Dutch fisherfolk by the sea (79x48cm-31x19in) s. pair. 18-Dec-2 John Nicholson, Haslemere #1222

£1250 $2063 €1813 Waiting the return of the fleet (90x124cm-35x49in) s. 1-Jul-3 Bearnes, Exeter #517/R est:600-900

GARVIE, T Bowman (1859-1944) British

£531 $850 €770 At the beach (30x47cm-12x19in) s.d.34 s.i.verso. 16-May-3 Skinner, Boston #358/R

GARZI, Luigi (1638-1721) Italian

£11538 $18115 €18000 Holy Family with other Saints (150x120cm-59x47in) 14-Dec-2 Artcurial Briest, Paris #15/R est:30000

Works on paper

£420 $600 €630 Standing male nude holding a sword and a shield (52x31cm-20x12in) black red chk. 23-Jan-3 Swann Galleries, New York #104/R

GARZOLINI, Giuseppe (1850-1938) Italian

£603 $977 €850 Autunno in montagna (27x41cm-11x16in) s. i.verso. 22-May-3 Stadion, Trieste #251

£739 $1197 €1000 Veduta di Buttrio (30x50cm-12x20in) s. s.i.verso. 22-May-3 Stadion, Trieste #398/R

£780 $1264 €1100 Una fontana, Spagna. Gabo de Gata, Spagna. s.d.1878 i.verso pair. 22-May-3 Stadion, Trieste #353/R

GARZONI, Giovanna (1600-1670) Italian

£39241 $61215 €62000 Birds (34x27cm-13x11in) tempera W/C vellum set of 6. 19-Oct-2 Semenzato, Venice #492/R est:55000-65000

GASCOIGNE, Rosalie (1917-1999) New Zealander

Prints

£2143 $3300 €3215 Close owly (100x70cm-39x28in) s.d.90 num.XXXVII/XLV screen print. 8-Sep-2 Sotheby's, Melbourne #110/R est:3000-4000 (A.D 6000)

Sculpture

£43825 $71873 €65738 Downbeat (122x79cm-48x31in) s.i.d.1977 verso reflective road signs board prov.exhib. 4-Jun-3 Deutscher-Menzies, Melbourne #22/R est:80000-100000 (A.D 110000)

Works on paper

£5754 $9552 €9803 Find the ball (15x91cm-6x36in) s.verso collage on wood. 10-Jun-3 Shapiro, Sydney #45/R est:10000-15000 (A.D 14500)

£9319 $14165 €13979 Norco cows (35x51cm-14x20in) init.d.76 verso collage wood prov.exhib.lit. 28-Aug-2 Deutscher-Menzies, Melbourne #145/R est:18000-25000 (A.D 26000)

£23657 $35957 €35486 Rose red city 4 (123x179cm-48x70in) s.i.d.1991-93 timber composition board diptych prov.exhib.lit. 28-Aug-2 Deutscher-Menzies, Melbourne #26/R est:70000-100000 (A.D 66000)

£31429 $49343 €47144 Cat tracks (60x55cm-24x22in) s.i.d.1989 verso sawn wood crates plywood prov.exhib.lit. 25-Nov-2 Christie's, Melbourne #39/R est:50000-70000 (A.D 88000)

£103571 $159500 €155357 Streetwise (135x100cm-53x39in) init.d.1986 i.verso reflective road signage on board prov.exhib. 8-Sep-2 Sotheby's, Melbourne #12/R est:200000-300000 (A.D 290000)

GASIOROWSKI, Gerard (1930-1986) French

£642 $988 €1020 Conciergerie de Paris. Coin de la Grande Place, Bruxelles (10x15cm-4x6in) postcard htd acrylic pair. 26-Oct-2 Cornette de St.Cyr, Paris #134/R

£679 $1046 €1080 Font Romeu. Civaux (10x15cm-4x6in) postcard htd acrylic pair. 26-Oct-2 Cornette de St.Cyr, Paris #133/R

£1875 $2981 €2700 La grande tombe (54x81cm-21x32in) s.i.d.1971 verso acrylic. 29-Apr-3 Artcurial Briest, Paris #496/R est:2000-2500

Sculpture

£1042 $1656 €1500 La guerre, tenete de l'armee Canadienne (21x30x25cm-8x12x10in) s. mixed media wood box prov. 29-Apr-3 Artcurial Briest, Paris #497 est:1500-2000

GASKELL, Anna (20th C) American?

Photographs

£2866 $4500 €4299 Lizzie Siddle (20x25cm-8x10in) s.d.verso chromogenic col print. 21-Apr-3 Phillips, New York #25/R est:4000-6000

£17500 $28000 €26250 Untitled no.5 (127x102cm-50x40in) s.d.1996 col coupler print mounted on cintra prov.exhib.lit. 15-May-3 Christie's, Rockefeller NY #338/R est:15000-20000

GASKIN, Arthur Joseph (1862-1928) British

Works on paper

£840 $1302 €1260 Study of head of youth (22x30cm-9x12in) s.d.1891 chk pencil prov. 2-Oct-2 Bonhams, Knowle #31

£5500 $8800 €8250 Head study of a youth (23x30cm-9x12in) s.d.1891 red chk pencil prov.exhib. 11-Mar-3 Bonhams, New Bond Street #67/R est:1000-1500

GASPAR, Cecil (20th C) American

£1807 $3000 €2620 Tilled fields (51x61cm-20x24in) s. i.verso. 11-Jun-3 Butterfields, San Francisco #4342/R est:3000-4000

GASPAR, Victor (?) Belgian?

£278 $442 €400 Sous-bois (65x80cm-26x31in) s. 29-Apr-3 Campo, Vlaamse Kaai #125

GASPARD, Léon (1882-1964) French

£1282 $2013 €2000 Un pont a Nijni (28x31cm-11x12in) s. cardboard. 10-Dec-2 Campo, Vlaamse Kaai #468 est:500-600
£1923 $3000 €2885 Team no.21 Russia (18x18cm-7x7in) 9-Nov-2 Altermann Galleries, Santa Fe #115
£3526 $5500 €5289 Old peasant woman (20x15cm-8x6in) s. indis i. canvas on board prov.lit. 9-Nov-2 Santa Fe Art, Santa Fe #92/R est:8000-10000
£3846 $6000 €5769 Arab street scene (20x20cm-8x8in) s. canvas on board prov.lit. 9-Nov-2 Santa Fe Art, Santa Fe #91/R est:8000-10000
£4167 $6500 €6251 Peking street scene (18x25cm-7x10in) s. oil silk on board prov.lit. 9-Nov-2 Santa Fe Art, Santa Fe #90/R est:8000-12000
£4487 $7000 €6731 Russian peasant lady (25x15cm-10x6in) artist board. 20-Sep-2 Du Mouchelle, Detroit #2019/R est:2500-3000
£7006 $11000 €10509 Winter landscape, Russia (22x27cm-9x11in) s. canvasboard prov. 20-Nov-2 Christie's, Los Angeles #31/R est:6000-8000
£14013 $22000 €21020 Girl in pink shawl (22x34cm-9x13in) s.i.d.1922 canvasboard prov. 20-Nov-2 Christie's, Los Angeles #19/R est:20000-30000
£41935 $65000 €62903 Russian village in winter (27x35cm-11x14in) s.d.1911 canvasboard. 4-Dec-2 Sotheby's, New York #155/R est:30000-50000

Works on paper

£1958 $3250 €2839 Woman and children in a town. Woman and two children (18x15cm-7x6in) s. pencil pastel pair prov. 11-Jun-3 Butterfields, San Francisco #4133/R est:4000-6000

GASPARE DI BENEDETTO DA PESARO (15th C) Italian

£256410 $397436 €400000 Madonna and Child with Saints (121x143cm-48x56in) tempera board polyptych prov.lit. 4-Dec-2 Christie's, Rome #476/R

GASPARI, Luciano (1913-) Italian

£1013 $1580 €1600 Garden 2 (87x110cm-34x43in) s. 19-Oct-2 Semenzato, Venice #139/R

GASQ, Paul Jean Baptiste (1860-1944) French

Sculpture

£1399 $2336 €2000 Berger et mouton (70cm-28in) s. brown pat bronze. 25-Jun-3 Artcurial Briest, Paris #43/R est:900-1000

GASSAR, F (19th C) ?

Sculpture

£2378 $3900 €3567 Hunting dogs attacking a grizzly bear (79x43cm-31x17in) s.i. bronze oval base. 8-Feb-3 Neal Auction Company, New Orleans #512/R est:1200-2000

GASSER, Henry (1909-1981) American

Works on paper

£409 $650 €614 Western wall (18x27cm-7x11in) s.i. W/C. 7-Mar-3 Skinner, Boston #544/R
£625 $1000 €938 Boats at dock (20x28cm-8x11in) s. W/C. 11-Jan-3 James Julia, Fairfield #437 est:800-1200
£769 $1200 €1154 Laundry line (19x23cm-7x9in) s.i. W/C. 9-Nov-2 Sloan, North Bethesda #546/R
£796 $1250 €1194 Sandy beach with red fishing shanty and other buildings (20x25cm-8x10in) s. W/C. 19-Apr-3 James Julia, Fairfield #263/R
£1125 $1800 €1631 Bay Side village with rolling hills (55x74cm-22x29in) s. W/C with tooling graphite. 16-May-3 Skinner, Boston #204/R est:2500-3500
£1558 $2400 €2337 Parisian street scenes (22x19cm-9x7in) s.i. W/C gouache three. 4-Sep-2 Christie's, Rockefeller NY #348/R est:1200-1800

GASSER, Leonardo (1831-?) Italian

£3500 $5845 €5250 Thoughtful moment (56x46cm-22x18in) s.d.1871. 18-Jun-3 Christie's, Kensington #111/R est:2500-3500

GASSIES, Jean Baptiste Georges (1829-1919) French

£786 $1226 €1179 Lake Katrine (18x27cm-7x11in) s.d.1884 panel prov. 9-Nov-2 Galerie Gloggner, Luzern #59/R (S.FR 1800)

GASSIES, Jean Bruno (1786-1832) French

£1899 $3000 €2849 Boy in an interior with a top hat (46x37cm-18x15in) prov. 1-Apr-3 Christie's, Rockefeller NY #361/R est:3000-5000

GASTALDI, Andrea (1826-1889) Italian

£6129 $9500 €9194 Duke d'este mourning death (199x240cm-78x94in) 29-Oct-2 Sotheby's, New York #30/R est:15000-20000

GASTAUD, Pierre (1920-) French

£282 $446 €423 Abstract (61x38cm-24x15in) s. 18-Nov-2 Waddingtons, Toronto #221/R (C.D 700)
£641 $1006 €1000 Z6 (81x100cm-32x39in) s. s.i.d.62 verso. 24-Nov-2 Laurence Calmels, Paris #133/R
£769 $1208 €1200 Vibrations interieures (74x47cm-29x19in) s.d.60 s.i.d.verso. 24-Nov-2 Laurence Calmels, Paris #134/R
£962 $1510 €1500 Untitled (73x92cm-29x36in) s.i. 24-Nov-2 Laurence Calmels, Paris #132/R

GASTE, Constant Georges (1869-1910) French

£1352 $2082 €2150 Portrait d'arabe barbu (35x26cm-14x10in) s.i.d.1903 panel. 27-Oct-2 Muizon & Le Coent, Paris #34/R

GASTEIGER, Anna Sophie (1878-1954) German

£323 $500 €485 Floral still life (66x56cm-26x22in) s. painted c.1920. 8-Dec-2 Toomey, Oak Park #624/R
£548 $850 €822 Floral still life (46x56cm-18x22in) s. painted c.1920. 8-Dec-2 Toomey, Oak Park #702/R
£1410 $2144 €2200 Colourful petunias (65x82cm-26x32in) s. 11-Jul-2 Hugo Ruef, Munich #662/R est:2200
£1603 $2436 €2500 Still life of corn poppies in a vase (60x46cm-24x18in) s. lit. 11-Jul-2 Allgauer, Kempten #2488/R

GASTEIGER, Jacob (1953-) Austrian

£1772 $2747 €2800 Untitled (87x87cm-34x34in) s.i.d.2000 verso acrylic. 24-Sep-2 Wiener Kunst Auktionen, Vienna #299/R est:2500-3500

GASTEMANS, Émile (1883-1956) Belgian

£382 $603 €550 Villageois devant un chateau (59x59cm-23x23in) cardboard. 28-Apr-3 Amberes, Antwerp #282
£1497 $2380 €2200 Landscape in Andalusia with farmer and bulls near city (101x110cm-40x43in) s. 24-Mar-3 Bernaerts, Antwerp #191/R est:3000-3700
£2177 $3461 €3200 Women at work in docks (60x80cm-24x31in) s.d.1926. 24-Mar-3 Bernaerts, Antwerp #181/R est:3000-4000

Works on paper

£314 $484 €500 Danseuse Espagnole (48x64cm-19x25in) s. W/C. 22-Oct-2 Campo, Vlaamse Kaai #506

GASTINE, Camille Auguste (1819-1867) French

Works on paper

£439 $685 €650 Etude pour la visitation (45x30cm-18x12in) crayon htd gouache prov. 31-Mar-3 Piasa, Paris #90/R

GASTINEAU, Henry (1791-1876) British

Works on paper

£250 $398 €375 Sugar loaf. Skyrrid Mountains, Monmouthshire (9x14cm-4x6in) sepia wash dr. 6-Mar-3 Clevedon Sale Rooms #515
£260 $434 €377 Curling pond, Fascally (20x30cm-8x12in) init. W/C. 24-Jun-3 Bonhams, Knightsbridge #125
£350 $557 €525 View near Rhaidyr, Rednorshire. Abbey Church, Neath (9x14cm-4x6in) sepia wash dr pair. 6-Mar-3 Clevedon Sale Rooms #512
£450 $716 €675 Crickhowel Castle, Brecknockshire. Kilgerran Castle, Pembrokeshire (9x14cm-4x6in) sepia wash dr pair. 6-Mar-3 Clevedon Sale Rooms #514
£500 $795 €750 Caercennin Castle, Caermarthenshire. Harbour entrance Fishguard (9x14cm-4x6in) sepia wash dr pair. 6-Mar-3 Clevedon Sale Rooms #513
£550 $897 €798 Easby Abbey on the Swale (19x27cm-7x11in) W/C scratching out over pencil. 21-Jul-3 Bonhams, Bath #4/R
£650 $1034 €975 Margam Church, Glamorganshire. Cloisters of Margam Abbey (9x14cm-4x6in) sepia wash dr pair. 6-Mar-3 Clevedon Sale Rooms #509/R
£650 $1034 €975 Remains of Llandaff Castle, Glamorganshire. Remains of the Priory (9x14cm-4x6in) sepia wash dr pair. 6-Mar-3 Clevedon Sale Rooms #511
£680 $1081 €1020 Kenarth Bridge on the Teify, Cardinganshire. Builth, Breconshire (9x14cm-4x6in) sepia wash dr pair. 6-Mar-3 Clevedon Sale Rooms #508/R

£850 $1352 €1275 Town Hall, Llantwit Major, Glamorganshire. Ostermouth Castle (9x14cm-4x6in) sepia wash dr pair. 6-Mar-3 Clevedon Sale Rooms #510/R

£1800 $2952 €2700 Park near Middleham Castle, Yorkshire, King Henry VI, part III, act IV, scene V (26x37cm-10x15in) s.d.1840 i.verso W/C. 4-Feb-3 Bonhams, Leeds #286 est:600-800

£2600 $4264 €3900 Grange, Cumberland (61x91cm-24x36in) s.d.1855 pencil W/C. 4-Feb-3 Bonhams, Leeds #285 est:1200-1800

GASTINI, Marco (1938-) Italian

Sculpture

£1935 $3058 €3000 February 15th. Acireale plan (65x65x2cm-26x26x1in) s.i.d.72 verso acrylic plexiglas two prov. 18-Dec-2 Christie's, Rome #204/R

GASTO, Pedro (1908-1997) Spanish

£774 $1223 €1200 Blue actor (49x34cm-19x13in) s. board. 18-Dec-2 Ansorena, Madrid #226/R

GASTON, Roy (?) British?

Works on paper

£550 $803 €825 Shane's Castle, Co. Antrim (38x51cm-15x20in) s. W/C. 12-Jun-2 John Ross, Belfast #192

GATAULINA, Mileuscha Ravilevna (1971-) Balkan

£371 $579 €557 Chrysanthemums (70x65cm-28x26in) mono. s.i. verso. 6-Nov-2 Dobiaschofsky, Bern #3369/R (S.FR 850)

GATCH, Lee (1902-1968) American

£671 $1100 €973 Classic (20x69cm-8x27in) s.i. canvasboard prov. 1-Jun-3 Wright, Chicago #178/R est:2000-3000

GATCHEEF, Alexi Peterovitch (?) Russian?

Sculpture

£1563 $2500 €2345 Sculpture (28x28cm-11x11in) bronze. 10-Jan-3 Du Mouchelle, Detroit #1045/R est:2500-3500

GATERMANN, Karl (1883-1959) German

£418 $647 €660 Lubeck in the snow (51x67cm-20x26in) s.d.19 board. 28-Sep-2 Hans Stahl, Hamburg #113/R

GATKE, Heinrich (19th C) ?

Works on paper

£282 $437 €440 Rowing boat making its way towards sailing ship (11x16cm-4x6in) s.d. pencil htd white. 7-Dec-2 Ketterer, Hamburg #11/R

GATSCHET, Niklaus (1736-1817) Swiss

Works on paper

£699 $1090 €1049 Ruines du Chateau de Resti (35x60cm-14x24in) W/C Indian ink. 20-Nov-2 Fischer, Luzern #2615/R est:1800-2500 (S.FR 1600)

GATTA, Saverio della (?-1829) Italian

£1724 $2724 €2500 Tarantella dance (23x17cm-9x7in) s.d.1800 tempera paper. 3-Apr-3 Porro, Milan #1/R

Works on paper

£380 $600 €600 Musician from Calabria (27x19cm-11x7in) i. gouache. 28-Nov-2 Tajan, Paris #46/R

GATTEAUX, Jacques Edouard (1788-1881) French

Works on paper

£609 $944 €950 Academie d'homme tenant un baton (60x45cm-24x18in) chl stump chk. 4-Dec-2 Piasa, Paris #129

£1154 $1788 €1800 Academie d'homme, bras gauche tendu (60x45cm-24x18in) s.i.verso chl chk stump. 4-Dec-2 Piasa, Paris #128/R

GATTI, Annibale (1828-1909) Italian

£23810 $37857 €35000 Allegory of Drama (120x170cm-47x67in) s. 18-Mar-3 Finarte, Milan #108/R

GATTIKER, Hermann (1865-1950) Swiss

£308 $450 €462 G Duttweiler Park (45x70cm-18x28in) s. 17-Jun-2 Philippe Schuler, Zurich #7410 (S.FR 700)

£354 $566 €531 Ruins on island (20x28cm-8x11in) s. board. 17-Mar-3 Philippe Schuler, Zurich #8441 (S.FR 750)

£522 $809 €783 Summer landscape on the Grimsel (62x91cm-24x36in) s. 9-Dec-2 Philippe Schuler, Zurich #3814 (S.FR 1200)

GATTUSO, Paul (20th C) American

£239 $375 €359 Swimming Rockport (64x76cm-25x30in) s. 22-Nov-2 Skinner, Boston #358/R

GAUCI, M (fl.1810-1846) British

Prints

£65000 $104650 €97500 Orchidaceae of Mexico and Guatemala (72x53cm-28x21in) hand col lithographs 40 first edition of 125 folio prov. 7-May-3 Sotheby's, London #1/R est:40000-60000

GAUD, A Henriquet (19/20th C) French

£3500 $5495 €5250 Basket of eggs, frying pan, bottle and a joint of ham on a table (46x61cm-18x24in) s. 21-Nov-2 Christie's, Kensington #87/R est:2000-3000

GAUD, Léon (1844-1908) Swiss

£602 $969 €903 Farmstead (17x26cm-7x10in) s. board. 7-May-3 Dobiaschofsky, Bern #568/R (S.FR 1300)

£3217 $4987 €4826 Retour de peche sur le Leman (33x49cm-13x19in) s. prov. 7-Dec-2 Galerie du Rhone, Sion #454/R est:3500-4500 (S.FR 7400)

GAUDAIRE-THOR, Jean (1947-) French

£972 $1536 €1400 Sanam (81x100cm-32x39in) s.i.d.verso lit. 27-Apr-3 Perrin, Versailles #152/R

GAUDEFROY, Alphonse (1845-1936) French

£15823 $24684 €25000 Atelier du sculpteur Dalou (74x90cm-29x35in) s.i. 18-Oct-2 Raboiurdin & Choppin de Janvry, Paris #26/R est:3500

£37975 $60000 €56963 Studio of Jules Dalou (74x90cm-29x35in) s.i.d.87. 24-Apr-3 Sotheby's, New York #55/R est:18000-25000

GAUDEZ, Adrien Étienne (1845-1902) French

Sculpture

£1154 $1812 €1800 Esmeralda (64cm-25in) i. brown pat.bronze. 21-Nov-2 Van Ham, Cologne #1215/R est:600

£1935 $3000 €2903 Figure of a girl in lacy dress holding flowers (58cm-23in) s. brown pat. bronze. 7-Dec-2 Selkirks, St. Louis #567/R est:3000-3500

£2200 $3432 €3300 Le belluaire (93cm-37in) s. brown pat bronze. 9-Apr-3 Sotheby's, London #206/R est:2500-3500

GAUDIER-BRZESKA, Henri (1891-1915) French

Sculpture

£8000 $12560 €12000 Duck (12cm-5in) bronze conceived 1914 prov.lit. 22-Nov-2 Christie's, London #74/R est:3000-5000

£9500 $15580 €14250 Ornamental mask (76cm-30in) mun.2/6 green pat. bronze cast 1969-70 exhib.lit. 6-Jun-3 Christie's, London #179/R est:8000-12000

Works on paper

£486 $773 €700 Nu debout (51x38cm-20x15in) ink dr. 29-Apr-3 Artcurial Briest, Paris #86

£800 $1248 €1200 Vulture (21x14cm-8x6in) chl double-sided. 15-Oct-2 Bonhams, Knightsbridge #119/R

£1100 $1716 €1650 Peacock. Falcon (21x14cm-8x6in) chl double-sided. 15-Oct-2 Bonhams, Knightsbridge #122/R est:800-1200

£2200 $3388 €3300 Standing male nude (37x25cm-15x10in) s. pen black ink prov. 5-Sep-2 Christie's, Kensington #520/R est:1500-2000

£2200 $3608 €3300 At exercise (25x35cm-10x14in) pen ink prov. 3-Jun-3 Sotheby's, Olympia #10/R est:500-700

GAUERMANN, Friedrich (1807-1862) Austrian

£1370 $2137 €2000 Study of hunting dog (21x28cm-8x11in) paper. 10-Apr-3 Van Ham, Cologne #1437/R est:2200

£2721 $4327 €4000 Horse (20x22cm-8x9in) s. board. 18-Mar-3 Finarte, Milan #221/R

£2740 $4274 €4000 Study of young bull (20x26cm-8x10in) paper. 10-Apr-3 Van Ham, Cologne #1438/R est:2200

£4965 $8043 €7000 Angler (24x17cm-9x7in) board. 22-May-3 Dorotheum, Vienna #123/R est:7000-8000

£9615 $15096 €15000 Pasture in the high mountains (43x32cm-17x13in) paper on canvas exhib. 25-Nov-2 Hassfurther, Vienna #41/R est:12000-15000

£22000 $36080 €33000 Zwei baren an einer quelle - two bears by a spring (31x39cm-12x15in) panel. 3-Jun-3 Sotheby's, London #12/R est:8000-12000

£44872 $70449 €70000 Hohensalzburg castle (30x42cm-12x17in) paper on canvas lit.exhib. 25-Nov-2 Hassfurther, Vienna #42/R est:65000-85000

£88608 $140000 €140000 Drover at Zellersee (102x147cm-40x58in) s.d.1862. 28-Nov-2 Dorotheum, Vienna #105/R est:120000-160000

GAUFFIER, Louis (1761-1801) French
£400 $624 €600 View of the Villa Frascati (22x38cm-9x15in) 10-Sep-2 Bonhams, Knightsbridge #256/R
Works on paper
£5247 $8500 €7871 Cornelia presenting her two young sons (34x52cm-13x20in) i. chk pen ink wash htd white prov. 22-Jan-3 Christie's, Rockefeller NY #98/R est:8000

GAUGAIN, Philip A (attrib) (fl.1783-1847) British
£450 $702 €653 Portrait of a gentleman (75x62cm-30x24in) i.verso oval. 28-Mar-3 ELR Auctions, Sheffield #220/R

GAUGENGIGL, Ignaz Marcel (1855-1932) German
£323 $474 €500 Advances (39x31cm-15x12in) s. panel. 20-Jun-2 Dr Fritz Nagel, Stuttgart #767/R
£3145 $5000 €4718 Artist's self portrait (103x74cm-41x29in) prov. 7-Mar-3 Skinner, Boston #558/R est:5000-7000

GAUGUIN, Jean René (1881-1961) Danish
Sculpture
£4766 $7960 €6911 Jockey jumping over a horse (29x32cm-11x13in) dark brown pat.bronze incl. wood socle prov.lit. 17-Jun-3 Rasmussen, Copenhagen #85/R est:60000-80000 (D.KR 50000)
£12082 $19089 €18123 Youth - rider on horseback (64cm-25in) brown pat.bronze st.f.N.O.Schmidt lit. 1-Apr-3 Rasmussen, Copenhagen #84/R est:30000-50000 (D.KR 130000)

GAUGUIN, Paul (1848-1903) French
£170000 $283900 €246500 La ferme de la Groue a Osny (38x46cm-15x18in) s.d.83 prov.exhib.lit. 25-Jun-3 Christie's, London #108/R est:120000-160000
£621118 $1000000 €931677 Oies (60x73cm-24x29in) s.d.89 prov.exhib.lit. 7-May-3 Christie's, Rockefeller NY #17/R est:1000000-1500000
£1400000 $2338000 €2100000 Village sous la neige (76x66cm-30x26in) s. painted c.1894 prov.exhib.lit. 23-Jun-3 Sotheby's, London #18/R est:1300000-1800000
£1739130 $2800000 €2608695 Nature morte a l'estampe japonaise (32x55cm-13x22in) s.d.88 prov.exhib.lit. 7-May-3 Christie's, Rockefeller NY #4/R est:2500000-3500000
£2692308 $4200000 €4038462 Cabane sous les arbres (72x43cm-28x17in) s.d.92 prov.exhib.lit. 6-Nov-2 Christie's, Rockefeller NY #9/R est:3500000-5500000
£6800000 $11356001 €10200000 Incantation or L'Apparition (66x76cm-26x30in) s.d.1902 prov.exhib.lit. 23-Jun-3 Sotheby's, London #16/R est:7000000-9000000
Prints
£2051 $3200 €3077 Auti te pape (27x43cm-11x17in) i.num. woodcut. 5-Nov-2 Christie's, Rockefeller NY #15/R est:4000-6000
£2128 $3447 €3000 Manao tupapau (27x42cm-11x17in) mono.i. woodcut. 20-May-3 Dorotheum, Vienna #111/R est:3000-3200
£2222 $3533 €3200 Miseres humaines (29x23cm-11x9in) s.d. lithograph zinc. 5-May-3 Ketterer, Munich #31/R est:1200-1500
£2308 $3600 €3462 Les cigales et les fourmis (20x27cm-8x11in) lithograph second edition of 2. 18-Sep-2 Swann Galleries, New York #8/R est:3000-5000
£2586 $4085 €3879 Portrait de Stephane Mallarme (18x14cm-7x6in) etching drypoint prov.lit. 28-Apr-3 Bukowskis, Stockholm #425/R est:30000-40000 (S.KR 34000)
£2800 $4368 €4200 L'universe est cree (23x37cm-9x15in) woodcut. 10-Oct-2 Sotheby's, London #41/R est:4000-6000
£2917 $4638 €4200 Bretonnes a la barriere (17x21cm-7x8in) s. lithograph zinc. 5-May-3 Ketterer, Munich #28/R est:1200-1500
£3077 $4862 €4800 Portrait de Stephane Mallarme. etching. 14-Nov-2 Libert, Castor, Paris #96 est:1250
£3526 $5500 €5289 Noa Noa (39x27cm-15x11in) i.num.72 woodcut edition of 100. 5-Nov-2 Christie's, Rockefeller NY #14/R est:5000-7000
£4167 $6625 €6000 Nave Nave Fenua - terre delicieuse (35x20cm-14x8in) mono.i. woodcut. 5-May-3 Ketterer, Munich #32/R est:2500-3500
£5282 $8768 €7500 Le char a boeufs (19x29cm-7x11in) init.num. wood engraving. 12-Jun-3 Piasa, Paris #77/R
£7394 $12275 €10500 Maruru, merci (20x35cm-8x14in) wood engraving. 12-Jun-3 Piasa, Paris #72/R
£7639 $12146 €11000 Bretonnes a la barriere (15x22cm-6x9in) s. lithograph zince. 5-May-3 Ketterer, Munich #27/R est:3000-3500
£7639 $12146 €11000 Les vieilles filles a Arles (19x20cm-7x8in) s. lithograph zinc. 5-May-3 Ketterer, Munich #29/R est:2500-3500
£8257 $13789 €11973 Les jours de dieu (14x18cm-6x7in) woodcut. 20-Jun-3 Kornfeld, Bern #39/R est:20000 (S.FR 18000)
£8716 $14555 €12638 Femme cueillant des fruits et oviri (13x11cm-5x4in) woodcut. 20-Jun-3 Kornfeld, Bern #38/R est:20000 (S.FR 19000)
£9174 $15321 €13302 Le calvaire breton (15x23cm-6x9in) mono.i. woodcut. 20-Jun-3 Kornfeld, Bern #41/R est:25000 (S.FR 20000)
£10811 $17405 €16217 Noa, Noa - l'Univers est cree (20x35cm-8x14in) mono.i. col woodcut lit. 7-May-3 AB Stockholms Auktionsverk #1211/R est:140000-160000 (S.KR 140000)
£10915 $18120 €15500 Planche au diable cornu (17x29cm-7x11in) one of 30 wood engraving. 12-Jun-3 Piasa, Paris #76/R
£12579 $20000 €18869 Manao Tupapau (18x27cm-7x11in) s.num.Ep.82 lithograph edition of 100. 29-Apr-3 Christie's, Rockefeller NY #404/R est:25000-35000
£13836 $22000 €20754 Nave nave fenua (35x20cm-14x8in) woodcut printed in ochre ink. 3-Mar-3 Swann Galleries, New York #19/R est:30000-50000
£15278 $24292 €22000 Manao Tupapau (18x27cm-7x11in) s.mono.i. lithograph. 5-May-3 Ketterer, Munich #33/R est:13000-15000
£15385 $24000 €23078 Bouddha (29x22cm-11x9in) mono.num.12 olive green woodcut prov. 5-Nov-2 Christie's, Rockefeller NY #16/R est:28000-32000
£15596 $26046 €22614 Elle pense au revenant - l'esprit (20x36cm-8x14in) col woodcut. 20-Jun-3 Kornfeld, Bern #35/R est:35000 (S.FR 34000)
£16514 $27578 €23945 Miseres humaines (19x30cm-7x12in) i. woodcut. 20-Jun-3 Kornfeld, Bern #40/R est:30000 (S.FR 36000)
£17123 $26884 €25000 Calvaire breton (16x25cm-6x10in) mono.i. engraving prov. 15-Apr-3 Laurence Calmels, Paris #4288/R est:6000
£17431 $29110 €25275 L'univers est cree (20x36cm-8x14in) col woodcut. 20-Jun-3 Kornfeld, Bern #33/R est:40000 (S.FR 38000)
£17606 $29225 €25000 Oviri, sauvage (20x12cm-8x5in) wood engraving. 12-Jun-3 Piasa, Paris #73/R
£18349 $30642 €26606 Le diable parle (20x36cm-8x14in) col woodcut. 20-Jun-3 Kornfeld, Bern #34/R est:40000 (S.FR 40000)
£19718 $32732 €28000 Nave nave fenua, terre delicieuse (36x20cm-14x8in) i. wood engraving. 12-Jun-3 Piasa, Paris #71/R
£25229 $42133 €36582 Le char aboeuf - souvenir de Bretagne (17x29cm-7x11in) mono.i. woodcut W/C col pen. 20-Jun-3 Kornfeld, Bern #42/R est:60000 (S.FR 55000)
£29487 $46000 €44231 Noa noa (36x21cm-14x8in) col woodcut edition of 25-30. 18-Sep-2 Swann Galleries, New York #9/R est:45000-65000
Sculpture
£1266 $1975 €2000 La petite Parisienne (27cm-11in) s. brown pat.bronze. 15-Oct-2 Dorotheum, Vienna #153/R est:2800-3800
£273292 $440000 €409938 Spirit (69x28cm-27x11in) mono. oak relief exec.c.1894 prov.exhib.lit. 6-May-3 Sotheby's, New York #9/R est:250000-350000
Works on paper
£3402 $5409 €5000 Cavalier et tete de profil. Cavalier (17x14cm-7x6in) crayon double-sided. 24-Mar-3 Tajan, Paris #184/R
£11801 $19000 €17702 Tete de Tahitienne. Tete d'homme (31x20cm-12x8in) pen ink W/C double-sided. 7-May-3 Sotheby's, New York #133/R est:18000-25000
£12247 $19105 €18371 Tahiti female head and head of man - possibly self portrait (31x20cm-12x8in) pen Indian ink two dr together prov.exhib.lit. 18-Sep-2 Kunsthallen, Copenhagen #21/R est:85000 (D.KR 145000)
£17000 $28390 €25500 Femmes de Martinique (13x11cm-5x4in) W/C chl. pencil. 26-Jun-3 Christie's, London #362/R est:10000-15000
£878378 $1370270 €1300000 Tete de tahitienne, de profil a gauche (30x20cm-12x8in) mono. pastel crayon htd gouache exhib.lit. 26-Mar-3 Piasa, Paris #120/R est:700000

GAUGUIN, Paul (attrib) (1848-1903) French
£4000 $6520 €6000 Portrait of young girl wearing pink dress, seated with dog in landscape (83x128cm-33x50in) 12-Feb-3 Bonhams, Knightsbridge #328/R est:4000-6000

GAUGUIN, Pola (1883-1961) Danish
£1175 $1880 €1763 Judgement of Paris (32x45cm-13x18in) s.d.30. 17-Mar-3 Blomqvist, Oslo #394/R est:16000-18000 (N.KR 13500)

GAUL, August (1869-1921) German
Sculpture
£1266 $2000 €2000 Bear lying down (8cm-3in) s. brown pat.bronze. 29-Nov-2 Villa Grisebach, Berlin #630/R est:2000-2500
£1392 $2200 €2200 Goose (7cm-3in) s. black brown pat.bronze. 29-Nov-2 Villa Grisebach, Berlin #631/R est:2000-2500
£1528 $2414 €2200 Donkey (10x14x4cm-4x6x2in) s. brown pat.bronze marble socle. 26-Apr-3 Dr Lehr, Berlin #147/R est:2200
£1709 $2700 €2700 Pig (4cm-2in) s. black brown pat.bronze. 29-Nov-2 Villa Grisebach, Berlin #632/R est:2000-2500
£1835 $2900 €2900 Donkey nibbling back leg (6x7x4cm-2x3x2in) s. dark brown pat.bronze marble socle Cast.H Noack Berlin. 30-Nov-2 Bassenge, Berlin #6264/R est:2400
£1841 $2890 €2762 Two recumbent goats (24x43cm-9x17in) s. bronze. 25-Nov-2 Stephan Welz, Johannesburg #212/R est:9000-12000 (SA.R 28000)
£2174 $3565 €3000 Two ducks (14cm-6in) s. brown pat.bronze stone socle Cast. Noack Berlin. 31-May-3 Villa Grisebach, Berlin #137/R est:3000-4000

£2394 $3855 €3400 Lion cub (19cm-7in) s.d.93 dark brown pat.bronze. 9-May-3 Schloss Ahlden, Ahlden #723/R est:2800
£2885 $4471 €4500 Trotting donkey (4x12x5cm-2x5x2in) s.mono. bronze marble socle exhib.lit. 4-Dec-2 Lempertz, Koln #723/R est:4000
£3077 $4769 €4800 Seated lion cub (24x12x2cm-9x5x1in) s.d.1898 bronze marble socle Cast.H.Noack Berlin exhib.lit. 4-Dec-2 Lempertz, Koln #722/R est:4000
£7246 $11884 €10000 Girl riding donkey (15cm-6in) st.sig. dark brown pat.bronze prov. 29-May-3 Lempertz, Koln #624/R est:5000

GAUL, Gilbert (1855-1919) American
£3503 $5500 €5255 Village by a pond (30x41cm-12x16in) s. canvas on board. 10-Dec-2 Doyle, New York #41/R est:2000-3000
£5031 $8000 €7547 American revolutionaries (53x36cm-21x14in) s. prov. 5-Mar-3 Sotheby's, New York #7/R est:8000-12000
£6169 $9500 €9254 Watching the burros (61x86cm-24x34in) s.i. 24-Oct-2 Shannon's, Milford #211/R est:6000-8000
£12903 $20000 €19355 Apple picker (33x27cm-13x11in) s.d.1880. 29-Oct-2 Sotheby's, New York #156/R est:3000-5000
£14103 $22000 €21155 Indian meditation (76x102cm-30x40in) s. prov.lit. 9-Nov-2 Santa Fe Art, Santa Fe #86/R est:30000-50000
£22078 $34000 €33117 Looking out to sea (46x61cm-18x24in) s. painted c.1910 prov. 24-Oct-2 Shannon's, Milford #51/R est:12000-18000
£22581 $35000 €33872 Mexican gamblers (51x76cm-20x30in) s. prov. 5-Dec-2 Christie's, Rockefeller NY #184/R est:20000-30000

GAUL, Gustave (1836-1888) Austrian
£1768 $2900 €2652 Merry maker (130x86cm-51x34in) s.d.1886. 8-Feb-3 Neal Auction Company, New Orleans #537/R est:2000-4000

GAUL, Winfred (1928-) German
£2885 $4471 €4500 O T (95x80cm-37x31in) s. oil dispersion painted 1956 prov.lit. 6-Dec-2 Ketterer, Munich #170/R est:5000-7000
£3846 $5962 €6000 O T 30-10-57 (65x95cm-26x37in) s. s.d.57 verso prov. 6-Dec-2 Ketterer, Munich #171/R est:8000-10000

GAULD, David (1865-1936) British
£860 $1359 €1290 Two Ayrshire cows at the edge of a field (51x76cm-20x30in) s. 7-Apr-3 Bonhams, Bath #116/R
£1005 $1628 €1457 Cattle in field (51x76cm-20x30in) s. 26-May-3 Rasmussen, Copenhagen #1471/R (D.KR 10500)
£1250 $1950 €1875 Calf resting (29x44cm-11x17in) s. 10-Apr-3 Bonhams, Edinburgh #88/R est:1000-1500
£1300 $2106 €1950 Farm scene (50x60cm-20x24in) s. 23-Jan-3 Bonhams, Edinburgh #318 est:1500-2000
£2900 $4524 €4350 Cattle watering beneath trees (72x92cm-28x36in) s. 17-Oct-2 Bonhams, Edinburgh #264/R est:3000-5000
£3000 $4650 €4500 Ayrshire calves in a summer landscape (50x60cm-20x24in) s. 5-Dec-2 Bonhams, Edinburgh #44/R est:4000-6000
£3200 $4960 €4800 Ayshire calves (30x46cm-12x18in) s. prov. 31-Oct-2 Christie's, London #106/R est:3000-5000
£4600 $7130 €6900 Ayrshire calves in a barn (56x76cm-22x30in) s. 5-Dec-2 Bonhams, Edinburgh #47/R est:6000-8000
£6000 $9120 €9000 Calves (61x91cm-24x36in) s. 28-Aug-2 Sotheby's, London #883/R est:6000-8000
£8000 $12400 €12000 Water mill (62x77cm-24x30in) s. 31-Oct-2 Christie's, London #107/R est:7000-10000
£19000 $29450 €28500 New bonnet (35x25cm-14x10in) s. board. 6-Dec-2 Lyon & Turnbull, Edinburgh #107/R est:3000-5000

GAULLI, Giovanni Battista (attrib) (1639-1709) Italian
£11000 $18370 €15950 Portrait of a Cardinal (66x56cm-26x22in) i. 11-Jul-3 Christie's, Kensington #209/R est:5000-8000

GAULT, Jacques Joseph de (18th C) French
Miniatures
£4200 $6804 €6300 Lady in classical robes (5cm-2xin) en grisaille with green leather travelling case. 22-May-3 Bonhams, New Bond Street #33/R est:300-500

GAUNT, W Norman (1918-) British
£250 $390 €375 January day at Ingleborough (63x76cm-25x30in) s. 10-Apr-3 Tennants, Leyburn #1069
£309 $479 €464 Polperro Harbour, Cornwall (50x61cm-20x24in) s. masonite. 3-Dec-2 Ritchie, Toronto #3057/R (C.D 750)
£350 $550 €525 Two huntsmen and hounds (61x121cm-24x48in) s. 21-Nov-2 Tennants, Leyburn #780
£420 $655 €630 Huntsman on a bay hunter coming out of a wood (61x76cm-24x30in) s. canvas panel. 10-Apr-3 Tennants, Leyburn #1067/R
£450 $702 €675 Preparing for the start with spectators. Seven dismounted riders (61x91cm-24x36in) s. canvas panel pair. 10-Apr-3 Tennants, Leyburn #1062
£500 $785 €750 Two racehorses over the fence (60x75cm-24x30in) s. 21-Nov-2 Tennants, Leyburn #784
£500 $785 €750 Racehorse going over the fence. Two racehorses neck and neck (61x51cm-24x20in) s. two. 21-Nov-2 Tennants, Leyburn #789
£500 $780 €750 Preparing for the start. Studies of show jumping and horse racing (60x122cm-24x48in) s. pair. 10-Apr-3 Tennants, Leyburn #1060
£500 $780 €750 Workhorse watering. Study of two workhorses (61x76cm-24x30in) s. canvas panel pair. 10-Apr-3 Tennants, Leyburn #1064
£550 $858 €825 Huntsman and hounds on a moorland. Huntsman on a white hunter (50x61cm-20x24in) one s. cotton canvas panel one canvas panel pair. 10-Apr-3 Tennants, Leyburn #1061
£600 $942 €900 Horse and cart with farm workers (61x76cm-24x30in) s. canvas on board. 21-Nov-2 Tennants, Leyburn #790
£600 $936 €900 Returning from exercise at Middleham stable (50x61cm-20x24in) s.i. canvas panel. 10-Apr-3 Tennants, Leyburn #1063
£700 $1099 €1050 Polo players (61x76cm-24x30in) s. canvas on board. 21-Nov-2 Tennants, Leyburn #785/R
£700 $1092 €1050 Men on horseback crossing a river. Horse and cart and figures on a beach (61x76cm-24x30in) s. one canvas on board pair. 10-Apr-3 Tennants, Leyburn #1057
£800 $1256 €1200 Willie Carson on Mukddaam, winner of the Garden Suite racing club Maiden Stakes, Newmarket (76x101cm-30x40in) s. 21-Nov-2 Tennants, Leyburn #787/R
£800 $1248 €1200 Woman feeding poultry. Child feeding poultry. Child playing a clarinet (51x61cm-20x24in) s. canvasboard three. 10-Apr-3 Tennants, Leyburn #1075
£800 $1248 €1200 Donkeys and figures on a beach (50x61cm-20x24in) s. canvasboard sold with another similar. 10-Apr-3 Tennants, Leyburn #1076
£800 $1248 €1200 Gypsy running a horse (51x61cm-20x24in) s. canvasboard sold with another similar. 10-Apr-3 Tennants, Leyburn #1079/R
£900 $1413 €1350 Huntsman in a wood (61x76cm-24x30in) s. canvas on board pair. 21-Nov-2 Tennants, Leyburn #781
£900 $1413 €1350 Two riders approaching a ditch. Racehorse in snow (61x76cm-24x30in) s. canvas on board. 21-Nov-2 Tennants, Leyburn #788
£900 $1413 €1350 Loch Torridon. Going for a jaunt on Arran (61x76cm-24x30in) s. canvas on board two. 21-Nov-2 Tennants, Leyburn #840
£950 $1492 €1425 Dowies Balry Moor (60x122cm-24x48in) s. 21-Nov-2 Tennants, Leyburn #839/R
£1100 $1727 €1650 Racehorse with jockey up (76x89cm-30x35in) canvas on board. 21-Nov-2 Tennants, Leyburn #778 est:200-300
£1100 $1727 €1650 Racehorse awaiting the start (61x122cm-24x48in) s. canvas on board. 21-Nov-2 Tennants, Leyburn #786 est:300-500
£1400 $2198 €2100 Cycling on the promenade. Donkey rides (51x61cm-20x24in) s. canvas on board two. 21-Nov-2 Tennants, Leyburn #861/R est:300-400
£2200 $3454 €3300 Herd of horses in a street (76x101cm-30x40in) s. 21-Nov-2 Tennants, Leyburn #783/R est:300-400
£2400 $3768 €3600 Donkey rides on the beach. making sand castle (61x122cm-24x48in) s. canvas on board two. 21-Nov-2 Tennants, Leyburn #782/R est:400-600
£3000 $4710 €4500 Children on donkeys at the seaside. Donkeys and deckchair (61x91cm-24x36in) s. canvas on board two. 21-Nov-2 Tennants, Leyburn #779 est:300-400

Works on paper
£300 $468 €450 Prince Philip carriage driving at Holker Hall (45x69cm-18x27in) s. gouache. 10-Apr-3 Tennants, Leyburn #880/R
£350 $546 €525 Huntsman (45x69cm-18x27in) s. W/C bodycol. 10-Apr-3 Tennants, Leyburn #888
£450 $707 €675 Going out at Epsom (55x71cm-22x28in) s. W/C gouache. 21-Nov-2 Tennants, Leyburn #678
£500 $785 €750 Huntsman. Going over a hedge (45x69cm-18x27in) s. W/C bodycol two. 21-Nov-2 Tennants, Leyburn #675
£500 $785 €750 Milling around at the start of point to point meeting. Out for a morning ride (45x69cm-18x27in) s. W/C gouache two. 21-Nov-2 Tennants, Leyburn #677
£500 $830 €725 Lunesdale harriers (32x48cm-13x19in) s. gouache on canvasboard. 12-Jun-3 Christie's, Kensington #30/R
£550 $864 €825 Harbour, Whitehaven. Drawn carts on a beach (48x61cm-19x24in) s. W/C gouache. 21-Nov-2 Tennants, Leyburn #665
£550 $864 €825 String enjoying seawater. December day in snow (45x69cm-18x27in) s. W/C two. 21-Nov-2 Tennants, Leyburn #674
£580 $905 €870 Study of sailing vessels in a harbour (50x63cm-20x25in) s. W/C gouache sold with four others similar. 10-Apr-3 Tennants, Leyburn #828
£650 $1021 €975 Coming home at sundown. Returning from the fishing banks at Heysham (46x69cm-18x27in) s. W/C gouache two. 21-Nov-2 Tennants, Leyburn #680
£650 $1040 €975 Huntman. Stop for a chat (30x48cm-12x19in) s.i.on mount gouache on linen pair. 14-Mar-3 Gardiner & Houlgate, Bath #72/R
£750 $1178 €1125 Out on the country. Coming up to the start (45x69cm-18x27in) s. W/C pair. 21-Nov-2 Tennants, Leyburn #673

GAUQUIE, Henri (1858-1927) French
Sculpture
£962 $1510 €1500 Figure of a mower (49cm-19in) s. green pat bronze marble base. 16-Dec-2 Bernaerts, Antwerp #201 est:1500-1800

GAUSACHS, Jose (1891-?) Spanish
£757 $1226 €1150 Coastal landscape (55x65cm-22x26in) s. 21-Jan-3 Ansorena, Madrid #58/R

GAUSE, Wilhelm (1853-1916) German
Works on paper
£283 $439 €450 Countryfolk in Lemberg (21x33cm-8x13in) s. pencils. pencil. 1-Oct-2 Dorotheum, Vienna #165/R

GAUSH, Alexander Fedorovich (1873-1947) Russian
£800 $1296 €1200 Portrait of bearded Izvozchik (54x46cm-21x18in) s.i. 20-May-3 Sotheby's, Olympia #395/R

GAUSSEN, Adolphe-Louis (1871-1954) French
£2838 $4427 €4200 Quais de Marseille (32x40cm-13x16in) s. panel. 26-Mar-3 Millon & Associes, Paris #70/R
£4196 $7007 €6000 La ciotat (60x81cm-24x32in) s. 27-Jun-3 Claude Aguttes, Neuilly #43/R est:5000-7000

GAUSSON, Leo (1860-1944) French
£346 $533 €550 Mill (38x46cm-15x18in) s.d.99. 27-Oct-2 Muizon & Le Coent, Paris #58
£597 $920 €950 Meule de foin (32x46cm-13x18in) prov. 27-Oct-2 Muizon & Le Coent, Paris #59/R
£1258 $1962 €2000 Paysage (16x23cm-6x9in) st.sig. cardboard painted c.1890. 11-Oct-2 Binoche, Paris #67/R
£1761 $2747 €2800 Chemin tournant (27x35cm-11x14in) st.sig. panel. 11-Oct-2 Binoche, Paris #68/R

GAUTHIER, Dominique (20th C) French
Works on paper
£972 $1546 €1400 Sans titre (154x138cm-61x54in) s.d.1982 verso mixed media canvas on panel. 29-Apr-3 Artcurial Briest, Paris #571 est:1200-1500

GAUTHIER, Jean Marc (20th C) French?
Works on paper
£302 $483 €420 Beau et con a la fois (99x99cm-39x39in) s.d.89 mixed media wood panel. 18-May-3 Neret-Minet, Paris #215

GAUTHIER, Joachim (1897-1988) Canadian
£300 $469 €450 Farmyard at Green lake, Haliburton (30x38cm-12x15in) s.i.verso canvas on board. 25-Mar-3 Ritchie, Toronto #80/R (C.D 700)
£412 $638 €618 October snowfall, Papineau River (30x37cm-12x15in) s. canvas on board. 3-Dec-2 Joyner, Toronto #417 est:1000-1500 (C.D 1000)
£429 $670 €644 Rocky shore of Lake Superior (61x76cm-24x30in) s. board. 25-Mar-3 Ritchie, Toronto #96/R est:1500-2500 (C.D 1000)
£444 $729 €666 Spruce Point, Haliburton (30x37cm-12x15in) s. board. 3-Jun-3 Joyner, Toronto #311/R est:800-1200 (C.D 1000)
£533 $875 €800 Morning, Blackfish Bay, Lake Kamaniskeg (30x37cm-12x15in) s. board prov. 3-Jun-3 Joyner, Toronto #485 est:1000-1500 (C.D 1200)
£622 $1020 €933 Waterfall on the Rockingham River (30x37cm-12x15in) s. board prov. 3-Jun-3 Joyner, Toronto #534 est:1000-1500 (C.D 1400)
£644 $1004 €934 Ontario farm (30x38cm-12x15in) s.i. board. 26-Mar-3 Walker's, Ottawa #220/R est:1000-1500 (C.D 1500)
£711 $1166 €1067 Athabaska Glacier, Jasper National Park (50x60cm-20x24in) s. board prov. 3-Jun-3 Joyner, Toronto #484 est:1500-2000 (C.D 1600)
Works on paper
£400 $656 €600 Georgian Bay (37x50cm-15x20in) s. W/C prov. 3-Jun-3 Joyner, Toronto #365/R est:1000-1500 (C.D 900)
£889 $1458 €1334 In the Ottawa valley. Coming storm (26x36cm-10x14in) s. W/C two. 3-Jun-3 Joyner, Toronto #467 est:800-1200 (C.D 2000)

GAUTHIER, Joseph Stany (1883-1969) French
£486 $792 €700 Port de Treboul (46x61cm-18x24in) s. 19-Jul-3 Thierry & Lannon, Brest #390

GAUTHIER, Oscar (1921-) French
£823 $1284 €1300 Composition (31x23cm-12x9in) s.d.1952 verso. 20-Oct-2 Charbonneaux, Paris #129/R est:700-800
£1132 $1755 €1800 Composition (92x60cm-36x24in) s. 30-Oct-2 Artcurial Briest, Paris #673 est:1200-1500
£1192 $1943 €1800 Feu et cendres (92x65cm-36x26in) s.d.1985. 3-Feb-3 Cornette de St.Cyr, Paris #424/R
Works on paper
£506 $790 €800 Composition (50x32cm-20x13in) s.d.57 gouache. 20-Oct-2 Charbonneaux, Paris #59 est:1000-1200

GAUTHIER, Paul (1937-) Canadian
£356 $583 €534 Rockingham swamp (30x37cm-12x15in) s. board. 3-Jun-3 Joyner, Toronto #381/R (C.D 800)
£533 $875 €800 Mountain peaks in Banff Nation Park (40x50cm-16x20in) s. board. 3-Jun-3 Joyner, Toronto #382/R est:1000-1200 (C.D 1200)

GAUTIER D'AGOTY, Jacques Fabien (attrib) (1710-1781) French
£2837 $4596 €4000 Portrait de Marie Antoinette (71x56cm-28x22in) exhib.prov. 21-May-3 Piasa, Paris #365/R est:6000-8000

GAUTIER D'AGOTY, Pierre Edouard (1775-1871) French
Miniatures
£2300 $3588 €3450 British officer possibly of Commissiariat wearing dark blue uniform (6cm-2xin) s. gold frame hair mono.verso oval. 5-Nov-2 Bonhams, New Bond Street #104/R est:1600-1800

GAUTIER, Albert (?-1938) French
£347 $552 €500 Ruine de temple grec (23x33cm-9x13in) s.i. panel. 30-Apr-3 Tajan, Paris #100

GAUTIER, Louis Francois Léon (1855-1947) French
£1486 $2319 €2200 Vue d'Avignon depuis Villeneuve-les-Avignon. Porte Thiers a Avignon (9x17cm-4x7in) s.i.d.1902 cardboard two. 27-Mar-3 Christie's, Paris #180/R

GAUVREAU, Pierre (1922-) Canadian
Works on paper
£570 $850 €855 Composition (16x19cm-6x7in) s.d.50 ink. 26-Jun-2 Iegor de Saint Hippolyte, Montreal #44 (C.D 1300)

GAUZY, Jeanne L (1886-1968) French
£372 $592 €540 Nude of boy (56x67cm-22x26in) s. 4-Mar-3 Ansorena, Madrid #314/R

GAVARDIE, Jean de (1909-1961) French
Works on paper
£385 $604 €600 Nature morte au citron vert (11x46cm-4x18in) s. gouache. 24-Nov-2 Lesieur & Le Bars, Le Havre #63

GAVARNI, Paul (1804-1866) French
Works on paper
£270 $422 €400 Coquette au miroir (21x17cm-8x7in) crayon chl. 27-Mar-3 Maigret, Paris #148
£284 $443 €426 Resting mountain hunters (15x13cm-6x5in) s. W/C over pencil. 6-Nov-2 Dobiaschofsky, Bern #1144/R (S.FR 650)
£321 $456 €520 Cantinieres jouant aux cartes (18x25cm-7x10in) crayon. 17-Mar-2 Galerie de Chartres, Chartres #38
£322 $500 €483 New year (29x23cm-11x9in) s. pen ink. 29-Oct-2 Sotheby's, New York #56/R
£461 $770 €650 Femme enveloppee dans un chale danseuse fumant le cigare (15x9cm-6x4in) i. W/C gouache black crayon. 19-Jun-3 Piasa, Paris #156a
£545 $866 €800 Pierrot a la statuette (29x20cm-11x8in) s. w htd gouache. 24-Mar-3 Tajan, Paris #151/R
£633 $1000 €1000 Polichinelle (28x22cm-11x9in) s.i. W/C wash htd white gouache. 28-Nov-2 Tajan, Paris #127/R
£638 $1066 €900 Homme au bonnet rouge (19x14cm-7x6in) s. W/C gouache pen grey wash. 19-Jun-3 Piasa, Paris #156/R
£645 $1000 €968 After the ball (23x16cm-9x6in) s. pencil gouache black ink prov. 29-Oct-2 Sotheby's, New York #54/R est:600-800
£709 $1100 €1064 Waiter and patron. Portrait of a gentleman seated (19x16cm-7x6in) s. black chk two. 29-Oct-2 Sotheby's, New York #55/R est:800-1200
£748 $1190 €1100 Retour de l'Inde (30x20cm-12x8in) indis.sig.i. W/C gouache exhib. 24-Mar-3 Tajan, Paris #159
£748 $1190 €1100 Qui va m'adorer? (29x20cm-11x8in) s.i. W/C gouache pen ink. 24-Mar-3 Tajan, Paris #157
£774 $1200 €1161 Un homme deguise comme pierrot (31x21cm-12x8in) s.i. pencil W/C wash htd white. 29-Oct-2 Sotheby's, New York #52/R est:400-600
£816 $1298 €1200 Fin du spectacle (32x22cm-13x9in) s. W/C gouache pen ink exhib. 24-Mar-3 Tajan, Paris #153

£884 $1406 €1300 Musicien ambulant (29x20cm-11x8in) W/C gouache pen ink. 24-Mar-3 Tajan, Paris #156
£953 $1515 €1400 Coloriste en carnaval (30x20cm-12x8in) s.i. W/C gouache pen ink. 24-Mar-3 Tajan, Paris #158
£967 $1500 €1451 Viscount. Fisherman (28x21cm-11x8in) s.i. pencil W/C wash htd white two exhib. 29-Oct-2 Sotheby's, New York #51/R est:3000-4000
£1020 $1621 €1500 Homme au gibus (31x20cm-12x8in) s. W/C pen ink htd gouache. 24-Mar-3 Tajan, Paris #149
£1097 $1700 €1646 Sur le chemin de Toulon. One spoke to her (33x21cm-13x8in) s.i. pencil W/C gouache htd white two. 29-Oct-2 Sotheby's, New York #53/R est:2000-3000
£1497 $2380 €2200 Loup rose et loup bleu (15x20cm-6x8in) s. W/C over crayon exhib. 24-Mar-3 Tajan, Paris #154

GAVARNI, Paul (attrib) (1804-1866) French
Works on paper
£353 $546 €550 Allaitement (18x14cm-7x6in) crayon. 4-Dec-2 Piasa, Paris #125

GAVENCKY, Frank J (1888-?) American
£625 $1000 €938 Carmel coast (51x61cm-20x24in) s. board. 11-Jan-3 Harvey Clar, Oakland #1213

GAVREL, Genevieve (1909-) French
£566 $872 €900 Port de Kelibia (33x45cm-13x18in) s. s.i.verso. 23-Oct-2 Rabourdin & Choppin de Janvry, Paris #200/R

GAW, William Alexander (1891-1973) American
£1452 $2250 €2178 Shirley poppies (61x41cm-24x16in) s.d.59. 29-Oct-2 John Moran, Pasadena #709 est:2000-3000
£2096 $3500 €3039 Tank house 1939 (46x56cm-18x22in) s. 17-Jun-3 John Moran, Pasadena #71 est:3000-5000
£2395 $4000 €3473 Summer home 1944 (46x56cm-18x22in) i.verso prov. 17-Jun-3 John Moran, Pasadena #70 est:3000-5000

GAWELL, Oskar (1888-1955) Austrian
Works on paper
£252 $392 €400 Woman with basket and sack (50x38cm-20x15in) s.i. Indian ink W/C lit. 20-Sep-2 Karlheinz Kaupp, Staufen #2175/R
£277 $432 €440 Portrait of Asian woman (47x32cm-19x13in) s.i. lit. W/C gouache pastel. 20-Sep-2 Karlheinz Kaupp, Staufen #2177/R
£566 $883 €900 Couple harvesting (44x32cm-17x13in) s. lit. 20-Sep-2 Karlheinz Kaupp, Staufen #2180/R
£755 $1177 €1200 Portrait of young woman with veil over face (38x31cm-15x12in) s. lit. 20-Sep-2 Karlheinz Kaupp, Staufen #2174/R
£755 $1177 €1200 Portrait of young woman with black hair (42x34cm-17x13in) mono. lit. W/C pastel. 20-Sep-2 Karlheinz Kaupp, Staufen #2176/R

GAY, August (1890-1949) American
£6369 $10000 €9554 Three figures in a wooded landscape (16x24cm-6x9in) s. board. 19-Nov-2 Butterfields, San Francisco #8249/R est:12000-16000
£10828 $17000 €16242 Rocks and waves (28x36cm-11x14in) s. masonite prov. 19-Nov-2 Butterfields, San Francisco #8248/R est:20000-25000

GAY, Edward (1837-1928) American
£705 $1100 €1058 Riverine landscape with birch trees (41x30cm-16x12in) s. board. 1-Aug-2 Eldred, East Dennis #795/R
£750 $1200 €1088 Windy day (30x46cm-12x18in) s.d.1910. 16-May-3 Skinner, Boston #215/R
£833 $1300 €1250 Pastoral landscape (34x57cm-13x22in) s.d.79 board. 13-Apr-3 Butterfields, Los Angeles #7000 est:1000-1500
£943 $1500 €1415 Fishing along the stream (51x76cm-20x30in) s. 5-Mar-3 Doyle, New York #29/R est:2000-4000
£1026 $1600 €1539 Summer landscape with pool of water in foreground (15x25cm-6x10in) s.d.1910. 15-Oct-2 Winter Associates, Plainville #135 est:2000-4000
£1299 $2000 €1949 Autumn landscape (77x63cm-30x25in) s. prov. 4-Sep-2 Christie's, Rockefeller NY #358/R est:3000-5000
£2273 $3250 €3410 Dutch landscape with windmill (48x43cm-19x17in) s. board. 11-Dec-1 Lincoln, Orange #459
£2373 $3750 €3560 Landscape (56x69cm-22x27in) s. prov. 24-Apr-3 Shannon's, Milford #225/R est:3000-5000
£3165 $5000 €4748 Hudson Valley School landscape (74x91cm-29x36in) s. 26-Apr-3 Thomaston Place, Thomaston #147
£4221 $6500 €6332 Spring blossoms (43x64cm-17x25in) s. 24-Oct-2 Shannon's, Milford #168/R est:3000-5000
£5063 $8000 €7595 Fishing on a summer day (43x69cm-17x27in) s.d.86. 24-Apr-3 Shannon's, Milford #16/R est:8000-12000

GAY, George Howell (1858-1931) American
£813 $1300 €1220 New England coastal view by moonlight (46x102cm-18x40in) s. 12-Jan-3 William Jenack, New York #379
£3165 $5000 €4748 Breaking waves (51x76cm-20x30in) s. 24-Apr-3 Shannon's, Milford #192/R est:4000-6000
Works on paper
£377 $600 €566 Coastal view with distant vessels (30x55cm-12x22in) s. W/C. 7-Mar-3 Skinner, Boston #326/R
£382 $600 €573 Seascape with multiple waves crashing against rocks and two-mast sailboat (25x51cm-10x20in) s. W/C. 19-Apr-3 James Julia, Fairfield #252/R
£481 $750 €722 Along the shore (43x67cm-17x26in) s.d.1901 W/C. 20-Sep-2 Sloan, North Bethesda #350/R
£637 $1000 €956 Autumnal landscape (45x70cm-18x28in) s. W/C. 22-Nov-2 Skinner, Boston #76/R est:2000-3000
£665 $1050 €998 Landscape with road and stone fence (33x53cm-13x21in) s. W/C. 18-Nov-2 Schrager Galleries, Milwaukee #623
£828 $1300 €1242 Breaking surf (25x51cm-10x20in) s. W/C on board. 10-Dec-2 Doyle, New York #30/R est:2500-3500
£875 $1400 €1313 Beach scene (28x58cm-11x23in) s. W/C. 11-Jan-3 James Julia, Fairfield #337a est:1750-2250
£959 $1400 €1439 Breaking waves (38x94cm-15x37in) s. W/C. 3-Nov-1 North East Auctions, Portsmouth #231/R

GAY, Walter (1856-1937) American
£7692 $12154 €12000 Interior of castle (54x65cm-21x26in) s. 18-Nov-2 Sotheby's, Paris #70/R est:4000
£8446 $13176 €12500 Bouquet de fleurs dans un interieur (58x36cm-23x14in) s. 25-Mar-3 Chochon-Barre & Allardi, Paris #128/R est:10000-11500
£12903 $20000 €19355 Vaux le Vicomte (54x65cm-21x26in) s.i. board prov. 4-Dec-2 Sotheby's, New York #52/R est:20000-30000
£17742 $27500 €26613 Council chamber Fontainebleau (60x73cm-24x29in) s. prov.exhib. 4-Dec-2 Sotheby's, New York #51/R est:20000-30000
£21986 $36716 €31000 Salon du Chateau de Reveillon (54x66cm-21x26in) s. board. 20-Jun-3 Piasa, Paris #32/R est:15000-18000

GAY, Walter (attrib) (1856-1937) American
£457 $750 €663 Coppersmith (43x33cm-17x13in) bears sig board. 4-Jun-3 Doyle, New York #59

GAYA, Ramon (1910-) Spanish
Works on paper
£323 $510 €500 Boy in profile (18x10cm-7x4in) s.d.1947 pencil dr. 17-Dec-2 Segre, Madrid #113/R

GAYNOR, Gertie (20th C) ?
£450 $729 €675 Othello and Desdemona (76x102cm-30x40in) s.i. 23-Jan-3 Christie's, Kensington #104

GAYRARD, Joseph Raymond Paul (1807-1855) French
Sculpture
£1700 $2652 €2550 Monkey steeplechase (23x23cm-9x9in) s. brown pat. bronze. 6-Nov-2 Sotheby's, Olympia #181/R est:1500-2000

GAZE, Harold (20th C) American
Works on paper
£1050 $1754 €1523 Peter and Prue on Mercury (23x15cm-9x6in) W/C. 25-Jun-3 Brightwells, Leominster #1001/R est:1000-1500
£2070 $3250 €3105 Fairies and flowers (32x25cm-13x10in) s.d.1935 pencil W/C prov. 19-Nov-2 Butterfields, San Francisco #8064/R est:3000-5000
£2866 $4500 €4299 Dragonfly fairy (34x27cm-13x11in) s.d.1934 W/C gouache ink. 20-Nov-2 Christie's, Los Angeles #84/R est:3000-5000
£3185 $5000 €4778 Fairies and bubbles. Fairy among trees (37x29cm-15x11in) s.d.1944 W/C gouache ink double-sided. 20-Nov-2 Christie's, Los Angeles #83/R est:3000-5000
£4777 $7500 €7166 Fairies and bubbles (35x27cm-14x11in) s.d.1945 pencil ink W/C prov. 19-Nov-2 Butterfields, San Francisco #8065/R est:3000-5000

GAZZERA, Romano (1908-1985) Italian
£1282 $2013 €2000 Peugeot heading East (13x50cm-5x20in) s. cardboard on canvas painted 1965. 23-Nov-2 Meeting Art, Vercelli #196/R

GAZZERI, E (19/20th C) Italian
Sculpture
£1274 $1988 €1911 Mythological male figure (89cm-35in) s. alabaster. 5-Aug-2 Rasmussen, Vejle #609/R est:20000 (D.KR 15000)

GAZZERI, Ernesto (19/20th C) Italian
Sculpture
£12195 $20000 €17683 Lovers (97cm-38in) marble with marble pedestal prov. 4-Jun-3 Doyle, New York #513/R est:20000-25000

GDANIETZ, Wilhelm (1893-1962) German
£288 $453 €450 Fisherman mending net (70x80cm-28x31in) s. canvas on board. 21-Nov-2 Van Ham, Cologne #1630

GEACH, Portia (1873-1959) Australian
£538 $817 €807 La fete (15x28cm-6x11in) s. canvas on board. 27-Aug-2 Goodman, Sydney #30 (A.D 1500)

GEAR, Mabel (1900-) British
£900 $1494 €1305 Yorkshire terrier (41x46cm-16x18in) s.d.1923. 10-Jun-3 David Lay, Penzance #120/R
Works on paper
£280 $437 €420 Study of a terrier (31x25cm-12x10in) s. pastel. 26-Mar-3 Sotheby's, Olympia #153/R
£350 $553 €525 Secret (17x22cm-7x9in) s. pencil col chk wash. 28-Nov-2 Christie's, Kensington #295/R
£350 $553 €525 Springer spaniel (22x17cm-9x7in) s. black white chk. 28-Nov-2 Christie's, Kensington #361/R
£360 $587 €540 Scottish west highland terrier (25x17cm-10x7in) s. W/C gouache. 12-Feb-3 Bonhams, Knightsbridge #103/R
£552 $900 €828 Good friends (30x23cm-12x9in) s. W/C bodycol. 11-Feb-3 Bonhams & Doyles, New York #51/R est:1000-1500
£900 $1467 €1350 Toby (31x28cm-12x11in) s.i. pastel chl htd gouache. 12-Feb-3 Bonhams, Knightsbridge #114/R
£1000 $1630 €1500 Best friends (39x34cm-15x13in) s. pastel chk. 12-Feb-3 Bonhams, Knightsbridge #100/R est:700-900
£1700 $2652 €2550 Bathtime (9x15cm-4x6in) s. pencil htd white. 20-Sep-2 Dee Atkinson & Harrison, Driffield #655/R est:300-400

GEAR, William (1915-1997) British
£2000 $3160 €3000 Abstract (40x30cm-16x12in) s.d.89. 27-Nov-2 Sotheby's, Olympia #185/R est:2000-3000
£2400 $3720 €3600 Summer landscape (91x61cm-36x24in) s.d.79 s.i.d.verso. 4-Dec-2 Christie's, Kensington #606/R est:3000-5000
£2402 $3507 €3603 Winter hedgerow (99x81cm-39x32in) s.d.1951 s.i.d. verso prov. 4-Jun-2 Germann, Zurich #14/R est:5000-7000 (S.FR 5500)
£3200 $5248 €4800 Composition, blue centre (47x62cm-19x24in) s.d.49 s.i.d.Avril 49 verso exhib. 3-Jun-3 Sotheby's, Olympia #274/R est:3000-4000
£3600 $5904 €5220 Summer landscape (76x63cm-30x25in) s.d.51 s.i.d.51 verso prov.lit. 4-Jun-3 Sotheby's, London #30/R est:3000-5000
Works on paper
£300 $480 €450 Suchow (41x28cm-16x11in) s.d.88 col ink. 14-Mar-3 Gardiner & Houlgate, Bath #27/R
£320 $496 €480 Red and green abstract (38x26cm-15x10in) s.d.53 col ink. 4-Dec-2 Christie's, Kensington #356/R
£780 $1295 €1170 Abstract composition (48x33cm-19x13in) s.d.1948 W/C. 10-Jun-3 Bonhams, Leeds #119
£1000 $1580 €1500 Abstract shapes (30x49cm-12x19in) s.d.48 W/C crayon. 27-Nov-2 Sotheby's, Olympia #318/R est:1000-1500
£2500 $3951 €3750 Abstract shapes (29x46cm-11x18in) s.d.47 gouache. 27-Nov-2 Sotheby's, Olympia #317/R est:2500-3500
£4000 $6240 €6000 Abstract composition (29x48cm-11x19in) s.d.47 gouache W/C. 12-Sep-2 Sotheby's, Olympia #146/R est:4000-6000

GEARHART, Frances Hammell (1869-1958) American
Prints
£1774 $2750 €2661 October splendour (25x20cm-10x8in) s.i. colour block prov. 29-Oct-2 John Moran, Pasadena #802 est:2000-3000
Works on paper
£903 $1500 €1309 Forest stream (44x34cm-17x13in) s. pencil W/C gouache prov. 11-Jun-3 Butterfields, San Francisco #4185/R est:2000-3000

GEBAUER, C D (1777-1831) German
£431 $698 €625 Some travellers resting at a Cossack camp (41x51cm-16x20in) init. 26-May-3 Rasmussen, Copenhagen #1479/R (D.KR 4500)

GEBEL, Mathes (attrib) (16th C) German
Sculpture
£6500 $10205 €9750 Nobleman (8cm-3in) boxwood prov.lit. 10-Dec-2 Sotheby's, London #82/R est:5000-8000

GEBHARD, Albert (1869-1937) Finnish
£443 $691 €700 Carrara (34x15cm-13x6in) s.d.16.4.1898. 12-Sep-2 Hagelstam, Helsinki #920
£510 $811 €750 The convalescent (43x33cm-17x13in) s. 27-Feb-3 Hagelstam, Helsinki #866/R
£4748 $7597 €6600 Lullaby (80x59cm-31x23in) s.d.1899 exhib.lit. 17-May-3 Hagelstam, Helsinki #90/R est:6000
Works on paper
£392 $643 €600 Sunday in Lovisa (62x78cm-24x31in) s. W/C. 9-Feb-3 Bukowskis, Helsinki #236/R
£823 $1300 €1300 Aleksis Kivi (41x30cm-16x12in) s. Indian ink. 30-Nov-2 Hagelstam, Helsinki #77/R

GEBHARD, Johannes (1894-1976) Finnish
£264 $407 €420 Sibbo (50x63cm-20x25in) s. 24-Oct-2 Hagelstam, Helsinki #1017
£980 $1608 €1500 Coastal breakers (50x65cm-20x26in) s. 9-Feb-3 Bukowskis, Helsinki #238/R est:700

GEBHARDT, Eduard K F von (1838-1925) German
£342 $534 €500 Portrait of a scholar (47x38cm-19x15in) bears sig. board. 10-Apr-3 Van Ham, Cologne #1439
£588 $965 €900 Lazarus poor (40x49cm-16x19in) s. board. 5-Feb-3 Neumeister, Munich #708

GEBHARDT, Karl (1860-1917) German
£385 $604 €600 Dominican monk writing at window (47x34cm-19x13in) s.d.84 panel. 21-Nov-2 Van Ham, Cologne #1632

GEBLER, Otto Friedrich (attrib) (1838-1917) German
£3846 $5962 €6000 Young herdsman with sheep in front of stall door (20x26cm-8x10in) i. 4-Dec-2 Neumeister, Munich #738/R est:5000

GEBURSCH, Theo (1890-1958) German
£360 $590 €500 Autumnal still life (75x50cm-30x20in) mono.d.1947 i. verso. 4-Jun-3 Reiss & Sohn, Konigstein #372/R

GECELLI, Johannes (1925-) German
£347 $549 €500 Thing in the middle (53x69cm-21x27in) i.d.1960 verso gouache board. 26-Apr-3 Dr Lehr, Berlin #151/R
£411 $650 €650 Untitled (50x37cm-20x15in) s.d.1983 acrylic. 29-Nov-2 Villa Grisebach, Berlin #633/R
£646 $1028 €950 Oval room (61x47cm-24x19in) s.d.67 tempera. 28-Mar-3 Bolland & Marotz, Bremen #610/R
£1887 $2906 €3000 Female figure (139x99cm-55x39in) s.d.1962. 26-Oct-2 Dr Lehr, Berlin #119/R est:4000
£2083 $3292 €3000 Composition in maroon (180x200cm-71x79in) s.d.1985/86 acrylic exhib. 26-Apr-3 Dr Lehr, Berlin #150/R est:3000
£2899 $4754 €4000 Kore (130x100cm-51x39in) s.d.64 verso s.i.d.1964 stretcher hessian exhib. 31-May-3 Villa Grisebach, Berlin #357/R est:4000-6000
Works on paper
£503 $775 €800 Untitled abstract composition with figure (61x48cm-24x19in) s.d.1963 gouache board. 26-Oct-2 Dr Lehr, Berlin #122/R
£833 $1292 €1300 Untitled (58x81cm-23x32in) s.d.63 gouache Indian ink bodycol board. 3-Dec-2 Lempertz, Koln #150/R

GECHTER, J F T (1796-1844) French
Sculpture
£2100 $3255 €3150 Dray horse in traces (16cm-6in) pat.bronze. 30-Oct-2 Mallams, Oxford #589/R est:800-1200

GECHTER, Jean François Theodore (1796-1844) French
Sculpture
£2258 $3500 €3387 Death of Harold (41cm-16in) s.d.1837 dark brown pat. bronze lit. 29-Oct-2 Sotheby's, New York #245/R est:1500-2000
£5500 $9185 €7975 St George and the Dragon (37x34cm-15x13in) s.i.d.1842 dk brown pat bronze. 8-Jul-3 Sotheby's, London #198/R est:3000-5000
£10000 $15600 €15000 Death of Charles the Bold (56x47cm-22x19in) s.st.f.De Braux brown pat bronze. 5-Nov-2 Sotheby's, London #145/R est:10000-15000

GECHTOFF, Leonid (19/20th C) American
£556 $900 €834 Trees in winter (64x76cm-25x30in) s. 24-Jan-3 Freeman, Philadelphia #206/R

GEDDES, Andrew (1783-1844) British
£1900 $2964 €2850 Portrait of William Hay Leight at his desk. Portrait of his wife (49x39cm-19x15in) s.d.1839 pair. 10-Apr-3 Bonhams, Edinburgh #75 est:2000-3000

GEDDES, Ewan (?-1935) British
Works on paper
£250 $418 €363 Ancient door with a artist sketching (24x16cm-9x6in) s.d.84 W/C stopping out. 26-Jun-3 Mellors & Kirk, Nottingham #792

GEDDES, Margaret (1914-) British
£500 $820 €750 Abstract composition (71x91cm-28x36in) s.d.December 1967 stretcher. 3-Jun-3 Sotheby's, Olympia #304/R

GEDDES, William (1841-1884) British
£1800 $2898 €2700 Study for 'The Dookin hole' (23x35cm-9x14in) mono. board prov. 20-Feb-3 Christie's, London #342/R

GEDLEK, Ludwig (1847-?) Austrian
£1158 $1923 €1679 Hunting (18x24cm-7x9in) s. panel. 16-Jun-3 Lilla Bukowskis, Stockholm #933 est:20000-25000 (S.KR 15000)
£2358 $3656 €3750 Camp with mounted soldiers (15x23cm-6x9in) s. panel one of pair. 29-Oct-2 Dorotheum, Vienna #216/R est:2200-2500
£2358 $3656 €3750 Patrol (15x23cm-6x9in) s. panel. 29-Oct-2 Dorotheum, Vienna #217/R est:2200-2500
£4717 $7358 €7500 On reconnaisance (20x31cm-8x12in) s. prov.lit. 20-Sep-2 Karlheinz Kaupp, Staufen #1875/R est:7500

GEEFS, Adrian (19th C) Dutch
£420 $697 €420 Peniche amarree au coucher du soleil (35x27cm-14x11in) s. 16-Jun-3 Horta, Bruxelles #4

GEENS, Louis (1835-1906) Belgian
£506 $790 €800 Grenadier (20x15cm-8x6in) s. panel. 15-Oct-2 Horta, Bruxelles #279

GEER, Carl Johan de (1938-) Swedish
Prints
£2733 $4263 €4100 Violated flag (67x47cm-26x19in) s.d.1967 serigraph. 5-Nov-2 Bukowskis, Stockholm #339/R est:8000-10000 (S.KR 39000)

GEER, Maximilian von (1690-1768) German
Works on paper
£12346 $20000 €18519 Gardens of the new Schloss Schleissheim with fountains and old Schloss in distance (20x14cm-8x6in) gouache vellum on leather prov. 21-Jan-3 Sotheby's, New York #93/R est:30000
£12346 $20000 €18519 Badenburg at Nymphenburg (20x14cm-8x6in) gouache vellum on leather prov. 21-Jan-3 Sotheby's, New York #92 est:30000
£12346 $20000 €18519 Fountains in the gardens of the Nymphenburg (20x14cm-8x6in) gouache vellum on leather prov. 21-Jan-3 Sotheby's, New York #97/R est:30000
£12346 $20000 €18519 Nymphenburg from the West with gondola in foreground (20x14cm-8x6in) gouache vellum on panel prov. 21-Jan-3 Sotheby's, New York #96/R est:30000
£12346 $20000 €18519 Schloss Lustheim (20x14cm-8x6in) gouache vellum on leather prov. 21-Jan-3 Sotheby's, New York #95/R est:30000
£12346 $20000 €18519 Fountains in the west gardens of Nymphenburg (20x14cm-8x6in) gouache vellum on leather prov. 21-Jan-3 Sotheby's, New York #94/R est:30000
£12346 $20000 €18519 Starnberger See (20x14cm-8x6in) gouache vellum on leather prov. 21-Jan-3 Sotheby's, New York #99/R est:30000

GEERARDS, Jasper (17th C) Dutch
£64748 $103597 €90000 Pronk still life of a roemer, partly peeled lemon, a lobster on a pewter plate (74x97cm-29x38in) s. prov.exhib.lit. 14-May-3 Christie's, Amsterdam #189/R est:40000-60000

GEERLINGS, Gerald Kenneth (1897-1998) American
Prints
£2258 $3500 €3387 Black magic - New York (37x27cm-15x11in) s.i.d.1929 etching aquatint. 25-Sep-2 Christie's, Rockefeller NY #19/R est:4000-6000

GEERLINGS, Jacob Hendrik (1839-1959) Dutch
£1783 $2782 €2800 Gele riders (47x55cm-19x22in) s. 6-Nov-2 Vendue Huis, Gravenhage #509/R est:2700-3000

GEERTSEN, Henri (1892-1969) Belgian
£253 $395 €400 Mediterranean city view (24x33cm-9x13in) s. panel. 21-Oct-2 Bernaerts, Antwerp #507/R
£316 $494 €500 Dog cage (88x54cm-35x21in) s. 21-Oct-2 Bernaerts, Antwerp #740
£411 $642 €650 Inner courtyard in the snow (70x95cm-28x37in) s. 21-Oct-2 Bernaerts, Antwerp #508/R

GEERTSEN, Ib (1919-) Danish
£254 $394 €381 Concrete composition (35x27cm-14x11in) s.indis.i.d.58 verso. 1-Oct-2 Rasmussen, Copenhagen #217 (D.KR 3000)
£345 $528 €518 Blue-yellow (92x73cm-36x29in) s.d.1985 verso. 24-Aug-2 Rasmussen, Havnen #2223 (D.KR 4000)
£447 $711 €671 Green landscape (28x23cm-11x9in) s.d.1968 verso. 10-Mar-3 Rasmussen, Vejle #650/R (D.KR 4800)
£836 $1322 €1254 Composition (59x85cm-23x33in) s.i.d.1949 stretcher double-sided. 1-Apr-3 Rasmussen, Copenhagen #338/R (D.KR 9000)

GEEX DELAVALLEE (attrib) (17th C) Belgian
£3846 $5962 €6000 Bain de Diane. Persee et muses (56x72cm-22x28in) copper pair. 6-Dec-2 Millon & Associes, Paris #23/R est:9000

GEFFCKEN, Walter (1872-1950) German
£342 $534 €500 Elegant figures in salon (46x40cm-18x16in) s. board. 10-Apr-3 Van Ham, Cologne #1440

GEGERFELT, Wilhelm von (1844-1920) Swedish
£323 $510 €485 Coastal landscape with houses (32x51cm-13x20in) indis.sig. panel. 30-Nov-2 Goteborg Auktionsverk, Sweden #143/R (S.KR 4600)
£385 $609 €578 Southern street scene with figures walking (31x26cm-12x10in) st.sig. i.verso panel. 16-Nov-2 Crafoord, Lund #46/R (S.KR 5500)
£508 $813 €737 French landscape (41x56cm-16x22in) s.d.76 panel. 18-May-3 Anders Antik, Landskrona #75 (S.KR 6500)
£512 $809 €768 Winter landscape in evening glow (56x35cm-22x14in) s. 30-Nov-2 Goteborg Auktionsverk, Sweden #144/R (S.KR 7300)
£781 $1241 €1172 Winter landscape with woman (81x61cm-32x24in) s.d.1870. 3-Mar-3 Lilla Bukowskis, Stockholm #553 (S.KR 10500)
£864 $1417 €1253 Southern street scene with figures (33x27cm-13x11in) stamped sig. panel. 4-Jun-3 AB Stockholms Auktionsverk #2263/R (S.KR 11000)
£1312 $2034 €1968 Washing day (45x64cm-18x25in) s. 4-Dec-2 AB Stockholms Auktionsverk #1676/R est:25000-30000 (S.KR 18500)
£1312 $2034 €1968 Quay with figures, Venice in sunshine (38x33cm-15x13in) st.sig. 4-Dec-2 AB Stockholms Auktionsverk #1778/R est:15000-18000 (S.KR 18500)
£1335 $2190 €1936 Coastal landscape with southern town (98x165cm-39x65in) s. 4-Jun-3 AB Stockholms Auktionsverk #2098/R est:15000-20000 (S.KR 17000)
£1348 $2089 €2022 Winter landscape with evening red (60x102cm-24x40in) s.d.77. 3-Dec-2 Bukowskis, Stockholm #201/R est:25000-30000 (S.KR 19000)
£1348 $2089 €2022 Evening sunshine, Venice (54x35cm-21x14in) s. 8-Dec-2 Uppsala Auktionskammare, Uppsala #92/R est:15000-20000 (S.KR 19000)
£1375 $2255 €1994 Couple in walking in twilight landscape (61x110cm-24x43in) s. 4-Jun-3 AB Stockholms Auktionsverk #2129/R est:15000-20000 (S.KR 17500)
£1418 $2199 €2127 Landscape with buildings by water, evening sunshine (100x166cm-39x65in) s. 4-Dec-2 AB Stockholms Auktionsverk #1566/R est:25000-30000 (S.KR 20000)
£1418 $2199 €2127 Seascape with fishermen in boat, evening glow (98x74cm-39x29in) s. 4-Dec-2 AB Stockholms Auktionsverk #1712/R est:20000-25000 (S.KR 20000)
£1702 $2638 €2553 Sunset (69x100cm-27x39in) s. 3-Dec-2 Bukowskis, Stockholm #377/R est:35000-40000 (S.KR 24000)
£1773 $2748 €2660 Sunset (12x21cm-5x8in) s. panel. 3-Dec-2 Bukowskis, Stockholm #376/R est:20000-25000 (S.KR 25000)
£1807 $2963 €2620 Venetian quay (44x64cm-17x25in) s. 4-Jun-3 AB Stockholms Auktionsverk #2162/R est:20000-25000 (S.KR 23000)
£1899 $3000 €3000 Ferme en Normandie (41x61cm-16x24in) s.d.77 panel. 1-Dec-2 Peron, Melun #52b
£2128 $3298 €3192 Twilight on the Mediterranean (55x80cm-22x31in) s. 3-Dec-2 Bukowskis, Stockholm #375/R est:40000-50000 (S.KR 30000)
£2624 $4067 €3936 Venetian quay (42x66cm-17x26in) s. 4-Dec-2 AB Stockholms Auktionsverk #1703/R est:30000-35000 (S.KR 37000)
£3103 $5027 €4499 From the outskirts of Venice at sunset (78x99cm-31x39in) s. 26-May-3 Bukowskis, Stockholm #68/R est:35000-40000 (S.KR 40000)
£3142 $5153 €4556 Venice (43x61cm-17x24in) s. 4-Jun-3 AB Stockholms Auktionsverk #2262/R est:50000-60000 (S.KR 40000)
£3453 $5525 €4800 Vue de Venise (40x56cm-16x22in) s. 14-May-3 Rabourdin & Choppin de Janvry, Paris #55/R est:6000-6500
£3456 $5669 €5011 Venetian quay (65x92cm-26x36in) s/. 4-Jun-3 AB Stockholms Auktionsverk #2087/R est:35000-40000 (S.KR 44000)
£3830 $5936 €5745 Boats at dusk (84x120cm-33x47in) s. 3-Dec-2 Bukowskis, Stockholm #291/R est:50000-70000 (S.KR 54000)
£5106 $7915 €7659 Harbour view with figures (65x99cm-26x39in) s. 3-Dec-2 Bukowskis, Stockholm #374/R est:60000-80000 (S.KR 72000)
£5816 $9014 €8724 Terrace by Tracimeno Lake (82x125cm-32x49in) s. 3-Dec-2 Bukowskis, Stockholm #290/R est:70000-90000 (S.KR 82000)
£12413 $20109 €17999 Celebration fireworks, Venice (94x145cm-37x57in) s. 26-May-3 Bukowskis, Stockholm #186/R est:175000-200000 (S.KR 160000)

GEHBE, Eduard (1845-1933) German
£1026 $1610 €1600 Still life with flowers and grapes (77x107cm-30x42in) s. 21-Nov-2 Dorotheum, Vienna #179/R est:2000-3000

GEHR, Ferdinand (1896-1996) Swiss
£1346 $2087 €2100 Desenzano, Umberto I Square (25x36cm-10x14in) s.d.1924 tempera paper. 5-Dec-2 Stadion, Trieste #739/R est:1000
Works on paper
£279 $441 €419 Face of Christ, Immaculata and Holy Frank of Sales (54x58cm-21x23in) chl W/C collage exec.1955. 26-Nov-2 Hans Widmer, St Gallen #1118 (S.FR 650)
£873 $1362 €1310 Cloud (13x23cm-5x9in) mono. pastel chk. 6-Nov-2 Hans Widmer, St Gallen #109/R est:2000-3600 (S.FR 2000)
£4803 $7493 €7205 Rose (34x25cm-13x10in) s.d.89 W/C. 6-Nov-2 Hans Widmer, St Gallen #21/R est:8000-12000 (S.FR 11000)

GEHRI, Karl (1850-1922) Swiss?
£1991 $3205 €2887 Bear in wine cellar (108x201cm-43x79in) s.d.1903. 9-May-3 Dobiaschofsky, Bern #182/R est:5500 (S.FR 4300)

GEHRIG, Jakob (1846-1922) German
£519 $774 €800 Wagons in evening landscape (30x60cm-12x24in) s.i.d.73 panel. 27-Jun-2 Neumeister, Munich #2717/R
£952 $1514 €1400 Lagoon, Venice (23x31cm-9x12in) s. panel. 19-Mar-3 Neumeister, Munich #561/R est:1000

GEHRMAN, Paul (1861-?) German
£256 $397 €400 Spring day in the wood (50x60cm-20x24in) s. 6-Dec-2 Michael Zeller, Lindau #768
£282 $468 €400 Lively Danzig with Kranentor in moonlight (80x120cm-31x47in) s. 14-Jun-3 Arnold, Frankfurt #745/R
£548 $855 €800 Harbour, canal and old town of Konigsberg by moonlight (80x120cm-31x47in) s. 10-Apr-3 Van Ham, Cologne #1441/R

GEHRY, Frank (20th C) American
Sculpture
£2373 $3750 €3560 Sitting beaver chair (83x83x81cm-33x33x32in) corrugated cardboard executed 1988 prov. 13-Nov-2 Sotheby's, New York #132/R est:1800-2200
£3165 $5000 €4748 Carumba chair (79x129x137cm-31x51x54in) corrugated cardboard executed 1988 prov. 13-Nov-2 Sotheby's, New York #103/R est:6000-8000
£10127 $16000 €15191 Log lamp (18x251x18cm-7x99x7in) wood metal light bulbs electrical transformer prov. 13-Nov-2 Sotheby's, New York #133/R est:5000-7000
£12500 $20000 €18750 Snake lamp (170x33x8cm-67x13x3in) hand painted gouache papier mache modeled paper electrical unit. 14-May-3 Sotheby's, New York #165/R est:10000-15000
£17405 $27500 €26108 Snakes lamps (38x168x10cm-15x66x4in) s. hand painted gouache on papier mache in two parts prov. 13-Nov-2 Sotheby's, New York #102/R est:12000-18000
£20570 $32500 €30855 Snake lamp (60x109x71cm-24x43x28in) colorcore wood wire incandescent light executed c.1982 prov. 13-Nov-2 Sotheby's, New York #101/R est:18000-25000
£53797 $85000 €80696 Fish lamp, boat house (109x48x36cm-43x19x14in) glass electrical fixture prov. 13-Nov-2 Sotheby's, New York #113/R est:5000-7000

GEIBEL, Casimir (1839-1896) German
£3064 $4841 €4596 Farmers and horses in field (67x101cm-26x40in) s.i. 2-Dec-2 Rasmussen, Copenhagen #1339/R est:40000 (D.KR 36000)

GEIGER, Ernst (1876-1965) Swiss
£699 $1090 €1049 Bielern lake in the autumn light (21x38cm-8x15in) s.d.1941 board. 8-Nov-2 Dobiaschofsky, Bern #128/R est:2000 (S.FR 1600)
£1288 $2034 €1932 Bielersee with Peter island (33x41cm-13x16in) s.d.1911. 29-Nov-2 Zofingen, Switzerland #2885 est:4500 (S.FR 3000)
£1288 $2034 €1932 On Bielersee (46x37cm-18x15in) s.d.41. 29-Nov-2 Zofingen, Switzerland #2886/R est:4500 (S.FR 3000)
£1643 $2695 €2382 Autumn reeds (65x56cm-26x22in) s. 4-Jun-3 Fischer, Luzern #1248/R est:3000-4000 (S.FR 3500)
£1965 $3066 €2948 Island beach (38x46cm-15x18in) s.d.23. 8-Nov-2 Dobiaschofsky, Bern #130/R est:3800 (S.FR 4500)
£2790 $4408 €4185 View from Rapf of Biel coastal landscape (65x56cm-26x22in) s.i.d.1945. 29-Nov-2 Zofingen, Switzerland #2884/R est:9500 (S.FR 6500)
£5240 $8175 €7860 Bieler lake landscape in the evening (46x55cm-18x22in) s. i.verso. 8-Nov-2 Dobiaschofsky, Bern #127/R est:14000 (S.FR 12000)
£7860 $12262 €11790 Autumn afternoon (51x66cm-20x26in) s.d.1918. 8-Nov-2 Dobiaschofsky, Bern #117/R est:20000 (S.FR 18000)

GEIGER, Karl Joseph (1822-1905) Austrian
£1154 $1800 €1731 Allegorical mythological scene with blind bearded man (183x152cm-72x60in) s. 22-Sep-2 Jeffery Burchard, Florida #99
£2200 $3454 €3300 Mozart directing imaginary actors from the operas Don Giovanni and magic flute (50x71cm-20x28in) i.on stretcher prov. 21-Nov-2 Christie's, Kensington #54/R est:2000-3000
Works on paper
£270 $422 €400 Heideroslein (27x20cm-11x8in) s.i. pencil W/C. 28-Mar-3 Dorotheum, Vienna #327
£629 $975 €1000 The twelve months (106x102cm-42x40in) W/C pencil paper on board. 1-Oct-2 Dorotheum, Vienna #180/R
£2500 $4100 €3750 Allegorie des lebens - allegory of the cycle of life (49x66cm-19x26in) s.d.1884 W/C pencil. 3-Jun-3 Sotheby's, London #9/R est:3000-4000

GEIGER, Richard (1870-1945) Austrian
£360 $562 €540 Nymph and satyr (67x87cm-26x34in) s. canvas on board. 8-Apr-3 Bonhams, Knightsbridge #295/R
£420 $680 €630 Captive audience (75x99cm-30x39in) s. 23-Jan-3 Christie's, Kensington #107
£769 $1208 €1200 La danseuse au tambourin (80x60cm-31x24in) s. 16-Dec-2 Gros & Delettrez, Paris #118/R
£861 $1309 €1292 After the curtain falls (103x75cm-41x30in) s. 27-Aug-2 Rasmussen, Copenhagen #1953/R (D.KR 10000)
£1300 $2119 €1950 Reclining female nude (84x121cm-33x48in) s. 13-Feb-3 Christie's, Kensington #53/R est:1000-1500
Works on paper
£280 $437 €420 Lady holding a spaniel, reclining on a polar bear rug (52cm-20in circular) s. W/C over pencil. 17-Sep-2 Rosebery Fine Art, London #676

GEIGER, Robert (1859-1903) German
£468 $730 €702 Portrait of a nun (43x56cm-17x22in) s.d.83 canvas on board. 28-Mar-3 Aspire, Cleveland #38/R

GEIGER, Rupprecht (1908-) German
£8861 $14000 €14000 Red-pale green (90x90cm-35x35in) s. stretcher acrylic. 30-Nov-2 Villa Grisebach, Berlin #421/R est:10000-15000
£23386 $36949 €36950 311/60 (106x116cm-42x46in) s.d.60 verso i. stretcher exhib. 30-Nov-2 Villa Grisebach, Berlin #422/R est:18000-22000

GEIGER, Willi (1878-1971) German
Works on paper
£897 $1310 €1400 End of all things (18x18cm-7x7in) s.d.02 Indian ink wash. 4-Jun-2 Karl & Faber, Munich #251/R

GEIGER-WEISSHAUPT, Fanny von (1861-1931) German
£494 $765 €770 Nymphenburg, Schlossallee (97x73cm-38x29in) s. 5-Dec-2 Schopman, Hamburg #571

GEILLE DE SAINT LEGER, Léon (1864-?) French
£513 $805 €800 Voilier a quai (46x29cm-18x11in) s.i.d.91. 16-Dec-2 Millon & Associes, Paris #144/R
£1195 $1840 €1900 Chameliers (38x61cm-15x24in) s. 23-Oct-2 Rabourdin & Choppin de Janvry, Paris #135/R

GEIRNAERT, Jozef (1791-1859) Belgian
£5036 $8058 €7000 Les musiciens ambulants (140x112cm-55x44in) s. 13-May-3 Palais de Beaux Arts, Brussels #76/R est:7000-10000

GEISMAR, F (20th C) ?
Works on paper
£1474 $2315 €2300 Musee de Vesoul (30x47cm-12x19in) s.d.1913 W/C. 25-Nov-2 Rieunier, Bailly-Pommery, Mathias, Paris #7/R

GEISS, Otto (20th C) German?
£769 $1192 €1200 Still life of partly peeled apple with wine glass (50x41cm-20x16in) s.d.1995 panel. 6-Dec-2 Auktionhaus Georg Rehm, Augsburg #8044/R
Works on paper
£513 $795 €800 Female nude (62x48cm-24x19in) s.d.2002 gouache. 6-Dec-2 Auktionhaus Georg Rehm, Augsburg #8043/R

GEISSER, Johann Josef (1824-1894) Swiss
£326 $505 €489 Paysage des Prealpes vaudoises (30x50cm-12x20in) paper on canvas. 7-Dec-2 Galerie du Rhone, Sion #319/R (S.FR 750)

£558 $882 €837 Girl with posy sitting with goats and cows (36x46cm-14x18in) s. 29-Nov-2 Zofingen, Switzerland #2337 (S.FR 1300)
£699 $1090 €1049 Sunny wooded landscape (63x49cm-25x19in) 6-Nov-2 Dobiaschofsky, Bern #573/R (S.FR 1600)
£798 $1309 €1157 Cows on shore of Lake Geneva (44x66cm-17x26in) s. 4-Jun-3 Fischer, Luzern #2105/R est:1800-2500 (S.FR 1700)
£917 $1449 €1376 Mountain landscape with lake and cows (101x81cm-40x32in) s. 14-Nov-2 Stuker, Bern #239/R est:800-1000 (S.FR 2100)
£1200 $2004 €1800 Swiss alpine lake (33x46cm-13x18in) s. 18-Jun-3 Christie's, Kensington #60/R est:1500-2000

GEISSLER-ROHRBACH, Senta (1902-) German
Works on paper
£440 $687 €700 Women and animals in landscape (28x35cm-11x14in) s. W/C pencil Indian ink. 11-Oct-2 Winterberg, Heidelberg #1146

GEIST, August Christian (1835-1868) German
£353 $554 €550 Two travellers before mountain range (43x54cm-17x21in) 21-Nov-2 Van Ham, Cologne #1633
£974 $1451 €1500 River landscape with hillside ruins (25x31cm-10x12in) s.d.1853. 26-Jun-2 Neumeister, Munich #738/R

GEITLINGER, Ernst (1895-1972) German
£633 $1000 €1000 Fox (48x63cm-19x25in) s.d.52 oil Indian ink chk paper on board. 29-Nov-2 Villa Grisebach, Berlin #636/R

GELBENEGGER, Franz (1875-1933) Austrian
£450 $698 €675 Horses resting (38x52cm-15x20in) s.i.d.1902 board. 3-Dec-2 Bonhams, Knightsbridge #5/R

GELDER, Nicolaes van (1620-1677) Flemish
£110000 $183700 €159500 Strawberries in blue and white Chinese porcelain bowl. Lobster and partle peeled lemon on a stone le (57x43cm-22x17in) s.d.1662 pair exhib.lit. 9-Jul-3 Christie's, London #43/R est:80000-120000

GELDEREN, G van (?) Belgian
£348 $543 €550 Nature morte au canard, aux poussins et aux champignons (43x63cm-17x25in) 16-Sep-2 Amberes, Antwerp #262

GELDEREN, Simon van (1905-1986) Belgian
£314 $484 €500 Vase de lys et lilas (60x50cm-24x20in) s. 22-Oct-2 Campo & Campo, Antwerp #293
£374 $595 €550 Nature morte au homard (80x100cm-31x39in) s. 18-Mar-3 Galerie Moderne, Brussels #526
£475 $736 €750 Port de peche (70x100cm-28x39in) s. 24-Sep-2 Galerie Moderne, Brussels #873
£503 $775 €800 Vendeurs de graphique sur les rives de la Seine a Paris (60x75cm-24x30in) s. 22-Oct-2 Campo & Campo, Antwerp #291
£660 $1049 €950 Nature morte au chrysanthemes (80x60cm-31x24in) s. 29-Apr-3 Campo & Campo, Antwerp #318
£701 $1093 €1100 Cour de ferme (60x72cm-24x28in) s. 11-Nov-2 Horta, Bruxelles #711

GELDORP, Georg (attrib) (c.1595-1665) Flemish
£5500 $9185 €7975 Portrait of of a young lady, wearing a black dress and ruff beside a chair (82x65cm-32x26in) i.d.1624 panel prov. 8-Jul-3 Sotheby's, Olympia #331/R est:5000-7000

GELDORP, Gortzius (1553-1618) Flemish
£2548 $3975 €4000 Portrait of a man wearing a black costume (58x39cm-23x15in) mono.i.d.1619 prov.exhib.lit. 5-Nov-2 Sotheby's, Amsterdam #135/R est:5000-7000

GELIBERT, Gaston (1850-1931) French
£2975 $4700 €4700 L'envol du canard (65x80cm-26x31in) s. 1-Dec-2 Peron, Melun #137

GELIBERT, Jules-Bertrand (1834-1916) French
£674 $1125 €950 Becasse (32x23cm-13x9in) mono.d.18. 20-Jun-3 Piasa, Paris #53 est:1200-1500
£2468 $3900 €3900 Le lapin qui fume (61x50cm-24x20in) s. 1-Dec-2 Peron, Melun #138
£2778 $4500 €4028 Setters flushing mallards (81x66cm-32x26in) s.d.1879. 21-May-3 Doyle, New York #206/R est:5000-7000

GELLEE, Claude (c.1600-1682) French
Prints
£1859 $2937 €2900 La danse au bord de l'eau. etching. 14-Nov-2 Libert, Castor, Paris #13 est:2250
£1859 $2937 €2900 Le bouvier. etching. 14-Nov-2 Libert, Castor, Paris #15/R est:2850
£2244 $3545 €3500 POnt de bois. eau forte. 13-Nov-2 Piasa, Paris #75/R
£4808 $7596 €7500 Le troupeau en marche par un temps orgeux. etching. 14-Nov-2 Libert, Castor, Paris #16 est:1850
Works on paper
£256 $400 €384 Wooded coastal landscape with figures (38x48cm-15x19in) 21-Sep-2 Nadeau, Windsor #228/R
£3526 $5465 €5500 Scene de brigandage (9x14cm-4x6in) pe ink. 4-Dec-2 Piasa, Paris #47/R
£52469 $85000 €78704 Mercury returning the cattle of Admetus to Apollo (17x24cm-7x9in) s.i.d.1671 chk pen ink htd white prov.exhib.lit. 22-Jan-3 Christie's, Rockefeller NY #61/R est:100000
£202703 $316216 €300000 Chasse d'Ascagne (24x31cm-9x12in) i. pen ink wash htd gouache. 26-Mar-3 Piasa, Paris #38/R est:100000-120000

GELLEE, Claude (after) (c.1600-1682) French
£5500 $8579 €8250 Capriccio of a Mediterranean port with the Villa Medici (102x134cm-40x53in) 19-Sep-2 Christie's, Kensington #186/R est:5000-7000
£6000 $9360 €9000 Pastoral landscape with drovers and cattle fording a river before a classical portico (74x98cm-29x39in) 8-Apr-3 Sotheby's, Olympia #250/R est:6000-8000
£8500 $13259 €12750 Capriccio of a Mediterranean port with the Villa Medici (102x137cm-40x54in) 19-Sep-2 Christie's, Kensington #199/R est:5000-7000

GELLER, Johann Nepomuk (1860-1954) Austrian
£1786 $2804 €2679 Market scene (32x38cm-13x15in) s. oil ink card. 25-Nov-2 Christie's, Melbourne #295/R est:5000-8000 (A.D 5000)
£3191 $5170 €4500 Market place (27x40cm-11x16in) s. board. 22-May-3 Dorotheum, Vienna #112/R est:5000-5500

GELLI, Odoardo (1852-1933) Italian
£1700 $2771 €2550 Woman in a wine cellar (31x21cm-12x8in) s. board. 29-Jan-3 Sotheby's, Olympia #280/R est:1500-2000
£2203 $3216 €3305 Interior with young woman (31x20cm-12x8in) s. panel. 17-Jun-2 Philippe Schuler, Zurich #4342/R est:5000-7000 (S.FR 5000)

GELPKE, Ludwig (1897-?) Swiss
£485 $707 €728 Still life of flowers (36x34cm-14x13in) mono.d.46 panel. 17-Jun-2 Philippe Schuler, Zurich #7412 (S.FR 1100)

GEMITO, Vincenzo (1852-1929) Italian
Sculpture
£3000 $4710 €4500 Testa di bambino - bust of a child (42cm-17in) s. brown pat. bronze on marble base lit. 10-Dec-2 Sotheby's, London #163/R est:3000-5000
£3000 $4710 €4500 Pescatorello (32cm-13in) s. brown pat. bronze veined black marble base. 10-Dec-2 Sotheby's, London #165/R est:2500-3000
£3000 $5010 €4350 Bust of Jean-Louis Ernest Meissonier (23cm-9in) s. brown pat bronze st.f.Gemito Napoli. 8-Jul-3 Sotheby's, London #223/R est:3000-5000
£3200 $5344 €4640 Idiota (40cm-16in) s. dk brown pat bronze incl blk veined marble base st.f.Gemito. 8-Jul-3 Sotheby's, London #226/R est:3000-5000
£13000 $20280 €19500 Narcissus, after the Antique (62cm-24in) st.num.145 brown pat bronze. 5-Nov-2 Sotheby's, London #186/R est:10000-15000
£20000 $31400 €30000 Bust of Giuseppe Verdi (56cm-22in) s. brown pat. bronze. 10-Dec-2 Sotheby's, London #162/R est:20000-25000

GEMMELL, Michael (1950-) Irish
£1258 $1962 €2000 Top fields (30x30cm-12x12in) s. 17-Sep-2 Whyte's, Dublin #91/R est:1000-1500

GEN-PAUL (1895-1975) French
£385 $596 €600 Composition (44x33cm-17x13in) s. oil chk pastel lit. 6-Dec-2 Karlheinz Kaupp, Staufen #2132/R
£922 $1494 €1300 Christ (55x33cm-22x13in) s. painted c.1950. 21-May-3 Cornette de St.Cyr, Paris #45/R
£1122 $1785 €1650 Mon fils (35x27cm-14x11in) s.d.46 s.i.verso isorel panel. 26-Feb-3 Artcurial Briest, Paris #280 est:1200-1500
£1135 $1838 €1600 Visage du Christ (55x33cm-22x13in) s. panel painted c.1950. 21-May-3 Cornette de St.Cyr, Paris #46/R est:1500-2000
£1224 $1947 €1800 Fleurs (55x33cm-22x13in) s.d.61 panel. 26-Feb-3 Artcurial Briest, Paris #281 est:1800-2200
£1646 $2600 €2600 Cavalier (38x25cm-15x10in) s. masonite. 29-Nov-2 Drouot Estimations, Paris #103
£1761 $2730 €2800 Fleurs des champs (55x33cm-22x13in) s. panel painted c.1948-50. 30-Oct-2 Artcurial Briest, Paris #304/R est:2500-3000
£1809 $2930 €2550 Gaby (55x46cm-22x18in) s. d.fevrier 51 verso. 21-May-3 Cornette de St.Cyr, Paris #43/R est:1200-1500
£1835 $2900 €2900 Don Quichotte (41x27cm-16x11in) s. masonite. 29-Nov-2 Drouot Estimations, Paris #104

£1986 $3217 €2800 Christ en croix (100x37cm-39x15in) s. s.i.d.verso panel. 21-May-3 Cornette de St.Cyr, Paris #47/R est:3000-5000
£2013 $3119 €3200 Bouquet de fleurs (73x60cm-29x24in) s. painted c.1935. 30-Oct-2 Artcurial Briest, Paris #305/R est:3800-4500
£2279 $3623 €3350 Fleurs (65x50cm-26x20in) s. painted c.1940. 26-Feb-3 Artcurial Briest, Paris #279/R est:4500-6000
£2420 $3776 €3800 Picador (31x22cm-12x9in) s. panel. 10-Nov-2 Eric Pillon, Calais #226/R
£2532 $4000 €4000 Aux courses (50x65cm-20x26in) s. 2-Dec-2 Tajan, Paris #122
£2866 $4471 €4500 Petite Paulette (61x50cm-24x20in) s. painted c.1930. 10-Nov-2 Eric Pillon, Calais #72/R
£2949 $4629 €4600 Le violoncelliste (40x26cm-16x10in) s. panel. 16-Dec-2 Chochon-Barre & Allardi, Paris #63/R est:4500-5000
£3185 $4968 €5000 Vase de fleurs (55x33cm-22x13in) s. panel. 10-Nov-2 Eric Pillon, Calais #234/R
£3191 $5330 €4500 Clown (55x33cm-22x13in) s. 20-Jun-3 Piasa, Paris #186/R est:5000-8000
£3401 $5408 €5000 Portrait de Jean Pierre Graval (55x46cm-22x18in) s.d.1928 s.verso. 28-Feb-3 Joron-Derem, Paris #32/R
£3654 $5663 €5700 Aux courses (51x64cm-20x25in) s. 6-Dec-2 Rieunier, Bailly-Pommery, Mathias, Paris #91/R
£5068 $7905 €7500 Course de chevaux (50x65cm-20x26in) s. 25-Mar-3 Chochon-Barre & Allardi, Paris #130/R est:7500-8000
£5975 $9261 €9500 La course cyclist a Montmartre (65x81cm-26x32in) s. painted c.1950. 30-Oct-2 Artcurial Briest, Paris #306/R est:10000-12000
£6552 $10483 €9500 Le clown (92x61cm-36x24in) s. 12-Mar-3 E & Eve, Paris #111/R est:5000-7000
£6944 $11042 €10000 Portrait de Jean Dehelly dans l'ecole des femmes (91x60cm-36x24in) s. painted c.1927-1928 lit. 29-Apr-3 Artcurial Briest, Paris #190/R est:10000-12000
£6944 $11458 €10000 L'homme au chapeau noire, portrait du Dr Coudert (55x46cm-22x18in) s.d.24 lit. 2-Jul-3 Artcurial Briest, Paris #645/R est:10000-12000
£9028 $14896 €13000 La Java (65x54cm-26x21in) s. s.i.verso painted c.1926-27 lit. 2-Jul-3 Artcurial Briest, Paris #647/R est:12000-15000
£9603 $15652 €14500 Violoncelliste (114x78cm-45x31in) s. 3-Feb-3 Cornette de St.Cyr, Paris #301/R est:15000
£9655 $15255 €14000 Violoniste (92x60cm-36x24in) s. 4-Apr-3 Tajan, Paris #186/R est:18000
£10993 $17919 €16600 Violoniste (90x58cm-35x23in) s.d.1925. 3-Feb-3 Cornette de St.Cyr, Paris #302/R est:12000
£11146 $17389 €17500 Paris, Montmartre, Rue Lepic (65x81cm-26x32in) s. painted 1925. 10-Nov-2 Eric Pillon, Calais #70/R
£11218 $17612 €17500 Nu (65x81cm-26x32in) s. painted c.1927-28 exhib.lit. 10-Dec-2 Artcurial Briest, Paris #503/R est:18000-22000
£11724 $18641 €17000 Le violoniste (93x60cm-37x24in) s. 5-Mar-3 Doutrebente, Paris #71/R est:10000
£13141 $20631 €20500 Fillette a la poupee (73x60cm-29x24in) s. painted c.1926 lit. 10-Dec-2 Artcurial Briest, Paris #504/R est:20000-25000
£13291 $21000 €21000 Violoniste (92x60cm-36x24in) s. 27-Nov-2 Blanchet, Paris #92/R est:20000
£26259 $42014 €36500 O Sole Mio (92x65cm-36x26in) s. s.i.d.verso. 14-May-3 Blanchet, Paris #91/R est:25000-30000
£27885 $43779 €43500 Coup de Beaujolais, auto-portrait (92x60cm-36x24in) s.d.28 i.verso prov.exhib.lit. 10-Dec-2 Artcurial Briest, Paris #502/R est:30000-40000

Works on paper

£263 $427 €400 Portrait de Sanz Martinez (27x22cm-11x9in) s.i.d.5 novembre ink pen dr. 22-Jan-3 Tajan, Paris #184
£263 $427 €400 Le violoniste (33x25cm-13x10in) gouache. 22-Jan-3 Tajan, Paris #185
£263 $427 €400 Les cavaliers (22x28cm-9x11in) gouache. 22-Jan-3 Tajan, Paris #189
£312 $496 €450 Portrait d'homme (27x19cm-11x7in) s.i.d.25 Nov.52 graphite dr. 29-Apr-3 Artcurial Briest, Paris #188
£312 $496 €450 Christ en croix (41x31cm-16x12in) s. W/C Indian ink exec.c.1955. 29-Apr-3 Artcurial Briest, Paris #189
£346 $536 €550 Marin a la buvette (27x21cm-11x8in) s. crayon ink dr. 7-Oct-2 Claude Aguttes, Neuilly #38
£385 $596 €600 En caleche (20x28cm-8x11in) s. col crayon dr. 6-Dec-2 Rieunier, Bailly-Pommery, Mathias, Paris #80
£403 $648 €600 La rose (30x22cm-12x9in) s.d.1960 ink dr. 23-Feb-3 Lesieur & Le Bars, Le Havre #62
£409 $634 €650 Christ en Croix (43x34cm-17x13in) s. mixed media. 7-Oct-2 Claude Aguttes, Neuilly #276
£411 $645 €600 Portrait de Michele (31x23cm-12x9in) s.d.74 crayolor. 21-Apr-3 Rabourdin & Choppin de Janvry, Paris #149
£426 $689 €600 Maternite (29x20cm-11x8in) s. pastel. 21-May-3 Cornette de St.Cyr, Paris #42/R
£428 $714 €620 La danse (28x20cm-11x8in) s. chl gouache. 9-Jul-3 Cornette de St.Cyr, Paris #172
£449 $704 €700 Cycliste (20x12cm-8x5in) s. W/C. 15-Dec-2 Eric Pillon, Calais #253/R
£461 $770 €650 Courses de chevaux (27x38cm-11x15in) s. pastel. 23-Jun-3 Claude Boisgirard, Paris #179/R
£475 $741 €750 Guitariste (63x26cm-25x10in) s. col crayon Chinese ink brush. 20-Oct-2 Chayette & Cheval, Paris #10
£494 $800 €750 Femme accoudee (26x21cm-10x8in) W/C pair. 22-Jan-3 Tajan, Paris #186
£537 $864 €800 Portrait (25x20cm-10x8in) s. ink dr. 23-Feb-3 Lesieur & Le Bars, Le Havre #63
£541 $843 €800 Violoniste (33x15cm-13x6in) s. wax crayon dr. 28-Mar-3 Charbonneaux, Paris #75
£566 $877 €900 Rue Ravignan (41x30cm-16x12in) s.i. pastel. 4-Oct-2 Tajan, Paris #106
£566 $877 €900 Polo a bagatelle (41x52cm-16x20in) s.i. Indian ink. 4-Oct-2 Tajan, Paris #105
£576 $944 €800 Don Quichotte (48x40cm-19x16in) s. ink pastel. 4-Jun-3 Marc Kohn, Paris #55/R
£601 $950 €950 Course de chevaux a Auteuil (26x37cm-10x15in) s.i. col crayon dr. 29-Nov-2 Drouot Estimations, Paris #99
£634 $1060 €920 Portrait (33x23cm-13x9in) s. chl W/C gouache. 9-Jul-3 Cornette de St.Cyr, Paris #170
£641 $1006 €1000 Danseur au violon (26x21cm-10x8in) s. col crayon. 15-Dec-2 Eric Pillon, Calais #251/R
£641 $1006 €1000 Vue de Paris (50x63cm-20x25in) s. W/C. 12-Dec-2 Rabourdin & Choppin de Janvry, Paris #76/R
£662 $1079 €1000 Bouquet de tournesols (43x30cm-17x12in) s. mixed media. 1-Feb-3 Claude Aguttes, Neuilly #239/R
£694 $1097 €1000 Arthur Grumaux (39x27cm-15x11in) s.i. pen dr. 25-Apr-3 Piasa, Paris #105
£723 $1172 €1100 Le clown (24x20cm-9x8in) s.d.45 gouache. 22-Jan-3 Tajan, Paris #188
£789 $1279 €1200 Les courses (21x30cm-8x12in) crayolors. 22-Jan-3 Tajan, Paris #183
£851 $1421 €1200 Les clowns musiciens (63x48cm-25x19in) s. mixed media. 23-Jun-3 Claude Boisgirard, Paris #182
£897 $1400 €1346 Polo players (51x64cm-20x25in) s. W/C. 10-Nov-2 Selkirks, St. Louis #590 est:1500-2000
£940 $1513 €1400 Course de chevaux (48x63cm-19x25in) s. mixed media. 23-Feb-3 Mercier & Cie, Lille #238/R
£962 $1510 €1500 Le violoncelliste (42x29cm-17x11in) s. crayolor. 16-Dec-2 Chochon-Barre & Allardi, Paris #62/R est:1000-1200
£993 $1609 €1400 Montmartre (46x37cm-18x15in) s. gouache. 21-May-3 Cornette de St.Cyr, Paris #43a/R
£1013 $1580 €1600 Gare de Vic (49x63cm-19x25in) s. W/C. 20-Oct-2 Chayette & Cheval, Paris #9/R
£1043 $1628 €1565 La Croisette, Cannes (50x66cm-20x26in) s.i. gouache chk. 16-Sep-2 Philippe Schuler, Zurich #3028/R est:1500-2000 (S.FR 2400)
£1118 $1812 €1700 Nogent sur Marne (21x27cm-8x11in) s. gouache. 22-Jan-3 Tajan, Paris #190 est:460-750
£1184 $1918 €1800 Les musiciens (27x21cm-11x8in) s. gouache pair. 22-Jan-3 Tajan, Paris #187 est:460-750
£1200 $1860 €1800 Les courses (47x61cm-19x24in) s. gouache. 5-Dec-2 Christie's, Kensington #176/R est:800-1200
£1204 $1938 €1806 Les jockeys (49x64cm-19x25in) s. mixed media. 7-May-3 Dobiaschofsky, Bern #573/R est:4000 (S.FR 2600)
£1218 $1912 €1900 Corrida (32x42cm-13x17in) s. gouache. 21-Nov-2 Neret-Minet, Paris #23/R
£1224 $1947 €1800 Le violoniste (50x64cm-20x25in) s. 2-Mar-3 Lombrail & Teucquam, Paris #174/R
£1282 $2013 €2000 Cavaliers (47x63cm-19x25in) s. gouache. 13-Dec-2 Piasa, Paris #141/R
£1282 $2013 €2000 Course de chevaux (34x48cm-13x19in) s. gouache. 15-Dec-2 Eric Pillon, Calais #256/R
£1382 $2238 €2100 Au polo (48x65cm-19x26in) s. W/C prov. 22-Jan-3 Tajan, Paris #193 est:1500-1800
£1500 $2505 €2250 Les cyclistes (49x65cm-19x26in) s. W/C gouache. 26-Jun-3 Christie's, London #388/R est:400-600
£1519 $2400 €2400 Moulin Rouge (49x64cm-19x25in) s. gouache. 27-Nov-2 Blanchet, Paris #107/R
£1565 $2488 €2300 Rentree au paddock (49x65cm-19x26in) s. gouache prov. 24-Mar-3 Claude Boisgirard, Paris #177/R
£1748 $2919 €2500 La Seine et Notre-Dame (48x63cm-19x25in) s. W/C ink. 26-Jun-3 Tajan, Paris #60/R est:3000-4600
£1888 $3153 €2700 Joueurs de Polo (48x60cm-19x24in) s. W/C ink gouache. 26-Jun-3 Tajan, Paris #61/R est:3000-4600
£1961 $3216 €3000 Deux attelages (48x63cm-19x25in) s.i. gouache. 9-Feb-3 Anaf, Lyon #110/R
£2075 $3217 €3300 Maternite Algerienne (65x50cm-26x20in) s.i.d.30 W/C pencil. 30-Oct-2 Artcurial Briest, Paris #207/R est:2800-3200
£2346 $3331 €3800 Cavaliers (47x62cm-19x24in) s. gouache W/C. 16-Mar-3 Eric Pillon, Calais #241/R
£2431 $3865 €3500 Scene de paddock (49x64cm-19x25in) s. gouache W/C graphite. 29-Apr-3 Artcurial Briest, Paris #187/R est:2000-3000
£2885 $4529 €4500 Cannes, cavaliers sur La Croisette (49x65cm-19x26in) s.i. gouache W/C. 15-Dec-2 Eric Pillon, Calais #203/R
£2930 $4571 €4600 Aux courses (50x65cm-20x26in) s. gouache. 10-Nov-2 Eric Pillon, Calais #207/R
£3057 $4769 €4800 Aux courses (50x65cm-20x26in) s. gouache. 10-Nov-2 Eric Pillon, Calais #206/R
£3087 $4970 €4600 Le paddock (48x63cm-19x25in) s.i. gouache. 23-Feb-3 Lesieur & Le Bars, Le Havre #61/R
£5306 $8437 €7800 Promenade en Caleche (49x60cm-19x24in) s.i. gouache W/C pencil. 26-Feb-3 Artcurial Briest, Paris #51/R est:5000-6000

GENBERG, Anton (1862-1939) Swedish

£270 $418 €405 Landscape in autumn colours, Kallror (33x41cm-13x16in) s. panel. 8-Dec-2 Uppsala Auktionskammare, Uppsala #171 (S.KR 3800)
£525 $830 €788 Mountain landscape with cattle, sheep and horses grazing (85x116cm-33x46in) s,. 16-Nov-2 Crafoord, Lund #5 (S.KR 7500)
£565 $886 €848 View of Fiskebackskil (42x62cm-17x24in) s.d.31. 16-Dec-2 Lilla Bukowskis, Stockholm #121 (S.KR 8000)

£567 $879 €851 Street scene, Visby (66x82cm-26x32in) s.i.d.1923. 8-Dec-2 Uppsala Auktionskammare, Uppsala #131/R (S.KR 8000)
£600. $942 €900 Spring brook in evening glow (73x91cm-29x36in) s.d. 16-Dec-2 Lilla Bukowskis, Stockholm #674 (S.KR 8500)
£633 $1051 €918 Northern summer landscape with red cottages (49x69cm-19x27in) s. 16-Jun-3 Lilla Bukowskis, Stockholm #1187 (S.KR 8200)
£687 $1086 €1031 Rio della Pieta, Venice (61x50cm-24x20in) s.d.94. 27-Nov-2 Falkkloos, Malmo #77732/R (S.KR 9800)
£772 $1282 €1119 Torneaahamn (60x80cm-24x31in) s.d.1911. 16-Jun-3 Lilla Bukowskis, Stockholm #1003 (S.KR 10000)
£811 $1346 €1176 Northern landscape (65x54cm-26x21in) s. 16-Jun-3 Lilla Bukowskis, Stockholm #515 (S.KR 10500)
£931 $1508 €1350 Winter landscape (61x81cm-24x32in) s.d.1912. 26-May-3 Bukowskis, Stockholm #107/R (S.KR 12000)
£993 $1539 €1490 Sun over the mountains - winter landscape with farm (90x117cm-35x46in) s.d.1916. 4-Dec-2 AB Stockholms Auktionsverk #1585/R (S.KR 14000)
£1301 $2056 €1952 Afternoon sunshine over snow covered mountains near Aare (73x100cm-29x39in) s.i.d.1911. 5-Apr-3 Rasmussen, Havnen #2025/R est:20000 (D.KR 14000)
£1702 $2638 €2553 View of Zinkensdamm, Stockholm (50x70cm-20x28in) s. panel. 3-Dec-2 Bukowskis, Stockholm #338/R est:20000-25000 (S.KR 24000)
£1791 $2901 €2687 Sunny autumn landscape with farm, horse and cart (59x89cm-23x35in) s.d.89. 3-Feb-3 Lilla Bukowskis, Stockholm #921 est:12000-15000 (S.KR 25000)
£1915 $2968 €2873 River landscape in evening, Aare (81x166cm-32x65in) s.d.1927. 3-Dec-2 Bukowskis, Stockholm #84/R est:25000-30000 (S.KR 27000)
£2715 $4399 €3937 Landscape with boy (70x90cm-28x35in) s.i.d.95. 26-May-3 Bukowskis, Stockholm #130/R est:40000-50000 (S.KR 35000)

GENDEBIEN, Louis (1882-1946) Belgian
£276 $436 €400 Port de peche (55x65cm-22x26in) s. 2-Apr-3 Vanderkindere, Brussels #527/R
£276 $436 €400 Bateaux de peche a Zeebrugge (33x41cm-13x16in) s. d.1935 verso canvas on cardboard. 2-Apr-3 Vanderkindere, Brussels #524/R

GENDRON, Ernest August (1817-1881) French
£849 $1325 €1350 Couple enlace (46x38cm-18x15in) s.d.1846. 14-Oct-2 Thierry & Lannon, Brest #115

GENDRON, Pierre (1934-) Canadian
£350 $539 €525 Zenada (63x51cm-25x20in) s. prov. 22-Oct-2 Iegor de Saint Hippolyte, Montreal #41 (C.D 850)

GENEGEN, Jos van (1857-1936) Belgian
£342 $538 €500 Paysage avec fermes (34x53cm-13x21in) s. 15-Apr-3 Galerie Moderne, Brussels #367
£449 $696 €700 Maisons dans la prairie (45x65cm-18x26in) s. 3-Dec-2 Campo & Campo, Antwerp #309
£897 $1364 €1400 Nature morte aux fleurs (70x90cm-28x35in) s. 27-Aug-2 Galerie Moderne, Brussels #313

GENELLI, Bonaventura (1798-1868) German
Works on paper
£1451 $2250 €2177 Prometheus (37x45cm-15x18in) s.i.d.1885 pencil W/C prov.exhib. 29-Oct-2 Sotheby's, New York #111/R est:1000-1500

GENERALIC, Ivan (1914-) Yugoslavian
£1593 $2484 €2500 Repas des moissonneurs (28x38cm-11x15in) prov. 5-Nov-2 Tajan, Paris #47/R
£3503 $5465 €5500 Marche aux bestiaux (47x71cm-19x28in) s.d.1961 prov. 5-Nov-2 Tajan, Paris #45/R est:3800-4800

GENERALIC, Josip (1936-) Yugoslavian
£334 $554 €484 Winter afternoon snowball fight (24x32cm-9x13in) s.d.1970 acrylic canvas on masonite. 10-Jun-3 Ritchie, Toronto #149/R (C.D 750)
£533 $885 €773 Couple with horse and sleigh. Summer picnic (42x28cm-17x11in) s.d.1970 acrylic canvas on board two. 10-Jun-3 Ritchie, Toronto #148/R est:1000-1500 (C.D 1200)

GENESEN, Frans van (1887-1945) Dutch
£348 $570 €480 Riviere a travers la ville (70x60cm-28x24in) s. 27-May-3 Campo & Campo, Antwerp #246
£692 $1079 €1100 Canal view (70x80cm-28x31in) s. 23-Sep-2 Bernaerts, Antwerp #26/R

GENEVRAY, Louis (1867-?) French
£1600 $2480 €2400 Bigoudennes au lavoir (50x61cm-20x24in) s.d.1922. 5-Dec-2 Christie's, Kensington #10/R est:2000-3000

GENGEMBRE, Joseph Z (19th C) French
Works on paper
£412 $650 €650 Portrait du Duc d'Aumale (20x31cm-8x12in) s.d. W/C crayon htd gouache. 28-Nov-2 Tajan, Paris #165

GENGYO, Miyagi (1817-1880) Japanese
Prints
£4487 $7000 €6731 Camera view, balloon (38x25cm-15x10in) s. col print. 25-Mar-3 Christie's, Rockefeller NY #358/R est:3000-3500

GENICOT, Robert Albert (1890-1981) French
£276 $461 €400 Bougival (38x55cm-15x22in) s.d.1923 s.i.d.verso. 9-Jul-3 Millon & Associes, Paris #159

GENIES, Carole (20th C) French
Works on paper
£298 $486 €450 Roxanne (130x89cm-51x35in) s. mixed media canvas. 1-Feb-3 Claude Aguttes, Neuilly #295/R

GENILLION, Jean Baptiste François (1750-1829) French
£11151 $18288 €15500 Vue de la ville de Naples (32x40cm-13x16in) 5-Jun-3 Fraysse & Associes, Paris #14/R est:6000-8000

GENIN, Lucien (1894-1958) French
£828 $1292 €1300 Paris, Notre-Dame (24x19cm-9x7in) s. 10-Nov-2 Eric Pillon, Calais #136/R
£880 $1365 €1400 La Place Pigalle (24x32cm-9x13in) s. cardboard. 4-Oct-2 Tajan, Paris #107 est:1000-1500
£1226 $1913 €1839 Notre Dame (46x55cm-18x22in) s. 6-Nov-2 AB Stockholms Auktionsverk #940/R est:20000-25000 (S.KR 17500)
£1401 $2186 €2200 Paris, rue animee (54x65cm-21x26in) s. 10-Nov-2 Eric Pillon, Calais #131/R
£2621 $4167 €3800 Bateaux au port de Marseille (60x73cm-24x29in) s. 5-Mar-3 Doutrebente, Paris #62/R est:5000-6000
£3145 $4874 €5000 Paris, notre Dame et les quais (60x73cm-24x29in) s. 30-Oct-2 Artcurial Briest, Paris #307 est:3000-4000
£4043 $6549 €5700 Place animee (60x73cm-24x29in) s. 26-May-3 Joron-Derem, Paris #67/R est:4000-6000
£4167 $6875 €6000 Paris, Place de l'Opera (60x73cm-24x29in) s. 2-Jul-3 Artcurial Briest, Paris #646/R est:6000-8000
Works on paper
£408 $649 €600 Bicetre, les roulottes (38x45cm-15x18in) s.i. W/C gouache. 26-Feb-3 Fraysse & Associes, Paris #20/R
£419 $663 €650 Les quais pres de Notre-Dame (25x36cm-10x14in) s. gouache. 17-Dec-2 Rossini, Paris #27
£504 $806 €700 Rue de Paris animee (23x31cm-9x12in) s. gouache. 13-May-3 Vanderkindere, Brussels #91
£556 $789 €900 Paris, barques en bord de Seine (21x25cm-8x10in) s. gouache. 16-Mar-3 Eric Pillon, Calais #238/R
£574 $896 €850 Port (18x23cm-7x9in) s. gouache W/C. 26-Mar-3 Millon & Associes, Paris #32/R
£621 $1037 €900 La Place du Tertre a Montmartre (34x25cm-13x10in) s. gouache. 10-Jul-3 Artcurial Briest, Paris #95
£719 $1151 €1000 Les roulottes (37x45cm-15x18in) s. W/C gouache. 18-May-3 Eric Pillon, Calais #97/R
£764 $1192 €1200 Rue du vieux Paris (30x23cm-12x9in) s. gouache. 10-Nov-2 Eric Pillon, Calais #139/R
£955 $1490 €1500 Paris, porte Saint-Martin (22x26cm-9x10in) s. gouache. 10-Nov-2 Eric Pillon, Calais #132/R
£1026 $1610 €1600 Villefranche (24x33cm-9x13in) s.i.d.47 gouache. 13-Dec-2 Piasa, Paris #258/R
£1720 $2683 €2700 Casino au bord de lac (31x41cm-12x16in) s. gouache. 10-Nov-2 Eric Pillon, Calais #133/R
£2083 $3313 €3000 Le port de Cassis (31x40cm-12x16in) s.d.38 gouache. 29-Apr-3 Artcurial Briest, Paris #184/R est:2000-3000
£2756 $4328 €4300 Canotiers sur les bords de Marne (62x52cm-24x20in) s. gouache. 24-Nov-2 Lesieur & Le Bars, Le Havre #64

GENIS, René (1922-) French
£764 $1192 €1200 Bordeaux, quais et docks (54x73cm-21x29in) s. 10-Nov-2 Eric Pillon, Calais #186/R
£791 $1266 €1100 Etang en bresse (50x74cm-20x29in) s. 18-May-3 Eric Pillon, Calais #139/R
£1139 $1800 €1800 Tros cheminees (46x55cm-18x22in) s. painted c.1954. 26-Nov-2 Camard, Paris #113/R
£1401 $2186 €2200 Brest, charbonnages sur le port (65x81cm-26x32in) s. painted 1954. 10-Nov-2 Eric Pillon, Calais #184/R
£1529 $2385 €2400 Gelee blanche pres de l'ecluse (54x81cm-21x32in) s. d.1956 verso. 10-Nov-2 Eric Pillon, Calais #185/R
£1852 $2630 €3000 Cueillette dans le verger (73x92cm-29x36in) s. 16-Mar-3 Eric Pillon, Calais #175/R

GENISSON, Jules Victor (1805-1860) Belgian
£450 $734 €675 Figures in a church (33x25cm-13x10in) s. 13-Feb-3 David Lay, Penzance #424/R
£1096 $1710 €1600 Interieur d'eglise (42x34cm-17x13in) s.d.1834. 14-Apr-3 Horta, Bruxelles #156 est:1200-1800
£2051 $3179 €3200 Interior of Liege cathedral (79x65cm-31x26in) s.d.1853 prov. 7-Dec-2 Ketterer, Hamburg #86/R est:4500-5000

GENN, Robert (1936-) Canadian
£216 $344 €313 After the rain (46x61cm-18x24in) s. s.i.d.1968 verso panel. 1-May-3 Heffel, Vancouver #25/R (C.D 500)
£216 $344 €313 Afternoon, November (46x61cm-18x24in) s. s.i.verso board. 1-May-3 Heffel, Vancouver #26/R (C.D 500)
£221 $347 €332 Hilltop, Galiano (20x25cm-8x10in) s.i.d.1978 panel. 25-Nov-2 Hodgins, Calgary #3/R (C.D 550)
£222 $364 €322 Low tide, Porspoder, Brittany (28x36cm-11x14in) 1-Jun-3 Levis, Calgary #43 (C.D 500)
£261 $410 €392 Warm surprise (20x25cm-8x10in) s.i. panel. 25-Nov-2 Hodgins, Calgary #250/R (C.D 650)
£324 $516 €470 Highland wilderness (20x25cm-8x10in) s. s.i.verso panel. 1-May-3 Heffel, Vancouver #27/R (C.D 750)
£606 $921 €909 Autumn on Atlin Lake (61x76cm-24x30in) acrylic. 4-Jul-2 Heffel, Vancouver #8 (C.D 1400)
£643 $1015 €965 Beaver pond in winter, Manning Park (61x76cm-24x30in) d.1972. 1-Dec-2 Levis, Calgary #30/R (C.D 1600)
£779 $1184 €1169 Six men and an umaik (61x122cm-24x48in) board. 4-Jul-2 Heffel, Vancouver #9 est:1500-2500 (C.D 1800)
£1144 $1819 €1716 Warm forest (25x30cm-10x12in) s.i.d. board prov. 23-Mar-3 Hodgins, Calgary #90/R est:600-900 (C.D 2700)
£1146 $1753 €1719 Bella coola (61x91cm-24x36in) 24-Aug-2 Heffel, Vancouver #10 est:2000-3000 (C.D 2750)
£1780 $2830 €2670 Prideaux islet (75x90cm-30x35in) s.i. 23-Mar-3 Hodgins, Calgary #48/R est:2000-3000 (C.D 4200)
£2000 $3280 €2900 Canada, western skyline (60x120cm-24x47in) s.i.d.1968 prov. 9-Jun-3 Hodgins, Calgary #10/R est:3000-4000 (C.D 4500)

GENNAI, Guido (1895-?) Italian
Works on paper
£290 $475 €400 Arco a San Gimignano (51x38cm-20x15in) s. W/C. 27-May-3 Finarte, Milan #152/R

GENNARELLI, A (20th C) Italian
Sculpture
£1100 $1760 €1650 Female bust with headdress (24cm-9in) s. green pat. bronze ivory. 15-May-3 Christie's, Kensington #449/R est:1200-1500

GENNARELLI, Amedeo (20th C) Italian
Sculpture
£1274 $1987 €2000 Kneeling woman (48x25x39cm-19x10x15in) st.f.AG brown green pat bronze. 6-Nov-2 Tajan, Paris #15
£2568 $4005 €3800 Jeune fille nue assise (40x50x17cm-16x20x7in) s. white marble. 26-Mar-3 Millon & Associes, Paris #164/R

GENNARI, Benedetto (16/17th C) Italian
Works on paper
£629 $900 €944 Lot and his daughters (18x27cm-7x11in) pen ink red chk. 23-Jan-3 Swann Galleries, New York #102/R

GENNARI, Benedetto (younger) (1633-1715) Italian
£8966 $14166 €13000 Saint John the Baptist (74x62cm-29x24in) 5-Apr-3 Finarte Semenzato, Milan #79/R est:9000

GENNARI, Cesare (1637-1688) Italian
Works on paper
£700 $1099 €1050 Young man (13x10cm-5x4in) red chk. 11-Dec-2 Sotheby's, Olympia #64/R

GENNARI, Cesare (attrib) (1637-1688) Italian
Works on paper
£886 $1400 €1400 Studies (40x28cm-16x11in) sanguine double-sided. 28-Nov-2 Tajan, Paris #16/R
£4400 $7348 €6380 Study of a tree within a landscape with two figures (21x29cm-8x11in) pen brown ink prov. 9-Jul-3 Bonhams, Knightsbridge #19/R est:800-1200

GENOELS, Abraham (1640-1723) Flemish
Works on paper
£828 $1292 €1300 Rocky Italianate landscape with figures resting by a stream (7x12cm-3x5in) s. pen black ink grey wash. 5-Nov-2 Sotheby's, Amsterdam #96/R
£955 $1490 €1500 Classical landscape with figures among buildings by a lake (11x16cm-4x6in) s. pen black ink grey wash prov.exhib. 5-Nov-2 Sotheby's, Amsterdam #98/R est:1000-1500

GENOESE SCHOOL (?) Italian
Works on paper
£5200 $8112 €7800 Kyrenia (10x23cm-4x9in) i.verso W/C. 11-Apr-3 Keys, Aylsham #490/R est:600-800

GENOESE SCHOOL (17th C) Italian
£5500 $8579 €8250 Portrait of a gentleman, in red robes (67x51cm-26x20in) 19-Sep-2 Christie's, Kensington #235/R est:5000-8000
£7233 $11283 €11500 Terrace wit figures (98x125cm-39x49in) 8-Oct-2 Christie's, Paris #22/R est:10000
Works on paper
£7099 $10080 €11500 Battle scene (13x30cm-5x12in) dr. 17-Mar-2 Galerie de Chartres, Chartres #45

GENOUD, Nanette (1907-1987) Swiss
£278 $447 €417 Village square with fountain (45x38cm-18x15in) s.d.1940 panel. 7-May-3 Dobiaschofsky, Bern #3279 (S.FR 600)
£349 $545 €524 Citadelle sur l'eau (45x55cm-18x22in) s.d.48 i. verso panel. 6-Nov-2 Dobiaschofsky, Bern #575/R (S.FR 800)

GENOVES, Juan (1930-) Spanish
£8500 $13855 €12750 Izqierda, derecha (100x100cm-39x39in) s.d.67. 3-Feb-3 Sotheby's, Olympia #170/R est:3000-4000
£14013 $22000 €21020 Face to the wall (95x124cm-37x49in) s.d.67 prov. 20-Nov-2 Christie's, Rockefeller NY #119/R est:20000-25000
Works on paper
£1500 $2355 €2250 Untitled (69x49cm-27x19in) s.d.67 mixed media. 15-Apr-3 Bonhams, Knightsbridge #158/R est:600-800

GENT, Joannes B N van (1891-1974) Dutch
£240 $350 €360 Still life with thistle and Chinese lanterns (61x51cm-24x20in) s. 10-May-2 Skinner, Boston #362/R
£282 $454 €400 Flowers in a brass pot (58x99cm-23x39in) s. 6-May-3 Vendu Notarishuis, Rotterdam #216/R
£965 $1524 €1448 Rhododendrons in a ginger jar (48x68cm-19x27in) s. 1-Apr-3 Stephan Welz, Johannesburg #423/R est:10000-15000 (SA.R 12000)

GENTAN, Shimada (1778-1840) Japanese
Works on paper
£3459 $5500 €5189 Peacock and peony (114x50cm-45x20in) s. ink col gold silk hanging scroll prov.lit. 24-Mar-3 Christie's, Rockefeller NY #42/R est:3000-4000

GENTH, Lillian (1876-1953) American
£370 $600 €555 House in landscape (15x20cm-6x8in) board. 25-Jan-3 Susanin's, Chicago #5016

GENTHE, Arnold (1869-1942) American
Photographs
£2110 $3250 €3165 Greta Garbo (35x26cm-14x10in) i. photograph. 22-Oct-2 Sotheby's, New York #136/R est:4000-6000
£2760 $4250 €4140 No.2 Madonna (34x26cm-13x10in) s.i. photograph. 22-Oct-2 Sotheby's, New York #135/R est:4000-6000
£2922 $4500 €4383 Window and stairway of the old Ursuline Convent, New Orleans (33x24cm-13x9in) warm toned print lit. 22-Oct-2 Sotheby's, New York #156/R est:3000-5000
£5519 $8500 €8279 Street of gamblers, San Francisco (27x34cm-11x13in) i.verso warm toned photograph exhib.lit. 22-Oct-2 Sotheby's, New York #133/R est:4000-6000

GENTILE, Luigi Salvatore (18/19th C) Italian
Works on paper
£350 $550 €525 Landscape with ruins (46x76cm-18x30in) s. gouache. 21-Nov-2 Shelley, Hendersonville #960/R
£7343 $12262 €10500 Eruption du 2 juin 1806 (50x77cm-20x30in) gouache. 27-Jun-3 Claude Aguttes, Neuilly #25/R est:5000-6000

GENTILINI, Aldo (1911-1982) Italian
£261 $418 €400 Composition (80x60cm-31x24in) s. 4-Jan-3 Meeting Art, Vercelli #576

GENTILINI, Franco (1909-1981) Italian
£2179 $3422 €3400 Figures (22x21cm-9x8in) s.d.1943. 20-Nov-2 Pandolfini, Florence #14/R
£5128 $8051 €8000 Acrobats (47x32cm-19x13in) s.d.73 tempera collage paper on canvas lit. 19-Nov-2 Finarte, Milan #32/R
£10759 $17000 €17000 Girl (35x25cm-14x10in) s. cardboard on canvas painted 1958 exhib.lit. 30-Nov-2 Farsetti, Prato #671/R est:22000
£10968 $17329 €17000 Homage to Carrieri (40x31cm-16x12in) s.i. cardboard on canvas painted 1965 prov.lit. 18-Dec-2 Christie's, Rome #313/R est:22000
£11565 $18388 €17000 Pulcinella and coloured handkerchiefs (26x39cm-10x15in) s. oil sand card on canvas. 1-Mar-3 Meeting Art, Vercelli #757
£11613 $18348 €18000 Suburbs (63x74cm-25x29in) s.d.1940 s.verso prov. 18-Dec-2 Christie's, Rome #236/R est:18000
£15603 $25277 €22000 Cattedrale - N.3 (41x33cm-16x13in) s. oil sand prov.exhib.lit. 26-May-3 Christie's, Milan #317/R est:18000-22000
£22222 $35333 €32000 Cathedral in Monreale (41x36cm-16x14in) s. painted 1953 prov.lit. 1-May-3 Meeting Art, Vercelli #595 est:30000
Works on paper
£699 $1090 €1049 Portrait of an officer (31x21cm-12x8in) s. Indian ink W/C oil. 6-Nov-2 Dobiaschofsky, Bern #576/R (S.FR 1600)
£962 $1510 €1500 Female nude (23x30cm-9x12in) s. Chinese ink. 21-Nov-2 Finarte, Rome #121
£1020 $1622 €1500 Cathedral wth girl (27x28cm-11x11in) s.d.1966 Chinese ink. 1-Mar-3 Meeting Art, Vercelli #707
£1554 $2424 €2300 Two young women (33x24cm-13x9in) s. mixed media exec.1966. 28-Mar-3 Farsetti, Prato #8/R

GENTILS, Vic (1919-1997) Belgian
Sculpture
£2014 $3223 €2800 Composition (80x50x2cm-31x20x1in) s.d.63 verso felt wood prov.lit. 17-May-3 De Vuyst, Lokeren #186/R est:3000-4000
£2128 $3553 €3000 Land 17 (58x58cm-23x23in) s.verso assemblage. 17-Jun-3 Palais de Beaux Arts, Brussels #588/R est:3000-4000
£2692 $4173 €4200 Going to a party (50cm-20in) s.i.d.70 painted wood prov.lit. 3-Dec-2 Christie's, Amsterdam #64/R est:3000-5000
£3597 $5755 €5000 Composition (144x24cm-57x9in) s.d.64 verso wood ivory prov. 17-May-3 De Vuyst, Lokeren #576/R est:5000-6000
£5128 $7949 €8000 War lovers (130cm-51in) s.i.d.1969 painted wood exhib.lit. 3-Dec-2 Christie's, Amsterdam #65/R est:8000-12000
£8966 $14345 €13000 Warlovers (128x76cm-50x30in) s.i. num.23/69 col wood exec.1969 exhib.lit. 15-Mar-3 De Vuyst, Lokeren #484/R est:12000-16000
Works on paper
£5556 $8833 €8000 Composition (70x32cm-28x13in) s.d.1966 verso mixed media triptych. 29-Apr-3 Campo, Vlaamse Kaai #127/R est:7500-8500

GENTZ, Ismael (1862-1914) German
Works on paper
£324 $531 €450 Portrait of the artist, Hans Gude (35x28cm-14x11in) s.i.d.1901 pencil. 4-Jun-3 Reiss & Sohn, Konigstein #234/R
£432 $708 €600 Portrait of the artist Friedrich Kallmorgen (34x26cm-13x10in) s.i.d.1908 pencil. 4-Jun-3 Reiss & Sohn, Konigstein #235/R

GENTZ, Karl Wilhelm (1822-1890) German
£323 $490 €485 Tangier coast (22x28cm-9x11in) init. board prov. 28-Aug-2 Deutscher-Menzies, Melbourne #447/R (A.D 900)
£1987 $3140 €3100 Oriental scene (40x31cm-16x12in) s. board. 16-Nov-2 Lempertz, Koln #1468/R est:3500
£3590 $5672 €5600 Young Nubier (37x32cm-15x13in) s.d.1853 board. 16-Nov-2 Lempertz, Koln #1467/R est:5000

GENZKEN, Isa (1948-) German?
Sculpture
£15000 $24000 €22500 Saal - hall (203x87x84cm-80x34x33in) s.i.d.1987 concrete steel wire construction prov.exhib. 14-May-3 Sotheby's, New York #378/R est:15000-20000

GENZMER, Berthold (1858-?) German
£4114 $6500 €6500 Village youth (81x113cm-32x44in) s. 28-Nov-2 Dorotheum, Vienna #46/R est:7000-8500

GEO-FOURRIER, Georges (1898-1966) French
Works on paper
£266 $420 €420 Bretonnes a l'eglise (21x24cm-8x9in) mono. Chinese ink W/C. 1-Dec-2 Livinec, Gaudcheau & Jezequel, Rennes #39/R
£458 $747 €660 Le marin de Douarnenez (29x18cm-11x7in) s. W/C. 19-Jul-3 Thierry & Lannon, Brest #56
£694 $1132 €1000 Femmes de Quimper de dos (21x26cm-8x10in) chl crayon. 19-Jul-3 Thierry & Lannon, Brest #36
£903 $1472 €1300 Ste Anne La Palue (26x34cm-10x13in) gouache. 19-Jul-3 Thierry & Lannon, Brest #88/R
£1319 $2151 €1900 Maison du pecheur a Porz Carn a St Guenole (24x38cm-9x15in) s. gouache. 19-Jul-3 Thierry & Lannon, Brest #89/R est:1000-1200

GEO-LACHAUX, Georges Marius (1891-?) French
£625 $1019 €900 Douarnenez, pecheur aux paniers sur le mole (55x46cm-22x18in) s.d.1932. 19-Jul-3 Thierry & Lannon, Brest #355

GEOFFROY, Adolphe Louis (1844-1915) French
Sculpture
£1325 $2159 €2000 Panthere rugissant I (39x44cm-15x17in) st.f.Susse brown black pat bronze exec.c.1910. 31-Jan-3 Rabourdin & Choppin de Janvry, Paris #162/R

GEOFFROY, Henry Jules Jean (1853-1924) French
£256 $395 €384 Coming ashore - couple with child and dog (32x46cm-13x18in) s. 4-Sep-2 Kunsthallen, Copenhagen #132/R (D.KR 3000)
£13793 $22069 €20000 Ecolier embarasse (82x62cm-32x24in) s.d.1908. 14-Mar-3 Libert, Castor, Paris #47/R est:12000
Works on paper
£3041 $4743 €4500 Enfants et jeune femme aux parapluies (47x40cm-19x16in) s. col crayon. 26-Mar-3 Rieunier, Paris #8/R

GEOGHEGAN, Trevor (1946-) Irish
£548 $860 €800 Autumn landscape (64x31cm-25x12in) s.i. s.d.1992 verso prov. 15-Apr-3 De Veres Art Auctions, Dublin #100q
£1250 $1987 €1800 Coming up to the gap (66x76cm-26x30in) s. i.d.1993 verso acrylic prov. 29-Apr-3 Whyte's, Dublin #18/R est:1800-2200
£2464 $4041 €3400 Forest light VII (76x76cm-30x30in) s.d.1987 s.i.d.verso. 28-May-3 Bonhams & James Adam, Dublin #95/R est:3000-4000

GEORGANDAS, Dimitrios (c.1851-1933) Greek
£4000 $6320 €6000 Saint Constantine and Saint Helen (30x40cm-12x16in) 1-Apr-3 Bonhams, New Bond Street #14 est:2500-3500

GEORGE, Adrian (1944-) British
Works on paper
£750 $1215 €1125 Dressing room (120x80cm-47x31in) s.d.1982 pastel. 20-May-3 Bonhams, Knightsbridge #186/R

GEORGE, Ernest (1839-1922) British
Works on paper
£300 $474 €450 Marseilles (14x22cm-6x9in) init.i. W/C. 26-Nov-2 Bonhams, Knightsbridge #249/R
£302 $486 €450 View of Huy (26x19cm-10x7in) s.d.1875 W/C. 18-Feb-3 Vanderkindere, Brussels #31
£340 $541 €510 Alger (27x39cm-11x15in) s.i. W/C. 4-Mar-3 Bearnes, Exeter #327
£580 $905 €870 Louvaine (33x23cm-13x9in) s.i.d.1876. 9-Oct-2 Andrew Hartley, Ilkley #632
£650 $1066 €975 Dinan, figures in the street (23x15cm-9x6in) s.i. W/C. 5-Feb-3 John Nicholson, Haslemere #1002

GEORGE, Gregory (19th C) Australian?
£823 $1267 €1235 Goodwin Sands, morning, after a storm (36x51cm-14x20in) 26-Oct-2 Heffel, Vancouver #16 est:2500-3500 (C.D 2000)

GEORGE, J (19th C) British
£2620 $4087 €3930 Woman on donkey on woodland track (72x127cm-28x50in) s. 20-Nov-2 Fischer, Luzern #1073/R est:7000-9000 (S.FR 6000)

GEORGE, Jean-Pierre (?) Swiss
£524 $817 €786 Landscape in Tessin - Lake Maggiore (22x32cm-9x13in) s. board prov. 9-Nov-2 Galerie Gloggner, Luzern #60/R (S.FR 1200)

GEORGE, Jessie Louise (fl.1908-1918) British
Works on paper
£300 $462 €450 Whitby at low tide (31x52cm-12x20in) s.d.1896 W/C htd white. 22-Oct-2 Bonhams, Knightsbridge #30/R
£450 $752 €653 Low tide, Whitby (30x53cm-12x21in) s.d.1896 W/C. 26-Jun-3 Richardson & Smith, Whitby #524

GEORGE, Louis Henri (19th C) French
£961 $1499 €1442 Mont Blanc in summer (32x24cm-13x9in) s.d.90 board. 6-Nov-2 Dobiaschofsky, Bern #577/R (S.FR 2200)

GEORGE, Ouida (20th C) American
£484 $750 €726 Two young ladies in a row boat on lily pond (76x102cm-30x40in) s. 1-Oct-2 Arthur James, Florida #95

£613 $950 €920 Jade willow (89x130cm-35x51in) s.d.88 s.i.d.on stretcher. 1-Oct-2 Arthur James, Florida #94
£613 $950 €920 Portrait of Mrs MacAusland (122x91cm-48x36in) s.d.May 1990. 1-Oct-2 Arthur James, Florida #96
£903 $1400 €1355 Young lady on tiger rug (102x76cm-40x30in) s.d.1990. 1-Oct-2 Arthur James, Florida #97

GEORGE, Patrick (1923-) British
£900 $1413 €1350 Opposite bank (84x210cm-33x83in) exhib. 15-Apr-3 Bonhams, Knightsbridge #206/R

GEORGE, Thomas (1918-) American
£463 $750 €695 Sea bells (208x208cm-82x82in) s. s.i.d.1984 verso. 24-Jan-3 Freeman, Philadelphia #242/R

GEORGE-JULLIARD, Jean Philippe (1818-1888) Swiss
£437 $681 €656 Les lavandieres (31cm-12in circular) s. paper on board. 6-Nov-2 Dobiaschofsky, Bern #578/R (S.FR 1000)
£617 $900 €926 Burg Valera and Kollegial Church in Sitten (30x46cm-12x18in) mono. paper on board. 17-Jun-2 Philippe Schuler, Zurich #4270/R (S.FR 1400)
£655 $1022 €983 Stone ridge (15x47cm-6x19in) mono. paper on board. 20-Nov-2 Fischer, Luzern #2088/R est:1600-1800 (S.FR 1500)
£657 $1078 €953 Treetops (29x41cm-11x16in) mono. paper on board. 4-Jun-3 Fischer, Luzern #2107/R (S.FR 1400)
£661 $965 €992 Fortress above lake (34x50cm-13x20in) mono. panel. 17-Jun-2 Philippe Schuler, Zurich #4269/R (S.FR 1500)
£705 $1050 €1058 Landscape near Arthez (24x38cm-9x15in) mono. board. 25-Jun-2 Koller, Zurich #6560/R (S.FR 1600)
£1408 $2310 €2042 Trees above the Vierwaldstattersee (67x53cm-26x21in) mono. canvas on pavatex. 4-Jun-3 Fischer, Luzern #1220/R est:3000-4000 (S.FR 3000)
£1408 $2310 €2042 Grape harvest (46x64cm-18x25in) s. 4-Jun-3 Fischer, Luzern #1231/R est:3000-4500 (S.FR 3000)
£1528 $2384 €2292 View of Weggis towards Pilatus (62x92cm-24x36in) s. 8-Nov-2 Dobiaschofsky, Bern #26/R est:4500 (S.FR 3500)
£1795 $2818 €2800 Vue de Geneve (47x69cm-19x27in) 21-Nov-2 Neret-Minet, Paris #82
£2830 $4585 €5010 Lac des quatre cantons (70x100cm-28x39in) s. 26-May-3 Sotheby's, Zurich #2/R est:6000-9000 (S.FR 6000)

GEORGE-LEGRAND, Louis (1801-1883) Swiss
£1304 $2035 €1956 Hilly wooded landscape with vie of lake (70x95cm-28x37in) s. 16-Sep-2 Philippe Schuler, Zurich #3368 est:2100-3500 (S.FR 3000)

GEORGES, Alain (20th C) French
£255 $400 €383 Constantinople (25x33cm-10x13in) s. 28-Jul-2 William Jenack, New York #199

GEORGES, Charles E (19/20th C) British
Works on paper
£460 $736 €690 Cottage beside a stream with a blossoming hawthorn (53x76cm-21x30in) s. W/C. 13-Mar-3 Duke & Son, Dorchester #106

GEORGES, Claude (1929-1988) French
£347 $549 €500 Composition (65x81cm-26x32in) s.d. 27-Apr-3 Perrin, Versailles #11
£641 $1006 €1000 Untitled (65x92cm-26x36in) s.d.72. 24-Nov-2 Laurence Calmels, Paris #135/R
£1026 $1610 €1600 Untitled (54x65cm-21x26in) s.d.56 s.i.d.verso. 24-Nov-2 Laurence Calmels, Paris #138/R

GEORGES, Jean (1890-?) French
£788 $1229 €1150 Marseilles harbour (17x36cm-7x14in) s. panel pair. 10-Apr-3 Schopman, Hamburg #702

GEORGI, Edwin (1896-1964) American
Works on paper
£932 $1500 €1398 Bust in profile of young woman (48x36cm-19x14in) gouache exhib. 10-May-3 Illustration House, New York #123/R est:1500-3000
£1410 $2200 €2115 Woman leaving as a man smokes in bed (56x41cm-22x16in) gouache. 9-Nov-2 Illustration House, New York #156/R est:1500-2500

GEORGI, Friedrich Otto (1819-1874) German
£500 $780 €750 Sinai Desert (32x52cm-13x20in) s.d.1856. 15-Oct-2 Sotheby's, London #204/R

GEORGI, Walter (1871-1924) German
£256 $397 €400 Head portrait of a man facing left and viewed in three-quarters profile (50x43cm-20x17in) s.d.92 canvas on masonite. 4-Dec-2 Neumeister, Munich #741/R
£943 $1453 €1500 Bad weather on the Brittany coast (68x89cm-27x35in) s.d.1914. 26-Oct-2 Quittenbaum, Hamburg #94/R est:1800
£3521 $5845 €5000 Portrait of a lady with bouquet of flowers at the shore with sailing boats (94x75cm-37x30in) s. 14-Jun-3 Arnold, Frankfurt #748/R est:800

GEORGIADIS, Nicholas (20th C) Continental
£900 $1422 €1350 Architectonic forms (65x49cm-26x19in) 1-Apr-3 Bonhams, New Bond Street #114
£2000 $3160 €3000 Fisherman's hut by the sea. 1-Apr-3 Bonhams, New Bond Street #115 est:2000-3000

GERALIS, Apostolos (1886-1983) Greek
£4800 $7440 €7200 Watering plants (32x23cm-13x9in) s.d.917 canvasboard. 2-Oct-2 Sotheby's, London #105/R est:2000
£5000 $7900 €7500 Card reader (48x62cm-19x24in) 1-Apr-3 Bonhams, New Bond Street #27 est:5000-7000
£18000 $27900 €27000 Playful moment (115x77cm-45x30in) s. 2-Oct-2 Sotheby's, London #34/R est:18000-25000

GERALIS, Loucas (1875-1958) Greek
£2600 $4108 €3900 View of the Acropolis (31x43cm-12x17in) 1-Apr-3 Bonhams, New Bond Street #68 est:2000-3000

GERARD, Baron François (1770-1837) French
£8228 $13000 €13000 Portrait du Roi Charles X (85x72cm-33x28in) oval prov. 27-Nov-2 Christie's, Paris #55/R est:6000-8000
Works on paper
£21605 $35000 €32408 Young woman adorning a statue of Empress Josephine with flowers, the greenhouse at Malmaison (14x22cm-6x9in) s. W/C paper on board. 23-Jan-3 Sotheby's, New York #105a/R est:40000-60000

GERARD, Baron François (circle) (1770-1837) French
£5500 $8635 €8250 Portrait of a gentleman, in a landscape (55x46cm-22x18in) bears sig. 12-Dec-2 Sotheby's, London #196/R est:4000-6000
£9000 $14130 €13500 Portrait of a lady standing, wearing a white dress and pink wrap, in a landscape (172x89cm-68x35in) 13-Dec-2 Christie's, Kensington #194/R est:2500-3500

GERARD, Baron François (studio) (1770-1837) French
£9091 $15182 €13000 Portrait d'homme (64x53cm-25x21in) 25-Jun-3 Sotheby's, Paris #70/R est:6000-9000

GERARD, Gaston (1859-?) French
£503 $800 €755 Portrait of a child (27x22cm-11x9in) s. panel. 7-Mar-3 Skinner, Boston #261/R
£601 $949 €902 Still life (30x27cm-12x11in) indis.s. board. 3-Apr-3 Heffel, Vancouver #32/R (C.D 1400)

GERARD, Lucien (1852-1935) Belgian
£127 $199 €200 L'etranger (50x61cm-20x24in) s. 11-Nov-2 Horta, Bruxelles #589
£377 $588 €550 Le repos bien merite (36x24cm-14x9in) s. panel. 14-Apr-3 Horta, Bruxelles #477
£1111 $1789 €1700 Le partage equitable (29x23cm-11x9in) s. 20-Jan-3 Horta, Bruxelles #95 est:2000-3000

GERARD, Lucien Grand (1880-1970) Belgian?
£378 $585 €600 Portrait de femme (46x38cm-18x15in) s.d. panel. 4-Oct-2 Tajan, Paris #113

GERARD, Marguerite (1761-1837) French
£10494 $17000 €15741 Regrets merites (31x27cm-12x11in) prov.lit. 23-Jan-3 Sotheby's, New York #205/R est:20000
£47256 $77500 €70884 L'accouchee or le dernier venu (63x51cm-25x20in) s. prov.lit. 29-May-3 Sotheby's, New York #142/R est:60000-80000

GERARD, Pascal (1941-) French
£637 $994 €1000 Conversation dans le parc (54x65cm-21x26in) s. 10-Nov-2 Eric Pillon, Calais #120/R

GERARD, Robert Ulderic (1920-2000) Belgian
£1079 $1727 €1500 Jeux d'enfants dans la sabliere (104x132cm-41x52in) s. 19-May-3 Horta, Bruxelles #373 est:1200-1800

GERARD, Simonin (?) Belgian
£1635 $2551 €2600 Farmhouse interior with figures. Farmhouse interior with woman at work and man (80x60cm-31x24in) s. pair. 23-Sep-2 Bernaerts, Antwerp #231/R est:3000-4000

GERARD, Theodore (1829-1895) Belgian

£654	$1052	€1000	Le puits (30x40cm-12x16in) s. panel. 20-Jan-3 Horta, Bruxelles #51
£784	$1263	€1200	Interieur flamand (46x38cm-18x15in) s. 14-Jan-3 Vanderkindere, Brussels #44
£2532	$4000	€4000	Le premier rayon de soleil (27x20cm-11x8in) s. panel. 26-Nov-2 Palais de Beaux Arts, Brussels #364a/R est:4000-5000
£3349	$5426	€4856	Interior scene with young girl writing letter (42x30cm-17x12in) s.d.82. 26-May-3 Rasmussen, Copenhagen #1205/R est:50000 (D.KR 35000)
£3800	$6232	€5700	Feeding the chicks (47x33cm-19x13in) s.d.64 verso panel prov. 3-Jun-3 Sotheby's, London #154/R est:4000-6000
£4000	$6280	€6000	Un bouquet de dahlia (101x70cm-40x28in) s.d.1890. 21-Nov-2 Christie's, Kensington #90/R est:5000-7000
£4000	$6480	€6000	Biscuit thief (48x35cm-19x14in) s.d.76. 20-May-3 Sotheby's, Olympia #372/R est:4000-6000
£4167	$6458	€6500	Propos galants (81x56cm-32x22in) s. 9-Dec-2 Horta, Bruxelles #140/R est:7000-9000
£10791	$17266	€15000	Small knitter (51x42cm-20x17in) s.d.1868 panel prov. 17-May-3 De Vuyst, Lokeren #430/R est:17000-20000
£13605	$21633	€20000	La visite (80x117cm-31x46in) s. 18-Mar-3 Vanderkindere, Brussels #15/R est:7500-10000
£14013	$21860	€22000	L'anniversaire de grand-mere (73x58cm-29x23in) s. panel. 11-Nov-2 Horta, Bruxelles #153 est:15000-20000
£22013	$33899	€35000	Young artist (70x54cm-28x21in) s.d.1866 panel prov. 23-Oct-2 Christie's, Amsterdam #110/R est:8000-12000

GERARDIN, Roland Marie (1907-1935) French

£2098	$3504	€3000	L'abandon (142x159cm-56x63in) s. 26-Jun-3 Tajan, Paris #309 est:3000-4000

GERASCH, August (1822-1894) Austrian

£433	$671	€650	Portrait of bearded man (31x39cm-12x15in) s.d.69. 24-Sep-2 Koller, Zurich #6563/R (S.FR 1000)

GERASCH, Franz (1822-1908) Austrian

Works on paper

£315	$450	€473	Young woman sitting victorious over a dragon defending a treasure (40x34cm-16x13in) s. pen ink wash. 23-Jan-3 Swann Galleries, New York #382/R
£541	$843	€800	On the walls of Donau city (18x22cm-7x9in) s. W/C. 28-Mar-3 Dorotheum, Vienna #191/R

GERBER, Carl (1839-?) German

£458	$737	€650	Dog and wasp (27x41cm-11x16in) s. panel lit. 9-May-3 Schloss Ahlden, Ahlden #1481/R
£458	$737	€650	Cats (27x41cm-11x16in) s. panel lit. 9-May-3 Schloss Ahlden, Ahlden #1482/R
£759	$1177	€1200	Wild boar in snowy wood (20x28cm-8x11in) s. panel. 25-Sep-2 Neumeister, Munich #580/R
£1712	$2671	€2500	Wild boar in winter wood (20x18cm-8x7in) s. panel. 10-Apr-3 Dorotheum, Vienna #122/R est:2500-2700

GERBER, Theo (1928-) Swiss

Works on paper

£323	$507	€485	Untitled (14x21cm-6x8in) s.d.1974 gouache. 23-Nov-2 Burkhard, Luzern #6/R (S.FR 740)

GERBIER D'OUVILLY, Balthasar (1593-1667) Flemish

£5500	$8745	€8250	Portrait of a gentleman wearing a green tunic (71x62cm-28x24in) 19-Mar-3 Sotheby's, London #10/R est:6000-8000

GERBINO, Rosario Urbino (1900-1972) American

£325	$475	€488	Backyard, winter. s.d.1934. 10-May-2 Skinner, Boston #202/R
£1484	$2300	€2226	Reclining nude female (48x76cm-19x30in) s. 28-Sep-2 Charlton Hall, Columbia #176/R est:3000-4000

GERCKEN, Graham (?) American

£248	$400	€372	Afternoon light Cox river (38x48cm-15x19in) board. 9-May-3 Douglas, South Deerfield #9
£256	$400	€384	Grand Canyon Cliffscape (58x46cm-23x18in) board. 11-Apr-3 Douglas, South Deerfield #2

GERDES, Ludwig (1954-) German

£1410	$2214	€2200	Black painting 3 (120x200cm-47x79in) s.d.87 verso exhib. 11-Dec-2 Artcurial Briest, Paris #810/R est:2200

GERE, Charles M (1869-1957) British

Works on paper

£480	$744	€720	Extensive river landscape (22x41cm-9x16in) mono. pencil W/C. 4-Dec-2 Christie's, Kensington #42

GERELL, Greta (1898-1982) Swedish

£320	$508	€480	Still life of flowers in jug (66x54cm-26x21in) s.d.42 panel. 2-Mar-3 Uppsala Auktionskammare, Uppsala #300/R (S.KR 4300)
£385	$601	€578	Still life of exotic instrument (42x34cm-17x13in) s.d.70 cardboard. 5-Nov-2 Bukowskis, Stockholm #218/R (S.KR 5500)
£434	$678	€651	Still life of statuette (35x28cm-14x11in) s.d.40 panel. 5-Nov-2 Bukowskis, Stockholm #211/R (S.KR 6200)
£596	$929	€894	Still life of eggs (19x24cm-7x9in) s.d.73 cardboard. 5-Nov-2 Bukowskis, Stockholm #215/R (S.KR 8500)
£631	$984	€947	Girl with lantern (73x53cm-29x21in) s. 5-Nov-2 Bukowskis, Stockholm #214/R (S.KR 9000)
£736	$1148	€1104	Still life of books (33x41cm-13x16in) s.d.72 cardboard. 5-Nov-2 Bukowskis, Stockholm #216/R (S.KR 10500)
£876	$1367	€1314	Still life of coffee cup and pumpkin (24x33cm-9x13in) s.d.77 panel. 5-Nov-2 Bukowskis, Stockholm #217/R (S.KR 12500)
£927	$1538	€1344	Black Oliver (32x41cm-13x16in) s.d.68 cardboard lit. 16-Jun-3 Lilla Bukowskis, Stockholm #992 (S.KR 12000)
£1086	$1694	€1629	Barns (73x93cm-29x37in) s. 5-Nov-2 Bukowskis, Stockholm #213/R est:8000-10000 (S.KR 15500)

Works on paper

£350	$547	€525	Facades (29x29cm-11x11in) s. gouache. 5-Nov-2 Bukowskis, Stockholm #212/R (S.KR 5000)

GERGELY, Porge (1858-1930) Hungarian

£828	$1308	€1200	Weekly market in Budapest (14x20cm-6x8in) s.d.907 s.i. verso panel. 5-Apr-3 Hans Stahl, Hamburg #6/R

GERHARD, Adolf (1910-1975) German?

£577	$900	€866	Continental river landscape with figures (61x81cm-24x32in) s. 18-Sep-2 Boos Gallery, Michigan #278a/R

GERHARDINGER, Constantin (1888-1970) German

£2468	$3677	€3800	Winter landscape by Samerberg (35x50cm-14x20in) s. masonite. 26-Jun-2 Neumeister, Munich #739/R est:2500

GERHARDT, Karl (1853-1940) American

£949	$1500	€1424	Dixie (36x51cm-14x20in) s.i.verso canvasboard. 16-Nov-2 New Orleans Auction, New Orleans #1555/R est:1200-1800

GERHARTZ, Dan (1965-) American?

£10274	$15000	€15411	At the garden door (183x81cm-72x32in) 18-May-2 Altermann Galleries, Santa Fe #244/R

GERICAULT, Theodore (1791-1824) French

£129032	$203871	€200000	Etude de peau de panthere (48x58cm-19x23in) panel painted c.1812 prov.lit. 18-Dec-2 Tajan, Paris #58/R

Prints

£5634	$9352	€8000	Le retour de Russie (44x36cm-17x14in) s. lithograph. 14-Jun-3 Hauswedell & Nolte, Hamburg #1200/R est:8000
£16026	$25321	€25000	Deux chevaux gris pommele se battant dans un ecurie. lithograph. 14-Nov-2 Libert, Castor, Paris #99/R est:7500
£32372	$51147	€50500	Boxeurs. lithograph. 14-Nov-2 Libert, Castor, Paris #97/R est:37500

Works on paper

£2703	$4216	€4000	Etude (12x20cm-5x8in) crayon exhib.lit. 31-Mar-3 Piasa, Paris #77
£3291	$5200	€5200	Etude de danseuses antiques (20x31cm-8x12in) pierre noire prov.exhib. 29-Nov-2 Claude Boisgirard, Paris #15/R
£3846	$5962	€6000	Foule se pressant autour d'un homme a terre (23x34cm-9x13in) crayon. 4-Dec-2 Piasa, Paris #145/R
£4938	$8000	€7407	Sketch for battle scene (18x20cm-7x8in) pen ink over chk. 21-Jan-3 Sotheby's, New York #130/R est:15000
£7407	$12000	€11111	Nude woman bathing (20x13cm-8x5in) pencil pen ink wash prov.exhib.lit. 22-Jan-3 Christie's, Rockefeller NY #103/R est:20000
£17419	$27000	€26129	Couple (15x23cm-6x9in) chl. 29-Oct-2 Sotheby's, New York #5/R est:30000-40000
£26923	$41731	€42000	Feuille d'etudes (29x19cm-11x7in) pen wash lit. 4-Dec-2 Libert, Castor, Paris #29/R
£28481	$45000	€45000	Cuirassier appuye sur son cheval (26x18cm-10x7in) W/C pen ink over crayon. 27-Nov-2 Camard, Paris #14/R est:60000
£37037	$60000	€55556	Three men restraining a horse (22x32cm-9x13in) chk pen ink htd white exhib.lit. 22-Jan-3 Christie's, Rockefeller NY #102/R est:70000
£70513	$109295	€110000	Homme vu de dos (25x18cm-10x7in) i. crayon W/C prov.lit. 4-Dec-2 Libert, Castor, Paris #31/R est:80000-100000

GERICAULT, Theodore (circle) (1791-1824) French

£18000	$28260	€27000	Momento mori of a skull and bones (27x33cm-11x13in) 13-Dec-2 Christie's, Kensington #195/R est:2000-3000

GERINI, Lorenzo di Niccolo (circle) (15th C) Italian

£8500	$13345	€12750	Martyrdom of Saint Lawrence (25x19cm-10x7in) panel double-sided. 11-Dec-2 Christie's, London #95/R est:10000-15000

GERINI, Niccolo di Pietro (?-1415) Italian
£70000 $116900 €101500 Crucifixion (26x78cm-10x31in) tempera gold ground panel predella prov.lit. 10-Jul-3 Sotheby's, London #29/R est:60000-80000

GERLACH, Everett C (20th C) American
£375 $600 €563 Old barnyard (51x61cm-20x24in) s. 15-Mar-3 Jeffery Burchard, Florida #54/R

GERLE, Aron (1860-1930) Swedish
£320 $508 €480 Sunset over tarn (95x115cm-37x45in) s.d.1901. 2-Mar-3 Uppsala Auktionskammare, Uppsala #329 (S.KR 4300)

GERMAIN, Jacques (1915-2001) French
£426 $689 €600 Petite composition (15x12cm-6x5in) mono. canvas on isorel. 23-May-3 Camard, Paris #180
£581 $917 €900 Composition abstraite (50x60cm-20x24in) s.d.66 s.d.verso. 18-Dec-2 Digard, Paris #211/R
£818 $1267 €1300 Composition (35x22cm-14x9in) s. 7-Oct-2 Claude Aguttes, Neuilly #278
£943 $1462 €1500 Composition (41x33cm-16x13in) s.d.64 paper on canvas. 30-Oct-2 Artcurial Briest, Paris #674 est:1200-1500
£1088 $1731 €1600 Composition (22x16cm-9x6in) s.d.1969 verso. 24-Mar-3 Claude Boisgirard, Paris #102/R
£1259 $2102 €1800 Composition (60x73cm-24x29in) s. 25-Jun-3 Claude Aguttes, Neuilly #163/R est:1830-2200
£1507 $2366 €2200 Sans titre (81x100cm-32x39in) mono. 21-Apr-3 Rabourdin & Choppin de Janvry, Paris #206 est:3000-4000
£1987 $3080 €3100 Composition (98x130cm-39x51in) s.d.1975 prov. 7-Dec-2 Cornette de St.Cyr, Paris #82/R
£2532 $4000 €4000 Composition abstraite (72x99cm-28x39in) s.d.67 verso. 26-Nov-2 Camard, Paris #125/R
£3087 $4970 €4600 Composition (73x92cm-29x36in) s.d.1956. 23-Feb-3 Mercier & Cie, Lille #111/R
£3205 $4968 €5000 Composition (161x130cm-63x51in) s.d.1980 s.i.d.verso. 7-Dec-2 Cornette de St.Cyr, Paris #80/R
£3356 $5403 €5000 Promenade bleue (80x100cm-31x39in) s. 23-Feb-3 Mercier & Cie, Lille #112/R
£3797 $6000 €6000 Composition (130x161cm-51x63in) s. s.d.65 verso. 26-Nov-2 Camard, Paris #126/R est:9000
£4304 $6800 €6800 Untitled (97x130cm-38x51in) s.d.61. 26-Nov-2 Camard, Paris #124/R

Works on paper
£256 $403 €400 Composition abstraite (41x32cm-16x13in) st.mono. Chinese ink exec.c.1947. 20-Nov-2 Binoche, Paris #33
£288 $453 €450 Composition abstraite (40x32cm-16x13in) st.mono Chinese ink exec.c.1946. 20-Nov-2 Binoche, Paris #32

GERMAIN, Jean (1900-?) French
£323 $500 €468 Place du Terne Monmartre (38x46cm-15x18in) board. 7-Dec-2 South Bay, Long Island #66/R

GERMAIN, Jean-Baptiste (1841-1910) French

Sculpture
£1020 $1622 €1500 Hercule et les ecuries d'Augias (80cm-31in) s. pat.bronze. 19-Mar-3 Hotel des Ventes Mosan, Brussels #226 est:1200-1300
£2405 $3800 €3608 Psyche and infant (56cm-22in) i. bronze. 24-Apr-3 Christie's, Rockefeller NY #186/R est:4000-6000

GERMAIN-THILL, Alphonse Leon Antoine (1873-1925) French
£2027 $3162 €3000 View of Fez (35x50cm-14x20in) s.i.d.1920 cardboard. 28-Mar-3 Claude Aguttes, Neuilly #215/R est:2500
£2390 $3681 €3800 Portraits de jeunes filles (24x82cm-9x32in) 23-Oct-2 Rabourdin & Choppin de Janvry, Paris #65/R

GERMAN SCHOOL
£5944 $8500 €8916 Madonna and Child (28x22cm-11x9in) panel. 22-Jan-3 Doyle, New York #79/R

GERMAN SCHOOL, 15th C

Prints
£5500 $9075 €7975 Apocalypsis Sancti Johannis (27x20cm-11x8in) hand col woodcut exec.c.1465. 1-Jul-3 Sotheby's, London #27/R est:6000-8000

GERMAN SCHOOL, 16th C
£7233 $11211 €11500 Virgin's death (153x100cm-60x39in) board. 7-Oct-2 Ansorena, Madrid #5/R
£7237 $11724 €11000 Virgin's death (153x100cm-60x39in) board painted c.1520. 21-Jan-3 Ansorena, Madrid #91/R est:9000
£8503 $13520 €12500 Saint Ambroise and Saint Stephen (126x52cm-50x20in) panel painted c.1500. 23-Mar-3 Herbette, Doullens #15/R
£11972 $19275 €17000 Flagellation of Christ (96x76cm-38x30in) panel. 10-May-3 Berlinghof, Heidelberg #180/R est:22000
£12821 $20256 €20000 The risen Christ saying farewell to the eleven apostles (126x85cm-50x33in) panel. 16-Nov-2 Lempertz, Koln #1056/R est:8000
£16026 $25160 €25000 Jesus preaching (66x80cm-26x31in) panel pair. 14-Dec-2 Artcurial Briest, Paris #26/R est:35000
£31126 $50735 €47000 Reclining female nude (77x123cm-30x48in) panel. 3-Feb-3 Chambelland & Giafferi, Paris #304/R est:3000

GERMAN SCHOOL, 16th/17th C
£10135 $15811 €15000 Portrait of a young prince in black court dress (180x100cm-71x39in) canvas on panel lit.prov. one of pair. 27-Mar-3 Dorotheum, Vienna #295/R est:15000-20000
£10135 $15811 €15000 Portrait of young prince in black court dress, allegedly Charles of Austria (180x100cm-71x39in) canvas on panel one of pair. 27-Mar-3 Dorotheum, Vienna #296/R est:15000-20000

GERMAN SCHOOL, 17th C

Sculpture
£10704 $17769 €15200 Vendangeur ou chemineau (23cm-9in) ivory oval wood socle. 16-Jun-3 Anaf, Lyon #61/R est:12000-13000
£96774 $152903 €150000 Lion attacking horse (25x30x25cm-10x12x10in) bronze wooden base prov.exhib. 17-Dec-2 Tajan, Paris #102/R est:150000-200000
£114583 $181042 €165000 Chasseurs de nuit (28x17x15cm-11x7x6in) bronze pair prov. 25-Apr-3 Beaussant & Lefèvre, Paris #79/R est:75000-85000

Works on paper
£20833 $33125 €30000 Triumph of Neptune (12x23cm-5x9in) pen wash prov. 5-May-3 Ketterer, Munich #234/R est:700-900

GERMAN SCHOOL, 18th C
£5000 $7850 €7500 Travellers on a rocky embankment with a ferry departing (64x91cm-25x36in) s. 10-Dec-2 Bonhams, New Bond Street #152/R est:5000-7000
£5033 $8104 €7500 Portrait of King George III, as a young boy when Prince Wales (77x65cm-30x26in) prov. 18-Feb-3 Sotheby's, Amsterdam #409/R est:3000-4000
£5449 $8554 €8500 Shepherds by the river (49x60cm-19x24in) 14-Dec-2 Artcurial Briest, Paris #69
£6376 $10265 €9500 Hunting still life with a dog, hare, ducks and pigeons (96x126cm-38x50in) s. 18-Feb-3 Sotheby's, Amsterdam #934b/R est:2500-3500
£6723 $10421 €10085 Holy Family (34x25cm-13x10in) s. cardboard. 6-Dec-2 Kieselbach, Budapest #180/R (H.F 2500000)
£6987 $10900 €10481 Lake landscaped with herders resting in the foreground (82x125cm-32x49in) panel. 20-Nov-2 Fischer, Luzern #1141/R est:5000-7000 (S.FR 16000)
£7643 $11924 €12000 Young nobleman (86x65cm-34x26in) 6-Nov-2 Hugo Ruef, Munich #955/R est:1500

Sculpture
£4828 $7676 €7000 Dancing satyr (46cm-18in) silver sold with base. 7-Mar-3 Semenzato, Venice #185/R

GERMAN SCHOOL, 19th C
£1667 $2583 €2600 Portrait (70x83cm-28x33in) mono. 5-Dec-2 Schopman, Hamburg #533 est:2200
£10494 $17000 €15741 Massive oak tree in extensive mountain landscape (37x48cm-15x19in) paper on board painted c.1820. 22-Jan-3 Christie's, Rockefeller NY #123/R est:15000

GERMAN, Horacio (20th C) ?
£187 $302 €281 Big loaf (79x59cm-31x23in) s.d.1955. 21-Jan-3 Louis Morton, Mexico #34/R (M.P 3200)

GERMANA, Mimmo (1944-1992) Italian
£1154 $1788 €1800 Untitled (55x75cm-22x30in) s.i.d.1988 verso. 4-Dec-2 Finarte, Milan #549/R
£1203 $1876 €1900 Bather (55x75cm-22x30in) s. acrylic card painted 1990. 14-Sep-2 Meeting Art, Vercelli #365/R
£2564 $4026 €4000 Untitled (60x80cm-24x31in) s.d.1990. 23-Nov-2 Meeting Art, Vercelli #112/R
£3125 $4969 €4500 Gitano (200x180cm-79x71in) s.i.d.1983 verso. 29-Apr-3 Wiener Kunst Auktionen, Vienna #481/R est:3000-6000

Works on paper
£538 $839 €850 Bather (56x77cm-22x30in) s.d.1990 mixed media card. 14-Sep-2 Meeting Art, Vercelli #100/R
£962 $1510 €1500 Figure (75x105cm-30x41in) s.d.1991 mixed media. 21-Nov-2 Finarte, Rome #164/R
£2500 $3875 €3900 Miro in water. Portrait of EC. Untitled (45cm-18in circular) s.d.1992 mixed media board triptych. 4-Dec-2 Finarte, Milan #543/R

GERMANA, Mimmo and PALADINO, Mimmo (20th C) Italian

Works on paper

£1519 $2370 €2400 Mimmo and Mimmo (48x66cm-19x26in) s. felt-tip pen collage. 14-Sep-2 Meeting Art, Vercelli #711/R

GERMASCHEFF, Michail (attrib) (1868-1930) Russian

£300 $486 €450 Troika driver (19x28cm-7x11in) s. canvasboard. 23-Jan-3 Christie's, Kensington #118

GERMAY, A (19/20th C) French

Sculpture

£1083 $1700 €1625 Solitude (46cm-18in) s. alabaster. 23-Nov-2 Jackson's, Cedar Falls #247/R est:1250-1750

£1300 $2093 €1885 Figure of a exotic semi draped female figure (53cm-21in) s. alabaster marble. 12-May-3 Joel, Victoria #519 est:1000-1500 (A.D 3250)

GERMENIS, Vasilis (1896-1966) Greek

£3000 $4740 €4500 Male torso (50x61cm-20x24in) 1-Apr-3 Bonhams, New Bond Street #35 est:3000-5000

£3800 $5890 €5700 Sewing by the window (40x30cm-16x12in) s. board. 2-Oct-2 Sotheby's, London #88/R

£7500 $11850 €11250 Sailing out (65x100cm-26x39in) 1-Apr-3 Bonhams, New Bond Street #31 est:5000-7000

GERNEZ, Paul Elie (1888-1948) French

£694 $1104 €1000 Les meules, soleil jaune, campagne du nord (17x24cm-7x9in) s.d.1910 cardboard. 29-Apr-3 Artcurial Briest, Paris #173/R

£2436 $3776 €3800 Nature morte, petit dejeuner (54x63cm-21x25in) s. 7-Dec-2 Cornette de St.Cyr, Paris #65/R

£2900 $4611 €4350 Femme vue de dos (46x38cm-18x15in) s. board prov. 20-Mar-3 Sotheby's, Olympia #159/R est:2500-3500

£3567 $5564 €5600 Coupe de fruits (46x55cm-18x22in) s.d.1915 panel. 10-Nov-2 Eric Pillon, Calais #44/R

Works on paper

£310 $518 €450 L'entree du port d'Honfleur (29x46cm-11x18in) s. chl wax crayon dr. 10-Jul-3 Artcurial Briest, Paris #16

£774 $1223 €1200 Paysage a Cleville (27x45cm-11x18in) s.i.d.42 W/C. 18-Dec-2 Ferri, Paris #52/R

£994 $1510 €1550 Honfleur (17x22cm-7x9in) s. chl dr. 16-Aug-2 Deauville, France #13/R

£2270 $3677 €3200 Le hameau (44x59cm-17x23in) s. pastel. 21-May-3 Cornette de St.Cyr, Paris #53/R est:3000-3500

£2564 $3897 €4000 Honfleur (25x32cm-10x13in) s.d. W/C prov. 16-Aug-2 Deauville, France #15/R

£7051 $10718 €11000 Plage de Trouville (38x48cm-15x19in) s.i. s.d.1936 verso pastel exhib.lit. 16-Aug-2 Deauville, France #58/R est:10000

GEROME, François (20th C) French?

£267 $425 €401 Moulin rouge (41x30cm-16x12in) s.i. painted c.1960. 2-Mar-3 Toomey, Oak Park #729/R

£353 $550 €530 Paris street scene with figures, cars and Arc de Triomphe (71x107cm-28x42in) s. 18-Sep-2 Alderfer's, Hatfield #256

£491 $800 €737 L'Arc les Champs Elysees, Paris (61x76cm-24x30in) painted c.1940. 14-Feb-3 Du Mouchelle, Detroit #2041/R

GEROME, Jean Léon (1824-1904) French

£1100 $1672 €1650 Bishop Belzunce of Marseille making a vow to the sacred heart (31x23cm-12x9in) 29-Aug-2 Christie's, Kensington #188/R est:500-800

£19445 $30917 €28000 Portrait presume de madame la Baronne Nathaniel de Rothschild (50x36cm-20x14in) s. panel. 30-Apr-3 Tajan, Paris #15/R est:10000

£48077 $75962 €75000 Le roi candaule (20x32cm-8x13in) s.d.1858 paper on canvas prov.lit. 18-Nov-2 Tajan, Paris #35/R est:30000-46000

£50633 $80000 €75950 Les deux augures (65x50cm-26x20in) s. prov.lit. 24-Apr-3 Sotheby's, New York #45/R est:80000-120000

£260000 $434200 €390000 First kiss of the sun (54x100cm-21x39in) s. canvas on board prov.exhib.lit. 19-Jun-3 Christie's, London #20/R est:200000-300000

£380000 $634600 €570000 Le porte de la mosquee El Hasaein au Caire - Doorway to the mosque El Assaneyn in Cario (54x44cm-21x17in) s. panel painted 1866 prov.exhib.lit. 19-Jun-3 Christie's, London #18/R est:70000-90000

£420000 $701400 €630000 Anaute avec deux chiens whippets (36x25cm-14x10in) s. panel painted 1867 prov.lit. 19-Jun-3 Christie's, London #22/R est:100000-150000

£435484 $675000 €653226 Solomon's wall Jerusalem - Wailing wall (92x74cm-36x29in) s. prov.exhib.lit. 29-Oct-2 Sotheby's, New York #49/R est:600000-800000

£529032 $835871 €820000 Retour de chasse (74x60cm-29x24in) s. painted c.1878 prov.exhib.lit. 19-Dec-2 Claude Aguttes, Neuilly #126/R est:300000-400000

£1000000 $1640000 €1500000 Interieur grec, le Gynecce (64x89cm-25x35in) s.d.MDCCCL. 3-Jun-3 Sotheby's, London #134/R est:400000-600000

Sculpture

£1700 $2652 €2550 Expiring Eagle of Waterloo (18cm-7in) s.num.X283 gilt bronze st.Siot lit. 9-Apr-3 Sotheby's, London #161/R est:1500-2000

£2465 $4068 €3550 La danseuse a la pomme (26cm-10in) s. gilt bronze sold with onyx socle Cast Siot Decauville. 1-Jul-3 Rossini, Paris #50/R

£2803 $4372 €4400 Danse (35cm-14in) gilt pat bronze Cast Siot onyx socle. 10-Nov-2 Eric Pillon, Calais #38/R

£3200 $4992 €4800 La joueuse de boules (32cm-13in) s.st.Siot gilt bronze green onyx socle lit. 9-Apr-3 Sotheby's, London #131/R est:2500-3500

£3597 $5899 €5000 Bacchante (60cm-24in) s.st.f.Siot gold pat bronze lit. 3-Jun-3 Piasa, Paris #32/R est:5000-6000

£5063 $8000 €7595 Caesar crossing the Rubicon (37cm-15in) i. bronze. 24-Apr-3 Christie's, Rockefeller NY #338/R est:8000-12000

£5500 $8580 €8250 Pursuit (25x18cm-10x7in) s.num.5837 brown green pat bronze st.Siot lit. 9-Apr-3 Sotheby's, London #181/R est:5000-7000

£9000 $14040 €13500 Anacreon, amour et bacchus (171cm-67in) s.num.872 brown pat bronze faux marble base st.f.F Barbedienne. 9-Apr-3 Sotheby's, London #136/R est:10000-15000

£17949 $28179 €28000 Danseuse mauresque (53cm-21in) s.st.f.Siot bronze ivory lapis lazuli socle prov. 10-Dec-2 Tajan, Paris #174/R est:40000

£51724 $82759 €75000 Danseuse a la pomme (93x56cm-37x22in) s.i. num.T711 gilded green pat bronze ivory Cast Siot lit. 15-Mar-3 De Vuyst, Lokeren #422/R

Works on paper

£13000 $21710 €19500 Homme portant un turban (27x16cm-11x6in) i. pencil executed c.1856-57 exhib. 19-Jun-3 Christie's, London #17/R est:6000-8000

GEROME, Jean Léon (after) (1824-1904) French

Sculpture

£9712 $15928 €13500 La danse ou danseuse a la pomme (51cm-20in) i.num.Z400 ivory gold pat bronze prov.lit. 4-Jun-3 Tajan, Paris #262/R est:16000-22000

GEROME, Jean Léon (studio) (1824-1904) French

£4221 $6500 €6332 Collaboration, Corneille and Moliere (24x32cm-9x13in) s. panel. 4-Sep-2 Christie's, Rockefeller NY #310/R est:6000-8000

GERRARD, Charles F (19th C) Australian

£5590 $9000 €8385 Coastal view of yachts under sail (33x58cm-13x23in) s.d.1886 board. 23-Feb-3 Skinner, Boston #31/R est:10000-15000

GERRITS, Gerrit Jacobus (1893-1965) Dutch

£481 $755 €750 Girl sitting with doll (71x61cm-28x24in) s. exhib. 25-Nov-2 Glerum, Amsterdam #130

GERRY, Samuel Lancaster (1813-1891) American

£692 $1100 €1038 Paddling across (15x24cm-6x9in) s. board prov. 7-Mar-3 Skinner, Boston #289/R

£1282 $2000 €1923 Paddling across (13x23cm-5x9in) s. panel. 22-Sep-2 Jeffery Burchard, Florida #20

£2500 $4000 €3750 Couple on a path at a wooded clearing with sailboats on a lake (46x30cm-18x12in) s. 16-May-3 York Town, York #959 est:3500-4500

£2581 $4000 €3872 Lake scene near mountains (48x33cm-19x13in) s. canvas on cardboard. 16-Jul-2 Arthur James, Florida #370

£2839 $4400 €4259 Couple strolling on a wooded path beside a lake (30x46cm-12x18in) s. 2-Nov-2 North East Auctions, Portsmouth #54/R est:4000-5000

£5195 $8000 €7793 Caldwell, Lake George (53x76cm-21x30in) s.d.1838 prov. 24-Oct-2 Shannon's, Milford #48/R est:8000-12000

GERRY, Samuel Lancaster (attrib) (1813-1891) American

£881 $1400 €1322 Lake George (20x41cm-8x16in) s. prov. 7-Mar-3 Skinner, Boston #286/R est:800-1200

GERTLER, Mark (1891-1939) British

£6500 $10660 €9750 Spanish scene (41x51cm-16x20in) painted c.1934. 3-Jun-3 Sotheby's, Olympia #62/R est:2000-3000

£15000 $24600 €22500 Tulips in a vase (51x25cm-20x10in) prov.exhib. 6-Jun-3 Christie's, London #27/R est:10000-15000

£38000 $62320 €57000 Silver vase (56x46cm-22x18in) s.d.30 prov. 6-Jun-3 Christie's, London #26/R est:25000-35000

Works on paper

£3100 $5146 €4495 Head study for nude with mandolin (20x20cm-8x8in) s.d.1934 chl dr. 10-Jun-3 David Lay, Penzance #253/R est:3000-4000

£5000 $8200 €7500 Portrait of Alice Edwards (45x30cm-18x12in) s.d.29 black crayon prov. 6-Jun-3 Christie's, London #25/R est:4000-6000

GERTLER, Mark (attrib) (1891-1939) British
Works on paper
£500 $785 €750 Artist and sleeping model in a studio (47x37cm-19x15in) pencil dr. 10-Dec-2 Lane, Penzance #58/R

GERTNER, Johan Vilhelm (1818-1871) Danish
£287 $465 €416 Portrait of professor Henriette Conradine Drejer (25x21cm-10x8in) init.d.1841. 26-May-3 Rasmussen, Copenhagen #1299/R (D.KR 3000)

GERTSCH, Franz (1930-) Swiss
£655 $1022 €983 Sunny path through trees (48x40cm-19x16in) s.d.46 panel. 8-Nov-2 Dobiaschofsky, Bern #169/R (S.FR 1500)
Prints
£23853 $39835 €34587 Natascha III (116x94cm-46x37in) s.i. col woodcut. 20-Jun-3 Kornfeld, Bern #46/R est:60000 (S.FR 52000)
£27523 $45963 €39908 Natascha III (105x90cm-41x35in) s. col woodcut. 20-Jun-3 Kornfeld, Bern #45/R est:60000 (S.FR 60000)

GERVAIS, Eugène (19th C) French
£897 $1409 €1400 Usine a Blois (60x73cm-24x29in) s. 11-Dec-2 Maigret, Paris #160

GERVAIS, Lise (1933-1998) Canadian
£650 $1021 €975 Composition (68x54cm-27x21in) s.d.65 d. verso prov. 12-Dec-2 Iegor de Saint Hippolyte, Montreal #33 (C.D 1600)
£2621 $4141 €3932 La croix du sud (69x61cm-27x24in) s.d.62 prov. 18-Nov-2 Sotheby's, Toronto #79/R est:3000-5000 (C.D 6500)
£3556 $5831 €5334 Evolution naturelle (127x102cm-50x40in) s.d.1959 masonite prov. 27-May-3 Sotheby's, Toronto #188/R est:6000-8000 (C.D 8000)

GERVAIS, Paul Jean (1859-1936) French
£3200 $5216 €4640 Portrait de femme en pied (61x35cm-24x14in) bears sig. 16-Jul-3 Sotheby's, Olympia #238/R est:1800-2500

GERVEX, Henri (1852-1929) French
£6282 $9926 €9800 Jeune femme en bord de mer (198x117cm-78x46in) s.d. exhib. 18-Nov-2 Tajan, Paris #206/R est:15000-18000
£9028 $14354 €13000 Jeune femme a sa toilette (25x20cm-10x8in) s. panel lit. 29-Apr-3 Artcurial Briest, Paris #153/R est:12000-15000
Works on paper
£538 $834 €850 Femme nue assise (30x22cm-12x9in) mono. graphite. 28-Sep-2 Cornette de St.Cyr, Paris #161
£4577 $7599 €6500 Etude d'enfants (40x73cm-16x29in) s.d.95 pastel paper on canvas. 11-Jun-3 Beaussant & Lefèvre, Paris #55/R est:2000-3000

GERWIN, K (20th C) German
Works on paper
£1083 $1733 €1570 Gun emplacement, Germany (49x42cm-19x17in) s.d.1944 W/C. 13-May-3 Watson's, Christchurch #88/R est:3000-6000 (NZ.D 3000)

GERY-GALY, Marguerite (20th C) French
£1216 $1897 €1800 Le peinture et son modele (100x111cm-39x44in) s. 25-Mar-3 Chochon-Barre & Allardi, Paris #132/R est:2000-2800

GERZ, Jochen (1940-) German
Works on paper
£380 $600 €600 Periple (21x26cm-8x10in) s.d.1972 verso ink on perspex prov. 26-Nov-2 Sotheby's, Amsterdam #291/R

GERZSO, Gunther (1915-2000) Mexican
£41401 $65000 €62102 Legendary landscape (60x81cm-24x32in) s.d.64 s.i.d.verso prov.lit. 19-Nov-2 Sotheby's, New York #97/R est:60000
£60510 $95000 €90765 Umbral (49x65cm-19x26in) s.d.64 s.i.d.verso masonite prov. 19-Nov-2 Sotheby's, New York #11/R est:60000
Sculpture
£4093 $6385 €6140 Pajaro mitologico (40x14cm-16x6in) s.d.1988 num.1/6 bronze prov.lit. 17-Oct-2 Louis Morton, Mexico #105/R est:70000-80000 (M.P 65000)
£10191 $16000 €15287 Similar (58x78x6cm-23x31x2in) s.d.94 num.4/6 pat bronze prov.lit. 19-Nov-2 Sotheby's, New York #96/R est:30000
£10828 $17000 €16242 Similar (58x78x6cm-23x31x2in) s.d.94 num.3/6 bronze prov.exhib. 20-Nov-2 Christie's, Rockefeller NY #34/R est:20000-30000

GESNE, Jean Victor Albert de (1834-1903) French
£690 $1062 €1035 Landscape with two dogs (61x50cm-24x20in) s. 27-Oct-2 Anders Antik, Landskrona #60/R (S.KR 10000)

GESNE, Jean Victor Albert de (attrib) (1834-1903) French
£296 $491 €420 Three hunting dogs quietly waiting (53x46cm-21x18in) 14-Jun-3 Arnold, Frankfurt #723/R

GESSI, Francesco (1588-1649) Italian
£2535 $4208 €3600 St Peter penitent (100x75cm-39x30in) 11-Jun-3 Dorotheum, Vienna #240/R est:4000-7000

GESSI, Francesco (circle) (1588-1649) Italian
£5500 $8635 €8250 Vestal Virgin Tuccia (130x100cm-51x39in) 10-Dec-2 Bonhams, New Bond Street #110/R est:2000-4000

GESSNER, Conrad (1764-1826) Swiss
£1717 $2661 €2576 Hunting party (74x92cm-29x36in) s.d.1807. 3-Oct-2 Koller, Zurich #3140/R est:5000-7000 (S.FR 4000)

GESSNER, Robert S (1908-1982) Swiss
£1048 $1645 €1572 Game 20 (48x48cm-19x19in) acrylic panel. 25-Nov-2 Germann, Zurich #112/R est:2800-3500 (S.FR 2400)
Works on paper
£306 $480 €459 Ibiza postcards (11x11cm-4x4in) s.i.d.1981 gouache. 23-Nov-2 Burkhard, Luzern #4 (S.FR 700)
£524 $823 €786 Composition (18x26cm-7x10in) s.d.1955 W/C. 23-Nov-2 Burkhard, Luzern #3/R (S.FR 1200)

GESSNER, Salomon (1730-1788) Swiss
£2113 $3465 €3064 Mythical figures in wood (40x27cm-16x11in) panel. 4-Jun-3 Fischer, Luzern #1211/R est:5000-6000 (S.FR 4500)

GESSNITZER, C (19th C) German?
£1200 $1824 €1800 Busy waterway (47x69cm-19x27in) s. with another work by same hand two. 29-Aug-2 Christie's, Kensington #10/R est:1000-1500

GESSNITZER, Joseph (19th C) Austrian
£320 $531 €480 Continental harbour scene (52x94cm-20x37in) s. 10-Jun-3 Bonhams, Knightsbridge #35/R

GESTEL, Leo (1881-1941) Dutch
£1218 $1851 €1900 Figures escaping down stairway exit (53x68cm-21x27in) s. paper on board lit. 11-Jul-2 Allgauer, Kempten #2491/R
£1773 $2872 €2500 Paris (56x43cm-22x17in) s.i. mixed media prov. 26-May-3 Glerum, Amsterdam #85/R est:4000-6000
£30216 $49554 €42000 Still life with tiger lilies (33x25cm-13x10in) s. painted c.1912-13 prov. 3-Jun-3 Christie's, Amsterdam #237/R est:28000-35000
£50633 $80000 €80000 Mallorca (55x62cm-22x24in) s.i.d.1914 i.d.verso prov. 26-Nov-2 Sotheby's, Amsterdam #95/R est:60000-80000
£82278 $130000 €130000 Still life with fruit and flowers (63x90cm-25x35in) s.d.1911 s.i.on stretcher prov. 26-Nov-2 Sotheby's, Amsterdam #90/R est:120000-180000
£136691 $224173 €190000 Still life with peonies (70x55cm-28x22in) s.d.13. 3-Jun-3 Christie's, Amsterdam #241/R est:120000-160000
£288462 $447115 €450000 Landweg in Bergen (110x146cm-43x57in) s.d.1912 s.i.d.verso prov.exhib.lit. 3-Dec-2 Christie's, Amsterdam #211/R est:350000-450000
Works on paper
£461 $747 €650 Fishing girl (33x26cm-13x10in) chk. 26-May-3 Glerum, Amsterdam #62/R
£709 $1149 €1000 Hilly landscape with farm and cows on the meadow (44x60cm-17x24in) chk. 26-May-3 Glerum, Amsterdam #34/R
£780 $1264 €1100 Harbour view (49x35cm-19x14in) s.d.37 W/C. 26-May-3 Glerum, Amsterdam #2/R
£962 $1510 €1500 Gentleman and lady (26x20cm-10x8in) mono. W/C. 25-Nov-2 Glerum, Amsterdam #153 est:400-600
£1690 $2721 €2400 Horses (13x20cm-5x8in) s.d.28 pencil pastel gouache. 7-May-3 Vendue Huis, Gravenhage #547/R est:400-600
£1795 $2782 €2800 Farmer at work (70x86cm-28x34in) s.d.1919 black chk. 3-Dec-2 Christie's, Amsterdam #8/R est:2000-3000
£1806 $2979 €2600 Belgian refugees (61x83cm-24x33in) s.i.d.1914 chl W/C prov.exhib. 1-Jul-3 Christie's, Amsterdam #378 est:1000-1500
£2158 $3540 €3000 De vlucht uit Belgie (39x31cm-15x12in) s.i.d.1914 pastel W/C. 3-Jun-3 Christie's, Amsterdam #39/R est:2000-3000
£3846 $5962 €6000 Gitana (57x48cm-22x19in) s.i. pastel W/C executed c.1914. 3-Dec-2 Christie's, Amsterdam #6/R est:8000-12000
£4114 $6500 €6500 Mart te Nijmegen (26x20cm-10x8in) s.i.d.08 W/C pastel. 26-Nov-2 Sotheby's, Amsterdam #103/R est:4000-6000
£7595 $12000 €12000 Two ladies in Amsterdam (24x17cm-9x7in) s. gouache W/C. 26-Nov-2 Sotheby's, Amsterdam #122/R est:12000-15000

£47468 $75000 €75000 Femme a sa toilette (48x54cm-19x21in) pastel prov. 26-Nov-2 Sotheby's, Amsterdam #85/R est:20000-30000

GETTE, Paul Armand (1927-) French
£694 $1104 €1000 Composition (81x100cm-32x39in) s.d.62 prov. 29-Apr-3 Artcurial Briest, Paris #572
Works on paper
£1282 $2013 €2000 Calcinations (65x52cm-26x20in) mixed media paper froisse panel prov.exhib. 24-Nov-2 Laurence Calmels, Paris #139/R

GETTY, Francis E (?) ?
£344 $550 €499 The Saco (26x35cm-10x14in) i.verso canvasboard. 16-May-3 Skinner, Boston #300/R

GEUDENS, Albert (?) Belgian
£377 $588 €550 Interieur a la table dressee (65x56cm-26x22in) s. 14-Apr-3 Horta, Bruxelles #282

GEUDTNER, Anna (1844-?) German
£3526 $5571 €5500 Hunting still life (102x43cm-40x17in) s. two. 16-Nov-2 Lempertz, Koln #1469/R est:4000

GEVERS, René (c.1869-?) Belgian
£490 $789 €750 Peniches au crepuscule (27x38cm-11x15in) s. panel. 20-Jan-3 Horta, Bruxelles #332

GEYER, Fritz (1875-1947) German
£1753 $2560 €2700 Lively market in Nurnberg (79x67cm-31x26in) s. board. 15-Jun-2 Hans Stahl, Hamburg #23/R

GEYER, Georg (1823-1912) Austrian
Works on paper
£270 $422 €400 Landscape with farmstead (38x48cm-15x19in) s.d.908 W/C. 28-Mar-3 Dorotheum, Vienna #254/R

GEYER, Herman (19th C) American
£1274 $2000 €1911 Wintry day in the Adirondacks (56x91cm-22x36in) s. 10-Dec-2 Doyle, New York #15/R est:2000-3000

GEYER, Walter Bruno (1922-) German
£253 $395 €400 Composition (94x93cm-37x37in) s. 18-Oct-2 Dr Fritz Nagel, Stuttgart #115/R

GEYGER, Ernst Moritz (1861-1941) German
Sculpture
£2500 $3875 €3750 Classical archer (63cm-25in) s.i. brown pat bronze rec. base. 29-Oct-2 Bonhams, New Bond Street #175/R est:3000-4000
£4516 $7000 €6774 Mirror (44cm-17in) init. silver electroplated bronze on malachite base prov. 29-Oct-2 Sotheby's, New York #251/R est:6000-8000

GEYP, Adriaan Marinus (1855-1926) Dutch
£986 $1587 €1400 Het Kleine Loo, achter Huis ten Bosch, Den Haag (73x58cm-29x23in) s. 7-May-3 Vendue Huis, Gravenhage #23/R
£2303 $3730 €3500 Country romance (96x141cm-38x56in) s. 21-Jan-3 Christie's, Amsterdam #199/R est:4000-6000

GFELLER, Werner (1895-1985) Swiss?
£509 $820 €738 Still life of flowers (39x45cm-15x18in) s. board. 9-May-3 Dobiaschofsky, Bern #178/R (S.FR 1100)
£742 $1158 €1113 Meadow landscape with fir trees (33x39cm-13x15in) s.i.verso canvas on masonite. 8-Nov-2 Dobiaschofsky, Bern #158/R (S.FR 1700)
£1019 $1640 €1478 Margarites (19x27cm-7x11in) s.indis.d. panel. 9-May-3 Dobiaschofsky, Bern #176/R est:1400 (S.FR 2200)

GHEDUZZI, Cesare (1894-1944) Italian
£680 $1082 €1000 Countryside in summer, Piemonte (30x44cm-12x17in) s. board. 1-Mar-3 Meeting Art, Vercelli #19
£1020 $1622 €1500 Cottage in the mountains (30x45cm-12x18in) s. board. 1-Mar-3 Meeting Art, Vercelli #171

GHEDUZZI, Giuseppe (1889-1957) Italian
£516 $831 €774 Alpine landscape (53x63cm-21x25in) s.d.10.10.1929 s.i.verso board. 12-May-3 Stephan Welz, Johannesburg #27 est:3000-5000 (SA.R 6000)
£533 $858 €800 Two women on a path carrying baskets (35x64cm-14x25in) s. board. 12-May-3 Stephan Welz, Johannesburg #26 est:3000-5000 (SA.R 6200)
£884 $1406 €1300 Valpelline (33x45cm-13x18in) s. board. 18-Mar-3 Finarte, Milan #184/R
£1538 $2415 €2400 Courtyard (25x36cm-10x14in) s. board. 10-Dec-2 Della Rocca, Turin #272/R
£1923 $3019 €3000 Courtyard (25x36cm-10x14in) s. board. 10-Dec-2 Della Rocca, Turin #379/R

GHEDUZZI, Ugo (1853-1925) Italian
£1701 $2704 €2500 Lights in the under-growth (46x66cm-18x26in) s.d.1911 cardboard. 1-Mar-3 Meeting Art, Vercelli #257

GHEERAERTS, Marcus (younger-style) (1561-1635) Belgian
£7800 $12168 €11700 Portrait of Queen Elizabeth I (61x46cm-24x18in) 11-Nov-2 Trembath Welch, Great Dunmow #458/R est:5000-7000
£12000 $18720 €18000 Portrait of a lady in Elizabethan costume (61x51cm-24x20in) 9-Oct-2 Woolley & Wallis, Salisbury #293/R est:4000-6000

GHELARDUCCI, Giulio (1883-1970) Italian
£321 $503 €500 Corrado Carapelli at the Circeo (44x32cm-17x13in) s.d.1952 card on canvas prov. 16-Dec-2 Pandolfini, Florence #322

GHENT, Peter (1856-1911) British
Works on paper
£350 $557 €525 Welsh coast, Harlech, N Wales (48x74cm-19x29in) s. 18-Mar-3 Capes Dunn, Manchester #450
£420 $680 €630 Shepherd's home, Carneth Llewellyn (34x49cm-13x19in) s. W/C. 21-Jan-3 Bonhams, Knightsbridge #48/R

GHERARDI, Cristoforo (attrib) (1508-1556) Italian
Works on paper
£700 $1099 €1050 Decorative grotesque designs (33x8cm-13x3in) pen ink pair after Raphael. 11-Dec-2 Sotheby's, Olympia #16/R

GHERARDINI, Alessandro (1655-1723) Italian
Works on paper
£1119 $1600 €1679 Study of a Saint seen from below (21x17cm-8x7in) red chk. 23-Jan-3 Swann Galleries, New York #105/R est:1000-1500

GHERRI-MORO, Bruno (1899-1967) Italian
£258 $407 €387 Val d'Herens with the village La Sage (60x81cm-24x32in) s.i. 29-Nov-2 Zofingen, Switzerland #2889 (S.FR 600)
£610 $1001 €885 Snowy mountain landscape with stream (60x80cm-24x31in) s. 4-Jun-3 Fischer, Luzern #1209/R (S.FR 1300)
Works on paper
£272 $433 €400 Venice (29x40cm-11x16in) s.d.62 W/C. 1-Mar-3 Stadion, Trieste #377

GHEYN, Jacob de III (c.1596-?) Dutch
Prints
£2025 $3200 €3200 Apostle Paul (30x20cm-12x8in) etching. 29-Nov-2 Bassenge, Berlin #5286/R est:3000
Works on paper
£10885 $17307 €16000 Prophets (26x1cm-10x0in) i. pen ink pair prov. 24-Mar-3 Tajan, Paris #15/R

GHEZ, Gilles (1945-) French
Works on paper
£304 $474 €450 Hommage a l'Afrique (70x80cm-28x31in) s.d.1981 mixed media prov. 28-Mar-3 Charbonneaux, Paris #77

GHEZZI, Giuseppe (attrib) (1634-1721) Italian
Works on paper
£633 $1000 €1000 Beggar (14x9cm-6x4in) Chinese ink. 2-Dec-2 Finarte, Milan #103

GHEZZI, Pier Leone (1674-1755) Italian
Works on paper
£1014 $1581 €1500 Padre Giuseppe Maria de Bologna (31x22cm-12x9in) i. pen ink prov. 31-Mar-3 Piasa, Paris #24
£1284 $2003 €1900 Maestro Carlo Banderaro in Frascati (26x19cm-10x7in) i. pen ink prov. 31-Mar-3 Piasa, Paris #23/R
£2113 $3401 €3000 Clement XI seque la processione in Piazza San Pietro (23x35cm-9x14in) blk pencil htd white pencil. 12-May-3 Sotheby's, Milan #47/R est:3000-4000
£52469 $85000 €78704 Portrait of Serafino and Francesco Falsacapa at table (16x26cm-6x10in) i. chk pen ink prov.lit. 22-Jan-3 Christie's, Rockefeller NY #38/R est:50000

GHIATZA, D (20th C) French?
Sculpture
£1069 $1785 €1550 Composition (123cm-48in) s.d.3/1969 bronze oak socle. 9-Jul-3 Millon & Associes, Paris #213b/R est:1200-1500

GHIGLIA, Oscar (1876-1945) Italian
£12025 $19000 €19000 Arum lilies and oranges (23x28cm-9x11in) s.d.924 verso cardboard prov.lit. 26-Nov-2 Christie's, Rome #197/R
£13291 $21000 €21000 Portrait of Paulo with green umbrella (34x31cm-13x12in) s.d.919 cardboard exhib.lit. 26-Nov-2 Christie's, Rome #201/R est:20000-30000

GHIGLIA, Paulo (1905-1979) Italian
£962 $1510 €1500 Portrait of veiled girl (50x37cm-20x15in) s. board. 16-Dec-2 Pandolfini, Florence #248/R
£1161 $1835 €1800 Under the parasol (36x45cm-14x18in) s.d.1951 board. 18-Dec-2 Finarte, Milan #184/R

GHIGLIERI, Lorenzo E (1931-) American
Sculpture
£2070 $3250 €3105 Trouble behind (53cm-21in) s.d.1983 num.6/22 brown pat bronze st.f.Valley Bronze. 19-Nov-2 Butterfields, San Francisco #8123/R est:3000-5000
£2244 $3500 €3366 Abraham Lincoln (197x121cm-78x48in) s.d.1979 brown pat. bronze i.f.Maiden. 12-Apr-3 Weschler, Washington #550/R est:10000-15000

GHIGLION-GREEN, Maurice (1913-) French
£1035 $1635 €1500 Jardin du mas de la Mitoune (38x55cm-15x22in) s. s.i.on stretcher. 4-Apr-3 Tajan, Paris #67/R
£1103 $1743 €1600 Jour de Noel (46x55cm-18x22in) s. s.i.on stretcher. 4-Apr-3 Tajan, Paris #81/R

GHIKA, Nicolas (1906-1994) Greek
£19000 $29450 €28500 Interior with easel III (89x116cm-35x46in) s. prov.exhib.lit. 2-Oct-2 Sotheby's, London #53/R est:20000-30000
Works on paper
£600 $930 €900 Study of nude (35x26cm-14x10in) s.d.59 pencil. 2-Oct-2 Sotheby's, London #95/R
£600 $930 €900 Conservatory (32x50cm-13x20in) s.d.1960 pencil. 2-Oct-2 Sotheby's, London #101/R
£600 $930 €900 Sketch of face (30x23cm-12x9in) s.d.55 pencil. 2-Oct-2 Sotheby's, London #97/R
£900 $1395 €1350 Chair and props (31x20cm-12x8in) s.d.60 pencil. 2-Oct-2 Sotheby's, London #100/R
£900 $1395 €1350 Face in profile (32x22cm-13x9in) s.d.55 pencil. 2-Oct-2 Sotheby's, London #99/R
£3000 $4650 €4500 Athens balcony (27x37cm-11x15in) s. W/C gouache. 2-Oct-2 Sotheby's, London #52/R est:6000

GHIOZZI, Renzo (1907-) Italian
£1076 $1678 €1700 Composition (100x70cm-39x28in) s. acrylic. 19-Oct-2 Semenzato, Venice #115/R

GHISOLFI, Enrico (1837-1918) Italian
£3526 $5535 €5500 Stone pit (62x93cm-24x37in) s. exhib. 10-Dec-2 Della Rocca, Turin #280 est:4000
£11613 $18348 €18000 Harvest on Barolo hills (107x190cm-42x75in) s.d.1865 exhib. 18-Dec-2 Finarte, Milan #92/R est:17000

GHISOLFI, Giovanni (1632-1683) Italian
£13207 $20339 €21000 Reunion de personnages pres des ruines d'un temple antique (68x89cm-27x35in) 25-Oct-2 Tajan, Paris #37/R est:1000-13000
£18868 $29245 €30000 Capriccio of Roman ruins and sacrifice to Mars (94x131cm-37x52in) prov. 2-Oct-2 Dorotheum, Vienna #9/R est:15000-20000

GHISOLFI, Giovanni (attrib) (1632-1683) Italian
£4054 $6324 €6000 Combat de Balaham (81x60cm-32x24in) 26-Mar-3 Pierre Berge, Paris #24/R

GHISOLFI, Giovanni (circle) (1632-1683) Italian
£4878 $8000 €7317 Architectural capriccio with figures by a cove (96x134cm-38x53in) prov. 30-May-3 Christie's, Rockefeller NY #20/R est:10000-15000
£4878 $8000 €7317 Architectural capriccio with figures by a statue and a fountain (96x134cm-38x53in) prov. 30-May-3 Christie's, Rockefeller NY #21/R est:10000-15000
£4878 $8000 €7317 Architectural capriccio with figures amongst ruins (96x134cm-38x53in) prov. 30-May-3 Christie's, Rockefeller NY #22/R est:10000-15000
£7500 $11700 €11250 Capriccio of a classical palace with figures (65x83cm-26x33in) 10-Apr-3 Christie's, Kensington #259/R est:3000-5000
£13000 $20150 €19500 Architectural capriccio with the raising of Lazaus (90x105cm-35x41in) canvas on masonite. 30-Oct-2 Bonhams, New Bond Street #176/R est:12000-15000

GHIVARELLO, Benedetto (1882-1955) Italian
£340 $541 €500 View of village (34x24cm-13x9in) s.d.1935 card on masonite. 1-Mar-3 Meeting Art, Vercelli #174
£374 $595 €550 Landscape (22x26cm-9x10in) s.d.1944 cardboard. 1-Mar-3 Meeting Art, Vercelli #48
£449 $704 €700 Mountainous landscape (35x44cm-14x17in) s. cardboard. 10-Dec-2 Della Rocca, Turin #267/R

GHOBERT, Bernard (20th C) ?
Works on paper
£302 $468 €480 Tiroir (19x19cm-7x7in) s. col pencil dr. 5-Oct-2 De Vuyst, Lokeren #155

GHOLAMI, M (?) ?
£316 $494 €500 Still life of fruit with insects and birds (79x59cm-31x23in) s. 14-Sep-2 Weidler, Nurnberg #6745

GHY-LEMM (20th C) French
£278 $458 €400 Homme noir assis (46x55cm-18x22in) s. 1-Jul-3 Claude Aguttes, Neuilly #128/R
£278 $458 €400 Vente publique. Chez le modiste (50x60cm-20x24in) s. double-sided. 1-Jul-3 Claude Aguttes, Neuilly #131/R
£417 $688 €600 Parc des butes Chaumont (50x65cm-20x26in) s. i.verso. 1-Jul-3 Claude Aguttes, Neuilly #124/R
£590 $974 €850 La plage aux cabines de bains et aux parasols (27x42cm-11x17in) s. panel. 1-Jul-3 Claude Aguttes, Neuilly #129/R

GIACCO, Francis (1955-) Australian
£421 $662 €632 Interior with figure reading (41x45cm-16x18in) d.7.4.80 s.verso. 15-Apr-3 Lawson Menzies, Sydney #162/R est:750-1500 (A.D 1100)
£786 $1225 €1179 Watson's Bay (49x48cm-19x19in) s.d.85. 11-Nov-2 Deutscher-Menzies, Melbourne #152/R (A.D 2200)

GIACHI, E (19th C) Italian
£7911 $12736 €11867 Proposal in an interior (75x49cm-30x19in) s.d.1891. 12-May-3 Stephan Welz, Johannesburg #420/R est:25000-35000 (SA.R 92000)

GIACOMELLI, Mario (1925-2000) Italian
Photographs
£1800 $2916 €2700 Paesaggio libera (18x40cm-7x16in) st.i.verso silver print exec.c.1960. 22-May-3 Sotheby's, London #111/R est:1800-2200

GIACOMELLI, Vincenzo (1841-1890) Italian
£5634 $9239 €8169 Market in Venice (68x95cm-27x37in) s.d.1877. 4-Jun-3 Fischer, Luzern #1046/R est:4000-6000 (S.FR 12000)

GIACOMETTI, Alberto (1901-1966) Swiss
£110000 $183700 €159500 Femme debout (55x29cm-22x11in) indis sig. painted c.1949 prov.exhib. 25-Jun-3 Christie's, London #200/R est:110000-130000
£403727 $650000 €605591 Portrait de Diego en gris (81x65cm-32x26in) s.d.1957 prov.exhib.lit. 7-May-3 Christie's, Rockefeller NY #26/R est:700000-1000000
Prints
£1781 $2778 €2600 Rimbaud vu par les peintres (29x25cm-11x10in) s. eau forte lit. 10-Apr-3 Finarte Semenzato, Rome #25/R
£2297 $3584 €3400 Vase of flowers (27x20cm-11x8in) s. eau forte. 28-Mar-3 Farsetti, Prato #315/R
£2778 $4389 €4000 L'atelier aux outeilles (41x56cm-16x22in) s.num.56/100 lithograph. 26-Apr-3 Cornette de St.Cyr, Paris #37/R est:2000-3000
£2830 $4500 €4245 Dans l'atelier (26x20cm-10x8in) s.num.40/50 etching. 2-May-3 Sotheby's, New York #162 est:2500-3500
£2945 $4800 €4418 Reclining woman (41x29cm-16x11in) s. num.55/90 lithograph exec.1960. 13-Feb-3 Christie's, Rockefeller NY #69/R
£2949 $4600 €4424 Studio with Annette (26x20cm-10x8in) s.num.15/111 verso etching card stock two on one sheet. 7-Nov-2 Swann Galleries, New York #648/R est:5000-8000
£3526 $5500 €5289 Nude facing front (34x14cm-13x6in) s.num.17/50 etching. 5-Nov-2 Christie's, Rockefeller NY #161/R est:3500-4500
£3944 $6546 €5600 Personnage dans l'atelier (55x36cm-22x14in) s. lithograph. 14-Jun-3 Hauswedell & Nolte, Hamburg #1201/R est:4000
£37615 $62817 €54542 Les pieds dans le plat (13x9cm-5x4in) s.i. copperplate. 20-Jun-3 Kornfeld, Bern #47/R est:50000 (S.FR 82000)

Sculpture

£5396 $8633 €7500 Coloquinte (21cm-8in) plaster lamp prov. 15-May-3 Sotheby's, Paris #113/R
£8993 $14388 €12500 Chandeliers (9cm-4in) plaster pair prov.lit. 15-May-3 Sotheby's, Paris #95/R
£9317 $15000 €13976 Lampe trepied a etoile (41cm-16in) black pat. bronze prov.lit. 7-May-3 Sotheby's, New York #301/R est:18000-25000
£13924 $21582 €22000 Petite tete d'Ottilia (5cm-2in) s.num.5/6 brown pat bronze conceived 1935 st.f.L.Thinot lit. 28-Sep-2 Christie's, Paris #17/R est:22000-26000
£14460 $23137 €20100 Amphore (33cm-13in) plaster prov.lit. 15-May-3 Sotheby's, Paris #119/R
£19872 $30801 €31000 Lampe trepied a etoile (40cm-16in) gilt pat bronze exec.c.1936 lit. 9-Dec-2 Piasa, Paris #46/R est:20000-30000
£20833 $32500 €31250 Lampadaire aux feuillies (147cm-58in) green pat. bronze executed c.1935-37 prov.lit. 6-Nov-2 Sotheby's, New York #229/R est:30000-40000
£21000 $35070 €30450 Tete de Meduse (25cm-10in) bronze executed c.1936-37 prov.lit. 24-Jun-3 Sotheby's, London #159/R est:10000-15000
£22436 $34776 €35000 Lampe feuilles (39cm-15in) num.601 gilt pat bronze lit. 9-Dec-2 Piasa, Paris #43/R est:20000-25000
£24359 $37756 €38000 Lampe feuille (39cm-15in) num.601 gilt pat bronze lit. 9-Dec-2 Piasa, Paris #44/R est:20000-25000
£25316 $39241 €40000 Tete de Simone de Beauvoir, petite tete sur double socle (13cm-5in) s.num.3/8 brown pat bronze conceived c.1946 st.f.Susse lit. 28-Sep-2 Christie's, Paris #15/R est:25000-35000
£25468 $40748 €35400 Masks (23x16cm-9x6in) plaster pair prov.lit. 15-May-3 Sotheby's, Paris #136/R
£26187 $41899 €36400 Balustre (70cm-28in) terracotta prov.lit. 15-May-3 Sotheby's, Paris #138/R
£27698 $44317 €38500 Vase (36cm-14in) plaster zinc prov.lit. 15-May-3 Sotheby's, Paris #120/R
£29487 $45705 €46000 Lampe a tete de femme (50cm-20in) gilt pat bronze exec.c.1936 lit. 9-Dec-2 Piasa, Paris #45/R est:30000-40000
£29817 $49794 €43235 Lampe, tete de femme (51cm-20in) bronze lit. 20-Jun-3 Kornfeld, Bern #55/R est:70000 (S.FR 65000)
£30380 $47089 €48000 Homme sur socle (8cm-3in) s.num.6/8 gold pat bronze conceived 1940-41 st.f.L.Thinot lit. 28-Sep-2 Christie's, Paris #21/R est:18000-24000
£34161 $55000 €51242 Lampadaire tete de femme (155cm-61in) i. gold pat. bronze prov.exhib.lit. 7-May-3 Sotheby's, New York #303/R est:25000-35000
£35000 $57400 €52500 Tete de Meduse (24cm-9in) pat bronze exec.c.1935 prov.lit. 5-Feb-3 Sotheby's, London #176/R est:45000
£36000 $55440 €54000 Tete de Simon Berard (19cm-7in) i.num.3/6 bronze conceived 1971 prov.lit. 22-Oct-2 Sotheby's, London #197/R est:12000-15000
£36709 $56899 €58000 Tete de femme sur socle, Marie-Laure de Noailles (12cm-5in) s.num.6/8 gold pat bronze conceived 1946 st.f.Thinot lit. 28-Sep-2 Christie's, Paris #20/R est:18000-24000
£39240 $60822 €62000 Figurine avec bras (11cm-4in) s.num.1/8 pat bronze. 28-Sep-2 Christie's, Paris #19/R est:25000-35000
£41139 $63766 €65000 Figurine (15x5x6cm-6x2x2in) s.num.7/8 brown pat bronze conceived c.1950 st.f.Susse. 28-Sep-2 Christie's, Paris #10/R est:50000-70000
£44304 $68671 €70000 Petit buste sur double socle (11cm-4in) s.num.6/8 brown pat bronze conceived 1940-41 st.f.L.Thinot lit. 28-Sep-2 Christie's, Paris #16/R est:30000-40000
£75949 $117722 €120000 Tete de femme, Flora Mayo (30x23x9cm-12x9x4in) s.num.5/8 green pat bronze conceived 1927 st.f.Susse lit. 28-Sep-2 Christie's, Paris #22/R est:10000-15000
£82278 $127532 €130000 Petit buste de Silvio sur double socle (18x12x11cm-7x5x4in) s.num.8/8 green pat bronze conceived 1942-43 st.f.M Pastori lit. 28-Sep-2 Christie's, Paris #14/R est:30000-40000
£85443 $132437 €135000 Femme, composition surrealiste (55x32x8cm-22x13x3in) s.num.6/6 brown pat bronze conceived 1927 st.f.Susse lit. 28-Sep-2 Christie's, Paris #1/R est:25000-35000
£85443 $132437 €135000 Composition (39x27x27cm-15x11x11in) s.num.7/8 brown pat bronze conceived 1927 st.f.Susse lit. 28-Sep-2 Christie's, Paris #4/R est:40000-60000
£101266 $156962 €160000 Composition cubiste (67x45x39cm-26x18x15in) s.num.7/8 green brown pat bronze conceived c.1926 st.f.Susse lit. 28-Sep-2 Christie's, Paris #3/R est:60000-80000
£110759 $171677 €175000 Femme (39x16x8cm-15x6x3in) s.num.4/6 brown pat bronze conceived 1928 st.f.Susse lit. 28-Sep-2 Christie's, Paris #2/R est:30000-40000
£120253 $186392 €190000 Buste d'homme sur socle (54x12x10cm-21x5x4in) s.num.5/8 brown pat bronze conceived c.1949-50 st.f.Susse lit. 28-Sep-2 Christie's, Paris #8/R est:140000-180000
£132911 $206013 €210000 Femme debout (22x6x8cm-9x2x3in) s.num.7/8 brown pat bronze conceived c.1950 st.f.Susse lit. 28-Sep-2 Christie's, Paris #12/R est:100000-150000
£139241 $215823 €220000 Figurine debout (23x6x10cm-9x2x4in) s.num.7/8 brown pat bronze conceived c.1946 st.f.Susse lit. 28-Sep-2 Christie's, Paris #18/R est:100000-150000
£158228 $245253 €250000 Buste de Marie-Laure (30x9x12cm-12x4x5in) s.num.7/8 green brown pat bronze conceived c.1946 st.f.Susse lit. 28-Sep-2 Christie's, Paris #24/R est:100000-150000
£227848 $353165 €360000 Buste de Diego sur tigc (33x13x13cm-13x5x5in) s.num.7/8 green brown pat bronze conceived c.1952 st.f.Susse lit. 28-Sep-2 Christie's, Paris #6/R est:200000-300000
£265823 $412025 €420000 Figurine (28x9x10cm-11x4x4in) s.num.8/8 green brown pat bronze conceived c.1947 st.f.Susse lit. 28-Sep-2 Christie's, Paris #11/R est:120000-160000
£379747 $588608 €600000 Buste de Diego (26x20x11cm-10x8x4in) s.num.5/8 brown pat bronze conceived 1954 st.f.Susse. 28-Sep-2 Christie's, Paris #5/R est:300000-400000
£434783 $700000 €652175 Buste de Diego, epaules longues (34cm-13in) s. num.3/6 brown black pat bronze prov. 7-May-3 Christie's, Rockefeller NY #30/R est:900000-1200000
£506329 $784810 €800000 Petit buste sur colonne (152x21x22cm-60x8x9in) s.num.8/8 green brown pat bronze conceived c.1952 st.f.Susse lit. 28-Sep-2 Christie's, Paris #7/R est:280000-320000
£506329 $784810 €800000 Femme degout (49x9x16cm-19x4x6in) s.num.5/8 brown pat bronze conceived c.1952 st.f.Susse lit. 28-Sep-2 Christie's, Paris #9/R est:250000-350000
£550000 $918500 €797500 Petit buste sur colonne (152cm-60in) s.i.num.8/8 st.f.Susse brown green pat bronze exec.1974 lit. 24-Jun-3 Christie's, London #70/R est:200000-300000
£613924 $951582 €970000 Buste d'homme (46x26x15cm-18x10x6in) s.num.2/8 green brown pat bronze conceived 1961 st.f.Susse lit. 28-Sep-2 Christie's, Paris #23/R est:350000-450000
£1012658 $1569620 €1600000 La cage, premier version (90x32x35cm-35x13x14in) s.num.3/8 green brown pat bronze conceived 1950 st.f.Susse lit. 28-Sep-2 Christie's, Paris #13/R est:600000-800000
£1217949 $1900000 €1826924 Figurine dans une boite entre deux boites qui sont des maisons (54cm-21in) i.num.2/6 gold brown pat. bronze i.f.Alexis Rudier prov.exhib.lit. 5-Nov-2 Sotheby's, New York #36/R est:2000000-3000000
£2236025 $3600000 €3354038 Homme qui marche III (46cm-18in) s.st.f.Rudier num.3/6 pat bronze prov.exhib.lit. 7-May-3 Christie's, Rockefeller NY #25/R est:3000000-4000000

Works on paper

£3497 $5840 €5071 Sketch for a window (49x68cm-19x27in) chl leather prov. 24-Jun-3 Koller, Zurich #18/R est:8000-12000 (S.FR 7730)
£5161 $8155 €8000 Portrait d'homme (29x21cm-11x8in) graphite dr prov.lit. 20-Dec-2 Ribeyre & Baron, Paris #44/R
£5882 $9824 €8529 Flowers in front of buildings (31x39cm-12x15in) s. pencil w/C prov. 24-Jun-3 Koller, Zurich #17/R est:15000-25000 (S.FR 13000)
£5963 $9959 €8646 Portrait d'Olivier larronde, appuyant sa tete contre la main (28x22cm-11x9in) pencil lit. 20-Jun-3 Kornfeld, Bern #51/R est:15000 (S.FR 13000)
£8145 $13602 €11810 Mountain landscape (25x34cm-10x13in) mono. W/C prov. 24-Jun-3 Koller, Zurich #27/R est:18000-22000 (S.FR 18000)
£8257 $13789 €11973 Portrait d'Olivier Larronde, assis deriere son bureau (28x22cm-11x9in) pencil lit. 20-Jun-3 Kornfeld, Bern #52/R est:15000 (S.FR 18000)
£8743 $14601 €12677 Capolago d'inverno (26x34cm-10x13in) mono. W/C over pencil prov. 24-Jun-3 Koller, Zurich #28/R est:28000-35000 (S.FR 19320)
£10092 $16853 €14633 Portrait d'Olivier Larronde, souriant, en profil (28x22cm-11x9in) pencil lit. 20-Jun-3 Kornfeld, Bern #49/R est:20000 (S.FR 22000)
£10550 $17619 €15298 L'avenue (36x25cm-14x10in) s.d.1956 ink prov. 20-Jun-3 Kornfeld, Bern #48/R est:25000 (S.FR 23000)
£10897 $17000 €16346 Personnage dans un interieur (29x42cm-11x17in) s.d.1959 graphite. 6-Nov-2 Sotheby's, New York #260/R est:15000-20000
£12000 $20040 €17400 Bouquet de fleurs (30x21cm-12x8in) pen ink prov. 24-Jun-3 Christie's, London #2/R est:5000-7000
£12000 $20040 €17400 Tete byzantine (33x25cm-13x10in) pencil prov. 24-Jun-3 Christie's, London #22/R est:4000-6000
£13043 $21391 €18000 Nature morte (33x25cm-13x10in) pencil prov.exhib.lit. 29-May-3 Lempertz, Koln #626/R est:18000-19000
£13761 $22982 €19953 Portrait d'Olivier Larronde, assis, au salon (28x22cm-11x9in) pencil lit. 20-Jun-3 Kornfeld, Bern #50/R est:25000 (S.FR 30000)

£15000 $25050 €21750 Tete byzantine (33x26cm-13x10in) pencil prov. 24-Jun-3 Christie's, London #21/R est:4000-6000
£17000 $28390 €24650 Portrait de Pierre Reverdy (50x33cm-20x13in) pencil prov. 24-Jun-3 Christie's, London #15/R est:8000-12000
£17000 $28390 €24650 Deux tetes egyptiennes (27x21cm-11x8in) pen ink prov. 24-Jun-3 Christie's, London #27/R est:8000-12000
£18634 $30000 €27951 Arbre. Etude de figures (50x36cm-20x14in) s.d.50 pencil double-sided prov. 7-May-3 Sotheby's, New York #302/R est:12000-18000
£26000 $43420 €37700 Nature morte aux fruits (26x35cm-10x14in) pencil prov. 24-Jun-3 Christie's, London #13/R est:14000-18000
£30000 $50100 €43500 Annette dans l'atelier (35x22cm-14x9in) col crayon prov. 24-Jun-3 Christie's, London #28/R est:10000-15000
£32000 $52480 €48000 Portrait de femme (49x32cm-19x13in) s.d.1955 pencil prov. 5-Feb-3 Sotheby's, London #175/R est:45000
£32000 $53440 €46400 Portrait de Teriade (43x27cm-17x11in) pencil prov. 24-Jun-3 Christie's, London #1/R est:18000-24000
£33654 $52500 €50481 Tete d'homme and tete de femme (40x30cm-16x12in) s. pencil double-sided. 6-Nov-2 Sotheby's, New York #289/R est:15000-20000

GIACOMETTI, Alberto and Diego (20th C) Swiss
Sculpture

£21118 $34000 €31677 Paire de grandes cariatides (33cm-13in) st.sig. brown pat. bronze pair cast c.1964 prov. 8-May-3 Christie's, Rockefeller NY #211/R est:20000-30000
£38608 $61000 €61000 Etoile (146cm-57in) s. brown pat bronze lamp exec.c.1936 lit. 26-Nov-2 Camard, Paris #110/R est:55000
£41139 $65000 €65000 Tete de femme (181cm-71in) brown green pat bronze lamp prov.lit. 26-Nov-2 Camard, Paris #109/R est:70000
£43478 $70000 €65217 Paire de lampes a tete de femme (52cm-20in) green brown pat. bronze pair cast c.1960 prov.lit. 8-May-3 Christie's, Rockefeller NY #212/R est:70000-90000
£44872 $70000 €67308 Lampadaire tete de femme (155cm-61in) brown pat. bronze prov.lit. 7-Nov-2 Christie's, Rockefeller NY #321/R est:70000-90000
£44872 $70000 €67308 Lampadire orne d'une pomme de pin (155cm-61in) gold pat. bronze cast c.1960 prov.lit. 7-Nov-2 Christie's, Rockefeller NY #323/R est:70000-90000
£46099 $74681 €65000 Lamp (51cm-20in) brown pat bronze exec.c.1951 prov. 20-May-3 Christie's, Paris #67/R est:18000-22000
£52662 $84259 €73200 Console (75x100x27cm-30x39x11in) cast iron prov.exhib.lit. 15-May-3 Sotheby's, Paris #125/R
£60897 $95000 €91346 Lampadaire tete de femme (155cm-61in) brown pat. bronze prov.lit. 7-Nov-2 Christie's, Rockefeller NY #320/R est:70000-90000
£65217 $105000 €97826 Lampadaire orne d'une pomme de pin (155cm-61in) gold pat. bronze cast c.1960 prov.lit. 8-May-3 Christie's, Rockefeller NY #209/R est:60000-80000
£65248 $105702 €92000 Tete de Gorgone II (24x26x17cm-9x10x7in) s.st.f.Susse brown pat bronze exec.c.1965 after J M Frank prov. 20-May-3 Christie's, Paris #56/R est:30000-50000
£163121 $264255 €230000 Abstract firedogs (34x29x39cm-13x11x15in) gilt pat bronze pair. 20-May-3 Christie's, Paris #71/R est:100000-150000

GIACOMETTI, Augusto (1877-1947) Swiss

£18100 $30226 €26245 Self portrait in Basque beret (55x55cm-22x22in) s.i.d.1947 verso prov.exhib.lit. 24-Jun-3 Koller, Zurich #42/R est:40000-60000 (S.FR 40000)
£65502 $102838 €98253 Roses (32x45cm-13x18in) s.i.d.1930 prov.lit. 25-Nov-2 Sotheby's, Zurich #69/R est:100000-120000 (S.FR 150000)

Works on paper

£1913 $2965 €2870 Sketch for window. pencil. 4-Dec-2 Koller, Zurich #154a est:4000-6000 (S.FR 4400)
£2096 $3270 €3144 Gethsemane (18cm-7in circular) mono. pencil htd white. 6-Nov-2 Hans Widmer, St Gallen #102/R est:3400-5800 (S.FR 4800)
£5150 $8137 €7725 Abstract (25x17cm-10x7in) pastel prov. 26-Nov-2 Phillips, Zurich #65/R est:12000-15000 (S.FR 12000)
£6009 $9494 €9014 Abstract (15x17cm-6x7in) pastel prov. 26-Nov-2 Phillips, Zurich #66/R est:8000-12000 (S.FR 14000)
£6957 $10783 €10436 House on slope (17x25cm-7x10in) W/C prov. double-sided. 4-Dec-2 Koller, Zurich #156/R est:8000-12000 (S.FR 16000)
£17467 $27249 €26201 Woman working III (31x31cm-12x12in) s. W/C lit. 6-Nov-2 Hans Widmer, St Gallen #103/R est:22000-35000 (S.FR 40000)
£40724 $68010 €59050 Eruption of Etna (47x47cm-19x19in) mono. pastel. 24-Jun-3 Koller, Zurich #31/R est:50000-80000 (S.FR 90000)

GIACOMETTI, Diego (1902-1985) Swiss
Sculpture

£3125 $5156 €4500 Tete de chien (14cm-6in) brown pat bronze exhib. 2-Jul-3 Artcurial Briest, Paris #688/R est:5000-7000
£3200 $4928 €4800 Tete de lionne (7cm-3in) st. bronze prov.lit. 22-Oct-2 Sotheby's, London #190/R est:2000-3000
£3526 $5500 €5289 Petites grenouilles (3cm-1in) one mono. dark brown pat. bronze pair prov.lit. 6-Nov-2 Sotheby's, New York #232/R est:6000-8000
£3600 $5544 €5400 Petite souris (12cm-5in) st. bronze prov. 22-Oct-2 Sotheby's, London #192/R est:4000-6000
£4500 $6930 €6750 Tete de chat (12cm-5in) st.sig. bronze prov. 22-Oct-2 Sotheby's, London #191/R est:5000-7000
£6410 $10000 €9615 Porte-manteau (47cm-19in) st.mono. dark green pat. bronze prov. 6-Nov-2 Sotheby's, New York #240/R est:10000-15000
£7362 $12000 €11043 La dompteuse, pied de lamp (36cm-14in) green pat. bronze prov.lit. 12-Feb-3 Sotheby's, New York #69/R est:15000-20000
£7975 $13000 €11963 La dompteuse, pied de lampe (36cm-14in) st. green pat. bronze prov.lit. 12-Feb-3 Sotheby's, New York #70/R est:15000-20000
£8200 $12628 €12300 Grenouille sur une feuille (15cm-6in) st.sig. bronze prov. 22-Oct-2 Sotheby's, London #196/R est:9000-12000
£9000 $13860 €13500 Homme solitaire a la coupe (29cm-11in) i. bronze conceived c.1975 prov. 22-Oct-2 Sotheby's, London #195/R est:8000-12000
£9615 $15000 €14423 Basset sur terrasse (7x29cm-3x11in) st.sig. green brown pat. bronze prov. 7-Nov-2 Christie's, Rockefeller NY #327/R est:8000-12000
£10256 $16000 €15384 Oiseau volant au soleil (10x21cm-4x8in) st.sig. green brown pat. bronze prov. 7-Nov-2 Christie's, Rockefeller NY #326/R est:10000-15000
£11538 $18115 €18000 Cheval (27x26x7cm-11x10x3in) st.sig. brown green pat bronze prov. 10-Dec-2 Artcurial Briest, Paris #499/R est:20000-30000
£12057 $19532 €17000 Chaise (95x41x50cm-37x16x20in) chair iron concrete plaster. 23-May-3 Camard, Paris #140/R est:10000-15000
£15385 $24000 €23078 Coupe a l'oiseau (17cm-7in) i. dark green pat. bronze prov. 6-Nov-2 Sotheby's, New York #233/R est:15000-20000
£17483 $29196 €25000 Tabouret de coiffeuse a la Harpie (57cm-22in) s. pat bronze prov.lit. 30-Jun-3 Artcurial Briest, Paris #80/R est:25000-35000
£20833 $32500 €31250 Bougeoir aux chauves-souris (33cm-13in) st.i. dark brown pat. bronze prov. 6-Nov-2 Sotheby's, New York #239/R est:20000-30000
£21154 $33212 €33000 Coupelle aux chiens (11x15x24cm-4x6x9in) s. green pat bronze prov. 10-Dec-2 Artcurial Briest, Paris #498/R est:20000-30000
£22436 $35000 €33654 Mangeoire pour oiseaux (50cm-20in) st. dark green pat. bronze prov. 6-Nov-2 Sotheby's, New York #231/R est:20000-30000
£23853 $39835 €34587 Lampe a quatre feuilles (62x16x17cm-24x6x7in) i. pat.bronze lit. 20-Jun-3 Kornfeld, Bern #56/R est:60000 (S.FR 52000)
£24845 $40000 €37268 Autruche sur socle (51cm-20in) brown green pat. bronze cast c.1970 prov.lit. 8-May-3 Christie's, Rockefeller NY #210/R est:40000-60000
£25000 $41750 €36250 Chat maitre d'hotel (30cm-12in) s. brown pat. bronze prov. 25-Jun-3 Christie's, London #189/R est:25000-35000
£26923 $42269 €42000 Pied de lampe (45cm-18in) plaster lit. 10-Dec-2 Piasa, Paris #213/R est:30000
£28000 $45920 €42000 Autruche (51cm-20in) st.mono. green brown pat bronze prov.lit. 4-Feb-3 Christie's, London #308/R est:30000
£28000 $45920 €42000 Table grecque (45x83x83cm-18x33x33in) bronze glass prov.lit. 5-Feb-3 Sotheby's, London #184/R est:35000
£28000 $45920 €42000 Table grecque (45x83x83cm-18x33x33in) bronze glass prov.lit. 5-Feb-3 Sotheby's, London #183/R est:35000
£28440 $47495 €41238 Lampe a forme de bougeoir (20cm-8in) pat.bronze lit. 20-Jun-3 Kornfeld, Bern #58/R est:15000 (S.FR 62000)
£28846 $45000 €43269 Table carcasse, modele bas au double plateau (44x129x86cm-17x51x34in) mono.i. green pat. bronze executed c.1980 prov.lit. 6-Nov-2 Sotheby's, New York #226/R est:40000-60000
£29487 $46295 €46000 Pied de lampe (45cm-18in) plaster lit. 10-Dec-2 Piasa, Paris #214/R est:30000
£30769 $47692 €48000 Coffee table with frogs (41x58x39cm-16x23x15in) st.sig. grey green pat bronze glass exec.c.1963 prov.exhib.lit. 4-Dec-2 Lempertz, Koln #33/R est:55000-60000
£30968 $48000 €46452 L'autruche (21cm-8in) green pat. bronze ostrich egg prov. 8-Dec-2 Wright, Chicago #189/R est:30000-40000
£31056 $50000 €46584 Table berceau, deuxieme version (40x156x43cm-16x61x17in) brown pat. bronze conceived c.1970 prov.lit. 7-May-3 Sotheby's, New York #304/R est:60000-80000
£32000 $53440 €46400 Petit gueridon aux harpies cree pour Cecil Beaton (44x45cm-17x18in) green brown pat. bronze conceived c.1955 prov.lit. 25-Jun-3 Christie's, London #190/R est:25000-35000
£32051 $50000 €48077 L'autruche (53cm-21in) mono. dark brown pat. bronze prov.lit. 6-Nov-2 Sotheby's, New York #241/R est:35000-45000
£32110 $53624 €46560 Chair (81x48x39cm-32x19x15in) iron bronze leather lit. 20-Jun-3 Kornfeld, Bern #60/R est:80000 (S.FR 70000)
£33654 $52500 €50481 Table berceau, deuxieme version (40x116x43cm-16x46x17in) mono.i. green pat. bronze executed c.1970 prov.lit. 6-Nov-2 Sotheby's, New York #227/R est:60000-80000
£35000 $57400 €52500 Table carcasse (43x126x82cm-17x50x32in) green pat bronze prov.lit. 4-Feb-3 Christie's, London #309/R est:45000
£37000 $60680 €55500 Peti gueridon-arbre (46cm-18in) bronze granite one of 6 prov.lit. 5-Feb-3 Sotheby's, London #182/R

£37267 $60000 €55901 La promenade des amis (62cm-24in) st.sig. black green pat. bronze cast 1980 prov. 8-May-3 Christie's, Rockefeller NY #214/R est:80000-100000
£37411 $59857 €52000 Table (43x125x80cm-17x49x31in) s.i. green pat.bronze glass prov.lit. 19-May-3 Tajan, Paris #126/R est:60000-80000
£38000 $62320 €57000 Table-feuilles (52x56x56cm-20x22x22in) mono. bronze glass prov.lit. 5-Feb-3 Sotheby's, London #181/R est:55000
£39490 $62000 €59235 Portmaneau (171cm-67in) s. bronze executed c.1965 prov. 11-Dec-2 Phillips, New York #5/R est:30000-50000
£41667 $65000 €62501 Chat maitre d'hotel (30cm-12in) i. brown pat. bronze conceived 1961 prov.lit. 6-Nov-2 Sotheby's, New York #242/R est:50000-70000
£41667 $65000 €62501 Chat maitre-d'hotel (30cm-12in) st.sig brown pat. bronze executed 1967 prov.lit. 7-Nov-2 Christie's, Rockefeller NY #335/R est:45000-65000
£43166 $69066 €60000 Chairs (94cm-37in) pat.bronze suede lit. 19-May-3 Tajan, Paris #125/R est:60000-65000
£43269 $67500 €64904 Table feuilles, modele bas aux grenouilles (52x56x56cm-20x22x22in) i. green pat. bronze prov.lit. 6-Nov-2 Sotheby's, New York #225/R est:70000-90000
£44872 $70000 €67308 Paysage, la promenade des amis (33x40cm-13x16in) st. green brown pat. bronze executed c.1967 prov. 7-Nov-2 Christie's, Rockefeller NY #329/R est:50000-70000
£49679 $77500 €74519 Cage aux oiseau (49x31cm-19x12in) st. green pat. bronze prov. 6-Nov-2 Sotheby's, New York #236/R est:40000-60000
£49689 $80000 €74534 Arbre de vie (79x67x17cm-31x26x7in) s. brown green pat. bronze cast c.1978 prov.lit. 8-May-3 Christie's, Rockefeller NY #213/R est:80000-120000
£51282 $80000 €76923 Paire de fauteuil a tete de lionnes (82cm-32in) green black brown pat. bronze two chairs cast c.1980 prov.lit. 7-Nov-2 Christie's, Rockefeller NY #325/R est:80000-120000
£54487 $85000 €81731 Console (90x84x25cm-35x33x10in) dark green pat. bronze prov. 6-Nov-2 Sotheby's, New York #228/R est:80000-120000
£70922 $114894 €100000 Standard lamp (148cm-58in) pat bronze prov. 20-May-3 Christie's, Paris #69/R est:40000-50000
£78014 $126383 €110000 Standard lamp (148cm-58in) pat bronze prov. 20-May-3 Christie's, Paris #70/R est:40000-50000
£80275 $134060 €116399 Table basse avec pietement en X, deuxieme version (48x67x131cm-19x26x52in) lit. bronze glass. 20-Jun-3 Kornfeld, Bern #57/R est:150000 (S.FR 175000)
£96154 $150000 €144231 Grande table basse de milieu au ruban et aux arbustes (47x144x56cm-19x57x22in) brown green bronze glass top executed c.1976 prov.lit. 7-Nov-2 Christie's, Rockefeller NY #322/R est:150000-200000
£110092 $183853 €159633 Table aux deux oiseaux (47x71cm-19x28in) bronze glass lit. 20-Jun-3 Kornfeld, Bern #61/R est:250000 (S.FR 240000)

GIACOMETTI, Diego (after) (1902-1985) Swiss
Works on paper
£8000 $13120 €12000 Rencontre (175x240cm-69x94in) mono. hand-woven wool pile rug one of 100 prov. 4-Feb-3 Christie's, London #304/R est:12000

GIACOMETTI, Giovanni (1868-1934) Swiss
£15021 $23734 €22532 White horses (32x41cm-13x16in) i. verso canvas over board prov.exhib.lit. 28-Nov-2 Christie's, Zurich #33/R est:40000-60000 (S.FR 35000)
£17904 $27930 €26856 Portrait of the boy, Giovanni Persenico (21x18cm-8x7in) mono.d.11 prov.lit. 6-Nov-2 Hans Widmer, St Gallen #53/R est:25000-39000 (S.FR 41000)
£85837 $135622 €128756 Nebbia (70x60cm-28x24in) mono. s.i.verso painted c.1910 prov.exhib.lit. 26-Nov-2 Phillips, Zurich #59/R est:190000-220000 (S.FR 200000)
£87336 $137118 €131004 Plazetta (80x65cm-31x26in) mono. s.i.d.1929 verso prov.lit. 25-Nov-2 Sotheby's, Zurich #68/R est:200000-250000 (S.FR 200000)
£135371 $212533 €203057 Stampa (86x93cm-34x37in) mono. s.i.d.1927 verso prov.lit. 25-Nov-2 Sotheby's, Zurich #67/R est:250000-300000 (S.FR 310000)
Prints
£2358 $3821 €4175 Mother and child II - Annetta and Bruno (20x19cm-8x7in) s.i. woodcut lit. 26-May-3 Sotheby's, Zurich #89/R est:5000-8000 (S.FR 5000)
£2489 $4156 €3609 Inverno (20x20cm-8x8in) mono.i. woodcut prov. 24-Jun-3 Koller, Zurich #385/R est:2800-3800 (S.FR 5500)
£3231 $5041 €4847 I figli della luce - sun children (15x15cm-6x6in) s. col woodcut prov.lit. 6-Nov-2 Hans Widmer, St Gallen #9/R est:5000-9000 (S.FR 7400)
£5660 $9170 €10019 Alberto in profile (13x10cm-5x4in) i. linocut lit. 26-May-3 Sotheby's, Zurich #54/R est:8000-12000 (S.FR 12000)
Works on paper
£3167 $5290 €4592 San Salvatore (17x24cm-7x9in) W/C. 24-Jun-3 Koller, Zurich #36/R est:8000-12000 (S.FR 7000)
£6114 $9537 €9171 Room with crib (24x18cm-9x7in) mono. W/C prov. 6-Nov-2 Hans Widmer, St Gallen #25/R est:14000-22000 (S.FR 14000)
£6787 $11335 €9841 Ponte Capriasca (22x26cm-9x10in) mono.d.1918 W/C. 24-Jun-3 Koller, Zurich #37/R est:18000-25000 (S.FR 15000)
£7240 $12090 €10498 Spoleto (22x28cm-9x11in) mono.i.d.25. IV. 31 W/C. 24-Jun-3 Koller, Zurich #38/R est:15000-20000 (S.FR 16000)
£8145 $13602 €11810 Summer road (25x34cm-10x13in) s.mono. w/C. 24-Jun-3 Koller, Zurich #35/R est:18000-25000 (S.FR 18000)
£12017 $18987 €18026 Pila, Maloja (22x28cm-9x11in) i. verso W/C over pencil. 28-Nov-2 Christie's, Zurich #31/R est:25000-35000 (S.FR 28000)
£12876 $20343 €19314 Piz Materdell (23x27cm-9x11in) mono. W/C over pencil prov. 28-Nov-2 Christie's, Zurich #32/R est:25000-35000 (S.FR 30000)
£20601 $32549 €30902 Silvaplan lake (36x49cm-14x19in) pencil W/C exhib. 26-Nov-2 Phillips, Zurich #68/R est:25000-30000 (S.FR 48000)
£23605 $37296 €35408 St Moritz lake (36x49cm-14x19in) pencil W/C exhib. 26-Nov-2 Phillips, Zurich #69/R est:25000-30000 (S.FR 55000)

GIACOYA, Mario (1951-) Uruguayan
£321 $500 €482 Sillas con flores (118x96cm-46x38in) 6-Aug-2 Galleria Y Remates, Montevideo #46

GIALLINA (1857-1939) Greek
Works on paper
£1200 $1956 €1800 View of the Acropolis (15x31cm-6x12in) s. W/C. 29-Jan-3 Sotheby's, Olympia #288/R est:800-1200

GIALLINA, Angelos (1857-1939) Greek
£6500 $10270 €9750 Parthenon. Porch of Caryatids (24x34cm-9x13in) two. 1-Apr-3 Bonhams, New Bond Street #4 est:7000-10000
Works on paper
£750 $1223 €1125 Lakeside landscape, Greece (18x33cm-7x13in) s.d.94 pencil W/C. 13-Feb-3 Christie's, Kensington #262/R
£1700 $2652 €2550 View of Achilleion Corfu (25x38cm-10x15in) indis sig. W/C. 15-Oct-2 Sotheby's, London #48/R est:1000-1500
£1800 $2808 €2700 Distant view of the Citadel of Corfu (38x71cm-15x28in) s. W/C over pencil. 15-Oct-2 Sotheby's, London #49/R est:1200-1800
£2000 $3120 €3000 View of Corfu (28x57cm-11x22in) s. W/C over pencil. 15-Oct-2 Sotheby's, London #53/R est:2000-3000
£2200 $3432 €3300 View of Corfu (24x48cm-9x19in) s. W/C on card. 15-Oct-2 Sotheby's, London #52/R est:2000-3000
£2778 $4417 €4000 View of the coast of Corfu (38x72cm-15x28in) s. pencil W/C. 29-Apr-3 Christie's, Amsterdam #99/R est:3000-5000
£3200 $4992 €4800 Quayside, Corfu (36x51cm-14x20in) s. W/C. 18-Oct-2 Keys, Aylsham #654/R est:2500-3000
£3200 $5088 €4800 Island of Pontikonissi and Vlacherna, Corfu, Greece (39x74cm-15x29in) s. W/C. 29-Apr-3 Bonhams, New Bond Street #132/R est:2500-3500
£3500 $5460 €5250 San Giorgio Maggiore Venice (39x73cm-15x29in) s. W/C over pencil. 15-Oct-2 Sotheby's, London #50/R est:4000-6000
£3500 $5425 €5250 View of Corfu (27x45cm-11x18in) s. W/C. 2-Oct-2 Sotheby's, London #84/R est:3000-5000
£3600 $5724 €5400 Figures on a track, the interior of Corfu (40x72cm-16x28in) s. W/C. 29-Apr-3 Bonhams, New Bond Street #133/R est:2500-3500
£4800 $7488 €7200 View of the Acropolis (22x49cm-9x19in) s. W/C. 15-Oct-2 Sotheby's, London #19/R est:2000-3000
£5200 $8060 €7800 View of Corfu (23x41cm-9x16in) s. W/C. 2-Oct-2 Sotheby's, London #83/R est:3000-5000
£10000 $15600 €15000 Rocky coastline (41x94cm-16x37in) s. W/C over pencil htd bodycol. 15-Oct-2 Sotheby's, London #51/R est:3000-5000
£11000 $17160 €16500 View of the Parthenon (48x91cm-19x36in) s. W/C over pencil prov. 15-Oct-2 Sotheby's, London #16/R est:5000-7000
£15000 $23250 €22500 View of Corfu (38x72cm-15x28in) s. W/C gouache. 2-Oct-2 Sotheby's, London #86/R est:8000-12000

GIAMBASTIANI, Lida M (20th C) American?
£301 $475 €452 Abstract figure in red hat (127x94cm-50x37in) s. 5-Apr-3 Harvey Clar, Oakland #1301

GIAMBOLOGNA (after) (c.1529-1608) Italian
Sculpture
£4895 $7000 €7343 Bull (36cm-14in) bronze marble base. 22-Jan-3 Doyle, New York #173/R

GIAMBOLOGNA-SUSINI (studio) (17th C) Italian
Sculpture
£11728 $19000 €17592 Mercury (46cm-18in) olive-golden pat bronze lit. 23-Jan-3 Sotheby's, New York #200/R est:12000

GIAMPEDI, Giuseppe (18th C) Italian
Works on paper
£440 $682 €700 View of the Temple of Peace (24x36cm-9x14in) s. W/C. 29-Oct-2 Finarte, Milan #446

GIANI, Felice (1760-1823) Italian
Works on paper
£253 $400 €400 Classical scene with figures (20x27cm-8x11in) pen wash. 29-Nov-2 Bassenge, Berlin #5640
£642 $1001 €950 Holy Family (20x27cm-8x11in) i. chk pen ink wash. 27-Mar-3 Christie's, Paris #43/R
£878 $1370 €1300 Studies of Madonna with Child (19x26cm-7x10in) pen ink wash over crayon. 26-Mar-3 Piasa, Paris #17/R

GIANI, Giovanni (1866-1937) Italian
£3401 $5408 €5000 Interior with mandolin player (41x30cm-16x12in) s. cardboard. 1-Mar-3 Meeting Art, Vercelli #78
Works on paper
£374 $595 €550 Painter (44x29cm-17x11in) s. pencil. 1-Mar-3 Meeting Art, Vercelli #52

GIANLISI, Antonio (younger) (1677-1727) Italian
£10000 $15800 €14500 Still life with metal vase and clock. Still life with metal vase and tray (72x92cm-28x36in) pair. 5-Apr-3 Finarte Semenzato, Milan #136/R est:22000
£11000 $18370 €15950 Grapes in a basket with sweetmeats on a salver on a draped table (67x97cm-26x38in) 9-Jul-3 Bonhams, New Bond Street #47/R est:5000-7000

GIANNACCINI, Ilio (1897-1968) Italian
£400 $608 €600 Spanish beauty (70x50cm-28x20in) s. canvas on board. 29-Aug-2 Christie's, Kensington #190

GIANNI (?) Italian
£11076 $17500 €17500 View of Naples (31x160cm-12x63in) s.d.1861. 29-Nov-2 Coutau Begarie, Paris #13/R

GIANNI, Ettore (?) Italian
Works on paper
£962 $1500 €1443 Italian coastal views (28x43cm-11x17in) s. W/C gouache pair. 12-Oct-2 Neal Auction Company, New Orleans #181/R est:1500-2500

GIANNI, Gerolamo (1837-1887) Italian
£1000 $1550 €1500 Grand Harbour, Malta (13x33cm-5x13in) s.d.1873 board. 25-Sep-2 Hamptons Fine Art, Godalming #477/R est:1000-1500
£2200 $3498 €3300 H.M.S Revenge with troops crowding her bow (26x51cm-10x20in) board. 29-Apr-3 Bonhams, New Bond Street #165/R est:2000-3000
£3500 $5670 €5250 Gozo boat in St Paul's Bay, Malta (32x48cm-13x19in) s.indis.d.188 board lit. 21-May-3 Christie's, Kensington #653/R est:2000-3000
£4800 $7632 €7200 Manoel Island and Valletta from Gzira, Malta (30x46cm-12x18in) s.d.1869 board. 29-Apr-3 Bonhams, New Bond Street #162/R est:4000-6000
£20000 $31200 €30000 View of the three cities across the Grand Harbour, Valleta (51x122cm-20x48in) s.d.1876 prov. 15-Oct-2 Sotheby's, London #110/R est:20000-30000

GIANNI, Gerolamo (attrib) (1837-1887) Italian
£900 $1458 €1350 Heavy swell in St Paul's Bay, Malta (12x36cm-5x14in) board. 21-May-3 Christie's, Kensington #654/R
£1400 $2268 €2100 Harbour scenes, Valetta (23x63cm-9x25in) board pair. 21-May-3 Christie's, Kensington #651/R est:1500-2000

GIANNI, Giuseppe (1829-1885) Italian
£449 $682 €700 Wooing of the bride (74x50cm-29x20in) s. lit. 11-Jul-2 Allgauer, Kempten #2492/R

GIANNI, Umberto (19/20th C) Italian
£472 $750 €708 Venetian canal view (51x76cm-20x30in) s.d.1909. 7-Mar-3 Skinner, Boston #342/R

GIANPIETRINO (1493-1540) Italian
£6383 $10085 €9575 Madonna and Child (52x40cm-20x16in) panel. 2-Dec-2 Rasmussen, Copenhagen #1631/R est:100000 (D.KR 75000)
£40268 $64832 €60000 Madonna and Child (55x40cm-22x16in) board. 19-Feb-3 Semenzato, Venice #206/R est:100000
£50676 $79054 €75000 Madonna and Child (52x41cm-20x16in) panel. 27-Mar-3 Dorotheum, Vienna #37/R est:20000-25000
£136986 $213699 €205479 Female nude in red coat (60x46cm-24x18in) panel prov.lit.exhib. 28-Mar-3 Koller, Zurich #3009/R est:170000-220000 (S.FR 300000)

GIANQUINTO, Alberto (1929-) Italian
£651 $1015 €950 Wild strawberries (20x30cm-8x12in) init. cardboard. 10-Apr-3 Finarte Semenzato, Rome #141/R
£1795 $2818 €2800 Magnolia (90x65cm-35x26in) init.d.1968 s.i.d.verso. 21-Nov-2 Finarte, Rome #283/R
Works on paper
£315 $492 €460 Interior with reclining figure (20x25cm-8x10in) init. ink. 10-Apr-3 Finarte Semenzato, Rome #85

GIAQUINTO, Corrado (c.1690-1765) Italian
£13208 $20472 €21000 Holy Family with saints. prov. 2-Oct-2 Dorotheum, Vienna #73/R est:22000-25000
£13462 $20865 €21000 Male nude (65x45cm-26x18in) 4-Dec-2 Christie's, Rome #479/R est:6000-9000
£30000 $50100 €43500 Joseph revealing his identity to his brother (48x38cm-19x15in) 9-Jul-3 Christie's, London #87/R est:20000-30000

GIAQUINTO, Corrado (attrib) (c.1690-1765) Italian
£21341 $35000 €32012 Gods of Mt Olympus (50x31cm-20x12in) paper on canvas modello prov. 5-Feb-3 Christie's, Rockefeller NY #313/R est:8000-12000

GIAQUINTO, Corrado (studio) (c.1690-1765) Italian
£5000 $8350 €7250 Assumption of the Virgin (49x38cm-19x15in) 8-Jul-3 Sotheby's, Olympia #446/R est:5000-7000

GIAQUINTO, Corrado (style) (c.1690-1765) Italian
£11500 $17825 €17250 Resurrection of Christ (46x38cm-18x15in) 30-Oct-2 Bonhams, New Bond Street #159/R est:2000-3000

GIARDELLO, G (19/20th C) Italian
£1676 $2665 €2514 Interior scene with young Italian woman wearing red dress (98x66cm-39x26in) s. 5-Mar-3 Rasmussen, Copenhagen #1735 est:10000-12000 (D.KR 18000)

GIARDELLO, Giuseppe (19th C) Italian
£833 $1292 €1300 Fishermen in Naples (33x16cm-13x6in) s. board. 4-Dec-2 Finarte, Rome #783
£1090 $1711 €1700 Amalfi coast (57x74cm-22x29in) s. board. 16-Dec-2 Pandolfini, Florence #59

GIARDIELLO, Giuseppe (19/20th C) Italian
£1100 $1716 €1650 Figures and beached vessels on a beach, Naples in the distance (49x67cm-19x26in) s. canvas on board. 17-Sep-2 Rosebery Fine Art, London #567 est:1200-1800
£1279 $1995 €1919 Fishing boat off Capri (17x30cm-7x12in) s. panel. 28-Mar-3 Koller, Zurich #3154/R est:2500-3500 (S.FR 2800)
£1279 $1995 €1919 Fishermen on the coast of Naples (17x30cm-7x12in) s. panel. 28-Mar-3 Koller, Zurich #3155/R est:2500-3500 (S.FR 2800)
£3241 $5121 €4700 In front of the tavern (51x105cm-20x41in) s. 5-Apr-3 Hans Stahl, Hamburg #60/R est:1100

GIARDINO, Pasquale (20th C) ?
£714 $1107 €1071 Nude and cat (91x71cm-36x28in) 29-Oct-2 Lawson Menzies, Sydney #46/R (A.D 2000)
£786 $1218 €1179 Melbourne docks (66x81cm-26x32in) s.d.95. 29-Oct-2 Lawson Menzies, Sydney #128 (A.D 2200)
£929 $1458 €1394 Untitled (61x76cm-24x30in) prov. 25-Nov-2 Christie's, Melbourne #459 est:2500-3500 (A.D 2600)
£932 $1416 €1398 Pink dragonfly (76x60cm-30x24in) 28-Aug-2 Deutscher-Menzies, Melbourne #205/R est:3000-4000 (A.D 2600)
£1195 $1960 €1793 Cavorting in the garden (59x59cm-23x23in) s.i.d.1987 verso. 4-Jun-3 Deutscher-Menzies, Melbourne #343/R est:2000-3000 (A.D 3000)
Works on paper
£573 $872 €860 Abstract (26x32cm-10x13in) s. pastel gouache. 28-Aug-2 Deutscher-Menzies, Melbourne #396/R (A.D 1600)
£876 $1437 €1314 Cat and the owl (59x66cm-23x26in) s.d.94 gouache pastel. 4-Jun-3 Deutscher-Menzies, Melbourne #180/R (A.D 2200)

£876 $1437 €1314 Alice in Wonderland (76x56cm-30x22in) s.d.95 gouache pastel. 4-Jun-3 Deutscher-Menzies, Melbourne #376/R (A.D 2200)

GIAUQUE, Fernand (1895-1973) Swiss
£370 $596 €555 Red table (48x60cm-19x24in) s. board. 7-May-3 Dobiaschofsky, Bern #585 (S.FR 800)
£417 $671 €626 Autumn shoreline (55x127cm-22x50in) s.d.59. 7-May-3 Dobiaschofsky, Bern #581/R (S.FR 900)
£556 $894 €806 Early spring at Ligerz (50x58cm-20x23in) s. 9-May-3 Dobiaschofsky, Bern #91/R (S.FR 1200)
£880 $1416 €1276 Le Vully (54x64cm-21x25in) s.d.46. 9-May-3 Dobiaschofsky, Bern #188/R est:2800 (S.FR 1900)

GIBB, H W Phelan (1870-1948) British
£250 $390 €375 Desolation Point, Exmoor (51x76cm-20x30in) s. s.i.d.April 1925 verso. 17-Sep-2 Rosebery Fine Art, London #520/R
£270 $429 €405 Standing female nude (54x28cm-21x11in) s. 18-Mar-3 Rosebery Fine Art, London #867/R
Works on paper
£550 $858 €825 Mussel gatherers (37x50cm-15x20in) pencil W/C. 12-Sep-2 Sotheby's, Olympia #47/R
£550 $858 €825 Bathers (47x34cm-19x13in) s. col chk gouache. 12-Sep-2 Sotheby's, Olympia #57/R

GIBB, John (1831-1909) New Zealander
£18293 $27988 €27440 Milford Sounds (60x90cm-24x35in) s.d.1886. 21-Aug-2 Dunbar Sloane, Auckland #18/R est:50000-80000 (NZ.D 60000)
£23794 $36881 €35691 Swagman beside fire drinking tea, alongside Bealey River, South Island (75x126cm-30x50in) s.d.1888. 4-Dec-2 Dunbar Sloane, Auckland #12/R est:100000-140000 (NZ.D 74000)

GIBB, John (attrib) (1831-1909) New Zealander
£596 $931 €894 Old limeworks, Cosair Bay (29x44cm-11x17in) 27-Mar-3 International Art Centre, Auckland #150/R (NZ.D 1700)

GIBB, Lewis Taylor (20th C) British
£280 $434 €420 Mountain landscape (42x51cm-17x20in) 3-Dec-2 Bonhams, Knightsbridge #245

GIBB, T H (19th C) British
£702 $1067 €1053 Royal stag on Benvenue (59x44cm-23x17in) s.i.d.1884 verso. 19-Aug-2 Joel, Victoria #256 est:800-1200 (A.D 2000)

GIBB, Thomas Henry (1833-?) British
£460 $722 €690 On the Bourmont (31x46cm-12x18in) s. s.i.verso. 16-Dec-2 Bonhams, Bury St Edmunds #543

GIBB, W M (1859-1931) New Zealander
£230 $327 €345 Mt. Cook (29x42cm-11x17in) s. board. 20-Mar-2 Watson's, Christchurch #181/R (NZ.D 750)
Works on paper
£358 $523 €537 New Bridgton Sandhills (33x46cm-13x18in) s. W/C. 12-Sep-1 Watson's, Christchurch #16/R est:1500-2500 (NZ.D 1200)

GIBB, William Menzies (1859-1931) New Zealander
£361 $578 €523 Pastoral landscape (35x44cm-14x17in) s. board. 13-May-3 Watson's, Christchurch #7/R (NZ.D 1000)
£542 $866 €786 Tranquil landscape (28x40cm-11x16in) s. 13-May-3 Watson's, Christchurch #74/R (NZ.D 1500)
Works on paper
£289 $462 €419 Mount Taranaki with cows and farm settlement (15x22cm-6x9in) s. W/C. 13-May-3 Watson's, Christchurch #39/R (NZ.D 800)
£460 $653 €690 Styx River (21x36cm-8x14in) s. W/C. 20-Mar-2 Watson's, Christchurch #103/R (NZ.D 1500)

GIBBINGS, Robert John (1889-1958) British
£350 $585 €508 French cafe scene (20x13cm-8x5in) panel. 24-Jun-3 Neal & Fletcher, Woodbridge #372

GIBBONS, C I (19th C) ?
Works on paper
£1373 $2142 €2060 Toronto (43x94cm-17x37in) s.i.d.1905 i.d.verso col pencil prov. 25-Mar-3 Ritchie, Toronto #155/R est:2000-3000 (C.D 3200)
£1459 $2276 €2189 Kingston (33x58cm-13x23in) s.i.d.1906 col pencil graphite. 25-Mar-3 Ritchie, Toronto #157/R est:2000-3000 (C.D 3400)
£1824 $2846 €2736 Chippewa (34x75cm-13x30in) s.i. col pencil prov. 25-Mar-3 Ritchie, Toronto #156/R est:2000-3000 (C.D 4250)
£1824 $2846 €2736 Jasmine (41x82cm-16x32in) s.i.d.1908 col pencil graphite. 25-Mar-3 Ritchie, Toronto #158/R est:2000-3000 (C.D 4250)
£2039 $3181 €3059 John Hanlan (41x75cm-16x30in) s.d.1908 i.verso col pencil graphite prov. 25-Mar-3 Ritchie, Toronto #159/R est:2000-3000 (C.D 4750)

GIBBONS, Goodwin (?) British
£260 $411 €377 Angler beside a river (30x41cm-12x16in) s. board. 22-Jul-3 Gorringes, Lewes #1636

GIBBONS, Ruth (?) ?
Works on paper
£260 $406 €390 Afternoon break, two terriers in a woodland (20x15cm-8x6in) s.d.87 W/C. 23-Sep-2 Bonhams, Chester #851

GIBBONS, William (19th C) British
£900 $1395 €1350 Departing for sea (35x59cm-14x23in) s.d.1880. 24-Sep-2 Rowley Fine Art, Newmarket #352/R
£1100 $1782 €1650 Racing cutters running into the estuary at Dartmouth (36x61cm-14x24in) s.d.1880. 21-May-3 Christie's, Kensington #626/R est:800-1200
£1700 $2652 €2550 Harbour scene, possibly Polperro (44x75cm-17x30in) s.d.1881 board. 9-Oct-2 Woolley & Wallis, Salisbury #213/R est:750-1000

GIBBS, Anthony (1951-) British
£280 $434 €420 Rural scene with sweeping meadows (48x97cm-19x38in) s. 6-Dec-2 Biddle & Webb, Birmingham #405/R
£280 $448 €420 View of African plain with figures of rhino (48x79cm-19x31in) s. 10-Jan-3 Biddle & Webb, Birmingham #350
£420 $609 €630 Extensive rural landscape with sheep, passing sprint (51x91cm-20x36in) s.d.77. 3-May-2 Biddle & Webb, Birmingham #524

GIBBS, George (1870-1942) American
£3727 $6000 €5591 Motoring through a soggy autumnal landscape (56x74cm-22x29in) indis.sig. canvas on panel painted c.1910. 10-May-3 Illustration House, New York #70/R est:3000-5000

GIBBS, James (19th C) British
Works on paper
£280 $445 €420 Figures on a rutted tracking passing through woodland (20x33cm-8x13in) s.d.1840 W/C. 18-Mar-3 Capes Dunn, Manchester #469

GIBBS, Len (1929-) Canadian
£1087 $1696 €1813 Driller (39x66cm-15x26in) s. s.i.d.1978 acrylic board. 13-Apr-3 Levis, Calgary #37/R est:2000-2500 (C.D 2500)

GIBBS, Thomas Binney (1870-?) British
£514 $801 €750 Landscape with cows by water (30x46cm-12x18in) s. 10-Apr-3 Dorotheum, Vienna #180/R
Works on paper
£1300 $2016 €1950 At the gallery. Outside the Palace (17x13cm-7x5in) one mono. one s.d.1913 W/C gouache two. 3-Dec-2 Sotheby's, Olympia #172/R est:500-700

GIBERT, Lucien (1904-1988) French
£937 $1528 €1350 Nature morte au magnum de champagne (53x76cm-21x30in) s. panel. 19-Jul-3 Thierry & Lannon, Brest #337/R

GIBNEY, Arthur (20th C) Irish
Works on paper
£1208 $1945 €1800 Morning light, Venice. Tourists on steps, Venice (25x38cm-10x15in) s. one d.1985 one d.1986 W/C pair. 18-Feb-3 Whyte's, Dublin #156/R est:1200-1500

GIBON, Sengai (1750-1837) Japanese?
Works on paper
£5000 $8350 €7250 Hotei yawning (98x26cm-39x10in) i. ink hanging scroll. 18-Jun-3 Christie's, London #280/R est:3000-5000

GIBSON, Bessie (1868-1961) Australian
£556 $789 €900 Bateaux a quai (19x24cm-7x9in) s. panel. 16-Mar-3 Eric Pillon, Calais #101/R

GIBSON, Charles Dana (1867-1944) American
Works on paper
£488 $800 €708 Football (19x38cm-7x15in) s. pen ink. 5-Jun-3 Swann Galleries, New York #103/R
£573 $900 €860 Woman rising from chair (25x20cm-10x8in) s. pen ink. 14-Dec-2 Weschler, Washington #691/R est:700-900

£2795 $4500 €4193 Couple in interior with trunk arriving (53x91cm-21x36in) s. pen ink. 10-May-3 Illustration House, New York #159/R est:5000-8000
£6410 $10000 €9615 Gentleman butterfly flitting among pretty girl flowers (46x71cm-18x28in) s. pen ink. 9-Nov-2 Illustration House, New York #90/R est:7500-10000

GIBSON, George (1904-) American/British
Works on paper
£581 $900 €872 Agoura tapestry (53x74cm-21x29in) s.d.69 i.verso W/C prov. 29-Oct-2 John Moran, Pasadena #769
£1592 $2500 €2388 Fisherman along the coast (47x60cm-19x24in) s.i. W/C prov. 19-Nov-2 Butterfields, San Francisco #8353/R est:3000-5000

GIBSON, John (1790-1866) British
Sculpture
£19000 $29830 €28500 Cupid disguised as a shepherd boy (192cm-76in) white marble on red column prov.lit. 10-Dec-2 Sotheby's, London #145/R est:15000-20000

GIBSON, Thomas (1680-1751) British
£28000 $46480 €42000 Portrait of the Hon Mrs William Townshend, in black and red masquerade dress (127x102cm-50x40in) prov.lit. 10-Jun-3 Christie's, London #11/R est:7000-10000

GIBSON, Thomas (attrib) (1680-1751) British
£5800 $9164 €8700 Portrait of Vice Admiral Sir John Baker (127x102cm-50x40in) prov. 26-Nov-2 Christie's, London #9/R est:4000-6000

GIBSON, Walter Hamilton (1850-1896) American
Works on paper
£382 $600 €573 Rocky pasture (20x28cm-8x11in) s.d.86 W/C. 22-Nov-2 Skinner, Boston #84/R

GIBSON, William Alfred (1866-1931) British
£450 $702 €675 Cartmell (19x24cm-7x9in) s. 17-Oct-2 Bonhams, Edinburgh #227
£550 $891 €825 Pastoral scene (13x22cm-5x9in) s. canvasboard. 20-May-3 Sotheby's, Olympia #282/R
£553 $862 €830 Mill (26x35cm-10x14in) s. panel. 15-Oct-2 Stephan Welz, Johannesburg #390/R est:10000-15000 (SA.R 9000)
£750 $1193 €1125 Katwyk, Holland (51x61cm-20x24in) s. prov. 6-Mar-3 Christie's, Kensington #151/R
£1200 $1872 €1800 On the Ayrshire coast (64x77cm-25x30in) s. prov. 17-Sep-2 Sotheby's, Olympia #32/R est:1200-1800
£1200 $1908 €1800 Angler on the edge of a lake (40x51cm-16x20in) s. panel. 6-Mar-3 Christie's, Kensington #150/R est:1000-1500
£1500 $2280 €2250 River landscape (30x40cm-12x16in) board. 28-Aug-2 Sotheby's, London #986/R est:1500-2000
£1900 $2888 €2850 Canal scene (27x35cm-11x14in) s. canvas on board. 28-Aug-2 Sotheby's, London #984/R est:1500-2000
£3200 $5184 €4800 Winter in Holland (51x61cm-20x24in) s. 23-May-3 Lyon & Turnbull, Edinburgh #25/R est:1000-1500

GICQUEL, Joelle (20th C) French
£2727 $4555 €3900 Les fenetres de l'ame (81x60cm-32x24in) s. 25-Jun-3 Claude Aguttes, Neuilly #192 est:3900-4000

GIDE, François Theophile Etienne (1822-1890) French
£2115 $3215 €3300 La mort de Tancrede (81x100cm-32x39in) s. 10-Jul-2 Rabourdin & Choppin de Janvry, Paris #101/R est:3300-3500

GIEL, Frans van (1892-1975) Belgian
£449 $704 €700 Girl with mandolin (47x47cm-19x19in) s. panel. 16-Dec-2 Bernaerts, Antwerp #322
£545 $855 €850 Landscape. s. 16-Dec-2 Bernaerts, Antwerp #848
£1026 $1610 €1600 Young farmer's wife at work (67x76cm-26x30in) s. 16-Dec-2 Bernaerts, Antwerp #859 est:750-1000
£1795 $2836 €2800 Interior with figures at a breakfast table (113x163cm-44x64in) s.d.68. 18-Nov-2 Bernaerts, Antwerp #416/R est:2000-3000
£1923 $2981 €3000 Symbol of the Campine (123x165cm-48x65in) s. 7-Dec-2 De Vuyst, Lokeren #352/R est:3500-4500

GIERSING, Harald (1881-1927) Danish
£633 $1007 €950 Figures on the way to church (45x48cm-18x19in) mono. 10-Mar-3 Rasmussen, Vejle #629/R (D.KR 6800)
£1208 $1909 €1812 Spring in the garden, Lindevej (39x44cm-15x17in) i.verso artist's board exhib. 1-Apr-3 Rasmussen, Copenhagen #33/R est:12000-15000 (D.KR 13000)
£2002 $3343 €2903 Self-portrait (38x31cm-15x12in) mono. artist board exhib.prov. 17-Jun-3 Rasmussen, Copenhagen #75/R est:15000-20000 (D.KR 21000)
£2742 $4360 €4113 The garden at Lindvej, 1911 (66x84cm-26x33in) mono. panel exhib. 26-Feb-3 Kunsthallen, Copenhagen #286/R est:40000 (D.KR 30000)
£3259 $5182 €4889 Study of football players, 1917 (52x70cm-20x28in) canvas on black painted plywood prov.lit. 4-Mar-3 Museumsbygningen, Copenhagen #537/R est:40000-45000 (D.KR 35000)
£22862 $35436 €34293 Lady seated in front of guitar - portrait of the artist's sister Ida (129x107cm-51x42in) painted 1923-24 prov.exhib.lit. 1-Oct-2 Rasmussen, Copenhagen #121/R est:250000 (D.KR 270000)
Works on paper
£302 $462 €453 Kain (30x23cm-12x9in) mono.d.3-03 pencil. 24-Aug-2 Rasmussen, Havnen #2250 (D.KR 3500)
£321 $495 €482 Self portrait (24x22cm-9x9in) i. verso W/C painted 1915. 23-Oct-2 Kunsthallen, Copenhagen #30 (D.KR 3800)

GIES, Emil (1872-?) German
£268 $412 €420 Barock house (23x34cm-9x13in) s.d.1916 board. 5-Sep-2 Arnold, Frankfurt #773/R
Works on paper
£349 $545 €524 Twin sisters (66x67cm-26x26in) s.d.1908 pastel. 6-Nov-2 Dobiaschofsky, Bern #583 (S.FR 800)

GIES, Joseph W (1860-1935) American
£512 $850 €742 Landscape with sheep (18x23cm-7x9in) s. board. 11-Jun-3 Boos Gallery, Michigan #589/R

GIES, Ludwig (1887-1966) German
Sculpture
£1844 $2987 €2600 Face of Christi (18x10x5cm-7x4x2in) i. bronze one sided relief pewter. 24-May-3 Van Ham, Cologne #199/R est:2000

GIESE, Marie (c.1865-1945) German
£261 $429 €400 Blind man's bluff (44x118cm-17x46in) s.d.Dec.96. 29-Mar-3 Dannenberg, Berlin #577/R

GIESECKE, Wilhelm and THIELE, Rudolf (19/20th C) Austrian/German
Sculpture
£6090 $9561 €9500 Bustes d'Arabes (70cm-28in) s. polychrome bronze wood socle pair. 11-Dec-2 Hotel des Ventes Mosan, Brussels #233/R est:7900-8100

GIESSEN, Johannes Theodorus (1900-1983) Dutch
£255 $397 €400 Houses behind dunes (65x95cm-26x37in) init. 6-Nov-2 Vendue Huis, Gravenhage #62

GIETL, Josua von (1847-1922) German
£553 $863 €880 Autumnal landscape with two hunters (25x36cm-10x14in) s. board. 9-Oct-2 Michael Zeller, Lindau #698/R

GIEZENDANNER, Babeli (1831-1905) German
Works on paper
£1834 $2861 €2751 Peasants with cattle near Schelleschotte, Churfirsten (10x17cm-4x7in) pencil pen W/C. 6-Nov-2 Hans Widmer, St Gallen #84/R est:3500-7000 (S.FR 4200)
£2009 $3134 €3014 Peasants with cattle up in the mountains (9x14cm-4x6in) pen W/C. 6-Nov-2 Hans Widmer, St Gallen #82/R est:3000-6000 (S.FR 4600)
£2620 $4087 €3930 Taking the cattle up to the mountains (16x25cm-6x10in) i. W/C pen. 6-Nov-2 Hans Widmer, St Gallen #61/R est:500-9000 (S.FR 6000)
£5677 $8856 €8516 Peasants and cattle in mountains (29x38cm-11x15in) i. W/C pen. 6-Nov-2 Hans Widmer, St Gallen #59/R est:12000-18000 (S.FR 13000)
£7424 $11581 €11136 Toggenburg farmstead with garden (22x35cm-9x14in) pen W/C paper on board. 6-Nov-2 Hans Widmer, St Gallen #83/R est:10000-16000 (S.FR 17000)
£7860 $12262 €11790 Peasants and cattle in mountains (35x48cm-14x19in) i. W/C pen. 6-Nov-2 Hans Widmer, St Gallen #60/R est:12000-20000 (S.FR 18000)

GIFFORD, Charles H (1839-1904) American
£3057 $4800 €4586 Evening harbour scene with fishing boats under sail (23x36cm-9x14in) s. 26-Jul-2 Eldred, East Dennis #519/R est:4000-6000
£3822 $6000 €5733 Rocky coastal beach scene with two figure in a boat (23x43cm-9x17in) s. board. 26-Jul-2 Eldred, East Dennis #535/R est:6000-8000
£6197 $8800 €9296 Study, figure boat (18x36cm-7x14in) 8-Aug-1 Barridorf, Portland #157/R est:5000-7000
£6688 $10500 €10032 Small sailboats and other boats approaching a seaside cliff (15x30cm-6x12in) s.d.69. 22-Nov-2 Eldred, East Dennis #831/R est:4000-6000
£19481 $30000 €29222 Gay head, Martha's Vineyard (15x25cm-6x10in) s.d.76 prov. 24-Oct-2 Shannon's, Milford #35/R est:5000-7000

GIFFORD, John (19th C) British
£1380 $2250 €2070 Three setters after the hunt (91x70cm-36x28in) s. 11-Feb-3 Bonhams & Doyles, New York #131 est:4000-6000
£1935 $3000 €2903 Hunting dogs in landscape with dead game and creel (91x71cm-36x28in) s. 2-Nov-2 North East Auctions, Portsmouth #91/R
£3600 $5976 €5400 Two setters with dead game in a landscape (61x92cm-24x36in) s. 10-Jun-3 Bonhams, Leeds #155/R est:1500-2000
£3750 $6000 €5625 Good day's work (61x91cm-24x36in) s. 14-May-3 Butterfields, San Francisco #1162/R est:4000-6000

GIFFORD, Sanford Robinson (1823-1880) American
£13548 $21000 €20322 Sketch of the Golden Horn, Constantinople (16x30cm-6x12in) init.d.May 1869 prov.lit. 5-Dec-2 Christie's, Rockefeller NY #50/R est:25000-35000
£20645 $32000 €30968 Looking down from Sargent Mountain, Mt. Desert (23x49cm-9x19in) bears estate st. verso prov. 5-Dec-2 Christie's, Rockefeller NY #6/R est:40000-60000
£24516 $38000 €36774 View of Catskills (20x12cm-8x5in) init.d.60 canvas on masonite prov. 3-Dec-2 Phillips, New York #3/R est:40000-60000
£27097 $42000 €40646 High Tor-Matlock Dale, New York (23x19cm-9x7in) i.on stretcher painted c.1855. 3-Dec-2 Phillips, New York #11/R est:25000-45000
£31646 $50000 €47469 Kauterskill Falls (38x28cm-15x11in) s.d.1846 oil on paper prov.exhib. 24-Apr-3 Shannon's, Milford #56/R est:50000-75000
£38710 $60000 €58065 Isola Bella in Lago Maggiore (20x34cm-8x13in) s. oil pencil paper on canvas. 5-Dec-2 Christie's, Rockefeller NY #64/R est:30000-50000
£38961 $60000 €58442 Kaaterskill Creek, looking up at South Mountain at the Catskills (33x28cm-13x11in) s. prov. 24-Oct-2 Shannon's, Milford #59/R est:20000-30000
£51613 $80000 €77420 Cardinal's coach on the Campagna (9x18cm-4x7in) canvas on panel prov.exhib.lit. 5-Dec-2 Christie's, Rockefeller NY #33/R est:25000-35000
£54839 $85000 €82259 Stelvio Road (25x21cm-10x8in) i.d.1868 prov.exhib.lit. 3-Dec-2 Phillips, New York #6/R est:30000-50000
£58065 $90000 €87098 Near Venice (27x41cm-11x16in) paper on canvas prov.exhib.lit. 5-Dec-2 Christie's, Rockefeller NY #57/R est:60000-80000
£109677 $170000 €164516 On the Nile, Gebel Shekh Hereedee (43x79cm-17x31in) s.d.1872 s.i.d.verso oil pencil prov.exhib.lit. 5-Dec-2 Christie's, Rockefeller NY #62/R est:250000-350000
£135484 $210000 €203226 Sketch on the Nile (19x33cm-7x13in) i.d.69 prov.exhib.lit. 3-Dec-2 Phillips, New York #30/R est:100000-150000
£277419 $430000 €416129 Sketch of Mount Chocorua (24x39cm-9x15in) s. painted c.1854-63 prov.exhib.lit. 3-Dec-2 Phillips, New York #22/R est:250000-350000
£296296 $480000 €444444 Mouth of the Shrewsbury River (29x48cm-11x19in) s.d.July 20 1867 s.i.verso prov.lit. 22-May-3 Christie's, Rockefeller NY #4/R est:150000-250000
£335484 $520000 €503226 Mote Mountain from Echo Lake, New Hampshire (26x43cm-10x17in) s. canvas on board prov. 5-Dec-2 Christie's, Rockefeller NY #12/R est:300000-500000
Works on paper
£385 $600 €578 Rocky coastal scene (18x25cm-7x10in) s. 1-Aug-2 Eldred, East Dennis #932/R
£385 $600 €578 Rocky coastal scene (18x25cm-7x10in) s. 1-Aug-2 Eldred, East Dennis #933/R

GIFFORD, Sanford Robinson (attrib) (1823-1880) American
£629 $1000 €944 Paddling on the lake (25x36cm-10x14in) 7-Mar-3 Skinner, Boston #284/R
£2031 $3250 €2945 Old mill in autumn, upstate New York view (13x18cm-5x7in) board. 16-May-3 Skinner, Boston #55/R est:3500-4500

GIGANTE, Ercole (1815-1860) Italian
£3200 $4960 €4800 Fishing craft off the Island of Capri (25x38cm-10x15in) s. pair. 31-Oct-2 Christie's, Kensington #464/R est:800-1200
£7500 $12525 €10875 Amalfi, the Convento dei Cappuccini (36x56cm-14x22in) s. 8-Jul-3 Sotheby's, Olympia #504/R est:6000-8000
£24828 $39228 €36000 Villa Reale, Naples (37x43cm-15x17in) s.d.1847 lit. 3-Apr-3 Porro, Milan #67/R est:50000

GIGANTE, Giacinto (1806-1876) Italian
£27586 $43586 €40000 Naples from San Martino (35x26cm-14x10in) d.1843 lit. 3-Apr-3 Porro, Milan #61/R est:50000
£44304 $70000 €70000 Sunset at Bacoli (50x69cm-20x27in) prov.lit. 26-Nov-2 Christie's, Rome #288/R est:60000-80000
Works on paper
£4000 $6320 €5800 Venus Temple in Baia (29x20cm-11x8in) W/C. 3-Apr-3 Porro, Milan #62/R
£4828 $7628 €7000 Landscape with saint praying (29x22cm-11x9in) W/C lit. 3-Apr-3 Porro, Milan #60/R
£9494 $15000 €15000 Bell tower in Gaeta (40x28cm-16x11in) i. W/C card. 26-Nov-2 Christie's, Rome #289/R est:20000
£19310 $30510 €28000 Paestum temples (49x33cm-19x13in) s.d.1854 W/C lit. 3-Apr-3 Porro, Milan #66/R est:40000

GIGANTE, Giacinto (attrib) (1806-1876) Italian
£4088 $6336 €6500 Landscape (41x54cm-16x21in) s. 29-Oct-2 Finarte, Milan #408/R est:3000-3500
Works on paper
£3797 $6000 €6000 View of Naples (20x35cm-8x14in) s.d.1833 W/C card. 26-Nov-2 Christie's, Rome #112 est:5000-8000

GIGER, Hans-Rudolf (1940-) Swiss
£9955 $16624 €14435 Year change - fantasy composition (100x140cm-39x55in) air brush acrylic. 24-Jun-3 Koller, Zurich #73/R est:18000-25000 (S.FR 22000)
£12534 $20932 €18174 A Jodorowsky's Dune I (69x99cm-27x39in) s.i. airbrush paper. 24-Jun-3 Koller, Zurich #72/R est:12000-20000 (S.FR 27700)
£19231 $29808 €30000 Passage X (200x140cm-79x55in) acrylic wood painted 1971 prov.exhib.lit. 4-Dec-2 Dorotheum, Vienna #9/R est:40000-50000
Sculpture
£1179 $1839 €1769 Death's-head (13x19x13cm-5x7x5in) s.d.75 gouache skull. 8-Nov-2 Dobiaschofsky, Bern #277/R est:4000 (S.FR 2700)

GIGLI, Ormond (1925-) American?
Photographs
£2532 $4000 €3798 Girl in the window (50x51cm-20x20in) s.d.1960 num.53/100 col coupler print. 22-Apr-3 Christie's, Rockefeller NY #109/R est:4000-6000

GIGLI, Roberto (19/20th C) Italian
Works on paper
£681 $1076 €1022 From the Forum, Rome (53x37cm-21x15in) s.i. W/C. 2-Dec-2 Rasmussen, Copenhagen #1835/R (D.KR 8000)
£1200 $1920 €1800 Temple of Saturn, the Forum, Rome. Arch of Septimus Severus, Rome (52x35cm-20x14in) s. W/C two. 11-Mar-3 Bonhams, New Bond Street #4/R est:1000-1500

GIGNOUS, Eugenio (1850-1906) Italian
£2390 $3681 €3800 View of Gignese (35x27cm-14x11in) s. canvas on cardboard. 23-Oct-2 Finarte, Milan #108/R
£3899 $6005 €6200 Washing (18x33cm-7x13in) s. board. 23-Oct-2 Finarte, Milan #69/R est:6000-7000
£6884 $11290 €9500 Paesaggio montano con laghetto (50x26cm-20x10in) s. 27-May-3 Finarte, Milan #54/R est:10000-11000

GIGNOUS, Lorenzo (1862-c.1954) Italian
£340 $541 €500 Mountainous landscape (10x22cm-4x9in) s. 1-Mar-3 Meeting Art, Vercelli #178
£556 $894 €834 Summer landscape with lake (18x28cm-7x11in) s. board prov. 7-May-3 Dobiaschofsky, Bern #589 (S.FR 1200)
£566 $872 €900 Wooded landscape with peasant woman (30x43cm-12x17in) s. cardboard. 28-Oct-2 Il Ponte, Milan #313
£755 $1162 €1200 Figures in the wood (16x23cm-6x9in) s. board. 23-Oct-2 Finarte, Milan #189/R
£1020 $1622 €1500 Autumn landscape (48x68cm-19x27in) s.d.1926 canvas on cardboard. 1-Mar-3 Meeting Art, Vercelli #112
£1935 $3058 €3000 View of Pallanza (45x74cm-18x29in) s. exhib. 18-Dec-2 Finarte, Milan #146/R est:3500
£8805 $13560 €14000 Sesto Calende (98x190cm-39x75in) s. 23-Oct-2 Finarte, Milan #115/R est:14000-15000

GIGUERE, George (20th C) ?
£2950 $4750 €4425 Grizzly bear rushed Indian with rifle (23x74cm-9x29in) s.d. 10-May-3 Illustration House, New York #177/R est:2000-4000

GIKOL, Ruth (1913-1983) American
£440 $700 €660 Street scene (66x97cm-26x38in) s. painted c.1940. 2-Mar-3 Toomey, Oak Park #783/R

GIL GALLANGO, Felipe (1838-1938) Spanish
£416 $607 €640 Seville (31x40cm-12x16in) s. cardboard. 17-Jun-2 Ansorena, Madrid #131/R
£629 $981 €1000 View of Seville (24x30cm-9x12in) s. cardboard. 8-Oct-2 Ansorena, Madrid #446/R
£5753 $8975 €8400 Street in Seville (40x28cm-16x11in) s. cardboard. 8-Apr-3 Ansorena, Madrid #35/R est:840

GIL GARCIA, J (20th C) Spanish
£403 $648 €600 Roses (35x70cm-14x28in) s.d.1922. 18-Feb-3 Durán, Madrid #561/R

GIL MARTIN, Daniel (1946-) Spanish
£1474 $2329 €2300 Instrument (50x34cm-20x13in) s. board. 13-Nov-2 Ansorena, Madrid #31/R

GIL MONTEJANO, Jose Antonio (1850-1906) Spanish
£1509 $2355 €2400 Aranjuez (33x21cm-13x8in) s. board. 17-Sep-2 Segre, Madrid #71/R

GIL Y GIL, Juan (1900-1984) Spanish
£317 $504 €460 Dancer (65x54cm-26x21in) s. 4-Mar-3 Ansorena, Madrid #117/R

GIL, Ignacio (1913-) Spanish
£568 $829 €852 Dov'e Pabre - Ibiza (38x46cm-15x18in) s. 4-Jun-2 Germann, Zurich #767 (S.FR 1300)
£2484 $4073 €3800 Figures in Majorca (38x46cm-15x18in) 5-Feb-3 Arte, Seville #767/R

GILARDI, Piero (1942-) Italian
Sculpture
£1161 $1835 €1800 Stones (12x31x23cm-5x12x9in) foam. 18-Dec-2 Christie's, Rome #48
Works on paper
£886 $1382 €1400 Computur stone (50x50cm-20x20in) s.i.d.1999 verso. 14-Sep-2 Meeting Art, Vercelli #714/R

GILARDI, Silvano (1933-) Italian
£347 $552 €500 Portrait of the painter Alessadri (60x50cm-24x20in) s.i.d.1956 verso board. 1-May-3 Meeting Art, Vercelli #264

GILBERT and GEORGE (20th C) British
Photographs
£6635 $10218 €10550 Singing sculpture (214x267cm-84x105in) s. num.15/20 offset diptych. 26-Oct-2 Cornette de St.Cyr, Paris #172/R
£32812 $52500 €49218 Coming to the cross (244x201cm-96x79in) s.i.d.1982 16 hand col photographs prov.exhib.lit. 14-May-3 Sotheby's, New York #335/R est:50000-70000
£38000 $58520 €57000 Moon youth (61x50cm-24x20in) s.i.d.1982 s.d.verso sixteen hand dyed gelatin silver prints. 23-Oct-2 Christie's, London #174/R est:35000-45000
£43750 $70000 €65625 Spat on (190x350cm-75x138in) s.i.d.1996 twelve hand dyed gelatin silver print prov. 15-May-3 Christie's, Rockefeller NY #345/R est:70000-90000
£45000 $73800 €67500 Hanging (242x202cm-95x80in) s.d.1988 i.num.1-16 verso col photo sixteen parts prov. 7-Feb-3 Sotheby's, London #132/R est:30000-40000
£50000 $82000 €75000 Tree naked (254x495cm-100x195in) twenty one hand col photographs executed 1991 prov.exhib. 5-Feb-3 Christie's, London #27/R est:60000-80000
£110759 $175000 €166139 Night view (150x120cm-59x47in) s.i.d.1978 nine hand col gelatin silver prints prov.exhib.lit. 13-Nov-2 Christie's, Rockefeller NY #68/R est:120000-180000
£150000 $240000 €225000 Day (200x160cm-79x63in) s.i.d.1978 col gelatin silver print set of 16 prov.lit. 14-May-3 Christie's, Rockefeller NY #59/R est:150000-200000
£164557 $260000 €246836 Coming (185x154cm-73x61in) gelatin silver print set of nine executed 1975 prov.lit. 14-Nov-2 Christie's, Rockefeller NY #435/R est:140000-180000
Works on paper
£1400 $2338 €2030 World of Gilbert and George, the storyboard (20x29cm-8x11in) s.num.6 ink wash. 24-Jun-3 Sotheby's, Olympia #53/R est:1000-1500
£2690 $4250 €4035 Westminster cross (118x110cm-46x43in) s.i.d.1981 postcards mounted on paperboard. 22-Apr-3 Butterfields, San Francisco #6074/R est:3000-5000

GILBERT, Alfred (1854-1934) British
Sculpture
£5500 $8580 €8250 Winged victory (39cm-15in) brown pat bronze sardonyx sphere stone plinth. 9-Apr-3 Sotheby's, London #99/R est:2000-3000
£13500 $21735 €20250 Perseus arming (36cm-14in) s. bronze prov.exhib.lit. 20-Feb-3 Christie's, London #151/R est:25000

GILBERT, Arthur (1819-1895) British
£513 $811 €800 Night on th seashore (12x17cm-5x7in) cardboard. 18-Nov-2 Tajan, Paris #25
£950 $1549 €1425 Mountain sheep on the Slingaehan Valley (25x18cm-10x7in) s.d.1889. 28-Jan-3 Gorringes, Lewes #1699/R
£1200 $1848 €1800 Rain cloud passing off (18x25cm-7x10in) s. 5-Sep-2 Christie's, Kensington #125/R est:1500-2000
£1400 $2282 €2100 Near Chilworth, Surrey (16x24cm-6x9in) indis sig. i.verso board. 12-Feb-3 Bonhams, Knightsbridge #265/R est:700-1000
£1500 $2310 €2250 Loch scene at sunset (41x81cm-16x32in) s. 3-Sep-2 Gorringes, Lewes #2309/R est:1000-1500
£2500 $3850 €3750 Night, a highland home (18x25cm-7x10in) s.d.1884. 5-Sep-2 Christie's, Kensington #124/R est:1500-2000
£2600 $4264 €3900 Marlow from the Thames (22x36cm-9x14in) s.indis.d.1867 prov. 29-May-3 Christie's, Kensington #117/R est:3000-4000

GILBERT, Arthur Hill (1894-1970) American
£266 $425 €399 Sierra rocky lake. init. canvas on board. 11-Jan-3 Harvey Clar, Oakland #1218
£621 $1000 €932 Cypress in Monterey coastal (20x25cm-8x10in) s. canvasboard. 18-Feb-3 John Moran, Pasadena #2a
£1250 $2000 €1875 Carmel coast (12x16cm-5x6in) board. 14-Mar-3 Du Mouchelle, Detroit #2007/R est:1500-2000
£2560 $4250 €3712 Haystacks (41x51cm-16x20in) s. 11-Jun-3 Butterfields, San Francisco #4220/R est:4000-6000
£4518 $7500 €6551 Monterey Farm (66x76cm-26x30in) s. prov. 11-Jun-3 Butterfields, San Francisco #4219/R est:6000-8000

GILBERT, Bess (1897-1965) American
£1198 $2000 €1737 Exposition building San Diego, Balboa Park (30x23cm-12x9in) s. canvasboard. 17-Jun-3 John Moran, Pasadena #9a est:700-1100

GILBERT, Dennis (1922-) British
£280 $451 €420 Girl knitting (100x74cm-39x29in) s. 18-Feb-3 Bonhams, Knightsbridge #156
£400 $632 €600 Port des arts (51x61cm-20x24in) s. 27-Nov-2 Sotheby's, Olympia #276/R

GILBERT, Horace W (1855-?) British
£1700 $2737 €2550 Snowdon from Llugwy Valley (43x58cm-17x23in) s.d.1894. 9-May-3 Mallams, Oxford #161/R est:1200-1500

GILBERT, John (19th C) British
Works on paper
£833 $1300 €1250 Ivanhoe. gouache pastel. 21-Sep-2 Harvey Clar, Oakland #1418

GILBERT, Michel Gerard (1914-) French
£577 $917 €866 Le petite dejeuner (30x40cm-12x16in) s.d.49 composition board. 4-Mar-3 Deutscher-Menzies, Melbourne #232/R (A.D 1500)

GILBERT, Sir John (1817-1897) British
£400 $624 €600 Musketeers on horseback (41x61cm-16x24in) s.d.1865. 17-Sep-2 Sotheby's, Olympia #185/R
£2692 $4227 €4200 King Henry IV (116x77cm-46x30in) s.d.1845 exhib.lit. 15-Dec-2 Mercier & Cie, Lille #344/R est:4500
£6600 $10230 €9900 Naseby (122x183cm-48x72in) s.d.1872-3 exhib. 2-Oct-2 Bonhams, Knowle #73/R est:6000-8000
Works on paper
£280 $454 €420 Triumphal procession lead by an Angel (20x16cm-8x6in) W/C htd white. 21-Jan-3 Bonhams, Knightsbridge #163/R

GILBERT, Stephen (1910-) British
£480 $744 €720 Abstract (33x41cm-13x16in) 4-Oct-2 Mallams, Oxford #541

Prints
£3387 $5250 €5081 Figure composition with woman standing (49x37cm-19x15in) s.d.49 prov. 1-Oct-2 Rasmussen, Copenhagen #84/R est:40000 (D.KR 40000)
Works on paper
£550 $897 €825 Abstract composition (21x27cm-8x11in) s. ink wash. 3-Feb-3 Sotheby's, Olympia #161/R
£705 $1093 €1100 Figure (32x24cm-13x9in) s.d.47 pencil brush ink. 3-Dec-2 Christie's, Amsterdam #111/R est:1000-1500

GILBERT, Victor (1847-1933) French
£3593 $6000 €5210 First steps (46x55cm-18x22in) s. prov. 22-Jun-3 Freeman, Philadelphia #35/R est:8000-12000
£3797 $5886 €6000 L'heure du the (34x26cm-13x10in) s. panel. 27-Sep-2 Rabourdin & Choppin de Janvry, Paris #54/R est:8000-8500
£3797 $6000 €6000 Femme nettoyant sa cuisine (46x38cm-18x15in) s. panel. 1-Dec-2 Peron, Melun #28
£4630 $7454 €6945 Balloons (55x46cm-22x18in) s. 7-May-3 Dobiaschofsky, Bern #591/R est:19000 (S.FR 10000)
£4790 $8000 €6946 Hungry companion (46x55cm-18x22in) s. prov. 22-Jun-3 Freeman, Philadelphia #34/R est:10000-15000
£6000 $9720 €9000 Flower seller (35x27cm-14x11in) s. 20-May-3 Sotheby's, Olympia #408/R est:1500-2000
£8861 $14000 €13292 Paris vegetable vendor (38x46cm-15x18in) s. panel. 17-Nov-2 CRN Auctions, Cambridge #63/R
£8861 $14000 €13292 Marchande de violettes (35x27cm-14x11in) s. panel. 24-Apr-3 Sotheby's, New York #146/R est:10000-15000
£9677 $15290 €15000 Elegante dans la foret (35x26cm-14x10in) s.panel. 19-Dec-2 Claude Aguttes, Neuilly #70/R
£16774 $26503 €26000 Fenaison (46x56cm-18x22in) s. 19-Dec-2 Claude Aguttes, Neuilly #30/R est:18000
£24193 $37500 €36290 Quai aux fleurs (61x50cm-24x20in) s.i. 29-Oct-2 Sotheby's, New York #88/R est:40000-60000
Works on paper
£4717 $7358 €7500 Fleuriste au parapluie rouge (22x16cm-9x6in) s. W/C htd gouache. 9-Oct-2 Lombrail & Teucquam, Paris #2/R

GILBERY, M (?) ?
£968 $1529 €1500 Rabbin (76x58cm-30x23in) s. panel exhib. 18-Dec-2 Digard, Paris #126/R

GILCHREST, Joan (1918-) British
£280 $437 €406 Good gossip at Mousehole (19x14cm-7x6in) init. oil paper on card. 27-Mar-3 Lane, Penzance #159
£440 $735 €638 Bank Penzance (16x12cm-6x5in) mono. prov. 19-Jun-3 Lane, Penzance #214
£500 $780 €750 Titus in my greenhouse (15x10cm-6x4in) mono. i.verso board. 17-Oct-2 David Lay, Penzance #1420
£540 $837 €810 Still life, comport of garlic and fruit (122x155cm-48x61in) init. card. 26-Sep-2 Lane, Penzance #274
£650 $1014 €975 View from my greenhouse with Titus (18x23cm-7x9in) mono. i.verso board. 17-Oct-2 David Lay, Penzance #1419
£650 $1014 €943 Dreaming at Mousehole (18x13cm-7x5in) init. board. 27-Mar-3 Lane, Penzance #49
£660 $1030 €957 Rough sea at Mousehole with kitten (18x13cm-7x5in) mono. board. 27-Mar-3 Lane, Penzance #214
£740 $1154 €1073 Windy day at St, Ives (18x16cm-7x6in) init. board prov. 27-Mar-3 Lane, Penzance #160/R
£800 $1248 €1200 Dreaming at Mousehole. Windy day at St Ives (17x17cm-7x7in) init. board two. 5-Nov-2 Bristol Auction Rooms #867
£860 $1436 €1247 Fishing boat before cottages (18x13cm-7x5in) init. board. 19-Jun-3 Lane, Penzance #145/R
£880 $1470 €1276 Fishing boats before a village (18x11cm-7x4in) init. board. 19-Jun-3 Lane, Penzance #170/R
£900 $1503 €1305 Watching the fleet sail (13x23cm-5x9in) init. board. 19-Jun-3 Lane, Penzance #5/R
£1050 $1628 €1575 Cat napping (51x48cm-20x19in) init. 26-Sep-2 Lane, Penzance #186 est:1000-1500
£1050 $1754 €1523 Sailing (12x17cm-5x7in) mono. board. 19-Jun-3 Lane, Penzance #402 est:500-600
£1100 $1705 €1650 Sunflowers at Mousehole (107x86cm-42x34in) init. 26-Sep-2 Lane, Penzance #141 est:400-600
£1150 $1794 €1725 Ben and Willy at Mousehole (47x32cm-19x13in) init. board. 5-Nov-2 Bristol Auction Rooms #879/R est:300-400
£1250 $1938 €1875 Still life, vase of wild roses (104x145cm-41x57in) init.board. 26-Sep-2 Lane, Penzance #275/R est:600-800
£1600 $2672 €2320 Alice, fishing boat (18x25cm-7x10in) mono. board. 19-Jun-3 Lane, Penzance #220/R est:700-800
£2000 $3100 €3000 Harbour side cottages (140x140cm-55x55in) s. board. 26-Sep-2 Lane, Penzance #276 est:1500-2000
£2000 $3140 €3000 Jack, Ben and Willy at Mousehole (47x32cm-19x13in) init. board. 10-Dec-2 Lane, Penzance #55/R est:1800-2500
£2600 $4030 €3900 Birds in Paradise Hayle (183x155cm-72x61in) init. board. 26-Sep-2 Lane, Penzance #10/R est:1750-2000
£3400 $5304 €4930 Magnolias at Mousehole (61x71cm-24x28in) init. board. 27-Mar-3 Lane, Penzance #110/R est:2000-3000

GILCHRIST, Joan (fl.1885-1913) British
£2500 $3900 €3625 Abandoned lighthouse (60x60cm-24x24in) init. board. 27-Mar-3 Lane, Penzance #10/R est:1500-2000

GILCHRIST, Philip Thomson (1865-1956) British
£250 $415 €363 The fal (41x61cm-16x24in) s.d.1900. 10-Jun-3 David Lay, Penzance #121

GILDEMEISTER, Max (1872-1934) German
£612 $973 €900 Sailing boat by Wannsee shore (47x68cm-19x27in) s. 28-Mar-3 Bolland & Marotz, Bremen #451/R
£1144 $1876 €1750 Autumn wood (115x70cm-45x28in) s. 29-Mar-3 Dannenberg, Berlin #578/R est:400

GILDEMEISTER-LOECH, E (19/20th C) German
£314 $491 €500 Still life with cup and milk bottle. mono. panel. 21-Sep-2 Bolland & Marotz, Bremen #368/R

GILDEWART, Friedrich Vordemberge (1899-1962) Dutch
Works on paper
£1147 $1813 €1790 Composition (26x31cm-10x12in) W/C exec.1953. 12-Nov-2 Babuino, Rome #233/R

GILDOR, Jacob (1948-) Israeli
£1379 $2207 €2000 Jerusalem a travers le temps (86x111cm-34x44in) s. canvas in 9 parts. 12-Mar-3 Rabourdin & Choppin de Janvry, Paris #222/R
£2278 $3600 €3417 Frishman Beach scene (61x79cm-24x31in) s.d.1969 s.i.d.verso. 27-Apr-3 Sotheby's, Tel Aviv #100/R est:4000-6000

GILE, Selden Connor (1877-1947) American
£2866 $4500 €4299 View of a harbour (23x30cm-9x12in) canvasboard prov. 19-Nov-2 Butterfields, San Francisco #8240/R est:5000-7000
£2866 $4500 €4299 Sea and rocks (19x23cm-7x9in) board painted c.1932 prov. 19-Nov-2 Butterfields, San Francisco #8241/R est:5000-7000
£3503 $5500 €5255 Tabletop still life (12x13cm-5x5in) s.d.40 canvasboard prov.exhib. 19-Nov-2 Butterfields, San Francisco #8254/R est:5000-7000
£6024 $10000 €8735 Green and pink hills (30x37cm-12x15in) s.d.32 board prov. 11-Jun-3 Butterfields, San Francisco #4257/R est:12000-15000
£9554 $15000 €14331 Green and pink hills (30x37cm-12x15in) s.d.32 board prov.exhib. 19-Nov-2 Butterfields, San Francisco #8239/R est:15000-20000
£10241 $17000 €14849 Rockridge Quarry (41x30cm-16x12in) exhib.lit. 11-Jun-3 Butterfields, San Francisco #4256/R est:15000-20000
£10843 $18000 €15722 Joss House (76x61cm-30x24in) s.d.28 canvas on masonite. 11-Jun-3 Butterfields, San Francisco #4262/R est:20000-30000
£11465 $18000 €17198 Waterfall in the woods (49x61cm-19x24in) s.d.28 board. 20-Nov-2 Christie's, Los Angeles #124/R est:10000-15000
£11465 $18000 €17198 Vibrant hillside (30x41cm-12x16in) s. prov. 19-Nov-2 Butterfields, San Francisco #8238/R est:20000-30000
£25904 $43000 €37561 Song of Marin (38x46cm-15x18in) s.d.32 prov. 11-Jun-3 Butterfields, San Francisco #5254/R est:25000-35000
£36145 $60000 €52410 Belvedere Cove looking through Raccoon Straits to San Francisco Bay (38x46cm-15x18in) s.d.29 board. 11-Jun-3 Butterfields, San Francisco #4252/R est:35000-45000
Works on paper
£2866 $4500 €4299 Farm houses, Marin (25x23cm-10x9in) s.d.35 W/C prov. 19-Nov-2 Butterfields, San Francisco #8243/R est:5000-7000
£4777 $7500 €7166 Cattle watering (38x49cm-15x19in) s.d.31 W/C prov. 19-Nov-2 Butterfields, San Francisco #8242/R est:5000-7000

GILES, Carl (1916-1995) British
Works on paper
£700 $1085 €1050 Men are all the same - no fashion sense whatsoever. Don't believe everything you read in the paper's (24x52cm-9x20in) s.i. pen ink two. 24-Sep-2 Bonhams, Knightsbridge #154/R

GILES, E D (19/20th C) ?
£1139 $1800 €1800 La course (30x46cm-12x18in) s.d.1907. 26-Nov-2 Palais de Beaux Arts, Brussels #192/R est:1800-2500

GILES, Geoffrey Douglas (1857-1941) British
£700 $1106 €1015 Two horses and a spaniel (51x61cm-20x24in) s.d.1886. 22-Jul-3 Sworder & Son, Bishops Stortford #371/R
£800 $1248 €1200 End of the hunt (29x34cm-11x13in) s.d.1925 board. 8-Oct-2 Sotheby's, Olympia #404/R

GILES, H P (19th C) American
£399 $650 €599 Woods in autumn (30x38cm-12x15in) s. panel. 1-Feb-3 Thomaston Place, Thomaston #53
£982 $1600 €1473 Winter landscape (43x56cm-17x22in) s. 1-Feb-3 Thomaston Place, Thomaston #16

GILES, James William (attrib) (1801-1870) British
£4200 $6510 €6300 View of King's College, Aberdeen, with figures (48x71cm-19x28in) 31-Oct-2 Christie's, London #24/R est:3000-5000

GILES, Tony (1925-) British
£300 $489 €450 Three spires (51x66cm-20x26in) s. board. 13-Feb-3 David Lay, Penzance #149
£370 $603 €555 Harbour (51x66cm-20x26in) s. board. 13-Feb-3 David Lay, Penzance #147
£380 $619 €570 Boats in a harbour (53x97cm-21x38in) s. board. 13-Feb-3 David Lay, Penzance #148
£440 $682 €660 Polperro harbour (142x251cm-56x99in) s. board. 26-Sep-2 Lane, Penzance #206
£520 $811 €780 Cornish coast (41x99cm-16x39in) s. board. 17-Oct-2 David Lay, Penzance #1515
£520 $811 €780 Stoney bridge (36x43cm-14x17in) s.i.d.1989 board. 16-Oct-2 David Lay, Penzance #259/R
£700 $1092 €1050 Goodnight Camborne (71x91cm-28x36in) s. i.verso. 17-Oct-2 David Lay, Penzance #1520
Works on paper
£320 $499 €480 Fantasy artwork for a GWR poster (56x41cm-22x16in) s.i.d.1984 gouache. 16-Oct-2 David Lay, Penzance #303/R
£380 $619 €570 Forty steps, Taunton (53x76cm-21x30in) s.i.d.1972 W/C. 13-Feb-3 David Lay, Penzance #377
£400 $624 €600 Brown queen (36x43cm-14x17in) s.i.d.1983 W/C. 16-Oct-2 David Lay, Penzance #298
£500 $835 €725 Viaduct at St. Stephens - Old Brunel piers (38x56cm-15x22in) s.d.25.2.82 mixed media. 19-Jun-3 Lane, Penzance #66
£700 $1092 €1050 Clay wagons, Burngullow (38x48cm-15x19in) s.i.d.84 verso gouache ink. 16-Oct-2 David Lay, Penzance #229

GILFORD, P (?) ?
£469 $751 €680 Gundogs by basket (30x40cm-12x16in) 18-May-3 Anders Antik, Landskrona #13 (S.KR 6000)

GILIOLI, Émile (1911-1977) French
Sculpture
£1800 $2844 €2700 Untitled (30cm-12in) s.d.1948 gold pat bronze metal base. 3-Apr-3 Christie's, Kensington #178/R
£2244 $3522 €3500 Forme (27cm-11in) s.d.59 white marble onyx base. 10-Dec-2 Piasa, Paris #144/R
£2244 $3522 €3500 Priere (36cm-14in) s.d.58 num.1/5 lead onyx socle exhib.lit. 10-Dec-2 Piasa, Paris #452/R
£2500 $4125 €3600 Sans titre (34x40x31cm-13x16x12in) s. col marble exec.c.1960. 1-Jul-3 Artcurial Briest, Paris #779/R est:4000-6000
£2564 $4026 €4000 Volume (40cm-16in) s.d.1958 white marble. 10-Dec-2 Piasa, Paris #143/R
£3034 $4855 €4400 Chateau (34x41cm-13x16in) s. pol white marble exec.1961 prov.exhib.lit. 15-Mar-3 De Vuyst, Lokeren #487/R est:4000-6000
£3205 $5032 €5000 Rencontre (33x15cm-13x6in) s. num.1/6 gilt pat bronze Cast Susse exhib. 24-Nov-2 Laurence Calmels, Paris #298/R
£3522 $5459 €5600 Le coq (46x36x15cm-18x14x6in) s. poli bronze. 30-Oct-2 Artcurial Briest, Paris #492/R est:6000-8000
£4167 $6542 €6500 Fleur blanche (18cm-7in) s.d.48 marble. 10-Dec-2 Piasa, Paris #453/R
£6090 $9561 €9500 Tete de guerrier (33x35cm-13x14in) s. num.1/3 black pat bronze Cast Susse. 24-Nov-2 Laurence Calmels, Paris #299/R
£20513 $32205 €32000 Untitled (19cm-7in) Baccarat crystal. 10-Dec-2 Piasa, Paris #145/R est:3000
Works on paper
£385 $604 €600 Violoniste assis (54x37cm-21x15in) s.i.d.1964 ink dr. 10-Dec-2 Piasa, Paris #150
£483 $806 €700 Personnage (48x37cm-19x15in) s.i.d.46 chl dr. 10-Jul-3 Artcurial Briest, Paris #289
£513 $805 €800 Forme (65x53cm-26x21in) s.i.d.168 chl dr. 10-Dec-2 Piasa, Paris #151
£513 $805 €800 Composition (65x50cm-26x20in) s.d.58 pastel. 10-Dec-2 Piasa, Paris #456
£577 $906 €900 Composition geometrique (65x51cm-26x20in) s.i.d.1965 chl dr. 10-Dec-2 Piasa, Paris #149
£591 $951 €880 Femme (60x45cm-24x18in) s. crayon dr. 23-Feb-3 Mercier & Cie, Lille #56
£769 $1208 €1200 Composition (64x47cm-25x19in) s.d.1949 pastel. 15-Dec-2 Perrin, Versailles #19/R
£872 $1405 €1300 Abstraction (50x64cm-20x25in) s. pastel. 23-Feb-3 Mercier & Cie, Lille #54/R
£903 $1435 €1300 Composition (31x49cm-12x19in) s.d.53 gouache pencil. 29-Apr-3 Artcurial Briest, Paris #574/R est:1200-1500
£962 $1510 €1500 Composition (65x49cm-26x19in) s.d.1956 chl. 10-Dec-2 Piasa, Paris #454
£1250 $2063 €1800 Composition (63x48cm-25x19in) s.d.1951 gouache crayon. 1-Jul-3 Artcurial Briest, Paris #780/R est:800-1000
£1282 $2013 €2000 Visage profil (64x51cm-25x20in) s.i.d.1965 chl dr. 10-Dec-2 Piasa, Paris #148
£1795 $2818 €2800 Untitled (65x50cm-26x20in) s.i.d.1962 chl dr. 10-Dec-2 Piasa, Paris #147
£1923 $3019 €3000 Untitled (64x50cm-25x20in) s.i.d.1968 chl crayon dr. 10-Dec-2 Piasa, Paris #146
£1923 $3019 €3000 Profil de femme (65x50cm-26x20in) s.d.57 chl. 10-Dec-2 Piasa, Paris #455

GILKERSON, William (20th C) American
£764 $1200 €1146 John Paul Jones pursued in the sloop providence (25x33cm-10x13in) mono. 26-Jul-2 Eldred, East Dennis #610/R est:1500-1800
Works on paper
£3344 $5250 €5016 Fourth of July at Herschel Island (33x46cm-13x18in) s. W/C. 26-Jul-2 Eldred, East Dennis #536/R est:3500-4500

GILL, Edmund (1820-1894) British
£600 $978 €900 River landscape with angler and water mill beyond (30x46cm-12x18in) s.d.1859. 28-Jan-3 Gorringes, Lewes #1716
£620 $1017 €930 River in full spate (20x15cm-8x6in) s.d.86 s.i.d.1886 verso canvas on board. 29-May-3 Christie's, Kensington #129/R
£1400 $2296 €2100 Mountain waterfall (25x33cm-10x13in) s. s.d.1885 verso. 5-Jun-3 Christie's, Kensington #679/R est:800-1200
£2177 $3440 €3266 Figures resting at a waterfall, Wales (41x30cm-16x12in) s.d.1862 board. 18-Nov-2 Waddingtons, Toronto #121/R est:3000-4000 (C.D 5400)
£3400 $5304 €5100 Welsh waterfall scenes (23x17cm-9x7in) one s.d.1862 panel pair. 26-Mar-3 Sotheby's, Olympia #36/R est:1200-1800
£7317 $12000 €10976 Falls on the Clyde (112x86cm-44x34in) s.indis.d.186. 5-Feb-3 Christie's, Rockefeller NY #206/R est:7000-9000
£11500 $18285 €17250 North country waterfall (41x61cm-16x24in) s.indis.d. 27-Feb-3 Bonhams, Chester #366/R est:800-1200

GILL, Edmund Ward (fl.1843-1868) British
£800 $1264 €1200 Scene on the Clyde (23x18cm-9x7in) s.verso panel. 17-Dec-2 Gorringes, Lewes #1405

GILL, Edward (19th C) British
£2500 $3950 €3750 Extensive wooded river landscape in the evening with cattle watering (50x71cm-20x28in) s. 7-Apr-3 David Duggleby, Scarborough #399 est:2000-2500

GILL, Eric (1882-1940) British
Prints
£2600 $4134 €3900 Nativity, who were the first to cry Noell? animals all it befell (43x48cm-17x19in) wood black print. 26-Feb-3 Sotheby's, Olympia #82/R est:1000-1500
Works on paper
£350 $539 €525 Head of a woman (29x24cm-11x9in) s. pencil. 5-Sep-2 Christie's, Kensington #501/R
£3000 $4650 €4500 Seated male nude (21x17cm-8x7in) pencil brown crayon. 24-Sep-2 Bonhams, New Bond Street #30 est:500-700

GILL, Madge (1882-1961) British
Works on paper
£2160 $3500 €3240 Untitled (63x50cm-25x20in) s.d.November 2 1951 pen ink board prov. 27-Jan-3 Christie's, Rockefeller NY #34/R est:3000-4000
£2778 $4500 €4167 Untitled (63x50cm-25x20in) s.d.March 25 1952 verso pen ink board prov. 27-Jan-3 Christie's, Rockefeller NY #33/R est:3000-4000

GILL, Samuel Thomas (1818-1880) Australian
Works on paper
£2857 $4486 €4286 Diggers wedding in Melbourne (13x22cm-5x9in) init.i.d.1852 W/C gouache. 25-Nov-2 Christie's, Melbourne #415/R est:8000-10000 (A.D 8000)
£3203 $4900 €4805 On the Sturt, Coromandel Valley, South Australia (22x27cm-9x11in) init. W/C. 25-Aug-2 Sotheby's, Paddington #190/R est:9000-12000 (A.D 9000)

GILL, Samuel Thomas (attrib) (1818-1880) Australian
£274 $420 €411 Cattle drinking from King River Australia (44x75cm-17x30in) init. 21-Aug-2 Dunbar Sloane, Auckland #66/R (NZ.D 900)

GILL, W W (19th C) British
£603 $916 €905 River landscape with boy watching bird, England (28x41cm-11x16in) s. 27-Aug-2 Rasmussen, Copenhagen #1888/R (D.KR 7000)

GILL, William (19th C) British
£2200 $3498 €3300 Bob cherry. Swing (32x22cm-13x9in) s.i.d.1864 pair. 18-Mar-3 Bonhams, New Bond Street #32/R est:1500-2000

GILL, William W (19th C) British
£640 $1018 €928 Figure on a wayside path (22x31cm-9x12in) board pair. 22-Mar-3 Lacy Scott, Bury St.Edmunds #473
£650 $1014 €975 Figures crossing stone bridge over waterfall (23x18cm-9x7in) s. 15-Oct-2 Gorringes, Lewes #2106/R

GILLBERG, Jacob Axel (1769-1845) Swedish
Miniatures
£1900 $3116 €2755 Gustav IV Adolph, King of Sweden (6cm-2in circular) s.d.1803 gold frame prov.exhib.lit. 3-Jun-3 Christie's, London #85/R est:800-1200

GILLEMANS, Jan Pauwel (elder) (1618-1675) Flemish
£2830 $4387 €4500 Putti with fruit outside Renaissance palace (62x71cm-24x28in) panel. 2-Oct-2 Dorotheum, Vienna #369/R est:3000-4000

GILLEMANS, Jan Pauwel (elder-circle) (1618-1675) Flemish
£5000 $7800 €7500 Still life with a lobster, grapes, melon and roemer (58x82cm-23x32in) bears sig. 8-Apr-3 Sotheby's, Olympia #189/R est:5000-7000

GILLEMANS, Jan Pauwel (younger) (1651-1704) Flemish
£18000 $28080 €27000 Still life of fruit in basket with parrot in landscape (59x52cm-23x20in) s. 10-Apr-3 Sotheby's, London #51/R est:8000

GILLEMANS, Peter Mathys (?-1692) Flemish
£8974 $14090 €14000 Fruit, bottle and wine on stone ledge (44x55cm-17x22in) s. 16-Dec-2 Rabourdin & Choppin de Janvry, Paris #171/R est:25000

GILLES, Piet (1908-) Dutch
£818 $1259 €1300 Barques sur l'etang (77x80cm-30x31in) s. 22-Oct-2 Galerie Moderne, Brussels #745
£1069 $1657 €1700 Snow-covered shore (77x71cm-30x28in) s.d.1944. 5-Oct-2 De Vuyst, Lokeren #156 est:1700-2000

GILLES, Werner (1894-1961) German
£2899 $4754 €4000 City of the dead (43x60cm-17x24in) s. i. verso prov. 29-May-3 Lempertz, Koln #632/R est:5000-6000
£5072 $8319 €7000 Schwarzenbach II (34x52cm-13x20in) s.d.1950 board prov. 29-May-3 Lempertz, Koln #634/R est:8000-10000
£5128 $7949 €8000 Evening in Le Brusc (51x67cm-20x26in) s. paper on board prov. 4-Dec-2 Lempertz, Koln #733/R est:8000-10000
£5128 $7949 €8000 Boats in harbour (31x43cm-12x17in) s. oil tempera board. 4-Dec-2 Lempertz, Koln #734/R est:6000
£5797 $9507 €8000 Sailing ships in harbour (38x58cm-15x23in) s. canvas on panel. 29-May-3 Lempertz, Koln #633/R est:9000
£8333 $13667 €11500 Gorge 3 (33x46cm-13x18in) s.d.1954 tempera prov.exhib. 29-May-3 Lempertz, Koln #635/R est:10000-12000
Works on paper
£296 $461 €470 Female nude with flower (48x33cm-19x13in) s. prov.lit. 20-Sep-2 Karlheinz Kaupp, Staufen #2136/R
£429 $666 €670 Woman on donkey in town (35x27cm-14x11in) s.d. brush. 7-Dec-2 Hauswedell & Nolte, Hamburg #668/R
£513 $795 €800 Three men by sea (46x62cm-18x24in) Indian ink. 7-Dec-2 Ketterer, Hamburg #295/R
£629 $981 €1000 Figures in a landscape (42x58cm-17x23in) brush ink wash executed c.1945-50. 9-Oct-2 Sotheby's, London #231/R est:1500-2000
£647 $1036 €900 Fishermen on beach (49x62cm-19x24in) s. Indian ink. 15-May-3 Neumeister, Munich #701/R
£823 $1300 €1300 Fishermen in boats (48x62cm-19x24in) s.d.1954 i. verso Indian ink brush wash. 29-Nov-2 Villa Grisebach, Berlin #637/R est:600-700
£993 $1609 €1400 Untitled - three figures (42x55cm-17x22in) s. W/C Indian ink. 24-May-3 Van Ham, Cologne #204/R
£1132 $1743 €1800 River landscape II (36x48cm-14x19in) s.d.1958 W/C board. 26-Oct-2 Dr Lehr, Berlin #123/R est:2400
£1474 $2285 €2300 Boats on beach (48x63cm-19x25in) s. W/C prov. 4-Dec-2 Lempertz, Koln #735/R est:2200

GILLESPIE, George K (1924-1996) British
£650 $1007 €975 Irish cathedral (33x38cm-13x15in) s. board. 2-Oct-2 John Ross, Belfast #280
£750 $1163 €1125 Blarney Castle, Co. Cork (25x30cm-10x12in) s. board. 4-Dec-2 John Ross, Belfast #113
£1000 $1550 €1500 On the coast (20x25cm-8x10in) s. board. 4-Dec-2 John Ross, Belfast #96 est:1000-1200
£1300 $2015 €1950 Feeding chickens, Donegal (20x33cm-8x13in) s. board. 2-Oct-2 John Ross, Belfast #54 est:1000-1200
£1300 $2067 €1950 By the river Lagan (25x30cm-10x12in) s. 5-Mar-3 John Ross, Belfast #237 est:800-1000
£1605 $2279 €2600 Muckish river Co. Donegal (48x76cm-19x30in) s. 14-Mar-2 Woodwards, Cork #196
£1795 $2818 €2800 Homestead (28x41cm-11x16in) s. panel. 19-Nov-2 Whyte's, Dublin #141/R est:3000-4000
£1879 $3026 €2800 Blarney Castle, Co Cork (25x30cm-10x12in) s. s.i.verso board. 18-Feb-3 Whyte's, Dublin #7/R est:1500-2000
£1918 $3011 €2800 On Glendun River, Cushendun, Co. Antrim (46x61cm-18x24in) s. i.verso. 15-Apr-3 De Veres Art Auctions, Dublin #111/R est:3000-4000
£2000 $2920 €3000 In the Killaries, Co. Galway (46x61cm-18x24in) s. 12-Jun-2 John Ross, Belfast #69 est:1600-1800
£2013 $3242 €3000 Stormy clouds, Ballynakill, Connemara (41x51cm-16x20in) s. i.verso. 18-Feb-3 Whyte's, Dublin #147 est:4000-5000
£2148 $3458 €3200 Loch Bawn, Connemara (30x41cm-12x16in) s. 18-Feb-3 Whyte's, Dublin #149/R est:2000-3000
£2192 $3441 €3200 Lake in Donegal (39x50cm-15x20in) s. 15-Apr-3 De Veres Art Auctions, Dublin #223/R est:3000-4000
£2244 $3478 €3500 Trout stream, Inverbeg, Co Connemara (40x50cm-16x20in) s. 3-Dec-2 Bonhams & James Adam, Dublin #82/R est:3000-5000
£2308 $3577 €3600 Cottage in the Mournes (41x51cm-16x20in) s. 3-Dec-2 Bonhams & James Adam, Dublin #122/R est:3000-5000
£2400 $3720 €3600 Donegal landscape (45x61cm-18x24in) s. board. 4-Dec-2 John Ross, Belfast #29 est:1800-2000
£2568 $4005 €3800 Garron Head, Co. Antrim (45x62cm-18x24in) s. 26-Mar-3 James Adam, Dublin #89/R est:3500-5000
£2800 $4340 €4200 Fishing, Co. Donegal (50x61cm-20x24in) s. 4-Dec-2 John Ross, Belfast #127 est:1500-1800
£3000 $4770 €4500 Cattle grazing by the Lagan (61x91cm-24x36in) s. 5-Mar-3 John Ross, Belfast #113 est:2500-3000
£3459 $5396 €5500 Killary, Connemara, County Galway (51x76cm-20x30in) s. i.verso. 17-Sep-2 Whyte's, Dublin #139/R est:6000-7000
£3899 $6083 €6200 River Esk, near Barnsmore, County Donegal (61x91cm-24x36in) s. i.verso. 17-Sep-2 Whyte's, Dublin #15/R est:6000-8000
£4653 $7398 €6700 Mournes and Shimna River, County Down (61x91cm-24x36in) s. board. 29-Apr-3 Whyte's, Dublin #113/R est:7000-9000
£6042 $9606 €8700 Cashla River, Connemara (61x91cm-24x36in) s. 29-Apr-3 Whyte's, Dublin #115/R est:5000-7000
£7692 $12077 €12000 In the Rosses, County Donegal (76x102cm-30x40in) s. 19-Nov-2 Whyte's, Dublin #75/R est:8000-10000
£9615 $15096 €15000 Stream in the Partry Mountains, County Mayo (61x91cm-24x36in) s. i.verso prov. 19-Nov-2 Whyte's, Dublin #81/R est:6000-8000

GILLESPIE, Rowan (1953-) Irish?
Sculpture
£1013 $1570 €1600 Man and woman (18cm-7in) s.d.1981 bronze. 24-Sep-2 De Veres Art Auctions, Dublin #137/R est:1000-1500
£1076 $1668 €1700 Crouching female figure (10cm-4in) s.d.86 bronze. 24-Sep-2 De Veres Art Auctions, Dublin #138 est:1000-1500
£16500 $26400 €24750 Reclining bodyscape (79cm-31in) s.i.d.1996 num.5/9 polished bronze. 15-May-3 Christie's, London #94/R est:3500

GILLET, Edgar (20th C) French
£430 $702 €650 La plage (50x65cm-20x26in) s. 1-Feb-3 Claude Aguttes, Neuilly #120

GILLET, Edward Frank (1874-1927) British
Works on paper
£480 $758 €720 Late (54x36cm-21x14in) W/C. 28-Nov-2 Bonhams, Knightsbridge #111/R

GILLET, Ernest (?) French
£654 $1072 €1000 Nature morte aux crustaces (70x92cm-28x36in) s. 9-Feb-3 Anaf, Lyon #112/R

GILLET, Frank (20th C) British
Works on paper
£450 $716 €675 Lemon, Blue Sleeves, horse jumping a fence (46x45cm-18x18in) W/C. 29-Apr-3 Rowley Fine Art, Newmarket #466

GILLET, Frederic (1814-1884) Swiss
£878 $1370 €1300 Vue de faintaisie de port de mer (22x32cm-9x13in) s. panel. 30-Mar-3 Anaf, Lyon #372/R

GILLET, Numa (1868-?) French
£436 $684 €680 Bretonnes sur le sentier (27x33cm-11x13in) s. 15-Dec-2 Thierry & Lannon, Brest #385

GILLET, Roger Edgar (1924-2003) French
£686 $1090 €1029 Composition (61x46cm-24x18in) s. prov. 26-Feb-3 Kunsthallen, Copenhagen #113/R (D.KR 7500)
£1192 $1943 €1800 Demoiselles (130x195cm-51x77in) s. painted 1971 prov. 3-Feb-3 Cornette de St.Cyr, Paris #427/R
£1208 $1945 €1800 Composition (130x98cm-51x39in) s.d.1958. 23-Feb-3 Mercier & Cie, Lille #110/R
£3311 $5397 €5000 Untitled (200x300cm-79x118in) s.d.1968. 3-Feb-3 Cornette de St.Cyr, Paris #428/R

Works on paper
£304 $480 €480 Brulage (23x33cm-9x13in) s.d.59 mixed media. 27-Nov-2 Blanchet, Paris #136/R

GILLI, Claude (1938-) French
£633 $1000 €1000 Pinceau (66x22cm-26x9in) s. acrylic panel. 2-Dec-2 Tajan, Paris #245
£1122 $1785 €1650 Coulee (43x33cm-17x13in) s. s.d.1967 verso panel. 24-Mar-3 Cornette de St.Cyr, Paris #46
£2778 $4416 €4000 Les Dimanches de Ville-d'Avray (67x130cm-26x51in) s.d.60 oil collage. 29-Apr-3 Artcurial Briest, Paris #366/R est:3800-4500
£3473 $5521 €5000 Flipper (145x114cm-57x45in) s.d.60. 29-Apr-3 Artcurial Briest, Paris #365/R est:4500-5500
Sculpture
£1831 $3039 €2600 Peinture bleue et noire (143cm-56in) s.d.83 polychrome wood. 18-Jun-3 Anaf, Lyon #28/R est:2500-2800
£10417 $16563 €15000 Souvenir ex-voto (120x60x25cm-47x24x10in) painted wood various objects photos lit. 29-Apr-3 Artcurial Briest, Paris #358/R est:3800-12000
Works on paper
£937 $1481 €1350 Sans titre (29x20cm-11x8in) s.d. collage. 27-Apr-3 Perrin, Versailles #81/R est:1000-1200
£952 $1514 €1400 Coeur bleu (27x21cm-11x8in) s.d.1963 collage. 24-Mar-3 Cornette de St.Cyr, Paris #45/R
£5128 $8051 €8000 Nu et bouquet (145x80cm-57x31in) s. s.d.64 verso asemblage. 11-Dec-2 Artcurial Briest, Paris #738/R est:12000
£7394 $12275 €10500 Le trayas (128x192cm-50x76in) s.i.d.XII 64 verso paint cut out panel. 18-Jun-3 Anaf, Lyon #46/R est:3000-4000

GILLIAM, Sam (1933-) American
£764 $1200 €1146 Untitled (25x32cm-10x13in) acrylic prov. 14-Dec-2 Weschler, Washington #737/R est:500-700
Works on paper
£1923 $3000 €2885 Branches (137x122cm-54x48in) s.d.1976 verso mixed media. 22-Sep-2 Susanin's, Chicago #5017/R est:1000-1500

GILLIAND, Vincent (20th C) Swiss
£278 $447 €417 Ferme vigneronne la Boilataz (32x41cm-13x16in) s. 7-May-3 Dobiaschofsky, Bern #3285 (S.FR 600)

GILLIES, Bill (20th C) American
Works on paper
£4969 $8000 €7454 Nancy Drew discovering book in back of clock (36x33cm-14x13in) s. gouache. 10-May-3 Illustration House, New York #131/R est:5000-8000

GILLIES, Sir William George (1898-1973) British
£1500 $2385 €2250 Wooded landscape (46x56cm-18x22in) s. 6-Mar-3 Christie's, Kensington #219/R est:2000-3000
£1800 $2754 €2700 Evening sky, East Lothian (21x24cm-8x9in) s.d.1922. 22-Aug-2 Bonhams, Edinburgh #1125/R est:1200-1800
£1900 $2907 €2850 Still life of vase, shell and feather (34x48cm-13x19in) s. board. 22-Aug-2 Bonhams, Edinburgh #964/R est:2500-3000
£3000 $4650 €4500 Still life (51x61cm-20x24in) s. 31-Oct-2 Christie's, London #126/R est:5000-8000
£4200 $6426 €6300 Still life of jug and fruit (40x49cm-16x19in) s. 22-Aug-2 Bonhams, Edinburgh #1167/R est:4000-6000
£4200 $6678 €6300 Border farmhouse (40x51cm-16x20in) s. 6-Mar-3 Christie's, Kensington #218/R est:3000-5000
£5200 $7956 €7800 Bridge and cottages (46x75cm-18x30in) s. 22-Aug-2 Bonhams, Edinburgh #975/R est:4000-6000
£6000 $9300 €9000 Still life, study in grey (82x99cm-32x39in) s. board prov.exhib.lit. 31-Oct-2 Christie's, London #126a est:6000-10000
£12000 $18720 €18000 Still life with Salamon's seal (50x74cm-20x29in) s. exhib. 14-Apr-3 Sotheby's, London #91/R est:12000-18000
Works on paper
£400 $664 €580 Carrington (26x36cm-10x14in) s. pencil. 13-Jun-3 Lyon & Turnbull, Edinburgh #93
£620 $967 €930 Above Portmore (11x18cm-4x7in) s.i.verso pencil sold with another similar. 17-Oct-2 Bonhams, Edinburgh #97
£650 $1014 €975 Near Pathhead (29x45cm-11x18in) s. pen ink. 10-Apr-3 Bonhams, Edinburgh #14/R
£700 $1092 €1050 Fearnon, Loch Tay (24x30cm-9x12in) s. pen ink. 10-Apr-3 Bonhams, Edinburgh #17/R
£880 $1373 €1320 Torquhan (25x35cm-10x14in) s. pencil. 17-Oct-2 Bonhams, Edinburgh #82
£1000 $1590 €1500 Artist's cottage at Temple (30x38cm-12x15in) s. pen ink. 6-Mar-3 Christie's, Kensington #222/R est:1000-1500
£1100 $1749 €1650 Temple village (25x35cm-10x14in) s. pen ink. 6-Mar-3 Christie's, Kensington #221/R est:700-1000
£1350 $2106 €2025 Plenploth, near Fountainhall (25x35cm-10x14in) s.d.1956 pencil laid down. 17-Oct-2 Bonhams, Edinburgh #87 est:400-600
£1400 $2226 €2100 Border town (25x35cm-10x14in) s. pen ink W/C. 6-Mar-3 Christie's, Kensington #220/R est:1000-1500
£1500 $2325 €2250 Lyne (15x35cm-6x14in) s.d.58 W/C dr. 5-Oct-2 Shapes, Edinburgh #251 est:600-800
£2000 $3060 €3000 Evening landscape (34x42cm-13x17in) s.d.1938 W/C. 22-Aug-2 Bonhams, Edinburgh #1054/R est:2000-3000
£2400 $3720 €3600 Between Temple and Carrington. Sunset (34x49cm-13x19in) s. one W/C brush ink one W/C bodycol pair prov.exhib. 31-Oct-2 Christie's, London #158/R est:2000-3000
£2500 $3875 €3750 Welsh farmhouse (48x64cm-19x25in) pen ink W/C. 6-Dec-2 Lyon & Turnbull, Edinburgh #59/R est:2000-3000
£2600 $4030 €3900 West Highland loch (25x36cm-10x14in) s. W/C pen ink. 5-Oct-2 Shapes, Edinburgh #373 est:2000-3000
£3200 $4960 €4800 Garden, Temple under snow (35x84cm-14x33in) s. pen ink grisaille exhib. 6-Dec-2 Lyon & Turnbull, Edinburgh #66/R est:3000-5000
£4400 $6732 €6600 Landscape in fire (55x71cm-22x28in) s. i.verso W/C over pencil. 22-Aug-2 Bonhams, Edinburgh #969/R est:2500-3500
£6000 $9720 €9000 Balquhidder (55x76cm-22x30in) s. pen ink grisaille. 23-May-3 Lyon & Turnbull, Edinburgh #85/R est:2000-3000
£6200 $10044 €9300 Letterfearn (33x65cm-13x26in) s. pen ink W/C. 23-May-3 Lyon & Turnbull, Edinburgh #81/R est:4000-6000
£7500 $12150 €11250 From the cottage window, temple (70x100cm-28x39in) s. pencil W/C. 23-May-3 Lyon & Turnbull, Edinburgh #61/R est:3000-5000

GILLIG, Jacob (1636-1701) Dutch
£2870 $4650 €4162 Still life of fish (40x50cm-16x20in) s.d.1666. 26-May-3 Bukowskis, Stockholm #398/R est:40000-50000 (S.KR 37000)
£8000 $12560 €12000 Pike and carp with nets beside a barrel on a brick wall (39x32cm-15x13in) s.d.1686 panel prov. 10-Dec-2 Bonhams, New Bond Street #279/R est:6000-8000

GILLOT, Claude (1673-1722) French
Works on paper
£8000 $13360 €11600 Les quatre ages de la vie - Seven figures in a garden, one digging with a spade (15x20cm-6x8in) pen ink prov.lit. 8-Jul-3 Christie's, London #67/R est:3000-5000

GILLOT, Eugène Louis (1868-1925) French
£255 $403 €383 Soldier in blue uniform from World War I (59x49cm-23x19in) s.d.1916. 2-Dec-2 Rasmussen, Copenhagen #1785/R (D.KR 3000)
£443 $700 €700 La Seine a Paris (33x41cm-13x16in) s.i. 1-Dec-2 Peron, Melun #69
£3574 $5648 €5361 Pavillon de Flora, Tuileries, Seine, Paris (66x54cm-26x21in) s. 2-Dec-2 Rasmussen, Copenhagen #1194/R est:40000-50000 (D.KR 42000)

GILLOUAYE, Andre (?) French
£338 $537 €490 Le port de Sauzon a Belle Ile (54x73cm-21x29in) s. 10-Mar-3 Thierry & Lannon, Brest #164

GILLRAY, James (1757-1815) British
Prints
£2600 $4030 €3900 John Bull taking a luncheon (26x36cm-10x14in) hand col etching. 4-Dec-2 Bonhams, New Bond Street #108/R est:1000-1500
£10000 $15500 €15000 Caricatures (34x47cm-13x19in) etching album. 5-Dec-2 Sotheby's, London #78/R est:5000-7000

GILMAN, Harold (1876-1919) British
£21000 $32550 €31500 Horse hair chaise longue (35x29cm-14x11in) init. board prov.exhib. 4-Dec-2 Sotheby's, London #52/R est:12000-18000
£55000 $90200 €82500 In the nursery, Snargate Rectory (53x43cm-21x17in) s. painted c.1908 prov.exhib. 6-Jun-3 Christie's, London #14/R est:60000-80000
£165000 $270600 €247500 Nude standing by a bed (36x25cm-14x10in) init. painted c.1916 prov. 6-Jun-3 Christie's, London #13/R est:30000-50000
£240000 $372000 €360000 Tea in the bedsitter (63x76cm-25x30in) prov. 4-Dec-2 Sotheby's, London #20/R est:35000-45000
Works on paper
£900 $1423 €1350 Landscape in Norway (28x44cm-11x17in) s. pen black ink W/C pencil prov.exhib. 27-Nov-2 Sotheby's, Olympia #31/R est:1000-1500

GILPIN, Rev William (1724-1804) British
Works on paper
£260 $406 €390 View of the Wye valley (14x21cm-6x8in) W/C. 26-Mar-3 Woolley & Wallis, Salisbury #70/R

£300 $465 €450 Castle and cattle in a picturesque landscape (15x24cm-6x9in) st.init. pen ink sepia wash. 2-Oct-2 George Kidner, Lymington #108/R
£320 $496 €480 River scene with temple and bridge (14x23cm-6x9in) st.init. pen ink sepia wash. 2-Oct-2 George Kidner, Lymington #109/R

GILPIN, Sawrey (1733-1807) British
Works on paper
£275 $446 €413 Ewe and her lambs (10x13cm-4x5in) init. W/C. 21-May-3 Bonhams, Knightsbridge #89/R

GILPIN, Sawrey (circle) (1733-1807) British
£6500 $10271 €9750 Dog resting in a landscape (89x115cm-35x45in) 28-Nov-2 Sotheby's, London #201/R est:5000-8000

GILROY, John William (1868-1944) British
£700 $1120 €1050 Primrose day (75x60cm-30x24in) s.d.1903 s.i.verso. 7-Jan-3 Bonhams, Knightsbridge #189/R
£2900 $4843 €4205 Apprentice (32x39cm-13x15in) s. panel. 17-Jun-3 Anderson & Garland, Newcastle #447/R est:1000-1800

GILSE, Marie Slager van (1891-1968) Belgian
£347 $573 €500 Cows by a forest pond (38x51cm-15x20in) s. 1-Jul-3 Christie's, Amsterdam #162

GILSI, Fritz (1878-1961) Swiss
£258 $407 €387 Lady sitting in a garden sewing (54x38cm-21x15in) s. 26-Nov-2 Hans Widmer, St Gallen #1124 (S.FR 600)
£773 $1221 €1160 Children's festival in St Galler (41x33cm-16x13in) s.d.04 board. 26-Nov-2 Hans Widmer, St Gallen #1122/R est:900-1800 (S.FR 1800)

GILSOUL, Victor (1867-1939) Belgian
£504 $806 €700 Paysage avec moulins a vent (27x37cm-11x15in) s. 13-May-3 Galerie Moderne, Brussels #323
£556 $883 €800 Chaumiere au bord de l'eau (25x38cm-10x15in) s. 29-Apr-3 Campo, Vlaamse Kaai #131
£566 $877 €900 Ecluse de Coloma sur la Weert en face de Tamise (31x27cm-12x11in) s. panel. 1-Oct-2 Palais de Beaux Arts, Brussels #473
£955 $1490 €1500 Vieux pont de Dordrecht (13x16cm-5x6in) s. panel. 10-Nov-2 Eric Pillon, Calais #85/R
£1655 $2648 €2400 On the edge of the village (73x100cm-29x39in) s. 15-Mar-3 De Vuyst, Lokeren #132/R est:2000-3000
£2390 $3704 €3800 Mechelen quay (55x71cm-22x28in) s. 5-Oct-2 De Vuyst, Lokeren #544/R est:3500-4500

GILSOUL-HOPPE, Ketty (1868-1939) Belgian
Works on paper
£360 $576 €500 Le pecheur (30x39cm-12x15in) s. W/C. 13-May-3 Vanderkindere, Brussels #169
£621 $1000 €950 Les nenuphars en fleurs (43x76cm-17x30in) s. W/C. 20-Jan-3 Horta, Bruxelles #45

GILST, Aanout van (1898-1981) Dutch
£268 $415 €402 Warm glow on a winter's night (61x51cm-24x20in) s. 3-Dec-2 Ritchie, Toronto #3065/R (C.D 650)

GIMENO Y ARASA, Francisco (1858-1927) Spanish
£4000 $6280 €6000 Paisaje con ovejas - landscape with sheep (45x61cm-18x24in) s.d.85 prov. 19-Nov-2 Sotheby's, London #45/R est:5000-7000
£6000 $9420 €9000 Recojiendo madera - gathering wood (46x55cm-18x22in) s.i.d.87 prov. 19-Nov-2 Sotheby's, London #44/R est:6000-8000
£12000 $18840 €18000 Camino forestal - forest path (28x46cm-11x18in) s. prov. 19-Nov-2 Sotheby's, London #46/R est:12000-18000
£30449 $47804 €47500 Boy in highchair (35x39cm-14x15in) prov.lit. 16-Dec-2 Castellana, Madrid #460/R est:18000
Works on paper
£483 $768 €700 Shelter (30x21cm-12x8in) s. wash pencil. 4-Mar-3 Ansorena, Madrid #662/R

GIMENO, Andres (1879-1927) Spanish
£578 $919 €850 Bullfight (14x18cm-6x7in) s. panel. 24-Mar-3 Fraysse & Associes, Paris #48/R

GIMIGNANI, Giacinto (1611-1681) Italian
£8966 $14166 €13000 Bacchanal (88x116cm-35x46in) 5-Apr-3 Finarte Semenzato, Milan #121/R est:15000
Works on paper
£1418 $2369 €2000 Le matyre de Saint Erasme (20x13cm-8x5in) pen brown ink brown wash prov. 19-Jun-3 Piasa, Paris #3/R est:2000

GIMIGNANI, Giacinto (attrib) (1611-1681) Italian
£18919 $29514 €28000 Two men playing with ball - or two men fighting (72x60cm-28x24in) prov. 27-Mar-3 Dorotheum, Vienna #11/R est:4000-7000

GIMMI, Wilhelm (1886-1965) Swiss
£610 $1001 €885 Nu assis peignoir (32x22cm-13x9in) s. board lit. 4-Jun-3 Fischer, Luzern #2110/R (S.FR 1300)
£1090 $1656 €1700 Still life with flowers, fruit and books (32x41cm-13x16in) mono.d.49 board. 11-Jul-2 Allgauer, Kempten #2494/R
£1132 $1811 €1698 Nue assis sur fond bleu (34x28cm-13x11in) s. lit. 17-Mar-3 Philippe Schuler, Zurich #4524/R est:2000-2500 (S.FR 2400)
£1222 $2040 €1772 Bather (37x45cm-15x18in) s. 24-Jun-3 Koller, Zurich #76 est:2700-3500 (S.FR 2700)
£1233 $1801 €1850 Femme de dos, epaules decouvertes (46x38cm-18x15in) s.d.1926. 17-Jun-2 Philippe Schuler, Zurich #4271/R est:4000-5000 (S.FR 2800)
£1310 $2044 €1965 Female nude kneeling on the bed (46x38cm-18x15in) s.d.63. 8-Nov-2 Dobiaschofsky, Bern #120/R est:4600 (S.FR 3000)
£1810 $3023 €2625 Cirque Medrano (33x41cm-13x16in) s. prov. 24-Jun-3 Koller, Zurich #55/R est:4000-7000 (S.FR 4000)
£2146 $3391 €3219 Still life with peaches (46x55cm-18x22in) s. 28-Nov-2 Christie's, Zurich #62/R est:3000-5000 (S.FR 5000)
£2174 $3370 €3261 Jardin a Aix en Provence (54x65cm-21x26in) s.d.1925 lit. 4-Dec-2 Koller, Zurich #148/R est:6000-9000 (S.FR 5000)
£2420 $3776 €3800 Femme se coiffant (46x38cm-18x15in) s. 7-Nov-2 Claude Aguttes, Neuilly #47/R est:4000-5000
£2830 $4585 €5010 Modele assis (46x38cm-18x15in) s. lit. 26-May-3 Sotheby's, Zurich #117/R est:6000-8000 (S.FR 6000)
£2830 $4585 €5010 Nu de dos (46x38cm-18x15in) s. 26-May-3 Sotheby's, Zurich #136/R est:7000-9000 (S.FR 6000)
£3493 $5485 €5240 Les oliviers pres de Villeneuve les Avignon (33x41cm-13x16in) s. panel prov.lit. 25-Nov-2 Sotheby's, Zurich #76/R est:8000-12000 (S.FR 8000)
£3991 $6545 €5787 Arlequin assis, un genou replie (65x54cm-26x21in) s. lit.prov. 4-Jun-3 Fischer, Luzern #1238/R est:6000-7500 (S.FR 8500)
Works on paper
£306 $487 €450 Nus au bain (23x22cm-9x9in) s. graphite ink wash. 24-Mar-3 Claude Boisgirard, Paris #53
£370 $577 €555 Woman sewing in park (18x12cm-7x5in) s. W/C pencil. 16-Sep-2 Philippe Schuler, Zurich #3199 (S.FR 850)
£957 $1484 €1436 Village in southern France (27x36cm-11x14in) s.d.1929 W/C paper on board. 4-Dec-2 Koller, Zurich #143/R est:800-1200 (S.FR 2200)

GIMOND, Marcel (1891-1961) French
Sculpture
£6383 $10340 €9000 Tete de femme (51cm-20in) num.3/8 pat bronze cire perdue Biscoglia height with base. 26-May-3 Joron-Derem, Paris #138/R est:4000-6000

GINAIN, Louis Eugène (1818-1886) French
£1148 $1860 €1665 Cavaliers Arabes acceptant du lait dans le Desert (70x55cm-28x22in) study. 26-May-3 Rasmussen, Copenhagen #1324/R est:12000-15000 (D.KR 12000)

GINDERTAEL, Roger van (1899-1982) Belgian
£411 $642 €650 Vase fleuri (46x38cm-18x15in) s. 15-Oct-2 Horta, Bruxelles #396
£1027 $1603 €1500 Composition a la table dressee (64x49cm-25x19in) paper sold with a photo. 14-Apr-3 Horta, Bruxelles #52 est:1800-2200
Works on paper
£377 $588 €550 La tricoteuse (33x25cm-13x10in) mono. chl dr sold with a catalogue. 14-Apr-3 Horta, Bruxelles #53

GINE, Alexander Vasilievitsch (1830-1880) Russian
£17405 $27500 €26108 Woodland lake by moonlight (59x74cm-23x29in) s.d.1877. 24-Apr-3 Sotheby's, New York #111/R est:35000-45000
£28000 $43960 €42000 Coastal view with ship (62x98cm-24x39in) s.d.1861. 20-Nov-2 Sotheby's, London #40/R est:25000-30000

GINER BUENO, Luis (1935-) Spanish
£329 $533 €500 Beach (28x18cm-11x7in) s. board. 21-Jan-3 Durán, Madrid #653/R
£329 $533 €500 Fishermen (28x18cm-11x7in) s. board. 21-Jan-3 Durán, Madrid #652/R
£625 $1013 €950 Fisherme o the beach (46x65cm-18x26in) s. 21-Jan-3 Durán, Madrid #606/R

GINKEL, Paul van (20th C) Canadian
£482 $757 €723 Red storm (60x45cm-24x18in) s.i.d.1992. 25-Nov-2 Hodgins, Calgary #124/R (C.D 1200)

GINNEKEN, Matthieu van (1811-1888) Dutch
£1064 $1723 €1500 Coq, poulets et poussins sur la basse-cour (38x47cm-15x19in) panel. 26-May-3 Amberes, Antwerp #90

GINNER, Charles (1878-1952) British
Works on paper
£850 $1369 €1275 Study for spring day at Boscastle (43x29cm-17x11in) pencil sold with two others by the same hand. 14-Jan-3 Bonhams, Knightsbridge #23/R
£2900 $4727 €4205 On the Avon near Bath (39x28cm-15x11in) s.i.d.1926 pen ink W/C. 21-Jul-3 Bonhams, Bath #29/R est:2000-3000

GINNETT, Louis (1875-1946) British
£1111 $1844 €1611 Love (63x52cm-25x20in) s.d.1900 i.verso. 16-Jun-3 Waddingtons, Toronto #126/R est:1500-2000 (C.D 2500)

GINOVART, Josep (?) Mexican
Works on paper
£504 $786 €756 Sin titulo (65x95cm-26x37in) s. mixed media masonite prov. 17-Oct-2 Louis Morton, Mexico #165 est:10000-12000 (M.P 8000)
£504 $786 €756 Sin titulo (26x21cm-10x8in) s. mixed media masonite prov. 17-Oct-2 Louis Morton, Mexico #172 est:10000-12000 (M.P 8000)

GINOVSZKY, Joseph (1800-1857) Austrian
£2270 $3678 €3292 Gentlemen Company. s.d.1838. 24-May-3 Dorotheum, Prague #38/R est:100000-150000 (C.KR 100000)

GINSBORG, Michael (1956-) Austrian
£380 $619 €570 Poisons (184x100cm-72x39in) s.i.d.1979 verso acrylic canvas on board shaped. 3-Feb-3 Sotheby's, Olympia #144/R

GINSBURG, Yankel (20th C) American
Works on paper
£1154 $1800 €1731 Still life of fruit (61x47cm-24x19in) s.d.LXXI mixed media. 14-Sep-2 Weschler, Washington #645/R est:500-1000

GINSIG, Markus (1909-) Swiss
£365 $576 €548 In the rose garden (36x48cm-14x19in) s.i.verso. 29-Nov-2 Zofingen, Switzerland #2892 (S.FR 850)

GIOBEL, Elsa (19/20th C) Swedish?
£656 $1090 €951 Dusk (37x24cm-15x9in) s.d.07. 16-Jun-3 Lilla Bukowskis, Stockholm #158 (S.KR 8500)
£741 $1231 €1074 Spring evening (55x45cm-22x18in) s.d.1905. 16-Jun-3 Lilla Bukowskis, Stockholm #157 (S.KR 9600)

GIOJA, Belisario (1829-1906) Italian
Works on paper
£380 $600 €600 Peasant with donkey (36x26cm-14x10in) s. W/C card. 26-Nov-2 Christie's, Rome #33

GIOJA, Theresia von (19th C) Austrian
£411 $641 €600 After the duel (95x114cm-37x45in) i. verso. 10-Apr-3 Dorotheum, Vienna #38/R est:1200-1600

GIOLDASIS, Dimitrios (1897-?) Greek
£6800 $10744 €10200 Pafsilipo park in Karditsa, under snow (66x91cm-26x36in) 1-Apr-3 Bonhams, New Bond Street #28 est:6000-8000

GIOLI, Francesco (1849-1922) Italian
£943 $1453 €1500 Wood (12x18cm-5x7in) s. board. 23-Oct-2 Finarte, Milan #141/R
£4638 $7606 €6400 Conversazione in giardino (39x30cm-15x12in) s.d.92 board. 27-May-3 Finarte, Milan #47/R est:5000-6000
Works on paper
£321 $497 €500 Nymph (25x7cm-10x3in) s. mixed media. 4-Dec-2 Finarte, Rome #736

GIOLI, Luigi (1854-1947) Italian
£2215 $3500 €3500 Wood in Fauglia (34x53cm-13x21in) s.d.92 prov. 26-Nov-2 Christie's, Rome #184/R
£3871 $6116 €6000 Landscape with figures (38x46cm-15x18in) s. 18-Dec-2 Finarte, Milan #22/R est:7000
£4000 $6360 €6000 View of the Theseum with the acropolis beyond, Athens (40x60cm-16x24in) s. 29-Apr-3 Bonhams, New Bond Street #129/R est:4000-6000
£6918 $10654 €11000 Tuscan cow-boy (44x64cm-17x25in) s. 23-Oct-2 Finarte, Milan #66/R est:12000-13000

GIONFRA, Ortensio (1918-) Italian
£833 $1317 €1300 Vase of flowers (60x80cm-24x31in) s. 15-Nov-2 Farsetti, Prato #82/R

GIONIMA, Antonio (1697-1732) Italian
Works on paper
£1800 $2826 €2700 Triumph of David. Male study (21x30cm-8x12in) i. pen ink double-sided prov.lit. 11-Dec-2 Sotheby's, Olympia #133/R est:1500-2000

GIORDA, Patrice (1952-) French
£764 $1215 €1100 Etude no 1 pour la reparation des bancs (90x80cm-35x31in) s.i.d.verso acrylic prov. 29-Apr-3 Artcurial Briest, Paris #608
£1944 $3091 €2800 Le voyage no 10, la passerelle (130x195cm-51x77in) s. i.d.verso acrylic prov. 29-Apr-3 Artcurial Briest, Paris #607/R est:2000-2500
£3773 $5849 €6000 La grande institution (145x210cm-57x83in) s.verso. 4-Oct-2 Tajan, Paris #110 est:2500-3000

GIORDANI, Giovanni (1884-1969) Italian
Works on paper
£248 $402 €350 Ritratto d'uomo (63x49cm-25x19in) s. W/C. 22-May-3 Stadion, Trieste #299

GIORDANO (?) Italian
£5806 $9000 €8709 Grapes (72x67cm-28x26in) s.d.1868 prov. 29-Oct-2 Sotheby's, New York #20/R est:15000-20000

GIORDANO DI PALMA, Léon Jean (1886-?) French
£935 $1534 €1300 Souq anime (26x35cm-10x14in) s. panel. 4-Jun-3 Tajan, Paris #268 est:1000-1200
£4317 $7079 €6000 Animation a l'entree du souq (65x81cm-26x32in) s. 4-Jun-3 Tajan, Paris #267/R est:7000-8000

GIORDANO, Felice (1880-1964) Italian
£544 $865 €800 Street with cart and horses (24x19cm-9x7in) s. board. 18-Mar-3 Finarte, Milan #44/R
£692 $1065 €1100 Street in Sorrento (23x29cm-9x11in) s. board. 23-Oct-2 Finarte, Milan #185/R
£774 $1223 €1200 Festive day in Naples (24x18cm-9x7in) s. board. 18-Dec-2 Finarte, Milan #161/R
£870 $1426 €1200 Paesaggio con ruscello e figure (19x23cm-7x9in) s. panel. 27-May-3 Finarte, Milan #29/R est:1200-1400
£950 $1501 €1425 Harbour town, Capri (56x74cm-22x29in) s. 14-Nov-2 Christie's, Kensington #106/R
£968 $1529 €1500 WInter landscape (34x43cm-13x17in) s. board. 18-Dec-2 Finarte, Milan #31
£976 $1600 €1415 Sunset over fishing boats (36x51cm-14x20in) bears sig. 4-Jun-3 Doyle, New York #60 est:800-1200
£1773 $2748 €2660 Still life of fish (92x126cm-36x50in) s. 4-Dec-2 AB Stockholms Auktionsverk #1870/R est:22000-25000 (S.KR 25000)
£1950 $3003 €3100 Toledo Street, Naples (43x60cm-17x24in) s. 23-Oct-2 Finarte, Milan #19/R
£2041 $3245 €3000 Exit from San Carlo's Theatre, Naples (40x50cm-16x20in) s. 18-Mar-3 Finarte, Milan #85/R
£4058 $6655 €5600 Terrazza di Capri (48x58cm-19x23in) s.d.1938. 27-May-3 Finarte, Milan #30/R est:2000-2500
£4430 $7000 €7000 Capri at night (69x49cm-27x19in) s. 26-Nov-2 Christie's, Rome #165/R est:9000

GIORDANO, Luca (1632-1705) Italian
£21951 $36000 €32927 Rest on the flight into Egypt (146x189cm-57x74in) s. painted with studio prov. 29-May-3 Sotheby's, New York #87/R est:40000-60000
£42683 $70000 €64025 Destruction of Jerusalem (201x178cm-79x70in) prov. 29-May-3 Sotheby's, New York #86/R est:40000-60000
£80000 $125600 €120000 Madonna and Child with sould in Purgatory (207x155cm-81x61in) bears sig. prov.lit. 11-Dec-2 Christie's, London #99/R est:40000-60000
£97484 $150126 €155000 Centauruses fighting (216x256cm-85x101in) lit. 23-Oct-2 Finarte, Rome #532/R est:120000-130000

GIORDANO, Luca (attrib) (1632-1705) Italian
£20833 $32917 €30000 Man (61x49cm-24x19in) 23-Apr-3 Rabourdin & Choppin de Janvry, Paris #68/R est:12000

GIORDANO, Luca (circle) (1632-1705) Italian
£10000 $16700 €14500 Astronomer resting his hands upon a celestial globe (101x74cm-40x29in) 9-Jul-3 Bonhams, New Bond Street #65/R est:2000-3000

GIORDANO, Luca (style) (1632-1705) Italian
£5962 $9301 €9480 Biblical scene (120x180cm-47x71in) 22-Sep-2 Semenzato, Venice #277/R est:8000-11000

GIORGETTI, Angelo (1899-1952) Swiss
£644 $1017 €966 Still life with apples, grapes and nuts on a white cloth (52x63cm-20x25in) s. 29-Nov-2 Zofingen, Switzerland #2893/R est:1200 (S.FR 1500)
£1135 $1771 €1703 Mountain lake in summer (65x80cm-26x31in) s.d.1942. 6-Nov-2 Dobiaschofsky, Bern #590/R est:3000 (S.FR 2600)

GIORGIONE (style) (1477-1510) Italian
£16667 $25833 €25001 The child Jupiter suckling the goat Althea (42x82cm-17x32in) 3-Dec-2 Bukowskis, Stockholm #430/R est:60000-80000 (S.KR 235000)

GIOTTO, Ambrogio Bondone (style) (1266-1336) Italian
£40000 $66800 €58000 Crucifixon with the Magdalene at the foot of the cross, Saint Peter and Saint Catherine (70x69cm-28x27in) gold ground panel portable triptych prov. 9-Jul-3 Christie's, London #76/R est:50000-70000

GIOVAGNOLI, Luca (1963-) Italian
Works on paper
£556 $889 €850 I could have taken you (60x60cm-24x24in) s. s.i.d.2001 mixed media collage on canvas. 4-Jan-3 Meeting Art, Vercelli #580

GIOVANI, Marco (1964-) Italian
Works on paper
£1418 $2298 €2000 Untitled (200x105cm-79x41in) s.d.2002 verso grafitti. 20-May-3 Porro, Milan #25/R est:3000-3200

GIOVANNI DA BOLOGNA (after) (14th C) Italian
Sculpture
£24825 $40217 €35996 Woman bathing (46cm-18in) pat.bronze incl.marble socle. 26-May-3 Bukowskis, Stockholm #981/R est:60000-70000 (S.KR 320000)

GIOVANNI D'ALEMAGNA (?-1450) Italian
£132911 $210000 €210000 Madonna of Humility (31x27cm-12x11in) tempera gold board prov. 29-Nov-2 Semenzato, Venice #405/R est:280000-310000

GIOVANNI DI ILARIO DA PARMA (15th C) Italian
£13121 $21255 €18500 Saint Agapius and the Martyrs (158x154cm-62x61in) i.d. 1496 tempera. 20-May-3 Babuino, Rome #1/R est:10000-12000

GIOVANNI, M (19/20th C) American
£2327 $3700 €3491 Rolling hills (81x102cm-32x40in) s. painted c.1933. 7-Mar-3 Jackson's, Cedar Falls #744/R est:200-300

GIOVANOPOULOS, Paul (20th C) American
£299 $475 €449 Black child peering from under American flag (51x76cm-20x30in) s. panel. 1-Mar-3 Thomaston Place, Thomaston #132

GIRALDEZ Y PENALVER, Adolfo (c.1840-1920) Spanish
£545 $850 €818 Puerto de Alicante (30x18cm-12x7in) s.i. painted c.1880 panel. 9-Oct-2 Doyle, New York #42
£1351 $2108 €2000 Caiz harbour (60x100cm-24x39in) s. 25-Mar-3 Durán, Madrid #106/R

GIRAN-MAX, Léon (1867-1927) French
£324 $518 €450 Un poupon (15x17cm-6x7in) s.i.d.1897 cardboard. 15-May-3 Christie's, Paris #124/R
£1384 $2145 €2200 Petit garcon sur la rive (73x60cm-29x24in) s. 4-Oct-2 Tajan, Paris #111 est:1500-1800
£3019 $4709 €4800 Les coquelicots (81x100cm-32x39in) s.d.1908. 9-Oct-2 Lombrail & Teucquam, Paris #4/R
£6452 $10194 €10000 Voilier a la sortie du port de Marseille (94x104cm-37x41in) s. painted 1919. 19-Dec-2 Claude Aguttes, Neuilly #219/R est:7000

GIRARD, Georges (1917-) French
£568 $886 €852 La table provencale (54x65cm-21x26in) s. i.d.1959 verso. 6-Nov-2 Dobiaschofsky, Bern #591/R (S.FR 1300)

GIRARD, Karine Firmin (1965-) French
£252 $392 €400 Beach (20x27cm-8x11in) s. 8-Oct-2 Ansorena, Madrid #404/R
£377 $589 €600 Playing on the beach (25x35cm-10x14in) s. 8-Oct-2 Ansorena, Madrid #423/R
£685 $1068 €1000 Dimanche au Bois-de-Boulogne (45x53cm-18x21in) s. 14-Apr-3 Glerum, Amsterdam #92/R
£719 $1151 €1000 Scene de rue a Paris (46x55cm-18x22in) s. 13-May-3 Palais de Beaux Arts, Brussels #342
£755 $1162 €1200 Beach scene (60x81cm-24x32in) s. 22-Oct-2 Durán, Madrid #683/R
£1027 $1603 €1500 Au Grand Boulevard (44x54cm-17x21in) s. 14-Apr-3 Glerum, Amsterdam #94/R est:1800-2200
£1438 $2315 €2200 Le Moulin Rouge anime (46x55cm-18x22in) s. 14-Jan-3 Vanderkindere, Brussels #166 est:2500-3500

GIRARD, Marie Firmin (1838-1921) French
£1341 $2200 €1944 Parisian street scene (25x30cm-10x12in) s. oil over pen, canvas on board. 4-Jun-3 Doyle, New York #50 est:4000-6000

GIRARD, Patrice (20th C) French?
Works on paper
£801 $1258 €1250 Transparences (82x82cm-32x32in) s.i.d. mixed media collage panel. 15-Dec-2 Perrin, Versailles #161/R

GIRARD, Raymond (1942-) Canadian
£261 $407 €435 Chateau richer (30x41cm-12x16in) s. s.i.verso board. 13-Apr-3 Levis, Calgary #448/R (C.D 600)

GIRARDET, Edouard-Henri (1819-1880) Swiss
Works on paper
£550 $853 €825 Interior with woman sewing (18x23cm-7x9in) s.d.1877 W/C dr. 1-Oct-2 Capes Dunn, Manchester #818/R

GIRARDET, Edouard-Henri (attrib) (1819-1880) Swiss
£463 $745 €695 In conversation on the mountain pasture (19x27cm-7x11in) 7-May-3 Dobiaschofsky, Bern #594/R (S.FR 1000)

GIRARDET, Eugène Alexis (1853-1907) French
£833 $1358 €1200 La Mer Morte vue du Mont des Oliviers (27x41cm-11x16in) s.d.1899 cardboard. 19-Jul-3 Thierry & Lannon, Brest #338
£1042 $1698 €1500 Le Trez-Hir (26x41cm-10x16in) panel. 19-Jul-3 Thierry & Lannon, Brest #130 est:1200-1500
£2264 $3600 €3396 Desert caravan encampment by moonlight (25x41cm-10x16in) s. panel. 22-Mar-3 New Orleans Auction, New Orleans #412/R est:4000-7000
£2770 $4322 €4100 L'anier, Biskara, Sidi Sersour (27x41cm-11x16in) s.i.d.9 Dbre 1895 panel. 31-Mar-3 Rossini, Paris #31/R
£5128 $8051 €8000 Campement (32x54cm-13x21in) s. 10-Dec-2 Renaud, Paris #8/R est:9000
£5806 $9000 €8709 Leaving the market (68x109cm-27x43in) s. 30-Oct-2 Christie's, Rockefeller NY #99/R est:12000-16000
Works on paper
£576 $944 €800 Portail de maison a Constantine (22x14cm-9x6in) s.i.d.1881 W/C. 4-Jun-3 Tajan, Paris #179

GIRARDET, Jules (1856-1946) French/Swiss
£466 $740 €699 La roseraie de Bagatelle (38x52cm-15x20in) s. 5-Mar-3 Rasmussen, Copenhagen #1841/R (D.KR 5000)

GIRARDET, Karl (1813-1871) Swiss
£696 $1078 €1044 Lively river delta (21x37cm-8x15in) mono. paper on board. 9-Dec-2 Philippe Schuler, Zurich #3815/R (S.FR 1600)
£2619 $4164 €3850 Chateau-Thierry, enfants au bord de la riviere (17x36cm-7x14in) mono. panel. 26-Feb-3 Artcurial Briest, Paris #115/R est:3000-5000
£2778 $4472 €4028 Landscape with herd of goats (17x25cm-7x10in) s. 9-May-3 Dobiaschofsky, Bern #14/R est:5500 (S.FR 6000)
£6604 $10698 €11688 Washerwomen at water's edge (30x51cm-12x20in) s.s. 26-May-3 Sotheby's, Zurich #17/R est:6000-8000 (S.FR 14000)

GIRARDET, Léon (1857-1895) French
Works on paper
£314 $515 €480 Portrait au jardin (38x47cm-15x19in) s. W/C. 7-Feb-3 Oger, Dumont, Paris #19/R
£442 $703 €650 La presentation au grand perre (45x28cm-18x11in) s. i. verso W/C. 19-Mar-3 Neumeister, Munich #357/R
£900 $1404 €1350 Begging (43x53cm-17x21in) s. W/C. 26-Mar-3 Sotheby's, Olympia #251/R

GIRARDET, Leopold Henri (1848-1904) Swiss
£742 $1158 €1113 Young washerwoman at spring (22x18cm-9x7in) s. board. 6-Nov-2 Dobiaschofsky, Bern #592/R (S.FR 1700)

GIRARDET, Paul Armand (1859-?) French
£1056 $1701 €1500 Chaumiere en bord d'etang (51x91cm-20x36in) s.d.1914. 12-May-3 Lesieur & Le Bars, Le Havre #42/R

GIRARDIN, Nicole (1933-) French
£1950 $3022 €3100 Bouquet rose et blanc (27x27cm-11x11in) s. 30-Oct-2 Coutau Begarie, Paris #142/R

GIRARDOT (?) ?
£1106 $1748 €1659 River landscape with boats and industrial buildings (12x20cm-5x8in) s.d.1881. 2-Dec-2 Rasmussen, Copenhagen #1496/R est:15000 (D.KR 13000)

GIRARDOT, Ernest Gustave (fl.1860-1893) British
£1700 $2771 €2465 Rural Felicity (36x30cm-14x12in) s.d.1869 s.i.verso. 16-Jul-3 Sotheby's, Olympia #203/R est:1000-1500

GIRARDOT, Henri (1878-1937) French
£355 $592 €500 Arbres en Dauphine (50x61cm-20x24in) s. 23-Jun-3 Delvaux, Paris #171

GIRARDOT, Louis Auguste (1858-1933) French
Works on paper
£1603 $2516 €2500 La belle algeroise (32x24cm-13x9in) s. col crayon. 16-Dec-2 Gros & Delettrez, Paris #151/R est:2000-3000

GIRAUD, Jean (20th C) French
Works on paper
£1379 $2179 €2000 Blueberry (57x43cm-22x17in) s. Chinese ink. 7-Apr-3 Claude Aguttes, Neuilly #139/R

GIRAUD, Pierre Francois Eugène (1806-1881) French
£5484 $8500 €8226 Spanish beauty with a fan (81x59cm-32x23in) s. prov. 30-Oct-2 Christie's, Rockefeller NY #182/R est:10000-15000
£8000 $13120 €12000 Finding Moses (51x74cm-20x29in) s.d.1856 prov. 3-Jun-3 Sotheby's, London #159/R est:6000-8000
£24306 $38646 €35000 Napolitaines a l'enfant (200x241cm-79x95in) s. prov. 30-Apr-3 Tajan, Paris #21/R est:30000

GIRAUDON, Henri (19th C) French
£314 $487 €500 Quai de Seine anime (21x16cm-8x6in) s.i.d.1879. 30-Oct-2 Coutau Begarie, Paris #91/R

GIRAULT DE PRANGEY, Joseph Philibert (19th C) French
Photographs
£2200 $3564 €3300 Kaire, Gmr Ebn Touloun fenetre (12x19cm-5x7in) two images on one daguerreotype. 20-May-3 Christie's, London #27/R est:3500-4500
£3500 $5670 €5250 Jeronda Temple d'apollon (12x19cm-5x7in) daguerreotype. 20-May-3 Christie's, London #37/R est:7000-10000
£4500 $7290 €6750 Bosphore, nord au dela de Pera (9x8cm-4x3in) daguerreotype. 20-May-3 Christie's, London #48/R est:1200-1800
£4800 $7776 €7200 Kaire, Gmr Ebn Touloun, barque du minaret (8x9cm-3x4in) daguerreotype. 20-May-3 Christie's, London #35/R est:1800-2400
£4800 $7776 €7200 Constantinople, pavillon pres du Serail (9x8cm-4x3in) daguerreotype. 20-May-3 Christie's, London #47/R est:2500-3500
£5000 $8100 €7500 Untitled, central pavilion of the Tuileries Palace, Paris (12x9cm-5x4in) daguerreotype lit. 20-May-3 Christie's, London #2/R est:6000-9000
£5500 $8910 €8250 Scutari, Grande Mosquee (9x8cm-4x3in) daguerreotype. 20-May-3 Christie's, London #46/R est:6000-9000
£6000 $9720 €9000 Aphrodisias, Temple de Venus, chapiteau (9x12cm-4x5in) daguerreotype. 20-May-3 Christie's, London #42/R est:900-1200
£6500 $10530 €9750 Kaire, Gmr Ebn Touloun, minaret (8x9cm-3x4in) daguerreotype. 20-May-3 Christie's, London #32/R est:1200-1800
£7000 $11340 €10500 Vieux Kaire cactus raquette (9x8cm-4x3in) st. daguerreotype. 20-May-3 Christie's, London #20/R est:1200-1800
£7000 $11340 €10500 Aphrodisias, colonnes torses (9x8cm-4x3in) daguerreotype. 20-May-3 Christie's, London #39/R est:1800-2400
£7000 $11340 €10500 Baalbec, petit temple, exterieur (12x9cm-5x4in) daguerreotype. 20-May-3 Christie's, London #66/R est:1800-2400
£7000 $11340 €10500 Edfou, figure, bas relief (19x12cm-7x5in) daguerreotype. 20-May-3 Christie's, London #76/R est:7000-12000
£7500 $12150 €11250 Cedres du Liban (9x12cm-4x5in) daguerreotype. 20-May-3 Christie's, London #51/R est:1800-2400
£8000 $12960 €12000 Toscanella lion etrusque (8x9cm-3x4in) daguerreotype lit. 20-May-3 Christie's, London #5/R est:2500-3500
£8000 $12960 €12000 Kaire, Bmr Ebn Touloun, mendiants (9x8cm-4x3in) daguerreotype. 20-May-3 Christie's, London #34/R est:9000-12000
£8500 $13770 €12750 Aphrodisias, figure et fragments (9x12cm-4x5in) daguerreotype. 20-May-3 Christie's, London #41/R est:900-1200
£8500 $13770 €12750 Alep, pres bab antakieh (19x12cm-7x5in) daguerreotype. 20-May-3 Christie's, London #52/R est:9000-12000
£8500 $13770 €12750 Baalbec pris des Carrieres au sud ouest (12x19cm-5x7in) daguerreotype. 20-May-3 Christie's, London #53/R est:9000-12000
£8500 $13770 €12750 Beni, hacan tombeau (8x9cm-3x4in) daguerreotype. 20-May-3 Christie's, London #71/R est:600-900
£8500 $13770 €12750 Untitled, twin capitals and entablature detail (19x12cm-7x5in) two images on one daguerreotype. 20-May-3 Christie's, London #77/R est:7000-10000
£9000 $14580 €13500 Alexandrie, Datiers (9x8cm-4x3in) daguerreotype. 20-May-3 Christie's, London #19/R est:1800-2400
£9000 $14580 €13500 Kaire, Gmr Ebn Touloun, minaret (9x8cm-4x3in) daguerreotype. 20-May-3 Christie's, London #31/R est:3000-4000
£9500 $15390 €14250 Baalbec, petite temple exterieur entablement (19x12cm-7x5in) daguerreotype. 20-May-3 Christie's, London #65/R est:3500-4500
£9500 $15390 €14250 Untitled, Jerusalem, Church of the Holy Sepulchre (9x16cm-4x6in) daguerreotype lit. 20-May-3 Christie's, London #83/R est:3000-4000
£10000 $16200 €15000 Kaire, Gmr Ebn Touloun (19x12cm-7x5in) daguerreotype. 20-May-3 Christie's, London #25/R est:20000-30000
£10000 $16200 €15000 Jerusalem, tombeaux, Josaphat (12x19cm-5x7in) daguerreotype. 20-May-3 Christie's, London #85/R est:15000-20000
£11000 $17820 €16500 Baalbec, peristyle (9x24cm-4x9in) daguerreotype. 20-May-3 Christie's, London #57/R est:4000-6000
£11000 $17820 €16500 Baalbec, cour hexagone (9x24cm-4x9in) daguerreotype. 20-May-3 Christie's, London #59/R est:6000-9000
£11000 $17820 €16500 Baalbec, petit temple a l'ouest (6x11cm-2x4in) daguerreotype. 20-May-3 Christie's, London #67/R est:1800-2400
£12000 $19440 €18000 Athenes, Tour des Vents (8x9cm-3x4in) daguerreotype. 20-May-3 Christie's, London #14/R est:3000-4000
£12000 $19440 €18000 Aphrodisias, enfants (9x12cm-4x5in) daguerreotype lit. 20-May-3 Christie's, London #40/R est:3000-4000
£12000 $19440 €18000 Baalbec, peristyle (24x9cm-9x4in) daguerreotype. 20-May-3 Christie's, London #58/R est:12000-18000
£12000 $19440 €18000 Djebel Selseleh, petit temple (8x9cm-3x4in) daguerreotype. 20-May-3 Christie's, London #79/R est:100-1800
£13000 $21060 €19500 Phile, temple decouvert (9x8cm-4x3in) daguerreotype lit. 20-May-3 Christie's, London #78/R est:1200-1800
£13000 $21060 €19500 Untitled, Jerusalem, village of Siloam (9x24cm-4x9in) daguerreotype. 20-May-3 Christie's, London #84/R est:12000-18000
£15000 $24300 €22500 Untitled, frozen fountain of the Chateau d'Eau (9x12cm-4x5in) daguerreotype lit. 20-May-3 Christie's, London #1/R est:9000-12000
£15000 $24300 €22500 Milet, theatre antique chapiteau (12x19cm-5x7in) daguerreotype. 20-May-3 Christie's, London #43/R est:20000-30000
£16000 $25920 €24000 Kaire, Gmr el Bordeni minaret (24x9cm-9x4in) daguerreotype. 20-May-3 Christie's, London #23/R est:20000-30000
£16000 $25920 €24000 Kaire, Gmr Ebn Touloun, Port Nord (24x9cm-9x4in) daguerreotype. 20-May-3 Christie's, London #24/R est:20000-30000
£16000 $25920 €24000 Kaire, Gmr Ebn Touloun fenetre (19x12cm-7x5in) daguerreotype. 20-May-3 Christie's, London #26/R est:30000-40000
£16000 $25920 €24000 Kaire, Gmr Ebn Touloun, minaret (24x9cm-9x4in) daguerreotype. 20-May-3 Christie's, London #36/R est:20000-30000
£16000 $25920 €24000 Baalec, petit temple ouest et sud (24x19cm-9x7in) daguerreotype. 20-May-3 Christie's, London #63/R est:4000-6000
£17000 $27540 €25500 Tivoli, Villa d'Este, Cypres (24x9cm-9x4in) daguerreotype. 20-May-3 Christie's, London #9/R est:20000-30000
£17000 $27540 €25500 Athenes, Temple Victoire aptere (19x12cm-7x5in) daguerreotype. 20-May-3 Christie's, London #12/R est:25000-35000
£17000 $27540 €25500 Bosphore, nord pecheries (8x9cm-3x4in) daguerreotype. 20-May-3 Christie's, London #45/R est:3000-4000
£17000 $27540 €25500 Baalbec, Grand Temple, colonnade (19x12cm-7x5in) daguerreotype. 20-May-3 Christie's, London #54/R est:9000-12000
£17000 $27540 €25500 Baalec petit temple, porte (19x12cm-7x5in) daguerreotype. 20-May-3 Christie's, London #64/R est:4000-6000
£18000 $29160 €27000 Kaire, Gmr Ebn Touloun, cour-fenetre (19x12cm-7x5in) two images on one daguerreotype. 20-May-3 Christie's, London #29/R est:20000-30000
£18000 $29160 €27000 Baalbec, Grand Temple, entablement (9x24cm-4x9in) daguerreotype. 20-May-3 Christie's, London #55/R est:20000-30000
£18000 $29160 €27000 Karnac, obelisque (9x8cm-4x3in) daguerreotype. 20-May-3 Christie's, London #73/R est:2500-3500
£19000 $30780 €28500 Kaire, Gmr Ebn Toulon, sculptures, pilattier (9x8cm-4x3in) daguerreotype. 20-May-3 Christie's, London #33/R est:1800-2400
£19000 $30780 €28500 Baalbec Grande Cour carree, niche (19x12cm-7x5in) i. daguerreotype. 20-May-3 Christie's, London #61/R est:7000-12000
£19000 $30780 €28500 Sakara, pyramide (8x9cm-3x4in) daguerreotype lit. 20-May-3 Christie's, London #70/R est:1200-1800
£20000 $32400 €30000 Tivoli, Villa d'Este (9x24cm-4x9in) daguerreotype. 20-May-3 Christie's, London #10/R est:25000-35000
£24000 $38880 €36000 Untitled, Jerusalem, inside the walls of the city (9x24cm-4x9in) daguerreotype. 20-May-3 Christie's, London #82/R est:30000-40000
£24000 $38880 €36000 Jerusalem, tombeaux des rois (12x19cm-5x7in) daguerreotype. 20-May-3 Christie's, London #86/R est:9000-12000
£25000 $40500 €37500 A la Douy (24x19cm-9x7in) init.i. daguerreotype exec.c.1841. 20-May-3 Christie's, London #3/R est:30000-40000
£26000 $42120 €39000 Rome, Ponte Rotto (9x24cm-4x9in) daguerreotype. 20-May-3 Christie's, London #7/R est:20000-30000
£26000 $42120 €39000 Kaire, Gmr Ebn Touloun, nef interieur (9x8cm-4x3in) daguerreotype. 20-May-3 Christie's, London #30/R est:5000-7000
£26000 $42120 €39000 Baalbec, prise de la porte sud ouest (9x24cm-4x9in) daguerreotype. 20-May-3 Christie's, London #56/R est:12000-18000
£28000 $45360 €42000 Athenes, Temple de Minerve Poliade (12x19cm-5x7in) daguerreotype. 20-May-3 Christie's, London #15/R est:20000-30000

£28000 $45360 €42000 Fouah, pris de l'ile (9x24cm-4x9in) daguerreotype. 20-May-3 Christie's, London #21/R est:35000-50000
£28000 $45360 €42000 Aphrodisias, Temple de Venus, chapiteau (9x12cm-4x5in) daguerreotype. 20-May-3 Christie's, London #38/R est:3000-4000
£32000 $51840 €48000 Constantinople, serail pris de Pera (9x24cm-4x9in) daguerreotype. 20-May-3 Christie's, London #44/R est:40000-60000
£32000 $51840 €48000 Baalbec, Grande Cour Carree Gran de cotes (12x19cm-5x7in) daguerreotype. 20-May-3 Christie's, London #60/R est:20000-30000
£32000 $51840 €48000 Jerusalem, Mosquee haram el Cherif, prise du nord (12x19cm-5x7in) daguerreotype. 20-May-3 Christie's, London #81/R est:30000-40000
£38000 $61560 €57000 Kaire, Gmr Ebn Toulon fenetre (19x12cm-7x5in) daguerreotype. 20-May-3 Christie's, London #28/R est:30000-40000
£40000 $64800 €60000 Alexandrie, Mosquee Nabedemiane (19x24cm-7x9in) daguerreotype. 20-May-3 Christie's, London #18/R est:50000-80000
£40000 $64800 €60000 Untitled, palm trees on the Nile (9x24cm-4x9in) daguerreotype. 20-May-3 Christie's, London #68/R est:6000-9000
£48000 $77760 €72000 Rosette, rue est publiee (24x19cm-9x7in) two images on one daguerreotype. 20-May-3 Christie's, London #22/R est:60000-90000
£48000 $77760 €72000 Damas, Iwan (24x19cm-9x7in) daguerreotype. 20-May-3 Christie's, London #50/R est:60000-90000
£65000 $105300 €97500 Gournah, tete de colosse (8x9cm-3x4in) daguerreotype. 20-May-3 Christie's, London #75/R est:2500-3500
£70000 $113400 €105000 Jerusalem, Grande Mosque, prise du palais du pacha (19x24cm-7x9in) daguerreotype. 20-May-3 Christie's, London #80/R est:70000-90000
£75000 $121500 €112500 Athenes, Temple de Minerve Poliade Facade Ouest (19x24cm-7x9in) daguerreotype. 20-May-3 Christie's, London #16/R est:90000-120000
£85000 $137700 €127500 Constantinople, Surudje (12x9cm-5x4in) daguerreotype. 20-May-3 Christie's, London #49/R est:9000-12000
£90000 $145800 €135000 Rome, Temple de Vesta (9x24cm-4x9in) daguerreotype. 20-May-3 Christie's, London #8/R est:50000-80000
£110000 $178200 €165000 Baalbec, Temple circulaire, detail interieur (19x24cm-7x9in) daguerreotype. 20-May-3 Christie's, London #62/R est:20000-30000
£140000 $226800 €210000 Athenes, Parthenon Facade et Colonnade Nord (19x24cm-7x9in) daguerreotype. 20-May-3 Christie's, London #11/R est:60000-90000
£150000 $243000 €225000 Gournah, temple colonne (19x12cm-7x5in) daguerreotype. 20-May-3 Christie's, London #74/R est:20000-30000
£170000 $275400 €255000 Memphis, tete de Sesostris (19x12cm-7x5in) daguerreotype. 20-May-3 Christie's, London #69/R est:25000-35000
£280000 $453600 €420000 Rome, Colonne Trajane (24x9cm-9x4in) daguerreotype. 20-May-3 Christie's, London #6/R est:50000-70000
£350000 $567000 €525000 Karnac, pylone, pris de l'ouest (24x19cm-9x7in) daguerreotype. 20-May-3 Christie's, London #72/R est:90000-120000
£500000 $810000 €750000 Athenes, Temple de Jupiter Olympien pris de l'est (19x24cm-7x9in) daguerreotype. 20-May-3 Christie's, London #13/R est:90000-120000

GIRIBALDI, E (?) ?
£1176 $1894 €1800 Navire en detresse (34x54cm-13x21in) panel. 18-Jan-3 Neret-Minet, Paris #151

GIRIEUD, Pierre (1876-1940) French
£2986 $4748 €4300 Paysage de Montagne (38x46cm-15x18in) s.i.d.1909 cardboard. 29-Apr-3 Artcurial Briest, Paris #166/R est:2000-3000

GIRIN, David Eugène (1848-1917) French
£472 $755 €708 Cello player (41x32cm-16x13in) s. 17-Mar-3 Philippe Schuler, Zurich #8636 (S.FR 1000)

GIRKE, Raimund (1930-) German
£993 $1609 €1400 Untitled (56x110cm-22x43in) 24-May-3 Van Ham, Cologne #207/R
£1090 $1689 €1700 Untitled (70x81cm-28x32in) painted 1955/1956 prov. 7-Dec-2 Van Ham, Cologne #184/R est:2500
£2128 $3447 €3000 Untitled - white composition (81x113cm-32x44in) 24-May-3 Van Ham, Cologne #206/R est:3500

Works on paper
£532 $862 €750 Untitled (31x25cm-12x10in) s.d.75 versogouache pencil board. 24-May-3 Van Ham, Cologne #208/R
£5769 $8942 €9000 Unititled (76x65cm-30x26in) s.d.stretcher mixed media cotton prov. 3-Dec-2 Lempertz, Koln #155/R est:10000-12000

GIRODET DE ROUCY TRIOSON, Anne Louis (1767-1824) French
£2866 $4471 €4500 Untitled (32x24cm-13x9in) 6-Nov-2 Gioffredo, Nice #50/R

GIRODON, Gabriel Charles (1884-1941) French
£540 $863 €750 Portrait presume de Paul Poiret (38x46cm-15x18in) s.d.08 s.i.d.1908 verso. 15-May-3 Christie's, Paris #326/R

GIRONCOLI, Bruno (1936-) Austrian

Sculpture
£32432 $50595 €48000 Untitled (185x78x155cm-73x31x61in) col polyester lit. 25-Mar-3 Wiener Kunst Auktionen, Vienna #12/R est:48000-55000

Works on paper
£638 $1034 €900 Untitled (20x14cm-8x6in) biro pen Indian ink. 20-May-3 Dorotheum, Vienna #231/R
£3797 $6000 €6000 My daughter Ina and child (73x103cm-29x41in) s. mixed media metallic col board. 27-Nov-2 Dorotheum, Vienna #285/R est:5800-8700
£4730 $7378 €7000 Untitled (82x107cm-32x42in) s. Indian ink metallic col squared paper lit. 25-Mar-3 Wiener Kunst Auktionen, Vienna #28/R est:7000-12000
£5072 $8319 €7000 Untitled (81x107cm-32x42in) s.i. ink metallic paint lit. 27-May-3 Wiener Kunst Auktionen, Vienna #198/R est:7000-12000

GIRONELLA, Alberto (1929-1999) Mexican
£13699 $21507 €20000 Franco Lezcano in his study (137x180cm-54x71in) s.d.65-66 prov.exhib. 15-Apr-3 Laurence Calmels, Paris #4287/R est:12000

Works on paper
£928 $1484 €1346 Mujer (25x33cm-10x13in) s.d.1971 Indian ink W/C. 15-May-3 Louis Morton, Mexico #151/R est:18000-20000 (M.P 15000)
£19108 $30000 €28662 Degas visits Sonia (130x195cm-51x77in) s.d.86-88 mixed media collage canvas on panel prov.exhib. 20-Nov-2 Christie's, Rockefeller NY #36/R est:45000-60000

GIRONIERE, Yves Benoist (20th C) French

Sculpture
£1572 $2437 €2500 Cavalier sautant un obstacle (36x37cm-14x15in) s. pat bronze Cast Susse. 6-Oct-2 Livinec, Gaudcheau & Jezequel, Rennes #81/R
£2500 $3900 €3750 Racehorses and jockeys at the finish (25x97cm-10x38in) s. brown pat. bronze. 6-Nov-2 Sotheby's, Olympia #175/R est:3000-5000

Works on paper
£288 $441 €450 Trois joueurs de polo sur leur monture (35x53cm-14x21in) s. W/C cardboard. 23-Aug-2 Deauville, France #192/R

GIROT, Louis Joseph (?) French

Works on paper
£289 $451 €460 Chiens de chasse (24x35cm-9x14in) W/C. 14-Oct-2 Blache, Grenoble #81

GIROUX, Henri (1951-) Canadian
£200 $328 €290 Sleigh ride (25x30cm-10x12in) s.i. 9-Jun-3 Hodgins, Calgary #13/R (C.D 450)

GIRTIN, Thomas (1775-1802) British

Works on paper
£5500 $8689 €8250 Marlow, Buckinghamshire, from across the river Thames (10x14cm-4x6in) W/C over pencil prov. 28-Nov-2 Sotheby's, London #254/R est:6000-8000
£6000 $9840 €8700 Banqueting Hall, Keniworth Castle, Warwickshire (57x46cm-22x18in) s. pencil pen ink W/C gum arabic prov.lit. 5-Jun-3 Christie's, London #89/R est:5000-8000
£90000 $149400 €135000 Mynnydd Mawr, North Wales (27x40cm-11x16in) s.d.1799 i.verso pencil W/C prov.exhib. 11-Jun-3 Christie's, London #1/R est:80000-120000
£420000 $663600 €630000 Jedburgh Abbey from the South East (42x55cm-17x22in) s. W/C over pencil htd bodycol. 28-Nov-2 Sotheby's, London #16/R est:200000-300000

GIRTIN, Thomas (attrib) (1775-1802) British

Works on paper
£1000 $1630 €1500 Near Lyme Regis (19x25cm-7x10in) pencil W/C sold with two others by different hands. 30-Jan-3 Lawrence, Crewkerne #615/R

GIRTIN, Thomas and TURNER, Joseph Mallord William (19th C) British

Works on paper

£3500 $5740 €5075 Interior of Raglan Castle, South Wales (26x20cm-10x8in) i. pencil blue wash prov. 5-Jun-3 Christie's, London #33/R est:4000-6000

£3800 $6232 €5510 River landscape. Sunlight on a river valley (24x37cm-9x15in) i. pencil W/C two after John Robert Cozens. 5-Jun-3 Christie's, London #32/R est:3500-4500

GISBERT, Antonio (1835-1901) Spanish

£2095 $3268 €3100 Jeune elegante au chapeau fleuri (41x31cm-16x12in) s. panel. 31-Mar-3 Rossini, Paris #29/R

£5960 $9715 €9000 Portrait of lady with whip (72x58cm-28x23in) s. 11-Feb-3 Segre, Madrid #60/R

GISCHIA, Léon (1903-1991) French

£1293 $2055 €1900 Composition 12F (60x50cm-24x20in) s. s.i.d.1972-74 verso. 1-Mar-3 Meeting Art, Vercelli #656

£2553 $4136 €3600 Alberi intrecciati (100x73cm-39x29in) s. prov. 26-May-3 Christie's, Milan #326/R est:4000-6000

£2581 $4077 €4000 Figures and ball (65x81cm-26x32in) s. painted 1967 prov. 18-Dec-2 Christie's, Rome #90/R

Works on paper

£385 $604 €600 Composition (46x55cm-18x22in) s. mixed media card on canvas. 23-Nov-2 Meeting Art, Vercelli #77

GISEL, A (19th C) ?

£1224 $1947 €1800 Gros horloge a Rouen (116x89cm-46x35in) s. 23-Mar-3 Herbette, Doullens #7/R

GISELA, Josef (1851-1899) Austrian

£12658 $20000 €20000 Devotion in St Stefan (41x34cm-16x13in) s. panel. 28-Nov-2 Dorotheum, Vienna #213/R est:20000-26000

GISIKO-SPARCK, Ida (1859-1940) Swedish

£559 $888 €839 Drying the fishing nets (42x67cm-17x26in) s. 5-Mar-3 Rasmussen, Copenhagen #1986/R (D.KR 6000)

GISLANDER, William (1890-1937) Swedish

£372 $592 €558 Landscape with birds (69x79cm-27x31in) s.d.26 prov. 10-Mar-3 Rasmussen, Vejle #538/R (D.KR 4000)

£391 $625 €567 Swans in flight (90x140cm-35x55in) s. 18-May-3 Anders Antik, Landskrona #49 (S.KR 5000)

£559 $888 €839 Geese in coastal meadow (45x59cm-18x23in) s.d.1933. 5-Mar-3 Rasmussen, Copenhagen #1857/R (D.KR 6000)

GISMONDI, Paolo (1612-1685) Italian

Works on paper

£1646 $2600 €2600 Musiciens sur une balustrade (10x12cm-4x5in) black chk pen brown ink brown wash sold with 5 drs by other hands. 27-Nov-2 Christie's, Paris #62/R est:1500-2000

GISPEN, Willem Hendrik (1890-1968) Dutch

£255 $397 €400 Eastern house (80x65cm-31x26in) s.d.63. 6-Nov-2 Vendue Huis, Gravenhage #169

GISSING, Roland (1895-1967) Canadian

£437 $716 €656 Kananaskis Valley (30x41cm-12x16in) s. i.d.1957 verso board. 6-Feb-3 Heffel, Vancouver #026/R (C.D 1100)

£462 $725 €693 Autumn gold (30x40cm-12x16in) s.i. board. 25-Nov-2 Hodgins, Calgary #128/R (C.D 1150)

£522 $820 €783 Kootenay Valley (30x40cm-12x16in) s.i.d.1956 board. 25-Nov-2 Hodgins, Calgary #328/R (C.D 1300)

£522 $814 €870 Promise of spring (41x51cm-16x20in) s. prov. 13-Apr-3 Levis, Calgary #38/R est:1500-2000 (C.D 1200)

£565 $882 €943 Evening after rain (61x91cm-24x36in) s. 13-Apr-3 Levis, Calgary #39 est:1500-2000 (C.D 1300)

£602 $946 €903 St Mary's Lake (30x40cm-12x16in) s.i.d.1954 board. 25-Nov-2 Hodgins, Calgary #42/R (C.D 1500)

£606 $964 €879 Near Cardston (29x39cm-11x15in) s. board prov. 1-May-3 Heffel, Vancouver #29/R (C.D 1400)

£697 $1080 €1046 Winter sunset (55x76cm-22x30in) s. 24-Sep-2 Ritchie, Toronto #3176/R (C.D 1700)

£741 $1148 €1112 Hills West of De Winter (45x60cm-18x24in) s. 3-Dec-2 Joyner, Toronto #277/R est:2000-3000 (C.D 1800)

£763 $1198 €1145 Lake near Morley (40x50cm-16x20in) s.i. 25-Nov-2 Hodgins, Calgary #151/R est:1800-2200 (C.D 1900)

£800 $1312 €1160 Near Kootenay Bay (30x40cm-12x16in) s.i. board. 9-Jun-3 Hodgins, Calgary #127/R est:1500-2000 (C.D 1800)

£858 $1339 €1244 Hills west of De Winton (46x61cm-18x24in) s.i. 26-Mar-3 Walker's, Ottawa #257/R est:2000-3000 (C.D 2000)

£884 $1387 €1326 Untitled - summer clouds (48x60cm-19x24in) s. 25-Nov-2 Hodgins, Calgary #81/R est:2250-2750 (C.D 2200)

£889 $1458 €1289 In Glacier Park (40x50cm-16x20in) s.i.d.1961 board. 9-Jun-3 Hodgins, Calgary #42/R est:1800-2200 (C.D 2000)

£889 $1458 €1289 Bow River below Castle Mountain (60x75cm-24x30in) s. 9-Jun-3 Hodgins, Calgary #276/R est:2500-3000 (C.D 2000)

£1022 $1676 €1482 Racehorse River near Fort Steele (30x40cm-12x16in) s.i. board. 9-Jun-3 Hodgins, Calgary #268/R est:1500-1800 (C.D 2300)

£1044 $1650 €1566 Freeze up (56x76cm-22x30in) 1-Dec-2 Levis, Calgary #31/R est:3000-4000 (C.D 2600)

£1067 $1749 €1547 Winter afternoon (50x65cm-20x26in) s.i. 9-Jun-3 Hodgins, Calgary #64/R est:2250-2750 (C.D 2400)

£1200 $1968 €1740 Kicking Horse River (30x40cm-12x16in) s.i.d.1960 board. 9-Jun-3 Hodgins, Calgary #269/R est:1500-1800 (C.D 2700)

£1422 $2332 €2062 Clouds over the hills (50x60cm-20x24in) s.i. 9-Jun-3 Hodgins, Calgary #348/R est:2000-2500 (C.D 3200)

£1446 $2270 €2169 Winter sunset (55x75cm-22x30in) s.i.d.1949. 25-Nov-2 Hodgins, Calgary #352/R est:3000-3500 (C.D 3600)

Works on paper

£482 $757 €723 Lake in the Rockies (35x41cm-14x16in) s. pastel. 25-Nov-2 Hodgins, Calgary #187/R (C.D 1200)

£723 $1142 €1085 Lake Louise (43x36cm-17x14in) d.1927 W/C. 1-Dec-2 Levis, Calgary #31a/R est:1200-1500 (C.D 1800)

GISSON, Andre (1910-) French/American

£360 $587 €522 Vase de fleurs (29x21cm-11x8in) s. 21-Jul-3 Bonhams, Bath #35/R

£625 $1000 €938 Sunny day in the park (61x76cm-24x30in) s. 16-Mar-3 Butterfields, San Francisco #1017 est:2000-3000

£769 $1200 €1154 Floral still life (51x41cm-20x16in) s. 9-Oct-2 Doyle, New York #44

£833 $1300 €1250 Stroll through the gardens (23x30cm-9x12in) s. 9-Oct-2 Doyle, New York #45

£958 $1600 €1389 Flower market, Notre Dame (51x61cm-20x24in) s. 22-Jun-3 Freeman, Philadelphia #140/R est:1500-2500

£962 $1500 €1443 Floral still life. Still life with pottery and fruit (30x23cm-12x9in) s. pair. 9-Oct-2 Doyle, New York #46 est:1200-1800

£1115 $1750 €1673 Still life with flowers (61x51cm-24x20in) s. 20-Nov-2 Boos Gallery, Michigan #486/R est:1500-2500

£1132 $1800 €1698 Floral still life (61x30cm-24x12in) s. 22-Mar-3 New Orleans Auction, New Orleans #407/R est:2000-4000

£1154 $1800 €1731 At the museum (30x41cm-12x16in) s. 9-Oct-2 Doyle, New York #47 est:1500-2500

£1154 $1800 €1731 Beach scene with figures (41x51cm-16x20in) s. prov. 12-Apr-3 Weschler, Washington #539/R est:1500-2500

£1200 $1944 €1800 Two nudes on balcony (28x35cm-11x14in) s. prov. 20-May-3 Sotheby's, Olympia #72/R est:400-600

£1218 $1900 €1827 Figures along the seashore (61x30cm-24x12in) s. 12-Apr-3 Weschler, Washington #540/R est:1500-2500

£1312 $2100 €1902 In the meadow (61x92cm-24x36in) s. 16-May-3 Skinner, Boston #329/R est:2000-4000

£1352 $2096 €2028 Carousel (61x91cm-24x36in) s. 24-Sep-2 Maynards, Vancouver #370/R est:3000-5000 (C.D 3300)

£1377 $2300 €1997 Street scene with figures (28x36cm-11x14in) s. pair. 22-Jun-3 Freeman, Philadelphia #141/R est:1500-2500

£1667 $2600 €2501 Paris street scene (41x51cm-16x20in) s. 30-Mar-3 Susanin's, Chicago #6081/R est:1000-1500

£1772 $2800 €2658 Park landscape with carousel and figures (61x91cm-24x36in) s. 22-Apr-3 Arthur James, Florida #117

£2244 $3500 €3366 Carrousel (41x51cm-16x20in) s. 30-Mar-3 Simpson's, Houston #190

£2465 $3500 €3698 Paris Arc de Triumph (61x91cm-24x36in) 4-Apr-2 Caddigan, Hanover #1

£2564 $4000 €3846 April in Paris (61x91cm-24x36in) 9-Nov-2 Altermann Galleries, Santa Fe #226

£2813 $4500 €4220 Figures picnicking by the Seine (61x91cm-24x36in) s. 15-Mar-3 Selkirks, St. Louis #678/R est:4000-5000

£3025 $4750 €4538 Mother and daughter seated in a garden (24x30cm-9x12in) s. 10-Dec-2 Doyle, New York #241/R est:2000-3000

Works on paper

£812 $1300 €1177 Walk in the tide waters (25x35cm-10x14in) s. W/C htd white graphite. 16-May-3 Skinner, Boston #312/R est:1800-2200

GIUFFRIDA, Joselita (20th C) Italian

£486 $768 €700 Que ne quiero verla (50x50cm-20x20in) s.d. s.i.d.verso acrylic prov. 28-Apr-3 Cornette de St.Cyr, Paris #404

GIULIANI, G (?) Italian

Works on paper

£1083 $1689 €1700 Ruelle animee au Caire (49x28cm-19x11in) s. W/C. 11-Nov-2 Horta, Bruxelles #542 est:1500-2000

GIULIANI, Giovanni (1893-1965) Italian

£338 $527 €500 Abstract composition (78x48cm-31x19in) s.d.61 prov. 26-Mar-3 Finarte Semenzato, Milan #131/R

GIULIANI, Maria Letizia (1908-1985) Italian

Works on paper

£256 $397 €400 Angels (167x125cm-66x49in) sepia ink Chinese ink cardboard. 4-Dec-2 Finarte, Rome #12/R

GIUNTA, Joseph (1911-2001) Canadian
£224 $351 €336 Terra incognita (20x25cm-8x10in) s. s.i.d.68 verso board. 10-Dec-2 Pinneys, Montreal #7 (C.D 550)
£285 $447 €428 Abstraction (25x20cm-10x8in) s.d.67 verso board. 10-Dec-2 Pinneys, Montreal #212 (C.D 700)
£369 $575 €554 March break up, Laurentians Que (30x41cm-12x16in) s. i.verso panel. 10-Sep-2 Iegor de Saint Hippolyte, Montreal #52 (C.D 900)
£391 $606 €587 Autumn, ste, Genevieve, Que (50x60cm-20x24in) s. board. 3-Dec-2 Joyner, Toronto #458 (C.D 950)
£432 $665 €648 Summer landscape, Val David, Quebec (31x41cm-12x16in) s.d.51 panel. 22-Oct-2 Iegor de Saint Hippolyte, Montreal #43 (C.D 1050)
£435 $679 €653 Autumn Laurentians near Ste Adele, Que (30x40cm-12x16in) s. init.i.verso panel. 30-Jul-2 Iegor de Saint Hippolyte, Montreal #69 (C.D 1080)
£435 $679 €653 Sous-bois, Mt Royal, Que (66x51cm-26x20in) s. i.verso. 30-Jul-2 Iegor de Saint Hippolyte, Montreal #70 (C.D 1080)
£610 $957 €915 Flower arrangement (41x51cm-16x20in) s.d.47 i.verso board. 10-Dec-2 Pinneys, Montreal #167 (C.D 1500)
£617 $951 €926 Old French Canadian homestead, Ste Adele (31x41cm-12x16in) s. panel. 22-Oct-2 Iegor de Saint Hippolyte, Montreal #44/R (C.D 1500)

GIUNTOTARDI, Philippe (1768-1831) Italian
Works on paper
£2365 $3689 €3500 Landscape with the Vesuvius (54x75cm-21x30in) graphite W/C. 27-Mar-3 Christie's, Paris #155/R
£6000 $10020 €8700 View of the Ponte Lucano and the tomb of the Plautii (27x38cm-11x15in) s.d.1810 W/C blk chk prov. 9-Jul-3 Sotheby's, London #68/R est:2500-3500

GIUSEPPE, di (20th C) Italian
£503 $785 €800 Woman with flowers (40x50cm-16x20in) 23-Sep-2 Dr Fritz Nagel, Stuttgart #7012/R

GIUSTI, Guglielmo (1824-1916) Italian
Works on paper
£1216 $1897 €1800 Monk by the Amalfitana (24x39cm-9x15in) s. W/C. 28-Mar-3 Dorotheum, Vienna #255/R est:2000-2500

GIUSTI, Salvatore (1773-1845) Italian
£1300 $2080 €1950 Still life of flowers displayed in a decanter (40x23cm-16x9in) s.d.1828 panel pair. 13-May-3 Bonhams, Knightsbridge #84/R est:1200-1800

GIUSTO, Faust (1867-1941) Italian
£1157 $1863 €1736 Fishermen in the Gulf of Naples (50x70cm-20x28in) s. 7-May-3 Dobiaschofsky, Bern #596/R est:2500 (S.FR 2500)
£1500 $2385 €2250 Paris in the snow (46x76cm-18x30in) s. 20-Mar-3 Christie's, Kensington #27/R est:2000-3000

GJEDSTED, Rolf (1947-) Danish
£280 $445 €420 Kiss of a butterfly (80x100cm-31x39in) s. acrylic. 29-Apr-3 Kunsthallen, Copenhagen #162 (D.KR 3000)
£326 $508 €489 Abstract composition - Spanish dance. s. painted 1999-2002. 11-Nov-2 Rasmussen, Vejle #98 (D.KR 3800)
£334 $557 €484 Butterfly morning (90x120cm-35x47in) s. d.1998-2002 verso. 17-Jun-3 Rasmussen, Copenhagen #129/R (D.KR 3500)
£381 $637 €552 The mission - loves' landscape (88x120cm-35x47in) s. init.d.1996-98 verso. 17-Jun-3 Rasmussen, Copenhagen #166 (D.KR 4000)
£391 $610 €587 Dance - composition (110x160cm-43x63in) s. i.d.1994-99 verso. 5-Aug-2 Rasmussen, Vejle #370/R (D.KR 4600)
£418 $661 €627 Dreaming lotus (100x100cm-39x39in) s. d.1998 verso cardboard on canvas. 1-Apr-3 Rasmussen, Copenhagen #329/R (D.KR 4500)
£431 $668 €647 White rain (120x100cm-47x39in) s. 4-Dec-2 Kunsthallen, Copenhagen #140 (D.KR 5000)
£458 $764 €664 Untitled (25x117cm-10x46in) s. acrylic paper on panel triptych. 17-Jun-3 Rasmussen, Copenhagen #127 (D.KR 4800)
£465 $734 €698 Where the angels dance (100x120cm-39x47in) s. 1-Apr-3 Rasmussen, Copenhagen #369/R (D.KR 5000)
£508 $787 €762 Love at 5 o'clock in the afternoon (100x120cm-39x47in) s. d.1999-2001 verso. 1-Oct-2 Rasmussen, Copenhagen #210/R (D.KR 6000)
£508 $787 €762 White rain (103x155cm-41x61in) s. d.1997-2001 verso. 1-Oct-2 Rasmussen, Copenhagen #241/R (D.KR 6000)
£715 $1194 €1037 Love landscape (140x100cm-55x39in) s. s.d.1999 verso cardboard on canvas. 17-Jun-3 Rasmussen, Copenhagen #120/R (D.KR 7500)

GJEMRE, Per (1864-1928) Norwegian
£2443 $3958 €3665 Landscape from Stjernero - girl raking hay (43x66cm-17x26in) s.i.d.1906. 26-May-3 Grev Wedels Plass, Oslo #6/R est:8000-10000 (N.KR 27000)

GJERDEVIK, Niels Erik (1962-) Norwegian
£320 $509 €480 Composition - INGN (80x130cm-31x51in) s.d.1993 verso. 26-Feb-3 Kunsthallen, Copenhagen #128 (D.KR 3500)
£511 $808 €767 Aeroplane composition (80x90cm-31x35in) s.d.1988 verso. 1-Apr-3 Rasmussen, Copenhagen #317/R (D.KR 5500)
£591 $922 €887 Composition (110x90cm-43x35in) s.d.84-85. 18-Sep-2 Kunsthallen, Copenhagen #276/R (D.KR 7000)

GJESDAL, Herman (attrib) (19/20th C) Norwegian
£290 $453 €435 Spring thaw (49x75cm-19x30in) s,. 23-Sep-2 Blomqvist, Lysaker #1067 (N.KR 3400)

GLACKENS, William (1870-1938) American
£4167 $6500 €6251 Central Park (43x53cm-17x21in) s. chk prov. 21-Sep-2 Pook & Pook, Downington #219/R est:1500-2500
£5975 $9500 €8963 View of a park (23x16cm-9x6in) panel prov. 4-Mar-3 Christie's, Rockefeller NY #56/R est:7000-9000
£6289 $10000 €9434 Apples on a checkered cloth (18x23cm-7x9in) prov. 4-Mar-3 Christie's, Rockefeller NY #68/R est:7000-9000
£16975 $27500 €25463 Pear, persimmons and grapes (18x27cm-7x11in) s.i. prov. 21-May-3 Sotheby's, New York #163/R est:20000-30000
£22013 $35000 €33020 Window (39x30cm-15x12in) prov. 4-Mar-3 Christie's, Rockefeller NY #70/R est:20000-30000
£26235 $42500 €39353 Pears and grapes (36x41cm-14x16in) painted c.1916 prov.exhib. 21-May-3 Sotheby's, New York #55/R est:30000-50000
£45161 $70000 €67742 Hammock (31x39cm-12x15in) init. exhib. 5-Dec-2 Christie's, Rockefeller NY #95/R est:60000-80000
£58642 $95000 €87963 Flowers with checkered background (60x50cm-24x20in) painted c.1935 prov.exhib.lit. 21-May-3 Sotheby's, New York #54/R est:60000-80000
£103125 $165000 €154688 Rockport, Mass 1936 no.3, beach scene. s.i.verso board. 11-Jan-3 James Julia, Fairfield #100
Works on paper
£1465 $2300 €2198 Dinner party (11x11cm-4x4in) s. i.verso ink collage exec.c.1907. 19-Nov-2 Wright, Chicago #103/R est:1500-2000
£8176 $13000 €12264 Bathing beach (25x36cm-10x14in) s. W/C chl executed 1914. 5-Mar-3 Sotheby's, New York #86/R est:8000-12000
£13889 $22500 €20834 Park near factory - park scene on the Delaware (23x34cm-9x13in) i. W/C gouache black chk executed 1900 prov. 21-May-3 Sotheby's, New York #60/R est:12000-18000
£54839 $85000 €82259 Paris cafe (41x28cm-16x11in) s. W/C chl executed c.1899 prov.exhib. 4-Dec-2 Sotheby's, New York #21/R est:40000-60000
£61290 $95000 €91935 Discussing art, literature and music - cafe scene (18x28cm-7x11in) s.i. ink chl on board executed c.1899 prov.exhib.lit. 4-Dec-2 Sotheby's, New York #20/R est:25000-35000
£103226 $160000 €154839 Old Legros at my side would comment upon it as mere clap-trap - The balcony (28x35cm-11x14in) s. ink on board executed c.1899 prov.exhib.lit. 4-Dec-2 Sotheby's, New York #8/R est:50000-70000
£129032 $200000 €193548 O'Rourke tried to climb through the ropes, but was pulled back (36x28cm-14x11in) s.i. chl on board executed c.1905 prov.exhib.lit. 4-Dec-2 Sotheby's, New York #7/R est:75000-100000

GLADWELL, Rodney (1934-) British
£313 $500 €470 Rodeo (58x79cm-23x31in) s.d.69 board. 8-Jan-3 Doyle, New York #67/R

GLAIN, Pascal Léon (18th C) French
Works on paper
£897 $1391 €1400 Portrait d'homme en buste (64x50cm-25x20in) i.verso pastel. 4-Dec-2 Piasa, Paris #98/R

GLAIZE, Auguste Barthelemy (1807-1893) French
£809 $1277 €1214 Homer surrounded by people listening on board a vessel (24x33cm-9x13in) sketch. 2-Dec-2 Rasmussen, Copenhagen #1780/R (D.KR 9500)

GLAIZE, Pierre Paul Léon (1842-1932) French
Works on paper
£253 $400 €400 Femme nue assise, les bras ecartes (31x19cm-12x7in) s. crayon. 28-Nov-2 Tajan, Paris #176

GLANSDORFF, Hubert (1877-1964) Belgian

£380	$592	€600	Vase fleuri (54x79cm-21x31in) s.d.28. 15-Oct-2 Horta, Bruxelles #7
£517	$822	€750	Vase de fleurs (60x80cm-24x31in) s.d.14. 4-Mar-3 Palais de Beaux Arts, Brussels #339
£621	$993	€900	Anemones (46x38cm-18x15in) s. 15-Mar-3 De Vuyst, Lokeren #135
£719	$1151	€1000	Vase fleuri de tulipes (59x99cm-23x39in) s. 19-May-3 Horta, Bruxelles #371
£833	$1308	€1300	Nature morte aux anemones (60x80cm-24x31in) s.d.1939. 19-Nov-2 Vanderkindere, Brussels #444
£1600	$2544	€2400	Chrysenthemes (60x85cm-24x33in) s.d.24 prov. 20-Mar-3 Sotheby's, Olympia #61/R est:1200-1800
£1731	$2717	€2700	Vase de fleurs (102x120cm-40x47in) s.d.1938. 19-Nov-2 Vanderkindere, Brussels #34/R est:2500-3750
£1799	$2878	€2500	Grand vase de fleurs en porcelaine de Chine (150x100cm-59x39in) s.d.23. 13-May-3 Vanderkindere, Brussels #68/R est:2500-3500
£2734	$4374	€3800	Grand vase de fleurs (100x120cm-39x47in) s.d.42. 13-May-3 Vanderkindere, Brussels #60 est:2500-3500

GLANSDORP, Aart (1903-1989) Dutch

£255	$397	€400	Still life of flowers (62x60cm-24x24in) s. 6-Nov-2 Vendue Huis, Gravenhage #102a
£637	$994	€1000	Still life (39x49cm-15x19in) s. 6-Nov-2 Vendue Huis, Gravenhage #102/R

GLARNER, Fritz (1899-1972) American/Swiss

£282	$462	€409	Naples (15x23cm-6x9in) mono.d.916 board prov. 4-Jun-3 Fischer, Luzern #2132/R (S.FR 600)
£376	$616	€545	Untitled (37x44cm-15x17in) prov. double-sided. 4-Jun-3 Fischer, Luzern #2127/R (S.FR 800)
£423	$693	€613	Portrait of girl - niece of artist (45x41cm-18x16in) prov. 4-Jun-3 Fischer, Luzern #2133/R (S.FR 900)
£469	$770	€680	Head of young woman (31x33cm-12x13in) s.d.26 board prov. 4-Jun-3 Fischer, Luzern #2120/R (S.FR 1000)
£563	$924	€816	Stone bridge in city (61x50cm-24x20in) prov. 4-Jun-3 Fischer, Luzern #2122/R (S.FR 1200)
£704	$1155	€1021	Girl with slide in hair (39x31cm-15x12in) prov. 4-Jun-3 Fischer, Luzern #2123/R est:1600-1800 (S.FR 1500)
£845	$1386	€1225	Stairway and red roof (54x45cm-21x18in) prov. 4-Jun-3 Fischer, Luzern #2121/R est:2200-2400 (S.FR 1800)
£845	$1386	€1225	Still life with white lilies (73x54cm-29x21in) prov. 4-Jun-3 Fischer, Luzern #2130/R est:2000-2200 (S.FR 1800)
£845	$1386	€1225	Portrait of man with green scarf and cigarette (100x81cm-39x32in) prov. 4-Jun-3 Fischer, Luzern #2131/R est:2000-2200 (S.FR 1800)
£939	$1540	€1362	Still life with cane and small vase (44x53cm-17x21in) prov. 4-Jun-3 Fischer, Luzern #2128/R est:2200-2400 (S.FR 2000)
£1048	$1635	€1572	Still life with vase of flowers and orange book (54x46cm-21x18in) board prov. 20-Nov-2 Fischer, Luzern #1304/R est:2500-3500 (S.FR 2400)
£5579	$8815	€8369	Study of Tondo (51x32cm-20x13in) s.d.1962 chl chk. 26-Nov-2 Phillips, Zurich #91/R est:8000-10000 (S.FR 13000)
£91743	$153211	€133027	Relational painting 1953, No 65 (74x68cm-29x27in) s.d.1953 s.i. verso prov.lit.exhib. 20-Jun-3 Kornfeld, Bern #62/R est:200000 (S.FR 200000)

Works on paper

£1073	$1695	€1610	Composition (26x21cm-10x8in) mono.d.1945 chl prov. 26-Nov-2 Phillips, Zurich #92/R est:2500-3500 (S.FR 2500)
£4292	$6781	€6438	Study for relational painting (87x66cm-34x26in) chl. 26-Nov-2 Phillips, Zurich #93/R est:10000-15000 (S.FR 10000)
£13734	$21700	€20601	Rythme de New-York (64x49cm-25x19in) pencil chk W/C exhib. 26-Nov-2 Phillips, Zurich #89/R est:15000-20000 (S.FR 32000)

GLASER, E (19/20th C) ?

£325	$484	€500	Fortress ruin high up in Neuffen (25x46cm-10x18in) i.verso board. 28-Jun-2 Sigalas, Stuttgart #796/R

GLASGOW, Berni (19th C) American

£764	$1200	€1146	On the subway, new York City (30x40cm-12x16in) s. masonite. 22-Nov-2 Skinner, Boston #322/R est:2000-3000

GLASS, Hamilton (19/20th C) British

Works on paper

£390	$624	€585	Coastal village with figures to side, church beyond (29x44cm-11x17in) s. W/C. 29-Jan-3 Wingetts, Wrexham #205/R

GLASS, James Hamilton (1820-1885) British

Works on paper

£1800	$2826	€2700	On birns Water, East Lothian. On Salton Water, East Lothian (48x72cm-19x28in) s. W/C pair. 21-Nov-2 Tennants, Leyburn #631 est:600-800

GLASS, John Hamilton (fl.1890-1925) British

£750	$1223	€1125	Portrait of a wolfhound (47x62cm-19x24in) i.verso. 12-Feb-3 Bonhams, Knightsbridge #142/R

Works on paper

£280	$437	€420	Forth from Dysart (43x31cm-17x12in) s. W/C gouache. 12-Sep-2 Bonhams, Edinburgh #337
£300	$477	€450	By the burn (31x46cm-12x18in) s. pencil W/C. 6-Mar-3 Christie's, Kensington #86/R
£450	$716	€675	Shepherd with his flock on a wooded track (49x74cm-19x29in) s. W/C. 6-Mar-3 Christie's, Kensington #171/R
£650	$1086	€943	Two figures sitting in meadow. Sheep grazing by a river (41x56cm-16x22in) s. pair. 8-Jul-3 Bonhams, Knightsbridge #63/R

GLASS, John W (?-1885) British

£260	$403	€390	Wolf-hound (48x63cm-19x25in) i.verso. 25-Sep-2 Hamptons Fine Art, Godalming #329

GLASS, Margaret (1950-) British

Works on paper

£260	$434	€377	Early morning Ramshot (33x48cm-13x19in) init.d.90 pastel. 20-Jun-3 Keys, Aylsham #570
£280	$456	€420	Runton Beach (36x48cm-14x19in) init.d.92 pastel. 14-Feb-3 Keys, Aylsham #534/R
£280	$456	€420	Pinmill foreshore (36x48cm-14x19in) init.d.91 pastel. 14-Feb-3 Keys, Aylsham #535
£300	$468	€450	Sunlight and showers (41x56cm-16x22in) s.d.93 pastel. 11-Apr-3 Keys, Aylsham #608
£300	$468	€450	Low tide, Woodbridge (41x51cm-16x20in) s.d.90 pastel. 11-Apr-3 Keys, Aylsham #609/R
£360	$580	€540	Snow over Ipswich railyard and docks (49x76cm-19x30in) init.d.73 pastel. 14-Jan-3 Bonhams, Ipswich #350

GLASS, William Mervyn (1885-1965) British

£320	$531	€464	Shipping off the west coats (45x61cm-18x24in) board. 13-Jun-3 Lyon & Turnbull, Edinburgh #10
£1700	$2635	€2550	Dutchmans Cap, Iona (33x41cm-13x16in) init.d.1922 panel. 6-Dec-2 Lyon & Turnbull, Edinburgh #102 est:800-1200
£2700	$4212	€4050	Iona, Loch-na-keal, looking to Ben More (36x44cm-14x17in) init. board. 10-Apr-3 Bonhams, Edinburgh #157/R est:2000-3000
£4500	$7020	€6750	Iona (23x33cm-9x13in) s.d.1920 canvasboard prov. 14-Apr-3 Sotheby's, London #116/R est:2000-3000

GLATTACKER, Adolf (1878-1971) German

£755	$1177	€1200	Suicide of Lucretia (67x49cm-26x19in) mono.d.1966 board. 20-Sep-2 Karlheinz Kaupp, Staufen #1910

GLATTE, Adolf (1866-1920) German

£497	$800	€746	Grove of trees, figure in field (30x38cm-12x15in) s. board. 22-Feb-3 Brunk, Ashville #740/R

GLATTER, Armin (1861-?) Hungarian

£268	$416	€402	Sewing I (43x32cm-17x13in) painted c.1900. 3-Dec-2 SOGA, Bratislava #96/R (SL.K 17000)
£268	$416	€402	Sewing II (43x32cm-17x13in) painted c.1900. 3-Dec-2 SOGA, Bratislava #97/R (SL.K 17000)

GLATTFELDER, Hansjorg (1939-) Swiss

£524	$765	€786	J.1 (27x42cm-11x17in) s.i.d.1999 verso acrylic canvas on panel. 4-Jun-2 Germann, Zurich #768 (S.FR 1200)
£524	$765	€786	D.1 (27x42cm-11x17in) s.i.d.1998 verso acrylic canvas on panel. 4-Jun-2 Germann, Zurich #769 (S.FR 1200)
£786	$1234	€1179	Untitled (56x76cm-22x30in) s.d.1987 tempera. 23-Nov-2 Burkhard, Luzern #170/R (S.FR 1800)

GLATZ, Oszkar (1872-1958) Hungarian

£699	$1090	€1049	Girl resting (36x49cm-14x19in) s.d.1928. 11-Apr-3 Kieselbach, Budapest #54/R est:250000 (H.F 250000)
£1237	$1917	€1856	Girl with a doll (50x38cm-20x15in) s. 6-Dec-2 Kieselbach, Budapest #40/R (H.F 460000)
£1238	$1932	€1857	Girl by the well, 1929 (50x64cm-20x25in) s.d.1929. 11-Sep-2 Kieselbach, Budapest #179/R (H.F 480000)
£1479	$2293	€2219	Girl with a tankard (70x50cm-28x20in) s. 6-Dec-2 Kieselbach, Budapest #85/R (H.F 550000)
£1748	$2709	€2622	Girl with a lamb (55x70cm-22x28in) s. 6-Dec-2 Kieselbach, Budapest #41/R (H.F 650000)
£2064	$3220	€3096	Grandfather, 1924 (100x69cm-39x27in) s.d.1924. 11-Sep-2 Kieselbach, Budapest #136/R (H.F 800000)
£2064	$3220	€2993	Girls outside (47x62cm-19x24in) s. 13-Sep-2 Mu Terem Galeria, Budapest #170/R est:400000 (H.F 800000)
£2151	$3335	€3119	Daydreamer (50x37cm-20x15in) s. 9-Dec-2 Mu Terem Galeria, Budapest #140/R est:500000 (H.F 800000)
£2451	$3823	€3677	Girl in sunny hillside (70x48cm-28x19in) s. 11-Sep-2 Kieselbach, Budapest #76/R (H.F 950000)
£2451	$3823	€3554	Reading child (62x47cm-24x19in) s. 13-Sep-2 Mu Terem Galeria, Budapest #169/R est:750000 (H.F 950000)

£3353 $5231 €5030 Girl with doll (90x70cm-35x28in) s.d.1937. 11-Apr-3 Kieselbach, Budapest #15/R est:200000 (H.F 1200000)
£5916 $9170 €8874 Early spring (50x70cm-20x28in) s. 6-Dec-2 Kieselbach, Budapest #24/R (H.F 2200000)

Works on paper

£1006 $1569 €1459 Riverside in spring (37x52cm-15x20in) s. pastel. 12-Apr-3 Mu Terem Galeria, Budapest #197/R est:180000 (H.F 360000)

GLATZER, Simon (1890-1945) Russian

£385 $604 €600 Scene de ghetto (46x38cm-18x15in) s. 12-Dec-2 Rabourdin & Choppin de Janvry, Paris #123

GLAUBACHER, Franz (1896-1974) Yugoslavian

£1151 $1842 €1600 Meadows (54x64cm-21x25in) s. board. 14-May-3 Dorotheum, Linz #405 est:2400-2600
£1154 $1823 €1800 Meadow landscape (47x61cm-19x24in) s. board. 18-Nov-2 Dorotheum, Linz #274 est:3600-4000
£1282 $2026 €2000 Farmstead in early spring (50x63cm-20x25in) s. panel. 18-Nov-2 Dorotheum, Linz #273/R est:4000-4400

Works on paper

£360 $576 €500 Braunau (22x26cm-9x10in) s.d.39 W/C. 14-May-3 Dorotheum, Linz #440/R
£791 $1266 €1100 Linz (18x24cm-7x9in) s.d.1960 W/C. 14-May-3 Dorotheum, Linz #439/R

GLAUBER, Jan (1656-1703) Dutch

£6081 $9486 €9000 Allegory - Ceres as personification of summer (60x74cm-24x29in) bears sig. prov. 27-Mar-3 Dorotheum, Vienna #174/R est:9000-15000

GLAUBER, Jan (attrib) (1656-1703) Dutch

£1313 $1995 €1970 Paysage Italien (77x98cm-30x39in) 3-Jul-2 Naón & Cia, Buenos Aires #16 est:1500-1800

GLAUBER, Johannes (1646-1726) Dutch

Works on paper

£1146 $1789 €1800 Arcadian landscape with two figures on a road by a monument (30x25cm-12x10in) brush grey ink wash prov. 5-Nov-2 Sotheby's, Amsterdam #93/R est:2000-3000
£1146 $1789 €1800 Arcadian landscape with woman mourning by a sarcophagus (30x26cm-12x10in) brush grey ink wash prov. 5-Nov-2 Sotheby's, Amsterdam #94/R est:2000-3000

GLAUBER, Johannes (attrib) (1646-1726) Dutch

£2200 $3520 €3300 Figures before a ruined arch (77x59cm-30x23in) 7-Jan-3 Bonhams, Knightsbridge #72/R est:2000-3000
£4000 $6680 €5800 Classical landscape with Diana and her nymphs hunting (89x134cm-35x53in) 8-Jul-3 Sotheby's, Olympia #414/R est:4000-6000

GLAUNER, Karl (1902-) Swiss

£262 $409 €393 Bettmeralp with Mischabel (74x64cm-29x25in) s. 20-Nov-2 Fischer, Luzern #2091/R (S.FR 600)

GLAUS, Alfred (1890-1971) Swiss

£278 $447 €417 Mountain landscape on the Sense (50x65cm-20x26in) s. 7-May-3 Dobiaschofsky, Bern #598 (S.FR 600)
£873 $1362 €1310 Niesen (50x65cm-20x26in) s. 20-Nov-2 Fischer, Luzern #2092/R est:2000-2500 (S.FR 2000)

GLAZUNOV, Ilya (1930-) Russian

£581 $900 €872 Winter landscape with funeral procession (51x137cm-20x54in) s. i.verso. 7-Dec-2 Selkirks, St. Louis #745/R
£774 $1200 €1161 Portrait of a young woman wearing a bonnet (99x69cm-39x27in) s.d.1978. 7-Dec-2 Selkirks, St. Louis #744/R est:500-700

GLEASON, Joe Duncan (1881-1959) American

Works on paper

£599 $1000 €869 Sweeping the sea lanes (15x18cm-6x7in) s.d.45 W/C prov. 17-Jun-3 John Moran, Pasadena #89 est:1000-2000
£778 $1300 €1128 Crash boats, army rescue boats in action (18x23cm-7x9in) s. W/C prov. 17-Jun-3 John Moran, Pasadena #86 est:1500-2000
£838 $1400 €1215 Vosper P.T. in action (20x25cm-8x10in) s. W/C prov. 17-Jun-3 John Moran, Pasadena #85 est:1500-2500

GLEESON, James Timothy (1915-) Australian

£620 $986 €930 Magus 4 (15x12cm-6x5in) s. board. 5-May-3 Sotheby's, Melbourne #193/R (A.D 1600)
£659 $1048 €989 Masks (17x11cm-7x4in) s. board. 5-May-3 Sotheby's, Melbourne #222 (A.D 1700)
£714 $1121 €1071 Dream keeper III (15x12cm-6x5in) s. board. 25-Nov-2 Christie's, Melbourne #454 (A.D 2000)
£800 $1288 €1160 Variation on the wanderer theme (14x12cm-6x5in) s. board. 12-May-3 Joel, Victoria #262/R est:2000-3000 (A.D 2000)
£893 $1411 €1340 Wanderer in landscape VII (12x14cm-5x6in) s. board. 18-Nov-2 Goodman, Sydney #46/R (A.D 2500)
£964 $1524 €1446 Two figures in Psychoscape (20x14cm-8x6in) s. board. 26-Nov-2 Sotheby's, Melbourne #127/R est:3000-5000 (A.D 2700)
£996 $1564 €1494 Icarus (15x12cm-6x5in) s. board. 15-Apr-3 Lawson Menzies, Sydney #240/R est:2000-3000 (A.D 2600)
£996 $1564 €1494 Prometheus on Mt. Olympus (15x12cm-6x5in) s. board. 15-Apr-3 Lawson Menzies, Sydney #242/R est:2000-3000 (A.D 2600)
£1068 $1633 €1602 Untitled (15x18cm-6x7in) s. board painted c.1965. 26-Aug-2 Sotheby's, Paddington #589/R est:5000-7000 (A.D 3000)
£1071 $1693 €1607 Male nude in surrealist landscape (19x14cm-7x6in) s. board. 18-Nov-2 Joel, Victoria #234 est:3000-5000 (A.D 3000)
£1073 $1684 €1610 Jason (15x12cm-6x5in) s. board. 15-Apr-3 Lawson Menzies, Sydney #241/R est:2000-3000 (A.D 2800)
£1163 $1849 €1745 Psychoscape (20x14cm-8x6in) s. board. 5-May-3 Sotheby's, Melbourne #194/R est:3000-5000 (A.D 3000)
£1260 $2003 €1890 Figure in a psychoscape (15x12cm-6x5in) s. board prov. 5-May-3 Sotheby's, Melbourne #191/R est:3000-5000 (A.D 3250)
£1301 $2055 €1886 Odysseus III (11x15cm-4x6in) s. i.verso board. 22-Jul-3 Lawson Menzies, Sydney #125/R est:2000-3000 (A.D 3200)
£1316 $2000 €1974 Fantasy (14x12cm-6x5in) s. board. 19-Aug-2 Joel, Victoria #355/R est:3000-5000 (A.D 3750)
£1336 $2110 €2313 Man in surrealscape (15x12cm-6x5in) s. board. 1-Apr-3 Goodman, Sydney #33 est:3500-4500 (A.D 3500)
£1500 $2370 €2250 Wanderer in rain (19x24cm-7x9in) s. canvasboard prov. 26-Nov-2 Sotheby's, Melbourne #131/R est:5000-8000 (A.D 4200)
£1550 $2465 €2325 Odysseus no 7 (14x12cm-6x5in) s. i.verso. 5-May-3 Sotheby's, Melbourne #330/R est:2000-4000 (A.D 4000)
£1577 $2397 €2366 Figure in surrealist landscape (15x19cm-6x7in) s. composition board prov. 28-Aug-2 Deutscher-Menzies, Melbourne #174/R est:2500-3500 (A.D 4400)
£1615 $2568 €2423 Variation on the wanderer theme II (15x12cm-6x5in) s. composition board. 4-Mar-3 Deutscher-Menzies, Melbourne #179/R est:3500-5000 (A.D 4200)
£1637 $2505 €2456 Surfer I (19x14cm-7x6in) s. board. 25-Aug-2 Sotheby's, Paddington #179 est:3000-6000 (A.D 4600)
£1679 $2652 €2909 Nude in psychoscape (14x12cm-6x5in) s. board. 1-Apr-3 Goodman, Sydney #42/R (A.D 4400)
£1786 $2768 €2679 Titan VIII (19x14cm-7x6in) s. board. 29-Oct-2 Lawson Menzies, Sydney #12/R est:3000-5000 (A.D 5000)
£1786 $2804 €2679 Psychoscape (15x12cm-6x5in) s. 25-Nov-2 Christie's, Melbourne #391/R est:5000-7000 (A.D 5000)
£1846 $2935 €2769 Variation on the wanderer theme I (15x12cm-6x5in) s. composition board. 4-Mar-3 Deutscher-Menzies, Melbourne #178/R est:3500-5000 (A.D 4800)
£1857 $2934 €2786 Figure in pschoscape (19x14cm-7x6in) s. board. 18-Nov-2 Goodman, Sydney #129 est:5000-7000 (A.D 5200)
£2132 $3390 €3198 Searcher (15x12cm-6x5in) s. i.verso board. 5-May-3 Sotheby's, Melbourne #329/R est:3000-5000 (A.D 5500)
£2143 $3364 €3215 Sentinel VI (20x16cm-8x6in) s.verso board painted c.1969. 25-Nov-2 Christie's, Melbourne #280/R est:5000-7000 (A.D 6000)
£2623 $4250 €3803 Wanderer I. Wanderer III (15x13cm-6x5in) s. board. 21-May-3 Doyle, New York #32/R est:1200-1600
£3203 $4900 €4805 Dream (39x29cm-15x11in) s.d.67 canvas on board prov. 25-Aug-2 Sotheby's, Paddington #128/R est:8000-12000 (A.D 9000)
£7143 $11214 €10715 Icarus legend (15x11cm-6x4in) s.i. board 10 panels. 25-Nov-2 Christie's, Melbourne #76/R est:20000-30000 (A.D 20000)
£9231 $14677 €13847 An ordered flow (133x178cm-52x70in) s.d.95 s.i.verso. 4-Mar-3 Deutscher-Menzies, Melbourne #53/R est:26000-30000 (A.D 24000)
£11429 $18057 €17144 Armourer (152x204cm-60x80in) s.d.85 prov.exhib.lit. 26-Nov-2 Sotheby's, Melbourne #48/R est:25000-35000 (A.D 32000)

Works on paper

£537 $817 €806 Remember Lots wife (56x44cm-22x17in) s.i.d.76 pencil collage ink wash pen ink exhib. 28-Aug-2 Deutscher-Menzies, Melbourne #359/R (A.D 1500)
£677 $1111 €1016 Exploitation of the chance meeting (42x29cm-17x11in) s.d.76 ink wash pen collage exhib. 4-Jun-3 Deutscher-Menzies, Melbourne #133/R (A.D 1700)
£860 $1308 €1290 Orchestra III (76x57cm-30x22in) s.d.76 pencil collage ink wash pen ink exhib. 28-Aug-2 Deutscher-Menzies, Melbourne #358/R (A.D 2400)
£958 $1427 €1437 Fantasy in figure one (49x36cm-19x14in) s. pen ink W/C prov. 27-Aug-2 Christie's, Melbourne #217/R est:3000-4000 (A.D 2500)

GLEGHORN, Thomas (1925-) Australian

£356 $544 €534 Harbour (61x122cm-24x48in) i.verso board painted 1959 prov. 26-Aug-2 Sotheby's, Paddington #599 est:3000-5000 (A.D 1000)
£387 $611 €581 Evocation of the entombment (61x91cm-24x36in) s.d.58 i.verso board. 27-Nov-2 Deutscher-Menzies, Melbourne #154/R est:2000-4000 (A.D 1080)

£1139 $1742 €1709 Corner of Ainsley's Corner (122x122cm-48x48in) s. s.i.verso painted 1974 prov. 26-Aug-2 Sotheby's, Paddington #583 est:4000-6000 (A.D 3200)

GLEHN, Jane de (1873-1961) British

Works on paper

£449 $700 €674 In the park, New York (20x25cm-8x10in) s. gouache. 1-Aug-2 Eldred, East Dennis #464/R

GLEHN, Wilfred Gabriel de (1870-1951) British

£1250 $2063 €1813 Portrait of Mrs Annie Melhuish Whitworth (91x73cm-36x29in) s.d.1936. 1-Jul-3 Bearnes, Exeter #518/R est:1000-1500
£1800 $2970 €2610 River Arun, West Sussex (66x76cm-26x30in) 3-Jul-3 Christie's, Kensington #459 est:2000-3000
£5000 $7800 €7500 View of the Cornish coast (63x76cm-25x30in) s.d.1918. 12-Sep-2 Sotheby's, Olympia #84/R est:2000-3000
£5000 $7900 €7500 Nude in a classical landscape (71x56cm-28x22in) s. 27-Nov-2 Sotheby's, Olympia #234/R est:5000-7000
£5400 $8370 €8100 Portrait of a seated model (75x62cm-30x24in) s. 29-Oct-2 Henry Adams, Chichester #504/R est:6000-8000
£12000 $18840 €18000 St. Tropez (48x61cm-19x24in) s. 22-Nov-2 Christie's, London #16/R est:12000-18000
£16129 $25000 €24194 Vieux port sur la Seine, Normandy (64x77cm-25x30in) s. i.verso prov. 29-Oct-2 Sotheby's, New York #86/R est:25000-35000

GLEICH, Joanna (1959-) Polish

£903 $1426 €1300 Untitled (150x130cm-59x51in) s.d.01 s.d. verso. 24-Apr-3 Dorotheum, Vienna #288/R

GLEICH, John (1879-?) German

£306 $483 €459 Char a boeuf (27x35cm-11x14in) s. cardboard. 17-Nov-2 Koller, Geneva #1246 (S.FR 700)
£425 $662 €620 Sailing ship in worsening weather (51x64cm-20x25in) s. 10-Apr-3 Schopman, Hamburg #703
£2138 $3336 €3400 Two Indian women on market square (50x50cm-20x20in) s. 20-Sep-2 Karlheinz Kaupp, Staufen #1856/R est:1100
£2830 $4415 €4500 Inner courtyard of Indian temple with seated Sikhs (67x60cm-26x24in) s. 20-Sep-2 Karlheinz Kaupp, Staufen #1854/R est:1400
£2893 $4513 €4600 Ruins of Amber (64x50cm-25x20in) s. i. verso. 20-Sep-2 Karlheinz Kaupp, Staufen #1858/R est:1400
£3396 $5298 €5400 Temple entrance in Puri, India (63x50cm-25x20in) s. i. verso. 20-Sep-2 Karlheinz Kaupp, Staufen #1855/R est:1500
£3522 $5494 €5600 Riverside Indian temple (80x100cm-31x39in) s. 20-Sep-2 Karlheinz Kaupp, Staufen #1860/R est:1500

GLEICHEN, Lady Helena (1873-1947) British

Works on paper

£360 $587 €540 Hauling timber (88x137cm-35x54in) s.i. chl wash. 30-Jan-3 Lawrence, Crewkerne #660

GLEICHEN-RUSSWURM, Heinrich Ludwig von (1836-1901) German

£1195 $1864 €1900 Walkers in woodland (23x32cm-9x13in) s. panel. 19-Sep-2 Dr Fritz Nagel, Stuttgart #933/R est:1000

GLEICHMANN, Otto (1887-1963) German

£2692 $4173 €4200 Couple (19x16cm-7x6in) s.d.19 W/C Indian ink. 4-Dec-2 Lempertz, Koln #737/R est:3500
£10870 $17826 €15000 Woman making herself beautiful (70x63cm-28x25in) s.d.1928 i. stretcher exhib. 31-May-3 Villa Grisebach, Berlin #237/R est:9000-12000

Works on paper

£685 $1068 €1000 Walking with foal (18x23cm-7x9in) s.d. pencil. 11-Apr-3 Winterberg, Heidelberg #1039/R est:980
£6159 $10101 €8500 Still life with shapes (16x12cm-6x5in) s.i.d.1920 gouache board exhib. 31-May-3 Villa Grisebach, Berlin #235/R est:3500-4500

GLEIM, Eduard (1812-1899) German

£2381 $3786 €3500 Mountain landscape with travellers on path (7x122cm-3x48in) s.d.69. 19-Mar-3 Neumeister, Munich #565/R est:4000

GLEIZE, Leon (19th C) French?

Works on paper

£1090 $1700 €1635 Femme nue (23x30cm-9x12in) s.d.1883 pencil. 19-Sep-2 Swann Galleries, New York #373/R est:2000-3000

GLEIZES, Albert (1881-1953) French

£9500 $15010 €14250 Composition bleue (44x36cm-17x14in) s.d.48 board. 3-Apr-3 Christie's, Kensington #121/R
£10204 $16224 €15000 Rue animee a Prague (85x96cm-33x38in) s.d.1904. 24-Mar-3 Coutau Begarie, Paris #200/R est:20000
£11950 $18522 €19000 Composition rouge brun (45x38cm-18x15in) s.d.48 panel. 30-Oct-2 Artcurial Briest, Paris #347/R est:20000-30000
£28000 $44240 €42000 Composition aux oeufs (71x58cm-28x23in) s.d.1921 prov.exhib.lit. 3-Apr-3 Christie's, Kensington #127/R est:20000-30000
£42000 $70140 €60900 Spirale brun et vert (168x78cm-66x31in) s.d.32-33 prov.exhib. 25-Jun-3 Christie's, London #199/R est:50000-60000

Works on paper

£1325 $2159 €2000 Composition (26x14cm-10x6in) s. gouache cardboard. 1-Feb-3 Claude Aguttes, Neuilly #209 est:3050-4575
£2500 $3850 €3750 La femme au gant (26x20cm-10x8in) s.d.20 pencil prov.exhib.lit. 23-Oct-2 Sotheby's, Olympia #693/R est:3000-4000
£3774 $6000 €5661 Etude pour composition a quatre elements (27x21cm-11x8in) pencil htd chk exec.1923 prov.lit. 27-Feb-3 Christie's, Rockefeller NY #32/R
£3800 $6042 €5700 Composition (35x28cm-14x11in) s.d.22 gouache. 20-Mar-3 Sotheby's, Olympia #86/R est:3000-4000
£4172 $6801 €6300 Composition (19x10cm-7x4in) s.i.d.1942 gouache W/C cardboard. 3-Feb-3 Chambelland & Giafferi, Paris #331/R est:2000
£4500 $6930 €6750 Autoportrait (17x15cm-7x6in) s.d.1935 gouache card prov.exhib.lit. 23-Oct-2 Sotheby's, Olympia #691/R est:2000-3000
£4861 $8021 €7000 Composition (34x26cm-13x10in) s.d.49 gouache oil. 2-Jul-3 Artcurial Briest, Paris #662/R est:7000-9000
£4965 $8291 €7000 Composition (29x16cm-11x6in) mono. gouache exec.c.1935. 23-Jun-3 Claude Boisgirard, Paris #125/R est:7000-8000
£5500 $8470 €8250 New York (18x14cm-7x6in) s.d.15 pen ink. 23-Oct-2 Sotheby's, Olympia #692/R est:4000-6000
£5769 $8942 €9000 Ciel et Terre (38x47cm-15x19in) s.d.38 gouache prov.lit. 4-Dec-2 Pierre Berge, Paris #23/R
£6250 $9938 €9000 Composition cubiste (48x31cm-19x12in) s. gouache exec.c.1930-31. 29-Apr-3 Campo & Campo, Antwerp #129/R est:10000-15000
£6923 $10869 €10800 Paysage cubiste (18x24cm-7x9in) s.d.13 ink dr. 11-Dec-2 Artcurial Briest, Paris #539/R est:10000
£7547 $12000 €11321 Figure en gloire (39x19cm-15x7in) s. gouache board prov. 27-Feb-3 Christie's, Rockefeller NY #34/R est:16000
£8000 $12320 €12000 Nature morte or oranges et poivrons (50x70cm-20x28in) s.d.44 gouache prov.exhib.lit. 22-Oct-2 Sotheby's, London #241/R est:9000-12000
£8597 $14357 €12466 Figure, cubist (37x25cm-15x10in) s.d.20. 24-Jun-3 Koller, Zurich #131/R est:3500-5000 (S.FR 19000)
£10646 $16928 €15650 Poeme onirique (27x21cm-11x8in) s.d.22 gouache. 26-Feb-3 Artcurial Briest, Paris #73/R est:7000-8000
£11511 $18417 €16000 Le ciel et la terre (37x46cm-15x18in) s.d. gouache exhib.lit. 18-May-3 Eric Pillon, Calais #266/R
£12000 $18480 €18000 Composition (43x35cm-17x14in) s.d.1921 gouache prov.lit. 22-Oct-2 Sotheby's, London #179/R est:10000-12000
£23077 $36231 €36000 Femme ux betes (39x24cm-15x9in) s.i.d.1913 wash gouache prov.lit. 10-Dec-2 Pierre Berge, Paris #40/R est:30000

GLENAVY, Lady Beatrice (1883-1970) British

Works on paper

£641 $1006 €1000 Little girl standing, with fairies playing by her feet (23x12cm-9x5in) mono.d.September 1923 W/C. 19-Nov-2 Hamilton Osborne King, Dublin #437/R

GLENDENING, Alfred Augustus (19th C) British

£755 $1162 €1200 Landscape with river and small punt (20x38cm-8x15in) mono.d.1888. 26-Oct-2 Quittenbaum, Hamburg #10/R
£1800 $2790 €2700 Woodcutter (60x90cm-24x35in) init.d.1884. 3-Dec-2 Sotheby's, Olympia #140/R est:2000-3000
£2006 $3250 €2909 Capel-Curig, North Wales (41x66cm-16x26in) s. prov. 21-May-3 Doyle, New York #179/R est:4000-6000
£2600 $4134 €3900 Sunset (20x38cm-8x15in) init.d.88. 6-Mar-3 Christie's, Kensington #458/R est:1200-1800
£2700 $4509 €3915 River landscape with cattle, fishermen - Hurley on the Thames (25x41cm-10x16in) init.d.93. 24-Jun-3 Neal & Fletcher, Woodbridge #378/R est:2500-3500
£3500 $5495 €5250 Shepherd driving sheep near the coast (30x51cm-12x20in) s.d.03. 19-Nov-2 Bonhams, New Bond Street #117/R est:2000-3000
£3800 $5966 €5700 River scene with a figure by a cottage (30x51cm-12x20in) s. 19-Nov-2 Bonhams, New Bond Street #118/R est:2000-3000
£4600 $7176 €6900 Drover with cattle in a river valley (61x50cm-24x20in) s. 8-Apr-3 Bonhams, Knightsbridge #156/R est:5000-7000
£5500 $9020 €8250 Angler on the bank of a river (30x51cm-12x20in) s.d.09 prov. 29-May-3 Christie's, Kensington #151/R est:4000-6000
£8917 $14000 €13376 Cattle grazing. In the hay fields (25x41cm-10x16in) init. one d.91 two prov. 10-Dec-2 Doyle, New York #168/R est:7000-10000
£10000 $15600 €15000 Cornfield, Isle of Wight (61x91cm-24x36in) s.init.d.1870 prov. 26-Mar-3 Woolley & Wallis, Salisbury #206/R est:10000-15000

GLENDENING, Alfred Augustus (jnr) (1861-1907) British

£360 $565 €540 River landscape at dusk (24x48cm-9x19in) init.d.1880 panel. 16-Apr-3 Christie's, Kensington #633
£1400 $2296 €2100 Morning, North Wales (9x24cm-4x9in) board. 4-Feb-3 Bonhams, Leeds #397 est:600-800

£1500 $2370 €2250 River landscape with cattle watering and a castle nearby (40x30cm-16x12in) init.d.86. 7-Apr-3 Bonhams, Bath #97/R est:1500-2000
£2200 $3674 €3190 Mill at sunset. Sheep in a park (21x17cm-8x7in) init.d.73 board pair. 17-Jun-3 Bonhams, New Bond Street #68/R est:1800-2500
£2667 $4427 €3867 Figure outside a cottage by a duck pond (41x30cm-16x12in) init.d.98. 16-Jun-3 Waddingtons, Toronto #155/R est:4000-6000 (C.D 6000)
£4400 $6820 €6600 Extensive river landscape with figures in a boat, cattle and village beyond (8x15cm-3x6in) init. 9-Dec-2 Lawrences, Bletchingley #1871/R est:2000-3000
£4600 $7452 €6900 Fishing on the Thames (27x40cm-11x16in) 20-May-3 Sotheby's, Olympia #216/R est:2000-3000
£5000 $8100 €7500 Path on the river bank (51x38cm-20x15in) s. 20-May-3 Sotheby's, Olympia #251/R est:1000-1500
£5500 $8580 €8250 Rest from the harvest (41x62cm-16x24in) init.d.83. 26-Mar-3 Sotheby's, Olympia #91/R est:2000-3000
£5500 $9185 €7975 View in Cumberland (61x50cm-24x20in) s. 17-Jun-3 Bonhams, New Bond Street #69/R est:6000-8000
£6000 $9420 €9000 Coastal scene with two young girls picking primroses. Children with a dog on sunlit path (26x36cm-10x14in) init.d.85 pair. 19-Nov-2 Bonhams, Leeds #217 est:6000-8000
£7800 $12246 €11700 Summer wooded landscape with two girls blackberrying (41x31cm-16x12in) init.d.97. 19-Nov-2 Bonhams, Leeds #218/R est:4000-5000
£9200 $14352 €13800 Ponty Gyfing, Capel Curig, North Wales (39x65cm-15x26in) s. 26-Mar-3 Sotheby's, Olympia #90/R est:4000-6000

GLENDENING, Alfred Augustus (snr) (?-c.1910) British
£6900 $11247 €10350 Ferry, Isleworth on Thames (39x24cm-15x9in) s.i.d.09. 11-Feb-3 Fellows & Sons, Birmingham #59/R est:5000-8000

GLENNIE, Arthur (1803-1890) British
Works on paper
£350 $578 €508 Mountainous Italian landscape (39x64cm-15x25in) s. pencil W/C scratching out. 3-Jul-3 Christie's, Kensington #72/R
£620 $980 €930 View of Postum with cattle in the foreground (18x32cm-7x13in) s. W/C. 26-Nov-2 Bonhams, Knightsbridge #62/R

GLEYRE, Charles (1806-1874) Swiss
£19182 $29541 €30500 Minerve entouree de Trois Graces (45x29cm-18x11in) panel canvas on board lit. 27-Oct-2 Muizon & Le Coent, Paris #39/R

GLINDONI, Henry Gillard (1852-1913) British
£444 $738 €644 Simon the cellarer (36x46cm-14x18in) s. 16-Jun-3 Waddingtons, Toronto #127/R est:1000-1500 (C.D 1000)

GLINTENKAMP, Hendrik (1887-1946) American
£5063 $8000 €7595 New York Harbor (51x61cm-20x24in) s. prov. 24-Apr-3 Shannon's, Milford #167/R est:8000-12000

GLINZ, Theo (1890-1962) Swiss
£429 $678 €644 Anemones in a blue vase (56x41cm-22x16in) s. 26-Nov-2 Hans Widmer, St Gallen #1134 (S.FR 1000)
£437 $681 €656 Farmstead (48x54cm-19x21in) s.d.1923 i. verso. 6-Nov-2 Dobiaschofsky, Bern #596/R (S.FR 1000)
£611 $954 €917 Summer bouquet (49x49cm-19x19in) s. panel. 6-Nov-2 Hans Widmer, St Gallen #80/R (S.FR 1400)
£655 $1022 €983 Flowers in vase (69x51cm-27x20in) s. panel. 6-Nov-2 Hans Widmer, St Gallen #86/R (S.FR 1500)
£1373 $2170 €2060 Still life with phlox (100x120cm-39x47in) s. panel. 26-Nov-2 Hans Widmer, St Gallen #1131 est:2400-4200 (S.FR 3200)
£1834 $2861 €2751 Romanshorn harbour (82x120cm-32x47in) s. panel. 6-Nov-2 Hans Widmer, St Gallen #95/R est:4000-6500 (S.FR 4200)

GLISENTI, X (19th C) Italian?
£9607 $15179 €14411 Father and daughter playing in elegant surroundings (59x77cm-23x30in) s. 14-Nov-2 Stuker, Bern #253/R est:2500-3000 (S.FR 22000)

GLOCKNER, Hermann (1889-1987) German
£314 $484 €500 Folding red/white (21x30cm-8x12in) mono.d.1977 verso tempera paper. 26-Oct-2 Dr Lehr, Berlin #126/R
£3188 $5229 €4400 Triangular elevations (70x50cm-28x20in) s.i.d.1980 verso tempera folded paper exhib. 31-May-3 Villa Grisebach, Berlin #211/R est:3000-4000
£4028 $6364 €5800 Triangles on red (50x72cm-20x28in) s.i.d. verso tempera folded paper. 26-Apr-3 Dr Lehr, Berlin #155/R est:4000
Works on paper
£1806 $2853 €2600 Green spiral (43x61cm-17x24in) mono.i.d.28/7/83 verso wax. 26-Apr-3 Dr Lehr, Berlin #157/R est:1000
£2292 $3621 €3300 Untitled (33x45cm-13x18in) s.d.1958 verso Indian ink tempera. 26-Apr-3 Dr Lehr, Berlin #154/R est:1500

GLOD, Adam (20th C) ?
£299 $464 €449 View of Tatras mountain (68x90cm-27x35in) board painted c.1935. 1-Oct-2 SOGA, Bratislava #8/R est:19000 (SL.K 19000)

GLODKOWSKI, O (?) ?
£298 $462 €447 Still life of lobster, fruit and nuts on table (33x49cm-13x19in) s. 28-Sep-2 Rasmussen, Havnen #2054 (D.KR 3500)

GLOECKNER, Michael (1915-1989) German/American
£250 $400 €363 Haiti No 4 (50x50cm-20x20in) init. s.i.d.1977 verso. 16-May-3 Skinner, Boston #371/R
£481 $750 €722 First spring light (104x91cm-41x36in) mono. s.i.d.Feb 1967 verso. 15-Oct-2 Winter Associates, Plainville #153

GLOEDEN, Wilhelm von (1886-1931) German
Photographs
£1923 $3000 €2885 Male nude seated on rock, Taormina (30x27cm-12x11in) s.i.d. platinum palladium. 21-Oct-2 Swann Galleries, New York #276/R est:3000-5000
£2025 $3200 €3038 Jugendlicher siziliander (22x16cm-9x6in) albumen print prov.lit. 24-Apr-3 Phillips, New York #88/R est:3000-4000

GLOERSEN, Jakob (1852-1912) Norwegian
£2618 $4110 €3927 Winter landscape with river (64x89cm-25x35in) s.d.1908. 21-Nov-2 Grev Wedels Plass, Oslo #68/R est:30000-40000 (N.KR 30000)

GLOGUEN, J (?) American?
£962 $1500 €1395 Racing cutter under sail (51x61cm-20x24in) s. 28-Mar-3 Eldred, East Dennis #602/R est:800-1200

GLOSER, Gerhard (1947-) Austrian
£464 $756 €700 Figures (42x60cm-17x24in) mono.d.2002 tempera board. 28-Jan-3 Dorotheum, Vienna #315/R

GLOSSOP, Allerley (1870-1955) South African
£288 $450 €432 Morning mists (50x40cm-20x16in) s.i. 11-Nov-2 Stephan Welz, Johannesburg #148 (SA.R 4500)

GLOUTCHENKO, Nicholai Petrovitch (1902-1977) Russian
£1154 $1812 €1800 Still life in interior (84x56cm-33x22in) s. panel. 12-Dec-2 Rabourdin & Choppin de Janvry, Paris #30/R

GLOVER, John (1767-1849) British
£300 $471 €450 Suffolk river landscape with cattle watering (48x66cm-19x26in) 13-Dec-2 Keys, Aylsham #690/R
£8140 $12942 €12210 West Water, the Lake District (50x65cm-20x26in) 5-May-3 Sotheby's, Melbourne #309/R est:10000-15000 (A.D 21000)
£8897 $13612 €13346 Wooded landscape (52x70cm-20x28in) 25-Aug-2 Sotheby's, Paddington #80/R est:25000-30000 (A.D 25000)
£19573 $29947 €29360 Italy, about twenty miles from Rome (76x114cm-30x45in) painted 1838 prov.exhib. 26-Aug-2 Sotheby's, Paddington #558/R est:40000-60000 (A.D 55000)
£21429 $33857 €32144 Castle at Otricoli (74x112cm-29x44in) 26-Nov-2 Sotheby's, Melbourne #58/R est:40000-60000 (A.D 60000)
£250000 $395000 €375000 Montacute, Bothwell (76x114cm-30x45in) s.d.1838 prov.exhib.lit. 26-Nov-2 Sotheby's, Melbourne #51/R est:1000000-1500000 (A.D 700000)
Works on paper
£1700 $2720 €2550 Fishing the weir pool (20x30cm-8x12in) W/C. 11-Mar-3 Bonhams, New Bond Street #46/R est:1000-1500
£1700 $2805 €2465 Cattle grazing in an extensive landscape (75x61cm-30x24in) pencil W/C. 3-Jul-3 Christie's, Kensington #130/R est:700-1000
£2200 $3608 €3300 Windermere (32x41cm-13x16in) pencil W/C. 4-Feb-3 Bonhams, Leeds #270 est:1500-2000
£3244 $5126 €4866 St. Laurent ruins. Lake Boisana, Italy (23x32cm-9x13in) i. W/C pair. 2-Apr-3 Christie's, Melbourne #2/R est:5000-7000 (A.D 8500)
£3244 $5126 €4866 Shepherds with a flock and a ruin on the banks of a lock with distant mountains (15x20cm-6x8in) W/C. 2-Apr-3 Christie's, Melbourne #44/R est:4000-6000 (A.D 8500)
£8812 $13130 €13218 Windsor Castle (76x115cm-30x45in) i. W/C pencil prov. 27-Aug-2 Christie's, Melbourne #102/R est:15000-20000 (A.D 23000)

GLOVER, John (attrib) (1767-1849) British

Works on paper

£360 $587 €540 Trees beside a path (28x38cm-11x15in) W/C. 28-Jan-3 Gorringes, Lewes #1600

GLUCK, Anselm (1950-) Austrian

£728 $1187 €1100 Untitled (49x40cm-19x16in) acrylic. 28-Jan-3 Dorotheum, Vienna #243/R

GLUCK, John (?) ?

£1394 $2203 €2091 Nude model (70x100cm-28x39in) s. 5-Apr-3 Rasmussen, Havnen #2105 est:3000 (D.KR 15000)

GLUCKLICH, Simon (1863-1943) German

£1690 $2806 €2400 Coquette in white summer dress (51x34cm-20x13in) s. panel. 14-Jun-3 Arnold, Frankfurt #751/R est:600

GLUCKMAN, Judith (1915-1961) South African

£295 $460 €443 African figurines with a scull. Woman sweeping (71x94cm-28x37in) s. board double-sided. 15-Oct-2 Stephan Welz, Johannesburg #194 est:1500-2000 (SA.R 4800)

GLUCKMANN, Grigory (1898-1973) American/Russian

£1274 $2000 €1911 Arranging her hair (46x33cm-18x13in) s. board prov. 19-Nov-2 Butterfields, San Francisco #8346/R est:2000-3000

£1419 $2214 €2100 Female nude (28x34cm-11x13in) s. panel. 28-Mar-3 Delvaux, Paris #45

£1796 $3000 €2604 Fruit and ceramic (32x41cm-13x16in) s. board prov. 18-Jun-3 Christie's, Los Angeles #90/R est:3000-5000

£2259 $3750 €3276 In the foyer (37x29cm-15x11in) s. panel prov. 11-Jun-3 Butterfields, San Francisco #4306/R est:3000-5000

£2500 $3926 €3750 Seated woman a decollette (37x49cm-15x19in) s. 20-Nov-2 Sotheby's, London #67/R est:2500-3500

£2838 $4427 €4200 Women and children (50x61cm-20x24in) s. 28-Mar-3 Delvaux, Paris #44/R est:2500

Works on paper

£791 $1226 €1250 Conversation romantique (21x15cm-8x6in) sepai gouache vellum. 29-Sep-2 Eric Pillon, Calais #28/R

GLUD, Wilfred Peter (1872-1946) Danish

£306 $496 €444 Nude female in chair by window (80x100cm-31x39in) s.d.39. 24-May-3 Rasmussen, Havnen #4313 (D.KR 3200)

GLUSING, Martin Franz (1885-1956) German

£374 $595 €550 Fishing boat in North Sea (60x80cm-24x31in) s. i. verso. 28-Mar-3 Bolland & Marotz, Bremen #548/R

£897 $1391 €1400 Finkenwarder fishing boats in the moonlight (80x120cm-31x47in) s.d.1927. 7-Dec-2 Hans Stahl, Hamburg #140/R

GLYDE, Henry George (1906-1998) Canadian

£442 $698 €663 Fulking, West Sussex, England (25x30cm-10x12in) d.1974 canvasboard. 1-Dec-2 Levis, Calgary #35/R (C.D 1100)

£803 $1269 €1205 Low tide near Active Pass, BC (33x41cm-13x16in) d.1954 paperboard. 1-Dec-2 Levis, Calgary #32/R est:2000-2500 (C.D 2000)

£843 $1333 €1265 Farm buildings, Saanich BC (28x36cm-11x14in) canvasboard. 1-Dec-2 Levis, Calgary #34/R est:1500-2000 (C.D 2100)

£978 $1604 €1418 Fulking, West Sussex, England (25x30cm-10x12in) s.i.d.1974 board. 9-Jun-3 Hodgins, Calgary #31/R est:1200-1800 (C.D 2200)

£1949 $3099 €2924 Old barn, Salmon Arm, BC (45x60cm-18x24in) s.i. 23-Mar-3 Hodgins, Calgary #22/R est:2500-3500 (C.D 4600)

£2008 $3153 €3012 Camp, Alaska Highway, north west of Whitehorse, St Elias Range (25x35cm-10x14in) s.i.d.1943 board prov. 25-Nov-2 Hodgins, Calgary #82/R est:3000-3500 (C.D 5000)

£3072 $4885 €4608 White Man's Pass, Canadian Rockies (60x75cm-24x30in) s.i. 23-Mar-3 Hodgins, Calgary #52/R est:3000-4000 (C.D 7250)

£6780 $10780 €10170 Country coffee shop (60x75cm-24x30in) s.i. 23-Mar-3 Hodgins, Calgary #104/R est:3500-5000 (C.D 16000)

Works on paper

£241 $378 €362 Canadian Rockies, near Louise (26x36cm-10x14in) s.d.1986 W/C. 25-Nov-2 Hodgins, Calgary #149/R (C.D 600)

£311 $510 €467 Old church by Bedforshire (39x56cm-15x22in) s. W/C chl. 3-Jun-3 Joyner, Toronto #565 (C.D 700)

£361 $567 €542 Female figure (56x38cm-22x15in) s.d.1966 ink W/C double-sided. 25-Nov-2 Hodgins, Calgary #337/R (C.D 900)

£489 $802 €734 In county Durham, England (41x50cm-16x20in) s.d.51 W/C ink. 3-Jun-3 Joyner, Toronto #209/R est:1200-1500 (C.D 1100)

£522 $814 €870 Untitled - reclining nude (38x58cm-15x23in) s. W/C prov. 13-Apr-3 Levis, Calgary #40/R est:1200-1500 (C.D 1200)

£622 $1020 €933 Cowboys at Canmore (26x37cm-10x15in) s.d.44 W/C prov. 3-Jun-3 Joyner, Toronto #483 est:1200-1500 (C.D 1400)

£756 $1239 €1096 Durham, England (40x51cm-16x20in) s.d.1949 W/C. 9-Jun-3 Hodgins, Calgary #167/R est:1750-2000 (C.D 1700)

£1689 $2770 €2534 Alaska highway, Yukon (36x38cm-14x15in) s.d.43 W/C. 3-Jun-3 Joyner, Toronto #572 est:1200-1500 (C.D 3800)

GMELIN, Johann (1810-1854) German

£8176 $12673 €13000 Palermo and Mt Pellegrino (70x96cm-28x38in) panel prov. 2-Oct-2 Dorotheum, Vienna #69/R est:13000-18000

GNOLI, Domenico (1933-1970) Italian

£4000 $6200 €6000 Piccolo uomo con una sciarpa rossa (49x39cm-19x15in) oil plaster on canvas exhib. 5-Dec-2 Christie's, Kensington #173/R est:5000-7000

£25000 $38500 €37500 Cattedrale e cavallo (168x74cm-66x29in) s.d.60 tempera sand prov. 22-Oct-2 Christie's, London #7/R est:25000-35000

£30000 $50100 €43500 Boy resting at a table (70x119cm-28x47in) s.d.60 acrylic sand prov.lit. 26-Jun-3 Sotheby's, London #206/R est:25000-35000

£170000 $265200 €255000 Shoulder (160x140cm-63x55in) s.i.d.1969 verso acrylic sand on canvas prov.exhib.lit. 21-Oct-2 Sotheby's, London #42/R est:190000-250000

Works on paper

£903 $1400 €1355 Wicked roberry (41x30cm-16x12in) s.i. pen ink. 28-Sep-2 Charlton Hall, Columbia #717/R

GOBAILLE, Jean (?) French?

£283 $439 €450 Bouquet de fleurs (50x60cm-20x24in) s. 6-Oct-2 Livinec, Gaudcheau & Jezequel, Rennes #54

GOBAUT, Gaspard (1814-1882) French

Works on paper

£2237 $3624 €3400 Armee en campagne (51x92cm-20x36in) s. W/C. 22-Jan-3 Tajan, Paris #20 est:1500-1800

GOBER, Robert (1954-) American

£35000 $57400 €52500 Untitled (24x32cm-9x13in) s.d.88 verso fabric paint felt tip pen flannel prov.exhib. 7-Feb-3 Sotheby's, London #153/R est:18000-25000

Photographs

£36709 $58000 €55064 Untitled (50x40cm-20x16in) s.d.1999 num.2/5 verso toned gelatin silver print prov.exhib. 13-Nov-2 Christie's, Rockefeller NY #57/R est:50000-70000

Prints

£16456 $26000 €24684 Untitled (29x24cm-11x9in) s.d.1994-95 num. platinum palladium print prov.exhib.lit. 14-Nov-2 Christie's, Rockefeller NY #307/R est:12000-18000

Sculpture

£25000 $41750 €37500 Bag of donuts (28x16x15cm-11x6x6in) s.d.1989 paper dough rhoplex 12 donuts 1/8 prov.lit. 26-Jun-3 Christie's, London #1/R est:30000-50000

£25316 $40000 €37974 Red shoe (8x8x20cm-3x3x8in) st.sig.d.1990 num.25/30 coloured wax prov.lit. 13-Nov-2 Sotheby's, New York #494/R est:40000-60000

£110000 $180400 €165000 Two breasts (21x18x10cm-8x7x4in) wax pigment in 2 parts exec.1990 prov. 6-Feb-3 Sotheby's, London #49/R est:180000

£126582 $200000 €189873 Untitled - dog bed (28x96x76cm-11x38x30in) s. i.d.1987 verso hand woven rattan cotton flannel fabric paint. 13-Nov-2 Christie's, Rockefeller NY #58/R est:350000-450000

£284810 $450000 €427215 Inverted sink (168x260x61cm-66x102x24in) plaster wood wire lath steel semi-gloss enamel paint prov.exhib. 13-Nov-2 Christie's, Rockefeller NY #26/R est:500000-700000

£411392 $650000 €617088 Untitled (60x44x28cm-24x17x11in) s.d.1990 verso beeswax pigment human hair prov.exhib.lit. 13-Nov-2 Christie's, Rockefeller NY #56/R est:1000000-1500000

Works on paper

£6962 $11000 €10443 Untitled (20x13cm-8x5in) s.d.86 graphite executed 1986 prov.exhib. 14-Nov-2 Christie's, Rockefeller NY #312/R est:18000-22000

£9494 $15000 €14241 Untitled (28x35cm-11x14in) s.d.85 graphite prov.exhib. 14-Nov-2 Christie's, Rockefeller NY #310/R est:15000-20000

£18987 $30000 €28481 Untitled - trees (16x27cm-6x11in) fabric paint chl on linen prov. 14-Nov-2 Christie's, Rockefeller NY #308/R est:50000-70000

GOBER, Robert and WOOL, Christopher (20th C) American

Photographs

£22152 $35000 €33228 Untitled (35x28cm-14x11in) s.d.1988 num.9/10 silver print prov.exhib.lit. 13-Nov-2 Christie's, Rockefeller NY #55/R est:60000-80000

GOBERT, Pierre (attrib) (1662-1744) French
£1773 $2961 €2500 Portrait presume de la Marquise de la Roche-sur-Yon (81x65cm-32x26in) 18-Jun-3 Tajan, Paris #122 est:3000-4000
£7500 $11700 €11250 Portrait of Charlotte d'Orleans, Duchess Modena (74x59cm-29x23in) oval. 10-Apr-3 Christie's, Kensington #193/R est:5000-8000

GOBERT, Pierre (style) (1662-1744) French
£3773 $5811 €6000 Portrait de Louise Bernardine de Durfort pres d'une fontaine (131x98cm-52x39in) i. 25-Oct-2 Tajan, Paris #3/R est:2000-3000

GOBIET, Bernhard (1892-?) German
£769 $1215 €1200 Roman theatre in Taormina with Mount Etna (63x83cm-25x33in) s.d.1932. 15-Nov-2 Reiss & Sohn, Konigstein #29/R

GOBILLARD, Paule (1869-1946) French
£645 $1019 €1000 Jardiniere (29x46cm-11x18in) s. 18-Dec-2 Ferri, Paris #53/R
£689 $1151 €1000 Vue de Marrakech (27x35cm-11x14in) init.d.38 cardboard. 10-Jul-3 Artcurial Briest, Paris #164
£903 $1427 €1400 Gondole (32x21cm-13x8in) 18-Dec-2 Ferri, Paris #68/R
£968 $1529 €1500 Fez, entree de la ville (38x48cm-15x19in) 18-Dec-2 Ferri, Paris #66/R
£1097 $1733 €1700 Vase de dahlias (39x52cm-15x20in) paint. 18-Dec-2 Ferri, Paris #62/R
£1613 $2548 €2500 Bassin du parc (37x46cm-15x18in) s. 18-Dec-2 Ferri, Paris #69/R
£1923 $3019 €3000 Femme cousant (73x60cm-29x24in) s. 15-Dec-2 Thierry & Lannon, Brest #386
£2581 $4077 €4000 Vase de lilas (81x65cm-32x26in) 18-Dec-2 Ferri, Paris #67/R est:6000
£3226 $5097 €5000 Fillette et sa nurse (40x36cm-16x14in) 18-Dec-2 Ferri, Paris #71/R
£5161 $8155 €8000 Paysage aux cypres (46x55cm-18x22in) s. 18-Dec-2 Ferri, Paris #64/R
£7742 $12232 €12000 A la campagne (50x61cm-20x24in) s. 18-Dec-2 Ferri, Paris #70/R est:15000
£13548 $21406 €21000 Volant (92x65cm-36x26in) s. 18-Dec-2 Ferri, Paris #59/R est:25000
Works on paper
£516 $815 €800 Landscape (26x45cm-10x18in) pastel. 18-Dec-2 Ferri, Paris #56/R
£516 $815 €800 Femme au transat (24x31cm-9x12in) W/C dr. 18-Dec-2 Ferri, Paris #55/R
£1032 $1631 €1600 Paysage a l riviere (30x23cm-12x9in) st.mono. W/C. 18-Dec-2 Ferri, Paris #54/R

GOBL, Camilla (attrib) (1871-1965) Austrian
£256 $405 €400 Snow covered autumn landscape (64x48cm-25x19in) 18-Nov-2 Dorotheum, Linz #275/R

GOBLAIN, Antoine Louis (1779-?) French
Works on paper
£884 $1406 €1300 Chateau de nantouillet (19x24cm-7x9in) s. W/C. 24-Mar-3 Tajan, Paris #79/R

GODARD (19/20th C) French
Sculpture
£8000 $12640 €12000 Bubble dance (52cm-20in) silvered bronze. 14-Nov-2 Christie's, Kensington #299/R est:5000-7000

GODARD, A (19/20th C) French
Sculpture
£1656 $2700 €2401 Nude with pet dog (56x33cm-22x13in) bronze. 18-Jul-3 Du Mouchelle, Detroit #2006/R est:3500-4500

GODARD, Gabriel (1933-) ?
£283 $450 €425 Bord de mer (100x100cm-39x39in) s.d.70 i.verso. 7-Mar-3 Skinner, Boston #531/R

GODCHAUX (?) ?
£633 $981 €1000 Barque dans la tempete (65x54cm-26x21in) s. 29-Sep-2 Eric Pillon, Calais #23/R
£8333 $13083 €13000 Voiliers sur le Bosphore (62x92cm-24x36in) s. 16-Dec-2 Gros & Delettrez, Paris #251/R est:3000-4500

GODCHAUX, Alfred (1835-1895) French
£1806 $2854 €2800 Landscape (51x73cm-20x29in) s. 17-Dec-2 Segre, Madrid #59/R
£2201 $3412 €3500 Le torrent (73x101cm-29x40in) s. 4-Oct-2 Tajan, Paris #115/R est:3000-3800

GODCHAUX, Emil (1860-?) Austrian?
£1049 $1752 €1500 Silhouette pres d'une riviere de montagne (54x65cm-21x26in) s. 26-Jun-3 Tajan, Paris #212 est:1500-2000
£1447 $2228 €2300 Grand voilier en remorque a l'entree d'un port (62x92cm-24x36in) s. 27-Oct-2 Lesieur & Le Bars, Le Havre #84/R
£1795 $2818 €2800 Cavaliers (22x41cm-9x16in) s. panel. 10-Dec-2 Tajan, Paris #182/R

GODCHAUX, Roger (1878-1958) French
£550 $858 €825 Drover and sheep on an Alpine track (34x26cm-13x10in) s. 26-Mar-3 Hamptons Fine Art, Godalming #213
£2200 $3498 €3300 Summer flowers in a vase on a step (92x65cm-36x26in) s. 20-Mar-3 Christie's, Kensington #36a/R est:2000-3000
Sculpture
£5000 $7800 €7500 Elephant with Mahout (28x29cm-11x11in) s.st.f.Susse green brown pat bronze lit. 5-Nov-2 Sotheby's, London #135/R est:4000-6000

GODDARD, Barrie (1941-) American
Works on paper
£1588 $2462 €2382 Brachina, October morning light (152x274cm-60x108in) i.d.1973 verso synthetic polymer paint canvas. 3-Dec-2 Shapiro, Sydney #79/R est:3000-5000 (A.D 4400)

GODDARD, James (fl.1811-1842) British
Works on paper
£1600 $2496 €2400 Temple of Minerva at Sunium (39x53cm-15x21in) s.d.1833 W/C. 15-Oct-2 Sotheby's, London #34/R est:1000-1500

GODDARD, Louis Charles (fl.1901-1921) British
Works on paper
£650 $1027 €975 Portrait of a young lady with blonde hair a landscape beyond. s. W/C pair. 13-Nov-2 Halls, Shrewsbury #356/R

GODDARD, William Charles (19th C) British
Works on paper
£260 $424 €390 Conway Castle from the foreshore (33x60cm-13x24in) s.d.1898 W/C over pencil htd white. 17-Feb-3 Bonhams, Bath #108

GODDERIS, Jack (1916-1971) Belgian
£252 $387 €400 Marine crepusculaire (75x130cm-30x51in) s. 22-Oct-2 Campo, Vlaamse Kaai #124
£347 $552 €500 Nature morte aux harengs (80x100cm-31x39in) s. 29-Apr-3 Campo & Campo, Antwerp #132/R
£374 $595 €550 Paysage d'hiver (70x85cm-28x33in) s. 18-Mar-3 Campo, Vlaamse Kaai #99
£382 $607 €550 Le port d'Anvers (70x80cm-28x31in) s.d.1942 exhib. 29-Apr-3 Campo & Campo, Antwerp #131
£629 $969 €1000 L'Escaut a Tamise (75x130cm-30x51in) s. 22-Oct-2 Campo, Vlaamse Kaai #514

GODEFROY (19/20th C) French
£16500 $25575 €24750 Lute a tambourine, panpipe and other instruments (69x120cm-27x47in) s.d.62 pair. 30-Oct-2 Christie's, Kensington #92/R est:6000-8000

GODEFROY, Robert (1928-) French
Sculpture
£2885 $4413 €4500 Tete de cheval (44cm-17in) i. num.3/8 bronze. 23-Aug-2 Deauville, France #244 est:4800
£3974 $6081 €6200 Tetes de chevaux. i. num.7/8 bronze. 23-Aug-2 Deauville, France #243/R est:6200

GODEL, Carl (1870-1948) Austrian
Works on paper
£321 $497 €500 Teufenback in upper Steiermark (37x51cm-15x20in) s.d.1926 W/C. 5-Dec-2 Dorotheum, Graz #103/R

GODET, Henri (1863-1937) French
Sculpture
£2400 $3744 €3600 Figurative inkwell (19x33cm-7x13in) s.num.U174 gilt bronze st.f.Siot-Decauville. 5-Nov-2 Sotheby's, London #182/R est:1500-2000

GODET, Julius (fl.1844-1894) British

£287 $445 €431 On the Llugwy, North Wales (51x76cm-20x30in) s. 24-Sep-2 Maynards, Vancouver #360 (C.D 700)

GODET, Pierre (20th C) French

£6761 $10885 €9600 Deauville, sur la plage (54x65cm-21x26in) s.d.82. 12-May-3 Lesieur & Le Bars, Le Havre #43

GODFRINON, Ernest (1878-1927) Belgian

£411 $642 €650 Effets de lumiere a Aix-en-Provence (24x30cm-9x12in) mono.d.09 s.i.verso. 16-Sep-2 Horta, Bruxelles #331

£791 $1266 €1100 Bouquets de dahlias (64x74cm-25x29in) s. 19-May-3 Horta, Bruxelles #414

GODGOLDT, Georghy (1915-1975) French

£1389 $2208 €2000 Battle (56x84cm-22x33in) s. cardboard painted 1948 lit. 1-May-3 Meeting Art, Vercelli #345

GODIE, Lee (20th C) American

Works on paper

£340 $500 €510 Woman in grapevines (71x53cm-28x21in) mixed media. 23-Jun-2 Susanin's, Chicago #5060/R

£340 $500 €510 Bouquet of flowers (51x28cm-20x11in) s. mixed media. 23-Jun-2 Susanin's, Chicago #5061/R

£1156 $1700 €1734 Woman in blue (86x81cm-34x32in) mixed media. 23-Jun-2 Susanin's, Chicago #5059/R est:600-800

GODLEVSKY, Ivan (1908-) Russian

£1382 $2238 €2100 Port de plaisance (60x81cm-24x32in) 27-Jan-3 Millon & Associes, Paris #29

GODWARD, John William (1858-1922) British

£4747 $7500 €7500 Beaute Orientale a l'eventail (62x75cm-24x30in) mono. 26-Nov-2 Palais de Beaux Arts, Brussels #193/R est:7500-10000

£25000 $41500 €37500 Study, Reverie (25x23cm-10x9in) mono. prov.exhib.lit. 12-Jun-3 Sotheby's, London #216/R est:25000-35000

£57000 $90630 €85500 Cleonice (50x40cm-20x16in) s.d.1913. 18-Mar-3 Bonhams, New Bond Street #91/R est:20000-30000

£65000 $104650 €97500 Venus binding her hair (113x228cm-44x90in) prov.exhib.lit. 20-Feb-3 Christie's, London #284/R est:120000

£68000 $107440 €102000 Carina (50x40cm-20x16in) i.d.verso prov.lit. 2-Dec-2 Sotheby's, London #105/R est:30000-40000

£120000 $199200 €180000 Idleness (51x101cm-20x40in) s.d.1907. 12-Jun-3 Sotheby's, London #35/R est:120000-180000

£170000 $282200 €255000 Reverie (126x76cm-50x30in) s.d.12 prov.lit. 12-Jun-3 Sotheby's, London #40/R est:180000-220000

£180000 $298800 €270000 Reverie (100cm-39in circular) s.d.1910 prov.lit. 11-Jun-3 Christie's, London #16/R est:200000-300000

GODWIN, Frank (1889-1959) American

Works on paper

£1739 $2800 €2609 Group of gangsters relaxing in interior (41x61cm-16x24in) s. W/C gouache exec.c.1930. 10-May-3 Illustration House, New York #105/R est:2000-4000

GODWIN, Mary (1887-1960) British

£380 $619 €551 At the fair (60x50cm-24x20in) s. 21-Jul-3 Bonhams, Bath #33/R

GODWIN, Ted (1933-) Canadian

£522 $825 €783 Fall reflection (30x41cm-12x16in) d.1990 woodboard. 1-Dec-2 Levis, Calgary #311/R (C.D 1300)

£913 $1424 €1523 Wild rice, lily pads and summer breezes 9 (61x76cm-24x30in) s.i.verso canvas on board prov. 13-Apr-3 Levis, Calgary #40a/R est:2000-2500 (C.D 2100)

GOEBEL, August Wilhelm (1883-?) German

Sculpture

£6918 $10792 €11000 Allegory of the muses (110x65cm-43x26in) s. dark grey pat.bronze pair. 20-Sep-2 Schloss Ahlden, Ahlden #632/R est:14000

GOEBEL, Carl (1824-1899) Austrian

Works on paper

£432 $691 €600 Portrait of Furst Thurn und Taxis (28x19cm-11x7in) s.d.851 W/C. 14-May-3 Dorotheum, Linz #464/R

£503 $780 €800 Young peasant in traditional costume (33x24cm-13x9in) s. W/C. 1-Oct-2 Dorotheum, Vienna #195/R

£743 $1159 €1100 Young peasants ploughing (27x42cm-11x17in) s. i. verso W/C. 28-Mar-3 Dorotheum, Vienna #214/R

£750 $1170 €1125 Morning ride (42x59cm-17x23in) s. W/C. 5-Nov-2 Bonhams, New Bond Street #18a

£1081 $1686 €1600 Country girl going up to alpine pasture (39x28cm-15x11in) s. W/C. 28-Mar-3 Dorotheum, Vienna #179/R est:1800-2000

£1149 $1792 €1700 Young Dalmatian man (47x36cm-19x14in) s. W/C. 28-Mar-3 Dorotheum, Vienna #211/R est:1600-2000

GOEBEL, Rod (1946-1993) American

£1731 $2700 €2597 Taos Pueblo evening (41x61cm-16x24in) 9-Nov-2 Altermann Galleries, Santa Fe #187

£12685 $20550 €18393 Fire and flower (122x107cm-48x42in) 23-May-3 Altermann Galleries, Santa Fe #173

GOEDHART, Jan Catharinus Adriaan (1893-1975) Dutch

Works on paper

£282 $454 €400 Moored sea ship (25x35cm-10x14in) s.d.1914 W/C. 6-May-3 Vendu Notarishuis, Rotterdam #66

GOEDVRIEND, Theodor Franciscus (1879-1969) Dutch

£317 $510 €450 Still life with pumpkins (71x59cm-28x23in) s. board. 7-May-3 Vendue Huis, Gravenhage #24

£428 $693 €650 Mushrooms (48x68cm-19x27in) s. board. 21-Jan-3 Christie's, Amsterdam #461

GOENEUTTE, Norbert (1854-1894) French

£16026 $25160 €25000 Jeune femme a sa couture (35x25cm-14x10in) s.d.1893 cardboard. 10-Dec-2 Artcurial Briest, Paris #462/R est:18000-25000

£28846 $44712 €45000 Enfants jouant sur la plage (45x55cm-18x22in) s.i.d.1883 panel exhib. 5-Dec-2 Gros & Delettrez, Paris #87/R est:30000

Works on paper

£450 $711 €653 Le dejeuner, Paris (24x29cm-9x11in) s. pen ink. 22-Jul-3 Bonhams, Knightsbridge #182/R

£1509 $2355 €2400 Soupe du matin (42x58cm-17x23in) s.i.d.1881 crayon prov.exhib.lit. 11-Oct-2 Binoche, Paris #113

GOEREE, Jan (1670-1731) Dutch

Works on paper

£268 $412 €420 Waag at Alkmaar (14x19cm-6x7in) red chk grey ink grey wash prov. 3-Sep-2 Christie's, Amsterdam #82/R

GOERG, Edouard (1893-1969) French

£1862 $3110 €2700 Des femmes et des fleurs (65x54cm-26x21in) s. 9-Jul-3 Millon & Associes, Paris #192/R est:2500-4000

£1923 $3019 €3000 Poitrine fleurie (65x54cm-26x21in) s. s.verso. 22-Nov-2 Millon & Associes, Paris #99/R

£2387 $3772 €3700 La fenetre sur la campagne (65x46cm-26x18in) s. s.d.verso. 17-Dec-2 Rossini, Paris #83/R

£2400 $3816 €3600 L'amoureux (65x54cm-26x21in) s. s.i.d.Septembre 57 verso. 20-Mar-3 Sotheby's, Olympia #209/R est:3000-4000

£4650 $7254 €7300 Bouquet rouge (73x60cm-29x24in) s. i.d.1963 verso. 10-Nov-2 Eric Pillon, Calais #204/R

£5063 $8000 €8000 Portrait (55x46cm-22x18in) s. s.i.verso exhib. 27-Nov-2 Blanchet, Paris #86

Works on paper

£735 $1168 €1080 Promenade dans la campagne (31x49cm-12x19in) s.d.45 gouache. 26-Feb-3 Artcurial Briest, Paris #98

£2166 $3378 €3400 Nu assis (48x31cm-19x12in) s.d.1946 gouache pastel. 10-Nov-2 Eric Pillon, Calais #205/R

GOERG-LAURESCH, Louis (1885-1950) Swiss

£660 $1057 €990 Printemps (81x100cm-32x39in) s. i. verso. 17-Mar-3 Philippe Schuler, Zurich #8443 (S.FR 1400)

GOERING (19th C) German?

Works on paper

£1724 $2741 €2500 Foret (35x52cm-14x20in) s.d.188 W/C. 7-Mar-3 Rabourdin & Choppin de Janvry, Paris #18/R est:2500-3000

GOERNER, E (?) French?

£6000 $9540 €8700 On guard (44x33cm-17x13in) s. panel. 29-Apr-3 Henry Adams, Chichester #338 est:4000-6000

GOETING, Jan (1918-1984) Dutch

Works on paper

£318 $497 €500 Photographer (51x51cm-20x20in) s. gouache. 6-Nov-2 Vendue Huis, Gravenhage #210

GOETSCH, Gustave (1877-1969) American

£481 $750 €722 Autumn landscape. s.d.1948. 10-Nov-2 Selkirks, St. Louis #820

£577 $900 €866 Self portrait, red skullcap (25x20cm-10x8in) s.d.1964 canvasboard prov. 10-Nov-2 Selkirks, St. Louis #818

£1026 $1600 €1539 Floral still life (41x51cm-16x20in) s. canvasboard. 10-Nov-2 Selkirks, St. Louis #821 est:800-1200

£1154 $1800 €1731 Artist's studio (25x20cm-10x8in) s.d.65 masonite prov. 10-Nov-2 Selkirks, St. Louis #819 est:1000-1500

Works on paper

£272 $425 €408 Harbour scene (28x38cm-11x15in) s.d.60 pastel. 10-Nov-2 Selkirks, St. Louis #816a

GOETSCH, Joseph (1728-1793) German

Sculpture

£1154 $1754 €1800 Resurrection of Christ (31cm-12in) painted gilded wood. 11-Jul-2 Hugo Ruef, Munich #1260/R est:1800

GOETZ, Gottfried Bernhard (1708-1774) German

Works on paper

£280 $400 €420 Saint John the Baptist (8x6cm-3x2in) pen ink wash htd white. 23-Jan-3 Swann Galleries, New York #340/R
£764 $1215 €1100 St Nicholas triumphing over the vices (21x15cm-8x6in) i. pen over pencil wash gouache. 5-May-3 Ketterer, Munich #248/R

GOETZ, Henri (1909-1989) French

£400 $632 €600 Composition (65x50cm-26x20in) s. 3-Apr-3 Christie's, Kensington #263/R
£576 $921 €800 Composition (28x36cm-11x14in) s. oil mixed media paper on panel. 18-May-3 Eric Pillon, Calais #277/R
£631 $984 €947 Au pays des phenomenes (57x65cm-22x26in) s.d.1984 verso. 5-Nov-2 Bukowskis, Stockholm #316/R (S.KR 9000)
£631 $984 €947 Les hauts de Montecarle (55x65cm-22x26in) s. 5-Nov-2 Bukowskis, Stockholm #318/R (S.KR 9000)
£662 $1079 €1000 Diplomate coquelicots (50x65cm-20x26in) s.d.1986. 1-Feb-3 Claude Aguttes, Neuilly #185/R
£806 $1257 €1209 Atterisage su un lieu partage (65x54cm-26x21in) s.d.1984 verso. 5-Nov-2 Bukowskis, Stockholm #317/R (S.KR 11500)
£927 $1511 €1400 Composition aux formes bleues (73x92cm-29x36in) s. painted 1988. 3-Feb-3 Cornette de St.Cyr, Paris #436
£1154 $1812 €1800 Plateau de la justice (54x65cm-21x26in) s.d.75 prov. 16-Dec-2 Charbonneaux, Paris #256/R est:2000-3000
£1176 $1929 €1800 Scene nautique (60x73cm-24x29in) s. i. oil. 9-Feb-3 Anaf, Lyon #113/R
£1837 $2920 €2700 Monument (65x81cm-26x32in) s. oil stone painted 1985 prov. 24-Mar-3 Claude Boisgirard, Paris #164
£2089 $3258 €3300 Saint Blaise (65x81cm-26x32in) s. i.d.1967 verso lit. 20-Oct-2 Charbonneaux, Paris #133/R est:4000-4500
£2436 $3824 €3800 Untitled (54x65cm-21x26in) s. 24-Nov-2 Laurence Calmels, Paris #141/R
£2564 $4026 €4000 Plateau de la justice (54x65cm-21x26in) s. s.i.d.1970 verso prov.lit. 24-Nov-2 Laurence Calmels, Paris #140/R
£3546 $5922 €5000 Composition (114x146cm-45x57in) s.d. prov.lit. 23-Jun-3 Claude Boisgirard, Paris #149/R est:6000-7000
£4808 $7548 €7500 Untitled (76x61cm-30x24in) s. prov.lit. 24-Nov-2 Laurence Calmels, Paris #142/R

Works on paper

£320 $496 €480 Composition (24x39cm-9x15in) s. gouache paper on canvas. 3-Dec-2 Bonhams, Knightsbridge #282/R
£321 $503 €500 Composition au tronc (15x19cm-6x7in) s.d.41 W/C. 13-Dec-2 Piasa, Paris #132
£483 $806 €700 Composition (22x37cm-9x15in) s.d.48 pastel. 10-Jul-3 Artcurial Briest, Paris #292
£513 $805 €800 Composition (25x32cm-10x13in) s. pastel. 16-Dec-2 Charbonneaux, Paris #150
£629 $1025 €950 Composition surrealiste (12x21cm-5x8in) s. pen dr. 31-Jan-3 Charbonneaux, Paris #98
£633 $981 €1000 Composition (50x65cm-20x26in) s. pastel paper on canvas. 28-Sep-2 Cornette de St.Cyr, Paris #320 est:1000-1200
£641 $1006 €1000 Composition (42x62cm-17x24in) s. pastel. 16-Dec-2 Charbonneaux, Paris #149
£674 $1125 €950 Composition (55x41cm-22x16in) s.d. graphite. 23-Jun-3 Claude Boisgirard, Paris #112/R
£865 $1359 €1350 Composition (16x25cm-6x10in) s.d.46 W/C. 13-Dec-2 Piasa, Paris #133
£884 $1406 €1300 Noisel (50x65cm-20x26in) s. mixed media exec.1963 prov. 24-Mar-3 Claude Boisgirard, Paris #165
£909 $1518 €1300 Composition (50x65cm-20x26in) s. pastel cardboard on canvas. 25-Jun-3 Claude Aguttes, Neuilly #273/R
£927 $1511 €1400 Composition (50x65cm-20x26in) s. pastel paper on canvas. 1-Feb-3 Claude Aguttes, Neuilly #309/R
£993 $1619 €1500 Composition (73x99cm-29x39in) s. pastel. 31-Jan-3 Charbonneaux, Paris #99 est:1500-2000
£1026 $1673 €1550 Sans titre (50x65cm-20x26in) s.d.1989 pastel cardboard on canvas. 1-Feb-3 Claude Aguttes, Neuilly #227/R est:1500-2000
£1035 $1635 €1500 Composition (80x100cm-31x39in) s. pastel on canvas. 4-Apr-3 Tajan, Paris #257
£1042 $1656 €1500 Untitled (50x65cm-20x26in) s.d.1958 wax crayon. 1-May-3 Meeting Art, Vercelli #472
£1497 $2380 €2200 Composition (46x62cm-18x24in) s. pastel oil. 26-Feb-3 Artcurial Briest, Paris #456 est:1000-1200
£1747 $2725 €2621 Untitled (47x56cm-19x22in) s. 6-Nov-2 Dobiaschofsky, Bern #600/R est:4700 (S.FR 4000)

GOETZE, Martin (1865-?) German

Sculpture

£1006 $1570 €1600 Whispering woman (43cm-17in) s. brown pat.bronze. 20-Sep-2 Schloss Ahlden, Ahlden #630/R

GOETZE, Sigismund (1866-1939) British

£800 $1272 €1200 Bamburgh Sands, Northumberland (41x61cm-16x24in) s. 6-Mar-3 Christie's, Kensington #494/R
£8000 $13360 €11600 Zouaves - Portrait of Francis and Philip Mond, sons of Emile Mond, Esq (150x109cm-59x43in) s.d.1907. 17-Jun-3 Bonhams, New Bond Street #97/R est:6000-8000

GOETZE, T (19th C) German

£897 $1364 €1400 Landscape near Brannenburg in the Inn valley (92x122cm-36x48in) s.d.1878. 11-Jul-2 Hugo Ruef, Munich #663/R

GOFF, Bruce Alonzo (1904-1982) American

Sculpture

£5161 $8000 €7742 Door from Price house, Bartlesville Oklahoma (93x34cm-37x13in) cast welded metal. 8-Dec-2 Wright, Chicago #265/R est:9000-12000

GOFF, Frederick E J (1855-1931) British

£600 $936 €900 Thames at Nuneaton (53x71cm-21x28in) s.i. 26-Mar-3 Hamptons Fine Art, Godalming #111
£1500 $2340 €2250 Off Greenwich and Windsor Castle (10x15cm-4x6in) s. pair. 9-Oct-2 Andrew Hartley, Ilkley #663/R est:1500-2000

Works on paper

£300 $495 €435 Burnham on Crouch (20x15cm-8x6in) s.i. W/C. 1-Jul-3 Bonhams, Norwich #111/R
£360 $562 €540 Thames with fishing boats and shipping (64x33cm-25x13in) s.d. 9-Oct-2 Andrew Hartley, Ilkley #660
£400 $608 €600 Shipping on the Thames (58x33cm-23x13in) s.d.1895 W/C. 14-Aug-2 Andrew Hartley, Ilkley #585
£600 $984 €900 Fishing smack off the coast (64x33cm-25x13in) s.indis d. W/C htd white. 5-Feb-3 Goldings, Lincolnshire #278
£900 $1467 €1350 Greenwich. Tower Bridge (10x15cm-4x6in) s. W/C pair. 7-Feb-3 Dee Atkinson & Harrison, Driffield #740
£1000 $1540 €1500 Broadway wharf, Limehouse (15x11cm-6x4in) s.i. W/C. 22-Oct-2 Sworder & Son, Bishops Stortford #688/R est:1000-1500
£1000 $1670 €1450 Westminster. Tower Bridge (11x15cm-4x6in) s.i. W/C pair. 18-Jun-3 Sotheby's, Olympia #93/R est:1000-1500
£1100 $1705 €1650 St. Paul's from bankside (25x35cm-10x14in) s.i. W/C. 24-Sep-2 Bonhams, Knightsbridge #210/R est:500-700
£1100 $1782 €1650 Off Greenwich (11x15cm-4x6in) s.i. pencil W/C. 21-May-3 Christie's, Kensington #478/R est:1000-1500
£1150 $1794 €1725 Westminster (11x14cm-4x6in) s.i. W/C. 26-Mar-3 Hamptons Fine Art, Godalming #103/R est:500-700
£1200 $1848 €1800 St Paul's from Blackfriars (16x11cm-6x4in) s.i. W/C. 22-Oct-2 Sworder & Son, Bishops Stortford #689/R est:1200-1500
£1200 $1848 €1800 Tower Bridge (11x15cm-4x6in) s.i. W/C. 22-Oct-2 Sworder & Son, Bishops Stortford #690/R est:1200-1600
£1300 $2132 €1950 Limehouse and River Thames, extensive river landscape (28x46cm-11x18in) s. W/C. 5-Feb-3 Goldings, Lincolnshire #223
£1400 $2184 €2100 Dusk at stand on the Green (11x15cm-4x6in) s.i. W/C htd white. 5-Nov-2 Bonhams, New Bond Street #141/R est:1000-1500
£1500 $2400 €2250 Pall Mall street scene. View of Gloucester Cathedral from river Severn (15x11cm-6x4in) s.i. W/C pair. 11-Mar-3 Bonhams, New Bond Street #92/R est:1000-1200
£1500 $2505 €2175 Westminster (11x14cm-4x6in) s.i. W/C. 18-Jun-3 Sotheby's, Olympia #92/R est:1500-2000
£1700 $2652 €2550 View of Westminster from the Thames (11x15cm-4x6in) s.i. W/C htd bodycol. 17-Sep-2 Sotheby's, Olympia #140/R est:1500-2000
£2000 $3140 €3000 Below London Bridge (17x25cm-7x10in) s.i. W/C. 16-Dec-2 Sotheby's, Olympia #131/R est:2000-3000
£2400 $3912 €3480 Tower Bridge. Off Greenwich (11x15cm-4x6in) s.i. pencil W/C htd white pair. 17-Jul-3 Tennants, Leyburn #718/R est:1200-1500
£2500 $4000 €3750 Lambeth Palace. Westminster Abbey. Tower Bridge. Lime House (12x15cm-5x6in) s.i. W/C htd white four. 11-Mar-3 Bonhams, New Bond Street #91/R est:2500-3500
£3200 $5056 €4640 Westminster. Blackfriars Bridge (23x30cm-9x12in) s. W/C pair. 22-Jul-3 Gorringes, Lewes #1640/R est:3000-5000
£3800 $6080 €5700 Westminster Bridge, dusk (34x74cm-13x29in) s.i. W/C. 11-Mar-3 Bonhams, New Bond Street #94/R est:3500-5000
£4200 $6720 €6300 Westminster, sunset (27x49cm-11x19in) s.i. W/C bodycol. 11-Mar-3 Bonhams, New Bond Street #93/R est:2000-3000
£6500 $10530 €9750 Below London Bridge. Westminster (12x15cm-5x6in) s.i. W/C htd white pair. 22-Jan-3 Bonhams, New Bond Street #359/R est:1200-1800

GOFF, Lloyd Lozes (1917-1982) American

£577 $900 €866 Untitled (41x51cm-16x20in) paper. 19-Oct-2 David Dike, Dallas #210/R

£1346 $2100 €2019 Islete Pueblo Water Tower (30x41cm-12x16in) paper painted c.1943. 19-Oct-2 David Dike, Dallas #244/R est:3000-5000

Works on paper

£833 $1300 €1250 Mexican village (33x56cm-13x22in) W/C. 19-Oct-2 David Dike, Dallas #272/R

GOFFINON, Aristide (1881-1952) Belgian

£432 $691 €600 Vase fleuri (50x60cm-20x24in) s. 19-May-3 Horta, Bruxelles #9

GOGARTEN, Heinrich (1850-1911) German

£823 $1275 €1300 Snowy winter wood with figures walking and skating on frozen stream (27x21cm-11x8in) s. panel. 25-Sep-2 Neumeister, Munich #583/R

£1529 $2385 €2400 Oberfohring church in winter (41x32cm-16x13in) s. 6-Nov-2 Hugo Ruef, Munich #1108/R est:1500

£1569 $2573 €2400 Westphalian landscape (37x49cm-15x19in) s.d.1889 panel. 8-Feb-3 Hans Stahl, Hamburg #53/R est:2900

£1582 $2453 €2500 Winter evening (40x50cm-16x20in) s. 28-Sep-2 Hans Stahl, Hamburg #59/R est:2700

GOGH, Vincent van (1853-1890) Dutch

£480769 $750000 €721154 Mere et enfant (43x34cm-17x13in) canvasboard painted March 1885 prov.exhib.lit. 5-Nov-2 Sotheby's, New York #55/R est:500000-700000

£3000000 $5010000 €4350000 Une liseuse de romans (73x93cm-29x37in) painted 1888 prov.exhib.lit. 24-Jun-3 Christie's, London #55/R est:3000000-4000000

£3800000 $6346000 €5510000 Nature morte, vase avec oeillets (41x32cm-16x13in) painted 1890 prov.exhib.lit. 24-Jun-3 Christie's, London #54/R est:3000000-5000000

Works on paper

£198758 $320000 €298137 Sien nursing baby (48x38cm-19x15in) s. gouache W/C black chk prov.exhib.lit. 8-May-3 Christie's, Rockefeller NY #112/R est:220000-280000

£269231 $420000 €403847 Pollard willow (38x56cm-15x22in) W/C gouache pen ink painted 27 July 1882 prov.exhib.lit. 6-Nov-2 Christie's, Rockefeller NY #3/R est:600000-800000

£390000 $639600 €585000 Six pines near the enclosure wall (25x33cm-10x13in) chl pencil exec.1889 prov.lit. 6-Feb-3 Christie's, London #413/R est:400000

£750000 $1252500 €1087500 La maison de Vincent a Arles (13x21cm-5x8in) pen ink exec.1888 double-sided with letter verso prov.exhib.lit. 24-Jun-3 Christie's, London #52/R est:700000-1000000

GOGO, Felix (19/20th C) Belgian

£283 $442 €450 Ruelle (61x49cm-24x19in) 14-Oct-2 Amberes, Antwerp #157

£496 $804 €700 Toledo (55x73cm-22x29in) 26-May-3 Amberes, Antwerp #35

£1887 $2943 €3000 Nu assis vu de dos (64x52cm-25x20in) 14-Oct-2 Amberes, Antwerp #156

GOGOIS, Pierre (1935-) French

£1026 $1610 €1600 Coucher de soleil sur Venise (46x61cm-18x24in) s. 16-Dec-2 Charbonneaux, Paris #257/R est:1500-1800

GOGOS, Basil (20th C) American

Works on paper

£311 $500 €467 Woman having nightmare of drunken soldiers carrying her away (46x69cm-18x27in) s. gouache en grisaille. 20-Feb-3 Illustration House, New York #70/R

GOHL, Edward Heinrich (1862-?) American

£321 $500 €482 Game keeper's cottage, Cernay la Ville, France (41x51cm-16x20in) s.i.stretcher. 22-Sep-2 Jeffery Burchard, Florida #120

GOHLER, Hermann (1874-?) German

£417 $646 €650 Figures on landing stage outside palace gardens (58x67cm-23x26in) s. i.d.1945 verso panel. 5-Dec-2 Neumeister, Munich #2795/R

GOINGS, Ralph (1928-) American

£23734 $37500 €35601 Perth diner still life (66x91cm-26x36in) s.d.80 s.i.d.verso prov.lit. 13-Nov-2 Sotheby's, New York #256/R est:40000-60000

£60127 $95000 €90191 Interior (91x133cm-36x52in) s. i.d.1972 verso prov. 13-Nov-2 Sotheby's, New York #254/R est:60000-80000

£69620 $110000 €104430 Sizzle kitchen (102x102cm-40x40in) s.d.1971 s.d.verso prov.exhib.lit. 14-Nov-2 Christie's, Rockefeller NY #167/R est:70000-90000

£175000 $280000 €262500 Blue chip (114x132cm-45x52in) s.d.1969 verso prov.exhib.lit. 15-May-3 Christie's, Rockefeller NY #163/R est:180000-220000

Works on paper

£9375 $15000 €14063 Gem top (28x38cm-11x15in) s.d.75 s.i.d.verso W/C prov.lit. 15-May-3 Christie's, Rockefeller NY #165/R est:12000-18000

GOIS, Étienne (1731-1823) French

Sculpture

£108974 $168910 €170000 Doulur (58x28x22cm-23x11x9in) s.d.1764 white marble lit. 9-Dec-2 Rabourdin & Choppin de Janvry, Paris #48/R est:45000

GOIS, Étienne (attrib) (1731-1823) French

Works on paper

£443 $691 €700 Scene de sacrifice (21x35cm-8x14in) pen wash. 18-Oct-2 Rabourdin & Choppin de Janvry, Paris #89

GOITINO, Yuyo (1935-) Uruguayan

£385 $604 €600 Untitled (46x22cm-18x9in) s. board. 16-Dec-2 Castellana, Madrid #980/R

£449 $704 €700 Untitled (45x36cm-18x14in) s. cardboard. 16-Dec-2 Castellana, Madrid #971/R

GOLA, Emilio (1852-1923) Italian

Works on paper

£811 $1249 €1217 Portrait of young woman with mirror (95x77cm-37x30in) s. pastel after Titian. 4-Sep-2 Kunsthallen, Copenhagen #137/R (D.KR 9500)

£3261 $5348 €4500 Villa tra gli alberi (51x61cm-20x24in) s. pastel. 27-May-3 Finarte, Milan #55/R est:4500-5500

GOLDBERG, David (20th C) Irish?

£255 $397 €400 French farmhouse (25x34cm-10x13in) s.d.01. 6-Nov-2 James Adam, Dublin #100/R

£255 $397 €400 Yellow field, Le Monteleut (30x40cm-12x16in) s.d.01. 6-Nov-2 James Adam, Dublin #102/R

£880 $1461 €1250 Road through cornfield, Le Montelut (34x44cm-13x17in) mono. 10-Jun-3 James Adam, Dublin #196/R est:400-600

GOLDBERG, Eric (1890-1969) Canadian

£202 $319 €303 Mending nets (46x58cm-18x23in) s. board prov. 14-Nov-2 Heffel, Vancouver #264 (C.D 500)

£203 $319 €305 Still life of flowers (61x46cm-24x18in) s. board prov. 10-Dec-2 Pinneys, Montreal #195 (C.D 500)

£292 $462 €438 Fandango (41x56cm-16x22in) s. board prov. 14-Nov-2 Heffel, Vancouver #216 (C.D 725)

£313 $494 €470 Friday night (51x61cm-20x24in) s. board. 14-Nov-2 Heffel, Vancouver #265 (C.D 775)

£403 $637 €605 Old chapel (50x61cm-20x24in) s. board prov. 14-Nov-2 Heffel, Vancouver #167/R est:700-900 (C.D 1000)

£565 $892 €848 Beach scene (61x91cm-24x36in) s. board prov. 14-Nov-2 Heffel, Vancouver #208/R est:800-1200 (C.D 1400)

£1233 $1973 €1850 Picnic (61x78cm-24x31in) s.i.verso board prov. 15-May-3 Heffel, Vancouver #83/R est:1000-1500 (C.D 2750)

£1613 $2548 €2420 Wedding (53x69cm-21x27in) s. masonite prov. 18-Nov-2 Sotheby's, Toronto #172/R est:2000-2500 (C.D 4000)

Works on paper

£206 $317 €309 Two boys with fish (61x51cm-24x20in) s. W/C. 22-Oct-2 Iegor de Saint Hippolyte, Montreal #45 (C.D 500)

GOLDBERG, Gustav Adolf (1848-1911) German

£2157 $3451 €3300 Young boy in frock coat with hunting dog (117x65cm-46x26in) s.d.1883 lit. 10-Jan-3 Allgauer, Kempten #1602/R est:2500

GOLDBERG, Len (20th C) American

£264 $425 €396 Seated young woman with camera (36x28cm-14x11in) s. acrylic chl pencil. 20-Feb-3 Illustration House, New York #71/R

GOLDBERG, Michael (1924-) American

£438 $700 €657 Dreams (30x20cm-12x8in) s. paper. 18-May-3 Butterfields, Los Angeles #7052

Works on paper

£1463 $2400 €2121 Abstract composition (45x55cm-18x22in) s. mixed media oil collage. 5-Jun-3 Swann Galleries, New York #105/R est:1800-2200

GOLDBLATT, Sidney (1919-) South African

£295 $460 €443 Slipway (36x59cm-14x23in) s. board. 15-Oct-2 Stephan Welz, Johannesburg #198 est:2000-3000 (SA.R 4800)

£301 $485 €452 An interior (30x36cm-12x14in) s. board. 12-May-3 Stephan Welz, Johannesburg #322 est:1800-2400 (SA.R 3500)
£305 $483 €458 Man and wildebeest in an extensive landscape (45x29cm-18x11in) s. acrylic pen ink board. 1-Apr-3 Stephan Welz, Johannesburg #215 est:2000-3000 (SA.R 3800)

GOLDEN, Grace (1904-) British
Works on paper
£400 $656 €600 St Clement Lane and Strand (28x28cm-11x11in) s. ink W/C prov. 3-Jun-3 Sotheby's, Olympia #15/R

GOLDEN, Rolland (1931-) American
£475 $750 €713 Trumpet player (51x38cm-20x15in) s.d.68 board. 16-Nov-2 New Orleans Auction, New Orleans #1578
£633 $1000 €950 Trombone player (51x38cm-20x15in) s.d.62 board. 16-Nov-2 New Orleans Auction, New Orleans #1577/R
Works on paper
£506 $800 €759 Farm (53x74cm-21x29in) s.d.68 W/C. 5-Apr-3 Neal Auction Company, New Orleans #361
£769 $1200 €1154 Nineteenth century shadow, twentieth century light (56x76cm-22x30in) s.d.74 W/C. 12-Oct-2 Neal Auction Company, New Orleans #1384

GOLDFARB, Shirley (20th C) ?
£544 $865 €800 Untitled (194x295cm-76x116in) s.d.59 verso. 3-Mar-3 Marc Kohn, Paris #32/R

GOLDFARB, Walter (1964-) Brazilian
Works on paper
£13415 $22000 €20123 Give her to drink (155x208cm-61x82in) s.d.2002 verso chl tempera wool thread embroidery prov.exhib. 28-May-3 Christie's, Rockefeller NY #47/R est:22000-28000

GOLDIE, Charles Alphonse (20th C) British
£404 $638 €606 Breton girl writing (44x53cm-17x21in) s. prov. 18-Nov-2 Waddingtons, Toronto #94/R (C.D 1000)
£766 $1210 €1149 Breton woman peeling apples. Breton boy in kitchen interior (61x46cm-24x18in) pair prov. 18-Nov-2 Waddingtons, Toronto #95/R (C.D 1900)

GOLDIE, Charles Frederick (1870-1947) New Zealander
Works on paper
£1273 $1960 €1910 Aeroplane (15x15cm-6x6in) init.i. pencil dr. 4-Sep-2 Dunbar Sloane, Wellington #67/R est:4000-8000 (NZ.D 4200)
£4754 $7843 €6893 Portrait of Nagaheke - or Perira te Kahikura (19x12cm-7x5in) s.i. pencil. 1-Jul-3 Peter Webb, Auckland #14/R est:8000-12000 (NZ.D 13500)
£5282 $8715 €7659 Portrait of a Maori boy (20x16cm-8x6in) s.i. pencil crayon. 1-Jul-3 Peter Webb, Auckland #16/R est:8000-12000 (NZ.D 15000)
£8099 $13363 €11744 Portrait of Guide Sophia - The heroine of Tarawera (24x20cm-9x8in) s.i. pencil. 1-Jul-3 Peter Webb, Auckland #15/R est:8000-12000 (NZ.D 23000)

GOLDIE, Geoffrey (20th C) ?
£378 $620 €567 Bathers (122x95cm-48x37in) s.d.1999 s.i.d.1999 verso composition board. 4-Jun-3 Deutscher-Menzies, Melbourne #371/R (A.D 950)

GOLDIN, Alice (1925-) South African
£258 $402 €387 Winter landscape (69x48cm-27x19in) s.d.66. 15-Oct-2 Stephan Welz, Johannesburg #202 est:2000-3000 (SA.R 4200)

GOLDIN, Nan (1953-) American
Photographs
£2244 $3522 €3500 Self-portrait in the Hotel de la Bretonnerie (69x101cm-27x40in) s.i.d.1997 cibachrome prov.exhib. 11-Dec-2 Artcurial Briest, Paris #779/R
£2400 $4008 €3480 Vivienne in the green dress, NYC (61x51cm-24x20in) s.i.d.1980 num.5/25 verso cibachrome lit. 24-Jun-3 Sotheby's, Olympia #137/R est:2000-3000
£2532 $4000 €3798 Chisato in bonbage, Tokyo (102x102cm-40x40in) cibachrome mounted on aluminum executed 1994 prov. 12-Nov-2 Phillips, New York #175/R est:8000-12000
£2597 $4000 €3896 John Heys as Diana Vreeland, New York City (51x61cm-20x24in) s.i.d.1990 verso cibachrome print prov.exhib. 25-Oct-2 Phillips, New York #165/R est:4000-6000
£2600 $4342 €3770 Christine on the train, Austria (41x61cm-16x24in) s.i.d.1993 num.6/25 cibachrome lit. 24-Jun-3 Sotheby's, Olympia #130/R est:2000-3000
£2800 $4676 €4060 Kana with her lizard, Tokyo (69x101cm-27x40in) s.i.d.1994 num.4/15 verso cibachrome prov.lit. 24-Jun-3 Sotheby's, Olympia #126/R est:3000-4000
£3000 $5010 €4350 Self portrait in the Hotel de la Bretonnerie, Paris (69x101cm-27x40in) s.i.d.1997 num.1/15 verso cibachrome prov.exhib. 24-Jun-3 Sotheby's, Olympia #125/R est:3000-4000
£3000 $5010 €4350 Philippe H and Suzanne kissing at Euthanasia, NYC (66x98cm-26x39in) s.i.d.1981 num.7/25 verso cibachrome print prov.lit. 26-Jun-3 Sotheby's, London #282/R est:3000-4000
£3077 $4769 €4800 Valeri's back, L Hotel, Paris (100x68cm-39x27in) s.i.d.1999 num.5/15 col photograph. 3-Dec-2 Christie's, Amsterdam #386/R est:4500-5500
£3165 $5000 €4748 Ivy in the Boston Garden, Boston (48x32cm-19x13in) s.i.d.1973 num.10/18 gelatin silver print lit. 22-Apr-3 Christie's, Rockefeller NY #125/R est:3000-5000
£3800 $6194 €5700 Bruce in the car, NYC (69x100cm-27x39in) s.i.d.1981 num.14/25 verso cibachrome print prov. 3-Feb-3 Sotheby's, Olympia #14/R est:4000-6000
£4487 $7089 €6731 Bruce in his red car, NYC 1981 (69x101cm-27x40in) s.num.16/25 verso C-print prov. 28-Apr-3 Bukowskis, Stockholm #1017/R est:60000-80000 (S.KR 59000)
£4487 $7089 €6731 Guy at Wigstock 1991 (101x69cm-40x27in) s.num.13/25 verso C-print prov. 28-Apr-3 Bukowskis, Stockholm #1018/R est:60000-80000 (S.KR 59000)
£5000 $8000 €7500 Jody in my bath tub, Sag Harbor (70x102cm-28x40in) s.i.d.1999 num.15 verso cibachrome prov. 16-May-3 Phillips, New York #215/R est:5000-7000
£5063 $8000 €7595 Self portrait, in the mirror (51x61cm-20x24in) s.i.d.1980 verso photograph prov.lit. 24-Apr-3 Phillips, New York #50/R est:10000-15000
£5380 $8500 €8070 Joey dressed for wigstock (41x51cm-16x20in) s.i.d.1991 num.18/25 c-print prov. 13-Nov-2 Sotheby's, New York #427/R
£5380 $8500 €8070 Sky on the twilight of Philippine's death, Winterthur, Switzerland (79x102cm-31x40in) s.i.d.1997 verso cibachrome prov.exhib.lit. 12-Nov-2 Phillips, New York #160/R est:10000-15000
£5932 $9372 €8898 Volcano at dawn, Stromboli, 1996 (70x102cm-28x40in) s.num.6/15 verso cibachrome prov. 28-Apr-3 Bukowskis, Stockholm #898/R est:50000-60000 (S.KR 78000)
£6028 $9766 €8500 At the bar - Toon, C and So (77x101cm-30x40in) s.i.d.1992 num.5/25 verso cibachrome. 26-May-3 Christie's, Milan #229/R est:7000-10000
£6944 $11458 €10000 Kathe in the Tub, West Berlin (69x101cm-27x40in) s.i.d.1984 num.9/25 verso cibachrome prov.exhib.lit. 3-Jul-3 Christie's, Paris #121/R est:10000-15000
£6962 $11000 €10443 Sky on the day of Phillipines death winterhur, 1997. s.i.d.1997 num.2/5 cibachrome print. 14-Nov-2 Christie's, Rockefeller NY #479/R est:12000-18000
£7500 $12000 €11250 Amanda in the sauna, Hotel Savoy, Berlin (69x101cm-27x40in) s.i.d.1993 num.12/15 silver dye bleach process print. 15-May-3 Christie's, Rockefeller NY #407/R est:8000-12000
£7595 $12000 €11393 Self portrait in my blue bathroom, Berlin (70x101cm-28x40in) s.i.d.1991 num.9/25 silver dye bleach print. 14-Nov-2 Christie's, Rockefeller NY #478/R est:10000-15000
£8228 $13000 €12342 Kathe in the tub, West Berlin (69x101cm-27x40in) c-print executed 1984 prov.exhib. 13-Nov-2 Sotheby's, New York #146/R est:6000-8000
£8500 $14195 €12325 Stromboli at dawn, Naples (76x102cm-30x40in) s.i.d.1986 num.13/15 cibachrome prov.lit. 27-Jun-3 Christie's, London #268/R est:8000-12000
£8750 $14000 €13125 Amanda on my fortuny, Berlin (69x100cm-27x39in) s.i.d.1993 num.18/25 verso c-print prov. 14-May-3 Sotheby's, New York #388/R est:8000-12000
£8766 $13500 €13149 Jimmy Paulette and Misty in the taxi, New York City (41x62cm-16x24in) s.i.d.1991 num.3/25 verso cibachrome print prov.lit. 25-Oct-2 Phillips, New York #167/R est:3000-8000
£10976 $18000 €16464 Chiclet doing her makeup (68x106cm-27x42in) s.verso cibachrome edition of 3. 10-Feb-3 Swann Galleries, New York #98/R est:20000-25000

£12025 $19000 €18038 Self portrait on the train - Germany (66x98cm-26x39in) s.i.d.1992 num.9/25 verso silver dye bleach print prov.exhib.lit. 14-Nov-2 Christie's, Rockefeller NY #477/R est:10000-15000
£13291 $21000 €19937 Guido at the dock, Venice, Italy (76x102cm-30x40in) s.i.d.1998 cibachrome prov.exhib.lit. 12-Nov-2 Phillips, New York #161/R est:8000-12000
£14000 $23380 €20300 Yogo and C putting on make-up, second tip, Bangkok (66x98cm-26x39in) s.i.d.1992 num.5/15 verso cibachrome print prov. 26-Jun-3 Sotheby's, London #110/R est:8000-12000

GOLDINGHAM, James A (fl.1870-1881) British
£3400 $5610 €4930 Fools make fools (61x86cm-24x34in) mono.d.1898. 2-Jul-3 Sotheby's, Olympia #320/R est:3000-5000

GOLDSCHEIDER (19/20th C) Austrian
Sculpture
£1258 $2101 €1800 Salome (64cm-25in) s. green pat terracotta. 25-Jun-3 Artcurial Briest, Paris #36/R est:300-500

GOLDSCHEIDER, Friedrich (1845-1897) Austrian/French
Sculpture
£1655 $2714 €2300 Buste d'un beaute Orientale (46cm-18in) s.num.1424/150/5 polychrome terracotta exec.c.1900. 4-Jun-3 Tajan, Paris #269/R est:2500-3000

GOLDSCHMIDT, Gertrudis (1912-1994) Venezuelan
Sculpture
£10191 $16000 €15287 Untitled (50x82x8cm-20x32x3in) painted iron wire chains exec.1983 prov.exhib.lit. 19-Nov-2 Sotheby's, New York #48/R est:30000
£63694 $100000 €95541 Trunk 2 (143x30cm-56x12in) stainless steel metal assemblage exec.1975 prov.exhib.lit. 20-Nov-2 Christie's, Rockefeller NY #46/R est:100000-150000

GOLDSCHMIDT, Hilde (1897-1980) Austrian?
Works on paper
£411 $642 €650 Little dog (44x29cm-17x11in) s.d.1920 W/C bodycol paper on board. 15-Oct-2 Dorotheum, Vienna #47/R
£700 $1148 €1050 Street in Kitzbuehl (33x23cm-13x9in) s.d.58 crayon col chk. 3-Jun-3 Sotheby's, Olympia #219/R

GOLDSMITH, Walter (fl.1880-1898) British
£10000 $16600 €15000 Windsor Castle from the Thames (122x153cm-48x60in) mono. 10-Jun-3 Christie's, London #136/R est:12000-18000

GOLDSWORTHY, Andy (1956-) British
Photographs
£3504 $5466 €5256 Calm-Knotweek stalks, Derwent Water, Cumbria. col. photoes two parts prov. 5-Nov-2 Bukowskis, Stockholm #478/R est:30000-40000 (S.KR 50000)

GOLDTHWAIT, Harold (19th C) British
£299 $500 €434 Vase of roses (76x66cm-30x26in) 29-Jun-3 Butterfields, Los Angeles #7016/R
£380 $543 €570 Returning home near Godalming (24x36cm-9x14in) s. i.verso mahogany panel. 11-Apr-2 Mellors & Kirk, Nottingham #547
£828 $1275 €1300 River landscape with figures (49x64cm-19x25in) s. 4-Sep-2 James Adam, Dublin #70/R est:800-1000
Works on paper
£850 $1420 €1233 View of a farm in a valley (24x37cm-9x15in) s. panel three. 17-Jun-3 Rosebery Fine Art, London #458/R

GOLKAR, Ali (1948-) Iranian
£769 $1200 €1154 Untitled (102x76cm-40x30in) painted c.1995. 11-Apr-3 Du Mouchelle, Detroit #91/R est:1700-1900

GOLLER, Bruno (1901-) German
£6646 $10500 €10500 Garden in bloom (74x61cm-29x24in) s.d.1922. 30-Nov-2 Villa Grisebach, Berlin #140/R est:12000-15000
£16026 $24840 €25000 Landscape with willows (91x78cm-36x31in) s. prov. 4-Dec-2 Lempertz, Koln #738/R est:25000-30000

GOLLER, Josef (1868-1930) German
Works on paper
£405 $632 €600 Venus seated between two pillars and holding mirror. mixed media. 26-Mar-3 Hugo Ruef, Munich #297/R

GOLLINGS, William Elling (1878-1932) American
£3205 $5000 €4808 Headin for camp (46x76cm-18x30in) s.d.1912 prov.lit. 9-Nov-2 Santa Fe Art, Santa Fe #141/R est:15000-20000
£10323 $16000 €15485 Observation point (26x21cm-10x8in) s.i.d.06 canvas on board prov. 5-Dec-2 Christie's, Rockefeller NY #183/R est:20000-30000
£22581 $35000 €33872 Cowboy on horse (25x36cm-10x14in) s.d.1913 prov. 4-Dec-2 Sotheby's, New York #146/R est:30000-50000

GOLLON, Chris (1953-) British
£750 $1238 €1088 Feast (183x61cm-72x24in) s. board. 3-Jul-3 Christie's, Kensington #587/R

GOLOMB, Curtis (1963-) Canadian
Works on paper
£609 $950 €1015 Jasper afternoon (98x72cm-39x28in) s.i. W/C paper on board prov. 13-Apr-3 Levis, Calgary #41/R est:1800-2400 (C.D 1400)

GOLOVIN, Aleksandr (1863-1930) Russian
Works on paper
£12000 $19440 €18000 Costume design for Fyodor Chaliapin in the role of Tonio (38x27cm-15x11in) s.i.d.1918 pen ink W/C htd gouache pencil. 21-May-3 Sotheby's, London #138/R est:3000-5000

GOLTZ, Walter (1875-1956) American
£519 $800 €779 Cornshocks. Pumpkins (30x38cm-12x15in) s. canvasboard pair prov. 24-Oct-2 Shannon's, Milford #225/R

GOLTZIUS, Hendrik (1558-1616) Dutch
Works on paper
£19108 $29809 €30000 Holy Family (10x8cm-4x3in) pen brown ink wash htd white lit. 5-Nov-2 Sotheby's, Amsterdam #8/R est:20000-30000

GOLTZIUS, Hendrik (circle) (1558-1616) Dutch
£5807 $9175 €9000 Holy Family (44x35cm-17x14in) panel. 18-Dec-2 Tajan, Paris #8/R est:12000

GOLUB, Leon Albert (1922-) American
£2848 $4500 €4272 Pinochet saluting (43x58cm-17x23in) s. i.d.1977 verso acrylic burlap prov. 13-Nov-2 Sotheby's, New York #557/R est:10000-15000

GOMAR Y GOMAR, Antonio (1853-1911) Spanish
£574 $896 €850 Landscape (35x20cm-14x8in) board. 25-Mar-3 Durán, Madrid #95/R

GOMERY, Emeric (1902-1969) French/Hungarian
Works on paper
£283 $441 €425 Female nude (63x48cm-25x19in) s.d.1959 W/C Indian ink brush. 16-Sep-2 Philippe Schuler, Zurich #3029 (S.FR 650)

GOMES, Micha (20th C) British?
Works on paper
£400 $620 €600 Greyhound (22x25cm-9x10in) s.d.20/2/02 pencil W/C wash. 4-Dec-2 John Ross, Belfast #229

GOMEZ JARAMILLO, Ignacio (1910-1970) Colombian
Works on paper
£420 $656 €630 On the beach (30x60cm-12x24in) s.i.d.1954 W/C. 6-Nov-2 AB Stockholms Auktionsverk #928/R (S.KR 6000)

GOMEZ MARTIN, Enrique (19th C) Spanish
£597 $932 €950 Soldiers (27x21cm-11x8in) s. board pair. 23-Sep-2 Durán, Madrid #77/R
£818 $1275 €1300 Battle scenes (11x27cm-4x11in) s. panel pair. 23-Sep-2 Durán, Madrid #79/R
£1603 $2532 €2500 Cavalry (72x24cm-28x9in) s. pair. 14-Nov-2 Arte, Seville #342/R

GOMEZ MAYORGA, Guillermo (1887-1962) Mexican
£1248 $1971 €1872 Farm (19x36cm-7x14in) s. 26-Nov-2 Louis Morton, Mexico #78/R (M.P 20000)
£1637 $2554 €2456 Paisaje (20x40cm-8x16in) s. masonite. 17-Oct-2 Louis Morton, Mexico #33/R est:35000-40000 (M.P 26000)

£1889 $2947 €2834 Paisaje (20x40cm-8x16in) s. masonite. 17-Oct-2 Louis Morton, Mexico #137/R est:35000-40000 (M.P 30000)
£3463 $5403 €5195 Bouquet de flores (42x60cm-17x24in) s. 17-Oct-2 Louis Morton, Mexico #57/R est:60000-65000 (M.P 55000)
£5038 $7859 €7557 Paisaje (40x70cm-16x28in) s. 17-Oct-2 Louis Morton, Mexico #63/R est:85000-90000 (M.P 80000)
£16373 $25542 €24560 Ameca (100x60cm-39x24in) s. 17-Oct-2 Louis Morton, Mexico #76/R est:160000-170000 (M.P 260000)

GOMEZ MIR, Eugenio (19/20th C) Spanish
£419 $663 €650 Landscape with buildings (20x33cm-8x13in) s. board. 18-Dec-2 Ansorena, Madrid #13/R

GOMEZ Y GIL, Guillermo (1862-1942) Spanish
£574 $896 €850 Water carriers (80x45cm-31x18in) s.d.91. 25-Mar-3 Durán, Madrid #728/R
£753 $1175 €1100 Seascape (25x29cm-10x11in) s. canvas on cardboard. 8-Apr-3 Ansorena, Madrid #25/R
£755 $1177 €1200 Seascape (27x32cm-11x13in) s. 23-Sep-2 Durán, Madrid #93/R
£755 $1177 €1200 Seascape (27x32cm-11x13in) s. 23-Sep-2 Durán, Madrid #92/R
£881 $1374 €1400 Seascape (22x30cm-9x12in) s. 23-Sep-2 Durán, Madrid #90/R
£1806 $2854 €2800 Gallant scene (100x65cm-39x26in) s. 17-Dec-2 Durán, Madrid #168/R
£3448 $5448 €5000 Seascape (73x101cm-29x40in) s. 7-Apr-3 Castellana, Madrid #49/R

GOMEZ, Marco Antonio (1910-1972) American/Mexican
£1442 $2250 €2163 Canyon at night (61x76cm-24x30in) s. s.i.verso prov. 9-Nov-2 Santa Fe Art, Santa Fe #174/R est:5000-7000
£1603 $2500 €2405 Hell raisers (61x76cm-24x30in) s. s.i.verso prov. 9-Nov-2 Santa Fe Art, Santa Fe #175/R est:5000-7000

GOMEZ, Maria (1953-) Spanish
Works on paper
£276 $436 €400 School, swimming-pool, trees (34x50cm-13x20in) s.i.d.1979 pencil dr prov. 1-Apr-3 Segre, Madrid #215/R

GOMEZ-GIMENO, Ricardo (1892-1954) Spanish
£692 $1079 €1100 Castel Moron d'Albret (27x33cm-11x13in) s. i.verso board. 23-Sep-2 Durán, Madrid #95/R
£705 $1114 €1100 Castel Moron d'Albret (27x33cm-11x13in) s. i.verso board. 19-Nov-2 Durán, Madrid #81/R
£881 $1374 €1400 Chateau de Montignac (56x46cm-22x18in) s.d.1932 board. 23-Sep-2 Durán, Madrid #96/R
Works on paper
£629 $981 €1000 Portrait of old man (47x30cm-19x12in) s.d.1929 dr. 23-Sep-2 Durán, Madrid #97/R

GOMOT, S (19/20th C) French
£2532 $3924 €4000 Navires au port (38x55cm-15x22in) s.i. pair. 27-Sep-2 Rabourdin & Choppin de Janvry, Paris #13/R est:4600-4800

GOMZE, Paul (1870-1949) Belgian
£278 $434 €440 Ferme animee (60x75cm-24x30in) s. panel double-sided. 16-Sep-2 Horta, Bruxelles #353

GONCHAROV, Grigory Andreyevich (1913-) Russian
£444 $738 €644 Maternity (78x140cm-31x55in) s.d.1975 s.i.verso lit. 16-Jun-3 Waddingtons, Toronto #344/R est:1000-1500 (C.D 1000)

GONDOUIN, Emmanuel (1883-1934) French
Works on paper
£347 $552 €500 Maternite (27x21cm-11x8in) st. graphite dr. 29-Apr-3 Artcurial Briest, Paris #85

GONG XIAN (1599-1689) Chinese
Works on paper
£27195 $44872 €39433 Cottage by the spring river (191x48cm-75x19in) s.i. ink satin hanging scroll. 6-Jul-3 Christie's, Hong Kong #478/R est:400000-500000 (HK.D 350000)
£54390 $89744 €78866 Landscape (206x52cm-81x20in) s.i. ink silk hanging scroll lit. 6-Jul-3 Christie's, Hong Kong #422/R est:500000-600000 (HK.D 700000)

GONI SUAREZ, Lorenzo (1911-1992) Spanish
Works on paper
£302 $471 €480 Aquelarre (34x23cm-13x9in) ink dr. 8-Oct-2 Ansorena, Madrid #510/R

GONIN, Francesco (1808-1889) Italian
£51282 $80513 €80000 Attacking Rome (133x105cm-52x41in) s.d.1852 lit. 16-Dec-2 Pandolfini, Florence #118/R est:75000

GONNER, Maximilian (1875-1921) German?
£276 $419 €430 Hohentwiel (40x75cm-16x30in) s.i.d.1907. 31-Aug-2 Geble, Radolfzell #633

GONNER, Rudolf (1872-1926) German
£314 $484 €500 Triest harbour (60x80cm-24x31in) s.d.23 i. verso. 23-Oct-2 Neumeister, Munich #642/R

GONS, F (19th C) Belgian
£2553 $4136 €3600 La Place Verte a Anvers (83x57cm-33x22in) panel. 26-May-3 Amberes, Antwerp #36

GONS, Frans (19th C) Belgian
£1783 $2800 €2675 Spilt ink (61x76cm-24x30in) s. panel. 14-Dec-2 Weschler, Washington #622/R est:3000-5000

GONTARD, Moris (1940-) French
£694 $1097 €1000 Quelques objets insolites dans ce doux paysage (110x115cm-43x45in) s.d. acrylic painted wood prov. 27-Apr-3 Perrin, Versailles #155/R
£868 $1372 €1250 Un froid inexplicable s'etait glisse (97x130cm-38x51in) s.d. acrylic prov. 27-Apr-3 Perrin, Versailles #157/R

GONTCHAROVA, Natalia (1881-1962) Russian
£12000 $18840 €18000 Still life of vase with flowers (22x16cm-9x6in) s. init.i.verso board. 20-Nov-2 Sotheby's, London #117/R est:6000-8000
£13462 $20865 €21000 Still life of roses and jasmin (35x24cm-14x9in) s. prov. 4-Dec-2 Lempertz, Koln #739/R est:8000-10000
£15000 $23550 €22500 Floral still life (22x16cm-9x6in) init. 20-Nov-2 Sotheby's, London #118/R est:10000-15000
£19872 $31199 €31000 Auto-portrait (61x46cm-24x18in) s. painted c.1930-32. 10-Dec-2 Pierre Berge, Paris #48/R est:30000
£45000 $70650 €67500 Still life of flowers (65x41cm-26x16in) s. 20-Nov-2 Sotheby's, London #188/R est:30000-40000
£55000 $86350 €82500 Still life of vase with flowers (55x55cm-22x22in) init. 20-Nov-2 Sotheby's, London #189/R est:30000-40000
£410000 $664200 €615000 Bathing boys, simultaneous perception (79x71cm-31x28in) i. 21-May-3 Sotheby's, London #135/R est:150000-200000
Works on paper
£440 $682 €700 Composition (28x20cm-11x8in) s. W/C exec.c.1950. 30-Oct-2 Artcurial Briest, Paris #20
£833 $1300 €1250 Seated cavalry officer (28x21cm-11x8in) s.i. W/C over pencil. 19-Sep-2 Swann Galleries, New York #375/R
£1380 $2304 €2000 Danseuse, projet de costume pour le ballet Sur le Borystheme (30x19cm-12x7in) bears i. W/C graphite htd gold felt tip. 10-Jul-3 Artcurial Briest, Paris #77/R est:1500-2000
£2098 $3504 €3000 Sans titre (24x16cm-9x6in) s. W/C. 26-Jun-3 Tajan, Paris #92/R est:3000-4000
£5595 $9343 €8000 St femme, projet de costume pour le ballet (55x42cm-22x17in) s. W/C gouache prov. 26-Jun-3 Tajan, Paris #87/R est:8000-10000
£5807 $9175 €9000 Untitled (27x19cm-11x7in) s. W/C exhib. 18-Dec-2 Tajan, Paris #44/R est:12000
£6294 $10511 €9000 Paysage (25x17cm-10x7in) s. W/C painted c.1920. 26-Jun-3 Tajan, Paris #91/R est:4000-6000
£6993 $11678 €10000 Composition geometrique (25x17cm-10x7in) s. W/C exec.c.1918-1920 lit. 26-Jun-3 Tajan, Paris #90/R est:4000-6000
£10490 $17518 €15000 Composition rayonniste (26x18cm-10x7in) mono. W/C exec.c.1920 prov.exhib. 26-Jun-3 Tajan, Paris #89/R est:7000-9000
£11888 $19853 €17000 Paysage rayonniste (27x19cm-11x7in) s. W/C exec.c.1920. 26-Jun-3 Tajan, Paris #88/R est:6000-8000
£15385 $25693 €22000 La danseuse (77x54cm-30x21in) s. gouache collage paper on canvas prov.exhib. 26-Jun-3 Tajan, Paris #86/R est:15000-20000
£36328 $56672 €54492 Scenes out of the life of Saints (86x76cm-34x30in) s. mixed media. 11-Apr-3 Kieselbach, Budapest #26/R est:13000000 (H.F 13000000)

GONTIER, Clement (19th C) French
£2893 $4484 €4600 Grand bouquet de fleurs sur entablement (81x65cm-32x26in) s. oval. 6-Oct-2 Livinec, Gaudcheau & Jezequel, Rennes #72/R

GONZAGA, Giovanfrancesco (1921-) Italian
£673 $1057 €1050 Big chestnut tree (40x30cm-16x12in) s. s.i.d.1990 verso. 23-Nov-2 Meeting Art, Vercelli #149/R
£949 $1481 €1500 Mushrooms and chestnuts (30x40cm-12x16in) s. s.i.d.1997 verso. 14-Sep-2 Meeting Art, Vercelli #927/R
£962 $1510 €1500 Horse (50x70cm-20x28in) s. s.i.d.1982 verso tempera cardboard. 23-Nov-2 Meeting Art, Vercelli #210/R
£1076 $1678 €1700 Knight (40x30cm-16x12in) s. s.i.d.1987 verso. 14-Sep-2 Meeting Art, Vercelli #970/R

£1090 $1711 €1700 Warrior in the snow (40x30cm-16x12in) s. s.i.d.1990 verso. 23-Nov-2 Meeting Art, Vercelli #185/R
£1111 $1778 €1700 Mushrooms and grapes (30x40cm-12x16in) s. s.i.verso. 4-Jan-3 Meeting Art, Vercelli #44
£1242 $1987 €1900 Rider (40x50cm-16x20in) s. s.i.verso. 4-Jan-3 Meeting Art, Vercelli #708
£1282 $2013 €2000 Picador (55x40cm-22x16in) s. s.i.verso. 23-Nov-2 Meeting Art, Vercelli #397/R
£1307 $2092 €2000 Fruit in under-growth (40x50cm-16x20in) s. painted 1990. 4-Jan-3 Meeting Art, Vercelli #502
£1307 $2092 €2000 Soldier (50x40cm-20x16in) s. painted 1990. 4-Jan-3 Meeting Art, Vercelli #723
£1307 $2092 €2000 Farms in Maremma (50x40cm-20x16in) s. s.i.d.1987 verso. 4-Jan-3 Meeting Art, Vercelli #733
£1319 $2098 €1900 Knight of Savoy galloping (50x40cm-20x16in) s. s.i.d.1991 verso. 1-May-3 Meeting Art, Vercelli #26
£1373 $2196 €2100 Stallion (50x40cm-20x16in) s. s.i.d.1990 verso. 4-Jan-3 Meeting Art, Vercelli #73
£1389 $2208 €2000 Rider in the desert (50x40cm-20x16in) s. painted 1989. 1-May-3 Meeting Art, Vercelli #310
£1519 $2370 €2400 Tuscan cowboy on the seashore (50x40cm-20x16in) s. 14-Sep-2 Meeting Art, Vercelli #976/R
£1538 $2415 €2400 Two horses (50x60cm-20x24in) s. s.i.d.1997 verso. 23-Nov-2 Meeting Art, Vercelli #242/R
£1987 $3120 €3100 Soldiers (70x50cm-28x20in) s. 23-Nov-2 Meeting Art, Vercelli #413/R
£2041 $3245 €3000 Desert knight (50x40cm-20x16in) s. painted 1990. 1-Mar-3 Meeting Art, Vercelli #744
£2353 $3765 €3600 Tuscan cow-boy riding (60x80cm-24x31in) s. 4-Jan-3 Meeting Art, Vercelli #511
£2381 $3786 €3500 Cowboy riding (50x40cm-20x16in) s. 1-Mar-3 Meeting Art, Vercelli #470
£2639 $4196 €3800 Fruit in interior with red background (50x70cm-20x28in) s. painted 1970. 1-May-3 Meeting Art, Vercelli #572
£3333 $5300 €4800 Two figures (50x60cm-20x24in) s. 1-May-3 Meeting Art, Vercelli #322

Works on paper
£327 $523 €500 Hussar (40x30cm-16x12in) s. s.i.verso mixed media card. 4-Jan-3 Meeting Art, Vercelli #125

GONZAGA, Pietro di Gottardo (attrib) (1751-1831) Italian
Works on paper
£705 $1093 €1100 Interior of gothic church (46x29cm-18x11in) pen ink wash. 4-Dec-2 Piasa, Paris #17

GONZALES, Marcel (19/20th C) ?
£352 $567 €500 Nus cubistes (25x32cm-10x13in) s. 11-May-3 Thierry & Lannon, Brest #252
£458 $737 €650 Nus au chaton (65x50cm-26x20in) s. 11-May-3 Thierry & Lannon, Brest #253

GONZALES, Roberta (1909-1976) French
£270 $422 €400 Still life 2 (33x55cm-13x22in) s.d.64 i.d.verso. 28-Mar-3 Charbonneaux, Paris #85/R
£405 $632 €600 Voliere 1 (50x73cm-20x29in) s.d.61 i.d.verso. 28-Mar-3 Charbonneaux, Paris #86
£592 $959 €900 Young woman (54x37cm-21x15in) s. cardboard. 21-Jan-3 Durán, Madrid #88/R

GONZALES, Xavier (1898-1993) American
£481 $750 €722 Woodlands (56x76cm-22x30in) board. 19-Oct-2 David Dike, Dallas #292/R
Works on paper
£228 $350 €342 Mystic (53x74cm-21x29in) s. W/C gouache. 27-Oct-2 Grogan, Boston #103
£228 $350 €342 Flotilla (56x71cm-22x28in) s. gouache. 27-Oct-2 Grogan, Boston #104

GONZALEZ ALACREU, Juan (1937-) Spanish
£1452 $2294 €2250 Fishermen by boats (60x81cm-24x32in) s. 17-Dec-2 Durán, Madrid #187/R

GONZALEZ BRAVO, Justo (1944-) Spanish
Works on paper
£305 $494 €430 Untitled (23x20cm-9x8in) s.d.1964 gouache. 24-May-3 Van Ham, Cologne #215/R
£1135 $1838 €1600 Untitled (545x65cm-215x26in) s. s.d. verso mixed media canvas. 24-May-3 Van Ham, Cologne #213/R est:2200

GONZALEZ MARCOS, Angel (1900-1977) Spanish
£411 $641 €600 Halt (70x100cm-28x39in) s. s.i.verso. 8-Apr-3 Ansorena, Madrid #38/R
£414 $658 €600 Bull scene (74x60cm-29x24in) s. i.verso. 4-Mar-3 Ansorena, Madrid #123/R
£473 $738 €700 Cattle (73x100cm-29x39in) s. s.i.verso. 25-Mar-3 Durán, Madrid #682/R
£507 $791 €750 Cattle scene (64x100cm-25x39in) s. s.i.verso. 25-Mar-3 Durán, Madrid #681/R
Works on paper
£268 $432 €400 Bulls (49x64cm-19x25in) s. gouache. 18-Feb-3 Durán, Madrid #1110/R
£274 $427 €400 Bull fight (50x74cm-20x29in) s. gouache cardboard. 8-Apr-3 Ansorena, Madrid #630/R
£329 $533 €500 Bulls (42x62cm-17x24in) s. gouache. 21-Jan-3 Ansorena, Madrid #334/R
£403 $648 €600 Last round (64x50cm-25x20in) s. s.d.verso gouache. 18-Feb-3 Durán, Madrid #597/R
£968 $1529 €1500 Bull fight (76x106cm-30x42in) s. gouache cardboard. 18-Dec-2 Ansorena, Madrid #383/R

GONZALEZ PEREZTORENA, Fermin (19th C) Spanish
£417 $658 €650 Landscape with cattle (73x133cm-29x52in) s.d.1872. 13-Nov-2 Ansorena, Madrid #343/R

GONZALEZ POBLETE, Daniel (1944-) Spanish
£2372 $3747 €3700 Nude and apple (42x32cm-17x13in) s. board. 13-Nov-2 Ansorena, Madrid #29/R est:3500

GONZALEZ SERRANO, Manuel (1917-1960) Mexican
£10976 $18000 €15915 Naturaleza muerta con torito (61x46cm-24x18in) s. masonite painted c.1944 prov.exhib. 27-May-3 Sotheby's, New York #92
£16079 $25727 €23315 Pescador (50x70cm-20x28in) s. 15-May-3 Louis Morton, Mexico #98/R est:290000-310000 (M.P 260000)

GONZALEZ ZAPATERO, Rafael (1953-) Spanish
£397 $648 €600 Perdrix (60x80cm-24x31in) 11-Feb-3 Castellana, Madrid #371/R

GONZALEZ, Carmelo (?) ?
£7643 $12000 €11465 Colonial interior (76x137cm-30x54in) s.d.58 s.i.d.verso prov. 20-Nov-2 Christie's, Rockefeller NY #113/R est:15000-20000

GONZALEZ, Juan Antonio (1842-1914) Spanish
£38710 $60000 €58065 Duel (94x138cm-37x54in) s.d.1880. 29-Oct-2 Sotheby's, New York #80/R est:80000-120000

GONZALEZ, Julio (1876-1942) Spanish
£15000 $24450 €22500 Untitled (21x11cm-8x4in) oil pencil panel painted c.1941-42 prov.exhib. 3-Feb-3 Christie's, London #162/R est:25000
Sculpture
£3919 $6114 €5800 Fleur (20x20x10cm-8x8x4in) tin prov. 28-Mar-3 Charbonneaux, Paris #162
£51282 $80000 €76923 Grande Venus (34cm-13in) num.1/9 brown pat bronze executed c.1936-37 prov.lit. 5-Nov-2 Phillips, New York #136/R est:80000-120000
£58000 $96860 €84100 Masque Montserrat criant (49cm-19in) s.i. brown pat. bronze st.f.R Gonzalez exhib.lit. 25-Jun-3 Christie's, London #226/R est:25000-35000
£236025 $380000 €354038 Femme assise I (92cm-36in) s.i. brown pat bronze lit. 7-May-3 Christie's, Rockefeller NY #28/R est:400000-600000
£1987180 $3100000 €2980770 Homme gothique (55cm-22in) s.indis d.1937 welded iron prov.lit. 6-Nov-2 Christie's, Rockefeller NY #39/R est:1500000-2000000
Works on paper
£3774 $6000 €5661 Abstraction. Femme (32x25cm-13x10in) init.d.39 crayon chl double-sided. 27-Feb-3 Christie's, Rockefeller NY #35/R est:7000
£7547 $12000 €11321 Untitled (25x16cm-10x6in) init.d.1937 pen ink wax crayon prov. 27-Feb-3 Christie's, Rockefeller NY #39/R est:15000
£10000 $16400 €15000 Tete et geranium (17x16cm-7x6in) init.d.1936 gouache W/C pen ink prov.lit. 6-Feb-3 Christie's, London #450/R est:15000

GONZALEZ, Zacarias (1923-) Spanish
Works on paper
£597 $932 €950 Peasnat girls (69x50cm-27x20in) s.d.1950 gouache. 17-Sep-2 Segre, Madrid #131/R

GONZALEZ-TORRES, Felix (1957-1996) Cuban
Photographs
£17000 $27880 €25500 Untitled - Venezia (19x24cm-7x9in) s.i.d.1988 verso C-print jigsaw in plastic bag num.2/3 prov.exhib. 6-Feb-3 Christie's, London #712/R est:12000-16000
£43750 $70000 €65625 Untitled - sand (32x39cm-13x15in) s.d.1994 num.3/12 photogravures portfolio 8 parts. 15-May-3 Christie's, Rockefeller NY #323/R est:60000-80000

£82278 $130000 €123417 Untitled - a couple (30x56cm-12x22in) s.i.d.1991 num,1/1 1/2 verso c-print jigsaw puzzles two. 13-Nov-2 Christie's, Rockefeller NY #5/R est:80000-120000

Sculpture
£46875 $75000 €70313 Untitled (336cm-132in) 24 ten watt lightbulbs executed 1993 prov.exhib.lit. 15-May-3 Phillips, New York #3/R est:70000-90000
£108974 $170000 €163461 Untitled (39x74cm-15x29in) offset on paper endless copies executed 1990 prov.exhib.lit. 11-Nov-2 Phillips, New York #6/R est:150000-200000
£165000 $270600 €247500 Untitled (30x6cm-12x2in) one white extension cord 44 feet 24 light bulbs executed 1992. 5-Feb-3 Christie's, London #12/R est:100000-150000

Works on paper
£9375 $15000 €14063 Untitled graph - blood work (32x24cm-13x9in) s.i.d.1990 graphite gouache prov.lit. 15-May-3 Christie's, Rockefeller NY #321/R est:15000-20000

GONZALO, Alberto (1954-) Spanish
£755 $1177 €1200 Dogon (116x89cm-46x35in) s.i.d.1989 verso. 8-Oct-2 Ansorena, Madrid #625/R
£755 $1177 €1200 Sweating at college (116x89cm-46x35in) s.i.d.1990 verso. 8-Oct-2 Ansorena, Madrid #640/R

GONZALVEZ, A R (19th/20th C) Spanish
£1290 $2039 €2000 Flowers (101x45cm-40x18in) s.d.1899. 17-Dec-2 Durán, Madrid #643/R
£1290 $2039 €2000 Flowers and willows (101x45cm-40x18in) s.d.1901. 17-Dec-2 Durán, Madrid #644/R
£1290 $2039 €2000 Flowers and doves (101x45cm-40x18in) s.d.1899. 17-Dec-2 Durán, Madrid #645/R

GONZALVO Y PEREZ, Pablo (1830-1896) Spanish
£1132 $1743 €1800 Interior (48x63cm-19x25in) 22-Oct-2 Durán, Madrid #120/R

GOOCH, James (fl.1819-1837) British
£660 $1016 €990 Portrait of a gentleman, with a white terrier (51x39cm-20x15in) s. 5-Sep-2 Christie's, Kensington #65/R

GOOCH, Thomas (1750-1802) British
£5000 $8000 €7500 Countess (64x76cm-25x30in) s.d.1789. 13-Mar-3 Duke & Son, Dorchester #260/R est:1500-3000

GOOCH, Thomas (attrib) (1750-1802) British
£1350 $2201 €2025 Three beagles in a landscape (19x24cm-7x9in) prov. 29-Jan-3 Dreweatt Neate, Newbury #175/R est:1200-1800

GOOD, Clement (1810-1896) Danish
Works on paper
£500 $795 €750 Passing frigates (56x92cm-22x36in) s.d.1893 W/C htd white. 29-Apr-3 Bonhams, Knightsbridge #53/R

GOOD, Leonard (1907-) American
£255 $400 €383 Uprooted (28x36cm-11x14in) s. canvasboard exhib. sold with a dr by the same artist. 23-Nov-2 Jackson's, Cedar Falls #361/R
£414 $650 €621 Bouquet in tall vase (61x46cm-24x18in) s. canvas on wood panel. 23-Nov-2 Jackson's, Cedar Falls #319/R

GOODACRE, Glenna (20th C) American
Sculpture
£962 $1500 €1443 Little sister (20cm-8in) bronze. 9-Nov-2 Altermann Galleries, Santa Fe #123
£1026 $1600 €1539 Little brother (20cm-8in) bronze. 9-Nov-2 Altermann Galleries, Santa Fe #122
£1603 $2500 €2405 Taos bus stop (20cm-8in) bronze. 9-Nov-2 Altermann Galleries, Santa Fe #121
£1917 $3105 €2780 Charity (28cm-11in) bronze. 23-May-3 Altermann Galleries, Santa Fe #198
£3549 $5750 €5146 Sacagawea study (18x18cm-7x7in) bronze. 23-May-3 Altermann Galleries, Santa Fe #126
£4808 $7500 €7212 Little pawns (97cm-38in) bronze. 9-Nov-2 Altermann Galleries, Santa Fe #120

GOODALL, Edward (1795-1870) British
Works on paper
£173 $275 €251 Parliament Buildings, Victoria (23x50cm-9x20in) s. W/C. 1-May-3 Heffel, Vancouver #32/R (C.D 400)
£173 $275 €251 Parliament Buildings, Victoria, British Columbia (26x34cm-10x13in) s.i. W/C prov. 1-May-3 Heffel, Vancouver #33/R (C.D 400)
£173 $275 €251 Parliament Buildings and Carolling Towers, Victoria (24x31cm-9x12in) s. W/C prov. 1-May-3 Heffel, Vancouver #34/R (C.D 400)
£195 $309 €283 Okanagan lake bridge, Kelowna, BC (23x34cm-9x13in) s.i. W/C prov. 1-May-3 Heffel, Vancouver #31/R (C.D 450)
£260 $413 €377 Lake scene (29x25cm-11x10in) s. W/C prov. 1-May-3 Heffel, Vancouver #30/R (C.D 600)
£281 $447 €407 Rogers Pass, BC (30x48cm-12x19in) s.i. W/C prov. 1-May-3 Heffel, Vancouver #36/R (C.D 650)

GOODALL, Edward Alfred (1819-1908) British
£13100 $20437 €19650 Evening market in Constantinople (43x61cm-17x24in) s.d.1857. 6-Nov-2 Dobiaschofsky, Bern #602/R est:32000 (S.FR 30000)
£27027 $42162 €40000 View of the little mosque of Saint Sophie (61x43cm-24x17in) s.d.1857. 28-Mar-3 Claude Aguttes, Neuilly #185/R est:40000-60000

Works on paper
£240 $372 €360 Figures at a well in the desert (14x34cm-6x13in) s. W/C prov. 3-Dec-2 Sotheby's, Olympia #126/R
£1000 $1560 €1500 Church of san Pietro di Castello, Venice (52x37cm-20x15in) W/C. 5-Nov-2 Bonhams, New Bond Street #87/R est:800-1200
£1300 $2080 €1950 Arab encampment on the edge of a city (36x74cm-14x29in) s. W/C. 13-Mar-3 Duke & Son, Dorchester #130/R est:1000-2000
£3000 $4770 €4500 Giralda, Seville (47x35cm-19x14in) W/C over pencil htd bodycol. 19-Mar-3 Sotheby's, London #219/R est:1000-1500

GOODALL, Frederick (1822-1904) British
£500 $795 €750 At the well (30x54cm-12x21in) mono.d.1870. 6-Mar-3 Christie's, Kensington #576/R
£560 $874 €840 Arab nomads near the sea (38x91cm-15x36in) mono.d.1884. 17-Oct-2 Lawrence, Crewkerne #498/R
£600 $948 €870 Flight into Egypt (41x61cm-16x24in) mono.d.1884-97. 22-Jul-3 Gorringes, Lewes #1653
£678 $1078 €1017 Portrait of John Vooght as a child (20x15cm-8x6in) s.d.1851 board. 18-Mar-3 Maynards, Vancouver #17/R (C.D 1600)
£800 $1312 €1200 Sunset over the pyramids (38x76cm-15x30in) mono. 29-May-3 Christie's, Kensington #207/R
£1000 $1590 €1500 Italian woman and child (23x19cm-9x7in) s.d.1863 panel. 6-Mar-3 Christie's, Kensington #547/R est:1200-1800
£1000 $1580 €1500 Study of an Arab standing near a well (54x35cm-21x14in) mono.d.1859/70. 7-Apr-3 Bonhams, Bath #121/R est:1000-1500
£1800 $2772 €2700 Camel train (56x39cm-22x15in) mono.d.1870 prov. 5-Sep-2 Christie's, Kensington #239/R est:1000-1500
£2025 $3200 €3038 Family of farmers crossing the desert (38x91cm-15x36in) mono.d.1888. 1-Apr-3 Christie's, Rockefeller NY #198/R est:4000-6000
£2200 $3674 €3190 Age and infancy (22x31cm-9x12in) s.d.1852 panel. 17-Jun-3 Bonhams, New Bond Street #82/R est:2000-3000
£3000 $4680 €4500 Figures at an oasis before the pyramids at sunset (38x69cm-15x27in) mono.d.1896. 11-Apr-3 Keys, Aylsham #641/R est:3500-4500
£40000 $64400 €60000 Palm grove (183x114cm-72x45in) mono.d.1894 prov.exhib.lit. 20-Feb-3 Christie's, London #159/R est:80000
£70968 $110000 €106452 Finding of Moses (152x114cm-60x45in) init.d.1885 prov. 30-Oct-2 Christie's, Rockefeller NY #42/R est:120000-160000

Works on paper
£400 $632 €580 Study for the time for roses (11x7cm-4x3in) mono.d.Feb 11th 1878 W/C bodycol. 22-Jul-3 Bonhams, Knightsbridge #190/R
£1538 $2415 €2400 Wayworn (18x13cm-7x5in) s.d.1853 W/C over pencil prov. 19-Nov-2 Whyte's, Dublin #97/R est:1500-2000
£1719 $2750 €2579 Figures in an Egyptian landscape with pyramids (13x28cm-5x11in) W/C. 18-May-3 Jeffery Burchard, Florida #98/R est:2800-3200

GOODALL, Frederick (attrib) (1822-1904) British
£420 $664 €630 Toy seller (17x24cm-7x9in) mono.d.48 board. 7-Apr-3 Bonhams, Bath #129/R

GOODALL, John Edward (fl.1877-1891) British
Works on paper
£380 $592 €570 Untitled (14x20cm-6x8in) s. pencil W/C htd white. 19-Sep-2 Christie's, Kensington #154
£2200 $3586 €3190 Ennuis, young lady seated on a Regency sofa (34x51cm-13x20in) s. pencil W/C. 17-Jul-3 Tennants, Leyburn #767/R est:2200-2500

GOODALL, John Strickland (1908-1996) British
Works on paper
£350 $546 €525 Governess (15x23cm-6x9in) s.d.95 pencil W/C pen ink gum arabic. 17-Oct-2 Christie's, Kensington #57/R

£480 $758 €720 On a beach (20x25cm-8x10in) s. W/C htd white. 27-Nov-2 Hamptons Fine Art, Godalming #179
£480 $749 €720 Piano player (15x20cm-6x8in) s. W/C htd white. 26-Mar-3 Hamptons Fine Art, Godalming #72
£520 $827 €780 Kitten (16x19cm-6x7in) s. W/C htd white. 25-Feb-3 Bonhams, Knightsbridge #58/R
£600 $954 €900 Do take care (14x19cm-6x7in) s. W/C bodycol. 25-Feb-3 Bonhams, Knightsbridge #57/R
£1550 $2527 €2325 Bracing walk. Sunday afternoon. Picnic (18x24cm-7x9in) s. W/C bodycol set of three. 29-Jan-3 Dreweatt Neate, Newbury #40 est:200-300

GOODALL, Walter (1830-1889) British
Works on paper
£533 $885 €773 Ferry (32x47cm-13x19in) s.d.1877 W/C. 16-Jun-3 Waddingtons, Toronto #86/R est:1000-1500 (C.D 1200)

GOODAY, Leslie (20th C) British
£500 $775 €750 Bellamine (34x45cm-13x18in) s. acrylic collage on board. 4-Dec-2 Christie's, Kensington #592/R

GOODE, Henry (1882-1966) American
£422 $700 €612 Desert in bloom (36x76cm-14x30in) s.d.40. 14-Jun-3 Jackson's, Cedar Falls #29/R

GOODE, Mervyn (1938-) American
£300 $465 €450 High summer (53x76cm-21x30in) s. 29-Oct-2 Henry Adams, Chichester #518

GOODIN, Walter (1907-1992) British
£550 $858 €825 Yorkshire landscape (61x82cm-24x32in) s. board. 10-Apr-3 Tennants, Leyburn #1010
£600 $978 €870 North landing at Flamborough Head, near Bridlington (59x75cm-23x30in) s. board. 17-Jul-3 Tennants, Leyburn #821/R
£750 $1170 €1125 Harbour scene (53x74cm-21x29in) s. 28-Mar-3 Dee Atkinson & Harrison, Driffield #666/R
£1600 $2496 €2400 Toward the Humer (21x29cm-8x11in) s.d.1981 board. 20-Sep-2 Dee Atkinson & Harrison, Driffield #611/R est:1000-1500

GOODMAN, Arthur Jule (fl.1902-1913) British
Works on paper
£394 $610 €591 Scotch soldier (56x34cm-22x13in) pencil. 1-Oct-2 SOGA, Bratislava #151/R est:25000 (SL.K 25000)

GOODMAN, H K (fl.1845-1850) American
£8176 $13000 €12264 Portrait of a man writing (76x107cm-30x42in) 29-Apr-3 Doyle, New York #17/R est:10000-15000

GOODMAN, Kathleen (20th C) British
Works on paper
£380 $619 €570 Portrait of Gillian (8x5cm-3x2in) s. W/C executed c.1931. 14-Feb-3 Keys, Aylsham #512

GOODMAN, Robert Gwelo (1871-1939) British
Works on paper
£322 $508 €483 Bridge over an estuary (24x38cm-9x15in) i.verso W/C. 1-Apr-3 Stephan Welz, Johannesburg #166 est:2000-3000 (SA.R 4000)
£338 $533 €507 Near Cape Town (23x30cm-9x12in) init. i.verso pastel. 1-Apr-3 Stephan Welz, Johannesburg #167 est:2000-3000 (SA.R 4200)

GOODNIGHT, Veryl (1947-) American
Sculpture
£2244 $3500 €3366 Privileged lady (56cm-22in) bronze. 9-Nov-2 Altermann Galleries, Santa Fe #175
£2564 $4000 €3846 Common goals (53cm-21in) bronze. 9-Nov-2 Altermann Galleries, Santa Fe #174
£16026 $25000 €24039 No turning back (163cm-64in) bronze. 9-Nov-2 Altermann Galleries, Santa Fe #176

GOODRICH, William R E (1887-1956) British
£300 $492 €450 Farmyard scene with labourer loading a horse drawn hay cart (22x31cm-9x12in) s.d.1929. 10-Feb-3 David Duggleby, Scarborough #570

GOODRICH, William Wells (19th C) American
£344 $550 €499 Still life with pears and grapes (41x28cm-16x11in) s.d.1859. 17-May-3 CRN Auctions, Cambridge #4

GOODSIR, Agnes (1865-1939) Australian
£775 $1233 €1163 Vase of flowers (35x25cm-14x10in) s. canvasboard exhib. 5-May-3 Sotheby's, Melbourne #280 (A.D 2000)

GOODWIN, Albert (1845-1932) British
£500 $785 €750 Corfe Castle, landscape with figures (25x36cm-10x14in) s.d. board. 13-Dec-2 Moore Allen & Innocent, Cirencester #521
£700 $1120 €1050 Eastern landscape at sunset. Moonlit coastal view (13x22cm-5x9in) s. board pair. 7-Jan-3 Bonhams, Knightsbridge #156/R
£3400 $5406 €5100 Venice (23x36cm-9x14in) s.i. card. 29-Apr-3 Gorringes, Lewes #2252
£4000 $6360 €6000 Folkestone (25x36cm-10x14in) s.i. card. 29-Apr-3 Gorringes, Lewes #2250
£4500 $7515 €6525 Thames at Windsor (33x48cm-13x19in) s.d.1889 board. 17-Jun-3 Bonhams, New Bond Street #73/R est:1000-1500
£5800 $9222 €8700 Sail in sight (25x35cm-10x14in) s.i. oil over pencil. 19-Mar-3 Sotheby's, London #208/R est:2000-3000
Works on paper
£450 $698 €675 Berrynarbour, N Devon (22x30cm-9x12in) s.mono.i. ink W/C over pencil htd bodycol prov. 2-Oct-2 Bonhams, Knowle #53
£600 $930 €900 Nijegen, Rhine (17x25cm-7x10in) s.i. pen ink W/C htd white. 3-Dec-2 Sotheby's, Olympia #103/R
£800 $1336 €1160 French river view (13x20cm-5x8in) mono.d.10 W/C. 24-Jun-3 Bonhams, Knightsbridge #1/R
£880 $1382 €1320 View of St. Paul's Cathedral from the South Bank of the Thames (24x34cm-9x13in) s.i.d.99 pencil W/C. 16-Apr-3 Christie's, Kensington #993/R
£900 $1404 €1350 Monaco (24x35cm-9x14in) mono.i.d.88 W/C. 17-Sep-2 Sotheby's, Olympia #108/R
£900 $1404 €1350 Dartmoor (25x37cm-10x15in) s.d.1905 pencil W/C scratching out prov. 27-Mar-3 Christie's, Kensington #138/R
£950 $1463 €1425 Sheep on the Downs (25x36cm-10x14in) mono.d.90 W/C. 22-Oct-2 Sworder & Son, Bishops Stortford #701/R
£1000 $1560 €1500 Gorge of the Teign, Dartmoor (16x23cm-6x9in) s.i. pencil W/C htd white. 18-Sep-2 Dreweatt Neate, Newbury #66/R est:500-700
£1100 $1704 €1650 Lucerne, Dawn (18x27cm-7x11in) s.i. W/C htd scratching out. 3-Dec-2 Sotheby's, Olympia #104/R est:600-800
£1200 $1956 €1800 Stratly on Thames. Bosham (18x23cm-7x9in) one s. pair. 28-Jan-3 Gorringes, Lewes #1598/R est:1200-1500
£1266 $2000 €1899 Bit of a Beachy Head (23x33cm-9x13in) s. pastel chk. 16-Nov-2 Harvey Clar, Oakland #1315
£1400 $2184 €2100 Certosa near Florence (24x34cm-9x13in) mono.d.73 W/C. 26-Mar-3 Hamptons Fine Art, Godalming #35/R est:1200-1800
£1600 $2496 €2400 Herstmonceux, East Sussex (18x25cm-7x10in) s.i. pencil W/C bodycol prov.lit. 27-Mar-3 Christie's, Kensington #129/R est:2000-3000
£1800 $2916 €2700 Sprite of the storm (35x51cm-14x20in) s.i.d.1909 W/C prov. 20-May-3 Sotheby's, Olympia #268/R est:2000-3000
£2000 $3120 €3000 St. Cross Hospital and church, Winchester (36x51cm-14x20in) s.i. W/C. 5-Nov-2 Bonhams, New Bond Street #146/R est:1500-2000
£2400 $3648 €3600 Phantom ship (26x35cm-10x14in) s.d.99 W/C scratching out. 15-Aug-2 Bonhams, New Bond Street #443/R est:1500-2000
£2400 $3840 €3600 Stonehenge at dusk (28x41cm-11x16in) s.i.d.1909 W/C. 11-Mar-3 Bonhams, New Bond Street #95/R est:1200-1800
£3000 $4980 €4500 Ali Baba and the forty thieves (36x25cm-14x10in) s. i.verso W/C scratching out prov. 12-Jun-3 Sotheby's, London #271/R est:3000-4000
£3500 $5810 €5250 Windsor Castle (26x37cm-10x15in) s. W/C over pencil htd bodycol prov.exhib. 12-Jun-3 Sotheby's, London #159/R est:4000-6000
£5000 $8300 €7500 Clovelly (25x36cm-10x14in) s.i. W/C bodycol. 12-Jun-3 Bonhams, New Bond Street #663/R est:4000-6000
£7800 $12714 €11700 Wells Cathedral with children beside a lake (36x51cm-14x20in) mono. W/C. 28-Jan-3 Gorringes, Lewes #1577/R est:2500-3500

GOODWIN, Albert (attrib) (1845-1932) British
Works on paper
£750 $1185 €1125 Wells (18x24cm-7x9in) bears sig. W/C gouache. 27-Nov-2 Hamptons Fine Art, Godalming #114
£850 $1318 €1275 Iffley Mill on the Tahmes (23x33cm-9x13in) mono. W/C. 4-Oct-2 Mallams, Oxford #468

GOODWIN, Arthur C (1866-1929) American
£1899 $3000 €2849 Copley Sq, Boston (38x46cm-15x18in) exhib. 17-Nov-2 CRN Auctions, Cambridge #33/R
£2070 $3250 €3105 In the park (102x107cm-40x42in) 22-Nov-2 Skinner, Boston #327/R est:3000-5000
£2070 $3250 €3105 Summer in the city (102x127cm-40x50in) 22-Nov-2 Skinner, Boston #338/R est:3000-5000
£2778 $4500 €4028 Stream in Autumn (64x76cm-25x30in) s. 21-May-3 Doyle, New York #112/R est:3000-5000
£10191 $16000 €15287 Winter, Park Street, Boston (71x91cm-28x36in) s.d.89. 22-Nov-2 Skinner, Boston #326/R est:18000-22000
£18182 $28000 €27273 Park Street Church (76x91cm-30x36in) s. prov.exhib. 24-Oct-2 Shannon's, Milford #139/R est:20000-30000

Works on paper

£304 $475 €456 New Hampshire landscape (46x61cm-18x24in) pastel. 18-Sep-2 Alderfer's, Hatfield #279/R
£312 $500 €452 Portrait of Rosalee Goodyear under a parasol (48x27cm-19x11in) pastel paper on board prov. 16-May-3 Skinner, Boston #166/R
£385 $600 €578 Winter landscape (46x61cm-18x24in) s. pastel. 18-Sep-2 Alderfer's, Hatfield #291
£417 $650 €626 Landscape with stream and buildings in distance (43x58cm-17x23in) s. pastel. 18-Sep-2 Alderfer's, Hatfield #283/R
£1019 $1600 €1529 Afternoon in the Boston public garden (33x48cm-13x19in) s. pastel paperboard. 10-Dec-2 Doyle, New York #68/R est:3000-5000
£1558 $2400 €2337 Copley Square, Boston (32x48cm-13x19in) s. pastel on board. 4-Sep-2 Christie's, Rockefeller NY #346/R est:1500-2500
£2065 $3200 €3098 Paper mill, Neponset river (48x61cm-19x24in) s.d.May 1909 i.verso pastel board prov.exhib. 3-Dec-2 Christie's, Rockefeller NY #596/R est:3000-5000

GOODWIN, Betty (1923-) Canadian

£1404 $2091 €2106 Figure and chair (66x50cm-26x20in) s.d.93/94 laser. 26-Jun-2 Iegor de Saint Hippolyte, Montreal #47 (C.D 3200)

Prints

£2632 $3921 €3948 Two vests (60x79cm-24x31in) s.i.d.1972 num.3-10 etching. 26-Jun-2 Iegor de Saint Hippolyte, Montreal #48/R (C.D 6000)

Works on paper

£2016 $3185 €3024 Series on flux IX (23x33cm-9x13in) s.d.1965 W/C prov. 14-Nov-2 Heffel, Vancouver #9/R est:5000-7000 (C.D 5000)

GOODWIN, Harry (?-1925) British

£3100 $4836 €4650 Waiting for the ferry, river Wey, Guildford (89x183cm-35x72in) mono.d.75. 10-Sep-2 Bonhams, Knightsbridge #189/R est:3000-4000

Works on paper

£300 $486 €450 Bluebell wood (33x50cm-13x20in) s.d.1889 W/C. 21-Jan-3 Bonhams, Knightsbridge #278/R
£540 $842 €810 Breithorn at the head of Lauterbrunnen (36x52cm-14x20in) mono.d.1898 i.verso W/C. 6-Nov-2 Bonhams, Chester #520
£800 $1304 €1200 View of Berne (35x53cm-14x21in) mono.i.d.1897 W/C. 29-Jan-3 Sotheby's, Olympia #166/R
£800 $1304 €1200 Sunset glow on the Jungfrau (52x36cm-20x14in) mono. W/C. 29-Jan-3 Sotheby's, Olympia #173/R
£800 $1248 €1200 Alpine scene (35x53cm-14x21in) mono.d.1898 W/C htd white. 25-Mar-3 Bonhams, Knightsbridge #55/R
£950 $1482 €1425 Valley of Sertig (34x50cm-13x20in) mono. i.d.79 verso mixed media paper on board. 26-Mar-3 Hamptons Fine Art, Godalming #77
£1400 $2282 €2100 Mont Blanc from Finhaut (51x34cm-20x13in) mono.d.1906 W/C. 29-Jan-3 Sotheby's, Olympia #172/R est:900-1200

GOODWIN, Phillip R (1882-1935) American

£13924 $22000 €20886 Mystic silence - figure in a canoe (30x41cm-12x16in) s. prov. 3-Apr-3 Christie's, Rockefeller NY #135/R est:3000-5000
£16129 $25000 €24194 Hunting scene (74x94cm-29x37in) init. prov. 4-Dec-2 Sotheby's, New York #151/R est:15000-25000
£34810 $55000 €50475 Luck catch (91x64cm-36x25in) s. painted c.1910-16 prov.exhib.lit. 26-Jul-3 Coeur d'Alene, Hayden #137/R est:50000-80000
£35032 $55000 €52548 Cowboy watering geraniums with a black cat (76x51cm-30x20in) s. prov. 19-Nov-2 Butterfields, San Francisco #8087/R est:15000-20000
£37975 $60000 €55064 There's that six point bull (61x84cm-24x33in) s. lit. 26-Jul-3 Coeur d'Alene, Hayden #84/R est:50000-75000
£41139 $65000 €59652 Two fishermen in a birch canoe (91x61cm-36x24in) s. prov.exhib.lit. 26-Jul-3 Coeur d'Alene, Hayden #55/R est:50000-80000
£47468 $75000 €68829 Waiting out the storm (91x64cm-36x25in) s. prov.exhib.lit. 26-Jul-3 Coeur d'Alene, Hayden #56/R est:50000-80000
£60127 $95000 €87184 Fishing at the rapids (91x64cm-36x25in) s. prov.exhib.lit. 26-Jul-3 Coeur d'Alene, Hayden #138/R est:50000-80000
£80128 $125000 €116186 Unexpected game (79x102cm-31x40in) 13-Oct-2 Cobbs, Peterborough #476

Works on paper

£4717 $7500 €7076 Bear hunters (13x19cm-5x7in) s. W/C gouache pencil. 5-Mar-3 Sotheby's, New York #143/R est:1200-1800
£5063 $8000 €7341 Gun for the man who knows (58x33cm-23x13in) s. chl. 26-Jul-3 Coeur d'Alene, Hayden #17/R est:4000-6000
£5063 $8000 €7341 Browsing (36x51cm-14x20in) s. W/C prov. 26-Jul-3 Coeur d'Alene, Hayden #26/R est:8000-12000

GOODWIN, Richard (1953-) Australian

Works on paper

£343 $531 €515 Untitled (209x156cm-82x61in) s.d.83 pencil chl paper on canvas. 3-Dec-2 Shapiro, Sydney #76 (A.D 950)
£981 $1530 €1700 Leichardt (170x320cm-67x126in) s.d.88 mixed media prov. 31-Mar-3 Goodman, Sydney #62 (A.D 2600)

GOODWIN, Richard Labarre (1840-1910) American

Works on paper

£513 $800 €770 Two hanging woodcocks (48x36cm-19x14in) s. W/C. 30-Mar-3 Susanin's, Chicago #6108/R

GOODWIN, Sidney (1867-1944) British

Works on paper

£300 $462 €450 Off Swanage (30x48cm-12x19in) s. W/C. 22-Oct-2 Bonhams, Bath #54
£500 $725 €750 Farm workers horses and chickens in a courtyard (36x30cm-14x12in) s.d.1898 W/C. 1-Jun-2 Hogben, Folkstone #186
£500 $779 €750 Hastings (30x49cm-12x19in) init.d.1902 pencil W/C. 19-Sep-2 Christie's, Kensington #58
£550 $798 €825 Panoramic landscape scene with ploughman and horses (36x30cm-14x12in) s.d.1899 W/C. 1-Jun-2 Hogben, Folkstone #187
£650 $1021 €975 Herdsmen with cattle and sheep crossing the moor (31x48cm-12x19in) s.d.1901 W/C. 16-Dec-2 Bonhams, Bury St Edmunds #387/R
£750 $1193 €1125 Harvesting (25x41cm-10x16in) s. W/C prov. 19-Mar-3 John Nicholson, Haslemere #1067

GOOL, Jan van (1685-1763) Dutch

£2878 $4604 €4000 Extensive wooded landscape with shepherds and flock with dog (113x70cm-44x28in) 13-May-3 Sotheby's, Amsterdam #86/R est:6000-8000
£4777 $7452 €7500 Wooded landscape with a herdsman and shepherdess resting with flocks (44x62cm-17x24in) s.d. panel. 6-Nov-2 Christie's, Amsterdam #32/R est:4000-6000
£5732 $8943 €9000 Herdsmen and their sheep, goats and cows in a hilly landscape, village with a church beyond (35x49cm-14x19in) s. panel prov. 5-Nov-2 Sotheby's, Amsterdam #247/R est:6000-8000

GOOR, Gaston (20th C) ?

£1529 $2385 €2400 Homere et les bergers (81x120cm-32x47in) panel. 6-Nov-2 Gioffredo, Nice #46/R

GOOR, Jan van (?-1694) Dutch

£1982 $2894 €2973 Portait of Cornelia de Ryck at easel (46x38cm-18x15in) s.d.1689 prov. 17-Jun-2 Philippe Schuler, Zurich #4343/R est:4000-6000 (S.FR 4500)

GOOSEY, G Turland (?) British

£720 $1123 €1080 Low tide, St Ives (20x25cm-8x10in) s. board. 17-Oct-2 David Lay, Penzance #1422
£900 $1395 €1350 Glimpse of St Ives harbour (122x91cm-48x36in) s. canvasboard. 26-Sep-2 Lane, Penzance #146
£900 $1395 €1350 Fishing boats in harbour, possibly St Ives (30x41cm-12x16in) s. board. 31-Oct-2 Duke & Son, Dorchester #296/R

GOOZEE, Dan (1943-) American

£1056 $1700 €1584 Evening light near Ramona (30x41cm-12x16in) s. 18-Feb-3 John Moran, Pasadena #125 est:1000-1500

GOPAS, Rudolph (1913-1982) New Zealander

£4167 $6500 €6251 Seated female figure study (101x74cm-40x29in) s.d.1959 board. 8-Apr-3 Peter Webb, Auckland #140/R est:12000-18000 (NZ.D 12000)

Works on paper

£510 $800 €765 Pahiatua landscape (37x50cm-15x20in) s.i.d.1949 W/C. 10-Dec-2 Peter Webb, Auckland #90/R est:2000-3000 (NZ.D 1600)
£545 $840 €818 Farm scene near Pahiatua (38x55cm-15x22in) s.i. W/C. 4-Sep-2 Dunbar Sloane, Wellington #118 est:2000-4000 (NZ.D 1800)
£815 $1271 €1223 At the Cromwell races. W/C. 7-Nov-2 International Art Centre, Auckland #90/R est:2500-3500 (NZ.D 2600)
£965 $1505 €1448 George Road in spring (44x57cm-17x22in) W/C prov.exhib. 27-Mar-3 International Art Centre, Auckland #46/R (NZ.D 2750)
£1354 $2125 €2031 Harbour scene with sunflowers (37x49cm-15x19in) pastel W/C. 10-Dec-2 Peter Webb, Auckland #76/R est:3500-4500 (NZ.D 4250)
£1520 $2371 €2280 Mountain landscape (42x55cm-17x22in) s.d.1953 W/C. 17-Sep-2 Peter Webb, Auckland #171/R est:4000-5000 (NZ.D 5000)
£1608 $2492 €2412 Untitled (88x87cm-35x34in) s.d.67 mixed media. 4-Dec-2 Dunbar Sloane, Auckland #27/R est:4000-8000 (NZ.D 5000)
£2089 $3051 €3134 Lyttelton Wharf (61x46cm-24x18in) s.d. W/C. 12-Sep-1 Watson's, Christchurch #72/R est:7500-12000 (NZ.D 7000)

GORANSSON, Ake (1902-1942) Swedish

£5551 $8771 €8327 Houses by the sea (27x36cm-11x14in) st.sig. canvas on panel prov.exhib.lit. 28-Apr-3 Bukowskis, Stockholm #205a/R est:30000-40000 (S.KR 73000)
£6692 $10573 €10038 Porcelain bowl on book (23x29cm-9x11in) st.sig. canvas on panel painted 1930-32 prov.exhib.lit. 28-Apr-3 Bukowskis, Stockholm #201/R est:70000-80000 (S.KR 88000)
£8365 $13217 €12548 Meadows among knob of rocks (28x37cm-11x15in) st.sig. prov.exhib. 28-Apr-3 Bukowskis, Stockholm #202/R est:60000-80000 (S.KR 110000)
£13900 $22378 €20850 Girl wearing yellow in doorway (48x38cm-19x15in) stamped sig. painted 1933/37 exhib.lit. 7-May-3 AB Stockholms Auktionsverk #856/R est:150000-160000 (S.KR 180000)
£14829 $23430 €22244 Woman with palette (34x25cm-13x10in) st.sig. painted 1933-37 canvas on panel prov.exhib.lit. 28-Apr-3 Bukowskis, Stockholm #205/R est:100000-125000 (S.KR 195000)

Works on paper

£461 $733 €692 Boy sleeping (27x21cm-11x8in) pencil. 3-Mar-3 Lilla Bukowskis, Stockholm #720 (S.KR 6200)

GORBATOFF, K (1876-1945) Russian

Works on paper

£3200 $5248 €4800 View of Capri (35x46cm-14x18in) s. pencil W/C bodycol. 5-Jun-3 Christie's, Kensington #941 est:300-500

GORBATOFF, Konstantin (1876-1945) Russian

£11000 $17380 €16500 View of Bethlehem (21x29cm-8x11in) s. panel. 26-Nov-2 Christie's, Kensington #25/R est:5000-7000
£11000 $17380 €16500 Street scene, Jerusalem (21x29cm-8x11in) s. panel. 26-Nov-2 Christie's, Kensington #26/R est:5000-7000
£30000 $47400 €45000 Winter view of the Kremlin, Moscow (70x100cm-28x39in) s. panel. 26-Nov-2 Christie's, Kensington #19/R est:15000-20000

GORBITZ, Johan (1782-1853) Norwegian

£691 $1154 €1002 Lake landscape with rowing boat (33x42cm-13x17in) s/ panel. 18-Jun-3 Grev Wedels Plass, Oslo #176 (N.KR 8000)
£865 $1367 €1298 Portrait of young man (8x9cm-3x4in) s.d.1824 cardboard. 2-Dec-2 Blomqvist, Oslo #335/R (N.KR 10000)
£1908 $2977 €2862 Landscape from the Savoy mountains (35x45cm-14x18in) s. i.verso panel. 21-Oct-2 Blomqvist, Oslo #324/R est:30000-40000 (N.KR 22000)

GORCHOV, Ron (1930-) American

£263 $400 €395 Abstract composition (99x74cm-39x29in) s.d.1965. 18-Aug-2 Jeffery Burchard, Florida #89/R

GORDIGIANI, Edoardo (1866-1961) Italian

£878 $1370 €1300 Garden in Rome (48x48cm-19x19in) s. painted 1954. 28-Mar-3 Farsetti, Prato #401/R
£1603 $2516 €2500 Self-portrait (60x85cm-24x33in) 16-Dec-2 Pandolfini, Florence #230/R
£1923 $3019 €3000 Still life with teapot (57x60cm-22x24in) s.d.41 prov. 16-Dec-2 Pandolfini, Florence #247/R

GORDIGIANI, Michele (1835-1909) Italian

£1290 $2039 €2000 Garden (24x31cm-9x12in) board. 18-Dec-2 Finarte, Milan #185/R
£2179 $3422 €3400 Portrait of girl (40x32cm-16x13in) oval. 16-Dec-2 Pandolfini, Florence #81/R

GORDILLO, Luis (1939-) Spanish

Works on paper

£345 $545 €500 Composition (15x21cm-6x8in) s.d.58 pencil. 1-Apr-3 Segre, Madrid #181/R
£440 $678 €700 Head (33x27cm-13x11in) s.d.60 gouache. 28-Oct-2 Segre, Madrid #128/R
£484 $765 €750 Woman (21x16cm-8x6in) i.d.58 ink. 17-Dec-2 Segre, Madrid #130/R
£500 $730 €770 Untitled (32x42cm-13x17in) s. gouache. 17-Jun-2 Ansorena, Madrid #299/R
£513 $810 €800 Untitled (34x26cm-13x10in) s.d.60 gop. 13-Nov-2 Ansorena, Madrid #462/R
£516 $815 €800 Untitled (21x16cm-8x6in) s.d.58 ink. 17-Dec-2 Segre, Madrid #129/R
£526 $853 €800 Composition (34x27cm-13x11in) s.d.60 gouache. 21-Jan-3 Durán, Madrid #714/R
£548 $866 €850 Untitled (34x26cm-13x10in) s.d.60 ink wash. 17-Dec-2 Segre, Madrid #133/R
£552 $872 €800 Abstraction (33x26cm-13x10in) s.d.60 ink wash. 1-Apr-3 Segre, Madrid #182/R
£566 $872 €900 Untitled (33x27cm-13x11in) s.d.60 gouache ink. 28-Oct-2 Segre, Madrid #130/R
£655 $1035 €950 Woman (21x15cm-8x6in) s.d.58 ink dr. 1-Apr-3 Segre, Madrid #183/R
£943 $1453 €1500 Untitled (42x31cm-17x12in) s.d.60 ink wash. 28-Oct-2 Segre, Madrid #129/R
£968 $1529 €1500 Abstraction (33x27cm-13x11in) s.d.60 gouache ink. 17-Dec-2 Segre, Madrid #132/R
£1032 $1631 €1600 Abstraction (33x27cm-13x11in) s.d.60 wash. 17-Dec-2 Segre, Madrid #134/R
£1053 $1705 €1600 Untitled (62x16cm-24x6in) s.d.89 mixed media. 21-Jan-3 Ansorena, Madrid #306/R
£5000 $7900 €7800 Untitled (96x75cm-38x30in) s.d.1990 mixed media board. 14-Nov-2 Arte, Seville #471/R

GORDIN, Sidney (1918-) American

Works on paper

£414 $650 €621 August 74-2 (40x32cm-16x13in) collage prov. 19-Nov-2 Wright, Chicago #177/R

GORDON, Arthur (19th C) British

£850 $1326 €1275 Putney on Thames (41x61cm-16x24in) s.d.05 s.i.d.verso. 7-Nov-2 Christie's, Kensington #139/R

Works on paper

£420 $685 €630 Mall, Hammersmith (38x51cm-15x20in) s.i.d.1897 W/C. 29-Jan-3 Sotheby's, Olympia #189/R
£500 $790 €750 Near Godlaming. Thames view with sailing barges (23x36cm-9x14in) s.d.1905 W/C pair. 24-Apr-3 Mallams, Cheltenham #274/R

GORDON, Douglas (1966-) British

Photographs

£3165 $5000 €4748 Never, never (61x76cm-24x30in) laser print on c-type paper executed 2000 prov.lit. 12-Nov-2 Phillips, New York #167/R est:8000-10000
£5903 $9740 €8500 Croque mort (133x91cm-52x36in) s. num.2/13 C-print prov. 3-Jul-3 Christie's, Paris #122/R est:10000-15000
£9000 $14760 €13500 Tattoo, for reflection (75x81cm-30x32in) s.i.d.1997 num.4/4 verso cibachrome print prov.lit. 7-Feb-3 Sotheby's, London #102/R est:6000-8000
£12658 $20000 €18987 Never, never (61x76cm-24x30in) digital c-print exec.2000 in two parts prov. 13-Nov-2 Sotheby's, New York #431/R est:20000-30000
£15000 $23100 €22500 Never neve, black negative mirrored. Never never, white negative mirrored (63x78cm-25x31in) s.num.8/13 two digital chromagenic print prov. 23-Oct-2 Christie's, London #182/R est:15000-20000

Works on paper

£34810 $55000 €52215 The end - bird man of Alcatraz (180x239cm-71x94in) solvent based ink on linen executed 1995-2000 prov.exhib. 14-Nov-2 Christie's, Rockefeller NY #346/R est:30000-40000

GORDON, Hortense Mattice (1889-1961) Canadian

£301 $473 €452 Chalet on the water's edge (23x28cm-9x11in) s. panel. 25-Nov-2 Hodgins, Calgary #389/R (C.D 750)
£1975 $3062 €2963 Untitled (69x49cm-27x19in) s. board prov. 3-Dec-2 Joyner, Toronto #210/R est:5000-7000 (C.D 4800)
£3247 $5162 €4708 Venetian canal (71x41cm-28x16in) s. painted c.1960-61 sold with an invitation and essay exhib. 1-May-3 Heffel, Vancouver #37/R est:2500-3000 (C.D 7500)

GORDON, Leon (1889-1943) American

£4348 $7000 €6522 Three men greeting woman with parasol (97x86cm-38x34in) painted c.1915 prov. 10-May-3 Illustration House, New York #72/R est:5000-7000

GORDON, Sir John Watson (1788-1864) British

£847 $1338 €1271 Portrait of Thomas Campbell, sculptor of Edinburgh (77x63cm-30x25in) prov. 18-Nov-2 Waddingtons, Toronto #176/R est:1000-1500 (C.D 2100)
£900 $1413 €1350 Portrait of Cuthbert Watson of Ovington, Yorkshire (127x102cm-50x40in) s.d.1858 prov. 21-Nov-2 Tennants, Leyburn #740/R
£950 $1549 €1378 Portrait of Lorne Campbell (76x64cm-30x25in) 17-Jul-3 Thomson, Roddick & Medcalf, Carlisle #131/R

GORDON, Sir John Watson (attrib) (1788-1864) British
£400 $656 €600 Portrait of Kalitza Janet Erskine Christian Hay (49x42cm-19x17in) canvas on board oval. 5-Jun-3 Christie's, Kensington #578/R
£900 $1485 €1305 Portrait of James Blackwell Praed of Tyringham (75x61cm-30x24in) prov. 2-Jul-3 Sotheby's, Olympia #27/R

GORDON, Sir John Watson (circle) (1788-1864) British
£6000 $9120 €9000 Young highland with Aberdeen in the distance (126x89cm-50x35in) 28-Aug-2 Sotheby's, London #897/R est:6000-8000

GORDON-CUMMING, Constance Frederika (1837-1924) British
Works on paper
£650 $1040 €975 Figures on a riverside track. The windmill (36x50cm-14x20in) one s.d.1866 W/C htd white pair. 11-Mar-3 Bonhams, New Bond Street #100/R

GORDON-CUMMING, Constance Frederika (attrib) (1837-1924) British
Works on paper
£1800 $2808 €2700 Benares (39x62cm-15x24in) s.i. W/C with three other Indian views four. 9-Oct-2 Woolley & Wallis, Salisbury #68/R est:600-800

GORDY, Robert (20th C) American
£1923 $3000 €2885 Et in arcadia (84x124cm-33x49in) s.d.Feb 10 79 acrylic. 12-Oct-2 Neal Auction Company, New Orleans #665/R est:5000-7000
Works on paper
£481 $750 €722 Untitled (75x57cm-30x22in) s.d. col magic. 14-Oct-2 Butterfields, San Francisco #1263/R
£1481 $2400 €2222 Rimbauds dream series (74x53cm-29x21in) s.d.73 marker. 24-Jan-3 New Orleans Auction, New Orleans #1051/R est:2500-4000

GORDYN, Hermanus Gerardus (1932-) Dutch
£4676 $7669 €6500 16 Augustus (100x70cm-39x28in) s.d.67. 3-Jun-3 Christie's, Amsterdam #387/R est:2500-3500

GORE, Frederick (1913-) British
£1500 $2370 €2250 January, Elm Park (51x61cm-20x24in) s. canvasboard prov. 27-Nov-2 Hamptons Fine Art, Godalming #384/R est:1500-2000
£2200 $3564 €3300 Laburnham, Elm Park Gardens (60x50cm-24x20in) s. 20-May-3 Bonhams, Knightsbridge #56/R est:2500-3500
£2700 $4428 €4050 Saint Berthe, les baux (63x81cm-25x32in) s.i.d.1960 stretcher. 3-Jun-3 Sotheby's, Olympia #179/R est:3000-4000
£2800 $4564 €4200 Saint Berthe, Les Baux (64x81cm-25x32in) i.d.1960 verso. 28-Jan-3 Gorringes, Lewes #1669/R est:3000-5000
£2800 $4368 €4200 Stubble fields, Bonnieux (61x76cm-24x30in) s. s.i.d.on stretcher. 27-Mar-3 Christie's, Kensington #496/R est:3000-5000
£2800 $4536 €4200 Vase of Provencal flowers (76x64cm-30x25in) s. 20-May-3 Bonhams, Knightsbridge #57/R est:3000-5000
£2800 $4676 €4060 Hibiscus on a covered terrace, July (81x102cm-32x40in) s. prov. 24-Jun-3 Bonhams, New Bond Street #87/R est:3000-5000
£3500 $5775 €5075 Olive trees before Puig Mayor, Majorca (65x81cm-26x32in) s. 3-Jul-3 Christie's, Kensington #471/R est:3000-5000
£3600 $5832 €5400 Sunflowers and cavaillou melons (81x63cm-32x25in) s. 20-May-3 Bonhams, Knightsbridge #60/R est:3000-5000
£3800 $6346 €5510 From a window in the rue de l'Aude, Paris (76x91cm-30x36in) s. s.i.d.1979 overlap prov. 24-Jun-3 Bonhams, New Bond Street #94/R est:3500-4500
£4000 $6200 €6000 Vinyards, October, below the Luberton (69x91cm-27x36in) s.d.92. 4-Oct-2 Mallams, Oxford #573/R est:4000-6000
£4200 $6552 €6300 Mediterranean landscape (76x91cm-30x36in) s. 27-Mar-3 Christie's, Kensington #493/R est:4000-6000
£4200 $6930 €6090 Valley of the Calavon, Bonnieux (81x91cm-32x36in) s.d.88. 3-Jul-3 Christie's, Kensington #473/R est:3000-5000
£4500 $7515 €6525 Olive grove in a Mediterranean summer landscape (76x102cm-30x40in) s. 24-Jun-3 Bonhams, New Bond Street #86/R est:5000-7000
£4600 $7544 €6900 Vineyard, Alleins (71x91cm-28x36in) s. i.d.1972 verso prov. 3-Jun-3 Sotheby's, Olympia #211/R est:5000-7000
£5500 $8745 €8250 Poppy field, Lacoste in the background (73x76cm-29x30in) s.d.2000. 26-Feb-3 Sotheby's, Olympia #341/R est:4000-6000
£6000 $9540 €9000 Venice from the Guidecca (71x97cm-28x38in) s.d.59 board prov. 26-Feb-3 Sotheby's, Olympia #342/R est:6000-8000
£9500 $15009 €14250 Fields of flowers St Remy de Provence (61x81cm-24x32in) s. s.i.stretcher. 27-Nov-2 Sotheby's, Olympia #258/R est:6000-8000
£12000 $18960 €18000 St Martin-les-Eaux, Haute Alpes de Provence (92x122cm-36x48in) s. s.i.d.1979 verso. 27-Nov-2 Sotheby's, Olympia #288/R est:10000-15000

GORE, Ken (1911-) American
£321 $487 €500 Coastal village (60x75cm-24x30in) s. panel. 11-Jul-2 Hugo Ruef, Munich #666

GORE, Spencer (1878-1914) British
£8000 $13120 €12000 Crossroads, Neuville, Dieppe (76x51cm-30x20in) painted c.1906 prov.exhib.lit. 6-Jun-3 Christie's, London #16/R est:10000-15000
£52000 $85280 €78000 Sunset, Letchworth, with man and dog (51x61cm-20x24in) s.i.d.1912 s.on stretcher prov.exhib. 6-Jun-3 Christie's, London #15/R est:25000-35000
Works on paper
£1300 $2028 €1950 Singer at the Old Bedford (35x23cm-14x9in) col chk ink prov. 12-Sep-2 Sotheby's, Olympia #59/R est:400-600

GORE, William Crampton (1871-1946) Irish
£652 $1070 €900 Irish landscape (29x45cm-11x18in) canvasboard. 28-May-3 Bonhams & James Adam, Dublin #55/R
£2532 $3924 €4000 Weir at Vaucluse, France (36x45cm-14x18in) s.d.Nov 1912 board prov. 25-Sep-2 James Adam, Dublin #116/R est:4000-5000

GORE, William Henry (fl.1880-1916) British
£32143 $50786 €48215 Sympathy (76x56cm-30x22in) s. exhib. 26-Nov-2 Sotheby's, Melbourne #224/R est:80000-120000 (A.D 90000)

GORE-BOOTH, Colum Robert (1913-1959) Irish
£604 $972 €900 Landscape with wind swept trees and flowering gorse (51x61cm-20x24in) s. board. 18-Feb-3 Whyte's, Dublin #206/R

GORG, Jurgen (1951-) German
£1700 $2754 €2550 Drew Grazian (100x80cm-39x31in) s.i. 20-May-3 Bonhams, Knightsbridge #138 est:400-600
£1700 $2754 €2550 Der Kavalieu (110x80cm-43x31in) s.i.d.88. 20-May-3 Bonhams, Knightsbridge #185/R est:400-600
£2200 $3564 €3300 Venezians (140x100cm-55x39in) s.i.d.88. 20-May-3 Bonhams, Knightsbridge #182/R est:400-600
Works on paper
£291 $460 €460 Jeannette (70x52cm-28x20in) s.d.1990 i. verso pastel pencil brush. 30-Nov-2 Arnold, Frankfurt #194/R
£450 $698 €675 Spiegelling, studies of semi clad female forms (36x28cm-14x11in) s.i.d.82 pencil pastel. 24-Sep-2 Anderson & Garland, Newcastle #400

GORGE, Paul Eugène (1856-1941) Belgian
£352 $567 €500 Farmer's interior with woman at work (55x70cm-22x28in) s. 12-May-3 Bernaerts, Antwerp #49

GORGUET, Auguste (1862-1927) French
£800 $1248 €1200 Portrait of Madame Richard (32x21cm-13x8in) s.i.d.1893 panel. 26-Mar-3 Sotheby's, Olympia #194/R
£950 $1549 €1378 Girl with wild flowers (43x36cm-17x14in) s. 21-Jul-3 Bonhams, Bath #88/R

GORI, Affortunato (19/20th C) Italian
Sculpture
£7200 $11448 €10800 Oriental dancer (45cm-18in) s. gilt bronze. 27-Feb-3 Sotheby's, Olympia #171/R est:6000-7000

GORI, Georges (20th C) French
Sculpture
£1747 $2900 €2533 Jeune femme au chiens (51x79cm-20x31in) s. silvered metal marble base. 14-Jun-3 Jackson's, Cedar Falls #464/R est:1000-2000

GORI, Gino Paolo (1911-1991) Italian
£385 $604 €600 San Lorenzo (60x26cm-24x10in) s. 16-Dec-2 Pandolfini, Florence #369

GORIN, Jean (1899-1981) French
£2800 $4424 €4200 Composition (50x50cm-20x20in) s.i.d.1971 acrylic wood board prov.exhib. 3-Apr-3 Christie's, Kensington #220/R
£4200 $6636 €6300 Spatio-temporelle 46 (96x100cm-38x39in) s.i.d.1968 acrylic wood board. 3-Apr-3 Christie's, Kensington #218/R

GORKY, Arshile (1904-1948) American
£15000 $24000 €22500 Untitled (23x5cm-9x2in) painted 1936-38 prov. 16-May-3 Phillips, New York #169/R est:25000-35000
£48750 $78000 €73125 Composition (16x27cm-6x11in) painted c.1946 prov.exhib.lit. 16-May-3 Phillips, New York #170/R est:90000-120000
£547945 $854795 €800000 Etude pour le tableau de Canberra (35x52cm-14x20in) s.verso exhib. 14-Apr-3 Laurence Calmels, Paris #4077/R est:1200000

Works on paper
£5313 $8500 €7970 Abstraction (28x22cm-11x9in) graphite exec.1935 prov. 15-May-3 Christie's, Rockefeller NY #146/R
£13699 $21507 €20000 Untitled (32x51cm-13x20in) chl exhib. 15-Apr-3 Laurence Calmels, Paris #4290/R est:15000
£13699 $21507 €20000 Untitled (31x36cm-12x14in) pen exhib. 15-Apr-3 Laurence Calmels, Paris #4291/R est:15000
£26712 $41938 €39000 Untitled (49x32cm-19x13in) ink exhib. 15-Apr-3 Laurence Calmels, Paris #4292/R
£31507 $49466 €46000 Untitled (78x56cm-31x22in) pen ink exhib. 15-Apr-3 Laurence Calmels, Paris #4289/R est:20000
£44304 $70000 €66456 Untitled (49x63cm-19x25in) s. graphite prov.exhib. 14-Nov-2 Christie's, Rockefeller NY #127/R est:40000-60000
£75000 $120000 €112500 Untitled (51x67cm-20x26in) s.d.44 graphite crayon prov. 14-May-3 Sotheby's, New York #123/R est:150000-200000
£284810 $450000 €427215 Study for orators III (53x71cm-21x28in) graphite chk executed 1946-47 prov. 12-Nov-2 Sotheby's, New York #3/R est:600000-800000
£395570 $625000 €593355 Untitled (43x58cm-17x23in) s.d.43 pastel pen ink prov.exhib.lit. 12-Nov-2 Sotheby's, New York #2/R est:600000-800000

GORMAN, Richard Borthwick (1933-) Canadian
£944 $1473 €1369 Abstraction in red and blue (127x81cm-50x32in) s.d.1958. 26-Mar-3 Walker's, Ottawa #427/R est:1500-2000 (C.D 2200)

GORMLEY, Anthony (1950-) British
Sculpture
£60000 $100200 €90000 Total Stranger III (193x56x30cm-76x22x12in) init.i.d.1996 num.3/345 cast iron air prov.exhib. 26-Jun-3 Christie's, London #39/R est:25000-35000
£72000 $118080 €108000 Quantum cloud XXI (230x143x116cm-91x56x46in) stainless steel bars exec.2000 prov.exhib. 6-Feb-3 Sotheby's, London #46/R est:120000
Works on paper
£3200 $5344 €4640 Torso (19x14cm-7x6in) s.i.d.92 verso pigment prov. 24-Jun-3 Sotheby's, Olympia #24/R est:1000-1500

GORNIK, Friedrich (1877-1943) Austrian
Sculpture
£3797 $6000 €5696 Woman knitting (28x23x23cm-11x9x9in) dore bronze. 15-Nov-2 Du Mouchelle, Detroit #2057/R est:5000-6000

GORO V AGYAFALVA, Lajos (younger) (1865-1904) Hungarian
£347 $506 €521 In Puszta I (21x31cm-8x12in) cardboard painted c.1900. 4-Jun-2 SOGA, Bratislava #107/R est:7000 (SL.K 22000)
£410 $598 €615 In Puszta II (21x31cm-8x12in) cardboard painted c.1900. 4-Jun-2 SOGA, Bratislava #108/R est:7000 (SL.K 26000)

GORP, Henri Nicolas van (attrib) (1756-1819) French
£1032 $1631 €1600 Young mother with child (24x20cm-9x8in) panel. 18-Dec-2 Piasa, Paris #43

GORRIN, Ulysse (20th C) French
£828 $1316 €1200 Barques au sec aux environs de St Cado (54x73cm-21x29in) s. 10-Mar-3 Thierry & Lannon, Brest #108/R

GORTAZAR, Alfonso (1955-) Spanish
£1419 $2243 €2200 Man in landscape (162x130cm-64x51in) s.d.1987 s.d.verso prov.exhib. 17-Dec-2 Segre, Madrid #197/R

GORTER, Arnold Marc (1866-1933) Dutch
£1656 $2583 €2600 Vordense brook (31x41cm-12x16in) s. 6-Nov-2 Vendue Huis, Gravenhage #491/R est:2500-3000
£1736 $2865 €2500 Cows grazing by a stream in a wooded landscape (50x40cm-20x16in) s. prov. 1-Jul-3 Christie's, Amsterdam #92/R est:2000-3000
£1842 $2984 €2800 After the rain (116x156cm-46x61in) s. 21-Jan-3 Christie's, Amsterdam #130/R est:3000-5000
£2083 $3312 €3000 Vordense beek - cows in a meadow near a stream (46x56cm-18x22in) s. 29-Apr-3 Christie's, Amsterdam #157/R est:3000-4000
£2264 $3487 €3600 Cows in a sunny autumn landscape (40x49cm-16x19in) s. 22-Oct-2 Sotheby's, Amsterdam #111/R est:4000-6000
£2623 $4250 €3803 Vordense Beek (61x79cm-24x31in) s. 21-May-3 Doyle, New York #189/R est:2500-3500
£4827 $7675 €7000 Vordense beek (101x135cm-40x53in) s. 10-Mar-3 Sotheby's, Amsterdam #163/R est:6000-8000
£20548 $32260 €30000 Spring blossoms (113x154cm-44x61in) s. 15-Apr-3 Sotheby's, Amsterdam #113/R est:8000-12000

GORUS, Pieter (1881-1941) Belgian
£321 $497 €500 Barn and farm (35x40cm-14x16in) s. 7-Dec-2 De Vuyst, Lokeren #136
£609 $956 €950 Paysage a la ferme (41x43cm-16x17in) s. 19-Nov-2 Vanderkindere, Brussels #98
£696 $1079 €1100 Bucherons (70x55cm-28x22in) s. 24-Sep-2 Galerie Moderne, Brussels #933
£1069 $1657 €1700 Lane with travellers and cows (44x47cm-17x19in) s. 5-Oct-2 De Vuyst, Lokeren #157 est:1700-2000

GORY, Affortunato (fl.1895-1925) Italian
Sculpture
£1655 $2615 €2400 Femme dans le vent (67cm-26in) s. gold pat bronze white marble. 2-Apr-3 Vanderkindere, Brussels #564/R est:1500-2500
£2158 $3540 €3000 Comedie (42x82x18cm-17x32x7in) s. ivory gold pat bronze marble socle gilt wood. 3-Jun-3 Piasa, Paris #34/R est:3000-3500
£3438 $5500 €5157 Dance with castanets. s. silver bronze Carrara marble base. 11-Jan-3 Harvey Clar, Oakland #1438

GOS, Albert (1852-1942) Swiss
£262 $414 €393 Chapelle (41x33cm-16x13in) s. 17-Nov-2 Koller, Geneva #1294 (S.FR 600)
£278 $447 €417 Castor and Pollux in Wallis (20x20cm-8x8in) s. 7-May-3 Dobiaschofsky, Bern #3292 (S.FR 600)
£349 $552 €524 Matterhorn (28x23cm-11x9in) s. board. 14-Nov-2 Stuker, Bern #256 (S.FR 800)
£524 $817 €786 Pointe de la Maya (55x46cm-22x18in) s. 8-Nov-2 Dobiaschofsky, Bern #96/R (S.FR 1200)
£611 $966 €917 Landscape with lake in spring (90x121cm-35x48in) s. 14-Nov-2 Stuker, Bern #254 (S.FR 1400)
£926 $1491 €1389 Cattle by hut on mountain pasture (40x32cm-16x13in) s. 7-May-3 Dobiaschofsky, Bern #601/R (S.FR 2000)
£1048 $1656 €1572 Mountain landscape with moonlit lake (100x121cm-39x48in) s. 14-Nov-2 Stuker, Bern #255 est:800-1200 (S.FR 2400)
£1310 $2044 €1965 Mont Rose, Zermatt (36x46cm-14x18in) s. i.d.1882 verso panel. 6-Nov-2 Dobiaschofsky, Bern #603/R est:1400 (S.FR 3000)
£2174 $3370 €3261 Summer in Kander valley (148x114cm-58x45in) s. 9-Dec-2 Philippe Schuler, Zurich #3816/R est:6000-8000 (S.FR 5000)

GOS, François (1880-1975) Swiss
£393 $613 €590 Lac de Morat (65x81cm-26x32in) s. 8-Nov-2 Dobiaschofsky, Bern #163/R (S.FR 900)
£1217 $1887 €1826 Cervin et Riffelsee (50x62cm-20x24in) s. 7-Dec-2 Galerie du Rhone, Sion #478/R est:4000-6000 (S.FR 2800)
£2083 $3354 €3125 Mont Rose (64x81cm-25x32in) s. 7-May-3 Dobiaschofsky, Bern #604/R est:1500 (S.FR 4500)

GOSE, Francisco Xavier (1876-1915) Spanish
Works on paper
£373 $611 €570 Stroll (23x30cm-9x12in) dr htd. 5-Feb-3 Arte, Seville #762/R

GOSLING, William (1824-1883) British
£260 $406 €390 Group of sheep in a landscape (19x29cm-7x11in) s. arched top. 8-Apr-3 Bristol Auction Rooms #568/R
£600 $954 €900 Boy fishing from a bridge (43x61cm-17x24in) 30-Apr-3 Halls, Shrewsbury #311/R
£1000 $1580 €1500 At shiplake on Thames (18x33cm-7x13in) s. i.verso. 18-Dec-2 Mallams, Oxford #690/R est:1000-1200
Works on paper
£500 $810 €750 Bolney Court, near Henley-on-Thames (24x47cm-9x19in) s.d.1879 W/C. 20-May-3 Sotheby's, Olympia #186/R

GOSSE, Sylvia (1881-1968) British
£250 $390 €375 Cows by a stream (45x61cm-18x24in) s. prov. 10-Apr-3 Tennants, Leyburn #1009
£280 $437 €420 Figures resting among haystacks (23x35cm-9x14in) s. board. 10-Apr-3 Tennants, Leyburn #1008
£480 $763 €720 Lady reclining on a chaise lounge in an interior (44x75cm-17x30in) s. paper. 18-Mar-3 Rosebery Fine Art, London #837
Works on paper
£260 $406 €390 Walk through the park on a spring day (19x30cm-7x12in) s. pen ink gouache. 18-Sep-2 Dreweatt Neate, Newbury #65a
£700 $1092 €1050 Reading the paper (43x34cm-17x13in) s. pastel pencil W/C. 12-Sep-2 Sotheby's, Olympia #71/R
£1400 $2156 €2100 Three women in an interior, the jay walker (22x25cm-9x10in) s. pen brush col ink. 5-Sep-2 Christie's, Kensington #528/R est:500-700
£1800 $2808 €2700 Industrial skyline at night (31x26cm-12x10in) s.d.09 chk gouache. 12-Sep-2 Sotheby's, Olympia #92/R est:700-900

GOTCH, Bernard Cecil (1876-1940) British
Works on paper
£250 $403 €375 Holywell Street, Oxford looking west with horse and cart (36x23cm-14x9in) s. W/C. 9-May-3 Mallams, Oxford #14/R
£460 $713 €690 Holywell Street, Oxford (23x36cm-9x14in) s. W/C. 4-Oct-2 Mallams, Oxford #500/R

GOTCH, Thomas Cooper (1854-1931) British
£2900 $4495 €4350 High Veldt, South Africa (28x48cm-11x19in) s.i. pair. 3-Dec-2 Sworder & Son, Bishops Stortford #947/R est:800-1200
£38000 $61180 €57000 Alleluya (51x67cm-20x26in) prov.exhib. 20-Feb-3 Christie's, London #238/R est:35000
Works on paper
£1200 $2004 €1740 Longship Lighthouse off Landsend (29x40cm-11x16in) s. W/C. 19-Jun-3 Lane, Penzance #245/R est:1200-1500
£5000 $7850 €7500 Music lesson (42x34cm-17x13in) s. pastel. 10-Dec-2 Lane, Penzance #155/R est:7000-9000

GOTH, Moricz (1873-1944) Hungarian
£651 $1015 €950 Forest in winter (40x59cm-16x23in) s. board. 14-Apr-3 Glerum, Amsterdam #151/R
£2763 $4476 €4200 Harbour of Douarnenez, France (36x46cm-14x18in) s.d.1924 canvas on plywood. 21-Jan-3 Christie's, Amsterdam #422/R est:3000-5000

GOTH, Sarika (1900-) Hungarian
£1282 $2013 €2000 Dolls (60x90cm-24x35in) s.d.1948. 25-Nov-2 Glerum, Amsterdam #96/R est:600-1000

GOTLIB, Henryk (1890-1966) Polish
£600 $966 €900 Figures on a path (61x52cm-24x20in) s. 14-Jan-3 Bonhams, Knightsbridge #69/R
£900 $1386 €1350 Three figures and a dog (61x51cm-24x20in) s. 23-Oct-2 Hamptons Fine Art, Godalming #188/R

GOTSCH, Friedrich Karl (1900-1984) Danish
£5797 $9507 €8000 Children with goat (60x59cm-24x23in) mono. s.i.d.1948 verso. 31-May-3 Villa Grisebach, Berlin #239/R est:8000-12000
£10127 $16000 €16000 Large bouquet (80x60cm-31x24in) mono. s.i.d.1927 verso. 27-Nov-2 Dorotheum, Vienna #26/R est:18000-24000
Works on paper
£1268 $2104 €1800 View out of the window (59x46cm-23x18in) s.d. W/C gouache. 14-Jun-3 Hauswedell & Nolte, Hamburg #1205/R est:1800
£1474 $2285 €2300 Red star (71x53cm-28x21in) mono. w/C over pencil prov. 7-Dec-2 Ketterer, Hamburg #356/R est:2800-3200

GOTT, Hans (1883-?) German
£338 $527 €500 Pre-alpine landscape in evening (31x46cm-12x18in) s. board. 26-Mar-3 Hugo Ruef, Munich #106
£468 $767 €650 Interior with portrait (71x50cm-28x20in) s.d.12 chipboard. 5-Jun-3 Dorotheum, Salzburg #501/R

GOTT, Joseph (1785-1860) British
Sculpture
£4000 $6680 €5800 Boy snatching a greyhound puppy from it's mother (47cm-19in) s. terracotta incl blk marble base glazed domed vitrine. 8-Jul-3 Sotheby's, London #175/R est:3000-5000
£4600 $7176 €6900 The deluge, possibly (54cm-21in) s. white marble brown marble plinth. 9-Apr-3 Sotheby's, London #87/R est:3000-5000
£18000 $28260 €27000 Little red riding hood (121cm-48in) s. white marble. 10-Dec-2 Sotheby's, London #148/R est:20000-25000

GOTTESLEBEN, Hans (1860-?) German
£553 $874 €830 Copf eines alen Mannes (50x42cm-20x17in) s. exhib. 2-Dec-2 Rasmussen, Copenhagen #1794/R (D.KR 6500)

GOTTLIEB, Adolph (1903-1974) American
£40625 $65000 €60938 Off white (229x122cm-90x48in) s.i.d.1973 verso acrylic prov. 15-May-3 Christie's, Rockefeller NY #171/R est:70000-90000
£40625 $65000 €60938 Black spread (61x46cm-24x18in) s.d.1961 verso oil paper on canvas prov. 14-May-3 Sotheby's, New York #113/R est:12000-18000
£120253 $190000 €180380 New year (183x104cm-72x41in) s. i.d.1965 verso prov. 13-Nov-2 Sotheby's, New York #219/R est:80000-120000
£531250 $850000 €796875 Blast II (229x114cm-90x45in) s. painted 1957 prov.exhib.lit. 15-May-3 Christie's, Rockefeller NY #106/R est:150000-200000
Works on paper
£15000 $24000 €22500 Untitled 8 (60x47cm-24x19in) s.i.d.1970 ink collage prov. 15-May-3 Christie's, Rockefeller NY #112/R est:15000-20000
£37975 $60000 €56963 Illuminated crypt (79x56cm-31x22in) s. gouache executed 1947 prov. 14-Nov-2 Christie's, Rockefeller NY #126/R est:30000-40000

GOTTLIEB, Harry (1895-?) American
£359 $575 €539 Dead trees (56x76cm-22x30in) s. 11-Jan-3 James Julia, Fairfield #369
Works on paper
£223 $350 €335 Dinner party (27x34cm-11x13in) s. W/C ink. 22-Nov-2 Skinner, Boston #194/R

GOTTLIEB, Leopold (1883-1934) Polish
£4679 $7347 €7300 Portrait d'Andre Gide (80x72cm-31x28in) s.i.d.25. 10-Dec-2 Renaud, Paris #55/R
Works on paper
£272 $433 €400 Femme a la toilette (37x28cm-15x11in) s. black crayon double-sided. 3-Mar-3 Claude Boisgirard, Paris #51
£448 $717 €650 Portrait presume de Chagall (34x27cm-13x11in) s. pierre noire dr. 12-Mar-3 Rabourdin & Choppin de Janvry, Paris #45/R
£1392 $2172 €2200 Travaux a l'atelier (44x29cm-17x11in) s. mixed media. 16-Sep-2 Horta, Bruxelles #23
£3185 $4968 €5000 Cinq personnages dans un atelier (44x28cm-17x11in) s. chl pastel. 6-Nov-2 Claude Boisgirard, Paris #22/R est:5000-6000

GOTTLIEB, Moritz (1856-1879) Polish
Sculpture
£1282 $2013 €2000 Synagogue (33x26cm-13x10in) mono. bronze relief. 12-Dec-2 Rabourdin & Choppin de Janvry, Paris #94/R

GOTTLOB, Fernand Louis (1873-?) French
Works on paper
£1156 $1839 €1700 Paysages mediterraneens (54x37cm-21x15in) s. one i.verso W/C pair. 24-Mar-3 Coutau Begarie, Paris #220/R

GOTTSCHALK, Albert (1866-1906) Danish
£596 $941 €894 From the naval shipyard (34x34cm-13x13in) exhib.prov. 2-Dec-2 Rasmussen, Copenhagen #1217/R (D.KR 7000)
£851 $1345 €1277 From a fishing village (24x31cm-9x12in) prov.exhib. 2-Dec-2 Rasmussen, Copenhagen #1269/R (D.KR 10000)
£936 $1479 €1404 Nature morte with scull (39x50cm-15x20in) exhib. 2-Dec-2 Rasmussen, Copenhagen #1220/R (D.KR 11000)
£991 $1595 €1487 Stone wall, Tisvilde Hegn (47x65cm-19x26in) s. 22-Feb-3 Rasmussen, Havnen #2014 (D.KR 11000)

GOTTSCHALK, Max (20th C) American
£276 $425 €414 Portrait of Edmund Wuerpel (61x46cm-24x18in) s. board painted c.1920. 8-Sep-2 Treadway Gallery, Cincinnati #645/R

GOTTSCHALL, Rene Willy (1933-) Swiss
£694 $1118 €1006 Nature morte au raisin (50x65cm-20x26in) s. i. verso. 7-May-3 Dobiaschofsky, Bern #606/R est:1400 (S.FR 1500)
£2778 $4472 €4028 Le portail (54x65cm-21x26in) s. i.d.84 verso. 7-May-3 Dobiaschofsky, Bern #605/R est:800 (S.FR 6000)

GOTTWALD, Frederick C (1860-1941) American
£5380 $8500 €8070 Gloucester Harbor (51x61cm-20x24in) s. exhib. 24-Apr-3 Shannon's, Milford #66/R est:5000-7000

GOTZ, Karl Otto (1914-) German
£11594 $19014 €16000 Kapsyl II (70x90cm-28x35in) s. s.i.d.1962 verso prov. 28-May-3 Lempertz, Koln #150/R est:18000
Works on paper
£2372 $3676 €3700 Untitled (29x25cm-11x10in) s. gouache board prov. 3-Dec-2 Lempertz, Koln #161/R est:2400
£3404 $5515 €4800 Composition (69x99cm-27x39in) s. s.i.d. verso gouache board. 24-May-3 Van Ham, Cologne #212/R est:7000
£28481 $45000 €45000 Untitled (81x100cm-32x39in) s. s.i.d.1953 verso mixed media prov. 29-Nov-2 Villa Grisebach, Berlin #85/R est:45000-50000

GOTZINGER, Hans (1867-1941) Austrian
Works on paper
£503 $780 €800 Upper St Veit (29x19cm-11x7in) s. W/C. 1-Oct-2 Dorotheum, Vienna #355/R
£743 $1159 €1100 Sollenstein, Ybbs (31x32cm-12x13in) s.d.1923 W/C. 28-Mar-3 Dorotheum, Vienna #280/R
£755 $1170 €1200 Matias Church in Budapest (29x19cm-11x7in) s. W/C paper on board. 1-Oct-2 Dorotheum, Vienna #254/R

GOTZL, Vincenc (20th C) Czechoslovakian
£709 $1099 €1064 Bunch of flowers (70x48cm-28x19in) 1-Oct-2 SOGA, Bratislava #140/R est:45000 (SL.K 45000)

GOTZLOFF, Carl (1799-1866) German
£370 $596 €555 Two travelling musicians with flute and bagpipes (26x21cm-10x8in) s. W/C. 7-May-3 Dobiaschofsky, Bern #1134/R (S.FR 800)
£3521 $5669 €5000 View over the Arno of houses in Florence (47x59cm-19x23in) s. metal. 7-May-3 Michael Zeller, Lindau #718/R est:3500
£4878 $8000 €7317 Temple of Segesta, Sicily (34x49cm-13x19in) s.i. 29-May-3 Sotheby's, New York #38/R est:8000-12000

£15823 $24525 €25000 Campagna landscape with bridge over river (29x39cm-11x15in) s.d.1820 canvas on panel. 25-Sep-2 Neumeister, Munich #582/R est:6000
£16463 $27000 €24695 View of Naples from Posillipo with mount Vesuvius beyond (65x103cm-26x41in) s. i.verso. 29-May-3 Sotheby's, New York #40/R est:15000-20000
Works on paper
£423 $701 €600 Taormina (13x24cm-5x9in) i.d.5.Mai 23 s. verso pencil. 12-Jun-3 Hauswedell & Nolte, Hamburg #350/R
£2025 $3139 €3200 Garibaldi's soldiers in discussion (21x15cm-8x6in) i. W/C over pencil htd white. 25-Sep-2 Neumeister, Munich #401/R est:1500
£3481 $5396 €5500 Pilgrim procession for the feast of Madonna dell'Arco (22x34cm-9x13in) s. W/C over pencil. 25-Sep-2 Neumeister, Munich #400/R est:3800

GOUBIE, Jean Richard (1842-1899) French
£4245 $6791 €5900 La rencontre des cavaliers (35x43cm-14x17in) s.d.1897. 14-May-3 Rabourdin & Choppin de Janvry, Paris #7/R est:6000-7000
£12057 $20135 €17000 La halte (38x46cm-15x18in) s. 20-Jun-3 Piasa, Paris #55/R est:15000-18000

GOUDIE, Alexander (1933-) British
£900 $1395 €1350 Self portrait with paint brushes (90x80cm-35x31in) s. 6-Dec-2 Lyon & Turnbull, Edinburgh #39/R
£1200 $1944 €1800 Colonsay rabbits (96x91cm-38x36in) s. 23-May-3 Lyon & Turnbull, Edinburgh #62 est:500-800
£1350 $2106 €2025 Still life of a jug of yellow daisies (34x27cm-13x11in) s. board. 17-Oct-2 Bonhams, Edinburgh #77/R est:500-800
£3100 $4836 €4650 Still life of red apples in a bowl (50x45cm-20x18in) s. 28-Mar-3 Bonhams, Edinburgh #143 est:2000-3000
£3600 $5616 €5400 Still life with mantel clock, photograph, candle and fruit (75x100cm-30x39in) 28-Mar-3 Bonhams, Edinburgh #142/R est:3000-5000
£5500 $8580 €8250 Cocktails (62x74cm-24x29in) s. 28-Mar-3 Bonhams, Edinburgh #144/R est:3000-5000
Works on paper
£400 $624 €600 Green angel (54x63cm-21x25in) s. col chk. 17-Sep-2 Sotheby's, Olympia #76/R
£450 $698 €675 Feather boa (40x38cm-16x15in) s. pastel. 6-Dec-2 Lyon & Turnbull, Edinburgh #64

GOUGELET, J (?) French?
£1205 $2000 €1747 Music lesson (56x46cm-22x18in) s. 14-Jun-3 Jackson's, Cedar Falls #368/R est:500-700

GOUILLET, Jules (1826-?) French
£3881 $6055 €5822 Still life with flowers (73x100cm-29x39in) s.d.1884. 28-Mar-3 Koller, Zurich #3132/R est:5000-8000 (S.FR 8500)

GOULBORN, Cecilia (19/20th C) British
Works on paper
£420 $655 €630 Trophy painting of salmon, killed by L J Richardson-Gardner (38x112cm-15x44in) s. W/C. 15-Oct-2 Gorringes, Lewes #2211

GOULD, Alexander Carruthers (1870-1948) British
£880 $1399 €1320 View on Exmoor (63x76cm-25x30in) s.d.1937. 27-Feb-3 Greenslade Hunt, Taunton #1304/R
£900 $1503 €1305 Sunbury weir, River Thames (43x58cm-17x23in) s. 20-Jun-3 Keys, Aylsham #690
Works on paper
£480 $763 €720 Porlock weir, Somerset (25x35cm-10x14in) s. W/C. 29-Apr-3 Bonhams, Knightsbridge #3/R

GOULD, David (fl.1885-1930) British
£330 $541 €495 Chat with an old friend (30x23cm-12x9in) mono.d.1904. 5-Jun-3 Christie's, Kensington #657/R
Works on paper
£540 $853 €810 Autumn evening - Thirlmere lake 1900 (49x75cm-19x30in) s. W/C htd white. 7-Apr-3 Bonhams, Bath #23/R

GOULD, Francis Carruthers (1844-1925) British
Works on paper
£452 $700 €678 Procession of British Royalty (23x36cm-9x14in) s. pen ink card. 25-Sep-2 Doyle, New York #37/R

GOULD, John Howard (1929-) Canadian
Works on paper
£975 $1550 €1463 Actress in quilted jacket (60x50cm-24x20in) s. mixed media prov. 23-Mar-3 Hodgins, Calgary #112/R est:1000-1500 (C.D 2300)
£1244 $2041 €1866 Woman sleeping (95x64cm-37x25in) s. mixed media prov. 3-Jun-3 Joyner, Toronto #177/R est:2000-3000 (C.D 2800)

GOULD, William Buelow (1803-1853) Australian
£1429 $2257 €2144 Hare, pheasant and two snipe (60x49cm-24x19in) linen on board prov.exhib.lit. 17-Nov-2 Sotheby's, Paddington #40/R est:7000-10000 (A.D 4000)
£3214 $5079 €4821 Falls of the Clyde, view of Corri-Linn (75x63cm-30x25in) s. canvas on board prov.exhib.lit. 17-Nov-2 Sotheby's, Paddington #39/R est:10000-15000 (A.D 9000)

GOULDEN, Jean (20th C) ?
£476 $757 €700 Nature morte au pot de fleurs sur fond de paysage (86x50cm-34x20in) s. panel prov. 28-Feb-3 Tajan, Paris #16

GOULDING, Tim (1945-) Irish
£514 $807 €750 Standing stones (77x77cm-30x30in) mono.d.91 oil on paper. 15-Apr-3 De Veres Art Auctions, Dublin #75/R
£2083 $3312 €3000 Beara, near the Allihies, West Cork (51x41cm-20x16in) init.d.1980. 29-Apr-3 Whyte's, Dublin #17/R est:1500-2000
Works on paper
£445 $695 €650 Autumn tints, 3 (31x20cm-12x8in) init. W/C. 8-Apr-3 James Adam, Dublin #131/R

GOULDSMITH, Harriet (1787-1863) British
£3000 $4740 €4500 View of Hampstead Heath looking towards Cannon Place (14x23cm-6x9in) i.d.1818 verso board. 26-Nov-2 Christie's, London #67/R est:2000-3000

GOULINAT, Jean Gabriel (1883-1972) French
£446 $696 €700 Allee des Muriers (46x54cm-18x21in) s.panel. 7-Nov-2 Chochon-Barre & Allardi, Paris #162

GOUMOIS, William de (1865-1941) Swiss
£262 $409 €393 Sailing ship at sea (42x57cm-17x22in) s.i.d.1901 board. 20-Nov-2 Fischer, Luzern #2095/R (S.FR 600)

GOUNAROPOULOS, Georges (1889-1977) Greek
£4487 $6821 €7000 Bather (24x19cm-9x7in) s. panel. 16-Aug-2 Deauville, France #134/R
£8000 $12640 €12000 Female nude (54x65cm-21x26in) 1-Apr-3 Bonhams, New Bond Street #62 est:8000-10000
£11000 $17380 €16500 Nymph (73x54cm-29x21in) 1-Apr-3 Bonhams, New Bond Street #42 est:10000-12000
£15000 $23250 €22500 Dreamscape (81x121cm-32x48in) s.d.65 board. 2-Oct-2 Sotheby's, London #71/R est:15000-20000
£19000 $29450 €28500 Women in dream landscape (82x108cm-32x43in) s. board. 2-Oct-2 Sotheby's, London #127/R est:15000-20000
Works on paper
£2500 $3875 €3750 Nude (84x58cm-33x23in) s. crayon chl. 2-Oct-2 Sotheby's, London #111/R

GOUPIL, Jules Adolphe (1839-1883) French
£9554 $15000 €14331 La lecon de musique (119x83cm-47x33in) s. 21-Nov-2 Sotheby's, New York #179/R est:20000-30000

GOUPY, Joseph (?-1782) French
Works on paper
£900 $1503 €1305 Paul preaching in Athens (19x24cm-7x9in) init. gouache. 9-Jul-3 Bonhams, Knightsbridge #16/R

GOURDON, Robert (attrib) (1820-?) French
£1923 $2981 €3000 Extensive landscape with thatched building (85x91cm-33x36in) canvas on panel. 5-Dec-2 Dr Fritz Nagel, Stuttgart #654/R est:1300

GOURLEY, Alan Stenhouse (1909-1991) British
£280 $431 €420 Venetian lagoon scene (25x35cm-10x14in) board. 22-Oct-2 Bonhams, Ipswich #306
£280 $437 €420 Gondolas moored towards the salute (62x76cm-24x30in) s. board. 27-Mar-3 Christie's, Kensington #494
£300 $468 €450 Pumpkins at the well (63x76cm-25x30in) s. 27-Mar-3 Christie's, Kensington #491/R
£380 $593 €570 Canal, Venice (46x58cm-18x23in) s. board. 27-Mar-3 Christie's, Kensington #490
£400 $624 €600 Houses of Parliament (61x76cm-24x30in) s. board. 27-Mar-3 Christie's, Kensington #492/R

£480 $792 €696 Gondoliers, Venice (46x61cm-18x24in) s. board. 3-Jul-3 Christie's, Kensington #468/R
Works on paper
£280 $431 €420 Fishing (25x35cm-10x14in) indis.sig. gouache. 5-Sep-2 Christie's, Kensington #525

GOUSSEV, Vladimir (1957-) Russian
£250 $388 €375 Girls in the garden (22x27cm-9x11in) s. 29-Sep-2 John Nicholson, Haslemere #20
£500 $775 €750 Chickens (41x33cm-16x13in) s. 8-Dec-2 John Nicholson, Haslemere #120/R
£550 $853 €825 On the beach (35x37cm-14x15in) s. 8-Dec-2 John Nicholson, Haslemere #121/R
£600 $930 €900 Beginning of autumn (50x40cm-20x16in) s. 29-Sep-2 John Nicholson, Haslemere #86/R
£608 $949 €900 On the bridge (55x46cm-22x18in) s. 25-Mar-3 Durán, Madrid #735/R
£700 $1085 €1050 Girl in a boat (50x40cm-20x16in) s. 29-Sep-2 John Nicholson, Haslemere #87/R
£800 $1240 €1200 On the shore (61x50cm-24x20in) s. 8-Dec-2 John Nicholson, Haslemere #123/R
£811 $1265 €1200 Poppy field (54x65cm-21x26in) s. 25-Mar-3 Durán, Madrid #734/R
£1300 $2015 €1950 On the gangways (50x65cm-20x26in) s. 8-Dec-2 John Nicholson, Haslemere #117/R
£1400 $2170 €2100 Between the mallows (46x55cm-18x22in) s. 8-Dec-2 John Nicholson, Haslemere #118/R
£1800 $2790 €2700 On the shore of the lake (61x46cm-24x18in) s. 8-Dec-2 John Nicholson, Haslemere #115/R
£1900 $2945 €2850 Spring near Moscow (55x46cm-22x18in) s. 29-Sep-2 John Nicholson, Haslemere #33/R

GOUWE, Adriaan Herman (1875-1965) Dutch
£313 $516 €450 Plough team (25x36cm-10x14in) s.d.09 s.stretcher. 1-Jul-3 Christie's, Amsterdam #578/R
£701 $1079 €1100 Plough team (22x40cm-9x16in) s. 3-Sep-2 Christie's, Amsterdam #359
£780 $1264 €1100 Summer landscape with houses and trees (12x20cm-5x8in) s. board. 26-May-3 Glerum, Amsterdam #106
£1019 $1590 €1600 Tahiti (49x64cm-19x25in) s.verso. 6-Nov-2 Vendue Huis, Gravenhage #72/R est:1000-1200

GOUWELOOS, Charles (1867-?) Belgian
£308 $484 €450 Maison de Meunier a Pede (33x40cm-13x16in) s. 15-Apr-3 Galerie Moderne, Brussels #399

GOUWELOOS, Jean (1868-1943) Belgian
£327 $526 €500 Cote mediterraneenne (46x60cm-18x24in) s. 14-Jan-3 Vanderkindere, Brussels #99
£478 $745 €750 Lavandiere au bord du cours d'eau (39x46cm-15x18in) s. 11-Nov-2 Horta, Bruxelles #676
£514 $801 €750 Vase fleuri de roses sauvages (70x58cm-28x23in) s. 14-Apr-3 Horta, Bruxelles #237
£523 $842 €800 Elegante au chignon (55x38cm-22x15in) s. 20-Jan-3 Horta, Bruxelles #22
£526 $853 €800 Les bouches de l'escaut (30x40cm-12x16in) s. panel. 21-Jan-3 Galerie Moderne, Brussels #245
£655 $1048 €950 Pleine mer (38x58cm-15x23in) s. 15-Mar-3 De Vuyst, Lokeren #140
£701 $1093 €1100 Elegante au chignon (55x38cm-22x15in) s. 11-Nov-2 Horta, Bruxelles #675
£1379 $2207 €2000 Satisfaction (120x80cm-47x31in) s. 17-Mar-3 Horta, Bruxelles #188 est:2500-3500
£1700 $2822 €1700 Nu de face, debout (50x37cm-20x15in) s. 16-Jun-3 Horta, Bruxelles #439 est:2000-2500
£1899 $2943 €3000 Barques de peche au bord de canal (37x87cm-15x34in) s. 24-Sep-2 Galerie Moderne, Brussels #884/R
£2553 $4034 €3830 Interior scene with woman in deep thoughts (61x50cm-24x20in) s. 2-Dec-2 Rasmussen, Copenhagen #1735/R est:30000-50000 (D.KR 30000)
£2564 $3974 €4000 Composition au vase fleuri et a la figurine (80x60cm-31x24in) s. 9-Dec-2 Horta, Bruxelles #209/R est:4500-5500
£3946 $6273 €5800 Elegante assise (60x50cm-24x20in) s. 18-Mar-3 Vanderkindere, Brussels #37/R est:6000-8000

GOUY (attrib) (18th C) ?
Works on paper
£321 $497 €500 Jeune paysanne et enfant dans un etable (33x23cm-13x9in) s.d.1766 sanguine. 4-Dec-2 Piasa, Paris #78

GOVAERTS, Abraham (1589-1626) Flemish
£9000 $14040 €13500 Judgement of Midas (28x54cm-11x21in) i.verso copper. 10-Apr-3 Sotheby's, London #3/R
£19231 $29808 €30000 Scene de chasse dans un bois (33x51cm-13x20in) panel. 6-Dec-2 Millon & Associes, Paris #5/R est:45000

GOVAERTS, Abraham (attrib) (1589-1626) Flemish
£7234 $12081 €10200 Alexandre et Diogene (51x65cm-20x26in) copper. 18-Jun-3 Tajan, Paris #76/R est:8000-10000
£26000 $40820 €39000 Woodland landscape with figures and waggons on the outskirts of a village (53x83cm-21x33in) panel. 10-Dec-2 Sotheby's, Olympia #362/R est:6000-8000

GOVAERTS, Abraham (circle) (1589-1626) Flemish
£8696 $14261 €12000 Paysage boise anime de personnages (30x40cm-12x16in) panel prov.exhib. 27-May-3 Palais de Beaux Arts, Brussels #294/R est:12500-17000

GOVAERTS, Abraham and FRANCKEN, Frans II (17th C) Flemish
£12500 $20875 €18125 Wooded landscape with the judgement of Midas (41x55cm-16x22in) copper. 9-Jul-3 Christie's, London #1/R est:12000-18000

GOVAERTS, Jean (1898-1985) Belgian
£261 $421 €400 Vase de fleurs (70x60cm-28x24in) s. 14-Jan-3 Vanderkindere, Brussels #82
£359 $579 €550 Eglise de Ciergnon (50x60cm-20x24in) s. 14-Jan-3 Vanderkindere, Brussels #76
£752 $1210 €1150 La mer (97x130cm-38x51in) s. 14-Jan-3 Vanderkindere, Brussels #35

GOVE, Gregory (1967-) American
£316 $500 €474 Untitled (104x58cm-41x23in) s. acrylic prov. 1-Dec-2 Susanin's, Chicago #5005/R

GOVERTSZ, Dirck (attrib) (1571-1643) Dutch
£6028 $10067 €8500 Nature morte aux gibiers, fruits et legumes sur un entablement (118x122cm-46x48in) 18-Jun-3 Tajan, Paris #80/R est:8000-12000

GOW, Andrew Carrick (1848-1920) British
Works on paper
£1290 $2000 €1935 Preparing for the hunt. Laboratory (35x26cm-14x10in) s.d.1862 one s.d.1983 pencil gouache. 29-Oct-2 Sotheby's, New York #126/R est:1000-1500

GOWANS, George Russell (1843-1924) British
£480 $754 €720 Near Stonehaven (35x52cm-14x20in) 17-Apr-3 Bonhams, Edinburgh #349

GOWIN, Emmet (1941-) American
Photographs
£3000 $4800 €4500 Edith, Danville, Virginia (14x18cm-6x7in) with sig.i.d.1969 verso silver print. 15-May-3 Swann Galleries, New York #423/R est:2500-3500

GOWING, Lawrence (1918-1991) British
£900 $1422 €1350 Lugs mill, Colwall 1929 (33x28cm-13x11in) s. i.verso board exhib. 7-Apr-3 Bonhams, Bath #68/R

GOY, Auguste (?) French
Works on paper
£282 $454 €400 Paysage au gardien de vaches pres de la riviere (22x38cm-9x15in) s. pastel. 11-May-3 Thierry & Lannon, Brest #295

GOYA Y LUCIENTES, Francisco Jose de (1746-1828) Spanish
£400000 $668000 €580000 Appearance of the Virgen del Pilar to Saint James (47x33cm-19x13in) prov.exhib.lit. 9-Jul-3 Christie's, London #72/R est:400000-600000
£2839506 $4600000 €4259259 Still life of dead hares (45x63cm-18x25in) prov.exhib.lit. 24-Jan-3 Christie's, Rockefeller NY #136/R est:2000000-3000000
Prints
£2532 $3924 €4000 El sueno de la razon produce monstruos (21x15cm-8x6in) etching aquatint. 27-Sep-2 Venator & Hansten, Koln #1277/R est:3000
£6731 $10433 €10500 Old woman on swing (19x12cm-7x5in) etching. 7-Dec-2 Hauswedell & Nolte, Hamburg #671/R est:14000
£20183 $33706 €29265 One can't tell you why (15x20cm-6x8in) etching wash drypoint prov. 20-Jun-3 Kornfeld, Bern #64/R est:50000 (S.FR 44000)
£50000 $77500 €75000 Los caprichos. etching album. 5-Dec-2 Sotheby's, London #19/R est:40000-60000
£50459 $84266 €73166 One can't look (14x21cm-6x8in) etching wash drypoint prov. 20-Jun-3 Kornfeld, Bern #63/R est:65000 (S.FR 110000)

GOYA Y LUCIENTES, Francisco Jose de (circle) (1746-1828) Spanish
£11111 $18000 €16667 Portrait of lady (84x62cm-33x24in) prov.lit. 23-Jan-3 Sotheby's, New York #136/R est:15000

GOYEN, Jan van (1596-1656) Dutch
£27439 $45000 €41159 Rural landscape with peasants and a drover by a track, village beyond (56x73cm-22x29in) indis.init. panel prov.exhib.lit. 30-May-3 Christie's, Rockefeller NY #14/R est:20000-30000
£29680 $46301 €44520 Extensive flat landscape (33x51cm-13x20in) i.d.1647 panel prov.lit. 28-Mar-3 Koller, Zurich #3034/R est:70000-100000 (S.FR 65000)
£30216 $48345 €42000 Dune landscape with peasants conversing by a farm (25x39cm-10x15in) panel prov.exhib.lit. 14-May-3 Christie's, Amsterdam #183/R est:35000-45000
£31447 $48742 €50000 Dutch river landscape (28x40cm-11x16in) panel lit.prov. 2-Oct-2 Dorotheum, Vienna #84/R est:50000-70000
£44025 $68239 €70000 Farmhouse among the dunes (38x58cm-15x23in) panel prov. lit. 2-Oct-2 Dorotheum, Vienna #83/R est:70000-90000
£45000 $75150 €65250 Winter and Summer landscapes (15cm-6in circular) one s.d.1627 one s. panel pair prov.exhib.lit. 10-Jul-3 Sotheby's, London #16/R est:60000-80000
£50000 $78500 €75000 Winter landscape with figures skating and sledging outside a village (29cm-11in circular) s.indis.d.162 panel prov. 12-Dec-2 Sotheby's, London #19/R est:30000-40000
£60000 $93600 €90000 Two riders and other figures with distant view of the church of Nieder-Elten (59x73cm-23x29in) s. panel oval prov.exhib.lit. 10-Apr-3 Sotheby's, London #63/R est:60000
£111111 $180000 €166667 Dune landscape with peasants by a track (89x126cm-35x50in) s.d.1634 prov.exhib.lit. 24-Jan-3 Christie's, Rockefeller NY #15/R est:200000-300000

Works on paper
£774 $1200 €1161 Landscape with trees (12x13cm-5x5in) black chk. 3-Dec-2 Christie's, Rockefeller NY #56/R
£3086 $5000 €4629 View of the Abbey at Elten (9x16cm-4x6in) i. chk wash prov.lit. 21-Jan-3 Sotheby's, New York #141/R est:5000
£7343 $12262 €10500 Paysage fluvial anime (12x20cm-5x8in) mono.d.1652 black crayon grey wash. 27-Jun-3 Claude Aguttes, Neuilly #5/R est:6000-7000
£8025 $13000 €12038 Houses and mill on riverbank (11x19cm-4x7in) mono.d.1653 chk wash prov.exhib.lit. 21-Jan-3 Sotheby's, New York #140/R est:12000
£8917 $13911 €14000 Hamlet near a stream with two figures on a bridge (12x18cm-5x7in) pen brown ink grey wash prov. 5-Nov-2 Sotheby's, Amsterdam #39/R est:15000-20000
£8917 $13911 €14000 Castle at Cleves, seen from the east (10x16cm-4x6in) black chk grey wash prov.exhib.lit. 5-Nov-2 Sotheby's, Amsterdam #40/R est:4000-6000
£14013 $21860 €22000 Polder landscape (12x19cm-5x7in) mono.d.1653 black chk grey wash prov.exhib.lit. 5-Nov-2 Sotheby's, Amsterdam #46/R est:25000-35000

GOYEN, Jan van (circle) (1596-1656) Dutch
£9494 $14715 €15000 Rhein landscape with castle (49x72cm-19x28in) mono.d.164 panel prov.lit. 25-Sep-2 Neumeister, Munich #481/R est:15000

GOYEN, Jan van (style) (1596-1656) Dutch
£5000 $8050 €7500 River landscape with fishing boats and other shipping (32x37cm-13x15in) mono.d.16 panel. 20-Feb-3 Christie's, Kensington #276/R est:1000-1500

GOYO, Hashiguchi (1880-1921) Japanese
Prints
£2564 $4000 €3846 Woman holding a towel (46x30cm-18x12in) s. silver-mica ground col woodcut. 25-Mar-3 Christie's, Rockefeller NY #399/R est:4000-6000

GOZZARD, J Walter (1888-1950) British
£400 $668 €580 Rural scene with farm girl at the river's edge and ferryman in his boat (51x76cm-20x30in) s. 25-Jun-3 Goldings, Lincolnshire #383
£550 $919 €798 Figures on a path beside cottages and a pond. Drover on a path (51x76cm-20x30in) s. pair. 24-Jun-3 Rowley Fine Art, Newmarket #358
£720 $1116 €1080 A gleam of sunshine. A moorland road (49x76cm-19x30in) s. i. stretcher pair. 2-Oct-2 Bonhams, Knowle #66
£798 $1300 €1197 Untitled (43x56cm-17x22in) 14-Feb-3 Du Mouchelle, Detroit #2095/R

GRAAE, Marie (19th C) Danish?
£328 $501 €492 Interior scene with grand piano (64x79cm-25x31in) 24-Aug-2 Rasmussen, Havnen #2048 (D.KR 3800)

GRAAT, Barend (attrib) (1628-1709) Flemish
£6369 $9936 €10000 Portrait of a gentleman and his wife and their children in a garden setting (121x110cm-48x43in) prov.exhib.lit. 5-Nov-2 Sotheby's, Amsterdam #79/R est:12000-18000

GRABACH, John R (1886-1981) American
£1138 $1900 €1650 Last of the snow (44x31cm-17x12in) s. canvas on board. 22-Jun-3 Freeman, Philadelphia #114/R est:1500-2500
£4777 $7500 €7166 Plaza cab man (36x47cm-14x19in) s. 22-Nov-2 Skinner, Boston #339/R est:400-600

GRABER, Margit (1895-1993) Hungarian
£1084 $1690 €1572 Still life (40x57cm-16x22in) canvas on cardboard lit. 13-Sep-2 Mu Terem Galeria, Budapest #82/R est:360000 (H.F 420000)
£2193 $3421 €3290 Kecskemet (58x72cm-23x28in) s. cardboard. 11-Sep-2 Kieselbach, Budapest #148/R (H.F 850000)

GRABER, Otto (1885-1952) German
£519 $790 €800 Village (36x41cm-14x16in) s. board. 6-Jul-2 Berlinghof, Heidelberg #205

GRABHEIN, Wilhelm (1859-1931) German
£487 $726 €750 Two dogs chasing cat (37x25cm-15x10in) s. 27-Jun-2 Neumeister, Munich #2727

GRABMAYER, Franz (1927-) German
£3481 $5500 €5500 Wooded landscape (145x160cm-57x63in) s.d.1986 verso prov. 27-Nov-2 Dorotheum, Vienna #315/R est:7000-10000

Works on paper
£1111 $1767 €1600 Untitled (100x70cm-39x28in) s. mixed media. 29-Apr-3 Wiener Kunst Auktionen, Vienna #505/R est:1600-2000

GRABONE, Arnold (1896-1981) German
£261 $429 €400 Wayside cross in high mountains (80x100cm-31x39in) s. 6-Feb-3 Weidler, Nurnberg #306/R
£288 $438 €450 Wayside shrine in the mountains (50x58cm-20x23in) s. 11-Jul-2 Hugo Ruef, Munich #667/R
£299 $476 €440 Fishing boats at dusk (50x60cm-20x24in) s. i. verso. 20-Mar-3 Neumeister, Munich #2579
£299 $476 €440 Storm off Capri (80x70cm-31x28in) s. i. verso. 20-Mar-3 Neumeister, Munich #2580
£308 $477 €480 Summer morning in Tyrol (59x79cm-23x31in) s. i. verso prov. 7-Dec-2 Ketterer, Hamburg #192/R
£338 $527 €500 Mountain settlement in Tyrol (70x90cm-28x35in) i. 31-Mar-3 Dr Fritz Nagel, Stuttgart #7014/R
£385 $596 €600 In the autumn (80x70cm-31x28in) s. i.d.1960 verso. 6-Dec-2 Michael Zeller, Lindau #712/R
£411 $638 €650 Mountain village (70x100cm-28x39in) s. i. verso. 26-Sep-2 Neumeister, Munich #2685/R
£411 $641 €600 Hochfilz pasture, Stubai (70x80cm-28x31in) s. 11-Apr-3 Sigalas, Stuttgart #352
£422 $629 €650 High mountains with alpine hut (80x70cm-31x28in) s. 28-Jun-2 Sigalas, Stuttgart #797/R
£443 $687 €700 Mountain landscape (82x110cm-32x43in) s. lit. 27-Sep-2 Auktionhaus Georg Rehm, Augsburg #8040/R
£455 $677 €700 High mountain chapel (80x70cm-31x28in) s. i. verso. 27-Jun-2 Neumeister, Munich #2679/R
£637 $994 €1000 Ships on silt (50x60cm-20x24in) s. 6-Nov-2 Hugo Ruef, Munich #1109/R
£646 $1028 €950 Tyrolean mountain farmstead (82x125cm-32x49in) s. 20-Mar-3 Neumeister, Munich #2577

GRABWINKLER, Peter (1885-1943) Austrian
Works on paper
£377 $585 €600 Water nymph and sleeping girl (56x54cm-22x21in) s. W/C. 1-Oct-2 Dorotheum, Vienna #332/R

GRACE, A L (19th C) British
£850 $1394 €1275 Back home at last (63x76cm-25x30in) s. i.verso. 29-May-3 Christie's, Kensington #282/R

GRACE, Gerald (1918-) American
£299 $475 €434 Wet sands (16x20cm-6x8in) s. board painted c.1950. 4-May-3 Treadway Gallery, Cincinnati #544/R

GRACE, James Edward (1851-1908) British
£270 $421 €405 Harbour scene with figures tending a fishing boat (36x64cm-14x25in) s.d.1881. 23-Sep-2 Bonhams, Chester #1002

GRACIA, Manuel de (1937-) Spanish
£690 $1097 €1000 Sopelena beach (27x35cm-11x14in) s. s.i.verso. 4-Mar-3 Ansorena, Madrid #139/R
£759 $1206 €1100 Aranjuez (26x34cm-10x13in) s. s.i.verso. 4-Mar-3 Ansorena, Madrid #140/R
£2323 $3670 €3600 Roadworks in the Arenal, Bilbao (60x73cm-24x29in) s. s.i.verso. 18-Dec-2 Ansorena, Madrid #67/R

GRADA, Antonio de (1858-1938) Swiss?
£408 $644 €612 Hunting still life with pheasants (113x56cm-44x22in) s.d.1907. 29-Nov-2 Zofingen, Switzerland #2450 (S.FR 950)
£524 $817 €786 Piz Padella near Samaden (44x35cm-17x14in) s.d.1910 canvas on panel. 20-Nov-2 Fischer, Luzern #2098/R (S.FR 1200)

GRADA, Raffaele de (1885-1957) Italian
£279 $441 €419 Mountain way with last cover of snow (27x40cm-11x16in) s. 29-Nov-2 Zofingen, Switzerland #2456 (S.FR 650)
£568 $886 €852 Autumn stream landscape (26x24cm-10x9in) s.d.1909 board. 20-Nov-2 Fischer, Luzern #2099 (S.FR 1300)
£611 $954 €917 Southern landscape with houses (26x36cm-10x14in) s. panel. 6-Nov-2 Dobiaschofsky, Bern #613/R (S.FR 1400)
£655 $1022 €983 Small village beneath cloudy skies (21x27cm-8x11in) s. panel. 20-Nov-2 Fischer, Luzern #2100/R est:500-700 (S.FR 1500)
£1087 $1696 €1631 Autumn landscape (56x43cm-22x17in) s.d.1916. 16-Sep-2 Philippe Schuler, Zurich #3513/R est:2000-2500 (S.FR 2500)
£1502 $2373 €2253 View of a sun-drenched pergola in an upper Italien mountain village (64x88cm-25x35in) prov. 29-Nov-2 Zofingen, Switzerland #2453 est:6500 (S.FR 3500)
£1717 $2712 €2576 Autumn time at sea (73x100cm-29x39in) s.d.1908 hessian. 29-Nov-2 Zofingen, Switzerland #2455 est:2500 (S.FR 4000)
£1852 $2981 €2778 Glacier in the Alps (45x65cm-18x26in) s. 7-May-3 Dobiaschofsky, Bern #608/R est:4000 (S.FR 4000)
£2096 $3270 €3144 Mountain stream in winter (80x102cm-31x40in) s. 6-Nov-2 Dobiaschofsky, Bern #612/R est:7000 (S.FR 4800)
£2365 $3689 €3500 Bathers (48x48cm-19x19in) s. tempera paper. 28-Mar-3 Farsetti, Prato #212/R
£2402 $3747 €3603 Summer landscape (65x50cm-26x20in) s. 6-Nov-2 Dobiaschofsky, Bern #614/R est:4000 (S.FR 5500)
£2821 $4372 €4400 Bergamo, part of the Old Walls Path (63x47cm-25x19in) canvas on board painted 1939 exhib. 4-Dec-2 Finarte, Milan #326/R
£3013 $4730 €4700 Stream (50x80cm-20x31in) s.d.1916. 23-Nov-2 Meeting Art, Vercelli #246/R
£3057 $4769 €4586 Paesaggio toscano (40x59cm-16x23in) s.d.1940 exhib. 6-Nov-2 Dobiaschofsky, Bern #611/R est:7000 (S.FR 7000)
£3165 $4937 €5000 Alpine refuge (48x76cm-19x30in) s. 14-Sep-2 Meeting Art, Vercelli #946/R
£4292 $6781 €6438 Farm buildings in Tuscany landscape (71x90cm-28x35in) s. board. 29-Nov-2 Zofingen, Switzerland #2454/R est:10000 (S.FR 10000)
£4861 $7826 €7292 Winter landscape (82x94cm-32x37in) s. i. stretcher. 7-May-3 Dobiaschofsky, Bern #607/R est:8000 (S.FR 10500)
£6419 $10014 €9500 San Miniato (55x65cm-22x26in) s. painted1927 exhib.lit. 26-Mar-3 Finarte Semenzato, Milan #302/R
£7692 $12077 €12000 Landscape (65x80cm-26x31in) s.d.1927. 19-Nov-2 Finarte, Milan #199/R
Works on paper
£613 $981 €920 Siena (29x33cm-11x13in) s. W/C over Indian ink. 17-Mar-3 Philippe Schuler, Zurich #4032 est:700-900 (S.FR 1300)
£1020 $1622 €1500 Farm (33x45cm-13x18in) s. W/C. 1-Mar-3 Meeting Art, Vercelli #752

GRADISCHNIG, Ernst (1949-) Austrian
Works on paper
£556 $878 €800 Houses in Djerba (45x35cm-18x14in) s.i.d.84 mixed media board. 24-Apr-3 Dorotheum, Vienna #202/R

GRADL, Hermann (1883-1964) German
£1014 $1581 €1500 Hilly green valley (70x90cm-28x35in) s. 26-Mar-3 Hugo Ruef, Munich #109/R est:1500

GRADY, Napoleone (1860-1949) Italian
£314 $484 €500 Anthony and Cleopatra (46x39cm-18x15in) s. 28-Oct-2 Il Ponte, Milan #336
£340 $541 €500 Seascape with fishermen (8x13cm-3x5in) s. board. 18-Mar-3 Finarte, Milan #75/R
£480 $749 €720 Lac d'Iseo (50x37cm-20x15in) mono. i. verso board. 6-Nov-2 Dobiaschofsky, Bern #615/R (S.FR 1100)
£578 $919 €850 Towards Savona (13x22cm-5x9in) s. board. 18-Mar-3 Finarte, Milan #161/R

GRAEB, Karl Georg Anton (1816-1884) German
£2390 $3728 €3800 Gothic church in riverside city (27x21cm-11x8in) s. board. 21-Sep-2 Bolland & Marotz, Bremen #484/R est:3800
Works on paper
£4000 $6240 €6000 Athens in ancient time (19x44cm-7x17in) s. W/C over pencil. 15-Oct-2 Sotheby's, London #18/R est:3000-5000

GRAEF, Oscar (1861-1912) German
£1139 $1766 €1800 Dachau piglet meal (80x105cm-31x41in) s.i. 25-Sep-2 Neumeister, Munich #584/R est:2000

GRAEFF, Werner (1901-1964) German
£2319 $3803 €3200 Blutu (80x80cm-31x31in) s.i.d.1972 cotton. 29-May-3 Lempertz, Koln #641/R est:4000

GRAEFLE, Albert (1807-1889) German
£1026 $1600 €1539 Portrait of a young boy in profile (37x32cm-15x13in) s. 12-Apr-3 Weschler, Washington #543/R est:700-900

GRAEME, Colin (fl.1858-1910) British
£350 $571 €525 English setter and terrier in landscape (38x48cm-15x19in) 7-Feb-3 Dee Atkinson & Harrison, Driffield #693
£700 $1141 €1050 Portrait of a collie (30x25cm-12x10in) s.d.95. 12-Feb-3 Bonhams, Knightsbridge #107/R
£740 $1236 €1073 Pheasants in a winter landscape. Grouse in a moorland landscape (30x25cm-12x10in) s. pair. 24-Jun-3 Bonhams, Knowle #89
£780 $1295 €1170 Terrier (24x18cm-9x7in) s. 10-Jun-3 Bonhams, Leeds #163/R
£900 $1404 €1350 Polly, portrait of horse in a stable (44x60cm-17x24in) s.i.d.1901. 8-Oct-2 Bonhams, Knightsbridge #174/R
£1100 $1793 €1595 Gypsy (40x56cm-16x22in) s.d.99. 16-Jul-3 Sotheby's, Olympia #96/R est:1000-2000
£1300 $2054 €1950 Gordon setters in a landscape (30x46cm-12x18in) s. 2-Dec-2 Gorringes, Lewes #2613 est:400-600
£1450 $2291 €2175 Two spaniels with a duck on the river bank (39x49cm-15x19in) s.d.1900. 7-Apr-3 David Duggleby, Scarborough #365/R est:1000-1500
£1700 $2771 €2465 Rest from hunting (51x76cm-20x30in) s.d.99. 16-Jul-3 Sotheby's, Olympia #95/R est:1000-1500
£1750 $2818 €2625 English pointer and Gordon setter standing amongst heather with stormy sky (30x40cm-12x16in) s. 20-Feb-3 Thos Mawer, Lincoln #437/R est:800-1200
£1800 $2736 €2700 Head studies of dogs (21x15cm-8x6in) s.d.92 pair. 28-Aug-2 Sotheby's, London #907/R est:2000-3000
£2057 $3250 €3086 Four hounds in a stream (56x76cm-22x30in) s.d.93. 26-Apr-3 Jeffery Burchard, Florida #69
£2100 $3234 €3150 Study of four dark bay and chestnut hunters in a landscape (56x57cm-22x22in) s.i. 23-Oct-2 Hampton & Littlewood, Exeter #463/R est:1000-1500
£2200 $3652 €3190 Spaniel putting a mallard up (41x51cm-16x20in) s. 12-Jun-3 Christie's, Kensington #301/R est:2000-3000
£2500 $3950 €3750 Day's bag (51x61cm-20x24in) 28-Nov-2 Christie's, Kensington #367/R est:2000-3000
£3600 $5796 €5400 Red and white setter and a Gordon setter, pointing game in a landscape (39x59cm-15x23in) s. 15-Jan-3 Cheffins Grain & Comins, Cambridge #417/R
£4800 $7584 €7200 Waiting for the keeper (41x51cm-16x20in) s.d.86. 28-Nov-2 Christie's, Kensington #151/R est:3000-4000
£4800 $7440 €7200 Study of a pointer with dead gamebirds and rifle. Study of a setter (49x39cm-19x15in) s. pair. 1-Oct-2 Fellows & Sons, Birmingham #1/R est:1200-1800

GRAF, Carl C (1892-1947) American
£1039 $1600 €1559 Child with watering can (15x20cm-6x8in) board painted c.1930. 8-Sep-2 Treadway Gallery, Cincinnati #621/R est:1500-2500

GRAF, F (19/20th C) German
£4500 $6975 €6750 Panoramic view of Frankfurt with the bridge across the Main to Frankfurt-Sachsenhausen (39x52cm-15x20in) s.d.1827 panel. 30-Oct-2 Christie's, Kensington #71/R est:3000-5000

GRAF, Hans (1654-1710) Austrian
£4403 $6824 €7000 Mountainous river landscape with castle and travellers (48x63cm-19x25in) s. prov. 2-Oct-2 Dorotheum, Vienna #204/R est:7000-10000

GRAF, J (?) ?
£513 $800 €770 Forest scenes (30x41cm-12x16in) panel pair. 14-Sep-2 Weschler, Washington #578/R

GRAF, Ludwig Ferdinand (1868-1932) Austrian
£4114 $6500 €6500 Girl in green dress (83x65cm-33x26in) s.d.1926 lit. 26-Nov-2 Wiener Kunst Auktionen, Vienna #113/R est:4000-8000

£5797 $9507 €8000 Cigale Bay (54x75cm-21x30in) s.d.1926 i.verso canvas on panel lit. 27-May-3 Wiener Kunst Auktionen, Vienna #45/R est:8000-14000
£6757 $10541 €10000 Fencers (101x101cm-40x40in) s.d.1919 canvas on panel lit. 25-Mar-3 Wiener Kunst Auktionen, Vienna #129/R est:6000-9000

GRAF, Oskar (1870-1958) German
£310 $493 €450 Apple blossom by Bodensee near Constance (72x91cm-28x36in) s.d.1948. 8-Mar-3 Arnold, Frankfurt #592/R

GRAF, Otto (1882-?) German
£385 $596 €600 View of Baden on summer day (50x60cm-20x24in) s.d.1922. 6-Dec-2 Michael Zeller, Lindau #773
£755 $1177 €1200 Young herdsman playing flute by the Rhine (45x50cm-18x20in) s.d.1915 board. 11-Oct-2 Winterberg, Heidelberg #1161

GRAF, Philip (1874-?) German
£1351 $2108 €2000 Spring in the Bavarian pre-Alps (70x100cm-28x39in) s.i. 28-Mar-3 Ketterer, Hamburg #38/R est:2200-2500

GRAFF, Anton (1736-1813) German/Swiss
£1871 $3068 €2600 Copies of the two angels from Raffael's Sixtine Madonna (60x48cm-24x19in) two. 4-Jun-3 Reiss & Sohn, Konigstein #140/R est:800
£4277 $6586 €6800 Portrait of Caroline von Westrell (75x58cm-30x23in) canvas on board. 23-Oct-2 Finarte, Rome #449/R
£8333 $13167 €13000 Self portrait (66x53cm-26x21in) prov. 16-Nov-2 Lempertz, Koln #1035/R est:13000
£24000 $40080 €34800 Portrait of Friedrich August, Elector and later King of Saxony (86x68cm-34x27in) s.d.1768 verso prov.exhib.lit. 10-Jul-3 Sotheby's, London #203/R est:10000-15000
£95000 $149150 €142500 Group portrait of the daughters of Johann Julius von Vieth (86x72cm-34x28in) prov.exhib.lit. 11-Dec-2 Christie's, London #75/R est:50000-70000

GRAFTON, Robert W (1876-1936) American
£258 $400 €387 Stevedore, New Orleans Dock scene. Figures (13x13cm-5x5in) pencil sketch double-sided prov. 7-Dec-2 Neal Auction Company, New Orleans #479
£316 $500 €474 Portrait of Mary Fisher (97x102cm-38x40in) s.d. canvas on board. 1-Dec-2 Susanin's, Chicago #5043/R
£2096 $3250 €3144 Venetian canal scene (51x41cm-20x16in) s.d.1905 prov. 7-Dec-2 Neal Auction Company, New Orleans #486/R est:5000-7000
£31410 $49000 €47115 Wash day, the old French court yard, New Orleans (61x51cm-24x20in) s.d.1916. 12-Oct-2 Neal Auction Company, New Orleans #514/R est:12000-18000

GRAGERA, Leopoldo (20th C) Spanish?
£289 $469 €440 Still life with lemons and perdrix (73x60cm-29x24in) s.d.1962. 21-Jan-3 Ansorena, Madrid #862/R

GRAHAM, Anne Marie (1925-) Australian
£690 $1083 €1035 Kuranda Station (39x49cm-15x19in) s.d.1990. 15-Apr-3 Lawson Menzies, Sydney #260/R est:2000-3000 (A.D 1800)
£714 $1121 €1071 Bali scene (47x63cm-19x25in) s.d.77. 25-Nov-2 Christie's, Melbourne #323/R (A.D 2000)
£2326 $3698 €3489 Loved fruit market (155x155cm-61x61in) s.d.94 s.i.verso prov. 5-May-3 Sotheby's, Melbourne #206/R est:6000-9000 (A.D 6000)

GRAHAM, Charles S (attrib) (1852-1911) American
Works on paper
£417 $650 €626 Black man in a tree with Spanish moss, two ladies below (33x25cm-13x10in) s.d.1889 mixed media. 10-Nov-2 Selkirks, St. Louis #824/R

GRAHAM, Colin D (1915-) Canadian
£341 $539 €512 Side street (30x41cm-12x16in) d.1999 acrylic. 1-Dec-2 Levis, Calgary #36/R (C.D 850)
£533 $875 €773 Quiet evening (60x90cm-24x35in) s.i. 9-Jun-3 Hodgins, Calgary #107/R est:1500-2500 (C.D 1200)

GRAHAM, David (1926-) British
£700 $1092 €1050 Monet in his garden (111x61cm-44x24in) s. 27-Mar-3 Christie's, Kensington #609/R

GRAHAM, F (19th C) British?
£1379 $2193 €2000 Hay wagon with figures and horses on a country road. Winter landscape (75x127cm-30x50in) s. pair. 4-Mar-3 Mealy's, Castlecomer #972/R est:2000-3000

GRAHAM, George (1881-1949) British
£250 $408 €375 Nude figures in a wood (25x38cm-10x15in) s. 14-Feb-3 Keys, Aylsham #927
£556 $900 €834 Dock scene (25x36cm-10x14in) s. 24-Jan-3 Freeman, Philadelphia #186/R
£800 $1328 €1200 Wood with two children (31x41cm-12x16in) s. 10-Jun-3 Bonhams, Leeds #179/R
Works on paper
£360 $565 €540 Bolton Castle, Wensleydale (49x74cm-19x29in) s. i.verso pencil W/C. 19-Nov-2 Bonhams, Leeds #66/R

GRAHAM, James Lillie (1873-?) Canadian
£366 $574 €549 Waiting for her husband's return (61x54cm-24x21in) s.d.1913 prov. 10-Dec-2 Pinneys, Montreal #199 (C.D 900)

GRAHAM, Peter (1836-1921) British
£300 $465 €450 Coastal landscape with yachts at sea (28x43cm-11x17in) s.d.1898. 2-Nov-2 Shapes, Edinburgh #305/R
£380 $631 €551 Highland cattle in a mountain landscape (70x90cm-28x35in) s.d.1896. 13-Jun-3 Lyon & Turnbull, Edinburgh #1
£4000 $6360 €6000 As sunshine cleareth mist away (122x92cm-48x36in) s.d.1916 s.i.verso. 6-Mar-3 Christie's, Kensington #92/R est:4000-6000

GRAHAM, Peter (1959-) British
£260 $424 €390 English roses (88x114cm-35x45in) s. 28-Jan-3 Bristol Auction Rooms #463/R
£430 $701 €645 Magical table (92x81cm-36x32in) s. 28-Jan-3 Bristol Auction Rooms #464
£500 $815 €750 Star fruit (93x81cm-37x32in) s. 28-Jan-3 Bristol Auction Rooms #465
£540 $880 €810 Japanese print with flowers (59x74cm-23x29in) s.d.98. 28-Jan-3 Bristol Auction Rooms #467/R

GRAHAM, Robert (1938-) American
Sculpture
£2331 $3800 €3497 Moca, torso (27cm-11in) st.sig. pat bronze. 13-Feb-3 Christie's, Rockefeller NY #266/R
£2404 $3750 €3606 Female torso (28x11x11cm-11x4x4in) s.i. bronze. 14-Oct-2 Butterfields, San Francisco #2102/R est:4000-6000
£3548 $5500 €5322 Untitled (23x61x61cm-9x24x24in) wax wood synthetic fabric in plexiglas box executed 1970 prov. 26-Sep-2 Christie's, Rockefeller NY #781/R est:4000-6000
£7500 $12000 €11250 Single head (46x30x30cm-18x12x12in) bronze copper base executed 1963 prov. 14-May-3 Sotheby's, New York #164/R est:4000-6000
£18987 $30000 €28481 Elisa (147x48x71cm-58x19x28in) polymer plaster copper bronze base executed 1995 prov. 13-Nov-2 Sotheby's, New York #287/R est:20000-30000

GRAHAM, Robert Alexander (1873-1946) American
£3313 $5500 €4804 Melting snow, Colorado foothills, no 7 (63x76cm-25x30in) s. i.verso prov. 11-Jun-3 Butterfields, San Francisco #4124/R est:7000-10000

GRAHAME, Pierre (1938-1996) Belgian
£1013 $1580 €1600 Pensee (64x63cm-25x25in) s.d.70 i.d.verso panel. 16-Oct-2 Hotel des Ventes Mosan, Brussels #269 est:1200-1600

GRAHL, August (1791-1868) German
Miniatures
£1100 $1694 €1650 Emma Natalia von Carlowitz nee von Zehmen (16cm-6xin) init. gilt metal mount leather easel frame rec. 24-Oct-2 Sotheby's, Olympia #97/R est:800-1200

GRAHN, Hjalmar (1882-1949) Swedish
£282 $443 €409 Harbour. prov. 15-Dec-2 Anders Antik, Landskrona #35 (S.KR 4000)
£754 $1177 €1131 View from Slussen (65x54cm-26x21in) s. canvas on board prov. 13-Sep-2 Lilla Bukowskis, Stockholm #478 (S.KR 11000)

GRAILLON, Cesar (1831-?) French
Sculpture
£2857 $4543 €4200 Interior scene (46x33cm-18x13in) s.d.1880 polychrome terracotta relief. 23-Mar-3 Herbette, Doullens #247/R

GRAILLY, Victor de (1804-1889) French
£2188 $3500 €3282 Peasants on a country road with a lake and hills beyond (53x73cm-21x29in) 14-May-3 Butterfields, San Francisco #1105/R est:4000-6000
£4688 $7500 €7032 Landscape with figures and cattle on a path with a waterfall beyond (55x74cm-22x29in) sold with a companion. 14-May-3 Butterfields, San Francisco #1106/R est:8000-12000

GRAILLY, Victor de (attrib) (1804-1889) French
£531 $850 €770 Animated country scene with figures and livestock by a river (55x74cm-22x29in) 16-May-3 Skinner, Boston #53/R
£1321 $2100 €1982 Travelers with livestock on the road overlooking the bay (54x73cm-21x29in) i.verso. 7-Mar-3 Skinner, Boston #281/R est:2000-3000
£1497 $2500 €2171 Washington's house and tomb at Mount Vernon (40x53cm-16x21in) 22-Jun-3 Freeman, Philadelphia #72/R est:2000-3000
£5063 $8000 €7595 The oxbow (46x61cm-18x24in) prov. 24-Apr-3 Shannon's, Milford #127/R est:6000-8000

GRAMATTE, Walter (19/20th C) ?
Works on paper
£11268 $18704 €16000 Self portrait with telegraph poles (49x40cm-19x16in) s.d.21 W/C Indian ink. 14-Jun-3 Hauswedell & Nolte, Hamburg #1208/R est:16000

GRAMMATICA, Antiveduto (1571-1626) Italian
£8974 $13910 €14000 Cleopatra's death (86x70cm-34x28in) 4-Dec-2 Christie's, Rome #447/R est:18000

GRAMMER, George (1898-1982) American
£1763 $2750 €2645 Driftwood (71x91cm-28x36in) 19-Oct-2 David Dike, Dallas #150/R est:1500-3000
Works on paper
£1122 $1750 €1683 Store fronts (38x64cm-15x25in) W/C executed c.1948. 19-Oct-2 David Dike, Dallas #152/R est:1500-3000

GRAN, Daniel (1694-1757) Austrian
£11321 $17547 €18000 The art of war (48x87cm-19x34in) prov.lit. 2-Oct-2 Dorotheum, Vienna #246/R est:18000-25000
Works on paper
£14583 $23188 €21000 St Elisabeth of Portugal giving out alms (32x20cm-13x8in) pen over pencil lit. 5-May-3 Ketterer, Munich #253/R est:1000-1200

GRAN, Enrique (1928-) Spanish
£472 $736 €750 Madrid (10x19cm-4x7in) s. sid1965 verso board. 23-Sep-2 Durán, Madrid #171/R

GRANCHI-TAYLOR, Achille (1857-1921) French
Works on paper
£694 $1132 €1000 Les deux marins (25x19cm-10x7in) s. W/C chl. 19-Jul-3 Thierry & Lannon, Brest #57
£1373 $2211 €1950 Le jeune mousse (34x22cm-13x9in) s. W/C mixed media. 11-May-3 Thierry & Lannon, Brest #84 est:1200-1500

GRAND-CARTERET, Jean Albert (1903-) French
Works on paper
£586 $926 €850 Woman (63x48cm-25x19in) s. pastel. 3-Apr-3 Hagelstam, Helsinki #1016/R

GRANDE, Giovanni (1887-1937) Italian
£1020 $1622 €1500 The Tanaro (69x100cm-27x39in) s.d.1927. 1-Mar-3 Meeting Art, Vercelli #90

GRANDE, Severin (1869-1934) Norwegian
£439 $693 €659 Portrait of Henrik Sorensen (80x61cm-31x24in) s.d.1909. 17-Dec-2 Grev Wedels Plass, Oslo #218 (N.KR 5000)
£600 $937 €900 Norwegian mountain landscape, summer (99x111cm-39x44in) s.d.11. 11-Nov-2 Rasmussen, Vejle #711/R (D.KR 7000)

GRANDEE, Joe (1929-1976) American
£1282 $2000 €1923 Indian Hunters (51x61cm-20x24in) masonite painted c.1973. 19-Oct-2 David Dike, Dallas #200/R est:1000-2000
£3526 $5500 €5289 His last hunt (79x104cm-31x41in) 9-Nov-2 Altermann Galleries, Santa Fe #89
Works on paper
£368 $600 €534 Trail of the long rifles (43x33cm-17x13in) W/C. 18-Jul-3 Du Mouchelle, Detroit #2013/R
£675 $1100 €979 Fast shoot (58x48cm-23x19in) W/C. 18-Jul-3 Du Mouchelle, Detroit #2011/R est:800-1200

GRANDEMANGE, Camille Auguste (attrib) (1875-1934) French
£961 $1499 €1442 Portrait of blonde girl (50x39cm-20x15in) i.d.1900. 6-Nov-2 Dobiaschofsky, Bern #617/R (S.FR 2200)

GRANDGERARD, Lucien Henri (1880-1965) French
£773 $1221 €1160 In the dressing-room (56x46cm-22x18in) s.i.d.1963 verso panel. 29-Nov-2 Zofingen, Switzerland #2457/R (S.FR 1800)
Works on paper
£321 $503 €500 Danseuse (45x37cm-18x15in) s. pastel. 16-Dec-2 Millon & Associes, Paris #23/R
£321 $503 €500 Danseuse devant un miroir (45x37cm-18x15in) s. pastel. 16-Dec-2 Millon & Associes, Paris #24

GRANDHOMME, Paul and MOREAU, Gustave (19th C) French
£35256 $54647 €55000 Plaintes du poete (17x11cm-7x4in) s.i. enamel copper lit. 5-Dec-2 Gros & Delettrez, Paris #88/R est:40000

GRANDI, Francesco de (1968-) Italian
£1338 $2221 €1900 Piattoforma (40x50cm-16x20in) s.i.d.2001 verso. 10-Jun-3 Finarte Semenzato, Milan #354/R est:1500-2000

GRANDI, Giuseppe (1843-1897) Italian
Sculpture
£1290 $2000 €1935 Marshall Ney (30cm-12in) s. brown pat. bronze prov.exhib. 29-Oct-2 Sotheby's, New York #252/R est:2000-3000

GRANDIO, Constantino (1923-1977) Spanish
Works on paper
£315 $492 €460 Donkey (29x19cm-11x7in) s. wash. 8-Apr-3 Ansorena, Madrid #609/R
£483 $768 €700 Vase of flowers (24x15cm-9x6in) s. W/C. 4-Mar-3 Ansorena, Madrid #664

GRANDMAISON, Nickola de (1892-1978) Canadian/Russian
£301 $473 €452 Quiet trail (30x40cm-12x16in) s.i. board. 25-Nov-2 Hodgins, Calgary #340/R (C.D 750)
Works on paper
£370 $577 €616 Untitled - Portrait of a young lady (36x28cm-14x11in) pastel. 13-Apr-3 Levis, Calgary #25b/R (C.D 850)
£597 $919 €896 Tete d'Indien (24x19cm-9x7in) s. pastel chl cardboard. 22-Oct-2 Iegor de Saint Hippolyte, Montreal #25/R (C.D 1450)
£803 $1269 €1205 Portrait of Rev MacLaurin (36x28cm-14x11in) pastel sandpaper. 1-Dec-2 Levis, Calgary #19a/R (C.D 2000)
£2222 $3644 €3222 Mrs Herebert Papisot, beaver bone (31x24cm-12x9in) i. pastel. 9-Jun-3 Hodgins, Calgary #301/R est:4000-5000 (C.D 5000)
£3139 $5022 €4709 Indian portrait (70x53cm-28x21in) s. pastel prov.lit. 15-May-3 Heffel, Vancouver #134/R est:8000-10000 (C.D 7000)
£3213 $5076 €4820 Indian with amulet on cobalt beads (58x48cm-23x19in) pastel sandpaper. 1-Dec-2 Levis, Calgary #18a/R est:10000-12000 (C.D 8000)
£5381 $8610 €8072 Papoose (30x23cm-12x9in) s. pastel prov. 15-May-3 Heffel, Vancouver #133/R est:5500-7500 (C.D 12000)
£11017 $17517 €16526 Indian portrait (58x46cm-23x18in) s. pastel. 23-Mar-3 Hodgins, Calgary #66/R est:8000-12000 (C.D 26000)

GRANDMAISON, Oreste de (1932-1985) Canadian
£400 $656 €580 Pole pine (20x25cm-8x10in) s.i. board. 9-Jun-3 Hodgins, Calgary #343/R (C.D 900)
£413 $644 €689 July storm, Alberta (23x30cm-9x12in) s. canvasboard prov. 13-Apr-3 Levis, Calgary #27 est:900-1200 (C.D 950)
£435 $678 €725 Hidden pool (36x46cm-14x18in) s. s.i.verso hard board. 13-Apr-3 Levis, Calgary #26/R est:900-1200 (C.D 1000)
£622 $1020 €902 Autumn sundown, Alberta (30x40cm-12x16in) s.i. prov. 9-Jun-3 Hodgins, Calgary #296/R est:1100-1400 (C.D 1400)
£667 $1093 €967 Snow caps (35x45cm-14x18in) s. 9-Jun-3 Hodgins, Calgary #200/R est:1100-1400 (C.D 1500)
£723 $1135 €1085 Lilies in late afternoon (40x50cm-16x20in) s.i.d. board. 25-Nov-2 Hodgins, Calgary #350/R (C.D 1800)
£844 $1385 €1224 River scene (55x70cm-22x28in) s. prov. 9-Jun-3 Hodgins, Calgary #35/R est:1500-2000 (C.D 1900)
£844 $1385 €1224 Avalanche snow (35x45cm-14x18in) s.i. board. 9-Jun-3 Hodgins, Calgary #62/R est:1500-2000 (C.D 1900)
£1022 $1676 €1482 Stormy sunset, Alberta (45x60cm-18x24in) s.i. board. 9-Jun-3 Hodgins, Calgary #61/R est:2000-2500 (C.D 2300)
£2034 $3234 €3051 Chinook Alberta (45x60cm-18x24in) s.i. board. 23-Mar-3 Hodgins, Calgary #106/R est:1500-2000 (C.D 4800)

GRANDMOULIN, Leandre (1873-1957) ?
Sculpture
£1218 $1912 €1900 Femme accroupie (120cm-47in) s.d.1909 red pat plaster. 19-Nov-2 Vanderkindere, Brussels #121/R est:750-1000
£3165 $5000 €5000 Mere et enfants (40x45x33cm-16x18x13in) s.d.1912 marble. 26-Nov-2 Palais de Beaux Arts, Brussels #330/R est:5000-7500

GRANDON, Charles (1691-1762) French
£45161 $71355 €70000 Portrait de Leonard Batheon de Vertyrieu (80x65cm-31x26in) s.i.d.1745. 18-Dec-2 Piasa, Paris #65/R est:30000

GRANDSIRE, Pierre Eugène (1825-1905) French
£620 $1011 €930 Harbour at sunset (54x45cm-21x18in) s. chl col chk. 29-Jan-3 Dreweatt Neate, Newbury #22

GRANDVILLE, Jean Ignace (1803-1847) French
Works on paper
£3243 $5059 €4800 Untitled. pen dr set of 11. 27-Mar-3 Maigret, Paris #250/R

GRANELL, Eugenio F (1912-2001) Spanish
£9589 $15055 €14000 Heure d'ete (28x18cm-11x7in) s.d.46 cardboard. 15-Apr-3 Laurence Calmels, Paris #4293/R
£10638 $17234 €15000 Contrabandistas pasando la frontera (38x46cm-15x18in) s.d.1973 prov.exhib. 20-May-3 Segre, Madrid #145/R est:11000
£17123 $26884 €25000 Oiseau edifie son paysage (76x61cm-30x24in) s.d.53. 15-Apr-3 Laurence Calmels, Paris #4294/R est:5000
£19178 $30110 €28000 Head of Indian (71x50cm-28x20in) s.d.44 i.verso. 15-Apr-3 Laurence Calmels, Paris #4295/R

GRANER Y ARRUFI, Luis (1863-1929) Spanish
£5660 $8774 €9000 Dusk in the harbour (77x102cm-30x40in) s. 7-Oct-2 Ansorena, Madrid #55/R
£16000 $25120 €24000 Vista nocturna - night scene (81x93cm-32x37in) s.d.1924. 19-Nov-2 Sotheby's, London #49/R est:6000-8000

GRANER, Ernst (1865-1943) Austrian
Works on paper
£338 $527 €500 Courtyard of house at Schonlaterngasse 7 (32x25cm-13x10in) s.i.d.31 W/C. 28-Mar-3 Dorotheum, Vienna #328/R
£696 $1100 €1100 Karskirche in winter (36x29cm-14x11in) s. W/C. 26-Nov-2 Wiener Kunst Auktionen, Vienna #143/R
£755 $1170 €1200 Entrance to the Oberen Belvedere (30x22cm-12x9in) s.d.11 W/C. 1-Oct-2 Dorotheum, Vienna #258/R
£943 $1462 €1500 Little castle in park (39x51cm-15x20in) s.d.18 W/C board. 1-Oct-2 Dorotheum, Vienna #282/R est:1800-2200
£1013 $1570 €1600 Cafe Fetzer in Vienna (40x52cm-16x20in) s.d.14 W/C htd white. 25-Sep-2 Neumeister, Munich #403/R
£1014 $1581 €1500 Children in village cemetery at Hafnerbach near Melk (48x39cm-19x15in) s. W/C board. 28-Mar-3 Dorotheum, Vienna #292/R est:1600-1800
£1132 $1755 €1800 Plankengasse with Michael Church (26x29cm-10x11in) s. W/C. 1-Oct-2 Dorotheum, Vienna #315/R est:3600-4000
£1258 $1950 €2000 Doorway of old town hall in Wipplingerstrasse (29x20cm-11x8in) s.i. verso W/C. 1-Oct-2 Dorotheum, Vienna #256/R est:3000-3200
£1351 $2108 €2000 Church (15x18cm-6x7in) s.d.1912 W/C. 28-Mar-3 Dorotheum, Vienna #331/R est:800-1000
£2390 $3704 €3800 Petersplatz in Vienna (42x33cm-17x13in) s.d.94 W/C. 1-Oct-2 Dorotheum, Vienna #257/R est:3800-4000
£2436 $3824 €3800 Cecco Beppe strolling (42x55cm-17x22in) s. W/C. 10-Dec-2 Della Rocca, Turin #365/R est:3000
£2830 $4387 €4500 Lusthaus in the Prater (27x43cm-11x17in) s. W/C. 1-Oct-2 Dorotheum, Vienna #243/R est:4000-4500
£4717 $7311 €7500 Main square in Perchtoldsdorf (52x69cm-20x27in) s.d.1909 W/C board. 1-Oct-2 Dorotheum, Vienna #251/R est:6500-8500

GRANERI, Giovanni Michele (circle) (18th C) Italian
£10000 $16700 €14500 Elegant family beside a gig, with peasants making merry outside an inn (72x98cm-28x39in) mono. 11-Jul-3 Christie's, Kensington #247/R est:6000-8000

GRANET, François Marius (1775-1849) French
£1560 $2418 €2340 L'escalier du vouvent (19x14cm-7x6in) panel. 4-Dec-2 AB Stockholms Auktionsverk #2043/R est:10000-15000 (S.KR 22000)
£7692 $12154 €12000 L'interieur de couvent de la Place Barberini a Rome (129x98cm-51x39in) prov.lit. 18-Nov-2 Tajan, Paris #3/R est:12000-15000
Works on paper
£2025 $3200 €3200 Une moine mendiant. Arche. Paysage. Ane. Moine priant. Homme (12x8cm-5x3in) i.verso pen brown ink brown wash W/C six on one mount. 27-Nov-2 Christie's, Paris #238/R est:2000-3000
£2564 $3974 €4000 Prise d'habit de M.lle de Lavalliere (23x39cm-9x15in) W/C over pen. 4-Dec-2 Libert, Castor, Paris #32/R
£5068 $7905 €7500 Moines admirant le coucher de soleil (13x19cm-5x7in) s. pen ink wash over crayon. 26-Mar-3 Piasa, Paris #66/R

GRANET, François Marius (attrib) (1775-1849) French
£4500 $7515 €6750 Interior of the choir in the Capuchin Church in Piazza Barbrini, Rome (100x75cm-39x30in) 18-Jun-3 Christie's, Kensington #152/R est:6000-8000

GRANFELT, Erik (1919-1990) Finnish
£358 $552 €570 Two women (25x20cm-10x8in) s. painted 1966. 24-Oct-2 Hagelstam, Helsinki #1062
£563 $907 €800 Still life of knife and orange (54x73cm-21x29in) 10-May-3 Bukowskis, Helsinki #216/R
£915 $1501 €1400 Boy sitting down (91x72cm-36x28in) s.d.66. 9-Feb-3 Bukowskis, Helsinki #240/R

GRANQUIST, Karl (?) Swedish
£823 $1284 €1235 Calm (24x30cm-9x12in) s.d.68 prov. 13-Sep-2 Lilla Bukowskis, Stockholm #452 (S.KR 12000)

GRANT, A (?) British
Works on paper
£650 $1021 €975 View of Christchurch Bay with Highcliffe Castle (20x27cm-8x11in) s.d.1783 W/C. 16-Apr-3 George Kidner, Lymington #92/R
£1400 $2198 €2100 View of Christchurch Bay with figures on the cliffs at Highcliffe (35x52cm-14x20in) W/C. 16-Apr-3 George Kidner, Lymington #93/R est:1500-2500
£2200 $3454 €3300 View of Highcliffe Castle with horse and carriage on the drive (47x64cm-19x25in) W/C. 16-Apr-3 George Kidner, Lymington #94/R est:2500-3500

GRANT, Alistair (1925-) British
£1300 $2002 €1950 Boulogne I (122x122cm-48x48in) s.i.verso exhib. 5-Sep-2 Christie's, Kensington #751/R est:1500-2000

GRANT, Blanche (1874-1948) American
£1603 $2500 €2405 Touch me not mountain (51x41cm-20x16in) s. i. verso board prov.lit. 9-Nov-2 Santa Fe Art, Santa Fe #182/R est:3500-4000

GRANT, Carleton (fl.1885-1899) British
Works on paper
£280 $434 €420 Beach at high tide (30x18cm-12x7in) s.d.1896 W/C htd white. 4-Dec-2 Christie's, Kensington #60
£320 $496 €480 Tarring the hull before Conway Castle (41x86cm-16x34in) s. W/C. 26-Sep-2 Lane, Penzance #138
£440 $695 €660 Sunlight and shadow (15x22cm-6x9in) s.d.1901 W/C htd white. 26-Nov-2 Bonhams, Knightsbridge #192/R
£560 $874 €812 Rowing boats in a harbour (18x28cm-7x11in) s.d.98 W/C bodycol. 3-Jul-3 Duke & Son, Dorchester #89/R
£650 $1073 €943 Fisherman mending a net by the shore (28x43cm-11x17in) s.d.98 W/C bodycol. 3-Jul-3 Duke & Son, Dorchester #90/R
£900 $1403 €1350 Low tide in Llandudno, Wales (19x28cm-7x11in) s.d.1897 pencil W/C htd white. 19-Sep-2 Christie's, Kensington #162/R est:500-700

GRANT, Donald (1930-) British
£1656 $2699 €2500 Rhinoceros (66x105cm-26x41in) s. 28-Jan-3 Dorotheum, Vienna #202/R est:2600-3000
£2000 $3100 €3000 Serval cat (25x30cm-10x12in) s. board prov. 4-Dec-2 Christie's, Kensington #478/R est:600-800
£3800 $5928 €5700 Elephant emerging (71x117cm-28x46in) s. 27-Mar-3 Christie's, Kensington #542/R est:4000-6000
£4200 $6930 €6090 Tiger - distinguished company (71x147cm-28x58in) s. prov. 3-Jul-3 Christie's, Kensington #509/R est:3000-5000
£4500 $7425 €6525 Tiger growling (51x76cm-20x30in) s. 3-Jul-3 Christie's, Kensington #510/R est:3000-4000
£5900 $9145 €8850 Pair of eland (61x91cm-24x36in) s. prov. 4-Dec-2 Christie's, Kensington #477/R est:2000-3000
£12000 $18600 €18000 Cheetah (60x89cm-24x35in) s. 4-Dec-2 Christie's, Kensington #479/R est:2000-3000
£20000 $32800 €30000 Herd of elephants (101x152cm-40x60in) s. 3-Jun-3 Sotheby's, Olympia #156/R est:10000-15000

GRANT, Duncan (1885-1978) British
£2000 $3160 €3000 Spanish dancers (145x112cm-57x44in) board. 27-Nov-2 Sotheby's, Olympia #238/R est:2000-3000
£2000 $3120 €3000 Study of Clive Bell at Charleston Manor (27x26cm-11x10in) s. oil paper on board. 27-Mar-3 Christie's, Kensington #428 est:1000-1500
£3800 $5928 €5700 Roman model (62x48cm-24x19in) s.i.d.1935 board prov. 27-Mar-3 Christie's, Kensington #431/R est:3000-5000

£4200 $6552 €6300 Harbour with a figure and boats (41x51cm-16x20in) s.d.1924 canvas on board prov. 10-Apr-3 Tennants, Leyburn #1129/R est:1500-2000
£5000 $7950 €7500 Auxerre (36x45cm-14x18in) s. indis d. board. 26-Feb-3 Sotheby's, Olympia #250/R est:5000-7000
£6500 $10140 €9750 Gazebo, Charleston (56x46cm-22x18in) init. i.d.1942 verso prov. 27-Mar-3 Christie's, Kensington #479/R est:5000-7000
£12500 $20500 €18750 Under the vine (76x51cm-30x20in) s.d.46 prov. 6-Jun-3 Christie's, London #24/R est:7000-10000
£13000 $21320 €19500 Woodland (63x44cm-25x17in) board painted c.1912 prov.exhib. 6-Jun-3 Christie's, London #20/R est:6000-8000
£19000 $29450 €28500 Flowers against abstract (74x60cm-29x24in) s.d.69 prov.exhib. 4-Dec-2 Sotheby's, London #71/R est:15000-20000

Works on paper
£320 $509 €480 Still life of ornaments (46x30cm-18x12in) s.d.74 W/C. 29-Apr-3 Gorringes, Lewes #2051
£400 $624 €600 Reclining male nude (54x74cm-21x29in) pencil gouache paper on canvas. 15-Oct-2 Bonhams, Knightsbridge #214/R
£550 $858 €825 Standing male nude (60x36cm-24x14in) init.d.48 chl. 15-Oct-2 Bonhams, Knightsbridge #153/R
£650 $1034 €975 Design for a fan (30x54cm-12x21in) s. pencil oil. 26-Feb-3 Sotheby's, Olympia #182/R
£650 $1014 €975 Firle place design (25x12cm-10x5in) pencil gouache executed 1950 prov. 27-Mar-3 Christie's, Kensington #354/R
£900 $1395 €1350 Still life with jug and knife (44x60cm-17x24in) s.d.60 pencil crayon W/C bodycol prov. 4-Dec-2 Christie's, Kensington #277/R
£900 $1404 €1350 Two figures on a beach (38x55cm-15x22in) s.d.29 W/C crayon. 27-Mar-3 Christie's, Kensington #276/R
£1100 $1716 €1650 Two nude figures with dog (13x25cm-5x10in) s.d.66 W/C pen. 15-Oct-2 Bonhams, Knightsbridge #121/R est:700-1000
£1300 $2171 €1885 Study for boys leapfrogging (55x37cm-22x15in) gouache black chk. 24-Jun-3 Bonhams, New Bond Street #29/R est:1500-2000
£1500 $2475 €2175 Madonna and child with musicians (58x47cm-23x19in) s.i.d.1925 pencil W/C bodycol. 3-Jul-3 Christie's, Kensington #265/R est:1000-1500
£2000 $3100 €3000 Madonna and Christ with musicians (48x46cm-19x18in) init.d.25 i.verso crayon W/C prov. 4-Dec-2 Christie's, Kensington #243/R est:2000-3000
£3200 $5056 €4800 Picnic (34x51cm-13x20in) s. gouache col crayon executed c.1928 prov.exhib. 27-Nov-2 Sotheby's, Olympia #32/R est:1500-2000
£3500 $5425 €5250 Seated nude (26x20cm-10x8in) init. black biro W/C bodycol and another W/C by the same hand. 4-Dec-2 Christie's, Kensington #246/R est:1500-2000

GRANT, Duncan (attrib) (1885-1978) British
£300 $489 €435 Two standing nudes (43x27cm-17x11in) board. 15-Jul-3 Bonhams, Knightsbridge #173

GRANT, Frederick M (1886-1959) American
£3065 $4750 €4598 Gypsy wagon (76x76cm-30x30in) s. painted c.1920. 8-Dec-2 Toomey, Oak Park #681/R est:6000-8000
£9740 $15000 €14610 Japanese screen (102x127cm-40x50in) s. painted c.1920. 8-Sep-2 Treadway Gallery, Cincinnati #577b/R est:15000-25000

GRANT, Gordon (1875-1962) American
£4013 $6100 €6020 Turn of the tide, New England harbour (64x76cm-25x30in) s. 17-Aug-2 North East Auctions, Portsmouth #1094/R est:5000-8000
£4276 $6500 €6414 Clipper ship (56x97cm-22x38in) s. 17-Aug-2 North East Auctions, Portsmouth #1092/R est:5000-8000

Works on paper
£290 $475 €421 Man reading newspaper with seated woman in an interior (29x39cm-11x15in) s. pen ink wash. 5-Jun-3 Swann Galleries, New York #107/R
£4717 $7500 €7076 Lobsterman in a dory (30x46cm-12x18in) s.d.1938 W/C. 1-Mar-3 North East Auctions, Portsmouth #763/R

GRANT, Ian Macdonald (1904-1993) British
Works on paper
£750 $1170 €1125 Two nudes (56x44cm-22x17in) s.d.1946 col chk. 12-Sep-2 Sotheby's, Olympia #90/R

GRANT, J Jeffrey (1883-1960) American
£313 $500 €470 Street scene (33x38cm-13x15in) s. canvasboard. 11-Jan-3 Susanin's, Chicago #5020/R
£313 $500 €470 Salamanca (33x38cm-13x15in) s. canvasboard. 11-Jan-3 Susanin's, Chicago #5021/R
£2250 $3600 €3375 Summer cottages (76x91cm-30x36in) s. 11-Jan-3 Susanin's, Chicago #5019/R est:2000-3000

Works on paper
£313 $500 €470 Sailboat (41x33cm-16x13in) s. W/C. 11-Jan-3 Susanin's, Chicago #5022/R

GRANT, James Ardern (1885-1973) British
£700 $1148 €1050 Portrait of Helen Rostron (76x51cm-30x20in) s. exhib. 3-Jun-3 Sotheby's, Olympia #53/R

GRANT, Keith (1930-) British
£850 $1352 €1275 Reflections in a lake night (100x121cm-39x48in) 18-Mar-3 Bonhams, Knightsbridge #81

Works on paper
£350 $578 €508 Sunset forest lake (53x79cm-21x31in) mixed media prov. 3-Jul-3 Christie's, Kensington #553

GRANT, Sir Francis (1810-1878) British
£15000 $23850 €22500 John Drlyell, Master of the Puckeridge hounds on a bay hunter with a hound in a landscape (61x84cm-24x33in) prov. 19-Mar-3 Sotheby's, London #116/R est:15000-20000

GRANUM, Einar (1920-1992) Norwegian
£519 $820 €779 Child sitting on a potty (61x50cm-24x20in) s.d.52 panel. 2-Dec-2 Blomqvist, Oslo #429/R (N.KR 6000)

GRANVAL, Charles (19/20th C) ?
£524 $828 €786 Market scene in Tunis (46x33cm-18x13in) s.i.d.1890. 14-Nov-2 Stuker, Bern #263/R (S.FR 1200)

GRAOVAC, Nikola (1907-) Yugoslavian
£1418 $2255 €2127 Summer afternoon (55x66cm-22x26in) s.cyrillic. 8-Mar-3 Dorotheum, Prague #155/R est:28000-42000 (C.KR 65000)

GRARD, Georges (1901-1984) Belgian
Sculpture
£1026 $1590 €1600 Femme assise arrangeant sa coiffure (19cm-7in) s. bronze executed 1942 lit. 3-Dec-2 Christie's, Amsterdam #52/R est:1200-1600

GRASDORP, Willem (1678-1723) Dutch
£8805 $13648 €14000 Still life (67x56cm-26x22in) prov.lit. 2-Oct-2 Dorotheum, Vienna #120/R est:14000-18000

GRASHOF, Otto (1812-1876) German
£4487 $7045 €7000 Mounted cossacks (146x103cm-57x41in) s.d.1840. 21-Nov-2 Van Ham, Cologne #1640/R est:12000

Works on paper
£1410 $2214 €2200 Portraits of Moorish soldiers (20x15cm-8x6in) mono.i. W/C pastel prov. two. 21-Nov-2 Van Ham, Cologne #1639 est:3000

GRASMAIR, Johann Georg Dominikus (1690-1751) Austrian
£641 $1006 €1000 Crowning Madonna through the Holy Trinity with four worshipping Saints (31x18cm-12x7in) i.verso en grisaille canvas on board. 21-Nov-2 Dorotheum, Vienna #54/R
£705 $1107 €1100 Blessed Virgin with Child with worshipping from four saints (35x21cm-14x8in) i.verso en grisaille canvas on board. 21-Nov-2 Dorotheum, Vienna #53/R

GRASS-MICK (1873-1963) French
£1027 $1603 €1500 Paysage corse (65x50cm-26x20in) 8-Apr-3 Gioffredo, Nice #177

Works on paper
£342 $534 €500 Moulin rouge (22x17cm-9x7in) col crayon dr. 8-Apr-3 Gioffredo, Nice #173

GRASS-MICK, Augustin (1873-1963) French
£1090 $1689 €1700 Portrait de Cezanne (49x32cm-19x13in) init.i. cardboard. 9-Dec-2 Beaussant & Lefèvre, Paris #51/R
£1259 $2102 €1800 Animation dans un rue a Menton (26x24cm-10x9in) mono.i. isorel. 26-Jun-3 Tajan, Paris #211/R est:2000-3000

Works on paper
£1053 $1705 €1600 La nuit chez bruant (21x27cm-8x11in) s.i. Indian ink wash W/C prov. 22-Jan-3 Tajan, Paris #40/R est:2000-3000

GRASSEL, Franz (1861-1948) German
£901 $1405 €1352 Cottage interior with woman by window (60x50cm-24x20in) s.d.1888. 11-Nov-2 Rasmussen, Vejle #697/R (D.KR 10500)
£2745 $4502 €4200 Black Forest woman in room (60x49cm-24x19in) s. bears d.1882. 8-Feb-3 Hans Stahl, Hamburg #18/R est:4800
£2949 $4571 €4600 Five white ducks on pond (22x32cm-9x13in) s. board. 6-Dec-2 Michael Zeller, Lindau #772/R est:500

GRASSERE, Gerard Joseph (1915-1993) Dutch
£321 $497 €500 Mother and child (40x50cm-16x20in) s. s.d.1934 verso. 3-Dec-2 Christie's, Amsterdam #325/R
£321 $497 €500 Aanbidding (49x39cm-19x15in) s. 3-Dec-2 Christie's, Amsterdam #329/R
£556 $917 €800 Fireplace (28x32cm-11x13in) s.d.40 prov. 1-Jul-3 Christie's, Amsterdam #363/R
£609 $944 €950 House in a landscape (50x60cm-20x24in) s. s.verso. 3-Dec-2 Christie's, Amsterdam #326/R
£897 $1391 €1400 Moulin rouge (40x50cm-16x20in) s. board. 3-Dec-2 Christie's, Amsterdam #327/R est:1000-1500
£2105 $3411 €3200 Girl at a table with fruits and a teapot (70x80cm-28x31in) s. board. 21-Jan-3 Christie's, Amsterdam #469/R est:2000-3000
Works on paper
£321 $497 €500 Schipbreuk - shipwreck (27x34cm-11x13in) s.d.55 gouache W/C prov. 3-Dec-2 Christie's, Amsterdam #331/R
£481 $745 €750 Clowns (33x21cm-13x8in) s.d.51 gouache. 3-Dec-2 Christie's, Amsterdam #328/R
£641 $994 €1000 Woman with bottle (47x37cm-19x15in) gouache prov. 3-Dec-2 Christie's, Amsterdam #330/R est:500-700

GRASSET, Edmond (1852-1880) French
£1722 $2790 €2497 Young well dressed couple looking at marble sculptures, Louvre (55x46cm-22x18in) s. 26-May-3 Rasmussen, Copenhagen #1337/R est:15000 (D.KR 18000)

GRASSET, Eugène (1841-1917) Swiss
£1154 $1812 €1800 View of Venice (41x62cm-16x24in) init. board. 16-Dec-2 Pandolfini, Florence #98/R

GRASSI, Nicola (1662-1748) Italian
Works on paper
£743 $1159 €1100 Immaculate Conception (31x22cm-12x9in) chk. 27-Mar-3 Christie's, Paris #39/R

GRASSI, Nicola (attrib) (1662-1748) Italian
£12329 $19233 €18000 Jacob watering Laban's herd (65x83cm-26x33in) prov. 10-Apr-3 Schopman, Hamburg #574 est:7000

GRASSI, Teresa (1878-?) Italian
£274 $427 €400 Naples with boats on beach (12x21cm-5x8in) s. panel. 10-Apr-3 Van Ham, Cologne #1450

GRASSL, Otto (1891-?) German
£390 $569 €600 Musicians (32x23cm-13x9in) s. lit. 14-Jun-2 Auktionhaus Georg Rehm, Augsburg #8037/R

GRASSMANN, Gunther (1900-1993) German
£1370 $2137 €2000 Children playing in the snow in front of a house (74x60cm-29x24in) s.d.29 lit. 10-Apr-3 Allgauer, Kempten #2783/R est:3400

GRASSO, Alfio (1945-) Italian
£327 $523 €500 Masks (90x100cm-35x39in) s. s.i.verso. 4-Jan-3 Meeting Art, Vercelli #716

GRASSY, Giuseppe (1755-1838) Austrian
£2785 $4344 €4400 Bather (30x40cm-12x16in) bears sig. copper. 14-Sep-2 Bergmann, Erlangen #717/R est:4000
Miniatures
£4200 $6888 €6090 Holy Roman Empress Maria Ludovica, holding a letter addressed to her brother (7cm-3xin) i. ormolu frame oval. 3-Jun-3 Christie's, London #84/R est:3000-5000

GRATCHEFF, Alexei Petrovitch (1780-1850) Russian
Sculpture
£1757 $2741 €2600 Troika (11cm-4in) i. brown pat.bronze Cast.C.F.Woerffel St Petersburg. 25-Mar-3 Dorotheum, Vienna #181/R est:2000-3000

GRATCHEFF, Georgi (attrib) (1860-1893) Russian
Sculpture
£3659 $6000 €5306 Russian warrior after battle (64x56x3cm-25x22x1in) s.i. bronze. 7-Jun-3 Neal Auction Company, New Orleans #71/R est:4000-6000

GRATE, Eric (1896-1983) Swedish
Sculpture
£1977 $3124 €2966 Spring (58cm-23in) s. green pat.bronze st.f.H Bergman sold with stone socle. 28-Apr-3 Bukowskis, Stockholm #238/R est:12000-15000 (S.KR 26000)
£4485 $6996 €6728 Duo - Dido and Aeneas (41cm-16in) s.d.1929 pat.bronze incl. stone base st.f.Bergman lit. 6-Nov-2 AB Stockholms Auktionsverk #614/R est:25000-30000 (S.KR 64000)
£4563 $7209 €6845 Navigare necesse est (36cm-14in) s.num.4/6 dark pat.bronze st.f.H Bergman cire perdue marble socle. 28-Apr-3 Bukowskis, Stockholm #240/R est:40000-50000 (S.KR 60000)
£5256 $8199 €7884 Sparrow god (48cm-19in) s.i.num.1/4 pat.bronze st.f.Valsuani cire perdue prov.exhib.lit. 6-Nov-2 AB Stockholms Auktionsverk #626/R est:100000-120000 (S.KR 75000)
£6564 $10568 €9846 Mediterranean idols (41cm-16in) s.num.2/4 pat.bronze incl. stone socle sf.f.Bergman cire perdue. 7-May-3 AB Stockholms Auktionsverk #721/R est:30000-35000 (S.KR 85000)
Works on paper
£927 $1492 €1391 King Ubu preparing for his entrance (33x23cm-13x9in) s. gouache wash. 7-May-3 AB Stockholms Auktionsverk #836/R (S.KR 12000)

GRATHWOL, Ray Anthony (1900-1992) American
£224 $350 €336 Tranquility (61x91cm-24x36in) s. board. 28-Mar-3 Aspire, Cleveland #36/R
£227 $350 €341 Untitled (58x43cm-23x17in) s. board. 25-Oct-2 Aspire, Cleveland #26
£259 $420 €389 Twilight landscape (46x61cm-18x24in) board. 23-Jan-3 Aspire, Cleveland #25

GRATTAN, George (1787-1819) British
£4730 $7378 €7000 Labourers return (34x39cm-13x15in) panel lit. 26-Mar-3 James Adam, Dublin #14/R est:4000-6000

GRATZ, Theodor (1859-1947) German
£881 $1374 €1400 Ammersee with Kloster Andechs in autumn (44x62cm-17x24in) s. 21-Sep-2 Bolland & Marotz, Bremen #485/R

GRAU SANTOS, Julian (1937-) Spanish
£881 $1356 €1400 Self-portrait at the piano (54x46cm-21x18in) s.d.72 cardboard exhib. 22-Oct-2 Durán, Madrid #164/R
£1053 $1705 €1600 Portrait of young woman (56x46cm-22x18in) s. 21-Jan-3 Ansorena, Madrid #157/R
£1346 $2127 €2100 Portrait of young woman (56x46cm-22x18in) s. s.i.verso. 13-Nov-2 Ansorena, Madrid #101/R
£2411 $3906 €3400 Frutas y flores (33x24cm-13x9in) s. prov. 20-May-3 Segre, Madrid #162/R est:2100
£2872 $4480 €4250 Interior with flowers and fruit (81x65cm-32x26in) s.d.93-94. 25-Mar-3 Durán, Madrid #190/R
£6897 $10897 €10000 Garden (73x92cm-29x36in) s. prov. 1-Apr-3 Segre, Madrid #167/R est:7500
Works on paper
£331 $526 €480 Square (51x38cm-20x15in) s.d.74 W/C gouache. 4-Mar-3 Ansorena, Madrid #659/R

GRAU, Ricardo (1907-1970) Peruvian
£4487 $6955 €7000 Ofrenda (62x83cm-24x33in) s. 9-Dec-2 Horta, Bruxelles #214/R est:8000-12000

GRAU-SALA, Emile (1911-1975) Spanish
£3871 $6116 €6000 Interior with flowers (28x33cm-11x13in) s. s.i.d.1967 verso cardboard. 17-Dec-2 Durán, Madrid #128/R
£6000 $9480 €9300 Cafe Charbon (37x45cm-15x18in) s. 18-Dec-2 Ansorena, Madrid #77/R
£7595 $12000 €12000 Music lesson (70x35cm-28x14in) s. i.d.1960 verso. 2-Dec-2 Tajan, Paris #153/R
£9000 $14310 €13500 Le port d'Honfleur (54x73cm-21x29in) s. painted c.1950. 20-Mar-3 Sotheby's, Olympia #135/R est:6000-8000
£9259 $13148 €15000 Nympheas (33x46cm-13x18in) s. 16-Mar-3 Eric Pillon, Calais #180/R
£9615 $15096 €15000 Apres-midi en musique (81x30cm-32x12in) s.d.1957 verso. 15-Dec-2 Eric Pillon, Calais #190/R
£9936 $15599 €15500 Rue de village pavoisee (33x55cm-13x22in) s. 13-Dec-2 Piasa, Paris #22/R est:9000
£11392 $18000 €18000 Coucher de soleil sur la Baie de Cannes (40x70cm-16x28in) s. 2-Dec-2 Tajan, Paris #152/R
£12057 $19532 €17000 Les lapins roses et blancs (54x65cm-21x26in) s. s.i.d.verso. 21-May-3 Cornette de St.Cyr, Paris #95/R est:5000-20000
£13423 $21611 €20000 Trois coquettes (41x33cm-16x13in) s.d.39 board. 18-Feb-3 Durán, Madrid #234/R est:17000
£14103 $22282 €22000 Conversation in the garden (61x50cm-24x20in) s. prov. 15-Nov-2 Laurence Calmels, Paris #18a/R est:20000
£15000 $23100 €22500 Les jumelles (73x60cm-29x24in) s. 22-Oct-2 Sotheby's, London #166/R est:12000-15000
£15068 $23507 €22000 Circus in the park (61x88cm-24x35in) s. 8-Apr-3 Ansorena, Madrid #231/R est:19500
£15385 $25693 €22000 Les repasseuses (50x61cm-20x24in) s. s.i.d.verso prov. 26-Jun-3 Tajan, Paris #285/R est:23000-25000

£16149 $26000 €24224 La reussite (51x65cm-20x26in) s. s.i.d.1959 verso prov. 7-May-3 Sotheby's, New York #410/R est:20000-30000
£16197 $26887 €23000 Chez le Bougnat, Paris (55x47cm-22x19in) s. s.i.d.verso. 15-Jun-3 Anaf, Lyon #96/R est:22000-26000
£16456 $25506 €26000 Jeune fille preparant un bouquet de fleurs (65x54cm-26x21in) s. 29-Sep-2 Eric Pillon, Calais #252/R
£19000 $29260 €28500 Courses a Deauville (54x65cm-21x26in) s. s.i.verso. 22-Oct-2 Sotheby's, London #165/R est:15000-20000
£20513 $32205 €32000 Gouter en famille (55x65cm-22x26in) s.d.1969 verso. 15-Dec-2 Eric Pillon, Calais #188/R
£24000 $40080 €34800 Place a Paris (50x100cm-20x39in) s. 24-Jun-3 Sotheby's, London #198/R est:18000-20000
£25000 $40000 €36250 Two young girls at the piano (99x81cm-39x32in) s. 17-May-3 Selkirks, St. Louis #250/R est:15000-20000
£31447 $49057 €50000 Three graces (81x65cm-32x26in) s.i.d.37. 23-Sep-2 Durán, Madrid #202/R est:45000

Works on paper

£316 $500 €500 Hommage a Raoul Dufy (23x29cm-9x11in) s.d.1965 ink collage dr. 27-Nov-2 Blanchet, Paris #104
£606 $958 €940 Figures (24x27cm-9x11in) s. W/C gouache. 18-Dec-2 Ansorena, Madrid #264/R
£613 $968 €950 Young woman (13x12cm-5x5in) s. ink dr. 18-Dec-2 Ansorena, Madrid #957/R
£685 $1075 €1000 Etude de portraits (35x25cm-14x10in) s.i.d.decembre 1974 W/C. 21-Apr-3 Raboudin & Choppin de Janvry, Paris #190
£1069 $1668 €1700 Reclining female nude (28x22cm-11x9in) s. col dr. 23-Sep-2 Durán, Madrid #134/R
£1144 $1842 €1750 Femme dans un interieur (37x26cm-15x10in) s. W/C. 14-Jan-3 Vanderkindere, Brussels #114 est:1500-2500
£1161 $1835 €1800 Lady with bird (20x28cm-8x11in) s.d.1936 W/C pastel pencil. 17-Dec-2 Segre, Madrid #112/R
£1195 $1840 €1900 Spring (38x29cm-15x11in) s. gouache lit. 22-Oct-2 Durán, Madrid #148/R
£1748 $2919 €2500 Jeune fille s'appretant (38x26cm-15x10in) s. gouache. 26-Jun-3 Tajan, Paris #150 est:1200-1500
£2387 $3772 €3700 First trip of Wagner to Paris (21x15cm-8x6in) W/C. 18-Dec-2 Ansorena, Madrid #234/R
£3691 $5943 €5500 At the races (24x31cm-9x12in) s.d.62 W/C gouache. 18-Feb-3 Durán, Madrid #215/R
£3691 $5943 €5500 Seashore (54x44cm-21x17in) s. gouache. 18-Feb-3 Durán, Madrid #240/R
£3871 $6116 €6000 Looking at the sea (47x63cm-19x25in) s.d.1971 W/C. 17-Dec-2 Durán, Madrid #218/R
£4730 $7378 €7000 Marchande de fleurs (48x28cm-19x11in) s.i.d.1946 W/C gouache. 28-Mar-3 Claude Aguttes, Neuilly #132b/R est:6000
£5513 $8600 €8270 Parisian park (65x47cm-26x19in) s.d.36 gouache. 20-Sep-2 Sloan, North Bethesda #403/R est:2000-3000
£6250 $9750 €9375 French village (55x45cm-22x18in) s.d.36 gouache. 20-Sep-2 Sloan, North Bethesda #404/R est:2000-3000
£8176 $12673 €13000 Scene de cirque (37x45cm-15x18in) s. pastel gouache. 30-Oct-2 Artcurial Briest, Paris #337/R est:12000-15000
£9119 $14135 €14500 Femme nue devant le miroir (85x65cm-33x26in) s. pastel paper on canvas. 7-Oct-2 Claude Aguttes, Neuilly #214/R
£9434 $14717 €15000 Tailor's study (49x64cm-19x25in) s.d.37 gouache. 23-Sep-2 Durán, Madrid #194/R est:15000
£13245 $21589 €20000 Circus (37x45cm-15x18in) s. mixed media board. 11-Feb-3 Segre, Madrid #153/R est:19000

GRAUBNER, Gotthard (1930-) German

£4487 $7090 €7000 Nimisis (27x27cm-11x11in) s.i.d.1996 verso acrylic oil linen on foam cushion. 14-Nov-2 Neumeister, Munich #783/R est:6200-7000

Works on paper

£566 $906 €849 Untitled (48x49cm-19x19in) s.d. W/C. 17-Mar-3 Philippe Schuler, Zurich #4035 est:1500-1800 (S.FR 1200)

GRAUER, William C (1896-1985) American

£288 $450 €432 Medieval, Spanish and Moorish faces (58x89cm-23x35in) s. board exhib. 28-Mar-3 Aspire, Cleveland #27/R
£941 $1450 €1412 Untitled (122x91cm-48x36in) acrylic board. 25-Oct-2 Aspire, Cleveland #17 est:1800-2200

GRAUSS, Geert (1882-1929) Dutch

£7801 $12638 €11000 Female sitting in front of a mirror (100x75cm-39x30in) s.d.18. 26-May-3 Glerum, Amsterdam #58/R est:5500-6500

GRAUVOGEL, Georg (20th C) German

£270 $422 €400 Rottach-Egern with Tegernsee (91x70cm-36x28in) 26-Mar-3 Hugo Ruef, Munich #110

GRAVE, Josua de (17/18th C) Dutch

Works on paper

£306 $477 €480 Military encampment near Mont Saint Andre (15x19cm-6x7in) s.id.1675 pen brown ink grey wash prov. 5-Nov-2 Sotheby's, Amsterdam #117/R

GRAVEL, Francine (1944-) Canadian

£192 $303 €288 Jeux d'enfants (46x61cm-18x24in) s.d.1995 s.i.d.verso prov. 14-Nov-2 Heffel, Vancouver #182 (C.D 475)
£402 $635 €603 Learning to fly (61x51cm-24x20in) d.1986 oil mixed media. 1-Dec-2 Levis, Calgary #37/R (C.D 1000)
£649 $1032 €941 Heralds of spring (102x152cm-40x60in) s.d.1995. 1-May-3 Heffel, Vancouver #40/R (C.D 1500)

GRAVEROL, A (1865-1949) French

Works on paper

£256 $400 €384 Woman as a grapevine, ready for harvest (13x25cm-5x10in) init. W/C. 28-Mar-3 Aspire, Cleveland #52/R
£256 $400 €384 Whimsical image of a woman in green, strung as an instrument (10x20cm-4x8in) init. W/C. 28-Mar-3 Aspire, Cleveland #53/R
£256 $400 €384 Beauty in a garden, surrounded by apple blossoms, Cupid and winged heads (15x25cm-6x10in) init. W/C. 28-Mar-3 Aspire, Cleveland #54/R
£304 $475 €456 Four beauties, each girl with different coloured hair, walking next to a pond (18x25cm-7x10in) init. W/C. 28-Mar-3 Aspire, Cleveland #55/R

GRAVES, Abbott Fuller (1859-1936) American

£1210 $1900 €1815 New England fisherman with white beard and tattoo, and young girl (51x46cm-20x18in) s. 19-Apr-3 James Julia, Fairfield #193/R est:3000-5000
£25806 $40000 €38709 Roses (51x61cm-20x24in) s. 5-Dec-2 Christie's, Rockefeller NY #41/R est:20000-30000
£30864 $50000 €46296 Gardener (70x50cm-28x20in) s. 22-May-3 Christie's, Rockefeller NY #40/R est:50000-70000

Works on paper

£1474 $2300 €2211 Untitled (33x25cm-13x10in) s. pastel graphite. 20-Sep-2 Du Mouchelle, Detroit #2106/R est:1000-1500
£1635 $2600 €2453 Tropical landscape, Bermuda (40x25cm-16x10in) s. pastel. 7-Mar-3 Skinner, Boston #403/R est:3000-5000
£5346 $8500 €8019 End of the garden (33x51cm-13x20in) s. i.verso W/C board prov. 5-Mar-3 Sotheby's, New York #1/R est:12000-18000

GRAVES, Abbott Fuller (attrib) (1859-1936) American

£1000 $1540 €1500 Gentleman gardening in a courtyard (71x51cm-28x20in) s. 3-Sep-2 Gorringes, Lewes #2290 est:1000-1500

GRAVES, Michael (1934-) American

Works on paper

£897 $1400 €1346 Collage (28x24cm-11x9in) s.d.1981 mixed media. 30-Mar-3 Butterfields, Los Angeles #1455/R est:700-900

GRAVES, Morris (1910-2001) American

£2548 $4000 €3822 Mango seed (15x19cm-6x7in) s.d.68 tempera paper prov. 20-Nov-2 Christie's, Los Angeles #115/R est:4000-6000
£9554 $15000 €14331 Spirit bird no 34 (33cm-13in circular) s.d.79 i.d.verso tempera paper on paper prov. 20-Nov-2 Christie's, Los Angeles #118/R est:15000-25000
£16975 $27500 €25463 Bouquet (37x32cm-15x13in) s.i. tempera pastel on paper painted 1949 prov.exhib. 21-May-3 Sotheby's, New York #43/R est:8000-12000

Works on paper

£3846 $6000 €5769 Priest with chalice head. gouache pastel. 21-Sep-2 Harvey Clar, Oakland #1469

GRAVES, Nancy (1940-1995) American

Sculpture

£13750 $22000 €20625 Astron (176x102x69cm-69x40x27in) s.i.d.VI-87 painted rusted steel prov. 14-May-3 Sotheby's, New York #427/R est:18000-22000

GRAVES, Shirrell Watson (c.1884-1954) American

Works on paper

£282 $450 €409 Magnolia (53x79cm-21x31in) s. W/C. 17-May-3 New Orleans Auction, New Orleans #940/R

GRAVIER, A de (19th C) ?

£1042 $1656 €1500 Promenade a cheval dans les Alpes (50x60cm-20x24in) s.d.1877. 30-Apr-3 Tajan, Paris #89 est:1500-2000

GRAY, Cedric (fl.1880) British

£988 $1600 €1482 Highlands with deer and sheep (46x66cm-18x26in) s.d.97. 24-Jan-3 New Orleans Auction, New Orleans #185/R est:1000-1500

GRAY, Claude W (1880-1940) Canadian
£739 $1153 €1233 Father Hennepin, Jesuit priest, taking leave of a la salle to discover Mississippi (82x102cm-32x40in) s.d.1924 board double-sided. 13-Apr-3 Levis, Calgary #42/R est:2000-2500 (C.D 1700)

GRAY, Cleve (1918-) American
£353 $550 €530 Woman tree (36x38cm-14x15in) s.d.68. 18-Sep-2 Alderfer's, Hatfield #304

GRAY, Douglas Stannus (1890-1959) British
£360 $583 €540 Shoreham Harbour (24x41cm-9x16in) exhib. 20-May-3 Sotheby's, Olympia #31/R
£400 $620 €600 Still life with vase of carnations (46x36cm-18x14in) s. 4-Dec-2 Christie's, Kensington #450
£700 $1106 €1015 Still life of flowers on a table (51x61cm-20x24in) s. board. 22-Jul-3 Gorringes, Lewes #1717
£1000 $1650 €1450 Garden at 102 King's Avenue, Clapham (26x35cm-10x14in) panel prov. 3-Jul-3 Christie's, Kensington #434/R est:1000-1500
£1100 $1672 €1650 Girl reclined on blanket in a park (25x46cm-10x18in) prov. 16-Aug-2 Keys, Aylsham #694/R

GRAY, Eileen (20th C) British
Sculpture
£54217 $90000 €81326 Screen (170cm-67in) white painted perforated steel 4 panels exec.c.1930 prov.exhib.lit. 11-Jun-3 Phillips, New York #23/R est:50000-70000
£93373 $155000 €140060 Screen (214cm-84in) white painted wood exec.c.1922-25 prov.lit. 11-Jun-3 Phillips, New York #22/R est:200000-300000

GRAY, Elizabeth (20th C) American?
Works on paper
£1013 $1600 €1520 Widgeon by moonlight (51x71cm-20x28in) s. W/C gouache on board prov. 3-Apr-3 Christie's, Rockefeller NY #192/R est:1000-1500

GRAY, George (18/19th C) British
£288 $453 €450 Children in meadow with haystacks (32x42cm-13x17in) s. 23-Nov-2 Arnold, Frankfurt #730/R

GRAY, H Barnard (attrib) (fl.1844-1871) British
£260 $411 €390 Evening on a coast (70x127cm-28x50in) 27-Nov-2 Hamptons Fine Art, Godalming #404

GRAY, Henry Percy (1869-1952) American
£14331 $22500 €21497 Farm beneath Mt Tamalpais (51x61cm-20x24in) s. 19-Nov-2 Butterfields, San Francisco #8153/R est:25000-35000
£22590 $37500 €32756 Sun dappled oaks with Mount Tamalpais in the distance (61x76cm-24x30in) s. prov. 11-Jun-3 Butterfields, San Francisco #4188/R est:25000-35000
Works on paper
£3012 $5000 €4367 Indian Boy Rock, Arizona (24x35cm-9x14in) s. pencil W/C. 11-Jun-3 Butterfields, San Francisco #4323/R est:5000-7000
£5689 $9500 €8249 Oaks in California landscape (23x33cm-9x13in) s. W/C. 17-Jun-3 John Moran, Pasadena #83 est:7000-9000
£10191 $16000 €15287 Landscape with oak tree (41x14cm-16x6in) init. W/C on a s.d.Jan 7 1949 personal letter prov. 19-Nov-2 Butterfields, San Francisco #8131/R est:6000-8000
£12048 $20000 €17470 Dunes at Monterey (28x36cm-11x14in) s. W/C prov. 11-Jun-3 Butterfields, San Francisco #4187/R est:12000-18000
£12903 $20000 €19355 Poppies and lupine in eucalyptus coastal landscape (41x51cm-16x20in) s.d.1928 W/C prov. 29-Oct-2 John Moran, Pasadena #680 est:20000-30000

GRAY, Jack L (1927-1981) American
£1711 $2600 €2567 Out of New Bedford (18x28cm-7x11in) s. board. 17-Aug-2 North East Auctions, Portsmouth #198/R
£18868 $30000 €28302 New York Harbor at sunset (67x102cm-26x40in) s. prov. 5-Mar-3 Sotheby's, New York #96/R est:20000-30000
£30864 $50000 €44753 On deck, Barque Medway (91x153cm-36x60in) s.d.82 i.verso prov. 29-Jul-3 Christie's, Rockefeller NY #188/R est:35000-55000

GRAY, Kate (fl.1870-1987) British
£900 $1395 €1350 Young artist (50x39cm-20x15in) s. 26-Sep-2 Mellors & Kirk, Nottingham #706/R
£950 $1549 €1425 Grandfathers art class (48x38cm-19x15in) s. 14-Feb-3 Keys, Aylsham #532/R
£950 $1558 €1425 Reading lesson (61x51cm-24x20in) s. 29-May-3 Christie's, Kensington #264/R

GRAY, Monica F (fl.1898-1919) British
£1994 $3250 €2991 Wolvey chatterbox. Wolvey juggler (22x20cm-9x8in) s. panel pair. 11-Feb-3 Bonhams & Doyles, New York #205/R est:1500-2000

GRAY, Norah Neilson (1882-1931) British
£500 $770 €750 Charwoman (112x86cm-44x34in) prov.exhib. 5-Sep-2 Christie's, Kensington #320/R
£1700 $2771 €2550 Michaelmas daisies (164x72cm-65x28in) 14-Feb-3 Lyon & Turnbull, Edinburgh #155

GRAY, Una (20th C) American
£253 $400 €380 Sunset scene with country house. painted c.1930. 16-Nov-2 Harvey Clar, Oakland #1260

GRAY, William (19th C) British
£1454 $2166 €2181 Unter the Lyne (28x38cm-11x15in) s.d.1853. 25-Jun-2 Koller, Zurich #6480/R est:3500-5500 (S.FR 3300)

GRAZIA, Ettore de (1909-1982) American
£409 $650 €614 Portrait of a man and woman (23x28cm-9x11in) s. board diptych. 2-Mar-3 Toomey, Oak Park #703/R

GRAZIANI, Francesco (17th C) Italian
£1800 $2934 €2700 Cavalry charge (18x32cm-7x13in) 12-Feb-3 Bonhams, Knightsbridge #42/R est:2000-3000
£3493 $5520 €5240 Battle scene (72x95cm-28x37in) prov. 17-Nov-2 Koller, Geneva #1248/R (S.FR 8000)

GRAZIANI, Francesco (attrib) (17th C) Italian
£2200 $3674 €3190 Cavalry battle (15x50cm-6x20in) 11-Jul-3 Christie's, Kensington #260/R est:2000-3000

GRAZIANI, Pietro (18th C) Italian
£3500 $5460 €5250 Landscape with cavalry skirmish (21x71cm-8x28in) prov. 8-Oct-2 Sotheby's, Olympia #373/R est:4000-6000
£7855 $12883 €11390 Battle scene (31x41cm-12x16in) 4-Jun-3 AB Stockholms Auktionsverk #2534/R est:25000-30000 (S.KR 100000)
£13000 $21710 €18850 River landscapes with cavalry crossing a bridge (25x51cm-10x20in) pair. 8-Jul-3 Sotheby's, Olympia #429/R est:6000-8000

GRAZIANI, Pietro (attrib) (18th C) Italian
£4895 $8175 €7000 Charge de cavalerie devant une ville fortifiee (48x64cm-19x25in) 27-Jun-3 Piasa, Paris #12/R est:4000-6000

GRAZZINI, Renzo (1912-1989) Italian
£321 $503 €500 Roses in black background (42x47cm-17x19in) board. 16-Dec-2 Pandolfini, Florence #340

GREASON, William (1884-?) American
£301 $500 €436 Old Hamburg Bridge (38x51cm-15x20in) s. 11-Jun-3 Boos Gallery, Michigan #587/R
£452 $750 €655 Winter landscape (61x91cm-24x36in) s.d.1944. 11-Jun-3 Boos Gallery, Michigan #586/R
£781 $1250 €1172 Misty evening, Port Clyde, Maine (46x71cm-18x28in) s. 15-Mar-3 Jeffery Burchard, Florida #39/R

GREATHEAD, Aston (1921-) New Zealander
£230 $327 €345 Roundup at Kowhai (61x90cm-24x35in) s. board prov. 20-Mar-2 Watson's, Christchurch #65/R (NZ.D 750)

GREAVES, Derrick (1927-) British
£1800 $2880 €2700 Moon and sleeping girl (155x143cm-61x56in) s.i. on overlap acrylic painted 1972. 15-May-3 Lawrence, Crewkerne #1020 est:400-600
£2400 $3744 €3600 Still life (152x95cm-60x37in) acrylic. 25-Mar-3 Bonhams, New Bond Street #144/R est:1500-2000
£4800 $7440 €7200 Mother and child asleep (76x127cm-30x50in) s. 4-Dec-2 Sotheby's, London #73/R est:5000-8000
Works on paper
£1500 $2369 €2250 Artist's son (37x55cm-15x22in) s. brush ink prov. 27-Nov-2 Sotheby's, Olympia #194/R est:800-1200
£2200 $3476 €3300 Study for a steel worker (52x36cm-20x14in) s. black chk prov. 27-Nov-2 Sotheby's, Olympia #193/R est:1500-2000

GREAVES, W (19/20th C) British
£1164 $1851 €1746 Landscape with rapids (51x76cm-20x30in) s.d.1876. 10-Mar-3 Rasmussen, Vejle #540/R est:10000 (D.KR 12500)

GREAVES, Walter (1846-1930) British
£1500 $2340 €2250 View of the Thames from Lindsey House (23x29cm-9x11in) board prov. 25-Mar-3 Bonhams, New Bond Street #19/R est:800-1200

£1600 $2496 €2400 Queen's Road, Chelsea (22x31cm-9x12in) s.i. board prov. 25-Mar-3 Bonhams, New Bond Street #30/R est:1800-2200
£2000 $3080 €3000 Thames nocturn, Lindsey Wharf (68x51cm-27x20in) 5-Sep-2 Christie's, Kensington #537/R est:2000-3000
£50000 $83000 €75000 James Abbott McNeill Whistler on the window's walk at his house in Lindsey Row, Chelsea (91x45cm-36x18in) s.d.1871 exhib. 11-Jun-3 Christie's, London #11/R est:50000-80000

Works on paper
£260 $424 €390 Full-length study of lady with parasol (26x18cm-10x7in) pastel dr. 17-Feb-3 Bonhams, Bath #37
£700 $1085 €1050 Cadogan Pier, Chelsea (24x32cm-9x13in) s. pencil crayon pen black ink grey wash. 4-Dec-2 Christie's, Kensington #257/R
£800 $1240 €1200 South west corner of Oakley Street. Old Battersea Bridge (26x22cm-10x9in) s.i. pencil crayon pen black ink grey wash pair. 4-Dec-2 Christie's, Kensington #258/R
£1500 $2445 €2250 Self portrait (14x10cm-6x4in) s. wash dr over pencil. 17-Feb-3 Bonhams, Bath #36/R est:300-500

GREAVES, William (fl.1882-1920) British
£500 $795 €750 Haymaking (41x61cm-16x24in) s. i.verso. 6-Mar-3 Mitchells, Cockermouth #820/R
£600 $978 €900 Harvest (25x41cm-10x16in) s. board. 29-Jan-3 Sotheby's, Olympia #193/R
£975 $1628 €1414 Potato gatherers (23x38cm-9x15in) s. board. 18-Jun-3 Andrew Hartley, Ilkley #1193/R

GREBBER, Pieter de (1600-c.1655) Dutch
£40000 $66800 €58000 Marriage portrait, with lady and gentleman seated on a carpet at base of tree (150x131cm-59x52in) init.d.1645. 10-Jul-3 Sotheby's, London #22/R est:40000-60000

GREBE, Fritz (1850-?) German
£545 $855 €850 Shepherd with flock in autumn wood (35x49cm-14x19in) s. board. 21-Nov-2 Van Ham, Cologne #1641
£833 $1292 €1300 Cows and sheep on beach (61x91cm-24x36in) s. lit. 7-Dec-2 Hans Stahl, Hamburg #80/R
£4500 $7155 €6750 Norwegian fjord (87x132cm-34x52in) s. 20-Mar-3 Christie's, Kensington #174/R est:2500-3500

GREBER, Henri Léon (1855-1941) French
Sculpture
£2000 $3140 €3000 Athlete (43cm-17in) s.i. green pat. bronze on a green marble plinth. 10-Dec-2 Sotheby's, London #167/R est:2500-3500

GREC, Stephane le (1924-) French
£446 $696 €700 Vase de fleurs (41x33cm-16x13in) s. panel. 10-Nov-2 Eric Pillon, Calais #264/R

GRECO, Alberto (1931-1965) ?
Works on paper
£1154 $1823 €1800 Homage to Picasso (46x73cm-18x29in) s.d.59 collage. 19-Nov-2 Durán, Madrid #159/R
£2055 $3205 €3000 Angelus Angelus (49x64cm-19x25in) s. mixed media collage. 8-Apr-3 Ansorena, Madrid #258/R

GRECO, El (1541-1614) Spanish
Works on paper
£180000 $279000 €270000 St. John the Baptist. St. John the Evangelist (14x5cm-6x2in) pen ink wash htd white pair prov.exhib.lit. 9-Dec-2 Bonhams, New Bond Street #101 est:200000-400000

GRECO, El (attrib) (1541-1614) Spanish
£5283 $8242 €8400 Portrait (20x18cm-8x7in) 21-Sep-2 Semenzato, Venice #133/R est:5000-6000
£28679 $44740 €45600 Burial of Christ (45x34cm-18x13in) 21-Sep-2 Semenzato, Venice #135/R est:40000-50000

GRECO, El (style) (1541-1614) Spanish
£6098 $10000 €9147 Crucifixon (61x39cm-24x15in) 29-May-3 Sotheby's, New York #125/R est:10000-15000
£92593 $150000 €138890 Saint Francis in meditation (96x76cm-38x30in) 23-Jan-3 Sotheby's, New York #240/R est:60000

GRECO, Emilio (1913-1995) Italian
£946 $1523 €1419 Still life of flowers and fruit (69x90cm-27x35in) s. prov. 12-May-3 Stephan Welz, Johannesburg #438/R est:12000-18000 (SA.R 11000)

Sculpture
£3191 $5170 €4500 Nanda (34x28x25cm-13x11x10in) gypsum exec.1943-44. 26-May-3 Christie's, Milan #63/R est:5000-7000
£3395 $5500 €4923 Donna Seduta (38cm-15in) s. blk pat bronze incl composition base. 21-May-3 Doyle, New York #34/R est:6000-9000
£6410 $10064 €10000 Girl (30cm-12in) s. brown pat bronze exec.1949. 21-Nov-2 Finarte, Rome #222/R est:10000-12000
£9317 $15000 €13976 Christo (61cm-24in) i. brown pat. bronze prov.lit. 7-May-3 Sotheby's, New York #377/R est:20000-30000
£12000 $18720 €18000 Figure accoccolata - crouching figure II (52cm-20in) i. bronze ppl. 21-Oct-2 Sotheby's, London #17/R est:15000-20000
Works on paper
£950 $1510 €1425 Portrait of a woman (55x42cm-22x17in) s.i.d.1954 pen ink four. 26-Feb-3 Sotheby's, Olympia #130/R est:600-800
£1216 $1897 €1800 Female nude (50x69cm-20x27in) s.d.1974 Chinese ink lit. 26-Mar-3 Finarte Semenzato, Milan #263/R
£1486 $2319 €2200 Female nude (70x51cm-28x20in) s.d.1977 Chinese ink lit. 26-Mar-3 Finarte Semenzato, Milan #264/R
£1554 $2424 €2300 Female nudes (51x70cm-20x28in) s.d. Chinese ink lit. 26-Mar-3 Finarte Semenzato, Milan #271/R
£1892 $2951 €2800 Female nude (51x70cm-20x28in) s.d.1978 Chinese ink lit. 26-Mar-3 Finarte Semenzato, Milan #272/R

GRECO, Gennaro (attrib) (1663-1714) Italian
£2709 $4281 €4200 Paysans devant un temple (34x47cm-13x19in) 20-Dec-2 Tajan, Paris #22/R est:4000

GREDER, Ulf (1949-) Swedish
£1173 $1876 €1701 Picnic (80x99cm-31x39in) s.i.d.1990 verso. 18-May-3 Anders Antik, Landskrona #53 est:5000 (S.KR 15000)

GREEN, Alan (1932-) British
Works on paper
£420 $656 €630 Drawing No.288 (58x53cm-23x21in) s.d.88 mixed media prov. 6-Nov-2 AB Stockholms Auktionsverk #844/R (S.KR 6000)

GREEN, Alfred H (fl.1844-1862) British
£980 $1617 €1421 Learning the alphabet (20x24cm-8x9in) mono. panel. 1-Jul-3 Bearnes, Exeter #503/R
£1500 $2310 €2250 Gypsy dance (71x91cm-28x36in) s.d.1874. 5-Sep-2 Christie's, Kensington #282/R est:2000-3000

GREEN, Anthony (1939-) British
£600 $990 €870 Yellow rose bush (51cm-20xin) s.i.d.94 board shaped. 3-Jul-3 Christie's, Kensington #641/R

GREEN, Charles (1840-1898) British
Works on paper
£1200 $1860 €1800 Last glass (34x24cm-13x9in) s.d.1871 pencil W/C. 26-Sep-2 Mellors & Kirk, Nottingham #620/R est:1000-1500
£1400 $2184 €2100 Courtship (28x36cm-11x14in) s.d.1878 pencil W/C. 19-Sep-2 Christie's, Kensington #1/R est:700-1000

GREEN, Charles Lewis (1844-1915) American
£897 $1400 €1346 Harbour scene (20x30cm-8x12in) s. 28-Mar-3 Eldred, East Dennis #559/R est:600-900
£1026 $1600 €1539 Man with scythe (20x30cm-8x12in) s. 28-Mar-3 Eldred, East Dennis #560/R est:600-900
£1795 $2800 €2693 Landscape with brook (76x51cm-30x20in) s. 28-Mar-3 Eldred, East Dennis #561/R est:1000-2000
£2945 $4300 €4418 Villagers on country road approaching a town (25x36cm-10x14in) s. panel. 3-Nov-1 North East Auctions, Portsmouth #270/R

GREEN, Denise (1946-) American
£2682 $3996 €4023 Free reign (121x12cm-48x5in) s.i.d.1990 verso prov.exhib. 27-Aug-2 Christie's, Melbourne #273/R est:7000-10000 (A.D 7000)
£3065 $4567 €4598 American Rhapsody (121x121cm-48x48in) s. i.d.1990 verso prov.exhib. 27-Aug-2 Christie's, Melbourne #226/R est:8000-12000 (A.D 8000)
£3393 $5293 €5090 Story, legend (157x111cm-62x44in) s.i.d.2000 verso. 11-Nov-2 Deutscher-Menzies, Melbourne #61/R est:6000-9000 (A.D 9500)

GREEN, Elizabeth (fl.1817) British
Works on paper
£1100 $1716 €1650 Bowder stone, Borrowdale, Cumbria. s.i.d.Sep 11.1817 W/C set of three. 5-Nov-2 Bonhams, New Bond Street #28/R est:1200-1800

GREEN, Elizabeth Shippen (1871-1954) American
Works on paper
£4348 $7000 €6522 Man hanging up a bird house (61x38cm-24x15in) s. chl exhib. 10-May-3 Illustration House, New York #39/R est:3000-6000

GREEN, Frank Russell (1856-1940) British
£1333 $2213 €1933 Waiting for the coach at Ye Kings Arms Inn (51x76cm-20x30in) s. 16-Jun-3 Waddingtons, Toronto #151/R est:4000-5000 (C.D 3000)

GREEN, George Pycock Everett (fl.1841-1873) British
Works on paper
£300 $465 €450 Bolton Abbey, rural landscape (31x50cm-12x20in) s.i. W/C. 1-Nov-2 Moore Allen & Innocent, Cirencester #219

GREEN, Ghiglion (20th C) ?
£892 $1391 €1400 En aout en Provence (38x46cm-15x18in) s. 5-Nov-2 Tajan, Paris #43/R

GREEN, Gregory (1959-) American
Sculpture
£1100 $1837 €1595 Nuclear device num 2, London, 239 plutonium, 15 kilotons. mixed media prov. 26-Jun-3 Sotheby's, London #294/R est:600-800

GREEN, Margaret (20th C) British
£350 $578 €508 Quiet evening (41x51cm-16x20in) s. board. 3-Jul-3 Christie's, Kensington #685/R

GREEN, Mike (1941-) New Zealander
Works on paper
£641 $980 €962 Dinning table (87x123cm-34x48in) s.d.90 W/C prov. 26-Aug-2 Sotheby's, Paddington #680 est:800-1200 (A.D 1800)
£1210 $1851 €1815 Bed, painting and two chairs - with suitcases (80x123cm-31x48in) s.d.92 W/C prov. 26-Aug-2 Sotheby's, Paddington #612 est:1000-1500 (A.D 3400)

GREEN, Richard Crafton (19th C) British
£360 $565 €540 An interior scene with a young girl peeling apples (46x36cm-18x14in) s.d.1869. 19-Nov-2 Bonhams, Leeds #211
£15190 $24000 €22785 Reading lesson (44x32cm-17x13in) painted 1890. 23-Apr-3 Christie's, Rockefeller NY #141/R est:25000-35000

GREEN, Roland (1896-1972) British
£800 $1248 €1200 Red grouse (48x73cm-19x29in) s. 14-Apr-3 Sotheby's, London #47/R
£1550 $2418 €2325 Late arrival. Mallard rising (36x24cm-14x9in) s. pair. 25-Mar-3 Gildings, Market Harborough #390 est:700-1000
Works on paper
£260 $406 €390 Study of lapwings (10x15cm-4x6in) s. W/C. 18-Oct-2 Keys, Aylsham #601
£260 $403 €390 Kingfisher (14x10cm-6x4in) s. W/C bodycol sold with another by the same hand. 30-Sep-2 Bonhams, Ipswich #290
£260 $434 €377 Greyheaded bush shrike (25x20cm-10x8in) s. W/C prov. 20-Jun-3 Keys, Aylsham #624
£300 $465 €450 Bittern (13x19cm-5x7in) s. W/C. 30-Sep-2 Bonhams, Ipswich #315
£300 $468 €450 Hobby hawk (18x30cm-7x12in) s. W/C. 11-Apr-3 Keys, Aylsham #593/R
£300 $468 €450 Grouse over a moorland (38x51cm-15x20in) s. W/C. 26-Mar-3 Hamptons Fine Art, Godalming #82
£300 $501 €435 Mallard rising from a broad (36x51cm-14x20in) s. W/C. 20-Jun-3 Keys, Aylsham #620
£320 $486 €480 Blue tits on snow covered branches (20x20cm-8x8in) s. W/C. 16-Aug-2 Keys, Aylsham #570/R
£340 $541 €510 Eagle in flight in cloudy skies (53x64cm-21x25in) s. W/C. 1-May-3 Locke & England, Leamington Spa #179/R
£350 $546 €525 Mallard rising (23x15cm-9x6in) s. W/C. 11-Apr-3 Keys, Aylsham #591
£350 $546 €525 Linnet on gorse (33x23cm-13x9in) s. W/C. 11-Apr-3 Keys, Aylsham #595
£350 $585 €508 On the mud flats, Braydon Water (36x48cm-14x19in) s. W/C. 20-Jun-3 Keys, Aylsham #622
£400 $624 €600 Snipe in flight over water (28x38cm-11x15in) s. W/C. 18-Oct-2 Keys, Aylsham #602/R
£420 $701 €609 Mallard in flight over a broad (25x36cm-10x14in) s. W/C. 20-Jun-3 Keys, Aylsham #625
£450 $734 €675 Bee eaters (30x23cm-12x9in) s. W/C. 14-Feb-3 Keys, Aylsham #620/R
£480 $744 €720 Hint of frost in the air (35x52cm-14x20in) s. W/C. 30-Sep-2 Bonhams, Ipswich #312
£480 $782 €720 Male and female pheasants in a woodland clearing (15x28cm-6x11in) s. W/C. 14-Feb-3 Keys, Aylsham #621/R
£480 $802 €696 Grouse in flight over highlands (30x43cm-12x17in) s. W/C. 20-Jun-3 Keys, Aylsham #623/R
£500 $835 €725 Geese in flight over a Scottish loch (36x48cm-14x19in) W/C prov. 20-Jun-3 Keys, Aylsham #621
£780 $1217 €1170 Geese in flight (36x51cm-14x20in) s. W/C. 11-Apr-3 Keys, Aylsham #596/R
£800 $1216 €1200 Mallard rising above the sea (51x33cm-20x13in) s. W/C. 16-Aug-2 Keys, Aylsham #568/R
£800 $1304 €1200 Swans in flight over sea (38x48cm-15x19in) s. W/C. 14-Feb-3 Keys, Aylsham #618/R
£875 $1330 €1313 Swans in flight over the sea (36x56cm-14x22in) s. W/C. 16-Aug-2 Keys, Aylsham #567/R
£1000 $1580 €1500 Robins nest (36x25cm-14x10in) s. W/C. 13-Nov-2 Halls, Shrewsbury #349/R est:400-500
£1250 $2038 €1875 Enemies of the British honey bee (66x43cm-26x17in) s.d.1912 W/C. 14-Feb-3 Keys, Aylsham #619/R est:500-700
£1400 $2212 €2100 Short eared owl in flight (35x50cm-14x20in) s. W/C. 28-Nov-2 Bonhams, Knightsbridge #18/R est:1500-2000

GREEN, Valentine (1739-1813) British
Prints
£4200 $6510 €6300 Philosopher showing an experiment on the air pump (49x59cm-19x23in) mezzotint after Joseph Wright of Derby. 4-Dec-2 Bonhams, New Bond Street #112/R est:1000-1500

GREEN, William (1760-1823) British
Works on paper
£500 $780 €750 At Rosthwaite (14x19cm-6x7in) s.d.1806 W/C. 10-Apr-3 Tennants, Leyburn #839

GREEN, William Bradford (1871-1945) American
£245 $400 €368 Fountain (99x74cm-39x29in) s.d.1920 board. 2-Feb-3 Grogan, Boston #54
£307 $500 €461 Portrait of a robed woman. Floral still life (61x46cm-24x18in) s. double-sided. 2-Feb-3 Grogan, Boston #18

GREENALL, Robert (20th C) British
Works on paper
£250 $393 €375 Crofts and haystacks (46x46cm-18x18in) mixed media. 13-Dec-2 Keys, Aylsham #349

GREENAWAY, Kate (1846-1901) British
£1800 $2862 €2700 Girl in a doorway carrying a basket of eggs (15x10cm-6x4in) init. board. 29-Apr-3 Gorringes, Lewes #2022
Works on paper
£949 $1500 €1424 Young girl with feathered hat (15x10cm-6x4in) init.d.1898 pencil W/C. 2-Apr-3 Doyle, New York #37/R est:800-1200
£2000 $3160 €3000 Waking (9x13cm-4x5in) init. pen ink W/C. 7-Apr-3 Bonhams, Bath #29/R est:2000-3000
£2600 $4108 €3900 Two at a sile (23x26cm-9x10in) W/C prov.exhib. 2-Dec-2 Sotheby's, London #48/R est:1500-2000

GREENAWAY, Kate (attrib) (1846-1901) British
Works on paper
£250 $400 €363 Knitting (11x14cm-4x6in) init. mixed media W/C prov. 16-May-3 Skinner, Boston #19/R

GREENBAUM, Joseph David (1864-1940) American
£481 $750 €722 Lily ponds in Stow Lake. 21-Sep-2 Harvey Clar, Oakland #1513
£920 $1500 €1334 Landscape (46x61cm-18x24in) 18-Jul-3 Du Mouchelle, Detroit #1164/R est:1600-2400

GREENE, Albert van Nesse (1887-?) American
£1442 $2250 €2163 Schuylkill canal house (64x76cm-25x30in) s. 18-Sep-2 Alderfer's, Hatfield #344/R est:4000-6000
£1946 $3250 €2822 Trees in a winter landscape (56x66cm-22x26in) s. 22-Jun-3 Freeman, Philadelphia #143/R est:4000-6000
£3365 $5250 €5048 Gray day (66x81cm-26x32in) s. 18-Sep-2 Alderfer's, Hatfield #334/R est:5000-7000
£3871 $6000 €5807 Riverscape (46x58cm-18x23in) s. board prov. 8-Dec-2 Freeman, Philadelphia #160/R est:4000-6000

GREENE, Balcomb (1904-1990) American
£1389 $2250 €2014 Composition (91x122cm-36x48in) s. prov. 21-May-3 Doyle, New York #12/R est:800-1200

GREENE, Bruce (1953-) American
£5128 $8000 €7692 Critic (61x91cm-24x36in) 9-Nov-2 Altermann Galleries, Santa Fe #74
£9589 $14000 €14384 Matters of philosophy (71x102cm-28x40in) 18-May-2 Altermann Galleries, Santa Fe #159/R
£10648 $17250 €15440 A long way from the wagon (76x86cm-30x34in) 23-May-3 Altermann Galleries, Santa Fe #54

GREENE, Daniel E (1934-) American
£362 $550 €543 Sailboats on the sound (66x81cm-26x32in) s.d.1964. 15-Aug-2 Doyle, New York #46

GREENE, Gertrude (1904-1956) American
Works on paper
£2229 $3500 €3344 36-01 (8x12cm-3x5in) s. collage exhib. 19-Nov-2 Wright, Chicago #144/R est:2000-3000

GREENE, John Beasley (19th C) American
Photographs
£8974 $14179 €14000 Thebes, le colosse de gauche (34x26cm-13x10in) s.d.num.l.107 albumin print prov. 16-Nov-2 Christie's, Paris #62/R est:8000-10000

GREENE, Milton H (1922-1985) American
Photographs
£2200 $3564 €3300 Marilyn Monroe removing a stocking (50x40cm-20x16in) s.num.38/125 verso brown toned silver print prov. 22-May-3 Sotheby's, London #182/R est:1000-1500

GREENE, Thomas Garland (?) Canadian?
£247 $385 €371 Haycart (26x28cm-10x11in) s. canvasboard. 25-Mar-3 Ritchie, Toronto #76 (C.D 575)

GREENHALGH, Thomas (19th C) British
Works on paper
£700 $1085 €1050 Windsor Castle (49x74cm-19x29in) s. W/C. 30-Sep-2 Bonhams, Ipswich #313/R

GREENHAM, Peter (1909-1992) British
£280 $440 €420 Chaumont, Haute-Marne (26x32cm-10x13in) canvasboard prov.exhib. 10-Dec-2 Lane, Penzance #183
£320 $499 €480 Portrait of Frank Dohearty, headmaster of Lancing College (70x58cm-28x23in) init. 15-Oct-2 Bonhams, Knightsbridge #169
£480 $749 €696 Canal landscape (52x70cm-20x28in) s.d.1924 cardboard. 27-Mar-3 Lane, Penzance #264
£1100 $1705 €1650 Port Meadow, Oxford (22x26cm-9x10in) init. s.i.verso board. 3-Dec-2 Bonhams, Knightsbridge #3/R est:700-900
£1500 $2324 €2250 Tide going out (17x18cm-7x7in) init. board exhib. 4-Dec-2 Sotheby's, London #50 est:600-800
£2200 $3432 €3300 Railway journey (45x66cm-18x26in) init. board prov.exhib. 25-Mar-3 Bonhams, New Bond Street #89/R est:1000-1500
£3600 $5580 €5400 Still with tea pot and inkwell (23x30cm-9x12in) init. set of four. 4-Dec-2 Sotheby's, London #45/R est:1000-1500
£3600 $5580 €5400 Savoy Alps (30x38cm-12x15in) init. board. 4-Dec-2 Sotheby's, London #47/R est:800-1200
£3600 $5580 €5400 View across Oxford towards Tom Tower from St. Mary's (38x54cm-15x21in) init. canvas on board. 4-Dec-2 Sotheby's, London #60/R est:1500-2000

GREENHAM, Robert Duckworth (1906-1975) British
£380 $597 €570 Universe, abstract (41x51cm-16x20in) s. i.d.1973 verso board. 15-Apr-3 Bonhams, Knightsbridge #144/R
£480 $749 €720 Portrait of Martha Hunt (51x41cm-20x16in) s. 17-Sep-2 Bonhams, Knightsbridge #16/R
£650 $1014 €975 Child of 60s (61x25cm-24x10in) s. board. 27-Mar-3 Christie's, Kensington #558/R
£780 $1256 €1170 Portrait of a woman (25x20cm-10x8in) board. 18-Feb-3 Bonhams, Knightsbridge #31/R
£800 $1256 €1200 St. Ives Bay, approaching rain (25x35cm-10x14in) s. indis d. board exhib. 15-Apr-3 Bonhams, Knightsbridge #147/R
£950 $1501 €1425 Portrait of a young lady (51x27cm-20x11in) s.d.40 board. 27-Nov-2 Sotheby's, Olympia #87/R est:1000-1500
£1190 $1976 €2029 Untitled - Portrait of a female (26x21cm-10x8in) s.d.44 verso. 10-Jun-3 Shapiro, Sydney #10/R est:4000-6000 (A.D 3000)

GREENHILL, Harold (1914-) Australian
£1400 $2254 €2100 Girl with cat (44x25cm-17x10in) s.d.51 board. 6-May-3 Christie's, Melbourne #232/R est:2000-4000 (A.D 3500)

GREENLEAF, Jacob (1887-1968) American
£528 $850 €792 Hilly summer landscape (51x61cm-20x24in) s.d.1944. 18-Feb-3 Arthur James, Florida #447

GREENLEES, James (fl.1860-1903) British
£450 $720 €675 Inverlochy Castle, Invernesshire (61x92cm-24x36in) s.d.1887 i.verso. 11-Mar-3 Bonhams, Knightsbridge #106/R

GREENWOOD, Ethan Allen (attrib) (1779-1856) American
£1069 $1700 €1550 Portrait of Benjamin Bernard Appleton and his fiancee. pair. 3-May-3 Van Blarcom, South Natick #198

GREENWOOD, Joseph H (1857-1927) American
£472 $750 €708 Forest's edge (51x40cm-20x16in) s.d.94. 7-Mar-3 Skinner, Boston #395/R

GREENWOOD, Marion (1909-1970) American
Works on paper
£881 $1400 €1322 Santiago Cucuchouchu (51x36cm-20x14in) s. chl exec.c.1932. 2-Mar-3 Toomey, Oak Park #630/R

GREENWOOD, Orlando (1892-1989) British
£550 $919 €798 Durham in the snow (25x25cm-10x10in) s. 17-Jun-3 Bonhams, Knightsbridge #150
£1600 $2464 €2400 Still life with tulips (69x45cm-27x18in) studio st.stretcher prov. 5-Sep-2 Christie's, Kensington #727/R est:1500-2000
£2000 $3280 €3000 Love and the butterfly (61x71cm-24x28in) s.d.1923 prov. 3-Jun-3 Sotheby's, Olympia #83/R est:1000-1500
£3800 $5890 €5700 Piano solo (74x60cm-29x24in) prov. 4-Dec-2 Christie's, Kensington #432/R est:1500-2000

GREER, A D (1904-1998) American
£962 $1500 €1443 Red roses (43x56cm-17x22in) 9-Nov-2 Altermann Galleries, Santa Fe #211
£1347 $2250 €1953 Floral still life, roses in a pink vase (91x76cm-36x30in) s. 17-Jun-3 John Moran, Pasadena #169 est:2500-3000
£1603 $2500 €2405 Mountain lake (46x61cm-18x24in) 19-Oct-2 David Dike, Dallas #279/R est:2500-5000
£1923 $3000 €2885 Floral with chrysanthemums (76x64cm-30x25in) 9-Nov-2 Altermann Galleries, Santa Fe #209
£1986 $2900 €2979 Yellow roses of Texas (76x91cm-30x36in) 18-May-2 Altermann Galleries, Santa Fe #254/R

GREER, Aubrey Dale (1904-1998) American
£839 $1300 €1259 Floral still life (56x66cm-22x26in) s. prov. 29-Oct-2 John Moran, Pasadena #714
£1032 $1600 €1548 Connecticut (61x76cm-24x30in) s. prov. 29-Oct-2 John Moran, Pasadena #713 est:2500-4000

GREF, Franz Heinrich (1872-1957) German
£276 $436 €400 Flowers in dark jug (45x40cm-18x16in) mono.d. 2-Apr-3 Dr Fritz Nagel, Stuttgart #9083/R

GREFE, Konrad (1823-1917) Austrian
£1441 $2248 €2162 Old tree by stream in a storm (158x208cm-62x82in) s.d.1858. 6-Nov-2 Dobiaschofsky, Bern #619/R est:5000 (S.FR 3300)
£3521 $5845 €5000 Sylvan landscape with rocks and torrent (158x208cm-62x82in) s.d.1858. 11-Jun-3 Dorotheum, Vienna #161/R est:5500-7500

GREFFE, Léon (1881-1949) French
£637 $993 €1000 Fete foraine (38x46cm-15x18in) s. 5-Nov-2 Tajan, Paris #23/R
£764 $1192 €1200 Place au village (39x41cm-15x16in) s. 5-Nov-2 Tajan, Paris #22/R

GREGERSEN, Emil (1921-1993) Danish
£595 $928 €893 Still life of objects on table (85x92cm-33x36in) s. 5-Aug-2 Rasmussen, Vejle #304/R (D.KR 7000)
£815 $1271 €1223 Positano (97x146cm-38x57in) s.d.51 exhib. 11-Nov-2 Rasmussen, Vejle #68/R (D.KR 9500)

GREGERSEN, Julius (1860-1953) German
£1052 $1662 €1578 Ship's portrait - Gerda af Goteborg (55x75cm-22x30in) s.d.13/8 1910. 30-Nov-2 Goteborg Auktionsverk, Sweden #377/R est:20000 (S.KR 15000)

GREGG, Paul (1876-1949) American
£510 $800 €765 Miner (61x56cm-24x22in) s.d.1928. 23-Nov-2 Jackson's, Cedar Falls #114/R

GREGOIRE, J (1887-1960) Dutch
£962 $1490 €1500 Conversation du tonnelier et de la porteuse de lait avec charrett attelee (58x49cm-23x19in) s.d.1842 panel. 9-Dec-2 Horta, Bruxelles #50 est:1500-2000

GREGOIRE, Jan (1887-1960) Dutch
£347 $573 €500 Street in Cannes (59x43cm-23x17in) prov.lit. 1-Jul-3 Christie's, Amsterdam #313

GREGOIRE, Jean-Louis (1840-1890) French
Sculpture
£1282 $2026 €2000 Alsace (44cm-17in) d.1871 terracotta lit. 18-Nov-2 Sotheby's, Paris #411/R
£1400 $2170 €2100 Une jeune paysanne (48cm-19in) s. brown pat. bronze. 26-Sep-2 Mellors & Kirk, Nottingham #791/R est:1000-1400
£1410 $2200 €2115 Figure of Hera (58cm-23in) s. bronze. 22-Sep-2 Susanin's, Chicago #5056/R est:2000-4000

£1862 $2961 €2793 Two women studying a letter (54x40cm-21x16in) s. gilded bronze sold with black marble socle. 10-Mar-3 Rasmussen, Vejle #1193/R est:25000 (D.KR 20000)
£3797 $6000 €5696 Figure of Psyche (74cm-29in) i. bronze on plinth. 24-Apr-3 Christie's, Rockefeller NY #213/R est:4000-6000
£5696 $9000 €8544 Group of three putti (58cm-23in) i. 24-Apr-3 Christie's, Rockefeller NY #330/R est:10000-15000

GREGOOR, Gillis Smak (1770-1843) Dutch
£2158 $3453 €3000 Milkmaid and her cows in a farmyard (30x42cm-12x17in) s. panel. 14-May-3 Christie's, Amsterdam #158/R est:2000-3000

GREGOR-GRIESHABER, Riccarda (20th C) German?
£310 $490 €450 Rendez vous (80x100cm-31x39in) board. 2-Apr-3 Dr Fritz Nagel, Stuttgart #9084/R

GREGORIEV, Nikolai (1880-1943) Russian
£4500 $7066 €6750 Windy day on the skating rink. Skating in the spring (73x55cm-29x22in) s.d.1937 i.verso pair. 20-Nov-2 Sotheby's, London #142/R est:5000-7000

GREGORIO, Giuseppe de (1920-) Italian
£486 $773 €700 Untitled (60x80cm-24x31in) s. 1-May-3 Meeting Art, Vercelli #418

GREGOROVIUS, Michel Christoph (19th C) German
Works on paper
£2113 $3401 €3000 Danzig shipyards with panoramic view of the city (65x45cm-26x18in) s. i.d.14.Dec.1846 verso gouache lit. 9-May-3 Schloss Ahlden, Ahlden #1412/R est:3800

GREGORY, Angela (1903-1990) American
Works on paper
£397 $650 €596 Iris (28x23cm-11x9in) init. W/C. 8-Feb-3 Neal Auction Company, New Orleans #370

GREGORY, Arthur V (1867-1957) Australian
Works on paper
£313 $489 €470 Australian passenger steam ship (34x58cm-13x23in) s.d.87 gouache. 10-Nov-2 Dunbar Sloane, Auckland #19 est:1000-2000 (NZ.D 1000)

GREGORY, Charles (1810-1896) British
Works on paper
£2600 $3952 €3900 Royal yacht Squadron's headquarters and promenade at Cowes (30x49cm-12x19in) s.d.1861 W/C htd white. 15-Aug-2 Bonhams, New Bond Street #401/R est:2000-3000

GREGORY, Charles (1850-1920) British
Works on paper
£2000 $3320 €3000 San Remo (49x34cm-19x13in) s. W/C bodycol. 12-Jun-3 Sotheby's, London #219/R est:2000-3000

GREGORY, Edward James (1850-1909) British
Works on paper
£1000 $1560 €1500 Portrait of Aline Henderson, seated on a swing (59x43cm-23x17in) init.d.94 pencil W/C htd bodycol prov. 19-Sep-2 Christie's, Kensington #7/R est:1200-1800
£2200 $3542 €3300 Reclining female nude (29x56cm-11x22in) s.i. chk prov. 20-Feb-3 Christie's, London #282/R

GREGORY, George (1849-1938) British
£460 $736 €690 Riverscape with anglers, blacksmiths beyond (41x66cm-16x26in) s.d.1885. 11-Mar-3 Gorringes, Lewes #2305
£700 $1169 €1015 Sailing barges in an estuary (30x47cm-12x19in) s.d.1882. 17-Jun-3 Anderson & Garland, Newcastle #482/R
£2400 $3912 €3600 Canal scene, Rotterdam (51x76cm-20x30in) s.d.1885. 11-Feb-3 Bonhams, Knowle #122/R est:1500-2000
Works on paper
£270 $451 €392 Prison hulk (14x24cm-6x9in) s.d.1890 W/C. 18-Jun-3 Sotheby's, Olympia #98/R
£300 $474 €450 Figures in conversation on a country lane (23x43cm-9x17in) s.d.1922 W/C. 13-Nov-2 Halls, Shrewsbury #358/R
£750 $1140 €1125 Off the Royal yacht squadron at Cowes (28x44cm-11x17in) s.d.1911 W/C. 15-Aug-2 Bonhams, New Bond Street #233/R

GREGORY, George (19th C) British
£6000 $9300 €9000 H.M.S Victory at her moorings in Portsmouth Harbour, H.M.S Duke of Wellington (56x102cm-22x40in) s.d.1883. 31-Oct-2 Christie's, Kensington #484/R est:6000-8000

GREGORY, Robert (1881-1918) Irish
£6410 $10064 €10000 Still life of flowers, in a white vase (60x45cm-24x18in) i.verso. 19-Nov-2 Hamilton Osborne King, Dublin #577/R est:4000-6000

GREIFFENHAGEN, Maurice (1862-1931) British
Works on paper
£300 $468 €435 Press gang with captain and sailors. s. W/C bodycol. 27-Mar-3 Lane, Penzance #340

GREIG, Catherine H (fl.1895-1904) British
£520 $822 €780 Courting jays (46x61cm-18x24in) s. 28-Nov-2 Bonhams, Knightsbridge #45/R

GREIG, Donald (1916-) British
Works on paper
£290 $473 €435 Snow in the lane, Avonwick (36x51cm-14x20in) s. W/C. 14-Feb-3 Keys, Aylsham #449

GREIG, John R (19/20th C) British
£900 $1395 €1350 The little Dutch girl (72x59cm-28x23in) s. prov. 5-Dec-2 Bonhams, Edinburgh #1
Works on paper
£950 $1511 €1425 Homewards, fisherfolk in Brittany (25x37cm-10x15in) s.i. mixed media. 6-Mar-3 Christie's, Kensington #134/R

GREIL, Alois (1841-1902) Austrian
£284 $443 €426 Going to market (26x18cm-10x7in) s.d.894 oil W/C. 20-Nov-2 Fischer, Luzern #2470 (S.FR 650)
Works on paper
£284 $443 €426 Girl and children in front of fusilier sitting on bench (23x15cm-9x6in) s.d.895. 20-Nov-2 Fischer, Luzern #2469/R (S.FR 650)
£1930 $3126 €2895 Broadside singers (20x27cm-8x11in) s.d.878 pencil W/C. 24-May-3 Dorotheum, Prague #231/R est:18000-27000 (C.KR 85000)

GREINER, Otto (1869-1916) German
£1410 $2059 €2200 Portrait of artist's wife (49x39cm-19x15in) mono.d.07 panel. 4-Jun-2 Karl & Faber, Munich #81/R est:2000
Works on paper
£291 $460 €460 Kneeling female nude with raised arms (55x39cm-22x15in) mono.d.1910 ochre. 29-Nov-2 Bassenge, Berlin #5902
£316 $500 €500 Standing female nude (59x40cm-23x16in) col chks. 29-Nov-2 Bassenge, Berlin #5903
£479 $748 €700 Female nude (33x44cm-13x17in) mono.d.23.7.04 col chk over pencil. 11-Apr-3 Winterberg, Heidelberg #393/R
£806 $1250 €1209 Landscape with houses, Grunwald (27x39cm-11x15in) i.d.19.9.89 pencil W/C chl. exhib. 29-Oct-2 Sotheby's, New York #108/R est:800-1200
£967 $1500 €1451 Standing male nude (48x30cm-19x12in) init.d.96 black red chk prov.exhib. 29-Oct-2 Sotheby's, New York #100/R est:3000-5000
£1346 $2127 €2100 Reclining female nude (46x30cm-18x12in) mono.d.1896 ochre htd white. 15-Nov-2 Reiss & Sohn, Konigstein #278/R est:3000
£1408 $2338 €2000 Study for Gaa (48x32cm-19x13in) Indian ink chk. 14-Jun-3 Hauswedell & Nolte, Hamburg #1211/R est:2500
£1935 $3000 €2903 Studies for Odysseus and Sirens (49x37cm-19x15in) s.i.d.1901 pencil col chk sold with lithograph. 29-Oct-2 Sotheby's, New York #98/R est:3000-5000
£1935 $3000 €2903 Standing male nude with studies of hands (46x29cm-18x11in) s.d.93 pencil htd white. 29-Oct-2 Sotheby's, New York #101/R est:800-1200
£7742 $12000 €11613 Study of a man with raised arms. Prometheus and Athena creating man (65x30cm-26x12in) init.d.97 pencil red chk two exhib. 29-Oct-2 Sotheby's, New York #99/R est:3000-4000

GREIS, Otto (1913-2001) German
£3478 $5704 €4800 Wind (80x80cm-31x31in) s.d.77 s.i.d. Marz 77 verso prov. 28-May-3 Lempertz, Koln #155/R est:4000

GREIVE, Johan Conrad (jnr) (1837-1891) Dutch
£3774 $5811 €6000 Shipping in a stiff breeze (47x65cm-19x26in) s. prov. 22-Oct-2 Sotheby's, Amsterdam #3/R est:4000-6000

£20548 $32260 €30000 Fishing boats at anchor on the Ij near Amsterdam (72x111cm-28x44in) s. 15-Apr-3 Sotheby's, Amsterdam #156/R est:20000-50000

GRELLE, Martin (1954-) American
£1781 $2600 €2672 The Matterhorn (46x61cm-18x24in) 18-May-2 Altermann Galleries, Santa Fe #201/R
£2397 $3500 €3596 Lords of the land (41x76cm-16x30in) 18-May-2 Altermann Galleries, Santa Fe #150/R
£4795 $7000 €7193 Headin' them home (51x76cm-20x30in) 18-May-2 Altermann Galleries, Santa Fe #143/R
£8442 $13000 €12663 Telling the tale (61x76cm-24x30in) 25-Oct-2 Morris & Whiteside, Hilton Head Island #31 est:13000-15000
£9578 $14750 €14367 New wealth (51x91cm-20x36in) 25-Oct-2 Morris & Whiteside, Hilton Head Island #20 est:13000-15000
£11538 $18000 €17307 Passing through the hole (76x102cm-30x40in) 9-Nov-2 Altermann Galleries, Santa Fe #77
£14198 $23000 €20587 Warrior down (91x102cm-36x40in) 23-May-3 Altermann Galleries, Santa Fe #23

GREMLICH, Adolf (1915-1971) German
£3493 $5450 €5240 Irises in vase with butterfly (65x53cm-26x21in) s.d.1969 board. 6-Nov-2 Hans Widmer, St Gallen #56/R est:4000-7000 (S.FR 8000)

GRENIER, François (19/20th C) French
£946 $1476 €1400 Shepherdess with sheep (70x100cm-28x39in) s. 25-Mar-3 Durán, Madrid #693/R
£10323 $16310 €16000 Shepherdess with sheep in the stable (70x100cm-28x39in) s. 18-Dec-2 Ansorena, Madrid #148/R est:1600

GRENIER, Henri (20th C) French
Works on paper
£535 $834 €850 View of Paris (34x49cm-13x19in) s. gouache. 8-Oct-2 Ansorena, Madrid #584
£645 $1019 €1000 View of Paris (33x48cm-13x19in) s. gouache. 17-Dec-2 Durán, Madrid #139/R
£645 $1019 €1000 View of Paris (33x48cm-13x19in) s. gouache. 17-Dec-2 Durán, Madrid #138/R

GRENNESS, Johannes (1875-1963) Danish
£344 $558 €499 Still life of flowers (65x66cm-26x26in) s. 24-May-3 Rasmussen, Havnen #2224/R (D.KR 3600)
£360 $580 €540 Woman reading (43x51cm-17x20in) s. 22-Feb-3 Rasmussen, Havnen #2025/R (D.KR 4000)

GREPPI, Antonio (19th C) Italian
£2400 $3816 €3600 Venetian house on the canal (52x35cm-20x14in) s. 20-Mar-3 Christie's, Kensington #48/R est:2000-3000

GRESELY, Gabriel (1712-1756) French
£12766 $21319 €18000 Trompe-l'oeil au violon et aux gravures (85x65cm-33x26in) s. 23-Jun-3 Beaussant & Lefèvre, Paris #269 est:5000-6000

GRESLEY, Frank (1855-1936) British
£520 $801 €780 Rural scene with figures, geese and thatched cottage (30x45cm-12x18in) s. 22-Oct-2 Bonhams, Bath #87
Works on paper
£400 $636 €600 Cattle in a meadow before a country house (17x26cm-7x10in) s. W/C. 5-Mar-3 Bonhams, Bury St Edmunds #298
£440 $713 €660 Preparing to go fishing (18x26cm-7x10in) s. W/C. 21-May-3 Bonhams, Knightsbridge #7/R
£480 $782 €696 Young woman outside a thatched cottage near a stream (62x47cm-24x19in) s. W/C. 17-Jul-3 Tennants, Leyburn #769
£650 $1053 €975 Cottage in a rural setting (18x27cm-7x11in) s. W/C. 21-May-3 Bonhams, Knightsbridge #86/R
£1000 $1660 €1450 Children outside a Derbyshire cottage (27x18cm-11x7in) s. pencil W/C. 10-Jun-3 Mellors & Kirk, Nottingham #799/R est:400-600

GRESLEY, Harold (1892-1967) British
Works on paper
£300 $477 €450 Welsh coastal scene (37x54cm-15x21in) s. W/C. 18-Mar-3 Rosebery Fine Art, London #844/R
£800 $1328 €1160 Monsal Dale Derbyshire (27x36cm-11x14in) s. pencil W/C. 10-Jun-3 Mellors & Kirk, Nottingham #796/R
£1200 $1956 €1800 Bluebell woods at Ingleby, Derbyshire (29x34cm-11x13in) s. pencil W/C htd white. 13-Feb-3 Mellors & Kirk, Nottingham #770
£1400 $2282 €2100 River landscape in summer, with cattle crossing a bridge, near cottages (36x54cm-14x21in) s. W/C htd white. 29-Jan-3 Hampton & Littlewood, Exeter #365/R est:500-600

GRESLEY, James S (1829-1908) British
Works on paper
£280 $437 €406 On the Wye (11x18cm-4x7in) s.d.1865 W/C. 27-Mar-3 Neales, Nottingham #913
£310 $484 €450 Dovedale, Derbyshire (12x18cm-5x7in) s.d.1871 W/C. 27-Mar-3 Neales, Nottingham #914
£340 $530 €493 Ambergate, Derbyshire (11x8cm-4x3in) s. W/C. 27-Mar-3 Neales, Nottingham #915
£360 $562 €522 Near Bakewell, Derbyshire (12x18cm-5x7in) s.d.71 W/C. 27-Mar-3 Neales, Nottingham #912
£380 $593 €551 Pont-y-Pair, Betws-y-coed, North Wales (13x20cm-5x8in) s. W/C. 27-Mar-3 Neales, Nottingham #911
£580 $916 €870 Mother and child beside a thatched cottage with calves in the foreground. Cattle by a river (19cm-7in circular) s. W/C pair. 2-Dec-2 Bonhams, Bath #12
£580 $916 €870 Farmhouse in a wooded landscape. Bolton Abbey on the Wharfe (19cm-7in circular) s. W/C pair. 2-Dec-2 Bonhams, Bath #14
£680 $1061 €1020 Summer wooded river landscape with figure, horse and cattle (38x51cm-15x20in) s.d.1891 W/C. 18-Oct-2 Keys, Aylsham #656/R

GRETHE, Carlos (1864-1913) German
£256 $397 €400 Church in the dunes (57x81cm-22x32in) s. i. verso. 5-Dec-2 Dr Fritz Nagel, Stuttgart #655/R
£314 $491 €500 North Sea fisherman (49x66cm-19x26in) s. i. verso. 19-Sep-2 Dr Fritz Nagel, Stuttgart #935/R
£484 $711 €750 Ships in harbour (26x35cm-10x14in) mono. i. verso canvas on board. 20-Jun-2 Dr Fritz Nagel, Stuttgart #768/R

GRETZNER, Harold (1902-1977) American
Works on paper
£581 $900 €872 Gretzner's green house (53x71cm-21x28in) s. i.verso W/C prov. 29-Oct-2 John Moran, Pasadena #687a

GREUX, Amadee Paul (1836-?) French
£286 $454 €420 Scene de rue (33x24cm-13x9in) s. 24-Mar-3 Thierry & Lannon, Brest #93

GREUZE, Jean-Baptiste (1725-1805) French
£40123 $65000 €60185 Portrait of a gentleman, possibly Nicolas Pierre Baptiste Anselme (69x59cm-27x23in) panel prov.lit. 24-Jan-3 Christie's, Rockefeller NY #121/R est:60000-80000
£49383 $80000 €74075 Study of an olld man (40x32cm-16x13in) prov.lit. 23-Jan-3 Sotheby's, New York #94/R est:60000-80000
£109756 $180000 €164634 Jeune fille a la colombe - young girl holding a dove (65x54cm-26x21in) prov.exhib.lit. 30-May-3 Christie's, Rockefeller NY #39/R est:10000-15000
£119718 $198732 €170000 Jeune fille pensive (41x33cm-16x13in) panel. 16-Jun-3 Claude Aguttes, Neuilly #23/R est:60000-80000
Works on paper
£878 $1370 €1300 Nu feminin (29x11cm-11x4in) sanguine. 26-Mar-3 Piasa, Paris #68
£3291 $5134 €5200 Etude de femme voilee (25x19cm-10x7in) i. sanguine. 18-Oct-2 Raboürdin & Choppin de Janvry, Paris #80/R
£7000 $11690 €10150 Couple with a child escaping from a burning house (48x34cm-19x13in) black chk ink wash htd white corner made up prov. 8-Jul-3 Christie's, London #69/R est:7000-10000
£49102 $82000 €71198 Head of a young lady (38x30cm-15x12in) red chk prov.exhib. 21-Jun-3 Selkirks, St. Louis #1052/R est:25000-30000

GREUZE, Jean-Baptiste (attrib) (1725-1805) French
Works on paper
£321 $506 €500 Portrait of young woman wearing pearl necklace (17x12cm-7x5in) ochre. 15-Nov-2 Reiss & Sohn, Konigstein #145/R
£1892 $2951 €2800 Chien marchant vers la droite (28x43cm-11x17in) i. chk stump prov. 27-Mar-3 Christie's, Paris #107/R

GREUZE, Jean-Baptiste (studio) (1725-1805) French
£10976 $18000 €16464 Young girl holding a dove (42x33cm-17x13in) prov.lit. 29-May-3 Sotheby's, New York #29/R est:10000-15000

GREVENBROECK, Alessandro (18th C) Italian
£3103 $4934 €4500 View of harbour (51x71cm-20x28in) 9-Mar-3 Semenzato, Venice #7/R

GREVENBROECK, Alessandro (attrib) (18th C) Italian
£10625 $17000 €15938 Sea battle with galleons and ships. Capriccio landscape (42x70cm-17x28in) pair. 14-May-3 Butterfields, San Francisco #1015/R est:7000-10000

GREVENBROECK, Orazio (17/18th C) Dutch
£1335 $2190 €1936 Mediterranean harbour scene with vessels (16x30cm-6x12in) copper. 4-Jun-3 AB Stockholms Auktionsverk #2549/R est:15000-20000 (S.KR 17000)
£9756 $16000 €14634 Unloading of the ship in an imaginary port (122x196cm-48x77in) prov. 29-May-3 Sotheby's, New York #110/R est:15000-20000
£26000 $43420 €37700 Capricci of Mediterranean harbours, moored shipping and figures on quay (27x54cm-11x21in) silvered copper four prov. 9-Jul-3 Bonhams, New Bond Street #31/R est:30000-40000

GREY, Charles (?-1892) British
£331 $510 €520 Portrait of a young bearded gentleman (23x18cm-9x7in) s.i. paper. 4-Sep-2 James Adam, Dublin #87/R
£700 $1106 €1050 Portrait of a gentleman with a spaniel believed to be Frederick Pilkington (93x77cm-37x30in) s.d.1850. 12-Nov-2 Bonhams, Knightsbridge #226/R

GREY, H (19th C) British?
£1200 $1908 €1800 Figures before a cottage in an extensive landscape (46x81cm-18x32in) s. pair. 6-Mar-3 Christie's, Kensington #446/R est:1000-1200

GREY, Kate (attrib) (19th C) British
£1000 $1640 €1500 Minding the baby (51x61cm-20x24in) 29-May-3 Christie's, Kensington #276/R est:1000-1500

GREY, Roger de (1918-) British
Works on paper
£550 $875 €825 Cascading stream between fir trees (127x91cm-50x36in) mono. W/C. 19-Mar-3 John Nicholson, Haslemere #1122/R

GREY-SMITH, Guy (1916-1981) Australian
£3488 $5547 €5232 Selby (90x59cm-35x23in) s.d.77 s.i.verso board. 5-May-3 Sotheby's, Melbourne #233/R est:5000-12000 (A.D 9000)

GRIBBLE, Bernard Finegan (1873-1962) British
£1100 $1727 €1650 Sinking of the German fleet. Scapa Flow on Saturday June 21 st. (61x86cm-24x34in) s. two. 16-Dec-2 Sotheby's, Olympia #169/R est:1000-1500
Works on paper
£320 $506 €480 Boat manufacturing at the Bristol docks (40x57cm-16x22in) s.i. W/C over pencil. 26-Nov-2 Bonhams, Knightsbridge #85
£480 $778 €720 Britannia and her adversary neck and neck in the Channel (32x44cm-13x17in) s. pencil W/C. 21-May-3 Christie's, Kensington #493/R
£586 $950 €850 Homage to ship design, Sovereign of the seas off Dover, a Tudor warship (39x56cm-15x22in) s. pencil pen ink W/C framed as one. 29-Jul-3 Christie's, Rockefeller NY #100/R

GRIBBON, Edward C (1898-1931) Irish
£833 $1308 €1300 Evian les bains (51x66cm-20x26in) s. 19-Nov-2 Whyte's, Dublin #34/R

GRIEKEN, Jef van (1950-) Belgian
£897 $1391 €1400 Chateau dans la brume (100x120cm-39x47in) s. 9-Dec-2 Horta, Bruxelles #402

GRIENT, Cornelis de (1691-1783) Dutch
Works on paper
£318 $497 €500 Harbour scene (21x28cm-8x11in) pen black ink brown wash. 5-Nov-2 Sotheby's, Amsterdam #229/R

GRIEPENKERL, Christian (1839-1916) German
£1795 $2818 €2800 Binding her sandals (40x31cm-16x12in) s. 10-Dec-2 Dorotheum, Vienna #168/R est:2800-3400

GRIER, Sir Edmond Wyly (1862-1957) British
£944 $1473 €1416 Corner of my dad's studio on Leader Lane (24x35cm-9x14in) i.verso panel prov. 25-Mar-3 Ritchie, Toronto #57/R est:400-600 (C.D 2200)

GRIES, Karl (20th C) German
£256 $390 €400 Resurrection of Christ (46x59cm-18x23in) s. panel. 11-Jul-2 Hugo Ruef, Munich #671

GRIESEL, Hennie (20th C) ?
£295 $460 €443 Still life with copper vessels on a table (70x96cm-28x38in) s. canvas on board. 15-Oct-2 Stephan Welz, Johannesburg #213 est:2000-2500 (SA.R 4800)

GRIESHABER, Helmut A P (1909-1981) German
Prints
£2276 $3596 €3300 Red bloom (53x39cm-21x15in) s.i.d.15.2.59 col woodcut. 2-Apr-3 Dr Fritz Nagel, Stuttgart #9347/R est:1500
£2276 $3596 €3300 Baby VI (49x70cm-19x28in) s. num.9/20 col woodcut board. 2-Apr-3 Dr Fritz Nagel, Stuttgart #9417/R est:2500
£2621 $4141 €3800 The red couple (76x65cm-30x26in) s. col woodcut board. 2-Apr-3 Dr Fritz Nagel, Stuttgart #9434/R est:1500
£2621 $4141 €3800 Woman with peacock (82x70cm-32x28in) s. num.44/70 col woodcut board. 2-Apr-3 Dr Fritz Nagel, Stuttgart #9435/R est:1500
£2658 $4120 €4200 Siamese cats (49x44cm-19x17in) s.i. col woodcut. 28-Sep-2 Ketterer, Hamburg #593/R est:2900-3200
£2754 $4516 €3800 Autumn (61x57cm-24x22in) s. col woodcut. 29-May-3 Lempertz, Koln #643/R est:3500
£2949 $4571 €4600 Ploughing (20x33cm-8x13in) s.d. woodcut. 7-Dec-2 Hauswedell & Nolte, Hamburg #690/R est:2600
£3793 $5993 €5500 Bird (47x46cm-19x18in) s.d. col woodcut. 2-Apr-3 Dr Fritz Nagel, Stuttgart #9426/R est:3800
£4138 $6538 €6000 Evening (61x67cm-24x26in) s. num.5/20 col woodcut board. 2-Apr-3 Dr Fritz Nagel, Stuttgart #9418/R est:3500
£5862 $9262 €8500 Summer (95x120cm-37x47in) s. col woodcut board. 2-Apr-3 Dr Fritz Nagel, Stuttgart #9382/R est:9000
£7586 $11986 €11000 Sandpit (100x120cm-39x47in) s. col woodcut board. 2-Apr-3 Dr Fritz Nagel, Stuttgart #9401/R est:10000
£8966 $14166 €13000 Hen - in fighting stance (75x89cm-30x35in) s. col woodcut. 2-Apr-3 Dr Fritz Nagel, Stuttgart #9392/R est:9000
£9655 $15255 €14000 Ulmo (90x110cm-35x43in) s. woodcut board. 2-Apr-3 Dr Fritz Nagel, Stuttgart #9365/R est:7000
£10345 $16345 €15000 Autumn (91x95cm-36x37in) s. col woodcut. 2-Apr-3 Dr Fritz Nagel, Stuttgart #9441/R est:9800
Works on paper
£338 $527 €500 Portrait of Wolfgang Frankenstein (26x20cm-10x8in) s.i.d.7/VIII/79 W/C col pen. 28-Mar-3 Ketterer, Hamburg #147/R
£828 $1308 €1200 Chrisopherus (42x30cm-17x12in) s.d.28.III.59 col chk tempera. 2-Apr-3 Dr Fritz Nagel, Stuttgart #9368/R
£1154 $1788 €1800 Tsarevitsch (52x38cm-20x15in) col chk. 7-Dec-2 Hauswedell & Nolte, Hamburg #676 est:2200
£1154 $1788 €1800 Tsarina (52x39cm-20x15in) col chk. 7-Dec-2 Hauswedell & Nolte, Hamburg #677 est:2200
£1154 $1788 €1800 Prince and princesses (52x39cm-20x15in) col chk. 7-Dec-2 Hauswedell & Nolte, Hamburg #679/R est:2200
£1603 $2484 €2500 Scythe and flute player (63x41cm-25x16in) i. mixed media canvas. 7-Dec-2 Hauswedell & Nolte, Hamburg #682/R est:3000
£3846 $5962 €6000 Spring (36x46cm-14x18in) s.d. col chk. 7-Dec-2 Hauswedell & Nolte, Hamburg #675/R est:6500
£4138 $6538 €6000 Mythological couple (77x56cm-30x22in) s. silver pen. 2-Apr-3 Dr Fritz Nagel, Stuttgart #9431/R est:8000

GRIEVE, Alec (?-1933) British
£270 $421 €405 Steamer off the coast (23x33cm-9x13in) mono.d.1920 canvas on board. 12-Sep-2 Bonhams, Edinburgh #324
£270 $421 €405 Nature's lullaby (50x60cm-20x24in) mono.d.1931. 12-Sep-2 Bonhams, Edinburgh #334

GRIEVE, W (?) British
£280 $448 €406 Cattle watering (51x76cm-20x30in) s. 17-May-3 Thomson Roddick & Medcalf, Edinburgh #652/R
£500 $800 €725 River scene with village (46x61cm-18x24in) s. 17-May-3 Thomson Roddick & Medcalf, Edinburgh #650/R

GRIFFA, Giorgio (1936-) Italian
£481 $745 €750 Untitled (68x100cm-27x39in) painted 1978 prov. 4-Dec-2 Finarte, Milan #574/R
£510 $811 €750 Flight (70x70cm-28x28in) s.d.1966-67 verso. 1-Mar-3 Meeting Art, Vercelli #513

GRIFFIER, Jan (17/18th C) Dutch
£1300 $2028 €1950 Eagle with a hare in a wooded landscape (120x104cm-47x41in) s. 10-Sep-2 Bonhams, Knightsbridge #197d/R est:1500-2000
£28571 $45429 €42000 Extensive Rhine landscape with boats (37x49cm-15x19in) s.d.1710 copper. 28-Mar-3 Bolland & Marotz, Bremen #406/R est:11000

GRIFFIER, Jan (elder) (1652-1718) Dutch
£20567 $31879 €30851 Rhen landscape with the hermit Antonius (49x39cm-19x15in) s. panel prov.exhib. 4-Dec-2 AB Stockholms Auktionsverk #2008/R est:50000-60000 (S.KR 290000)

GRIFFIER, Jan (younger) (fl.1738-1773) British
£3453 $5525 €4800 Hen protecting her chickens from a hawk, by a ruin (116x99cm-46x39in) prov. 14-May-3 Christie's, Amsterdam #150/R est:2500-3500

GRIFFIER, Robert (1688-1750) British
£6608 $9648 €9912 Rhine landscape with ships and figures (47x56cm-19x22in) s. prov. 17-Jun-2 Philippe Schuler, Zurich #4344/R est:8000-12000 (S.FR 15000)
£8219 $12822 €12000 Idyllic river landscape with ships and herders on shore (39x48cm-15x19in) s. 10-Apr-3 Van Ham, Cologne #1213/R est:24000
£11321 $17547 €18000 Ice skaters (22x31cm-9x12in) 2-Oct-2 Dorotheum, Vienna #177/R est:18000-24000
£14865 $23189 €22000 River landscape with basket weavers (74x110cm-29x43in) s. 27-Mar-3 Dorotheum, Vienna #94/R est:22000-28000

GRIFFIER, Robert (style) (1688-1750) British
£12079 $19448 €18000 Winterlandscape with a figure skating on the ice. Landscape with horsemen and hunters (111x190cm-44x75in) two. 18-Feb-3 Sotheby's, Amsterdam #366/R est:7000-10000

GRIFFIN, David (20th C) American
£1849 $2700 €2774 Girl in rose garden (61x76cm-24x30in) 18-May-2 Altermann Galleries, Santa Fe #229/R

GRIFFIN, James Martin (1850-?) British
£449 $700 €674 Forest scene. board. 21-Sep-2 Harvey Clar, Oakland #1514

GRIFFIN, Keith Alastair (1927-) British
£700 $1085 €1050 Mayflower II retracing the steps of her ancestor, off Cape Cod (61x91cm-24x36in) s. 31-Oct-2 Christie's, Kensington #558/R

GRIFFIN, Thomas Bailey (1858-1918) American
£438 $700 €635 Mountain stream landscape (48x36cm-19x14in) s. 17-May-3 CRN Auctions, Cambridge #5
£472 $750 €708 Delaware water gap (23x30cm-9x12in) s. i.stretcher. 29-Apr-3 Doyle, New York #18
£962 $1500 €1443 On the Gusquehunna River. s. i.verso. 19-Oct-2 Harvey Clar, Oakland #1412a

GRIFFIN, Walter (1861-1935) American
£2404 $3750 €3606 Marchande de legumes, Paimpol, France (48x64cm-19x25in) s.d.1895 s.i.verso. 1-Aug-2 Eldred, East Dennis #916/R est:3000-5000

GRIFFING, Robert (20th C) American
£2055 $3000 €3083 The stone (23x30cm-9x12in) 18-May-2 Altermann Galleries, Santa Fe #88/R
£2055 $3000 €3083 The player (23x30cm-9x12in) 18-May-2 Altermann Galleries, Santa Fe #89/R
£9494 $15000 €13766 Ottawa chief (36x28cm-14x11in) s. 26-Jul-3 Coeur d'Alene, Hayden #25/R est:8000-12000
£11039 $17000 €16559 They came this way (46x30cm-18x12in) 25-Oct-2 Morris & Whiteside, Hilton Head Island #40 est:13000-15000
£41139 $65000 €59652 How could things get any worse ? (91x127cm-36x50in) s. 26-Jul-3 Coeur d'Alene, Hayden #100/R est:60000-90000

GRIFFITH, Frank (1889-1979) British
£600 $936 €900 Shipyard smiths - Sunderland (63x76cm-25x30in) studio st. 27-Mar-3 Christie's, Kensington #564/R

GRIFFITH, Louis Oscar (1875-1956) American
£2147 $3500 €3221 Country path (58x74cm-23x29in) board. 2-Feb-3 Simpson's, Houston #395

GRIFFITH, Marie Osthaus (20th C) American/German
£475 $750 €689 Summer landscape (36x51cm-14x20in) s. 5-Apr-3 DeFina, Austinburg #1293

GRIFFITH, Moses (1747-1819) British
Works on paper
£300 $468 €450 Gynt du on the river Cynlach near Tan-y-Brokeh (22x32cm-9x13in) W/C over pencil htd bodycol. 26-Mar-3 Sotheby's, Olympia #41/R
£520 $848 €780 North view of Fountains Abbey. West view of Fountains Abbey (15x21cm-6x8in) pen ink W/C two. 29-Jan-3 Dreweatt Neate, Newbury #99
£600 $942 €900 View of the Dee near Pentir. Windings of the Dee and Bala Lake (20x32cm-8x13in) one i. W/C over pencil prov. pair. 20-Nov-2 Sotheby's, Olympia #2/R
£900 $1414 €1350 Distant view of the Eife Hills. Dolbadarin Castle (20x31cm-8x12in) W/C over pencil htd bodycol pair. 20-Nov-2 Sotheby's, Olympia #5/R est:1000-1500
£900 $1414 €1350 Nant Mill in Caernarvonshire. Pont-Y-Pair Over river Llugwy (21x33cm-8x13in) W/C over pencil htd bodycol pair. 20-Nov-2 Sotheby's, Olympia #7/R est:1000-1500
£950 $1491 €1425 Castle Dinas Bran, Denbighshire (22x16cm-9x6in) W/C over pencil. 20-Nov-2 Sotheby's, Olympia #40/R est:600-800
£5000 $7950 €7500 Malvern Hills from Bevere, Worcestershire (25x40cm-10x16in) i.verso pen ink W/C over pencil prov.exhib. 19-Mar-3 Sotheby's, London #145/R est:1000-1500

GRIFFITHS, C J (19th C) British
£450 $711 €675 Woodcock in flight (60x51cm-24x20in) s.d.1849. 28-Nov-2 Christie's, Kensington #30/R

GRIFFITHS, Harley Cameron (1908-1981) Australian
£214 $327 €321 View of the Goulburn River (76x101cm-30x40in) s.d.57 i.verso prov. 26-Aug-2 Sotheby's, Paddington #606 (A.D 600)
£534 $844 €801 Still life, camellias in a glass vase (45x35cm-18x14in) s.d.51 board. 7-Apr-3 Shapiro, Sydney #449 (A.D 1400)
£569 $871 €854 Pensacola, Spain (45x51cm-18x20in) s.d.55 i.verso board prov. 26-Aug-2 Sotheby's, Paddington #767 est:800-1200 (A.D 1600)

GRIFFITHS, James (1825-1896) Canadian
Works on paper
£287 $445 €431 Still life with pineapple and fruits (18x24cm-7x9in) s. W/C pencil prov. 24-Sep-2 Ritchie, Toronto #3066/R (C.D 700)
£847 $1338 €1271 Mixed bouquet (16x22cm-6x9in) s. W/C. 14-Nov-2 Heffel, Vancouver #118/R est:2500-3500 (C.D 2100)

GRIFFITHS, John (19th C) British
Works on paper
£1016 $1596 €1524 Still life with flowers (42x30cm-17x12in) s. W/C. 10-Dec-2 Pinneys, Montreal #53 est:2500-3500 (C.D 2500)

GRIFFITHS, W T (?) British
£4500 $7425 €6525 Polperro Harbour (76x127cm-30x50in) s. 1-Jul-3 Bonhams, Norwich #227/R est:5000-8000

GRIFFITHS, Wilf Frank (1917-) Canadian
£171 $271 €257 River in Haliburton (61x76cm-24x30in) s. s.i.verso board prov. 14-Nov-2 Heffel, Vancouver #245 (C.D 425)

GRIGGS, Samuel W (1827-1898) American
£1401 $2200 €2102 Summer day on the mountain lake (46x76cm-18x30in) s.d.79. 14-Dec-2 Weschler, Washington #668/R est:2500-3500
£2019 $3250 €3029 Trains passing through the valley (109x109cm-43x43in) s.d.1874. 20-Jan-3 Arthur James, Florida #80
£2202 $3500 €3303 Conway on the Sago (41x66cm-16x26in) s. prov. 7-Mar-3 Skinner, Boston #294/R est:1500-3000
£3365 $5250 €5048 River valley (36x60cm-14x24in) s.d.1881. 9-Nov-2 Sloan, North Bethesda #589/R est:500-700

GRIGORESCO, Nicolas (1838-1907) Rumanian
£723 $1114 €1150 Paysans roumains (20x36cm-8x14in) paper. 27-Oct-2 Muizon & Le Coent, Paris #31/R

GRIGORESCO, Nicolas (attrib) (1838-1907) Rumanian
£1210 $1888 €1900 Girl's portrait (46x35cm-18x14in) s. board. 6-Nov-2 Hugo Ruef, Munich #1110/R est:1500

GRIGORIEV, Boris (1886-1939) Russian
£13000 $20540 €19500 Portrait of a lady in a hat (41x33cm-16x13in) s.d.1931. 26-Nov-2 Christie's, Kensington #38/R est:3000-5000
£17405 $27500 €26108 Landscape with mountains in the distance (51x70cm-20x28in) s. 24-Apr-3 Sotheby's, New York #119/R est:20000-30000
£22000 $34540 €33000 Haystacks (49x62cm-19x24in) s. 20-Nov-2 Sotheby's, London #82/R est:18000-25000
£25000 $40500 €37500 Faces at a window (64x54cm-25x21in) s. prov. 21-May-3 Sotheby's, London #172/R est:25000-35000
£28000 $45360 €42000 Woman of Bourg de Butz (73x54cm-29x21in) s.verso i.on stretcher. 21-May-3 Sotheby's, London #173/R est:20000-25000
£40000 $62800 €60000 Still life of flowers and green shutters (73x60cm-29x24in) s. 20-Nov-2 Sotheby's, London #141/R est:20000-30000
Works on paper
£1139 $1800 €1800 Girl with doll (30x23cm-12x9in) s. dr. 1-Dec-2 Bukowskis, Helsinki #246/R est:1500-2000
£3200 $5184 €4800 Girl on the grass (12x23cm-5x9in) s.d.1918 Indian ink W/C prov. 21-May-3 Sotheby's, London #139/R est:1500-2000

£6000 $9720 €9000 Five Brazilian boys (38x49cm-15x19in) s. gouache. 21-May-3 Sotheby's, London #174/R est:6000-8000

GRILL, Oswald (1878-1969) Austrian
£3793 $6069 €5500 Traces in the snow (80x6cm-31x2in) s.d.44. 11-Mar-3 Dorotheum, Vienna #93/R est:1500-2200

GRILO, Sarah (1921-) Argentinian
£976 $1600 €1464 Sin titulo (42x63cm-17x25in) s. s.i.verso oil ink painted c.1965 prov. 28-May-3 Christie's, Rockefeller NY #158/R est:2000-3000

GRIM, Maurice (1890-1968) French
£637 $993 €1000 Paradis terrestre (38x46cm-15x18in) s. cardboard. 5-Nov-2 Tajan, Paris #11/R

GRIMALDI, Giovanni Francesco (1606-1680) Italian
Works on paper
£1800 $2826 €2700 Saint John the Evangelist (44x28cm-17x11in) s.i. pen ink over black chk. 11-Dec-2 Sotheby's, Olympia #88/R est:2000-3000
£1900 $2983 €2850 Panoramic river landscape with monastic buildings in the distance (21x30cm-8x12in) bears sig pen ink prov. 11-Dec-2 Sotheby's, Olympia #99/R est:1500-1800

GRIMALDI, Giovanni Francesco (attrib) (1606-1680) Italian
£6000 $9420 €9000 Woodec landscape with figures making merry (65x77cm-26x30in) 13-Dec-2 Christie's, Kensington #266/R est:7000-10000

GRIMANI, Guido (1871-1933) Italian
£496 $804 €700 Vicolo orientale (25x16cm-10x6in) s. board. 22-May-3 Stadion, Trieste #372/R
£532 $862 €750 Barche in Sacchetta (16x25cm-6x10in) s. board. 22-May-3 Stadion, Trieste #191/R
£1915 $3102 €2700 Pescatori in laguna (31x46cm-12x18in) s. canvas on board. 22-May-3 Stadion, Trieste #337/R est:2500-3500

GRIMELUND, Johannes Martin (1842-1917) Norwegian
£633 $1025 €950 River landscape (31x41cm-12x16in) s. panel. 27-Jan-3 Blomqvist, Lysaker #1070/R (N.KR 7000)
£851 $1319 €1277 Soleil couchant, Brehat (33x46cm-13x18in) s.d.1910. 4-Dec-2 AB Stockholms Auktionsverk #1913/R (S.KR 12000)
£1038 $1640 €1557 From Le Mexico - docks at Antwerp (46x65cm-18x26in) s.d.1883 i.stretcher. 2-Dec-2 Blomqvist, Oslo #317/R (N.KR 12000)
£1211 $1913 €1817 Fishing on calm lake (38x55cm-15x22in) s.d.1877. 2-Dec-2 Blomqvist, Oslo #362/R est:20000-22000 (N.KR 14000)
£1471 $2324 €2207 From Fjallbacka - coastal scene with boats (47x66cm-19x26in) s.d.11-9-89. 2-Dec-2 Blomqvist, Oslo #321/R est:15000-18000 (N.KR 17000)
£1579 $2495 €2369 Harbour scene, Holland (34x65cm-13x26in) s.indis.i.d.1884. 17-Dec-2 Grev Wedels Plass, Oslo #146/R est:20000-30000 (N.KR 18000)
£1817 $2870 €2726 Le Seine a Rouen (50x80cm-20x31in) s. i.stretcher. 2-Dec-2 Blomqvist, Oslo #350/R est:16000-20000 (N.KR 21000)

GRIMM, Arthur (1883-1948) German
£2877 $4488 €4200 Baden Baden (67x78cm-26x31in) s.d. 11-Apr-3 Winterberg, Heidelberg #1071/R est:5600
£5822 $9082 €8500 Hollerbach (65x80cm-26x31in) s.d. 11-Apr-3 Winterberg, Heidelberg #1070/R est:5600

GRIMM, Paul (1892-1974) American
£313 $500 €470 Scene at sunset (51x61cm-20x24in) s. board. 18-May-3 Butterfields, Los Angeles #7030
£375 $600 €563 Pleasant Vista (51x61cm-20x24in) s. i.verso board. 18-May-3 Butterfields, Los Angeles #7025
£438 $700 €657 Desert Vista (20x25cm-8x10in) s. board. 18-May-3 Butterfields, Los Angeles #7024
£466 $750 €699 Desert verbena (20x25cm-8x10in) s. board prov. 18-Feb-3 John Moran, Pasadena #8
£531 $850 €797 South Fork, Palisades Glacier (41x51cm-16x20in) s.verso board. 18-May-3 Butterfields, Los Angeles #7031
£700 $1100 €1050 Eucalyptus trees (76x51cm-30x20in) s. board. 19-Nov-2 Butterfields, San Francisco #8317/R
£807 $1300 €1211 Morning in the harbour, San Diego (23x30cm-9x12in) s. prov. board. 18-Feb-3 John Moran, Pasadena #157a
£875 $1400 €1313 Temple Crag, Palisades Glacier (51x61cm-20x24in) s. i.d.July 67 verso board. 18-May-3 Butterfields, Los Angeles #7028 est:1500-2500
£932 $1500 €1398 San Jacinto desert verbena (20x25cm-8x10in) s. board prov. 18-Feb-3 John Moran, Pasadena #7 est:1000-1500
£994 $1600 €1491 Eucalyptus trees (30x23cm-12x9in) s. board. 18-Feb-3 John Moran, Pasadena #93 est:2000-3000
£1056 $1700 €1584 Smoke tree ranch, Palm Springs, Calif (23x30cm-9x12in) s. i.d.1948 verso board. 18-Feb-3 John Moran, Pasadena #94 est:1000-2000
£1078 $1800 €1563 Landscape, winter on the desert (41x51cm-16x20in) s. i.verso. 17-Jun-3 John Moran, Pasadena #171 est:2000-3000
£1083 $1700 €1625 Peaceful harbour (66x102cm-26x40in) s. 19-Nov-2 Butterfields, San Francisco #8316/R est:2000-3000
£1097 $1700 €1646 In the valley's (51x61cm-20x24in) s. 29-Oct-2 John Moran, Pasadena #691 est:2500-3500
£1161 $1800 €1742 Chino Canyon and San Jacinto (51x61cm-20x24in) s. board. 28-Sep-2 Charlton Hall, Columbia #538/R est:2500-3500
£1180 $1900 €1770 Golden sycamore (23x30cm-9x12in) s. board. 18-Feb-3 John Moran, Pasadena #22a est:1000-1500
£1198 $2000 €1737 Landscape, among the smoke trees (51x61cm-20x24in) s. i.verso. 17-Jun-3 John Moran, Pasadena #172 est:2000-3000
£1452 $2250 €2178 Temple Crags, Palisades Glacier (61x76cm-24x30in) s. 29-Oct-2 John Moran, Pasadena #751 est:3000-4000
£1497 $2500 €2171 Barn and eucalyptus in landscape (33x41cm-13x16in) s. board prov. 17-Jun-3 John Moran, Pasadena #27a est:2000-3000
£1647 $2750 €2388 Landscape, Sentinels (71x91cm-28x36in) s. i.verso prov. 17-Jun-3 John Moran, Pasadena #180 est:3000-5000
£1796 $3000 €2604 Eucalyptus landscape, nature's sentinel (61x76cm-24x30in) s. i.verso. 17-Jun-3 John Moran, Pasadena #162 est:4000-6000
£1946 $3250 €2822 Eucalyptus landscape - rooted silence (76x102cm-30x40in) s.i.d.1945 prov. 17-Jun-3 John Moran, Pasadena #13 est:3000-5000
£2019 $3250 €3029 Colourful sand dunes (61x76cm-24x30in) s. i.verso prov. 18-Feb-3 John Moran, Pasadena #156 est:3000-4000
£2019 $3250 €3029 Glacier Palisades (51x61cm-20x24in) s. i.verso. 18-Feb-3 John Moran, Pasadena #157 est:2000-3000
£2484 $4000 €3726 La Crescenta foothills (30x41cm-12x16in) s. i.d.1934 verso masonite. 18-Feb-3 John Moran, Pasadena #22 est:2500-3500
£2640 $4250 €3960 Restful lane (61x76cm-24x30in) s. i.d.1946 verso. 18-Feb-3 John Moran, Pasadena #45 est:7000-9000
£3727 $6000 €5591 Peaceful ranch (61x76cm-24x30in) s. i.verso. 18-Feb-3 John Moran, Pasadena #41 est:6000-8000
£3846 $6000 €5769 Sierra golden autumn. board. 21-Sep-2 Harvey Clar, Oakland #1505
£3915 $6500 €5677 Old San Jacinto (76x102cm-30x40in) s. i.verso i. on stretcher prov. 11-Jun-3 Butterfields, San Francisco #4337/R est:3000-5000
£4194 $6500 €6291 Cabin in atmospheric landscape (46x61cm-18x24in) s. board. 29-Oct-2 John Moran, Pasadena #630a est:3000-5000
£4516 $7000 €6774 Late afternoon (58x79cm-23x31in) s. 29-Oct-2 John Moran, Pasadena #630b est:5000-7000

GRIMM, Samuel Hieronymus (1733-1794) Swiss
Works on paper
£419 $650 €629 Cottage and small bridge in a landscape (16x28cm-6x11in) black chk pen black ink W/C. 3-Dec-2 Christie's, Rockefeller NY #57/R
£3600 $5724 €5400 Roche Abbey, Yorkshire (23x33cm-9x13in) s. s.verso prov.exhib. 19-Mar-3 Sotheby's, London #142/R est:3000-4000

GRIMM, Stanley (1891-1966) British
£650 $1073 €943 Still life with vase of flowers (76x63cm-30x25in) s. 3-Jul-3 Christie's, Kensington #486/R

GRIMMER, Abel (1573-1619) Flemish
£14634 $24000 €21951 Moated tower with farmhouses (16x37cm-6x15in) panel. 30-May-3 Christie's, Rockefeller NY #17/R est:10000-15000

GRIMMER, Abel (circle) (1573-1619) Flemish
£9554 $14904 €15000 Church interior with a funeral procession (35x46cm-14x18in) bears sig.d.1599 panel. 5-Nov-2 Sotheby's, Amsterdam #251/R est:10000-15000
£12000 $18840 €18000 Church interior with figures (47x72cm-19x28in) panel. 12-Dec-2 Sotheby's, London #171/R est:12000-18000

GRIMMER, Jacob (studio) (1526-1589) Flemish
£12000 $18720 €18000 Village with elegant figures approaching on horseback (42x56cm-17x22in) panel prov. 9-Apr-3 Bonhams, New Bond Street #11/R est:4000-6000

GRIMONT, Odette (20th C) French
£374 $595 €550 Port breton (38x46cm-15x18in) s.on stretcher. 24-Mar-3 Coutau Begarie, Paris #238

GRIMOU, Alexis (attrib) (1680-1740) French
£839 $1401 €1200 Portrait d'homme soulevant son chapeau (41x37cm-16x15in) 27-Jun-3 Piasa, Paris #62
£1130 $1752 €1695 Portrait of woman wearing felt hat (70x60cm-28x24in) 9-Dec-2 Philippe Schuler, Zurich #3817/R est:4000-4500 (S.FR 2600)

GRIMSHAW, Atkinson (1836-1893) British
£4300 $6622 €6450 Swanston Street, Melbourne, between the lights (30x46cm-12x18in) s. s.i.verso photographic base paper on canvas. 5-Sep-2 Christie's, Kensington #201/R est:5000-7000
£4800 $7392 €7200 Home of the heron (60x91cm-24x36in) s.i. 5-Sep-2 Christie's, Kensington #202/R est:3000-5000

£26000 $43160 €39000 Ghyll Beck Bridge, Barden, Yorkshire (91x71cm-36x28in) s.d.1885 i.verso prov. 10-Jun-3 Christie's, London #143/R est:20000-30000
£34000 $53720 €51000 On the Esk at Whitby (29x44cm-11x17in) s.d.1877 board prov. 26-Nov-2 Christie's, London #133/R est:18000-25000
£36000 $56520 €54000 Whitby harbour my moonlight (28x43cm-11x17in) i.verso artists board prov. 16-Dec-2 Sotheby's, London #75/R est:40000-60000
£40000 $66800 €58000 Bridge (61x91cm-24x36in) s. s.i.verso. 17-Jun-3 Bonhams, New Bond Street #75/R est:40000-60000
£56000 $88480 €84000 Liverpool docks by moonlight (34x44cm-13x17in) s.d.92. 7-Apr-3 David Duggleby, Scarborough #419/R est:30000-40000
£65625 $105000 €98438 Autumn scene of tree lined street with woman near a stone wall (64x76cm-25x30in) s. i.verso. 16-May-3 York Town, York #998 est:25000-35000
£70000 $116200 €105000 Roundhay lake, Leeds (46x69cm-18x27in) s.d.5.93 s.i.d.verso prov. 12-Jun-3 Sotheby's, London #213/R est:70000-90000
£75000 $118500 €112500 Autumnal evening glow (30x51cm-12x20in) s.d.1882 board. 2-Dec-2 Sotheby's, London #29/R est:50000-70000
£76786 $121321 €115179 Liverpool Docks by moonlight (60x91cm-24x36in) s. prov. 26-Nov-2 Sotheby's, Melbourne #233/R est:200000-300000 (A.D 215000)
£78000 $123240 €117000 December moonlight (76x63cm-30x25in) s.d.1885 s.i.d.verso. 26-Nov-2 Christie's, London #134/R est:60000-80000
£82000 $129560 €123000 Liverpool by gaslight (58x90cm-23x35in) s. s.i.verso prov. 26-Nov-2 Christie's, London #135/R est:60000-100000
£91000 $142870 €136500 Lane scene, possibly a view of Knostrop Hall, Leeds (47x36cm-19x14in) s.d.1880 board on panel prov. 19-Nov-2 Bonhams, Leeds #249 est:60000-80000
£129032 $200000 €193548 Gourock, near the Clyde shipping dock (61x93cm-24x37in) s. s.i.verso prov. 29-Oct-2 Sotheby's, New York #157/R est:200000-300000
£130000 $208000 €195000 Chelsea street (30x25cm-12x10in) s.d.1885 s.i.d.1885 verso prov. 15-May-3 Lawrence, Crewkerne #998/R est:70000-90000
£180000 $289800 €270000 Harbour flare (76x127cm-30x50in) s.d.1879 s.i.d.on stretcher prov.exhib.lit. 19-Feb-3 Christie's, London #20/R est:200000-300000
£206000 $344020 €298700 Autumn gold - woman passing a walled townhouse at twilight (75x63cm-30x25in) s.d.1888 i.verso. 17-Jun-3 Anderson & Garland, Newcastle #458/R est:40000-70000
£309677 $480000 €464516 Spirit of night (82x122cm-32x48in) s.d.1879 prov.exhib. 30-Oct-2 Christie's, Rockefeller NY #34/R est:220000-280000

Works on paper
£20000 $33200 €30000 Autumn sunlight (26x42cm-10x17in) s. i.verso W/C. 12-Jun-3 Sotheby's, London #209/R est:12000-18000

GRIMSHAW, Louis (1870-1943) British
£14000 $21700 €21000 Sunderland with boats at dusk with the lights on the boats (31x46cm-12x18in) s.d.99. 25-Sep-2 John Nicholson, Haslemere #1021/R est:5000-8000

GRINEAU, Bryan de (1882-1957) French
Works on paper
£2000 $3080 €3000 Vintage Bentley Tourer at full throttle (44x60cm-17x24in) s.d.1937 crayon W/C gouache. 23-Oct-2 Hampton & Littlewood, Exeter #428/R est:1000-1500

GRINNELL, George Victor (1878-1946) American
£6329 $10000 €9494 Old mystic vista (76x91cm-30x36in) s. i.verso. 24-Apr-3 Shannon's, Milford #58/R est:5000-7000

GRIOT, Francois Marie (1951-) French
£313 $509 €450 Scheherazade et le sultan (80x60cm-31x24in) s. panel. 19-Jul-3 Thierry & Lannon, Brest #202
£317 $510 €450 La boite de Pandore (73x60cm-29x24in) s.d.28.02.03 acrylic panel. 11-May-3 Thierry & Lannon, Brest #257

GRIPS, Charles Joseph (1825-1920) Belgian
£17964 $30000 €26048 Woman in interior preparing a meal (44x33cm-17x13in) s.d.1862 panel. 22-Jun-3 Freeman, Philadelphia #9/R est:5000-8000

GRIS, Juan (1887-1927) Spanish
£300000 $501000 €450000 Compotier, carafe et livre ouvert (50x65cm-20x26in) s. painted 1925 prov.exhib.lit. 23-Jun-3 Sotheby's, London #23/R est:300000-400000
£321678 $537203 €460000 Pipe, tabac, verre et journal (38x46cm-15x18in) s.d.2-19 prov.exhib.lit. 30-Jun-3 Artcurial Briest, Paris #50/R

Works on paper
£3800 $6004 €5700 Costume design (27x18cm-11x7in) s.i. pencil chl wax crayon gouache prov.exhib. 3-Apr-3 Christie's, Kensington #78/R
£19725 $32940 €28601 Compotier et verre (24x31cm-9x12in) chk prov. 20-Jun-3 Kornfeld, Bern #65/R est:40000 (S.FR 43000)
£26923 $42269 €42000 At the races (35x26cm-14x10in) s. crayon felt-tip pen htd gouache dr. 16-Dec-2 Rabourdin & Choppin de Janvry, Paris #131/R est:60000

GRIS, Juan (attrib) (1887-1927) Spanish
Works on paper
£1448 $2345 €2200 Le medecin, projet d'illustration. Etude de personnages (39x31cm-15x12in) s. gouache black crayon double-sided. 22-Jan-3 Tajan, Paris #115 est:2500-3000

GRISENKO, Nikolas (1856-1900) Russian
£7000 $10990 €10500 Imperial yacht The Aurora moored off the Black Sea coast (41x27cm-16x11in) s. board. 20-Nov-2 Sotheby's, London #46/R est:2000-3000

GRISET, Ernest (attrib) (1844-1907) French
Works on paper
£350 $571 €525 Frogs, snakes and newts atop a tree stump (13x23cm-5x9in) s. pen ink dr W/C. 7-Feb-3 Dee Atkinson & Harrison, Driffield #744

GRISON, François Adolphe (1845-1914) French
£480 $749 €720 Stag and roe deer (51x61cm-20x24in) s. prov. 9-Nov-2 Galerie Gloggner, Luzern #65/R (S.FR 1100)
£1135 $1771 €1703 At the alchemist (19x24cm-7x9in) s. panel prov. 9-Nov-2 Galerie Gloggner, Luzern #64/R est:1400-1600 (S.FR 2600)
£1761 $2923 €2500 Promenade a dos d'ane (39x23cm-15x9in) s. panel. 13-Jun-3 Rabourdin & Choppin de Janvry, Paris #115/R est:3000-3500
£6550 $10349 €9825 Apres le combat (41x33cm-16x13in) s. 17-Nov-2 Koller, Geneva #1255/R est:30000 (S.FR 15000)

GRISOT, Pierre (1911-1995) French
£417 $646 €650 Jeune danseuse assise (27x21cm-11x8in) s. panel. 7-Dec-2 De Vuyst, Lokeren #139/R
£542 $890 €830 Baigneuse dans un paysage (35x27cm-14x11in) s. masonite. 7-Feb-3 Oger, Dumont, Paris #94/R
£620 $955 €930 Jeune fille assise (23x18cm-9x7in) s. board. 22-Oct-2 Bonhams, Bath #96
£692 $1072 €1100 Jeune femme se promenant (33x26cm-13x10in) s. 5-Oct-2 De Vuyst, Lokeren #159
£933 $1549 €1353 Parisienne (27x22cm-11x9in) s. masonite prov. 16-Jun-3 Waddingtons, Toronto #271/R est:800-1200 (C.D 2100)
£1034 $1728 €1500 Elegante a l'ombrelle (27x22cm-11x9in) s. isorel. 9-Jul-3 Millon & Associes, Paris #131/R est:1500-1800
£1069 $1785 €1550 Elegantes au cafe (35x27cm-14x11in) s. isorel. 9-Jul-3 Millon & Associes, Paris #130/R est:1500-1800
£1092 $1757 €1550 Jeune femme au parapluie (35x27cm-14x11in) s. 11-May-3 Lombrail & Teucquam, Paris #230/R
£1092 $1757 €1550 Parisienne pres de la Tour Eiffel (27x22cm-11x9in) s. isorel. 11-May-3 Lombrail & Teucquam, Paris #231/R
£1127 $1814 €1600 Elegante pres de la riviere (27x22cm-11x9in) s. isorel. 11-May-3 Lombrail & Teucquam, Paris #233/R
£1151 $1842 €1600 Nu assis (35x26cm-14x10in) s. panel. 18-May-3 Eric Pillon, Calais #104/R
£1235 $1753 €2000 Jeune fille dans le parc (35x27cm-14x11in) s. panel. 16-Mar-3 Eric Pillon, Calais #193/R
£1358 $1928 €2200 Ballerines (38x46cm-15x18in) s. 16-Mar-3 Eric Pillon, Calais #192/R
£1847 $2882 €2900 Paris, promeneurs sur les quais (27x22cm-11x9in) s. panel. 10-Nov-2 Eric Pillon, Calais #127/R
£1852 $2630 €3000 Jeune fille aux courses (45x46cm-18x18in) s. panel. 16-Mar-3 Eric Pillon, Calais #195/R
£2374 $3799 €3300 Les deux jeunes filles dans le parc (55x46cm-22x18in) s. 18-May-3 Eric Pillon, Calais #103/R

GRISOT, Pierre (attrib) (1911-1995) French
£270 $451 €392 Circus (60x49cm-24x19in) s.d.1967 board. 24-Jun-3 Rowley Fine Art, Newmarket #371

GRITCHENKO, Alexis (1883-1977) Russian
£1450 $2262 €2175 Vieux Paris (45x40cm-18x16in) s. board. 17-Sep-2 Rosebery Fine Art, London #561 est:400-600
£3000 $4860 €4500 Rocky Breton coast line (73x100cm-29x39in) s. board. 21-May-3 Sotheby's, London #94/R est:3000-5000

GRITSCHKER-KUNZENDORF, Anna (1871-?) German
£700 $1169 €1015 Portrait of Agnes von Glasgow (201x101cm-79x40in) s.d.1899. 17-Jun-3 Rosebery Fine Art, London #469/R

GRITTEN, Henry C (1818-1873) British
£562 $894 €843 Highland scene with cattle (30x43cm-12x17in) s.d.1872 prov. 5-May-3 Sotheby's, Melbourne #345 (A.D 1450)

GRIVOLAS, Antoine (1843-1902) French
£1306 $2050 €1959 Still life of flowers (69x51cm-27x20in) s. 16-Dec-2 Lilla Bukowskis, Stockholm #533 est:6000-8000 (S.KR 18500)

GROB, Konrad (1828-1904) Swiss
£655 $1028 €983 Kerenzerberg (36x48cm-14x19in) s. s.i. verso. 25-Nov-2 Sotheby's, Zurich #19/R (S.FR 1500)
£2315 $3727 €3473 Children playing in meadow (50x75cm-20x30in) s.i. 7-May-3 Dobiaschofsky, Bern #610/R est:7500 (S.FR 5000)

GROBE, German (1857-1938) German
£816 $1298 €1200 Fiskare - coastal landscape with vessels (53x38cm-21x15in) s.d.1896. 24-Mar-3 Bukowskis, Helsinki #375/R
£1056 $1701 €1500 Fisherwomen on the dunes (38x48cm-15x19in) s.d.33 board. 6-May-3 Vendu Notarishuis, Rotterdam #125/R est:1500-2000
£2113 $3401 €3000 Fishing boat in the surf (58x78cm-23x31in) s. 7-May-3 Vendue Huis, Gravenhage #477/R est:3000-5000
£3459 $5327 €5500 Bomschuiten in the breakers (39x50cm-15x20in) s. panel. 23-Oct-2 Christie's, Amsterdam #183/R est:2500-3000

GROEBER, Hermann (1865-1935) German
£701 $1093 €1100 Village landscape (25x33cm-10x13in) s. board. 6-Nov-2 Hugo Ruef, Munich #111/R

GROEN, Geoffrey de (1938-) Australian
Works on paper
£1083 $1679 €1625 Slithy toves (137x135cm-54x53in) s.i.d.verso synthetic polymer paint canvas prov. 3-Dec-2 Shapiro, Sydney #91/R est:2500-3500 (A.D 3000)

GROEN, Hendrik Pieter (1886-1964) Dutch
£461 $746 €700 Afbraak Delftschevaart, Rotterdam (33x40cm-13x16in) s. s.i.d.Oct 1922 verso canvas on panel. 21-Jan-3 Christie's, Amsterdam #346
£4605 $7461 €7000 Horse drawn cart a quay along the river Maas, Rotterdam (61x89cm-24x35in) s. 21-Jan-3 Christie's, Amsterdam #351/R est:4000-6000

GROENESTEIN, Jan (19th C) Dutch
£496 $804 €700 Rokin in Amsterdam (36x47cm-14x19in) s.d.49 panel. 26-May-3 Glerum, Amsterdam #35/R
£694 $1146 €1000 Bullfight (29x64cm-11x25in) s. board prov. 1-Jul-3 Christie's, Amsterdam #580/R

GROENEVELD, Cornelius (1882-1952) Dutch
£1193 $1850 €1790 Moored boats near village shore (56x70cm-22x28in) s. prov. 3-Dec-2 Ritchie, Toronto #3061/R est:2000-2500 (C.D 2900)
£1317 $2041 €1976 Nieuvwkoop (76x100cm-30x39in) s. prov. 3-Dec-2 Ritchie, Toronto #3060/R est:3000-4000 (C.D 3200)
£1931 $3013 €2800 Motherly attention (76x61cm-30x24in) s. prov. 26-Mar-3 Walker's, Ottawa #9/R est:2500-3500 (C.D 4500)

GROENEWEGEN, Adrianus Johannes (1874-1963) Dutch
£516 $800 €774 Old homestead, Gravehagen, Holland (20x25cm-8x10in) s. painted c.1910. 8-Dec-2 Toomey, Oak Park #623/R

GROENEWEGEN, Gerrit (1754-1826) Dutch
£252 $390 €400 Coastal scene (9x13cm-4x5in) s. sepia. 4-Nov-2 Glerum, Amsterdam #93

GROENEWEGEN, Gerrit (circle) (1754-1826) Dutch
Works on paper
£6369 $9936 €10000 Fishing boats by a pier (26x41cm-10x16in) bears sig.d.1792 pen brown ink W/C. 5-Nov-2 Sotheby's, Amsterdam #109/R est:800-1200

GROENEWEGEN, Pieter Anthonisz van (?-1658) Dutch
£11950 $18522 €19000 Italian landscape with ruins of classical buildings and figures at a well (29x38cm-11x15in) s. panel prov. 4-Nov-2 Glerum, Amsterdam #13/R est:10000-15000

GROESBECK, Dan Sayre (1878-1950) American
£778 $1300 €1128 Pirates in sword fight (46x53cm-18x21in) oil mixed media. 17-Jun-3 John Moran, Pasadena #81 est:1500-2000

GROH, Gundi (20th C) Austrian
£316 $494 €500 In the stocking cupboard (14x19cm-6x7in) s.d.1989 masonite. 15-Oct-2 Dorotheum, Vienna #260/R
£380 $592 €600 Concentrated power (23x16cm-9x6in) s.d.1991 masonite. 15-Oct-2 Dorotheum, Vienna #261/R
£570 $889 €900 Beautiful evening (19x20cm-7x8in) s.i.d.1992 masonite. 15-Oct-2 Dorotheum, Vienna #262/R

GROL, Henny van (1957-) Dutch
Sculpture
£1111 $1833 €1600 Two sea lions (34cm-13in) bronze stone base prov. 1-Jul-3 Christie's, Amsterdam #590/R est:400-600

GROLIG, Curt Victor Clemens (1805-1863) German
£3400 $5644 €4930 Busy quayside with an artist sketching (41x50cm-16x20in) s.d.1830. 10-Jun-3 Mellors & Kirk, Nottingham #871/R est:2000-4000
£3782 $5862 €5900 Algerian harbour with fortress (32x46cm-13x18in) s. prov. 7-Dec-2 Ketterer, Hamburg #87/R est:4000-4500
£5102 $8112 €7500 Un port d'Orient (32x48cm-13x19in) s. 24-Mar-3 Rabourdin & Choppin de Janvry, Paris #133/R est:7500-9000

GROLL, Albert Lorey (1866-1952) American
£313 $500 €470 Country landscape with figure and house on hill (41x30cm-16x12in) s. 15-Mar-3 Jeffery Burchard, Florida #73/R
£629 $1000 €944 Arizona mountains scene (15x20cm-6x8in) s. board prov. 5-Mar-3 Sotheby's, New York #138/R est:800-1200
£1090 $1700 €1635 Landscapes (10x13cm-4x5in) board four. 19-Oct-2 David Dike, Dallas #199/R est:2500-5000
£4808 $7500 €7212 Landscape near Hopi village, New Mexico (71x91cm-28x36in) s. prov. 9-Nov-2 Santa Fe Art, Santa Fe #69/R est:15000-20000

GROLL, Andreas (attrib) (1850-1907) Austrian
£3145 $4906 €5000 Allegories of the virtues (90cm-35in circular) tondo four. 23-Sep-2 Wiener Kunst Auktionen, Vienna #65a est:4000-6000
£7547 $11774 €12000 Allegory of music (470x230cm-185x91in) ceiling painting. 23-Sep-2 Wiener Kunst Auktionen, Vienna #65/R est:4000-8000

GROLLERON, Paul Louis Narcisse (1848-1901) French
£833 $1300 €1250 Helmet maker (18x13cm-7x5in) s. panel. 9-Oct-2 Doyle, New York #48
£976 $1600 €1415 Wounded soldier (28x20cm-11x8in) s. panel. 4-Jun-3 Doyle, New York #61 est:1500-2500
£1761 $2923 €2500 Le sergent Tanviray (33x46cm-13x18in) s.d.94. 13-Jun-3 Rabourdin & Choppin de Janvry, Paris #73/R est:2500-3000
£2188 $3500 €3282 The toll (56x46cm-22x18in) s. canvasboard. 14-May-3 Butterfields, San Francisco #1116/R est:4000-6000

GROLMAN, Johannes Paul Costantinus (1841-1927) Dutch
£563 $907 €800 Large church of Alkmaar (17x13cm-7x5in) s. panel. 7-May-3 Vendue Huis, Gravenhage #371/R
£2483 $3948 €3600 Interior view of a synagogue in Nijkerk (40x50cm-16x20in) s. s.i.verso. 10-Mar-3 Sotheby's, Amsterdam #160 est:1200-1800

GROM-ROTTMAYER, Hermann (1877-1953) Austrian
£509 $820 €764 Family pleasures (109x84cm-43x33in) s.d.12. 7-May-3 Dobiaschofsky, Bern #611/R (S.FR 1100)

GROMAIRE, Marcel (1892-1971) French
£1795 $2782 €2800 Pot jaune (41x33cm-16x13in) init. s.i.d.1919 verso lit. 9-Dec-2 Beaussant & Lefèvre, Paris #55/R
£2041 $3245 €3000 Tete d'homme (15x10cm-6x4in) s.d.1923 panel prov.exhib.lit. 26-Feb-3 Artcurial Briest, Paris #301/R est:2500-3000
£3650 $5767 €5475 Chateau dans les Sapins (41x33cm-16x13in) s.d.1934 panel prov. 28-Apr-3 Bukowskis, Stockholm #299/R est:40000-60000 (S.KR 48000)
£5769 $9058 €9000 Soleil couchant, maree montante (54x65cm-21x26in) s.d.1955 s.i.d.verso exhib.lit. 10-Dec-2 Piasa, Paris #63/R est:5000-7000
£6565 $10438 €9650 Paysage rocheux (38x46cm-15x18in) s.d.1943 s.i.d.1943 verso prov.lit. 26-Feb-3 Artcurial Briest, Paris #300/R est:6000-7000
£8861 $13823 €14000 La ronde des feuilles (54x65cm-21x26in) s.d.1966 prov.lit. 20-Oct-2 Claude Boisgirard, Paris #22/R est:9000-12000
£9231 $14492 €14400 Hangara a bateaux (54x65cm-21x26in) s.d.1948 s.i.d.1948 verso prov.exhib.lit. 11-Dec-2 Artcurial Briest, Paris #533/R est:12000
£12349 $19882 €18400 Brouette (65x81cm-26x32in) s.d.1961 prov.exhib.lit. 23-Feb-3 Mercier & Cie, Lille #2544/R est:25000
£17949 $28179 €28000 Meditant (81x65cm-32x26in) s.d.1963 s.i.d.verso prov.exhib.lit. 10-Dec-2 Piasa, Paris #217/R
£21656 $33783 €34000 Paysage de Montrouge (100x81cm-39x32in) s. painted 1929. 6-Nov-2 Gioffredo, Nice #51/R
£25001 $39001 €37000 Deux baigneuses (81x65cm-32x26in) s.d.53 prov.exhib.lit. 26-Mar-3 Tajan, Paris #38/R
£28369 $45957 €40000 Nu assis au divan rouge (65x54cm-26x21in) s.d.1968 s.i.d.verso prov. 26-May-3 Christie's, Milan #287/R est:20000-30000

£30769 $48308 €48000 Paris au printemps (81x100cm-32x39in) s.d.1956 s.i.d.verso prov.exhib.lit. 10-Dec-2 Piasa, Paris #215/R est:35000
£33974 $53340 €53000 Emigrants (130x162cm-51x64in) s.d.1958 s.i.d.verso prov.exhib.lit. 10-Dec-2 Piasa, Paris #216/R est:60000
£34591 $55000 €51887 Marchande de fruits (81x100cm-32x39in) s.d.1953 prov.exhib.lit. 27-Feb-3 Christie's, Rockefeller NY #79/R est:30000-40000

Prints

£2324 $3858 €3300 Le couple (23x18cm-9x7in) s.num.one of 50 engraving vellum. 12-Jun-3 Piasa, Paris #81/R

Works on paper

£457 $750 €686 Seated nude with stockings (33x25cm-13x10in) s.d.1950 India ink. 5-Feb-3 Doyle, New York #84/R
£461 $746 €700 Vue de village (33x25cm-13x10in) s.d.1940 pen Indian ink dr. 22-Jan-3 Tajan, Paris #146
£464 $756 €700 Nue, debout (33x25cm-13x10in) s.d.1952 Indian ink dr. 1-Feb-3 Claude Aguttes, Neuilly #244/R
£613 $968 €950 Nu feminin accoude (32x25cm-13x10in) s.d. pen Indian ink. 17-Dec-2 Rossini, Paris #29
£735 $1168 €1080 Nu tourne vers la gauche (25x33cm-10x13in) st.sig. ink dr. 26-Feb-3 Artcurial Briest, Paris #58
£735 $1168 €1080 Nu, tourne vers la droite (25x33cm-10x13in) st.sig. ink dr exec.c.1948. 26-Feb-3 Artcurial Briest, Paris #59
£789 $1279 €1200 Nu allonge (25x32cm-10x13in) s. pen Indian ink. 22-Jan-3 Tajan, Paris #147
£818 $1267 €1300 Offrande a l'amour (24x31cm-9x12in) s. pen Indian ink dr. 30-Oct-2 Artcurial Briest, Paris #208
£822 $1290 €1200 Nu assis (33x25cm-13x10in) s.d. ink dr prov. 21-Apr-3 Rabourdin & Choppin de Janvry, Paris #94/R
£828 $1308 €1200 Nu (33x25cm-13x10in) s.d.1958 ink. 2-Apr-3 Christie's, Paris #5/R
£897 $1409 €1400 Nu assis (32x25cm-13x10in) s.d.1943 Chinese ink dr. 10-Dec-2 Piasa, Paris #62/R
£962 $1510 €1500 Etude de nu (32x25cm-13x10in) s.d.1958 Chinese ink dr exhib. 10-Dec-2 Piasa, Paris #425
£962 $1510 €1500 Etude e nu (33x25cm-13x10in) s.d.1956 Chinese ink. 10-Dec-2 Piasa, Paris #423
£972 $1546 €1400 Scene de cafe (27x21cm-11x8in) s.d.1924 ink dr. 29-Apr-3 Artcurial Briest, Paris #87/R est:1200-1500
£1064 $1723 €1500 Nu (31x24cm-12x9in) s.d. ink. 21-May-3 Cornette de St.Cyr, Paris #66/R est:1500-1800
£1065 $1714 €1598 Nu debut (26x14cm-10x6in) s.d.1927 Indian ink wash. 7-May-3 Dobiaschofsky, Bern #1615/R est:3500 (S.FR 2300)
£1154 $1812 €1800 Nu assis (31x24cm-12x9in) s.d.1938 Chinese ink dr. 10-Dec-2 Piasa, Paris #61/R
£1181 $1948 €1700 Nu (25x33cm-10x13in) d.6.7.71 verso ink dr. 2-Jul-3 Artcurial Briest, Paris #709/R est:1800-2000
£1282 $2013 €2000 Etude de nu (33x25cm-13x10in) s.d.1954 Chinese ink dr. 10-Dec-2 Piasa, Paris #419
£1300 $2015 €1950 Nu assis. Deux hommes (32x23cm-13x9in) s.d.1926 pen ink paper on card two. 5-Dec-2 Christie's, Kensington #98/R est:1000-1500
£1667 $2617 €2600 Etude de nu (33x25cm-13x10in) s.d.1958 chi dr. 10-Dec-2 Piasa, Paris #59/R est:4000
£1678 $2803 €2400 Jeune femme allongee (24x32cm-9x13in) s.d. pen dr. 27-Jun-3 Claude Aguttes, Neuilly #91/R est:1000-1500
£1727 $2763 €2400 Nu allonge, jambe repliee (25x32cm-10x13in) s.d. Indian ink dr. 18-May-3 Eric Pillon, Calais #200/R
£1795 $2818 €2800 Nu assis (32x25cm-13x10in) s.d.1944 Chinese ink dr. 10-Dec-2 Piasa, Paris #60/R
£1799 $2878 €2500 Nu debout (32x25cm-13x10in) s.d. Indian ink dr. 18-May-3 Eric Pillon, Calais #203/R
£1871 $2974 €2750 Nu (25x33cm-10x13in) s.d.1961 Indian ink dr. 26-Feb-3 Artcurial Briest, Paris #57/R est:2000-3000
£1871 $2993 €2600 Nu allonge (25x33cm-10x13in) s.d. Indian ink dr. 18-May-3 Eric Pillon, Calais #199/R
£1923 $3019 €3000 Etude de nu (33x25cm-13x10in) s.d.1944 Chinese ink prov. 10-Dec-2 Piasa, Paris #417
£1923 $3019 €3000 Etude de nu (33x25cm-13x10in) s.d.1956 Chinese ink dr. 10-Dec-2 Piasa, Paris #422
£1955 $3070 €3050 Modele nu (34x26cm-13x10in) s.d.1953 Chinese ink. 15-Dec-2 Lombrail & Teucquam, Paris #13/R
£2885 $4529 €4500 Etude de nu (25x32cm-10x13in) s.d.194 Chinese ink prov. 10-Dec-2 Piasa, Paris #418/R
£2885 $4529 €4500 Etude de nu (25x33cm-10x13in) s.d.1960. 10-Dec-2 Piasa, Paris #427/R
£4487 $7045 €7000 Etude de nu (33x26cm-13x10in) s.d.1954 Chinese ink dr. 10-Dec-2 Piasa, Paris #421/R est:4000
£5627 $8891 €8441 Femme nue couchee (35x48cm-14x19in) s.d.1941 Indian ink W/C. 28-Apr-3 Bukowskis, Stockholm #298/R est:60000-80000 (S.KR 74000)
£9615 $15096 €15000 Harlem, rue (32x44cm-13x17in) s.d.1951 W/C Chinese ink prov.exhib. 10-Dec-2 Piasa, Paris #420/R est:8000
£17949 $28179 €28000 Atelier du peintre (33x43cm-13x17in) s.d.1956 W/C ink prov.exhib. 10-Dec-2 Piasa, Paris #416/R est:8000

GRONCKEL, Vital Jean de (1820-1890) Belgian

£759 $1185 €1200 Portrait d'elegante au ruban rose (108x86cm-43x34in) s.d.1848. 16-Sep-2 Horta, Bruxelles #457

GRONDHOUT, Willem Adrianus (1878-1934) Dutch

£637 $994 €1000 City view of Amsterdam with Nicolas church (33x52cm-13x20in) s. 6-Nov-2 Vendue Huis, Gravenhage #16/R

GRONE, Ferdinand E (fl.1888-1919) British

Works on paper

£260 $429 €377 Gathering the turnips (22x31cm-9x12in) s. W/C. 1-Jul-3 Bonhams, Norwich #106

GRONE, Ferdinand E (attrib) (fl.1888-1919) British

Works on paper

£400 $620 €600 Rural landscape with sheep grazing and a town in the distance (47x35cm-19x14in) s. pastel. 1-Oct-2 Fellows & Sons, Birmingham #170/R

GRONHOLM, Paul (1907-1992) Finnish

£289 $448 €460 Landscape from France (50x65cm-20x26in) s.d.68. 6-Oct-2 Bukowskis, Helsinki #174/R
£475 $779 €660 Still life (45x35cm-18x14in) s. 5-Jun-3 Hagelstam, Helsinki #985/R

GRONMYRA, Oscar (1874-1911) Norwegian

£340 $523 €510 Woman and boat by shore (90x65cm-35x26in) s. painted 1902. 28-Oct-2 Blomqvist, Lysaker #1067/R (N.KR 4000)
£381 $583 €572 Snowy weather (40x64cm-16x25in) s. panel painted 1907. 26-Aug-2 Blomqvist, Lysaker #1124/R (N.KR 4400)

GRONVALL, Sven (1908-1975) Finnish

£252 $387 €400 Town (32x53cm-13x21in) s.d.1974. 24-Oct-2 Hagelstam, Helsinki #864

GROOMS, Red (1937-) American

£3548 $5500 €5322 Portrait of Paul Suttman (213x85cm-84x33in) s. painted 1964 prov. 26-Sep-2 Christie's, Rockefeller NY #766/R est:7000-9000

Prints

£2065 $3200 €3098 Little Italy (65x90cm-26x35in) s.num.27/90 col lithograph three dimensional. 25-Sep-2 Christie's, Rockefeller NY #283/R est:4000-6000
£2761 $4500 €4142 Hot-dog vendor (85x67cm-33x26in) s.d.1994 lithograph linocut. 13-Feb-3 Christie's, Rockefeller NY #268/R

Sculpture

£3459 $5500 €5189 Fats Domino (44x52x44cm-17x20x17in) s.num.43/54 cut out col lithograph plexiglas box. 2-May-3 Sotheby's, New York #454/R est:2500-3500
£4717 $7500 €7076 Charlie Chaplin (58x47x30cm-23x19x12in) s.num.69/75 cut out col lithograph plexiglas box. 2-May-3 Sotheby's, New York #455/R est:4000-6000
£10323 $16000 €15485 Lucius Quintus Cincinnatus Lamar (41x43x15cm-16x17x6in) s.d.65 painted wood construction. 26-Sep-2 Christie's, Rockefeller NY #760/R est:18000-25000
£17187 $27500 €25781 Hot dog table (119x112x19cm-47x44x7in) s.d.65 wagon col felt tip pen paper light fixture prov. 14-May-3 Sotheby's, New York #195/R est:14000-18000

Works on paper

£503 $800 €755 Activity on the street (36x48cm-14x19in) s.d.1968 felt-tip pen. 18-Mar-3 Arthur James, Florida #59
£1090 $1700 €1635 Street scene Yugoslavia (65x48cm-26x19in) s.d.1968 W/C felt tip pen pencil two sheet of paper prov. 5-Nov-2 Doyle, New York #57/R est:2000-3000

GROOMS, Reginald L (1900-) American

£974 $1500 €1461 Repose (46x56cm-18x22in) s. 8-Sep-2 Treadway Gallery, Cincinnati #565/R est:2000-3000

GROOT (?) ?

£889 $1476 €1289 Drawbridge on the canal (50x70cm-20x28in) s. 16-Jun-3 Waddingtons, Toronto #243/R est:2000-3000 (C.D 2000)

GROOT, Adrianus Martinus de (1870-?) Dutch

£1539 $2447 €2309 New York Harbour by night. s. 5-May-3 Rasmussen, Vejle #303/R est:12000-15000 (D.KR 16500)

GROOT, Annemarie de (1952-) Dutch

£526 $853 €800 Nude with masks (120x100cm-47x39in) s.d.92 acrylic prov. 21-Jan-3 Christie's, Amsterdam #490

GROOT, Frans Arnold Breuhaus de (1824-1872) Belgian

£1266 $1975 €2000 Moored flat-bottomed boats at the quay with figures (25x34cm-10x13in) s.d.46 panel. 21-Oct-2 Glerum, Amsterdam #101/R est:3000-5000

GROOT, Gerardus Hendrikus de (1878-1947) Dutch

£288 $449 €420 Village view with fields in the foreground (29x49cm-11x19in) s. 14-Apr-3 Glerum, Amsterdam #126

GROOT, Maurits de (1880-1934) Dutch

£268 $417 €420 Farmer's wife (113x75cm-44x30in) s. 5-Nov-2 Vendu Notarishuis, Rotterdam #50

GROOT, W E van (?) Dutch?

£800 $1272 €1200 Figure close to a mill with stream (38x61cm-15x24in) s. panel. 20-Mar-3 Ewbank, Send #406

GROOTE, A de (19/20th C) ?

£600 $948 €900 Figures skating on a Dutch waterway (38x58cm-15x23in) s. panel. 14-Nov-2 Christie's, Kensington #154

£1400 $2212 €2100 Figures skating by farm buildings in Dutch winter landscape (71x91cm-28x36in) s. panel arched top. 14-Nov-2 Christie's, Kensington #85 est:300-500

GROOTH, George Christoph (studio) (1716-1749) Russian

£26377 $42731 €38247 Empress Elisabeth of Russia on horseback. 26-May-3 Bukowskis, Stockholm #455/R est:100000-150000 (S.KR 340000)

GROPPER, William (1897-1977) American

£5844 $9000 €8766 Man on the floor, stockmarket (91x71cm-36x28in) s. painted c.1935 prov. 8-Sep-2 Treadway Gallery, Cincinnati #664/R est:6000-8000

£6169 $9500 €9254 Senate group (51x64cm-20x25in) s. painted c.1935 prov. 8-Sep-2 Treadway Gallery, Cincinnati #665/R est:6000-8000

£7547 $12000 €11321 Senate hearing (43x66cm-17x26in) s. board. 4-Mar-3 Christie's, Rockefeller NY #105/R est:10000-15000

£15094 $24000 €22641 United Nations securities council (46x77cm-18x30in) s. 4-Mar-3 Christie's, Rockefeller NY #102/R est:12000-18000

Works on paper

£649 $1000 €974 Politicians (35x51cm-14x20in) brush ink prov.exhib. 4-Sep-2 Christie's, Rockefeller NY #369/R est:1000-1500

GROS, Jean Louis (1793-1879) French

£15854 $26000 €22988 Paisaje con puente de Madera (33x45cm-13x18in) s.d.1842 paper on canvas exhib. 27-May-3 Sotheby's, New York #137

£47256 $77500 €68521 Grutas de Cacahuamilpa (101x131cm-40x52in) s.d.1835 prov.exhib.lit. 27-May-3 Sotheby's, New York #49

GROSAJT, Alain (1943-) Belgian

£1111 $1767 €1600 Abstraction (146x114cm-57x45in) s. d.1986 verso. 29-Apr-3 Campo & Campo, Antwerp #137/R est:1800-2200

GROSE, Daniel C (1838-1890) American

£1097 $1700 €1646 Hudson river landscape (38x61cm-15x24in) s.d. 8-Dec-2 Toomey, Oak Park #693/R est:2000-3000

GROSPERIN, Claude (1936-1977) French

£802 $1140 €1300 Cavaliers sur la plage (50x61cm-20x24in) s. 16-Mar-3 Eric Pillon, Calais #225/R

GROSS, Adalbert (1835-1914) Hungarian

£505 $783 €758 View of Grand Canal in Venice (30x46cm-12x18in) painted c.1880. 3-Dec-2 SOGA, Bratislava #113/R (SL.K 32000)

GROSS, Anthony (1905-1984) British

£700 $1148 €1050 French landscape (94x76cm-37x30in) s.d.58 canvas on board. 3-Jun-3 Sotheby's, Olympia #289/R

£2200 $3432 €3300 Creyssens church in the meadow (92x132cm-36x52in) s.d.1976 prov. 12-Sep-2 Sotheby's, Olympia #64/R est:2000-3000

Works on paper

£750 $1230 €1125 Les causses (39x56cm-15x22in) s.i.d.1982 ink W/C sold with a W/C by Robin Darwin. 6-Jun-3 Christie's, London #83/R

GROSS, Chaim (1904-1991) American

Sculpture

£974 $1500 €1461 Mother and children playing (13cm-5in) s.num.1/12 blue green pat bronze exec.c.1960 sold with base prov. 8-Sep-2 Treadway Gallery, Cincinnati #670/R est:2000-3000

£2710 $4200 €4065 Handstand (34cm-13in) s.num.1/6 brown pat bronze exec.c.1963. 3-Dec-2 Christie's, Rockefeller NY #609/R est:2000-4000

£2760 $4250 €4140 Mother and child (30cm-12in) s.num.1/6 green brown pat bronze exec.c.1960 prov. 8-Sep-2 Treadway Gallery, Cincinnati #667/R est:5000-7000

£11950 $19000 €17925 Acrobats (193cm-76in) i.num.N2 dark brown pat. bronze prov. 5-Mar-3 Sotheby's, New York #84/R est:15000-25000

Works on paper

£274 $450 €397 Circus acrobats num 4 (33x26cm-13x10in) s.d. W/C pen ink. 5-Jun-3 Swann Galleries, New York #109a/R

£335 $550 €486 Provincetown trees (55x41cm-22x16in) s.d. W/C. 5-Jun-3 Swann Galleries, New York #109/R

GROSS, Frantisek (1909-1985) Czechoslovakian

£2618 $4162 €3927 Man machines (60x49cm-24x19in) s.d.47 board. 8-Mar-3 Dorotheum, Prague #123/R est:80000-120000 (C.KR 120000)

£6981 $11099 €10472 Interior (60x49cm-24x19in) s.d.47 board. 8-Mar-3 Dorotheum, Prague #122/R est:120000-180000 (C.KR 320000)

GROSS, George (20th C) American

Works on paper

£3727 $6000 €5591 Three prostitutes in police holding cell (41x30cm-16x12in) s. W/C exec.c.1955. 10-May-3 Illustration House, New York #128/R est:7000-9000

GROSS, Michael (1920-) Israeli

£15127 $23900 €22691 Crevice in the ground (121x89cm-48x35in) s. painted 1966 lit. 27-Apr-3 Sotheby's, Tel Aviv #74/R est:18000-25000

£16456 $26000 €24684 Untitled (80x81cm-31x32in) s. painted c.1970. 27-Apr-3 Sotheby's, Tel Aviv #79/R est:15000-20000

GROSS, Peter Alfred (1849-1914) American

£513 $800 €770 Farmhouse and trees (41x51cm-16x20in) s.verso board painted c.1890. 18-Sep-2 Alderfer's, Hatfield #352

GROSSE, Franz Theodore (1829-1891) German

£576 $921 €800 Historical allegories of the history of the House of Solm (33x23cm-13x9in) one s.d.1857 paper prov. two. 17-May-3 Lempertz, Koln #1289/R

GROSSER, Maurice (20th C) ?

£617 $1000 €926 Chapel at platanias (38x56cm-15x22in) s. s.i.d.66 verso prov. 24-Jan-3 Freeman, Philadelphia #221/R est:100-200

GROSSFURSTIN, Olga Nikolajewna (1822-1892) Russian

£3691 $5942 €5500 Elegant figures in a boat accompanying (56x79cm-22x31in) 18-Feb-3 Sotheby's, Amsterdam #479/R est:1000-2000

GROSSI, Proferio (1923-2000) Italian

£538 $839 €850 Still life (50x70cm-20x28in) s.d.1960 masonite. 14-Sep-2 Meeting Art, Vercelli #923/R

GROSSMANN, Rudolf (1882-1941) German

£1026 $1497 €1600 Cannes palms (52x70cm-20x28in) s. panel. 4-Jun-2 Karl & Faber, Munich #257/R est:2500

£2778 $4389 €4000 Street in Bruges (41x37cm-16x15in) s. i. verso. 26-Apr-3 Dr Lehr, Berlin #165/R est:5000

Works on paper

£1154 $1788 €1800 Igor Strawinsky conducting (48x31cm-19x12in) s. Indian ink brush over pencil. 4-Dec-2 Lempertz, Koln #753/R est:2000

GROSSMULLER, Rudolf (20th C) German

£382 $596 €600 High mountain landscape (100x150cm-39x59in) s. 6-Nov-2 Hugo Ruef, Munich #1112

£1250 $1987 €1800 High mountain landscape (100x150cm-39x59in) s. 29-Apr-3 Wiener Kunst Auktionen, Vienna #585/R est:1200-2000

GROSSO, Alfonso (1893-1983) Spanish

£1923 $3038 €3000 Portrait of lady (96x75cm-38x30in) s. 14-Nov-2 Arte, Seville #395/R

GROSSO, Giacomo (1860-1938) Italian

£8176 $12591 €13000 Portrait of ladyy with fan (114x81cm-45x32in) s.d.909. 23-Oct-2 Finarte, Milan #83/R est:14000-15000

GROSSO, Orlando (1882-1968) Italian

£2027 $3162 €3000 Parades (36x48cm-14x19in) s.d.1930 board. 28-Mar-3 Farsetti, Prato #662

£3716 $5797 €5500 Morning (69x79cm-27x31in) s. 28-Mar-3 Farsetti, Prato #682

GROSZ, George (1893-1959) American/German

£2089	$3258	€3300	Standing female nude (74x48cm-29x19in) paper prov. 18-Oct-2 Dr Fritz Nagel, Stuttgart #507/R est:4300
£5000	$7700	€7500	Before the bath (51x40cm-20x16in) s.d.40 s.verso canvasboard prov.lit. 23-Oct-2 Sotheby's, Olympia #676/R est:6000-8000
£5252	$8613	€7300	Kneeling nude (46x59cm-18x23in) oil W/C paper. 6-Jun-3 Ketterer, Munich #43/R est:6000-8000
£5310	$8390	€7700	Artist and model (48x62cm-19x24in) s. board. 5-Apr-3 Hans Stahl, Hamburg #74/R est:8000
£22436	$35000	€33654	Lotte Schmalhausen auf dem Tisch sitzend, mid angezogenen Beinen (86x67cm-34x26in) s.d.1928 s.d.verso prov.exhib. 7-Nov-2 Christie's, Rockefeller NY #273/R est:40000-60000
£54487	$85000	€81731	Zeitideen - ideas of the time (80x60cm-31x24in) canvas on board painted 1929 prov.exhib.lit. 6-Nov-2 Sotheby's, New York #210/R est:30000-50000

Prints

£2658	$4200	€4200	Self portrait - for Charlie Chaplin (49x34cm-19x13in) s.i. photo lithograph. 30-Nov-2 Villa Grisebach, Berlin #273/R est:3000-3500
£13836	$21585	€22000	Gott mit uns (65x48cm-26x19in) s. lithograph deluxe portfolio. 9-Oct-2 Sotheby's, London #441/R est:12500-15500

Works on paper

£253	$400	€400	Plant study (27x20cm-11x8in) pen. 29-Nov-2 Villa Grisebach, Berlin #643/R
£274	$425	€411	Lady at candle lit desk (23x18cm-9x7in) s. ink W/C. 16-Jul-2 Arthur James, Florida #334
£755	$1162	€1200	Seated female nude (42x24cm-17x9in) s. pencil. 26-Oct-2 Dr Lehr, Berlin #138/R
£818	$1259	€1300	Berlin sausage seller (15x10cm-6x4in) d.27.10.12 pencil. 26-Oct-2 Dr Lehr, Berlin #137/R
£833	$1317	€1200	Man with barrel organ (18x12cm-7x5in) s.i.d.Juli 19 pencil. 26-Apr-3 Dr Lehr, Berlin #169/R
£845	$1403	€1200	Landscape (13x25cm-5x10in) s.d. chk. 14-Jun-3 Hauswedell & Nolte, Hamburg #1215/R
£962	$1500	€1443	New York park scene (46x61cm-18x24in) s. pen ink. 21-Sep-2 Rachel Davis, Shaker Heights #261 est:3000-5000
£1087	$1783	€1500	Railway line (15x21cm-6x8in) s.d.1912 chl. 29-May-3 Lempertz, Koln #651/R est:1200
£1232	$2020	€1700	Woman's head (38x28cm-15x11in) s.d.29.11.27 Indian ink. 29-May-3 Lempertz, Koln #652/R est:2500
£1384	$2131	€2200	Erotic scene (46x60cm-18x24in) i. st.sig. verso pencil. 26-Oct-2 Dr Lehr, Berlin #139/R est:1500
£1408	$2338	€2000	Seated woman wearing headscarf (63x47cm-25x19in) s.d. pencil. 14-Jun-3 Hauswedell & Nolte, Hamburg #1219/R est:2500
£1528	$2400	€2292	Reclining nude (32x41cm-13x16in) pencil prov. 25-Nov-2 Germann, Zurich #90/R est:4000-6000 (S.FR 3500)
£1831	$3039	€2600	Love games (14x23cm-6x9in) s.i. pen. 14-Jun-3 Hauswedell & Nolte, Hamburg #1216/R est:3000
£2051	$3200	€3077	Tanzlokal (32x24cm-13x9in) s. brush black ink. 19-Sep-2 Swann Galleries, New York #381/R est:3500-5000
£2051	$3200	€3077	Garnet Lake, New York (39x50cm-15x20in) s.i. W/C exec.c.1935. 18-Sep-2 Swann Galleries, New York #48/R est:3000-5000
£2244	$3522	€3500	Reclining figure (38x29cm-15x11in) s. Chinese ink exec.1915 lit. 21-Nov-2 Finarte, Rome #172/R
£2323	$3670	€3600	Artist (65x53cm-26x21in) ink exec.c.1926. 18-Dec-2 Christie's, Rome #118/R
£2400	$3818	€3600	Woman undressing (61x48cm-24x19in) st.sig. pencil exec.c.1940. 20-Mar-3 Sotheby's, Olympia #80/R est:3000-4000
£2642	$4200	€3963	Figures (67x43cm-26x17in) s.d.27 brush ink exec.1927 prov. 27-Feb-3 Christie's, Rockefeller NY #29/R
£3165	$4905	€5000	Reclining female nude (40x59cm-16x23in) s.i. prov. 28-Sep-2 Ketterer, Hamburg #216/R est:5000-6000
£3333	$5167	€5200	Street with hanged man (29x19cm-11x7in) s. chl. 7-Dec-2 Hauswedell & Nolte, Hamburg #715/R est:6000
£3600	$5868	€5400	Reclining nude (37x56cm-15x22in) s. pen ink col ink W/C. 3-Feb-3 Bonhams, New Bond Street #34/R est:4000-6000
£3819	$6035	€5500	Before tea (59x46cm-23x18in) i. verso pen brush Indian ink. 26-Apr-3 Dr Lehr, Berlin #170/R est:7000
£4054	$6324	€6000	Back from the market (59x46cm-23x18in) s. gouache. 26-Mar-3 Finarte Semenzato, Milan #270/R
£4487	$6955	€7000	In the outdoors (60x46cm-24x18in) st.sig. i. Indian ink prov. 4-Dec-2 Lempertz, Koln #754/R est:7500
£4487	$6955	€7000	The day after (59x46cm-23x18in) s.i.d.37 i.d. verso Indian ink. 4-Dec-2 Lempertz, Koln #756/R est:7000-9000
£4808	$7452	€7500	Female nude with hat in the dunes (50x39cm-20x15in) st.sig. W/C cardboard exec.1940 prov. 6-Dec-2 Ketterer, Munich #115/R est:7500-8500
£5405	$8432	€8000	Undressing nude (65x49cm-26x19in) W/C card. 26-Mar-3 Finarte Semenzato, Milan #332/R
£5696	$9000	€9000	Untitled (64x50cm-25x20in) s.i. pen exhib. 30-Nov-2 Villa Grisebach, Berlin #274/R est:7000-8000
£6522	$10696	€9000	Lady Hamilton posing for Sir William Hamilton (59x47cm-23x19in) s. Indian ink. 31-May-3 Villa Grisebach, Berlin #224/R est:7000-9000
£6731	$10433	€10500	A retrieved Reformation (64x46cm-25x18in) s.i. W/C. 7-Dec-2 Hauswedell & Nolte, Hamburg #717/R est:12500
£6897	$10897	€10000	Freed workers - worker uprising (65x53cm-26x21in) st.sig. Indian ink brush board. 2-Apr-3 Dr Fritz Nagel, Stuttgart #9341/R est:9800
£8228	$13000	€13000	The intoxicated ship (52x65cm-20x26in) i. i. verso pen W/C lit.exhib. six. 30-Nov-2 Villa Grisebach, Berlin #276/R est:5000-6000
£8805	$13736	€14000	Tiergarten, Berlin (49x37cm-19x15in) s.i. pen ink executed c.1922 prov. 9-Oct-2 Sotheby's, London #215/R est:20000-30000
£9434	$14528	€15000	Strolling people (59x48cm-23x19in) s. i. verso W/C pen. 26-Oct-2 Dr Lehr, Berlin #136/R est:8000
£10256	$15897	€16000	Street (19x28cm-7x11in) i. pen W/C over pencil. 7-Dec-2 Hauswedell & Nolte, Hamburg #716/R est:14000
£10897	$17000	€16346	Mann (29x22cm-11x9in) s. i.verso pen ink. 14-Oct-2 Butterfields, San Francisco #2012/R est:2500-3500
£14085	$23380	€20000	Three officials for George Kaiser (35x38cm-14x15in) i. W/C Indian ink brush exhib. 14-Jun-3 Hauswedell & Nolte, Hamburg #1218/R est:25000
£15493	$25718	€22000	Figures playing cards at round table (21x27cm-8x11in) s.d. Indian ink. 14-Jun-3 Hauswedell & Nolte, Hamburg #1217/R est:25000
£15500	$23870	€23250	Der heimliche kaiser - industrialist Hugo Stinnes (64x48cm-25x19in) st.sig. verso brush ink executed 1920 prov.exhib. 22-Oct-2 Sotheby's, London #218/R est:14000-18000
£18000	$27720	€27000	Alter mann und krankenschwester - old man and nurse (60x46cm-24x18in) s.d.1928 W/C pen brush ink prov. 22-Oct-2 Sotheby's, London #219/R est:12000-15000
£18405	$30000	€27608	Sie haben etwas entdeckt - They found something (62x46cm-24x18in) s.i.d.1946 verso W/C pen ink prov.exhib. 12-Feb-3 Sotheby's, New York #86/R est:30000-40000
£24359	$38000	€36539	Lieb vaterland, magst ruhig sein (46x62cm-18x24in) indis sig. pen India ink executed 1922 prov.lit. 7-Nov-2 Christie's, Rockefeller NY #131/R est:18000-22000
£25000	$38500	€37500	Kutschers gehilfe Berliner Strassenszene - Carter's man, Berlin - Berlin street scene (66x47cm-26x19in) s. W/C pencil executed c.1928 prov. 22-Oct-2 Sotheby's, London #221/R est:25000-35000
£25000	$41000	€37500	Masked ball (65x52cm-26x20in) s.i.d.1927 W/C pencil prov. 6-Feb-3 Christie's, London #461/R est:35000
£41139	$65000	€65000	People on the street (45x58cm-18x23in) s.d.1919 brush. 29-Nov-2 Villa Grisebach, Berlin #58/R est:30000-35000
£60000	$100200	€87000	Gesellschaft - gathering (38x49cm-15x19in) s.d.Okt 1916 w, brush ink prov.exhib.lit. 24-Jun-3 Sotheby's, London #264/R est:60000-80000
£175000	$292250	€253750	Ecce Homo (50x38cm-20x15in) s. W/C pen brush black ink spritztechnik exec.1921 prov.lit. 24-Jun-3 Christie's, London #33/R est:80000-120000
£270000	$440100	€405000	Quer durch Berlin N (42x30cm-17x12in) s.d.1919 W/C pen ink prov.exhib.lit. 3-Feb-3 Christie's, London #13/R est:100000-150000

GROTH, Jan (20th C) Danish

Works on paper

£384	$599	€576	Composition (64x90cm-25x35in) pencil executed 1986. 23-Sep-2 Blomqvist, Lysaker #1057 (N.KR 4500)
£427	$666	€641	Composition (64x90cm-25x35in) s. pencil executed 1987. 23-Sep-2 Blomqvist, Lysaker #1058 (N.KR 5000)
£929	$1468	€1394	Compositions (62x88cm-24x35in) s.d.71 chk three prov. 1-Apr-3 Rasmussen, Copenhagen #325 (D.KR 10000)

GROTH, Johann Christoph (attrib) (1688-1764) German

£3226	$4742	€5000	Portrait of Carl Alexander, Herzog von Wurttemberg (147x113cm-58x44in) 20-Jun-2 Dr Fritz Nagel, Stuttgart #712/R est:5000

GROTH, Vilhelm (1842-1899) Danish

£324	$502	€486	Figure on woodland path (39x43cm-15x17in) s.d.1897. 28-Sep-2 Rasmussen, Havnen #2077 (D.KR 3800)
£340	$530	€510	Path through Frederiksvaerk woods (41x56cm-16x22in) s.d.1893 exhib. 5-Aug-2 Rasmussen, Vejle #185/R (D.KR 4000)
£2534	$3953	€3801	Summer's day by the fjord with children playing at water's edge (84x69cm-33x27in) s.d.1889. 23-Sep-2 Rasmussen, Vejle #84/R est:30000 (D.KR 30000)

GROTKOVSKY, Jan (1902-1961) Czechoslovakian

£347	$538	€521	Sunrise in High Tatras (80x59cm-31x23in) painted c.1925. 3-Dec-2 SOGA, Bratislava #5/R (SL.K 22000)

Works on paper

£394	$559	€591	After storm (50x39cm-20x15in) pastel exec.c.1935. 26-Mar-2 SOGA, Bratislava #10/R (SL.K 25000)

GROUMELLEC, Loic le (1958-) French

£903 $1490 €1300 Les megalithes noirs (48x65cm-19x26in) s.i.d.1986 acrylic paper lit. 3-Jul-3 Christie's, Paris #52/R
£1266 $2000 €2000 Megalithes et maison (42x29cm-17x11in) oil lacquer painted 1990 prov.exhib. 27-Nov-2 Tajan, Paris #108/R
£1266 $2000 €2000 Croix (25x25cm-10x10in) s.i.d.1990 verso oil lacquer prov. 27-Nov-2 Tajan, Paris #109/R
£1304 $2139 €1800 Megalithes (25x25cm-10x10in) s.i.d.1988 verso paint lacquer prov. 27-May-3 Tajan, Paris #71/R est:2000-2500
£1304 $2139 €1800 Megalithe (25x25cm-10x10in) s.i.d.1989 verso paint lacquer prov. 27-May-3 Tajan, Paris #72/R est:2000-2500

Works on paper

£1736 $2743 €2500 Megalithes et maison (35x35cm-14x14in) s.i.d.verso. 28-Apr-3 Cornette de St.Cyr, Paris #450 est:2000-2500

GROUX, Charles de (1825-1870) Belgian

£1342 $2161 €2000 Jeune femme et ses enfants a l'eglise (23x18cm-9x7in) s. panel. 18-Feb-3 Vanderkindere, Brussels #237
£1646 $2567 €2600 Regrets (80x54cm-31x21in) s. 15-Oct-2 Horta, Bruxelles #112
£6329 $9873 €10000 Distributing the bread (83x107cm-33x42in) 21-Oct-2 Bernaerts, Antwerp #82/R est:10000-12000

Works on paper

£577 $906 €900 Le marchand de marrons (30x44cm-12x17in) s. chl W/C gouache dr. 10-Dec-2 Vanderkindere, Brussels #68

GROUX, Henry de (1867-1930) Belgian

£3425 $5377 €5000 Portrait de Charles Baudelaire (67x54cm-26x21in) s. panel lit. 15-Apr-3 Laurence Calmels, Paris #4094/R

Works on paper

£596 $972 €900 Christ (65x50cm-26x20in) s. pastel. 17-Feb-3 Horta, Bruxelles #79
£1701 $2704 €2500 Paysage surrealiste anime (74x90cm-29x35in) s.d.1900 pastel. 18-Mar-3 Vanderkindere, Brussels #100/R est:2500-4000

GROUX, Henry de (attrib) (1867-1930) Belgian

Works on paper

£10274 $16130 €15000 Portrait de Charles Baudelaire (73x52cm-29x20in) d.1907 pastel cardboard. 15-Apr-3 Laurence Calmels, Paris #4093/R est:400

GROVE, Nordahl (1822-1885) Danish

£900 $1368 €1350 Deer grazing in a park at dusk (33x47cm-13x19in) s.d.1862 s.i.verso. 29-Aug-2 Christie's, Kensington #116
£931 $1480 €1397 From Jyllinge, Roskilde Fjord (44x66cm-17x26in) s.d.1872. 5-Mar-3 Rasmussen, Copenhagen #2062/R (D.KR 10000)
£1021 $1614 €1532 The gunpowder house in Hellebaek (43x61cm-17x24in) s.d.55. 2-Dec-2 Rasmussen, Copenhagen #1802/R est:12000 (D.KR 12000)
£1100 $1804 €1650 Collecting sand at the bend by the lake (58x79cm-23x31in) s.d.58. 5-Jun-3 Christie's, Kensington #677/R est:1000-1500

GROVER, Oliver Dennett (1861-1927) American

£903 $1400 €1355 Venetian September day, boats leaving Chioggia, italy (15x28cm-6x11in) s.d. 8-Dec-2 Toomey, Oak Park #625/R
£10191 $16000 €15287 View of horticulture buildings from Wooded Island (38x46cm-15x18in) s.d.1893. 10-Dec-2 Doyle, New York #103/R est:12000-18000

GROVES, John (?) British?

£1100 $1782 €1650 M.V Author in the Clyde (59x100cm-23x39in) s.d.82. 21-Jan-3 Bonhams, New Bond Street #183/R est:200-300
£2300 $3726 €3450 M.V Astronomer in the Falklands (60x90cm-24x35in) s.d.83. 21-Jan-3 Bonhams, New Bond Street #184/R est:400-600

GRUAU, René (1910-) French?

£350 $585 €508 Silhouette of a woman in colours (13x10cm-5x4in) s. 13-Jul-3 Lots Road, London #350

GRUBACS, Carlo (19th C) Italian

£5479 $8548 €8219 Interior of St Marks Church, Venice (21x27cm-8x11in) s.d.1843. 28-Mar-3 Koller, Zurich #3145/R est:17000-22000 (S.FR 12000)
£8219 $12822 €12329 St Marks Place, Venice (21x27cm-8x11in) s.d.1845. 28-Mar-3 Koller, Zurich #3144/R est:17000-22000 (S.FR 18000)
£17000 $26520 €25500 Piazetta and Doges Palace. Santa Maria de la Salute (33x27cm-13x11in) s. pair. 17-Sep-2 Sotheby's, Olympia #280/R est:10000-15000

Works on paper

£2432 $3795 €3600 St Mark's church in Venice (14x19cm-6x7in) s. W/C. 28-Mar-3 Dorotheum, Vienna #218/R est:1400-1600

GRUBACS, Carlo (attrib) (19th C) Italian

£1019 $1600 €1529 Scene in Venice (10x8cm-4x3in) panel. 10-Dec-2 Doyle, New York #208/R est:3000-4000

GRUBACS, Giovanni (1829-1919) Italian

£7269 $10830 €10904 Canale Grande and S Maria della Salute (51x74cm-20x29in) bears s. i. verso. 25-Jun-2 Koller, Zurich #6708 est:800-1400 (S.FR 16500)
£7269 $10830 €10904 Doges Palace and St Marks Square (50x73cm-20x29in) bears sig. i. verso. 25-Jun-2 Koller, Zurich #6709 est:800-1400 (S.FR 16500)

GRUBAS, Marco (1839-1910) Italian

£1027 $1603 €1500 Doges Palace and Campanile (14x26cm-6x10in) s. panel one of pair. 10-Apr-3 Dorotheum, Vienna #28/R est:1600-2000
£1027 $1603 €1500 View from St Marks Square of St Giorgio Maggiore (14x26cm-6x10in) s. panel one of pair. 10-Apr-3 Dorotheum, Vienna #29/R est:1600-2000

GRUBER, Francis (1912-1948) French

£3000 $4650 €4500 Fleur des champs (55x46cm-22x18in) s.d.1934 board. 5-Dec-2 Christie's, Kensington #56/R est:3000-5000
£7000 $10780 €10500 Le canal (82x65cm-32x26in) s.d.1946 prov. 23-Oct-2 Sotheby's, Olympia #616/R est:7000-9000
£10072 $16115 €14000 L'homme nu (116x89cm-46x35in) s.d. exhib.lit. 18-May-3 Eric Pillon, Calais #156/R
£17361 $28646 €25000 Nu au gilet rouge assis (113x86cm-44x34in) s.d. exhib. 1-Jul-3 Rossini, Paris #91/R

GRUBER, Franz Xaver (1801-1862) Austrian

£3082 $4808 €4500 Gutenstein, Niederosterreich (27x40cm-11x16in) s.i.d.1850 i. verso paper on board. 10-Apr-3 Dorotheum, Vienna #153/R est:6000-7000

GRUBER, Hannes (1928-) Swiss

£558 $882 €837 Group of houses in Bund landscape (56x76cm-22x30in) s.d.77 tempera paper. 26-Nov-2 Hans Widmer, St Gallen #1136/R (S.FR 1300)

Works on paper

£300 $475 €450 Composition (35x48cm-14x19in) s. pastel chk. 26-Nov-2 Hans Widmer, St Gallen #1137/R (S.FR 700)

GRUBER-GLEICHENBERG, Franz (1886-1940) Austrian

£1517 $2428 €2200 Village in Montafon (71x62cm-28x24in) s.i. prov. 11-Mar-3 Dorotheum, Vienna #32/R est:2400-3200
£1795 $2782 €2800 Worthersee (37x49cm-15x19in) s. i. verso. 5-Dec-2 Dorotheum, Graz #19/R est:1800

GRUEBER, Albrecht (1847-1888) German

£750 $1162 €1125 Proposal (37x30cm-15x12in) s.i. 3-Dec-2 Sotheby's, Olympia #254/R
£1408 $2310 €2042 Roccoco scene with man and woman holding dog (37x30cm-15x12in) s.d.72. 4-Jun-3 Fischer, Luzern #1154/R est:3000-4500 (S.FR 3000)

GRUELLE, Richard Buckner (1851-1914) American

Works on paper

£1234 $1900 €1851 Country path at sunset (25x36cm-10x14in) s. W/C exec.c.1890 lit. 8-Sep-2 Treadway Gallery, Cincinnati #555/R est:2000-3000

GRUN, Jules Alexandre (1868-1934) French

£5359 $8790 €8200 Poupee verte (116x89cm-46x35in) s.d.1928. 7-Feb-3 Oger, Dumont, Paris #97/R

GRUN, Maurice (1869-1947) French

£1241 $1986 €1800 Bouquet de fleurs (46x38cm-18x15in) mono.d.1902. 12-Mar-3 Libert, Castor, Paris #116 est:800-1000
£1517 $2412 €2200 Jeunes ecoliers les devoirs a la maison (33x41cm-13x16in) s. 10-Mar-3 Thierry & Lannon, Brest #109/R
£4583 $7471 €6600 Partie de cartes devant l'atre (130x160cm-51x63in) s. 19-Jul-3 Thierry & Lannon, Brest #131 est:6000-7000

GRUNBAUM, Laurent A (1791-1852) Austrian

Miniatures

£1000 $1540 €1500 Young gentleman in a blue cloak (9cm-4xin) s. gilt metal bezel oval exec.c.1830. 24-Oct-2 Sotheby's, Olympia #81/R est:1200-1500

GRUND, Johann (1808-1887) Austrian
£2200 $3520 €3300 At the well. Travellers in a coastal landscape (55x68cm-22x27in) s.d.1874 pair. 11-Mar-3 Bonhams, Knightsbridge #83/R est:2000-2500

GRUND, Norbert Joseph Carl (1717-1767) Czechoslovakian
£1392 $2158 €2200 Peasant family resting on roadside (12x17cm-5x7in) panel. 25-Sep-2 Neumeister, Munich #482/R est:1500
£1728 $2834 €2506 Hunting party with falcons (41x30cm-16x12in) panel. 4-Jun-3 AB Stockholms Auktionsverk #2561/R est:25000-30000 (S.KR 22000)
£6289 $9748 €10000 Landscape with ruined wall and muleteer (18x23cm-7x9in) panel. 2-Oct-2 Dorotheum, Vienna #229/R est:10000-14000
£17568 $27405 €26000 Tobias and the angel. Hagar and the angel in the desert (21x26cm-8x10in) panel two prov.lit. 27-Mar-3 Dorotheum, Vienna #235/R est:20000-30000

GRUND, Norbert Joseph Carl (attrib) (1717-1767) Czechoslovakian
£1197 $1987 €1700 Miraculous draught of fishes (14x17cm-6x7in) panel. 11-Jun-3 Dorotheum, Vienna #461/R est:400-600
£3226 $5097 €5000 Paysan au repos (25x21cm-10x8in) panel. 20-Dec-2 Tajan, Paris #67/R

GRUNDIG, Hans (1901-1958) German
£903 $1426 €1300 Tree lined country track (55x60cm-22x24in) i. verso board. 26-Apr-3 Dr Lehr, Berlin #174/R

GRUNDMANN, Basilius (attrib) (1726-1798) German
£1757 $2741 €2600 Winter landscape with ice skaters (23x29cm-9x11in) panel prov. one of pair. 27-Mar-3 Dorotheum, Vienna #411/R est:2500-3300

GRUNDMANN, Hedwig (1894-1987) German
£2394 $3855 €3400 Houses and streets (82x41cm-32x16in) s.i. tempera gouache linen prov. 9-May-3 Schloss Ahlden, Ahlden #1565/R est:3400

GRUNDTVIG, L (1836-?) Danish
£1022 $1584 €1533 Portraits of gentleman and lady (84x68cm-33x27in) s. one d.1869 one d.1880 oval pair. 28-Sep-2 Rasmussen, Havnen #2040 est:5000-8000 (D.KR 12000)

GRUNDTVIG, Ludvig (1836-?) Danish
£1411 $2272 €2117 Portrait of lady. Portrait of gentleman (84x68cm-33x27in) s.d.1869 and 1880 oval pair. 19-Jan-3 Hindemae, Ullerslev #7328/R est:18000 (D.KR 16000)

GRUNENWALD, Alexander Rudolf (1849-1890) German
£1268 $2041 €1800 Figures outside tavern (50x65cm-20x26in) s.i.d.1873 canvas on panel lit. 9-May-3 Schloss Ahlden, Ahlden #1378/R est:1800

GRUNENWALD, Jakob (1822-1896) German
£3243 $5059 €4800 Resting during harvest (34x52cm-13x20in) mono. 26-Mar-3 Hugo Ruef, Munich #114 est:900

GRUNENWALD, Jakob (attrib) (1822-1896) German
£1090 $1711 €1700 Flute playing shepherd with girl and flock (38x30cm-15x12in) 21-Nov-2 Van Ham, Cologne #1644 est:2000

GRUNER, Elioth (1882-1939) Australian
£1447 $2243 €2171 Waimangu Valley and geyser (34x45cm-13x18in) s.d.1931. 4-Dec-2 Dunbar Sloane, Auckland #70/R est:5000-10000 (NZ.D 4500)
£4286 $6729 €6429 Storm clouds (19x24cm-7x9in) s.d.1931 i.verso board prov. 25-Nov-2 Christie's, Melbourne #69/R est:12000-15000 (A.D 12000)
£4962 $7840 €7443 Summer pastoral (24x36cm-9x14in) s. board. 2-Apr-3 Christie's, Melbourne #21/R est:10000-15000 (A.D 13000)
£5018 $7627 €7527 Hills near Canberra (37x44cm-15x17in) s.d.1937 canvasboard prov.exhib. 28-Aug-2 Deutscher-Menzies, Melbourne #75/R est:15000-20000 (A.D 14000)
£5357 $8464 €8036 Ploughing (23x28cm-9x11in) s. canvas on board painted c.1916-18. 27-Nov-2 Deutscher-Menzies, Melbourne #60/R est:16000-20000 (A.D 15000)
£5536 $8746 €8304 Landscape (32x43cm-13x17in) s.d.1929 panel prov. 17-Nov-2 Sotheby's, Paddington #35/R est:10000-15000 (A.D 15500)
£8846 $14065 €13269 Spring morning (44x40cm-17x16in) painted c.1917 prov. 4-Mar-3 Deutscher-Menzies, Melbourne #102/R est:30000-40000 (A.D 23000)
£9924 $15679 €14886 Summer Idyll (45x30cm-18x12in) s.d.1930 i.verso board prov. 2-Apr-3 Christie's, Melbourne #6/R est:15000-20000 (A.D 26000)
£11494 $17126 €17241 Yellow roses (60x50cm-24x20in) s.d.1925. 27-Aug-2 Christie's, Melbourne #77/R est:14000-18000 (A.D 30000)

GRUNERT, Eugen (1856-?) German
£1027 $1603 €1500 Newmark in the evening (103x154cm-41x61in) s. 10-Apr-3 Van Ham, Cologne #1453/R est:3000

GRUNEWALD, Arthur (1887-?) German
£353 $536 €550 Still life of fruit (91x144cm-36x57in) s. 11-Jul-2 Hugo Ruef, Munich #675
£385 $585 €600 Still life of vegetables (87x173cm-34x68in) s. 11-Jul-2 Hugo Ruef, Munich #674

GRUNEWALD, Dietrich (20th C) Irish?
£342 $534 €500 Middle Eastern harbour (91x122cm-36x48in) s. 8-Apr-3 James Adam, Dublin #79/R

GRUNEWALD, Isaac (1889-1946) Swedish
£1296 $2022 €1944 Drain-pipe and barrel (33x24cm-13x9in) s. tempera panel. 6-Nov-2 AB Stockholms Auktionsverk #549/R est:22000-25000 (S.KR 18500)
£1429 $2371 €2072 Northern landscape (54x65cm-21x26in) s. 16-Jun-3 Lilla Bukowskis, Stockholm #75 est:25000-30000 (S.KR 18500)
£1472 $2296 €2208 Still life of vegetables (37x46cm-15x18in) s. panel. 6-Nov-2 AB Stockholms Auktionsverk #541/R est:30000-35000 (S.KR 21000)
£1749 $2763 €2624 The flight (34x24cm-13x9in) s. canvas on board. 28-Apr-3 Bukowskis, Stockholm #153/R est:30000-35000 (S.KR 23000)
£1892 $2952 €2838 Still life of fruit in bowl (26x32cm-10x13in) s. 5-Nov-2 Bukowskis, Stockholm #225/R est:15000-18000 (S.KR 27000)
£2077 $3365 €3116 Still life of amaryllis (45x56cm-18x22in) s. 3-Feb-3 Lilla Bukowskis, Stockholm #548/R est:30000-40000 (S.KR 29000)
£2085 $3357 €3128 Amaryllis (34x40cm-13x16in) s. panel. 7-May-3 AB Stockholms Auktionsverk #649/R est:15000-20000 (S.KR 27000)
£2735 $4321 €4103 Still life of amaryllis (41x33cm-16x13in) s. 27-Nov-2 Falkkloos, Malmo #77757/R est:40000 (S.KR 39000)
£2857 $4600 €4286 Still life of amaryllis (41x33cm-16x13in) s. panel. 7-May-3 AB Stockholms Auktionsverk #725/R est:30000-40000 (S.KR 37000)
£2966 $4686 €4449 French landscape (38x47cm-15x19in) s. panel. 28-Apr-3 Bukowskis, Stockholm #21/R est:30000-35000 (S.KR 39000)
£3083 $4810 €4625 From Saltsjobaden (46x55cm-18x22in) s. 5-Nov-2 Bukowskis, Stockholm #64/R est:22000-25000 (S.KR 44000)
£3089 $4973 €4634 Still life of anemones (55x38cm-22x15in) s. 7-May-3 AB Stockholms Auktionsverk #886/R est:50000-60000 (S.KR 40000)
£3552 $5719 €5328 The blue barrel (65x54cm-26x21in) s. 7-May-3 AB Stockholms Auktionsverk #855/R est:45000-50000 (S.KR 46000)
£3714 $5794 €5571 Fruit trees in blossom, La Valle de Bievres (46x38cm-18x15in) s.d.22 panel exhib. 5-Nov-2 Bukowskis, Stockholm #83/R est:50000-75000 (S.KR 53000)
£4234 $6562 €6351 Portrait of young woman wearing blue dress (57x43cm-22x17in) i. sketch verso prov. 1-Oct-2 Rasmussen, Copenhagen #119/R est:60000-80000 (D.KR 50000)
£4479 $7211 €6719 Sigrid at the easel (46x38cm-18x15in) s. exhib. 7-May-3 AB Stockholms Auktionsverk #913/R est:60000-80000 (S.KR 58000)
£4695 $7324 €7043 Still life of amaryllis (46x38cm-18x15in) s. panel. 5-Nov-2 Bukowskis, Stockholm #10/R est:50000-55000 (S.KR 67000)
£5174 $8330 €7761 Still life of red amaryllis and yellow tulips (38x46cm-15x18in) s. panel. 7-May-3 AB Stockholms Auktionsverk #747/R est:40000-50000 (S.KR 67000)
£5466 $8527 €8199 Figure with blue back (55x46cm-22x18in) 5-Nov-2 Bukowskis, Stockholm #83d/R est:50000-60000 (S.KR 78000)
£5483 $8827 €8225 Still life of amaryllis (42x33cm-17x13in) s. panel. 7-May-3 AB Stockholms Auktionsverk #754/R est:60000-80000 (S.KR 71000)
£6027 $9402 €9041 Still life of garlic, fruit and flowers (72x59cm-28x23in) s. exhib. 5-Nov-2 Bukowskis, Stockholm #66/R est:100000-125000 (S.KR 86000)
£6171 $9750 €9257 Still life of amaryllis (73x59cm-29x23in) s. 27-Nov-2 Falkkloos, Malmo #77823/R est:80000 (S.KR 88000)
£6844 $10814 €10266 Still life of chrysanthemums (66x55cm-26x22in) s. panel. 28-Apr-3 Bukowskis, Stockholm #16a/R est:100000-125000 (S.KR 90000)
£8365 $13217 €12548 Still life of amaryllis (55x45cm-22x18in) s. panel. 28-Apr-3 Bukowskis, Stockholm #180c/R est:70000-80000 (S.KR 110000)
£9110 $14212 €13665 Still life of flowers (91x73cm-36x29in) s. 6-Nov-2 AB Stockholms Auktionsverk #530/R est:180000-200000 (S.KR 130000)
£9266 $14919 €13899 Still life of amaryllis (100x80cm-39x31in) s. 7-May-3 AB Stockholms Auktionsverk #746/R est:125000-150000 (S.KR 120000)
£9460 $14758 €14190 Baron James Ensor (120x87cm-47x34in) s. exhib.lit. 5-Nov-2 Bukowskis, Stockholm #202/R est:100000-150000 (S.KR 135000)

£12355 $19892 €18533 Interior scene with Sigrid and Ivan (55x46cm-22x18in) s. 7-May-3 AB Stockholms Auktionsverk #789/R est:150000-180000 (S.KR 160000)
£12411 $19238 €18617 Susanna in the Bath (92x72cm-36x28in) s. 8-Dec-2 Uppsala Auktionskammare, Uppsala #218/R est:100000-125000 (S.KR 175000)
£14716 $22957 €22074 Woman by waterfall - from the Paradise series (129x50cm-51x20in) s.d.43 tempera panel. 5-Nov-2 Bukowskis, Stockholm #115/R est:100000-125000 (S.KR 210000)
£15209 $24030 €22814 The Moroccan - nude female model on sofa (84x100cm-33x39in) s.d.1936 exhib.lit. 28-Apr-3 Bukowskis, Stockholm #162/R est:200000-250000 (S.KR 200000)
£21724 $33889 €32586 Woman by spring - from the Paradise serie (130x120cm-51x47in) s.d.43 tempera panel. 5-Nov-2 Bukowskis, Stockholm #118/R est:250000-300000 (S.KR 310000)
£25228 $39355 €37842 From the Susanna suite (200x245cm-79x96in) s. tempera. 5-Nov-2 Bukowskis, Stockholm #210/R est:275000-300000 (S.KR 360000)
£26616 $42053 €39924 The artist Joseph Hecht (117x88cm-46x35in) s. painted 1915 exhib.lit. 28-Apr-3 Bukowskis, Stockholm #25/R est:400000-500000 (S.KR 350000)
£35739 $55753 €53609 Still life of flowers (100x70cm-39x28in) s. panel. 5-Nov-2 Bukowskis, Stockholm #166a/R est:375000-400000 (S.KR 510000)
£57143 $92000 €85715 Sigrid and beautiful flowers in vases (116x89cm-46x35in) s. painted c.1915. 7-May-3 AB Stockholms Auktionsverk #699/R est:600000-800000 (S.KR 740000)
£121673 $192243 €182510 Bathers at Fano (130x170cm-51x67in) s. painted 1917 exhib.lit. 28-Apr-3 Bukowskis, Stockholm #161/R est:1800000-2000000 (S.KR 1600000)
£175193 $273301 €262790 The hunter (73x54cm-29x21in) s.d.16 prov.exhib.lit. 5-Nov-2 Bukowskis, Stockholm #121/R est:1500000-1700000 (S.KR 2500000)

Works on paper

£353 $554 €530 Model (32x49cm-13x19in) s. Indian ink. 16-Dec-2 Lilla Bukowskis, Stockholm #866 (S.KR 5000)
£386 $641 €560 Serviteur de Cleopatre (38x25cm-15x10in) s. mixed media. 16-Jun-3 Lilla Bukowskis, Stockholm #416 (S.KR 5000)
£522 $793 €783 French landscape (23x31cm-9x12in) s. W/C. 16-Aug-2 Lilla Bukowskis, Stockholm #589 (S.KR 7600)
£537 $870 €806 Arab on horseback (47x30cm-19x12in) s. mixed media. 3-Feb-3 Lilla Bukowskis, Stockholm #841 (S.KR 7500)
£818 $1300 €1227 Coastal landscape (63x47cm-25x19in) s. gouache. 3-Mar-3 Lilla Bukowskis, Stockholm #308 (S.KR 11000)
£841 $1312 €1262 Kostschei in The Firebird - stage sketch (48x37cm-19x15in) s. mixed media executed 1926 lit. 6-Nov-2 AB Stockholms Auktionsverk #742/R (S.KR 12000)
£1086 $1694 €1629 View of the garden (65x50cm-26x20in) s. pastel. 5-Nov-2 Bukowskis, Stockholm #95/R est:20000-25000 (S.KR 15500)
£1141 $1802 €1712 At the restaurant (20x27cm-8x11in) s. W/C. 28-Apr-3 Bukowskis, Stockholm #14/R est:20000-25000 (S.KR 15000)
£1141 $1802 €1712 Woman (33x21cm-13x8in) s. W/C pencil. 28-Apr-3 Bukowskis, Stockholm #159/R est:10000-12000 (S.KR 15000)
£1158 $1865 €1737 Male models (35x25cm-14x10in) s. W/C. 7-May-3 AB Stockholms Auktionsverk #737/R est:18000-20000 (S.KR 15000)
£1158 $1865 €1737 Summer -1919 (18x27cm-7x11in) s.i. i.verso W/C exhib. 7-May-3 AB Stockholms Auktionsverk #767/R est:10000-12000 (S.KR 15000)
£1166 $1819 €1749 Fire bird (47x37cm-19x15in) s. W/C costume sketch exhib. 13-Sep-2 Lilla Bukowskis, Stockholm #507 est:6000-8000 (S.KR 17000)
£1236 $2051 €1792 Nude model (42x25cm-17x10in) s. red chk. 16-Jun-3 Lilla Bukowskis, Stockholm #142 est:12000-15000 (S.KR 16000)
£1369 $2163 €2054 Composition with figures (34x50cm-13x20in) s. W/C. 28-Apr-3 Bukowskis, Stockholm #157/R est:25000-30000 (S.KR 18000)
£1597 $2523 €2396 Southern landscape (34x50cm-13x20in) s.i.d.2 juli 1926 W/C. 28-Apr-3 Bukowskis, Stockholm #13/R est:20000-25000 (S.KR 21000)
£1597 $2523 €2396 The lion and the horse (40x36cm-16x14in) s. gouache W/C exhib. 28-Apr-3 Bukowskis, Stockholm #20/R est:30000-40000 (S.KR 21000)
£1962 $3061 €2943 Female nude (27x21cm-11x8in) s. W/C. 6-Nov-2 AB Stockholms Auktionsverk #628/R est:20000-25000 (S.KR 28000)
£2102 $3280 €3153 Southern landscape (47x62cm-19x24in) s. W/C. 5-Nov-2 Bukowskis, Stockholm #116/R est:35000-40000 (S.KR 30000)
£4345 $6778 €6518 On the beach (49x65cm-19x26in) s. W/C. 5-Nov-2 Bukowskis, Stockholm #62/R est:40000-50000 (S.KR 62000)

GRUNEWALD, Mathias (style) (1455-1528) German

£5484 $8665 €8500 Crucifixion (48x32cm-19x13in) panel. 19-Dec-2 Delvaux, Paris #81/R

GRUNFELD (19th C) ?

£1409 $2269 €2100 Paysage anime (51x65cm-20x26in) s. 23-Feb-3 Lesieur & Le Bars, Le Havre #66/R

GRUNFELD, Ludwig (fl.1840-1875) Austrian

£890 $1389 €1300 Travellers in summer alpine valleys (32x39cm-13x15in) s.d.8/41 two. 10-Apr-3 Van Ham, Cologne #1454

GRUNFELD, Thomas (1956-) German

Sculpture

£6000 $9240 €9000 Misfit - St. Bernhard (60x120x70cm-24x47x28in) taxidermy executed 1994 prov.exhib. 22-Oct-2 Sotheby's, London #479/R est:8000-12000
£26000 $43420 €37700 Misfit - cow (152x190x80cm-60x75x31in) taxidermy executed 1997 prov.exhib.lit. 27-Jun-3 Christie's, London #277/R est:12000-15000

GRUNHUT, Isidoro (1862-?) Italian

£1195 $1900 €1733 Portrait of two young boys (61x74cm-24x29in) s.d.1893. 3-May-3 Van Blarcom, South Natick #93/R

GRUNLER, Ehregott (1797-1881) German

£308 $477 €480 Johann Wolfgang von Goethe with the Schiller's skull (87x68cm-34x27in) s. 5-Dec-2 Neumeister, Munich #2798

GRUNSTEN, Harry N (1902-) Canadian

£444 $729 €666 Storm over Shickshock Mountains, Gaspe. Day perce rock, Gaspe (22x27cm-9x11in) s. board pair. 3-Jun-3 Joyner, Toronto #389/R est:800-1200 (C.D 1000)

GRUNSWEIGH, Nathan (1880-c.1970) Polish

£1348 $2250 €1900 Le pre Catalan (50x65cm-20x26in) s. i.verso. 17-Jun-3 Claude Boisgirard, Paris #59/R est:1800-2200
£1418 $2369 €2000 Un coin de banlieue (54x65cm-21x26in) s.d. 17-Jun-3 Claude Boisgirard, Paris #58/R est:2000-2500

GRUNWALD, Bela Ivanyi (1867-1940) Hungarian

£788 $1150 €1182 In Puszta (50x60cm-20x24in) painted c.1930. 4-Jun-2 SOGA, Bratislava #118/R est:38000 (SL.K 50000)
£963 $1493 €1445 At steppe (100x69cm-39x27in) painted c.1939. 3-Dec-2 SOGA, Bratislava #114/R est:55000 (SL.K 61000)
£1339 $2075 €2009 In front of the house (50x60cm-20x24in) painted c.1920. 1-Oct-2 SOGA, Bratislava #126/R est:38000 (SL.K 85000)
£1882 $2918 €2729 Road leading next to a farm (100x72cm-39x28in) s. card. 9-Dec-2 Mu Terem Galeria, Budapest #171/R est:650000 (H.F 700000)
£2286 $3543 €3315 Gathering clouds over the Hungarian Plain (71x100cm-28x39in) s. 9-Dec-2 Mu Terem Galeria, Budapest #165/R est:800000 (H.F 850000)
£2420 $3752 €3509 Before the storm (52x67cm-20x26in) s. 9-Dec-2 Mu Terem Galeria, Budapest #142/R est:600000 (H.F 900000)
£2580 $4024 €3741 Grange (70x100cm-28x39in) s. panel. 13-Sep-2 Mu Terem Galeria, Budapest #78/R est:650000 (H.F 1000000)
£4681 $7489 €7022 Summer day in the field (56x74cm-22x29in) s. exec.c.1910. 16-May-3 Kieselbach, Budapest #58/R (H.F 1600000)
£4902 $7646 €7353 Still life with flowers (60x50cm-24x20in) s. 11-Sep-2 Kieselbach, Budapest #137/R (H.F 1900000)
£5676 $8854 €8514 Large still life with flowers, 1930 (131x151cm-52x59in) s.d.1930. 11-Sep-2 Kieselbach, Budapest #68/R (H.F 2200000)
£7223 $11268 €10835 Girls from Kecskmet, 1912 (70x71cm-28x28in) s. cardboard. 11-Sep-2 Kieselbach, Budapest #12/R (H.F 2800000)
£7530 $11671 €10919 Still life of fruit and flower (71x101cm-28x40in) s. exhib. 9-Dec-2 Mu Terem Galeria, Budapest #130/R est:190000 (H.F 2800000)
£7530 $11671 €10919 In the valley (56x87cm-22x34in) s. 9-Dec-2 Mu Terem Galeria, Budapest #213/R est:1900000 (H.F 2800000)
£10319 $16098 €14963 Sunlit outskirts of the village (59x64cm-23x25in) s. 13-Sep-2 Mu Terem Galeria, Budapest #45/R est:750000 (H.F 4000000)
£14000 $22960 €21000 On the Lido (48x70cm-19x28in) s.i. indis d. board. 3-Jun-3 Sotheby's, London #102/R est:15000-20000
£30739 $47953 €44572 Landscape in Nagybanya (90x100cm-35x39in) 12-Apr-3 Mu Terem Galeria, Budapest #100/R est:4000000 (H.F 11000000)

GRUNWALD, Bela Ivanyi (attrib) (1867-1940) Hungarian

£441 $626 €662 Bathing (80x97cm-31x38in) painted c.1930. 26-Mar-2 SOGA, Bratislava #132/R (SL.K 28000)

GRUNWALD, Carl (1907-1968) German

£321 $497 €500 Orpheus and Euripides (22x15cm-9x6in) s. board. 4-Dec-2 Lempertz, Koln #758/R

GRUPPE, Charles Paul (1860-1940) American
£520 $868 €754 Corner in the pasture (24x34cm-9x13in) s.i. s.verso board. 17-Jun-3 Rosebery Fine Art, London #530/R
£531 $850 €797 An old friend of mine. Composition Carnegie Hall, still life with violin (41x51cm-16x20in) s. 1-Jan-3 Nadeau, Windsor #79
£641 $1000 €962 River landscape with birch trees (51x30cm-20x12in) s. 22-Sep-2 Jeffery Burchard, Florida #30b
£781 $1250 €1172 Dutch woodsman (25x36cm-10x14in) s. 11-Jan-3 James Julia, Fairfield #228 est:2500-3000
£789 $1279 €1200 Fetching water from the well (38x48cm-15x19in) s. 21-Jan-3 Christie's, Amsterdam #272 est:700-900
£820 $1287 €1230 Figure on horseback in a wooded landscape (27x20cm-11x8in) s. board. 16-Dec-2 Bonhams, Bury St Edmunds #522/R
£920 $1500 €1380 Small red sailed schooner isolated in golden sea (28x53cm-11x21in) 1-Feb-3 Thomaston Place, Thomaston #138
£968 $1500 €1452 Rocky coastline with distant ship (30x41cm-12x16in) s. 7-Dec-2 Selkirks, St. Louis #251/R est:2500-3000
£1118 $1800 €1677 October day (36x51cm-14x20in) s. 15-Jan-3 Boos Gallery, Michigan #655/R est:1250-1750
£1210 $1900 €1815 Autumn stream with high banks having tall trees (64x74cm-25x29in) s. 19-Apr-3 James Julia, Fairfield #93/R est:4000-6000
£1290 $2000 €1935 Fishing shacks along the shore (30x41cm-12x16in) s. 7-Dec-2 Selkirks, St. Louis #252/R est:2500-3500
£1751 $2750 €2627 Seascape with sailboat in distance with light grey ocean and sunlit grey sky (30x41cm-12x16in) s. board. 19-Apr-3 James Julia, Fairfield #94/R est:2500-3500
£1783 $2782 €2800 Rider on tow-path (50x67cm-20x26in) s. 6-Nov-2 Vendue Huis, Gravenhage #492/R est:1200-1600
£2000 $3200 €3000 Near the Hague, Holland (25x36cm-10x14in) s. i.verso board. 11-Jan-3 James Julia, Fairfield #227 est:2500-3500
£2273 $3500 €3410 On the farm (41x61cm-16x24in) s. 4-Sep-2 Christie's, Rockefeller NY #337/R est:3000-5000
£3013 $4700 €4520 Winter stream scene (76x91cm-30x36in) s. 1-Aug-2 Eldred, East Dennis #796/R est:2000-2500
£5519 $8500 €8279 Brook in spring (46x61cm-18x24in) s. 24-Oct-2 Shannon's, Milford #166/R est:7000-9000

Works on paper
£592 $959 €900 Farmhouse by a brook, dunes in the distance (33x48cm-13x19in) s. black chk W/C htd white. 21-Jan-3 Christie's, Amsterdam #145
£688 $1100 €1032 Landscape with sheep grazing (36x33cm-14x13in) s. W/C gouache. 17-May-3 Pook & Pook, Downington #386/R est:1000-1200
£944 $1500 €1416 Dutch harbour (33x48cm-13x19in) s. W/C gouache. 7-Mar-3 Skinner, Boston #526/R est:1000-1500

GRUPPE, Emile A (1896-1978) American
£1274 $2000 €1911 Schooner pulling dingy off Wingaersheek beach (30x41cm-12x16in) s. s.i.verso board. 19-Apr-3 James Julia, Fairfield #32/R est:2000-3000
£1592 $2500 €2388 Beach scene with young girl playing in sand and other figures (30x41cm-12x16in) s. board. 19-Apr-3 James Julia, Fairfield #31/R est:3000-4000
£1783 $2800 €2675 Gloucester Harbor (30x25cm-12x10in) s. i.d.1935 verso canvasboard. 22-Nov-2 Skinner, Boston #348/R est:600-800
£2051 $3200 €3077 Birch in a landscape (46x51cm-18x20in) s. 20-Sep-2 Sloan, North Bethesda #485/R est:4000-6000
£2187 $3500 €3171 On fish (61x51cm-24x20in) s. i.verso. 16-May-3 Skinner, Boston #287/R est:4000-6000
£2188 $3500 €3282 Snow scene (30x41cm-12x16in) s. i.verso board. 15-Mar-3 Jeffery Burchard, Florida #122/R
£2229 $3500 €3344 Rocky shoreline with surf fisherman (46x51cm-18x20in) s. indis.i.verso. 19-Apr-3 James Julia, Fairfield #30/R est:6000-8000
£2244 $3500 €3366 Gloucester harbour (41x51cm-16x20in) s. canvasboard. 22-Sep-2 Jeffery Burchard, Florida #30
£2250 $3600 €3263 Bathers (51x41cm-20x16in) s. 17-May-3 CRN Auctions, Cambridge #48
£2478 $3965 €3717 Meadow brook (61x76cm-24x30in) s. board. 11-Jan-3 James Julia, Fairfield #65 est:7000-9000
£2516 $4000 €3774 Gloucester harbour (46x51cm-18x20in) s. 7-Mar-3 Skinner, Boston #492/R est:4000-6000
£2543 $4070 €3815 Morning Stuart Beach, Florida (64x76cm-25x30in) s. i.on stretcher. 11-Jan-3 James Julia, Fairfield #66 est:6000-8000
£2861 $4750 €4148 Reflection (25x20cm-10x8in) s. i.verso panel prov. 11-Jun-3 Butterfields, San Francisco #4073/R est:3000-5000
£3125 $5000 €4531 Naples Beach Florida (46x61cm-18x24in) s. canvasboard. 16-May-3 Skinner, Boston #310/R est:3000-5000
£3185 $5000 €4778 Rocky coastline with seagulls over crashing waves in morning light (61x71cm-24x28in) s. s.i.d.1976 on stretcher. 19-Apr-3 James Julia, Fairfield #29/R
£3281 $5250 €4922 Winter, a brook with large covered banks (30x41cm-12x16in) s.verso board. 11-Jan-3 James Julia, Fairfield #67 est:4000-6000
£3459 $5500 €5189 Gloucester morning (61x51cm-24x20in) s. s.i.d.1960 verso. 7-Mar-3 Skinner, Boston #476/R est:3000-5000
£3503 $5500 €5255 Vermont winter (41x51cm-16x20in) s. s.i.verso canvasboard prov. 10-Dec-2 Doyle, New York #71/R est:3000-4000
£3822 $6000 €5733 Early spring landscape with mountains and wooded hills showing the last of the snow (41x51cm-16x20in) s. 19-Apr-3 James Julia, Fairfield #28/R est:5000-7000
£3896 $6000 €5844 Morning, Rockport (51x61cm-20x24in) s. prov. 24-Oct-2 Shannon's, Milford #8/R est:4000-6000
£4194 $6500 €6291 Nymphs (25x20cm-10x8in) s. board exhib. 3-Dec-2 Christie's, Rockefeller NY #597/R est:3000-5000
£4221 $6500 €6332 Men at work (51x61cm-20x24in) s. prov. 24-Oct-2 Shannon's, Milford #6/R est:5000-7000
£5128 $8000 €7692 Untitled, dock scene (61x51cm-24x20in) 18-Oct-2 Du Mouchelle, Detroit #2071/R est:6000-9000
£5696 $9000 €8544 Gloucester Harbor (76x91cm-30x36in) s. i.verso prov. 24-Apr-3 Shannon's, Milford #37/R est:8000-12000
£5844 $9000 €8766 Morning, Gloucester Harbour (76x91cm-30x36in) s. prov. 24-Oct-2 Shannon's, Milford #54/R est:9000-12000
£5975 $9500 €8963 Birches, Gloucester harbour (63x76cm-25x30in) s. 7-Mar-3 Skinner, Boston #463/R est:6000-8000
£6200 $9858 €9300 Gloucester morning (77x91cm-30x36in) s. i.verso. 29-Apr-3 Bonhams, New Bond Street #186/R est:5000-8000
£6369 $10000 €9554 Sugar bush, winter landscape (76x91cm-30x36in) s. i.stretcher prov. 19-Nov-2 Butterfields, San Francisco #8050/R est:8000-12000
£6627 $11000 €9609 Bright Gloucester Bay (76x91cm-30x36in) s. i.verso prov. 11-Jun-3 Butterfields, San Francisco #4083/R est:6000-8000
£7792 $12000 €11688 Winter in Gloucester (76x91cm-30x36in) s. prov. 24-Oct-2 Shannon's, Milford #112/R est:12000-18000
£7895 $12000 €11843 Harbour scene with three sailboats (41x30cm-16x12in) s. board. 17-Aug-2 North East Auctions, Portsmouth #1095/R
£8387 $13000 €12581 Nymph in a wooded landscape (81x102cm-32x40in) s. painted c.1928. 8-Dec-2 Toomey, Oak Park #717/R est:20000-30000
£15569 $26000 €22575 Rocky neck, East Gloucester (30x41cm-12x16in) s. s.i.verso board prov.exhib. 22-Jun-3 Freeman, Philadelphia #112/R est:15000-25000

Works on paper
£7595 $12000 €11393 Rockport Beach (64x76cm-25x30in) s. i.v, prov. 24-Apr-3 Shannon's, Milford #10/R est:8000-12000

GRUPPEL, Carl Maria (?) ?
£272 $433 €400 The postman (24x21cm-9x8in) s. copper. 24-Mar-3 Bernaerts, Antwerp #15/R

GRUS, Jaroslav (1891-1981) Czechoslovakian
£454 $736 €681 Landscape with village (27x33cm-11x13in) s.d.1926 board. 24-May-3 Dorotheum, Prague #124/R est:20000-30000 (C.KR 20000)

Works on paper
£330 $522 €495 Motif with a train (60x86cm-24x34in) s.d. mixed media. 30-Nov-2 Dorotheum, Prague #156/R (C.KR 16000)

GRUST, F G (1889-?) Dutch
£962 $1500 €1443 Dutch family interior (64x76cm-25x30in) 18-Oct-2 Du Mouchelle, Detroit #2290/R est:2000-3000
£1250 $2000 €1875 Mother and child on Holland shore (63x76cm-25x30in) s. 18-May-3 Butterfields, Los Angeles #7047 est:2000-3000

GRUTTEFIEN, Elisabeth (19th C) German
£1224 $1947 €1800 Norwegian landscape in spring (80x120cm-31x47in) s. 25-Feb-3 Dorotheum, Vienna #82/R est:1800-2200

GRUTZKE, Johannes (1937-) German
Works on paper
£1806 $2853 €2600 Krimhild and Brunhilda (145x98cm-57x39in) s.i.d.1.3.87 pastel board. 26-Apr-3 Dr Lehr, Berlin #178/R est:3500

GRUTZNER, Eduard von (1846-1925) German
£1037 $1700 €1556 Good brew. s. paper on panel. 31-May-3 Harvey Clar, Oakland #1161
£1863 $3000 €2795 Noon day nap (27x22cm-11x9in) s. panel. 23-Feb-3 Butterfields, Los Angeles #7010 est:1000-1500
£2411 $3906 €3400 Portrait of a monk (21x15cm-8x6in) s.d.13 panel. 22-May-3 Dorotheum, Vienna #151/R est:4000-5000
£3712 $5419 €5568 Smiling monk carrying basket (40x30cm-16x12in) s.d.1907 prov. 4-Jun-2 Germann, Zurich #74/R est:9000-12000 (S.FR 8500)
£3797 $6000 €6000 Falstaff (33x25cm-13x10in) s.d.1904 panel. 28-Nov-2 Dorotheum, Vienna #137/R est:6500-8500
£3822 $5885 €6000 Monk (33x25cm-13x10in) s.d.1905 panel. 5-Sep-2 Arnold, Frankfurt #776/R est:8000
£6289 $9686 €10000 Der Feinschmecker (21x15cm-8x6in) s.d.1895 panel prov.lit. 23-Oct-2 Christie's, Amsterdam #90/R est:10000-15000
£7547 $11774 €12000 Brother monk tasting wine (21x16cm-8x6in) s.d.72 panel. 19-Sep-2 Dr Fritz Nagel, Stuttgart #937/R est:12000
£7547 $11623 €12000 Falstaff (33x28cm-13x11in) s.d.1916 panel prov. 23-Oct-2 Christie's, Amsterdam #91/R est:10000-15000
£16352 $25509 €26000 A little accident (52x42cm-20x17in) s.d.96. 19-Sep-2 Dr Fritz Nagel, Stuttgart #936/R est:15000
£19424 $31079 €27000 St Ottmar of St Gallen (80x62cm-31x24in) s.d.1920 prov.lit. 17-May-3 Lempertz, Koln #1398/R est:28000

£34615 $53654 €54000 Scene from Faust (75x100cm-30x39in) s.d.1897. 5-Dec-2 Dr Fritz Nagel, Stuttgart #656/R
Works on paper
£442 $703 €650 Old man in top hat (25x20cm-10x8in) s.d.90 pencil wash. 19-Mar-3 Neumeister, Munich #359

GRUYTER, Jacob Willem (1856-1908) Dutch
£573 $883 €900 Bomschuiten on the beach at dusk (71x101cm-28x40in) s. 3-Sep-2 Christie's, Amsterdam #292
£855 $1386 €1300 Aan de Noordzee (34x54cm-13x21in) s.d.87 s. verso. 21-Jan-3 Christie's, Amsterdam #136/R est:600-800
£1034 $1644 €1500 Boats in an estuary (30x50cm-12x20in) s. s.d.1883 verso. 10-Mar-3 Sotheby's, Amsterdam #157/R est:1000-1500

GRYEFF, Adriaen de (1670-1715) Flemish
£1806 $2854 €2800 Venus and Adonis in landscape (20x26cm-8x10in) s. panel. 18-Dec-2 Renaud, Paris #48/R
£2703 $4216 €4000 Still life with dead rooster and wildfowl (60x57cm-24x22in) s. prov. 27-Mar-3 Dorotheum, Vienna #377/R est:3000-5000
£3459 $5327 €5500 Sainte Marie Madeleine repentante (24x33cm-9x13in) mono. panel. 25-Oct-2 Tajan, Paris #71/R est:5000-7000
£4140 $6376 €6500 Hunting still life with a spaniel watching a bag of hare and songbirds (18x14cm-7x6in) init. panel. 3-Sep-2 Christie's, Amsterdam #31/R est:2500-3500
£4140 $6459 €6500 Hinting still life with a swan, deer, birds and two dogs (28x41cm-11x16in) s. panel prov. 5-Nov-2 Sotheby's, Amsterdam #37/R est:6000-8000
£4403 $6824 €7000 Gallant scene in the pantry (27x37cm-11x15in) board. 7-Oct-2 Ansorena, Madrid #43/R
£4605 $7461 €7000 Gallant scene in the panntry (27x37cm-11x15in) mono. board. 21-Jan-3 Ansorena, Madrid #90/R
£4828 $7676 €7000 Dogs resting during hunt (25x31cm-10x12in) s. board. 4-Mar-3 Ansorena, Madrid #55/R
£5290 $8359 €8200 Still life with dead game (58x73cm-23x29in) s. 20-Dec-2 Tajan, Paris #74/R est:7000

GRYNT, Pieter (19/20th C) Scandinavian
£7000 $11480 €10500 Bater ankret opp pa fjorden - boat moored in a fjord (101x151cm-40x59in) s. 3-Jun-3 Sotheby's, London #266/R est:4000-6000

GSCHEIDEL, Martin (1857-?) German
£287 $448 €431 Thatched houses and figures by water's edge (58x90cm-23x35in) s. 23-Sep-2 Rasmussen, Vejle #275/R (D.KR 3400)

GSCHOSMANN, Ludwig (c.1901-1988) German
£325 $494 €500 Extensive landscape with figures resting (60x80cm-24x31in) s. 5-Jul-2 Weidler, Nurnberg #8737/R
£348 $540 €550 Hunt (68x79cm-27x31in) s. 27-Sep-2 Weidler, Nurnberg #8709/R
£411 $641 €600 Picnic on Starnberg Lake (60x80cm-24x31in) s. lit. 10-Apr-3 Allgauer, Kempten #2785/R
£449 $704 €700 Tegernsee (90x100cm-35x39in) 23-Nov-2 Arnold, Frankfurt #734/R
£489 $812 €709 Schliersee (69x79cm-27x31in) s. s.i.verso. 16-Jun-3 Waddingtons, Toronto #294/R est:1200-1400 (C.D 1100)
£806 $1274 €1209 At the ball (81x71cm-32x28in) s. 18-Nov-2 Waddingtons, Toronto #261/R est:2000-2500 (C.D 2000)
£1146 $1789 €1800 Venice (60x80cm-24x31in) s. 6-Nov-2 Hugo Ruef, Munich #1116/R est:1200

GSELL, Laurent (1860-1944) French
£385 $604 €600 Coucher de soleil a Rogny (38x59cm-15x23in) s.d.1942. 24-Nov-2 Lesieur & Le Bars, Le Havre #69
£7595 $12000 €11393 Workmen (149x99cm-59x39in) s. 24-Apr-3 Sotheby's, New York #163/R est:12000-18000

GU DASHEN (17th C) Chinese
Works on paper
£3497 $5769 €5071 Landscape (124x64cm-49x25in) s.i. ink hanging scroll after MI FU. 6-Jul-3 Christie's, Hong Kong #458/R est:50000-70000 (HK.D 45000)

GUACCI, Michelangelo (1910-1967) Italian
£532 $862 €750 Bacco (17x13cm-7x5in) s.d.66 panel. 22-May-3 Stadion, Trieste #363/R
£567 $919 €800 Ballerina (24x18cm-9x7in) s.d.65 board. 22-May-3 Stadion, Trieste #368/R
Works on paper
£638 $1034 €900 Colpo di vento (36x48cm-14x19in) s.d.67 W/C. 22-May-3 Stadion, Trieste #360/R

GUAITAMACCHI, Jonathan (1961-) British/Italian
£2838 $4427 €4200 Central street (90x130cm-35x51in) s.i.d.2001 verso. 26-Mar-3 Finarte Semenzato, Milan #175/R
Works on paper
£5248 $8502 €7400 Passaggio (70x207cm-28x81in) s.i.d.2002 verso mixed media canvas. 20-May-3 Porro, Milan #26/R est:7200-7400

GUALA, Pier Francesco (attrib) (1698-1757) Italian
£2600 $4082 €3900 Allegory of architecture (80x60cm-31x24in) 10-Dec-2 Bonhams, New Bond Street #198/R est:3000-5000

GUAN LIANG (1899-1985) Chinese
£6993 $11538 €10140 Memorial hall of the 72 revolutioners (47x39cm-19x15in) s. painted c.1950 exhib. 6-Jul-3 Christie's, Hong Kong #147/R est:100000-120000 (HK.D 90000)
£10101 $16667 €14646 Landscape (50x39cm-20x15in) s. painted c.1940. 6-Jul-3 Christie's, Hong Kong #146/R est:120000-150000 (HK.D 130000)
Works on paper
£1399 $2308 €2029 Opera figures (94x59cm-37x23in) s.d.1979 col ink scroll. 6-Jul-3 Christie's, Hong Kong #224/R est:20000-30000 (HK.D 18000)

GUAN TONG (attrib) (10th C) Chinese
Works on paper
£34965 $57692 €50699 Waiting for the ferry (127x48cm-50x19in) s.i.d.1111 ink silk hanging scroll with separate hanging scroll. 6-Jul-3 Christie's, Hong Kong #443/R est:500000-700000 (HK.D 450000)

GUAN WEI (1957-) Australian/Chinese
Works on paper
£1071 $1671 €1607 Yellow bowl (86x46cm-34x18in) init. s.i.d.16.9.1990 verso synthetic polymer paint canvas. 11-Nov-2 Deutscher-Menzies, Melbourne #17/R est:3000-4000 (A.D 3000)
£1500 $2340 €2250 Carrot (86x46cm-34x18in) init. s.i.d.13.9.90 verso synthetic polymer paint canvas. 11-Nov-2 Deutscher-Menzies, Melbourne #16/R est:3000-4000 (A.D 4200)
£1692 $2691 €2538 Shoe (127x48cm-50x19in) s.d.92 s.i.d.1992.2.3. verso synthetic polymer paint prov. 4-Mar-3 Deutscher-Menzies, Melbourne #184/R est:5000-7000 (A.D 4400)

GUAN YU (1962-) Chinese
Works on paper
£306 $487 €450 Reve de nuit (40x40cm-16x16in) st.sig. mixed media. 24-Mar-3 Coutau Begarie, Paris #340
£306 $487 €450 Regard des songes (33x34cm-13x13in) st.sig. mixed media. 24-Mar-3 Coutau Begarie, Paris #338

GUANSE, Antonio (1926-) Spanish
£342 $534 €500 Waves VI (65x54cm-26x21in) s.d.89 s.i.verso. 8-Apr-3 Ansorena, Madrid #296/R
£581 $917 €900 Atelier III (65x54cm-26x21in) s.d.75. 18-Dec-2 Ansorena, Madrid #223/R
Works on paper
£308 $481 €450 Burnt land (64x49cm-25x19in) s.d.81 mixed media cardboard. 8-Apr-3 Ansorena, Madrid #295/R
£321 $501 €475 Sunny landscape (40x50cm-16x20in) s. gouache lit. 25-Mar-3 Durán, Madrid #115/R

GUARANA, F (?) Italian
£1899 $3000 €3000 Quay from saint mark's (25x35cm-10x14in) s. 27-Nov-2 Finarte, Milan #11/R

GUARANA, Jacopo (attrib) (1720-1808) Italian
Works on paper
£380 $600 €600 Putto volant, tenant une couronne (23x30cm-9x12in) i.verso col chk. 27-Nov-2 Christie's, Paris #84

GUARDABASSI, Guerrino (1841-?) Italian
£452 $750 €655 Landscape with a boy. Landscape with a girl (28x18cm-11x7in) s. s.verso pair. 11-Jun-3 Boos Gallery, Michigan #550/R
Works on paper
£305 $500 €442 Young flute player (51x33cm-20x13in) s.i. W/C htd white. 4-Jun-3 Doyle, New York #62
£377 $600 €566 Flower vendor (41x30cm-16x12in) s. W/C gouache paperboard. 7-Mar-3 Skinner, Boston #242/R
£400 $632 €600 Cardinal admiring a portrait of the Madonna and Child (50x37cm-20x15in) s. W/C bodycol. 26-Nov-2 Bonhams, Knightsbridge #219/R

GUARDI, Francesco (1712-1793) Italian

£18000 $28260 €27000 Isola della Beata Vergine del Rosario, Venice (12x19cm-5x7in) prov. 11-Dec-2 Christie's, London #122/R

£21053 $34105 €32000 Education of the Virgin (44x34cm-17x13in) 21-Jan-3 Ansorena, Madrid #101/R est:30000

£21951 $36000 €32927 Capriccio with buildings, fishing boat and gondolas in the foreground (18x24cm-7x9in) prov. 29-May-3 Sotheby's, New York #60a/R est:40000-60000

£28049 $46000 €42074 Capriccio with a church and tower, fishing boat and gondolas in the foreground (18x24cm-7x9in) panel prov. 29-May-3 Sotheby's, New York #60/R est:40000-60000

£37037 $60000 €55556 Capriccio of ruins in the Venetian Lagoon (18x43cm-7x17in) canvas on panel pair prov.exhib.lit. 24-Jan-3 Christie's, Rockefeller NY #167/R est:60000-80000

£42000 $65520 €63000 Capriccio of the Venetian lagoon with obelisk (21x30cm-8x12in) 10-Apr-3 Sotheby's, London #98/R est:30000-40000

£115000 $192050 €166750 Architectural capriccio with figures before a ruined arch (23x18cm-9x7in) prov. 10-Jul-3 Sotheby's, London #58/R est:20000-30000

£155000 $258850 €224750 Architectural capriccio with figures before an open door (23x17cm-9x7in) prov. 10-Jul-3 Sotheby's, London #59/R est:15000-20000

£240000 $374400 €360000 Capriccio of buildings on the laguna with figures by a ruined arch (56x42cm-22x17in) prov. 9-Apr-3 Christie's, London #116/R est:60000-80000

£720000 $1130400 €1080000 Entrance to the Grand Canal (84x129cm-33x51in) prov.exhib.lit. 11-Dec-2 Christie's, London #123/R est:400000-600000

Works on paper

£60000 $100200 €87000 View of the Rio dei Mendicant, Venice (18x26cm-7x10in) pen brown ink wash red chk blk chk study verso prov. 9-Jul-3 Sotheby's, London #52/R est:60000-80000

GUARDI, Francesco (attrib) (1712-1793) Italian

£2448 $3500 €3672 Rustic house beside lagoon (27x42cm-11x17in) prov.lit. 22-Jan-3 Doyle, New York #106

£5500 $8525 €8250 Venice, view of the Piazzetta with San Giorgio Maggiore in distance (27x38cm-11x15in) 31-Oct-2 Sotheby's, Olympia #196/R est:6000-8000

£10569 $16699 €15325 Capriccios, piazza with figures and a domed church beyond. View through the ruin (73x58cm-29x23in) pair prov. 22-Jul-3 Lawson Menzies, Sydney #291/R est:11000-15000 (A.D 26000)

£54000 $90180 €78300 Capriccio of ruins on the Venetian laguna with washerwoman and other figures (17x23cm-7x9in) panel. 11-Jul-3 Christie's, Kensington #264/R est:10000-15000

Works on paper

£1950 $3003 €3100 San Marco's square (21x27cm-8x11in) pen dr. 28-Oct-2 Il Ponte, Milan #156/R

£1950 $3003 €3100 Saint Gmignano church (25x21cm-10x8in) pen dr. 28-Oct-2 Il Ponte, Milan #157/R est:700

GUARDI, Francesco (studio) (1712-1793) Italian

£11111 $17556 €16000 View of San Jacopo di Paludo (19x26cm-7x10in) 25-Apr-3 Beaussant & Lefèvre, Paris #19/R est:4000-6000

GUARDI, Francesco (style) (1712-1793) Italian

£5063 $8000 €7595 Venetian view (57x75cm-22x30in) 1-Apr-3 Christie's, Rockefeller NY #356/R est:10000-15000

GUARDI, Giacomo (1764-1835) Italian

£11511 $18417 €16000 Rialto bridge in Venice (70x98cm-28x39in) canvas on panel prov. 17-May-3 Lempertz, Koln #1055/R est:18000

£14198 $23000 €21297 View of San Giorgio (16x22cm-6x9in) prov. 23-Jan-3 Sotheby's, New York #132/R est:30000

£15000 $25050 €21750 The Piazzetta, Venice looking towards St Mark's Square (29x29cm-11x11in) 9-Jul-3 Bonhams, New Bond Street #33/R est:5000-7000

Works on paper

£3800 $5966 €5700 View of the Canal by Ca'Foscari, Venice (11x18cm-4x7in) s. i.verso bodycol. 13-Dec-2 Christie's, Kensington #297/R est:1000-1500

£5500 $9185 €7975 Ruined building over a canal with two figures. Imaginary view of the Venetian Lagoon (46x31cm-18x12in) black chk pen ink wash two. 8-Jul-3 Christie's, London #58/R est:6000-8000

£5800 $9686 €8410 Rialto Bridge, Venice (15x24cm-6x9in) bodycol. 8-Jul-3 Christie's, London #59/R est:3000-5000

£6331 $10129 €8800 Venetian scene (15x25cm-6x10in) s.i. verso gouache. 17-May-3 Lempertz, Koln #1226/R est:3000

£7500 $11775 €11250 Fondamenta Quintavalle, Venice. Fondamenta dei Mendicanti, Venice (11x18cm-4x7in) s.i. bodycol pair. 13-Dec-2 Christie's, Kensington #296/R est:2000-3000

£12821 $19872 €20000 Capriccios (46x31cm-18x12in) pen ink wash set of 4. 4-Dec-2 Piasa, Paris #16/R est:25000

£14634 $24000 €21951 View of the Piazza San Marco, Venice (15x25cm-6x10in) i.verso gouache. 29-May-3 Sotheby's, New York #156/R est:10000-15000

£15854 $26000 €23781 View of San Giorgio Maggiore, Venice (15x24cm-6x9in) i. gouache. 29-May-3 Sotheby's, New York #155/R est:10000-15000

GUARDI, Giacomo (attrib) (1764-1835) Italian

£21384 $32931 €34000 View of the Piazzetta. View of Campo SS. Giovanni and Paolo (45x72cm-18x28in) pair. 23-Oct-2 Finarte, Rome #527/R est:32000-35000

Works on paper

£2600 $4342 €3770 Figures strolling in a piazza. gouache. 9-Jul-3 Bonhams, Knightsbridge #9/R est:700-1000

GUARDI, Giovanni Antonio (1698-1760) Italian

Works on paper

£3086 $5000 €4629 Design for altarpiece (23x17cm-9x7in) i. pen ink wash over chk. 21-Jan-3 Sotheby's, New York #76/R est:4500

£43210 $70000 €64815 Magus (26x19cm-10x7in) chk prov.lit. 22-Jan-3 Christie's, Rockefeller NY #48/R est:60000

GUARIENTI, Carlo (1923-) Italian

Works on paper

£1560 $2528 €2200 Composition (123x128cm-48x50in) s.d.87 mixed media masonite. 26-May-3 Christie's, Milan #87 est:2500-3000

GUARINO DA SOLOFRA, Francesco (1611-1654) Italian

£15517 $24517 €22500 Judith (25x20cm-10x8in) copper prov.lit. 3-Apr-3 Porro, Milan #9/R est:40000

£24828 $39228 €36000 Saint Onofrio (115x93cm-45x37in) prov.lit. 3-Apr-3 Porro, Milan #13/R est:50000

£26897 $42497 €39000 Saint Lucy (28cm-11in circular) copper prov.lit. 3-Apr-3 Porro, Milan #8/R est:55000

£141379 $223379 €205000 Joseph interpreting the pharaoh's dreams (128x155cm-50x61in) prov.lit. 3-Apr-3 Porro, Milan #12/R est:250000

GUARISCO, Elizabeth M (1955-) American

Sculpture

£5195 $8000 €7793 Spirit of competition (41cm-16in) bronze. 25-Oct-2 Morris & Whiteside, Hilton Head Island #167 est:8000-10000

GUARLOTTI, Giovanni (1869-1954) Italian

£1410 $2214 €2200 Cows at pasture (37x51cm-15x20in) s. cardboard. 10-Dec-2 Della Rocca, Turin #286/R

GUARNIDO, Juan (20th C) French?

Works on paper

£586 $926 €850 Blacksad (30x21cm-12x8in) s. graphite. 7-Apr-3 Claude Aguttes, Neuilly #41/R

£724 $1144 €1050 Blacksad (30x21cm-12x8in) s. graphite dr. 7-Apr-3 Claude Aguttes, Neuilly #40/R

GUARNIERI, Guido (1886-?) Italian

£321 $497 €500 Landscape in Friuli (40x50cm-16x20in) s. board. 5-Dec-2 Stadion, Trieste #854

GUASCH, Javier (?) ?

£1342 $2161 €2000 Interior with figure (81x66cm-32x26in) s. 18-Feb-3 Durán, Madrid #1152/R

GUASTALLA, Pierre (1891-1968) French

£739 $1190 €1050 Le grand cedre (65x50cm-26x20in) s. 11-May-3 Thierry & Lannon, Brest #362

£1408 $2268 €2000 Paysage breton (33x55cm-13x22in) s. 11-May-3 Thierry & Lannon, Brest #181 est:1200-1500

£1667 $2617 €2600 Vallee (52x66cm-20x26in) s. 15-Dec-2 Thierry & Lannon, Brest #388

£1795 $2818 €2800 YTrois Mages (60x73cm-24x29in) s. 15-Dec-2 Thierry & Lannon, Brest #139

GUAY, Gabriel (1848-?) French

£851 $1319 €1277 Lavandieres pres de Saint-Omer, Pas-de-Calais (56x69cm-22x27in) s. 4-Dec-2 AB Stockholms Auktionsverk #1873/R (S.KR 12000)

GUAY, le (19th C) French?
Miniatures
£1351 $2108 €2000 Portrait d'homme (6x5cm-2x2in) s. 26-Mar-3 Pierre Berge, Paris #78/R

GUAYASAMIN, Oswaldo (1919-1999) Ecuadorian
£10377 $16085 €16500 Pain (98x53cm-39x21in) s. 7-Oct-2 Ansorena, Madrid #81/R est:16500
£14024 $23000 €20335 Paisaje de quito (75x120cm-30x47in) s. painted c.1970 prov. 27-May-3 Sotheby's, New York #148
£28662 $45000 €42993 Faith procession (69x53cm-27x21in) s. painted 1945 prov.lit. 20-Nov-2 Christie's, Rockefeller NY #73/R est:30000-40000
£35032 $55000 €52548 Pain (98x67cm-39x26in) s. painted c.1956 prov.lit. 20-Nov-2 Christie's, Rockefeller NY #75/R est:40000-50000
Works on paper
£1282 $2000 €1923 Untitled, preparatory drawing (46x61cm-18x24in) s.i.d.1960 ink pencil gouache. 14-Oct-2 Butterfields, San Francisco #2144/R est:3000-5000
£3659 $6000 €5489 Sin titulo (50x37cm-20x15in) s.d.1943 W/C pencil prov. 28-May-3 Christie's, Rockefeller NY #92/R est:8000-10000

GUAZZO, Andreina Crepet (1909-) Italian
£326 $535 €450 San Antonio di Ranverso (37x52cm-15x20in) traces sig. panel. 27-May-3 Finarte, Milan #129/R

GUBA, Rudolf (1884-1950) German
£314 $484 €500 Fishing boat (49x58cm-19x23in) s. board on panel. 26-Oct-2 Quittenbaum, Hamburg #12/R
£346 $533 €550 Fishing boats (52x81cm-20x32in) s. 26-Oct-2 Quittenbaum, Hamburg #13/R

GUBBELS, Klaas (1934-) Dutch
£3741 $6135 €5200 Remember (120x105cm-47x41in) init.d.95 verso prov. 3-Jun-3 Christie's, Amsterdam #361/R est:4500-5500

GUBLER, Max (1898-1973) Swiss
£755 $1208 €1133 Self portrait at easel (43x35cm-17x14in) oil chk. 17-Mar-3 Philippe Schuler, Zurich #4326/R est:2000-3000 (S.FR 1600)
£1739 $2696 €2609 Standing nude in studio (65x54cm-26x21in) prov.lit. 4-Dec-2 Koller, Zurich #142/R est:6000-8000 (S.FR 4000)
£5652 $8761 €8478 Self portrait (73x60cm-29x24in) prov.lit. 4-Dec-2 Koller, Zurich #140/R est:8000-15000 (S.FR 13000)
£5677 $8288 €8516 Surb valley, Unterengstringen landscape (51x61cm-20x24in) prov.exhib.lit. 4-Jun-2 Germann, Zurich #62/R est:15000-25000 (S.FR 13000)
£6438 $10172 €9657 Venice (38x46cm-15x18in) s.d.49 lit. 26-Nov-2 Phillips, Zurich #78/R est:15000-20000 (S.FR 15000)
£6604 $10698 €11688 Hung up fish (115x81cm-45x32in) s.d. prov.exhib.lit. 26-May-3 Sotheby's, Zurich #96/R est:20000-40000 (S.FR 14000)
£7339 $12257 €10642 Seated woman in white dress (110x80cm-43x31in) s.i.d.1929 prov.exhib. 20-Jun-3 Kornfeld, Bern #66/R est:20000 (S.FR 16000)
£8491 $13755 €15029 Reclining pheasant (50x61cm-20x24in) s. prov.exhib.lit. 26-May-3 Sotheby's, Zurich #97/R est:18000-25000 (S.FR 18000)
£8584 $13562 €12876 Venice (50x61cm-20x24in) s.d.49 lit. 26-Nov-2 Phillips, Zurich #80/R est:20000-25000 (S.FR 20000)
£10435 $16278 €15653 Still life with Etruscan mask and plaster statuette (130x162cm-51x64in) lit.exhib.prov. 16-Sep-2 Philippe Schuler, Zurich #3369/R est:24000-28000 (S.FR 24000)
£10730 $16953 €16095 Small summer landscape with wine field in Unterengstringen (38x46cm-15x18in) lit. 26-Nov-2 Phillips, Zurich #81/R est:25000-30000 (S.FR 25000)
£10870 $16848 €16305 Limmat landscape, melting snow (130x162cm-51x64in) prov.lit. 4-Dec-2 Koller, Zurich #129/R est:30000-50000 (S.FR 25000)
£11354 $17825 €17031 Woman seated in front of easel (120x97cm-47x38in) prov.lit. 25-Nov-2 Germann, Zurich #82/R est:25000-30000 (S.FR 26000)
£12227 $19197 €18341 Poppies and corn (120x97cm-47x38in) prov.exhib.lit. 25-Nov-2 Germann, Zurich #81/R est:30000-35000 (S.FR 28000)
£13974 $21939 €20961 Still life with fruit bowl, glass vase and thistles (89x116cm-35x46in) i. verso prov.exhib.lit. 25-Nov-2 Germann, Zurich #69/R est:30000-35000 (S.FR 32000)
£14480 $24181 €20996 Quarry (114x146cm-45x57in) prov.lit. 24-Jun-3 Koller, Zurich #52/R est:40000-50000 (S.FR 32000)
£15721 $22952 €23582 Nighttime landscape with gas works (50x61cm-20x24in) s.d.1950 prov.exhib.lit. 4-Jun-2 Germann, Zurich #61/R est:20000-30000 (S.FR 36000)
£16514 $27578 €23945 Harvest near Unterengstringen (116x146cm-46x57in) exhib. 20-Jun-3 Kornfeld, Bern #68/R est:40000 (S.FR 36000)
£17195 $28715 €24933 Summer landscape, view of Schlieren (128x154cm-50x61in) prov.lit. 24-Jun-3 Koller, Zurich #59/R est:45000-60000 (S.FR 38000)
£18349 $30642 €26606 Winter landscape, Kloster Fahr (97x130cm-38x51in) exhib. 20-Jun-3 Kornfeld, Bern #67/R est:40000 (S.FR 40000)
Works on paper
£617 $900 €926 Three men in waiting room (34x22cm-13x9in) s. chl study verso. 17-Jun-2 Philippe Schuler, Zurich #4182/R (S.FR 1400)

GUCCIONE, Piero (1925-) Italian
£9615 $15096 €15000 Suburbs (100x80cm-39x31in) s.d.1960. 23-Nov-2 Meeting Art, Vercelli #364/R est:15000
Works on paper
£1844 $2987 €2600 Stagno di montagna - Ragusa - dopo il tramonto (37x49cm-15x19in) i.d.14.10.73 pastel tempera pencil. 26-May-3 Christie's, Milan #69/R est:1800-2200

GUDE, Hans Fredrik (1825-1903) Norwegian
£1483 $2329 €2225 Berchtesgaden - street scene (38x52cm-15x20in) s. 25-Nov-2 Blomqvist, Lysaker #1088/R est:30000-35000 (N.KR 17000)
£2531 $3973 €3797 Man rowing at Chiemsee (25x14cm-10x6in) init.i.d.24 aug 67 i.verso lit. 21-Nov-2 Grev Wedels Plass, Oslo #2/R est:30000-40000 (N.KR 29000)
£2700 $4401 €3915 Stormy landscape (26x41cm-10x16in) s.d.1880. 16-Jul-3 Sotheby's, Olympia #141/R est:600-800
£3401 $5408 €5000 Venetian harbour (24x38cm-9x15in) s.d.16 Mai 1894 paper on canvas. 19-Mar-3 Neumeister, Munich #570/R est:2000
£3620 $5864 €5430 Waterfall (35x30cm-14x12in) init.d.45. 26-May-3 Grev Wedels Plass, Oslo #127/R est:50000-70000 (N.KR 40000)
£4539 $7035 €6809 Lake landscape with figures (32x48cm-13x19in) s.d.1856. 3-Dec-2 Bukowskis, Stockholm #165/R est:50000-60000 (S.KR 64000)
£4867 $7982 €7057 Suphellebreen, Fjaerland - mountain landscape (35x49cm-14x19in) s.i.d.2 de Sept 1849 paper on panel prov. 2-Jun-3 Blomqvist, Oslo #162/R est:100000 (N.KR 53000)
£10560 $17319 €15312 Seascape with yacht (36x40cm-14x16in) s.d.1897 exhib.lit. 2-Jun-3 Blomqvist, Oslo #106/R est:140000-180000 (N.KR 115000)
£10993 $17039 €16490 Landscape with figures by brook (57x86cm-22x34in) s.d.1869. 3-Dec-2 Bukowskis, Stockholm #166/R est:200000-300000 (S.KR 155000)
£13925 $22280 €20888 Landscape from Faeste near Moss (39x64cm-15x25in) s.d.1893. 17-Mar-3 Blomqvist, Oslo #329/R est:120000-150000 (N.KR 160000)
£22624 $36652 €33936 Fishing with closing net from boat (50x75cm-20x30in) s.d.1873. 26-May-3 Grev Wedels Plass, Oslo #92/R est:250000-300000 (N.KR 250000)
£25152 $39237 €37728 Washing at the edge of water - possibly Bodensee in Germany (51x79cm-20x31in) s. painted 1882. 21-Oct-2 Blomqvist, Oslo #306/R est:200000-250000 (N.KR 290000)
£27419 $42500 €41129 Fishing party at sunrise (76x107cm-30x42in) s.d.1873. 29-Oct-2 Sotheby's, New York #122/R est:60000-80000
£27434 $43345 €41151 Salmon fishing (45x64cm-18x25in) s.d.1848. 28-Apr-3 Blomqvist, Oslo #320/R est:250000-350000 (N.KR 310000)
Works on paper
£1623 $2564 €2435 Vessels by coast (20x42cm-8x17in) s.d.1893 pencil wash. 17-Dec-2 Grev Wedels Plass, Oslo #1459/R est:15000-20000 (N.KR 18500)
£5410 $8494 €8115 Coastal landscape from Torekov (36x53cm-14x21in) s.i.d.1890 W/C. 21-Nov-2 Grev Wedels Plass, Oslo #1/R est:30000-50000 (N.KR 62000)

GUDE, Hans Fredrik and TIDEMAND, Adolph (19th C) Norwegian
£445026 $698691 €667539 The bridal voyage on the Hardangerfjord (45x66cm-18x26in) s.d.1853 lit. 21-Nov-2 Grev Wedels Plass, Oslo #41/R est:5000000-7000000 (N.KR 5100000)

GUDERNA, Ladislav (1921-) Czechoslovakian
£663 $1028 €995 In the bar (37x50cm-15x20in) oil tempera cardboard painted 1976. 3-Dec-2 SOGA, Bratislava #88/R (SL.K 42000)
Works on paper
£284 $414 €426 Spaceman (33x48cm-13x19in) mixed media board. 4-Jun-2 SOGA, Bratislava #239a/R est:12000 (SL.K 18000)
£599 $850 €899 Woman (106x65cm-42x26in) pastel mixed media board exec.1970. 26-Mar-2 SOGA, Bratislava #110/R est:48000 (SL.K 38000)

GUDGEON, Ralston (1910-1984) British
Works on paper
£360 $569 €522 Two for joy, pair of magpies on the branches of a silver birch tree (45x55cm-18x22in) s. W/C. 22-Jul-3 Bonhams, Knightsbridge #52a
£400 $620 €600 Black cock (50x60cm-20x24in) s. pencil W/C bodycol. 26-Sep-2 Mellors & Kirk, Nottingham #649/R
£420 $651 €630 Red grouse (50x63cm-20x25in) s. pencil W/C bodycol. 26-Sep-2 Mellors & Kirk, Nottingham #641/R
£420 $651 €630 Cock Pheasant (47x61cm-19x24in) s. pencil W/C bodycol. 26-Sep-2 Mellors & Kirk, Nottingham #642
£440 $682 €660 Lapwings (49x61cm-19x24in) s. pencil W/C bodycol. 26-Sep-2 Mellors & Kirk, Nottingham #643/R

GUDIASHVILI, Lado (1896-1980) Russian
Works on paper
£3000 $4860 €4500 Young women and horses (26x20cm-10x8in) s. pencil. 21-May-3 Sotheby's, London #154/R est:3000-5000

GUDIN, H (19th C) French
£1538 $2415 €2400 Barques de peche (13x20cm-5x8in) s. panel. 19-Nov-2 Servarts Themis, Bruxelles #101
£1923 $3019 €3000 Clair de lune sur la mer (13x21cm-5x8in) s. panel. 19-Nov-2 Servarts Themis, Bruxelles #103

GUDIN, Henriette (1825-?) French
£314 $525 €450 Les voiles (30x50cm-12x20in) s. 26-Jun-3 Tajan, Paris #197
£705 $1093 €1100 Clair de lune sur la mer (13x20cm-5x8in) s. panel. 9-Dec-2 Beaussant & Lefèvre, Paris #54/R
£1049 $1490 €1700 Barques de pecheurs au clair de lune (13x20cm-5x8in) s. panel. 16-Mar-3 Eric Pillon, Calais #5/R
£1300 $2171 €1885 Beached fishing boat, sunset. Shrimping (12x18cm-5x7in) s. pair. 17-Jun-3 Bonhams, New Bond Street #111/R est:1500-2000
£1358 $1928 €2200 Barques et voiliers pres du rivage (21x13cm-8x5in) s. panel. 16-Mar-3 Eric Pillon, Calais #2/R
£1600 $2512 €2400 Fishing boats at sunset (13x21cm-5x8in) s. panel. 21-Nov-2 Tennants, Leyburn #758/R est:1000-1500
£1603 $2516 €2500 Barques de peche pres du rivage (14x21cm-6x8in) s. panel. 15-Dec-2 Eric Pillon, Calais #12/R
£1700 $2754 €2550 Fishermen heading out to sea (24x40cm-9x16in) s. panel. 21-May-3 Christie's, Kensington #668/R est:2000-3000
£2025 $3200 €3200 Depart. Retour de peche (13x20cm-5x8in) s. panel pair. 2-Dec-2 Tajan, Paris #38
£2025 $3200 €3200 Bateaux a maree basse (14x20cm-6x8in) s. panel. 2-Dec-2 Rieunier, Paris #45/R
£2244 $3478 €3500 Retour de peche (13x21cm-5x8in) s. panel. 9-Dec-2 Beaussant & Lefèvre, Paris #53/R
£3288 $5162 €4800 Shipping in a calm (13x21cm-5x8in) s. panel. 15-Apr-3 Sotheby's, Amsterdam #29/R est:3000-5000

GUDIN, Hermine (19th C) French
£1322 $1969 €1983 Ships off coast in moonlight (23x33cm-9x13in) s. panel. 25-Jun-2 Koller, Zurich #6513 est:800-1200 (S.FR 3000)

GUDIN, Theodore (1802-1880) French
£845 $1361 €1200 Fishing boats and yachts at the quay, city view beyond (18x28cm-7x11in) s. panel. 12-May-3 Bernaerts, Antwerp #196/R
£1233 $1923 €1800 Sea battle at night (41x57cm-16x22in) s.d.29 Mai 1859. 10-Apr-3 Dorotheum, Vienna #220/R est:1800-2400
£1887 $2925 €3000 Beach on stormy sea (31x47cm-12x19in) s.d.1863 panel. 29-Oct-2 Dorotheum, Vienna #22/R est:2800-3200
£5200 $8060 €7800 Coaster unloading at dusk off the Brittany coast (32x49cm-13x19in) s.i.d.1865 panel. 31-Oct-2 Christie's, Kensington #470/R est:3500-5000
£5594 $9343 €8000 L'incendie du Kent (98x136cm-39x54in) 27-Jun-3 Claude Aguttes, Neuilly #46/R est:8000-10000
Works on paper
£297 $425 €446 Shipwreck victims hailing a rescue vessel (8x13cm-3x5in) s.d.1860 brush ink wash. 23-Jan-3 Swann Galleries, New York #309/R

GUDIN, Theodore (attrib) (1802-1880) French
£1560 $2606 €2200 Marine (28x35cm-11x14in) bears sig.d.1856. 23-Jun-3 Beaussant & Lefèvre, Paris #301/R est:2000-2200

GUDNASON, Svavar (1909-1988) Icelandic
£558 $881 €837 Composition (48x40cm-19x16in) s.d.1950 oil stick. 1-Apr-3 Rasmussen, Copenhagen #231/R (D.KR 6000)

GUDNI, Georg (1961-) Icelandic
£656 $1057 €984 Landscape (50x50cm-20x20in) s.d.1989 verso. 7-May-3 AB Stockholms Auktionsverk #963/R (S.KR 8500)

GUE, David John (1836-1917) American
£1560 $2450 €2340 Beach scene with greenish blue waves breaking on sandy shore (30x46cm-12x18in) s. 19-Apr-3 James Julia, Fairfield #264a/R est:2000-4000

GUE, David John (attrib) (1836-1917) American
£2273 $3250 €3410 Moonlight marinescape (25x36cm-10x14in) s. board. 11 Dec-1 Lincoln, Orange #473/R

GUEGAN, Yvonne (1915-) French
£316 $494 €500 Nature morte a la bouteille (55x46cm-22x18in) s. isorel. 15-Sep-2 Etude Bailleul, Bayeux #134/R
£380 $592 €600 Les anemones (41x33cm-16x13in) s.d.1974. 15-Sep-2 Etude Bailleul, Bayeux #131/R

GUEGUEN, Suzanne (20th C) French
Works on paper
£295 $463 €460 Procession (28x38cm-11x15in) s. gouache. 15-Dec-2 Thierry & Lannon, Brest #329

GUELDRY, Charles Albert (1884-1973) French
£629 $981 €1000 Channel with shallops (34x27cm-13x11in) s. 20-Sep-2 Millon & Associes, Paris #122/R

GUEQUIER, Georges (?) Belgian
£3800 $5966 €5700 Final chapter (70x50cm-28x20in) s.d.1917. 21-Nov-2 Christie's, Kensington #31/R est:2000-3000

GUERARD, Amedee (1824-1908) French
£2553 $3957 €3830 Mother and child with bunch of grapes (113x84cm-44x33in) s.d.63 prov.exhib. 3-Dec-2 Bukowskis, Stockholm #180/R est:30000-40000 (S.KR 36000)

GUERARD, Bernard von (1780-1836) German
Works on paper
£1622 $2530 €2400 Portrait of Grafen Ludwig Lebzeltern (15x11cm-6x4in) s. W/C. 28-Mar-3 Dorotheum, Vienna #368/R est:200-2500

GUERARD, Eugène von (1811-1901) Austrian
£21352 $32669 €32028 Wakatipu, with Mount Earnslaw (37x65cm-15x26in) s.d.1878 prov.exhib. 26-Aug-2 Sotheby's, Paddington #553/R est:80000-120000 (A.D 60000)
£24911 $38114 €37367 Mr Andrew Wittles residence at Apollo Bay with Cape Patton in the distance (23x31cm-9x12in) s.d.1859 i.verso exhib. 25-Aug-2 Sotheby's, Paddington #55/R est:70000-90000 (A.D 70000)
£28571 $44857 €42857 Shipwreck off coast (61x86cm-24x34in) s. prov. 25-Nov-2 Christie's, Melbourne #83/R est:80000-120000 (A.D 80000)
£89147 $141744 €133721 Cathedral Mount, valley of the Acheron River, Victoria (56x76cm-22x30in) s.d.1863 prov. 5-May-3 Sotheby's, Melbourne #149/R est:250000-350000 (A.D 230000)

GUERBILSKY, Andre (20th C) Russian
£400 $632 €600 Reclining female nude (33x46cm-13x18in) s. 14-Nov-2 Christie's, Kensington #16/R

GUERCINO (1591-1666) Italian
Works on paper
£6500 $10140 €9750 Noah directing animals into his ark (21x28cm-8x11in) pen brown ink prov. 17-Oct-2 Lawrence, Crewkerne #382/R est:7000-10000

GUERCINO, Giovanni Francesco (1591-1666) Italian
Works on paper
£2233 $3483 €3550 Bearded man (19x16cm-7x6in) pen. 21-Sep-2 Dannenberg, Berlin #540/R est:300
£3200 $5344 €4640 Study of a sleeping child (25x19cm-10x7in) red chk stumping prov. 9-Jul-3 Sotheby's, London #46/R est:2500-3500
£4400 $6908 €6600 Head study of a moustachioed man in a hat (8x6cm-3x2in) pen ink prov. 11-Dec-2 Sotheby's, Olympia #35/R est:1500-2000
£4500 $7515 €6525 Portrait of a bearded man (13x8cm-5x3in) pen brown ink red chk framing lines prov. 9-Jul-3 Bonhams, Knightsbridge #1/R est:2000-3000
£5500 $8635 €8250 Cleopatra (23x15cm-9x6in) pen ink prov.lit. 11-Dec-2 Sotheby's, Olympia #62/R est:2000-3000

£5625 $9000 €8438 Woman churning butter (25x19cm-10x7in) pen ink paper laid down. 14-May-3 Butterfields, San Francisco #1004/R est:10000-15000
£6081 $9486 €9000 Study of young woman (18x14cm-7x6in) pen ink prov. 27-Mar-3 Christie's, Paris #71/R
£6757 $10541 €10000 Portrait of bearded man (19x15cm-7x6in) pen ink prov. 27-Mar-3 Maigret, Paris #47/R
£8025 $13000 €12038 Study of young woman (13x16cm-5x6in) pen ink prov. 21-Jan-3 Sotheby's, New York #49/R est:15000
£9000 $15030 €13050 Caricature of a man in a hat in profile (14x13cm-6x5in) pen brown ink prov.exhib. 8-Jul-3 Christie's, London #36/R est:2000-3000
£9259 $15000 €13889 Mars, Venus and Cupid (24x34cm-9x13in) i. pen ink prov. 21-Jan-3 Sotheby's, New York #51/R est:20000
£15000 $25050 €21750 Landscape with a tree and two travellers near a pond and distant buildings (19x27cm-7x11in) bears i. red chk. 9-Jul-3 Sotheby's, London #35/R est:20000-30000
£18000 $30060 €26100 Madonna and child (22x18cm-9x7in) pen brown ink wash prov. 9-Jul-3 Sotheby's, London #32/R est:12000-18000
£43210 $70000 €64815 Susannah and the elders (29x31cm-11x12in) i. pen ink prov. 21-Jan-3 Sotheby's, New York #54/R est:90000
£50000 $83500 €72500 Bathsheba attended by her maid (25x18cm-10x7in) pen brown ink. 8-Jul-3 Christie's, London #37/R est:30000-50000
£52469 $85000 €78704 Young woman holding sieve (23x30cm-9x12in) chk prov. 21-Jan-3 Sotheby's, New York #43/R est:40000
£67901 $110000 €101852 Seated youthreading (30x21cm-12x8in) chk prov.lit. 22-Jan-3 Christie's, Rockefeller NY #26/R est:80000

GUERCINO, Giovanni Francesco (attrib) (1591-1666) Italian
Works on paper
£839 $1325 €1300 Head of young man (16x20cm-6x8in) i. pen ink prov. 19-Dec-2 Delvaux, Paris #77/R
£3916 $5600 €5874 Three monks in prayer witnessing a vision of the Virgin and child (34x27cm-13x11in) pen ink. 23-Jan-3 Swann Galleries, New York #65/R est:3000-5000

GUERCINO, Giovanni Francesco (circle) (1591-1666) Italian
£5500 $9185 €7975 Cleopatra (117x95cm-46x37in) 11-Jul-3 Christie's, Kensington #221/R est:4000-6000
£6500 $10140 €9750 Madonna and Child (73x61cm-29x24in) 10-Apr-3 Christie's, Kensington #234/R est:6000-8000

GUERCIOS, Carlo del (19/20th C) Italian?
£478 $750 €717 Theatre scene (102x163cm-40x64in) d.1917. 13-Dec-2 Du Mouchelle, Detroit #1361/R

GUERIN, Armand (1913-1983) French
£307 $491 €461 Paris in winter (64x80cm-25x31in) s. masonite. 17-Mar-3 Philippe Schuler, Zurich #8640 (S.FR 650)
£319 $497 €500 Rue (60x73cm-24x29in) s. panel. 5-Nov-2 Tajan, Paris #126
£510 $795 €800 Place Vendome (60x73cm-24x29in) s. panel. 5-Nov-2 Tajan, Paris #111
£510 $795 €800 Place Vendome (60x73cm-24x29in) s. panel. 5-Nov-2 Tajan, Paris #110/R
£552 $872 €800 Charette Odoul (73x60cm-29x24in) s. panel. 4-Apr-3 Tajan, Paris #114
£573 $894 €900 Ile de la Cite (60x72cm-24x28in) s. panel. 5-Nov-2 Tajan, Paris #114
£573 $894 €900 Pont aerien sous la neige (65x81cm-26x32in) s. panel. 5-Nov-2 Tajan, Paris #121/R
£577 $900 €866 Barges (64x81cm-25x32in) s. masonite prov. 9-Oct-2 Doyle, New York #50
£605 $944 €950 Place de la Concorde (60x73cm-24x29in) s. panel. 5-Nov-2 Tajan, Paris #113/R

GUERIN, Charles (1875-1939) French
£709 $1184 €1000 Femme se drapant (82x65cm-32x26in) mono. s.d.verso. 23-Jun-3 Delvaux, Paris #132
£1293 $2055 €1900 Nu a sa coiffure (80x81cm-31x32in) s.d.1900 exhib. 26-Feb-3 Artcurial Briest, Paris #169 est:1500-2200

GUERIN, Ernest (1887-1952) French
Works on paper
£441 $680 €662 Femme de la Presquie, Bretagne (23x15cm-9x6in) s. gouache. 28-Oct-2 Blomqvist, Lysaker #1068 (N.KR 5200)
£620 $1035 €899 Dolmen pres ploumarmel carmac bretagne. Recontre sur lad dune penmarc'y (25x33cm-10x13in) s.i. pencil gouache pair. 11-Jul-3 Bracketts, Tunbridge Wells #779
£897 $1409 €1400 Bretagne (17x23cm-7x9in) s.i. W/C. 15-Dec-2 Thierry & Lannon, Brest #55
£897 $1409 €1400 Bretagne, Notre-Dame de Lotivy (15x22cm-6x9in) s.i. W/C gouache. 15-Dec-2 Eric Pillon, Calais #116/R
£915 $1474 €1300 Trois Bretonnes dans la lande (15x8cm-6x3in) s. W/C. 11-May-3 Thierry & Lannon, Brest #85
£949 $1489 €1480 Femme (22x15cm-9x6in) s.i. W/C pastel. 15-Dec-2 Thierry & Lannon, Brest #33
£1154 $1812 €1800 Village en Bretagne (17x22cm-7x9in) s.i. W/C. 15-Dec-2 Thierry & Lannon, Brest #56
£1266 $1962 €2000 Chaumieres en Bretagne (26x33cm-10x13in) s. W/C. 29-Sep-2 Eric Pillon, Calais #186/R
£1282 $1987 €2000 Maisons bretonnes (21x26cm-8x10in) s.i. W/C. 7-Dec-2 Martinot & Savignat, Pontoise #145
£1456 $2256 €2300 Chaumiere dans le morbihan (18x23cm-7x9in) s. W/C gouache. 29-Sep-2 Eric Pillon, Calais #185/R
£2238 $3737 €3200 Paysage a l'eglise Tronoen St Jean Trolimon Bretagne (52x71cm-20x28in) s.i. W/C prov. 26-Jun-3 Tajan, Paris #49/R est:3500-4000
£3141 $4931 €4900 Sainte-Marine Benodet (38x46cm-15x18in) s.i. W/C. 15-Dec-2 Thierry & Lannon, Brest #57/R
£3333 $5433 €4800 Retour du pardon de Plovan (36x45cm-14x18in) s. W/C. 19-Jul-3 Thierry & Lannon, Brest #58/R est:2500-3000
£3592 $5782 €5100 Notre Dame de Rocamadour et chaloupes sardinieres at Camaret (38x55cm-15x22in) s.i. W/C. 11-May-3 Thierry & Lannon, Brest #86/R est:3500-4000
£4859 $7823 €6900 Procession en Bregagne - Notre Dame de la Joie (37x54cm-15x21in) s.i. W/C. 11-May-3 Thierry & Lannon, Brest #87/R est:3500-3800
£6944 $11319 €10000 Jour de fete a Ste Marine (70x120cm-28x47in) W/C triptych. 19-Jul-3 Thierry & Lannon, Brest #60 est:10000-12000

GUERIN, François (?-1791) French
£18000 $28080 €27000 Allegory of Painting. Allegory of Architecture (55x65cm-22x26in) s.d.1749 pair prov. 10-Apr-3 Sotheby's, London #89/R est:18000

GUERIN, Gabriel (1869-1916) French
£506 $770 €780 Vue de village (65x44cm-26x17in) s.d.1903. 7-Jul-2 Lombrail & Teucquam, Paris #59/R

GUERIN, Jean Urbain (1760-1836) French
Miniatures
£1100 $1727 €1650 Young gentleman in a blue coat (8cm-3xin) s. gilt metal mount oval. 10-Dec-2 Christie's, London #135/R est:600-800
£1300 $2028 €1950 Gentleman wearing brown coat with brass buttons white waistcoat (8cm-3xin) s.d. gilt frame red velvet reverse oval. 5-Nov-2 Bonhams, New Bond Street #40/R est:1000-1500
£2482 $4021 €3500 Le Duc d'Enghein (7x6cm-3x2in) s.ivory hair copper surround. 21-May-3 Piasa, Paris #327/R est:3000-4000
Works on paper
£1451 $2250 €2177 Portrait of a gentleman (21x16cm-8x6in) init.d.1828 pencil gouache ink prov. 29-Oct-2 Sotheby's, New York #40/R est:1000-1500
£1538 $2569 €2200 Autoportrait (20x16cm-8x6in) i. W/C gouache oval. 25-Jun-3 Sotheby's, Paris #72/R est:1000-1500

GUERIN, Paulin Jean Baptiste (1783-1855) French
£3165 $5000 €5000 Sainte Famille attristee par le presentiment de la Passion du sauveur (189x156cm-74x61in) s.d.1829. 27-Nov-2 Christie's, Paris #62/R

GUERIN, Pierre Narcisse (attrib) (1774-1833) French
Works on paper
£317 $500 €500 Tete de femme portant une coiffe (13x14cm-5x6in) crayon stump double-sided. 28-Nov-2 Tajan, Paris #177
£1216 $1897 €1800 Agrippine maudit Neron (36x47cm-14x19in) i. i.verso pierre noire chk. 27-Mar-3 Maigret, Paris #184/R

GUERIN, Therese (fl.1886-1908) French
£5944 $9927 €8500 Bouquet de roses (81x144cm-32x57in) s. 27-Jun-3 Claude Aguttes, Neuilly #51/R est:8000-12000

GUERINAU, Richard (20th C) French?
Works on paper
£331 $523 €480 Chant des Stryges (42x29cm-17x11in) s. Chinese ink. 7-Apr-3 Claude Aguttes, Neuilly #43
£607 $959 €880 Chant des Stryges (50x35cm-20x14in) s. Chinese ink. 7-Apr-3 Claude Aguttes, Neuilly #44/R

GUERMACHEV, Mikhail Mikhailovich (1867-1930) Russian
£580 $916 €870 Snow covered avenue of trees at dusk (46x56cm-18x22in) s. prov. 27-Nov-2 Bonhams, Knowle #247
£1502 $2343 €2178 Sunset through snowy trees (55x65cm-22x26in) s. prov. 26-Mar-3 Walker's, Ottawa #40/R est:3000-4000 (C.D 3500)

£1944 $3208 €2800 Les bouleaux a l'automne (54x64cm-21x25in) s. 1-Jul-3 Rossini, Paris #92/R
£2000 $3100 €3000 Sunlit trees (54x46cm-21x18in) s. 3-Dec-2 Sotheby's, Olympia #271/R est:500-700

GUEROULT, Maurice (1875-?) French
Works on paper
£578 $919 €850 Promenade en bateau-mouche sur la Seine (37x46cm-15x18in) W/C gouache cardboard. 24-Mar-3 Coutau Begarie, Paris #234/R

GUERRA, Giovanni (1544-1618) Italian
Works on paper
£570 $900 €900 Une homme, entoure de quatre autres (17x12cm-7x5in) i. black chk pen brown ink brown wash. 27-Nov-2 Christie's, Paris #28/R

GUERRA, Giovanni (attrib) (1544-1618) Italian
Works on paper
£1216 $1897 €1800 Annunciation (16x11cm-6x4in) pen ink wash octagonal. 26-Mar-3 Piasa, Paris #7/R

GUERRANT, Roger (1930-1977) French
£1410 $2214 €2200 Pommiers (64x80cm-25x31in) s.d.65 masonite. 24-Nov-2 Lesieur & Le Bars, Le Havre #71/R
Works on paper
£810 $1304 €1150 Composition botanique (46x54cm-18x21in) s.d.70 gouache. 12-May-3 Lesieur & Le Bars, Le Havre #44/R

GUERRERO GALVAN, Jesus (1910-1973) Mexican
£5038 $7859 €7557 Nina con paloma (70x60cm-28x24in) s.d.1956. 17-Oct-2 Louis Morton, Mexico #93/R est:120000-130000 (M.P 80000)
£7317 $12000 €10610 Mujer (81x71cm-32x28in) s.d.1957. 27-May-3 Sotheby's, New York #84
£47771 $75000 €71657 Kids with racket (90x65cm-35x26in) s.i.d.1936 s.i.d.verso board prov. 19-Nov-2 Sotheby's, New York #82/R

GUERRERO MALAGON, Cecilio (1909-1996) Spanish
£789 $1279 €1200 Toledo (20x46cm-8x18in) s. board. 21-Jan-3 Durán, Madrid #1188
£855 $1386 €1300 Procession (65x33cm-26x13in) s. board. 21-Jan-3 Durán, Madrid #1276
£1053 $1705 €1600 Washerwomen in the village (21x46cm-8x18in) s. board. 21-Jan-3 Durán, Madrid #1187/R

GUERRERO, Jose (1914-1992) Spanish
£481 $760 €750 Shapes (15x39cm-6x15in) s.d.1984 paper. 19-Nov-2 Durán, Madrid #627/R
£759 $1206 €1100 Tracks (13x31cm-5x12in) s.d.1984 card. 4-Mar-3 Ansorena, Madrid #238/R
£1195 $1864 €1900 Shapes (12x32cm-5x13in) s.d.1984 card. 23-Sep-2 Durán, Madrid #143/R
£5724 $9044 €8300 Untitled (64x51cm-25x20in) s.d.1976 gouache prov. 1-Apr-3 Segre, Madrid #188/R
Works on paper
£455 $664 €700 Red and black (22x15cm-9x6in) s.i. mixed media. 17-Jun-2 Ansorena, Madrid #101/R
£3750 $6000 €5625 Series solitarios no.2 (63x49cm-25x19in) s. W/C pencil. 16-Mar-3 Butterfields, San Francisco #1077 est:400-600

GUERRERO, Manuel Ruiz (1864-1917) Spanish
£577 $912 €900 Saint Hildephonsus' market, Madrid (25x16cm-10x6in) s.i. board. 19-Nov-2 Durán, Madrid #121/R

GUERRESCHI, Giuseppe (1929-1985) Italian
£1282 $2013 €2000 Portrait of Max (100x70cm-39x28in) s.i.d.1970 verso acrylic. 19-Nov-2 Finarte, Milan #231/R
£1677 $2650 €2600 Woman (150x110cm-59x43in) s.i.d.975 verso exhib. 18-Dec-2 Christie's, Rome #69/R

GUERRIER, Raymond (1920-) French
£400 $636 €600 Vache (73x92cm-29x36in) s. i. on stretcher. 18-Mar-3 Rosebery Fine Art, London #860
£414 $658 €600 Hiver en Provence (54x73cm-21x29in) s. 5-Mar-3 Doutrebente, Paris #63/R
£465 $768 €670 Les arbres aux collines bleues (60x73cm-24x29in) s. 1-Jul-3 Rossini, Paris #93
£674 $1091 €950 Canal Saint Martin (59x73cm-23x29in) s. 23-May-3 Camard, Paris #167/R
£700 $1099 €1050 Murcia, Spain (73x92cm-29x36in) s. i.stretcher prov. 10-Dec-2 Rosebery Fine Art, London #602/R
£745 $1206 €1050 Pont de Bir-Hakem (72x92cm-28x36in) s. 23-May-3 Camard, Paris #168/R

GUERRIERI, Giovanni Francesco (1589-1655) Italian
£5500 $8580 €8250 Rabbit, mallard and other birds hanging above a stone ledge (49x64cm-19x25in) s.d.1657 panel. 10-Apr-3 Christie's, Kensington #241/R est:5000-8000

GUERY, Armand (1850-1912) French
£573 $836 €860 Country landscape with shepherd and flock (20x26cm-8x10in) s. panel. 17-Jun-2 Philippe Schuler, Zurich #4345/R (S.FR 1300)
£1456 $2300 €2300 Berger et son troupeau (20x26cm-8x10in) s. panel. 1-Dec-2 Peron, Melun #76
£4196 $7007 €6000 Temps gris sur la Vuippe (100x81cm-39x32in) s.d.1902 exhib. 27-Jun-3 Claude Aguttes, Neuilly #33/R est:6000-8000
£4430 $7000 €7000 Berger et ses moutons pres des meules (81x116cm-32x46in) s.d.1911. 1-Dec-2 Peron, Melun #173

GUFFENS, Godfried (1823-1901) Belgian
£19355 $30000 €29033 Rouget de lisle singing the Marseillaise (130x187cm-51x74in) s.d.1849. 29-Oct-2 Sotheby's, New York #28/R est:40000-60000

GUGEL, K A (19th C) German
£774 $1138 €1200 Young lady (67x55cm-26x22in) s. 24-Jun-2 Dr Fritz Nagel, Stuttgart #6024/R

GUGEL, Karl Adolf (1820-1885) German
£1293 $2055 €1900 Young orange seller (88x70cm-35x28in) s.i.d.1871. 19-Mar-3 Neumeister, Munich #572/R est:2000
£1923 $3019 €3000 Young beauty (67x55cm-26x22in) s.d.1872. 10-Dec-2 Dorotheum, Vienna #33/R est:3400-3800
£2365 $3689 €3500 Italian girl and boy with musical instruments (114x93cm-45x37in) s. 26-Mar-3 Hugo Ruef, Munich #112 est:3500

GUGG, Hugo (1878-1956) German
£285 $450 €450 Friedrichs Castle in Apulien (40x51cm-16x20in) s.d.1951 board. 29-Nov-2 Bolland & Marotz, Bremen #798/R

GUGGENBERGER, Theodor Otto Michael (1866-1929) German
£288 $438 €450 Extensive wooded landscape (24x39cm-9x15in) s. board lit. 11-Jul-2 Allgauer, Kempten #2497/R
£408 $649 €600 Upper Bavarian mountain village (60x75cm-24x30in) s. 28-Mar-3 Bolland & Marotz, Bremen #455/R

GUGGENBICHLER, Johann Meinrad (1649-1723) Austrian
Sculpture
£4392 $6851 €6500 St Joseph (43cm-17in) lime wood. 25-Mar-3 Dorotheum, Vienna #60/R est:5500-6500
£5068 $7905 €7500 Christ as the good shepherd (115cm-45in) lime wood gold painted. 25-Mar-3 Dorotheum, Vienna #129/R est:8000-9000

GUHR, Richard (1873-1956) German
£3500 $5845 €5250 Triumphant return (41x25cm-16x10in) init.d.1897 tempera W/C gold leaf over pencil board. 18-Jun-3 Christie's, Kensington #71/R est:4000-6000

GUICHARD, Joseph Benoit (1806-1880) French
Works on paper
£439 $685 €650 Autoportrait de l'artiste adolescent (23x20cm-9x8in) s.d.1821 pierre noire. 25-Mar-3 Chochon-Barre & Allardi, Paris #3/R

GUIDA, Federico (1969-) Italian
£2095 $3268 €3100 Figures (120x90cm-47x35in) s.d.2000 verso. 26-Mar-3 Finarte Semenzato, Milan #142/R
£4167 $6458 €6500 She plays the piano, he plays the trumpet (190x140cm-75x55in) s.i.d.1997 verso canvas on board. 4-Dec-2 Finarte, Milan #449/R
Works on paper
£1667 $2583 €2600 Untitled (115x150cm-45x59in) s.d.1999 verso mixed media on canvas. 4-Dec-2 Finarte, Milan #451/R
£2482 $4021 €3500 Untitled (130x110cm-51x43in) s.d.2001 mixed media canvas. 20-May-3 Porro, Milan #27/R est:4000-4300

GUIDA, Giovanni (1837-?) Italian
£5442 $8653 €8000 Villa on Lake Maggiore with figures (44x88cm-17x35in) s. 18-Mar-3 Finarte, Milan #91/R

GUIDI, Virgilio (1892-1984) Italian
£1154 $1812 €1800 Venice (40x50cm-16x20in) s. s.verso. 20-Nov-2 Pandolfini, Florence #69/R
£1218 $1924 €1900 Big head (40x30cm-16x12in) s.i.d.1968. 15-Nov-2 Farsetti, Prato #327/R

£1282 $2013 €2000 Saint Mark's (40x50cm-16x20in) s. 19-Nov-2 Finarte, Milan #99
£1290 $2039 €2000 Saint Giorgio, Venice (40x50cm-16x20in) s. s.i.verso prov. 18-Dec-2 Christie's, Rome #139/R
£1438 $2301 €2200 San Giorgio, Venice (40x50cm-16x20in) s. 4-Jan-3 Meeting Art, Vercelli #501
£1538 $2385 €2400 Mask (75x61cm-30x24in) s. lit. 5-Dec-2 Stadion, Trieste #801/R
£1582 $2468 €2500 Saint Giorgio, Venice (40x50cm-16x20in) s. s.i.verso. 14-Sep-2 Meeting Art, Vercelli #925/R
£1667 $2633 €2600 Tragic mask (60x50cm-24x20in) s. s.i.d.1970 verso. 15-Nov-2 Farsetti, Prato #119/R
£1709 $2666 €2700 Big heads (60x50cm-24x20in) s. s.i.d.1973. 14-Sep-2 Meeting Art, Vercelli #974/R
£1806 $2871 €2600 Big heads (50x40cm-20x16in) s. s.i.verso. 1-May-3 Meeting Art, Vercelli #189
£2041 $3245 €3000 Saint Mark's Venice (30x40cm-12x16in) s. 1-Mar-3 Meeting Art, Vercelli #753
£2179 $3422 €3400 Saint Mark's (50x60cm-20x24in) s. lit. 19-Nov-2 Finarte, Milan #254/R
£2785 $4400 €4400 Saint Mark's (50x60cm-20x24in) s. i.verso painted 1972. 30-Nov-2 Farsetti, Prato #632
£2848 $4500 €4500 Studio interior (50x60cm-20x24in) s. i.verso painted 1971. 30-Nov-2 Farsetti, Prato #631/R
£4387 $6932 €6800 Judgement (140x100cm-55x39in) s. s.d.1960 verso exhib.lit. 18-Dec-2 Christie's, Rome #281/R
£4387 $6932 €6800 Judgement (140x100cm-55x39in) s. s.d.1960 verso exhib.lit. 18-Dec-2 Christie's, Rome #280/R
£5484 $8665 €8500 Figure in the space (70x89cm-28x35in) s. painted 1958 exhib.lit. 18-Dec-2 Christie's, Rome #266/R est:4000
£5769 $9058 €9000 Figure (50x60cm-20x24in) s. s.d.1956 verso. 19-Nov-2 Finarte, Milan #190/R
£6329 $10000 €10000 Meeting (50x42cm-20x17in) s. board painted 1944. 30-Nov-2 Farsetti, Prato #639/R est:13000
£7447 $12064 €10500 Figura in grigio (60x50cm-24x20in) s. s.d.56 verso prov.exhib. 26-May-3 Christie's, Milan #314/R est:8000-10000
£7742 $12232 €12000 Present condition (100x140cm-39x55in) painted 1957 exhib.lit. 18-Dec-2 Christie's, Rome #264/R
£8163 $12980 €12000 Roman landscape (49x59cm-19x23in) s. board painted 1925 lit. 1-Mar-3 Meeting Art, Vercelli #488 est:12000
£8974 $14090 €14000 Saint Mark's (70x110cm-28x43in) s. painted 1961 lit. 23-Nov-2 Meeting Art, Vercelli #116/R est:13000
£9032 $14271 €14000 Saint Giorgio (50x75cm-20x30in) s. painted 1940 prov.exhib.lit. 18-Dec-2 Christie's, Rome #276/R est:20000
£13548 $21406 €21000 Bridge on the river (50x60cm-20x24in) s. s.d.1956 cardboard prov.exhib.lit. 18-Dec-2 Christie's, Rome #277/R
£23718 $34628 €37000 Figure in the light (145x175cm-57x69in) s. painted 1951 prov.exhib.lit. 5-Jun-2 Il Ponte, Milan #89/R est:30000-40000
£33974 $53340 €53000 Sowing (120x90cm-47x35in) s. board painted 1929 prov.lit. 19-Nov-2 Finarte, Milan #227/R est:48000-54000

GUIDON, J (19th C) ?
£346 $540 €550 Arbres en fleurs (46x61cm-18x24in) s. 9-Oct-2 Marc Kohn, Paris #26

GUIETTE, René (1893-1976) Belgian
£1258 $1937 €2000 Oiseau gris (50x40cm-20x16in) s. panel. 22-Oct-2 Campo, Vlaamse Kaai #516
£1418 $2369 €2000 Nature morte a la cruche et a la pendule (49x63cm-19x25in) 23-Jun-3 Amberes, Antwerp #98
£6090 $9439 €9500 Paysage de banlieue (60x73cm-24x29in) s. painted c.1929-30 prov.exhib.lit. 3-Dec-2 Christie's, Amsterdam #36/R est:7500-9500
£7692 $12077 €12000 Couple a l'homme (73x54cm-29x21in) s. prov. 10-Dec-2 Vanderkindere, Brussels #75/R est:5000-7500

Works on paper
£278 $442 €400 Figure d'homme (56x40cm-22x16in) s.d.1947 dr. 29-Apr-3 Campo & Campo, Antwerp #138
£313 $497 €450 Abstraction en rose (54x33cm-21x13in) s.d.1961 mixed media. 29-Apr-3 Campo & Campo, Antwerp #139
£451 $718 €650 Signe de Zen (51x31cm-20x12in) s. mixed media. 29-Apr-3 Campo & Campo, Antwerp #140/R
£481 $745 €750 Composition (60x42cm-24x17in) s.d.21.6.61 mixed media cardboard prov. 3-Dec-2 Christie's, Amsterdam #120/R
£486 $773 €700 Lettres Orientals (51x33cm-20x13in) s.d.1961 mixed media. 29-Apr-3 Campo & Campo, Antwerp #145
£556 $883 €800 Saule etete (54x39cm-21x15in) s.d.1951 mixed media. 29-Apr-3 Campo & Campo, Antwerp #147
£570 $900 €900 Composition (56x44cm-22x17in) s.d.18-XII-59 mixed media. 26-Nov-2 Palais de Beaux Arts, Brussels #241
£642 $1001 €950 Fleur du mur (49x39cm-19x15in) s.i.d.54 mixed media. 28-Mar-3 Charbonneaux, Paris #88/R
£694 $1104 €1000 Abstraction (40x50cm-16x20in) s. mixed media. 29-Apr-3 Campo & Campo, Antwerp #146
£705 $1093 €1100 Composition (62x39cm-24x15in) s.i.d.62 W/C sand lit. 7-Dec-2 De Vuyst, Lokeren #141
£764 $1215 €1100 Abstraction en blanc (50x32cm-20x13in) s.d.1961 mixed media. 29-Apr-3 Campo & Campo, Antwerp #141
£764 $1215 €1100 Composition graphique (50x33cm-20x13in) s.d.1961 mixed media. 29-Apr-3 Campo & Campo, Antwerp #142
£764 $1215 €1100 Signes orientaux (62x41cm-24x16in) s.d.1961 mixed media. 29-Apr-3 Campo & Campo, Antwerp #618
£764 $1215 €1100 Langue orientale (61x41cm-24x16in) s.d.1961 mixed media. 29-Apr-3 Campo & Campo, Antwerp #619
£833 $1308 €1300 Composition (74x54cm-29x21in) s.d.27-XII-62 col pigment. 16-Dec-2 Charbonneaux, Paris #259
£1806 $2871 €2600 Reveries (45x60cm-18x24in) s.d.1949 gouache. 29-Apr-3 Campo & Campo, Antwerp #143 est:750-1000

GUIGNARD, Alberto da Veiga (1896-1962) Brazilian
£35032 $55000 €52548 Landscape by Ouro Preto (42x50cm-17x20in) s.d.1958 panel prov. 20-Nov-2 Christie's, Rockefeller NY #13/R est:60000-80000

GUIGNE, Alexis Eugène (1839-?) French
Works on paper
£372 $580 €550 Village en Ile-de-France (23x28cm-9x11in) s. w. 27-Mar-3 Maigret, Paris #215

GUIGNET, Jean Adrien (1816-1854) French
Works on paper
£676 $1054 €1000 Personnage oriental (33x25cm-13x10in) s. 26-Mar-3 Piasa, Paris #109/R

GUIGON, Charles-Louis (1807-1882) Swiss
£1748 $2920 €2500 Vue de l'entree du Chateau de Marilly pres de'Evian (38x47cm-15x19in) i.verso paper on cardboard. 25-Jun-3 Sotheby's, Paris #87/R est:3000-4000

GUIGOU, Paul (1834-1871) French
£12903 $20387 €20000 Vue de l'Huveaune (26x16cm-10x6in) s.d.68 panel prov. 18-Dec-2 Ferri, Paris #72 est:30000

GUIGUET, François Joseph (1860-1937) French
£1582 $2500 €2500 Portrait de Marie (35x27cm-14x11in) s.d.1905. 1-Dec-2 Anaf, Lyon #91

GUILBERT, Narcisse (1878-1942) French
£392 $631 €600 Le chateau de la Marquise de Sevigne (71x75cm-28x30in) s. exhib. 20-Jan-3 Horta, Bruxelles #487

GUILBERT, Paul Louis (1886-?) French
£292 $427 €450 Dance (30x45cm-12x18in) s. cardboard. 17-Jun-2 Ansorena, Madrid #246/R

GUILFOYLE, Josephine (20th C) ?
£331 $517 €520 First meeting (75x60cm-30x24in) s. 6-Nov-2 James Adam, Dublin #133/R
£331 $517 €520 Istrabraq - portrait of a horse (61x44cm-24x17in) s. pastel. 6-Nov-2 James Adam, Dublin #130/R

GUILLAIN, Marthe (1890-1974) Belgian
£475 $741 €750 Conversation devat 'Chez Juliette' (54x65cm-21x26in) s. 16-Sep-2 Horta, Bruxelles #20
£552 $877 €800 Femme assise dans un interieur (65x50cm-26x20in) s. 4-Mar-3 Palais de Beaux Arts, Brussels #340
£601 $938 €950 Fete foraine (54x65cm-21x26in) s.d.35. 16-Sep-2 Horta, Bruxelles #18

GUILLAUME, Albert (1873-1942) French
£3165 $4905 €5000 La sieste (53x66cm-21x26in) s. panel. 27-Sep-2 Rabourdin & Choppin de Janvry, Paris #41/R est:6500-7000

GUILLAUMET, Gustave (1840-1887) French
£1613 $2548 €2500 Campement Oriental (28x29cm-11x11in) st.sig. canvas on cardboard. 17-Dec-2 Rossini, Paris #86
£1798 $2949 €2500 Scene de campement (19x28cm-7x11in) s. 4-Jun-3 Tajan, Paris #275/R est:2500-3000
£2200 $3674 €3300 Arab caravan in the desert (17x48cm-7x19in) s. 18-Jun-3 Christie's, Kensington #182/R est:2000-3000

Works on paper
£355 $592 €500 Deux etudes de personnages drapes (22x13cm-9x5in) chl white chk. 19-Jun-3 Piasa, Paris #163

GUILLAUMIN, A (19/20th C) French
£1362 $2233 €1975 Sunlit coastal plain (60x81cm-24x32in) s. 4-Jun-3 Fischer, Luzern #2139/R est:2500-3000 (S.FR 2900)

GUILLAUMIN, Armand (1841-1927) French
£3374 $5500 €5061 Paysage de la Creuse (25x33cm-10x13in) s. painted c.1910. 12-Feb-3 Sotheby's, New York #17/R est:7000-9000
£3500 $5565 €5250 Perdrix rouge, nature morte (50x38cm-20x15in) s. painted c.1905. 20-Mar-3 Sotheby's, Olympia #40/R est:4000-6000
£6115 $10029 €8500 Mediterranean bay (27x35cm-11x14in) s.i. 3-Jun-3 Christie's, Amsterdam #37/R est:5000-7000

£7911 $12263 €12500 Le Puy Barriou (32x48cm-13x19in) s. painted c.1910 prov. 28-Sep-2 Christie's, Paris #15/R est:16000-22000
£11218 $17612 €17500 Bord de mer a Agay (60x73cm-24x29in) s. painted c.1903 prov.lit. 10-Dec-2 Pierre Berge, Paris #17/R est:25000
£12422 $20000 €18633 St. Palais la pierriere (73x92cm-29x36in) s.d.99 prov. 7-May-3 Sotheby's, New York #397/R est:25000-35000
£12658 $20000 €18987 View of a valley, summertime (54x65cm-21x26in) s. prov. 22-Apr-3 Butterfields, San Francisco #6000/R est:25000-35000
£15094 $24000 €22641 Rochers au Trayas (65x81cm-26x32in) s. painted c.1915 prov. 27-Feb-3 Christie's, Rockefeller NY #16/R est:35000
£16129 $25484 €25000 Paysage de la Creuse (54x65cm-21x26in) s. lit. 19-Dec-2 Claude Aguttes, Neuilly #155/R est:30000
£16770 $27000 €25155 Nature morte et pommes (34x42cm-13x17in) s. painted c.1905. 7-May-3 Sotheby's, New York #153/R est:30000-40000
£18000 $29520 €27000 Gouffre saulnier, Crozant (54x65cm-21x26in) s. painted c.1898 prov.lit. 4-Feb-3 Christie's, London #245/R est:30000
£18000 $29520 €27000 Vallee de la Creuse et Puy Barriou (65x81cm-26x32in) s. painted c.1922 prov.lit. 5-Feb-3 Sotheby's, London #223/R est:30000
£18000 $30060 €26100 Le pont Charraud (65x80cm-26x31in) painted c.1905 prov.lit. 25-Jun-3 Christie's, London #140/R est:18000-25000
£18710 $29562 €29000 Femme a la couture (73x60cm-29x24in) s. prov.exhib. 18-Dec-2 Tajan, Paris #32/R est:30000-50000
£19355 $30581 €30000 Paysanne et son enfant sur un chemin (55x67cm-22x26in) s. prov. 18-Dec-2 Tajan, Paris #30/R est:40000
£21000 $34440 €31500 Paysage d'ete a Damiette (60x73cm-24x29in) s. painted c.1885 prov.lit. 5-Feb-3 Sotheby's, London #227/R est:30000
£22000 $36080 €33000 Saint-Palais, POinte de la Perriere (50x64cm-20x25in) s. painted c.1893 prov.exhib.lit. 4-Feb-3 Christie's, London #218/R est:15000
£25000 $39250 €39000 Promenade au bord de l'eau (54x65cm-21x26in) s. lit. 13-Dec-2 Piasa, Paris #9/R est:42000
£25000 $41000 €37500 Paysage du Midi (73x92cm-29x36in) s. painted c.1905. 4-Feb-3 Christie's, London #293/R est:35000
£25806 $40774 €40000 Paysanne pres d'une chaumiere (60x73cm-24x29in) s. double-sided prov. 18-Dec-2 Tajan, Paris #29/R est:60000
£27215 $43000 €43000 Rocher de la fileuse (73x92cm-29x36in) s. i.d.1907 verso prov. 29-Nov-2 Villa Grisebach, Berlin #5/R est:50000-70000
£30000 $46200 €45000 Nature morte au pichet (34x44cm-13x17in) s. painted c.1905 prov.exhib.lit. 22-Oct-2 Sotheby's, London #199/R est:22000-25000
£31690 $52606 €45000 Le rocher rouge a Agay (73x92cm-29x36in) s. painted c.1900 prov.lit. 12-Jun-3 Tajan, Paris #15/R est:45000-55000
£32000 $53440 €46400 Les ruines du chateau, Crozant (65x81cm-26x32in) s. i.verso painted c.1905 prov.lit. 25-Jun-3 Christie's, London #114/R est:18000-24000
£34161 $55000 €51242 Paysage de l'Ile de France (55x46cm-22x18in) s. painted c.1875. 7-May-3 Sotheby's, New York #107/R est:40000-50000
£36585 $57439 €54878 La roche de l'Echo, Crozant (72x81cm-28x32in) s. 12-Dec-2 Iegor de Saint Hippolyte, Montreal #36 (C.D 90000)
£48077 $75000 €72116 Le brusc (60x92cm-24x36in) s. painted c.1902 prov.lit. 6-Nov-2 Sotheby's, New York #179/R est:80000-120000
£51282 $80000 €76923 La moulin bouchardon a Crozant (78x93cm-31x37in) s. painted c.1895 prov. 7-Nov-2 Christie's, Rockefeller NY #204/R est:80000-120000
£64103 $100000 €96155 Nature morte a la marmite (46x55cm-18x22in) s.d.67 prov.exhib.lit. 6-Nov-2 Sotheby's, New York #112/R est:25000-30000
£86538 $135000 €129807 La Seine (65x81cm-26x32in) s.d.2.73 prov. 7-Nov-2 Christie's, Rockefeller NY #202/R est:100000-150000
£105000 $172200 €157500 Port sur l'Oise a Compiegne (50x61cm-20x24in) s.d.77 prov. 5-Feb-3 Sotheby's, London #121/R est:90000

Works on paper
£570 $900 €900 Meule de foin (10x17cm-4x7in) s.d.87 crayon pastel dr. 26-Nov-2 Camard, Paris #9
£833 $1292 €1300 Portrait de petite fille (43x36cm-17x14in) chl. 8-Dec-2 Feletin, Province #191/R
£1335 $2190 €1936 Paysage aux environs de Moret (19x26cm-7x10in) s. pastel. 4-Jun-3 AB Stockholms Auktionsverk #2492/R est:12000-15000 (S.KR 17000)
£3816 $6182 €5800 Madame Guillaumin et sa fille Marguerite (30x37cm-12x15in) s.d.94 i.verso pastel lit. 22-Jan-3 Tajan, Paris #74/R est:6000-8000
£4934 $7994 €7500 Les bords de la Creuse (45x61cm-18x24in) s. pastel prov. 22-Jan-3 Tajan, Paris #75/R est:7000-8000
£29814 $48000 €44721 Madame Guillamin avec Madeleine (60x47cm-24x19in) s.d.89 pastel paper on board prov.lit. 8-May-3 Christie's, Rockefeller NY #110/R est:40000-60000
£35256 $55000 €52884 Le lecture de Mme Guillaumin (52x68cm-20x27in) s. pastel executed 1889 prov.lit. 7-Nov-2 Christie's, Rockefeller NY #108/R est:30000-40000

GUILLAUMIN, Armand (younger) (1875-1955) French
£1780 $2830 €2670 Brittany coast (53x66cm-21x26in) init.d.1901. 18-Mar-3 Maynards, Vancouver #6/R est:3000-4000 (C.D 4200)

GUILLE, Captain J D (20th C) British
£1227 $2000 €1841 Hunt near the sea (40x50cm-16x20in) s. paper on board. 11-Feb-3 Bonhams & Doyles, New York #257/R est:2000-3000

GUILLEMET, Jean Baptiste Antoine (1843-1918) French
£1065 $1714 €1598 Carriere de Chantilly (54x72cm-21x28in) s. i. stretcher. 7-May-3 Dobiaschofsky, Bern #615/R est:2200 (S.FR 2300)
£1400 $2282 €2030 Farmyard (38x46cm-15x18in) s. 16-Jul-3 Sotheby's, Olympia #220/R est:1000-1500
£1667 $2683 €2501 Landscape with lake and church (46x55cm-18x22in) s.i. bears d.1884. 7-May-3 Dobiaschofsky, Bern #616/R est:2800 (S.FR 3600)
£1892 $2951 €2800 Entree du village (24x33cm-9x13in) s. painted 1893. 28-Mar-3 Claude Aguttes, Neuilly #39/R
£2568 $4005 €3800 Regates au large (17x25cm-7x10in) s. panel. 28-Mar-3 Claude Aguttes, Neuilly #40/R
£5000 $8150 €7500 By the sea, Normandy (64x114cm-25x45in) s. 29-Jan-3 Sotheby's, Olympia #327/R est:5000-7000
£6090 $9561 €9500 Saint Vaast La Hougue (37x54cm-15x21in) s. lit. 11-Dec-2 Maigret, Paris #128/R est:3000-5000

GUILLEMIN, A (19/20th C) French
£4906 $7555 €7800 Aux abords de la mosquee (180x158cm-71x62in) s. 23-Oct-2 Rabourdin & Choppin de Janvry, Paris #118/R

GUILLEMIN, Alexandre Marie (1817-1880) French
£2089 $3300 €3300 Flower in the hair of the mother (43x32cm-17x13in) s. panel. 29-Nov-2 Bolland & Marotz, Bremen #700/R est:3900

GUILLEMIN, Émile Coriolan Hippolyte (1841-1907) French
Sculpture
£13000 $20280 €19500 Femme Indienne, figure debout, porte-lumiere (248cm-98in) s.d.1872 brown pat bronze glass iron column st.f.F.Barbedienne. 5-Nov-2 Sotheby's, London #195/R est:10000-15000

GUILLEMINET, Claude (1821-1860) French
£1019 $1600 €1529 Barnyard scene with chickens, rooster and pheasant. s. 22-Nov-2 Skinner, Boston #21/R
£1346 $2113 €2100 Scenes de basse-cour (17x32cm-7x13in) s. panel pair. 15-Dec-2 Lombrail & Teucquam, Paris #2/R
£2025 $3200 €3200 La basse cour (18x24cm-7x9in) s. panel pair. 1-Dec-2 Peron, Melun #31
£2793 $4524 €4050 In the poultry yard (34x23cm-13x9in) s. pair panel. 25-May-3 Uppsala Auktionskammare, Uppsala #106/R est:15000-20000 (S.KR 36000)

GUILLERMO, Juan (1916-1968) Spanish
£2516 $3925 €4000 Fisherman with cock (100x81cm-39x32in) s. s.i.verso. 23-Sep-2 Durán, Madrid #209/R

GUILLERY, Franz (1863-1933) German
£353 $546 €550 Fishing boats by San Giorgio Maggiore (60x80cm-24x31in) s. 5-Dec-2 Neumeister, Munich #2800/R

GUILLON, Adolphe-Irenee (attrib) (1829-1896) French
£469 $750 €680 Mountain flutist (27x21cm-11x8in) s. panel. 16-May-3 Skinner, Boston #16/R

GUILLONNET, Octave Denis Victor (1872-1967) French
£325 $511 €488 Meeting at the fountain (13x17cm-5x7in) s. board. 10-Dec-2 Pinneys, Montreal #47 (C.D 800)
£7372 $11574 €11500 Drapeaux de la fete (45x30cm-18x12in) s.i. 10-Dec-2 Tajan, Paris #183/R est:6000
£8500 $13090 €12750 Femmes au jardin (73x60cm-29x24in) s. 23-Oct-2 Sotheby's, Olympia #633/R est:5000-7000

GUILLOU, Alfred (1844-1926) French
£2361 $3849 €3400 Bretonnes et leurs enfants au bord de la ria au soleil couchant (24x33cm-9x13in) s. panel. 19-Jul-3 Thierry & Lannon, Brest #133 est:3000-4000
£4085 $6576 €5800 Ramasseuse de goemon (91x64cm-36x25in) c.1900. 11-May-3 Thierry & Lannon, Brest #182/R est:2000-2200
£4620 $7300 €7300 Client entreprenant (146x115cm-57x45in) s. 26-Nov-2 Camard, Paris #54/R est:9100
£5674 $9191 €8000 Le client entreprenant (146x115cm-57x45in) s. 23-May-3 Camard, Paris #25/R est:7600-9100
£14565 $23887 €20100 Le petit frere (113x91cm-44x36in) s. painted c.1913. 27-May-3 Artcurial Briest, Paris #98/R est:8000-10000

GUILLOUX, Charles Victor (1866-1946) French
£417 $688 €600 Reflets de peupliers dans le canal (46x35cm-18x14in) s. 1-Jul-3 Rossini, Paris #95/R
£1090 $1711 €1700 Chaumieres (27x41cm-11x16in) s. 15-Dec-2 Thierry & Lannon, Brest #389

£2152 $3357 €3400 Pont Alexandre III, coucher de soleil (24x47cm-9x19in) s.d.1903. 20-Oct-2 Anaf, Lyon #160/R
£8904 $13890 €13000 Coucher du soleil a Herblay (33x54cm-13x21in) s.d.1902i. verso i. stretcher. 10-Apr-3 Schopman, Hamburg #575 est:700

Works on paper

£516 $815 €800 Largue Roche a maree basse (27x40cm-11x16in) gouache. 17-Dec-2 Rossini, Paris #31

GUIMARAES, Jose de (1939-) Portuguese

£5380 $8500 €8500 Untitled (56x38cm-22x15in) s. prov. 26-Nov-2 Sotheby's, Amsterdam #53/R est:1000-1500
£9353 $14964 €13000 Composition avec femme (100x80cm-39x31in) s.d.84. 13-May-3 Palais de Beaux Arts, Brussels #337 est:750-1000

GUINAND, René (1892-1984) Swiss

£2402 $3795 €3603 Plaine d'Aire (70x95cm-28x37in) s. painted 1937. 17-Nov-2 Koller, Geneva #1210 (S.FR 5500)

GUINART, Francisco (19/20th C) Spanish

£855 $1386 €1300 Gypsy area in Granada (61x50cm-24x20in) s. 21-Jan-3 Ansorena, Madrid #281/R
£1711 $2771 €2600 Aigua Blava beach, Costa Brava (60x75cm-24x30in) s. s.i.verso. 21-Jan-3 Ansorena, Madrid #76/R
£2387 $3772 €3700 Big fair, Breda (61x75cm-24x30in) s. s.i.verso. 18-Dec-2 Ansorena, Madrid #373/R
£2692 $4254 €4200 Beach on the Costa Brava (60x75cm-24x30in) s. s.i.verso. 13-Nov-2 Ansorena, Madrid #178/R

GUINEA, Anselmo de (1855-1906) French

£18868 $29057 €30000 Young shepherdess (87x59cm-34x23in) s. 22-Oct-2 Durán, Madrid #276/R est:30000

Works on paper

£1781 $2778 €2600 Roman woman (58x44cm-23x17in) s. chl dr. 8-Apr-3 Ansorena, Madrid #236/R

GUINEGAULT, G P (1893-?) French

£317 $510 €450 L'echouage de la chaloupe sardiniere (55x46cm-22x18in) s. 11-May-3 Thierry & Lannon, Brest #364

Works on paper

£423 $680 €600 Depart pour la peche a I'lle d'Yeu (41x59cm-16x23in) s. pastel. 11-May-3 Thierry & Lannon, Brest #296

GUINEGAULT, Georges P (1893-?) French

Works on paper

£340 $547 €520 Jeune femme assoupie (29x59cm-11x23in) s. mixed media. 20-Jan-3 Horta, Bruxelles #486

GUINHALD, Bernard de (1885-?) French

£261 $421 €400 Vue de Martigues (33x55cm-13x22in) s. 20-Jan-3 Horta, Bruxelles #484

GUINNESS, Lindy (1941-) British

£1400 $2212 €2030 Stone landscape, Inis Meain, Arran Islands (59x74cm-23x29in) s.d.89. 22-Jul-3 Sotheby's, Olympia #98 est:300-500

GUINNESS, May (1863-1955) British

Works on paper

£500 $800 €750 Mount of Olives (18x26cm-7x10in) s. s.i.verso pencil pastel. 15-May-3 Christie's, Kensington #218/R
£950 $1511 €1425 Afternoon tea (30x22cm-12x9in) s. pastel. 5-Mar-3 John Ross, Belfast #63

GUINO, Richard (1890-1973) French

Sculpture

£1475 $2360 €2050 Idyle (18x28x11cm-7x11x4in) s.st.f. black brown pat bronze. 18-May-3 Charbonneaux, Paris #224/R est:2200-2500
£31646 $49367 €50000 Grande maternite (96x84x47cm-38x33x19in) s. green brown pat.bronze Cast.Susse freres Paris prov.lit. 31-Jul-2 Tajan, Paris #13/R est:50000-60000

Works on paper

£320 $509 €480 Etude de femme (33x42cm-13x17in) s. sanguine prov. 20-Mar-3 Sotheby's, Olympia #19/R

GUINO, Richard and RENOIR, Pierre Auguste (20th C) French

Sculpture

£3548 $5500 €5322 Tete de femme (16cm-6in) s. brown green pat. bronze. 26-Sep-2 Christie's, Rockefeller NY #538/R est:7000-9000
£6000 $9240 €9000 Tete de petite Venus (10cm-4in) num.2/3 brown pat bronze exec.c.1963 prov. 23-Oct-2 Sotheby's, Olympia #664/R est:6000-8000
£12500 $20625 €18000 Petite Venus debout ou Venus a la pomme (59cm-23in) s.st.f.C. Valsuani brown pat bronze lit. 2-Jul-3 Artcurial Briest, Paris #635/R est:20000-25000

GUINOVART, Jose (1927-) Spanish

£586 $926 €850 Abstraction (28x20cm-11x8in) s. paper. 1-Apr-3 Segre, Madrid #217/R
£993 $1619 €1500 Cos de Mar. s. oil mixed media board painted 1992 prov. 11-Feb-3 Segre, Madrid #237/R
£1170 $1896 €1650 Untitled (50x35cm-20x14in) s.d.2002 paper on canvas. 20-May-3 Segre, Madrid #147/R est:1350
£1192 $1943 €1800 Sota blue (37x26cm-15x10in) s. s.i.d.1992 verso oil mixed media board prov. 11-Feb-3 Segre, Madrid #238/R
£1854 $3023 €2800 Gran Cap (98x69cm-39x27in) s.d.1987 oil gouache wax crayon prov. 11-Feb-3 Segre, Madrid #226/R
£2258 $3568 €3500 Cap de Creus 103 (66x73cm-26x29in) s.d.1991 oil mixed media plastic board prov.exhib. 17-Dec-2 Segre, Madrid #159/R
£2390 $3728 €3800 Untitled (60x70cm-24x28in) s. oil earth panel on board. 17-Sep-2 Segre, Madrid #173/R

Works on paper

£1006 $1550 €1600 Untitled (47x35cm-19x14in) s.d.2002 W/C collage chl paper on canvas lit. 28-Oct-2 Segre, Madrid #146/R
£1258 $1962 €2000 Composition (34x40cm-13x16in) s. mixed media on canvas. 8-Oct-2 Ansorena, Madrid #630/R

GUION, Molly (1910-) American

£269 $450 €390 Chrysanthemums and autumn leaves (64x76cm-25x30in) s. 22-Jun-3 Jeffery Burchard, Florida #58/R

GUIRAMAND, Paul (1926-) French

£774 $1200 €1161 Flower baskets (102x76cm-40x30in) s. painted c.1960. 8-Dec-2 Toomey, Oak Park #810/R
£2013 $3119 €3200 Le village, rose (73x92cm-29x36in) s. 30-Oct-2 Artcurial Briest, Paris #390 est:4000-6000

Works on paper

£280 $467 €400 Au lavoir (42x56cm-17x22in) s. gouache. 26-Jun-3 Tajan, Paris #179/R
£692 $1072 €1100 Composition au bouquet (47x59cm-19x23in) s. W/C. 3-Nov-2 Feletin, Province #86/R

GUIRAND DE SCEVOLA, Lucien (1871-1950) French

£290 $461 €420 Barques sardinieres sous voiles (34x42cm-13x17in) s. canvas on cardboard. 10-Mar-3 Thierry & Lannon, Brest #114/R
£377 $604 €566 Baigneuse (32x22cm-13x9in) s. 17-Mar-3 Philippe Schuler, Zurich #8639 (S.FR 800)
£613 $950 €920 Portrait of a woman in beaded head-dress and red coat (64x53cm-25x21in) s. 2-Nov-2 North East Auctions, Portsmouth #1151a/R

Works on paper

£1042 $1646 €1500 Bouquet (91x71cm-36x28in) s. pastel. 25-Apr-3 Piasa, Paris #112/R est:2000

GUIRAUD-RIVIERE, M (1881-?) French

Sculpture

£5500 $8690 €8250 Stella (62cm-24in) s. bronze. 14-Nov-2 Christie's, Kensington #267/R est:5000-8000
£12000 $18960 €18000 Rose of Baghdad (81cm-32in) s. bronze. 14-Nov-2 Christie's, Kensington #268/R est:12000-15000

GUIRAUD-RIVIERE, Maurice (1881-?) French

Sculpture

£4088 $6377 €6500 Danseuse au ballon (66cm-26in) s. silver pat.bronze marble socle. 9-Oct-2 Lombrail & Teucquam, Paris #12/R

GUISE, C J (19/20th C) ?

£1401 $2200 €2102 Portrait of the ship The Beran (30x58cm-12x23in) s. i.d.1893 verso panel. 19-Apr-3 James Julia, Fairfield #101/R est:1500-2500

GUKEI, Sumiyoshi (attrib) (1631-1705) Japanese

Works on paper

£1013 $1600 €1600 Le dernier entretien de Genni et Fujitsubo avant son depart en retraite (35x102cm-14x40in) ink polychrome. 29-Nov-2 Tajan, Paris #84 est:2500-2800

GULACSY, Lajos (1882-1932) Hungarian

£4192 $6539 €6288 Vision (18x23cm-7x9in) s. board. 11-Apr-3 Kieselbach, Budapest #149/R est:1200000-1500000 (H.F 1500000)
£15370 $23977 €22287 Street detail (34x47cm-13x19in) s. board. 12-Apr-3 Mu Terem Galeria, Budapest #140/R est:3000000 (H.F 5500000)

£215141 $333468 €322712 It is snowing in Nakonxipan - one day snow (96x48cm-38x19in) s. 6-Dec-2 Kieselbach, Budapest #30/R (H.F 80000000)
£255479 $395993 €370445 Lady playing on an old instrument (97x68cm-38x27in) s. card exhib.lit. 9-Dec-2 Mu Terem Galeria, Budapest #52/R est:28000000 (H.F 95000000)

Works on paper
£615 $959 €923 Love (7x12cm-3x5in) s. Indian ink. 11-Apr-3 Kieselbach, Budapest #148/R est:90000-220000 (H.F 220000)
£1285 $2005 €1928 Self portrait dressed as Pierrot (21x16cm-8x6in) s. pencil. 11-Apr-3 Kieselbach, Budapest #180/R est:460000 (H.F 460000)
£7266 $11334 €10899 Young girl with black silken scarf and golden brooch (20x13cm-8x5in) s. mixed media. 11-Apr-3 Kieselbach, Budapest #31/R est:650000-2600000 (H.F 2600000)

GULBECK, A (?) ?
£425 $663 €638 Seascape with vessels (89x135cm-35x53in) s. 5-Aug-2 Rasmussen, Vejle #2334 (D.KR 5000)

GULBRANSSON, Olaf (1873-1958) Norwegian
Works on paper
£364 $556 €546 The violinist (22x14cm-9x6in) s. Indian ink. 26-Aug-2 Blomqvist, Lysaker #1125/R (N.KR 4200)
£634 $1052 €900 Composition (28x22cm-11x9in) i. Indian ink. 14-Jun-3 Hauswedell & Nolte, Hamburg #1222/R
£641 $974 €1000 Portrait of man with hands clasped (19x11cm-7x4in) s.d.50 pen. 11-Jul-2 Hugo Ruef, Munich #889/R
£897 $1364 €1400 Cartoon strip (35x25cm-14x10in) s. pen. 11-Jul-2 Hugo Ruef, Munich #890/R

GULDBRANDSEN, Frits (1813-1849) Danish
£3172 $5043 €4758 The artist in his study, Gammel Frederiksborggade (30x24cm-12x9in) i.verso. 5-May-3 Rasmussen, Vejle #345/R est:5000 (D.KR 34000)

GULLICHSEN, Alvar (1961-) Finnish
£1032 $1631 €1600 Zeitbarometer (100x71cm-39x28in) s.verso. 19-Dec-2 Hagelstam, Helsinki #838/R est:1500

GULLVAG, Hakon (1959-) Norwegian
£6428 $10542 €9321 Composition with figures (148x190cm-58x75in) s. s.d.1989 verso. 2-Jun-3 Blomqvist, Oslo #196/R est:70000-90000 (N.KR 70000)

GULLY, John (1819-1888) New Zealander
Works on paper
£848 $1307 €1272 Head of the lake, sunset (30x44cm-12x17in) s. W/C prov. 4-Sep-2 Dunbar Sloane, Wellington #157 est:1000-2000 (NZ.D 2800)
£1552 $2282 €2328 Arthur's Pass (16x29cm-6x11in) s. W/C prov. 19-Jun-2 Watson's, Christchurch #28/R est:5000-7500 (NZ.D 4750)
£2219 $3461 €3329 Mount Cook in mid-summer with three figures beside the dry glacier bed (58x42cm-23x17in) s. W/C. 17-Sep-2 Peter Webb, Auckland #129/R est:15000-20000 (NZ.D 7300)
£2456 $3832 €3684 Lake Hayes, Otago (29x52cm-11x20in) s.d.1882 W/C. 27-Mar-3 International Art Centre, Auckland #141/R est:7000-10000 (NZ.D 7000)
£5016 $7824 €7524 Stage coach in Arthur's Pass (34x62cm-13x24in) s.d.1886 W/C. 7-Nov-2 International Art Centre, Auckland #139/R est:18000-26000 (NZ.D 16000)
£5224 $7627 €7836 Mitre Peak. s.d.1863 W/C. 12-Sep-1 Watson's, Christchurch #48/R est:20000-30000 (NZ.D 17500)
£8232 $12595 €12348 Lake Wakatipu, Queenstown (47x63cm-19x25in) s.d.1863 W/C. 21-Aug-2 Dunbar Sloane, Auckland #41/R est:28000-35000 (NZ.D 27000)

GUMERY, Adolphe (1861-1943) French
£5500 $9185 €8250 Dans le jardin (41x33cm-16x13in) s. 18-Jun-3 Christie's, Kensington #105/R est:6000-8000

GUMMERUS-GUMMERUS, Olga (1876-?) Finnish?
Works on paper
£854 $1333 €1350 Interior (39x53cm-15x21in) s.d.1906 gouache. 15-Sep-2 Bukowskis, Helsinki #192/R

GUMMESSON, Per (1858-1928) Swedish
£301 $476 €452 Winter wood (100x54cm-39x21in) s.d.95. 16-Nov-2 Crafoord, Lund #75/R (S.KR 4300)

GUNARSA, Nyoman (1944-) Indonesian
£6993 $11538 €10140 Dancers (148x148cm-58x58in) mono.d.1990. 6-Jul-3 Christie's, Hong Kong #53/R est:90000-120000 (HK.D 90000)

GUNAWAN, Hendra (1918-1983) Javanese
£19884 $30621 €29826 View of a landscape (102x194cm-40x76in) s. 27-Oct-2 Christie's, Hong Kong #89/R est:280000-350000 (HK.D 240000)
£49710 $76553 €74565 Two women and a child by the beach (80x140cm-31x55in) s.d.80 prov. 27-Oct-2 Christie's, Hong Kong #88/R est:280000-380000 (HK.D 600000)
£50505 $83333 €73232 Catching flea (155x91cm-61x36in) s.i.d.63 canvas on board prov. 6-Jul-3 Christie's, Hong Kong #65/R est:260000-350000 (HK.D 650000)
£66045 $108974 €95765 Mother and child (139x80cm-55x31in) s.d.80. 6-Jul-3 Christie's, Hong Kong #64/R est:300000-400000 (HK.D 850000)
£108780 $179487 €157731 Durian festival (148x95cm-58x37in) s.d.80 prov. 6-Jul-3 Christie's, Hong Kong #63/R est:380000-450000 (HK.D 1400000)
£149130 $229660 €223695 Vegetable sellers on the beach (140x179cm-55x70in) s.i.d.75 s.i.verso prov.lit. 27-Oct-2 Christie's, Hong Kong #86/R est:700000-900000 (HK.D 1800000)
£155400 $256410 €225330 Kuda lumping (147x297cm-58x117in) s.d.73 lit. 6-Jul-3 Christie's, Hong Kong #66/R est:2000000-3000000 (HK.D 2000000)
£198840 $306214 €298260 Feasting at the beach (136x263cm-54x104in) s.d.73. 27-Oct-2 Christie's, Hong Kong #87/R est:2400000-4000000 (HK.D 2400000)

GUNDERSEN, Gunnar S (1921-1983) Norwegian
£2207 $3399 €3311 Composition (58x51cm-23x20in) s. acrylic panel painted 1959. 28-Oct-2 Blomqvist, Lysaker #1070 est:15000-18000 (N.KR 26000)
£8651 $13668 €12977 Composition 2 (131x90cm-52x35in) s.d.64 acrylic exhib. 2-Dec-2 Blomqvist, Oslo #439/R est:120000-150000 (N.KR 100000)
£9083 $14351 €13625 Composition 5 (101x100cm-40x39in) s.d.64 i.stretcher acrylic exhib. 2-Dec-2 Blomqvist, Oslo #448/R est:100000-120000 (N.KR 105000)

Works on paper
£1211 $1913 €1817 Composition (31x36cm-12x14in) s. mixed media executed c.1959. 2-Dec-2 Blomqvist, Oslo #417/R est:7000-9000 (N.KR 14000)

GUNDLACH, Henry (1884-1965) German
£513 $795 €800 Hanstedt landscape (52x70cm-20x28in) s.d.1940. 5-Dec-2 Schopman, Hamburg #621
£782 $1244 €1150 Farmstead on Sylt (50x60cm-20x24in) s.d.37. 28-Mar-3 Bolland & Marotz, Bremen #550/R

GUNDORFF, Georg Valdemar (1876-?) Danish
£1210 $1925 €1815 Coastal landscape with three women in the dunes (39x49cm-15x19in) s.d.1919. 10-Mar-3 Rasmussen, Vejle #558/R est:12000 (D.KR 13000)

GUNN, Herbert James (1893-1964) British
£32000 $49600 €48000 From Cap d'Antibes (46x61cm-18x24in) s. i.overlap exhib. 31-Oct-2 Christie's, London #156/R est:25000-35000

GUNSAM, Karl Joseph (1900-1972) Austrian
£3077 $4831 €4800 Flowers (61x46cm-24x18in) s. lit. 25-Nov-2 Hassfurther, Vienna #43/R est:6000-7000
£5072 $8319 €7000 Still life of flowers (72x59cm-28x23in) s.d.57. 27-May-3 Wiener Kunst Auktionen, Vienna #57/R est:5000-8000
Works on paper
£962 $1519 €1500 Lake in Salzkammergut (52x69cm-20x27in) s.d.50 W/C. 12-Nov-2 Dorotheum, Vienna #164/R est:900-1300

GUNTER, Irwin (19th C) German
£1300 $2054 €1950 Extensive seascape with distant sailing boats (99x150cm-39x59in) s. 13-Nov-2 Halls, Shrewsbury #411/R est:800-1200

GUNTHER, Ernst (1910-1990) Swiss
Sculpture
£1834 $2861 €2751 Young woman with jug (174cm-69in) i. clay. 20-Nov-2 Fischer, Luzern #1432/R est:2000-2500 (S.FR 4200)

GUNTHER, Erwin (1864-1927) German
£849 $1325 €1350 Steamer in Hamburg harbour (52x62cm-20x24in) s. lit. 20-Sep-2 Karlheinz Kaupp, Staufen #2091/R

£1057 $1544 €1586 Coastal landscape (67x100cm-26x39in) s.i.d. 17. 17-Jun-2 Philippe Schuler, Zurich #4370/R (S.FR 2400)
£2372 $3676 €3700 Hamburg harbour (73x137cm-29x54in) s.i.d.1919 prov. 7-Dec-2 Ketterer, Hamburg #47/R est:3000-3500

GUNTHER, Herta (1934-) German
Works on paper
£278 $439 €400 Two women on the pull (21x18cm-8x7in) s. chl col chk board. 26-Apr-3 Dr Lehr, Berlin #181/R
£417 $658 €600 Waiting room (45x37cm-18x15in) s.d.1989 chl pastel chk board. 26-Apr-3 Dr Lehr, Berlin #180/R

GUNTHER, Joseph (1820-?) German
£811 $1305 €1217 Southern river landscape (37x49cm-15x19in) s.d.1878. 22-Feb-3 Rasmussen, Havnen #2086/R (D.KR 9000)

GUNTHER, Peter Georg (fl.1820-1830) Danish
Works on paper
£431 $655 €647 The Tiber near Engelsborg, fishermen in foreground (30x43cm-12x17in) s.i.d.1822 pen W/C. 27-Aug-2 Rasmussen, Copenhagen #1665/R (D.KR 5000)

GUNTHER-NAUMBURG, Otto (1856-1941) German
£256 $397 €400 Rocky coastal landscape (30x45cm-12x18in) s. panel. 7-Dec-2 Dannenberg, Berlin #666/R
£679 $1052 €1019 Dutch countryside I (34x69cm-13x27in) tempera cardboard painted c.1890. 3-Dec-2 SOGA, Bratislava #176/R (SL.K 43000)
£679 $1052 €1019 Dutch countryside II (34x69cm-13x27in) tempera cardboard painted c.1890. 3-Dec-2 SOGA, Bratislava #177/R (SL.K 43000)
£3797 $6000 €6000 Castle bridge, Berlin (38x50cm-15x20in) s.i.d.87 exhib.lit. 30-Nov-2 Villa Grisebach, Berlin #116 est:3000-3500

GUNZ, Engelbert (1908-) Swiss
£261 $407 €392 Cows on lake shore (17x40cm-7x16in) s. board. 16-Sep-2 Philippe Schuler, Zurich #6620 (S.FR 600)
£261 $407 €392 Peasant women in field (17x40cm-7x16in) s. board. 16-Sep-2 Philippe Schuler, Zurich #6621 (S.FR 600)

GUO CHUANZHANG (1912-) Chinese
Works on paper
£725 $1188 €1000 Clouds in Huangshan mountains (124x65cm-49x26in) s. sela Indian ink hanging scroll. 30-May-3 Dr Fritz Nagel, Stuttgart #1258/R

GUO WEI (1960-) Chinese
£3396 $5230 €5400 Mosquito season 2 (160x100cm-63x39in) s.d.2000 exhib. 26-Oct-2 Cornette de St.Cyr, Paris #178/R

GUO YIZONG (1940-) Chinese
Works on paper
£362 $594 €500 Lotus (144x80cm-57x31in) i. seals Indian ink col hanging scroll. 30-May-3 Dr Fritz Nagel, Stuttgart #1194/R
£471 $772 €650 Flowers (86x112cm-34x44in) s.d.1988 seals Indian ink col. 30-May-3 Dr Fritz Nagel, Stuttgart #1229/R

GURDON, Nora (1881-1974) Australian
£354 $539 €531 Dandenongs (25x34cm-10x13in) s. board. 28-Aug-2 Deutscher-Menzies, Melbourne #406/R (A.D 990)
£393 $620 €590 Mediterranean harbour (24x18cm-9x7in) s. board. 18-Nov-2 Joel, Victoria #244/R est:1000-1200 (A.D 1100)
£1075 $1634 €1613 View from the Dandenongs (45x60cm-18x24in) s. 28-Aug-2 Deutscher-Menzies, Melbourne #238/R est:3500-4500 (A.D 3000)

GURLITT, Louis (1812-1897) German
£2721 $4327 €4000 Mountain lake - possibly Lake Garda (51x71cm-20x28in) bears sig.d.42. 19-Mar-3 Neumeister, Munich #573/R est:4000
£4190 $6662 €6285 Italian landscape with view towards mountains, two girls in foreground (87x126cm-34x50in) 10-Mar-3 Rasmussen, Vejle #180/R est:50000 (D.KR 45000)
£4965 $8043 €7000 View in southern Italy (42x65cm-17x26in) s.i. 22-May-3 Dorotheum, Vienna #9/R est:7000-9000
£5587 $8883 €8381 Coastal landscape from the bay near Palermo, Scicily (27x43cm-11x17in) s.d.1848. 5-Mar-3 Rasmussen, Copenhagen #1572/R est:50000-75000 (D.KR 60000)

GURLITT, Louis (attrib) (1812-1897) German
£1410 $2186 €2200 Italian mountain landscape (34x46cm-13x18in) 5-Dec-2 Dr Fritz Nagel, Stuttgart #657/R est:4000

GURSCHNER, Herbert (1901-1975) Austrian
£7246 $11884 €10000 Spring in Tyrol (42x54cm-17x21in) s. 27-May-3 Wiener Kunst Auktionen, Vienna #47/R est:8000-12000

GURSKY, Andreas (1955-) German
Photographs
£4000 $6680 €5800 Ratingen (31x49cm-12x19in) cibachrome print prov.lit. 26-Jun-3 Sotheby's, London #283/R est:4000-6000
£7595 $12000 €11393 Hoesel (91x80cm-36x31in) s.i.d.84 num.1/10 c-print prov. 13-Nov-2 Sotheby's, New York #441/R est:15000-20000
£10000 $16400 €15000 Singapore II (80x60cm-31x24in) s.d.15.1.2000 verso s.i.d.98 num.1/8 verso cibachrome print prov. 7-Feb-3 Sotheby's, London #122/R est:6000-8000
£13750 $22000 €20625 Schnorchler (59x75cm-23x30in) s.i.d.1988 num.12/12 cibachrome print prov.lit. 14-May-3 Sotheby's, New York #395/R est:18000-25000
£13924 $22000 €20886 Porto Bahnhof (51x61cm-20x24in) s.i.d.1988 num.6/8 col coupler print prov.exhib. 14-Nov-2 Christie's, Rockefeller NY #415/R est:18000-22000
£14000 $21560 €21000 Kairo, diptychon (87x52cm-34x20in) s.i.d.10.7.1993 c-print lit. 23-Oct-2 Christie's, London #200/R est:8000-12000
£15500 $25885 €22475 Singapore II (80x60cm-31x24in) s.i.d.97 num.17/25 cibachrome print prov.lit. 27-Jun-3 Christie's, London #259/R est:8000-12000
£26582 $42000 €39873 Autobahn mettmann (180x219cm-71x86in) col coupler print mounted on plexiglas executed 1993 prov.exhib. 14-Nov-2 Christie's, Rockefeller NY #413/R est:60000-80000
£30625 $49000 €45938 Siemens, Augsburg (133x328cm-52x129in) four c-prints mounted in plexiglas executed 1993 prov. 16-May-3 Phillips, New York #127/R est:60000-80000
£42000 $70140 €63000 Untitled III (186x222cm-73x87in) s.i.d.96 1/6 verso chromogenic col print prov.lit. 25-Jun-3 Sotheby's, London #2/R est:60000-80000
£44304 $70000 €66456 Niagara Falls (104x87cm-41x34in) s. col coupler print executed 1989 prov.exhib.lit. 14-Nov-2 Christie's, Rockefeller NY #414/R est:70000-90000
£46000 $75440 €69000 Porto Bahnof (146x168cm-57x66in) s.d.1988 num.3/4 verso cibachrome print prov.lit. 7-Feb-3 Sotheby's, London #110/R est:40000-60000
£46000 $76820 €66700 Hong Kong port (116x90cm-46x35in) s.i.d.94 num.5/6 verso cibachrome print prov.exhib. 26-Jun-3 Sotheby's, London #118/R est:30000-40000
£50000 $80000 €75000 Maloja (211x717cm-83x282in) s.i.d.89 num.4/4 col coupler print prov.exhib. 15-May-3 Christie's, Rockefeller NY #349/R est:40000-60000
£80000 $123200 €120000 Charles de Gaulle (140x187cm-55x74in) s.i.d.92 num.3/4 verso cibachrome print prov.lit. 22-Oct-2 Sotheby's, London #307/R est:50000-120000
£95000 $146300 €142500 Hong Kong stock Exchange II (207x319cm-81x126in) i.num.5/6 chromagenic print executed 1998 prov.lit. 23-Oct-2 Christie's, London #192/R est:120000-180000
£110000 $180400 €165000 Albertville (165x197cm-65x78in) s.i.d.1992 num.1/4 verso cibachrome print prov.lit. 7-Feb-3 Sotheby's, London #123/R est:60000-80000
£141026 $220000 €211539 Turner collection, London (176x213cm-69x84in) s.i. chromogenic col print executed 1995 prov.exhib. 11-Nov-2 Phillips, New York #9/R est:150000-200000
£256250 $410000 €384375 Klitschko (207x261cm-81x103in) chromogenic col print executed 1999 prov.exhib. 15-May-3 Phillips, New York #7/R est:250000-350000

GURVICH, Jose (1927-1974) Lithuanian
£1346 $2100 €2019 Naturaleza muerta en colores puros (34x46cm-13x18in) d.57 cardboard prov. 30-Jul-2 Galleria Y Remates, Montevideo #46 est:2000-2500
£4906 $7800 €7359 Urban composition (57x61cm-22x24in) s.d.52 cardboard. 2-Mar-3 Galleria Y Remates, Montevideo #74/R
£5688 $9100 €8532 Building (38x39cm-15x15in) s.d.62 cardboard. 5-Jan-3 Galleria Y Remates, Montevideo #94/R
£7317 $12000 €10976 From the series: Canto a la vida y a la naturaleza (50x69cm-20x27in) s.d.1956 cardboard prov. 28-May-3 Christie's, Rockefeller NY #100/R est:14000-16000

Works on paper
£256 $400 €384 Naturaleza muerta I (8x11cm-3x4in) s. W/C. 30-Jul-2 Galleria Y Remates, Montevideo #49/R

£256 $400 €384 Landscape (13x9cm-5x4in) s.d.1960 ink. 10-Oct-2 Galleria Y Remates, Montevideo #22/R
£353 $550 €530 Reading II (18x12cm-7x5in) s. ink W/C prov. 10-Oct-2 Galleria Y Remates, Montevideo #23/R
£545 $850 €818 San Marcos (17x22cm-7x9in) s. W/C. 30-Jul-2 Galleria Y Remates, Montevideo #48/R
£641 $1000 €962 Almuerzo en el cerro (12x19cm-5x7in) s.d.1959 W/C. 30-Jul-2 Galleria Y Remates, Montevideo #47/R
£764 $1200 €1146 Embrace (18x25cm-7x10in) s.d.61 pencil W/C. 20-Nov-2 Galleria Y Remates, Montevideo #21/R
£4615 $7200 €6923 Mates (54x67cm-21x26in) s.d.57 prov. 10-Oct-2 Galleria Y Remates, Montevideo #72/R
£7927 $13000 €11891 Muerte de Sara (48x34cm-19x13in) s.d.1969 gouache prov.lit. 28-May-3 Christie's, Rockefeller NY #105/R est:12000-16000

GUSMAROLI, Riccardo (1963-) Italian
£2553 $4136 €3600 Untitled (125x138cm-49x54in) s. map. 20-May-3 Porro, Milan #28/R est:3500-3700
Works on paper
£1702 $2757 €2400 Golfo dell'asinara (75x114cm-30x45in) s.d.1999 paper on map paper. 26-May-3 Christie's, Milan #103/R est:2000-2500

GUSSONI, Vittorio (1893-1968) Italian
£1064 $1723 €1500 Angurie (40x40cm-16x16in) s. panel. 22-May-3 Stadion, Trieste #182/R est:600-800
£1064 $1723 €1500 Meloni sul tavolo (40x40cm-16x16in) s. panel. 22-May-3 Stadion, Trieste #181/R est:600-800
£1195 $1840 €1900 Portrait of woman in Via Fiori Chiari (49x39cm-19x15in) s. 28-Oct-2 Il Ponte, Milan #321
£1844 $2987 €2600 Sulla spiaggia (60x50cm-24x20in) s. panel. 22-May-3 Stadion, Trieste #179/R est:1000-1500

GUSSOW, Karl (1843-1907) German
£1479 $2381 €2100 Girl in traditional costume (38x29cm-15x11in) s.i.d.1880 panel lit. 9-May-3 Schloss Ahlden, Ahlden #1480/R est:1700

GUSSOW, Karl (attrib) (1843-1907) German
£503 $785 €800 Girl in traditional costume (39x31cm-15x12in) i. 23-Sep-2 Dr Fritz Nagel, Stuttgart #7054/R

GUSTAT, E W (20th C) ?
£344 $550 €516 Untitled (91x61cm-36x24in) s. 16-May-3 Du Mouchelle, Detroit #180/R

GUSTAVSON, Henry (1864-?) American
£258 $400 €387 Hidden forest (46x61cm-18x24in) s. 7-Dec-2 Harvey Clar, Oakland #1332

GUSTAVSSON, Mats (1951-) Swedish
Works on paper
£736 $1148 €1104 Man (37x27cm-15x11in) W/C. 6-Nov-2 AB Stockholms Auktionsverk #895/R (S.KR 10500)

GUSTON, Philip (1913-1980) American
£156250 $250000 €234375 Window (76x99cm-30x39in) panel painted 1969 prov. 14-May-3 Sotheby's, New York #162/R est:125000-175000
£1075949 $1700000 €1613924 Painted in bed (151x264cm-59x104in) s. s.i.d.1973 verso prov.exhib.lit. 12-Nov-2 Sotheby's, New York #29/R est:1200000-1800000
Prints
£2065 $3200 €3098 Street (57x77cm-22x30in) s.d.1970 num.76/120 lithograph. 25-Sep-2 Christie's, Rockefeller NY #284/R est:2000-3000
Works on paper
£28125 $45000 €42188 Solitary II (41x54cm-16x21in) s.d.70 black ink prov.exhib. 14-May-3 Sotheby's, New York #160/R est:30000-40000
£75000 $120000 €112500 Untitled (58x74cm-23x29in) init.d.1980 black ink prov.exhib. 14-May-3 Sotheby's, New York #161/R est:50000-70000

GUTAHAZA, Gyula Nemeth (19th C) Hungarian
£256 $405 €400 Peasant market with horses and carts (25x35cm-10x14in) s. 15-Nov-2 Reiss & Sohn, Konigstein #32

GUTFREUND, Otto (1889-1927) Czechoslovakian
Sculpture
£1449 $2377 €2000 Female head (20cm-8in) s. pat.bronze prov.exhib. 29-May-3 Lempertz, Koln #656/R est:2000
£1910 $3036 €2750 Femme nue allongee (13x27x13cm-5x11x5in) brown pat bronze prov.exhib.lit. 29-Apr-3 Artcurial Briest, Paris #206/R est:3000-4000
£2069 $3269 €3000 Don Quixote (38cm-15in) s. brown green pat.bronze. 2-Apr-3 Dr Fritz Nagel, Stuttgart #9339/R est:3800
£5435 $8913 €7500 Cello player (47cm-19in) dark pat.bronze prov.exhib. 29-May-3 Lempertz, Koln #655/R est:8000-10000
Works on paper
£243 $386 €350 Etude de nus (21x17cm-8x7in) studio st.verso ink dr exec.c.1912 prov. 29-Apr-3 Artcurial Briest, Paris #207
£372 $580 €558 Nude girl (23x20cm-9x8in) i.d.1920 pencil dr. 12-Oct-2 Dorotheum, Prague #243 (C.KR 18000)
£620 $967 €930 Dance (14x11cm-6x4in) Indian ink dr double-sided. 12-Oct-2 Dorotheum, Prague #184/R (C.KR 30000)
£929 $1450 €1394 Head of a man (36x26cm-14x10in) mono. pastel chl. 12-Oct-2 Dorotheum, Prague #204/R (C.KR 45000)

GUTHRIE, James (1859-1930) British
£500 $815 €750 Portrait of Stoddart Walker. Portrait of his wife (56x40cm-22x16in) pair. 29-Jan-3 Sotheby's, Olympia #236/R
£15000 $24300 €22500 Portrait of Miss Robina Spencer (179x68cm-70x27in) s.d.91 lit. 23-May-3 Lyon & Turnbull, Edinburgh #69/R est:15000-20000
£21000 $32130 €31500 Stone breaker (31x38cm-12x15in) s.d.1886 exhib. 22-Aug-2 Bonhams, Edinburgh #1108/R est:20000-30000

GUTIERREZ DE LA VEGA, Jose (?-1865) Spanish
£1923 $3038 €3000 Saint Catalina (116x89cm-46x35in) 14-Nov-2 Arte, Seville #274/R
£2244 $3522 €3500 Biblical scene (145x104cm-57x41in) 19-Nov-2 Castellana, Madrid #499/R
£4516 $7135 €7000 Saint Rufina (49x37cm-19x15in) s. 18-Dec-2 Ansorena, Madrid #97/R est:7000

GUTIERREZ DIEZ, Maria del Carmen (1952-) Spanish
£338 $527 €500 Figures (97x130cm-38x51in) s.d.77. 25-Mar-3 Durán, Madrid #9/R

GUTIERREZ MONTIEL, Juan (1934-) Spanish
£377 $589 €600 Alfonso XII (91x60cm-36x24in) s.d.1972. 8-Oct-2 Ansorena, Madrid #609/R

GUTIERREZ SOLANA, Jose (1886-1945) Spanish
£110000 $172700 €165000 Mascaras de pueblo - masks in the town (55x71cm-22x28in) s. painted c.1935 prov.exhib.lit. 19-Nov-2 Sotheby's, London #33/R est:60000-80000
Works on paper
£8500 $13346 €12750 Esperando la sopa - queuing for soup (21x28cm-8x11in) s. pen ink executed c.1910-12. 19-Nov-2 Sotheby's, London #36/R est:2000-3000
£11000 $17270 €16500 Traperos de el rastro - rag and bone men at el rastro (28x23cm-11x9in) s. pen ink executed 1925 prov. 19-Nov-2 Sotheby's, London #34/R est:3000-5000
£24000 $37680 €36000 Murga Gaditana I - carnival in Cadiz (32x42cm-13x17in) s. col crayon conte prov. executed c.1935. 19-Nov-2 Sotheby's, London #31/R est:7000-10000
£24000 $37680 €36000 Murga gaditana II - carnival in Cadiz (32x42cm-13x17in) s. col crayon conte executed c.1935 prov. 19-Nov-2 Sotheby's, London #32/R est:7000-10000
£38000 $59660 €57000 Carnaval de mascaras - masked performers (36x48cm-14x19in) s. black crayon conte prov. 19-Nov-2 Sotheby's, London #35/R est:7000-10000

GUTIERREZ, Ernesto (1873-1934) Spanish
£1207 $1931 €1750 Stroll (50x62cm-20x24in) s.i. 11-Mar-3 Castellana, Madrid #17/R
£1935 $3058 €3000 Madrid seen from Las Vistillas (50x62cm-20x24in) s. 18-Dec-2 Castellana, Madrid #37/R

GUTKNECHT, Anton (20th C) American
£1242 $2000 €1863 Sunset coastal (36x48cm-14x19in) s. 18-Feb-3 John Moran, Pasadena #75a est:2500-4000

GUTMAN, Nachum (1898-1978) Israeli
£256 $403 €400 Cheder (46x36cm-18x14in) s. cardboard. 12-Dec-2 Rabourdin & Choppin de Janvry, Paris #50
£288 $453 €450 La lecture (55x46cm-22x18in) s. 24-Nov-2 Chayette & Cheval, Paris #312
£316 $519 €440 Benediction de la lune (45x35cm-18x14in) s. oil gouache paper. 3-Jun-3 Tajan, Paris #36
£550 $858 €825 Moored vessels (60x73cm-24x29in) s. 15-Oct-2 Bonhams, Knightsbridge #145/R
£34177 $54000 €51266 Harbour scene (61x81cm-24x32in) init. board prov. 27-Apr-3 Sotheby's, Tel Aviv #27/R est:40000-60000
Works on paper
£288 $453 €450 Shtetel (39x46cm-15x18in) s. gouache. 12-Dec-2 Rabourdin & Choppin de Janvry, Paris #51

£4430 $7000 €6645 Summer meal in garden (36x54cm-14x21in) s. W/C on card prov. 27-Apr-3 Sotheby's, Tel Aviv #5/R est:7000-9000

GUTTUSO, Renato (1912-1987) Italian

£2083 $3312 €3000 Portrait of man from Calabria (54x54cm-21x21in) s.i.d.1937 board. 1-May-3 Meeting Art, Vercelli #320
£3613 $5708 €5600 Boxer (75x54cm-30x21in) s. tempera chl paper on canvas prov. 18-Dec-2 Christie's, Rome #34/R
£3901 $6319 €5500 Abbraccio (39x50cm-15x20in) s.i. tempera paper on canvas prov. 26-May-3 Christie's, Milan #334/R est:4000-6000
£7092 $11489 €10000 Barca sul Nilo (50x40cm-20x16in) s. s.i.d.59 verso prov. 26-May-3 Christie's, Milan #138/R est:7000-10000
£7372 $11647 €11500 Hands (51x36cm-20x14in) s. s.verso. 15-Nov-2 Farsetti, Prato #296/R est:7500
£8974 $13910 €14000 Artichokes (48x76cm-19x30in) s. painted 1966-67 prov. 4-Dec-2 Finarte, Milan #334/R est:16000
£15603 $25277 €22000 Nude (60x65cm-24x26in) s. lit. 26-May-3 Christie's, Milan #129/R est:12000-13000
£16026 $25160 €25000 Boiled eggs on the table (54x65cm-21x26in) s. painted 1972 lit. 23-Nov-2 Meeting Art, Vercelli #250/R est:25000
£17730 $28723 €25000 Retata - Portella della ginestra (30x40cm-12x16in) s. prov.exhib.lit. 26-May-3 Christie's, Milan #353/R est:20000-25000
£18987 $30000 €30000 Cup and bottle (50x65cm-20x26in) s. painted 1958 lit. 30-Nov-2 Farsetti, Prato #660/R est:35000
£28082 $43808 €41000 Village with red sky (79x100cm-31x39in) s. s.d.1956 verso. 10-Apr-3 Finarte Semenzato, Rome #212/R est:42000

Works on paper

£897 $1434 €1300 Reclining female nude (23x30cm-9x12in) s. Chinese ink. 11-Mar-3 Babuino, Rome #218/R
£1026 $1610 €1600 Study of dancers (32x47cm-13x19in) s.d.1952 mixed media. 21-Nov-2 Finarte, Rome #177
£1282 $2013 €2000 Gymnastics (35x50cm-14x20in) s. pencil exec.1983. 21-Nov-2 Finarte, Rome #131/R
£1282 $1987 €2000 Bacchante (48x32cm-19x13in) s.i. mixed media. 5-Dec-2 Stadion, Trieste #728/R
£1361 $2163 €2000 Figures (33x45cm-13x18in) s. pencil chl. 1-Mar-3 Meeting Art, Vercelli #725
£1689 $2635 €2500 Woman (50x28cm-20x11in) s.d.58 Chinese ink gouache. 28-Mar-3 Farsetti, Prato #213/R
£1757 $2741 €2600 Bust of woman (55x46cm-22x18in) s.i.d.1966 gouache pencil collage card on canvas. 28-Mar-3 Farsetti, Prato #7/R
£1923 $2981 €3000 Feminine profile (62x43cm-24x17in) s.d.1968 Chinese ink. 4-Dec-2 Finarte, Milan #207/R
£2041 $3245 €3000 Nude (26x30cm-10x12in) Chinese ink tempera W/C. 1-Mar-3 Meeting Art, Vercelli #718
£2051 $3221 €3200 Scrapyard (51x75cm-20x30in) s.d.1978 felt-tip pen dr paper on cardboard. 23-Nov-2 Meeting Art, Vercelli #203/R
£2230 $3478 €3300 Woman (34x25cm-13x10in) s.d.60 Chinese ink W/C. 26-Mar-3 Finarte Semenzato, Milan #38/R
£2436 $3824 €3800 Kiss (51x36cm-20x14in) s. Chinese ink W/C lit. 19-Nov-2 Finarte, Milan #27/R
£2564 $4026 €4000 Figures (27x36cm-11x14in) i.d.1946 Chinese ink double-sided exhib. 19-Nov-2 Finarte, Milan #15/R
£2740 $4274 €4000 Peasant scene (33x44cm-13x17in) s. pencil chl. 10-Apr-3 Finarte Semenzato, Rome #106/R
£2885 $4471 €4500 Composition (56x50cm-22x20in) s. W/C Indian ink. 6-Dec-2 Hauswedell & Nolte, Hamburg #145/R est:5000
£3108 $4849 €4600 Nudes (50x70cm-20x28in) s. Chinese ink dr paper on canvas on cardboard. 28-Mar-3 Farsetti, Prato #290/R
£3425 $5342 €5000 Water carriers (50x70cm-20x28in) s. ink W/C card double-sided. 10-Apr-3 Finarte Semenzato, Rome #109/R
£3973 $6197 €5800 Figures in the woods (51x73cm-20x29in) s. Chinese ink W/C exec.1971. 10-Apr-3 Finarte Semenzato, Rome #259/R
£4178 $6518 €6100 Beach (50x50cm-20x20in) s. ink W/C lead lit. 10-Apr-3 Finarte Semenzato, Rome #105/R est:5000
£4452 $6945 €6500 Battle (70x100cm-28x39in) s. graphite tempera card. 10-Apr-3 Finarte Semenzato, Rome #256/R est:6500
£5556 $8833 €8000 Car wreck (37x51cm-15x20in) s.d.1978 mixed media card. 1-May-3 Meeting Art, Vercelli #566

GUY, Louis (1824-1886) French

£633 $1000 €1000 Faisans (39x46cm-15x18in) s.d.1862. 1-Dec-2 Anaf, Lyon #95
£732 $1113 €1098 North African man wearing white clothing (24x15cm-9x6in) s.d.1883 panel. 27-Aug-2 Rasmussen, Copenhagen #1629/R (D.KR 8500)

GUY, Seymour (1824-1910) American

£10390 $16000 €15585 Little shopper (30x25cm-12x10in) s. prov. 24-Oct-2 Shannon's, Milford #84/R est:10000-15000
£27778 $45000 €41667 Young girl reading (67x56cm-26x22in) mono.d.1877 prov. 21-May-3 Sotheby's, New York #211/R est:25000-35000

GUYNIER, Jean (1630-1707) French

£2821 $4428 €4400 Portrait d'un gentilhomme a la cuirasse (73x60cm-29x24in) s.d.1693 verso oval. 19-Nov-2 Vanderkindere, Brussels #13/R est:2000-3000

GUYOMARD, Gerard (1936-) French

£646 $1028 €950 L'homme assis (100x73cm-39x29in) s.i.d.74 verso acrylic. 26-Feb-3 Artcurial Briest, Paris #400
£916 $1447 €1420 Composition aux personnages (73x54cm-29x21in) s.d.83 acrylic prov. 18-Dec-2 Digard, Paris #58/R
£1293 $2055 €1900 Polyphonie bucolique (117x89cm-46x35in) s.d.1997 acrylic. 24-Mar-3 Cornette de St.Cyr, Paris #70/R

GUYOT, Georges Lucien (1885-1973) French

Sculpture

£5032 $7951 €7800 Ours marchant (19cm-7in) s.i. pat.bronze Cast.Susses Freres. 17-Dec-2 Claude Aguttes, Neuilly #44/R est:3000-4500
£5674 $9191 €8000 Lionne allongee se lechant la patte (13x29x12cm-5x11x5in) s. brown green pat bronze cire perdue. 23-May-3 Camard, Paris #102/R est:3800-4500
£15828 $25324 €22000 Babouin (41x13x22cm-16x5x9in) s. black pat.bronze. 19-May-3 Tajan, Paris #51/R est:16000-18000
£28058 $44892 €39000 Les amours royaux (40x93x25cm-16x37x10in) s. black pat.bronze. 19-May-3 Tajan, Paris #52/R est:40000-45000

Works on paper

£586 $833 €950 Poules (18x23cm-7x9in) s. W/C. 16-Mar-3 Eric Pillon, Calais #49/R
£789 $1279 €1200 Tiger (41x51cm-16x20in) s. chl W/C brush ink. 21-Jan-3 Christie's, Amsterdam #416/R est:500-700
£1026 $1610 €1600 Panthere noire se lechant (26x43cm-10x17in) s. chl pastel. 20-Nov-2 Claude Boisgirard, Paris #14
£1915 $3102 €2700 Jaguars (21x31cm-8x12in) s. W/C Indian ink board on board. 23-May-3 Camard, Paris #79 est:1500-2200

GUYOT, Henri (20th C) French

£335 $493 €520 Course (46x65cm-18x26in) s. 23-Jun-2 Chambelland & Giafferi, Paris #73/R

GUYOT, Louise (19th C) French

£1603 $2500 €2405 River landscapes with figures and boats (43x61cm-17x24in) s. pair. 21-Sep-2 Nadeau, Windsor #47/R est:3000-5000

GUYS, Constantin (1802-1892) French

Works on paper

£256 $403 €400 Cavalier et sa monture (15x13cm-6x5in) st.sig. ink col crayon. 21-Nov-2 Neret-Minet, Paris #21
£266 $420 €399 Horse and carriage (16x23cm-6x9in) pen ink wash prov. 26-Nov-2 Hans Widmer, St Gallen #1142 (S.FR 620)
£285 $450 €450 Etude de femme voilee (17x13cm-7x5in) W/C pen ink over crayon. 28-Nov-2 Tajan, Paris #167
£309 $488 €464 Two men with horse in front of carriage with two ladies (20x25cm-8x10in) pen ink W/C. 26-Nov-2 Hans Widmer, St Gallen #1143 (S.FR 720)
£347 $573 €500 Les deux mondaines (17x12cm-7x5in) brown ink wash. 1-Jul-3 Rossini, Paris #27
£370 $573 €555 La taverne (14x18cm-6x7in) st. pencil ink prov. 7-Dec-2 Galerie du Rhone, Sion #108/R (S.FR 850)
£377 $581 €600 Lorette (17x12cm-7x5in) ink dr prov. 27-Oct-2 Muizon & Le Coent, Paris #45/R
£435 $674 €653 Prostituees et leur souteneur. Scene napoleonienne. pencil ink dr pair prov. 7-Dec-2 Galerie du Rhone, Sion #109/R (S.FR 1000)
£461 $746 €700 L'attelage (20x27cm-8x11in) Indian ink wash prov. 22-Jan-3 Tajan, Paris #14/R
£550 $897 €825 Battle of Inkerman (20x46cm-8x18in) i. pencil ink. 29-Jan-3 Sotheby's, Olympia #321/R
£556 $917 €800 Deux femmes sur le pas d'une porte (20x15cm-8x6in) i.verso col ink wash. 1-Jul-3 Rossini, Paris #22
£625 $1031 €900 Elegante a la capeline (18x14cm-7x6in) wash W/C. 1-Jul-3 Rossini, Paris #30
£638 $1066 €900 Les trois lorettes (15x18cm-6x7in) Indian ink brown wash W/C. 20-Jun-3 Piasa, Paris #41b
£680 $1082 €1000 Deux danseuse dans un cabaret (19x27cm-7x11in) W/C pen ink over crayon. 24-Mar-3 Tajan, Paris #135/R
£680 $1082 €1000 Femme de face (19x13cm-7x5in) wash over crayon. 24-Mar-3 Tajan, Paris #147
£694 $1146 €1000 Deux femmes en robes courtes au cabaret (17x18cm-7x7in) wash crayon. 1-Jul-3 Rossini, Paris #26
£696 $1078 €1044 Le cavalier anglais (14x21cm-6x8in) wash over pencil Indian ink prov. 9-Dec-2 Philippe Schuler, Zurich #4163 (S.FR 1600)
£705 $1093 €1100 Scene de rue (12x16cm-5x6in) ink wash exhib. 9-Dec-2 Beaussant & Lefèvre, Paris #56/R
£705 $1093 €1100 Deux lorettes (17x23cm-7x9in) pen ink wsh. 4-Dec-2 Piasa, Paris #126
£750 $1200 €1125 Group of officers. Man on horse back (17x13cm-7x5in) pen ink brown wash two. 14-May-3 Doyle, New York #32 est:500-700
£773 $1221 €1160 Two riders (12x14cm-5x6in) wash pen ink dr. 29-Nov-2 Zofingen, Switzerland #2340 (S.FR 1800)
£833 $1375 €1200 Elegante au manchon (19x15cm-7x6in) W/C. 1-Jul-3 Rossini, Paris #21/R
£833 $1375 €1200 Elegante (29x22cm-11x9in) pen brown ink wash graphite. 1-Jul-3 Rossini, Paris #23/R
£833 $1375 €1200 La discussion, Quatre femmes et un homme (18x22cm-7x9in) pen brown ink black wash. 1-Jul-3 Rossini, Paris #29

£864 $1227 €1400 Jeune fille au piano (14x19cm-6x7in) Chinese ink wash dr. 16-Mar-3 Eric Pillon, Calais #81/R
£870 $1348 €1305 La cavalcade (20x32cm-8x13in) W/C wash Indian ink prov. 9-Dec-2 Philippe Schuler, Zurich #4164/R (S.FR 2000)
£880 $1416 €1320 Two women in theatre box (19x13cm-7x5in) Indian ink wash. 7-May-3 Dobiaschofsky, Bern #1139/R (S.FR 1900)
£972 $1604 €1400 Deux femmes au salon (23x30cm-9x12in) pen brown ink wash graphite. 1-Jul-3 Rossini, Paris #25/R
£1020 $1621 €1500 Elegante de profil (19x12cm-7x5in) W/C over crayon. 24-Mar-3 Tajan, Paris #145
£1043 $1617 €1565 La Daumont Imperial au bois (12x27cm-5x11in) W/C Indian ink prov. 9-Dec-2 Philippe Schuler, Zurich #4162/R est:2000-2500 (S.FR 2400)
£1111 $1578 €1800 Cafe de Tous les Plaisirs (21x29cm-8x11in) W/C wash. 16-Mar-3 Eric Pillon, Calais #82/R
£1184 $1918 €1800 Caleche a Constantinople (25x33cm-10x13in) W/C Indian ink prov. 22-Jan-3 Tajan, Paris #10/R est:2000-3000
£1225 $1948 €1800 Femme debout (25x18cm-10x7in) W/C pen ink. 24-Mar-3 Tajan, Paris #131
£1225 $1948 €1800 Femme au chale rouge (21x13cm-8x5in) W/C over crayon. 24-Mar-3 Tajan, Paris #146
£1319 $2177 €1900 Jeune femme au bouquet dans une loge de theatre (15x14cm-6x6in) W/C exhib. 1-Jul-3 Rossini, Paris #24/R
£1361 $2164 €2000 Couple (28x20cm-11x8in) W/C over crayon. 24-Mar-3 Tajan, Paris #137
£1361 $2164 €2000 Femme au corset lace (23x18cm-9x7in) W/C pen ink. 24-Mar-3 Tajan, Paris #138/R
£1389 $2292 €2000 Elegante au manchon soulevant sa robe (39x25cm-15x10in) pen brown ink W/C exhib. 1-Jul-3 Rossini, Paris #16/R
£1389 $2292 €2000 Groupe de trois femmes et deux soldats (19x28cm-7x11in) pen col wash exhib. 1-Jul-3 Rossini, Paris #20/R
£1528 $2521 €2200 Femme au bouquet dans une loge (13x15cm-5x6in) W/C. 1-Jul-3 Rossini, Paris #15/R
£1652 $2561 €2478 Le carosse de S M la Reine Victoria tournant sous les arbres (22x39cm-9x15in) W/C exhib.prov. 9-Dec-2 Philippe Schuler, Zurich #4161/R est:4000-5000 (S.FR 3800)
£1667 $2750 €2400 Couple de buveurs et servante (20x33cm-8x13in) pen col ink wash. 1-Jul-3 Rossini, Paris #28/R
£1710 $2771 €2600 Cavalier et cavaliere, en fond, un attelage (19x30cm-7x12in) W/C prov. 22-Jan-3 Tajan, Paris #8/R est:3000-4000
£1776 $2877 €2700 Cortege d'officiers a cheval, en fond un defile de troupes (22x32cm-9x13in) mono.i. W/C Indian ink prov. 22-Jan-3 Tajan, Paris #13/R est:3000-4000
£1776 $2877 €2700 Deux elegantes a l'ombrelle dans un caleche (25x33cm-10x13in) W/C Indian ink prov. 22-Jan-3 Tajan, Paris #15/R est:3000-4000
£1800 $3006 €2610 Queen Victoria's carriage in a park (22x39cm-9x15in) W/C over pen brown ink prov.exhib. 9-Jul-3 Sotheby's, London #140/R est:2000-3000
£1842 $2984 €2800 Groupes de femmes Europeennes, Espagnoles et Orientales (25x33cm-10x13in) W/C Indian ink prov. 22-Jan-3 Tajan, Paris #12/R est:2000-3000
£1905 $3029 €2800 Hommes en galante compagnie (14x21cm-6x8in) W/C over crayon. 24-Mar-3 Tajan, Paris #136
£1905 $3029 €2800 Femme assise dans un fauteuil (20x16cm-8x6in) W/C pen ink. 24-Mar-3 Tajan, Paris #143/R
£1905 $3029 €2800 Deux hommes et une femme conversant (19x16cm-7x6in) pen ink W/C. 24-Mar-3 Tajan, Paris #141/R
£1905 $3029 €2800 Femme en robe noire decolletee (33x21cm-13x8in) W/C pen ink. 24-Mar-3 Tajan, Paris #139/R
£2000 $3160 €3100 Elegantes (20x28cm-8x11in) ink wash. 18-Dec-2 Ferri, Paris #73
£2041 $3245 €3000 Elegantes passant devant un cafe (16x21cm-6x8in) W/C pen ink. 24-Mar-3 Tajan, Paris #133/R
£2041 $3245 €3000 Femme relevant le bas de sa robe (24x17cm-9x7in) W/C. 24-Mar-3 Tajan, Paris #140/R
£2361 $3896 €3400 Deux elegantes (26x19cm-10x7in) col ink wash. 1-Jul-3 Rossini, Paris #18/R
£2381 $3786 €3500 Deux femmes et un homme dans un cafe (15x18cm-6x7in) W/C pen ink. 24-Mar-3 Tajan, Paris #132
£2721 $4327 €4000 Quatre figures (16x13cm-6x5in) s. W/C pen ink. 24-Mar-3 Tajan, Paris #142/R
£3092 $5009 €4700 Espagnoles a la mantille et hidalgo (33x25cm-13x10in) W/C Indian ink prov. 22-Jan-3 Tajan, Paris #11/R est:4000-5000
£3402 $5409 €5000 Filles (14x20cm-6x8in) mono. pen ink wash. 24-Mar-3 Tajan, Paris #152/R
£3742 $5950 €5500 Femme a l'ombrelle (27x18cm-11x7in) W/C pen ink. 24-Mar-3 Tajan, Paris #130/R
£4082 $6491 €6000 Attelage au galop (20x31cm-8x12in) pen ink W/C. 24-Mar-3 Tajan, Paris #134/R
£4082 $6491 €6000 Rencontre pendant la promenade (22x35cm-9x14in) W/C pen ink. 24-Mar-3 Tajan, Paris #148/R
£5102 $8112 €7500 Caleche (20x30cm-8x12in) W/C pen ink over crayon prov. 24-Mar-3 Tajan, Paris #144/R

GUYS, Constantin (attrib) (1802-1892) French
Works on paper
£449 $704 €700 Portrait de femme (19x12cm-7x5in) ink wash. 13-Dec-2 Piasa, Paris #136
£580 $934 €870 Figures in a horse drawn carriage (15x20cm-6x8in) pen ink W/C. 19-Feb-3 Mallams, Oxford #347
£1200 $1872 €1800 Study of a woman in a red dress (40x23cm-16x9in) W/C over pencil prov. 26-Mar-3 Sotheby's, Olympia #256/R est:1200-1800

GUZMAN, Juan Bautista de (19th C) Spanish
£6000 $9540 €9000 Farwell (141x89cm-56x35in) s.d.90. 20-Mar-3 Christie's, Kensington #86/R est:4000-6000

GUZZARDI, Giuseppe (?-1914) Italian
£470 $771 €705 Drummer ready for battle (30x21cm-12x8in) s. 5-Jun-3 Christie's, Kensington #632
£861 $1309 €1292 Girl wearing white silk dress holding a fan (29x20cm-11x8in) s. 27-Aug-2 Rasmussen, Copenhagen #1630/R (D.KR 10000)

GUZZARDI, Rudolph (1903-1962) Italian/American
£577 $900 €866 Firenze (20x25cm-8x10in) canvasboard painted c.1950. 19-Oct-2 David Dike, Dallas #348/R

GWERK, Edmund (1895-1956) Czechoslovakian
Works on paper
£441 $626 €662 Train (20x28cm-8x11in) pastel pencil exec.c.1928-32. 26-Mar-2 SOGA, Bratislava #46/R (SL.K 28000)

GWYNNE, Marjorie Campbell (1886-1958) Australian
£600 $966 €870 Prickly pears (44x46cm-17x18in) s. 12-May-3 Joel, Victoria #314/R est:800-1200 (A.D 1500)

GWYNNE-JONES, Allan (1892-1982) British
£7400 $11692 €11100 Field poppies and hawkweed (31x44cm-12x17in) s.d.1934 i. verso. 4-Apr-3 Moore Allen & Innocent, Cirencester #656/R est:3000-5000

GYANINY, Geo (?) ?
£316 $500 €500 Rue de Moufti, Tunis (35x27cm-14x11in) s. panel. 28-Nov-2 Piasa, Paris #35
£816 $1298 €1200 Rue de Moufti, Tunisie (35x27cm-14x11in) s. panel. 24-Mar-3 Rabourdin & Choppin de Janvry, Paris #209/R

GYARMATHY, Tihamer (1915-) Hungarian
£2064 $3220 €3096 Hot afternoon, 1983 (91x81cm-36x32in) s.verso. 11-Sep-2 Kieselbach, Budapest #121/R (H.F 800000)
£2420 $3752 €3630 Middle ages (80x70cm-31x28in) s. 6-Dec-2 Kieselbach, Budapest #128/R (H.F 900000)
£2689 $4168 €3899 Relations (70x60cm-28x24in) s.i.d.984 verso lit. 9-Dec-2 Mu Terem Galeria, Budapest #107/R est:950000 (H.F 1000000)
£6454 $10004 €9358 Looking upward (50x40cm-20x16in) s.i.d.949 verso. 9-Dec-2 Mu Terem Galeria, Budapest #96/R est:1100000 (H.F 2400000)

GYENES, Gitta (1888-1960) Hungarian
£1748 $2709 €2535 Water-mill (47x57cm-19x22in) s. 9-Dec-2 Mu Terem Galeria, Budapest #166/R est:420000 (H.F 650000)

GYLDEN, Emma (1835-1874) Finnish
£1069 $1657 €1700 Winter landscape (28x49cm-11x19in) s. 6-Oct-2 Bukowskis, Helsinki #175/R est:700

GYNGELL, Albert (fl.1873-1892) British
£1900 $2945 €2850 Bank of wild flowers, near Malvern (89x58cm-35x23in) s.d.1892. 6-Dec-2 Biddle & Webb, Birmingham #264

GYOKUDO, Uragami (1745-1820) Japanese
Works on paper
£50314 $80000 €75471 Half the sky is misty rain (156x73cm-61x29in) s.d.1813 ink hanging scroll lit. 24-Mar-3 Christie's, Rockefeller NY #22/R est:50000-70000

GYOKURAN, Ikeno (1728-1784) Japanese
Works on paper
£252 $400 €378 Chrysanthemum (106x28cm-42x11in) s. ink hanging scroll. 24-Mar-3 Christie's, Rockefeller NY #24/R

GYOKUSHIN (19th C) Japanese
Sculpture
£3400 $5678 €4930 Lantern-vendor carrying a mass of lanterns on a stick (26cm-10in) s. ivory group. 18-Jun-3 Christie's, London #144 est:2000-3000

GYOKUSHU, Kuwayama (1746-1799) Japanese
Works on paper
£1384 $2200 €2076 Chrysanthemum. Bamboo in wind (124x28cm-49x11in) s. ink hanging scrolls pair. 24-Mar-3 Christie's, Rockefeller NY #31/R est:2000-3000

GYSBRECHTS, Franciscus (17th C) Dutch
£3659 $6000 €5489 Still life of a gilt ewer, gilt plate, prints and writing materials all resting on a draped table (84x59cm-33x23in) 29-May-3 Sotheby's, New York #118/R est:8000-12000

GYSELMAN, Warner (1827-?) Dutch
£1700 $2686 €2550 Winter landscape (14x20cm-6x8in) s. panel. 2-Dec-2 Bonhams, Bath #148/R est:600-800

GYSELS, Pieter (1621-1690) Flemish
£17073 $28000 €25610 Village scene with peasants strolling by a river bank (21x26cm-8x10in) copper. 30-May-3 Christie's, Rockefeller NY #16/R est:10000-15000
£27439 $45000 €41159 Village kermesse with horse-drawn cart in the foreground (18x24cm-7x9in) indis.s.i. copper. 30-May-3 Christie's, Rockefeller NY #15/R est:8000-12000
£36000 $56160 €54000 Vertumnus and Pomona set within the grounds of a villa (26x35cm-10x14in) copper prov. 10-Apr-3 Sotheby's, London #4/R est:20000
£75862 $119862 €110000 Paysage fluvial avec marche au poisson (26x38cm-10x15in) panel prov.lit. 2-Apr-3 Marc Kohn, Paris #17/R est:140000-160000

GYSELS, Pieter (attrib) (1621-1690) Flemish
£1154 $1800 €1731 Still life (53x74cm-21x29in) canvas on masonite. 20-Oct-2 Susanin's, Chicago #5049/R est:2000-3000
£17500 $27475 €26250 Village scene with figures bleaching linen in the foreground (30x41cm-12x16in) panel. 10-Dec-2 Sotheby's, Olympia #363/R est:6000-8000

GYSELS, Pieter and IMMENRAET, Philips Augustyn (17th C) Flemish
£16438 $25644 €24000 Resting in the park after the hunt (118x158cm-46x62in) prov. 8-Apr-3 Ansorena, Madrid #113/R est:24000

GYSIS, Nicolas (1842-1901) Greek
£2600 $4030 €3900 Woman in profile (8x7cm-3x3in) init. prov. 2-Oct-2 Sotheby's, London #78/R
£4025 $6279 €6400 Portrait of girl (30x21cm-12x8in) s. board lit. 20-Sep-2 Schloss Ahlden, Ahlden #1307/R est:6500
£4870 $7256 €7500 Farmstead (26x20cm-10x8in) mono. canvas on board. 26-Jun-2 Neumeister, Munich #745/R est:1500
£6494 $9675 €10000 Young woman sewing (18x14cm-7x6in) mono. i. verso. 26-Jun-2 Neumeister, Munich #744/R est:2000
£150000 $232500 €225000 Mourning in the forester's cottage (94x123cm-37x48in) s.d.1881 prov.exhib.lit. 2-Oct-2 Sotheby's, London #26/R est:150000-200000
Sculpture
£1700 $2635 €2550 Grief (13cm-5in) painted plaster exec.c.1898 prov. 2-Oct-2 Sotheby's, London #10/R
£2000 $3100 €3000 Girl shivering (14cm-6in) painted plaster exec.c.1898 prov. 2-Oct-2 Sotheby's, London #9/R
£3000 $4650 €4500 Grief (13cm-5in) painted plaster prov. 2-Oct-2 Sotheby's, London #8/R
£3000 $4650 €4500 Woman by spring (20cm-8in) painted plaster exec.c.1898 prov. 2-Oct-2 Sotheby's, London #6/R
£3200 $4960 €4800 Man grappling with animal (16cm-6in) painted plaster exec.c.1898 prov. 2-Oct-2 Sotheby's, London #7/R
Works on paper
£10000 $15500 €15000 Three drapery studies (21x25cm-8x10in) init. pencil chk set of 3. 2-Oct-2 Sotheby's, London #15/R est:6000-8000

GYURKOVITS, Frantisek (1876-1968) Hungarian?
£394 $575 €591 Still life with flowers (96x82cm-38x32in) painted c.1935. 4-Jun-2 SOGA, Bratislava #16/R est:22000 (SL.K 25000)
£441 $644 €662 In the garden (72x83cm-28x33in) painted c.1925. 4-Jun-2 SOGA, Bratislava #15/R est:28000 (SL.K 28000)

HAAG, Carl (1820-1915) German
Works on paper
£500 $800 €750 Fish market, Rome; a busy street under an archway with monks buying fish (59x43cm-23x17in) s.d.1849 W/C. 11-Mar-3 Bonhams, Oxford #48/R
£1200 $1884 €1800 Arabs and camels resting in the desert (18x51cm-7x20in) s.d.1867 pencil W/C. 16-Apr-3 Christie's, Kensington #1073/R est:300-500
£1500 $2445 €2250 Armenian priest (77x56cm-30x22in) W/C htd bodycol arched top prov. 29-Jan-3 Sotheby's, Olympia #272/R est:1500-2500
£1600 $2496 €2400 Bedwaeen outpost (48x33cm-19x13in) s.i. W/C pencil. 17-Oct-2 Lawrence, Crewkerne #411/R est:1500-2000
£1600 $2496 €2400 Courtyard in Cairo (24x34cm-9x13in) s.i.d.1859 W/C pencil. 17-Oct-2 Lawrence, Crewkerne #412 est:2000-3000
£2800 $4536 €4200 Hassan Ben Moosa, a Bedowee of the Howareen Tribe (37x26cm-15x10in) s. W/C scratching out. 23-Jan-3 Christie's, Kensington #339/R est:700-1000
£3000 $4680 €4500 Coffee bearer (29x22cm-11x9in) s. W/C over pencil htd bodycol. 15-Oct-2 Sotheby's, London #166/R est:1500-2000

HAAG, Jean Paul (19th C) French
£1965 $3066 €2948 Poultry yard (21x26cm-8x10in) s. 20-Nov-2 Fischer, Luzern #1094/R est:4600-5000 (S.FR 4500)

HAAGA, Eduard (19th C) German
£268 $432 €400 Church on a winter's night (25x17cm-10x7in) panel prov. 18-Feb-3 Sotheby's, Amsterdam #298

HAAGE, Jean (19th C) French
£340 $568 €493 Portrait of an officer (63x54cm-25x21in) indis sig.d.1897. 8-Jul-3 Bonhams, Knightsbridge #235/R

HAAGEN, Joris van der (c.1615-1669) Dutch
£19000 $31730 €27550 Wooded landscape with a stag hunt (37x50cm-15x20in) s. panel prov. 9-Jul-3 Christie's, London #40/R est:10000-15000

HAALA, Anton (19th C) Austrian
£400 $628 €600 Portrait of a gentleman in black coat and cravat. Portrait of a gentleman seated (27x21cm-11x8in) s.d.1838-39 panel pair. 16-Apr-3 Christie's, Kensington #555/R

HAALAND, Erling (20th C) Norwegian
£297 $458 €446 Coastal landscape with steam boat (34x60cm-13x24in) s. painted 1932. 28-Oct-2 Blomqvist, Lysaker #1077 (N.KR 3500)
£401 $626 €602 Steam boat by the coast (34x60cm-13x24in) s. painted 1932. 23-Sep-2 Blomqvist, Lysaker #1068 (N.KR 4700)

HAALAND, Lars Laurits (1855-1938) Norwegian
£1645 $2517 €2468 Sailing vessel by the coast (27x40cm-11x16in) s. painted 1910. 26-Aug-2 Blomqvist, Lysaker #1136/R est:18000-22000 (N.KR 19000)
£3122 $4871 €4683 Boat in outport (33x80cm-13x31in) s.d.1913. 21-Oct-2 Blomqvist, Oslo #311/R est:40000-50000 (N.KR 36000)
£3122 $5120 €4527 Seascape with boat in rough seas (45x70cm-18x28in) s.d.1901. 2-Jun-3 Blomqvist, Oslo #211/R (N.KR 34000)
£3413 $5324 €5120 Among the islets (69x134cm-27x53in) s. 23-Sep-2 Blomqvist, Lysaker #1069/R est:50000-60000 (N.KR 40000)
£3620 $5864 €5430 Pilot boat by rugged coast (39x55cm-15x22in) s.d.1905. 26-May-3 Grev Wedels Plass, Oslo #8/R est:30000-50000 (N.KR 40000)
£5882 $9294 €8823 Coastal landscape with boats (65x120cm-26x47in) s.d.1921. 2-Dec-2 Blomqvist, Oslo #314/R est:50000-60000 (N.KR 68000)
£6887 $11295 €9986 Regatta with small boats in fresh breeze (56x81cm-22x32in) s.indis.d.190. 2-Jun-3 Blomqvist, Oslo #30/R est:80000-100000 (N.KR 75000)

HAALAND, Tore (20th C) Norwegian
£654 $1027 €981 Composition (59x63cm-23x25in) 25-Nov-2 Blomqvist, Lysaker #1091/R (N.KR 7500)

HAALKE, Hjalmar (1894-1964) Norwegian
£316 $499 €474 Spring evening, Lillehammer (46x55cm-18x22in) s.d.1951 i.verso exhib. 17-Dec-2 Grev Wedels Plass, Oslo #238 (N.KR 3600)
£368 $582 €552 Schoolboy musician with tuba (70x50cm-28x20in) init.d.1953. 17-Dec-2 Grev Wedels Plass, Oslo #239/R (N.KR 4200)

HAAN, J K de (18th C) Flemish
£1939 $3142 €2812 Still life of fruit (47x38cm-19x15in) s. panel. 25-May-3 Uppsala Auktionskammare, Uppsala #9/R est:20000-25000 (S.KR 25000)

HAANEN, Adriana (1814-1895) Dutch
£5063 $7899 €8000 Still life with fruit on a plinth (39x33cm-15x13in) s.d.1845 panel. 21-Oct-2 Glerum, Amsterdam #192/R est:5000-7000
£15278 $24292 €22000 Worthy tribute (76x101cm-30x40in) s. exhib. 29-Apr-3 Christie's, Amsterdam #205/R est:30000-50000

£40278 $64042 €58000 Roses by a stream (39x54cm-15x21in) s. panel. 29-Apr-3 Christie's, Amsterdam #203/R est:40000-60000
£50314 $77484 €80000 Roses in a basket (51x64cm-20x25in) s. 23-Oct-2 Christie's, Amsterdam #108/R est:40000-60000
£86806 $138021 €125000 July rozen (72x100cm-28x39in) s.d.1862 px/. 29-Apr-3 Christie's, Amsterdam #190/R est:70000-90000

HAANEN, Cecil van (1844-1914) Dutch
£897 $1391 €1400 Half-length portrait of a girl with gauze scarf around her neck (55x45cm-22x18in) s.d.1884 canvas on canvas. 4-Dec-2 Neumeister, Munich #748/R

HAANEN, Elisabeth Alida (1809-1845) Dutch
£3145 $4843 €5000 Kitchen scene (53x45cm-21x18in) s.d.1836. 22-Oct-2 Sotheby's, Amsterdam #47/R est:5000-8000

HAANEN, Georg Gillis van (1807-1876) Dutch
£352 $567 €500 Portrait of a gentleman with book (38x20cm-15x8in) s. panel. 7-May-3 Vendue Huis, Gravenhage #358
£1509 $2340 €2400 Landscape at dusk (34x59cm-13x23in) s.d.1855. 29-Oct-2 Dorotheum, Vienna #85/R est:2400-2600
£4452 $6945 €6500 Figures on a frozen river in front of a ruin (20x26cm-8x10in) s. panel prov. 14-Apr-3 Glerum, Amsterdam #15/R est:2500-3500

HAANEN, Remi van (1812-1894) Dutch
£1538 $2385 €2400 River landscape with windmill in evening sun (18x32cm-7x13in) s.d.890. 5-Dec-2 Dr Fritz Nagel, Stuttgart #658/R est:1500
£3165 $5000 €5000 Landscape with figures (41x56cm-16x22in) s. oil over pencil panel. 28-Nov-2 Dorotheum, Vienna #195/R est:5000-6000
£3546 $5745 €5000 Dutch landscape in moonlight (18x32cm-7x13in) s.d.890. 22-May-3 Dorotheum, Vienna #58/R est:4500-5000
£5380 $8500 €8500 Mill near Theist (48x64cm-19x25in) 28-Nov-2 Dorotheum, Vienna #27/R est:8500-9500
£7500 $11700 €11250 Sunset over the Bosphorus (72x111cm-28x44in) s. 15-Oct-2 Sotheby's, London #81/R est:8000-12000
Works on paper
£743 $1159 €1100 On the water (33x53cm-13x21in) s. W/C. 28-Mar-3 Dorotheum, Vienna #236/R

HAAR, Herman van der (1867-1938) Dutch
£300 $465 €450 Corn stooks in a field (34x51cm-13x20in) s. 22-Jul-2 Bonhams, Bury St Edmunds #436

HAAREN, Dirk Johannes van (1878-1953) Dutch
£379 $603 €550 Cows in a landscape (15x22cm-6x9in) s. panel. 10-Mar-3 Sotheby's, Amsterdam #138

HAARLEM SCHOOL (17th C) Dutch
£38790 $62839 €56246 Vanitas scene with Jesus as a child, Resurrection scene in background (66x51cm-26x20in) panel prov. 26-May-3 Bukowskis, Stockholm #390/R est:600000-800000 (S.KR 500000)

HAARTMAN, Axel (1877-1969) Finnish
£471 $772 €720 Landscape with elder (32x40cm-13x16in) s.d.1944. 9-Feb-3 Bukowskis, Helsinki #243/R
£497 $815 €760 Flowers in vase (74x59cm-29x23in) s.i.d.1960. 9-Feb-3 Bukowskis, Helsinki #242/R
£556 $911 €850 Green landscape (55x45cm-22x18in) s.i.d.1957. 9-Feb-3 Bukowskis, Helsinki #247/R
£588 $965 €900 Colourful garden (44x40cm-17x16in) s.i.d.1961. 9-Feb-3 Bukowskis, Helsinki #244/R
£696 $1086 €1100 On the park bench - old lady resting (75x64cm-30x25in) s.d.1941. 12-Sep-2 Hagelstam, Helsinki #986/R
£719 $1151 €1000 Aabo (28x40cm-11x16in) s. 17-May-3 Hagelstam, Helsinki #159/R
£752 $1233 €1150 Quiet bay (58x48cm-23x19in) s.i.d.1922. 9-Feb-3 Bukowskis, Helsinki #246/R
£792 $1228 €1260 Landscape from Kimito skerries (58x82cm-23x32in) s.i.d.1951. 6-Oct-2 Bukowskis, Helsinki #176/R
£850 $1393 €1300 Winter in Naadendal (64x47cm-25x19in) s.i.d.1950. 9-Feb-3 Bukowskis, Helsinki #245/R
£863 $1381 €1200 Aabo (60x50cm-24x20in) s.d.1908. 17-May-3 Hagelstam, Helsinki #160/R
£1408 $2268 €2000 Coastal landscape from Kimito (106x79cm-42x31in) s.i.d.1951 board. 10-May-3 Bukowskis, Helsinki #178/R est:1000-1500

HAAS, Ernst (1921-1986) ?
Photographs
£2435 $3750 €3653 Grand Central Station, New York (16x24cm-6x9in) photograph lit. 22-Oct-2 Sotheby's, New York #199/R est:2000-3000

HAAS, Johannes Hubertus Leonardus de (1832-1908) Flemish
£1310 $2083 €1900 Summer landscape with cows by trees (31x47cm-12x19in) s. panel. 8-Mar-3 Arnold, Frankfurt #596/R est:800
£1769 $2812 €2600 Castle and landscape (45x64cm-18x25in) s. panel. 24-Mar-3 Bernaerts, Antwerp #54/R est:1000-1500
£1887 $2906 €3000 Cows in a meadow (29x38cm-11x15in) s.d.50 panel. 22-Oct-2 Sotheby's, Amsterdam #100/R est:3000-5000
£2115 $3279 €3300 Cows at the shore (31x47cm-12x19in) s. panel. 7-Dec-2 De Vuyst, Lokeren #527/R est:3500-4500
£3767 $5877 €5500 Troupeau au coucher e soleil (83x65cm-33x26in) s. panel. 14-Apr-3 Horta, Bruxelles #217/R est:5000-7000
£4444 $7378 €6444 Cows in a pasture (70x91cm-28x36in) s. panel. 16-Jun-3 Waddingtons, Toronto #254a/R est:4000-5000 (C.D 10000)
£7547 $11623 €12000 Cows in a sunlit river landscape. Cows in a meadow (61x49cm-24x19in) s. panel pair prov. 23-Oct-2 Christie's, Amsterdam #207/R est:14000-18000

HAAS, Johannes Hubertus Leonardus de and ROFFIAEN, Jean (19th C) Flemish
£1806 $2871 €2600 Cattle grazing by a sandy track in summer near Genck (24x34cm-9x13in) s.i. panel. 29-Apr-3 Christie's, Amsterdam #24/R est:3000-4000

HAAS, M F H de (1832-1895) Dutch
£5944 $8500 €8916 Marinescape with figures at rocky cliff (30x48cm-12x19in) s. board. 11-Dec-1 Lincoln, Orange #466

HAAS, Mauritz F H de (1832-1895) Dutch
£1266 $2000 €1899 After the storm (23x46cm-9x18in) s. i.verso prov. 24-Apr-3 Shannon's, Milford #178/R est:2000-3000
£1519 $2400 €2279 Ships near a rocky coast (18x25cm-7x10in) s. board prov. 24-Apr-3 Shannon's, Milford #1/R est:3000-5000
£5901 $9500 €8852 Narranganset, coastal scene with sailboats (36x56cm-14x22in) prov.exhib. 18-Feb-3 John Moran, Pasadena #52 est:6000-8000
£8642 $14000 €12531 Dutch fishing craft off the coast (35x51cm-14x20in) s.d.1880. 29-Jul-3 Christie's, Rockefeller NY #149/R est:6000-8000
£9877 $16000 €14322 Distant sails (36x61cm-14x24in) s. 29-Jul-3 Christie's, Rockefeller NY #151/R est:7000-9000
£15190 $24000 €22785 Sailing by moonlight (46x76cm-18x30in) s. 24-Apr-3 Shannon's, Milford #103/R est:15000-25000
£22785 $36000 €34178 View off the coast (61x102cm-24x40in) s. prov. 24-Apr-3 Shannon's, Milford #60/R est:20000-30000
£27273 $42000 €40910 Schooner off the coast (51x51cm-20x20in) s. prov. 24-Oct-2 Shannon's, Milford #88/R est:20000-30000

HAAS, Michel (1934-) ?
Works on paper
£1154 $1812 €1800 Untitled (137x125cm-54x49in) s. mixed media prov. 15-Dec-2 Perrin, Versailles #156/R
£1793 $2833 €2600 Mother and child (102x128cm-40x50in) mixed media prov. 4-Apr-3 Tajan, Paris #259/R

HAAS, Richard (1936-) American
Works on paper
£1076 $1700 €1614 Indian treaty room, old executive office building. Borough Hall, Brooklyn (94x69cm-37x27in) s.d.86 pastel pencil board prov. 13-Nov-2 Sotheby's, New York #257/R est:1800-2200

HAAS, William F de (1830-1880) Dutch
£19014 $27000 €28521 Distant sails (38x66cm-15x26in) 8-Aug-1 Barridorf, Portland #161/R est:20000-30000

HAASE, Ludwig (1868-1944) Austrian
Works on paper
£576 $921 €800 View of Linz across river (21x28cm-8x11in) s. W/C. 14-May-3 Dorotheum, Linz #456/R

HAASE, Ove (1894-1989) Danish
£686 $1070 €1029 Still life of yellow roses in glass vase (53x41cm-21x16in) s.d.1920-21. 11-Nov-2 Rasmussen, Vejle #566/R (D.KR 8000)

HAAXMAN, Pieter (1854-1937) Dutch
£29000 $45530 €43500 Daydreams (105x205cm-41x81in) s. prov. 19-Nov-2 Sotheby's, London #129/R est:20000-30000

HAAXMAN, Pieter Alardus (1814-1887) Dutch
£694 $1146 €1000 Serenade (23x20cm-9x8in) s. panel. 1-Jul-3 Christie's, Amsterdam #30

HABBE, Nicolai (1827-1889) Danish
£559 $899 €839 From an Italian prison (21x17cm-8x7in) metal. 22-Feb-3 Rasmussen, Havnen #2357/R (D.KR 6200)

HABER, Robert (1929-) South African
Works on paper
£250 $408 €363 View of Table mountain, Cape Town (52x73cm-20x29in) s. gouache htd white. 17-Jul-3 Tennants, Leyburn #742

HABER, Shamai (1922-1995) Polish
£400 $636 €600 Abstract composition (64x50cm-25x20in) s.d.59 acrylic gold paint. 18-Mar-3 Bonhams, Knightsbridge #84

HABERJAHN, Gabriel (1890-1956) Swiss
£324 $522 €486 La Thielle bei Yverdon (50x70cm-20x28in) s. i. verso. 7-May-3 Dobiaschofsky, Bern #620/R (S.FR 700)

HABERMANN, Franz von (1788-1866) Czech/Austrian
Works on paper
£4000 $6480 €6000 Military scene (50x72cm-20x28in) s. indis i. W/C. 21-May-3 Sotheby's, London #11/R est:4000-6000

HABERMANN, Hugo von (1849-1929) German
£256 $397 €400 Judith (60x51cm-24x20in) s.d.75. 5-Dec-2 Neumeister, Munich #2802/R

HABL, Willy (1888-1964) German
£260 $379 €400 North sea coastal scene with four men pushing a boat onto land (34x42cm-13x17in) s. 15-Jun-2 Hans Stahl, Hamburg #179

HACCOU, Johannes Cornelis (1798-1839) Dutch
Works on paper
£705 $1093 €1100 Dutch sailing ship off coast (17x23cm-7x9in) s.d.1819 or 1829 W/C prov. 7-Dec-2 Ketterer, Hamburg #7/R

HACKAERT, Jan (1629-1699) Dutch
£12739 $19873 €20000 Wooded river landscape with fishermen and a man with a donkey (68x57cm-27x22in) s. prov. 5-Nov-2 Sotheby's, Amsterdam #294/R est:20000-30000

HACKAERT, Jan (attrib) (1629-1699) Dutch
£7000 $10850 €10500 Stag shooting. Duck shooting (45x35cm-18x14in) panel prov. two. 6-Dec-2 Lyon & Turnbull, Edinburgh #20/R est:6000-8000
Works on paper
£455 $650 €683 Village at the edge of a wooded landscape (28x33cm-11x13in) pen black ink col wash. 23-Jan-3 Swann Galleries, New York #201/R

HACKAERT, Jan (circle) (1629-1699) Dutch
£6800 $11356 €9860 Wooded landscape with sportsman and dog. A stag hunt with three sportsmen (44x35cm-17x14in) bears sig. panel. 9-Jul-3 Bonhams, New Bond Street #154/R est:8000-12000

HACKENBERGER, Dolores (?) American?
£264 $425 €396 Farmhouse with quilts on the wash line with barn in the background (58x28cm-23x11in) s.i. 21-Feb-3 York Town, York #1285

HACKENSOLLNER, Camillo (19th C) Austrian
£1338 $2154 €1900 Hunting celebration (103x137cm-41x54in) s.d.1857. 10-May-3 Berlinghof, Heidelberg #243/R est:1500

HACKER, Arthur (1858-1919) British
£7296 $11528 €10944 Study for imprisoned spring (42x32cm-17x13in) init.i. panel prov. 3-Apr-3 Heffel, Vancouver #39/R est:16000-20000 (C.D 17000)
£65000 $107900 €97500 Musicienne du silence (102x127cm-40x50in) s.d.1900 exhib.lit. 11-Jun-3 Christie's, London #15/R est:50000-70000
£80000 $127200 €120000 Imprisoned spring (92x71cm-36x28in) s.i.d.1911 exhib. 19-Mar-3 Sotheby's, London #279/R est:40000-60000

HACKER, Eugen (19th C) German
£377 $589 €600 Landscape with river and farmstead (16x21cm-6x8in) s. panel. 20-Sep-2 Karlheinz Kaupp, Staufen #2083

HACKER, Horst (1842-1906) German
£288 $447 €450 Fjord landscape on spring day (29x50cm-11x20in) s.i. 6-Dec-2 Michael Zeller, Lindau #777
£513 $795 €800 Gosau lake with view of the Dachstein mountains (59x85cm-23x33in) i. i.verso canvas on canvas. 4-Dec-2 Neumeister, Munich #749
£2017 $3268 €2925 Evening at the graveyard (91x135cm-36x53in) s.i. prov. 25-May-3 Uppsala Auktionskammare, Uppsala #54/R est:15000-20000 (S.KR 26000)

HACKERT, Carl Ludwig (1740-1800) German
£1408 $2338 €2000 River landscape by moonlight (29x39cm-11x15in) s.d.1777 gouache paper on card. 11-Jun-3 Dorotheum, Vienna #151/R est:2500-3500

HACKERT, E (?) ?
Works on paper
£1203 $1900 €1805 Antechamber of the King's apartment in the Castle of Sagan (209x295cm-82x116in) i. W/C bodycol htd gold prov.lit. 1-Apr-3 Christie's, Rockefeller NY #386/R est:2000-3000

HACKERT, Jacob Philippe (1737-1807) German
£10690 $16890 €15500 Harvest at San Leucio (42x58cm-17x23in) i.d.1790 tempera card. 3-Apr-3 Porro, Milan #37/R est:22000
£140000 $233800 €203000 Rome, a distant view of Saint Peter's Basilica and the Vatican (77x91cm-30x36in) s.i.d.1770 prov.lit. 10-Jul-3 Sotheby's, London #64/R est:140000-180000
£250000 $417500 €362500 Panoramic landscape in Roman Campagna with distant prospect of Villa Albani (121x168cm-48x66in) s.d.1779. 10-Jul-3 Sotheby's, London #62/R est:150000-200000
Works on paper
£4200 $6678 €6300 Resting figure with dog under trees (66x51cm-26x20in) pen sepia W/C. 29-Apr-3 Sworder & Son, Bishops Stortford #382/R est:1500-2000
£5500 $9185 €7975 View of the River Po from the church of the Madonna del Pillone near Turin (34x45cm-13x18in) s.i. pencil grey wash. 8-Jul-3 Christie's, London #109/R est:3000-5000
£6800 $10812 €10200 Resting figures with a dog under a tree (66x50cm-26x20in) i. pen sepia W/C. 29-Apr-3 Sworder & Son, Bishops Stortford #383/R est:2000-3000

HACKMAN, Frederick James (fl.1908) British
£360 $569 €540 Mermaid, Rye (36x46cm-14x18in) s. 2-Dec-2 Gorringes, Lewes #2711

HACKSTOUN, William (fl.1896-1916) British
Works on paper
£1100 $1749 €1650 Lodge (34x44cm-13x17in) s.d.1889 pencil W/C. 6-Mar-3 Christie's, Kensington #148/R est:400-600

HADDEN, Nellie (fl.1885-1920) British
Works on paper
£1380 $2250 €2070 Blenheim spaniel by a door (24x30cm-9x12in) s. W/C. 11-Feb-3 Bonhams & Doyles, New York #193/R est:1000-1500
£3000 $4980 €4500 Royal favourites, Windsor (30x45cm-12x18in) init.d.1900 W/C. 12-Jun-3 Bonhams, New Bond Street #664/R est:3000-5000

HADDON, David W (fl.1884-1914) British
£270 $427 €405 Cornish fisher (33x23cm-13x9in) s.i.d.1889 panel. 24-Apr-3 Richardson & Smith, Whitby #202
£300 $471 €450 Portrait of a bearded gentleman (42x32cm-17x13in) s. board. 10-Dec-2 Lane, Penzance #217
£340 $534 €510 Grandpa's knee (12x14cm-5x6in) init. panel. 25-Nov-2 Bonhams, Chester #911
£340 $530 €510 Fisherman (59x49cm-23x19in) s. canvasboard oval. 26-Mar-3 Sotheby's, Olympia #27/R
£400 $632 €600 North Sea fisher (33x23cm-13x9in) s.i. panel. 24-Apr-3 Richardson & Smith, Whitby #207
£400 $668 €580 Cottage interior with old man seated by a window (23x18cm-9x7in) s. 20-Jun-3 Keys, Aylsham #752/R
£580 $916 €870 Scenes depicting figures in an interior (23x18cm-9x7in) s. board pair. 24-Apr-3 Richardson & Smith, Whitby #136
£920 $1472 €1380 Fish sale, portrait of a fisherman reading the Herald newspaper (29x22cm-11x9in) s.i. s.d.1890 verso. 11-Mar-3 David Duggleby, Scarborough #200/R
£1000 $1650 €1450 Little inquisitive (44x28cm-17x11in) s. s.i.d.1891 verso board. 1-Jul-3 Bearnes, Exeter #507/R est:600-900

HADDON, Trevor (1864-1941) British
£420 $664 €630 Fountain of the mosque, Cordoba (60x39cm-24x15in) s. 14-Nov-2 Bonhams, Edinburgh #327
£897 $1409 €1400 Peasants taking cattle to market in Gerona (47x39cm-19x15in) s. 21-Nov-2 Van Ham, Cologne #1649

£897 $1391 €1400 Jeune bergere et ses moutons (61x91cm-24x36in) 3-Dec-2 Campo & Campo, Antwerp #109
£1150 $1875 €1725 Venetian water carriers (54x75cm-21x30in) s. 11-Feb-3 Dickinson, Davy & Markham, Brigg #710/R est:300-500

HADENFELDT, Christian (1883-?) German
Works on paper
£481 $745 €750 Ship in Hamburg harbour (39x48cm-15x19in) s.i.d.1930 W/C board prov. 7-Dec-2 Ketterer, Hamburg #51/R

HADERER, Gerhard (?) Austrian
Works on paper
£949 $1472 €1500 Cigarette seller (25x29cm-10x11in) s. W/C pencil. 24-Sep-2 Wiener Kunst Auktionen, Vienna #338/R

HADJIMICHAIL, Theofilos (1871-1933) Greek
£30000 $47400 €45000 Amphora with flowers, Duck and cock (80x58cm-31x23in) double-sided painted c.1930. 1-Apr-3 Bonhams, New Bond Street #70 est:30000-40000

HAEBERLIN, Carl von (1832-1911) German
£943 $1472 €1500 Old blacksmith (22x25cm-9x10in) mono.d.83 canvas on board. 19-Sep-2 Dr Fritz Nagel, Stuttgart #938/R est:1800

HAEFLIGER, Leopold (1929-1989) Swiss
£262 $409 €393 Red landscape (30x40cm-12x16in) prov. 9-Nov-2 Galerie Gloggner, Luzern #74/R (S.FR 600)
£307 $497 €445 Girl's portrait (26x14cm-10x6in) s.d.1956 board prov. 24-May-3 Galerie Gloggner, Luzern #52 (S.FR 650)
£349 $545 €524 Autumn landscape (28x29cm-11x11in) s.d.74. 9-Nov-2 Galerie Gloggner, Luzern #67 (S.FR 800)
£371 $579 €557 Fasnacht - Old lady (30x20cm-12x8in) s.d.75 prov. 9-Nov-2 Galerie Gloggner, Luzern #69/R (S.FR 850)
£415 $647 €623 Winter landscape (24x40cm-9x16in) s.d.71 prov. 9-Nov-2 Galerie Gloggner, Luzern #68 (S.FR 950)
£472 $746 €708 Winter landscape with farmhouse and frozen lake (45x75cm-18x30in) s.d.1963. 29-Nov-2 Zofingen, Switzerland #2894 (S.FR 1100)
£480 $749 €720 Crucifixion with Maria and the Apostle John (46x25cm-18x10in) s.d.1961 panel prov. 9-Nov-2 Galerie Gloggner, Luzern #72 (S.FR 1100)
£524 $817 €786 Portrait of Anna Haefliger, wife of the artist (81x60cm-32x24in) s.d.75 prov. 9-Nov-2 Galerie Gloggner, Luzern #16 (S.FR 1200)
£655 $1022 €983 Landscape with pair of riders (75x95cm-30x37in) s.d.54 fibreboard prov. 9-Nov-2 Galerie Gloggner, Luzern #73/R (S.FR 1500)
£849 $1375 €1231 Park landscape with mansion (26x40cm-10x16in) s.d.74 board prov. 24-May-3 Galerie Gloggner, Luzern #57/R (S.FR 1800)
£1528 $2384 €2292 Crayfish on white cloth (52x67cm-20x26in) s.d.87. 20-Nov-2 Fischer, Luzern #1290/R est:4000-6000 (S.FR 3500)
£1698 $2751 €2462 Winter landscape (50x66cm-20x26in) s.d.82 prov. 24-May-3 Galerie Gloggner, Luzern #55 est:2500-2800 (S.FR 3600)
£1698 $2751 €2462 Waiter (73x46cm-29x18in) s.d.82 prov. 24-May-3 Galerie Gloggner, Luzern #56/R est:4000-4500 (S.FR 3600)
£1981 $3209 €2872 Burial (51x63cm-20x25in) s.d.73 prov. 24-May-3 Galerie Gloggner, Luzern #45 est:2800-3500 (S.FR 4200)
£4009 $6495 €5813 Boucherie (61x46cm-24x18in) s.d.70 prov. 24-May-3 Galerie Gloggner, Luzern #54/R est:3000-3500 (S.FR 8500)
Works on paper
£429 $678 €644 Clown (60x32cm-24x13in) s.d.1967 mixed media. 29-Nov-2 Zofingen, Switzerland #2895 (S.FR 1000)

HAEFLIGER, Paul (1914-1982) Australian/German
£268 $421 €402 Still life (26x33cm-10x13in) s.i.verso board. 15-Apr-3 Lawson Menzies, Sydney #151/R (A.D 700)
£287 $451 €431 Park building seen through gateway (25x40cm-10x16in) init. canvasboard prov. 15-Apr-3 Lawson Menzies, Sydney #245/R (A.D 750)
£300 $483 €450 Three figures (43x62cm-17x24in) s.d.68 board. 14-Jan-3 Bonhams, Knightsbridge #44
Works on paper
£264 $419 €396 Secret (46x29cm-18x11in) s.d.50 gouache. 5-May-3 Sotheby's, Melbourne #328 (A.D 680)

HAEFTEN, Nicolas van (attrib) (1663-1715) Dutch
£2270 $3518 €3405 Visit from the vicar (59x71cm-23x28in) 4-Dec-2 AB Stockholms Auktionsverk #1961/R est:35000-40000 (S.KR 32000)

HAEHNEL, Ernst Julius (1811-1891) German
Sculpture
£1400 $2184 €2100 Portrait statuette of Michelangelo (54cm-21in) s.i.d.1878 brown pat bronze lit. 9-Apr-3 Sotheby's, London #138/R est:1500-2500

HAELEN, John A (fl.1920-1930) American
£4487 $7000 €6731 Man carrying woman ashore as natives transport cargo (71x112cm-28x44in) s.d.1925. 9-Nov-2 Illustration House, New York #177/R est:4000-6000

HAEN, Abraham de I (17th C) Dutch
£13422 $21609 €20000 Landscape with chickens, turkey and a rabbit (171x203cm-67x80in) s.d.1638 prov.lit. 18-Feb-3 Sotheby's, Amsterdam #245/R est:15000-20000

HAENEL, Eduard G (19/20th C) ?
£633 $1000 €950 Forest landscape with ducks taking off (69x99cm-27x39in) painted c.1910. 15-Nov-2 Du Mouchelle, Detroit #2037/R

HAENSBERGEN, Jan van (1642-1705) Dutch
£3000 $4710 €4500 Italianate landscape with nymphs bathing (20x27cm-8x11in) panel prov.lit. 16-Dec-2 Sotheby's, London #38/R est:3000-4000
£3165 $4905 €5000 Woman bathing in rocky landscape (26x34cm-10x13in) panel. 25-Sep-2 Neumeister, Munich #484/R est:8000
£4400 $6820 €6600 Landscape with Venus and Cupid surprised by satyrs (19x24cm-7x9in) init. copper. 31-Oct-2 Sotheby's, Olympia #70/R est:2000-3000

HAERLE, Johann (19th C) Austrian
£321 $487 €500 Religious tableau from Rinn/Inntal (156x87cm-61x34in) s. canvas on panel. 11-Jul-2 Hugo Ruef, Munich #680/R

HAES, Carlos de (1829-1898) Spanish
£892 $1391 €1400 Landscape near Piedra, Spain (25x36cm-10x14in) 6-Nov-2 Vendue Huis, Gravenhage #553/R
£2308 $3646 €3600 Mill (30x39cm-12x15in) s. 14-Nov-2 Arte, Seville #378/R
£4605 $7461 €7000 Pond (24x32cm-9x13in) s. board. 21-Jan-3 Durán, Madrid #155/R
£4934 $7993 €7500 Landscape (15x22cm-6x9in) s. board. 21-Jan-3 Ansorena, Madrid #189/R est:6500
£11711 $18971 €17800 Well (33x50cm-13x20in) lit. 21-Jan-3 Ansorena, Madrid #170/R est:10800
Works on paper
£390 $632 €550 La Pizarra (23x30cm-9x12in) s.i.d.1857 pencil sketch. 20-May-3 Segre, Madrid #1/R est:450
£897 $1417 €1300 Landscape with river and house (19x29cm-7x11in) s.d.1880 pencil dr. 1-Apr-3 Segre, Madrid #29/R

HAES, Carlos de (attrib) (1829-1898) Spanish
£680 $1061 €1020 Landscape study (22x14cm-9x6in) bears sig. 26-Mar-3 Sotheby's, Olympia #191/R

HAESE, Gunter (1924-) German
Sculpture
£5513 $8545 €8600 Arcis (30x20x20cm-12x8x8in) s. brass phosphorous bronze wood socle. 3-Dec-2 Lempertz, Koln #166/R est:6000-7000

HAESEKER, Alexandra (20th C) Canadian
Works on paper
£636 $1011 €954 Dog walk, cross country (75x75cm-30x30in) s.d.1980 W/C in two parts prov. 23-Mar-3 Hodgins, Calgary #86/R est:1500-2000 (C.D 1500)

HAFELFINGER, Eugen (1898-1979) Swiss
Works on paper
£655 $956 €983 Tavern (34x26cm-13x10in) s. mixed media panel. 4-Jun-2 Germann, Zurich #771/R (S.FR 1500)

HAFFEN, Yvonne Jean (?) French?
Works on paper
£411 $650 €650 Pecheurs sur les quais de Seine (24x30cm-9x12in) s. chl crayon. 1-Dec-2 Livinec, Gaudcheau & Jezequel, Rennes #38d

HAFFENRICHTER, Hans (20th C) German?
£432 $691 €600 Morning light. s. i. stretcher. 15-May-3 Neumeister, Munich #447/R

HAFFNER, Felix (1818-1875) French
£3425 $5377 €5000 At the village fountain (131x98cm-52x39in) s. prov. 15-Apr-3 Sotheby's, Amsterdam #84/R est:3000-5000

HAFFNER, Léon (1881-1972) French
£2655 $4222 €3850 Fregate du 18eme croisant les cotes Africaines (158x99cm-62x39in) s. panel. 4-Mar-3 Livinec, Gaudcheau & Jezequel, Rennes #420

Works on paper
£353 $554 €550 Deux-mats sous voiles (39x79cm-15x31in) s. gouache. 15-Dec-2 Thierry & Lannon, Brest #330
£377 $581 €600 Yacht vu par l'avant (44x32cm-17x13in) s. gouache. 27-Oct-2 Lesieur & Le Bars, Le Havre #240
£408 $658 €580 Sloop grand largue tribord amures (43x31cm-17x12in) s. gouache. 11-May-3 Thierry & Lannon, Brest #315
£423 $680 €600 Caravelle sous voiles (25x17cm-10x7in) s. gouache. 11-May-3 Thierry & Lannon, Brest #314
£503 $775 €800 Yacht (40x80cm-16x31in) s. gouache pochoir. 27-Oct-2 Lesieur & Le Bars, Le Havre #355/R
£566 $877 €900 Voiliers en mer (39x77cm-15x30in) s. gouache. 3-Nov-2 Feletin, Province #120
£609 $956 €950 Regate (44x32cm-17x13in) s. gouache. 24-Nov-2 Lesieur & Le Bars, Le Havre #72/R
£878 $1370 €1300 Trois-mats (40x80cm-16x31in) s.i. gouache. 26-Mar-3 Millon & Associes, Paris #31/R
£1410 $2214 €2200 Trois mats (39x79cm-15x31in) s. W/C gouache. 16-Dec-2 Millon & Associes, Paris #188/R est:1200-1800
£2628 $4126 €4100 La regate (79x39cm-31x15in) s. W/C gouache. 16-Dec-2 Millon & Associes, Paris #187/R est:1200-1800

HAFNER, Charles Andrew (1888-?) American
£401 $650 €602 Autumn's gift (51x61cm-20x24in) s.d.1952. 24-Jan-3 Freeman, Philadelphia #227/R

HAFSTROM, Jan (1937-) Swedish
£1369 $2163 €2054 Landscape score (42x81cm-17x32in) s.d.1979-80 acrylic paper prov.exhib. 28-Apr-3 Bukowskis, Stockholm #997a/R est:18000-20000 (S.KR 18000)
£1542 $2405 €2313 Purple (100x100cm-39x39in) s.d.1981 verso oil on wood construction. 6-Nov-2 AB Stockholms Auktionsverk #900/R est:25000-30000 (S.KR 22000)

Sculpture
£2453 $3826 €3680 Untitled (116x86x12cm-46x34x5in) s.d.1989 verso object oil wood construction. 6-Nov-2 AB Stockholms Auktionsverk #901/R est:50000-60000 (S.KR 35000)

Works on paper
£1521 $2403 €2282 Diptych (84x120cm-33x47in) mixed media assemblage panel executed 1979-80. 28-Apr-3 Bukowskis, Stockholm #996/R est:20000-25000 (S.KR 20000)

HAFTEN, Nicolas van (c.1663-1715) French
£1266 $2000 €2000 Oyster dinner (15x13cm-6x5in) mono. panel prov. 27-Nov-2 Christie's, Paris #4/R

HAGAN, Robert (1947-) Australian
£279 $457 €405 Draught horses ploughing (122x244cm-48x96in) s. 3-Jun-3 Lawson Menzies, Sydney #896 (A.D 700)
£300 $468 €450 Pinmoll, Suffolk (41x51cm-16x20in) s.d.92. 27-Mar-3 Christie's, Kensington #462

HAGARTY, Clara (1871-1958) Canadian
£370 $574 €555 Dusk over a marsh (26x34cm-10x13in) s.d.10 board. 3-Dec-2 Joyner, Toronto #447 (C.D 900)

HAGARTY, Mary S (fl.1885-1938) British
Works on paper
£300 $474 €450 Woodland glade (35x25cm-14x10in) s. W/C. 26-Nov-2 Bonhams, Knightsbridge #200/R
£320 $499 €480 On the rows, Chester (24x34cm-9x13in) init. W/C. 6-Nov-2 Bonhams, Chester #316
£320 $499 €480 Off to school (18x30cm-7x12in) s. W/C. 10-Apr-3 Tennants, Leyburn #898
£420 $664 €630 Salisbury Cathedral under evening light (40x29cm-16x11in) s. W/C. 26-Nov-2 Bonhams, Knightsbridge #199/R
£600 $954 €900 Ponies on Dartmoor (28x38cm-11x15in) s. W/C. 27-Feb-3 Greenslade Hunt, Taunton #1270/R

HAGARTY, Parker (1859-1934) British
£350 $549 €525 View of the river Ogmore (24x36cm-9x14in) s. panel. 20-Nov-2 Sotheby's, Olympia #32/R
£480 $744 €720 Derwentwater (68x90cm-27x35in) s. 25-Sep-2 Peter Wilson, Nantwich #35

HAGBERG, Rune (1924-) Swedish
£502 $808 €753 W10 (40x15cm-16x6in) init. tempera canvas in wooden box prov. 7-May-3 AB Stockholms Auktionsverk #980/R (S.KR 6500)
Works on paper
£334 $540 €484 Composition (74x100cm-29x39in) s. mixed media. 25-May-3 Uppsala Auktionskammare, Uppsala #271 (S.KR 4300)

HAGBORG, August (1852-1925) Swedish
£583 $909 €875 Jetty by calm water (43x53cm-17x21in) study. 13-Sep-2 Lilla Bukowskis, Stockholm #413 (S.KR 8500)
£621 $1005 €900 Fisherfamily on beach (41x21cm-16x8in) s.i. panel. 25-May-3 Uppsala Auktionskammare, Uppsala #114/R (S.KR 8000)
£776 $1257 €1125 Landscape with fence, Dalaro (55x76cm-22x30in) s. 26-May-3 Bukowskis, Stockholm #170/R (S.KR 10000)
£857 $1337 €1286 Fisherfolk by watercourse (26x40cm-10x16in) s. panel exhib. 13-Sep-2 Lilla Bukowskis, Stockholm #529 (S.KR 12500)
£1259 $2065 €1750 Evening sun (72x93cm-28x37in) s. 4-Jun-3 Bukowskis, Helsinki #478/R est:900
£1396 $2262 €2024 Young beauty (40x30cm-16x12in) s. panel. 26-May-3 Bukowskis, Stockholm #163/R est:15000-20000 (S.KR 18000)
£1885 $3092 €2733 Oyster gatherers (56x46cm-22x18in) s. 4-Jun-3 AB Stockholms Auktionsverk #2133/R est:30000-40000 (S.KR 24000)
£2095 $3393 €3038 Landscape at sunset (80x120cm-31x47in) s. 26-May-3 Bukowskis, Stockholm #73/R est:30000-35000 (S.KR 27000)
£2553 $3957 €3830 At the shoemaker's workshop (74x64cm-29x25in) s. prov.exhib. 3-Dec-2 Bukowskis, Stockholm #282/R est:20000-22000 (S.KR 36000)
£2638 $4273 €3825 Mussel gatherer in Brittany (82x59cm-32x23in) s. 25-May-3 Uppsala Auktionskammare, Uppsala #118/R est:30000-40000 (S.KR 34000)
£2908 $4507 €4362 Fisherman on beach, Normandy (71x59cm-28x23in) s. panel. 4-Dec-2 AB Stockholms Auktionsverk #1576/R est:18000-20000 (S.KR 41000)
£3103 $5027 €4499 Mussel gatherer, Brittany (73x54cm-29x21in) s. 26-May-3 Bukowskis, Stockholm #74/R est:30000-40000 (S.KR 40000)
£13548 $21000 €20322 Daydreaming on the beach (77x121cm-30x48in) s. 29-Oct-2 Sotheby's, New York #120/R est:30000-40000
£21722 $35190 €31497 The farewell (97x130cm-38x51in) 26-May-3 Bukowskis, Stockholm #76/R est:200000-250000 (S.KR 280000)

HAGEDORN, Friedrich (19th C) German?
Works on paper
£13000 $20540 €19500 View at Rio de Janeiro (54x81cm-21x32in) s. W/C over pencil htd bodycol. 15-Nov-2 Sotheby's, London #84/R est:3000-4000

HAGEDORN, Karl (1889-1969) British
£900 $1476 €1350 Gypsy caravans (60x81cm-24x32in) s.d.47. 3-Jun-3 Sotheby's, Olympia #55/R
Works on paper
£370 $592 €555 Beach at Molyvos (33x51cm-13x20in) s. W/C. 11-Mar-3 Gorringes, Lewes #2424

HAGEDORN-OLSEN, Jeppe (1929-) Danish
£362 $554 €543 Landscape (64x90cm-25x35in) s.d.48. 24-Aug-2 Rasmussen, Havnen #2162 (D.KR 4200)
£397 $607 €596 Harbour scene (75x96cm-30x38in) s. 24-Aug-2 Rasmussen, Havnen #2169 (D.KR 4600)

HAGEDORN-OLSEN, Thorvald (1902-1996) Danish
£280 $445 €420 Fjord landscape (26x54cm-10x21in) s. 29-Apr-3 Kunsthallen, Copenhagen #227 (D.KR 3000)
£305 $509 €442 The Three Graces (28x34cm-11x13in) s. canvas on masonite. 17-Jun-3 Rasmussen, Copenhagen #204 (D.KR 3200)
£306 $477 €459 Man and woman at outdoor cafe (47x56cm-19x22in) s. 5-Aug-2 Rasmussen, Vejle #288/R (D.KR 3600)
£408 $636 €612 Landscape with farms and cattle (50x60cm-20x24in) s. 5-Aug-2 Rasmussen, Vejle #292/R (D.KR 4800)
£429 $669 €644 Interior scene with figures (61x81cm-24x32in) s.d.44. 11-Nov-2 Rasmussen, Vejle #69/R (D.KR 5000)
£595 $940 €893 Coastal landscape from Rorvig Harbour (53x71cm-21x28in) s.d.42. 5-Apr-3 Rasmussen, Havnen #4183/R (D.KR 6400)

HAGEDORN-OLSEN, Thorvald (attrib) (1902-1996) Danish
£254 $394 €381 Kortinge Nor near Munkebo (50x65cm-20x26in) s. 1-Oct-2 Rasmussen, Copenhagen #324 (D.KR 3000)

HAGELGANS, Michael Christoph Emanuel (attrib) (1725-1766) German
£3774 $5849 €6000 Portrait of young prince with armour and ermine cloak (74x59cm-29x23in) prov. 2-Oct-2 Dorotheum, Vienna #194/R est:4000-7000

HAGELSTAM, Hjalmar (20th C) Finnish

£295 $484 €410 Landscape (48x58cm-19x23in) s.d.1938. 5-Jun-3 Hagelstam, Helsinki #934

HAGEMAN, Victor (1868-1938) Belgian

£5696 $9000 €9000 Automne (75x100cm-30x39in) s.d.93 exhib. 26-Nov-2 Palais de Beaux Arts, Brussels #101/R est:8700-12500
£6329 $10000 €10000 Champ d'avoine dans la brume (60x80cm-24x31in) s.indis.d.94. 26-Nov-2 Palais de Beaux Arts, Brussels #103/R est:10000-12500
£6962 $11000 €11000 La tricoteuse dans les champs (90x45cm-35x18in) s.d.91. 26-Nov-2 Palais de Beaux Arts, Brussels #102/R est:10000-12500

Works on paper

£360 $576 €500 Paysanne (108x62cm-43x24in) s. mixed media. 13-May-3 Palais de Beaux Arts, Brussels #260
£1392 $2200 €2200 Matelots hindous (105x36cm-41x14in) mono. mixed media paper on canvas diptych. 26-Nov-2 Palais de Beaux Arts, Brussels #104/R est:1750-2500
£1646 $2600 €2600 Matelots hindous (70x100cm-28x39in) s. mixed media paper on canvas. 26-Nov-2 Palais de Beaux Arts, Brussels #106/R est:2500-3700
£4930 $7937 €7000 Shepherd with flock in landscape (70x118cm-28x46in) s. W/C. 12-May-3 Bernaerts, Antwerp #38/R est:4000-5000

HAGEMANN, Godefroy de (1820-1877) French

£2000 $3180 €3000 An Arab market with a mosque beyond (80x61cm-31x24in) s.d.86. 29-Apr-3 Bonhams, New Bond Street #102/R est:2000-3000
£4967 $8096 €7500 Scene de la vie paysanne (62x83cm-24x33in) s. 16-Feb-3 Mercier & Cie, Lille #223/R est:10000-12000

HAGEMANN, Oskar H (1888-1984) German

£426 $689 €600 Man carrying child on shoulders (69x36cm-27x14in) s.d.63 panel. 24-May-3 Van Ham, Cologne #224/R

HAGEMANS, Maurice (1852-1917) Belgian

£460 $718 €690 Tranquil river bank with angler (90x45cm-35x18in) s. 23-Sep-2 Bonhams, Chester #928
£633 $987 €1000 Paysage (27x45cm-11x18in) s. 15-Oct-2 Vanderkindere, Brussels #105
£850 $1411 €850 Laboureur et son chien (20x33cm-8x13in) s. 16-Jun-3 Horta, Bruxelles #69
£890 $1389 €1300 Le troupeau (40x53cm-16x21in) s. 14-Apr-3 Horta, Bruxelles #80
£1097 $1733 €1700 Bergers et troupeau traversant la foret (42x28cm-17x11in) s. 17-Dec-2 Palais de Beaux Arts, Brussels #545/R est:1750-2500
£1644 $2564 €2400 Au soleil couchant (41x70cm-16x28in) s. i.verso. 14-Apr-3 Horta, Bruxelles #78 est:3000-4000
£2353 $3788 €3600 Les moutons sous les cerisiers (30x50cm-12x20in) s. 20-Jan-3 Horta, Bruxelles #154 est:3000-4000
£2878 $4604 €4000 Verger en fleurs (48x72cm-19x28in) s. 13-May-3 Palais de Beaux Arts, Brussels #78/R est:4000-6000
£7325 $11427 €11500 Environs de Dinant, le matin (80x127cm-31x50in) s.d.1880. 11-Nov-2 Horta, Bruxelles #102/R est:10000-15000

Works on paper

£348 $543 €550 Sous-bois anime (14x20cm-6x8in) s. W/C. 15-Oct-2 Vanderkindere, Brussels #97
£369 $594 €550 Chemin creux anime (29x18cm-11x7in) s. W/C. 18-Feb-3 Vanderkindere, Brussels #22
£377 $588 €550 Fagoteuse et son ane dans un chemin creux (23x10cm-9x4in) s. W/C. 14-Apr-3 Horta, Bruxelles #82
£464 $756 €700 Berger et troupeau (12x24cm-5x9in) s. W/C. 17-Feb-3 Horta, Bruxelles #235
£484 $765 €750 Voiliers en mer (52x78cm-20x31in) s. W/C. 17-Dec-2 Palais de Beaux Arts, Brussels #541
£576 $921 €800 Retour de paturage (18x26cm-7x10in) s.d.1913 verso W/C. 19-May-3 Horta, Bruxelles #303
£582 $908 €850 Brume sur l'etang (21x25cm-8x10in) s. W/C. 14-Apr-3 Horta, Bruxelles #81
£638 $1066 €900 Paysage anime (54x40cm-21x16in) s. mixed media. 18-Jun-3 Hotel des Ventes Mosan, Brussels #185
£655 $1042 €950 Paysan labourant (28x45cm-11x18in) s.d.1885 W/C gouache. 4-Mar-3 Palais de Beaux Arts, Brussels #342
£680 $1082 €1000 Promenade en foret (18x24cm-7x9in) s. W/C paper on board. 19-Mar-3 Hotel des Ventes Mosan, Brussels #184
£694 $1104 €1000 Ferme au bord de l'eau (34x50cm-13x20in) s. W/C. 29-Apr-3 Campo, Vlaamse Kaai #141
£899 $1439 €1250 Cour de ferme animee (14x24cm-6x9in) s. W/C gouache. 13-May-3 Vanderkindere, Brussels #138
£935 $1496 €1300 Troupeau de vaches pres de la meule (16x56cm-6x22in) s. W/C. 19-May-3 Horta, Bruxelles #302 est:800-1200
£1176 $1894 €1800 Le laboureur (27x54cm-11x21in) s. W/C. 20-Jan-3 Horta, Bruxelles #153 est:2500-3000
£1218 $1888 €1900 Vaches s'abreuvant (26x46cm-10x18in) s. W/C. 9-Dec-2 Horta, Bruxelles #208 est:2000-3000
£1379 $2193 €2000 Peasant woman with her cattle in an evening landscape (33x53cm-13x21in) s. W/C gouache. 10-Mar-3 Sotheby's, Amsterdam #108/R est:1300-1600
£1410 $2214 €2200 Vache a la riviere (58x110cm-23x43in) s. W/C. 11-Dec-2 Hotel des Ventes Mosan, Brussels #220 est:1800-2200
£1438 $2244 €2100 Troupeau au clair de lune (59x30cm-23x12in) s. W/C. 14-Apr-3 Horta, Bruxelles #79 est:1800-2200
£1439 $2302 €2000 Fermiere et ses vaches au pre (30x59cm-12x23in) s. W/C gouache. 13-May-3 Vanderkindere, Brussels #65 est:2000-3000
£1448 $2317 €2100 Les ramasseuses de pommes de terre (34x49cm-13x19in) s.d.1884 W/C. 17-Mar-3 Horta, Bruxelles #91 est:1800-2200
£1655 $2647 €2300 Vachere et son troupeau au bord de l'eau (32x48cm-13x19in) s. W/C. 13-May-3 Vanderkindere, Brussels #180/R est:2000-3000
£1667 $2617 €2600 Fermiere et sa vache au bord du ruisseau (25x24cm-10x9in) s. W/C. 10-Dec-2 Vanderkindere, Brussels #121 est:800-1200
£1699 $2736 €2600 Troupeau au bord de l'eau (60x88cm-24x35in) s. W/C sold with a catalogue. 20-Jan-3 Horta, Bruxelles #152/R est:3000-5000
£1795 $2836 €2800 Landscape with shepherdess near the farm (41x63cm-16x25in) s. W/C gouache. 18-Nov-2 Bernaerts, Antwerp #315/R est:2000-2200
£1899 $2962 €3000 Berger et troupeau de moutons (131x83cm-52x33in) s. W/C. 16-Sep-2 Horta, Bruxelles #108/R
£2000 $3320 €2000 Avant l'orage (60x88cm-24x35in) s. 16-Jun-3 Horta, Bruxelles #68 est:2000-3000
£2800 $4648 €2800 Coucher de soleil (33x53cm-13x21in) s. 16-Jun-3 Horta, Bruxelles #67 est:3000-4000
£3291 $5200 €5200 Bord d'etang avec pecheur (60x83cm-24x33in) s. W/C. 26-Nov-2 Palais de Beaux Arts, Brussels #327/R est:3000-4000
£3597 $5755 €5000 Berger et moutons traversant le verger (120x80cm-47x31in) s. gouache. 13-May-3 Palais de Beaux Arts, Brussels #83/R est:5000-7500
£3797 $5924 €6000 Fermiere faisant boire une vache dans une mare (92x135cm-36x53in) s. mixed media. 16-Sep-2 Horta, Bruxelles #107/R

HAGEMANS, Paul (1884-1959) Belgian

£268 $417 €420 Chemin anime en Ardennes (30x40cm-12x16in) s. panel. 11-Nov-2 Horta, Bruxelles #106
£329 $513 €520 Allegorie royale (60x60cm-24x24in) s. panel. 16-Sep-2 Horta, Bruxelles #109
£483 $772 €700 A Anseremme (40x50cm-16x20in) s. 17-Mar-3 Horta, Bruxelles #93
£484 $765 €750 Moutons a l'abreuvoir (40x38cm-16x15in) s. panel. 17-Dec-2 Galerie Moderne, Brussels #812
£709 $1184 €1000 Maison dans la prairie (32x35cm-13x14in) s. panel. 17-Jun-3 Palais de Beaux Arts, Brussels #582/R
£764 $1192 €1200 Bateau de peche au carenage a Zeebruges (25x32cm-10x13in) s. panel. 11-Nov-2 Horta, Bruxelles #105
£828 $1324 €1200 Apres l'orage (70x80cm-28x31in) s. 17-Mar-3 Horta, Bruxelles #92
£993 $1658 €1400 Femmes au bord d'un etang (36x30cm-14x12in) s. panel oval. 17-Jun-3 Palais de Beaux Arts, Brussels #581/R
£1923 $2981 €3000 Vase fleuri de roses sur fond de chinoiseries (60x60cm-24x24in) s. 9-Dec-2 Horta, Bruxelles #207/R est:4000-6000
£2358 $3656 €3750 Le petit marche en provence (60x70cm-24x28in) s. panel. 1-Oct-2 Palais de Beaux Arts, Brussels #477/R est:3750-5000
£6051 $9439 €9500 Les derniers preparatifs (120x70cm-47x28in) s. panel. 11-Nov-2 Horta, Bruxelles #104/R est:9000-14000

Works on paper

£288 $449 €420 Le port d'Anvers (22x30cm-9x12in) s. mixed media. 14-Apr-3 Horta, Bruxelles #293
£305 $497 €460 Dans les champs (20x25cm-8x10in) s. mixed media. 17-Feb-3 Horta, Bruxelles #238
£305 $497 €460 Pecheur a la ligne (20x25cm-8x10in) s. mixed media. 17-Feb-3 Horta, Bruxelles #237
£464 $756 €700 Promenade au bord de l'etang (42x31cm-17x12in) s. mixed media. 17-Feb-3 Horta, Bruxelles #236
£1538 $2415 €2400 Elegante assise (25x19cm-10x7in) s. W/C. 10-Dec-2 Vanderkindere, Brussels #123 est:500-750

HAGEMEISTER, Karl (1848-1933) German

£1824 $2846 €2700 Landscape (48x60cm-19x24in) s. lit. 28-Mar-3 Karrenbauer, Konstanz #1735 est:1000
£5380 $8500 €8500 Lakeshore (69x99cm-27x39in) s.d.1896. 30-Nov-2 Villa Grisebach, Berlin #117/R est:5000-7000
£7770 $12122 €11500 Summer woodland lake (72x119cm-28x47in) s.d.93. 28-Mar-3 Karrenbauer, Konstanz #1737 est:1500
£8446 $13176 €12500 Autumnal woodland pond (109x165cm-43x65in) s. lit. 28-Mar-3 Karrenbauer, Konstanz #1728/R est:1500

Works on paper

£5000 $7800 €7400 Water lilies on pond (90x60cm-35x24in) s. mixed media. 28-Mar-3 Karrenbauer, Konstanz #1736 est:1000

HAGEN, Else (1914-) Norwegian

£2168 $3382 €3252 Masks (100x100cm-39x39in) s. s.d.stretcher painted 1981-82-83. 21-Oct-2 Blomqvist, Oslo #404/R est:35000-40000 (N.KR 25000)
£3287 $5194 €4931 Two figures with arms raised (100x100cm-39x39in) s. 2-Dec-2 Blomqvist, Oslo #458/R est:30000-35000 (N.KR 38000)

HAGEN, Johann van der (1676-1745) Dutch
£633 $981 €1000 View of city (26x45cm-10x18in) i. panel. 27-Sep-2 Dr Fritz Nagel, Leipzig #3933/R
£5000 $8100 €7500 French and British men-o'war in a swell after dark (65x49cm-26x19in) 21-May-3 Christie's, Kensington #514/R est:6000-8000

HAGEN, Theodor (1842-1919) German
£3043 $4748 €4565 Village street near Weimar (91x137cm-36x54in) s. prov. 16-Sep-2 Philippe Schuler, Zurich #3473/R est:8000-12000 (S.FR 7000)

HAGEN, William van der (attrib) (?-1745) British
£35000 $55650 €52500 Prospect of Hinwick House, Bedfordshire (111x154cm-44x61in) i. prov.lit. 19-Mar-3 Sotheby's, London #65/R est:25000-40000

HAGENAUER, Franz (1906-1986) Austrian
Sculpture
£949 $1472 €1500 Ram (15x25cm-6x10in) brass. 25-Sep-2 Wiener Kunst Auktionen, Vienna #433/R
£1139 $1800 €1800 Giraffe (32cm-13in) sheet brass. 26-Nov-2 Dorotheum, Vienna #320/R est:1500-2000
£1528 $2429 €2200 Schnauzer (13cm-5in) brass Cast.WHW. 29-Apr-3 Wiener Kunst Auktionen, Vienna #233/R est:1500-2500
£1772 $2800 €2800 Dachsund (59cm-23in) sheet brass. 26-Nov-2 Dorotheum, Vienna #322/R est:1800-2200
£1799 $2878 €2500 Dancer (41cm-16in) alpaca nickel brass socle. 15-May-3 Neumeister, Munich #126/R est:1600-1800
£1986 $3217 €2800 Tennis player (23cm-9in) i. brass. 21-May-3 Dorotheum, Vienna #232/R est:1500-2000
£2083 $3312 €3000 Dachsund (14cm-6in) brass CastWHW. 29-Apr-3 Wiener Kunst Auktionen, Vienna #232/R est:800-1800
£2244 $3545 €3500 Lower arm with hand (30cm-12in) i. verso alpaka. 14-Nov-2 Neumeister, Munich #453/R est:3200-3600
£4167 $6583 €6500 Female mask (50x38cm-20x15in) i. verso alpaka. 14-Nov-2 Neumeister, Munich #451/R est:5000-5500
£4167 $6583 €6500 Male mask (50x29cm-20x11in) i. verso alpaka. 14-Nov-2 Neumeister, Munich #452/R est:5000-6000
£7692 $12154 €12000 Dancer (119cm-47in) i. brass. 14-Nov-2 Neumeister, Munich #450/R est:10000-12000
£8108 $12649 €12000 Head on hand (68cm-27in) nickel metal Cast.WHW. 25-Mar-3 Wiener Kunst Auktionen, Vienna #70/R est:10000-20000
£12000 $19200 €18000 Human head (52cm-20in) bronze. 15-May-3 Christie's, Kensington #435/R est:3000-5000

HAGENAUER, Karl (1898-1956) Austrian
Sculpture
£949 $1500 €1500 Fox (31cm-12in) brass. 26-Nov-2 Dorotheum, Vienna #318/R est:1500-2000
£1111 $1767 €1600 Horse (15x22cm-6x9in) brass Cast.WHW, Hagenauer Wien. 29-Apr-3 Wiener Kunst Auktionen, Vienna #230/R est:1500-2500
£1702 $2757 €2400 Standing female nude (29cm-11in) s. brass. 21-May-3 Dorotheum, Vienna #237/R est:2400-3400
£1844 $2987 €2600 Greyhound (25cm-10in) s. brass. 21-May-3 Dorotheum, Vienna #240/R est:1500-2000
£6400 $10176 €9600 Hunting group (25x70cm-10x28in) dark pat. bronze. 27-Feb-3 Sotheby's, Olympia #189/R est:4000-5000
Works on paper
£694 $1097 €1000 Composition (44x60cm-17x24in) pencil transparent paper. 24-Apr-3 Dorotheum, Vienna #13/R

HAGENBEEK, Charles (1870-?) ?
£3000 $4920 €4500 Resting sheep and cattle with their herder (89x119cm-35x47in) mono. lit. 5-Jun-3 Christie's, Kensington #776/R est:1000-1500

HAGENLOCHER, Karl Wilhelm von (1909-) German?
£292 $435 €450 Impressionist landscape (60x70cm-24x28in) 28-Jun-2 Sigalas, Stuttgart #799/R

HAGER, Marie (20th C) German?
£1164 $1816 €1700 Peasant cart in winter wood (75x86cm-30x34in) s. 10-Apr-3 Schopman, Hamburg #673 est:2000

HAGER, R A (19/20th C) Austrian
£881 $1400 €1322 Pleasant cows (76x61cm-30x24in) s. 22-Mar-3 New Orleans Auction, New Orleans #105/R est:1800-2500

HAGERBAUMER, David (1921-) American
Works on paper
£797 $1300 €1196 Winter shadows, ruffed grouse (53x74cm-21x29in) s.d.1960 W/C. 16-Feb-3 Butterfields, San Francisco #2109 est:1000-1500
£920 $1500 €1380 Bear river marsh, mallards (41x55cm-16x22in) s.d.1959 W/C. 16-Feb-3 Butterfields, San Francisco #2087 est:1000-1500
£1043 $1700 €1565 In the pines, California quail (37x48cm-15x19in) s.d.1960 W/C. 16-Feb-3 Butterfields, San Francisco #2081 est:1000-1500
£1104 $1800 €1656 In to roost, Canada geese (53x74cm-21x29in) s.d.1960 W/C. 16-Feb-3 Butterfields, San Francisco #2104 est:1000-1500
£1807 $3000 €2620 Ducks over water. Ducks over water (56x76cm-22x30in) one s.d.1998 one s.d.1988 W/C pair prov. 11-Jun-3 Butterfields, San Francisco #4138a/R est:3000-5000

HAGERUP, Nels (1864-1922) American
£411 $650 €617 Moonrise over Pacific. s. 5-Apr-3 Harvey Clar, Oakland #1337
£469 $750 €704 Seascape at sunset (36x56cm-14x22in) s. 16-Mar-3 Butterfields, San Francisco #1031
£692 $1100 €1038 California seascape (46x76cm-18x30in) s. 3-May-3 Harvey Clar, Oakland #1209
£736 $1200 €1104 Seascape (30x56cm-12x22in) s. 16-Feb-3 Butterfields, San Francisco #2105
£807 $1300 €1211 Seascape (41x71cm-16x28in) s. canvas on canvas. 18-Feb-3 John Moran, Pasadena #125a
£2201 $3500 €3302 Before the Golden Gate (46x102cm-18x40in) s. 3-May-3 Harvey Clar, Oakland #1208
£3025 $4750 €4538 Sunset on the California coast (66x117cm-26x46in) s. prov. 19-Nov-2 Butterfields, San Francisco #8147/R est:3000-5000

HAGG, Jacob (1839-1931) Swedish
£877 $1385 €1316 Spanish fishing boats at Cadiz (25x35cm-10x14in) s.d.1887. 30-Nov-2 Goteborg Auktionsverk, Sweden #151/R (S.KR 12500)
£2595 $4100 €3893 Fast sailing boat Emma (53x73cm-21x29in) s.d.1874. 27-Nov-2 Falkkloos, Malmo #77635/R est:35000 (S.KR 37000)
£25601 $41474 €37121 The steam corvette Freja (150x120cm-59x47in) s.d.1907 lit. 26-May-3 Bukowskis, Stockholm #98/R est:150000-175000 (S.KR 330000)
Works on paper
£400 $668 €580 Shipping in a harbour (26x39cm-10x15in) s.d.1883 W/C. 18-Jun-3 Sotheby's, Olympia #119/R
£618 $939 €927 Full sail (46x33cm-18x13in) s.d.1912 W/C. 16-Aug-2 Lilla Bukowskis, Stockholm #792 (S.KR 9000)
£780 $1209 €1170 Three-master in high seas (35x50cm-14x20in) s. W/C. 4-Dec-2 AB Stockholms Auktionsverk #1746/R (S.KR 11000)
£1435 $2325 €2081 Sailing vessels with union flag (22x33cm-9x13in) s. W/C. 26-May-3 Bukowskis, Stockholm #97/R est:15000-20000 (S.KR 18500)

HAGGER, Brian (1935-) British
£480 $763 €720 Wilton Arms (50x60cm-20x24in) s.d.1974. 18-Mar-3 Bonhams, Knightsbridge #86
£550 $875 €825 Munster Road (71x91cm-28x36in) s.d.1973. 18-Mar-3 Bonhams, Knightsbridge #85

HAGGIN, Ben Ali (1882-1951) American
£566 $900 €849 Portrait of Gordon Grant (102x76cm-40x30in) s.i.d.1932. 7-Mar-3 Skinner, Boston #553/R

HAGHE, Louis (1806-1885) Belgian
Works on paper
£385 $600 €578 Cathedral interior (36x28cm-14x11in) s.d.1865 W/C. 30-Mar-3 Susanin's, Chicago #6095/R
£417 $650 €626 Confirmation scene, Rome (44x30cm-17x12in) init. gouache W/C exec.c.1870. 19-Sep-2 Swann Galleries, New York #387/R
£475 $793 €689 Transept of the Cathedral of Tournay, in Belgium, with clergy and figures (74x53cm-29x21in) s.d.1868 W/C bodycol. 25-Jun-3 Goldings, Lincolnshire #364
£550 $836 €825 Italien peasants in landscapes (33x23cm-13x9in) s. one d.1853 W/C pair. 16-Aug-2 Keys, Aylsham #589/R
£680 $1061 €1020 Reading the new play (25x34cm-10x13in) s. W/C htd bodycol. 25-Mar-3 Bonhams, Knightsbridge #215/R
£880 $1373 €1320 Continental procession (42x27cm-17x11in) s.d.1851 W/C bodycol. 5-Nov-2 Bonhams, New Bond Street #88/R
£900 $1440 €1350 Quentin Matsys Well, Antwerp Cathedral, Belgium (34x25cm-13x10in) s.d.1865 W/C bodycol. 11-Mar-3 Bonhams, New Bond Street #6/R

HAGN, Ludwig von (1819-1898) German
£1646 $2551 €2600 Rococco figures in palace parkland (90x130cm-35x51in) 25-Sep-2 Neumeister, Munich #589/R est:3000

HAGN, Richard von (1850-c.1890) German
£2671 $4167 €3900 View from Langeness towards Fohr (58x82cm-23x32in) s.d.1921. 10-Apr-3 Schopman, Hamburg #672a est:1500

HAGONDOKOFF, Constantin (1934-) ?
Works on paper
£952 $1514 €1400 Rialto (24x30cm-9x12in) s. W/C over pen. 24-Mar-3 Coutau Begarie, Paris #291/R

HAGUE, Arthur Anderson (?) British
£250 $390 €375 Collecting hay (40x51cm-16x20in) s. 26-Mar-3 Sotheby's, Olympia #114/R
£1550 $2542 €2325 Friends in the meadow (51x76cm-20x30in) s. 5-Jun-3 Christie's, Kensington #652/R est:400-600

HAGUE, J Edward Homerville (fl.1884-1917) British
£480 $782 €720 Fizz (36x26cm-14x10in) s.d.1887. 12-Feb-3 Bonhams, Knightsbridge #104/R

HAGUE, Joshua Anderson (1850-1916) British
£400 $668 €580 Extensive landscape with hayfield in the foreground (38x51cm-15x20in) s. 18-Jun-3 Andrew Hartley, Ilkley #1126
£650 $1014 €975 Rest among the cornstocks (51x40cm-20x16in) s. 10-Sep-2 Bonhams, Knightsbridge #216/R
£1240 $1946 €1860 Bridge over rushing waters (91x71cm-36x28in) s. 24-Jul-2 Walker's, Ottawa #24/R est:5000-6000 (C.D 3000)
£1401 $2200 €2102 Hayfield (71x127cm-28x50in) s. 22-Nov-2 Skinner, Boston #308/R est:1800-2200

HAGUE, Louis (19th C) ?
Works on paper
£280 $437 €420 Figures in a cathedral (32x22cm-13x9in) s.d.1863 W/C. 9-Oct-2 Woolley & Wallis, Salisbury #102/R

HAHN, Emanuel (1881-1926) Canadian
Sculpture
£2889 $4738 €4334 Man and woman (58cm-23in) s. bronze wooden base executed c.1911-12 prov.exhib.lit. 27-May-3 Sotheby's, Toronto #174/R est:6000-8000 (C.D 6500)
£3427 $5415 €5141 Contemplation (67cm-26in) green pat. bronze prov.exhib. 18-Nov-2 Sotheby's, Toronto #154/R est:9000-12000 (C.D 8500)

HAHN, Gustav Adolphe (1811-1872) German
£1538 $2415 €2400 Nurnberg (78x104cm-31x41in) s.d.1867. 23-Nov-2 Arnold, Frankfurt #737/R est:1600
£2581 $3794 €4000 Wechselburg Church near Rochlitz in Sachsen (73x56cm-29x22in) s.d.1854. 20-Jun-2 Dr Fritz Nagel, Stuttgart #771/R est:5000

HAHN, Henriette (1862-?) Danish
Works on paper
£466 $740 €699 Studies of models and trees (74x64cm-29x25in) s. pencil 11 in one frame. 5-Mar-3 Rasmussen, Copenhagen #2129 (D.KR 5000)

HAHN, Joseph (1839-1906) German
£261 $418 €400 Mill on the Maisach surrounded by trees (20x26cm-8x10in) s. indis.i.d.1898 verso board lit. 10-Jan-3 Allgauer, Kempten #1606/R
£4430 $6867 €7000 Ziegelei Reifenstuel in Bogenhausen (60x112cm-24x44in) s.d.1870. 25-Sep-2 Neumeister, Munich #590/R est:6000

HAHN, Sylvia (20th C) Canadian?
£279 $435 €419 Kingston (27x22cm-11x9in) s. s.i.verso board. 25-Mar-3 Ritchie, Toronto #70/R (C.D 650)
£356 $583 €516 Outer Islands. Parry dound (28x38cm-11x15in) board. 1-Jun-3 Levis, Calgary #46/R (C.D 800)

HAID, Georg (1861-1935) German?
£302 $471 €480 Sailing yacht in storm (47x57cm-19x22in) s.d.1924 i. verso panel. 9-Oct-2 Michael Zeller, Lindau #709/R

HAIDER, Hermann (1938-) Austrian
£897 $1418 €1400 Still life of flowers (80x100cm-31x39in) s.d. 18-Nov-2 Dorotheum, Linz #280
£962 $1519 €1500 Still life of flowers (80x100cm-31x39in) s.d. 18-Nov-2 Dorotheum, Linz #279/R est:2600-3000
£1007 $1612 €1400 Landscape (50x66cm-20x26in) mono.d.62. 14-May-3 Dorotheum, Linz #406/R

HAIER, Joseph (1816-1891) Austrian
£545 $850 €818 Portrait of a boy with his spaniel (99x74cm-39x29in) s. 21-Sep-2 Pook & Pook, Downington #103/R
£1325 $2147 €1988 Before the learned (73x94cm-29x37in) s. 3-Feb-3 Lilla Bukowskis, Stockholm #568 est:10000-12000 (S.KR 18500)
£2421 $3849 €3632 Dorfmaler - interior from the village artist's studio, with his children looking on (69x55cm-27x22in) s.i.d.1882. 5-Mar-3 Rasmussen, Copenhagen #1741/R est:30000 (D.KR 26000)

HAIG, Axel Herman (1835-1921) Swedish
Works on paper
£400 $624 €600 Cloisters San Juan de Los Reyes, Toledo (35x25cm-14x10in) mono.i.d.21/6/ 1883 W/C. 6-Nov-2 Bonhams, Chester #384
£460 $718 €690 Cordova - cathedral interior (34x24cm-13x9in) mono.d.1883 W/C. 6-Nov-2 Bonhams, Chester #382
£660 $1030 €990 Scene Toledo Cathedral (34x24cm-13x9in) mono.d.1883 W/C. 6-Nov-2 Bonhams, Chester #381
£1000 $1560 €1500 Segovia, Spain (46x29cm-18x11in) mono.i.d.1886 W/C. 6-Nov-2 Bonhams, Chester #380/R est:500-700
£1000 $1590 €1500 Children being lectured in a Mosque, Cairo (26x37cm-10x15in) mono.d.1890 W/C htd white. 29-Apr-3 Bonhams, New Bond Street #105/R est:1200-1800
£1050 $1638 €1575 Street in Toledo (48x28cm-19x11in) mono.i.d.1888 W/C. 6-Nov-2 Bonhams, Chester #383/R est:300-500
£1200 $1872 €1800 Cloisters, Tarragona (48x31cm-19x12in) mono.d.1895 W/C. 9-Oct-2 Woolley & Wallis, Salisbury #140/R est:600-800
£1500 $2385 €2250 Shoemakers, Cairo (25x37cm-10x15in) mono.i.d.1899 W/C htd white. 29-Apr-3 Bonhams, New Bond Street #104/R est:1200-1800
£1650 $2574 €2475 Church of San Salvador, Seville (28x24cm-11x9in) mono.d.1883 W/C. 6-Nov-2 Bonhams, Chester #386/R est:300-500
£2200 $3432 €3300 Eastern doorway, Seville (36x18cm-14x7in) mono.d.1883 W/C. 6-Nov-2 Bonhams, Chester #385 est:400-500

HAIG, Earl (20th C) British
£1300 $2002 €1950 Dryburgh Banks in summer (84x91cm-33x36in) s. i.verso. 5-Sep-2 Christie's, Kensington #642 est:700-1000
Works on paper
£300 $498 €450 Study for olive trees and terrace (29x39cm-11x15in) s. W/C. 10-Jun-3 Sworder & Son, Bishops Stortford #486/R
£300 $498 €450 Tweed from the Holmes (32x49cm-13x19in) s. W/C. 10-Jun-3 Sworder & Son, Bishops Stortford #487/R

HAIGH, Alfred Grenfell (1870-1963) British
£1200 $1872 €1800 Sun stream (51x61cm-20x24in) s.i.d.1945. 6-Nov-2 Sotheby's, Olympia #94/R est:800-1200
£3100 $4929 €4650 Pair of black and white, and brown and white skewbald ponies with terrier in paddock (47x61cm-19x24in) s.d.1903. 18-Mar-3 Rosebery Fine Art, London #900/R est:1500-2000

HAIKIN, John (?) Irish?
£541 $834 €850 Farmer and child (53x46cm-21x18in) board. 4-Sep-2 James Adam, Dublin #69

HAILEY, Clarence (fl.1914-1916) British
£680 $1061 €1020 Willonyx with jockey up (44x60cm-17x24in) s.i. 26-Mar-3 Sotheby's, Olympia #101/R

HAINARD, Philippe (1879-1938) Swiss
£524 $817 €786 Soleil couchant (37x46cm-15x18in) s.d.1922 i. stretcher. 6-Nov-2 Dobiaschofsky, Bern #629/R (S.FR 1200)

HAINARD, Robert (1906-1999) Swiss
Sculpture
£1806 $2907 €2619 Wild boar (19cm-7in) s.num.13/20 green black pat bronze. 9-May-3 Dobiaschofsky, Bern #175/R est:3600 (S.FR 3900)
£1852 $2981 €2685 Badger sitting (12x21cm-5x8in) s. st.f.M Pastori dark pat bronze. 9-May-3 Dobiaschofsky, Bern #173/R est:4000 (S.FR 4000)

HAINARD-ROTEN, Germaine (1902-1990) German
£655 $1022 €983 Summer meadows (60x73cm-24x29in) s.d.45. 6-Nov-2 Dobiaschofsky, Bern #630 (S.FR 1500)

HAINDL-LAPOIRIE, Elfy (1907-1969) Austrian
£1410 $2228 €2200 Still life with fruit (81x65cm-32x26in) s. 12-Nov-2 Dorotheum, Vienna #159/R est:2000-2600

HAINE, Desire Victor Felix (1900-1989) Belgian
Works on paper
£342 $534 €500 Bords de Sambre (65x50cm-26x20in) s.d.43 chl dr. 14-Apr-3 Horta, Bruxelles #367

HAINES, Frederick Stanley (1879-1960) Canadian
£321 $508 €482 Two sisters (36x43cm-14x17in) d.1920 paperboard. 1-Dec-2 Levis, Calgary #38/R (C.D 800)

£489 $802 €734 Bridge near Port Sidney (21x26cm-8x10in) s. panel. 3-Jun-3 Joyner, Toronto #493 est:1000-1500 (C.D 1100)
£558 $870 €837 Mackeral sky (25x30cm-10x12in) s. masonite. 25-Mar-3 Ritchie, Toronto #103/R est:600-800 (C.D 1300)
£622 $1020 €933 Black birch and flaming maples, 1950 (40x50cm-16x20in) s. board. 3-Jun-3 Joyner, Toronto #247/R est:1500-1800 (C.D 1400)
£667 $1093 €1001 Cedar valley (40x50cm-16x20in) s. canvasboard double-sided. 3-Jun-3 Joyner, Toronto #8/R est:1500-1800 (C.D 1500)
£858 $1339 €1287 Late summer (41x51cm-16x20in) s.i.d.1955 board. 25-Mar-3 Ritchie, Toronto #91/R est:1200-1800 (C.D 2000)
£907 $1433 €1361 Southwest corner, Seythes Island (25x20cm-10x8in) s. board prov. 14-Nov-2 Heffel, Vancouver #221/R est:1500-2000 (C.D 2250)
£1333 $2187 €2000 Looking up the valley below field (25x36cm-10x14in) s. panel. 3-Jun-3 Joyner, Toronto #204/R est:3000-4000 (C.D 3000)
£1481 $2296 €2222 Georgian Bay (50x65cm-20x26in) s. board. 3-Dec-2 Joyner, Toronto #114/R est:1500-2000 (C.D 3600)
£9677 $15290 €14516 Northern landscape (107x136cm-42x54in) s. panel prov.exhib. 18-Nov-2 Sotheby's, Toronto #180/R est:10000-12000 (C.D 24000)

Works on paper

£333 $546 €500 Floral study (40x50cm-16x20in) s. gouache on board. 3-Jun-3 Joyner, Toronto #475 (C.D 750)

HAINES, Richard (1906-1984) American

£217 $350 €326 Mesa land (38x56cm-15x22in) s. s.i.verso. 23-Feb-3 Butterfields, Los Angeles #7025
£1198 $2000 €1737 Modernist harbour scene, morning tide (76x91cm-30x36in) i. prov. 17-Jun-3 John Moran, Pasadena #137 est:1000-2000

HAINS, Raymond (1926-) French

£4717 $7311 €7500 Sans titre (62x47cm-24x19in) s.d.1974 verso torn poster steel sheet. 30-Oct-2 Artcurial Briest, Paris #577 est:6000-9000

Sculpture

£2639 $4196 €3800 Seita (41x32cm-16x13in) s.d.2000 verso paint wood plastic. 29-Apr-3 Artcurial Briest, Paris #542/R est:2200-2500
£3103 $5183 €4500 Seita (41x32x5cm-16x13x2in) s.i.d.verso plastic painted wood. 9-Jul-3 Cornette de St.Cyr, Paris #297/R est:4000-5000
£7547 $12000 €11321 Saffa (114x85x6cm-45x33x2in) s. painted wood multiple exec.c.1966-8. 29-Apr-3 Christie's, Rockefeller NY #614/R est:7000-9000
£8163 $12980 €12000 Saffa (100x41x15cm-39x16x6in) s.d.1970 verso painted wood prov. 24-Mar-3 Cornette de St.Cyr, Paris #73/R est:10000
£10000 $16700 €14500 Saffa (95x79x12cm-37x31x5in) s. acrylic on wood executed 1971 prov. 27-Jun-3 Christie's, London #169/R est:7000-10000

Works on paper

£3000 $4920 €4500 Untitled (106x106cm-42x42in) s.d.1976 verso decollage metal prov. 7-Feb-3 Sotheby's, London #199/R est:5000-7000
£4800 $7824 €7200 Le chat (29x17cm-11x7in) s.d.1957 decollage on paper. 3-Feb-3 Sotheby's, Olympia #92/R est:3000-4000
£5000 $7700 €7500 Untitled (54x62cm-21x24in) s.d.1965 decollage metal prov. 22-Oct-2 Sotheby's, London #345/R est:4000-6000
£5500 $8470 €8250 Untitled (105x105cm-41x41in) s.d.1976 verso decollage on metal prov. 22-Oct-2 Sotheby's, London #346/R est:5000-7000
£8013 $12580 €12500 Coucou bazar (98x98cm-39x39in) s.i.d.verso torn poster on canvas. 16-Dec-2 Charbonneaux, Paris #260/R est:7000-9000
£10000 $16700 €14500 Untitled (70x76cm-28x30in) s.d.62 decollage canvas prov. 26-Jun-3 Sotheby's, London #170/R est:8000-12000
£11458 $18906 €16500 Sans titre (100x100cm-39x39in) s.d.1963 verso torn poster prov. 1-Jul-3 Artcurial Briest, Paris #526/R est:15000-20000
£11500 $19205 €16675 Untitled (101x99cm-40x39in) s.d.1961 decollage metal prov. 26-Jun-3 Sotheby's, London #163/R est:6000-8000
£11915 $19898 €16800 Composition (100x93cm-39x37in) s.verso torn poster. 18-Jun-3 Pierre Berge, Paris #93/R est:8000-9000
£12821 $20128 €20000 Untitled (81x63cm-32x25in) s.d.1961 torn posters prov. 11-Dec-2 Artcurial Briest, Paris #735/R est:15000
£15000 $24600 €22500 Untitled (117x106cm-46x42in) s.d.1965 verso decollage metal prov. 7-Feb-3 Sotheby's, London #197/R est:8000-12000
£19048 $30286 €28000 Coucou bazar (85x93cm-33x37in) s.i.d.1973 verso torn posters on canvas. 24-Mar-3 Cornette de St.Cyr, Paris #61/R est:30000

HAITE, George Charles (1855-1924) British

Works on paper

£300 $468 €450 River landscape (36x60cm-14x24in) s.d.5th Oct 1900 W/C bodycol. 25-Mar-3 Bonhams, Knightsbridge #45/R
£300 $480 €450 Eastern street scene with figures (29x32cm-11x13in) s. W/C. 11-Mar-3 Bonhams, Oxford #26/R
£420 $664 €630 Curio shop, Tangier (36x33cm-14x13in) s. W/C bodycol. 13-Nov-2 Halls, Shrewsbury #367/R
£800 $1248 €1200 Boat ashore, Villefranche. Venetian doorway (24x39cm-9x15in) s. pair prov. 17-Sep-2 Sotheby's, Olympia #109/R
£1600 $2528 €2400 Waiting for the ferry at Dortracht (46x89cm-18x35in) s.d.1890 W/C bodycol. 26-Nov-2 Bonhams, Knightsbridge #238/R est:1200-1800

HAITE, William (attrib) (19th C) British

£583 $950 €875 Country landscape with figures resting on a path (25x34cm-10x13in) board. 16-Feb-3 Butterfields, San Francisco #2050

HAJAMADI, Fariba (1957-) Iranian

Works on paper

£339 $532 €509 Untitled (214x234cm-84x92in) mixed media diptych. 16-Dec-2 Lilla Bukowskis, Stockholm #678 (S.KR 4800)

HAJDU, Étienne (1907-1996) French

Sculpture

£1180 $1900 €1770 Untitled (41x60cm-16x24in) brass. 23-Feb-3 Butterfields, Los Angeles #7034 est:1000-2000
£4808 $7548 €7500 Untitled (27cm-11in) s. gilt pat bronze exec.1970. 10-Dec-2 Piasa, Paris #154/R
£5806 $9000 €8709 Femme en noire (80cm-31in) s.d.60 black marble prov.exhib. 26-Sep-2 Christie's, Rockefeller NY #544/R est:8000-12000
£5938 $9500 €8907 Aube (63x44x16cm-25x17x6in) i.d.1968 num.1-4 brown black pat. bronze prov. 14-May-3 Sotheby's, New York #116/R est:5000-7000
£10256 $16103 €16000 Olga (45x16cm-18x6in) s.d.1975 white marble exhib. 10-Dec-2 Piasa, Paris #152/R
£16026 $25160 €25000 Catherine (44cm-17in) s.d.1974 onyx exhib. 10-Dec-2 Piasa, Paris #153/R est:3500

Works on paper

£316 $491 €500 Sans titre (90x62cm-35x24in) s.d. Indian ink. 28-Sep-2 Cornette de St.Cyr, Paris #330

HAJEK, Otto Herbert (1927-) Czechoslovakian

Works on paper

£949 $1472 €1500 Colour path (62x44cm-24x17in) s.d.1964 Indian ink gouache monotype paper on board. 28-Sep-2 Ketterer, Hamburg #422/R est:2000-2200

HAJEK-HALKE, Heinz (1898-1983) ?

Photographs

£2192 $3419 €3200 Nude model (40x30cm-16x12in) s.i. verso gelatin silver. 12-Apr-3 Lempertz, Koln #75/R est:3000
£2482 $4021 €3500 Ripe fruit (24x18cm-9x7in) silver gelatin. 23-May-3 Van Ham, Cologne #106/R est:3500
£5346 $8286 €8500 Eve song (24x18cm-9x7in) gelatin silver lit. 2-Nov-2 Lempertz, Koln #27/R est:6000-8000
£11321 $17547 €18000 Black and white nude (24x17cm-9x7in) s. verso gelatin silver lit. 2-Nov-2 Lempertz, Koln #28/R est:12000-15000

HAK, Ton (1946-) Dutch?

Sculpture

£2158 $3540 €3000 La deuxieme dance (57cm-22in) s.num. bronze. 3-Jun-3 Christie's, Amsterdam #178/R est:3000-5000
£2302 $3776 €3200 Liggend beeld (65cm-26in) s.num. bronze. 3-Jun-3 Christie's, Amsterdam #199/R est:3000-5000

HAKE, Claes (1945-) Swedish

Sculpture

£1261 $1968 €1892 Feffe (58cm-23in) s.num.VI/VI green pat.bronze incl wood socle. 6-Nov-2 AB Stockholms Auktionsverk #748/R est:8000-10000 (S.KR 18000)

HAKES, J A (fl.1870-1880) British

£380 $593 €570 Portrait of the paddle steamer, Powerful (36x46cm-14x18in) s.d.1916. 10-Sep-2 David Duggleby, Scarborough #366

HAKEWILL, Henry (1771-1830) British

Works on paper

£2200 $3498 €3300 Aston House, with garden views (20x28cm-8x11in) black ink over pencil set of four. 20-Mar-3 Sotheby's, London #330/R est:600-800

HAKUIN, Ekaku (1685-1768) Japanese

Works on paper

£6289 $10000 €9434 Daruma crossing the Yangtze river on a reed (27x43cm-11x17in) sealed ink hanging scroll. 24-Mar-3 Christie's, Rockefeller NY #12/R est:4500-5500

£10692 $17000 €16038 Hotei admiring the moon (34x54cm-13x21in) sealed ink hanging scroll. 24-Mar-3 Christie's, Rockefeller NY #11/R est:4000-6000
£17610 $28000 €26415 Hotei (46x82cm-18x32in) s. ink hanging scroll. 24-Mar-3 Christie's, Rockefeller NY #13/R est:5000-7000
£28302 $45000 €42453 Hoteil as a naked monk (54x63cm-21x25in) sealed ink hanging scroll. 24-Mar-3 Christie's, Rockefeller NY #14/R est:5000-7000

HALA, Jan (1890-1959) Czechoslovakian
£945 $1380 €1418 Children at fire (19x26cm-7x10in) double-sided painted c.1926-28. 4-Jun-2 SOGA, Bratislava #11/R est:48000 (SL.K 60000)
£947 $1468 €1421 Woman from Vazec (52x30cm-20x12in) painted 1929. 3-Dec-2 SOGA, Bratislava #15/R est:60000 (SL.K 60000)
£1231 $1909 €1847 Vazec village (34x49cm-13x19in) cardboard painted 1947. 3-Dec-2 SOGA, Bratislava #14/R est:75000 (SL.K 78000)

HALAPY, Janus (1893-1960) Hungarian
£782 $1221 €1173 Cherry tree - blossoming (60x80cm-24x31in) s. 11-Apr-3 Kieselbach, Budapest #1/R (H.F 280000)

HALASZ-HRADIL, Elemir (1873-1948) Czechoslovakian
£315 $460 €473 Pile of hay (24x28cm-9x11in) painted c.1940. 4-Jun-2 SOGA, Bratislava #39/R est:18000 (SL.K 20000)

HALAUSKA, Ludwig (1827-1882) German
£1135 $1771 €1703 Summer river landscape in the mountains (39x48cm-15x19in) s.d.856. 6-Nov-2 Dobiaschofsky, Bern #3397/R est:5000 (S.FR 2600)
£2025 $3200 €3200 Part of Oberbayern (81x54cm-32x21in) s. i.verso. 28-Nov-2 Dorotheum, Vienna #208/R est:3000-4000
£3205 $4968 €5000 Mountain lake in Austria (26x42cm-10x17in) s.d.855 paper on board. 4-Dec-2 Neumeister, Munich #753/R est:2400

HALBERG-KRAUSS, Fritz (1874-1951) German
£473 $738 €700 Chiemsee landscape (24x36cm-9x14in) s. panel. 26-Mar-3 Hugo Ruef, Munich #117
£513 $805 €800 Extensive country landscape near Dachau (44x60cm-17x24in) s.d.1916. 21-Nov-2 Van Ham, Cologne #1652
£701 $1079 €1100 Dachauer Moos in summer (35x57cm-14x22in) s.i. 5-Sep-2 Arnold, Frankfurt #779/R
£704 $1169 €1000 Grazing cows at river bank (28x43cm-11x17in) s.i. board. 14-Jun-3 Arnold, Frankfurt #759/R
£748 $1190 €1100 Herder with cows by woodland pond (38x50cm-15x20in) s. board. 19-Mar-3 Neumeister, Munich #579 est:800
£844 $1258 €1300 Flock of sheep in storm (15x17cm-6x7in) s. i. verso panel. 26-Jun-2 Neumeister, Munich #748
£903 $1328 €1400 Mountain lake (71x100cm-28x39in) s.i. 20-Jun-2 Dr Fritz Nagel, Stuttgart #772/R
£1013 $1600 €1600 Meadow landscape with hay wagons (15x31cm-6x12in) s. panel. 30-Nov-2 Berlinghof, Heidelberg #324 est:1200
£1039 $1548 €1600 Still pond with trees and cattle on shore (15x24cm-6x9in) s. panel. 26-Jun-2 Neumeister, Munich #747/R
£1083 $1689 €1700 Harvesting (28x42cm-11x17in) s. board. 6-Nov-2 Hugo Ruef, Munich #1126/R est:1200
£1282 $1949 €2000 Lower mountain landscape with moorland lake (28x42cm-11x17in) s. board. 11-Jul-2 Hugo Ruef, Munich #683/R est:600
£1351 $2108 €2000 Frauenisel on summer day (38x51cm-15x20in) s.i. board. 27-Mar-3 Dr Fritz Nagel, Stuttgart #809/R est:1500
£2911 $4513 €4600 Freisinger Moos (77x69cm-30x27in) s. 25-Sep-2 Neumeister, Munich #592/R est:3500

HALBIQUE, Roger Charles (1900-1977) Algerian
£4167 $6542 €6500 Grande fete a Bab Dekaken a Fez (50x63cm-20x25in) s. panel. 16-Dec-2 Gros & Delettrez, Paris #39/R est:6000-8000

HALD, Edward (1883-1980) Swedish
£1862 $3016 €2700 Women sunbathing (60x49cm-24x19in) s.d.1920 panel. 25-May-3 Uppsala Auktionskammare, Uppsala #235/R est:30000-35000 (S.KR 24000)
£6657 $10385 €9986 Figures in landscape (65x100cm-26x39in) s.d.1913 panel exhib.lit. 5-Nov-2 Bukowskis, Stockholm #54/R est:60000-80000 (S.KR 95000)

Works on paper
£349 $566 €506 Nude woman in landscape (26x21cm-10x8in) s.d.1914 W/C. 25-May-3 Uppsala Auktionskammare, Uppsala #234/R (S.KR 4500)
£741 $1163 €1112 The birth (98x69cm-39x27in) s.d.1921 mixed media panel. 16-Dec-2 Lilla Bukowskis, Stockholm #120/R (S.KR 10500)

HALE, Bernard (1812-1875) British
Works on paper
£280 $459 €420 South landing Flamborough (18x33cm-7x13in) s.d.April 1867 W/C. 10-Feb-3 David Duggleby, Scarborough #560

HALE, John (1863-1955) British
£800 $1296 €1200 Still life of irises, roses and other flowers (75x23cm-30x9in) s. canvasboard. 21-May-3 Bonhams, Knightsbridge #183/R

HALE, William Matthew (1837-1929) British
£500 $785 €750 Fishing boats in a rough sea (18x37cm-7x15in) s. board pair. 16-Dec-2 Bonhams, Bury St Edmunds #514
£545 $845 €850 Steep English coast near Ebbe with beach fisherman and their boats (61x107cm-24x42in) s. 7-Dec-2 Dannenberg, Berlin #669/R

HALEN, Francisco de Paula van (?-1887) Spanish
£649 $948 €1000 Untitled (50x64cm-20x25in) s. 12-Jun-2 Castellana, Madrid #256/R
£812 $1185 €1250 Landscape (50x64cm-20x25in) s. 12-Jun-2 Castellana, Madrid #9/R
Works on paper
£302 $471 €480 Black jockey (26x20cm-10x8in) s. wax crayon. 17-Sep-2 Segre, Madrid #306/R

HALFPENNY, Joseph (1748-1811) British
Works on paper
£600 $990 €870 Kirkham Priory, Yorkshire (30x38cm-12x15in) i.verso pencil pen grey ink W/C. 3-Jul-3 Christie's, Kensington #88/R

HALGO, A (?) ?
Sculpture
£1500 $2385 €2250 Bellerophon riding on the back of Pegasus (74cm-29in) s. bronze. 4-Mar-3 Bearnes, Exeter #532/R est:1500-2000

HALICKA, Alice (1895-1975) Polish
£1986 $3316 €2800 Scene d'interieur (29x25cm-11x10in) s. cardboard. 17-Jun-3 Claude Boisgirard, Paris #62/R est:2500-3000
£2690 $4303 €3900 Mere et fillette dans un interieur (41x33cm-16x13in) s. 12-Mar-3 Rabourdin & Choppin de Janvry, Paris #162/R
£2695 $4501 €3800 Nature morte (45x81cm-18x32in) s. painted c.1930. 23-Jun-3 Delvaux, Paris #128/R est:2500-3000
£7092 $11844 €10000 Composition a la guitaire (66x51cm-26x20in) s.d. 17-Jun-3 Claude Boisgirard, Paris #60/R est:10000-12000
£8163 $12980 €12000 Composition cubiste (50x61cm-20x24in) s.d. 3-Mar-3 Claude Boisgirard, Paris #53 est:10000-12000
Works on paper
£833 $1317 €1300 Marchand d'habits. Retour de synagogue (33x24cm-13x9in) s. one i. verso gouache over pencil two. 14-Nov-2 Neumeister, Munich #577/R

HALID (20th C) Turkish
£8163 $12980 €12000 Sur le Bosphore au clair du lune (27x61cm-11x24in) s. 24-Mar-3 Rabourdin & Choppin de Janvry, Paris #132/R est:1200-1500

HALL, Anne Marie (1945-) Australian
£464 $733 €696 Feral hunters (91x119cm-36x47in) s.d.69 i.verso. 18-Nov-2 Joel, Victoria #338 est:800-1000 (A.D 1300)

HALL, Christopher (1930-) British
£280 $434 €420 Via Garibaldi, Montpelupone (28x24cm-11x9in) s.d.1991 board. 3-Dec-2 Bonhams, Knightsbridge #176
£300 $483 €450 The Calvary, Braganza (46x39cm-18x15in) s.d.1982 board exhib. 14-Jan-3 Bonhams, Knightsbridge #53
£550 $858 €825 Farm building in a landscape (24x36cm-9x14in) s.d.June 1967 board. 15-Oct-2 Bonhams, Knightsbridge #44/R

HALL, Clifford (1904-1973) British
£260 $411 €377 Street scene (30x30cm-12x12in) s. panel prov. 28-Jul-3 David Duggleby, Scarborough #295/R
£400 $620 €600 Portrait of Hanna (41x28cm-16x11in) canvasboard prov. 4-Dec-2 Christie's, Kensington #410
£660 $1016 €990 Late afternoon, Cheyne Row (29x39cm-11x15in) s. board. 22-Oct-2 Bonhams, Bath #83
£750 $1215 €1125 Paighton Beach (25x36cm-10x14in) s. board. 20-May-3 Bonhams, Knightsbridge #170/R
£800 $1312 €1200 Wrapped bather, lying down (20x30cm-8x12in) s. board. 3-Jun-3 Sotheby's, Olympia #205/R
£900 $1395 €1350 One afternoon (35x43cm-14x17in) board prov. 4-Dec-2 Christie's, Kensington #423/R est:700-1000
£1200 $1896 €1800 Ernie of Conduit Street (61x45cm-24x18in) s. 27-Nov-2 Sotheby's, Olympia #235/R est:1200-1800
£1200 $1908 €1800 Brighton (24x35cm-9x14in) s. s.i.d.August 1950 verso. 26-Feb-3 Sotheby's, Olympia #325/R est:1200-1800
£1900 $3021 €2850 Late afternoon, Cheyne Row (29x39cm-11x15in) s.d.August 1944 verso exhib. 26-Feb-3 Sotheby's, Olympia #240/R est:800-1200

£2600 $4108 €3900 Bathers (76x102cm-30x40in) s.d.72 board. 27-Nov-2 Sotheby's, Olympia #292/R est:2000-3000

HALL, Doris (?) American
£314 $500 €471 Seated woman with vase of flowers (91x58cm-36x23in) s. 8-Mar-3 Harvey Clar, Oakland #1328

HALL, Edward (1922-1991) British
£1200 $1980 €1740 Lilie's on the roof (71x91cm-28x36in) s.d.1972 s.i.on stretcher. 3-Jul-3 Christie's, Kensington #690/R est:500-700

HALL, Frederick (1860-1948) British
£300 $474 €435 Mounted jockeys on a race course (30x46cm-12x18in) s. 22-Jul-3 Gorringes, Lewes #1542
£350 $571 €525 Switzerland, bernese oberland from near Murren (32x40cm-13x16in) s. board prov. 29-Jan-3 Dreweatt Neate, Newbury #129
£800 $1256 €1200 Open landscape with distant farmstead (48x61cm-19x24in) s. 13-Dec-2 Keys, Aylsham #691
£1700 $2771 €2550 Summer landscape, Great Barrington, in the Cotswolds (40x32cm-16x13in) s. i.verso panel. 29-Jan-3 Hampton & Littlewood, Exeter #398/R est:1500-2000
£1900 $2945 €2850 Morning on the South Downs (81x99cm-32x39in) s. board. 26-Sep-2 Lane, Penzance #240/R est:2000-3000
£2600 $4030 €3900 Christine (91x43cm-36x17in) s.i.d.1893 prov. 3-Dec-2 Bonhams, New Bond Street #11/R est:2000-3000
£10300 $15965 €15450 Portrait of a young peasant girl (20x31cm-8x12in) s.d.1886 panel. 1-Oct-2 Fellows & Sons, Birmingham #102/R est:150-250

HALL, George Henry (1825-1913) American
£1250 $2000 €1875 Children carrying fruit (94x74cm-37x29in) 16-Mar-3 Butterfields, San Francisco #1024 est:1000-1500
£1875 $3000 €2719 Portrait of a lady with a rose (56x42cm-22x17in) s.d.1887. 16-May-3 Skinner, Boston #87/R est:3000-5000
£4375 $7000 €6563 Young woman with grapes and watermelon (69x51cm-27x20in) s. 15-Mar-3 Eldred, East Dennis #344/R est:10000-15000
£4545 $7000 €6818 Little flower arranger (69x56cm-27x22in) s.d.1901 prov. 24-Oct-2 Shannon's, Milford #146/R est:7000-9000
£27097 $42000 €40646 In a rug bazaar, Cairo (121x88cm-48x35in) s.d.1877 prov.exhib. 5-Dec-2 Christie's, Rockefeller NY #51/R est:40000-60000

HALL, George Lothian (1825-1888) British
Works on paper
£900 $1422 €1305 Rocky coastal scenes with stormy waters. Coastal scene with beached hulk (30x48cm-12x19in) s.d.1868 W/C pair. 22-Jul-3 Lawrences, Bletchingley #1330/R

HALL, H R (fl.1895-1902) British
£780 $1271 €1131 Landscape with highland cattle (55x80cm-22x31in) s. 16-Jul-3 James Thompson, Kirby Lonsdale #287
£1900 $3116 €2850 Glencoe (76x127cm-30x50in) s. 29-May-3 Christie's, Kensington #85/R est:2000-3000
£2400 $3768 €3600 On the look out, Arab caravan in the desert (76x152cm-30x60in) s. s.i.verso. 21-Nov-2 Tennants, Leyburn #847/R est:1000-1500

HALL, Haines (1903-1977) American
Works on paper
£807 $1300 €1211 Guests arrive for Christmas dinner at a southern mansion (48x56cm-19x22in) s. W/C exec.c.1950. 10-May-3 Illustration House, New York #67/R

HALL, Harry (1814-1882) British
£1800 $2988 €2610 Cymbal, chestnut racehorse in a stable (43x53cm-17x21in) i. prov. 12-Jun-3 Christie's, Kensington #42/R est:2000-3000
£2200 $3432 €3300 Chopette, a bay racehorse in a stable (41x52cm-16x20in) s.i.d.1871. 26-Mar-3 Sotheby's, Olympia #141/R est:2000-3000
£2419 $3823 €3750 Dr Negro (50x61cm-20x24in) 18-Dec-2 Castellana, Madrid #4/R
£2800 $4424 €4200 Bay racehorse in a stable (43x53cm-17x21in) 28-Nov-2 Christie's, Kensington #120/R est:3000-5000
£4200 $6636 €6300 Prince Charlie in stable (41x51cm-16x20in) 27-Nov-2 Christie's, London #71/R est:3000-5000
£4800 $7488 €7200 Apology, liver chestnut racehorse (59x76cm-23x30in) s.d.1874 prov.lit. 8-Oct-2 Sotheby's, Olympia #399/R est:6000-8000
£14500 $23345 €21750 Study of a racehorse, possibley Fisherman (85x117cm-33x46in) s.d.1857-8. 19-Feb-3 Rupert Toovey, Partridge Green #88/R est:4000-6000
£22000 $34760 €33000 Prince Charlie held by his jockey (75x113cm-30x44in) s.i.d.1874 prov. 27-Nov-2 Christie's, London #69/R est:10000-15000

HALL, Henry R (?) British
£250 $380 €375 Highland cattle returning to the homestead (50x75cm-20x30in) s. s.i.verso. 4-Jul-2 Mellors & Kirk, Nottingham #850

HALL, J (?) ?
Works on paper
£300 $465 €450 Iron clippership Gauntlet of Glasgow, Capt John McGregor (43x57cm-17x22in) s.i. W/C. 24-Sep-2 Bonhams, Knightsbridge #41/R
£380 $589 €570 Full rigged ship City of Mobile off the Perch Rock Fort (50x72cm-20x28in) s.i. pencil W/C htd white. 31-Oct-2 Christie's, Kensington #362/R

HALL, James (1869-1917) American
£420 $650 €630 Hunting dog with pheasant (38x51cm-15x20in) s. 20-Jul-2 New Orleans Auction, New Orleans #753/R

HALL, John Alexander (1914-) Canadian
£1864 $2964 €2796 Tools (45x68cm-18x27in) s.i.d.1997 acrylic prov. 23-Mar-3 Hodgins, Calgary #26/R est:3000-4000 (C.D 4400)

HALL, Kenneth (1913-1946) British
£900 $1404 €1350 Howland Street (50x61cm-20x24in) s. s.i.d.stretcher prov. 17-Sep-2 Rosebery Fine Art, London #549
Works on paper
£1667 $2750 €2400 Self portrait (50x35cm-20x14in) s. W/C exhib. 7-Jul-3 Hamilton Osborne King, Dublin #195/R est:800-1200

HALL, Lady Edna Clarke (1879-1979) British
Works on paper
£650 $1034 €975 Atalanta's race (29x39cm-11x15in) W/C two lit. 26-Feb-3 Sotheby's, Olympia #54/R

HALL, Lindsay Bernard (1859-1935) Australian/British
£281 $427 €422 Pensive nun (59x45cm-23x18in) s. 19-Aug-2 Joel, Victoria #224 (A.D 800)

HALL, Nigel (1943-) British/Australian
Works on paper
£742 $1166 €1113 Composition No 158 (76x100cm-30x39in) s.i.d.1980 chl prov. 25-Nov-2 Germann, Zurich #95/R est:1800-2200 (S.FR 1700)

HALL, Oliver (1869-1957) British
£335 $559 €486 Tree landscape, North Wales (38x53cm-15x21in) s. 25-Jun-3 Goldings, Lincolnshire #335
£420 $676 €630 Bullock in a pasture with woodland and cottages (56x76cm-22x30in) 18-Feb-3 Rosebery Fine Art, London #652
£600 $936 €900 Welsh mountains (56x76cm-22x30in) s. 11-Sep-2 Bonhams, Newport #333
£700 $1113 €1050 Distant view of Loch Linnhi (61x76cm-24x30in) s. exhib. 6-Mar-3 Christie's, Kensington #127/R
£750 $1170 €1125 Mill house, Avila (56x77cm-22x30in) s. 27-Mar-3 Christie's, Kensington #523/R
£850 $1335 €1275 Bullock in a pasture with woodland and cottages (56x76cm-22x30in) s. 10-Dec-2 Rosebery Fine Art, London #594

HALL, Patrick (1906-1992) British
£380 $589 €600 Childs prayer (60x45cm-24x18in) s. i.verso. 24-Sep-2 De Veres Art Auctions, Dublin #129
Works on paper
£280 $459 €420 Estuary at Ulverston (39x56cm-15x22in) s. pencil W/C. 4-Feb-3 Bonhams, Leeds #295

HALL, Percy (20th C) Irish?
Works on paper
£479 $748 €700 Bogland (72x80cm-28x31in) s. mixed media. 8-Apr-3 James Adam, Dublin #170/R

HALL, Peter Adolphe (1739-1793) Swedish
Miniatures
£3000 $5010 €4350 Lady with a garland of flowers in her hair (6cm-2xin) rec. gilt metal frame oval exec.c.1785. 25-Jun-3 Sotheby's, Olympia #20/R est:2000-3000

HALL, Peter Adolphe (attrib) (1739-1793) Swedish
Miniatures
£3000 $4860 €4500 Lady wearing blue dress (5cm-2xin) gold mounted bonbonniere. 22-May-3 Bonhams, New Bond Street #57/R est:3000-5000

HALL, Richard (1860-1943) French
£313 $475 €470 Vaso con flores y fruto (32x26cm-13x10in) s.d.1925 board. 3-Jul-2 Naón & Cia, Buenos Aires #65

HALL, Richard (1857-1942) Swedish
£284 $440 €426 Portrait of the artist Carl Johansson (30x22cm-12x9in) s.i.d.1891 panel. 4-Dec-2 AB Stockholms Auktionsverk #1574/R (S.KR 4000)

HALL, Sydney Prior (1842-1922) British
Works on paper
£641 $1006 €1000 Studies of land leaguers (35x23cm-14x9in) i.verso pencil pair framed as one. 19-Nov-2 Hamilton Osborne King, Dublin #552/R

HALL, T W (19th C) British
£3200 $4896 €4800 Pigger, Edinburgh (52x42cm-20x17in) s.i.indis d. set of five. 22-Aug-2 Bonhams, Edinburgh #1002/R est:3000-5000

HALL, Thomas P (fl.1837-1867) British
£620 $1029 €930 Portrait of a young lady at a window (29x24cm-11x9in) s.d.1858. 10-Jun-3 Bonhams, Knightsbridge #192/R

HALL, Wendall (20th C) American
£478 $750 €717 Unhitching the horse. s.d.1983. 14-Dec-2 Charlton Hall, Columbia #462/R

HALL, William Henry (?-1880) British
Works on paper
£270 $427 €405 Coastal scene with sailing vessels and downburst of rain (32x54cm-13x21in) s.d.1876 W/C. 27-Nov-2 Bonhams, Knowle #188

HALLAM, Joseph Sydney (1898-1953) Canadian
£412 $638 €618 Kennebunkport (30x40cm-12x16in) s. panel. 3-Dec-2 Joyner, Toronto #457 est:1000-1500 (C.D 1000)
£576 $893 €864 October afternoon (60x75cm-24x30in) s. 3-Dec-2 Joyner, Toronto #268/R est:1500-2000 (C.D 1400)

HALLE, William (1912-) British
£1200 $1872 €1800 View of Battersea (61x76cm-24x30in) 12-Sep-2 Sotheby's, Olympia #108/R est:400-600

HALLER, Hermann (1880-1950) Swiss
Sculpture
£11792 $19104 €20873 Girl with hands above head (115cm-45in) gold brown pat.bronze prov.lit. 26-May-3 Sotheby's, Zurich #94/R est:25000-30000 (S.FR 25000)

HALLER, Michael (attrib) (19th C) Austrian
£822 $1282 €1200 Shepherd on river bank (26x34cm-10x13in) bears s.d.1881 one of pair. 10-Apr-3 Dorotheum, Vienna #84/R
£822 $1282 €1200 Prayer (26x34cm-10x13in) one of pair. 10-Apr-3 Dorotheum, Vienna #85/R

HALLER, Roman (1920-) Austrian
£972 $1536 €1400 Vanishing moon (45x60cm-18x24in) s. i.d.1986 stretcher. 24-Apr-3 Dorotheum, Vienna #218/R
£1266 $1975 €2000 Coloured circles in large sky (60x50cm-24x20in) s.d.1969 i. verso. 15-Oct-2 Dorotheum, Vienna #169/R est:1700-2600

HALLET, Andre (1890-1959) Belgian
£276 $439 €400 Rive Kisenyi - Lac Kivu (39x47cm-15x19in) s.i. verso panel. 4-Mar-3 Palais de Beaux Arts, Brussels #336
£306 $487 €450 Riviere en Afrique (50x60cm-20x24in) s.verso. 18-Mar-3 Vanderkindere, Brussels #25
£321 $503 €500 L'automne (53x28cm-21x11in) s. panel. 11-Dec-2 Hotel des Ventes Mosan, Brussels #288
£346 $533 €550 Port de peche (45x37cm-18x15in) s.d.1918 panel. 22-Oct-2 Galerie Moderne, Brussels #756
£374 $595 €550 Etang au parc d'Avroy a Liege (14x19cm-6x7in) panel. 19-Mar-3 Hotel des Ventes Mosan, Brussels #244
£461 $770 €650 Les vaches au pre (33x40cm-13x16in) s. panel. 18-Jun-3 Hotel des Ventes Mosan, Brussels #216
£481 $745 €750 Environs de Leopoldville. Bord de lac anime (34x40cm-13x16in) s. panel pair. 9-Dec-2 Horta, Bruxelles #31
£532 $888 €750 Museum of Tervuren with park view (38x46cm-15x18in) s. panel. 23-Jun-3 Bernaerts, Antwerp #177/R
£609 $944 €950 Effets de lumiere sur un etang (59x69cm-23x27in) s. 9-Dec-2 Horta, Bruxelles #30
£641 $994 €1000 Premieres gelees (50x65cm-20x26in) s. panel. 7-Dec-2 De Vuyst, Lokeren #146/R
£719 $1180 €1000 Vue d'Aketi, Congo (40x50cm-16x20in) s. i.verso. 3-Jun-3 Christie's, Amsterdam #36/R est:1000-1500
£750 $1245 €750 Vue du parc national Albert (35x60cm-14x24in) s.d.1934 panel. 16-Jun-3 Horta, Bruxelles #346
£755 $1209 €1050 Environs de Marseille (50x61cm-20x24in) s. cardboard. 13-May-3 Vanderkindere, Brussels #234 est:750-1000
£764 $1192 €1200 Barque sur l'Ourthe (59x68cm-23x27in) s. panel. 11-Nov-2 Horta, Bruxelles #614
£800 $1328 €800 Buste d'africaine (67x61cm-26x24in) s. panel. 16-Jun-3 Horta, Bruxelles #347
£823 $1284 €1300 Lavoir (38x45cm-15x18in) s. s.i.d.1919 verso panel. 15-Oct-2 Horta, Bruxelles #115
£966 $1545 €1400 Kutu warriers, Bomputu Congo (60x70cm-24x28in) s. 15-Mar-3 De Vuyst, Lokeren #147/R
£1007 $1612 €1400 Cap Ferrant, jardin de la Comtesse de Breteuil (37x46cm-15x18in) s. board painted 1919. 17-May-3 De Vuyst, Lokeren #196/R
£1026 $1610 €1600 Etude, jeune negresse (50x41cm-20x16in) s. s.i.verso panel. 11-Dec-2 Hotel des Ventes Mosan, Brussels #256 est:1400-1600
£1258 $1950 €2000 Dans un village Kutu, Bomputu, Zaire (79x70cm-31x28in) s.i. verso lit. 1-Oct-2 Palais de Beaux Arts, Brussels #479/R est:2000-2500
£1384 $2145 €2200 Maison du passeur au canal de louvain (60x70cm-24x28in) s. 5-Oct-2 De Vuyst, Lokeren #463/R est:3000-3600
£1392 $2172 €2200 Vue animee du port d'Ostende (80x102cm-31x40in) s. 16-Sep-2 Horta, Bruxelles #188/R
£1887 $2925 €3000 Automne (70x80cm-28x31in) s. painted 1940. 5-Oct-2 De Vuyst, Lokeren #161/R est:2800-3000
£2051 $3179 €3200 L'Estacade du port d'Ostende (80x100cm-31x39in) s.i.d.1928 prov. 3-Dec-2 Christie's, Amsterdam #29/R est:2600-3000
£2158 $3453 €3000 Grand Place, Bruxelles (71x60cm-28x24in) s. d.1920 verso. 13-May-3 Palais de Beaux Arts, Brussels #79/R est:3000-4000
£2483 $3972 €3600 Sweet waters of Out-Heverlee (60x70cm-24x28in) s. panel. 15-Mar-3 De Vuyst, Lokeren #145/R est:2200-2500

HALLETT, Dorothy S (fl.1913-30) British
Works on paper
£320 $493 €480 Portrait of a Pekingese, Ya-tze of Greystones (41x33cm-16x13in) s. pastel. 3-Sep-2 Gorringes, Lewes #2099/R
£700 $1141 €1050 Kos of Kneesworth (40x31cm-16x12in) s.i. pastel. 12-Feb-3 Bonhams, Knightsbridge #126/R

HALLETT, Hendricks (1847-1921) American
Works on paper
£416 $650 €624 Dune scene (53x43cm-21x17in) s. W/C. 1-Aug-2 Eldred, East Dennis #1088/R
£429 $700 €644 Marblehead Neck (33x48cm-13x19in) s. W/C. 2-Feb-3 Grogan, Boston #60

HALLEY, H (19/20th C) ?
£1586 $2506 €2300 Le Tower Bridge a Londres (33x41cm-13x16in) s.d.1919 cardboard. 2-Apr-3 Vanderkindere, Brussels #519/R est:400-500

HALLEY, Peter (1953-) American
£13125 $21000 €19688 Orange prison (119x112cm-47x44in) s.d.2002 acrylic rollatex on canvas in two parts prov.exhib. 14-May-3 Sotheby's, New York #437/R est:25000-35000
£18987 $30000 €28481 Matrix (213x173cm-84x68in) acrylic day-glo metal acrylic rollatex painted 1999 prov.exhib. 13-Nov-2 Sotheby's, New York #478/R est:35000-45000
£31646 $50000 €47469 Brute (229x236cm-90x93in) day-glo acrylic acrylic rol-a-tex on canvas painted 1993 prov. 12-Nov-2 Sotheby's, New York #67/R est:60000-80000
£53125 $85000 €79688 Rectangular prison with smokestack (184x316cm-72x124in) acrylic day-glo acrylic metal roll-a-tex on canvas painted 1987. 15-May-3 Phillips, New York #33/R est:80000-120000
Sculpture
£13194 $21771 €19000 Portrait of JCC (115x89x9cm-45x35x4in) s.d.1997 verso acrylic Day-glo acrylic Roll-a-Tex canvas prov. 3-Jul-3 Christie's, Paris #27/R est:20000-30000

HALLIDAY, Brian (?) New Zealander
£269 $392 €404 Lifting clouds, Remarkables, Queenstown (48x64cm-19x25in) s. 12-Sep-1 Watson's, Christchurch #50 est:700-1200 (NZ.D 900)
£1211 $1888 €1817 Summer walk, Ohawe Akaroa Harbour (50x60cm-20x24in) s. board. 27-Mar-3 International Art Centre, Auckland #125/R est:3000-4000 (NZ.D 3450)

HALLIDAY, T (?) ?
£561 $887 €842 Nude (91x61cm-36x24in) s. 26-Nov-2 Louis Morton, Mexico #49/R (M.P 9000)

HALLMAN, Adolf (1893-1968) Swedish
£2523 $3936 €3785 Times Square, New York (101x150cm-40x59in) painted 1950s exhib. 5-Nov-2 Bukowskis, Stockholm #274/R est:25000-30000 (S.KR 36000)

HALLMAN, Gustaf (1800-1865) Swedish
Works on paper
£659 $1068 €956 King Karl XIV Johan (9x7cm-4x3in) s.d.1820 gouache. 26-May-3 Bukowskis, Stockholm #504a/R (S.KR 8500)

HALLMAN, Magnus (1745-1822) Swedish
£340 $530 €510 Saint Birgitta. i.verso. 5-Aug-2 Rasmussen, Vejle #2061 (D.KR 4000)

HALLMARK, George (1949-) American
£10035 $15455 €15053 Avant-hier (122x91cm-48x36in) 25-Oct-2 Morris & Whiteside, Hilton Head Island #118 est:18000-20000

HALLOWELL, George Hawley (1871-1926) American
Works on paper
£2830 $4500 €4245 Woods supper (48x66cm-19x26in) s. W/C on board prov.exhib. 4-Mar-3 Christie's, Rockefeller NY #88/R est:6000-8000

HALLSTROM, Carl (1850-1929) Swedish
£377 $581 €600 Moonlight (47x82cm-19x32in) s. 27-Oct-2 Bukowskis, Helsinki #321/R
£949 $1481 €1500 In the forest (68x102cm-27x40in) s.d.1887. 15-Sep-2 Bukowskis, Helsinki #332/R est:1800

HALLSTROM, Eric (1893-1946) Swedish
£439 $685 €659 The wash-house in snow (54x66cm-21x26in) s. exhib.prov. 13-Sep-2 Lilla Bukowskis, Stockholm #416 (S.KR 6400)
£480 $730 €720 Autumn landscape with buildings (24x36cm-9x14in) s. 16-Aug-2 Lilla Bukowskis, Stockholm #31 (S.KR 7000)
£561 $875 €842 Boy reading (70x81cm-28x32in) s. painted 1937. 6-Nov-2 AB Stockholms Auktionsverk #652/R (S.KR 8000)
£701 $1093 €1052 Autumn (45x55cm-18x22in) s. panel painted 1939 exhib. 6-Nov-2 AB Stockholms Auktionsverk #653/R (S.KR 10000)
£806 $1257 €1209 Window towards the woods (50x43cm-20x17in) s. panel painted 1935. 6-Nov-2 AB Stockholms Auktionsverk #667/R (S.KR 11500)
£951 $1502 €1427 Riddarfjarden and Norrmalarstrand (20x34cm-8x13in) s. panel painted 1920s. 28-Apr-3 Bukowskis, Stockholm #86/R (S.KR 12500)
£989 $1562 €1484 Bandy players at Edsviken (26x35cm-10x14in) s. canvas on panel exhib. 28-Apr-3 Bukowskis, Stockholm #83/R (S.KR 13000)
£1120 $1803 €1680 French town scene with park (43x43cm-17x17in) indis sig.i.d.29. 7-May-3 AB Stockholms Auktionsverk #835/R est:8000-10000 (S.KR 14500)
£1296 $2022 €1944 Poppies (73x60cm-29x24in) s. exhib. 6-Nov-2 AB Stockholms Auktionsverk #662/R est:15000-20000 (S.KR 18500)
£1402 $2186 €2103 In the studio (52x64cm-20x25in) s. 5-Nov-2 Bukowskis, Stockholm #177/R est:20000-25000 (S.KR 20000)
£1489 $2309 €2234 From Stockholm (34x49cm-13x19in) s. cardboard on panel. 8-Dec-2 Uppsala Auktionskammare, Uppsala #220/R est:20000-30000 (S.KR 21000)
£1597 $2523 €2396 Children playing, Aakero (67x83cm-26x33in) s. painted 1943 exhib. 28-Apr-3 Bukowskis, Stockholm #180a/R est:30000-40000 (S.KR 21000)
£1636 $2601 €2454 From Guldgrand (69x82cm-27x32in) s. 3-Mar-3 Lilla Bukowskis, Stockholm #13 est:25000-30000 (S.KR 22000)
£1892 $2952 €2838 The lock in Beaucaire (54x73cm-21x29in) s. painted 1926. 6-Nov-2 AB Stockholms Auktionsverk #679/R est:30000-40000 (S.KR 27000)
£2102 $3280 €3153 Pulling up the boats (64x74cm-25x29in) s. canvas on panel. 5-Nov-2 Bukowskis, Stockholm #93b/R est:35000-40000 (S.KR 30000)
£2523 $3936 €3785 Small town in France (47x45cm-19x18in) s. panel. 6-Nov-2 AB Stockholms Auktionsverk #687/R est:20000-25000 (S.KR 36000)
£2780 $4476 €4170 The sailing boat (63x78cm-25x31in) s. exhib.lit. 7-May-3 AB Stockholms Auktionsverk #815/R est:30000-35000 (S.KR 36000)
£3475 $5595 €5213 Southern landscape (27x23cm-11x9in) s. 7-May-3 AB Stockholms Auktionsverk #751/R est:60000-80000 (S.KR 45000)
£4563 $7209 €6845 From Polhemsgatan, Stockholm (60x74cm-24x29in) s.d.1930 prov.exhib.lit. 28-Apr-3 Bukowskis, Stockholm #91/R est:60000-80000 (S.KR 60000)
£28031 $43728 €42047 Southern Bergen from Malartorget (37x45cm-15x18in) s.i. panel prov.exhib.lit. 5-Nov-2 Bukowskis, Stockholm #93c/R est:400000-450000 (S.KR 400000)
£29432 $45915 €44148 Street in Strangnas (51x70cm-20x28in) s.d.17 prov.exhib.lit. 5-Nov-2 Bukowskis, Stockholm #26b/R est:300000-350000 (S.KR 420000)
Works on paper
£520 $828 €780 The artist's daughter Christina (42x52cm-17x20in) s. pastel prov. 3-Mar-3 Lilla Bukowskis, Stockholm #781 (S.KR 7000)
£565 $886 €848 In the garden (41x49cm-16x19in) s. pastel. 16-Dec-2 Lilla Bukowskis, Stockholm #38 (S.KR 8000)
£1141 $1802 €1712 Newly fallen snow (49x63cm-19x25in) s. pastel exhib. 28-Apr-3 Bukowskis, Stockholm #82/R est:20000-25000 (S.KR 15000)

HALLSTROM, Staffan (1914-1976) Swedish
£502 $808 €753 Double-dealing (23x29cm-9x11in) init. d.1967 verso. 7-May-3 AB Stockholms Auktionsverk #970/R (S.KR 6500)
£3042 $4806 €4563 Late autumn (91x116cm-36x46in) s. exhib. 28-Apr-3 Bukowskis, Stockholm #279/R est:30000-35000 (S.KR 40000)
£5792 $9324 €8688 Homeward journey (104x115cm-41x45in) init.d.65 exhib. 7-May-3 AB Stockholms Auktionsverk #1066/R est:60000-80000 (S.KR 75000)

HALMHUBER, Heinrich (1852-1908) German
Works on paper
£252 $392 €400 Scenes from ceiling painting (23x32cm-9x13in) s.i.d.1881 W/C board. 9-Oct-2 Michael Zeller, Lindau #710/R

HALMI, Arthur (1866-1939) Hungarian
£252 $400 €378 Artist's son at easel. oval. 22-Mar-3 Nadeau, Windsor #443
£2322 $3622 €3483 Little girl (54x34cm-21x13in) s. board. 11-Sep-2 Kieselbach, Budapest #55/R (H.F 900000)

HALNON, Frederick James (1881-?) British
Sculpture
£1300 $2002 €1950 Bacchante (35cm-14in) s. bronze marble base. 28-Oct-2 Sotheby's, Olympia #79/R est:1200-1800

HALONEN, Arttu (1885-1965) Finnish
Sculpture
£1690 $2721 €2400 Mother and child (40cm-16in) s.d.1913 bronze. 10-May-3 Bukowskis, Helsinki #2/R est:800-1000

HALONEN, Eino (1915-1941) Finnish
Sculpture
£1709 $2700 €2700 Female nude (62cm-24in) s. bronze. 30-Nov-2 Hagelstam, Helsinki #13/R est:2000

HALONEN, Emil (1875-1950) Finnish
Sculpture
£1329 $2100 €2100 Kyllikki (34cm-13in) s.d.1941 bronze. 1-Dec-2 Bukowskis, Helsinki #3/R est:1200-1400
£1511 $2417 €2100 Boy with water lily (26cm-10in) s.d.1909 bronze. 17-May-3 Hagelstam, Helsinki #12/R est:1000

HALONEN, Kalle (1899-1947) Finnish
£475 $741 €750 Boats on beach (65x54cm-26x21in) s. 12-Sep-2 Hagelstam, Helsinki #829/R

HALONEN, Pekka (1865-1933) Finnish
£1962 $3061 €3100 I Jaaskisdrakt - the artist's wife Maija in interior (49x41cm-19x16in) painted c.1905. 15-Sep-2 Bukowskis, Helsinki #196/R est:2500
£2621 $4141 €3800 Waterfall (70x44cm-28x17in) 3-Apr-3 Hagelstam, Helsinki #844/R est:3500
£3097 $4893 €4800 View across the sea (80x48cm-31x19in) 19-Dec-2 Hagelstam, Helsinki #800
£5755 $9209 €8000 View of fields (58x78cm-23x31in) s.d.1913. 17-May-3 Hagelstam, Helsinki #117/R est:8000
£6209 $10183 €9500 Coastal cliffs (61x46cm-24x18in) s.d.1925. 9-Feb-3 Bukowskis, Helsinki #249/R est:9000
£6329 $10000 €10000 Kivikoski - river through large stones (73x51cm-29x20in) s.d.1916 board exhib.lit. 1-Dec-2 Bukowskis, Helsinki #63/R est:11000-13000
£6329 $10000 €10000 Coastal cliffs (61x54cm-24x21in) s.d.1908 lit. 1-Dec-2 Bukowskis, Helsinki #65/R est:10000-12000
£7483 $11898 €11000 Summer's day (46x37cm-18x15in) s.d.1923. 24-Mar-3 Bukowskis, Helsinki #76/R est:8000
£8544 $13500 €13500 Sawing the logs (57x33cm-22x13in) s.d.1909 canvas on board. 1-Dec-2 Bukowskis, Helsinki #67/R est:7000-8000

£13291 $21000 €21000 White roses (76x53cm-30x21in) s.d.1913 lit. 30-Nov-2 Hagelstam, Helsinki #126/R est:20000

HALPERN, Jacques (1925-) ?

£3425 $5377 €5000 Untitled (60x73cm-24x29in) s.d.47 cardboard. 15-Apr-3 Laurence Calmels, Paris #4221/R

HALPERN, Stanislau (1919-1969) ?

£800 $1304 €1200 Untitled (120x120cm-47x47in) s. 3-Feb-3 Sotheby's, Olympia #81/R

HALPERT, Samuel (1884-1930) American

£1730 $2750 €2595 Country landscape (51x61cm-20x24in) 5-Mar-3 Doyle, New York #30/R est:2500-3500

£10191 $16000 €15287 Interior scene with still life of flowers (70x60cm-28x24in) s.d.20 prov. 14-Dec-2 Weschler, Washington #708/R est:3000-5000

HALPIN, Janet Cruise (20th C) Irish?

£296 $491 €420 Decorative male sitting (74x59cm-29x23in) s. 10-Jun-3 James Adam, Dublin #60/R

HALS, Frans (elder) (c.1580-1666) Dutch

£1604938 $2600000 €2407407 Portrait of a gentleman in a black coat and cape holding gloves (108x80cm-43x31in) prov.exhib.lit. 23-Jan-3 Sotheby's, New York #37a/R est:2000000-3000000

HALS, Frans (style) (16/17th C) Dutch

£18065 $28000 €27098 Portrait of a gentleman, holding a pair of gloves (86x66cm-34x26in) prov.exhib.lit. 2-Oct-2 Christie's, Rockefeller NY #164/R est:8000-12000

HALS, Harmen (1611-1669) Dutch

£1800 $2790 €2700 Interior scene with peasants singing and woman playing recorder (36x27cm-14x11in) mono. i.verso panel. 31-Oct-2 Sotheby's, Olympia #52/R est:2000-3000

£5063 $8000 €8000 Inn interior (36x36cm-14x14in) indis.mono. panel prov. 27-Nov-2 Christie's, Paris #7/R est:10000-15000

HALSALL, William Formby (1841-1919) American

£3503 $5500 €5255 Evening harbour scene with departing brig (61x91cm-24x36in) s. 26-Jul-2 Eldred, East Dennis #530/R est:7000-9000

HALSEY, William (19/20th C) American

£308 $475 €462 Ocean sunset (30x46cm-12x18in) s. painted c.1900. 8-Sep-2 Treadway Gallery, Cincinnati #609/R

HALSMAN, Philippe (1906-1972) American

Photographs

£4808 $7500 €7212 Albert Einstein (50x42cm-20x17in) s.i. silver. 21-Oct-2 Swann Galleries, New York #152/R est:7000-10000

HALSTEINSON, Johannes (attrib) (17th C) Norwegian?

£380 $615 €570 Woman threading a needle (43x42cm-17x17in) s. 27-Jan-3 Blomqvist, Lysaker #1071 (N.KR 4200)

HALSWELLE, Keeley (1832-1891) British

£3000 $4770 €4500 Early rise, delivering the lumber at dawn (107x184cm-42x72in) s.d.1880. 4-Mar-3 Bonhams, Knightsbridge #282/R est:2000-3000

£4800 $7296 €7200 Head of Loch Awe and Kilchurn Castle (61x91cm-24x36in) s.d.1888 s.i.on stretcher. 28-Aug-2 Sotheby's, London #919/R est:3000-4000

£6000 $9540 €9000 Breezy common, Thorpeness (104x179cm-41x70in) s.d.1888 prov. 18-Mar-3 Bonhams, New Bond Street #50/R est:6000-9000

£100000 $161000 €150000 Play scene in Hamlet (142x254cm-56x100in) s.d.1878 prov.exhib.lit. 20-Feb-3 Christie's, London #242/R est:60000

HAMACHER, Willy (1865-1909) German

£382 $589 €600 Coastal view along the French Riviera (101x127cm-40x50in) s. 3-Sep-2 Christie's, Amsterdam #151

HAMAGUCHI, Yozo (1909-) Japanese

Prints

£1887 $3000 €2831 Poplar (20x27cm-8x11in) s.num.42/50 col mezzotint. 29-Apr-3 Christie's, Rockefeller NY #474/R est:3500-4500

£1899 $3000 €2849 Blue glass (23x33cm-9x13in) s.d.1957 num.9/50 col mezzotint. 12-Nov-2 Doyle, New York #231/R est:4000-6000

£2013 $3200 €3020 Bowl of cherries (46x62cm-18x24in) s.num.43/50 col aquatint. 7-Mar-3 Skinner, Boston #56/R est:700-900

£2244 $3500 €3366 Cherries (38x28cm-15x11in) s.num.45/75 col mezzotint. 5-Nov-2 Christie's, Rockefeller NY #163/R est:5000-7000

£2483 $3923 €3600 Still life of cherries in bowl (57x46cm-22x18in) s.i. num.2/2 col aquatint. 2-Apr-3 Dr Fritz Nagel, Stuttgart #9478/R est:1100

£2500 $3875 €3750 Black cherry (20x27cm-8x11in) s.num.12/50 mezzotint. 5-Dec-2 Sotheby's, London #133/R est:3000-4000

£2516 $4000 €3774 Fourteen cherries (53x25cm-21x10in) s.num.2/50 col mezzotint. 29-Apr-3 Christie's, Rockefeller NY #475/R est:3500-4500

£2673 $4250 €4010 Bottle with one and one quarter lemons (62x474cm-24x187in) s.i. hand col mezzotint. 2-May-3 Sotheby's, New York #166/R est:5000-7000

£5346 $8500 €8019 Watermelon (23x54cm-9x21in) s.num.16/150 mezzotint. 2-May-3 Sotheby's, New York #174/R est:6000-8000

£11511 $18417 €16000 Roofs of Paris (15x20cm-6x8in) s.i. num.36/50 col mezzotint lit. 15-May-3 Neumeister, Munich #449/R est:5000-6000

HAMALAINEN, Vaino (1876-1940) Finnish

£408 $649 €600 Berghalls Church (50x42cm-20x17in) s.d.1917. 27-Feb-3 Hagelstam, Helsinki #912/R

£440 $682 €700 At the spinning-wheel (39x31cm-15x12in) s. 6-Oct-2 Bukowskis, Helsinki #194/R

£503 $775 €800 Lady (42x38cm-17x15in) s.d.1904. 24-Oct-2 Hagelstam, Helsinki #973

£667 $1027 €1060 Home beach (38x55cm-15x22in) s. 24-Oct-2 Hagelstam, Helsinki #923

£680 $1082 €1000 Interior (53x42cm-21x17in) s.d.1907. 24-Mar-3 Bukowskis, Helsinki #100/R

£1392 $2200 €2200 Wind coming from the west (39x31cm-15x12in) s. canvas on board. 1-Dec-2 Bukowskis, Helsinki #68/R est:2000-2300

£1655 $2647 €2300 Beached boats (43x76cm-17x30in) s.d.1909. 17-May-3 Hagelstam, Helsinki #148/R est:2500

£1690 $2721 €2400 Coastal landscape, Hogland (32x41cm-13x16in) s.i.d.28. 10-May-3 Bukowskis, Helsinki #35/R est:2000-2300

£2152 $3400 €3400 Girl having picked mushrooms (61x50cm-24x20in) s.d.1921 exhib. 30-Nov-2 Hagelstam, Helsinki #110/R est:2500

HAMBACH, Johann Michael (attrib) (17th C) German

£3459 $5327 €5500 Nature morte a la coupe de poires et plats d'etain (65x81cm-26x32in) 25-Oct-2 Tajan, Paris #83/R est:2300-3000

HAMBACH, Johann Michael (circle) (17th C) German

£7000 $11690 €10150 Stoneware jug on pewter salver and other objects on a table (35x46cm-14x18in) panel. 9-Jul-3 Bonhams, New Bond Street #173/R est:5000-7000

HAMBIDGE, Jay (1867-1924) Canadian

£7547 $12000 €11321 Central Park mall (51x70cm-20x28in) s. 5-Mar-3 Sotheby's, New York #62/R est:10000-15000

Works on paper

£932 $1500 €1398 Italian religious procession (53x41cm-21x16in) s.d. W/C en grisaille. 10-May-3 Illustration House, New York #161/R est:1500-3000

HAMBLE, M (20th C) ?

Works on paper

£260 $395 €390 Harbour scene with various shipping (25x36cm-10x14in) s.d.1918 W/C. 17-Sep-2 Henry Adams, Chichester #128

HAMBLIN, E C (1833-1902) British

£300 $468 €450 Anglers by a Highland river (60x92cm-24x36in) s. 15-Sep-2 Lots Road, London #332

HAMBLIN, Sturtevant J (attrib) (fl.1837-1856) American

£11585 $19000 €16798 Portrait of a girl in blue, holding a fan (53x38cm-21x15in) 8-Jun-3 Skinner, Boston #80/R est:7000-9000

HAMBLIN-SMITH, M J (20th C) British

£300 $477 €450 Old Easter's dreaming youth pan seated in a woodland landscape at twilight (36x47cm-14x19in) oil on paper. 6-Mar-3 Bonhams, Cornwall #738

HAMBLING, Maggi (1945-) British

£340 $541 €510 Lovers. s.i.d.77/78 acrylic on paper. 18-Mar-3 Bonhams, Knightsbridge #89

£360 $576 €540 Before sunrise (48x61cm-19x24in) s.d. 8-Jan-3 Brightwells, Leominster #1096

£1200 $2004 €1740 Lady singing (76x61cm-30x24in) s.i.d.July-August 1972 verso. 17-Jun-3 Rosebery Fine Art, London #537/R est:300-400

£1800 $2826 €2700 Welsh black heifer (53x43cm-21x17in) s.d.86 i.verso. 20-Nov-2 Sotheby's, Olympia #54/R est:600-800

Works on paper

£480 $802 €696 Sunset (60x48cm-24x19in) s.i.d.88 W/C exhib. 17-Jun-3 Bonhams, Knightsbridge #70/R

£600 $1002 €870 Sunrise (47x60cm-19x24in) s.d.12.8.91 W/C. 17-Jun-3 Bonhams, Knightsbridge #13/R
£700 $1085 €1050 Sunrise, Hadleigh, Suffolk (61x48cm-24x19in) s.d.13.9.91/2 W/C ink. 30-Sep-2 Bonhams, Ipswich #354/R
£700 $1113 €1050 Untitled (101x64cm-40x25in) s.i. mixed media. 18-Mar-3 Bonhams, Knightsbridge #87
£750 $1193 €1125 Falling bull (82x61cm-32x24in) s. chl. 18-Mar-3 Bonhams, Knightsbridge #88

HAMBOURG, Andre (1909-1999) French
£1899 $2962 €3000 Paysage (27x35cm-11x14in) s. painted c.1935. 20-Oct-2 Chayette & Cheval, Paris #71/R
£2177 $3461 €3200 Pont-neuf (38x46cm-15x18in) s. painted c.1937. 24-Mar-3 Claude Boisgirard, Paris #50/R
£2244 $3522 €3500 Apres-midi a saint-Remy de Provence (22x35cm-9x14in) s. i.verso. 15-Dec-2 Lombrail & Teucquam, Paris #15/R
£2329 $3656 €3400 Palette de l'artiste representant des voiliers (28x41cm-11x16in) s.i.d.1993. 21-Apr-3 Rabourdin & Choppin de Janvry, Paris #144/R est:3000-3500
£2600 $4134 €3900 Beau temps calme (22x28cm-9x11in) s. init.i.verso prov. 20-Mar-3 Sotheby's, Olympia #136/R est:3000-5000
£2724 $4250 €4086 Temps doux a Deauville (11x24cm-4x9in) s. init.i.d.1988 verso prov. 14-Oct-2 Butterfields, San Francisco #2000/R est:3000-5000
£2785 $4400 €4400 La Seine et Notre-Dame (50x61cm-20x24in) s.d.1926. 2-Dec-2 Tajan, Paris #81/R
£3205 $4968 €5000 Torse de jeune fille rousse (55x46cm-22x18in) s. s.i.d.1931 verso prov.lit. 9-Dec-2 Beaussant & Lefèvre, Paris #61/R
£3694 $5763 €5800 Venise, Riva degli Schiavohi (27x34cm-11x13in) s.i.d. init. verso. 7-Nov-2 Claude Aguttes, Neuilly #48/R est:6000-7000
£3774 $6000 €5661 Entree du port a Deauville (16x27cm-6x11in) s. init.i.d.1968 verso prov. 27-Feb-3 Christie's, Rockefeller NY #88/R est:6000
£3819 $6073 €5500 Les regates (22x35cm-9x14in) s. i.d.1956 verso. 29-Apr-3 Artcurial Briest, Paris #268/R est:6000-8000
£4140 $6500 €6210 La lecon d'equitation dans la carriere en autumne (8x20cm-3x8in) s. init.i.verso prov. 10-Dec-2 Doyle, New York #242/R est:6000-8000
£5096 $8000 €7644 Trouville, le port (4x7cm-2x3in) s. init.i.verso prov. 10-Dec-2 Doyle, New York #243/R est:4000-6000
£5135 $8011 €7600 Mauresque d'Alger (55x46cm-22x18in) s.i.d.1934 lit. 28-Mar-3 Claude Aguttes, Neuilly #213/R est:9000
£5208 $8229 €7500 Entree du port (27x35cm-11x14in) s. 25-Apr-3 Piasa, Paris #12/R
£7200 $11448 €10800 Maree Haute, beau temps (38x46cm-15x18in) s. init.i.d.1964 verso prov. 20-Mar-3 Sotheby's, Olympia #144/R est:7000-9000
£7292 $12031 €10500 Al la grande cour, Honfleur (81x100cm-32x39in) s.i.d.1977 s.i.verso. 2-Jul-3 Artcurial Briest, Paris #712/R est:12000-16000
£8176 $13000 €12264 Petit voilier rouge (16x22cm-6x9in) s. init.i.verso prov. 27-Feb-3 Christie's, Rockefeller NY #90/R est:7000
£8904 $13979 €13000 Bouquet de fleurs (72x60cm-28x24in) s. s.i.d.1949 verso. 21-Apr-3 Rabourdin & Choppin de Janvry, Paris #143/R est:12000-13000
£9494 $14715 €15000 Soleil, maree basse a Trouville (54x65cm-21x26in) s. init.i.verso prov. 28-Sep-2 Christie's, Paris #29/R est:12000-18000
£10000 $16000 €15000 Premiere de planches a voile dans l'estuaire de la touques (65x81cm-26x32in) s.d.1977 i.verso. 14-May-3 Butterfields, San Francisco #1178/R est:8000-12000
£12739 $19873 €20000 Soleil a maree basse sur la plage de Trouville (54x65cm-21x26in) s. i.verso. 10-Nov-2 Eric Pillon, Calais #105/R
£15878 $24770 €23500 Famille marocaine (60x73cm-24x29in) s.i. 28-Mar-3 Claude Aguttes, Neuilly #212/R est:6000-9000
Works on paper
£230 $373 €350 Venise (3x10cm-1x4in) mono. pen dr prov. 22-Jan-3 Tajan, Paris #62
£338 $527 €500 Echouee dans un port (23x32cm-9x13in) s.i. ink wash. 28-Mar-3 Delvaux, Paris #59a
£496 $804 €700 Le Photographe (30x30cm-12x12in) s.d.1972 pen. 23-May-3 Camard, Paris #158
£986 $1637 €1400 La plage (17x23cm-7x9in) s. col crayon dr. 16-Jun-3 Oger, Dumont, Paris #26
£994 $1510 €1550 Honfleur (40x60cm-16x24in) s.i. pastel ink exec.1949 exhib. 16-Aug-2 Deauville, France #50/R
£1026 $1590 €1600 Alger (19x28cm-7x11in) s.i.d.1943 ink dr htd wash. 9-Dec-2 Beaussant & Lefèvre, Paris #57/R
£1186 $1803 €1850 Chalutier a quai (29x21cm-11x8in) s.i.d.1975 Chinese ink wash. 16-Aug-2 Deauville, France #49
£4487 $7045 €7000 Foire du Trone (85x176cm-33x69in) s.i.d.1959 W/C. 15-Dec-2 Lombrail & Teucquam, Paris #17/R

HAMBRESIN, Albrecht (1850-1937) Belgian
Sculpture
£1497 $2380 €2200 Bust of young oriental woman (68cm-27in) s. green pat.bronze Cast.Compagnie des Bronzes. 24-Mar-3 Bernaerts, Antwerp #43/R est:2500-3000

HAMBUCHEN, Wilhelm (1869-1939) German
£302 $465 €480 Fishing boats by shore (39x49cm-15x19in) s. board. 23-Oct-2 Neumeister, Munich #650
£350 $550 €525 Day's sailing on the river (35x48cm-14x19in) s. 16-Apr-3 Christie's, Kensington #835
£476 $757 €700 Sailing boats on North Sea (51x61cm-20x24in) s. 28-Mar-3 Bolland & Marotz, Bremen #457/R
£769 $1208 €1200 Sylt (30x40cm-12x16in) s. board. 21-Nov-2 Van Ham, Cologne #1653
£1667 $2633 €2600 Unloading the catch (67x86cm-26x34in) s. 16-Nov-2 Lempertz, Koln #1471 est:1000

HAMEL, Michel (20th C) French
Works on paper
£2431 $3840 €3500 Poussieres d'anges (82x68cm-32x27in) pastel gras. 28-Apr-3 Cornette de St.Cyr, Paris #409 est:3500-4000

HAMEL, Otto (1866-1950) German
£253 $392 €400 Square in front of town hall, Bremen (71x91cm-28x36in) i. 27-Sep-2 Dr Fritz Nagel, Leipzig #3950/R
£345 $545 €500 Bremen town square (71x91cm-28x36in) i. 5-Apr-3 Dr Fritz Nagel, Leipzig #3964/R
£409 $638 €650 Versailles park (52x67cm-20x26in) s.d.1912. 21-Sep-2 Berlinghof, Heidelberg #124
£510 $795 €800 Chioggia near Venice (28x38cm-11x15in) s. 6-Nov-2 Hugo Ruef, Munich #1127/R
£696 $1100 €1100 Interior view of Ottobeuren monastery (92x72cm-36x28in) s. 30-Nov-2 Berlinghof, Heidelberg #325/R

HAMEL, Theophile (1817-1870) Canadian
£3333 $5467 €5000 Portrait of Joseph Charles Tache (120x90cm-47x35in) arched corners prov. 3-Jun-3 Joyner, Toronto #356/R est:10000-15000 (C.D 7500)

HAMEL, Willem (1860-1924) Dutch
£411 $600 €617 Dutch street scene (61x51cm-24x20in) s.d.49. 3-Nov-1 North East Auctions, Portsmouth #1011/R

HAMER, Edward (1877-1960) American
£351 $550 €527 Harvest time (41x51cm-16x20in) s. canvasboard. 23-Nov-2 Jackson's, Cedar Falls #88/R

HAMERTON, Robert Jacob (fl.1831-1858) British
Works on paper
£340 $524 €510 Kidwelly Castle, Wales (34x49cm-13x19in) s.d.1835 W/C. 5-Sep-2 Morphets, Harrogate #377

HAMILTON, Ann (1956-) American
Photographs
£8861 $14000 €13292 Untitled (11x11cm-4x4in) black/white photograph in 3 parts prov. 13-Nov-2 Sotheby's, New York #501/R est:18000-22000
£10127 $16000 €15191 Untitled (11x11cm-4x4in) black/white photograph in 3 parts prov. 13-Nov-2 Sotheby's, New York #500/R est:18000-22000
£10759 $17000 €16139 Untitled (11x11cm-4x4in) black/white photograph exec.1993 prov. 13-Nov-2 Sotheby's, New York #499/R est:18000-22000
Sculpture
£9375 $15000 €14063 Slaughter (10x47x35cm-4x19x14in) silk organza cotton thread oil in four parts executed 1997. 14-May-3 Sotheby's, New York #350/R est:20000-30000

HAMILTON, Carl Wilhelm de (1668-1754) Austrian
£28000 $46760 €40600 Forest floor still lifes with butterflies, grasshopper and snails (37x29cm-15x11in) copper pair. 9-Jul-3 Christie's, London #56/R est:30000-50000

HAMILTON, Carl Wilhelm de (attrib) (1668-1754) Austrian
£1892 $2951 €2800 Still life with thistle plant, reptiles, snail and insects (37x28cm-15x11in) canvas on board. 27-Mar-3 Dr Fritz Nagel, Stuttgart #769/R est:2600

HAMILTON, Eva H (1880-1959) British
£3472 $5521 €5000 Estuary, Malahide (44x44cm-17x17in) i.on stretcher exhib. 29-Apr-3 Whyte's, Dublin #37/R est:5000-7000
£10000 $16000 €15000 Summer's day in the west (51x61cm-20x24in) init. 16-May-3 Sotheby's, London #73/R est:10000-15000

HAMILTON, Frank Moss (1930-) American
Works on paper
£315 $500 €473 Beyond the reef, Lahaina, Maui, Hawaii (55x75cm-22x30in) s.i. W/C board. 7-Mar-3 Skinner, Boston #438/R

HAMILTON, Gavin (attrib) (1723-1798) British
£3145 $4874 €5000 St John the Evangelist (103x82cm-41x32in) 2-Oct-2 Dorotheum, Vienna #6/R est:5000-7000

HAMILTON, Gustavus (1739-1775) Irish
Miniatures
£696 $1100 €1100 Portrait of a lady in a blue dress (4x3cm-2x1in) W/C oval giltwood and gesso frame. 27-Nov-2 James Adam, Dublin #102/R
£2300 $3588 €3450 Mr and Mrs Blair he wearing grey coat with gold buttons she decollete dress (4cm-2xin) s.d.176. gold frame blue glass border plaited hair oval pair. 5-Nov-2 Bonhams, New Bond Street #51/R est:1000-1500

HAMILTON, Hamilton (1847-1928) American/British
£9494 $15000 €14241 Story time (30x51cm-12x20in) s. 24-Apr-3 Shannon's, Milford #76/R est:15000-20000

HAMILTON, Hildegard (1906-) American
£710 $1100 €1065 Grammercy Park (46x38cm-18x15in) s.i.d. 8-Dec-2 Toomey, Oak Park #619/R

HAMILTON, Hugh Douglas (1739-1808) British
£3500 $5600 €5250 Portrait of gentleman, beleived to be Robert La Touche (20x15cm-8x6in) panel. 15-May-3 Christie's, London #13/R est:3000-5000
Works on paper
£750 $1170 €1125 Portrait of an officer (27x22cm-11x9in) s.d.1770 i.verso black col chk oval. 17-Sep-2 Rosebery Fine Art, London #635/R
£1611 $2593 €2400 Portrait (25x22cm-10x9in) s.d.1770 i.verso pastel prov. 18-Feb-3 Whyte's, Dublin #100/R est:2500-3500
£2564 $3974 €4000 Portrait, purportedly of Princess Elizabeth (35x29cm-14x11in) pastel oval. 3-Dec-2 Bonhams & James Adam, Dublin #18/R est:2000-3000
£8000 $12800 €12000 Portrait of John Viscount Crosbie. Portrait of of his wife. Lady Diana Sackville (24x19cm-9x7in) i. pastel over pencil pair. 16-May-3 Sotheby's, London #18/R est:4000-6000

HAMILTON, Hugh Douglas (attrib) (1739-1808) British
Works on paper
£440 $678 €660 Portrait of lady (15x13cm-6x5in) pen ink chk oval. 25-Oct-2 Gorringes, Lewes #878
£1000 $1560 €1500 Portrait of a lady three quarter length (24x19cm-9x7in) pastel. 26-Mar-3 Hamptons Fine Art, Godalming #39/R est:1000-1500

HAMILTON, James (1819-1878) American
£1146 $1800 €1719 Gale (61x102cm-24x40in) s.i. 10-Dec-2 Doyle, New York #29/R est:2000-3000
£1529 $2400 €2294 Ship at sea, sunset (53x76cm-21x30in) s. i.indis d.1973 verso. 10-Dec-2 Doyle, New York #28/R est:3000-4000
£3395 $5500 €4923 Shore at twilight (53x76cm-21x30in) c.1867 prov.exhib. 21-May-3 Doyle, New York #56/R est:3000-5000
£3892 $6500 €5643 Sunset on the Nile (76x127cm-30x50in) s.d.69. 22-Jun-3 Freeman, Philadelphia #93/R est:4000-6000
£3896 $6000 €5844 Ships in a gale (30x61cm-12x24in) s. s.d.1875 verso prov. 24-Oct-2 Shannon's, Milford #62/R est:6000-8000

HAMILTON, James Whitelaw (1860-1932) British
£880 $1373 €1320 Upland pastures (26x33cm-10x13in) s. panel. 10-Apr-3 Bonhams, Edinburgh #93
£900 $1377 €1350 River scene, autumn (48x60cm-19x24in) s. 22-Aug-2 Bonhams, Edinburgh #1168
£962 $1510 €1500 Village by the North Sea (60x50cm-24x20in) s. 23-Nov-2 Arnold, Frankfurt #740/R est:1200
£1600 $2608 €2320 Scottish fishing village (60x50cm-24x20in) s. 16-Jul-3 Sotheby's, Olympia #137/R est:800-1200
£2000 $3140 €3000 Hoisting the sails (36x46cm-14x18in) s. 16-Apr-3 Christie's, Kensington #851/R est:2000-3000

HAMILTON, Johann Georg de (1672-1737) Flemish
£24000 $37440 €36000 Spaniels guarding wildfowl and songbirds. Whippets guarding hare (89x99cm-35x39in) pair. 10-Apr-3 Sotheby's, London #68/R est:18000

HAMILTON, Ken (20th C) Irish
£900 $1395 €1350 By the rock pool (50x40cm-20x16in) s. 4-Dec-2 John Ross, Belfast #66
£900 $1395 €1350 Fine day for fixing the thatch (30x40cm-12x16in) s. board. 4-Dec-2 John Ross, Belfast #231
£1141 $1837 €1700 Portrait of a woman (41x30cm-16x12in) s. board. 18-Feb-3 Whyte's, Dublin #229/R est:1500-2000
£1350 $2093 €2025 Still life (36x46cm-14x18in) s. 2-Oct-2 John Ross, Belfast #61 est:1800-2000

HAMILTON, Letitia (1878-1964) British
£1042 $1656 €1500 Country churchyard (30x25cm-12x10in) init. canvas on board. 29-Apr-3 Whyte's, Dublin #107/R est:2000-3000
£1100 $1826 €1595 Purple and gold (12x17cm-5x7in) init. panel prov. 10-Jun-3 Mellors & Kirk, Nottingham #850/R est:300-500
£1944 $3092 €2800 Yachts on a fine day (8x13cm-3x5in) init. board pair prov. 29-Apr-3 Whyte's, Dublin #30/R est:2000-3000
£2051 $3221 €3200 Rock of Cashel (39x36cm-15x14in) init. panel. 19-Nov-2 Hamilton Osborne King, Dublin #451/R est:1500-2500
£2222 $3533 €3200 Donkey's (21x25cm-8x10in) panel prov. 29-Apr-3 Whyte's, Dublin #3/R est:3000-4000
£2639 $4354 €3800 St. Edmundsbury on the Liffey, seen through beech trees (30x40cm-12x16in) canvasboard. 7-Jul-3 Hamilton Osborne King, Dublin #212/R est:1000-1500
£2685 $4322 €4000 Ireland's eye (11x17cm-4x7in) init. i.verso canvasboard. 18-Feb-3 Whyte's, Dublin #1/R est:2000-3000
£2778 $4417 €4000 Portmarnock (20x25cm-8x10in) init. canvasboard prov.exhib. 29-Apr-3 Whyte's, Dublin #2/R est:4000-6000
£2953 $4754 €4400 Glimpse of houses and trees on a windy day (32x42cm-13x17in) init. panel. 18-Feb-3 Whyte's, Dublin #70/R est:3000-5000
£3800 $6080 €5700 Dunbrody Abbey. Co Wexford (30x41cm-12x16in) board prov. 16-May-3 Sotheby's, London #75/R est:4000-6000
£3974 $6240 €6200 Bridge of Sighs, Venice (24x20cm-9x8in) init. board. 19-Nov-2 Whyte's, Dublin #148/R est:4000-5000
£4348 $7130 €6000 Ireland's eye, Howth (11x17cm-4x7in) init, board pair prov. 28-May-3 Bonhams & James Adam, Dublin #132/R est:6000-10000
£4808 $7548 €7500 Fisherman's cottage, Dunmanus Bay, co Cork. Dunmanus Bay (13x18cm-5x7in) one init. board pair. 19-Nov-2 Hamilton Osborne King, Dublin #448/R est:3000-5000
£5500 $8800 €8250 Upper town, Nazare (51x61cm-20x24in) init. 16-May-3 Sotheby's, London #77/R est:2000-3000
£6000 $9300 €9000 Monastery, Valdemosa (51x61cm-20x24in) mono. 2-Oct-2 John Ross, Belfast #155 est:4000-5000
£6216 $9697 €9200 West of Ireland village (21x25cm-8x10in) init. board. 26-Mar-3 James Adam, Dublin #106/R est:4000-6000
£6604 $10302 €10500 People in the park (24x25cm-9x10in) init. board. 17-Sep-2 Whyte's, Dublin #107/R est:5000-7000
£8389 $13507 €12500 Riverside landscape (36x46cm-14x18in) init. canvas on board. 18-Feb-3 Whyte's, Dublin #18/R est:8000-10000
£9434 $14717 €15000 Harbour, Dubrovnik (51x66cm-20x26in) init. i.verso exhib. 17-Sep-2 Whyte's, Dublin #67/R est:8000-10000
£10507 $17232 €14500 Twelve Pins, Connemara, from Roundstone Harbour (51x60cm-20x24in) init. 28-May-3 Bonhams & James Adam, Dublin #53/R est:12000-16000
£10897 $16891 €17000 Ponte della Paglia, Venice (55x63cm-22x25in) init. 3-Dec-2 Bonhams & James Adam, Dublin #58/R est:6000-9000
£18000 $28800 €27000 Evening, Lake Garda (51x66cm-20x26in) init. 16-May-3 Sotheby's, London #72/R est:12000-18000

HAMILTON, Mary Riter (1873-1954) Canadian
£583 $933 €875 On the sand, White Rock, BC (24x45cm-9x18in) s. i.verso board painted c.1915. 15-May-3 Heffel, Vancouver #157 est:800-1200 (C.D 1300)

HAMILTON, Philipp Ferdinand de (1664-1750) Flemish
£8068 $12505 €12102 Albino pheasant (29x36cm-11x14in) s. board pair. 6-Dec-2 Kieselbach, Budapest #78/R (H.F 3000000)
£11737 $18309 €17606 Fox in poultry yard (77x88cm-30x35in) s.d.1746. 11-Apr-3 Kieselbach, Budapest #174/R est:4200000 (H.F 4200000)

HAMILTON, Philipp Ferdinand de (attrib) (1664-1750) Flemish
£1831 $3039 €2600 Still life with dead game birds (31x44cm-12x17in) bear i. prov. 11-Jun-3 Dorotheum, Vienna #397/R est:1000-1500
£2273 $3386 €3500 Still life with hunting dogs and slain game (82x110cm-32x43in) canvas on board. 28-Jun-2 Sigalas, Stuttgart #803/R
£3169 $5261 €4500 Hunting still life (73x88cm-29x35in) prov. 11-Jun-3 Dorotheum, Vienna #411/R est:3000-5000
£4403 $6824 €7000 Duck, King Charles hound and parrot in park setting (51x71cm-20x28in) 2-Oct-2 Dorotheum, Vienna #265/R est:4000-7000

HAMILTON, Philipp Ferdinand de (circle) (1664-1750) Flemish
£6040 $9724 €9000 Hind (94x120cm-37x47in) 18-Feb-3 Sotheby's, Amsterdam #263/R est:6000-8000

HAMILTON, Philipp Ferdinand de (style) (1664-1750) Flemish
£8000 $13360 €11600 Tigress and her cub (144x193cm-57x76in) 8-Jul-3 Sotheby's, Olympia #477/R est:10000-15000

HAMILTON, Richard (1922-) British
£288 $438 €432 Languid floating flower (50x46cm-20x18in) 16-Aug-2 Lilla Bukowskis, Stockholm #154 (S.KR 4200)

Photographs
£4500 $7380 €6750 Instant painting (70x56cm-28x22in) s.num.3/17 col photo prov.lit. 7-Feb-3 Sotheby's, London #131/R est:5000-7000
Prints
£2166 $3400 €3249 Fashion plate (75x60cm-30x24in) i. col offset lithograph screenprint collage pochoir. 21-Nov-2 Swann Galleries, New York #68/R est:3500-5000
£2692 $4200 €4038 My Marilyn (62x83cm-24x33in) s.d.66 num.29/75 col screenprint. 5-Nov-2 Christie's, Rockefeller NY #386/R est:3000-5000
£3526 $5500 €5289 Release (70x94cm-28x37in) s.num.148/150 col screenprint collage. 5-Nov-2 Christie's, Rockefeller NY #387/R est:4000-6000
£4200 $6510 €6300 Self portrait (39x26cm-15x10in) i. etching aquatint engraving. 2-Oct-2 Christie's, Kensington #46/R est:800-1200
£4200 $6510 €6300 Ex-position (31x21cm-12x8in) auuatint drypoint engraving. 2-Oct-2 Christie's, Kensington #48/R est:800-1200
£4600 $7130 €6900 Reaper (28x37cm-11x15in) s.num.10/25 aquatint. 2-Oct-2 Christie's, Kensington #45/R est:1000-1500
£5200 $8060 €7800 Adonis in Y fronts (68x83cm-27x33in) s.d.1963 num.35/40 screenprints. 2-Oct-2 Christie's, Kensington #51/R est:2000-3000
£9200 $14260 €13800 Her's is a lush situation (27x35cm-11x14in) s. etching collage silver foil. 2-Oct-2 Christie's, Kensington #49/R est:1200-1600

HAMILTON, Theodore (20th C) American
£255 $400 €383 Walk in the snow (61x46cm-24x18in) s. 28-Jul-2 Butterfields, San Francisco #3080

HAMILTON, Vereker (fl.1886-1914) British
£750 $1163 €1125 View across roof tops in the snow, possibly from the artist's studio (66x56cm-26x22in) s. 31-Oct-2 Duke & Son, Dorchester #231

HAMILTON, William (1751-1801) British
£7500 $11850 €11250 Portrait of Mrs Siddons as Euphrasia in the Grecian Daughter (67x48cm-26x19in) unlined canvas prov. 26-Nov-2 Christie's, London #36/R est:8000-12000

HAMILTON, William (20th C) American
£385 $600 €578 California desert scene (41x61cm-16x24in) s. 29-Mar-3 Charlton Hall, Columbia #641/R

HAMMAD, Mahmoud (1923-1988) Syrian
£1900 $3021 €2850 Mother and child (18x16cm-7x6in) s. i.d.1961 verso acrylic wood panel. 30-Apr-3 Sotheby's, London #140/R est:1500-2000
£3800 $6042 €5700 Figures (89x74cm-35x29in) s.d.61 board. 30-Apr-3 Sotheby's, London #139/R est:3000-5000

HAMMAN, Edouard-Jean-Conrad (1819-1888) Belgian
£2785 $4344 €4400 Famille sur un balcon (50x65cm-20x26in) s. 15-Oct-2 Horta, Bruxelles #42/R

HAMMAN, Edouard-Michel-Ferdinand (1850-?) French
£900 $1396 €1350 Sheep on a clifftop (60x80cm-24x31in) s. 3-Dec-2 Sotheby's, Olympia #242/R est:1000-1200

HAMME, Peter van (1880-1936) German
£261 $418 €400 Woman on bank of Cheimsee (37x45cm-15x18in) s.i.d.03 double-sided lit. 10-Jan-3 Allgauer, Kempten #1607/R

HAMMEE, Antoine van (1836-1903) Flemish
£255 $392 €400 Moored rowing boats (22x27cm-9x11in) s. canvas on panel. 3-Sep-2 Christie's, Amsterdam #154
£550 $897 €825 Roman street scene (36x51cm-14x20in) s.d.73 panel. 29-Jan-3 Sotheby's, Olympia #278/R

HAMMELL, Will (1888-?) American
Works on paper
£1210 $1900 €1815 Untitled (47x33cm-19x13in) s. pen ink W/C three illustrations prov. 22-Nov-2 Skinner, Boston #214/R est:600-800

HAMMER, Christian Gottlob (1779-1864) German
Works on paper
£538 $834 €850 Kupferberg ruins (23x29cm-9x11in) s.d.1829 W/C tempera. 27-Sep-2 Auktionhaus Georg Rehm, Augsburg #8047

HAMMER, Guido (20th C) German
Works on paper
£280 $437 €440 Head of deer before woodland background (45x31cm-18x12in) s.d.1893 W/C bodycol. 5-Nov-2 Hartung & Hartung, Munich #5067/R

HAMMER, Hans Jorgen (1815-1882) Danish
£388 $589 €582 Evening in Ariccia (27x23cm-11x9in) mono.d.1877 prov. 27-Aug-2 Rasmussen, Copenhagen #1708/R (D.KR 4500)
£478 $775 €693 Model study of a young man holding a leaf (110x103cm-43x41in) s.d.1843. 26-May-3 Rasmussen, Copenhagen #1514/R (D.KR 5000)

HAMMER, Max (1930-) German
£449 $696 €700 Still life with colourful roses (70x60cm-28x24in) s.d.1947 board. 6-Dec-2 Michael Zeller, Lindau #782/R

HAMMER, William (1821-1889) German
£5161 $8000 €7742 Basket of strawberries and peaches on a stone ledge (37x44cm-15x17in) painted 1856. 30-Oct-2 Christie's, Rockefeller NY #110/R est:10000-15000

HAMMERSHOI, Svend (1873-1948) Danish
£466 $740 €699 Koldinghus seen from the other side of the lake (50x45cm-20x18in) s. panel possibly painted 1918 exhib. 5-Mar-3 Rasmussen, Copenhagen #2036/R (D.KR 5000)
£512 $789 €768 Rosenborg Palace (55x45cm-22x18in) init. panel. 4-Sep-2 Kunsthallen, Copenhagen #116/R (D.KR 6000)
£766 $1210 €1149 View towards the spire at Helligand's Church (46x37cm-18x15in) init.d.26 panel. 2-Dec-2 Rasmussen, Copenhagen #1218/R (D.KR 9000)
£766 $1210 €1149 View with tree tops (63x59cm-25x23in) 30-Nov-2 Rasmussen, Havnen #2126/R (D.KR 9000)
£851 $1345 €1277 Rosenborg Palace (389x132cm-153x52in) painted 1932-1934 exhib. 2-Dec-2 Rasmussen, Copenhagen #1223/R (D.KR 10000)
£1617 $2555 €2426 View across roof tops at Nybodger (62x76cm-24x30in) mono.d.03 prov. 27-Nov-2 Museumsbygningen, Copenhagen #85/R est:5000 (D.KR 19000)

HAMMERSHOI, Vilhelm (1864-1916) Danish
£2489 $3933 €3734 Heath landscape with avenue in background, Lyngby (15x27cm-6x11in) i.verso. 13-Nov-2 Kunsthallen, Copenhagen #37/R est:18000 (D.KR 29000)
£6891 $10474 €10337 Landscape study from Haraldskaer paper mill by Vejle river (18x25cm-7x10in) painted 1883 prov. 27-Aug-2 Rasmussen, Copenhagen #1503/R est:25000-35000 (D.KR 80000)
£7656 $12402 €11101 Portrait of Miss Becker, later Mrs Knud Faber (55x45cm-22x18in) exhib.prov. 26-May-3 Rasmussen, Copenhagen #1156/R est:75000 (D.KR 80000)
£12744 $19881 €19116 From a corner of a farm (34x36cm-13x14in) init. painted 1883 prov. 5-Aug-2 Rasmussen, Vejle #87/R est:100000-150000 (D.KR 150000)
£12920 $19638 €19380 From a baker's shop (53x35cm-21x14in) study. 27-Aug-2 Rasmussen, Copenhagen #1445/R est:150000 (D.KR 150000)
£50000 $82000 €75000 Interior, strandgade (67x63cm-26x25in) prov.exhib.lit. 3-Jun-3 Sotheby's, London #227/R est:50000-70000
£167598 $266480 €251397 Interior from Strandgade 30, lady seen from behind by window (43x50cm-17x20in) 5-Mar-3 Rasmussen, Copenhagen #1527/R est:2000000 (D.KR 1800000)
£238298 $376511 €357447 Sitting room - doors open to a room behind with piano and stool (36x32cm-14x13in) init. prov. 2-Dec-2 Rasmussen, Copenhagen #1129/R est:2000000-2500000 (D.KR 2800000)
Works on paper
£29330 $46634 €43995 Interior scene with lady at piano, Bredgade 25 (37x29cm-15x11in) chl executed 1910. 10-Mar-3 Rasmussen, Vejle #18/R est:50000-75000 (D.KR 315000)

HAMMERSHOJ, Frank (1940-) Danish
£372 $592 €558 Composition (121x121cm-48x48in) init. 10-Mar-3 Rasmussen, Vejle #623/R (D.KR 4000)
£372 $592 €558 Composition with still life on table (90x80cm-35x31in) init. 10-Mar-3 Rasmussen, Vejle #628/R (D.KR 4000)

HAMMERSTAD, John Olsen (1842-1925) American
£503 $800 €755 Coastal scene with sailboats (41x61cm-16x24in) s. painted c.1900. 4-May-3 Treadway Gallery, Cincinnati #458/R
£844 $1300 €1266 Woodland stream (46x66cm-18x26in) s. 8-Sep-2 Treadway Gallery, Cincinnati #636/R
£1097 $1700 €1646 Crashing waves (86x170cm-34x67in) s. painted c.1880. 8-Dec-2 Toomey, Oak Park #661/R est:2500-3500

HAMMERSTIEL, Robert (1933-) ?
£2207 $3531 €3200 Before dusk (109x100cm-43x39in) mono. 11-Mar-3 Dorotheum, Vienna #253/R est:1300-2000

HAMMOCK, Earl G (1896-1971) American
£481 $750 €722 Untitled - autumn landscape (74x81cm-29x32in) s. masonite panel prov. 9-Nov-2 Santa Fe Art, Santa Fe #238/R

HAMMOND, Arthur Henry Knighton (1875-1970) British
Works on paper
£300 $429 €450 Queen Mary in Liverpool Dock's (24x34cm-9x13in) s. W/C. 28-Feb-2 Greenslade Hunt, Taunton #409
£300 $429 €450 In the stable yard (32x49cm-13x19in) s. W/C. 28-Feb-2 Greenslade Hunt, Taunton #410
£320 $522 €480 Ventimilia (30x38cm-12x15in) s.i. 13-Feb-3 David Lay, Penzance #138/R
£340 $527 €510 Cattle on a farm (56x77cm-22x30in) s. W/C. 25-Sep-2 Hamptons Fine Art, Godalming #150/R
£370 $562 €555 Rio S Trevaso (46x64cm-18x25in) s.d.1929 W/C. 16-Aug-2 Keys, Aylsham #555
£400 $636 €600 Sunny morning on Druids Hill (54x76cm-21x30in) s. i.verso W/C. 18-Mar-3 Bonhams, Sevenoaks #227
£480 $749 €720 Flowers in bright profusion dancing (48x59cm-19x23in) s. W/C exhib. 9-Oct-2 Woolley & Wallis, Salisbury #148/R
£500 $745 €750 Unloading a boat on a quayside (35x51cm-14x20in) s. W/C. 27-Jun-2 Greenslade Hunt, Taunton #735/R
£700 $1001 €1050 Sunbathers (34x49cm-13x19in) s.i. gouache W/C. 11-Apr-2 Mellors & Kirk, Nottingham #541
£900 $1287 €1350 Ploughman and team resting in a field (51x74cm-20x29in) s. pencil W/C. 28-Feb-2 Greenslade Hunt, Taunton #408/R
£1000 $1490 €1500 Italian fishing boats (48x72cm-19x28in) s. W/C. 27-Jun-2 Greenslade Hunt, Taunton #731/R est:500-800
£1400 $2226 €2100 Resting in the shade, scene at a horse show (55x76cm-22x30in) s. W/C. 27-Feb-3 Greenslade Hunt, Taunton #1277/R est:700-900

HAMMOND, Arthur J (1875-1947) American
£323 $500 €485 Moonlight, Carmel Dunes (28x36cm-11x14in) s. board. 2-Nov-2 North East Auctions, Portsmouth #31/R
£975 $1550 €1463 Seascape dune scene of children playing (38x48cm-15x19in) 3-May-3 Van Blarcom, South Natick #193/R

HAMMOND, Bill (1947-) New Zealander
£1061 $1633 €1592 Versuvio wall (25x20cm-10x8in) s.i.d.1992 acrylic on music paper. 4-Sep-2 Dunbar Sloane, Wellington #55/R est:1100-2000 (NZ.D 3500)
£3860 $6021 €5790 Head bone (120x79cm-47x31in) s.d.1989 acrylic paper. 27-Mar-3 International Art Centre, Auckland #40/R est:20000-30000 (NZ.D 11000)
£6079 $9483 €9119 Twist and crawl (90x58cm-35x23in) s.d.1984. 17-Sep-2 Peter Webb, Auckland #94/R est:35000-50000 (NZ.D 20000)
£6369 $10000 €9554 Crime watch (105x157cm-41x62in) s.i.d.1990 acrylic two wallpaper sections. 10-Dec-2 Peter Webb, Auckland #36/R est:30000-40000 (NZ.D 20000)
£6667 $10267 €10001 Boulder Bay 4 (40x60cm-16x24in) s.i.d.2001. 4-Sep-2 Dunbar Sloane, Wellington #26/R est:24000-30000 (NZ.D 22000)
£9722 $15167 €14583 Meantime; organ donor swappa crate 3 (50x160cm-20x63in) s.i.d.1989 acrylic paper. 8-Apr-3 Peter Webb, Auckland #68/R est:25000-35000 (NZ.D 28000)
£9722 $15167 €14583 Plain 3 (31x65cm-12x26in) s.d.1997 acrylic board. 8-Apr-3 Peter Webb, Auckland #72/R est:26000-35000 (NZ.D 28000)
£16667 $25667 €25001 Black robin (27x164cm-11x65in) s.i.d.1996. 4-Sep-2 Dunbar Sloane, Wellington #22a/R est:50000-70000 (NZ.D 55000)
£18541 $28924 €27812 Zoomorphic detail (59x39cm-23x15in) s.i.d.1999. 17-Sep-2 Peter Webb, Auckland #93/R est:60000-85000 (NZ.D 61000)
£54140 $85000 €81210 Placemakers II (210x190cm-83x75in) s.i.d.1996 acrylic prov. 10-Dec-2 Peter Webb, Auckland #31/R est:180000-220000 (NZ.D 170000)
Works on paper
£282 $440 €423 M.V.A (14x8cm-6x3in) init.i.d.1987 pencil sketch. 5-Nov-2 Peter Webb, Auckland #162/R (NZ.D 900)
£457 $700 €686 Playing the drums (48x36cm-19x14in) s.d.1988 pencil dr. 21-Aug-2 Dunbar Sloane, Auckland #68 est:1000-2000 (NZ.D 1500)

HAMMOND, G (?) British
Works on paper
£600 $930 €900 Haymakers, gathering hay on to a horse drawn cart (18x12cm-7x5in) s. i.verso W/C. 1-Oct-2 Fellows & Sons, Birmingham #142/R

HAMMOND, George F (1855-?) American
Works on paper
£281 $450 €407 Seascape (63x99cm-25x39in) s.i.d.1911 W/C. 16-May-3 Skinner, Boston #104/R
£375 $600 €544 Mt Assinniboine, Alberta, Canada (74x53cm-29x21in) s.d.1910 W/C gouache. 16-May-3 Skinner, Boston #130/R

HAMMOND, Horace (fl.1902-1939) British
Works on paper
£460 $727 €667 Near Welford on Avon (29x44cm-11x17in) s. W/C. 22-Jul-3 Bristol Auction Rooms #310/R
£620 $961 €930 Gypsy encampment (27x43cm-11x17in) s. pencil W/C htd white. 26-Sep-2 Mellors & Kirk, Nottingham #639/R
£1500 $2340 €2250 Meet (18x25cm-7x10in) s. W/C bodycol. 10-Oct-2 Greenslade Hunt, Taunton #573/R est:1200-1600

HAMMOND, Jane (1950-) American
£6329 $10000 €9494 Untitled (193x190cm-76x75in) s. i.d.1991 verso prov.exhib. 13-Nov-2 Sotheby's, New York #150/R est:8000-12000

HAMMOND, John A (1843-1939) Canadian
£320 $499 €480 Outward bound (22x42cm-9x17in) s.i. board prov. 15-Oct-2 Bonhams, Knightsbridge #94
£589 $925 €884 Dutch home (20x28cm-8x11in) init.i.verso board. 10-Dec-2 Pinneys, Montreal #159 (C.D 1450)
£595 $976 €893 Fishing boats, Allens Creek, NB (25x35cm-10x14in) s.d.1931 s.i.verso board. 6-Feb-3 Heffel, Vancouver #028/R (C.D 1500)
£602 $952 €903 Bow River Falls, CPR (13x20cm-5x8in) d.1903 panel. 1-Dec-2 Levis, Calgary #39/R (C.D 1500)
£756 $1239 €1134 Fish weirs, St. John, N.B (27x45cm-11x18in) s.i. verso board. 3-Jun-3 Joyner, Toronto #317/R est:1200-1500 (C.D 1700)
£823 $1276 €1235 Mist effect, the Bay of Fundy (14x21cm-6x8in) s.d.1893 panel. 3-Dec-2 Joyner, Toronto #141/R est:1500-2000 (C.D 2000)
£1121 $1794 €1682 Low tide, Bay of Funfy (89x56cm-35x22in) s. i.d.1893 board prov. 15-May-3 Heffel, Vancouver #189/R est:3000-4000 (C.D 2500)
£1156 $1895 €1734 Saint John Harbour (32x47cm-13x19in) s. indis d. board. 3-Jun-3 Joyner, Toronto #251/R est:3000-4400 (C.D 2600)
£1345 $2152 €2018 Fishermen's houses, St. John (52x64cm-20x25in) s.d.1925 i.verso board prov. 15-May-3 Heffel, Vancouver #169/R est:2000-3000 (C.D 3000)
£1600 $2624 €2400 Herring fishing (42x57cm-17x22in) s. indis d. panel. 3-Jun-3 Joyner, Toronto #138/R est:3000-5000 (C.D 3600)
£2222 $3644 €3333 St. John Harbour, New Brunswick (31x60cm-12x24in) s. 3-Jun-3 Joyner, Toronto #80/R est:3000-5000 (C.D 5000)
£3556 $5831 €5334 Maket slip, St. John, N.B (75x100cm-30x39in) s.d.1926 canvas on board prov. 3-Jun-3 Joyner, Toronto #95/R est:8000-12000 (C.D 8000)
£8871 $14016 €13307 Fishing boats at sea (79x105cm-31x41in) s.d.1893 prov. 18-Nov-2 Sotheby's, Toronto #101/R est:10000-15000 (C.D 22000)
Works on paper
£222 $364 €322 Ships at sail (23x32cm-9x13in) ink wash. 9-Jun-3 Hodgins, Calgary #374/R (C.D 500)

HAMMOND, Miss Gertrude Demain (1862-1953) British
Works on paper
£750 $1215 €1125 Proposal (35x25cm-14x10in) s.d.1908 W/C. 21-Jan-3 Bonhams, Knightsbridge #62/R
£940 $1466 €1410 Queen of hearts (22x35cm-9x14in) s.indis.d. W/C htd gouache exhib. 17-Oct-2 Lawrence, Crewkerne #424/R

HAMMOND, Robert John (fl.1882-1911) British
£450 $720 €675 Cattle watering in a small pool by a country road (25x35cm-10x14in) s. 13-May-3 Bonhams, Knightsbridge #56/R
£880 $1470 €1276 Worcestershire cottage with children by the garden gate (30x45cm-12x18in) s.d.1912 i.on stretcher. 23-Jun-3 Bonhams, Bath #149
£1450 $2262 €2175 Blackberry gatherers, Somersetshire (32x22cm-13x9in) s.d.1890. 25-Mar-3 Gildings, Market Harborough #428/R est:1000-1500
£1500 $2325 €2250 Figure and ducks beside a pack horse bridge. Shepherd and sheep on road (20x41cm-8x16in) s. two. 31-Oct-2 Duke & Son, Dorchester #306/R est:600-1200
£3200 $5120 €4800 Feeding the chickens (40x60cm-16x24in) pair. 13-May-3 Bonhams, Knightsbridge #174/R est:1500-2000

HAMON, Jean Louis (1821-1874) French
£19355 $30000 €29033 Night (41x31cm-16x12in) s.i.d.1868 prov.exhib.lit. 29-Oct-2 Sotheby's, New York #25/R est:30000-40000

HAMPE, Guido (1839-1902) German
£1224 $1947 €1800 View of Wetterhorn and Rosenlauigletsch (34x49cm-13x19in) s.d.72. 25-Feb-3 Dorotheum, Vienna #162/R est:2000-2400

£1408 $2310 €2042 Landscape with fortress and chapels (49x71cm-19x28in) s. 4-Jun-3 Fischer, Luzern #1132/R est:3500 (S.FR 3000)

HAMPEL, Carl (c.1887-1942) Australian
£246 $373 €369 Misty morn (39x49cm-15x19in) s. canvas on board. 19-Aug-2 Joel, Victoria #149 (A.D 700)
£263 $400 €395 Inlet (48x58cm-19x23in) s. canvasboard. 19-Aug-2 Joel, Victoria #286 (A.D 750)

HAMPEL, Sigmund Walter (1868-1949) Austrian
£3930 $6131 €5895 Portrait of young woman in Renaissance dress before landscape (90x72cm-35x28in) s. panel. 20-Nov-2 Fischer, Luzern #1187/R est:10000-14000 (S.FR 9000)
Works on paper
£380 $592 €600 Temptation of St Anthony (33x28cm-13x11in) s. W/C gouache over pencil grid board. 15-Oct-2 Dorotheum, Vienna #29

HAMPSHIRE, Ernest Llewellyn (1882-?) British
£363 $573 €545 Near Colyton, Devon (51x76cm-20x30in) s. i.stretcher. 18-Nov-2 Waddingtons, Toronto #102/R (C.D 900)
£449 $700 €674 River landscape. s. 19-Oct-2 Harvey Clar, Oakland #1398

HAMPSON, Roger (?) British
£280 $434 €420 Corner off-licence (28x23cm-11x9in) s. board. 1-Oct-2 Capes Dunn, Manchester #707
£290 $458 €435 Back Vernon Street, Bolton (58x89cm-23x35in) 18-Dec-2 Mallams, Oxford #634

HAMPTON, John Wade (1918-2000) American
£2246 $3750 €3257 Mustanger (46x61cm-18x24in) s.d.1969. 21-Jun-3 Selkirks, St. Louis #186/R est:5000-6000

HAMSUN, Regine (20th C) Norwegian
£366 $575 €549 Self portrait after Botticelli (120x81cm-47x32in) s. 25-Nov-2 Blomqvist, Lysaker #1095 (N.KR 4200)

HAMSUN, Tore (1912-1995) Norwegian
£351 $554 €527 Field landscape, South of Norway (51x98cm-20x39in) s.d.93 i.verso exhib. 17-Dec-2 Grev Wedels Plass, Oslo #223/R (N.KR 4000)
£368 $582 €552 Light summer's day (64x80cm-25x31in) s.d.91 i.verso exhib. 17-Dec-2 Grev Wedels Plass, Oslo #222 (N.KR 4200)

HAMZA, Hans (1879-1945) Austrian
£1772 $2800 €2800 Farmer girl with flowers (19x14cm-7x6in) s. panel. 28-Nov-2 Dorotheum, Vienna #197/R est:2400-2600
£4965 $8043 €7000 Market in Hauptplatz in Wiener Neustadt (10x16cm-4x6in) s. panel. 22-May-3 Dorotheum, Vienna #168/R est:6500-7000

HAMZA, Johann (1850-1927) German
£2532 $4000 €4000 Curious (26x20cm-10x8in) s.i. panel. 28-Nov-2 Dorotheum, Vienna #203/R est:6500-8500
£11159 $17296 €16739 Carpenter's workshop (32x37cm-13x15in) s.i. 3-Oct-2 Koller, Zurich #3109/R est:26000-32000 (S.FR 26000)

HAMZA, Johann (attrib) (1850-1927) German
£732 $1149 €1098 Queen's treasures (46x36cm-18x14in) s.d.1872 board. 10-Dec-2 Pinneys, Montreal #45 (C.D 1800)

HAN MIN (20th C) Chinese
Works on paper
£471 $772 €650 Girl riding horse and leading another (92x49cm-36x19in) i.d.1988 seals Indian ink col hanging scroll. 30-May-3 Dr Fritz Nagel, Stuttgart #1263/R

HANAU, Hendricus Joannes Petrus (attrib) (1830-1900) Dutch
£372 $603 €539 The Crucifixion (110x85cm-43x33in) i.d.1865 verso. 25-May-3 Uppsala Auktionskammare, Uppsala #49 (S.KR 4800)

HANCOCK, Charles (1795-1868) British
£320 $499 €480 Terriers by the steps to a barn (19x27cm-7x11in) panel prov. 26-Mar-3 Hamptons Fine Art, Godalming #147

HANCOCK, Herbert (attrib) (1830-1882) Canadian
£184 $288 €276 A few autumn tinks (21x34cm-8x13in) mono.d.1873 s.i.d.verso. 10-Sep-2 Iegor de Saint Hippolyte, Montreal #53 (C.D 450)

HAND, Thomas (?-1804) British
£400 $652 €600 Winter landscape with skaters outside a cottage (15x20cm-6x8in) panel. 29-Jan-3 Hampton & Littlewood, Exeter #415/R

HANDKE, Johann Christoph (1694-1774) Czechoslovakian
£1800 $2790 €2700 Young man contemplating whilst reading (41x31cm-16x12in) indis.sig.d.17. 30-Oct-2 Bonhams, New Bond Street #171/R est:2000-3000

HANDLER, Richard (1932-) Austrian
£1006 $1560 €1600 Still life of flowers (63x60cm-25x24in) s. panel. 29-Oct-2 Dorotheum, Vienna #215/R est:1600-1800
£1370 $2137 €2000 Flowers (100x74cm-39x29in) s. 10-Apr-3 Dorotheum, Vienna #98/R est:2400-2800
£1479 $2381 €2100 Still life of flowers with insect (74x55cm-29x22in) s. panel. 7-May-3 Michael Zeller, Lindau #725/R est:1800

HANDLER, Rolf (1938-) German
Works on paper
£277 $426 €440 Girl with bow in hair (54x42cm-21x17in) s.d.1995 gouache collage on board. 26-Oct-2 Dr Lehr, Berlin #145/R

HANDLER-STEINFEST, Herta (1940-) Austrian
£697 $1122 €990 Extensive summer landscape (47x79cm-19x31in) s. panel. 7-May-3 Michael Zeller, Lindau #724/R

HANDMANN, Emanuel (1718-1781) Swiss
£873 $1362 €1310 Portrait of Barbara Salome Steiger (81x65cm-32x26in) s.d.1758 verso. 8-Nov-2 Dobiaschofsky, Bern #12/R (S.FR 2000)
£2403 $3797 €3605 Portraits of the married couple Emanuel Frielrich Sprungli-Hemmann (53x40cm-21x16in) s.i.d.1772 verso prov. pair. 29-Nov-2 Zofingen, Switzerland #2341/R est:6500 (S.FR 5600)
£3052 $5005 €4425 Portrait of French officer (82x65cm-32x26in) 4-Jun-3 Fischer, Luzern #1203/R est:3000-4000 (S.FR 6500)

HANDY, John (fl.1787-1791) British
£300 $465 €450 Woodland landscape (23x28cm-9x11in) 25-Sep-2 John Nicholson, Haslemere #1047

HANEDOES, Louwrens (1822-1905) Dutch
£2055 $3205 €3000 Extensive summer mountain landscape (91x133cm-36x52in) s. 10-Apr-3 Van Ham, Cologne #1464/R est:3500

HANFT, Willy (1888-?) German
£282 $454 €400 Yellow and orange flowers in blue vase (38x33cm-15x13in) s. board. 7-May-3 Michael Zeller, Lindau #726/R

HANGER, Max (1874-1955) German
£301 $467 €470 Three cockerels (17x12cm-7x5in) s. panel lit. 6-Dec-2 Karlheinz Kaupp, Staufen #2236
£306 $477 €459 Poultry in country landscape (11x19cm-4x7in) s. panel. 6-Nov-2 Dobiaschofsky, Bern #632/R (S.FR 700)
£308 $481 €450 Behind the chicken coop (6x10cm-2x4in) s. panel. 10-Apr-3 Van Ham, Cologne #1458
£310 $500 €465 Chickens (16x21cm-6x8in) s. board. 23-Feb-3 Butterfields, Los Angeles #7066
£328 $511 €492 Poultry yard (8x15cm-3x6in) s.i. board. 6-Nov-2 Dobiaschofsky, Bern #633/R (S.FR 750)
£371 $579 €557 Poultry in yard (11x16cm-4x6in) s.i. board. 6-Nov-2 Dobiaschofsky, Bern #634/R (S.FR 850)
£377 $589 €600 Poultry yard (12x15cm-5x6in) s. board. 21-Sep-2 Dannenberg, Berlin #566/R
£417 $633 €650 Two pheasants (24x18cm-9x7in) s. panel. 31-Aug-2 Geble, Radolfzell #634/R
£446 $696 €700 Poultry yard (15x30cm-6x12in) s. panel. 6-Nov-2 Hugo Ruef, Munich #1123/R
£446 $696 €700 Poultry (12x19cm-5x7in) s. panel. 6-Nov-2 Hugo Ruef, Munich #1124
£475 $750 €750 Poultry yard (10x26cm-4x10in) panel lit. 29-Nov-2 Schloss Ahlden, Ahlden #1205/R
£478 $745 €750 Poultry yard (6x24cm-2x9in) s. panel. 6-Nov-2 Hugo Ruef, Munich #1122/R
£484 $711 €750 Poultry yard (21x21cm-8x8in) s. panel. 20-Jun-2 Dr Fritz Nagel, Stuttgart #770/R
£513 $779 €800 Poultry yard (18x24cm-7x9in) s.i. panel. 31-Aug-2 Geble, Radolfzell #635/R
£517 $817 €750 Pheasant in high mountain wood (23x17cm-9x7in) s. panel. 5-Apr-3 Hans Stahl, Hamburg #7/R
£680 $1082 €1000 Peacock with poultry (16x21cm-6x8in) s.i. panel lit. 21-Mar-3 Auktionhaus Georg Rehm, Augsburg #8033/R
£705 $1107 €1100 Poultry yard (18x23cm-7x9in) s. panel. 21-Nov-2 Van Ham, Cologne #1651
£710 $1043 €1100 Peacock and turkey scaring poultry (13x26cm-5x10in) s.i. panel. 20-Jun-2 Dr Fritz Nagel, Stuttgart #769/R
£759 $1177 €1200 Pheasants in autumnal forest clearing (24x18cm-9x7in) s. panel. 25-Sep-2 Neumeister, Munich #588/R
£892 $1391 €1400 Idyllic backyard with hens and poultry (30x40cm-12x16in) s.i. panel. 7-Nov-2 Allgauer, Kempten #2831/R
£912 $1423 €1450 Pheasant in moorland (21x16cm-8x6in) s. panel. 9-Oct-2 Michael Zeller, Lindau #706/R

HANGER, Max (attrib) (1874-1955) German
£1132 $1721 €1698 Birds feeding (60x94cm-24x37in) bears sig.d.1911. 16-Aug-2 Lilla Bukowskis, Stockholm #261 est:10000 (S.KR 16500)
£2585 $4110 €3800 Poultry (60x94cm-24x37in) i.d.1911 canvas on panel. 19-Mar-3 Neumeister, Munich #575/R est:2000

HANICH, Davos (1922-) French
£577 $906 €900 Aphrodite (65x54cm-26x21in) s. i.d.1954 verso exhib. 24-Nov-2 Laurence Calmels, Paris #143/R

HANISCH, Alois (1866-1937) Austrian
£493 $794 €700 Still life with teapot and decanter (34x89cm-13x35in) s.d.1920. 7-May-3 Vendue Huis, Gravenhage #149/R

HANKE, Henry Aloysius (1901-1989) Australian
£300 $456 €450 Phlox in a vase by pots and a statuette on a draped table (38x46cm-15x18in) s.d.40. 29-Aug-2 Christie's, Kensington #215
£575 $902 €863 Chrysanthemums and vase (50x45cm-20x18in) s. prov. 15-Apr-3 Lawson Menzies, Sydney #24/R est:1500-3000 (A.D 1500)
£687 $1085 €1031 Gypsy (48x58cm-19x23in) s. 1-Apr-3 Lawson Menzies, Sydney #567 (A.D 1800)
£1138 $1798 €1650 Untitled - reclining nude (69x90cm-27x35in) s.d.85 prov. 22-Jul-3 Lawson Menzies, Sydney #100/R est:5000-7000 (A.D 2800)

HANKES, J F (fl.1838-1859) British
£420 $651 €630 Country scene with milkmaid, cows and sheep (42x52cm-17x20in) s.d.1848. 24-Sep-2 Anderson & Garland, Newcastle #531

HANKINS, Abraham (1903-1963) American
£419 $650 €629 Kee off the grass (39x29cm-15x11in) s. i.verso board. 8-Dec-2 Freeman, Philadelphia #119/R
£958 $1600 €1389 Still life (46x61cm-18x24in) 22-Jun-3 Freeman, Philadelphia #147a/R est:1000-1500

HANKO, Fukuda (1804-1864) Japanese
Works on paper
£6918 $11000 €10377 Chinese landscapes (158x71cm-62x28in) s. one d.1864 ink col silk hanging scroll triptych prov.lit. 24-Mar-3 Christie's, Rockefeller NY #63/R est:4000-6000

HANLON, Father Jack (1913-1968) Irish
£2466 $3871 €3600 Madonna with praying figure (43x35cm-17x14in) s.d.46 i.verso board. 15-Apr-3 De Veres Art Auctions, Dublin #258 est:1400-1800
£3333 $5167 €5200 Still life of summer flowers (46x30cm-18x12in) s. 3-Dec-2 Thomas Adams, Dublin #375
£3490 $5619 €5200 Early summer (46x33cm-18x13in) s. i.stretcher. 18-Feb-3 Whyte's, Dublin #16/R est:6000-8000
£5694 $9054 €8200 Christ falls for the first time (51x56cm-20x22in) s. prov. 29-Apr-3 Whyte's, Dublin #36/R est:4000-6000
Prints
£6040 $9725 €9000 Near Grasse, Provence (38x55cm-15x22in) s.d.1945 i.verso. 18-Feb-3 Whyte's, Dublin #69/R est:8000-10000
Works on paper
£816 $1321 €1150 Interior of Jerpoint Abbey (33x50cm-13x20in) s. W/C. 20-May-3 Mealy's, Castlecomer #1326/R est:700-1100
£822 $1290 €1200 Interior still life (34x48cm-13x19in) s.d.65 W/C. 15-Apr-3 De Veres Art Auctions, Dublin #4 est:1000-1500
£915 $1290 €1500 Still life of a bowl of pears (28x38cm-11x15in) W/C prov. 5-Feb-2 Thomas Adams, Dublin #355
£1062 $1667 €1550 Continental village (34x48cm-13x19in) s.d.65 W/C. 15-Apr-3 De Veres Art Auctions, Dublin #3/R est:1000-1500
£1096 $1721 €1600 Golden cage (39x55cm-15x22in) s.d.1962 W/C prov. 15-Apr-3 De Veres Art Auctions, Dublin #101/R est:1500-2000
£2013 $3242 €3000 Through the winter (29x39cm-11x15in) s. W/C prov. with another work by same artist two. 18-Feb-3 Whyte's, Dublin #10/R est:1800-2200
£2013 $3242 €3000 Bathers and boats on the Riviera (33x50cm-13x20in) s. W/C. 18-Feb-3 Whyte's, Dublin #66/R est:2000-2600
£2083 $3312 €3000 Brasserie Dupont, Paris (39x29cm-15x11in) s. W/C. 29-Apr-3 Whyte's, Dublin #72/R est:2000-3000
£2148 $3458 €3200 Cafe Florida, France (28x38cm-11x15in) s. W/C. 18-Feb-3 Whyte's, Dublin #17/R est:3000-4000
£6757 $10541 €10000 Eviction (56x78cm-22x31in) gouache prov. 26-Mar-3 James Adam, Dublin #77/R est:800-1200

HANLY, Patrick (1932-) New Zealander
£1216 $1897 €1824 Willing child observing the innocent (51x66cm-20x26in) s.d.1991 s.i.d.verso oil on broken composition. 17-Sep-2 Peter Webb, Auckland #144/R est:4000-6000 (NZ.D 4000)
£3472 $5417 €5208 Vacation; three fold screen (160x40cm-63x16in) s.d.1985 three hinged boards exhib. 8-Apr-3 Peter Webb, Auckland #33/R est:15000-25000 (NZ.D 10000)
£13380 $22077 €19401 Pure painting 12 (91x91cm-36x36in) s.i.d.1976 i.d.verso enamel on board prov. 1-Jul-3 Peter Webb, Auckland #24/R est:35000-55000 (NZ.D 38000)
£18293 $27988 €27440 Golden age series, red and black 1978/79 (90x90cm-35x35in) s.d.78 board. 21-Aug-2 Dunbar Sloane, Auckland #11/R est:50000-90000 (NZ.D 60000)
Works on paper
£283 $455 €425 Wood bouquet (68x64cm-27x25in) s.d.92 mixed media wood. 7-May-3 Dunbar Sloane, Auckland #49/R (NZ.D 800)
£697 $1073 €1046 Awake Aotearoa - Fall of Icarus (74x62cm-29x24in) s.i.d.1993 pencil pen. 4-Sep-2 Dunbar Sloane, Wellington #136 est:1500-2500 (NZ.D 2300)
£1585 $2614 €2298 I am (59x43cm-23x17in) s.i.d.1970 i.s.verso W/C collage screenprint. 1-Jul-3 Peter Webb, Auckland #1/R est:7000-9000 (NZ.D 4500)
£3859 $5981 €5789 Torso A (26x27cm-10x11in) s.d. mixed media. 4-Dec-2 Dunbar Sloane, Auckland #29/R est:13000-18000 (NZ.D 12000)

HANMANN, Inger (20th C) Danish
£259 $396 €389 Composition in blue, white, black (290x440cm-114x173in) s.d.90 enamel metal three parts. 24-Aug-2 Rasmussen, Havnen #2225/R (D.KR 3000)

HANN, George (20th C) British
£500 $780 €750 French street scene (51x43cm-20x17in) s. board. 15-Oct-2 Gorringes, Lewes #2162

HANNA, W (?) ?
£600 $924 €900 Highland landscape with cattle beside stream (61x107cm-24x42in) s. 7-Sep-2 Shapes, Edinburgh #477

HANNAFORD, Charles (19/20th C) British
Works on paper
£260 $434 €377 British naval war ship being towed into port by steam and paddle tug boat (38x70cm-15x28in) W/C htd white. 17-Jun-3 Rosebery Fine Art, London #620
£386 $606 €579 Fishing boats at sunset (35x53cm-14x21in) s. W/C. 10-Dec-2 Pinneys, Montreal #105 (C.D 950)

HANNAFORD, Charles A (fl.1919-1935) British
Works on paper
£260 $406 €390 Wherry on Barton Broad (28x43cm-11x17in) s. W/C. 18-Oct-2 Keys, Aylsham #610/R

HANNAFORD, Charles E (1863-1955) British
Works on paper
£280 $442 €406 Doone Valley (43x69cm-17x27in) s. W/C. 23-Jul-3 Mallams, Oxford #121/R
£356 $590 €516 Rising mist, pass of Glencoe, Argyllshire, Scotland (44x69cm-17x27in) s.i. W/C. 16-Jun-3 Waddingtons, Toronto #72/R (C.D 800)
£383 $605 €575 Boats on the Grand Canal, Venice (32x38cm-13x15in) s. W/C. 18-Nov-2 Waddingtons, Toronto #59/R (C.D 950)
£390 $608 €585 Wreckage in heavy seas at Great Tor, Gower (37x66cm-15x26in) s.d.91 W/C pencil. 11-Sep-2 Bonhams, Newport #217

HANNAFORD, Michael (1832-1891) Canadian
£2044 $3353 €3066 Riverscape with Canoeists by a rapid (45x90cm-18x35in) s.d.1880 prov. 3-Jun-3 Joyner, Toronto #243/R est:3000-5000 (C.D 4600)

HANNAH, Eva (20th C) Australian?
£697 $1143 €1011 Tulips III (104x89cm-41x35in) s.d.93. 3-Jun-3 Lawson Menzies, Sydney #887 (A.D 1750)

HANNANOW, Wasili (20th C) ?
£577 $906 €900 Goal (81x100cm-32x39in) mono. s.i.d.1991 verso. 21-Nov-2 Dorotheum, Vienna #342/R

HANNAUX, Emmanuel (1855-1934) French
Sculpture
£4747 $7358 €7500 Le poete et la sirene (56x53cm-22x21in) s. gold pat bronze Cast Susse Freres. 29-Sep-2 Eric Pillon, Calais #103/R

HANNAUX, Paul (1899-1954) French
£709 $1184 €1000 Vue de Tolede (81x130cm-32x51in) s.i. 17-Jun-3 Claude Boisgirard, Paris #64/R

HANNEMAN, Adriaen (1601-1671) Dutch
£20000 $33400 €29000 Portrait of Edward Hyde, 1st Earl of Clardendon, half-length (92x74cm-36x29in) octagonal prov.lit. 9-Jul-3 Bonhams, New Bond Street #37/R est:8000-12000

HANNEMAN, Adriaen (studio) (1601-1671) Dutch
£16500 $26071 €24750 Portrait of Henry Stuart, Duke of Gloucester, when a boy (67x53cm-26x21in) prov.lit. 28-Nov-2 Sotheby's, London #145/R est:8000-12000

HANNEMAN, Adriaen (style) (1601-1671) Dutch
£30000 $46800 €45000 Portrait of a Rabbi, wearing a red jacket and a fur hat (68x58cm-27x23in) i. 8-Apr-3 Sotheby's, Olympia #139/R est:2000-3000

HANNO, Carl von (1901-1953) Norwegian
£340 $523 €510 Yard in Kristiania (60x50cm-24x20in) s. painted c.1922. 28-Oct-2 Blomqvist, Lysaker #1082 (N.KR 4000)
£444 $692 €666 Boats by jetty (46x55cm-18x22in) s. panel. 23-Sep-2 Blomqvist, Lysaker #1072 (N.KR 5200)
£724 $1173 €1086 Boy seated wearing national costume from Setesdalen (66x61cm-26x24in) s.d.32. 26-May-3 Grev Wedels Plass, Oslo #113/R (N.KR 8000)

HANNO, Fritz (19th C) German
£1316 $2132 €2000 Still life with white roses and a fan (41x32cm-16x13in) s.i.d.84 s. verso. 21-Jan-3 Christie's, Amsterdam #124/R est:2000-3000

HANNON, Theodore (1851-1916) Belgian
Works on paper
£753 $1175 €1100 Vues de Capri (3x12cm-1x5in) s.d.89 W/C set of five in one frame. 14-Apr-3 Horta, Bruxelles #429

HANNOT, Johannes (17th C) Dutch
£47000 $78490 €68150 Still life of fruits, suspended from ring and blue ribbon with butterfly and fly (72x57cm-28x22in) prov. 10-Jul-3 Sotheby's, London #125/R est:30000-50000

HANOTEAU, Hector (1823-1890) French
£1474 $2315 €2300 Paysage a l'etang (50x73cm-20x29in) s. 16-Dec-2 Millon & Associes, Paris #145/R est:1200-1500

HANOTEAU, Hector (attrib) (1823-1890) French
£435 $674 €653 Family round fire (46x56cm-18x22in) s. 9-Dec-2 Philippe Schuler, Zurich #8643 (S.FR 1000)

HANRATH, John Otto (1882-1944) Dutch
£256 $403 €400 White pot with flowers (82x89cm-32x35in) s.d.37 i.verso. 25-Nov-2 Glerum, Amsterdam #10

HANSCH, Anton (1813-1876) Austrian
£2848 $4500 €4500 Farm building with figures (50x70cm-20x28in) s. 28-Nov-2 Dorotheum, Vienna #216/R est:4500-5000
£4965 $8043 €7000 View of Salzburg (100x142cm-39x56in) s.d.876. 22-May-3 Dorotheum, Vienna #102/R est:7000-10000
£5975 $9321 €9500 Mountain landscape (103x140cm-41x55in) s.d.863. 23-Sep-2 Wiener Kunst Auktionen, Vienna #48/R est:2500-5000

HANSCH, Anton (circle) (1813-1876) Austrian
£5674 $9191 €8000 View of Graz (103x141cm-41x56in) 22-May-3 Dorotheum, Vienna #14/R est:7000-9000

HANSCH, Johannes (1875-1945) German
£476 $757 €700 Landscape with trees (43x59cm-17x23in) panel. 28-Mar-3 Bolland & Marotz, Bremen #456

HANSCHE, Reinhold (1867-?) German
£493 $778 €740 Lion with his catch, three hunters pointing (70x100cm-28x39in) s. 5-Apr-3 Rasmussen, Havnen #2026 (D.KR 5300)

HANSCHKE, Ulrich (attrib) (1944-) German
£704 $1134 €1000 Impression Berchtesgaden (40x60cm-16x24in) i. verso board. 7-May-3 Michael Zeller, Lindau #1097/R

HANSEN, Al (1927-1995) American
£313 $494 €450 Untitled (48x32cm-19x13in) s.d.1991 collage. 24-Apr-3 Dorotheum, Vienna #279/R
Works on paper
£313 $494 €450 Untitled (48x32cm-19x13in) s.d.1991 collage. 24-Apr-3 Dorotheum, Vienna #278/R
£737 $1143 €1150 Untitled - Hershey's (19x19cm-7x7in) collage masonite. 6-Dec-2 Hauswedell & Nolte, Hamburg #149/R

HANSEN, Alfred J (19/20th C) New Zealander
Works on paper
£280 $437 €420 Stage coach, Otira Gorge (34x50cm-13x20in) s.d.1902 W/C. 6-Aug-2 Peter Webb, Auckland #72/R (NZ.D 950)

HANSEN, Anton (1891-1960) Danish
Works on paper
£743 $1175 €1115 Social realistic scene (26x22cm-10x9in) s.d.1918 Indian ink W/C pencil. 1-Apr-3 Rasmussen, Copenhagen #42/R (D.KR 8000)

HANSEN, Armin Carl (1886-1957) American
£4459 $7000 €6689 Moon peeking through dark clouds (18x23cm-7x9in) s. canvasboard prov. 19-Nov-2 Butterfields, San Francisco #8186/R est:5000-7000
£54217 $90000 €78615 Doldrums, tropical calm (76x91cm-30x36in) s.i. i. on stretcher prov. 11-Jun-3 Butterfields, San Francisco #4212/R est:80000-120000
£152866 $240000 €229299 After dinner (63x76cm-25x30in) s. i.stretcher prov. 19-Nov-2 Butterfields, San Francisco #8199/R est:100000-150000

HANSEN, Armin Carl (attrib) (1886-1957) American
£1156 $1700 €1734 Still life (48x38cm-19x15in) board. 23-Jun-2 Susanin's, Chicago #5105/R est:500-600

HANSEN, Arne L (1921-) Danish
£276 $422 €414 Composition (100x80cm-39x31in) init.d.50. 24-Aug-2 Rasmussen, Havnen #2224 (D.KR 3200)
£325 $514 €488 Frost (81x102cm-32x40in) init.d.58 s.d.58 verso. 1-Apr-3 Rasmussen, Copenhagen #506 (D.KR 3500)
£466 $722 €699 Farm frost II (79x94cm-31x37in) init.d.58 s.d.58 verso. 1-Oct-2 Rasmussen, Copenhagen #290 (D.KR 5500)
£667 $1114 €967 Landscape, Norrbotten (60x140cm-24x55in) init. s.d.57 verso. 17-Jun-3 Rasmussen, Copenhagen #105/R (D.KR 7000)

HANSEN, Bjorn T (1942-) Danish
£372 $587 €558 Spanish red earth (130x97cm-51x38in) s.d.1985 verso. 1-Apr-3 Rasmussen, Copenhagen #384/R (D.KR 4000)
£550 $853 €825 The 9th of April (80x115cm-31x45in) s.verso. 1-Oct-2 Rasmussen, Copenhagen #225/R (D.KR 6500)

HANSEN, Carel Lodewyk (1765-1840) Dutch
£863 $1381 €1200 Interior with a peasant reading to three listeners (26x21cm-10x8in) init. panel. 14-May-3 Christie's, Amsterdam #160/R est:1500-2500

HANSEN, Constantin (1804-1880) Danish
£372 $587 €558 Portrait of young man (27x21cm-11x8in) panel. 5-Apr-3 Rasmussen, Havnen #2157 (D.KR 4000)
£698 $1110 €1047 The artist's daughter Elise (23x22cm-9x9in) painted 1868. 5-Mar-3 Rasmussen, Copenhagen #1776/R (D.KR 7500)
£1676 $2665 €2514 Landscape from Cortal Schwabach, Tyrol (27x25cm-11x10in) s.stretcher prov. 5-Mar-3 Rasmussen, Copenhagen #1875/R est:15000-20000 (D.KR 18000)
£1818 $2945 €2636 Art's genius (37x27cm-15x11in) s. stretcher painted c.1858. 26-May-3 Rasmussen, Copenhagen #1128/R est:25000 (D.KR 19000)
£12432 $20016 €18648 Vesta Temple and Piazza Bocca della Verita (39x51cm-15x20in) s. painted 1839 prov.lit. 26-Feb-3 Museumsbygningen, Copenhagen #40/R est:75000-100000 (D.KR 138000)
£36313 $57737 €54470 Double portrait of Kristiane Hansen and Marie Kobke standing by sewing table (114x94cm-45x37in) s.d.1869 exhib.prov. 5-Mar-3 Rasmussen, Copenhagen #1545/R est:350000-400000 (D.KR 390000)

HANSEN, Ejnar (1884-1965) American/Danish
£240 $400 €348 Arroyo landscape (30x41cm-12x16in) s. board prov. 17-Jun-3 John Moran, Pasadena #202
£269 $450 €390 Landscape, near Brookside Park, Pasadena (30x41cm-12x16in) s. board prov. 17-Jun-3 John Moran, Pasadena #204

HANSEN, Hans (1874-1948) Danish
£340 $538 €510 Flowering peonies (72x92cm-28x36in) s.d.1920 exhib. 2-Dec-2 Rasmussen, Copenhagen #1446/R (D.KR 4000)

HANSEN, Hans (1853-1947) British

£360 $565 €540 Fisherfolk on the quay (28x34cm-11x13in) 17-Apr-3 Bonhams, Edinburgh #339

Works on paper

£320 $509 €480 Dutch church interior (36x23cm-14x9in) s. W/C. 29-Apr-3 Bonhams, Knightsbridge #67/R

£520 $827 €780 Market scene (17x24cm-7x9in) s. W/C. 25-Feb-3 Bonhams, Knightsbridge #156/R

HANSEN, Hans (attrib) (1769-1828) Danish

£2213 $3496 €3320 Portrait of Ove Rammel Sehested (70x54cm-28x21in) oval prov. 2-Dec-2 Rasmussen, Copenhagen #1682/R est:15000-20000 (D.KR 26000)

HANSEN, Hans Nikolaj (1853-1923) Danish

£310 $503 €465 Man and woman walking with wheelbarrow on wet road (51x57cm-20x22in) init.d.1903. 25-Jan-3 Rasmussen, Havnen #2017 (D.KR 3500)

£600 $937 €900 Breakfast being served - scene from a bedroom (58x76cm-23x30in) init.d.1902. 11-Nov-2 Rasmussen, Vejle #532/R (D.KR 7000)

£766 $1240 €1111 Lady enjoying the view of the sea (26x52cm-10x20in) mono.d.87. 26-May-3 Rasmussen, Copenhagen #1422/R (D.KR 8000)

£936 $1479 €1404 Nude woman inside witchcraft circle (65x80cm-26x31in) init.d.1891. 30-Nov-2 Rasmussen, Havnen #2274/R (D.KR 11000)

HANSEN, Harald (1890-1967) Danish

£254 $394 €381 Ambelteuse - coastal landscape (60x79cm-24x31in) s.indis.d. 1-Oct-2 Rasmussen, Copenhagen #332 (D.KR 3000)

£384 $610 €576 Snake tamer, Djelma el Fna, Marrakech (100x120cm-39x47in) s.d.48-49. 26-Feb-3 Kunsthallen, Copenhagen #274 (D.KR 4200)

HANSEN, Heinrich (1821-1890) Danish

£574 $930 €832 Interior from the Cathedral in Seville (32x27cm-13x11in) init.i. panel. 26-May-3 Rasmussen, Copenhagen #1288/R (D.KR 6000)

£931 $1480 €1397 Church interior with monk (43x35cm-17x14in) 5-Mar-3 Rasmussen, Copenhagen #1688/R (D.KR 10000)

£1053 $1705 €1527 Southern church interior with monk (42x36cm-17x14in) init.d.77. 26-May-3 Rasmussen, Copenhagen #1338/R (D.KR 11000)

£1267 $1976 €1901 Church interior from Santa Maria della Gracia in Milan (65x52cm-26x20in) init.d.82. 23-Sep-2 Rasmussen, Vejle #221/R est:20000 (D.KR 15000)

£8387 $13000 €12581 Interior of the Doge's Palace (56x49cm-22x19in) prov. 29-Oct-2 Sotheby's, New York #21/R est:18000-25000

£12258 $19000 €18387 Interior, Copenhagen (56x48cm-22x19in) prov. 29-Oct-2 Sotheby's, New York #22/R est:20000-30000

£15000 $24600 €22500 Interior, Lubeck (58x51cm-23x20in) s.i.d.73. 3-Jun-3 Sotheby's, London #225/R est:8000-12000

£57872 $91438 €86808 Summer's day at Hojbro Plads with fisherwomen selling fish (42x63cm-17x25in) init.d.67 study prov. 2-Dec-2 Rasmussen, Copenhagen #1166/R est:500000-600000 (D.KR 680000)

HANSEN, Herman Wendelborg (1854-1924) American

Works on paper

£219 $350 €329 London street scene with figures at a fruit stand (11x16cm-4x6in) init.d.May 89 pencil. 16-Mar-3 Butterfields, San Francisco #1030

£10274 $15000 €15411 Buffalo hunt (33x43cm-13x17in) W/C. 18-May-2 Altermann Galleries, Santa Fe #57/R

£20833 $32500 €31250 Apaches on Santa Fe trail (58x89cm-23x35in) s.d.19 W/C prov.lit. 9-Nov-2 Santa Fe Art, Santa Fe #150/R est:25000-35000

£21795 $34000 €32693 Scout (58x89cm-23x35in) s.d.1921 W/C prov. 9-Nov-2 Santa Fe Art, Santa Fe #151/R est:25000-35000

HANSEN, J T (1848-1912) Danish

£1106 $1748 €1659 Steps in Italy (20x15cm-8x6in) s. i.verso pa/. 2-Dec-2 Rasmussen, Copenhagen #1318/R est:5000 (D.KR 13000)

£1712 $2756 €2568 Temple ruins (52x27cm-20x11in) s.i. 22-Feb-3 Rasmussen, Havnen #2360/R est:15000-20000 (D.KR 19000)

Works on paper

£450 $725 €675 From a monastery (23x32cm-9x13in) s.i.d.1891 W/C. 22-Feb-3 Rasmussen, Havnen #2264 (D.KR 5000)

£1081 $1741 €1622 Temple ruins in Pompeii (23x34cm-9x13in) s.i.d.1886 W/C. 22-Feb-3 Rasmussen, Havnen #2009/R est:4000 (D.KR 12000)

HANSEN, Jens Peter Helge (1934-) Danish

£338 $527 €507 Outside town (80x105cm-31x41in) s.d.1974 verso. 18-Sep-2 Kunsthallen, Copenhagen #168 (D.KR 4000)

HANSEN, Job (1899-1960) Dutch

£4676 $7669 €6500 Landscape (60x50cm-24x20in) s.i.verso oil on plywood painted c.1925-30. 3-Jun-3 Christie's, Amsterdam #261/R est:5000-7000

£7092 $11489 €10000 Still life of flowers (58x48cm-23x19in) s.1938 petrol board. 26-May-3 Glerum, Amsterdam #122/R est:2500-3000

HANSEN, Jorgen Teik (1947-) Danish

£335 $529 €503 View with tea-pot (100x81cm-39x32in) init.i.d.80 verso. 1-Apr-3 Rasmussen, Copenhagen #343 (D.KR 3600)

HANSEN, Josef Theodor (1848-1912) Danish

£420 $667 €630 Street scene, Athens (22x16cm-9x6in) s.i.d.1894. 5-May-3 Rasmussen, Vejle #554/R (D.KR 4500)

£839 $1325 €1300 Taormina theatre (52x69cm-20x27in) s.d.1907-17. 18-Dec-2 Finarte, Milan #129/R

£1399 $2225 €2099 Church interior from St Zeno, Verona (52x35cm-20x14in) s.i.d.1885. 5-May-3 Rasmussen, Vejle #551/R est:20000 (D.KR 15000)

£1862 $2961 €2793 Acropolis (24x32cm-9x13in) s.i.d.1882. 5-Mar-3 Rasmussen, Copenhagen #1576/R est:20000-25000 (D.KR 20000)

£2793 $4496 €4190 Interior from Pompeii (37x48cm-15x19in) s.i.d.1905. 22-Feb-3 Rasmussen, Havnen #2371/R est:30000 (D.KR 31000)

£14432 $22947 €21648 View of the Forum towards Campigdoglio (77x55cm-30x22in) s.d.1905. 5-Mar-3 Rasmussen, Copenhagen #1577/R est:60000-80000 (D.KR 155000)

HANSEN, Kjeld (1919-) Danish

£344 $558 €499 Riders (60x68cm-24x27in) s. 24-May-3 Rasmussen, Havnen #4182 (D.KR 3600)

HANSEN, Knud (1934-1988) Danish

£353 $547 €530 Street scene with figures (92x73cm-36x29in) init.d.82. 4-Dec-2 Kunsthallen, Copenhagen #193 (D.KR 4100)

HANSEN, Knut (1876-1926) Danish

£294 $471 €450 Portrait of woman with hat (52x27cm-20x11in) s. board lit. 10-Jan-3 Allgauer, Kempten #1608/R

HANSEN, Lars (1813-1872) Danish

£340 $538 €510 Portrait of lady (81x61cm-32x24in) s.d.1857. 2-Dec-2 Rasmussen, Copenhagen #1673/R (D.KR 4000)

HANSEN, Markus (20th C) American?

Works on paper

£4762 $7571 €7000 Curtain in my own dirt (77x102cm-30x40in) s.d.2001 verso dust under glass. 24-Mar-3 Cornette de St.Cyr, Paris #184/R

HANSEN, Niels (1880-1946) Danish

£559 $888 €839 Still life of flowers in vase and fruit (95x95cm-37x37in) s.d.1921. 10-Mar-3 Rasmussen, Vejle #27 (D.KR 6000)

HANSEN, Niels Christian (1834-1922) Danish

£3352 $5330 €5028 Interior scene with the sisters Hedvig, Agnes and Mathilde Ahlefeldt Laurvig (123x88cm-48x35in) s.d.1868 prov. 5-Mar-3 Rasmussen, Copenhagen #1561/R est:40000 (D.KR 36000)

HANSEN, Peter (1868-1928) Danish

£353 $568 €530 Country road through woods, summer (29x40cm-11x16in) mono. 19-Jan-3 Hindemae, Ullerslev #7513/R (D.KR 4000)

£409 $645 €614 Sheep on woodland path (41x52cm-16x20in) init.d.1904. 2-Dec-2 Rasmussen, Copenhagen #1479/R (D.KR 4800)

£450 $725 €675 Kitchen interior with stove and copper saucepans (50x60cm-20x24in) s. 22-Feb-3 Rasmussen, Havnen #2003 (D.KR 5000)

£761 $1172 €1142 Enghave Square, early spring (46x61cm-18x24in) mono. painted 1908. 23-Oct-2 Kunsthallen, Copenhagen #165/R (D.KR 9000)

£772 $1204 €1158 Fjord landscape with jetty (31x38cm-12x15in) mono.d.1919. 11-Nov-2 Rasmussen, Vejle #638/R (D.KR 9000)

£947 $1440 €1421 Field workers near Brescia, Lago di Garda (80x100cm-31x39in) init. 27-Aug-2 Rasmussen, Copenhagen #1442/R (D.KR 11000)

£1053 $1705 €1527 Children playing (49x49cm-19x19in) init. 26-May-3 Rasmussen, Copenhagen #1442/R (D.KR 11000)

£1418 $2283 €2127 Young boy seated by the sea, Southern Fyn (43x57cm-17x22in) init. 11-May-3 Hindemae, Ullerslev #362/R est:15000-20000 (D.KR 15000)

£1895 $2880 €2843 Driving the pigs outside (64x77cm-25x30in) s.d.1904 exhib.prov. 27-Aug-2 Rasmussen, Copenhagen #1444/R est:15000-20000 (D.KR 22000)

£1954 $3048 €2931 View across Svanninge Hills (55x68cm-22x27in) init. 5-Aug-2 Rasmussen, Vejle #111/R est:25000 (D.KR 23000)

Works on paper
£466 $742 €699 Figures in boat (48x59cm-19x23in) init. W/C exhib. 29-Apr-3 Kunsthallen, Copenhagen #269/R (D.KR 5000)

HANSEN, Rob (?) Danish?
£355 $574 €533 Interior scene with woman (46x32cm-18x13in) s,. 25-Jan-3 Rasmussen, Havnen #2077 (D.KR 4000)

HANSEN, Sigvard (1859-1938) Danish
£511 $807 €767 Heather landscape and horse and wagon (70x100cm-28x39in) s.d.1911 exhib. 2-Dec-2 Rasmussen, Copenhagen #1309/R (D.KR 6000)
£652 $1036 €978 Small girl in snow in front of house in the Alps (43x60cm-17x24in) s.i.d.1914-1916. 5-Mar-3 Rasmussen, Copenhagen #1886 (D.KR 7000)
£722 $1127 €1083 Wooded landscape, winter (53x72cm-21x28in) s.d.1918. 5-Aug-2 Rasmussen, Vejle #230/R (D.KR 8500)
£766 $1240 €1111 Bare trees by the coast in spring (57x47cm-22x19in) mono.d.85. 26-May-3 Rasmussen, Copenhagen #1435/R (D.KR 8000)
£1132 $1766 €1800 House in the country with sea beyond (35x50cm-14x20in) s.i.d.1921. 9-Oct-2 Michael Zeller, Lindau #715/R est:1800
£1531 $2480 €2220 Young man sharpening his scythe in an orchard (40x63cm-16x25in) mono.i.d.Juni 88. 26-May-3 Rasmussen, Copenhagen #1109/R est:8000-10000 (D.KR 16000)

HANSEN-AARSLEV, Jens (1848-?) Danish
£383 $620 €555 Interior scene with woman seen from behind (48x39cm-19x15in) s. 26-May-3 Rasmussen, Copenhagen #1544/R (D.KR 4000)

HANSEN-REISTRUP, Karl (1863-1929) Danish
Works on paper
£280 $445 €420 Parisian town scene with horses and carts outside wine merchant (32x48cm-13x19in) s.d.1905 W/C. 5-May-3 Rasmussen, Vejle #605/R (D.KR 3000)

HANSON, Duane (1925-1996) American
Sculpture
£63291 $100000 €94937 Flea market vendor. polychromed bronze hair sunglasses fabric executed 1990. 14-Nov-2 Christie's, Rockefeller NY #335/R est:100000-150000
£112500 $180000 €168750 Policeman (183x45x38cm-72x18x15in) autobody filler fiberglass paint accessories executed 1993 prov. 15-May-3 Christie's, Rockefeller NY #370/R est:200000-300000
£187500 $300000 €281250 Housewife (112x89x155cm-44x35x61in) fiberglass oil hair fabric curlers armchair exec.1969-70 prov. 14-May-3 Christie's, Rockefeller NY #22/R est:300000-400000

HANSON, Rolf (1953-) Swedish
£2433 $3845 €3650 Onban - composition (123x121cm-48x48in) s.d.1991 verso panel. 28-Apr-3 Bukowskis, Stockholm #956/R est:15000-18000 (S.KR 32000)
£6657 $10385 €9986 Aragona (183x367cm-72x144in) d.1986 verso panel exhib. 6-Nov-2 AB Stockholms Auktionsverk #890/R est:100000-125000 (S.KR 95000)

HANSTEEN, Asta (1824-1908) Norwegian
£2941 $4647 €4412 Woman with roses in her hair (94x78cm-37x31in) s.d.1853. 2-Dec-2 Blomqvist, Oslo #338/R est:20000-25000 (N.KR 34000)

HANSTEEN, Nils (1855-1912) Norwegian
£303 $464 €455 Calm evening (18x27cm-7x11in) s. painted 1898. 26-Aug-2 Blomqvist, Lysaker #1148 (N.KR 3500)
£432 $721 €626 Sailing vessel in harbour (18x24cm-7x9in) s.d.1884 mahogany panel. 18-Jun-3 Grev Wedels Plass, Oslo #179/R (N.KR 5000)
£1377 $2259 €1997 Sailing ship towing rowboat (38x63cm-15x25in) s.d.1899. 2-Jun-3 Blomqvist, Oslo #95/R est:18000-22000 (N.KR 15000)
£1821 $2841 €2732 Landscape from Oslo fjord (30x60cm-12x24in) s.d.1887. 21-Oct-2 Blomqvist, Oslo #300/R est:25000-30000 (N.KR 21000)
£3214 $5271 €4660 Evening by the fjord (73x129cm-29x51in) s.i.d.1877 lit. 2-Jun-3 Blomqvist, Oslo #93/R est:50000-60000 (N.KR 35000)
Works on paper
£259 $433 €376 Ship wreck (30x23cm-12x9in) s.d.94 mixed media. 18-Jun-3 Grev Wedels Plass, Oslo #28/R (N.KR 3000)

HANTAI, Simon (1922-) French
£9589 $15055 €14000 Untitled (88x83cm-35x33in) s.i.d.1950. 15-Apr-3 Laurence Calmels, Paris #4298/R est:12000
£10063 $15597 €16000 Sans titre (54x49cm-21x19in) mono.d.71 prov. 30-Oct-2 Artcurial Briest, Paris #464/R est:5000-6000
£12026 $18760 €19000 Sans titre (106x157cm-42x62in) s. 31-Jul-2 Tajan, Paris #54/R est:25000-30000
£21795 $34218 €34000 Untitled (102x77cm-40x30in) s.d.1964 prov. 15-Dec-2 Perrin, Versailles #58/R est:30000
£31250 $51562 €45000 Sans titre (102x86cm-40x34in) mono.d.69 exhib. 1-Jul-3 Artcurial Briest, Paris #547/R est:40000-50000
£41096 $64521 €60000 Rosee solidifiee (71x100cm-28x39in) s.d.1950-51 exhib.lit. 15-Apr-3 Laurence Calmels, Paris #4297/R est:40000
Works on paper
£17123 $26884 €25000 Regarde dans mes yeux, je te cherche, ne me chasse pas (46x35cm-18x14in) mono.i.d.52 wax paint prov.exhib.lit. 15-Apr-3 Laurence Calmels, Paris #4296/R est:10000

HANULA, Jozef (1863-1944) Czechoslovakian
Works on paper
£252 $368 €378 Villager (20x13cm-8x5in) pencil. 4-Jun-2 SOGA, Bratislava #25/R est:12000 (SL.K 16000)

HANZEN, Aleksei Vasilievich (1876-1937) Russian
£6000 $9720 €9000 Sailing at half mast (70x100cm-28x39in) s. 21-May-3 Sotheby's, London #65/R est:5000-7000
£11709 $18500 €18500 House by the sea (75x91cm-30x36in) s. 1-Dec-2 Bukowskis, Helsinki #247/R est:3000-5000
£12000 $18840 €18000 Cavern entrance. Rowing boats moored at night (73x90cm-29x35in) s. two. 20-Nov-2 Sotheby's, London #48/R est:2000-3000

HAPPEL, Peter (1813-1854) German
£950 $1577 €950 Ciel d'orage (25x36cm-10x14in) s. panel. 16-Jun-3 Horta, Bruxelles #464

HAQUETTE, Georges Jean Marie (1854-1906) French
£1389 $2208 €2000 Les pecheurs (27x35cm-11x14in) s. 29-Apr-3 Christie's, Amsterdam #104/R est:2500-3500
£2250 $3668 €3375 Waiting for the catch (74x54cm-29x21in) s.d.1882. 13-Feb-3 Christie's, Kensington #183/R est:1200-1800

HARA, Jacques (1933-) French
£276 $436 €400 Village en hiver (27x22cm-11x9in) s. ss.i.verso. 4-Apr-3 Tajan, Paris #87
£287 $447 €450 Devant la mairie (27x35cm-11x14in) s. s.i.verso. 5-Nov-2 Tajan, Paris #137
£350 $547 €550 Neige tombant (27x35cm-11x14in) s. s.i.verso. 5-Nov-2 Tajan, Paris #136

HARA, Katsuro (1889-1966) Japanese
£1656 $2583 €2600 Promeneurs dans le parc (73x100cm-29x39in) s. 10-Nov-2 Eric Pillon, Calais #160/R

HARANGHY, Jeno (1894-1951) Hungarian
£2555 $3960 €3705 Summer in the zoo (104x130cm-41x51in) s. 9-Dec-2 Mu Terem Galeria, Budapest #203/R est:650000 (H.F 950000)

HARBUZ, Ann (1908-) Canadian
£196 $305 €326 Mom plastering Log House (43x62cm-17x24in) s.d.1981 acrylic prov. 13-Apr-3 Levis, Calgary #459/R (C.D 450)

HARDEN, John (1772-1847) British
Works on paper
£900 $1503 €1305 Valley of Hawshead (13x18cm-5x7in) s.d.1837 verso monotone W/C. 20-Jun-3 Keys, Aylsham #395

HARDENBERGH, Gerard R (1855-1915) American
Works on paper
£683 $1100 €1025 Fish below the surface with detailed border (30x51cm-12x20in) s.d.1889. 22-Feb-3 Pook & Pook, Downington #148/R

HARDER, J (?) ?
£431 $655 €647 Norwegian fjord landscape with vessels ands workers (70x105cm-28x41in) s. 27-Aug-2 Rasmussen, Copenhagen #1918/R (D.KR 5000)
£1233 $1923 €1800 Blooming heather (83x120cm-33x47in) s. 10-Apr-3 Dorotheum, Vienna #20/R est:1800-2200

HARDERS, J (19/20th C) ?
£524 $822 €786 Breakers (80x120cm-31x47in) s. 25-Nov-2 Blomqvist, Lysaker #1097 (N.KR 6000)

HARDERS, Johannes (1871-1950) German
£1139 $1766 €1800 Ships in Hamburg harbour (85x120cm-33x47in) s. 28-Sep-2 Hans Stahl, Hamburg #199 est:1900

HARDEY, Mrs Richard (c.1800-1860) American
£350 $557 €525 Portrait of Ann Marie Harunhaer (91x76cm-36x30in) i.verso. 18-Mar-3 Capes Dunn, Manchester #524

HARDIE, Charles Martin (1858-1916) British
£600 $930 €900 Daydreaming (23x13cm-9x5in) init.d.88 board. 5-Dec-2 Bonhams, Edinburgh #35
£650 $1014 €975 Ferryman (24x34cm-9x13in) init.d.88. 17-Oct-2 Bonhams, Edinburgh #166
£2200 $3366 €3300 In the gloaming (33x46cm-13x18in) init. 22-Aug-2 Bonhams, Edinburgh #1087 est:2500-3500
£2484 $4000 €3726 Young girl and boy fishing in a stream (61x91cm-24x36in) s.d.1882. 20-Jan-3 Arthur James, Florida #135
£3900 $6396 €5850 Ford on the south Esk (102x127cm-40x50in) s.d.1913. 29-May-3 Christie's, Kensington #103/R est:1000-1500

HARDIE, Charles Martin (attrib) (1858-1916) British
Works on paper
£580 $945 €870 Edinburgh flower seller (51x41cm-20x16in) mono. W/C. 1-Feb-3 Shapes, Edinburgh #318/R

HARDIE, Martin (1875-1952) British
Works on paper
£340 $551 €510 Waiting for the story teller, Bab Guissa, Fez (36x25cm-14x10in) s.d.1928 W/C. 21-May-3 Bonhams, Knightsbridge #12/R

HARDIME, Pieter (1677-1758) Flemish
£7000 $10990 €10500 Roses, narcissi, tulips and other flowers in a brozen vase on stone ledge (87x96cm-34x38in) 10-Dec-2 Bonhams, New Bond Street #122/R est:5000-7000
£7692 $11923 €12000 Nature morte aux fleurs et aux fruits (61x53cm-24x21in) copper. 3-Dec-2 Campo & Campo, Antwerp #112/R est:14000-18000
£11000 $17270 €16500 Roses, tulips and other flowers in a glass vase on a stone ledge (73x99cm-29x39in) 10-Dec-2 Bonhams, New Bond Street #269/R est:5000-7000

HARDIME, Pieter (attrib) (1677-1758) Flemish
£10791 $17266 €15000 Bouquet de fleurs sur un entablement (83x69cm-33x27in) 15-May-3 Christie's, Paris #527/R est:15000-20000

HARDIME, Simon (1672-1737) Flemish
£3500 $5845 €5075 Roses, tulips, narcissi and other flowers in a glass vase on a ledge (47x37cm-19x15in) 9-Jul-3 Bonhams, New Bond Street #7/R est:4000-6000
£5500 $8635 €8250 Roses, morning glory and other flowers in a basket on a ledge (78x97cm-31x38in) 13-Dec-2 Christie's, Kensington #131/R est:4500-6500

HARDING, C (1792-1866) American
£4000 $6520 €6000 Fishing boats off shore in a storm (63x76cm-25x30in) s.d.1828 two. 29-Jan-3 Dreweatt Neate, Newbury #192/R est:1500-2000

HARDING, Charles T (19th C) British
£1218 $1888 €1900 Moonlight (31x35cm-12x14in) s.d.1826 panel. 7-Dec-2 De Vuyst, Lokeren #151/R est:2000-2500

HARDING, Chester (1792-1866) American
£1258 $2000 €1887 Portrait of Miss Biddle of Philadelphia (81x61cm-32x24in) s.i.verso. 1-Mar-3 North East Auctions, Portsmouth #700/R est:2000-3000

HARDING, Chester (attrib) (1792-1866) American
£976 $1600 €1415 Portrait of a seated gentleman (74x61cm-29x24in) 8-Jun-3 Skinner, Boston #301/R est:1500-2500

HARDING, Emily P (19th C) British?
£1600 $2464 €2400 Still life of fishes, fruit, flowers, eggs and game (64x76cm-25x30in) s.d.1893. 3-Sep-2 Gorringes, Lewes #2141 est:2000-3000

HARDING, George Perfect (1780-1853) British
Works on paper
£320 $515 €480 Mrs Mary Robinson as Perdita (22x17cm-9x7in) pastel panel. 15-Jan-3 Cheffins Grain & Comins, Cambridge #348/R

HARDING, James Duffield (1798-1863) British
Works on paper
£250 $408 €375 Boulder strewn stream in a rugged landscape (24x34cm-9x13in) s.d.1857 verso W/C. 29-Jan-3 Hampton & Littlewood, Exeter #356
£400 $632 €600 Windsor Castle from lower meadow (21x29cm-8x11in) pencil W/C. 7-Apr-3 Bonhams, Bath #8
£620 $967 €930 Moorish gateway leading to the Great Square of the Viva Rambla (10x15cm-4x6in) W/C. 5-Nov-2 Bonhams, New Bond Street #23/R
£1097 $1700 €1646 On the Italian lakes (36x53cm-14x21in) s.d.1860 pencil W/C gouache prov. 29-Oct-2 Sotheby's, New York #149/R est:1000-1500

HARDING, Meyer (1964-) Brazilian
£1064 $1723 €1500 Untitled (50x70cm-20x28in) s.d.2001 verso. 20-May-3 Porro, Milan #29/R est:2000-2200

HARDING, Samuel A (20th C) British
Works on paper
£260 $411 €390 Cornish coastal landscape (30x25cm-12x10in) s. W/C. 2-Dec-2 Gorringes, Lewes #2769

HARDORFF, Herman Rudolf (1816-1907) German
£1038 $1660 €1557 River landscape with sailing ships (50x76cm-20x30in) s.d.1862. 17-Mar-3 Philippe Schuler, Zurich #4615 (S.FR 2200)

HARDRICK, John W (1891-1968) American
£584 $900 €876 Floral still life (25x20cm-10x8in) board painted c.1940. 8-Sep-2 Treadway Gallery, Cincinnati #663/R
£881 $1400 €1322 Winter landscape (46x61cm-18x24in) board painted c.1940. 2-Mar-3 Toomey, Oak Park #742/R
£881 $1400 €1322 Floral still life (25x20cm-10x8in) board painted c.1940. 2-Mar-3 Toomey, Oak Park #745/R
£1509 $2400 €2264 Winter stream (23x30cm-9x12in) board painted c.1940. 2-Mar-3 Toomey, Oak Park #743/R est:1000-2000
£2097 $3250 €3146 Floral still life (61x76cm-24x30in) s.d. board. 8-Dec-2 Toomey, Oak Park #740/R est:4500-6500
£2516 $4000 €3774 Floral still life (24x30cm-9x12in) s.d. board. 4-May-3 Treadway Gallery, Cincinnati #606/R est:4500-6500

HARDS, Charles G (attrib) (fl.1883-1891) British
£5449 $8609 €8500 Young girls and dogs playing in a garden (54x58cm-21x23in) 12-Nov-2 Mealy's, Castlecomer #1055/R

HARDWICK, John Jessop (1831-1917) British
Works on paper
£1250 $2025 €1813 Still life with roses in a blue and white willow patterned jug (25x20cm-10x8in) s. W/C. 21-May-3 Edgar Horn, Eastbourne #212/R est:200-300

HARDWICK, Melbourne H (1857-1916) American
£563 $900 €845 Horse and wagon on beach (25x36cm-10x14in) s. board. 11-Jan-3 James Julia, Fairfield #483 est:1000-1500
£1274 $2000 €1911 Gloucester Rocks (68x58cm-27x23in) s. 22-Nov-2 Skinner, Boston #347/R est:1000-2000

HARDY, Andre (1887-1986) French?
£342 $533 €540 Le vieux manoir (63x94cm-25x37in) s. isorel. 15-Sep-2 Etude Bailleul, Bayeux #169
£380 $592 €600 Le chemin creux (29x36cm-11x14in) s. cardboard laid down. 15-Sep-2 Etude Bailleul, Bayeux #170
£380 $592 €600 Le pressoir (28x37cm-11x15in) s. cardboard. 15-Sep-2 Etude Bailleul, Bayeux #171/R
£538 $839 €850 Les moissons (66x92cm-26x36in) s. isorel. 15-Sep-2 Etude Bailleul, Bayeux #166/R
£570 $889 €900 Le Vieux Douet, entre Proussy et St-Pierre la Vieille (29x36cm-11x14in) s. cardboard. 15-Sep-2 Etude Bailleul, Bayeux #164
£949 $1481 €1500 Autoportrait (56x44cm-22x17in) s. paper. 15-Sep-2 Etude Bailleul, Bayeux #161/R
£1076 $1678 €1700 Le retour du bateau (26x36cm-10x14in) s. isorel. 15-Sep-2 Etude Bailleul, Bayeux #165/R

HARDY, Anna Eliza (1839-1934) American
£12676 $18000 €19014 Peonies (43x56cm-17x22in) 8-Aug-1 Barridorf, Portland #58/R est:18000-22000

HARDY, Cyril (19th C) British
Works on paper
£200 $332 €290 Continental market scene (35x51cm-14x20in) s. W/C. 16-Jun-3 Waddingtons, Toronto #50/R (C.D 450)

£270 $443 €405 Middle Eastern street scene (28x38cm-11x15in) s. W/C. 4-Feb-3 Bonhams, Chester #588
£378 $627 €548 Mosque of Algiers (36x51cm-14x20in) s. W/C prov. 16-Jun-3 Waddingtons, Toronto #67/R (C.D 850)

HARDY, David (attrib) (fl.1855-1870) British
£1900 $3021 €2850 By the hearth (20x30cm-8x12in) panel. 18-Mar-3 Bonhams, New Bond Street #63/R est:600-900

HARDY, Dudley (1865-1922) British
£650 $1021 €975 Unloading the morning's catch (61x48cm-24x19in) s.d.1901. 10-Dec-2 Pinneys, Montreal #32 (C.D 1600)
£1778 $2951 €2578 By the quay (62x49cm-24x19in) s.d.1901. 16-Jun-3 Waddingtons, Toronto #150/R est:4000-4500 (C.D 4000)
£2800 $4396 €4200 The album (40x30cm-16x12in) s.d.94. 16-Dec-2 Sotheby's, London #79/R est:3000-4000

Works on paper
£400 $644 €580 Fish sellers (18x38cm-7x15in) s. W/C. 12-May-3 Joel, Victoria #266 est:1000-1500 (A.D 1000)
£500 $770 €750 Saaba player (25x36cm-10x14in) s. gouache. 23-Oct-2 Hamptons Fine Art, Godalming #79/R
£850 $1335 €1275 Bird merchant (51x76cm-20x30in) indis sig. pencil W/C. 16-Apr-3 Christie's, Kensington #1010/R
£1250 $2025 €1875 Fisherfolk at low tide (24x35cm-9x14in) s. bodycol. 21-Jan-3 Bonhams, Knightsbridge #253/R est:800-1200
£3000 $4650 €4500 Sorting the catch (37x51cm-15x20in) s. W/C bodycol. 2-Oct-2 Bonhams, Knowle #33/R est:800-1200

HARDY, Frederick Daniel (1826-1911) British
£700 $1120 €1050 Seamstresses in an interior of Cranbrook school (67x108cm-26x43in) s.d.1883 stretcher. 11-Mar-3 Bonhams, Knightsbridge #259/R
£1600 $2496 €2400 Card player (32x41cm-13x16in) panel. 8-Oct-2 Bonhams, Knightsbridge #281/R est:1200-1800
£2600 $4316 €3900 Visitor anticipated (53x27cm-21x11in) s.d.1893. 10-Jun-3 Christie's, London #87/R est:3000-5000
£3400 $5338 €5100 Story time (25x30cm-10x12in) s.d.1894. 19-Nov-2 Bonhams, New Bond Street #143/R est:3000-4000
£7000 $11270 €10500 My studio (25x39cm-10x15in) s.d.1898 board on panel prov.exhib. 20-Feb-3 Christie's, London #123/R
£8200 $13448 €12300 Reading a letter (39x55cm-15x22in) s.d.1890. 4-Jun-3 Bonhams, Chester #384/R est:4000-6000
£11000 $18260 €16500 Dame school (34x53cm-13x21in) s.d.1889 prov. 10-Jun-3 Christie's, London #86/R est:6000-10000
£20000 $32200 €30000 After the party (69x109cm-27x43in) s.d.1871 prov.exhib.lit. 20-Feb-3 Christie's, London #101/R est:25000

HARDY, Frederick Daniel (attrib) (1826-1911) British
£350 $567 €525 Waiting for the arrival (41x56cm-16x22in) s.d.1896. 23-Jan-3 Christie's, Kensington #288
£2162 $3589 €3135 Interior scene with figures (31x42cm-12x17in) bears sig.d.1895. 16-Jun-3 Lilla Bukowskis, Stockholm #510 est:8000-10000 (S.KR 28000)

HARDY, Heywood (1843-1933) British
£800 $1272 €1200 Shepherd and his sheep in a moorland landscape (20x40cm-8x16in) s. indis d. 27-Feb-3 Greenslade Hunt, Taunton #1290/R
£850 $1411 €1233 Head of a St. Bernard (51x61cm-20x24in) s. 12-Jun-3 Christie's, Kensington #278/R
£4435 $7008 €6653 Watchman (55x39cm-22x15in) s.d.1873. 18-Nov-2 Waddingtons, Toronto #146/R est:7000-7500 (C.D 11000)
£8000 $12480 €12000 Meynell hunt, with Charles West on Comet and George on Red Prince (39x62cm-15x24in) s.d.1915. 10-Apr-3 Tennants, Leyburn #1051/R est:8000-12000
£11268 $16000 €16902 Out for a hunt, portrait of Thomas Dominic (94x117cm-37x46in) 8-Aug-1 Barridorf, Portland #88/R est:15000-25000
£13000 $20670 €19500 Morning refreshment (25x36cm-10x14in) s. prov. 18-Mar-3 Bonhams, New Bond Street #53/R est:6000-8000
£14000 $21980 €21000 Glass before the start (51x77cm-20x30in) s. prov. 19-Nov-2 Bonhams, New Bond Street #125/R est:10000-15000
£14000 $22260 €21000 Driving a bargain (30x48cm-12x19in) s. 18-Mar-3 Bonhams, New Bond Street #52/R est:4000-6000
£16456 $26000 €24684 Busy day by the Swan (51x77cm-20x30in) s. prov. 23-Apr-3 Christie's, Rockefeller NY #116/R est:25000-35000
£17722 $28000 €26583 Morning ride (81x102cm-32x40in) s.d.1900. 23-Apr-3 Christie's, Rockefeller NY #5/R est:30000-40000
£20000 $33200 €30000 Morecambe Sands (46x84cm-18x33in) s. 12-Jun-3 Sotheby's, London #287/R est:20000-30000
£24000 $37680 €36000 Narrow miss at the crossroads (51x77cm-20x30in) s. prov. 19-Nov-2 Bonhams, New Bond Street #124/R est:15000-20000
£26000 $41080 €39000 Asking the way (61x51cm-24x20in) s. 26-Nov-2 Christie's, London #88/R est:15000-20000
£27000 $44010 €39150 Gone to ground (58x84cm-23x33in) s. prov. 17-Jul-3 Tennants, Leyburn #891/R est:25000-30000
£29000 $45240 €43500 Hounds of the Tickham hunt, Kent (77x162cm-30x64in) s. 6-Nov-2 Sotheby's, Olympia #157/R est:25000-40000
£32000 $50560 €48000 Sunday ride (46x61cm-18x24in) s. 2-Dec-2 Sotheby's, London #89/R est:30000-50000
£38000 $63080 €57000 Secret letter (87x133cm-34x52in) s. 10-Jun-3 Christie's, London #145/R est:40000-60000
£45000 $75150 €65250 After the morning gallop (53x78cm-21x31in) s.d.1907. 17-Jun-3 Bonhams, New Bond Street #63/R est:20000-30000
£52000 $84760 €75400 Meet (51x77cm-20x30in) s. prov. 17-Jul-3 Tennants, Leyburn #890/R est:12000-18000

Works on paper
£590 $915 €885 Huntsman at a crossroads in winter (24x33cm-9x13in) W/C over pencil. 2-Oct-2 Bonhams, Knowle #20

HARDY, Heywood (attrib) (1843-1933) British
£2977 $4704 €4466 Untitled, girls on the shore (24x30cm-9x12in) board prov. 7-Apr-3 Shapiro, Sydney #425/R est:3000-5000 (A.D 7800)

HARDY, James (19th C) British
£330 $525 €495 Shipping scene, castle beyond (40x51cm-16x20in) s. panel. 27-Feb-3 Greenslade Hunt, Taunton #1321
£480 $730 €720 Shipping in rough water (30x38cm-12x15in) s. 16-Aug-2 Keys, Aylsham #498
£610 $1000 €885 Marine battle (71x91cm-28x36in) s. panel. 7-Jun-3 Neal Auction Company, New Orleans #255 est:1000-1500
£650 $1053 €975 Merchantmen at sea (61x91cm-24x36in) s. 23-Jan-3 Christie's, Kensington #76/R
£750 $1178 €1125 Dutch barges in choppy waters (41x51cm-16x20in) s. panel. 16-Apr-3 Christie's, Kensington #900/R
£900 $1395 €1350 Bombardment of Algiers (56x76cm-22x30in) s. panel. 31-Oct-2 Christie's, Kensington #450/R
£976 $1600 €1464 Naval battle (69x91cm-27x36in) s. panel. 8-Feb-3 Neal Auction Company, New Orleans #860/R est:2000-3000
£1100 $1705 €1650 American frigate and racing schooner. Dutch barges in coastal waters (40x51cm-16x20in) s. panel pair. 31-Oct-2 Christie's, Kensington #3446/R est:600-800
£1500 $2325 €2250 Dutch warship anchored offshore. Barges transferring the cargo (41x51cm-16x20in) s. panel pair. 31-Oct-2 Christie's, Kensington #447/R est:400-600

HARDY, James (jnr) (1832-1889) British
£1050 $1712 €1575 Preparing dinner (28x46cm-11x18in) s. 29-Jan-3 Sotheby's, Olympia #130/R est:1000-1500
£2500 $4050 €3750 Dead game in a landscape (39x55cm-15x22in) s.d.1876. 22-May-3 Christie's, London #35/R est:2500-3500
£4500 $7020 €6750 Huntsman at rest, figure with two retrievers (49x76cm-19x30in) 10-Sep-2 David Duggleby, Scarborough #360/R est:3500-4000
£7600 $11552 €11400 End of the day (23x18cm-9x7in) s.d.74 s.verso panel. 28-Aug-2 Sotheby's, London #860/R est:5000-7000

Works on paper
£250 $385 €375 Still life of dead game (31x42cm-12x17in) s. W/C over pencil gum arabic. 3-Sep-2 Bristol Auction Rooms #503
£950 $1558 €1425 Reed gatherers in a rowing boat with dogs swimming (22x45cm-9x18in) s. W/C. 2-Jun-3 David Duggleby, Scarborough #265/R
£1450 $2262 €2175 Brace of grouse. Partridge and woodpigeon (21x32cm-8x13in) s.d.69 W/C pair. 6-Nov-2 Bonhams, Chester #478/R est:1500-2000
£1900 $2888 €2850 Still life of dead game (48x66cm-19x26in) s.d.1862 W/C gouache. 28-Aug-2 Sotheby's, London #815/R est:1500-2000
£8000 $12720 €12000 Out on the moors (53x86cm-21x34in) s.d.77 pencil W/C htd white. 6-Mar-3 Christie's, Kensington #56/R est:10000-15000
£17000 $26520 €25500 Waiting for the guns (70x52cm-28x20in) s.d.71 W/C prov. 14-Apr-3 Sotheby's, London #23/R est:10000-15000

HARDY, James (jnr-attrib) (1832-1889) British
£850 $1386 €1233 Spaniel retrieving a pheasant (56x43cm-22x17in) 17-Jul-3 Tennants, Leyburn #880/R

HARDY, James (snr) (1801-1879) British
£1300 $2067 €1950 Scenes in Stirlingshire (16x34cm-6x13in) s.d.1862 board pair. 6-Mar-3 Christie's, Kensington #42/R est:1500-2500

HARDY, Janes (20th C) British
£350 $553 €525 Sailing barges at sea with town beyond (38x49cm-15x19in) s. panel. 4-Apr-3 Moore Allen & Innocent, Cirencester #689
£680 $1074 €1020 Barges and shipping off coast (30x40cm-12x16in) s. panel pair. 4-Apr-3 Moore Allen & Innocent, Cirencester #682
£700 $1085 €1050 Naval engagement off a port (61x76cm-24x30in) s. panel. 25-Sep-2 Hamptons Fine Art, Godalming #366
£800 $1232 €1200 Warships at anchor (70x90cm-28x35in) s. plywood. 22-Oct-2 Bonhams, Bath #117

HARDY, Mrs Richard (19th C) British
£270 $427 €405 Portrait of Mrs Walton (67x53cm-26x21in) oval. 26-Nov-2 Bonhams, Oxford #69
£320 $506 €480 Portrait of Hannah Hudson (75x60cm-30x24in) oval. 26-Nov-2 Bonhams, Oxford #68

HARDY, Robert (1952-) British
£260 $413 €390 Tree and house (24x30cm-9x12in) s. 18-Mar-3 Bonhams, Knightsbridge #92
£380 $604 €570 Orange tree (33x43cm-13x17in) s. board. 18-Mar-3 Bonhams, Knightsbridge #94

HARDY, Thomas Bush (1842-1897) British
£329 $510 €494 Coast at Pevensey (30x51cm-12x20in) s.d.1897 board. 3-Dec-2 Ritchie, Toronto #3042/R (C.D 800)
£500 $810 €750 At the quayside (43x33cm-17x13in) s.d.87. 21-May-3 Christie's, Kensington #622/R
£520 $827 €780 Making for harbour. Jetty on the French coast (25x37cm-10x15in) s.d.1897 board. 4-Mar-3 Bonhams, Knightsbridge #295/R
£700 $1134 €1015 Fisherfolk by jetty and boats on calm water (16x22cm-6x9in) 29-Jul-3 Holloways, Banbury #336/R
£1000 $1620 €1500 Waiting for the catch (34x25cm-13x10in) s.d.1884. 23-May-3 Lyon & Turnbull, Edinburgh #42/R est:1000-1500

Works on paper
£242 $382 €363 Figures on the beach watching a ship in distress (19x28cm-7x11in) s.d.1889 W/C. 18-Nov-2 Waddingtons, Toronto #72/R (C.D 600)
£280 $445 €420 Coastal scene with shipping (30x23cm-12x9in) s.d.1896. 18-Mar-3 Capes Dunn, Manchester #451
£300 $498 €450 Shipping scene (9x14cm-4x6in) indis sig. W/C. 10-Jun-3 Bonhams, Leeds #89
£303 $476 €455 Llan Stephen Castle, South Wales (12x17cm-5x7in) s.i.d.1879 gouache. 25-Nov-2 Christie's, Melbourne #334/R (A.D 850)
£380 $604 €570 Harbour scene (27x95cm-11x37in) s.d.1890 W/C. 2-Mar-3 Lots Road, London #348
£380 $623 €570 Shipping off the coast (15x36cm-6x14in) s. W/C. 10-Feb-3 David Duggleby, Scarborough #565
£380 $616 €551 Fishing boats off the harbour (10x15cm-4x6in) s. 23-May-3 Dee Atkinson & Harrison, Driffield #694/R
£380 $616 €551 Shipping leaving Folkestone Harbour (24x44cm-9x17in) s.d.1887 W/C. 29-Jul-3 Henry Adams, Chichester #498/R
£400 $620 €600 Coming in with the tide (31x50cm-12x20in) s.i. W/C bodycol. 30-Sep-2 Bonhams, Ipswich #331/R
£400 $620 €600 Harbour bar (38x107cm-15x42in) s.i. W/C htd bodycol. 31-Oct-2 Christie's, Kensington #355
£409 $650 €614 Folkstone (23x50cm-9x20in) s.i.d.1899 W/C gouache. 7-Mar-3 Skinner, Boston #336/R
£480 $749 €720 Shipping off the coast with ruined castle (44x72cm-17x28in) s.d.1889 W/C. 10-Sep-2 David Duggleby, Scarborough #138
£500 $795 €750 Broadstairs fishing boats by the jetty (20x38cm-8x15in) s. i.verso. 19-Mar-3 John Nicholson, Haslemere #1051/R
£520 $827 €780 Calais, shipping off the coast (13x18cm-5x7in) s.i. W/C. 18-Mar-3 Sworder & Son, Bishops Stortford #430/R
£540 $842 €810 Fishing vessels and fishermen in a boat in choppy seas (36x36cm-14x14in) s.d.1889 W/C. 10-Sep-2 David Duggleby, Scarborough #215
£550 $858 €825 Fishing fleet off a coast (46x74cm-18x29in) s.d.1891 W/C. 11-Apr-3 Keys, Aylsham #454/R
£550 $891 €825 Boulogne pier (23x70cm-9x28in) s.i.d.1892 pen brown ink W/C. 21-May-3 Christie's, Kensington #458/R
£550 $869 €825 Nearing sunset Katwyk (19x30cm-7x12in) s.d.1894 W/C. 5-Apr-3 Windibank, Dorking #182/R
£600 $948 €900 Running into harbour during a gale (31x50cm-12x20in) s.i.d.1879 W/C htd white. 26-Nov-2 Bonhams, Knightsbridge #162a/R
£600 $972 €900 Off Calais pier (22x16cm-9x6in) s.d.889 W/C. 21-May-3 Christie's, Kensington #469/R
£607 $953 €911 Wreck of Jubtetuse (21x69cm-8x27in) s.i.d.1890 W/C gouache. 25-Nov-2 Christie's, Melbourne #269/R (A.D 1700)
£621 $993 €900 Busy waters (28x37cm-11x15in) s. W/C. 12-Mar-3 James Adam, Dublin #150/R
£622 $1033 €902 On the breakwall (21x36cm-8x14in) s.d.1893 W/C. 10-Jun-3 Ritchie, Toronto #6/R est:600-900 (C.D 1400)
£650 $1001 €975 Shipping in a squall, fishermen by the water edge (12x18cm-5x7in) s. W/C. 5-Sep-2 Morphets, Harrogate #366/R
£720 $1145 €1080 Broadstairs (16x24cm-6x9in) s.i. W/C htd white. 5-Mar-3 Bonhams, Bury St Edmunds #270/R
£750 $1178 €1125 Leaving harbour (22x45cm-9x18in) s.d.1895 W/C. 16-Dec-2 Sotheby's, Olympia #106/R
£750 $1223 €1088 Fishing boats and other shipping off a harbour at Scarborough (35x46cm-14x18in) bears sig.d1890 pencil W/C scratching out. 17-Jul-3 Tennants, Leyburn #701/R
£800 $1272 €1200 Off Whitby (49x74cm-19x29in) s.i.d.1891 W/C. 4-Mar-3 Bearnes, Exeter #342/R
£800 $1232 €1200 Boats on the Kensington gravel pit (6x10cm-2x4in) s. i.d.1889 verso W/C. 22-Oct-2 Bonhams, Knightsbridge #155/R
£820 $1304 €1230 Return of the fleet (12x17cm-5x7in) bears sig.i.d.95 W/C htd white. 4-Mar-3 Bonhams, Knightsbridge #241/R
£850 $1326 €1275 On the Maas. In the North Sea (22x34cm-9x13in) s.i.d.1873 pencil W/C pair. 17-Oct-2 Christie's, Kensington #160/R
£850 $1318 €1275 Calais Pier (15x30cm-6x12in) s.i.d.896 pencil W/C htd white. 31-Oct-2 Christie's, Kensington #327/R
£850 $1377 €1275 Streamer and a barque off a harbour entrance (19x32cm-7x13in) s. W/C. 21-Jan-3 Bonhams, New Bond Street #161/R
£860 $1342 €1290 Rough water, Sark (21x33cm-8x13in) s.d.1889 W/C. 5-Nov-2 Bristol Auction Rooms #921/R
£891 $1389 €1337 Katwijk am zee (43x68cm-17x27in) s.i. W/C htd white. 15-Oct-2 Stephan Welz, Johannesburg #381/R est:6000-9000 (SA.R 14500)
£900 $1413 €1350 Entering port (21x70cm-8x28in) s.d.1896 W/C. 16-Dec-2 Sotheby's, Olympia #109/R
£940 $1476 €1410 Naval frigates and other vessels off the coast. Fishing pinks (15x44cm-6x17in) s.d.1896 W/C pencil bodycol pair. 15-Apr-3 Bonhams, Knowle #88
£950 $1473 €1425 Royal Albert hulk in the Hamoaze, 1890 (63x102cm-25x40in) s.i.d.1890 W/C htd bodycol. 31-Oct-2 Christie's, Kensington #352/R
£1100 $1727 €1650 Trafalgar (23x33cm-9x13in) s.d.1882 W/C. 16-Dec-2 Sotheby's, Olympia #110/R est:1000-1500
£1100 $1804 €1650 Stormy seascape with sailing ships and shipwreck (51x73cm-20x29in) W/C. 10-Feb-3 Robin Fenner, Tavistock #671/R est:550-650
£1100 $1749 €1650 Fishing boats off a shoreline (25x41cm-10x16in) bears sig. d.1864 W/C. 30-Apr-3 Halls, Shrewsbury #243/R est:800-1200
£1200 $1848 €1800 Fluelen, Lake Lucerne (31x49cm-12x19in) s.i. W/C. 22-Oct-2 Bonhams, Knightsbridge #43/R est:1000-1500
£1200 $1860 €1800 Off the East Coast (37x98cm-15x39in) s.i.d.890 pen ink W/C htd white. 31-Oct-2 Christie's, Kensington #344/R est:1500-2500
£1200 $1944 €1800 Fishing fleet heading out to sea (23x32cm-9x13in) s.d.1873 W/C bodycol. 21-May-3 Christie's, Kensington #461/R est:600-800
£1200 $2004 €1740 Sailing ships off the coast (64x95cm-25x37in) s.d.1892 W/C. 9-Jul-3 George Kidner, Lymington #138/R est:1000-1500
£1300 $2106 €1950 After rain, Dutch hay barges (19x48cm-7x19in) s.i.d.1871 W/C. 21-May-3 Christie's, Kensington #463/R est:1000-1500
£1300 $2067 €1950 Shipping off a jetty (13x44cm-5x17in) s. indis d. W/C. 27-Feb-3 Greenslade Hunt, Taunton #1247/R est:500-800
£1300 $2132 €1950 Off the French coast (13x15cm-5x6in) s.d.1875 W/C. 5-Feb-3 John Nicholson, Haslemere #981 est:500-800
£1400 $2268 €2100 Harbour, North Shields (44x69cm-17x27in) s.i.d.1891 W/C htd white. 22-Jan-3 Bonhams, New Bond Street #348/R est:1500-2000
£1400 $2282 €2100 Yarmouth pier, off Dover (24x51cm-9x20in) s.d.1894 W/C htd white two. 11-Feb-3 Bonhams, Knowle #45 est:600-900
£1500 $2325 €2250 H.M.S Duke of Wellington, Portsmouth Harbour (25x17cm-10x7in) s.i.d.1890 pencil W/C bodycol. 31-Oct-2 Christie's, Kensington #356/R est:1500-2500
£1500 $2355 €2250 Dutch harbour scene (22x65cm-9x26in) s.d.1891 W/C htd bodycol. 16-Dec-2 Sotheby's, Olympia #108/R est:1000-1500
£1600 $2480 €2400 On the Maas (15x34cm-6x13in) s.i.d.94 pencil W/C htd bodycol pair. 31-Oct-2 Christie's, Kensington #351/R est:1200-1800
£1600 $2528 €2400 Low tide (25x41cm-10x16in) s.d.1883 W/C. 18-Dec-2 Mallams, Oxford #585/R est:600-800
£1600 $2592 €2400 On the Dutch coast (17x25cm-7x10in) s.i. pencil W/C. 21-May-3 Christie's, Kensington #462/R est:700-900
£1600 $2672 €2320 Fishing vessels on the shore (22x32cm-9x13in) s.d.1882 W/C htd bodycol. 18-Jun-3 Sotheby's, Olympia #83/R est:800-1200
£1700 $2584 €2550 Hulks in Portsmouth Harbour (48x36cm-19x14in) s.i.d.1895 W/C. 15-Aug-2 Bonhams, New Bond Street #227/R est:700-1000
£1800 $2826 €2700 Hazy morning off Greenwich (43x68cm-17x27in) s.i. indis sig. W/C. 16-Dec-2 Sotheby's, Olympia #107/R est:2000-5000
£1900 $3078 €2850 On the Scheldt (12x17cm-5x7in) s.d.1880 W/C htd white. 22-Jan-3 Bonhams, New Bond Street #357/R est:1000-1500
£2200 $3630 €3190 Drover and sheep in an extensive coastal landscape (43x68cm-17x27in) s.d.1895 W/C htd white. 1-Jul-3 Bonhams, Norwich #92/R est:800-1200
£2300 $3657 €3450 Barges in an estuary. Return of the fishing fleet. s. W/C pair. 30-Apr-3 Halls, Shrewsbury #230/R est:1200-1800
£2400 $3864 €3600 Greenwich Pier, stormy weather (24x51cm-9x20in) s. i.verso W/C. 15-Jan-3 Cheffins Grain & Comins, Cambridge #385/R
£2400 $3864 €3600 Shipping off the Port of Dort (29x47cm-11x19in) s.d.1881 W/C. 15-Jan-3 Cheffins Grain & Comins, Cambridge #386/R
£2500 $3875 €3750 Calais Pier (40x70cm-16x28in) s.i.d.1874 pencil W/C bodycol. 31-Oct-2 Christie's, Kensington #353/R est:2500-3500
£2500 $3900 €3625 At the mouth of the Tyne (33x49cm-13x19in) s.d.1875 i.verso W/C. 28-Mar-3 ELR Auctions, Sheffield #199/R est:1000-1500
£2600 $3952 €3900 Unloading the catch (23x69cm-9x27in) s.d.1890 W/C bodycol scratching out. 15-Aug-2 Bonhams, New Bond Street #431/R est:3000-5000
£2600 $4108 €3900 Boulogne harbour (46x69cm-18x27in) s. W/C. 29-Nov-2 Dee Atkinson & Harrison, Driffield #869/R est:1500-2500
£2600 $4134 €3900 Fishing boats off Calais harbour (39x79cm-15x31in) s.i.d.1889 W/C. 20-Mar-3 Martel Maides, Guernsey #161/R est:1500-2000
£2600 $4134 €3900 Coastal scene, low tide (13x44cm-5x17in) s. indis d. W/C. 27-Feb-3 Greenslade Hunt, Taunton #1246/R est:500-800
£2800 $4312 €4200 On the Scheldt. Off Flushing (22x70cm-9x28in) s.i.d.1896 W/C pair. 23-Oct-2 Hamptons Fine Art, Godalming #50/R est:1000-1500
£3000 $4560 €4500 Off Treport (33x49cm-13x19in) s.i.d.1878 W/C htd bodycol. 15-Aug-2 Bonhams, New Bond Street #427/R est:3000-5000
£3000 $4800 €4500 Calais pier (36x53cm-14x21in) s.i.d.1891 W/C htd bodycol. 13-Mar-3 Duke & Son, Dorchester #85/R est:800-1500

£3200 $5344 €4640 Shipping in the English Channel. Shipping off the coast (26x73cm-10x29in) s.d.1890 pencil W/C htd white pair. 26-Jun-3 Mellors & Kirk, Nottingham #835/R est:2500-3000
£4000 $6360 €6000 Fishing boats off Calais. In Portsmouth Harbour (41x61cm-16x24in) one s.d.1895 W/C htd bodycol one sketch pair. 30-Apr-3 Halls, Shrewsbury #228/R est:3000-4000
£4800 $7440 €7200 Summer's eve, Scheveningen (53x95cm-21x37in) s.i.d.1874-80 pencil W/C bodycol. 31-Oct-2 Christie's, Kensington #354/R est:3000-5000
£5500 $8690 €8250 At Scarbro. Fishing boats and other sailing vessels off Whitby (28x71cm-11x28in) s.d.1890 W/C pair. 13-Nov-2 Halls, Shrewsbury #361 est:3000-5000

HARDY, Thomas Bush (attrib) (1842-1897) British
Works on paper
£272 $425 €408 Untitled country road (23x33cm-9x13in) W/C. 29-Mar-3 Charlton Hall, Columbia #220/R
£290 $452 €435 Busy estuary scene (21x32cm-8x13in) s.i. W/C. 13-Sep-2 Lyon & Turnbull, Edinburgh #55/R
£300 $468 €450 Clearing a wreck (23x48cm-9x19in) bears sig.i. W/C pencil bodycol laid down. 17-Oct-2 Lawrence, Crewkerne #395/R
£400 $624 €600 Venice (12x21cm-5x8in) pencil W/C. 18-Sep-2 Dreweatt Neate, Newbury #25
£645 $1000 €968 Vessels at rough seas (43x66cm-17x26in) s.i. W/C. 28-Sep-2 Charlton Hall, Columbia #578/R
£700 $1113 €1050 Watching the boats (24x72cm-9x28in) bears sig.d.1890 W/C. 4-Mar-3 Bonhams, Knightsbridge #235/R

HARDY, Thomas le (fl.1793-1807) British
Miniatures
£1188 $1900 €1723 Portrait of a British officer (5x5cm-2x2in) mono. 17-May-3 New Orleans Auction, New Orleans #5/R est:1400-1800

HARDY, W J (fl.1845-1856) British
£550 $875 €825 Riverside scene with cattle (28x38cm-11x15in) board. 2-Mar-3 Lots Road, London #350a

HARDY, William F (19th C) British
£350 $574 €525 Rustic beauty (25x20cm-10x8in) s.d.77. 5-Jun-3 Christie's, Kensington #639/R

HARE, Channing (1899-1976) American
£258 $400 €387 Sunflower (46x38cm-18x15in) s.d.1971 masonite. 1-Oct-2 Arthur James, Florida #426

HARE, David (1917-1992) American
Sculpture
£3165 $5000 €4748 Rain cloud sun (79cm-31in) s.d.52 steel bronze on wood base. 24-Apr-3 Shannon's, Milford #175/R est:5000-7000

HARE, John (20th C) American
Works on paper
£220 $350 €330 Beached dory, evening (24x30cm-9x12in) s. W/C. 7-Mar-3 Skinner, Boston #477/R

HARE, John Knowles (1882-1947) American
£637 $1000 €956 End of winter (76x102cm-30x40in) s. i.verso. 22-Nov-2 Skinner, Boston #292/R est:700-900
Works on paper
£242 $375 €363 Landscape with cottages by water's edge (23x28cm-9x11in) s. W/C. 3-Nov-2 Van Blarcom, South Natick #259
£406 $650 €589 At the docks (44x34cm-17x13in) s. W/C gouache. 16-May-3 Skinner, Boston #282/R

HARE, Julius (1859-1932) British
£860 $1367 €1290 Figures on the shore, Cemaes Bay (46x85cm-18x33in) s.i.d.95. 27-Feb-3 Bonhams, Chester #345

HAREUX, Ernest Victor (1847-1909) French
£641 $974 €1000 High mountain valley by moonlight with cows in front of alpine hut (162x132cm-64x52in) s.d.1908 lit. 11-Jul-2 Allgauer, Kempten #2500/R

HARGAN, Joe (?) ?
£600 $936 €900 Cafe Guerbois, The Sensualists (100x90cm-39x35in) s.d. 17-Sep-2 Bonhams, Knightsbridge #151/R

HARGENS, Charles (1893-) American
£1026 $1600 €1539 Studio of George Sotter, Holicong, PA (30x41cm-12x16in) s. board. 18-Sep-2 Alderfer's, Hatfield #346/R est:800-1200
£1154 $1800 €1731 Across the plains (20x18cm-8x7in) s. board. 18-Sep-2 Alderfer's, Hatfield #342/R est:800-1200

HARGITT, Edward (1835-1895) British
£450 $711 €675 Figures seated on the grass with mill house beyond (29x44cm-11x17in) s. panel. 26-Nov-2 Bonhams, Oxford #39/R
£2200 $3476 €3300 Goat herd and flock overlooking a loch scene (57x80cm-22x31in) s.d.1863. 27-Nov-2 Bonhams, Knowle #251 est:2000-2500
£6048 $9556 €9072 Conway Castle, North Wales (137x183cm-54x72in) s.d.Jan 1885. 18-Nov-2 Waddingtons, Toronto #183/R est:15000-20000 (C.D 15000)

HARGRAVE, Gordon (fl.c.1890-1920) British
Works on paper
£280 $442 €420 Evening hour, Blisworth, 1907 (25x36cm-10x14in) s. W/C. 2-Dec-2 Gorringes, Lewes #2692

HARGREAVES, Lucy (fl.1880-1930) British
£820 $1304 €1230 An incident in the hunt (26x35cm-10x14in) init.indis.d.09 s.i.stretcher. 27-Feb-3 Bonhams, Chester #398/R

HARGREAVES, Thomas (1774-1846) British
Miniatures
£2200 $3608 €3190 Anne Earle in white dress (9x7cm-4x3in) s.d.1811 gilt metal frame rectangular. 3-Jun-3 Christie's, London #177/R est:1000-1500

HARGREAVES, Thomas (attrib) (1774-1846) British
Miniatures
£700 $1162 €1015 Portrait of a lady (8x5cm-3x2in) i.verso oval case. 12-Jun-3 Gorringes, Lewes #1585

HARING, Keith (1958-1990) American
£904 $1500 €1311 Stylized figure (76x102cm-30x40in).d.1989 b. 11-Jun-3 Boos Gallery, Michigan #569/R est:2500-5000
£3671 $5727 €5800 Untitled (86x114cm-34x45in) tempera feltpen board. 18-Oct-2 Dr Fritz Nagel, Stuttgart #512/R est:5800
£7188 $11500 €10782 Two figures enclosing a heart, over three figures (61x38cm-24x15in) i. acrylic maker panel. 17-May-3 Pook & Pook, Downington #91/R est:4000-5000
£10870 $17827 €15000 Spiritual (97x126cm-38x50in) tempera felt panel. 27-May-3 Tajan, Paris #60/R est:15000-20000
£14375 $23000 €21563 Dog (128x96cm-50x38in) s.d.86 acrylic silkscreen prov.lit. 15-May-3 Christie's, Rockefeller NY #387/R est:12000-18000
£15000 $24000 €22500 Untitled - in pink (49x49cm-19x19in) mono.d.Dec 29 1984 verso acrylic canvas on board prov. 14-May-3 Sotheby's, New York #456/R est:10000-15000
£18065 $28000 €27098 Untitled (98x131cm-39x52in) s. i.d.1982 verso acrylic brush ink prov. 26-Sep-2 Christie's, Rockefeller NY #818/R est:35000-45000
£22152 $35000 €33228 Gil's dream (91x61cm-36x24in) s.i.d.1989 acrylic prov. 13-Nov-2 Sotheby's, New York #559/R est:25000-35000
£35484 $55000 €53226 Little bad wolf (76x76cm-30x30in) s. i.d.Oct 10 1984 verso acrylic prov. 26-Sep-2 Christie's, Rockefeller NY #815/R est:50000-70000
£50000 $82000 €75000 Mickey mouse (127x193cm-50x76in) s.i.d.June 18 1981 verso acrylic two parts. 7-Feb-3 Sotheby's, London #171/R est:30000-40000
£75949 $120000 €113924 Untitled (152x152cm-60x60in) s.d.1985 overlap acrylic prov. 13-Nov-2 Sotheby's, New York #563/R est:125000-175000
£108974 $170000 €163461 Untitled (152x152cm-60x60in) s.d.May 3 1988 acrylic prov. 11-Nov-2 Phillips, New York #29/R est:100000-150000
Prints
£1442 $2250 €2163 From Pop Shop I (30x38cm-12x15in) s.d.num.47/200 col silkscreen. 14-Oct-2 Butterfields, San Francisco #1266/R est:1500-2000
£1740 $2750 €2610 From flowers no.1 (100x130cm-39x51in) s.d.1990 num.12/15 col silkscreen. 22-Apr-3 Butterfields, San Francisco #2282/R est:3000-5000
£2128 $3447 €3000 Untitled (107x126cm-42x50in) s.d.83 num.26/100 serigraph prov. 26-May-3 Christie's, Milan #12/R est:3000-3500
£2201 $3500 €3302 Best buddies (55x70cm-22x28in) bears another sig.num.47/200 col screenprint. 2-May-3 Sotheby's, New York #460/R est:3000-4000
£2756 $4272 €4300 Pyramid of people (101x81cm-40x32in) s.d.1985 col lithograph. 7-Dec-2 Van Ham, Cologne #208/R est:3300

£2857 $4600 €4286 Composition (57x57cm-22x22in) s.d.88 num.89/100 col silkscreen. 7-May-3 AB Stockholms Auktionsverk #1212/R est:25000-30000 (S.KR 37000)
£3194 $5046 €4791 Untitled 2 (78x97cm-31x38in) s.num.44/60 col lithograph lit. 28-Apr-3 Bukowskis, Stockholm #427/R est:30000-40000 (S.KR 42000)
£4403 $7000 €6605 Untitled V (107x127cm-42x50in) s.d.num.68/100 col screenprint. 2-May-3 Sotheby's, New York #456/R est:6000-8000
£9615 $15000 €14423 Apocolypse, New York, George Mulder Fine Arts (96x96cm-38x38in) s.num. col screenprints set of ten. 5-Nov-2 Christie's, Rockefeller NY #388/R est:10000-15000
£10692 $17000 €16038 Flowers suite, New York (100x130cm-39x51in) s.d.num.74/100 col screenprint set of five plastic portfolio. 29-Apr-3 Christie's, Rockefeller NY #616/R est:15000-20000
£10759 $17000 €16139 Retrospect (117x209cm-46x82in) s.d.1989 num.43/75 col silkscreen. 22-Apr-3 Butterfields, San Francisco #2279/R est:15000-20000
£18868 $30000 €28302 Growing (102x76cm-40x30in) s.d.num.95/100 col screenprint set of five. 2-May-3 Sotheby's, New York #458/R est:20000-30000

Sculpture
£3459 $5362 €5500 Chirro et torro (54x32cm-21x13in) s.d.88 luminous glass plexiglas pair. 30-Oct-2 Artcurial Briest, Paris #681/R est:3000-4000
£11538 $18000 €17307 Totem (184cm-72in) s.d.num.17/35 col plywood metal. 5-Nov-2 Christie's, Rockefeller NY #389/R est:15000-20000

Works on paper
£385 $604 €600 Keith Haring Stedelijk Museum (34x26cm-13x10in) s. felt-pen exec.1986. 25-Nov-2 Glerum, Amsterdam #188
£625 $1000 €906 Blue figures (11x14cm-4x6in) s.d.88 ink. 16-May-3 Skinner, Boston #380/R est:1500-2000
£828 $1382 €1200 Personnage dansant (13x9cm-5x4in) s.d.87 felt tip. 9-Jul-3 Cornette de St.Cyr, Paris #298/R
£1100 $1705 €1650 Homo decorans - det dekorerende menneske (21x29cm-8x11in) s.i.d.1985 black felt tip pen prov. 5-Dec-2 Christie's, Kensington #228/R est:1000-2000
£1572 $2437 €2500 Untitled (22x15cm-9x6in) s.d.89 felt-tip pen. 5-Oct-2 De Vuyst, Lokeren #165/R est:2600-3000
£1887 $2925 €3000 Man with heart head (28x21cm-11x8in) s.d.89 black marker. 30-Oct-2 Artcurial Briest, Paris #598 est:2300-3000
£2166 $3400 €3249 Untitled, spaceship and figure (23x23cm-9x9in) felt tip marker black ink. 21-Nov-2 Swann Galleries, New York #70/R est:2000-3000
£2187 $3500 €3281 Dancing dogs (23x24cm-9x9in) s.i.d.82 black marker. 14-May-3 Sotheby's, New York #455/R est:8000-12000
£2187 $3500 €3171 Party time (28x22cm-11x9in) s.d.86 ink. 16-May-3 Skinner, Boston #379/R est:2000-3000
£2201 $3412 €3500 Jongle-two figures (25x20cm-10x8in) s.d.89 black marker. 30-Oct-2 Artcurial Briest, Paris #599/R est:2300-3000
£2244 $3522 €3500 Untitled (33x24cm-13x9in) s.i.d.1986 col ink prov. 15-Dec-2 Perrin, Versailles #152/R
£2264 $3509 €3600 Mickey (26x21cm-10x8in) s.i. felt dr cardboard. 30-Oct-2 Artcurial Briest, Paris #469/R est:3000-4000
£2436 $3824 €3800 Untitled (31x22cm-12x9in) s.d.1985 Chinese ink dr prov. 15-Dec-2 Perrin, Versailles #153/R
£2564 $3974 €4000 Subway drawing (104x74cm-41x29in) white chk canvas on canvas on board. 7-Dec-2 Van Ham, Cologne #207/R est:4300
£2600 $4342 €3770 Cow (29x39cm-11x15in) s.i.d.89 felt tip prov. 24-Jun-3 Sotheby's, Olympia #65/R est:2000-3000
£2625 $4200 €3938 Untitled (48x61cm-19x24in) black marker on poster board executed c.1984 prov. 16-May-3 Phillips, New York #146/R est:8000-12000
£2826 $4380 €4239 Subway-drawing - dog (105x57cm-41x22in) chk. 4-Dec-2 Koller, Zurich #204/R est:6000-9000 (S.FR 6500)
£2848 $4443 €4500 Subway drawing (123x91cm-48x36in) chk. 18-Oct-2 Dr Fritz Nagel, Stuttgart #514/R est:4500
£3061 $4867 €4500 Untitled (22x35cm-9x14in) mono. felt-tip pen. 24-Mar-3 Cornette de St.Cyr, Paris #95/R
£3103 $4903 €4500 Subway drawing (124x90cm-49x35in) chk. 2-Apr-3 Dr Fritz Nagel, Stuttgart #9468/R est:4100
£3500 $5530 €5250 Untitled (107x74cm-42x29in) chk. 3-Apr-3 Christie's, Kensington #236/R
£3671 $5727 €5800 Untitled (34x25cm-13x10in) s.i.d.1986 Indian ink W/C. 18-Oct-2 Dr Fritz Nagel, Stuttgart #513/R est:5800
£4069 $6429 €5900 Untitled (97x126cm-38x50in) tempera feltpen panel. 2-Apr-3 Dr Fritz Nagel, Stuttgart #9469/R est:5800
£4539 $7035 €6809 Untitled (36x44cm-14x17in) s.d.83 Indian ink. 8-Dec-2 Uppsala Auktionskammare, Uppsala #286/R est:40000-50000 (S.KR 64000)
£5062 $8100 €7593 Untitled (48x61cm-19x24in) black marker on poster board executed c.1984 prov. 16-May-3 Phillips, New York #147/R est:8000-12000
£5072 $8319 €7000 Subway drawing (113x75cm-44x30in) chk board. 28-May-3 Lempertz, Koln #160/R est:8000
£5380 $8500 €8500 Untitled (57x73cm-22x29in) s.d.Oct 3- 1984 verso ink. 26-Nov-2 Sotheby's, Amsterdam #247/R est:4000-6000
£5696 $9000 €8544 Angel (23x24cm-9x9in) s.d.82 marker. 13-Nov-2 Sotheby's, New York #565/R est:9000-12000
£5696 $9000 €9000 Untitled (39x52cm-15x20in) s.d.Feb 28 83 i.verso sumai ink. 26-Nov-2 Sotheby's, Amsterdam #249/R est:6000-8000
£6028 $9766 €8500 Subway drawing (206x103cm-81x41in) chk board on canvas. 24-May-3 Van Ham, Cologne #228/R est:7000
£6250 $10000 €9375 Untitled (185x189cm-73x74in) silkscreen ink on fabric executed 1988 prov. 15-May-3 Christie's, Rockefeller NY #394/R est:10000-15000
£6646 $10500 €10500 Subway drawing (120x83cm-47x33in) chk dr exec.1982 prov. 27-Nov-2 Tajan, Paris #93/R est:6000-7000
£8844 $14061 €13000 Untitled (120x89cm-47x35in) pastel card. 1-Mar-3 Meeting Art, Vercelli #430 est:12000
£10625 $17000 €15938 Untitled - boombox (102x123cm-40x48in) sumi ink on foamcore executed 1984 prov. 15-May-3 Christie's, Rockefeller NY #395/R est:12000-18000
£12025 $19000 €18038 Untitled (61x48cm-24x19in) s.d.85 marker prov. 13-Nov-2 Sotheby's, New York #561/R est:12000-18000
£12500 $20625 €18000 Les voleurs de pyramides (94x67cm-37x26in) s.i.d.83 felt tip. 1-Jul-3 Artcurial Briest, Paris #542/R est:20000-25000
£23750 $38000 €35625 Untitled (76x108cm-30x43in) s.d.Jan 21-82 ink prov. 15-May-3 Christie's, Rockefeller NY #392/R est:25000-30000
£26250 $42000 €39375 Untitled (56x76cm-22x30in) s.d.Nov 27.81 black marker prov. 16-May-3 Phillips, New York #151/R est:40000-60000

HARLAMOFF, Alexis (1842-1915) Russian
£9000 $14580 €13500 Village in the South of France (32x23cm-13x9in) s. board. 21-May-3 Sotheby's, London #64/R est:5000-7000
£14000 $22680 €21000 Scene from a midsummers night's dream (78x62cm-31x24in) s. 21-May-3 Sotheby's, London #62/R est:15000-20000
£16000 $26720 €24000 Head of a young girl (32x24cm-13x9in) s. panel. 18-Jun-3 Christie's, Kensington #114/R est:8000-12000
£41778 $69351 €60578 Mignon (47x37cm-19x15in) s. prov. 16-Jun-3 Waddingtons, Toronto #346/R est:80000-120000 (C.D 94000)
£44304 $70000 €66456 Jeune fille couchee (61x89cm-24x35in) s. 24-Apr-3 Sotheby's, New York #59/R est:70000-90000
£58065 $90000 €87098 Flower girl (92x74cm-36x29in) s.d.1878 prov. 30-Oct-2 Christie's, Rockefeller NY #52/R est:100000-150000
£77419 $120000 €116129 Pink bonnet (55x44cm-22x17in) s. prov. 30-Oct-2 Christie's, Rockefeller NY #48/R est:120000-160000

HARLESTON, Edwin Augustus (1881-1932) American
£3153 $4950 €4730 Young black boy holding red rose to nose and wearing black outfit with hat (25x20cm-10x8in) board. 19-Apr-3 James Julia, Fairfield #41a/R est:800-1000

HARLEY, Herbert E (fl.1884-1908) British
£1200 $1920 €1800 Portrait of a lady seated in a garden sewing (36x15cm-14x6in) s.d.94 panel. 11-Mar-3 Bonhams, Knightsbridge #116/R est:500-700

HARLFINGER, Fanny (1873-1954) Austrian?
£463 $745 €695 Madonna (100x100cm-39x39in) s.i.d.1919. 7-May-3 Dobiaschofsky, Bern #624/R (S.FR 1000)

HARLFINGER, Richard (1873-1943) Austrian
£647 $1062 €900 Adjudicator (85x110cm-33x43in) s.d.1917. 5-Jun-3 Dorotheum, Salzburg #500/R

HARLOW, George Henry (1787-1819) British

Works on paper
£1800 $2826 €2700 Portrait of Benjamin Robert Haydon (25x20cm-10x8in) s.i.d.1815 pencil chk prov. 21-Nov-2 Christie's, London #14/R est:2000-3000

HARLOW, George Henry (attrib) (1787-1819) British
£302 $478 €453 Celestial beauty (44x36cm-17x14in) 18-Nov-2 Waddingtons, Toronto #87/R (C.D 750)
£480 $782 €720 Group portrait of three sisters (24x19cm-9x7in) panel. 13-Feb-3 Mellors & Kirk, Nottingham #810
£8000 $13280 €12000 Portrait of a gentleman, possibly a member of the Wellesley family (91x71cm-36x28in) prov. 10-Jun-3 Christie's, London #41/R est:8000-12000

HARMAR, Fairlie (1876-1945) British
£320 $499 €480 Shell collectors (76x97cm-30x38in) s. 15-Oct-2 Bonhams, Knightsbridge #168

HARMER, Alexander F (1856-1925) American
£2690 $4250 €3901 Moving on (30x36cm-12x14in) s. board. 26-Jul-3 Coeur d'Alene, Hayden #239/R est:8000-12000

£5120 $8500 €7424 Beyond these infinities lies gold (61x91cm-24x36in) mono. i.verso. 11-Jun-3 Butterfields, San Francisco #4193/R est:10000-15000

HARMON, Annie (1855-1930) American

£1090 $1700 €1635 Orange meadow. board. 21-Sep-2 Harvey Clar, Oakland #1516

HARMON, Charles (1859-1936) American

£321 $500 €482 Mountain lake scene (41x51cm-16x20in) s. 21-Sep-2 Harvey Clar, Oakland #1645
£353 $550 €530 Mountainous landscape (74x114cm-29x45in) s.d.1899. 20-Sep-2 Freeman, Philadelphia #63/R
£417 $650 €626 California redwoods (36x25cm-14x10in) s. board prov. 20-Sep-2 Freeman, Philadelphia #53/R
£1154 $1800 €1731 Crashing waves at the Golden Gate. 21-Sep-2 Harvey Clar, Oakland #1545

HARMS, Anton Friedrich (1695-1745) German

£8000 $12560 €12000 Plate of herrings on an urn, trout and a lobsters, bottle of olive oil on a draped table (92x81cm-36x32in) s.d.1734 prov. 13-Dec-2 Christie's, Kensington #144/R est:8000-12000

HARMS, Edith Margaret (1870-1943) British

Works on paper

£620 $986 €930 Still life of pink roses in a pottery jug (53x33cm-21x13in) s.d.1903 W/C. 30-Apr-3 Hampton & Littlewood, Exeter #463/R

HARMS, Johannes Oswald (1643-1708) German

£7742 $12000 €11613 Capriccio of classical ruins with figures and fountain (87x134cm-34x53in) 2-Oct-2 Christie's, Rockefeller NY #139/R est:7000-10000
£12579 $19497 €20000 Winter landscape with frozen river (63x88cm-25x35in) s.d.1674. 2-Oct-2 Dorotheum, Vienna #231/R est:20000-30000

HARNETT, B J (19th C) American

£4140 $6500 €6210 View of the Golden Gate (81x152cm-32x60in) prov. 19-Nov-2 Butterfields, San Francisco #8139/R est:3000-5000

HARNETT, William Michael (1848-1892) American

£5405 $8432 €8000 Still life with plums spilling out of bag. s.d.1881. 26-Mar-3 Hugo Ruef, Munich #121/R est:8000
£11950 $19000 €17925 Still life for William Ignatius Blemly (30x20cm-12x8in) mono. painted c.1877 prov.lit. 5-Mar-3 Sotheby's, New York #35/R est:15000-20000
£23457 $38000 €35186 Still life with fruit and vase (12x9cm-5x4in) mono. s.i.on stretcher. 22-May-3 Christie's, Rockefeller NY #11/R est:30000-50000
£64516 $100000 €96774 Two quinces (31x27cm-12x11in) s.d.1877 prov.exhib. 5-Dec-2 Christie's, Rockefeller NY #44/R est:120000-180000

HARNEY, Paul E (1850-1915) American

£321 $500 €482 Portrait of a monk (30x25cm-12x10in) s. canvasboard prov. 10-Nov-2 Selkirks, St. Louis #841/R
£353 $550 €530 Chickens (25x33cm-10x13in) s.d.1911 canvasboard prov. 10-Nov-2 Selkirks, St. Louis #843/R
£359 $600 €521 Interior scene of an old man warming his hands near a stove (30x41cm-12x16in) s.d.1884. 21-Jun-3 Selkirks, St. Louis #154/R
£481 $750 €722 Chickens (20x25cm-8x10in) s. 10-Nov-2 Selkirks, St. Louis #843a
£545 $850 €818 Portrait of a monk seated at a table (28x23cm-11x9in) s.d.1896. 10-Nov-2 Selkirks, St. Louis #842/R
£689 $1150 €999 Chickens (25x36cm-10x14in) s.d.1913. 21-Jun-3 Selkirks, St. Louis #155 est:800-1000
£833 $1300 €1250 Portrait of a monk resting his head (41x30cm-16x12in) s.d.1896 prov. 10-Nov-2 Selkirks, St. Louis #844
£1410 $2200 €2115 Chickens in a farmyard (18x23cm-7x9in) s. 10-Nov-2 Selkirks, St. Louis #840/R est:1000-1500

Works on paper

£513 $800 €770 Gateway to Old Peltingill home farm in Bath, Maine (28x38cm-11x15in) s.d. W/C dr. 14-Sep-2 Selkirks, St. Louis #129

HARPER, Charles (1943-) Irish

£2083 $3312 €3000 Limescape (95x102cm-37x40in) s.d.1998 s.i.verso acrylic. 29-Apr-3 Whyte's, Dublin #140/R est:3000-4000
£2278 $3532 €3600 Girl (65x55cm-26x22in) init.d.1965 board. 25-Sep-2 James Adam, Dublin #117/R est:1500-2000
£2609 $4278 €3600 Homage to Dan O'Neill (102x76cm-40x30in) 28-May-3 Bonhams & James Adam, Dublin #67/R est:4000-6000
£2703 $4216 €4000 Exuberant landscape (110x120cm-43x47in) s.d.March 2000 acrylic on linen. 26-Mar-3 James Adam, Dublin #98/R est:4000-6000

Works on paper

£597 $932 €950 Head (44x57cm-17x22in) i.verso mixed media. 17-Sep-2 Whyte's, Dublin #76/R
£1923 $3019 €3000 Public race (71x57cm-28x22in) s.i.d.1993 W/C pastel pen ink. 19-Nov-2 Whyte's, Dublin #25/R est:3000-4000

HARPER, Edward Steel (1878-1951) British

£240 $400 €348 Portrait of a distinguished gentleman (102x76cm-40x30in) mono. canvasboard. 22-Jun-3 Jeffery Burchard, Florida #94/R
£750 $1170 €1125 Lake side in spring. Field landscape (46x30cm-18x12in) mono. one d.1916 one d.1914 with another by same hand three. 26-Mar-3 Hamptons Fine Art, Godalming #139

HARPER, Frank R (1908-) American

£932 $1500 €1398 Ponce de Leon pauses at spring for drink (56x46cm-22x18in) s. 20-Feb-3 Illustration House, New York #75/R est:1000-1500

HARPER, Henry Andrew (1835-1900) British

Works on paper

£300 $462 €450 Ruins in an Italian landscape (25x35cm-10x14in) s.d.1869 W/C. 22-Oct-2 Bonhams, Knightsbridge #52/R
£320 $499 €480 Pools of Solomon, near Bethlehem (36x26cm-14x10in) s.d.1899 W/C. 25-Mar-3 Bonhams, Knightsbridge #56/R
£321 $508 €482 Landscape (46x72cm-18x28in) s.d.1881 W/C. 27-Nov-2 Deutscher-Menzies, Melbourne #269/R est:1000-1500 (A.D 900)
£480 $758 €720 Sea of Galilee from the Heights of Fiberias (25x35cm-10x14in) s.d.1896 W/C. 27-Nov-2 Peter Wilson, Nantwich #116
£500 $795 €750 Sphinx at Giza, Egypt (56x77cm-22x30in) s.d.1892 W/C. 29-Apr-3 Bonhams, New Bond Street #96
£850 $1326 €1275 Smyrna from the sea (22x48cm-9x19in) s.i.d.1872 W/C prov. 15-Oct-2 Sotheby's, London #97/R
£1400 $2268 €2100 Sea of Tiberies, from Gardara. View of Sinai, Egypt (11x20cm-4x8in) one s.d.93 one s.d.1895 pencil W/C. 23-Jan-3 Christie's, Kensington #373/R est:500-700
£1800 $2862 €2700 Sea of Galilea (25x36cm-10x14in) s.i.d.1896 W/C htd white. 29-Apr-3 Bonhams, New Bond Street #89/R est:2000-3000
£2000 $3120 €3000 Figures on a street in Jerusalem (36x25cm-14x10in) s.i. W/C over pencil htd bodycol. 15-Oct-2 Sotheby's, London #118/R est:2000-3000

HARPER, Melinda (1965-) Australian

£996 $1564 €1494 Untitled 1996 (61x55cm-24x22in) s. verso. 15-Apr-3 Lawson Menzies, Sydney #79/R est:1800-2500 (A.D 2600)
£1938 $3081 €2907 Untitled (76x76cm-30x30in) s.d.2001 verso. 5-May-3 Sotheby's, Melbourne #265/R est:3000-5000 (A.D 5000)
£2063 $3425 €3516 Untitled (30x25cm-12x10in) s.d.1995 verso. 10-Jun-3 Shapiro, Sydney #88/R est:1800-2200 (A.D 5200)
£2299 $3609 €3449 Untitled (121x100cm-48x39in) s. i.d.1999 verso. 15-Apr-3 Lawson Menzies, Sydney #11/R est:3000-5000 (A.D 6000)
£3049 $4817 €4421 Untitled 2002 (122x112cm-48x44in) s.d.2002 verso. 22-Jul-3 Lawson Menzies, Sydney #5/R est:3000-5000 (A.D 7500)
£4264 $6779 €6396 Untitled (183x152cm-72x60in) s.d.2002 verso. 5-May-3 Sotheby's, Melbourne #189/R est:7000-10000 (A.D 11000)
£4643 $7243 €6965 Untitled (122x112cm-48x44in) prov. 11-Nov-2 Deutscher-Menzies, Melbourne #60/R est:5000-7000 (A.D 13000)

HARPER, Miles (fl.1935) British

Works on paper

£290 $473 €435 Devil (31x10cm-12x4in) s.d.34 pen ink W/C. 30-Jan-3 Lawrence, Crewkerne #659/R

HARPER, Thomas (1820-1889) British

Works on paper

£260 $403 €390 Figures on the rocks at Tynemouth (12x37cm-5x15in) init.d.1871 W/C. 24-Sep-2 Anderson & Garland, Newcastle #307

HARPIGNIES, Henri (1819-1916) French

£641 $974 €1000 Mountain lake with boat and figures (24x18cm-9x7in) s.d.89 canvas on board. 11-Jul-2 Allgauer, Kempten #2501/R
£750 $1178 €1125 Washerwoman on the shore (28x34cm-11x13in) indis sig.d.4 Sept 1869 board. 16-Apr-3 Christie's, Kensington #595/R
£1081 $1686 €1600 Chemin dans la colline (22x14cm-9x6in) s.d.1910 i.verso. 26-Mar-3 Rieunier, Paris #14/R
£1181 $1924 €1700 Paysage de la Cote d'Azur dans les environs de menton (21x27cm-8x11in) s. 19-Jul-3 Thierry & Lannon, Brest #340 est:1700-2000
£1268 $2104 €1800 Paysage nuageux (22x33cm-9x13in) s. s.i.verso. 11-Jun-3 Beaussant & Lefèvre, Paris #61/R est:2000-2500
£1538 $2431 €2400 Mountain path on sunny evening (19x26cm-7x10in) s. panel prov. 15-Nov-2 Reiss & Sohn, Konigstein #34/R est:3000
£2000 $3280 €3000 Au bord du Lac, St Prive (25x33cm-10x13in) s. prov. 3-Jun-3 Sotheby's, London #137/R est:3000-4000
£2174 $3391 €3261 Landscape with castle (35x55cm-14x22in) s. 16-Sep-2 Philippe Schuler, Zurich #3475/R est:7000-9000 (S.FR 5000)

£2500 $3950 €3750 Sunlit pool with herons on the bank (36x86cm-14x34in) s.d.1903. 18-Dec-2 Mallams, Oxford #686/R est:3000-4000
£3038 $4800 €4800 Chasseur et son chien (46x55cm-18x22in) s.d.1904. 29-Nov-2 Drouot Estimations, Paris #72
£4321 $7000 €6265 Woman at rest beneath a tree (69x97cm-27x38in) s.d.93. 21-May-3 Doyle, New York #201/R est:10000-15000
£4577 $7599 €6500 Saint-Prive, Yonne (33x46cm-13x18in) s.d. 11-Jun-3 Beaussant & Lefèvre, Paris #62/R est:6000-8000
£6000 $9420 €9000 Les bords de l'aumance (31x50cm-12x20in) s. 19-Nov-2 Sotheby's, London #154/R est:6000-8000
£7424 $11581 €11136 Village confirmation (41x33cm-16x13in) s.d.1860. 20-Nov-2 Fischer, Luzern #1078/R est:8000-12000 (S.FR 17000)
£9494 $15000 €14241 Les bords de I'Allier (51x62cm-20x24in) s.d.89 prov. 23-Apr-3 Christie's, Rockefeller NY #69/R est:12000-16000
£9607 $14987 €14411 Retour a la ferme (41x31cm-16x12in) s. 20-Nov-2 Fischer, Luzern #1079/R est:7000-9000 (S.FR 22000)
£12000 $19200 €18000 Bords de l'Allier (51x61cm-20x24in) s.i.verso. 13-Mar-3 Duke & Son, Dorchester #250/R

Works on paper
£253 $400 €400 Sous-bois (4x8cm-2x3in) s.d.1908 wash. 28-Nov-2 Tajan, Paris #211
£265 $432 €400 Paysage anime de personnages (4x8cm-2x3in) s.d.1909 pen grey wash dr. 16-Feb-3 Mercier & Cie, Lille #247a
£458 $750 €700 Arbres (14x22cm-6x9in) s.i.d.1906 wash. 7-Feb-3 Oger, Dumont, Paris #24
£469 $750 €680 Twilight along the lane (16x17cm-6x7in) s.d.1871 W/C. 16-May-3 Skinner, Boston #44/R
£500 $780 €750 Tree trunks at St. Prive (42x27cm-17x11in) s.i.d.1908 chl. 17-Oct-2 Christie's, Kensington #64
£500 $800 €750 St Prive. s.i. chl dr. 12-Jan-3 William Jenack, New York #333
£527 $853 €800 Sous-bois (15x23cm-6x9in) s. chl dr. 22-Jan-3 Tajan, Paris #22
£538 $839 €850 Peniche sur la Seine a Rouen (23x33cm-9x13in) s. W/C. 16-Sep-2 Horta, Bruxelles #211
£608 $949 €900 Figures sur un chemin (5x9cm-2x4in) s.d.08 brush Chinese ink wash over crayon. 26-Mar-3 Piasa, Paris #110
£633 $1000 €950 Hilly landscape with a lake in the foreground (143x229cm-56x90in) s.d.1909 pencil W/C. 1-Apr-3 Christie's, Rockefeller NY #377a/R
£650 $1053 €975 Menton, Cote d'Azur (28x19cm-11x7in) s.i. pencil W/C. 23-Jan-3 Christie's, Kensington #346/R
£764 $1192 €1200 Saint Cloud in Seine valley (14x17cm-6x7in) mono. W/C. 6-Nov-2 Hugo Ruef, Munich #1381/R
£986 $1568 €1450 Paysage au soleil couchant (14x22cm-6x9in) s.d.1902 W/C. 26-Feb-3 Artcurial Briest, Paris #116
£1081 $1686 €1600 L'ile aux cypres (5x8cm-2x3in) mono. W/C. 31-Mar-3 Rossini, Paris #15
£1083 $1689 €1700 Vaches s'abreuvant au soleil couchant (36x52cm-14x20in) s.d.1882 W/C. 7-Nov-2 Claude Aguttes, Neuilly #49 est:1500-1800
£1603 $2484 €2500 Bords de riviere (18x27cm-7x11in) mono. W/C over crayon. 4-Dec-2 Piasa, Paris #138/R
£1923 $3000 €2885 Wooded landscape by lake (41x33cm-16x13in) s. W/C prov. 5-Nov-2 Arthur James, Florida #360
£2436 $3776 €3800 Vue de la cathedrale de Chartres (26x18cm-10x7in) s.i.d. 88 W/C over crayon. 4-Dec-2 Piasa, Paris #142/R
£3000 $5010 €4500 Le village de Saint Prive (37x54cm-15x21in) s.i.d.1883 pencil W/C. 18-Jun-3 Christie's, Kensington #15/R est:4000-6000
£4000 $6360 €6000 Le valon (26x37cm-10x15in) s.d.1858 W/C prov. 20-Mar-3 Christie's, Kensington #4/R est:4000-6000
£6173 $10000 €9260 Hilly landscape (17x25cm-7x10in) s.d.94 pencil W/C. 22-Jan-3 Christie's, Rockefeller NY #115/R est:6000
£6757 $10541 €10000 Cheminee dans un interieur (23x16cm-9x6in) W/C over crayon. 28-Mar-3 Delvaux, Paris #117 est:1000

HARR, Karl Erik (1940-) Norwegian
£877 $1386 €1316 In the month of August (47x55cm-19x22in) s.d.80. 17-Dec-2 Grev Wedels Plass, Oslo #225/R (N.KR 10000)

Works on paper
£312 $477 €468 Trollfjord battle (69x49cm-27x19in) s. gouache W/C study executed 1972. 26-Aug-2 Blomqvist, Lysaker #1150/R (N.KR 3600)
£320 $490 €480 Coastal landscape (42x62cm-17x24in) s. mixed media executed 1969. 26-Aug-2 Blomqvist, Lysaker #1149 (N.KR 3700)

HARRADEN, Richard Bankes (1778-1862) British
£500 $825 €725 A Prospect of Wimpole House and Park, Cambridgeshire (36x53cm-14x21in) i.stretcher. 2-Jul-3 Sotheby's, Olympia #113/R

HARRADEN, Richard Bankes (attrib) (1778-1862) British
£3500 $5565 €5250 Magdalen spire, Oxford (65x76cm-26x30in) 6-Mar-3 Christie's, Kensington #392/R est:2000-3000

HARRI, Juhani (1939-) Finnish
Works on paper
£2278 $3600 €3600 The moon is going up (90x70cm-35x28in) s.d.90 collage. 1-Dec-2 Bukowskis, Helsinki #317/R est:3500-4000

HARRIES, Hywel (1921-) British
£1450 $2262 €2175 Salem Revisited (66x77cm-26x30in) s.d.69 board. 11-Sep-2 Bonhams, Newport #417/R est:1000-1500

HARRIGAN, James (1937-) British
£460 $736 €667 Country garden (35x48cm-14x19in) s. 17-May-3 Thomson Roddick & Medcalf, Edinburgh #693

HARRINGTON, Charles (1865-1943) British
Works on paper
£340 $530 €510 Approaching storm (35x47cm-14x19in) s. W/C. 25-Mar-3 Bonhams, Knightsbridge #144
£350 $578 €508 Broken bank of the Mersey (26x37cm-10x15in) s.d.23 pencil W/C. 3-Jul-3 Christie's, Kensington #133
£450 $702 €675 Summer pasture (62x46cm-24x18in) s. W/C. 26-Mar-3 Hamptons Fine Art, Godalming #48
£480 $763 €720 Open landscape with the Downs in the distance (25x36cm-10x14in) s. W/C. 29-Apr-3 Gorringes, Lewes #2092
£550 $891 €825 Brighton from the race course (27x36cm-11x14in) s.d.23 W/C. 20-May-3 Sotheby's, Olympia #36/R
£650 $1073 €943 On the River Ouse, Sussex (26x37cm-10x15in) s.d.24 pencil W/C prov. 3-Jul-3 Christie's, Kensington #107
£680 $1054 €1020 Tewkesbury Elms (27x37cm-11x15in) s.d.22 W/C over pencil htd white. 2-Oct-2 Bonhams, Knowle #41
£1000 $1590 €1500 Distant view of Chichester, Sussex (28x38cm-11x15in) s. W/C over pencil. 19-Mar-3 Sotheby's, London #205/R est:600-800
£1020 $1581 €1530 On the Ouse (30x48cm-12x19in) s.d.27 W/C over pencil. 2-Oct-2 Bonhams, Knowle #43 est:200-300

HARRINGTON, William (?) ?
Works on paper
£340 $482 €550 Northside Cork (48x33cm-19x13in) s.d. pencil wash. 29-Mar-2 Woodwards, Cork #175

HARRIS, Brent (1956-) Australian
£1714 $2674 €2571 Moonboy too (98x81cm-39x32in) s.i.d.93 verso linen. 11-Nov-2 Deutscher-Menzies, Melbourne #58/R est:3000-5000 (A.D 4800)
£3571 $5500 €5357 Territory (190x152cm-75x60in) s.d.93 verso oil on linen. 8-Sep-2 Sotheby's, Melbourne #51/R est:3000-4000 (A.D 10000)

HARRIS, Charles Gordon (1891-?) American
£562 $900 €815 Sand dunes, Westport point (63x76cm-25x30in) s. i.verso. 16-May-3 Skinner, Boston #268/R

Works on paper
£377 $600 €566 Rocky coast (47x61cm-19x24in) s. W/C. 7-Mar-3 Skinner, Boston #490/R

HARRIS, Edmund J (19th C) American
£1656 $2750 €2401 Mountain lake landscape (76x51cm-30x20in) s. prov. 11-Jun-3 Boos Gallery, Michigan #405/R est:2000-3000

HARRIS, Edwin (1855-1906) British
£3800 $6194 €5700 Seamstress (77x64cm-30x25in) s.d.1878 s.verso. 29-Jan-3 Sotheby's, Olympia #228/R est:4000-6000
£4000 $6200 €6000 Portrait of a man (20x15cm-8x6in) s. panel. 3-Dec-2 Bonhams, New Bond Street #8/R est:1000-1500
£8000 $12640 €12000 Reflective moment (51x41cm-20x16in) s. 27-Nov-2 Bonhams, Knowle #230 est:1500-2500
£14000 $21840 €21000 In the greenhouse (51x41cm-20x16in) s. s.i.verso exhib. 27-Mar-3 Christie's, Kensington #418/R est:8000-12000

Works on paper
£520 $811 €780 River landscape (35x53cm-14x21in) s.d.1949 W/C pair. 26-Mar-3 Sotheby's, Olympia #158/R

HARRIS, George (19/20th C) British
£280 $440 €420 Lumber cart outside the Royal Oak Inn (22x32cm-9x13in) s.d.1894. 10-Dec-2 Bristol Auction Rooms #997
£500 $785 €750 Homeward bound through snow at sunset. Mother and child near a wooded pool (26x37cm-10x15in) s. pair. 10-Dec-2 Bristol Auction Rooms #996/R

HARRIS, George Walter (fl.1864-1893) British
£380 $635 €551 Still life of fruit (30x59cm-12x23in) s. 9-Jul-3 George Kidner, Lymington #167/R

HARRIS, H (19th C) British
£450 $702 €675 Chepstow Castle, Wye Valley with figures and boats (37x66cm-15x26in) s. 10-Sep-2 Bonhams, Knightsbridge #172/R

HARRIS, Henry (1805-1865) British
£870 $1400 €1305 Landscape with village, cattle and boats on the water (76x127cm-30x50in) s. 22-Feb-3 Pook & Pook, Downington #308/R est:1000-1500

HARRIS, Henry (1852-1926) British
£280 $431 €420 Rural river landscape with cattle (20x35cm-8x14in) s. 22-Oct-2 Bonhams, Bath #251
£280 $431 €420 Near Lynmouth, Devon (19x31cm-7x12in) s. 22-Oct-2 Bonhams, Bath #252
£280 $431 €420 Tanker lady, north Wales (20x37cm-8x15in) s.d.1891. 22-Oct-2 Bonhams, Bath #255
£280 $442 €420 Tintern Abbey (37x67cm-15x26in) s.i.verso. 12-Nov-2 Bonhams, Knightsbridge #187
£300 $462 €450 Country lane near Clovelly (87x55cm-34x22in) s. 22-Oct-2 Bonhams, Bath #246
£300 $477 €450 Logging at sunset in an extensive landscape (19x46cm-7x18in) s. board. 4-Mar-3 Bristol Auction Rooms #303/R
£320 $493 €480 Gipsy camp near Clovelly (87x52cm-34x20in) s. 22-Oct-2 Bonhams, Bath #250
£340 $568 €493 Chepstow Castle and the Wye Bridge looking towards Tutshill (32x63cm-13x25in) s. 17-Jun-3 Bristol Auction Rooms #491
£360 $554 €540 Coming home, timber wagon in a rural landscape (52x65cm-20x26in) s. 22-Oct-2 Bonhams, Bath #247
£360 $554 €540 Ludford Mill, Ludlow (26x44cm-10x17in) s. 22-Oct-2 Bonhams, Bath #253
£380 $585 €570 Cottages in north Wales (26x45cm-10x18in) 22-Oct-2 Bonhams, Bath #254
£400 $616 €600 St Clement, Truro, Cornwall (29x50cm-11x20in) s. 22-Oct-2 Bonhams, Bath #249
£400 $628 €600 Wreckers, Cornwall (21x43cm-8x17in) s. i.verso. 10-Dec-2 Bristol Auction Rooms #986a/R
£480 $739 €720 Brownlow's haunted castle, Cheshire (29x50cm-11x20in) s. 22-Oct-2 Bonhams, Bath #243
£560 $890 €840 Views on the Frome, near Bristol (23x19cm-9x7in) pair. 4-Mar-3 Bristol Auction Rooms #300
£600 $954 €900 Landscape with cattle drinking from a river in foreground (40x75cm-16x30in) s. 6-Mar-3 Clevedon Sale Rooms #134
£760 $1269 €1102 Riverside farm with cattle. Cottage by a stone bridge with figures (32x53cm-13x21in) s. pair. 17-Jun-3 Bristol Auction Rooms #489/R
£820 $1304 €1230 Chepstow Castle. Tintern Abbey, Monmouthshire (13x20cm-5x8in) s. pair. 4-Mar-3 Bristol Auction Rooms #301
£880 $1382 €1320 Tintern Abbey. Ardrosson Castle (33x51cm-13x20in) s. pair. 10-Dec-2 Bristol Auction Rooms #984/R
£1150 $1806 €1725 Barge leaving a lock. Cattle watering in a wooded stream (36x61cm-14x24in) s. pair. 10-Dec-2 Bristol Auction Rooms #985/R est:500-700

HARRIS, James (1810-1887) British
£1500 $2340 €2250 Oystermouth Castle, Glamorgan. Traveller with his hound near Oystermouth (25x32cm-10x13in) one s.one panel. 9-Apr-3 Cheffins Grain & Comins, Cambridge #696/R est:250-350

Works on paper
£850 $1343 €1275 Barque floundering in heavy seas (28x48cm-11x19in) s.d.67 W/C. 13-Nov-2 Halls, Shrewsbury #336/R

HARRIS, Jeffrey (1949-) New Zealander
£627 $978 €941 Girl's head no.8 (68x41cm-27x16in) oil pastel. 7-Nov-2 International Art Centre, Auckland #9/R est:2500-3500 (NZ.D 2000)
£1042 $1625 €1563 Couple with baby (45x45cm-18x18in) hardboard. 8-Apr-3 Peter Webb, Auckland #95/R est:3000-4000 (NZ.D 3000)
£1274 $2000 €1911 German cousins (137x144cm-54x57in) s.d.1974 i.verso. 10-Dec-2 Peter Webb, Auckland #68/R est:4000-6000 (NZ.D 4000)
£2229 $3500 €3344 Lorraine (216x182cm-85x72in) s.i.d.1984 acrylic. 10-Dec-2 Peter Webb, Auckland #67/R est:7000-9000 (NZ.D 7000)

Works on paper
£251 $391 €377 Judith (22x32cm-9x13in) s.i.d.1979 pencil dr. 5-Nov-2 Peter Webb, Auckland #5/R (NZ.D 800)
£704 $1162 €1021 Two figures in a landscape (57x77cm-22x30in) s.d.1979 pastel. 1-Jul-3 Peter Webb, Auckland #11/R est:2500-3500 (NZ.D 2000)
£789 $1232 €1184 Figures (42x68cm-17x27in) s.d.70 mixed media board. 27-Mar-3 International Art Centre, Auckland #16/R (NZ.D 2250)
£833 $1300 €1250 Two figures (27x38cm-11x15in) s.d.1997 pastel. 8-Apr-3 Peter Webb, Auckland #151/R (NZ.D 2400)
£955 $1500 €1433 Untitled (102x150cm-40x59in) s.d.1988 pastel. 10-Dec-2 Peter Webb, Auckland #112/R est:4000-6000 (NZ.D 3000)

HARRIS, Lawren Phillips (1910-) Canadian
£258 $402 €387 Lakeshore near Port Hope (20x25cm-8x10in) s. board. 25-Mar-3 Ritchie, Toronto #112 (C.D 600)

HARRIS, Lawren Stewart (1885-1970) Canadian
£1681 $2690 €2522 L.S.H Holdings no.39 (38x46cm-15x18in) board prov. 15-May-3 Heffel, Vancouver #183/R est:2000-3000 (C.D 3750)
£2691 $4305 €4037 L.S.H Holdings no.145 (93x49cm-37x19in) s.d.1958 board prov. 15-May-3 Heffel, Vancouver #185/R est:3000-4000 (C.D 6000)
£2823 $4460 €4235 Untitled Lsh no.146 (76x112cm-30x44in) prov. 14-Nov-2 Heffel, Vancouver #7/R est:5000-7000 (C.D 7000)
£4032 $6371 €6048 Untitled Lsh no.37 (60x76cm-24x30in) board prov. 14-Nov-2 Heffel, Vancouver #6/R est:4000-6000 (C.D 10000)
£6667 $10933 €10001 Laurentian landscape (20x25cm-8x10in) s. init.verso board prov. 27-May-3 Sotheby's, Toronto #152/R est:15000-20000 (C.D 15000)
£7661 $12105 €11492 Abstraction LSH no.97 (102x140cm-40x55in) i.verso painted c.1958 prov.exhib.lit. 14-Nov-2 Heffel, Vancouver #197/R est:12000-15000 (C.D 19000)
£8969 $14350 €13454 Pinting (112x127cm-44x50in) s.i.d.September 1958 prov.exhib.lit. 15-May-3 Heffel, Vancouver #90/R est:10000-15000 (C.D 20000)
£12851 $20177 €19277 Rocky mountain icefields (30x18cm-12x7in) prov.exhib. 25-Nov-2 Hodgins, Calgary #357a/R est:45000-55000 (C.D 32000)
£18145 $28669 €27218 Toronto outskirts, houses group no.VI (27x36cm-11x14in) s.verso panel prov.lit. 14-Nov-2 Heffel, Vancouver #125/R est:50000-60000 (C.D 45000)
£22222 $36444 €33333 Trapper's shack, North shore (26x34cm-10x13in) panel. 3-Jun-3 Joyner, Toronto #122/R est:50000-60000 (C.D 50000)
£24664 $39462 €36996 Lake Simcoe (27x36cm-11x14in) s. s.i.verso panel prov. 15-May-3 Heffel, Vancouver #175/R est:45000-55000 (C.D 55000)
£24691 $38272 €37037 Sand Lake, Algoma (26x34cm-10x13in) s. s.i.verso board. 3-Dec-2 Joyner, Toronto #50/R est:60000-80000 (C.D 60000)
£33333 $54667 €50000 Maligne Lake, Rocky Mts (26x34cm-10x13in) s. panel prov. 3-Jun-3 Joyner, Toronto #98/R est:60000-80000 (C.D 75000)
£33333 $54667 €50000 Algoma sketch CVII (27x36cm-11x14in) s. s.i.verso panel prov.exhib. 27-May-3 Sotheby's, Toronto #31/R est:50000-70000 (C.D 75000)
£34274 $54153 €51411 Mongoose Lake, Algoma II, Algoma sketches XI (27x24cm-11x9in) s.i. s.verso panel painted c.1920 prov.lit. 14-Nov-2 Heffel, Vancouver #84/R est:65000-85000 (C.D 85000)
£34979 $54218 €52469 Falls, Montreal River, Algoma (26x32cm-10x13in) s. i.d.1918 verso board prov.exhib.lit. 3-Dec-2 Joyner, Toronto #21/R est:60000-80000 (C.D 85000)
£35556 $58311 €53334 Wenchemna, lake Rocky Mts, mountain (30x37cm-12x15in) s.verso board lit. 3-Jun-3 Joyner, Toronto #84/R est:80000-100000 (C.D 80000)
£40000 $65600 €60000 Algoma sketch XLII (27x35cm-11x14in) s.i.verso panel prov.lit. 27-May-3 Sotheby's, Toronto #77/R est:70000-90000 (C.D 90000)
£45267 $70165 €67901 In the white mountains (45x55cm-18x22in) s. board painted c.1934-35 prov.lit. 3-Dec-2 Joyner, Toronto #45/R est:50000-60000 (C.D 110000)
£48387 $76452 €72581 North shore, Lake Superior, Lake Superior sketch LXVIII (30x38cm-12x15in) s.i.verso panel prov. 14-Nov-2 Heffel, Vancouver #93/R est:100000-120000 (C.D 120000)
£68548 $108306 €102822 Building the ice house, Hamilton (27x32cm-11x13in) s.i.d.1912 panel prov.lit. 14-Nov-2 Heffel, Vancouver #20/R est:100000-125000 (C.D 170000)
£78629 $124234 €117944 Tumbling glacier, Berg Lake (30x38cm-12x15in) s.i.d.1928-29 panel prov.exhib.lit. 14-Nov-2 Heffel, Vancouver #79/R est:175000-185000 (C.D 195000)
£80000 $131199 €120000 In the ward (27x29cm-11x11in) s. board prov.lit. 3-Jun-3 Joyner, Toronto #74/R est:100000-120000 (C.D 180000)
£80717 $129148 €121076 Mountains after rain, Jasper Park (46x56cm-18x22in) s. s.i.verso masonite pianted c.1934-41 prov. 15-May-3 Heffel, Vancouver #124/R est:125000-175000 (C.D 180000)
£241935 $382258 €362903 In the ward - grocery store (81x96cm-32x38in) s.d.1920 prov.exhib.lit. 14-Nov-2 Heffel, Vancouver #75/R est:600000-800000 (C.D 600000)
£246914 $382716 €370371 Snowfall (90x110cm-35x43in) s.d.20 prov.exhib.lit. 3-Dec-2 Joyner, Toronto #52/R est:600000-800000 (C.D 600000)

Works on paper
£1411 $2230 €2117 House (18x24cm-7x9in) pencil dr. prov. 14-Nov-2 Heffel, Vancouver #83/R est:4000-6000 (C.D 3500)
£1564 $2424 €2346 Mount Washington, New Hampshire (21x26cm-8x10in) pencil executed c.1934-38 prov.exhib. 3-Dec-2 Joyner, Toronto #167/R est:2500-3500 (C.D 3800)
£1600 $2624 €2400 Baffin Island (18x24cm-7x9in) pencil prov. 3-Jun-3 Joyner, Toronto #145/R est:2500-3500 (C.D 3600)
£1728 $2679 €2592 Mount Edith Cavell (17x24cm-7x9in) pencil executed c.1926 prov. 3-Dec-2 Joyner, Toronto #37/R est:4000-6000 (C.D 4200)

£2105 $3137 €3158 Entrance to Clyde inlet, Baffin (19x24cm-7x9in) graphite prov. 26-Jun-2 Iegor de Saint Hippolyte, Montreal #49 (C.D 4800)
£4889 $8018 €7334 House, Duke St, Toronto (21x29cm-8x11in) ink htd white exhib.lit. 3-Jun-3 Joyner, Toronto #120/R est:6000-8000 (C.D 11000)

HARRIS, Marian D (1904-) American
£2032 $3250 €3048 Still life of a copper vase with white calla lilies (112x99cm-44x39in) s. 17-May-3 Pook & Pook, Downington #396/R est:3500-4000

HARRIS, Maude (fl.1883-1936) British
Works on paper
£889 $1476 €1289 Children playing on a beach (33x41cm-13x16in) s. pastel pencil prov. 16-Jun-3 Waddingtons, Toronto #28/R est:2000-2500 (C.D 2000)

HARRIS, Moses (1731-1785) British
Works on paper
£60000 $96600 €90000 Entomoligical drawings (25x20cm-10x8in) num. W/C drs 150 manuscript leaves 39 lit. 7-May-3 Sotheby's, London #62/R est:40000-60000

HARRIS, Pam (20th C) Irish?
£704 $1169 €1000 Arrier (51x51cm-20x20in) s.i.d.99 verso. 10-Jun-3 James Adam, Dublin #285/R est:1000-1500
£959 $1496 €1400 Union painting no 12 (51x51cm-20x20in) s.verso. 8-Apr-3 James Adam, Dublin #62/R
£1096 $1710 €1600 Union painting, no 14 (76x76cm-30x30in) s.i.d.2001 verso. 8-Apr-3 James Adam, Dublin #50/R est:1700-1900

HARRIS, Peter Alfred (20th C) Canadian?
£343 $536 €515 Flowers (68x61cm-27x24in) s. masonite prov. 25-Mar-3 Ritchie, Toronto #166/R (C.D 800)

HARRIS, Robert (1849-1919) Canadian
£340 $524 €510 Mrs Joseph Hanson (75x60cm-30x24in) s.d.1897 i.verso. 22-Oct-2 Bonhams, Bath #230
£492 $762 €738 Golf links, Lake Placid (14x20cm-6x8in) s. panel prov. 24-Sep-2 Ritchie, Toronto #3143/R (C.D 1200)
Works on paper
£225 $349 €338 Watching the miracle (27x19cm-11x7in) s.i. W/C card. 24-Sep-2 Ritchie, Toronto #3068/R (C.D 550)

HARRIS, Robert G (1911-) American
£1118 $1800 €1677 Family entering church (58x46cm-23x18in) s. 19-Feb-3 Illustration House, New York #219/R est:2000-3000
£1491 $2400 €2237 Children singing in church (51x46cm-20x18in) s. 19-Feb-3 Illustration House, New York #221/R est:2000-3000

HARRIS, Sam Hyde (1889-1977) American
£1347 $2250 €1953 Landscape, sands of time (41x51cm-16x20in) i.verso canvasboard prov. 17-Jun-3 John Moran, Pasadena #183 est:1000-2000
£1398 $2250 €2097 Barn in eucalyptus, hazy day (41x51cm-16x20in) s. canvasboard. 18-Feb-3 John Moran, Pasadena #48 est:3000-4000
£1656 $2750 €2401 Arroyo variety (39x51cm-15x20in) st.sig. canvasboard. 11-Jun-3 Butterfields, San Francisco #4284/R est:3000-5000
£1708 $2750 €2562 Green outbuilding (18x23cm-7x9in) s. i.verso canvasboard prov. 18-Feb-3 John Moran, Pasadena #12 est:1000-1500
£1796 $3000 €2604 Sunshine and shadow (51x61cm-20x24in) s. 18-Jun-3 Christie's, Los Angeles #69/R est:4000-6000
£2484 $4000 €3726 Desert jewel (56x71cm-22x28in) s. i.stretcher. 18-Feb-3 John Moran, Pasadena #132a est:3000-5000
£2532 $4000 €3671 Mountain goat (64x76cm-25x30in) s. 26-Jul-3 Coeur d'Alene, Hayden #21/R est:5000-10000
£2640 $4250 €3960 Product of irrigation (41x51cm-16x20in) s. i.verso canvasboard. 18-Feb-3 John Moran, Pasadena #25a est:2500-3500
£2742 $4250 €4113 Memory of spring (46x61cm-18x24in) st. i.verso masonite prov. 29-Oct-2 John Moran, Pasadena #655a est:3500-4500
£2742 $4250 €4113 Capistrano Cottage (46x61cm-18x24in) st. i.verso prov. 29-Oct-2 John Moran, Pasadena #655b est:3000-4000
£2844 $4750 €4124 Landscape - restless wind (41x51cm-16x20in) s. i.verso canvasboard. 17-Jun-3 John Moran, Pasadena #39 est:3000-4500
£2994 $5000 €4341 Landscape with barn (41x51cm-16x20in) s. i.verso canvasboard prov. 17-Jun-3 John Moran, Pasadena #182 est:2500-3500
£4516 $7000 €6774 California landscape (41x51cm-16x20in) s. masonite prov. 29-Oct-2 John Moran, Pasadena #757 est:4000-6000

HARRIS, Steve (?) ?
£376 $587 €564 Barrell in window (45x62cm-18x24in) s. board. 7-Nov-2 International Art Centre, Auckland #119/R est:1200-2000 (NZ.D 1200)
£376 $587 €564 Billy can (43x61cm-17x24in) s. board. 7-Nov-2 International Art Centre, Auckland #120/R est:1200-2000 (NZ.D 1200)
£964 $1524 €1446 Still life with red tin (30x86cm-12x34in) s. board prov. 27-Nov-2 Deutscher-Menzies, Melbourne #156/R est:2500-3500 (A.D 2700)
£1930 $3011 €2895 Red apples (43x56cm-17x22in) s. board. 27-Mar-3 International Art Centre, Auckland #142/R est:6500-7500 (NZ.D 5500)
£2632 $4105 €3948 Old tin box (30x86cm-12x34in) s. board. 27-Mar-3 International Art Centre, Auckland #6/R est:5000-7000 (NZ.D 7500)
£2798 $4477 €4057 Clear water (60x60cm-24x24in) s. acrylic painted 2001. 13 May-3 Watson's, Christchurch #59/R est:7000-9000 (NZ.D 7750)
£2807 $4379 €4211 Lightly painted vase (44x58cm-17x23in) board. 27-Mar-3 International Art Centre, Auckland #10/R est:6000-8000 (NZ.D 8000)

HARRIS, William E (1856-1929) British
£500 $780 €750 Landscape with figure pulling a wheelbarrow (59x100cm-23x39in) s. 23-Apr-3 Rupert Toovey, Partridge Green #75/R
£550 $891 €825 Broken path, Sutton Park, Warwickshire (41x61cm-16x24in) s.d.1881 i.verso. 23-Jan-3 Christie's, Kensington #233
£550 $858 €825 Boating on the River Thames near Windsor (40x61cm-16x24in) s.d.1894. 26-Mar-3 Sotheby's, Olympia #113/R
£1000 $1560 €1500 View across a Llyn in Snowdonia (50x75cm-20x30in) s. 11-Sep-2 Bonhams, Newport #251 est:1200-1800
£1350 $2120 €2025 Children fishing on the Lledr (61x102cm-24x40in) s.d.1882. 19-Nov-2 Bonhams, Leeds #248 est:1500-2000
Works on paper
£450 $734 €675 Brigantine tug and London steamboat on Limehouse Beach (36x53cm-14x21in) s.d.1895 i.verso W/C pencil htd bodycol. 11-Feb-3 Bonhams, Knowle #38
£550 $858 €825 Trawler and tugboats in a harbour (48x35cm-19x14in) s.d.1896 W/C. 9-Oct-2 Woolley & Wallis, Salisbury #35/R

HARRISON, Anthony (20th C) British
£500 $780 €750 Harvesting (19x30cm-7x12in) s.d.1913 canvas on panel. 7-Nov-2 Christie's, Kensington #168/R

HARRISON, Charles Harmony (1842-1902) British
Works on paper
£250 $408 €375 Norfolk riverside church by moonlight (20x33cm-8x13in) s. W/C. 14-Feb-3 Keys, Aylsham #614
£900 $1467 €1350 Quiet corner of the Broads (56x86cm-22x34in) s.d.1878 W/C. 14-Feb-3 Keys, Aylsham #616/R
£1300 $2119 €1950 Norfolk wooded landscape with figure, cattle and boats (51x86cm-20x34in) s.d.1876 W/C. 14-Feb-3 Keys, Aylsham #617/R est:1000-1400
£1900 $3173 €2755 Wherry near a Norfolk mill in summer (25x41cm-10x16in) s.d.1881 W/C. 20-Jun-3 Keys, Aylsham #627/R est:1200-1600
£2000 $3120 €3000 Figures on a river bank with yacht beside Belaugh church (46x69cm-18x27in) s.d.1890 W/C. 18-Oct-2 Keys, Aylsham #604/R est:1000-1500

HARRISON, Chris Galvin (20th C) Danish?
£549 $856 €824 Balticum Painting (100x120cm-39x47in) s.d.2000 verso. 18-Sep-2 Kunsthallen, Copenhagen #165/R (D.KR 6500)
£718 $1120 €1077 Nocturne (80x100cm-31x39in) s.i.d.99/2000 verso. 18-Sep-2 Kunsthallen, Copenhagen #275/R (D.KR 8500)

HARRISON, Christopher John (1945-) British
£420 $638 €630 Trompe l'oeil - two faience two handle pilgrims flask (79x53cm-31x21in) mono. board. 13-Aug-2 Canterbury Auctions, UK #104/R

HARRISON, Claude (1922-) British
£503 $800 €755 Last round (25x30cm-10x12in) s.d.1984 i.d.verso board. 7-Mar-3 Skinner, Boston #630/R
£850 $1326 €1275 Swimmers (51x61cm-20x24in) s. board. 27-Mar-3 Christie's, Kensington #567/R
£1250 $1950 €1875 Tribute to the Commedia dell Arte (51x61cm-20x24in) s. i.d.2000 verso board. 26-Mar-3 Hamptons Fine Art, Godalming #247/R est:600-800
£1400 $2184 €2100 Points of views (40x50cm-16x20in) s.d.2000 s.d.verso board. 27-Mar-3 Christie's, Kensington #560/R est:1000-1500

HARRISON, Clifford (20th C) British
£1400 $2184 €2100 Russian chinaware on a shelf (50x76cm-20x30in) init.d.1972 board prov. 12-Sep-2 Sotheby's, Olympia #67/R est:1000-1500
£2200 $3432 €3300 Ornamental terrine from the swan service (55x76cm-22x30in) init.d.1974 board prov. 12-Sep-2 Sotheby's, Olympia #66/R est:1000-1500

HARRISON, Frederick Clifford (20th C) British
£800 $1240 €1200 Still Life with delft horse and two plates (43x79cm-17x31in) s. panel. 29-Oct-2 Gorringes, Lewes #1266/R

HARRISON, George (19/20th C) British
£980 $1548 €1470 September afternoon (102x127cm-40x50in) s. 27-Nov-2 Bonhams, Knowle #215
£2500 $4075 €3750 September afternoon (100x125cm-39x49in) 14-Feb-3 Lyon & Turnbull, Edinburgh #124

HARRISON, J (19th C) British
Works on paper
£407 $638 €611 Untitled (49x75cm-19x30in) s. W/C. 10-Dec-2 Pinneys, Montreal #64 (C.D 1000)

HARRISON, J C (1898-1985) British
Works on paper
£2150 $3419 €3225 Seated Monk with open book and snuff box with magpie on his shoulder (45x33cm-18x13in) s. W/C. 24-Mar-3 Trembath Welch, Great Dunmow #503/R est:1500-2500

HARRISON, John Cyril (1898-1985) British
Works on paper
£500 $790 €750 Gyr falcons (54x38cm-21x15in) s. pencil W/C. 28-Nov-2 Christie's, Kensington #40/R
£500 $815 €750 Cape sea eagle (43x61cm-17x24in) s. W/C. 14-Feb-3 Keys, Aylsham #613/R
£700 $1085 €1050 Black terns over Hickling Broad (36x57cm-14x22in) s. W/C bodycol. 30-Sep-2 Bonhams, Ipswich #318
£700 $1106 €1015 Skein of pink footed geese (47x33cm-19x13in) s. W/C. 22-Jul-3 Bonhams, Knightsbridge #62/R
£750 $1193 €1125 Whooper swans on the Ouse Washes (44x55cm-17x22in) s. W/C. 26-Feb-3 Cheffins Grain & Comins, Cambridge #545/R
£780 $1240 €1170 Little terns on the Ouse Washes (44x55cm-17x22in) s. W/C. 26-Feb-3 Cheffins Grain & Comins, Cambridge #560/R
£900 $1395 €1350 Blackcock in the Cairngorms (38x56cm-15x22in) s. W/C bodycol. 30-Sep-2 Bonhams, Ipswich #319
£900 $1404 €1350 Mallards alighting (23x32cm-9x13in) s,d.1929 W/C. 6-Nov-2 Sotheby's, Olympia #139/R est:1000-1500
£900 $1485 €1305 Pheasant (43x67cm-17x26in) s. W/C. 1-Jul-3 Bonhams, Norwich #95/R
£1000 $1560 €1500 Grouse disturbed by a Golden Eagle (55x75cm-22x30in) s. W/C. 17-Sep-2 Bonhams, Sevenoaks #252 est:1000-1500
£1000 $1580 €1450 Male and female pintails (32x46cm-13x18in) s. W/C htd white. 22-Jul-3 Bonhams, Knightsbridge #63/R est:1000-1500
£1050 $1712 €1575 Pair of teal upon a lake (27x37cm-11x15in) s. pencil W/C. 29-Jan-3 Dreweatt Neate, Newbury #96/R est:800-1200
£1100 $1738 €1595 Foraging snipe (22x13cm-9x5in) s. W/C. 22-Jul-3 Bonhams, Knightsbridge #61/R est:600-800
£1350 $2228 €1958 Widgeon landing in a sunset in the highlands (33x47cm-13x19in) s. W/C. 1-Jul-3 Bonhams, Norwich #103/R est:1000-1500
£1900 $2945 €2850 Partridge on the Norfolk coast (38x55cm-15x22in) s. W/C. 30-Sep-2 Bonhams, Ipswich #359/R est:1200-1800
£1900 $3021 €2850 Capercaillie displaying (75x56cm-30x22in) s. pencil W/C bodycol prov. 6-Mar-3 Christie's, Kensington #126/R est:1200-1800
£1900 $2964 €2850 Woodcock alighting (47x32cm-19x13in) s. W/C. 6-Nov-2 Sotheby's, Olympia #144/R est:1000-2000
£2000 $3040 €3000 Golden eagle (44x56cm-17x22in) s. W/C. 28-Aug-2 Sotheby's, London #841/R est:2000-3000
£2000 $3120 €3000 Study of grouse in flight over heather covered moorland (36x51cm-14x20in) s. W/C. 18-Oct-2 Keys, Aylsham #625/R est:1500-2000
£2000 $3100 €3000 Flying geese, Skye (55x76cm-22x30in) s. W/C over pencil. 30-Sep-2 Bonhams, Ipswich #358/R est:1800-2500
£2000 $3120 €3000 High above the ocean, golden eagles (55x77cm-22x30in) s. W/C over pencil prov. 14-Apr-3 Sotheby's, London #45/R est:2000-3000
£2000 $3320 €2900 Decollatus and mellanistic pheasant. Principalis and mongolicus pheasant (35x50cm-14x20in) s.i. pencil W/C bodycol pair. 12-Jun-3 Christie's, Kensington #139/R est:2000-4000
£2600 $4030 €3900 Flight of blackcock over the river (56x77cm-22x30in) s. W/C. 30-Sep-2 Bonhams, Ipswich #357/R est:1800-2500
£3000 $4680 €4500 Osprey plunging (77x59cm-30x23in) s. W/C over pencil prov. 14-Apr-3 Sotheby's, London #38/R est:1500-2000
£3100 $4836 €4650 Grouse in Highland setting watching an approaching Golden Eagle (51x74cm-20x29in) s. W/C. 18-Oct-2 Keys, Aylsham #624/R est:3000-5000

HARRISON, John Cyril (attrib) (1898-1985) British
£650 $1021 €975 Mallard rising over river, early morning (48x74cm-19x29in) s.d. 13-Dec-2 Keys, Aylsham #668/R

HARRISON, Sarah Cecilia (1863-1941) British
£6000 $9600 €9000 Portrait of a lady in velvet coat (42x33cm-17x13in) init.d.1901. 16-May-3 Sotheby's, London #51/R est:3000-5000
£9177 $14225 €14500 Blayney R.T Balfour and Madeline his wife (91x73cm-36x29in) 25-Sep-2 James Adam, Dublin #65/R est:7000-10000

HARRISON, Ted (1926-) Canadian
£1205 $1904 €1808 Paddle wheeler (30x38cm-12x15in) d.1980 acrylic paperboard. 1-Dec-2 Levis, Calgary #40/R est:1500-2000 (C.D 3000)
£1244 $2041 €1804 Caribou antlers (91x61cm-36x24in) acrylic on board. 1-Jun-3 Levis, Calgary #49/R est:3500-4500 (C.D 2800)
£1411 $2230 €2117 Great eclipse (91x122cm-36x48in) s.i.verso acrylic on board painted c.1972 prov. 14-Nov-2 Heffel, Vancouver #198/R est:4000-5000 (C.D 3500)
£1867 $3061 €2801 Flowing ice (90x120cm-35x47in) s. acrylic painted 1982. 3-Jun-3 Joyner, Toronto #374/R est:2500-3500 (C.D 4200)
£1957 $3052 €3263 Deer in flight (122x91cm-48x36in) s. i.d.1984 verso acrylic. 13-Apr-3 Levis, Calgary #43a/R est:4000-5000 (C.D 4500)
£2000 $3280 €2900 Evening ice flows (61x91cm-24x36in) acrylic on board. 1-Jun-3 Levis, Calgary #48/R est:3500-4500 (C.D 4500)

HARRISON, Thomas Alexander (1853-1930) American
£2564 $4000 €3846 Twilight (41x61cm-16x24in) s. 5-Nov-2 Arthur James, Florida #455
£4516 $7000 €6774 Aurore (51x96cm-20x38in) prov. 3-Dec-2 Phillips, New York #46/R est:8000-12000
£12346 $20000 €18519 Seascape (73x150cm-29x59in) s. prov. 22-May-3 Christie's, Rockefeller NY #59/R est:25000-35000

HARRITON, Abraham (1893-1986) American
£267 $425 €401 Encounter (46x61cm-18x24in) s. 7-Mar-3 Skinner, Boston #612/R
£637 $1000 €956 Landscape with five nudes frolicking next to water and rocks (89x127cm-35x50in) s. s.i.verso prov. 19-Apr-3 James Julia, Fairfield #306/R

HARROWING, Walter (fl.1877-1904) British
£250 $400 €375 Head of a bay hunter (44x39cm-17x15in) s.d.1900. 15-May-3 Lawrence, Crewkerne #946/R
£1850 $2886 €2775 Bay hunter, saddled, in a stable yard (61x71cm-24x28in) s.d.1886 pair. 6-Nov-2 Bonhams, Chester #496/R est:2000-3000

HARSANYI, Charles (1905-1973) American
£478 $750 €717 Storm over Wic Wac (56x76cm-22x30in) s. i.verso masonite. 22-Nov-2 Skinner, Boston #264/R
£542 $850 €813 White giant (54x46cm-21x18in) s. s.i.d.1950 verso. 22-Nov-2 Skinner, Boston #268/R
£828 $1300 €1242 Reflections (69x79cm-27x31in) s. masonite. 22-Nov-2 Skinner, Boston #266/R est:1000-1500
£968 $1500 €1452 Afternoon in January 1945 (66x79cm-26x31in) s. s.i.d.1945 verso prov. 29-Oct-2 John Moran, Pasadena #798 est:800-1200

HARSHE, Robert Bartholomew (1879-1938) American
£314 $500 €471 Peonies (56x76cm-22x30in) estate st.verso board painted c.1930. 2-Mar-3 Toomey, Oak Park #654/R

HART, Conway Weston (attrib) (fl.1849-1869) British
£2000 $2980 €3000 Drummer boy (76x63cm-30x25in) bears sig. 27-Jun-2 Greenslade Hunt, Taunton #744/R est:200-300

HART, George Overbury (1868-1933) American
Works on paper
£1132 $1800 €1698 Shipboard revelry, crossing the line (20x33cm-8x13in) s.i.d.Feb.1916 W/C pen. 1-Mar-3 North East Auctions, Portsmouth #699/R

HART, James MacDougal (1828-1901) American
£343 $550 €515 Farmer with oxcart and two oxen (36x58cm-14x23in) s. 15-Mar-3 Eldred, East Dennis #415/R
£1465 $2300 €2198 Cows at pasture (51x41cm-20x16in) s. 22-Nov-2 Skinner, Boston #63/R est:2500-3500
£1951 $3043 €2927 Landscape (30x48cm-12x19in) 9-Nov-2 Altermann Galleries, Santa Fe #193
£2866 $4500 €4299 Bend in the river (23x30cm-9x12in) s. 10-Dec-2 Doyle, New York #12/R est:5000-7000
£3822 $6000 €5733 Threatening weather (82x59cm-32x23in) s. prov. 19-Nov-2 Butterfields, San Francisco #8014/R est:4000-6000
£7742 $12000 €11613 Path by river (22x38cm-9x15in) s.d.1862. 3-Dec-2 Phillips, New York #9/R est:8000-12000
£61728 $100000 €92592 Loon Lake, Adirondacks (117x198cm-46x78in) s. prov. 22-May-3 Christie's, Rockefeller NY #9/R est:100000-150000

HART, Kevin Pro (1928-) Australian
£314 $477 €471 Dragonfly (14x18cm-6x7in) s. board. 27-Aug-2 Goodman, Sydney #2 (A.D 875)

£357 $564 €536 Ants (14x46cm-6x18in) s. board. 18-Nov-2 Goodman, Sydney #169 (A.D 1000)
£393 $609 €590 Scrub country, broken hill (18x44cm-7x17in) s. board. 29-Oct-2 Lawson Menzies, Sydney #112 (A.D 1100)
£430 $624 €645 Boys at the water hole (33x48cm-13x19in) s. 10-Dec-1 Goodman, Sydney #451 (A.D 1200)
£458 $714 €687 Two horse race (15x15cm-6x6in) s. board. 21-Oct-2 Australian Art Auctions, Sydney #83 (A.D 1300)
£458 $714 €687 Hill end (29x39cm-11x15in) s. board. 21-Oct-2 Australian Art Auctions, Sydney #88 (A.D 1300)
£478 $784 €693 Landscape (16x23cm-6x9in) s. board. 3-Jun-3 Lawson Menzies, Sydney #703 (A.D 1200)
£478 $784 €693 Reflections in the stream (21x29cm-8x11in) s. board. 3-Jun-3 Lawson Menzies, Sydney #705 (A.D 1200)
£493 $769 €740 Menindee landscape (30x50cm-12x20in) s. board. 21-Oct-2 Australian Art Auctions, Sydney #136 (A.D 1400)
£500 $775 €750 Creek scene (28x44cm-11x17in) s. board. 29-Oct-2 Lawson Menzies, Sydney #205 (A.D 1400)
£520 $837 €754 Landscape (14x14cm-6x6in) s. board. 12-May-3 Joel, Victoria #367 est:1000-1500 (A.D 1300)
£526 $800 €789 Misty moonlight reflections (52x59cm-20x23in) s.d.64 board. 19-Aug-2 Joel, Victoria #254 est:1000-1500 (A.D 1500)
£536 $830 €804 Three bushmen on a bench (24x27cm-9x11in) s. board. 29-Oct-2 Lawson Menzies, Sydney #127/R (A.D 1500)
£536 $846 €804 Dragon fly (15x14cm-6x6in) s. cardboard. 18-Nov-2 Goodman, Sydney #25 (A.D 1500)
£563 $879 €845 Blue lake, Broken Hill (23x30cm-9x12in) s. board. 21-Oct-2 Australian Art Auctions, Sydney #151 (A.D 1600)
£571 $886 €857 Day at the races (14x14cm-6x6in) s. board. 29-Oct-2 Lawson Menzies, Sydney #306 (A.D 1600)
£573 $905 €992 Settler's camp (39x40cm-15x16in) s. board. 1-Apr-3 Goodman, Sydney #102 (A.D 1500)
£592 $899 €888 Putter (17x19cm-7x7in) s. board. 27-Aug-2 Goodman, Sydney #4 (A.D 1650)
£597 $980 €896 Pipcan country (40x47cm-16x19in) s. i.verso composition board. 4-Jun-3 Deutscher-Menzies, Melbourne #338/R (A.D 1500)
£611 $965 €917 Sharpening the shears (15x15cm-6x6in) s. board. 7-Apr-3 Australian Art Auctions, Sydney #65 (A.D 1600)
£643 $996 €965 Black stump (34x48cm-13x19in) s. board. 29-Oct-2 Lawson Menzies, Sydney #275 (A.D 1800)
£643 $1015 €965 River bank (44x34cm-17x13in) s. board. 27-Nov-2 Deutscher-Menzies, Melbourne #183/R est:1500-2000 (A.D 1800)
£687 $1085 €996 Playing in the street (21x30cm-8x12in) s. 7-Apr-3 Australian Art Auctions, Sydney #99 (A.D 1800)
£717 $1039 €1076 Under the trees (29x40cm-11x16in) s. board. 10-Dec-1 Goodman, Sydney #482 (A.D 2000)
£720 $1159 €1044 Bark hut (24x29cm-9x11in) s. board. 12-May-3 Joel, Victoria #380 est:1200-1500 (A.D 1800)
£760 $1223 €1140 Fish and chips (21x29cm-8x11in) s. board. 6-May-3 Christie's, Melbourne #292/R est:1500-2000 (A.D 1900)
£775 $1208 €1163 Majestic bouquet (43x24cm-17x9in) s. pva. 21-Oct-2 Australian Art Auctions, Sydney #118 (A.D 2200)
£788 $1198 €1182 Old well (23x35cm-9x14in) s.d.1971 composition board. 28-Aug-2 Deutscher-Menzies, Melbourne #437/R (A.D 2200)
£801 $1266 €1388 Outback station (22x25cm-9x10in) s. board. 1-Apr-3 Goodman, Sydney #40 (A.D 2100)
£813 $1285 €1179 Outside the homestead (22x14cm-9x6in) s. oil on paper. 22-Jul-3 Lawson Menzies, Sydney #218/R est:1500-2500 (A.D 2000)
£839 $1326 €1454 Green beetle (21x29cm-8x11in) s. board. 1-Apr-3 Goodman, Sydney #1 (A.D 2200)
£857 $1354 €1286 Mining town (32x32cm-13x13in) s. board. 27-Nov-2 Deutscher-Menzies, Melbourne #178/R est:2500-3500 (A.D 2400)
£877 $1386 €1520 Ants (19x19cm-7x7in) s. board. 1-Apr-3 Goodman, Sydney #4/R (A.D 2300)
£896 $1299 €1344 Town (28x38cm-11x15in) s.i. board. 10-Dec-1 Goodman, Sydney #481 (A.D 2500)
£932 $1416 €1398 Insects (44x34cm-17x13in) s.d.76 board. 27-Aug-2 Goodman, Sydney #67 (A.D 2600)
£932 $1416 €1398 Yellow firework flowers (88x88cm-35x35in) s.d.75. 27-Aug-2 Goodman, Sydney #202 (A.D 2600)
£956 $1568 €1434 Landscape and car parts (30x25cm-12x10in) s. i.verso composition board. 4-Jun-3 Deutscher-Menzies, Melbourne #300/R est:1500-2000 (A.D 2400)
£956 $1568 €1434 Cove, Sydney (30x20cm-12x8in) s. prov. 4-Jun-3 Deutscher-Menzies, Melbourne #335/R (A.D 2400)
£992 $1567 €1719 Dragonfly (35x28cm-14x11in) s. board. 1-Apr-3 Goodman, Sydney #12/R est:1500-2500 (A.D 2600)
£1004 $1525 €1506 Knock off time, South Mine (48x41cm-19x16in) s.i.d.80 board. 27-Aug-2 Goodman, Sydney #88 est:2500-3500 (A.D 2800)
£1036 $1699 €1554 Menindee landscape (49x57cm-19x22in) s. i.verso composition board prov. 4-Jun-3 Deutscher-Menzies, Melbourne #301/R est:2000-3000 (A.D 2600)
£1039 $1580 €1559 Mine men (25x26cm-10x10in) s. board. 27-Aug-2 Goodman, Sydney #96 est:2000-3000 (A.D 2900)
£1056 $1648 €1584 Rainbow creek (61x78cm-24x31in) s. 21-Oct-2 Australian Art Auctions, Sydney #78 (A.D 3000)
£1057 $1670 €1533 Waterbirds (25x25cm-10x10in) s.d.74 board. 22-Jul-3 Lawson Menzies, Sydney #223/R est:1200-2200 (A.D 2600)
£1069 $1689 €1604 Majestic bouquet (43x26cm-17x10in) s. board. 7-Apr-3 Australian Art Auctions, Sydney #106 (A.D 2800)
£1111 $1689 €1667 Birds on the creek (29x37cm-11x15in) s. board. 27-Aug-2 Goodman, Sydney #15 est:2500-3500 (A.D 3100)
£1145 $1809 €1718 Outback woolshed (30x44cm-12x17in) s. board. 1-Apr-3 Lawson Menzies, Sydney #438 est:3300-4300 (A.D 3000)
£1147 $1743 €1721 Landscape (49x59cm-19x23in) s. composition board. 28-Aug-2 Deutscher-Menzies, Melbourne #433/R est:3000-4000 (A.D 3200)
£1203 $1913 €1805 Broken Hill Street (29x30cm-11x12in) s.i. board. 3-Mar-3 Lawson Menzies, Sydney #355 est:1200-2000 (A.D 3200)
£1231 $1957 €1847 Mining camp (29x29cm-11x11in) s. composition board. 4-Mar-3 Deutscher-Menzies, Melbourne #201/R est:1800-2200 (A.D 3200)
£1232 $2008 €1848 The judgement (50x60cm-20x24in) s. board. 3-Feb-3 Lawson Menzies, Sydney #439 est:3500-4500 (A.D 3400)
£1275 $2091 €1913 Flower study (31x23cm-12x9in) s. canvas on board prov. 4-Jun-3 Deutscher-Menzies, Melbourne #336/R est:1000-1500 (A.D 3200)
£1286 $2031 €1929 Waterbirds (30x61cm-12x24in) s. board. 27-Nov-2 Deutscher-Menzies, Melbourne #188/R est:2200-3000 (A.D 3600)
£1300 $2093 €1885 Red roof (29x29cm-11x11in) s. board. 12-May-3 Joel, Victoria #287 est:1500-2000 (A.D 3250)
£1321 $2088 €1982 Watching the trials (21x29cm-8x11in) s. board. 18-Nov-2 Joel, Victoria #231 est:1800-2200 (A.D 3700)
£1333 $2027 €2000 Grasshopper and plant (60x45cm-24x18in) s. board. 19-Aug-2 Joel, Victoria #166 est:2000-3000 (A.D 3800)
£1357 $2144 €2036 Yabbie trappers (29x48cm-11x19in) s. board. 18-Nov-2 Goodman, Sydney #118 est:3500-4500 (A.D 3800)
£1360 $2190 €1972 Camp by the creek (24x29cm-9x11in) s. board. 12-May-3 Joel, Victoria #375 est:2000-4000 (A.D 3400)
£1362 $2070 €2043 Flower study (61x45cm-24x18in) s.d.89 board. 28-Aug-2 Deutscher-Menzies, Melbourne #438/R est:2000-3000 (A.D 3800)
£1362 $2070 €2043 South Mine, Broken Hill (44x44cm-17x17in) s. board. 27-Aug-2 Goodman, Sydney #27/R est:3000-4000 (A.D 3800)
£1404 $2133 €2106 Geebung polo club (59x66cm-23x26in) s.d.65 board. 19-Aug-2 Joel, Victoria #278 est:2000-3000 (A.D 4000)
£1423 $2248 €2063 Flowers in red vase (21x44cm-8x17in) s. board. 22-Jul-3 Lawson Menzies, Sydney #219/R est:3500-4500 (A.D 3500)
£1429 $2257 €2144 Miner series (48x40cm-19x16in) s.d.73 board. 18-Nov-2 Goodman, Sydney #76 est:4000-6000 (A.D 4000)
£1431 $2260 €2478 Emu creek (44x75cm-17x30in) s. board. 1-Apr-3 Goodman, Sydney #60b est:3000-4000 (A.D 3750)
£1434 $2179 €2151 Yabbie bar (23x30cm-9x12in) s. 28-Aug-2 Deutscher-Menzies, Melbourne #255/R est:2000-3000 (A.D 4000)
£1434 $2352 €2151 Visiting the station wrecks (23x27cm-9x11in) s. board. 4-Jun-3 Deutscher-Menzies, Melbourne #302/R est:1500-2000 (A.D 3600)
£1470 $2234 €2205 Hold up (31x44cm-12x17in) s. board. 27-Aug-2 Goodman, Sydney #232 est:2500-3500 (A.D 4100)
£1500 $2415 €2175 Windmill (30x39cm-12x15in) s. board. 12-May-3 Joel, Victoria #234 est:2000-3000 (A.D 3750)
£1607 $2539 €2411 Sheep yards (39x49cm-15x19in) s. board. 18-Nov-2 Goodman, Sydney #38/R est:3200-4200 (A.D 4500)
£1613 $2452 €2420 Shearing sheds (50x60cm-20x24in) s.d.86 board. 27-Aug-2 Goodman, Sydney #176/R est:4500-6500 (A.D 4500)
£1692 $2690 €2538 Dragon fly (39x29cm-15x11in) s.d.1999 board. 3-Mar-3 Lawson Menzies, Sydney #354 est:1500-2000 (A.D 4500)
£1750 $2765 €2625 Dragon fly with ants (48x31cm-19x12in) s. board. 18-Nov-2 Goodman, Sydney #126 est:5000-8000 (A.D 4900)
£1786 $2768 €2679 Emu creek (40x72cm-16x28in) s. board. 29-Oct-2 Lawson Menzies, Sydney #53/R est:4000-5000 (A.D 5000)
£1800 $2898 €2610 Mulga Bill (39x49cm-15x19in) s. board. 12-May-3 Joel, Victoria #227/R est:3000-5000 (A.D 4500)
£1829 $2891 €2652 Water hole (55x77cm-22x30in) s.i.d.76 canvas on board. 22-Jul-3 Lawson Menzies, Sydney #224/R est:4000-6000 (A.D 4500)
£1857 $2934 €2786 Rabitter's camp (58x69cm-23x27in) s.d.74 board. 26-Nov-2 Sotheby's, Melbourne #115/R est:2500-4500 (A.D 5200)
£1916 $3008 €2874 Mulga Bill (60x30cm-24x12in) s.i.d.76 board. 15-Apr-3 Lawson Menzies, Sydney #18/R est:4000-6000 (A.D 5000)
£1923 $3057 €2885 Huts by the creek (30x45cm-12x18in) s. canvas on board prov. 4-Mar-3 Deutscher-Menzies, Melbourne #202/R est:3500-5000 (A.D 5000)
£1964 $3103 €2946 Smoko in the crib (90x120cm-35x47in) s. board. 18-Nov-2 Joel, Victoria #155 est:5000-7000 (A.D 5500)
£2033 $3211 €2948 Miner's houses 2 (45x59cm-18x23in) s. board. 22-Jul-3 Lawson Menzies, Sydney #217/R est:5000-7000 (A.D 5000)
£2236 $3533 €3242 Dead insect (60x49cm-24x19in) s. i.verso. 22-Jul-3 Lawson Menzies, Sydney #225/R est:5000-7000 (A.D 5500)
£2393 $3781 €3590 Picnic racing scene (44x59cm-17x23in) s. board. 18-Nov-2 Goodman, Sydney #12/R est:3000-5000 (A.D 6700)
£2439 $3854 €3537 Miners houses (45x49cm-18x19in) s. board. 22-Jul-3 Lawson Menzies, Sydney #134/R est:5000-7000 (A.D 6000)
£2509 $3814 €3764 Man in a tub (45x61cm-18x24in) s.d.69 i.verso. 28-Aug-2 Deutscher-Menzies, Melbourne #436/R est:2800-3600 (A.D 7000)
£2516 $3975 €3774 Campsite (91x91cm-36x36in) s.d.76 prov. 27-Nov-2 Deutscher-Menzies, Melbourne #186/R est:4000-6000 (A.D 7045)
£2689 $4410 €4034 Auction in the droving days (46x46cm-18x18in) s.i. composition board prov. 4-Jun-3 Deutscher-Menzies, Melbourne #294/R est:4000-6000 (A.D 6750)
£2874 $4511 €4311 Pittwater (75x75cm-30x30in) s.i. board. 15-Apr-3 Lawson Menzies, Sydney #17/R est:5000-7000 (A.D 7500)
£2874 $4511 €4311 Race meeting (44x70cm-17x28in) s.d.74 board. 15-Apr-3 Lawson Menzies, Sydney #199/R est:6000-8000 (A.D 7500)
£2982 $4533 €4473 Discussion under the dig tree (59x69cm-23x27in) s. board. 19-Aug-2 Joel, Victoria #271/R est:2500-3500 (A.D 8500)

£3257 $5113 €4886 Race meeting (44x60cm-17x24in) s. 15-Apr-3 Lawson Menzies, Sydney #206/R est:6000-10000 (A.D 8500)
£3626 $5729 €5439 Bishop (51x41cm-20x16in) s. 7-Apr-3 Australian Art Auctions, Sydney #138 (A.D 9500)
£4135 $6575 €6203 Wildflowers in red pot (73x58cm-29x23in) s. 3-Mar-3 Lawson Menzies, Sydney #365 est:3500-4500 (A.D 11000)
£4483 $7083 €7766 Eureka stockade (56x109cm-22x43in) s. board. 1-Apr-3 Goodman, Sydney #17 est:7000-12000 (A.D 11750)
£8244 $12530 €12366 The landing (122x122cm-48x48in) s.i.d.73 composition board. 28-Aug-2 Deutscher-Menzies, Melbourne #256/R est:10000-15000 (A.D 23000)
£34000 $54740 €51000 Banjo Patterson mural (90x120cm-35x47in) s.i.d.73-74 board in five parts prov. 6-May-3 Christie's, Melbourne #122/R est:60000-80000 (A.D 85000)

Sculpture

£1300 $2093 €1885 Four faces of the miner (38cm-15in) i. bronze. 12-May-3 Joel, Victoria #268 est:1800-2500 (A.D 3250)

Works on paper

£268 $420 €402 Dying insect (16x24cm-6x9in) s.i. W/C ink. 25-Nov-2 Christie's, Melbourne #324 (A.D 750)
£430 $654 €645 Plate layers (16x23cm-6x9in) s.i.d.73 W/C. 28-Aug-2 Deutscher-Menzies, Melbourne #434/R (A.D 1200)
£611 $965 €917 Camp (45x44cm-18x17in) s. monotype. 7-Apr-3 Australian Art Auctions, Sydney #83 (A.D 1600)

HART, Salomon Alexander (1806-1881) British

£380 $600 €570 Fall mountain and lake scene (56x91cm-22x36in) s.d.73. 26-Apr-3 Thomaston Place, Thomaston #132
£1389 $2236 €2084 Portrait of young Queen Victoria (121x80cm-48x31in) s.d.1842. 7-May-3 Dobiaschofsky, Bern #626/R est:2700 (S.FR 3000)

HART, Thomas (?-1886) British

Works on paper

£300 $498 €435 Wreck on the Lizard coast (33x58cm-13x23in) s. W/C. 10-Jun-3 David Lay, Penzance #490
£300 $498 €435 Mines at Botallack (36x61cm-14x24in) s. W/C. 10-Jun-3 David Lay, Penzance #491
£500 $780 €750 Polpier Cove and The Stags, Lizard (20x36cm-8x14in) s. i.verso W/C. 17-Oct-2 David Lay, Penzance #1489
£600 $936 €900 Mont St Michel (23x33cm-9x13in) s. W/C. 15-Oct-2 Gorringes, Lewes #2272
£1000 $1590 €1500 View of St. Michael's Mount (52x80cm-20x31in) s. W/C. 29-Apr-3 Bonhams, Knightsbridge #52/R est:800-1200

HART, William Howard (1863-?) American

£4908 $8000 €7362 Upper John's Brook (61x51cm-24x20in) s. 16-Feb-3 Butterfields, San Francisco #2093 est:1800-2250

HART, William MacDougal (1823-1894) American

£2548 $4000 €3822 River landscape with grazing cows beside a cottage (41x61cm-16x24in) s. indis d. 14-Dec-2 Weschler, Washington #661/R est:7000-9000
£2597 $4000 €3896 Lake Windermere (30x46cm-12x18in) s.d.1852 panel. 4-Sep-2 Christie's, Rockefeller NY #357/R est:3000-5000
£4491 $7500 €6512 By the old wall (28x43cm-11x17in) s. 22-Jun-3 Jeffery Burchard, Florida #32/R est:8000-12000
£5161 $8000 €7742 On the Maine coast (23x41cm-9x16in) s. canvas on board painted c.1860 prov. 3-Dec-2 Phillips, New York #5/R
£11465 $18000 €17198 Land in Keene Valley, Vermont (33x61cm-13x24in) s. prov. 19-Nov-2 Butterfields, San Francisco #8001/R est:12000-16000
£20645 $32000 €30968 Grand manan (24x46cm-9x18in) s. painted c.1860. 3-Dec-2 Phillips, New York #27/R est:25000-45000

HARTA, Felix Albrecht (1884-1970) Hungarian/Austrian

£1367 $2242 €1900 Summer landscape (60x73cm-24x29in) s.d.1932. 5-Jun-3 Dorotheum, Salzburg #588/R est:2000-3000
£6597 $10490 €9500 Still life with books (56x69cm-22x27in) 29-Apr-3 Wiener Kunst Auktionen, Vienna #577/R est:6500-8000
£7372 $11574 €11500 Flowers (52x61cm-20x24in) s. 25-Nov-2 Hassfurther, Vienna #46/R est:9000-11000

HARTE, Glynn Boyd (20th C) British

Works on paper

£850 $1318 €1275 Le Bois de moutiers (25x20cm-10x8in) mono. gouache gessoed panel sold with two others. 24-Sep-2 Bonhams, New Bond Street #132

HARTE, J A (fl.1872) British?

£8500 $13685 €12750 Waiting at the cottage door (50x39cm-20x15in) s.d.72 prov. 20-Feb-3 Christie's, London #222/R est:6000-8000

HARTIG, Carl Christoph (1888-?) Swiss

£944 $1492 €1416 Portrait of lady wearing hat (90x70cm-35x28in) s. 13-Nov-2 Kunsthallen, Copenhagen #51/R (D.KR 11000)

HARTIG, Hans (1873-?) German

£202 $319 €303 Figures loading cart in continental town (69x49cm-27x19in) s. 18-Nov-2 Waddingtons, Toronto #256/R (C.D 500)
£440 $687 €700 Jetty (50x70cm-20x28in) s. board. 21-Sep-2 Bolland & Marotz, Bremen #488/R
£523 $858 €800 Pommer landscape (28x42cm-11x17in) board. 8-Feb-3 Hans Stahl, Hamburg #93/R
£769 $1215 €1200 New-Warp on the Stettiner Haff (55x71cm-22x28in) s.i. board. 14-Nov-2 Neumeister, Munich #578/R
£769 $1192 €1200 Landscape (47x60cm-19x24in) mono.d.14.XI.05 board. 7-Dec-2 Hans Stahl, Hamburg #81/R
£884 $1406 €1300 Low tide on the Ostsee coast (49x71cm-19x28in) s. i. verso board. 28-Mar-3 Bolland & Marotz, Bremen #458/R

HARTIGAN, Paul (20th C) New Zealander?

£1562 $2437 €2343 Travelling companion (59x248cm-23x98in) s.i.d.1994 verso enamel board exhib. 8-Apr-3 Peter Webb, Auckland #156/R est:4500-7000 (NZ.D 4500)

HARTING, Lloyd (1901-1976) American

Works on paper

£641 $1000 €962 Unwanted ones (28x36cm-11x14in) s. graphite W/C gouache prov.lit. 9-Nov-2 Santa Fe Art, Santa Fe #111/R est:3000-5000
£1763 $2750 €2645 Desperate race (38x56cm-15x22in) s. graphite W/C gouache prov.lit. 9-Nov-2 Santa Fe Art, Santa Fe #112/R est:4000-6000
£2343 $3795 €3397 Round up (36x53cm-14x21in) W/C. 23-May-3 Altermann Galleries, Santa Fe #122

HARTLAND, Henry Albert (1840-1893) Irish

Works on paper

£268 $417 €420 Rocky coastal inlet (17x34cm-7x13in) s. W/C. 6-Nov-2 James Adam, Dublin #96/R
£300 $477 €450 Ravine near Arthog, Wales (34x51cm-13x20in) s. W/C. 27-Feb-3 Bonhams, Chester #342
£366 $531 €575 Stroll near Carrigrohane (33x49cm-13x19in) W/C. 29-May-2 Woodwards, Cork #204
£550 $891 €825 River views (17x25cm-7x10in) s. W/C pair. 21-Jan-3 Bonhams, Knightsbridge #228/R
£828 $1201 €1300 Peaceful riverside study (25x50cm-10x20in) W/C. 29-May-2 Woodwards, Cork #201
£2319 $3803 €3200 Irish homestead (47x75cm-19x30in) s. W/C. 28-May-3 Bonhams & James Adam, Dublin #32/R est:3000-5000

HARTLEY, Alex (1963-) British

Photographs

£5000 $7700 €7500 Untitled - model (110x170cm-43x67in) col photograph glass MDF executed 1994 prov. 23-Oct-2 Christie's, London #181/R est:5000-7000

HARTLEY, Marsden (1877-1943) American

£25806 $40000 €38709 Ski signs (56x71cm-22x28in) s. i.d.1939-40 verso board prov.exhib.lit. 4-Dec-2 Sotheby's, New York #83/R est:40000-60000
£58065 $90000 €87098 Trees by a lake (25x36cm-10x14in) board painted 1941 prov. 4-Dec-2 Sotheby's, New York #82/R est:100000-150000
£67901 $110000 €101852 Scouting the fish boat (71x56cm-28x22in) board painted c.1939-40 prov.exhib.lit. 21-May-3 Sotheby's, New York #80/R est:80000-120000
£70968 $110000 €106452 Near santa Fe (32x79cm-13x31in) prov. 5-Dec-2 Christie's, Rockefeller NY #132/R est:120000-180000
£103226 $160000 €154839 Still life (51x40cm-20x16in) s.d.1921 panel prov.exhib. 4-Dec-2 Sotheby's, New York #69/R est:125000-175000
£111111 $180000 €166667 Landscape no.27 (30x23cm-12x9in) board painted c.1908 prov.exhib. 21-May-3 Sotheby's, New York #120/R est:200000-300000
£167742 $260000 €251613 Still life with bananas (51x41cm-20x16in) s. painted c.1911-12 prov.exhib.lit. 4-Dec-2 Sotheby's, New York #68/R est:100000-150000
£191358 $310000 €287037 Sail movement (51x41cm-20x16in) s. panel painted 1916 prov.exhib.lit. 21-May-3 Sotheby's, New York #12/R est:300000-500000
£222222 $360000 €333333 Composition (49x39cm-19x15in) board painted 1913 prov.exhib.lit. 21-May-3 Sotheby's, New York #17/R est:200000-300000
£253086 $410000 €379629 Flowers from a lonely child (51x41cm-20x16in) s.i.d.1935-36 canvasboard prov.exhib. 21-May-3 Sotheby's, New York #113/R est:300000-400000
£393548 $610000 €590322 Still life with flowers (81x65cm-32x26in) painted c.1928 prov.exhib.lit. 4-Dec-2 Sotheby's, New York #61/R est:300000-500000
£548387 $850000 €822581 Mont sainte-Victoire (81x100cm-32x39in) prov.exhib.lit. 5-Dec-2 Christie's, Rockefeller NY #144/R est:1000000-1500000

Prints

£1635 $2600 €2453 Number two Dreitorspitze (31x40cm-12x16in) s.i.d.1934 lithograph edition of 150. 7-Mar-3 Skinner, Boston #57/R est:3000-5000

Works on paper

£8805 $14000 €13208 Aix-en-Provence (48x61cm-19x24in) s.d.27 pencil prov.exhib.lit. 5-Mar-3 Sotheby's, New York #76/R est:15000-25000

£20062 $32500 €30093 Near aix-en-provence (71x53cm-28x21in) ink pencil executed c.1928 prov.exhib.lit. 21-May-3 Sotheby's, New York #7/R est:30000-50000

£21605 $35000 €32408 Vinalhaven (46x61cm-18x24in) crayon chk paperboard executed c.1938 prov.exhib.lit. 21-May-3 Sotheby's, New York #6/R est:30000-50000

HARTLEY, Rachel (1884-?) American

£535 $850 €803 On the beach (41x65cm-16x26in) s. 7-Mar-3 Skinner, Boston #503/R

£1104 $1700 €1656 Greenwich Village (51x41cm-20x16in) canvasboard prov. 24-Oct-2 Shannon's, Milford #228/R est:1500-2500

HARTMAN (?) ?

£2244 $3478 €3500 Stream (92x73cm-36x29in) s. 4-Dec-2 Pierre Berge, Paris #141/R

HARTMAN, Anne Franciscus (1904-1975) Dutch

£625 $1031 €900 Sluice in a Dutch village (55x65cm-22x26in) s.d.46. 1-Jul-3 Christie's, Amsterdam #102/R

HARTMAN, Mauno (1930-) Finnish

Works on paper

£381 $625 €530 Jonna (29x54cm-11x21in) s.d.1982 verso chk nature material. 4-Jun-3 Bukowskis, Helsinki #286/R

HARTMAN, Sydney K (1863-1929) American

£250 $400 €375 Harbour scene (25x33cm-10x13in) s. 17-May-3 Pook & Pook, Downington #200d

HARTMANN, Bertram (1882-1960) American

£579 $950 €840 Beach scene (18x23cm-7x9in) s.d. canvasboard. 5-Jun-3 Swann Galleries, New York #116/R

Works on paper

£793 $1300 €1150 View of New York (56x38cm-22x15in) s. W/C. 5-Jun-3 Swann Galleries, New York #117/R

HARTMANN, Carl (1818-1857) German

£800 $1328 €1200 Portrait of a young boy (43x33cm-17x13in) s.d.1848 board painted oval. 10-Jun-3 Bonhams, Knightsbridge #222/R

HARTMANN, George T (?-1934) American

£315 $500 €473 Autumnal arrangement, still life with mums and oak leaves (51x41cm-20x16in) s.d.35 canvasboard. 7-Mar-3 Skinner, Boston #555/R

HARTMANN, Hugo Friedrich (1870-1960) German

£321 $503 €500 River (35x42cm-14x17in) s. 23-Nov-2 Arnold, Frankfurt #744/R

HARTMANN, Johann Jacob (1680-1730) Czechoslovakian

£10390 $15481 €16000 Hunting party at rest in wood (32x39cm-13x15in) 26-Jun-2 Neumeister, Munich #633/R est:10000

HARTMANN, Sylvia von (20th C) ?

Works on paper

£320 $531 €464 Night tree (83x58cm-33x23in) s.d.1993 mixed media. 13-Jun-3 Lyon & Turnbull, Edinburgh #106

HARTMANN, Werner (1903-1981) Swiss

£480 $749 €720 Figure walking in autumn landscape (32x41cm-13x16in) s. pavatex. 20-Nov-2 Fischer, Luzern #2108/R (S.FR 1100)

HARTMANN, Wilhelm (1793-1862) Swiss

Works on paper

£1106 $1748 €1659 Gentlemen and ladies walking by Swiss mountain lake (21x30cm-8x12in) s.d.837 W/C. 2-Dec-2 Rasmussen, Copenhagen #1840/R est:15000 (D.KR 13000)

HARTMANN, Wolfgang (1600-1663) Swedish/German

Prints

£2837 $4397 €4256 The Royal Residence, Stockholm (42x64cm-17x25in) copper plate engraving printed on two sheets lit. 3-Dec-2 Bukowskis, Stockholm #548/R est:50000-75000 (S.KR 40000)

HARTRATH, Lucie (1868-1962) American

£6452 $10000 €9678 Close of the day (46x51cm-18x20in) s. painted c.1910. 8-Dec-2 Toomey, Oak Park #649/R est:12000-15000

HARTRICK, Archibald Standish (1864-1950) British

£300 $468 €450 Gardener resting on his fork (91x61cm-36x24in) s. 10-Apr-3 Tennants, Leyburn #1121

£950 $1482 €1425 Hurdle maker (40x56cm-16x22in) s. i.verso board. 10-Apr-3 Tennants, Leyburn #1120/R

Works on paper

£380 $608 €570 Portrait of Sgt James Mustard at Coronation of King George V (29x21cm-11x8in) s.i.d.1911 pe chl chk exhib. 15-May-3 Lawrence, Crewkerne #852

HARTSON, Walter C (1866-?) British

£446 $700 €669 Early moonrise (41x51cm-16x20in) s. 14-Dec-2 Weschler, Washington #666/R

HARTUNG, Hans (1904-1989) French/German

£4114 $6377 €6500 P1973-B19 (74x104cm-29x41in) i.d.13 aout 1973 verso acrylic cardboard prov. 28-Sep-2 Cornette de St.Cyr, Paris #331/R est:10000-12000

£5031 $7799 €8000 P10-1976-H9 (39x59cm-15x23in) acrylic pastel cardboard prov.lit. 30-Oct-2 Artcurial Briest, Paris #571/R est:6000-7000

£5072 $8319 €7000 P 1960 (73x50cm-29x20in) s.d.60 acrylic board prov. 28-May-3 Lempertz, Koln #165/R est:7000-8000

£5346 $8286 €8500 T 1989-A50 (65x54cm-26x21in) mono.i.verso lit. 30-Oct-2 Artcurial Briest, Paris #570/R est:8000-12000

£5674 $9191 €8000 Hvplar (100x72cm-39x28in) s.d. i.d.18/2/82 verso acrylic varnish. 23-May-3 Binoche, Paris #70 est:10000-12000

£6329 $10000 €10000 T-1982-U 19 (92x65cm-36x26in) s.d.82 verso i. stretcher acrylic. 30-Nov-2 Villa Grisebach, Berlin #370/R est:10000-14000

£6792 $10460 €10800 T1981-R26 (61x38cm-24x15in) s.d.1981 acrylic. 26-Oct-2 Cornette de St.Cyr, Paris #7/R est:12000

£6962 $11000 €11000 T-1976-E 3 (92x65cm-36x26in) mono.d.76 verso acrylic. 30-Nov-2 Villa Grisebach, Berlin #368/R est:14000-18000

£7008 $10932 €10512 Composition (35x24cm-14x9in) s.d.55 prov. 6-Nov-2 AB Stockholms Auktionsverk #956/R est:80000-100000 (S.KR 100000)

£7609 $12478 €10500 P 1960 (64x95cm-25x37in) s.i.d.2/12/62 i. verso oil chk board prov. 28-May-3 Lempertz, Koln #164/R est:7000

£8108 $12649 €12000 H9 (40x60cm-16x24in) acrylic oil pastel card painted 1976. 26-Mar-3 Finarte Semenzato, Milan #346/R

£8511 $13787 €12000 P 1967-117 (89x66cm-35x26in) s.d.67 i.d.verso tempera pastel graffiti board. 26-May-3 Christie's, Milan #167/R est:7000-10000

£8654 $12635 €13500 P1967-A52 (73x99cm-29x39in) s.d.1967 acrylic col crayon cardboard. 5-Jun-2 Il Ponte, Milan #107/R est:12000-14000

£10145 $16638 €14000 P 1953 (65x48cm-26x19in) s.d.53 oil chk. 28-May-3 Lempertz, Koln #163/R est:18000-20000

£10417 $16458 €15000 Composition P (50x65cm-20x26in) s.d. i.verso acrylic grattage cardboard prov. 27-Apr-3 Perrin, Versailles #45/R est:15000-18000

£10443 $16500 €16500 T1982-R4 (81x100cm-32x39in) s.d.1982 acrylic. 27-Nov-2 Tajan, Paris #35/R

£10897 $16891 €17000 P 40 - 1981 H (75x105cm-30x41in) mono.d.81 acrylic board. 3-Dec-2 Lempertz, Koln #175/R est:18000-20000

£11594 $19014 €16000 P 1970 A 35 (104x72cm-41x28in) s.d.70 i.d. verso oil chk sprayed Indian ink board prov. 31-May-3 Villa Grisebach, Berlin #337/R est:20000-25000

£13333 $21200 €19600 T1982-R31 (92x73cm-36x29in) mono.d.1982 acrylic. 24-Mar-3 Cornette de St.Cyr, Paris #6/R

£17308 $27173 €27000 T1965-R10 (73x60cm-29x24in) s.d.65. 19-Nov-2 Finarte, Milan #195/R est:10000-16000

£18590 $29186 €29000 T1961-H48 (72x92cm-28x36in) s.d.1971. 23-Nov-2 Meeting Art, Vercelli #120/R est:25000

£19608 $31373 €30000 T1980-K24 (97x146cm-38x57in) s.i.d.1980 verso acrylic. 4-Jan-3 Meeting Art, Vercelli #629 est:30000

£20470 $32956 €30500 Composition (70x48cm-28x19in) s.d.1950 oil pastel. 23-Feb-3 Mercier & Cie, Lille #63/R est:26000

£21740 $35653 €30000 T 1967 H 17 (65x81cm-26x32in) s.d.1967 prov. 27-May-3 Tajan, Paris #16/R est:15000-20000

£25532 $41362 €36000 PN-27 1950 (48x72cm-19x28in) s.d.50 oil pastel paper prov. 26-May-3 Christie's, Milan #249/R est:30000-40000

£38462 $59615 €60000 T 1963 R 9 (180x111cm-71x44in) s.d.63 i. stretcher. 3-Dec-2 Lempertz, Koln #172/R est:65000-80000

£43165 $69065 €60000 T-1951-20 (50x73cm-20x29in) s.d. i. stretcher prov. 15-May-3 Neumeister, Munich #704/R est:50000-60000

£55128 $86551 €86000 T1946-6 (31x60cm-12x24in) s.d.1946 panel prov.lit. 15-Dec-2 Perrin, Versailles #66/R est:70000

£131034 $207034 €190000 T1948-43 (81x100cm-32x39in) s. painted 1948 prov. 2-Apr-3 Christie's, Paris #9/R est:180000

Works on paper

£2931 $4895 €4250 Composition (37x25cm-15x10in) s.i.d. pastel cardboard prov. 9-Jul-3 Cornette de St.Cyr, Paris #299/R est:4500-5000
£3346 $5286 €5019 Untitled - painted stone (6x11cm-2x4in) s.d.56 Indian ink. 1-Apr-3 Rasmussen, Copenhagen #246/R est:5000 (D.KR 36000)
£3793 $5993 €5500 Untitled (50x64cm-20x25in) s.d. i.d.29-8-86 verso col chk board. 2-Apr-3 Dr Fritz Nagel, Stuttgart #9480/R est:6000
£3797 $6000 €6000 P 58-61 (49x65cm-19x26in) s.d.58 i. verso chl board. 30-Nov-2 Villa Grisebach, Berlin #367/R est:6000-8000
£3819 $6302 €5500 P 1962-HH 5119 (19x14cm-7x6in) s.i.d.3/4/62 crayon col wax pastel exhib. 1-Jul-3 Artcurial Briest, Paris #789/R est:6000-9000
£4789 $7949 €6800 Composition (49x74cm-19x29in) s.d.60 wax pastel crayon. 18-Jun-3 Anaf, Lyon #47/R est:10000-12000
£4828 $7628 €7000 P1960-294 (77x57cm-30x22in) s.d.60 pastel prov. 2-Apr-3 Christie's, Paris #17/R
£5128 $8051 €8000 Composition (30x24cm-12x9in) s.d.1958 pastel chl. 15-Dec-2 Eric Pillon, Calais #269/R
£5449 $8554 €8500 Composition (56x45cm-22x18in) s.d.1959 pastel wax crayon prov. 15-Dec-2 Perrin, Versailles #61/R
£5862 $9262 €8500 P1953-HH5 105 (65x48cm-26x19in) s.d.53 pastel prov. 2-Apr-3 Christie's, Paris #16/R est:18000
£5903 $9740 €8500 PM 1961-36 (37x27cm-15x11in) s.d.61 wax col pastel crayon. 1-Jul-3 Artcurial Briest, Paris #788/R est:6000-8000
£6000 $10020 €8700 P 1959-158 (68x76cm-27x30in) s.d.59 i.d.1959 verso pastel prov. 26-Jun-3 Sotheby's, London #190/R est:6000-8000
£7000 $11480 €10500 P 1957-57 (65x50cm-26x20in) s.d.57 i.verso pastel. 7-Feb-3 Sotheby's, London #226/R est:8000-12000
£8333 $12667 €13000 Composition (50x65cm-20x26in) s.d.1958 pastel. 16-Aug-2 Deauville, France #65/R est:15000
£9058 $14855 €12500 P 1959-95 (37x26cm-15x10in) s.d.59 i. verso chk chl pencil prov. 30-May-3 Villa Grisebach, Berlin #69/R est:8000-10000
£10897 $17109 €17000 Untitled (49x72cm-19x28in) s.d.61 pastel wax crayon. 24-Nov-2 Laurence Calmels, Paris #144/R est:15000
£14103 $21859 €22000 Untitled (50x65cm-20x26in) s.d.1957 chk chl dr W/C pencil cardboard prov. 6-Dec-2 Ketterer, Munich #176/R est:20000-25000
£14744 $22853 €23000 Composition (48x73cm-19x29in) s.d.48 col chk board prov. 3-Dec-2 Lempertz, Koln #173/R est:25000-28000
£17931 $28331 €26000 P1953-HH5 104 (48x65cm-19x26in) s.d.53 pastel cardboard prov. 2-Apr-3 Christie's, Paris #7/R est:38000
£17949 $28179 €28000 P.53.40 (47x70cm-19x28in) s.d.1953 pastel lit. 15-Dec-2 Perrin, Versailles #59/R est:25000
£19444 $30722 €28000 Sans titre (24x19cm-9x7in) s.d. graphite pastel tempera prov.lit. 27-Apr-3 Perrin, Versailles #32/R est:2000-25000
£22000 $36740 €31900 P1948-HH4900 (48x72cm-19x28in) s.d.1948 pastel ink. 27-Jun-3 Christie's, London #120/R est:14000-18000

HARTUNG, Heinrich (1851-1919) German

£1026 $1610 €1600 Shepherd with flock in Luneberger Heide (84x63cm-33x25in) s.d.81. 21-Nov-2 Van Ham, Cologne #1656 est:1500
£1987 $3120 €3100 Wooded river landscape with swan (66x48cm-26x19in) s.d.91. 21-Nov-2 Van Ham, Cologne #1655/R est:4000
£2778 $4472 €4028 Landscape with farmstead (39x53cm-15x21in) s. canvas on panel. 7-May-3 Dobiaschofsky, Bern #627/R est:7000 (S.FR 6000)

HARTUNG, Heinrich (1888-1966) German

£1918 $2992 €2800 Nurburg in summer Eifel landscape (75x93cm-30x37in) s.d.1942 panel. 10-Apr-3 Van Ham, Cologne #1465/R est:1900

HARTUNG, Johann (19th C) German

£800 $1328 €1160 Mischievous kittens in the kitchen. Kittens at tea time (31x15cm-12x6in) s. panel pair. 16-Jun-3 Waddingtons, Toronto #290/R est:2500-3000 (C.D 1800)

HARTUNG, Karl (1908-1967) German

Sculpture

£2244 $3478 €3500 Bull (7cm-3in) st.sig. brown pat.bronze exhib. 3-Dec-2 Lempertz, Koln #171/R est:7000-8000
£18841 $30899 €26000 Standing (46cm-18in) red brown pat.bronze. 31-May-3 Villa Grisebach, Berlin #295/R est:20000-30000

Works on paper

£580 $951 €800 Figural composition (39x61cm-15x24in) s. s.i. verso chk. 31-May-3 Villa Grisebach, Berlin #829/R
£705 $1093 €1100 Figure in studio (25x35cm-10x14in) s. W/C wax chk. 6-Dec-2 Hauswedell & Nolte, Hamburg #153/R

HARTWELL, George (attrib) (1815-1901) American

£8176 $13000 €12264 Portrait of a young woman holding a rose (69x53cm-27x21in) painted c.1845 lit. 1-Mar-3 North East Auctions, Portsmouth #533/R est:10000-15000

HARTWICH, Herman (1853-1926) American

£1408 $2310 €2042 Women gathering sticks in southern Tyrol (53x38cm-21x15in) s.i.d.1887. 4-Jun-3 Fischer, Luzern #1158/R est:2400-2800 (S.FR 3000)

HARTWICK, George Gunther (attrib) (19th C) American

£528 $850 €792 Two men viewing a river landscape (38x48cm-15x19in) 23-Feb-3 Skinner, Boston #4/R

HARTWIG, Heinie (1937-) American

£252 $400 €378 Country sunset. s. 8-Mar-3 Harvey Clar, Oakland #1152
£256 $400 €384 Indian encampment, dusk (13x28cm-5x11in) s. board. 20-Sep-2 Freeman, Philadelphia #112/R
£272 $425 €408 Mountain lake (15x28cm-6x11in) s. masonite. 14-Sep-2 Selkirks, St. Louis #131
£272 $425 €408 Teepees in landscape at dusk (15x30cm-6x12in) s. masonite. 14-Sep-2 Selkirks, St. Louis #133
£272 $425 €408 River and mountains (13x28cm-5x11in) s. board. 20-Sep-2 Freeman, Philadelphia #88/R
£353 $550 €530 Above the canyon (15x28cm-6x11in) s. masonite. 14-Sep-2 Selkirks, St. Louis #132
£370 $600 €555 Indian camp under sunset skies (51x76cm-20x30in) s. board. 24-Jan-3 Freeman, Philadelphia #184/R
£484 $750 €726 Wilderness home (43x58cm-17x23in) s. i.verso masonite. 7-Dec-2 Neal Auction Company, New Orleans #859/R
£513 $800 €770 Camp at early dawn (15x28cm-6x11in) s. masonite. 12-Oct-2 Neal Auction Company, New Orleans #1425
£599 $1000 €869 Indians in landscape (15x30cm-6x12in) s. i.verso. 17-Jun-3 John Moran, Pasadena #106 est:1000-1500
£609 $950 €914 Teepees near a mountain lake (51x76cm-20x30in) s. masonite. 14-Sep-2 Selkirks, St. Louis #130
£1065 $1650 €1598 Day of rest (53x84cm-21x33in) s. masonite. 21-Jul-2 Jeffery Burchard, Florida #88/R
£1218 $1900 €1827 Indians camping by a mountain lake. 21-Sep-2 Harvey Clar, Oakland #1517
£1603 $2500 €2405 Indian encampment (61x91cm-24x36in) s. panel prov. 9-Nov-2 Santa Fe Art, Santa Fe #140/R est:4000-6000
£2244 $3500 €3366 Indian encampment (58x43cm-23x17in) s. masonite. 12-Oct-2 Neal Auction Company, New Orleans #1424/R est:1500-2000
£2404 $3750 €3606 Cold winter (8x8cm-3x3in) s. panel prov. 9-Nov-2 Santa Fe Art, Santa Fe #139/R est:3000-4000
£6962 $11000 €10095 Majestic mountain (76x114cm-30x45in) s. board. 26-Jul-3 Coeur d'Alene, Hayden #231/R est:5000-10000

HARTWIG, Max (1873-1939) German

£458 $732 €700 Red deer on forest edge (58x74cm-23x29in) s. 10-Jan-3 Allgauer, Kempten #1611/R

HARTZ, Lauritz (1903-1987) Danish

£677 $1050 €1016 Summer house, Nordstrand (64x80cm-25x31in) init. 1-Oct-2 Rasmussen, Copenhagen #329/R (D.KR 8000)
£1267 $1976 €1901 Trees, early spring (68x84cm-27x33in) init.d.1964 exhib. 18-Sep-2 Kunsthallen, Copenhagen #31/R est:15000 (D.KR 15000)
£1487 $2349 €2231 Landscape with trees and bushes (58x79cm-23x31in) init. 1-Apr-3 Rasmussen, Copenhagen #556/R est:15000 (D.KR 16000)
£1689 $2635 €2534 Landscape, Gronnehave (66x80cm-26x31in) init.d.64 exhib. 18-Sep-2 Kunsthallen, Copenhagen #32/R est:18000 (D.KR 20000)

HARUNOBU, Suzuki (1724-1770) Japanese

Prints

£11538 $18000 €17307 Beauty seated holding a pipe, a kamuro next to her (28x21cm-11x8in) col print. 25-Mar-3 Christie's, Rockefeller NY #10/R est:18000-22000

HARVEG, Rino (1918-) Norwegian

£346 $530 €519 Landscape from Nesland in Rauland (73x92cm-29x36in) s. panel painted 1943-44. 26-Aug-2 Blomqvist, Lysaker #1151 (N.KR 4000)

HARVEN, Alice de (?) ?

Works on paper

£513 $795 €800 Jeune fille et son chat (62x50cm-24x20in) s. pastel oval. 9-Dec-2 Horta, Bruxelles #330

HARVEY, Alice and Isabella (19th C) Irish?

Works on paper

£1042 $1656 €1500 Topographical landscapes of Donegal (37x61cm-15x24in) s.i.d.1854 W/C pen ink set of 9. 29-Apr-3 Whyte's, Dublin #177/R est:1500-2000

HARVEY, G (20th C) American

£2885 $4500 €4328 San Francisco de le Espado (61x51cm-24x20in) 9-Nov-2 Altermann Galleries, Santa Fe #228

£5449 $8500 €8174 Yellow awning (33x25cm-13x10in) 9-Nov-2 Altermann Galleries, Santa Fe #222
£16026 $25000 €24039 When chores are done (61x91cm-24x36in) 9-Nov-2 Altermann Galleries, Santa Fe #62

HARVEY, George (1800-1878) American
£3313 $5500 €4804 Peaches in a basket. Pears and grapes. Plums. (29x44cm-11x17in) s. one d.1909 five prov. 11-Jun-3 Butterfields, San Francisco #4024/R est:4000-6000
Works on paper
£2642 $4200 €3963 Florida Keys (23x39cm-9x15in) s. W/C. 4-Mar-3 Christie's, Rockefeller NY #20/R est:6000-8000

HARVEY, Gerald (1933-) American
£3082 $4500 €4623 Johnson Creek (51x61cm-20x24in) 18-May-2 Altermann Galleries, Santa Fe #207/R
£5137 $7500 €7706 Old Spicewood Spring road (61x91cm-24x36in) 18-May-2 Altermann Galleries, Santa Fe #206/R
£5195 $8000 €7793 Cow hoss from the spade (28x36cm-11x14in) 25-Oct-2 Morris & Whiteside, Hilton Head Island #177 est:7000-9000
£10274 $15000 €15411 59th and Fifth Avenue (30x23cm-12x9in) 18-May-2 Altermann Galleries, Santa Fe #241/R
Sculpture
£2466 $3600 €3699 Those that plunder (43cm-17in) one of 30 bronze. 18-May-2 Altermann Galleries, Santa Fe #157/R

HARVEY, Gertrude (1889-?) British
£400 $668 €580 Farm at Lelant Cornwall (33x39cm-13x15in) s. oil paper on board. 19-Jun-3 Lane, Penzance #210/R

HARVEY, H J (?) British
£300 $489 €450 Still life study of blue bowl holding orange marigolds (31x25cm-12x10in) s.i. 11-Feb-3 Fellows & Sons, Birmingham #11/R

HARVEY, H W (19th C) British
Works on paper
£660 $1023 €990 View of Nevis from Bapitere roads, St Kitts (33x43cm-13x17in) s. init.i.d.May 1825 verso W/C. 16-Jul-2 Bearnes, Exeter #416
£1650 $2508 €2475 Sea battle scenes between English and French men-o-war (60x86cm-24x34in) indis sig.d.1844 W/C pair. 17-Sep-2 Henry Adams, Chichester #108 est:800-1200
£2800 $4536 €4200 Glorious first of June (63x90cm-25x35in) s. one d.1844 pencil W/C pair. 21-May-3 Christie's, Kensington #417/R est:3000-5000

HARVEY, Harold (1874-1941) British
£600 $942 €900 Portrait of a seated lady, believed to be Gertrude Harvey (38x25cm-15x10in) init.i. 12-Dec-2 Richardson & Smith, Whitby #433
£3500 $5460 €5250 Outside the blacksmith's shop (25x36cm-10x14in) s.indis.d.1913. 17-Oct-2 David Lay, Penzance #1448/R est:3000-5000
£5000 $7750 €7500 Boatyard (71x97cm-28x38in) s.d.1921 panel prov.lit. 26-Sep-2 Lane, Penzance #295/R est:8000-12000
£7000 $10920 €10150 Spring in Cornwall (30x41cm-12x16in) s.d.1909 exhib.lit. 27-Mar-3 Lane, Penzance #65/R est:7000-8000
£12500 $19375 €18750 At the end of the day, mother with baby in a cradle (170x127cm-67x50in) s. 26-Sep-2 Lane, Penzance #50/R est:13000-16000
£15000 $23550 €22500 Feeding time (30x35cm-12x14in) s.d.08 lit. 22-Nov-2 Christie's, London #39/R est:15000-20000
£27000 $44280 €39150 One summer's day (76x61cm-30x24in) s.d.18 board. 4-Jun-3 Sotheby's, London #7/R est:15000-20000

HARVEY, John Rabone (1862-1933) British
£281 $443 €422 Men working in field with horses (43x50cm-17x20in) s. 30-Nov-2 Goteborg Auktionsverk, Sweden #180/R (S.KR 4000)

HARVEY, Marion Roger Hamilton (1886-1971) British
£2301 $3750 €3452 Rab, portrait of an English setter (51x67cm-20x26in) s. 11-Feb-3 Bonhams & Doyles, New York #229/R est:1500-2000
Works on paper
£300 $468 €450 Terrier (20x15cm-8x6in) s. ink W/C laid down. 10-Apr-3 Bonhams, Edinburgh #80
£360 $558 €540 Shelite, standing (40x46cm-16x18in) s. pastel. 7-Dec-2 Shapes, Edinburgh #305/R
£380 $593 €570 Sandy, long haired ginger cat (46x32cm-18x13in) s. chk. 10-Apr-3 Bonhams, Edinburgh #117
£400 $624 €600 Sooty and Smokey, long haired cats (39x49cm-15x19in) s. chk. 10-Apr-3 Bonhams, Edinburgh #118
£1227 $2000 €1841 Wei Elfann of Giffnock. Champion Yu-Fai of Giffnock, Pekinese portrait (29x41cm-11x16in) s.i. pastel black chk two prov. 11-Feb-3 Bonhams & Doyles, New York #233 est:1200-1800

HARVEY, Russell (1904-1963) South African
£1548 $2492 €2322 Portrait of a girl. Portrait of a boy (23x13cm-9x5in) s. board pair. 12-May-3 Stephan Welz, Johannesburg #72 est:2000-4000 (SA.R 18000)

HARVEY, Sir George (attrib) (1806-1876) British
£750 $1253 €1088 Young princes conversing in interior (53x79cm-21x31in) 20-Jun-3 Keys, Aylsham #769/R

HARWAY, John (19/20th C) British
£605 $962 €908 Gig with figures on beach (59x38cm-23x15in) s. 10-Mar-3 Rasmussen, Vejle #513/R (D.KR 6500)

HARWOOD, John (fl.1818-1829) British
£800 $1240 €1200 Crowded steamer coming into Ramsgate (43x53cm-17x21in) 31-Oct-2 Christie's, Kensington #457/R

HARWOOD, Lloyd (20th C) New Zealander
£825 $1286 €1238 Lady and the lighthouse (17x26cm-7x10in) s.d.2003 oil paint stick board. 27-Mar-3 International Art Centre, Auckland #3/R (NZ.D 2350)

HARWOOD, Lucy (1893-1972) British
£280 $468 €406 Sheep and labs in a landscape (61x49cm-24x19in) s.d.1939 verso. 19-Jun-3 Lane, Penzance #368
£320 $499 €464 Portrait of a young man. Study of a young auburn haired woman (14x11cm-6x4in) double-sided. 27-Mar-3 Neales, Nottingham #1032
£420 $655 €609 Still life of flowers and fruit (22x20cm-9x8in) 27-Mar-3 Neales, Nottingham #1028/R

HARY, Gyula (1864-?) Hungarian
£2048 $3276 €3072 Seashore in Italy (80x60cm-31x24in) s. 16-May-3 Kieselbach, Budapest #51/R (H.F 700000)

HARZE, Leopold (1831-1893) Belgian
Sculpture
£949 $1481 €1500 Homme se rasant (22x23cm-9x9in) s. terracotta hexagonal base. 16-Oct-2 Hotel des Ventes Mosan, Brussels #161 est:500-600
£5674 $9475 €8000 Dorine, bust de jeune femme. gilt bronze red marble sold with 2 candelabras. 17-Jun-3 Palais de Beaux Arts, Brussels #37/R est:6250-7500

HARZIC, Auguste F (1902-?) Algerian
£939 $1540 €1362 Paysage 25 (60x81cm-24x32in) s.d.Fevrier 1971. 4-Jun-3 Fischer, Luzern #2146/R est:1200-1500 (S.FR 2000)

HASBROUCK, Dubois Fenelon (1860-1934) American
£1013 $1600 €1520 Springtime, near Kingston, NY (33x48cm-13x19in) s.d.86 board. 17-Nov-2 CRN Auctions, Cambridge #48/R
£1258 $2000 €1887 Summer. Winter (10x14cm-4x6in) s.d.1895 board pair. 7-Mar-3 Skinner, Boston #263/R est:700-900

HASCH, Carl (1834-1897) Austrian
£577 $894 €900 Boat trip on Zellersee at the foot of the Grossglockner (20x29cm-8x11in) s. panel. 5-Dec-2 Dorotheum, Graz #20/R
£1438 $2358 €2200 Mountain lake in evening light with woman by shack (58x86cm-23x34in) s. 8-Feb-3 Hans Stahl, Hamburg #20/R est:2300

HASEGAWA, Kiyoshi (1891-1980) Japanese
Prints
£2083 $3250 €3125 Table devant la fenetre (33x25cm-13x10in) s.num.16/50 mezzotint executed c.1954/55. 21-Sep-2 Rachel Davis, Shaker Heights #80/R est:2500-3500

HASELTINE, Herbert (1877-1962) American
Sculpture
£8228 $13000 €11931 Citron - horse head (33cm-13in) s.d.1937 gold pat. bronze prov. 26-Jul-3 Coeur d'Alene, Hayden #92/R est:12000-18000
£29032 $45000 €43548 Suffolk punch stallion, Sudbourne premier (27cm-11in) gilt bronze gold pat. green marble base. 4-Dec-2 Sotheby's, New York #100/R est:25000-35000

HASELTINE, William Stanley (1835-1900) American
£129032 $200000 €193548 Rocks at Narragansett, Rhode Island (31x56cm-12x22in) init. prov. 5-Dec-2 Christie's, Rockefeller NY #30/R est:200000-300000
Works on paper
£10968 $17000 €16452 Great Head, Mt. Desert (38x55cm-15x22in) init.i. ink wash over pencil prov.exhib. 5-Dec-2 Christie's, Rockefeller NY #59/R est:10000-15000

HASEMANN, Wilhelm Gustav Friederich (1850-1913) German
£2516 $3925 €4000 Black Forest landscape (17x24cm-7x9in) s. panel prov. 19-Sep-2 Dr Fritz Nagel, Stuttgart #939/R est:1200
£9859 $14000 €14789 New kittens (64x51cm-25x20in) 8-Aug-1 Barridorf, Portland #32/R est:9000-12000
£11644 $18164 €17000 Two women resting in grass, Black Forest village beyond (46x37cm-18x15in) s. i. stretcher. 11-Apr-3 Winterberg, Heidelberg #400/R est:7400

HASENCLEVER, Johann Peter (1810-1853) German
£8974 $13910 €14000 Examination of Hieronymous Jobs (75x90cm-30x35in) s.d.1839 lit. 4-Dec-2 Neumeister, Munich #759/R est:15000

HASENPFLUG, Carl George Adolph (1802-1858) German
£15385 $23846 €24000 View of church ruins in winter (59x71cm-23x28in) s.d.1848. 4-Dec-2 Neumeister, Munich #760/R est:3500

HASLEN, Ken (?) ?
£419 $650 €629 View of sailboats in harbor (69x79cm-27x31in) s. 28-Sep-2 Thomaston Place, Thomaston #21

HASLUND, Ludvig (1847-1902) Norwegian
£341 $532 €512 Bridge by rapids (29x44cm-11x17in) s. 23-Sep-2 Blomqvist, Lysaker #1075 (N.KR 4000)

HASLUND, Otto (1842-1917) Danish
£255 $403 €383 Portrait of a child (48x40cm-19x16in) s.d.1904 exhib. 2-Dec-2 Rasmussen, Copenhagen #1276/R (D.KR 3000)
£2553 $4034 €3830 Two boys and a dog in Dyrehaven (56x92cm-22x36in) s.d.1884. 2-Dec-2 Rasmussen, Copenhagen #1103/R est:30000-40000 (D.KR 30000)
£2842 $4320 €4263 Poor people out collecting pine-cones for fire (101x121cm-40x48in) s.d.1889 exhib. 27-Aug-2 Rasmussen, Copenhagen #1892/R est:25000 (D.KR 33000)

HASS, Fritz (1902-?) German
£270 $422 €400 Winter landscape (30x40cm-12x16in) s. panel. 26-Mar-3 Hugo Ruef, Munich #301

HASS, Sigfred (1848-1908) Danish/German
£426 $660 €639 Norwegian coastal landscape in moonlight (64x96cm-25x38in) s.d.85. 28-Sep-2 Rasmussen, Havnen #2055/R (D.KR 5000)
£465 $725 €698 Wooded landscape with figure in spring (66x98cm-26x39in) s.d.90. 23-Sep-2 Rasmussen, Vejle #89/R (D.KR 5500)

HASSALL, John (1868-1948) British
Works on paper
£400 $620 €600 Nobody asked you to come (35x25cm-14x10in) s.i. card pen ink W/C. 25-Sep-2 Hamptons Fine Art, Godalming #258/R
£3000 $4740 €4500 Seven dwarfs (54x76cm-21x30in) s. W/C exhib. 2-Dec-2 Sotheby's, London #54/R est:5000-7000

HASSAM, Childe (1859-1935) American
£17405 $27500 €25237 West course, Maidstone (20x28cm-8x11in) s. 26-Jul-3 Coeur d'Alene, Hayden #217/R est:15000-25000
£19753 $32000 €29630 Incoming tide (84x94cm-33x37in) s.d.1919 init.d.verso prov. 22-May-3 Christie's, Rockefeller NY #58/R est:40000-60000
£240741 $390000 €361112 Walk around the Island (27x36cm-11x14in) s.d.1890 prov.exhib.lit. 21-May-3 Sotheby's, New York #56/R est:250000-350000
£339506 $550000 €509259 Rooftop garden, Paris (25x37cm-10x15in) s.d.1888 panel prov. 22-May-3 Christie's, Rockefeller NY #48/R est:300000-500000
£348387 $540000 €522581 Autumn boulevard, Paris (47x47cm-19x19in) s. exhib. 5-Dec-2 Christie's, Rockefeller NY #56/R est:500000-700000
Prints
£1887 $3000 €2831 Billboards, New York (12x16cm-5x6in) s. etching. 2-May-3 Sotheby's, New York #17/R est:2000-3000
£2201 $3500 €3302 House on Main Street, Easthampton (41x79cm-16x31in) s.i.d.1922 etching. 30-Apr-3 Doyle, New York #196/R est:1000-1500
£2215 $3500 €3323 Easthampton (19x29cm-7x11in) s.i. etching executed c.1917. 12-Nov-2 Doyle, New York #234/R est:1500-2500
£6918 $11000 €10377 Lion Gardiner House, Easthampton (25x36cm-10x14in) s.i. etching. 2-May-3 Sotheby's, New York #18/R est:8000-12000
Works on paper
£9615 $15000 €14423 Rustic landscape with bridge over a stream (33x38cm-13x15in) s.d.1901 W/C. 1-Aug-2 Eldred, East Dennis #988/R est:20000-40000
£11728 $19000 €17592 Horses of Actaeon, Montauk (22x29cm-9x11in) s.d.September 25 1921 W/C gouache prov. 21-May-3 Sotheby's, New York #139/R est:20000-30000
£15432 $25000 €23148 Home sweet home cottage (19x32cm-7x13in) s.i.d.1917 W/C gouache pencil on joined paper. 21-May-3 Sotheby's, New York #138/R est:15000-25000
£18750 $30000 €27188 Beal's Camp, Montauk (22x28cm-9x11in) s.i.d.1921 W/C prov. 16-May-3 Skinner, Boston #246/R est:50000-75000
£30645 $47500 €45968 Sunset, Old Lyme (23x29cm-9x11in) s.d.1916 W/C prov.exhib. 4-Dec-2 Sotheby's, New York #3/R est:40000-60000
£37037 $60000 €55556 Canterbury (36x25cm-14x10in) s.d.1889 W/C pencil gouache prov. 21-May-3 Sotheby's, New York #137/R est:25000-35000

HASSAM, Childe (attrib) (1859-1935) American
Works on paper
£701 $1100 €1052 Naples waterfront with tall stucco sided buildings and small boat (33x23cm-13x9in) s. W/C. 19-Apr-3 James Julia, Fairfield #251/R est:1500-2500

HASSAN, Muhammad (19th C) Persian
£24476 $40874 €35000 Portrait de jeune femme (142x90cm-56x35in) s. canvas laid down. 26-Jun-3 Claude Boisgirard, Paris #254/R

HASSE, Isa (1884-1962) German
£443 $700 €700 Remberti tunnel at night (55x65cm-22x26in) mono. 29-Nov-2 Bolland & Marotz, Bremen #514/R

HASSEBRAUK, Ernst (1905-1974) German
£1122 $1638 €1750 Still life of peonies (77x99cm-30x39in) s. mixed media. 4-Jun-2 Karl & Faber, Munich #260/R est:3500
Works on paper
£833 $1317 €1200 Still life with wine glass (57x73cm-22x29in) s. mixed media board. 26-Apr-3 Dr Lehr, Berlin #186/R
£903 $1426 €1300 Still life with boxes (50x70cm-20x28in) s. mixed media board. 26-Apr-3 Dr Lehr, Berlin #187/R

HASSELBERG, Per (1850-1894) Swedish
Sculpture
£3928 $6441 €5696 The frog (39cm-15in) s. white marble incl. stone base lit. 4-Jun-3 AB Stockholms Auktionsverk #2380/R est:30000-40000 (S.KR 50000)
£4610 $7145 €6915 The frog (39cm-15in) s. white marble incl. stone base sold with pedestal. 4-Dec-2 AB Stockholms Auktionsverk #1827/R est:20000-25000 (S.KR 65000)

HASSELHORST, Johann Heinrich (1825-1904) German
Works on paper
£629 $975 €1000 Brother and sister (39x33cm-15x13in) s.d.1888 pencil oval. 1-Oct-2 Dorotheum, Vienna #105

HASSELL, H E (?) British?
Works on paper
£480 $730 €720 Moonlight in Camaes (48x69cm-19x27in) s. i.verso W/C. 14-Aug-2 Andrew Hartley, Ilkley #588

HASSELL, Hilton Macdonald (1910-1980) Canadian
£389 $603 €584 Conifer contrast, Madawaska (86x61cm-34x24in) s. masonite. 24-Sep-2 Ritchie, Toronto #3172a/R (C.D 950)
£569 $893 €854 Rue d'Auteuil, Quebec (46x56cm-18x22in) s. i.verso board. 10-Dec-2 Pinneys, Montreal #168 (C.D 1400)
£1244 $2041 €1866 Harbour, Country Down, Ireland (70x120cm-28x47in) s. board. 3-Jun-3 Joyner, Toronto #325/R est:2000-3000 (C.D 2800)
£1610 $2560 €2415 Eskimo settlement, Eastern Arctic (60x90cm-24x35in) s.i. acrylic on board prov. 23-Mar-3 Hodgins, Calgary #81/R est:2500-3500 (C.D 3800)
£1728 $2679 €2592 Children of Connemara (65x100cm-26x39in) s. board prov. 3-Dec-2 Joyner, Toronto #230/R est:2000-2500 (C.D 4200)

HASSELT, Willem van (1882-1963) Dutch
£478 $745 €750 Village by water (30x60cm-12x24in) s. panel. 7-Nov-2 Chochon-Barre & Allardi, Paris #165

HASSENTEUFEL, Hans (1887-1943) German
£321 $503 €500 Female nude before mountain landscape (100x80cm-39x31in) s. 21-Nov-2 Van Ham, Cologne #1657
£986 $1637 €1400 Female half-nude standing (101x70cm-40x28in) s. 14-Jun-3 Arnold, Frankfurt #762/R
£1800 $2826 €2700 Mandolin player (86x71cm-34x28in) i. 16-Apr-3 Christie's, Kensington #777/R est:2000-3000
£3600 $5616 €5400 Nude with water jug (100x70cm-39x28in) s.i. 26-Mar-3 Sotheby's, Olympia #285/R est:2000-3000

HASSETT, W R (19th C) American
£599 $1000 €869 Kentucky forest (23x30cm-9x12in) s.i.d.83 verso panel. 21-Jun-3 Charlton Hall, Columbia #516/R est:400-600

HASSLER, Carl von (1887-1962) American
£1763 $2750 €2645 Taos Indian (61x46cm-24x18in) s. prov. 9-Nov-2 Santa Fe Art, Santa Fe #44/R est:4000-6000
£3313 $5500 €4804 Autumn in Tesuque, New Mexico (49x66cm-19x26in) s. cardboard. 11-Jun-3 Butterfields, San Francisco #4122/R est:5000-7000
£3915 $6500 €5677 Snow in Pojoaque Valley, New Mexico (36x51cm-14x20in) s. board. 11-Jun-3 Butterfields, San Francisco #4123/R est:4000-6000

HASTAIRE (1946-) French
£556 $878 €800 Hommage a James Ensor (60x60cm-24x24in) s. s.i.d.verso acrylic collage. 28-Apr-3 Cornette de St.Cyr, Paris #411
£728 $1187 €1100 Fragments du XXeme siecle (60x60cm-24x24in) s. s.i.verso acrylic collage. 3-Feb-3 Cornette de St.Cyr, Paris #439
£949 $1472 €1500 Fragments du XXeme siecle, hommage a Warhol (60x60cm-24x24in) s. s.i.verso acrylic collage. 28-Sep-2 Cornette de St.Cyr, Paris #333 est:1200-1500
£1108 $1717 €1750 Fragments du XXeme siecle, Magritte (60x60cm-24x24in) s. s.i.d.verso acrylic collage. 28-Sep-2 Cornette de St.Cyr, Paris #332 est:1200-1500

HASTINGS, Edward (fl.1804-1827) British
£1500 $2445 €2175 Death of the poet Chatterton (61x74cm-24x29in) s. prov.lit. 21-Jul-3 Sotheby's, London #343/R est:2000-3000

HASTINGS, Matthew (1834-1919) American
£1299 $2000 €1949 In Arcadia (56x46cm-22x18in) s. painted c.1870. 8-Sep-2 Treadway Gallery, Cincinnati #527/R est:4000-6000

HASUI, Kawase (1883-1957) Japanese
Prints
£2201 $3500 €3302 Night rain, Teradomari (39x26cm-15x10in) s. col woodcut. 24-Mar-3 Christie's, Rockefeller NY #219/R est:2500-3000
£2830 $4500 €4245 Evening snow (30x28cm-12x11in) s. woodcut. 24-Mar-3 Christie's, Rockefeller NY #217/R est:5000-7000
£3500 $5845 €5075 Ryotei villa by the pine tree pond (19x48cm-7x19in) s. 18-Jun-3 Christie's, London #353/R est:3500-3800
£3774 $6000 €5661 River bank, Komagata (26x39cm-10x15in) s. col woodcut. 24-Mar-3 Christie's, Rockefeller NY #211/R est:2500-3000
£3800 $6346 €5510 Small boat in the rain (19x38cm-7x15in) s. 18-Jun-3 Christie's, London #354/R est:3500-3800
Works on paper
£2564 $4000 €3846 Lingering snow at Urayasu (53x50cm-21x20in) s.d.1945 W/C pencil. 25-Mar-3 Christie's, Rockefeller NY #395/R est:4000-6000
£2564 $4000 €3846 Kisoji Suhara in rain (57x42cm-22x17in) s.i.d.1951 W/C. 25-Mar-3 Christie's, Rockefeller NY #396/R est:4000-6000
£5769 $9000 €8654 Iwai Bridge at Sakiyama, Tochigi prefecture (57x41cm-22x16in) s. W/C. 25-Mar-3 Christie's, Rockefeller NY #394/R est:4000-6000

HASZARD, Rhona (1901-1931) New Zealander
£7879 $12133 €11819 London street scene (35x25cm-14x10in) s. canvas on board. 4-Sep-2 Dunbar Sloane, Wellington #71/R est:3000-4000 (NZ.D 26000)

HATCH, Lorenzo James (1857-1914) American
£353 $550 €530 Clouds gathering over a hillside (41x51cm-16x20in) s.d.1904. 20-Sep-2 Freeman, Philadelphia #121/R

HATFIELD, J A (19th C) British
Sculpture
£3484 $5400 €5226 Group of grapplers (74cm-29in) s.d.1862 bronze wooden plinth. 2-Oct-2 Christie's, Rockefeller NY #729/R est:5000-7000

HATHERELL, William (1855-1928) British
Works on paper
£800 $1328 €1200 Summer girl (19x30cm-7x12in) s.i. pencil sold with dr. by Percy Angelo Staynes lit. 12-Jun-3 Sotheby's, London #270/R

HATOUM, Mona (1952-) Palestinian
Photographs
£18000 $30060 €26100 Roadworks, performance-still (76x108cm-30x43in) num.10/15 verso gelatin silver print aluminium prov.lit. 26-Jun-3 Sotheby's, London #297/R est:18000-25000
Sculpture
£4375 $7000 €6563 Rubber mat (3x78x56cm-1x31x22in) rubber silicone executed 1996 prov. 14-May-3 Sotheby's, New York #349/R est:8000-12000
£6452 $10000 €9678 Rubber mat (3x78x55cm-1x31x22in) silicone rubber executed 1996 prov.exhib. 26-Sep-2 Christie's, Rockefeller NY #895/R est:10000-15000

HATTAM, Harold Bickford (1913-1994) Australian
£3365 $5351 €5048 Boats and shore, Shoreham (66x81cm-26x32in) s.d.84 i.verso. 4-Mar-3 Deutscher-Menzies, Melbourne #65/R est:6000-8000 (A.D 8750)
£6923 $11008 €10385 Sand dunes, Shoreham (99x121cm-39x48in) s. 4-Mar-3 Deutscher-Menzies, Melbourne #64/R est:10000-14000 (A.D 18000)

HATTENDORF, H (19th C) American
Works on paper
£581 $900 €872 Landscape with a cart by the river (30x46cm-12x18in) s. W/C. 7-Dec-2 Neal Auction Company, New Orleans #450 est:900-1200

HATTERSLEY, Frederick William (1859-?) British
Works on paper
£400 $616 €600 Preparing for a move (34x24cm-13x9in) s. W/C. 22-Oct-2 Bonhams, Knightsbridge #176/R
£600 $924 €900 Criccieth beach, North Wales (24x35cm-9x14in) s. W/C. 22-Oct-2 Bonhams, Knightsbridge #158/R
£600 $948 €900 Shepherds resting with their flock of sheep (24x34cm-9x13in) s. W/C. 27-Nov-2 Peter Wilson, Nantwich #134/R
£1000 $1550 €1500 Figures on a beach sorting the day's catch. Beach scene with fishermen (26x36cm-10x14in) s. pencil W/C pair. 4-Dec-2 Christie's, Kensington #54/R est:400-600
£1850 $2812 €2775 Hauling boats for repair. Good catch (25x33cm-10x13in) s.d.1920 W/C pair. 16-Aug-2 Keys, Aylsham #592/R

HATTON, E W (fl.1845-1859) British
Miniatures
£1100 $1716 €1650 Miss George wearing low cut blue dress with white gauze trim pink ribbon (8cm-3xin) s.d.1853 verso gilded frame oval. 5-Nov-2 Bonhams, New Bond Street #129/R est:800-1200

HATTON, Irene (fl.1937) British
Works on paper
£244 $373 €366 Adam and Eve (54x36cm-21x14in) s. W/C. 21-Aug-2 Dunbar Sloane, Auckland #559 (NZ.D 800)

HATVANY, Ferencz (1881-1958) Hungarian
£2581 $4000 €3872 Floral still life (94x89cm-37x35in) s. 28-Sep-2 Charlton Hall, Columbia #183/R est:5000-7000

HATZ, Felix (1904-1999) Swedish
£420 $656 €630 Landscape (38x46cm-15x18in) s.d.45 panel. 6-Nov-2 AB Stockholms Auktionsverk #715/R (S.KR 6000)

HAU, Woldemar (1816-1895) Russian
Works on paper
£4200 $6804 €6300 Portrait of Grand Duchess Alexandre Alexandrovna (16x11cm-6x4in) s.d.1845 pencil W/C htd white. 21-May-3 Sotheby's, London #1/R est:2500-3500
£4200 $6804 €6300 Portrait of a lady by a piano (24x19cm-9x7in) s.d.1846 W/C htd white. 21-May-3 Sotheby's, London #12/R est:4000-6000

£4200 $6888 €6300 Two children seated on a perambulator (27x21cm-11x8in) s.d.1841 pencil W/C htd white. 5-Jun-3 Christie's, Kensington #859/R est:300-900

HAUBTMANN, Michael (1843-1921) German/Czech
£4225 $6803 €6000 View over ruins to Etna (77x123cm-30x48in) s.d.1882. 7-May-3 Michael Zeller, Lindau #730/R est:3500

HAUCHECORNE, Philippe (1907-1976) French
£1370 $2151 €2000 Nadja (50x73cm-20x29in) s.i.d.62. 15-Apr-3 Laurence Calmels, Paris #4232/R

HAUCK, Friedrich Ludwig (1718-1801) German
£1056 $1701 €1500 Portrait of nobleman (85x69cm-33x27in) s.i.d.1766 verso. 7-May-3 Michael Zeller, Lindau #569/R est:1500

HAUG, Robert von (1857-1922) German
£577 $894 €900 Soldiers with horses in morning landscape (23x37cm-9x15in) s. board. 5-Dec-2 Dr Fritz Nagel, Stuttgart #659/R
£696 $1086 €1100 Man feeding horses (48x43cm-19x17in) s.d.1907 tempera. 18-Oct-2 Dr Fritz Nagel, Stuttgart #163/R
£755 $1177 €1200 Cavalry in extensive dune landscape (73x117cm-29x46in) s.d.16. 19-Sep-2 Dr Fritz Nagel, Stuttgart #940/R

HAUGEN-SORENSEN, Arne (1932-) Danish
£689 $1047 €1034 Abstract animal composition (29x22cm-11x9in) init.d.88. 3-Sep-2 Museumsbygningen, Copenhagen #520/R (D.KR 8000)
£1056 $1647 €1584 Composition (33x41cm-13x16in) init.d.72. 18-Sep-2 Kunsthallen, Copenhagen #142/R est:8000 (D.KR 12500)
£2695 $4258 €4043 Composition with reclining woman (70x70cm-28x28in) s.d.78-79. 1-Apr-3 Rasmussen, Copenhagen #214/R est:20000 (D.KR 29000)
£6041 $9545 €9062 Erotic figure composition with man and woman (97x195cm-38x77in) s.d.84. 1-Apr-3 Rasmussen, Copenhagen #193/R est:80000 (D.KR 65000)

Works on paper
£320 $509 €480 Composition (38x28cm-15x11in) init.d.85. 26-Feb-3 Kunsthallen, Copenhagen #71 (D.KR 3500)

HAUGEN-SORENSEN, Jorgen (1934-) Danish
Sculpture
£1605 $2503 €2408 Figure (59cm-23in) mono.d.60 bronze. 18-Sep-2 Kunsthallen, Copenhagen #199/R est:15000 (D.KR 19000)

HAUGHTON, Moses (attrib) (18/19th C) British
£1100 $1716 €1650 Hope. Peace (22x27cm-9x11in) oil metal on panel oval pair. 7-Nov-2 Christie's, Kensington #222/R est:800-1200

HAUGHTON, Wilfred (1921-) Irish
Works on paper
£360 $526 €540 Cows grazing by a haystack (25x36cm-10x14in) s. pastel. 12-Jun-2 John Ross, Belfast #280

HAUKANESS, Lars (1863-1929) Canadian
£391 $610 €653 French Indian woman from Berens Rivers Reservation, Manitoba (25x36cm-10x14in) s. canvasboard prov. 13-Apr-3 Levis, Calgary #45/R est:900-1200 (C.D 900)

HAUKELAND, Arnold (1920-1983) Norwegian
Sculpture
£13841 $21869 €20762 Dynamite (121x26x47cm-48x10x19in) s.d.61 bronze exhib.lit. 2-Dec-2 Blomqvist, Oslo #440/R est:100000-140000 (N.KR 160000)

HAUMONT, Emile Richard (19/20th C) French
£795 $1295 €1200 Bretonne se rendant a l'eglise (104x80cm-41x31in) s.d.84. 2-Feb-3 Muizon & Le Coent, Paris #46

HAUNOLD, Carl (1832-1911) Austrian
£440 $682 €700 Eisenerz church, Steiermark (33x39cm-13x15in) mono. canvas on masonite. 29-Oct-2 Dorotheum, Vienna #163/R
£609 $926 €950 Alpine landscape (32x50cm-13x20in). 31-Aug-2 Geble, Radolfzell #636/R
£694 $1104 €1000 Trees (33x27cm-13x11in) 29-Apr-3 Wiener Kunst Auktionen, Vienna #533/R
£1090 $1722 €1700 Evening on the Donau near Deutsch Altenburg (20x33cm-8x13in) mono. i.d.1899 verso board. 16-Nov-2 Lempertz, Koln #1473/R est:1500

HAUNSTETTER, Josef (20th C) German?
£449 $696 €700 Sunlit Watzmann on summer's day (81x105cm-32x41in) s. 6-Dec-2 Michael Zeller, Lindau #784/R

HAUPTMANN, Ivo (1886-1973) German
£392 $643 €600 North Sea (31x41cm-12x16in) W/C. 8-Feb-3 Hans Stahl, Hamburg #127
£1132 $1766 €1800 Still life with pears (33x46cm-13x18in) s.d.46. 21-Sep-2 Bolland & Marotz, Bremen #705/R
£1831 $3039 €2600 Still life of flowers (65x54cm-26x21in) mono.d. 14-Jun-3 Hauswedell & Nolte, Hamburg #1224/R est:2500

Works on paper
£481 $760 €750 View of Agnetendorf from Wiesenstein (46x50cm-18x20in) s.d.1921 W/C over chk. 15-Nov-2 Reiss & Sohn, Konigstein #540/R
£575 $943 €880 Antibes (33x42cm-13x17in) W/C. 8-Feb-3 Hans Stahl, Hamburg #128/R
£641 $1013 €1000 Bathers (50x41cm-20x16in) s.d.1921 W/C over chk. 15-Nov-2 Reiss & Sohn, Konigstein #538/R
£779 $1138 €1200 Winter in Switzerland (38x46cm-15x18in) s.d.1963 W/C. 15-Jun-2 Hans Stahl, Hamburg #185/R
£948 $1554 €1450 Lakeside (32x41cm-13x16in) s.d.1958 brush. 8-Feb-3 Hans Stahl, Hamburg #129/R est:750
£974 $1422 €1500 Harbour scene with sailing boats near the jetty (38x46cm-15x18in) s.d.1968 W/C. 15-Jun-2 Hans Stahl, Hamburg #184/R

HAUPTMANN, Ivo (attrib) (1886-1973) German
£2009 $3154 €3014 Landscape (38x42cm-15x17in) s.d.1920 board double-sided. 25-Nov-2 Germann, Zurich #730/R est:1500-1800 (S.FR 4600)

HAUPTMANN, Karl (1880-1947) German
£568 $886 €852 Crossroads in the mountains (60x50cm-24x20in) s. panel. 6-Nov-2 Dobiaschofsky, Bern #636/R (S.FR 1300)
£769 $1192 €1200 Winter's day in the Black Forest (24x34cm-9x13in) s. lit. 6-Dec-2 Karlheinz Kaupp, Staufen #2028/R
£929 $1441 €1450 Extensive sunny winter landscape (26x39cm-10x15in) s. board lit. 6-Dec-2 Karlheinz Kaupp, Staufen #2320/R
£1026 $1590 €1600 Lake in snowy Black Forest (50x70cm-20x28in) s. lit. 6-Dec-2 Karlheinz Kaupp, Staufen #2041/R est:500
£1310 $2070 €1965 Black Forest in winter (32x41cm-13x16in) s. board. 14-Nov-2 Stuker, Bern #272/R est:3500-4000 (S.FR 3000)
£1410 $2186 €2200 Heavy snow in Black Forest valley (71x90cm-28x35in) s. lit. 6-Dec-2 Karlheinz Kaupp, Staufen #2352 est:2100
£1474 $2285 €2300 Snow-covered Black Forest landscape in sunlight (70x90cm-28x35in) s. 4-Dec-2 Neumeister, Munich #761/R est:2500
£1761 $2835 €2500 Woodland (70x80cm-28x31in) s.d.35 i. verso panel. 9-May-3 Schloss Ahlden, Ahlden #1532/R est:3200
£1887 $2943 €3000 Black Forest valley with farmsteads in evening (42x64cm-17x25in) s.d.17 lit. 20-Sep-2 Karlheinz Kaupp, Staufen #2044/R est:3500
£1899 $3000 €3000 Black Forest winter landscape with farmhouses in the sunshine (70x90cm-28x35in) s.d.37. 30-Nov-2 Geble, Radolfzell #666 est:3000
£1931 $3051 €2800 Snowy Black Forest landscape (61x71cm-24x28in) s. 2-Apr-3 Dr Fritz Nagel, Stuttgart #9477/R est:3900
£2230 $3478 €3300 Snowy winter landscape near Bernau in the Black Forest (70x89cm-28x35in) s.d.37. 27-Mar-3 Dr Fritz Nagel, Stuttgart #814/R est:3000
£4088 $6377 €6500 First snow on Schauinsland (70x90cm-28x35in) s. lit. 20-Sep-2 Karlheinz Kaupp, Staufen #1958/R est:5000

HAUS, Hendrik Manfried (1803-1843) Dutch
Works on paper
£529 $772 €794 Skaters on winter canal (19x25cm-7x10in) s.d.1839 W/C. 17-Jun-2 Philippe Schuler, Zurich #4802/R (S.FR 1200)

HAUSDORF, Georg (20th C) German
£281 $450 €422 Winter landscape (64x76cm-25x30in) s. 15-Mar-3 Selkirks, St. Louis #672/R

HAUSEN, Werner von (1870-1951) Finnish
£264 $409 €420 Ice in spring (35x49cm-14x19in) s.d.1942. 6-Oct-2 Bukowskis, Helsinki #180/R
£294 $482 €450 Summer idyll (40x59cm-16x23in) s.d.1898. 9-Feb-3 Bukowskis, Helsinki #250/R

HAUSER, Carry (1895-1985) Austrian
Works on paper
£285 $444 €450 Diana Bad (13x19cm-5x7in) mono. gouache. 15-Oct-2 Dorotheum, Vienna #74/R
£285 $444 €450 Happy Easter (14x9cm-6x4in) gouache. 15-Oct-2 Dorotheum, Vienna #71/R

£288 $456 €450 Jesus child (21x13cm-8x5in) s. pen brush Indian ink gouache board. 12-Nov-2 Dorotheum, Vienna #91/R
£288 $456 €450 Under the clouds (30x48cm-12x19in) mono.i.d.66 chk. 12-Nov-2 Dorotheum, Vienna #208/R
£288 $472 €400 Self portrait (23x17cm-9x7in) s.d.21 W/C. 5-Jun-3 Dorotheum, Salzburg #819/R
£331 $540 €500 Boys swimming in the sea (30x44cm-12x17in) s.i.d.84 pencil W/C. 28-Jan-3 Dorotheum, Vienna #225/R
£475 $741 €750 Pirano from the air (39x29cm-15x11in) s.i.mono.d.30 pencil W/C. 15-Oct-2 Dorotheum, Vienna #75/R
£475 $741 €750 Self (48x35cm-19x14in) s.i.mono.d.31. 15-Oct-2 Dorotheum, Vienna #77/R
£521 $823 €750 Girl - head (28x20cm-11x8in) s.mono.i.d.56 biro W/C. 24-Apr-3 Dorotheum, Vienna #153/R
£563 $918 €850 Konni from Frankfurt (39x27cm-15x11in) mono.i.d.59 mixed media. 28-Jan-3 Dorotheum, Vienna #124/R
£1042 $1646 €1500 Portrait of girl (22x16cm-9x6in) mono.d.23 pencil W/C bodycol. 24-Apr-3 Dorotheum, Vienna #63/R est:1600-2000

HAUSER, Johann (1926-1996) German
Works on paper
£617 $1000 €926 Untitled (20x29cm-8x11in) s.d.27.9.1972 col pencil prov. 27-Jan-3 Christie's, Rockefeller NY #105/R est:2500-3000
£617 $1000 €926 Lion head (22x30cm-9x12in) s.d.12.7.93 pencil prov.exhib. 27-Jan-3 Christie's, Rockefeller NY #106/R est:1500-2000
£617 $1000 €926 Untitled - square (29x39cm-11x15in) s. col pencil sold with etching. 27-Jan-3 Christie's, Rockefeller NY #107/R est:2000-2500
£828 $1324 €1200 Four armed Caspar (28x21cm-11x8in) s.d.22.4.67 col pen two. 11-Mar-3 Dorotheum, Vienna #198/R est:600-850
£926 $1500 €1389 Untitled - elephant (20x30cm-8x12in) s. pencil prov.exhib. 27-Jan-3 Christie's, Rockefeller NY #110/R est:3000-5000
£926 $1500 €1389 Untitled - grey shark (22x30cm-9x12in) s. graphite crayon prov.exhib. 27-Jan-3 Christie's, Rockefeller NY #112/R est:3000-5000
£1235 $2000 €1853 Red square (22x30cm-9x12in) s.d.4.7.1973 crayon pencil prov.exhib. 27-Jan-3 Christie's, Rockefeller NY #108/R est:2500-3000

HAUSER, John (1859-1913) American
£2201 $3500 €3302 Visit in camp, Pine Ridge Reservation South Dakota (30x46cm-12x18in) s.d.1909 i.verso canvas on board prov. 5-Mar-3 Sotheby's, New York #158/R est:8000-12000
£2673 $4250 €4010 Chief Big Ghost, Sioux (30x20cm-12x8in) s.d.1912 s.d.verso board prov. 5-Mar-3 Sotheby's, New York #159/R est:6000-8000
£9677 $15000 €14516 Sioux encampment, Porcupine (30x46cm-12x18in) s.d.1910 canvas on board prov. 5-Dec-2 Christie's, Rockefeller NY #157/R est:15000-25000

Works on paper
£2244 $3500 €3366 Indian on horse back taking aim in desert landscape (28x20cm-11x8in) s. gouache. 20-Oct-2 Jeffery Burchard, Florida #28/R
£3145 $5000 €4718 Pueblo Village (46x30cm-18x12in) s.i.d.1905 W/C gouache. 5-Mar-3 Sotheby's, New York #129/R est:6000-8000
£3571 $5500 €5357 Indian rider (33x23cm-13x9in) s.d.1902 gouache. 8-Sep-2 Treadway Gallery, Cincinnati #577/R est:8000-10000
£3774 $6000 €5661 Chief blue horse (36x25cm-14x10in) s.d.1905 s.i.verso W/C gouache paper on board. 5-Mar-3 Sotheby's, New York #131/R est:4000-6000

HAUSER, Renée-Yolande (1919-) Swiss
£261 $404 €392 Dried flowers (80x60cm-31x24in) s. masonite. 9-Dec-2 Philippe Schuler, Zurich #8725 (S.FR 600)
£349 $545 €524 Dried summer flowers in vase (61x35cm-24x14in) s. panel. 6-Nov-2 Dobiaschofsky, Bern #637/R (S.FR 800)

HAUSERMANN, Charles (1886-1938) Swiss
£330 $528 €495 Still life (45x66cm-18x26in) mono. 17-Mar-3 Philippe Schuler, Zurich #8445 (S.FR 700)

HAUSFELDT, Hans (1902-1977) German
£252 $392 €400 Figures by Ploer See (29x43cm-11x17in) board. 21-Sep-2 Bolland & Marotz, Bremen #604/R

HAUSHALTER, George M (1862-?) American
£313 $500 €470 Portrait of a young boy (46x36cm-18x14in) s. 11-Jan-3 James Julia, Fairfield #538

HAUSMANN, Gustav (1827-1899) German
£2564 $4000 €3846 Lauter Brennenthal River Valley, Switzerland. 21-Sep-2 Harvey Clar, Oakland #1404
£3082 $4808 €4900 High mountain landscape (80x124cm-31x49in) mono.d.1863 lit. 20-Sep-2 Schloss Ahlden, Ahlden #1120/R est:4500

HAUSMANN, Raoul (1886-1971) Austrian
£2536 $4159 €3500 12 July 1960 (92x73cm-36x29in) mono.d.60 i.d.12.VII.59 verso exhib. 29-May-3 Lempertz, Koln #657/R est:3600

HAUSTRAETE, Gaston (1878-1949) Belgian
£355 $561 €550 Coin de Bruxelles (54x65cm-21x26in) s. 17-Dec-2 Palais de Beaux Arts, Brussels #547
£360 $576 €500 Bords d'etang au coucher du soleil (67x63cm-26x25in) s. 19-May-3 Horta, Bruxelles #53/R
£385 $596 €600 Bateaux de peche a Blankenberge (50x60cm-20x24in) s.d.24. 9-Dec-2 Horta, Bruxelles #323
£419 $663 €650 Village ardennais (80x70cm-31x28in) s. 17-Dec-2 Galerie Moderne, Brussels #638
£445 $695 €650 Automne (50x82cm-20x32in) s. 14-Apr-3 Horta, Bruxelles #9
£458 $737 €700 Vase de fleurs (58x73cm-23x29in) s.d.1919 panel. 14-Jan-3 Vanderkindere, Brussels #58
£506 $790 €800 Vue du moulin (50x40cm-20x16in) s. 16-Sep-2 Horta, Bruxelles #410
£753 $1175 €1100 Coucher de soleil sur l'etang (66x81cm-26x32in) s.d.1900. 14-Apr-3 Horta, Bruxelles #8
£755 $1170 €1200 Elegante devant le miroir (100x80cm-39x31in) s.d.1926. 1-Oct-2 Palais de Beaux Arts, Brussels #482
£1042 $1719 €1500 Sailing vessels on a rough sea by a pier (80x100cm-31x39in) s. 1-Jul-3 Christie's, Amsterdam #148/R est:1500-2000
£1079 $1727 €1500 Bouquet de fleurs sur une table (70x80cm-28x31in) s.d.32. 13-May-3 Palais de Beaux Arts, Brussels #263 est:1500-2000
£1258 $2051 €1900 Vase chinois fleuri (120x100cm-47x39in) s.d.24. 17-Feb-3 Horta, Bruxelles #122
£2158 $3453 €3000 Vue de Parc de Bruxelles sous la neige (53x64cm-21x25in) s. 19-May-3 Horta, Bruxelles #52/R est:3000-4000

HAUTEKIET, Edmond (?) ?
£540 $863 €750 Plage d'hiver (85x125cm-33x49in) s. 13-May-3 Palais de Beaux Arts, Brussels #264/R

HAUTH, Emil van (1899-1974) German
£1972 $3175 €2800 City (32x41cm-13x16in) s. panel lit. 9-May-3 Schloss Ahlden, Ahlden #1547/R est:2800

HAUTRIVE, Mathilde Marguerite (1881-1963) French
£1336 $2097 €1950 Peniche sur la Seine a Bougival (50x65cm-20x26in) s.d.1936 s.verso. 21-Apr-3 Rabourdin & Choppin de Janvry, Paris #151 est:800-1000

Works on paper
£449 $704 €700 Lac au Bois de Vincennes (37x45cm-15x18in) s. gouache. 16-Dec-2 Chochon-Barre & Allardi, Paris #70

HAVARD, James (1937-) American
Works on paper
£1258 $2000 €1887 Hopi mask (40x32cm-16x13in) s.d. mixed media board. 4-May-3 Treadway Gallery, Cincinnati #568/R est:3000-5000

HAVEKOST, Eberhard (1967-) American
£12025 $19000 €18038 Driver 2 (130x90cm-51x35in) s.i.d.01 verso prov.exhib. 14-Nov-2 Christie's, Rockefeller NY #322/R est:15000-20000

HAVELKA, Roman (1877-1950) Czechoslovakian
£268 $419 €402 Winter landscape (17x24cm-7x9in) s. cardboard. 12-Oct-2 Dorotheum, Prague #69 (C.KR 13000)

HAVELL, Alfred C (1855-1928) British
£943 $1546 €1367 Horse and buggy with dog (29x55cm-11x22in) s. 4-Jun-3 AB Stockholms Auktionsverk #2462/R (S.KR 12000)
£15500 $25110 €23250 Steeplechasing, traditionally identified as Racing in Ireland (76x128cm-30x50in) mono. prov. 22-May-3 Christie's, London #20/R est:8000-12000

HAVELL, Edmund (jnr) (1819-1894) British
£2500 $3850 €3750 Lace seller (43x35cm-17x14in) s.d.1864 painted oval. 5-Sep-2 Christie's, Kensington #305/R est:1000-1500

HAVELL, R (19th C) ?
Prints
£4444 $7200 €6444 Black skimmer or shearwater (53x53cm-21x21in) hand col etching engraving aquatint after J J Audubon. 22-May-3 Sotheby's, New York #886
£6296 $10200 €9129 Florida cormorant (50x67cm-20x26in) hand col etching aquatint engraving after J J Audubon. 22-May-3 Sotheby's, New York #882
£7037 $11400 €10204 Gannet (63x96cm-25x38in) hand col etching aquatint engraving after J J Audubon. 22-May-3 Sotheby's, New York #887
£8889 $14400 €12889 Frigate pelican (38x66cm-15x26in) hand col etching engraving aquatint after J J Audubon. 22-May-3 Sotheby's, New York #885
£19259 $31200 €27926 Hooping crane (95x63cm-37x25in) hand col etching engraving aquatint after J J Audubon. 22-May-3 Sotheby's, New York #883

£25926 $42000 €37593 Wood ibiss (38x25cm-15x10in) hand col etching aquatint engraving after J J Audubon. 22-May-3 Sotheby's, New York #880
£29630 $48000 €42964 Hooping crane (99x66cm-39x26in) hand col etching aquatint engraving after J J Audubon. 22-May-3 Sotheby's, New York #884
£62963 $102000 €91296 Snowy heron or white egret (65x53cm-26x21in) hand col etching engraving after J J Audubon. 22-May-3 Sotheby's, New York #881

HAVELL, Robert (19th C) British
Prints
£2609 $4200 €3914 Rose breasted grosbeak (65x52cm-26x20in) hand col engraving aquatint after John James Audubon. 16-Jan-3 Christie's, Rockefeller NY #10/R est:4000-6000
£2981 $4800 €4472 American goldfinch (50x31cm-20x12in) hand col engraving aquatint after John James Audubon. 16-Jan-3 Christie's, Rockefeller NY #7/R est:2000-3000
£4348 $7000 €6522 Falco Washingtoniensis (97x65cm-38x26in) hand col engraving aquatint after John James Audubon. 16-Jan-3 Christie's, Rockefeller NY #5/R est:4000-6000
£8696 $14000 €13044 Black bellied darter (98x65cm-39x26in) hand col engraving aquatint after John James Audubon. 16-Jan-3 Christie's, Rockefeller NY #13/R est:12000-16000
£9317 $15000 €13976 White heron (65x97cm-26x38in) hand col engraving aquatint after John James Audubon. 16-Jan-3 Christie's, Rockefeller NY #15/R est:18000-22000
£34161 $55000 €51242 American white pelican (97x66cm-38x26in) hand col engraving aquatint after John James Audubon. 16-Jan-3 Christie's, Rockefeller NY #12/R est:40000-60000

HAVELL, William (1782-1857) British
Works on paper
£700 $1155 €1015 View on the River Wye near Monmouth (51x69cm-20x27in) i.verso W/C over pencil htd scratching out. 2-Jul-3 Sotheby's, Olympia #221/R
£900 $1431 €1350 Harbour at Mumbai Bombay, India (19x48cm-7x19in) W/C prov. 29-Apr-3 Bonhams, New Bond Street #63/R

HAVEN, Franklin de (1856-1934) American
£478 $750 €717 Twilight (30x40cm-12x16in) s. indis d. 22-Nov-2 Skinner, Boston #78/R
£710 $1100 €1065 Sheep at twilight (50x86cm-20x34in) s.d.1892. 3-Dec-2 Christie's, Rockefeller NY #601/R
£818 $1300 €1227 Wash day (41x51cm-16x20in) s.d. 2-Mar-3 Toomey, Oak Park #605/R
£897 $1400 €1346 Farmer plowing a field (41x51cm-16x20in) s.d.1897. 14-Sep-2 Weschler, Washington #612/R est:1000-1500
£1161 $1800 €1742 Rocky coast (61x76cm-24x30in) s. 3-Dec-2 Christie's, Rockefeller NY #599/R est:2000-3000

HAVERMAET, Charles van (fl.1895-1911) British
£949 $1481 €1500 Sweet relax (23x42cm-9x17in) s. panel. 15-Oct-2 Horta, Bruxelles #200

HAVERMANN, Hendrik Johannes (1857-1928) Dutch
£833 $1308 €1300 Reclining nude woman (39x74cm-15x29in) s. 25-Nov-2 Glerum, Amsterdam #164/R

HAVERS, Alice (1850-1890) British
£3000 $4680 €4500 Tis a very good world (36x42cm-14x17in) s. prov. 17-Sep-2 Sotheby's, Olympia #181/R est:3000-5000

HAVERTY, Joseph Patrick (1794-1864) British
£3478 $5704 €4800 Portrait of the children of John J Blake (60x50cm-24x20in) 28-May-3 Bonhams & James Adam, Dublin #21/R est:5000-8000

HAVET, Henri-Charles-Julien (1862-1913) French
£612 $978 €850 Campement dans le desert, Orientaliste (31x45cm-12x18in) s. panel. 19-May-3 Horta, Bruxelles #178

HAVILAND, Paul (1880-1950) American
Photographs
£1899 $3000 €2849 New York at night (16x18cm-6x7in) photogravure prov.lit. 25-Apr-3 Phillips, New York #204/R est:1500-2500

HAVLICEK, Vincenz (1864-1914) Austrian
Works on paper
£314 $487 €500 Landscape with farmsteads and mountains beyond (16x24cm-6x9in) W/C paper on board. 1-Oct-2 Dorotheum, Vienna #344/R
£472 $731 €750 Mountain landscape (74x58cm-29x23in) s.d.1912. 1-Oct-2 Dorotheum, Vienna #151/R
£1216 $1897 €1800 Krems and the Donau (20x35cm-8x14in) s. W/C. 28-Mar-3 Dorotheum, Vienna #275/R est:1200-1500

HAVSTEEN-MIKKELSEN, Sven (1912-1999) Danish
£803 $1237 €1205 Jesus on the Cross (40x51cm-16x20in) init. 23-Oct-2 Kunsthallen, Copenhagen #135/R (D.KR 9500)
£1106 $1748 €1659 Landscape with houses against blue sky (38x54cm-15x21in) init. 27-Nov-2 Museumsbygningen, Copenhagen #546/R est:6000-8000 (D.KR 13000)
£1394 $2203 €2091 Evening sky, autumn 1953, Haroy, west coast of Norway (39x51cm-15x20in) init. 1-Apr-3 Rasmussen, Copenhagen #575/R est:12000-15000 (D.KR 15000)

HAWAY, Georges (1941-) Belgian
£340 $569 €480 La Batte a Liege (50x60cm-20x24in) s. 18-Jun-3 Hotel des Ventes Mosan, Brussels #259

HAWES, Charles (?-1998) American
Works on paper
£1026 $1600 €1539 Nude burlesque dancer backstage applying talcum to breast (56x36cm-22x14in) s. gouache. 9-Nov-2 Illustration House, New York #134/R est:1000-3000

HAWKINS, Dennis (1925-) British
£800 $1312 €1200 Orient yellow and violet (122x76cm-48x30in) s.d.1964 i.verso board on panel sold with W/C by same hand. 6-Jun-3 Christie's, London #114/R

HAWKINS, Edward Mack Curtis (1877-?) American
£253 $400 €367 Twilight (18x25cm-7x10in) board. 5-Apr-3 DeFina, Austinburg #1302
£380 $600 €551 Harp of the winds (18x25cm-7x10in) s.d.1912 board. 5-Apr-3 DeFina, Austinburg #1304

HAWKINS, G M (20th C) ?
£1100 $1793 €1650 Lido, Margate (50x76cm-20x30in) s.d.1929. 17-Feb-3 Bonhams, Bath #111 est:300-400

HAWKINS, H F Weaver (1893-1977) Australian/British
£430 $654 €645 Untitled (49x40cm-19x16in) s.d.51 i.verso composition board. 28-Aug-2 Deutscher-Menzies, Melbourne #211/R (A.D 1200)
£430 $654 €645 High wind (45x38cm-18x15in) s.d.59 i.verso composition board. 28-Aug-2 Deutscher-Menzies, Melbourne #212/R (A.D 1200)
£430 $654 €645 Activity (44x36cm-17x14in) s.d.58 i.verso composition board. 28-Aug-2 Deutscher-Menzies, Melbourne #213/R (A.D 1200)
£860 $1308 €1290 Salome (49x40cm-19x16in) s.d.47 canvasboard. 28-Aug-2 Deutscher-Menzies, Melbourne #210/R (A.D 2400)
£1938 $3081 €2907 Cultivating (42x59cm-17x23in) s.d.43 s.i.verso board. 5-May-3 Sotheby's, Melbourne #261/R est:5000-8000 (A.D 5000)
£2688 $4085 €4032 Pilot, atomic power (44x37cm-17x15in) s.i.verso board painted c.1947. 28-Aug-2 Deutscher-Menzies, Melbourne #208/R est:8000-12000 (A.D 7500)
£4480 $6810 €6720 Group with reproduction (44x54cm-17x21in) s.d.50 i.verso canvasboard. 28-Aug-2 Deutscher-Menzies, Melbourne #207/R est:10000-14000 (A.D 12500)
£8462 $13454 €12693 Full tilt (61x78cm-24x31in) s.d.54 composition board exhib.lit. 4-Mar-3 Deutscher-Menzies, Melbourne #94/R est:25000-35000 (A.D 22000)
Works on paper
£357 $561 €536 Good samaritan (50x24cm-20x9in) s.d.55 gouache pencil prov.exhib. 25-Nov-2 Christie's, Melbourne #451/R (A.D 1000)
£1008 $1602 €1512 Footballers I (55x75cm-22x30in) s.d.66 W/C. 5-May-3 Sotheby's, Melbourne #279/R est:2500-3500 (A.D 2600)
£1163 $1849 €1745 Steeple chase (54x70cm-21x28in) s.d.68 ink W/C. 5-May-3 Sotheby's, Melbourne #277/R est:2000-3000 (A.D 3000)

HAWKINS, Henry (19th C) British
£24000 $38640 €36000 Crucifixion (115x183cm-45x72in) prov.exhib.lit. 20-Feb-3 Christie's, London #218/R est:50000

HAWKINS, James (20th C) British
Works on paper
£400 $632 €600 Mountain loch (30x53cm-12x21in) W/C collage. 18-Dec-2 Mallams, Oxford #592/R

HAWKINS, Louis Welden (1849-1910) British
£586 $938 €850 Landscape with little donkeys (24x32cm-9x13in) s.i. panel. 15-Mar-3 De Vuyst, Lokeren #153
£1702 $2689 €2553 Girl with knitting, houses in background (53x81cm-21x32in) s. panel. 2-Dec-2 Rasmussen, Copenhagen #1754/R est:25000 (D.KR 20000)
Works on paper
£3038 $4739 €4800 La fileuse (44x28cm-17x11in) s. W/C gouache exec.c.1895. 20-Oct-2 Mercier & Cie, Lille #331/R est:4500-5000

HAWKINS, O John (1935-) Canadian
£741 $1148 €1112 Colour and light show (80x120cm-31x47in) s. acrylic painted 1989 prov. 3-Dec-2 Joyner, Toronto #297/R est:1000-1500 (C.D 1800)

HAWKINS, William (1895-1990) American
£18519 $30000 €27779 Willard Hotel (122x152cm-48x60in) s.i. enamel on masonite painted c.1987 prov.exhib.lit. 27-Jan-3 Christie's, Rockefeller NY #93/R est:30000-40000
£21605 $35000 €32408 Jerusalem (117x152cm-46x60in) s.i. enamel on masonite prov. 27-Jan-3 Christie's, Rockefeller NY #85/R est:40000-60000

HAWKINSON, Tim (1960-) American
Sculpture
£5000 $8000 €7500 Perspector - mirror self portrait (104x34x8cm-41x13x3in) s.d.1999 verso polyurethane foam on mirrored surface prov. 14-May-3 Sotheby's, New York #321/R est:10000-15000

HAWKSETT, John (attrib) (19th C) Irish
£600 $930 €900 Visionary (40x32cm-16x13in) s.i.verso. 3-Dec-2 Sotheby's, Olympia #55/R

HAWKSWORTH, William Thomas Martin (1853-1935) British
£450 $738 €675 Country lane scene with figures (33x61cm-13x24in) s. 7-Feb-3 Biddle & Webb, Birmingham #85

HAWLEY, Hughson (1850-1936) American
Works on paper
£250 $400 €375 View of the Wellington Inn, with figures, a cart, a donkey and market stall (18x20cm-7x8in) s.d.1872 W/C. 13-Mar-3 Duke & Son, Dorchester #121
£700 $1064 €1050 Exeter Cathedral (76x58cm-30x23in) s.d.1915 pencil W/C htd white. 4-Jul-2 Mellors & Kirk, Nottingham #811

HAWLEY, Peter (20th C) American
Works on paper
£2795 $4500 €4193 Boy pouring sugar from cart as mother shops (53x43cm-21x17in) s. gouache board. 10-May-3 Illustration House, New York #132/R est:5000-7000

HAWORTH, Bobs Cogill (1904-1988) Canadian
£186 $292 €279 Autumn showers (51x64cm-20x25in) s. board. 24-Jul-2 Walker's, Ottawa #229/R (C.D 450)
£311 $510 €451 Untitled - rolling hills (51x64cm-20x25in) acrylic board. 1-Jun-3 Levis, Calgary #51/R (C.D 700)
£333 $546 €500 Black fleet rides an Atlantic swell (50x62cm-20x24in) s. acrylic board. 3-Jun-3 Joyner, Toronto #377/R (C.D 750)
£489 $802 €709 Northern reflections (50x63cm-20x25in) s. acrylic board. 9-Jun-3 Hodgins, Calgary #198/R est:900-1200 (C.D 1100)
£543 $848 €906 Untitled - self portrait (64x56cm-25x22in) s. bears i. prov. 13-Apr-3 Levis, Calgary #47/R est:1800-2200 (C.D 1250)
Works on paper
£206 $319 €309 Quebec landscape (25x35cm-10x14in) s.d.39 pencil prov. 3-Dec-2 Joyner, Toronto #406 (C.D 500)

HAWORTH, Peter (1889-1986) Canadian
£356 $583 €534 October fiesta (50x62cm-20x24in) s. board. 3-Jun-3 Joyner, Toronto #376/R (C.D 800)
£435 $678 €725 Sanctuary lake (56x76cm-22x30in) s. i.verso board prov. 13-Apr-3 Levis, Calgary #46/R est:1500-2000 (C.D 1000)
£3111 $5102 €4667 Pitit de gras, Cape Breton (57x62cm-22x24in) s. exhib. 3-Jun-3 Joyner, Toronto #171/R est:3000-4000 (C.D 7000)
£3333 $5467 €5000 St. Irenee (57x62cm-22x24in) s. 3-Jun-3 Joyner, Toronto #146/R est:4000-6000 (C.D 7500)
Works on paper
£322 $502 €483 Fog, Little Anse, Cape Breton (37x56cm-15x22in) s. W/C. 25-Mar-3 Ritchie, Toronto #120 (C.D 750)
£444 $729 €666 Tress (49x47cm-19x19in) s. W/C. 3-Jun-3 Joyner, Toronto #370/R est:600-800 (C.D 1000)

HAWTHORNE, Charles W (1872-1930) American
£2215 $3500 €3323 Blond boy (36x28cm-14x11in) estate st. prov. 24-Apr-3 Shannon's, Milford #214/R est:3000-5000
£17742 $27500 €26613 Provincetown Harbour (43x49cm-17x19in) s. panel prov. 4-Dec-2 Sotheby's, New York #49/R est:15000-20000

HAXTON, Elaine Alys (1909-1999) Australian
£607 $935 €911 Pisa (23x13cm-9x5in) board. 3-Sep-2 Shapiro, Sydney #383 est:2000-3000 (A.D 1700)
£615 $978 €923 Avalon beach (18x40cm-7x16in) board painted c.1984. 4-Mar-3 Deutscher-Menzies, Melbourne #97/R (A.D 1600)
£766 $1203 €1149 Self portrait (48x40cm-19x16in) s. board prov. 15-Apr-3 Lawson Menzies, Sydney #157/R est:2500-3500 (A.D 2000)
£1290 $1961 €1935 Boy at boatshed, Pittwater (30x20cm-12x8in) bears another sig. board prov. 28-Aug-2 Deutscher-Menzies, Melbourne #225/R est:4000-6000 (A.D 3600)
£2033 $3211 €2948 Harlequin on horseback (45x35cm-18x14in) s.d.55 board. 22-Jul-3 Lawson Menzies, Sydney #152/R est:5000-7000 (A.D 5000)
£5714 $8857 €8571 Harlequin and horse (90x45cm-35x18in) s. board lit. 29-Oct-2 Lawson Menzies, Sydney #8/R est:20000-24000 (A.D 16000)
£8366 $13721 €12549 Girl with drawing (56x45cm-22x18in) s. composition board. 4-Jun-3 Deutscher-Menzies, Melbourne #57/R est:25000-30000 (A.D 21000)
Works on paper
£358 $545 €537 Umbrella Street, Japan (35x44cm-14x17in) s.d.69 W/C pastel pen ink prov. 28-Aug-2 Deutscher-Menzies, Melbourne #322/R (A.D 1000)
£464 $733 €696 Casse Noisette, 2nd scene (51x34cm-20x13in) s.i. pen ink gouache. 27-Nov-2 Deutscher-Menzies, Melbourne #216/R est:1500-2000 (A.D 1300)
£1214 $1919 €1821 Sailing on Pittwater (35x25cm-14x10in) s.d.70 i.verso mixed media. 26-Nov-2 Sotheby's, Melbourne #126/R est:1500-2500 (A.D 3400)

HAY, Bernard (1864-?) British/Italian
£513 $795 €800 Neapolitan fisher-boy peeling an orange (40x24cm-16x9in) s.i. 7-Dec-2 Dannenberg, Berlin #670/R
£513 $795 €800 Young Neapolitan girl with grapes in a basket (40x24cm-16x9in) s.i. 7-Dec-2 Dannenberg, Berlin #671/R
£881 $1365 €1400 Southern Italian coastal landscape (29x17cm-11x7in) s. panel. 29-Oct-2 Dorotheum, Vienna #67/R
£1100 $1793 €1650 Portrait of an Italian beauty (46x27cm-18x11in) s.i. panel. 29-Jan-3 Sotheby's, Olympia #281/R est:800-1200
£1700 $2754 €2550 Coast of Capri (61x105cm-24x41in) s. 20-May-3 Sotheby's, Olympia #385/R est:1000-1500
£1800 $2808 €2700 Off the coast, Southern Italy (78x48cm-31x19in) s. 17-Sep-2 Sotheby's, Olympia #203/R est:1200-1500
£1900 $3021 €2850 Along the Amalfi coast (40x25cm-16x10in) s.d.1906. 20-Mar-3 Christie's, Kensington #61/R est:2000-3000
£2000 $3160 €3000 Backstreet in Capri (45x30cm-18x12in) s. 14-Nov-2 Christie's, Kensington #298/R est:1200-1500

HAY, Cecil (1889-?) British
£580 $916 €870 Still life (50x60cm-20x24in) s.d.29. 14-Nov-2 Bonhams, Edinburgh #323
£600 $954 €900 Flowers and ceramics (51x61cm-20x24in) s.d.29 prov. 6-Mar-3 Christie's, Kensington #184/R

HAY, Charlotte (1798-?) Swedish
£2878 $4604 €4000 La Benediction (94x81cm-37x32in) s. 13-May-3 Vanderkindere, Brussels #49 est:2000-3000

HAY, Darlene (20th C) Canadian?
£578 $948 €838 Sage by road, early morning (109x145cm-43x57in) 1-Jun-3 Levis, Calgary #52/R est:900-1200 (C.D 1300)

HAY, George (1831-1913) British
£350 $557 €525 Haymaking (33x61cm-13x24in) s. indis d. canvasboard. 6-Mar-3 Christie's, Kensington #485/R

HAY, Peter Alexander (1866-1952) British
Works on paper
£5242 $8282 €7863 Kelpie (103x68cm-41x27in) s.d.1906 W/C. 18-Nov-2 Waddingtons, Toronto #170/R est:8000-10000 (C.D 13000)

HAY, Ralph W (fl.1919-1921) British
£300 $489 €450 Fife fishing village (37x52cm-15x20in) 14-Feb-3 Lyon & Turnbull, Edinburgh #108

HAY, Thomas Marjoribanks (1862-1921) British
£460 $750 €690 Glen Lednock, Comrie (23x33cm-9x13in) 14-Feb-3 Lyon & Turnbull, Edinburgh #84
Works on paper
£280 $454 €420 Noss Head Lighthouse, Cathness (15x22cm-6x9in) s.i. W/C. 21-Jan-3 Bonhams, Knightsbridge #288/R
£280 $445 €420 On the Lednach Camrie (36x53cm-14x21in) s.i.d.89 W/C. 30-Apr-3 Halls, Shrewsbury #234/R
£280 $445 €420 Loch Awe (25x46cm-10x18in) s.i.d.89 W/C htd white. 30-Apr-3 Halls, Shrewsbury #235/R
£280 $465 €406 Cattle on the wetlands (34x48cm-13x19in) s. W/C. 13-Jun-3 Lyon & Turnbull, Edinburgh #135
£380 $623 €570 Scottish moor (21x8cm-8x3in) s. W/C. 7-Jun-3 Shapes, Edinburgh #367
£420 $651 €630 River Tay, near Dunkeld, Perthshire (35x25cm-14x10in) s.d.XIII W/C. 24-Sep-2 Bonhams, Knightsbridge #232/R
£900 $1431 €1350 Highland Clachan. Approaching storm (18x25cm-7x10in) init.i. W/C. 30-Apr-3 Halls, Shrewsbury #227/R

HAY, William M (fl.1852-1881) British
£3000 $4680 €4500 Girl of Madiera (173x114cm-68x45in) s.d.87. 17-Sep-2 Sotheby's, Olympia #157/R est:3000-5000

HAY-CAMPBELL, Charles Duncan (1867-1936) New Zealander
£364 $560 €546 Harbour scene with man in wooden dinghy (59x49cm-23x19in) s. board. 4-Sep-2 Dunbar Sloane, Wellington #134 est:1000-2000 (NZ.D 1200)

HAYD, Karl (1882-1945) Austrian
£417 $658 €650 Dolls (34x48cm-13x19in) s. board. 18-Nov-2 Dorotheum, Linz #282/R

HAYDEN, Harold (20th C) American
£255 $400 €383 Untitled (16x20cm-6x8in) s.i.d. board. 19-Nov-2 Wright, Chicago #170/R

HAYDEN, Henri (1883-1970) French
£791 $1298 €1100 Girl with cat (46x38cm-18x15in) s. s.verso prov. 3-Jun-3 Christie's, Amsterdam #29/R est:1000-1500
£1139 $1800 €1800 Paysage du midi (38x46cm-15x18in) s. cardboard on canvas. 27-Nov-2 Lemoine & Ferrando, Paris #98/R est:1500-2000
£1154 $1812 €1800 Bouquet de roses blanches (30x46cm-12x18in) s. 13-Dec-2 Piasa, Paris #137
£1923 $2981 €3000 Paysage du midi (38x46cm-15x18in) s. plywood. 3-Dec-2 Christie's, Amsterdam #33/R est:2000-3000
£2517 $4102 €3800 Paysage vert (34x46cm-13x18in) s.d.1959. 3-Feb-3 Cornette de St.Cyr, Paris #303/R
£2885 $4529 €4500 Paysage mediterraneen (54x65cm-21x26in) s. 16-Dec-2 Rabourdin & Choppin de Janvry, Paris #45/R
£3265 $5192 €4800 Paysage du Rousillon d'Apt (46x65cm-18x26in) s.d.44 cardboard. 26-Feb-3 Artcurial Briest, Paris #205/R est:4000-4500
£4014 $6382 €5900 Nature morte aux pipes et a la revue de Paris (45x52cm-18x20in) s. cardboard. 24-Mar-3 Coutau Begarie, Paris #208/R
£4966 $7945 €7200 Lavandieres au bord de la riviere (49x64cm-19x25in) s. 12-Mar-3 Rabourdin & Choppin de Janvry, Paris #126/R
£5000 $7950 €7500 Nature morte (38x46cm-15x18in) s. board prov. 20-Mar-3 Sotheby's, Olympia #70/R est:5000-7000
£7000 $11130 €10500 Nature morte a l'artichaut (55x65cm-22x26in) s.d.52 s.d.verso prov. 20-Mar-3 Sotheby's, Olympia #65/R est:4000-6000
£22152 $35000 €35000 Nature morte (54x65cm-21x26in) s.d.1914 exhib. 29-Nov-2 Drouot Estimations, Paris #123/R est:25000
Works on paper
£720 $1174 €1080 Port Breton (29x23cm-11x9in) s. W/C over pencil executed c.1913 prov. 3-Feb-3 Bonhams, New Bond Street #14/R est:800-1200
£828 $1382 €1200 Paysage (31x48cm-12x19in) s.d. W/C Indian ink. 10-Jul-3 Artcurial Briest, Paris #17

HAYDON, Benjamin Robert (1786-1846) British
Works on paper
£300 $486 €450 Crowds watching a burning ship (23x34cm-9x13in) wash sketch verso double-sided. 21-Jan-3 Bonhams, Knightsbridge #65/R
£1800 $2970 €2610 Study of Wilkie's hand (29x22cm-11x9in) i. blk chk. 2-Jul-3 Sotheby's, Olympia #178/R est:300-400

HAYDON, Benjamin Robert (attrib) (1786-1846) British
£400 $668 €580 Falstaff with his friends (62x74cm-24x29in) 25-Jun-3 Cheffins, Cambridge #765

HAYE, Reinier de la (1640-1684) Dutch
£1282 $2013 €2000 Drinking coffee (40x35cm-16x14in) s. panel. 23-Nov-2 Arnold, Frankfurt #746/R est:6000

HAYEK, Hans von (1869-1940) Austrian
£725 $1188 €1000 Tropical valley (45x60cm-18x24in) s. i. stretcher prov. 29-May-3 Lempertz, Koln #658/R
£2083 $3437 €3000 Volendam fisherman looking over the harbour (80x60cm-31x24in) s.d.1906. 1-Jul-3 Christie's, Amsterdam #113/R est:1500-2000

HAYES, Arthur E (19th C) British
Works on paper
£320 $509 €480 Rural landscape (25x34cm-10x13in) s. W/C. 29-Apr-3 Bonhams, Knightsbridge #97a

HAYES, Claude (1852-1922) British
Works on paper
£260 $413 €390 Haymaking (26x35cm-10x14in) s. W/C. 4-Mar-3 Bearnes, Exeter #390
£260 $434 €377 Haymaking at Tewkesbury (24x30cm-9x12in) s. W/C. 25-Jun-3 Bonhams, Bury St Edmunds #494
£270 $419 €405 Child fishing from a bridge (23x15cm-9x6in) s.d.91 W/C. 31-Oct-2 Duke & Son, Dorchester #184
£320 $509 €480 Canal with barges (25x15cm-10x6in) s. W/C. 5-Mar-3 John Ross, Belfast #215
£340 $530 €510 River scene with cattle (20x43cm-8x17in) s. W/C. 9-Apr-3 Andrew Hartley, Ilkley #920
£350 $550 €525 Summer pastoral (35x51cm-14x20in) s. W/C. 15-Apr-3 Bonhams, Knowle #83
£360 $572 €540 Landscape with shepherd and flock near a windmill, farmstead, horse and cart (65x98cm-26x39in) s. W/C over pencil. 19-Mar-3 Rupert Toovey, Partridge Green #128/R
£380 $543 €570 Sheep grazing in a meadow, building beyond (18x25cm-7x10in) s. W/C. 28-Feb-2 Greenslade Hunt, Taunton #386/R
£380 $593 €570 Old Mill, Snettisham, Suffolk (31x46cm-12x18in) s. W/C. 9-Oct-2 Woolley & Wallis, Salisbury #26/R
£380 $627 €551 Cooling stream (22x34cm-9x13in) s. W/C. 1-Jul-3 Bearnes, Exeter #432/R
£412 $638 €618 Stroll by a mountain ringed lake (25x73cm-10x29in) s. W/C. 3-Dec-2 Ritchie, Toronto #3008/R est:900-1200 (C.D 1000)
£420 $655 €630 Horse and rider in a rural landscape (25x16cm-10x6in) s. pencil W/C htd white. 19-Sep-2 Christie's, Kensington #72
£456 $711 €684 View of a windmill and figure in a landscape (53x75cm-21x30in) s. W/C. 17-Sep-2 Peter Webb, Auckland #191/R est:1500-2500 (NZ.D 1500)
£460 $731 €690 Portrait of a young girl (25x17cm-10x7in) s. W/C. 5-Mar-3 Bonhams, Bury St Edmunds #250/R
£500 $790 €750 Near Walberwick (25x33cm-10x13in) s. W/C exhib. 13-Nov-2 Halls, Shrewsbury #362/R
£500 $815 €725 Landscape with sheep (23x34cm-9x13in) s. W/C. 16-Jul-3 Sotheby's, Olympia #48/R
£550 $869 €825 Figures amongst corn stocks (24x35cm-9x14in) s. W/C. 26-Nov-2 Bonhams, Knightsbridge #20/R
£597 $932 €950 Landscape (25x37cm-10x15in) s.d.1892 i.verso W/C htd white prov. 17-Sep-2 Whyte's, Dublin #60
£620 $967 €930 Good hay making day (23x34cm-9x13in) s. W/C htd white. 17-Oct-2 Christie's, Kensington #13
£700 $1085 €1050 Shepherd and his daughter (34x51cm-13x20in) s. W/C. 24-Sep-2 Bonhams, Knightsbridge #164/R
£755 $1177 €1200 Shepherding a flock of sheep. Gathering kelp. s. W/C pair. 17-Sep-2 Thomas Adams, Dublin #1
£1208 $1945 €1800 Rider leading a pack of horses down a country lane (27x36cm-11x14in) s. W/C over pencil. 18-Feb-3 Whyte's, Dublin #105/R est:1800-2200
£2436 $3849 €3800 Woodcutter in landscape with other figures (54x72cm-21x28in) s. W/C. 12-Nov-2 Mealy's, Castlecomer #1315
£3000 $4980 €4500 Haymaking (52x74cm-20x29in) s. W/C. 12-Jun-3 Bonhams, New Bond Street #651/R est:3000-5000

HAYES, David (20th C) American?
Sculpture
£1159 $1900 €1681 Dancing woman (130x48x89cm-51x19x35in) bronze prov. 1-Jun-3 Wright, Chicago #262/R est:3000-4000

HAYES, Edward (attrib) (1797-1864) British
£1656 $2550 €2600 Portrait of a young military officer (74x62cm-29x24in) 4-Sep-2 James Adam, Dublin #83/R est:4000-6000

HAYES, Edwin (1820-1904) British
£709 $1107 €1050 Off Kinsale harbour (8x23cm-3x9in) s. board. 26-Mar-3 James Adam, Dublin #2/R est:1000-1500
£1266 $1962 €2000 Sailing vessels nearing shore (15x20cm-6x8in) s. board. 25-Sep-2 James Adam, Dublin #111/R est:2500-3000
£2000 $3160 €3000 Bringing in the catch (18x30cm-7x12in) s. panel. 6-Apr-3 Lots Road, London #370/R est:1800-2200
£2686 $4217 €4029 Shipping in the channel (46x71cm-18x28in) s. 24-Jul-2 Walker's, Ottawa #22/R est:7000-8000 (C.D 6500)
£2800 $4564 €4200 Leaving harbour, stormy seas (23x32cm-9x13in) 14-Feb-3 Lyon & Turnbull, Edinburgh #34

£2866 $4500 €4299 Fishing in rough waters (41x61cm-16x24in) s. board. 23-Nov-2 Jackson's, Cedar Falls #19/R est:3000-5000
£3500 $5600 €5250 Schooner leaving Portsmouth Harbour (31x46cm-12x18in) s. i. indis d. verso prov. 16-May-3 Sotheby's, London #32/R est:4000-6000
£4000 $6480 €6000 Fishermen off the harbour mouth at Margate (36x61cm-14x24in) s. 21-May-3 Christie's, Kensington #606/R est:3000-5000
£4808 $7452 €7500 Sailing ships near harbour (45x68cm-18x27in) s. 3-Dec-2 Bonhams & James Adam, Dublin #21/R est:8000-10000
£5063 $7848 €8000 Sailing boats (31x62cm-12x24in) s. 25-Sep-2 James Adam, Dublin #69a/R est:6000-9000
£5128 $8051 €8000 In the North Sea (30x50cm-12x20in) s. panel prov. 19-Nov-2 Whyte's, Dublin #66/R est:5000-7000
£6711 $10805 €10000 Sailing ships nearing harbour (46x69cm-18x27in) s. 18-Feb-3 Whyte's, Dublin #91/R est:10000-12000
£6918 $10792 €11000 Harbour mouth (41x56cm-16x22in) s.d.1851. 17-Sep-2 Whyte's, Dublin #118/R est:9000-10000

Works on paper

£440 $695 €660 Fishing boat in a choppy sea with other vessels on the horizon (14x27cm-6x11in) s. W/C bodycol. 7-Apr-3 Bonhams, Bath #13
£541 $843 €800 Fishing smacks in choppy seas (19x27cm-7x11in) s. W/C. 26-Mar-3 James Adam, Dublin #1/R
£1689 $2804 €2449 Fishing boats off the coast (16x34cm-6x13in) s.d.86 W/C. 16-Jun-3 Waddingtons, Toronto #188/R est:1000-1500 (C.D 3800)
£1892 $2951 €2800 Stormy weather off the rocks, Howth, Ireland (21x48cm-8x19in) s. W/C. 26-Mar-3 James Adam, Dublin #3/R est:2500-3000
£1900 $3021 €2850 Sailing barge in a choppy sea (36x72cm-14x28in) s.d.1871 W/C. 26-Feb-3 Cheffins Grain & Comins, Cambridge #513/R
£2000 $3140 €3000 Yarmouth fishing boats leaving Gorleston (27x37cm-11x15in) s.i. W/C. 16-Dec-2 Sotheby's, Olympia #93/R est:1000-2000
£3481 $5396 €5500 Fishing boats (49x71cm-19x28in) s. W/C. 25-Sep-2 James Adam, Dublin #122/R est:4000-6000

HAYES, F William (1848-1918) British

£1000 $1550 €1500 Landscape with cattle watering (48x100cm-19x39in) s. 26-Sep-2 Mellors & Kirk, Nottingham #700/R est:800-1200
£1795 $2800 €2693 Evening on the Severn (102x168cm-40x66in) s.i.verso. 12-Apr-3 Weschler, Washington #506/R est:4000-6000

HAYES, Michael Angelo (1820-1877) British

Works on paper

£1150 $1898 €1668 Dragoons No. 3 (40x30cm-16x12in) i. pen ink W/C over pencil htd bodycol. 2-Jul-3 Sotheby's, Olympia #278/R est:1000-1500

HAYET, Louis (1854-1940) French

£346 $540 €550 Nature morte au pichet (16x22cm-6x9in) st.sig. cardboard lit. 11-Oct-2 Binoche, Paris #105
£377 $589 €600 Sous-bois (16x22cm-6x9in) cardboard lit. 11-Oct-2 Binoche, Paris #103
£535 $834 €850 Atelier du peintre a Cormeilles (12x17cm-5x7in) st.sig. cardboard lit. 11-Oct-2 Binoche, Paris #12/R
£629 $981 €1000 Village (17x12cm-7x5in) s. cardboard lit. 11-Oct-2 Binoche, Paris #58/R
£660 $1030 €1050 Roses tremieres (22x15cm-9x6in) s.d.1934 lit. 11-Oct-2 Binoche, Paris #14/R
£723 $1128 €1150 Marche (12x16cm-5x6in) s.d.1930 lit. 11-Oct-2 Binoche, Paris #55/R
£755 $1177 €1200 Etude de chats (37x52cm-15x20in) st.sig. cardboard lit. 11-Oct-2 Binoche, Paris #15/R
£818 $1275 €1300 Entree du village (22x16cm-9x6in) st.sig. cardboard lit. 11-Oct-2 Binoche, Paris #74/R
£943 $1472 €1500 Branches (16x22cm-6x9in) st.sig. cardboard lit. 11-Oct-2 Binoche, Paris #70/R
£1321 $2060 €2100 Nature morte aux fruits (17x12cm-7x5in) s.d.1935 canvas on cardboard lit. 11-Oct-2 Binoche, Paris #104
£1380 $2304 €2000 Place animee (19x28cm-7x11in) s. panel lit. 10-Jul-3 Artcurial Briest, Paris #132/R est:2000-3000
£1384 $2158 €2200 Place de la Concorde (20x13cm-8x5in) st.sig. lit. 11-Oct-2 Binoche, Paris #61
£1572 $2453 €2500 Femme cousant (20x11cm-8x4in) st.sig. cardboard lit. 11-Oct-2 Binoche, Paris #57/R
£1761 $2747 €2800 Toits (22x27cm-9x11in) st.sig. panel lit. 11-Oct-2 Binoche, Paris #60/R
£1887 $2943 €3000 Paysage (44x32cm-17x13in) st.sig. cardboard painted c.1895 lit. 11-Oct-2 Binoche, Paris #26/R
£2013 $3140 €3200 Etude de ciel (19x24cm-7x9in) st.sig. cardboard lit. 11-Oct-2 Binoche, Paris #21/R
£2013 $3140 €3200 Femme repassant (17x11cm-7x4in) st.sig. cardboard lit. 11-Oct-2 Binoche, Paris #56/R
£2830 $4415 €4500 Drac (67x95cm-26x37in) s.d.1901 cardboard on canvas exhib.lit. 11-Oct-2 Binoche, Paris #65/R
£3019 $4709 €4800 Paysage (25x52cm-10x20in) st.sig. cardboard lit. 11-Oct-2 Binoche, Paris #18/R
£3333 $5200 €5300 Paysage (31x47cm-12x19in) st.sig. cardboard lit. 11-Oct-2 Binoche, Paris #16/R
£4403 $6868 €7000 Deux femmes a la fenetre (51x37cm-20x15in) st.sig. cardboard lit. 11-Oct-2 Binoche, Paris #62/R est:8000-12000
£11950 $18642 €19000 Etude de ciel gris (27x45cm-11x18in) st.sig. cardboard painted 1888 lit. 11-Oct-2 Binoche, Paris #25/R est:12000-15000

Works on paper

£230 $373 €350 Personnages assis. st.sig. one htd col drs pair in one frame. 22-Jan-3 Tajan, Paris #47
£252 $392 €400 Etude de femme (17x10cm-7x4in) st.sig. crayon lit. 11-Oct-2 Binoche, Paris #82
£252 $392 €400 Etude de nurses au jardin public (15x23cm-6x9in) st.sig. W/C lit. 11-Oct-2 Binoche, Paris #102
£283 $442 €450 Comedien en costume rouge (18x23cm-7x9in) st.sig. crayon chl lit. 11-Oct-2 Binoche, Paris #37/R
£314 $491 €500 Spectacle (17x21cm-7x8in) s. col crayon exhib.lit. 11-Oct-2 Binoche, Paris #36
£314 $491 €500 Etude de femmes (15x23cm-6x9in) mono. W/C lit. 11-Oct-2 Binoche, Paris #101/R
£377 $589 €600 Projection publique (18x22cm-7x9in) st.sig. col crayon exhib.lit. 11-Oct-2 Binoche, Paris #50
£440 $687 €700 Homme debout de profil. Homme assis de dis (14x10cm-6x4in) st.sig. W/C crayon. 11-Oct-2 Binoche, Paris #33/R
£472 $736 €750 Au musee (19x12cm-7x5in) st.sig. W/C lit. 11-Oct-2 Binoche, Paris #6/R
£472 $736 €750 Marche (26x23cm-10x9in) st.sig. crayon lit. 11-Oct-2 Binoche, Paris #77/R
£503 $785 €800 Homme a la casquette assis. Homme au chapeau (14x10cm-6x4in) st.sig. W/C crayon pair lit. 11-Oct-2 Binoche, Paris #34/R
£503 $785 €800 Hommes assis (14x10cm-6x4in) W/C crayon pair. 11-Oct-2 Binoche, Paris #30/R
£503 $785 €800 Femme a l'ombrelle. Homme assis sur la plage (16x10cm-6x4in) st.sig. W/C crayon pair. 11-Oct-2 Binoche, Paris #29/R
£503 $785 €800 Paris, scene de rue (13x19cm-5x7in) s. crayon lit. 11-Oct-2 Binoche, Paris #45/R
£503 $785 €800 Homme assis sur banc public (19x15cm-7x6in) st.sig. crayon chl lit. 11-Oct-2 Binoche, Paris #88/R
£535 $834 €850 Scene de rue, Paris (13x19cm-5x7in) s. crayon lit. 11-Oct-2 Binoche, Paris #46/R
£566 $883 €900 Interior of museum, Louvre (22x18cm-9x7in) s. W/C lit. 11-Oct-2 Binoche, Paris #8/R
£566 $883 €900 Homme age assis sur un banc. Femme agee assise sur un banc (14x10cm-6x4in) st.sig. W/C crayon pair. 11-Oct-2 Binoche, Paris #31/R
£566 $883 €900 Hommes a la casquette sur la plage (13x10cm-5x4in) W/C crayon pair. 11-Oct-2 Binoche, Paris #32/R
£566 $883 €900 Homme assis. Femme assise (15x10cm-6x4in) st.sig. W/C crayon pair. 11-Oct-2 Binoche, Paris #27/R
£629 $981 €1000 Scene de rue, Paris (13x19cm-5x7in) s. crayon. 11-Oct-2 Binoche, Paris #49/R
£692 $1079 €1100 Riviere (9x16cm-4x6in) st.sig. W/C lit. pair. 11-Oct-2 Binoche, Paris #97
£696 $1100 €1100 Paysage (13x21cm-5x8in) st.sig. W/C. 26-Nov-2 Camard, Paris #36
£755 $1177 €1200 Scene de rue, Paris (13x19cm-5x7in) s. crayon lit. 11-Oct-2 Binoche, Paris #43
£786 $1226 €1250 Pont au change (16x12cm-6x5in) st.sig. W/C lit. 11-Oct-2 Binoche, Paris #99/R
£818 $1275 €1300 Concert (16x21cm-6x8in) s. col crayon exhib.lit. 11-Oct-2 Binoche, Paris #52/R
£881 $1374 €1400 Quatorze Juillet aux lampions (16x21cm-6x8in) s. col crayon exhib.lit. 11-Oct-2 Binoche, Paris #54/R
£943 $1472 €1500 Bord de l'eau (12x18cm-5x7in) st.sig. W/C lit. 11-Oct-2 Binoche, Paris #10/R
£975 $1521 €1550 DEux marchandes (10x17cm-4x7in) s. W/C lit. 11-Oct-2 Binoche, Paris #11/R
£1038 $1619 €1650 Marche du Temple (45x63cm-18x25in) st.sig. crayon lit. 11-Oct-2 Binoche, Paris #40/R
£1069 $1668 €1700 Interior (12x16cm-5x6in) s. W/C exhib.lit. 11-Oct-2 Binoche, Paris #3/R
£1069 $1668 €1700 Chemin (21x18cm-8x7in) mono. mixed media lit. 11-Oct-2 Binoche, Paris #23/R
£1069 $1668 €1700 Funerailles de Victor Hugo (18x21cm-7x8in) s. col crayon exhib.lit. 11-Oct-2 Binoche, Paris #53/R
£1132 $1766 €1800 Bouquet de fleurs (15x10cm-6x4in) st.sig. W/C lit. 11-Oct-2 Binoche, Paris #96
£1258 $1962 €2000 Mat (18x12cm-7x5in) st.sig. W/C lit. 11-Oct-2 Binoche, Paris #4/R
£1384 $2158 €2200 Fete a Menilmontant (18x21cm-7x8in) s. W/C exhib.lit. 11-Oct-2 Binoche, Paris #2/R
£1447 $2257 €2300 Jardin (22x19cm-9x7in) mono. mixed media lit. 11-Oct-2 Binoche, Paris #24/R
£1572 $2453 €2500 Au bord de l'Oise (26x35cm-10x14in) st.sig. W/C exhib.lit. 11-Oct-2 Binoche, Paris #5/R

HAYLLAR, Edith (1860-1948) British

£320000 $515200 €480000 Summer shower (53x44cm-21x17in) s.d.1883 panel prov.exhib.lit. 20-Feb-3 Christie's, London #104/R est:200000

HAYLLAR, J (19th C) British

Works on paper

£1923 $2808 €3000 Feeding mother (49x34cm-19x13in) s.d.1868 W/C. 10-Jun-2 Thomas Adams, Dublin #351

HAYLLAR, James (1829-1920) British

£1645 $2550 €2468 Interior with grandson on grandfather's lap (112x86cm-44x34in) s.d.1878. 24-Sep-2 Koller, Zurich #6606 est:4000-6000 (S.FR 3800)

£3800 $6232 €5510 Village gossip. Reformed character (34x25cm-13x10in) s.d.1877 oil on paper pair. 5-Jun-3 Christie's, London #138/R est:2000-3000
£7000 $11060 €10500 Keeping out the cold (112x87cm-44x34in) s. prov. 26-Nov-2 Christie's, London #128/R est:8000-12000
£7000 $11130 €10500 As careful as a mother (114x86cm-45x34in) s.d.1878 exhib. 6-Mar-3 Christie's, Kensington #558/R est:8000-12000
£35000 $56350 €52500 Only daughter (112x152cm-44x60in) s.d.1875 prov.exhib.lit. 20-Feb-3 Christie's, London #100/R est:30000

HAYLLAR, Jessica (1858-1940) British
£120000 $193200 €180000 Coming event (57x47cm-22x19in) s.d.1886 prov.exhib.lit. 20-Feb-3 Christie's, London #267/R est:150000

HAYLLAR, Kate (fl.1883-1898) British
Works on paper
£42000 $67620 €63000 Thing of beauty is a joy forever (34x25cm-13x10in) s.d.1890 pencil pen ink W/C htd white prov.exhib. 20-Feb-3 Christie's, London #263/R est:30000

HAYLLAR, Mary (fl.1880-1885) British
£22000 $35420 €33000 For a good boy (41x29cm-16x11in) s.d.1880 prov.exhib. 20-Feb-3 Christie's, London #262/R est:18000

HAYLLOR, J (19th C) British
£265 $411 €398 Tides reach with cottages (19x28cm-7x11in) s.d.September 2 1893 board. 26-Sep-2 Locke & England, Leamington Spa #334

HAYLS, John (circle) (?-1679) British
£10500 $16695 €15750 Portrait of two children, one in satin gown and the other in nursery clothes (130x105cm-51x41in) 19-Mar-3 Sotheby's, London #23/R est:6000-8000

HAYMAN, Francis (1708-1776) British
£10000 $15800 €15000 Portrait of Sir Henry Paulet Saint-John in landscape with gun and spaniel (77x104cm-30x41in) i. prov.lit. 27-Nov-2 Christie's, London #23/R est:10000-15000

HAYMAN, Patrick (1915-1988) British
£550 $875 €825 Mother and child valley and hills (39x29cm-15x11in) s. board. 18-Mar-3 Bonhams, Knightsbridge #100
£650 $1034 €975 Holy Family (33x43cm-13x17in) s. 18-Mar-3 Bonhams, Knightsbridge #99
£1300 $2067 €1950 Bride and groom (51x63cm-20x25in) s. board. 18-Mar-3 Bonhams, Knightsbridge #103 est:700-1000
£3000 $4770 €4500 Blind man (50x60cm-20x24in) s. 18-Mar-3 Bonhams, Knightsbridge #101 est:500-700
Works on paper
£280 $445 €420 Townscape at dusk with mother and child (28x22cm-11x9in) s.d.57 gouache. 18-Mar-3 Bonhams, Knightsbridge #102
£420 $655 €630 Birds and trees (13x18cm-5x7in) s. ink W/C prov. 16-Oct-2 David Lay, Penzance #292/R
£528 $871 €766 Clam tips near St. Anstell (12x21cm-5x8in) s.d.1957 ink gouache W/C. 1-Jul-3 Peter Webb, Auckland #97/R est:2000-3000 (NZ.D 1500)

HAYMSON, John (1902-1980) American
£314 $500 €471 New York stock exchange (76x61cm-30x24in) s. 5-Mar-3 Doyle, New York #31/R

HAYNES, Douglas Hector (1936-) Canadian
£201 $317 €302 Winter forms (84x71cm-33x28in) d.1959 acrylic. 1-Dec-2 Levis, Calgary #313/R (C.D 500)

HAYNES, John William (fl.1852-1882) British
£582 $908 €850 Faggot gatherer in evening light by edge of wood (38x76cm-15x30in) bears sig. 10-Apr-3 Van Ham, Cologne #1468/R
£2500 $3900 €3750 First, the only one (36x46cm-14x18in) s. i.d.1859 verso. 6-Nov-2 Bonhams, Chester #446/R est:2000-3000
£4500 $7515 €6525 Fisherman's home (64x76cm-25x30in) s.d.80 s.i.verso. 17-Jun-3 Bonhams, New Bond Street #56/R est:5000-7000

HAYS, Barton S (1826-1914) American
£774 $1200 €1161 Apples and peaches on a table top (36x51cm-14x20in) s. 29-Oct-2 John Moran, Pasadena #623
£2548 $4000 €3822 Still life with grapes, peaches and pears (30x46cm-12x18in) s. prov. 19-Nov-2 Butterfields, San Francisco #8007/R est:3000-5000

HAYS, Dan (1966-) British
£950 $1548 €1425 Guinea pig (16x22cm-6x9in) s.d.2000 verso. 3-Feb-3 Sotheby's, Olympia #38/R est:400-600

HAYS, George Arthur (1854-1934) American
£892 $1400 €1338 Landscape of Flagstaff, Maine with tall mountains and winding stream (46x61cm-18x24in) s. 19-Apr-3 James Julia, Fairfield #19/R est:1500-2500

HAYS, George Arthur (attrib) (1854-1934) American
£974 $1500 €1461 Landscape with cows (38x48cm-15x19in) 6-Sep-2 Douglas, South Deerfield #3

HAYS, William Jacob (snr) (1830-1875) American
£5161 $8000 €7742 Dakota Badlands (35x62cm-14x24in) oil pencil board painted 1860. 3-Dec-2 Phillips, New York #39/R est:10000-15000
£14194 $22000 €21291 Basket of strawberries (24x22cm-9x9in) s.d.1859 board prov. 5-Dec-2 Christie's, Rockefeller NY #18/R est:15000-25000
£32258 $50000 €48387 Buffalo hunt (66x122cm-26x48in) s.d.1872 prov.exhib. 5-Dec-2 Christie's, Rockefeller NY #158/R est:30000-50000

HAYTER, John (1800-1891) British
£2800 $4424 €4200 Portrait of Edward Norman. Portrait of Mrs Edward Norman (91x72cm-36x28in) pair. 12-Nov-2 Bonhams, Knightsbridge #246/R est:2500-3500
Works on paper
£700 $1141 €1015 Portraits of Mr and Mrs William Angerstein (45x30cm-18x12in) s.d.1844 s.d.1845 col.chk. brown paper pair prov. 21-Jul-3 Sotheby's, London #482

HAYTER, Sir George (1792-1871) British
£11000 $17490 €16500 Portrait of Queen Victoria, seated in ceremonial robes (89x67cm-35x26in) s.d.1838 prov. 6-Mar-3 Christie's, Kensington #376/R est:5000-8000
£16667 $27833 €23500 Portrait de la Comtesse Arthur de la Bourdonnaye (198x163cm-78x64in) s.d.1830. 18-Jun-3 Piasa, Paris #14/R est:25000-28000

HAYTER, Sir George (attrib) (1792-1871) British
£280 $434 €420 Portrait of a gentleman full length with his dog (46x33cm-18x13in) 30-Sep-2 Sotheby's, Olympia #544/R
£400 $652 €600 Portrait of a gentleman with his dog (45x35cm-18x14in) 29-Jan-3 Dreweatt Neate, Newbury #174
£1200 $1920 €1800 Portrait of Elizabeth Grant (76x64cm-30x25in) 11-Mar-3 Gorringes, Lewes #2368 est:1000-1500

HAYTER, Stanley William (1901-1988) British
£1923 $2981 €3000 Untitled (73x60cm-29x24in) s.d.53. 3-Dec-2 Lempertz, Koln #176/R est:3000
£3600 $5940 €5220 Composition (73x60cm-29x24in) s.d.53. 3-Jul-3 Christie's, Kensington #746/R est:2800-3500
£4528 $6974 €7200 Aerial landscape (114x161cm-45x63in) s.d.1956 prov. 26-Oct-2 Cornette de St.Cyr, Paris #17/R
£4528 $6974 €7200 Composition (120x120cm-47x47in) s.d.1959. 26-Oct-2 Cornette de St.Cyr, Paris #18/R
£6090 $9561 €9500 Coquilles (100x81cm-39x32in) s.d.67 i.verso. 24-Nov-2 Laurence Calmels, Paris #145/R est:6000
Works on paper
£550 $869 €825 Untitled study (48x64cm-19x25in) s.d.61 W/C pastel prov. 27-Nov-2 Sotheby's, Olympia #210/R
£4110 $6452 €6000 Untitled (27x22cm-11x9in) s.d.35 oil gouache grattage panel. 15-Apr-3 Laurence Calmels, Paris #4299/R
£4795 $7527 €7000 Untitled (30x41cm-12x16in) s.d.36 gouache paper on canvas on panel. 15-Apr-3 Laurence Calmels, Paris #4300/R

HAYWARD, Alfred Frederick William (1856-1939) British
£276 $425 €414 Apples (20x20cm-8x8in) s. 27-Oct-2 Grogan, Boston #19
£300 $495 €435 White mallow in a vase (34x23cm-13x9in) s.d.1893. 1-Jul-3 Bearnes, Exeter #485
£1100 $1804 €1650 Sloe and strawberries (46x33cm-18x13in) s. 5-Feb-3 John Nicholson, Haslemere #1071 est:900-1200

HAYWARD, Alfred Frederick William (attrib) (1856-1939) British
£250 $398 €375 Christmas roses (13x38cm-5x15in) 6-Mar-3 Christie's, Kensington #637/R

HAYWARD, Alfred Robert (1875-1971) British
£280 $468 €406 Beach scene with boats (40x50cm-16x20in) s.d.96. 9-Jul-3 George Kidner, Lymington #161/R
£2000 $3100 €3000 Still life with poppies (51x41cm-20x16in) s. prov. 4-Dec-2 Christie's, Kensington #460/R est:1500-2000

HAYWARD, Arthur (1889-1971) British
£1800 $2988 €2610 Artist's studios, Porthmeor, St Ives (25x41cm-10x16in) s. panel. 10-Jun-3 David Lay, Penzance #241/R est:1800-2400
£6200 $9796 €9300 Early morning, St Ives (28x23cm-11x9in) s. board exhib. 27-Nov-2 Sotheby's, Olympia #82/R est:2000-3000
Works on paper
£380 $619 €551 Deckchairs looking out to sea (24x33cm-9x13in) s.d.1954 W/C. 15-Jul-3 Bonhams, Knightsbridge #159

HAYWARD, John Samuel (1778-1822) British
Works on paper
£300 $492 €450 Ben Lomond from Loch Lomond (30x43cm-12x17in) pencil W/C. 5-Jun-3 Christie's, Kensington #934/R

HAZARD, Arthur Merton (1872-1930) American
£637 $1000 €956 Reclining nude with a bird in her hand (74x91cm-29x36in) s. prov. 19-Nov-2 Butterfields, San Francisco #8348/R

HAZARD, William Garnet (1903-) Canadian
Works on paper
£181 $285 €272 Bouquet of mums and daisies (25x33cm-10x13in) W/C. 1-Dec-2 Levis, Calgary #42/R (C.D 450)
£201 $317 €302 Floral bouquet (25x30cm-10x12in) W/C. 1-Dec-2 Levis, Calgary #41/R (C.D 500)
£413 $649 €620 Village in winter, street activity (36x48cm-14x19in) s. W/C double-sided. 24-Jul-2 Walker's, Ottawa #407/R est:1200-1600 (C.D 1000)
£472 $736 €708 Floral still life (35x43cm-14x17in) s. W/C. 25-Mar-3 Ritchie, Toronto #86/R est:1500-2000 (C.D 1100)
£537 $843 €806 Georgian Bay in summer. Fishing boats in harbour (33x46cm-13x18in) s. W/C double-sided. 24-Jul-2 Walker's, Ottawa #205/R est:1500-2000 (C.D 1300)
£620 $973 €930 Still life with flowers and fruit. Boats in dry-dock (46x58cm-18x23in) s. W/C double-sided. 24-Jul-2 Walker's, Ottawa #424/R est:1600-2000 (C.D 1500)

HAZELHUST, Ernest William (1866-1949) British
Works on paper
£250 $398 €375 Loch Lomond (23x33cm-9x13in) s. i.verso W/C. 30-Apr-3 Halls, Shrewsbury #222
£280 $459 €420 West Country mooring beside boathouses and other quayside buildings (38x51cm-15x20in) s. W/C. 6-Feb-3 Amersham Auction Rooms, UK #286a
£300 $474 €450 Earl of Huntleys House, Edinburgh (51x36cm-20x14in) s. W/C. 2-Dec-2 Gorringes, Lewes #2754
£420 $664 €630 Rowing out in the morning (34x52cm-13x20in) init. W/C. 26-Nov-2 Bonhams, Knightsbridge #24/R

HAZELTON, Mary Brewster (1868-1953) American
£937 $1500 €1359 Springtime (51x41cm-20x16in) s.d.98. 16-May-3 Skinner, Boston #234/R est:2500-3500

HAZLEDINE, Alfred (1876-1954) Belgian
£641 $994 €1000 Paysage hivernal (53x75cm-21x30in) s. canvas on panel. 9-Dec-2 Horta, Bruxelles #216
£1346 $2087 €2100 Transport de bois dans un paysage enneige (44x61cm-17x24in) s. 9-Dec-2 Horta, Bruxelles #215 est:2500-3500

HE BAILI (1945-) Chinese
Works on paper
£7382 $12179 €10704 Miniature landscapes (16x21cm-6x8in) s. ink scroll set of four. 6-Jul-3 Christie's, Hong Kong #336/R est:70000-90000 (HK.D 95000)

HE HAIXIA (1908-) Chinese
Works on paper
£362 $594 €500 Bamboo and narcissus (44x67cm-17x26in) s.d.1985 seals Indian ink col prov. 30-May-3 Dr Fritz Nagel, Stuttgart #1220/R
£580 $951 €800 Mountain landscape with fishing boat (69x44cm-27x17in) i.d.1987 seal Indian ink col hanging scroll. 30-May-3 Dr Fritz Nagel, Stuttgart #1189/R
£580 $951 €800 Pine tree and rocks (70x50cm-28x20in) i.d.1977 seals Indian ink col hanging scroll. 30-May-3 Dr Fritz Nagel, Stuttgart #1224/R
£2174 $3565 €3000 Great Wall of China (139x69cm-55x27in) i. seals Indian ink col hanging scroll. 30-May-3 Dr Fritz Nagel, Stuttgart #1270/R est:1000-1500

HE HUAISHUO (1941-) Chinese
Works on paper
£4878 $7707 €7317 Heavy seas (66x75cm-26x30in) s.i.d.1983 ink col. 28-Apr-3 Sotheby's, Hong Kong #525/R est:60000-80000 (HK.D 60000)

HE JIAYING (1957-) Chinese
Works on paper
£725 $1188 €1000 Kneeling girl with chicks (68x68cm-27x27in) s. seals Indian ink col hanging scroll. 30-May-3 Dr Fritz Nagel, Stuttgart #1293/R
£870 $1426 €1200 Seated young woman (91x54cm-36x21in) s. seals Indian ink col hanging scroll. 30-May-3 Dr Fritz Nagel, Stuttgart #1238/R
£942 $1545 €1300 Girl reading (68x68cm-27x27in) s. seal Indian ink col hanging scroll. 30-May-3 Dr Fritz Nagel, Stuttgart #1292/R
£1159 $1901 €1600 Reclining female nude (96x89cm-38x35in) i. seals Indian ink col hanging scroll. 30-May-3 Dr Fritz Nagel, Stuttgart #1239/R est:800-1200

HEADE, Martin Johnson (1819-1904) American
£24691 $40000 €37037 Red rose with rosebud (30x23cm-12x9in) s. prov. 21-May-3 Sotheby's, New York #201/R est:50000-70000
£41935 $65000 €62903 Queen of roses (41x26cm-16x10in) s. prov.lit. 5-Dec-2 Christie's, Rockefeller NY #19/R est:80000-120000
£135484 $210000 €203226 Two hunters in a landscape (31x61cm-12x24in) s.d.62 prov.exhib.lit. 4-Dec-2 Sotheby's, New York #113/R est:200000-300000
£503226 $780000 €754839 Orchid and two hummingbirds (40x51cm-16x20in) s.d.72 panel prov.exhib.lit. 3-Dec-2 Phillips, New York #38/R est:500000-750000

HEADLAM, Kristin (1953-) Australian
£1680 $2705 €2520 Forest (121x152cm-48x60in) with sig.d.1991 prov. 6-May-3 Christie's, Melbourne #246/R est:2500-3500 (A.D 4200)

HEALY, Henry (1909-1985) Irish?
£959 $1505 €1400 Haymaking (50x39cm-20x15in) s. canvasboard prov. 15-Apr-3 De Veres Art Auctions, Dublin #147/R est:1500-2000
£1069 $1668 €1700 Howth harbour (36x46cm-14x18in) s. board. 17-Sep-2 Whyte's, Dublin #19 est:2000-2500
£1154 $1788 €1800 Evening light (48x58cm-19x23in) s. board. 3-Dec-2 Thomas Adams, Dublin #391
£1611 $2593 €2400 Edge of the forest (51x61cm-20x24in) s. board. 18-Feb-3 Whyte's, Dublin #192/R est:1500-2000
£1835 $2845 €2900 Calm before the storm (49x59cm-19x23in) s. board. 25-Sep-2 James Adam, Dublin #38/R est:3000-4000
£2051 $3221 €3200 Fairview Park (51x61cm-20x24in) s. i.d.1976 verso board. 19-Nov-2 Whyte's, Dublin #108/R est:2500-3000
£2174 $3565 €3000 Coastal farmstead near Lettermore (34x54cm-13x21in) s. board. 28-May-3 Bonhams & James Adam, Dublin #98/R est:3000-4000

HEALY, Thomas Cantwell (1820-1873) American
£1625 $2600 €2356 Portrait of Mrs Rezin Pleasants Bowie (86x69cm-34x27in) s.i.d.May 10 1860. 17-May-3 New Orleans Auction, New Orleans #926/R est:3000-5000

HEAPHY, Charles (1822-1881) New Zealander
Works on paper
£3860 $6021 €5790 European gathering in the Hauraki Gulf (14x22cm-6x9in) W/C. 27-Mar-3 International Art Centre, Auckland #95/R est:15000-25000 (NZ.D 11000)

HEAPHY, Thomas Frank (1813-1873) British
£900 $1440 €1350 Portrait of a young girl (25x17cm-10x7in) s.i.d.1863 board. 11-Mar-3 Bonhams, Knightsbridge #183/R

HEARD, Joseph (1799-1859) British
£6875 $11000 €9969 Brig "Ituna" at sea (71x102cm-28x40in) s.d.1835. 16-May-3 Skinner, Boston #107/R est:2000-4000

HEARD, Joseph (attrib) (1799-1859) British
£909 $1445 €1364 Canadian brigantine in arctic waters (53x73cm-21x29in) 1-May-3 Waddingtons, Toronto #155/R est:2000-3000 (C.D 2100)
£4800 $7776 €7200 Brig Tom Tough sailing close hauled under close-reefed topsail off the Skerries, Anglesey (53x76cm-21x30in) 21-Jan-3 Bonhams, New Bond Street #227/R est:2000-3000
£7200 $11376 €10800 Brig Rapid inward bound for Liverpool off Point Lynas (57x83cm-22x33in) 28-Nov-2 Sotheby's, London #104/R est:3000-5000

HEARMAN, Louise (1963-) Australian

£1769 $2813 €2654 Untitled, no 699 (43x35cm-17x14in) s.i.d.98 verso board. 4-Mar-3 Deutscher-Menzies, Melbourne #70/R est:5000-7000 (A.D 4600)
£2692 $4281 €4038 Untitled, no 655 (68x91cm-27x36in) s.i.d.98 verso composition board. 4-Mar-3 Deutscher-Menzies, Melbourne #69/R est:8000-12000 (A.D 7000)
£3461 $5504 €5192 Untitled, no 555 (91x68cm-36x27in) s.i.d.96 verso composition board. 4-Mar-3 Deutscher-Menzies, Melbourne #67/R est:10000-15000 (A.D 9000)
£3846 $6115 €5769 Untitled, no 389 (59x89cm-23x35in) s.i.d.1994. 4-Mar-3 Deutscher-Menzies, Melbourne #66/R est:10000-15000 (A.D 10000)
£6154 $9785 €9231 Untitled, no 817 (61x76cm-24x30in) s.i.d.2000 verso board. 4-Mar-3 Deutscher-Menzies, Melbourne #68/R est:8000-12000 (A.D 16000)

Works on paper

£279 $457 €419 Untitled, child no 351 (28x20cm-11x8in) s.d.91 verso chl prov. 4-Jun-3 Deutscher-Menzies, Melbourne #282/R (A.D 700)
£615 $978 €923 Untitled (33x38cm-13x15in) pastel. 4-Mar-3 Deutscher-Menzies, Melbourne #71/R (A.D 1600)

HEARNE, Thomas (1744-1817) British

Works on paper

£1300 $2158 €1950 Appleby Castle, Cumberland (30x46cm-12x18in) s. W/C over pencil. 12-Jun-3 Sotheby's, London #132/R est:1500-2000
£1800 $2826 €2700 Infirmary chapel, Ely looking east (15x22cm-6x9in) i.verso pencil W/C prov. 21-Nov-2 Christie's, London #35/R est:2000-3000
£6800 $9724 €10200 Lymington (21x27cm-8x11in) pencil W/C prov.exhib.lit. 22-Jan-3 Christie's, London #10/R

HEARNE, Thomas (attrib) (1744-1817) British

Works on paper

£420 $651 €630 Near Maidstone, Kent (52x42cm-20x17in) i.d.Aug 11 1807 verso pencil pen brown ink wash. 4-Dec-2 Christie's, Kensington #32

HEARTFIELD, John (1891-1968) German

Photographs

£6646 $10500 €10500 The cross was not yet heavy enough (27x27cm-11x11in) i. verso silver gelatin lit.exhib. 28-Nov-2 Villa Grisebach, Berlin #1209/R est:4000-6000

HEAT, Conrad (1767-1826) British

£993 $1619 €1500 Marie Antoinette praying (50x42cm-20x17in) s. 11-Feb-3 Segre, Madrid #58/R

HEATH, Adrian (1920-1992) British

£300 $501 €435 Composition in yellow (25x24cm-10x9in) init.d.74 oil pastel pencil. 17-Jun-3 Bonhams, Knightsbridge #58
£550 $891 €825 Moon (25x20cm-10x8in) prov.exhib. 20-May-3 Bonhams, Knightsbridge #115/R
£1150 $1794 €1725 Untitled (18x10cm-7x4in) s.i.verso board. 16-Oct-2 David Lay, Penzance #333/R
£2000 $3120 €3000 Untitled (30x40cm-12x16in) s.d.58 verso prov. 25-Mar-3 Bonhams, New Bond Street #138/R est:2000-3000
£11000 $18040 €15950 Untitled (91x101cm-36x40in) s.d.58 prov. 4-Jun-3 Sotheby's, London #73/R est:8000-12000

Works on paper

£400 $628 €600 Untitled (75x55cm-30x22in) s.d.62 gouache ink. 15-Apr-3 Bonhams, Knightsbridge #155/R
£450 $752 €653 Untitled (76x56cm-30x22in) s.d.74 W/C pencil wax crayon. 17-Jun-3 Bonhams, Knightsbridge #128/R

HEATH, Claude (1964-) British

Works on paper

£1200 $2004 €1740 Untitled (69x49cm-27x19in) s.i.d.25.8.95 ball point pen. 24-Jun-3 Sotheby's, Olympia #23/R est:1200-1800

HEATH, David (20th C) American

Photographs

£9146 $15000 €13719 Vengeful sister (19x25cm-7x10in) s.i. silver print edition 7/10. 10-Feb-3 Swann Galleries, New York #91/R est:3500-4500

HEATH, Edda Maxwell (1875-1972) American

£387 $600 €581 Flower fields below Mt Tamalpias (20x25cm-8x10in) s. board. 29-Oct-2 John Moran, Pasadena #602

HEATH, Frank Gascoigne (1873-1936) British

£750 $1223 €1125 Alpine village (23x28cm-9x11in) s. 13-Feb-3 David Lay, Penzance #165
£7500 $12075 €11250 Woodlands glade (49x59cm-19x23in) s. prov. 15-Jan-3 Cheffins Grain & Comins, Cambridge #440/R
£8125 $13000 €12188 Sporting stories (51x61cm-20x24in) s.d.1918. 14-May-3 Butterfields, San Francisco #1151/R est:6000-8000
£16000 $25760 €24000 Girls playing on a boat (49x59cm-19x23in) s. prov. 15-Jan-3 Cheffins Grain & Comins, Cambridge #441/R

HEATH, Mel (1930-) Canadian

Works on paper

£932 $1482 €1398 Mountain high (53x71cm-21x28in) s. W/C. 23-Mar-3 Hodgins, Calgary #63/R est:700-900 (C.D 2200)

HEATH, William (1795-1840) British

£704 $1134 €1000 Scene de cour (61x50cm-24x20in) s. 12-May-3 Lesieur & Le Bars, Le Havre #47/R

Works on paper

£400 $636 €600 Swing Bridge over Pent, Dover (15x23cm-6x9in) W/C gum arabic. 4-Mar-3 Bonhams, Knightsbridge #267

HEATHER, Marjorie (1904-1989) British

Works on paper

£320 $518 €464 Election fever (27x39cm-11x15in) s. pen ink W/C. 20-May-3 Dreweatt Neate, Newbury #209/R

HEAVYSIDE, John Smith (?) British

£700 $1085 €1050 Landscape and figures (46x35cm-18x14in) board. 25-Sep-2 Hamptons Fine Art, Godalming #338/R

HEBALD, Milton (1917-) American

Sculpture

£1019 $1600 €1529 Dancing nude (79cm-31in) i. brown pat. bronze. 24-Nov-2 Butterfields, San Francisco #2669/R est:1500-2000

HEBBAR, Kattingeri Krishna (1911-1996) Indian

£426 $672 €639 Dance - Indian musicians playing to a dressed up cow (58x75cm-23x30in) 2-Dec-2 Rasmussen, Copenhagen #1506/R (D.KR 5000)
£4662 $7692 €6760 Mother and child (77x92cm-30x36in) s.d.63. 6-Jul-3 Christie's, Hong Kong #73/R est:65000-85000 (HK.D 60000)
£6000 $9360 €9000 Mother and child (61x76cm-24x30in) s.d.1952. 17-Oct-2 Bonhams, Knightsbridge #576/R est:6000-8000

HEBERT, Adrien (1890-1967) Canadian

£356 $583 €534 La baie des trepasses, 1913 (26x34cm-10x13in) canvasboard prov.lit. 3-Jun-3 Joyner, Toronto #474 (C.D 800)
£494 $760 €741 Sous-bois (38x46cm-15x18in) s. 22-Oct-2 Iegor de Saint Hippolyte, Montreal #46 (C.D 1200)
£741 $1141 €1112 Chemin et vue du fleuve (43x54cm-17x21in) s. 22-Oct-2 Iegor de Saint Hippolyte, Montreal #47 (C.D 1800)
£2376 $3730 €3564 Port of Montreal (51x61cm-20x24in) s. canvas on board. 24-Jul-2 Walker's, Ottawa #208/R est:2000-2500 (C.D 5750)

HEBERT, Henri (1884-1950) Canadian

Sculpture

£1230 $1918 €1845 Sacre-Coeur (51x23x14cm-20x9x6in) s. bronze exec.c.1920 Cast Hohwiller. 10-Sep-2 Iegor de Saint Hippolyte, Montreal #55 (C.D 3000)

Works on paper

£236 $369 €354 Nude study of a man (69x43cm-27x17in) mono.i. graphite. 25-Mar-3 Ritchie, Toronto #151 (C.D 550)

HEBERT, Louis Philippe (1850-?) Canadian

Sculpture

£7661 $12105 €11492 Fleur des bois (54x41x16cm-21x16x6in) s.i.d.1897 bronze lit. 14-Nov-2 Heffel, Vancouver #56/R est:20000-25000 (C.D 19000)

HECHT, Hendrick van der (1841-1901) Belgian

£272 $433 €400 La cour de ferme (26x32cm-10x13in) s. panel. 18-Mar-3 Campo, Vlaamse Kaai #250
£300 $471 €450 By the lock gates (31x40cm-12x16in) s. 21-Nov-2 Tennants, Leyburn #834

£504 $806 €700 Bord de riviere animee (83x62cm-33x24in) mono.d.94. 13-May-3 Vanderkindere, Brussels #58
£577 $894 €900 View of Halle (37x28cm-15x11in) mono.d.1875 panel prov.exhib. 7-Dec-2 De Vuyst, Lokeren #340
£791 $1266 €1100 Paysage aux vaches et chevres (46x65cm-18x26in) s. 13-May-3 Vanderkindere, Brussels #129
£2179 $3422 €3400 Le vaches au paturage (80x105cm-31x41in) s. 10-Dec-2 Campo, Vlaamse Kaai #519 est:2800-3300

HECHT, Zoltan (1890-1968) American/Hungarian
£613 $950 €920 Seated nude (76x46cm-30x18in) s. painted c.1940. 8-Dec-2 Toomey, Oak Park #792/R

HECK, Claes Dircksz van der (17th C) Dutch
£8917 $13911 €14000 Extensive river landscape with travellers by a road, castle beyond (51x66cm-20x26in) s.d.1641 panel. 6-Nov-2 Christie's, Amsterdam #59/R est:15000-25000

HECKE, Arthur van (1924-) French
£256 $403 €400 Ecume (23x27cm-9x11in) exhib. 16-Dec-2 Charbonneaux, Paris #301
£436 $702 €650 Entree du port (27x22cm-11x9in) s. 23-Feb-3 Mercier & Cie, Lille #90
£446 $696 €700 Sous-bois (22x27cm-9x11in) s. 10-Nov-2 Eric Pillon, Calais #278/R
£604 $972 €900 Marine (46x55cm-18x22in) s. 23-Feb-3 Mercier & Cie, Lille #96/R
£899 $1439 €1250 Le port (55x46cm-22x18in) s. 18-May-3 Eric Pillon, Calais #223/R
£955 $1490 €1500 Nature morte au vase et au compotier (54x65cm-21x26in) s. 10-Nov-2 Eric Pillon, Calais #276/R
£955 $1490 €1500 Paysage pres de Dunkerque (46x55cm-18x22in) s. 10-Nov-2 Eric Pillon, Calais #275/R
£1042 $1646 €1500 Composition (73x100cm-29x39in) s.d.61. 25-Apr-3 Piasa, Paris #193
£1074 $1729 €1600 Marine (46x55cm-18x22in) s. 23-Feb-3 Mercier & Cie, Lille #109
£2148 $3458 €3200 Mais que fait le camion jaune dans les rochers? (89x145cm-35x57in) i.verso painted c.1969 exhib. 23-Feb-3 Mercier & Cie, Lille #94/R
£4228 $6807 €6300 Fin de l'automne (100x81cm-39x32in) s. 23-Feb-3 Mercier & Cie, Lille #95/R

Works on paper
£483 $778 €720 Portrait de jeune femme (55x42cm-22x17in) s. W/C. 23-Feb-3 Mercier & Cie, Lille #249/R
£637 $994 €1000 Port (41x48cm-16x19in) s. W/C. 10-Nov-2 Eric Pillon, Calais #277/R

HECKE, Jan van den and QUELLINUS, Erasmus II (17th C) Flemish
£10135 $15811 €15000 Garland of roses, carnations, narcissus, poppies and other flowers (57x42cm-22x17in) prov.lit. 27-Mar-3 Dorotheum, Vienna #145/R est:15000-20000

HECKE, Willem van (1893-1976) Belgian
£308 $477 €480 Composition (19x29cm-7x11in) s.d.1962 paper on panel lit. 7-Dec-2 De Vuyst, Lokeren #358
£314 $487 €500 Figure of a woman standing (23x17cm-9x7in) s.d.1951 paper on panel. 5-Oct-2 De Vuyst, Lokeren #374
£355 $592 €500 Personnages dans un paysage (18x25cm-7x10in) s.d.1941 paper. 17-Jun-3 Palais de Beaux Arts, Brussels #630
£451 $718 €650 Figure sur fond jaune (37x27cm-15x11in) s.d.1967 paper. 29-Apr-3 Campo & Campo, Antwerp #319
£504 $806 €700 Figure (24x21cm-9x8in) s.d.1966. 17-May-3 De Vuyst, Lokeren #372
£540 $863 €750 Figure (36x27cm-14x11in) s. paper. 17-May-3 De Vuyst, Lokeren #371
£545 $845 €850 Two figures (19x28cm-7x11in) s.d.1963 paper on panel lit. 7-Dec-2 De Vuyst, Lokeren #356
£683 $1094 €950 Composition (39x29cm-15x11in) s.d.1969 paper on panel. 17-May-3 De Vuyst, Lokeren #373
£683 $1094 €950 Seascape (20x26cm-8x10in) s.d.1939 paper. 17-May-3 De Vuyst, Lokeren #374
£881 $1365 €1400 Mother and child (40x31cm-16x12in) s. paper on panel. 5-Oct-2 De Vuyst, Lokeren #373/R
£971 $1554 €1350 Family (35x26cm-14x10in) s.d.1969 paper on panel. 17-May-3 De Vuyst, Lokeren #370/R est:1400-1600
£1154 $1788 €1800 Structure (36x27cm-14x11in) s.d.1966 paper on panel. 7-Dec-2 De Vuyst, Lokeren #357 est:1200-1400

Works on paper
£582 $908 €850 Les joueurs de cartes (21x25cm-8x10in) s.d.1937 mixed media. 14-Apr-3 Horta, Bruxelles #329

HECKEL, August von (1824-1883) German
£17610 $27296 €28000 Judith with head of Holofernes (232x317cm-91x125in) s. prov. 2-Oct-2 Dorotheum, Vienna #192/R est:30000-35000

HECKEL, Erich (1883-1970) German
£5072 $8319 €7000 Cloud (31x45cm-12x18in) s.i.d.19 tempera over chk paper on board prov. 31-May-3 Villa Grisebach, Berlin #186/R est:7000-9000
£17089 $27000 €27000 Landscape with goats (82x96cm-32x38in) s.d.25 prov.exhib. 30-Nov-2 Villa Grisebach, Berlin #232/R est:35000-45000
£21739 $35652 €30000 Autumn landscape (60x70cm-24x28in) s.d.48 s.i.d. stretcher tempera prov. 29-May-3 Lempertz, Koln #659/R est:30000-32000
£31250 $49687 €45000 Girls in wood (26x33cm-10x13in) s.i.d. W/C pencil. 5-May-3 Ketterer, Munich #870/R est:30000-40000
£400000 $668000 €580000 Landstrasse. Winter landscape (68x79cm-27x31in) s.d.13 double-sided prov.exhib.lit. 24-Jun-3 Christie's, London #61/R est:300000-400000
£750000 $1170000 €1125000 Kinder im freien - Children in a landscape (61x68cm-24x27in) s.d.09 s.i.on stretcher prov.exhib.lit. 9-Oct-2 Sotheby's, London #20/R est:800000-1000000
£800000 $1336000 €1160000 Sitzender weiblicher Akt. Das weisse Haus, Moritzburg (70x59cm-28x23in) painted c.1909 init.d.10 verso double-sided prov.lit. 24-Jun-3 Christie's, London #63/R est:900000-1200000

Prints
£1646 $2600 €2600 Sunrise (25x32cm-10x13in) s.d. woodcut. 29-Nov-2 Villa Grisebach, Berlin #654/R est:2000-2500
£1944 $3092 €2800 Bathing huts (26x32cm-10x13in) s.i.d. lithograph. 5-May-3 Ketterer, Munich #850/R est:2000-3000
£1944 $3092 €2800 In fourth class (32x27cm-13x11in) s.mono.i.d. lithograph. 5-May-3 Ketterer, Munich #867/R est:1200-1500
£2044 $3250 €3066 Bildnis E H (36x28cm-14x11in) s.d.17 woodcut. 7-Mar-3 Skinner, Boston #59a/R est:1800-2200
£2138 $3336 €3400 Mann in der ebene (61x48cm-24x19in) s.d.1917 woodcut. 9-Oct-2 Sotheby's, London #444/R est:2000-3000
£2174 $3565 €3000 Sunrise (25x32cm-10x13in) s.d. woodcut. 31-May-3 Villa Grisebach, Berlin #185/R est:3500-4500
£2215 $3434 €3500 Figure kneeling on rock (50x31cm-20x12in) s.d.14 woodcut. 27-Sep-2 Venator & Hansten, Koln #1701/R est:4500
£2222 $3533 €3200 Woman at window (32x26cm-13x10in) s.mono.d. lithograph sketch verso. 5-May-3 Ketterer, Munich #851/R est:2000-3000
£2292 $3644 €3300 Girl's head (33x26cm-13x10in) s.d. lithograph. 5-May-3 Ketterer, Munich #858/R est:1500-2000
£2390 $3728 €3800 Madchen am meer (61x48cm-24x19in) s.d.1918 woodcut. 9-Oct-2 Sotheby's, London #445/R est:3500-4500
£2500 $3875 €3750 Parksee (32x27cm-13x11in) s.d.1914 drypoint. 5-Dec-2 Sotheby's, London #136/R est:3000-4000
£2639 $4196 €3800 Village street (27x33cm-11x13in) s.mono.i.d. lithograph. 5-May-3 Ketterer, Munich #849/R est:3000-4000
£2641 $4384 €3750 Tired (46x34cm-18x13in) s. woodcut. 14-Jun-3 Hauswedell & Nolte, Hamburg #1243/R est:5000
£2778 $4417 €4000 Woman in the street (33x27cm-13x11in) s.i.d. lithograph. 5-May-3 Ketterer, Munich #861/R est:1500-1700
£2817 $4676 €4000 Stralsund (31x35cm-12x14in) s.d. woodcut. 14-Jun-3 Hauswedell & Nolte, Hamburg #1239/R est:4500
£2848 $4500 €4500 Snow scene (43x29cm-17x11in) s.d. woodcut. 30-Nov-2 Villa Grisebach, Berlin #195/R est:3000-4000
£3000 $4650 €4500 Stralsund (30x35cm-12x14in) s.d.1912 woodcut. 5-Dec-2 Sotheby's, London #135/R est:3500-4500
£3019 $4709 €4800 Mude (46x33cm-18x13in) s. woodcut. 9-Oct-2 Sotheby's, London #447/R est:3500-4500
£3169 $5261 €4500 Reclining figure (18x11cm-7x4in) s.d. col woodcut. 14-Jun-3 Hauswedell & Nolte, Hamburg #1240/R est:4500
£3237 $5309 €4500 Mude (47x33cm-19x13in) s. woodcut. 3-Jun-3 Christie's, Amsterdam #437/R est:5000-7000
£3333 $5300 €4800 Bearded man (44x36cm-17x14in) s.i.d.08 lithograph. 5-May-3 Ketterer, Munich #852/R est:1500-2000
£3472 $5521 €5000 Portrait of E H (36x30cm-14x12in) s.d. woodcut. 5-May-3 Ketterer, Munich #874/R est:2000-3000
£3472 $5521 €5000 Man on the plains (38x27cm-15x11in) s.i.d.1918 woodcut. 5-May-3 Ketterer, Munich #869/R est:1500-2000
£3873 $6430 €5500 Woman reading (33x34cm-13x13in) s.i.d. woodcut. 14-Jun-3 Hauswedell & Nolte, Hamburg #1238/R est:4500
£4167 $6625 €6000 Reader (33x23cm-13x9in) s.d. woodcut. 5-May-3 Ketterer, Munich #853/R est:2000-3000
£5556 $8833 €8000 Tightrope walkers (25x20cm-10x8in) s.i.d. drypoint prov. 5-May-3 Ketterer, Munich #865/R est:1500-1700
£5903 $9385 €8500 Woman sitting cross legged (33x27cm-13x11in) s.mono.d. lithograph. 5-May-3 Ketterer, Munich #855/R est:3000-4000
£6111 $9717 €8800 Tired (46x33cm-18x13in) s. woodcut. 5-May-3 Ketterer, Munich #871/R est:2500-3500
£6250 $9938 €9000 Figure praying (42x22cm-17x9in) s.mono.i.d. woodcut. 5-May-3 Ketterer, Munich #857/R est:2500-3500
£6410 $9936 €10000 Tired figure (46x34cm-18x13in) s. woodcut. 7-Dec-2 Hauswedell & Nolte, Hamburg #737/R est:10000
£7394 $12275 €10500 Woman (26x21cm-10x8in) s.i.d. woodcut. 14-Jun-3 Hauswedell & Nolte, Hamburg #1244/R est:12000
£7639 $12146 €11000 Nude (33x18cm-13x7in) s.d. lithograph prov. 5-May-3 Ketterer, Munich #862/R est:5000-7000
£9028 $14354 €13000 Two girls (21x20cm-8x8in) s.i.d. woodcut. 5-May-3 Ketterer, Munich #866/R est:2500-3000
£9374 $14905 €13500 Dancer in dressing room (38x28cm-15x11in) s.d. lithograph. 5-May-3 Ketterer, Munich #868/R est:3000-4000
£9722 $15458 €14000 Scene in wood (27x33cm-11x13in) s.d. lithograph. 5-May-3 Ketterer, Munich #863/R est:3000-5000
£9722 $15458 €14000 By the water (27x33cm-11x13in) s.i.d. lithograph. 5-May-3 Ketterer, Munich #864/R est:5000-7000

£10417 $16563 €15000 Woman with mirror (42x23cm-17x9in) s.mono.i.d. woodcut. 5-May-3 Ketterer, Munich #856/R est:4000-6000
£11111 $17667 €16000 Variety scene (25x32cm-10x13in) s. col lithograph. 5-May-3 Ketterer, Munich #872/R est:5000-8000
£15217 $24957 €21000 Two girls in studio (18x24cm-7x9in) s.d.10 woodcut prov. 30-May-3 Villa Grisebach, Berlin #23/R est:24000-28000
£17949 $27821 €28000 Reclining woman (18x38cm-7x15in) s.i.d. col lithograph. 7-Dec-2 Hauswedell & Nolte, Hamburg #732/R est:15000
£86957 $142609 €120000 Standing child - Franzi (37x28cm-15x11in) s.d.1911 col woodcut prov. 30-May-3 Villa Grisebach, Berlin #28/R est:130000-160000
£87156 $145550 €126376 Standing Franzi - standing child (37x28cm-15x11in) s.d.11 col woodcut. 20-Jun-3 Kornfeld, Bern #69/R est:200000 (S.FR 190000)
£130000 $202800 €195000 Liegende (62x44cm-24x17in) s.d.09 black blue red woodcut. 10-Oct-2 Sotheby's, London #46/R est:140000-160000
£160256 $248397 €250000 Franzi reclining (20x23cm-8x9in) s.i.d. col woodcut. 7-Dec-2 Hauswedell & Nolte, Hamburg #736/R est:125000

Works on paper

£1946 $3134 €2900 Actor (31x23cm-12x9in) s.i.d.53 W/C pencil brush. 21-Feb-3 Sigalas, Stuttgart #895/R est:3400
£2089 $3237 €3300 Waterside village (39x24cm-15x9in) s.i.d. W/C. 28-Sep-2 Hans Stahl, Hamburg #18/R est:3000
£2308 $3577 €3600 Winter landscape (48x63cm-19x25in) s.i.d.41 W/C chk. 4-Dec-2 Lempertz, Koln #765/R est:4000-5000
£2660 $4309 €3750 Lilies (63x48cm-25x19in) s.i.d.61 W/C pencil. 24-May-3 Van Ham, Cologne #238/R est:5500
£3205 $4968 €5000 Autumnal Bodensee landscape (54x69cm-21x27in) s.d.43 W/C over pencil. 4-Dec-2 Lempertz, Koln #766/R est:5000-6000
£3418 $5400 €5400 View of Bodensee (31x43cm-12x17in) s.d.48 pencil black white W/C. 29-Nov-2 Sigalas, Stuttgart #1206 est:4800
£3481 $5500 €5500 The pianist (43x34cm-17x13in) s.d.21 Indian ink brush W/C over chk prov. 30-Nov-2 Villa Grisebach, Berlin #175/R est:7500-8500
£3797 $5886 €6000 Dune landscape in winter (47x60cm-19x24in) s.i.d.53/54 prov. 28-Sep-2 Hans Stahl, Hamburg #16 est:7000
£3986 $6536 €5500 Dark tree (56x69cm-22x27in) s.i.d.48 W/C chk. 31-May-3 Villa Grisebach, Berlin #277/R est:6000-8000
£4037 $5733 €6500 Two brothers (61x48cm-24x19in) s.i.d.49 Indian ink pen lit. 23-Mar-2 Geble, Radolfzell #591/R est:6200
£4362 $7023 €6500 Manuel (42x36cm-17x14in) s.i.d.31 W/C. 21-Feb-3 Sigalas, Stuttgart #893/R est:7500
£4630 $7454 €6945 Plants in broken jug (63x49cm-25x19in) s.d.40 W/C. 7-May-3 Dobiaschofsky, Bern #629/R est:15000 (S.FR 10000)
£4718 $7596 €6700 Wooded hillside I (51x68cm-20x27in) s.d.43 W/C board. 10-May-3 Berlinghof, Heidelberg #943/R est:3600
£5208 $8281 €7500 Head of young man (19x10cm-7x4in) mono.d. s.d. verso gouache over pencil. 5-May-3 Ketterer, Munich #873/R est:4000-6000
£5435 $8913 €7500 Lake in Tessin (31x43cm-12x17in) s.i.d.58 W/C bodycol over pencil prov. 29-May-3 Lempertz, Koln #666/R est:8000-10000
£6475 $10360 €9000 Lago Maggiore (61x50cm-24x20in) s.i.d.62 W/C over pencil. 15-May-3 Neumeister, Munich #266/R est:8000-9000
£6475 $10619 €9000 Mountains near Salzburg (51x70cm-20x28in) s.i.d. W/C white over pencil prov. 6-Jun-3 Ketterer, Munich #79/R est:9000-12000
£6475 $10619 €9000 Landscape - Ennstal Alps near Admont in Austria (48x63cm-19x25in) s.i.d. W/C white over pencil prov. 6-Jun-3 Ketterer, Munich #78/R est:9000-12000
£6506 $10279 €9759 Still life of lilies in vase (46x36cm-18x14in) s.d.19 W/C pencil. 1-Apr-3 Rasmussen, Copenhagen #50/R est:75000-100000 (D.KR 70000)
£6604 $10302 €10500 Landschaft in Italien - Italian landscape (45x60cm-18x24in) s.d.31 W/C over pencil prov. 9-Oct-2 Sotheby's, London #126/R est:15000-20000
£6944 $11042 €10000 Washing (29x41cm-11x16in) s.d. W/C pencil chk. 5-May-3 Ketterer, Munich #859/R est:20000-30000
£6962 $11000 €11000 Nude seated on beach (36x44cm-14x17in) s. W/C Indian ink brush double-sided prov. 30-Nov-2 Villa Grisebach, Berlin #167/R est:12500-15000
£7692 $11923 €12000 On the Drau (52x68cm-20x27in) s.i.d.40 W/C over pencil prov. 4-Dec-2 Lempertz, Koln #767/R est:12000-14000
£8451 $13859 €12254 Tulips and narcissi in pot II (57x46cm-22x18in) s.d.28 W/C. 4-Jun-3 Fischer, Luzern #1171/R est:18000-22000 (S.FR 18000)
£8451 $14028 €12000 Two figures on beach (59x46cm-23x18in) s.i.d. W/C gouache over graphite. 14-Jun-3 Hauswedell & Nolte, Hamburg #1227/R est:12000
£8544 $13500 €13500 Tulips and wooden figure (69x49cm-27x19in) mono.i.d.36 W/C over pencil. 30-Nov-2 Villa Grisebach, Berlin #247/R est:12000-14000
£8608 $13600 €13600 Girls waiting (31x43cm-12x17in) s.i.d.1956 W/C. 30-Nov-2 Geble, Radolfzell #718 est:13500
£8696 $14261 €12000 Magician (64x48cm-25x19in) s.i.d.54 W/C over pencil prov. 29-May-3 Lempertz, Koln #665/R est:12000
£8803 $14613 €12500 River valley between mountains (36x43cm-14x17in) s.i.d. W/C carpenter's pencil. 14-Jun-3 Hauswedell & Nolte, Hamburg #1228/R est:12000
£10256 $15897 €16000 Flowers in front of painted wall (62x51cm-24x20in) s.i.d.32 gouache. 4-Dec-2 Lempertz, Koln #763/R est:18000
£11392 $18000 €18000 Houses by water (31x36cm-12x14in) s.i.d.12 W/C over chk. 30-Nov-2 Villa Grisebach, Berlin #190/R est:18000-24000
£14085 $23380 €20000 The Alster (40x49cm-16x19in) s.i.d.Juni 1913 W/C over pencil. 14-Jun-3 Hauswedell & Nolte, Hamburg #1226/R est:18000
£14493 $23768 €20000 Salzburg (53x69cm-21x27in) iis.i.d.40 W/C over pencil prov. 31-May-3 Villa Grisebach, Berlin #241/R est:20000-30000
£17610 $27472 €28000 Uferlandschaft - Coast landscape (45x62cm-18x24in) s.d.22 W/C chl prov. 9-Oct-2 Sotheby's, London #103/R est:40000-60000
£22152 $35000 €35000 At the seaside (33x50cm-13x20in) s.i.d.13 i.verso W/C gouache over graphite prov. 29-Nov-2 Villa Grisebach, Berlin #33/R est:35000-40000
£24516 $38735 €38000 Femme en bord de mer (39x34cm-15x13in) s. W/C. 19-Dec-2 Delvaux, Paris #16/R est:20000
£24648 $40915 €35000 Nude coming hair (33x29cm-13x11in) s.i.d. carpenter's pencil W/C bodycol chk double-sided. 14-Jun-3 Hauswedell & Nolte, Hamburg #1225/R est:38000
£41026 $63590 €64000 Young woman with cat (35x50cm-14x20in) s.i.d.11 W/C gouache col chk pencil prov.lit. 4-Dec-2 Lempertz, Koln #25/R est:60000-70000
£72464 $118841 €100000 Reclining figure (32x29cm-13x11in) s.i. crayons W/C gouache board prov. 30-May-3 Villa Grisebach, Berlin #21/R est:65000-75000

HECKENDORF, Franz (1888-1962) German

£1282 $2026 €2000 Saint Tropez (45x70cm-18x28in) si.d.1954 canvas on board. 14-Nov-2 Neumeister, Munich #579/R est:1200-1500
£1329 $2073 €2100 Seine landscape (26x30cm-10x12in) s.d.30/31 panel lit. 14-Sep-2 Bergmann, Erlangen #761/R est:1900
£1667 $2583 €2600 People strolling along shore (21x32cm-8x13in) s.d.23 i. verso panel prov. 4-Dec-2 Lempertz, Koln #775/R est:2500
£1698 $2649 €2700 Sunflowers in vase (100x75cm-39x30in) s.d.28 lit. 20-Sep-2 Karlheinz Kaupp, Staufen #1917/R est:3500
£3205 $4968 €5000 Flowers (70x60cm-28x24in) s.d.18. 4-Dec-2 Lempertz, Koln #774/R est:4000
£3623 $5942 €5000 Flowers in vase and cactus (70x60cm-28x24in) s.d.22 prov. 31-May-3 Villa Grisebach, Berlin #263/R est:8000-10000
£3623 $5942 €5000 Still life of flowers (63x63cm-25x25in) s.d.58 masonite. 31-May-3 Villa Grisebach, Berlin #268/R est:5000-7000
£3986 $6536 €5500 Arrival of Columbus (80x100cm-31x39in) s. 31-May-3 Villa Grisebach, Berlin #267/R est:5000-6000
£4167 $6583 €6000 Panorama de Constantinople (60x80cm-24x31in) s.i.d.1916. 25-Apr-3 Piasa, Paris #13/R
£4430 $7000 €7000 Still life with fruit and flowers (80x100cm-31x39in) s. panel lit. 29-Nov-2 Schloss Ahlden, Ahlden #1405/R est:8500
£5063 $8000 €8000 Landscape near Ragusa (90x120cm-35x47in) s.d.23 s.i. verso. 30-Nov-2 Villa Grisebach, Berlin #299/R est:9000-12000
£5797 $9507 €8000 Village by mountain lake (70x100cm-28x39in) s. bears d.1957. 31-May-3 Villa Grisebach, Berlin #264/R est:7000-9000
£7692 $11923 €12000 Mountain landscape with lake (77x59cm-30x23in) s.d.1919 canvas on fibreboard. 6-Dec-2 Ketterer, Munich #82/R est:12000-15000

Works on paper

£1408 $2268 €2000 Farmstead front garden (30x47cm-12x19in) s.d.1960 lit. 9-May-3 Schloss Ahlden, Ahlden #1543/R est:1400

HEDA, Gerrit Willemsz (c.1620-1702) Dutch

£28302 $43868 €45000 Still life with oysters, nautilus goblet (58x79cm-23x31in) panel lit. 2-Oct-2 Dorotheum, Vienna #122/R est:40000-50000
£130000 $217100 €188500 An overturned silver tumbler and a roemer on a pewter plate, Facon-de-Venise wine glass (59x84cm-23x33in) s. panel. 9-Jul-3 Christie's, London #46/R est:40000-60000

HEDA, Gerrit Willemsz (circle) (c.1620-1702) Dutch

£16783 $24000 €25175 Still life with roemer, peeled lemon and meat pie (38x49cm-15x19in) panel exhib. 22-Jan-3 Doyle, New York #114/R est:10000

HEDA, Willem Claesz (1594-1680) Dutch

£10063 $15597 €16000 Still life with overturned silver tazza, wine glass, lemon, bread (58x72cm-23x28in) bears i. panel. 2-Oct-2 Dorotheum, Vienna #174/R est:15000-20000

HEDA, Willem Claesz (circle) (1594-1680) Dutch

£20000 $33400 €29000 Half-filled roemer, glass, overturned tazza, other objects on half draped table (58x72cm-23x28in) s.d.1642 panel. 9-Jul-3 Bonhams, New Bond Street #77/R est:20000-30000

HEDA, Willem Claesz (style) (1594-1680) Dutch
£7137 $11562 €10349 Still life of wineglass, bread and fish (64x83cm-25x33in) 26-May-3 Bukowskis, Stockholm #400a/R est:80000-100000 (S.KR 92000)

HEDBERG, Kalle (1894-1959) Swedish
£953 $1496 €1430 Sleeping (81x60cm-32x24in) s.d.29. 16-Dec-2 Lilla Bukowskis, Stockholm #50 (S.KR 13500)

HEDDEGHEM, Alice van (fl.1906-1927) British
£400 $620 €600 Still life with roses and syringia (39x115cm-15x45in) s. 26-Sep-2 Mellors & Kirk, Nottingham #675/R

HEDINGER, Elise (1854-?) American
£566 $883 €900 Harvest (71x100cm-28x39in) s.i.d.17 lit. 20-Sep-2 Schloss Ahlden, Ahlden #1285/R

HEDLEY, Johnson (attrib) (1848-1914) British
£750 $1185 €1125 Prize cow (48x66cm-19x26in) s. 24-Apr-3 Richardson & Smith, Whitby #62

HEDLEY, Ralph (c.1851-1913) British
£950 $1568 €1378 Darning by the fire (51x40cm-20x16in) s.d.09. 2-Jul-3 Sotheby's, Olympia #312/R
£1700 $2669 €2550 Portrait of J G Wilson and his son A A Wilson (76x63cm-30x25in) s.d.1902. 21-Nov-2 Tennants, Leyburn #743/R est:300-500
£2083 $3250 €3125 Time for bed (84x74cm-33x29in) 9-Oct-2 Doyle, New York #54/R est:4000-6000
£4800 $7536 €7200 Portrait of John George Wilson, seated on a low wall holding a fishing rod (153x102cm-60x40in) 21-Nov-2 Tennants, Leyburn #742/R est:2000-3000
£10000 $15600 €15000 Uncle Toby and the dicky bird society (52x60cm-20x24in) s.d.1897. 26-Mar-3 Sotheby's, Olympia #140/R est:6000-9000

HEDLUND, Bjorn (1953-) Swedish
£1296 $2022 €1944 Composition (150x130cm-59x51in) s.d.1986. 6-Nov-2 AB Stockholms Auktionsverk #809/R est:10000-12000 (S.KR 18500)

HEDRICK, Ron (20th C) Canadian
£435 $678 €725 Street hockey (61x76cm-24x30in) s. i.verso prov. 13-Apr-3 Levis, Calgary #48/R est:1200-1500 (C.D 1000)

HEDSTROM, Newton Samuel (1914-) Australian
£676 $1035 €1014 City (72x95cm-28x37in) s. board prov. 25-Aug-2 Sotheby's, Paddington #163/R est:1500-2500 (A.D 1900)

HEEKS, Willy (1951-) American
Works on paper
£355 $550 €533 Habitat (137x102cm-54x40in) init.d.1990 mixed media prov. 25-Sep-2 Doyle, New York #39/R

HEEL, Jan van (1898-1991) Dutch
£1197 $1927 €1700 Mountain landscape (49x59cm-19x23in) s.d.55. 7-May-3 Vendue Huis, Gravenhage #214/R est:1000-1200
£1439 $2360 €2000 Mountainous landscape (60x50cm-24x20in) s. s. on stretcher. 3-Jun-3 Christie's, Amsterdam #60/R est:2000-3000
£1806 $2979 €2600 Spain (50x60cm-20x24in) s.d.56 s.i.stretcher prov.exhib. 1-Jul-3 Christie's, Amsterdam #410/R est:2000-3000
£1944 $3208 €2800 Dog (60x50cm-24x20in) s. s.i.verso prov. 1-Jul-3 Christie's, Amsterdam #420/R est:3000-5000
£2038 $3180 €3200 Rocking-chairs (59x49cm-23x19in) s. 5-Nov-2 Vendu Notarishuis, Rotterdam #125/R est:1600-1800
£2436 $3776 €3800 Landschap III (70x100cm-28x39in) s. si.d.verso. 3-Dec-2 Christie's, Amsterdam #283/R est:4000-6000
£2675 $4173 €4200 Small square in Paris with merry-go-round (48x38cm-19x15in) s. s.i.d.49 verso prov. 6-Nov-2 Vendue Huis, Gravenhage #252/R est:3000-4000
£3822 $5962 €6000 Toy (60x50cm-24x20in) s.d.83 prov. 6-Nov-2 Vendue Huis, Gravenhage #251/R est:3000-4000
£4808 $7452 €7500 Self portrait as a clown (60x50cm-24x20in) s. executed c.1935 prov. 3-Dec-2 Christie's, Amsterdam #202/R est:6000-8000
£5036 $8259 €7000 Landscape XXX (100x90cm-39x35in) s.d.64 s.i.d.on stretcher exhib. 3-Jun-3 Christie's, Amsterdam #390/R est:3000-5000
£8974 $13910 €14000 Clown (101x101cm-40x40in) s.d.35 prov. 3-Dec-2 Christie's, Amsterdam #197/R est:14000-18000
Works on paper
£828 $1292 €1300 Paris interior (31x24cm-12x9in) s.d.49 gouache prov. 6-Nov-2 Vendue Huis, Gravenhage #190/R
£1799 $2950 €2500 Stilleven met vlinder - still life with butterfly (48x31cm-19x12in) s.d.67 pen ink gouache. 3-Jun-3 Christie's, Amsterdam #389/R est:1500-2000
£2302 $3776 €3200 Orange bird (31x48cm-12x19in) s.d.April 15 67 gouache ballpoint on newpaper. 3-Jun-3 Christie's, Amsterdam #388/R est:1500-2000

HEEL, Johann Peter (attrib) (1696-1767) German
Sculpture
£1824 $2846 €2700 Bust of grieving saint (29cm-11in) wood gold silver. 26-Mar-3 Hugo Ruef, Munich #1486/R est:1200

HEEM, Cornelis de (1631-1695) Dutch
£12658 $20000 €20000 Still life with fruit and water glass (39x30cm-15x12in) s. panel prov. 26-Nov-2 Wiener Kunst Auktionen, Vienna #7/R est:20000-40000

HEEM, Cornelis de (attrib) (1631-1695) Dutch
£10897 $17109 €17000 Still life of grapes, oysters and other fruit (51x41cm-20x16in) 21-Nov-2 Van Ham, Cologne #1365/R est:16000

HEEM, Cornelis de (style) (1631-1695) Dutch
£5500 $9185 €7975 Partly peeled lemon on a pewter plate, plums, cherries and other fruit on a table (40x55cm-16x22in) 11-Jul-3 Christie's, Kensington #56/R est:6000-8000
£6500 $10140 €9750 Grapes, plums, peach a melon and cherries on a stone ledge, with a snails (34x27cm-13x11in) panel. 10-Apr-3 Christie's, Kensington #96/R est:4000-6000
£12739 $19618 €20000 Peaches and grapes with roses and other flowers in a glass vase (34x39cm-13x15in) init. 3-Sep-2 Christie's, Amsterdam #23/R est:3000-5000

HEEM, Jan Davidsz de (1606-1684) Dutch
£62000 $97340 €93000 Still life of porcelain vase, flowers, acorns and fruit (44x35cm-17x14in) bears sig. panel prov. 12-Dec-2 Sotheby's, London #24/R est:30000-50000
£64748 $103597 €90000 Still life with fruit, leaves, tiger moth and other flowers (46x74cm-18x29in) s.d.1653. 13-May-3 Sotheby's, Amsterdam #47/R est:70000-90000
£280000 $439600 €420000 Still life of fruit on a silver plate, and crayfish on a table (27x39cm-11x15in) s.d. panel prov.lit. 12-Dec-2 Sotheby's, London #25/R est:300000-500000

HEEM, Jan Davidsz de (attrib) (1606-1684) Dutch
£1489 $2309 €2234 Still life of flowers and fruit (32x25cm-13x10in) bears sig. 3-Dec-2 Bukowskis, Stockholm #454/R est:15000-20000 (S.KR 21000)

HEEM, Jan Davidsz de (style) (1606-1684) Dutch
£8108 $12649 €12000 Still life with gilt cup in form of bunch of grapes, fruit, dragonfly and snail (69x88cm-27x35in) 18th C prov. 27-Mar-3 Dorotheum, Vienna #396/R est:16000-24000

HEEM, Jan Jansz de (circle) (1650-1695) Dutch
£10135 $15811 €15000 Still life with oranges, cherries, pomegranate and glass of wine. mono.i. 27-Mar-3 Dorotheum, Vienna #180/R est:14000-18000

HEEM, de (style) (17th C) Dutch
£16000 $24960 €24000 Still life with fruit and lobster on a table (80x100cm-31x39in) 14-Apr-3 Hamilton Osborne King, Dublin #1471/R est:10000-15000

HEEMSKERK, Egbert van (17/18th C) Dutch
£549 $900 €824 Boors carousing in a tavern (57x82cm-22x32in) panel. 5-Feb-3 Christie's, Rockefeller NY #294/R
£645 $948 €1000 Peasant sitting at table in tavern (26x20cm-10x8in) panel. 20-Jun-2 Dr Fritz Nagel, Stuttgart #713/R
£870 $1348 €1305 Les fumeurs de pipe (31x26cm-12x10in) s. 7-Dec-2 Galerie du Rhone, Sion #83/R (S.FR 2000)
£2800 $4368 €4200 Peasants smoking and drinking in an interior (42x59cm-17x23in) 9-Apr-3 Bonhams, New Bond Street #59/R est:3000-5000
£2821 $4372 €4400 Two smokers in a tavern (27x22cm-11x9in) panel. 4-Dec-2 Neumeister, Munich #604/R est:4000
£3205 $4968 €5000 Weeping family at the death bed (45x62cm-18x24in) panel lit. 4-Dec-2 Neumeister, Munich #603/R est:4500

HEEMSKERK, Egbert van (attrib) (17/18th C) Dutch
£490 $775 €735 Cheating at cards (26x22cm-10x9in) indis.sig. panel. 16-Nov-2 Crafoord, Lund #31/R (S.KR 7000)
£800 $1288 €1200 Doctor's surgery (41x33cm-16x13in) 20-Feb-3 Christie's, Kensington #86/R

HEEMSKERK, Egbert van (elder) (1610-1680) Dutch
£3355 $5402 €5000 Peasants drinking and smoking (16x11cm-6x4in) s. panel prov. 18-Feb-3 Sotheby's, Amsterdam #203/R est:1500-2000
£7500 $11625 €11250 Peasant smoking, drinking and playing cards in a tavern (54x72cm-21x28in) prov. 30-Oct-2 Christie's, Kensington #25/R est:5000-7000

HEEMSKERK, Egbert van (elder-attrib) (1610-1680) Dutch
£1790 $2793 €2685 Tavern scene (18x26cm-7x10in) panel. 6-Nov-2 Dobiaschofsky, Bern #640/R est:2800 (S.FR 4100)

HEEMSKERK, Egbert van (younger) (1634-1704) Dutch
£1034 $1593 €1551 Interior from an inn (34x46cm-13x18in) panel. 27-Oct-2 Anders Antik, Landskrona #127/R est:20000-25000 (S.KR 15000)
£1541 $2404 €2250 Peasants in tavern (27x35cm-11x14in) 10-Apr-3 Van Ham, Cologne #1217/R est:3500
£2000 $3340 €2900 Tavern interior with boors eating, drinking and smoking (35x45cm-14x18in) 8-Jul-3 Sotheby's, Olympia #376/R est:2000-3000
£4000 $6680 €5800 Village Fair (41x57cm-16x22in) 9-Jul-3 Bonhams, New Bond Street #188/R est:3000-5000
£5068 $7905 €7500 Meeting at the inn (11x18cm-4x7in) mono.d.1698 panel pair. 28-Mar-3 Delvaux, Paris #125/R est:8000
£5096 $7949 €8000 Peasants singing, making music and drinking in a tavern (76x63cm-30x25in) prov. 5-Nov-2 Sotheby's, Amsterdam #1/R est:8000-12000
£16981 $26321 €27000 Peasants drinking in an inn (56x76cm-22x30in) prov. 7-Oct-2 Ansorena, Madrid #28/R est:27000

HEEMSKERK, Egbert van (younger-attrib) (1634-1704) Dutch
£1241 $2011 €1799 Lesson at school (23x31cm-9x12in) i.verso panel prov. 25-May-3 Uppsala Auktionskammare, Uppsala #44/R est:20000-25000 (S.KR 16000)
£2115 $3321 €3300 Peasants in tavern (27x33cm-11x13in) 21-Nov-2 Van Ham, Cologne #1366/R est:4500

HEEMSKERK, Hendrik van (17th C) Dutch
£8917 $13911 €14000 Still life of grapes, peaches and a nut on a draped table (37x48cm-15x19in) s. panel prov. 5-Nov-2 Sotheby's, Amsterdam #296/R est:15000-20000

HEEMSKERK, Jacob Eduard van Beest (1828-1894) Dutch
£704 $1134 €1000 Fishing boat on sea (12x20cm-5x8in) s. panel. 7-May-3 Vendue Huis, Gravenhage #395
£1887 $2906 €3000 Shipping off the coast (67x95cm-26x37in) s. 22-Oct-2 Sotheby's, Amsterdam #8/R est:3000-4000
£4403 $6780 €7000 Return of the squadron of Prince Hendrik of the Netherlands by the English coast in 1874 (55x75cm-22x30in) s. panel prov. 23-Oct-2 Christie's, Amsterdam #64/R est:8000-12000

HEEMSKERK, Marten Jacobsz van Veen (1498-1574) Dutch
Works on paper
£23226 $36000 €34839 Horse tamer of Monte Cavallo (20x23cm-8x9in) pen ink dr. exhib. 2-Nov-2 North East Auctions, Portsmouth #102/R est:40000-60000

HEER, Margaretha de (17th C) German
Works on paper
£4140 $6459 €6500 Cockerels and chickens in a farmyard (30x25cm-12x10in) s. gouache vellum prov.exhib. 5-Nov-2 Sotheby's, Amsterdam #146/R est:7000-9000
£7643 $11924 €12000 Study of flowers, insects and shells (17x23cm-7x9in) s.d.1665 W/C gouache gum arabic vellum prov. 5-Nov-2 Sotheby's, Amsterdam #141/R est:6000-8000

HEERDEN, Louis van (1941-) South African
Works on paper
£288 $450 €432 Passage through a French garden, no 8 (76x56cm-30x22in) s. pastel exec.c.1988/89 exhib. 11-Nov-2 Stephan Welz, Johannesburg #535 (SA.R 4500)

HEERDEN, Piet van (1917-1991) South African
£215 $335 €323 Autumn trees (44x34cm-17x13in) s. canvas on board. 15-Oct-2 Stephan Welz, Johannesburg #488 est:3000-5000 (SA.R 3500)
£461 $719 €692 Klapmuts (27x59cm-11x23in) s. board. 15-Oct-2 Stephan Welz, Johannesburg #489 est:3000-5000 (SA.R 7500)
£499 $803 €749 Cape Dutch Farm House amongst tress (40x50cm-16x20in) s.d.54 board. 12-May-3 Stephan Welz, Johannesburg #204 est:5000-7000 (SA.R 5800)
£533 $858 €800 Onweerslandskap met huise (19x34cm-7x13in) s. board. 12-May-3 Stephan Welz, Johannesburg #192 est:4000-6000 (SA.R 6200)
£723 $1143 €1085 Edge of town (24x34cm-9x13in) s.d.57 canvasboard. 1-Apr-3 Stephan Welz, Johannesburg #212 est:3000-5000 (SA.R 9000)
£801 $1249 €1202 Morning landscape, Springbok (45x60cm-18x24in) s. i.verso canvas on board. 11-Nov-2 Stephan Welz, Johannesburg #553 (SA.R 12500)
£1025 $1599 €1538 Namaqualand landscape (24x28cm-9x11in) s. canvas on board. 11-Nov-2 Stephan Welz, Johannesburg #532/R est:7000-10000 (SA.R 16000)
£1290 $2077 €1935 Namaqualand landscape with a dirt road (29x40cm-11x16in) s.d.50. 12-May-3 Stephan Welz, Johannesburg #450/R est:6000-9000 (SA.R 15000)
£1290 $2077 €1935 Extensive Namaqualand landscape with mountains in the distance (34x44cm-13x17in) s.d.60 canvas on board. 12-May-3 Stephan Welz, Johannesburg #451/R est:6000-9000 (SA.R 15000)
£1505 $2423 €2258 Mother and children in a garden (39x48cm-15x19in) s.d.49. 12-May-3 Stephan Welz, Johannesburg #512/R est:6000-9000 (SA.R 17500)
£1892 $3046 €2838 View down du Toit's Kloof (44x58cm-17x23in) s. canvas on board. 12-May-3 Stephan Welz, Johannesburg #589/R est:7000-10000 (SA.R 22000)
£1892 $3046 €2838 Farmlands with snow covered mountains (38x49cm-15x19in) s. canvas on board. 12-May-3 Stephan Welz, Johannesburg #591 est:6000-8000 (SA.R 22000)
£2322 $3738 €3483 Boland Mountains (34x44cm-13x17in) s. canvas on board. 12-May-3 Stephan Welz, Johannesburg #578/R est:7000-10000 (SA.R 27000)
£3267 $5261 €4901 Namaqualand in spring (44x65cm-17x26in) s. canvas on board. 12-May-3 Stephan Welz, Johannesburg #483/R est:18000-24000 (SA.R 38000)
£3783 $6091 €5675 Namaqualand daisies in an extensive landscape (39x49cm-15x19in) s. canvas on board. 12-May-3 Stephan Welz, Johannesburg #484/R est:20000-30000 (SA.R 44000)
£3869 $6230 €5804 Extensive spring landscape Namaqualand (50x75cm-20x30in) s.d.1967 canvas on board. 12-May-3 Stephan Welz, Johannesburg #482/R est:25000-35000 (SA.R 45000)

HEEREBAART, Georgius (1829-1915) Dutch
£2516 $3874 €4000 Haycart near the field (35x45cm-14x18in) s. panel. 22-Oct-2 Sotheby's, Amsterdam #29/R est:4000-6000
£12500 $19875 €18000 Dutch country life (23x34cm-9x13in) s. panel pair. 29-Apr-3 Christie's, Amsterdam #4/R est:10000-15000

HEEREMANS, Karl (?) ?
Works on paper
£290 $461 €420 Errants (63x49cm-25x19in) s. s.i.verso mixed media. 4-Mar-3 Ansorena, Madrid #257

HEEREMANS, Thomas (fl.1660-1697) Dutch
£3269 $5067 €5100 Village by the river (67x61cm-26x24in) 6-Dec-2 Maigret, Paris #62/R est:5000
£8500 $13260 €12750 Riverside village with peasants in rowing boats (48x66cm-19x26in) s.d.1677 prov. 9-Apr-3 Bonhams, New Bond Street #8/R est:5000-7000
£8710 $13761 €13500 Village by river (46x62cm-18x24in) s.d.1669 panel. 18-Dec-2 Piasa, Paris #40/R est:7000
£8966 $14255 €13000 River landscape (67x61cm-26x24in) 4-Mar-3 Ansorena, Madrid #58/R est:12000
£9500 $14725 €14250 Winter landscape with figures before an inn (20x26cm-8x10in) s.d.1671 panel. 31-Oct-2 Sotheby's, Olympia #67/R est:4000-6000
£10135 $15811 €15000 Merry making peasants in village (25x31cm-10x12in) s.d.1661 panel. 27-Mar-3 Dorotheum, Vienna #189/R est:15000-20000

HEEREMANS, Thomas (attrib) (fl.1660-1697) Dutch
£3000 $4650 €4500 Townsfolk skating and sledding on a frozen lake before a building (22x26cm-9x10in) indis init. panel. 30-Oct-2 Christie's, Kensington #30/R est:2000-3000
£6000 $10020 €8700 Winter landscape (26x35cm-10x14in) bears sig. panel. 8-Jul-3 Sotheby's, Olympia #410/R est:6000-8000

HEERFORDT, Anna Cathrine Christine (1839-1910) Danish
£746 $1187 €1119 Still life of red and white flowers with beech leaves (49x37cm-19x15in) s.d.1905. 5-May-3 Rasmussen, Vejle #578/R (D.KR 8000)
£788 $1261 €1182 Still life of roses (58x69cm-23x27in) init. 13-Jan-3 Rasmussen, Vejle #45/R (D.KR 9000)

HEERFORDT, Ida Marie Margrethe (1834-1887) Danish
£1119 $1780 €1679 Grape vine with blue and green grapes (50x45cm-20x18in) s.d.1878 exhib. 5-May-3 Rasmussen, Vejle #580/R est:12000 (D.KR 12000)

HEERSCHOP, Hendrik (attrib) (1620-1672) Flemish
£9459 $14757 €14000 Philosopher (31x26cm-12x10in) panel prov. 27-Mar-3 Dorotheum, Vienna #210/R est:8000-12000

HEERUP, Henry (1907-1993) Danish
£299 $475 €449 Figure composition (24x31cm-9x12in) s.d.7-8 Juli 47. 29-Apr-3 Kunsthallen, Copenhagen #45/R (D.KR 3200)
£299 $475 €449 The big tree, winter (22x16cm-9x6in) s.verso plywood. 29-Apr-3 Kunsthallen, Copenhagen #201/R (D.KR 3200)
£394 $630 €591 Hilly landscape (32x34cm-13x13in) cardboard. 13-Jan-3 Rasmussen, Vejle #266/R (D.KR 4500)
£508 $813 €762 Chimney sweep (27x40cm-11x16in) s. cardboard. 13-Jan-3 Rasmussen, Vejle #267/R (D.KR 5800)
£622 $1008 €902 Composition with rainbow (33x27cm-13x11in) 24-May-3 Rasmussen, Havnen #4158/R (D.KR 6500)
£652 $1036 €978 Woodland scene with white shape (71x48cm-28x19in) panel. 10-Mar-3 Rasmussen, Vejle #716/R (D.KR 7000)
£1101 $1706 €1652 Figure composition (34x35cm-13x14in) s.verso plywood. 1-Oct-2 Rasmussen, Copenhagen #67/R est:15000 (D.KR 13000)
£1101 $1706 €1652 Composition (33x30cm-13x12in) s.verso plywood. 1-Oct-2 Rasmussen, Copenhagen #68/R est:15000 (D.KR 13000)
£1136 $1886 €1647 Ornaments (42x33cm-17x13in) s. panel painted c.1950. 12-Jun-3 Kunsthallen, Copenhagen #30/R est:12000 (D.KR 12000)
£1301 $2056 €1952 Erotic figure composition (33x41cm-13x16in) s. painted c.1950. 1-Apr-3 Rasmussen, Copenhagen #107/R est:15000-20000 (D.KR 14000)
£1493 $2373 €2240 The pyramid man (38x50cm-15x20in) s. panel painted c.1950. 29-Apr-3 Kunsthallen, Copenhagen #41/R est:15000 (D.KR 16000)
£2239 $3471 €3359 Profile of the moon (51x70cm-20x28in) s.d.75 masonite prov. 4-Dec-2 Kunsthallen, Copenhagen #99/R est:30000 (D.KR 26000)
£2462 $4087 €3570 Happy girl (38x53cm-15x21in) s. painted c.1950. 12-Jun-3 Kunsthallen, Copenhagen #1/R est:25000 (D.KR 26000)
£2498 $3872 €3747 The doll child (72x112cm-28x44in) s.d.78 masonite exhib. 4-Dec-2 Kunsthallen, Copenhagen #106/R est:30000 (D.KR 29000)
£3253 $5139 €4880 Female Turkish dancer (81x53cm-32x21in) s. painted c.1960. 1-Apr-3 Rasmussen, Copenhagen #106/R est:40000 (D.KR 35000)
£3726 $5775 €5589 Girl cyclist - erotic figure composition (56x80cm-22x31in) s.d.1970 masonite. 1-Oct-2 Rasmussen, Copenhagen #99/R est:50000 (D.KR 44000)
£4234 $6562 €6351 Horse and wagon - war situation (86x96cm-34x38in) s.d.45 plywood lit. 1-Oct-2 Rasmussen, Copenhagen #101/R est:50000 (D.KR 50000)
£5214 $8291 €7821 Love (110x123cm-43x48in) s. exhib. 10-Mar-3 Rasmussen, Vejle #762/R est:60000-80000 (D.KR 56000)
£5490 $8564 €8235 Bathers (75x125cm-30x49in) s.d.1976 masonite prov. 18-Sep-2 Kunsthallen, Copenhagen #81/R est:70000 (D.KR 65000)
£7449 $11844 €11174 Eve and the snake (102x102cm-40x40in) s.d.1936 exhib. 10-Mar-3 Rasmussen, Vejle #775/R est:100000-125000 (D.KR 80000)
£18587 $29368 €27881 The jester's ballad (110x140cm-43x55in) s.d.48 painted on coal sack exhib.prov. 1-Apr-3 Rasmussen, Copenhagen #116/R est:200000 (D.KR 200000)

Sculpture
£1270 $1969 €1905 Owl (28x23x20cm-11x9x8in) granite. 1-Oct-2 Rasmussen, Copenhagen #96/R est:12000-15000 (D.KR 15000)
£6475 $10619 €9000 Donkey with a basket (30cm-12in) painted granite executed c.1950 prov. 3-Jun-3 Christie's, Amsterdam #194/R est:9000-12000
£6530 $10382 €9795 Figure (54cm-21in) chalk stone exec.c.1945-50. 29-Apr-3 Kunsthallen, Copenhagen #92/R est:75000 (D.KR 70000)
£9141 $14534 €13712 Female head (67cm-26in) granite exhib. 26-Feb-3 Kunsthallen, Copenhagen #23/R est:125000 (D.KR 100000)
£9294 $14684 €13941 The wheel of hearts (65x69x11cm-26x27x4in) s. painted sandstone executed 1947-48 exhib.prov. 1-Apr-3 Rasmussen, Copenhagen #117/R est:80000-100000 (D.KR 100000)
£11008 $17062 €16512 The stone man (72x45x30cm-28x18x12in) granite executed 1948-49 prov. 1-Oct-2 Rasmussen, Copenhagen #73/R est:75000-100000 (D.KR 130000)

Works on paper
£299 $475 €449 Horse and cart (27x39cm-11x15in) s.d.7 Juli 56 crayon. 29-Apr-3 Kunsthallen, Copenhagen #43/R (D.KR 3200)
£299 $475 €449 The Negro and Madonna (15x21cm-6x8in) s. crayon. 29-Apr-3 Kunsthallen, Copenhagen #51/R (D.KR 3200)
£299 $475 €449 The dog artist (15x20cm-6x8in) s. crayon. 29-Apr-3 Kunsthallen, Copenhagen #52/R (D.KR 3200)
£336 $534 €504 Cow waving (29x39cm-11x15in) s.i.d.22 Juni 60 crayon. 29-Apr-3 Kunsthallen, Copenhagen #46/R (D.KR 3600)
£336 $534 €504 Composition (30x31cm-12x12in) s. crayon. 29-Apr-3 Kunsthallen, Copenhagen #48/R (D.KR 3600)
£336 $534 €504 Bathing girl (15x21cm-6x8in) s. crayon. 29-Apr-3 Kunsthallen, Copenhagen #49/R (D.KR 3600)
£392 $623 €588 The Queen (39x28cm-15x11in) s.i.d.19-20 Maj crayon. 29-Apr-3 Kunsthallen, Copenhagen #44/R (D.KR 4200)
£392 $623 €588 Istanbul (27x40cm-11x16in) s.d.18 maj 1954 crayon. 29-Apr-3 Kunsthallen, Copenhagen #47/R (D.KR 4200)
£429 $682 €644 Young bird (21x15cm-8x6in) s. crayon. 29-Apr-3 Kunsthallen, Copenhagen #50/R (D.KR 4600)
£429 $682 €644 Freedom - I want to come (21x15cm-8x6in) s. crayon. 29-Apr-3 Kunsthallen, Copenhagen #53/R (D.KR 4600)
£465 $734 €698 Faaborg, 14-15 okt.73 (25x40cm-10x16in) dr. 1-Apr-3 Rasmussen, Copenhagen #349 (D.KR 5000)
£933 $1483 €1400 Figure composition with Charlie Rivel (50x62cm-20x24in) s.d.1960 crayon. 29-Apr-3 Kunsthallen, Copenhagen #54/R (D.KR 10000)

HEES, Gerrit van (attrib) (1629-c.1701) Flemish
£5000 $8350 €7250 Landscape with figures on a road near a woodland village (50x68cm-20x27in) panel prov. 8-Jul-3 Sotheby's, Olympia #408/R est:2000-3000

HEFELE, J F (?-1710) German
Works on paper
£3200 $5312 €4800 Parrot and a dog by some fruit. Monkey and a jay by some fruit (13x16cm-5x6in) gouache pair. 12-Jun-3 Sotheby's, London #114/R est:3000-5000

HEFFERTON, Phillip (20th C) American
£741 $1200 €1112 Painting of George Washington on a dollar bill (122x170cm-48x67in) exhib. 24-Jan-3 New Orleans Auction, New Orleans #1066/R est:700-1000
£1667 $2600 €2501 Untitled (122x170cm-48x67in) exhib.prov. 20-Sep-2 New Orleans Auction, New Orleans #1407/R

HEFFNER, Karl (1849-1925) German
£300 $456 €450 Vessels moored on a river at dusk (27x35cm-11x14in) s. panel. 29-Aug-2 Christie's, Kensington #253
£357 $532 €550 Sunset on lakeshore (22x33cm-9x13in) s. 26-Jun-2 Neumeister, Munich #752
£385 $585 €600 Fishing boats in bay (26x34cm-10x13in) s. board. 11-Jul-2 Hugo Ruef, Munich #687/R
£520 $842 €754 Figure in horsedrawn cart in wooded landscape (15x12cm-6x5in) s. panel. 24-May-3 Windibank, Dorking #295
£641 $1013 €1000 Viaduct near Roman (20x31cm-8x12in) s. canvas on panel. 15-Nov-2 Reiss & Sohn, Konigstein #35/R
£671 $1100 €973 Hunters in a river landscape (38x56cm-15x22in) s. 4-Jun-3 Doyle, New York #63 est:2000-3000
£681 $1076 €1022 View towards a fishing village (47x67cm-19x26in) s. 2-Dec-2 Rasmussen, Copenhagen #1392/R (D.KR 8000)
£700 $1099 €1050 Village on an estuary (71x96cm-28x38in) s. 16-Apr-3 Christie's, Kensington #717
£881 $1374 €1400 By the river - in England (26x34cm-10x13in) s. panel. 11-Oct-2 Winterberg, Heidelberg #545/R
£900 $1467 €1350 House on the river (79x119cm-31x47in) s. 13-Feb-3 Christie's, Kensington #171/R
£1026 $1590 €1600 Lower Rhineland river landscape (66x95cm-26x37in) s. 5-Dec-2 Dr Fritz Nagel, Stuttgart #660/R est:1200
£1392 $2200 €2088 View of men fishing nets in marshlands (43x61cm-17x24in) s. 26-Apr-3 Thomaston Place, Thomaston #117
£1447 $2242 €2300 Seaside town (56x75cm-22x30in) s. 2-Nov-2 Hans Stahl, Toestorf #10/R est:1700
£1550 $2511 €2248 Figure in rowing boat with church and buildings on riverbank (47x73cm-19x29in) s. 24-May-3 Windibank, Dorking #296/R est:1400-1600
£2103 $3323 €3155 North German landscape with busy river in the evening (80x100cm-31x39in) s. 26-Nov-2 Hans Widmer, St Gallen #1149/R est:4500-8000 (S.FR 4900)
£3632 $5884 €5448 English landscape (80x130cm-31x51in) s. 24-May-3 Dorotheum, Prague #43/R est:160000-280000 (C.KR 160000)
£4000 $6200 €6000 On the edge of the wood (35x85cm-14x33in) s. 6-Dec-2 Lyon & Turnbull, Edinburgh #101/R est:2000-3000

HEGEDUS, Endre (1913-) Hungarian
£3227 $5002 €4841 December (44x50cm-17x20in) 6-Dec-2 Kieselbach, Budapest #186/R (H.F 1200000)

HEGENBARTH, Emanuel (1868-1923) German
£2564 $3974 €4000 Summer's day in the country (100x149cm-39x59in) s. 5-Dec-2 Dr Fritz Nagel, Stuttgart #661/R est:4000
Works on paper
£504 $806 €700 Pan - magazine cover (43x37cm-17x15in) i. verso gouache chk. 15-May-3 Neumeister, Munich #103/R

HEGENBARTH, Josef (1884-1962) German
£4717 $7264 €7500 Poultry (29x35cm-11x14in) panel. 26-Oct-2 Dr Lehr, Berlin #155/R est:6000
Works on paper
£225 $328 €350 Restaurant (14x20cm-6x8in) s. Indian ink brush pen. 4-Jun-2 Karl & Faber, Munich #266
£417 $609 €650 Collection of animals (30x22cm-12x9in) s. Indian ink brush pen. 4-Jun-2 Karl & Faber, Munich #265
£431 $699 €647 Wild boars (34x43cm-13x17in) s. mixed media. 24-May-3 Dorotheum, Prague #229/R est:10000-15000 (C.KR 19000)
£449 $696 €700 Hen (39x35cm-15x14in) s. i. verso Indian ink pen brush. 4-Dec-2 Lempertz, Koln #776/R
£513 $795 €800 Resting deer (37x40cm-15x16in) s. i.verso gouache double-sided. 4-Dec-2 Neumeister, Munich #515/R
£1056 $1754 €1500 Girl's head (45x33cm-18x13in) s. i. verso W/C pen. 14-Jun-3 Hauswedell & Nolte, Hamburg #1250/R est:1000
£1197 $1987 €1700 Man's head (43x34cm-17x13in) s. Indian ink brush W/C tempera. 14-Jun-3 Hauswedell & Nolte, Hamburg #1251/R est:1200
£2564 $4051 €4000 Pedestrians (35x24cm-14x9in) s. glue board. 15-Nov-2 Reiss & Sohn, Konigstein #542/R est:2000
£2722 $4300 €4300 Cafe concert (31x43cm-12x17in) s. mixed media board. 30-Nov-2 Bassenge, Berlin #6312/R est:4000
£3165 $5000 €5000 Watching the giraffes in the zoo (39x29cm-15x11in) s. mixed media board. 30-Nov-2 Bassenge, Berlin #6313/R est:4000

HEGER, Heinrich Anton (1832-1888) German
£2041 $3245 €3000 Room in the Doges Palace, Venice (54x45cm-21x18in) s.i. panel. 19-Mar-3 Neumeister, Munich #581/R est:2000

HEGG, Teresa (fl.1872-1893) British
Works on paper
£650 $1086 €943 Still life of white roses and poppies (37x53cm-15x21in) s. W/C. 24-Jun-3 Bonhams, Knightsbridge #156/R

HEGI, Johann Salomon (1814-1896) Swiss
Works on paper
£1300 $2067 €1950 Mexican family outside their hut (29x40cm-11x16in) s. W/C. 29-Apr-3 Bonhams, New Bond Street #218/R est:1000-1500

HEGI, Johann Salomon (attrib) (1814-1896) Swiss
Works on paper
£1859 $2881 €2900 Mexican scene (23x32cm-9x13in) bears sig. W/C. 6-Dec-2 Maigret, Paris #52 est:2200

HEIBERG, Astri Welhaven (1881-1967) Norwegian
£302 $505 €438 Woman and flowers (53x46cm-21x18in) init. panel. 18-Jun-3 Grev Wedels Plass, Oslo #181 (N.KR 3500)

HEIBERG, Jean (1884-1976) Norwegian
£436 $685 €654 Landscape (61x76cm-24x30in) s. 25-Nov-2 Blomqvist, Lysaker #1112/R (N.KR 5000)
£542 $879 €813 Landscape (61x76cm-24x30in) s. panel. 27-Jan-3 Blomqvist, Lysaker #1078/R (N.KR 6000)
£15385 $24923 €23078 From Brevik - two boys on fence (89x117cm-35x46in) s.d.1918. 26-May-3 Grev Wedels Plass, Oslo #44/R est:150000-200000 (N.KR 170000)

HEICKE, Joseph (1811-1861) Austrian
£2177 $3461 €3200 On the alpine pasture (52x68cm-20x27in) s. 25-Feb-3 Dorotheum, Vienna #159/R est:2500-3000

HEICKE, Joseph (attrib) (1811-1861) Austrian
£705 $1107 €1100 Shepherd with his herd on the way to drink (58x70cm-23x28in) 10-Dec-2 Dorotheum, Vienna #54/R
£890 $1398 €1300 Hunters resting before view of Schloss Taufer in southern Tyrol (55x68cm-22x27in) 16-Apr-3 Dorotheum, Salzburg #69/R

HEICKELL, Arthur (1873-1958) Finnish
£252 $390 €400 Landscape from Paijanne (40x50cm-16x20in) s. 6-Oct-2 Bukowskis, Helsinki #182/R
£272 $433 €400 Graveyard (45x65cm-18x26in) s. 24-Mar-3 Bukowskis, Helsinki #84/R
£275 $450 €420 Autumn (40x50cm-16x20in) s. 9-Feb-3 Bukowskis, Helsinki #254/R
£283 $436 €450 Lake landscape (40x50cm-16x20in) s. 24-Oct-2 Hagelstam, Helsinki #909
£289 $446 €460 Beach (40x50cm-16x20in) s. 24-Oct-2 Hagelstam, Helsinki #980
£306 $487 €450 View across the sea (40x50cm-16x20in) s. 24-Mar-3 Bukowskis, Helsinki #86/R
£314 $484 €500 Pielisjarvi (53x81cm-21x32in) s. 24-Oct-2 Hagelstam, Helsinki #954
£314 $484 €500 Landscape (34x50cm-13x20in) s. 24-Oct-2 Hagelstam, Helsinki #850
£314 $487 €500 The red villa (45x65cm-18x26in) s. 6-Oct-2 Bukowskis, Helsinki #183/R
£316 $494 €500 Washing clothes (36x51cm-14x20in) s. 15-Sep-2 Bukowskis, Helsinki #202/R
£317 $501 €460 Lake landscape (40x50cm-16x20in) s. 3-Apr-3 Hagelstam, Helsinki #1055
£329 $513 €520 River landscape (48x68cm-19x27in) s. 12-Sep-2 Hagelstam, Helsinki #922
£340 $541 €500 Birches on the beach (51x40cm-20x16in) s.d.05. 24-Mar-3 Bukowskis, Helsinki #87/R
£355 $561 €550 Landscape (40x50cm-16x20in) s. 19-Dec-2 Hagelstam, Helsinki #846
£358 $552 €570 Sunset (46x66cm-18x26in) s. 27-Oct-2 Bukowskis, Helsinki #184/R
£374 $614 €520 Coastal landscape (48x65cm-19x26in) s. 5-Jun-3 Hagelstam, Helsinki #1013
£408 $649 €600 Pine trees on coastal cliff (67x83cm-26x33in) s. 24-Mar-3 Bukowskis, Helsinki #85/R
£418 $652 €660 Landscape with trees and lake, Esbo (65x80cm-26x31in) s. 12-Sep-2 Hagelstam, Helsinki #978/R
£428 $659 €680 Cottage on shore (48x65cm-19x26in) s. 27-Oct-2 Bukowskis, Helsinki #185/R
£440 $678 €700 Landscape (63x97cm-25x38in) s. 24-Oct-2 Hagelstam, Helsinki #1056
£453 $697 €720 Cottage in Urjala (64x79cm-25x31in) s.i. 27-Oct-2 Bukowskis, Helsinki #186/R
£483 $763 €700 Coastal cliffs (40x58cm-16x23in) s. 3-Apr-3 Hagelstam, Helsinki #868
£490 $804 €750 Coastal landscape with pine trees (45x64cm-18x25in) s. 9-Feb-3 Bukowskis, Helsinki #253/R
£523 $858 €800 View from Paijanne (55x81cm-22x32in) s. 9-Feb-3 Bukowskis, Helsinki #251/R
£752 $1233 €1150 Wash day (40x50cm-16x20in) s. 9-Feb-3 Bukowskis, Helsinki #252/R

HEIDE, Alfred (1855-?) German
Works on paper
£269 $423 €420 Hamburg Harbour (46x64cm-18x25in) s. mixed media board. 23-Nov-2 Arnold, Frankfurt #748

HEIDE, Ella (?) Danish?
£280 $445 €420 Dune landscape with lighthouse (35x52cm-14x20in) s.i. 5-May-3 Rasmussen, Vejle #632 (D.KR 3000)

HEIDE, Johannes Wilhelm van der (1878-1957) Dutch
£1783 $2746 €2800 Cows in a sunlit meadow (36x35cm-14x14in) s. cardboard exhib. 3-Sep-2 Christie's, Amsterdam #277/R est:2000-3000
£1986 $3099 €2900 Cows in summer landscape (32x40cm-13x16in) s. board. 10-Apr-3 Van Ham, Cologne #1472/R est:1800

HEIDECK, Carl Wilhelm von (1788-1861) German
£15068 $23507 €22000 Russian and polish cavalry in field camp (72x87cm-28x34in) d.1834. 10-Apr-3 Van Ham, Cologne #1471/R est:9000

HEIDECK, Carl Wilhelm von (attrib) (1788-1861) German
£16438 $25644 €24000 Soldiers in village (71x87cm-28x34in) d.1834. 10-Apr-3 Van Ham, Cologne #1480/R est:9000

HEIDEKEN, Per Gustaf von (1781-1864) Swedish
£420 $664 €630 Figure and horse in a barn interior (29x24cm-11x9in) indis.sig. panel. 27-Nov-2 Hamptons Fine Art, Godalming #454

HEIDER, Hans (1861-1947) German
£377 $581 €600 Ramersdorf Church in Munich (37x67cm-15x26in) s.i. 23-Oct-2 Neumeister, Munich #655/R

HEIGEL, Joseph (1780-1837) German
Miniatures
£9500 $14915 €14250 Reise family, Comte de Reiset and his eldest son. Comtesse de Reiset and her younger son seated (12x16cm-5x6in) s. gilt wood frame pair prov.lit. 10-Dec-2 Christie's, London #228/R est:6000-8000

HEIGHTON, Brent (1954-) Canadian
Works on paper
£562 $888 €843 Power of the mountain (79x107cm-31x42in) W/C. 1-Dec-2 Levis, Calgary #43/R (C.D 1400)

HEIJBERG, Johannes Gerardus (1869-1952) Dutch
£2420 $3776 €3800 Soldiers in a waiting room (45x60cm-18x24in) s. 6-Nov-2 Vendue Huis, Gravenhage #510/R est:2000-3000
Works on paper
£657 $1078 €953 Young man wearing blue hat (70x55cm-28x22in) s. W/C htd white. 4-Jun-3 Fischer, Luzern #2469/R (S.FR 1400)

HEIJBOER, Anton (20th C) Dutch?
Works on paper
£538 $850 €850 Wat is de zon weer aardig voor ons (78x106cm-31x42in) s. W/C chk. 26-Nov-2 Palais de Beaux Arts, Brussels #406

HEIKKA, Earle E (1910-1941) American
Sculpture
£1582 $2500 €2294 Glassing the north slope (33cm-13in) bronze. 26-Jul-3 Coeur d'Alene, Hayden #44/R est:3000-5000
£1761 $2800 €2642 Standing cowboy (53cm-21in) i. bronze marble base i.f.JHM Classic. 5-Mar-3 Sotheby's, New York #149/R est:4000-6000

HEIKKILA, Erkki (1933-) Finnish
£331 $543 €460 Female nude (92x72cm-36x28in) s.d.75. 4-Jun-3 Bukowskis, Helsinki #296/R

HEIKKILA, Kustaa (1870-1937) Finnish
£3291 $5200 €5200 Fishermen hauling in the seine in Karelen (70x150cm-28x59in) s. 30-Nov-2 Hagelstam, Helsinki #100/R est:5000

HEIL, Charles Emile (1870-1953) American
Works on paper
£323 $500 €485 Black throated blue warbler (23x15cm-9x6in) s. W/C graphite prov. 2-Nov-2 North East Auctions, Portsmouth #88

HEIL, Daniel van (1604-1662) Flemish
£3354 $5500 €5031 Italianate landscape with fishermen by a river with a bridge (33x42cm-13x17in) init. panel prov. 5-Feb-3 Christie's, Rockefeller NY #262/R est:3000-5000
£6849 $10685 €10000 Cavaliers au bord d'une cascade avec ruines (72x114cm-28x45in) mono. 14-Apr-3 Horta, Bruxelles #193/R est:12000-15000

HEIL, Daniel van (attrib) (1604-1662) Flemish
£8276 $13241 €12000 De brand van Troje (164x240cm-65x94in) 17-Mar-3 Amberes, Antwerp #247/R

HEIL, Theodore van (fl.1668-1692) Flemish
£7000 $11690 €10150 Winter landscape with travellers and figures skating on a lake, village beyond (59x82cm-23x32in) 9-Jul-3 Bonhams, New Bond Street #18/R est:8000-12000

HEILBUTH, Ferdinand (1826-1889) French
£1410 $2200 €2115 Cardinal's arrival (84x61cm-33x24in) init. 9-Oct-2 Doyle, New York #55 est:4000-6000
£4000 $6680 €6000 La rasquette (34x57cm-13x22in) s. 18-Jun-3 Christie's, Kensington #134/R est:2000-3000
£6875 $11000 €10313 Figures on a terrace overlooking Rome, St Peters in the distance (84x129cm-33x51in) s. 14-May-3 Butterfields, San Francisco #1107/R est:10000-150000
£6962 $10861 €11000 Letter (115x145cm-45x57in) s.d.1858. 21-Oct-2 Bernaerts, Antwerp #90/R est:10000-15000
Works on paper
£302 $486 €450 Offrandes (37x46cm-15x18in) s. W/C. 18-Feb-3 Vanderkindere, Brussels #35
£567 $948 €800 Tete de femme de profil (21x19cm-8x7in) init. W/C prov. 20-Jun-3 Piasa, Paris #30/R
£1631 $2724 €2300 Elegante sur la plage (37x53cm-15x21in) s.i. W/C. 23-Jun-3 Beaussant & Lefèvre, Paris #314/R est:1500-2000

HEILIGER, Bernhard (1915-1995) German
Sculpture
£2899 $4754 €4000 Small figure (28x8x10cm-11x3x4in) brown pat.bronze prov.exhib.lit. 28-May-3 Lempertz, Koln #168/R est:6500
£6159 $10101 €8500 Bird torso (110cm-43in) s.d.69 brown pat.bronze Cast.W.Fussel 1 Berlin 10. 31-May-3 Villa Grisebach, Berlin #326/R est:6000-8000
£6203 $9800 €9800 Head of a figure I (28cm-11in) mono.d.49 aluminium exhib. 30-Nov-2 Villa Grisebach, Berlin #356/R est:4000-5000

HEILMANN, Anton Paul (1830-1912) Austrian
Works on paper
£629 $975 €1000 Barock house in landscaped gardens (45x74cm-18x29in) s. W/C. 1-Oct-2 Dorotheum, Vienna #336/R

HEILMANN, Flora (1872-1944) Danish
£266 $431 €399 Flowers in vase (50x35cm-20x14in) s.d.1915. 25-Jan-3 Rasmussen, Havnen #2024/R (D.KR 3000)

HEILMANN, Gerhard (1859-1946) Danish
£335 $543 €486 Still life of fruit (32x23cm-13x9in) init.d.85. 24-May-3 Rasmussen, Havnen #2288 (D.KR 3500)

HEILMANN, Karl (1881-) German
£226 $350 €339 Snow scene with chalet (76x122cm-30x48in) s. painted 1919. 6-Dec-2 Eldred, East Dennis #1036/R

HEILMAYER, Karl (1829-1908) German
£897 $1409 €1400 Florentine landscape in evening light (42x61cm-17x24in) s.d.1856. 21-Nov-2 Van Ham, Cologne #1658/R
£949 $1472 €1500 Evening near Bozen (75x55cm-30x22in) s.d.1899. 25-Sep-2 Neumeister, Munich #596/R est:1500
£1013 $1570 €1600 Venice by moonlight (16x27cm-6x11in) s.d.71 panel. 25-Sep-2 Neumeister, Munich #597/R est:1200
£1056 $1701 €1500 St Bartholome with Funtensee Grundseetauern and Schonfeldspitze (28x39cm-11x15in) s.d.1863. 7-May-3 Vendue Huis, Gravenhage #375/R est:1500-2000
£2532 $4000 €4000 Bozen at evening time (75x55cm-30x22in) i.verso. 28-Nov-2 Dorotheum, Vienna #38/R est:4500-5000

HEIM, François Joseph (1787-1865) French
£6757 $10541 €10000 Prise du Temple de Jerusalem (57x74cm-22x29in) 26-Mar-3 Tajan, Paris #101/R est:12000
Works on paper
£2903 $4500 €4355 Portrait of the Duke of Nemours (33x18cm-13x7in) mono. pencil black white chk. 29-Oct-2 Sotheby's, New York #18/R est:1000-1500

HEIM, François Joseph (circle) (1787-1865) French
£11189 $18686 €16000 La victoire des Turcs a Nicopolis (70x115cm-28x45in) i.verso. 25-Jun-3 Tajan, Paris #87/R est:8000-12000

HEIMBACH, Christian Wolfgang (1613-1678) German
£15711 $25766 €22781 Charlotte, Countess of Hohenloe (21x15cm-8x6in) i.d.1652 copper. 4-Jun-3 AB Stockholms Auktionsverk #2519/R est:50000-70000 (S.KR 200000)
£15711 $25766 €22781 Philippa Sabina, Countess of Hohenlohe (21x15cm-8x6in) i.d.1653 copper. 4-Jun-3 AB Stockholms Auktionsverk #2521/R est:50000-70000 (S.KR 200000)

HEIMBUECHER, Elizabeth (20th C) American
£321 $500 €482 Wooded autumn landscape (61x51cm-24x20in) s. 10-Nov-2 Selkirks, St. Louis #846/R

HEIMERDINGER, Friedrich (1817-1882) Italian/German
£720 $1174 €1080 Hanging bird on a cigar box lid (23x18cm-9x7in) s. i.verso. 29-Jan-3 Brightwells, Leominster #872/R

HEIMERL, Josef (19/20th C) Austrian
£338 $527 €500 Two kittens (20x25cm-8x10in) s. 26-Mar-3 Hugo Ruef, Munich #127/R
£505 $783 €758 Small dog in kitchen (39x90cm-15x35in) painted c.1900. 3-Dec-2 SOGA, Bratislava #165/R (SL.K 32000)
£642 $1001 €950 Two puppies playing (20x25cm-8x10in) s. 26-Mar-3 Hugo Ruef, Munich #126/R

HEIN, Alois Raimond (1852-1936) Austrian
£609 $926 €950 Still life of fruit (30x23cm-12x9in) s.i. panel. 31-Aug-2 Geble, Radolfzell #638/R
£609 $926 €950 Still life of flowers (30x23cm-12x9in) s.i. panel. 31-Aug-2 Geble, Radolfzell #639

HEIN, Eduard (19th C) German
£641 $1006 €1000 Bacharach am Rhein (68x97cm-27x38in) s. 21-Nov-2 Van Ham, Cologne #1659/R
£641 $1006 €1000 Stolzenfels am Rhein (69x98cm-27x39in) s. 21-Nov-2 Van Ham, Cologne #1660/R
£818 $1275 €1300 Vierwaldstattersee with Tell chapel (47x65cm-19x26in) s. 9-Oct-2 Michael Zeller, Lindau #723/R
£837 $1222 €1256 Winter landscape with stream, figures and animals (94x131cm-37x52in) s.i. 17-Jun-2 Philippe Schuler, Zurich #4346 (S.FR 1900)

HEIN, Eduard (jnr) (19/20th C) German
£605 $962 €908 Winter landscape with house, river and birds in flight at sunset (36x28cm-14x11in) s. 5-Mar-3 Rasmussen, Copenhagen #1917/R (D.KR 6500)

HEIN, Marie Vlielander (1871-1955) Dutch
£352 $567 €500 Still life of flowers (43x28cm-17x11in) s. 7-May-3 Vendue Huis, Gravenhage #173/R

HEINE, Harry (1928-) Canadian
Works on paper
£699 $1112 €1049 Trawler off Macaulay Point, Victoria, Vancouver Island (35x53cm-14x21in) s.i. W/C. 23-Mar-3 Hodgins, Calgary #117/R est:750-1000 (C.D 1650)

HEINE, Thomas Theodor (1867-1948) German
£321 $468 €500 The patron (38x35cm-15x14in) mono.i. Indian ink pen over pencil bodycol. 4-Jun-2 Karl & Faber, Munich #273
Works on paper
£385 $562 €600 Studio visit (26x29cm-10x11in) s. Indian ink brush pen over pencil bodycol. 4-Jun-2 Karl & Faber, Munich #272
£545 $845 €850 Zepplin oak in Klein Butzig (30x23cm-12x9in) mono. W/C Indian in pencil bodycol. 7-Dec-2 Ketterer, Hamburg #244/R
£577 $912 €900 Oktoberfest (20x22cm-8x9in) s.mono.i. Indian ink over pencil htd white. 14-Nov-2 Neumeister, Munich #581/R

HEINEFETTER, Johann (1815-1902) German
£1401 $2186 €2200 Laden donkey with figures high up with view of a southern bay (31x40cm-12x16in) s.d.1874 board lit. 7-Nov-2 Allgauer, Kempten #2833/R est:2900

HEINEL, Eduard (1835-1895) German
£1233 $1923 €1800 Fishermen and women dancing on Capri beach in the evening (47x62cm-19x24in) s. panel lit. 10-Apr-3 Allgauer, Kempten #2796/R est:1000

HEINEMANN, Reinhardt (1895-1967) German
Works on paper
£372 $592 €558 Composition (44x53cm-17x21in) s.d.20/1-1939 W/C. 10-Mar-3 Rasmussen, Vejle #763 (D.KR 4000)

HEINER, Meyer (1953-) German
£1064 $1723 €1500 Head of Apollo (60x50cm-24x20in) s. s.d.98 verso. 20-May-3 Dorotheum, Vienna #285/R est:1400-1600
£1064 $1723 €1500 Head of Aphrodite (60x50cm-24x20in) s. s.d.1995 verso. 20-May-3 Dorotheum, Vienna #286/R est:1400-1600

HEINES, H (19th C) Dutch
£709 $1099 €1064 Coastal landscape (14x17cm-6x7in) s.d.91 panel. 4-Dec-2 AB Stockholms Auktionsverk #1892/R (S.KR 10000)

HEINESEN, Zakarias (1936-) Danish
£953 $1592 €1382 Landscape, Funningur (70x90cm-28x35in) s.d.83. 17-Jun-3 Rasmussen, Copenhagen #170/R (D.KR 10000)

HEINISCH, A (?) ?
£442 $689 €663 Figures and buildings by the bank (57x75cm-22x30in) s. 5-Aug-2 Rasmussen, Vejle #2303 (D.KR 5200)

HEINISCH, Barbara (1944-) German
£1090 $1689 €1700 Movement with Sybille. s.d.82 one i. tempera triptych prov. 7-Dec-2 Van Ham, Cologne #218/R est:1800

HEINISCH, Karl Adam (1847-1923) German
£2042 $3288 €2900 Hay harvest (18x27cm-7x11in) s.i. panel lit. 9-May-3 Schloss Ahlden, Ahlden #1426/R est:2900
£7042 $11549 €10211 Village idyll with stream (15x26cm-6x10in) s.d.1881 panel. 4-Jun-3 Fischer, Luzern #1142/R est:15000-18000 (S.FR 15000)

HEINONEN, Aarre (1906-) Finnish
£621 $981 €900 Composition (33x46cm-13x18in) s.d.1974. 3-Apr-3 Hagelstam, Helsinki #899

HEINRICH, Ernst (1896-1969) German
£1560 $2528 €2200 Putting on make up (51x39cm-20x15in) s. s.i.d.1923 verso board. 24-May-3 Van Ham, Cologne #248/R est:2400

HEINRICH, Franz (1802-1890) German
Works on paper
£600 $972 €900 Interior of the Vatican, Rome (35x48cm-14x19in) s. pencil W/C bodycol. 23-Jan-3 Christie's, Kensington #364/R
£1197 $1987 €1700 Dala dell'Illiade in the Galleria Palatina, Florence (42x60cm-17x24in) s. w/C. 12-Jun-3 Hauswedell & Nolte, Hamburg #354/R est:1200

HEINRICH-HANSEN, Adolf (1859-1925) Danish
£1772 $2818 €2658 Exterior with dog and puppies at the food dish (50x70cm-20x28in) s. 5-May-3 Rasmussen, Vejle #609/R est:10000-12000 (D.KR 19000)

HEINS (?) ?
£4321 $7086 €6265 Young girl with parrot (75x62cm-30x24in) s.d.1722 July 19. 4-Jun-3 AB Stockholms Auktionsverk #2545/R est:45000-50000 (S.KR 55000)

HEINSDORFF, Emil Ernst (1887-1948) German
£487 $711 €750 Idyllic mountain landscape (51x39cm-20x15in) s.d.1922/23 panel. 14-Jun-2 Auktionhaus Georg Rehm, Augsburg #8044/R

HEINSIUS, Johann Ernst (1740-1812) German
£2600 $4056 €3900 Portrait of the comtesse de Bernicourt with a rose in her hand (84x67cm-33x26in) i.verso. 10-Apr-3 Christie's, Kensington #162/R est:2000-3000

HEINSIUS, Johann Ernst (attrib) (1740-1812) German
£3846 $5962 €6000 Portrait d'homme tenant un medaillon (73x60cm-29x24in) 6-Dec-2 Millon & Associes, Paris #70/R

HEINTZ, Joseph (elder) (1564-1609) Swiss
£13100 $20699 €19650 Abigail before David (173x280cm-68x110in) 14-Nov-2 Stuker, Bern #276/R est:40000-50000 (S.FR 30000)
Works on paper
£900 $1404 €1350 Scene of execution (15x13cm-6x5in) pen ink wash over black chk. 9-Apr-3 Bonhams, New Bond Street #145

HEINTZ, Joseph (elder-circle) (1564-1609) Swiss
£7483 $11898 €11000 Woman's portrait - possibly Philippine Le Roy, Dame de Ravels (25x19cm-10x7in) copper. 19-Mar-3 Neumeister, Munich #440/R est:6000

HEINTZ, Joseph (elder-style) (1564-1609) Swiss
£13413 $20925 €20120 Diana and Aktaeon (107x200cm-42x79in) 11-Apr-3 Kieselbach, Budapest #145/R est:4800000 (H.F 4800000)

HEINTZ, Richard (1871-1929) Belgian
£417 $654 €650 La meule et la ferme (15x20cm-6x8in) d.1919 i.verso panel. 11-Dec-2 Hotel des Ventes Mosan, Brussels #251
£609 $956 €950 Gros temps aqueduc (22x29cm-9x11in) s. i.d.1912 verso cardboard. 11-Dec-2 Hotel des Ventes Mosan, Brussels #301
£980 $1578 €1500 Vue de village ardennais (24x32cm-9x13in) s.d.1896 cardboard. 20-Jan-3 Horta, Bruxelles #75 est:1800-2200
£1769 $2812 €2600 Jeux d'ombres en foret (48x60cm-19x24in) s. prov.lit. 19-Mar-3 Hotel des Ventes Mosan, Brussels #238 est:2800-4200
£1905 $3029 €2800 La vieille barque, Sorrente (33x48cm-13x19in) s. s.i.d.sept 07 verso panel lit. 19-Mar-3 Hotel des Ventes Mosan, Brussels #309/R est:2900-3500
£1923 $3019 €3000 Temps de pluie a Sy (30x38cm-12x15in) s. s.i.verso. 11-Dec-2 Hotel des Ventes Mosan, Brussels #317a est:1900-2100
£2313 $3678 €3400 Vue de Nassogne (45x55cm-18x22in) s. i.d.1926 verso panel. 19-Mar-3 Hotel des Ventes Mosan, Brussels #251 est:4200-5600
£2313 $3678 €3400 Horizon (25x34cm-10x13in) s. canvas on panel. 19-Mar-3 Hotel des Ventes Mosan, Brussels #319 est:3600-3800
£2564 $4026 €4000 Solitude, a Sy (54x73cm-21x29in) s.d.04 i.verso. 11-Dec-2 Hotel des Ventes Mosan, Brussels #271/R est:4000-6000
£2857 $4543 €4200 Bord de l'Ourthe (14x19cm-6x7in) s. s.i.d.1915 verso panel. 19-Mar-3 Hotel des Ventes Mosan, Brussels #305/R est:3500-4000
£3205 $5032 €5000 Apres midi de decembre, Angleur (100x74cm-39x29in) s.d.1904 i.d.verso. 11-Dec-2 Hotel des Ventes Mosan, Brussels #261/R est:4500-5000

HEINZE, Adolph (1887-1958) American
£318 $500 €477 Mountain landscape with cabin (36x28cm-14x11in) s.verso canvasboard. 23-Nov-2 Jackson's, Cedar Falls #94/R
£411 $650 €617 Mountain ranch (71x81cm-28x32in) s. 1-Dec-2 Susanin's, Chicago #5155/R
£414 $650 €621 Majestic peaks (30x41cm-12x16in) s. canvasboard. 23-Nov-2 Jackson's, Cedar Falls #68/R

£1032 $1600 €1548 Firs against majesty (81x76cm-32x30in) s. 28-Sep-2 Charlton Hall, Columbia #546/R est:500-800
£2435 $3750 €3653 Glimpse of the harbour (71x71cm-28x28in) s. board prov. 24-Oct-2 Shannon's, Milford #29/R est:3000-5000

HEISIG, Bernhard (1925-) Polish
£5031 $7748 €8000 Gulper See at night (50x60cm-20x24in) s. s.i.d.1996 verso. 26-Oct-2 Dr Lehr, Berlin #165/R est:6000
£10507 $17232 €14500 Old houses in Warnau - on the Havel (60x80cm-24x31in) s. s. verso s.i.d.84 stretcher prov. 31-May-3 Villa Grisebach, Berlin #368/R est:15000-20000

Works on paper
£556 $878 €800 Gudrun II (59x42cm-23x17in) s. pencil board. 26-Apr-3 Dr Lehr, Berlin #197/R
£603 $977 €850 Girl (48x36cm-19x14in) s. Indian ink W/C. 24-May-3 Van Ham, Cologne #251/R

HEISKA, Joonas (1873-1937) Finnish
£354 $553 €560 Stones on the beach (25x34cm-10x13in) 15-Sep-2 Bukowskis, Helsinki #205/R
£386 $610 €560 Farmyard (34x40cm-13x16in) s. 3-Apr-3 Hagelstam, Helsinki #957
£475 $779 €660 Cows (37x32cm-15x13in) s. 5-Jun-3 Hagelstam, Helsinki #845/R
£755 $1170 €1200 Boats on shore (37x58cm-15x23in) 6-Oct-2 Bukowskis, Helsinki #187/R
£897 $1417 €1300 View of the sea (18x48cm-7x19in) s. 3-Apr-3 Hagelstam, Helsinki #956/R

HEISS, Johann (1640-1704) German
£15108 $24173 €21000 Death of Dido (82x99cm-32x39in) prov. 17-May-3 Lempertz, Koln #1059/R est:30000
£25899 $41439 €36000 Gathering of Gods (82x106cm-32x42in) MONO.D.1578. 17-May-3 Lempertz, Koln #1060/R est:15000

HEITER, Michael M (1883-?) American
£886 $1400 €1329 Autumn landscape (41x51cm-16x20in) s. 17-Nov-2 CRN Auctions, Cambridge #67a/R

HEITINGER, Paul (1841-1920) German
£252 $387 €400 Enjoying the ice (43x60cm-17x24in) s.i.d.1901. 23-Oct-2 Neumeister, Munich #657/R
£959 $1496 €1400 Bodensee (18x30cm-7x12in) s. i. verso panel. 10-Apr-3 Dorotheum, Vienna #67 est:1600-1800
£1538 $2385 €2400 Landscape by moonlight with village by lakeside (48x70cm-19x28in) s. 4-Dec-2 Neumeister, Munich #763/R est:1000

HEKKING, Carel Josephus Antonius (1826-?) Dutch
£7534 $11753 €11000 Herders with cattle in wooded landscape (57x78cm-22x31in) s.d.1850 panel. 10-Apr-3 Van Ham, Cologne #1477/R est:7000

HEKKING, J A (1830-1903) American
£4465 $7100 €6698 Untitled, landscape with cows and pond (51x86cm-20x34in) 28-Feb-3 Douglas, South Deerfield #2

HEKKING, Joseph Antonio (1830-1903) American
£506 $800 €759 Winter landscape (33x23cm-13x9in) canvasboard. 15-Nov-2 Du Mouchelle, Detroit #2028/R

HELBERGER, Alfred Hermann (1871-1946) German
£500 $790 €750 Norwegian landscape (68x87cm-27x34in) s. prov. 3-Apr-3 Christie's, Kensington #109/R
£500 $790 €750 Norwegian landscape (49x60cm-19x24in) mono. prov. 3-Apr-3 Christie's, Kensington #115/R
£500 $790 €750 Mountains II (71x89cm-28x35in) mono. painted 1914 prov. 3-Apr-3 Christie's, Kensington #113/R
£2848 $4500 €4500 Norwegian landscape (94x140cm-37x55in) mono. 30-Nov-2 Villa Grisebach, Berlin #330/R est:3000-4000

HELBIG, Walter (1878-1965) German
£343 $542 €515 Portrait of a young lady (65x49cm-26x19in) s. 26-Nov-2 Hans Widmer, St Gallen #1151 (S.FR 800)
£1223 $1907 €1835 Mountain lake (59x46cm-23x18in) s. s.i.d. stretcher panel. 6-Nov-2 Hans Widmer, St Gallen #91/R est:2800-4800 (S.FR 2800)
£1528 $2384 €2292 Collina al lago (70x82cm-28x32in) s.d.45 i. stretcher. 6-Nov-2 Hans Widmer, St Gallen #22/R est:3500-7500 (S.FR 3500)
£1747 $2725 €2621 Women bathing in lake (62x66cm-24x26in) s.d.47 s.i.d. stretcher. 6-Nov-2 Hans Widmer, St Gallen #90/R est:3500-7000 (S.FR 4000)
£4292 $6781 €6438 Foreign town (85x95cm-33x37in) s.d.41 s.i.verso. 26-Nov-2 Hans Widmer, St Gallen #1150 est:8000-12000 (S.FR 10000)
£5652 $9270 €7800 Grotto I (57x43cm-22x17in) s. s.i. stretcher. 31-May-3 Villa Grisebach, Berlin #280/R est:4000-6000
£8584 $13562 €12876 Standing nude in landscape (113x80cm-44x31in) s.d.23 prov.exhib. 28-Nov-2 Christie's, Zurich #77/R est:20000-25000 (S.FR 20000)

HELBING, Ferenc (1870-1958) Hungarian
£1816 $2834 €2633 Dream of Emese (70x99cm-28x39in) s. lit. 12-Apr-3 Mu Terem Galeria, Budapest #28/R est:600000 (H.F 650000)

HELCK, Peter (1897-?) American
£6410 $10000 €9615 Motorists asking directions at town's centre (53x66cm-21x26in) s. casein board. 9-Nov-2 Illustration House, New York #127/R est:7000-10000

HELD, Al (1928-) American
Prints
£2439 $4000 €3537 Straits of Magellan (102x127cm-40x50in) hard ground etching lithograph. 1-Jun-3 Wright, Chicago #318/R est:5000-7000
Works on paper
£5096 $8000 €7644 Untitled (19x24cm-7x9in) liquitex board prov. 19-Nov-2 Wright, Chicago #236/R est:7000-9000

HELD, Alma M (1898-1988) American
£637 $1000 €956 Fall landscape (36x25cm-14x10in) s. i.verso artists board. 23-Nov-2 Jackson's, Cedar Falls #89/R
£701 $1100 €1052 Summer light Cape Cod (25x36cm-10x14in) i.verso artists board. 23-Nov-2 Jackson's, Cedar Falls #86/R
£1210 $1900 €1815 Landscape near Iowa city (25x36cm-10x14in) s. i.verso artists board. 23-Nov-2 Jackson's, Cedar Falls #87/R est:1000-1500

HELD, John (jnr) (1889-1958) American
Works on paper
£745 $1200 €1118 Man in beat up car gazes longingly at new model (18x25cm-7x10in) s. pen ink. 20-Feb-3 Illustration House, New York #78/R est:1500-2000
£1863 $3000 €2795 Mr Globe playing a saxophone (23x18cm-9x7in) s. pen ink W/C exec.c.1920. 10-May-3 Illustration House, New York #8/R est:3000-5000
£15385 $24000 €23078 Woman training a bulldog to sit up (46x36cm-18x14in) s. gouache. 9-Nov-2 Illustration House, New York #15/R est:10000-15000

HELDER, Johannes (1842-1913) Dutch
£348 $543 €550 Chickens (38x45cm-15x18in) s.d.1912. 21-Oct-2 Glerum, Amsterdam #74/R

HELDNER, Collette Pope (1902-1996) American
£481 $750 €722 Marchand's tin shop, rue Royale, New Orleans (51x41cm-20x16in) s. s.i.d.1932 verso board. 22-Sep-2 Jeffery Burchard, Florida #57
£570 $900 €855 Swamp Idyl, Louisiana Bayou country (61x76cm-24x30in) s. s.i.verso. 5-Apr-3 Neal Auction Company, New Orleans #348
£577 $900 €866 Swamp Idyll (61x122cm-24x48in) s. 20-Sep-2 New Orleans Auction, New Orleans #1231/R est:1000-1500
£577 $900 €866 Old slave quarters, rue Royale, Vieux Carre, New Orleans (13x10cm-5x4in) s. s.i.d.1933 verso board. 12-Oct-2 Neal Auction Company, New Orleans #600/R
£609 $950 €914 Swamp idyll, Louisiana bayou country (86x56cm-34x22in) s. s.i.verso. 12-Oct-2 Neal Auction Company, New Orleans #1410
£610 $1000 €885 Swamp Idyll, Louisiana Bayou Country (61x102cm-24x40in) s. s.i.verso. 7-Jun-3 Neal Auction Company, New Orleans #402/R est:1500-2500
£897 $1400 €1346 Hot Tamale Vendor, Vieux Carre, New Orleans (13x10cm-5x4in) s. s.i.d.1933 verso board. 12-Oct-2 Neal Auction Company, New Orleans #601/R est:1200-1800
£1282 $2000 €1923 Old courtyard, South Stockholme (46x36cm-18x14in) s. 20-Sep-2 New Orleans Auction, New Orleans #1232/R est:2000-4000
£1299 $2000 €1949 Swamp idyll, Louisiana bayou country (41x51cm-16x20in) s.i. board painted c.1950. 8-Sep-2 Treadway Gallery, Cincinnati #658/R est:1000-2000
£2405 $3800 €3608 New Orleans courtyard with a Creole woman (51x41cm-20x16in) s. board. 5-Apr-3 Neal Auction Company, New Orleans #334/R est:2000-3000

HELDNER, Knute (1884-1952) American
£1069 $1700 €1604 Pioneers (12x23cm-5x9in) s. board painted c.1925. 4-May-3 Treadway Gallery, Cincinnati #564/R est:2500-4500
£1161 $1800 €1742 Cabin in the bayou (41x51cm-16x20in) s. 7-Dec-2 Neal Auction Company, New Orleans #482/R est:2000-3000
£1923 $3000 €2885 Bayou landscape (41x51cm-16x20in) s. 12-Oct-2 Neal Auction Company, New Orleans #642/R est:2500-3500

£1923 $3000 €2885 Louisiana bayou with fisherman and cabin (41x51cm-16x20in) s. 12-Oct-2 Neal Auction Company, New Orleans #661/R est:3000-5000
£2244 $3500 €3366 Going to mass no 10 (61x43cm-24x17in) s. i.verso artist board. 12-Oct-2 Neal Auction Company, New Orleans #641/R est:4000-6000

HELDT, Werner (1904-1954) German
£9494 $15000 €15000 City street at night (63x80cm-25x31in) panel prov.exhib. 30-Nov-2 Villa Grisebach, Berlin #284/R est:20000-30000
Works on paper
£1250 $1975 €1800 Almond trees on Mallorca (31x47cm-12x19in) mono.d.1935 s.i. verso. 26-Apr-3 Dr Lehr, Berlin #203/R est:2000
£2264 $3487 €3600 Still life with houses (31x43cm-12x17in) mno.d.1950 chl wash. 26-Oct-2 Dr Lehr, Berlin #166/R est:4500
£2465 $4092 €3500 Lakeside Berlin (30x41cm-12x16in) mono.i.d.1948 Indian ink brush exhib. 14-Jun-3 Hauswedell & Nolte, Hamburg #1252/R est:3000
£2564 $3974 €4000 Composition - helmet (48x62cm-19x24in) mono.d.1950 chl. 7-Dec-2 Hauswedell & Nolte, Hamburg #742/R est:5000
£2778 $4389 €4000 Still life at window (42x49cm-17x19in) mono.d.1949 W/C. 26-Apr-3 Dr Lehr, Berlin #205/R est:5000
£2917 $4608 €4200 Woman at window (62x47cm-24x19in) chl. 26-Apr-3 Dr Lehr, Berlin #204/R est:3600
£5063 $8000 €8000 Still life at window with geometric forms (30x35cm-12x14in) mono.d.50 prov. 30-Nov-2 Villa Grisebach, Berlin #358/R est:8000-10000
£7246 $11884 €10000 Berlin by the sea (62x48cm-24x19in) mono.d.48 i. verso chl prov.exhib. 29-May-3 Lempertz, Koln #672/R est:12000-14000
£13768 $22580 €19000 Uproar (73x99cm-29x39in) mono.d.48 chl prov.exhib. 30-May-3 Villa Grisebach, Berlin #63/R est:15000-20000
£19565 $32087 €27000 Street still life (48x61cm-19x24in) mono.d.49 i. verso W/C Indian ink brush chl prov.exhib. 29-May-3 Lempertz, Koln #673/R est:22000-25000

HELENIUS, Ester (1875-1955) Finnish
£748 $1190 €1100 Old bridge (61x50cm-24x20in) s.d.37. 24-Mar-3 Bukowskis, Helsinki #92/R
Works on paper
£1266 $2000 €2000 The girl from Vederlax (34x39cm-13x15in) s. mixed media executed c.1896-98 lit. 30-Nov-2 Hagelstam, Helsinki #83/R est:1500

HELENIUS, Jorma (1955-) Finnish
£1509 $2325 €2400 Winter (45x36cm-18x14in) s. 24-Oct-2 Hagelstam, Helsinki #1038 est:1000
£2390 $3681 €3800 Birch grove (40x52cm-16x20in) s. 24-Oct-2 Hagelstam, Helsinki #1033 est:1000
£2676 $4308 €3800 Oak grove (63x94cm-25x37in) s. 10-May-3 Bukowskis, Helsinki #59/R est:4000-5000
£4214 $6489 €6700 Landscape (58x82cm-23x32in) s. 24-Oct-2 Hagelstam, Helsinki #1027 est:2000

HELFFERICH, Frans (1871-1941) Dutch
£266 $415 €420 Hens in the yard (17x23cm-7x9in) s. panel. 21-Oct-2 Glerum, Amsterdam #224

HELINCK, Gustave (1884-1954) Belgian
£321 $503 €500 Marine (74x126cm-29x50in) s. 10-Dec-2 Campo, Vlaamse Kaai #231
£411 $642 €650 Paysage enneige (40x48cm-16x19in) s. 15-Oct-2 Horta, Bruxelles #344
£414 $662 €600 Depart des pecheurs (90x125cm-35x49in) s. 17-Mar-3 Horta, Bruxelles #124
£545 $845 €850 Depart des pecheurs (90x125cm-35x49in) s. 9-Dec-2 Horta, Bruxelles #351

HELION, Jean (1904-1987) French
£2199 $3562 €3100 Les toits (46x55cm-18x22in) mono.d.61 s.i.d.61 verso. 26-May-3 Joron-Derem, Paris #72/R est:3000
£2857 $4543 €4200 La chute au cafe (38x55cm-15x22in) mono.d.74 s.d.verso acrylic. 26-Feb-3 Artcurial Briest, Paris #525/R est:3000-3500
£5769 $9058 €9000 Composition (65x50cm-26x20in) s.d.26 prov.lit. 10-Dec-2 Piasa, Paris #223/R
£13462 $21135 €21000 Nature morte aux citrons (50x65cm-20x26in) init.d.29 paper on canvas prov.exhib.lit. 10-Dec-2 Piasa, Paris #221/R est:12000
£17000 $27710 €25500 Floralie (130x185cm-51x73in) s.i.d.67 verso prov.exhib. 3-Feb-3 Sotheby's, Olympia #185/R est:6000-8000
£17308 $27173 €27000 Formes trouees (46x65cm-18x26in) s.d.29 paper on canvas prov.exhib. 10-Dec-2 Piasa, Paris #222/R est:8000
£24359 $37756 €38000 Construction (66x50cm-26x20in) s.d.1929 cardboard exhib.lit. 9-Dec-2 Piasa, Paris #51/R est:15000-20000
£63830 $103404 €90000 Etude de tete (39x28cm-15x11in) studio st.verso panel prov.exhib. 21-May-3 Cornette de St.Cyr, Paris #72/R est:90000-110000
£92199 $149362 €130000 L'homme au chapeau (57x49cm-22x19in) s.d.verso prov.exhib. 21-May-3 Cornette de St.Cyr, Paris #71/R est:130000-150000
Works on paper
£769 $1208 €1200 Trois figures a New York (12x18cm-5x7in) s.d.1945 verso ink dr prov. 15-Dec-2 Perrin, Versailles #93/R
£949 $1472 €1500 Instrument sur un gueridon (45x64cm-18x25in) s.d. gouache. 28-Sep-2 Cornette de St.Cyr, Paris #162 est:2000-2500
£1156 $1839 €1700 Le songe (22x30cm-9x12in) mono.d.27.IV.79 W/C pastel ink. 26-Feb-3 Artcurial Briest, Paris #526/R est:1500-1800
£1560 $2528 €2200 Masque (26x20cm-10x8in) s.i.d. wash ink. 21-May-3 Cornette de St.Cyr, Paris #77/R est:2500-3000
£1603 $2516 €2500 Scene de rue a New York (12x19cm-5x7in) s.d.1944 W/C double-sided prov. 15-Dec-2 Perrin, Versailles #87/R
£1698 $2649 €2700 Figure complexe (35x27cm-14x11in) s.d.1937 ink crayon lit. 11-Oct-2 Binoche, Paris #137
£1736 $2760 €2500 Equilibre (14x16cm-6x6in) d.33 s.i.d.33 verso W/C ink. 29-Apr-3 Artcurial Briest, Paris #109/R est:3000-4000
£2903 $4587 €4500 Deux journaliers (23x31cm-9x12in) s.d.47 col crayon dr prov. 19-Dec-2 Ruellan, Paris #124/R
£3846 $5962 €6000 Equilibre (22x27cm-9x11in) s.i.d.1934 gouache W/C ink. 7-Dec-2 Cornette de St.Cyr, Paris #79/R est:8000
£4236 $6693 €6100 Composition (24x31cm-9x12in) s.i.d. ink W/C prov.exhib. 27-Apr-3 Perrin, Versailles #53/R est:4500-5000
£6410 $9936 €10000 Composition (19x25cm-7x10in) s.d.1932 gouache ink graphite. 7-Dec-2 Cornette de St.Cyr, Paris #78/R est:6000-8000
£6939 $11033 €10200 Equilibre (23x30cm-9x12in) s.d.35 W/C ink graphite. 26-Feb-3 Artcurial Briest, Paris #91/R est:7500-8500

HELL, Johan van (1889-1952) Dutch
£22152 $35000 €35000 Strand (75x87cm-30x34in) s.d.1925. 26-Nov-2 Sotheby's, Amsterdam #105a/R est:9000-12000

HELLEMANS, P J (20th C) ?
£2025 $3200 €3200 Moutons dans un paysage montagneux (64x53cm-25x21in) panel. 2-Dec-2 Amberes, Antwerp #1341a

HELLEMANS, Pierre (1787-1845) Belgian
£1156 $1839 €1700 River landscape with castle on river bank (24x31cm-9x12in) s. panel. 25-Feb-3 Dorotheum, Vienna #60/R est:2600-2800
£14194 $22426 €22000 Jeune berger au repos (43x36cm-17x14in) indis.sig. panel. 18-Dec-2 Tajan, Paris #57/R est:15000

HELLESEN, Hanne (1801-1844) Danish
£2973 $4786 €4460 Still life of flowers and fruit on ledge (39x47cm-15x19in) s.d.1832. 22-Feb-3 Rasmussen, Havnen #2074/R est:12000-15000 (D.KR 33000)

HELLESEN, Thorwald (1888-1937) Danish
Works on paper
£5714 $9086 €8400 Composition (44x28cm-17x11in) s. gouache. 26-Feb-3 Artcurial Briest, Paris #74 est:1500-1800

HELLEU, Jean (1894-1985) French
£2414 $3814 €3500 Hamble river near Southampton (46x61cm-18x24in) s. 4-Apr-3 Tajan, Paris #147/R

HELLEU, Paul-Cesar (1859-1927) French
Prints
£1923 $3000 €2885 Madame Letellier reading (55x34cm-22x13in) s. col drypoint exec.c.1890. 7-Nov-2 Swann Galleries, New York #438/R est:4000-6000
£1923 $3019 €3000 Elegante au chapeau (64x48cm-25x19in) s. drypoint. 13-Dec-2 Peschetau-Badin Godeau & Leroy, Paris #14
£2013 $3200 €3020 Madame Georges Menier (52x35cm-20x14in) s. col drypoint executed c.1900. 1-May-3 Swann Galleries, New York #324/R est:4000-6000
£2600 $4030 €3900 Femme au chapeau et collier de peries (68x48cm-27x19in) s. drypoint. 3-Dec-2 Christie's, London #135/R est:2000-3000
£2692 $4227 €4200 Elegante aux cheveux roux et chapeau. s. drypoint. 11-Dec-2 Maigret, Paris #30/R est:900-1000
Works on paper
£1351 $2108 €2000 Portrait de Arline Chase (48x29cm-19x11in) i. crayon sanguine. 26-Mar-3 Piasa, Paris #130/R
£2414 $3862 €3500 Mlle Marie. Jeune femme se tenant les mains (61x39cm-24x15in) col crayon double-sided. 12-Mar-3 Libert, Castor, Paris #120/R est:4000-5000
£2564 $3974 €4000 Femme accoudee (51x39cm-20x15in) crayon dr prov. 7-Dec-2 Cornette de St.Cyr, Paris #26/R est:5000
£2727 $4200 €4091 Young girl with a hat (63x49cm-25x19in) s. red black white chk paper on card. 4-Sep-2 Christie's, Rockefeller NY #317/R est:6000-8000

£3662 $6079 €5200 Portrait de femme (30x22cm-12x9in) s. col crayon dr. 11-Jun-3 Beaussant & Lefèvre, Paris #63/R est:5500-6000
£4088 $6377 €6500 Jeune femme de profil a gauche (31x25cm-12x10in) s. crayons. 10-Oct-2 Ribeyre & Baron, Paris #47/R est:7000-9000
£4403 $6868 €7000 Jeune femme de trois quarts a droite (42x35cm-17x14in) s. crayons. 10-Oct-2 Ribeyre & Baron, Paris #48/R est:10000-12000
£4808 $7548 €7500 Femme endormie aux mains jointes (41x48cm-16x19in) s. sanguine. 16-Dec-2 Eric Coutrier, Paris #65/R
£5500 $8690 €8250 Portrait de Margaret Kelly (57x76cm-22x30in) s.i. crayon. 3-Apr-3 Christie's, Kensington #26/R
£5696 $8886 €9000 Jeune femme assise (45x30cm-18x12in) s. sanguine chk. 20-Oct-2 Claude Boisgirard, Paris #8/R est:9000-12000
£5769 $9058 €9000 Femme en buste a la capeline (53x42cm-21x17in) s. chl col crayon. 16-Dec-2 Eric Coutrier, Paris #64/R
£5862 $9379 €8500 Elegante de trois quart face (59x49cm-23x19in) s. col crayon chk. 12-Mar-3 Libert, Castor, Paris #122/R est:4000-5000
£7692 $12077 €12000 Femme a la capeline (71x57cm-28x22in) s. chl col crayon. 16-Dec-2 Eric Coutrier, Paris #62/R est:15000
£7931 $12690 €11500 Elegante appuyee sur une chaise (86x50cm-34x20in) s. col crayon chk. 12-Mar-3 Libert, Castor, Paris #123/R est:4000-5000
£8276 $13241 €12000 Femme de profil et tete de femme (73x58cm-29x23in) s. col crayon. 12-Mar-3 Libert, Castor, Paris #121/R est:4000-5000
£8975 $14180 €14000 La lecture au salon (38x52cm-15x20in) s. chl sanguine htd white prov. 18-Nov-2 Tajan, Paris #183/R est:15000-20000
£11000 $18370 €15950 Portrait of an elegant woman wearing a hat, leaning on a chair (94x57cm-37x22in) s. col chk htd white prov. 8-Jul-3 Christie's, London #93/R est:12000-16000
£15385 $24154 €24000 Pli Watteau (71x51cm-28x20in) s. crayon dr. 16-Dec-2 Eric Coutrier, Paris #63/R est:15000

HELLGREWE, Rudolf (1860-?) German
£321 $497 €500 Mark landscape (31x47cm-12x19in) s. board prov. 7-Dec-2 Ketterer, Hamburg #169/R
£321 $497 €500 Mark lake landscape (80x120cm-31x47in) s. lit. 6-Dec-2 Karlheinz Kaupp, Staufen #2056
£353 $546 €550 Mark lake landscape in the evening (65x100cm-26x39in) s. lit. 6-Dec-2 Karlheinz Kaupp, Staufen #2023/R
£353 $546 €550 Mark lake landscape (80x120cm-31x47in) s. lit. 6-Dec-2 Karlheinz Kaupp, Staufen #2043
£385 $596 €600 Woodland by lake in Mark landscape (70x100cm-28x39in) s. lit. 6-Dec-2 Karlheinz Kaupp, Staufen #2031
£385 $596 €600 Mark lake in evening light (75x130cm-30x51in) s. lit. 6-Dec-2 Karlheinz Kaupp, Staufen #2054
£385 $596 €600 First October snows in evening landscape (100x80cm-39x31in) s. lit. 6-Dec-2 Karlheinz Kaupp, Staufen #2345/R
£2532 $4000 €4000 Mediterranean coast (184x234cm-72x92in) s. 29-Nov-2 Coutau Begarie, Paris #6

HELLHOF, Heinrich (1868-1914) German
£1362 $2151 €2043 The girls from Skagen (80x113cm-31x44in) s.d.1913. 2-Dec-2 Rasmussen, Copenhagen #1301/R est:15000 (D.KR 16000)

HELLINGRATH, Berthold (1877-?) German
£545 $861 €850 Marienkirche, Danzig on sunny winter afternoon (47x51cm-19x20in) s. board. 15-Nov-2 Reiss & Sohn, Konigstein #36/R

HELLMAN, Ake (1915-) Finnish
£302 $496 €420 Still life of vegetables and jug (32x46cm-13x18in) s. 5-Jun-3 Hagelstam, Helsinki #991/R

HELLMEIER, Otto (1908-) German
£253 $392 €400 Wetterstein view (20x29cm-8x11in) s. i. verso masonite. 26-Sep-2 Neumeister, Munich #2737
£256 $390 €400 Chiemsee (40x50cm-16x20in) s. panel. 11-Jul-2 Hugo Ruef, Munich #690
£316 $491 €500 Village of Solb (25x34cm-10x13in) s. i. verso masonite. 26-Sep-2 Neumeister, Munich #2736/R
£325 $484 €500 Still life of roses (24x17cm-9x7in) s. panel. 27-Jun-2 Neumeister, Munich #2740
£325 $484 €500 Still life of flowers (35x25cm-14x10in) s. panel. 27-Jun-2 Neumeister, Munich #2741
£519 $774 €800 Country garden in Raisting (35x50cm-14x20in) s. i. verso panel. 27-Jun-2 Neumeister, Munich #2739/R
£544 $865 €800 Iffeldorf (21x31cm-8x12in) s. board. 20-Mar-3 Neumeister, Munich #2640/R

HELLNER, Julius (20th C) German
£385 $604 €600 Shepherd with flock in autumnal landscape (93x149cm-37x59in) s.i. 23-Nov-2 Arnold, Frankfurt #750/R

HELLSTROM, Carl (1841-1916) Swedish
£315 $498 €473 Man on horseback, Skaane 1710 (60x43cm-24x17in) s. 16-Nov-2 Crafoord, Lund #29/R (S.KR 4500)

HELLWAG, Rudolf (1867-1942) German
£850 $1343 €1275 Cornish fishing village (58x74cm-23x29in) s. 17-Dec-2 Gorringes, Lewes #1495/R

HELLWEGER, Franz (1812-1880) Austrian
£609 $943 €914 Resting on the Flight (16x20cm-6x8in) mono. board. 9-Dec-2 Philippe Schuler, Zurich #8644 (S.FR 1400)

HELMAN, Robert (1910-) French
£500 $815 €750 Untitled (55x46cm-22x18in) s.d.1963 i.verso. 3-Feb-3 Sotheby's, Olympia #78/R
£500 $815 €750 La foret (130x95cm-51x37in) 3-Feb-3 Sotheby's, Olympia #209/R
£600 $978 €900 Untitled (81x100cm-32x39in) s. 3-Feb-3 Sotheby's, Olympia #77/R

HELMANTEL, Henk (1945-) Dutch
£7092 $11489 €10000 Still life of a door (41x35cm-16x14in) s.d.1972 panel. 26-May-3 Glerum, Amsterdam #256/R est:10000-15000
£8974 $13910 €14000 Geertekerk - utrecht (58x42cm-23x17in) s.d.1878 s.i.d.verso board. 3-Dec-2 Christie's, Amsterdam #190/R est:15000-20000
£15827 $25957 €22000 Sint Janskerk te Utrecht, naar het Zuid-westen (77x64cm-30x25in) s.d.1984 s.i.verso board. 3-Jun-3 Christie's, Amsterdam #213/R est:20000-30000
£16026 $25160 €25000 Still life with an apple, grapes and a glass vase (35x45cm-14x18in) s.d.2001 board. 25-Nov-2 Glerum, Amsterdam #242/R est:15000-20000
£20513 $31795 €32000 Still life with fruit (75x95cm-30x37in) s.d.1986 masonite prov. 3-Dec-2 Sotheby's, Amsterdam #4/R est:32000-45000
£20513 $31795 €32000 Stilleven met valappeltjes (56x47cm-22x19in) s.d.1996 s.d.verso board. 3-Dec-2 Christie's, Amsterdam #191/R est:20000-30000

HELMBERGER, Adolf (1885-1967) Austrian
£611 $954 €917 Wolfgangsee in summer (32x41cm-13x16in) s.d.1952. 6-Nov-2 Dobiaschofsky, Bern #644/R (S.FR 1400)
£705 $1114 €1100 Oeschinensee with Blumlisalp, Switzerland (41x36cm-16x14in) s. board. 18-Nov-2 Dorotheum, Linz #284/R
£1517 $2428 €2200 Early spring (60x50cm-24x20in) s.d.1938. 11-Mar-3 Dorotheum, Vienna #75/R est:1300-1600
£1583 $2532 €2200 Matterhorn (88x117cm-35x46in) s.d.1920. 14-May-3 Dorotheum, Klagenfurt #5/R est:500
£1747 $2725 €2621 Still life of flowers with Christmas roses (51x41cm-20x16in) s.d.1951 board. 6-Nov-2 Dobiaschofsky, Bern #643/R est:1600 (S.FR 4000)
£1799 $2950 €2500 View from Ostra in Gfohl in Waldviertel (76x85cm-30x33in) s.d.1931. 5-Jun-3 Dorotheum, Salzburg #542/R est:5000-6500
£3378 $5270 €5000 St Wolfgang (50x71cm-20x28in) s.d.1949. 25-Mar-3 Wiener Kunst Auktionen, Vienna #123/R est:4000-8000
£3597 $5899 €5000 Furberg near St Gilgen, (75x85cm-30x33in) s.d.1942 i.verso. 5-Jun-3 Dorotheum, Salzburg #543/R est:6000-7000
£4148 $6472 €6222 Winter landscape by Wolfgangsee (73x98cm-29x39in) s.d.1954. 6-Nov-2 Dobiaschofsky, Bern #642/R est:3600 (S.FR 9500)
£4676 $7669 €6500 Winter morning (70x100cm-28x39in) s.d.1930 i.verso. 5-Jun-3 Dorotheum, Salzburg #544/R est:6000-7000
Works on paper
£705 $1107 €1100 Mountain lake. Tree trunk (24x18cm-9x7in) s.d.1905 gouache. 21-Nov-2 Van Ham, Cologne #1662

HELMBREKER, Theodor (attrib) (1633-1696) Flemish
£2411 $3906 €3400 Peasants eating outside a homestead (71x94cm-28x37in) 21-May-3 James Adam, Dublin #18/R est:4000-5000

HELMBREKER, Theodor (circle) (1633-1696) Flemish
£13000 $20410 €19500 Village with peasants herding cattle, mountains landscape beyond (82x117cm-32x46in) 13-Dec-2 Christie's, Kensington #89/R est:7000-10000

HELME, Helge (1894-1987) Danish
£279 $441 €419 Girl drinking milk (46x38cm-18x15in) s.d.42. 1-Apr-3 Rasmussen, Copenhagen #582 (D.KR 3000)
£287 $465 €416 Young woman reading (24x18cm-9x7in) s. 26-May-3 Rasmussen, Copenhagen #1446 (D.KR 3000)
£293 $474 €440 Model asleep (17x22cm-7x9in) s. 25-Jan-3 Rasmussen, Havnen #2138 (D.KR 3300)
£301 $488 €452 Nude model asleep with blue blanket (22x36cm-9x14in) s. 25-Jan-3 Rasmussen, Havnen #2202/R (D.KR 3400)
£304 $474 €456 Seated nude model (106x78cm-42x31in) s. 23-Sep-2 Rasmussen, Vejle #2168 (D.KR 3600)
£340 $530 €510 Female nude on white cloth (35x27cm-14x11in) s. 5-Aug-2 Rasmussen, Vejle #69/R (D.KR 4000)
£341 $528 €512 Seated girl wearing white dress (47x38cm-19x15in) s. 28-Sep-2 Rasmussen, Havnen #2022 (D.KR 4000)
£343 $535 €515 Seated nude model (46x38cm-18x15in) s. 11-Nov-2 Rasmussen, Vejle #510/R (D.KR 4000)
£343 $535 €515 Young girl seated by potted plants (65x54cm-26x21in) s. 11-Nov-2 Rasmussen, Vejle #516/R (D.KR 4000)
£343 $535 €515 Nature study with nude woman (27x23cm-11x9in) s. 11-Nov-2 Rasmussen, Vejle #518/R (D.KR 4000)
£355 $553 €533 Reading the letter (35x27cm-14x11in) s. 23-Sep-2 Rasmussen, Vejle #159/R (D.KR 4200)
£373 $593 €560 Young girl wearing hat, reading (35x30cm-14x12in) s. 5-May-3 Rasmussen, Vejle #648/R (D.KR 4000)

£390	$604	€585	Portrait of young woman seated with red shawl (40x29cm-16x11in) s. 1-Oct-2 Rasmussen, Copenhagen #277/R (D.KR 4600)
£442	$689	€663	Female nude seated on white cloth (30x22cm-12x9in) s. 5-Aug-2 Rasmussen, Vejle #67/R (D.KR 5200)

Prints

£419	$666	€629	Portrait of young nude girl (35x27cm-14x11in) s. 10-Mar-3 Rasmussen, Vejle #44 (D.KR 4500)

HELMONT, Lucas van Gassel (attrib) (c.1480-c.1570) Flemish

£496	$829	€700	La Vierge a l'Enfant dans un paysage (22x34cm-9x13in) panel. 18-Jun-3 Tajan, Paris #56

HELMONT, Matheus van (1623-1679) Flemish

£8280	$12917	€13000	Peasant woman and a young man eating and drinking at a table (41x58cm-16x23in) s. prov.exhib.lit. 5-Nov-2 Sotheby's, Amsterdam #10/R est:15000-20000
£22642	$35094	€36000	Peasants drinking and making music in village square (77x118cm-30x46in) copper. 2-Oct-2 Dorotheum, Vienna #95/R est:25000-45000
£24828	$39228	€36000	La fete des Rois (58x82cm-23x32in) s. 2-Apr-3 Marc Kohn, Paris #14/R est:40000-44000

HELMONT, Matheus van (attrib) (1623-1679) Flemish

£2347	$3850	€3403	Peasant with pipe and jug stepping away from fireplace (22x16cm-9x6in) copper. 4-Jun-3 Fischer, Luzern #1023/R est:5000-6000 (S.FR 5000)
£8000	$13360	€11600	Interior scene with two ladies at their devotions amidst witch's sabbath (50x68cm-20x27in) bears sig. panel. 9-Jul-3 Bonhams, New Bond Street #107/R est:7000-9000

HELMONT, Zeger Jacob van (attrib) (1683-1726) Flemish

£487	$750	€731	Portrait of the artist (41x32cm-16x13in) 4-Sep-2 Christie's, Rockefeller NY #224/R
£2568	$4005	€3800	Self portrait (40x32cm-16x13in) 27-Mar-3 Dorotheum, Vienna #177/R est:3000-5000

HELNWEIN, Gottfried (1948-) Austrian

£4138	$6621	€6000	Untitled blue (200x150cm-79x59in) s. oil acrylic. 11-Mar-3 Dorotheum, Vienna #254/R est:12000-17000

Works on paper

£1192	$1943	€1800	Untitled (32x20cm-13x8in) s.d.72 pencil. 28-Jan-3 Dorotheum, Vienna #251/R est:1800-2400
£1250	$1975	€1800	Girl's face with plaster (34x18cm-13x7in) s.d.72 pencil. 24-Apr-3 Dorotheum, Vienna #220/R

HELPMAN, John Robert Crichton (1814-?) British

Works on paper

£850	$1326	€1275	Parthenon (28x38cm-11x15in) s. W/C over pencil prov. 15-Oct-2 Sotheby's, London #3/R

HELPS, Francis (fl.1910-1940) British

£250	$408	€375	Study of a nude lady seated (81x64cm-32x25in) 14-Feb-3 Keys, Aylsham #508
£800	$1264	€1200	Figures in classical landscape (44x59cm-17x23in) 27-Nov-2 Sotheby's, Olympia #98/R

HELST, Bartholomeus van der (attrib) (1613-1670) Dutch

£8922	$14453	€12937	Portrait of gentleman (100x86cm-39x34in) prov.exhib.lit. 26-May-3 Bukowskis, Stockholm #412/R est:125000-150000 (S.KR 115000)

HELST, Bartholomeus van der (circle) (1613-1670) Dutch

£5000	$8350	€7250	Portrait of a young lady, half-length in a red dress holding a minature (77x62cm-30x24in) oval. 9-Jul-3 Bonhams, New Bond Street #157/R est:5000-7000

HELSTED, Axel (1847-1907) Danish

£266	$431	€399	Church interior with figures (82x57cm-32x22in) s.d.1885. 25-Jan-3 Rasmussen, Havnen #2111/R (D.KR 3000)
£574	$930	€832	Interior scene with Italian girls (52x43cm-20x17in) s.i.d.1879 panel. 24-May-3 Rasmussen, Havnen #2234/R (D.KR 6000)
£1292	$1964	€1938	The botanist (50x61cm-20x24in) s. 27-Aug-2 Rasmussen, Copenhagen #1460/R est:15000 (D.KR 15000)
£1532	$2420	€2298	Bathing girls on Hornbaek beach (45x58cm-18x23in) 2-Dec-2 Rasmussen, Copenhagen #1433/R est:12000-15000 (D.KR 18000)

HELSTED, Vigo (1861-1926) Danish

£262	$404	€393	Breakers by Klitmolle Strand (40x57cm-16x22in) s. 26-Oct-2 Rasmussen, Havnen #2087 (D.KR 3100)
£321	$501	€482	Ship wrecked - fog is lifting, Hirtshals (38x59cm-15x23in) s.i.d.1894. 23-Sep-2 Rasmussen, Vejle #103/R (D.KR 3800)
£473	$757	€710	Summer morning with large swell, Agger (39x60cm-15x24in) s.d.1907. 13-Jan-3 Rasmussen, Vejle #84/R (D.KR 5400)

HELT-STOCADE, Nicolaes (attrib) (1614-1669) Flemish

£17730	$27482	€26595	Interior scene with woman seated (133x148cm-52x58in) prov. 4-Dec-2 AB Stockholms Auktionsverk #1949/R est:250000-300000 (S.KR 250000)

HEM, Piet van der (1885-1961) Dutch

£789	$1279	€1200	Portrait of Mata Hari (50x35cm-20x14in) s. prov. 21-Jan-3 Christie's, Amsterdam #401/R est:1500-2000
£1401	$2186	€2200	Hare (49x64cm-19x25in) s. 6-Nov-2 Vendue Huis, Gravenhage #121/R est:2000-3000
£1528	$2521	€2200	Still life with flowers in a ginger jar, Cologne pot and cherries (40x50cm-16x20in) s. 1-Jul-3 Christie's, Amsterdam #379/R est:2500-3500
£3947	$6395	€6000	Fox and its prey (70x90cm-28x35in) s. prov. 21-Jan-3 Christie's, Amsterdam #432/R est:4000-6000
£6707	$10262	€10061	Bullfighting (79x98cm-31x39in) s. 21-Aug-2 Dunbar Sloane, Auckland #70/R est:20000-30000 (NZ.D 22000)

Works on paper

£288	$453	€450	Teun de Klepperman op Vrijersvoeten (50x35cm-20x14in) s. Indian ink htd white. 25-Nov-2 Glerum, Amsterdam #53/R
£298	$483	€420	America weather Nat (45x34cm-18x13in) s. Indian ink blue pencil htd white. 26-May-3 Glerum, Amsterdam #120/R
£481	$755	€750	Mr A W Kamp (50x37cm-20x15in) s.i. W/C. 25-Nov-2 Glerum, Amsterdam #16/R
£481	$755	€750	Tourism in the Netherlands (50x35cm-20x14in) s. Indian ink htd white. 25-Nov-2 Glerum, Amsterdam #22/R
£481	$755	€750	Saint and the quotas (50x35cm-20x14in) s.i. Indian ink blue pencil htd white. 25-Nov-2 Glerum, Amsterdam #59/R
£545	$855	€850	Rivalry between car and track (50x35cm-20x14in) s. Indian ink htd white. 25-Nov-2 Glerum, Amsterdam #55/R
£1026	$1610	€1600	Recovery in the bag (50x35cm-20x14in) s. Indian ink blue pencil htd white. 25-Nov-2 Glerum, Amsterdam #57/R est:500-700
£11392	$18000	€18000	Parijs nachtcafe (32x47cm-13x19in) s. ink pencil prov. 26-Nov-2 Sotheby's, Amsterdam #104/R est:18000-22000

HEMBERG, Elli (1896-1994) Swedish

£618	$995	€927	Composition 14 (55x46cm-22x18in) stamped i.verso. 7-May-3 AB Stockholms Auktionsverk #930/R (S.KR 8000)

HEMERY, Paul (1921-) French

£470	$756	€700	Composition abstraite (61x73cm-24x29in) s.d.1970. 23-Feb-3 Mercier & Cie, Lille #106
£570	$918	€850	Figure (66x81cm-26x32in) s.d.1965. 23-Feb-3 Mercier & Cie, Lille #107

Works on paper

£604	$972	€900	Paysage (125x100cm-49x39in) s. pastel. 23-Feb-3 Mercier & Cie, Lille #93

HEMESLEY, J (19th C) British?

£1000	$1560	€1500	Ploughing in olden times (48x86cm-19x34in) s.d.1859. 11-Apr-3 Keys, Aylsham #627/R est:1000-1500

HEMESSEN, Jan van (attrib) (1504-1566) Flemish

£6129	$9684	€9500	Portrait de femme au voile rose (35x25cm-14x10in) panel. 18-Dec-2 Tajan, Paris #9/R

HEMING, Arthur (1870-1940) Canadian

£1689	$2770	€2534	Fishing by the falls (30x50cm-12x20in) s.d.32. 3-Jun-3 Joyner, Toronto #283/R est:2000-3000 (C.D 3800)

HEMINGWAY, Andrew (1955-) British

£14957	$23782	€22436	Store house (145x107cm-57x42in) s. tempera board painted 1984 prov.exhib. 6-Mar-3 Heffel, Vancouver #43/R est:40000-50000 (C.D 35000)

HEMINGWAY, J (19th C) British

£1700	$2669	€2550	Portrait of Mr Thomas Hemingway and his wife (122x87cm-48x34in) pair. 21-Nov-2 Tennants, Leyburn #735a/R est:600-800

HEMKEN, Willem de Haas (1831-1911) Dutch

Works on paper

£1083	$1668	€1700	Daily activities on the quay in Hoorn (25x36cm-10x14in) s. pencil W/C htd white. 3-Sep-2 Christie's, Amsterdam #106/R est:1000-1500

HEMMRICH, Georg (1896-?) German
£449 $682 €700 Street scene in Cairo (44x35cm-17x14in) s. panel. 11-Jul-2 Hugo Ruef, Munich #692/R
£479 $748 €700 Bavarian alpine village with stage coach (14x18cm-6x7in) s.i. panel lit. 10-Apr-3 Allgauer, Kempten #2799/R

HEMPEL, Joseph von (attrib) (1800-1871) Austrian
£385 $596 €600 Jesus and St Anthony (48x28cm-19x11in) 5-Dec-2 Dorotheum, Graz #21

HEMPEL, Simon (19th C) Danish?
£340 $538 €510 Seascape at Helgoland (44x70cm-17x28in) s.d.1876. 30-Nov-2 Rasmussen, Havnen #2247 (D.KR 4000)

HEMPTINNE, G de (19th C) Belgian
£1497 $2380 €2200 Nature morte aux fleurs (55x84cm-22x33in) s.d.1888 pair. 18-Mar-3 Galerie Moderne, Brussels #594/R est:2000-3000

HEMSLEY, William (1819-1906) British
£250 $405 €375 Bookworm (61x51cm-24x20in) s.i. 23-Jan-3 Christie's, Kensington #111
£452 $700 €678 Genre scene with mother, a new baby with brother and angry girl (30x23cm-12x9in) i.verso prov.exhib. 3-Nov-2 Van Blarcom, South Natick #307
£750 $1200 €1125 Feeding the rabbits (22x17cm-9x7in) s.verso panel. 11-Mar-3 Bonhams, Knightsbridge #268/R
£900 $1422 €1305 Good news, interior scene with mother reading a letter to a child. i. panel. 22-Jul-3 Lawrences, Bletchingley #1541
£1500 $2340 €2250 Autumn (21x17cm-8x7in) s.i. panel. 7-Nov-2 Christie's, Kensington #237/R est:1000-1500
£1600 $2656 €2320 Porridge (15x13cm-6x5in) s. panel. 12-Jun-3 Gorringes, Lewes #1664 est:600-800
£2200 $3498 €3300 Threading the needle. Reading lesson (20x15cm-8x6in) init. panel pair. 6-Mar-3 Christie's, Kensington #545/R est:2500-3500
£2258 $3568 €3387 Girl with rabbit (30x23cm-12x9in) s. exhib. 18-Nov-2 Waddingtons, Toronto #129/R est:3500-4500 (C.D 5600)
£3600 $5904 €5400 Truant detected (56x46cm-22x18in) s.d.1853 panel exhib. 29-May-3 Christie's, Kensington #258/R est:3000-5000
£5400 $8424 €8100 Breakfast party (44x37cm-17x15in) s.i.verso. 6-Nov-2 Bonhams, Chester #543/R est:2000-3000
£9209 $14550 €13814 Village school (52x66cm-20x26in) s. board. 15-Nov-2 Naón & Cia, Buenos Aires #61/R

HEMSLEY, William (attrib) (1819-1906) British
£650 $1001 €975 Learning to read (23x28cm-9x11in) panel. 24-Oct-2 Christie's, Kensington #138/R

HEMUS, Charles (1849-1925) New Zealander
£1592 $2500 €2388 Portrait of Princess Ahiri (52x52cm-20x20in) s.d.1906. 10-Dec-2 Peter Webb, Auckland #25/R est:8000-12000 (NZ.D 5000)

HEMY, Bernard Benedict (1845-1913) British
£270 $421 €405 Beached vessel with figures and lighthouse beyond (30x61cm-12x24in) s. 17-Sep-2 Rosebery Fine Art, London #503
£288 $444 €432 Fishing in a rowboat (30x46cm-12x18in) 26-Oct-2 Heffel, Vancouver #19 (C.D 700)
£380 $635 €551 Shipwreck in King Edwards Bay, Tynemouth (26x46cm-10x18in) s. board. 17-Jun-3 Anderson & Garland, Newcastle #448
£950 $1444 €1425 Shipping scenes on the Tyne (15x23cm-6x9in) s. board pair. 15-Aug-2 Bonhams, New Bond Street #341/R
£1000 $1560 €1500 Shipping on the Tyne with figures in the foreground (41x61cm-16x24in) s.d.1892. 25-Mar-3 Bonhams, Leeds #655 est:1000-1500
£1200 $1884 €1800 Shipping on the river Tyne (61x91cm-24x36in) s. 19-Nov-2 Bonhams, Leeds #189/R est:800-1000
Works on paper
£850 $1335 €1275 Cullercoats Bay, Northumberland (42x58cm-17x23in) s. W/C htd bodycol. 16-Dec-2 Sotheby's, Olympia #55/R
£1000 $1580 €1500 Clipper ship and other vessels at North Shields (35x52cm-14x20in) s. W/C. 28-Nov-2 Martel Maides, Guernsey #40/R est:1000-1500

HEMY, Bernard Benedict (attrib) (1845-1913) British
£300 $489 €450 River scene with steamship, tug boats and fishing vessels (25x28cm-10x11in) s. board. 7-Feb-3 Dee Atkinson & Harrison, Driffield #702/R

HEMY, Charles Napier (1841-1917) British
£400 $632 €600 Coming into shore (44x67cm-17x26in) paper. 12-Nov-2 Bonhams, Knightsbridge #172/R
£1500 $2355 €2250 Passing squall, Falmouth (46x85cm-18x33in) init.d.1907. 16-Dec-2 Sotheby's, Olympia #103/R est:1000-1500
£1600 $2608 €2400 Clearing (47x86cm-19x34in) s. indis d. 29-Jan-3 Dreweatt Neate, Newbury #185/R est:1500-2000
£2482 $3848 €3723 The coming storm (66x96cm-26x38in) init. 4-Dec-2 AB Stockholms Auktionsverk #1888/R est:50000-60000 (S.KR 35000)
£11000 $17820 €16500 Along shore fishermen (56x76cm-22x30in) s.d.1890 s.i.verso prov. 22-Jan-3 Bonhams, New Bond Street #394/R est:10000-15000
£13500 $20520 €20250 Falmouth Regatta (33x48cm-13x19in) s.d.1885 board. 15-Aug-2 Bonhams, New Bond Street #445/R est:5000-8000
£14250 $22230 €20663 Along shore fisherman. i.d.1890 verso. 27-Mar-3 Lane, Penzance #150/R est:16000-20000
Works on paper
£280 $456 €420 Iron buoy (20x30cm-8x12in) mono. W/C. 13-Feb-3 David Lay, Penzance #60
£280 $456 €420 Church interior (20x33cm-8x13in) init.d.1874. 13-Feb-3 David Lay, Penzance #61
£1200 $1872 €1800 Plymouth (42x54cm-17x21in) init.d.1909 W/C htd white sold with another by the same hand. 17-Oct-2 Lawrence, Crewkerne #431/R est:800-1200
£2200 $3410 €3300 Rolling sea (46x67cm-18x26in) init.d.1904 W/C bodycol. 31-Oct-2 Christie's, Kensington #395/R est:1500-2000
£4000 $6240 €6000 Racing yacht running from the mark (46x71cm-18x28in) init.d.1903 W/C. 17-Oct-2 David Lay, Penzance #1449/R est:5000-8000

HEMY, Thomas Marie (1852-1937) British
£600 $996 €900 River Wier with Durham Cathedral and castle in the background (48x90cm-19x35in) s. indis d. 10-Jun-3 Bonhams, Leeds #157
£2100 $3507 €3045 Young girl skipping and other figures conversing in a sunlit cobbled yard (63x79cm-25x31in) s. indis d. 17-Jun-3 Anderson & Garland, Newcastle #468/R est:2000-3000
Works on paper
£280 $434 €420 Sea view, Isle of White (52x74cm-20x29in) s.d.1923 W/C. 24-Sep-2 Anderson & Garland, Newcastle #319

HENAULT, Casimir (1836-?) French
£400 $628 €600 Flower arranger (35x24cm-14x9in) s.i.verso panel. 16-Apr-3 Christie's, Kensington #793/R

HENCK, Sophie Ernestine (1822-1893) Danish
£1014 $1581 €1521 Still life of fruit on stone ledge (38x46cm-15x18in) s. 23-Sep-2 Rasmussen, Vejle #149/R est:15000 (D.KR 12000)

HENCKEL, Karl (1877-?) German
£1026 $1590 €1600 At the loom (98x90cm-39x35in) s. 5-Dec-2 Schopman, Hamburg #574 est:1600

HENCKEL, Peter Holst (1966-) Danish
£525 $814 €788 Ion binding (150x120cm-59x47in) s.d.86 verso. 1-Oct-2 Rasmussen, Copenhagen #149/R (D.KR 6200)

HENDERICHS, F von (19th C) German
£252 $392 €400 Wild boars hunting (33x44cm-13x17in) i. 23-Sep-2 Dr Fritz Nagel, Stuttgart #7097/R
£764 $1260 €1100 Poultry, peacock, black cock and grey hen by a pond (15x41cm-6x16in) s. panel. 1-Jul-3 Christie's, Amsterdam #547

HENDERSON, Arthur Edward (1870-1956) British
Works on paper
£1500 $2340 €2250 Interior of Hagia Sophia, Constantinople (48x18cm-19x7in) s. W/C over pencil htd bodycol prov. 15-Oct-2 Sotheby's, London #70/R est:1500-2000

HENDERSON, Elsie Marion (1880-1967) British
£280 $468 €406 Still life with geraniums (45x63cm-18x25in) board. 17-Jun-3 Bonhams, Knightsbridge #92
£320 $531 €464 Pine forest, Guernsey looking towards Herm (75x50cm-30x20in) 12-Jun-3 Martel Maides, Guernsey #21/R

HENDERSON, J F (?) ?
£3191 $5330 €4500 Jeunes pecheurs sur des rochers au bord de la mer (69x98cm-27x39in) 23-Jun-3 Amberes, Antwerp #101

HENDERSON, James (1871-1951) Canadian
£944 $1473 €1416 Spring landscape (20x25cm-8x10in) s. panel. 25-Mar-3 Ritchie, Toronto #58/R est:2000-2500 (C.D 2200)
£978 $1604 €1418 Qu'appelle Valley (20x25cm-8x10in) s. board. 9-Jun-3 Hodgins, Calgary #297/R est:1750-2250 (C.D 2200)
£2667 $4373 €4001 Golden autumn, Qu'Appelle Valley (60x75cm-24x30in) s. 3-Jun-3 Joyner, Toronto #153/R est:7000-9000 (C.D 6000)
£2667 $4373 €4001 Valley road (25x30cm-10x12in) s. s.i.verso board prov. 27-May-3 Sotheby's, Toronto #206/R est:3000-4000 (C.D 6000)

£2889 $4738 €4334 Close of day (51x61cm-20x24in) s. s.i.verso prov. 27-May-3 Sotheby's, Toronto #14/R est:5000-7000 (C.D 6500)

HENDERSON, John (1860-1924) British
£800 $1240 €1200 Still life with chrysanthemums in a vase (61x46cm-24x18in) s. 2-Nov-2 Shapes, Edinburgh #313/R
£1650 $2591 €2475 Incoming tide on the Scottish coast (65x98cm-26x39in) s. 10-Dec-2 Lane, Penzance #288 est:300-500

HENDERSON, Joseph (1832-1908) British
£1500 $2325 €2250 Fresh breeze off Kintyre (33x55cm-13x22in) s. i.stretcher. 6-Dec-2 Lyon & Turnbull, Edinburgh #46 est:600-800
£2200 $3366 €3300 Tattie pickers on the coast (44x60cm-17x24in) s. 22-Aug-2 Bonhams, Edinburgh #1052 est:700-1000
£2700 $4131 €4050 Fishing boats, evening, on the West Coast (36x61cm-14x24in) s. 22-Aug-2 Bonhams, Edinburgh #1081 est:2500-4000
£2800 $4256 €4200 Fishermen pulling in the nets (46x61cm-18x24in) indis sig. 28-Aug-2 Sotheby's, London #998/R est:2000-3000
£3200 $4864 €4800 On the shore (45x61cm-18x24in) s. 28-Aug-2 Sotheby's, London #1005/R est:3000-5000
£5500 $8580 €8250 Collecting bait (72x98cm-28x39in) s. 28-Mar-3 Bonhams, Edinburgh #132/R est:4000-6000
£5800 $8816 €8700 Children playing on the shore (66x96cm-26x38in) 28-Aug-2 Sotheby's, London #995/R est:3000-5000
£5800 $9048 €8700 Returning home (89x64cm-35x25in) s. 17-Oct-2 Bonhams, Edinburgh #261/R est:2000-3000
£6000 $9540 €9000 Beach at Ballantae (46x76cm-18x30in) s. exhib. 6-Mar-3 Christie's, Kensington #152/R est:3000-5000
£12000 $18240 €18000 Summer clouds (72x91cm-28x36in) s. 28-Aug-2 Sotheby's, London #987/R est:10000-15000

HENDERSON, Joseph Morris (1863-1936) British
£400 $640 €600 Coastal scene (31x46cm-12x18in) s. 13-May-3 Bonhams, Sevenoaks #342/R
£480 $778 €720 Summer grazing (28x44cm-11x17in) s. 23-Jan-3 Bonhams, Edinburgh #333
£650 $1034 €975 Highland river (51x66cm-20x26in) s. prov. 6-Mar-3 Christie's, Kensington #130/R
£700 $1092 €1050 Ayrshire cove (32x42cm-13x17in) 17-Oct-2 Bonhams, Edinburgh #195
£820 $1337 €1230 On the Steuchar (25x35cm-10x14in) s. board. 1-Feb-3 Shapes, Edinburgh #388/R
£1000 $1600 €1500 Low tide (46x69cm-18x27in) s. 13-May-3 Bonhams, Sevenoaks #338/R est:1000-1500
£1100 $1716 €1650 River near Ballatter (18x25cm-7x10in) s. board. 17-Sep-2 Sotheby's, Olympia #46/R est:1200-1800
£1200 $2004 €1740 Scottish homestead (31x42cm-12x17in) s. 26-Jun-3 Mellors & Kirk, Nottingham #895/R est:600-800
£1300 $2028 €1950 On the Stinchar (18x25cm-7x10in) s. board prov. 17-Sep-2 Sotheby's, Olympia #55/R est:1000-1500
£1500 $2430 €2250 At Benderloch, Argyllshire (50x75cm-20x30in) s. 23-May-3 Lyon & Turnbull, Edinburgh #53 est:800-1200
£1600 $2480 €2400 Summer sea (44x67cm-17x26in) s. 5-Dec-2 Bonhams, Edinburgh #102 est:1500-2000
£1600 $2592 €2400 On the Ayrshire coast (51x75cm-20x30in) s. 23-May-3 Lyon & Turnbull, Edinburgh #4 est:600-800

HENDERSON, Keith (1883-?) British
£450 $693 €675 Still life of mixed fruit, silver and glassware (61x77cm-24x30in) s. 23-Oct-2 Hamptons Fine Art, Godalming #175/R

HENDERSON, Leslie (1895-1988) American
£822 $1200 €1233 Wissahickson winter, from Rittentown to Park Drive Manor (41x51cm-16x20in) s.d.3-17-56. 3-Nov-1 North East Auctions, Portsmouth #266a/R
£1226 $1900 €1839 Wissahickon winter (41x51cm-16x20in) s.d.3-17-56 i.verso canvasboard. 8-Dec-2 Freeman, Philadelphia #139/R est:1200-1800
£3253 $4750 €4880 Winter in Fairmount Park, Rittenhouse village (64x76cm-25x30in) s.d.1-10-45. 3-Nov-1 North East Auctions, Portsmouth #266/R

HENDERSON, Louise (1912-1994) New Zealander
£940 $1467 €1410 Flowers in a blue vase (52x35cm-20x14in) s.d.1987. 7-Nov-2 International Art Centre, Auckland #60/R est:2500-3500 (NZ.D 3000)
£2120 $3413 €3180 Self portrait 'Belle Tournure' (87x58cm-34x23in) s. board. 7-May-3 Dunbar Sloane, Auckland #35/R est:5500-7500 (NZ.D 6000)
£2778 $4333 €4167 Still life (59x45cm-23x18in) s.d.1985 board. 8-Apr-3 Peter Webb, Auckland #99/R est:8000-12000 (NZ.D 8000)
Works on paper
£470 $734 €705 Abstract (27x39cm-11x15in) s.d.1985 mixed media. 5-Nov-2 Peter Webb, Auckland #131/R est:1000-1500 (NZ.D 1500)
£702 $1116 €1053 Abstract from the seasons series (62x43cm-24x17in) s.i. W/C. 25-Feb-3 Peter Webb, Auckland #26 est:2500-3500 (NZ.D 2000)
£940 $1467 €1410 Untitled (40x58cm-16x23in) s.d.1968 W/C. 7-Nov-2 International Art Centre, Auckland #12/R est:3000-5000 (NZ.D 3000)
£1111 $1733 €1667 Bush (37x54cm-15x21in) s.d.1972 W/C. 8-Apr-3 Peter Webb, Auckland #153/R est:2500-3500 (NZ.D 3200)
£1448 $2216 €2172 Lake Craigieburn (33x44cm-13x17in) s. W/C. 21-Aug-2 Dunbar Sloane, Auckland #7/R est:5000-8000 (NZ.D 4750)
£2982 $4653 €4473 North Canterbury landscape (47x52cm-19x20in) s. W/C. 27-Mar-3 International Art Centre, Auckland #77/R est:8000-12000 (NZ.D 8500)

HENDERSON, William (fl.1874-1892) British
£1000 $1580 €1500 Grazing sheep near Goathland (48x64cm-19x25in) s. 24-Apr-3 Richardson & Smith, Whitby #150/R est:1000-1500

HENDERYCKX, Leopold (1888-1960) Belgian
Works on paper
£690 $1090 €1000 La legende d'Uylenspiegel (63x63cm-25x25in) s. W/C. 2-Apr-3 Vanderkindere, Brussels #77/R

HENDRICKX, Henri François Joseph (1817-1894) Belgian
Works on paper
£5000 $8350 €7250 Running of the first races at Brussels (45x72cm-18x28in) blk chk W/C bodycol. 9-Jul-3 Sotheby's, London #81/R est:2500-3500

HENDRICKX, Jos (1906-1971) Belgian
Works on paper
£302 $468 €480 Woman (151x60cm-59x24in) st.mono. W/C chl brown chk. 5-Oct-2 De Vuyst, Lokeren #168

HENDRIKS, Willem (1828-1891) Dutch
£289 $474 €419 Untitled - fruit trees in full bloom (30x41cm-12x16in) 1-Jun-3 Levis, Calgary #53/R (C.D 650)
£289 $474 €419 Untitled - cattle in pasture (30x41cm-12x16in) 1-Jun-3 Levis, Calgary #54/R (C.D 650)
£302 $486 €450 Nature morte aux tomates (55x70cm-22x28in) s.d.1941. 18-Feb-3 Galerie Moderne, Brussels #363/R
£455 $714 €683 Cattle in a sunny pasture (53x61cm-21x24in) s.verso. 24-Jul-2 Walker's, Ottawa #8/R est:1500-2000 (C.D 1100)
£479 $753 €700 Nature morte aux tomates (55x70cm-22x28in) s.d.1941. 15-Apr-3 Galerie Moderne, Brussels #409
£577 $900 €866 Spring landscape with cottage and figure (51x76cm-20x30in) s. 18-Sep-2 Jackson's, Cedar Falls #757/R
£613 $1000 €920 Canal bank, Holland (30x41cm-12x16in) s. 16-Feb-3 Jeffery Burchard, Florida #28
£656 $1016 €984 Cows by the river (51x61cm-20x24in) s. 24-Sep-2 Maynards, Vancouver #363/R est:1500-2000 (C.D 1600)
£702 $1103 €1053 Cattle resting in the orchard (51x71cm-20x28in) s. 24-Jul-2 Walker's, Ottawa #1/R est:2000-2500 (C.D 1700)
£887 $1402 €1331 Woman tending cows in a spring meadow (61x91cm-24x36in) s. 18-Nov-2 Waddingtons, Toronto #196/R est:1000-1500 (C.D 2200)

HENDRIKS, Wybrand (1744-1831) Dutch
£5755 $9209 €8000 Still life with fruit, flowers, butterfly, fly and ants (66x50cm-26x20in) mono. panel. 13-May-3 Sotheby's, Amsterdam #50/R est:8000-8250
Works on paper
£4846 $7075 €7269 Still life with flowers, fruit and insects (43x33cm-17x13in) s.d.1782. 17-Jun-2 Philippe Schuler, Zurich #4803/R est:4000-5000 (S.FR 11000)

HENDSCHEL, Albert (1834-1883) German
£926 $1491 €1389 Catching butterflies (14x11cm-6x4in) board. 7-May-3 Dobiaschofsky, Bern #633/R (S.FR 2000)
Works on paper
£324 $538 €460 Dancing elf (18x7cm-7x3in) pencil. 12-Jun-3 Hauswedell & Nolte, Hamburg #356/R

HENGARTNER, Johan Baptist (c.1830-1895) German
Works on paper
£323 $459 €520 Girl with jug (62x46cm-24x18in) i. verso mixed media. 23-Mar-2 Geble, Radolfzell #547/R

HENGELER, Adolf (1863-1927) German
£397 $648 €600 Congratulator (50x40cm-20x16in) oval. 28-Jan-3 Dorotheum, Vienna #14/R
£409 $650 €614 Youthful caricature (51x51cm-20x20in) s. board painted c.1880. 2-Mar-3 Toomey, Oak Park #707/R

Works on paper
£833 $1267 €1300 Lower Alp landscape with Putto on toboggan (36x35cm-14x14in) s.d.10 gouache. 11-Jul-2 Allgauer, Kempten #2293/R

HENGGE, Joseph (1890-1970) German
£481 $731 €750 Portrait of the famous conductor Hans Knappersbusch (94x68cm-37x27in) s. 11-Jul-2 Allgauer, Kempten #2511/R

HENGST, Oswald (1870-1938) Austrian
£481 $755 €750 Tyrolean farmhouse (30x23cm-12x9in) s. 21-Nov-2 Dorotheum, Vienna #209/R

HENKE, Ulrich (1896-?) German
£325 $474 €500 Still life with fruit (39x58cm-15x23in) s.d.32 s.verso lit. 15-Jun-2 Hans Stahl, Hamburg #128

HENKEL, Ceasar Carl Hans (19/20th C) ?
£3300 $5115 €4950 Naive topographical view of Umata, Eastern Province, South Africa (107x183cm-42x72in) s.d.1913. 31-Oct-2 Duke & Son, Dorchester #334/R

HENKEL, Manfred (1936-1988) German
£566 $883 €900 Pforzheim (190x158cm-75x62in) s.i. verso. 21-Sep-2 Dannenberg, Berlin #559/R

HENLEY, Lionel Charles (1843-?) British
£479 $748 €700 The interlude (36x25cm-14x10in) s.d.1898. 10-Apr-3 Dorotheum, Vienna #119/R

HENLEY, W B (?) ?
£410 $623 €615 Angling at the bend of the river (51x77cm-20x30in) s. 29-Aug-2 Christie's, Kensington #96

HENNAH, Joseph Edward (1897-) British
£500 $770 €750 Polperro harbour (28x41cm-11x16in) s. board sold with another by the same hand. 5-Sep-2 Christie's, Kensington #579

HENNE, Joachim (attrib) (fl.1700-1702) German
Sculpture
£19000 $29830 €28500 Virgin and child with Joseph and St. John (17x13cm-7x5in) ivory relief lit. 10-Dec-2 Sotheby's, London #78/R est:10000-15000

HENNEBELLE, Pierre (1926-) French
£443 $691 €700 La plage (41x32cm-16x13in) s. 20-Oct-2 Mercier & Cie, Lille #359
£1076 $1678 €1700 Mer ou plaine (64x80cm-25x31in) s. d.75 verso. 20-Oct-2 Mercier & Cie, Lille #360 est:1800

HENNEBERGER, August Philipp (1902-) German
Works on paper
£363 $566 €530 Timber yard near Bavarian village (36x50cm-14x20in) s. W/C. 11-Apr-3 Winterberg, Heidelberg #1113

HENNEKYN, David (attrib) (fl.1665-1969) Dutch
£24000 $37440 €36000 Grapes on the vine, peach and an orange in a blue and white porcelain bowl (65x60cm-26x24in) bears sig. 9-Apr-3 Christie's, London #60/R est:15000-25000

HENNELL, Thomas (1903-1945) British
Works on paper
£600 $954 €900 Lime and frost (30x48cm-12x19in) s.d.1942 sold with dr. 26-Feb-3 Sotheby's, Olympia #118/R

HENNER, Jean Jacques (1829-1905) French
£1179 $1839 €1769 Reclining female nude in landscape (30x41cm-12x16in) s.i. verso board. 20-Nov-2 Fischer, Luzern #1103/R est:3000-4000 (S.FR 2700)
£1218 $1900 €1827 Landscape with reclining female nude (30x46cm-12x18in) s. panel. 18-Sep-2 Boos Gallery, Michigan #177/R est:1000-1500
£1257 $2100 €1823 Lady in profile (41x32cm-16x13in) s. panel. 22-Jun-3 Freeman, Philadelphia #33/R est:2000-3000
£1420 $2016 €2300 Portrait de femme a la robe rouge (27x22cm-11x9in) s. 16-Mar-3 Eric Pillon, Calais #76/R
£1485 $2316 €2228 Reclining female nude (56x91cm-22x36in) s.i. 6-Nov-2 Dobiaschofsky, Bern #646/R est:2800 (S.FR 3400)
£2373 $3750 €3560 Reclining nude in a landscape (36x64cm-14x25in) s. panel. 2-Apr-3 Doyle, New York #41/R est:5000-7000
£2454 $4000 €3558 Reclining nude in a landscape (25x41cm-10x16in) panel. 18-Jul-3 Du Mouchelle, Detroit #2004/R est:3000-5000
£3038 $4800 €4557 Auburn haired beauty in profile with book (56x48cm-22x19in) s. 16-Nov-2 New Orleans Auction, New Orleans #336/R est:3000-5000

HENNER, Jean Jacques (attrib) (1829-1905) French
£503 $775 €800 Adam and Eve (15x23cm-6x9in) canvas on board prov. 28-Oct-2 Il Ponte, Milan #276/R
£881 $1356 €1400 Head of girl (28x23cm-11x9in) s. cardboard on board. 28-Oct-2 Il Ponte, Milan #234/R

HENNESSEY, Frank Charles (1893-1941) Canadian
Works on paper
£414 $633 €621 March day, Gastineau River (22x29cm-9x11in) pastel. 24-Aug-2 Rasmussen, Havnen #2070 (D.KR 4800)
£889 $1458 €1334 Serene reflection (34x44cm-13x17in) s.d.35 pastel. 3-Jun-3 Joyner, Toronto #588 est:1500-2000 (C.D 2000)
£1022 $1676 €1533 Rocky banks and stream (32x44cm-13x17in) s.d.39 pastel. 3-Jun-3 Joyner, Toronto #564 est:1500-2000 (C.D 2300)

HENNESSY, Patrick (1915-1980) Irish
£6090 $9439 €9500 Wild land, Connemara (62x74cm-24x29in) s. 3-Dec-2 Bonhams & James Adam, Dublin #47/R est:10000-15000
£10968 $17000 €16452 White cliffs of Etretat (91x160cm-36x63in) s. i.d.10-10-65 verso. 21-Jul-2 Jeffery Burchard, Florida #24/R
£13356 $20969 €19500 Marine encounter (64x77cm-25x30in) s. exhib. 15-Apr-3 De Veres Art Auctions, Dublin #145/R est:20000-30000
Works on paper
£3019 $4709 €4800 Kinsale (39x23cm-15x9in) s.i.d.1941 verso W/C prov. 17-Sep-2 Whyte's, Dublin #149/R est:3000-3500

HENNESSY, William John (1839-1917) British
£3300 $5214 €4785 Mrs W.M Hennessey and her sister Miss Maher (10x15cm-4x6in) mono.d.1870 i.verso board. 23-Jul-3 Mallams, Oxford #265/R est:800-1200
Works on paper
£1250 $2000 €1813 Secret (37x46cm-15x18in) s.d.1889 pastel. 16-May-3 Skinner, Boston #139/R est:2000-4000

HENNIG, Albert (1907-1998) German
Works on paper
£256 $397 €400 Abstract composition (13x17cm-5x7in) s.d.1983 W/C felt-tip pen board. 7-Dec-2 Van Ham, Cologne #219/R
£347 $549 €500 Untitled abstract landscape (26x31cm-10x12in) s.d.1986 W/C board. 26-Apr-3 Dr Lehr, Berlin #211/R
£417 $658 €600 Winter in Annaberg (17x23cm-7x9in) s.d.1978 W/C board. 26-Apr-3 Dr Lehr, Berlin #209/R
£685 $1068 €1000 Sun over city (24x29cm-9x11in) s.d. W/C feltpen. 11-Apr-3 Winterberg, Heidelberg #1116 est:980

HENNIG, Erich (1875-?) German
£279 $438 €419 Seated woman (91x62cm-36x24in) s.stretcher. 25-Nov-2 Blomqvist, Lysaker #1114/R (N.KR 3200)

HENNIG, Gustav Adolph (1797-1869) German
£759 $1177 €1200 Anna Thecla Kraft (34x29cm-13x11in) i. 27-Sep-2 Dr Fritz Nagel, Leipzig #3932/R
£1761 $2712 €2800 Portrait d'un jeune garcon. Portrait d'une jeune fille (27x11cm-11x4in) s. pair. 25-Oct-2 Tajan, Paris #99 est:2000-3000

HENNIG, Otto (1871-1920) Norwegian
£288 $452 €432 Cow in the mountains (60x86cm-24x34in) s. 25-Nov-2 Blomqvist, Lysaker #1115/R (N.KR 3300)
£316 $513 €474 Cattle at watering place (48x65cm-19x26in) s. 27-Jan-3 Blomqvist, Lysaker #1081/R (N.KR 3500)
£341 $532 €512 Spring evening by the fjord, Bygdo (61x75cm-24x30in) s. painted 1912. 23-Sep-2 Blomqvist, Lysaker #1078/R (N.KR 4000)
£406 $678 €589 Cold winter evening (48x72cm-19x28in) s. i.stretcher. 18-Jun-3 Grev Wedels Plass, Oslo #183/R (N.KR 4700)
£509 $784 €764 Spring evening by the fjord, Bygdo (61x75cm-24x30in) s. painted 1912. 28-Oct-2 Blomqvist, Lysaker #1085 (N.KR 6000)
£619 $1010 €929 A sunny day in autumn (66x36cm-26x14in) s. 17-Feb-3 Blomqvist, Lysaker #1076/R (N.KR 7000)
£890 $1397 €1335 River landscape (67x96cm-26x38in) s. 25-Nov-2 Blomqvist, Lysaker #1116 (N.KR 10200)

HENNIGS, Gosta von (1866-1941) Swedish
£1017 $1607 €1526 Ballet dancers (62x51cm-24x20in) mono.d.1919 prov. 27-Nov-2 Falkkloos, Malmo #77671/R (S.KR 14500)
£19395 $31420 €28123 Tramway horses (123x132cm-48x52in) s.d.1904 prov.lit. 26-May-3 Bukowskis, Stockholm #79/R est:100000-125000 (S.KR 250000)

HENNING, Adolf (1809-1900) German

£1319 $2177 €1900 Portrait of a young girl in a white dress (30x26cm-12x10in) s.d.1848 s.verso sold with two portraits by the same hand. 1-Jul-3 Christie's, Amsterdam #43/R est:1000-1500

£1646 $2551 €2600 Southern landscape with palm trees by water (32x47cm-13x19in) s. 25-Sep-2 Neumeister, Munich #598/R est:2500

£5449 $8609 €8500 Children of the artist (69x50cm-27x20in) s.d.1858 prov. 16-Nov-2 Lempertz, Koln #1475/R est:8000

HENNING, Anton (?) ?

Works on paper

£441 $643 €662 Queen bee (110x135cm-43x53in) mono.d.1989 mixed media exhib. 17-Jun-2 Philippe Schuler, Zurich #4371 (S.FR 1000)

£573 $836 €860 Untitled (131x104cm-52x41in) mono.d.1988 mixed media board. 17-Jun-2 Philippe Schuler, Zurich #4030 (S.FR 1300)

£1057 $1544 €1586 Icon in bed III (190x160cm-75x63in) mono.d.1989 mixed media. 17-Jun-2 Philippe Schuler, Zurich #4372 (S.FR 2400)

HENNING, Cristian (attrib) (1741-1822) Dutch

Works on paper

£1783 $2782 €2800 Farmyard birds (43x64cm-17x25in) gouache. 5-Nov-2 Sotheby's, Amsterdam #144/R est:2500-3500

HENNING, Gerhard (1880-1967) Swedish

Sculpture

£1257 $2061 €1823 Nude woman (28cm-11in) s.d.1923 dark pat.bronze Cast.Rasmussen cire perdue. 4-Jun-3 AB Stockholms Auktionsverk #2391/R est:10000-12000 (S.KR 16000)

£2323 $3671 €3485 Reclining woman (20x31cm-8x12in) s.d.1926 num.IV black pat.bronze sold with socle st.f.Rasmussen. 1-Apr-3 Rasmussen, Copenhagen #83/R est:20000 (D.KR 25000)

£4478 $7343 €6493 Sonja - reclining woman (41cm-16in) s. pat.bronze Cast H Bergman cire perdue. 4-Jun-3 AB Stockholms Auktionsverk #2365/R est:40000-50000 (S.KR 57000)

£12546 $19823 €18819 Reclining nude woman (43x57x23cm-17x22x9in) s.num.1 pat.bronze incl.black painted veneer base lit. 1-Apr-3 Rasmussen, Copenhagen #75/R est:75000-100000 (D.KR 135000)

HENNING, John (1771-1851) British

Sculpture

£3400 $5406 €5100 Portrait of James Watt (7cm-3in) s.d.1809 glass paste relief. 20-Mar-3 Sotheby's, London #60/R est:400-600

HENNING, Walton W (fl.1886-1887) British

Works on paper

£440 $700 €660 Double portrait of Harriet and Eliza Bennett (18x14cm-7x6in) W/C on ivory. 29-Apr-3 Sworder & Son, Bishops Stortford #407/R

HENNINGER, Manfred (1894-1986) German

£741 $1193 €1112 Forest clearing (88x115cm-35x45in) s. 7-May-3 Dobiaschofsky, Bern #635/R (S.FR 1600)

£1034 $1634 €1500 Swabian summer landscape (43x57cm-17x22in) i. stretcher masonite. 2-Apr-3 Dr Fritz Nagel, Stuttgart #9471/R est:1500

£1241 $1961 €1800 Indian (47x25cm-19x10in) s.i.d. masonite. 2-Apr-3 Dr Fritz Nagel, Stuttgart #9470/R est:1400

£1519 $2370 €2400 Stilll life of cactus (46x61cm-18x24in) s. i. verso. 18-Oct-2 Dr Fritz Nagel, Stuttgart #519/R est:2800

£1586 $2506 €2300 Still life of flowers (66x85cm-26x33in) s. 2-Apr-3 Dr Fritz Nagel, Stuttgart #9474/R

£1655 $2615 €2400 Bathers by Max Eyth lake (35x55cm-14x22in) s.d.1948. 2-Apr-3 Dr Fritz Nagel, Stuttgart #9472/R est:1800

£2276 $3596 €3300 Upper Italian lake landscape (58x82cm-23x32in) s. board prov. 2-Apr-3 Dr Fritz Nagel, Stuttgart #9473/R est:4500

£3623 $5942 €5000 Ibiza (53x64cm-21x25in) s.d.1934 i. verso prov. 31-May-3 Villa Grisebach, Berlin #250/R est:5000-6000

Works on paper

£345 $545 €500 Figures in wood (28x32cm-11x13in) s.d.25.9.1946 ochre. 2-Apr-3 Dr Fritz Nagel, Stuttgart #9102/R

£621 $981 €900 Three male nudes (49x62cm-19x24in) s.d. pastel prov. 2-Apr-3 Dr Fritz Nagel, Stuttgart #9103/R

HENNINGS, Ernest Martin (1886-1956) American

£7643 $12000 €11465 Cloudburst (30x36cm-12x14in) s. canvas on board prov. 20-Nov-2 Christie's, Los Angeles #107/R est:10000-15000

£14103 $22000 €21155 Fishermen of Chioggia, Italy (51x61cm-20x24in) s. prov.lit. 9-Nov-2 Santa Fe Art, Santa Fe #190/R est:20000-30000

£16129 $25000 €24194 Yellowing Aspen (37x36cm-15x14in) s. canvasboard prov. 5-Dec-2 Christie's, Rockefeller NY #186/R est:30000-50000

£58065 $90000 €87098 Indian riders entering an Aspen grove (41x51cm-16x20in) s. prov. 29-Oct-2 John Moran, Pasadena #707a est:40000-60000

£61644 $90000 €92466 Young Taos chief (76x76cm-30x30in) 18-May-2 Altermann Galleries, Santa Fe #35/R

£83871 $130000 €125807 Towering Aspen (51x51cm-20x20in) s. i.stretcher prov. 29-Oct-2 John Moran, Pasadena #705 est:50000-70000

Prints

£2987 $4750 €4481 Rabbit hunters (25x25cm-10x10in) s.i. col relief print. 7-Mar-3 Skinner, Boston #63/R est:600-800

HENNINGS, Johann Friedrich (1838-1899) German

£2089 $3237 €3300 Moonlit harbour - possibly Venice (80x72cm-31x28in) s. 25-Sep-2 Neumeister, Munich #599/R est:3000

£9574 $14840 €14361 A stroll in the palace gardens (110x65cm-43x26in) s. 3-Dec-2 Bukowskis, Stockholm #182/R est:100000-125000 (S.KR 135000)

HENNINGSEN, Erik (1855-1930) Danish

£258 $393 €387 Two small girls wearing summer dresses (25x21cm-10x8in) sketch prov. 27-Aug-2 Rasmussen, Copenhagen #1583 (D.KR 3000)

£340 $530 €510 Town scene with two children (35x23cm-14x9in) s. 5-Aug-2 Rasmussen, Vejle #89 (D.KR 4000)

£429 $669 €644 Summer's day in the garden, figures at table in background (34x27cm-13x11in) mono. 11-Nov-2 Rasmussen, Vejle #691/R (D.KR 5000)

£431 $655 €647 Garden in red and green (32x23cm-13x9in) prov. 27-Aug-2 Rasmussen, Copenhagen #1786/R (D.KR 5000)

£638 $1009 €957 Woman winding wool in cottage (32x26cm-13x10in) init.d.76. 2-Dec-2 Rasmussen, Copenhagen #1305/R (D.KR 7500)

£686 $1070 €1029 Landscape with nude man and woman (80x62cm-31x24in) init.verso. 11-Nov-2 Rasmussen, Vejle #517/R (D.KR 8000)

£745 $1184 €1118 Girl seated wearing green head scarf (35x26cm-14x10in) mono. 5-Mar-3 Rasmussen, Copenhagen #1928/R (D.KR 8000)

£851 $1345 €1277 Party at the Students' Club (33x27cm-13x11in) study prov. 2-Dec-2 Rasmussen, Copenhagen #1729/R (D.KR 10000)

£892 $1400 €1338 Stroget at Christmas, Copenhagen view (32x42cm-13x17in) mono. 22-Nov-2 Skinner, Boston #323/R est:1800-2200

£1723 $2618 €2585 Small children by a cake stall in evening (66x54cm-26x21in) s.d.1880 exhib. 27-Aug-2 Rasmussen, Copenhagen #1910/R est:20000-25000 (D.KR 20000)

£2931 $4484 €4397 Goodbye on the quay (60x48cm-24x19in) s. 24-Aug-2 Rasmussen, Havnen #2325/R est:20000-30000 (D.KR 34000)

£5551 $8548 €8327 The Bridegroom's speech to the Bride (56x69cm-22x27in) s. 4-Sep-2 Kunsthallen, Copenhagen #117/R est:75000 (D.KR 65000)

Works on paper

£335 $543 €486 Man kneeling in landscape by the coast (19x14cm-7x6in) s. W/C. 26-May-3 Rasmussen, Copenhagen #1600/R (D.KR 3500)

£698 $1110 €1047 Girl from Fanoe (22x17cm-9x7in) mono.i.d.1883 pencil W/C. 5-Mar-3 Rasmussen, Copenhagen #2161/R (D.KR 7500)

HENNINGSEN, Frants (1850-1908) Danish

£259 $396 €389 Fisherman with red scarf (54x43cm-21x17in) s.d.1880. 24-Aug-2 Rasmussen, Havnen #2117 (D.KR 3000)

£289 $451 €434 Seascape from Hellebaek with Kullen in background (32x48cm-13x19in) mono. 5-Aug-2 Rasmussen, Vejle #271/R (D.KR 3400)

£370 $596 €555 Portrait of the philosopher Velazquez (89x50cm-35x20in) mono. 19-Jan-3 Hindemae, Ullerslev #7331/R (D.KR 4200)

£459 $744 €666 Portrait of seated woman (25x18cm-10x7in) mono.d.86 mahogany. 24-May-3 Rasmussen, Havnen #2158/R (D.KR 4800)

£510 $795 €765 Summer landscape with manor house in background (25x35cm-10x14in) mono.d.12 september 1886. 5-Aug-2 Rasmussen, Vejle #211/R (D.KR 6000)

£6475 $10360 €9000 Repos sur les champs (41x33cm-16x13in) mono.d.74. 17-May-3 De Vuyst, Lokeren #438/R est:10000-12000

HENNO, Louis (1907-1990) Belgian

£360 $576 €500 Bouquet de fleurs (100x80cm-39x31in) s. 13-May-3 Vanderkindere, Brussels #47

HENOCK, Arthur (?) British?

Works on paper

£520 $754 €780 Falls on the North Teign, evening (33x51cm-13x20in) s. W/C. 3-May-2 Biddle & Webb, Birmingham #325

HENRI, Robert (1865-1929) American

£481 $750 €722 Four figures (23x18cm-9x7in) estate st. sepia ink dr. 14-Sep-2 Selkirks, St. Louis #136

£6790 $11000 €10185 Old houses in Normandie (65x81cm-26x32in) prov.exhib.lit. 21-May-3 Sotheby's, New York #156/R est:12000-18000
£179012 $290000 €268518 Portrait of Cara in a red dress (61x51cm-24x20in) s. prov. 22-May-3 Christie's, Rockefeller NY #57/R est:180000-240000
£259259 $420000 €388889 Berna escudero (61x51cm-24x20in) s.verso painted 1922 prov.exhib.lit. 21-May-3 Sotheby's, New York #59/R est:125000-175000

Works on paper
£223 $350 €335 Double self portrait (17x12cm-7x5in) pen ink prov. 14-Dec-2 Weschler, Washington #716/R
£224 $350 €336 Portrait of man in a rain hat (34x25cm-13x10in) crayon prov. 12-Apr-3 Weschler, Washington #591/R
£299 $475 €449 Atlantic City (12x18cm-5x7in) s.i.d.88 pen ink graphite. 20-Mar-3 Skinner, Bolton #739/R
£976 $1600 €1415 Reclining nude (49x31cm-19x12in) estate init. W/C brush ink wash. 5-Jun-3 Swann Galleries, New York #119/R est:2000-3000
£1341 $2200 €1944 View from a louvre window, Paris (23x15cm-9x6in) i. pencil exec.c.1894. 5-Jun-3 Swann Galleries, New York #118/R est:1000-1500
£7407 $12000 €11111 Woodland scene, Monhegan, Maine (30x51cm-12x20in) s. s.verso pastel executed 1918 prov.exhib. 21-May-3 Sotheby's, New York #82/R est:10000-15000
£8642 $14000 €12963 Stone wall with woods (32x50cm-13x20in) s. pastel executed 1918 prov.exhib. 21-May-3 Sotheby's, New York #81/R est:10000-15000
£13580 $22000 €20370 Under the trees Monhegan (32x50cm-13x20in) s. s.i.verso pastel prov.exhib. 21-May-3 Sotheby's, New York #22/R est:12000-18000

HENRICH, Albert (1899-1971) German
£577 $894 €900 Still life with apple, peaches and jug (40x50cm-16x20in) s. 7-Dec-2 Van Ham, Cologne #220/R

HENRICHSEN, Carsten (1824-1897) Danish
£338 $527 €507 Landscape view (40x53cm-16x21in) mono.d.1867. 23-Sep-2 Rasmussen, Vejle #67/R (D.KR 4000)
£345 $524 €518 Angler by waterway in wood at sunset (43x64cm-17x25in) 27-Aug-2 Rasmussen, Copenhagen #1855/R (D.KR 4000)
£372 $592 €558 Landscape from Julebaek with view towards Kronborg (27x40cm-11x16in) mono.d.1854. 5-Mar-3 Rasmussen, Copenhagen #1976/R (D.KR 4000)
£391 $622 €587 Summer landscape with woman seated by road (50x71cm-20x28in) mono.d.1873. 10-Mar-3 Rasmussen, Vejle #263/R (D.KR 4200)
£426 $672 €639 Fjord landscape in evening light (28x39cm-11x15in) mono.d.1854. 2-Dec-2 Rasmussen, Copenhagen #1248 (D.KR 5000)
£493 $769 €740 Fjord landscape with houses and figures (50x71cm-20x28in) mono.d.1870. 5-Aug-2 Rasmussen, Vejle #207/R (D.KR 5800)
£638 $1034 €957 Watering the cattle (49x69cm-19x27in) mono.d.1864. 25-Jan-3 Rasmussen, Havnen #2227 (D.KR 7200)
£709 $1127 €1064 Landscape from Hellebaek (43x61cm-17x24in) mono.d.1872. 5-May-3 Rasmussen, Vejle #353/R (D.KR 7600)
£745 $1184 €1118 Rowing boat on lake, late afternoon (70x95cm-28x37in) mono.d.1869. 5-Mar-3 Rasmussen, Copenhagen #2058/R (D.KR 8000)

HENRICI, John H (1874-1958) American
£409 $650 €614 Fireside (25x35cm-10x14in) s.i. 7-Mar-3 Skinner, Boston #312/R
£625 $1000 €938 Four street urchins (46x61cm-18x24in) s. 15-Mar-3 Eldred, East Dennis #419/R

HENRIET, Israel (attrib) (1590-1661) French
Works on paper
£475 $750 €750 Figures pres d'une fontaine (8x16cm-3x6in) i.d.1622 verso pen ink crayon. 28-Nov-2 Tajan, Paris #12

HENRIKSEN, Harald (1883-1960) Danish
£272 $424 €408 View of a pleasure boat harbour (70x82cm-28x32in) s. 5-Aug-2 Rasmussen, Vejle #113/R (D.KR 3200)

HENRIKSEN, Henry J (1936-) Norwegian
£289 $444 €434 Wonder/reflection (61x51cm-24x20in) s. 28-Oct-2 Blomqvist, Lysaker #1087 (N.KR 3400)

HENRIKSEN, William (1880-1964) Danish
£270 $435 €405 Farm with girl and dog (43x35cm-17x14in) s. 22-Feb-3 Rasmussen, Havnen #2033 (D.KR 3000)
£315 $508 €473 From Nyboder (41x56cm-16x22in) s. 22-Feb-3 Rasmussen, Havnen #2011 (D.KR 3500)
£488 $790 €732 Interior scene with sunshine through window (48x38cm-19x15in) s. 25-Jan-3 Rasmussen, Havnen #2074 (D.KR 5500)
£513 $800 €770 Hansbjerg Mose (28x43cm-11x17in) s.i.d.1931. 20-Sep-2 New Orleans Auction, New Orleans #506/R
£957 $1550 €1388 Sunshine in the blue sitting room (48x38cm-19x15in) s. 26-May-3 Rasmussen, Copenhagen #1425/R (D.KR 10000)

HENRIKSSON, Harry (?) Finnish?
£782 $1244 €1150 Landscape from Aabo (70x90cm-28x35in) s.d.43. 24-Mar-3 Bukowskis, Helsinki #95/R

HENRION, Armand (1875-?) Belgian
£420 $685 €609 Pierrot head study (18x14cm-7x6in) board. 17-Jul-3 Tennants, Leyburn #921
£961 $1499 €1442 Clown with pipe (18x14cm-7x6in) s. panel. 6-Nov-2 Dobiaschofsky, Bern #649/R (S.FR 2200)
Works on paper
£253 $395 €400 Pierrot triste (26x21cm-10x8in) s. mixed media oval. 16-Sep-2 Horta, Bruxelles #286

HENRIQUEL, Louis Pierre (1797-1892) French
Works on paper
£517 $822 €750 Helene de Mecklembours, Duchesse d'Orleans (28x20cm-11x8in) s.i. graphite dr exec.c.1835 sold with an engraving. 5-Mar-3 Oger, Dumont, Paris #18

HENRIQUES, Sally (1815-1886) Danish
£44789 $68079 €67184 Female model in front of mirror (88x62cm-35x24in) s.d.20.10.41. 27-Aug-2 Rasmussen, Copenhagen #1419/R est:150000-250000 (D.KR 520000)

HENRY (?) ?
£13500 $21060 €20250 Venice by moonlight (59x89cm-23x35in) indis.sig. 6-Nov-2 Dreweatt Neate, Newbury #317/R est:400-600

HENRY, Barclay (fl.1891-1940) British
£420 $689 €630 Crofters drying their nets (23x38cm-9x15in) s.d.1916. 10-Feb-3 David Duggleby, Scarborough #611
£980 $1597 €1421 Fishing from a boat (58x89cm-23x35in) s.d.1889. 17-Jul-3 Thomson, Roddick & Medcalf, Carlisle #125/R

HENRY, Edward (?) ?
£3247 $5000 €4871 Ocean (20x25cm-8x10in) s. panel prov.exhib. 24-Oct-2 Shannon's, Milford #192/R est:5000-7000

HENRY, Edward Lamson (1841-1919) American
£17742 $27500 €26613 Huckster (22x29cm-9x11in) s. board prov.exhib. 4-Dec-2 Sotheby's, New York #132/R est:15000-20000
Works on paper
£373 $600 €560 Scene of salesman with horse and carriage stopped at roadside talking with woman (33x53cm-13x21in) s. W/C. 22-Feb-3 Brunk, Ashville #393/R

HENRY, George (1859-1943) British
£5200 $8060 €7800 Beside the lake (51x61cm-20x24in) s.d.1918. 6-Dec-2 Lyon & Turnbull, Edinburgh #106/R est:5000-7000
£18000 $27360 €27000 Japanese family in an interior (29x25cm-11x10in) panel. 28-Aug-2 Sotheby's, London #1069a est:10000-15000
Works on paper
£3000 $4560 €4500 On the moor (28x49cm-11x19in) s. W/C bodycol. 28-Aug-2 Sotheby's, London #1068/R est:3000-5000
£3600 $5508 €5400 In the woods (24x19cm-9x7in) gouache. 22-Aug-2 Bonhams, Edinburgh #1177/R est:2000-3000

HENRY, Grace (1868-1953) British
£2179 $3422 €3400 Plane trees, France (46x55cm-18x22in) s. board prov. 19-Nov-2 Whyte's, Dublin #147/R est:2000-4000
£2500 $4000 €3750 Path to the lake (51x61cm-20x24in) s. 16-May-3 Sotheby's, London #76/R est:2000-3000
£2899 $4754 €4000 Polyanthus (35x24cm-14x9in) s. board. 28-May-3 Bonhams & James Adam, Dublin #143/R est:3000-4000
£3270 $5102 €5200 Red sail, Venice (23x30cm-9x12in) init. board. 17-Sep-2 Whyte's, Dublin #64/R est:5000-7000
Works on paper
£850 $1360 €1275 Woman of Connemara (25x33cm-10x13in) init. pencil W/C. 15-May-3 Christie's, Kensington #216/R

HENRY, H (19th C) French
£3077 $4831 €4800 Essayage d'escarpins (79x50cm-31x20in) s. 10-Dec-2 Tajan, Paris #179/R

HENRY, Harry Raymond (1882-1974) American
£870 $1400 €1305 Stream in foothill landscape (30x41cm-12x16in) s. board prov. 18-Feb-3 John Moran, Pasadena #138 est:1500-2500
£1161 $1800 €1742 Through the trees (41x51cm-16x20in) s. i.verso. 29-Oct-2 John Moran, Pasadena #720 est:2000-3000

HENRY, James Levin (1855-?) British
£1400 $2156 €2100 Dutch canal (32x46cm-13x18in) s. 23-Oct-2 Hamptons Fine Art, Godalming #141/R est:1500-1800

HENRY, Jules (19th C) ?
£272 $433 €400 Musician (38x31cm-15x12in) s.d.1849. 1-Mar-3 Stadion, Trieste #382

HENRY, Marjorie (?) British?
£445 $699 €650 Mountain landscape (14x18cm-6x7in) s. canvas on board prov. 15-Apr-3 De Veres Art Auctions, Dublin #5/R
£600 $954 €900 Still life (56x50cm-22x20in) s. board. 5-Mar-3 John Ross, Belfast #6
£900 $1431 €1350 Still life (60x50cm-24x20in) s. board. 5-Mar-3 John Ross, Belfast #249

HENRY, Maurice (1907-1984) French
£1677 $2650 €2600 Pensee non controlee (100x81cm-39x32in) s. s.i.d.1971 verso acrylic prov. 18-Dec-2 Christie's, Rome #70/R
£1702 $2757 €2400 Nulle part (55x46cm-22x18in) s.d.75 s.i.d.verso. 26-May-3 Christie's, Milan #176/R est:2500-3500
Works on paper
£1370 $2151 €2000 Untitled (32x25cm-13x10in) s. ink. 15-Apr-3 Laurence Calmels, Paris #4316/R
£1370 $2151 €2000 Untitled (33x25cm-13x10in) s. ink. 15-Apr-3 Laurence Calmels, Paris #4318/R est:1200
£1507 $2366 €2200 Untitled (32x25cm-13x10in) s. ink. 15-Apr-3 Laurence Calmels, Paris #4317/R
£1918 $3011 €2800 Untitled (32x25cm-13x10in) ink. 15-Apr-3 Laurence Calmels, Paris #4320/R est:1200
£2740 $4301 €4000 Portrait caricatural d'Andre Breton (17x22cm-7x9in) s. wash ink. 15-Apr-3 Laurence Calmels, Paris #4319/R est:1500
£12329 $19233 €18000 Portrait des surrealistes (50x32cm-20x13in) s. ink lit. 14-Apr-3 Laurence Calmels, Paris #4015/R est:1500

HENRY, Michel (1928-) French
£304 $475 €456 Sous les palmes (23x33cm-9x13in) s. i.on stretcher prov. 5-Nov-2 Arthur James, Florida #106
£353 $575 €530 Verdure (20x25cm-8x10in) s. prov. 2-Feb-3 Simpson's, Houston #208a
£545 $850 €818 Myostis et peaches (46x38cm-18x15in) s. i.on stretcher prov. 5-Nov-2 Arthur James, Florida #105
£641 $1000 €962 Coquelicots de France (41x51cm-16x20in) s. i.verso prov. 20-Sep-2 Sloan, North Bethesda #412/R est:1500-2000
£1282 $2000 €1923 Fleurs des champs (132x99cm-52x39in) s. i.stretcher prov. 5-Nov-2 Arthur James, Florida #110
£1538 $2400 €2307 Marguerite et poppies (91x74cm-36x29in) s. i.verso prov. 5-Nov-2 Arthur James, Florida #109/R

HENRY, Olive (1902-1989) British
£260 $403 €390 Concerto harmony (45x37cm-18x15in) board. 4-Dec-2 John Ross, Belfast #272
£704 $1169 €1000 Pomp (34x45cm-13x18in) s. board. 10-Jun-3 James Adam, Dublin #178/R est:600-800
£1250 $1987 €1800 On stage (51x41cm-20x16in) s. i.verso oil graphite canvas on board prov. 29-Apr-3 Whyte's, Dublin #226/R est:1500-2000
Works on paper
£250 $365 €375 South of France (25x36cm-10x14in) s. W/C. 12-Jun-2 John Ross, Belfast #30
£288 $449 €420 Boats in harbour (27x36cm-11x14in) s. W/C. 8-Apr-3 James Adam, Dublin #128/R
£380 $555 €570 By the water fountain (28x38cm-11x15in) s. W/C. 12-Jun-2 John Ross, Belfast #303

HENRY, Paul (1876-1958) Irish
£472 $736 €684 Autumn landscape with three horses (53x102cm-21x40in) s.i.d.1998. 26-Mar-3 Walker's, Ottawa #444/R est:1200-1600 (C.D 1100)
£15000 $24000 €22500 Near Coomasaharn (25x33cm-10x13in) s. board. 15-May-3 Christie's, London #45/R est:20000-30000
£17000 $27200 €25500 Clare Island from Achill (31x44cm-12x17in) s. 16-May-3 Sotheby's, London #102/R est:15000-20000
£19178 $30110 €28000 Cottages in a windswept mountain landscape (38x46cm-15x18in) s. prov. 15-Apr-3 De Veres Art Auctions, Dublin #224/R est:30000-40000
£20000 $32000 €30000 Sunset in the Mourne Mountains (27x38cm-11x15in) s. board exhib. 15-May-3 Christie's, London #50/R est:20000-30000
£21739 $35652 €30000 Keel Village, Achill Island 1911 (45x51cm-18x20in) s. prov.exhib. 28-May-3 Bonhams & James Adam, Dublin #86/R est:30000-40000
£23000 $36800 €34500 Killary bay (33x41cm-13x16in) s. panel exhib. 15-May-3 Christie's, London #46/R est:30000-50000
£25000 $38750 €37500 Trees, Co. Wicklow (46x61cm-18x24in) s. 2-Oct-2 John Ross, Belfast #163 est:25000-27500
£30000 $48000 €45000 Ballyeighan, Birr (61x51cm-24x20in) s.d.1913 prov. 15-May-3 Christie's, London #48/R est:30000-50000
£30000 $48000 €45000 Sunshine and shadow (40x51cm-16x20in) s. prov. 16-May-3 Sotheby's, London #88/R est:25000-35000
£36000 $57600 €54000 Bog by the sea (38x45cm-15x18in) s. 16-May-3 Sotheby's, London #101/R est:20000-30000
£38000 $60800 €57000 Connemara (33x39cm-13x15in) s. board prov. 16-May-3 Sotheby's, London #85/R est:25000-35000
£48551 $79623 €67000 Slievemore, Achill (36x40cm-14x16in) s. board. 28-May-3 Bonhams & James Adam, Dublin #51/R est:40000-60000
Works on paper
£2973 $4638 €4400 Mushrooms on a hill (37x21cm-15x8in) i.verso gouache paper on board prov. 26-Mar-3 James Adam, Dublin #60/R est:3000-5000

HENRY, Paul (attrib) (1876-1958) Irish
£14000 $22400 €21000 Keem Bay, Achill (38x46cm-15x18in) 16-May-3 Sotheby's, London #103/R est:15000-20000

HENRY, William (1812-1884) British
Works on paper
£252 $400 €378 Navigating small islands (53x66cm-21x26in) s. W/C exec.c.1959. 2-Mar-3 Toomey, Oak Park #640/R
£299 $475 €449 Mercado (41x51cm-16x20in) s.d. i.verso casein board. 2-Mar-3 Toomey, Oak Park #638/R

HENS, Ben (1936-) Dutch
Works on paper
£269 $423 €420 Composition (97x68cm-38x27in) s.d.66 gouache. 25-Nov-2 Glerum, Amsterdam #239

HENS, Frans (1856-1928) Belgian
£633 $987 €1000 Plue sur l'Escaut (52x63cm-20x25in) prov. 16-Sep-2 Amberes, Antwerp #214
£1389 $2208 €2000 Barques echouees au bord de l'Escaut (100x100cm-39x39in) s. 29-Apr-3 Campo & Campo, Antwerp #148/R est:2250-2750

HENSCHEL, Gallus Emil (1865-?) German
Works on paper
£282 $437 €440 Farmer's cottage near Ahrenshoop (28x38cm-11x15in) s.i.d.1910 W/C htd white. 7-Dec-2 Dannenberg, Berlin #677/R

HENSEL, Wilhelm (1794-1861) German
£6987 $10900 €10481 Portrait of Fanny Mendelssohn Bartholdy (129x103cm-51x41in) 6-Nov-2 Dobiaschofsky, Bern #650/R est:5000 (S.FR 16000)

HENSEL, Wilhelm (attrib) (1794-1861) German
£7500 $11700 €11250 Family concert (77x118cm-30x46in) prov. 10-Apr-3 Tennants, Leyburn #940/R est:5000-7000

HENSELMANN, Wilhelm (?) German?
£260 $387 €400 Restaurant in city park (54x73cm-21x29in) s. i. verso. 27-Jun-2 Neumeister, Munich #2744/R

HENSHALL, John Henry (1856-1928) British
Works on paper
£620 $973 €930 Kindergarten (25x36cm-10x14in) s. W/C. 24-Jul-2 Walker's, Ottawa #20/R est:2000-3000 (C.D 1500)
£751 $1171 €1089 Young tutor (25x37cm-10x15in) s. W/C. 26-Mar-3 Walker's, Ottawa #46/R est:1000-1500 (C.D 1750)
£1300 $2028 €1950 May we come in ? (20x29cm-8x11in) s. pencil W/C scratching out. 27-Mar-3 Christie's, Kensington #16 est:1200-1800
£2200 $3586 €3190 Difficult lesson (25x36cm-10x14in) s. W/C. 16-Jul-3 Sotheby's, Olympia #116/R est:2000-3000
£2500 $3951 €3750 This is the way we go to school (27x37cm-11x15in) s.i. W/C. 2-Dec-2 Sotheby's, London #53/R est:2500-3500

HENSHAW, Frederick Henry (1807-1891) British
£500 $795 €750 An overshot mill (74x62cm-29x24in) s.d.1856. 4-Mar-3 Bearnes, Exeter #474/R
£600 $912 €900 Summer wooded river landscape with cattle watering (28x33cm-11x13in) s.d.1882. 16-Aug-2 Keys, Aylsham #621/R
£600 $948 €900 Feeding rabbits (23x33cm-9x13in) s. 12-Nov-2 Bonhams, Knightsbridge #146/R
£680 $1081 €1020 Sheep and figures in a landscape (25x35cm-10x14in) s.d.1841. 4-Mar-3 Bearnes, Exeter #475/R
£2100 $3339 €3150 Mountain pass (28x38cm-11x15in) s.i0 verso panel. 4-Mar-3 Bearnes, Exeter #471/R est:800-1200

£2600 $4056 €3900 Gypsy encampment (76x63cm-30x25in) s.d.1844 panel. 8-Oct-2 Bonhams, Knightsbridge #94/R est:2000-3000
£3200 $5056 €4800 Forest or Arden, Warwickshire (57x94cm-22x37in) s.d.1845 exhib. 2-Dec-2 Bonhams, Bath #108/R est:4000-6000
£4800 $7344 €7200 Corstorphine, near Edinburgh (63x54cm-25x21in) s.i. 22-Aug-2 Bonhams, Edinburgh #997/R est:5000-8000

HENSHAW, Frederick Henry (attrib) (1807-1891) British
£2000 $3260 €3000 Wooded landscape with figures, cattle and sheep walking along tree-lined path (33x24cm-13x9in) i.verso board. 11-Feb-3 Fellows & Sons, Birmingham #42/R est:800-1200

HENSHAW, Glenn Cooper (1881-1946) American
Works on paper
£224 $350 €336 Portrait of an elderly man with cane (55x43cm-22x17in) s.d.12 chl pastel. 12-Apr-3 Weschler, Washington #584/R
£597 $950 €896 New York harbour (14x10cm-6x4in) s. pastel exec.c.1910. 4-May-3 Treadway Gallery, Cincinnati #539/R

HENSLEY, Jackson (20th C) American
£7692 $12000 €11538 Aspens (102x183cm-40x72in) s. prov.lit. 9-Nov-2 Santa Fe Art, Santa Fe #185/R est:10000-20000

HENSLEY, Marie (c.1856-1911) British
Works on paper
£420 $680 €630 Peonies (23x42cm-9x17in) s.d.1898 pencil W/C. 23-Jan-3 Christie's, Kensington #309

HENSON, Bill (1955-) Australian
Photographs
£1505 $2288 €2258 Untitled (103x67cm-41x26in) type C col photo edition 10. 28-Aug-2 Deutscher-Menzies, Melbourne #286/R est:3500-4500 (A.D 4200)
£1643 $2563 €2465 Untitled (107x89cm-42x35in) s.i.d.num.7/20 type C col photo. 11-Nov-2 Deutscher-Menzies, Melbourne #13/R est:4000-5000 (A.D 4600)
£1857 $2860 €2786 Image from untitled (106x88cm-42x35in) type c colour photograph. 8-Sep-2 Sotheby's, Melbourne #44/R est:3000-5000 (A.D 5200)
£1929 $2970 €2894 Image from untitled (107x88cm-42x35in) type c colour photograph. 8-Sep-2 Sotheby's, Melbourne #35/R est:3000-5000 (A.D 5400)
£2000 $3220 €2900 Untitled (106x86cm-42x34in) photograph. 12-May-3 Joel, Victoria #325 est:5000-6000 (A.D 5000)
£2091 $3430 €3137 Untitled (78x65cm-31x26in) s.i.num. type C col photo edition 10 lit. 4-Jun-3 Deutscher-Menzies, Melbourne #101/R est:4500-6500 (A.D 5250)
£2439 $3854 €3537 Untitled (91x70cm-36x28in) type c colour photograph. 22-Jul-3 Lawson Menzies, Sydney #17/R est:4500-6000 (A.D 6000)
£2643 $4070 €3965 Image from untitled (179x121cm-70x48in) type c colour photograph. 8-Sep-2 Sotheby's, Melbourne #43/R est:4000-6000 (A.D 7400)
£2789 $4573 €4184 Untitled (106x86cm-42x34in) s.i.d. type C col photo. 4-Jun-3 Deutscher-Menzies, Melbourne #100/R est:4500-6000 (A.D 7000)
£2880 $4637 €4320 Untitled (100x65cm-39x26in) type C col. photograph num.7/17. 6-May-3 Christie's, Melbourne #245/R est:4000-6000 (A.D 7200)
£3200 $5152 €4800 Untitled (101x66cm-40x26in) type c col photograph num.4/10. 6-May-3 Christie's, Melbourne #253/R est:4000-6000 (A.D 8000)

HENSTENBURGH, Herman (1667-1726) Dutch
Works on paper
£8710 $13761 €13500 Birds by fountains (37x27cm-15x11in) s. gouache pair. 18-Dec-2 Renaud, Paris #56/R est:12000
£14000 $23380 €20300 Thistles, daisies and mushrooms by pond with snake, lizard and frog with various insects (41x32cm-16x13in) s. gouache gum arabic vellum prov.exhib.lit. 9-Jul-3 Sotheby's, London #114/R est:20000-30000
£18000 $30060 €26100 Urn garlanded with flowers, fruit, hazelnuts and insects and snails on stone ledge (44x34cm-17x13in) s. W/C gouache gum arabic traces blk chk vellum prov.exhib.lit. 9-Jul-3 Sotheby's, London #112/R est:25000-35000

HENSTENBURGH, Herman (attrib) (1667-1726) Dutch
Works on paper
£2817 $4676 €4000 Still life of flowers (43x30cm-17x12in) 12-Jun-3 Hauswedell & Nolte, Hamburg #278/R est:5000

HENTZE, C (20th C) ?
Works on paper
£461 $747 €650 Surreal scene (25x277cm-10x109in) s.d.15 W/C Indian ink paper on board. 24-May-3 Van Ham, Cologne #254
£709 $1149 €1000 Figures in landscape (25x27cm-10x11in) s.d.1920/21 verso W/C Indian ink col chk. 24-May-3 Van Ham, Cologne #253/R

HENZE, Robert (1827-1906) German
Sculpture
£1439 $2302 €2000 Bacchantal scene (97x89cm-38x35in) s.i. pat.bronze wall relief. 19-May-3 Dorotheum, Vienna #279/R est:3500-3800

HENZELL, Isaac (1815-1876) British
£600 $942 €900 Wayside conversation (35x46cm-14x18in) s.d.1876. 16-Apr-3 Christie's, Kensington #757
£1150 $1829 €1725 Boys fishing. Maid and dog by a country lane (24x18cm-9x7in) s.d.1845 panel pair. 27-Feb-3 Bonhams, Chester #377/R est:1200-1800
£1400 $2198 €2100 River landscape with a boy and his dog tending cattle (72x92cm-28x36in) s. 21-Nov-2 Tennants, Leyburn #797/R est:1000-1500
£1800 $3006 €2610 Boy herding goats, sheep and cattle on a hillside overlooking a river (44x59cm-17x23in) s.d.53 panel. 17-Jun-3 Anderson & Garland, Newcastle #479/R est:2000-3000

HENZIROSS, Eugen (1877-1961) ?
£306 $477 €459 Fisherman (50x61cm-20x24in) s. 6-Nov-2 Dobiaschofsky, Bern #651/R (S.FR 700)

HEPPENER, Johannes Jacobus (attrib) (1826-1898) Dutch
£1433 $2321 €2150 Landscape with figures by house (63x91cm-25x36in) 3-Feb-3 Lilla Bukowskis, Stockholm #552 est:20000-25000 (S.KR 20000)

HEPPER, G (1839-1868) British
£1800 $3006 €2610 Street scene with figures outside a millners (28x40cm-11x16in) s.d.1864 panel. 17-Jun-3 Bonhams, New Bond Street #57/R est:2000-3000

HEPPER, George (1839-1868) British
£3200 $5088 €4800 Ghillie's companions (30x34cm-12x13in) s.d.67 panel. 6-Mar-3 Christie's, Kensington #106/R est:2000-4000

HEPPLE, John Wilson (1886-1939) British
£350 $546 €525 Figure on a bridge in a mountainous lakeland landscape (28x43cm-11x17in) s.d.1913. 20-Sep-2 Richardson & Smith, Whitby #74

HEPPLE, Robert Norman (1908-1994) British
£1900 $2926 €2850 Queen Mother (51x51cm-20x20in) studio st.verso board. 5-Sep-2 Christie's, Kensington #597/R est:1000-1500

HEPPLE, Wilson (1853-1937) British
£600 $948 €900 Mixed pickles (43x53cm-17x21in) s.d.1889 monochrome. 2-Dec-2 Bonhams, Bath #151/R
£650 $1007 €975 Bay mare and her foal by a tree and a river bank (24x34cm-9x13in) s.d.1901 panel. 24-Sep-2 Anderson & Garland, Newcastle #516/R
£700 $1064 €1050 Rural scenes with figures and work horses (38x48cm-15x19in) s. pair. 14-Aug-2 Andrew Hartley, Ilkley #679
£800 $1264 €1200 Mare and foal in an orchard (25x34cm-10x13in) s.d.1901 panel. 28-Nov-2 Christie's, Kensington #143/R
£850 $1326 €1275 Portrait of horse, Zill (70x50cm-28x20in) s.d.1894. 14-Sep-2 Cumbria Auction Rooms, UK #56/R
£1550 $2449 €2325 Kittens and canvases (29x16cm-11x6in) s. panel. 7-Apr-3 Bonhams, Bath #117/R est:800-1200
£1800 $2808 €2700 Harvesting. Man and horses by an arched bridge (38x48cm-15x19in) s. pair. 20-Sep-2 Richardson & Smith, Whitby #118 est:1800-2200
£2300 $3611 €3450 Two kittens playing beside a kutani tea service (25x36cm-10x14in) s. 19-Nov-2 Bonhams, Leeds #180/R est:2000-3000
£2700 $4185 €4050 Jewel thieves (28x39cm-11x15in) s.d.1913 i.stretcher. 24-Sep-2 Anderson & Garland, Newcastle #515/R est:2000-3000
£7362 $12000 €11043 Dodger (28x39cm-11x15in) s.i.d.81. 11-Feb-3 Bonhams & Doyles, New York #171/R est:3000-5000
Works on paper
£1200 $2004 €1740 Portraits of kittens (17x13cm-7x5in) s.d.1913 W/C pair. 17-Jun-3 Anderson & Garland, Newcastle #234/R est:600-800

£2800 $4676 €4060 Jewel thieves, three kittens playing with pearl necklace (37x55cm-15x22in) s.d.1921 W/C. 17-Jun-3 Anderson & Garland, Newcastle #233/R est:3000-5000

HEPWORTH, Dame Barbara (1903-1975) British

£14000 $21980 €21000 Construction I (86x101cm-34x40in) s.d.1965 s.i.d.verso oil pencil on gesso board prov.lit. 22-Nov-2 Christie's, London #92/R est:15000-20000
£15000 $23250 €22500 Atlantic form (61x43cm-24x17in) s.d.1963 oil pencil on board. 4-Oct-2 Mallams, Oxford #586/R est:6000-8000
£23000 $35650 €34500 Stone form (33x53cm-13x21in) s.d.1961 oil pencil board. 4-Oct-2 Mallams, Oxford #585/R est:6000-8000

Sculpture

£3800 $5928 €5700 Hand in a relaxed position (31cm-12in) init.d.1950 bronze. 12-Sep-2 Sotheby's, Olympia #136/R est:2000-3000
£6211 $10000 €9317 Two forms domino (21cm-8in) i.d.1969 num.3/9 gold pat. bronze prov.lit. 7-May-3 Sotheby's, New York #316/R est:10000-15000
£12500 $19625 €18750 Mincarlo (16cm-6in) init.d.1971 num.3/12 18 caret yellow gold prov. 22-Nov-2 Christie's, London #46/R est:12000-18000
£32051 $50000 €48077 Idol (77cm-30in) s.i.d.1971 num.8/9 polished bronze cast 1971 prov.exhib. 7-Nov-2 Christie's, Rockefeller NY #342/R est:60000-80000
£204969 $330000 €307454 Figure (183cm-72in) i.d.1964 num.6/6 brown green pat. bronze exhib.lit. 7-May-3 Sotheby's, New York #341/R est:200000-300000

HER, G (?) ?

£1025 $1599 €1538 Five old men (91x136cm-36x54in) indis.sig. 11-Nov-2 Stephan Welz, Johannesburg #425/R est:8000-12000 (SA.R 16000)

HERALD, James Watterson (1859-1914) British

£980 $1588 €1470 Figures in a village street (31x23cm-12x9in) 23-May-3 Lyon & Turnbull, Edinburgh #30a
£1900 $3078 €2850 Moonlight (28x34cm-11x13in) 23-May-3 Lyon & Turnbull, Edinburgh #14a est:1500-2000

Works on paper

£250 $390 €375 Stained glass window (57x45cm-22x18in) pastel oval. 10-Oct-2 Bonhams, Edinburgh #341
£250 $390 €375 Young violinist (14x9cm-6x4in) pastel. 10-Oct-2 Bonhams, Edinburgh #340
£280 $437 €420 In the harbour (11x15cm-4x6in) init. W/C. 10-Apr-3 Bonhams, Edinburgh #102
£280 $437 €420 Promenade (12x12cm-5x5in) pencil. 10-Apr-3 Bonhams, Edinburgh #138
£300 $468 €450 Stepping carefully (16x11cm-6x4in) pencil. 17-Oct-2 Bonhams, Edinburgh #185
£320 $525 €480 Portrait of a girl (28x19cm-11x7in) s. pastel bodycol. 5-Jun-3 Christie's, Kensington #851/R
£500 $780 €750 Woman with fan (17x9cm-7x4in) s. gouache col chk. 17-Sep-2 Sotheby's, Olympia #80/R
£550 $842 €825 Windmill (20x14cm-8x6in) s.d.88 gouache W/C. 22-Aug-2 Bonhams, Edinburgh #1104
£1100 $1804 €1650 Street scene with figures and horses before a church (25x36cm-10x14in) bears i.verso W/C. 4-Jun-3 Bonhams, Chester #420 est:200-300
£2000 $3040 €3000 Cattle resting in the shade (38x48cm-15x19in) s. pastel. 28-Aug-2 Sotheby's, London #1067/R est:2000-3000
£2800 $4284 €4200 George Street, Edinburgh (20x14cm-8x6in) s.d.88 W/C gouache. 22-Aug-2 Bonhams, Edinburgh #1102/R est:1500-2000
£2800 $4396 €4200 Indoor flower market (27x22cm-11x9in) s. W/C bodycol. 10-Dec-2 Rosebery Fine Art, London #676/R est:1000-1500
£3350 $5193 €5025 Arboath street scene, with fisherfolk at work (36x48cm-14x19in) s. pastel W/C. 7-Dec-2 Shapes, Edinburgh #312/R est:2000-3000
£3900 $6084 €5850 On the quay (27x31cm-11x12in) s. W/C htd white. 10-Apr-3 Bonhams, Edinburgh #83/R est:1000-1500
£4500 $6975 €6750 Going to school (30x40cm-12x16in) s.d.1890 W/C. 31-Oct-2 Christie's, London #101/R est:3000-4000
£4938 $7605 €7407 Quayside, Harwich (31x38cm-12x15in) W/C. 26-Oct-2 Heffel, Vancouver #21 est:6000-8000 (C.D 12000)
£12000 $18240 €18000 Buffalo Bill at Arbroth (45x63cm-18x25in) s. W/C. 28-Aug-2 Sotheby's, London #1063/R est:10000-15000

HERALD, James Watterson (attrib) (1859-1914) British

Works on paper

£2000 $3100 €3000 Sweetie shop (27x37cm-11x15in) pastel dr. 24-Sep-2 Patersons, Paisley #433

HERAMB, Thore (1916-) Norwegian

£806 $1242 €1209 At the ward (125x150cm-49x59in) s. painted 1938. 28-Oct-2 Blomqvist, Lysaker #1088 (N.KR 9500)
£1035 $1574 €1553 Composition (51x65cm-20x26in) s.d.58 panel. 31-Aug-2 Grev Wedels Plass, Oslo #51/R (N.KR 12000)
£1493 $2419 €2240 Composition (50x65cm-20x26in) s.d.60 panel. 26-May-3 Grev Wedels Plass, Oslo #109/R est:15000-20000 (N.KR 16500)
£6018 $9508 €9027 Soria Moria Palace (71x146cm-28x57in) s.d.58 exhib. 28-Apr-3 Blomqvist, Oslo #385/R est:60000-80000 (N.KR 68000)

HERAULT-COYPEL, Magdelene (17th C) French

£8451 $14028 €12000 Homme assis a sa table de travail la main posee sur un livre ouvert (114x86cm-45x34in) s. lit. 15-Jun-3 Anaf, Lyon #120/R est:10000-12000

HERAUT, Henri (1894-?) French

£962 $1510 €1500 Mere et enfant (55x46cm-22x18in) s. 16-Dec-2 Chochon-Barre & Allardi, Paris #71 est:1300-1500

HERBERT OF MUCKROSS, Mrs (?) British

Works on paper

£900 $1404 €1350 Torc and Devil's Island. Dundag Rocks and Torc. Muckross (35x53cm-14x21in) W/C set of three. 14-Apr-3 Sotheby's, London #52/R

HERBERT, Albert Henry (20th C) British

£300 $501 €435 Woman seated on a seaside promenade reading (60x75cm-24x30in) s. 17-Jun-3 Anderson & Garland, Newcastle #355/R
£310 $518 €450 Fish quay, North Shields (60x60cm-24x24in) s. board. 17-Jun-3 Anderson & Garland, Newcastle #351
£370 $618 €537 Grey Street, Newcastle looking towards the Theatre Royal (51x38cm-20x15in) s. panel. 17-Jun-3 Anderson & Garland, Newcastle #353a/R
£700 $1169 €1015 Panoramic view of North Shields Harbour (91x121cm-36x48in) s.d.1974. 17-Jun-3 Anderson & Garland, Newcastle #352/R

Works on paper

£270 $451 €392 Figures at the corner of Blackett street and Northumberland Street, Newcastle (44x31cm-17x12in) s.d.1938 W/C. 17-Jun-3 Anderson & Garland, Newcastle #345
£270 $451 €392 Tyne looking across to Redheads (36x52cm-14x20in) s.d.1974 i.verso W/C. 17-Jun-3 Anderson & Garland, Newcastle #346

HERBERT, Alfred (?-1861) British

Works on paper

£820 $1345 €1230 Fishing vessels off Seaton (13x39cm-5x15in) init.d.1845 pencil W/C. 4-Feb-3 Bonhams, Leeds #222

HERBERT, Arthur John (1834-1856) British

£6000 $9960 €9000 Painters walk, Hampstead Heath (47x31cm-19x12in) s.d.1855 i.verso. 12-Jun-3 Sotheby's, London #272/R est:7000-10000

HERBERT, Harold Brocklebank (1892-1945) Australian

Works on paper

£351 $533 €527 Buffalo boulders (36x34cm-14x13in) s.d.1933 W/C. 19-Aug-2 Joel, Victoria #202 est:1000-1500 (A.D 1000)

HERBERT, John Rogers (1810-1890) British

£1300 $2119 €1885 Plea (45x61cm-18x24in) s.d.1835 panel. 16-Jul-3 Sotheby's, Olympia #40/R est:1000-1500
£1550 $2434 €2325 Desert scene (87x170cm-34x67in) 16-Dec-2 Bonhams, Bury St Edmunds #550/R est:1200-1500
£2603 $4060 €3800 Arabian shepherds at oasis (86x168cm-34x66in) s.d.1885. 8-Apr-3 Ansorena, Madrid #238/R
£32000 $51520 €48000 Our Saviour subject to His parents at Nazareth (102x158cm-40x62in) s.d.1860 prov.exhib.lit. 20-Feb-3 Christie's, London #133/R est:50000

HERBERT, John Rogers (attrib) (1810-1890) British

£1800 $2790 €2700 Elizabeth Lady Mellor and her two elder children (127x102cm-50x40in) 29-Oct-2 Gorringes, Lewes #1256/R est:2000-3000

HERBERT, Sidney (1854-1914) British

£8966 $14166 €13000 Scene from the Eneide (133x188cm-52x74in) s.d.1870 i.d.1870 verso. 5-Apr-3 Finarte Semenzato, Milan #20/R est:7000

HERBERTE, E B (fl.1860-1893) British

£7500 $12150 €11250 Coach changing horses outside an inn. London to St Albans coach (3x46cm-1x18in) s.d.1879 pair. 22-May-3 Christie's, London #61/R est:4000-6000
£8000 $12960 €12000 Meet. On the scent. Full cry. Death (30x46cm-12x18in) s.d.1890 four. 22-May-3 Christie's, London #60/R est:7000-10000

Works on paper
£280 $426 €420 Hunting scenes (10x13cm-4x5in) s.d.1882 sic W/C in one frame. 16-Aug-2 Keys, Aylsham #578

HERBERTE, Edward Benjamin (fl.1860-1893) British
£900 $1422 €1350 Heading for the fence (30x25cm-12x10in) s.d.1883. 28-Nov-2 Bonhams, Knightsbridge #109/R
£4500 $7110 €6750 Meet. gone to ground (41x61cm-16x24in) s. pair. 28-Nov-2 Christie's, Kensington #81/R est:5000-7000
£15000 $23400 €22500 The 1885 Grand National - Valentine's Brook (76x127cm-30x50in) s.d.1885 sold with a hand drawn key by same hand. 6-Nov-2 Sotheby's, Olympia #71/R est:15000-20000

HERBIG, Otto (1889-1971) German
Works on paper
£449 $696 €700 Boats under trees (65x45cm-26x18in) s.d.22 col chk wash double-sided. 4-Dec-2 Lempertz, Koln #777/R
£943 $1453 €1500 Nude with masks (76x71cm-30x28in) s.d.1953 pastel chk. 26-Oct-2 Quittenbaum, Hamburg #101/R est:1200
£962 $1519 €1500 Tessin landscape (48x62cm-19x24in) s.d.1926 pastel chk paper on board. 14-Nov-2 Neumeister, Munich #583/R

HERBIN, Auguste (1882-1960) French
£9459 $14757 €14000 Chemin des Carrieres (54x73cm-21x29in) s. prov. 26-Mar-3 Tajan, Paris #33/R
£9677 $15290 €15000 Notre-Dame de Paris (81x100cm-32x39in) s. prov.exhib. 18-Dec-2 Tajan, Paris #74/R est:15000-20000
£12179 $19122 €19000 Composition geometrique (50x36cm-20x14in) cardboard painted c.1920-21 prov. 10-Dec-2 Pierre Berge, Paris #52/R est:25000
£13100 $20568 €19650 Composition (65x54cm-26x21in) s. prov.lit. 25-Nov-2 Germann, Zurich #23/R est:40000-50000 (S.FR 30000)
£13912 $22119 €20450 Apres la pluie a la Roche-Guyon (60x73cm-24x29in) s. exhib.lit. 26-Feb-3 Artcurial Briest, Paris #159/R est:15000-18000
£17177 $27311 €25250 Construction (73x60cm-29x24in) s.d.32 prov.exhib.lit. 26-Feb-3 Artcurial Briest, Paris #298/R est:13000-15000
£18590 $28814 €29000 Abstract composition (60x73cm-24x29in) s. i. stretcher prov.exhib. 4-Dec-2 Lempertz, Koln #778/R est:25000-30000
£19000 $29260 €28500 Venus I (100x81cm-39x32in) s.d.1945 s.on stretcher prov.exhib. 22-Oct-2 Sotheby's, London #354/R est:18000-25000
£20513 $32205 €32000 Mer I (81x60cm-32x24in) s.i.d.1945 prov.lit. 10-Dec-2 Piasa, Paris #235/R est:30000
£20513 $32205 €32000 Air-Feu IV (92x73cm-36x29in) s.i.d.1944 prov.exhib.lit. 10-Dec-2 Piasa, Paris #234/R est:40000
£24476 $40874 €35000 Composition (73x53cm-29x21in) s.d.38 prov.lit. 30-Jun-3 Artcurial Briest, Paris #52a/R est:40000-60000
£28000 $46760 €40600 Fruit (100x81cm-39x32in) s.i.d.1945 prov. 25-Jun-3 Christie's, London #219/R est:30000-40000
£30769 $48000 €46154 Nature morte aux azalees (60x76cm-24x30in) s. painted 1904 prov. 7-Nov-2 Christie's, Rockefeller NY #279/R est:45000-65000
£30769 $48308 €48000 Lune I (92x73cm-36x29in) s.i.d.1945 prov.lit. 10-Dec-2 Piasa, Paris #230/R est:30000
£30769 $48308 €48000 Terre-Eau II (92x60cm-36x24in) s.i.d.1944 prov.exhib.lit. 10-Dec-2 Piasa, Paris #232/R est:35000
£35256 $54647 €55000 Air-feu III (92x60cm-36x24in) s.i.d.1944 lit. 9-Dec-2 Piasa, Paris #38/R est:30000-40000
£41667 $65417 €65000 Terre-Eau I (92x73cm-36x29in) s.i.d.1944 prov.lit. 10-Dec-2 Piasa, Paris #229/R est:35000
£41667 $65417 €65000 Venus III (81x65cm-32x26in) s.i.d.1945 prov.lit. 10-Dec-2 Piasa, Paris #233/R est:35000
£47000 $78490 €68150 Le soleil et les planetes (130x97cm-51x38in) s.d.1941 prov.exhib.lit. 26-Jun-3 Sotheby's, London #159/R est:40000-60000
£51282 $79487 €80000 Louis Carre I (100x81cm-39x32in) s.d.1944 lit. 9-Dec-2 Piasa, Paris #37/R est:60000-80000
£54487 $85545 €85000 Pain et vin II (73x54cm-29x21in) s.i.d.1944 prov.lit. 10-Dec-2 Piasa, Paris #228/R est:35000
£60897 $95000 €91346 Bien (130x89cm-51x35in) s.i.d.1952 prov.exhib.lit. 7-Nov-2 Christie's, Rockefeller NY #340/R est:80000-120000
£70513 $110705 €110000 Christ (195x130cm-77x51in) s.i.d.1944 exhib.lit. 10-Dec-2 Piasa, Paris #231/R est:80000
£98000 $163660 €142100 La place Maubert (65x54cm-26x21in) s. painted 1907 prov.exhib.lit. 24-Jun-3 Sotheby's, London #147/R est:70000-100000
£102564 $160000 €153846 Paysage en corse (60x73cm-24x29in) s. painted 1907 prov. 6-Nov-2 Sotheby's, New York #180/R est:100000-150000

Works on paper
£878 $1370 €1300 Urban landscape (31x22cm-12x9in) s. pencil. 26-Mar-3 Finarte Semenzato, Milan #90/R
£1111 $1766 €1600 Nu penche vu de dos (27x18cm-11x7in) s. graphite estompe dr. 29-Apr-3 Artcurial Briest, Paris #103/R est:1800-2200
£1154 $1812 €1800 Etude pour air et feu (30x23cm-12x9in) s.i.d.1944 graphite dr prov. 10-Dec-2 Piasa, Paris #398
£1282 $2013 €2000 Etude pour pain et vin (27x22cm-11x9in) s.i.d.1944 graphite dr prov. 10-Dec-2 Piasa, Paris #396
£1603 $2516 €2500 Etude pour air et feu (22x32cm-9x13in) s.i.d.1944 graphite dr prov. 10-Dec-2 Piasa, Paris #397/R
£3205 $5032 €5000 Composition abstraite (35x25cm-14x10in) s. W/C. 10-Dec-2 Piasa, Paris #98/R
£3526 $5535 €5500 Soleil et plantes (34x26cm-13x10in) s.d.1941 gouache W/C prov. 10-Dec-2 Piasa, Paris #373
£3526 $5535 €5500 Composition (32x23cm-13x9in) s. W/C gouache exec.1937 prov. 10-Dec-2 Piasa, Paris #394/R
£4808 $7548 €7500 Composition (35x24cm-14x9in) s.d.31 W/C. 10-Dec-2 Piasa, Paris #106/R
£4861 $7729 €7000 Composition sur le theme jazz (23x31cm-9x12in) s.d.36 W/C gouache graphite. 29-Apr-3 Artcurial Briest, Paris #117/R est:5000-7000
£5128 $8051 €8000 Composition (32x23cm-13x9in) s. W/C exec.1937 prov. 10-Dec-2 Piasa, Paris #392 est:7000
£5449 $8554 €8500 Air, feu (36x27cm-14x11in) s.d.1944 gouache prov. 10-Dec-2 Piasa, Paris #383/R
£5769 $9058 €9000 Femme II (36x27cm-14x11in) s.i.d.1944 prov. 10-Dec-2 Piasa, Paris #387/R
£5769 $9058 €9000 Air, feu I (36x27cm-14x11in) s.d.1944 gouache prov. 10-Dec-2 Piasa, Paris #386/R est:7000
£5769 $9058 €9000 Homme II (36x27cm-14x11in) s.i.d.1944 gouache prov. 10-Dec-2 Piasa, Paris #390/R
£5769 $9058 €9000 Homme I (36x27cm-14x11in) s.i.d.1944 gouache prov. 10-Dec-2 Piasa, Paris #389/R est:6000
£6090 $9561 €9500 Composition geometrique (34x26cm-13x10in) s. W/C. 10-Dec-2 Piasa, Paris #105/R
£6410 $10064 €10000 Composition geometrique (32x23cm-13x9in) s. W/C. 10-Dec-2 Piasa, Paris #101/R est:8000-10000
£6410 $10064 €10000 Composition (35x27cm-14x11in) s.d.1941 gouache W/C prov. 10-Dec-2 Piasa, Paris #369 est:8000
£6410 $10064 €10000 Femme I (36x27cm-14x11in) s.i.d.1944 gouache prov. 10-Dec-2 Piasa, Paris #388/R est:6000
£6410 $10064 €10000 Composition (32x23cm-13x9in) s. gouache exec.1937 prov. 10-Dec-2 Piasa, Paris #393/R est:7000
£6731 $10567 €10500 Air, feu II (36x27cm-14x11in) s.i.d.1944 gouache prov. 10-Dec-2 Piasa, Paris #385/R est:7000
£7051 $11071 €11000 Bailleux I (28x36cm-11x14in) s.d.1942 gouache prov. 10-Dec-2 Piasa, Paris #379/R est:10000
£7692 $12077 €12000 Composition (34x26cm-13x10in) s.d.40 gouache W/C prov. 10-Dec-2 Piasa, Paris #367 est:9000
£7692 $12077 €12000 Air, feu (27x36cm-11x14in) s.i.d.1944 prov. 10-Dec-2 Piasa, Paris #384/R est:8000
£8333 $13083 €13000 Air, feu (36x27cm-14x11in) s.i.d.1944 gouache. 10-Dec-2 Piasa, Paris #100/R est:6000-8000
£8333 $13083 €13000 Trigo (38x27cm-15x11in) s.d.1942 gouache prov. 10-Dec-2 Piasa, Paris #368 est:10000
£8333 $13083 €13000 Composition (27x36cm-11x14in) s.d.1942 gouache W/C prov. 10-Dec-2 Piasa, Paris #372 est:10000
£8333 $13083 €13000 Composition (35x25cm-14x10in) s.d.38 gouache W/C prov. 10-Dec-2 Piasa, Paris #366/R est:7000
£8654 $13413 €13500 Trigo II (34x26cm-13x10in) s.d.1942 gouache lit. 9-Dec-2 Piasa, Paris #36/R
£8654 $13587 €13500 Pain, vin (36x24cm-14x9in) s.i.d.1944 gouache. 10-Dec-2 Piasa, Paris #99/R est:10000
£8654 $13587 €13500 Papa, maman, bebe (36x25cm-14x10in) s.d.1943 gouache cardboard prov. 10-Dec-2 Piasa, Paris #377/R est:8000
£8974 $13910 €14000 Composition sur les mots nuits-voile 6 (35x42cm-14x17in) s.d.1943 gouache. 9-Dec-2 Piasa, Paris #33/R est:10000-12000
£9615 $14904 €15000 Pain, vin (36x24cm-14x9in) s.i.d.1944 gouache. 9-Dec-2 Piasa, Paris #34/R est:8000-10000
£9615 $15096 €15000 Air, feu (36x27cm-14x11in) s.i.d.1944 gouache. 10-Dec-2 Piasa, Paris #104/R est:8000-10000
£9615 $15096 €15000 Christ II (36x24cm-14x9in) s.d.1943 gouache prov. 10-Dec-2 Piasa, Paris #374 est:12000
£9615 $15096 €15000 Pain, vin (35x24cm-14x9in) s.i.d.1944 gouache prov. 10-Dec-2 Piasa, Paris #382/R est:10000
£9615 $15096 €15000 Louis Carre 5 (32x25cm-13x10in) s.d.1944 gouache prov.exhib. 10-Dec-2 Piasa, Paris #381/R est:9000
£9615 $15096 €15000 Homme, femme (36x22cm-14x9in) s.d.1944 gouache prov. 10-Dec-2 Piasa, Paris #391/R est:6000
£9936 $15599 €15500 Bailleux II (28x36cm-11x14in) s.d.1942 gouache W/C prov. 10-Dec-2 Piasa, Paris #370 est:10000
£9936 $15599 €15500 Nez (26x34cm-10x13in) s.d.1943 gouache prov. 10-Dec-2 Piasa, Paris #376/R est:8000
£10256 $15897 €16000 Louis Carre I (27x36cm-11x14in) s.i.d.1944 gouache. 9-Dec-2 Piasa, Paris #35/R est:6000-8000
£10256 $16103 €16000 Air, feu (27x36cm-11x14in) s.i.d.1944 gouache. 10-Dec-2 Piasa, Paris #103/R est:8000
£10256 $16103 €16000 Composition (27x35cm-11x14in) s.d.1942 gouache prov. 10-Dec-2 Piasa, Paris #378/R est:9000
£10256 $16103 €16000 Louis Carre 3 (25x20cm-10x8in) s.d.1944 gouache prov. 10-Dec-2 Piasa, Paris #380/R est:8000
£10577 $16606 €16500 Louis Carre II (27x36cm-11x14in) s.d.1944 gouache. 10-Dec-2 Piasa, Paris #97/R est:8000
£10897 $17109 €17000 Christ I (36x26cm-14x10in) s.d.1943 gouache prov. 10-Dec-2 Piasa, Paris #375/R est:12000
£14744 $23147 €23000 Composition sur les mots nuit-voile 8 (35x42cm-14x17in) s.d.1943 i.verso gouache prov. 10-Dec-2 Piasa, Paris #371/R est:12000

HERBO, Fernand (1905-1995) French
£504 $806 €700 Le port, quai anime (16x22cm-6x9in) s. panel. 18-May-3 Eric Pillon, Calais #122/R
£769 $1169 €1200 Maree basse a Saint-Gilles-Croix-de-Vie (60x81cm-24x32in) s. 16-Aug-2 Deauville, France #137/R
£863 $1381 €1200 Vase de fleurs (81x65cm-32x26in) s. 18-May-3 Eric Pillon, Calais #140/R

£881	$1365	€1400	Remorqueur a Rouen (65x81cm-26x32in) s. 30-Oct-2 Artcurial Briest, Paris #360
£1266	$1962	€2000	Le remorqueur pres du rivage (60x73cm-24x29in) s. 29-Sep-2 Eric Pillon, Calais #253/R
£1290	$2039	€2000	En route vers la mer (46x55cm-18x22in) s. 18-Dec-2 Ferri, Paris #75
£1678	$2635	€2450	Noirmoutier (60x80cm-24x31in) s. s.i.verso. 21-Apr-3 Rabourdin & Choppin de Janvry, Paris #39/R est:1800-2000
£1790	$2542	€2900	Honfleur, port et Lieutenance (65x50cm-26x20in) s. 16-Mar-3 Eric Pillon, Calais #235/R
£1900	$3097	€2850	Bateaux sortant du port (60x81cm-24x32in) s. 3-Feb-3 Bonhams, New Bond Street #96/R est:2000-3000

Works on paper

£329	$533	€500	Bateaux a l'entree du port de Honfleur (25x33cm-10x13in) s. W/C. 22-Jan-3 Tajan, Paris #53
£356	$559	€520	Le petit pont (14x19cm-6x7in) s. gouache exec.c.1938. 21-Apr-3 Rabourdin & Choppin de Janvry, Paris #152
£528	$850	€750	Honfleur, le port - Barques a quai (28x44cm-11x17in) s.i.d.1935. 11-May-3 Thierry & Lannon, Brest #316
£662	$1079	€1000	Port et bateaux a quai (42x60cm-17x24in) s.d. W/C. 31-Jan-3 Charbonneaux, Paris #104/R
£692	$1072	€1100	Vue de Normandie (48x65cm-19x26in) s. W/C gouache. 4-Oct-2 Tajan, Paris #119
£1049	$1490	€1700	Port de Honfleur (30x47cm-12x19in) s. W/C. 16-Mar-3 Eric Pillon, Calais #163/R

HERBO, Léon (1850-1907) Belgian

£260	$434	€377	Still life of chrysanthemum in a Chinese vase with a bowl of fruit and a jug (59x33cm-23x13in) s. 23-Jun-3 Bonhams, Bath #236
£278	$442	€400	Reverie (43x53cm-17x21in) s. canvas on panel. 29-Apr-3 Campo & Campo, Antwerp #625
£288	$447	€450	Jeune fille (36x27cm-14x11in) s. panel. 3-Dec-2 Campo & Campo, Antwerp #116/R
£828	$1292	€1300	Homme vetu de rouge fumant une cigarette (46x36cm-18x14in) s. panel. 11-Nov-2 Horta, Bruxelles #66
£892	$1391	€1400	Elegante Orientale (36x27cm-14x11in) s.d.1894 panel. 11-Nov-2 Horta, Bruxelles #65
£959	$1496	€1400	Elegante a la rose (37x27cm-15x11in) s. panel. 14-Apr-3 Horta, Bruxelles #58
£1026	$1610	€1600	Nature morte au journal (54x66cm-21x26in) s.d.74. 19-Nov-2 Servarts Themis, Bruxelles #115
£1135	$1783	€1703	La femme de l'artiste (65x51cm-26x20in) s.d.1881 panel. 25-Nov-2 Germann, Zurich #135/R est:3000-5000 (S.FR 2600)
£1266	$1975	€2000	Landscape with reclining nude (39x28cm-15x11in) s.d.1879 panel. 21-Oct-2 Bernaerts, Antwerp #142/R est:2000-2500
£1911	$2981	€3000	Orientale (62x50cm-24x20in) s. 11-Nov-2 Horta, Bruxelles #64 est:3700-6200
£2179	$3422	€3400	Dame a la lecture assise dans un interieur (77x62cm-30x24in) 25-Nov-2 Amberes, Antwerp #170
£3200	$5344	€4800	Afternoon walk (79x59cm-31x23in) s. 18-Jun-3 Christie's, Kensington #110/R est:2000-3000
£5769	$8942	€9000	Les cerises (82x95cm-32x37in) s. 3-Dec-2 Campo & Campo, Antwerp #115/R est:9000-10000
£17949	$28179	€28000	La rose de perse (75x100cm-30x39in) s. prov. 16-Dec-2 Gros & Delettrez, Paris #404/R est:25000-35000

HERBST, Adolf (1909-1983) Swiss

£657	$1078	€953	Standing figure (44x29cm-17x11in) s. board prov. 4-Jun-3 Fischer, Luzern #2150/R (S.FR 1400)
£896	$1452	€1299	Girl wearing hat (61x38cm-24x15in) s.d.82 prov. 24-May-3 Galerie Gloggner, Luzern #58/R (S.FR 1900)
£1087	$1696	€1631	Silvia (61x46cm-24x18in) s.d.1955 exhib. 16-Sep-2 Philippe Schuler, Zurich #3370/R est:3500-4500 (S.FR 2500)
£1226	$1987	€1778	Femme au voile (65x46cm-26x18in) s.d.82 prov. 24-May-3 Galerie Gloggner, Luzern #59/R est:2500-2800 (S.FR 2600)
£1651	$2675	€2922	Female nude in studio (65x46cm-26x18in) s. prov. 26-May-3 Sotheby's, Zurich #100/R est:3500-4500 (S.FR 3500)
£1717	$2712	€2576	Interior (65x46cm-26x18in) s.d.59. 26-Nov-2 Phillips, Zurich #31/R est:4000-6000 (S.FR 4000)
£1792	$2868	€2688	Interior with flower still life (65x46cm-26x18in) s.d. 17-Mar-3 Philippe Schuler, Zurich #4526/R est:4000-5000 (S.FR 3800)

HERBST, Thomas (1848-1915) German

£1538	$2385	€2400	Path between trees (56x36cm-22x14in) board prov. 7-Dec-2 Ketterer, Hamburg #139/R est:2000-2200
£1688	$2465	€2600	Landscape with fence (30x35cm-12x14in) board. 15-Jun-2 Hans Stahl, Hamburg #187/R
£2338	$3413	€3600	Forest path by sunlight (73x57cm-29x22in) painted c.1910. 15-Jun-2 Hans Stahl, Hamburg #186/R
£3038	$4709	€4800	Peasant woman in north German landscape (34x23cm-13x9in) s. canvs on panel. 28-Sep-2 Hans Stahl, Hamburg #148/R est:5000

HERBSTOFFER, Peter Rudolf Karl (1821-1876) French

£769	$1208	€1200	The duel (27x36cm-11x14in) s.d.1866 panel. 21-Nov-2 Van Ham, Cologne #1665/R

HERCK, Jacobus Melchior van (fl.1678-1735) Flemish

£17000	$26690	€25500	Portrait of Maria Luisa of Savoy, Queen of Spain, in a garland of flowers with putti (164x121cm-65x48in) prov. 13-Dec-2 Christie's, Kensington #262/R est:8000-12000

HERCK, Jacobus Melchior van (attrib) (fl.1678-1735) Flemish

£2200	$3542	€3300	Roses, parrot tulips and other flowers in a vase with a silver plate on partly draped table (57x47cm-22x19in) 20-Feb-3 Christie's, Kensington #75/R est:2500-3500

HERD, Richard (attrib) (1836-1920) British

£480	$773	€696	River Llugwy, Bettws-y-Coed, North Wales (29x22cm-11x9in) board. 12-May-3 Joel, Victoria #395 est:1200-1500 (A.D 1200)
£640	$1030	€928	Old bridge Patterdale, Cumberland (19x30cm-7x12in) board. 12-May-3 Joel, Victoria #373 est:1200-1500 (A.D 1600)

HERDIES, Olivier (1906-1993) French?

Works on paper

£270	$435	€405	Poisson volant (50x65cm-20x26in) s.d.1953 Indian ink exhib. 7-May-3 AB Stockholms Auktionsverk #881/R (S.KR 3500)
£280	$437	€420	Dance (63x48cm-25x19in) s.d.59 Indian ink. 6-Nov-2 AB Stockholms Auktionsverk #772/R (S.KR 4000)
£280	$437	€420	Composition in black (48x63cm-19x25in) s.d.57 Indian ink exhib. 6-Nov-2 AB Stockholms Auktionsverk #781/R (S.KR 4000)
£309	$481	€464	Untitled (64x49cm-25x19in) s.i.d.1961 pastel. 13-Sep-2 Lilla Bukowskis, Stockholm #910 (S.KR 4500)
£315	$492	€473	Composition in blue (49x64cm-19x25in) s.d.54 W/C exhib. 6-Nov-2 AB Stockholms Auktionsverk #771/R (S.KR 4500)
£350	$547	€525	Jazz (63x48cm-25x19in) s.d.1957 Indian ink exhib. 6-Nov-2 AB Stockholms Auktionsverk #773/R (S.KR 5000)
£350	$547	€525	Composition (25x32cm-10x13in) s. pastel executed 1960. 6-Nov-2 AB Stockholms Auktionsverk #777/R (S.KR 5000)
£385	$601	€578	Composition in colour (64x50cm-25x20in) s.d.1961 mixed media exhib. 6-Nov-2 AB Stockholms Auktionsverk #784/R (S.KR 5500)
£385	$601	€578	View in red (38x30cm-15x12in) init.d.1948 W/C exhib. 6-Nov-2 AB Stockholms Auktionsverk #789/R (S.KR 5500)
£420	$656	€630	Composition in yellow (22x27cm-9x11in) s.d.48 W/C exhib. 6-Nov-2 AB Stockholms Auktionsverk #770/R (S.KR 6000)
£420	$656	€630	Hommage a Gene Krupa (50x65cm-20x26in) s.d.14.1.70 W/C exhib. 6-Nov-2 AB Stockholms Auktionsverk #787/R (S.KR 6000)
£456	$711	€684	Abstract composition (38x46cm-15x18in) s.d.1950 Indian ink exhib. 6-Nov-2 AB Stockholms Auktionsverk #782/R (S.KR 6500)
£491	$765	€737	Black composition (49x64cm-19x25in) s.d.1953 Indian ink exhib. 6-Nov-2 AB Stockholms Auktionsverk #780/R (S.KR 7000)
£491	$765	€737	Composition in black (38x45cm-15x18in) s.d.1948 Indian ink. 6-Nov-2 AB Stockholms Auktionsverk #783/R (S.KR 7000)
£701	$1093	€1052	La ville rouge (37x44cm-15x17in) init.d.48 gouache exhib. 6-Nov-2 AB Stockholms Auktionsverk #786/R (S.KR 10000)
£1051	$1640	€1577	Composition (38x45cm-15x18in) init. W/C executed 1948 exhib. 6-Nov-2 AB Stockholms Auktionsverk #768/R est:12000-15000 (S.KR 15000)
£1261	$1968	€1892	Composition in grey and black (38x45cm-15x18in) init. W/C executed 1946 exhib. 6-Nov-2 AB Stockholms Auktionsverk #769/R est:8000-10000 (S.KR 18000)
£1752	$2733	€2628	Composition in colour (137x195cm-54x77in) s. exhib. 6-Nov-2 AB Stockholms Auktionsverk #788/R est:18000-20000 (S.KR 25000)

HERDLE, George Linton (1868-1922) American

Works on paper

£255	$400	€383	Landscape with cottage and windmill (30x43cm-12x17in) s. W/C. 14-Dec-2 Charlton Hall, Columbia #455

HERDMAN, Robert (1828-1888) British

£1564	$2424	€2346	Samson (90x70cm-35x28in) mono.d.1854. 3-Dec-2 Ritchie, Toronto #3020/R est:3000-5000 (C.D 3800)
£1800	$2808	€2700	At the well (92x72cm-36x28in) 17-Sep-2 Sotheby's, Olympia #8/R est:1000-1500
£2095	$3393	€3038	Heather from the hills, Anan (60x45cm-24x18in) mono.d.1864 panel. 25-May-3 Uppsala Auktionskammare, Uppsala #67/R est:25000-30000 (S.KR 27000)
£2400	$3792	€3600	Little messenger (28x24cm-11x9in) init.d.1860 exhib. 7-Apr-3 Bonhams, Bath #124/R est:1500-2000
£6000	$9300	€9000	Jeanie Deans's visit to Effie Deans (64x77cm-25x30in) mono. board prov. 31-Oct-2 Christie's, London #59/R est:4000-6000

HERDMAN, Robert Duddingstone (1863-1922) British
Works on paper
£650 $1014 €975 Spanish Contadina (16cm-6in circular) mono. W/C htd white. 17-Oct-2 Bonhams, Edinburgh #150/R

HERDMAN, W G (1805-1882) British
Works on paper
£1050 $1701 €1575 St. Nicholas church and Chapel Street Liverpool (23x45cm-9x18in) W/C. 21-Jan-3 Bonhams, New Bond Street #153/R est:250-350

HERDMAN, William Gavin (1805-1882) British
£1700 $2703 €2550 In Edinburgh, the high street, Leith Wynd and Canongate (42x76cm-17x30in) s.d.1856 i.on stretcher. 6-Mar-3 Christie's, Kensington #103/R est:1500-2000
Works on paper
£260 $413 €390 Captain Dawson's House, and Custom's Water Street, Liverpool (15x20cm-6x8in) init. W/C painted with family. 27-Feb-3 Bonhams, Chester #358
£900 $1467 €1305 St. Nicholas Church, called locally the Seaman's church (31x46cm-12x18in) pencil pen ink W/C htd white. 17-Jul-3 Tennants, Leyburn #714/R

HERDMAN-SMITH, Robert (1879-?) British
Works on paper
£280 $445 €420 Estuary, Lelant, Cornwall (30x38cm-12x15in) s. i.mount W/C. 18-Mar-3 Capes Dunn, Manchester #466
£862 $1345 €1293 Entrance to Arab Bazaar Cairo (38x32cm-15x13in) s. W/C. 7-Nov-2 International Art Centre, Auckland #123/R est:4000-6000 (NZ.D 2750)

HEREDERO, Antonio (1918-) Spanish
Works on paper
£535 $834 €850 Grove (66x94cm-26x37in) s. W/C. 23-Sep-2 Durán, Madrid #72/R

HERGE (1907-1983) Belgian
Works on paper
£4138 $6621 €6000 Tintin et Milou (35x30cm-14x12in) s.i.d.75 W/C pen ink dr prov. 15-Mar-3 De Vuyst, Lokeren #155/R est:5500-6500

HERGENRODER, Georg Heinrich (1736-1794) German
£6757 $10541 €10000 Interior of cave with ancient monuments and figures (52x64cm-20x25in) s.d.1780 panel. 27-Mar-3 Dorotheum, Vienna #232/R est:9000-12000

HERGER, Edmund (1860-1907) German
£449 $704 €700 Vase of flowers (68x49cm-27x19in) 16-Dec-2 Pandolfini, Florence #115

HERGET, Herbert (20th C) American
£503 $800 €755 Hopi pot maker (51x23cm-20x9in) s. canvasboard. 5-Mar-3 Sotheby's, New York #127/R
£1101 $1750 €1652 Indian artist (26x40cm-10x16in) s. canvasboard. 5-Mar-3 Sotheby's, New York #135/R est:2000-3000
Works on paper
£455 $700 €683 Borrowing some eggs (46x30cm-18x12in) s. gouache exec.c.1920. 8-Sep-2 Treadway Gallery, Cincinnati #630/R

HERING, Georg Wilhelm Richard (1884-1936) Dutch
£350 $546 €550 Portrait of a lady with single rose in her hand (91x79cm-36x31in) s.d.1921. 6-Nov-2 Vendue Huis, Gravenhage #9
£3103 $4934 €4500 Fishermen in the harbour of Volendam (61x75cm-24x30in) s.d.1930. 10-Mar-3 Sotheby's, Amsterdam #344/R est:2000-3000

HERING, George Edwards (1805-1879) British
£516 $831 €774 At the river side (44x55cm-17x22in) s. 12-May-3 Stephan Welz, Johannesburg #7/R est:5000-8000 (SA.R 6000)
£1394 $2174 €2091 Mountain landscape with sheep by water (47x100cm-19x39in) s.d.1857. 23-Sep-2 Rasmussen, Vejle #243/R est:20000 (D.KR 16500)

HERING, George Edwards (attrib) (1805-1879) British
£4000 $6240 €6000 View of the fortress of Rumeli Hisari on the Bosphorus from Anadolu Hisari hill (37x46cm-15x18in) oil paper on board. 15-Oct-2 Sotheby's, London #85/R est:4000-6000

HERING, Harry (1887-1949) American
£305 $500 €458 Canoeing in the mountains (41x51cm-16x20in) s. masonite. 5-Feb-3 Doyle, New York #67/R

HERING, Thomas M (19th C) British
Works on paper
£260 $411 €390 Somerset House from the South Bank (27x45cm-11x18in) s.d.1891 W/C over pencil htd white. 27-Nov-2 Bonhams, Knowle #177

HERIOT, George (1766-1844) Canadian
Works on paper
£380 $600 €570 Taymouth Creek, Perthshire (11x17cm-4x7in) i.verso W/C. 26-Nov-2 Bonhams, Knightsbridge #43/R
£407 $638 €611 Mount Orgueil Castle, Jersey, Channel Islands (11x18cm-4x7in) W/C. 10-Dec-2 Pinneys, Montreal #134 (C.D 1000)
£427 $670 €641 Arundel Castle, Sussex (11x18cm-4x7in) W/C. 10-Dec-2 Pinneys, Montreal #171 (C.D 1050)

HERISSON, Louis François (1811-1859) French
£1800 $2880 €2700 Elegant lady sitting for a portrait (58x71cm-23x28in) s.d.1849 oval. 13-May-3 Bonhams, Knightsbridge #311a est:1500-2000

HERKENRATH, Peter (1900-1992) German
£1090 $1689 €1700 Geometric figures (60x40cm-24x16in) s. oil pencil board. 7-Dec-2 Van Ham, Cologne #221/R est:2500
£1603 $2484 €2500 Untitled - Cipressa (43x55cm-17x22in) s. s.i. verso. 3-Dec-2 Lempertz, Koln #182/R est:3500
£7372 $11426 €11500 Untitled - composition with yellow (130x100cm-51x39in) s. i. stretcher. 3-Dec-2 Lempertz, Koln #181/R est:4000-5000
Works on paper
£321 $497 €500 Profile of girl seated (52x37cm-20x15in) s. W/C gouache. 7-Dec-2 Van Ham, Cologne #222

HERKOMER, Hubert von (1849-1914) British
£550 $864 €825 Portrait of a bearded gentleman (123x99cm-48x39in) init. 21-Nov-2 Tennants, Leyburn #745
Works on paper
£270 $451 €392 Portrait of a young woman wearing a pink cap (31x23cm-12x9in) init.d.88 W/C. 17-Jun-3 Anderson & Garland, Newcastle #221/R
£620 $1011 €930 Away away (50x38cm-20x15in) s.d.1880 pencil W/C htd white. 29-Jan-3 Dreweatt Neate, Newbury #37/R
£6000 $9420 €9000 Old gardener (15x20cm-6x8in) init. pencil bodycol gum arabic scratching out prov.lit. 21-Nov-2 Christie's, London #89/R est:4000-6000

HERLAND, Emma (1856-1947) French
£972 $1585 €1400 Interieur de ferme (55x43cm-22x17in) s. 19-Jul-3 Thierry & Lannon, Brest #341
£986 $1587 €1400 Le Fret, barques au sec (38x55cm-15x22in) s. 11-May-3 Thierry & Lannon, Brest #365

HERMAN, Carl (?) British
£300 $474 €450 View of the old town and South Bay, Scarborough from St Mary's Churchyard (40x60cm-16x24in) s.d.1946. 7-Apr-3 David Duggleby, Scarborough #367/R

HERMAN, Josef (1911-1999) British
£1600 $2496 €2400 Lifting blocks (13x18cm-5x7in) board. 15-Oct-2 Bonhams, Knightsbridge #125/R est:1200-1800
£2000 $3140 €3000 Still life of a lemon with pots and peeler (32x51cm-13x20in) canvasboard. 20-Nov-2 Sotheby's, Olympia #70/R est:1200-1800
£2700 $4266 €4050 Mending the sails (25x35cm-10x14in) 2-Dec-2 Bonhams, Bath #53/R est:1200-1800
£3500 $5494 €5250 Still life of flowers (54x44cm-21x17in) 20-Nov-2 Sotheby's, Olympia #82/R est:3000-5000
£3800 $6346 €5510 Couple by a wall (35x45cm-14x18in) prov. 24-Jun-3 Bonhams, New Bond Street #74/R est:3000-5000
£4200 $6552 €6300 Still life with tulips (44x27cm-17x11in) board. 27-Mar-3 Christie's, Kensington #638/R est:2000-3000
£5000 $8350 €7250 Peasant family, sic (45x60cm-18x24in) s.i.d.1968 verso prov. 24-Jun-3 Bonhams, New Bond Street #76/R est:4000-6000
£7000 $10920 €10500 In the little harbour (51x66cm-20x26in) s.i.verso prov. 27-Mar-3 Christie's, Kensington #588/R est:5000-7000
£8000 $13120 €12000 Miners' bus (61x76cm-24x30in) exhib. 3-Jun-3 Sotheby's, Olympia #141/R est:8000-12000

£10500	$16275	€15750	Mexican township (71x91cm-28x36in) s.i.d.1967 verso prov. 3-Dec-2 Bonhams, New Bond Street #77/R est:6000-8000
£12000	$18720	€18000	Last hours of the day (71x91cm-28x36in) s.i.verso prov. 25-Mar-3 Bonhams, New Bond Street #105/R est:8000-12000

Works on paper

£300	$473	€450	Two miners seated (17x19cm-7x7in) pen ink W/C. 27-Nov-2 Sotheby's, Olympia #263/R
£300	$477	€450	Two fishermen and a boat (19x23cm-7x9in) pen. black ink wash over pencil. 18-Mar-3 Rosebery Fine Art, London #884
£350	$549	€525	Woman ironing (17x21cm-7x8in) W/C gouache over chl. 20-Nov-2 Sotheby's, Olympia #63/R
£350	$574	€525	Fisherman on a bridge (24x19cm-9x7in) pen brush ink prov. 6-Jun-3 Christie's, London #59
£380	$627	€551	Fisherfolk on the quay (16x22cm-6x9in) pencil brush ink. 3-Jul-3 Christie's, Kensington #522
£400	$620	€600	Husband and wife (25x20cm-10x8in) s. pen brush black ink W/C bodycol prov. 4-Dec-2 Christie's, Kensington #310/R
£400	$620	€600	Family with basket of fish (19x25cm-7x10in) s. pen brush black ink felt tip pen prov. 4-Dec-2 Christie's, Kensington #312/R
£400	$644	€600	Two Arabs seated on a wall (16x22cm-6x9in) pen wash prov. 14-Jan-3 Bonhams, Knightsbridge #64/R
£400	$644	€600	Feeding the ducks (17x22cm-7x9in) pen ink. 18-Feb-3 Bonhams, Knightsbridge #14/R
£400	$644	€600	Sleeping figure (17x22cm-7x9in) pen ink. 18-Feb-3 Bonhams, Knightsbridge #17/R
£420	$676	€630	Two fisherman (17x22cm-7x9in) pen ink. 14-Jan-3 Bonhams, Knightsbridge #4/R
£440	$686	€660	Joseph's model, abstract (24x19cm-9x7in) W/C bodycol. 11-Sep-2 Bonhams, Newport #395
£450	$702	€675	Seagull at Aldeburgh (19x26cm-7x10in) W/C gouache. 11-Sep-2 Bonhams, Newport #397
£450	$711	€675	Standing miner (20x12cm-8x5in) brush ink wash over pencil. 27-Nov-2 Sotheby's, Olympia #265/R
£450	$752	€653	Landscape at night (24x41cm-9x16in) indis.i.d. pen ink wash. 17-Jun-3 Bonhams, Knightsbridge #218/R
£475	$741	€713	In the classroom (20x25cm-8x10in) s. pen ink col chk prov. 27-Mar-3 Christie's, Kensington #586/R
£480	$754	€720	Head of a man (26x20cm-10x8in) ink. 20-Nov-2 Sotheby's, Olympia #62/R
£480	$758	€720	Raking (19x24cm-7x9in) W/C ink over pencil. 2-Dec-2 Bonhams, Bath #41/R
£500	$780	€750	Miners resting (17x22cm-7x9in) pencil brush ink. 27-Mar-3 Christie's, Kensington #587
£500	$795	€750	Study of four standing figures (20x25cm-8x10in) pen blue ink W/C. 18-Mar-3 Capes Dunn, Manchester #416
£520	$811	€780	Arab figures (17x22cm-7x9in) pen ink black wash prov. 17-Sep-2 Bonhams, Knightsbridge #46/R
£550	$858	€825	Josef's other model (24x18cm-9x7in) pencil W/C. 11-Sep-2 Bonhams, Newport #396
£550	$863	€825	Village street (20x21cm-8x8in) W/C col chk chl. 20-Nov-2 Sotheby's, Olympia #65/R
£550	$853	€825	Seated man with glass of wine (24x18cm-9x7in) s. pen brush black ink W/C bodycol prov. 4-Dec-2 Christie's, Kensington #313/R
£600	$936	€900	Three men (18x23cm-7x9in) pen ink. 11-Sep-2 Bonhams, Newport #391
£600	$936	€900	Three miners sat before a colliery (11x18cm-4x7in) pen ink W/C. 11-Sep-2 Bonhams, Newport #393
£600	$936	€900	Gypsies on the road (17x21cm-7x8in) pencil wash dr. 11-Sep-2 Bonhams, Newport #399
£600	$936	€900	Contemplative figure (14x17cm-6x7in) pen sepia ink wash executed c.1955. 11-Sep-2 Bonhams, Newport #390
£600	$990	€870	Windmill. Man and wife (23x17cm-9x7in) pencil brush ink col chks. 3-Jul-3 Christie's, Kensington #528/R
£620	$967	€930	Anchor fished out of the sea at Dunwich, Suffolk coast (19x24cm-7x9in) W/C. 11-Sep-2 Bonhams, Newport #403
£680	$1074	€1020	Drying the nets (17x22cm-7x9in) pen wash over pencil. 2-Dec-2 Bonhams, Bath #42/R
£700	$1092	€1050	Woman of Taos, New Mexico (24x18cm-9x7in) W/C bodycol. 11-Sep-2 Bonhams, Newport #394
£700	$1092	€1050	Peasants in a field in Burgundy (20x25cm-8x10in) pen ink wash dr. 11-Sep-2 Bonhams, Newport #404
£700	$1127	€1050	Three figures (17x22cm-7x9in) W/C. 14-Jan-3 Bonhams, Knightsbridge #2/R
£750	$1177	€1125	Woman bending. Miner (21x17cm-8x7in) ink pair. 20-Nov-2 Sotheby's, Olympia #61/R
£750	$1177	€1125	Village scene with figures. Going to the pub (19x24cm-7x9in) chl pair. 20-Nov-2 Sotheby's, Olympia #64/R
£750	$1208	€1125	Walking the dog (19x24cm-7x9in) pen ink prov. 14-Jan-3 Bonhams, Knightsbridge #8/R
£750	$1170	€1125	Farmworkers at sunrise (19x25cm-7x10in) s. pen brush ink W/C prov. 27-Mar-3 Christie's, Kensington #585/R
£820	$1279	€1230	Miner after work (25x19cm-10x7in) wash dr. 11-Sep-2 Bonhams, Newport #402
£850	$1403	€1233	Man in fish and chips shop (24x19cm-9x7in) black biro brush ink bodycol prov. 3-Jul-3 Christie's, Kensington #525/R
£900	$1414	€1350	Washerwomen. Figures in a street (17x18cm-7x7in) chl pair. 20-Nov-2 Sotheby's, Olympia #60/R est:400-600
£900	$1449	€1350	Man and dog (24x19cm-9x7in) W/C. 14-Jan-3 Bonhams, Knightsbridge #204/R
£950	$1463	€1425	Returning home (18x22cm-7x9in) s. pen brush black ink W/C prov. 5-Sep-2 Christie's, Kensington #613
£950	$1491	€1425	Two fisherwomen (46x28cm-18x11in) W/C gouache pencil. 20-Nov-2 Sotheby's, Olympia #85/R est:800-1200
£1100	$1804	€1650	Planting the fields (20x25cm-8x10in) pen ink wash prov. 3-Jun-3 Sotheby's, Olympia #142/R est:400-600
£1200	$1848	€1800	Sorting the nets (18x23cm-7x9in) s. pen brush black ink W/C pastel prov. 5-Sep-2 Christie's, Kensington #631/R est:400-600
£1200	$1932	€1800	Greek village (19x25cm-7x10in) W/C. 14-Jan-3 Bonhams, Knightsbridge #206/R est:800-1000
£1250	$1950	€1875	Two minners at Ystradgyniais (17x21cm-7x8in) pen ink dr. 11-Sep-2 Bonhams, Newport #401 est:600-800
£1400	$2296	€2100	Two miners one with a pole (21x27cm-8x11in) c.1944-55 pen Indian ink wash exhib. 2-Jun-3 David Duggleby, Scarborough #282/R est:300-500
£1600	$2464	€2400	Fishermen seated on the sea wall (20x24cm-8x9in) s. pen brush black ink pastel prov. 5-Sep-2 Christie's, Kensington #607/R est:400-600

HERMAN, Sali (1898-1993) Australian/Swiss

£351	$533	€527	Gentle giant (48x42cm-19x17in) s.d.24. 19-Aug-2 Joel, Victoria #257 est:2000-3000 (A.D 1000)
£385	$600	€578	Landscape in the Swartland (46x58cm-18x23in) s. 20-Oct-2 Susanin's, Chicago #5089/R
£687	$1085	€1031	Landscape (44x59cm-17x23in) s. 1-Apr-3 Lawson Menzies, Sydney #439 (A.D 1800)
£714	$1129	€1071	Figure in alpine meadow holding an Edelwiss flower (49x42cm-19x17in) s.d.24. 27-Nov-2 Deutscher-Menzies, Melbourne #214/R est:3000-4500 (A.D 2000)
£1214	$1918	€1821	Tree lined road (45x61cm-18x24in) s.d.77 canvas on board. 27-Nov-2 Deutscher-Menzies, Melbourne #145/R est:3200-5000 (A.D 3400)
£1571	$2483	€2357	Captain (91x71cm-36x28in) s.d.78. 27-Nov-2 Deutscher-Menzies, Melbourne #147/R est:4500-6000 (A.D 4400)
£2299	$3609	€3449	Mustering sheep (50x60cm-20x24in) s.d.63. 15-Apr-3 Lawson Menzies, Sydney #202/R est:7000-12000 (A.D 6000)
£2857	$4486	€4286	Industry (70x135cm-28x53in) s.d.59 prov.exhib. 25-Nov-2 Christie's, Melbourne #105/R est:12000-18000 (A.D 8000)
£4643	$7336	€6965	Suburbia (44x65cm-17x26in) s.d.1944. 17-Nov-2 Sotheby's, Paddington #1/R est:18000-28000 (A.D 13000)
£5000	$7900	€7500	Farmhouse (45x65cm-18x26in) s.d.80. 27-Nov-2 Deutscher-Menzies, Melbourne #39/R est:10000-15000 (A.D 14000)
£5426	$8628	€8139	Back Lane, Paddington (47x59cm-19x23in) s. prov. 5-May-3 Sotheby's, Melbourne #162/R est:14000-20000 (A.D 14000)
£5426	$8628	€8139	Aboriginal burial ground (81x122cm-32x48in) s.d.62/64. 5-May-3 Sotheby's, Melbourne #212/R est:8000-12000 (A.D 14000)
£6429	$10093	€9644	Chopping wood (100x136cm-39x54in) s. prov. 25-Nov-2 Christie's, Melbourne #17/R est:15000-20000 (A.D 18000)
£8000	$12880	€12000	Paddington (63x81cm-25x32in) s.d.75 prov. 6-May-3 Christie's, Melbourne #91/R est:20000-30000 (A.D 20000)
£8140	$12942	€12210	Solitary building (74x94cm-29x37in) s.d.68 prov.exhib.lit. 5-May-3 Sotheby's, Melbourne #38/R est:18000-25000 (A.D 21000)
£9195	$13701	€13793	Autumn in Victoria street (40x44cm-16x17in) s.d.46 board prov.exhib.lit. 27-Aug-2 Christie's, Melbourne #83/R est:30000-40000 (A.D 24000)
£12456	$19057	€18684	Alley cat (37x49cm-15x19in) s.d.50 prov. 25-Aug-2 Sotheby's, Paddington #46/R est:25000-35000 (A.D 35000)
£18605	$29581	€27908	Woolloomooloo (61x136cm-24x54in) s.d.73 prov. 5-May-3 Sotheby's, Melbourne #21/R est:60000 (A.D 48000)
£27132	$43140	€40698	Red house (101x127cm-40x50in) s.d.65 prov.exhib.lit. 5-May-3 Sotheby's, Melbourne #14/R est:40000-60000 (A.D 70000)

HERMANJAT, Abraham (1862-1932) Swiss

£1217	$1887	€1826	Les diablerets (22x35cm-9x14in) init. cardboard. 7-Dec-2 Galerie du Rhone, Sion #479 est:3500-4500 (S.FR 2800)
£1745	$2792	€2618	Summer lake landscape with bathers (33x38cm-13x15in) s.d. 17-Mar-3 Philippe Schuler, Zurich #4528/R est:3000-5000 (S.FR 3700)

Works on paper

£326	$505	€489	Paysage campagnard (20x28cm-8x11in) mono. pencil W/C gouache. 7-Dec-2 Galerie du Rhone, Sion #400/R (S.FR 750)

HERMANN, Emil (1870-1966) American

£577	$900	€866	Plains Indian girl wading in water (10x20cm-4x8in) board. 19-Oct-2 David Dike, Dallas #88/R

HERMANN, Ernst (1846-1914) German

Works on paper

£1295	$2072	€1800	Acropolis, Athens (24x39cm-9x15in) s.d.8/VI 74 w/C over pencil. 17-May-3 Lempertz, Koln #1292/R est:1800

HERMANN, Hans (1813-1890) German

£1127	$1870	€1600	Lively market scene (36x24cm-14x9in) s.d.1886 board. 14-Jun-3 Arnold, Frankfurt #768/R est:1800

HERMANN, Johann (1794-1880) Austrian

£629	$981	€1000	Portrait of Marie Lacroix (53x42cm-21x17in) i.d.1837 verso one of pair. 19-Sep-2 Dr Fritz Nagel, Stuttgart #943/R

£629 $981 €1000 Portrait of Gustav Dofour (53x42cm-21x17in) i.d.1838 verso one of pair. 19-Sep-2 Dr Fritz Nagel, Stuttgart #944/R

HERMANN, Leo (19th C) French
£2329 $3750 €3494 At rest in the park (15x18cm-6x7in) s. panel. 20-Jan-3 Arthur James, Florida #809

HERMANN, Leo (attrib) (19th C) French
£449 $700 €674 Watering flowers (18x13cm-7x5in) bears sig. panel. 9-Oct-2 Doyle, New York #57

HERMANN, Ludwig (1812-1881) German
£1132 $1766 €1800 Rugen coast (66x96cm-26x38in) s.d.1841. 19-Sep-2 Dr Fritz Nagel, Stuttgart #942/R est:1800
£4800 $7488 €7200 Scheilde at Anvers (71x97cm-28x38in) s.d.1860. 26-Mar-3 Sotheby's, Olympia #221/R est:5000-7000
£5200 $8112 €7800 Danzig (68x96cm-27x38in) s.d.1863. 26-Mar-3 Sotheby's, Olympia #220/R est:5000-7000
£12000 $18840 €18000 On the quayside, Cologne. On the shore, Zuider Zee (68x97cm-27x38in) one s.d.1866 pair. 19-Nov-2 Bonhams, New Bond Street #34/R est:8000-12000

HERMANN, M (1897-?) German
£1645 $2550 €2468 Still life of flowers in venetian glass vase (118x63cm-46x25in) s. panel. 24-Sep-2 Koller, Zurich #6556/R est:2500-3500 (S.FR 3800)

HERMANN, Woldemar (1807-1878) German
Works on paper
£288 $460 €400 Southern Italian riverside town (17x24cm-7x9in) s. w/C. 17-May-3 Lempertz, Koln #1291

HERMANN-PAUL (1874-1940) French
£1554 $2424 €2300 Elegante au chien (33x41cm-13x16in) mono. panel. 25-Mar-3 Chochon-Barre & Allardi, Paris #136/R est:3000-3200

HERMANNS, Heinrich (1862-1942) German
£288 $453 €450 Gondolas off Venice (10x18cm-4x7in) s.d.92 panel. 21-Nov-2 Van Ham, Cologne #1668
£545 $855 €850 Sailing boats off Venice (9x15cm-4x6in) s. panel two. 21-Nov-2 Van Ham, Cologne #1667
£897 $1409 €1400 Spring on the Lagoon, Venice (10x32cm-4x13in) s. board. 21-Nov-2 Van Ham, Cologne #1669/R
Works on paper
£616 $962 €900 Canalside factory in Ruhr (36x58cm-14x23in) s. W/C. 10-Apr-3 Van Ham, Cologne #1481
£753 $1175 €1100 Steelworks in the Ruhr (45x60cm-18x24in) s. W/C. 10-Apr-3 Van Ham, Cologne #1480/R
£753 $1175 €1100 Steel factory (43x58cm-17x23in) s. W/C. 10-Apr-3 Van Ham, Cologne #1482
£1079 $1727 €1500 Lake Garda near Stresa, Vaeno (31x43cm-12x17in) s. gouache. 17-May-3 Lempertz, Koln #1293/R est:1500

HERMANS, Charles (1839-1924) Belgian
£440 $678 €700 Marchands d'oignons (142x107cm-56x42in) s. 22-Oct-2 Campo, Vlaamse Kaai #519/R
£769 $1192 €1200 La lecture (21x29cm-8x11in) bears sig. panel. 9-Dec-2 Horta, Bruxelles #327
£863 $1381 €1200 Boutique a Tunis (37x33cm-15x13in) s. 19-May-3 Horta, Bruxelles #462
£4966 $7895 €7200 Jeune elegante a l'eventail (58x42cm-23x17in) s. 4-Mar-3 Palais de Beaux Arts, Brussels #354/R est:4900-6900
£29677 $46890 €46000 Le bal masque (123x81cm-48x32in) s. 17-Dec-2 Palais de Beaux Arts, Brussels #558/R est:30000-40000
£132911 $210000 €199367 At the masquerade (37x47cm-15x19in) s. 24-Apr-3 Sotheby's, New York #77/R est:80000-120000

HERMANS, J J (?) ?
£253 $395 €400 L'allee du Lanteern - hof en automne (34x44cm-13x17in) 16-Sep-2 Amberes, Antwerp #215

HERMANS, Lievin (19/20th C) Belgian?
Works on paper
£690 $1103 €1000 Homme a son bureau (58x39cm-23x15in) s.d.1906 pastel. 17-Mar-3 Horta, Bruxelles #230

HERMANS, Paul (1898-1972) Belgian
£272 $433 €400 Paysage Orientaliste anime (55x70cm-22x28in) 18-Mar-3 Galerie Moderne, Brussels #153/R
£276 $441 €400 Man singing (45x37cm-18x15in) s. 15-Mar-3 De Vuyst, Lokeren #156

HERMANSEN, O A (1849-1897) Danish
£1872 $2958 €2808 Roses and other flowers in vase (34x27cm-13x11in) s.d.1876. 2-Dec-2 Rasmussen, Copenhagen #1457/R est:25000 (D.KR 22000)

HERMANSEN, Olaf August (1849-1897) Danish
£2828 $4638 €4101 Autumn landscape, Malardalen (80x53cm-31x21in) s.d.94. 4-Jun-3 AB Stockholms Auktionsverk #2256/R est:15000-18000 (S.KR 36000)

HERMANUS, Paul (1859-1911) Belgian
£261 $421 €400 Coucher de soleil sur le petit port (31x41cm-12x16in) s. canvas on panel. 20-Jan-3 Horta, Bruxelles #140
£764 $1215 €1100 Paysage hollandais avec tour (28x40cm-11x16in) s. panel. 29-Apr-3 Campo & Campo, Antwerp #149/R
£1258 $1937 €2000 Village zelandais (39x47cm-15x19in) s. panel. 22-Oct-2 Campo & Campo, Antwerp #133
£1300 $2158 €1300 Ruelle animee a Bruges (46x32cm-18x13in) s. panel. 16-Jun-3 Horta, Bruxelles #419
£1307 $2105 €2000 Lavandiere pres du moulin (32x55cm-13x22in) s. panel. 20-Jan-3 Horta, Bruxelles #139 est:2500-3500
£1690 $2721 €2400 Figures by Katwijk church (33x27cm-13x11in) panel. 7-May-3 Vendue Huis, Gravenhage #476/R est:2500-3000

HERMELIN, Olof (1827-1913) Swedish
£461 $715 €692 Cattle by barn (55x100cm-22x39in) s. 8-Dec-2 Uppsala Auktionskammare, Uppsala #59/R (S.KR 6500)
£543 $880 €787 Fishing village (51x79cm-20x31in) s.d.9/7 1895. 25-May-3 Uppsala Auktionskammare, Uppsala #147/R (S.KR 7000)
£579 $909 €869 Early spring morning (33x56cm-13x22in) s. 16-Dec-2 Lilla Bukowskis, Stockholm #130 (S.KR 8200)
£635 $997 €953 Twilight in the skerries (36x60cm-14x24in) s. 16-Dec-2 Lilla Bukowskis, Stockholm #453 (S.KR 9000)
£780 $1209 €1170 Going away at night, Skagen (43x60cm-17x24in) s.d.99. 4-Dec-2 AB Stockholms Auktionsverk #1623/R (S.KR 11000)
£786 $1288 €1140 Earl spring morning - coastal scene with figures (33x56cm-13x22in) s. 4-Jun-3 AB Stockholms Auktionsverk #2156/R (S.KR 10000)
£943 $1546 €1367 Fishing village with boat houses and children on jetty (54x80cm-21x31in) s.d.90. 4-Jun-3 AB Stockholms Auktionsverk #2090/R (S.KR 12000)
£960 $1498 €1440 Landscape, Orbyhus in Upland (54x80cm-21x31in) s. 13-Sep-2 Lilla Bukowskis, Stockholm #619 (S.KR 14000)
£1094 $1717 €1641 Time for sowing (29x55cm-11x22in) s. 16-Dec-2 Lilla Bukowskis, Stockholm #131/R est:12000-15000 (S.KR 15500)
£1100 $1804 €1595 Mountain landscape with cottages (53x80cm-21x31in) s.d.1900. 4-Jun-3 AB Stockholms Auktionsverk #2231/R est:15000-18000 (S.KR 14000)
£2121 $3478 €3075 Summer landscape from Langangen's farm, Stocksund (53x80cm-21x31in) s.d.1911. 4-Jun-3 AB Stockholms Auktionsverk #2161/R est:15000-20000 (S.KR 27000)
£2226 $3250 €3339 Stream in winter (74x112cm-29x44in) s. 3-Nov-1 North East Auctions, Portsmouth #990/R
£2638 $4273 €3825 Nasby Lake in Sodermanland (50x80cm-20x31in) s. 26-May-3 Bukowskis, Stockholm #131/R est:20000-25000 (S.KR 34000)
£2695 $4177 €4043 Spring landscape from Skuttunge, Uppland with woman on path (54x80cm-21x31in) s.d.1901. 3-Dec-2 Bukowskis, Stockholm #146/R est:18000-20000 (S.KR 38000)

HERMES, Erich (1881-1971) Swiss
£352 $525 €528 Fisherman mending net (53x40cm-21x16in) s.d.1902. 25-Jun-2 Koller, Zurich #6676 (S.FR 800)

HERMES, Gertrude (1901-1983) British
Works on paper
£360 $572 €540 Waterlilies (30x23cm-12x9in) s. i.d.1947 col chk sold with a companion. 5-Mar-3 Bonhams, Bury St Edmunds #285/R

HERNANDEZ MOMPO, Manuel (1927-1992) Spanish
£2358 $3679 €3750 Preparing a party (27x35cm-11x14in) s.d.65 paper. 23-Sep-2 Durán, Madrid #197/R
£5405 $8432 €8000 Composition (35x49cm-14x19in) s. card. 25-Mar-3 Durán, Madrid #186/R
£5806 $9000 €8709 Vagabond (99x61cm-39x24in) s.i. painted c.1955. 8-Dec-2 Toomey, Oak Park #829/R est:600-800
£6410 $10128 €10000 Landscape with clouds (52x73cm-20x29in) s.d.1980 board lit. 19-Nov-2 Durán, Madrid #236/R
£10063 $15497 €16000 Composition (51x66cm-20x26in) s.d.965 board. 22-Oct-2 Durán, Madrid #273/R
Works on paper
£1887 $2906 €3000 Untitled (16x24cm-6x9in) s.d.1964 wax crayon. 28-Oct-2 Segre, Madrid #140/R
£3901 $6319 €5500 Calle con gente (72x50cm-28x20in) s.d.1974 col pencil. 20-May-3 Segre, Madrid #155/R est:5000

£5319 $8617 €7500 Gente en el campo (48x68cm-19x27in) s.d.1974 W/C pastel ink. 20-May-3 Segre, Madrid #148/R est:6000
£6291 $10255 €9500 Untitled (38x55cm-15x22in) s.d.1962 gouache wax crayon prov.lit. 11-Feb-3 Segre, Madrid #222/R est:4800
£15101 $24312 €22500 Village celebrating (52x65cm-20x26in) s.d.76 mixed media card. 18-Feb-3 Durán, Madrid #206/R

HERNANDEZ PIJUAN, Juan (1931-) Spanish
£8861 $14000 €14000 Flor II (147x162cm-58x64in) s.i.d.1991 prov. 27-Nov-2 Tajan, Paris #94/R est:10000-12000
£22925 $36451 €33700 Paisatge amb llum blanca (150x225cm-59x89in) s.d.90 i.d.verso prov. 26-Feb-3 Artcurial Briest, Paris #427/R est:15000-20000
Works on paper
£530 $864 €800 Cloud (27x20cm-11x8in) s.d.1991 gouache. 11-Feb-3 Segre, Madrid #213/R
£755 $1177 €1200 Study of fruit (63x49cm-25x19in) s.d.1972 pencil dr. 8-Oct-2 Ansorena, Madrid #478/R

HERNANDEZ SANZ, Agustin (1931-) Spanish
£833 $1317 €1300 Castle in Madrid (54x63cm-21x25in) s. 13-Nov-2 Ansorena, Madrid #282/R

HERNANDEZ XOCHITIOTZIN, Desidero (1922-) Mexican
£2393 $3733 €3590 Ofrenda a pepito y pepita (78x58cm-31x23in) s.d.1952 masonite. 17-Oct-2 Louis Morton, Mexico #38/R est:40000-58000 (M.P 38000)

HERNANDEZ, D (1856-1932) Peruvian
£2692 $4227 €4200 Portrait of gypsy girl (29x21cm-11x8in) s.i.d.1879. 23-Nov-2 Arnold, Frankfurt #753/R est:300

HERNANDEZ, Daniel (1856-1932) Peruvian
£2404 $3798 €3750 Young lady (41x32cm-16x13in) s. board. 19-Nov-2 Durán, Madrid #237/R
£2987 $4660 €4750 Misfortune n the street (47x31cm-19x12in) s.i.d.1878. 23-Sep-2 Durán, Madrid #230/R
£8442 $13000 €12663 Stolen kisses (51x38cm-20x15in) s. panel painted c.1890. 8-Sep-2 Treadway Gallery, Cincinnati #522/R est:10000-20000
Works on paper
£1316 $2132 €2000 Theatre scene (53x35cm-21x14in) s. W/C. 21-Jan-3 Durán, Madrid #148/R

HERNANDEZ, Julio Lopez (1930-) Spanish
Sculpture
£8065 $12742 €12500 Hope in the books (53x78x80cm-21x31x31in) s.d.1980 num.3/6 bronze polyester lit. 17-Dec-2 Segre, Madrid #155/R est:12500

HERNANDEZ, Luis (20th C) Spanish?
£2740 $4301 €4000 Femme dans l'arbre (42x32cm-17x13in) s.d.1944. 15-Apr-3 Laurence Calmels, Paris #4305/R est:150

HERNANDEZ, Mariano (1928-) Spanish
£641 $1006 €1000 Dragon (150x150cm-59x59in) s.d.73 acrylic. 24-Nov-2 Laurence Calmels, Paris #147/R
Works on paper
£321 $503 €500 Composition fantasmagorique (58x76cm-23x30in) s.d.91 W/C Chinese ink. 24-Nov-2 Laurence Calmels, Paris #146/R

HERNANDEZ, Miguel (1893-1957) Spanish
£1235 $2000 €1853 Untitled (72x61cm-28x24in) s.d.49 board prov.exhib. 27-Jan-3 Christie's, Rockefeller NY #30/R est:4000-6000
£1507 $2366 €2200 Reve de la Vierge (23x18cm-9x7in) s. i.verso. 15-Apr-3 Laurence Calmels, Paris #4301/R
£2055 $3226 €3000 Souvenir Inca (46x55cm-18x22in) s. i.verso mixed media on canvas exhib. 15-Apr-3 Laurence Calmels, Paris #4302/R
£2397 $3764 €3500 Portrait d'Andre Breton (55x46cm-22x18in) s.d.52 panel. 15-Apr-3 Laurence Calmels, Paris #4303/R
£4012 $6500 €6018 Untitled (27x47cm-11x19in) s.d.47 prov.exhib. 27-Jan-3 Christie's, Rockefeller NY #28/R est:4000-6000
£5247 $8500 €7871 Passage Ronce Paris (81x99cm-32x39in) s.d.1948 s.i.verso prov.exhib. 27-Jan-3 Christie's, Rockefeller NY #26/R est:7000-9000

HERNANDEZ, Sergio (1957-) Mexican
£9446 $14736 €14169 Apocalipsis (120x150cm-47x59in) s. prov. 17-Oct-2 Louis Morton, Mexico #79/R est:170000-190000 (M.P 150000)
£15924 $25000 €23886 Night flowers (140x180cm-55x71in) prov. 19-Nov-2 Sotheby's, New York #134/R
Works on paper
£2350 $3760 €3408 Untitled (49x68cm-19x27in) s. mixed media hand-cut paper. 15-May-3 Louis Morton, Mexico #46/R est:45000-55000 (M.P 38000)
£4573 $7500 €6860 Sin titulo (91x150cm-36x59in) ink paper on canvas exec.1989 prov. 28-May-3 Christie's, Rockefeller NY #52/R est:8000-10000

HERNANDEZ, Victor (1827-1901) Spanish
£440 $713 €660 Still life of carnations and asparagus fern in a glass vase (61x51cm-24x20in) s. 21-May-3 Bonhams, Knightsbridge #186

HEROLD, Georg (1947-) German
£280 $437 €420 2130 (24x18cm-9x7in) mono.d.87 acrylic screws. 6-Nov-2 AB Stockholms Auktionsverk #965/R (S.KR 4000)
Sculpture
£1282 $1987 €2000 Untitled (48x40x16cm-19x16x6in) s.i.d.85 verso brick epoxy canvas lit. 3-Dec-2 Lempertz, Koln #183/R est:2000
Works on paper
£1812 $2971 €2500 Untitled (30x24cm-12x9in) s.d.88 stretcher caviar galvanised copper silver acrylic. 28-May-3 Lempertz, Koln #175/R est:2200

HEROLD, Hans (1923-) Canadian
£975 $1550 €1463 Weekend at little Bear Lake (90x90cm-35x35in) s.i.d.1982 acrylic. 23-Mar-3 Hodgins, Calgary #107/R est:1000-1250 (C.D 2300)

HEROLD, Jacques (1910-1987) Rumanian
£2759 $4607 €4000 Beatrice et Dante (55x38cm-22x15in) s. s.i.d.1948 verso prov.exhib.lit. 10-Jul-3 Artcurial Briest, Paris #291/R est:4500-5000
£7534 $11829 €11000 Cristallisation de la foret (60x73cm-24x29in) s.d.46 panel. 15-Apr-3 Laurence Calmels, Paris #4309/R est:15000
Works on paper
£329 $520 €510 Composition surrealiste (45x35cm-18x14in) s. gouache. 18-Dec-2 Digard, Paris #72/R
£851 $1421 €1200 La fleur d'eau (35x27cm-14x11in) s. s.i.d.verso mixed media. 18-Jun-3 Pierre Berge, Paris #111/R
£2055 $3226 €3000 Visage (32x24cm-13x9in) s.d.42 W/C ink. 15-Apr-3 Laurence Calmels, Paris #4308/R

HERON, Hilary (1923-) Irish
Sculpture
£3478 $5704 €4800 Two figures in relief (45x45cm-18x18in) s.verso lead plaque. 28-May-3 Bonhams & James Adam, Dublin #115/R est:4000-6000

HERON, James (fl.1880-1919) British
Works on paper
£300 $474 €450 Scottish coastal landscape (36x53cm-14x21in) s.d.1892 W/C. 2-Dec-2 Gorringes, Lewes #2576

HERON, Patrick (1920-1999) British
£15000 $24600 €22500 Dull brown with green and white (30x41cm-12x16in) s.i.d.Oct 1962exhib. 6-Jun-3 Christie's, London #111/R est:10000-15000
£27000 $42390 €40500 Blue disc, Chinese vermillion (51x23cm-20x9in) s. i.d.59 prov. 22-Nov-2 Christie's, London #95/R est:12000-18000
£35000 $54950 €52500 Disc fragments in red (122x132cm-48x52in) s. i.d.1965 prov.exhib. 22-Nov-2 Christie's, London #96/R est:25000-35000
£36000 $56520 €54000 Storm at St. Ives (20x61cm-8x24in) s.d.52 s.i.d.verso prov. 22-Nov-2 Christie's, London #94/R est:25000-35000
£85000 $139400 €123250 Pink table with lamp and jug (71x91cm-28x36in) s.d.1948 prov.exhib.lit. 4-Jun-3 Sotheby's, London #29/R est:25000-35000
Works on paper
£9500 $14725 €14250 Chinese lantern (42x51cm-17x20in) gouache exhib. 3-Dec-2 Bonhams, New Bond Street #116/R est:3000-4000
£9500 $14820 €14250 Foursquare - pink in violet, pink in orange, with lemon and turquoise (57x78cm-22x31in) s.i.d.July 25 1966 gouache. 25-Mar-3 Bonhams, New Bond Street #125/R est:6000-8000

HEROULT, Antoine Desire (1802-1853) French
Works on paper
£1242 $1999 €1900 Port de Bayonne (58x87cm-23x34in) s.d.1843 W/C over pen. 18-Jan-3 Neret-Minet, Paris #150/R

HERP, Willem van (attrib) (17/18th C) Flemish
£2532 $4000 €4000 Mars seeking Minerva (59x74cm-23x29in) copper. 29-Nov-2 Bolland & Marotz, Bremen #653/R est:4900
£5195 $8052 €7793 Neptune's banquet (29x36cm-11x14in) copper. 24-Sep-2 Koller, Zurich #6438/R est:12000-15000 (S.FR 12000)

HERP, Willem van (elder) (1614-1677) Flemish
£8000 $12560 €12000 David before Saul (62x84cm-24x33in) panel prov. 13-Dec-2 Christie's, Kensington #71/R est:6000-8000
£26000 $40560 €39000 Biblical scene (88x105cm-35x41in) copper. 10-Apr-3 Sotheby's, London #32/R est:6000-8000

HERPEL, Franz (1850-?) German
£314 $491 €500 Boat. s. 21-Sep-2 Bolland & Marotz, Bremen #493/R

HERPFER, Fritz (1883-1936) German
£255 $397 €400 Still life with flowers and plate (67x56cm-26x22in) s. 6-Nov-2 Hugo Ruef, Munich #1136/R
£314 $515 €480 View of Notre Dame in Paris (35x27cm-14x11in) s.d.26 board. 5-Feb-3 Neumeister, Munich #721

HERR, Michael (1591-1661) German
£7962 $12420 €12500 Hunting scene (59x90cm-23x35in) mono.d.1624. 6-Nov-2 Hugo Ruef, Munich #943/R est:1800

HERR, Michael (attrib) (1591-1661) German
Works on paper
£1622 $2530 €2400 God sends his angels out (17x21cm-7x8in) i. pen wash. 27-Mar-3 Dr Fritz Nagel, Stuttgart #696/R est:1000

HERREMANS, L (c.1858-?) Belgian
£6329 $10000 €10000 L'eglise de la Chapelle a Bruxelles (71x48cm-28x19in) 2-Dec-2 Amberes, Antwerp #1342

HERREMANS, Lievin (c.1858-1907) Belgian
£601 $938 €950 Depart des voiliers (60x48cm-24x19in) s. 15-Oct-2 Horta, Bruxelles #394

HERRER, Cesar de (1868-1919) Spanish
£769 $1208 €1200 Views of Venice (18x11cm-7x4in) s. board two. 21-Nov-2 Van Ham, Cologne #1670/R
£838 $1308 €1215 At the market place (28x36cm-11x14in) s. 12-Apr-3 Mu Terem Galeria, Budapest #67/R est:190000 (H.F 300000)
£1032 $1610 €1496 Man with hat (82x30cm-32x12in) s. 13-Sep-2 Mu Terem Galeria, Budapest #143/R est:240000 (H.F 400000)
£1345 $2084 €1950 Venetian lagoon (47x34cm-19x13in) s. 9-Dec-2 Mu Terem Galeria, Budapest #53/R est:350000 (H.F 500000)
£1806 $2817 €2619 Torcello (37x48cm-15x19in) s. 13-Sep-2 Mu Terem Galeria, Budapest #15/R est:350000 (H.F 700000)
£1882 $2918 €2823 Ladies in the box (58x78cm-23x31in) s. 6-Dec-2 Kieselbach, Budapest #116/R (H.F 700000)
£4248 $6967 €6500 St Mark's Square, Venice in summer (47x86cm-19x34in) s.i.d.97. 29-Mar-3 Dannenberg, Berlin #589/R est:300

HERRERO, Abel (1971-) Cuban
£2057 $3332 €2900 Aerodinamic brothers (105x145cm-41x57in) 20-May-3 Porro, Milan #31/R est:3500-3700

HERRERO, Jesus (20th C) Spanish
£313 $506 €475 Mountains (65x50cm-26x20in) s. 21-Jan-3 Durán, Madrid #60/R

HERRERO, Mari Puri (1942-) Spanish
£897 $1417 €1300 Holy Friday (25x33cm-10x13in) s. prov.lit. 1-Apr-3 Segre, Madrid #162/R

HERRFELDT, Marcel René von (1890-1965) French
£608 $949 €900 Young woman wearing wide brimmed hat (56x46cm-22x18in) s. 26-Mar-3 Hugo Ruef, Munich #130/R
£1731 $2717 €2700 Nude on rock by sea (110x84cm-43x33in) s. 21-Nov-2 Van Ham, Cologne #1671/R est:1800
Works on paper
£429 $678 €644 Reclining female nude with net stockings (29x38cm-11x15in) s. gouache. 29-Nov-2 Zofingen, Switzerland #2468 (S.FR 1000)

HERRING (19th C) British
£1150 $1748 €1725 Three horses in a farmyard, with mallard in the foreground (24x29cm-9x11in) bears sig. 13-Aug-2 Gildings, Market Harborough #252/R est:1200-1800

HERRING, J F (19/20th C) British
£3000 $4800 €4500 Farmstead (21x28cm-8x11in) bears sig. 14-Mar-3 Du Mouchelle, Detroit #2220/R est:4500-6500
Works on paper
£580 $928 €870 Equestrian study (23x30cm-9x12in) d.1856 W/C. 10-Jan-3 Biddle & Webb, Birmingham #375

HERRING, J F (jnr) (1815-1907) British
£4375 $7000 €6563 View of stable interior (25x36cm-10x14in) s. 12-Jan-3 William Jenack, New York #412

HERRING, J F (snr) (1795-1865) British
£2564 $4026 €4000 Joining the hunt (40x60cm-16x24in) bear sig. 19-Nov-2 Hamilton Osborne King, Dublin #424/R est:2000-3000
£3526 $5535 €5500 Frightened by the train (40x60cm-16x24in) bears sig. 19-Nov-2 Hamilton Osborne King, Dublin #424a/R est:2000-3000

HERRING, James and ROTHERMEL, Peter Frederick (attrib) (19th C) American
£8766 $13500 €13149 George Washington and his generals at the Battle of Yorktown (107x91cm-42x36in) oval. 24-Oct-2 Shannon's, Milford #92/R est:20000-30000

HERRING, John Frederick (jnr) (1815-1907) British
£1795 $2818 €2800 Racehorse with jockey up, in a landscape. Mother and child (29x37cm-11x15in) indis.sig. panel double-sided. 19-Nov-2 Hamilton Osborne King, Dublin #420/R est:2000-3000
£3000 $4710 €4500 Two dogs in a stable interior (35x42cm-14x17in) s.d.1845 board. 19-Nov-2 Bonhams, New Bond Street #62/R est:3000-5000
£3145 $5000 €4718 Duke of Grafton's Bolivar in a stable (56x69cm-22x27in) s.i.d.1840 prov. 30-Apr-3 Sotheby's, New York #560/R est:7000-10000
£3200 $4992 €4800 In a farmyard (15x21cm-6x8in) s.indisd. 26-Mar-3 Hamptons Fine Art, Godalming #255/R est:2500-3500
£3333 $4800 €5000 Farmyard scenes. board 5 in one frame. 15-Jan-3 Christie's, Rockefeller NY #149/R est:8000
£3544 $5600 €5316 Horses in farmyard (22x30cm-9x12in) s. board. 15-Nov-2 Naón & Cia, Buenos Aires #62/R
£3828 $6201 €5551 Ducks by waterhole. Sow with piglets surrounded of chickens and a cockerel (39x51cm-15x20in) s. oval pair. 26-May-3 Rasmussen, Copenhagen #1315/R est:40000 (D.KR 40000)
£4000 $6280 €6000 Returning home (37x51cm-15x20in) s. 19-Nov-2 Bonhams, New Bond Street #64/R est:3000-5000
£4000 $6320 €6000 Farmyard scene (36x51cm-14x20in) s. 28-Nov-2 Bonhams, Knightsbridge #95/R est:4000-6000
£4500 $7470 €6525 Horses, pigs and chickens in a farmyard (24x34cm-9x13in) s. oil board arched top. 12-Jun-3 Christie's, Kensington #86/R est:3000-5000
£6200 $9734 €9300 Horses and cattle watering beside a barn (30x41cm-12x16in) s. 19-Nov-2 Bonhams, New Bond Street #63/R est:4000-6000
£6500 $10270 €9750 The plough team (36x51cm-14x20in) s,. 26-Nov-2 Christie's, London #145/R est:6000-8000
£8000 $13280 €12000 Horses and ducks by a farm pond (38x51cm-15x20in) s.d.1851. 10-Jun-3 Christie's, London #146/R est:10000-15000
£8000 $13360 €11600 Farmyard scene with a hunt passing in the distance (41x61cm-16x24in) s. 17-Jun-3 Bonhams, New Bond Street #43/R est:10000-15000
£10000 $16600 €15000 Plough team (38x52cm-15x20in) s.d.1851. 12-Jun-3 Sotheby's, London #280/R est:10000-15000
£14500 $22620 €21750 Farmyard scenes (42x61cm-17x24in) s. pair. 10-Apr-3 Tennants, Leyburn #1048/R est:15000-20000
£15000 $23400 €22500 Horses and figures resting. Mares and foals with cattle and sheep (41x61cm-16x24in) s. pair. 10-Apr-3 Tennants, Leyburn #1047/R est:15000-20000
£16500 $26070 €24750 Horses sheltering under trees. Horses, chickens, sow and piglets in farmyard (31x46cm-12x18in) one s. pair. 26-Nov-2 Christie's, London #143/R est:12000-18000
£62000 $100440 €93000 Touchstone winning the 1836 Doncaster Cup, with other horses (58x78cm-23x31in) s.i.d.1836 prov. 22-May-3 Christie's, London #39/R est:70000-100000
Works on paper
£320 $506 €480 Farmyard scene with horses, poultry and pigs (20x30cm-8x12in) s. W/C htd white. 27-Nov-2 Bonhams, Knowle #195
£460 $727 €690 Horses on a rural track (18x28cm-7x11in) s.d.1843 W/C. 26-Nov-2 Bonhams, Knightsbridge #49a/R
£1400 $2240 €2100 Horses in a stable (23x33cm-9x13in) s.d.1847 W/C two. 13-Mar-3 Duke & Son, Dorchester #168/R est:800-1200

HERRING, John Frederick (jnr-attrib) (1815-1907) British
£800 $1328 €1160 Livestock in a farmyard, a fox hunt beyond (41x61cm-16x24in) bears sig. 12-Jun-3 Gorringes, Lewes #1690
£1210 $1900 €1815 Halt (61x61cm-24x24in) 23-Nov-2 Pook & Pook, Downington #102/R est:1500-2500
£1656 $2600 €2484 Return (61x61cm-24x24in) 23-Nov-2 Pook & Pook, Downington #101/R est:1500-2500

HERRING, John Frederick (snr) (1795-1865) British
£813 $1276 €1220 Resting sheep (32cm-13in circular) s.d.1848 canvas on board. 10-Dec-2 Pinneys, Montreal #41 est:3000-4000 (C.D 2000)
£1923 $3019 €3000 Escaping horse (60x51cm-24x20in) 10-Dec-2 Della Rocca, Turin #368/R est:2500
£2690 $4250 €4035 Whalebone (36x46cm-14x18in) s.i.d.1810 prov. 22-Apr-3 Arthur James, Florida #355
£3000 $4770 €4500 Cow and calf in a stall (24x29cm-9x11in) s. panel. 19-Mar-3 Sotheby's, London #107/R est:6000-8000
£4167 $6500 €6251 Mare and foal (36x46cm-14x18in) s.d.18 panel. 9-Nov-2 Sloan, North Bethesda #586/R est:10000-15000

£6410 $10000 €9615 Farm yard with horses (111x94cm-44x37in) s. 9-Nov-2 Sloan, North Bethesda #587/R est:30000-40000
£7000 $11690 €10150 Study of two horses heads (25x30cm-10x12in) 17-Jun-3 Bonhams, New Bond Street #48a
£7500 $12150 €11250 Chestnut in a stable (36x44cm-14x17in) s.d.1834 prov.exhib. 22-May-3 Christie's, London #57/R est:8000-12000
£8000 $12640 €12000 Head of grey Arab (25x36cm-10x14in) init.d.1851 panel prov. 27-Nov-2 Christie's, London #52/R est:8000-12000
£9500 $15009 €14250 Bay hunter in a loose box (35x50cm-14x20in) s. 28-Nov-2 Sotheby's, London #208/R est:12000-16000
£15000 $23700 €22500 Racehorse in a stable with a groom (27x34cm-11x13in) s.i. 28-Nov-2 Christie's, Kensington #128/R est:15000-20000
£15000 $24300 €22500 Little Wonder, winner of the Derby (35x46cm-14x18in) s.d.1840 panel prov.exhib. 22-May-3 Christie's, London #58/R est:7000-10000
£16000 $25440 €24000 Mr William Orde's bay filly Bees-wing in a loose box (35x45cm-14x18in) s.i. prov. 19-Mar-3 Sotheby's, London #115/R est:10000-15000
£20000 $31400 €30000 At the water's edge (31x26cm-12x10in) panel pair prov. 19-Nov-2 Bonhams, New Bond Street #60/R est:20000-30000
£20000 $32400 €30000 Birmingham, winner of the 1830 St Leger Stakes, in a stable (25x30cm-10x12in) s.i.d.1830 panel prov. 22-May-3 Christie's, London #9/R est:10000-15000
£23000 $37260 €34500 Glaucus, bay racehorse in a stable (25x30cm-10x12in) s.d.1840 panel prov. 22-May-3 Christie's, London #40/R est:25000-35000
£24000 $38880 €36000 Mango, winner of the 1837 St Leger Stakes, in a stable (25x30cm-10x12in) s.i.d.1837 panel prov. 22-May-3 Christie's, London #8/R est:10000-15000
£25000 $39250 €37500 Ducks and ducklings beside a stream (41x36cm-16x14in) s.d.1850 panel prov. 19-Nov-2 Bonhams, New Bond Street #72/R est:20000-30000
£35000 $55650 €52500 Gentleman out shooting with a setter and a pointer (44x70cm-17x28in) s. 19-Mar-3 Sotheby's, London #113/R est:35000-45000
£40000 $63200 €60000 Mr O'Brien Jonathan Wild with jockey up (56x76cm-22x30in) indis.s. prov. 27-Nov-2 Christie's, London #66/R est:40000-60000
£50000 $78000 €75000 Coaching scene outside the Philpots Inn, Meopham (91x132cm-36x52in) s.d.1860. 6-Nov-2 Sotheby's, Olympia #46/R est:50000-70000
£60000 $95400 €90000 Summer (61x91cm-24x36in) s.d. prov.exhib. 19-Mar-3 Sotheby's, London #248/R est:60000-80000
£470000 $714400 €705000 Halt (107x183cm-42x72in) s.d.1852. 28-Aug-2 Sotheby's, London #1049/R est:300000-500000

HERRLEIN, Johann Peter (attrib) (1722-1799) German
£943 $1462 €1500 St John the Evangelist with eagle (70x85cm-28x33in) 2-Oct-2 Dorotheum, Vienna #245/R est:1800-2800

HERRMANN, Frank S (1866-1942) American
£521 $859 €750 Pleasurable day at the beach (47x65cm-19x26in) s.d.1925 cardboard. 1-Jul-3 Christie's, Amsterdam #77
£1781 $2778 €2600 At the shoemakers in Venice (24x35cm-9x14in) s.i.d.92 panel. 10-Apr-3 Dorotheum, Vienna #6/R est:2500-3000
Works on paper
£796 $1250 €1194 Dunes near The Hague with some pink flowers (30x33cm-12x13in) s.d.1919 W/C. 19-Apr-3 James Julia, Fairfield #307/R

HERRMANN, Hans (1858-1942) German
£833 $1292 €1300 River landscape (39x31cm-15x12in) s.i. canvas on board. 4-Dec-2 Lempertz, Koln #779/R
£1346 $2127 €2100 Still life with fish (40x32cm-16x13in) s.d.1887 panel exhib. 16-Nov-2 Lempertz, Koln #1476/R est:2500
£1667 $2617 €2600 Fish market on Zuidersee (68x96cm-27x38in) s.d.1903. 21-Nov-2 Van Ham, Cologne #1673/R est:2500
£1948 $2844 €3000 Fish market in Amsterdam (48x32cm-19x13in) s. i.verso panel. 15-Jun-2 Hans Stahl, Hamburg #83/R
£2564 $4026 €4000 Flowermarket in Amsterdam (78x60cm-31x24in) s. 21-Nov-2 Van Ham, Cologne #1672/R est:6000
£5696 $8829 €9000 Avenue in large Dutch city with horse drawn carriages and figures (58x51cm-23x20in) s.d.1895. 25-Sep-2 Neumeister, Munich #600/R est:1200
Works on paper
£475 $750 €750 Fishing smack on Neustadt quay (46x38cm-18x15in) s. W/C. 29-Nov-2 Bolland & Marotz, Bremen #709/R
£683 $1094 €950 Fishing boats in the Amsterdam harbour (28x39cm-11x15in) s.i. pencil board prov. 17-May-3 Lempertz, Koln #1294/R

HERRMANN, Karl (1813-1881) German
£1389 $2236 €2084 Lorelei (91x78cm-36x31in) 7-May-3 Dobiaschofsky, Bern #637/R est:5000 (S.FR 3000)

HERRMANN, Willy (1895-1963) German
£301 $470 €440 Mark landscape with lake and hayricks (71x101cm-28x40in) s. 9-Apr-3 Neumeister, Munich #679/R
£321 $503 €500 Lake landscape with trees in Mark (81x111cm-32x44in) s. 21-Nov-2 Van Ham, Cologne #1674
£449 $696 €700 Mecklenburg landscape with haystacks (82x100cm-32x39in) s. 7-Dec-2 Dannenberg, Berlin #679/R
£449 $696 €700 Harvelpartie with view from the trees (60x80cm-24x31in) s. masonite. 7-Dec-2 Dannenberg, Berlin #680/R
£597 $932 €950 Cornstooks in field (60x80cm-24x31in) s. 21-Sep-2 Dannenberg, Berlin #563/R
£1266 $2000 €2000 Sunny autumn day (160x180cm-63x71in) s. lit. 29-Nov-2 Schloss Ahlden, Ahlden #1320/R est:1900

HERRMANN-LEON, Charles (1838-1908) French
£409 $650 €614 On the lookout (27x35cm-11x14in) s. 7-Mar-3 Skinner, Boston #441/R

HERRMANSTORFER, Josef (1817-1901) German
£544 $865 €800 Hay harvest (17x24cm-7x9in) s.d.1892 panel. 20-Mar-3 Neumeister, Munich #2643/R

HERSANT, Julien (19th C) French
£2397 $3764 €3500 Fleur dechardon (24x19cm-9x7in) s.d.1870. 15-Apr-3 Laurence Calmels, Paris #4307/R est:150-200
£3288 $5162 €4800 Paix par les droits politiques des femmes, temple de la paix (87x117cm-34x46in) s.d.1883 panel. 15-Apr-3 Laurence Calmels, Paris #4306/R

HERSCHEND, Oscar (1853-1891) Danish
£306 $477 €459 Coastal landscape with boats (26x41cm-10x16in) s. 5-Aug-2 Rasmussen, Vejle #262 (D.KR 3600)
£350 $560 €525 Figures and horses by farm, windmill in background (39x59cm-15x23in) s.d.79 and 84. 13-Jan-3 Rasmussen, Vejle #148/R (D.KR 4000)
£406 $625 €609 Landscape from Raabjerg Mile (40x66cm-16x26in) mono.d.82. 26-Oct-2 Rasmussen, Havnen #2058/R (D.KR 4800)
£598 $921 €897 Life-boat on the beach (75x99cm-30x39in) mono.i.d.89. 4-Sep-2 Kunsthallen, Copenhagen #107/R (D.KR 7000)

HERSENT, Louis (attrib) (1777-1860) French
£1338 $2128 €2007 Gustav Vasa saying Good-bye to his people (46x55cm-18x22in) 3-Mar-3 Lilla Bukowskis, Stockholm #368 est:12000-15000 (S.KR 18000)

HERSSEN, Alexandre van (17th C) Flemish
£2830 $4387 €4500 Landscape with travellers and three horse carriage (38x47cm-15x19in) lit. 2-Oct-2 Dorotheum, Vienna #329/R est:4500-6000

HERST, Auguste-Clement (1825-?) French
£800 $1248 €1200 Gamekeeper's cottage (50x66cm-20x26in) s. indis d. 26-Mar-3 Sotheby's, Olympia #167/R

HERTEL, Albert (1843-1912) German
£633 $987 €1000 Courtyard in Berlin (40x33cm-16x13in) s.i.d.1897 panel lit. 14-Sep-2 Bergmann, Erlangen #730/R
£633 $1000 €1000 Near Nice (41x25cm-16x10in) canvas on panel. 29-Nov-2 Bassenge, Berlin #5925/R
£3800 $5928 €5700 Zoo (91x129cm-36x51in) s.d.1906. 17-Sep-2 Sotheby's, Olympia #271/R est:4000-6000
£4747 $7500 €7500 Procession to church in Bad Hofgastein (73x110cm-29x43in) s.d.1885. 28-Nov-2 Dorotheum, Vienna #5/R est:8500-9500

HERTER, Adele (1869-1946) American
£8805 $14000 €13208 Allium and queen Anne's lace (46x30cm-18x12in) s. pair prov. 5-Mar-3 Sotheby's, New York #5/R est:15000-25000

HERTER, Albert (1871-1950) American
Works on paper
£3293 $5500 €4775 Evening walk (51x41cm-20x16in) s. W/C gouache on board prov. 17-Jun-3 John Moran, Pasadena #53 est:7000-9000

HERTER, Ernst Gustav (1846-1917) German
Sculpture
£1195 $1864 €1900 Frederick the Great (48cm-19in) s.i.d.1891 dark brown pat.bronze. 20-Sep-2 Schloss Ahlden, Ahlden #1659/R est:1400

HERTERICH, Ludwig Ritter von (1856-1932) German
Works on paper
£609 $926 €950 Hunt (70x100cm-28x39in) s. i.d.1920 verso mixed media. 11-Jul-2 Hugo Ruef, Munich #892/R

HERTERVIG, Lars (1830-1902) Norwegian
Works on paper
£4671 $7381 €7007 Midday light. Study of clouds (21x30cm-8x12in) s.d.1858 W/C double-sided. 2-Dec-2 Blomqvist, Oslo #391/R est:40000-50000 (N.KR 54000)
£6071 $9471 €9107 House by road (23x16cm-9x6in) rem.sig. gouache W/C exhib.lit. 21-Oct-2 Blomqvist, Oslo #457/R est:35000-45000 (N.KR 70000)
£23934 $38294 €35901 Landscape with alpine dairy farm (32x49cm-13x19in) init.d.1856 indis.sig.d.1874 mixed media. 17-Mar-3 Blomqvist, Oslo #402/R est:200000-250000 (N.KR 275000)
£62446 $97415 €93669 Marsh landscape with tall trees and root in foreground (42x39cm-17x15in) s.indis.d.18. gouache W/C mixed media exhib.lit. 21-Oct-2 Blomqvist, Oslo #462/R est:350000-450000 (N.KR 720000)

HERTLING, Wilhelm Jakob (1849-1926) German
Works on paper
£1282 $1987 €2000 English girl near Nymphenburg Castle (56x73cm-22x29in) s. gouache over pencil. 4-Dec-2 Neumeister, Munich #516/R est:2000

HERTZ, Mogens (1909-1990) Danish
£254 $391 €381 Summer landscape (27x41cm-11x16in) s.d.50 cardboard. 23-Oct-2 Kunsthallen, Copenhagen #38 (D.KR 3000)
£274 $436 €411 View towards a church (28x46cm-11x18in) s.stretcher masonite exhib. 26-Feb-3 Kunsthallen, Copenhagen #276 (D.KR 3000)
£324 $522 €486 View with house (33x46cm-13x18in) s. masonite. 22-Feb-3 Rasmussen, Havnen #2296 (D.KR 3600)
£366 $581 €549 Autumn harvest, /Bornholm (27x46cm-11x18in) s. 26-Feb-3 Kunsthallen, Copenhagen #268 (D.KR 4000)
£372 $587 €558 Coastal landscape with view of sea, Bornholm (25x39cm-10x15in) s.d.50 panel. 1-Apr-3 Rasmussen, Copenhagen #589/R (D.KR 4000)
£425 $663 €638 Street scene, Bornholm (26x40cm-10x16in) s. 5-Aug-2 Rasmussen, Vejle #290/R (D.KR 5000)
£465 $734 €698 Harbour view from Bornholm (60x93cm-24x37in) s.d.1940. 5-Apr-3 Rasmussen, Havnen #4210/R (D.KR 5000)
£483 $764 €725 View across the sea, Bornholm (38x61cm-15x24in) s. 5-Apr-3 Rasmussen, Havnen #4212/R (D.KR 5200)
£604 $954 €906 Still life of fruit, bust and flowers (56x83cm-22x33in) s.d.48. 1-Apr-3 Rasmussen, Copenhagen #97/R (D.KR 6500)
£612 $948 €918 Summer's day by farm, Bornholm (38x62cm-15x24in) s.d.57. 4-Dec-2 Kunsthallen, Copenhagen #313 (D.KR 7100)
£616 $1022 €893 Still life of objects on table (60x70cm-24x28in) s.d.42 masonite. 12-Jun-3 Kunsthallen, Copenhagen #277/R (D.KR 6500)
£653 $1038 €980 White houses by the sea (38x61cm-15x24in) s. 29-Apr-3 Kunsthallen, Copenhagen #229/R (D.KR 7000)
£686 $1090 €1029 Still life (56x67cm-22x26in) 26-Feb-3 Kunsthallen, Copenhagen #241/R (D.KR 7500)
£690 $1055 €1035 Farm (65x100cm-26x39in) s.d.58. 24-Aug-2 Rasmussen, Havnen #2292/R (D.KR 8000)
£724 $1122 €1086 Coastal landscape with house and figures (26x47cm-10x19in) s. 28-Sep-2 Rasmussen, Havnen #2006 (D.KR 8500)
£819 $1253 €1229 Woman in lounger (81x100cm-32x39in) s. 24-Aug-2 Rasmussen, Havnen #2054/R (D.KR 9500)
£868 $1381 €1302 Figures at Gudhjem Harbour (44x52cm-17x20in) s. 26-Feb-3 Kunsthallen, Copenhagen #244/R (D.KR 9500)
£947 $1440 €1421 Thatched farm in evening light (60x92cm-24x36in) s.d.57. 3-Sep-2 Museumsbygningen, Copenhagen #558/R (D.KR 11000)
£1034 $1583 €1551 Village street with figures, Bornholm (54x74cm-21x29in) s. 24-Aug-2 Rasmussen, Havnen #2157 est:7000-10000 (D.KR 12000)
£1069 $1689 €1604 From Kongen's Nytorv (47x60cm-19x24in) s.d.46 panel. 1-Apr-3 Rasmussen, Copenhagen #521/R (D.KR 11500)
£1115 $1762 €1673 Farmyard with geese in foreground (50x74cm-20x29in) s. 1-Apr-3 Rasmussen, Copenhagen #495/R est:12000-15000 (D.KR 12000)
£1141 $1757 €1712 Street scene with figures, Gudhjem (54x65cm-21x26in) s. 23-Oct-2 Kunsthallen, Copenhagen #25/R est:12000 (D.KR 13500)
£1144 $1910 €1659 Still life of flowers, fruit and jug (52x72cm-20x28in) s.d.54 exhib.prov. 17-Jun-3 Rasmussen, Copenhagen #86/R est:15000-20000 (D.KR 12000)
£1244 $1940 €1866 Winter's day with figures at Gudhjem, sea in background (55x73cm-22x29in) s. 11-Nov-2 Rasmussen, Vejle #64/R est:15000 (D.KR 14500)
£1705 $2830 €2472 Street scene with figures, Gudhjem (116x97cm-46x38in) s.d.58. 12-Jun-3 Kunsthallen, Copenhagen #251/R est:20000 (D.KR 18000)
£1716 $2866 €2488 Fishermen returning home in evening, Gudhjem (73x116cm-29x46in) s.d.55 prov. 17-Jun-3 Rasmussen, Copenhagen #71/R est:20000-30000 (D.KR 18000)

HERTZBERG, Halfdan (1857-1890) Norwegian
Sculpture
£1447 $2344 €2171 Street boy whistling (130cm-51in) s. plaster prov. 27-Jan-3 Blomqvist, Lysaker #1083/R est:25000-30000 (N.KR 16000)

HERVE, Isabelle (20th C) French
£295 $472 €410 Mer automnale (50x50cm-20x20in) s. acrylic. 18-May-3 Neret-Minet, Paris #224/R
£396 $633 €550 Morceaux de vie (80x40cm-31x16in) s. acrylic. 18-May-3 Neret-Minet, Paris #49/R
£468 $748 €650 Les deux freres (80x80cm-31x31in) s. acrylic. 18-May-3 Neret-Minet, Paris #142/R

HERVE, Jacques (1905-) French
£550 $836 €825 Anemones in a vase aside figurine (70x60cm-28x24in) s. 29-Aug-2 Christie's, Kensington #43/R

HERVE, Jules R (1887-1981) French
£565 $892 €848 Sick boy (22x26cm-9x10in) s. board prov.exhib. 18-Nov-2 Waddingtons, Toronto #227/R (C.D 1400)
£577 $906 €900 Le bapteme (50x60cm-20x24in) s. paper on panel. 11-Dec-2 Hotel des Ventes Mosan, Brussels #317c
£971 $1554 €1350 Vieil homme (22x14cm-9x6in) s. isorel. 16-May-3 Lombrail & Teucquam, Paris #236
£1000 $1570 €1500 Near the Arc de Triomphe (27x22cm-11x9in) s. 15-Apr-3 Bonhams, Knightsbridge #7/R est:500-700
£1210 $1911 €1815 Quai a Paris en hiver (22x27cm-9x11in) s. board. 18-Nov-2 Waddingtons, Toronto #239/R est:3000-3500 (C.D 3000)
£1274 $1987 €2000 Paris, jardin des Tuileries (22x27cm-9x11in) s. 10-Nov-2 Eric Pillon, Calais #99/R
£1276 $2016 €1850 Jeune couple (27x22cm-11x9in) s. s.verso cardboard. 4-Apr-3 Tajan, Paris #183
£1378 $2178 €2150 Paris, les quais de Seine (33x41cm-13x16in) s. 14-Nov-2 Credit Municipal, Paris #56/R est:1500-1800
£1548 $2400 €2322 Jardin en Louvre (22x27cm-9x11in) s. s.verso. 26-Sep-2 Christie's, Rockefeller NY #557/R est:2000-3000
£1613 $2548 €2420 Off to the hunt (27x22cm-11x9in) s. 18-Nov-2 Waddingtons, Toronto #238/R est:3500-4000 (C.D 4000)
£1687 $2750 €2531 Fountain in the jardin de Luxembourg (33x41cm-13x16in) s. 16-Feb-3 Butterfields, San Francisco #2072 est:1800-2250
£1728 $2454 €2800 Rue animee (27x22cm-11x9in) s. 16-Mar-3 Eric Pillon, Calais #204/R
£1800 $2898 €2700 Les petits amis (45x53cm-18x21in) s. s.i.verso. 14-Jan-3 Bonhams, Knightsbridge #146/R est:1000-2000
£1911 $2981 €3000 Sortie d'eglise (33x41cm-13x16in) s. s.i.verso. 8-Nov-2 Pierre Berge, Paris #4
£1975 $3200 €2864 Ballerinas (23x28cm-9x11in) S. 21-May-3 Doyle, New York #231/R est:1500-2000
£2000 $3240 €3000 Village wedding (44x53cm-17x21in) s. s.verso. 20-May-3 Bonhams, Knightsbridge #123/R est:1000-1500
£2037 $2893 €3300 Paris, quais et Pont-Neuf (46x55cm-18x22in) s. 16-Mar-3 Eric Pillon, Calais #213/R
£2044 $3394 €2964 Porte St. Denis, Paris (46x56cm-18x22in) s. 16-Jun-3 Waddingtons, Toronto #279/R est:4000-6000 (C.D 4600)
£2308 $3623 €3600 Rue de village animee de figures (47x39cm-19x15in) s. 15-Dec-2 Mercier & Cie, Lille #387/R est:3000
£2405 $3800 €3800 Quais de Notre-Dame (44x54cm-17x21in) s. 2-Dec-2 Tajan, Paris #36
£2532 $3949 €4000 La chorale du Dimanche (38x46cm-15x18in) s. 15-Oct-2 Regis & Thiollet, Argentuil #91
£2848 $4443 €4500 Paris, les quais, les bouquinistes (46x55cm-18x22in) s. 20-Oct-2 Mercier & Cie, Lille #329/R est:4500-5000
£2851 $4248 €4277 Place de la Concorde et terrace des Tuilleries (54x65cm-21x26in) s. 26-Jun-2 Iegor de Saint Hippolyte, Montreal #50/R (C.D 6500)
£2885 $4529 €4500 Foyer (38x46cm-15x18in) s. 15-Dec-2 Mercier & Cie, Lille #386/R
£2930 $4571 €4600 Paris, marche aux fleurs (32x40cm-13x16in) s. 10-Nov-2 Eric Pillon, Calais #100/R
£2949 $4629 €4600 Promeneurs au Parc du Luxembourg (46x55cm-18x22in) s. 15-Dec-2 Lombrail & Teucquam, Paris #7/R
£2975 $4641 €4700 Procession dans le village (46x38cm-18x15in) s. board. 20-Oct-2 Galerie de Chartres, Chartres #149 est:2500-3000
£3049 $4787 €4574 Place de la Concorde, Paris (44x53cm-17x21in) s. 10-Dec-2 Pinneys, Montreal #59 est:5000-7000 (C.D 7500)
£3086 $4753 €4629 Restaurant (51x65cm-20x26in) 26-Oct-2 Heffel, Vancouver #22 est:3000-4000 (C.D 7500)
£3103 $4934 €4500 Place de la Concorde animee (54x65cm-21x26in) s. 7-Mar-3 Rabourdin & Choppin de Janvry, Paris #6/R est:4000-4500
£3262 $5285 €4600 La sortie du Bapteme (46x38cm-18x15in) s. 26-May-3 Joron-Derem, Paris #71/R est:3000-35000
£3439 $5366 €5400 Paris, Place de la Concorde (46x55cm-18x22in) s. 10-Nov-2 Eric Pillon, Calais #96/R
£3617 $6040 €5100 Le passage du facteur a Langres (41x33cm-16x13in) s. i.verso. 20-Jun-3 Piasa, Paris #156/R est:3000-4000

£3800 $6194 €5700 L'arc de Trimphe (53x64cm-21x25in) s. s.verso. 3-Feb-3 Bonhams, New Bond Street #95/R est:1000-1500
£4000 $6520 €6000 Les tuileries (73x92cm-29x36in) s. 3-Feb-3 Bonhams, New Bond Street #94/R est:2000-3000
£4000 $6440 €6000 Cafe Tuileries (78x59cm-31x23in) s. 14-Jan-3 Bonhams, Knightsbridge #149/R est:2000-3000
£4717 $7500 €7076 Scene de Paris (46x54cm-18x21in) s. s.verso prov. 27-Feb-3 Christie's, Rockefeller NY #96/R est:6000
£4755 $7941 €6800 Dimanche au village (39x46cm-15x18in) s. 27-Jun-3 Claude Aguttes, Neuilly #66/R est:4000-6000
£5704 $9469 €8100 Vente aux encheres dans un village (65x81cm-26x32in) s. 11-Jun-3 Beaussant & Lefèvre, Paris #65/R est:5000-6000

HERVE-MATHE, Jules Alfred (1868-1953) French
Works on paper
£1250 $2037 €1800 Thornier sous voile a Concarneau (44x30cm-17x12in) s. W/C. 19-Jul-3 Thierry & Lannon, Brest #61 est:1500-1800

HERVENS, Jacques (1890-1928) Belgian
£288 $447 €450 Pichet fleuri de roses (65x51cm-26x20in) s.d.1925. 9-Dec-2 Horta, Bruxelles #447

HERVIER, Adolphe (1818-1879) French
£1861 $2885 €2792 Riverside farmstead (66x45cm-26x18in) s. 24-Sep-2 Koller, Zurich #6507/R est:1500-2000 (S.FR 4300)

HERVIEU, Louise (1878-1954) French
£414 $662 €600 Bouquet de fleurs et cerises sur une table (58x44cm-23x17in) s. graphite chl. 12-Mar-3 Libert, Castor, Paris #119
Works on paper
£443 $700 €700 Nature morte aux fruits et carafe (49x63cm-19x25in) s. pastel. 26-Nov-2 Camard, Paris #56
£531 $844 €780 Nature morte aux coquillages (64x49cm-25x19in) s. chl grattage dr. 26-Feb-3 Artcurial Briest, Paris #24
£571 $909 €840 Nature morte au bouquet (64x49cm-25x19in) s. chl grattage dr. 26-Feb-3 Artcurial Briest, Paris #25

HERVO, Vaino (1894-1974) Finnish
£425 $697 €650 Flowers in vase (73x55cm-29x22in) s.d.52. 9-Feb-3 Bukowskis, Helsinki #255/R

HERWERDEN, Jacob Dirk van (1806-1879) Dutch
£10101 $16667 €14646 Solo rivier Res Marlioen, Java (25x36cm-10x14in) s.d.55 panel. 6-Jul-3 Christie's, Hong Kong #22/R est:130000-180000 (HK.D 130000)

HERWIJNEN, Jan van (1889-1965) Dutch
£573 $894 €900 Latyrus (20x30cm-8x12in) init. 6-Nov-2 Vendue Huis, Gravenhage #576

HERZGER, Walter (20th C) German
£3671 $5800 €5800 Still life with peaches on a dish and flower vase (49x63cm-19x25in) s.i.verso. 30-Nov-2 Geble, Radolfzell #668 est:5800

HERZIG, Gottfried (1870-1922) Swiss
£322 $509 €483 Farmer boy sitting in the field (50x40cm-20x16in) s.d.1898. 29-Nov-2 Zofingen, Switzerland #2898/R (S.FR 750)

HERZIG, Heinrich (1887-1964) Swiss
£611 $954 €917 Spring on the Rhine (23x37cm-9x15in) s.d.51 panel. 6-Nov-2 Hans Widmer, St Gallen #15/R (S.FR 1400)
£742 $1158 €1113 Gamsberg from Palfries (26x35cm-10x14in) s.d.1939 i. verso board. 6-Nov-2 Hans Widmer, St Gallen #137/R (S.FR 1700)
£773 $1221 €1160 In the Rhein valley (34x45cm-13x18in) s. panel. 26-Nov-2 Hans Widmer, St Gallen #1170 est:1000-2400 (S.FR 1800)
£786 $1226 €1179 Strela pass (37x39cm-15x15in) s. s.i. verso board. 6-Nov-2 Hans Widmer, St Gallen #36/R (S.FR 1800)
£786 $1234 €1179 Appenzell landscape (55x67cm-22x26in) s. s.i. verso panel. 25-Nov-2 Germann, Zurich #732/R est:1500-2000 (S.FR 1800)
£830 $1303 €1245 Appenzell countryside (39x51cm-15x20in) s. s.d. verso panel. 25-Nov-2 Germann, Zurich #733/R est:1000-1500 (S.FR 1900)
£1747 $2725 €2621 Rhine valley (41x43cm-16x17in) s.d.1948 s.i. verso board. 6-Nov-2 Hans Widmer, St Gallen #79/R est:1800-3600 (S.FR 4000)
Works on paper
£258 $407 €387 Landscape with tree near pond (31x23cm-12x9in) s.d.1914 gouache. 26-Nov-2 Hans Widmer, St Gallen #1167 (S.FR 600)
£429 $678 €644 Lion house in Rheineck (30x32cm-12x13in) s.d.1955 W/C over pencil. 26-Nov-2 Hans Widmer, St Gallen #1165 (S.FR 1000)

HERZIG, Heinrich (attrib) (1887-1964) Swiss
£429 $678 €644 Three scenes in a cafe (82x48cm-32x19in) panel. 26-Nov-2 Hans Widmer, St Gallen #1172 (S.FR 1000)

HERZOG, August (1885-1959) German
£759 $1177 €1200 Birkenstein (30x40cm-12x16in) s.d.1916 i. verso board. 25-Sep-2 Neumeister, Munich #602/R

HERZOG, August (attrib) (1885-1959) German
£633 $981 €1000 Kallmunz on the Naab and Vils (70x54cm-28x21in) i.d.1928. 25-Sep-2 Neumeister, Munich #601/R

HERZOG, Hermann (1832-1932) American/German
£395 $600 €593 In the alps (46x30cm-18x12in) s. pastel paper on board. 18-Aug-2 Jeffery Burchard, Florida #93/R
£903 $1400 €1355 Mountain landscape with stream (18x30cm-7x12in) s. board. 2-Nov-2 North East Auctions, Portsmouth #38/R
£1807 $3000 €2620 Landscape with cattle (46x58cm-18x23in) s. 11-Jun-3 Boos Gallery, Michigan #545/R est:6000-8000
£2830 $4500 €4245 Cattle in the woods (53x71cm-21x28in) s. i.verso. 7-Mar-3 Skinner, Boston #277/R est:5000-7000
£3526 $5500 €5289 Fishermen off a quay (56x79cm-22x31in) s. 14-Sep-2 Weschler, Washington #611/R est:6000-8000
£3614 $6000 €5240 Waves crashing on a rocky coast (33x47cm-13x19in) s.d.1901 canvas on board. 11-Jun-3 Butterfields, San Francisco #4020/R est:4000-6000
£3643 $5683 €5465 German landscape with house and wanderer (50x73cm-20x29in) s. 21-Oct-2 Blomqvist, Oslo #348/R est:35000-45000 (N.KR 42000)
£4268 $7000 €6402 Alpine landscape with cows (53x76cm-21x30in) s.d.1868. 8-Feb-3 Neal Auction Company, New Orleans #262/R est:12000-18000
£5682 $8750 €8523 Deer on the mountain ledge (53x76cm-21x30in) s. prov. 24-Oct-2 Shannon's, Milford #115/R est:12000-18000
£8861 $14000 €13292 Spring at the mill (56x71cm-22x28in) s. 24-Apr-3 Shannon's, Milford #55/R est:12000-18000
£10692 $17000 €16038 Departure (50x72cm-20x28in) s. prov. 5-Mar-3 Sotheby's, New York #29/R est:12000-18000
£20968 $32500 €31452 Florida live oaks with deer (37x46cm-15x18in) s. prov. 4-Dec-2 Sotheby's, New York #111/R est:15000-20000
£25806 $40000 €38709 Landscape with lake and mountains (64x92cm-25x36in) indis.sig. painted c.1890 prov. 3-Dec-2 Phillips, New York #32/R est:45000-65000
£25926 $42000 €38889 Florida sunset (63x48cm-25x19in) s. 22-May-3 Christie's, Rockefeller NY #5/R est:25000-35000

HERZOG, Jakob (1867-1959) Swiss
£739 $1146 €1109 Winterthur (57x64cm-22x25in) s.d.1922. 9-Dec-2 Philippe Schuler, Zurich #8727 (S.FR 1700)

HESLING, Bernard (1905-1987) Australian
£346 $546 €502 King and queen (81x42cm-32x17in) s.d.67 vitreouse enamel on metal. 22-Jul-3 Lawson Menzies, Sydney #139/R (A.D 850)
£477 $753 €827 Hey diddle diddle (41x84cm-16x33in) s.d.72 enamel metal sold with a book. 1-Apr-3 Goodman, Sydney #99/R (A.D 1250)
£569 $899 €825 Australian motifs (55x55cm-22x22in) vitreous enamel on metal. 22-Jul-3 Lawson Menzies, Sydney #138/R est:1500-2000 (A.D 1400)
£651 $1023 €977 Untitled (53x90cm-21x35in) s. enamel metal plate on board. 15-Apr-3 Lawson Menzies, Sydney #237/R est:2000-3000 (A.D 1700)

HESS, Eugen (1824-1862) German
£1900 $2944 €2850 Returning from the hunt (70x59cm-28x23in) s.d.1855. 3-Dec-2 Sotheby's, Olympia #252/R est:1000-1500

HESS, Florence (1891-1974) British
£500 $770 €750 Still life study of flowers in a vase (23x28cm-9x11in) s. board. 24-Oct-2 Richardson & Smith, Whitby #466

HESS, Heinrich Maria von (1798-1863) German
Works on paper
£2593 $4200 €3890 Allegories of Faith, Hope and Charity (32x36cm-13x14in) s.d.1819 graphite pen ink htd white. 22-Jan-3 Christie's, Rockefeller NY #119/R

HESS, Johann Michael (1768-1830) German
£10811 $16865 €16000 Tancred and Clorinda (105x86cm-41x34in) s.d.1817. 27-Mar-3 Dorotheum, Vienna #245/R est:6000-8000

HESS, Ludwig (1760-1800) Swiss
£1493 $2494 €2165 Landscape with mountain and fortress (34x50cm-13x20in) panel. 24-Jun-3 Koller, Zurich #1/R est:3000-5000 (S.FR 3300)
Works on paper
£873 $1362 €1310 Landscape with lake (25x37cm-10x15in) s.d.1788 gouache. 8-Nov-2 Dobiaschofsky, Bern #20/R (S.FR 2000)

HESS, Marcel (1791-1835) Belgian
£329 $533 €500 Interieur a la cheminee (70x55cm-28x22in) s. 21-Jan-3 Galerie Moderne, Brussels #191

HESS, Marcel (1878-1948) Belgian
£300 $468 €450 Still life of flowers in a vase (44x38cm-17x15in) s. board. 9-Oct-2 Woolley & Wallis, Salisbury #314/R
£423 $680 €600 Still life of flowers (60x50cm-24x20in) s. board lit. 9-May-3 Schloss Ahlden, Ahlden #1388
Works on paper
£274 $427 €400 L'heure de la sieste (53x44cm-21x17in) s. mixed media. 14-Apr-3 Horta, Bruxelles #501
£360 $576 €500 Portrait de S.A.R la Reine Astrid (64x47cm-25x19in) s. pastel. 13-May-3 Vanderkindere, Brussels #92

HESS, Peter von (1792-1871) German
£809 $1277 €1214 Riders in moonlight (23x22cm-9x9in) mono. panel. 2-Dec-2 Rasmussen, Copenhagen #1655/R (D.KR 9500)
£28000 $43960 €42000 Don Cossacks with French captives (38x49cm-15x19in) s.d.1819 panel. 20-Nov-2 Sotheby's, London #14/R est:18000-25000

HESS, Sara M (1880-?) American
£774 $1200 €1161 Garden path (28x36cm-11x14in) s. board painted c.1920. 8-Dec-2 Toomey, Oak Park #614/R

HESS, Stanley (1923-) American
£335 $525 €503 Fragment, legend of the true cross (33x53cm-13x21in) s.d.57 s.i.verso. 23-Nov-2 Jackson's, Cedar Falls #344/R

HESSE, Alexandre (1806-1879) French
£1346 $2127 €2100 Portrait d'homme (64x55cm-25x22in) s.d.1877 oval. 17-Nov-2 Herbette, Doullens #46/R

HESSE, Eva (1936-1970) American
£140000 $229600 €210000 Untitled (155x105cm-61x41in) s.d.64 prov.exhib.lit. 5-Feb-3 Christie's, London #6/R est:100000-150000
Sculpture
£227848 $360000 €341772 Untitled (20x20cm-8x8in) s.d.1967 metal over steel washers wood prov.lit. 13-Nov-2 Christie's, Rockefeller NY #41/R est:300000-400000

HESSE, Henri-Joseph (1781-1849) French
Works on paper
£567 $948 €800 Portrait de son fils Alexandre Hesse (53x38cm-21x15in) i. chl estompe white chk. 19-Jun-3 Piasa, Paris #171

HESSE, Hermann (1877-1962) German
£5240 $8175 €7860 Red and green (23x27cm-9x11in) s.d.24 i. verso W/C over pencil. 6-Nov-2 Dobiaschofsky, Bern #655/R est:10000 (S.FR 12000)
Works on paper
£641 $1013 €1000 Houses in Tessin (7x12cm-3x5in) mono.d.3i W/C over Indian ink. 15-Nov-2 Reiss & Sohn, Konigstein #546/R
£673 $983 €1050 Dusk in Tessin (4x5cm-2x2in) i. W/C pen. 4-Jun-2 Karl & Faber, Munich #276
£949 $1500 €1500 Houses in Tessin (6x90cm-2x35in) mono.d.1931 W/C Indian ink. 30-Nov-2 Arnold, Frankfurt #251/R est:1200
£1135 $1771 €1703 Enthralling night (8x10cm-3x4in) s.i. W/C. 6-Nov-2 Hans Widmer, St Gallen #35/R est:1500-2600 (S.FR 2600)
£1418 $2298 €2000 Tessin landscape (18x25cm-7x10in) s.d.1920 i. verso W/C. 20-May-3 Dorotheum, Vienna #142/R est:2500-3000
£1655 $2647 €2300 Transition (4x5cm-2x2in) i. W/C pen two. 15-May-3 Neumeister, Munich #271/R est:1500-1800
£1921 $2997 €2882 Tessin landscape at dusk (8x11cm-3x4in) pen W/C. 6-Nov-2 Dobiaschofsky, Bern #657/R est:4800 (S.FR 4400)
£2192 $3419 €3200 Houses in Montagnola (15x11cm-6x4in) mono. W/C pen. 11-Apr-3 Winterberg, Heidelberg #1127/R est:2950
£3433 $5425 €5150 Blue cloud over the village (18x13cm-7x5in) s.d.20 W/C. 29-Nov-2 Zofingen, Switzerland #2470/R est:9500 (S.FR 8000)
£5380 $8500 €8500 Montagnola scenes (11x12cm-4x5in) pen W/C four. 27-Nov-2 Dorotheum, Vienna #15/R est:7000-9000
£6962 $11000 €11000 Montagnola (31x24cm-12x9in) s.d.12 Mai 25 W/C. 27-Nov-2 Dorotheum, Vienna #14/R est:8000-12000

HESSE, Ludwig Ferdinand (1795-1876) German
Works on paper
£775 $1286 €1100 Fountain monument in square in park landscape. s.d.1821 wash pen. 12-Jun-3 Hauswedell & Nolte, Hamburg #357/R

HESSELBOM, Otto (1848-1913) Swedish
£439 $668 €659 Landscape with red cottage (42x55cm-17x22in) s. canvas on panel exhib. 16-Aug-2 Lilla Bukowskis, Stockholm #671 (S.KR 6400)
£480 $730 €720 Farm yard with figures (38x48cm-15x19in) s. 16-Aug-2 Lilla Bukowskis, Stockholm #642 (S.KR 7000)
£1280 $2074 €1856 Field of dandelions (56x35cm-22x14in) s.d.1905 paper on cardboard lit. 26-May-3 Bukowskis, Stockholm #121/R est:20000-25000 (S.KR 16500)
£1296 $2126 €1879 Autumn walk (60x46cm-24x18in) s.d.1889. 4-Jun-3 AB Stockholms Auktionsverk #2239/R est:15000-20000 (S.KR 16500)
£9574 $14840 €14361 Winter landscape with snow, evening light, Koppom (89x71cm-35x28in) s.d.1903 exhib.lit. 3-Dec-2 Bukowskis, Stockholm #6/R est:100000-125000 (S.KR 135000)

HESSING, Gustav (1909-1981) Rumanian
£3481 $5500 €5500 Girl sitting in landscape (127x90cm-50x35in) s.d. 27-Nov-2 Dorotheum, Vienna #202/R est:6000-9500
£11392 $18000 €18000 Clown (170x96cm-67x38in) s.d.1952 verso. 27-Nov-2 Dorotheum, Vienna #196/R est:10000-14000
£12162 $18973 €18000 Still life (81x101cm-32x40in) mono.d.39 i. verso. 25-Mar-3 Wiener Kunst Auktionen, Vienna #127/R est:15000-25000
Works on paper
£601 $938 €950 Portrait (63x47cm-25x19in) mono. pastel chk. 15-Oct-2 Dorotheum, Vienna #196/R
£621 $993 €900 Nice flecks of colour (49x64cm-19x25in) s. W/C. 11-Mar-3 Dorotheum, Vienna #167/R
£897 $1418 €1400 Boats (44x59cm-17x23in) s.d.46 W/C gouache. 12-Nov-2 Dorotheum, Vienna #156/R

HESSL, Gustav August (1849-1926) Austrian
£1208 $1945 €1800 Market day (23x32cm-9x13in) s. panel. 18-Feb-3 Sotheby's, Amsterdam #314/R est:450-500

HESSMERT, Karl (1869-?) German
£333 $523 €520 View through trees of summer park with silhouette of town (70x80cm-28x31in) s. 21-Nov-2 Van Ham, Cologne #1675
£622 $1008 €902 Breakers (64x94cm-25x37in) s. 24-May-3 Rasmussen, Havnen #2113/R (D.KR 6500)
£708 $1146 €1027 Spring landscape with horses, cows and sheep grazing (77x97cm-30x38in) s. prov. 24-May-3 Galerie Gloggner, Luzern #61/R (S.FR 1500)

HESTER, Joy (1920-1960) Australian
Works on paper
£8462 $13454 €12693 Lovers (33x25cm-13x10in) s.d.55 ink wash chl prov. 4-Mar-3 Deutscher-Menzies, Melbourne #21/R est:18000-25000 (A.D 22000)

HETSCH, Philippe Friedrich von (attrib) (1758-1839) German
£1013 $1570 €1600 Cornelia, mother of Gracchen (43x48cm-17x19in) 25-Sep-2 Neumeister, Munich #487/R

HETTICH, Eugen (1848-1888) German
£1149 $1792 €1700 River valley (114x143cm-45x56in) s.i.d.1877. 27-Mar-3 Dr Fritz Nagel, Stuttgart #815/R est:1700
£1603 $2484 €2500 Rocky river shore (114x143cm-45x56in) s.i.d.1877. 5-Dec-2 Dr Fritz Nagel, Stuttgart #662/R est:3300

HETTINGA TROMP, Tjitske Geertruida Maria van (1872-1962) Dutch
£347 $573 €500 Still life with stoneware (31x40cm-12x16in) mono.d.1948 prov. 1-Jul-3 Christie's, Amsterdam #262/R

HETTINGER, Johann Georg (18th C) Austrian
£1923 $3019 €3000 Old lady examining coin by candlelight (109x78cm-43x31in) s. canvas on canvas lit. 21-Nov-2 Dorotheum, Vienna #44/R est:4500-6000

HETZ, Carl (1828-1899) German
£1410 $2144 €2200 Young woman with fish on plate (74x59cm-29x23in) s. 11-Jul-2 Hugo Ruef, Munich #696/R est:1200

HETZEL, George (1826-1899) American
£962 $1500 €1443 Dark wooded landscape with figures (30x23cm-12x9in) s.indis.d.1813 board. 18-Sep-2 Alderfer's, Hatfield #326 est:800-1200
£3800 $5890 €5700 Forest track and stream (102x152cm-40x60in) s.d.1889. 26-Sep-2 Lane, Penzance #210/R est:3800-5000

HEUBERGER, Felix (20th C) ?
£1410 $2228 €2200 Traunsee (70x83cm-28x33in) s.d.1933. 12-Nov-2 Dorotheum, Vienna #100/R

HEUR, Cornelis Joseph de (1707-1762) Flemish
Works on paper
£743 $1159 €1100 Bacchus et Silene (56x33cm-22x13in) crayon htd chk. 31-Mar-3 Piasa, Paris #50

HEUSCH, Jacob de (1657-1701) Dutch
£4878 $8000 €7073 River landscape with travellers on a path (66x90cm-26x35in) indis.sig. 4-Jun-3 Christie's, Rockefeller NY #191/R est:8000-12000
£7051 $11141 €11000 Coastal landscape with fishermen (33x46cm-13x18in) s. panel. 16-Nov-2 Lempertz, Koln #1040/R est:12000

HEUSCH, Willem de (1638-1692) Dutch
£4026 $6482 €6000 Southern landscape with travellers beside a bridge over a river (53x74cm-21x29in) indis sig.d. panel prov.lit. 18-Feb-3 Sotheby's, Amsterdam #239/R est:6000-8000
£12346 $20000 €18519 River landscape with peasants (36x47cm-14x19in) s. panel prov.lit. 23-Jan-3 Sotheby's, New York #252/R est:30000
Works on paper
£705 $1114 €1100 Southern river landscape with ruins (19x27cm-7x11in) mnoo.d.1669 w/C. 16-Nov-2 Lempertz, Koln #1237/R

HEUSCH, Willem de (attrib) (1638-1692) Dutch
£789 $1232 €1184 Returning home (42x59cm-17x23in) 27-Mar-3 International Art Centre, Auckland #189/R (NZ.D 2250)
Works on paper
£510 $795 €800 Italianate landscape (14x20cm-6x8in) pen brown ink wash over black chk prov. 5-Nov-2 Sotheby's, Amsterdam #100/R

HEUSER, Carl (19th C) German
£2800 $4368 €4200 Good smoke. Good read (16x12cm-6x5in) s. board pair. 26-Mar-3 Sotheby's, Olympia #282a/R est:3000-4000

HEUSER, Christian (1862-1942) German
£1400 $2184 €2100 Portrait of a gentleman smoking an ornate pipe (16x12cm-6x5in) s. panel. 10-Sep-2 Bonhams, Knightsbridge #70/R est:800-1200

HEUSINGER, Johann (1769-1846) German
Miniatures
£1500 $2310 €2250 Empress Alexandra Feodorovan (12cm-5xin) rec. giltwood frame oval exec.c.1820 after G von Kugelgen. 24-Oct-2 Sotheby's, Olympia #26/R est:1000-1500

HEUSSLER, Ernst Georg (1903-) ?
£371 $579 €557 Carnaval (100x110cm-39x43in) s. 6-Nov-2 Dobiaschofsky, Bern #3411 (S.FR 850)

HEUVEL, Karel Jan van den (1913-1991) Dutch
£278 $442 €400 Nature morte (65x80cm-26x31in) s. 29-Apr-3 Campo & Campo, Antwerp #880
£313 $497 €450 Table dressee (36x46cm-14x18in) panel. 29-Apr-3 Campo & Campo, Antwerp #877
£333 $530 €480 La recolte (36x46cm-14x18in) s. 29-Apr-3 Campo & Campo, Antwerp #856
£347 $552 €500 La recolte (26x34cm-10x13in) paper. 29-Apr-3 Campo & Campo, Antwerp #863
£380 $600 €600 Paysage fluvial (80x100cm-31x39in) s. 26-Nov-2 Palais de Beaux Arts, Brussels #401
£382 $607 €550 Nature morte aux fleurs (80x65cm-31x26in) s. 29-Apr-3 Campo & Campo, Antwerp #310
£451 $718 €650 Petit fille a la table (25x34cm-10x13in) s. paper. 29-Apr-3 Campo & Campo, Antwerp #876
£521 $828 €750 Cafe Flore (36x46cm-14x18in) s. panel. 29-Apr-3 Campo & Campo, Antwerp #864
£590 $939 €850 Jeune femme au chapeau (80x65cm-31x26in) s. 29-Apr-3 Campo & Campo, Antwerp #309

HEUZE, Edmond (1884-1967) French
£863 $1381 €1200 Canotage au Bois de Boulogne (50x61cm-20x24in) s. 14-May-3 Blanchet, Paris #73/R

HEWARD, Prudence (1896-1947) Canadian
£5778 $9476 €8667 Autumn, Knowlton, P.Q (31x36cm-12x14in) painted c.1940 panel prov. 27-May-3 Sotheby's, Toronto #63/R est:3000-4000 (C.D 13000)

HEWIN, George (19th C) ?
£7500 $12450 €10875 Full rigger Chieftain of Bangor outward bound from Liverpool off Great Orme's Head, North Wales (70x91cm-28x36in) s.i.d.1841. 12-Jun-3 Christie's, London #515/R est:3000-5000

HEWITT, Beatrice Pauline (1907-) British
£300 $501 €435 Builth Bridge, winter landscape (37x44cm-15x17in) s. i.verso board. 19-Jun-3 Lane, Penzance #153
£300 $501 €435 Brecon, panoramic landscape (37x47cm-15x19in) i.verso board. 19-Jun-3 Lane, Penzance #154

HEWITT, Henry (1818-1875) British
£320 $499 €480 Figure in a punt (63x96cm-25x38in) s.d.1871. 17-Sep-2 Bonhams, Ipswich #376
£1100 $1793 €1650 By the waterfall (23x37cm-9x15in) s.d.1848 board. 29-Jan-3 Sotheby's, Olympia #108/R est:400-600

HEWITT, Henry (attrib) (1818-1875) British
£1150 $1829 €1725 Outside the cottage. Path beside the river (28x38cm-11x15in) bears sig.d.1843 panel pair. 18-Mar-3 Bonhams, Sevenoaks #204 est:650-850

HEWTON, Randolph Stanley (1888-1960) Canadian
£1975 $3062 €2963 Spring break up (50x60cm-20x24in) s. 3-Dec-2 Joyner, Toronto #16/R est:3000-4000 (C.D 4800)
£2444 $4009 €3666 Dominion Square, Montreal (18x23cm-7x9in) s. board. 3-Jun-3 Joyner, Toronto #23/R est:3000-5000 (C.D 5500)
£3696 $5765 €6163 Untitled - snowy mountains (36x41cm-14x16in) s. prov. 13-Apr-3 Levis, Calgary #49/R est:12000-15000 (C.D 8500)
£4115 $6379 €6173 Les jardins du Luxembourg, Paris (17x23cm-7x9in) s. board. 3-Dec-2 Joyner, Toronto #412 est:1000-1500 (C.D 10000)

HEY, Paul (1867-1952) German
£1083 $1668 €1700 Coach trip on sunny afternoon (27x30cm-11x12in) 5-Sep-2 Arnold, Frankfurt #785 est:600
£1731 $2683 €2700 Journey in the carriage - farmer's wife with daughter in sunny hilly landscape (28x30cm-11x12in) s. 4-Dec-2 Neumeister, Munich #767/R est:2200
£2734 $4374 €3800 Hay harvest (75x94cm-30x37in) s. gouache board. 17-May-3 Lempertz, Koln #1296/R est:4000
Works on paper
£541 $843 €800 Vienna, Volksgarten (21x29cm-8x11in) s.i. verso W/C. 28-Mar-3 Dorotheum, Vienna #358/R

HEYBERGER, Stephan (17th C) German
Works on paper
£621 $981 €900 Wild boar hunt (19x26cm-7x10in) s.i. 4-Apr-3 Venator & Hansten, Koln #1488

HEYBOER, Anton (1924-) Dutch
£313 $497 €450 Quatre femmes (76x106cm-30x42in) s. paper on canvas. 29-Apr-3 Campo, Vlaamse Kaai #146
£319 $517 €450 Three figures (39x49cm-15x19in) s. 26-May-3 Glerum, Amsterdam #317/R
£458 $737 €650 Figures (53x63cm-21x25in) s. 6-May-3 Vendu Notarishuis, Rotterdam #33
£1154 $1788 €1800 Untitled (56x65cm-22x26in) s.d.1975. 3-Dec-2 Christie's, Amsterdam #359/R est:1800-2200
Works on paper
£283 $436 €450 De passionele liefde (78x106cm-31x42in) s. W/C. 22-Oct-2 Campo, Vlaamse Kaai #153
£291 $471 €410 Genuine love keeps the man - genuine love keeps the woman (49x69cm-19x27in) s.d.1983 mixed media. 26-May-3 Glerum, Amsterdam #324/R
£298 $483 €420 Four woman (62x94cm-24x37in) s.d.1980 mixed media. 26-May-3 Glerum, Amsterdam #325/R
£599 $964 €850 Fat ladies on the beach (78x106cm-31x42in) s. W/C pastel. 7-May-3 Vendue Huis, Gravenhage #232/R

HEYDEN, Carl (1845-1933) German
£641 $1006 €1000 Boy with sister and mother in kitchen (61x79cm-24x31in) s. 21-Nov-2 Van Ham, Cologne #1677
£1218 $1888 €1900 Midday meal in the farmer's kitchen (80x91cm-31x36in) s. canvas on canvas. 4-Dec-2 Neumeister, Munich #768/R est:1200

HEYDEN, J C J van der (1928-) Dutch
£10897 $16891 €17000 Untitled (45x61cm-18x24in) s.d.66 on stretcher oil on two canvas diptych. 3-Dec-2 Christie's, Amsterdam #353/R est:10000-15000

HEYDEN, Jacobus Cornelis Johannes van der (1928-) Dutch
£310 $493 €450 Polder landscape with a windmill (40x30cm-16x12in) s. 10-Mar-3 Sotheby's, Amsterdam #365

HEYDEN, Jan van der (1637-1712) Dutch

£29582 $45852 €44373 Riverside landscape with a castle (48x58cm-19x23in) 6-Dec-2 Kieselbach, Budapest #72/R (H.F 11000000)
£32212 $51861 €48000 Hawking party returning to a castle beside a river (49x62cm-19x24in) indis sig.d. panel prov.exhib.lit. 18-Feb-3 Sotheby's, Amsterdam #227/R est:45000-55000
£35000 $58450 €50750 View of a canal with a village beyond, possibly the Vecht near Maarssen (46x60cm-18x24in) panel prov.lit. 9-Jul-3 Christie's, London #39/R est:30000-50000

HEYDEN, Jan van der and VELDE, Adriaen van de (17th C) Dutch

£30000 $50100 €43500 River landscape with a fortified castle and bridge (70x57cm-28x22in) panel prov.lit. 9-Jul-3 Christie's, London #52/R est:30000-50000

HEYDEN, Otto (1820-1897) German

£458 $750 €700 Market place in northern Africa (23x35cm-9x14in) s. board on panel. 8-Feb-3 Hans Stahl, Hamburg #96/R
£2778 $4417 €4000 In the shade on the banks of the River Nile (25x42cm-10x17in) s. 29-Apr-3 Christie's, Amsterdam #71/R est:3500-4500

HEYDENDAHL, Friedrich Joseph Nicolai (1844-1906) German

£483 $768 €700 Lower Rhineland village on winter evening (32x24cm-13x9in) s. panel. 8-Mar-3 Arnold, Frankfurt #606/R
£870 $1357 €1305 Dutch landscape in winter with frozen lake (16x32cm-6x13in) s. panel. 16-Sep-2 Philippe Schuler, Zurich #3477/R (S.FR 2000)
£1032 $1610 €1548 Evening in the village (65x95cm-26x37in) s. 11-Sep-2 Kieselbach, Budapest #166/R (H.F 400000)
£1233 $1923 €1800 Winter landscape (66x95cm-26x37in) s. 10-Apr-3 Van Ham, Cologne #1487/R est:1600
£2000 $3200 €3000 Fishing boat in a Norwegian fjord by moonlight (94x132cm-37x52in) s. 7-Jan-3 Bonhams, Knightsbridge #246/R est:2000-3000
£6115 $9784 €8500 Sangliers en foret (94x130cm-37x51in) s. 13-May-3 Palais de Beaux Arts, Brussels #189/R est:8700-11500

HEYENBROCK, Johan Coenrad Hermann (1871-1948) Dutch

£2803 $4372 €4400 Metal foundry (51x76cm-20x30in) s. i.verso. 6-Nov-2 Vendue Huis, Gravenhage #71/R est:5000-6000
£7006 $10790 €11000 Scheepswerf en machinefabriek Burgerhout, Rotterdam (101x202cm-40x80in) s. s.i.verso. 3-Sep-2 Christie's, Amsterdam #330 est:3000-5000

Works on paper

£625 $1013 €950 Workers in a coal factory (46x62cm-18x24in) s. pastel. 21-Jan-3 Christie's, Amsterdam #285
£2303 $3730 €3500 Gieterij Nering Bogel, Deventer (73x100cm-29x39in) s. col chk pastel. 21-Jan-3 Christie's, Amsterdam #275 est:1200-1600

HEYER (?) ?

£674 $1051 €1124 Untitled - In the trenches (23x29cm-9x11in) s.d.1917 prov. 13-Apr-3 Levis, Calgary #463/R est:400-500 (C.D 1550)

HEYER, Arthur (1872-1931) German

£479 $748 €700 Hen with chicks (4x44cm-2x17in) s. 10-Apr-3 Dorotheum, Vienna #238/R
£600 $936 €900 Mother and kitten (40x50cm-16x20in) with sig. 26-Mar-3 Sotheby's, Olympia #266/R
£629 $975 €1000 Cat with pot plant (38x48cm-15x19in) s. 29-Oct-2 Dorotheum, Vienna #162/R
£700 $1120 €1050 White cats with a Biedermeier clock (85x70cm-33x28in) 11-Mar-3 Bonhams, Knightsbridge #228/R
£750 $1185 €1125 Keeping a distance (56x69cm-22x27in) s. board. 14-Nov-2 Christie's, Kensington #227/R
£800 $1296 €1200 Two white kittens (50x70cm-20x28in) s. 20-May-3 Sotheby's, Olympia #415/R
£850 $1343 €1275 Friends at play. Close shave (55x68cm-22x27in) s. two. 14-Nov-2 Christie's, Kensington #43/R
£1000 $1560 €1500 Cat on table (55x68cm-22x27in) s. 17-Sep-2 Sotheby's, Olympia #226/R est:1000-1500
£1544 $2485 €2300 Chatons jouant devant lapendule (61x81cm-24x32in) s. 18-Feb-3 Vanderkindere, Brussels #8/R
£1840 $3000 €2760 Sound asleep (55x68cm-22x27in) s. 11-Feb-3 Bonhams & Doyles, New York #215/R est:2000-3000
£1963 $3200 €2945 Old and the young (50x70cm-20x28in) s. 11-Feb-3 Bonhams & Doyles, New York #213/R est:2500-3500
£4800 $7776 €7200 Curiosity (56x69cm-22x27in) s. 20-May-3 Sotheby's, Olympia #389/R est:3000-4000

HEYERDAHL, Hans Olaf (1857-1913) Norwegian

£519 $795 €779 Man with moustache (61x46cm-24x18in) s. painted 1897. 26-Aug-2 Blomqvist, Lysaker #1170/R (N.KR 6000)
£3287 $5194 €4931 Drying the nets by old boat house (36x48cm-14x19in) s.d.1877 panel. 2-Dec-2 Blomqvist, Oslo #346/R est:35000-40000 (N.KR 38000)
£3643 $5683 €5465 Young boy (50x36cm-20x14in) s.d.84 panel. 21-Oct-2 Blomqvist, Oslo #340/R est:40000-60000 (N.KR 42000)
£5190 $8201 €7785 Children tobogganing (27x20cm-11x8in) s. panel. 2-Dec-2 Blomqvist, Oslo #312/R est:40000-60000 (N.KR 60000)
£5637 $8794 €8456 Woman in interior - possibly artist's wife Christine (22x16cm-9x6in) s.i.d.1882 panel. 21-Oct-2 Blomqvist, Oslo #314/R est:70000-90000 (N.KR 65000)
£10860 $17593 €16290 From Aasgaardstrand with figures (64x103cm-25x41in) s.d.08. 26-May-3 Grev Wedels Plass, Oslo #131/R est:150000-200000 (N.KR 120000)
£18584 $29363 €27876 Double portrait of two young boys - Ingar and Einar Skavland (54x67cm-21x26in) s. exhib.lit. 28-Apr-3 Blomqvist, Oslo #318/R est:200000-300000 (N.KR 210000)

HEYERMANS, Jean Arnould (1837-1892) Belgian

£1728 $2834 €2506 Loves me, loves me not! (58x44cm-23x17in) s. 4-Jun-3 AB Stockholms Auktionsverk #2414/R est:20000-25000 (S.KR 22000)
£3200 $5056 €4800 Fond memories (86x71cm-34x28in) s. 14-Nov-2 Christie's, Kensington #26 est:2000-4000

HEYL, Marinus (1836-1931) Dutch

£342 $534 €500 Landscape with woman carrying bundle of wood (33x65cm-13x26in) s. panel. 14-Apr-3 Glerum, Amsterdam #138/R
£411 $641 €600 Village on a river (29x54cm-11x21in) s. panel. 14-Apr-3 Glerum, Amsterdam #139/R

HEYL, Siegfried (20th C) ?

£769 $1208 €1200 Flowers in vase (47x37cm-19x15in) s. 21-Nov-2 Van Ham, Cologne #1679

HEYLIGERS, Antoon François (1828-1897) Dutch

£3000 $5010 €4350 Town crier, Bruges (27x33cm-11x13in) s.d.1860 panel. 17-Jun-3 Bonhams, New Bond Street #5/R est:2500-3500

HEYLIGERS, Hendrik (1877-1967) Dutch

£1172 $1876 €1700 Enfants a la mer (38x46cm-15x18in) s. 17-Mar-3 Horta, Bruxelles #183 est:600-800

HEYMANN, Marius (19th C) ?

£1053 $1705 €1527 Still life of melon, peaches and flowers on ledge (29x38cm-11x15in) s.d.1848 panel. 26-May-3 Rasmussen, Copenhagen #1225/R (D.KR 11000)

HEYMANS, Adriaan Josef (1839-1921) Flemish

£362 $594 €500 Paysage (6x12cm-2x5in) s. 27-May-3 Campo & Campo, Antwerp #105
£374 $595 €550 Le champ de ble a l'ombrelle (30x46cm-12x18in) s. 18-Mar-3 Campo, Vlaamse Kaai #108
£674 $1125 €950 Paysage de neige (9x10cm-4x4in) s. panel. 17-Jun-3 Palais de Beaux Arts, Brussels #583/R
£818 $1267 €1300 Paysage au clair de lune (19x28cm-7x11in) s. panel. 1-Oct-2 Palais de Beaux Arts, Brussels #485
£949 $1481 €1500 Landscape with mill and farm (26x38cm-10x15in) s. panel. 21-Oct-2 Bernaerts, Antwerp #24/R est:1500-2000
£2446 $3914 €3400 Impression lumineuse avant l'orage (60x77cm-24x30in) s. 19-May-3 Horta, Bruxelles #158 est:4000-6000
£2897 $4634 €4200 Longboats in Papendrecht (32x54cm-13x21in) s. panel exhib.lit. 15-Mar-3 De Vuyst, Lokeren #416/R est:4000-5000
£3268 $5261 €5000 Les dunes (60x73cm-24x29in) s. 20-Jan-3 Horta, Bruxelles #229 est:5000-6500
£3503 $5465 €5500 Coucher de soleil sur l'attelage (40x46cm-16x18in) s. 11-Nov-2 Horta, Bruxelles #204/R est:7500-10000
£3846 $5962 €6000 View of the surroundings of Kalmthout (60x78cm-24x31in) s. 7-Dec-2 De Vuyst, Lokeren #429/R est:6000-7000
£6329 $10000 €10000 Matinee tiede au hameau (38x47cm-15x19in) s. 26-Nov-2 Palais de Beaux Arts, Brussels #332/R est:10000-15000

HEYMANS, Eduard (1912-1972) Dutch

Works on paper

£1154 $1788 €1800 Diluviaal Bewijs (165x300cm-65x118in) s.i.d.20.8.61 verso mixed media. 3-Dec-2 Christie's, Amsterdam #175/R est:1800-2200

HEYN, Karl (1834-1906) German

£962 $1510 €1500 High mountains with village (126x100cm-50x39in) s.d.80. 21-Nov-2 Dorotheum, Vienna #137/R est:3000-3600

HEYNES, Theodoor (1920-1990) Dutch

Works on paper

£426 $689 €600 Still life with flowers in glazed pots (39x55cm-15x22in) s. W/C. 26-May-3 Glerum, Amsterdam #154/R

HEYNSIUS, Kees (1890-?) Dutch
£276 $439 €400 People at a market (31x45cm-12x18in) s. board. 10-Mar-3 Sotheby's, Amsterdam #312

HEYRAULT, Louis Robert (19th C) French
£3688 $6159 €5200 Chasse a courre (54x73cm-21x29in) one s.d.1846 panel pair. 20-Jun-3 Piasa, Paris #45/R est:6000-8000
£3901 $6514 €5500 Chasse a courre (54x73cm-21x29in) one s.d.1848 panel pair. 20-Jun-3 Piasa, Paris #46/R est:6000-8000

HEYS, Ward (19th C) British
Works on paper
£280 $437 €420 View of Grasmere (44x44cm-17x17in) s.d.92 pencil W/C. 19-Sep-2 Christie's, Kensington #46

HEYSEN, Nora (1911-) Australian
£1400 $2254 €2100 Native flower posy (22x12cm-9x5in) s. i.verso cardboard. 6-May-3 Christie's, Melbourne #285 est:3500-4500 (A.D 3500)
£5364 $7992 €8046 Still life (48x44cm-19x17in) s. canvasboard prov. 27-Aug-2 Christie's, Melbourne #22/R est:14000-18000 (A.D 14000)
£5376 $8172 €8064 Still life (40x29cm-16x11in) s.d.1935 board. 27-Aug-2 Goodman, Sydney #110/R est:3000-6000 (A.D 15000)
£8185 $12523 €12278 Still life of dahlias in a jug (40x33cm-16x13in) s. prov. 25-Aug-2 Sotheby's, Paddington #42/R est:15000-20000 (A.D 23000)
Works on paper
£246 $385 €369 Lede (46x29cm-18x11in) s.d.56 conte. 21-Oct-2 Australian Art Auctions, Sydney #111 (A.D 700)

HEYSEN, Sir Hans (1877-1968) Australian
£717 $1039 €1076 Gum trees and the Flinders Rangers (15x24cm-6x9in) s. pen ink wash pastel board. 10-Dec-1 Goodman, Sydney #486 (A.D 2000)
£12800 $20608 €19200 Flower piece (61x51cm-24x20in) s.d.1925 prov.exhib. 6-May-3 Christie's, Melbourne #23/R est:20000-30000 (A.D 32000)
Works on paper
£321 $508 €482 White gums (25x31cm-10x12in) s. i.verso pencil. 27-Nov-2 Deutscher-Menzies, Melbourne #249 est:1000-1500 (A.D 900)
£429 $677 €644 Landscape with goats (30x39cm-12x15in) s. chl prov. 17-Nov-2 Sotheby's, Paddington #75 est:1500-3000 (A.D 1200)
£498 $742 €747 Landscape (17x29cm-7x11in) pencil. 27-Aug-2 Christie's, Melbourne #342 est:1000-1500 (A.D 1300)
£640 $1030 €960 Hillside town (21x31cm-8x12in) s. W/C gouache. 6-May-3 Christie's, Melbourne #283 est:1000-1500 (A.D 1600)
£1219 $1852 €1829 Landscape, Mount Torrens (25x36cm-10x14in) s. W/C. 27-Aug-2 Goodman, Sydney #107 est:3000-5000 (A.D 3400)
£1281 $1960 €1922 Gum trees (37x29cm-15x11in) s.d.43 W/C pastel. 25-Aug-2 Sotheby's, Paddington #197 est:1500-2500 (A.D 3600)
£1357 $2144 €2036 Quiet stream (23x25cm-9x10in) s.d.98 W/C. 27-Nov-2 Deutscher-Menzies, Melbourne #247/R est:4000-6000 (A.D 3800)
£1423 $2178 €2135 Gathering storm clouds, Flinders Ranges (51x63cm-20x25in) s.d.1958 i.verso chl chk prov. 26-Aug-2 Sotheby's, Paddington #598 est:4000-6000 (A.D 4000)
£1600 $2576 €2400 Study for cattle and gum (30x39cm-12x15in) s. pencil prov. 6-May-3 Christie's, Melbourne #367 est:3000-4000 (A.D 4000)
£1754 $2667 €2631 Hilltops study (25x17cm-10x7in) s. W/C. 19-Aug-2 Joel, Victoria #274/R est:5000-6000 (A.D 5000)
£1754 $2667 €2631 Copse (25x33cm-10x13in) s.d.07 W/C. 19-Aug-2 Joel, Victoria #296 est:6000-8000 (A.D 5000)
£1769 $2813 €2654 Haystack (28x37cm-11x15in) s. chl prov. 4-Mar-3 Deutscher-Menzies, Melbourne #101/R est:5000-7000 (A.D 4600)
£2321 $3644 €3482 Loggers (26x36cm-10x14in) s. pencil. 25-Nov-2 Christie's, Melbourne #351/R est:7000-10000 (A.D 6500)
£2490 $3710 €3735 Sheep grazing (30x39cm-12x15in) s.d.1944 W/C pencil. 27-Aug-2 Christie's, Melbourne #221/R est:3000-5000 (A.D 6500)
£2862 $4523 €4293 Bullock Dray and drive, homeward bound (28x39cm-11x15in) s.d.1911 W/C. 2-Apr-3 Christie's, Melbourne #19/R est:5000-8000 (A.D 7500)
£3036 $4766 €4554 White gum, Ambleside (31x39cm-12x15in) s.d.1968 W/C prov. 25-Nov-2 Christie's, Melbourne #218/R est:7000-10000 (A.D 8500)
£3600 $5724 €5400 Early morning, Ambleside (38x52cm-15x20in) s.d.1923 i.d.verso W/C. 29-Apr-3 Bonhams, New Bond Street #8/R est:3000-5000
£3876 $6163 €5814 Stockman on a country road (29x38cm-11x15in) s. W/C. 5-May-3 Sotheby's, Melbourne #292/R est:10000-15000 (A.D 10000)
£4093 $6262 €6140 In the field, ploughing (38x52cm-15x20in) s.d.1923 W/C. 26-Aug-2 Sotheby's, Paddington #651/R est:8000-12000 (A.D 11500)
£4301 $6538 €6452 Cows grazing (36x43cm-14x17in) s. W/C prov. 27-Aug-2 Goodman, Sydney #129/R est:12000-18000 (A.D 12000)
£5200 $8372 €7800 Landscape at Hahndorf, Adelaide Hills (32x40cm-13x16in) s. pencil W/C. 6-May-3 Christie's, Melbourne #111/R est:10000-15000 (A.D 13000)
£5357 $8411 €8036 Eucalyptus, drover and cattle water (41x53cm-16x21in) s.d.1931 W/C. 25-Nov-2 Christie's, Melbourne #84/R est:15000-18000 (A.D 15000)
£6870 $10855 €10305 Timberworkers making tea (32x39cm-13x15in) s.d.1915 W/C. 2-Apr-3 Christie's, Melbourne #11/R est:12000-18000 (A.D 18000)
£7117 $10890 €10676 Cows in the pasture (48x61cm-19x24in) s.d.1936 W/C. 25-Aug-2 Sotheby's, Paddington #70/R est:20000-30000 (A.D 20000)
£7968 $13068 €11952 Woodside pastoral (32x40cm-13x16in) s.i.d.1938 W/C. 4-Jun-3 Deutscher-Menzies, Melbourne #62/R est:12000-18000 (A.D 20000)

HEYWORTH, Alfred (1926-1976) British
Works on paper
£260 $413 €390 Approaching rain, Walberswick. s.d.67 W/C. 2-Mar-3 ELR Auctions, Sheffield #192

HIBBARD, Aldro Thompson (1886-1972) American
£2500 $4000 €3750 Bass rocks (46x66cm-18x26in) s. board. 11-Jan-3 James Julia, Fairfield #204 est:5000-8000
£3459 $5500 €5189 Winter landscape with distant farm (45x61cm-18x24in) s. canvasboard. 7-Mar-3 Skinner, Boston #459/R est:6000-8000
£3750 $6000 €5438 Sunset, winter (18x23cm-7x9in) s. board. 16-May-3 Skinner, Boston #262/R est:1500-3000
£3906 $6250 €5664 Winter scene (46x64cm-18x25in) s. board. 17-May-3 CRN Auctions, Cambridge #14
£4167 $6500 €6251 Winter landscape (45x61cm-18x24in) s. canvasboard. 9-Nov-2 Sloan, North Bethesda #592/R est:6000-8000
£4487 $7000 €6731 Vermont hills (41x51cm-16x20in) s. canvasboard. 9-Nov-2 Sloan, North Bethesda #591/R est:6000-8000
£4516 $7000 €6774 Winter day (61x81cm-24x32in) s. 28-Sep-2 Charlton Hall, Columbia #545/R est:5000-8000
£5988 $10000 €8683 New England Valley (41x50cm-16x20in) s. canvas on board. 18-Jun-3 Christie's, Los Angeles #99/R est:3000-5000
£6369 $10000 €9554 Snowy valley (96x127cm-38x50in) s. 20-Nov-2 Christie's, Los Angeles #64/R est:12000-18000
£12500 $20000 €18125 Lake Louise (77x91cm-30x36in) s. prov. 16-May-3 Skinner, Boston #236/R est:12000-15000
£15663 $26000 €22711 River in autumn, no 4 (61x81cm-24x32in) s.i.verso prov. 11-Jun-3 Butterfields, San Francisco #4084/R est:10000-15000
£19578 $32500 €28388 Snowy morning (76x91cm-30x36in) s. prov. 11-Jun-3 Butterfields, San Francisco #4074/R est:10000-15000
£19872 $31000 €29808 Schooners near a rocky north shore or a Maine harbour (36x43cm-14x17in) s. 1-Aug-2 Eldred, East Dennis #810/R est:9000-12000

HIBBERT, Phyllis I (1903-) British
Works on paper
£300 $468 €450 Vase of flowers (25x30cm-10x12in) s. W/C. 18-Sep-2 James Thompson, Kirby Lonsdale #161
£600 $936 €900 Roses, foxgloves, larkspur and clematis in a bowl (53x75cm-21x30in) s. W/C. 6-Nov-2 Bonhams, Chester #357
£700 $1092 €1050 Vase of summer flowers (55x75cm-22x30in) s. 31-Jul-2 James Thompson, Kirby Lonsdale #13/R

HIBEL, Edna (1917-) American
£1282 $2000 €1923 Road to Tonafico (23x33cm-9x13in) s. i.verso particle board. 20-Oct-2 Jeffery Burchard, Florida #30/R
£1603 $2500 €2405 Floral still life (76x102cm-30x40in) s. board. 18-Sep-2 Alderfer's, Hatfield #391/R est:900-1200
Works on paper
£478 $750 €717 Peach tree (34x25cm-13x10in) s. W/C gouache. 22-Nov-2 Skinner, Boston #171/R

HICK, Jacqueline (1920-) Australian
£2222 $3311 €3333 Wedding (71x101cm-28x40in) s.i. verso oil gold leaf on board pair. 27-Aug-2 Christie's, Melbourne #257/R est:6000-8000 (A.D 5800)

HICKEY, Dale (1937-) Australian
£714 $1114 €1071 Window (46x39cm-18x15in) oil pastel prov. 11-Nov-2 Deutscher-Menzies, Melbourne #10/R (A.D 2000)
£3214 $5078 €4821 Untitled 1985 (121x121cm-48x48in) s.verso oil enamel prov.exhib. 27-Nov-2 Deutscher-Menzies, Melbourne #7/R est:10000-15000 (A.D 9000)
£7857 $12100 €11786 Black (182x182cm-72x72in) s.d.93. 8-Sep-2 Sotheby's, Melbourne #27/R est:12000-18000 (A.D 22000)
£8571 $13371 €12857 Untitled (182x182cm-72x72in) s.d.1986 oil enamel linen. 11-Nov-2 Deutscher-Menzies, Melbourne #42/R est:20000-30000 (A.D 24000)
£10853 $17256 €16280 Five on yellow (183x183cm-72x72in) s.d.92 oil enamel prov. 5-May-3 Sotheby's, Melbourne #138/R est:20000-30000 (A.D 28000)

Works on paper
£571 $891 €857 Skull and easel (29x42cm-11x17in) s.d.89 pastel. 11-Nov-2 Deutscher-Menzies, Melbourne #105/R (A.D 1600)

HICKEY, Desmond (20th C) British?
£769 $1192 €1200 Raining in Stephen's Green (46x61cm-18x24in) s.d. 17-Jul-2 Woodwards, Cork #252
£796 $1242 €1250 Conversation at Keel, Achill (49x60cm-19x24in) s. board. 6-Nov-2 James Adam, Dublin #39/R
Works on paper
£741 $1067 €1200 Punchestown the last furlong (46x61cm-18x24in) s. 25-Apr-2 Woodwards, Cork #248

HICKEY, Patrick (1927-1999) Irish
£1528 $2429 €2200 Bananas (56x76cm-22x30in) s.i. oil on paper exhib. 29-Apr-3 Whyte's, Dublin #60/R est:2500-3500
£3221 $5187 €4800 Melon slice and apples (81x41cm-32x16in) s.d.1996 board exhib. 18-Feb-3 Whyte's, Dublin #60/R est:3500-4500
Works on paper
£473 $738 €700 Old larch tree (75x56cm-30x22in) s.d.February 28 83 ink prov. 26-Mar-3 James Adam, Dublin #131/R
£480 $744 €720 Watercourse, Co Wicklow (51x74cm-20x29in) s.i.d.1969 W/C. 31-Oct-2 Duke & Son, Dorchester #161
£513 $795 €800 Houses across the valley, with olive trees (71x49cm-28x19in) s.i. mixed media exhib. 3-Dec-2 Bonhams & James Adam, Dublin #108/R

HICKEY, Thomas (1741-1824) British
£4400 $6952 €6600 Portrait of a young officer (26x20cm-10x8in) prov. 28-Nov-2 Sotheby's, London #177/R est:3000-5000

HICKEY, Thomas (attrib) (1741-1824) British
£650 $1066 €975 Half-length portrait of a young child (30x25cm-12x10in) oval. 4-Feb-3 Sworder & Son, Bishops Stortford #166/R

HICKIN, George (fl.1858-1877) British
£400 $640 €600 Gathering fire wood (47x41cm-19x16in) s.d.1899. 7-Jan-3 Bonhams, Knightsbridge #19
Works on paper
£560 $851 €840 Chickens and ducks on a river bank (18x28cm-7x11in) W/C. 14-Aug-2 Andrew Hartley, Ilkley #554

HICKIN, George Arthur (19th C) British
£750 $1230 €1125 In the heart of Wales (49x75cm-19x30in) s. 3-Jun-3 Bonhams, Oxford #56/R

HICKS, Edward (1780-1849) American
£198758 $320000 €298137 Washington at the Delaware (32x32cm-13x13in) i. prov.exhib.lit. 16-Jan-3 Christie's, Rockefeller NY #398/R est:200000-300000

HICKS, G E (1824-1914) British
£9000 $14940 €13050 Portrait of a girl holding dead linnet in her arms (58x43cm-23x17in) s. 12-Jun-3 Hobbs Parker, Ashford #482/R est:2000-3000

HICKS, George Elgar (1824-1914) British
£17000 $27370 €25500 Cloud with silver lining (127x102cm-50x40in) s.d.1890 i.verso prov.exhib.lit. 20-Feb-3 Christie's, London #269/R est:15000
Works on paper
£900 $1467 €1350 Gypsy girl (32x43cm-13x17in) s.d.1874 W/C. 11-Feb-3 Fellows & Sons, Birmingham #129/R
£3200 $5152 €4800 Latest arrival (38x27cm-15x11in) init. pencil chk htd white prov.exhib.lit. 20-Feb-3 Christie's, London #119/R

HICKS, Morley (1877-1959) American
£248 $400 €372 Bailey Harbour No.8 (41x51cm-16x20in) s.d. s.i.verso board. 20-Jan-3 Schrager Galleries, Milwaukee #665

HICKS, Thomas (1823-1890) American
£1687 $2750 €2531 The home stretch, trout all sold. s.d.1864. 1-Feb-3 Thomaston Place, Thomaston #91

HICKS, Thomas (after) (1823-1890) American
Prints
£3727 $6000 €5591 Abraham Lincoln (66x49cm-26x19in) lithograph after Thomas Hicks. 16-Jan-3 Christie's, Rockefeller NY #2/R est:6000-8000

HIDALGO DE CAVIEDES, Hipolito (1902-1996) Spanish
£3289 $5329 €5000 Girl with doves (100x75cm-39x30in) s. 21-Jan-3 Ansorena, Madrid #299/R est:5000

HIDER, Frank (1861-1933) British
£280 $448 €420 High tide on the Cornish coast (29x50cm-11x20in) s. 7-Jan-3 Gildings, Market Harborough #413/R
£321 $500 €482 Untitled seaside cliffs (28x48cm-11x19in) s. 29-Mar-3 Charlton Hall, Columbia #124/R
£420 $664 €630 Rocky coastal landscape at sunset with sailing ships (39x60cm-15x24in) s.d.1912. 4-Apr-3 Moore Allen & Innocent, Cirencester #691/R
£480 $749 €720 Fisherfolk on a beach by their boats (43x33cm-17x13in) s. 11-Apr-3 Keys, Aylsham #628/R
£620 $980 €930 Dusk, fishing boats at low tide. Coastal scene with boats (30x51cm-12x20in) pair. 29-Nov-2 Dee Atkinson & Harrison, Driffield #819
£700 $1106 €1050 Autumn in the highlands. Vessels off a rocky coastline (30x51cm-12x20in) s. i.verso pair. 14-Nov-2 Christie's, Kensington #193/R
£1800 $2916 €2700 Highland views (29x50cm-11x20in) s. board pair. 20-May-3 Sotheby's, Olympia #180/R est:500-700

HIDER, M C (19/20th C) ?
£420 $651 €630 Sunrise and sunset (28x48cm-11x19in) s. pair. 25-Sep-2 Wintertons, Lichfield #583/R

HIEBLOT, Eugene (1886-1953) French?
£390 $601 €620 Le paquebot Colombie (33x40cm-13x16in) s. panel. 27-Oct-2 Lesieur & Le Bars, Le Havre #200/R

HIENONEN, Erkki (1933-) Finnish
£317 $510 €450 Composition (62x50cm-24x20in) s.d.87. 10-May-3 Bukowskis, Helsinki #230/R
£759 $1200 €1200 Winter (116x81cm-46x32in) s.d.68-86. 1-Dec-2 Bukowskis, Helsinki #319/R
£823 $1300 €1300 Flight (116x89cm-46x35in) s.d.69. 1-Dec-2 Bukowskis, Helsinki #318/R

HIER, Auguste van (19/20th C) Dutch?
£400 $620 €600 Fishing smacks in harbour (61x91cm-24x36in) s. 6-Oct-2 Lots Road, London #356

HIERSCH-MINERBI, Joachim (1834-?) Austrian
£769 $1192 €1200 Harbour by moonlight with buildings, figures and sailing ships (23x53cm-9x21in) s. panel. 4-Dec-2 Neumeister, Munich #769/R est:1000

HIETANEN, Reino (1932-) Finnish
Works on paper
£296 $458 €470 Coastal rocks (34x34cm-13x13in) s.d.79 mixed media. 6-Oct-2 Bukowskis, Helsinki #189/R
£324 $518 €450 Composition (34x38cm-13x15in) s.d.1939 mixed media. 17-May-3 Hagelstam, Helsinki #176/R
£340 $541 €500 Composition (62x48cm-24x19in) s.d.1961 collage. 24-Mar-3 Bukowskis, Helsinki #97/R
£359 $590 €550 Tree (34x38cm-13x15in) s.d.1985 mixed media. 9-Feb-3 Bukowskis, Helsinki #257/R
£380 $600 €600 Composition (25x30cm-10x12in) s.d.1976 mixed media. 30-Nov-2 Hagelstam, Helsinki #178/R

HIFLER, A (?) ?
£1346 $2087 €2100 Fishermen coming back (68x105cm-27x41in) s. 5-Dec-2 Stadion, Trieste #699/R

HIGGINS, Charles (1897-?) British
£320 $499 €480 Abstract figure (75x30cm-30x12in) panel. 17-Sep-2 Bonhams, Knightsbridge #68
£1300 $2055 €1950 Le Saint des fauves (107x77cm-42x30in) s. board. 27-Nov-2 Sotheby's, Olympia #306/R est:600-800

HIGGINS, Eugene (1874-1958) American
Works on paper
£346 $550 €519 Fire (54x42cm-21x17in) s. i.verso W/C gouache. 7-Mar-3 Skinner, Boston #602/R

HIGGINS, George F (19th C) American
£736 $1200 €1104 Boaters beneath bridge (56x41cm-22x16in) s. 2-Feb-3 Grogan, Boston #57
£2516 $4000 €3774 Valley farm (86x66cm-34x26in) s.d.1874. 7-Mar-3 Skinner, Boston #276/R est:2000-2500

HIGGINS, Robert B (1943-) Irish?
£500 $775 €750 Pheasants, Greyabbey Estate, Co. Down (58x80cm-23x31in) s. 4-Dec-2 John Ross, Belfast #193

£700 $1085 €1050 In the Mournes (76x122cm-30x48in) s. 2-Oct-2 John Ross, Belfast #105

Works on paper

£320 $496 €480 Cottage near the Mournes (25x56cm-10x22in) s. W/C. 2-Oct-2 John Ross, Belfast #32
£340 $496 €510 Ballyquinton Point from Strangford (25x53cm-10x21in) s. W/C. 12-Jun-2 John Ross, Belfast #43
£350 $543 €525 Over Donegal (56x76cm-22x30in) s. W/C. 2-Oct-2 John Ross, Belfast #110
£380 $589 €570 Mallards over the River Quoile, Downpatrick (56x71cm-22x28in) s. W/C. 4-Dec-2 John Ross, Belfast #252
£450 $716 €675 Near the Mournes (50x76cm-20x30in) s. W/C. 5-Mar-3 John Ross, Belfast #88

HIGGINS, Violet Moore (?) American

Works on paper

£683 $1100 €1025 Young girl riding swing (30x30cm-12x12in) s. pen ink gouache chl. 10-May-3 Illustration House, New York #37/R
£705 $1100 €1058 Young girl holding Christmas wreath (43x30cm-17x12in) s. W/C. 9-Nov-2 Illustration House, New York #2/R
£994 $1600 €1491 Woman and child undersea (48x33cm-19x13in) s. ink. 20-Feb-3 Illustration House, New York #79/R est:1000-1500

HIGGINS, Wilfred (1893-1978) British

£2100 $3276 €3150 Portrait of swinging light (38x48cm-15x19in) s. 10-Sep-2 Louis Taylor, Stoke on Trent #1146/R

HIGGS, Avis (?) New Zealander?

Works on paper

£242 $373 €363 Grant road, Thorndon (34x49cm-13x19in) s. W/C. 4-Sep-2 Dunbar Sloane, Wellington #153 (NZ.D 800)

HIGGS, Cecil (1906-1986) South African

£197 $307 €296 Still life (24x34cm-9x13in) s.d.57. 15-Oct-2 Stephan Welz, Johannesburg #442 est:3000-5000 (SA.R 3200)
£723 $1143 €1085 Rock pool composition (34x44cm-13x17in) s. board. 1-Apr-3 Stephan Welz, Johannesburg #454/R est:7000-10000 (SA.R 9000)

HIGHAM, Thomas B (20th C) American

£1474 $2300 €2211 Quaker meeting house, Sandwich, Mass (46x51cm-18x20in) s. i.verso board. 1-Aug-2 Eldred, East Dennis #1092/R est:1500-2500

HIGHMORE, Anthony (1719-1799) British

Works on paper

£250 $395 €375 Lady at needlework (11x7cm-4x3in) pencil. 26-Nov-2 Bonhams, Knightsbridge #147

HIGUERO, Enrique Marin (1876-?) Spanish

Works on paper

£621 $987 €900 Granada (17x10cm-7x4in) s. W/C. 4-Mar-3 Ansorena, Madrid #696/R
£1195 $1864 €1900 Alhambra patio (51x35cm-20x14in) s. W/C. 8-Oct-2 Ansorena, Madrid #535/R
£1282 $2026 €2000 Alhambra (16x10cm-6x4in) s. W/C 4 in one frame. 19-Nov-2 Durán, Madrid #147/R
£1452 $2294 €2250 View of Toledo (35x53cm-14x21in) s. W/C. 17-Dec-2 Durán, Madrid #152/R
£1474 $2329 €2300 Madrid seen from Toledo bridge (47x32cm-19x13in) s. W/C. 13-Nov-2 Ansorena, Madrid #190/R
£1923 $3038 €3000 View of Toledo (52x38cm-20x15in) s.i. W/C. 19-Nov-2 Durán, Madrid #194/R

HILAIRE, Camille (1916-1988) French

£1852 $2630 €3000 Piano et violoncelle (33x46cm-13x18in) s. 16-Mar-3 Eric Pillon, Calais #242/R
£3546 $5745 €5000 Le quatuor (73x92cm-29x36in) s. s.i.d.verso. 23-May-3 Binoche, Paris #83 est:5000-6000
£3597 $5755 €5000 Femme assise a sa coiffeuse (60x60cm-24x24in) s.d.verso. 18-May-3 Eric Pillon, Calais #150/R
£3949 $6161 €6200 Bord de riviere au printemps (46x55cm-18x22in) s. 10-Nov-2 Eric Pillon, Calais #217/R
£4177 $6516 €6600 Maree haute (81x65cm-32x26in) s. s.i.verso prov. 20-Oct-2 Anaf, Lyon #162/R
£6369 $9936 €10000 Concours hippique (81x130cm-32x51in) s. painted 1957. 10-Nov-2 Eric Pillon, Calais #215/R
£6815 $10632 €10700 Canal a Venise (73x92cm-29x36in) s. 10-Nov-2 Eric Pillon, Calais #218/R

Works on paper

£314 $487 €500 Nu a la fenetre (38x28cm-15x11in) s. W/C pencil. 30-Oct-2 Artcurial Briest, Paris #270
£397 $624 €620 Bord de mer (37x45cm-15x18in) s. pastel. 24-Nov-2 Lesieur & Le Bars, Le Havre #75
£544 $865 €800 Roseaux (30x23cm-12x9in) s. W/C gouache. 24-Mar-3 Coutau Begarie, Paris #297
£544 $865 €800 Barque (47x61cm-19x24in) s. gouache. 24-Mar-3 Coutau Begarie, Paris #296
£563 $935 €800 L'etang (28x38cm-11x15in) s. W/C ink prov. 11-Jun-3 Beaussant & Lefèvre, Paris #69
£955 $1490 €1500 Nu feminin (29x39cm-11x15in) W/C. 6-Nov-2 Gioffredo, Nice #62/R
£1274 $1987 €2000 Nu allonge (48x35cm-19x14in) s. W/C. 10-Nov-2 Eric Pillon, Calais #233/R
£1293 $2055 €1900 Orchestre (39x54cm-15x21in) s. gouache. 24-Mar-3 Coutau Begarie, Paris #295/R
£1439 $2302 €2000 Bord de riviere (49x34cm-19x13in) s. W/C. 18-May-3 Eric Pillon, Calais #224/R

HILAIRE, Jean Baptiste (1753-1822) French

Works on paper

£1296 $2100 €1944 Fete champetre with girl on a swing (32x26cm-13x10in) gouache vellum. 21-Jan-3 Sotheby's, New York #191/R est:2000

HILBERT, Jaro (20th C) French?

£1613 $2548 €2420 Three Bedouins (131x155cm-52x61in) s.d.1939 prov. 18-Nov-2 Waddingtons, Toronto #237/R est:3000-5000 (C.D 4000)

HILDEBRAND, Ferdinand Theodor (1804-1874) German

Works on paper

£705 $1114 €1100 Self portrait (22x17cm-9x7in) d.May 1829 i. verso pencil. 16-Nov-2 Lempertz, Koln #1333
£10494 $17000 €15741 Artist's studio in Rome (19x11cm-7x4in) i. pencil W/C prov. 22-Jan-3 Christie's, Rockefeller NY #125/R est:6000

HILDEBRANDT, Eduard (1818-1869) German

Works on paper

£316 $500 €500 Junks off Shanghai (15x22cm-6x9in) mono W/C on pencil board. 29-Nov-2 Bassenge, Berlin #5926
£651 $1015 €950 Busy street in Cairo (36x27cm-14x11in) s. W/C lit. 10-Apr-3 Allgauer, Kempten #2618/R
£949 $1500 €1500 Nagasaki harbour in Japan (26x37cm-10x15in) s.i. W/C. 29-Nov-2 Sigalas, Stuttgart #1091/R est:1500
£2800 $4536 €4200 Jerusalem from the mount of Olives (27x41cm-11x16in) s.i.d.1852 W/C. 20-May-3 Sotheby's, Olympia #361/R est:2000-3000

HILDEBRANDT, Eduard (attrib) (1818-1869) German

Works on paper

£350 $553 €525 Pagodas by a river at sunset (22x30cm-9x12in) W/C over pencil htd bodycol. 15-Nov-2 Sotheby's, London #20a/R

HILDEBRANDT, Howard Logan (1872-1958) American

£409 $650 €614 Portrait of a little girl (77x64cm-30x25in) s. 7-Mar-3 Skinner, Boston #564/R
£479 $800 €695 Portrait of a seated lady (91x96cm-36x38in) s. 22-Jun-3 Freeman, Philadelphia #139/R

HILDEBRANDT, Howard Logan (attrib) (1872-1958) American

£5833 $9100 €8750 Picnic (61x48cm-24x19in) s. artist board exhib. 8-Nov-2 York Town, York #687a

HILDER, J J (1881-1916) Australian

Works on paper

£3077 $4892 €4616 Boat house (14x22cm-6x9in) s.d.1912 W/C. 4-Mar-3 Deutscher-Menzies, Melbourne #138/R est:9000-12000 (A.D 8000)

HILDER, Jesse Jewhurst (1881-1916) Australian

Works on paper

£382 $603 €662 Bondi (10x19cm-4x7in) s.d.1904 W/C. 1-Apr-3 Goodman, Sydney #14 (A.D 1000)
£679 $1072 €1019 Lennox Bridge (26x36cm-10x14in) s. W/C prov. 17-Nov-2 Sotheby's, Paddington #16/R est:3000-5000 (A.D 1900)
£763 $1206 €1145 Gathering clouds, Dora Creek (26x26cm-10x10in) s. W/C. 7-Apr-3 Shapiro, Sydney #424/R (A.D 2000)
£843 $1256 €1265 Ti trees (20x27cm-8x11in) s. W/C. 27-Aug-2 Christie's, Melbourne #250 est:2000-4000 (A.D 2200)
£920 $1370 €1380 White bridge (20x24cm-8x9in) s. W/C. 27-Aug-2 Christie's, Melbourne #289 est:2000-4000 (A.D 2400)
£1139 $1742 €1709 Interior of Albers home at Gordon (27x19cm-11x7in) s. W/C prov. 25-Aug-2 Sotheby's, Paddington #169/R est:3000-5000 (A.D 3200)
£4198 $6634 €6297 Boy with calf in meadow (13x29cm-5x11in) s. i.verso W/C prov.exhib.lit. 2-Apr-3 Christie's, Melbourne #53/R est:5000-8000 (A.D 11000)

HILDER, Richard (1813-1852) British

£477 $753 €716 Landscape with figures (36x46cm-14x18in) s.d.1844. 30-Nov-2 Goteborg Auktionsverk, Sweden #183/R (S.KR 6800)
£620 $967 €930 Woodland landscape with pond and figures (31x33cm-12x13in) panel prov. 26-Mar-3 Sotheby's, Olympia #6/R
£1000 $1650 €1450 Droving cattle and sheep (29x40cm-11x16in) panel. 2-Jul-3 Sotheby's, Olympia #92/R est:1000-1500
£1200 $1896 €1800 Winter landscape with a figure on a path before a cottage (25x34cm-10x13in) s. panel. 2-Dec-2 Bonhams, Bath #125/R est:800-1200
£1500 $2430 €2250 Woded river landscape with figures on a country path (30x40cm-12x16in) s. panel prov. 23-May-3 Lyon & Turnbull, Edinburgh #7/R est:1000-1500
£3000 $4800 €4500 Figure on horseback on a country track. Gathering brushwood (24x19cm-9x7in) panel pair. 15-May-3 Lawrence, Crewkerne #919/R est:2000-3000

HILDER, Rowland (1905-1993) British

£3080 $4805 €4620 Suffolk farm (51x61cm-20x24in) s. board. 15-Oct-2 Bonhams, Knightsbridge #6/R est:3000-5000

Works on paper

£360 $562 €540 Greenwich reach (12x21cm-5x8in) s. W/C htd white. 15-Oct-2 Bonhams, Knightsbridge #203/R
£420 $655 €630 Barns on the Isle of Grain (8x25cm-3x10in) s.d.1987 pen W/C. 15-Oct-2 Bonhams, Knightsbridge #206/R
£450 $752 €653 Faversham Creek (17x25cm-7x10in) s. W/C. 18-Jun-3 Sotheby's, Olympia #127/R
£500 $770 €750 House at a harbour side (51x61cm-20x24in) s. pen ink wash gouache. 23-Oct-2 Hamptons Fine Art, Godalming #75
£720 $1130 €1080 Tug and liner (45x52cm-18x20in) s. W/C. 16-Dec-2 Bonhams, Bury St Edmunds #419/R
£750 $1178 €1125 Scottish fishing village (25x36cm-10x14in) s. W/C. 15-Apr-3 Bonhams, Knightsbridge #205/R
£1300 $2132 €1950 Ploughing the fields (17x23cm-7x9in) s. ink W/C gouache. 3-Jun-3 Sotheby's, Olympia #107/R est:1000-1500
£1400 $2198 €2100 Farm in Yorkshire (34x50cm-13x20in) s. W/C. 15-Apr-3 Bonhams, Knightsbridge #15/R est:800-1200
£1400 $2296 €2100 Farm cart (23x33cm-9x13in) s. ink W/C gouache. 3-Jun-3 Sotheby's, Olympia #106/R est:1500-2000
£2400 $3912 €3600 Figures in an autumn landscape (48x48cm-19x19in) s. gouache. 28-Jan-3 Gorringes, Lewes #1666/R est:1200-1500
£2400 $3936 €3600 Oast houses (37x54cm-15x21in) s. ink W/C gouache. 3-Jun-3 Sotheby's, Olympia #108/R est:2500-3500

HILER, Hilaire (1898-1966) American/French

Works on paper

£305 $500 €442 Untitled abstraction (20x15cm-8x6in) s. gouache prov. 1-Jun-3 Wright, Chicago #158/R
£396 $650 €574 Untitled abstraction (13x10cm-5x4in) s. gouache prov. 1-Jun-3 Wright, Chicago #157/R

HILES, Bartram (1872-1927) British

£480 $782 €720 On a harbour quay (51x38cm-20x15in) 14-Feb-3 Lyon & Turnbull, Edinburgh #103

HILGERS, Carl (1818-1890) German

£1667 $2617 €2600 Shipwreck (39x52cm-15x20in) s.d.1849. 21-Nov-2 Van Ham, Cologne #1681/R est:2800
£1795 $2818 €2800 Soldiers by tent in winter landscape (19x23cm-7x9in) s. panel. 21-Nov-2 Van Ham, Cologne #1680/R est:1800
£8219 $12822 €12000 Dutch winter landscape (40x58cm-16x23in) s. panel. 10-Apr-3 Van Ham, Cologne #1488/R est:8000

Sculpture

£1111 $1789 €1700 Orpheus (53cm-21in) s. dark pat bronze. 20-Jan-3 Horta, Bruxelles #302 est:1200-1800

HILGERS, Georg (attrib) (1879-1944) German

£670 $1085 €972 Shepherd boy in the mountains (108x135cm-43x53in) s. 26-May-3 Rasmussen, Copenhagen #1267 (D.KR 7000)

HILL, Adrian (1897-1977) British

£340 $558 €510 West country boy (49x60cm-19x24in) s. board. 9-Feb-3 Lots Road, London #352
£450 $738 €675 Bourton on the Water (50x60cm-20x24in) s. canvasboard prov. 3-Jun-3 Sotheby's, Olympia #101/R
£550 $902 €825 Connemara (63x76cm-25x30in) s. board prov. 3-Jun-3 Sotheby's, Olympia #99/R

Works on paper

£850 $1309 €1275 Railway cutting on the Lens and Arras railway (20x28cm-8x11in) s.i. pen ink W/C sold with a dr by the same artist. 5-Sep-2 Christie's, Kensington #744

HILL, Andrew Putnam (1853-1922) American

£503 $800 €755 Canyon pass (91x66cm-36x26in) s. board painted c.1915. 2-Mar-3 Toomey, Oak Park #611/R

HILL, Carl Frederik (1849-1911) Swedish

£3142 $5153 €4556 Landscape from Skaane (24x33cm-9x13in) painted c.1870 prov. 4-Jun-3 AB Stockholms Auktionsverk #2281/R est:50000-60000 (S.KR 40000)
£62844 $103064 €91124 Evening idyll - landscape from Fontainebleau (42x63cm-17x25in) s.d.75 lit. 4-Jun-3 AB Stockholms Auktionsverk #2303/R est:800000-1000000 (S.KR 800000)

Works on paper

£621 $1005 €900 Centaur (17x21cm-7x8in) i.verso Indian ink lit. 26-May-3 Bukowskis, Stockholm #178/R (S.KR 8000)
£1474 $2388 €2137 Woman posing (22x14cm-9x6in) chk sketch prov. 26-May-3 Bukowskis, Stockholm #179/R est:4000-5000 (S.KR 19000)
£1552 $2514 €2250 Dancers (21x28cm-8x11in) Indian ink chk prov. 26-May-3 Bukowskis, Stockholm #180/R est:20000-25000 (S.KR 20000)
£1629 $2639 €2362 Three graces (21x24cm-8x9in) Indian ink chk prov. 26-May-3 Bukowskis, Stockholm #181/R est:20000-25000 (S.KR 21000)
£1631 $2528 €2447 Hissing cat (33x42cm-13x17in) s.d.1865 pencil htd white after M P Korner lit. 4-Dec-2 AB Stockholms Auktionsverk #1603/R est:10000-12000 (S.KR 23000)
£2514 $4123 €3645 Elephants (17x21cm-7x8in) crayon prov. 4-Jun-3 AB Stockholms Auktionsverk #2300/R est:30000-40000 (S.KR 32000)
£2979 $4617 €4469 Drawing from the time of sickness (51x66cm-20x26in) Indian ink. 3-Dec-2 Bukowskis, Stockholm #103/R est:25000-30000 (S.KR 42000)
£3103 $5027 €4499 The waterfall (17x20cm-7x8in) chk. 26-May-3 Bukowskis, Stockholm #177/R est:15000-20000 (S.KR 40000)
£3299 $5411 €4784 Fantasy animal near waterfall (17x21cm-7x8in) s. crayon exhib. 4-Jun-3 AB Stockholms Auktionsverk #2180/R est:60000-80000 (S.KR 42000)
£3511 $5441 €5267 Evening glow - landscape (17x21cm-7x8in) col crayon. 4-Dec-2 AB Stockholms Auktionsverk #1626/R est:40000-45000 (S.KR 49500)
£3569 $5781 €5175 Exotic landscape with elephants (16x21cm-6x8in) chk exhib. 26-May-3 Bukowskis, Stockholm #174/R est:20000-25000 (S.KR 46000)
£3972 $6156 €5958 Seascape (20x32cm-8x13in) s. W/C prov. 4-Dec-2 AB Stockholms Auktionsverk #1628/R est:60000-80000 (S.KR 56000)
£13964 $22622 €20248 Walking in the spring (69x53cm-27x21in) s.d.75 pencil. 26-May-3 Bukowskis, Stockholm #176/R est:80000-100000 (S.KR 180000)

HILL, David Octavius (attrib) (1802-1870) British

£600 $954 €900 Figure in a Scottish landscape with Comrie and Strathearn beyond (63x107cm-25x42in) prov. 6-Mar-3 Christie's, Kensington #47/R

HILL, David Octavius and ADAMSON, Robert (19th C) British

Photographs

£3145 $4874 €5000 Newhaven, Fisher Women (13x19cm-5x7in) i. verso calotype lit. 31-Oct-2 Van Ham, Cologne #12/R est:5500

HILL, Derek (1916-2000) British

£500 $800 €750 Portrait of a gentleman, a former ambassador to the United States (101x81cm-40x32in) two. 15-May-3 Lawrence, Crewkerne #1011
£700 $1120 €1050 Field near Buis les Baronnies (30x30cm-12x12in) prov. 15-May-3 Christie's, Kensington #173/R
£800 $1280 €1200 Young man seated (49x65cm-19x26in) s. prov. 15-May-3 Christie's, Kensington #174/R
£900 $1431 €1350 Head and shoulders portrait study of girl in white jumper (48x36cm-19x14in) mono. board. 7-Mar-3 Biddle & Webb, Birmingham #228
£900 $1440 €1350 Sermoneta from Ninfa. Torre d'alto, Sermoneta (14x20cm-6x8in) one oil board one tempera board by Lelia Caetani two. 15-May-3 Christie's, Kensington #175/R
£1013 $1570 €1600 Corfu sunset (16x24cm-6x9in) mono. 25-Sep-2 James Adam, Dublin #6/R est:1000-1500
£1050 $1680 €1575 Meenawn Cliffs, Achill; ode to Graham Sutherland (46x61cm-18x24in) 15-May-3 Christie's, Kensington #170/R est:500-1000
£1200 $1848 €1800 Valley at Dundonnell (41x55cm-16x22in) prov. 5-Sep-2 Christie's, Kensington #667/R est:2000-3000
£1300 $2028 €1950 Wicklow Hills (17x25cm-7x10in) board exhib. 18-Sep-2 Dreweatt Neate, Newbury #160/R est:600-800
£1500 $2369 €2250 Wicklow Hills (16x23cm-6x9in) board exhib. 27-Nov-2 Sotheby's, Olympia #51/R est:1200-1800

£2000 $3100 €3000 Tory 1995, from my hut (20x28cm-8x11in) mono.d.1995 verso board. 4-Dec-2 John Ross, Belfast #177 est:2000-2500
£2200 $3498 €3300 Chamber music (27x51cm-11x20in) mono. i.verso. 26-Feb-3 Sotheby's, Olympia #225/R est:2000-3000
£2500 $3875 €3750 Tor More, Tory Island (71x122cm-28x48in) exhib. 4-Dec-2 Christie's, Kensington #543/R est:3000-5000
£2500 $4000 €3750 View from Bagazzano, Tuscany. Lady in red hat (25x30cm-10x12in) board two. 15-May-3 Christie's, Kensington #176/R est:600-800
£3000 $4800 €4500 Venice from La Luna Hotel (70x49cm-28x19in) init. indis d. board prov.exhib. 16-May-3 Sotheby's, London #126/R est:3000-5000
£3200 $5120 €4800 Glendowan, Donegal (29x33cm-11x13in) init. board painted 1957 prov.exhib. 15-May-3 Christie's, London #36/R est:3500
£3500 $5600 €5250 Miss Pye's washing day (43x33cm-17x13in) prov. 15-May-3 Christie's, Kensington #172/R est:1500-2000

HILL, Edward Rufus (1852-c.1908) American
£982 $1600 €1473 View of the Yosemite valley with Half Dome in the distance (34x27cm-13x11in) s. canvas on board. 16-Feb-3 Butterfields, San Francisco #2084 est:600-800

HILL, Edward Rufus (attrib) (1852-c.1908) American
£1039 $1600 €1559 Wooded landscape (56x84cm-22x33in) 27-Oct-2 Grogan, Boston #72 est:800-1200

HILL, Ernest F (20th C) British
Works on paper
£400 $624 €600 Polperro (18x27cm-7x11in) s. W/C. 26-Mar-3 Hamptons Fine Art, Godalming #47

HILL, Howard (19th C) American
£323 $500 €485 Country landscape (20x30cm-8x12in) s. 3-Dec-2 Christie's, Rockefeller NY #584/R
£687 $1100 €1031 Standoff (36x55cm-14x22in) s. 16-Mar-3 Butterfields, San Francisco #1026 est:2000-3000
£719 $1200 €1043 Chickens and roosters in barnyard (23x18cm-9x7in) s. prov. 17-Jun-3 John Moran, Pasadena #13a est:1500-2000
£1406 $2250 €2039 Ducks, ducklings and barnyard fowl (25x36cm-10x14in) s. 17-May-3 CRN Auctions, Cambridge #6
£2229 $3500 €3344 Chickens in a river landscape (31x41cm-12x16in) s. prov. 19-Nov-2 Butterfields, San Francisco #8018/R est:3000-5000

HILL, J E (19/20th C) British?
£5975 $9201 €9500 Jeune fille au plateau de fleurs. Jeune musicienne a la jetee de roses (63x38cm-25x15in) s.d.1904 panel pair. 23-Oct-2 Rabourdin & Choppin de Janvry, Paris #123/R est:12000

HILL, James John (1811-1882) British
£1507 $2351 €2261 Mother with two children and small dog (36x30cm-14x12in) mono.d.75 panel. 28-Mar-3 Koller, Zurich #3107/R est:4000-7000 (S.FR 3300)
£1875 $3000 €2813 On the way to market (91x71cm-36x28in) s. 14-May-3 Butterfields, San Francisco #1140/R est:4000-6000
£3000 $4650 €4500 Portrait of a lady in the countryside (77x63cm-30x25in) s.d.1871. 3-Dec-2 Sotheby's, Olympia #57/R est:3000-5000
£3629 $5734 €5444 Harvest girl (91x71cm-36x28in) prov. 18-Nov-2 Waddingtons, Toronto #156/R est:10000-15000 (C.D 9000)

HILL, James Stevens (1854-1921) British
£260 $424 €390 Still life with flowers in a glass vase (35x30cm-14x12in) s. 13-Feb-3 Mellors & Kirk, Nottingham #802

HILL, Jean (19th C) British
£264 $409 €420 Paysage d'hiver au moulin (50x80cm-20x31in) s. 1-Oct-2 Palais de Beaux Arts, Brussels #486/R
£291 $454 €460 Retour du marche (52x80cm-20x31in) s. 16-Sep-2 Horta, Bruxelles #285

HILL, Joan (?) ?
£753 $1183 €1100 Chemin de campagne anime (27x40cm-11x16in) s. 15-Apr-3 Galerie Moderne, Brussels #405

HILL, John (19th C) British
Prints
£15000 $24150 €22500 Exotic botany (48x29cm-19x11in) hand col engravings 35 first edition folio lit. 7-May-3 Sotheby's, London #64/R est:12000-20000

HILL, John Henry (1839-1922) American/British
Works on paper
£312 $500 €452 Hepatica (21x30cm-8x12in) s.d.1905 W/C gouache. 16-May-3 Skinner, Boston #88/R
£1667 $2600 €2501 Forest scene with stone bridge and creek (29x24cm-11x9in) s. W/C gouache paper on board prov. 12-Apr-3 Weschler, Washington #555/R est:1000-1500

HILL, John William (1812-1879) American
Works on paper
£7407 $12000 €10740 Gone fishing (18x25cm-7x10in) s. W/C. 21-May-3 Doyle, New York #94/R est:12000-18000
£70968 $110000 €106452 Broadway looking South from Liberty Street (44x63cm-17x25in) s.d.1831 W/C prov. 4-Dec-2 Sotheby's, New York #110/R est:30000-50000

HILL, John William and John Henry (19th C) American
Works on paper
£12963 $21000 €18796 Untitled. W/C pen ink pencil thirty four. 21-May-3 Doyle, New York #60/R est:6000-8000
£12963 $21000 €18796 Untitled. W/C pen ink pencil thirty two. 21-May-3 Doyle, New York #65/R est:6000-8000
£13580 $22000 €19691 Untitled. W/C pen ink pencil thirty. 21-May-3 Doyle, New York #61/R est:6000-8000
£14013 $22000 €21020 Untitled. W/C dr. album. 10-Dec-2 Doyle, New York #2/R est:6000-8000
£14013 $22000 €21020 Untitled. W/C dr. album. 10-Dec-2 Doyle, New York #3/R est:6000-8000
£15287 $24000 €22931 Untitled. W/C dr. various subjects album. 10-Dec-2 Doyle, New York #13/R est:6000-8000
£16049 $26000 €23271 Untitled. W/C pen ink pencil thirty one. 21-May-3 Doyle, New York #62/R est:6000-8000
£16561 $26000 €24842 Untitled. W/C various subjects album. 10-Dec-2 Doyle, New York #1/R est:6000-8000

HILL, Justus (19th C) British
£700 $1092 €1050 Thames at Kew (46x61cm-18x24in) s. 7-Nov-2 Christie's, Kensington #136/R

HILL, Laura (19th C) American
£1180 $1900 €1770 Fruit still life (46x69cm-18x27in) s. 23-Feb-3 Skinner, Boston #53/R est:800-1200

HILL, Mabel M (1872-1956) New Zealander
£400 $624 €600 Still life of zinnias (25x36cm-10x14in) s. 15-Oct-2 Gorringes, Lewes #2206
Works on paper
£500 $795 €750 Still life of Iceland poppies (51x38cm-20x15in) s.d.1929 W/C. 29-Apr-3 Bonhams, New Bond Street #2

HILL, Margot (20th C) British
Works on paper
£260 $408 €390 Antique shop (43x62cm-17x24in) mixed media canvas on board. 15-Apr-3 Bonhams, Knightsbridge #55

HILL, Nina (1877-1970) British
£365 $562 €580 Sailing boats in harbour (38x28cm-15x11in) s. 27-Oct-2 Bukowskis, Helsinki #322/R

HILL, Robin (1932-) Australian
Works on paper
£456 $693 €684 Pink and white cockatoos (60x51cm-24x20in) s.i.d.68 W/C. 19-Aug-2 Joel, Victoria #204 est:1000-1200 (A.D 1300)
£800 $1304 €1160 Major Mitchell cockatoos (46x46cm-18x18in) s.d.95 W/C. 21-Jul-3 Sotheby's, London #766/R

HILL, Rowland (1919-) British
£350 $511 €525 Old Cavehill Road, Belfast (36x51cm-14x20in) s.d.1939 board. 12-Jun-2 John Ross, Belfast #157
£380 $555 €570 On the road home, Donegal (33x51cm-13x20in) s.d.1938 board. 12-Jun-2 John Ross, Belfast #246
£423 $668 €660 Glynn village (28x44cm-11x17in) s.i. board. 12-Nov-2 Mealy's, Castlecomer #1255
£500 $795 €750 Corner of Lough Neagh (35x50cm-14x20in) s. board. 5-Mar-3 John Ross, Belfast #231
£850 $1318 €1275 Cottages, Donegal (50x76cm-20x30in) s. 4-Dec-2 John Ross, Belfast #145
£850 $1386 €1233 Farmstead (36x45cm-14x18in) s. board. 15-Jul-3 Bonhams, Knightsbridge #109/R
£1000 $1590 €1500 Thatched cottages, Donegal (50x61cm-20x24in) s. 5-Mar-3 John Ross, Belfast #208 est:500-600
£1250 $1988 €1875 Corn field (45x61cm-18x24in) s. 5-Mar-3 John Ross, Belfast #119 est:600-700

£1449 $2377 €2000 Murlough Bay (46x61cm-18x24in) s. 28-May-3 Bonhams & James Adam, Dublin #57/R est:1500-2000
£1450 $2262 €2175 Coastal inlet with rowboats, cottages and mountains beyond (51x76cm-20x30in) s. 6-Nov-2 Bonhams, Chester #490 est:300-500
£1611 $2593 €2400 Cottages by the sea (51x76cm-20x30in) s. 18-Feb-3 Whyte's, Dublin #208/R est:2000-3000
£1900 $3040 €2850 Connemara (51x76cm-20x30in) s. 15-May-3 Christie's, Kensington #179/R est:1500-2000
£2821 $4428 €4400 Landscape with fishermen (61x91cm-24x36in) s. 19-Nov-2 Whyte's, Dublin #139/R est:4500-5500

Works on paper
£250 $398 €375 Sheephaven Bay, County Donegal (25x35cm-10x14in) s. W/C. 5-Mar-3 John Ross, Belfast #233
£280 $434 €420 Narrow - water castle, Co. Down (20x35cm-8x14in) s.d.1941 W/C. 4-Dec-2 John Ross, Belfast #74
£300 $477 €450 Connemara (23x33cm-9x13in) s. W/C. 5-Mar-3 John Ross, Belfast #104
£1042 $1656 €1500 Sheephaven Bay, County Donegal. Landscape with coastal inlet (25x37cm-10x15in) s. W/C htd white pair. 29-Apr-3 Whyte's, Dublin #191/R est:1500-2000
£1950 $3042 €2925 Horse guards (28x39cm-11x15in) s.d.1930 W/C. 26-Mar-3 Hamptons Fine Art, Godalming #93 est:800-1000
£2400 $3888 €3480 Grand Canal, Venice (30x46cm-12x18in) s.d.1912 W/C. 1-Aug-3 Dee Atkinson & Harrison, Driffield #652 est:300-400

HILL, Rowland Henry (1873-1952) British

Works on paper
£320 $502 €480 Sheep beside a moorland road, possibly a scene on the North Yorkshire Moors (19x26cm-7x10in) s.d.1934 pencil W/C. 19-Nov-2 Bonhams, Leeds #122
£400 $624 €600 Shambles, York (35x25cm-14x10in) s.d.1912 W/C. 10-Sep-2 David Duggleby, Scarborough #247
£500 $780 €750 Sheephaven Bay, Co Donegal (25x36cm-10x14in) s. W/C pencil. 17-Sep-2 Goldings, Lincolnshire #607
£600 $960 €900 Moorland track (20x27cm-8x11in) s.d.1934 W/C. 11-Mar-3 David Duggleby, Scarborough #46
£880 $1373 €1320 Valley village (24x34cm-9x13in) s. W/C. 10-Sep-2 David Duggleby, Scarborough #166
£900 $1422 €1350 Ellerby Hotel (18x25cm-7x10in) s.d.1929 W/C. 24-Apr-3 Richardson & Smith, Whitby #190/R
£1050 $1638 €1575 Moorland landscape with figures and horse and cart (27x39cm-11x15in) s.d.1930 W/C. 10-Sep-2 David Duggleby, Scarborough #205 est:1000-1200
£1100 $1716 €1650 Horse and cart in extensive moorland landscape (28x41cm-11x16in) s.d.1934 W/C htd white. 10-Sep-2 David Duggleby, Scarborough #181/R est:1000-1500
£1100 $1738 €1650 Imposing dwelling, possibly Ugthorpe (25x33cm-10x13in) s.d.1927 W/C. 24-Apr-3 Richardson & Smith, Whitby #75/R est:500-600
£1950 $3042 €2925 November evening, shepherd with dog and flock (30x23cm-12x9in) s.d.1918 i.verso W/C. 10-Sep-2 David Duggleby, Scarborough #278 est:1200-1500
£2200 $3586 €3300 Runswick Bay, Yorkshire; coastal scene with row of cottages and figures (37x25cm-15x10in) s.d.1931 i.verso W/C. 11-Feb-3 Fellows & Sons, Birmingham #128/R est:400-600
£2200 $3652 €3300 Quayside at Whitby with figures and a horse and cart (25x35cm-10x14in) indis sig. pencil W/C bodycol htd white. 10-Jun-3 Bonhams, Leeds #92 est:500-700
£2950 $4602 €4425 National Gallery and St Martin's in the Fields' (27x37cm-11x15in) s.d.1921 W/C. 10-Sep-2 David Duggleby, Scarborough #242/R est:1000-1500

HILL, Samuel (19th C) American?
£6918 $11000 €10377 Ohio of Salem (46x61cm-18x24in) i.d.August 1851 in the style of George Ropes. 1-Mar-3 North East Auctions, Portsmouth #485/R est:5000-8000

HILL, Sterling (20th C) American
£633 $1000 €950 Winner's circle (71x91cm-28x36in) s.d.1934. 17-Nov-2 CRN Auctions, Cambridge #5/R

HILL, Thomas (1829-1908) American
£850 $1385 €1275 Fireside prayers (26x35cm-10x14in) s.d.98 board. 29-Jan-3 Sotheby's, Olympia #208/R est:400-600
£3313 $5500 €4804 Forest path (53x36cm-21x14in) paperboard prov. 11-Jun-3 Butterfields, San Francisco #4177/R est:6000-8000
£4217 $7000 €6115 Little girl and a cow near a pasture (61x30cm-24x12in) s. prov. 11-Jun-3 Butterfields, San Francisco #4161/R est:6000-8000
£7453 $12000 €11180 Bright Angel Trail, Grand Canyon of the Colorado Thomas Hill (36x51cm-14x20in) s. panel on board. 18-Feb-3 John Moran, Pasadena #54 est:15000-20000
£9036 $15000 €13102 Fishing in a mountain stream (36x29cm-14x11in) s. board double-sided prov. 11-Jun-3 Butterfields, San Francisco #4176/R est:10000-15000
£10241 $17000 €14849 Boulder-strewn forest stream (55x37cm-22x15in) s. paper on canvas prov. 11-Jun-3 Butterfields, San Francisco #4173/R est:8000-12000
£13253 $22000 €19217 Waterfall in the Sierras (52x35cm-20x14in) s. paper on board prov. 11-Jun-3 Butterfields, San Francisco #4172/R est:10000-15000
£15924 $25000 €23886 Cows and two boys with a fishing pole on a path, marin (56x89cm-22x35in) s.d.1877 prov. 19-Nov-2 Butterfields, San Francisco #8152/R est:25000-35000
£20062 $32500 €30093 Yosemite valley (47x65cm-19x26in) s. 21-May-3 Sotheby's, New York #216/R est:20000-30000
£22293 $35000 €33440 Geysers, Sonoma, California (46x61cm-18x24in) s. prov. 19-Nov-2 Butterfields, San Francisco #8132/R est:30000-50000
£24691 $40000 €37037 Rocky mountains (46x86cm-18x34in) s.d.1869. 21-May-3 Sotheby's, New York #215/R est:25000-35000
£26899 $42500 €39004 Yosemite Valley (61x51cm-24x20in) s.d.1894 prov. 26-Jul-3 Coeur d'Alene, Hayden #196/R est:25000-40000
£108434 $180000 €157229 Fisherman and his dog on the bank of the Merced River, Yosemite (90x135cm-35x53in) s.d.1895 prov. 11-Jun-3 Butterfields, San Francisco #4165/R est:150000-200000
£123457 $200000 €185186 Emerald Bay, Lake Tahoe (69x115cm-27x45in) s.d.1883 prov.exhib. 22-May-3 Christie's, Rockefeller NY #30/R est:80000-120000

HILL, Thomas (attrib) (1829-1908) American
£2500 $4000 €3750 Liona Oaks, Alameda County, California (39x72cm-15x28in) bears sig.d.1871. 16-Mar-3 Butterfields, San Francisco #1025 est:2500-3500

HILL, Thomas (1852-1926) British
£800 $1248 €1200 Apple blossom (56x44cm-22x17in) s.d.1884. 26-Mar-3 Hamptons Fine Art, Godalming #156

HILL, William A (1886-1969) American
£263 $400 €395 High Street, Marblehead (46x61cm-18x24in) s. 17-Aug-2 North East Auctions, Portsmouth #146

HILLARD, William H (1888-1951) American
£6289 $10000 €9434 On Beaver Pond, Kinsman Notch (92x61cm-36x24in) s. 7-Mar-3 Skinner, Boston #297/R est:3000-5000

HILLENIUS, Jaap (1934-1999) Dutch
£674 $1091 €950 Water along stones (50x55cm-20x22in) i.verso. 26-May-3 Glerum, Amsterdam #159/R

HILLER, Heinrich (19th C) German
£302 $471 €480 Konigssee on warm summer day (83x133cm-33x52in) s. lit. 20-Sep-2 Schloss Ahlden, Ahlden #1154/R
£962 $1490 €1500 Harbour with steamer (56x90cm-22x35in) s. lit. 6-Dec-2 Karlheinz Kaupp, Staufen #2330/R est:800

HILLER-FOELL, Maria (1880-1943) German
£759 $1200 €1200 Reclining nude (65x101cm-26x40in) s.d.1916. 27-Nov-2 Dr Fritz Nagel, Stuttgart #3208/R

HILLERSBERG, Lars (1937-) Swedish

Works on paper
£266 $421 €399 Stalin and Jan Myrdal (31x24cm-12x9in) s.d.73 mixed media. 28-Apr-3 Bukowskis, Stockholm #919/R (S.KR 3500)
£353 $554 €530 Posthum Modernism (80x99cm-31x39in) s.d.88 mixed media. 16-Dec-2 Lilla Bukowskis, Stockholm #326 (S.KR 5000)
£395 $625 €593 The street (74x87cm-29x34in) s.d.60 Indian ink htd white panel. 28-Apr-3 Bukowskis, Stockholm #921/R (S.KR 5200)
£541 $870 €812 The town (40x58cm-16x23in) Indian ink panel. 7-May-3 AB Stockholms Auktionsverk #1033/R (S.KR 7000)
£541 $870 €812 The town (43x61cm-17x24in) s. Indian ink panel. 7-May-3 AB Stockholms Auktionsverk #1034/R (S.KR 7000)
£1158 $1865 €1737 Newspaper reader (45x40cm-18x16in) s.d.65 Indian ink. 7-May-3 AB Stockholms Auktionsverk #1032/R est:5000-6000 (S.KR 15000)
£1261 $1968 €1892 Interurbant (51x42cm-20x17in) s.d.69 mixed media collage lit. 5-Nov-2 Bukowskis, Stockholm #345/R est:7000-9000 (S.KR 18000)

£1331 $2077 €1997 The war between people and cars (49x73cm-19x29in) s.d.76 mixed media. 5-Nov-2 Bukowskis, Stockholm #347/R est:20000-25000 (S.KR 19000)
£1682 $2624 €2523 First, second, third (54x60cm-21x24in) s.d.76 mixed media collage. 5-Nov-2 Bukowskis, Stockholm #346/R est:25000-30000 (S.KR 24000)
£2281 $3605 €3422 The bank robbery (66x93cm-26x37in) s.d.76 collage assemblage. 28-Apr-3 Bukowskis, Stockholm #918/R est:10000-12000 (S.KR 30000)

HILLESTROM, Per (1733-1816) Swedish
£3404 $5277 €5106 Christina Gyllenstierna giving her letter to Christian II (43x51cm-17x20in) s. prov. 3-Dec-2 Bukowskis, Stockholm #412/R est:60000-80000 (S.KR 48000)
£6950 $10773 €10425 Interior from Falu Mine (51x67cm-20x26in) s.d.1798. 4-Dec-2 AB Stockholms Auktionsverk #1619/R est:50000-60000 (S.KR 98000)
£7092 $10993 €10638 Scene from Orlando Furioso (39x32cm-15x13in) panel prov. 3-Dec-2 Bukowskis, Stockholm #410a/R est:100000-125000 (S.KR 100000)
£7463 $12239 €10821 Wingaakers - Boer - cottage interior (33x40cm-13x16in) s. 4-Jun-3 AB Stockholms Auktionsverk #2137/R est:50000-60000 (S.KR 95000)
£8248 $13527 €11960 The smithy (36x43cm-14x17in) panel prov.lit. 4-Jun-3 AB Stockholms Auktionsverk #2138/R est:40000-50000 (S.KR 105000)
£9819 $16104 €14238 Still life of fish in pewter dish (46x53cm-18x21in) 4-Jun-3 AB Stockholms Auktionsverk #2141/R est:140000-160000 (S.KR 125000)
£22498 $36447 €32622 Young girl with candlelight in her pantry looking for something (40x32cm-16x13in) s. panel prov.exhib.lit. 26-May-3 Bukowskis, Stockholm #365/R est:200000-225000 (S.KR 290000)

HILLESTROM, Per (attrib) (1733-1816) Swedish
£900 $1403 €1350 Barn interior with peasants round a fire (36x48cm-14x19in) indis.sig. 19-Sep-2 Christie's, Kensington #141 est:1000-1500
£3688 $5716 €5532 Still life of bread, fish and oysters (62x79cm-24x31in) 3-Dec-2 Bukowskis, Stockholm #411/R est:50000-60000 (S.KR 52000)

HILLFON, Curt (1943-) Swedish
£266 $421 €399 Composition with two sticks (100x82cm-39x32in) s. acrylic. 30-Nov-2 Goteborg Auktionsverk, Sweden #541/R (S.KR 3800)
£303 $467 €455 Composition with half a frame floating (100x82cm-39x32in) s.d.1988. 27-Oct-2 Anders Antik, Landskrona #508/R (S.KR 4400)

HILLFON, Hertha (1921-) Swedish
Sculpture
£3924 $6122 €5886 Head (90x78x52cm-35x31x20in) terracotta. 6-Nov-2 AB Stockholms Auktionsverk #911/R est:40000-50000 (S.KR 56000)

HILLGRUND, Bengt (1935-) Swedish
£1332 $2105 €1998 Still life of bowl, bottles and eggs (92x83cm-36x33in) s.d.81. 27-Nov-2 Falkkloos, Malmo #77542/R est:15000 (S.KR 19000)

HILLHOUSE, May (1908-1989) South African
£2580 $4025 €3870 Tribe (82x101cm-32x40in) s.d.70 prov. 15-Oct-2 Stephan Welz, Johannesburg #458/R est:30000-40000 (SA.R 42000)

HILLIARD, Nicholas (1547-1619) British
Miniatures
£6000 $9420 €9000 Anne of Denmark (4cm-2xin) vellum on card prov. 10-Dec-2 Christie's, London #47/R est:3000-5000
£105000 $172200 €152250 Gentleman in a black doublet and cloak with high collar (5cm-2xin) i.d.1577 vellum tortoiseshell frame oval prov.exhib.lit. 3-Jun-3 Christie's, London #51/R est:15000-25000

HILLIARD, William Henry (1836-1905) American
£938 $1500 €1360 Landscape with figure on the road (25x41cm-10x16in) s. 17-May-3 CRN Auctions, Cambridge #18

HILLIARD, William Henry (attrib) (1836-1905) American
£259 $425 €389 Wandering brook (46x41cm-18x16in) 8-Feb-3 Neal Auction Company, New Orleans #928

HILLIER, H D (19th C) British
£1447 $2300 €2171 Loch Maree, Ross-shire. Beneath the crags of Ben Venue, Perthshire (43x33cm-17x13in) s. s.i.verso pair. 18-Mar-3 Doyle, New York #30/R est:2500-3500
£3300 $5049 €4950 Ben Cruachan from Inverlocky (51x76cm-20x30in) s. s.i.verso. 22-Aug-2 Bonhams, Edinburgh #1060/R est:2500-3500

HILLIER, Tristram (1905-1983) British
£10000 $15700 €15000 Monastery and fountain at El Toboso (51x76cm-20x30in) s. i.d.1958 0n stretcher prov. 22-Nov-2 Christie's, London #87/R est:7000-10000

HILLIKER, H (19th C) American
£1647 $2700 €2388 Portrait of a lady wearing a lace bonnet (79x61cm-31x24in) 8-Jun-3 Skinner, Boston #357/R est:1500-2000

HILLINGFORD, Robert Alexander (1825-1904) British
£1887 $3000 €2831 Secret rendezvous (76x50cm-30x20in) s. 5-Mar-3 Christie's, Rockefeller NY #60/R est:3000-5000
£4610 $7145 €6915 Scene from 17th Century English History (61x91cm-24x36in) s. prov. 3-Dec-2 Bukowskis, Stockholm #325/R est:70000-80000 (S.KR 65000)
£4800 $7584 €7200 Captain Ramsay saving the guns, Fuentes, D'onoro, 1811 (47x61cm-19x24in) s. exhib. 2-Dec-2 Sotheby's, London #69/R est:3500-5000
£6200 $9858 €9300 Battle of Waterloo (48x74cm-19x29in) s. i.verso. 29-Apr-3 Gorringes, Lewes #2307

HILLS, Anna A (1882-1930) American
£1056 $1700 €1584 Crashing waves on rocks (30x41cm-12x16in) i.verso board prov. 18-Feb-3 John Moran, Pasadena #134 est:1000-2000
£2246 $3750 €3257 Landscape (28x36cm-11x14in) s.d. board. 17-Jun-3 John Moran, Pasadena #49 est:3000-4000
£2994 $5000 €4341 Sparkling waves breaking on rocks (25x48cm-10x19in) s. canvasboard prov. 17-Jun-3 John Moran, Pasadena #19 est:6000-8000
£10828 $17000 €16242 Springtime, Banning, California (25x36cm-10x14in) s.d.1916 indis.i.verso paperboard prov. 19-Nov-2 Butterfields, San Francisco #8195/R est:6000-8000
£14331 $22500 €21497 Winding river, near San Bernardino (51x77cm-20x30in) s.d.1924 i.stretcher prov. 19-Nov-2 Butterfields, San Francisco #8194/R est:12000-15000

HILLS, Laura Coombs (1859-1952) American
£4167 $6500 €6251 Sweet peas and roses (41x36cm-16x14in) s. i.verso. 1-Aug-2 Eldred, East Dennis #824/R est:9000-12000
Works on paper
£4375 $7000 €6344 Little boy in a sailor suit (59x50cm-23x20in) s. pastel. 16-May-3 Skinner, Boston #140/R est:3000-5000
£5000 $8000 €7250 Three roses (23x20cm-9x8in) s. pastel prov. 16-May-3 Skinner, Boston #172/R est:6000-8000
£6289 $10000 €9434 Tulips (31x27cm-12x11in) s. pastel board prov. 5-Mar-3 Sotheby's, New York #3/R est:10000-15000
£8437 $13500 €12234 Poppies (53x45cm-21x18in) s. pastel prov. 16-May-3 Skinner, Boston #173/R est:10000-15000
£15000 $24000 €21750 Daffodils (45x38cm-18x15in) s. pastel prov. 16-May-3 Skinner, Boston #171/R est:10000-15000

HILLS, Robert (1769-1844) British
Works on paper
£260 $411 €377 Sheep resting on a grassy bank overlooking a lake (23x33cm-9x13in) s. pencil W/C. 23-Jul-3 Mallams, Oxford #163/R
£276 $450 €414 Fallow deer (30x42cm-12x17in) s.d.1809 pencil W/C. 16-Feb-3 Butterfields, San Francisco #2027
£550 $847 €825 In the fields (15x20cm-6x8in) W/C. 23-Oct-2 Hamptons Fine Art, Godalming #60/R
£1200 $1896 €1800 Pigs in a farmyard (18x25cm-7x10in) indis sig. W/C. 2-Dec-2 Bonhams, Bath #11/R est:800-1200
£1850 $2868 €2775 Deer by a woodland stream (39x49cm-15x19in) W/C. 30-Sep-2 Bonhams, Ipswich #349/R est:2000-2500
£2900 $4611 €4350 Peaceful farmyard (48x73cm-19x29in) s.d.1806 W/C. 4-Mar-3 Bearnes, Exeter #396/R est:1000-1500
£8000 $12480 €12000 Village in snow (51x71cm-20x28in) s.d.1817 W/C scratching. 5-Nov-2 Bonhams, New Bond Street #66/R est:5000-8000

HILMAR, Jiri (1937-) Czechoslovakian
Sculpture
£1087 $1783 €1500 Untitled (171x44x7cm-67x17x3in) s.d.87 verso wood prov.lit. 28-May-3 Lempertz, Koln #179/R est:2500

HILSOE, Hans (20th C) Danish
£254 $391 €381 Coastal landscape, Hornbaek (61x87cm-24x34in) s. 26-Oct-2 Rasmussen, Havnen #2168 (D.KR 3000)
£550 $864 €825 Interior scene (57x44cm-22x17in) s. prov. 10-Dec-2 Rosebery Fine Art, London #527/R

£640 $1017 €960 Interior scene with woman at window (68x53cm-27x21in) s. prov. 26-Feb-3 Kunsthallen, Copenhagen #533/R (D.KR 7000)
£1397 $2221 €2096 Interior scene with peep into dining room (50x60cm-20x24in) s. 5-Mar-3 Rasmussen, Copenhagen #2046/R est:12000 (D.KR 15000)

HILSON, Jessie M (fl.1890-1900) British
Works on paper
£260 $406 €390 Elizabeth Castle (20x37cm-8x15in) s. W/C. 26-Mar-3 Bonhams & Langlois, Jersey #146

HILTON, Bo (1961-) British
£290 $450 €435 Marianne - St. Clements Hall (30x25cm-12x10in) s.i.d.19.8.00 verso. 1-Oct-2 Bonhams, Leeds #332
£360 $572 €540 Brighton (25x30cm-10x12in) 26-Feb-3 Sotheby's, Olympia #331/R
£410 $636 €615 Brighton Pier, late afternoon (25x30cm-10x12in) s. i.d.20.2.2000 verso board. 1-Oct-2 Bonhams, Leeds #330
£500 $770 €750 Brighton beach, late afternoon (32x42cm-13x17in) s. s.i.d.22.9.00 verso board. 5-Sep-2 Christie's, Kensington #677/R
£800 $1232 €1200 Maritime festival, Penzance (31x46cm-12x18in) s. board. 5-Sep-2 Christie's, Kensington #680/R

HILTON, Henry (fl.1880-1888) British
£1250 $1938 €1875 Feeding chickens (44x37cm-17x15in) s.d.78. 2-Oct-2 Bonhams, Knowle #84 est:500-800

HILTON, John William (1904-1983) American
£613 $950 €920 Passing storm (30x41cm-12x16in) s. i.verso board prov. 29-Oct-2 John Moran, Pasadena #729
£839 $1300 €1259 Spirit of spring (30x41cm-12x16in) s. i.verso board prov. 29-Oct-2 John Moran, Pasadena #730
£875 $1400 €1313 Palm Springs landscape. s. masonite. 12-Jan-3 William Jenack, New York #429
£1069 $1700 €1604 City of refuge, Hawaii (51x76cm-20x30in) s. i.d.verso board. 2-Mar-3 Toomey, Oak Park #684/R est:1000-2000
£1452 $2250 €2178 Joy in the dunes (46x61cm-18x24in) s. i.verso masonite. 29-Oct-2 John Moran, Pasadena #774 est:2000-3000
£2329 $3750 €3494 San Jacinto, Snow Creek (76x61cm-30x24in) s.d.1938 board prov. 18-Feb-3 John Moran, Pasadena #132 est:3000-4000

HILTON, Ned (20th C) American
£1497 $2500 €2171 Landscape, la madrugada (61x76cm-24x30in) s. i.verso prov. 17-Jun-3 John Moran, Pasadena #121 est:3000-4000

HILTON, Roger (1911-1975) British
£9000 $13950 €13500 Figure 1972 (91x76cm-36x30in) s.verso prov.exhib. 4-Dec-2 Sotheby's, London #84/R est:10000-15000
Works on paper
£580 $969 €841 Standing nude (28x21cm-11x8in) ink dr. prov. 19-Jun-3 Lane, Penzance #149
£2000 $3120 €3000 Cat (38x53cm-15x21in) init.d.73 gouache. 16-Oct-2 David Lay, Penzance #221/R est:2000-2500
£4000 $6240 €6000 Nude with red (36x53cm-14x21in) s.d.73 gouache pencil. 16-Oct-2 David Lay, Penzance #276/R est:2500-3500
£4200 $6888 €6300 Untitled (45x38cm-18x15in) init.d.X/74 gouache col chk prov. 6-Jun-3 Christie's, London #194/R est:2500-3500
£5500 $8525 €8250 Reclining figure (27x37cm-11x15in) init.i.d.74 gouache chl. 3-Dec-2 Bonhams, New Bond Street #114/R est:4000-6000
£6000 $9300 €9000 Seated figure (47x37cm-19x15in) init.d.2. 75 gouache chl. 3-Dec-2 Bonhams, New Bond Street #115/R est:4000-6000
£6000 $9840 €9000 Reclining female figure (38x54cm-15x21in) init.d.73 crayon gouache prov. 6-Jun-3 Christie's, London #196/R est:3000-5000

HILTON, Rose (1931-) British
£300 $468 €450 Figures at a table (23x25cm-9x10in) s. board. 16-Oct-2 David Lay, Penzance #277/R
£380 $593 €570 Chess players (41x41cm-16x16in) s. s.i.verso. 16-Oct-2 David Lay, Penzance #225/R
£400 $624 €580 Welsh landscape (25x30cm-10x12in) s.i.verso. 27-Mar-3 Lane, Penzance #175/R
£650 $1086 €943 Godrevy winter (24x32cm-9x13in) s.i. panel. 19-Jun-3 Lane, Penzance #35/R
£950 $1549 €1425 Dinner party (51x56cm-20x22in) s.i.d.1983 verso. 13-Feb-3 David Lay, Penzance #142/R
£1600 $2496 €2400 Yellow pot. s.d.1983 board. 16-Oct-2 David Lay, Penzance #238/R est:800-1200
£2500 $3900 €3625 Vase of anemones (51x51cm-20x20in) s.i.verso prov. 27-Mar-3 Lane, Penzance #25/R est:2000-2500
Works on paper
£290 $484 €421 Woman reading in an interior (19x25cm-7x10in) s. pastel. 19-Jun-3 Lane, Penzance #94
£1200 $1872 €1800 Cat (13x18cm-5x7in) init. W/C exhib. 16-Oct-2 David Lay, Penzance #240/R est:300-500

HILTON, William (jnr-attrib) (1786-1839) British
£2308 $3646 €3600 Portrait of gentleman (125x102cm-49x40in) prov. 12-Nov-2 Mealy's, Castlecomer #1040/R

HILTUNEN, Eila (1922-) Finnish
Sculpture
£1329 $2100 €2100 The money tree (21cm-8in) bronze. 1-Dec-2 Bukowskis, Helsinki #291/R est:1800-2000
£36076 $57000 €57000 The dancer (182cm-72in) painted wood. 1-Dec-2 Bukowskis, Helsinki #290/R est:20000-25000

HILVERDINK, Eduard Alexander (1846-1891) Dutch
£1282 $1949 €2000 Winter scene with city gate and figures (25x21cm-10x8in) s. panel. 17-Aug-2 Hans Stahl, Toestorf #40/R est:3500
£1831 $2948 €2600 Figures by the gate of an old guesthouse in Achterburgwal in Amsterdam (34x25cm-13x10in) s. panel. 7-May-3 Vendue Huis, Gravenhage #385/R est:2500-3000
£9589 $15055 €14000 Snowy view of the Smedestraat (67x56cm-26x22in) s.d.89 prov. 15-Apr-3 Sotheby's, Amsterdam #60/R est:8000-12000

HILVERDINK, Johannes (1813-1902) Dutch
£655 $1042 €950 Fishermen near the seaside in an evening landscape (19x15cm-7x6in) s. panel. 10-Mar-3 Sotheby's, Amsterdam #100/R est:300-500
£5189 $8406 €7524 Dutch winter landscape (60x86cm-24x34in) s. prov. 24-May-3 Galerie Gloggner, Luzern #62/R est:5800-6500 (S.FR 11000)
Works on paper
£395 $639 €600 Coastal scene (30x47cm-12x19in) s.d.1894 pencil W/C. 21-Jan-3 Christie's, Amsterdam #100
£764 $1260 €1100 Fishermen tending to their nets at sunset (44x63cm-17x25in) s.d.1853 pencil pen ink W/C. 1-Jul-3 Christie's, Amsterdam #23/R

HINCKLEY, Thomas H (1813-1896) American
£5479 $8000 €8219 Cows in landscape with farmhouse in distance (66x91cm-26x36in) s.indis.d.1855. 3-Nov-1 North East Auctions, Portsmouth #814/R est:3500-4500
£5732 $9000 €8598 In the pasture (102x137cm-40x54in) s.d.1837. 22-Nov-2 Skinner, Boston #82/R est:10000-15000

HINCZ, Gyula (1904-) Hungarian
£2064 $3220 €2993 Still life (90x100cm-35x39in) s.d.966 verso. 13-Sep-2 Mu Terem Galeria, Budapest #107/R est:750000 (H.F 800000)

HIND, William George Richardson (1833-1888) Canadian
Works on paper
£1070 $1658 €1605 Evening return, Mingan (17x26cm-7x10in) W/C prov. 3-Dec-2 Joyner, Toronto #209/R est:3000-4000 (C.D 2600)

HINDENLANG, Charles (1894-1960) Swiss
£773 $1221 €1160 Sculpture in the park (28x21cm-11x8in) s.verso board. 29-Nov-2 Zofingen, Switzerland #2901/R est:2200 (S.FR 1800)
Works on paper
£278 $447 €403 View from window (30x22cm-12x9in) mono.d.14 W/C over pencil. 7-May-3 Dobiaschofsky, Bern #641/R (S.FR 600)

HINDER, Francis Henry Critchley (1906-1992) Australian
£317 $494 €476 To the right (24x28cm-9x11in) s. oil pencil. 21-Oct-2 Australian Art Auctions, Sydney #146 (A.D 900)
£17082 $26135 €25623 Over the bridge (95x74cm-37x29in) s.d.1957 board exhib. 25-Aug-2 Sotheby's, Paddington #40/R est:20000-30000 (A.D 48000)
Sculpture
£3032 $4700 €4548 Dark image (46x37x18cm-18x15x7in) i.verso luminal kinetic electric motors col lights perspex prov. 3-Dec-2 Shapiro, Sydney #40/R est:8000-12000 (A.D 8400)
Works on paper
£438 $718 €657 Man at work (22x22cm-9x9in) s.d.38 i.verso pencil gouache. 4-Jun-3 Deutscher-Menzies, Melbourne #365/R (A.D 1100)
£690 $1083 €1035 Marconi-trans-Atlantic (21x30cm-8x12in) s.d.57 felt pen exhib. 15-Apr-3 Lawson Menzies, Sydney #117/R est:2000-3000 (A.D 1800)
£786 $1234 €1179 Study for Art Critics (38x51cm-15x20in) s.d.40 pencil prov.exhib. 25-Nov-2 Christie's, Melbourne #452/R est:2000-3000 (A.D 2200)

HINDLEY, Godfrey C (fl.1876-1914) British
£1100 $1826 €1595 Table to tell (35x50cm-14x20in) s.d.1883. 13-Jun-3 Lyon & Turnbull, Edinburgh #120 est:500-800
£1595 $2600 €2393 After the duel (46x64cm-18x25in) 14-Feb-3 Du Mouchelle, Detroit #2038/R est:2000-2500

HINDS, Will (20th C) American
£2258 $3500 €3387 Horse on farm (25x33cm-10x13in) s. 7-Dec-2 Neal Auction Company, New Orleans #514/R est:3500-4500
£2439 $4000 €3659 Forgotten lane (43x33cm-17x13in) s. artist board. 8-Feb-3 Neal Auction Company, New Orleans #396/R est:5000-6000
£2439 $4000 €3537 Melrose plantation (28x36cm-11x14in) s. 7-Jun-3 Neal Auction Company, New Orleans #425/R est:4500-5500
£3846 $6000 €5769 Country road (51x38cm-20x15in) s. masonite. 12-Oct-2 Neal Auction Company, New Orleans #684/R est:6000-8000
£4006 $6250 €6009 Mallards in Louisiana bayou (23x38cm-9x15in) s. masonite. 12-Oct-2 Neal Auction Company, New Orleans #685/R est:3500-4500

HINE, Harry T (1845-1941) British
Works on paper
£250 $390 €375 Coastal scene (19x43cm-7x17in) s. W/C. 26-Mar-3 Sotheby's, Olympia #85/R
£320 $496 €480 Shepherd and sheep on a road and mountainous valley (34x35cm-13x14in) s. W/C. 25-Sep-2 John Nicholson, Haslemere #879
£620 $967 €930 Coastal view with boats in harbour by a jetty (36x53cm-14x21in) s.d.1878 W/C. 11-Apr-3 Keys, Aylsham #461/R

HINE, Henry George (1811-1895) British
Works on paper
£400 $620 €600 Shepherd and sheep in an extensive landscape (20x33cm-8x13in) s.d.1872 W/C. 31-Oct-2 Duke & Son, Dorchester #136/R
£580 $905 €870 On the beach (15x24cm-6x9in) s.d.1865 W/C. 25-Mar-3 Bonhams, Knightsbridge #2/R
£600 $948 €870 Cuckmere Haven from the Downs (46x84cm-18x33in) s.d.1885 W/C. 22-Jul-3 Sworder & Son, Bishops Stortford #398/R
£660 $1030 €990 Brighton Beach with fishing boats and fishermen (13x24cm-5x9in) s.d.1865 W/C. 6-Nov-2 Bonhams, Chester #479

HINE, Lewis W (1879-1940) American
Photographs
£1899 $3000 €3000 Disillusioned - after a few years work in the textile mills (25x20cm-10x8in) i. verso silver gelatin lit.exhib. 28-Nov-2 Villa Grisebach, Berlin #1221/R est:4000-6000
£2025 $3200 €3038 Mechanic and turbine, General Electric Company (27x36cm-11x14in) s.verso gelatin silver print prov.exhib. 25-Apr-3 Phillips, New York #212/R est:3000-5000
£2532 $4000 €3798 Office boy, 11 years old, works in law office, Mobile Alabama (12x17cm-5x7in) i.verso gelatin silver print prov. 25-Apr-3 Phillips, New York #3/R est:10000-15000
£2658 $4200 €3987 Italian immigrant family looking for lost luggage (24x19cm-9x7in) gelatin silver print prov.lit. 24-Apr-3 Phillips, New York #91/R est:2500-3500
£3671 $5800 €5507 Italian immigrant, East Side (24x19cm-9x7in) gelatin silver print prov.lit. 24-Apr-3 Phillips, New York #92/R est:2500-3500
£4747 $7500 €7121 Empire State Building (17x12cm-7x5in) i.verso gelatin silver print prov.exhib.lit. 25-Apr-3 Phillips, New York #8/R est:25000-35000
£5696 $9000 €8544 Slide, Kelly, slide! playground stuff (28x50cm-11x20in) i.verso gelatin silver print prov.exhib. 25-Apr-3 Phillips, New York #67/R est:3000-5000
£8861 $14000 €13292 Worker, Empire State building (23x30cm-9x12in) i.d.1930 verso photograph. 23-Apr-3 Sotheby's, New York #70/R est:15000-20000
£14557 $23000 €21836 Girl at factory loom (26x34cm-10x13in) s.i.verso gelatin silver print prov. 25-Apr-3 Phillips, New York #65/R est:3000-5000

HINE, William Egerton (1926-) British
Works on paper
£320 $506 €480 Runswick village, Yorkshire (33x51cm-13x20in) s.d.1909 W/C. 2-Dec-2 Gorringes, Lewes #2656

HINES, Frederick (19/20th C) British
£900 $1404 €1350 In the springtime (77x117cm-30x46in) s.d.1880 s.i.d.verso. 7-Nov-2 Christie's, Kensington #201/R
Works on paper
£350 $557 €525 Rural scene with cattle (25x36cm-10x14in) s. W/C. 7-Mar-3 Biddle & Webb, Birmingham #119
£400 $652 €600 Mother and child at riverside feeding ducks (36x25cm-14x10in) s. W/C. 14-Feb-3 Keys, Aylsham #502/R
£500 $810 €750 Girl feeding ducks (52x36cm-20x14in) s. bodycol. 21-Jan-3 Bonhams, Knightsbridge #59/R
£650 $1027 €975 Figures with sheep in a landscape setting (23x53cm-9x21in) s. W/C pair. 18-Dec-2 John Nicholson, Haslemere #1135/R
£780 $1217 €1170 Woodland scene with young country maiden collecting firewood (53x36cm-21x14in) s.d. W/C. 16-Oct-2 Brightwells, Leominster #1168
£1200 $1920 €1800 Harvesting by moonlight (56x38cm-22x15in) s. W/C. 11-Mar-3 Gorringes, Lewes #2400/R est:1200-1800

HINES, Theodore (fl.1876-1889) British
£290 $447 €435 Kilchurn castle, Loch Awe with lady. 7-Sep-2 Shapes, Edinburgh #537
£450 $702 €675 Girl beside a lake in a wooded landscape (45x81cm-18x32in) s. 10-Sep-2 Bonhams, Knightsbridge #13
£500 $815 €725 Burnham Beeches (46x81cm-18x32in) s. 16-Jul-3 Sotheby's, Olympia #59/R
£577 $900 €866 Derby bridge (61x104cm-24x41in) s. 29-Mar-3 Charlton Hall, Columbia #159/R
£600 $948 €870 On the waters of Luss, Loch Lomond (23x43cm-9x17in) s. s.i.d.96 verso. 24-Jul-3 John Nicholson, Haslemere #1201/R
£737 $1194 €1069 Highland home near Strathspey (31x41cm-12x16in) s.verso. 25-May-3 Uppsala Auktionskammare, Uppsala #73/R (S.KR 9500)
£750 $1200 €1125 River landscape with figures punting, possibly Henley Lock on Thames (39x60cm-15x24in) s. 7-Jan-3 Bonhams, Knightsbridge #137/R
£1200 $1908 €1800 Ellen's Isle, Loch Katrine (41x30cm-16x12in) s. s.i.verso. 6-Mar-3 Christie's, Kensington #71/R est:600-800
£1400 $2156 €2100 Wargrave-on-Thames (51x76cm-20x30in) s. 5-Sep-2 Christie's, Kensington #170/R est:800-1200

HINKLE, Clarence Keiser (1880-1960) American
£4790 $8000 €6946 Street scene, Old Summerland (25x33cm-10x13in) s. i.verso board. 17-Jun-3 John Moran, Pasadena #136 est:3000-5000
£17516 $27500 €26274 Portrait of a lady (91x76cm-36x30in) s. prov.exhib.lit. 19-Nov-2 Butterfields, San Francisco #8175/R est:10000-15000
Works on paper
£701 $1100 €1052 Cottage garden (18x25cm-7x10in) s. W/C gouache. 20-Nov-2 Christie's, Los Angeles #117/R
£774 $1200 €1161 Lone pine (36x51cm-14x20in) s. W/C prov. 29-Oct-2 John Moran, Pasadena #688a
£994 $1600 €1491 Floral still life (16x12cm-6x5in) s. W/C prov. 18-Feb-3 John Moran, Pasadena #83a est:1500-2500

HINSBERGER, Alexis (1907-1996) ?
£321 $500 €482 Chanteurs Catalans (61x46cm-24x18in) s. s.i.verso. 22-Sep-2 Jeffery Burchard, Florida #39

HINTERHOLZER, Franz (1851-?) German?
£321 $503 €500 Landscape near Salzburg (21x27cm-8x11in) s. board. 21-Nov-2 Dorotheum, Vienna #144/R
£321 $503 €500 Mountain view in the autumn evening (19x29cm-7x11in) s. board. 21-Nov-2 Dorotheum, Vienna #145/R
£468 $767 €650 Woodland way in Leopoldskroner Weiher in Salzburg (30x41cm-12x16in) s. board. 5-Jun-3 Dorotheum, Salzburg #528/R

HINTERMEISTER, Henry (1897-1972) American
£774 $1200 €1161 Duck hunting (61x46cm-24x18in) s. 7-Dec-2 Selkirks, St. Louis #238 est:1000-1500
£1118 $1800 €1677 General George C Marshall in uniform (69x53cm-27x21in) s. 19-Feb-3 Illustration House, New York #223/R est:2000-3000
£1242 $2000 €1863 Boy awaits judge's assessment of his calf (71x53cm-28x21in) s. 19-Feb-3 Illustration House, New York #203/R est:3000-4000
£1242 $2000 €1863 Fisherman distracted by young woman artist (53x71cm-21x28in) s. 19-Feb-3 Illustration House, New York #235/R est:3000-4000
£1491 $2400 €2237 Boy, girl and dog with lambs (71x53cm-28x21in) s. 19-Feb-3 Illustration House, New York #204/R est:2500-3500
£1553 $2500 €2330 Fisherman daydreams while listening to radio, bears attracted to cooking smells (56x71cm-22x28in) s. 19-Feb-3 Illustration House, New York #226/R est:2500-3500
£1553 $2500 €2330 Fisherman reaching far into stream to net fish (53x71cm-21x28in) s. 19-Feb-3 Illustration House, New York #229/R est:3000-5000
£1677 $2700 €2516 Boy grooming calf, proud grandfather looking on (71x53cm-28x21in) s. 19-Feb-3 Illustration House, New York #206/R est:2000-3000
£2019 $3250 €3029 Fisherman climbs over fence to avoid angered bull (53x71cm-21x28in) s. 19-Feb-3 Illustration House, New York #227/R est:2500-3500

£2019 $3250 €3029 Fisherman's cooking attracts mother bear and cubs (56x71cm-22x28in) s. 19-Feb-3 Illustration House, New York #228/R est:2500-3500
£2174 $3500 €3261 Boy greets newborn foal (71x53cm-28x21in) s. 19-Feb-3 Illustration House, New York #205/R est:2500-3500
£2329 $3750 €3494 Boy, dog and grandfather in buckboard, circus train in background (71x53cm-28x21in) s. 19-Feb-3 Illustration House, New York #202/R est:3000-6000
£2532 $4000 €3798 Childhood days (53x71cm-21x28in) s. prov. 24-Apr-3 Shannon's, Milford #202/R est:2500-3500
£2640 $4250 €3960 Boy and dog harvesting vegetables for needy European children (71x53cm-28x21in) s. 19-Feb-3 Illustration House, New York #207/R est:2500-3500
£2795 $4500 €4193 Boys preparing for take-off in homemade airplane (71x53cm-28x21in) s. 19-Feb-3 Illustration House, New York #208/R est:4000-8000
£3481 $5500 €5047 Mallard marsh (61x46cm-24x18in) s. 26-Jul-3 Coeur d'Alene, Hayden #28/R est:3000-5000
£4348 $7000 €6522 Boy on raft waving to passing train (71x53cm-28x21in) s. 19-Feb-3 Illustration House, New York #201/R est:4000-6000
£4747 $7500 €6883 Pat (61x76cm-24x30in) s. 26-Jul-3 Coeur d'Alene, Hayden #243/R est:5000-8000

Works on paper
£2545 $4250 €3690 Figure in landscape - Tryst (66x51cm-26x20in) s. pastel. 17-Jun-3 John Moran, Pasadena #58 est:5000-7000

HINTERSEHER, Josef (1873-1955) German
Sculpture
£4838 $7500 €7257 Youth with stag (72cm-28in) s. brown pat. bronze st.f.Guss prov.exhib. 29-Oct-2 Sotheby's, New York #249/R est:4000-6000

HINTON, Walter Haskell (20th C) American
£1069 $1700 €1604 Illustration for Western story (74x84cm-29x33in) s. painted c.1940. 2-Mar-3 Toomey, Oak Park #687/R est:2000-3000

HINTZE, Johann Heinrich (1800-1860) German
Works on paper
£2245 $3569 €3300 Interior of Biedermeier salon (18x26cm-7x10in) s. W/C htd white. 19-Mar-3 Neumeister, Munich #362 est:1400
£5696 $9000 €9000 Panorama of Unter den Linden in Berlin (16x69cm-6x27in) s. pen wash bodycol. 29-Nov-2 Bassenge, Berlin #5810/R est:9500

HINZ, Johann Georg (1630-1688) German
£18000 $28260 €27000 Still life of nautilus cup, glasses, fruit in a bowl and hazelnuts (67x81cm-26x32in) 12-Dec-2 Sotheby's, London #158/R est:20000-30000

HINZ, Johann Georg (attrib) (fl.1666-1700) German
£9434 $14623 €15000 Still life with ewer, venetian glasses and fruit in silver bowl (52x58cm-20x23in) 2-Oct-2 Dorotheum, Vienna #47/R est:15000-25000
£19355 $30581 €30000 Still life with copper, jug and orange (88x52cm-35x20in) bears mono. panel. 18-Dec-2 Tajan, Paris #27/R est:30000-35000

HIOLLE, Ernest Eugène (1834-1886) French
Sculpture
£1451 $2250 €2177 Bust of Carpeaux (46cm-18in) s.i. terracotta prov. 29-Oct-2 Sotheby's, New York #225/R est:3000-5000

HIPPLE, J W (19th C) ?
£1100 $1694 €1650 Tranquil stretch of the river (62x91cm-24x36in) s. 5-Sep-2 Christie's, Kensington #116/R est:1000-1500

HIQUILY, Philippe (1925-) French
Sculpture
£2516 $3899 €4000 Arachnee (84x16x14cm-33x6x6in) silver brass socle prov.lit. 30-Oct-2 Artcurial Briest, Paris #685/R est:5000-7000

HIRALDEZ DE ACOSTA, Marcos (1830-?) Spanish
£1572 $2453 €2500 Portrait of gentleman (125x98cm-49x39in) s.d.1865. 23-Sep-2 Durán, Madrid #165/R

HIRANKUL, Sujarit (1956-1982) Thai
£1657 $2552 €2486 Houses by the river (73x88cm-29x35in) s.d.74 s.i.d.verso. 27-Oct-2 Christie's, Hong Kong #63/R est:22000-32000 (HK.D 20000)

HIRD, W (19th C) European
£1200 $1908 €1800 Scotch homestead (76x126cm-30x50in) s. 4-Mar-3 Bearnes, Exeter #456/R est:800-1200

HIREMY-HIRSCHL, Adolph (1860-1933) Hungarian
£650 $1053 €975 Portrait of a young woman (63x50cm-25x20in) 20-May-3 Sotheby's, Olympia #393/R

Works on paper
£967 $1500 €1451 Reclining female nude (31x48cm-12x19in) i. chl black white chk. 29-Oct-2 Sotheby's, New York #104/R est:600-800
£1935 $3000 €2903 Studies for st. Cecilia. Woman from the back (24x33cm-9x13in) pencil black white chk two prov. 29-Oct-2 Sotheby's, New York #105/R est:700-900

HIROSE, Satoshi (1963-) Japanese
Works on paper
£633 $987 €1000 Both side painting - blue (150x150cm-59x59in) s.d.1995 mixed media. 21-Oct-2 Bernaerts, Antwerp #669

HIROSHIGE (19th C) Japanese
Prints
£2051 $3221 €3200 Halte. s. print. 16-Dec-2 Beaussant & Lefèvre, Paris #205
£3077 $4831 €4800 Halte. s.print. 16-Dec-2 Beaussant & Lefèvre, Paris #211/R

HIROSHIGE, Ando I (1797-1858) Japanese
Prints
£1923 $3000 €2885 Actor Ichikawa Danjuro VII (20x18cm-8x7in) s.i. silver highlights print. 25-Mar-3 Christie's, Rockefeller NY #135/R est:3000-3500
£1923 $3000 €2885 Goten Hill, Shinagawa (36x24cm-14x9in) s. col print. 25-Mar-3 Christie's, Rockefeller NY #210/R est:2000-4000
£1923 $3000 €2885 Seven Ri Beach, Sagami province (37x24cm-15x9in) s. col print. 25-Mar-3 Christie's, Rockefeller NY #263/R est:3000-5000
£2051 $3200 €3077 Otsuki plain, Kai Province (37x25cm-15x10in) s. col print. 25-Mar-3 Christie's, Rockefeller NY #224/R est:3000-3500
£2244 $3500 €3366 Eight views of the Sumida river, night rain, Masaki (23x34cm-9x13in) s. col print. 25-Mar-3 Christie's, Rockefeller NY #182/R est:3500-5500
£2244 $3500 €3366 Pagoda of Zojoji Temple, Akabane (36x24cm-14x9in) s. col print. 25-Mar-3 Christie's, Rockefeller NY #206/R est:2000-4000
£2436 $3800 €3654 Open garden, Hachiman Shrine, Fukagawa (36x25cm-14x10in) s. col print. 25-Mar-3 Christie's, Rockefeller NY #203/R est:2000-4000
£2436 $3800 €3654 Shinobazu Pond, Ueno (37x13cm-15x5in) s. col print. 25-Mar-3 Christie's, Rockefeller NY #237/R est:3000-5000
£2564 $4000 €3846 Actor Ichikawa Danjuro VII (21x20cm-8x8in) s.i. silver highlights print. 25-Mar-3 Christie's, Rockefeller NY #137/R est:4000-5000
£2564 $4000 €3846 Autumn moon, Seto (25x38cm-10x15in) s. col print. 25-Mar-3 Christie's, Rockefeller NY #196/R est:3000-4000
£2600 $4108 €3900 Family crossing a small bridge in the mist (25x38cm-10x15in) s. col print. 13-Nov-2 Christie's, London #16/R est:3000-3500
£2692 $4200 €4038 Armour hanging pine, Hakkei slope (36x24cm-14x9in) s. col print. 25-Mar-3 Christie's, Rockefeller NY #202/R est:2000-4000
£2885 $4500 €4328 Kasumigaseki (37x26cm-15x10in) s. col print. 25-Mar-3 Christie's, Rockefeller NY #208/R est:2000-4000
£3077 $4800 €4616 Hauling canal boats, Yotsugi road (35x24cm-14x9in) s. col print. 25-Mar-3 Christie's, Rockefeller NY #201/R est:2000-4000
£3077 $4800 €4616 Motofuji, Meguro (36x24cm-14x9in) s. col print. 25-Mar-3 Christie's, Rockefeller NY #205/R est:2000-4000
£3077 $4800 €4616 Town prosperous with Tanabata festival (36x25cm-14x10in) s.num. col print. 25-Mar-3 Christie's, Rockefeller NY #209/R est:3000-5000
£3077 $4800 €4616 Eitai Bridge, Tsukuda island (37x25cm-15x10in) s. col print. 25-Mar-3 Christie's, Rockefeller NY #212/R est:2000-4000
£3205 $5000 €4808 Egoyomi surimono with a pocket watch (21x19cm-8x7in) s.i.d.1823 col print. 25-Mar-3 Christie's, Rockefeller NY #138/R est:5000-7000
£3205 $5000 €4808 Takamiya, station 65 (24x36cm-9x14in) s. print. 25-Mar-3 Christie's, Rockefeller NY #167/R est:5000-7000
£3205 $5000 €4808 Mannen Bridge, Fukagawa (37x25cm-15x10in) s. col print. 25-Mar-3 Christie's, Rockefeller NY #197/R est:5000-7000
£3205 $5000 €4808 Kominato Bay, Awa Province (36x25cm-14x10in) s. col print. 25-Mar-3 Christie's, Rockefeller NY #220/R est:5000-7000
£3526 $5500 €5289 Moon pine, Ueno Temple precincts (36x24cm-14x9in) s. col print. 25-Mar-3 Christie's, Rockefeller NY #198/R est:4500-5500
£3526 $5500 €5289 Mount Yuga, Bizen Province (24x35cm-9x14in) s. col print. 25-Mar-3 Christie's, Rockefeller NY #229/R est:6000-8000
£3846 $6000 €5769 Kiyomizu, famous places of Kyoto (26x38cm-10x15in) s. col print. 25-Mar-3 Christie's, Rockefeller NY #189/R est:6000-8000

£4167 $6500 €6251 Listening to insects (25x38cm-10x15in) s. col print. 25-Mar-3 Christie's, Rockefeller NY #183/R est:4000-6000
£5128 $8000 €7692 Karuizawa, station 19 (24x36cm-9x14in) s. col print. 25-Mar-3 Christie's, Rockefeller NY #164/R est:8000-12000
£5128 $8000 €7692 Ebbtide, Shibaura (25x38cm-10x15in) s. col print prov. 25-Mar-3 Christie's, Rockefeller NY #184/R est:3000-3500
£5449 $8500 €8174 Cherry blossoms at night in Nakanocho in the Yoshiwara (26x38cm-10x15in) s. col print. 25-Mar-3 Christie's, Rockefeller NY #185/R est:3500-4000
£5449 $8500 €8174 Crossing a bridge in the snow (37x25cm-15x10in) s. col print. 25-Mar-3 Christie's, Rockefeller NY #235/R est:9000-11000
£6410 $10000 €9615 Treasury of loyal retainers (25x37cm-10x15in) s. col prints sixteen. 25-Mar-3 Christie's, Rockefeller NY #233/R est:10000-15000
£6410 $10000 €9615 Moon (35x25cm-14x10in) s. col print. 25-Mar-3 Christie's, Rockefeller NY #234/R est:10000-15000
£6410 $10000 €9615 Plum garden, Kamata (36x25cm-14x10in) s. col print. 25-Mar-3 Christie's, Rockefeller NY #216/R est:6000-8000
£7692 $12000 €11538 Cherry trees in full bloom, Arashiyama (25x38cm-10x15in) s. col print. 25-Mar-3 Christie's, Rockefeller NY #190/R est:12000-15000
£8333 $13000 €12500 Cicada and morning glory (38x13cm-15x5in) s.i. print. 25-Mar-3 Christie's, Rockefeller NY #242/R est:10000-15000
£8974 $14000 €13461 Wind and waves at Naruto, Awa province (36x26cm-14x10in) s. col print. 25-Mar-3 Christie's, Rockefeller NY #221/R est:7000-9000
£9615 $15000 €14423 Taikobashi and setting-sun hill, Meguro (36x24cm-14x9in) s. col print. 25-Mar-3 Christie's, Rockefeller NY #215/R est:10000-15000
£9615 $15000 €14423 Crescent moon (39x17cm-15x7in) s. col print prov. 25-Mar-3 Christie's, Rockefeller NY #238/R est:15000-20000
£10256 $16000 €15384 Asakusa rice fields during the cock festival (36x24cm-14x9in) s. col print. 25-Mar-3 Christie's, Rockefeller NY #199/R est:5000-7000
£14103 $22000 €21155 Evening snow, Asakusa (26x19cm-10x7in) s. col print triptych. 25-Mar-3 Christie's, Rockefeller NY #251/R est:15000-20000
£41667 $65000 €62501 Seba, station 32 (23x37cm-9x15in) s. col print. 25-Mar-3 Christie's, Rockefeller NY #168/R est:65000-85000
£70513 $110000 €105770 Fireworks, Ryogoku (36x24cm-14x9in) s. col print. 25-Mar-3 Christie's, Rockefeller NY #213/R est:70000-90000

HIRSCH, Auguste Alexandre (1833-1912) French
£4113 $6376 €6170 The love letter (116x89cm-46x35in) s. prov. 3-Dec-2 Bukowskis, Stockholm #181/R est:50000-70000 (S.KR 58000)

HIRSCH, Christian Gotthard (1889-1977) German
£252 $392 €400 St Blasien, Black Forest (32x50cm-13x20in) s.d.1964 i. verso tempera pastel lit. 20-Sep-2 Karlheinz Kaupp, Staufen #2181

HIRSCH, Joseph (1910-1981) American
£1069 $1700 €1604 Kites on the levee (43x64cm-17x25in) s. acrylic prov. 18-Mar-3 Arthur James, Florida #98
£2329 $3750 €3494 Men pausing from excavation work (64x28cm-25x11in) s. painted c.1940. 10-May-3 Illustration House, New York #147/R est:3000-5000

Works on paper
£221 $350 €332 Memorial (64x41cm-25x16in) s. W/C. 5-Apr-3 Neal Auction Company, New Orleans #591
£239 $375 €359 Southern landscape (39x48cm-15x19in) s. W/C. 22-Nov-2 Skinner, Boston #239/R
£380 $600 €570 World War II vintage navy pilot refuels his biplane (48x28cm-19x11in) s. W/C board. 26-Apr-3 Thomaston Place, Thomaston #575

HIRSCH, Karl Jakob (1892-?) German
£2264 $3487 €3600 Hiddensee landscape (67x90cm-26x35in) mono. 26-Oct-2 Dr Lehr, Berlin #169/R est:3000

HIRSCHBERG, Carl (1854-1923) American
£1006 $1600 €1509 Brook bridge (51x71cm-20x28in) s. s.i.d.1916 verso. 7-Mar-3 Skinner, Boston #393/R est:1800-2200

HIRSCHFELD, Al (1903-2003) American
Works on paper
£1887 $3000 €2831 Bruce Springsteen (175x135cm-69x53in) s.i. Indian ink over pencil executed c.2002. 30-Apr-3 Doyle, New York #203/R est:3000-4000
£2484 $4000 €3726 Crew and actor on an industrial film set (51x46cm-20x18in) s. pen ink. 10-May-3 Illustration House, New York #21/R est:4000-7000
£2564 $4000 €3846 Writer pauses outside of Broadway theatres (33x33cm-13x13in) s. pen ink wash en grisaille prov. 9-Nov-2 Illustration House, New York #69/R est:4000-6000
£3526 $5500 €5289 Katherine Hepburn and Sir Laurence Olivier with Emmy award (58x51cm-23x20in) s. pen ink. 9-Nov-2 Illustration House, New York #68/R est:4500-6000

HIRSCHFELD, Emil Benediktoff (1867-1922) Russian
£310 $493 €450 Sous bois la Clairiere (55x38cm-22x15in) s. canvas on panel. 10-Mar-3 Thierry & Lannon, Brest #116
£347 $566 €500 Petite barque sous voiles (12x16cm-5x6in) s. panel. 19-Jul-3 Thierry & Lannon, Brest #344

HIRSCHFELD-MACK, Ludwig (1893-1964) Australian/German
Works on paper
£1085 $1726 €1628 Abstract composition (17x25cm-7x10in) s.d.1940 W/C pencil. 5-May-3 Sotheby's, Melbourne #237 est:2000-3000 (A.D 2800)
£1218 $1852 €1827 Abstract (25x17cm-10x7in) s.d.1940 W/C exhib. 28-Aug-2 Deutscher-Menzies, Melbourne #171/R est:3000-4000 (A.D 3400)
£1290 $1961 €1935 Abstract (21x27cm-8x11in) s.d.1940 W/C exhib. 28-Aug-2 Deutscher-Menzies, Melbourne #170/R est:3000-4000 (A.D 3600)
£1354 $2221 €1963 Abstract (21x27cm-8x11in) i. W/C conte ink exec.c.1961. 4-Jun-3 Deutscher-Menzies, Melbourne #364/R est:1000-2000 (A.D 3400)

HIRSCHING, August (1889-1962) German
£875 $1400 €1313 Interior scene with young female in front of a mirror (43x30cm-17x12in) s.d.1922 s.verso board. 15-Mar-3 Jeffery Burchard, Florida #62/R

HIRST, Damien (1965-) British
£2690 $4250 €4035 Spin paintings (15x9cm-6x4in) s.i.verso one acrylic paper one gouache painted c.1995 prov. 13-Nov-2 Sotheby's, New York #404/R
£3800 $6346 €5510 Untitled, spin painting (45cm-18in circular) acrylic paper prov. 24-Jun-3 Sotheby's, Olympia #6/R est:4000-6000
£4000 $6560 €6000 Untitled (46cm-18in circular) st.i. verso acrylic paper one of 50 prov. 6-Feb-3 Christie's, London #735/R est:5000-7000
£5500 $9185 €7975 Untitled, spin painting (45cm-18in circular) acrylic paper prov. 24-Jun-3 Sotheby's, Olympia #5/R est:4000-6000
£6329 $10000 €9494 Mini spin painting (63x63cm-25x25in) acrylic on paper executed 2001. 12-Nov-2 Phillips, New York #194/R est:10000-15000
£7000 $11690 €10150 Benflourex (8x19cm-3x7in) s.i.verso gloss paint prov.lit. 26-Jun-3 Sotheby's, London #103/R est:5000-7000
£10000 $16700 €14500 Avidin-hemocyanin (25x30cm-10x12in) s.i.verso gloss paint prov.lit. 26-Jun-3 Sotheby's, London #104/R est:10000-15000
£90000 $147600 €135000 Gorgeous concentric beautiful charity begins at home, exploding orange painting (213x213cm-84x84in) household gloss paint painted 2002 prov. 6-Feb-3 Sotheby's, London #45/R est:70000
£110000 $183700 €165000 Happy Fun (119x84cm-47x33in) exc.1994 prov.lit. 25-Jun-3 Sotheby's, London #45/R est:100000-150000
£112500 $180000 €168750 Untitled (107x122cm-42x48in) yellow gloss household paint butterflies on canvas prov. 15-May-3 Phillips, New York #37/R est:200000-250000
£130000 $213200 €195000 Nocturne (76x123cm-30x48in) gloss household paint butterflies painted 2000 oval prov. 6-Feb-3 Sotheby's, London #47/R est:180000
£164557 $260000 €246836 Aicar diphosphate (170x201cm-67x79in) i.verso gloss household paint painted 1992 prov.exhib. 13-Nov-2 Sotheby's, New York #134/R est:150000-200000
£220000 $360800 €330000 Oo you are lovely (122x122cm-48x48in) gloss household paint and butterflies painted 1998 prov. 5-Feb-3 Christie's, London #9/R est:150000-200000
£230000 $384100 €345000 Naja Naja Sputatrix (234x295cm-92x116in) household gloss paint canvas exc.2000 prov.lit. 25-Jun-3 Sotheby's, London #46/R est:200000-300000
£240000 $400800 €360000 Or love (213cm-84in circular) butterflies and household gloss paint exc.1998-99 prov. 25-Jun-3 Sotheby's, London #6/R est:250000-350000
£303797 $480000 €455696 Beauty is in the eye of the beholder (213cm-84in circular) butterflies gloss household paint on canvas executed 1998. 12-Nov-2 Sotheby's, New York #58/R est:500000-700000

Prints
£2000 $3340 €2900 Liver, bacon, onions, SP (152x101cm-60x40in) s. col silkscreen edition of 150. 24-Jun-3 Sotheby's, Olympia #8/R est:1500-2000

£12658 $20000 €18987 Last supper (152x102cm-60x40in) s. set of thirteen screenprints executed 1999 prov. 14-Nov-2 Christie's, Rockefeller NY #351/R est:20000-30000
£17500 $28000 €26250 Last supper (152x102cm-60x40in) set of 13 col screenprints executed 1999 prov. 15-May-3 Christie's, Rockefeller NY #411/R est:20000-30000

Sculpture
£156250 $250000 €234375 Untitled (56x94x10cm-22x37x4in) mixed media sculpture fiberboard wood steel glass fish formaldhyd. 14-May-3 Sotheby's, New York #306/R est:80000-120000

HIRT, Heinrich (1841-1902) German
£12338 $18383 €19000 Making dolls clothes (50x39cm-20x15in) s.i. lit. 26-Jun-2 Neumeister, Munich #757/R est:4000

HIRT, Heinrich (attrib) (1841-1902) German
£3103 $4903 €4500 Young woman rocking child in cradle (49x38cm-19x15in) s. 5-Apr-3 Hans Stahl, Hamburg #9/R est:4500

HIRTH DU FRENES, Rudolf (1846-1916) German
£487 $726 €750 Acrobats outside village tavern (24x31cm-9x12in) s. 26-Jun-2 Neumeister, Munich #758/R
£1392 $2158 €2200 Three girls reading book (33x43cm-13x17in) s. 25-Sep-2 Neumeister, Munich #604/R est:2500
£2632 $4263 €4000 Interior von dem Insel Marken (52x32cm-20x13in) s. exhib. 21-Jan-3 Christie's, Amsterdam #315/R est:4000-6000

HIRTZ, Albert (?) ?
£348 $550 €550 Marche en Bretagne (46x55cm-18x22in) s. 1-Dec-2 Livinec, Gaudcheau & Jezequel, Rennes #77

HIRZEL, Heinrich (1729-1790) Swiss
£741 $1193 €1112 Country landscape with peasants (18x21cm-7x8in) s.i.d.1762. 7-May-3 Dobiaschofsky, Bern #643 (S.FR 1600)

HIS, René Charles Edmond (1877-1960) French
£700 $1169 €1015 View from the heights (31x40cm-12x16in) s. 17-Jun-3 Gildings, Market Harborough #438/R
£750 $1170 €1125 Calmer waters (33x47cm-13x19in) s. prov. 25-Mar-3 Bonhams, Leeds #566
£769 $1208 €1200 Bord de l'Eure (46x55cm-18x22in) s. 21-Nov-2 Neret-Minet, Paris #36/R
£1582 $2500 €2500 Bord de riviere (27x35cm-11x14in) s. 1-Dec-2 Peron, Melun #102
£1650 $2706 €2475 Quiet stretch of the river (33x46cm-13x18in) s. 5-Jun-3 Christie's, Kensington #700/R est:1000-1500
£1850 $2886 €2775 Matin d'ete a St. Moray (61x81cm-24x32in) s.d.1935 prov. 25-Mar-3 Bonhams, Leeds #567/R est:1500-2000
£2532 $4000 €4000 Bord de riviere (60x81cm-24x32in) s. 1-Dec-2 Peron, Melun #180
£2800 $4368 €4200 Bords de L'eure (46x55cm-18x22in) s. 26-Mar-3 Sotheby's, Olympia #279/R est:1500-2000
£3250 $5330 €4875 Summer's day at the banks of the river (53x74cm-21x29in) s. 5-Jun-3 Christie's, Kensington #701/R est:2000-3000

HISCOX, George (1840-1909) British
Works on paper
£480 $787 €720 River Blythe, Suffolk (26x38cm-10x15in) s. W/C. 4-Jun-3 Bonhams, Chester #399

HISER, Margaret F (19th C) American
Works on paper
£769 $1200 €1154 Rose and the morning glory (33x23cm-13x9in) i.d.April 30 1859 W/C theorem. 21-Sep-2 Pook & Pook, Downington #40/R

HISLOP, Andrew (fl.1880-1903) British
£350 $567 €525 Fishing village (49x74cm-19x29in) s. 20-May-3 Sotheby's, Olympia #250/R

HISLOP, Margaret Ross (1894-1972) British
£500 $795 €750 Still life with vase of flowers (41x51cm-16x20in) s. board. 6-Mar-3 Christie's, Kensington #216/R

HITCHCOCK, Harold (1914-) British
Works on paper
£320 $496 €480 Figures in a garden (79x57cm-31x22in) mono.d.1962 W/C. 3-Dec-2 Bonhams, Knightsbridge #294/R

HITCHCOCK, Lucius Wolcott (1868-1942) American
Works on paper
£1118 $1800 €1677 Artist carrying canvas, children watching (64x43cm-25x17in) s.d. chl board lit. 10-May-3 Illustration House, New York #42/R est:1500-2500

HITCHENS, Alfred (1861-?) British
Works on paper
£380 $604 €570 Portrait of Miss Agnesi Evans (42x34cm-17x13in) s.d.1894 pastel. 26-Feb-3 Cheffins Grain & Comins, Cambridge #502

HITCHENS, Ivon (1893-1979) British
£10000 $16000 €15000 November painting II (38x71cm-15x28in) s. 8-Jan-3 Brightwells, Leominster #1087 est:15000-20000
£15000 $23250 €22500 Gentle spring (58x62cm-23x24in) painted 1933. 4-Dec-2 Sotheby's, London #41/R est:18000-25000
£16000 $25600 €24000 Autumn larchwood (38x71cm-15x28in) s.d.1946. 8-Jan-3 Brightwells, Leominster #1089/R est:15000-20000
£18000 $27900 €27000 There he her met (53x132cm-21x52in) s. s.i.stretcher. 4-Dec-2 Sotheby's, London #90/R est:15000-20000
£21000 $33600 €31500 Steam at Burton (38x104cm-15x41in) s. 8-Jan-3 Brightwells, Leominster #1088/R est:15000-20000
£21000 $35070 €30450 Willow no 1 (43x109cm-17x43in) s.d.67 prov. 24-Jun-3 Bonhams, New Bond Street #105/R est:15000-20000
£25000 $41000 €37500 Orange and pink poppies (84x51cm-33x20in) s. prov. 6-Jun-3 Christie's, London #167/R est:10000-15000
£31000 $50840 €44950 Grey mill pool (41x92cm-16x36in) s. painted 1950 prov.exhib. 4-Jun-3 Sotheby's, London #71/R est:15000-20000
£34000 $52700 €51000 River Rother, near Stedham (45x110cm-18x43in) s.d.1964 prov. 3-Dec-2 Bonhams, New Bond Street #97/R est:15000-20000
£55000 $86350 €82500 Spring flowers and blue teapot (74x61cm-29x24in) studio st. verso painted c.1934 prov.exhib. 22-Nov-2 Christie's, London #75/R est:25000-35000

Works on paper
£500 $775 €750 Three nudes (36x25cm-14x10in) i.indis d. pen ink dr. 1-Oct-2 Bonhams, Leeds #304
£750 $1208 €1125 Seated female nude (27x20cm-11x8in) pen. 14-Jan-3 Bonhams, Knightsbridge #58/R

HITCHENS, John (1940-) British
£300 $477 €450 Open space (28x54cm-11x21in) s. s.i.d.Jan 61 on stretcher. 4-Mar-3 Bearnes, Exeter #446/R
£320 $522 €464 Downland clouds (48x69cm-19x27in) s.d.1971. 17-Jul-3 Thomson, Roddick & Medcalf, Carlisle #165/R
£650 $1007 €975 Greenfields under grey (46x107cm-18x42in) s. s.i.d.1963 on stretcher prov. 4-Dec-2 Christie's, Kensington #557
£1200 $1848 €1800 June greenhouse (63x89cm-25x35in) s. s.i.verso. 5-Sep-2 Christie's, Kensington #704/R est:800-1200

HITTELL, Charles Joseph (1861-1938) American
£1708 $2750 €2562 Mission San Francisco Solano (23x38cm-9x15in) s.d.1907 i.verso canvas on canvas prov.exhib. 18-Feb-3 John Moran, Pasadena #52b est:2000-3000

HITZLER, Franz (1946-) German
£385 $608 €600 Untitled (61x45cm-24x18in) s.d.1982 acrylic paper on board. 14-Nov-2 Neumeister, Munich #791/R
£935 $1496 €1300 Untitled (178x99cm-70x39in) s.d. board. 15-May-3 Neumeister, Munich #708/R
£1603 $2532 €2500 Red creature (124x100cm-49x39in) s.d.1974. 14-Nov-2 Neumeister, Munich #789/R est:1000-1200

Works on paper
£288 $460 €400 Untitled (71x53cm-28x21in) s. verso mixed media exhib. 15-May-3 Neumeister, Munich #707/R
£288 $460 €400 Untitled (35x25cm-14x10in) s.d. verso Indian ink brush chl pencil bodycol. 15-May-3 Neumeister, Munich #709/R
£302 $483 €420 Untitled (53x36cm-21x14in) s.d. i. verso oil gouache monotype. 15-May-3 Neumeister, Munich #712/R
£396 $633 €550 Untitled (61x41cm-24x16in) oil gouache chl pencil prov. 15-May-3 Neumeister, Munich #710/R
£540 $863 €750 Untitled (90x70cm-35x28in) s.d. verso mixed media. 15-May-3 Neumeister, Munich #706/R

HIXON, William J (attrib) (fl.1825-1857) British
Works on paper
£800 $1312 €1160 Fisherman and donkey returning home (29x37cm-11x15in) s.d.1831 W/C. 7-Jun-3 Shapes, Edinburgh #371/R

HJELM, Fanny (1858-1944) Swedish
£1312 $2034 €1968 Lake landscape (39x55cm-15x22in) s. 3-Dec-2 Bukowskis, Stockholm #289/R est:12000-15000 (S.KR 18500)

HJERLOW, Ragnvald (1863-1947) Norwegian
£567 $890 €851 Autumn evening (40x55cm-16x22in) s. 25-Nov-2 Blomqvist, Lysaker #1121 (N.KR 6500)

HJERSING, Arne (1860-1926) Norwegian

£866 $1325 €1299 Summer evening, Lillehammer (43x71cm-17x28in) s. 26-Aug-2 Blomqvist, Lysaker #1171/R (N.KR 10000)

HJERTEN, Sigrid (1885-1948) Swedish

£6388 $10093 €9582 Model with yellow necklace (46x38cm-18x15in) s. panel. 28-Apr-3 Bukowskis, Stockholm #151/R est:60000-80000 (S.KR 84000)

£9506 $15019 €14259 Still life of flowers (92x73cm-36x29in) painted 1930s. 28-Apr-3 Bukowskis, Stockholm #147/R est:150000-175000 (S.KR 125000)

£10512 $16398 €15768 Still life of statuette (47x38cm-19x15in) s. 5-Nov-2 Bukowskis, Stockholm #83c/R est:175000-200000 (S.KR 150000)

£11913 $18584 €17870 Ivan at the table (64x54cm-25x21in) 5-Nov-2 Bukowskis, Stockholm #82/R est:175000-200000 (S.KR 170000)

£12263 $19131 €18395 The red crane (72x61cm-28x24in) s. panel. 6-Nov-2 AB Stockholms Auktionsverk #741/R est:175000-200000 (S.KR 175000)

£14716 $22957 €22074 Ivan in front of window looking out (58x42cm-23x17in) s. painted 1914 exhib.lit. 6-Nov-2 AB Stockholms Auktionsverk #585/R est:250000-300000 (S.KR 210000)

£14716 $22957 €22074 Still life of flowers and cockerel (65x54cm-26x21in) s. panel exhib.lit. 5-Nov-2 Bukowskis, Stockholm #119/R est:150000-200000 (S.KR 210000)

£19305 $31081 €28958 The studio terrace in Paris (61x50cm-24x20in) s. exhib. 7-May-3 AB Stockholms Auktionsverk #911/R est:250000-300000 (S.KR 250000)

£20322 $31703 €30483 Landscape from Alvastra (55x74cm-22x29in) s. exhib. 5-Nov-2 Bukowskis, Stockholm #166/R est:300000-350000 (S.KR 290000)

£20463 $32946 €30695 Landscape with cypresses (73x92cm-29x36in) 7-May-3 AB Stockholms Auktionsverk #749/R est:175000-200000 (S.KR 265000)

£30133 $47008 €45200 Woman wearing yellow blouse (64x49cm-25x19in) st.i. painted 1919. 6-Nov-2 AB Stockholms Auktionsverk #721/R est:275000-300000 (S.KR 430000)

£210231 $327961 €315347 The children (153x161cm-60x63in) s. painted 1914 prov.exhib.lit. 6-Nov-2 AB Stockholms Auktionsverk #630/R est:2000000-2500000 (S.KR 3000000)

Works on paper

£1962 $3061 €2943 Figures in landscape (40x33cm-16x13in) s. W/C. 6-Nov-2 AB Stockholms Auktionsverk #627/R est:30000-35000 (S.KR 28000)

£8059 $12572 €12089 Beach umbrellas, Alassio (50x65cm-20x26in) s. gouache executed c.1917 exhib.lit. 5-Nov-2 Bukowskis, Stockholm #83b/R est:70000-80000 (S.KR 115000)

£19011 $30038 €28517 The beach, Alassio (50x64cm-20x25in) s. gouache. 28-Apr-3 Bukowskis, Stockholm #214/R est:250000-275000 (S.KR 250000)

HJORTH, Bror (1894-1968) Swedish

£15603 $24184 €23405 The old Rattviks road in Sjugare (63x51cm-25x20in) s. 8-Dec-2 Uppsala Auktionskammare, Uppsala #209/R est:150000-200000 (S.KR 220000)

£52558 $81990 €78837 Love scene I (177x68cm-70x27in) s. polychrome painted wood prov.lit. 5-Nov-2 Bukowskis, Stockholm #219/R est:700000-800000 (S.KR 750000)

Sculpture

£1261 $1968 €1892 Lovers (20cm-8in) s.d.1956 num.1/10 painted plaster. 5-Nov-2 Bukowskis, Stockholm #70/R est:8000-10000 (S.KR 18000)

£1261 $1968 €1892 Reclining woman (10cm-4in) s. dark pat.bronze. 5-Nov-2 Bukowskis, Stockholm #140/R est:20000-25000 (S.KR 18000)

£1261 $1968 €1892 Woman asleep (26cm-10in) s. terracotta prov. 5-Nov-2 Bukowskis, Stockholm #142/R est:12000-15000 (S.KR 18000)

£1822 $2842 €2733 Lovers (16cm-6in) s.num.3/9 painted terracotta executed 1935-1950. 5-Nov-2 Bukowskis, Stockholm #73a/R est:15000-18000 (S.KR 26000)

£2102 $3280 €3153 Reclining woman (18cm-7in) s.num.2 painted terracotta. 5-Nov-2 Bukowskis, Stockholm #143/R est:10000-12000 (S.KR 30000)

Works on paper

£789 $1230 €1184 Lion (23x31cm-9x12in) pencil. 13-Sep-2 Lilla Bukowskis, Stockholm #746 (S.KR 11500)

£841 $1312 €1262 Old man seated in wicker work chair (65x30cm-26x12in) s. chl. 5-Nov-2 Bukowskis, Stockholm #75/R (S.KR 12000)

£1822 $2842 €2733 Boy seated in wicker work chair (29x19cm-11x7in) s. pencil prov. 5-Nov-2 Bukowskis, Stockholm #76/R est:15000-20000 (S.KR 26000)

HJORTH-NIELSEN, Soren (1901-1983) Danish

£354 $564 €531 Mountain landscape, Spain (50x61cm-20x24in) init. 5-May-3 Rasmussen, Vejle #51/R (D.KR 3800)

£575 $896 €863 Houses by road (53x75cm-21x30in) init. 11-Nov-2 Rasmussen, Vejle #29/R (D.KR 6700)

£676 $1041 €1014 Wood in summer (74x92cm-29x36in) init. 26-Oct-2 Rasmussen, Havnen #2216 (D.KR 8000)

£839 $1401 €1217 View across green fields (60x73cm-24x29in) init. s.i.d.1947 verso. 17-Jun-3 Rasmussen, Copenhagen #179/R (D.KR 8800)

£1292 $2003 €1938 Summer landscape, Asserbo (65x92cm-26x36in) init. 4-Dec-2 Kunsthallen, Copenhagen #344/R est:8000 (D.KR 15000)

£1610 $2672 €2335 Summer landscape, Falsted 1956-58 (73x93cm-29x37in) init. 12-Jun-3 Kunsthallen, Copenhagen #272/R est:8000 (D.KR 17000)

HJORTZBERG, Olle (1872-1959) Swedish

£565 $886 €848 Southern landscape with figures (54x65cm-21x26in) s.d.1951 panel. 16-Dec-2 Lilla Bukowskis, Stockholm #861 (S.KR 8000)

£706 $1123 €1059 Hyacinths (35x27cm-14x11in) s.d.48 panel. 3-Mar-3 Lilla Bukowskis, Stockholm #28 (S.KR 9500)

£788 $1277 €1182 Southern European landscape (46x39cm-18x15in) s. panel. 3-Feb-3 Lilla Bukowskis, Stockholm #711 (S.KR 11000)

£834 $1384 €1209 Southern landscape with figures (50x61cm-20x24in) s.d.1951 panel. 16-Jun-3 Lilla Bukowskis, Stockholm #522 (S.KR 10800)

£1297 $2050 €1946 Still life of urn and bowl (51x62cm-20x24in) s.d.1946 panel. 30-Nov-2 Goteborg Auktionsverk, Sweden #149/R est:15000 (S.KR 18500)

£1807 $2963 €2620 Still life of fruit (38x46cm-15x18in) s. 4-Jun-3 AB Stockholms Auktionsverk #2081/R est:30000-35000 (S.KR 23000)

£2482 $3848 €3723 Wild flowers - Karleksort (62x51cm-24x20in) s.d.48 prov. 3-Dec-2 Bukowskis, Stockholm #130/R est:45000-50000 (S.KR 35000)

£2482 $3848 €3723 Flowers by window (64x53cm-25x21in) s.d.1949 panel. 4-Dec-2 AB Stockholms Auktionsverk #1727/R est:40000-50000 (S.KR 35000)

£2483 $4022 €3600 Still life of flowers (61x51cm-24x20in) s.d.47 panel. 26-May-3 Bukowskis, Stockholm #187/R est:40000-50000 (S.KR 32000)

£3404 $5277 €5106 Summer flowers in pot on window ledge (38x46cm-15x18in) s. 3-Dec-2 Bukowskis, Stockholm #118/R est:35000-40000 (S.KR 48000)

£3535 $5797 €5126 Still life of roses (56x47cm-22x19in) s. panel. 4-Jun-3 AB Stockholms Auktionsverk #2082/R est:40000-45000 (S.KR 45000)

£3546 $5496 €5319 Still life of roses in silver vase (55x45cm-22x18in) s.d.1942 panel. 3-Dec-2 Bukowskis, Stockholm #1/R est:50000-70000 (S.KR 50000)

£3546 $5496 €5319 Summer meadow (53x65cm-21x26in) s.d.48 panel. 3-Dec-2 Bukowskis, Stockholm #128/R est:50000-60000 (S.KR 50000)

£3546 $5496 €5319 Still life of photograph and pink roses in glass jug (65x54cm-26x21in) s.d.1942 panel. 4-Dec-2 AB Stockholms Auktionsverk #1704/R est:50000-60000 (S.KR 50000)

£3546 $5496 €5319 Roman lady (111x71cm-44x28in) s.i.d.1903. 4-Dec-2 AB Stockholms Auktionsverk #1714/R est:50000-60000 (S.KR 50000)

£4255 $6596 €6383 Spring flowers in pot (50x62cm-20x24in) s.d.1950 prov. 3-Dec-2 Bukowskis, Stockholm #19/R est:60000-70000 (S.KR 60000)

£6206 $10054 €8999 Dahlias in glass vase (46x36cm-18x14in) s.d.1926 panel. 26-May-3 Bukowskis, Stockholm #23/R est:80000-100000 (S.KR 80000)

£7447 $11543 €11171 Still life of with wild flowers (61x50cm-24x20in) s.d.41. 3-Dec-2 Bukowskis, Stockholm #18/R est:80000-100000 (S.KR 105000)

£8922 $14453 €12937 Still life of wood anemones and common hepaticas (51x62cm-20x24in) s.d.48 panel. 26-May-3 Bukowskis, Stockholm #187a/R est:70000-80000 (S.KR 115000)

£9427 $15460 €13669 Still life of yellow roses in silver vase (65x50cm-26x20in) s.d.1946 panel. 4-Jun-3 AB Stockholms Auktionsverk #2109/R est:60000-80000 (S.KR 120000)

£34911 $56555 €50621 Midsummer wild flowers (100x81cm-39x32in) s.d.1942 panel prov. 26-May-3 Bukowskis, Stockholm #122/R est:250000-300000 (S.KR 450000)

Works on paper

£483 $768 €725 Backyard (45x37cm-18x15in) s.i.d.47 W/C. 3-Mar-3 Lilla Bukowskis, Stockholm #215 (S.KR 6500)

£1418 $2199 €2127 Tulips (37x48cm-15x19in) s.d.1958 W/C. 3-Dec-2 Bukowskis, Stockholm #23/R est:25000-30000 (S.KR 20000)

£1702 $2638 €2553 Yellow roses (34x25cm-13x10in) s.d.57 W/C. 3-Dec-2 Bukowskis, Stockholm #117/R est:20000-22000 (S.KR 24000)

£1807 $2963 €2620 Bouquet of hare-bells and daisies (33x25cm-13x10in) s.d.1951 W/C. 4-Jun-3 AB Stockholms Auktionsverk #2111/R est:15000-18000 (S.KR 23000)

HLAVACEK, Anton (1842-1926) Austrian
£479 $748 €700 Mondsee (24x31cm-9x12in) s. board. 10-Apr-3 Dorotheum, Vienna #97/R
£1633 $2596 €2400 Street scene in Vienna (42x51cm-17x20in) i.verso board. 25-Feb-3 Dorotheum, Vienna #190/R est:2500-3000
£1646 $2600 €2600 View of Habsburg and the Aare valley (80x180cm-31x71in) s. 28-Nov-2 Dorotheum, Vienna #139/R est:3800-5000
£2899 $4754 €4000 Molvena Lake and Brenta mountains (47x64cm-19x25in) s. 27-May-3 Hassfurther, Vienna #44/R est:3400-3800
£4348 $7130 €6000 Mountain lake (79x101cm-31x40in) s. 27-May-3 Wiener Kunst Auktionen, Vienna #27/R est:5000-8000
Works on paper
£503 $780 €800 Traunstein at dusk (14x21cm-6x8in) s. W/C. 1-Oct-2 Dorotheum, Vienna #352/R

HLINA, Ladislav (1947-) German
Sculpture
£1069 $1668 €1700 Wild boar (56cm-22in) dark brown pat.bronze. 20-Sep-2 Schloss Ahlden, Ahlden #642/R est:1400
£1195 $1864 €1900 Young flautist (61cm-24in) dark brown pat.bronze. 20-Sep-2 Schloss Ahlden, Ahlden #652/R est:1800
£1241 $1974 €1800 Two young goats play fighting (63cm-25in) s. bronze. 8-Mar-3 Arnold, Frankfurt #245/R est:2400
£1831 $2948 €2600 Girl with ducklings (108cm-43in) s. dark brown pat.bronze. 9-May-3 Schloss Ahlden, Ahlden #715/R est:1900
£1831 $2948 €2600 Girl with lamb (112cm-44in) dark brown pat.bronze. 9-May-3 Schloss Ahlden, Ahlden #716/R est:1900
£3077 $4831 €4800 Donkey (76cm-30in) i. dark brown pat.bronze. 21-Nov-2 Van Ham, Cologne #1221/R est:3300

HLINOMAZ, Josef (?) ?
£873 $1387 €1310 Sea landscape (70x50cm-28x20in) s. bears d. 8-Mar-3 Dorotheum, Prague #135/R est:8000-12000 (C.KR 40000)

HLITO, Alfredo (1923-1993) Argentinian
£3503 $5500 €5255 Composition (99x49cm-39x19in) s.d.59 prov. 19-Nov-2 Sotheby's, New York #109/R est:15000
£5311 $8390 €7967 Monument (180x45cm-71x18in) s.d.89 acrylic. 15-Nov-2 Naón & Cia, Buenos Aires #15/R

HLOZNIK, Ferdinand (1921-) Czechoslovakian
£332 $514 €498 In cafe (32x45cm-13x18in) tempera paper painted 1958. 3-Dec-2 SOGA, Bratislava #86/R (SL.K 21000)

HLOZNIK, Vincent (1919-1997) Czechoslovakian
£504 $781 €756 Circus (28x36cm-11x14in) tempera paper. 1-Oct-2 SOGA, Bratislava #104/R est:32000 (SL.K 32000)
£599 $928 €899 Horses on pastures (42x58cm-17x23in) tempera board. 1-Oct-2 SOGA, Bratislava #102/R est:50000 (SL.K 38000)
£1024 $1587 €1536 Don Quixote (48x19cm-19x7in) board. 1-Oct-2 SOGA, Bratislava #101/R est:60000 (SL.K 65000)
£1150 $1633 €1725 In coffee house III (33x49cm-13x19in) board painted 1949. 26-Mar-2 SOGA, Bratislava #105/R est:55000 (SL.K 73000)
£1181 $1725 €1772 Sleeping (41x65cm-16x26in) oil tempera board. 4-Jun-2 SOGA, Bratislava #93/R est:45000 (SL.K 75000)
£2520 $3579 €3780 Apocalypse (54x75cm-21x30in) tempera gouache painted 1946. 26-Mar-2 SOGA, Bratislava #103/R est:95000 (SL.K 160000)
Sculpture
£1307 $1856 €1961 Melancholy (28cm-11in) epoxy marble base exec.1947. 26-Mar-2 SOGA, Bratislava #106/R est:38000 (SL.K 83000)
Works on paper
£379 $587 €569 Mused (60x42cm-24x17in) W/C exec.1943. 3-Dec-2 SOGA, Bratislava #80/R (SL.K 24000)
£882 $1252 €1323 Figures (59x84cm-23x33in) W/C ink exec.1961. 26-Mar-2 SOGA, Bratislava #107/R est:35000 (SL.K 56000)
£1339 $1955 €2009 Don Quixote and Sancho Panza (63x48cm-25x19in) pastel. 4-Jun-2 SOGA, Bratislava #92/R est:85000 (SL.K 85000)

HLUNGWANE, Jackson Mbhazima (1923-) South African
Sculpture
£1290 $2077 €1935 Bird (153cm-60in) wood. 12-May-3 Stephan Welz, Johannesburg #540/R est:15000-20000 (SA.R 15000)

HOAD, Norman (20th C) ?
£419 $700 €608 Goodwood - the final furlong (46x61cm-18x24in) s. 29-Jun-3 Butterfields, Los Angeles #7046/R

HOAR, Steve (20th C) Canadian
Sculpture
£1124 $1765 €1686 Rolling thunder (75cm-30in) s. num.4/20 bronze with wood base. 25-Nov-2 Hodgins, Calgary #79/R est:2500-3000 (C.D 2800)

HOARE, Thomas (attrib) (18th C) British
Works on paper
£347 $573 €500 Portrait of a gentleman of the Needham family (40x30cm-16x12in) pastel. 7-Jul-3 Hamilton Osborne King, Dublin #73/R
£800 $1248 €1200 Portrait of a man of the Needham Family in full wig and waistcoat (60x46cm-24x18in) pastel sold with a companion. 14-Apr-3 Hamilton Osborne King, Dublin #1452/R

HOARE, William (1706-1799) British
Works on paper
£800 $1320 €1160 Portrait of a lady (59x44cm-23x17in) d.1749 pastel paper on panel. 2-Jul-3 Sotheby's, Olympia #154/R
£800 $1320 €1160 Portrait of a lady (59x44cm-23x17in) pastel paper on canvas. 2-Jul-3 Sotheby's, Olympia #155/R
£2800 $4424 €4200 Portrait of a lady (57x42cm-22x17in) pastel paper on canvas. 28-Nov-2 Sotheby's, London #214/R est:3000-4000

HOARE, William (attrib) (1706-1799) British
£880 $1364 €1320 Elizabeth Warburton (73x58cm-29x23in) 1-Nov-2 Moore Allen & Innocent, Cirencester #405/R

HOBART OF MONKS ELEIGH, John R (fl.1829-1858) British
£1600 $2528 €2400 Brown racehorse with a spaniel by his side in a park (38x44cm-15x17in) s.d.1830. 28-Nov-2 Christie's, Kensington #140/R est:800-1200

HOBART, Clark (1868-1948) American
£3106 $5000 €4659 Along the riverbank (28x41cm-11x16in) s.d.97 canvasboard. 18-Feb-3 John Moran, Pasadena #95b est:3000-5000

HOBBEMA, Meindert (1638-1709) Dutch
£18868 $29245 €30000 River landscape (51x68cm-20x27in) prov.lit. 2-Oct-2 Dorotheum, Vienna #85/R est:25000-35000

HOBBEMA, Meindert (attrib) (1638-1709) Dutch
£7692 $12000 €11538 Wooded landscape with villagers and cottages (76x105cm-30x41in) panel. 9-Nov-2 Sloan, North Bethesda #564/R est:25000-35000
£16216 $25297 €24000 Ruined castle near pond in oak forest (40x53cm-16x21in) i. panel. 27-Mar-3 Dorotheum, Vienna #142/R est:9000-14000

HOBBY, Jess (20th C) American
£774 $1200 €1161 Midwestern landscape (71x84cm-28x33in) s. painted c.1920. 8-Dec-2 Toomey, Oak Park #686/R
£1069 $1700 €1604 Midwestern landscape (71x84cm-28x33in) s. painted c.1920. 2-Mar-3 Toomey, Oak Park #565/R est:2500-4500

HOBDAY, William Armfield (1771-1831) British
Miniatures
£2900 $4524 €4350 Young gentleman wearing dark grey coat cream waistcoat frilled white cravat (7cm-3xin) gilt frame blue glass verso oval. 5-Nov-2 Bonhams, New Bond Street #66/R est:2500-3500

HOBERMAN, Nicky (1967-) South African
£3200 $5344 €4640 Sweet pickle (91x91cm-36x36in) prov. 24-Jun-3 Sotheby's, Olympia #17/R est:1500-2000

HOBLEY, Edward George (1866-1916) British
£638 $989 €957 Harvesting by farm (92x71cm-36x28in) s.d.1897. 4-Dec-2 AB Stockholms Auktionsverk #1859/R (S.KR 9000)

HOBSON, Cecil J (1874-1918) British
Works on paper
£1900 $3135 €2755 In full bloom (54x26cm-21x10in) s.d.09 pencil W/C gum arabic scratching out. 3-Jul-3 Christie's, Kensington #28/R est:1000-1500

HOCH, Franz Xaver (1869-1916) German
£321 $487 €500 Extensive hilly landscape with view of a village (80x105cm-31x41in) s. d.1913 verso lit. 11-Jul-2 Allgauer, Kempten #2517/R

HOCH, Hannah (1889-1979) German
£449 $700 €674 Landscape (28x38cm-11x15in) s.d.1944 canvasboard. 29-Mar-3 Charlton Hall, Columbia #157/R
Works on paper
£382 $603 €550 Untitled abstract composition (21x30cm-8x12in) spray Indian ink board. 26-Apr-3 Dr Lehr, Berlin #219/R

£633 $1000 €1000 Flower woman with cat's eyes (21x13cm-8x5in) mono.d.IX/73 collage. 30-Nov-2 Bassenge, Berlin #6322/R
£652 $1070 €900 Composition (18x16cm-7x6in) mono. W/C Indian ink. 31-May-3 Villa Grisebach, Berlin #570/R
£696 $1100 €1100 Still life of flowers (13x10cm-5x4in) mono.d.64 collage board. 30-Nov-2 Bassenge, Berlin #6321/R
£719 $1180 €1000 The poet (14x20cm-6x8in) mono.i. W/C over Indian ink. 4-Jun-3 Reiss & Sohn, Konigstein #400/R
£2113 $3507 €3000 Til is ill (32x27cm-13x11in) mono. s.i. verso W/C bodycol. 14-Jun-3 Hauswedell & Nolte, Hamburg #1255/R est:3500
£3038 $4800 €4800 Flowers in vase (61x48cm-24x19in) s.i s.d.1932 verso W/C board. 30-Nov-2 Villa Grisebach, Berlin #336/R est:3000-4000
£3819 $6035 €5500 Above the clouds (31x23cm-12x9in) mono.i.d.1971 s.i.d. verso collage board. 26-Apr-3 Dr Lehr, Berlin #218/R est:7000
£3889 $6144 €5600 Colourful wall (66x52cm-26x20in) mono.d.1961 s.i.d. verso. 26-Apr-3 Dr Lehr, Berlin #217/R est:7000

HOCHARD, Gaston (1863-1913) French
£281 $443 €422 Danseus Russes (43x62cm-17x24in) s. cardboard. 30-Nov-2 Goteborg Auktionsverk, Sweden #184/R (S.KR 4000)

HOCHECKER, Franz (1730-1782) German
£3247 $4838 €5000 Elegant hunting party amongst trees with waterfall (25x30cm-10x12in) 26-Jun-2 Neumeister, Munich #635/R est:4000

HOCHECKER, Franz (circle) (1730-1782) German
£5000 $7750 €7500 River landscape with ferry, trade vessels and bridge (55x77cm-22x30in) 30-Oct-2 Bonhams, New Bond Street #170/R est:5000-7000

HOCHMANN, Franz Gustav (1861-?) German
£759 $1200 €1200 Thoughtful moment (61x80cm-24x31in) s. lit. 29-Nov-2 Schloss Ahlden, Ahlden #1371/R

HOCHSCHARTNER, Ernst (1877-1947) Austrian
£576 $944 €800 Reclining female nude (88x148cm-35x58in) s.d.1910. 5-Jun-3 Dorotheum, Salzburg #483/R

HOCK, Daniel (1858-1934) Austrian
£2025 $3200 €3200 Unlucky cupid (114x81cm-45x32in) s.i.d.1880. 28-Nov-2 Dorotheum, Vienna #82/R est:3000-4000
£2025 $3200 €3200 Angel with fruit or flowers (151x66cm-59x26in) s.d.1896 four. 26-Nov-2 Wiener Kunst Auktionen, Vienna #127/R est:1200-3000

HOCKELMANN, Antonius (1937-) German
£808 $1252 €1260 Landscape (80x100cm-31x39in) s.d.92. 7-Dec-2 Van Ham, Cologne #228/R
£1154 $1788 €1800 Goethe (38cm-15xin) i. s.d.1999 verso acrylic aluminium foil glue. 3-Dec-2 Lempertz, Koln #193/R est:2000

Works on paper
£385 $596 €600 Mask (70x50cm-28x20in) s. wax crayon. 7-Dec-2 Van Ham, Cologne #231
£507 $832 €700 Untitled (65x50cm-26x20in) s.d.1997 col chk gouache Indian ink. 28-May-3 Lempertz, Koln #185/R
£577 $894 €900 Untitled (50x70cm-20x28in) s.d.1995 wax crayon acrylic. 7-Dec-2 Van Ham, Cologne #229/R

HOCKEN, Marion Grace (1922-1987) British
£280 $437 €420 Sea bream's head (10x13cm-4x5in) s.d.1947 board. 16-Oct-2 David Lay, Penzance #330
£400 $644 €600 Still life with lilies, fuschias and delphiniums (64x77cm-25x30in) s. 18-Feb-3 Bonhams, Knightsbridge #20/R

HOCKERT, Johan (1826-1866) Swedish
£296 $465 €444 Girl wearing national costume (33x28cm-13x11in) mono.d.1850. 16-Dec-2 Lilla Bukowskis, Stockholm #180 (S.KR 4200)

HOCKEY, Patrick (1948-1992) Australian
£286 $452 €497 Victorian lady (44x44cm-17x17in) s. board. 1-Apr-3 Goodman, Sydney #95 (A.D 750)
£307 $457 €461 Cattlemen of the North, Western Australia (45x55cm-18x22in) s.d.76 prov. 27-Aug-2 Christie's, Melbourne #272 (A.D 800)
£466 $676 €699 Man with emu (59x90cm-23x35in) s. board. 10-Dec-1 Goodman, Sydney #406 (A.D 1300)
£538 $817 €807 Tennis (75x99cm-30x39in) s. acrylic board. 27-Aug-2 Goodman, Sydney #33 (A.D 1500)
£2907 $4622 €4361 Prize bull (90x118cm-35x46in) s.d.71. 5-May-3 Sotheby's, Melbourne #350/R est:5000-7000 (A.D 7500)

HOCKNER, Rudolf (1864-1942) German
£497 $785 €720 Woodland pond in late autumn (12x21cm-5x8in) board. 5-Apr-3 Hans Stahl, Hamburg #120/R
£660 $1017 €1050 Winter landscape (23x31cm-9x12in) s. board. 26-Oct-2 Quittenbaum, Hamburg #16/R
£779 $1138 €1200 View of old Hamburg with square, streets, figures and carts in middle (12x18cm-5x7in) s. board on panel. 15-Jun-2 Hans Stahl, Hamburg #190
£1090 $1689 €1700 Wedel, village street (223x30cm-88x12in) s. board. 5-Dec-2 Schopman, Hamburg #634 est:1650
£1172 $1852 €1700 Windmill in winter (34x50cm-13x20in) s.d.1929 board. 5-Apr-3 Quittenbaum, Hamburg #90/R est:2200
£1233 $1923 €1800 Klovensteen (30x45cm-12x18in) s. board. 10-Apr-3 Schopman, Hamburg #679 est:2000
£1410 $2186 €2200 Finkenwerder harbour entrance (28x45cm-11x18in) s.d.1913 panel. 5-Dec-2 Schopman, Hamburg #632 est:2500
£1603 $2484 €2500 Niendorf (45x65cm-18x26in) s.d.1936. 5-Dec-2 Schopman, Hamburg #631 est:3200
£4276 $6756 €6200 Meadow landscape near Wedel (52x72cm-20x28in) s.d.1938. 5-Apr-3 Quittenbaum, Hamburg #92/R est:2800
£4690 $7410 €6800 Behind the mill in Wedel (53x73cm-21x29in) s.d.1937. 5-Apr-3 Quittenbaum, Hamburg #91/R est:2800

HOCKNEY, David (1937-) British
£29000 $48430 €42050 Picture of a still life on a table (61x60cm-24x24in) acrylic painted 1965 prov.lit. 27-Jun-3 Christie's, London #192/R est:30000-40000
£30000 $50100 €43500 Erection (122x91cm-48x36in) s.i.verso board painted 1961 prov. 27-Jun-3 Christie's, London #194/R est:30000-40000
£56250 $90000 €84375 Man with wings and rocks (61x61cm-24x24in) s.d.63 verso s.on stretcher prov.lit. 14-May-3 Sotheby's, New York #207/R est:100000-150000
£75000 $115500 €112500 Saleman (61x31cm-24x12in) s.i.d.63 i.on stretcher prov. 23-Oct-2 Christie's, London #101/R est:60000-80000
£88608 $140000 €132912 Man thinking (91x63cm-36x25in) s.d.62 i.verso oil pencil prov.exhib. 14-Nov-2 Christie's, Rockefeller NY #147/R est:150000-200000
£110000 $183700 €159500 Red bridge (91x61cm-36x24in) s.i.d.1989 verso acrylic prov.exhib. 26-Jun-3 Sotheby's, London #224/R est:100000-150000
£175000 $280000 €262500 Snake (183x183cm-72x72in) oil chk graphite letterset painted 1962 prov.exhib.lit. 14-May-3 Christie's, Rockefeller NY #19/R est:250000-350000
£348101 $550000 €522152 Diving board with still water on blue paper (183x217cm-72x85in) init.d.78 col pressed paper pulp prov.lit. 12-Nov-2 Sotheby's, New York #45/R est:500000-700000
£1645570 $2600000 €2468355 Portrait of Nick Wilder (183x183cm-72x72in) s. i.d.1966 verso acrylic prov.exhib.lit. 13-Nov-2 Christie's, Rockefeller NY #51/R est:2500000-3500000

Photographs
£4000 $6200 €6000 David and Ann on the subway (100x69cm-39x27in) s.num.11 photo-collage. 5-Dec-2 Sotheby's, London #213/R est:5000-7000
£5660 $8774 €9000 Gregory loading his camera, Kyoto (44x26cm-17x10in) s.i.d.1983 photo collage 11 C-prints. 31-Oct-2 Van Ham, Cologne #147/R est:8000
£5696 $9000 €8544 Ian washing his hair (74x81cm-29x32in) s.i.d.1983 colour photocollage prov.lit. 13-Nov-2 Sotheby's, New York #535/R est:6000-8000
£10000 $16500 €14500 Grand Canyon with my shadow (94x157cm-37x62in) s.i.d.1982 photo collage prov. 3-Jul-3 Christie's, Kensington #621/R est:4000-6000

Prints
£1740 $2750 €2610 Horizontal dogs (39x46cm-15x18in) s.d.1995 num.37/80 col etching aquatint. 22-Apr-3 Butterfields, San Francisco #2294/R est:3000-4000
£1899 $3000 €2849 Still life that has an elaborate silver frame (71x57cm-28x22in) col lithograph. 22-Apr-3 Butterfields, San Francisco #2285/R est:2500-3500
£1923 $3000 €2885 Gorge d'Incre (55x69cm-22x27in) s.d.num.32/68 col lithograph silkscreen. 14-Oct-2 Butterfields, San Francisco #1278/R est:4000-6000
£1923 $3000 €2885 Homage to Michelangelo (59x79cm-23x31in) s.d.num.24/200 black red etching. 5-Nov-2 Christie's, Rockefeller NY #397/R est:3000-5000
£1923 $3000 €2885 Two Pembroke Studio chairs (48x56cm-19x22in) s.d.num.30/98 col lithograph. 5-Nov-2 Christie's, Rockefeller NY #400/R est:3500-4500
£2000 $3120 €3000 Celia musing (102x74cm-40x29in) s.d.1979 num.78/100 lithograph. 10-Oct-2 Sotheby's, London #253/R est:2000-2500
£2000 $3120 €3000 Hollywood collection, picture of Melrose Avenue in an ornate gold frame (77x56cm-30x22in) s.d.1965 col lithograph. 25-Mar-3 Sotheby's, London #176/R est:2000-2500

£2038 $3200 €3057 Sunflower I (46x38cm-18x15in) s.d.1995 num.56/80 etching aquatint. 21-Nov-2 Swann Galleries, New York #79/R est:2500-3500
£2083 $3250 €3125 Image of Celia study (58x45cm-23x18in) s.d.num.28/60 col etching aquatint lithograph. 14-Oct-2 Butterfields, San Francisco #1277/R est:2500-3500
£2100 $3297 €3150 My bonnie lies over the ocean (51x51cm-20x20in) s. etching aquatint collage. 17-Apr-3 Christie's, Kensington #51/R est:1500-2000
£2200 $3410 €3300 Apples, grapes, lemons on a table (43x55cm-17x22in) s.d.1988 num.26/91 print. 4-Dec-2 Bonhams, New Bond Street #321/R est:2500-3500
£2200 $3630 €3190 Figure by a curtain (50x64cm-20x25in) s.d.num.1/75 col lithograph silkscreen. 1-Jul-3 Sotheby's, London #186/R est:2000-2500
£2200 $3630 €3190 Parade, Metropolitan Opera New York (202x102cm-80x40in) s. col screenprint. 2-Jul-3 Christie's, London #88 est:1500-2000
£2400 $3720 €3600 Three black flowers (27x21cm-11x8in) s.num.35/50 hand made print executed c.1986. 5-Dec-2 Sotheby's, London #209/R est:1800-2200
£2400 $3960 €3480 Snow, from the Weather Series (86x72cm-34x28in) s.i.d.num.49/98 col lithograph screenprint. 2-Jul-3 Christie's, London #256/R est:2000-3000
£2404 $3750 €3606 Two Pembroke Studio chairs (47x56cm-19x22in) s.d.84 num.81/98 col lithograph. 14-Oct-2 Butterfields, San Francisco #1276/R est:3000-5000
£2516 $4000 €3774 Tres, end of triple (113x80cm-44x31in) s.d.num.5/35 col lithograph. 2-May-3 Sotheby's, New York #473/R est:3000-4000
£2532 $4000 €3798 Marguerites (24x18cm-9x7in) s.d.1973 col etching. 22-Apr-3 Butterfields, San Francisco #2289/R est:5500-6500
£2564 $4000 €3846 Black white plant (78x92cm-31x36in) s.d.num.11/35 etching aquatint. 5-Nov-2 Christie's, Rockefeller NY #408/R est:5000-7000
£2724 $4250 €4086 Pembroke Studio with blue chairs and lamp (47x56cm-19x22in) s.d.84 num.7/98 col lithograph. 14-Oct-2 Butterfields, San Francisco #1275/R est:4000-6000
£2724 $4250 €4086 Studio (90x111cm-35x44in) s.d.num.21 col digital inkjet edition of 45. 14-Oct-2 Butterfields, San Francisco #1279/R est:3500-5500
£2800 $4368 €4200 Brooke Hopper (97x71cm-38x28in) s.d.1976 num.9/92 lithograph. 10-Oct-2 Sotheby's, London #245/R est:1000-1200
£2857 $4514 €4286 Mist (72x63cm-28x25in) s.d.73 num.34/98 lithograph. 26-Nov-2 Sotheby's, Melbourne #248/R est:8000-12000 (A.D 8000)
£2867 $4358 €4301 Celia (98x84cm-39x33in) s.d.1980 num.38/100 lithograph. 28-Aug-2 Deutscher-Menzies, Melbourne #290/R est:7000-10000 (A.D 8000)
£3000 $4650 €4500 W.H Auden (27x23cm-11x9in) s.d.1970 num.3/8 drypoint. 5-Dec-2 Sotheby's, London #207/R est:2000-3000
£3000 $4650 €4500 Vertical dogs (39x46cm-15x18in) s.d.1995 num.80/80 col etching aquatint. 5-Dec-2 Sotheby's, London #211/R est:3000-4000
£3000 $4710 €4500 Hypnotist (65x57cm-26x22in) s.num.32/50 red black etching. 17-Apr-3 Christie's, Kensington #52/R est:3000-4000
£3000 $4950 €4350 Sunflower I (38x46cm-15x18in) s.d.num.44/80 etching aquatint. 1-Jul-3 Sotheby's, London #184a/R est:2000-2500
£3200 $4928 €4800 Red pot (36x22cm-14x9in) s.d.1986 num.58/60 col photocopy. 24-Oct-2 Christie's, Kensington #74/R est:1500-2000
£3205 $5032 €5000 Picture of Melrose Avenue (76x56cm-30x22in) s.d.1965 num.84/85 col lithograph. 21-Nov-2 Finarte, Rome #100/R
£3500 $5460 €5250 Flowers made of paper and black ink (99x95cm-39x37in) s.i.d.1971 lithograph. 10-Oct-2 Sotheby's, London #248/R est:4000-6000
£3600 $5616 €5400 Picture of still life that has silver frame (77x56cm-30x22in) s.i.d. col lithograph. 31-Mar-3 Bonhams, New Bond Street #347/R est:3500-4500
£3800 $5928 €5700 Brenda with cigarette (87x56cm-34x22in) s.d.1998 num.12/35 etching. 10-Oct-2 Sotheby's, London #250/R est:1500-2000
£3846 $6000 €5769 Bora Bora (88x122cm-35x48in) s.d.num.46/100 col lithograph. 5-Nov-2 Christie's, Rockefeller NY #399/R est:6000-8000
£3854 $6013 €5781 Bora Bora (88x120cm-35x47in) s.num.79/100 col lithograph 1980 lit. 6-Nov-2 AB Stockholms Auktionsverk #1011/R est:50000-60000 (S.KR 55000)
£4000 $6600 €5800 Not so good mist (92x75cm-36x30in) s.i.d.num.2/2 col lithograph. 1-Jul-3 Sotheby's, London #185/R est:5000-7000
£4403 $7000 €6605 Red flowers and green leaves, separate (35x43cm-14x17in) s.d.num.69/70 col copier handmade print two sheets. 2-May-3 Sotheby's, New York #471/R est:4000-5000
£4487 $7000 €6731 Pretty tulips (72x50cm-28x20in) s.i.d. col lithograph edition of 200. 5-Nov-2 Christie's, Rockefeller NY #393/R est:5000-7000
£4487 $7000 €6731 Table flowable (112x145cm-44x57in) s.d.num.AP VI/X col lithograph edition of 50. 5-Nov-2 Christie's, Rockefeller NY #405/R est:9000-12000
£4487 $7000 €6731 Twelve-fifteen (112x145cm-44x57in) s.d.num.50/50 col lithograph. 5-Nov-2 Christie's, Rockefeller NY #406/R est:8000-10000
£4500 $6975 €6750 Living room and terrace, July 1986 (43x56cm-17x22in) s.d.68 num.32/60 col office copier. 3-Dec-2 Christie's, London #131/R est:5000-7000
£4500 $6975 €6750 Petty tulips (72x51cm-28x20in) s.i.d.1969 num.122/200 col lithograph. 5-Dec-2 Sotheby's, London #210/R est:4500-5000
£4800 $7920 €6960 Pretty tulips (73x51cm-29x20in) i.d.1970 col lithograph. 2-Jul-3 Christie's, London #89/R est:4000-5000
£5031 $8000 €7547 Celia on an office chair (69x54cm-27x21in) s.d.num.6/60 col etching aquatint. 29-Apr-3 Christie's, Rockefeller NY #618/R est:9000-12000
£5400 $8370 €8100 Rue de Seine (54x43cm-21x17in) s.d.1971 num.78/150 etching. 5-Dec-2 Sotheby's, London #212/R est:6000-8000
£5449 $8500 €8174 Rain, from Weather Series (100x80cm-39x31in) s.i.d.num.74/98 col lithograph. 5-Nov-2 Christie's, Rockefeller NY #394/R est:4000-6000
£5449 $8500 €8174 Snow, from Weather Series (102x85cm-40x33in) s.d.num.V col lithograph. 5-Nov-2 Christie's, Rockefeller NY #395/R est:5000-7000
£6731 $10500 €10097 Van Gogh chair (95x88cm-37x35in) s.d.num.11/35 col etching aquatint. 5-Nov-2 Christie's, Rockefeller NY #407/R est:8000-10000
£6918 $11000 €10377 Celia with green plant (75x100cm-30x39in) s.d.num.23/90 col lithograph. 2-May-3 Sotheby's, New York #468/R est:9000-12000
£7051 $11000 €10577 Contrejour in the French style (99x91cm-39x36in) s.d.num.4/75 col etching aquatint. 5-Nov-2 Christie's, Rockefeller NY #396/R est:10000-15000
£8500 $13260 €12750 Water made thick and thin lines (50x69cm-20x27in) s.d.1978-80 num.29/40 col lithograph. 10-Oct-2 Sotheby's, London #257/R est:6000-8000
£8974 $14000 €13461 Water made of thick and thin lines and light blue washes (65x86cm-26x34in) s.d.num.AP XI col lithograph. 5-Nov-2 Christie's, Rockefeller NY #398/R est:10000-12000
£9000 $14850 €13050 Lithographic water made of lines, crayon and blue wash (74x87cm-29x34in) s.d.1978-1980 num.48/48 col lithograph. 2-Jul-3 Christie's, London #86/R est:7000-10000
£9500 $15675 €13775 Lithographic water made of lines, crayon and two blue washed (55x75cm-22x30in) s.d.num.61/85 col lithograph. 2-Jul-3 Christie's, London #257/R est:6000-9000
£10063 $16000 €15095 Water made of lines, crayon and blue washes without green wash (75x87cm-30x34in) s.d.num.AP VII col lithograph. 2-May-3 Sotheby's, New York #475/R est:10000-12000
£10692 $17000 €16038 Views of hotel well II (75x93cm-30x37in) s.d.num.30/75 col lithograph. 2-May-3 Sotheby's, New York #469/R est:14000-18000
£13836 $22000 €20754 Pembroke studio interior (118x140cm-46x55in) s.d.84 num.38/70 col lithograph. 29-Apr-3 Christie's, Rockefeller NY #619/R est:15000-20000
£15385 $24000 €23078 Hotel Acatlan, second day (73x193cm-29x76in) s.d.num.19/98 col lithograph two sheets. 5-Nov-2 Christie's, Rockefeller NY #402/R est:25000-35000
£18000 $28080 €27000 Amaryllis in vase (127x91cm-50x36in) s.d.1984/85 num.XIV/XVI lithograph. 25-Mar-3 Sotheby's, London #180/R est:20000-30000
£20570 $32500 €30855 Gregory in the pool (82x127cm-32x50in) init.d.1978 col print paper pulp. 22-Apr-3 Butterfields, San Francisco #2290/R est:50000-70000
£25157 $40000 €37736 Rake's progress (51x63cm-20x25in) s.num. etching col aquatint set of 16 portfolio slipcase. 29-Apr-3 Christie's, Rockefeller NY #617/R est:40000-60000
£25641 $40000 €38462 Caribbean tea time (121x447cm-48x176in) s.num.32/36 col lithograph collage double-sided 4 panel screen. 5-Nov-2 Christie's, Rockefeller NY #403/R est:40000-60000

Works on paper
£1974 $3197 €3000 My dog Stanley (29x44cm-11x17in) s.i. pencil dr two joined sheets. 22-Jan-3 Tajan, Paris #234/R est:3000-5000
£2097 $3250 €3146 Portrait of a young man. s. ink dr. 7-Dec-2 Harvey Clar, Oakland #1341
£3000 $4710 €4500 Chuck (43x35cm-17x14in) init.d.1975 pen ink. 19-Nov-2 Bonhams, Leeds #91/R est:2000-3000
£3500 $5460 €5250 Scrabble game (135x98cm-53x39in) s.i.d.1983 photo collage. 10-Oct-2 Sotheby's, London #251/R est:4000-5000
£4200 $6510 €6300 Palm tree (34x42cm-13x17in) init.d.67 pencil. 4-Dec-2 Christie's, Kensington #337/R est:3000-5000

£7000 $10780 €10500 Still life with flowers (27x20cm-11x8in) init.i.d.65 pen black ink crayon prov.exhib. 5-Sep-2 Christie's, Kensington #740/R est:6000-8000
£7500 $12300 €11250 Study for stillness (34x49cm-13x19in) init.i.d.62pen ink prov.exhib. 6-Jun-3 Christie's, London #67/R est:8000-12000
£8000 $13360 €11600 Celia (76x56cm-30x22in) mono.i.d.May 21.1984 ink double-sided prov. 27-Jun-3 Christie's, London #191/R est:10000-15000
£8200 $13694 €11890 Crawling insects (25x36cm-10x14in) init.i. ink W/C exec.c.1960 prov.exhib. 26-Jun-3 Sotheby's, London #222/R est:6000-8000
£8500 $13260 €12750 Luncheon at the British Embassy Tokyo (115x209cm-45x82in) s.i.d.1983 photo collage. 10-Oct-2 Sotheby's, London #252/R est:4000-5000
£13948 $22039 €20922 Drawing of a camel without a head (34x49cm-13x19in) s.d.1962 s.i.d.1962 verso W/C crayon prov. 3-Apr-3 Heffel, Vancouver #43/R est:30000-35000 (C.D 32500)
£15625 $25000 €23438 Wayne Sleep (43x35cm-17x14in) s.d.1971 ink. 14-May-3 Sotheby's, New York #260a/R est:8000-12000
£17000 $27880 €25500 Cecil Beaton (42x34cm-17x13in) s.i.d.69 pencil prov. 6-Jun-3 Christie's, London #191/R est:15000-20000
£18000 $30060 €26100 Drawing of a camel without a head (33x49cm-13x19in) init.d.62 s.i.d.verso crayon pencil W/C prov. 27-Jun-3 Christie's, London #188/R est:18000-24000
£25316 $40000 €37974 Flowers (43x35cm-17x14in) init.d.78 col pencil prov. 14-Nov-2 Christie's, Rockefeller NY #176/R est:40000-60000
£33000 $54120 €49500 Bank, Palm Springs (35x43cm-14x17in) init.i.d.68 col pencil prov.lit. 7-Feb-3 Sotheby's, London #249/R est:30000-40000
£34810 $55000 €52215 Study for a closer grand canyon IV, Isis Temple (50x65cm-20x26in) init.d.98 col wax crayon prov.exhib. 14-Nov-2 Christie's, Rockefeller NY #177/R est:60000-80000

HODDER, Albert (fl.1880-1895) British
£800 $1256 €1200 Beach scene (33x65cm-13x26in) s.d.1880. 16-Dec-2 Sotheby's, Olympia #75/R

HODDLE, Robert (1794-1881) Australian
Works on paper
£6452 $9806 €9678 Surveying party en route to Bong-bong (26x40cm-10x16in) i. W/C exec.c.1830. 28-Aug-2 Deutscher-Menzies, Melbourne #96/R est:22000-26000 (A.D 18000)

HODEL, Ernst (elder) (1852-1902) Swiss
£429 $669 €644 Mountain lake with tourist boat and cliff (158x115cm-62x45in) s.i.d.1886. 11-Nov-2 Rasmussen, Vejle #657/R (D.KR 5000)
£568 $886 €852 Wetterhorn (67x52cm-26x20in) s. 20-Nov-2 Fischer, Luzern #2116/R (S.FR 1300)

HODEL, Ernst (younger) (1881-1955) Swiss
£271 $422 €407 Lotschental (38x51cm-15x20in) s. panel. 20-Nov-2 Fischer, Luzern #2117/R (S.FR 620)
£283 $453 €425 Snowy mountain village in Wallis (51x77cm-20x30in) s. 17-Mar-3 Philippe Schuler, Zurich #8448 (S.FR 600)
£283 $453 €425 Mountain landscape (60x69cm-24x27in) s. 17-Mar-3 Philippe Schuler, Zurich #8449 (S.FR 600)
£472 $755 €708 Engadin winter landscape (53x75cm-21x30in) s. 17-Mar-3 Philippe Schuler, Zurich #8446 (S.FR 1000)
£611 $954 €917 Saas Fee (49x64cm-19x25in) s. board exhib. 8-Nov-2 Dobiaschofsky, Bern #100/R (S.FR 1400)
£694 $1118 €1006 Lauterbrunnen valley with Oberhorn Lake (78x108cm-31x43in) s. i.verso. 9-May-3 Dobiaschofsky, Bern #124/R (S.FR 1500)

HODGDON, Sally (?) American
Works on paper
£839 $1300 €1259 Parrot in fruit tree (36x30cm-14x12in) calligraphic pen. 2-Nov-2 North East Auctions, Portsmouth #730/R est:3500-5500

HODGDON, Sylvester Phelps (1830-1906) American
£3503 $5500 €5255 Winter, Park Street, Boston (30x40cm-12x16in) s.d.1879. 22-Nov-2 Skinner, Boston #89/R est:800-1200

HODGE, Francis Edwin (1883-1949) British
Works on paper
£2000 $3120 €3000 Number please! (32x36cm-13x14in) W/C over pencil. 12-Sep-2 Sotheby's, Olympia #220/R est:500-700

HODGE, Helen (1870-1958) American
£241 $400 €349 Kansas landscape (61x76cm-24x30in) s. 14-Jun-3 Jackson's, Cedar Falls #30/R

HODGES, Charles Howard (attrib) (1764-1837) British
£1401 $2186 €2200 Portrait of Ester Sara Elisabeth Rijgersbos, half length (72x58cm-28x23in) 6-Nov-2 Christie's, Amsterdam #48/R est:700-900

HODGES, J Sydney Willis (1829-1900) British
Works on paper
£800 $1240 €1200 Lord Hood of Avalon as a midshipman with Bombay beyond (43x30cm-17x12in) mono. pencil W/C. 31-Oct-2 Christie's, Kensington #384/R

HODGES, Jim (1957-) American
Works on paper
£2532 $4000 €3798 Study for corner corner (43x28cm-17x11in) aluminium exec.1999 prov. 13-Nov-2 Sotheby's, New York #403/R
£8228 $13000 €12342 Diary of flowers. pen ink on paper napkins executed 1993 prov. 12-Nov-2 Phillips, New York #186/R est:15000-20000

HODGES, T (19th C) British
Works on paper
£1200 $2004 €1740 St. Andrews Gold Club (20x13cm-8x5in) init.d.1880 W/C. 20-Jun-3 Keys, Aylsham #291 est:250-300
£2000 $3340 €2900 St. Andrews Golf Club (20x13cm-8x5in) init.d.1883 W/C. 20-Jun-3 Keys, Aylsham #290 est:250-300
£2400 $4008 €3480 Skipper, St. Andrews Golf Club (20x10cm-8x4in) init. monotone W/C. 20-Jun-3 Keys, Aylsham #289 est:250-300
£4500 $7515 €6525 Old Tom playing golf, at St. Andrews Golf Club (20x13cm-8x5in) init.d.86 monotone w,. 20-Jun-3 Keys, Aylsham #288/R est:400-500

HODGES, Walter Parry (1760-1845) British
Works on paper
£400 $624 €600 Country race meeting (35x49cm-14x19in) pen ink W/C. 26-Mar-3 Sotheby's, Olympia #92/R

HODGES, William (attrib) (1744-1797) British
£6500 $10270 €9750 Italianate river landscape with peasants in boat and fortified bridge beyond (45x62cm-18x24in) prov. 26-Nov-2 Christie's, London #59/R est:4000-6000
£30000 $47400 €45000 Seven dials, Covent Garden (99x125cm-39x49in) 28-Nov-2 Sotheby's, London #135/R est:10000-15000

HODGES, William (style) (1744-1797) British
£14000 $22260 €21000 Pacific islanders outside their hut (27x24cm-11x9in) 29-Apr-3 Bonhams, New Bond Street #20 est:500-800

HODGINS, Robert (1920-) South African
£1045 $1651 €1568 Can-can ce n'est pas gentil (55x55cm-22x22in) s.d.2002 i.verso. 1-Apr-3 Stephan Welz, Johannesburg #484/R est:7000-10000 (SA.R 13000)
£1419 $2284 €2129 Interviewing a hunk (50x75cm-20x30in) s.i.d.1998 verso. 12-May-3 Stephan Welz, Johannesburg #511/R est:12000-18000 (SA.R 16500)
£1966 $3066 €2949 Three men waiting (91x122cm-36x48in) s.i. i.d.1998/9 verso prov. 15-Oct-2 Stephan Welz, Johannesburg #495/R est:20000-30000 (SA.R 32000)
£2572 $4064 €3858 Bathers (45x75cm-18x30in) i.verso board exhib. 1-Apr-3 Stephan Welz, Johannesburg #485/R est:25000-35000 (SA.R 32000)
£3215 $5080 €4823 Death and the maiden (90x120cm-35x47in) s.i. i.d.1999/2000 verso lit. 1-Apr-3 Stephan Welz, Johannesburg #486/R est:35000-50000 (SA.R 40000)
Works on paper
£362 $572 €543 Two men watching boring T.V (36x53cm-14x21in) s.i.d.2000 W/C. 1-Apr-3 Stephan Welz, Johannesburg #483 est:4000-6000 (SA.R 4500)
£1032 $1661 €1548 Girl on a couch (54x36cm-21x14in) s.i.d.99 W/C. 12-May-3 Stephan Welz, Johannesburg #343 est:5000-8000 (SA.R 12000)
£2883 $4497 €4325 Fun fair (91x121cm-36x48in) s.d.1997 i.verso chl oil. 11-Nov-2 Stephan Welz, Johannesburg #511/R est:40000-60000 (SA.R 45000)

HODGKIN, Eliot (1905-1987) British
£2400 $3960 €3480 Interior at La Brande (17x32cm-7x13in) s.i. board prov. 3-Jul-3 Christie's, Kensington #491/R est:1000-1500
£4000 $6240 €6000 Conspirators (42x30cm-17x12in) s.d.68 board exhib. 27-Mar-3 Christie's, Kensington #531/R est:4000-6000
£9000 $14850 €13050 Apricot in paper (12x19cm-5x7in) s.d.25.65 tempera board prov. 3-Jul-3 Christie's, Kensington #495/R est:4000-6000
£12000 $19680 €17400 Dead leaves and bird's eggs (13x29cm-5x11in) s.d.12 VIII 66 tempera. 5-Jun-3 Christie's, London #195/R est:10000-15000

HODGKIN, Howard (1932-) British

£28000 $46760 €40600 On the beach (45x53cm-18x21in) board prov.exhib.lit. 24-Jun-3 Bonhams, New Bond Street #109/R est:30000-40000
£30000 $50100 €43500 Rain in Venice (61cm-24in circular) s.d.1985 i.verso oil on wood prov.exhib.lit. 27-Jun-3 Christie's, London #195/R est:30000-40000

Prints

£2000 $3140 €3000 Here we are in Croydon (55x77cm-22x30in) s.d.1979 hand col lithograph. 17-Apr-3 Christie's, Kensington #58/R est:1600-2200
£2038 $3200 €3057 Blue listening ear (48x65cm-19x26in) init.d.1986 num.36/100 hand col W/C gouache etching carborundum. 21-Nov-2 Swann Galleries, New York #84/R est:3500-5000
£2038 $3200 €3057 Red palm (108x135cm-43x53in) init.i. hand col W/C lithograph. 21-Nov-2 Swann Galleries, New York #85/R est:2500-3500
£2200 $3498 €3300 Indian tree (92x121cm-36x48in) init.d.1991 num.29/55 hand col etching. 18-Mar-3 Bonhams, Knightsbridge #111 est:1200-1800
£2759 $4248 €4139 A storm (52x61cm-20x24in) s.d.1977 num.96/100 col lithograph hand col in gouache. 27-Oct-2 Anders Antik, Landskrona #678/R est:20000-25000 (S.KR 40000)
£3019 $4800 €4529 For Bernard Jacobson (105x150cm-41x59in) s.num.9/80 col lithograph gouache crayon two sheets. 29-Apr-3 Christie's, Rockefeller NY #620/R est:5000-7000
£3548 $5500 €5322 For Bernard Jacobson (105x150cm-41x59in) s.num.55/80 hand col lithograph on two sheets. 25-Sep-2 Christie's, Rockefeller NY #291/R est:4000-6000
£3600 $5616 €5400 For Bernard Jacobon (106x150cm-42x59in) num.59/80 lithograph hand colouring. 25-Mar-3 Sotheby's, London #185/R est:3000-4000
£3800 $5928 €5700 David's pool (63x80cm-25x31in) init.d.1979-85 num.22/100 hand col etching aquatint. 10-Oct-2 Sotheby's, London #261/R est:3000-4000
£4403 $7000 €6605 For Bernard Jacobson (105x150cm-41x59in) s.d.num.15/80 col lithograph gouache wax crayon two sheets. 2-May-3 Sotheby's, New York #476/R est:5000-7000
£4500 $7020 €6750 Street palm (149x120cm-59x47in) init.d.1990-91 num.15/55 col etching. 10-Oct-2 Sotheby's, London #262/R est:4000-5000
£5000 $7800 €7500 Flowering palm (149x120cm-59x47in) init.d.1990-91 etching carborundum. 25-Mar-3 Sotheby's, London #187/R est:3000-4000
£6500 $10010 €9750 Venice evening (160x196cm-63x77in) init.d. num.16/60 etching aquatint col embossing on sixteen sheet. 24-Oct-2 Christie's, Kensington #79/R est:7000-10000
£7000 $10990 €10500 Venice night (160x196cm-63x77in) init.d.1995 etching aquatint on two sheets. 17-Apr-3 Christie's, Kensington #61/R est:7000-10000
£8200 $12792 €12300 Venice evening (160x196cm-63x77in) num.25/60 etching aquatint. 25-Mar-3 Sotheby's, London #186/R est:5000-7000
£8800 $13816 €13200 Venice evening (160x196cm-63x77in) init.d.1995 hand col etching aquatint. 17-Apr-3 Christie's, Kensington #60/R est:7000-10000

HODGKINS, Frances (1869-1947) New Zealander

£114841 $184894 €172262 Green jug and jade sea (75x64cm-30x25in) s. prov.exhib.lit. 7-May-3 Dunbar Sloane, Auckland #11/R est:300000-400000 (NZ.D 325000)
£142361 $222083 €213542 Still life with landscape (75x62cm-30x24in) s. painted c.1930 prov.exhib.lit. 8-Apr-3 Peter Webb, Auckland #45/R est:250000-350000 (NZ.D 410000)

Works on paper

£654 $929 €981 Yachting regatta (15x11cm-6x4in) init. W/C prov. 21-Nov-1 Watson's, Christchurch #59/R (NZ.D 2250)
£2744 $4198 €4116 Refugees (45x37cm-18x15in) W/C prov. 21-Aug-2 Dunbar Sloane, Auckland #10/R est:15000-25000 (NZ.D 9000)
£3939 $6067 €5909 Bridge, Dordrecht, Holland (23x25cm-9x10in) s.d.1907 W/C prov. 4-Sep-2 Dunbar Sloane, Wellington #42/R est:25000-35000 (NZ.D 13000)
£4200 $6678 €6300 Landscape with woodland and farm buildings (40x53cm-16x21in) i. gouache. 18-Mar-3 Rosebery Fine Art, London #855/R est:3000-4000
£7000 $11480 €10500 Maori women collecting water by a pool in a village landscape (26x22cm-10x9in) s.i. W/C. 10-Feb-3 Robin Fenner, Tavistock #633/R est:4000-6000
£19293 $29904 €28940 Still life (47x63cm-19x25in) s. pencil W/C gouache prov.exhib. 4-Dec-2 Dunbar Sloane, Auckland #28/R est:60000-80000 (NZ.D 60000)
£52083 $81250 €78125 Private bathing (55x76cm-22x30in) s. gouache exec.c.1935-1936 exhib.lit. 8-Apr-3 Peter Webb, Auckland #57/R est:150000-200000 (NZ.D 150000)
£52083 $81250 €78125 Cornish landscape (53x70cm-21x28in) s. gouache exec.c.1935-1936 priv. 8-Apr-3 Peter Webb, Auckland #58/R est:150000-200000 (NZ.D 150000)

HODGKINS, Frances and KEAN, Cissie (19/20th C) New Zealander/British

Works on paper

£606 $933 €909 European village scene (35x34cm-14x13in) W/C. 4-Sep-2 Dunbar Sloane, Wellington #77/R est:5000-10000 (NZ.D 2000)
£606 $933 €909 Ladies by a riverbank (37x28cm-15x11in) W/C. 4-Sep-2 Dunbar Sloane, Wellington #78/R est:5000-10000 (NZ.D 2000)

HODGKINS, William Matthew (1833-1898) New Zealander

Works on paper

£804 $1246 €1206 South Island lake and mountain scene (30x48cm-12x19in) W/C. 4-Dec-2 Dunbar Sloane, Auckland #46/R (NZ.D 2500)
£3055 $4735 €4583 Gold prospector with horse, South Island, westcoast River, with mountains (49x75cm-19x30in) s. W/C. 4-Dec-2 Dunbar Sloane, Auckland #21/R est:15000-20000 (NZ.D 9500)

HODGKINSON, Frank (1919-2001) Australian

£613 $913 €920 Abstract (88x64cm-35x25in) s.d.58 board. 27-Aug-2 Christie's, Melbourne #196 est:800-1200 (A.D 1600)
£1143 $1794 €1715 Projected wet (59x90cm-23x35in) s.d.58 i.verso board. 25-Nov-2 Christie's, Melbourne #271/R est:2000-3000 (A.D 3200)
£1286 $2031 €1929 Untitled (62x121cm-24x48in) s.d.1958 board. 17-Nov-2 Sotheby's, Paddington #59/R est:2000-4000 (A.D 3600)
£1533 $2284 €2300 Time past sensuality (82x101cm-32x40in) s.d.80 s.i.verso. 27-Aug-2 Christie's, Melbourne #236/R est:4000-6000 (A.D 4000)
£1643 $2596 €2465 No.11 (91x120cm-36x47in) s. i.verso board. 17-Nov-2 Sotheby's, Paddington #61/R est:2000-4000 (A.D 4600)
£1971 $2996 €2957 Darling harbour I (30x152cm-12x60in) s.d.86 i.verso. 28-Aug-2 Deutscher-Menzies, Melbourne #350/R est:3500-4500 (A.D 5500)
£2500 $3900 €3750 Walsh bay (127x107cm-50x42in) s. s.i.verso. 11-Nov-2 Deutscher-Menzies, Melbourne #89/R est:8000-10000 (A.D 7000)
£2857 $4457 €4286 Night fishing, Port Jakson IV (185x107cm-73x42in) s.d.87 s.i.d.verso. 11-Nov-2 Deutscher-Menzies, Melbourne #128/R est:9000-12000 (A.D 8000)

Works on paper

£268 $423 €402 Billabong (55x74cm-22x29in) s.d.80 gouache W/C. 27-Nov-2 Deutscher-Menzies, Melbourne #155/R (A.D 750)
£1495 $2287 €2243 Flashes of Dawn Sepik River (207x123cm-81x48in) s.d.March 1977 i.verso gouache W/C on ten sheets. 26-Aug-2 Sotheby's, Paddington #587 est:3000-5000 (A.D 4200)

HODGSON, David (1798-1864) British

£360 $565 €540 Figure by a stream outside a country cottage (31x25cm-12x10in) panel. 16-Dec-2 Bonhams, Bury St Edmunds #538
£750 $1170 €1125 Norfolk wooded landscape with cottages in distance (74x56cm-29x22in) 11-Apr-3 Keys, Aylsham #658/R

Works on paper

£5400 $8586 €8100 Drawings of Norwich (20x13cm-8x5in) two s. pen ink wash over pencil set of four. 19-Mar-3 Sotheby's, London #169/R est:2000-3000

HODGSON, George (1847-1921) British

Works on paper

£260 $404 €390 River Trent at Nottingham (35x51cm-14x20in) s. W/C gouache. 3-Dec-2 Sotheby's, Olympia #65/R
£340 $541 €510 Troutdale, Barrowdale, Cumberland (35x53cm-14x21in) s.i. W/C. 4-Mar-3 Bearnes, Exeter #424/R
£370 $614 €555 Woman and child on a rural path (36x54cm-14x21in) s. W/C. 10-Jun-3 Bonhams, Leeds #68

HODGSON, Walker (fl.1890s) British

Works on paper

£2200 $3542 €3300 Portrait of Frederic, Lord Leighton seated (41x36cm-16x14in) s.i.d.1892 chk wash prov.exhib. 20-Feb-3 Christie's, London #149/R

HODGSON, William Scott (1864-?) British

£480 $763 €720 Whitby Harbour (71x91cm-28x36in) s. 29-Apr-3 Gorringes, Lewes #2278

HODICKE, Karl Horst (1938-) German

£3022 $4835 €4200 Melon (80x100cm-31x39in) s.d.1996 verso acrylic. 15-May-3 Neumeister, Munich #459/R est:2500-3000

Works on paper

£769 $1192 €1200 Untitled (61x86cm-24x34in) mono.d.1978 gouache chl. 6-Dec-2 Hauswedell & Nolte, Hamburg #157/R

HODIENER, Hugo (1886-c.1935) German

Works on paper

£411 $642 €650 Mountain landscape (70x59cm-28x23in) s. gouache. 15-Oct-2 Dorotheum, Vienna #22/R

HODLER, Ferdinand (1853-1918) Swiss

£1267 $2116 €1837 Standing female nude (43x20cm-17x8in) oil chk prov. 24-Jun-3 Koller, Zurich #21/R est:3000-5000 (S.FR 2800)

£1762 $2626 €2643 Woman picking herbs (30x38cm-12x15in) board. 25-Jun-2 Koller, Zurich #6573/R est:3000-5000 (S.FR 4000)

£2423 $3610 €3635 Blumlisalp, Bernese Oberland (34x44cm-13x17in) board. 25-Jun-2 Koller, Zurich #6571 est:5000-7000 (S.FR 5500)

£6438 $10172 €9657 Disappointed soul (22x15cm-9x6in) s. indian ink blue on pencil prov. 28-Nov-2 Christie's, Zurich #38/R est:15000-20000 (S.FR 15000)

£20513 $32000 €30770 Lac de Thoune (30x41cm-12x16in) s. board. 30-Mar-3 Susanin's, Chicago #6058/R est:20000-30000

£20870 $32348 €31305 Taking the oath (120x60cm-47x24in) s. prov.lit. 4-Dec-2 Koller, Zurich #115/R est:30000-50000 (S.FR 48000)

£24017 $37707 €36026 Bull with Jungfrau in background (23x16cm-9x6in) mono. board. 25-Nov-2 Sotheby's, Zurich #25/R est:40000-60000 (S.FR 55000)

£34335 $54249 €51503 Le Fer a Cheval pres de Sixte (29x43cm-11x17in) s. paper on board prov. 28-Nov-2 Christie's, Zurich #28/R est:80000-120000 (S.FR 80000)

£43668 $68559 €65502 Bull by Lake Brienz (10x14cm-4x6in) s. prov.exhib.lit. 25-Nov-2 Sotheby's, Zurich #64/R est:100000-150000 (S.FR 100000)

£52752 $88096 €76490 Cows in meadow with view of Harder and Bodeli from Interlaken (16x24cm-6x9in) mono. board. 20-Jun-3 Kornfeld, Bern #72/R est:125000 (S.FR 115000)

£69869 $109694 €104804 Two chestnut trees (42x29cm-17x11in) s. prov.exhib. 25-Nov-2 Sotheby's, Zurich #39/R est:150000-200000 (S.FR 160000)

£85837 $135622 €128756 Portrait of Clara Battier (46x33cm-18x13in) s. prov.exhib.lit. 26-Nov-2 Phillips, Zurich #29/R est:200000-250000 (S.FR 200000)

£111588 $176309 €167382 Wetterhorn (27x35cm-11x14in) s. exhib.lit. 26-Nov-2 Phillips, Zurich #19/R est:120000-150000 (S.FR 260000)

£144796 $241810 €209954 Portrait of Valentine Gode Darel (42x41cm-17x16in) s.d.1909 prov.exhib. 24-Jun-3 Koller, Zurich #16/R est:180000-250000 (S.FR 320000)

£157205 $246812 €235808 Am Petit Saleve (35x24cm-14x9in) s. prov.exhib.lit. 25-Nov-2 Sotheby's, Zurich #65/R est:220000-260000 (S.FR 360000)

£171674 $271245 €257511 Love (65x155cm-26x61in) s. painted c.1907 prov.exhib. 26-Nov-2 Phillips, Zurich #44/R est:280000-350000 (S.FR 400000)

£386266 $610300 €579399 Excellence of form (120x88cm-47x35in) s. prov.exhib.lit. 26-Nov-2 Phillips, Zurich #33/R est:900000-1300000 (S.FR 900000)

£613208 $993396 €1085378 Le Grand Muveran (64x87cm-25x34in) s. prov.lit. 26-May-3 Sotheby's, Zurich #60/R est:1300000-1600000 (S.FR 1300000)

£1115880 $1763090 €1673820 Geneva lake with Mont-Blanc in the early morning (65x84cm-26x33in) s. prov. 26-Nov-2 Phillips, Zurich #54/R est:1500000-2000000 (S.FR 2600000)

Prints

£8155 $12884 €12233 Holy hour with six figures (63x103cm-25x41in) s.i. lithograph lit. 28-Nov-2 Christie's, Zurich #39/R est:12000-15000 (S.FR 19000)

Works on paper

£524 $828 €786 Homme debout avec bras leve (44x24cm-17x9in) s. 17-Nov-2 Koller, Geneva #1335/R (S.FR 1200)

£644 $1017 €966 Lady sitting (29x25cm-11x10in) pencil. 26-Nov-2 Hans Widmer, St Gallen #1177 est:1500-2600 (S.FR 1500)

£655 $1022 €983 Woman with outstretched arms (20x12cm-8x5in) s. pencil dr. 8-Nov-2 Dobiaschofsky, Bern #49/R (S.FR 1500)

£769 $1285 €1115 Study of two reclining figures (14x30cm-6x12in) pencil. 24-Jun-3 Koller, Zurich #22/R est:2000-3000 (S.FR 1700)

£830 $1211 €1245 Study for 'Jena' (30x44cm-12x17in) pencil prov. 4-Jun-2 Germann, Zurich #772 (S.FR 1900)

£873 $1371 €1310 Figure study - Holy Hour (27x11cm-11x4in) st.sig. pencil. 25-Nov-2 Sotheby's, Zurich #60/R est:2000-2500 (S.FR 2000)

£962 $1490 €1500 Couple lying down - nudes (25x42cm-10x17in) st.sig. pencil transparent paper. 4-Dec-2 Lempertz, Koln #781/R est:1800

£1019 $1640 €1478 Friends in the nude (34x40cm-13x16in) st.sig. pencil dr. 9-May-3 Dobiaschofsky, Bern #58/R (S.FR 2200)

£1202 $1899 €1803 Portrait of Adrian Lachenal (37x39cm-15x15in) st.sig. pencil. 28-Nov-2 Christie's, Zurich #27/R est:2000-4000 (S.FR 2800)

£1415 $2264 €2123 Man in hat with gun (23x11cm-9x4in) pencil squared paper. 17-Mar-3 Philippe Schuler, Zurich #4334/R est:2000-2500 (S.FR 3000)

£1528 $2460 €2216 Study of Eurythmie (30x26cm-12x10in) s. pencil dr. 9-May-3 Dobiaschofsky, Bern #56/R est:3300 (S.FR 3300)

£1630 $2380 €2445 Girl's portrait (23x18cm-9x7in) s.i. pencil. 17-Jun-2 Philippe Schuler, Zurich #4184/R est:2500-3000 (S.FR 3700)

£1717 $2712 €2576 Angel heads (32x27cm-13x11in) st.sig. Indian ink chl wash chk prov.exhib. two. 28-Nov-2 Christie's, Zurich #25/R est:4000-6000 (S.FR 4000)

£1717 $2712 €2576 Figure of a boy (49x15cm-19x6in) s. pencil prov. 28-Nov-2 Christie's, Zurich #36/R est:2500-3000 (S.FR 4000)

£1717 $2712 €2576 Standing female nude with outstretched arms (35x29cm-14x11in) st.sig. pencil prov. 28-Nov-2 Christie's, Zurich #37/R est:4000-6000 (S.FR 4000)

£4009 $6495 €7097 False spectre - figure study for 'truth' (27x10cm-11x4in) mono. verso pencil Indian ink W/C prov.exhib. 26-May-3 Sotheby's, Zurich #46/R est:6000-9000 (S.FR 8500)

£4525 $7557 €6561 Portrait of Clara Pasche Battier (59x44cm-23x17in) pencil tempera prov. 24-Jun-3 Koller, Zurich #19/R est:14000-18000 (S.FR 10000)

£5150 $8137 €7725 Study for unity (44x20cm-17x8in) pencil gouache oil. 26-Nov-2 Phillips, Zurich #13/R est:12000-15000 (S.FR 12000)

£8584 $13562 €12876 Watchmaker from Geneva (36x15cm-14x6in) s. Indian ink pencil prov. 28-Nov-2 Christie's, Zurich #26/R est:20000-25000 (S.FR 20000)

£12876 $20343 €19314 Female nude in green (44x23cm-17x9in) s. pencil oil paper on wood prov.exhib.lit. 26-Nov-2 Phillips, Zurich #12/R est:30000-40000 (S.FR 30000)

HODLER, Hermann (1888-1965) Swiss

£437 $690 €656 Beer hut in winter (72x85cm-28x33in) 14-Nov-2 Stuker, Bern #284/R (S.FR 1000)

HODR, Karel (1910-) Czechoslovakian

£270 $422 €400 Wasserburg (29x59cm-11x23in) s. i. verso board lit. 28-Mar-3 Karrenbauer, Konstanz #1747

HODSON, Samuel John (1836-1908) British

Works on paper

£320 $515 €480 Steps of St Marco Venice with numerous figures and boats (36x53cm-14x21in) W/C over pencil. 22-Feb-3 Hogben, Folkstone #180

HOEBER, Arthur (1854-1915) American

£1299 $2000 €1949 Fields at sunset (30x41cm-12x16in) s. 24-Oct-2 Shannon's, Milford #199/R est:1500-2000

£1935 $3000 €2903 Landscape view of woods and a pond (18x13cm-7x5in) s. panel. 2-Nov-2 North East Auctions, Portsmouth #29/R

£2968 $4600 €4452 Afternoon (61x51cm-24x20in) s. i.verso prov. 2-Nov-2 North East Auctions, Portsmouth #83/R est:2000-4000

£3548 $5500 €5322 Near Easthampton, Long Island (25x36cm-10x14in) s.i. prov. 2-Nov-2 North East Auctions, Portsmouth #33/R est:1500-2500

£3846 $6000 €5769 Tidewater stream (63x76cm-25x30in) s. i.verso. 14-Sep-2 Weschler, Washington #610/R est:3000-5000

HOEBRECHT, Pierre (1888-1966) Belgian

£759 $1185 €1200 Boulevards animes a Bruxelles sous l'occupation (56x87cm-22x34in) mono.d.1914-15 triptych. 10-Sep-2 Vanderkindere, Brussels #289

HOECK, Raymond van (1922-1992) Belgian

£252 $387 €400 Nature morte aux huitres et au saumon (55x65cm-22x26in) s. 22-Oct-2 Campo, Vlaamse Kaai #314

£252 $387 €400 Nature morte a la coupe de fruits et aux oiseaux morts (55x65cm-22x26in) s. 22-Oct-2 Campo, Vlaamse Kaai #315

HOECKE, Robert van den (attrib) (1622-1668) Flemish

£9819 $16104 €14238 The capture of the citadel (41x70cm-16x28in) bears init. 4-Jun-3 AB Stockholms Auktionsverk #2533/R est:60000-80000 (S.KR 125000)

HOECKER, Paul (1854-1910) German

£256 $403 €400 Two pierrots with opera glasses in box (35x46cm-14x18in) s. board portrait study verso. 21-Nov-2 Van Ham, Cologne #1682

HOEDT, Jan Hendrik Willem (1825-1868) Dutch
£1644 $2564 €2400 River landscape with anchored sailing boat near a farm (17x24cm-7x9in) s. panel. 14-Apr-3 Glerum, Amsterdam #31/R est:2500-3000

HOEDT, Pieter Louis (1832-1878) Dutch
Works on paper
£592 $959 €900 Cows in meadow. Sheep grazing (30x54cm-12x21in) s. pencil W/C bodycol pair. 21-Jan-3 Christie's, Amsterdam #153

HOEF, Abraham van der (attrib) (fl.1613-1649) Dutch
£2482 $3848 €3723 Battle scene (41x63cm-16x25in) init. panel. 3-Dec-2 Bukowskis, Stockholm #478/R est:30000-35000 (S.KR 35000)
£2600 $4030 €3900 Cavalry skirmish (42x65cm-17x26in) 30-Oct-2 Bonhams, New Bond Street #43/R est:2000-3000

HOEF, Frouke van der (1861-1949) Dutch
Works on paper
£321 $503 €500 Mushroom (45x64cm-18x25in) s.d.1921 batik. 25-Nov-2 Glerum, Amsterdam #112

HOEFEL, Johann Nepomuk (1786-1864) Austrian
£1210 $1876 €1815 After breakfast (52x44cm-20x17in) s. 6-Dec-2 Kieselbach, Budapest #17/R (H.F 450000)

HOEFFLER, Adolf (1826-1898) German
Works on paper
£377 $588 €550 Kronberg seen from Falkenstein (27x44cm-11x17in) s.i.d.26.Sept.82 pencil chk. 11-Apr-3 Winterberg, Heidelberg #403

HOEFNAGEL, Georg (1542-1600) Flemish
Works on paper
£158065 $249742 €245000 Mythological scene and still life (17x23cm-7x9in) mono.d.1590 gouache vellum on panel. 18-Dec-2 Beaussant & Lefèvre, Paris #20/R est:50000

HOEFNAGEL, Joris (17th C) Dutch
Works on paper
£40123 $65000 €60185 Naked savage (14x20cm-6x8in) bodycol htd gold. 22-Jan-3 Christie's, Rockefeller NY #85/R est:15000

HOEHME, Gerhard (1920-1990) German
£20513 $31795 €32000 Mondrian's garden - hommage (109x100cm-43x39in) s.d.59 s.i.d. verso canvas collage exhib. 3-Dec-2 Lempertz, Koln #195/R est:25000
Works on paper
£385 $596 €600 Abstract composition (21x30cm-8x12in) s.d.56 W/C ink board. 7-Dec-2 Van Ham, Cologne #234/R
£481 $745 €750 Untitled (34x27cm-13x11in) s.d.62 s.i.d.1962 verso pencil. 7-Dec-2 Van Ham, Cologne #235/R
£946 $1476 €1400 Untitled (29x20cm-11x8in) s.d. gouache over monotype board prov. 28-Mar-3 Ketterer, Hamburg #359/R

HOEHN, Alfred (1875-?) German
£256 $397 €400 Still life with poppies, teapot and lemons (54x44cm-21x17in) s.d.1927. 5-Dec-2 Schopman, Hamburg #576
£353 $554 €550 Girl in summer meadow (75x60cm-30x24in) s.d.1910. 23-Nov-2 Arnold, Frankfurt #755

HOEHN, Georg (attrib) (1812-1879) German
£472 $736 €750 Cows at ford (20x28cm-8x11in) panel. 19-Sep-2 Dr Fritz Nagel, Stuttgart #945/R

HOEK, Hans van (1947-) Dutch
£2878 $4719 €4000 Kruis tussen de bomen - cross between trees (169x160cm-67x63in) s.i.d.88 oil chk. 3-Jun-3 Christie's, Amsterdam #372/R est:4500-5500
Works on paper
£1899 $3000 €3000 Vijf figuren in landschap (57x77cm-22x30in) s.d.1994 W/C black chk. 26-Nov-2 Sotheby's, Amsterdam #65/R est:2000-3000
£1923 $2981 €3000 Freesia's (74x105cm-29x41in) s.i.d.1986 verso w/. 3-Dec-2 Christie's, Amsterdam #358/R est:3000-5000
£2051 $3179 €3200 Peelandschap (73x102cm-29x40in) s.i.d.89 verso chl W/C. 3-Dec-2 Christie's, Amsterdam #356/R est:3000-5000

HOENDERDOS, Jac Hendricus (1914-) Dutch
£1986 $3217 €2800 Terrace by the sea (46x55cm-18x22in) s. 26-May-3 Glerum, Amsterdam #156/R est:1000-1500

HOENIGSMANN, Rela (1865-?) German
£577 $894 €900 Small town (88x63cm-35x25in) s.i. 5-Dec-2 Neumeister, Munich #2812/R

HOEPFNER, Franz (19th C) German
£432 $708 €600 Idstein (40x30cm-16x12in) s. canvas on board. 4-Jun-3 Reiss & Sohn, Konigstein #144/R
£520 $827 €780 Nearing shore (37x49cm-15x19in) s.d.1879. 4-Mar-3 Bristol Auction Rooms #367/R
£2200 $3278 €3300 Nuns Chair, Douglas Head (41x61cm-16x24in) i.verso. 28-Jun-2 Chrystals Auctions, Isle of Man #158 est:300-500
£4500 $6975 €6750 Christmas goose fair, St. Matthews (107x69cm-42x27in) 6-Dec-2 Chrystals Auctions, Isle of Man #223 est:4000-6000

HOEPHNER, Franz (19th C) British?
£850 $1309 €1275 Coastal landscape with fisherfolk near a cottage and distant sailing boats (29x44cm-11x17in) s.d.86 i.verso. 23-Oct-2 Hampton & Littlewood, Exeter #442/R

HOERLE, Heinrich (1895-1936) German
£5797 $9507 €8000 Self portrait (40x30cm-16x12in) s.i. board prov.exhib. 29-May-3 Lempertz, Koln #675/R est:5000-6000
Works on paper
£3526 $5465 €5500 Two girls' heads (31x50cm-12x20in) s.i.d.1927/7 Indian ink oil bodycol board prov. 4-Dec-2 Lempertz, Koln #782/R est:6000-7000

HOERMAN, Carl (1885-?) American
£385 $600 €578 Adobe huts (33x38cm-13x15in) board. 19-Oct-2 David Dike, Dallas #218/R
£2388 $3750 €3582 Desert verbena in bloom (70x78cm-28x31in) s. 19-Nov-2 Butterfields, San Francisco #8319/R est:3000-5000

HOET, Gerard (elder) (1648-1733) Dutch
£9500 $14915 €14250 Rachel and Jacob, Rachel and Laban (19x24cm-7x9in) one s.d.1674 panel pair. 10-Dec-2 Bonhams, New Bond Street #261/R est:8000-12000

HOETERICKX, Émile (1858-1923) Belgian
£4483 $7172 €6500 Attraction (45x75cm-18x30in) s.d.1880. 15-Mar-3 De Vuyst, Lokeren #515/R est:7000-8000
Works on paper
£414 $658 €600 Scene de marche (49x35cm-19x14in) s. W/C gouache. 4-Mar-3 Palais de Beaux Arts, Brussels #344
£1862 $2979 €2700 Great market in Brussels (23x17cm-9x7in) s.i. W/C. 15-Mar-3 De Vuyst, Lokeren #159/R est:3000-3500
£2069 $3310 €3000 View of park in London (23x18cm-9x7in) s.i. W/C. 15-Mar-3 De Vuyst, Lokeren #158/R est:3000-3500

HOETGER, Bernhard (1874-1949) German
Sculpture
£2174 $3565 €3000 Girl with hoop (18cm-7in) bronze pat.bronze lit. 29-May-3 Lempertz, Koln #676/R est:2500
£2899 $4754 €4000 Man with stick (29cm-11in) s. brown pat.bronze. 29-May-3 Lempertz, Koln #677/R est:4200
£11594 $19014 €16000 Head of the dancer, Sent M'Ahesa (38cm-15in) s.i. verso artificial stone prov. 30-May-3 Villa Grisebach, Berlin #22/R est:12000-15000

HOETGER, Bernhard (attrib) (1874-1949) German
Sculpture
£3718 $5874 €5800 Girl with wind blown hair (31cm-12in) s.i. green grey pat.bronze. 16-Nov-2 Quittenbaum, Munich #233/R est:5800
£3846 $6077 €6000 Old man (30cm-12in) s. dark brown pat.bronze. 16-Nov-2 Quittenbaum, Munich #232 est:5800

HOEVE, Jan van (?) Dutch
£409 $638 €650 Still life (50x61cm-20x24in) s. board. 23-Sep-2 Durán, Madrid #154/R

HOEVEN, G E C Pruys van der (1839-1921) Dutch
Works on paper
£308 $481 €450 Portrait of a girl (56x40cm-22x16in) s. pastel. 14-Apr-3 Glerum, Amsterdam #179/R

HOEVENAAR, Cornelis Willem (elder) (1802-1873) Dutch

£789 $1279 €1200 Domestic duties (47x38cm-19x15in) s. 21-Jan-3 Christie's, Amsterdam #6 est:1200-1600

HOEVENAAR, Willem Pieter (1808-1863) Dutch

£10917 $17031 €16376 Figures round table (73x90cm-29x35in) s.d.1835. 6-Nov-2 Dobiaschofsky, Bern #662/R est:29000 (S.FR 25000)

HOEYDONCK, Paul van (1925-) Belgian

£345 $552 €500 Intelligent gas (20x60cm-8x24in) s. s.i.verso panel. 15-Mar-3 De Vuyst, Lokeren #343

Works on paper

£646 $1028 €950 Colonisation sur la Planete Zafir X-30 (61x61cm-24x24in) s.d.63 verso assemblage gold gouache. 18-Mar-3 Galerie Moderne, Brussels #537/R

£17610 $27119 €28000 Kyoto box (74x111cm-29x44in) s.d.1989 verso mixed media. 22-Oct-2 Campo, Vlaamse Kaai #653

HOFBAUER, Josef (1907-1998) German

£359 $590 €550 Four ducks on pond (18x24cm-7x9in) s. panel. 29-Mar-3 Dannenberg, Berlin #595/R

£390 $569 €600 Procession (13x18cm-5x7in) s. panel lit. 14-Jun-2 Auktionhaus Georg Rehm, Augsburg #8055

£425 $697 €650 Ducks and chickens by pond (13x18cm-5x7in) s. panel. 29-Mar-3 Dannenberg, Berlin #593/R

£425 $697 €650 Baby goat with chicks (12x17cm-5x7in) s. panel. 29-Mar-3 Dannenberg, Berlin #594/R

£425 $697 €650 Shepherd with flock at stable door (23x18cm-9x7in) s. panel. 29-Mar-3 Dannenberg, Berlin #596/R

£437 $690 €656 The rest (13x18cm-5x7in) panel. 14-Nov-2 Stuker, Bern #285 (S.FR 1000)

£458 $732 €700 Poultry at the village pond (16x21cm-6x8in) s. canvas on panel. 10-Jan-3 Allgauer, Kempten #1629/R

£510 $811 €750 Ducks and hens by pond (13x18cm-5x7in) s. panel lit. 21-Mar-3 Auktionhaus Georg Rehm, Augsburg #8038

£510 $811 €750 Romantic Chiemsee landscape (15x30cm-6x12in) s. panel lit. 21-Mar-3 Auktionhaus Georg Rehm, Augsburg #8039/R

£577 $894 €900 Hens and ducks at the pond (13x18cm-5x7in) s. panel. 7-Dec-2 Dannenberg, Berlin #683/R

£577 $894 €900 Extensive romantic landscape (13x18cm-5x7in) s. panel lit. 6-Dec-2 Auktionhaus Georg Rehm, Augsburg #8060/R

£629 $981 €1000 Cockerel and chickens (13x17cm-5x7in) s. 20-Sep-2 Karlheinz Kaupp, Staufen #1998/R

£654 $1046 €1000 Fisherman with boat on the Cheimsee with view of Fraueninsel (15x30cm-6x12in) s. canvas on panel. 10-Jan-3 Allgauer, Kempten #1627/R

£719 $1150 €1100 Loaded wagon and figures on path by stream (15x30cm-6x12in) s. canvas on panel. 10-Jan-3 Allgauer, Kempten #1628/R

£764 $1192 €1200 Ducks on pond (13x18cm-5x7in) s. panel lit. 8-Nov-2 Auktionhaus Georg Rehm, Augsburg #8062/R

£769 $1192 €1200 Chiemsee landscape with boat (13x18cm-5x7in) s. panel lit. 6-Dec-2 Auktionhaus Georg Rehm, Augsburg #8059/R

£784 $1255 €1200 Lower alpine landscape with hay-making by lake (20x40cm-8x16in) s. panel. 10-Jan-3 Allgauer, Kempten #1626/R

£784 $1255 €1200 Hay-making at Tegernsee (19x39cm-7x15in) s. panel. 10-Jan-3 Allgauer, Kempten #1625/R

£948 $1554 €1450 Tegernsee with peasants harvesting (20x40cm-8x16in) s. panel lit. 7-Feb-3 Auktionhaus Georg Rehm, Augsburg #8039/R

£955 $1490 €1500 Peasants harvesting hay in romantic landscape (40x20cm-16x8in) s. panel lit. 8-Nov-2 Auktionhaus Georg Rehm, Augsburg #8063/R est:1200

£962 $1490 €1500 Romantic landscape with stream, figures and animals (15x30cm-6x12in) s. panel lit. 6-Dec-2 Auktionhaus Georg Rehm, Augsburg #8061/R est:1500

£1069 $1668 €1700 Ducks and hens by pond (13x18cm-5x7in) s. 21-Sep-2 Dannenberg, Berlin #564/R est:650

HOFBAUER, Josef (jnr) (1948-) German

£372 $580 €550 Food market (13x18cm-5x7in) s. panel. 26-Mar-3 Hugo Ruef, Munich #137

HOFER, Candida (1944-) German

Photographs

£1935 $3000 €2903 Bibliotheque Nationale de France Paris I (52x41cm-20x16in) s.i.d.1998 num.5/6 verso color coupler print prov.exhib. 26-Sep-2 Christie's, Rockefeller NY #855/R est:3000-5000

£1944 $3091 €2800 Volkswagenwerk Wolfsburg (37x37cm-15x15in) s.num.2/6 verso cibachrome print prov. 29-Apr-3 Artcurial Briest, Paris #500/R est:1200-1500

£2452 $3800 €3678 Abteiberg St. Benediktusberg Vaals II (47x40cm-19x16in) s.i.d.1998 verso color coupler print prov.exhib. 26-Sep-2 Christie's, Rockefeller NY #854/R est:3000-5000

£2812 $4500 €4218 Museum fur volkerkunde dresden IV (85x85cm-33x33in) s.verso c-print executed 2000 prov. 16-May-3 Phillips, New York #198/R est:5000-7000

£2813 $4500 €4220 Biblioteque nationale de France, Paris I (46x39cm-18x15in) s.i.d.1998 num.3/6 col coupler print prov. 14-May-3 Sotheby's, New York #410/R est:5000-7000

£3125 $5000 €4688 Observatory Los Angeles I, 2000 (59x59cm-23x23in) s.verso cibachrome print prov. 14-May-3 Sotheby's, New York #412/R est:6000-8000

£3500 $5390 €5250 BNF Paris XVI (60x60cm-24x24in) s. col coupler print executed 1998 prov. 23-Oct-2 Christie's, London #193/R est:5000-7000

£3500 $5390 €5250 Bibliothek Medrid I (60x60cm-24x24in) s. col coupler print executed 2000 prov. 23-Oct-2 Christie's, London #194/R est:5000-7000

£5063 $8000 €7595 BNF Paris XXII (86x86cm-34x34in) s.verso c-print exec.1998 prov. 13-Nov-2 Sotheby's, New York #442/R est:9000-12000

£8125 $13000 €12188 Los Angeles Public Library IV (85x85cm-33x33in) s.verso c-print executed 2000 prov. 16-May-3 Phillips, New York #197/R est:5000-7000

HOFER, Heinrich (1825-1878) German

£961 $1499 €1442 Landscape with cattle by ford (46x58cm-18x23in) s.i.d.1858. 20-Nov-2 Fischer, Luzern #2119/R est:2000-2200 (S.FR 2200)

HOFER, Ignaz (19th C) ?

£2051 $3179 €3200 Landscape with Seggau Castle (56x75cm-22x30in) s.d.842 panel. 5-Dec-2 Dorotheum, Graz #22/R est:3200

HOFER, Karl (1878-1955) German

£13924 $21722 €22000 Portrait of old woman (38x30cm-15x12in) mono.d.1947 lit. 18-Oct-2 Dr Fritz Nagel, Stuttgart #528/R est:28000

£18987 $30000 €30000 Still life with candles (57x76cm-22x30in) mono.d.48 prov.exhib. 29-Nov-2 Villa Grisebach, Berlin #80/R est:35000-45000

£20513 $29949 €32000 Reading hour (76x81cm-30x32in) mono.d.53. 4-Jun-2 Karl & Faber, Munich #277/R est:35000-40000

£20886 $33000 €33000 Lonely harbour (100x80cm-39x31in) mono.d.50 i. stretcher prov.exhib.lit. 30-Nov-2 Villa Grisebach, Berlin #361/R est:35000-40000

£21519 $34000 €34000 Still life (43x59cm-17x23in) mono. prov. 30-Nov-2 Villa Grisebach, Berlin #350/R est:30000-40000

£24051 $38000 €38000 Seated half-nude (80x64cm-31x25in) mono.d.30 prov. 29-Nov-2 Villa Grisebach, Berlin #56/R est:50000-70000

£25316 $40000 €40000 Women's room (117x80cm-46x31in) mono. 30-Nov-2 Bassenge, Berlin #6324/R est:50000

£25316 $40000 €40000 Summer evening (100x82cm-39x32in) mono.d.50 prov.exhib.lit. 29-Nov-2 Villa Grisebach, Berlin #81/R est:40000-60000

£25316 $40000 €40000 Girl with vinyl record (91x71cm-36x28in) mono.d.54 prov.exhib. 27-Nov-2 Dorotheum, Vienna #38/R est:40000-70000

£25362 $41594 €35000 Sunflowers (100x65cm-39x26in) mono.d.47 prov.exhib. 31-May-3 Villa Grisebach, Berlin #285/R est:35000-45000

£26432 $38590 €39648 Gewri - Indian girl (70x51cm-28x20in) mono. board lit.prov. 17-Jun-2 Philippe Schuler, Zurich #4380/R est:50000-70000 (S.FR 60000)

£26582 $42000 €42000 Female at a window (81x73cm-32x29in) mono.d.43 i.verso prov.exhib.lit. 29-Nov-2 Villa Grisebach, Berlin #77/R est:40000-60000

£43478 $71304 €60000 Still life of flowers (112x85cm-44x33in) mono.d.33 i. stretcher prov. 30-May-3 Villa Grisebach, Berlin #54/R est:45000-55000

£49689 $80000 €74534 Blumenmadchen - flower girl (101x81cm-40x32in) init.d.35 prov.exhib.lit. 7-May-3 Sotheby's, New York #362/R est:100000-150000

£50725 $83188 €70000 Madonna del Piano - Tessin (63x90cm-25x35in) mono. i. stretcher prov.exhib. 30-May-3 Villa Grisebach, Berlin #56/R est:70000-90000

£53846 $83462 €84000 Girl drying herself and wearing turban (61x46cm-24x18in) mono.d.41 prov. 4-Dec-2 Lempertz, Koln #787/R est:70000-80000

£57554 $94388 €80000 Young Indian (99x75cm-39x30in) mono. i. stretcher prov.exhib. 6-Jun-3 Ketterer, Munich #47/R est:70000-90000

£84615 $131154 €132000 Wartende frau (82x67cm-32x26in) mono.d.36 prov.exhib. 4-Dec-2 Lempertz, Koln #16/R est:100000-120000

£85000 $138550 €127500 Landliches paar im mondlicht (102x106cm-40x42in) mono.d.38 prov.exhib. 3-Feb-3 Christie's, London #25/R est:100000-150000

£90000 $140400 €135000 Sitzender weiblicher akt - seated female nude (95x85cm-37x33in) mono. painted 1927 prov.exhib.lit. 9-Oct-2 Sotheby's, London #32/R est:100000-150000

£132912 $210000 €210000 Girl throwing flowers (104x81cm-41x32in) mono.d.45 s.i.verso prov. 29-Nov-2 Villa Grisebach, Berlin #65/R est:120000-150000

Works on paper
£1233 $1923 €1800 Two girls (40x30cm-16x12in) mono. pencil. 11-Apr-3 Winterberg, Heidelberg #1139/R est:2400
£1266 $2000 €2000 Couple (60x42cm-24x17in) mono. Indian ink. 29-Nov-2 Villa Grisebach, Berlin #666/R est:2500-3000
£1321 $2113 €1982 Girl with flowers (43x27cm-17x11in) mono. chl wash. 17-Mar-3 Philippe Schuler, Zurich #4039 est:2000-3000 (S.FR 2800)
£1582 $2453 €2500 Man with bird (26x17cm-10x7in) mono.i. graphite. 28-Sep-2 Ketterer, Hamburg #214/R est:2400-2800
£1761 $2747 €2800 Woman at a table (61x45cm-24x18in) mono. pencil executed c.1926 prov. 9-Oct-2 Sotheby's, London #234/R est:4000-6000
£1761 $2747 €2800 Young female nude II (59x40cm-23x16in) mono. chl executed 1924 prov. 9-Oct-2 Sotheby's, London #235/R est:3000-4000
£1795 $2621 €2800 Seated female nude (41x31cm-16x12in) mono. pencil chk. 4-Jun-2 Karl & Faber, Munich #278/R est:2000
£1899 $3000 €3000 Figures (52x38cm-20x15in) mono.i. chl wash. 30-Nov-2 Bassenge, Berlin #6325/R est:3500
£1899 $3000 €3000 Figures (52x38cm-20x15in) mono. chl wash. 30-Nov-2 Bassenge, Berlin #6326/R est:4000
£2013 $3140 €3200 Standing female nude holding cloth (32x25cm-13x10in) mono. wash pen sketch verso. 11-Oct-2 Winterberg, Heidelberg #1244/R est:2400
£2532 $4000 €4000 Woman in armchair (50x38cm-20x15in) mono. chl pencil. 30-Nov-2 Villa Grisebach, Berlin #346/R est:4000-6000
£3165 $5000 €5000 Girl's head (30x24cm-12x9in) mono. W/C. 30-Nov-2 Villa Grisebach, Berlin #207/R est:3500-4500
£3797 $6000 €6000 Head (60x42cm-24x17in) mono. W/C gouache over col chk sketch verso. 30-Nov-2 Villa Grisebach, Berlin #360a/R est:3500-4500

HOFF, Conrad (1816-1883) German
£2381 $3786 €3500 Venice by moonlight (36x29cm-14x11in) s. 19-Mar-3 Neumeister, Munich #587/R est:2200

HOFF, George Raynor (20th C) ?
Sculpture
£3943 $5993 €5915 Bust of Norman Lindsay (65cm-26in) st.num.19/70 bronze. 27-Aug-2 Goodman, Sydney #125/R est:12000-18000 (A.D 11000)

HOFF, Guy (1889-1962) American
Works on paper
£1242 $2000 €1863 Girl in green cloche hat (58x43cm-23x17in) s. pastel exec.c.1926 lit. 10-May-3 Illustration House, New York #121/R est:2000-4000

HOFF, Johann Friedrich (1835-1913) German
Works on paper
£788 $1261 €1182 Orpheus in the Under-world (40x76cm-16x30in) s. W/C arched. 13-Jan-3 Rasmussen, Vejle #213/R (D.KR 9000)

HOFF, Margo (1912-) American
Works on paper
£774 $1200 €1161 Dancers (25x20cm-10x8in) s. W/C painted c.1950 pair. 8-Dec-2 Toomey, Oak Park #765/R

HOFF, Tor (1925-1976) Norwegian
£826 $1355 €1198 Interior scene with young woman (80x60cm-31x24in) s.d.53. 2-Jun-3 Blomqvist, Oslo #199/R (N.KR 9000)
£1393 $2228 €2090 Composition in green, black and white (83x83cm-33x33in) s.d.1971 acrylic panel. 17-Mar-3 Blomqvist, Oslo #443/R est:22000-24000 (N.KR 16000)
£2611 $4178 €3917 Interior scene with seated nude (100x120cm-39x47in) s.d.55. 17-Mar-3 Blomqvist, Oslo #420/R est:35000-45000 (N.KR 30000)
£2618 $4110 €3927 Composition (60x73cm-24x29in) s.d.48. 21-Nov-2 Grev Wedels Plass, Oslo #69/R est:40000-60000 (N.KR 30000)

HOFFBAUER, Charles (attrib) (1875-1957) French
£1226 $1900 €1839 Cafe scene (18x36cm-7x14in) canvas on board painted c.1905. 8-Dec-2 Toomey, Oak Park #695/R est:1000-2000

HOFFMAN, A V (?) German
£215 $339 €323 Untitled (30x27cm-12x11in) s. board. 3-Apr-3 Heffel, Vancouver #45/R (C.D 500)

HOFFMAN, Adrian (19th C) German
£850 $1360 €1275 Still life of flowers (106x65cm-42x26in) s. 7-Jan-3 Bonhams, Knightsbridge #75/R

HOFFMAN, Belle (1889-?) American
£2760 $4250 €4140 Red cross fair (23x30cm-9x12in) s. board prov. 24-Oct-2 Shannon's, Milford #136/R est:2500-3500

HOFFMAN, Frank B (1888-1958) American
£4808 $7500 €7212 Mustang roundup (58x79cm-23x31in) s. prov.lit. 9-Nov-2 Santa Fe Art, Santa Fe #21/R est:10000-20000
£12821 $20000 €19232 Fox hunt (86x107cm-34x42in) 9-Nov-2 Altermann Galleries, Santa Fe #232

HOFFMAN, Frank V (1902-) American
£260 $400 €390 City towers (76x97cm-30x38in) s. board painted c.1960. 8-Sep-2 Treadway Gallery, Cincinnati #694/R
£327 $505 €491 Marina towers on the river (81x61cm-32x24in) s. 25-Oct-2 Aspire, Cleveland #14
£779 $1200 €1169 Marina Towers, on the river, Chicago (81x61cm-32x24in) s. painted c.1966. 8-Sep-2 Treadway Gallery, Cincinnati #698/R
£1039 $1600 €1559 Rural landscape. s. painted c.1935. 8-Sep-2 Treadway Gallery, Cincinnati #641/R est:1500-2500
£1169 $1800 €1754 Leda and the swan (168x173cm-66x68in) painted wood screen three panels exhib. 8-Sep-2 Treadway Gallery, Cincinnati #759/R est:1000-2000

Works on paper
£325 $500 €488 Glowacki's pharmacy, Milwaukee and Grand Ave, Chicago (36x51cm-14x20in) s. W/C exec.c.1960. 8-Sep-2 Treadway Gallery, Cincinnati #615/R

HOFFMAN, Harry Leslie (1871-1964) American
£223 $350 €335 Landscape in fall with tall trees lining curved dirt roads (61x51cm-24x20in) s.d.1952. 19-Apr-3 James Julia, Fairfield #289/R
£641 $1000 €962 Road in woods (60x50cm-24x20in) s.i.d.1952. 9-Nov-2 Sloan, North Bethesda #606/R
£1807 $3000 €2620 Indefatigable shore, Galapogos (46x51cm-18x20in) s. i.verso panel painted c.1923. 14-Jun-3 Jackson's, Cedar Falls #11/R est:2500-4500

HOFFMAN, Irwin D (20th C) American
£710 $1100 €1065 El jibato (51x58cm-20x23in) 4-Oct-2 Douglas, South Deerfield #3

HOFFMAN, Malvina (1887-1966) American
Sculpture
£1062 $1700 €1540 Cap (14cm-6in) s. green pat bronze sold with black metal plinth. 16-May-3 Skinner, Boston #158/R est:1500-2000
£5660 $9000 €8490 Tibetan jewel merchant (31cm-12in) i. brown pat. bronze prov.lit. 4-Mar-3 Christie's, Rockefeller NY #81/R est:4000-6000
£14194 $22000 €21291 Russian dancers (27x30cm-11x12in) i. green reddish brown pat. bronze. 5-Dec-2 Christie's, Rockefeller NY #109/R est:15000-25000
£29032 $45000 €43548 La frileuse (100cm-39in) i. green pat. bronze executed 1912. 5-Dec-2 Christie's, Rockefeller NY #80/R est:15000-25000

HOFFMAN, Martin (1935-) American
£705 $1100 €1058 Connection (152x203cm-60x80in) s.i.d.1973 verso acrylic prov. 14-Oct-2 Butterfields, San Francisco #2107/R est:3000-5000

HOFFMANN VON VESTENHOF, August (1849-?) German
£1200 $1860 €1800 Nude with rose (80x64cm-31x25in) s. 3-Dec-2 Sotheby's, Olympia #275/R est:1500-2000

HOFFMANN, Carl Heinrich (19th C) German
Works on paper
£302 $483 €420 Bull by tree and fence (20x28cm-8x11in) s.d.65 W/C. 13-May-3 Hartung & Hartung, Munich #4043/R

HOFFMANN, Carl and MEYER, Hannes (20th C) Swiss
Photographs
£7595 $12000 €12000 Co-op: interior (16x16cm-6x6in) i. verso silver gelatin lit.exhib. 28-Nov-2 Villa Grisebach, Berlin #1320/R est:3000-5000

HOFFMANN, Franz Jacob (1851-1903) German
£287 $441 €450 Deer in winter landscape (74x58cm-29x23in) s. 5-Sep-2 Arnold, Frankfurt #787

HOFFMANN, Josef (1831-1904) Austrian
£472 $731 €750 Salzkammergut (42x56cm-17x22in) s. i. verso. 29-Oct-2 Dorotheum, Vienna #9/R
£805 $1297 €1200 Ring-a-ring-of-roses (125x90cm-49x35in) s.d.1885. 18-Feb-3 Sotheby's, Amsterdam #321 est:1500-2000

Works on paper

£285 $444 €450 Little cupboards (15x21cm-6x8in) pencil transparent paper. 15-Oct-2 Dorotheum, Vienna #68/R

HOFFMANN, Josef (attrib) (1831-1904) Austrian

£268 $432 €400 Woodland park in spring (57x77cm-22x30in) s. 18-Feb-3 Sotheby's, Amsterdam #296/R
£342 $534 €500 Village with mill and mountain stream (27x35cm-11x14in) paper lit. 10-Apr-3 Allgauer, Kempten #2807/R

HOFFMANN, Oskar Adolfovitch (1851-1913) Russian

£542 $900 €786 Landscape with ploughman (18x28cm-7x11in) 11-Jun-3 Boos Gallery, Michigan #443/R est:1500-2500
£3239 $5215 €4600 Walking home (32x24cm-13x9in) s.d.84. 10-May-3 Bukowskis, Helsinki #397/R est:3000-4000
£12000 $18840 €18000 Venus by moonlight (175x124cm-69x49in) s.d.1908. 20-Nov-2 Sotheby's, London #62/R est:12000-18000

HOFFMANN-FALLERSLEBEN, Franz (1855-1927) German

£705 $1072 €1100 Landscape in northern Germany (31x25cm-12x10in) s.d.78 panel. 31-Aug-2 Geble, Radolfzell #640/R

HOFFNUNG, Gerard (1925-1959) British

Works on paper

£500 $790 €750 Beating a retreat (26x40cm-10x16in) s. W/C over pen ink. 26-Nov-2 Bonhams, Knightsbridge #262/R

HOFKER, Willem Gerard (1902-1981) Dutch

£308 $481 €450 City in the evening sun (14x20cm-6x8in) s. panel. 14-Apr-3 Glerum, Amsterdam #173/R
£892 $1373 €1400 Self portrait - a study (20x22cm-8x9in) s.d.1962 panel. 3-Sep-2 Christie's, Amsterdam #203a
£1210 $1864 €1900 Dressing after bath (35x22cm-14x9in) s.d.35. 3-Sep-2 Christie's, Amsterdam #205 est:1000-1500
£1844 $2987 €2600 Self portrait (50x34cm-20x13in) s.d.1965. 26-May-3 Glerum, Amsterdam #103/R est:2800-3800
£3057 $4708 €4800 Nude in front of mirror (39x21cm-15x8in) s.d.1935 prov. 3-Sep-2 Christie's, Amsterdam #260/R est:2500-3500
£3822 $5885 €6000 Chinese dolls (65x50cm-26x20in) s.d.1978. 3-Sep-2 Christie's, Amsterdam #202/R est:3000-5000
£14085 $21690 €21128 Re Remioth (34x25cm-13x10in) s.i.d.1938. 27-Oct-2 Christie's, Hong Kong #32/R est:55000-75000 (HK.D 170000)
£194250 $320513 €281663 Balinese beauties (75x49cm-30x19in) s.i.d.1943. 6-Jul-3 Christie's, Hong Kong #18/R est:500000-700000 (HK.D 2500000)

Works on paper

£541 $834 €850 Anticoli, Corrado (40x31cm-16x12in) s.i.d.1959 pencil black chk pastel with two other works by three. 3-Sep-2 Christie's, Amsterdam #211
£541 $834 €850 Wells Cathedral (28x38cm-11x15in) s.i.d.1974 pencil black brown chk with another work two. 3-Sep-2 Christie's, Amsterdam #212
£764 $1177 €1200 View of San Pietro, Assisi (42x33cm-17x13in) s.i.d.1955 black brown chk with two other works three. 3-Sep-2 Christie's, Amsterdam #210
£955 $1471 €1500 View of the Molo and the Palazzo Ducale from Bacino di San Marco, Venice (23x45cm-9x18in) s.i.d.1961 black brown chk W/C with another work by same hand two. 3-Sep-2 Christie's, Amsterdam #206/R est:1500-2000
£955 $1471 €1500 Ca' d'oro, Venetia (41x32cm-16x13in) s.i.d.1959 red black chk pastel with another by same hand two. 3-Sep-2 Christie's, Amsterdam #209 est:1500-2000
£2866 $4414 €4500 Girl asleep -a study (17x22cm-7x9in) s. pencil black brown chk W/C with five other works six. 3-Sep-2 Christie's, Amsterdam #207/R est:1200-1600
£2953 $4872 €4282 Women by temple gate (53x35cm-21x14in) s.d.1952 black chk W/C. 6-Jul-3 Christie's, Hong Kong #12/R est:6500-9500 (HK.D 38000)
£29526 $48718 €42813 Ni Gemblong, Klandis Bali (38x25cm-15x10in) s.i.d.1939 black chk pastel prov.exhib.lit. 6-Jul-3 Christie's, Hong Kong #19/R est:220000-280000 (HK.D 380000)
£33140 $51036 €49710 Under the banyan tree at the temple of the dead near the house in Abangan, Bali (47x30cm-19x12in) s.i.d.Sept 1941 conte crayon col pigment lit. 27-Oct-2 Christie's, Hong Kong #9/R est:140000-180000 (HK.D 400000)

HOFKUNST, Alfred (1942-) Austrian

Works on paper

£786 $1226 €1179 Light abstract composition with crabs and lobsters (34x25cm-13x10in) s.d.83 mixed media paper on canvas. 8-Nov-2 Dobiaschofsky, Bern #268/R (S.FR 1800)
£2183 $3188 €3275 Tapis (200x300cm-79x118in) s.d.1971/72 mixed media board prov. 4-Jun-2 Germann, Zurich #80/R est:8000-12000 (S.FR 5000)
£2620 $4114 €3930 Sunset I (150x170cm-59x67in) s.d.1980 pastel acrylic. 25-Nov-2 Sotheby's, Zurich #150/R est:6000-8000 (S.FR 6000)

HOFLAND, Thomas Christopher (1777-1843) British

£2600 $4316 €3900 Cromack waters (51x77cm-20x30in) prov.exhib. 10-Jun-3 Christie's, London #61/R est:3000-5000

HOFLEHNER, Rudolf (1916-1995) Austrian

Sculpture

£10638 $17234 €15000 Poros - Figure 12 K (73cm-29in) iron prov. 20-May-3 Dorotheum, Vienna #182/R est:9000-13000

Works on paper

£4430 $7000 €7000 Untitled (95x110cm-37x43in) s.d.48 mixed media. 27-Nov-2 Dorotheum, Vienna #231/R est:7000-9000

HOFLER, Max (1892-1963) British

£285 $436 €428 Severn near Newham (51x61cm-20x24in) s. painted c.1950 prov. 26-Aug-2 Sotheby's, Paddington #620 (A.D 800)

HOFMANN, Earl (20th C) American

£769 $1200 €1154 Third Avenue El, New York (41x30cm-16x12in) s.indis d. masonite. 20-Sep-2 Sloan, North Bethesda #477/R est:600-800

HOFMANN, Egon (1884-1972) Austrian

£1583 $2532 €2200 Mountain railway (34x47cm-13x19in) s. i. verso board. 14-May-3 Dorotheum, Linz #392/R est:2800-3200

HOFMANN, Hans (1880-1966) American/German

£6400 $10624 €6400 La visite de Cupidon (71x61cm-28x24in) s. 16-Jun-3 Horta, Bruxelles #40 est:3000-5000
£22581 $35000 €33872 Untitled - gulls with sailboats (63x76cm-25x30in) panel painted c.1942 prov. 26-Sep-2 Christie's, Rockefeller NY #714/R est:25000-35000
£81250 $130000 €121875 Black splash (56x66cm-22x26in) s.d.48 i.d.verso board prov. 14-May-3 Sotheby's, New York #120/R est:50000-70000
£125000 $200000 €187500 Red parable (152x122cm-60x48in) s.d.64 s.i.d.1964 verso prov. 14-May-3 Sotheby's, New York #152/R est:60000-80000
£187500 $300000 €281250 Frolocking (183x152cm-72x60in) s.d.65 s.i.d.1965 verso prov.exhib.lit. 14-May-3 Sotheby's, New York #129/R est:120000-180000
£284810 $450000 €427215 Opulence (102x127cm-40x50in) s.d.54 s.i.d.verso prov.exhib. 14-Nov-2 Christie's, Rockefeller NY #124/R est:250000-350000
£322785 $510000 €484178 Calliope - muse of epic poetry (193x152cm-76x60in) s.d.63 s.d.verso prov.exhib. 13-Nov-2 Christie's, Rockefeller NY #46/R est:300000-400000

Works on paper

£513 $810 €800 View of Enns (60x75cm-24x30in) s.d.1962 W/C. 18-Nov-2 Dorotheum, Linz #433/R
£3097 $4800 €4646 Provincetown (30x43cm-12x17in) mono.d.42 pen ink paper on board prov. 26-Sep-2 Christie's, Rockefeller NY #716/R est:6000-8000
£5128 $8000 €7692 Untitled (48x60cm-19x24in) s. gouache crayon executed c.1942 prov. 5-Nov-2 Doyle, New York #27/R est:10000-15000
£7500 $12000 €11250 Provincetown (36x43cm-14x17in) init.d.VII 22 41 black ink col crayon prov.exhib. 14-May-3 Sotheby's, New York #121/R est:15000-20000
£10127 $16000 €15191 Untitled - Provincetown (28x36cm-11x14in) s.d.IV 20.43 black ink crayon on paper prov. 13-Nov-2 Sotheby's, New York #214/R est:18000-22000
£18987 $30000 €28481 Evening (60x44cm-24x17in) gouache W/C crayon on paper executed 1943 prov. 13-Nov-2 Sotheby's, New York #213/R est:35000-45000

HOFMANN, Hermann (1920-) Swiss

£391 $610 €587 Winter IV (54x65cm-21x26in) s.d.1974. 16-Sep-2 Philippe Schuler, Zurich #3372 (S.FR 900)
£478 $746 €717 Blue night I (102x83cm-40x33in) s. panel. 16-Sep-2 Philippe Schuler, Zurich #6624 (S.FR 1100)
£522 $814 €783 Toscana (82x101cm-32x40in) s. 16-Sep-2 Philippe Schuler, Zurich #3373 (S.FR 1200)

HOFMANN, Jan Cornelis (1813-1882) Dutch

£701 $1093 €1100 Sailing ship in a storm. Boat in calm water (27x36cm-11x14in) s. panel two. 5-Nov-2 Vendu Notarishuis, Rotterdam #84/R

HOFMANN, Ludwig von (1861-1945) German
£1103 $1743 €1600 Coastal landscape (35x46cm-14x18in) mono. board. 2-Apr-3 Dr Fritz Nagel, Stuttgart #9109/R est:600
£1284 $2003 €1900 April sun (100x64cm-39x25in) s. 26-Mar-3 Hugo Ruef, Munich #138/R est:1200
£18841 $30899 €26000 Spring dance (108x69cm-43x27in) s.i.1905 s.i. stretcher. 31-May-3 Villa Grisebach, Berlin #115/R est:25000-35000
Works on paper
£316 $494 €500 Seated male nude (41x32cm-16x13in) s.d.Juli 1885 pencil. 18-Oct-2 Dr Fritz Nagel, Stuttgart #186/R
£316 $500 €500 Bathers (18x11cm-7x4in) mono. pencil wash. 29-Nov-2 Villa Grisebach, Berlin #670/R
£650 $1034 €975 Kneeling female nude (30x34cm-12x13in) init. pencil sold with chl sketches. 26-Feb-3 Sotheby's, Olympia #7/R
£949 $1500 €1500 Coastal landscape (24x36cm-9x14in) mono. pastel pencil. 29-Nov-2 Villa Grisebach, Berlin #671/R est:1000-1200
£3064 $4750 €4596 Bathers (24x37cm-9x15in) init. pastel. 29-Oct-2 Sotheby's, New York #112/R est:600-800

HOFMANS, Pieter (1642-1692) Flemish
£48000 $80160 €69600 Military encampment on the campus Martius before the Ponte Molle, Soracte beyond (229x308cm-90x121in) 9-Jul-3 Christie's, London #103/R est:20000-30000

HOFMEIER, Miriam McKinnie (1906-1987) American
£833 $1300 €1250 Skaters (81x71cm-32x28in) s.d.1949. 10-Nov-2 Selkirks, St. Louis #874/R

HOFMEISTER, Johannes (1914-1990) Danish
£396 $614 €594 Interior scene with figure (30x40cm-12x16in) init. panel. 4-Dec-2 Kunsthallen, Copenhagen #124/R (D.KR 4600)
£677 $1050 €1016 Landscape with figures, Hjorring 1952 (27x37cm-11x15in) init. masonite. 1-Oct-2 Rasmussen, Copenhagen #325/R (D.KR 8000)
£815 $1271 €1223 Landscape with figures (56x61cm-22x24in) init. 11-Nov-2 Rasmussen, Vejle #59/R (D.KR 9500)
£823 $1308 €1235 Landscape with figures (55x62cm-22x24in) init. masonite. 26-Feb-3 Kunsthallen, Copenhagen #359/R (D.KR 9000)
£935 $1458 €1403 Figure by pier (40x50cm-16x20in) init. s.i.verso panel. 5-Aug-2 Rasmussen, Vejle #310/R (D.KR 11000)
£1141 $1757 €1712 Figures in landscape (34x45cm-13x18in) init. panel. 23-Oct-2 Kunsthallen, Copenhagen #73/R est:10000 (D.KR 13500)
£1183 $1822 €1775 Coastal landscape with houses (60x69cm-24x27in) init. 26-Oct-2 Rasmussen, Havnen #2257 est:8000-12000 (D.KR 14000)
£1372 $2141 €2058 Landscape with figure (45x54cm-18x21in) init. masonite. 11-Nov-2 Rasmussen, Vejle #54/R est:15000 (D.KR 16000)
£2002 $3343 €2903 Figure by the sea (51x67cm-20x26in) init. plywood. 17-Jun-3 Rasmussen, Copenhagen #64/R est:20000-25000 (D.KR 21000)
Prints
£2271 $3588 €3407 La ville de Rapperschweil au bord du Lac de Zuric (16x26cm-6x10in) col etching. 14-Nov-2 Stuker, Bern #9160 est:3500-4500 (S.FR 5200)

Works on paper
£293 $448 €440 Spring (61x55cm-24x22in) init. crayon. 24-Aug-2 Rasmussen, Havnen #2291 (D.KR 3400)

HOFNER, Johann Baptist (attrib) (1832-1913) German
£1699 $2787 €2600 Portrait of a girl (45x34cm-18x13in) s.d.1860 canvas on canvas. 5-Feb-3 Neumeister, Munich #725/R est:1000

HOFNER, Johann Baptist and LENBACH, Franz von (19th C) German
£16352 $25509 €26000 Poultry yard with pigeon (92x120cm-36x47in) s.d.1898. 19-Sep-2 Dr Fritz Nagel, Stuttgart #947/R est:2500

HOFSCHEN, Edgar (1941-) German
£253 $392 €400 Modification used by men XXXI (40x50cm-16x20in) s.i.d.1971 prov.exhib. 28-Sep-2 Ketterer, Hamburg #512/R
£506 $800 €800 Modification (138x101cm-54x40in) d.1974 s. verso acrylic tempera panel. 30-Nov-2 Arnold, Frankfurt #257/R
Works on paper
£348 $550 €550 Landscape (70x60cm-28x24in) mixed media cloth. 30-Nov-2 Arnold, Frankfurt #256/R

HOGARTH, Arthur Paul (1917-) British
Works on paper
£280 $434 €420 Ex-chief Albert Luthuli (49x35cm-19x14in) s.i.d.56 pencil W/C. 3-Dec-2 Bonhams, Knightsbridge #99a
£420 $668 €630 Banff Springs Hotel, Alberta (45x58cm-18x23in) pencil W/C. 9-Mar-3 Lots Road, London #356/R

HOGARTH, William (attrib) (1697-1764) British
£16000 $25280 €24000 Portrait of lady with ribbon in her hair (56x46cm-22x18in) lit. 26-Nov-2 Christie's, London #20/R est:5000-8000

HOGENDORPS JACOB, Adrienne Jacqueline van (1857-1920) Dutch
£4403 $6780 €7000 White roses in a glass vase (52x42cm-20x17in) s.d.82 s.on stretcher. 23-Oct-2 Christie's, Amsterdam #29/R est:7000-9000

HOGER, Joseph (1801-1877) Austrian
Works on paper
£1258 $1950 €2000 Puchberg on Schneeberg (14x21cm-6x8in) s.d.186 W/C. 1-Oct-2 Dorotheum, Vienna #188/R est:1600-1800

HOGER, Rudolf A (1877-1930) Austrian
£644 $1017 €966 Afternoon dance company in the park (90x124cm-35x49in) s.d.1924. 26-Nov-2 Hans Widmer, St Gallen #1179 est:700-2200 (S.FR 1500)

HOGFELDT, Robert (1894-1986) Swedish
£297 $473 €446 Landscape with calm river (46x55cm-18x22in) s. panel. 3-Mar-3 Lilla Bukowskis, Stockholm #149 (S.KR 4000)
£329 $514 €494 In the bottle (55x46cm-22x18in) s. panel. 13-Sep-2 Lilla Bukowskis, Stockholm #576 (S.KR 4800)
£874 $1416 €1311 Susannah and the Elders (38x46cm-15x18in) s. panel. 3-Feb-3 Lilla Bukowskis, Stockholm #918 (S.KR 12200)
Works on paper
£283 $449 €425 Dog (19x24cm-7x9in) s. mixed media. 3-Mar-3 Lilla Bukowskis, Stockholm #137 (S.KR 3800)
£283 $449 €425 Family time (27x36cm-11x14in) s. W/C. 3-Mar-3 Lilla Bukowskis, Stockholm #141 (S.KR 3800)
£283 $449 €425 Saint George and the Dragon (38x43cm-15x17in) s. W/C. 3-Mar-3 Lilla Bukowskis, Stockholm #162 (S.KR 3800)
£287 $464 €431 The Trojan horse (40x55cm-16x22in) s. W/C. 3-Feb-3 Lilla Bukowskis, Stockholm #877 (S.KR 4000)
£288 $449 €432 Flirting (27x33cm-11x13in) s. W/C. 13-Sep-2 Lilla Bukowskis, Stockholm #288 (S.KR 4200)
£297 $473 €446 Troll playing violin (30x42cm-12x17in) s. W/C. 3-Mar-3 Lilla Bukowskis, Stockholm #138 (S.KR 4000)
£301 $476 €452 Summer enjoyment (18x36cm-7x14in) s. W/C. 16-Nov-2 Crafoord, Lund #71/R (S.KR 4300)
£310 $503 €450 Winter landscape with figures (29x37cm-11x15in) s. gouache. 25-May-3 Uppsala Auktionskammare, Uppsala #180 (S.KR 4000)
£355 $550 €533 The fairy having a stop for a smoke (30x24cm-12x9in) s. W/C. 8-Dec-2 Uppsala Auktionskammare, Uppsala #180 (S.KR 5000)
£401 $638 €602 Choir-singing (31x39cm-12x15in) s. W/C. 3-Mar-3 Lilla Bukowskis, Stockholm #146 (S.KR 5400)
£416 $662 €624 Rivals (23x32cm-9x13in) s. W/C. 3-Mar-3 Lilla Bukowskis, Stockholm #143 (S.KR 5600)
£446 $709 €669 Susanna in the bath (33x37cm-13x15in) s. W/C. 3-Mar-3 Lilla Bukowskis, Stockholm #145 (S.KR 6000)
£473 $766 €710 Music on the branch (23x35cm-9x14in) s. W/C. 3-Feb-3 Lilla Bukowskis, Stockholm #642 (S.KR 6600)
£520 $828 €780 Susanna and the Elders (30x43cm-12x17in) s. W/C. 3-Mar-3 Lilla Bukowskis, Stockholm #142 (S.KR 7000)
£550 $875 €825 The pig transport (36x51cm-14x20in) s. W/C. 3-Mar-3 Lilla Bukowskis, Stockholm #136 (S.KR 7400)
£781 $1241 €1172 Three troll girls dancing (28x35cm-11x14in) s. W/C. 3-Mar-3 Lilla Bukowskis, Stockholm #139 (S.KR 10500)
£818 $1300 €1227 Party evening (30x41cm-12x16in) s. W/C. 3-Mar-3 Lilla Bukowskis, Stockholm #163 (S.KR 11000)
£855 $1359 €1283 Troll girls bathing (31x37cm-12x15in) s. W/C. 3-Mar-3 Lilla Bukowskis, Stockholm #144 (S.KR 11500)

HOGGATT, William (1880-1961) British
£1700 $2839 €2465 Castletown Square, Isle of Man (33x33cm-13x13in) s. board. 26-Jun-3 Mellors & Kirk, Nottingham #890 est:200-300
£2200 $3278 €3300 Moorland farm (18x20cm-7x8in) s. 28-Jun-2 Chrystals Auctions, Isle of Man #161a est:2000-2800
£2200 $3410 €3300 Ploughing below Bradda Head (18x23cm-7x9in) s. board. 6-Dec-2 Chrystals Auctions, Isle of Man #173 est:1500-2000
Works on paper
£300 $483 €450 Silverburn, Isle of Man (52x70cm-20x28in) s. W/C. 11-May-3 Lots Road, London #332/R
£550 $853 €825 Lime quarry (13x18cm-5x7in) s. W/C. 6-Dec-2 Chrystals Auctions, Isle of Man #264
£1150 $1909 €1725 Rushen church from Ballakilly, Isle of Man (13x15cm-5x6in) s.d.1928 W/C. 12-Jun-3 Scarborough Perry Fine Arts, Hove #438
£1200 $1860 €1800 Stock yard, Ballakilley (28x38cm-11x15in) s. col chk. 6-Dec-2 Chrystals Auctions, Isle of Man #248c est:1200-1800
£1300 $1937 €1950 Nude bathers, Scolaby pool (23x25cm-9x10in) s. W/C. 28-Jun-2 Chrystals Auctions, Isle of Man #147 est:700-1000
£1450 $2161 €2175 Geese near Scolaby pool (25x23cm-10x9in) s. W/C. 28-Jun-2 Chrystals Auctions, Isle of Man #146 est:800-1000
£3200 $4960 €4800 Potato harvesters, Isle of Man (51x61cm-20x24in) s. W/C. 4-Oct-2 Mallams, Oxford #512 est:300-500
£3200 $4768 €4800 Feeding the sheep in Manx winter landscape (43x53cm-17x21in) s. col chk. 28-Jun-2 Chrystals Auctions, Isle of Man #174 est:1500-2000

£3700 $5735 €5550 From an orchan lane (20x28cm-8x11in) s. W/C two. 4-Oct-2 Mallams, Oxford #513
£4100 $6109 €6150 River landscape with nunnery (53x71cm-21x28in) s. W/C. 28-Jun-2 Chrystals Auctions, Isle of Man #197 est:2000-3000

HOGLER, Franz (1802-1855) Austrian
Sculpture
£1127 $1814 €1600 Karl Ludwig Graf Grunne (50cm-20in) s. brown pat.bronze. 7-May-3 Dorotheum, Vienna #258/R est:900-1400

HOGLEY, S E (fl.1874-1893) British
£360 $562 €540 Herder with Highland cattle (38x58cm-15x23in) s. 9-Oct-2 Andrew Hartley, Ilkley #776

HOGUE, Alexandre (1898-1994) American
£1442 $2250 €2163 Fiery furnace (71x51cm-28x20in) acrylic. 19-Oct-2 David Dike, Dallas #350/R est:2000-4000
£41667 $65000 €62501 Pulliam Bluffs, Chisos Mountains (102x142cm-40x56in) painted c.1984 exhib. 19-Oct-2 David Dike, Dallas #178/R est:75000-100000
Works on paper
£2564 $4000 €3846 Dath Grip, west of San Marcos (25x30cm-10x12in) pastel executed c.1924. 19-Oct-2 David Dike, Dallas #166/R est:4000-6000

HOGUET, Charles (1821-1870) French
£633 $981 €1000 Paysans dans la lande (27x34cm-11x13in) init. panel. 29-Sep-2 Eric Pillon, Calais #52/R
£779 $1161 €1200 Woodcutters in forest clearing (33x25cm-13x10in) s. 26-Jun-2 Neumeister, Munich #759/R
£968 $1423 €1500 Old windmill against cloudy evening skies (73x52cm-29x20in) s. 20-Jun-2 Dr Fritz Nagel, Stuttgart #774/R est:1500
£1250 $2063 €1800 Activities on the beach (60x92cm-24x36in) bears sig. 1-Jul-3 Christie's, Amsterdam #57 est:2000-3000
£1500 $2505 €2175 Preparing vegetables (32x43cm-13x17in) s. panel. 8-Jul-3 Bonhams, Knightsbridge #229/R est:1200-1800
£2600 $4056 €3900 Extensive landscape with windmill, pond and figure fishing from rock in the foreground (49x73cm-19x29in) s. indis d.1846. 8-Oct-2 Bonhams, Knightsbridge #300/R est:2000-3000
£5063 $8000 €7595 Straying from the herd (91x73cm-36x29in) s. 24-Apr-3 Sotheby's, New York #102/R est:12000-15000

HOHEI, Satake (?-1807) Japanese
Works on paper
£1069 $1700 €1604 Landscape (106x33cm-42x13in) s. ink col silk hanging scroll sold with another. 24-Mar-3 Christie's, Rockefeller NY #32/R est:1500-2500

HOHENBERG, Bodo von (17th C) German
Works on paper
£377 $585 €600 Oculata Fides (22x16cm-9x6in) s.i.d.1620 W/C pen. 1-Oct-2 Dorotheum, Vienna #66/R

HOHENBERG, Enrico (1834-1897) Italian
£3015 $4582 €4523 Still lives of fruit and chickens - fruit, birds and goldfish (56x69cm-22x27in) s. pair. 27-Aug-2 Rasmussen, Copenhagen #1802/R est:40000-45000 (D.KR 35000)

HOHENBERGER, E (19/20th C) Italian?
£2516 $3899 €4000 Still life with asters, pomegranate, melons and grapes (52x123cm-20x48in) s. 29-Oct-2 Dorotheum, Vienna #98/R est:1300-1600

HOHENBERGER, Franz (1867-1941) German
£1603 $2484 €2500 Still life of flowers and fruit (70x98cm-28x39in) s. 5-Dec-2 Schopman, Hamburg #523 est:2500

HOHENBUCHLER, Irene (20th C) Austrian
£1241 $1986 €1800 Ear and chair (35x99cm-14x39in) s.i.d.87 acrylic. 11-Mar-3 Dorotheum, Vienna #257/R est:1300-1700

HOHENLEITER, Francisco (1889-1968) Spanish
£1207 $1907 €1750 Rider (32x24cm-13x9in) s. i.verso. 7-Apr-3 Castellana, Madrid #427/R
£2200 $3432 €3300 Figures on a terrace with a cityscape beyond (80x99cm-31x39in) indis sig.d. 8-Oct-2 Bonhams, Knightsbridge #182/R est:2000-3000
£5806 $9174 €9000 Gypsies (78x56cm-31x22in) s.d.MCMXLVI. 17-Dec-2 Durán, Madrid #195/R
£8276 $13076 €12000 Little market in Sanlucar de Barrameda (81x100cm-32x39in) s.d. 7-Apr-3 Castellana, Madrid #52/R est:5000

HOHLIG, Georg (1879-1940) German
£390 $608 €620 Tree in snowy hill landscape (36x49cm-14x19in) s. 11-Oct-2 Winterberg, Heidelberg #1242

HOHLWEIN, Ludwig (1879-1949) German
Works on paper
£823 $1275 €1300 Fox hunt (23x23cm-9x9in) mono. i. verso Indian ink brush W/C htd white. 25-Sep-2 Neumeister, Munich #406/R
£1014 $1581 €1500 Wild ducks (43x42cm-17x17in) s.d.08 gouache. 26-Mar-3 Hugo Ruef, Munich #327/R est:1500

HOHNECK, Adolf (1812-1878) German
£576 $921 €800 Broken bottle (26x20cm-10x8in) s.i. 17-May-3 De Vuyst, Lokeren #202

HOHNEL, Wilhelm (1871-1941) Austrian
£385 $608 €600 Soldier with horses in winter landscape (23x32cm-9x13in) s. board. 18-Nov-2 Dorotheum, Linz #287/R
£791 $1266 €1100 Horses heads (30x25cm-12x10in) s. board. 14-May-3 Dorotheum, Linz #402/R
£1410 $2228 €2200 Cart horses (48x64cm-19x25in) s. 18-Nov-2 Dorotheum, Linz #288/R est:4000-4800

HOHNSTEDT, Peter Lanz (1872-1957) American
£387 $600 €581 Wooded lake scene (20x25cm-8x10in) s. board. 29-Oct-2 John Moran, Pasadena #605
£417 $650 €626 Spring in the hills (25x30cm-10x12in) panel. 19-Oct-2 David Dike, Dallas #303/R
£577 $900 €866 Texas bluebonnets (20x25cm-8x10in) 19-Oct-2 David Dike, Dallas #205/R
£822 $1200 €1233 Path in the woods with pine trees (71x56cm-28x22in) s. 3-Nov-1 North East Auctions, Portsmouth #274
£962 $1500 €1443 At the rapids (61x91cm-24x36in) 19-Oct-2 David Dike, Dallas #259a est:500-1000
£1840 $3000 €2760 Rocky mountain valley (51x61cm-20x24in) s. 2-Feb-3 Simpson's, Houston #360

HOIN, Claude (1750-1817) French
Works on paper
£3797 $6000 €6000 Portrait de jeune homme en buste (55x44cm-22x17in) col chk. 27-Nov-2 Christie's, Paris #202/R est:5000-7000

HOIN, Claude (attrib) (1750-1817) French
Works on paper
£321 $503 €500 Etude d'arbres (31x26cm-12x10in) i. pierre noire htd white. 13-Dec-2 Pierre Berge, Paris #7
£321 $503 €500 Etude d'arbres (32x27cm-13x11in) i. pierre noire htd white. 13-Dec-2 Pierre Berge, Paris #6
£353 $554 €550 Etude de porte (31x26cm-12x10in) i. pierre noire htd white double-sided. 13-Dec-2 Pierre Berge, Paris #12
£385 $604 €600 Paysage avec barriere (26x31cm-10x12in) i. pierre noire htd white. 13-Dec-2 Pierre Berge, Paris #5/R
£385 $604 €600 Paysage (25x31cm-10x12in) i. pierre noire htd white. 13-Dec-2 Pierre Berge, Paris #3
£385 $604 €600 Paysage (31x26cm-12x10in) i. pierre noire htd white. 13-Dec-2 Pierre Berge, Paris #14
£481 $755 €750 Paysage (26x31cm-10x12in) i. pierre noire htd white. 13-Dec-2 Pierre Berge, Paris #13
£577 $906 €900 Paysage avec porte (26x32cm-10x13in) i. pierre noire htd white. 13-Dec-2 Pierre Berge, Paris #8
£833 $1308 €1300 Vue du chateau vieux a Meudon (26x31cm-10x12in) i. pierre noire htd white. 13-Dec-2 Pierre Berge, Paris #11/R
£1026 $1610 €1600 Paysage avec pont (26x31cm-10x12in) i. pierre noire htd white. 13-Dec-2 Pierre Berge, Paris #1/R

HOINKIS, Ewald (1897-1960) German
Photographs
£2089 $3300 €3300 Untitled (26x19cm-10x7in) s.i. col lit.exhib. 28-Nov-2 Villa Grisebach, Berlin #1228/R est:3000-5000
£2340 $3791 €3300 Untitled - bowl with eggs (15x19cm-6x7in) gelatin silver prov. 23-May-3 Van Ham, Cologne #118/R est:3000
£2704 $4192 €4300 George Grosz (11x8cm-4x3in) i. verso silver gelatine lit.prov. 31-Oct-2 Van Ham, Cologne #155/R est:5000

HOITSU, Sakai (1761-1828) Japanese
Works on paper
£7547 $12000 €11321 Flowers of the four seasons (150x38cm-59x15in) s. ink col gold silk hanging scrolls pair. 24-Mar-3 Christie's, Rockefeller NY #35/R est:15000-20000

£10692 $17000 €16038 Tiger and peony. Chinese children playing (125x169cm-49x67in) s. ink col gold gold leaf two-panel screens pair lit. 24-Mar-3 Christie's, Rockefeller NY #89/R est:10000-15000

HOKE, Ann (20th C) American
£267 $425 €401 Floral still life (51x41cm-20x16in) s.d. 2-Mar-3 Toomey, Oak Park #557/R

HOKE, Giselbert (1927-) Austrian
Works on paper
£4255 $6894 €6000 Black goat (50x66cm-20x26in) s.i.d.10.9.83 mixed media. 20-May-3 Dorotheum, Vienna #255/R est:3600-4500

HOKINSON, Helen Elna (1893-1949) American
Works on paper
£559 $900 €839 Matron at pet store purchasing fish (28x18cm-11x7in) s. brush ink wash en grisaille. 20-Feb-3 Illustration House, New York #80/R

HOKKEI, Toyota (1780-1850) Japanese
Works on paper
£6918 $11000 €10377 Yamauba and Kintaro (91x35cm-36x14in) s. ink col silk hanging scroll. 24-Mar-3 Christie's, Rockefeller NY #29/R est:5000-7000

HOKSTAD, Oscar (1894-1982) Norwegian
£297 $466 €446 Farm (64x84cm-25x33in) s. 25-Nov-2 Blomqvist, Lysaker #1123 (N.KR 3400)
£345 $525 €518 The bay - view over Trondheimsfjorden (35x43cm-14x17in) s.d.1917 i.stretcher. 31-Aug-2 Grev Wedels Plass, Oslo #52 (N.KR 4000)

HOKUJU, Shotei (17/18th C) Japanese
Prints
£2244 $3500 €3366 Far view of sea at Shinagawa from Shiba Atagoyama (26x38cm-10x15in) s. print prov. 25-Mar-3 Christie's, Rockefeller NY #106/R est:3500-4500

HOKUSAI (1760-1849) Japanese
Prints
£3974 $6240 €6200 Poeme. s. print prov. 16-Dec-2 Beaussant & Lefèvre, Paris #202/R
£15862 $25221 €23000 Oban yoko-e (36x24cm-14x9in) s. 7-Mar-3 Piasa, Paris #255/R est:6000-8000

HOKUSAI, Katsushika (1760-1849) Japanese
£7051 $11000 €10577 Tone river, Shimosa province (19x26cm-7x10in) s. print. 25-Mar-3 Christie's, Rockefeller NY #104/R est:8000-12000
Prints
£2000 $3340 €2900 Village of Sekiya by the Sumida River (25x37cm-10x15in) s. from series Fugaku sanjurokkei. 18-Jun-3 Christie's, London #218/R est:2000-2200
£2200 $3674 €3190 Village of Sekiya by the Sumida river (26x37cm-10x15in) s. from series Fugaku sanjurokkei. 18-Jun-3 Christie's, London #217 est:2000-2200
£2564 $4000 €3846 Urashima entering the dragon palace (24x37cm-9x15in) s. print. 25-Mar-3 Christie's, Rockefeller NY #95/R est:4000-5000
£5000 $7900 €7500 Travellers and pack animals toiling up a steep slope (25x37cm-10x15in) s. col print prov. 13-Nov-2 Christie's, London #12/R est:5000-7000
£7692 $12000 €11538 Sangi Hitoshi (26x37cm-10x15in) s. print. 25-Mar-3 Christie's, Rockefeller NY #99/R est:6000-8000
£7692 $12000 €11538 Ono no Komachi (26x37cm-10x15in) s. col print prov. 25-Mar-3 Christie's, Rockefeller NY #100/R est:12000-18000
£8974 $14000 €13461 Ariwara no Narihira (26x38cm-10x15in) s. col print. 25-Mar-3 Christie's, Rockefeller NY #101/R est:10000-15000

HOKUSAI, Katsushika (attrib) (1760-1849) Japanese
Works on paper
£1019 $1590 €1600 Mountain scenes (99x40cm-39x16in) s.i. seal Indian ink col silk hanging scrolls pair. 9-Nov-2 Dr Fritz Nagel, Stuttgart #1854/R
£2215 $3500 €3500 Oiseau pose sur une culliere dans une vasque (27x44cm-11x17in) ink polychrome prov. 29-Nov-2 Tajan, Paris #49/R est:3500-4000

HOLAN, Karel (1893-1953) Czechoslovakian
£681 $1103 €1022 Rocks at Jeptiska (81x100cm-32x39in) s.d.50. 24-May-3 Dorotheum, Prague #79/R est:30000-45000 (C.KR 30000)

HOLBAK, Niels (1884-1954) Danish
£289 $451 €434 Street scene with figures and houses (32x48cm-13x19in) s. 5-Aug-2 Rasmussen, Vejle #2040/R (D.KR 3400)
£296 $456 €444 Street scene in Fano (44x52cm-17x20in) s. 26-Oct-2 Rasmussen, Havnen #2106 (D.KR 3500)
£383 $620 €555 Small girl baking apples (76x63cm-30x25in) s. 26-May-3 Rasmussen, Copenhagen #1328/R (D.KR 4000)

HOLBEIN, Hans (style) (15/16th C) German
£10500 $16695 €15750 Portrait of Henry VIII in a fur trimmed coat (75x58cm-30x23in) i. panel. 6-Mar-3 Christie's, Kensington #302/R est:3000-5000

HOLBEIN, Hans (younger-style) (1497-1543) German
£8500 $13515 €12750 Portrait of King Henry VIII (58x45cm-23x18in) panel prov. 19-Mar-3 Sotheby's, London #16/R est:7000-9000
£9000 $14310 €13500 Portrait of Thomas Cromwell, 1st. Earl of Essex (40x28cm-16x11in) i. panel prov.exhib.lit. 19-Mar-3 Sotheby's, London #11/R est:6000-8000

HOLBERTON, Wakeman (1839-1898) American
£2592 $4250 €3758 Rainbow trout and fishing reel beside a stream (33x48cm-13x19in) s.d.1888. 8-Jun-3 Skinner, Boston #189/R est:2000-3000

HOLBO, Kristen (1869-1953) Norwegian
£1641 $2740 €2379 Mountain landscape with flowers, possibly from Rondane (105x135cm-41x53in) s.d.14 i.verso. 18-Jun-3 Grev Wedels Plass, Oslo #185/R est:25000-30000 (N.KR 19000)

HOLD, Abel (1815-1891) British
£420 $659 €630 Gundog in a landscape (27x40cm-11x16in) s.i.d.1847 panel. 16-Apr-3 Christie's, Kensington #689
£580 $911 €870 Untitled (44x54cm-17x21in) 15-Apr-3 Bonhams, Chester #994
£1500 $2430 €2250 Day's bag (51cm-20in circular) s.d.1849. 23-Jan-3 Christie's, Kensington #58/R est:2000-3000

HOLDEN, John (20th C) British
Works on paper
£520 $811 €780 Fishing boats off Peel Castle, Isle of Man (34x65cm-13x26in) s.d.1901 pastel. 6-Nov-2 Bonhams, Chester #356

HOLDEN, Paul (20th C) British
£260 $421 €390 Bridge, Steadbally (46x60cm-18x24in) s. 20-May-3 Bonhams, Knightsbridge #98

HOLDER, Edward Henry (fl.1864-1917) British
£650 $1021 €975 Anglers on a riverbank, said to be on the Conway, North Wales (33x87cm-13x34in) s. 16-Apr-3 Christie's, Kensington #624/R
£922 $1429 €1383 Landscape with woman gathering firewood (33x55cm-13x22in) s.d.1878. 8-Dec-2 Uppsala Auktionskammare, Uppsala #47/R est:15000-18000 (S.KR 13000)
£1500 $2430 €2250 Lynton and Lynmouth from Haliday Hill (51x76cm-20x30in) s. 23-Jan-3 Christie's, Kensington #222 est:500-700
£4200 $6552 €6300 Thunderstorm passing over Lands End (102x76cm-40x30in) mono. arched top exhib. 7-Nov-2 Christie's, Kensington #170/R est:3000-5000

HOLDER, Frans van (1881-1919) Belgian
£759 $1185 €1200 Elegante au bord de la riviere (43x44cm-17x17in) s. panel. 16-Sep-2 Horta, Bruxelles #187

HOLDER, Geoffrey (1930-) American
£1166 $1900 €1749 Native boy (30x20cm-12x8in) d.1958 artist's board. 14-Feb-3 Du Mouchelle, Detroit #1033/R est:2000-3000

HOLDING, Henry James (1833-1872) British
£900 $1467 €1350 Afternoon by the sea (64x113cm-25x44in) s.d.1871. 29-Jan-3 Sotheby's, Olympia #89/R est:800-1200
Works on paper
£260 $426 €377 Stormy coastal seascape with figures on rocky shore, wreck beyond (51x69cm-20x27in) s.d.1869 W/C scratching out. 3-Jun-3 Capes Dunn, Manchester #73

HOLDREDGE, Ransome G (1836-1899) American

£932 $1500 €1398 Cows in landscape (20x36cm-8x14in) s. canvas on canvas prov. 18-Feb-3 John Moran, Pasadena #99 est:2000-3000
£1056 $1700 €1584 Stream in wooded landscape (23x36cm-9x14in) s. canvas on canvas prov. 18-Feb-3 John Moran, Pasadena #99a est:2000-3000
£1069 $1700 €1604 Misty river (56x91cm-22x36in) s. 8-Mar-3 Harvey Clar, Oakland #1203
£3012 $5000 €4367 Scene on the Van Dusen River, Humboldt County (23x30cm-9x12in) s. i.verso board prov. 11-Jun-3 Butterfields, San Francisco #4160/R est:3000-5000

HOLDREDGE, Ransome G (attrib) (1836-1899) American

£962 $1500 €1443 Trees by the river in the long afternoon. board. 21-Sep-2 Harvey Clar, Oakland #1518

HOLDSTOCK, Alfred Worsley (1820-1901) Canadian

£1016 $1596 €1524 Fishing near the waterfalls at autumn time (25x35cm-10x14in) board prov. 10-Dec-2 Pinneys, Montreal #143 est:2500-3500 (C.D 2500)

Works on paper

£1179 $1851 €1769 Indian encampment near the rapids (34x55cm-13x22in) pastel. 10-Dec-2 Pinneys, Montreal #154 est:2000-2500 (C.D 2900)
£1301 $2042 €1952 Lower falls (34x55cm-13x22in) i. pastel. 10-Dec-2 Pinneys, Montreal #151 est:2000-2500 (C.D 3200)

HOLENE, Bjorg (1947-) Norwegian

£3028 $4784 €4542 Twilight children and other creatures (210x130cm-83x51in) s.d.1983 canvas on panel exhib. 2-Dec-2 Blomqvist, Oslo #468/R est:40000-50000 (N.KR 35000)

HOLESCH, Denes de (?) Australian?

£214 $338 €321 Hunting scene (51x71cm-20x28in) s. 27-Nov-2 Deutscher-Menzies, Melbourne #270/R (A.D 600)

HOLGATE, Edwin Headley (1892-1977) Canadian

£4484 $7175 €6726 Low water, Morin Heights (22x27cm-9x11in) init. s.i.d.October 1967 panel prov. 15-May-3 Heffel, Vancouver #213/R est:10000-12000 (C.D 10000)
£10222 $16764 €15333 Portrait of Joan (32x40cm-13x16in) s.d.58 panel prov. 27-May-3 Sotheby's, Toronto #214/R est:9000-12000 (C.D 23000)
£11211 $17937 €16817 British aerodrome with Lancaster bombers (84x102cm-33x40in) painted c.1943-44 prov.lit. 15-May-3 Heffel, Vancouver #170/R est:20000-25000 (C.D 25000)
£42601 $68161 €63902 Nude (38x46cm-15x18in) s. s.i.verso painted c.1930 prov.lit. 15-May-3 Heffel, Vancouver #46/R est:60000-80000 (C.D 95000)

Prints

£3427 $5415 €5141 Bathers (12x11cm-5x4in) init. wood engraving prov.lit. 18-Nov-2 Sotheby's, Toronto #58/R est:3000-5000 (C.D 8500)

Works on paper

£3292 $5103 €4938 Reclining nude (53x74cm-21x29in) init. chl prov. 3-Dec-2 Joyner, Toronto #143/R est:8000-10000 (C.D 8000)

HOLIDAY, Gilbert (1879-1937) British

£9500 $15770 €13775 Grand National (46x61cm-18x24in) s. s.i.verso prov. 12-Jun-3 Christie's, Kensington #107/R est:8000-12000

Works on paper

£420 $697 €609 Community singing (22x16cm-9x6in) s.i. pencil. 12-Jun-3 Martel Maides, Guernsey #136/R
£700 $1162 €1015 Portrait of Giovanni Grasso (46x35cm-18x14in) i.d.11-3-1910 W/C bodycol. 12-Jun-3 Martel Maides, Guernsey #135
£3600 $5688 €5400 Unloading the coal boat at St Peter Port harbour, Guernsey (26x20cm-10x8in) s. W/C htd white. 28-Nov-2 Martel Maides, Guernsey #20/R est:700-900

HOLIDAY, Henry (1839-1927) British

Works on paper

£500 $825 €725 Head of a girl (21x17cm-8x7in) pencil. 2-Jul-3 Sotheby's, Olympia #317/R

HOLL, Frank (1845-1888) British

£45000 $71100 €67500 Wide wide world (76x64cm-30x25in) s.d.1873. 28-Nov-2 Sotheby's, London #31/R est:30000-50000

HOLL, Frank (attrib) (1845-1888) British

£285 $447 €428 Deep in thought (30x30cm-12x12in) 10-Dec-2 Pinneys, Montreal #87 (C.D 700)

HOLLAENDER, Alphons (1845-1923) German

£1667 $2433 €2600 Fishing village (38x28cm-15x11in) card. 5-Jun-2 Il Ponte, Milan #232/R
£3165 $5000 €5000 Spinning (13x22cm-5x9in) s. board. 26-Nov-2 Christie's, Rome #191/R

HOLLAIN, N F J (c.1761-?) French

£2215 $3456 €3500 La jeune femme et son enfant. Le chasseur et son fils (32x24cm-13x9in) s. panel pair. 20-Oct-2 Galerie de Chartres, Chartres #81 est:3500-4600

HOLLAMS, F Mabel (1877-1963) British

£650 $1079 €943 Sally, a saddled skewbald horse (33x45cm-13x18in) s.i. panel. 12-Jun-3 Christie's, Kensington #65/R
£798 $1300 €1197 Bubbles a Pekinese (25x35cm-10x14in) s.i. panel prov. 11-Feb-3 Bonhams & Doyles, New York #237/R est:2500-3500
£800 $1248 €1200 In the paddock (28x33cm-11x13in) s.verso canvasboard. 17-Oct-2 David Lay, Penzance #1456
£800 $1304 €1200 Bubbles (31x41cm-12x16in) s.i. panel. 12-Feb-3 Bonhams, Knightsbridge #111/R
£800 $1328 €1160 Willetta, bridled brown horse (32x45cm-13x18in) s.i. i.verso panel. 12-Jun-3 Christie's, Kensington #63/R
£850 $1343 €1275 Woggles, a yorkie. Okaye, a corgi (30x25cm-12x10in) s.i. panel two. 28-Nov-2 Christie's, Kensington #288/R
£900 $1404 €1350 Ur, a bay horse (36x46cm-14x18in) s.i.d.48 panel. 18-Sep-2 Dreweatt Neate, Newbury #180a/R
£900 $1422 €1350 Tiddleywinks, bridled grey hunter (30x44cm-12x17in) s.i.d.45 panel. 28-Nov-2 Christie's, Kensington #185/R
£900 $1404 €1350 Jimmy (39x50cm-15x20in) s.i.d.54 board. 26-Mar-3 Sotheby's, Olympia #144/R
£1000 $1490 €1500 Portrait of Staffordshire bull terrier Sally (44x33cm-17x13in) s.d.1948 board. 27-Jun-2 Greenslade Hunt, Taunton #768/R est:400-600
£1000 $1560 €1500 Chestnut racehorse with a jockey up in the colours of Mr J.S Austen (40x51cm-16x20in) s.d.1932 panel. 6-Nov-2 Sotheby's, Olympia #95/R est:1000-2000
£1104 $1800 €1656 Wilfred, study of a terrier (35x25cm-14x10in) s.i.d.37 panel. 11-Feb-3 Bonhams & Doyles, New York #204/R est:1500-2000
£1200 $1896 €1800 Bunny, a scottie (35x43cm-14x17in) s.i. panel. 28-Nov-2 Christie's, Kensington #334/R est:1500-2000
£1300 $2028 €1950 Air mail (40x50cm-16x20in) s.i.d.54 board. 26-Mar-3 Sotheby's, Olympia #103/R est:500-700
£1300 $2028 €1950 Martin (34x45cm-13x18in) s.i. board. 26-Mar-3 Sotheby's, Olympia #145/R est:500-700
£1300 $2028 €1950 Westcot (40x32cm-16x13in) s.i.d.1932 board. 26-Mar-3 Sotheby's, Olympia #147/R est:500-700
£1400 $2212 €2100 Sorrel, bridled chestnut horse (34x46cm-13x18in) s.i.d.37 panel. 28-Nov-2 Christie's, Kensington #149/R est:1500-2000
£1400 $2184 €2100 Eclipses (34x45cm-13x18in) s.i.d.36. 26-Mar-3 Sotheby's, Olympia #102/R est:500-700
£1400 $2184 €2100 Take Care (34x46cm-13x18in) s.d.35 panel. 26-Mar-3 Woolley & Wallis, Salisbury #155/R est:600-800
£1500 $2445 €2250 Henry a bay hunter (22x29cm-9x11in) s. panel. 28-Jan-3 Henry Adams, Chichester #460/R est:1500-2000
£1500 $2445 €2250 Sam a dark brown hunter (34x45cm-13x18in) s.d.37 panel. 28-Jan-3 Henry Adams, Chichester #461/R est:1500-2000
£1500 $2385 €2250 Peat, study of a horse's head. board. 29-Apr-3 Lawrences, Bletchingley #1435/R est:400-600
£1500 $2460 €2250 Before the race (30x34cm-12x13in) 3-Jun-3 Bonhams, Knightsbridge #62/R est:1500-2000
£1687 $2750 €2531 Javelin, a German shepherd (43x38cm-17x15in) s.i. panel. 11-Feb-3 Bonhams & Doyles, New York #227/R est:1500-2500
£1840 $3000 €2760 Bella, study of a dachshund (45x50cm-18x20in) s.i. panel. 11-Feb-3 Bonhams & Doyles, New York #226/R est:2000-3000
£1900 $3002 €2850 Wigmore, bridled hunter (33x45cm-13x18in) s.i.d.43 panel. 28-Nov-2 Christie's, Kensington #186/R est:1000-1500
£1950 $3023 €2925 Bradden, chestnut gelding (32x45cm-13x18in) s.i. panel. 29-Oct-2 Henry Adams, Chichester #593/R est:800-1000
£1963 $3200 €2945 French bulldog (25x17cm-10x7in) init. panel. 11-Feb-3 Bonhams & Doyles, New York #206/R est:2000-3000
£2000 $3120 €3000 Chestnut hunter in a field (34x50cm-13x20in) s.d.48. 26-Mar-3 Sotheby's, Olympia #149/R est:400-600
£2200 $3476 €3300 Drainpipe, a liver chestnut horse (33x46cm-13x18in) s.d.1933 panel. 28-Nov-2 Christie's, Kensington #148/R est:2200-2800
£2300 $3634 €3450 Toby and Chokey a bay hunter and black hunter (34x45cm-13x18in) s. board pair. 26-Nov-2 Bonhams, Oxford #55/R est:300-500
£2400 $3792 €3600 Robin, a saddled bay hunter (33x46cm-13x18in) s.i.d.1933 panel. 28-Nov-2 Christie's, Kensington #150/R est:2200-2800
£2400 $3768 €3600 Study of chestnut hunter (45x60cm-18x24in) s.d.53. 11-Dec-2 Rupert Toovey, Partridge Green #75/R

HOLLAND, George Herbert Buckingham (1901-) British

£350 $567 €525 Barges and other traffic by Tower Bridge (51x80cm-20x31in) s. 23-Jan-3 Christie's, Kensington #235/R

HOLLAND, James (1800-1870) British

£340 $527 €510 Evening after a thunderstorm, Venice (30x25cm-12x10in) s.i.d.1850 verso board. 4-Oct-2 Mallams, Oxford #549

£1000 $1640 €1500 Royal Mile, Edinburgh (58x46cm-23x18in) s.d.1853 board. 5-Jun-3 Christie's, Kensington #725/R est:400-600
£5500 $8580 €8250 Canal scene, Venice (54x39cm-21x15in) prov. exhib. 9-Oct-2 Woolley & Wallis, Salisbury #318/R est:4000-6000
£6800 $10608 €10200 Grand Canal, Venice (67x90cm-26x35in) i.verso prov.exhib. 9-Oct-2 Woolley & Wallis, Salisbury #319/R est:10000-15000
£22000 $34540 €33000 Serra Convent, Oporto (37x53cm-15x21in) s.d.1838 prov. 16-Dec-2 Sotheby's, London #71/R est:15000-20000
£30000 $49800 €45000 Colleoni monument, Venice (101x127cm-40x50in) s.d.1845 prov.exhib. 10-Jun-3 Christie's, London #73/R est:15000-25000

Works on paper
£250 $388 €375 On the Grand Canal, Venice (27x41cm-11x16in) W/C executed c.1850. 25-Sep-2 Peter Wilson, Nantwich #117/R
£1400 $2296 €2030 Venetian canal with two barges (29x21cm-11x8in) mono.d.35 pencil col chk htd white prov.exhib. 5-Jun-3 Christie's, London #105/R est:1200-1800
£2800 $4396 €4200 Leicester Gallery, Knole (28x43cm-11x17in) init.d.42 pencil W/C gum arabic bodycol. 21-Nov-2 Christie's, London #50/R est:3000-5000
£4500 $7380 €6525 Venice, with Santa Maria della Salute in the distance (32x53cm-13x21in) mono.i.d.1858 pencil W/C bodycol prov. 5-Jun-3 Christie's, London #163/R est:5000-8000
£5400 $8964 €8100 Greenwich Hospital from Greenwich Hill (26x22cm-10x9in) s. W/C over pencil htd stopping out prov. 12-Jun-3 Sotheby's, London #138/R est:4000-6000
£10500 $15015 €15750 Venetian canal (34x24cm-13x9in) pencil W/C gum htd white scratching out prov.exhib.lit. 22-Jan-3 Christie's, London #55/R est:8000

HOLLAND, James (attrib) (1800-1870) British
Works on paper
£320 $499 €480 Italian lake with boats and figures (25x36cm-10x14in) init. W/C bodycol. 17-Sep-2 Goldings, Lincolnshire #675

HOLLAND, John (18/19th C) British
£938 $1500 €1407 Sunset along a mountainous shore (86x137cm-34x54in) s. 15-Mar-3 Selkirks, St. Louis #89/R est:2000-3000
£2700 $4185 €4050 Herring fishing off Bradda Head (76x137cm-30x54in) s. monochrome. 6-Dec-2 Chrystals Auctions, Isle of Man #221 est:1200-1600
£2900 $4524 €4350 By a river (36x53cm-14x21in) 26-Mar-3 Hamptons Fine Art, Godalming #216/R est:2000-3000
£11000 $17050 €16500 Gathering firewood. Gathering seaweed (51x91cm-20x36in) s. pair. 6-Dec-2 Chrystals Auctions, Isle of Man #172 est:9000-12000

Works on paper
£500 $745 €750 Hauling in the catch (66x107cm-26x42in) s. chl monochrome. 28-Jun-2 Chrystals Auctions, Isle of Man #175

HOLLAND, John (snr) (fl.1831-1879) British
£620 $1029 €930 Three men resting by a river bank (31x46cm-12x18in) s. 10-Jun-3 Bonhams, Leeds #188
£1300 $2067 €1950 Les Autelets, Sark (28x43cm-11x17in) s.i. 20-Mar-3 Martel Maides, Guernsey #42/R est:1300-1500

HOLLAND, S S (fl.1877-1911) British
£2000 $3340 €2900 Evening on the wear with figures resting in the foreground (127x188cm-50x74in) s. 17-Jun-3 Anderson & Garland, Newcastle #445/R est:2000-3500

HOLLAND, Tom (1936-) American
£2724 $4250 €4086 Black fish series no 8 (122x155cm-48x61in) s.i.d.1991 verso epoxy aluminum fiberglass lit. 14-Oct-2 Butterfields, San Francisco #2114/R est:4000-6000

HOLLAND, W Harry (1941-) British
£900 $1431 €1350 Family on a beach (33x28cm-13x11in) s. board. 29-Apr-3 Peter Francis, Wales #15

HOLLANDER, Hendrik (1823-1884) Dutch
£696 $1086 €1100 Interior with young boy with hoop and dog (28x23cm-11x9in) s. panel. 21-Oct-2 Glerum, Amsterdam #80/R
£1100 $1727 €1650 Interior with a woman sewing by a window, spaniel at her feet (19x15cm-7x6in) s. panel. 21-Nov-2 Tennants, Leyburn #851/R est:600-800

HOLLAWAY, Antony (1928-2000) British
Sculpture
£1000 $1590 €1500 Blue and green spheres (47x47x13cm-19x19x5in) with sig.d.69 perspex. 18-Mar-3 Bonhams, Knightsbridge #109 est:800-1000

HOLLEGHA, Wolfgang (1929-) Austrian
£6962 $11000 €11000 Untitled (185x185cm-73x73in) s.d.1983. 27-Nov-2 Dorotheum, Vienna #278/R est:13000-19000
£9929 $16085 €14000 Untitled (92x105cm-36x41in) s. 20-May-3 Dorotheum, Vienna #265/R est:9000-12000

HOLLEMAN, Frida (1908-1999) Dutch
£764 $1260 €1100 Horse riders (40x30cm-16x12in) s. 1-Jul-3 Christie's, Amsterdam #575a

HOLLENBERG, Felix (1868-1946) German
£586 $926 €850 Extensive landscape (18x24cm-7x9in) mono.d.5.8.30 s.d. verso board. 2-Apr-3 Dr Fritz Nagel, Stuttgart #9110/R
£586 $926 €850 Killesberg in the evening (17x15cm-7x6in) mono. s.i.d. verso board. 2-Apr-3 Dr Fritz Nagel, Stuttgart #9111/R
£968 $1423 €1500 Autumnal landscape (70x99cm-28x39in) s.d.93. 20-Jun-2 Dr Fritz Nagel, Stuttgart #775/R est:2500

HOLLENSTEIN, Stephanie (1886-1944) Austrian
£7595 $12000 €12000 Lago Zoi, Dolomites (82x126cm-32x50in) s. 27-Nov-2 Dorotheum, Vienna #166/R est:12000-18000
Works on paper
£1646 $2600 €2600 Lago Zoi, Dolomites (13x21cm-5x8in) s. W/C. 27-Nov-2 Dorotheum, Vienna #167/R est:1200-1600

HOLLESTELLE, Jacob (1858-1920) Dutch
£2381 $3786 €3500 Beach by the Ebbe (40x80cm-16x31in) s. 25-Feb-3 Dorotheum, Vienna #230/R est:3500-4000

HOLLINGS, Anna (?) ?
£386 $602 €579 Love letters (76x61cm-30x24in) s. 27-Mar-3 International Art Centre, Auckland #5/R (NZ.D 1100)

HOLLINGSWORTH, C (20th C) British?
£900 $1431 €1350 On the stairs (69x53cm-27x21in) s. 6-Mar-3 Christie's, Kensington #603/R

HOLLINGSWORTH, Howard (20th C) American
£491 $800 €737 Mountain view (38x53cm-15x21in) canvas on board painted c.1930. 14-Feb-3 Du Mouchelle, Detroit #2175/R

HOLLINS, John (1798-1855) British
£400 $636 €600 Portrait of an aristocratic lady (91x71cm-36x28in) s.d.1844. 6-Mar-3 Bonhams, Cornwall #728

HOLLMANN, Charles (1877-1953) Dutch
£362 $586 €550 City in winter (57x61cm-22x24in) s. board. 21-Jan-3 Christie's, Amsterdam #442

HOLLOSY, Simon (1857-1918) Hungarian
£1291 $2001 €1937 Nude in the studio (73x53cm-29x21in) s. 6-Dec-2 Kieselbach, Budapest #68/R (H.F 480000)
£3493 $5450 €5240 River landscape in summer (100x100cm-39x39in) s.d.1916 prov. 9-Nov-2 Galerie Gloggner, Luzern #80/R est:4500-5000 (S.FR 8000)
£25150 $39234 €37725 Spring by the brook (100x100cm-39x39in) s.d.1916. 11-Apr-3 Kieselbach, Budapest #49/R est:8000000-9000000 (H.F 9000000)

HOLLOWAY, Charles Edward (1838-1897) British
£300 $492 €450 Hay barges and other vessels on the Thames (53x76cm-21x30in) s.d.1890. 5-Jun-3 Christie's, Kensington #736
£650 $1027 €975 Fishing boats running into harbour in a heavy swell (46x66cm-18x26in) s.d.81. 14-Nov-2 Christie's, Kensington #214

HOLLOWAY, Edward Stratton (?-1939) American
£579 $950 €869 Fishing boats at low tide (76x64cm-30x25in) s. 9-Feb-3 William Jenack, New York #293

HOLLYER, Gregory (19/20th C) British
£382 $600 €573 Under the beech tree, autumn (56x81cm-22x32in) s. 22-Nov-2 Skinner, Boston #276/R

HOLLYER, Maud (fl.1900-1910) British
Works on paper
£311 $516 €451 Tudor cottage and country garden (48x75cm-19x30in) s. W/C. 16-Jun-3 Waddingtons, Toronto #76/R (C.D 700)

HOLLYER, W P (1834-1922) British
£750 $1193 €1125 Head of a highland cow (71x71cm-28x28in) s.d.77 i.d.1877 verso. 6-Mar-3 Christie's, Kensington #70/R
£2200 $3498 €3300 Pass at Glencoe (102x152cm-40x60in) s.i.d. 6-Mar-3 Christie's, Kensington #54/R est:2000-3000

HOLLYWOOD, William (20th C) British
£1600 $2496 €2400 Widgeons (59x89cm-23x35in) s. 14-Apr-3 Hamilton Osborne King, Dublin #1507 est:1000-1500

HOLM, Astrid (1876-1937) Danish
£512 $814 €768 Still life of fruit on dish (43x38cm-17x15in) s. 10-Mar-3 Rasmussen, Vejle #652 (D.KR 5500)

HOLM, Christian Frederik Carl (1804-1846) Danish
£3873 $6236 €5500 Taking the cows up to the mountain pasture (72x98cm-28x39in) mono.d.1838. 9-May-3 Schloss Ahlden, Ahlden #1475/R est:5800

HOLM, Gosta (?) Swedish
Works on paper
£323 $510 €500 Troll in the forest (18x13cm-7x5in) s. W/C. 19-Dec-2 Hagelstam, Helsinki #899/R

HOLM, H G F (1803-1861) Danish
Works on paper
£698 $1110 €1047 View through Frederiksgade towards the Marble Church (22x33cm-9x13in) W/C pencil. 5-Mar-3 Rasmussen, Copenhagen #2086/R (D.KR 7500)
£2239 $3560 €3359 Schonberg's country home, Gammel Kongevej (12x18cm-5x7in) d.1834 W/C lit. 5-May-3 Rasmussen, Vejle #332/R est:18000 (D.KR 24000)

HOLM, Harald Martin (1866-1920) Danish
Works on paper
£478 $775 €693 French anemones in Chinese vase (57x48cm-22x19in) s. pastel exhib. 26-May-3 Rasmussen, Copenhagen #1230/R (D.KR 5000)

HOLM, Niels Emil Severin (1823-1863) Danish
£581 $894 €872 Scene from living in the country (20x28cm-8x11in) study painted 1855. 4-Sep-2 Kunsthallen, Copenhagen #15/R (D.KR 6800)
£1025 $1578 €1538 Herrevads Kloster in Skane, summer of 1852 (22x32cm-9x13in) s. lit. 4-Sep-2 Kunsthallen, Copenhagen #1/R est:10000 (D.KR 12000)

HOLM, P C and PETERSEN, L (19th C) Danish/German
£930 $1432 €1395 Ship's portrait of the barque Helios (75x67cm-30x26in) s.i.d.1861. 26-Oct-2 Rasmussen, Havnen #3129/R (D.KR 11000)
£2488 $4031 €3608 Portrait of the two master Schiller (47x65cm-19x26in) s.i.d.1853. 24-May-3 Rasmussen, Havnen #2277/R est:10000-15000 (D.KR 26000)

HOLM, Per Daniel (1835-1903) Swedish
£565 $886 €848 Sunday in summer (60x90cm-24x35in) s. 16-Dec-2 Lilla Bukowskis, Stockholm #608 (S.KR 8000)
£692 $1086 €1038 Mountain landscape with hunters (75x105cm-30x41in) s.d.1861. 16-Dec-2 Lilla Bukowskis, Stockholm #1028/R (S.KR 9800)

HOLMAN, Francis (1729-1790) British
£1400 $2268 €2100 Cutter Mermaid running into the fleet anchorage at the Downs (46x36cm-18x14in) s.d.1778 prov. 21-May-3 Christie's, Kensington #372/R est:1000-1500

HOLMBERG, August (attrib) (1851-1911) German
£1020 $1622 €1500 Reader (29x24cm-11x9in) s.d.1873. 18-Mar-3 Finarte, Milan #126/R

HOLMBERG-KROHN, Julie (1882-1956) Norwegian/Russian
£594 $915 €891 Blue still life of flowers with oranges (89x63cm-35x25in) s. painted 1914. 28-Oct-2 Blomqvist, Lysaker #1169/R (N.KR 7000)

HOLMBOE, Thorolf (1866-1935) Norwegian
£329 $510 €494 View from shore (51x65cm-20x26in) s. 3-Dec-2 Ritchie, Toronto #3106/R (C.D 800)
£382 $588 €573 Winter landscape with wagon on road (107x58cm-42x23in) s. painted 1893. 28-Oct-2 Blomqvist, Lysaker #1096/R (N.KR 4500)
£433 $662 €650 Sailing at night (32x48cm-13x19in) s. 26-Aug-2 Blomqvist, Lysaker #1184/R (N.KR 5000)
£487 $793 €731 View across Akerselven - river landscape (75x67cm-30x26in) s. canvas on panel. 17-Feb-3 Blomqvist, Lysaker #1078/R (N.KR 5500)
£561 $937 €813 Coastal landscape with geese (60x68cm-24x27in) s.d.1911. 18-Jun-3 Grev Wedels Plass, Oslo #186/R (N.KR 6500)
£647 $984 €971 Archipelago (38x46cm-15x18in) s. i.verso panel. 31-Aug-2 Grev Wedels Plass, Oslo #53/R (N.KR 7500)
£702 $1109 €1053 Landscape from Saro, west coast of Sweden (65x75cm-26x30in) s.i.d.1902. 17-Dec-2 Grev Wedels Plass, Oslo #233/R (N.KR 8000)
£707 $1160 €1025 Lighthouse by the sea (54x73cm-21x29in) s. 2-Jun-3 Blomqvist, Oslo #100/R (N.KR 7700)
£708 $1154 €1062 Coastal landscape at night (33x49cm-13x19in) s.d.1903 panel. 17-Feb-3 Blomqvist, Lysaker #1077/R (N.KR 8000)
£918 $1506 €1331 Sailing boat and breakers (55x85cm-22x33in) s.d.1919. 2-Jun-3 Blomqvist, Oslo #102/R (N.KR 10000)
£1134 $1781 €1701 Road through large trees (77x90cm-30x35in) s. 25-Nov-2 Blomqvist, Lysaker #1127/R est:20000-25000 (N.KR 13000)
£1178 $1849 €1767 Boat on the fjord (64x77cm-25x30in) s/. 25-Nov-2 Blomqvist, Lysaker #1125/R est:15000-18000 (N.KR 13500)
£1377 $2259 €1997 Two rowing boats at anchor (61x75cm-24x30in) s.d.04. 2-Jun-3 Blomqvist, Oslo #96/R est:18000-22000 (N.KR 15000)
£1644 $2597 €2466 Summer, sun, sail and steamer (40x49cm-16x19in) s. 2-Dec-2 Blomqvist, Oslo #386/R est:20000-25000 (N.KR 19000)
£1741 $2785 €2612 Winter landscape, evening (103x71cm-41x28in) s.d.1906. 17-Mar-3 Blomqvist, Oslo #373/R est:25000-35000 (N.KR 20000)
£1754 $2772 €2631 Pine trees at Bygdo (104x86cm-41x34in) s.d.1920 i.verso. 17-Dec-2 Grev Wedels Plass, Oslo #237/R est:20000-25000 (N.KR 20000)
£3114 $4920 €4671 Snowy landscape with bullfinch and urn (82x59cm-32x23in) s. 2-Dec-2 Blomqvist, Oslo #313/R est:20000-25000 (N.KR 36000)
£3509 $5544 €5264 Avenue of trees (82x109cm-32x43in) s.d.1920. 17-Dec-2 Grev Wedels Plass, Oslo #236/R est:30000-40000 (N.KR 40000)
£3905 $6014 €5858 Cormorant drying his wings (97x80cm-38x31in) s. 28-Oct-2 Blomqvist, Lysaker #1095/R est:15000-20000 (N.KR 46000)
£3982 $6451 €5973 Landscape from Aasgaardstrand (86x100cm-34x39in) s. 26-May-3 Grev Wedels Plass, Oslo #95/R est:50000-70000 (N.KR 44000)
£4352 $6963 €6528 Evening landscape from Rauer near Svenner (66x79cm-26x31in) s. i.stretcher. 17-Mar-3 Blomqvist, Oslo #369/R est:30000-40000 (N.KR 50000)
£5048 $8077 €7572 Boat in full sails along the coast (80x80cm-31x31in) s. 17-Mar-3 Blomqvist, Oslo #393/R est:20000-40000 (N.KR 58000)
£5430 $8796 €8145 House with garden and figures (70x80cm-28x31in) s.d.1915. 26-May-3 Grev Wedels Plass, Oslo #60/R est:30000 (N.KR 60000)

Works on paper
£260 $397 €390 Pilot by the coast (30x22cm-12x9in) s. W/C wash. 26-Aug-2 Blomqvist, Lysaker #1186/R (N.KR 3000)
£345 $525 €518 Two bullfinches (25x24cm-10x9in) s. pencil W/C. 31-Aug-2 Grev Wedels Plass, Oslo #54/R (N.KR 4000)
£467 $719 €701 Tenglo (33x48cm-13x19in) s. W/C pencil executed 1895. 28-Oct-2 Blomqvist, Lysaker #1097 (N.KR 5500)
£785 $1233 €1178 Landscape, Hanko (55x72cm-22x28in) s. pastel. 25-Nov-2 Blomqvist, Lysaker #1126/R (N.KR 9000)
£1396 $2192 €2094 Family of polar bears (68x78cm-27x31in) s. W/C. 25-Nov-2 Blomqvist, Lysaker #1128 est:15000-18000 (N.KR 16000)
£3911 $6218 €5867 Evening with horse chestnut in flower (61x57cm-24x22in) s.d.1912 W/C crayon Indian ink. 5-Mar-3 Rasmussen, Copenhagen #2047/R est:20000 (D.KR 42000)

HOLMEFJORD, Ingvald (20th C) Danish
£326 $519 €489 Blue figure (54x65cm-21x26in) init.d.96. 29-Apr-3 Kunsthallen, Copenhagen #77 (D.KR 3500)

HOLMES, Dwight (1900-1988) American
£288 $450 €432 Landscape (20x25cm-8x10in) board. 19-Oct-2 David Dike, Dallas #1/R
£481 $750 €722 Forest Park in the fall (18x25cm-7x10in) board. 19-Oct-2 David Dike, Dallas #316/R
£513 $800 €770 South Fork in Guadalupe (41x51cm-16x20in) 19-Oct-2 David Dike, Dallas #217/R
£513 $800 €770 Gulls (25x30cm-10x12in) board. 19-Oct-2 David Dike, Dallas #361/R
£641 $1000 €962 Bluebonnets (30x41cm-12x16in) board. 19-Oct-2 David Dike, Dallas #119/R
£1154 $1800 €1731 Mexico (61x76cm-24x30in) 19-Oct-2 David Dike, Dallas #340/R est:2000-3000
£1218 $1900 €1827 Bluebonnets near Fredericksburg, Texas (41x51cm-16x20in) canvasboard. 19-Oct-2 David Dike, Dallas #118/R est:1500-3000

HOLMES, Edward (?-1893) British
£1331 $2102 €1997 Landscape with girl and dog (44x52cm-17x20in) s. 16-Nov-2 Crafoord, Lund #50/R est:8000 (S.KR 19000)
£3250 $5330 €4875 Chasing the ducks (51x76cm-20x30in) s.d.1854. 29-May-3 Christie's, Kensington #255/R est:4000-6000

HOLMES, George Augustus (?-1911) British
£1500 $2340 €2250 Rivals (22x17cm-9x7in) s. 8-Apr-3 Bonhams, Knightsbridge #136/R est:1500-2000
£6000 $9420 €9000 Doctor (36x42cm-14x17in) init. board. 21-Nov-2 Clevedon Sale Rooms #223/R est:4000-6000

HOLMES, James (1777-1860) British
£3500 $5565 €5250 Right Honourable George Gordon Byron, Lord Byron (11x8cm-4x3in) s.i.d.12 April 1816. 4-Mar-3 Bearnes, Exeter #322/R est:400-600

HOLMES, James (attrib) (1777-1860) British
Works on paper
£800 $1240 €1200 Portrait of Lady Delamare (33x25cm-13x10in) W/C with two other portraits three. 30-Sep-2 Sotheby's, Olympia #552/R

HOLMES, Jan (1911-) American
£449 $700 €674 Melon eaters (38x102cm-15x40in) exhib. 19-Oct-2 David Dike, Dallas #134/R

HOLMES, John J (20th C) British
£700 $1085 €1050 Schooner Kirin sailing on the Clyde (50x100cm-20x39in) s. 31-Oct-2 Christie's, Kensington #413/R
£700 $1099 €1050 Cicely, Endeavour and Yankee (80x100cm-31x39in) s. i. on stretcher. 16-Dec-2 Sotheby's, Olympia #182/R
£700 $1169 €1015 Britannia racing in the Solent off Norris Castle (61x91cm-24x36in) s. i.on stretcher. 18-Jun-3 Sotheby's, Olympia #138/R
£1300 $2171 €1885 Britannia versus Westward off the Royal Solent Yacht Club (80x100cm-31x39in) s. i.on stretcher. 18-Jun-3 Sotheby's, Olympia #140/R est:800-1200

HOLMES, Marcus (1880-?) British
Works on paper
£460 $727 €690 Polperro harbour with sailing boats (33x51cm-13x20in) s. W/C. 4-Apr-3 Moore Allen & Innocent, Cirencester #443

HOLMES, Ralph (1876-1963) American
£719 $1200 €1043 Landscape, jagged mountains (36x46cm-14x18in) s. masonite. 17-Jun-3 John Moran, Pasadena #121b est:1000-1500
£1161 $1800 €1742 Landscape (81x71cm-32x28in) s. prov. 29-Oct-2 John Moran, Pasadena #634 est:2500-3500
£1198 $2000 €1737 River landscape (61x76cm-24x30in) s. prov. 17-Jun-3 John Moran, Pasadena #78a est:2500-3500
£1796 $3000 €2604 Landscape with road to the snow (61x71cm-24x28in) s. i.verso. 17-Jun-3 John Moran, Pasadena #68 est:1500-2000
£3871 $6000 €5807 Landing (86x91cm-34x36in) s. i.verso prov. 29-Oct-2 John Moran, Pasadena #766 est:4000-6000

HOLMES, Sharon Christian (1950-) Canadian
£207 $322 €344 Blue and Charlie (77x97cm-30x38in) s. i.d.1989 verso mixed media prov. 13-Apr-3 Levis, Calgary #464/R (C.D 475)

HOLMES, Sir Charles (1868-1936) British
£800 $1248 €1200 Easter snow showers cross furl (46x81cm-18x32in) s. 12-Sep-2 Sotheby's, Olympia #119/R
£1800 $2772 €2700 Harter Fell (51x61cm-20x24in) init.i.d.09 prov.exhib. 5-Sep-2 Christie's, Kensington #206/R est:800-1200

HOLMES, Walter (20th C) European
£260 $434 €377 Tynemouth beach at low tide (37x44cm-15x17in) s.i.d.Feb 74 verso. 17-Jun-3 Anderson & Garland, Newcastle #358

HOLMES, William H (1846-1933) American
Works on paper
£321 $500 €482 Flying clouds (22x28cm-9x11in) s. W/C. 20-Sep-2 Sloan, North Bethesda #360/R
£833 $1300 €1250 Distant view of Mt. Orizaba, Mexico (24x33cm-9x13in) s.i.d.June 1928 W/C. 20-Sep-2 Sloan, North Bethesda #359/R est:600-800

HOLMGREN, Vilhelm (1863-1943) Swedish
£336 $531 €504 Coastal landscape with woman bathing (45x53cm-18x21in) s. panel. 16-Nov-2 Crafoord, Lund #77/R (S.KR 4800)
Works on paper
£245 $387 €368 Oriental girl with string instrument (35x21cm-14x8in) W/C. 16-Nov-2 Crafoord, Lund #86/R (S.KR 3500)

HOLMLUND, Josephina (1827-1905) Swedish
£386 $595 €579 Moonlit landscape with boat and figures on jetty (52x66cm-20x26in) s.d.1862 i.stretcher. 27-Oct-2 Anders Antik, Landskrona #253 (S.KR 5600)
£392 $643 €600 Fjord landscape (58x42cm-23x17in) s. 9-Feb-3 Bukowskis, Helsinki #411/R
£469 $722 €704 Alpine landscape with wanderer (118x100cm-46x39in) 27-Oct-2 Anders Antik, Landskrona #237a (S.KR 6800)
£491 $776 €737 Landscape from Sognefjord, Norway (37x54cm-15x21in) s. 30-Nov-2 Goteborg Auktionsverk, Sweden #150/R (S.KR 7000)
£709 $1099 €1064 Fjord landscape with figures on the beach (63x93cm-25x37in) s.d.88. 4-Dec-2 AB Stockholms Auktionsverk #1762/R (S.KR 10000)
£857 $1337 €1286 Moonlit landscape with woman and cow (61x94cm-24x37in) s. 13-Sep-2 Lilla Bukowskis, Stockholm #410 (S.KR 12500)
£1059 $1662 €1589 Rowing trip on the fjord (32x50cm-13x20in) s. canvas on panel. 16-Dec-2 Lilla Bukowskis, Stockholm #879 est:5000-7000 (S.KR 15000)
£2292 $3713 €3438 Mountain landscape with cottage (82x118cm-32x46in) s.d.1882. 3-Feb-3 Lilla Bukowskis, Stockholm #524 est:25000-30000 (S.KR 32000)

HOLMSTROM, Tora Vega (1880-1967) Swedish
£371 $586 €557 Woman (34x33cm-13x13in) mono. 16-Nov-2 Crafoord, Lund #72/R (S.KR 5300)
£842 $1330 €1263 Still life of flowers in vase (71x61cm-28x24in) mono. prov. 27-Nov-2 Falkkloos, Malmo #77691/R (S.KR 12000)
£1407 $2223 €2111 Still life of fruit (43x38cm-17x15in) s.d.27 verso panel. 28-Apr-3 Bukowskis, Stockholm #135/R est:12000-15000 (S.KR 18500)
£1822 $2842 €2733 French voluntary soldier (46x40cm-18x16in) init. i.verso lit. 5-Nov-2 Bukowskis, Stockholm #35/R est:12000-15000 (S.KR 26000)
£1931 $3108 €2897 Woman holding baby (55x45cm-22x18in) panel. 7-May-3 AB Stockholms Auktionsverk #837/R est:10000-12000 (S.KR 25000)
£2034 $3213 €3051 The hills - mountain landscape (73x93cm-29x37in) mono. prov.lit. 27-Nov-2 Falkkloos, Malmo #77687/R est:30000 (S.KR 29000)

HOLMWOOD, John (1910-1987) New Zealander
£550 $919 €798 Beach with palm trees and hut (90x60cm-35x24in) s.d.60 board. 17-Jun-3 Bonhams, Knightsbridge #51/R
£2456 $3832 €3684 Raetihi country (74x106cm-29x42in) s. board. 27-Mar-3 International Art Centre, Auckland #50/R est:10000-15000 (NZ.D 7000)

HOLOPAINEN, Kaarlo Yrjo (19th C) Finnish
£510 $811 €750 Nature scene from Rantasalmi (49x31cm-19x12in) s.d.1891. 27-Feb-3 Hagelstam, Helsinki #1030

HOLROYD, Sir Charles (1861-1917) British
£1097 $1700 €1646 Pre-Raphaelite, neo-classical figures in a landscape (41x61cm-16x24in) s. panel. 2-Nov-2 North East Auctions, Portsmouth #49/R est:800-1200

HOLSCHER, Constantin (1861-1921) German
£3800 $6194 €5510 Boarding (77x97cm-30x38in) s.d.1893. 16-Jul-3 Sotheby's, Olympia #221/R est:2000-3000

HOLSOE, Carl (1863-1935) Danish
£380 $586 €570 Farmyard (27x36cm-11x14in) s. panel. 26-Oct-2 Rasmussen, Havnen #2246 (D.KR 4500)
£657 $1051 €986 Landscape with farms (26x36cm-10x14in) s. 13-Jan-3 Rasmussen, Vejle #185/R (D.KR 7500)
£680 $1060 €1020 Landscape view with half-timbered house (47x79cm-19x31in) s. exhib. 5-Aug-2 Rasmussen, Vejle #194/R (D.KR 8000)
£1717 $2712 €2576 Still life of hare, pheasants and herrings (100x76cm-39x30in) s. 13-Nov-2 Kunsthallen, Copenhagen #62/R est:20000 (D.KR 20000)
£4000 $6200 €6000 Woman in an interior (68x68cm-27x27in) 3-Dec-2 Sotheby's, Olympia #292/R est:4000-6000
£4248 $6627 €6372 Interior scene with lady embroidering by lamplight (47x47cm-19x19in) s. panel. 5-Aug-2 Rasmussen, Vejle #8/R est:50000 (D.KR 50000)
£7092 $10993 €10638 Interior scene with woman embroidering (47x47cm-19x19in) s. panel. 3-Dec-2 Bukowskis, Stockholm #364/R est:140000-150000 (S.KR 100000)

£8613 $13092 €12920 Girl standing by window (58x73cm-23x29in) s. exhib. 27-Aug-2 Rasmussen, Copenhagen #1454/R est:125000-150000 (D.KR 100000)
£13964 $22622 €20248 Drawing-room interior (57x50cm-22x20in) s. 26-May-3 Bukowskis, Stockholm #285/R est:80000-100000 (S.KR 180000)
£14468 $22860 €21702 Sunshine in corner of sitting room (53x42cm-21x17in) s. 2-Dec-2 Rasmussen, Copenhagen #1124/R est:200000 (D.KR 170000)
£14925 $24478 €21641 Interior scene with woman in doorway (53x46cm-21x18in) s. panel prov. 4-Jun-3 AB Stockholms Auktionsverk #2476/R est:100000-150000 (S.KR 190000)
£16312 $25284 €24468 Sunlit sitting room interior (48x43cm-19x17in) s. 4-Dec-2 AB Stockholms Auktionsverk #1883/R est:125000-150000 (S.KR 230000)
£18159 $28328 €27239 Dining room interior with table set and maid lighting candles (93x90cm-37x35in) s. 23-Sep-2 Rasmussen, Vejle #34/R est:200000 (D.KR 215000)
£20484 $32570 €30726 The artist's wife reading in a corner of the sitting room (57x54cm-22x21in) s. 5-Mar-3 Rasmussen, Copenhagen #1526/R est:175000-225000 (D.KR 220000)
£21277 $32979 €31916 Interior scene with woman sewing (59x63cm-23x25in) s,. 3-Dec-2 Bukowskis, Stockholm #308/R est:150000-175000 (S.KR 300000)
£27097 $42000 €40646 An interior with a stove and a view into dining room (70x60cm-28x24in) s. 30-Oct-2 Christie's, Rockefeller NY #6/R est:30000-40000
£28000 $45920 €42000 Interior I sollys - sunlit interior (68x79cm-27x31in) s. prov. 3-Jun-3 Sotheby's, London #213/R est:18000-25000
£30000 $49200 €45000 Laesende kvinde ved vindvet - reading in the morning light (95x80cm-37x31in) s. 3-Jun-3 Sotheby's, London #212/R est:30000-50000
£36000 $60120 €54000 Lady reading music in an interior (50x53cm-20x21in) s. prov. 19-Jun-3 Christie's, London #76/R est:18000-25000
£38492 $63126 €55813 Interior scene with lady seated at window (66x52cm-26x20in) s. 4-Jun-3 AB Stockholms Auktionsverk #2466/R est:300000-350000 (S.KR 490000)

HOLSOE, Niels (1865-1928) Danish
£298 $474 €447 Interior (55x45cm-22x18in) s.d.1917 panel. 10-Mar-3 Rasmussen, Vejle #535 (D.KR 3200)
£474 $720 €711 Interior from St Nikolai Church in Koge (87x56cm-34x22in) s.d.1909. 27-Aug-2 Rasmussen, Copenhagen #1710/R (D.KR 5500)

HOLST, Agda (1886-1976) Swedish
£297 $475 €431 Still life (52x39cm-20x15in) s.d.1932. 18-May-3 Anders Antik, Landskrona #91 (S.KR 3800)
£339 $532 €492 Still life. 15-Dec-2 Anders Antik, Landskrona #1008 (S.KR 4800)
£2510 $3965 €3765 Town scene with figures (48x63cm-19x25in) s.d.1917. 28-Apr-3 Bukowskis, Stockholm #85/R est:30000-40000 (S.KR 33000)

HOLST, Johan Gustaf von (1841-1917) Swedish
£1257 $2061 €1823 Landscape with dog and snipe (100x72cm-39x28in) s.d.81. 4-Jun-3 AB Stockholms Auktionsverk #2327/R est:18000-20000 (S.KR 16000)
£1277 $1979 €1916 Mallards in flight (89x74cm-35x29in) s. 4-Dec-2 AB Stockholms Auktionsverk #1590/R est:15000-20000 (S.KR 18000)
£1396 $2262 €2024 Portrait of a dachshund (34x26cm-13x10in) mono.d.1898. 25-May-3 Uppsala Auktionskammare, Uppsala #109/R est:10000-12000 (S.KR 18000)
£1560 $2418 €2340 Irish setter (35x28cm-14x11in) s. 4-Dec-2 AB Stockholms Auktionsverk #1631/R est:10000-15000 (S.KR 22000)

HOLST, Johannes (1880-1965) Swedish
£600 $978 €900 Cutty Sark at sea (61x51cm-24x20in) s.d.1945. 28-Jan-3 Gorringes, Lewes #1674
£723 $1143 €1085 Schooner on a stormy sea (53x68cm-21x27in) s.d.1930. 1-Apr-3 Stephan Welz, Johannesburg #428/R est:10000-15000 (SA.R 9000)
£1895 $3108 €2900 Sailing boats (42x64cm-17x25in) s.d.1917. 8-Feb-3 Hans Stahl, Hamburg #151/R est:2900
£2338 $3413 €3600 Four-mast barque Hera on a journey (68x100cm-27x39in) s.d.1910 canvas on canvas. 15-Jun-2 Hans Stahl, Hamburg #238/R
£2821 $4372 €4400 Three master at sea (52x70cm-20x28in) s.d.1933. 5-Dec-2 Schopman, Hamburg #655 est:4400
£3205 $4968 €5000 Threemaster, Helio, off the coast (93x135cm-37x53in) s.d.1919. 7-Dec-2 Hans Stahl, Hamburg #144/R est:6000
£3247 $4740 €5000 Quiet journey for the four-mast barque Parma (105x165cm-41x65in) s. i.verso. 15-Jun-2 Hans Stahl, Hamburg #236/R est:5500
£3767 $5877 €5500 Three master on the high seas (95x150cm-37x59in) s.d.1917. 10-Apr-3 Schopman, Hamburg #708 est:4000
£6164 $9616 €9000 Fully rigged ship, the Walkure (80x118cm-31x46in) s.d.1911. 10-Apr-3 Schopman, Hamburg #707/R est:9000

HOLST, Laurits (1848-1934) Danish
£552 $862 €828 Coastal landscape with sailing vessel (46x81cm-18x32in) s.d.74. 5-Aug-2 Rasmussen, Vejle #31/R (D.KR 6500)
£1900 $3173 €2755 Shipping off Gibraltar (41x69cm-16x27in) s.d.92. 17-Jun-3 Bonhams, New Bond Street #21/R est:2000-3000
£2979 $4706 €4469 Ship run aground in frozen waters (39x64cm-15x25in) s.d.87. 2-Dec-2 Rasmussen, Copenhagen #1423/R est:35000-40000 (D.KR 35000)

HOLSTAYN, Josef (20th C) German
£1200 $1956 €1800 Flowers in a basket and a bird's nest (60x49cm-24x19in) s.i. panel. 13-Feb-3 Christie's, Kensington #235/R est:1500-2500
£3425 $5342 €5000 Still life with roses, camellias, grapes, birds nest, butterflies (60x50cm-24x20in) s. 10-Apr-3 Dorotheum, Vienna #76/R est:6500-7500
£4516 $7000 €6774 Assorted flowers, fruit, insects, bird, nest and porcelain bowl (75x60cm-30x24in) s.i. 2-Oct-2 Christie's, Rockefeller NY #790/R est:3000-5000
£5755 $9209 €8000 Still life on main square in Linz (74x59cm-29x23in) s.d.75. 14-May-3 Dorotheum, Linz #388/R est:14000-18000

HOLSTEIN, Bent (1942-) Danish
£455 $755 €660 Golden wall II (100x81cm-39x32in) s.d.1987 verso. 12-Jun-3 Kunsthallen, Copenhagen #80/R (D.KR 4800)
£604 $954 €906 Nubian silver (100x81cm-39x32in) s.d.1986 verso. 1-Apr-3 Rasmussen, Copenhagen #311/R (D.KR 6500)
£861 $1335 €1292 From Grass Key (114x146cm-45x57in) s.d.1996 verso. 4-Dec-2 Kunsthallen, Copenhagen #250/R (D.KR 10000)
£1016 $1575 €1524 African Baroue I (147x114cm-58x45in) s.d.1983 verso prov. 1-Oct-2 Rasmussen, Copenhagen #194/R est:15000-20000 (D.KR 12000)

HOLSTEIN, Pieter (1934-) Dutch
£1154 $1788 €1800 Ten einder (60x70cm-24x28in) s. s.verso painted c.1967. 3-Dec-2 Christie's, Amsterdam #337/R est:1500-2000

HOLSTEYN, Pieter (elder) (1580-1662) Dutch
Works on paper
£1712 $2671 €2500 Oyster fishing (15x20cm-6x8in) mono. W/C Indian ink over pencil. 11-Apr-3 Winterberg, Heidelberg #98/R est:750
£1986 $3099 €2900 Gibbon (15x20cm-6x8in) mono. W/C over pencil. 11-Apr-3 Winterberg, Heidelberg #99/R est:750
£2192 $3419 €3200 Dromedary (15x17cm-6x7in) mono. W/C Indian ink over pencil. 11-Apr-3 Winterberg, Heidelberg #97/R est:850

HOLSTEYN, Pieter (younger) (1614-1687) Flemish
Works on paper
£385 $562 €600 Bird on branch (15x18cm-6x7in) mono. W/C Indian ink. 4-Jun-2 Karl & Faber, Munich #20/R
£385 $562 €600 Bird (15x20cm-6x8in) mono. W/C over pencil. 4-Jun-2 Karl & Faber, Munich #21/R
£385 $562 €600 Bird (15x19cm-6x7in) mono. W/C Indian ink over pencil. 4-Jun-2 Karl & Faber, Munich #24/R

HOLT, Alf Krohg (1919-) Norwegian
£289 $444 €434 Building workers (50x61cm-20x24in) s. 28-Oct-2 Blomqvist, Lysaker #1099 (N.KR 3400)

HOLT, E F (19th C) British
£1282 $2000 €1923 Farm animals (58x89cm-23x35in) s.d.1884. 22-Sep-2 Susanin's, Chicago #5040/R est:3000-5000

HOLT, Edwin Frederick (fl.1864-1897) British
£600 $954 €900 Cows in a barn (30x36cm-12x14in) s.d.1886. 6-Mar-3 Christie's, Kensington #592/R
£700 $1141 €1050 Feeding the sheep (51x61cm-20x24in) mono.d.1892. 29-Jan-3 Sotheby's, Olympia #109/R
£1098 $1800 €1592 Trip to the Farriers (51x76cm-20x30in) s.i.d.1892. 4-Jun-3 Doyle, New York #64 est:2000-3000
£1150 $1817 €1725 Village scene near Redbourn (60x92cm-24x36in) s.d.1893. 26-Nov-2 Bonhams, Oxford #49
£1500 $2490 €2175 Huntsman with pointers on a moor (51x76cm-20x30in) s.d.1883. 12-Jun-3 Christie's, Kensington #286/R est:1500-2000
£1600 $2528 €2400 Plough horses and a pony being shod outside a blacksmith. horses and figures outside a post office (45x60cm-18x24in) s.d.1881 pair. 26-Nov-2 Bonhams, Oxford #58 est:400-600

£7692 $12077 €12000 Hunting scene (70x90cm-28x35in) s. 19-Nov-2 Castellana, Madrid #69/R est:12000

HOLT, Herbert (1849-?) British
£280 $459 €406 Tower Bridge (50x60cm-20x24in) s. 1-Jun-3 Lots Road, London #367

HOLTE, Arthur Brandish (fl.1883-1894) British
£380 $619 €570 In the woodland glade (46x36cm-18x14in) s.d.1877 s.i.d.1877 verso. 13-Feb-3 Christie's, Kensington #101

HOLTE, Frank A (19th C) British
£270 $416 €405 Mountain landscape with a figure fishing in a river (41x58cm-16x23in) 24-Oct-2 Grant, Worcester #316/R

HOLTEN, Sofie (1858-1930) Danish
£426 $672 €639 Allegory of Winter and Spring (143x58cm-56x23in) s.indis.d.1890 exhib. 2-Dec-2 Rasmussen, Copenhagen #1501/R (D.KR 5000)
£1818 $2945 €2636 Woman in a vegetable garden, large cabbages in foreground (130x98cm-51x39in) s.i.d.85. 26-May-3 Rasmussen, Copenhagen #1325/R est:8000-15000 (D.KR 19000)

HOLTER, Wilhelm (1842-1916) Norwegian
£723 $1143 €1085 Crows on the beach (35x60cm-14x24in) s. 2-Dec-2 Rasmussen, Copenhagen #1290/R (D.KR 8500)

HOLTRUP, Jan (1917-) Dutch
£1911 $2981 €3000 Horses ploughing near Groesbeek (49x59cm-19x23in) s. 6-Nov-2 Vendue Huis, Gravenhage #34/R est:2500-3000
£2394 $3855 €3400 Limburg landscape with hay wagon (48x39cm-19x15in) s.d.50. 7-May-3 Vendue Huis, Gravenhage #105 est:1000-1500
£2548 $3975 €4000 Cattle in woody landscape (39x59cm-15x23in) s. 5-Nov-2 Vendu Notarishuis, Rotterdam #36/R est:800-1000

HOLTY, Carl (1900-1973) American
Works on paper
£793 $1300 €1150 Abstract still life (34x51cm-13x20in) s. col pastel exec.c.1940. 5-Jun-3 Swann Galleries, New York #125/R
£915 $1500 €1327 Untitled (20x15cm-8x6in) s.d. col gouache card stock three. 5-Jun-3 Swann Galleries, New York #126/R est:2000-3000
£1026 $1600 €1539 Seated angle (30x23cm-12x9in) gouache paper on card exec.c.1945. 19-Sep-2 Swann Galleries, New York #413/R est:1500-2500
£3185 $5000 €4778 Untitled (10x15cm-4x6in) s.d. ink. 19-Nov-2 Wright, Chicago #156/R est:5000-7000

HOLTZBECHER, Hans (1861-?) German
£850 $1393 €1300 Young girl with red flowers in hair (40x30cm-16x12in) s. 8-Feb-3 Hans Stahl, Hamburg #97/R est:1400
£1090 $1689 €1700 Portrait of a girl in the "Jugendstil" style (74x60cm-29x24in) s. lit. 7-Dec-2 Bergmann, Erlangen #771/R est:750

HOLUB, Georg (1861-1919) Czechoslovakian
£769 $1215 €1200 Alpine landscape (104x82cm-41x32in) s.d.1909. 12-Nov-2 Dorotheum, Vienna #20/R

HOLUBITSCHKA, Hansjorg (1960-) ?
£1900 $3097 €2850 Untitled - Volterra (160x240cm-63x94in) s.i.d.1996 verso prov. 3-Feb-3 Sotheby's, Olympia #33/R est:1000-1500

HOLY, Adrien (1898-1978) Swiss
£377 $604 €566 Bathers on the shore of the Maggia (33x46cm-13x18in) s.d. 17-Mar-3 Philippe Schuler, Zurich #8453 (S.FR 800)
£459 $715 €689 Drobak harbour, Norway (32x46cm-13x18in) s.d.38 board. 6-Nov-2 Hans Widmer, St Gallen #128/R (S.FR 1050)
£524 $817 €786 Harbour scene (35x56cm-14x22in) s.d.37 board. 8-Nov-2 Dobiaschofsky, Bern #81/R (S.FR 1200)
£568 $886 €852 Repos du modele (46x61cm-18x24in) s.d.48. 8-Nov-2 Dobiaschofsky, Bern #83/R (S.FR 1300)
£648 $1044 €940 Paysage de Haute Provence (54x72cm-21x28in) s. i.verso. 9-May-3 Dobiaschofsky, Bern #93/R (S.FR 1400)
£1135 $1771 €1703 L'interieur d'atelier (73x92cm-29x36in) s.d.47. 6-Nov-2 Hans Widmer, St Gallen #138/R est:1500-3500 (S.FR 2600)

HOLY, Miloslav (1897-1974) Czechoslovakian
£1033 $1611 €1550 Bouquet in vase (80x60cm-31x24in) s.d.34 exhib. 12-Oct-2 Dorotheum, Prague #111/R (C.KR 50000)

HOLYOAKE, Rowland (fl.1880-1911) British
£2200 $3674 €3190 Portrait of a young girl (33x28cm-13x11in) s. exhib. 24-Jun-3 Neal & Fletcher, Woodbridge #380/R est:800-1200

HOLYOAKE, William (1834-1894) British
£3200 $5312 €4800 Receiving the love note (52x41cm-20x16in) 10-Jun-3 Bonhams, Knightsbridge #224/R est:1000-1500

HOLZ, Johann Daniel (1867-1945) German
£417 $654 €650 Shepherdess with flock by autumn wood (71x108cm-28x43in) s. panel. 21-Nov-2 Van Ham, Cologne #1685
£545 $855 €850 Peasant woman with cows grazing in summer landscape (70x100cm-28x39in) s. 21-Nov-2 Van Ham, Cologne #1686
£629 $981 €1000 River with riders and horses on summer day (30x38cm-12x15in) s. lit. 20-Sep-2 Karlheinz Kaupp, Staufen #2032

HOLZAPFEL, Carl (1865-1926) German
£524 $817 €786 Shepherd's evening song (100x80cm-39x31in) s. 6-Nov-2 Dobiaschofsky, Bern #673/R (S.FR 1200)

HOLZAPFEL, Ludwig (20th C) German
£692 $1079 €1100 Rooftops of Munich (40x30cm-16x12in) s. panel. 20-Sep-2 Schloss Ahlden, Ahlden #1280/R

HOLZEL, Adolf (1853-1934) German
£380 $600 €600 Composition with figures and landscape - Japanese (17x19cm-7x7in) graphite prov. 27-Nov-2 Dr Fritz Nagel, Stuttgart #3087/R
£1013 $1600 €1600 Apparition (14x11cm-6x4in) pastel graphite prov.lit. 27-Nov-2 Dr Fritz Nagel, Stuttgart #3061/R est:1800
£1034 $1634 €1500 Woman with red headscarf (19x24cm-7x9in) s. board. 2-Apr-3 Dr Fritz Nagel, Stuttgart #9482/R est:2000
£3793 $5993 €5500 Bebenhausen (30x63cm-12x25in) s.d. prov. 2-Apr-3 Dr Fritz Nagel, Stuttgart #9481/R est:3000
£4138 $6538 €6000 Yellow angel (49x41cm-19x16in) board prov. 2-Apr-3 Dr Fritz Nagel, Stuttgart #9484/R est:9800
£5580 $9151 €7700 Harlequin (19x25cm-7x10in) s. board. 31-May-3 Villa Grisebach, Berlin #200/R est:8000-10000
£5660 $8830 €9000 Colourful composition (42x34cm-17x13in) board painted 1917-18 prov.exhib.lit. 9-Oct-2 Sotheby's, London #326/R est:12000-15000
£6604 $10302 €10500 Suffer the little children to come unto me (25x19cm-10x7in) st.verso board painted c.1912 prov.exhib.lit. 9-Oct-2 Sotheby's, London #343/R est:15000-20000
£7547 $11774 €12000 Woman on the River Amper - Journey home (67x81cm-26x32in) painted c.1904 prov.exhib.lit. 9-Oct-2 Sotheby's, London #369/R est:18000-25000
£15094 $23547 €24000 Sonnige hauser im moos - Sunny houses in the Fen (41x51cm-16x20in) s.i.d.1902 prov.exhib.lit. 9-Oct-2 Sotheby's, London #344/R est:18000-25000

Works on paper
£348 $550 €550 Two figures (30x21cm-12x8in) chk prov.lit. 27-Nov-2 Dr Fritz Nagel, Stuttgart #3074/R
£348 $550 €550 Couple with dog (10x7cm-4x3in) Indian ink pastel postcard prov. 27-Nov-2 Dr Fritz Nagel, Stuttgart #3114/R
£380 $600 €600 Circle composition with figure (15x12cm-6x5in) graphite chl prov. 27-Nov-2 Dr Fritz Nagel, Stuttgart #3055/R
£443 $700 €700 Figure composition (16x20cm-6x8in) chk prov. 27-Nov-2 Dr Fritz Nagel, Stuttgart #3175/R
£475 $741 €750 Composition (11x14cm-4x6in) chl pencil board prov. 18-Oct-2 Dr Fritz Nagel, Stuttgart #525/R
£475 $750 €750 Memory of the circus (15x12cm-6x5in) i. col chk graphite prov. 27-Nov-2 Dr Fritz Nagel, Stuttgart #3145/R
£504 $826 €700 Composition (12x15cm-5x6in) mono. graphite board prov. 4-Jun-3 Reiss & Sohn, Konigstein #406
£506 $800 €800 Two female nudes (30x21cm-12x8in) chk prov.lit. 27-Nov-2 Dr Fritz Nagel, Stuttgart #3073/R
£506 $800 €800 Abstract blooms (29x22cm-11x9in) graphite prov.lit. 27-Nov-2 Dr Fritz Nagel, Stuttgart #3158/R
£506 $800 €800 Self drawing (15x20cm-6x8in) graphite pastel board prov. 27-Nov-2 Dr Fritz Nagel, Stuttgart #3159/R
£570 $900 €900 Composition with three figures (30x21cm-12x8in) chk prov.lit. 27-Nov-2 Dr Fritz Nagel, Stuttgart #3075/R
£570 $900 €900 Figure and circle composition (11x12cm-4x5in) Indian ink pastel prov. 27-Nov-2 Dr Fritz Nagel, Stuttgart #3146/R
£629 $981 €1000 Inimitable painter's sport (27x21cm-11x8in) black chk excuted 1920 prov. 9-Oct-2 Sotheby's, London #383/R est:1500-3000
£633 $987 €1000 Adoration of the three Kings (14x11cm-6x4in) chl pencil prov. 18-Oct-2 Dr Fritz Nagel, Stuttgart #522/R
£696 $1100 €1100 Group of men (20x25cm-8x10in) graphite prov.lit. 27-Nov-2 Dr Fritz Nagel, Stuttgart #3198/R
£719 $1180 €1000 Chinese figures (11x14cm-4x6in) col pastel chk over pencil. 4-Jun-3 Reiss & Sohn, Konigstein #405/R
£755 $1177 €1200 Landscape with tress (23x17cm-9x7in) s.i.d.1902 chl prov.exhib.lit. 9-Oct-2 Sotheby's, London #374/R est:1800-2500
£755 $1177 €1200 Circle composition - landscape (11x14cm-4x6in) chl. 20-Sep-2 Sigalas, Stuttgart #1100/R
£759 $1200 €1200 Couple (11x10cm-4x4in) Indian ink pastel envelope prov. 27-Nov-2 Dr Fritz Nagel, Stuttgart #3106/R
£823 $1300 €1300 Composition (12x15cm-5x6in) graphite pastel prov. 27-Nov-2 Dr Fritz Nagel, Stuttgart #3107/R

£881 $1374 €1400 Figure and text - circles (33x21cm-13x8in) pen ink executed c.1912 prov.exhib.lit. 9-Oct-2 Sotheby's, London #382/R est:1000-1500

£886 $1400 €1400 Figures (19x15cm-7x6in) graphite pastel prov.lit. 27-Nov-2 Dr Fritz Nagel, Stuttgart #3088/R

£886 $1400 €1400 Standing and kneeling figure (14x11cm-6x4in) s. pastel chk prov.lit. 27-Nov-2 Dr Fritz Nagel, Stuttgart #3140/R

£897 $1391 €1400 Figural composition (31x19cm-12x7in) s. chl graphite. 7-Dec-2 Ketterer, Hamburg #270/R

£949 $1500 €1500 Figure on red - angel (14x11cm-6x4in) graphite pastel prov. 27-Nov-2 Dr Fritz Nagel, Stuttgart #3014/R est:1500

£949 $1500 €1500 Two figures with umbrella (14x11cm-6x4in) graphite pastel prov. 27-Nov-2 Dr Fritz Nagel, Stuttgart #3115/R est:1400

£1013 $1600 €1600 Figures in landscape (14x11cm-6x4in) s. Indian ink pastel. 27-Nov-2 Dr Fritz Nagel, Stuttgart #3004/R est:1600

£1013 $1600 €1600 Mother and child (11x14cm-4x6in) graphite pastel prov. 27-Nov-2 Dr Fritz Nagel, Stuttgart #3005/R est:1700

£1013 $1600 €1600 Figures (27x8cm-11x3in) pastel graphite prov. 27-Nov-2 Dr Fritz Nagel, Stuttgart #3123/R est:1600

£1013 $1600 €1600 Landscape (11x14cm-4x6in) pastel graphite prov.lit. 27-Nov-2 Dr Fritz Nagel, Stuttgart #3124/R est:1900

£1108 $1728 €1750 Couple (14x11cm-6x4in) Indian ink pastel board prov. 18-Oct-2 Dr Fritz Nagel, Stuttgart #523/R est:1900

£1108 $1750 €1750 Figures with circle ornamentation (27x20cm-11x8in) Indian ink prov.lit. 27-Nov-2 Dr Fritz Nagel, Stuttgart #3026/R est:1800

£1139 $1800 €1800 Adoration (14x11cm-6x4in) chk pastel prov.lit. 27-Nov-2 Dr Fritz Nagel, Stuttgart #3141/R est:1600

£1258 $1962 €2000 Schwarz umrandete grafitscheibe mit weisser mitte - Black bordered graphite plane with centre (11x14cm-4x6in) chl W/C executed c.1925-1930 prov. 9-Oct-2 Sotheby's, London #316/R est:3000-4000

£1266 $1975 €2000 Composition of figures (10x14cm-4x6in) Indian ink col chk W/C pencil. 18-Oct-2 Dr Fritz Nagel, Stuttgart #526/R est:2400

£1266 $2000 €2000 Figures in circle (10x16cm-4x6in) pastel graphite prov.lit. 27-Nov-2 Dr Fritz Nagel, Stuttgart #3045/R est:1900

£1266 $2000 €2000 Composition (11x14cm-4x6in) pastel graphite. 27-Nov-2 Dr Fritz Nagel, Stuttgart #3189/R est:1900

£1384 $2131 €2200 Figural composition (11x14cm-4x6in) pastel. 26-Oct-2 Dr Lehr, Berlin #174/R est:1800

£1392 $2172 €2200 Female nude (7x10cm-3x4in) col pen. 18-Oct-2 Dr Fritz Nagel, Stuttgart #524/R est:2400

£1517 $2397 €2200 Circle composition (11x14cm-4x6in) pastel graphite. 2-Apr-3 Dr Fritz Nagel, Stuttgart #9483/R est:2200

£1519 $2400 €2400 Figure composition with circle (12x16cm-5x6in) graphite pastel prov.lit. 27-Nov-2 Dr Fritz Nagel, Stuttgart #3046/R est:2400

£1519 $2400 €2400 Abstraction with brown centre (14x11cm-6x4in) pastel graphite prov.lit. 27-Nov-2 Dr Fritz Nagel, Stuttgart #3062/R est:2800

£1646 $2600 €2600 Composition with text (32x20cm-13x8in) d.18.6.1914 Indian ink prov.exhib.lit. 27-Nov-2 Dr Fritz Nagel, Stuttgart #3025/R est:3000

£1899 $3000 €3000 Ascending figures (14x11cm-6x4in) pastel prov.lit. 27-Nov-2 Dr Fritz Nagel, Stuttgart #3015/R est:3200

£1899 $3000 €3000 Annunciation (13x20cm-5x8in) pastel graphite prov.lit. 27-Nov-2 Dr Fritz Nagel, Stuttgart #3176/R est:3400

£2013 $3140 €3200 Ente und andere vogel - Duck and other birds (9x14cm-4x6in) col pencil on card executed c.1920-1925 prov. 9-Oct-2 Sotheby's, London #309/R est:4000-5000

£2201 $3434 €3500 Pelikan legt ei - Pelican laying an egg (9x14cm-4x6in) st.verso col pencil on card executed c.1920-25 prov. 9-Oct-2 Sotheby's, London #302/R est:4000-5000

£2642 $4121 €4200 Kleinteilige komposition mit figuren - Tessellated composition with figures (11x14cm-4x6in) st.verso pastel pencil executed c.1927-1928 prov.exhib. 9-Oct-2 Sotheby's, London #307/R est:6000-8000

£2642 $4121 €4200 Women at a grave (11x14cm-4x6in) pastel executed c.1930 prov.exhib. 9-Oct-2 Sotheby's, London #332/R est:6000-8000

£2848 $4500 €4500 Adoration (32x20cm-13x8in) pastel graphite tempera lit. 27-Nov-2 Dr Fritz Nagel, Stuttgart #3097/R est:700

£3019 $4709 €4800 Collage abstract accreted image (11x8cm-4x3in) st.verso collage on paper executed c.1913-16 prov.exhib. 9-Oct-2 Sotheby's, London #327/R est:4000-5000

£3145 $4906 €5000 Vogel - strauss - Bird ostrich (9x14cm-4x6in) s. st.verso pastel pencil on card prov. 9-Oct-2 Sotheby's, London #303/R est:4000-5000

£3145 $4906 €5000 Gockel - Cockerel (10x16cm-4x6in) st.verso pastel pencil executed c.1920-25 prov. 9-Oct-2 Sotheby's, London #304/R est:4000-5000

£3145 $4906 €5000 Schwan - Swan (9x14cm-4x6in) st.verso pastel pencil on card executed c.1920-25 prov. 9-Oct-2 Sotheby's, London #305/R est:4000-5000

£3145 $4906 €5000 Marchenvogel - Fairy-tale-bird (11x14cm-4x6in) st.verso col pencil pen ink executed c.1920-25 prov. 9-Oct-2 Sotheby's, London #306/R est:4000-5000

£3145 $4906 €5000 Abstract ornament (10x24cm-4x9in) i. pen brush ink executed 30th July 1898 prov. 9-Oct-2 Sotheby's, London #324/R est:3000-4000

£3145 $4906 €5000 Biblical scene, the sea of Galilee (15x23cm-6x9in) W/C brush pen ink executed c.1920 prov.exhib. 9-Oct-2 Sotheby's, London #330/R est:3000-4000

£3459 $5396 €5500 Ente -Duck (9x14cm-4x6in) st.verso pastel pencil on card executed c.1920-25 prov. 9-Oct-2 Sotheby's, London #301/R est:4000-5000

£3459 $5396 €5500 Phantastischer vogel - Fantastical bird (9x14cm-4x6in) pastel col pencil executed c.1920-1925 prov. 9-Oct-2 Sotheby's, London #310/R est:4000-5000

£3774 $5887 €6000 Esel - Donkey (9x14cm-4x6in) gouache col pencil executed c.1920-1925 prov. 9-Oct-2 Sotheby's, London #308/R est:4000-5000

£3797 $6000 €6000 Sailing boats off Knokke (110x125cm-43x49in) chl prov.lit. 27-Nov-2 Dr Fritz Nagel, Stuttgart #3032/R est:8000

£3797 $6000 €6000 Let the little children come unto me (129x109cm-51x43in) chl prov.lit. 27-Nov-2 Dr Fritz Nagel, Stuttgart #3033/R est:8500

£4088 $6377 €6500 Circle oval and triangle on white and green (10x15cm-4x6in) pastel executed c.1925-30 prov. 9-Oct-2 Sotheby's, London #331/R est:4500-6500

£4130 $6774 €5700 Composition (32x25cm-13x10in) pastel oil chk pencil. 31-May-3 Villa Grisebach, Berlin #198/R est:6000-8000

£5769 $8942 €9000 Figural composition (32x25cm-13x10in) s. mixed media lit. 6-Dec-2 Karlheinz Kaupp, Staufen #2302/R est:12000

£6475 $10619 €9000 Composition (32x25cm-13x10in) s. col chk prov. 6-Jun-3 Ketterer, Munich #58/R est:13000-15000

£6897 $10897 €10000 Figures with tree (30x42cm-12x17in) pastel prov. 2-Apr-3 Dr Fritz Nagel, Stuttgart #9485/R est:12000

£7547 $11774 €12000 Komposition, figuren in bergiger landschaft - Composition, figures in mountainous landscape (25x30cm-10x12in) pastel executed 1930 exhib. 9-Oct-2 Sotheby's, London #317/R est:18000-25000

£8805 $13736 €14000 Abstract ornament (33x21cm-13x8in) i. pen brush ink executed c.1898 prov.exhib.lit. 9-Oct-2 Sotheby's, London #325/R est:3000-4000

£9434 $14717 €15000 Skizzenbuch (18x11cm-7x4in) with sig pencil dr. in sketchbook executed 1883. 9-Oct-2 Sotheby's, London #346/R est:10000-15000

£12579 $19623 €20000 Composition - figures in a landscape (30x37cm-12x15in) s. pastel executed 1930 prov.exhib.lit. 9-Oct-2 Sotheby's, London #338/R est:30000-40000

£13836 $21585 €22000 Komposition - Agyptisches sommernachtsfest, rot gegen blau - Composition, Egyptian summer nights (25x30cm-10x12in) pastel pencil executed c.1925-30 prov.exhib.lit. 9-Oct-2 Sotheby's, London #318/R est:24000-28000

£13836 $21585 €22000 Composition with circle and figures in a landscape (30x46cm-12x18in) st.verso pastel executed 1930 prov.exhib.lit. 9-Oct-2 Sotheby's, London #339/R est:30000-40000

£26415 $41208 €42000 Dynamische kreisrhythmen - Dynamic circular rhythms (50x65cm-20x26in) st.verso pastels executed c.1930 prov.exhib.lit. 9-Oct-2 Sotheby's, London #329/R est:60000-90000

HOLZER, Jenny (1950-) American

£1384 $2200 €2076 Little queenie (53x59cm-21x23in) enamel on metal. 29-Apr-3 Christie's, Rockefeller NY #621/R est:3000-5000

Sculpture

£10625 $17000 €15938 Untitled - from the living series (13x74x5cm-5x29x2in) electronic LED sign red diodes executed 1983 prov. 14-May-3 Sotheby's, New York #380/R est:15000-20000

HOLZER, Joseph (1824-1876) Austrian

£321 $497 €500 Landscape with stream (25x43cm-10x17in) s. board. 5-Dec-2 Dorotheum, Graz #23/R

£1772 $2800 €2800 Mountain river with forest worker (52x42cm-20x17in) s. board. 28-Nov-2 Dorotheum, Vienna #222/R est:3000-3500

£6329 $10000 €10000 Zellersee with view of Zell am See and the Kitzsteinhorn (68x95cm-27x37in) s. 28-Nov-2 Dorotheum, Vienna #106/R est:11000-12000

HOLZL, Johann Felix (18th C) ?

£321 $497 €500 Sanci Aloysii (59x44cm-23x17in) s.d.1754 bears i. i. verso. 6-Dec-2 Michael Zeller, Lindau #688/R

HOLZMEISTER, Clemens (1886-1983) Austrian

Works on paper

£633 $1000 €1000 Ankara. Late summer (30x45cm-12x18in) s.i.d.1945 and 1950 W/C pair. 26-Nov-2 Wiener Kunst Auktionen, Vienna #175/R

HOM, Georg (1838-1911) German
£1603 $2484 €2500 Young chambermaid (117x71cm-46x28in) s. 5-Dec-2 Dr Fritz Nagel, Stuttgart #663/R est:2500

HOM, Poul (1905-1994) Danish
£283 $442 €425 Religious scene. s. fresco. 11-Nov-2 Rasmussen, Vejle #2000 (D.KR 3300)
£541 $833 €812 Portrait of boy (35x44cm-14x17in) s. 23-Oct-2 Kunsthallen, Copenhagen #98 (D.KR 6400)
£1016 $1575 €1524 Young girl reading (81x46cm-32x18in) s. 1-Oct-2 Rasmussen, Copenhagen #387/R est:6000 (D.KR 12000)
£1072 $1672 €1608 Mother and child, rooftops in background (100x140cm-39x55in) s. 11-Nov-2 Rasmussen, Vejle #70/R est:10000 (D.KR 12500)
£1371 $2180 €2057 Julie (97x70cm-38x28in) s. painted c.1958. 26-Feb-3 Kunsthallen, Copenhagen #253/R est:10000 (D.KR 15000)

HOMAN, Margot (1956-) Dutch
Sculpture
£3448 $5482 €5000 Male nude (76cm-30in) s. bronze marble metal base two. 10-Mar-3 Sotheby's, Amsterdam #343 est:300-500

HOMBURG, Jacob (19th C) French
£327 $510 €520 Portrait of Susanna Julianna Moogin (88x70cm-35x28in) i. verso. 21-Sep-2 Berlinghof, Heidelberg #117

HOME, Robert (1752-1834) British
Works on paper
£2400 $3744 €3600 Portrait of Mordant Ricketts (101x93cm-40x37in) gouache ivory. 17-Oct-2 Bonhams, Knightsbridge #149/R est:800-1200

HOME, Robert (attrib) (1752-1834) British
Miniatures
£3400 $5304 €5100 Colonel C King standing by his horse wearing uniform Bengal Light Cavalry (16cm-6xin) i.verso ormolu mount wood frame rec. lit. 5-Nov-2 Bonhams, New Bond Street #156/R est:1000-1500

HOMER, Winslow (1836-1910) American
£80247 $130000 €120371 Cornfield (34x56cm-13x22in) i. prov.exhib. 21-May-3 Sotheby's, New York #177/R est:150000-250000
£967742 $1500000 €1451613 Girl in the hammock (34x51cm-13x20in) s.d.1873 prov. 5-Dec-2 Christie's, Rockefeller NY #42/R est:1500000-2500000
Prints
£3797 $6000 €5696 Perils of the sea (41x53cm-16x21in) s. etching vellum executed c.1888. 12-Nov-2 Doyle, New York #246/R est:5000-7000
Works on paper
£3459 $5500 €5189 Map of Great Britain (29x20cm-11x8in) s.indis d. pencil executed c.1846 prov. 5-Mar-3 Sotheby's, New York #54/R est:1500-2000
£37037 $60000 €55556 On the mussel bed (25x46cm-10x18in) s. W/C chk prov.exhib. 21-May-3 Sotheby's, New York #178/R est:70000-90000
£98765 $160000 €148148 Dance of the woodsmen - camp in Canada (35x53cm-14x21in) s.d.97 W/C ink prov.exhib.lit. 21-May-3 Sotheby's, New York #51/R est:80000-120000
£180645 $280000 €270968 Berry picker (32x20cm-13x8in) init. pencil executed c.1878 prov.exhib. 4-Dec-2 Sotheby's, New York #14/R est:150000-250000
£197531 $320000 €296297 Breakwater (37x54cm-15x21in) s.d.1883 W/C pencil prov.exhib.lit. 22-May-3 Christie's, Rockefeller NY #39/R est:400000-600000
£234568 $380000 €351852 Small sloop (24x34cm-9x13in) s. W/C executed 1880 prov.exhib. 22-May-3 Christie's, Rockefeller NY #60/R est:400000-600000
£283871 $440000 €425807 Shady spot, Houghton Farm (18x22cm-7x9in) init.d.1878 W/C paper on board prov.exhib. 5-Dec-2 Christie's, Rockefeller NY #23/R est:250000-350000
£617284 $1000000 €925926 Fishing (18x22cm-7x9in) s.d.1878 W/C gouache prov.exhib. 21-May-3 Sotheby's, New York #170/R est:400000-600000

HOMER, Winslow (attrib) (1836-1910) American
Works on paper
£320 $499 €480 Montego Bay, Jamaica (30x20cm-12x8in) s.i.verso W/C. 20-Sep-2 Richardson & Smith, Whitby #37

HOMPE, G (19th C) ?
£255 $398 €383 Landscape with cattle by watering hole (31x40cm-12x16in) s. 5-Aug-2 Rasmussen, Vejle #2213 (D.KR 3000)

HON, Henri le (1809-1872) Belgian
£4167 $6625 €6000 Une bataille sur mer (75x104cm-30x41in) s.i.d.1841 panel1841. 29-Apr-3 Christie's, Amsterdam #25/R est:2500-3500

HONDECOETER, Gillis Claesz de (1570-1638) Dutch
£15000 $23400 €22500 Wooded river landscape with a huntsman on a tack, a village beyond (27x35cm-11x14in) init.d.1613 panel. 9-Apr-3 Christie's, London #4/R est:8000-12000
£16000 $25120 €24000 Rocky landscape with cattle and figures on a path (39x59cm-15x23in) mono.d.1632 panel. 12-Dec-2 Sotheby's, London #132/R est:12000-18000
£32000 $50240 €48000 Woode river landscape with travellers and dog. Woode river landscape with figures (20x26cm-8x10in) panel paie prov.exhib. 11-Dec-2 Christie's, London #31/R est:30000-40000

HONDECOETER, Gillis Claesz de (attrib) (1570-1638) Dutch
£1410 $2214 €2200 Peasant women milking cows by wood (63x81cm-25x32in) bears sig. 21-Nov-2 Van Ham, Cologne #1368/R est:2500

HONDECOETER, Gysbert Gillisz de (1604-1653) Dutch
£13522 $21094 €21500 Poultry yard (55x72cm-22x28in) mono. panel prov. 19-Sep-2 Dr Fritz Nagel, Stuttgart #876/R est:5000

HONDECOETER, Melchior de (1636-1695) Dutch
£1951 $3200 €2927 Kingfisher and songbirds by an overturned vase on a ledge (37x41cm-15x16in) prov. 5-Feb-3 Christie's, Rockefeller NY #251/R est:3000-5000
£12000 $20040 €17400 Still life of game with a knife upon a marble table-top and green cloth (73x64cm-29x25in) remains sig. 10-Jul-3 Sotheby's, London #149/R est:12000-18000
£95000 $149150 €142500 Forest floor still life with birds (68x59cm-27x23in) prov. 11-Dec-2 Christie's, London #63/R est:30000-50000

HONDECOETER, Melchior de (circle) (1636-1695) Dutch
£12000 $20040 €17400 Peacock, a peahen, poultry and other birds in a rocky landscape (102x132cm-40x52in) 11-Jul-3 Christie's, Kensington #68/R est:7000-10000

HONDECOETER, Melchior de (studio) (1636-1695) Dutch
£24438 $39589 €35435 Scene with white peacock and other birds (134x166cm-53x65in) bears sig. 26-May-3 Bukowskis, Stockholm #407/R est:100000-150000 (S.KR 315000)

HONDECOETER, Melchior de (style) (1636-1695) Dutch
£13876 $22478 €20120 Cockerel in fight with a turkey and other poultry (116x153cm-46x60in) prov. 26-May-3 Rasmussen, Copenhagen #1140/R est:150000 (D.KR 145000)

HONDIUS, Abraham (1625-1695) Dutch
£3200 $5024 €4800 Dogs fighting over dead stag in a landscape (36x41cm-14x16in) s.d.1662 panel. 13-Dec-2 Christie's, Kensington #69/R est:4000-6000
£3200 $5344 €4640 Dogs attacking a boar in a landscape (26x35cm-10x14in) s.d.1668 panel prov. 11-Jul-3 Christie's, Kensington #125/R est:2500-3500
£4000 $6240 €6000 Christ expelling the merchants from the temple. Christ and the woman taken in adultery (37x49cm-15x19in) panel pair. 8-Apr-3 Sotheby's, Olympia #145/R est:4000-6000
£4892 $7827 €6800 Swan being chased from nest by hounds. Stork frightened by hounds (28x35cm-11x14in) s. panel pair. 13-May-3 Sotheby's, Amsterdam #15/R est:8000-12000
£10000 $15600 €15000 Landscape with huntsman and hounds (85x140cm-33x55in) s.d.1685. 23-Sep-2 Bonhams, Bayswater #404/R est:6000-8000
£12000 $20040 €17400 Hounds attacking a stag (119x177cm-47x70in) s. prov. 10-Jul-3 Sotheby's, London #190/R est:15000-20000

HONDIUS, Gerrit (1891-1970) American/Dutch
£687 $1100 €996 Two woman. Three woman (76x51cm-30x20in) s. masonite two. 16-May-3 Skinner, Boston #188a/R
£875 $1400 €1269 Three figures. Still life with vegetables (53x49cm-21x19in) s. masonite two. 16-May-3 Skinner, Boston #195/R est:600-800
£1062 $1700 €1540 Girl with a vase. Two ladies (76x61cm-30x24in) s. masonite. 16-May-3 Skinner, Boston #197/R est:600-800

HONDT, Lambert de (17th C) Flemish
£1500 $2325 €2250 Military encampment with soldier and dog before tents (78x61cm-31x24in) 31-Oct-2 Sotheby's, Olympia #53/R est:1500-2000

HONE, David (20th C) British
£701 $1093 €1100 Still life with rose in silver vase (25x20cm-10x8in) s. 6-Nov-2 James Adam, Dublin #70/R est:300-500
£1203 $1864 €1900 Near Roundstone. Evening, Merrion Strand (25x18cm-10x7in) s.i.verso board pair. 25-Sep-2 James Adam, Dublin #75/R est:2000-4000
£2564 $4026 €4000 Sandymount Strand, looking toward Howth (36x46cm-14x18in) s. exhib.lit. 19-Nov-2 Whyte's, Dublin #138/R est:4000-5000
£2681 $4397 €3700 Children playing on beach at Sandymount (35x45cm-14x18in) s. 28-May-3 Bonhams & James Adam, Dublin #97/R est:3000-4000

HONE, Evie (1894-1955) Irish
£2800 $4564 €4200 Still life study of fruit, pot plant and oil lamp on a table (53x89cm-21x35in) s. 14-Feb-3 Keys, Aylsham #722 est:1500-2000
Works on paper
£822 $1290 €1200 Design for stained glass window, Greystones (23x9cm-9x4in) gouache prov. 15-Apr-3 De Veres Art Auctions, Dublin #271 est:800-1200
£900 $1314 €1350 Kilmalkin Church, Connemara (23x13cm-9x5in) mono. gouache on board design for stained glass. 12-Jun-2 John Ross, Belfast #270
£1301 $2043 €1900 Crane (36x24cm-14x9in) gouache. 15-Apr-3 De Veres Art Auctions, Dublin #257/R est:1800-2200
£1342 $2161 €2000 Angel playing instrument - design for stain glass (13x11cm-5x4in) gouache. 18-Feb-3 Whyte's, Dublin #113/R est:800-1000
£1346 $2113 €2100 Trees at Marley (21x17cm-8x7in) s. gouache board prov.exhib. 19-Nov-2 Whyte's, Dublin #3/R est:3000-4000
£1370 $2151 €2000 Marley wood (36x45cm-14x18in) W/C. 15-Apr-3 De Veres Art Auctions, Dublin #243/R est:2000-3000
£1635 $2551 €2600 Spider's Bay, Lough Mask, County Mayo (44x33cm-17x13in) i.verso gouache prov. 17-Sep-2 Whyte's, Dublin #69/R est:2000-3000
£2282 $3674 €3400 Pool in the wood at Marley, Rathfarnham (33x41cm-13x16in) i. gouache. 18-Feb-3 Whyte's, Dublin #14/R est:3000-4000

HONE, Horace (1756-1825) British
£500 $800 €750 Portrait of a gentleman in blue coat with white stock (13x10cm-5x4in) board. 15-May-3 Christie's, Kensington #137/R
Miniatures
£3800 $6232 €5510 Young lady in white dress (8cm-3xin) mono.d.1786 silver gilt frame oval. 3-Jun-3 Christie's, London #173/R est:2000-3000

HONE, Nathaniel I (1718-1784) British
£4231 $6727 €6347 Portrait of Captain Lambert Brabazon in uniform (76x63cm-30x25in) s.d.1784 exhib. 4-Mar-3 Deutscher-Menzies, Melbourne #104/R est:15000-20000 (A.D 11000)
£6000 $9600 €9000 Portrait of an artist wearing a blue waistcoat (68x56cm-27x22in) 16-May-3 Sotheby's, London #1/R est:4000-6000
£60000 $94800 €90000 Double portrait of General Richard Wilford and Sir Levett Hanson (137x137cm-54x54in) s.d.1777 pr. 26-Nov-2 Christie's, London #45/R est:70000-100000
Miniatures
£1300 $2002 €1950 Portrait of gentleman (5x3cm-2x1in) mono.d.1763 oval W/C. 25-Oct-2 Gorringes, Lewes #860
£2200 $3608 €3190 Young gentleman in a white coat with red velvet collar (3cm-1xin) mono.d.1762 enamel oval. 3-Jun-3 Christie's, London #33/R est:1200-1500
£2500 $3925 €3750 Gentleman in a mole coloured coat (4cm-2xin) mono.d.1748 enamel on copper. 10-Dec-2 Christie's, London #24/R est:800-1200
£3200 $5024 €4800 Young lady in black dress (4cm-2xin) s.d.1749 enamel on copper. 10-Dec-2 Christie's, London #25/R est:1500-2500
Works on paper
£1000 $1600 €1500 Portrait of young boy in blue suit and white hat (54x41cm-21x16in) init.d.76 pastel. 15-May-3 Christie's, London #23/R
£1800 $2988 €2700 Portrait of a boy, wearing a beige jacket and gold waistcoat (29x23cm-11x9in) pastel painted oval prov. 12-Jun-3 Sotheby's, London #113/R est:2000-3000

HONE, Nathaniel I (attrib) (1718-1784) British
£1200 $1872 €1800 Portrait of a lady (27x22cm-11x9in) panel. 17-Sep-2 Sotheby's, Olympia #88/R est:1200-1800

HONE, Nathaniel II (1831-1917) Irish
£2899 $4754 €4000 Coastal landscape. Portmarnock (31x46cm-12x18in) 28-May-3 Bonhams & James Adam, Dublin #20/R est:2500-3500
£13924 $20329 €22000 Near Kilrush, Co Clare. 21-May-2 Thomas Adams, Dublin #311/R
£35443 $54937 €56000 Harbour scene, Mediterranean (61x101cm-24x40in) init. prov. 25-Sep-2 James Adam, Dublin #55/R est:50000-80000
Works on paper
£759 $1177 €1200 Sand bunker (15x23cm-6x9in) W/C prov. 25-Sep-2 James Adam, Dublin #29 est:1200-1800
£1076 $1668 €1700 Landscape (11x19cm-4x7in) W/C prov. 25-Sep-2 James Adam, Dublin #28/R est:1800-2500
£1538 $2415 €2400 Sand bunker (16x24cm-6x9in) i.verso prov.lit. 19-Nov-2 Whyte's, Dublin #59 est:2000-2500

HONEGGER, Gottfried (1917-) Swiss
£4803 $7541 €7205 Biseautage (102x76cm-40x30in) s.d.1969 acrylic over board relief. 23-Nov-2 Burkhard, Luzern #49/R est:12000-16000 (S.FR 11000)
Sculpture
£1397 $2194 €2096 Untitled (26x26x13cm-10x10x5in) s. num.347/500 bronze. 23-Nov-2 Burkhard, Luzern #50/R est:1500-2000 (S.FR 3200)
£1727 $2832 €2400 Sculpture division 2 (55cm-22in) marble executed 1986 prov. 3-Jun-3 Christie's, Amsterdam #188/R est:2500-3500
£2882 $4525 €4323 Pole (89cm-35in) nickeled aluminium. 23-Nov-2 Burkhard, Luzern #47/R est:6000-7000 (S.FR 6600)
Works on paper
£284 $414 €426 Composition - New Year card (15x22cm-6x9in) s.i.d.1990/91 W/C. 4-Jun-2 Germann, Zurich #773 (S.FR 650)

HONEIN, Alphonse (19th C) American
£1218 $1900 €1827 Portrait of a lady (102x81cm-40x32in) s. prov. 12-Oct-2 Neal Auction Company, New Orleans #806/R est:1200-1800

HONEY, C Winifred (1892-1944) British
£239 $349 €359 Hay making (41x51cm-16x20in) s. 12-Sep-1 Watson's, Christchurch #4 (NZ.D 800)

HONG ZHU AN (1955-) Chinese
Works on paper
£3108 $5128 €4507 Five fish (150x150cm-59x59in) s. ink col rice paper. 6-Jul-3 Christie's, Hong Kong #45/R est:35000-45000 (HK.D 40000)

HONGYI (1880-1942) Chinese
Works on paper
£1626 $2569 €2439 Sutra (32x33cm-13x13in) s.d.1934 ink. 28-Apr-3 Sotheby's, Hong Kong #561/R est:20000-30000 (HK.D 20000)

HONIGBERGER, Ernst (?) German
£692 $1079 €1100 Portrait of young woman in Sieburg costume (43x64cm-17x25in) s. lit. 20-Sep-2 Karlheinz Kaupp, Staufen #1931/R

HONKANEN, J (20th C) Finnish
£329 $513 €520 Landscape (44x60cm-17x24in) s. 12-Sep-2 Hagelstam, Helsinki #967

HONORE, Henri (after) (?) French
Sculpture
£7692 $12077 €12000 La charmeuse de serpents (90cm-35in) s. gold brown pat bronze. 16-Dec-2 Gros & Delettrez, Paris #179/R est:10000-12000

HONSA, Jan (1876-1937) Czechoslovakian
£611 $971 €917 Winter landscape (44x30cm-17x12in) s. 8-Mar-3 Dorotheum, Prague #53/R est:26000-39000 (C.KR 28000)

HONTA, Renée (1894-1955) Irish
£5556 $8833 €8000 Nature morte aux fruits (53x64cm-21x25in) prov.exhib. 29-Apr-3 Whyte's, Dublin #101/R est:8000-10000

HONTHORST, Gerrit van (1590-1656) Dutch
£5000 $8350 €7250 The Toothextracter (145x214cm-57x84in) 9-Jul-3 Bonhams, New Bond Street #92/R est:4000-6000

HONTHORST, Gerrit van (after) (1590-1656) Dutch
£7382 $11885 €11000 Dentist (164x224cm-65x88in) prov.lit. 18-Feb-3 Sotheby's, Amsterdam #202/R est:7500-10000

HONTHORST, Gerrit van (studio) (1590-1656) Dutch
£5479 $8548 €8000 Portrait of Frederik Hendrik (52x44cm-20x17in) lit. 10-Apr-3 Van Ham, Cologne #1223/R est:1800
£9500 $15865 €13775 Merry violonist holding a roemer (80x64cm-31x25in) prov.lit. 8-Jul-3 Sotheby's, Olympia #383/R est:7000-10000

HONTHORST, Gerrit van (style) (1590-1656) Dutch
£159038 $257642 €230605 The Denial of Saint Peter (53x68cm-21x27in) 26-May-3 Bukowskis, Stockholm #386/R est:40000-50000 (S.KR 2050000)

HOOCH, Pieter de (1629-1681) Dutch
£80000 $125600 €120000 Interior with mother nursing her children before a fireplace (84x82cm-33x32in) prov.lit. 12-Dec-2 Sotheby's, London #35/R est:50000-70000

HOOCH, Pieter de (style) (1629-1681) Dutch
£40123 $65000 €60185 Elegant figures playing skittles in a landscaped park (67x73cm-26x29in) prov.exhib.lit. 24-Jan-3 Christie's, Rockefeller NY #49/R est:40000-60000

HOOD, Cherry (20th C) Australian?
Works on paper
£643 $996 €965 Portrait I (75x56cm-30x22in) s. W/C. 29-Oct-2 Lawson Menzies, Sydney #144 (A.D 1800)
£643 $996 €965 Portrait II (75x56cm-30x22in) W/C. 29-Oct-2 Lawson Menzies, Sydney #147 (A.D 1800)
£1149 $1805 €1724 Portrait (75x56cm-30x22in) s.d.2002 verso W/C. 15-Apr-3 Lawson Menzies, Sydney #74/R est:3500-4500 (A.D 3000)
£1533 $2406 €2300 Retriever (76x57cm-30x22in) s. i.d.2002 verso W/C. 15-Apr-3 Lawson Menzies, Sydney #5/R est:2000-3000 (A.D 4000)
£2033 $3211 €2948 Bedouin caanan dog no.6 (75x57cm-30x22in) s. i.d.2002 verso W/C. 22-Jul-3 Lawson Menzies, Sydney #16/R est:3000-5000 (A.D 5000)
£2107 $3308 €3161 Portrait 2000 (75x56cm-30x22in) s.d.2002 verso W/C. 15-Apr-3 Lawson Menzies, Sydney #6/R est:3000-4000 (A.D 5500)
£2383 $3693 €3575 Young man (160x102cm-63x40in) s.i.d.verso W/C. 3-Dec-2 Shapiro, Sydney #47/R est:6000-8000 (A.D 6600)
£2857 $4429 €4286 Portrait (151x102cm-59x40in) W/C. 29-Oct-2 Lawson Menzies, Sydney #5/R est:5500-6500 (A.D 8000)
£4286 $6771 €6429 Watermark 2001 (152x101cm-60x40in) W/C. 27-Nov-2 Deutscher-Menzies, Melbourne #9/R est:4500-6500 (A.D 12000)

HOOD, Ernest Burnett (1932-1988) British
£250 $410 €375 Cliffs, Isle of Whithorn (76x51cm-30x20in) s. 5-Jun-3 Christie's, Kensington #733
£320 $499 €480 Castle on promontary (50x60cm-20x24in) s. 13-Sep-2 Lyon & Turnbull, Edinburgh #8/R
£320 $522 €480 Scotia Bar, Glasgow (26x36cm-10x14in) 14-Feb-3 Lyon & Turnbull, Edinburgh #63
£360 $562 €540 Culzean Castle (25x35cm-10x14in) s. board. 13-Sep-2 Lyon & Turnbull, Edinburgh #23/R
£460 $754 €667 Mixed fruit and vase of flowers on a table (38x47cm-15x19in) s. board. 7-Jun-3 Shapes, Edinburgh #435
£700 $1092 €1050 Interior (27x18cm-11x7in) s. board. 13-Sep-2 Lyon & Turnbull, Edinburgh #128/R
£720 $1123 €1080 Still life of daisies (42x30cm-17x12in) s. 17-Oct-2 Bonhams, Edinburgh #75
£1700 $2652 €2550 Interior with the artist's wife (32x19cm-13x7in) s. prov. 14-Apr-3 Sotheby's, London #166/R est:1000-1500
Works on paper
£450 $702 €675 Kingston Bridge during construction (44x48cm-17x19in) s.d.69 pastel W/C. 13-Sep-2 Lyon & Turnbull, Edinburgh #88/R

HOOD, George Washington (1869-1949) American
£994 $1600 €1491 Seated mermaid and standing woman (43x30cm-17x12in) s. board exhib. 10-May-3 Illustration House, New York #36/R est:1200-1800

HOOD, Kenneth Edwin (1928-) Australian
£429 $673 €644 Victorian landscape (85x69cm-33x27in) s.d.61 board prov. 25-Nov-2 Christie's, Melbourne #464/R (A.D 1200)

HOODLESS, Harry (1913-1997) British
£850 $1377 €1275 M.V Defender in Liverpool Docks (69x98cm-27x39in) s.d.1957 board. 21-Jan-3 Bonhams, New Bond Street #191/R

HOOFT, Ina (1894-?) Dutch
£268 $417 €420 Varied still life with flowers, fruit and wall decoration (54x45cm-21x18in) s. prov. 5-Nov-2 Vendu Notarishuis, Rotterdam #71
£385 $604 €600 Still life with flowers, fruit and a picture (60x50cm-24x20in) s.d.46. 25-Nov-2 Glerum, Amsterdam #65

HOOG, Bernard de (1867-1943) Dutch
£280 $448 €420 Farmyard scene with female figures and chickens (51x33cm-20x13in) i. 10-Jan-3 Biddle & Webb, Birmingham #325
£348 $543 €550 Portrait of Mrs Spliethoff-Bouwer (136x109cm-54x43in) s.d.1918. 21-Oct-2 Glerum, Amsterdam #108/R
£1250 $2063 €1800 Yellow and white chrysanthemums (61x75cm-24x30in) s. prov. 1-Jul-3 Christie's, Amsterdam #95 est:2000-3000
£1600 $2672 €2320 Preparing a meal (25x30cm-10x12in) s. 17-Jun-3 Bonhams, New Bond Street #10/R est:1500-2000
£2179 $3400 €3269 Spinning yarn (99x79cm-39x31in) s. 22-Sep-2 Susanin's, Chicago #5042/R est:5000-7000
£2264 $3487 €3600 Musical moment (50x40cm-20x16in) s. 22-Oct-2 Sotheby's, Amsterdam #113/R est:4000-6000
£2394 $3855 €3400 Mother feeding baby on her lap with child watching (33x29cm-13x11in) s. 7-May-3 Vendue Huis, Gravenhage #446/R est:3000-5000
£2667 $4427 €3867 Happy family (41x30cm-16x12in) s. prov. 16-Jun-3 Waddingtons, Toronto #251/R est:5000-7000 (C.D 6000)
£3111 $5164 €4511 Happy family (51x61cm-20x24in) s. prov. 16-Jun-3 Waddingtons, Toronto #250/R est:7000-9000 (C.D 7000)
£3200 $5344 €4800 Girl sewing (41x30cm-16x12in) s. 18-Jun-3 Christie's, Kensington #49/R est:2500-3500
£3433 $5356 €4978 Mending time (50x40cm-20x16in) s. 26-Mar-3 Walker's, Ottawa #10/R est:7000-9000 (C.D 8000)
£4800 $8016 €7200 Young seamstress (41x32cm-16x13in) s. 18-Jun-3 Christie's, Kensington #48/R est:5000-7000
£5043 $8169 €7312 Interior scene with family (60x75cm-24x30in) s. prov. 25-May-3 Uppsala Auktionskammare, Uppsala #58/R est:25000-30000 (S.KR 65000)
£5600 $8904 €8400 Dutch interior with mother and child (79x99cm-31x39in) s. 4-Mar-3 Bearnes, Exeter #480/R est:4000-6000
£5903 $9740 €8500 Doctor's visit (95x126cm-37x50in) s. 1-Jul-3 Christie's, Amsterdam #99/R est:6000-8000
£15723 $24214 €25000 Washing day (100x80cm-39x31in) s. prov.lit. 23-Oct-2 Christie's, Amsterdam #189/R est:12000-16000

HOOG, Birger (1899-1929) Swedish
£1121 $1749 €1682 Vase with flowers (65x50cm-26x20in) s.d.26. 6-Nov-2 AB Stockholms Auktionsverk #735/R est:20000-25000 (S.KR 16000)

HOOGERHEYDEN, Engel (1740-1809) German
£20144 $32230 €28000 Batavian fleet under Vice Admiral Carel Hendrik Verhuell at Flushing (28x38cm-11x15in) s.d.1805 panel. 14-May-3 Christie's, Amsterdam #202/R est:8000-12000

HOOGSTEYNS, Jan (1935-) Belgian
£321 $503 €500 Nude sitting (55x45cm-22x18in) s. 25-Nov-2 Glerum, Amsterdam #193
£362 $586 €550 Her majesty (65x55cm-26x22in) s. 21-Jan-3 Christie's, Amsterdam #495/R
£694 $1104 €1000 Paysage d'hiver (75x90cm-30x35in) s. 29-Apr-3 Campo & Campo, Antwerp #636

HOOGSTRATEN, Samuel van (1627-1678) Flemish
£9554 $14904 €15000 Portrait of a gentleman, wearing a black coat with a white collar, holding gloves (80x64cm-31x25in) mono.d.1660 prov.exhib.lit. 5-Nov-2 Sotheby's, Amsterdam #303/R est:15000-20000
£65000 $108550 €94250 Young boy preparing to bathe in a stream, watched by a girl (95x75cm-37x30in) mono. arched top. 10-Jul-3 Sotheby's, London #24/R est:25000-35000

HOOK, James Clarke (1819-1907) British
£807 $1300 €1211 Midday rest by the shore (53x91cm-21x36in) s.d.1880. 19-Feb-3 Doyle, New York #39
£32000 $51520 €48000 Gull catcher (122x94cm-48x37in) mono.d.1877 prov.exhib.lit. 20-Feb-3 Christie's, London #202/R est:60000

HOOK, Sandy (1879-1960) French
Works on paper
£791 $1250 €1250 Le chemin de halage (54x65cm-21x26in) s.d.46 pastel. 27-Nov-2 Lemoine & Ferrando, Paris #111/R
£878 $1370 €1300 Bateaux dans un port (30x48cm-12x19in) s. W/C pair. 27-Mar-3 Maigret, Paris #297
£1034 $1645 €1500 Trois mats en route (46x68cm-18x27in) s. pastel gouache. 4-Mar-3 Livinec, Gaudcheau & Jezequel, Rennes #417
£2414 $3838 €3500 Le Saverne en manuuvre au port (54x86cm-21x34in) s.d.1919 gouache W/C. 4-Mar-3 Livinec, Gaudcheau & Jezequel, Rennes #418

HOOK, William C (1948-) American
£2244 $3500 €3366 Open field (61x76cm-24x30in) acrylic. 9-Nov-2 Altermann Galleries, Santa Fe #189

HOOPE, Cornelis Jan (1920-) Dutch
Works on paper
£298 $483 €420 View of a French street (53x38cm-21x15in) s. W/C. 26-May-3 Glerum, Amsterdam #110

HOOPER, John Horace (fl.1877-1899) British
£1282 $2013 €2000 Figure with geese in English landscape in evening (62x107cm-24x42in) s. s. verso. 23-Nov-2 Arnold, Frankfurt #762/R
£1400 $2338 €2030 Landscape with figure by a pool, near Godalming (61x92cm-24x36in) s.i. s.verso. 25-Jun-3 Bonhams, Bury St Edmunds #568/R est:1500-2000
£1800 $2808 €2700 Summer sunlight (60x105cm-24x41in) s. s.i.verso. 26-Mar-3 Sotheby's, Olympia #32/R est:2000-3000
£1800 $2916 €2700 Harvest scene, near Arundel (61x107cm-24x42in) s. s.i.verso. 20-May-3 Sotheby's, Olympia #218/R est:2000-3000
£1800 $2952 €2700 Old lock (61x107cm-24x42in) s. i.verso. 29-May-3 Christie's, Kensington #180/R est:2000-3000
£2300 $3726 €3450 Berkshire cornfield (91x152cm-36x60in) s. s.i.d. 20-May-3 Sotheby's, Olympia #265/R est:2000-3000
£2778 $4000 €4167 Summer afternoon (59x100cm-23x39in) s. 15-Jan-3 Christie's, Rockefeller NY #131/R

HOOPER, John Horace (attrib) (fl.1877-1899) British
£550 $858 €825 Punting (51x76cm-20x30in) s. 7-Nov-2 Christie's, Kensington #135/R

HOOPER, Luther (1849-1932) British
Works on paper
£580 $911 €870 Cattle by the river (46x72cm-18x28in) s. W/C. 16-Dec-2 Bonhams, Bury St Edmunds #421

HOORDE, C van (19th C) Belgian
£348 $543 €550 Nature morte aux fleurs (30x46cm-12x18in) 16-Sep-2 Amberes, Antwerp #263

HOORDE, Louis van (19th C) Belgian
£449 $696 €700 La declamation (38x50cm-15x20in) s. panel. 3-Dec-2 Campo & Campo, Antwerp #313

HOORICKX, Ernest (1859-1908) Belgian
£392 $631 €600 Le chemin ensoleille (32x50cm-13x20in) s. 20-Jan-3 Horta, Bruxelles #311

HOOTON, Margaret Minnett (20th C) American
£577 $900 €866 Penny for your thoughts (36x28cm-14x11in) 19-Oct-2 David Dike, Dallas #281/R
£801 $1250 €1202 Flood of 1908 (41x51cm-16x20in) 19-Oct-2 David Dike, Dallas #336/R
£1538 $2400 €2307 Texas State capital circa 1910 (41x51cm-16x20in) 19-Oct-2 David Dike, Dallas #113/R est:1200-2500

HOOYBERG, Elbert (1903-1984) Dutch
£3526 $5535 €5500 Fantasy picture of Nieuwe church and a market place (72x90cm-28x35in) s.d.1937. 25-Nov-2 Glerum, Amsterdam #165/R est:3000-4000

HOPE, E Lyn (fl.1940-1958) British
Works on paper
£1282 $1987 €2000 Hauling in the nets at Sligo (34x48cm-13x19in) s. gouache. 3-Dec-2 Bonhams & James Adam, Dublin #46/R est:1500-2000

HOPE, Gabrielle (1916-) New Zealander
Works on paper
£880 $1452 €1276 Karekare II (57x44cm-22x17in) W/C. 1-Jul-3 Peter Webb, Auckland #88/R est:2500-3500 (NZ.D 2500)

HOPE, Henry (?) New Zealander
£361 $578 €523 Jervois Rd, Ponsonby Auckland (60x78cm-24x31in) s. board. 13-May-3 Watson's, Christchurch #62/R (NZ.D 1000)

HOPE, James (1818-1892) American
£2372 $3700 €3558 Portraits of young girls (51x43cm-20x17in) i.verso pair. 21-Sep-2 Pook & Pook, Downington #72/R est:2000-4000
£4403 $7000 €6605 Study of Rainbow falls, Watkins Glen (91x76cm-36x30in) s.d.1872 i.verso prov. 4-Mar-3 Christie's, Rockefeller NY #5/R est:8000-12000

HOPE, John David (?) ?
£641 $994 €1000 Italian landscape (14x20cm-6x8in) i. verso. 9-Dec-2 Dr Fritz Nagel, Stuttgart #7015/R

HOPE, Laurence (1928-) Australian
£349 $555 €524 Portrait of a woman (44x50cm-17x20in) board. 5-May-3 Sotheby's, Melbourne #197 (A.D 900)

HOPE, Robert (1869-1936) British
£248 $400 €372 Portrait of a woman with a red scarf (36x25cm-14x10in) init. board. 15-Jan-3 Boos Gallery, Michigan #665/R
£300 $477 €450 Evening landscape (38x51cm-15x20in) s. 26-Feb-3 Sotheby's, Olympia #230/R
£380 $581 €570 Post office (23x33cm-9x13in) s. board. 22-Aug-2 Bonhams, Edinburgh #980
£450 $702 €675 Girl with guitar (24x20cm-9x8in) init. board. 13-Sep-2 Lyon & Turnbull, Edinburgh #76/R
£540 $826 €810 In Ettrickdale (26x34cm-10x13in) s. s.i.verso panel. 22-Aug-2 Bonhams, Edinburgh #991
£549 $900 €824 The mill pond, Cocksburns Path, Berwickshire, Scotland (41x51cm-16x20in) s. 8-Feb-3 Neal Auction Company, New Orleans #162/R
£600 $918 €900 Kirkhope Tower, Ettrickdale. Porch (11x15cm-4x6in) init. canvas on panel two. 22-Aug-2 Bonhams, Edinburgh #978
£700 $1071 €1050 The bridge (26x30cm-10x12in) s. canvas on panel. 22-Aug-2 Bonhams, Edinburgh #979
£750 $1148 €1125 Shepherd on a bridge (30x40cm-12x16in) s. 22-Aug-2 Bonhams, Edinburgh #982
£750 $1148 €1125 Borders townscape (24x29cm-9x11in) init. canvasboard. 22-Aug-2 Bonhams, Edinburgh #986
£780 $1193 €1170 Children playing by a harbour (18x24cm-7x9in) s. panel. 22-Aug-2 Bonhams, Edinburgh #990
£800 $1192 €1200 Tunny fisher, Concarneau (24x34cm-9x13in) s. s.i.verso board. 27-Jun-2 Greenslade Hunt, Taunton #762/R
£980 $1499 €1470 Poultry yard. Farmyard and river scene (12x13cm-5x5in) set of three. 22-Aug-2 Bonhams, Edinburgh #981
£980 $1539 €1470 Children feeding their rabbits (20x25cm-8x10in) s. board. 16-Dec-2 Bonhams, Bury St Edmunds #493/R
£1000 $1430 €1500 Willows at Knowes Mill, East Linton (43x59cm-17x23in) s. i.stretcher. 11-Apr-2 Mellors & Kirk, Nottingham #564/R est:1000-1500
£1000 $1550 €1500 Homewards at close of day (41x51cm-16x20in) s. 5-Dec-2 Bonhams, Edinburgh #129 est:1000-1500
£1050 $1607 €1575 Field workers (24x34cm-9x13in) s. panel. 22-Aug-2 Bonhams, Edinburgh #988 est:600-800
£1100 $1683 €1650 In harbour (23x19cm-9x7in) s. board. 22-Aug-2 Bonhams, Edinburgh #987/R est:300-500
£1300 $2028 €1950 On the river Dochart, Killin (35x51cm-14x20in) 14-Apr-3 Sotheby's, London #122/R est:1000-1500
£2100 $3339 €3150 Feeding the rabbits (20x25cm-8x10in) s. canvas on board. 6-Mar-3 Christie's, Kensington #112/R est:1200-1800
£2200 $3366 €3300 Breton quayside (23x27cm-9x11in) s. canvas on board. 22-Aug-2 Bonhams, Edinburgh #984/R est:400-600
£2200 $3366 €3300 Springtime, foot of the Eildons, Melrose (40x52cm-16x20in) s. s.i.verso. 22-Aug-2 Bonhams, Edinburgh #985 est:1000-1500
£3000 $4590 €4500 Girl in red (60x50cm-24x20in) s. 22-Aug-2 Bonhams, Edinburgh #989 est:600-800
£14103 $22000 €21155 Girl wearing a black hat (76x64cm-30x25in) s. 12-Oct-2 Neal Auction Company, New Orleans #535/R est:1500-2500

HOPFGARTEN, August Ferdinand (1807-1896) German
Works on paper
£417 $663 €600 Portrait of young woman (29x20cm-11x8in) chl over pencil chk. 5-May-3 Ketterer, Munich #294/R
£591 $939 €850 Heidelberg castle (21x27cm-8x11in) pencil. 5-May-3 Ketterer, Munich #300/R
£764 $1215 €1100 Man walking along, galloping horse (11x18cm-4x7in) i. W/C over pencil. 5-May-3 Ketterer, Munich #299/R
£2083 $3312 €3000 Portrait of the artist Senff, two Italian women strolling along (21x12cm-8x5in) i. pencil double-sided. 5-May-3 Ketterer, Munich #297/R est:300-400

HOPKIN, Robert (1832-1909) American
£368 $600 €552 Sailing ship at sea (36x51cm-14x20in) painted c.1885. 14-Feb-3 Du Mouchelle, Detroit #2045/R
£368 $600 €552 Seascape (30x46cm-12x18in) s. 2-Feb-3 Grogan, Boston #47
£920 $1500 €1334 Seascape (33x48cm-13x19in) 18-Jul-3 Du Mouchelle, Detroit #2007/R est:1000-1200
£1592 $2500 €2388 Sailing ships at night (51x61cm-20x24in) 13-Dec-2 Du Mouchelle, Detroit #2085/R est:2500-3500
£1840 $3000 €2668 Seascape with sailing ship (46x61cm-18x24in) 18-Jul-3 Du Mouchelle, Detroit #2008/R est:3000-4000

HOPKINS, Arthur (1848-1930) British
Works on paper
£540 $875 €783 Two children walking past autumnal bushes within a landscape (26x33cm-10x13in) s. W/C gouache. 21-May-3 Rupert Toovey, Partridge Green #1/R
£880 $1470 €1276 Young boy seated on a quay (28x19cm-11x7in) s.d.1878 W/C. 19-Jun-3 Lane, Penzance #198
£2400 $3840 €3600 RSVP (37x49cm-15x19in) s.d.1910 W/C. 11-Mar-3 Bonhams, New Bond Street #71/R est:1500-2000

HOPKINS, Frances Anne (1838-1919) British
Works on paper
£380 $608 €570 Figure with cows beside a building with trees and an extensive landscape (33x48cm-13x19in) mono.d.1911 W/C bodycol. 13-Mar-3 Duke & Son, Dorchester #125/R
£550 $880 €825 Washing in the river (25x36cm-10x14in) mono. W/C bodycol. 13-Mar-3 Duke & Son, Dorchester #132

HOPKINS, Mark (20th c) American
Sculpture
£1174 $1925 €1702 The elephant family (28x62cm-11x24in) s.d.94 pat.bronze. 4-Jun-3 Fischer, Luzern #1372/R est:2500-3500 (S.FR 2500)

HOPKINS, Milton W (attrib) (1789-1844) American
£2640 $4250 €3960 Portraits (66x56cm-26x22in) pair. 23-Feb-3 Skinner, Boston #152/R est:8000-12000

HOPKINS, William H (?-1892) British
£4487 $7045 €7000 Scene de chasse (34x58cm-13x23in) s. panel pair. 10-Dec-2 Campo, Vlaamse Kaai #247 est:2800-3200

HOPKINSON, Charles Sydney (1869-1962) American
£5263 $8000 €7895 Surf in morning sunlight (61x64cm-24x25in) s. 17-Aug-2 North East Auctions, Portsmouth #1230/R
Works on paper
£903 $1400 €1355 Seascapes (25x36cm-10x14in) one s. one init. W/C two. 2-Nov-2 North East Auctions, Portsmouth #46/R

HOPKINSON, William John (1887-?) Canadian
£565 $882 €943 Church at Canmore, Alta (25x30cm-10x12in) s. i.verso board. 13-Apr-3 Levis, Calgary #467/R est:250-350 (C.D 1300)

HOPLEY, Edward William John (1816-1869) British
£1000 $1590 €1500 Race for an apple (54x40cm-21x16in) i. 4-Mar-3 Bearnes, Exeter #459/R est:1000-1500

HOPPE, Carl (1897-1981) American
£449 $700 €674 Texas wildflower (20x28cm-8x11in) panel painted c.1964. 19-Oct-2 David Dike, Dallas #301/R
£1923 $3000 €2885 Giant cactus (51x61cm-20x24in) painted c.1957. 19-Oct-2 David Dike, Dallas #130/R est:3000-6000

HOPPE, Erik (1897-1968) Danish
£847 $1312 €1271 Houses on the outskirts of Copenhagen (70x75cm-28x30in) s. 1-Oct-2 Rasmussen, Copenhagen #331/R (D.KR 10000)
£1554 $2471 €2331 Figures in Sondermarken (50x72cm-20x28in) s. 26-Feb-3 Kunsthallen, Copenhagen #272/R est:20000 (D.KR 17000)
£1576 $2522 €2364 Landscape (54x68cm-21x27in) s. 13-Jan-3 Rasmussen, Vejle #273/R est:15000 (D.KR 18000)
£1828 $2907 €2742 Evening landscape, Sondermarken with sun in the back (66x80cm-26x31in) s. exhib. 26-Feb-3 Kunsthallen, Copenhagen #227/R est:25000 (D.KR 20000)
£1948 $3019 €2922 Green landscape, possibly Sondermarken (50x61cm-20x24in) s. 1-Oct-2 Rasmussen, Copenhagen #359/R est:30000 (D.KR 23000)
£2011 $3197 €3017 View towards houses, Wilders Square, Christianshavn (76x80cm-30x31in) s. prov. 26-Feb-3 Kunsthallen, Copenhagen #245/R est:20000 (D.KR 22000)
£2332 $3708 €3498 Figure in Sondermarken (39x47cm-15x19in) s. 29-Apr-3 Kunsthallen, Copenhagen #212/R est:20000 (D.KR 25000)
£2726 $4225 €4089 View across Wilders Plads (100x106cm-39x42in) s. 28-Sep-2 Rasmussen, Havnen #2202/R est:10000 (D.KR 32000)
£3043 $4686 €4565 Figure among trees, Sondermarken (73x100cm-29x39in) s. prov. 23-Oct-2 Kunsthallen, Copenhagen #26/R est:30000 (D.KR 36000)
Works on paper
£340 $530 €510 Landscape from Sondermarken with figures (43x54cm-17x21in) s. W/C. 5-Aug-2 Rasmussen, Vejle #289/R (D.KR 4000)

HOPPE, Ferdinand Theodor (1848-1890) German
£545 $855 €850 Portrait of young woman on Ostsee coast (37x22cm-15x9in) s. 21-Nov-2 Van Ham, Cologne #1687/R

HOPPENBROUWERS, Johannes Franciscus (1819-1866) Dutch
£1410 $2200 €2115 Winter landscape with ice fishermen (25x33cm-10x13in) s. panel. 21-Sep-2 Nadeau, Windsor #117/R est:3000-5000
£1538 $2415 €2400 Winter landscape (24x38cm-9x15in) s. panel. 15-Dec-2 Mercier & Cie, Lille #360
£1736 $2760 €2500 Snow covered pine trees in a winter landscape (12x18cm-5x7in) s. panel prov. 29-Apr-3 Christie's, Amsterdam #12/R est:4000-6000
£4717 $7264 €7500 Winter landscape with skaters near a koek en zopie (54x70cm-21x28in) s. 22-Oct-2 Sotheby's, Amsterdam #64/R est:7000-9000
£6289 $9686 €10000 Woodgatherers on the ice on a windy day (55x73cm-22x29in) s.d.52 panel. 23-Oct-2 Christie's, Amsterdam #121/R est:12000-18000

HOPPENBROUWERS, Johannes Franciscus and ROCHUSSEN, Charles (19th C) Dutch
£1316 $2132 €2000 Panoramic landscape with figures conversing in the foreground (47x63cm-19x25in) s. 21-Jan-3 Christie's, Amsterdam #9/R est:2000-3000

HOPPER, Dennis (1936-) American
Photographs
£15190 $24000 €22785 Double standard (41x61cm-16x24in) s.d.1961 num.15/15 gelatin. 14-Nov-2 Christie's, Rockefeller NY #482/R est:10000-15000

HOPPER, Edward (1882-1967) American
£838710 $1300000 €1258065 Clamdigger (62x76cm-24x30in) lit. 5-Dec-2 Christie's, Rockefeller NY #117/R est:1500000-2500000
Works on paper
£14286 $22000 €21429 Golfers (29x18cm-11x7in) s.d.99 pen ink pencil. 4-Sep-2 Christie's, Rockefeller NY #364/R est:3000-5000
£20645 $32000 €30968 Standing man with a moustache (28x19cm-11x7in) s.d.1901 W/C gray wash paper on board prov. 5-Dec-2 Christie's, Rockefeller NY #189/R est:20000-30000
£20968 $32500 €31452 Indian (29x18cm-11x7in) s.d.1901 pen ink pencil prov. 4-Dec-2 Sotheby's, New York #156/R est:15000-25000
£111111 $180000 €166667 Lime Rock Quarry II (36x51cm-14x20in) s.i. W/C paper on paperboard lit. 22-May-3 Christie's, Rockefeller NY #78/R est:250000-350000
£135802 $220000 €203703 House and trees, Gloucester (30x46cm-12x18in) s. i.verso chl executed 1922 prov. 22-May-3 Christie's, Rockefeller NY #71/R est:150000-250000
£290323 $450000 €435485 Oregon coast (50x70cm-20x28in) s. W/C prov.exhib.lit. 5-Dec-2 Christie's, Rockefeller NY #206/R est:500000-700000
£324074 $525000 €486111 House on hill top - house on dune, South Truro (36x51cm-14x20in) s. W/C prov.exhib.lit. 21-May-3 Sotheby's, New York #19/R est:500000-700000

HOPPER, John Horace (fl.1877-1899) British
£1100 $1793 €1650 Rural landscape at sunset, near Purley, Berks, with buildings and figures (90x60cm-35x24in) s. i.verso. 11-Feb-3 Fellows & Sons, Birmingham #1/R

HOPPNER, John (1758-1810) British
£409 $650 €614 Portrait of John Orchard (193x163cm-76x64in) 7-Mar-3 Jackson's, Cedar Falls #546/R
£3000 $4710 €4500 Bacchanalian muse (96cm-38in circular) feigned circle prov. 16-Apr-3 Christie's, Kensington #529/R est:4000-6000
£8500 $14110 €12750 Portrait of Lady Barbara Ashley Cooper in a white dress and black shawl, in a landscape (76x63cm-30x25in) prov.lit. 10-Jun-3 Christie's, London #39/R est:5000-8000
Works on paper
£260 $403 €390 Wooded landscape with traveller resting (39x54cm-15x21in) black chk grey wash htd white. 30-Oct-2 Bonhams, New Bond Street #196/R

HOPPNER, John (attrib) (1758-1810) British
£400 $652 €600 Portrait of John Earl of Kerry as a boy, wearing red (36x30cm-14x12in) oval. 28-Jan-3 Gorringes, Lewes #1726
£950 $1501 €1425 Portrait of a lady in a white dress (76x64cm-30x25in) 2-Dec-2 Gorringes, Lewes #2755/R
£1200 $1872 €1800 Portrait of Granville John Penn (128x103cm-50x41in) prov.lit. 7-Nov-2 Christie's, Kensington #63/R est:1000-1500
£1613 $2548 €2420 Portrait of a lady seated in a landscape (127x102cm-50x40in) 18-Nov-2 Waddingtons, Toronto #139/R est:4000-6000 (C.D 4000)

HOPS, Tom (1906-1976) German
£685 $1068 €1000 Venice (47x60cm-19x24in) s. panel. 10-Apr-3 Schopman, Hamburg #631

HOPTON, Gwendoline M (fl.1897-1913) British

£300 $501 €435 Breton market (16x23cm-6x9in) board. 19-Jun-3 Lane, Penzance #107
£400 $628 €600 Duck pond (44x58cm-17x23in) studio st. 10-Dec-2 Lane, Penzance #173

HOPWOOD, Henry Silkstone (1860-1914) British

£620 $973 €930 Picardy Farm (12x16cm-5x6in) s. canvasboard. 19-Nov-2 Bonhams, Leeds #108/R
£620 $973 €930 On the edge of the Sahara (12x16cm-5x6in) panel. 19-Nov-2 Bonhams, Leeds #112/R
£820 $1287 €1230 Dancing figure (12x16cm-5x6in) s.i. panel. 19-Nov-2 Bonhams, Leeds #116/R
£880 $1461 €1320 Early morning, Tunis (21x27cm-8x11in) s. canvas on board. 10-Jun-3 Bonhams, Leeds #198
£900 $1413 €1350 Sidi Okba, Algeria (12x16cm-5x6in) panel. 19-Nov-2 Bonhams, Leeds #113/R
£920 $1444 €1380 Letter writer, Biskra (16x12cm-6x5in) s. panel. 19-Nov-2 Bonhams, Leeds #111/R
£1000 $1570 €1500 Colonnade, Biskra (20x14cm-8x6in) i.d.1914 panel. 19-Nov-2 Bonhams, Leeds #114/R est:1000-1500
£1050 $1649 €1575 North African market scene (12x16cm-5x6in) i. panel. 19-Nov-2 Bonhams, Leeds #110/R est:1000-1200
£1200 $1884 €1800 On the sands (12x16cm-5x6in) panel. 19-Nov-2 Bonhams, Leeds #115/R est:1200-1800

HORACEK, Rudolf (1915-1986) ?

Works on paper

£1358 $2200 €2037 Untitled (87x62cm-34x24in) s. graphite col pencil prov.exhib. 27-Jan-3 Christie's, Rockefeller NY #115/R est:1500-2000
£1358 $2200 €2037 Untitled (60x44cm-24x17in) s. graphite col pencil prov. 27-Jan-3 Christie's, Rockefeller NY #117/R est:1500-2000

HORACIO (1912-1972) Mexican

£1923 $3000 €2885 Retrato de nina con pajaros. Nina con gatos y perros (60x46cm-24x18in) s. pair prov. 14-Oct-2 Butterfields, San Francisco #2127/R est:4000-6000
£14013 $22000 €21020 Portraits of girl (61x46cm-24x18in) s. painted c.1945 pair prov. 20-Nov-2 Christie's, Rockefeller NY #65/R est:10000-15000

HORANEK, Jaroslav (1925-1995) Czechoslovakian

£590 $956 €856 Target (60x46cm-24x18in) s.d.64 enamel oil panel. 24-May-3 Dorotheum, Prague #139/R est:18000-30000 (C.KR 26000)

HORBERG, Pehr (1746-1816) Swedish

£1277 $1979 €1916 Adoration of the Shepherds (44x30cm-17x12in) init.d.1791 panel. 3-Dec-2 Bukowskis, Stockholm #416/R est:12000-15000 (S.KR 18000)

HORDIJK, Gerard (1899-1958) Dutch

£758 $1206 €1100 Brug Chambord (65x81cm-26x32in) s. 10-Mar-3 Sotheby's, Amsterdam #241/R est:1000-1500

Works on paper

£414 $638 €650 Dancers (34x25cm-13x10in) s. brush black ink gouache. 3-Sep-2 Christie's, Amsterdam #381
£541 $845 €850 Horse race (15x20cm-6x8in) s. W/C. 5-Nov-2 Vendu Notarishuis, Rotterdam #114/R

HOREL, E Albert (1876-1964) French

£1132 $1743 €1800 Medina (64x92cm-25x36in) s. 23-Oct-2 Rabourdin & Choppin de Janvry, Paris #208/R

HOREMANS, J J (18th C) Flemish

£3200 $5344 €4640 Elegant company resting from a hunt before a palace (71x99cm-28x39in) s.d.1794 after P.Wouwerman. 8-Jul-3 Sotheby's, Olympia #417/R est:1000-2000

HOREMANS, Jan Josef (18th C) Flemish

£3275 $5109 €4913 Riotous card players in tavern (50x59cm-20x23in) 20-Nov-2 Fischer, Luzern #1033/R est:8000-12000 (S.FR 7500)
£8865 $14805 €12500 Scene d'interieur Hollandais avec un professeur de Clavecin (39x32cm-15x13in) s. 18-Jun-3 Tajan, Paris #84/R est:7000-8000

HOREMANS, Jan Josef (elder) (1682-1759) Flemish

£2866 $4471 €4500 Elegant company dancing and feasting on a terrace (47x60cm-19x24in) s.d.1719 prov. 6-Nov-2 Christie's, Amsterdam #37/R est:3000-5000
£7500 $11775 €11250 Lawyer's office (35x32cm-14x13in) s. 13-Dec-2 Christie's, Kensington #127/R est:5000-7000
£16000 $26720 €23200 Courtyard in a town with a mussel seller and other figures (47x60cm-19x24in) s. 11-Jul-3 Christie's, Kensington #110/R est:7000-10000

HOREMANS, Jan Josef (elder-attrib) (1682-1759) Flemish

£608 $949 €900 Interior scene with couple chatting (50x41cm-20x16in) 26-Mar-3 Rossini, Paris #116
£1701 $2704 €2500 Interior scene (49x58cm-19x23in) 24-Mar-3 Finarte Semenzato, Rome #491/R

HOREMANS, Jan Josef (younger) (1714-1790) Flemish

£1800 $2790 €2700 Family games (50x59cm-20x23in) 6-Dec-2 Lyon & Turnbull, Edinburgh #17/R est:1800-2500
£3396 $5264 €5400 Inn interior (63x76cm-25x30in) prov. 7-Oct-2 Ansorena, Madrid #50/R
£25000 $39000 €37500 Cauliflower, onions and peaches, jug on a table (44x61cm-17x24in) s.d.1773 panel prov. 9-Apr-3 Christie's, London #27/R est:25000-35000

HOREMANS, Peter Jacob (attrib) (1700-1776) Flemish

£1986 $3316 €2800 Scene de concert devant la terrasse d'un palais (47x59cm-19x23in) bears sig. 18-Jun-3 Tajan, Paris #79/R est:3500-4500

HORGNIES, Norbert Joseph (19th C) Belgian

£1400 $2240 €2100 Boys selling fish at a doorway (48x38cm-19x15in) s. 11-Mar-3 Gorringes, Lewes #2471/R est:1500-2000
£1889 $3136 €2739 Boy blowing on his soup. Boy kneeling in snow with bird and birdcage (19x15cm-7x6in) s. indis d. panel two prov. 10-Jun-3 Ritchie, Toronto #107/R est:2500-3500 (C.D 4250)

HORIK, Vladimir (1939-) Canadian

£339 $528 €509 Coin d'une village au bord du fleuve (20x25cm-8x10in) s. isorel. 30-Jul-2 Iegor de Saint Hippolyte, Montreal #74 (C.D 840)
£435 $679 €653 Haut plateau en Charlevoix (35x46cm-14x18in) s.d.1985 isorel. 30-Jul-2 Iegor de Saint Hippolyte, Montreal #75 (C.D 1080)
£2458 $3908 €3687 Overlooking the seaway (50x70cm-20x28in) s.i. board. 23-Mar-3 Hodgins, Calgary #78/R est:2000-3000 (C.D 5800)

HORLOR, George W (fl.1849-1891) British

£500 $780 €750 Pony, dogs and the day's bag in a moorland setting (34x44cm-13x17in) s.d.1886 panel. 10-Apr-3 Tennants, Leyburn #1043
£950 $1520 €1425 Highland scene with sheep and black cock (40x61cm-16x24in) s.d.1871. 7-Jan-3 Bonhams, Knightsbridge #227g/R
£1400 $2282 €2030 Bernese mountain dogs on guard over their flock (40x60cm-16x24in) s.d.1872. 21-Jul-3 Bonhams, Bath #79/R est:800-1200
£1450 $2262 €2175 Sheepdog tending a flock in a highland landscape (41x61cm-16x24in) s.d.1876. 10-Apr-3 Tennants, Leyburn #1044/R est:1000-1500
£1800 $2808 €2700 Dead game (43x64cm-17x25in) s.d.1845. 17-Sep-2 Sotheby's, Olympia #31/R est:800-1200
£1800 $2844 €2700 Bran, property of the author (23x30cm-9x12in) s.d.1877 i.d.verso board. 28-Nov-2 Christie's, Kensington #303/R est:500-800
£3000 $4680 €4500 Cattle by a pool in a moorland landscape (46x61cm-18x24in) s.d.1891. 10-Apr-3 Tennants, Leyburn #1045/R est:1500-2000
£3600 $5616 €5400 Highland landscapes, spaniels with the day's bag and spaniels and a pony (35x45cm-14x18in) s.d.1895 pair. 10-Apr-3 Tennants, Leyburn #1046/R est:2000-3000
£5000 $7800 €7500 Day's bag (91x52cm-36x20in) s. 14-Apr-3 Sotheby's, London #54/R est:5000-7000

HORLOR, George W (attrib) (fl.1849-1891) British

£1150 $1794 €1725 Setters with dead game in a mountain landscape (41x61cm-16x24in) 10-Apr-3 Tennants, Leyburn #1042/R est:600-800

HORLOR, J (19th C) British

£675 $1060 €1013 Mountainous Welsh landscapes with cattle and figures (50x60cm-20x24in) s. pair. 21-Nov-2 Clevedon Sale Rooms #265

HORLOR, Joseph (1809-1887) British

£366 $600 €549 Mill stream in the Scottish highlands (74x86cm-29x34in) s. 5-Feb-3 Doyle, New York #18/R
£400 $624 €600 Clovelly, north Devon (18x28cm-7x11in) s. s.i.verso board. 10-Apr-3 Tennants, Leyburn #985/R
£450 $733 €675 River landscape (33x51cm-13x20in) s. 29-Jan-3 Sotheby's, Olympia #110/R
£480 $778 €720 Fisherwoman on a rocky shore looking out to sea (20x34cm-8x13in) s. 23-May-3 Honiton Galleries, Honiton #714
£800 $1264 €1200 Ruined abbey in a river landscape with figures and cattle in the foreground (59x102cm-23x40in) s. 2-Dec-2 Bonhams, Bath #120/R
£850 $1385 €1275 Faggot gatherer (43x61cm-17x24in) s. 29-Jan-3 Sotheby's, Olympia #111/R est:600-800
£1700 $2805 €2465 At Carmarthen, the Vale of Towy. On the Irvon. At Abergwesyn on the Irvon.Trawler on shore (11x15cm-4x6in) three s. i.d.1853 board set of four. 1-Jul-3 Bearnes, Exeter #486/R est:800-1200

£2147 $3500 €3221 Coast of North Shields (28x48cm-11x19in) s.d.1867. 2-Feb-3 Simpson's, Houston #407

HORLOR, Joseph (attrib) (1809-1887) British
£3200 $5184 €4800 Travelers on a mountain path (89x142cm-35x56in) 20-May-3 Sotheby's, Olympia #198/R est:2000-3000

HORMANN, Theodor von (1840-1895) Austrian
£7092 $11489 €10000 Landscape in Lower Austria (23x40cm-9x16in) st.sig. verso panel. 22-May-3 Dorotheum, Vienna #42/R est:14000-15000
£8511 $13787 €12000 Residence with garden in the neighbourhood of St Polten (56x68cm-22x27in) s.d.82. 22-May-3 Dorotheum, Vienna #110/R est:8000-12000
£19565 $32087 €27000 Estate in spring (36x50cm-14x20in) 27-May-3 Wiener Kunst Auktionen, Vienna #42/R est:15000-25000
Works on paper
£972 $1546 €1400 Flower market in Place St Sulpice, Paris (17x20cm-7x8in) s.i. Indian ink. 29-Apr-3 Wiener Kunst Auktionen, Vienna #566/R est:500-1000
£1875 $2981 €2700 Shovelling snow (20x35cm-8x14in) W/C. 29-Apr-3 Wiener Kunst Auktionen, Vienna #570/R est:1500-3000

HORN, Rebecca (1944-) German
Sculpture
£5800 $8932 €8700 Thermometre a'amour (95x36x9cm-37x14x4in) crystal liquid metal butterflies text mount on wall prov. 22-Oct-2 Sotheby's, London #342/R est:4000-6000

HORN, Roni (1944-) American
Sculpture
£25316 $40000 €37974 When Dickinson shut her eyes (140x89x63cm-55x35x25in) plastic aluminium exec.1993 prov. 13-Nov-2 Sotheby's, New York #482/R est:40000-60000
Works on paper
£3503 $5500 €5255 Untitled (11x16cm-4x6in) pastel pigment cutout shapes pair prov. 19-Nov-2 Wright, Chicago #303/R est:4000-5000

HORNBROOK, Thomas L (1780-1850) British
£2600 $4030 €3900 Royal Naval frigate announcing its arrival in the Hamoaze, Plymouth Sounds (38x53cm-15x21in) 31-Oct-2 Christie's, Kensington #454/R est:1000-1500

HORNE, G C (19th C) ?
£1108 $1739 €1662 Portrait of the Rotomahana at sea (44x70cm-17x28in) s.d.1888. 25-Nov-2 Peter Webb, Auckland #51/R est:4000-7000 (NZ.D 3500)

HORNE, Sir William van (1843-1915) Canadian
£2311 $3790 €3467 Matapedia fishing camp (11x17cm-4x7in) init.d.89 board. 3-Jun-3 Joyner, Toronto #196/R est:1200-1500 (C.D 5200)

HORNEL, Edward Atkinson (1864-1933) British
£7000 $10920 €10500 Young girl with swans (41x50cm-16x20in) s.d.1917. 14-Apr-3 Sotheby's, London #147/R est:5000-7000
£7000 $10920 €10500 Summer day (50x40cm-20x16in) s.d.1919. 10-Apr-3 Bonhams, Edinburgh #176 est:4000-6000
£9000 $13770 €13500 In Brighouse Bay (60x50cm-24x20in) s.d.1929. 22-Aug-2 Bonhams, Edinburgh #1181/R est:8000-12000
£10000 $15200 €15000 Young Japanese girls gathering flowers (76x63cm-30x25in) s.d.1921. 28-Aug-2 Sotheby's, London #1070/R est:10000-15000
£10000 $15500 €15000 Lily pond. Gathering primroses (6x22cm-2x9in) one s.d.1918 one s. canvas on panel pair prov. 31-Oct-2 Christie's, London #155/R est:12000-18000
£10500 $16380 €15750 Picking primroses (62x75cm-24x30in) s.d.1920. 10-Apr-3 Bonhams, Edinburgh #173/R est:6000-8000
£12000 $18360 €18000 Gathering snowdrops in the woods (60x71cm-24x28in) s.d.1917. 22-Aug-2 Bonhams, Edinburgh #1069/R est:12000-18000
£22000 $33440 €33000 Head of Japanese girl (29x23cm-11x9in) s. panel. 28-Aug-2 Sotheby's, London #1068a est:10000-15000
£30000 $46500 €45000 Peacock feather (102x127cm-40x50in) s.d.1916. 31-Oct-2 Christie's, London #154/R est:35000-45000
£48000 $72960 €72000 Swan lake (61x61cm-24x24in) s.d.1905 prov.exhib. 28-Aug-2 Sotheby's, London #1064/R est:40000-60000
£50000 $77500 €75000 Easter eggs (77x63cm-30x25in) s.d.1901 exhib. 31-Oct-2 Christie's, London #153/R est:50000-80000

HORNEMAN, Christian (1765-1844) Danish
Miniatures
£1267 $1976 €1901 Portrait of actress and singer Caroline Jagemann (67x6cm-26x2in) s. gold frame prov. 23-Sep-2 Rasmussen, Vejle #3/R est:8000-10000 (D.KR 15000)

HORNEMANN, Friedrich Adolf (1813-1890) German
£4487 $6955 €7000 Gypsies playing for peasant family round table (90x122cm-35x48in) s.i. 5-Dec-2 Dr Fritz Nagel, Stuttgart #664/R est:5500

HORNER, Edwin (20th C) ?
£380 $592 €600 Southern French city (63x54cm-25x21in) s. masonite. 18-Oct-2 Dr Fritz Nagel, Stuttgart #183/R

HORNER, Eva (19/20th C) British
£250 $390 €375 Sheep shearing (23x33cm-9x13in) s.d.1901. 9-Apr-3 Andrew Hartley, Ilkley #959

HORNER, Friedrich (1800-1864) Swiss
£602 $969 €903 Autumn landscape with white building (25x31cm-10x12in) s. canvas on board. 7-May-3 Dobiaschofsky, Bern #664/R (S.FR 1300)
Works on paper
£920 $1454 €1380 Classical ruins in an extensive landscape. Piece of rough seas in a mountains bay (40x56cm-16x22in) s. W/C pair. 26-Nov-2 Bonhams, Oxford #13/R
£1135 $1794 €1703 Hilly landscape with ruins in Upper Italy (37x50cm-15x20in) mono. W/C. 14-Nov-2 Stuker, Bern #9559 est:2800-3400 (S.FR 2600)

HORNER, Johan (1711-1763) Danish
£1435 $2325 €2081 Portrait of nobleman wearing armour and red jacket (78x64cm-31x25in) 26-May-3 Rasmussen, Copenhagen #1279/R est:15000 (D.KR 15000)
£5957 $9413 €8936 Portrait of Thalia Storm (74x64cm-29x25in) i.d.1756 exhib.prov. 2-Dec-2 Rasmussen, Copenhagen #1144/R est:50000-75000 (D.KR 70000)

HORNERO, Concha (1949-) Spanish
£440 $678 €700 Transparences (130x98cm-51x39in) s. s.d.2000 verso oil marble powder. 28-Oct-2 Segre, Madrid #167/R

HORNIGK, Hans (1878-?) German?
£327 $536 €500 Lakeside house in summer (70x100cm-28x39in) s. 29-Mar-3 Dannenberg, Berlin #598/R

HORNOR, Thomas (c.1800-1844) British
Works on paper
£440 $686 €660 Egg gathering on the Gower (28x45cm-11x18in) s. W/C. 11-Sep-2 Bonhams, Newport #190

HORNUNG, Joseph (1792-1870) Swiss
£6552 $10483 €9500 King of Sweden meeting his daughter (128x99cm-50x39in) 17-Mar-3 Pandolfini, Florence #591/R est:12000

HORNUNG, Preben (1919-1989) Danish
£253 $395 €380 Composition (21x33cm-8x13in) mono.d.62 cardboard. 18-Sep-2 Kunsthallen, Copenhagen #40 (D.KR 3000)
£463 $722 €695 Trees in snow, Olsted (44x31cm-17x12in) init.d.66 s.i.d.1966 verso. 11-Nov-2 Rasmussen, Vejle #21/R (D.KR 5400)
£676 $1054 €1014 From my garden - Nov.1973 (41x41cm-16x16in) mono. 18-Sep-2 Kunsthallen, Copenhagen #103/R (D.KR 8000)
£931 $1480 €1397 Composition (43x73cm-17x29in) init. s.d.1960 verso. 10-Mar-3 Rasmussen, Vejle #642/R (D.KR 10000)
£1716 $2866 €2488 On the surface of water (60x73cm-24x29in) mono. mono.d.1983 verso. 17-Jun-3 Rasmussen, Copenhagen #48/R est:20000 (D.KR 18000)
£2602 $4112 €3903 Water surface (60x73cm-24x29in) mono. s.d.1982 verso exhib.prov. 1-Apr-3 Rasmussen, Copenhagen #314/R est:20000 (D.KR 28000)
£2710 $4200 €4065 Composition in black and white (112x79cm-44x31in) mono. s.i.d.1986 verso prov. 1-Oct-2 Rasmussen, Copenhagen #39/R est:18000-25000 (D.KR 32000)
£3048 $4725 €4572 In passing (180x123cm-71x48in) mono. s.d.1975 verso sketch for large picture prov. 1-Oct-2 Rasmussen, Copenhagen #214/R est:30000-40000 (D.KR 36000)

£10594 $16421 €15891 Railway theme (196x115cm-77x45in) mono.d.59 verso exhib. 4-Dec-2 Kunsthallen, Copenhagen #23/R est:100000 (D.KR 123000)

Works on paper

£338 $527 €507 Figure composition (60x46cm-24x18in) mono. red chk chl. 18-Sep-2 Kunsthallen, Copenhagen #98 (D.KR 4000)

HORNUNG-JENSEN, C (1882-1960) Danish

£431 $698 €625 Young woman seated on bench in Frederiksberg Garden (41x53cm-16x21in) mono. 26-May-3 Rasmussen, Copenhagen #1547 (D.KR 4500)

£521 $829 €782 The artist's wife Ellen at the summerhouse in Hornbaek (43x53cm-17x21in) prov. 5-Mar-3 Rasmussen, Copenhagen #2043/R (D.KR 5600)

£603 $916 €905 Evening with figures, artist's wife sewing (45x55cm-18x22in) s.d.36 exhib. 27-Aug-2 Rasmussen, Copenhagen #1877/R (D.KR 7000)

HORNUNG-JENSEN, Carl (1882-1960) Danish

£487 $775 €731 June landscape (53x76cm-21x30in) s. 18-Mar-3 Maynards, Vancouver #37/R (C.D 1150)

HORRIX, Hendrikus Mattheus (1845-1932) Dutch

£704 $1134 €1000 Woman with pot (20x12cm-8x5in) s. 7-May-3 Vendue Huis, Gravenhage #13

HORSBURGH, John (attrib) (1791-1869) British

£1613 $2548 €2500 Stormy sea (51x91cm-20x36in) s. 18-Dec-2 Finarte, Milan #130/R

HORSFALL, Robert Bruce (1869-?) American

Works on paper

£315 $500 €473 Upland sandpipers (34x24cm-13x9in) s.d.1925 W/C gouache. 7-Mar-3 Skinner, Boston #363/R

HORSKY, Emery Donaldson (1885-1964) American

£1207 $1955 €1750 Chinese cook (69x99cm-27x39in) 23-May-3 Altermann Galleries, Santa Fe #120

HORSLEY, Hopkins Horsley Hobday (1807-1890) British

£650 $1066 €975 Welsh pass (45x76cm-18x30in) 29-May-3 Christie's, Kensington #101/R

HORST, Gerrit Willemsz (1612-1652) Dutch

£650 $1014 €975 Penitant Magdalen (139x114cm-55x45in) 8-Apr-3 Bonhams, Knightsbridge #296/R

HORST, Gerrit Willemsz (attrib) (1612-1652) Dutch

£3597 $5755 €5000 Humiliation of King Ahab (134x184cm-53x72in) 14-May-3 Christie's, Amsterdam #139/R est:4000-6000

HORST, Horst P (1906-1999) German

Photographs

£1700 $2754 €2550 White sleeve. Peplum. Evening wear (50x40cm-20x16in) st. s.i. two d.1936 one d.1951verso silver print three prov.lit. 22-May-3 Sotheby's, London #171/R est:1500-2000

£2110 $3250 €3165 Mainboucher corset (24x19cm-9x7in) s.i.d.1939 photograph. 24-Oct-2 Sotheby's, New York #221/R est:3000-5000

£2179 $3378 €3400 Mainbocher corset (32x24cm-13x9in) s. s. verso gelatin silver lit. 6-Dec-2 Bassenge, Berlin #4730/R est:4000

£2195 $3600 €3293 Round the clock no 1 (23x19cm-9x7in) s. i.verso silver print. 10-Feb-3 Swann Galleries, New York #96/R est:5000-7000

£3084 $4750 €4626 Round the clock I (30x23cm-12x9in) s.i. photograph. 24-Oct-2 Sotheby's, New York #220/R est:4000-6000

£3165 $5000 €4748 Mainbocher corset (46x34cm-18x13in) with sig.i.d.1939 photograph. 23-Apr-3 Sotheby's, New York #239/R est:5000-7000

£3165 $5000 €4748 Round the clock I (46x36cm-18x14in) s.i.d.1987 photograph. 23-Apr-3 Sotheby's, New York #240/R est:5000-7000

£3374 $5500 €5061 Round the clock I, N.Y (45x35cm-18x14in) s.i.d.1987 gelatin silver print. 12-Feb-3 Christie's, Rockefeller NY #262/R est:6000-8000

£3797 $6000 €5696 Still life, wine bottle, NY (36x45cm-14x18in) s. s.i.d.verso num.6/10 platinum palladium print. 22-Apr-3 Christie's, Rockefeller NY #76/R est:10000-15000

£4500 $7290 €6750 Mainbocher corset, Paris (35x27cm-14x11in) s. i.d.verso silver print lit. 22-May-3 Sotheby's, London #172/R est:800-1200

HORST, Wilhelm (1852-?) German

£577 $906 €900 Faggott gatherer on woodland path (86x59cm-34x23in) s.d.1902. 23-Nov-2 Arnold, Frankfurt #763/R

HORTER, Earl (1881-1940) American

Works on paper

£477 $750 €716 Joy Valentine (38x53cm-15x21in) i.d.March 14 W/C pencil. 14-Dec-2 Weschler, Washington #715/R

£838 $1400 €1215 Reclining nude (27x38cm-11x15in) s.d.32 W/C. 22-Jun-3 Freeman, Philadelphia #166/R est:1000-1500

HORTON, Brian (1933-) British

Works on paper

£350 $553 €525 Cumbrian landscape with clouds (53x57cm-21x22in) s.d.1986 gouache exhib. 27-Nov-2 Sotheby's, Olympia #279/R

HORTON, Etty (fl.1882-1905) British

£256 $420 €371 Afternoon landscape (38x51cm-15x20in) s. 30-May-3 Aspire, Cleveland #44/R

£260 $426 €390 Horse and rider on river towpath (25x35cm-10x14in) 10-Feb-3 Bonhams, Bath #179

£550 $897 €825 Figures in a river landscape. Sheep in a river landscape (30x40cm-12x16in) s. pair. 12-Feb-3 Bonhams, Knightsbridge #266/R

£550 $913 €798 An Irish hound (51x61cm-20x24in) s. 12-Jun-3 Christie's, Kensington #263/R

£550 $919 €798 Figure in a lakeland landscape (51x76cm-20x30in) s. 8-Jul-3 Bonhams, Knightsbridge #41/R

£650 $1066 €975 Riverside rest (51x76cm-20x30in) s. 29-May-3 Christie's, Kensington #136/R

£1600 $2496 €2400 Summer days (41x61cm-16x24in) s. pair. 7-Nov-2 Christie's, Kensington #128/R est:1000-1500

HORTON, George (1859-1950) British

Works on paper

£280 $434 €420 Winter in Holland (35x24cm-14x9in) s. W/C. 24-Sep-2 Anderson & Garland, Newcastle #289

£310 $481 €465 Dordrecht harbour (32x24cm-13x9in) s. W/C. 24-Sep-2 Anderson & Garland, Newcastle #288

£310 $518 €450 Sailing barge on a Dutch canal (30x23cm-12x9in) s. W/C. 17-Jun-3 Anderson & Garland, Newcastle #239

£410 $685 €595 In Holland (31x27cm-12x11in) s.i. W/C. 17-Jun-3 Anderson & Garland, Newcastle #240/R

£1000 $1550 €1500 Schooner beached near South Shields with figures and horse-cart (50x70cm-20x28in) s. W/C. 24-Sep-2 Anderson & Garland, Newcastle #292/R est:300-450

HORTON, John M (1935-) Canadian

£346 $526 €519 Outbound Sieners - Fraser River (25x41cm-10x16in) board. 4-Jul-2 Heffel, Vancouver #12 (C.D 800)

£411 $625 €617 Evening tow (30x41cm-12x16in) 4-Jul-2 Heffel, Vancouver #11 (C.D 950)

HORTON, Percy (1897-1970) British

£340 $530 €510 Home farm, Firle (57x75cm-22x30in) board. 17-Sep-2 Bonhams, Knightsbridge #160/R

HORTON, William Samuel (1865-1936) American

£2201 $3500 €3302 La seine fumee blue. Apres-midi d'automne Suisse (44x55cm-17x22in) s.i. s.i.verso one on board one on panel. 5-Mar-3 Sotheby's, New York #94/R est:5000-7000

£3459 $5500 €5189 Biarritz, petites personnes sur la plage (44x55cm-17x22in) i.verso board. 5-Mar-3 Sotheby's, New York #48/R est:8000-12000

£4403 $7000 €6605 Vagues, Rochers, et petits personnes sur le plage (6x45cm-2x18in) s.i.verso panel. 5-Mar-3 Sotheby's, New York #46/R est:10000-15000

£7547 $12000 €11321 Evening lights, Broadstairs Harbor. Le ruisseau devant le chateau (63x76cm-25x30in) s.i. one on board panel two. 5-Mar-3 Sotheby's, New York #68/R est:6000-8000

£16129 $25000 €24194 Garden and bridge at Sonning (42x53cm-17x21in) i. board prov.exhib. 4-Dec-2 Sotheby's, New York #1/R est:15000-25000

Works on paper

£679 $1100 €985 Effects of Autumn, with Edmon Castle in the distance (46x61cm-18x24in) s. pastel. 21-May-3 Doyle, New York #81/R

HORUP, Inge (1958-) Danish

£325 $527 €471 Composition (88x108cm-35x43in) s.d.93 masonite. 24-May-3 Rasmussen, Havnen #4314 (D.KR 3400)

HORVATH, Andor (1876-?) Hungarian

£315 $488 €473 Drinking wine (24x35cm-9x14in) board painted c.1900. 1-Oct-2 SOGA, Bratislava #122/R est:12000 (SL.K 20000)

HORVATH, G A (19/20th C) Hungarian
£395 $612 €593 Corn cleaning (55x67cm-22x26in) painted c.1930. 3-Dec-2 SOGA, Bratislava #111/R (SL.K 25000)
£679 $1052 €1019 In the pub (58x76cm-23x30in) painted c.1935. 3-Dec-2 SOGA, Bratislava #110/R (SL.K 43000)

HORWARTER, Joseph Eugène (1854-1925) Austrian
£1258 $1962 €2000 Maid reading in elegant drawing room (72x45cm-28x18in) s. 9-Oct-2 Michael Zeller, Lindau #733/R est:2000
£1538 $2415 €2400 With grandmother (43x22cm-17x9in) s.i.verso canvas on board. 10-Dec-2 Dorotheum, Vienna #129/R est:1200-1400

HOSCH, Karl (1900-1972) Swiss
£261 $404 €392 Two oriental women (44x37cm-17x15in) s. canvas on board. 9-Dec-2 Philippe Schuler, Zurich #3818/R (S.FR 600)

HOSCHEDE-MONET, Blanche (1865-1947) French
£8156 $13621 €11500 Les environs de Giverny (65x81cm-26x32in) s.d. 23-Jun-3 Delvaux, Paris #123/R est:10000-15000
£11043 $18000 €16565 Bord de riviere (54x65cm-21x26in) s. 12-Feb-3 Sotheby's, New York #40/R est:15000-20000

HOSEMANN, Theodor (1807-1875) German
£2993 $4759 €4400 Artist sketching two country girls outdoors (64x80cm-25x31in) s.d.1873. 19-Mar-3 Neumeister, Munich #591/R est:4800
£3623 $5942 €5000 Rendezvous in the country (18x24cm-7x9in) mono.d.18 TH 53 board prov. 31-May-3 Villa Grisebach, Berlin #107/R est:5000-7000

HOSIASSON, Philippe (1898-1978) French
£426 $711 €600 Composition (33x41cm-13x16in) s.d. 23-Jun-3 Delvaux, Paris #163
£1346 $2113 €2100 Sans titre (81x61cm-32x24in) s.d. s.i.verso. 16-Dec-2 Charbonneaux, Paris #261/R est:1500-2000
Works on paper
£323 $510 €510 Composition (42x36cm-17x14in) s.i.d.162 W/C. 27-Nov-2 Blanchet, Paris #134

HOSKINS, Gayle Porter (1887-1962) American
£2065 $3200 €3098 Game for sale (79x58cm-31x23in) s. 3-Dec-2 Christie's, Rockefeller NY #573/R est:2000-3000
£2258 $3500 €3387 Bring back the game (79x56cm-31x22in) s. 3-Dec-2 Christie's, Rockefeller NY #572/R est:2000-3000
£2258 $3500 €3387 Leisurely afternoon (96x69cm-38x27in) s. 3-Dec-2 Christie's, Rockefeller NY #575/R est:2000-3000
£10897 $17000 €16346 Cowboy and Indian in close combat (81x58cm-32x23in) s. 9-Nov-2 Illustration House, New York #174/R est:20000-30000
Works on paper
£282 $450 €423 Destroyer escort (36x43cm-14x17in) s. W/C prov. 17-May-3 Pook & Pook, Downington #146/R

HOSKINS, John (17th C) British
Miniatures
£6000 $9360 €9000 George Villiers, Duke of Buckingham with blue sash of the Garter (6cm-2xin) init. W/C on vellum gilt frame oval prov. 5-Nov-2 Bonhams, New Bond Street #16/R est:6000-8000
£16000 $24960 €24000 Robert Carr, Earl of Somerset wearing armour with brass studs (3cm-1xin) vellum gold frame with tag engraved by John Hoskins oval. 5-Nov-2 Bonhams, New Bond Street #15/R est:8000-10000
£17500 $29050 €25375 Lady, possibly Mary Cromwell, wearing a pearl necklace (7x6cm-3x2in) s.d.1651 i.verso vellum oval. 10-Jun-3 Mellors & Kirk, Nottingham #530/R est:3000-5000

HOSMER, Harriet (1830-1908) American
Sculpture
£16168 $27000 €23444 Winged boy seated on a toadstool (102cm-40in) i. white marble with pedestal. 21-Jun-3 Selkirks, St. Louis #1004/R est:25000-35000
£22000 $36740 €31900 Sleeping faun (81x118cm-32x46in) s.i. white marble incl marble base. 8-Jul-3 Sotheby's, London #218/R est:20000-30000

HOSOTTE, Georges (1936-) French
£1795 $2782 €2800 Paysage pastoral (60x73cm-24x29in) s. 8-Dec-2 Feletin, Province #160

HOSSE, Adolf (1875-1958) German
£1582 $2468 €2500 Horse drawn sleigh in snowy village (100x140cm-39x55in) s. lit. 14-Sep-2 Bergmann, Erlangen #759/R

HOSSZU, Marton (1894-?) Czechoslovakian
£551 $783 €827 Portrait of a lady (55x60cm-22x24in) painted c.1925. 26-Mar-2 SOGA, Bratislava #126/R (SL.K 35000)

HOST, Oluf (1884-1966) Danish
£426 $672 €639 Fruit trees in blossom (31x37cm-12x15in) s.i.d.1909. 30-Nov-2 Rasmussen, Havnen #2209/R (D.KR 5000)
£694 $1076 €1041 Cow in meadow landscape (20x24cm-8x9in) init.i.indis.d.12 or 13 s.stretcher. 1-Oct-2 Rasmussen, Copenhagen #360/R (D.KR 8200)
£1693 $2625 €2540 Evening sky (47x48cm-19x19in) init. 1-Oct-2 Rasmussen, Copenhagen #135/R est:25000-35000 (D.KR 20000)
£1948 $3019 €2922 Orion - twilight landscape (28x34cm-11x13in) init. 1-Oct-2 Rasmussen, Copenhagen #270/R est:20000-25000 (D.KR 23000)
£2146 $3411 €3219 Autumn landscape with Grejersen's farm, Roe Sogn (60x81cm-24x32in) init.d.11/8. 29-Apr-3 Kunsthallen, Copenhagen #262/R est:35000 (D.KR 23000)
£2652 $4402 €3845 From the harbour at Gudhjem (47x58cm-19x23in) init. 12-Jun-3 Kunsthallen, Copenhagen #246/R est:30000 (D.KR 28000)
£3622 $6050 €5252 Midsummer Night's bonfire, Bognemark (81x146cm-32x57in) prov. 17-Jun-3 Rasmussen, Copenhagen #93/R est:40000-60000 (D.KR 38000)
£3810 $5906 €5715 Autumn landscape with mill, figures and blue sky (55x81cm-22x32in) init. 1-Oct-2 Rasmussen, Copenhagen #134/R est:40000-50000 (D.KR 45000)
£4182 $6608 €6273 Christmas Eve, Bognemark with Madonna and Child (50x65cm-20x26in) init. painted c.1940 lit. 1-Apr-3 Rasmussen, Copenhagen #69/R est:40000-50000 (D.KR 45000)
£4194 $7005 €6081 Bathers on the beach (55x81cm-22x32in) init. prov. 17-Jun-3 Rasmussen, Copenhagen #78/R est:30000 (D.KR 44000)
£5390 $8517 €8085 Osterlars Church (40x53cm-16x21in) init.d.23-3-49 prov. 1-Apr-3 Rasmussen, Copenhagen #81/R est:60000 (D.KR 58000)
£5970 $9493 €8955 Bognemark, Bornholm (38x65cm-15x26in) init. 29-Apr-3 Kunsthallen, Copenhagen #241/R est:40000 (D.KR 64000)
£7197 $11947 €10436 Sunset over Norresund (90x146cm-35x57in) init.d.63. 12-Jun-3 Kunsthallen, Copenhagen #270/R est:100000 (D.KR 76000)
Works on paper
£477 $796 €692 Round church and sketches (27x39cm-11x15in) Indian ink W/C gouache prov. 17-Jun-3 Rasmussen, Copenhagen #189/R (D.KR 5000)

HOSTEIN, Edouard (1804-1889) French
£700 $1106 €1050 Way home from market (49x74cm-19x29in) s.d.1845. 14-Nov-2 Christie's, Kensington #103/R

HOTEL, Albert (attrib) (19th C) German
£2051 $3118 €3200 Procession in mountain landscape (73x110cm-29x43in) s.d.1885. 11-Jul-2 Hugo Ruef, Munich #701/R est:900

HOTERE, Ralph (1931-) New Zealander
£4514 $7042 €6771 Northern motorway (58x63cm-23x25in) s.d.1960 i.verso canvas on board. 8-Apr-3 Peter Webb, Auckland #92/R est:8000-12000 (NZ.D 13000)
£5634 $9296 €8169 Winter Solstice (25x18cm-10x7in) s.i.d.1991 metallic paint gold leaf. 1-Jul-3 Peter Webb, Auckland #54/R est:10000-15000 (NZ.D 16000)
£7903 $12328 €11855 Me Tangi Kapa Ko to mate 1 to marama (51x38cm-20x15in) s.i.d.1972 oil on paper. 17-Sep-2 Peter Webb, Auckland #84/R est:25000-40000 (NZ.D 26000)
£8681 $13542 €13022 Biko (196x27cm-77x11in) s.d.1988 dyed silk panel. 8-Apr-3 Peter Webb, Auckland #93/R est:12000-18000 (NZ.D 25000)
£8772 $13684 €13158 Still life of lemons on a table (64x80cm-25x31in) s.d.1957 board. 27-Mar-3 International Art Centre, Auckland #29/R est:30000-40000 (NZ.D 25000)
£13678 $21337 €20517 Black painting, red cruciform (90x60cm-35x24in) i. s.d.1969 brolite on board. 17-Sep-2 Peter Webb, Auckland #90/R est:45000-65000 (NZ.D 45000)
£14583 $22750 €21875 Song cycle; a wind goes (120x45cm-47x18in) i.verso s.i.d.1975 on stretcher. 8-Apr-3 Peter Webb, Auckland #43/R est:40000-60000 (NZ.D 42000)
£19293 $29904 €28940 Black painting No 1 (122x61cm-48x24in) s.d.verso brolite lacquer board. 4-Dec-2 Dunbar Sloane, Auckland #20/R est:80000-120000 (NZ.D 60000)
£36458 $56875 €54687 Miserers Nobis from the Requiem series (122x122cm-48x48in) s.i.d.1974 i.verso. 8-Apr-3 Peter Webb, Auckland #44/R est:60000-80000 (NZ.D 105000)

£53191 $82979 €79787 Black Union Jack (240x180cm-94x71in) s.i.d.1986 acrylic on canvas. 17-Sep-2 Peter Webb, Auckland #91/R est:100000-150000 (NZ.D 175000)
£57878 $89711 €86817 Aurora/Aramoana (245x68cm-96x27in) s.i.d.1980-83 i.verso lacquer corrugated iron wood nails. 4-Dec-2 Dunbar Sloane, Auckland #14/R est:150000-200000 (NZ.D 180000)
£74841 $117500 €112262 Towards Aramoana, Alumin Politik, 1982 (120x85cm-47x33in) mono. acrylic board sash window prov. 10-Dec-2 Peter Webb, Auckland #32/R est:150000-220000 (NZ.D 235000)
£96831 $159771 €140405 Black window (121x85cm-48x33in) s.i.d.1983 acrylic board steel roofing rivets each window. 1-Jul-3 Peter Webb, Auckland #27/R est:230000-280000 (NZ.D 275000)

Prints
£1911 $3000 €2867 Manhire's midnight windows at Carey's Bar (52x37cm-20x15in) s.i.d.1980 etching. 10-Dec-2 Peter Webb, Auckland #3/R est:2500-3500 (NZ.D 6000)
£2150 $3375 €3225 Towards Aramoana, black window (53x37cm-21x15in) s.i.d.1984. 10-Dec-2 Peter Webb, Auckland #10/R est:3000-5000 (NZ.D 6750)
£2280 $3556 €3420 Winter solstice (75x53cm-30x21in) s.i.d.1991 num.9/10 lithograph. 17-Sep-2 Peter Webb, Auckland #70/R est:3000-5000 (NZ.D 7500)
£2432 $3793 €3648 Winter solstice (75x53cm-30x21in) s.i.d.1991 lithograph. 17-Sep-2 Peter Webb, Auckland #69/R est:3000-5000 (NZ.D 8000)
£2473 $3982 €3710 God Bless America (65x45cm-26x18in) s.d.1991 lithograph. 7-May-3 Dunbar Sloane, Auckland #2/R est:2500-4500 (NZ.D 7000)
£2807 $4379 €4211 In the labyrinth, from pine (53x37cm-21x15in) s.d.1984 lithograph gold. 27-Mar-3 International Art Centre, Auckland #8/R est:4500-6500 (NZ.D 8000)
£2807 $4379 €4211 This is black Union Jack (53x38cm-21x15in) s.d.1988 num.25/28 lithograph. 27-Mar-3 International Art Centre, Auckland #69/R est:2500-3500 (NZ.D 8000)
£2817 $4648 €4085 Untitled (75x52cm-30x20in) s.d.1992 num.2/18 lithograph. 1-Jul-3 Peter Webb, Auckland #6/R est:6000-8000 (NZ.D 8000)
£2827 $4551 €4241 Matauri Bay (54x44cm-21x17in) s.d.88 19/30 lithograph. 7-May-3 Dunbar Sloane, Auckland #13/R est:3500-5500 (NZ.D 8000)
£2951 $4604 €4427 This is a black Union Jack (53x37cm-21x15in) s.i.d.1988 lithograph. 8-Apr-3 Peter Webb, Auckland #4/R est:4000-6000 (NZ.D 8500)
£4299 $6750 €6449 Untitled (75x52cm-30x20in) s.d.1992 lithograph gold pigment pastel. 10-Dec-2 Peter Webb, Auckland #9/R est:7000-9000 (NZ.D 13500)

Works on paper
£408 $636 €612 Drawing for port chalmers paintings (18x33cm-7x13in) s.i.d.1972 pencil dr. 5-Nov-2 Peter Webb, Auckland #43 est:400-600 (NZ.D 1300)
£1216 $1897 €1824 Figure study - the rehearsal (34x32cm-13x13in) s.d.1969 ink. 17-Sep-2 Peter Webb, Auckland #124/R est:3500-4500 (NZ.D 4000)
£2070 $3250 €3105 Woman no.69 (54x32cm-21x13in) s.i. ink dr. 10-Dec-2 Peter Webb, Auckland #85/R est:7000-9000 (NZ.D 6500)
£2727 $4200 €4091 Female nude (27x18cm-11x7in) s.d.1965 ink dr. 4-Sep-2 Dunbar Sloane, Wellington #56/R est:4500-6000 (NZ.D 9000)
£2951 $4604 €4427 Window in Spain (32x22cm-13x9in) s.i.d.78 W/C. 8-Apr-3 Peter Webb, Auckland #46/R est:8000-12000 (NZ.D 8500)
£3537 $5482 €5306 Working drawing for a stainless steel painting (46x61cm-18x24in) s.i.d.1989 mixed media. 4-Dec-2 Dunbar Sloane, Auckland #54/R est:15000-25000 (NZ.D 11000)
£4861 $7583 €7292 Drawing for black painting (42x41cm-17x16in) s.i.d.1970 mixed media prov. 8-Apr-3 Peter Webb, Auckland #62/R est:15000-20000 (NZ.D 14000)
£5949 $9220 €8924 February May and the birds of ice; the moon drowns in its voices of water (45x56cm-18x22in) s.i.d.1972 W/C. 4-Dec-2 Dunbar Sloane, Auckland #34/R est:15000-25000 (NZ.D 18500)
£6529 $10250 €9794 Song cycle (38x27cm-15x11in) s.i.d.1976 W/C. 10-Dec-2 Peter Webb, Auckland #37/R est:15000-20000 (NZ.D 20500)
£7746 $12782 €11232 Drawing for song cycle (43x21cm-17x8in) s.i.d.1976 W/C. 1-Jul-3 Peter Webb, Auckland #38/R est:22000-26000 (NZ.D 22000)
£7774 $12516 €11661 Untitled (37x28cm-15x11in) s.d.93 mixed media. 7-May-3 Dunbar Sloane, Auckland #21/R est:20000-30000 (NZ.D 22000)

HOTTEBERT, Leon (19th C) Belgian?
£641 $1006 €1000 Portrait de femme a la tulipe (47x38cm-19x15in) s. 15-Dec-2 Mercier & Cie, Lille #385/R

HOTTENROTH, Woldemar (1802-1894) German
Works on paper
£472 $731 €750 Standing male nude (40x23cm-16x9in) pencil white chk. 4-Oct-2 Paul Kieffer, Pforzhiem #9356/R

HOTTENROTH, Woldemar (attrib) (1802-1894) German
£543 $842 €815 Landscape near Naples (59x93cm-23x37in) 9-Dec-2 Philippe Schuler, Zurich #3911/R (S.FR 1250)

HOTTINGER, William A (1890-?) American
£385 $600 €578 Seated woman looking up at the sky (48x30cm-19x12in) s. board. 18-Sep-2 Alderfer's, Hatfield #292

HOTTOT, Louis (1834-1905) French
Sculpture
£1600 $2464 €2400 Nubian woman holding a tray (86cm-34in) s. painted spelter. 28-Oct-2 Sotheby's, Olympia #10/R est:1500-2500
£3000 $4620 €4500 Figural clock group with Arab woman (108cm-43in) s. spelter. 28-Oct-2 Sotheby's, Olympia #26/R est:3000-5000

HOTTOT, Louis (after) (1834-1905) French
Sculpture
£5128 $8051 €8000 Arabe arme. Femme arabe aux bijoux (63x40cm-25x16in) s. plaque pair. 16-Dec-2 Gros & Delettrez, Paris #141/R est:3800-4500

HOTZENDORFF, Theodor von (1898-1974) German
£422 $629 €650 Forest interior (50x30cm-20x12in) mono. board study verso. 27-Jun-2 Neumeister, Munich #2749/R
£566 $883 €900 Spring evening in Chiemgau (52x86cm-20x34in) mono. i. verso panel. 21-Sep-2 Bolland & Marotz, Bremen #708/R
£1081 $1686 €1600 Grassau (54x110cm-21x43in) mono. 26-Mar-3 Hugo Ruef, Munich #134/R est:1600

HOU, Axel (1860-1948) Danish
£2627 $4203 €3941 Afternoon tea in the garden room (50x58cm-20x23in) s.d.1895. 13-Jan-3 Rasmussen, Vejle #10/R est:30000 (D.KR 30000)

HOUBEN, Charles (1871-1931) Belgian
£266 $415 €420 Travaux au potager (29x45cm-11x18in) s. panel. 16-Sep-2 Horta, Bruxelles #278
£336 $540 €500 Ecluse sur le Vesdre (48x73cm-19x29in) s. 18-Feb-3 Galerie Moderne, Brussels #280
£426 $711 €600 Paysage a la riviere (49x74cm-19x29in) s. 18-Jun-3 Hotel des Ventes Mosan, Brussels #254

HOUBEN, H (1858-1931) Belgian
£1064 $1723 €1500 Ruelle a Geel avec un berger de moutons (53x73cm-21x29in) 26-May-3 Amberes, Antwerp #45/R
£1384 $2158 €2200 Ramasseuse de bois mort dans un chemin forestier (58x74cm-23x29in) 14-Oct-2 Amberes, Antwerp #164
£1887 $2943 €3000 La rcolte (38x58cm-15x23in) 14-Oct-2 Amberes, Antwerp #163

HOUBEN, Henri (1858-1931) Belgian
£596 $972 €900 Zelandaise devant une ferme et une barque de peche (32x40cm-13x16in) 17-Feb-3 Amberes, Antwerp #210
£700 $1127 €1050 Shepherd with his flock of sheep approaching the town (54x63cm-21x25in) s. 14-Jan-3 Bonhams, Ipswich #378
£1560 $2528 €2200 Vaches dans la prairie (75x111cm-30x44in) 26-May-3 Amberes, Antwerp #44/R
£2319 $3803 €3200 L'entree de la femme (55x80cm-22x31in) s. 27-May-3 Campo, Vlaamse Kaai #110/R est:2000-2500
£2899 $4754 €4000 Rue de village a Zoersel a la tombee de la nuit (80x100cm-31x39in) s. 27-May-3 Campo, Vlaamse Kaai #111/R est:3000-3500
£3378 $5270 €5000 Personnages sur le quai dans un petit port hollandais (98x149cm-39x59in) s. 25-Mar-3 Campo & Campo, Antwerp #90/R est:6000-8000
£4054 $6324 €6000 Fermiere et animaux dans un paysage (96x137cm-38x54in) s. 25-Mar-3 Campo & Campo, Antwerp #91/R est:7000-8000
£6552 $10483 €9500 At the farmyard (70x101cm-28x40in) s. 15-Mar-3 De Vuyst, Lokeren #518/R est:9500-11000
£8333 $12917 €13000 Market with fish sellers at Walcheren (83x130cm-33x51in) s.i. 7-Dec-2 De Vuyst, Lokeren #440/R est:13000-15000

HOUBRAKEN, Arnold (attrib) (1660-1719) Dutch
£24000 $40080 €34800 Eliezer and Rebecca at the well. Jacob and Rachel at the well (53x64cm-21x25in) pair. 8-Jul-3 Sotheby's, Olympia #439/R est:8000-12000
Works on paper
£975 $1521 €1550 Men, women and children visiting baby Jesus (23x20cm-9x8in) pen wash. 11-Oct-2 Winterberg, Heidelberg #255/R

HOUBRAKEN, Niccolino van (attrib) (1660-1723) Italian
£4516 $7135 €7000 Flowers in landscape (93x75cm-37x30in) 18-Dec-2 Piasa, Paris #21 est:3000

HOUBRON, Frederic Anatole (1851-1908) French
Works on paper
£1439 $2302 €2000 Vue de la Seine a Conflans-Sainte-Honorine (19x33cm-7x13in) s.d.1900 mixed media panel. 13-May-3 Palais de Beaux Arts, Brussels #191/R est:2000-3000

HOUDON, Jean Antoine (1741-1828) French
Sculpture
£962 $1490 €1500 Deesse grecque (84cm-33in) s. bronze. 3-Dec-2 Campo & Campo, Antwerp #135/R est:1500-2000
£10897 $16891 €17000 Portrait de l'Imperatrice Josephine (56x25x24cm-22x10x9in) plaster exec.1806 prov.lit. 9-Dec-2 Rabourdin & Choppin de Janvry, Paris #97/R est:30000
£11538 $17885 €18000 Portrait de Jean Pierre Charles Le Noir (78x52x33cm-31x20x13in) plaster exec.1784 lit. 9-Dec-2 Rabourdin & Choppin de Janvry, Paris #59/R est:45000
£13462 $21269 €21000 Marquis de Mejanes (86cm-34in) s. pat plaster exec.c.1786 lit. 15-Nov-2 Beaussant & Lefèvre, Paris #134/R est:14000-17000
£13462 $20865 €21000 Portrait de madame Quesnay (68x28x28cm-27x11x11in) s. plaster pat terracotta lit. 9-Dec-2 Rabourdin & Choppin de Janvry, Paris #62/R est:22000
£14103 $21859 €22000 Portrait d'Honore-Gabriel Riquetti (88x65x39cm-35x26x15in) s.d.1791 painted terracotta prov. 9-Dec-2 Rabourdin & Choppin de Janvry, Paris #77/R est:45000
£16026 $24840 €25000 Portrait presume de la Duchesse de Chevreuse (76x48x24cm-30x19x9in) st.sig. plaster pat terracotta prov.exhib.lit. 9-Dec-2 Rabourdin & Choppin de Janvry, Paris #65/R est:45000
£22436 $34776 €35000 Portrait de Louise Brongniart (52x23x20cm-20x9x8in) plaster exec.1779 lit. 9-Dec-2 Rabourdin & Choppin de Janvry, Paris #70/R est:30000
£23077 $35769 €36000 Voltaire assis (37x14x20cm-15x6x8in) s.d.1778 plaster pat terracotta lit. 9-Dec-2 Rabourdin & Choppin de Janvry, Paris #106/R est:18000
£28846 $44712 €45000 Portrait de la Princesse de Salm (61x38x25cm-24x15x10in) s. white marble prov.lit. 9-Dec-2 Rabourdin & Choppin de Janvry, Paris #95/R
£41667 $64583 €65000 Portrait d'Anne-Ange Houdon (39x23x13cm-15x9x5in) pat plaster exec.1791 lit. 9-Dec-2 Rabourdin & Choppin de Janvry, Paris #68/R est:30000
£44872 $69551 €70000 Portrait de Rousseau a l'antique (58x26x24cm-23x10x9in) s.d.1780 pat bronze exhib.lit. 9-Dec-2 Rabourdin & Choppin de Janvry, Paris #105/R
£51282 $79487 €80000 Portrait de l'Abbe Jean Jacques Barthelemy (62x29x26cm-24x11x10in) s. pat. plaster prov.lit. 9-Dec-2 Rabourdin & Choppin de Janvry, Paris #64/R est:22000
£96154 $149038 €150000 Portrait de Voltaire a la francaise (60x42x32cm-24x17x13in) s.d.1778 terracotta exhib.lit. 9-Dec-2 Rabourdin & Choppin de Janvry, Paris #104/R est:45000
£115385 $178846 €180000 Portrait de Marie-Joseph Chenier (56x28x23cm-22x11x9in) terracotta exhib.lit. 9-Dec-2 Rabourdin & Choppin de Janvry, Paris #76/R est:60000
£403846 $634039 €630000 Portrait du Marquis de Bire (80cm-31in) s.d.1785 white marble prov. 13-Dec-2 Rossini, Paris #265/R est:60000-75000

HOUDON, Jean Antoine (after) (1741-1828) French
Sculpture
£5128 $7949 €8000 Volatire assis (35x18x27cm-14x7x11in) terracotta prov.exhib.lit. 9-Dec-2 Rabourdin & Choppin de Janvry, Paris #107/R
£12821 $19872 €20000 Portrait de Jean Antoine Nicolas Caritat (66x44x24cm-26x17x9in) terracotta exhib.lit. 9-Dec-2 Rabourdin & Choppin de Janvry, Paris #61/R est:15000

HOUDON, Jean Antoine (attrib) (1741-1828) French
Sculpture
£6757 $10541 €10136 Young woman with flowers and bow in her hair (82cm-32in) i.d.1779 white marble prov. 23-Sep-2 Rasmussen, Vejle #330/R est:50000 (D.KR 80000)
£16667 $25833 €26000 Portrait du Marquis Emmanuel de Pastoret (72x55x35cm-28x22x14in) plaster pat terracotta exhib.lit. 9-Dec-2 Rabourdin & Choppin de Janvry, Paris #75/R est:45000
£35256 $54647 €55000 King Charles (38x29x14cm-15x11x6in) white marble prov.lit. 9-Dec-2 Rabourdin & Choppin de Janvry, Paris #66/R est:45000

HOUDON, Jean Antoine (studio) (1741-1828) French
Sculpture
£6731 $10433 €10500 Portrait de Christoph Willibald von Gluck (69x37x30cm-27x15x12in) st.sig. plaster pat. terracotta lit. 9-Dec-2 Rabourdin & Choppin de Janvry, Paris #63/R
£14744 $22853 €23000 Portrait de Caludine Houdon (39x26x16cm-15x10x6in) plaster exhib.lit. 9-Dec-2 Rabourdin & Choppin de Janvry, Paris #69/R est:20000
£16000 $25120 €24000 Figure of winter (151cm-59in) plaster lit. 10-Dec-2 Sotheby's, London #139/R est:18000-25000
£17949 $27821 €28000 Portrait de madame Houdon (58x35x21cm-23x14x8in) plaster exec.1786 lit. 9-Dec-2 Rabourdin & Choppin de Janvry, Paris #67/R est:30000
£17949 $27821 €28000 Portrait de la Princesse de Salm (60x35x29cm-24x14x11in) s. plaster prov.exhib.lit. 9-Dec-2 Rabourdin & Choppin de Janvry, Paris #96/R est:30000
£46296 $75000 €69444 Benjamin Franklin (57cm-22in) s.d.1778 plaster prov.lit. 23-Jan-3 Sotheby's, New York #237/R est:40000

HOUEL, Jean (?) French
£6294 $10510 €9000 Scene paysanne (46x64cm-18x25in) i.d.1789 verso. 25-Jun-3 Artcurial Briest, Paris #491/R est:8000-12000
Works on paper
£26950 $45007 €38000 Les crateres de l'Etna (25x35cm-10x14in) gouache. 23-Jun-3 Beaussant & Lefèvre, Paris #86/R est:3000-4000

HOUGAARD, Henning (1922-1995) Swedish
£398 $649 €597 Winter landscape with fox (45x60cm-18x24in) s/. 17-Feb-3 Blomqvist, Lysaker #1079/R (N.KR 4500)
£1309 $2055 €1964 Crows (54x65cm-21x26in) s. 25-Nov-2 Blomqvist, Lysaker #1129/R est:12000-15000 (N.KR 15000)

HOUGH, William (fl.1857-1894) British
£6875 $11000 €10313 Still life with blackberries and ivy on a mossy bank (38x48cm-15x19in) s. 14-May-3 Butterfields, San Francisco #1163/R est:3000-5000
Works on paper
£1100 $1793 €1595 Still life of a plum. Still life of an apple (14x12cm-6x5in) s. W/C gouache pair. 16-Jul-3 Sotheby's, Olympia #54/R est:1000-1500

HOUGHTON, Arthur Boyd (1836-1875) British
£4000 $6440 €6000 Brother and sister of the artist playing chess (26x30cm-10x12in) prov.lit. 20-Feb-3 Christie's, London #261/R

HOUGHTON, J B (?) British?
Works on paper
£458 $700 €687 Portrait of Garibaldi. W/C. 26-Jul-2 Douglas, South Deerfield #1

HOUILON, Maurice (20th C) French
£296 $476 €420 La fete a Bury (38x46cm-15x18in) s.d.sept.1925. 11-May-3 Thierry & Lannon, Brest #368

HOURTAL, Henri (19/20th C) French
£449 $704 €700 A la porte de la ville (33x40cm-13x16in) s. panel. 16-Dec-2 Gros & Delettrez, Paris #364
£1361 $2163 €2000 Rue Quinquempois a Paris (53x45cm-21x18in) s. 21-Mar-3 Rieunier, Bailly-Pommery, Mathias, Paris #113/R

HOUS, B de (19/20th C) ?
£1200 $1896 €1800 Playing with mother (51x61cm-20x24in) s. 14-Nov-2 Christie's, Kensington #270/R est:600-800

HOUSER, Allan C (1915-1994) American
Sculpture
£2083 $3250 €3125 Jicarilla Apaches (23x13x5cm-9x5x2in) i. num.8/40 bronze prov.lit. 9-Nov-2 Santa Fe Art, Santa Fe #251/R est:4000-6000
£4063 $6500 €6095 Intimate conversations (25cm-10in) i. num.10/20 bronze. 13-Jan-3 Christie's, Rockefeller NY #56/R est:12000
£7500 $12000 €11250 Pensive maiden (36cm-14in) s. num.16/20 bronze. 13-Jan-3 Christie's, Rockefeller NY #55/R est:20000

HOUSSARD, Charles Claude (1884-1958) Belgian
£347 $559 €521 Marine- Mer du Nord (65x80cm-26x31in) s. i.d.1927 verso. 7-May-3 Dobiaschofsky, Bern #3329 (S.FR 750)

HOUSSAYE, Josephine (1840-?) French
£6000 $9420 €9000 Tapestry weavers (73x69cm-29x27in) s. 21-Nov-2 Christie's, Kensington #165/R est:6000-8000

HOUSSER, Yvonne McKague (1898-1996) Canadian
£378 $619 €567 Dazzling sun (50x31cm-20x12in) board painted c.1946 prov. 3-Jun-3 Joyner, Toronto #394/R (C.D 850)
£667 $1093 €1001 Haliburton woods (40x50cm-16x20in) s.d.1964 board. 3-Jun-3 Joyner, Toronto #351/R est:1000-1500 (C.D 1500)
£667 $1093 €967 Falling leaves (40x49cm-16x19in) s.i. paper on board. 9-Jun-3 Hodgins, Calgary #387/R est:1800-2200 (C.D 1500)
£2130 $3408 €3195 Moonlight on the little lake (30x41cm-12x16in) s. s.i.verso prov.exhib. 15-May-3 Heffel, Vancouver #217/R est:2500-3500 (C.D 4750)

Works on paper
£200 $328 €300 Red tile rooftops (22x27cm-9x11in) s. W/C ink. 3-Jun-3 Joyner, Toronto #478 (C.D 450)

HOUSTON, A (19th C) ?

Works on paper
£380 $627 €551 Figures fishing in a highland stream (25x43cm-10x17in) s. indis d. W/C. 3-Jul-3 Duke & Son, Dorchester #122/R

HOUSTON, Deryk (20th C) Canadian?
£378 $620 €548 Warm grass (76x76cm-30x30in) acrylic. 1-Jun-3 Levis, Calgary #55 (C.D 850)

HOUSTON, George (1869-1947) British
£390 $612 €585 By the loch (26x36cm-10x14in) 17-Apr-3 Bonhams, Edinburgh #332
£520 $811 €780 River landscape, Ayrshire (41x51cm-16x20in) s. 13-Sep-2 Lyon & Turnbull, Edinburgh #39/R
£800 $1328 €1160 Cattle in an open meadow (30x45cm-12x18in) s.d.94 pair. 13-Jun-3 Lyon & Turnbull, Edinburgh #14
£1400 $2296 €2100 Kilchurn Castle, Argyll (46x61cm-18x24in) s. 7-Jun-3 Shapes, Edinburgh #370/R est:800-1200
£1500 $2490 €2175 Waterfall in woodland (61x91cm-24x36in) s. 12-Jun-3 Gorringes, Lewes #1746 est:800-1200
£1600 $2448 €2400 An Ayrshire glen (45x60cm-18x24in) s. 22-Aug-2 Bonhams, Edinburgh #1175/R est:1800-2000
£1800 $2754 €2700 Banks o'Doon, Patna, Ayrshire (25x35cm-10x14in) s.i panel. 22-Aug-2 Bonhams, Edinburgh #949/R est:1200-1800
£1800 $2808 €2700 Shores of Loch Fyne (45x60cm-18x24in) s. 10-Apr-3 Bonhams, Edinburgh #167 est:2000-3000
£2000 $3040 €3000 View of a waterfall in a glen (46x61cm-18x24in) s.d.98. 28-Aug-2 Sotheby's, London #990/R est:1500-2000
£3200 $4992 €4800 Isle of Tiree (46x61cm-18x24in) s. 14-Apr-3 Sotheby's, London #128/R est:2000-3000
£4600 $6992 €6900 Loch Tay (46x61cm-18x24in) s. prov. 28-Aug-2 Sotheby's, London #994/R est:4000-6000
£15000 $23250 €22500 Returning from school (102x127cm-40x50in) s. 31-Oct-2 Christie's, London #98/R est:15000-20000

Works on paper
£750 $1170 €1125 Tamagawa, Japan (33x48cm-13x19in) s.i.d.1911 W/C gouache. 17-Oct-2 Bonhams, Edinburgh #163
£1000 $1530 €1500 Front and pier, Inveraray (35x50cm-14x20in) s. W/C over pencil. 22-Aug-2 Bonhams, Edinburgh #1084/R est:1000-1500
£1100 $1716 €1650 Rainy day, Inveraray (44x58cm-17x23in) s. W/C gouache over pencil. 17-Oct-2 Bonhams, Edinburgh #246 est:1000-1500

HOUSTON, Ian (1934-) British
£260 $403 €390 Farm at Angeja, northern Portugal (25x35cm-10x14in) s. board. 30-Sep-2 Bonhams, Ipswich #380
£280 $462 €406 Farm at paddock wood (22x28cm-9x11in) s. board. 1-Jul-3 Bonhams, Norwich #294
£350 $571 €525 Queen Galadrid passing Aldeburgh (23x33cm-9x13in) s. 14-Feb-3 Keys, Aylsham #548
£390 $608 €585 Last light, Peniche, Portugal (18x25cm-7x10in) s. 18-Oct-2 Keys, Aylsham #759/R
£450 $707 €675 Farm loke (23x33cm-9x13in) s. 13-Dec-2 Keys, Aylsham #728/R
£500 $770 €750 Paddock wood, Kent. Farm lane (23x28cm-9x11in) s. i.verso board two. 24-Oct-2 Christie's, Kensington #65/R
£550 $864 €825 Overy staithe (40x61cm-16x24in) s. board. 15-Apr-3 Bonhams, Knightsbridge #14/R
£600 $966 €900 Spanish fishing boats, Cullera (25x35cm-10x14in) s. board. 18-Feb-3 Bonhams, Knightsbridge #80/R
£650 $1073 €943 February sunlight on Halvergate Marshes (55x86cm-22x34in) s. board. 1-Jul-3 Bonhams, Norwich #284/R
£880 $1452 €1276 Farmland near Reedham, Norfolk (50x76cm-20x30in) s. board. 1-Jul-3 Bonhams, Norwich #285/R

Works on paper
£280 $456 €420 Pchniche Harbour (28x36cm-11x14in) s. W/C. 14-Feb-3 Keys, Aylsham #551/R

HOUSTON, John (1930-) British
£280 $456 €420 Gold-fish (60x91cm-24x36in) 14-Feb-3 Lyon & Turnbull, Edinburgh #150
£320 $522 €480 Sunset (26x26cm-10x10in) 14-Feb-3 Lyon & Turnbull, Edinburgh #45
£400 $648 €600 Cornfields, evening (8x10cm-3x4in) s.d.74 board exhib. 23-May-3 Lyon & Turnbull, Edinburgh #38
£580 $951 €870 Sunset with broken clouds (39x20cm-15x8in) s. 7-Jun-3 Shapes, Edinburgh #359/R
£600 $936 €900 Moon over the bay (66x71cm-26x28in) s. s.i.verso. 10-Apr-3 Tennants, Leyburn #1136/R
£680 $1115 €1020 Sunset with dark clouds (45x60cm-18x24in) s. 7-Jun-3 Shapes, Edinburgh #358/R
£850 $1411 €1233 Grurnard Bay, moonlight (20x20cm-8x8in) s. board exhib. 10-Jun-3 David Lay, Penzance #96/R
£980 $1529 €1470 Sunset (23x29cm-9x11in) s. 10-Apr-3 Bonhams, Edinburgh #57
£1350 $2106 €2025 Bathers at Trouville (35x35cm-14x14in) s. 10-Apr-3 Bonhams, Edinburgh #34/R est:800-1200
£1800 $3006 €2610 Yellow roses (35x25cm-14x10in) s. prov. 17-Jun-3 Anderson & Garland, Newcastle #389 est:1500-2500
£1900 $2945 €2850 Entrance to the shrine, Kyoto (29x29cm-11x11in) s.i.stretcher. 24-Sep-2 Anderson & Garland, Newcastle #406/R est:1500-2500
£2000 $3120 €3000 Low tide, Luskentyre, Harris (86x112cm-34x44in) s. 14-Apr-3 Sotheby's, London #174/R est:2000-3000
£2000 $3240 €3000 Flowers in a yellow vase (202x68cm-80x27in) s. 23-May-3 Lyon & Turnbull, Edinburgh #11/R est:2000-3000
£2100 $3255 €3150 Bass rock still life (75x75cm-30x30in) 5-Dec-2 Bonhams, Edinburgh #88/R est:1000-1500
£2400 $3888 €3600 Sunset over Dunnet Bay (111x100cm-44x39in) s.d.1972-73. 23-May-3 Lyon & Turnbull, Edinburgh #32/R est:2000-2500
£3000 $4560 €4500 Morning sea, Dieppe (127x152cm-50x60in) s.d.1978-80 prov.exhib. 28-Aug-2 Sotheby's, London #1032/R est:2000-3000
£3500 $5425 €5250 Blue still life (63x76cm-25x30in) s. exhib. 31-Oct-2 Christie's, London #186/R est:3000-5000
£3800 $6042 €5700 Flowrs on yellow (56x76cm-22x30in) s.d.1963 prov. 6-Mar-3 Christie's, Kensington #234/R est:2000-3000

Works on paper
£350 $557 €525 Loguivy sur mer, Brittany (18x28cm-7x11in) s. pencil W/C. 6-Mar-3 Christie's, Kensington #233/R
£400 $624 €600 By the window (21x34cm-8x13in) s. W/C. 17-Oct-2 Bonhams, Edinburgh #94
£680 $1040 €1020 Cornfields and sunset (17x24cm-7x9in) s.i.d.73 verso W/C gouache. 22-Aug-2 Bonhams, Edinburgh #1172

HOUSTON, John Adam (1812-1884) British
£800 $1248 €1200 Death of Count Warwick (66x50cm-26x20in) s.d.1873. 17-Sep-2 Sotheby's, Olympia #9/R
£3000 $4590 €4500 Skylark (60x90cm-24x35in) init.d.1861 exhib. 22-Aug-2 Bonhams, Edinburgh #951/R est:3000-5000

HOUSTON, John Adam (attrib) (1812-1884) British
£1040 $1674 €1508 Evening thoughts (26x20cm-10x8in) s.d. board. 12-May-3 Joel, Victoria #402 est:1500-2000 (A.D 2600)

HOUSTON, Robert (1891-1942) British
£340 $547 €510 Loch scene, summer (40x75cm-16x30in) s. 20-Feb-3 Bonhams, Edinburgh #335

HOUTHUESEN, Albert (1903-1979) British
£400 $636 €600 Swift river between rock walls (24x29cm-9x11in) s.i.d.October 72 board. 26-Feb-3 Sotheby's, Olympia #127/R
£450 $715 €675 Cloud over rocks (35x45cm-14x18in) s. i.d.1969 verso board. 26-Feb-3 Sotheby's, Olympia #128/R
£550 $858 €825 Sentinel Rock (64x76cm-25x30in) s.d.1975 acrylic board. 15-Oct-2 Gorringes, Lewes #2185/R
£550 $875 €825 Moonlit rocky coastline (19x24cm-7x9in) s. acrylic board. 29-Apr-3 Rowley Fine Art, Newmarket #406/R
£600 $954 €900 Seascape at sunset (24x34cm-9x13in) s. acrylic board. 29-Apr-3 Rowley Fine Art, Newmarket #407
£620 $961 €930 Spring squall (17x25cm-7x10in) s. i.verso board exhib. 1-Oct-2 Bonhams, Leeds #290
£650 $1066 €975 October coast (35x45cm-14x18in) s. i.d.1969 verso board. 3-Jun-3 Sotheby's, Olympia #228/R
£750 $1193 €1125 Castanets (24x34cm-9x13in) s. board. 26-Feb-3 Sotheby's, Olympia #133/R
£800 $1312 €1200 Sea at Prestatyn (21x28cm-8x11in) s. i.verso board. 3-Jun-3 Sotheby's, Olympia #230/R
£800 $1312 €1200 Moonlight (64x76cm-25x30in) i.d.April 1959 verso. 3-Jun-3 Sotheby's, Olympia #231/R
£1300 $2067 €1950 Tree in a snowy winter landscape (21x28cm-8x11in) s. acrylic board. 29-Apr-3 Rowley Fine Art, Newmarket #405/R est:500-700
£2600 $4134 €3900 Supper at Emmaus (76x106cm-30x42in) s.d.1927 verso canvas on board. 26-Feb-3 Sotheby's, Olympia #123/R est:600-800

£11000 $17490 €16500 Wreck of the Early Hope (95x128cm-37x50in) s. board. 26-Feb-3 Sotheby's, Olympia #136/R est:2000-3000
Works on paper
£360 $572 €540 Last will and Testament (45x59cm-18x23in) s. pastel prov. 26-Feb-3 Sotheby's, Olympia #124/R

HOUWAERT, Louis (1873-?) Belgian
£380 $592 €600 Femme dans un interieur (100x75cm-39x30in) s.d.1901. 15-Oct-2 Vanderkindere, Brussels #54

HOUYOUX, Léon (1856-?) Belgian
£261 $421 €400 La maison du Rouge-Cloitre en ete (50x65cm-20x26in) s.d.1935 panel. 20-Jan-3 Horta, Bruxelles #307
£283 $436 €450 Vue du lac et des collines a Roquebrune (30x40cm-12x16in) s. panel. 22-Oct-2 Campo & Campo, Antwerp #511
£305 $497 €460 Dimanche sur l'etang (38x55cm-15x22in) s. 17-Feb-3 Horta, Bruxelles #325

HOUZE, Florentin (1809-1905) Belgian
£282 $454 €400 Visiting the new mother (52x59cm-20x23in) panel. 12-May-3 Bernaerts, Antwerp #35
£408 $649 €600 La mort de Charles-Quint (28x35cm-11x14in) s. 18-Mar-3 Vanderkindere, Brussels #6

HOVE, Bartholomeus Johannes van (1790-1880) Dutch
£5479 $8603 €8000 View of Dutch town (42x33cm-17x13in) s. panel. 15-Apr-3 Sotheby's, Amsterdam #6/R est:6000-8000
£6164 $9678 €9000 View of a Dutch town in summer (34x48cm-13x19in) s.d.1858 panel prov. 15-Apr-3 Sotheby's, Amsterdam #155/R est:10000-15000
£6452 $10194 €9678 Under the oaken crown (53x42cm-21x17in) s.d.1833 panel. 18-Nov-2 Waddingtons, Toronto #203/R est:10000-15000 (C.D 16000)

HOVE, Hubertus van (1814-1865) Dutch
£5414 $8446 €8500 La genereuse servante (60x47cm-24x19in) s.d.1849 panel. 11-Nov-2 Horta, Bruxelles #226/R est:5000-7500

HOVE, Johannes Hubertus van (1827-1881) Dutch
£7547 $11698 €12000 The letter (68x56cm-27x22in) s. panel prov. 2-Oct-2 Dorotheum, Vienna #172/R est:8000-10000

HOVE, L van (?) ?
£629 $981 €1000 Dutch harbour (69x105cm-27x41in) s. i. verso. 9-Oct-2 Michael Zeller, Lindau #736/R
£1026 $1610 €1600 Village portuaire (66x103cm-26x41in) s. 19-Nov-2 Galerie Moderne, Brussels #301 est:1000-1500

HOVENDEN, Thomas (1840-1895) American/Irish
£21875 $35000 €32813 Wayside chat (83x62cm-33x24in) s.i.d.1875. 14-May-3 Butterfields, San Francisco #1150/R est:8000-120000
£24193 $37500 €36290 Special correspondent (36x51cm-14x20in) mono. prov. 4-Dec-2 Sotheby's, New York #126/R est:25000-35000

HOW, Beatrice (1867-1932) British
£2500 $3900 €3750 Femme devant la cheminee (43x36cm-17x14in) exhib. 7-Nov-2 Christie's, Kensington #231/R est:2000-3000
Works on paper
£500 $780 €750 Mere et enfant au bol bleu (21x16cm-8x6in) init. pastel. 13-Sep-2 Lyon & Turnbull, Edinburgh #28/R
£500 $825 €725 Enfant a la boule jaune (29x31cm-11x12in) s. pastel exhib. 3-Jul-3 Christie's, Kensington #251/R

HOWARD, Cecil de Blaquiere (1888-1956) American
Sculpture
£16049 $26000 €24074 Heavyweight boxer (76cm-30in) i. brown pat. bronze on green marble base lit. 22-May-3 Christie's, Rockefeller NY #66/R est:15000-25000

HOWARD, Edith Lucile (1885-1960) American
£313 $500 €470 Col d'Aspne'Pyrenees (28x36cm-11x14in) s. canvasboard. 18-May-3 Jeffery Burchard, Florida #9/R

HOWARD, Freda (20th C) British
£260 $421 €390 Flower seller St. Ives, Cornwall (48x58cm-19x23in) s.d.1957 board. 23-May-3 Honiton Galleries, Honiton #712

HOWARD, George James (1843-1911) British
£480 $749 €720 Bar Jadh Ranje, Najsick, Central India (20x36cm-8x14in) i.verso panel prov. 17-Sep-2 Sotheby's, Olympia #166/R
Works on paper
£800 $1256 €1200 Study of a reclining figure (93x37cm-37x15in) pencil red chk htd white prov. 21-Nov-2 Christie's, London #81/R

HOWARD, Henry (1769-1847) British
£2744 $4500 €4116 Birth of Venus (33x40cm-13x16in) i.verso. 29-May-3 Sotheby's, New York #16/R est:6000-8000

HOWARD, Hugh Huntington (1860-1927) American
£250 $410 €363 Rocky coast (74x99cm-29x39in) s. painted 1927. 30-May-3 Aspire, Cleveland #36/R

HOWARD, Humbert (1905-1990) American
£802 $1300 €1203 Still life with oranges (64x76cm-25x30in) s.d.70 board. 24-Jan-3 Freeman, Philadelphia #103/R est:1500-2500
£926 $1500 €1389 Seated figure (33x41cm-13x16in) s.d.69 board. 24-Jan-3 Freeman, Philadelphia #161/R est:400-600
£1667 $2600 €2501 Niform no.4 (81x53cm-32x21in) s.d.71 board exhib. 20-Sep-2 Freeman, Philadelphia #134/R est:300-500

HOWARD, John Langley (1902-) American
£1146 $1800 €1719 Storm at sea (41x36cm-16x14in) s. prov. 19-Nov-2 Butterfields, San Francisco #8339/R est:3000-5000

HOWARD, Ken (1932-) British
£380 $593 €570 Samford Spiney, evening (22x16cm-9x6in) s. canvasboard. 17-Sep-2 Bonhams, Knightsbridge #231/R
£480 $749 €720 Autumn landscape (14x21cm-6x8in) s. board. 17-Sep-2 Bonhams, Knightsbridge #233/R
£480 $778 €720 Low tide, Sennen (14x22cm-6x9in) s. canvas on board exhib. 20-May-3 Sotheby's, Olympia #147/R
£490 $764 €735 Richmond evening (14x22cm-6x9in) s. board prov. 25-Mar-3 Bonhams, Leeds #583
£550 $858 €825 Lorraine and the daffodils (25x20cm-10x8in) s. 17-Sep-2 Bonhams, Knightsbridge #41/R
£550 $869 €825 Mountain village (21x16cm-8x6in) s. canvas on board. 27-Nov-2 Sotheby's, Olympia #131/R
£600 $930 €900 Queen Elizabeth the second with tugs (25x35cm-10x14in) 4-Dec-2 Christie's, Kensington #538/R
£600 $936 €900 Venice (20x24cm-8x9in) s. board. 26-Mar-3 Hamptons Fine Art, Godalming #225
£600 $984 €900 Alpine village (25x20cm-10x8in) s. canvas on board. 3-Jun-3 Sotheby's, Olympia #185/R
£700 $1085 €1050 Copes in autumn (30x61cm-12x24in) 4-Dec-2 Christie's, Kensington #535/R
£700 $1092 €1050 Towards St. Paul's (51x61cm-20x24in) s. 27-Mar-3 Christie's, Kensington #503/R
£700 $1141 €1015 Harbour (25x30cm-10x12in) s. board. 15-Jul-3 Bonhams, Knightsbridge #5/R
£800 $1272 €1200 Street scene Rome (24x18cm-9x7in) s. board. 26-Feb-3 Sotheby's, Olympia #313/R
£800 $1312 €1200 Woman reclining (21x25cm-8x10in) s. canvas on board. 3-Jun-3 Sotheby's, Olympia #204/R
£850 $1343 €1275 Venice (20x26cm-8x10in) s. canvasboard. 27-Nov-2 Sotheby's, Olympia #113/R
£850 $1369 €1275 The Moors, Cornwall (13x22cm-5x9in) s. board sold with two others by the same hand. 14-Jan-3 Bonhams, Knightsbridge #65/R
£850 $1394 €1275 Venetian canal (30x25cm-12x10in) s. canvas on board. 3-Jun-3 Sotheby's, Olympia #182/R
£900 $1485 €1305 Facade, St. Paul's Cathedral, London (61x51cm-24x20in) s. 3-Jul-3 Christie's, Kensington #681/R
£950 $1501 €1425 Still life of potted plant (25x20cm-10x8in) s. canvas on card. 27-Nov-2 Sotheby's, Olympia #145/R est:600-800
£1000 $1580 €1500 Port scene (20x25cm-8x10in) s. canvas on board. 27-Nov-2 Sotheby's, Olympia #136/R est:1000-1500
£1000 $1570 €1500 Aberdeen shipyard (34x46cm-13x18in) s.i.d.50. 15-Apr-3 Bonhams, Knightsbridge #85/R est:600-800
£1000 $1650 €1450 Figures on a country lane (50x60cm-20x24in) 3-Jul-3 Christie's, Kensington #682/R est:700-1000
£1100 $1705 €1650 Looking towards Chelsea Wharf (71x90cm-28x35in) 4-Dec-2 Christie's, Kensington #531/R est:1200-1800
£1100 $1749 €1650 Thames at Battersea (22x28cm-9x11in) s. canvasboard. 26-Feb-3 Sotheby's, Olympia #328/R est:600-800
£1200 $1860 €1800 Figures in a square (51x63cm-20x25in) s. 4-Dec-2 Christie's, Kensington #534/R est:1000-1500
£1200 $1896 €1800 Near S Barnaby (25x15cm-10x6in) s. i.stretcher. 27-Nov-2 Sotheby's, Olympia #149/R est:1200-1800
£1200 $1884 €1800 Marazian beach in summer (14x60cm-6x24in) s. 10-Dec-2 Lane, Penzance #25/R est:1200-1500
£1200 $1872 €1800 Park Lane (25x30cm-10x12in) 27-Mar-3 Christie's, Kensington #522/R est:600-800
£1300 $2067 €1950 Summer flowers, mousehole (39x29cm-15x11in) s. canvasboard. 26-Feb-3 Sotheby's, Olympia #315/R est:800-1200
£1300 $2067 €1950 Newlyn (25x34cm-10x13in) s. canvasboard. 26-Feb-3 Sotheby's, Olympia #327/R est:700-900
£1300 $2067 €1950 St Magus, King and Martyr (122x30cm-48x12in) s. board. 29-Apr-3 Gorringes, Lewes #2241
£1400 $2170 €2100 Towards St. Paul's (61x51cm-24x20in) s.d.66. 4-Dec-2 Christie's, Kensington #533/R est:1500-2000
£1700 $2805 €2465 At the market stall (51x60cm-20x24in) s. 3-Jul-3 Christie's, Kensington #679/R est:700-1000

£1900 $3021 €2850 Celtic cross, winter (63x76cm-25x30in) s. 26-Feb-3 Sotheby's, Olympia #271/R est:1000-1500
£1900 $2964 €2850 View of the Thames from Richmond Hill (51x61cm-20x24in) s. 25-Mar-3 Bonhams, New Bond Street #65/R est:1500-2000
£2200 $3432 €3300 Southwall sidings. Church interior (46x182cm-18x72in) s. double-sided. 27-Mar-3 Christie's, Kensington #514/R est:1500-2500
£2600 $4056 €3900 Reclining female nude in the artist studio (46x36cm-18x14in) s. 25-Mar-3 Bonhams, New Bond Street #90/R est:2000-3000
£3100 $5177 €4495 Santa Magdalena de Pulpis, midday (50x60cm-20x24in) s. prov. 24-Jun-3 Bonhams, New Bond Street #79/R est:1500-2500
£3500 $5740 €5075 Church of St Edmund King and Martyr, Lombard Street at Clements Lane (183x91cm-72x36in) s.i. on the stretcher. 4-Jun-3 Sotheby's, London #59/R est:4000-6000
£3700 $5847 €5550 Sam Marco (26x35cm-10x14in) s. board. 27-Nov-2 Sotheby's, Olympia #118/R est:1200-1800
£4500 $7111 €6750 Studio (51x35cm-20x14in) s. 27-Nov-2 Sotheby's, Olympia #150/R est:2000-3000
£6000 $9840 €9000 Standing nude, the artist's studio (122x102cm-48x40in) s. 3-Jun-3 Sotheby's, Olympia #160/R est:6000-8000
£8000 $12480 €12000 St Martin-within-Ludgate, London (106x56cm-42x22in) s. i.stretcher board. 12-Sep-2 Sotheby's, Olympia #116/R est:4000-6000
£10000 $15800 €15000 Model in an artist's studio (122x92cm-48x36in) s. 27-Nov-2 Sotheby's, Olympia #228/R est:10000-15000

Works on paper

£350 $550 €525 Campo St. Srefano (20x25cm-8x10in) s. W/C prov. 10-Dec-2 Clarke Gammon, Guildford #1
£370 $618 €537 Moonrise - St. Quen's Bay (15x15cm-6x6in) s.i.d.25.7.80 gouache. 23-Jun-3 Bonhams, Bath #70
£420 $668 €630 Hampton Court (17x22cm-7x9in) s. pencil W/C. 26-Feb-3 Sotheby's, Olympia #210/R
£450 $702 €675 Morning light (13x18cm-5x7in) s. W/C. 15-Oct-2 Bonhams, Knightsbridge #116/R
£450 $738 €675 Newlyn harbour (17x23cm-7x9in) s.i. W/C. 3-Jun-3 Sotheby's, Olympia #175/R
£500 $805 €750 Leonard Slatkin in rehearsal at the Guildhall School of Music (20x29cm-8x11in) s.i.d.82 W/C. 14-Jan-3 Bonhams, Knightsbridge #16/R
£550 $891 €825 Marcia at Oriel (27x37cm-11x15in) s.d.85 W/C gouache exhib. 20-May-3 Sotheby's, Olympia #146/R
£600 $984 €900 Quay, Newlyn (24x18cm-9x7in) s.d.6 90 W/C gouache. 3-Jun-3 Sotheby's, Olympia #164/R
£800 $1272 €1200 Figures study (24x17cm-9x7in) s. pencil col chks. 26-Feb-3 Sotheby's, Olympia #316/R
£800 $1272 €1200 Nude (19x13cm-7x5in) s. W/C. 26-Feb-3 Sotheby's, Olympia #317/R
£800 $1312 €1200 Havana (23x20cm-9x8in) s. W/C. 3-Jun-3 Sotheby's, Olympia #165/R
£850 $1394 €1275 Seated nude (17x12cm-7x5in) s. W/C. 3-Jun-3 Sotheby's, Olympia #166/R
£1300 $2055 €1950 Venetian plaza (18x12cm-7x5in) s. W/C. 27-Nov-2 Sotheby's, Olympia #43/R est:500-700

HOWARD, Nellie C Hopps (1855-1956) American

£2108 $3500 €3057 Campfire at twilight with a buck at the edge of a clearing (38x76cm-15x30in) s.indis.d. prov. 11-Jun-3 Butterfields, San Francisco #4164/R est:4000-6000

HOWARD, Newton (1912-1984) American

£375 $600 €544 Belize lighthouse (33x43cm-13x17in) s.d.1970 board. 17-May-3 New Orleans Auction, New Orleans #950/R
£375 $600 €544 Belize village (33x43cm-13x17in) s.d.1970 board. 17-May-3 New Orleans Auction, New Orleans #951

HOWARD, Squire (fl.1882-1895) British

£650 $1086 €943 Harvesting scene with horse and cart (404x33cm-159x13in) s.d.1898. 18-Jun-3 Andrew Hartley, Ilkley #1113

HOWARD, William (17th C) British

£703 $1110 €1055 Mill on the canal (76x127cm-30x50in) 1-Dec-2 Levis, Calgary #225/R (C.D 1750)
£1000 $1620 €1500 Unloading the catch on the jetty at Whitby (61x91cm-24x36in) s. 21-May-3 Christie's, Kensington #684/R est:1200-1800
£1500 $2310 €2250 Figures in a Dutch town (76x127cm-30x50in) s. 5-Sep-2 Christie's, Kensington #261/R est:1000-1500

HOWDELL, Thomas (after) (18th C) American

Prints

£5280 $8500 €7920 South east view, New York City, America (47x65cm-19x26in) engraving exec.c.1763. 18-Jan-3 Sotheby's, New York #869/R est:3000-5000
£5901 $9500 €8852 South west view of New York City, America (47x65cm-19x26in) engraving exec.c.176. 18-Jan-3 Sotheby's, New York #870/R est:3000-5000

HOWE, Henry (attrib) (1816-1893) American

Works on paper

£897 $1400 €1346 View of Philadelphia's Walnut Street Dock (13x23cm-5x9in) pen ink wash prov. 12-Apr-3 Freeman, Philadelphia #22/R est:2000-3000

HOWE, L van (19th C) Dutch

£1027 $1603 €1500 Harbour (69x104cm-27x41in) s. 10-Apr-3 Dorotheum, Vienna #227/R est:1500-1700
£1224 $1947 €1800 View of Strassbourg (54x78cm-21x31in) s. 25-Feb-3 Dorotheum, Vienna #81/R est:2200-2400

HOWE, R (19th C) American

£2742 $4250 €4113 Still life with fruit, wine glass, decanter and caterpillar (33x36cm-13x14in) s. 29-Oct-2 Doyle, New York #12 est:2500-3500

HOWE, William Henry (1846-1929) American

£1406 $2250 €2109 On the beach, Egmond, Holland (58x81cm-23x32in) 16-May-3 Du Mouchelle, Detroit #2070/R est:1000-2000
£2344 $3750 €3399 Shepherdess (61x82cm-24x32in) s.d.97. 16-May-3 Skinner, Boston #74/R est:3000-5000

HOWELL, Peter (1932-) British

£280 $448 €406 Rubbing down (34x39cm-13x15in) s.d.73. 13-May-3 Bristol Auction Rooms #458/R
£310 $505 €465 Horses in the snow (50x60cm-20x24in) s.d.78. 28-Jan-3 Bristol Auction Rooms #486
£320 $522 €480 Mares and foals (75x90cm-30x35in) s.d.78. 28-Jan-3 Bristol Auction Rooms #488
£340 $554 €510 Sale ring, Tattersalls, Newmarket (44x59cm-17x23in) s. 28-Jan-3 Bristol Auction Rooms #485/R
£1925 $3100 €2888 Horse racing scene depicting 20 jockeys in bright silks on their mounts (97x135cm-38x53in) s. 22-Feb-3 Pook & Pook, Downington #204/R est:3000-5000

HOWELL, Raymond (20th C) American

£316 $500 €474 City dream (99x56cm-39x22in) s. 5-Apr-3 Harvey Clar, Oakland #1432

HOWELL, Samuel (fl.1828-1854) British

£350 $571 €508 Portrait of W.B. Charles Lee, M.P Grand Master of Provincial Grand Lodge, West Yorkshire (142x112cm-56x44in) i. 17-Jul-3 Tennants, Leyburn #799

HOWELLS, Bessie Curran (1885-1981) American

Works on paper

£321 $500 €482 Untitled (13x25cm-5x10in) W/C executed c.1909. 19-Oct-2 David Dike, Dallas #165/R

HOWELLS, Maud (19/20th C) British

£1450 $2378 €2175 Moment of contemplation (55x41cm-22x16in) s. 29-May-3 Christie's, Kensington #242/R est:1000-1500

Works on paper

£320 $496 €480 Love letter (38x31cm-15x12in) s. W/C. 24-Sep-2 Bonhams, Knightsbridge #166/R

HOWES, Jerome (20th C) American

£318 $500 €477 Trompe-l'oeil with quadrant, postcards and jagging wheel (61x46cm-24x18in) s. 22-Nov-2 Eldred, East Dennis #1136/R
£414 $650 €621 Yacht race with tugboat (51x76cm-20x30in) s. board. 26-Jul-2 Eldred, East Dennis #504/R
£414 $650 €621 Portrait of the American pilot boat No.12 Fannies (61x76cm-24x30in) s. 26-Jul-2 Eldred, East Dennis #507/R
£414 $650 €621 Schooner, Judith (41x61cm-16x24in) s. masonite. 22-Nov-2 Eldred, East Dennis #1062/R
£541 $850 €812 Catboat under sail (28x36cm-11x14in) s. board. 26-Jul-2 Eldred, East Dennis #226/R
£541 $850 €812 Two masted yacht under sail (41x64cm-16x25in) s. 26-Jul-2 Eldred, East Dennis #616/R
£705 $1100 €1058 Paddlesteamer America (51x76cm-20x30in) s. 28-Mar-3 Eldred, East Dennis #802/R
£737 $1150 €1106 Clipper ship Spitfire off Manomet Light (61x91cm-24x36in) s. board. 28-Mar-3 Eldred, East Dennis #603/R
£755 $1200 €1133 State of Maine, portrait of a steamship (61x91cm-24x36in) s. 7-Mar-3 Skinner, Boston #316/R
£833 $1300 €1250 Paddle steamer Oceanview of Bath (51x76cm-20x30in) s. 28-Mar-3 Eldred, East Dennis #521/R
£1019 $1600 €1529 Whale ships Essex and Chili of Nantucket (76x102cm-30x40in) s. 22-Nov-2 Eldred, East Dennis #653/R est:800-1200

HOWET, Marie (1897-1984) Belgian

£300 $471 €450 Still life with flowers and pomegranate (44x60cm-17x24in) s. 15-Apr-3 Bonhams, Knightsbridge #81/R

£440 $678 €700 Paysage par temps d'orage (50x60cm-20x24in) s. 22-Oct-2 Campo & Campo, Antwerp #512
£550 $891 €825 Young girl in a summer meadow (35x45cm-14x18in) s. 23-Jan-3 Christie's, Kensington #257/R
£1241 $1986 €1800 Dans ma cuisine a Rochehaut - Bouillon (70x60cm-28x24in) s. i. verso. 17-Mar-3 Horta, Bruxelles #227 est:1500-2000

Works on paper
£274 $427 €400 La table dressee (33x46cm-13x18in) s. W/C. 14-Apr-3 Horta, Bruxelles #399
£346 $536 €550 Village ardenais (48x60cm-19x24in) s.d.1929 gouache Indian ink. 5-Oct-2 De Vuyst, Lokeren #172

HOWEY, John William (1873-1938) British
£1200 $1896 €1800 Cattle at rest in a building (36x43cm-14x17in) s. prov. 24-Apr-3 Richardson & Smith, Whitby #87 est:1000-1500

Works on paper
£360 $569 €540 Figures on the quay, Whitby Harbour (18x23cm-7x9in) i.verso W/C. 24-Apr-3 Richardson & Smith, Whitby #191

HOWEY, Robert Leslie (1900-1981) British

Works on paper
£280 $437 €420 Ullswater (20x27cm-8x11in) s. W/C. 10-Sep-2 David Duggleby, Scarborough #220
£390 $608 €585 Derwent Water (14x19cm-6x7in) s. W/C htd bodycol. 10-Sep-2 David Duggleby, Scarborough #236
£700 $1127 €1050 Moonlit landscape, near Seathwaite (49x62cm-19x24in) s. W/C ink. 14-Jan-3 Bonhams, Knightsbridge #182
£1750 $2765 €2625 Storm over Runswick with Coble in the Bay (43x58cm-17x23in) s.d.69 mixed media. 24-Apr-3 Richardson & Smith, Whitby #160/R est:1500-2000

HOWIE, J (19th C) British
£800 $1248 €1200 Mango, winner of the Great St Leger (30x35cm-12x14in) i.d.1838 verso panel. 10-Apr-3 Tennants, Leyburn #1030/R

HOWIS, William (1804-1882) Irish
£1218 $1924 €1900 View on the Dargle (46x61cm-18x24in) init.d.1862 i.d.verso. 12-Nov-2 Mealy's, Castlecomer #1240

HOWITT, John Newton (1885-1958) American

Works on paper
£248 $400 €372 Older men, one with lollipop and one with bunny (64x89cm-25x35in) s. chl. 20-Feb-3 Illustration House, New York #82/R

HOWITT, Samuel (1765-1822) British

Works on paper
£300 $483 €450 Near Abingdon, Berkshire (13x20cm-5x8in) W/C prov. 15-Jan-3 Cheffins Grain & Comins, Cambridge #359/R
£500 $780 €750 Dead rabbit and woodcock (33x46cm-13x18in) s. W/C pencil. 17-Oct-2 Lawrence, Crewkerne #1571/R
£550 $869 €825 Coursing (22x34cm-9x13in) s. W/C. 28-Nov-2 Christie's, Kensington #312/R
£950 $1577 €1425 Study of a lion (18x26cm-7x10in) s. W/C. 12-Jun-3 Bonhams, New Bond Street #645/R

HOWLAND, Alfred Cornelius (1838-1909) American
£479 $700 €719 Cottages and pond in landscape at sunset (41x28cm-16x11in) s. 3-Nov-1 North East Auctions, Portsmouth #1190/R

HOWLEY, John Richard (1931-) Australian
£250 $390 €375 Landscape (37x41cm-15x16in) s.d.78 board. 11-Nov-2 Deutscher-Menzies, Melbourne #196/R (A.D 700)
£400 $644 €580 Turning a blind eye (90x119cm-35x47in) s.d.93 acrylic on board. 12-May-3 Joel, Victoria #310 est:800-1200 (A.D 1000)
£643 $1003 €965 Burning off (111x121cm-44x48in) s.d.78. 11-Nov-2 Deutscher-Menzies, Melbourne #164/R (A.D 1800)
£643 $1003 €965 Images (122x91cm-48x36in) s. board. 11-Nov-2 Deutscher-Menzies, Melbourne #190 (A.D 1800)
£786 $1225 €1179 Planets (82x183cm-32x72in) i.verso prov. 11-Nov-2 Deutscher-Menzies, Melbourne #181/R (A.D 2200)
£1000 $1560 €1500 Blue celestial (131x144cm-52x57in) s.d.78. 11-Nov-2 Deutscher-Menzies, Melbourne #165/R est:3000-4000 (A.D 2800)

HOWSON, Peter (1958-) British
£900 $1404 €1350 Dagger dance (32x26cm-13x10in) s. board prov. 14-Apr-3 Sotheby's, London #185/R
£1200 $1992 €1740 Moonlit figure (102x76cm-40x30in) 12-Jun-3 Gorringes, Lewes #1760 est:1200-1800
£1500 $2310 €2250 Scar face (40x30cm-16x12in) s. 5-Sep-2 Christie's, Kensington #587/R est:1500-2000
£3000 $4770 €4500 Embrace (122x91cm-48x36in) s.i.verso. 29-Apr-3 Gorringes, Lewes #2373
£6000 $9180 €9000 Last Mohican (183x122cm-72x48in) 22-Aug-2 Bonhams, Edinburgh #1096/R est:7000-10000
£17000 $26350 €25500 Pocket full of poesies (183x213cm-72x84in) s. s.i.stretcher prov.lit. 31-Oct-2 Christie's, London #212/R est:10000-15000

Works on paper
£600 $930 €900 Portrait of a young man (60x45cm-24x18in) s. chl col crayon. 4-Dec-2 Christie's, Kensington #305/R
£620 $967 €930 After the match (55x76cm-22x30in) pastel gouache. 15-Oct-2 Bonhams, Knightsbridge #204/R
£950 $1463 €1425 Portrait head (27x20cm-11x8in) s. pastel sold with another by the same artist. 5-Sep-2 Christie's, Kensington #591/R
£1200 $1908 €1800 Female nude, rear view (91x61cm-36x24in) s. chl pastel sold with another by same hand prov. 6-Mar-3 Christie's, Kensington #265/R est:600-800
£1250 $2063 €1813 Study of a male head (26x19cm-10x7in) s. chl pastel. 3-Jul-3 Christie's, Kensington #544/R est:1000-1500

HOYER, Edward (19th C) British
£750 $1253 €1088 High seas (41x61cm-16x24in) s.d.80. 18-Jun-3 Sotheby's, Olympia #42/R
£1800 $2790 €2700 Shipping on the Bosphorous by moonlight (76x127cm-30x50in) s. indis d. 31-Oct-2 Christie's, Kensington #482/R est:1500-2500

HOYER, P (19th C) British
£450 $684 €675 Masted steamer and sailing vessel with coastline beyond (59x90cm-23x35in) s. 15-Aug-2 Rupert Toovey, Partridge Green #1410/R

HOYLAND, John (1934-) British
£500 $825 €725 Abstract (75x54cm-30x21in) s.d.69 acrylic on paper. 3-Jul-3 Christie's, Kensington #729/R
£850 $1326 €1275 Untitled (75x55cm-30x22in) s.d.78 acrylic on paper prov. 25-Mar-3 Bonhams, New Bond Street #139/R
£2800 $4368 €4200 Abstract (213x213cm-84x84in) d.21.7.64. 27-Mar-3 Christie's, Kensington #647/R est:2500-3500

HOYNINGEN-HUENE, George (1900-1968) British

Photographs
£2597 $4000 €3896 Miriam Hopkins (25x20cm-10x8in) i.d.1934 verso photograph prov.exhib.lit. 24-Oct-2 Sotheby's, New York #86/R est:4000-6000
£3797 $6000 €5696 Agneta fisher, swimwear by Schiaparelli (21x26cm-8x10in) photograph prov.exhib.lit. 23-Apr-3 Sotheby's, New York #158/R est:6000-9000
£3797 $6000 €5696 Lee Miller in Lanvin Prelude (27x20cm-11x8in) s.i.d.1931 verso photograph prov.lit. 23-Apr-3 Sotheby's, New York #161/R est:5000-7000
£5696 $9000 €8544 Jean Barry (20x25cm-8x10in) s.i.d.1931 verso photograph prov.lit. 23-Apr-3 Sotheby's, New York #160/R est:7000-10000
£59740 $92000 €89610 Bathing suit, A J Izod, LTD, London (25x21cm-10x8in) i.d.1930 photograph prov.exhib.lit. 24-Oct-2 Sotheby's, New York #88/R est:20000-30000

HOYOLL, Philipp (1816-?) German
£1341 $2200 €2012 Over her shoulder (33x28cm-13x11in) s.d.1867. 5-Feb-3 Christie's, Rockefeller NY #190/R est:2000-3000

HOYOS, Therese Grafin (19th C) Austrian?

Works on paper
£458 $737 €650 Billiard room in Gutenstein Castle (24x23cm-9x9in) i. W/C. 7-May-3 Dorotheum, Vienna #314/R

HOYRUP, Carl (1893-1961) Danish
£311 $500 €467 Mallard duck and ducklings at waters edge (41x66cm-16x26in) s. 22-Feb-3 Brunk, Ashville #36/R
£456 $720 €684 Seascape with eiderducks landing (100x140cm-39x55in) s. 30-Nov-2 Goteborg Auktionsverk, Sweden #185/R (S.KR 6500)
£550 $913 €798 Setter on the scent (67x97cm-26x38in) s. 12-Jun-3 Christie's, Kensington #293/R

HOYT, E C (19th C) American
£295 $475 €443 Seascape, ship on stormy sea (30x46cm-12x18in) s. 22-Feb-3 Brunk, Ashville #325/R

HOYTE, J B C (1835-1913) New Zealander

Works on paper
£1280 $1959 €1920 New Zealand landscape with two boats (38x69cm-15x27in) s. W/C. 21-Aug-2 Dunbar Sloane, Auckland #101 est:4000-6000 (NZ.D 4200)

£2134 $3265 €3201 Surveyors campsite alongside river - South Island scene (26x43cm-10x17in) init. W/C. 21-Aug-2 Dunbar Sloane, Auckland #32/R est:6000-10000 (NZ.D 7000)
£3215 $4984 €4823 Boaters rowing on the sound with Maori huts, Mitre Peak in background (61x41cm-24x16in) s. W/C. 4-Dec-2 Dunbar Sloane, Auckland #39/R est:10500-15000 (NZ.D 10000)
£5776 $9242 €8375 Southern Lakes, New Zealand (35x59cm-14x23in) W/C prov. 13-May-3 Watson's, Christchurch #23/R est:15000-20000 (NZ.D 16000)

HOYTE, John Barr Clarke (1835-1913) New Zealander
Works on paper
£266 $416 €399 Garden palace, Sydney (25x42cm-10x17in) W/C. 7-Nov-2 International Art Centre, Auckland #124/R (NZ.D 850)
£436 $619 €654 Milford Sound (10x20cm-4x8in) init. W/C prov. 21-Nov-1 Watson's, Christchurch #57/R (NZ.D 1500)
£485 $747 €728 Road to Paihia (28x19cm-11x7in) s. W/C. 4-Sep-2 Dunbar Sloane, Wellington #130 est:1500-2500 (NZ.D 1600)
£581 $826 €872 Milford Sound (23x44cm-9x17in) s. W/C. 21-Nov-1 Watson's, Christchurch #105/R (NZ.D 2000)
£727 $1120 €1091 Lake and mountains scene (20x42cm-8x17in) s. W/C. 4-Sep-2 Dunbar Sloane, Wellington #141 est:1600-2500 (NZ.D 2400)
£784 $1223 €1176 Pink and white terraces (24x46cm-9x18in) s. W/C. 7-Nov-2 International Art Centre, Auckland #99 est:2500-4000 (NZ.D 2500)
£815 $1271 €1223 Southern homestead (13x28cm-5x11in) s. W/C. 7-Nov-2 International Art Centre, Auckland #160/R est:1500-2500 (NZ.D 2600)
£940 $1467 €1410 Lake Wakatipu (20x52cm-8x20in) s. W/C. 7-Nov-2 International Art Centre, Auckland #155/R est:3000-5000 (NZ.D 3000)
£1404 $2189 €2106 Whakapapa Geyser (46x36cm-18x14in) s. W/C. 27-Mar-3 International Art Centre, Auckland #128/R est:4000-8000 (NZ.D 4000)
£1930 $3011 €2895 Military camp scenes (15x23cm-6x9in) one s. W/C pair. 27-Mar-3 International Art Centre, Auckland #109/R est:2000-4000 (NZ.D 5500)
£2778 $4333 €4167 Constabulary, Drury (19x31cm-7x12in) init. W/C exec.c.1865 prov. 8-Apr-3 Peter Webb, Auckland #102/R est:9000-12000 (NZ.D 8000)
£3762 $5868 €5643 Cecil peak, Queenstown (35x47cm-14x19in) s. W/C. 7-Nov-2 International Art Centre, Auckland #136/R est:12000-16000 (NZ.D 12000)
£4559 $7112 €6839 Mitre Peak, Milford Sound (58x38cm-23x15in) s. W/C. 17-Sep-2 Peter Webb, Auckland #112/R est:18000-25000 (NZ.D 15000)
£4643 $7336 €6965 Sydney Harbour from the north shore looking east (35x70cm-14x28in) s. W/C prov. 17-Nov-2 Sotheby's, Paddington #29/R est:4000-6000 (A.D 13000)
£5714 $9029 €8571 Sydney Harbour (35x36cm-14x14in) s. W/C executed c.1880 prov. 17-Nov-2 Sotheby's, Paddington #30/R est:3000-5000 (A.D 16000)
£6079 $9483 €9119 Bay of Island (39x65cm-15x26in) s. W/C. 17-Sep-2 Peter Webb, Auckland #110/R est:25000-35000 (NZ.D 20000)
£6383 $9957 €9575 Entrance to the Whangarei Harbour (36x62cm-14x24in) s. W/C. 17-Sep-2 Peter Webb, Auckland #111/R est:25000-30000 (NZ.D 21000)
£10031 $15649 €15047 Milford Sound (53x95cm-21x37in) s. W/C. 7-Nov-2 International Art Centre, Auckland #95/R est:28000-40000 (NZ.D 32000)
£11433 $17492 €17150 Auckland Harbour (33x51cm-13x20in) s.d.1869 W/C prov. 21-Aug-2 Dunbar Sloane, Auckland #14/R est:25000-35000 (NZ.D 37500)

HOYTEMA, Theodoor van (1863-1917) Dutch
Works on paper
£286 $450 €429 Barnyard scene of chickens and turkey (48x58cm-19x23in) s. W/C gouache. 23-Nov-2 Pook & Pook, Downington #568/R
£1090 $1711 €1700 Flower field (12x18cm-5x7in) mono. pencil W/C sold with drawing by another hand. 25-Nov-2 Glerum, Amsterdam #168 est:150-250

HOYTON, Inez E (1903-1983) British
£480 $758 €720 Still life of a plant (45x29cm-18x11in) s. acrylic. 27-Nov-2 Sotheby's, Olympia #159/R

HRDLICKA, Alfred (1928-) Austrian
Sculpture
£2308 $3646 €3600 Back study (34x12x17cm-13x5x7in) mono. brown pat.bronze. 12-Nov-2 Dorotheum, Vienna #315/R est:3600-5000
£6962 $11000 €11000 Kaiserallee II - tree study (88x21x20cm-35x8x8in) mon. dark brown pat.bronze. 27-Nov-2 Dorotheum, Vienna #255/R est:9000-13000

Works on paper
£641 $994 €1000 Anna (40x29cm-16x11in) s.d.1974 Indian ink. 6-Dec-2 Hauswedell & Nolte, Hamburg #160/R
£949 $1472 €1500 First Aid post (47x60cm-19x24in) s.d.1976 sepia graphite. 24-Sep-2 Wiener Kunst Auktionen, Vienna #204/R
£1282 $2026 €2000 Study for the peasant wars (50x70cm-20x28in) s.d.1983 i. verso chk wash. 12-Nov-2 Dorotheum, Vienna #266/R est:2000-2600
£1282 $1987 €2000 Execution in Plotzensee (40x37cm-16x15in) s.d.1974 pen. 6-Dec-2 Hauswedell & Nolte, Hamburg #159/R
£1736 $2760 €2500 People (47x62cm-19x24in) s.d.1970 Indian ink. 29-Apr-3 Wiener Kunst Auktionen, Vienna #424/R est:2500-3500
£1986 $3217 €2800 Bertold Brecht - Mother Courage and her children (89x69cm-35x27in) s.d.1986 bister chk Indian ink brush exhib.prov. 20-May-3 Dorotheum, Vienna #283/R est:2000-2600
£1987 $3080 €3100 Interior - studio of Mr Rodin (76x57cm-30x22in) s.d.1982 W/C chl chk exhib. 3-Dec-2 Lempertz, Koln #200/R est:3000
£2372 $3676 €3700 Il puttino beating Lopez in the presence of Philip II (49x67cm-19x26in) s.d.1982 col chks chl exhib. 3-Dec-2 Lempertz, Koln #199/R est:2000

HRDY, Olinka (1902-1987) American
Works on paper
£854 $1400 €1238 Lilies (25x36cm-10x14in) s.d.1937 col pencil. 1-Jun-3 Wright, Chicago #187/R est:1000-1500

HRIPCENKO, Ivan (20th C) ?
£2083 $3312 €3000 Swans (91x150cm-36x59in) s.d.1988. 1-May-3 Meeting Art, Vercelli #328

HROCH, Vladimir (1907-1966) Czechoslovakian
£1136 $1772 €1704 St Vitus Cathedral (105x87cm-41x34in) s.d.1936. 12-Oct-2 Dorotheum, Prague #110/R est:40000-60000 (C.KR 55000)

HRUBY, Sergius (1869-1943) Austrian
Works on paper
£886 $1382 €1400 Two worlds (49x72cm-19x28in) s.d.20 Indian ink W/C. 15-Oct-2 Dorotheum, Vienna #55/R est:1200-1800

HSIAO CHIN (1935-) Chinese
£604 $954 €906 Before the tempest -33 (120x70cm-47x28in) s.d.1985 stretcher paper on canvas. 1-Apr-3 Rasmussen, Copenhagen #388/R (D.KR 6500)
£625 $994 €900 Jubbliniagione (90x50cm-35x20in) s.d.1969. 29-Apr-3 Campo & Campo, Antwerp #639
£935 $1534 €1300 Composition (50x70cm-20x28in) s.d.1961 s.i.d.verso. 3-Jun-3 Christie's, Amsterdam #99/R est:1200-1600
£1132 $1755 €1800 Le tao (100x70cm-39x28in) mono. i.d.verso. 4-Oct-2 Tajan, Paris #122 est:150
£1135 $1838 €1600 M-125-WN (70x90cm-28x35in) s.d.60 s.i.d.verso prov.exhib. 26-May-3 Christie's, Milan #184/R est:1000-1500

HSING CHAO (?) Chinese
Works on paper
£2201 $3390 €3500 Chevaux et palfreniers parmi les pins (200x90cm-79x35in) s.indis.d. 23-Oct-2 Piasa, Paris #344/R est:4000-5000

HU RUOSI (1916-) Chinese
Works on paper
£3089 $4881 €4634 Sparrows gathering at a plum blossom tree (120x55cm-47x22in) s.i.d.1941 ink col hanging scroll. 28-Apr-3 Sotheby's, Hong Kong #576/R est:30000-50000 (HK.D 38000)

HU SHAN YU (1909-1993) Chinese
£5051 $8333 €7324 Still life with fruit (50x61cm-20x24in) s. prov.exhib. 6-Jul-3 Christie's, Hong Kong #160/R est:80000-100000 (HK.D 65000)

HU SHUANGAN (1916-1988) Chinese
Works on paper
£580 $951 €800 Three tigers drinking (114x48cm-45x19in) s. seals Indian ink col hanging scroll. 30-May-3 Dr Fritz Nagel, Stuttgart #1152/R
£580 $951 €800 Scholar and tiger (110x47cm-43x19in) i.d.1943 seals Indian ink col hanging scroll. 30-May-3 Dr Fritz Nagel, Stuttgart #1155/R

HU YEFO (1908-) Chinese
Works on paper
£1554 $2564 €2253 Lady (17x51cm-7x20in) s. ink scroll. 6-Jul-3 Christie's, Hong Kong #379/R est:20000-30000 (HK.D 20000)
£4472 $7065 €6708 Turtledove (129x65cm-51x26in) s. ink col hanging scroll. 28-Apr-3 Sotheby's, Hong Kong #570/R est:55000-75000 (HK.D 55000)

HU YONGKAI (1945-) Chinese
Works on paper
£3730 $6154 €5409 Lotus (75x71cm-30x28in) s. ink scroll. 6-Jul-3 Christie's, Hong Kong #276/R est:45000-50000 (HK.D 48000)

HUA YAN (1682-1756) Chinese
Works on paper
£4274 $7051 €6197 Conversation amidst pine trees (131x35cm-52x14in) s.d.1732 ink col hanging scroll. 6-Jul-3 Christie's, Hong Kong #449/R est:60000-80000 (HK.D 55000)

HUANG BINHONG (1864-1955) Chinese
Works on paper
£11382 $17984 €17073 Autumn excursion (89x32cm-35x13in) s.i. ink col hanging scroll. 28-Apr-3 Sotheby's, Hong Kong #593/R est:150000-200000 (HK.D 140000)
£19512 $30829 €29268 Landscape of Yang Shuo (100x35cm-39x14in) s.i. ink col hanging scroll. 28-Apr-3 Sotheby's, Hong Kong #647/R est:100000-150000 (HK.D 240000)

HUANG YON WU (20th C) Chinese
Works on paper
£1379 $2193 €2000 Waves breaking round rock (141x68cm-56x27in) s.d.1933 ink. 7-Mar-3 Piasa, Paris #312/R est:1200-1500
£1379 $2193 €2000 Bird flying near tree in winter (49x116cm-19x46in) ink polychrome. 7-Mar-3 Piasa, Paris #316

HUANG YONGYU (1924-) Chinese
Works on paper
£1232 $2020 €1700 Scholar by river (46x48cm-18x19in) s.d.1986 seal Indian ink col hanging scroll. 30-May-3 Dr Fritz Nagel, Stuttgart #1165/R est:1500
£10569 $16699 €15854 Buddhist monk (144x89cm-57x35in) s.i.d.1990 ink col hanging scroll. 28-Apr-3 Sotheby's, Hong Kong #517/R est:80000-120000 (HK.D 130000)

HUANG ZHOU (1925-1997) Chinese
Works on paper
£3497 $5769 €5071 Donkeys (37x645cm-15x254in) s.i. ink scroll. 6-Jul-3 Christie's, Hong Kong #319/R est:60000-80000 (HK.D 45000)

HUANG, Anton (1935-1985) Javanese
£13256 $20414 €19884 Mimpi - dream (79x99cm-31x39in) s. indis d. 27-Oct-2 Christie's, Hong Kong #84/R est:80000-100000 (HK.D 160000)

HUARD, Marcel (20th C) French
£1151 $1842 €1600 Les enfants sur la plage (50x61cm-20x24in) s.d. panel. 18-May-3 Eric Pillon, Calais #42/R

HUART, Claude (20th C) French
£1069 $1700 €1550 Paysage a la Chaumiere (58x37cm-23x15in) s. panel. 10-Mar-3 Thierry & Lannon, Brest #170/R

HUAULT, Jean Pierre and Amy (attrib) (17/18th C) Swiss
Miniatures
£1500 $2460 €2175 Jupiter and Antiope, God disguised as a satyr revealing the beauty of a sleeping nymph (4x6cm-2x2in) enamel on copper octagonal prov. 3-Jun-3 Christie's, London #12/R est:1000-1500

HUAULT, Pierre (younger) (1647-1698) Swiss
Miniatures
£1500 $2460 €2175 William III, Prince of Orange (4cm-2xin) enamel on copper oval. 3-Jun-3 Christie's, London #4/R est:1500-2500

HUBACEK, Josef (1899-1931) Czechoslovakian
£1816 $2942 €2724 Cap Ferrat (65x100cm-26x39in) s.d.1931 III. 24-May-3 Dorotheum, Prague #78/R est:50000-75000 (C.KR 80000)

HUBACEK, William (19th C) American
£2410 $4000 €3495 Floral still life with roses (91x66cm-36x26in) s. prov. 11-Jun-3 Butterfields, San Francisco #4145/R est:5000-7000

HUBBARD, Bennett (1806-1870) British
£3049 $5000 €4574 Young boy with his favourite terrier (91x71cm-36x28in) s.d.Oct.1855 verso. 8-Feb-3 Neal Auction Company, New Orleans #107/R est:5000-7500

HUBBARD, Eric Hesketh (1892-1957) British
£360 $558 €540 Pool of London (46x61cm-18x24in) s. 3-Dec-2 Bonhams, Knightsbridge #28/R
£380 $593 €570 Manobier castle and church (45x60cm-18x24in) s. 11-Sep-2 Bonhams, Newport #329/R
£650 $1014 €975 White landscape (63x76cm-25x30in) s. exhib. 12-Sep-2 Sotheby's, Olympia #69/R

HUBBARD, John (1931-) American
£260 $424 €377 Casa Pilatos (88x105cm-35x41in) s.d.1991. 15-Jul-3 Bonhams, Knightsbridge #94
£350 $546 €525 Red haytor quarry no.2 (26x26cm-10x10in) sold with four limited edition Xmas cards exhib. 12-Sep-2 Sotheby's, Olympia #145/R
£350 $578 €508 Winter garden (67x53cm-26x21in) s.d.63 oil on paper prov. 3-Jul-3 Christie's, Kensington #723/R
Works on paper
£600 $930 €900 Garden scene (20x35cm-8x14in) s.d.1986 gouache prov.exhib. 4-Dec-2 Christie's, Kensington #334

HUBBARD, Whitney Myron (1875-1965) American
£226 $350 €339 Dense green forest landscape (36x28cm-14x11in) s. board. 7-Dec-2 South Bay, Long Island #175/R
£258 $400 €387 Dunes and sea (15x20cm-6x8in) init. board. 7-Dec-2 South Bay, Long Island #175a/R
£291 $450 €437 Brown rocks (20x25cm-8x10in) cardboard exhib. 7-Dec-2 South Bay, Long Island #170/R
£291 $450 €437 House and trees in winter. init. barlap. 7-Dec-2 South Bay, Long Island #173/R
£420 $650 €630 Woman in black hat (41x30cm-16x12in) s.d. 7-Dec-2 South Bay, Long Island #172/R
£613 $950 €920 Woman in garden with parasol (30x25cm-12x10in) 7-Dec-2 South Bay, Long Island #167/R
£1419 $2200 €2129 Sailboats in harbour (25x36cm-10x14in) artist board exhib. 7-Dec-2 South Bay, Long Island #180/R

HUBBELL, Henry Salem (1870-1949) American
£1572 $2437 €2500 Maison au toit rouge dans un paysage (27x41cm-11x16in) s. prov. 30-Oct-2 Artcurial Briest, Paris #141/R est:3000-3500

HUBBUCH, Karl (1891-1979) German
£13924 $22000 €22000 Four woman talking (38x47cm-15x19in) canvas on canvas painted c.1930/35 prov. 29-Nov-2 Villa Grisebach, Berlin #59/R est:22000-25000
£39855 $65362 €55000 Lona with flowers (100x95cm-39x37in) s. s.i.stretcher prov. 30-May-3 Villa Grisebach, Berlin #46/R est:70000-90000
£68000 $110840 €102000 Akt im Badezimmer (107x75cm-42x30in) s. canvas on board prov.exhib. 3-Feb-3 Christie's, London #17/R est:40000-60000
£150000 $234000 €225000 Die drillinge - Triplets (148x157cm-58x62in) s. painted c.1927 prov.exhib.lit. 9-Oct-2 Sotheby's, London #38/R est:150000-200000
Works on paper
£324 $522 €460 The apparition (18x26cm-7x10in) mono.i. pencil lit. 9-May-3 Schloss Ahlden, Ahlden #1553/R
£380 $592 €600 Woman yawning (40x32cm-16x13in) mono. chk. 18-Oct-2 Dr Fritz Nagel, Stuttgart #191/R
£411 $642 €650 Fishermen in Marseille (32x32cm-13x13in) s. Indian ink. 18-Oct-2 Dr Fritz Nagel, Stuttgart #192/R
£481 $755 €750 Study of seated woman (42x33cm-17x13in) pencil Chinese ink. 20-Nov-2 Pandolfini, Florence #30
£540 $885 €750 Floers (40x54cm-16x21in) s. W/C pencil board. 4-Jun-3 Reiss & Sohn, Konigstein #410/R
£696 $1100 €1100 At school (58x44cm-23x17in) mono. Indian ink brush over pencil lit. 29-Nov-2 Schloss Ahlden, Ahlden #1428/R
£786 $1226 €1250 Marquee with beer garden (34x39cm-13x15in) mono. pen study verso. 11-Oct-2 Winterberg, Heidelberg #1267/R
£870 $1426 €1200 Three female nudes (33x42cm-13x17in) st.sig. pencil. 31-May-3 Villa Grisebach, Berlin #579/R
£3000 $4920 €4500 Jobless (51x40cm-20x16in) init.i. W/C pen brush ink exec.c.1933 prov. 6-Feb-3 Christie's, London #462/R

£4430 $7000 €7000 Cake shop (45x59cm-18x23in) s. mixed media. 30-Nov-2 Villa Grisebach, Berlin #279/R est:7000-9000

HUBER, Adolf (20th C) German?
£253 $395 €400 Reutlingen park (62x96cm-24x38in) canvas on masonite. 18-Oct-2 Dr Fritz Nagel, Stuttgart #193/R

HUBER, Ernst (1895-1960) Austrian
£481 $760 €750 Flower bouquet (30x20cm-12x8in) s.d.1948 paste. 12-Nov-2 Dorotheum, Vienna #155/R
£545 $855 €850 Waterfall with goat herder (28x33cm-11x13in) s. veneer panel. 21-Nov-2 Dorotheum, Vienna #294/R
£1013 $1600 €1600 Venice (18x21cm-7x8in) mono. board. 26-Nov-2 Wiener Kunst Auktionen, Vienna #119/R est:1200-2500
£1223 $2006 €1700 Bunch of summer flowers in vase (59x45cm-23x18in) s.d.1940. 5-Jun-3 Dorotheum, Salzburg #773/R est:1600-2200
£1923 $3038 €3000 Gafra mosque square (78x100cm-31x39in) 12-Nov-2 Dorotheum, Vienna #89/R est:4500-6000
£2025 $3159 €3200 Flowers (45x53cm-18x21in) s.d.48 board. 15-Oct-2 Dorotheum, Vienna #116/R est:4000-5000
£2275 $3594 €3413 Bunch of summer flowers in a vase (91x70cm-36x28in) s. 26-Nov-2 Hans Widmer, St Gallen #1181/R est:900-2400 (S.FR 5300)
£2885 $4558 €4500 Figures outdoors - blue houses (82x105cm-32x41in) 12-Nov-2 Dorotheum, Vienna #116/R est:4500-6000
£3237 $5309 €4500 Southern coastal landscape, possibly near Taormina (28x40cm-11x16in) s. panel. 5-Jun-3 Dorotheum, Salzburg #545/R est:5600-7000
£5769 $9115 €9000 Park in Hollywood (60x73cm-24x29in) s. 12-Nov-2 Dorotheum, Vienna #185/R est:9000-10000
£6522 $10696 €9000 Larkspur (80x60cm-31x24in) prov. 27-May-3 Hassfurther, Vienna #45/R est:9000-10000
£6884 $11290 €9500 Village in Lower Austria (60x80cm-24x31in) prov. 27-May-3 Hassfurther, Vienna #46/R est:7000-9000
£8696 $14261 €12000 Bunch of flowers (60x50cm-24x20in) s. 27-May-3 Wiener Kunst Auktionen, Vienna #64/R est:12000-20000

Works on paper
£285 $444 €450 Smyrne (24x31cm-9x12in) s.i. pen brush Indian ink sepia. 15-Oct-2 Dorotheum, Vienna #56/R
£321 $503 €500 Olive grove (34x48cm-13x19in) s.d.25 W/C. 21-Nov-2 Dorotheum, Vienna #461/R
£545 $855 €850 Peonies in a vase (62x50cm-24x20in) s. W/C. 21-Nov-2 Dorotheum, Vienna #462/R
£662 $1079 €1000 Kram (46x60cm-18x24in) s.i.d.48 W/C. 28-Jan-3 Dorotheum, Vienna #107/R
£694 $1104 €1000 Farmstead (24x42cm-9x17in) s. W/C two. 29-Apr-3 Wiener Kunst Auktionen, Vienna #611/R
£903 $1426 €1300 Fishing boats in Caorle (47x62cm-19x24in) s.d.13.Juli 1955 W/C. 24-Apr-3 Dorotheum, Vienna #119/R
£917 $1431 €1376 Still life of flowers (62x48cm-24x19in) s. W/C. 6-Nov-2 Dobiaschofsky, Bern #674/R (S.FR 2100)
£1346 $1965 €2100 Winter in Wagrain (47x62cm-19x24in) s. W/C. 4-Jun-2 Karl & Faber, Munich #288 est:600
£1772 $2765 €2800 Dalmatien (51x73cm-20x29in) s.i.d.1923 Indian ink W/C bodycol. 15-Oct-2 Dorotheum, Vienna #40/R est:2200-2400
£2436 $3776 €3800 Dubrovnik harbour (46x60cm-18x24in) s.d.35 W/C bodycol. 5-Dec-2 Dorotheum, Graz #110/R est:3000

HUBER, Fritz (1894-1977) Swiss
£258 $407 €387 Idyllic scene at Griefensee (46x55cm-18x22in) s.i. 29-Nov-2 Zofingen, Switzerland #2915 (S.FR 600)

HUBER, Hans (attrib) (1813-1889) Austrian
£475 $736 €750 Summer landscape with approaching storm (21x26cm-8x10in) 25-Sep-2 Neumeister, Munich #606/R

HUBER, Jean (1721-1786) Swiss
£1057 $1544 €1586 Voltaire et les paysans (31x21cm-12x8in) panel prov. 17-Jun-2 Philippe Schuler, Zurich #4272/R (S.FR 2400)

HUBER, Jean-Daniel (1754-1845) Swiss
£3648 $5764 €5472 Shore of Lake Geneva with figures and animals (83x100cm-33x39in) s. 28-Nov-2 Christie's, Zurich #7/R est:7000-9000 (S.FR 8500)

HUBER, Léon (1858-1928) French
£2484 $4000 €3726 Still life with strawberries, pears, bottles of wine and cheese (48x64cm-19x25in) s. 19-Jan-3 Jeffery Burchard, Florida #76/R
£2949 $4571 €4600 Jeux de chatons (60x93cm-24x37in) s.d.1900. 9-Dec-2 Horta, Bruxelles #189/R est:5000-6000
£4510 $7396 €6900 Debacle (95x143cm-37x56in) s.d.1903. 9-Feb-3 Anaf, Lyon #144/R est:7000

HUBER, Otto (19/20th C) German
£573 $894 €900 Backyards in winter (61x55cm-24x22in) s. board. 6-Nov-2 Hugo Ruef, Munich #1149/R

HUBER, Thomas (1700-1779) German
£1701 $2704 €2500 Old man (37x31cm-15x12in) s.d.1741. 21-Mar-3 Millon & Associes, Paris #13/R

Works on paper
£1218 $1888 €1900 Stage (71x114cm-28x45in) s.i.d.95 W/C over pencil prov. 3-Dec-2 Lempertz, Koln #202/R est:2000

HUBER, Wilhelm (1787-1871) German
£6800 $11356 €9860 View of the bay of Baia near Naples, town of Pozzuoli beyond (60x83cm-24x33in) s.d.1840. 8-Jul-3 Sotheby's, Olympia #505/R est:5000-7000

HUBERT, Léon (1887-?) French
£633 $987 €1000 Le port de Villefranche (48x59cm-19x23in) s. 15-Oct-2 Vanderkindere, Brussels #94

HUBERTI, Antonio (Pseudonym) (1907-) French

Works on paper
£345 $548 €500 Femme au sein nu (65x54cm-26x21in) s. i.verso mixed media cardboard. 4-Mar-3 Livinec, Gaudcheau & Jezequel, Rennes #121

HUBERTI, Edouard Jules Joseph (1818-1880) Belgian
£833 $1308 €1300 Vase de fleurs (51x31cm-20x12in) s. 10-Dec-2 Vanderkindere, Brussels #106
£4138 $6621 €6000 L'oree de la foret (160x203cm-63x80in) s. lit. 15-Mar-3 De Vuyst, Lokeren #516/R est:6500-7500

HUBMANN, Monika (1950-) Austrian
£314 $484 €500 Still life with wine glass (100x100cm-39x39in) s.d.88. 22-Oct-2 Wiener Kunst Auktionen, Vienna #1139/R
£314 $484 €500 Shop window (100x100cm-39x39in) s.d.88. 22-Oct-2 Wiener Kunst Auktionen, Vienna #1152/R

HUBNER, Alois Hans (fl.1900-1910) Austrian
£903 $1426 €1300 The three Zinnen (105x125cm-41x49in) s.d.1909. 24-Apr-3 Dorotheum, Vienna #130/R

HUBNER, Carl Wilhelm (1814-1879) German
£2817 $4535 €4000 Young seducer (60x77cm-24x30in) s.d.1835. 10-May-3 Berlinghof, Heidelberg #248/R est:6600

HUBNER, Eduard (1842-1924) German
£840 $1335 €1260 Still life of objects on kitchen table (53x73cm-21x29in) s.d.97. 5-May-3 Rasmussen, Vejle #591/R (D.KR 9000)
£10000 $15700 €15000 Frauen von Capri - woman of Capri (101x177cm-40x70in) s.d.1874. 19-Nov-2 Sotheby's, London #122/R est:10000-15000

HUBNER, Heinrich (1869-1945) German
£696 $1100 €1100 Blue room (83x72cm-33x28in) s.d.1920. 30-Nov-2 Bassenge, Berlin #6342/R
£4648 $7483 €6600 The garden (80x91cm-31x36in) s. lit. 9-May-3 Schloss Ahlden, Ahlden #1536/R est:6800

HUBNER, Joseph (1817-?) German
£800 $1296 €1200 Figures unloading barges on an Alpine lake (48x65cm-19x26in) s.d.1851. 23-Jan-3 Christie's, Kensington #146/R

HUBNER, Julius (1842-1874) German
£691 $1085 €1037 Conversation over a good mug (24x19cm-9x7in) s.d.1871 board. 10-Dec-2 Pinneys, Montreal #31 (C.D 1700)

Works on paper
£1197 $1987 €1700 Golden age (9x17cm-4x7in) mono.i. pencil W/C htd bodycol. 12-Jun-3 Hauswedell & Nolte, Hamburg #362/R est:2000

HUBNER, Louis (fl.1740-1769) British
£7000 $11060 €10500 Duckwing game cock, chickens, pigeons and bullfinch in a landscape (98x123cm-39x48in) 28-Nov-2 Sotheby's, London #199/R est:8000-12000

HUBNER, Ulrich (1872-1932) German

Works on paper
£256 $397 €400 View of yacht harbour with town silhouette in background (22x31cm-9x12in) s.d.29 W/C. 7-Dec-2 Dannenberg, Berlin #687/R

HUBSCH, Francisca (1857-1944) German
£541 $843 €800 Small harbour on the Kantle (44x55cm-17x22in) s. board lit. 28-Mar-3 Karrenbauer, Konstanz #1749

HUBSCH, Hermann (1901-?) German
£256 $403 €400 Still life (65x49cm-26x19in) s. board. 23-Nov-2 Arnold, Frankfurt #764/R
HUCHET, Urbain (1930-) French?
£353 $568 €540 Le violoniste (65x54cm-26x21in) s. 19-Jan-3 Feletin, Province #178
HUCHTENBURGH, Jan van (1647-1733) Dutch
£5500 $8580 €8250 Cavalry skirmish (44x53cm-17x21in) s. prov.exhib. 10-Apr-3 Christie's, Kensington #110/R est:2000-3000
£15924 $24841 €25000 Battle at Blenheim, near Hochstadt (44x66cm-17x26in) s.i.d.1704. 5-Nov-2 Sotheby's, Amsterdam #242/R est:12000-18000
HUCHTENBURGH, Jan van (attrib) (1647-1733) Dutch
£13964 $22622 €20248 Battle scene by fortress (108x94cm-43x37in) bears indis sig. 26-May-3 Bukowskis, Stockholm #432/R est:80000-100000 (S.KR 180000)
HUCHTENBURGH, Jan van (circle) (1647-1733) Dutch
£12179 $19122 €19000 Massacre (175x296cm-69x117in) canvas on canvas. 21-Nov-2 Dorotheum, Vienna #50/R est:15000-26000
£14103 $22141 €22000 Massacre (175x296cm-69x117in) canvas on canvas. 21-Nov-2 Dorotheum, Vienna #51/R est:15000-26000
HUCKE, Edwin (18/19th C) American
£510 $800 €765 Brig Grand Turk of Salem (36x51cm-14x20in) s. 22-Nov-2 Eldred, East Dennis #1058/R
HUDECEK, Antonin (1872-1941) Czechoslovakian
£413 $652 €620 Dahlias (63x88cm-25x35in) paper. 30-Nov-2 Dorotheum, Prague #74 (C.KR 20000)
£2331 $3613 €3497 Shade (94x130cm-37x51in) painted c.1920-23. 1-Oct-2 SOGA, Bratislava #200/R est:148000 (SL.K 148000)
HUDECEK, Antonin (attrib) (1872-1941) Czechoslovakian
£300 $483 €450 Summer landscape (47x67cm-19x26in) s. canvasboard. 14-Jan-3 Bonhams, Knightsbridge #127/R
HUDECEK, Emy (1937-) Austrian
£1192 $1943 €1800 Diana (58x40cm-23x16in) mono.d.69 masonite. 28-Jan-3 Dorotheum, Vienna #175/R est:1500-2000
HUDECEK, Frantisek (1909-1990) Czechoslovakian
£6356 $10297 €9534 Chimney in a brick field (73x52cm-29x20in) s.d.43 board. 24-May-3 Dorotheum, Prague #129/R est:200000-300000 (C.KR 280000)
HUDLER, August (after) (19th C) German?
Sculpture
£2083 $3000 €3125 Adam (66cm-26in) pat bronze. 15-Jan-3 Christie's, Rockefeller NY #244/R
HUDSON RIVER SCHOOL, American
£4444 $7378 €6444 Sunset, Hudson Valley (81x122cm-32x48in) 16-Jun-3 Waddingtons, Toronto #11/R est:12000-16000 (C.D 10000)
HUDSON, Grace Carpenter (1865-1937) American
£6329 $10000 €9177 Friend of foe (53x43cm-21x17in) s. lit. 26-Jul-3 Coeur d'Alene, Hayden #202a/R est:10000-20000
£11321 $18000 €16982 Baby (26x20cm-10x8in) s.d.95 s.i.verso. 7-Mar-3 Skinner, Boston #352/R est:4000-6000
£26730 $42500 €40095 Basket weavers (36x46cm-14x18in) s.d.1906. 7-Mar-3 Skinner, Boston #353/R est:25000-35000
HUDSON, Hannah Maria (19th C) British?
£3125 $5000 €4531 Primitive portraits of a gentleman and a lady (76x64cm-30x25in) s.d.1833 pair. 17-May-3 CRN Auctions, Cambridge #35
HUDSON, Hannah Maria (attrib) (19th C) British?
£620 $998 €930 Portrait of a gentleman in black coat. Portrait of a lady leaning on a book (63x76cm-25x30in) two. 14-Jan-3 Bonhams, Knowle #329
HUDSON, Henry John (1881-1910) British
£3724 $6033 €5400 Interior scene with woman - Belle epoque (155x105cm-61x41in) mono.d.1893. 25-May-3 Uppsala Auktionskammare, Uppsala #111/R est:20000-25000 (S.KR 48000)
HUDSON, Thomas (1701-1779) British
£3500 $5565 €5250 Portrait of a lady wearing a grey dress (74x62cm-29x24in) painted oval prov. 19-Mar-3 Sotheby's, London #47/R est:3000-5000
HUDSON, Thomas (attrib) (1701-1779) British
£12000 $18480 €18000 Portrait of lady (124x99cm-49x39in) 25-Oct-2 Gorringes, Lewes #876
HUDSON, Thomas (circle) (1701-1779) British
£5000 $8300 €7250 Portrait of Catherine, wife of Edwyn Francis Stanhope of Stanwell (124x99cm-49x39in) i.d.1810. 16-Jun-3 Duke & Son, Dorchester #164 est:6000-10000
HUDSON, William (?-1847) British
£5556 $9000 €8056 Political debate between two Irishmen (76x51cm-30x20in) prov.lit. 21-May-3 Doyle, New York #75/R est:5000-7000
Works on paper
£350 $546 €525 Portrait of a young girl with a dog (16x11cm-6x4in) W/C bodycol on ivorine. 17-Oct-2 Christie's, Kensington #8
HUE, Charles Desire (1825-?) French
£5096 $8000 €7644 Restful afternoon (19x24cm-7x9in) s. 10-Dec-2 Doyle, New York #213/R est:4000-6000
£8917 $14000 €13376 Games of love (65x54cm-26x21in) s. pair. 21-Nov-2 Sotheby's, New York #176/R est:15000-20000
HUE, Jean François (attrib) (1751-1823) French
£1538 $2569 €2200 Paysage de riviere dans une foret (23x30cm-9x12in) panel. 27-Jun-3 Piasa, Paris #109/R est:2000-3000
£7500 $12525 €10875 Shipwreck in stormy seas with survivors at a campfire in the foreground (57x81cm-22x32in) 9-Jul-3 Bonhams, New Bond Street #121/R est:8000-12000
Works on paper
£567 $919 €800 Groupe de personnages dans une architecture antique, au crepuscule (20x25cm-8x10in) gouache. 23-May-3 Beaussant & Lefèvre, Paris #44
HUE, Madelaine (1882-1943) French
£974 $1500 €1461 Nature morte aux raisins (46x56cm-18x22in) s.i. board painted c.1940. 8-Sep-2 Treadway Gallery, Cincinnati #739/R est:800-1200
HUEBLER, Douglas (1924-1997) American
Works on paper
£10800 $18036 €15660 Working drawings (130x102cm-51x40in) i. two d.1976 one d.1975 col felt tip pencil text paper 3 prov. 26-Jun-3 Sotheby's, London #129/R est:4000-6000
HUELSENBECK, Richard (1892-?) German
£1859 $2714 €2900 Untitled (97x112cm-38x44in) s.d.41 s.d.verso. 5-Jun-2 Il Ponte, Milan #57
Works on paper
£385 $562 €600 Dada (80x90cm-31x35in) s.i.verso mixed media collage on canvas. 5-Jun-2 Il Ponte, Milan #28
HUET, J (?) French
£828 $1316 €1200 Rouen (50x73cm-20x29in) 9-Mar-3 Feletin, Province #212
HUET, Jacques (20th C) French?
£276 $433 €430 Plage animee en Normandie (45x54cm-18x21in) s. 24-Nov-2 Lesieur & Le Bars, Le Havre #78
HUET, Jean Baptiste (1745-1811) French
£1900 $3040 €2850 Courting couple in a garden (35x27cm-14x11in) panel with companion two. 11-Mar-3 Bonhams, Knightsbridge #246/R est:1000-1500
Works on paper
£532 $888 €750 Ane au repos (21x27cm-8x11in) s. black crayon white chk. 19-Jun-3 Piasa, Paris #98
£1103 $1766 €1600 Deux amours et un faune (14x20cm-6x8in) ink Chinese ink wash dr pair. 14-Mar-3 Libert, Castor, Paris #13/R
£1135 $1838 €1600 La colombe captive (18x22cm-7x9in) s.d.1776 W/C pen wash. 21-May-3 Piasa, Paris #356/R est:1500-2000

£1216 $1897 €1800 Etudes de vaches (25x36cm-10x14in) crayon chk. 26-Mar-3 Piasa, Paris #72/R
£1899 $3000 €3000 Paysage avec une chaumiere et deux personnages pechant (24x35cm-9x14in) i. col chk. 27-Nov-2 Christie's, Paris #200/R est:1200-1600

HUET, Jean Baptiste (attrib) (1745-1811) French
£2000 $3340 €2900 Still life with a marble putto holding a bowl with watch, book and three coins (23x19cm-9x7in) indis.sig.d. panel. 8-Jul-3 Sotheby's, Olympia #483/R est:2000-3000

Works on paper
£490 $700 €735 Young man and woman seated in a pastoral landscape (15x19cm-6x7in) pen ink wash. 23-Jan-3 Swann Galleries, New York #274/R
£621 $993 €900 Etude de boucs (18x24cm-7x9in) sanguine. 12-Mar-3 E & Eve, Paris #31
£811 $1265 €1200 Etude de cgiens et ours (32x25cm-13x10in) i. crayon. 27-Mar-3 Maigret, Paris #89/R
£946 $1476 €1400 Figure agee prechant (36x23cm-14x9in) pierre noire chk. 26-Mar-3 Piasa, Paris #44/R

HUET, Nicolas (younger) (1770-?) French

Works on paper
£3600 $6012 €5220 Exotic crow (40x30cm-16x12in) pen blk ink W/C. 9-Jul-3 Sotheby's, London #120/R est:4000-6000

HUET, Paul (1803-1869) French
£541 $843 €800 Ruisseau dans un sous-bois (31x21cm-12x8in) studio st.verso cardboard. 26-Mar-3 Piasa, Paris #107
£2051 $3241 €3200 Esquisse our gouffre (23x43cm-9x17in) cardboard. 18-Nov-2 Sotheby's, Paris #63/R
£2098 $3504 €3000 Paysage lacustre a la barque (18x28cm-7x11in) s. cardboard. 26-Jun-3 Tajan, Paris #199/R est:3000-3500
£2436 $3849 €3800 Vallee d'Apt (33x50cm-13x20in) panel prov. 18-Nov-2 Sotheby's, Paris #62/R
£2564 $4051 €4000 View of Royat (21x20cm-8x8in) paper on panel prov. 18-Nov-2 Sotheby's, Paris #64/R
£3462 $5469 €5400 Etude pour inondation (33x46cm-13x18in) prov. 18-Nov-2 Sotheby's, Paris #61/R

Works on paper
£261 $429 €400 Etude de tete et de calligraphie (15x11cm-6x4in) stuidio st. pen ink over crayon. 7-Feb-3 Piasa, Paris #133
£261 $429 €400 Paysage a l'aqueduc (22x34cm-9x13in) studio st. pen ink. 7-Feb-3 Piasa, Paris #136
£294 $482 €450 Scene troubadour (16x12cm-6x5in) studio st. W/C over crayon. 7-Feb-3 Piasa, Paris #132
£541 $843 €800 Paysage de Normandie (29x45cm-11x18in) i. crayon chk. 31-Mar-3 Piasa, Paris #87

HUF, Fritz (1888-1970) Swiss
£648 $1044 €972 Still life with flowers (54x39cm-21x15in) s.d.1943 board. 7-May-3 Dobiaschofsky, Bern #668/R (S.FR 1400)

HUFF, F A (?) American?

Works on paper
£789 $1200 €1184 Battle of Camperdown (51x71cm-20x28in) s.i. en grisaille. 17-Aug-2 North East Auctions, Portsmouth #566/R

HUFFMAN, Laton A (1854-1931) American

Photographs
£4430 $7000 €6424 Percy Williamson's ranch, breaks of Missouri, north Montana. Trail herd (25x38cm-10x15in) s.i. hand col photograph and collotype pair lit. 26-Jul-3 Coeur d'Alene, Hayden #9/R est:5000-8000

HUFTIER, Jean Paul (20th C) French?
£799 $1262 €1150 Le retour (162x177cm-64x70in) 28-Apr-3 Cornette de St.Cyr, Paris #415

HUG, Charles (1899-1979) Swiss
£873 $1362 €1310 Morning in Amsterdam (60x73cm-24x29in) s. s.i.d.1947 verso lit. 6-Nov-2 Hans Widmer, St Gallen #131/R (S.FR 2000)
£961 $1499 €1442 Malergarten in the evening light (65x92cm-26x36in) s.i. 8-Nov-2 Dobiaschofsky, Bern #110/R (S.FR 2200)
£1373 $2170 €2060 Peaches (19x24cm-7x9in) s. s.d.1948 verso pavatex prov. exhib.lit. 26-Nov-2 Phillips, Zurich #62/R est:900-1200 (S.FR 3200)

HUG, Fritz Rudolf (1921-1989) Swiss
£283 $438 €425 Cockerel (60x73cm-24x29in) material. 9-Dec-2 Philippe Schuler, Zurich #8733 (S.FR 650)
£284 $414 €426 Pony (45x55cm-18x22in) s. 4-Jun-2 Germann, Zurich #776 (S.FR 650)
£343 $542 €515 Rocky and dry stream bed (32x40cm-13x16in) s. masonite. 29-Nov-2 Zofingen, Switzerland #2918 (S.FR 800)
£348 $539 €522 Two hedgehogs (40x60cm-16x24in) s. 9-Dec-2 Philippe Schuler, Zurich #8734 (S.FR 800)
£391 $607 €587 Zurich (60x72cm-24x28in) s. 9-Dec-2 Philippe Schuler, Zurich #8735 (S.FR 900)
£463 $745 €671 Three bluetits (61x38cm-24x15in) s. 7-May-3 Dobiaschofsky, Bern #673/R (S.FR 1000)
£463 $745 €671 Deer (50x65cm-20x26in) s. 7-May-3 Dobiaschofsky, Bern #672 (S.FR 1000)
£472 $746 €708 Zurich parade ground (54x66cm-21x26in) s. masonite. 29-Nov-2 Zofingen, Switzerland #2919 (S.FR 1100)
£524 $817 €786 Reclining sow with four piglets (27x34cm-11x13in) s. board. 8-Nov-2 Dobiaschofsky, Bern #219/R (S.FR 1200)
£556 $894 €806 Margay (60x40cm-24x16in) s.i. 7-May-3 Dobiaschofsky, Bern #670/R (S.FR 1200)
£565 $876 €848 La fuite (70x200cm-28x79in) s.i. oil tempera cloth. 9-Dec-2 Philippe Schuler, Zurich #3819 (S.FR 1300)
£648 $1044 €940 Okapi (46x65cm-18x26in) s. 7-May-3 Dobiaschofsky, Bern #671/R (S.FR 1400)
£694 $1118 €1006 Munster Bridge and St Peter Church in Zurich (54x73cm-21x29in) s. panel. 9-May-3 Dobiaschofsky, Bern #186/R est:2000 (S.FR 1500)
£2620 $4114 €3930 Yehudi Menuhin (61x82cm-24x32in) s. 25-Nov-2 Sotheby's, Zurich #109/R est:6000-8000 (S.FR 6000)
£3472 $5590 €5034 View of the studio (69x100cm-27x39in) s.d.71-73 i.verso. 9-May-3 Dobiaschofsky, Bern #210/R est:7500 (S.FR 7500)

HUGE, Jurgan Frederick (1809-1878) American

Works on paper
£573 $900 €860 House with horse drawn carriage in foreground (43x53cm-17x21in) i.verso graphite. 23-Nov-2 Pook & Pook, Downington #53/R

HUGENTOBLER, Ivan Edwin (1886-1972) Swiss
£873 $1362 €1310 Horses head (49x39cm-19x15in) s.d.1947. 20-Nov-2 Fischer, Luzern #1281/R est:2500-3000 (S.FR 2000)
£2146 $3391 €3219 View of village street with cemetery and path to church (80x58cm-31x23in) s.d.1917. 26-Nov-2 Hans Widmer, St Gallen #1187/R est:5000-9500 (S.FR 5000)
£3004 $4747 €4506 Two friends (59x75cm-23x30in) s.d.1915. 26-Nov-2 Hans Widmer, St Gallen #1188/R est:7000-11000 (S.FR 7000)

Works on paper
£262 $409 €393 Horse's head (31x22cm-12x9in) s.d.1945 chl wash. 6-Nov-2 Dobiaschofsky, Bern #1660 (S.FR 600)
£262 $414 €393 Horse with foal (30x26cm-12x10in) mono. chl. 26-Nov-2 Hans Widmer, St Gallen #1191 (S.FR 610)
£262 $414 €393 Saddled horse rearing (26x23cm-10x9in) mono. chl. 26-Nov-2 Hans Widmer, St Gallen #1192 (S.FR 610)
£262 $414 €393 Two horse's heads in a team (25x22cm-10x9in) mono. chl. 26-Nov-2 Hans Widmer, St Gallen #1194 (S.FR 610)
£262 $414 €393 Three horses behind a fence (23x22cm-9x9in) s. chl htd white ink wash. 26-Nov-2 Hans Widmer, St Gallen #1195 (S.FR 610)
£262 $414 €393 White horse (25x24cm-10x9in) mono. chl pencil. 26-Nov-2 Hans Widmer, St Gallen #1197 (S.FR 610)
£262 $414 €393 Four horses (27x26cm-11x10in) chl wash ink dr. 26-Nov-2 Hans Widmer, St Gallen #1198 (S.FR 610)
£262 $414 €393 General Dufour on horse (24x20cm-9x8in) mono. i. chl wash ink dr. 26-Nov-2 Hans Widmer, St Gallen #1199 (S.FR 610)
£644 $1017 €966 Portrait of the horse of Warteck-Bierbrauerei in Basel (39x32cm-15x13in) W/C exec.1944. 29-Nov-2 Zofingen, Switzerland #2922 est:1900 (S.FR 1500)

HUGENTOBLER, Ivan Edwin (attrib) (1886-1972) Swiss
£529 $788 €794 Two mounted officers (30x38cm-12x15in) i.d.1958. 25-Jun-2 Koller, Zurich #6592 (S.FR 1200)

HUGGINS, William (1820-1884) British
£500 $835 €725 Game birds hanging in a larder (72x55cm-28x22in) s. 26-Jun-3 Mellors & Kirk, Nottingham #924
£920 $1472 €1380 Poultry (25x32cm-10x13in) s.d.1872 oil pencil board oval. 15-May-3 Lawrence, Crewkerne #980/R
£1800 $2952 €2700 Tabby cat (30cm-12in circular) s. board. 4-Jun-3 Bonhams, Chester #287/R est:1500-2000
£2000 $3080 €3000 Cactus and flowers (61x48cm-24x19in) indis.sig.d.1870 board prov. 5-Sep-2 Christie's, Kensington #337/R est:2500-3500

Works on paper
£1600 $2480 €2400 Cow and calf (43x53cm-17x21in) s.d.1863 W/C. 25-Sep-2 John Nicholson, Haslemere #920/R est:500-1000
£1700 $2754 €2550 Study of a lion and his pride (9x18cm-4x7in) s.d.1871 pencil red chk. 20-May-3 Sotheby's, Olympia #3/R est:300-500

HUGGINS, William John (1781-1845) British
£3800 $5966 €5700 Survivors rescued from a shipwreck in a storm (55x80cm-22x31in) s. 16-Dec-2 Sotheby's, Olympia #14/R est:4000-6000

£26316 $40000 €39474 Duke of York (43x56cm-17x22in) s.board set of five. 17-Aug-2 North East Auctions, Portsmouth #721/R est:15000-25000
£30000 $46500 €45000 Gallant encounter between H.M.S Boadicea and two French warship Le Duquay-Trouin (81x127cm-32x50in) s.d.1822. 31-Oct-2 Christie's, Kensington #441/R est:20000-30000

Works on paper
£420 $668 €630 NCS Castle Huntley in a storm (20x27cm-8x11in) i.verso W/C. 6-Mar-3 Clevedon Sale Rooms #152

HUGGINS, William John (attrib) (1781-1845) British
£500 $810 €750 Frigate hove-to and riding her anchors in a gale (43x53cm-17x21in) 21-May-3 Christie's, Kensington #551/R

HUGHES, Ardis (20th C) American
£4348 $7000 €6522 Silhouette artist with young mother and boy posing (91x71cm-36x28in) s. 10-May-3 Illustration House, New York #80/R est:3500-5000

HUGHES, Arthur (1832-1915) British
£400 $656 €600 Maid carrying a bunch of dried grasses (39x23cm-15x9in) s. panel. 4-Jun-3 Bonhams, Chester #382
£800 $1248 €1200 Boats going out (26x45cm-10x18in) s. panel. 8-Apr-3 Bonhams, Knightsbridge #228/R
£4500 $7470 €6750 Cliff searchers (29x46cm-11x18in) s. board prov.exhib.lit. 10-Jun-3 Christie's, London #92/R est:2500-3500
£5500 $8689 €8250 Returning home (49x75cm-19x30in) s. 2-Dec-2 Sotheby's, London #61/R est:5000-7000
£8387 $13000 €12581 Asleep in the woods (35x46cm-14x18in) s. 30-Oct-2 Christie's, Rockefeller NY #191/R est:10000-15000
£340000 $547400 €510000 Birthday picnic - Portrait of the children of William and Anne Pattinson of Felling (102x128cm-40x50in) s. painted arch prov.exhib.lit. 19-Feb-3 Christie's, London #11/R est:300000-500000

HUGHES, Arthur Ford (1856-?) British
Works on paper
£1800 $2880 €2700 Lesson in arcadia (65x105cm-26x41in) s. W/C prov. 11-Mar-3 Bonhams, New Bond Street #70/R est:2000-3000

HUGHES, Bill (1932-1992) American
£2244 $3500 €3366 Pumpkin patch (61x76cm-24x30in) 9-Nov-2 Altermann Galleries, Santa Fe #34

HUGHES, Daisy Marguerite (1883-1968) American
£2419 $3750 €3629 Houses in landscape (53x66cm-21x26in) s. prov. 29-Oct-2 John Moran, Pasadena #750 est:3000-5000

HUGHES, David Gordon (1957-) Irish
£1090 $1711 €1700 Still life with red poppies (43x43cm-17x17in) mono. 19-Nov-2 Whyte's, Dublin #121/R est:1500-2000

HUGHES, Edward (1832-1908) British
£4750 $7363 €7125 Incident in the life of Paganini (73x102cm-29x40in) s.d.1869. 2-Oct-2 Bonhams, Knowle #68/R est:6000-8000
£14000 $23240 €21000 Rescue (96x123cm-38x48in) s. 10-Jun-3 Christie's, London #121/R est:15000-20000

HUGHES, Edward John (1913-) Canadian
£6222 $10204 €9333 Koksilah river at Cowichan Bay (63x81cm-25x32in) s.d.1990 s.i.d.on stretcher acrylic prov. 27-May-3 Sotheby's, Toronto #50/R est:10000-15000 (C.D 14000)
£7556 $12391 €11334 Beside the public wharf, Crofton, BC (61x93cm-24x37in) s.d.1981 s.i.d. on stretcher acrylic prov. 27-May-3 Sotheby's, Toronto #127/R est:15000-20000 (C.D 17000)
£7661 $12105 €11492 Ship with a blue hull, Cowichan Bay, B.C (81x102cm-32x40in) s.d.1982 s.i.verso prov.lit. 18-Nov-2 Sotheby's, Toronto #121/R est:12000-16000 (C.D 19000)
£8444 $13849 €12666 Cowichan river. Cowichan River at Skutz Falls (102x81cm-40x32in) s.d.1988 one acrylic one graphite two prov. 27-May-3 Sotheby's, Toronto #51/R est:12000-16000 (C.D 19000)
£10222 $16764 €15333 Ferry at Crofton BC (61x93cm-24x37in) s.d.1981 s.i.d.verso prov. 27-May-3 Sotheby's, Toronto #123/R est:20000-25000 (C.D 23000)
£32258 $50968 €48387 Roberts Bay, BC (61x63cm-24x25in) s.i.d.1953 prov. 14-Nov-2 Heffel, Vancouver #40/R est:35000-45000 (C.D 80000)
£48889 $80178 €73334 Store at Allison Harbour, BC (62x80cm-24x31in) s.d.1955 prov.lit. 3-Jun-3 Joyner, Toronto #30/R est:100000-150000 (C.D 110000)
£85202 $136323 €127803 Courtenay, BC (91x102cm-36x40in) s.d.1950 s.i.d.verso prov.exhib.lit. 15-May-3 Heffel, Vancouver #99/R est:200000-250000 (C.D 190000)

Works on paper
£242 $382 €363 Mount Begbie (22x30cm-9x12in) s.i.d.1958 pencil dr. prov. 14-Nov-2 Heffel, Vancouver #136 (C.D 600)
£323 $510 €485 Low tide at Fulford harbour (22x30cm-9x12in) s.i.d.1967 pencil prov. 14-Nov-2 Heffel, Vancouver #41 (C.D 800)
£404 $646 €606 Late afternoon, Cooper's Cove (22x30cm-9x12in) s. s.i.d.1948 verso pencil prov. 15-May-3 Heffel, Vancouver #178/R est:1000-1500 (C.D 900)
£404 $646 €606 Gary Writing - artist brother (25x23cm-10x9in) s. W/C prov. 15-May-3 Heffel, Vancouver #192 est:600-800 (C.D 900)
£444 $701 €666 Above Ganges harbour (22x30cm-9x12in) s.i.d.1967 pencil. 14-Nov-2 Heffel, Vancouver #42 est:1000-1500 (C.D 1100)
£493 $789 €740 Fraser River near Cheam View (23x30cm-9x12in) s. s.i.d.1958 verso pencil prov. 15-May-3 Heffel, Vancouver #177/R est:1000-1500 (C.D 1100)
£897 $1435 €1346 Gsnges on Saltspring Island, BC (22x30cm-9x12in) s. s.i.d.1967 verso pencil prov. 15-May-3 Heffel, Vancouver #176/R est:1000-1500 (C.D 2000)
£1008 $1593 €1512 Namu Cannery (22x30cm-9x12in) s.i.d.1953 s.i.d.verso pencil prov. 14-Nov-2 Heffel, Vancouver #69/R est:1000-2000 (C.D 2500)
£1089 $1720 €1634 View of the Houses of Parliament (52x66cm-20x26in) s. s.i.verso pencil htd white prov.exhib. 18-Nov-2 Sotheby's, Toronto #159/R est:3000-5000 (C.D 2700)
£1109 $1752 €1664 Kelby logging Co, Cumshewa inlet, QCI (22x30cm-9x12in) s.i.d.1953 s.i.d.verso pencil prov. 14-Nov-2 Heffel, Vancouver #68/R est:1000-1500 (C.D 2750)
£1121 $1794 €1682 Dawson's Landing (30x22cm-12x9in) init.d.1953 s.i.d.verso pencil prov. 15-May-3 Heffel, Vancouver #191/R est:1500-2500 (C.D 2500)
£1290 $2039 €1935 Boat approaching the fog (44x30cm-17x12in) s.d.30 W/C prov. 18-Nov-2 Sotheby's, Toronto #155/R est:1500-2000 (C.D 3200)
£1333 $2187 €2000 Government house and parliament building. Winnipeg Fort Garry Hotel. Winnipeg views (28x37cm-11x15in) s. s.i.d.1956 verso graphite set of four prov. 27-May-3 Sotheby's, Toronto #196/R est:1800-2000 (C.D 3000)
£1371 $2166 €2057 Monument and chateau Laurier (46x61cm-18x24in) s.i.d.1956 W/C prov.lit. 18-Nov-2 Sotheby's, Toronto #160/R est:4000-6000 (C.D 3400)
£1915 $3026 €2873 Near the forest museum, Ducan (51x61cm-20x24in) s.d.1998 i.d.verso W/C prov. 18-Nov-2 Sotheby's, Toronto #36/R est:6000-8000 (C.D 4750)
£4222 $6924 €6333 Trees at Mill Bay. Young maples at Mill Bay, BC (27x34cm-11x13in) one s.d.1996 one s.d.1974 W/C graphite prov. 27-May-3 Sotheby's, Toronto #130/R est:7000-9000 (C.D 9500)

HUGHES, Edward Robert (1851-1914) British
£5000 $7950 €7500 Portrait of Major Norman Leith-Hay Clark (61x52cm-24x20in) s. prov. 19-Mar-3 Sotheby's, London #277/R est:5000-7000
£7000 $11270 €10500 Byram's Tryst (59x44cm-23x17in) s. prov.exhib. 20-Feb-3 Christie's, London #281/R

Works on paper
£3000 $4830 €4500 Study of young tennis player (48x24cm-19x9in) i. pencil W/C htd white prov. 20-Feb-3 Christie's, London #254/R
£19858 $30780 €29787 Nymph running away (93x73cm-37x29in) s.d.1898 W/C. 4-Dec-2 AB Stockholms Auktionsverk #1837/R est:30000-35000 (S.KR 280000)

HUGHES, Edwin (fl.1862-1892) British
£417 $650 €626 Toast (15x10cm-6x4in) s.d.1874 board. 20-Oct-2 Jeffery Burchard, Florida #18/R
£800 $1312 €1200 Artist's muse (30x41cm-12x16in) s.d.1872. 29-May-3 Christie's, Kensington #274/R
£850 $1326 €1275 Welcome interruption (51x34cm-20x13in) s.d.1888. 9-Oct-2 Woolley & Wallis, Salisbury #289/R

HUGHES, Edwin (attrib) (fl.1862-1892) British
£250 $407 €375 Beg sir! (36x30cm-14x12in) bears sig.d. 29-Jan-3 Sotheby's, Olympia #70/R

HUGHES, Eleanor (1882-1959) British
Works on paper
£211 $299 €317 Chancery Lane (38x16cm-15x6in) ink sketch. 21-Nov-1 Watson's, Christchurch #174/R (NZ.D 725)

£221 $314 €332 European Alpine village (24x30cm-9x12in) ink wash. 21-Nov-1 Watson's, Christchurch #130/R (NZ.D 760)
£320 $454 €480 Maori people. Early Christchurch cityscape (38x23cm-15x9in) s.d.06 ink dr double-sided. 21-Nov-1 Watson's, Christchurch #34/R (NZ.D 1100)

HUGHES, Ethel (19/20th C) British
Works on paper
£1500 $2355 €2250 Views with mothers, children and animals in Welford on Avon (28x39cm-11x15in) s. W/C over pencil pair. 15-Apr-3 Bonhams, Knowle #101 est:1000-1500

HUGHES, G J (19/20th C) British
Works on paper
£300 $468 €450 Jack Russel terrier barking at two cats sitting in a laudau (17x24cm-7x9in) s. W/C. 9-Oct-2 Woolley & Wallis, Salisbury #170/R

HUGHES, George Frederick (fl.1859-1883) British
£1550 $2542 €2325 Guarding the catch (51x67cm-20x26in) s.d.1883. 3-Jun-3 Bonhams, Oxford #54/R est:600-900

HUGHES, George H (fl.1894-1909) British
Works on paper
£460 $754 €690 Village scene with mother, girl and geese before thatched inn (50x73cm-20x29in) s. W/C. 4-Jun-3 Bonhams, Chester #328

HUGHES, H (19/20th C) British
£900 $1467 €1350 Portrait of mother and two children (76x63cm-30x25in) s.d.1848. 29-Jan-3 Sotheby's, Olympia #62/R est:300-400
£2600 $4056 €3900 Portrait of a young girl with her doll, in a landscape (35x29cm-14x11in) indis.sig.verso metal oval. 10-Apr-3 Tennants, Leyburn #1105/R est:400-600

HUGHES, John Joseph (?-1909) British
£260 $434 €377 Welsh valley by a cottage (44x66cm-17x26in) s. 8-Jul-3 Bonhams, Knightsbridge #53/R
£306 $475 €459 Woodland landscape with mountains and waterfall. 3-Nov-2 Van Blarcom, South Natick #291
£350 $560 €525 Welsh valley scene with figures and cattle by a cottage (44x66cm-17x26in) s. 7-Jan-3 Bonhams, Knightsbridge #241/R
£400 $612 €600 Study of cattle and drover outside cottage (36x64cm-14x25in) s. 22-Aug-2 Mallams, Cheltenham #252
£921 $1437 €1382 Blackberry picking in a country lane (35x52cm-14x20in) s. 15-Oct-2 Stephan Welz, Johannesburg #377/R est:4000-6000 (SA.R 15000)

HUGHES, Lester (20th C) American
£287 $450 €431 Horses fording a stream in western landscape (51x41cm-20x16in) s. 14-Dec-2 Charlton Hall, Columbia #738/R
£313 $500 €470 Cowboys in landscape (61x91cm-24x36in) s. 11-Jan-3 James Julia, Fairfield #687
£359 $600 €521 Heading out (38x76cm-15x30in) s. 21-Jun-3 Charlton Hall, Columbia #546/R
£385 $600 €578 Cowboys at sunset (61x76cm-24x30in) s. 29-Mar-3 Charlton Hall, Columbia #637/R
£417 $650 €626 Long ride home (41x51cm-16x20in) s. 29-Mar-3 Charlton Hall, Columbia #643

HUGHES, Patrick (1939-) British
£850 $1394 €1275 Jigsaw puzzle (51x61cm-20x24in) board prov. 3-Jun-3 Sotheby's, Olympia #305/R
£2400 $3744 €3600 Rainbow in a cage (123x184cm-48x72in) gloss paint board prov. 12-Sep-2 Sotheby's, Olympia #139/R est:2000-3000

HUGHES, Talbot (1869-1942) British
£700 $1141 €1015 Fashionable lady seated in an armchair applying a beauty spot (25x18cm-10x7in) s. indis d. panel. 17-Jul-3 Tennants, Leyburn #918/R
£3600 $5868 €5400 The love letter (25x20cm-10x8in) s.d.95 panel. 29-Jan-3 Sotheby's, Olympia #214/R est:2000-3000

HUGHES, Thomas John (attrib) (19th C) British
£320 $506 €480 Portrait of a gentleman (91x71cm-36x28in) 2-Dec-2 Gorringes, Lewes #2891

HUGHES, William (1842-1901) British
£320 $518 €464 Study of fruit (18x23cm-7x9in) s.d.1878. 1-Aug-3 Dee Atkinson & Harrison, Driffield #628
£480 $744 €720 Black grapes, apple, pear, stoneware jug and partridge (34x44cm-13x17in) s.d.1872 canvas on board. 2-Oct-2 Bonhams, Knowle #96
£700 $1141 €1015 Still life of dead game with pheasants and woodcock and autumn leaves (91x71cm-36x28in) 21-Jul-3 Sotheby's, London #839
£850 $1386 €1233 Still life of grapes (18x27cm-7x11in) s. 21-Jul-3 Sotheby's, London #141 est:600-800
£1400 $2282 €2030 Still life of grapes and berries. Still life with plums and a butterfly (18x23cm-7x9in) mono. pair. 21-Jul-3 Sotheby's, London #85 est:800-1200
£1429 $2257 €2144 Still life with apples and grapes (30x40cm-12x16in) s.d.1869 panel prov. 26-Nov-2 Sotheby's, Melbourne #229/R est:5000-8000 (A.D 4000)
£1600 $2608 €2320 Still life with game, an earthenware jug, gun and powder horn (89x68cm-35x27in) mono.d.1883. 21-Jul-3 Sotheby's, London #588/R est:1000-1500
£1800 $2934 €2610 Still life with pheasants and a gun by a chair with vases (35x28cm-14x11in) mono.d.1872 board. 21-Jul-3 Sotheby's, London #827 est:600-800
£1850 $2923 €2775 Still life of strawberries, grapes and other fruit in a basket (36x46cm-14x18in) s.d.1882. 2-Dec-2 Bonhams, Bath #169/R est:1500-2500
£2000 $3280 €3000 Fruit, and Admiral butterfly on a wooden ledge (66x51cm-26x20in) s.d.1887. 29-May-3 Christie's, Kensington #313/R est:2000-3000
£2200 $3586 €3190 Still life of fig and grapes (21x34cm-8x13in) s. 21-Jul-3 Sotheby's, London #139 est:800-1200
£2600 $4238 €3770 Still life of poultry and fruit (75x49cm-30x19in) s.d.1865. 21-Jul-3 Sotheby's, London #516/R est:3000-4000
£2800 $4564 €4060 Still life with fruit and heron (76x112cm-30x44in) mono.d.1865. 21-Jul-3 Sotheby's, London #609/R est:1200-1800
£3000 $5010 €4350 Garden's shed (23x20cm-9x8in) s.d.1868 exhib. 17-Jun-3 Bonhams, New Bond Street #49/R est:2000-3000
£3500 $5810 €5250 Like autumn fruit that mellowed long - Dryden (61x51cm-24x20in) s.d.1869 exhib. 10-Jun-3 Christie's, London #98/R est:4000-6000
£4984 $7875 €7476 Black grapes. White grapes (11x57cm-4x22in) s.d.1881 pair. 1-Apr-3 Stephan Welz, Johannesburg #413/R est:30000-50000 (SA.R 62000)
£5000 $8300 €7500 Grapes and oranges on a silver salver, decanter of wine on a ledge (51x61cm-20x24in) s.d.1867. 12-Jun-3 Sotheby's, London #238/R est:5000-7000

Works on paper
£800 $1304 €1160 Still lives of fruit (10x10cm-4x4in) W/C round pair. 21-Jul-3 Sotheby's, London #763/R

HUGHES-STANTON, Blair (1902-) British
£400 $656 €600 Reclining nude (47x75cm-19x30in) init.d.29. 3-Jun-3 Sotheby's, Olympia #201/R

HUGHES-STANTON, Sir Herbert (1870-1937) British
£400 $664 €600 Extensive landscape with shepherd and sheep in the foreground (50x68cm-20x27in) s.d.1914. 10-Jun-3 Bonhams, Leeds #186
£430 $671 €645 Harvest time (49x74cm-19x29in) s. s.indis.i.verso. 15-Oct-2 Stephan Welz, Johannesburg #392/R est:5000-8000 (SA.R 7000)
£480 $782 €696 View of Kalapationes, Corfu (21x28cm-8x11in) s. 21-Jul-3 Sotheby's, London #841
£800 $1304 €1160 Surrey landscape, a view near Albury (16x25cm-6x10in) s.i. board. 21-Jul-3 Sotheby's, London #611/R
£1100 $1793 €1595 Extensive landscape with distant estuary, possibly North Wales (72x91cm-28x36in) s.d.1915. 21-Jul-3 Sotheby's, London #830 est:500-700
£1200 $1956 €1740 Near Montreuil (44x59cm-17x23in) s.d.1922. 21-Jul-3 Sotheby's, London #587/R est:800-1200
£1250 $1988 €1875 Evening, Cagnes (39x49cm-15x19in) s.d.1931 exhib. 4-Mar-3 Bearnes, Exeter #457/R est:700-900
£1250 $1988 €1875 Road to Tobermory, Mull (34x44cm-13x17in) s.d.1934 exhib. 4-Mar-3 Bearnes, Exeter #458/R est:700-900
£1290 $2000 €1935 Lady near wooded shoreline (71x102cm-28x40in) s. 16-Jul-2 Arthur James, Florida #101

Works on paper
£260 $424 €390 River Meon, Tighfield, Hants (24x34cm-9x13in) s.d.1907 pencil W/C. 29-Jan-3 Dreweatt Neate, Newbury #1
£280 $456 €406 View of the Solent from the harvest field (48x58cm-19x23in) s. W/C. 21-Jul-3 Sotheby's, London #589
£350 $571 €508 Provencal landscape (37x53cm-15x21in) s. W/C. 21-Jul-3 Sotheby's, London #590
£420 $685 €609 Studland Bay, Dorset (34x49cm-13x19in) s.d.1921 W/C. 21-Jul-3 Sotheby's, London #840/R

HUGHTO, Darryl (1943-) American
£609 $950 €1015 Holy day (235x101cm-93x40in) s.i.d.1981 verso acrylic prov. 13-Apr-3 Levis, Calgary #311/R est:2000-3000 (C.D 1400)

HUGIN, Karl Otto (1887-1963) German

£655 $1035 €983 La goulette (49x61cm-19x24in) s.i. s.d.1926 verso. 14-Nov-2 Stuker, Bern #295/R est:2000-2500 (S.FR 1500)

£873 $1371 €1310 Woman reading newspaper (45x31cm-18x12in) s. 25-Nov-2 Sotheby's, Zurich #106/R est:2000-3000 (S.FR 2000)

HUGLEY, S E (?) British

£1900 $3078 €2850 On Sannoxburn, Glen Sannox (61x91cm-24x36in) s. i.verso. 23-May-3 Lyon & Turnbull, Edinburgh #2 est:600-800

HUGNET, Georges (1906-1974) French

£1044 $1650 €1650 L'oeil de l'eau (13x73cm-5x29in) mono.d.56 s.i.verso wood. 27-Nov-2 Lemoine & Ferrando, Paris #99/R est:1800-2200

Works on paper

£503 $780 €800 Decalcomanie (25x16cm-10x6in) mono. ink. 30-Oct-2 Artcurial Briest, Paris #255

£566 $877 €900 Decalcomanie (26x13cm-10x5in) mono. ink. 30-Oct-2 Artcurial Briest, Paris #254/R

HUGO, Jean (1894-1984) French

£700 $1106 €1050 Pimlico (30x46cm-12x18in) painted c.1954. 3-Apr-3 Christie's, Kensington #92/R

£1400 $2212 €2030 Mediterranean landscapes (4x7cm-2x3in) s. board pair. 22-Jul-3 Sotheby's, Olympia #274/R est:1500-2500

£2000 $3160 €3000 Place du vilage en Catalogne (225x271cm-89x107in) s. 3-Apr-3 Christie's, Kensington #99/R

£2200 $3476 €3190 Summer Carnival (46x27cm-18x11in) s.i.d.1953. 22-Jul-3 Sotheby's, Olympia #273/R est:2000-3000

£4516 $7135 €7000 Landscapes (8x13cm-3x5in) s.i. panel set of 6. 19-Dec-2 Bondu, Paris #8 est:4000

Works on paper

£559 $905 €850 Pool harbour (8x12cm-3x5in) s. gouache exhib. 22-Jan-3 Tajan, Paris #213/R

£592 $959 €900 La baie des Anges (5x13cm-2x5in) s. i.verso gouache exhib. 22-Jan-3 Tajan, Paris #211/R

£592 $959 €900 Phare et balise (5x8cm-2x3in) s. gouache. 22-Jan-3 Tajan, Paris #212/R

£629 $975 €1000 Paysage de bord de mer (21x15cm-8x6in) s.i. gouache sold with another by the same artist. 30-Oct-2 Artcurial Briest, Paris #260

£1053 $1705 €1600 Saint Hubert (11x16cm-4x6in) s. s.i.d.verso gouache. 22-Jan-3 Tajan, Paris #210/R est:1800-2000

£1757 $2741 €2600 La maison de Fontainebleau (22x16cm-9x6in) s.d.26 gouache prov. 31-Mar-3 Pierre Berge, Paris #35/R est:2200-3000

£3404 $5515 €4800 Comportant quatre vues agrestes. s. gouache four exec.c.1950 prov. 20-May-3 Christie's, Paris #61/R est:5500-7500

£3800 $6004 €5700 Cmargue en hiver (23x15cm-9x6in) s. gouache prov.exhib. 3-Apr-3 Christie's, Kensington #82/R

£4113 $6664 €5800 Illustrant des vues de marines. s. gouache four exec.c.1950 prov. 20-May-3 Christie's, Paris #60/R est:6500-8500

£4610 $7468 €6500 Paysage animes. s. one i. gouache four exec.c.1950 prov. 20-May-3 Christie's, Paris #64/R est:7000-8000

£5106 $8272 €7200 Vue d'une entree. Nature morte. Village. La derniere un paysage anime. s. gouache four exec.c.1950 prov. 20-May-3 Christie's, Paris #59/R est:8000-10000

£5319 $8617 €7500 Illustrant des vues de bateaux ou de maisons. five s. two i. one d.49 one d.50 gouache 6 catalogue exec.c.1950. 20-May-3 Christie's, Paris #62/R est:6500-8500

£5319 $8617 €7500 Natures mortes. s. three gouache one ink four exec.c.1950 prov. 20-May-3 Christie's, Paris #63/R est:8000-10000

HUGO, Valentine (1890-1968) French

Works on paper

£2821 $4372 €4400 Portrait de Dominique Eluard (37x28cm-15x11in) Chinese ink graphite htd gouache exec.c.1945. 4-Dec-2 Christie's, Paris #138/R est:8000

HUGO, Victor (1802-1885) French

Works on paper

£4430 $6911 €7000 Le ruisseau (6x7cm-2x3in) wash sepia ink prov. 16-Oct-2 Fraysse & Associes, Paris #48/R est:4000-6000

£35443 $56000 €56000 Souvenir de la lande (24x32cm-9x13in) s.i. pen ink Chinese ink. 29-Nov-2 Drouot Estimations, Paris #59/R est:60000

£151899 $236962 €240000 Le burg sans nom de Neckarsteinach (49x31cm-19x12in) s.d.avril 1857 sepia wash dr prov.exhib.lit. 16-Oct-2 Fraysse & Associes, Paris #49/R est:80000-120000

HUGUENIN, Viretaux-Henri-Edouard (1878-1958) Swiss

£480 $749 €720 Aletsch glacier in autumn (46x38cm-18x15in) s. 6-Nov-2 Dobiaschofsky, Bern #681/R (S.FR 1100)

£480 $749 €720 Motifs de la foret et du glacier d'Aletsch (54x65cm-21x26in) s.d.1937. 8-Nov-2 Dobiaschofsky, Bern #95/R (S.FR 1100)

£524 $817 €786 Vue de la Moosfluh, Riederalp (46x55cm-18x22in) s. 8-Nov-2 Dobiaschofsky, Bern #97/R (S.FR 1200)

HUGUES, Jean (20th C) French?

Sculpture

£2500 $3950 €3600 Femme assise a la fontaine (55cm-22in) s. col pat bronze. 25-Apr-3 Drouot Estimations, Paris #31 est:1200-1500

HUGUES, Victor Louis (1827-?) French

£871 $1376 €1350 Couple de bergers dans un paysage (25x32cm-10x13in) s.d.1853. 18-Dec-2 Ferri, Paris #78/R

HUGUET, Victor Pierre (1835-1902) French

£2236 $3510 €3354 Arabs forging a river as sunset approaches (37x46cm-15x18in) s. board prov. 10-Dec-2 Pinneys, Montreal #57 est:6000-10000 (C.D 5500)

£2703 $4216 €4000 Oriental scene (54x45cm-21x18in) s. lit. 28-Mar-3 Karrenbauer, Konstanz #1748/R est:750

£3750 $6000 €5625 Desert caravan (37x46cm-15x18in) s. panel. 14-May-3 Butterfields, San Francisco #1127/R est:6000-8000

£4000 $6280 €6000 Figures on a river bank (37x46cm-15x18in) s. panel. 21-Nov-2 Christie's, Kensington #194/R est:4000-6000

£4808 $7548 €7500 Halte au bord de l'oued (37x46cm-15x18in) s. panel. 16-Dec-2 Gros & Delettrez, Paris #190/R est:6000-7500

£10000 $15700 €15000 La chasse au faucon (53x77cm-21x30in) s. 19-Nov-2 Sotheby's, London #162/R est:6000-8000

£16000 $24960 €24000 Crossing the desert (66x87cm-26x34in) s. prov. 15-Oct-2 Sotheby's, London #191/R est:12000-18000

HUHTAMO, Kari (20th C) Finnish

Sculpture

£1329 $2100 €2100 Composition (90x70cm-35x28in) s.d.1980 stainless steel. 1-Dec-2 Bukowskis, Helsinki #293/R est:1700-2000

£1582 $2500 €2500 The thought (38x52cm-15x20in) s.d.1977 stainless steel. 1-Dec-2 Bukowskis, Helsinki #292/R est:1700-2000

HUIDOBRO LAPLANA, Luis (1870-1936) Spanish

£449 $709 €700 Landscape (24x34cm-9x13in) s. 13-Nov-2 Ansorena, Madrid #330/R

HUILLARD, Esther (19/20th C) French

Works on paper

£270 $422 €400 Elegante en noir au manchon (46x28cm-18x11in) mono. pastel. 31-Mar-3 Rossini, Paris #56

HUILLIOT, Pierre Nicolas (1674-1751) French

£6552 $10483 €9500 Singe au pied de bouquet (262x100cm-103x39in) 11-Mar-3 Christie's, Paris #247/R

HUILLIOT, Pierre Nicolas (attrib) (1674-1751) French

£4000 $6320 €6200 Nature morte au vase de fleurs sur entablement (82x65cm-32x26in) 18-Dec-2 Piasa, Paris #102/R

HUIN, Charles Alexis (18th C) German

Works on paper

£1622 $2530 €2400 Portrait of lady with muff (45x36cm-18x14in) pastel prov.lit. 27-Mar-3 Dorotheum, Vienna #427/R est:2500-3000

HUINEMAN, Kornelis Jacobus (1886-1952) Dutch

£775 $1247 €1100 Town view in winter with sea gulls near canal (73x58cm-29x23in) s.d.1929. 7-May-3 Vendue Huis, Gravenhage #48/R

HUISUM, A van (19th C) Dutch

£692 $1079 €1100 Seascape (47x68cm-19x27in) 23-Sep-2 Dr Fritz Nagel, Stuttgart #7001/R

HUITEL, Eloise Caroline (1827-1896) French

£4200 $6552 €6300 Harun-ar-rashid and the poet (65x70cm-26x28in) s. exhib. 15-Oct-2 Sotheby's, London #199/R est:5000-7000

HUITTI, Ilmari (1897-1960) Finnish

£258 $408 €400 Landscape (39x45cm-15x18in) s. 19-Dec-2 Hagelstam, Helsinki #882/R

£504 $826 €700 Woman spinning (64x53cm-25x21in) s.d.28. 4-Jun-3 Bukowskis, Helsinki #304/R

HULA, Anton (1896-1946) Austrian

£347 $549 €500 Roses in glass (40x30cm-16x12in) s.d.1943 masonite. 24-Apr-3 Dorotheum, Vienna #112/R

HULDAH, Cherry Jeffe (20th C) American
£429 $700 €644 Portrait of a lady (33x33cm-13x13in) painted c.1950. 14-Feb-3 Du Mouchelle, Detroit #2162/R
£538 $850 €807 Curtain call (61x51cm-24x20in) s. 5-Apr-3 DeFina, Austinburg #1354
£609 $950 €914 Young lady in orange (91x61cm-36x24in) s. s.d.1958 verso. 5-Nov-2 Arthur James, Florida #65
£3846 $6000 €5769 In the patio (102x91cm-40x36in) s. s.i.d.1979 verso prov. 5-Nov-2 Arthur James, Florida #64

HULETT, Charles Willard (1903-1971) American
£311 $500 €467 Sycamore landscape (41x51cm-16x20in) s. masonite prov. 18-Feb-3 John Moran, Pasadena #153

HULETT, Ralph (19/20th C) American
£258 $400 €387 Mountain dunes, Banff (51x76cm-20x30in) s. i.verso. 29-Oct-2 John Moran, Pasadena #771

HULINGS, Clark (1922-) American
£6494 $10000 €9741 Street in Naples (51x20cm-20x8in) 25-Oct-2 Morris & Whiteside, Hilton Head Island #110 est:12000-15000
£11392 $18000 €16518 Going to market (20x30cm-8x12in) s. 26-Jul-3 Coeur d'Alene, Hayden #205/R est:10000-20000
£13782 $21500 €20673 Village in Spain (51x76cm-20x30in) 9-Nov-2 Altermann Galleries, Santa Fe #218
£17742 $27500 €26613 Apodaca Hill, Santa Fe (41x61cm-16x24in) s.d.1971 prov. 4-Dec-2 Sotheby's, New York #147/R est:25000-45000
£22152 $35000 €32120 Green watering can (76x51cm-30x20in) s.d.1978 s.i.verso prov.exhib.lit. 26-Jul-3 Coeur d'Alene, Hayden #101/R est:30000-50000
£81169 $125000 €121754 Montmartre in the rain (64x91cm-25x36in) 25-Oct-2 Morris & Whiteside, Hilton Head Island #111 est:100000-110000

Works on paper
£2055 $3000 €3083 Konda, Turkey (43x64cm-17x25in) W/C. 18-May-2 Altermann Galleries, Santa Fe #257/R

HULK, Abraham (19th C) Dutch
£306 $487 €450 Marine au voilier (22x31cm-9x12in) s. panel. 18-Mar-3 Campo, Vlaamse Kaai #114
£700 $1155 €1015 Fishing vessels in heavy seas (13x20cm-5x8in) s.d.1855 panel. 3-Jul-3 Duke & Son, Dorchester #210/R
£828 $1308 €1200 Storm clouds gathering above sailing ships off the coast (25x35cm-10x14in) s. W/C gouache. 5-Apr-3 Hans Stahl, Hamburg #158/R
£2200 $3564 €3300 Onshore breeze off the Dutch coast (35x55cm-14x22in) 21-May-3 Christie's, Kensington #378/R est:1500-2500
£3000 $4860 €4500 Stiff breeze. Fishing barges at dusk (15x20cm-6x8in) s. panel pair. 21-May-3 Christie's, Kensington #376/R est:4000-6000
£9800 $16170 €14210 Fishing boats in harbour at dusk. Rowing boat coming ashore (19x29cm-7x11in) s. pair. 1-Jul-3 Bearnes, Exeter #494/R est:4000-6000

HULK, Abraham (jnr) (1851-1922) British
£260 $416 €390 Landscape with oak trees and farmhouse (61x51cm-24x20in) s. 11-Mar-3 Gorringes, Lewes #2308
£300 $468 €450 Huntsman in the woods near Windsor (44x34cm-17x13in) s. 19-Sep-2 John Bellman, Billingshurst #1368
£300 $468 €450 Village pond (76x51cm-30x20in) 8-Apr-3 Bonhams, Knightsbridge #264/R
£320 $512 €480 Countryside scene, with young girl by a stream and farmstead (36x60cm-14x24in) s. 11-Mar-3 David Duggleby, Scarborough #222
£320 $512 €480 Country hamlet with drover and sheep on the road (50x76cm-20x30in) s. 13-May-3 Bonhams, Knightsbridge #204/R
£350 $543 €525 Extensive landscape, with figures and village beyond (60x50cm-24x20in) s. 29-Oct-2 Henry Adams, Chichester #546
£360 $598 €540 Devon rocky coastal view (29x24cm-11x9in) s.i.verso. 10-Jun-3 Bonhams, Knightsbridge #193/R
£650 $988 €975 Feeding the chickens before a farmstead. Shepherdess with her flock (61x41cm-24x16in) s. pair. 29-Aug-2 Christie's, Kensington #203/R
£833 $1300 €1250 Figure in a landscape with stream (61x41cm-24x16in) s. 20-Sep-2 Sloan, North Bethesda #442/R est:1500-2500
£1242 $2037 €1900 Woodland road (35x25cm-14x10in) s. i.verso. 9-Feb-3 Bukowskis, Helsinki #412/R
£7758 $12568 €11249 Dutch fishing boats (37x53cm-15x21in) s. 26-May-3 Bukowskis, Stockholm #235/R est:30000-35000 (S.KR 100000)

Works on paper
£280 $445 €420 River landscape (34x45cm-13x18in) s. W/C. 29-Apr-3 Bonhams, Knightsbridge #26/R

HULK, Abraham (snr) (1813-1897) Dutch
£1572 $2421 €2500 Fishermen brining in the nets (20x25cm-8x10in) s. panel. 22-Oct-2 Sotheby's, Amsterdam #15/R est:3000-5000
£3000 $5010 €4500 Shipping off the Dutch coast (15x20cm-6x8in) s. panel. 18-Jun-3 Christie's, Kensington #55a/R est:3000-4000
£3158 $5116 €4800 Calm (20x30cm-8x12in) s. 21-Jan-3 Christie's, Amsterdam #72/R est:2500-3500
£3205 $4968 €5000 Bateaux de peche a maree basse (15x20cm-6x8in) s. panel. 5-Dec-2 Gros & Delettrez, Paris #10/R
£3400 $5678 €4930 On the Scheldt (17x25cm-7x10in) s. panel. 18-Jun-3 Sotheby's, Olympia #39/R est:2000-3000
£3500 $5565 €5250 Sailing boats off the Dutch coast (28x39cm-11x15in) panel. 20-Mar-3 Christie's, Kensington #149/R est:4000-6000
£3571 $5643 €5357 An evening calm (20x30cm-8x12in) s. panel. 26-Nov-2 Sotheby's, Melbourne #185/R est:10000-15000 (A.D 10000)
£4747 $7405 €7500 Marina with yachts and fishing boats (54x73cm-21x29in) 21-Oct-2 Bernaerts, Antwerp #141/R est:7500-9000
£4930 $7937 €7000 Fishing ships on the sea (25x40cm-10x16in) s. 7-May-3 Vendue Huis, Gravenhage #397/R est:7000-9000
£5500 $8965 €7975 Shipping in a calm sea (17x25cm-7x10in) s. panel. 16-Jul-3 Sotheby's, Olympia #188/R est:3000-5000
£6000 $9540 €9000 Hauling in the nets (30x41cm-12x16in) s. 20-Mar-3 Christie's, Kensington #148/R est:7000-10000
£6200 $10354 €8990 Fisherman and their boats at evening, other boats offshore (41x61cm-16x24in) s. prov. 18-Jun-3 Sotheby's, Olympia #38/R est:4000-6000
£6329 $10000 €9494 Shipping at Lowestoft (61x91cm-24x36in) s. prov. 3-Apr-3 Boos Gallery, Michigan #274/R est:15000-25000
£6849 $10753 €10000 Ships at anchor in a calm (24x32cm-9x13in) s. panel. 15-Apr-3 Sotheby's, Amsterdam #9/R est:3000-5000
£8000 $12560 €12000 Shipping in an estuary (25x17cm-10x7in) s. board prov. 19-Nov-2 Sotheby's, London #136/R est:6000-8000
£14000 $22960 €21000 Dutch coastal scenes with sailing vessels (18x25cm-7x10in) s. panel pair. 4-Feb-3 Sworder & Son, Bishops Stortford #137/R est:12000-15000
£15000 $25050 €22500 Shipping in a squall. Shipping in a calm (17x25cm-7x10in) s. panel pair. 19-Jun-3 Christie's, London #57/R est:15000-20000

Works on paper
£1384 $2131 €2200 Sailing vessels in a calm (13x21cm-5x8in) s. pencil W/C htd white. 23-Oct-2 Christie's, Amsterdam #78/R est:2500-3500
£1549 $2494 €2200 Ships on calm water (15x24cm-6x9in) s. W/C. 7-May-3 Vendue Huis, Gravenhage #403/R est:800-1000

HULK, Hendrik (1842-1937) Dutch
£1220 $2000 €1830 Beach with anchored fishing boats and fishermen (30x46cm-12x18in) s. 5-Feb-3 Christie's, Rockefeller NY #211/R est:3000-5000
£1911 $2943 €3000 Calm, a haybarge on the river (32x47cm-13x19in) prov. 3-Sep-2 Christie's, Amsterdam #280/R est:2500-3500
£4167 $6625 €6000 Sailing barges on a river. Vessel on a calm river (32x50cm-13x20in) s. panel pair. 29-Apr-3 Christie's, Amsterdam #10/R est:2500-3500

HULK, John Frederick (jnr) (1855-1913) Dutch
£634 $1020 €900 Ducks at the edge of the water (26x20cm-10x8in) s.d.92 panel. 7-May-3 Vendue Huis, Gravenhage #431/R
£1250 $2063 €1800 Sportsmen with their pointers at a pond (71x56cm-28x22in) s. plywood. 1-Jul-3 Christie's, Amsterdam #74/R est:700-900

HULK, John Frederick (snr) (1829-1911) Dutch
£1300 $2028 €1950 The pursuit (92x61cm-36x24in) s.d.92. 6-Nov-2 Sotheby's, Olympia #163/R est:1500-2000
£1494 $2181 €2300 View of city with figures on the quay (27x21cm-11x8in) s. panel. 19-Jun-2 Vendue Huis, Gravenhage #168/R
£5208 $8594 €7500 Daily activities along a Dutch canal (59x49cm-23x19in) s.d.1872. 1-Jul-3 Christie's, Amsterdam #56/R est:5000-7000
£13699 $21507 €20000 Town view Amsterdam (61x91cm-24x36in) s. i.verso. 15-Apr-3 Sotheby's, Amsterdam #157/R est:20000-30000
£14000 $21700 €21000 Haarlam (62x92cm-24x36in) s. 4-Dec-2 Christie's, London #34/R est:15000-20000

HULK, William F (1852-1906) British
£320 $531 €480 Drover and cattle on a country road (30x25cm-12x10in) s. 10-Jun-3 Bonhams, Knightsbridge #254/R
£573 $894 €900 Cow at the edge of ditch (29x24cm-11x9in) s. 6-Nov-2 Vendue Huis, Gravenhage #433
£603 $1007 €850 Fishing boats on the river (31x46cm-12x18in) s. 23-Jun-3 Bernaerts, Antwerp #28/R
£605 $944 €950 Landscape with cows (28x21cm-11x8in) s. 6-Nov-2 Vendue Huis, Gravenhage #434/R
£760 $1208 €1140 Cattle in watermeadows (20x14cm-8x6in) s. board pair. 27-Feb-3 Bonhams, Chester #378
£839 $1300 €1259 Cows at pasture (13x25cm-5x10in) s. board. 28-Sep-2 Charlton Hall, Columbia #551/R
£1210 $1888 €1900 Meadow with cows resting at the water (73x126cm-29x50in) s. 6-Nov-2 Vendue Huis, Gravenhage #432/R est:1500-2000
£2000 $3340 €2900 In the meadow (74x122cm-29x48in) s.d.78. 20-Jun-3 Keys, Aylsham #716/R est:1000-1500

HULL, Frederick William (1867-1953) British?
£250 $388 €375 Feeding chickens (25x36cm-10x14in) s. board. 2-Oct-2 John Ross, Belfast #186
£500 $775 €750 Lock gates on the Lagan (25x36cm-10x14in) s. board. 2-Oct-2 John Ross, Belfast #5
£600 $930 €900 Corn stacks in the Glens (25x36cm-10x14in) s. board. 2-Oct-2 John Ross, Belfast #185

HULL, James (1921-1990) British
£750 $1170 €1125 Abstract composition in black, yellow and white (84x38cm-33x15in) s.d.56 board. 15-Oct-2 Bonhams, Knightsbridge #212/R

HULL, John (20th C) American
£414 $650 €621 Valley of darkness (102x122cm-40x48in) s.d.1985 verso acrylic. 21-Nov-2 Swann Galleries, New York #86/R
£793 $1300 €1150 Brotherhood (61x81cm-24x32in) acrylic exhib. 1-Jun-3 Wright, Chicago #237/R est:1500-2000

HULL, Kata (20th C) American
£500 $800 €725 Midsummer (35x23cm-14x9in) s.i.d.1999 verso board. 16-May-3 Skinner, Boston #364/R

HULL, Marie (1890-1980) American
£1835 $2900 €2753 Rocky outcrop in the waves (30x51cm-12x20in) s. prov. 5-Apr-3 Neal Auction Company, New Orleans #329a/R est:3000-5000

HULL, William (1820-1880) British
Works on paper
£600 $942 €900 Welsh mountain stream (34x53cm-13x21in) s.d.1859 pencil W/C. 16-Apr-3 Christie's, Kensington #1041/R

HULLEY, Henry (fl.1783-1800) British
£1500 $2370 €2250 Wagon with team of eight outside a tavern (38x53cm-15x21in) s.d.1800. 2-Dec-2 Bonhams, Bath #124 est:1500-2000

HULLGREN, Oscar (1869-1948) Swedish
£1064 $1649 €1596 At the outer skerries (93x127cm-37x50in) s.d.1938 exhib. 4-Dec-2 AB Stockholms Auktionsverk #1650/R est:15000-18000 (S.KR 15000)

HULME, Frederick William (1816-1884) British
£1234 $1950 €1851 Watermill, Derbyshire (41x61cm-16x24in) s. 18-Nov-2 Schrager Galleries, Milwaukee #1294
£2500 $3950 €3750 Rest on the way to market (51x66cm-20x26in) s.d.1859 canvas on board. 26-Nov-2 Sotheby's, Melbourne #219/R est:8000-12000 (A.D 7000)
£3000 $4800 €4500 Surrey landscape (76x127cm-30x50in) s.d.1870. 11-Mar-3 Bonhams, Knightsbridge #322/R est:3000-5000
£28000 $44240 €42000 Sheep resting in woodland glade, traveller looking on (71x59cm-28x23in) s.d.1865 prov. 26-Nov-2 Christie's, London #123/R est:18000-25000

HULSDONCK, Jacob van (1582-1647) Flemish
£80000 $125600 €120000 Bunch of grapes on the vine (18x23cm-7x9in) s. copper prov. 11-Dec-2 Christie's, London #17/R est:40000-60000

HULSDONCK, Jacob van (attrib) (1582-1647) Flemish
£39161 $65399 €56000 Nature morte au panier d'abricots, prunes et raisins sur un entablement (49x71cm-19x28in) copper. 27-Jun-3 Piasa, Paris #19/R est:40000-50000

HULSDONCK, Jacob van (style) (1582-1647) Flemish
£12658 $20000 €20000 Basket with grapes, apricots, plums ad figs (55x71cm-22x28in) panel. 27-Nov-2 Christie's, Paris #3/R est:20000-30000

HULSEBOOM, Gerrit (attrib) (1784-1863) Dutch
£633 $987 €1000 Landscape with figures by a river (35x44cm-14x17in) panel. 21-Oct-2 Glerum, Amsterdam #140/R

HULSER, Joseph (1819-1850) German
£2397 $3740 €3500 Vierwaldstatter See (97x140cm-38x55in) s.d.1847. 10-Apr-3 Van Ham, Cologne #1492/R est:8000

HULST, Frans de (1610-1661) Flemish
£4808 $7548 €7500 Fortified tower on Dutch river (39x52cm-15x20in) panel oval. 21-Nov-2 Van Ham, Cologne #1369/R est:8500
£12579 $19497 €20000 Resting peasants outside village among dunes (41x53cm-16x21in) panel. 2-Oct-2 Dorotheum, Vienna #97/R est:20000-25000

HULSWIT, Jan (1766-1822) Dutch
£6369 $9936 €10000 Wooded landscape with houses, sheep and cow near a stream, and two shepherds paddling beyond (78x103cm-31x41in) 5-Nov-2 Sotheby's, Amsterdam #213/R est:7000-9000

HULTEN, C O (1916-) Swedish
£684 $1088 €1026 Echo of the beach (37x45cm-15x18in) s.d.58 panel. 3-Mar-3 Lilla Bukowskis, Stockholm #585 (S.KR 9200)

HULTEN, Carl Otto (1916-) Swedish
£2239 $3605 €3359 Meeting and transformation (65x81cm-26x32in) s.d.59. 7-May-3 AB Stockholms Auktionsverk #810/R est:25000-30000 (S.KR 29000)

Works on paper
£837 $1322 €1256 Bird woman - imaginary painting (33x45cm-13x18in) s. mixed media executed c.1950 exhib. 28-Apr-3 Bukowskis, Stockholm #258/R (S.KR 11000)

HUMBERT, Jean-Charles-Ferdinand (1813-1881) Swiss
£1217 $1899 €1826 Landscape with horses and sheep (44x61cm-17x24in) s. 16-Sep-2 Philippe Schuler, Zurich #3376/R est:2000-2400 (S.FR 2800)
£2778 $4472 €4028 Landscape with riders (33x49cm-13x19in) s.d.1849 masonite. 9-May-3 Dobiaschofsky, Bern #3/R est:7500 (S.FR 6000)
£2778 $4472 €4028 Cattle watering (79x128cm-31x50in) s.d.1879. 9-May-3 Dobiaschofsky, Bern #35/R est:8500 (S.FR 6000)

HUMBLOT, Robert (1907-1962) French
£694 $1104 €1000 Paysage des alpilles (27x35cm-11x14in) s. 29-Apr-3 Artcurial Briest, Paris #271
£1709 $2649 €2700 Vue de Bretagne (38x61cm-15x24in) s.d.56 prov. 28-Sep-2 Christie's, Paris #31/R est:3000-4500
£1795 $2782 €2800 Village (58x90cm-23x35in) s.d.43 prov. 3-Dec-2 Christie's, Amsterdam #31/R est:3000-5000
£1803 $2866 €2650 Nature morte au vase de roses (43x60cm-17x24in) s.d.56. 26-Feb-3 Artcurial Briest, Paris #340/R est:3000-4000
£2258 $3568 €3500 Barques de peche au port de Saint-Guenole (38x61cm-15x24in) s. 19-Dec-2 Claude Aguttes, Neuilly #170/R
£2414 $4031 €3500 Saint Guenole (61x38cm-24x15in) s. 9-Jul-3 Millon & Associes, Paris #195/R est:3000-4000
£2973 $4638 €4400 Bateaux a maree basse (50x73cm-20x29in) s.d.58. 26-Mar-3 Millon & Associes, Paris #104/R

HUME, Edith (fl.1862-1906) British
£1600 $2608 €2320 Gathering cockle shells (16x11cm-6x4in) init. board. 16-Jul-3 Sotheby's, Olympia #79/R est:800-1200
£1900 $2945 €2850 Fisher girl (26x20cm-10x8in) indis.sig. 5-Dec-2 Bonhams, Edinburgh #45/R est:700-900
£2500 $3875 €3750 Fisher girl unloading the catch (29x23cm-11x9in) s. panel. 5-Dec-2 Bonhams, Edinburgh #46/R est:1000-1500
£2800 $4452 €4200 Fishergirl (30x23cm-12x9in) s. panel. 6-Mar-3 Christie's, Kensington #582/R est:3000-5000

HUME, Edith (attrib) (fl.1862-1906) British
£1467 $2436 €2127 Gathering wild flowers (30x24cm-12x9in) panel. 16-Jun-3 Lilla Bukowskis, Stockholm #35 est:4000-5000 (S.KR 19000)

HUME, Gary (1962-) British
£32500 $52000 €48750 Girl boy, boy girl (209x142cm-82x56in) s.d.1991 enamel MDF board in two parts prov.exhib. 15-May-3 Phillips, New York #36/R est:50000-70000
£58000 $96860 €87000 Seahorse (221x170cm-87x67in) s.i.d.1997 verso enamel aluminium panel prov.exhib. 25-Jun-3 Sotheby's, London #4/R est:50000-70000
£85000 $130900 €127500 3 (305x241cm-120x95in) enamel paint on aluminium panel executed 2000 prov. 22-Oct-2 Sotheby's, London #315/R est:70000-100000

Works on paper
£280 $468 €406 Fuzzy snowman (27x19cm-11x7in) s.verso felt card. 24-Jun-3 Sotheby's, Olympia #27/R
£400 $652 €600 Fuzzy snowman (27x19cm-11x7in) s.verso fuzzy felt on card. 3-Feb-3 Sotheby's, Olympia #40/R est:300-500
£6000 $10020 €8700 Kate Moss (71x56cm-28x22in) s.i.d.00 verso felt tip pen glass on aluminium prov. 26-Jun-3 Sotheby's, London #291/R est:6000-8000
£12500 $20500 €18750 Rome V (147x95cm-58x37in) s.i.d.93 pastel prov. 7-Feb-3 Sotheby's, London #116/R est:8000-12000

HUME, Robert (1861-1937) British
£320 $531 €464 East Lothian Burn (27x23cm-11x9in) s. 13-Jun-3 Lyon & Turnbull, Edinburgh #90

HUMME, Julius (1825-1889) Canadian
£723 $1135 €1085 Sunset on the Black River (28x44cm-11x17in) mono.i. 25-Nov-2 Hodgins, Calgary #50/R (C.D 1800)
£1245 $1955 €1868 Basket weaving on the Black River (50x40cm-20x16in) mono.i. 25-Nov-2 Hodgins, Calgary #32/R est:1500-2000 (C.D 3100)
£1365 $2144 €2048 Road north of Orillia (29x44cm-11x17in) mono.i. canvas on board. 25-Nov-2 Hodgins, Calgary #49/R est:1500-1800 (C.D 3400)
Works on paper
£622 $1020 €933 Fishing by the rapids. Fishing on a quiet back water (20x27cm-8x11in) s.d.84 pair. 3-Jun-3 Joyner, Toronto #358/R est:1200-1500 (C.D 1400)

HUMMEL, Carl (1821-1907) German
£651 $1015 €950 Bushes in wood (36x51cm-14x20in) 11-Apr-3 Winterberg, Heidelberg #411
£9787 $15464 €14681 Landscape view of Capri (72x100cm-28x39in) s.d.1886 prov. 2-Dec-2 Rasmussen, Copenhagen #1142/R est:150000 (D.KR 115000)
Miniatures
£3200 $5248 €4640 Young lady holding her gauze white dress and light blue cashmere stole (7x9cm-3x4in) s.d.1810gilt metal frame rec. 3-Jun-3 Christie's, London #249/R est:2000-3000

HUMMEL, Carl de Bourdon (c.1769-1840) Austrian
Works on paper
£541 $843 €800 Portrait of young woman with curly hair (4cm-2in circular) s. W/C ivory. 28-Mar-3 Dorotheum, Vienna #361/R

HUMPHREY, Edward J (fl.1872-1889) British
Works on paper
£700 $1113 €1050 Cairo date seller (53x36cm-21x14in) s.d.1882 W/C. 29-Apr-3 Bonhams, New Bond Street #106

HUMPHREY, Florence (fl.1905-1940) British
£386 $603 €560 What shall we do ? (27x34cm-11x13in) s. panel exhib. 26-Mar-3 Walker's, Ottawa #85/R est:1000-1500 (C.D 900)

HUMPHREY, Jack Weldon (1901-1967) Canadian
£314 $502 €471 Coal harbour (38x55cm-15x22in) s. board. 15-May-3 Heffel, Vancouver #48 (C.D 700)
£1815 $2867 €2723 Flowers and checkerboard. Bearded man (76x59cm-30x23in) s. double-sided prov. 14-Nov-2 Heffel, Vancouver #100/R est:4500-6500 (C.D 4500)
£1815 $2867 €2723 Portrait of a girl with calendulas (60x49cm-24x19in) s. double-sided. 14-Nov-2 Heffel, Vancouver #181/R est:5000-6000 (C.D 4500)
Works on paper
£526 $784 €789 Abstraction (39x54cm-15x21in) s. gouache. 26-Jun-2 Iegor de Saint Hippolyte, Montreal #51 (C.D 1200)

HUMPHREY, Ozias (1742-1810) British
Miniatures
£1600 $2496 €2400 Mrs John Egerton seated besides an urn (23cm-9xin) i.d.1783 verso pencil crayon card rec. prov.lit. 5-Nov-2 Bonhams, New Bond Street #5/R est:500-700
£1700 $2652 €2550 Signor Venanzio Rauzzini with his hand tucked inside his waistcoat (21cm-8xin) i.verso pencil crayon paper rec. prov.lit. 5-Nov-2 Bonhams, New Bond Street #6/R est:500-700
£2100 $3402 €3150 Sir John MacPherson, Governor General of India (9cm-4xin) s.i.verso. 22-May-3 Bonhams, New Bond Street #112/R est:2000-3000
£3500 $5740 €5075 Young officer, probably of an Indian infantry regiment (5cm-2xin) s.d.1786 gold frame oval prov. 3-Jun-3 Christie's, London #137/R est:2500-3500

HUMPHREY, Thomas (1858-1927) Australian
£382 $603 €573 Distant hills (46x77cm-18x30in) s. 1-Apr-3 Lawson Menzies, Sydney #484 (A.D 1000)

HUMPHREYS, Ian (20th C) British
£280 $468 €406 Cup (45x40cm-18x16in) s.d.85. 17-Jun-3 Bonhams, Knightsbridge #11/R
£320 $518 €480 Green table (76x85cm-30x33in) 20-May-3 Bonhams, Knightsbridge #9/R
£440 $686 €660 Painted bird (101x75cm-40x30in) 17-Sep-2 Bonhams, Knightsbridge #152/R
Works on paper
£320 $499 €480 Two figures (21x31cm-8x12in) s. gouache. 17-Sep-2 Bonhams, Knightsbridge #35/R
£450 $702 €675 Standing figure (71x50cm-28x20in) s. gouache. 17-Sep-2 Bonhams, Knightsbridge #149/R

HUMPHRIES, Jacqueline (1960-) American
£1220 $2000 €1769 Four corners (183x183cm-72x72in) s.verso oil on linen prov. 1-Jun-3 Wright, Chicago #348/R est:2000-3000

HUMPHRISS, Charles Henry (1867-1934) British
Sculpture
£1000 $1600 €1450 Warrior (41cm-16in) s.i.d.1904 brown pat bronze sold with black marble base. 16-May-3 Skinner, Boston #133/R est:2200-2800
£1438 $2300 €2157 Pray to the great spirit. s. bronze. 12-Jan-3 William Jenack, New York #219
£5975 $9500 €8963 Warrior (41cm-16in) i. dark reddish brown pat. bronze i.f.Roman prov. 5-Mar-3 Sotheby's, New York #134/R est:12000-18000
£7051 $11000 €10577 Sundial (48x23x23cm-19x9x9in) i. bronze prov.lit. 9-Nov-2 Santa Fe Art, Santa Fe #191/R est:12000-17000
£14516 $22500 €21774 Appeal to the Great Spirit (79cm-31in) dark brown pat. bronze i.f.Roman prov.lit. 4-Dec-2 Sotheby's, New York #153/R est:12000-18000

HUNAEUS, Andreas (1814-1866) Danish
£279 $444 €419 Tyrolean singer (28x18cm-11x7in) i.verso. 5-Mar-3 Rasmussen, Copenhagen #1926/R (D.KR 3000)
£354 $563 €531 Young man with black jacket and white shirt (27x21cm-11x8in) prov. 5-Mar-3 Rasmussen, Copenhagen #2028 (D.KR 3800)

HUNDERTWASSER, Friedrich (1928-2000) Austrian
Prints
£1987 $3080 €3100 City-city (56x76cm-22x30in) s.num.83/350 col silk print exec.1979. 7-Dec-2 Van Ham, Cologne #248/R est:4500
£2025 $3139 €3200 City citizen (76x56cm-30x22in) s.i.d.28 III 94 col serigraph photo lithograph metal. 28-Sep-2 Ketterer, Hamburg #530/R est:3200-3500
£2025 $3200 €3200 Pacific steamers (52x39cm-20x15in) s.i. col woodcut. 30-Nov-2 Villa Grisebach, Berlin #435/R est:3000-3500
£2201 $3500 €3302 Good-bye from Africa (47x62cm-19x24in) s.d.num.70/70 col lithograph metal. 2-May-3 Sotheby's, New York #180/R est:3000-5000
£2201 $3500 €3302 La barca (67x42cm-26x17in) s.d.num.C/101/251 metal col screenprint. 2-May-3 Sotheby's, New York #181 est:2000-2500
£2201 $3500 €3302 Two clouds raining seven colours (29x51cm-11x20in) s.d.num.47/200 col woodcut. 2-May-3 Sotheby's, New York #184/R est:3000-5000
£2308 $3577 €3600 Sudsee II - journey by train to the sea (65x50cm-26x20in) s.d.1967 num.233/267 col lithograph. 7-Dec-2 Van Ham, Cologne #244/R est:3200
£2516 $4000 €3774 Meadowman, brown (32x24cm-13x9in) s.d.num.20/240 col etching aquatint. 2-May-3 Sotheby's, New York #187/R est:3000-4000
£2673 $4250 €4010 Two trees on board of regentag (37x51cm-15x20in) s.red chop num.47/200 col woodcut portfolio box. 2-May-3 Sotheby's, New York #183/R est:3000-5000
£2673 $4250 €4010 Rain falls far from us (37x51cm-15x20in) s.d.num.47/200 col woodcut. 2-May-3 Sotheby's, New York #185/R est:3000-5000
£2830 $4500 €4245 Meadowman, blue (32x24cm-13x9in) s.d.num.25/240 col etching aquatint. 2-May-3 Sotheby's, New York #186/R est:3000-4000
£2848 $4415 €4500 The rain falls far from us (37x51cm-15x20in) s.i.d.10.2.82 col woodcut gold. 28-Sep-2 Ketterer, Hamburg #525/R est:5000-6000
£2848 $4500 €4500 Town in town (44x63cm-17x25in) s. col serigraph. 30-Nov-2 Bassenge, Berlin #6344/R est:3000
£2950 $4719 €4100 Rainy day with Walter Kampmann (41x58cm-16x23in) s.i. num.67/170 col serigraph. 15-May-3 Neumeister, Munich #460/R est:2500-2800
£3077 $4769 €4800 Pacific steamer (57x41cm-22x16in) s.i.d.85 num.341/999 col woodcut. 6-Dec-2 Ketterer, Munich #205/R est:4800-5000
£3459 $5500 €5189 Kleine welten VI (27x23cm-11x9in) s. woodcut edition of 200. 2-May-3 Sotheby's, New York #189/R est:5000-7000
£3669 $6017 €5100 Testament in yellow (52x74cm-20x29in) s.i.d.24. Mai 1971 col silkscreen over silver foil. 6-Jun-3 Ketterer, Munich #130/R est:7400-7800

£3712 $5828 €5568 In the snow - Barnbach worship (37x44cm-15x17in) s.d.1987 col etching aquatint lit. 25-Nov-2 Germann, Zurich #426/R est:7000-9000 (S.FR 8500)

Works on paper

£556 $878 €800 Spiral. Head (15x10cm-6x4in) W/C postcard two. 24-Apr-3 Dorotheum, Vienna #163/R
£2800 $4340 €4200 Spirale fallen into downtown white garden (17x21cm-7x8in) s.i.d.1961 s.i.d.verso pen brush ink exhit.lit. 5-Dec-2 Christie's, Kensington #195/R est:2000-4000
£7000 $11690 €10150 Dalai Lama - flucht mit durchbohrter spirale (19x27cm-7x11in) s. W/C executed 1959 prov. 27-Jun-3 Christie's, London #131/R est:7000-9000
£48000 $78720 €72000 Funchal (45x62cm-18x24in) s.d.1973 s.i.d.verso W/C egg-tempera oil prov.exhib.lit. 6-Feb-3 Christie's, London #608/R est:30000-40000
£60000 $100200 €87000 Grune welle (44x63cm-17x25in) s.d.1972-73 s.i.d.verso W/C col pencil chk vinyl prov.exhib.lit. 27-Jun-3 Christie's, London #132/R est:30000-40000

HUNDT, Hermann Baptist (1894-1974) German

£1159 $1901 €1600 Concert (75x95cm-30x37in) s. 29-May-3 Lempertz, Koln #682/R est:2000

HUNGARIAN SCHOOL, 18th C

£441 $684 €662 St Barbara (38x25cm-15x10in) 1-Oct-2 SOGA, Bratislava #18/R est:35000 (SL.K 28000)
£583 $903 €875 St John (75x62cm-30x24in) 1-Oct-2 SOGA, Bratislava #19/R est:35000 (SL.K 37000)

HUNN, Tom (fl.1878-1908) British

Works on paper

£270 $429 €405 Spring time, Thorncombe, Surrey (33x51cm-13x20in) s.i. W/C. 5-Mar-3 Bonhams, Bury St Edmunds #311
£400 $632 €580 Country garden in Graffham, Sussex (33x50cm-13x20in) s.d.1906 W/C. 22-Jul-3 Bonhams, Knightsbridge #86/R
£620 $980 €930 Old Place, Lindfield (29x50cm-11x20in) s.d.1901 W/C. 26-Nov-2 Bonhams, Knightsbridge #48/R
£1300 $2080 €1950 Thames at Goring church and Mill, Oxfordshire (47x71cm-19x28in) s. W/C. 11-Mar-3 Bonhams, New Bond Street #75/R est:1500-2000

HUNT, Alan M (1947-) British

Works on paper

£503 $775 €800 Canards sur l'etang (27x34cm-11x13in) s. gouache. 22-Oct-2 Campo, Vlaamse Kaai #157

HUNT, Alfred William (1830-1896) British

Works on paper

£500 $780 €750 Heidelberg (25x35cm-10x14in) i.d.1850 verso pencil W/C. 17-Oct-2 Christie's, Kensington #127
£2400 $3936 €3480 Rokeby, Yorkshire (28x40cm-11x16in) pencil W/C scratching out prov. 5-Jun-3 Christie's, London #112/R est:2500-3500
£4400 $6864 €6600 View of Harlech Castle (33x51cm-13x20in) W/C. 15-Oct-2 Gorringes, Lewes #2178/R est:2500-3500

HUNT, Andrew (1790-1861) British

£300 $492 €450 Figures on stepping stones (43x60cm-17x24in) indis.s exhib. 4-Jun-3 Bonhams, Chester #294

HUNT, Bryan (1947-) American

£1720 $2700 €2580 Concorde window (29x22cm-11x9in) s.i.d. oil pastel rag paper prov. 19-Nov-2 Wright, Chicago #266/R est:3000-4000

Sculpture

£18987 $30000 €28481 Airship (20x103x13cm-8x41x5in) paper oil acrylic wood exec.1979 prov.exhib. 13-Nov-2 Sotheby's, New York #540/R est:30000-40000

HUNT, Cecil Arthur (1873-1965) British

Works on paper

£320 $499 €480 Bernina Pass, looking towards Switzerland (22x32cm-9x13in) s. i.verso pencil prov. 25-Mar-3 Gildings, Market Harborough #384
£420 $655 €630 Arisaig, Scotland (27x38cm-11x15in) s. W/C sold with another. 25-Mar-3 Gildings, Market Harborough #394
£900 $1404 €1350 Highland Head farm. English lakes (36x52cm-14x20in) s. W/C two. 5-Nov-2 Bonhams, New Bond Street #101/R

HUNT, Charles (attrib) (19th C) British

£750 $1163 €1125 Trial, an interior scene with two young children wearing mock wigs (16x22cm-6x9in) s. 5-Dec-2 Ambrose, Loughton #825/R

HUNT, Charles (jnr) (1829-1900) British

£1000 $1540 €1500 New pupil (25x37cm-10x15in) s. 5-Sep-2 Christie's, Kensington #273/R est:2000-3000
£2400 $3888 €3600 Judge and jury (16x24cm-6x9in) s.d.1866. 20-May-3 Sotheby's, Olympia #255/R est:1200-1800
£2500 $3900 €3750 Suitor (46x60cm-18x24in) s.d.83. 26-Mar-3 Sotheby's, Olympia #139/R est:2500-5000
£2857 $4514 €4286 Travelling artist (61x91cm-24x36in) 26-Nov-2 Sotheby's, Melbourne #213/R est:10000-15000 (A.D 8000)
£3036 $4675 €4554 Untitled - gentleman riding a horse pulled cart (75x114cm-30x45in) s.d.81 i.on stretcher verso. 3-Sep-2 Shapiro, Sydney #442/R est:8000-12000 (A.D 8500)

HUNT, Charles D (1840-1914) American

£1824 $2900 €2736 Mountain lake, autumn (44x68cm-17x27in) s.d.1874. 7-Mar-3 Skinner, Boston #269/R est:2000-2500
£3459 $5500 €5189 Open landscape with grazing cattle (34x59cm-13x23in) s.d.1866. 7-Mar-3 Skinner, Boston #265/R est:1500-2000

HUNT, Daisy Vere (?) British

Works on paper

£280 $434 €420 Continental town scene (36x51cm-14x20in) s. W/C pen ink. 1-Nov-2 Moore Allen & Innocent, Cirencester #339

HUNT, Edgar (1876-1953) British

£1300 $2028 €1950 Mallard drake by reeds (15x15cm-6x6in) s. board. 26-Mar-3 Hamptons Fine Art, Godalming #145/R est:1500-2000
£2800 $4452 €4200 Stable friends (18x25cm-7x10in) s. board. 6-Mar-3 Christie's, Kensington #564/R est:1500-2000
£5000 $7950 €7500 Chickens, chicks and pigeons (31x25cm-12x10in) s.d.1906. 18-Mar-3 Bonhams, New Bond Street #104/R est:5000-7000
£6500 $10205 €9750 Mother goat with her kids (28x38cm-11x15in) s.d.1945 canvasboard. 19-Nov-2 Bonhams, New Bond Street #131/R est:8000-12000
£7800 $12636 €11700 Three guinea pig's (22x30cm-9x12in) s.d.1901 panel prov. 20-May-3 Sotheby's, Olympia #38/R est:5000-7000
£8000 $12560 €12000 Pride of the roost (84x127cm-33x50in) s.d.1910. 19-Nov-2 Bonhams, New Bond Street #71/R est:10000-15000
£8200 $13612 €12300 Cockerel and chickens (19x23cm-7x9in) s.d.1913. 12-Jun-3 Sotheby's, London #283/R est:10000-15000
£10000 $16700 €14500 Goat and chickens inside a barn (26x33cm-10x13in) s.d.1913 panel. 17-Jun-3 Bonhams, New Bond Street #80/R est:10000-15000
£10000 $16700 €14500 Chickens in a barn (25x29cm-10x11in) s.d.1911 panel. 17-Jun-3 Bonhams, New Bond Street #81/R est:10000-15000
£11200 $18704 €16240 Poultry, pigeons and a goat in a farmyard (21x27cm-8x11in) s.d.1926. 17-Jun-3 Anderson & Garland, Newcastle #457/R est:8000-14000
£11377 $19000 €16497 Barnyard (30x41cm-12x16in) s.d.1938 prov. 22-Jun-3 Freeman, Philadelphia #43/R est:15000-25000
£11800 $19116 €17700 Pigeons and doves outside a cottage door (30x25cm-12x10in) s.d.1915 prov. 20-May-3 Sotheby's, Olympia #37/R est:6000-8000
£13100 $20437 €19650 Chickens. Rabbits and doves (20x28cm-8x11in) s. two. 20-Nov-2 Fischer, Luzern #1151/R est:30000-40000 (S.FR 30000)
£14500 $24215 €21025 Chickens and rabbits in a farmyard (36x30cm-14x12in) s. 17-Jun-3 Bonhams, New Bond Street #90/R est:10000-15000
£16500 $27555 €23925 Goats and chickens in an interior (61x91cm-24x36in) s.d.1904. 17-Jun-3 Bonhams, New Bond Street #79/R est:12000-18000
£18000 $28620 €27000 Pigeons and ducks. Rabbits and chickens by a hutch (25x20cm-10x8in) s.d.1915 pair prov. 18-Mar-3 Bonhams, New Bond Street #102/R est:15000-20000
£21000 $33390 €31500 Goats and chickens in a stable (61x91cm-24x36in) s.d.1906. 18-Mar-3 Bonhams, New Bond Street #103/R est:12000-18000
£22000 $36520 €33000 Chickens, chicks and doves. Rabbit hutch, with rabbits and chickens (29x39cm-11x15in) s.d.1921 pair. 10-Jun-3 Christie's, London #156/R est:25000-35000
£24000 $39840 €36000 Pony, donkey and chickens in a farmyard (36x46cm-14x18in) s.d.1923. 10-Jun-3 Christie's, London #155/R est:12000-18000
£28000 $44240 €42000 Duck and ducklings with doves by pond. Ducks and chickens feeding time (28x39cm-11x15in) s.d.1922 pair. 26-Nov-2 Christie's, London #142/R est:30000-40000
£31000 $50220 €46500 Feeding time (62x51cm-24x20in) s. 20-May-3 Sotheby's, Olympia #226/R est:18000-25000
£32000 $53120 €48000 Visiting the new arrivals (56x76cm-22x30in) s.d.1915. 12-Jun-3 Sotheby's, London #284/R est:30000-40000
£50000 $79000 €75000 Corner of the farmyard (76x61cm-30x24in) s.d.1916. 2-Dec-2 Sotheby's, London #72/R est:30000-40000

HUNT, Edgar (attrib) (1876-1953) British
£1923 $3000 €2885 Rooster and pigeons at farm. 21-Sep-2 Harvey Clar, Oakland #1405

HUNT, Edward Aubrey (1855-1922) British
£600 $960 €900 Harbour scenes with windmill, boats and figures (25x33cm-10x13in) s. board pair. 8-Jan-3 Brightwells, Leominster #1042
£650 $1027 €975 Blossom girl and sheep in a meadow (25x30cm-10x12in) s. i.d.1881 verso. 2-Dec-2 Gorringes, Lewes #2566
£700 $1078 €1050 Tranquil river landscape with figures in a punt (33x47cm-13x19in) s. 23-Oct-2 Hamptons Fine Art, Godalming #128/R
£1650 $2640 €2475 Fishing boat approaching the shore in a stiff breeze (90x70cm-35x28in) s.d.83 canvas on board. 11-Mar-3 Bonhams, Oxford #58/R est:500-800
£2100 $3402 €3150 On the stocks, boat building at Rye (44x63cm-17x25in) s. 21-May-3 Christie's, Kensington #682/R est:1000-1500
£3448 $5379 €5172 Farmyard with horses and chickens (34x54cm-13x21in) s.d.1923. 7-Nov-2 International Art Centre, Auckland #166/R est:8000-12000 (NZ.D 11000)

Works on paper
£620 $961 €930 Travellers and camels on a shore before town buildings (24x37cm-9x15in) s. W/C. 25-Sep-2 Hamptons Fine Art, Godalming #311/R

HUNT, Esther (1875-1951) American
£683 $1100 €1025 Chinese girl holding a feather fan (25x20cm-10x8in) s. board. 18-Feb-3 John Moran, Pasadena #6a

Works on paper
£1198 $2000 €1737 Chinese girl dressed in pink (23x20cm-9x8in) s. W/C. 17-Jun-3 John Moran, Pasadena #188 est:1500-2000

HUNT, Goanna (1983-) Australian

Works on paper
£1372 $2126 €2058 Untitled (25x40cm-10x16in) synthetic polymer paint board exhib. 3-Dec-2 Shapiro, Sydney #232/R est:3500-5000 (A.D 3800)

HUNT, John S (19th C) British

Sculpture
£6000 $10020 €8700 Lady on horseback holding a falcon with man alongside her (54cm-21in) silver. 25-Jun-3 Sotheby's, Olympia #270/R est:6000-8000

HUNT, Lynn Bogue (1878-1960) American
£2532 $4000 €3798 Western quail (36x30cm-14x12in) s. prov.lit. 3-Apr-3 Christie's, Rockefeller NY #219/R est:2000-3000
£3106 $5000 €4659 Ducks taking off, setting sun (79x56cm-31x22in) s. canvasboard painted c.1940. 10-May-3 Illustration House, New York #57/R est:4000-6000
£3333 $4800 €5000 Setters at point (76x55cm-30x22in) s. 15-Jan-3 Christie's, Rockefeller NY #170/R

HUNT, Reuben (19th C) British
£300 $459 €450 Asleep on duty (61x50cm-24x20in) s. 21-Aug-2 Bonhams, Knowle #231
£360 $554 €540 Chicken and goat (24x34cm-9x13in) s.d.1922. 22-Oct-2 Bonhams, Bath #263
£360 $554 €540 Disputing the way (24x34cm-9x13in) s. 22-Oct-2 Bonhams, Bath #264

HUNT, Richard (19th C) British

Sculpture
£2025 $3200 €3038 Winged form (69cm-27in) bronze. 1-Dec-2 Susanin's, Chicago #5009/R
£2532 $4000 €3798 Abstract (38x51x25cm-15x20x10in) s.num.1/9 bronze mahogany base. 1-Dec-2 Susanin's, Chicago #5135/R est:3000-5000

HUNT, Thomas (1854-1929) British

Works on paper
£2000 $3040 €3000 When the day of toil is done (60x90cm-24x35in) indis sig. W/C stopping out scratching out prov.exhib. 28-Aug-2 Sotheby's, London #1066/R est:2000-3000

HUNT, Thomas Lorraine (1882-1938) American
£931 $1500 €1397 Coastal scene (18x23cm-7x9in) s. paper. 23-Feb-3 Butterfields, Los Angeles #7067 est:2000-3000
£3822 $6000 €5733 Sierra Madre landscape (22x28cm-9x11in) s. paper prov. 20-Nov-2 Christie's, Los Angeles #18/R est:5000-7000
£6369 $10000 €9554 Winter splendour (52x62cm-20x24in) s. 20-Nov-2 Christie's, Los Angeles #65/R est:10000-15000
£22293 $35000 €33440 Harbour sails (36x43cm-14x17in) s. board prov. 20-Nov-2 Christie's, Los Angeles #78/R est:15000-25000

HUNT, Walter (1861-1941) British
£6000 $9420 €9000 Intruders (73x99cm-29x39in) s.d.1881. 19-Nov-2 Bonhams, New Bond Street #156/R est:6000-8000
£8000 $12560 €12000 Calves at a trough (30x40cm-12x16in) s.d.1920. 19-Nov-2 Bonhams, New Bond Street #157/R est:5000-7000
£9000 $14130 €13500 Calves at feeding time (30x40cm-12x16in) s.d.1911 prov. 19-Nov-2 Bonhams, New Bond Street #120/R est:6000-8000
£10000 $15700 €15000 Summertime in Devonshire (51x76cm-20x30in) s.d.1910. 19-Nov-2 Bonhams, New Bond Street #123/R est:12000-18000
£12000 $19560 €18000 Crofter's farmyard (49x75cm-19x30in) s.d.1903 s.verso. 30-Jan-3 Lawrence, Crewkerne #722/R est:12000-18000
£14500 $22765 €21750 Besieged (52x77cm-20x30in) s.d.1916. 19-Nov-2 Bonhams, New Bond Street #122/R est:10000-15000
£18000 $27360 €27000 Chase (101x152cm-40x60in) s.d.1912. 28-Aug-2 Sotheby's, London #876/R est:20000-30000
£20000 $32800 €30000 Calves, chickens and a cockerel (51x76cm-20x30in) s.d.1921. 29-May-3 Christie's, Kensington #216/R est:10000-15000

HUNT, William Henry (1790-1864) British
£850 $1394 €1275 Primula and a bird's nest on a mossy bank (18x23cm-7x9in) s.verso board. 29-May-3 Christie's, Kensington #317/R

Works on paper
£400 $616 €600 Still life of an apple and white grapes (18cm-7in circular) s. W/C. 3-Sep-2 Gorringes, Lewes #2097
£609 $950 €914 Herrings (10x16cm-4x6in) i.verso W/C gouache over pencil prov.exhib. 14-Sep-2 Weschler, Washington #596/R
£700 $1092 €1050 Young lady, at her leisure (10x6cm-4x2in) pencil prov. 27-Mar-3 Christie's, Kensington #21/R
£1600 $2576 €2400 Head of bearded man (21x15cm-8x6in) s. s.i.verso pencil W/C gum arabic prov. 20-Feb-3 Christie's, London #353/R
£2581 $4000 €3872 Study of a boxer (36x25cm-14x10in) s.i. pencil W/C gouache prov. 29-Oct-2 Sotheby's, New York #151/R est:3000-4000
£2600 $4082 €3900 Study of a young girl (16x20cm-6x8in) s. pencil W/C oval prov. 21-Nov-2 Christie's, London #91/R est:3000-5000
£2800 $4396 €4200 Still life white and black grapes and redcurrents (23x33cm-9x13in) s. pencil W/C bodycol gum arabic. 21-Nov-2 Christie's, London #61/R est:3000-5000
£3000 $4890 €4500 Primroses (33x36cm-13x14in) s. W/C htd bodycol. 29-Jan-3 Sotheby's, Olympia #54/R est:4000-6000
£3200 $5152 €4800 Still life with basket, nest, egg, red currants and ladybird (18x29cm-7x11in) s. pencil W/C gum arabic scratching out prov. 20-Feb-3 Christie's, London #127/R est:6000
£4000 $5720 €6000 Distant shipping beneath stormy skies (9x13cm-4x5in) s. wash prov.exhib.lit. 22-Jan-3 Christie's, London #45/R est:3500
£7500 $11925 €11250 Boy blowing bubbles (27x17cm-11x7in) s. W/C over pencil htd bodycol scratching out. 19-Mar-3 Sotheby's, London #151/R est:4000-6000

HUNT, William Holman (1827-1910) British
£7500 $12075 €11250 Group portrait of Mrs Davies with the Clark grandchildren (76x63cm-30x25in) prov. 20-Feb-3 Christie's, London #318/R
£600000 $966000 €900000 Il Dolce far niente (101x81cm-40x32in) mono.i.d.1866 s.i.verso prov.exhib. 19-Feb-3 Christie's, London #26/R est:800000-1200000

Works on paper
£1850 $2868 €2775 Comical sketch of musicians (8x6cm-3x2in) i.verso pen ink. 24-Sep-2 Rowley Fine Art, Newmarket #370/R

HUNT, William Morris (1824-1879) American
£7643 $12000 €11465 Ophelia (81x65cm-32x26in) mono. 22-Nov-2 Skinner, Boston #106/R est:7000-9000

Works on paper
£380 $612 €570 Lessons in cards (36x27cm-14x11in) s. W/C. 15-Jan-3 Cheffins Grain & Comins, Cambridge #370/R

HUNTEN, Emil (1827-1902) German
£1233 $1923 €1800 French messenger on horseback (23x46cm-9x18in) s.d.72. 10-Apr-3 Van Ham, Cologne #1493/R est:2600
£1429 $2214 €2144 Battle scene (101x92cm-40x36in) s. 24-Sep-2 Koller, Zurich #6567/R est:2400-3200 (S.FR 3300)

HUNTEN, Franz Johann Wilhelm (1822-1887) German
£611 $954 €917 Coastal scene (44x72cm-17x28in) s.d.1872. 6-Nov-2 Dobiaschofsky, Bern #686/R (S.FR 1400)
£921 $1492 €1400 Shipping in distress off a rocky coast (44x62cm-17x24in) s.d.1849. 21-Jan-3 Christie's, Amsterdam #65 est:800-1200
£1242 $1950 €1863 Barque amateur Charles H Harvey Cmdr, 1860 (43x64cm-17x25in) s. 22-Nov-2 Eldred, East Dennis #1110/R est:1000-1500
£2632 $4263 €4000 Stormy weather (63x74cm-25x29in) s.d.1851. 21-Jan-3 Christie's, Amsterdam #82/R est:3000-4000

HUNTEN, Richard (1867-?) German
£288 $447 €450 Elb impression (32x47cm-13x19in) s.i.d.95 canvas on board. 7-Dec-2 Hans Stahl, Hamburg #145
£414 $654 €600 Harbour (49x44cm-19x17in) s.d.1927. 5-Apr-3 Quittenbaum, Hamburg #96/R

HUNTER, Alexis (20th C) Australian
£868 $1354 €1302 Animal figure (18x23cm-7x9in) s.d.1985 verso prov. 8-Apr-3 Peter Webb, Auckland #155/R (NZ.D 2500)

HUNTER, Clementine (1887-1988) American
£366 $600 €549 Jesus and Mary (41x51cm-16x20in) mono. artist board. 8-Feb-3 Neal Auction Company, New Orleans #380/R
£416 $650 €624 Her cabin (30x41cm-12x16in) mono. oil silver gelatin print artist board. 12-Oct-2 Neal Auction Company, New Orleans #1436
£962 $1500 €1443 Two cats (36x46cm-14x18in) mono. canvasboard. 12-Oct-2 Neal Auction Company, New Orleans #694/R est:1500-2500
£1125 $1800 €1631 Saturday night at the Honky Tonk (38x41cm-15x16in) mono. board. 17-May-3 New Orleans Auction, New Orleans #949/R est:2000-4000
£1235 $2000 €1853 Saturday night (41x51cm-16x20in) mono.i. canvasboard. 24-Jan-3 New Orleans Auction, New Orleans #385/R est:2500-4000
£1358 $2200 €2037 Pickin cotton (28x58cm-11x23in) mono. board. 24-Jan-3 New Orleans Auction, New Orleans #383/R est:2000-4000
£1519 $2400 €2279 Couple dancing (38x41cm-15x16in) mono. board prov. 16-Nov-2 New Orleans Auction, New Orleans #1571/R est:2500-4000
£1605 $2600 €2408 Wedding (46x61cm-18x24in) mono. board prov. 24-Jan-3 New Orleans Auction, New Orleans #382/R est:2500-4000
£1605 $2600 €2408 Hauling cotton (41x51cm-16x20in) mono.i. canvasboard. 24-Jan-3 New Orleans Auction, New Orleans #384/R est:2500-4000
£1625 $2600 €2356 Pickin cotton (41x51cm-16x20in) mono. board. 17-May-3 New Orleans Auction, New Orleans #947/R est:2000-4000
£1667 $2600 €2501 Baptism (41x51cm-16x20in) mono. canvasboard. 12-Oct-2 Neal Auction Company, New Orleans #695/R est:2000-3000
£1677 $2750 €2516 Wash day (56x66cm-22x26in) mono. canvasboard. 8-Feb-3 Neal Auction Company, New Orleans #377/R est:2500-3500
£1728 $2800 €2592 Zinnias (46x36cm-18x14in) mono.i.d.1983 canvasboard prov. 24-Jan-3 New Orleans Auction, New Orleans #386/R est:3000-5000
£1750 $2800 €2538 Feeding the geese (41x61cm-16x24in) mono. board. 17-May-3 New Orleans Auction, New Orleans #948/R est:1800-2500
£1763 $2750 €2645 Women playing cards (41x51cm-16x20in) mono. canvasboard. 12-Oct-2 Neal Auction Company, New Orleans #688/R est:2000-3000
£1772 $2800 €2658 Angels (41x51cm-16x20in) mono. board prov. 16-Nov-2 New Orleans Auction, New Orleans #1572/R est:2500-4000
£1795 $2800 €2693 Pickin cotton (41x51cm-16x20in) mono. prov. 20-Sep-2 New Orleans Auction, New Orleans #1254/R est:2500-4000
£1852 $3000 €2778 Doctor scene (41x51cm-16x20in) mono.i. canvasboard prov. 24-Jan-3 New Orleans Auction, New Orleans #381/R est:3000-5000
£1859 $2900 €2789 Picking cotton (38x51cm-15x20in) mono. canvasboard. 12-Oct-2 Neal Auction Company, New Orleans #686 est:2500-3500
£1923 $3000 €2885 Zinnias (51x25cm-20x10in) mono. canvas panel. 20-Sep-2 New Orleans Auction, New Orleans #1251/R est:2500-4000
£1923 $3000 €2885 Nativity scene (41x51cm-16x20in) mono. board prov. 20-Sep-2 New Orleans Auction, New Orleans #1253/R est:2500-4000
£1935 $3000 €2903 Baptism (41x61cm-16x24in) 29-Oct-2 Doyle, New York #65 est:2000-3000
£2025 $3200 €3038 Cotton mill (41x51cm-16x20in) mono. board prov. 16-Nov-2 New Orleans Auction, New Orleans #1570/R est:2500-4000
£2083 $3250 €3125 Picking cotton (46x61cm-18x24in) mono. canvasboard. 12-Oct-2 Neal Auction Company, New Orleans #696 est:2500-3500
£2096 $3250 €3144 Cotton pickers (38x61cm-15x24in) mono. board. 7-Dec-2 Neal Auction Company, New Orleans #506/R est:2500-3500
£2138 $3400 €3207 Africa hut at Melrose Plantation (41x51cm-16x20in) i.verso board. 22-Mar-3 New Orleans Auction, New Orleans #1091/R est:2500-4000
£2244 $3500 €3366 Wash day (41x51cm-16x20in) mono. canvasboard. 12-Oct-2 Neal Auction Company, New Orleans #687 est:2000-3000
£2308 $3600 €3462 Buildings at Melrose (46x61cm-18x24in) mono. board. 20-Sep-2 New Orleans Auction, New Orleans #1252/R est:3000-5000
£2308 $3600 €3462 Washday (41x51cm-16x20in) mono. board. 12-Oct-2 Neal Auction Company, New Orleans #697/R est:2500-3500
£2404 $3750 €3606 Picking cotton (46x61cm-18x24in) mono. board. 12-Oct-2 Neal Auction Company, New Orleans #698/R est:2500-3500
£2405 $3800 €3608 Pecan picking (46x58cm-18x23in) mono. board prov. 16-Nov-2 New Orleans Auction, New Orleans #1573/R est:2500-4000
£2564 $4000 €3846 Fishing on Cane River (41x51cm-16x20in) mono. board prov. 20-Sep-2 New Orleans Auction, New Orleans #1255/R est:2500-4000

HUNTER, Colin (1841-1904) British
£4000 $6440 €6000 Fishing boat off the coast (81x13cm-32x5in) s. prov.lit. 20-Feb-3 Christie's, London #276/R

HUNTER, Colin (attrib) (1841-1904) British
£360 $601 €522 Drying the nets at lockside (28x58cm-11x23in) s.verso board. 26-Jun-3 Richardson & Smith, Whitby #624

HUNTER, Frances Tipton (1896-1957) American
£369 $575 €554 Sleeping baby (38x33cm-15x13in) s. pastel dr board. 14-Sep-2 Selkirks, St. Louis #137

Works on paper
£629 $1000 €944 Sleeping infant (41x33cm-16x13in) s. i.verso pastel paperboard exec.c.1920. 2-Mar-3 Toomey, Oak Park #692/R

HUNTER, Fred Leo (1858-1943) American
£267 $425 €401 Landscape with figures in a forest interior (43x51cm-17x20in) s. 7-Mar-3 Jackson's, Cedar Falls #623/R

HUNTER, George Leslie (1877-1931) British
£3000 $4560 €4500 Still life of chrysanthemums (51x41cm-20x16in) s. 28-Aug-2 Sotheby's, London #1079/R est:5000-7000
£4000 $6360 €6000 Artist's bedroom (41x47cm-16x19in) s. board prov. 6-Mar-3 Christie's, Kensington #209/R est:2000-3000
£7000 $10920 €10500 Largo (13x21cm-5x8in) s. panel. 10-Apr-3 Bonhams, Edinburgh #154/R est:3000-5000
£7500 $11850 €11250 Snowy landscape, St. Monans, Fife (12x21cm-5x8in) s.i.verso panel. 26-Nov-2 Sotheby's, Melbourne #235/R est:6000-8000 (A.D 21000)
£8393 $13261 €12590 Corn stooks and red roof (12x21cm-5x8in) s. panel. 26-Nov-2 Sotheby's, Melbourne #236/R est:6000-8000 (A.D 23500)
£9643 $15236 €14465 Mill stream (12x21cm-5x8in) bears sig panel. 26-Nov-2 Sotheby's, Melbourne #237/R est:6000-8000 (A.D 27000)
£15000 $22800 €22500 Still life of fruit and green jug (46x37cm-18x15in) init. s.i.d.1927. 28-Aug-2 Sotheby's, London #1077/R est:15000-20000
£15000 $23250 €22500 Spring flowers and fruit (61x51cm-24x20in) s. 31-Oct-2 Christie's, London #131/R est:15000-20000
£16000 $24800 €24000 Peaches and tankard (25x34cm-10x13in) s. panel prov. 31-Oct-2 Christie's, London #132/R est:10000-15000
£20000 $30400 €30000 Still life of flowers in a yellow jug (64x53cm-25x21in) s. i.on stretcher. 28-Aug-2 Sotheby's, London #1076/R est:20000-30000
£22000 $33440 €33000 View in the Cote D'Azur (55x46cm-22x18in) s. s.i.on stretcher painted c.1920. 28-Aug-2 Sotheby's, London #1078/R est:15000-20000
£24000 $36720 €36000 Lundin Lock, Fife (102x128cm-40x50in) s. prov. 22-Aug-2 Bonhams, Edinburgh #1128/R est:25000-35000
£25000 $39750 €37500 Still life with apples (40x48cm-16x19in) s. board. 6-Mar-3 Christie's, Kensington #210/R est:20000-30000
£30000 $45600 €45000 Old Arsenal in Venice (61x51cm-24x20in) s. 28-Aug-2 Sotheby's, London #1075/R est:30000-50000
£46000 $70380 €69000 Pink roses in a Chinese vase (46x30cm-18x12in) init. 22-Aug-2 Bonhams, Edinburgh #1071/R est:20000-30000

Works on paper
£1500 $2340 €2250 Seaside theatre, lower Largo, with a pink cloud (18x25cm-7x10in) pen ink W/C crayons prov. 14-Apr-3 Sotheby's, London #113/R est:1000-1500
£3400 $5202 €5100 Granny and her cat (35x26cm-14x10in) s. ink crayon W/C. 22-Aug-2 Bonhams, Edinburgh #1122/R est:2500-4000
£10500 $16380 €15750 St. Monance (52x38cm-20x15in) s. W/C pencil prov. 14-Apr-3 Sotheby's, London #112/R est:2500-3500

HUNTER, George Sherwood (1846-1919) British
£700 $1092 €1050 Dutch interior (46x30cm-18x12in) s. i.verso. 17-Oct-2 David Lay, Penzance #1098/R
£1500 $2415 €2250 Newlyn lighthouse (15x23cm-6x9in) prov. 20-Feb-3 Christie's, London #208/R
£1500 $2415 €2250 Newlyn (23x15cm-9x6in) prov. 20-Feb-3 Christie's, London #207/R
£2000 $3220 €3000 Study of sailor (23x15cm-9x6in) prov. 20-Feb-3 Christie's, London #209/R
£3000 $4890 €4500 Light, Volendan, Zuider Zee (43x29cm-17x11in) s.i.verso exhib. 29-Jan-3 Sotheby's, Olympia #227/R est:3000-5000

HUNTER, John F (1893-1951) British
£550 $803 €825 Blitz Square, Belfast (36x46cm-14x18in) board. 12-Jun-2 John Ross, Belfast #13
£700 $1022 €1050 Waterfall in the woodlands (46x56cm-18x22in) s. 12-Jun-2 John Ross, Belfast #159
£900 $1314 €1350 Boats at Toulon (46x56cm-18x22in) s. 12-Jun-2 John Ross, Belfast #188

Works on paper
£900 $1431 €1350 Kilkeel (53x68cm-21x27in) mixed media. 5-Mar-3 John Ross, Belfast #29

HUNTER, Leslie (1877-1931) British
£13000 $21060 €19500 Fifeshire village (25x30cm-10x12in) s. panel. 23-May-3 Lyon & Turnbull, Edinburgh #58/R est:6000-8000
£23000 $37260 €34500 Still life of fruit, bead and black bottle on table top (36x31cm-14x12in) s. 23-May-3 Lyon & Turnbull, Edinburgh #89/R est:6000-8000

£95000 $153900 €142500 Still life with flowers in a striped vase. Portrait of T J Honeyman in evening dress (103x76cm-41x30in) s. double-sided prov.lit. 23-May-3 Lyon & Turnbull, Edinburgh #93/R est:40000-60000

Works on paper

£2400 $3984 €3480 Flowers in a yellow jug (43x36cm-17x14in) s. chk wash. 10-Jun-3 David Lay, Penzance #98/R est:3000-5000
£11000 $17050 €16500 Street scene, Antibes (37x43cm-15x17in) s. pen ink col chk prov. 6-Dec-2 Lyon & Turnbull, Edinburgh #86/R est:3000-5000

HUNTER, Mary Sutherland (1899-?) British

£560 $935 €812 St. Ives (34x46cm-13x18in) s.d. board. 19-Jun-3 Lane, Penzance #408

HUNTER, Mary Young (1878-1936) British

Works on paper

£280 $431 €420 Portrait of Aline Margaret Scott-Elliot (21x17cm-8x7in) i.verso W/C. 22-Oct-2 Bonhams, Knightsbridge #167/R

HUNTER, Mason (1854-1921) British

£500 $780 €750 Squall in the Forth (24x35cm-9x14in) s. canvasboard. 10-Oct-2 Bonhams, Edinburgh #348
£650 $1060 €975 Reed cutter (45x30cm-18x12in) 14-Feb-3 Lyon & Turnbull, Edinburgh #145
£687 $1071 €996 Herring fishers, Tarbert (71x91cm-28x36in) s.i. exhib. 26-Mar-3 Walker's, Ottawa #62a/R est:1500-2000 (C.D 1600)
£800 $1272 €1200 Tarbert Bay, Loch Fyne (36x41cm-14x16in) s. board. 29-Apr-3 Gorringes, Lewes #2057
£1800 $2790 €2700 Pittenweem (26x39cm-10x15in) s. canvas on board. 5-Dec-2 Bonhams, Edinburgh #126 est:1800-2500
£2600 $4134 €3900 Grey, St. Monans, Fife (51x91cm-20x36in) s.d.09 i.verso exhib. 6-Mar-3 Christie's, Kensington #147/R est:3000-5000

HUNTER, Philip (1958-) Australian

£1085 $1726 €1628 Untitled No 4 (122x107cm-48x42in) s.d.98 verso. 5-May-3 Sotheby's, Melbourne #190 est:2800-3500 (A.D 2800)
£1214 $1919 €1821 Visit IV (159x128cm-63x50in) s.d.90 i.verso. 26-Nov-2 Sotheby's, Melbourne #143 est:3000-5000 (A.D 3400)
£1429 $2229 €2144 House for Herclitus (152x121cm-60x48in) s.i.d.95 verso. 11-Nov-2 Deutscher-Menzies, Melbourne #102/R est:4000-6000 (A.D 4000)

HUNTER, Robert (fl.1745-1803) Irish

£5942 $9745 €8200 Portrait of a militia officer in uniform (78x65cm-31x26in) s.d.1764 painted oval prov. 28-May-3 Bonhams & James Adam, Dublin #1/R est:4000-6000

HUNTER, Robert (1947-) Australian

£7527 $11441 €11291 Untitled (122x244cm-48x96in) init.d.86 verso board. 28-Aug-2 Deutscher-Menzies, Melbourne #39/R est:20000-30000 (A.D 21000)

Works on paper

£5714 $8914 €8571 Painting I (122x244cm-48x96in) init.i.d.89 verso synthetic polymer paint plyboard. 11-Nov-2 Deutscher-Menzies, Melbourne #43/R est:18000-24000 (A.D 16000)
£7143 $11000 €10715 Untitled (122x244cm-48x96in) init.d.1991 verso synthetic polymer on board. 8-Sep-2 Sotheby's, Melbourne #19/R est:15000-25000 (A.D 20000)

HUNTER, Tom (1965-) British

Photographs

£3200 $5216 €4800 After party (122x154cm-48x61in) s.i.d.2000 num.2/5 cibachrome print. 3-Feb-3 Sotheby's, Olympia #179/R est:1000-1500

HUNTINGTON WHITLOCK, Sarah (19th C) American

£12579 $20000 €18869 Frost comes (102x126cm-40x50in) s.i.d.1853. 5-Mar-3 Sotheby's, New York #115/R est:25000-35000

HUNTINGTON, Anna Hyatt (1876-1973) American

Sculpture

£1849 $2700 €2774 Centaur (28cm-11in) s. bronze. 3-Nov-1 North East Auctions, Portsmouth #299/R est:2000-3000
£2259 $3750 €3276 Pa don't care as long as we don't scratch (16cm-6in) s.i.d.1967 brown pat bronze. 11-Jun-3 Butterfields, San Francisco #4041/R est:3000-5000
£2405 $3800 €3608 Yawning panther (34cm-13in) i. reddish brown pat. bronze. 3-Apr-3 Christie's, Rockefeller NY #158/R est:4000-5000
£2710 $4200 €4065 Jaguar reaching (16cm-6in) s.num.142 brown pat bronze st.f.Gorham. 3-Dec-2 Christie's, Rockefeller NY #576/R est:2000-3000
£4500 $7020 €6750 Jaguar reaching (16cm-6in) s. green brown pat bronze st.Gorham. 9-Apr-3 Sotheby's, London #119/R est:3000-4000
£167665 $280000 €243114 Jaguar. Reaching jauar (109cm-43in) i. verdigris pat. bronze two prov. 18-Jun-3 Christie's, Los Angeles #70/R est:80000-120000

HUNTINGTON, Dwight W (19/20th C) American

Works on paper

£625 $1000 €906 On the scent (28x43cm-11x17in) s.d.1905 W/C gouache. 16-May-3 Skinner, Boston #126/R

HUNTINGTON, Elizabeth Hamilton Thayer (1878-1963) American

Works on paper

£260 $400 €390 Still life with roses (46x41cm-18x16in) s. pastel sold with a W/C by same hand. 27-Oct-2 Grogan, Boston #33

HUNTLEY, Isabel (1901-1982) Australian?

£464 $715 €696 Dresden (46x62cm-18x24in) s. board exhib. 3-Sep-2 Shapiro, Sydney #427 est:1500-2500 (A.D 1300)

HUNZIKER, Edwin (1901-1986) Swiss

£278 $447 €417 Summer coast (60x81cm-24x32in) s. 7-May-3 Dobiaschofsky, Bern #3337 (S.FR 600)

HUNZIKER, Max (1901-1976) Swiss

£370 $577 €555 Still life with cherries (38x46cm-15x18in) s. 16-Sep-2 Philippe Schuler, Zurich #3377/R (S.FR 850)

HUNZINGER, Werner (1816-c.1861) American

£1538 $2431 €2400 Still life with fruit and wine in goblet (31x26cm-12x10in) s.d.1837 copper. 16-Nov-2 Lempertz, Koln #1481/R est:2000

HUOT, Adolphe Joseph (1839-1883) French

Works on paper

£1613 $2500 €2420 Seated male nude. Female study. Male nude (63x43cm-25x17in) W/C col chk set of three one oil on board prov. 29-Oct-2 Sotheby's, New York #84/R est:1000-1500

HUOT, Charles Edouard (1855-1930) Canadian

£365 $569 €548 Ste-Catherine, porteneuf (14x22cm-6x9in) cardboard exec.c.1887. 25-Mar-3 Iegor de Saint Hippolyte, Montreal #62 (C.D 850)
£558 $870 €837 La tasse (25x33cm-10x13in) s. panel. 25-Mar-3 Iegor de Saint Hippolyte, Montreal #64 (C.D 1300)
£644 $1004 €966 Cour interieure du seminaire de Quebec (5x10cm-2x4in) panel exec.c.1905. 25-Mar-3 Iegor de Saint Hippolyte, Montreal #63 (C.D 1500)
£889 $1458 €1334 Hunter by a cascading river (35x50cm-14x20in) s. 3-Jun-3 Joyner, Toronto #257/R est:2500-3500 (C.D 2000)
£905 $1403 €1358 Man standing smoking pipe (29x14cm-11x6in) board prov. 3-Dec-2 Joyner, Toronto #405 est:1000-1500 (C.D 2200)
£1631 $2544 €2447 Interior court of the Quebec seminary (16x21cm-6x8in) cardboard exec.c.1905. 25-Mar-3 Iegor de Saint Hippolyte, Montreal #66 (C.D 3800)
£2060 $3214 €3090 Quebec et le traversier Le Polaris (26x42cm-10x17in) s. panel. 25-Mar-3 Iegor de Saint Hippolyte, Montreal #65/R (C.D 4800)

HUPET, Andre (1922-1993) Belgian?

Sculpture

£3774 $5811 €6000 Maitrise de Nimy (65cm-26in) s. stone. 22-Oct-2 Campo, Vlaamse Kaai #522/R

HUPIN, Jacques (17th C) French

£3774 $5849 €6000 Gilt ornamental dishes and silver bow on precious rug (88x117cm-35x46in) prov.lit. 2-Oct-2 Dorotheum, Vienna #289/R est:6000-8000
£20000 $31400 €30000 Still life of fruit in a bowl, ormolu plate and ewers on a draped carpet (116x118cm-46x46in) bears sig. 12-Dec-2 Sotheby's, London #208/R est:12000-18000

HURARD, Joseph Marius (1887-1956) French

£1307 $2144 €2000 Ribo Martiques. Burscons sous la neige (26x54cm-10x21in) s. i.verso panel pair. 9-Feb-3 Anaf, Lyon #145

HURD, Peter (1904-1984) American

£7372 $11500 €11058 My father's house (41x51cm-16x20in) 9-Nov-2 Altermann Galleries, Santa Fe #21

Works on paper

£801 $1250 €1202 El guitarron Juarez (15x13cm-6x5in) pen ink executed c.1959. 19-Oct-2 David Dike, Dallas #80/R

£1346 $2100 €2019 Exhibition, Chester County art Association (25x38cm-10x15in) ink. 9-Nov-2 Altermann Galleries, Santa Fe #22
£2123 $3100 €3185 New Mexico landscape (23x48cm-9x19in) W/C. 18-May-2 Altermann Galleries, Santa Fe #197/R
£2273 $3500 €3410 Well on the plains (28x46cm-11x18in) W/C. 25-Oct-2 Morris & Whiteside, Hilton Head Island #122 est:4000-5000
£5324 $8625 €7720 New Mexico rain (61x71cm-24x28in) W/C. 23-May-3 Altermann Galleries, Santa Fe #161
£6731 $10500 €10097 Navajo Lake (71x97cm-28x38in) W/C. 9-Nov-2 Altermann Galleries, Santa Fe #20

HURDLE, Robert (1918-) British
£480 $749 €720 Poppy field (76x92cm-30x36in) 17-Sep-2 Bonhams, Knightsbridge #123/R

HURLEY, Robert Newton (1894-1980) Canadian
Works on paper
£201 $315 €302 Untitled - composition (39x49cm-15x19in) s. W/C. 25-Nov-2 Hodgins, Calgary #422/R (C.D 500)
£283 $441 €471 Untitled - prairie harvest (30x41cm-12x16in) s.d.1964 W/C prov. 13-Apr-3 Levis, Calgary #51/R (C.D 650)
£283 $441 €471 Untitled - prairie slough (25x36cm-10x14in) s.d.1961 W/C paper board prov. 13-Apr-3 Levis, Calgary #53 (C.D 650)
£301 $473 €452 Prairie town with slough (27x34cm-11x13in) s.d.1962 W/C board. 25-Nov-2 Hodgins, Calgary #1/R (C.D 750)
£321 $504 €482 Prairie panorama (23x32cm-9x13in) s.d.1959 W/C board. 25-Nov-2 Hodgins, Calgary #253/R (C.D 800)
£321 $504 €482 Fisgard Lighthouse (32x36cm-13x14in) s.i.d.1971 W/C board. 25-Nov-2 Hodgins, Calgary #321/R (C.D 800)
£370 $577 €616 Clam bay (32x43cm-13x17in) s. s.i.verso W/C paper board prov. 13-Apr-3 Levis, Calgary #52/R (C.D 850)
£402 $631 €603 Saskatchewan sunset (14x19cm-6x7in) s.i.d.1950 W/C. 25-Nov-2 Hodgins, Calgary #28/R (C.D 1000)
£462 $729 €693 Saskatchewan harvest scene (23x36cm-9x14in) d.1960 W/C. 1-Dec-2 Levis, Calgary #45b/R (C.D 1150)
£511 $838 €741 Prairie nocturne (39x36cm-15x14in) s.d.1974 W/C. 9-Jun-3 Hodgins, Calgary #1/R est:600-800 (C.D 1150)
£582 $920 €873 Prairie sunset (33x43cm-13x17in) W/C paperboard. 1-Dec-2 Levis, Calgary #45/R (C.D 1450)
£600 $984 €870 Pasture gate, town and elevator (22x31cm-9x12in) s.d.1962 W/C. 9-Jun-3 Hodgins, Calgary #9/R est:600-800 (C.D 1350)

HURRY, Leslie (1909-1978) British
Works on paper
£350 $578 €508 Figures in a landscape (32x41cm-13x16in) s.d.Oct 1970 pencil W/C bodycol pen ink. 3-Jul-3 Christie's, Kensington #523/R
£480 $802 €696 Drawing at Chesters (37x21cm-15x8in) s.d.1946 W/C ink prov. 17-Jun-3 Bonhams, Knightsbridge #207
£700 $1085 €1050 Le Moulin Joyeux, Paris (42x51cm-17x20in) s.indis.i.d.38 W/C. 4-Dec-2 Christie's, Kensington #271

HURST, Hal (1863-1938) British
Works on paper
£400 $648 €600 Ships on a shore at low tide (39x49cm-15x19in) s. W/C. 21-May-3 Bonhams, Knightsbridge #51/R

HURT, Louis B (1856-1929) British
£800 $1272 €1200 Figures resting on a woodland path (33x22cm-13x9in) s. canvasboard. 6-Mar-3 Christie's, Kensington #62/R
£1600 $2544 €2400 Staffa. Storm over the highlands (14x28cm-6x11in) one s. one init. board two. 4-Mar-3 Bearnes, Exeter #427/R est:800-1200
£1800 $2862 €2700 Highland river landscape (32x48cm-13x19in) s. canvas on board. 6-Mar-3 Christie's, Kensington #63/R est:1500-2000
£2000 $3080 €3000 Highland cattle by a lochside (58x48cm-23x19in) s. 6-Sep-2 Richardson & Smith, Whitby #453
£2143 $3386 €3215 In the woods (51x81cm-20x32in) s.d.1882 s.i.verso. 26-Nov-2 Sotheby's, Melbourne #214/R est:8000-12000 (A.D 6000)
£2500 $3975 €3750 At Corrie, Arran. Tulloch (13x23cm-5x9in) init.i.d.Sept 03 board pair. 4-Mar-3 Bearnes, Exeter #426/R est:1000-1500
£3000 $4560 €4500 Highland cattle (21x31cm-8x12in) s. canvasboard. 28-Aug-2 Sotheby's, London #810/R est:1800-2500
£5957 $9651 €8400 Highland cattle in lake and mountain landscape (45x34cm-18x13in) s.d.1908. 21-May-3 James Adam, Dublin #15 est:3000-4000
£9494 $15000 €14241 Hills of Ross Shire, Glen Torridon (102x76cm-40x30in) s.d.86 s.i.d.verso. 23-Apr-3 Christie's, Rockefeller NY #82/R est:18000-25000
£10000 $15500 €15000 On the Loch Maree, Ross-shire (102x77cm-40x30in) s.d.1887 prov. 31-Oct-2 Christie's, London #84/R est:10000-15000
£10000 $15600 €15000 In the Highlands (33x48cm-13x19in) s. 14-Apr-3 Sotheby's, London #20/R est:10000-15000
£11000 $17490 €16500 Highland cattle watering by a loch (61x91cm-24x36in) s.d.1886. 6-Mar-3 Christie's, Kensington #64/R est:10000-15000
£12000 $18720 €18000 By the loch (41x61cm-16x24in) s.d.1911 i.verso. 14-Apr-3 Sotheby's, London #27/R est:10000-15000
£14000 $21280 €21000 Highland cattle in a landscape (62x102cm-24x40in) s. 28-Aug-2 Sotheby's, London #859/R est:15000-20000
£15000 $22800 €22500 Highland cattle and drovers in a glen (76x127cm-30x50in) s.d.1881. 28-Aug-2 Sotheby's, London #885/R est:15000-20000
£22500 $34200 €33750 Glen in Ardgour (61x101cm-24x40in) s. 28-Aug-2 Sotheby's, London #922/R est:15000-20000

HURTEN, Carl Ferdinand (1818-?) German
Works on paper
£280 $442 €420 Still life of an orchid (27x19cm-11x7in) s. bodycol. 26-Nov-2 Bonhams, Knightsbridge #263/R

HURTUBISE, Jacques (1939-) Canadian
£1084 $1713 €1626 Rosita (173x173cm-68x68in) d.1967 acrylic. 1-Dec-2 Levis, Calgary #314/R (C.D 2700)
£2460 $4009 €3690 Denise (127x127cm-50x50in) s.i.d.68 verso acrylic. 12-Feb-3 Iegor de Saint Hippolyte, Montreal #97/R (C.D 6100)

HUSAIN, Maqbool Fida (1915-) Indian
£4000 $6240 €6000 Young lady with drums (35x25cm-14x10in) s. board. 17-Oct-2 Bonhams, Knightsbridge #578/R est:4000-6000
£5806 $9174 €9000 Village (51x45cm-20x18in) s.d.1950 cardboard. 19-Dec-2 Ruellan, Paris #58/R
£11655 $19231 €16900 Fisherwoman (92x122cm-36x48in) s. acrylic. 6-Jul-3 Christie's, Hong Kong #92/R est:140000-180000 (HK.D 150000)
£13209 $21795 €19153 Chandramukhi (92x122cm-36x48in) s. acrylic. 6-Jul-3 Christie's, Hong Kong #91/R est:140000-180000 (HK.D 170000)
£19425 $32051 €28166 Sitar player (102x152cm-40x60in) s.d.79. 6-Jul-3 Christie's, Hong Kong #81/R est:200000-250000 (HK.D 250000)
Works on paper
£4000 $6360 €6000 Nudes (35x30cm-14x12in) s. gouache W/C. 2-May-3 Christie's, Kensington #569/R est:2000-3000
£5051 $8333 €7324 Horse (107x71cm-42x28in) s. W/C. 6-Jul-3 Christie's, Hong Kong #82/R est:45000-65000 (HK.D 65000)

HUSER, Heinrich A (?) German
£481 $755 €750 Woods on lakeshore (103x128cm-41x50in) s.d.96. 21-Nov-2 Van Ham, Cologne #1688/R

HUSKISSON, Robert (1820-1861) British
£100000 $161000 €150000 Titania asleep (30x36cm-12x14in) i.verso panel prov.exhib.lit. 19-Feb-3 Christie's, London #2/R est:70000-100000

HUSNER, Paul (1942-) Swiss
£1574 $2424 €2361 Chinese opera, Singapore (50x60cm-20x24in) s. s.i.verso. 27-Oct-2 Christie's, Hong Kong #17/R est:14000-18000 (HK.D 19000)

HUSOVSZKY, Janos (1883-1961) Hungarian
£2286 $3543 €3315 Winter market at Nagybanya (81x100cm-32x39in) s. 9-Dec-2 Mu Terem Galeria, Budapest #65/R est:600000 (H.F 850000)

HUSSAIN, Muhammad (19th C) Persian
Works on paper
£9000 $14310 €13500 Flowers, birds and butterflies. s. two signed by different artists d.1880-81 album page three. 30-Apr-3 Sotheby's, London #39/R est:2000-3000

HUSSEM, Willem (1900-1974) Dutch
£510 $795 €800 Flowers in ginger jar (39x31cm-15x12in) s.d.22 panel. 6-Nov-2 Vendue Huis, Gravenhage #173/R
£1056 $1701 €1500 Abstract composition (72x59cm-28x23in) s.d.51 verso. 7-May-3 Vendue Huis, Gravenhage #204/R est:1500-2000
£1358 $2118 €2352 Ke krekel (60x73cm-24x29in) s.verso prov. 31-Mar-3 Goodman, Sydney #194/R (A.D 3600)
£2518 $4129 €3500 Untitled (50x60cm-20x24in) init.d.57 canvas on board. 3-Jun-3 Christie's, Amsterdam #117/R est:4000-6000
£2675 $4173 €4200 Untitled (65x55cm-26x22in) studio st. verso prov. 6-Nov-2 Vendue Huis, Gravenhage #213/R est:1500-2000
£2734 $4483 €3800 Composition (33x26cm-13x10in) init.d.57. 3-Jun-3 Christie's, Amsterdam #115/R est:3000-5000
£3503 $5465 €5500 Nr B (60x60cm-24x24in) init.d.63 studio st. verso prov. 6-Nov-2 Vendue Huis, Gravenhage #214/R est:3000-5000
£4487 $6955 €7000 Composition (60x50cm-24x20in) init.d.63 board. 3-Dec-2 Christie's, Amsterdam #146/R est:3000-5000
£6962 $11000 €11000 Untitled (66x66cm-26x26in) init.d.63 prov. 26-Nov-2 Sotheby's, Amsterdam #264/R est:6000-9000
£7194 $11799 €10000 Untitled (120x150cm-47x59in) prov. 3-Jun-3 Christie's, Amsterdam #360/R est:10000-15000
Works on paper
£414 $658 €600 Untitled (32x25cm-13x10in) s.d.52. 10-Mar-3 Sotheby's, Amsterdam #465

HUSSEY, Giles (1710-1788) British
Works on paper
£19000 $29450 €28500 Portrait of Prince Charles Edward Stuart (26x19cm-10x7in) pencil pen grey ink wash feigned oval. 31-Oct-2 Christie's, London #6/R est:4000-6000

HUSSMANN, Albert Heinrich (1874-1946) German
Sculpture
£1149 $1792 €1700 Europa on bull (63cm-25in) s. dark pat.bronze marble socle. 27-Mar-3 Dr Fritz Nagel, Stuttgart #990/R est:2000
£1321 $2060 €2100 Europa on bull (61cm-24in) i. pat.bronze stone socle. 21-Sep-2 Bolland & Marotz, Bremen #214/R est:1100
£5769 $9058 €9000 Amazone on horseback (94cm-37in) s. bronze Cast.Gladenbeck Berlin. 23-Nov-2 Arnold, Frankfurt #368/R
£13000 $20280 €19500 Dying Amazon (82x40x38cm-32x16x15in) s.i. brown pat bronze lit. 5-Nov-2 Sotheby's, London #196/R est:8000-12000

HUSTON, William (19th C) American
£487 $750 €731 Coastal view (38x71cm-15x28in) s. 27-Oct-2 Grogan, Boston #63

HUSZAR, Vilmos (1884-1960) Dutch
£8446 $13176 €12500 Composition geometrique (54x54cm-21x21in) s. masonite. 26-Mar-3 Millon & Associes, Paris #144/R est:15000
£10319 $16098 €15479 Young woman with geometrical picture and bauhaus lamp (50x60cm-20x24in) s. 11-Sep-2 Kieselbach, Budapest #109/R (H.F 4000000)

HUTCHENS, Frank Townsend (1869-1937) American
£37975 $60000 €56963 Youth (76x64cm-30x25in) s. 24-Apr-3 Shannon's, Milford #123/R est:25000-35000

HUTCHESON, Tom (1924-) British
Works on paper
£300 $486 €450 Remembered place with burn (20x18cm-8x7in) s. mixed media on board. 20-May-3 Bonhams, Knightsbridge #172/R
£1650 $2756 €2393 Brulage with red (71x69cm-28x27in) s.d.73 mixed media. 20-Jun-3 Keys, Aylsham #424 est:100-150

HUTCHINS, Ernest J (19/20th C) Canadian
Works on paper
£258 $402 €374 Interior of Old Fort Garry (41x56cm-16x22in) s.i.d.08 W/C. 26-Mar-3 Walker's, Ottawa #473 (C.D 600)

HUTCHINSON, J (19/20th C) British
£750 $1193 €1125 White wings, study of a horse (30x41cm-12x16in) s.d.1902 pair. 30-Apr-3 Goldings, Lincolnshire #111/R

HUTCHINSON, Nick Hely (1955-) Irish
Works on paper
£650 $1007 €975 Sunny terrace, Paros (49x68cm-19x27in) init. gouache exhib. 4-Dec-2 Christie's, Kensington #330
£1026 $1610 €1600 Mountain sheep, Mayo (51x66cm-20x26in) init. i.verso gouache pastel prov. 19-Nov-2 Whyte's, Dublin #10/R est:800-1200

HUTCHINSON, Peter C (1935-1984) British
£310 $484 €465 Pheasants in a wooded landscape (58x91cm-23x36in) s.d.1982. 11-Apr-3 Keys, Aylsham #305

HUTCHISON, Frederick William (1871-1953) Canadian
£1235 $1914 €1853 Near Hudson Heights houses (25x30cm-10x12in) s. canvas on board. 3-Dec-2 Joyner, Toronto #423 est:600-800 (C.D 3000)
Works on paper
£1070 $1658 €1605 St. Urbain (9x15cm-4x6in) init.i. gouache prov. 3-Dec-2 Joyner, Toronto #240/R est:3000-3500 (C.D 2600)

HUTCHISON, Robert Gemmell (1855-1936) British
£3500 $5425 €5250 Toy balloon (41x30cm-16x12in) s. 31-Oct-2 Christie's, London #111/R est:4000-6000
£4000 $6200 €6000 Mother and child (61x46cm-24x18in) s. 31-Oct-2 Christie's, London #109/R est:5000-7000
£5000 $7750 €7500 Pink dress (46x36cm-18x14in) s. board. 6-Dec-2 Lyon & Turnbull, Edinburgh #65/R est:4000-6000
£6500 $10075 €9750 Young gate keeper (35x25cm-14x10in) s. exhib. 31-Oct-2 Christie's, London #112/R est:4000-6000
£6500 $10205 €9750 Pans, Machrihanish (9x13cm-4x5in) s. board prov. 16-Apr-3 George Kidner, Lymington #105/R est:3000-5000
£6600 $10296 €9900 Tired out (60x50cm-24x20in) s. prov. 10-Apr-3 Bonhams, Edinburgh #111/R est:5000-7000
£7200 $11232 €10800 Toy boat (25x30cm-10x12in) s. board. 10-Apr-3 Bonhams, Edinburgh #132/R est:6000-8000
£7800 $12090 €11700 Morning break (30x22cm-12x9in) s. board. 6-Dec-2 Lyon & Turnbull, Edinburgh #38/R est:6000-8000
£8000 $12480 €12000 Young fishers (14x17cm-6x7in) s. panel. 10-Apr-3 Bonhams, Edinburgh #153a/R est:8000-12000
£16500 $25575 €24750 Sailing the toy boat, Carnoustie (40x50cm-16x20in) s. 6-Dec-2 Lyon & Turnbull, Edinburgh #48/R est:18000-25000
£20000 $31200 €30000 Windy day by the coast (51x76cm-20x30in) s. 14-Apr-3 Sotheby's, London #136/R est:20000-30000
Works on paper
£1000 $1530 €1500 Beachcombing (31x39cm-12x15in) s. conte. 22-Aug-2 Bonhams, Edinburgh #1129/R est:1000-1500
£3500 $5425 €5250 Southerness, Dumfriesshire (39x49cm-15x19in) s. W/C bodycol. 31-Oct-2 Christie's, London #110/R est:3000-5000
£11500 $17595 €17250 Doubtful weather (60x50cm-24x20in) s. W/C. 22-Aug-2 Bonhams, Edinburgh #1083/R est:10000-15000

HUTH, Franz (attrib) (1876-?) German
£355 $522 €550 Peonies (79x58cm-31x23in) s. 24-Jun-2 Dr Fritz Nagel, Stuttgart #6018

HUTH, Julius (1838-1892) German
£700 $1120 €1050 Shipping in the Sound on a calm day (26x40cm-10x16in) s.d.76 panel. 13-May-3 Bonhams, Knightsbridge #57/R

HUTH, Willy Robert (1890-1977) German
£409 $630 €650 Spanish village street (24x31cm-9x12in) mono.d.1946 masonite. 26-Oct-2 Dr Lehr, Berlin #186/R
Works on paper
£347 $549 €500 Martel Schwichtenberg (42x57cm-17x22in) mono.i.d.1928 Indian ink. 26-Apr-3 Dr Lehr, Berlin #230/R
£915 $1520 €1300 Card players (49x37cm-19x15in) s.d. W/C pencil. 14-Jun-3 Hauswedell & Nolte, Hamburg #1266/R

HUTHER, Julius (1881-1954) German
£377 $581 €600 Lively beach scene (44x51cm-17x20in) s. board. 23-Oct-2 Neumeister, Munich #670/R
£432 $691 €600 Island woman (57x45cm-22x18in) s. board. 15-May-3 Neumeister, Munich #279/R
£463 $745 €695 Village in summer (70x90cm-28x35in) s.d.30. 7-May-3 Dobiaschofsky, Bern #675/R (S.FR 1000)
£719 $1151 €1000 Southsea Island woman (55x44cm-22x17in) s.d. board. 15-May-3 Neumeister, Munich #275/R
Works on paper
£417 $668 €580 Backyard on wash day (41x30cm-16x12in) s.d. W/C Indian ink board. 15-May-3 Neumeister, Munich #277/R

HUTIN, Charles-François (1715-1776) French
£35000 $54600 €52500 Portrait of a young woman holding a spaniel (78x56cm-31x22in) s.d.1767. 9-Apr-3 Christie's, London #76/R est:10000-15000

HUTRI, Armas (1922-) Finnish
Sculpture
£980 $1608 €1500 Sheltering from the wind (49cm-19in) s.d.1986 num.1/3 bronze. 9-Feb-3 Bukowskis, Helsinki #184/R est:1200
£1456 $2300 €2300 The tax payers (45cm-18in) s.d.74 num.2/3 bronze. 1-Dec-2 Bukowskis, Helsinki #295/R est:1700-2000
£1772 $2800 €2800 The butler (69cm-27in) s.d.1970 bronze. 1-Dec-2 Bukowskis, Helsinki #294/R est:2000-2300

HUTSON, Marshall C (fl.1930-40) British
Sculpture
£833 $1292 €1300 Student with portfolio (36cm-14in) bronze. 17-Jul-2 Woodwards, Cork #249
£897 $1391 €1400 Caryatid (86cm-34in) bronze. 17-Jul-2 Woodwards, Cork #250
£1218 $1888 €1900 Secret (61cm-24in) init. green pat. bronze. 17-Jul-2 Woodwards, Cork #247

HUTTE, Axel (1951-) ?
Photographs
£3000 $4620 €4500 Glacier des bossons (162x197cm-64x78in) s.d.1997 num.2/4 verso chromagenic print prov. 23-Oct-2 Christie's, London #213/R est:4000-6000
£5000 $7700 €7500 Maderaner Tal - waterfall (203x149cm-80x59in) s.d.1997 num.2/4 chromagenic print prov. 23-Oct-2 Christie's, London #210/R est:7000-10000

HUTTENBRENNER, Erni von (1874-1944) Austrian

£	$	€	Details
£2821	$4372	€4400	Napoleon on horseback crossing the St Bernhard's Pass (63x53cm-25x21in) s.d.1927 panel. 6-Dec-2 Michael Zeller, Lindau #793/R est:3200
£3020	$4862	€4500	Virgin and child with Saint Peter , Paul and Mary Magdalene (258x192cm-102x76in) s.d.1934 after Sir Anthony Van Dyck. 18-Feb-3 Sotheby's, Amsterdam #205 est:1500-2000

HUTTER, Wolfgang (1928-) Austrian

£	$	€	Details
£5696	$9000	€9000	Spring II (59x39cm-23x15in) s.d.91 masonite. 27-Nov-2 Dorotheum, Vienna #266/R est:9000-13000
£5696	$9000	€9000	Summer II (59x39cm-23x15in) s.d.91 masonite. 27-Nov-2 Dorotheum, Vienna #267/R est:9000-13000
£5696	$9000	€9000	Autumn II (59x39cm-23x15in) s.d.91 masonite. 27-Nov-2 Dorotheum, Vienna #268/R est:9000-13000
£5696	$9000	€9000	Winter II (59x39cm-23x15in) s.d.91 masonite. 27-Nov-2 Dorotheum, Vienna #269/R est:9000-13000

HUTTON, Thomas S (c.1865-1935) British

£	$	€	Details
£280	$456	€420	Durham City (9x13cm-4x5in) s. 12-Feb-3 Andrew Hartley, Ilkley #861
£450	$716	€675	Glen (61x91cm-24x36in) s. 6-Mar-3 Christie's, Kensington #128/R

Works on paper

£	$	€	Details
£280	$468	€406	Angler at Sligachan, Isle of Skye (37x53cm-15x21in) s. i.verso W/C. 17-Jun-3 Anderson & Garland, Newcastle #308/R
£314	$497	€471	Busy riverside town (23x34cm-9x13in) s. W/C htd scratching out. 26-Nov-2 Sotheby's, Melbourne #230/R est:700-900 (A.D 880)
£480	$744	€720	Seaton sluice harbour at low tide with coble in foreground (29x49cm-11x19in) s.d.1925 W/C. 24-Sep-2 Anderson & Garland, Newcastle #320/R
£500	$835	€725	Whitby Harbour (35x50cm-14x20in) s. indis d. W/C. 17-Jun-3 Anderson & Garland, Newcastle #307/R
£540	$837	€810	Bamburgh castle on a summer's day (32x53cm-13x21in) s. W/C. 24-Sep-2 Anderson & Garland, Newcastle #354/R
£640	$992	€960	View of Durham city across rooftops towards the castle (40x61cm-16x24in) s.d.1926 W/C. 24-Sep-2 Anderson & Garland, Newcastle #349/R
£650	$1014	€975	Staithes and Penny Nab (33x25cm-13x10in) s. W/C. 20-Sep-2 Richardson & Smith, Whitby #93

HUTTY, Alfred (1877-1954) American

Works on paper

£	$	€	Details
£1829	$3000	€2652	Deep south (41x43cm-16x17in) d.8.11.41 chl. 7-Jun-3 Neal Auction Company, New Orleans #353/R est:3000-5000

HUVEY, Joseph (19/20th C) French

£	$	€	Details
£284	$448	€426	Mountain lake with Eiger, Monch and Jungfrau (68x92cm-27x36in) s. 14-Nov-2 Stuker, Bern #300/R (S.FR 650)

HUYGELEN, Frans (1878-1940) Belgian

£	$	€	Details
£275	$442	€420	Composition aux roses et fruits rouges (80x70cm-31x28in) s. d.1933 verso panel. 20-Jan-3 Horta, Bruxelles #25

HUYGENS, François Joseph (1820-1908) Belgian

£	$	€	Details
£380	$592	€600	Nature morte a la rose et a la pensee (31x24cm-12x9in) s.d.1853. 16-Sep-2 Horta, Bruxelles #334
£892	$1391	€1400	Nature morte aux oiseaux (38x30cm-15x12in) s. panel. 11-Nov-2 Horta, Bruxelles #546
£1046	$1684	€1600	Nature morte aux roses en pensees (31x24cm-12x9in) s.d.1858 panel. 14-Jan-3 Vanderkindere, Brussels #41 est:400-600
£1635	$2551	€2600	Still life with grapes, coconut, bottle and wine glass (39x49cm-15x19in) s. panel. 19-Sep-2 Dr Fritz Nagel, Stuttgart #948/R est:1800

HUYGENS, Léon (19/20th C) Belgian

£	$	€	Details
£261	$421	€400	Le mole de Zeebrugge (30x40cm-12x16in) s.d.1912 panel. 14-Jan-3 Vanderkindere, Brussels #26
£2115	$3279	€3300	Snowy landscape (70x100cm-28x39in) s. 7-Dec-2 De Vuyst, Lokeren #155/R est:3300-4000

HUYS, Bernhard (1885-1973) German

£	$	€	Details
£304	$480	€480	Early spring evening on Weiherberg (30x38cm-12x15in) s.verso board. 29-Nov-2 Bolland & Marotz, Bremen #531
£380	$600	€600	Peat boat in Teufels fen at dusk (50x65cm-20x26in) s. board. 29-Nov-2 Bolland & Marotz, Bremen #530/R
£408	$649	€600	Farmstead in Teufelsmoor (50x70cm-20x28in) s. i. verso panel. 28-Mar-3 Bolland & Marotz, Bremen #345/R
£408	$649	€600	Spring on the Hamme (50x70cm-20x28in) s. panel. 28-Mar-3 Bolland & Marotz, Bremen #346/R
£411	$650	€650	Mill by the fen ditch (50x70cm-20x28in) s. i.d.1951 verso board. 29-Nov-2 Bolland & Marotz, Bremen #327/R
£411	$650	€650	Fens at dusk (70x50cm-28x20in) s.i.d.1959 verso. 29-Nov-2 Bolland & Marotz, Bremen #528/R
£429	$681	€630	Birche avenue at start of spring (50x70cm-20x28in) s. panel. 28-Mar-3 Bolland & Marotz, Bremen #344
£443	$700	€700	Evening in the fens (49x64cm-19x25in) s. d.71 verso board. 29-Nov-2 Bolland & Marotz, Bremen #525/R
£443	$700	€700	Cottage on the fens with birch trees in the evening (50x64cm-20x25in) s. board. 29-Nov-2 Bolland & Marotz, Bremen #526/R
£692	$1079	€1100	Farmstead on the Hamme on autumn evening (50x65cm-20x26in) s. panel. 21-Sep-2 Bolland & Marotz, Bremen #371/R
£696	$1100	€1100	Worpswede farmhouse in winter (50x69cm-20x27in) s. board. 29-Nov-2 Bolland & Marotz, Bremen #524/R
£1132	$1766	€1800	Worpswede farmstead in spring (75x93cm-30x37in) s. i.d. verso panel. 21-Sep-2 Bolland & Marotz, Bremen #369/R est:2200

HUYS, Modeste (1875-1932) Belgian

£	$	€	Details
£1667	$2583	€2600	Ruins in Westhoek (33x44cm-13x17in) s. board. 7-Dec-2 De Vuyst, Lokeren #156/R est:2400-2800
£4828	$7724	€7000	Snow in the spring (34x44cm-13x17in) s. mono.i.d.1921 verso panel. 15-Mar-3 De Vuyst, Lokeren #440/R est:7000-9000
£7092	$11844	€10000	Woodview with well and haystack (36x47cm-14x19in) s. 23-Jun-3 Bernaerts, Antwerp #183/R est:10000-15000
£8974	$14090	€14000	Paysage de la Lys (37x45cm-15x18in) s. 10-Dec-2 Campo, Vlaamse Kaai #257/R est:10000-15000
£14744	$22853	€23000	Autumn in the park (69x56cm-27x22in) s. mono.i.verso painted 1917. 7-Dec-2 De Vuyst, Lokeren #546/R est:24000-26000
£58865	$98305	€83000	Rats d'eau (81x107cm-32x42in) s. mono.i.d.21 verso. 23-Jun-3 Bernaerts, Antwerp #185 est:60000-70000

Works on paper

£	$	€	Details
£556	$894	€850	Course hippique (22x31cm-9x12in) mono. chl dr. 20-Jan-3 Horta, Bruxelles #28

HUYSEN, Hof (1900-) Dutch

£	$	€	Details
£577	$900	€866	Figures on horseback (61x51cm-24x20in) 18-Oct-2 Du Mouchelle, Detroit #1155/R

HUYSMANS, Cornelis (1648-1727) Flemish

£	$	€	Details
£3653	$5699	€5480	Landscape (59x82cm-23x32in) 28-Mar-3 Koller, Zurich #3074/R est:6000-8000 (S.FR 8000)
£9868	$15987	€15000	Landscape with classical figures (52x62cm-20x24in) exhib. 21-Jan-3 Ansorena, Madrid #96/R est:15000
£11321	$17547	€18000	Landscape with classical figures (52x62cm-20x24in) prov. 7-Oct-2 Ansorena, Madrid #32/R est:18000

HUYSMANS, Frans (1885-1954) Dutch

£	$	€	Details
£347	$573	€500	Tree in a dune landscape (29x34cm-11x13in) s. plywood. 1-Jul-3 Christie's, Amsterdam #390

HUYSMANS, Jacob (attrib) (1633-1680) Flemish

£	$	€	Details
£800	$1304	€1160	Portrait of a lady wearing a brown dress and pearl clasp (33x25cm-13x10in) panel. 21-Jul-3 Sotheby's, London #395

HUYSMANS, Jan Baptist (1826-1906) Belgian

£	$	€	Details
£955	$1490	€1500	Portrait of Josepha van de Lauter, wife of doctor Jacobus Petrus de Bruyn (105x79cm-41x31in) s.i.d.1852. 6-Nov-2 Vendue Huis, Gravenhage #471/R est:1500-2000
£1300	$2028	€1950	Turkish girl on a balcony (21x13cm-8x5in) s. panel. 10-Apr-3 Bonhams, Edinburgh #129/R est:1500-2000
£1572	$2421	€2500	Orientale tenant une rose (25x19cm-10x7in) s.d.1868 panel. 23-Oct-2 Rabourdin & Choppin de Janvry, Paris #68/R
£3500	$5530	€5250	En meditation (24x40cm-9x16in) s. panel. 7-Apr-3 Bonhams, Bath #132/R est:3000-4000

HUYSMANS, Jan Baptist (1654-1716) Flemish

£	$	€	Details
£2885	$4558	€4500	Chamber recital (49x37cm-19x15in) s.d.1697 panel. 18-Nov-2 Bernaerts, Antwerp #187/R est:4500-6000

HUYSUM, Jan van (1682-1749) Dutch

£	$	€	Details
£864198	$1400000	€1296297	Roses and other flowers in a terracotta vase with a bird's nest on marble ledge. Fruit and peonies (51x42cm-20x17in) s.i.d.1744 panel pair prov.lit. 24-Jan-3 Christie's, Rockefeller NY #147/R est:1500000-20000

HUYSUM, Jan van (style) (1682-1749) Dutch

£	$	€	Details
£5500	$9185	€8250	Roses, tulips and other summer flowers on a ledge (60x47cm-24x19in) panel. 18-Jun-3 Christie's, Kensington #39/R est:5000-7000
£10596	$17272	€16000	Bouquets (60x46cm-24x18in) panel pair. 31-Jan-3 Rabourdin & Choppin de Janvry, Paris #174/R est:13000

HUYSUM, Justus van (17/18th C) Dutch

£	$	€	Details
£2830	$4387	€4500	Ideal landscape (75x100cm-30x39in) 29-Oct-2 Artcurial Briest, Paris #27/R est:5500

HVIDBERG, Knud (1927-1986) Danish
£458 $764 €664 Black and tan (73x66cm-29x26in) s.d.63 verso. 17-Jun-3 Rasmussen, Copenhagen #29/R (D.KR 4800)

HYAKUSEN, Sakaki (1698-1753) Japanese
Works on paper
£503 $800 €755 Landscape (130x32cm-51x13in) s. ink col hanging scroll exhib. 24-Mar-3 Christie's, Rockefeller NY #17/R

HYATT, Derek (1931-) British
£280 $454 €420 Landscape (26x30cm-10x12in) board. 20-May-3 Bonhams, Knightsbridge #71/R
£280 $454 €420 Time moves across the move (31x36cm-12x14in) board prov. 20-May-3 Bonhams, Knightsbridge #74/R
£280 $456 €406 Winters glance (60x120cm-24x47in) board. 15-Jul-3 Bonhams, Knightsbridge #97
£300 $465 €450 End of the summer (35x41cm-14x16in) board prov.exhib. 1-Oct-2 Bonhams, Leeds #336
£380 $604 €570 Little owl among the limestone (75x91cm-30x36in) board. 18-Mar-3 Bonhams, Knightsbridge #124
£440 $713 €660 Bronze age moor from Hunger Hill, Hail and sunlight (38x151cm-15x59in) board prov. 20-May-3 Bonhams, Knightsbridge #72/R
£800 $1272 €1200 Meeting on the moor (122x121cm-48x48in) board. 18-Mar-3 Bonhams, Knightsbridge #122

HYBERT, Fabrice (1961-) French?
£1528 $2521 €2200 Sans titre (60x73cm-24x29in) s.i.d.1991 verso flourescent acrylic wax crayon. 1-Jul-3 Artcurial Briest, Paris #872/R est:2000-2500
Works on paper
£340 $541 €500 Radar (30x21cm-12x8in) s.d.1996 graphite felt-tip pen dr. 24-Mar-3 Cornette de St.Cyr, Paris #40/R

HYDE, Doug (1946-) American
Sculpture
£11644 $17000 €17466 Standing Indian woman (165cm-65in) bronze stone. 18-May-2 Altermann Galleries, Santa Fe #11/R

HYDE, Wayne (20th C) American
Sculpture
£898 $1500 €1302 They stood tall (51x41cm-20x16in) s.d.2002 painted bronze. 21-Jun-3 Charlton Hall, Columbia #595/R est:2000-3000
£1484 $2300 €2226 They stood tall, group of civil war soldiers (51x41cm-20x16in) s.d.2002 num.2/8 bronze black marble base. 28-Sep-2 Charlton Hall, Columbia #614/R est:3000-4000

HYDE, William (?-1925) British
Works on paper
£480 $763 €720 London street scene (15x22cm-6x9in) s.d.10 W/C. 25-Feb-3 Bonhams, Knightsbridge #159/R

HYDMAN-VALLIEN, Ulrika (1938-) Swedish
£463 $769 €671 Wild animals in wood (38x46cm-15x18in) s. panel. 16-Jun-3 Lilla Bukowskis, Stockholm #327 (S.KR 6000)
£580 $922 €870 Angels (51x40cm-20x16in) s. panel. 3-Mar-3 Lilla Bukowskis, Stockholm #304 (S.KR 7800)

HYLAND, Benedict A (19th C) British
£1595 $2600 €2393 Family of Clumber spaniels (61x77cm-24x30in) s. 11-Feb-3 Bonhams & Doyles, New York #162/R est:3000-5000

HYNAIS, Vojtech (1845-1925) Czechoslovakian
Works on paper
£1135 $1839 €1646 Boy nude study (40x22cm-16x9in) s.d.29 1884 pencil. 24-May-3 Dorotheum, Prague #216/R est:18000-30000 (C.KR 50000)

HYNAIS, Voytech (1854-1925) Czechoslovakian
£6545 $10406 €9818 Joan of Arc (55x36cm-22x14in) s.i.d.1890. 8-Mar-3 Dorotheum, Prague #13/R est:260000-370000 (C.KR 300000)
£9284 $14669 €13926 Female semi-nude (90x70cm-35x28in) s.indis.d. 30-Nov-2 Dorotheum, Prague #11/R est:400000-600000 (C.KR 450000)

HYNCKES, Raoul (1893-1973) Dutch
£637 $981 €1000 Village street in Belgium (52x65cm-20x26in) s. 3-Sep-2 Christie's, Amsterdam #398
£966 $1535 €1400 Landscape in Belgium (52x65cm-20x26in) i.verso. 10-Mar-3 Sotheby's, Amsterdam #292 est:1000-1500
£1319 $2177 €1900 Village street (48x62cm-19x24in) 1-Jul-3 Christie's, Amsterdam #373/R est:1800-2200
£2897 $4606 €4200 View of a river with a moored boat in the distance (41x56cm-16x22in) s. panel. 10-Mar-3 Sotheby's, Amsterdam #291/R est:2000-3000

HYNCKES-ZAHN, Marguerite (1897-1978) Dutch
£256 $403 €400 Still life with melon and a cup (34x49cm-13x19in) init. 25-Nov-2 Glerum, Amsterdam #73
£308 $483 €480 Still life with a laurel branch in a glass and fruit (45x31cm-18x12in) init. board. 25-Nov-2 Glerum, Amsterdam #150
£1090 $1711 €1700 Blue canvas (63x50cm-25x20in) init. i.verso. 25-Nov-2 Glerum, Amsterdam #48/R est:1000-1500

HYNER, Arend (1866-1916) Dutch
£478 $745 €750 Interior of farmhouse (66x54cm-26x21in) s. 6-Nov-2 Vendue Huis, Gravenhage #487

HYNES, Stephen (1944-) Canadian
£222 $364 €322 Promenades des gouveneurs, Quebec (40x60cm-16x24in) s.i.d.2000. 9-Jun-3 Hodgins, Calgary #209/R (C.D 500)
£281 $441 €422 One played a mouth organ the other a Jews harp, Rue St Andre, Quebec (40x50cm-16x20in) s.i.d.2000. 25-Nov-2 Hodgins, Calgary #359/R (C.D 700)
£301 $473 €452 Beaver foundations (50x40cm-20x16in) s.i. exhib. 25-Nov-2 Hodgins, Calgary #361/R (C.D 750)

HYPPOLITE, Hector (1894-1948) Haitian
£10274 $16130 €15000 Adoration de la Sainte Vierge (74x66cm-29x26in) i.verso cardboard exhib.lit. 15-Apr-3 Laurence Calmels, Paris #4310/R est:18000
£10959 $17205 €16000 Re Laucation Pa Pa Dom Balas (73x65cm-29x26in) s.i.verso cardboard lit. 15-Apr-3 Laurence Calmels, Paris #4315/R est:20000
£11644 $18281 €17000 Maitre Adani (74x65cm-29x26in) s. s.i.verso cardboard. 15-Apr-3 Laurence Calmels, Paris #4312/R est:18000
£17123 $26712 €25000 Ogoun Ferraille (51x70cm-20x28in) s. cardboard prov.exhib.lit. 14-Apr-3 Laurence Calmels, Paris #4013/R est:15000
£19178 $30110 €28000 Marinete Pie Che Che (51x70cm-20x28in) i. cardboard exhib.lit. 15-Apr-3 Laurence Calmels, Paris #4311/R est:18000
£21233 $33336 €31000 Mari Travo (52x69cm-20x27in) s.i. cardboard exhib.lit. 15-Apr-3 Laurence Calmels, Paris #4313/R est:20000
£23288 $36562 €34000 Dee (61x76cm-24x30in) s. s.i.verso cardboard lit. 15-Apr-3 Laurence Calmels, Paris #4314/R est:20000

HYRE, Laurent de la (1606-1656) French
£7500 $11775 €11250 Two winged putti in landscape (91x118cm-36x46in) 11-Dec-2 Christie's, London #79/R

HYRE, Laurent de la (attrib) (1606-1656) French
Works on paper
£612 $973 €900 Architecture animee (34x23cm-13x9in) pen ink wash over crayon. 21-Mar-3 Rieunier, Bailly-Pommery, Mathias, Paris #42

HYSING, Hans (attrib) (?-1723) Swedish
£1500 $2310 €2250 Portrait of a gentleman, in a red coat (76x63cm-30x25in) feigned oval. 5-Sep-2 Christie's, Kensington #26/R est:2000-3000

IACOPINO, Mimmo (1962-) Italian
£1418 $2298 €2000 Untitled (100x100cm-39x39in) s.d.2002 metro da banco tedesco. 20-May-3 Porro, Milan #32/R est:2200-2400

IACOVLEFF, Alexandre (1887-1938) French/Russian
£1646 $2600 €2600 Breakers (32x41cm-13x16in) s. panel. 1-Dec-2 Bukowskis, Helsinki #251/R est:1500-2000
£45000 $72900 €67500 Sleeping nude (41x100cm-16x39in) s.d.1929. 21-May-3 Sotheby's, London #115/R est:40000-60000
£150000 $235500 €225000 Portrait of the artist Boris Grigoriev (73x54cm-29x21in) exhib. 20-Nov-2 Sotheby's, London #115/R est:40000-60000
Works on paper
£800 $1296 €1200 Portrait of a Chinaman (42x28cm-17x11in) s.i.d.1919 sanguine. 21-May-3 Sotheby's, London #118/R
£955 $1490 €1500 Portrait d'homme (57x46cm-22x18in) s.d.1955 sanguine. 10-Nov-2 Eric Pillon, Calais #167/R
£2152 $3400 €3400 Seated boy (64x54cm-25x21in) s.i.d.1931 sanguine chl. 28-Nov-2 Piasa, Paris #1/R
£2405 $3800 €3608 Bambili-la Ganza (48x63cm-19x25in) s.i. indis d. W/C crayon. 3-Apr-3 Christie's, Rockefeller NY #182/R est:2000-3000
£3500 $5670 €5250 Young Chinese boy (61x48cm-24x19in) s.i.d.1919 sanguine. 21-May-3 Sotheby's, London #117/R est:3000-4000
£8000 $12960 €12000 Lake Albert, Africa (52x75cm-20x30in) s.i.d.1925 gouache on board exhib. 21-May-3 Sotheby's, London #116/R est:8000-12000

£9000 $14130 €13500 Young Japanese girl (63x51cm-25x20in) s.d.1919 chl sanguine. 20-Nov-2 Sotheby's, London #101/R est:4000-6000

IACURTO, Francesco (1908-) Canadian
£369 $575 €554 Autoportrait (21x14cm-8x6in) s.i.d.1940 panel. 10-Sep-2 Iegor de Saint Hippolyte, Montreal #56 (C.D 900)
£984 $1534 €1476 Spring, Quebec (25x30cm-10x12in) s.d.1964 cardboard. 10-Sep-2 Iegor de Saint Hippolyte, Montreal #58 (C.D 2400)
£1050 $1754 €1523 Street scene with carriages (51x61cm-20x24in) s.d.65. 18-Jun-3 Andrew Hartley, Ilkley #1129/R est:500-800
£1210 $1887 €1815 Bateau dans le port de Quebec (25x31cm-10x12in) s. isorel. 30-Jul-2 Iegor de Saint Hippolyte, Montreal #80 (C.D 3000)
£1301 $2042 €1952 Beauport, Quebec (51x41cm-20x16in) s.d.1945 i.verso. 10-Dec-2 Pinneys, Montreal #24 est:1000-1500 (C.D 3200)
£1399 $2155 €2099 Les pecheurs d'eperlan (40x50cm-16x20in) s.d.1972. 22-Oct-2 Iegor de Saint Hippolyte, Montreal #48 (C.D 3400)
£1535 $2287 €2303 Paysage (51x61cm-20x24in) s.d.1972. 26-Jun-2 Iegor de Saint Hippolyte, Montreal #54 (C.D 3500)
£2254 $3516 €3381 Scene maritime (50x60cm-20x24in) s.d.1960. 10-Sep-2 Iegor de Saint Hippolyte, Montreal #57/R (C.D 5500)
Works on paper
£435 $679 €653 Jeune fille (27x19cm-11x7in) s.d. sanguine. 30-Jul-2 Iegor de Saint Hippolyte, Montreal #79 (C.D 1080)

IALENTI, Antonio (1937-) Italian
£316 $494 €500 Countryside in Molise (50x70cm-20x28in) s. s.i.verso. 14-Sep-2 Meeting Art, Vercelli #160
£316 $494 €500 River Adda (50x70cm-20x28in) s. s.i.verso. 14-Sep-2 Meeting Art, Vercelli #445/R
£316 $494 €500 Big vase of flowers (60x45cm-24x18in) s. painted 1999. 14-Sep-2 Meeting Art, Vercelli #857
£316 $494 €500 Countryside in Abruzzo (50x70cm-20x28in) s. 14-Sep-2 Meeting Art, Vercelli #892/R
£327 $523 €500 Field with flowers (50x70cm-20x28in) s. 4-Jan-3 Meeting Art, Vercelli #219
£327 $523 €500 The Sesia (70x50cm-28x20in) s. s.i.verso. 4-Jan-3 Meeting Art, Vercelli #717
£347 $552 €500 Spring blooming (70x50cm-28x20in) s. 1-May-3 Meeting Art, Vercelli #272
£359 $575 €550 Seascape in Calabria (50x70cm-20x28in) s. 4-Jan-3 Meeting Art, Vercelli #500
£374 $595 €550 Vase of flowers (70x50cm-28x20in) s. painted 2000. 1-Mar-3 Meeting Art, Vercelli #761
£382 $607 €550 Vase of flowers (70x50cm-28x20in) s. s.i.verso. 1-May-3 Meeting Art, Vercelli #499
£382 $607 €550 Countryside in Abruzzo (50x70cm-20x28in) s.i.verso. 1-May-3 Meeting Art, Vercelli #497
£425 $680 €650 Vase of flowers (70x50cm-28x20in) s. s.i.verso. 4-Jan-3 Meeting Art, Vercelli #514
£521 $828 €750 Portofino (50x70cm-20x28in) s. painted 2001. 1-May-3 Meeting Art, Vercelli #60
£633 $987 €1000 Little house surrounded by flowers (70x100cm-28x39in) s. s.i.verso painted 2001. 14-Sep-2 Meeting Art, Vercelli #936/R
£641 $1006 €1000 Marine with flowers (70x99cm-28x39in) s. board painted 2001 oval. 23-Nov-2 Meeting Art, Vercelli #197/R
£654 $1046 €1000 Como lake (70x100cm-28x39in) s. s.i.verso. 4-Jan-3 Meeting Art, Vercelli #734
£680 $1082 €1000 Portofino (60x80cm-24x31in) s. painted 2001. 1-Mar-3 Meeting Art, Vercelli #501
£694 $1104 €1000 Countryside in Moise (70x100cm-28x39in) s. 1-May-3 Meeting Art, Vercelli #96
£719 $1150 €1100 Portofino (70x100cm-28x39in) s. 4-Jan-3 Meeting Art, Vercelli #523
£962 $1510 €1500 Countryside in Molise (100x140cm-39x55in) s. s.i.verso painted 2001 lit. 23-Nov-2 Meeting Art, Vercelli #471/R

IBANEZ BERNABE, Francisco Manuel (20th C) Spanish
Works on paper
£272 $430 €425 Goats in the life cycle (24x34cm-9x13in) s.d.1996 mixed media board. 14-Nov-2 Arte, Seville #444/R

IBANEZ DE ALDECOA, Julian (1866-1952) Spanish
£2308 $3646 €3600 Basque peasant woman (40x50cm-16x20in) s. board. 13-Nov-2 Ansorena, Madrid #105/R est:3600

IBANEZ, Jesus (1947-) Spanish
£3711 $5714 €5900 Taming seals (81x116cm-32x46in) s.d.1976 prov.exhib. 28-Oct-2 Segre, Madrid #182/R est:5900

IBBETSON, Julius Caesar (1759-1817) British
£278 $447 €417 Circus in the city (19x14cm-7x6in) s.d.1796 Indian ink pen brush W/C. 7-May-3 Dobiaschofsky, Bern #1143/R (S.FR 600)
£1100 $1726 €1650 View of Conway Castle (70x83cm-28x33in) bears sig. 20-Nov-2 Sotheby's, Olympia #9/R est:800-1200
£2000 $3120 €3000 Portrait of John Baines aged 22 (41x30cm-16x12in) i.d.1810. 7-Nov-2 Christie's, Kensington #43/R est:1200-1800
£8500 $13430 €12750 Farmyard with cattle, horse and figures. Figures and cattle by stream (28x38cm-11x15in) s.d.1805 panel pair. 26-Nov-2 Christie's, London #62/R est:6000-8000
£44000 $69960 €66000 Salmon fishery at Pony Aberglaslyn, North Wales (99x123cm-39x48in) s. prov.exhib.lit. 19-Mar-3 Sotheby's, London #63/R est:15000-20000
Works on paper
£300 $477 €450 Cottages in the lake District (13x21cm-5x8in) s. sepia. 25-Feb-3 John Taylors, Louth #454
£900 $1423 €1350 Milkmaid and cattle by a tree (21x29cm-8x11in) s. pen ink W/C. 28-Nov-2 Sotheby's, London #287/R est:1000-1500
£2000 $3160 €3000 Losing her calf (28x38cm-11x15in) W/C. 2-Dec-2 Gorringes, Lewes #2618/R est:1500-2000
£2400 $3744 €3600 Country dance. Street muscians. Dancing dogs. Exotic dancers (14x21cm-6x8in) W/C set of four. 5-Nov-2 Bonhams, New Bond Street #46/R est:800-1200

IBBETSON, Julius Caesar (attrib) (1759-1817) British
£300 $471 €450 Portrait of a lady, possibly Mrs Thompson, the artist's mother-in-law (26x23cm-10x9in) 21-Nov-2 Tennants, Leyburn #729/R
£408 $649 €600 Herder with cattle watering (56x46cm-22x18in) panel lit. 21-Mar-3 Auktionhaus Georg Rehm, Augsburg #8040
£533 $885 €773 Watermill and church in river valley (27x41cm-11x16in) panel prov. 10-Jun-3 Ritchie, Toronto #59/R est:1200-1600 (C.D 1200)

IBELS, Henri Gabriel (1867-1936) French
£377 $589 €600 Portrait de Madame (40x31cm-16x12in) s.i.d.1920 cardboard. 11-Oct-2 Binoche, Paris #126
Prints
£6538 $10331 €10200 Pierrefort 12. col lithograph. 13-Nov-2 Piasa, Paris #210/R est:2000-2500
Works on paper
£466 $661 €750 A la caserne (23x30cm-9x12in) s. chl Indian ink gouache. 20-Mar-2 Chayette & Cheval, Paris #53/R

IBORRA, Casimiro Lino (1857-1935) Spanish
£650 $1014 €975 Sheep in a barn (110x150cm-43x59in) s. 17-Sep-2 Sotheby's, Olympia #227/R

IBOU, Paul (1939-) Belgian
£278 $442 €400 Blackworld (120x120cm-47x47in) s.d.1976 verso. 29-Apr-3 Campo, Vlaamse Kaai #153

IBSEN, Immanuel (1887-1944) Danish
£343 $542 €515 Steamer at quay, Copenhagen (63x63cm-25x25in) s. 13-Nov-2 Kunsthallen, Copenhagen #81 (D.KR 4000)
£933 $1483 €1400 Portrait of young woman - Miss Lucie Tage-Jensen (100x75cm-39x30in) 29-Apr-3 Kunsthallen, Copenhagen #268/R (D.KR 10000)
£1894 $3144 €2746 Landscape, Venoe 1942 (88x110cm-35x43in) exhib.lit. 12-Jun-3 Kunsthallen, Copenhagen #278/R est:20000 (D.KR 20000)

ICART, Louis (1888-1950) French
£816 $1298 €1200 Ballerinas (61x49cm-24x19in) s.i. 27-Feb-3 Hagelstam, Helsinki #812
£3077 $4831 €4800 Femme accoudee sur un sofa (100x81cm-39x32in) 20-Nov-2 Claude Boisgirard, Paris #38/R est:4500
£4514 $7178 €6500 Elegantes au levrier Place de la Concorde (46x55cm-18x22in) s. 29-Apr-3 Artcurial Briest, Paris #198/R est:6100-7600
£4861 $7729 €7000 Elegantes et caleche devant Notre-Dame (46x55cm-18x22in) s. 29-Apr-3 Artcurial Briest, Paris #197/R est:6100-7600
£6149 $9592 €9100 La conversation au salon (61x50cm-24x20in) s. panel. 25-Mar-3 Chochon-Barre & Allardi, Paris #138/R est:6300-6500
Prints
£1763 $2750 €2645 Faust (58x39cm-23x15in) s. hand col etching aquatint drypoint. 30-Mar-3 Butterfields, Los Angeles #1009 est:1000-1500
£1852 $3000 €2778 Reclining nude (76x142cm-30x56in) s. print. 24-May-3 Susanin's, Chicago #19
£1887 $2925 €3000 Leda et le cygne (54x81cm-21x32in) s. aquatint eau forte. 30-Oct-2 Coutau Begarie, Paris #6/R
£2000 $3300 €2900 Smoke - fumeel (41x54cm-16x21in) s. etching drypoint. 1-Jul-3 Bearnes, Exeter #411/R est:2000-2500
£2564 $4000 €3846 Leda and the Swan (62x89cm-24x35in) s. hand col etching aquatint drypoint. 30-Mar-3 Butterfields, Los Angeles #1019/R est:4000-6000
£2564 $4000 €3846 Pink slippers (53x90cm-21x35in) s. hand col etching aquatint drypoint. 30-Mar-3 Butterfields, Los Angeles #1021/R est:4000-5000
£2658 $4200 €4200 Pur sang (55x98cm-22x39in) s. col drypoint eau forte exec.1938 lit. 26-Nov-2 Camard, Paris #97/R
£2848 $4500 €4272 Leda and the swan (53x81cm-21x32in) s. drypoint aquatint. 22-Apr-3 Butterfields, San Francisco #2145/R est:4000-6000
£3077 $4831 €4800 Pur-Sange (47x89cm-19x35in) s. col etching. 10-Dec-2 Vanderkindere, Brussels #88/R est:1250-1750
£5769 $9000 €8654 Can can (51x76cm-20x30in) s. hand col etching drypoint aquatint. 30-Mar-3 Butterfields, Los Angeles #1020/R est:6000-8000

Works on paper

£300 $480 €450 Statue of Liberty (47x35cm-19x14in) s. pencil dr. on tracing paper. 15-May-3 Christie's, Kensington #238/R

£400 $668 €580 Three elegant ladies in a chamber (51x41cm-20x16in) init. chl buff paper feigned oval. 17-Jun-3 Rosebery Fine Art, London #528/R

£800 $1280 €1200 Scenes with figures (48x32cm-19x13in) s. chl dr. two. 15-May-3 Christie's, Kensington #234/R

£1259 $2102 €1800 Pierrot et colombine (51x38cm-20x15in) s. chl. 26-Jun-3 Tajan, Paris #20/R est:1800-2000

£2214 $3498 €3321 Le panier de pommes (45x33cm-18x13in) s. pastel sold with another by the same artist. 7-Apr-3 Shapiro, Sydney #556/R est:6000-9000 (A.D 5800)

ICAZA, Ernesto (1866-1935) Mexican

£10976 $18000 €16464 Preparandose para la carrera parejera; El Tlacuelero (40x60cm-16x24in) s.d.1914 prov. 28-May-3 Christie's, Rockefeller NY #73/R est:22000-26000

IEFIMENKO, Viktor (1952-) Russian

£1400 $2170 €2100 Resting under the willow tree (61x50cm-24x20in) s. 8-Dec-2 John Nicholson, Haslemere #51/R

£1500 $2325 €2250 Sunny day (65x54cm-26x21in) s. 8-Dec-2 John Nicholson, Haslemere #50/R

£1500 $2325 €2250 Figures in a rowing boat with lilies (73x60cm-29x24in) s. 8-Dec-2 John Nicholson, Haslemere #52/R

IEGOROV, Alexei (1966-) Russian

£741 $1193 €1074 On the beach (70x60cm-28x24in) s.i. verso. 7-May-3 Dobiaschofsky, Bern #715/R (S.FR 1600)

IEPEREN, Johan Hendrik van (1909-1995) Dutch

£284 $460 €400 Farm with haystack (19x26cm-7x10in) s. board. 26-May-3 Glerum, Amsterdam #194/R

£355 $574 €500 Forest edge (40x50cm-16x20in) s. 26-May-3 Glerum, Amsterdam #201/R

£390 $632 €550 Farm with haystack (23x29cm-9x11in) s. board. 26-May-3 Glerum, Amsterdam #191

£411 $666 €580 Still life with stone jug and vase (20x25cm-8x10in) s. board. 26-May-3 Glerum, Amsterdam #202/R

£532 $862 €750 Portrait of a man (39x28cm-15x11in) s. board. 26-May-3 Glerum, Amsterdam #200

£603 $977 €850 Village view (60x60cm-24x24in) 26-May-3 Glerum, Amsterdam #169/R

£709 $1149 €1000 Portrait of a man (26x20cm-10x8in) s. board. 26-May-3 Glerum, Amsterdam #182/R

£922 $1494 €1300 Winter in Epe (17x23cm-7x9in) s. board painted 1942 lit. 26-May-3 Glerum, Amsterdam #192/R

£1064 $1723 €1500 Red flowers in a white vase (29x23cm-11x9in) s. board. 26-May-3 Glerum, Amsterdam #177/R est:800-1200

£1064 $1723 €1500 Forest path in Epe (27x37cm-11x15in) s. board. 26-May-3 Glerum, Amsterdam #184/R est:200-300

£3191 $5170 €4500 Still life with flowers in a vase (64x49cm-25x19in) s. board. 26-May-3 Glerum, Amsterdam #176/R est:2000-2500

£3262 $5285 €4600 Portrait of a lady (31x24cm-12x9in) s. board lit. 26-May-3 Glerum, Amsterdam #199/R est:1000-1500

Works on paper

£355 $574 €500 Snowy landscape with mill without blades and single farm (27x40cm-11x16in) gouache. 26-May-3 Glerum, Amsterdam #172/R

£355 $574 €500 Flowers in a vase (18x12cm-7x5in) s. gouache. 26-May-3 Glerum, Amsterdam #181/R

£355 $574 €500 Village street (31x39cm-12x15in) black chk W/C. 26-May-3 Glerum, Amsterdam #193/R

£390 $632 €550 Village view (31x41cm-12x16in) s. black chk gouache. 26-May-3 Glerum, Amsterdam #211

£532 $862 €750 Two clowns (27x40cm-11x16in) W/C. 26-May-3 Glerum, Amsterdam #168/R

£1064 $1723 €1500 Farm in the evening (49x64cm-19x25in) s. W/C. 26-May-3 Glerum, Amsterdam #190/R est:600-800

IERACE, Francesco (1854-?) Italian

Sculpture

£2709 $4226 €4280 Vittorio de Heisenhoff's wife portrait (40cm-16in) white marble. 15-Oct-2 Babuino, Rome #532/R

IEVGRAFOV, Dmitrii (1967-) Russian

£275 $426 €413 On Nevsky Avenue in Saint-Petersburg (44x37cm-17x15in) s. 8-Dec-2 John Nicholson, Haslemere #143/R

£350 $543 €525 On the quay near Annichkov Bridge in Saint-Petersburg (48x61cm-19x24in) s. 8-Dec-2 John Nicholson, Haslemere #144/R

IGLER, Gustav (1842-1908) Hungarian

£3096 $4829 €4644 Girl playing by the piano (67x51cm-26x20in) s. 11-Sep-2 Kieselbach, Budapest #31/R (H.F 1200000)

IGLESIAS SANZ, Antonio (1935-) Spanish

£369 $594 €550 Church (37x45cm-15x18in) s. 18-Feb-3 Durán, Madrid #101/R

£405 $632 €600 Rural street (55x46cm-22x18in) s. 25-Mar-3 Durán, Madrid #718/R

IGLESIAS, Cristina (1956-) ?

Sculpture

£4500 $7335 €6750 Untitled (120x80x21cm-47x31x8in) iron steel cement wood serigraphy in three parts executed 1988. 3-Feb-3 Sotheby's, Olympia #109/R est:3000-4000

£7000 $11410 €10500 Untitled (27x81cm-11x32in) iron steel cement executed 1987 prov.exhib. 3-Feb-3 Sotheby's, Olympia #107/R est:1500-2000

IHLE, I (20th C) German

£323 $474 €500 Stuttgart (66x85cm-26x33in) s. 20-Jun-2 Dr Fritz Nagel, Stuttgart #776/R

IHLEE, Rudolph (1883-1968) British

£600 $966 €900 Beneath the bridge (38x45cm-15x18in) board. 14-Jan-3 Bonhams, Knightsbridge #212/R

£800 $1272 €1200 Rocky valley (35x46cm-14x18in) s.d.1926 board. 26-Feb-3 Sotheby's, Olympia #232/R

Works on paper

£380 $593 €570 Seamstresses (19x24cm-7x9in) s. pastel. 12-Sep-2 Sotheby's, Olympia #48/R

IHLER, Carl (1897-?) Austrian

£481 $755 €750 Spring at Achensee (50x68cm-20x27in) s.d.25. 21-Nov-2 Dorotheum, Vienna #256/R

IHLY, Daniel (1854-1910) Swiss

£393 $613 €590 Landscape (33x52cm-13x20in) s. cardboard prov. 9-Nov-2 Galerie Gloggner, Luzern #82/R (S.FR 900)

£708 $1132 €1062 Still life with apples and cabbage head (43x60cm-17x24in) s.d. 17-Mar-3 Philippe Schuler, Zurich #4530 (S.FR 1500)

£3538 $5660 €5307 Champ de Coqueliers (65x129cm-26x51in) s. 17-Mar-3 Philippe Schuler, Zurich #4531/R est:4000-6000 (S.FR 7500)

IHRAN, Manne (1877-1917) Swedish

£496 $770 €744 Uppsala Palace (34x46cm-13x18in) s.d.1915 panel. 8-Dec-2 Uppsala Auktionskammare, Uppsala #166 (S.KR 7000)

£532 $824 €798 St Erik's spring from Saluhallen (55x35cm-22x14in) s.d.10 panel. 8-Dec-2 Uppsala Auktionskammare, Uppsala #167 (S.KR 7500)

IJJASZ, Gyula (1874-1943) Czechoslovakian

£315 $447 €473 In the garden (45x51cm-18x20in) cardboard painted c.1920. 26-Mar-2 SOGA, Bratislava #134/R (SL.K 20000)

IKE NO TAIGA (1723-1776) Japanese

Works on paper

£6918 $11000 €10377 Refrain from a Ming-dynasty poem (126x54cm-50x21in) s. ink col hanging scroll prov.lit. 24-Mar-3 Christie's, Rockefeller NY #20/R est:10000-15000

£26415 $42000 €39623 Mountain peak in spring haze (114x29cm-45x11in) s. ink hanging scroll prov.lit. 24-Mar-3 Christie's, Rockefeller NY #21/R est:12000-18000

IKEMURA, Leiko (1951-) ?

Works on paper

£524 $823 €786 Untitled (21x30cm-8x12in) chl. 23-Nov-2 Burkhard, Luzern #246/R (S.FR 1200)

IKKIDLUAK, Lucassie (1949-) North American

Sculpture

£1304 $2035 €2175 Musk ox (23x37x15cm-9x15x6in) green stone carving. 13-Apr-3 Levis, Calgary #57/R est:3500-4000 (C.D 3000)

IKONEN, Ilmari (1897-1953) Finnish

£366 $600 €560 Winter's day (50x65cm-20x26in) s.d.46. 9-Feb-3 Bukowskis, Helsinki #260/R

ILECKO, Jozef (1909-1986) Czechoslovakian

£284 $414 €426 Mother and child (39x37cm-15x15in) board painted c.1960. 4-Jun-2 SOGA, Bratislava #227/R est:15000 (SL.K 18000)

Works on paper
£268 $391 €402 Woman from Zdiar (37x28cm-15x11in) W/C. 4-Jun-2 SOGA, Bratislava #226/R est:17000 (SL.K 17000)
£394 $610 €591 Woman in scarf (34x23cm-13x9in) pastel exec.c.1935. 1-Oct-2 SOGA, Bratislava #75/R est:25000 (SL.K 25000)

ILG, Pius (1940-) Swiss
£1135 $1783 €1703 Untitled (100x100cm-39x39in) s. d.10.10.1999 acrylic. 23-Nov-2 Burkhard, Luzern #24/R est:200-3000 (S.FR 2600)

ILLINGWORTH, Leslie Gilbert (1902-1979) British
Works on paper
£360 $572 €540 Lady aviator (51x32cm-20x13in) s. pen ink. 26-Feb-3 Cheffins Grain & Comins, Cambridge #547/R

ILLINGWORTH, Michael (1932-1988) New Zealander
£12739 $20000 €19109 Pah Hill (106x90cm-42x35in) prov.exhib. 10-Dec-2 Peter Webb, Auckland #34/R est:40000-50000 (NZ.D 40000)

ILLSLEY, Bryan (20th C) British
£250 $390 €375 Fruit on a plate (23x30cm-9x12in) s. i.d.1972 verso board. 16-Oct-2 David Lay, Penzance #249
£400 $624 €600 Red on blue (33x41cm-13x16in) s.i.verso board. 16-Oct-2 David Lay, Penzance #254/R
£420 $655 €630 Three triangles (23x33cm-9x13in) s.i.d.1968 board. 16-Oct-2 David Lay, Penzance #252/R
£580 $905 €870 Bird figure (58x48cm-23x19in) s.verso board. 16-Oct-2 David Lay, Penzance #251/R
Works on paper
£350 $546 €525 Black and white drawing (43x46cm-17x18in) s.d.1968 s.i.verso dr. 16-Oct-2 David Lay, Penzance #255/R
£400 $624 €600 Bird above blue (89x69cm-35x27in) init.i.d.1983 mixed media. 16-Oct-2 David Lay, Penzance #256/R

ILSTED, Peter Vilhelm (1861-1933) Danish
£440 $677 €660 Study of an Arab (24x16cm-9x6in) cardboard. 26-Oct-2 Rasmussen, Havnen #2096/R (D.KR 5200)
£515 $814 €773 Interior scene with lady (22x31cm-9x12in) mono. cardboard. 17-Nov-2 Hindemae, Ullerslev #7668/R (D.KR 6000)
£603 $916 €905 Interior scene with children by petroleum lamp (32x23cm-13x9in) s. panel. 27-Aug-2 Rasmussen, Copenhagen #1908/R (D.KR 7000)
£680 $1060 €1020 Interior scene with table, mirror and chair (40x55cm-16x22in) mono. 5-Aug-2 Rasmussen, Vejle #1/R (D.KR 8000)
£1292 $1964 €1938 Model study (34x30cm-13x12in) prov. 27-Aug-2 Rasmussen, Copenhagen #1950/R est:12000-15000 (D.KR 15000)
£1323 $2130 €1985 Southern steps (45x32cm-18x13in) 11-May-3 Hindemae, Ullerslev #157/R est:20000 (D.KR 14000)
£1914 $3100 €2775 Street scene in Capri with woman (54x38cm-21x15in) s.d.1891. 26-May-3 Rasmussen, Copenhagen #1330/R est:20000 (D.KR 20000)
£2749 $4509 €3986 Self-portrait with hat (24x21cm-9x8in) mono.d.85 panel. 4-Jun-3 AB Stockholms Auktionsverk #2465/R est:20000-25000 (S.KR 35000)
£12259 $19615 €18389 Interior scene with woman and sunshine coming through window (49x44cm-19x17in) i.verso. 13-Jan-3 Rasmussen, Vejle #8/R est:150000 (D.KR 140000)
£25806 $40000 €38709 Open door (61x49cm-24x19in) mono.d.1912 panel. 30-Oct-2 Christie's, Rockefeller NY #9/R est:30000-40000
£26582 $42000 €39873 Young girls standing by a window in an interior (66x64cm-26x25in) mono.d.1906. 23-Apr-3 Christie's, Rockefeller NY #1/R est:30000-40000
£26701 $40586 €40052 Casual guests (69x92cm-27x36in) s.d.1887 exhib. 27-Aug-2 Rasmussen, Copenhagen #1452/R est:150000-200000 (D.KR 310000)
£30000 $49200 €45000 Ved vinduet - at the window (58x58cm-23x23in) prov. 3-Jun-3 Sotheby's, London #222/R est:30000-50000
Prints
£2013 $3200 €3020 Girl with a tray (49x40cm-19x16in) s. col mezzotint. 3-Mar-3 Swann Galleries, New York #31/R est:3000-5000
£3101 $4713 €4652 Girl seen from behind by window (34x27cm-13x11in) s.i. col etching. 28-Aug-2 Museumsbygningen, Copenhagen #92/R est:1200 (D.KR 36000)
£3145 $5000 €4718 Sunshine (34x27cm-13x11in) s. col mezzotint. 4-Mar-3 Swann Galleries, New York #358/R est:3000-5000

ILSTED, Peter Vilhelm (attrib) (1861-1933) Danish
£769 $1200 €1154 Interior with open door (50x28cm-20x11in) bears sig.verso i.stretcher. 9-Nov-2 Sloan, North Bethesda #576/R

ILTNERS, Edgars (1925-) Russian
£263 $407 €410 Rowers (63x41cm-25x16in) s.d.1955 double-sided. 7-Dec-2 Dannenberg, Berlin #689/R

ILYIN, Peter Alexander (1887-1958) American
£344 $550 €499 Mountain landscape (23x30cm-9x12in) s. board. 16-May-3 Skinner, Boston #239/R

IMANDT, Willem (1882-1967) Dutch
£972 $1604 €1400 Borobudur at dusk (61x80cm-24x31in) s. 1-Jul-3 Christie's, Amsterdam #295/R

IMHOF, Heinrich Maximilian (1798-1869) Swiss
Sculpture
£6731 $10433 €10500 Profile portrait of Johann Heinrich Dannecker (16x14cm-6x6in) alabaster on marble prov. 5-Dec-2 Dr Fritz Nagel, Stuttgart #773/R est:9000

IMHOF, Joseph A (1871-1955) American
£962 $1500 €1443 Mishongovi pueblo, N Arizona (20x28cm-8x11in) s. board. 18-Sep-2 Alderfer's, Hatfield #310 est:600-800
£2083 $3250 €3125 Ponderosa pine and yellow aspen (66x56cm-26x22in) s. i.verso. 18-Sep-2 Alderfer's, Hatfield #309 est:1000-1500
£2724 $4250 €4086 Poplars, San Juan Pueblo, New Mexico (61x43cm-24x17in) s.d.1947 s.i.verso. 18-Sep-2 Alderfer's, Hatfield #306 est:2000-3000
£3045 $4750 €4568 Portrait of Iron Tail Sioux, a Native American man (94x79cm-37x31in) s. board. 18-Sep-2 Alderfer's, Hatfield #307 est:2000-3000
£4808 $7500 €7212 Ute Indians on the warpath (94x69cm-37x27in) s. i.verso canvas on board prov. 9-Nov-2 Santa Fe Art, Santa Fe #113/R est:15000-20000

IMKAMP, Wilhelm (1906-1990) German
£633 $1000 €1000 View of Mainhardter mountain (54x64cm-21x25in) s.d.37. 29-Nov-2 Sigalas, Stuttgart #1215/R
£2564 $3974 €4000 Composition (62x43cm-24x17in) s.d.59 board on panel. 7-Dec-2 Van Ham, Cologne #251/R est:6500
Works on paper
£360 $576 €500 La - Lilla (38x31cm-15x12in) s.d. s.i.d. verso gouache Indian ink. 15-May-3 Neumeister, Munich #463/R

IMMENDORF, Jorg (1945-) German
£1899 $2962 €3000 Birth of the sculptor (100x80cm-39x31in) s.i.d.1991 prov. 18-Oct-2 Dr Fritz Nagel, Stuttgart #515/R est:5000
£5000 $8350 €7250 Komplizin (130x100cm-51x39in) s.i.d.90 prov. 26-Jun-3 Sotheby's, London #254/R est:5000-7000
£16456 $26000 €26000 Sons of the sun (88x66cm-35x26in) s.i.d.92. 27-Nov-2 Dorotheum, Vienna #107/R est:18000-25000
Prints
£2278 $3600 €3600 Howler (105x65cm-41x26in) s.d.88 acrylic linocut on canvas. 27-Nov-2 Dorotheum, Vienna #109/R est:3200-3800
Works on paper
£833 $1292 €1300 Stage set (21x31cm-8x12in) s.d.86 pencil W/C. 5-Dec-2 Dorotheum, Graz #112/R
£1812 $2971 €2500 Cafe Deutschland - partially built (41x29cm-16x11in) s.i.d.78 gouache. 31-May-3 Villa Grisebach, Berlin #840/R est:2500-3000

IMMERMAN, David (20th C) American
£223 $350 €335 177th Street, Bronx (25x30cm-10x12in) s.d.1937 i.verso. 22-Nov-2 Skinner, Boston #329/R

IMPARATO, Gerolamo (16/17th C) Italian
£7547 $11698 €12000 Adoration of the shepherds (129x99cm-51x39in) prov.lit. 7-Oct-2 Ansorena, Madrid #36/R est:12000
£7895 $12789 €12000 Adoration of the shepherds (129x99cm-51x39in) lit. 21-Jan-3 Ansorena, Madrid #93/R est:10000

IMPENS, Josse (1840-1905) Belgian
£411 $645 €600 Joueuse de mandoline (38x28cm-15x11in) s. 15-Apr-3 Galerie Moderne, Brussels #361
£690 $1103 €1000 Un moment de repos (33x20cm-13x8in) s. panel. 17-Mar-3 Horta, Bruxelles #168
£1200 $1992 €1200 Artiste a son chevalet (54x66cm-21x26in) s. 16-Jun-3 Horta, Bruxelles #397
£1282 $1949 €2000 Maternity (37x51cm-15x20in) s. panel. 27-Aug-2 Galerie Moderne, Brussels #310/R

IMPERIALI, Francesco (circle) (18th C) Italian
£6500 $10205 €9750 Madonna and Child (23x18cm-9x7in) copper. 13-Dec-2 Christie's, Kensington #248/R est:3000-4000

IMSCHOOT, Jules van (1821-1884) Flemish
£1100 $1793 €1650 Avoiding a live shell. Signaling the charge (22x32cm-9x13in) s.d.64 panel pair. 13-Feb-3 Christie's, Kensington #198/R est:1000-1500

INCE, Joseph Murray (1806-1859) British
£2200 $3432 €3300 Landscape on the Radnorshire Herefordshire borders (45x62cm-18x24in) 11-Sep-2 Bonhams, Newport #250/R est:1500-2000
£6500 $10010 €9750 Stockholm (101x127cm-40x50in) s.d.1836. 5-Sep-2 Christie's, Kensington #241/R est:7000-10000
Works on paper
£550 $908 €798 Queen's College, Cambridge (34x24cm-13x9in) s.d.1846 W/C. 1-Jul-3 Bonhams, Norwich #62/R
£950 $1587 €1378 Shepherding the flock home (19x32cm-7x13in) s.d.1839 W/C. 24-Jun-3 Bonhams, Knightsbridge #40/R
£1400 $2212 €2100 Figures fishing for trout from a bridge (18x31cm-7x12in) s. W/C over pencil htd bodycol. 28-Nov-2 Sotheby's, London #288/R est:800-1200

INCHBOLD, John William (1830-1888) British
£3000 $4740 €4500 Lake of Geneva, from the North (35x53cm-14x21in) s. 2-Dec-2 Sotheby's, London #60/R est:3000-4000

INCOLE, Albert (20th C) Belgian?
Works on paper
£479 $748 €700 Laque de Chine, danseuse Art Deco (75x40cm-30x16in) mono.d.1961 verso. 14-Apr-3 Horta, Bruxelles #275

INDEN, Ernst (1879-1945) German
£582 $908 €850 On the Olef near Gemund (60x80cm-24x31in) s. 10-Apr-3 Van Ham, Cologne #1496
£959 $1496 €1400 Boats in upper Italian harbour (50x40cm-20x16in) s.d.1907 canvas on panel. 10-Apr-3 Van Ham, Cologne #1495/R

INDIA, Bernardino (1528-1590) Italian
Works on paper
£4730 $7378 €7000 Noces de Cana (20x31cm-8x12in) i. chk pen ink wash prov. 27-Mar-3 Christie's, Paris #58/R

INDIAN SCHOOL
Works on paper
£14685 $21000 €22028 Botanical rendering (45x27cm-18x11in) i. W/C. 22-Jan-3 Doyle, New York #71

INDIAN SCHOOL, 19th C
£5096 $7389 €8000 Mado Singh II (76x61cm-30x24in) 31-May-2 Blanchet, Paris #34/R
£7962 $11545 €12500 Tukoji Rao Holkar II (154x93cm-61x37in) s. 31-May-2 Blanchet, Paris #30/R est:7500-9000

INDIAN SCHOOL, 20th C
£2038 $2955 €3200 Sawai Man Singh II (76x61cm-30x24in) 31-May-2 Blanchet, Paris #32/R
£12420 $18010 €19500 Portrait of Maharadja (145x86cm-57x34in) painted c.1930. 31-May-2 Blanchet, Paris #29/R est:7500-9000
Works on paper
£1465 $2124 €2300 Indian princes. gouache. 31-May-2 Blanchet, Paris #27/R

INDIANA, Robert (1928-) American
£29688 $47500 €44532 Decade autoportrait 1966 (61x61cm-24x24in) prov. 14-May-3 Sotheby's, New York #256/R est:30000-40000
£48750 $78000 €73125 Nonending nonagon (61x56cm-24x22in) s.i.d.1962 prov. 15-May-3 Christie's, Rockefeller NY #130/R est:60000-80000
£75949 $120000 €113924 Spring (152x127cm-60x50in) s.i.d.78 prov. 14-Nov-2 Christie's, Rockefeller NY #155/R est:120000-180000
£105769 $163942 €165000 Love (183x183cm-72x72in) acrylic prov. 5-Dec-2 Stadion, Trieste #732/R est:70000
£125000 $200000 €187500 Terre haute 2 (152x127cm-60x50in) s.i.d.1969 verso acrylic prov.exhib.lit. 15-May-3 Christie's, Rockefeller NY #128/R est:200000-300000
£164557 $260000 €246836 Love wall - black, red and yellow (60x50cm-24x20in) init.d.68 oil on four attached canvases prov. 14-Nov-2 Christie's, Rockefeller NY #134/R est:150000-200000
Prints
£5096 $8000 €7644 Garden of love suite (27x27cm-11x11in) s.d.num.85 silkscreen set of six. 19-Nov-2 Wright, Chicago #227/R est:9000-12000
£5975 $9500 €8963 Four panel love (80x80cm-31x31in) s.d.num.87/150 col screenprint four sheets. 2-May-3 Sotheby's, New York #479/R est:2500-3500
Sculpture
£21875 $35000 €32813 Nine (45x46x25cm-18x18x10in) st.sig. num.7/8 steel enamel prov. 15-May-3 Christie's, Rockefeller NY #198/R est:25000-35000
£24051 $38000 €36077 One (45x46x25cm-18x18x10in) st.sig.num.1/2 enamel on steel executed 1996 prov. 14-Nov-2 Christie's, Rockefeller NY #185/R est:35000-45000
£63291 $100000 €94937 Love (61x61x30cm-24x24x12in) st.sig.d.1966-97 stainless steel prov. 14-Nov-2 Christie's, Rockefeller NY #103/R est:70000-90000

INDONI, Filippo (1800-1884) Italian
£1572 $2421 €2500 Peasant woman (78x56cm-31x22in) s. 28-Oct-2 Il Ponte, Milan #328
£7500 $11775 €11250 Source of amusement (46x34cm-18x13in) s.d.1877 panel. 21-Nov-2 Christie's, Kensington #64/R est:4000-6000
Works on paper
£798 $1300 €1157 Tyrolean couple (61x79cm-24x31in) W/C. 18-Jul-3 Du Mouchelle, Detroit #2155/R est:1500-2000
£800 $1264 €1200 Boy and girl resting on an alpine path (52x36cm-20x14in) s. 2-Apr-3 Edgar Horn, Eastbourne #262/R
£860 $1402 €1290 Young girl and boy resting on an alpine path (37x52cm-15x20in) s. W/C. 11-Feb-3 Fellows & Sons, Birmingham #62/R
£900 $1413 €1350 Two Italian girls (75x53cm-30x21in) s.i. pencil W/C htd white. 19-Nov-2 Bonhams, Leeds #17
£2700 $4212 €4050 Courting couple by wayside. Young peasant in traditional costume (54x36cm-21x14in) s. W/C two. 6-Nov-2 Bonhams, Chester #450 est:1200-1800

INDONI, J (19/20th C) Italian?
£761 $1187 €1269 Tyrolean lovers (63x50cm-25x20in) i. prov. 13-Apr-3 Levis, Calgary #210a/R est:2500-3500 (C.D 1750)

INDREBO, Tone (1954-) Norwegian
£995 $1613 €1493 Remembrance IV (54x54cm-21x21in) s.d.96. 26-May-3 Grev Wedels Plass, Oslo #125/R (N.KR 11000)

INDUNO, Domenico (1815-1878) Italian
Works on paper
£6122 $9735 €9000 Rural interior with young housewife (38x29cm-15x11in) s. W/C prov. 18-Mar-3 Finarte, Milan #61/R est:12000

INDUNO, Gerolamo (1827-1890) Italian
£12903 $20000 €19355 Dancing lesson (45x60cm-18x24in) s.i.d.1868 prov.exhib. 29-Oct-2 Sotheby's, New York #24/R est:30000-40000
£17089 $27000 €27000 Soldier coming back (75x95cm-30x37in) s. 26-Nov-2 Christie's, Rome #219/R est:16000-20000
Works on paper
£10063 $15497 €16000 Winter landscape with figures (48x71cm-19x28in) s. W/C card. 23-Oct-2 Finarte, Milan #36/R est:20000-25000

INGANNI, Angelo (1807-1880) Italian
£4610 $7468 €6500 Giocando con la mamma (50x66cm-20x26in) s.d.1848. 22-May-3 Stadion, Trieste #267/R est:6000-8000
£5409 $8330 €8600 Young woman by fire (33x27cm-13x11in) s.d.1880. 28-Oct-2 Il Ponte, Milan #326/R est:3000

INGELS, Domien (1881-1946) ?
Sculpture
£2483 $3972 €3600 Greyhound (50x55cm-20x22in) s. wood. 15-Mar-3 De Vuyst, Lokeren #433/R est:4000-5000
£2590 $4144 €3600 Greyhound (25x15cm-10x6in) s.i. dark brown pat bronze. 17-May-3 De Vuyst, Lokeren #208/R est:1000-1400

INGEN, Hendrikus Alexander van (1846-1920) Dutch
£1724 $2741 €2500 Resting cows (50x85cm-20x33in) s.d.1915. 10-Mar-3 Sotheby's, Amsterdam #124 est:1000-1500

INGERL, Kurt (1935-1999) Austrian
£596 $972 €900 Structure 2 (50x50cm-20x20in) s.i.d.1978 verso lacquer masonite. 28-Jan-3 Dorotheum, Vienna #229/R
£795 $1295 €1200 Sequence 10 (50x50cm-20x20in) s.i.d.1978 lacquer masonite. 28-Jan-3 Dorotheum, Vienna #230/R

INGERMANN, Keith (?) ?
£248 $400 €372 House of the white pekinese (53x71cm-21x28in) s. i.verso masonite prov. 18-Feb-3 Arthur James, Florida #164

INGHAM, Bryan (1936-1997) British
£1600 $2624 €2400 Falmouth still life (25x30cm-10x12in) s.i.d.1985 verso oil collage board. 3-Jun-3 Sotheby's, Olympia #273/R est:800-1200
Works on paper
£650 $1014 €975 Untitled (10x5cm-4x2in) collage. 16-Oct-2 David Lay, Penzance #294
£1150 $1794 €1725 Flower piece, Tremayne (13x5cm-5x2in) s.i.d.1985 verso collage. 16-Oct-2 David Lay, Penzance #293/R est:300-400
£4000 $6240 €6000 St. Ives (86x146cm-34x57in) pencil W/C oil collage on board. 27-Mar-3 Christie's, Kensington #603/R est:4000-6000
£6800 $10608 €10200 Three jugs and a ship - summer (35x74cm-14x29in) mixed media on panel prov. 25-Mar-3 Bonhams, New Bond Street #121/R est:5000-7000

INGLEFIELD, Admiral Sir Edward Augustus (1820-1894) British
Works on paper
£850 $1352 €1275 H.M.S Erebus and H.M.S Terror entering the Melville Sound (11x15cm-4x6in) mono.i. W/C bodycol prov. 29-Apr-3 Bonhams, New Bond Street #177/R

INGLES, Jack (?) New Zealander?
£526 $821 €789 Bowl of flowers and green pot (54x44cm-21x17in) board. 27-Mar-3 International Art Centre, Auckland #191 (NZ.D 1500)

INGLIS, David N (?-1933) British
Works on paper
£1200 $1872 €1800 Portrait of Edward Mountbatten (59x47cm-23x19in) init.i. chl crayon W/C prov. 9-Oct-2 Woolley & Wallis, Salisbury #6/R est:500-700

INGLIS, Jane (?-1916) British
£1100 $1716 €1650 Stormy morning, coast of Donegal, Ireland (51x61cm-20x24in) s.d.1887 i.on stretcher. 7-Nov-2 Christie's, Kensington #166/R est:800-1200

INGLIS, Peter (20th C) American
£260 $400 €390 Interior of 44 West Newton Street, Boston, home of Mary Grant Price (30x61cm-12x24in) 27-Oct-2 Grogan, Boston #92

INGRAIN CARDENAS, Eloy (1927-) Spanish
£405 $632 €600 Cazorla (96x116cm-38x46in) s. 25-Mar-3 Durán, Madrid #156/R

INGRAM, William Ayerst (1855-1913) British
Works on paper
£380 $616 €570 Return of the herring boats (34x52cm-13x20in) s. W/C htd white. 21-May-3 Christie's, Kensington #452/R
£520 $811 €780 Return of the herring fleet (35x53cm-14x21in) s. W/C. 6-Nov-2 Bonhams, Chester #475
£606 $933 €909 Estuary of the Camel, near Padstow (41x85cm-16x33in) s. W/C. 4-Sep-2 Dunbar Sloane, Wellington #89/R est:3000-5000 (NZ.D 2000)

INGRES (style) (1780-1867) French
£4516 $7000 €6774 Odalisque, nude reclining on a bed (76x99cm-30x39in) 2-Nov-2 North East Auctions, Portsmouth #62/R est:2500-4500

INGRES, Jean Auguste Dominique (1780-1867) French
Prints
£3205 $5064 €5000 Odalisque. lithograph. 14-Nov-2 Libert, Castor, Paris #105/R est:3800
£3774 $6000 €5661 Odalisque (13x21cm-5x8in) lithograph. 3-Mar-3 Swann Galleries, New York #6/R est:5000-8000
Works on paper
£10885 $17307 €16000 Etude pour le vitrail de Saint-Philippe (236x15cm-93x6in) crayon prov.lit. 24-Mar-3 Tajan, Paris #126/R
£12346 $20000 €18519 Young nude woman (23x29cm-9x11in) s. pencil htd white prov. 22-Jan-3 Christie's, Rockefeller NY #108/R est:30000
£17230 $26878 €25500 Portrait de Jean Racine (22x16cm-9x6in) s.d.1845 crayon wash prov. 26-Mar-3 Piasa, Paris #103/R est:15000
£30864 $50000 €46296 Female nude with arms raised (45x16cm-18x6in) graphite prov.exhib. 22-Jan-3 Christie's, Rockefeller NY #107/R est:70000
£52469 $85000 €78704 Studies of hands and foot (31x23cm-12x9in) i. lead prov.lit. 22-Jan-3 Christie's, Rockefeller NY #106/R est:80000
£54000 $90180 €78300 Portrait of the actor, Monsieur Brochard (8x8cm-3x3in) s.d.1796 graphite round prov.exhib.lit. 9-Jul-3 Sotheby's, London #59/R est:50000-70000
£202531 $320000 €320000 Etude de nu, preparatoire pour l'ange en haut a gauche dans le voeu de Louis XIII (51x35cm-20x14in) i. pierre noire stump htd chk. 28-Nov-2 Tajan, Paris #105/R est:60000-80000

INGRES, Jean Auguste Dominique (attrib) (1780-1867) French
Works on paper
£641 $1000 €962 Hands (10x15cm-4x6in) s. pencil. 30-Mar-3 Susanin's, Chicago #6070/R
£3145 $4843 €5000 Man (36x26cm-14x10in) s. dr. 28-Oct-2 Il Ponte, Milan #224/R

INGUIMBERTY, Joseph (1896-1971) French
£3148 $4848 €4722 Paysage du Tonkin - landscape of Tonkin (54x74cm-21x29in) painted c.1938. 27-Oct-2 Christie's, Hong Kong #56/R est:30000-40000 (HK.D 38000)
£15540 $25641 €22533 Vietnamese women (198x154cm-78x61in) s.d.1935. 6-Jul-3 Christie's, Hong Kong #39/R est:240000-350000 (HK.D 200000)
£57995 $89312 €86993 Payes et personnages du Tonkin - Landscape and people of Tonkin (228x290cm-90x114in) s.d.1933 exhib. 27-Oct-2 Christie's, Hong Kong #50/R est:850000-1000000 (HK.D 700000)

INGVARSSON, Jarl (1955-) Swedish
£596 $929 €894 Evening News or the Express (35x27cm-14x11in) s.verso. 6-Nov-2 AB Stockholms Auktionsverk #896/R (S.KR 8500)

INIESTA, Felix (19th C) Spanish
£1572 $2421 €2500 Shepherdess with sheep (102x61cm-40x24in) s.d.91. 22-Oct-2 Durán, Madrid #256/R

INIGO, Manuel de (1930-) Spanish
£321 $506 €500 Resting (54x65cm-21x26in) s. s.i.verso. 19-Nov-2 Durán, Madrid #54/R

INJALBERT, Jean Antoine (1845-1933) French
Sculpture
£1026 $1590 €1600 Tete de fillette (38cm-15in) s. bronze. 3-Dec-2 Campo & Campo, Antwerp #136/R est:1000-1500

INLANDER, Henry (1925-1983) British
£360 $554 €540 Girl and window II (100x80cm-39x31in) s. 22-Oct-2 Bonhams, Bath #7

INNES (?) ?
£1600 $2496 €2400 Blue pool, Dorset (25x35cm-10x14in) indis.sig.d.1912 i.verso board. 18-Sep-2 Dreweatt Neate, Newbury #104/R

INNES, James Dickson (1887-1914) British
£520 $868 €754 Gull Rock, Zennor (37x48cm-15x19in) s.d.1909 i.verso. 19-Jun-3 Lane, Penzance #177
£6500 $10205 €9750 Blue pool, Dorset (25x35cm-10x14in) s.d.1912 i.verso panel. 22-Nov-2 Christie's, London #35/R est:7000-10000
Works on paper
£700 $1106 €1050 Borghese Gardens (35x24cm-14x9in) s. W/C. 26-Nov-2 Bonhams, Knightsbridge #164/R
£750 $1170 €1125 Romance (19x38cm-7x15in) pen ink W/C prov.exhib. 27-Mar-3 Christie's, Kensington #308/R
£1700 $2805 €2465 Mountains (20x35cm-8x14in) W/C. 3-Jul-3 Christie's, Kensington #298/R est:1800-2500

INNES, John (1863-1941) Canadian
£381 $603 €572 Buffalo on the prairies (20x30cm-8x12in) woodboard. 1-Dec-2 Levis, Calgary #45c/R (C.D 950)

INNESS, George (1825-1894) American
£2742 $4250 €4113 Woodland interior (23x36cm-9x14in) init.d. 8-Dec-2 Toomey, Oak Park #633/R est:6000-8000
£5660 $9000 €8490 Log (34x31cm-13x12in) board prov.lit. 4-Mar-3 Christie's, Rockefeller NY #10/R est:8000-12000
£16456 $26000 €24684 Opening in the woods with figure (30x46cm-12x18in) s. prov. 24-Apr-3 Shannon's, Milford #22/R est:12000-18000
£32812 $52500 €47577 Fishing (30x46cm-12x18in) s.d.1867 board prov.exhib.lit. 16-May-3 Skinner, Boston #79/R est:30000-50000
£45161 $70000 €67742 Twilight (51x77cm-20x30in) s.d.1875 prov.exhib.lit. 5-Dec-2 Christie's, Rockefeller NY #34/R est:70000-90000
£58065 $90000 €87098 View of St. Peter's, Rome (76x114cm-30x45in) s.d.1871 prov.lit. 4-Dec-2 Sotheby's, New York #117/R est:75000-100000
£123457 $200000 €185186 Niagara (41x61cm-16x24in) s.d.1885 panel prov.exhib.lit. 21-May-3 Sotheby's, New York #47/R est:200000-300000
£167742 $260000 €251613 Sunset (82x107cm-32x42in) s.d.1893 prov.exhib.lit. 4-Dec-2 Sotheby's, New York #120/R est:250000-350000

INNESS, George (attrib) (1825-1894) American
Works on paper
£783 $1300 €1135 On the Hudson (25x36cm-10x14in) pencil drawing. 13-Jun-3 Du Mouchelle, Detroit #2076/R

INNESS, George (jnr) (1853-1926) American
£1233 $1800 €1850 Chetolah (5x10cm-2x4in) 18-May-2 Altermann Galleries, Santa Fe #252/R

INNIS, David (20th C) British
£250 $390 €375 Roses (74x82cm-29x32in) board exhib. 27-Mar-3 Christie's, Kensington #482

INNOCENT, Ferenc (1859-?) Hungarian
£288 $447 €450 Young woman (35x25cm-14x10in) s. board. 6-Dec-2 Weidler, Nurnberg #8832/R

INNOCENT, Franck (1912-1983) French?
£863 $1381 €1200 Le ponton (60x81cm-24x32in) s.d. 14-May-3 Blanchet, Paris #120/R

INNOCENTI, Camillo (1871-1961) Italian
£349 $510 €524 La collation (22x16cm-9x6in) i. panel. 4-Jun-2 Germann, Zurich #780 (S.FR 800)
£419 $650 €629 Genre scene of two figures beside a hearth (33x25cm-13x10in) s. panel. 7-Dec-2 Selkirks, St. Louis #749/R
£613 $950 €920 Figures drinking beside a hearth (23x33cm-9x13in) s. panel. 7-Dec-2 Selkirks, St. Louis #750/R
£1923 $2981 €3000 White hat (45x32cm-18x13in) s. 4-Dec-2 Finarte, Rome #743/R
Works on paper
£553 $874 €830 Cardinal reading (14x11cm-6x4in) s.i. W/C prov. 2-Dec-2 Rasmussen, Copenhagen #1818/R (D.KR 6500)

INNOCENTI, Camillo (attrib) (1871-1961) Italian
£341 $531 €512 Blacksmith's fatherly delight (22x14cm-9x6in) s. paper on panel. 20-Nov-2 Fischer, Luzern #2132/R (S.FR 780)

INNOCENTI, G (19/20th C) Italian
£2067 $3142 €3101 Two judges of art (32x24cm-13x9in) s.d.71 panel. 27-Aug-2 Rasmussen, Copenhagen #1609/R est:15000-20000 (D.KR 24000)

INO, Pierre (1909-) French
£828 $1292 €1300 Souvenir du Chateau Ferrare (65x54cm-26x21in) s. prov. 7-Nov-2 Chochon-Barre & Allardi, Paris #170

INSHAW, David (1943-) British
Works on paper
£360 $562 €540 Life drawing, Sylvia (47x44cm-19x17in) pastel prov. 15-Oct-2 Bonhams, Knightsbridge #10/R

INSKIP, John Henry (?-1947) British
£2000 $3140 €3000 Children playing before Brandon Bridge (51x63cm-20x25in) s.d.84. 16-Dec-2 Bonhams, Bury St Edmunds #444/R est:1000-1500

INSLEY, Albert (1842-1937) American
£645 $1000 €968 Pastoral landscape (30x48cm-12x19in) s. 25-Sep-2 Doyle, New York #41/R
£800 $1328 €1160 Autumn afternoon (35x51cm-14x20in) s. 10-Jun-3 Ritchie, Toronto #90/R est:1800-2200 (C.D 1800)
£1753 $2700 €2630 Golden meadow (30x43cm-12x17in) s. painted c.1890. 8-Sep-2 Treadway Gallery, Cincinnati #535/R est:2500-3500
£2346 $3800 €3402 Off Cape Elizabeth, Maine (51x81cm-20x32in) s. i.stretcher prov.exhib. 21-May-3 Doyle, New York #85/R est:4000-6000

INTRAINA, Enrico Edoardo (1870-?) ?
£1161 $1835 €1800 Prealpi by Lecco (18x32cm-7x13in) s. cardboard. 18-Dec-2 Finarte, Milan #79

IOKI, Bunsai (1863-1906) Japanese
Works on paper
£2200 $3542 €3300 Group of figures taking respite in the gardens of Nikko (32x48cm-13x19in) s.i. W/C. 19-Feb-3 Sotheby's, Olympia #25/R

IONESCU, Gheorges (1912-) Rumanian
£1258 $2000 €1887 Violete (33x25cm-13x10in) s.i. board. 22-Mar-3 New Orleans Auction, New Orleans #416/R est:1800-2500

IPOLD, Rudolf (1873-1936) Austrian
£2535 $4208 €3600 The Ildefonso Altar (71x97cm-28x38in) s.d.1900 panel. 11-Jun-3 Dorotheum, Vienna #387/R est:2500-3500
Works on paper
£256 $403 €400 Portrait of child (5x7cm-2x3in) s. W/C ivory oval. 25-Nov-2 Dorotheum, Vienna #510
£288 $453 €450 Woman with fur collar (8x10cm-3x4in) s.d.1925 w/C. 25-Nov-2 Dorotheum, Vienna #506
£321 $503 €500 Woman with blue grey dress (7x10cm-3x4in) s. W/C oval. 25-Nov-2 Dorotheum, Vienna #509
£353 $554 €550 Girl's portrait (8x10cm-3x4in) s.d.1922 W/C oval. 25-Nov-2 Dorotheum, Vienna #498
£385 $604 €600 Woman wearing blue shawl (8x10cm-3x4in) s.d.1928 W/C oval. 25-Nov-2 Dorotheum, Vienna #497
£417 $654 €650 Woman wearing black dress (9x14cm-4x6in) s.d.1929 W/C possibly ivory oval. 25-Nov-2 Dorotheum, Vienna #495
£417 $654 €650 Woman wearing blue dress and beige shawl (8x10cm-3x4in) s.d.1928 W/C. 25-Nov-2 Dorotheum, Vienna #502/R
£417 $654 €650 Woman with roses (7x10cm-3x4in) s.d.19 W/C oval. 25-Nov-2 Dorotheum, Vienna #505/R
£417 $654 €650 Woman wearing blue dress (8x10cm-3x4in) s. W/C oval. 25-Nov-2 Dorotheum, Vienna #507
£449 $704 €700 Woman with fur collar (10x12cm-4x5in) s. W/C possibly ivory oval. 25-Nov-2 Dorotheum, Vienna #508
£513 $805 €800 Portrait of woman wearing blue hat with feathers (11x16cm-4x6in) s. W/C. 25-Nov-2 Dorotheum, Vienna #511/R

IPOUSTEGUY, Jean (1920-) French
Sculpture
£1042 $1656 €1500 Ombre de sein (45x30x17cm-18x12x7in) s.num.1/1 bronze Cast Blanchet prov.exhib. 29-Apr-3 Artcurial Briest, Paris #643/R est:1000-1500
£2739 $4273 €4300 Femme nue, les bras sur le buste (36cm-14in) s.d.1959 num.2/6 pat.bronze. 7-Nov-2 Claude Aguttes, Neuilly #52/R est:2500-3000
£2964 $4594 €4446 Bust surrounded by box (54x33x30cm-21x13x12in) s.d.1966 num.3/9 bronze. 1-Oct-2 Rasmussen, Copenhagen #48/R est:40000 (D.KR 35000)

IPPO, Mori (1798-1871) Japanese
Works on paper
£2025 $3200 €3200 Snowy landscape (133x48cm-52x19in) s. Indian ink scroll. 27-Nov-2 Wiener Kunst Auktionen, Vienna #230/R est:2500-5000

IPSEN, Poul Janus (1936-) Danish
£340 $538 €510 Inside-outside II (102x71cm-40x28in) s.i.d.96 verso. 27-Nov-2 Museumsbygningen, Copenhagen #722/R (D.KR 4000)
£593 $919 €890 My model II (102x87cm-40x34in) s.d.01/81 verso. 1-Oct-2 Rasmussen, Copenhagen #187/R (D.KR 7000)
£698 $1110 €1047 Inside-Outside II (102x71cm-40x28in) i.verso. 10-Mar-3 Rasmussen, Vejle #741/R (D.KR 7500)
£847 $1312 €1271 Miss Spanking (102x71cm-40x28in) s.i.verso prov. 1-Oct-2 Rasmussen, Copenhagen #143/R (D.KR 10000)
£1621 $2706 €2350 They will not see (145x145cm-57x57in) s. verso exhib. 17-Jun-3 Rasmussen, Copenhagen #32/R est:20000 (D.KR 17000)

IRANZO ALMONACID, Jose (1931-) Spanish
Works on paper
£1132 $1743 €1800 Composition (115x148cm-45x58in) s. mixed media board. 22-Oct-2 Durán, Madrid #130/R

IRELAND, Thomas Tayler (fl.1880-c.1927) British
£580 $905 €870 Pastoral scene with cattle (68x51cm-27x20in) s.d.1889. 25-Mar-3 Bonhams, Leeds #599
Works on paper
£300 $465 €450 Children playing in a woodland glade (51x33cm-20x13in) s. W/C. 6-Dec-2 Chrystals Auctions, Isle of Man #178
£350 $508 €525 Bluebells and primroses (36x25cm-14x10in) s. W/C. 3-May-2 Biddle & Webb, Birmingham #391
£440 $682 €660 Lake in wooded landscape (33x51cm-13x20in) s. W/C. 6-Dec-2 Chrystals Auctions, Isle of Man #176
£440 $722 €660 Woodland scene with lake and woman gathering firewood (35x40cm-14x16in) s. W/C. 4-Jun-3 Bonhams, Chester #403
£520 $806 €780 Stream in a woodland glade (33x51cm-13x20in) s. W/C. 6-Dec-2 Chrystals Auctions, Isle of Man #177
£520 $806 €780 Stream in woodland glade (33x51cm-13x20in) s. W/C. 6-Dec-2 Chrystals Auctions, Isle of Man #181

IRESON, Christopher (20th C) ?
£650 $1007 €975 Servant girl in a sunlit Italian garden (75x54cm-30x21in) s.d.III. 26-Sep-2 Mellors & Kirk, Nottingham #735/R
Works on paper
£1300 $2015 €1950 Venice evening on the Riva (24x29cm-9x11in) s.i. mixed media. 26-Sep-2 Mellors & Kirk, Nottingham #660/R est:700-900

IRISH SCHOOL, 18th C
£16667 $25833 €26000 Wooded landscape with two gentlemen conversing and huntsman (74x99cm-29x39in) 3-Dec-2 Bonhams & James Adam, Dublin #15/R est:8000-12000

IRISH SCHOOL, 19th C
£4000 $5720 €6000 Landing the catch. board. 20-Apr-2 Hogben, Folkstone #176 est:400-600
£6304 $10339 €8700 Eviction (63x75cm-25x30in) 28-May-3 Bonhams & James Adam, Dublin #4/R est:6000-8000

IRITZ, Sandor Iranyi (1890-1975) Hungarian
Works on paper
£722 $1127 €1047 Sheaf carriers (29x23cm-11x9in) s. pastel. 13-Sep-2 Mu Terem Galeria, Budapest #157/R est:100000 (H.F 280000)

IRMER, Carl (1834-1900) German
£1300 $2119 €1885 Island of Rugen (60x86cm-24x34in) s.d.74. 16-Jul-3 Sotheby's, Olympia #184/R est:1000-1500

IRMINGER, Valdemar (1850-1938) Danish
£254 $391 €381 Blind beggars (63x51cm-25x20in) mono.d.83. 26-Oct-2 Rasmussen, Havnen #2073/R (D.KR 3000)
£257 $401 €386 Noah leading the animals towards the Ark (70x87cm-28x34in) init. 11-Nov-2 Rasmussen, Vejle #707/R (D.KR 3000)
£297 $470 €446 Two guards resting by a tree (45x45cm-18x18in) init. 5-Apr-3 Rasmussen, Havnen #2168 (D.KR 3200)
£372 $592 €558 Portrait of the landscape artist Thorvald Niss (64x50cm-25x20in) s.i.d.1903. 5-Mar-3 Rasmussen, Copenhagen #1676/R (D.KR 4000)
£374 $583 €561 Biblical scene (89x76cm-35x30in) init.d.97 exhib. 5-Aug-2 Rasmussen, Vejle #70/R (D.KR 4400)
£931 $1480 €1397 Small devils steeling wine (63x48cm-25x19in) init.d.98 exhib. 5-Mar-3 Rasmussen, Copenhagen #1868/R (D.KR 10000)
£1095 $1751 €1643 The Christian arena (96x95cm-38x37in) init.i.d.02 exhib. 13-Jan-3 Rasmussen, Vejle #214/R est:20000 (D.KR 12500)
£1509 $2340 €2400 Cupid on the back of a roaring lion (42x62cm-17x24in) mono.d.08. 29-Oct-2 Dorotheum, Vienna #92/R est:3000-3500

IROLLI, Vincenzo (1860-1949) Italian
£1389 $2236 €2084 Italian market (19x28cm-7x11in) s. canvas on panel. 7-May-3 Dobiaschofsky, Bern #676/R est:3600 (S.FR 3000)
£1899 $3000 €3000 Still life with dead bird (155x75cm-61x30in) s. 26-Nov-2 Christie's, Rome #227/R
£2200 $3432 €3300 Portrait of a woman (40x31cm-16x12in) s. 17-Sep-2 Sotheby's, Olympia #285/R est:2500-3500
£3071 $4514 €4760 Rain (38x54cm-15x21in) 24-Jun-2 Babuino, Rome #351
£3846 $5962 €6000 Young mother with child (38x22cm-15x9in) s. 5-Dec-2 Dr Fritz Nagel, Stuttgart #666/R est:5000
£6289 $9686 €10000 Girl with flowers (63x46cm-25x18in) s. 28-Oct-2 Il Ponte, Milan #285/R est:6000
£6522 $10696 €9000 Ritratto di bimbo (34x30cm-13x12in) s. 27-May-3 Finarte, Milan #106/R est:8000-9000
£9434 $14528 €15000 Still life with fish (75x100cm-30x39in) s. 23-Oct-2 Finarte, Milan #150/R est:16000-20000
£11392 $18000 €18000 Cut plait (82x60cm-32x24in) s. prov.lit. 26-Nov-2 Christie's, Rome #268/R est:30000
£15823 $25000 €25000 Copper pan maker (68x103cm-27x41in) s. 26-Nov-2 Christie's, Rome #300/R est:40000
£16774 $26000 €25161 Far away thoughts (55x34cm-22x13in) s. 30-Oct-2 Christie's, Rockefeller NY #166/R est:10000-15000
£21519 $34000 €34000 Amongst flowers (77x137cm-30x54in) s. 26-Nov-2 Christie's, Rome #297/R est:20000-30000
£34177 $54000 €54000 Seated girl (160x50cm-63x20in) s. prov.lit. 26-Nov-2 Christie's, Rome #276/R est:45000-60000
Works on paper
£1064 $1723 €1500 Terrazza fiorita (41x60cm-16x24in) s. W/C board. 22-May-3 Stadion, Trieste #224/R est:1000-1500

IRONSIDE, Christopher (20th C) British
Works on paper
£440 $704 €660 View of Lansdowne circus in winter (25x33cm-10x13in) W/C. 8-Jan-3 Brightwells, Leominster #1086

IRONSIDE, Robin (1912-1965) British
Works on paper
£3000 $4770 €4500 New moon being born inside the old (34x55cm-13x22in) ink gouache exhib. 26-Feb-3 Sotheby's, Olympia #125/R est:800-1200

IRVIN, Albert (1922-) British
£600 $990 €870 With black (46x30cm-18x12in) s.d.64 prov. 3-Jul-3 Christie's, Kensington #737/R
Works on paper
£1200 $2004 €1740 Untitled, abstract (27x37cm-11x15in) s.d.81 W/C gouache. 24-Jun-3 Bonhams, New Bond Street #129/R est:800-1200

IRVIN, Fred (1914-) American
Works on paper
£2564 $4000 €3846 Newsboy standing to attention while policeman raises flag (48x33cm-19x13in) s. gouache. 9-Nov-2 Illustration House, New York #26/R est:2500-3500

IRVINE, Greg (1946-) Australian
£246 $373 €369 Indian courtyard (121x182cm-48x72in) mono. s.verso. 19-Aug-2 Joel, Victoria #194 (A.D 700)

IRVINE, James (1833-1899) British
£3800 $5776 €5700 Highland stream (76x109cm-30x43in) s.i.on stretcher. 28-Aug-2 Sotheby's, London #890/R est:2500-3500

IRVINE, Wilson (1869-1936) American
£1807 $3000 €2620 Autumn landscape (30x41cm-12x16in) s. prov. 11-Jun-3 Butterfields, San Francisco #4076/R est:3000-5000
£2410 $4000 €3495 Meandering stream (61x69cm-24x27in) s. prov. 11-Jun-3 Butterfields, San Francisco #4069/R est:5000-7000
£4790 $8000 €6946 Calm sea (55x65cm-22x26in) s. canvas on board. 18-Jun-3 Christie's, Los Angeles #94/R est:8000-12000
£7051 $11000 €10577 French quarter courtyard (30x41cm-12x16in) s. painted c.1927-28 lit. 12-Oct-2 Neal Auction Company, New Orleans #636/R est:6000-9000
£8974 $14000 €13461 Autumn landscape (64x76cm-25x30in) s. 1-Aug-2 Eldred, East Dennis #937a est:5000-7000
Works on paper
£258 $400 €387 White mountains (33x46cm-13x18in) s. pastel W/C double-sided. 2-Nov-2 North East Auctions, Portsmouth #39/R

IRVING, William C (1866-1943) British
£110000 $171600 €165000 Blaydon races - study for life (90x128cm-35x50in) s.d.1903 two. 6-Nov-2 Sotheby's, Olympia #82/R est:40000-60000
Works on paper
£480 $802 €696 Newbiggin fisherman (25x32cm-10x13in) s. indis d. W/C. 17-Jun-3 Anderson & Garland, Newcastle #222/R

IRWE, Knut (1912-) Swedish
£407 $643 €611 Landscape with line of birds (55x70cm-22x28in) s. panel. 30-Nov-2 Goteborg Auktionsverk, Sweden #547/R (S.KR 5800)

IRWIN, Gwyther (1931-) British
Works on paper
£450 $693 €675 Bauxite baby (96x22cm-38x9in) collage. 5-Sep-2 Christie's, Kensington #695

IRWIN, Wesley Fraser (1897-1976) Canadian
£370 $577 €616 Bowl of flowers (43x34cm-17x13in) s. s.i.verso board prov. 13-Apr-3 Levis, Calgary #476/R (C.D 850)

ISAAC, Terry A (1958-) American
£2690 $4250 €3901 Stripes on snow study (15x30cm-6x12in) s. acrylic. 26-Jul-3 Coeur d'Alene, Hayden #194/R est:3000-5000

ISAAKSZ, Isaac (17th C) Dutch
£4054 $6324 €6000 Portrait of a Roman Imperial (37x28cm-15x11in) panel prov. 27-Mar-3 Dorotheum, Vienna #209/R est:6000-10000

ISAAKSZ, Isaac (studio) (17th C) Dutch
£7547 $11698 €12000 Feast of Herod (128x265cm-50x104in) 2-Oct-2 Dorotheum, Vienna #164/R est:12000-16000

ISABEY, Eugène (1803-1886) French
£694 $1104 €1000 Scene de cour (58x73cm-23x29in) panel. 30-Apr-3 Tajan, Paris #5
£851 $1421 €1200 Portrait de femme (31x17cm-12x7in) init. panel after Rubens prov. 23-Jun-3 Beaussant & Lefèvre, Paris #316/R
£1274 $2000 €1911 Cotes Brehat (30x40cm-12x16in) s. 22-Nov-2 Skinner, Boston #391/R est:3000-5000
£1282 $1987 €2000 Portraits d'officiers (23x16cm-9x6in) s.d.1860 pair. 6-Dec-2 Rieunier, Bailly-Pommery, Mathias, Paris #52/R
£1752 $2750 €2628 Before the tomb (24x20cm-9x8in) s.d.75 prov. 10-Dec-2 Doyle, New York #185/R est:3000-5000
£1795 $2836 €2800 Scene de naufrage (37x50cm-15x20in) prov.exhib.lit. 18-Nov-2 Sotheby's, Paris #66/R

£2113 $3507 €3000 La maison des pecheurs. s. i.d.1838 verso lit. 11-Jun-3 Beaussant & Lefèvre, Paris #76/R est:3000-4000
£2222 $3578 €3333 Rocky coastline in the sun (35x61cm-14x24in) s. 7-May-3 Dobiaschofsky, Bern #677/R est:5500 (S.FR 4800)
£2532 $3949 €4000 Portrait de sa fille avec son chien (51x41cm-20x16in) prov.exhib. 18-Oct-2 Rabourdin & Choppin de Janvry, Paris #31/R
£2722 $4300 €4083 Boats in stormy weather off a Northern coast (43x64cm-17x25in) s.d.1856 panel. 16-Nov-2 New Orleans Auction, New Orleans #315/R est:5000-8000
£5578 $8869 €8200 Marine, soleil couchant (12x29cm-5x11in) s. paper on panel prov. 24-Mar-3 Fraysse & Associes, Paris #49/R
£7595 $12000 €11393 Departure for fishing (84x122cm-33x48in) s.d.62 prov. 24-Apr-3 Shannon's, Milford #133/R est:20000-30000

Works on paper
£360 $565 €540 Fishing boats on a beach at Etretat (11x17cm-4x7in) init.i. black lead. 11-Dec-2 Sotheby's, Olympia #294/R
£641 $1013 €1000 Vase aux deux perroquets (32x20cm-13x8in) W/C htd gouache prov. 18-Nov-2 Sotheby's, Paris #59/R
£719 $1151 €1000 Bateau de peche (16x23cm-6x9in) s.d.1841 W/C. 13-May-3 Vanderkindere, Brussels #6
£1014 $1581 €1500 Figures et bateaux pres des falaises (10x17cm-4x7in) W/C over crayon. 26-Mar-3 Piasa, Paris #94/R
£1149 $1792 €1700 Port a maree basse (12x21cm-5x8in) W/C gouache over crayon. 26-Mar-3 Piasa, Paris #95
£1195 $1852 €1900 Landscapes and marine studies (28x27cm-11x11in) W/C gour in one frame. 1-Oct-2 Dorotheum, Vienna #222/R est:1600-1800
£1351 $2108 €2000 Ramassage des coquillages a maree basse (9x19cm-4x7in) W/C gouache over crayon. 26-Mar-3 Piasa, Paris #96
£1375 $2200 €2063 Whispered secrets (33x23cm-13x9in) init. W/C. 14-May-3 Doyle, New York #41 est:1000-1500

ISABEY, Eugène (attrib) (1803-1886) French
£870 $1348 €1305 Coastal landscape with fishermen (35x61cm-14x24in) s. 9-Dec-2 Philippe Schuler, Zurich #8651 (S.FR 2000)
£897 $1409 €1400 Old buildings in small French city (24x18cm-9x7in) 21-Nov-2 Van Ham, Cologne #1690/R

Works on paper
£1761 $2730 €2800 Landscape and marine studies (24x39cm-9x15in) W/C six in one frame. 1-Oct-2 Dorotheum, Vienna #221/R est:2000-2500

ISABEY, Jean Baptiste (1767-1855) French
£19620 $31000 €31000 Couple descendant l'escalier de la tourelle du Chateau d'Harcourt (64x44cm-25x17in) s.d.1827 prov.exhib. 27-Nov-2 Christie's, Paris #65/R est:15000-20000

Miniatures
£1739 $2852 €2400 Portrait de Frederic Guillaume IV (8x6cm-3x2in) s. gilt bronze frame oval. 27-May-3 Palais de Beaux Arts, Brussels #324 est:1000-1200
£4194 $6626 €6500 Portrait de l'Imperatrice Josephine (5x3cm-2x1in) s.d.1804 oval. 18-Dec-2 Beaussant & Lefèvre, Paris #3/R
£6000 $9840 €8700 Claire de Morel-Vinde in a white muslin dress (6cm-2xin) s. gilt metal frame prov. 3-Jun-3 Christie's, London #124/R est:4000-6000
£7000 $10920 €10500 Young lady hair in ringlets seated in a chair wearing black decollete dress (20cm-8xin) s.d.1839 W/C paper set in hexagonal leather case rec. arched top. 5-Nov-2 Bonhams, New Bond Street #111/R est:7000-9000
£15000 $23550 €22500 Emperor Napoleon I of France wearing coronation robes (6cm-2xin) s. silver gilt frame oval prov.lit. 10-Dec-2 Christie's, London #119/R est:6000-8000

Works on paper
£629 $900 €944 Head of a young man, Monsieur Dumay (24x17cm-9x7in) s.i. brush ink. 23-Jan-3 Swann Galleries, New York #286/R
£650 $1021 €975 Girl seated on a canape holding a miniature in her hand (45x37cm-18x15in) i. black white chk prov. 13-Dec-2 Christie's, Kensington #322/R
£962 $1510 €1500 Portrait presume de la princesse de Polignac (24x19cm-9x7in) s. W/C. 14-Dec-2 Artcurial Briest, Paris #5/R
£1000 $1570 €1500 Portrait of a man said to be Louis Antoine de Saint Just (24x20cm-9x8in) s.i. black white chk oval lit. 13-Dec-2 Christie's, Kensington #324/R est:1000-1500
£3395 $5500 €5093 Portrait of young lady (25x20cm-10x8in) chl htd white oval. 21-Jan-3 Sotheby's, New York #175/R est:6000
£4516 $7135 €7000 Tombeau de Napoleon I (43x38cm-17x15in) s. pen ink wash. 18-Dec-2 Beaussant & Lefèvre, Paris #26/R
£5674 $9475 €8000 Portrait de femme dans un paysage (53x40cm-21x16in) i.d.1793 black crayon gouache. 19-Jun-3 Piasa, Paris #159/R est:5000-6000
£9494 $14810 €15000 Escalier de la grande tour (25x16cm-10x6in) s.d.1822 gouache. 20-Oct-2 Anaf, Lyon #163/R

ISABEY, Jean Baptiste (attrib) (1767-1855) French

Miniatures
£968 $1529 €1500 Portrait de Napoleon I (6cm-2in circular) 18-Dec-2 Beaussant & Lefèvre, Paris #8/R

ISAKSEN, Christen Holm (1877-1935) Danish
£286 $478 €415 Coastal landscape with bird mountain (19x24cm-7x9in) mono. artist's board. 17-Jun-3 Rasmussen, Copenhagen #169 (D.KR 3000)
£296 $459 €444 Risin and Kellingen - landscape from Faroe Islands (25x36cm-10x14in) mono. canvas on panel. 1-Oct-2 Rasmussen, Copenhagen #330 (D.KR 3500)

ISAKSON, Karl (1878-1922) Swedish
£887 $1374 €1331 Portrait of the artist Herman Osterlund (52x40cm-20x16in) i.d.1902 verso exhib. 4-Dec-2 AB Stockholms Auktionsverk #1764/R (S.KR 12500)
£1612 $2514 €2418 Head of woman (29x42cm-11x17in) i.verso exhib. 5-Nov-2 Bukowskis, Stockholm #190/R est:20000-25000 (S.KR 23000)
£3504 $5466 €5256 Nature morte (35x29cm-14x11in) with init. canvas on panel painted c.1911 exhib. 5-Nov-2 Bukowskis, Stockholm #186/R est:50000-60000 (S.KR 50000)
£7358 $11479 €11037 Nature morte (50x61cm-20x24in) lit. 5-Nov-2 Bukowskis, Stockholm #99/R est:80000-100000 (S.KR 105000)
£9294 $14684 €13941 Woodland road, Smaaland (68x48cm-27x19in) painted 1914-15 prov.exhib.lit. 1-Apr-3 Rasmussen, Copenhagen #4/R est:100000 (D.KR 100000)
£11431 $17718 €17147 Purple and yellow flowers (65x58cm-26x23in) painted 1913 exhib.lit. 1-Oct-2 Rasmussen, Copenhagen #115/R est:150000-200000 (D.KR 135000)
£18533 $29838 €27800 Flowers in vase and books on table (57x72cm-22x28in) painted 1918-1920 prov.exhib.lit. 7-May-3 AB Stockholms Auktionsverk #654/R est:175000-200000 (S.KR 240000)
£25402 $39373 €38103 Still life of potted plant, orange, jug and books (66x55cm-26x22in) painted c.1915 exhib.lit. 1-Oct-2 Rasmussen, Copenhagen #114/R est:200000-250000 (D.KR 300000)
£31599 $49926 €47399 Still life of green jug, books and stoneware pot (68x54cm-27x21in) painted c.1916 prov. 1-Apr-3 Rasmussen, Copenhagen #15/R est:200000-250000 (D.KR 340000)

ISAMBERT, Alphonse (1818-?) French
£1208 $1945 €1800 Artiste antique dans son atelier de poterie (73x60cm-29x24in) s.d.1852. 18-Feb-3 Vanderkindere, Brussels #491

ISARDA, Wajid (17th C) Indian?
£1200 $1908 €1740 Portrait of Aurangzeb on a terrace. i. painted c.1680. 1-May-3 Bonhams, Knightsbridge #111 est:1500-2000

ISBAK, Poul (1943-) Danish

Sculpture
£3101 $4806 €4652 Female torso (52x42x30cm-20x17x12in) marble. 4-Dec-2 Kunsthallen, Copenhagen #60/R est:35000 (D.KR 36000)
£3346 $5286 €5019 Chair with high back (93x62x37cm-37x24x15in) init.d.84-85 polished light marble. 1-Apr-3 Rasmussen, Copenhagen #178/R est:50000-75000 (D.KR 36000)

ISBEY, Annette (20th C) New Zealander
£627 $978 €941 Two horses and riders with small running figures (20x102cm-8x40in) s. linen. 7-Nov-2 International Art Centre, Auckland #140/R est:1800-2600 (NZ.D 2000)

ISBRAND, Victor (1897-1989) Danish
£297 $481 €431 From the Metro, Paris (50x60cm-20x24in) s. 24-May-3 Rasmussen, Havnen #4039 (D.KR 3100)
£410 $651 €615 From Menton (60x48cm-24x19in) s.i. 10-Mar-3 Rasmussen, Vejle #746 (D.KR 4400)
£604 $954 €906 Still life of jug and bowl with daisies (71x58cm-28x23in) s. 1-Apr-3 Rasmussen, Copenhagen #94/R (D.KR 6500)

ISCAN, Ferit (1931-1986) French
£1573 $2438 €2500 L'atelier (112x162cm-44x64in) s. acrylic. 4-Oct-2 Tajan, Paris #124 est:3000-3500

ISELI, Rolf (1934-) Swiss
£4803 $7541 €7205 Earth landscape - end landscape (102x150cm-40x59in) s.i.d.1980 acrylic earth prov. 25-Nov-2 Germann, Zurich #16/R est:12000-16000 (S.FR 11000)
Works on paper
£2174 $3565 €3000 Large sketch sheet St Romain (69x100cm-27x39in) s.d.84 W/C oil pastel chk pencil prov. 28-May-3 Lempertz, Koln #196/R est:3500
£2620 $4087 €3930 Untitled (78x56cm-31x22in) s.d.87 W/C pastel gouache chl. 8-Nov-2 Dobiaschofsky, Bern #262/R est:6000 (S.FR 6000)
£5677 $8913 €8516 Homme de terre (76x106cm-30x42in) s.i.d.1972 earth W/C oil pencil prov. 25-Nov-2 Germann, Zurich #14/R est:16000-20000 (S.FR 13000)
£7860 $12262 €11790 Orange composition with feathers (107x76cm-42x30in) s.i.d.77 feathers soil gouache pastel W/C exhib. 8-Nov-2 Dobiaschofsky, Bern #260/R est:15000 (S.FR 18000)

ISENBART, Marie Victor Émile (1846-1921) French
£1923 $3038 €3000 Les bucherons (50x65cm-20x26in) s. 18-Nov-2 Tajan, Paris #119/R est:3000-3800

ISENBRANDT, Adriaen (1490-1551) Flemish
£16774 $26000 €25161 St Catherine of Alexandria, with martyrdom scene beyond (39x32cm-15x13in) panel prov.exhib.lit. 2-Oct-2 Christie's, Rockefeller NY #137/R est:10000-15000

ISENBRANDT, Adriaen (circle) (1490-1551) Flemish
£10494 $17000 €15741 Holy family (9x15cm-4x6in) panel shaped top prov.lit. 24-Jan-3 Christie's, Rockefeller NY #28/R est:18000-22000

ISENBURGER, Eric (1902-1971) American/German
£1319 $2085 €1900 Still life with tulips and narcissi (85x68cm-33x27in) s.d.1923. 26-Apr-3 Dr Lehr, Berlin #231/R est:1500

ISGRO, Emilio (1936-) Spanish
Sculpture
£2710 $4281 €4200 Deleted book (40x60x11cm-16x24x4in) s.i.d.1970 book plexiglas. 18-Dec-2 Christie's, Rome #193/R est:6000
Works on paper
£272 $433 €400 Artist and Love (29x24cm-11x9in) s.i. mixed media cardboard. 1-Mar-3 Meeting Art, Vercelli #589
£321 $503 €500 Artist and love (29x24cm-11x9in) mixed media cardboard on cardboard. 23-Nov-2 Meeting Art, Vercelli #70
£347 $552 €500 Artist and mistake (29x24cm-11x9in) s.i. mixed media card. 1-May-3 Meeting Art, Vercelli #163

ISHERWOOD, Christopher (20th C) British
£340 $547 €510 Sailing boats at St Ives (23x33cm-9x13in) s. board. 19-Feb-3 Mallams, Oxford #435
£680 $1095 €1020 Rain and dogs, Wigan (33x43cm-13x17in) s. board. 19-Feb-3 Mallams, Oxford #434/R

ISHERWOOD, Jean de Courtenay (1911-) Australian
£575 $902 €863 Still life 1949 (49x38cm-19x15in) s. board. 15-Apr-3 Lawson Menzies, Sydney #166/R est:1500-2000 (A.D 1500)

ISHERWOOD, Lawrence (1917-1988) British
£250 $390 €375 Grand Canal, Venice (30x40cm-12x16in) s.i.d.1970 i.verso board after JMW Turner. 23-Sep-2 Bonhams, Chester #1013
£250 $390 €375 Grand Canal, Venice (25x35cm-10x14in) s. i.verso board after Turner. 23-Sep-2 Bonhams, Chester #1015
£260 $406 €390 Llanberis Pass, Caernarvonshire (45x60cm-18x24in) s.d.69 i.verso board. 23-Sep-2 Bonhams, Chester #1009
£260 $419 €390 Bolton (41x56cm-16x22in) s. board. 18-Feb-3 Bonhams, Knightsbridge #76/R
£270 $427 €405 Mary Hopkins (76x33cm-30x13in) s. s. verso board. 27-Nov-2 Peter Wilson, Nantwich #27
£280 $440 €420 Miner's bathtime (35x45cm-14x18in) s. board. 15-Apr-3 Bonhams, Knightsbridge #65
£320 $502 €480 Wigan sunset (20x25cm-8x10in) s. canvas on board. 25-Nov-2 Bonhams, Chester #995
£320 $502 €480 Four nudes (38x47cm-15x19in) s. i.verso board. 25-Nov-2 Bonhams, Chester #997
£350 $550 €525 Leigh skyline (61x76cm-24x30in) 10-Dec-2 Capes Dunn, Manchester #706
£360 $562 €540 House of Parliament, nocturne (29x39cm-11x15in) s.i.verso board. 23-Sep-2 Bonhams, Chester #1011
£440 $686 €660 Rain Eros, London (30x40cm-12x16in) s.i.d.69 verso board. 23-Sep-2 Bonhams, Chester #1016
£550 $902 €798 Land's End, coast scene with cliffs (46x61cm-18x24in) s.d.73 board. 3-Jun-3 Capes Dunn, Manchester #33/R
£580 $934 €841 Patti Boyd at Epstein's funeral (48x36cm-19x14in) s. board. 19-Feb-3 Peter Wilson, Nantwich #55
£620 $961 €930 Poppies - 83gns (44x34cm-17x13in) s. board. 25-Sep-2 Peter Wilson, Nantwich #96
£640 $1005 €960 Rain (37x106cm-15x42in) s.d.64 i.d.verso board. 25-Nov-2 Bonhams, Chester #998
£650 $1027 €975 St Martins in the Field London (47x62cm-19x24in) s. s. verso board. 27-Nov-2 Peter Wilson, Nantwich #74/R
£650 $1066 €943 Snow, Lime Street, Wigan (30x41cm-12x16in) s.d.73 board. 3-Jun-3 Capes Dunn, Manchester #34/R
£840 $1319 €1260 Rain (37x106cm-15x42in) s.d.64 i.verso board. 25-Nov-2 Bonhams, Chester #999
£850 $1318 €1275 Southport Beach (39x54cm-15x21in) s.d.1975 board. 25-Sep-2 Peter Wilson, Nantwich #95
Works on paper
£340 $537 €510 Southport beach (17x23cm-7x9in) s.d.1973 W/C. 27-Nov-2 Peter Wilson, Nantwich #112/R

ISHERWOOD, Lawrence (attrib) (1917-1988) British
£260 $406 €390 Bridge (34x44cm-13x17in) s. board. 9-Oct-2 Woolley & Wallis, Salisbury #162/R

ISKANDAR, Popo (1927-2000) Javanese
£2651 $4083 €3977 Patung primitif - primitive statue (75x65cm-30x26in) s.d.63 lit. 27-Oct-2 Christie's, Hong Kong #77/R est:30000-40000 (HK.D 32000)
£7770 $12821 €11267 Two leopards (100x131cm-39x52in) s.d.91 acrylic. 6-Jul-3 Christie's, Hong Kong #58/R est:45000-75000 (HK.D 100000)

ISKOWITZ, Gershon (1921-1988) Canadian
£866 $1377 €1256 Morning at Silver lake (86x107cm-34x42in) s.d.1961 i.verso prov. 1-May-3 Heffel, Vancouver #48/R est:3000-3500 (C.D 2000)
Works on paper
£288 $447 €432 Untitled (32x55cm-13x22in) s.d.78 W/C. 3-Dec-2 Joyner, Toronto #193/R (C.D 700)
£393 $616 €590 Parry Sounds series II (46x61cm-18x24in) s.d.65 W/C prov. 24-Jul-2 Walker's, Ottawa #225/R (C.D 950)

ISLE, Wolfgang (1945-) German
£285 $450 €450 Composition with bridal couple (180x160cm-71x63in) s.d.XI/89. 30-Nov-2 Arnold, Frankfurt #266/R

ISMAIL, Adham (1922-1963) Syrian
£4500 $7155 €6750 Family (122x91cm-48x36in) s.d.1959 acrylic board. 30-Apr-3 Sotheby's, London #148/R est:4000-6000

ISMAIL, Naim (1930-1979) Syrian
£4000 $6360 €6000 Two sleepers (127x77cm-50x30in) s.d.1969 i.verso. 30-Apr-3 Sotheby's, London #141/R est:5000-7000

ISNARD, Vivien (1946-) French?
£252 $390 €400 Sans titre (70x156cm-28x61in) s.d.1973 acrylic prov. 30-Oct-2 Artcurial Briest, Paris #686
£440 $682 €700 No 31 (160x208cm-63x82in) s.d.1973 i.verso acrylic prov. 30-Oct-2 Artcurial Briest, Paris #687

ISOM, Graham (1945-) British
£679 $964 €1100 Grand National 1991 (51x74cm-20x29in) s. 29-Mar-2 Woodwards, Cork #182/R
£700 $1106 €1050 The 210th St. Ledger, 1988 (76x102cm-30x40in) s. i.verso. 28-Nov-2 Christie's, Kensington #204/R
£850 $1343 €1275 Minster Sun beats Diminuendo, St. Ledger 1988 (51x76cm-20x30in) s. i.verso. 28-Nov-2 Christie's, Kensington #201/R

ISON, Graham (?) British?
£480 $749 €720 Lowther Stakes, York, 20th August 1998 (51x66cm-20x26in) s. 10-Apr-3 Tennants, Leyburn #1054
£550 $858 €825 July Cup, Newmarket, 7th July 1994 (51x61cm-20x24in) s. 10-Apr-3 Tennants, Leyburn #1053
£550 $858 €825 Queen Anne Stakes, Ascot, 4th June 1994 (51x61cm-20x24in) s. 10-Apr-3 Tennants, Leyburn #1055

ISOU, Isidore (1925-) French
£1258 $1950 €2000 Entretien avec Jean Cocteau (55x46cm-22x18in) s.d.89 acrylic. 30-Oct-2 Artcurial Briest, Paris #688 est:1200-1500

ISRAELI SCHOOL
£4878 $7659 €7317 Woman seated on a hillside (61x38cm-24x15in) s. 10-Dec-2 Pinneys, Montreal #70 est:200-400 (C.D 12000)

ISRAELS, Isaac (1865-1934) Dutch
£13699 $21507 €20000 Portrait of a lady (27x21cm-11x8in) s. panel. 15-Apr-3 Sotheby's, Amsterdam #226/R est:10000-15000

£18868 $29057 €30000 Kinderjuffrouw in de diergaarde, Den Haag (50x40cm-20x16in) s. painted c.1917 prov. 23-Oct-2 Christie's, Amsterdam #146/R est:30000-40000
£18868 $29057 €30000 Balalaika player (80x66cm-31x26in) s. painted c.1924 prov.lit. 22-Oct-2 Sotheby's, Amsterdam #221/R est:40000-60000
£22535 $36282 €32000 Portrait of young woman wearing hat (95x65cm-37x26in) s. 7-May-3 Michael Zeller, Lindau #751/R est:18000
£28481 $44430 €45000 Portrait of Max Liebermann (80x52cm-31x20in) s. 21-Oct-2 Glerum, Amsterdam #176/R est:30000-50000
£35032 $55000 €52548 Beach at Viareggio, 1927-34 (19x15cm-7x6in) s. 10-Dec-2 Doyle, New York #218/R est:30000-40000
£38194 $60729 €55000 Javanese woman seated (62x36cm-24x14in) s. painted c.1916 prov. 29-Apr-3 Christie's, Amsterdam #174/R est:50000-70000
£45139 $71771 €65000 Jardin du Luxembourg - jour d'ete a Paris (46x55cm-18x22in) s. painted c.1910-12 prov.exhib.lit. 29-Apr-3 Christie's, Amsterdam #181/R est:60000-80000
£47945 $75274 €70000 Walcheren boy (83x57cm-33x22in) s. painted 1897. 15-Apr-3 Sotheby's, Amsterdam #246/R est:80000-120000
£75342 $118288 €110000 Coiffer Sainte Catherine (73x60cm-29x24in) s. 15-Apr-3 Sotheby's, Amsterdam #235/R est:120000-180000
£88050 $135597 €140000 Une Parisienne (82x55cm-32x22in) s. board painted c.1905 prov.exhib.lit. 22-Oct-2 Sotheby's, Amsterdam #206/R est:140000-160000
£95890 $150548 €140000 Moulin de la Galette, Paris (82x57cm-32x22in) s. board on panel painted c.1904. 15-Apr-3 Sotheby's, Amsterdam #209/R est:90000-120000
£100629 $154969 €160000 At the scale cafe, The Hague (65x58cm-26x23in) s. painted c.1930 prov.lit. 22-Oct-2 Sotheby's, Amsterdam #217/R est:140000-160000
£144654 $222767 €230000 Revue girl - la cocotte - at the scala, The Hague (70x60cm-28x24in) s. prov. 22-Oct-2 Sotheby's, Amsterdam #212/R est:75000-90000

Prints

£2532 $3949 €4000 Cloakroom (50x65cm-20x26in) s.num.50/42 lithograph prov.lit. 21-Oct-2 Glerum, Amsterdam #162/R est:2500-3500

Works on paper

£270 $419 €405 Portrait of a lady in a hat (42x47cm-17x19in) st.sig. red crayon. 3-Dec-2 Bonhams, Knightsbridge #254
£2055 $3226 €3000 Three servant girls on the Prinsengracht, Amsterdam (45x67cm-18x26in) studio st. chl executed c.1893-93 prov. 15-Apr-3 Sotheby's, Amsterdam #126/R est:3000-5000
£3000 $4650 €4500 Market (29x37cm-11x15in) s. W/C. 5-Dec-2 Christie's, Kensington #60/R est:3000-5000
£3947 $6395 €6000 Javanese dancer (34x49cm-13x19in) s. black chk W/C prov. 21-Jan-3 Christie's, Amsterdam #241/R est:4000-6000
£5051 $8333 €7324 Before the ceremony (51x40cm-20x16in) s. W/C. 6-Jul-3 Christie's, Hong Kong #27/R est:60000-70000 (HK.D 65000)
£15068 $23658 €22000 Pancake day (74x61cm-29x24in) s. W/C. 15-Apr-3 Sotheby's, Amsterdam #241/R est:14000-18000
£24051 $37519 €38000 Punting on the Thames near Richmond (35x50cm-14x20in) s. W/C prov. 21-Oct-2 Glerum, Amsterdam #177/R est:40000-60000
£61644 $96781 €90000 View of the Noordeinde, The Hague (81x60cm-32x24in) s. W/C prov. 15-Apr-3 Sotheby's, Amsterdam #244/R est:90000-120000

ISRAELS, Isaac (attrib) (1865-1934) Dutch

£1312 $2100 €1902 By the carousel (32x39cm-13x15in) bears sig. board. 16-May-3 Skinner, Boston #342/R est:1000-1500

ISRAELS, Josef (1824-1911) Dutch

£2083 $3312 €3000 Oud vrouwtje (24x16cm-9x6in) s. panel prov. 29-Apr-3 Christie's, Amsterdam #130/R est:2500-3500
£2516 $3874 €4000 Rabbi (40x32cm-16x13in) s. panel prov.exhib. 23-Oct-2 Christie's, Amsterdam #205/R est:2000-3000
£2516 $3874 €4000 Reading a letter (31x22cm-12x9in) s. panel prov. 23-Oct-2 Christie's, Amsterdam #206/R est:4000-6000
£8219 $12904 €12000 Homeward bound (116x77cm-46x30in) s. 15-Apr-3 Sotheby's, Amsterdam #137/R est:5000-7000
£8219 $12822 €12000 Sorrow (36x43cm-14x17in) s. panel prov. 14-Apr-3 Glerum, Amsterdam #54/R est:10000-12000
£9434 $14528 €15000 Return of the fisherboats (31x44cm-12x17in) s. board on panel. 22-Oct-2 Sotheby's, Amsterdam #225/R est:15000-20000
£10063 $15497 €16000 Fishermen spreading a net (32x46cm-13x18in) s. panel prov.exhib.lit. 22-Oct-2 Sotheby's, Amsterdam #216/R est:15000-20000
£17031 $26568 €25547 After the storm (108x143cm-43x56in) 20-Nov-2 Fischer, Luzern #1093/R est:20000-25000 (S.FR 39000)
£27778 $44167 €40000 De aardappeloogs - peasant couple on a horse cart (84x121cm-33x48in) s. prov.exhib. 29-Apr-3 Christie's, Amsterdam #141/R est:35000-45000

Works on paper

£278 $458 €400 Coachman (41x29cm-16x11in) s. pencil black ink chl. 1-Jul-3 Christie's, Amsterdam #194
£288 $450 €432 Der Torweg (10x13cm-4x5in) s. chl. 30-Mar-3 Simpson's, Houston #192
£307 $500 €461 Torweg (10x15cm-4x6in) s. charcoal. 2-Feb-3 Simpson's, Houston #145a
£350 $546 €550 Fisherwoman (41x28cm-16x11in) s. pencil dr. 6-Nov-2 Vendue Huis, Gravenhage #541
£390 $569 €600 Two fisher women (18x25cm-7x10in) s. pencil dr. 19-Jun-2 Vendue Huis, Gravenhage #240/R
£791 $1266 €1100 Young woman sitting at window. Woman peeling potatoes (28x20cm-11x8in) s. pencil prov. two. 17-May-3 Lempertz, Koln #1298
£1081 $1686 €1600 Man in red coat reading at table (39x33cm-15x13in) s. W/C paper on board. 28-Mar-3 Dorotheum, Vienna #244/R est:1400-1600
£1370 $2151 €2000 Peasant woman in a landscape (23x31cm-9x12in) s.W/C. 15-Apr-3 Sotheby's, Amsterdam #105/R est:3000-5000
£2400 $3720 €3600 Knitting (44x31cm-17x12in) chk pastel W/C dr exec.c.1860. 3-Dec-2 SOGA, Bratislava #151/R est:190000 (SL.K 152000)
£2932 $4750 €4251 Woman sewing by a window (33x23cm-13x9in) s. W/C over pencil paper on board prov. 21-May-3 Doyle, New York #186/R est:5000-7000
£3185 $5000 €4778 Courting couple (6x10cm-2x4in) s. W/C htd white. 10-Dec-2 Doyle, New York #190/R est:6000-8000
£7097 $11000 €10646 Quiet moment (49x69cm-19x27in) s. W/C gouache prov. 30-Oct-2 Christie's, Rockefeller NY #114/R est:10000-15000
£7895 $12789 €12000 Onder de lamp - self portrait of the artist writing in his study (34x51cm-13x20in) s. pencil ink W/C prov.exhib.lit. 21-Jan-3 Christie's, Amsterdam #217/R est:6000-8000

ISSAIEV, Nicolas (1897-1977) French/Russian

£662 $1079 €1000 Jeune orientale (73x54cm-29x21in) s. 3-Feb-3 Cornette de St.Cyr, Paris #310
£3200 $5184 €4800 Young bride in red chair (73x54cm-29x21in) s. 21-May-3 Sotheby's, London #208/R est:2000-3000

ISSELMANN, Dik (20th C) American?

£353 $550 €530 Still life with flowers in a vase. 19-Oct-2 Harvey Clar, Oakland #1587
£616 $962 €900 Still life with fruit, tin jug and plate (40x70cm-16x28in) s.d.1942. 10-Apr-3 Van Ham, Cologne #1497

ISSELMANN, Ernst (1885-1916) German

Works on paper

£342 $534 €500 Industrial area in the Saarland (41x51cm-16x20in) s. W/C board. 10-Apr-3 Van Ham, Cologne #1499
£411 $641 €600 Industrial city in the Saarland (38x45cm-15x18in) s.d.1915 W/C paper on board. 10-Apr-3 Van Ham, Cologne #1498

ISSUPOFF, Alessio (1889-1957) Russian

£272 $433 €400 Hussards on the river (40x50cm-16x20in) s. 1-Mar-3 Stadion, Trieste #81
£10204 $16224 €15000 Reading in the garden (98x70cm-39x28in) s. 18-Mar-3 Finarte, Milan #1/R

ISTLER, Josef (1919-) Czechoslovakian

£532 $862 €750 Composition (50x39cm-20x15in) s.d.1971 verso acrylic panel. 24-May-3 Van Ham, Cologne #285/R
£576 $944 €800 Untitled (54x44cm-21x17in) s.d.67 oil on paper. 3-Jun-3 Christie's, Amsterdam #126/R
£1218 $1888 €1900 Composition (89x59cm-35x23in) s.d.1949 board prov. 3-Dec-2 Christie's, Amsterdam #140/R est:600-800

ISTOKOVITS, Kalman (1898-?) Hungarian

£1291 $2001 €1872 Storm over the hills (70x100cm-28x39in) s.d.1926. 9-Dec-2 Mu Terem Galeria, Budapest #164/R est:300000 (H.F 480000)

ISTRATI, Alexandre (1915-1991) Rumanian

£346 $536 €550 Composition (38x46cm-15x18in) s.d.67 s.verso prov. 30-Oct-2 Artcurial Briest, Paris #689
£513 $805 €800 Untitled (65x54cm-26x21in) s. s.d.1971 verso. 24-Nov-2 Laurence Calmels, Paris #155/R
£578 $919 €850 Composition (65x81cm-26x32in) s. s.d.1981 verso. 26-Feb-3 Artcurial Briest, Paris #507
£816 $1298 €1200 Composition (74x100cm-29x39in) s. s.d.1960 verso. 26-Feb-3 Artcurial Briest, Paris #511
£833 $1308 €1300 Untitled (46x55cm-18x22in) s. s.d.74 verso. 24-Nov-2 Laurence Calmels, Paris #161/R
£833 $1308 €1300 Composition (100x81cm-39x32in) s. 11-Dec-2 Maigret, Paris #174/R
£884 $1406 €1300 Composition (100x80cm-39x31in) 26-Feb-3 Artcurial Briest, Paris #497
£962 $1510 €1500 Untitled (81x65cm-32x26in) s. s.d.1959 verso. 24-Nov-2 Laurence Calmels, Paris #160/R
£1090 $1711 €1700 Untitled (50x61cm-20x24in) s. s.d.1963 verso. 24-Nov-2 Laurence Calmels, Paris #157/R

£1154 $1812 €1800 Untitled (100x100cm-39x39in) s.d.69 s.d.verso prov.exhib. 24-Nov-2 Laurence Calmels, Paris #166/R
£1282 $2013 €2000 Blanc et noir (65x81cm-26x32in) s.i. i.d.1966 verso. 24-Nov-2 Laurence Calmels, Paris #153/R
£1474 $2315 €2300 Untitled (92x66cm-36x26in) s. s.d.1965 verso prov. 24-Nov-2 Laurence Calmels, Paris #163/R
£1565 $2488 €2300 Sans titre (92x73cm-36x29in) s. s.d.1958 verso prov. 26-Feb-3 Artcurial Briest, Paris #498/R est:2000-2500
£1603 $2516 €2500 Untitled (196x130cm-77x51in) s. s.d.1968 verso prov.exhib. 24-Nov-2 Laurence Calmels, Paris #154/R
£1633 $2596 €2400 Les plus hauts mondes (130x97cm-51x38in) s.d.62 s.i.d.1962 verso prov. 26-Feb-3 Artcurial Briest, Paris #501 est:2200-2500
£1633 $2596 €2400 Sans titre (162x130cm-64x51in) s.d.54. 26-Feb-3 Artcurial Briest, Paris #505/R est:2500-3500
£1633 $2596 €2400 Composition (93x74cm-37x29in) s. s.d.1956 verso. 26-Feb-3 Artcurial Briest, Paris #509/R est:2000-2500
£1690 $2806 €2400 Sans titre (65x82cm-26x32in) s. s.i.verso paint. 18-Jun-3 Anaf, Lyon #49/R est:1500-1800
£1795 $2818 €2800 Untitled (100x100cm-39x39in) s. s.d.1965 verso prov.exhib. 24-Nov-2 Laurence Calmels, Paris #156/R
£1800 $3006 €2610 Untitled (92x73cm-36x29in) s. s.d.1986 verso. 24-Jun-3 Sotheby's, Olympia #95/R est:2000-3000
£1837 $2920 €2700 Composition (60x116cm-24x46in) s. s.d.1971 verso acrylic. 24-Mar-3 Claude Boisgirard, Paris #144/R
£1973 $3137 €2900 Stynx (130x97cm-51x38in) s.d.57 s.i.d.1957 verso exhib. 26-Feb-3 Artcurial Briest, Paris #500 est:2200-2500
£1987 $3120 €3100 Untitled (92x64cm-36x25in) s.d.58 prov.exhib. 24-Nov-2 Laurence Calmels, Paris #162/R
£2244 $3522 €3500 Harmonie en jaune (130x161cm-51x63in) s.d.56 prov.exhib. 24-Nov-2 Laurence Calmels, Paris #158/R
£2436 $3824 €3800 Untitled (150x150cm-59x59in) s. s.d.1971 prov. 24-Nov-2 Laurence Calmels, Paris #164/R
£2756 $4328 €4300 Untitled (73x92cm-29x36in) s. s.d.1977 verso prov.exhib. 24-Nov-2 Laurence Calmels, Paris #159/R
£3077 $4831 €4800 Symphonie gris (92x73cm-36x29in) s.d.61 s.i.d.verso prov.exhib. 24-Nov-2 Laurence Calmels, Paris #165/R
£3673 $5841 €5400 Sans titre (198x200cm-78x79in) s. s.d.1983 verso. 26-Feb-3 Artcurial Briest, Paris #506/R est:2000-2500
£4082 $6490 €6000 Une serie d'elans successifs (162x114cm-64x45in) s.d.61 s.i.d.1961 verso. 26-Feb-3 Artcurial Briest, Paris #504 est:2500-3000

Works on paper

£321 $503 €500 Untitled (28x31cm-11x12in) s.d.63 gouache. 24-Nov-2 Laurence Calmels, Paris #149/R
£321 $503 €500 Untitled (27x21cm-11x8in) s. gouache. 24-Nov-2 Laurence Calmels, Paris #152/R
£449 $704 €700 Untitled (40x30cm-16x12in) s.d.62 gouache. 24-Nov-2 Laurence Calmels, Paris #150/R
£449 $704 €700 Untitled (43x22cm-17x9in) s.d.62 gouache. 24-Nov-2 Laurence Calmels, Paris #151/R
£641 $1006 €1000 Untitled (40x30cm-16x12in) s.d.62 gouache. 24-Nov-2 Laurence Calmels, Paris #148/R

ISTVANFFY, Gabrielle Rainer (1877-1964) Hungarian

£420 $685 €630 Good rest (22x30cm-9x12in) s. paper sold with crayon study of a cat by the same hand. 13-Feb-3 Christie's, Kensington #221/R
£600 $948 €900 Stalking the prey (24x37cm-9x15in) s. 14-Nov-2 Christie's, Kensington #35/R

ITALIAN SCHOOL

£3774 $5811 €6000 Ricotta cheese eater (161x117cm-63x46in) 28-Oct-2 Il Ponte, Milan #6
£6394 $10167 €9591 Girl wearing Renaissance costume (40x30cm-16x12in) oil gold ground panel. 3-Mar-3 Lilla Bukowskis, Stockholm #427 est:10000-12000 (S.KR 86000)
£15278 $24139 €22000 From the life of a holy man (34x22cm-13x9in) tempera panel. 25-Apr-3 Beaussant & Lefèvre, Paris #5/R est:3000

Sculpture

£10959 $17096 €16000 Satyr and Bacchant (110x80x87cm-43x31x34in) bronze. 8-Apr-3 Ansorena, Madrid #933/R est:16000

Works on paper

£890 $1389 €1300 Kneeling saint surrounded by putti (34x28cm-13x11in) htd white sepia sketch verso. 11-Apr-3 Winterberg, Heidelberg #112/R est:980

ITALIAN SCHOOL, 15th C

£6114 $9537 €9171 Madonna and child (24x14cm-9x6in) panel. 20-Nov-2 Fischer, Luzern #1003/R est:12000-15000 (S.FR 14000)

ITALIAN SCHOOL, 16th C

£8503 $13520 €12500 Venus and Love (64x52cm-25x20in) mono. painted c.1580. 21-Mar-3 Millon & Associes, Paris #5/R est:8000
£17352 $27068 €26028 Young boy sitting by window with notebook (135x85cm-53x33in) panel. 28-Mar-3 Koller, Zurich #3042/R est:7000-12000 (S.FR 38000)
£33333 $52333 €52000 Madonna and Child (36x27cm-14x11in) panel. 14-Dec-2 Artcurial Briest, Paris #19/R est:10000

Works on paper

£5208 $8281 €7500 Marriage of Mary (52x40cm-20x16in) bears mono.d.1545 pen sepia wash htd opaque white paper on board. 5-May-3 Ketterer, Munich #351/R est:800-1000
£5903 $9385 €8500 Study of seated saint surrounded by angels (29x21cm-11x8in) pen double-sided prov. 5-May-3 Ketterer, Munich #360/R est:300-400
£6757 $10541 €10000 Bearded man in profile (26x17cm-10x7in) chk prov. 27-Mar-3 Christie's, Paris #184/R est:2000
£7292 $11594 €10500 Amazone on horseback with fighters (20x20cm-8x8in) pen wash paper on board prov. 5-May-3 Ketterer, Munich #365/R est:400-500
£156250 $248437 €225000 John the Evangelist (26x43cm-10x17in) pen. 5-May-3 Ketterer, Munich #355/R est:300-500

ITALIAN SCHOOL, 16th/17th C

£5578 $8869 €8200 Still life of flowers (102x76cm-40x30in) 19-Mar-3 Neumeister, Munich #444/R est:3000

Sculpture

£54545 $91091 €78000 Buste de Minerve (74cm-29in) porphyry exhib.lit. 25-Jun-3 Sotheby's, Paris #27/R est:60000-80000

ITALIAN SCHOOL, 17th C

£4138 $6621 €6000 Nativity (98x72cm-39x28in) 12-Mar-3 James Adam, Dublin #145/R est:6000-8000
£4895 $8175 €7000 La rencontre d'Eliezer et de Rebecca (71x62cm-28x24in) 25-Jun-3 Artcurial Briest, Paris #467/R est:4000-6000
£5183 $8500 €7775 Monkeys and parrots with a bunch of grapes and flowers (58x68cm-23x27in) 29-May-3 Sotheby's, New York #112/R est:10000-15000
£6053 $9805 €9200 Ruins with figures (63x48cm-25x19in) 21-Jan-3 Ansorena, Madrid #183/R
£6332 $9878 €9498 Biblical scene (104x172cm-41x68in) 6-Nov-2 Dobiaschofsky, Bern #689/R est:10000 (S.FR 14500)
£6824 $10646 €10100 Still lives (33x52cm-13x20in) pair. 26-Mar-3 Pierre Berge, Paris #22/R
£6966 $11006 €10100 Shepherds in landscape (37x63cm-15x25in) pair. 1-Apr-3 Babuino, Rome #46/R
£8163 $12980 €12000 Coastal landscape with classical ruins (104x124cm-41x49in) 19-Mar-3 Neumeister, Munich #443/R est:6000
£9251 $13507 €13877 Portait of man wearing turban (103x79cm-41x31in) 17-Jun-2 Philippe Schuler, Zurich #7334 est:2500-3000 (S.FR 21000)
£10256 $16103 €16000 Madonna and Child. panel. 19-Nov-2 Servarts Themis, Bruxelles #261/R est:6000
£11574 $18634 €17361 Old Master still life (106x204cm-42x80in) 7-May-3 Dobiaschofsky, Bern #679/R est:28000 (S.FR 25000)
£14286 $22000 €21429 Peacock in garden (157x112cm-62x44in) canvas on board. 23-Oct-2 Doyle, New York #81/R est:5000-7000
£15094 $23547 €24000 Death of Saint Joseph (101x123cm-40x48in) 20-Sep-2 Millon & Associes, Paris #623/R
£18868 $29434 €30000 Coastal view with vessels on a stormy sea (113x178cm-44x70in) 20-Sep-2 Millon & Associes, Paris #670/R est:35000-50000
£22930 $35771 €36000 Still lives of flowers (120x95cm-47x37in) pair. 7-Nov-2 Chochon-Barre & Allardi, Paris #18
£37736 $58868 €60000 Naval action (113x178cm-44x70in) pair. 20-Sep-2 Millon & Associes, Paris #670a/R est:65000-110000
£39568 $63309 €55000 Pan and nymph (88x132cm-35x52in) 14-May-3 Dorotheum, Linz #336/R est:2600-2900

Sculpture

£7692 $12846 €11000 Buste d'Empereur Romain (79cm-31in) white marble polychrome. 25-Jun-3 Sotheby's, Paris #11/R est:10000-15000
£20000 $31600 €30000 Crucifixion (110cm-43in) ivory wood marble. 14-Nov-2 Christie's, London #70/R est:15000-20000

Works on paper

£651 $1015 €950 Matthew the Evangelist (29x17cm-11x7in) mono.i.d. wash Indian ink. 11-Apr-3 Winterberg, Heidelberg #111
£753 $1175 €1100 Adoration of the Shepherds (34x25cm-13x10in) i. W/C pen over pencil. 11-Apr-3 Winterberg, Heidelberg #114/R
£19000 $31730 €27550 Figures binding the hands of a standing female (20x14cm-8x6in) red chk prov.lit. 8-Jul-3 Christie's, London #35/R est:2500-3500
£33333 $53000 €48000 Newest court of justice (53x33cm-21x13in) pen sepia brush opaque white over pen. 5-May-3 Ketterer, Munich #411/R est:1400-1800

ITALIAN SCHOOL, 17th/18th C

£6757 $10541 €10000 Jesus heals the lame (75x90cm-30x35in) panel one of pair. 28-Mar-3 Karrenbauer, Konstanz #1751/R
£10811 $16865 €16000 Sermon on the Mount (75x90cm-30x35in) panel one of pair. 28-Mar-3 Karrenbauer, Konstanz #1750/R est:2200

ITALIAN SCHOOL, 18th C

£3493 $5450 €5240 Sailing ships and galleys anchored off coast (108x140cm-43x55in) 20-Nov-2 Fischer, Luzern #1067/R est:8000-10000 (S.FR 8000)
£4545 $7000 €6818 Drover in extensive landscape (140x128cm-55x50in) 23-Oct-2 Doyle, New York #104 est:4000-6000
£5128 $7949 €8000 Wooded mountain landscape (195x132cm-77x52in) prov. 5-Dec-2 Dr Fritz Nagel, Stuttgart #613/R est:4000
£5240 $8175 €7860 Ascension of Maria (61x43cm-24x17in) 20-Nov-2 Fischer, Luzern #1014/R est:3500-4000 (S.FR 12000)
£5240 $8175 €7860 Caritas (131x180cm-52x71in) 20-Nov-2 Fischer, Luzern #1052/R est:12000-15000 (S.FR 12000)
£5346 $8286 €8500 Landscape with ruins and fishermen (82x126cm-32x50in) 29-Oct-2 Finarte, Milan #421/R est:5000-6000
£5405 $8432 €8000 Roman ruins with figures (27x31cm-11x12in) panel. 27-Mar-3 Dr Fritz Nagel, Stuttgart #766/R est:1200
£5479 $8548 €8000 St Jean Baptiste (45x37cm-18x15in) cardboard. 8-Apr-3 Gioffredo, Nice #60/R
£5535 $8523 €8800 Shipwreck scene (98x36cm-39x14in) 28-Oct-2 Il Ponte, Milan #127/R est:5000
£5793 $9500 €8690 Still life of flowers in a porcelain vase. Still life of flowers in a glass vase and apples (40x58cm-16x23in) pair. 29-May-3 Sotheby's, New York #152/R est:8000-12000
£6222 $10329 €9022 Alexander cutting the Gordian knot (49x74cm-19x29in) canvas on board. 10-Jun-3 Ritchie, Toronto #172/R est:2000-2500 (C.D 14000)
£6373 $9943 €10070 Saint Andrew's conversion (250x210cm-98x83in) 15-Oct-2 Babuino, Rome #150/R est:15000
£6481 $9204 €10500 Saint Cecily (62x73cm-24x29in) 17-Mar-2 Galerie de Chartres, Chartres #86/R
£6918 $10723 €11000 Capriccio (114x165cm-45x65in) 29-Oct-2 Finarte, Milan #409/R est:11000-12000
£7325 $11427 €11500 Still life of flowers (64x48cm-25x19in) 6-Nov-2 Hugo Ruef, Munich #953/R est:1500
£7586 $12138 €11000 Composition with flowers and pumpkins (76x88cm-30x35in) 17-Mar-3 Pandolfini, Florence #667/R
£9091 $15182 €13000 Meleagre et Atalante (85x56cm-33x22in) s. 25-Jun-3 Tajan, Paris #13/R est:12000-15000
£10135 $15811 €15000 Scenes of Venice (45x30cm-18x12in) pair. 27-Mar-3 Dr Fritz Nagel, Stuttgart #740/R est:3000
£14352 $23251 €20810 Veduta - Grand Canal, Venice (51x70cm-20x28in) 25-May-3 Uppsala Auktionskammare, Uppsala #3/R est:15000-20000 (S.KR 185000)
£26761 $38000 €40142 Architectural ruins with figures (94x117cm-37x46in) 8-Aug-1 Barridorf, Portland #152/R est:15000-20000
£32012 $52500 €48018 Slaying of Nessus by Hercules (142x154cm-56x61in) 29-May-3 Sotheby's, New York #114/R est:35000-45000
£32012 $52500 €48018 Education of Achilles by Chiron (142x154cm-56x61in) 29-May-3 Sotheby's, New York #115/R est:35000-45000
£32278 $50032 €51000 Holy Family with Infant St John the Baptist (102x81cm-40x32in) 25-Sep-2 Neumeister, Munich #492/R est:1800
£38961 $56883 €60000 Views with figures (36x77cm-14x30in) board pair. 17-Jun-2 Ansorena, Madrid #163/R est:4800
£92593 $150000 €138890 Saint Peter's, Rome, with Bernini's Colonnade and a procession in carriages (90x135cm-35x53in) 24-Jan-3 Christie's, Rockefeller NY #56/R est:80000-120000

Sculpture

£18706 $31240 €26750 Diane (73cm-29in) white marble exec.c.1700 lit. 25-Jun-3 Sotheby's, Paris #9/R est:12000-18000
£40000 $62800 €60000 Column (112cm-44in) marble. 10-Dec-2 Sotheby's, London #138/R est:6000-9000
£47552 $79413 €68000 Venus Medicis et Antinous de Belvedere (51cm-20in) brown pat bronze pair lit. 25-Jun-3 Sotheby's, Paris #25/R est:30000-40000

ITALIAN SCHOOL, 18th/19th C

£25175 $36000 €37763 Bacchanalian scene (65x75cm-26x30in) 22-Jan-3 Doyle, New York #87 est:5000

Sculpture

£4747 $7500 €7121 Cupid and Psyche (72cm-28in) alabaster. 24-Apr-3 Christie's, Rockefeller NY #294/R est:8000-12000

ITALIAN SCHOOL, 19th C

£3846 $6038 €6000 Romantic southern landscape with figures, river, trees and ruins (103x135cm-41x53in) 19-Nov-2 Hamilton Osborne King, Dublin #422/R est:3000-5000
£4403 $6780 €7000 Landscape in Lazio (84x128cm-33x50in) 23-Oct-2 Finarte, Milan #9/R est:5000-6000
£4697 $7563 €7000 Madonna and Child (58x40cm-23x16in) bears i.verso panel gold ground arched top. 18-Feb-3 Sotheby's, Amsterdam #189/R est:3000-4000
£5204 $8275 €7806 Paris and Helena (240x195cm-94x77in) 3-Mar-3 Lilla Bukowskis, Stockholm #371 est:40000-50000 (S.KR 70000)
£6000 $9420 €9000 Verona, panorama (41x56cm-16x22in) 21-Nov-2 Christie's, Kensington #154/R est:6000-8000
£6475 $10360 €9000 Madonna with child, Infant St John and angels (148x122cm-58x48in) 17-May-3 Lempertz, Koln #1067/R est:5000
£7000 $10920 €10500 Italianate landscape with figures on a terrace overlooking a village (72x91cm-28x36in) 9-Apr-3 Bonhams, New Bond Street #115/R est:6000-8000
£7143 $10429 €11000 Putti in wooded landscape (85x120cm-33x47in) 14-Jun-2 Auktionhaus Georg Rehm, Augsburg #8067/R est:5000
£11026 $17421 €17200 Portrait d'un des fils de Ferdinand 1er de Naples (150x117cm-59x46in) 15-Nov-2 Drouot Estimations, Paris #75/R est:6000-8000
£12830 $20015 €20400 Venetian scenes (61x81cm-24x32in) i. pair. 22-Sep-2 Semenzato, Venice #135/R est:7000-8000
£16892 $26351 €25000 Achille and Lycomede's daughters. Achille and Chiron (156x123cm-61x48in) pair. 31-Mar-3 Finarte Semenzato, Milan #501/R est:30000
£24000 $40080 €36000 Constantinople from above Bebek (116x195cm-46x77in) prov. 19-Jun-3 Christie's, London #2/R est:25000-35000

Sculpture

£5063 $8000 €7595 Bust of Caesar (83x61x159cm-33x24x63in) col marble socle square pedestal. 26-Nov-2 Christie's, Rockefeller NY #295 est:10000-15000
£7343 $12262 €10500 Grand groupe de laocoon (74x52cm-29x20in) brown pat bronze lit. 25-Jun-3 Sotheby's, Paris #5/R est:6000-8000
£7595 $12000 €11393 Group of the farnese bull (51cm-20in) bronze cast by M Amodio. 24-Apr-3 Christie's, Rockefeller NY #244/R est:12000-18000
£7742 $12232 €12000 Marcus Aurelius as Hercules (214cm-84in) Carrara marble sold wit base. 18-Dec-2 Ansorena, Madrid #1055/R est:12000
£8135 $12935 €12203 Figure seated on chair (174cm-69in) wood. 26-Feb-3 Kunsthallen, Copenhagen #567/R est:100000 (D.KR 89000)
£10000 $15600 €15000 Venus de medici (158cm-62in) s.Luisi marble executed c.1885. 8-Apr-3 Christie's, Melbourne #252/R est:15000-20000 (A.D 26000)
£11538 $18000 €17307 Group of dancing children (91x30cm-36x12in) s.Luisi marble executed c.1885. 8-Apr-3 Christie's, Melbourne #270/R est:15000-20000 (A.D 30000)
£12000 $18600 €18000 Cleopatra seated on a lion (89x56x51cm-35x22x20in) parcel gilt paste-set alabaster stepped base exec.c.1885. 1-Oct-2 Christie's, London #375/R est:12000-18000

ITALIAN SCHOOL, 19th/20th C

Sculpture

£7000 $10920 €10500 Young woman standing beside a well (156cm-61in) s. white marble lit. 5-Nov-2 Sotheby's, London #164/R est:7000-10000
£9677 $15290 €15000 Angels playing music (237x97cm-93x38in) bronze. 18-Dec-2 Ansorena, Madrid #1056/R est:15000

ITALIAN SCHOOL, 20th C

£7358 $11479 €11700 Views of Venice (84x105cm-33x41in) set of 4. 20-Sep-2 Semenzato, Venice #210/R

Sculpture

£6536 $10719 €10000 Ero (140cm-55in) alabaster marble sold with base. 9-Feb-3 Anaf, Lyon #87/R est:12000
£9032 $14000 €13548 Busts of Julius Caesar and Hadrian (93x66cm-37x26in) various marbles pair. 3-Dec-2 Christie's, Rockefeller NY #513/R est:10000-15000

Works on paper

£641 $1006 €1000 Women (28x19cm-11x7in) i. chl pair. 20-Nov-2 Pandolfini, Florence #24a

ITCHO, Hanabusa (attrib) (1652-1724) Japanese

Works on paper

£800 $1288 €1200 Kakemono (112x44cm-44x17in) s. ink silk. 19-Feb-3 Sotheby's, Olympia #1/R

ITEN, Hans (1874-1930) Swiss/British

£650 $1053 €975 Coastal landscape (16x21cm-6x8in) s. board. 20-May-3 Bonhams, Knightsbridge #11/R
£1400 $2240 €2100 Cornfield (15x21cm-6x8in) board. 15-May-3 Christie's, Kensington #232/R est:600-800
£2000 $3200 €3000 Orchard pathway (41x52cm-16x20in) s. board. 15-May-3 Christie's, Kensington #231/R est:1500-2000
£2500 $3975 €3750 Autumn in Belvoir Park (30x40cm-12x16in) s. board. 5-Mar-3 John Ross, Belfast #43 est:1200-1500
£2500 $4000 €3750 Clouds over bogland (46x56cm-18x22in) prov. 16-May-3 Sotheby's, London #131/R est:1200-1800
£3000 $4800 €4500 Cushendall, Co Antrim (28x35cm-11x14in) s. s.i.verso panel. 15-May-3 Christie's, Kensington #230/R est:3000-5000
£3000 $4770 €4500 Trees by the River Lagan (15x20cm-6x8in) s. board. 5-Mar-3 John Ross, Belfast #22 est:1200-1500

£3000 $4800 €4500 Day in Cushendell, Co Antrim (31x41cm-12x16in) s. panel. 15-May-3 Christie's, Kensington #201/R est:2000-3000

ITHAKISIOS, Vasilis (1878-1977) Greek

£3800 $6004 €5700 Sailing (43x55cm-17x22in) 1-Apr-3 Bonhams, New Bond Street #58 est:2500-3500
£7000 $11060 €10500 Mount Olympus (55x43cm-22x17in) 1-Apr-3 Bonhams, New Bond Street #61 est:3000-5000

ITO, Shinsui (1898-1972) Japanese
Prints

£2244 $3500 €3366 Underrobe (43x26cm-17x10in) s. num.11/200 verso mica ground col woodcut. 25-Mar-3 Christie's, Rockefeller NY #409/R est:3000-3500
£2564 $4000 €3846 Evening cool (44x26cm-17x10in) s. num.12/200 verso col woodcut. 25-Mar-3 Christie's, Rockefeller NY #407/R est:4000-6000
£3846 $6000 €5769 Snowstorm (44x27cm-17x11in) s.num.128/250 col woodcut. 25-Mar-3 Christie's, Rockefeller NY #404/R est:4000-6000
£3846 $6000 €5769 Snowy night (44x29cm-17x11in) s. num.25/200 verso col woodcut. 25-Mar-3 Christie's, Rockefeller NY #406/R est:6000-8000
£12821 $20000 €19232 After the bath (46x30cm-18x12in) s. num.26/50 verso col woodcut. 25-Mar-3 Christie's, Rockefeller NY #413/R est:12000-15000

ITO, Yoshihiko (1867-1942) Japanese
Works on paper

£286 $449 €429 Lantern (50x32cm-20x13in) s. W/C. 25-Nov-2 Christie's, Melbourne #337 (A.D 800)
£300 $489 €450 Mt Fuji at dawn (48x31cm-19x12in) s. W/C. 13-Feb-3 Mellors & Kirk, Nottingham #780
£314 $500 €471 Spring landscape with pagodas and cherry blossoms in full bloom (48x30cm-19x12in) s. W/C. 7-Mar-3 Jackson's, Cedar Falls #880/R
£377 $600 €566 Fall river landscape with boat and temple in the background (48x30cm-19x12in) s. W/C. 7-Mar-3 Jackson's, Cedar Falls #881/R
£398 $653 €577 Tranquil river (30x48cm-12x19in) s. W/C. 4-Jun-3 Deutscher-Menzies, Melbourne #419/R (A.D 1000)

ITTEN, Johannes (1888-1967) Swiss
Works on paper

£2949 $4571 €4600 Composition (29x37cm-11x15in) s.d.1923 pastel board. 4-Dec-2 Lempertz, Koln #789/R est:3000

ITTMAN, Hans (1914-) Dutch

£719 $1180 €1000 Untitled (95x120cm-37x47in) s. 3-Jun-3 Christie's, Amsterdam #90/R est:1000-1500

ITURRIA, Ignacio de (1949-) Uruguayan

£1069 $1700 €1604 Cadaques (24x19cm-9x7in) s.d.82. 2-Mar-3 Galleria Y Remates, Montevideo #91/R
£1859 $2900 €2789 Cadaques (46x38cm-18x15in) s.d.79. 30-Jul-2 Galleria Y Remates, Montevideo #71/R est:3500-4200
£2051 $3200 €3077 Woman in Cadaques (72x60cm-28x24in) s.d.79. 10-Oct-2 Galleria Y Remates, Montevideo #59/R
£2308 $3600 €3462 Immigrants (39x47cm-15x19in) s. pr. 10-Oct-2 Galleria Y Remates, Montevideo #60/R
£2564 $4000 €3846 Cadaques (74x61cm-29x24in) s.d.79. 10-Oct-2 Galleria Y Remates, Montevideo #58/R
£3333 $5200 €5000 Cadaques (72x62cm-28x24in) s. 10-Oct-2 Galleria Y Remates, Montevideo #57/R
£6731 $10500 €10097 Woman (114x146cm-45x57in) s.d.80. 10-Oct-2 Galleria Y Remates, Montevideo #56/R

IVACKOVIC, Djoka (1930-) Balkan

£556 $884 €800 Peinture 31 VIII (100x100cm-39x39in) i.d.verso. 29-Apr-3 Artcurial Briest, Paris #577

IVANOFF, Michail Philippovitch (1869-1930) Russian

£2975 $4700 €4700 Market in Nishni Novgorod (43x70cm-17x28in) s. board. 1-Dec-2 Bukowskis, Helsinki #250/R est:3000-4000

IVANOFF, Serge (1893-1983) Bulgarian

£4500 $7290 €6750 Portrait of a dandy in a top hat (61x51cm-24x20in) s.i.d.1939 prov. 21-May-3 Sotheby's, London #148/R est:4000-6000

IVANOV, A (20th C) Russian

£538 $839 €850 Priest (25x32cm-10x13in) s.d.1851. 15-Sep-2 Bukowskis, Helsinki #334/R

IVANOVICH, Ivan (?) Russian?

£340 $550 €510 Girl with headress (48x38cm-19x15in) 24-Jan-3 Douglas, South Deerfield #1

IVANOVITCH, Fedor (1765-1832) Russian

£18705 $29928 €26000 Catherine the Great in her study with companions (112x93cm-44x37in) s. 17-May-3 Hagelstam, Helsinki #28/R est:17000

IVARSON, Ivan (1900-1939) Swedish

£967 $1567 €1451 Landscape from Cagnes, South of France (42x52cm-17x20in) painted 1927. 3-Feb-3 Lilla Bukowskis, Stockholm #842 (S.KR 13500)
£1313 $2179 €1904 Cliffs and sea, Marstrand (48x60cm-19x24in) s.i.d.1925 exhib. 16-Jun-3 Lilla Bukowskis, Stockholm #71 est:25000-30000 (S.KR 17000)
£2857 $4600 €4286 Woman by trees (33x40cm-13x16in) exhib.prov. 7-May-3 AB Stockholms Auktionsverk #854/R est:25000-30000 (S.KR 37000)
£15058 $24243 €22587 Still life of flowers (69x49cm-27x19in) s. prov. 7-May-3 AB Stockholms Auktionsverk #825/R est:250000-300000 (S.KR 195000)
£17169 $26783 €25754 The large custom's house, Gothenburg (66x67cm-26x26in) s. prov.exhib. 5-Nov-2 Bukowskis, Stockholm #18/R est:300000-350000 (S.KR 245000)

Works on paper

£371 $615 €538 Woman (17x14cm-7x6in) s. chk. 16-Jun-3 Lilla Bukowskis, Stockholm #230 (S.KR 4800)
£1331 $2077 €1997 In the shadow of the tree (20x16cm-8x6in) s. W/C. 5-Nov-2 Bukowskis, Stockholm #16/R est:25000-30000 (S.KR 19000)

IVASCHENKO, Tatiana Anatolievna (20th C) Russian

£663 $1100 €961 Proposal accepted (91x61cm-36x24in) s. 14-Jun-3 Jackson's, Cedar Falls #210/R
£843 $1400 €1222 Sashinka and Sonichka (76x102cm-30x40in) s. 14-Jun-3 Jackson's, Cedar Falls #204/R est:1000-1500

IVENS, Renaat (1935-) Belgian
Works on paper

£517 $828 €750 Composition (45x65cm-18x26in) s.d.68 polymer panel. 15-Mar-3 De Vuyst, Lokeren #164

IVERS, W J (19/20th C) American?
Works on paper

£465 $725 €674 The Admiral (41x56cm-16x22in) s. W/C. 28-Mar-3 Eldred, East Dennis #650/R

IVERSEN, Kraesten (1886-1955) Danish

£429 $716 €622 Landscape, Bornholm (85x110cm-33x43in) init. s.stretcher prov. 17-Jun-3 Rasmussen, Copenhagen #168/R (D.KR 4500)
£633 $988 €950 View of the sea, Bornholm (90x120cm-35x47in) init. exhib. 18-Sep-2 Kunsthallen, Copenhagen #35 (D.KR 7500)
£638 $1009 €957 Still life of gladioli in blue vase and apples in bowl (81x64cm-32x25in) init. prov. 27-Nov-2 Museumsbygningen, Copenhagen #678/R (D.KR 7500)
£721 $1160 €1082 Winter landscape with boathouse by water (78x99cm-31x39in) init. 22-Feb-3 Rasmussen, Havnen #2309 (D.KR 8000)
£743 $1175 €1115 Evening by the sea at Svaneke - cliffs in foreground (55x100cm-22x39in) init. painted c.1955. 1-Apr-3 Rasmussen, Copenhagen #560/R (D.KR 8000)
£936 $1479 €1404 Wood with sunlit places (125x150cm-49x59in) i.stretcher painted c.1950 prov.exhib. 27-Nov-2 Museumsbygningen, Copenhagen #586/R (D.KR 11000)
£1394 $2203 €2091 Bay with fishing village in background, Iceland (106x178cm-42x70in) init. prov. 1-Apr-3 Rasmussen, Copenhagen #592/R est:15000-20000 (D.KR 15000)

IVES, Chauncey Bradley (1810-1894) American
Sculpture

£32258 $50000 €48387 Ideal figure with harp (130cm-51in) i. white marble with base prov. 4-Dec-2 Sotheby's, New York #139/R est:50000-70000

IWAN, Friedrich (1889-?) German
Works on paper

£255 $397 €400 View of Dominsel of Breslau (48x59cm-19x23in) s. W/C lit. 7-Nov-2 Allgauer, Kempten #2674/R

IWILL, Joseph (1850-1923) French

£347 $573 €500 Venise vue de la Lagune au crepuscule (15x30cm-6x12in) s. 1-Jul-3 Rossini, Paris #97
£590 $962 €850 Marine, soleil couchant (33x46cm-13x18in) s. 19-Jul-3 Thierry & Lannon, Brest #345

£764 $1207 €1100 Vieille porte a Moret (18x26cm-7x10in) s.d.98 cardboard. 25-Apr-3 Pisa, Paris #128/R
£793 $1300 €1190 Sailboats beached on the shore of a seaside town (41x32cm-16x13in) s. 5-Feb-3 Christie's, Rockefeller NY #200/R est:600-800

IZNARDO, Michele (20th C) French
£288 $460 €400 Paysage (19x60cm-7x24in) s. tempera oil wood. 18-May-3 Neret-Minet, Paris #143

IZQUIERDO CARVAJAL (?) Spanish
£1026 $1621 €1600 Collector (65x119cm-26x47in) s. 13-Nov-2 Ansorena, Madrid #98/R est:1600

IZQUIERDO, Maria (1906-1950) Mexican
£17316 $27706 €25108 El senor con caballo (44x59cm-17x23in) s.d.VII 41 masonite. 15-May-3 Louis Morton, Mexico #75/R est:265000-280000 (M.P 280000)

Works on paper
£9146 $15000 €13262 Mujeres en la carcel (22x28cm-9x11in) s.d.36 gouache. 27-May-3 Sotheby's, New York #79
£10191 $16000 €15287 Horses (28x39cm-11x15in) s.d.53 gouache prov. 19-Nov-2 Sotheby's, New York #115/R
£12102 $19000 €18153 Bathers (23x28cm-9x11in) s.d.38 gouache prov.exhib. 20-Nov-2 Christie's, Rockefeller NY #11/R est:15000-20000

IZSAK SIPOS, Szilard (1977-) Hungarian
£387 $604 €581 Sloe brush (200x120cm-79x47in) s. 11-Sep-2 Kieselbach, Budapest #124/R (H.F 150000)
£490 $765 €735 Briar (150x150cm-59x59in) s. 11-Sep-2 Kieselbach, Budapest #125/R (H.F 190000)

J B (?) ?
£600 $960 €900 Portrait of a young boy (40x32cm-16x13in) mono. 11-Mar-3 Bonhams, Knightsbridge #64/R

Sculpture
£5926 $9600 €8593 Fully rigged ship. American eagle and shield (8x20cm-3x8in) init. col engraved scrimshaw whale tooth double-sided exec.c.1860. 22-May-3 Sotheby's, New York #752

JAAKOLA, Alpo (1929-1997) Finnish
£392 $643 €600 The politician (36x32cm-14x13in) s. 9-Feb-3 Bukowskis, Helsinki #262/R
£510 $811 €750 Brunette (38x29cm-15x11in) s.d.78. 24-Mar-3 Bukowskis, Helsinki #105/R
£576 $921 €800 Seated figure (55x46cm-22x18in) s.d.1988 board. 17-May-3 Hagelstam, Helsinki #178/R
£601 $938 €950 Tower (70x93cm-28x37in) s.d.1974. 12-Sep-2 Hagelstam, Helsinki #1001
£719 $1179 €1100 Three women (70x55cm-28x22in) s.d.79. 9-Feb-3 Bukowskis, Helsinki #261/R
£1835 $2900 €2900 Water pictures (66x90cm-26x35in) s.d.62. 1-Dec-2 Bukowskis, Helsinki #321/R est:2200-2500

Works on paper
£327 $507 €520 In the field (49x33cm-19x13in) s.d.1966 W/C. 6-Oct-2 Bukowskis, Helsinki #197/R

JAATINEN, Eeli (1905-1970) Finnish
£327 $536 €500 Girl with jug (65x54cm-26x21in) s.d.1970. 9-Feb-3 Bukowskis, Helsinki #263/R

JABONEAU, Albert (19th C) French
£573 $894 €900 Trois mats par gros temps (51x76cm-20x30in) s. 11-Nov-2 Horta, Bruxelles #680

JABURG, Oltmann (1830-1908) German
£5714 $9086 €8400 The Duisburg (57x88cm-22x35in) s.d.1860. 28-Mar-3 Bolland & Marotz, Bremen #468/R est:11000
£7911 $12500 €12500 Bark Hohenstaufen (59x84cm-23x33in) s.d.1858. 29-Nov-2 Bolland & Marotz, Bremen #713/R est:14000

JACCARD, Christian (1939-) French
£417 $658 €600 Piece rouge calcinee (81x60cm-32x24in) s.i.verso acrylic. 28-Apr-3 Cornette de St.Cyr, Paris #419
£1250 $1988 €1800 Anonyme calcine 19th siecle (65x51cm-26x20in) meches lentes canvas on panel prov. 29-Apr-3 Artcurial Briest, Paris #459/R est:2000-2500

JACHIMOWICZ, Theodor (1800-1889) Austrian
£1392 $2200 €2200 Figures round table (70x95cm-28x37in) s.d.1874. 26-Nov-2 Wiener Kunst Auktionen, Vienna #123/R est:1200-2000

JACK, John (19/20th C) British
£377 $600 €566 On the Firth of Forth, Musselburgh (25x46cm-10x18in) board. 22-Mar-3 New Orleans Auction, New Orleans #109

JACK, Kenneth (1924-) Australian
£321 $508 €482 Melrose - Willochra Creek (43x59cm-17x23in) s.d.1965 board. 18-Nov-2 Joel, Victoria #265 est:1600-2000 (A.D 900)
£925 $1416 €1388 St. Arnaud, Victoria (91x122cm-36x48in) s.d.1964 prov. 26-Aug-2 Sotheby's, Paddington #673/R est:5000-8000 (A.D 2600)
£1352 $2069 €2028 Country town (81x122cm-32x48in) s.d.1962 board. 26-Aug-2 Sotheby's, Paddington #569/R est:5000-8000 (A.D 3800)
£1352 $2069 €2028 Outback town (91x122cm-36x48in) s.d.1964 board prov. 25-Aug-2 Sotheby's, Paddington #173 est:3000-5000 (A.D 3800)
£1514 $2483 €2271 Landscape (61x91cm-24x36in) s.d.1957 composition board. 4-Jun-3 Deutscher-Menzies, Melbourne #382/R est:1500-2000 (A.D 3800)

Works on paper
£214 $327 €321 View of Adelaide (33x45cm-13x18in) s.d.1951 W/C prov. 26-Aug-2 Sotheby's, Paddington #731 (A.D 600)
£226 $359 €339 Showery afternoon, Tilba (67x100cm-26x39in) s.d.1981 W/C pencil prov. 23-Mar-3 Goodman, Sydney #12 (A.D 600)
£249 $381 €374 Looking East along North Terrace, Adelaide (33x45cm-13x18in) s.d.1951 W/C prov. 26-Aug-2 Sotheby's, Paddington #575/R (A.D 700)
£558 $914 €837 Dusty day, Thargomindah, Queensland (33x52cm-13x20in) s.d.1992 i.verso W/C. 4-Jun-3 Deutscher-Menzies, Melbourne #380/R (A.D 1400)
£558 $914 €837 Afternoon shadows, Maryborough (36x54cm-14x21in) s.d.1992 W/C. 4-Jun-3 Deutscher-Menzies, Melbourne #381/R (A.D 1400)
£558 $914 €837 Canal, Murano, Italy (50x71cm-20x28in) s.d.1984 s.i.verso W/C pastel. 4-Jun-3 Deutscher-Menzies, Melbourne #383/R (A.D 1400)
£560 $885 €971 Twilight Sydney, Macquarie Street (67x100cm-26x39in) s. W/C pencil prov. 1-Apr-3 Goodman, Sydney #7/R (A.D 1470)
£928 $1467 €1392 Elmore, Victoria (42x77cm-17x30in) s.d.1992 s.i.verso W/C. 27-Nov-2 Deutscher-Menzies, Melbourne #254/R est:1800-2400 (A.D 2600)
£928 $1467 €1392 Kerang, Victoria (50x71cm-20x28in) s.d.1992 s.i.verso W/C. 27-Nov-2 Deutscher-Menzies, Melbourne #255/R est:1800-2400 (A.D 2600)

JACK, Richard (1866-1952) Canadian/British
£215 $335 €323 Portrait of Richard Peach Captn, ADC to Goc, 3rd CDN Division (47x37cm-19x15in) s.i. 25-Mar-3 Ritchie, Toronto #132 (C.D 500)
£410 $639 €615 Portrait de gentilhomme (70x56cm-28x22in) 10-Sep-2 Iegor de Saint Hippolyte, Montreal #62 (C.D 1000)
£3947 $5882 €5921 Paysage de l'Ouest Canadien (89x109cm-35x43in) 26-Jun-2 Iegor de Saint Hippolyte, Montreal #55/R (C.D 9000)

JACKEVICAITE, J (19/20th C) ?
£573 $836 €860 Sicilian herder (114x80cm-45x31in) s.i.d.1923. 17-Jun-2 Philippe Schuler, Zurich #7338/R (S.FR 1300)

JACKLIN, Marjorie (1895-1984) British

Works on paper
£480 $768 €720 Student of F W Booty. Fishing boats outside Whitby harbour (37x72cm-15x28in) s.d.1914 W/C. 11-Mar-3 David Duggleby, Scarborough #132/R

JACKS, Richard (?) ?
£280 $434 €420 Couvent des Cordeliers, Gambetta, Cahors (33x41cm-13x16in) s. board. 31-Oct-2 Duke & Son, Dorchester #329/R

JACKS, Robert (1943-) Australian
£1275 $2091 €1913 Cello (92x92cm-36x36in) s.i.d.1999 verso. 4-Jun-3 Deutscher-Menzies, Melbourne #349/R est:3500-4500 (A.D 3200)
£2713 $4314 €4070 Painting of H (183x152cm-72x60in) s.i.d.1998. 5-May-3 Sotheby's, Melbourne #267/R est:8000-12000 (A.D 7000)
£3214 $4982 €4821 Head of a harlequin (183x152cm-72x60in) s.verso. 29-Oct-2 Lawson Menzies, Sydney #35/R est:10000-15000 (A.D 9000)
£4107 $6489 €6161 Head of the harlequin (183x152cm-72x60in) s.d.1996 i.verso. 26-Nov-2 Sotheby's, Melbourne #30/R est:12000-18000 (A.D 11500)
£4286 $6771 €6429 Yellow flamenco (182x152cm-72x60in) s.d.2001 i.verso. 26-Nov-2 Sotheby's, Melbourne #40/R est:12000-18000 (A.D 12000)

Sculpture
£1143 $1783 €1715 Harmony in grey (81x45x31cm-32x18x12in) i.d.1996 num.7 painted timber. 11-Nov-2 Deutscher-Menzies, Melbourne #83/R est:3000-4000 (A.D 3200)
£1500 $2340 €2250 Harmony in red (84x34x30cm-33x13x12in) painted timber. 11-Nov-2 Deutscher-Menzies, Melbourne #84/R est:3000-4000 (A.D 4200)
Works on paper
£536 $799 €804 Wandering (76x57cm-30x22in) s.i.d.1999 W/C pencil. 27-Aug-2 Christie's, Melbourne #294 est:1500-2500 (A.D 1400)
£3036 $4736 €4554 Metropolis revisited (183x152cm-72x60in) s.i.d.1983 verso synthetic polymer paint canvas. 11-Nov-2 Deutscher-Menzies, Melbourne #37/R est:8000-12000 (A.D 8500)

JACKSON OF LIVERPOOL, William (style) (18th C) British
£7600 $12616 €11400 Frigate of the Blue Squadron off the coast (91x122cm-36x48in) 12-Jun-3 Sotheby's, London #43/R est:5000-7000

JACKSON, Albert Edward (1873-1952) British
£1250 $1975 €1875 Robin Hoods Bay (43x79cm-17x31in) s. 28-Nov-2 Richardson & Smith, Whitby #630
Works on paper
£540 $902 €783 Girl with pixies and elves offering fruits (28x20cm-11x8in) s. gouache W/C. 25-Jun-3 Brightwells, Leominster #999/R

JACKSON, Alexander Young (1882-1974) Canadian
£3086 $4784 €4629 Hasaga mine Red Lake (26x34cm-10x13in) s. panel double-sided. 3-Dec-2 Joyner, Toronto #180/R est:6000-8000 (C.D 7500)
£3292 $5103 €4938 Barn in Muskoka (26x34cm-10x13in) s. panel. 3-Dec-2 Joyner, Toronto #140/R est:8000-12000 (C.D 8000)
£3704 $5741 €5556 Rouge river, Grenville, Que, September (26x34cm-10x13in) s. panel. 3-Dec-2 Joyner, Toronto #215/R est:7000-9000 (C.D 9000)
£3704 $5741 €5556 Coastal scene, Newfoundland (26x34cm-10x13in) s. panel. 3-Dec-2 Joyner, Toronto #254/R est:7000-9000 (C.D 9000)
£3863 $6026 €5601 Canal du Loing at Charenton, France (27x34cm-11x13in) s.i. board prov.lit. 26-Mar-3 Walker's, Ottawa #230/R est:7000-9000 (C.D 9000)
£4036 $6457 €6054 Italian cemetery in Copper Cliff, Sudbury, Ontario (27x34cm-11x13in) s. s.i.verso panel prov. 15-May-3 Heffel, Vancouver #93/R est:10000-12000 (C.D 9000)
£4222 $6924 €6333 Hasaga mine, Red lake, Ont (26x34cm-10x13in) s. painted April 1952 prov. 3-Jun-3 Joyner, Toronto #121/R est:8000-10000 (C.D 9500)
£4260 $6816 €6390 Stream and marsh in wooded area, Sudbury, Ontario (27x34cm-11x13in) s. panel prov.lit. 15-May-3 Heffel, Vancouver #49/R est:10000-12000 (C.D 9500)
£4260 $6816 €6390 Farm at Combermere (27x34cm-11x13in) s. s.i.d.October 1961 verso panel prov. 15-May-3 Heffel, Vancouver #98/R est:8000-10000 (C.D 9500)
£4435 $7008 €6653 Low water, Rouge River near Grenville, Quebec (27x34cm-11x13in) s. s.i.verso panel prov. 18-Nov-2 Sotheby's, Toronto #82/R est:8000-10000 (C.D 11000)
£4435 $7008 €6653 Oatfield, Madoc. Ontario (27x34cm-11x13in) s.i. panel double-sided prov. 14-Nov-2 Heffel, Vancouver #144/R est:10000-12000 (C.D 11000)
£4444 $7289 €6666 Knob lake (27x34cm-11x13in) s. s.i.d.June 1961 verso prov. 27-May-3 Sotheby's, Toronto #60/R est:7000-9000 (C.D 10000)
£4444 $7289 €6666 Mount Robson from railroad (22x27cm-9x11in) s. s.i.d.1914 verso panel prov. 27-May-3 Sotheby's, Toronto #209/R est:12000-15000 (C.D 10000)
£4721 $7365 €6845 Lake Superior (27x34cm-11x13in) i. panel prov.lit. 26-Mar-3 Walker's, Ottawa #242/R est:7000-9000 (C.D 11000)
£4819 $7566 €7229 Winter, Ripon, Que (26x34cm-10x13in) s.i.d.1961 panel. 25-Nov-2 Hodgins, Calgary #84/R est:15000-18000 (C.D 12000)
£4819 $7614 €7229 Autumn in Algoma (25x33cm-10x13in) d.1937 panel. 1-Dec-2 Levis, Calgary #46/R est:15000-20000 (C.D 12000)
£4839 $7645 €7259 Bridge in Venice (22x27cm-9x11in) s. s.d.Jan 8 verso panel prov. 18-Nov-2 Sotheby's, Toronto #5/R est:7000-10000 (C.D 12000)
£4889 $8018 €7334 Creek, Sutton, Que (28x34cm-11x13in) s. s.i.d.Oct 1958 prov. 27-May-3 Sotheby's, Toronto #62/R est:7000-9000 (C.D 11000)
£5111 $8382 €7667 Wolfe lake, June - Rideau (26x34cm-10x13in) s. panel prov. 3-Jun-3 Joyner, Toronto #182/R est:7000-9000 (C.D 11500)
£5242 $8282 €7863 Starret - Olsen Mine. Red Lake (27x34cm-11x13in) s.i.d.1952 panel double-sided prov. 14-Nov-2 Heffel, Vancouver #130/R est:10000-15000 (C.D 13000)
£5242 $8282 €7863 Settler's cabin, Ottawa Valley (27x34cm-11x13in) s.i.d.1958 board prov. 14-Nov-2 Heffel, Vancouver #155/R est:10000-12000 (C.D 13000)
£5333 $8747 €8000 Cottage by the lake, winter, Algoma (26x34cm-10x13in) panel prov. 3-Jun-3 Joyner, Toronto #12/R est:8000-10000 (C.D 12000)
£5333 $8747 €8000 Old Woman Bay, Ancaster (26x34cm-10x13in) s.d.20 Nov 1879 canvas on board. 3-Jun-3 Joyner, Toronto #134/R est:12000-15000 (C.D 12000)
£5350 $8292 €8025 Lagoon, Georgian Bay, August,1946 (26x34cm-10x13in) s. panel prov. 3-Dec-2 Joyner, Toronto #86/R est:10000-12000 (C.D 13000)
£5830 $9327 €8745 Skeena River Country (22x27cm-9x11in) s. i.d.1926 verso panel prov.lit. 15-May-3 Heffel, Vancouver #36/R est:14000-16000 (C.D 13000)
£6173 $9568 €9260 Farm near Commander lake, Que, 1966 (26x34cm-10x13in) s. panel. 3-Dec-2 Joyner, Toronto #228/R est:8000-10000 (C.D 15000)
£6222 $10204 €9333 Agawa River, Algoma (27x34cm-11x13in) s.i.d.Oct 3 1955 panel prov. 27-May-3 Sotheby's, Toronto #150/R est:12000-15000 (C.D 14000)
£6222 $10204 €9333 Franklin, Great Bear lake (28x34cm-11x13in) s. s.i.d.1951 verso panel prov. 27-May-3 Sotheby's, Toronto #201/R est:12000-15000 (C.D 14000)
£6278 $10045 €9417 Vimy Mountain - Waterton Park, Alberta (27x34cm-11x13in) s. i.d.May 1951 verso panel prov.lit. 15-May-3 Heffel, Vancouver #47/R est:12000-14000 (C.D 14000)
£6452 $10194 €9678 Georgian Bay (27x34cm-11x13in) s. panel double-sided prov. 14-Nov-2 Heffel, Vancouver #86/R est:12000-15000 (C.D 16000)
£6584 $10206 €9876 Georgian Bay (26x34cm-10x13in) s. panel. 3-Dec-2 Joyner, Toronto #223/R est:10000-12000 (C.D 16000)
£6855 $10831 €10283 Village at dusk, Charlevoix, Quebec (21x27cm-8x11in) s.i.verso panel painted c.1925 prov. 14-Nov-2 Heffel, Vancouver #131/R est:15000-18000 (C.D 17000)
£6889 $11298 €10334 Go Home Bay, Georgian Bay, 1962 (26x34cm-10x13in) s. panel prov. 3-Jun-3 Joyner, Toronto #168/R est:10000-15000 (C.D 15500)
£7111 $11662 €10667 Landscape with haywagon and barn (25x33cm-10x13in) s. s.d.Aug 15 52 verso panel prov. 27-May-3 Sotheby's, Toronto #61/R est:12000-15000 (C.D 16000)
£7258 $11468 €10887 Windswept tree (27x34cm-11x13in) s.d. panel painted c.1942 prov. 14-Nov-2 Heffel, Vancouver #133/R est:10000-12000 (C.D 18000)
£7359 $11701 €10671 Coppermine country (27x34cm-11x13in) s. panel prov. 1-May-3 Heffel, Vancouver #49/R est:8000-10000 (C.D 17000)
£7819 $12119 €11729 Spring flood, Shefferville, Que (40x50cm-16x20in) s. prov. 3-Dec-2 Joyner, Toronto #66/R est:20000-25000 (C.D 19000)
£8065 $12742 €12098 Cowley, Alberta (27x34cm-11x13in) s. s.i.d.Nov 1937 panel prov.lit. 18-Nov-2 Sotheby's, Toronto #45/R est:12000-15000 (C.D 20000)
£8065 $12742 €12098 Farm, St Aubert (27x34cm-11x13in) s. s.i.d.April 1945 panel prov. 18-Nov-2 Sotheby's, Toronto #83/R est:12000-15000 (C.D 20000)
£8889 $14578 €13334 PincherCreek, Alberta Ranchlands (30x41cm-12x16in) s. i.verso panel prov.lit. 27-May-3 Sotheby's, Toronto #202/R est:15000-20000 (C.D 20000)
£9053 $14033 €13580 North country (26x34cm-10x13in) s.d.1938 panel double-sided. 3-Dec-2 Joyner, Toronto #132/R est:15000-20000 (C.D 22000)
£9053 $14033 €13580 Indian village, Kamloops (26x34cm-10x13in) s. panel double-sided. 3-Dec-2 Joyner, Toronto #165/R est:12000-15000 (C.D 22000)
£9073 $14335 €13610 Quebec barn in winter (22x27cm-9x11in) s. panel painted c.1925 prov.lit. 14-Nov-2 Heffel, Vancouver #94/R est:15000-18000 (C.D 22500)
£9073 $14335 €13610 Spring Coulee, Alberta (27x34cm-11x13in) i.d.1938 s.verso panel double-sided prov.lit. 14-Nov-2 Heffel, Vancouver #189/R est:20000-25000 (C.D 22500)
£9333 $15307 €13533 Rocky lake, Lake Superior (22x26cm-9x10in) s.i.d.1923 panel prov. 9-Jun-3 Hodgins, Calgary #59/R est:16000-20000 (C.D 21000)
£9778 $16036 €14667 Ogilvy Mt. Yukon (40x50cm-16x20in) s. 3-Jun-3 Joyner, Toronto #76/R est:20000-25000 (C.D 22000)
£10000 $16400 €15000 Winter - Bon Echo (22x27cm-9x11in) s. s.i. verso panel prov. 27-May-3 Sotheby's, Toronto #17/R est:8000-10000 (C.D 22500)

£11111 $18222 €16667 Floe ice, Lancaster Sound (22x25cm-9x10in) s.i.d.1927 double-sided panel prov.lit. 27-May-3 Sotheby's, Toronto #16/R est:15000-20000 (C.D 25000)
£12332 $19731 €18498 Les maisons abandonee (22x27cm-9x11in) s. i.d.1925 verso panel prov. 15-May-3 Heffel, Vancouver #23/R est:18000-22000 (C.D 27500)
£12332 $19731 €18498 Winter near Rimouski, Quebec (22x27cm-9x11in) s.i. s.verso panel painted c.1925 prov. 15-May-3 Heffel, Vancouver #24/R est:15000-18000 (C.D 27500)
£13453 $21525 €20180 Beaver lake, Algoma (51x63cm-20x25in) s. s.i.verso prov.lit. 15-May-3 Heffel, Vancouver #108/R est:30000-40000 (C.D 30000)
£14113 $22298 €21170 House with a blue roof, Harrington, Quebec (41x51cm-16x20in) s.i.d.1965 prov. 14-Nov-2 Heffel, Vancouver #29/R est:25000-35000 (C.D 35000)
£15451 $24103 €22404 Hills behind Ripon, Quebec (21x27cm-8x11in) s.i. panel prov.lit. 26-Mar-3 Walker's, Ottawa #218/R est:25000-30000 (C.D 36000)
£15638 $24239 €23457 Ranches near Pincher, Alberta (50x65cm-20x26in) s. prov. 3-Dec-2 Joyner, Toronto #111/R est:25000-30000 (C.D 38000)
£15695 $25112 €23543 Pngnirtung (22x27cm-9x11in) s.i.d.1927 s.verso prov.lit. 15-May-3 Heffel, Vancouver #34/R est:15000-20000 (C.D 35000)
£16461 $25514 €24692 Street, Colbalt, Oct 11th 1932 (21x26cm-8x10in) s. panel lit. 3-Dec-2 Joyner, Toronto #58/R est:20000-30000 (C.D 40000)
£17937 $28700 €26906 Baffin Island, Pangnirtung Pass with Mt Thor (41x51cm-16x20in) s. s.i.verso prov.lit. 15-May-3 Heffel, Vancouver #33/R est:30000-40000 (C.D 40000)
£20576 $31893 €30864 Hills at Ste Adele, Que (62x82cm-24x32in) s. 3-Dec-2 Joyner, Toronto #48/R est:50000-60000 (C.D 50000)
£22222 $34444 €33333 St. Tite des caps, Quebec (63x82cm-25x32in) s. prov. 3-Dec-2 Joyner, Toronto #18/R est:50000-60000 (C.D 54000)
£31111 $51022 €46667 Evening, Georgian Bay (51x63cm-20x25in) s. s.i.d.1913 stretcher prov. 27-May-3 Sotheby's, Toronto #149/R est:50000-70000 (C.D 70000)

Works on paper
£258 $402 €374 A.Y.'s Scandinavian chair studies (20x25cm-8x10in) ink dr. prov. 26-Mar-3 Walker's, Ottawa #270/R (C.D 600)
£429 $670 €622 Studies of horses and cabriole (11x20cm-4x8in) i.verso graphite dr. prov. 26-Mar-3 Walker's, Ottawa #232/R est:1500-2000 (C.D 1000)
£558 $870 €809 Horse and vehicles. Farm buildings (11x20cm-4x8in) graphite double-sided prov. 26-Mar-3 Walker's, Ottawa #217 est:1500-2000 (C.D 1300)
£558 $870 €809 Three geolettes (11x20cm-4x8in) graphite prov. 26-Mar-3 Walker's, Ottawa #258/R est:1500-2000 (C.D 1300)
£558 $870 €809 Port Dover (23x30cm-9x12in) graphite ink dr. prov. 26-Mar-3 Walker's, Ottawa #259/R est:1500-2000 (C.D 1300)
£558 $870 €809 Green sail (14x18cm-6x7in) s. graphite oil on card prov. 26-Mar-3 Walker's, Ottawa #261/R est:1200-1600 (C.D 1300)
£773 $1205 €1121 Georgian Bay studies (22x30cm-9x12in) graphite dr. double-sided prov. 26-Mar-3 Walker's, Ottawa #260/R est:1500-2000 (C.D 1800)
£901 $1406 €1306 Barnyard, Baie St. Paul (11x20cm-4x8in) graphite prov. 26-Mar-3 Walker's, Ottawa #216/R est:1500-2000 (C.D 2100)
£905 $1403 €1358 Chez nous (7x10cm-3x4in) two init. one i. ink dr. htd white set of four lit. 3-Dec-2 Joyner, Toronto #424 est:600-800 (C.D 2200)
£987 $1540 €1431 Solid old house, Quebec (12x20cm-5x8in) graphite dr. prov. 26-Mar-3 Walker's, Ottawa #231/R est:2000-2500 (C.D 2300)
£1416 $2209 €2053 Horse and vehicles. Farm buildings (11x20cm-4x8in) graphite dr. double-sided prov. 26-Mar-3 Walker's, Ottawa #237a/R est:1500-2000 (C.D 3300)
£1613 $2548 €2420 Old Dugouts between Kemmel and Vierstraat (18x24cm-7x9in) s.i.d.1917 graphite dr. prov. 14-Nov-2 Heffel, Vancouver #186/R est:2500-3000 (C.D 4000)
£1957 $3052 €3263 Somewhere, France (11x18cm-4x7in) s.i. graphite prov. 13-Apr-3 Levis, Calgary #65/R est:2500-3000 (C.D 4500)
£3556 $5831 €5334 Paperboard making (48x63cm-19x25in) s. gouache prov. 27-May-3 Sotheby's, Toronto #165/R est:10000-12000 (C.D 8000)

JACKSON, Alice (?) British?
£800 $1216 €1200 Study of cockerel and hens in a barn (24x33cm-9x13in) s. 10-Jul-2 Peter Wilson, Nantwich #74/R

JACKSON, Ashley (1940-) British
Works on paper
£400 $624 €600 Yorkshire Pennine Farm (55x74cm-22x29in) s.d.1977 W/C. 25-Mar-3 Bonhams, Leeds #552/R

JACKSON, Billy Morrow (20th C) American
£321 $500 €482 Prairie patchwork (66x89cm-26x35in) s. canvasboard. 14-Sep-2 Weschler, Washington #636/R

JACKSON, Elbert McGran (19/20th C) American
£477 $750 €716 Attic (61x79cm-24x31in) s. 23-Nov-2 Pook & Pook, Downington #159/R
£1677 $2700 €2516 Couple relaxing in living room (79x61cm-31x24in) s. painted c.1940. 10-May-3 Illustration House, New York #93/R est:3000-5000
£1863 $3000 €2795 Valet removing tired man's shoes (64x64cm-25x25in) s. painted c.1929. 10-May-3 Illustration House, New York #92/R est:2400-3200

JACKSON, Francis Ernest (1872-1945) British
£340 $534 €510 Journal (24x32cm-9x13in) board. 15-Apr-3 Bonhams, Knightsbridge #187

JACKSON, Frederick William (1859-1918) British
£340 $551 €493 River landscape (33x43cm-13x17in) s. board. 22-May-3 Richardson & Smith, Whitby #485
£400 $616 €600 Thatched farmstead with haystack (28x33cm-11x13in) init. board. 24-Oct-2 Richardson & Smith, Whitby #465/R
£850 $1309 €1275 Lady feeding geese in a field (36x46cm-14x18in) s. 3-Sep-2 Gorringes, Lewes #2284
£880 $1382 €1320 Cattle in a meadow under a harvest moon (25x35cm-10x14in) s. canvasboard. 19-Nov-2 Bonhams, Leeds #107
£940 $1504 €1410 Ludlow weir with the castle in the background (38x46cm-15x18in) s. exhib. 11-Mar-3 David Duggleby, Scarborough #243/R
Works on paper
£270 $427 €392 Moors, Whitby (20x28cm-8x11in) s. W/C. 23-Jul-3 Mallams, Oxford #114/R
£500 $790 €750 Sheep on the moors (33x46cm-13x18in) s. W/C. 24-Apr-3 Richardson & Smith, Whitby #90/R
£800 $1312 €1160 Farmer and cattle beside an old farm (36x23cm-14x9in) s. W/C. 6-Jun-3 Halls, Shrewsbury #736/R
£850 $1318 €1275 Extensive heathland landscape with a windmill (25x36cm-10x14in) s. i.verso W/C. 31-Oct-2 Duke & Son, Dorchester #174
£5500 $8689 €8250 Potato gathering (35x52cm-14x20in) s. bears i.verso W/C. 2-Dec-2 Sotheby's, London #86/R est:2500-3500

JACKSON, Frederick William (attrib) (1859-1918) British
£580 $916 €870 Lady with geese (36x43cm-14x17in) bears sig. 24-Apr-3 Richardson & Smith, Whitby #105

JACKSON, G (19th C) British
£2301 $3750 €3452 Portrait of a cavalier King Charles spaniel (53x61cm-21x24in) s.d.1838. 11-Feb-3 Bonhams & Doyles, New York #96/R est:1500-2000

JACKSON, George (19th C) British
£1290 $2000 €1935 Forest interior with sheep (56x91cm-22x36in) s.d. 8-Dec-2 Toomey, Oak Park #632/R est:2750-3750
£1951 $3200 €2829 Dogs outside kennels (51x61cm-20x24in) s.d.1839. 4-Jun-3 Christie's, Rockefeller NY #203/R est:3000-5000

JACKSON, Gilbert (attrib) (17th C) British
£16774 $26000 €25161 Standing portrait of a cavalier (208x119cm-82x47in) 2-Nov-2 North East Auctions, Portsmouth #125/R est:18000-24000

JACKSON, Gilbert (circle) (17th C) British
£8000 $13040 €11600 Portrait of a child, full-length wearing a white dress and coral necklace (104x84cm-41x33in) 21-Jul-3 Sotheby's, London #403/R est:4000-6000

JACKSON, Harry (1924-) American
Sculpture
£958 $1600 €1389 Ol'sabertooth (25cm-10in) sig.i.d.80 num.5/250 bronze st.f.WFS. 21-Jun-3 Selkirks, St. Louis #198 est:2500-3000
£1019 $1600 €1529 Iroquois guide II (36cm-14in) s.d.1980 bronze. 10-Dec-2 Doyle, New York #115/R est:3000-5000
£1096 $1600 €1644 Ol' Sabertooth (25cm-10in) one of 250 bronze. 18-May-2 Altermann Galleries, Santa Fe #168/R
£1433 $2250 €2150 Trapper II (38cm-15in) s.d.1992 brown pat bronze. 10-Dec-2 Doyle, New York #114/R est:3000-5000
£1712 $2500 €2568 Sacagawea II (43cm-17in) polychrome bronze. 18-May-2 Altermann Galleries, Santa Fe #164/R
£2055 $3000 €3083 Washakie II (46cm-18in) polychrome bronze. 18-May-2 Altermann Galleries, Santa Fe #165/R
£2130 $3450 €3089 Sunset washakie (46cm-18in) bronze polychrome. 23-May-3 Altermann Galleries, Santa Fe #31
£2695 $4500 €3908 Bustin'one (36cm-14in) s.d.1959 bronze. 21-Jun-3 Selkirks, St. Louis #207/R est:6000-8000
£2874 $4800 €4167 Washakie II (47cm-19in) i.d.1981 brown pat. bronze prov. 18-Jun-3 Christie's, Los Angeles #80/R est:5000-7000

£4259 $6900 €6176 Foreman (43cm-17in) bronze polychrome. 23-May-3 Altermann Galleries, Santa Fe #32
£5679 $9200 €8235 Marshal II (41x46x15cm-16x18x6in) bronze. 23-May-3 Altermann Galleries, Santa Fe #135
£5975 $9500 €8963 Foreman (43cm-17in) i. brown pat. bronze prov.lit. 5-Mar-3 Sotheby's, New York #154/R est:8000-12000
£6176 $10005 €8955 Ropin star (71cm-28in) bronze polychrome. 23-May-3 Altermann Galleries, Santa Fe #30
£7051 $11000 €10577 Dog soldier (64x64x43cm-25x25x17in) bronze polychrome. 9-Nov-2 Altermann Galleries, Santa Fe #168
£8873 $14375 €12866 John Wayne first model for the monument (64x56x18cm-25x22x7in) bronze. 23-May-3 Altermann Galleries, Santa Fe #33
£19178 $28000 €28767 The Marshall (74cm-29in) one of 40 bronze. 18-May-2 Altermann Galleries, Santa Fe #167/R
£22436 $35000 €33654 Marshal (74cm-29in) bronze. 9-Nov-2 Altermann Galleries, Santa Fe #166
£25478 $40000 €38217 Sacagawea, study for the monument (98cm-39in) s.d.1979 st.thumbprint brown pat bronze st.f.WFS prov. 20-Nov-2 Christie's, Los Angeles #111/R est:25000-35000
£37671 $55000 €56507 The Marshal polychrome (74cm-29in) bronze. 18-May-2 Altermann Galleries, Santa Fe #68/R

JACKSON, James Ranalph (1882-1975) Australian
£611 $965 €917 Carabella Point, morning (29x64cm-11x25in) s.d.1972 board prov. 7-Apr-3 Shapiro, Sydney #415 (A.D 1600)
£842 $1280 €1263 Rigging the boats, Sydney Harbour (36x44cm-14x17in) s. canvas on board. 19-Aug-2 Joel, Victoria #338 est:2000-3000 (A.D 2400)
£996 $1633 €1444 Folly Point, Cremorne (36x44cm-14x17in) s. board. 3-Jun-3 Lawson Menzies, Sydney #760 (A.D 2500)
£1047 $1664 €1571 Miner Homes, Wattle Flats, NSW (22x53cm-9x21in) s. canvasboard exhib. 5-May-3 Sotheby's, Melbourne #346 est:3000-5000 (A.D 2700)
£1138 $1798 €1650 Ships on the harbour (29x39cm-11x15in) s.d.1918 panel. 22-Jul-3 Lawson Menzies, Sydney #79/R est:3000-5000 (A.D 2800)
£1434 $2179 €2151 Evening Middle Harbour (44x59cm-17x23in) s. 27-Aug-2 Goodman, Sydney #100/R est:3000-5000 (A.D 4000)
£1500 $2415 €2175 Afternoon on the jetty (45x54cm-18x21in) s. board. 12-May-3 Joel, Victoria #394 est:4000-5000 (A.D 3750)
£1550 $2465 €2325 Bridge in sunlight (50x59cm-20x23in) s.d.29. 5-May-3 Sotheby's, Melbourne #293/R est:4000-6000 (A.D 4000)
£2439 $3854 €3537 Sydney Harbour from North Sydney (28x64cm-11x25in) s.d.75 board. 22-Jul-3 Lawson Menzies, Sydney #160/R est:5500-7500 (A.D 6000)
£2490 $3710 €3735 Old road to the spit (46x55cm-18x22in) s. canvas on board prov. 27-Aug-2 Christie's, Melbourne #218/R est:4000-6000 (A.D 6500)
£2500 $3900 €3750 Autumn sky, Sidney Harbour (46x61cm-18x24in) s. prov. 12-Sep-2 Sotheby's, Olympia #111/R est:2500-3500
£2500 $3875 €3750 Island schooners, Sydney harbour (49x60cm-19x24in) s. 29-Oct-2 Lawson Menzies, Sydney #7/R est:8000-12000 (A.D 7000)
£4264 $6779 €6396 On the bay; Victorian coastline (54x74cm-21x29in) s. 5-May-3 Sotheby's, Melbourne #177/R est:12000-18000 (A.D 11000)
£5916 $9347 €8874 North harbour Sydney (29x38cm-11x15in) s. board. 2-Apr-3 Christie's, Melbourne #8/R est:4000-6000 (A.D 15500)
£6375 $10454 €9563 From above Castle Rock, Sydney (56x66cm-22x26in) s. prov. 4-Jun-3 Deutscher-Menzies, Melbourne #68/R est:18000-24000 (A.D 16000)

JACKSON, John (1778-1831) British
£2400 $3816 €3600 Portrait of Sir Joshua Reynolds (15x12cm-6x5in) panel after Sir Joshua Reynolds. 19-Mar-3 Sotheby's, London #48/R est:1200-1800
£4200 $6678 €6300 Half-length portrait of John Flaxman (76x64cm-30x25in) prov. 30-Apr-3 Halls, Shrewsbury #308/R est:2000-3000
£11500 $18285 €17250 Portrait of Antonio Canova, seated, view of his studio beyond (127x101cm-50x40in) prov. 19-Mar-3 Sotheby's, London #61/R est:8000-12000

JACKSON, Kurt (1961-) British
Works on paper
£400 $652 €600 Landscape (36x25cm-14x10in) s.d.1987 mixed media. 13-Feb-3 David Lay, Penzance #282

JACKSON, Martin (1919-1986) American
£370 $600 €555 Enchanted doorway (28x38cm-11x15in) s. board. 24-Jan-3 Freeman, Philadelphia #204/R

JACKSON, Mary (1936-) British
£320 $506 €480 Bandstand (17x24cm-7x9in) canvas on board. 27-Nov-2 Sotheby's, Olympia #112/R

JACKSON, Raymond Allen (1927-) British
Works on paper
£390 $644 €566 I'm sure I was picked for polo (40x58cm-16x23in) s.i. pencil pen black ink W/C. 3-Jul-3 Christie's, Kensington #203/R
£400 $620 €600 Sorry, Monty, luv - could we do that again (45x75cm-18x30in) s. pen black ink W/C. 4-Dec-2 Christie's, Kensington #150/R

JACKSON, Ronald (1902-1992) Canadian
£302 $478 €453 Ready for launch (41x51cm-16x20in) s.i. s.verso acrylic on canvasboard. 14-Nov-2 Heffel, Vancouver #71 (C.D 750)
£578 $948 €838 Scene near Alaska (50x60cm-20x24in) s. board prov. 9-Jun-3 Hodgins, Calgary #33/R est:1000-1500 (C.D 1300)
£649 $1032 €941 Up Anyox way (76x61cm-30x24in) s. i.verso board. 1-May-3 Heffel, Vancouver #50/R (C.D 1500)
£675 $1106 €1013 Mists of Moresby Island, QCI (61x91cm-24x36in) s. i.verso canvasboard. 6-Feb-3 Heffel, Vancouver #030/R (C.D 1700)
£1290 $2115 €1935 Charlottes rain storm (61x91cm-24x36in) s. i.verso canvasboard. 6-Feb-3 Heffel, Vancouver #029/R est:2000-3000 (C.D 3250)

JACKSON, Samuel (1794-1869) British
Works on paper
£320 $506 €480 Arcadian landscape (29x20cm-11x8in) W/C. 7-Apr-3 Bonhams, Bath #5
£1800 $2844 €2700 Happy valley (19x25cm-7x10in) s. W/C prov. 27-Nov-2 Hamptons Fine Art, Godalming #172/R est:800-1200
£4300 $7138 €6450 St. Augustine's parade, Bristol (16x23cm-6x9in) s. W/C executed c.1825 prov. 12-Jun-3 Bonhams, New Bond Street #619/R est:4000-6000

JACKSON, Samuel Phillips (1830-1904) British
£550 $919 €798 Fishing boats in a harbour town (51x76cm-20x30in) s. 26-Jun-3 Richardson & Smith, Whitby #636
Works on paper
£270 $440 €405 Goats by an alpine waterfall (45x61cm-18x24in) W/C pencil htd bodycol. 30-Jan-3 Lawrence, Crewkerne #617/R
£276 $431 €414 Barge approaching a lock (36x58cm-14x23in) s.d.1877 W/C htd bodycol. 15-Oct-2 Stephan Welz, Johannesburg #378 est:3000-5000 (SA.R 4500)
£800 $1280 €1200 Evening, Ullswater. Early morning, Stag Head tarn (9x15cm-4x6in) W/C pair. 11-Mar-3 Bonhams, New Bond Street #81/R
£800 $1336 €1160 Frigate in distress (33x48cm-13x19in) mono. indis d. W/C. 20-Jun-3 Keys, Aylsham #459
£950 $1539 €1425 On the Hamoaze, Plymouth (9x15cm-4x6in) W/C gouache. 22-Jan-3 Bonhams, New Bond Street #363/R
£1400 $2282 €2100 Land's End (46x75cm-18x30in) s.d.1869 W/C htd white. 29-Jan-3 Dreweatt Neate, Newbury #107/R est:1200-1800
£1800 $2916 €2700 Mount Orgueil, Jersey, mid-day (9x15cm-4x6in) W/C gouache. 22-Jan-3 Bonhams, New Bond Street #360/R est:600-800
£2200 $3564 €3300 St. Pierre Port, Guernsey (9x15cm-4x6in) W/C gouache. 22-Jan-3 Bonhams, New Bond Street #362/R est:600-800
£2300 $3726 €3450 Entrance to Dartmouth Harbour (9x15cm-4x6in) W/C gouache. 22-Jan-3 Bonhams, New Bond Street #361/R est:600-800

JACKSON, William Franklin (1850-1936) American
£940 $1513 €1400 Landscape with trees reflected in water (51x61cm-20x24in) s. 18-Feb-3 Whyte's, Dublin #199/R
£1946 $3250 €2822 Lake Louise-Banff (69x81cm-27x32in) s. prov. 17-Jun-3 John Moran, Pasadena #127 est:3000-5000
£2844 $4750 €4124 Lake in wooded landscape (84x102cm-33x40in) s. 17-Jun-3 John Moran, Pasadena #126 est:5000-7000
£4140 $6500 €6210 Poppies and lupine on a river's edge (18x25cm-7x10in) s. canvasboard. 19-Nov-2 Butterfields, San Francisco #8217/R est:5000-7000
£8125 $13000 €11781 California poppies and lupines, Fair Oaks, Sacramento, California (36x66cm-14x26in) s. s.i.verso. 16-May-3 Skinner, Boston #242/R est:300-500

JACOB, Alexandre (1876-1972) French
£600 $936 €900 Bords marne (13x22cm-5x9in) s. board. 15-Oct-2 Bearnes, Exeter #404/R
£1000 $1560 €1500 Fin de journee (24x34cm-9x13in) s. canvas on board. 15-Oct-2 Bearnes, Exeter #403/R est:1000-1500
£1200 $1944 €1800 Tow path (19x15cm-7x6in) s. panel. 20-May-3 Sotheby's, Olympia #70/R est:500-700
£1450 $2262 €2175 Winter in Asnieres (32x40cm-13x16in) s. board. 15-Oct-2 Bearnes, Exeter #402/R est:1500-2000
£2000 $3240 €3000 Printempes a la ferme (26x24cm-10x9in) s.i.verso board. 20-May-3 Sotheby's, Olympia #71/R est:1000-1500
£2200 $3432 €3300 Apres la pluie, environs d'Amiens (37x44cm-15x17in) s. board. 15-Oct-2 Bearnes, Exeter #405/R est:1500-2000
£3200 $5184 €4800 River scene (27x35cm-11x14in) s. board. 20-May-3 Sotheby's, Olympia #68/R est:1000-2000
£4600 $7452 €6900 Elclaircie sur la neige (35x27cm-14x11in) s.i.verso board. 20-May-3 Sotheby's, Olympia #69/R est:1000-2000
£10000 $15600 €15000 Wild fowler (148x165cm-58x65in) s. arched. 15-Oct-2 Bearnes, Exeter #401/R est:4000-6000

JACOB, Emanuel (?) ?
£568 $891 €852 Untitled (55x46cm-22x18in) s.d.1962 exhib. 23-Nov-2 Burkhard, Luzern #197/R (S.FR 1300)

JACOB, Ernst (1895-1981) Austrian
Works on paper
£1667 $2633 €2600 Owl (75x47cm-30x19in) s.d.17 Marz 1914 pen Indian ink W/C gouache gold. 12-Nov-2 Dorotheum, Vienna #16/R est:2800-3400

JACOB, Ernst Emanuel (1917-1966) Swiss
£687 $1085 €1031 Don Quixote (162x140cm-64x55in) s.d.1964 exhib. 26-Nov-2 Hans Widmer, St Gallen #1203/R est:1600-4500 (S.FR 1600)
£1266 $1988 €1899 Table II (65x81cm-26x32in) s.d.1952 s.i.d. stretcher. 25-Nov-2 Germann, Zurich #68/R est:3000-4000 (S.FR 2900)
£2620 $3825 €3930 Improvisation (130x100cm-51x39in) s.d.1963 exhib. 4-Jun-2 Germann, Zurich #59/R est:6000-8000 (S.FR 6000)
£3275 $4782 €4913 Composition on yellow background (101x73cm-40x29in) s. s.i. verso exhib.lit. 4-Jun-2 Germann, Zurich #46/R est:4000-6000 (S.FR 7500)
Works on paper
£1572 $2468 €2358 Composition (120x72cm-47x28in) s. mixed media gold panel. 25-Nov-2 Germann, Zurich #102/R est:4000-6000 (S.FR 3600)

JACOB, Julius (younger) (1842-1929) German
Works on paper
£1132 $1755 €1800 Ruins in Rome in summer (46x31cm-18x12in) s.i.d.April 1875 W/C mixed media. 29-Oct-2 Dorotheum, Vienna #75/R est:1800-2200

JACOB, Max (1876-1944) French
Works on paper
£318 $497 €500 Saint-Benoit-sur-Loire (20x15cm-8x6in) W/C. 6-Nov-2 Gioffredo, Nice #52/R
£1250 $2037 €1800 Sur les bords de la riviere en Bretagne (27x36cm-11x14in) s.d.27 gouache. 19-Jul-3 Thierry & Lannon, Brest #268 est:2000-2600
£1268 $2041 €1800 L'adoration des mages (20x26cm-8x10in) s. mixed media. 11-May-3 Thierry & Lannon, Brest #122 est:1200-1500
£1479 $2381 €2100 Le vieux pont a Quimperle (30x38cm-12x15in) s.d.27 gouache. 11-May-3 Thierry & Lannon, Brest #121/R est:1200-1400
£2692 $4227 €4200 Market scene (27x35cm-11x14in) s.d.19 gouache. 24-Nov-2 Laurence Calmels, Paris #167/R

JACOB, Ned (1938-) American
£1688 $2600 €2532 Chief's blanket (61x25cm-24x10in) 25-Oct-2 Morris & Whiteside, Hilton Head Island #26 est:3000-4000
Works on paper
£287 $450 €431 Lighting up (18x15cm-7x6in) s. i.verso chl graphite exec.c.1967. 23-Nov-2 Jackson's, Cedar Falls #311/R
£355 $550 €533 Native Americans on horseback (58x48cm-23x19in) s. chl. 7-Dec-2 Selkirks, St. Louis #248/R
£516 $800 €774 Standing man with gun (53x43cm-21x17in) init. chl dr. 7-Dec-2 Selkirks, St. Louis #247/R

JACOB, Walter (1893-1964) German
£411 $638 €650 Sheep by the sea (23x31cm-9x12in) mono.d.1921 i. verso. 28-Sep-2 Ketterer, Hamburg #123/R
£66667 $109333 €92000 Self portrait as smoker (80x64cm-31x25in) bears mono.d.20 prov.exhib.lit. 31-May-3 Villa Grisebach, Berlin #216/R est:18000-24000
Works on paper
£313 $494 €450 Self portrait (51x43cm-20x17in) mono.d.1921 Indian ink brush. 26-Apr-3 Dr Lehr, Berlin #234/R

JACOBEY, Karoly (1825-1891) Hungarian
£2064 $3220 €3096 Farewell to Izabella (104x122cm-41x48in) s. 11-Sep-2 Kieselbach, Budapest #98/R (H.F 800000)

JACOBI, Lotte (1896-1990) American
Photographs
£1899 $3000 €2849 Light abstraction (25x20cm-10x8in) s. photograph. 23-Apr-3 Sotheby's, New York #185/R est:3000-5000
£2273 $3500 €3410 Photogenic (22x17cm-9x7in) s. photograph prov.exhib. 22-Oct-2 Sotheby's, New York #95/R est:3000-5000
£2848 $4500 €4500 Untitled - photogenic (35x28cm-14x11in) s. s.i. verso silver gelatin. 28-Nov-2 Villa Grisebach, Berlin #1240/R est:2000-2500

JACOBI, Marcus (1891-1969) Swiss
£393 $613 €590 Lake Thun with Stockhornkette (57x74cm-22x29in) s. 6-Nov-2 Dobiaschofsky, Bern #709/R (S.FR 900)

JACOBI, Otto Reinhard (1812-1901) German/Canadian
£741 $1148 €1112 Courtship (22x30cm-9x12in) s.d.1894 board prov. 3-Dec-2 Joyner, Toronto #271/R est:1200-1500 (C.D 1800)
£905 $1403 €1358 Gypsy family (25x45cm-10x18in) s.d.1876 prov. 3-Dec-2 Joyner, Toronto #243/R est:1800-2400 (C.D 2200)
Works on paper
£267 $415 €401 In the Laurentians (17x27cm-7x11in) s.d.1871 W/C prov.lit. 3-Dec-2 Joyner, Toronto #433 (C.D 650)
£267 $437 €401 Children at the water's edge (54x72cm-21x28in) s.d.1885 W/C. 3-Jun-3 Joyner, Toronto #16/R (C.D 600)
£281 $447 €407 Mountain and river (46x66cm-18x26in) s.d.1876 W/C prov. 1-May-3 Heffel, Vancouver #51/R (C.D 650)
£356 $583 €516 Sunset. Trees, high on the bank. W/C two various sizes. 9-Jun-3 Hodgins, Calgary #75/R (C.D 800)
£444 $729 €666 Rapids under a footbridge (41x29cm-16x11in) s.d.1875 W/C. 3-Jun-3 Joyner, Toronto #362/R est:1000-1500 (C.D 1000)
£451 $699 €677 Rapids (15x27cm-6x11in) s.d.1878 W/C prov.exhib. 24-Sep-2 Ritchie, Toronto #3074a (C.D 1100)
£602 $952 €903 Mountain waterfall. Mountain river with bridge (10x15cm-4x6in) one d.1870 one d.1874 W/C pair. 1-Dec-2 Levis, Calgary #49/R (C.D 1500)
£782 $1212 €1173 Lake scene in the Rockies (19x37cm-7x15in) s.d.1873 W/C sold with two W/C by M.Matthews and T.H. Wilkinson. 3-Dec-2 Joyner, Toronto #506 (C.D 1900)

JACOBI, Rudolf (1889-1972) American
Works on paper
£435 $713 €600 Seaside village (39x48cm-15x19in) s. gouache paper on board. 31-May-3 Villa Grisebach, Berlin #581/R

JACOBS, H (19/20th C) Belgian
Sculpture
£1419 $2214 €2100 Young woman wearing jewelry (55cm-22in) s.st.f.Charenton terracotta. 26-Mar-3 Millon & Associes, Paris #170/R

JACOBS, Herman (1936-) Belgian
£374 $595 €550 Seated man (73x100cm-29x39in) s. 24-Mar-3 Bernaerts, Antwerp #853
£411 $642 €650 Ancien interieur flamand (77x97cm-30x38in) 16-Sep-2 Amberes, Antwerp #217

JACOBS, J E (?) ?
£342 $538 €500 Femme dans un interieur (60x47cm-24x19in) s. panel. 15-Apr-3 Galerie Moderne, Brussels #378/R

JACOBS, Jacob Albertus Michael (1812-1879) Belgian
£440 $687 €700 View of Dieppe (22x40cm-9x16in) panel. 23-Sep-2 Bernaerts, Antwerp #666/R
£507 $832 €700 Lecon de musique (62x45cm-24x18in) s. panel. 27-May-3 Campo & Campo, Antwerp #115
£621 $1000 €950 Bateau de peche echoue (54x46cm-21x18in) s. 20-Jan-3 Horta, Bruxelles #48
Works on paper
£327 $526 €500 Scene de peche (17x27cm-7x11in) s. wash. 14-Jan-3 Vanderkindere, Brussels #106
£340 $541 €500 Fishing boats on beach (20x28cm-8x11in) s. W/C. 19-Mar-3 Neumeister, Munich #369

JACOBS, Michel (1877-1958) American
£449 $700 €674 Spring landscapes (56x69cm-22x27in) s. 9-Nov-2 Sloan, North Bethesda #615/R

JACOBS, Paul Emil (1802-1866) German
£8442 $12578 €13000 Judith with Holofernes (149x120cm-59x47in) s.d.1845 prov. 26-Jun-2 Neumeister, Munich #765/R est:17000

JACOBS, Valery (19/20th C) Belgian?
£316 $494 €500 Nature morte au vase fleuri (89x58cm-35x23in) 16-Sep-2 Amberes, Antwerp #218

JACOBSEN, A (19th C) ?
£592 $911 €888 Wooded landscape with figures and water (84x132cm-33x52in) s. 26-Oct-2 Rasmussen, Havnen #2050 (D.KR 7000)

JACOBSEN, Antonio (1850-1921) American

£1513	$2300	€2270	Sail and steamship on the high seas (64x89cm-25x35in) s. en grisaille. 17-Aug-2 North East Auctions, Portsmouth #511/R est:800-1200
£1582	$2500	€2373	Saratoga (36x61cm-14x24in) s.d.1907 board. 17-Nov-2 CRN Auctions, Cambridge #58/R
£2379	$3878	€3569	Lusitania (56x90cm-22x35in) s.d.1908 board. 12-Feb-3 Iegor de Saint Hippolyte, Montreal #104/R (C.D 5900)
£2469	$4000	€3580	American steamship, Seguranca (46x76cm-18x30in) s. indis.i. 21-May-3 Doyle, New York #58/R est:8000-10000
£2536	$3905	€3804	DFDS steamship Christine in rough seas (56x93cm-22x37in) s.i.d.1894. 26-Oct-2 Rasmussen, Havnen #3059/R est:30000-40000 (D.KR 30000)
£2740	$4000	€4110	Portuguese steamship, Peninsular (46x76cm-18x30in) prov.lit. 3-Nov-1 North East Auctions, Portsmouth #72/R est:4000-6000
£3226	$5000	€4839	View of New York , Philadelphia and Norfolk railroad barges (81x152cm-32x60in) s.d. board prov. 29-Oct-2 Doyle, New York #55 est:3000-4000
£3445	$5237	€5168	Ship's portrait of Christine (56x91cm-22x36in) s.i.d.1894. 27-Aug-2 Rasmussen, Copenhagen #1475/R est:40000-50000 (D.KR 40000)
£3571	$5500	€5357	Steamship Majestic (20x41cm-8x16in) s.d.1908 board prov. 24-Oct-2 Shannon's, Milford #203/R est:2500-3500
£3614	$6000	€5240	The Lusitania on the high seas (56x90cm-22x35in) s.d.1908 board. 11-Jun-3 Butterfields, San Francisco #4019/R est:8000-12000
£3618	$5500	€5427	Steamship, Apache (56x89cm-22x35in) s. board prov.lit. 17-Aug-2 North East Auctions, Portsmouth #875/R est:9000-15000
£3618	$5500	€5427	Steamship, Brunswick (76x152cm-30x60in) s.d.1914 board prov.lit. 17-Aug-2 North East Auctions, Portsmouth #1011/R est:8000-12000
£3704	$6000	€5556	Steamship Brazos at sea (48x88cm-19x35in) s.d.1913. 21-Jan-3 Christie's, Rockefeller NY #392/R
£3704	$6000	€5556	The Lenape (48x88cm-19x35in) s.d.1913 board. 21-Jan-3 Christie's, Rockefeller NY #391/R
£4276	$6500	€6414	French steam ship, La Lorraine (76x127cm-30x50in) s. prov.lit. 17-Aug-2 North East Auctions, Portsmouth #646/R est:8000-12000
£4384	$6400	€6576	British steamship (56x91cm-22x36in) s.d.1889 prov. 3-Nov-1 North East Auctions, Portsmouth #64/R est:8000-12000
£4384	$6400	€6576	Steamship, Carroll (48x91cm-19x36in) s.d.1918 prov.lit. 3-Nov-1 North East Auctions, Portsmouth #91/R est:8000-12000
£4452	$6500	€6678	British steamship, Aguan (56x91cm-22x36in) s.d.1889 prov.lit. 3-Nov-1 North East Auctions, Portsmouth #81/R est:5000-8000
£4605	$7000	€6908	Steamship, Monroe (76x127cm-30x50in) s.d.1903 prov. 17-Aug-2 North East Auctions, Portsmouth #649/R est:7000-10000
£4658	$7500	€6987	Fishing schooner Marie Gilbert (22x36cm-9x14in) s.i.d. board prov. 16-Jan-3 Christie's, Rockefeller NY #461/R est:7000-10000
£4777	$7500	€7166	Portrait of the steamship Cottage City (56x91cm-22x36in) s. 26-Jul-2 Eldred, East Dennis #523/R est:10000-15000
£4905	$7750	€7358	Ships at sea (46x76cm-18x30in) s.d.1906 board. 24-Apr-3 Shannon's, Milford #91/R est:10000-15000
£4934	$7500	€7401	Steamship, Mexico (56x91cm-22x36in) s.d.1902 prov.lit. 17-Aug-2 North East Auctions, Portsmouth #647/R est:8000-12000
£5063	$8000	€7595	US frigate Constitution (38x64cm-15x25in) s.d.1917 board. 30-Nov-2 Thomaston Place, Thomaston #73a
£5096	$7847	€8000	Helka under sea (30x54cm-12x21in) s.d.1887. 3-Sep-2 Christie's, Amsterdam #291/R est:8000-12000
£5479	$8000	€8219	French steamship, Havel (122x56cm-48x22in) s.d.1894 lit. 3-Nov-1 North East Auctions, Portsmouth #82/R est:4000-6000
£5479	$8000	€8219	British steamship, Gallia (56x89cm-22x35in) s. lit. 3-Nov-1 North East Auctions, Portsmouth #84/R est:10000-15000
£5479	$8000	€8219	German steamship, Capri (53x89cm-21x35in) s.d.1900 prov.lit. 3-Nov-1 North East Auctions, Portsmouth #85/R est:10000-15000
£5479	$8000	€8219	Steamship, Kroonland (46x76cm-18x30in) s.d.1905 lit. 3-Nov-1 North East Auctions, Portsmouth #86/R est:10000-15000
£5500	$8525	€8250	Danish steamer Hekla I outward bound for New York (56x91cm-22x36in) s.i.d.1882. 31-Oct-2 Christie's, Kensington #478/R est:5000-7000
£5592	$8500	€8388	Steamship, Monterey (46x74cm-18x29in) s.d.1901 prov.lit. 17-Aug-2 North East Auctions, Portsmouth #1010/R est:8000-12000
£5616	$8200	€8424	Steamship, General Whitney (46x79cm-18x31in) prov.lit. 3-Nov-1 North East Auctions, Portsmouth #80/R est:8000-12000
£5696	$9000	€8544	American bark, Onaway (30x48cm-12x19in) s.d.1915 board prov. 24-Apr-3 Shannon's, Milford #74/R est:6000-8000
£5822	$8500	€8733	Steamship, Rio Grande (56x91cm-22x36in) s.d.1900 prov.lit. 3-Nov-1 North East Auctions, Portsmouth #74/R est:10000-15000
£5822	$8500	€8733	Steamship, Black Warrior (89x137cm-35x54in) s.d.1853 canvas on board prov. 3-Nov-1 North East Auctions, Portsmouth #78/R est:3000-5000
£5822	$8500	€8733	Belgian steamship, Henry Eyde (56x91cm-22x36in) prov.lit. 3-Nov-1 North East Auctions, Portsmouth #83/R est:8000-12000
£5921	$9000	€8882	Ship, Wisconsin (56x91cm-22x36in) s.d.1876 lit. 17-Aug-2 North East Auctions, Portsmouth #813/R est:10000-15000
£6164	$9000	€9246	German steamship, Neckar (51x79cm-20x31in) s.d.1879 lit. 3-Nov-1 North East Auctions, Portsmouth #96/R est:10000-15000
£6369	$10000	€9554	Anslem, steam screw (56x90cm-22x35in) s.i.d.1899. 22-Nov-2 Skinner, Boston #124a/R est:10000-15000
£6369	$10000	€9554	Portrait of the steamship Czaritza (74x152cm-29x60in) s. board painted 1915. 19-Apr-3 James Julia, Fairfield #100/R est:10000-20000
£6507	$9500	€9761	Steamships, General Whitney and Neptune (48x81cm-19x32in) init.d.1886 canvas on board prov.lit. 3-Nov-1 North East Auctions, Portsmouth #95/R est:12000-15000
£6575	$9600	€9863	Steamship, Eureka (56x91cm-22x36in) s.d.1888 lit. 3-Nov-1 North East Auctions, Portsmouth #93/R est:8000-12000
£6579	$10000	€9869	Steam yacht, Winchester (56x91cm-22x36in) s.d.1908 board. 17-Aug-2 North East Auctions, Portsmouth #1072/R est:10000-15000
£6678	$9750	€10017	British steamship, Germanic (122x76cm-48x30in) s.d.1894 lit. 3-Nov-1 North East Auctions, Portsmouth #90/R est:6000-9000
£7407	$12000	€11111	The City of Everett (49x89cm-19x35in) s.i.d.1915 board. 21-Jan-3 Christie's, Rockefeller NY #389/R est:15000
£7407	$12000	€11111	Steamship Knickerbocker at sea (56x91cm-22x36in) s.i.d.1892. 21-Jan-3 Christie's, Rockefeller NY #394/R est:18000
£7534	$11000	€11301	Steamboat, Danville (56x91cm-22x36in) s.d.1906 board lit. 3-Nov-1 North East Auctions, Portsmouth #63/R est:12000-18000
£8000	$12400	€12000	German tanker Helios at sea (56x91cm-22x36in) s.i.d.1898/31. 31-Oct-2 Christie's, Kensington #477/R est:7000-9000
£8882	$13500	€13323	Steam yacht, Winchester (56x91cm-22x36in) s.d.1910 board sold with three pieces of ship's dinner service. 17-Aug-2 North East Auctions, Portsmouth #1070/R est:10000-15000
£8904	$13000	€13356	Ship, Shackamoxon (48x76cm-19x30in) s.d.1916 board lit. 3-Nov-1 North East Auctions, Portsmouth #94/R est:8000-12000
£8904	$13000	€13356	Prince George (76x46cm-30x18in) s.d.1909 board prov.lit. 3-Nov-1 North East Auctions, Portsmouth #98/R est:6000-9000
£9211	$14000	€13817	Auxilliary screw barque, Saint Ronans (76x127cm-30x50in) s.d.1883. 17-Aug-2 North East Auctions, Portsmouth #648/R est:15000-20000
£9589	$14000	€14384	British steamship, Columbo (46x91cm-18x36in) s. prov.lit. 3-Nov-1 North East Auctions, Portsmouth #79/R est:10000-15000
£9740	$15000	€14610	Rescue at sea (56x91cm-22x36in) i. 24-Oct-2 Shannon's, Milford #63/R est:15000-25000
£9740	$15000	€14610	Steamship, Saratoga (56x91cm-22x36in) s.i.d.1899. 24-Oct-2 Shannon's, Milford #64/R est:15000-25000
£10274	$15000	€15411	Sidewheel towboat, Anna (76x132cm-30x52in) s.d.1858. 3-Nov-1 North East Auctions, Portsmouth #77/R est:5000-8000
£10526	$16000	€15789	American four masted ship, Puritan (56x91cm-22x36in) s.d.1906 board. 17-Aug-2 North East Auctions, Portsmouth #1009/R est:12000-18000
£10811	$17405	€16217	Seascape with signal ship (71x102cm-28x40in) s.i.d.1912. 22-Feb-3 Rasmussen, Havnen #2367/R est:30000-50000 (D.KR 120000)
£11842	$18000	€17763	SS Egyptian Monarch (76x152cm-30x60in) s. lit. 17-Aug-2 North East Auctions, Portsmouth #812/R est:18000-24000
£15723	$25000	€23585	Shackamaxon (58x102cm-23x40in) s.d.1916 board prov.lit. 5-Mar-3 Sotheby's, New York #49/R est:20000-30000
£16438	$24000	€24657	Steamer, John P Jackson (81x137cm-32x54in) s.d.1860. 3-Nov-1 North East Auctions, Portsmouth #75/R est:15000-25000
£17123	$25000	€25685	Tugboat, Lewis Pulver (56x91cm-22x36in) s.d.1884 lit. 3-Nov-1 North East Auctions, Portsmouth #89/R est:15000-20000
£17808	$26000	€26712	Paddle wheel steamboat, Rip van Winkle (79x132cm-31x52in) s.d.1854 prov.lit. 3-Nov-1 North East Auctions, Portsmouth #76/R est:12000-18000
£18868	$30000	€28302	Schooner Olive (71x121cm-28x48in) s.d.1908 panel prov. 5-Mar-3 Sotheby's, New York #50/R est:15000-25000

JACOBSEN, Antonio (attrib) (1850-1921) American

£1100	$1727	€1650	Steamship Rex off a coastline (62x92cm-24x36in) 21-Nov-2 Tennants, Leyburn #750/R

JACOBSEN, August (1868-1955) Norwegian

£266	$420	€399	Wooded landscape near Sollerod lake (60x91cm-24x36in) s. 17-Nov-2 Hindemae, Ullerslev #7567/R (D.KR 3100)
£1769	$2813	€2654	Mother and child walking on woodland path by river (83x131cm-33x52in) s. 5-Mar-3 Rasmussen, Copenhagen #2061/R est:20000 (D.KR 19000)

JACOBSEN, David (1821-1871) Danish

£298	$471	€447	Interior of an outhouse (30x40cm-12x16in) prov. 2-Dec-2 Rasmussen, Copenhagen #1777/R (D.KR 3500)
£468	$740	€702	Two men smoking pipes (27x22cm-11x9in) s.i. 2-Dec-2 Rasmussen, Copenhagen #1510/R (D.KR 5500)

£483 $764 €725 Soldiers marching (14x38cm-6x15in) s. canvas on masonite. 5-Apr-3 Rasmussen, Havnen #2165 (D.KR 5200)

JACOBSEN, Egill (1910-1998) Danish

£315 $508 €473 Composition. s. 22-Feb-3 Rasmussen, Havnen #2233 (D.KR 3500)
£933 $1483 €1400 Mask composition (54x43cm-21x17in) init.d.81 paper. 29-Apr-3 Kunsthallen, Copenhagen #111/R (D.KR 10000)
£1206 $1869 €1809 Mask composition (54x43cm-21x17in) init.d.81. 4-Dec-2 Kunsthallen, Copenhagen #42/R est:18000 (D.KR 14000)
£4307 $6675 €6461 Masks in green (46x65cm-18x26in) init.d.57 verso. 4-Dec-2 Kunsthallen, Copenhagen #56/R est:60000 (D.KR 50000)
£4645 $7247 €6968 Cello 74 (65x42cm-26x17in) init.d.74 verso. 18-Sep-2 Kunsthallen, Copenhagen #92a est:65000 (D.KR 55000)
£5484 $8720 €8226 Green mask (46x65cm-18x26in) exhib.lit. 26-Feb-3 Kunsthallen, Copenhagen #3/R est:85000 (D.KR 60000)
£6581 $10464 €9872 Gart - composition (46x65cm-18x26in) init.d.59 verso prov.exhib.lit. 26-Feb-3 Kunsthallen, Copenhagen #55/R est:80000 (D.KR 72000)
£7621 $11812 €11432 Green mask composition (42x65cm-17x26in) init.d.58 and 65 prov. 1-Oct-2 Rasmussen, Copenhagen #90/R est:90000-100000 (D.KR 90000)
£7626 $12736 €11058 1 red and green (45x67cm-18x26in) init.i.d.1951 verso exhib. 17-Jun-3 Rasmussen, Copenhagen #3/R est:80000-100000 (D.KR 80000)
£9758 $15418 €14637 Improvisation (73x116cm-29x46in) init.d.1953-55 verso exhib.prov. 1-Apr-3 Rasmussen, Copenhagen #113/R est:100000-150000 (D.KR 105000)
£10256 $15897 €16000 Den gule mand - yellow man (116x89cm-46x35in) init.d.77 verso prov.lit. 3-Dec-2 Christie's, Amsterdam #319/R est:13000-16000
£10512 $16714 €15768 Spring (81x65cm-32x26in) init.verso exhib.lit. 26-Feb-3 Kunsthallen, Copenhagen #10/R est:150000 (D.KR 115000)
£12059 $18691 €18089 Mask in red (100x75cm-39x30in) init.d.1968 verso exhib.lit. 4-Dec-2 Kunsthallen, Copenhagen #21/R est:150000 (D.KR 140000)
£13514 $21081 €20271 The sea (81x65cm-32x26in) init.d.56 verso exhib.lit. 18-Sep-2 Kunsthallen, Copenhagen #3/R est:125000 (D.KR 160000)
£16365 $25366 €24548 Masks in brown, Cagnes (45x60cm-18x24in) prov.lit. 4-Dec-2 Kunsthallen, Copenhagen #58/R est:200000 (D.KR 190000)
£19517 $30836 €29276 Eof (117x73cm-46x29in) init.d.60 verso prov.exhib.lit. 1-Apr-3 Rasmussen, Copenhagen #111/R est:150000-200000 (D.KR 210000)
£24117 $37382 €36176 Dancing mask (96x73cm-38x29in) init.d.45 verso lit. 4-Dec-2 Kunsthallen, Copenhagen #89/R est:250000 (D.KR 280000)
£41133 $65402 €61700 Autumn (113x83cm-44x33in) init. verso exhib.lit. 26-Feb-3 Kunsthallen, Copenhagen #32/R est:400000 (D.KR 450000)
£43184 $66935 €64776 Yellow mask in brown (114x146cm-45x57in) init.i.d.70 verso prov.exhib.lit. 1-Oct-2 Rasmussen, Copenhagen #69/R est:350000-400000 (D.KR 510000)

Works on paper

£310 $481 €465 Blue mask (19x16cm-7x6in) init.d.82 crayon. 4-Dec-2 Kunsthallen, Copenhagen #46 (D.KR 3600)
£418 $661 €627 Mask composition (32x24cm-13x9in) s.d.75 crayon. 1-Apr-3 Rasmussen, Copenhagen #270/R (D.KR 4500)
£1208 $1909 €1812 Mask composition (42x26cm-17x10in) init.d.69 W/C chk Indian ink pen. 1-Apr-3 Rasmussen, Copenhagen #251/R est:15000 (D.KR 13000)
£1306 $2076 €1959 Mask composition (49x35cm-19x14in) init.d.86 W/C crayon pen on lithograph. 29-Apr-3 Kunsthallen, Copenhagen #15/R est:10000 (D.KR 14000)
£1351 $2108 €2027 Composition with mask (54x41cm-21x16in) init.d.81 W/C crayon Indian ink. 18-Sep-2 Kunsthallen, Copenhagen #43/R est:18000 (D.KR 16000)
£1394 $2203 €2091 Mask composition (58x39cm-23x15in) s.d.78 gouache Indian ink. 1-Apr-3 Rasmussen, Copenhagen #233/R est:15000 (D.KR 15000)
£2509 $3965 €3764 By the river (33x27cm-13x11in) init.i.d.51 W/C gouache prov.lit. 1-Apr-3 Rasmussen, Copenhagen #232/R est:20000-25000 (D.KR 27000)

JACOBSEN, Erik Lagoni (1930-) Danish

£861 $1335 €1292 Artist and muse (177x134cm-70x53in) s. 4-Dec-2 Kunsthallen, Copenhagen #243/R (D.KR 10000)

JACOBSEN, Georg (1887-1976) Danish

£5112 $8076 €7668 Still life of flowers, fruit and jugs (50x65cm-20x26in) s.stretcher painted c.1925. 1-Apr-3 Rasmussen, Copenhagen #7/R est:80000-100000 (D.KR 55000)

JACOBSEN, Ludvig (1890-1957) Danish

£272 $424 €408 Temptations of Jason (51x37cm-20x15in) s.d.23. 5-Aug-2 Rasmussen, Vejle #65/R (D.KR 3200)
£274 $427 €400 Comfortable sofa corner (29x32cm-11x13in) s. 10-Apr-3 Schopman, Hamburg #632/R
£279 $441 €419 Fredmans Epistel No.14 (62x76cm-24x30in) s. 1-Apr-3 Rasmussen, Copenhagen #547 (D.KR 3000)
£340 $538 €510 Don Ranudo de Cotribrados (87x111cm-34x44in) s. 30-Nov-2 Rasmussen, Havnen #2275/R (D.KR 4000)
£357 $557 €536 View of Tolero (47x53cm-19x21in) s.i.d.29. 5-Aug-2 Rasmussen, Vejle #85 (D.KR 4200)
£468 $740 €702 Assemblee dans un parc (78x130cm-31x51in) s. 30-Nov-2 Rasmussen, Havnen #2276/R (D.KR 5500)
£506 $785 €800 Children playing (52x54cm-20x21in) s. 28-Sep-2 Hans Stahl, Hamburg #91/R
£525 $841 €788 The confinement (85x112cm-33x44in) s. 13-Jan-3 Rasmussen, Vejle #186/R (D.KR 6000)
£559 $888 €839 Le joueur de flute a la campagne (99x127cm-39x50in) s. 10-Mar-3 Rasmussen, Vejle #34 (D.KR 6000)
£560 $890 €840 The amateur politician (64x55cm-25x22in) s. 5-May-3 Rasmussen, Vejle #85/R (D.KR 6000)
£653 $1038 €980 Interior scene with figures merrymaking (86x111cm-34x44in) s. 5-May-3 Rasmussen, Vejle #88/R (D.KR 7000)

JACOBSEN, Maren (20th C) ?

£312 $493 €468 Travellers (70x80cm-28x31in) s.d.2001 acrylic pastel. 26-Nov-2 Louis Morton, Mexico #112/R est:7000 (M.P 5000)

JACOBSEN, Robert (1912-1993) Danish

£4657 $7218 €6986 Figures in room (120x200cm-47x79in) s. painted serigraph mounted on canvas. 1-Oct-2 Rasmussen, Copenhagen #32/R est:60000 (D.KR 55000)

Sculpture

£1239 $2070 €1797 Woman and child (35cm-14in) init. iron. 17-Jun-3 Rasmussen, Copenhagen #39/R est:15000 (D.KR 13000)
£1270 $1969 €1905 Concrete sculpture (26cm-10in) init.i.num.5/5 black painted iron. 1-Oct-2 Rasmussen, Copenhagen #10/R est:20000-25000 (D.KR 15000)
£1415 $2208 €2123 Untitled (23cm-9in) init. black painted iron. 11-Nov-2 Rasmussen, Vejle #84/R est:15000-20000 (D.KR 16500)
£1430 $2388 €2074 Construction (53x30x45cm-21x12x18in) green pat.bronze. 17-Jun-3 Rasmussen, Copenhagen #47/R est:25000-30000 (D.KR 15000)
£1931 $3108 €2897 Untitled (19cm-7in) init. black pat.iron exhib. 7-May-3 AB Stockholms Auktionsverk #720/R est:30000-35000 (S.KR 25000)
£2793 $4441 €4190 Doll (50cm-20in) st.init. welded gilded iron. 10-Mar-3 Rasmussen, Vejle #682/R est:40000 (D.KR 30000)
£3166 $5034 €4749 Doll (44cm-17in) st.init. welded gilded iron. 10-Mar-3 Rasmussen, Vejle #683/R est:35000-40000 (D.KR 34000)
£3504 $5466 €5256 The rider (68cm-27in) init. pat iron executed 1964 prov.exhib. 6-Nov-2 AB Stockholms Auktionsverk #618/R est:80000-100000 (S.KR 50000)
£3532 $5580 €5298 Father, mother and child (58x63cm-23x25in) init. partly gilded iron. 1-Apr-3 Rasmussen, Copenhagen #282/R est:40000-50000 (D.KR 38000)
£4275 $6755 €6413 Concrete sculpture (43cm-17in) init. black painted iron. 1-Apr-3 Rasmussen, Copenhagen #195/R est:50000 (D.KR 46000)
£5927 $9187 €8891 Jeune Diable (32x28cm-13x11in) init. pat. welded iron decorated with enamel exec.1956 prov.exhib. 1-Oct-2 Rasmussen, Copenhagen #102/R est:75000-100000 (D.KR 70000)
£6063 $9641 €9095 The rider (69cm-27in) pat.iron exhib.prov. 29-Apr-3 Kunsthallen, Copenhagen #169/R est:75000 (D.KR 65000)
£7435 $11747 €11153 Untitled - concrete sculpture (157x79x69cm-62x31x27in) init. black painted iron executed 1987 prov. 1-Apr-3 Rasmussen, Copenhagen #183/R est:100000 (D.KR 80000)
£8049 $13362 €11671 Doll (48cm-19in) iron exec.c.1952. 12-Jun-3 Kunsthallen, Copenhagen #11/R est:100000 (D.KR 85000)
£8049 $13362 €11671 Construction (75cm-30in) init. black painted iron. 12-Jun-3 Kunsthallen, Copenhagen #48/R est:80000 (D.KR 85000)
£9141 $14534 €13712 Doll (35cm-14in) iron exhib.prov. 26-Feb-3 Kunsthallen, Copenhagen #22/R est:125000 (D.KR 100000)
£11854 $18374 €17781 L'Homme futur (57cm-22in) init. pat welded iron prov.exhib.lit. 1-Oct-2 Rasmussen, Copenhagen #104/R est:150000-200000 (D.KR 140000)
£11854 $18374 €17781 L'idole au Marteau (50cm-20in) init. welded pat iron executed 1955 prov.exhib.lit. 1-Oct-2 Rasmussen, Copenhagen #110/R est:150000-175000 (D.KR 140000)
£11854 $18374 €17781 Portrait de M.P. (62cm-24in) init. welded pat iron executed 1958 prov.exhib.lit. 1-Oct-2 Rasmussen, Copenhagen #112/R est:150000-175000 (D.KR 140000)

£12278 $19030 €18417 Sans titre (56cm-22in) init. welded pat iron executed 1951 prov.exhib.lit. 1-Oct-2 Rasmussen, Copenhagen #111/R est:150000-175000 (D.KR 145000)
£13941 $22026 €20912 Concrete scupture (93x50x48cm-37x20x19in) init. grey white pat iron. 1-Apr-3 Rasmussen, Copenhagen #151/R est:150000-200000 (D.KR 150000)
£15241 $23624 €22862 The Emperor's tailor (70cm-28in) init. welded pat iron executed 1957 prov.exhib.lit. 1-Oct-2 Rasmussen, Copenhagen #107/R est:200000-250000 (D.KR 180000)
£19196 $30521 €28794 Concrete sculpture (45cm-18in) st.init.num.66 black painted iron exhib.prov. 26-Feb-3 Kunsthallen, Copenhagen #7/R est:200000 (D.KR 210000)

Works on paper
£255 $398 €383 Composition (49x64cm-19x25in) mono. mixed media red paper. 5-Aug-2 Rasmussen, Vejle #364/R (D.KR 3000)
£255 $398 €383 Composition (49x64cm-19x25in) s. mixed media blue paper. 5-Aug-2 Rasmussen, Vejle #365/R (D.KR 3000)
£255 $398 €383 Composition (49x64cm-19x25in) s. mixed media black paper. 5-Aug-2 Rasmussen, Vejle #366/R (D.KR 3000)
£284 $441 €426 Composition (23x17cm-9x7in) s. crayon. 4-Dec-2 Kunsthallen, Copenhagen #66/R (D.KR 3300)
£284 $460 €426 Composition (42x30cm-17x12in) s. W/C. 25-Jan-3 Rasmussen, Havnen #2183 (D.KR 3200)
£366 $581 €549 Composition (21x16cm-8x6in) s. crayon. 26-Feb-3 Kunsthallen, Copenhagen #34 (D.KR 4000)
£366 $581 €549 Composition (50x73cm-20x29in) init. crayon. 26-Feb-3 Kunsthallen, Copenhagen #129 (D.KR 4000)
£388 $601 €582 Composition (25x32cm-10x13in) s. crayon. 4-Dec-2 Kunsthallen, Copenhagen #80 (D.KR 4500)
£411 $642 €650 Composition (50x60cm-20x24in) s.i.d.1961 chl. 16-Sep-2 Horta, Bruxelles #87
£428 $681 €642 Composition (86x60cm-34x24in) s. mixed media. 10-Mar-3 Rasmussen, Vejle #640/R (D.KR 4600)
£517 $801 €776 Composition (47x67cm-19x26in) s. gouache. 4-Dec-2 Kunsthallen, Copenhagen #35/R (D.KR 6000)
£606 $964 €909 Composition (65x50cm-26x20in) s. gouache. 29-Apr-3 Kunsthallen, Copenhagen #180/R (D.KR 6500)
£640 $1017 €960 Composition (96x67cm-38x26in) s. W/C. 26-Feb-3 Kunsthallen, Copenhagen #173/R (D.KR 7000)
£929 $1468 €1394 Composition (48x63cm-19x25in) s. gouache Indian ink. 1-Apr-3 Rasmussen, Copenhagen #260/R (D.KR 10000)
£1441 $2276 €2162 Composition (50x63cm-20x25in) s. gouache Indian ink prov. 1-Apr-3 Rasmussen, Copenhagen #264/R est:5000 (D.KR 15500)
£1487 $2349 €2231 Composition (93x63cm-37x25in) s. W/C Indian ink Japan paper on canvas. 1-Apr-3 Rasmussen, Copenhagen #234/R est:18000-20000 (D.KR 16000)
£1770 $2868 €2567 Composition (17x22cm-7x9in) s. crayon. 24-May-3 Rasmussen, Havnen #4154/R est:1500 (D.KR 18500)

JACOBSEN, Sophus (1833-1912) Norwegian
£1567 $2507 €2351 Man and rowing boat in moonlight (54x77cm-21x30in) s. 17-Mar-3 Blomqvist, Oslo #360/R est:25000-35000 (N.KR 18000)
£3269 $5133 €5100 Moonlit fisherman in boat on wooded lake (101x150cm-40x59in) s. 21-Nov-2 Van Ham, Cologne #1695/R est:10000
£5022 $7834 €7533 The magpie (97x150cm-38x59in) s. 20-Nov-2 Fischer, Luzern #1159/R est:6000-8000 (S.FR 11500)
£7051 $11071 €11000 Wild boar in snowy wood (129x159cm-51x63in) s. 21-Nov-2 Van Ham, Cologne #1696/R est:12000
£12217 $19792 €18326 Landscape with women in rowing boat (98x148cm-39x58in) s/. 26-May-3 Grev Wedels Plass, Oslo #128/R est:150000-200000 (N.KR 135000)
£16774 $26000 €25161 Gondoliers on the Grand Canal with a view of Santa Maria Maggiore, Venice (79x118cm-31x46in) s.d.66 prov. 30-Oct-2 Christie's, Rockefeller NY #207/R est:10000-15000

JACOBSON, John (1958-) Swedish
£1483 $2343 €2225 Untitled (72x144cm-28x57in) s. verso panel two in one frame prov. 28-Apr-3 Bukowskis, Stockholm #999/R est:10000-15000 (S.KR 19500)

JACOBSON, Norman (19/20th C) American
£2500 $3900 €3750 Three Indians (74x58cm-29x23in) s. panel painted c.1920 prov. 9-Nov-2 Santa Fe Art, Santa Fe #224/R est:6000-10000

JACOBSSON, Fritz (20th C) Finnish?
£1935 $3058 €3000 Untitled. 19-Dec-2 Hagelstam, Helsinki #952

JACOMIN, Jean Marie (1789-1858) French
£5696 $8886 €9000 Bully (93x75cm-37x30in) s. 21-Oct-2 Bernaerts, Antwerp #188/R est:7000-7500

JACOMIN, Marie Ferdinand (1843-1902) French
£759 $1200 €1200 La vie au bord de l'eau (38x46cm-15x18in) s. 1-Dec-2 Peron, Melun #54

JACOULET, Paul (1902-1960) French
Prints
£1765 $2700 €2648 Song of waves, Ponape, East Carolinas. s. i.verso col print. 21-Aug-2 Eldred, East Dennis #32/R est:2500-3500
£1765 $2700 €2648 Sandalwood smoke. s. i.verso col print. 21-Aug-2 Eldred, East Dennis #115/R est:2000-3000
£1830 $2800 €2745 Beauty of Yap and orchids, West Carolinas. s. i.verso col print. 21-Aug-2 Eldred, East Dennis #14/R est:2000-3000
£2157 $3300 €3236 Daughter of the chief. s. i.verso col print. 21-Aug-2 Eldred, East Dennis #139/R est:3000-4000
£2222 $3400 €3333 First love, Yap, West Carolina Islands. s. num.verso col print. 21-Aug-2 Eldred, East Dennis #38/R est:3000-4000
£2222 $3400 €3333 Dans la nature. s. num.64/350 verso col print. 21-Aug-2 Eldred, East Dennis #89/R est:3800-4200
£2222 $3400 €3333 Black lotus. s. i.verso col print. 21-Aug-2 Eldred, East Dennis #151/R est:3500-4500
£2222 $3400 €3333 Dancer. s. i.verso col print. 21-Aug-2 Eldred, East Dennis #154/R est:3000-4000
£2484 $3800 €3726 Yagourouh and Mio. s. i.verso gold flakes col print. 21-Aug-2 Eldred, East Dennis #47/R est:3500-4000
£2484 $3800 €3726 On Tinian Island. s. i.verso col print. 21-Aug-2 Eldred, East Dennis #153/R est:3500-4500
£2549 $3900 €3824 Substitute. s. i.verso col print. 21-Aug-2 Eldred, East Dennis #120/R est:3500-4500
£2549 $3900 €3824 Tragedy actress. s. i.verso col print. 21-Aug-2 Eldred, East Dennis #155/R est:3000-4000
£2745 $4200 €4118 Tattooed woman of Falalap, West Carolinas. s. i.verso col print. 21-Aug-2 Eldred, East Dennis #21/R est:4000-5000
£2745 $4200 €4118 Mango seller. s. i.verso col print. 21-Aug-2 Eldred, East Dennis #54/R est:3000-4000
£2876 $4400 €4314 The favourite. s. num.149/150 verso col print. 21-Aug-2 Eldred, East Dennis #83/R est:3600-4000
£2941 $4500 €4412 Flowers of the Distant Islands, South Seas. s. num.3/350 verso col print. 21-Aug-2 Eldred, East Dennis #60/R est:5000-6000
£3660 $5600 €5490 Song of waves (152x122cm-60x48in) i.num.DK mural 80 tiles with border tiles. 21-Aug-2 Eldred, East Dennis #32a/R est:1500-2500
£4641 $7100 €6962 Mysterious Pacific. s. i.verso col print. 21-Aug-2 Eldred, East Dennis #103/R est:7000-9000

JACQUART, Lucie (1882-1956) Belgian
£449 $696 €700 Bouquet d'anemones (38x46cm-15x18in) s. panel. 9-Dec-2 Horta, Bruxelles #251
£538 $850 €850 Fruits et bouquet d'immortelles (60x53cm-24x21in) s.d.1921. 26-Nov-2 Palais de Beaux Arts, Brussels #110/R

JACQUE, Charles Émile (1813-1894) French
£353 $550 €530 Sheepfold (25x33cm-10x13in) s. 9-Oct-2 Doyle, New York #60
£600 $948 €900 Shepherd and sheep by woodland edge in landscape (27x35cm-11x14in) s. canvas on panel. 4-Apr-3 Moore Allen & Innocent, Cirencester #627/R
£641 $1000 €962 Sheep in a manger (46x33cm-18x13in) s. 12-Apr-3 Weschler, Washington #528/R est:800-1200
£1218 $1912 €1900 Berger et moutons (32x46cm-13x18in) s. 15-Dec-2 Lombrail & Teucquam, Paris #3/R
£1475 $2330 €2300 Berger et son troupeau a l'abreuvoir (34x25cm-13x10in) s. panel. 18-Nov-2 Tajan, Paris #123 est:2400-3000
£1646 $2600 €2600 Stable interior (18x24cm-7x9in) bears sig. panel lit. 29-Nov-2 Schloss Ahlden, Ahlden #1339/R est:2400
£2000 $3040 €3000 Coq et poules (66x53cm-26x21in) s. 3-Jul-2 Naón & Cia, Buenos Aires #10/R est:3000-4000
£2927 $4800 €4244 La bergerie (45x63cm-18x25in) s. prov. 4-Jun-3 Christie's, Rockefeller NY #243/R est:6000-8000
£3009 $4845 €4514 Cows and geese (71x112cm-28x44in) s. paper on canvas. 7-May-3 Dobiaschofsky, Bern #707/R est:6800 (S.FR 6500)
£3333 $5133 €5300 Serrail (42x64cm-17x25in) s. prov. 28-Oct-2 Il Ponte, Milan #249/R
£3459 $5396 €5500 La bergere et son troupeau (37x46cm-15x18in) s. panel. 9-Oct-2 Lombrail & Teucquam, Paris #9/R
£4065 $6382 €6098 Shepherdess and sheep (51x66cm-20x26in) s.d.75 prov. 10-Dec-2 Pinneys, Montreal #50 est:22000-28000 (C.D 10000)
£4610 $7468 €6500 Flock of sheep on edge of forest (47x66cm-19x26in) s. panel. 22-May-3 Dorotheum, Vienna #192/R est:6000-7000
£5063 $8000 €7595 Shepherd and his flock in a moonlight landscape (81x65cm-32x26in) s. oil paper on canvas prov. 23-Apr-3 Christie's, Rockefeller NY #65/R est:15000-20000
£5174 $8175 €8175 Shepherdess with flock (42x30cm-17x12in) s. panel lit. 29-Nov-2 Schloss Ahlden, Ahlden #1334/R est:9500
£6000 $9420 €9000 Paysage avec vaches et moutons (46x70cm-18x28in) s. 19-Nov-2 Sotheby's, London #175/R est:4000-6000
£7143 $10643 €11000 Shepherd with flock in barn (46x67cm-18x26in) s. 26-Jun-2 Neumeister, Munich #764/R est:8000

Works on paper
£408 $649 €600 Moutons dans la bergerie (22x15cm-9x6in) s. W/C htd gouache. 24-Mar-3 Coutau Begarie, Paris #92

£443 $700 €700 Femme et son enfant face au coq (13x11cm-5x4in) st.sig. pen black ink. 1-Dec-2 Peron, Melun #58
£592 $959 €900 Le repas des paysans (20x26cm-8x10in) init. ink dr. 22-Jan-3 Tajan, Paris #1

JACQUE, Charles Emile (attrib) (1813-1894) French
£2264 $3487 €3600 Landscape with sheep (27x34cm-11x13in) s. board. 28-Oct-2 Il Ponte, Milan #259/R

JACQUELIN, Marguerite (19/20th C) French
£12025 $19000 €18038 Still life with flowers (105x140cm-41x55in) s. 24-Apr-3 Sotheby's, New York #151/R est:12000-18000

JACQUEMART, Alfred (1824-1896) French
Sculpture
£1026 $1610 €1600 Chien et tortue (16x18cm-6x7in) s. brown pat bronze. 10-Dec-2 Renaud, Paris #104/R
£1547 $2537 €2150 Le chien a la tortue (15cm-6in) s. bronze. 3-Jun-3 Thierry & Lannon, Brest #53
£3200 $4960 €4800 Bloodhound studying a tortoise (15x17cm-6x7in) bronze. 4-Oct-2 Moore Allen & Innocent, Cirencester #292/R est:500-800
£5000 $7900 €7250 Head of a hound (41x41cm-16x16in) cast iron round. 22-Jul-3 Sotheby's, Olympia #318/R est:2000-3000

JACQUEMART, Nelie (1841-1912) French
£962 $1510 €1500 Portrait de M Fauche (103x73cm-41x29in) s. 13-Dec-2 Piasa, Paris #144

JACQUES, C (19th C) French
£759 $1214 €1100 Interieur d'ecurie (73x116cm-29x46in) s. 17-Mar-3 Horta, Bruxelles #74

JACQUES, E (1874-1937) Belgian
£1447 $2286 €2171 Two young girls enjoying afternoon tea in drawing-room (51x78cm-20x31in) s. 2-Dec-2 Rasmussen, Copenhagen #1733/R est:25000 (D.KR 17000)

JACQUES, Emile (1874-1937) Belgian
£435 $713 €600 Deux femmes se reposant (50x80cm-20x31in) s. 27-May-3 Campo & Campo, Antwerp #116

JACQUES, François-Louis (1877-1937) Swiss
£262 $409 €393 Cows grazing in summer pasture (34x49cm-13x19in) s. 6-Nov-2 Dobiaschofsky, Bern #715/R (S.FR 600)

JACQUET, Alain (1939-) French
£1111 $1766 €1600 Detail du camouflage Lichtenstein hot dog (10x20cm-4x8in) s.i.d.1963 verso acrylic exhib.lit. 29-Apr-3 Artcurial Briest, Paris #403 est:1500-2000
£1497 $2380 €2200 Bird (102x102cm-40x40in) s.i.d.verso. 3-Mar-3 Marc Kohn, Paris #31/R
£2244 $3522 €3500 Image d'Epinal (89x73cm-35x29in) s.d.mars 62 verso prov. 16-Dec-2 Charbonneaux, Paris #263/R est:3500-4000
Photographs
£2222 $3534 €3200 Portrait de Pierre Restany (48x35cm-19x14in) s.i.d.64 verso cellulosique canvas. 29-Apr-3 Artcurial Briest, Paris #350/R est:3000-3500
Prints
£3994 $6150 €6350 Portrait of man (161x113cm-63x44in) s.d.1964 s.i.d.verso serigraph prov.lit. 26-Oct-2 Cornette de St.Cyr, Paris #64/R
£17089 $27000 €27000 Dejeuner sur l'herbe (175x196cm-69x77in) s.i.d.1964 serigraph on canvas diptych prov. 27-Nov-2 Tajan, Paris #78/R est:25000-30000

JACQUET, Gustave-Jean (1846-1909) French
£641 $1006 €1000 Printemps (46x33cm-18x13in) s. s.i.verso cardboard. 22-Nov-2 Millon & Associes, Paris #54
£1613 $2500 €2420 Portrait of a young auburn haired woman wearing a red dress (36x25cm-14x10in) s. 7-Dec-2 Selkirks, St. Louis #766/R est:3000-5000
£2160 $3500 €3132 Return from Market (46x25cm-18x10in) s.d.1872. 21-May-3 Doyle, New York #217/R est:8000-10000
£3000 $4740 €4500 Portrait of a young lady, wearing a dark coat (33x24cm-13x9in) s.i. 14-Nov-2 Christie's, Kensington #287/R est:2500-3500
£4088 $6296 €6500 Attentive reading (55x46cm-22x18in) s.d.1873. 22-Oct-2 Sotheby's, Amsterdam #85/R est:6000-8000
£5484 $8500 €8226 Young beauty (27x22cm-11x9in) s. panel prov. 3-Dec-2 Christie's, Rockefeller NY #619/R est:7000-9000
£7000 $11410 €10500 Portrait of a lady (31x23cm-12x9in) s. panel. 29-Jan-3 Sotheby's, Olympia #296/R est:2000-3000
£20000 $31400 €30000 La pavane (236x141cm-93x56in) s.d.1883 prov.exhib. 19-Nov-2 Bonhams, New Bond Street #168/R est:20000-30000

JACQUET, J (19th C) French
Sculpture
£2785 $4344 €4400 Mythological group with several figures (55cm-22in) s. black pat bronze Cast Vittoz. 21-Oct-2 Bernaerts, Antwerp #127/R est:4500-5400

JACQUETTE, Julia (1964-) American
£31250 $50000 €46875 Couples, kissing (183x183cm-72x72in) s.i.d.1998 verso prov. 14-May-3 Sotheby's, New York #444/R est:10000-15000

JADIN, Louis Godefroy (1805-1882) French
£1329 $2073 €2100 La grande allee de Rambouillet. s.d.1832. 20-Oct-2 Mercier & Cie, Lille #291 est:1500-2500

JAECKEL, Henry (19th C) German
£780 $1271 €1131 Cabin beneath the mountains (44x65cm-17x26in) s.d.1876. 16-Jul-3 Sotheby's, Olympia #144/R
£5128 $7949 €8000 Venice (85x95cm-33x37in) s. i. stretcher. 5-Dec-2 Schopman, Hamburg #525 est:6500

JAECKEL, Willy (1888-1944) German
£4348 $7130 €6000 Still life with flowers in vase in front of red cloth (55x74cm-22x29in) s.d.19 prov. 29-May-3 Lempertz, Koln #684/R est:5000-6000

JAEGER, Gotthilf (1871-?) German
Sculpture
£1948 $2844 €3000 Female nude drinking (52cm-20in) s. bronze marble socle. 14-Jun-2 Auktionhaus Georg Rehm, Augsburg #6089/R est:300

JAENISCH, Hans (1907-1989) German
£2405 $3728 €3800 May landscape (70x100cm-28x39in) s. i.d.1954 verso paper on panel. 28-Sep-2 Ketterer, Hamburg #367/R est:3000-4000
Sculpture
£1795 $2782 €2800 Mother and child (37x6x6cm-15x2x2in) bronze. 7-Dec-2 Hauswedell & Nolte, Hamburg #757/R est:1200
Works on paper
£392 $620 €620 Waiting (35x21cm-14x8in) mono.d.48 gouache Indian ink. 29-Nov-2 Villa Grisebach, Berlin #684/R

JAFFE, Lee (1957-) American
Works on paper
£596 $929 €894 Bullhead Catfish (75x53cm-30x21in) s.d.85 mixed media. 6-Nov-2 AB Stockholms Auktionsverk #953/R (S.KR 8500)

JAGER, Adeline (attrib) (1809-1897) German
£962 $1510 €1500 Still life of fruit (67x54cm-26x21in) s.d.1851. 21-Nov-2 Dorotheum, Vienna #93/R est:3000-3800

JAGER, Frederic (1957-) French?
Sculpture
£2421 $3753 €3850 Enfant cavalier (53x53cm-21x21in) num.1/8 brown pat bronze. 6-Oct-2 Livinec, Gaudcheau & Jezequel, Rennes #83/R

JAGGANNATH, Bindu Bihare (?) Indian
£4000 $6240 €6000 Krishna Darshan (61x66cm-24x26in) s. 17-Oct-2 Bonhams, Knightsbridge #538/R est:4000-6000

JAGGER, Charles (c.1770-1827) British
Miniatures
£1700 $2652 €2550 Augustus Frederick FitzGerald 3rd Duke of Leinster (9cm-4xin) silver gilt frame rec. prov. 5-Nov-2 Bonhams, New Bond Street #139/R est:1000-1200

JAGGER, David (fl.1917-1940) British
£440 $669 €660 Lamplight study - self portrait of the artist (46x36cm-18x14in) s. 13-Aug-2 Canterbury Auctions, UK #103
£1400 $2212 €2100 Miss Suzanne Grotrian (155x112cm-61x44in) s.d.34. 27-Nov-2 Sotheby's, Olympia #69/R est:1500-2000
Works on paper
£500 $800 €750 Off to the bull fight (60x42cm-24x17in) s.i.verso W/C. 19-May-3 Robin Fenner, Tavistock #303

JAGGER, Edith (fl.1932-1938) British
£400 $656 €600 Still life of flowers in a glass vase (44x29cm-17x11in) s. 3-Jun-3 Bonhams, Oxford #79/R

JAHN, Hans Emil (1834-1902) Norwegian
£1745 $2861 €2530 Regatta by the coast (78x107cm-31x42in) s.i.d.1887. 2-Jun-3 Blomqvist, Oslo #7/R est:20000-25000 (N.KR 19000)

JAINES, Melanies Z (20th C) ?
£360 $558 €540 Still life on a white tablecloth (70x55cm-28x22in) s. 3-Dec-2 Bonhams, Knightsbridge #110/R

JAIPUR SCHOOL (18th C) Indian
£12821 $20000 €19232 Jewelled woman before a palace gateway (30x22cm-12x9in) prov. 27-Mar-3 Christie's, Rockefeller NY #220/R est:25000-35000

JAKESCH, Alexander (1862-?) Czechoslovakian
£389 $650 €564 Parting (58x97cm-23x38in) s.d.1921. 29-Jun-3 Butterfields, Los Angeles #7028/R
£2903 $4268 €4500 City street, possibly Prague (120x87cm-47x34in) s.d.89. 20-Jun-2 Dr Fritz Nagel, Stuttgart #777/R est:1500
£5000 $7850 €7500 Old tow. Prague (121x88cm-48x35in) s.d.89. 21-Nov-2 Christie's, Kensington #125/R est:5000-7000

JAKOBIDES, Georg (1853-1932) Greek
£4430 $6911 €7000 Model in the studio (80x39cm-31x15in) i. 19-Oct-2 Semenzato, Venice #160/R est:7000-8000
£38000 $60040 €57000 Combing her locks (28x22cm-11x9in) 1-Apr-3 Bonhams, New Bond Street #25 est:25000-30000

JAKOBSSON, Fritz (1940-) Finnish
£1408 $2268 €2000 Still life of pears (26x33cm-10x13in) s. 10-May-3 Bukowskis, Helsinki #51/R est:2200-2500
£3797 $6000 €6000 Still life of currants (60x90cm-24x35in) s.d.1986. 1-Dec-2 Bukowskis, Helsinki #69/R est:5000-6000
Works on paper
£629 $969 €1000 Nude resting (21x30cm-8x12in) s.d.1990 dr. 27-Oct-2 Bukowskis, Helsinki #196/R
£1761 $2835 €2500 Common hepaticas (43x58cm-17x23in) s.d.1987 W/C. 10-May-3 Bukowskis, Helsinki #81/R est:2000-2300
£4051 $6400 €6400 After the hunt (95x68cm-37x27in) s.d.1987 W/C. 1-Dec-2 Bukowskis, Helsinki #70/R est:4000-4500

JAKOWLEFF, Michael (1880-1942) Russian
£288 $460 €400 Ruelle de Bruges (32x39cm-13x15in) s. d.14.V.1925 verso panel. 13-May-3 Vanderkindere, Brussels #121
£408 $649 €600 Plage animee a Heyst-sur-mer (30x39cm-12x15in) s.d.12-VIII-1926. 18-Mar-3 Vanderkindere, Brussels #28

JAKSIC, Ivana (1973-) Yugoslavian
£875 $1400 €1269 C.S. face (130x110cm-51x43in) s.d.01.02. 13-May-3 Sotheby's, Tel Aviv #101/R est:1500-2000
£1078 $1800 €1563 C.S right eye, cheek, part nose and lips (152x75cm-60x30in) s.d.99/00 verso. 25-Jun-3 Sotheby's, Moscow #217/R est:1800-2200
£1317 $2200 €1910 C.S part of the face, neck and serial number (180x100cm-71x39in) s.d.01. 25-Jun-3 Sotheby's, Moscow #218/R est:1800-2200

JAKUB, Frantisek (1875-1940) Czechoslovakian
£1589 $2574 €2304 Mother love (110x138cm-43x54in) s.d.22. 24-May-3 Dorotheum, Prague #52/R est:50000-75000 (C.KR 70000)

JALABERT, Charles François (1819-1901) French
£1631 $2577 €2447 Chiara - young Roman on a terrace with view of the Campagna (23cm-9in circular) s.i.d.1847/50 parquet. 29-Nov-2 Zofingen, Switzerland #2343/R est:4500 (S.FR 3800)

JAMAR, Armand (1870-1946) Belgian
£292 $464 €420 L'Enfer (38x46cm-15x18in) s.d.1954. 29-Apr-3 Campo & Campo, Antwerp #151
£302 $486 €450 Marine en soiree (38x46cm-15x18in) s.d.1925 panel. 18-Feb-3 Vanderkindere, Brussels #36
£315 $492 €460 La mer (50x60cm-20x24in) s.d.1924 panel. 14-Apr-3 Horta, Bruxelles #460
£316 $494 €500 Retour du pecheur (38x46cm-15x18in) s.d.1935. 15-Oct-2 Horta, Bruxelles #25
£340 $541 €500 Marine (35x50cm-14x20in) s.d.44 canvas on panel. 19-Mar-3 Hotel des Ventes Mosan, Brussels #312/R
£353 $554 €550 Ferme isolee en Campine (38x46cm-15x18in) s.d.8 oct 1942. 11-Dec-2 Hotel des Ventes Mosan, Brussels #250
£360 $576 €500 Winter landscape (55x75cm-22x30in) s.d.1935. 17-May-3 De Vuyst, Lokeren #213/R
£369 $594 €550 Barques dans le chenal (35x50cm-14x20in) s.d.1916 panel. 18-Feb-3 Vanderkindere, Brussels #41
£417 $654 €650 Vieille ferme en Brabant (55x75cm-22x30in) s.d.1943 i.verso. 11-Dec-2 Hotel des Ventes Mosan, Brussels #241
£435 $674 €653 Le glacier d'Argentieres (55x75cm-22x30in) s.1937. 7-Dec-2 Galerie du Rhone, Sion #139 (S.FR 1000)
£479 $748 €700 Martigues (37x29cm-15x11in) s.d.1936 i.verso panel. 14-Apr-3 Horta, Bruxelles #459
£503 $810 €750 Environs de Calais (38x46cm-15x18in) s.d.1932 panel. 18-Feb-3 Vanderkindere, Brussels #59
£504 $806 €700 Venise le soir (19x27cm-7x11in) s. panel. 19-May-3 Horta, Bruxelles #259
£532 $888 €750 Soleil couchant a la mer (34x44cm-13x17in) s.d.1938 panel. 18-Jun-3 Hotel des Ventes Mosan, Brussels #277
£540 $863 €750 View of Bruges (100x150cm-39x59in) s.d.1935. 17-May-3 De Vuyst, Lokeren #211/R
£545 $855 €850 Vue d'une vallee (29x37cm-11x15in) s.d.10 avril 1939 panel. 11-Dec-2 Hotel des Ventes Mosan, Brussels #260
£570 $889 €900 Marche mediterraneen (27x36cm-11x14in) s. 16-Sep-2 Horta, Bruxelles #511
£680 $1082 €1000 Le samovar (100x70cm-39x28in) s.d.1946 i. verso. 19-Mar-3 Hotel des Ventes Mosan, Brussels #283
£719 $1151 €1000 Voilier au port. Voilier dans l'estuaire (37x29cm-15x11in) s.d.1936 panel pair. 19-May-3 Horta, Bruxelles #260
£728 $1187 €1100 Sieste au soleil (75x54cm-30x21in) s.d.1914. 17-Feb-3 Horta, Bruxelles #27
£755 $1170 €1200 Pont Flamand in Bruges (100x150cm-39x59in) s. s.i.verso. 5-Oct-2 De Vuyst, Lokeren #179
£759 $1199 €1100 Legende flamande (37x45cm-15x18in) s. one d.21 fevr.1940 one d.28 fevr.1940 pair. 2-Apr-3 Vanderkindere, Brussels #96/R
£818 $1259 €1300 Vue de village en Bretagne (75x55cm-30x22in) s. 22-Oct-2 Campo & Campo, Antwerp #138
£962 $1490 €1500 Vue a Veere (76x56cm-30x22in) s.d.1921. 9-Dec-2 Horta, Bruxelles #66 est:1800-2200
£1107 $1783 €1650 Ruelle animee en Afrique du nord (61x50cm-24x20in) s.d.1923. 18-Feb-3 Vanderkindere, Brussels #27
£1156 $1839 €1700 Voiles a Venise (42x59cm-17x23in) s. canvas on panel i.d.1931 verso. 19-Mar-3 Hotel des Ventes Mosan, Brussels #242 est:1400-1800
£1392 $2172 €2200 Port de peche mediterraneen (38x46cm-15x18in) s.d.1923. 15-Oct-2 Horta, Bruxelles #24

JAMBOR, Louis (1884-1955) American
£1882 $2918 €2823 Afternoon tea in the garden (98x74cm-39x29in) s. 6-Dec-2 Kieselbach, Budapest #123/R (H.F 700000)

JAMES, Charles (20th C) British?
£1132 $1766 €1800 Reading (41x33cm-16x13in) s. board. 23-Sep-2 Durán, Madrid #149/R
£1161 $1835 €1800 Confidences (49x42cm-19x17in) s. board. 18-Dec-2 Ansorena, Madrid #360/R
£2534 $3953 €3750 Thoughtful lady (73x100cm-29x39in) s. canvas on board. 25-Mar-3 Durán, Madrid #107/R

JAMES, David (fl.1881-1898) British
£520 $811 €780 Breaking waves (43x69cm-17x27in) 19-Sep-2 Mallams, Cheltenham #243
£850 $1377 €1275 Waves crashing on a rocky shore (63x115cm-25x45in) s.d.74. 21-May-3 Christie's, Kensington #701/R
£1050 $1670 €1575 Coming in with the tide (49x75cm-19x30in) s.d.90 s.i.d.verso. 4-Mar-3 Bearnes, Exeter #447/R est:1000-1500
£1200 $1896 €1800 On a rocky shore (63x103cm-25x41in) 27-Nov-2 Hamptons Fine Art, Godalming #354 est:1200-1500
£1300 $2054 €1950 Sail assisted steamship in stormy sea (50x75cm-20x30in) s.d.77. 27-Nov-2 Bonhams, Brooks & Langlois, Jersey #94/R est:1300-1500
£1447 $2345 €2200 Coastal landscape (76x127cm-30x50in) s.d.70. 21-Jan-3 Ansorena, Madrid #75/R
£1600 $2432 €2400 Fishing fleet off the coast (76x127cm-30x50in) 15-Aug-2 Bonhams, New Bond Street #351/R est:800-1000
£1800 $2826 €2700 Rollers off a headland (46x76cm-18x30in) s.d.83. 16-Dec-2 Sotheby's, Olympia #138/R est:2000-3000
£2500 $3925 €3750 Evening tide (30x51cm-12x20in) s.d.1900. 16-Dec-2 Sotheby's, Olympia #136/R est:2500-3500
£4000 $6320 €6000 North Easter, coast of Devon (63x127cm-25x50in) s.d.89 i.verso. 2-Dec-2 Sotheby's, London #44/R est:4000-6000
£17000 $28220 €25500 Grey day off the Cornish Coast (63x127cm-25x50in) s.d.94 s.d.verso. 10-Jun-3 Christie's, London #82/R est:18000-25000

JAMES, Edward (1820-1877) British
Works on paper
£223 $350 €335 Schooner Laura A Dodd dismasted in the Bay of St. Lawrences (13x28cm-5x11in) s. W/C. 26-Jul-2 Eldred, East Dennis #502/R
£573 $900 €860 Schooner Laura Dodd (36x53cm-14x21in) s.d.1899 W/C. 14-Dec-2 CRN Auctions, Cambridge #167/R
£701 $1100 €1052 Schooner Laura a Dodd Capt, Lane at Bay-of-Island Newfoundland (36x53cm-14x21in) s. W/C. 26-Jul-2 Eldred, East Dennis #501/R est:1000-2000

£892 $1400 €1338 Schooner Laura A, Dodd entering Georgetown Bermuda (15x28cm-6x11in) s. W/C. 26-Jul-2 Eldred, East Dennis #500/R est:600-900

JAMES, Frederick (1857-1932) American
Works on paper
£267 $425 €401 Morning at Menemsha Creek (97x36cm-38x14in) s. W/C. 7-Mar-3 Jackson's, Cedar Falls #728/R

JAMES, George (attrib) (?-1795) British
£1290 $2039 €1935 Portrait of a lady, holding a coronet (126x83cm-50x33in) 18-Nov-2 Waddingtons, Toronto #99/R est:1500-2000 (C.D 3200)

JAMES, John Wells (1873-?) American
£1317 $2200 €1910 Mixed flowers in a vase (61x51cm-24x20in) s. canvas on board. 22-Jun-3 Freeman, Philadelphia #148/R est:2500-4000

JAMES, Louis (?) British
£1429 $2229 €2144 Window shopping (102x102cm-40x40in) s.d.68 s.i.d.68 verso. 11-Nov-2 Deutscher-Menzies, Melbourne #90/R est:4000-6000 (A.D 4000)
£2143 $3321 €3215 Jacaranda Valley, idyll for Rosie (152x183cm-60x72in) s.i.d.91 i.verso. 29-Oct-2 Lawson Menzies, Sydney #96 est:5500-8000 (A.D 6000)

JAMES, Louis Robert (1920-1997) Australian
£573 $872 €860 Abstract (53x45cm-21x18in) s.d.77 verso composition board. 28-Aug-2 Deutscher-Menzies, Melbourne #363/R (A.D 1600)
£605 $926 €908 Arcady (24x35cm-9x14in) s.d.61 s.i.d.verso prov. 25-Aug-2 Sotheby's, Paddington #172 est:2000-4000 (A.D 1700)
£1190 $1976 €2029 Yellow interior (101x101cm-40x40in) i. s.d.69 verso oil masonite on board. 10-Jun-3 Shapiro, Sydney #74/R est:3000-4000 (A.D 3000)
£1200 $1884 €1800 Still life with a cactus (65x76cm-26x30in) s. prov. 10-Dec-2 Rosebery Fine Art, London #610/R est:1500-2000
£1250 $1962 €1875 Arcady. Little Kingdom 5. Red mirage. Pink Landscape (18x25cm-7x10in) one s.d.62 s.i.d.62 verso three s.d.61 s.i.d.61 verso board 4. 25-Nov-2 Christie's, Melbourne #393/R est:2000-3000 (A.D 3500)
£1429 $2243 €2144 Sunspot (62x75cm-24x30in) s.d. s.i.d.67 verso board. 25-Nov-2 Christie's, Melbourne #273/R est:3000-4000 (A.D 4000)
£2400 $3864 €3600 Drift 12 (243x243cm-96x96in) s.i.d.69 acrylic oil triptych. 6-May-3 Christie's, Melbourne #75/R est:6000-9000 (A.D 6000)
£3831 $5709 €5747 Red night (100x126cm-39x50in) s.d.62 prov.exhib. 27-Aug-2 Christie's, Melbourne #84/R est:10000-15000 (A.D 10000)

JAMES, Roy Walter (1897-?) American
£509 $850 €738 Rice fields, Moorea Island (46x61cm-18x24in) s.i.d.1947 masonite. 17-Jun-3 John Moran, Pasadena #110a

JAMES, Will (1892-1942) American
Works on paper
£9494 $15000 €13766 Misunderstood mule (36x46cm-14x18in) s. chl prov.lit. 26-Jul-3 Coeur d'Alene, Hayden #34/R est:10000-15000

JAMES, William (fl.1754-1771) British
£82000 $136120 €123000 Venice, the entrance to the Grand Canal looking east (98x165cm-39x65in) prov.exhib.lit. 12-Jun-3 Sotheby's, London #107/R est:60000-80000

JAMES, William (attrib) (fl.1754-1771) British
£44000 $69080 €66000 Grand Canal looking south with Santa Maria della Carita (47x73cm-19x29in) 10-Dec-2 Bonhams, New Bond Street #195/R est:5000-7000

JAMES, William (circle) (fl.1754-1771) British
£4870 $7500 €7305 Venetian canal (46x63cm-18x25in) 23-Oct-2 Doyle, New York #78/R est:10000-15000

JAMESON, Cecil Stuart (fl.1910-1937) British
Works on paper
£400 $624 €600 Brighton beach (21x28cm-8x11in) W/C. 26-Mar-3 Woolley & Wallis, Salisbury #54/R

JAMESON, Frank (1898-1968) British
£280 $437 €420 Penryn River (56x66cm-22x26in) s. 17-Oct-2 David Lay, Penzance #1086
£450 $707 €675 Bathing in the lake (51x61cm-20x24in) s. 15-Apr-3 Bonhams, Knightsbridge #34/R
£740 $1236 €1073 Boats at anchor St. Ives harbour (39x49cm-15x19in) s. 19-Jun-3 Lane, Penzance #225/R
£1050 $1754 €1523 Breezy day St. Ives (34x44cm-13x17in) s. i.verso board. 19-Jun-3 Lane, Penzance #281 est:800-1200

JAMESON, Rosa (fl.1885-1895) British
Works on paper
£1100 $1716 €1650 Squirrels eating berries (51x43cm-20x17in) s. W/C. 17-Sep-2 Sotheby's, Olympia #123/R est:600-900

JAMESONE, George (attrib) (1587-1644) British
£17000 $26350 €25500 Portrait of a mother holding a fan, with a child (112x84cm-44x33in) i. panel. 30-Oct-2 Bonhams, New Bond Street #168/R est:6000-8000

JAMIESON, Alexander (1873-1937) British
£300 $468 €450 Sketch of famous staircase at Blois (41x32cm-16x13in) s.d.1911 i.verso panel. 17-Sep-2 Rosebery Fine Art, London #530/R
£480 $773 €720 Corner of the Palace of Versaille (32x40cm-13x16in) s.d.1912 panel. 20-Feb-3 Bonhams, Edinburgh #334
£729 $1203 €1050 Rue aux arcades (46x37cm-18x15in) s. panel. 1-Jul-3 Rossini, Paris #98/R
£800 $1312 €1200 Portrait of Biddy, the artist's wife (62x52cm-24x20in) panel. 3-Jun-3 Sotheby's, Olympia #31/R
£1100 $1738 €1650 Design for panel decoration at Chelsea Town Hall. Oil sketch (65x92cm-26x36in) prov.exhib. two. 1-Dec-2 Lots Road, London #340/R
£1200 $1968 €1800 San Gimigniano (29x34cm-11x13in) board. 3-Jun-3 Sotheby's, Olympia #35/R est:1200-1800
£1400 $2170 €2100 Landscape, with village beyond (36x28cm-14x11in) s. panel. 29-Oct-2 Henry Adams, Chichester #527/R est:1500-2000
£1450 $2262 €2175 Shepherd, S Valery sur Somme (38x46cm-15x18in) s. s.i.verso panel. 17-Oct-2 Bonhams, Edinburgh #229 est:800-1200

JAMIESON, F E (1895-1950) British
£260 $403 €390 Highland loch scene at sunset (49x75cm-19x30in) s. 24-Sep-2 Anderson & Garland, Newcastle #527/R
£300 $471 €450 Loch Ness. Loch Lomond (40x61cm-16x24in) one s.i.verso two. 15-Apr-3 Bonhams, Ipswich #305
£330 $518 €495 View of Loch Katrine. Loch Goil, Aryllshire (40x61cm-16x24in) one s. i.verso two. 15-Apr-3 Bonhams, Ipswich #314

JAMIESON, Frances E (1895-1950) British
£391 $602 €587 Garelock Head, NB (51x76cm-20x30in) 26-Oct-2 Heffel, Vancouver #23 (C.D 950)

JAMIESON, Frederick E (20th C) British
£270 $424 €405 Scottish loch and mountain landscape with cottage (41x56cm-16x22in) s. 13-Dec-2 Keys, Aylsham #681/R
£280 $440 €420 Extensive loch and mountain landscape (41x51cm-16x20in) s. 13-Dec-2 Keys, Aylsham #680

JAMIESON, Gil (1938-) Australian
£249 $381 €374 Man in a field (78x92cm-31x36in) s. board painted c.1968. 26-Aug-2 Sotheby's, Paddington #592 (A.D 700)

JAMIESON, Robert Kirkland (1881-1950) British
£320 $496 €480 Variation on the Theme by Ricci (101x126cm-40x50in) s.d.1933. 3-Dec-2 Bonhams, Knightsbridge #355

JAMINY, Chris (20th C) French
Works on paper
£621 $993 €900 Portrait du Baron Fould-Springer (38x25cm-15x10in) s.d.30 pastel paper on cardboard. 11-Mar-3 Christie's, Paris #254/R

JAMISON, Philip (1925-) American
Works on paper
£346 $550 €519 Farmhouse in winter (20x33cm-8x13in) s. W/C. 5-Mar-3 Doyle, New York #34/R
£629 $1000 €944 Winter landscape with farm building (48x74cm-19x29in) s. W/C. 7-Mar-3 Jackson's, Cedar Falls #635/R est:1000-1500

JAMMET, Yvonne (1900-1967) Irish
£694 $1104 €1000 Reader (76x61cm-30x24in) s.d.1955. 29-Apr-3 Whyte's, Dublin #69/R est:1000-1200

JAMNITZER, Christoph (attrib) (1563-1618) German
Works on paper
£11728 $19000 €17592 Dance of the Months (15x49cm-6x19in) i. chk pen ink wash htd white. 22-Jan-3 Christie's, Rockefeller NY #87/R est:8000

JAN, Elvire (1904-1996) French/Bulgarian
Works on paper
£350 $584 €500 Composition (40x80cm-16x31in) W/C. 26-Jun-3 Tajan, Paris #163
£612 $973 €900 Composition (47x68cm-19x27in) s.d.1979 W/C. 24-Mar-3 Claude Boisgirard, Paris #104

JANCE, Paul Claude (1840-?) French
£1572 $2452 €2358 Still life of roses (40x27cm-16x11in) s.i. 6-Nov-2 Dobiaschofsky, Bern #711/R est:3400 (S.FR 3600)

JANCO, Marcel (1895-1984) Israeli/Rumanian
£1267 $2116 €1837 Composition avec carre (35x50cm-14x20in) s. canvas on panel. 24-Jun-3 Koller, Zurich #155/R est:1500-2200 (S.FR 2800)
Sculpture
£1026 $1621 €1600 Relief (22x34cm-9x13in) s.i.d.1915/1950 verso num.1/5 brass copper aluminium. 14-Nov-2 Neumeister, Munich #799/R est:1800-2000
Works on paper
£1387 $2190 €2081 Study for a mural for the United Nation building (24x61cm-9x24in) s. gouache executed c.1950 prov. 27-Apr-3 Sotheby's, Tel Aviv #52/R est:1200-1800
£4375 $6956 €6300 Autoportrait (20x14cm-8x6in) s.d.922 Indian ink dr prov. 29-Apr-3 Artcurial Briest, Paris #240 est:4000-6000

JANCZAK, Jan (1938-) Polish
£283 $441 €425 Troubadour (44x59cm-17x23in) s.d.I.IV.74 masonite. 16-Sep-2 Philippe Schuler, Zurich #6461 (S.FR 650)

JANDI, David (1893-1944) Hungarian
£2151 $3335 €3227 Still life of sunflowers (50x70cm-20x28in) s. canvasboard. 6-Dec-2 Kieselbach, Budapest #53/R (H.F 800000)
Works on paper
£826 $1288 €1198 Bathers (25x33cm-10x13in) s. pastel. 13-Sep-2 Mu Terem Galeria, Budapest #33/R est:280000 (H.F 320000)
£826 $1288 €1198 In the barn (33x29cm-13x11in) s. pastel. 13-Sep-2 Mu Terem Galeria, Budapest #34/R est:250000 (H.F 320000)
£1006 $1569 €1459 Family (50x64cm-20x25in) s. pastel. 12-Apr-3 Mu Terem Galeria, Budapest #37/R est:300000 (H.F 360000)
£1076 $1667 €1614 Autumn in Nagybanyan (39x41cm-15x16in) s. pastel. 6-Dec-2 Kieselbach, Budapest #11/R (H.F 400000)
£1230 $1918 €1784 Bathers (36x52cm-14x20in) s.d.931 pastel. 12-Apr-3 Mu Terem Galeria, Budapest #36/R est:280000 (H.F 440000)

JANECEK, Ota (1919-1996) Czechoslovakian
£873 $1387 €1310 Still life (48x60cm-19x24in) s. board. 8-Mar-3 Dorotheum, Prague #104/R est:40000-60000 (C.KR 40000)
£1342 $2094 €2013 Sun and earth (75x54cm-30x21in) s.d.85. 12-Oct-2 Dorotheum, Prague #136/R est:40000-60000 (C.KR 65000)
£1446 $2255 €2169 Form (72x60cm-28x24in) s.d.64. 12-Oct-2 Dorotheum, Prague #156 est:40000-60000 (C.KR 70000)

JANERAND, Daniel du (1919-1990) French
£253 $395 €400 Paysage Provencal (39x51cm-15x20in) s. paper. 15-Sep-2 Feletin, Province #119

JANES, Alfred (1911-1999) British
£2300 $3588 €3450 Little Castus 1947 (39x30cm-15x12in) s. board. 11-Sep-2 Bonhams, Newport #341/R est:1000-1500

JANES, Norman (1892-1980) British
£650 $1014 €975 Blackfriars (56x76cm-22x30in) s. exhib. 27-Mar-3 Christie's, Kensington #501/R

JANIKOWSKI, Mieczyslaw Tadeusz (1912-1968) Polish
£1154 $1812 €1800 Untitled (54x65cm-21x26in) s.d.1957. 24-Nov-2 Laurence Calmels, Paris #168/R

JANIN, Jean (1899-1970) French
£570 $900 €900 Draperies sur la plage (54x65cm-21x26in) s. 27-Nov-2 Blanchet, Paris #51

JANIN, Louise (1893-1996) French
£966 $1613 €1400 Vent d'Avril (100x73cm-39x29in) s. panel. 10-Jul-3 Artcurial Briest, Paris #302/R est:1500-2000
£2885 $4529 €4500 Evasion (130x96cm-51x38in) s. i.verso masonite painted 1953. 22-Nov-2 Millon & Associes, Paris #132/R
Works on paper
£1205 $2000 €1747 Figures in a mythic landscape (117x147cm-46x58in) s. mixed media board prov. 11-Jun-3 Butterfields, San Francisco #4307/R est:3500-4500

JANIN, Paul (?) French?
£949 $1500 €1500 Place des Cordeliers (15x24cm-6x9in) s. i.verso cardboard. 1-Dec-2 Anaf, Lyon #99 est:1800-2000

JANK, Angelo (1868-c.1956) German
£370 $577 €540 Foxhunt with riders jumping a hedge (55x75cm-22x30in) s. lit. 10-Apr-3 Allgauer, Kempten #2818/R
£411 $638 €650 Horses clearing water jump (70x90cm-28x35in) s. prov. 28-Sep-2 Ketterer, Hamburg #18/R
£458 $760 €650 Hunting with hounds with cavalry (60x80cm-24x31in) s. 14-Jun-3 Arnold, Frankfurt #777/R
£506 $800 €800 Hunters with hounds, horses in mid jump (70x90cm-28x35in) s. 29-Nov-2 Bolland & Marotz, Bremen #715/R
£552 $872 €800 Riders jumping a fence (70x90cm-28x35in) s. 5-Apr-3 Hans Stahl, Hamburg #11/R
£775 $1286 €1100 Hunting with hounds (67x90cm-26x35in) s. 14-Jun-3 Arnold, Frankfurt #776/R

JANKOVIC, Jozef (1937-) Czechoslovakian
Works on paper
£567 $805 €851 CSR '68 (65x90cm-26x35in) gouache exec.1970. 26-Mar-2 SOGA, Bratislava #275/R (SL.K 36000)
£788 $1221 €1182 Head (82x70cm-32x28in) epoxy mixed media exec.c.1995-99. 1-Oct-2 SOGA, Bratislava #291/R est:50000 (SL.K 50000)

JANKOWSKI, Czeslaw Boris (attrib) (1862-1941) Polish
£400 $628 €600 Woodland nymph playing with a pipe (41x65cm-16x26in) s.d.1888. 16-Apr-3 Christie's, Kensington #763/R

JANKOWSKI, F Wilhelm (19th C) Austrian
£692 $1079 €1100 Melk on the Donau (55x68cm-22x27in) s. 21-Sep-2 Dannenberg, Berlin #571/R
£1683 $2659 €2525 View of Budapest (55x65cm-22x26in) init.d.1863. 30-Nov-2 Goteborg Auktionsverk, Sweden #186/R est:30000 (S.KR 24000)

JANKOWSKI, J Wilhelm (fl.1825-1861) Austrian
£300 $480 €450 Continental town view from across a river (26x47cm-10x19in) s. panel. 7-Jan-3 Bonhams, Knightsbridge #229/R
£483 $768 €700 Riverside city (30x40cm-12x16in) s. 8-Mar-3 Arnold, Frankfurt #612/R

JANKOWSKI, J Wilhelm (attrib) (fl.1825-1861) Austrian
£1088 $1731 €1600 Idyllic boat trip near Laxenburg Castle (55x68cm-22x27in) 25-Feb-3 Dorotheum, Vienna #181/R est:1300-1500

JANNECK, Franz Christoph (1703-1761) Austrian
£17597 $27275 €26396 Festivities in the castle (34x42cm-13x17in) s. i. verso copper. 3-Oct-2 Koller, Zurich #3062/R est:40000-50000 (S.FR 41000)

JANNY, Georg (1864-1935) Austrian
Works on paper
£311 $485 €467 Sailing boats at San Michele (27x19cm-11x7in) s.i. W/C. 6-Nov-2 Dobiaschofsky, Bern #712/R (S.FR 710)
£473 $738 €700 House on the Rax (40x50cm-16x20in) s.i. verso mixed media board. 28-Mar-3 Dorotheum, Vienna #263/R
£946 $1476 €1400 Village street (17x23cm-7x9in) s. gouache. 28-Mar-3 Dorotheum, Vienna #261/R

JANOSKA, Teodor (1891-1960) Czechoslovakian
£284 $414 €426 Three heads (71x58cm-28x23in) painted c.1930. 4-Jun-2 SOGA, Bratislava #35/R est:18000 (SL.K 18000)

JANS, Jan (?) Dutch
£556 $917 €800 View of the Singel, Amsterdam, with the Koepelkerk in the distance (30x40cm-12x16in) s. 1-Jul-3 Christie's, Amsterdam #143/R

JANS, Knud (1916-1985) Danish
£465 $734 €698 Story for children II (81x116cm-32x46in) s.d.1970 s.i.d.IX 1970 verso. 1-Apr-3 Rasmussen, Copenhagen #383/R (D.KR 5000)

JANSEM (1920-) French
Sculpture
£1282 $2000 €1923 Jeune femme assise (29x20x25cm-11x8x10in) s.num.1/6 brown pat bronze. 19-Sep-2 Swann Galleries, New York #457/R est:3000-5000

JANSEM, Jean (1920-1990) French

£1258	$1950	€2000	La procession (24x20cm-9x8in) s. oil ink paper. 30-Oct-2 Artcurial Briest, Paris #395/R est:2500-3000
£1350	$2201	€2025	Still life of a fish (49x73cm-19x29in) s. 3-Feb-3 Bonhams, New Bond Street #64/R est:1500-2000
£1563	$2500	€2345	Two seated women (41x27cm-16x11in) s. 18-May-3 Butterfields, Los Angeles #7017 est:1000-1500
£1763	$2750	€2645	Femmes dans la rue (91x72cm-36x28in) s. 13-Apr-3 Butterfields, Los Angeles #7116
£2911	$4600	€4600	Femmes de dos (41x27cm-16x11in) s.. 164. 29-Nov-2 Drouot Estimations, Paris #109/R
£2911	$4600	€4600	Personnages accroupis (46x33cm-18x13in) s. painted 1973. 29-Nov-2 Drouot Estimations, Paris #108/R
£3000	$4890	€4500	Deux femmes (46x33cm-18x13in) s. 3-Feb-3 Sotheby's, Olympia #192/R est:2000-3000
£3057	$4830	€4586	Cleaning fish (88x116cm-35x46in) s. 14-Nov-2 Stuker, Bern #318/R est:5000-6000 (S.FR 7000)
£3800	$6194	€5700	Hommes attables (54x65cm-21x26in) s. 3-Feb-3 Sotheby's, Olympia #191/R est:3000-4000
£6800	$11084	€10200	Figure group (116x89cm-46x35in) s. 3-Feb-3 Bonhams, New Bond Street #62/R est:5000-8000
£8228	$13000	€12342	Le pecheur (131x162cm-52x64in) s. prov. 22-Apr-3 Butterfields, San Francisco #6031/R est:15000-20000
£10897	$17000	€16346	Exercises, trois ballerines (163x129cm-64x51in) s.d.69 prov. 14-Oct-2 Butterfields, San Francisco #2028/R est:10000-15000
£12903	$20387	€20000	Femmes accroupies (130x162cm-51x64in) s. 19-Dec-2 Delvaux, Paris #47/R est:18000

Works on paper

£1079	$1727	€1500	Jeune femme assise (48x63cm-19x25in) s. Indian ink dr. 18-May-3 Eric Pillon, Calais #163/R
£1763	$2750	€2645	Jeune fille en pierrot (66x51cm-26x20in) s. i.verso W/C graphite prov. 14-Oct-2 Butterfields, San Francisco #2029/R est:2500-3500
£1899	$2962	€3000	Nu allonge (65x48cm-26x19in) s. W/C ink. 20-Oct-2 Anaf, Lyon #165a/R
£2083	$3250	€3125	Femme en repose (50x66cm-20x26in) s. ink gouache prov. 14-Oct-2 Butterfields, San Francisco #2027/R est:3000-5000
£2405	$3752	€3800	Nu s'etirant (48x62cm-19x24in) s. W/C ink. 20-Oct-2 Anaf, Lyon #165/R

JANSEN, Dirk (1878-1952) Dutch

£350	$567	€525	Shipping in a harbour (18x23cm-7x9in) s. panel. 20-May-3 Sotheby's, Olympia #373/R

JANSEN, Franz Maria (1885-1958) German

£577	$894	€900	Poster for fairy-tale publication (86x93cm-34x37in) s. oil gouache board. 7-Dec-2 Van Ham, Cologne #256

Works on paper

£609	$944	€950	Poster for an Indian temple (77x98cm-30x39in) s. gouache oil exec.1910. 7-Dec-2 Van Ham, Cologne #257

JANSEN, Hendrik Willebrord (1855-1908) Dutch

£1667	$2683	€2501	Fishermen on river (85x130cm-33x51in) s. 7-May-3 Dobiaschofsky, Bern #708/R est:7000 (S.FR 3600)
£2083	$3437	€3000	Sailing barges in a breeze (80x60cm-31x24in) s. 1-Jul-3 Christie's, Amsterdam #109/R est:1500-2000

JANSEN, Johannes Maurisz (1812-1857) Dutch

£775	$1247	€1100	Anglers by a castle moat (25x23cm-10x9in) s. panel. 6-May-3 Vendu Notarishuis, Rotterdam #88/R
£1233	$1936	€1800	Extensive landscape with a shepherd and travelers on a sandy (26x35cm-10x14in) s.d.1842 panel. 15-Apr-3 Sotheby's, Amsterdam #8/R est:1000-1500

JANSEN, Joseph (1829-1905) German

£641	$1013	€1000	Martinstine on the Nahe (46x38cm-18x15in) s. 16-Nov-2 Lempertz, Koln #1484/R

JANSEN, Willem George Frederick (1871-1949) Dutch

£655	$1035	€983	Small seascape. s. panel. 14-Nov-2 Stuker, Bern #319/R est:800-1200 (S.FR 1500)
£701	$1093	€1100	Village at the water (14x21cm-6x8in) s. panel. 6-Nov-2 Vendue Huis, Gravenhage #636
£828	$1292	€1300	City canal in winter (22x31cm-9x12in) s. 5-Nov-2 Vendu Notarishuis, Rotterdam #11
£1389	$2292	€2000	Binnendieze bij Uilenburgstraatje, 's-Hertogenbosch (41x50cm-16x20in) s. 1-Jul-3 Christie's, Amsterdam #140/R est:2000-3000
£1447	$2345	€2200	In the country (60x90cm-24x35in) s. 21-Jan-3 Christie's, Amsterdam #135/R est:2500-3500
£1447	$2345	€2200	Busy workers at a sandpit (40x56cm-16x22in) s. 21-Jan-3 Christie's, Amsterdam #138/R est:2500-3500
£1712	$2671	€2500	Woman in the country (50x40cm-20x16in) s. prov.exhib. 14-Apr-3 Glerum, Amsterdam #62/R est:2500-3500
£1793	$2851	€2600	Children playing in the street Maastricht (45x54cm-18x21in) s. i.on stretcher. 10-Mar-3 Sotheby's, Amsterdam #191/R est:2200-2500
£1944	$3092	€2800	Tending to the sheep (50x40cm-20x16in) indis sig. prov. 29-Apr-3 Christie's, Amsterdam #162/R est:2000-3000
£2358	$3702	€3537	The pearl fisher (58x94cm-23x37in) s. 12-Dec-2 Iegor de Saint Hippolyte, Montreal #39 (C.D 5800)
£2420	$3776	€3800	Village on polder canal in winter (49x58cm-19x23in) s. 6-Nov-2 Vendue Huis, Gravenhage #638/R est:3000-4000
£2516	$3874	€4000	View of a village along a river (41x61cm-16x24in) s. prov.lit. 23-Oct-2 Christie's, Amsterdam #188/R est:4000-6000
£2778	$4417	€4000	Shellgatherer on the beach (50x65cm-20x26in) s. 29-Apr-3 Christie's, Amsterdam #155/R est:4000-6000
£2830	$4358	€4500	Achter de boederij (42x61cm-17x24in) s. s.i.on stretcher prov. 23-Oct-2 Christie's, Amsterdam #184/R est:4500-5500

Works on paper

£845	$1361	€1200	Sand grinding (28x38cm-11x15in) s. W/C. 7-May-3 Vendue Huis, Gravenhage #29/R

JANSON, Co (?) Dutch

£379	$606	€550	Otira sun showers (24x34cm-9x13in) s.d.85 board. 13-May-3 Watson's, Christchurch #53/R (NZ.D 1050)

JANSON, Johannes (1729-1784) Dutch

£833	$1308	€1300	Cattle under trees in wood (38x31cm-15x12in) s.d.1768 panel. 21-Nov-2 Van Ham, Cologne #1383/R

Works on paper

£1026	$1621	€1600	Southern landscapes with figures (23x21cm-9x8in) s.d.1775 w/C two. 16-Nov-2 Lempertz, Koln #1249/R est:2000

JANSONS, Ivars (1939-) ?

£491	$747	€737	Rendezvous (43x55cm-17x22in) s. board. 19-Aug-2 Joel, Victoria #272 est:800-1000 (A.D 1400)
£561	$853	€842	At North Adelaide (49x59cm-19x23in) s. 19-Aug-2 Joel, Victoria #314 est:800-1000 (A.D 1600)
£691	$1092	€1002	Alpine scene (54x75cm-21x30in) s.d.72. 22-Jul-3 Lawson Menzies, Sydney #288/R est:1000-2000 (A.D 1700)

JANSSAUD, Mathurin (1857-1940) French

Works on paper

£417	$688	€600	Chapelle Bretonne (34x26cm-13x10in) s. pastel. 1-Jul-3 Rossini, Paris #33
£903	$1490	€1300	Matinee au pardon de Sainte Anne (21x31cm-8x12in) s. pastel. 1-Jul-3 Rossini, Paris #34/R
£972	$1604	€1400	Arrivee en barque pour le pardon (22x33cm-9x13in) s. pastel. 1-Jul-3 Rossini, Paris #32/R
£1620	$2608	€2300	Retour de peche au soleil couchant (25x32cm-10x13in) s. pastel. 11-May-3 Thierry & Lannon, Brest #64 est:1800-2000
£1736	$2830	€2500	Retour de peche pres du mole (22x33cm-9x13in) s. pastel. 19-Jul-3 Thierry & Lannon, Brest #93 est:2600-2800
£2041	$3245	€3000	Concarneau, retour de peche (31x39cm-12x15in) s. pastel paper on cardboard. 26-Feb-3 Artcurial Briest, Paris #29/R est:2500-3000
£2436	$3849	€3800	Depart de peche a Concarneau (45x55cm-18x22in) s. pastel. 18-Nov-2 Tajan, Paris #131/R est:3500-4600
£2532	$3924	€4000	Marins et Bretonnes sur le port au soleil couchant (36x53cm-14x21in) s. pastel. 29-Sep-2 Eric Pillon, Calais #190/R
£2759	$4607	€4000	Le retour des pecheurs (48x63cm-19x25in) s. pastel dr. 10-Jul-3 Artcurial Briest, Paris #21/R est:3500-4000
£2817	$4535	€4000	Concarneau, l'attente des Bretonnes (46x55cm-18x22in) s. pastel. 11-May-3 Thierry & Lannon, Brest #63/R est:4000-5000
£3239	$5215	€4600	Retour de peche (45x54cm-18x21in) s. pastel. 11-May-3 Thierry & Lannon, Brest #61/R est:4000-4500
£4231	$6642	€6600	Retour des pecheurs (48x63cm-19x25in) s. pastel. 15-Dec-2 Eric Pillon, Calais #124/R
£8099	$13039	€11500	Retour de peche au soleil couchant (48x64cm-19x25in) s. pastel. 11-May-3 Thierry & Lannon, Brest #62/R est:5000-6000

JANSSEN, Horst (1929-1995) German

£1258	$1937	€2000	Cat and mouse (30x21cm-12x8in) i.d.28.2.1986 chk. 26-Oct-2 Dr Lehr, Berlin #188/R est:1000

Works on paper

£262	$411	€393	Der stumme Schrei (28x19cm-11x7in) s. col pencil. 25-Nov-2 Blomqvist, Lysaker #1131 (N.KR 3000)
£341	$532	€512	Landscape, Oslo fjord (33x26cm-13x10in) s. pencil crayon executed 1971. 23-Sep-2 Blomqvist, Lysaker #1094 (N.KR 4000)
£417	$658	€600	Empty hours for Kerstin (30x40cm-12x16in) s.i.d.14.6.93 chk. 26-Apr-3 Dr Lehr, Berlin #242/R
£435	$674	€653	Matura (46x38cm-18x15in) mono.d.28.6.66 pencil. 4-Dec-2 Koller, Zurich #166/R (S.FR 1000)
£576	$921	€800	Landscape with setting sun (11x22cm-4x9in) s.d.2.3.81 col pencil. 15-May-3 Neumeister, Munich #464/R
£641	$994	€1000	I must come through myself (31x22cm-12x9in) s.i.d.8.1.85 W/C Indian ink. 3-Dec-2 Lempertz, Koln #212/R
£641	$994	€1000	Love! Love, say I! My beauty! Love for 30 Marks (38x32cm-15x13in) s.i.d.1966 pencil col pen. 6-Dec-2 Hauswedell & Nolte, Hamburg #175/R
£654	$1027	€981	Morning ritual (42x29cm-17x11in) s. W/C Indian ink. 25-Nov-2 Blomqvist, Lysaker #1132 (N.KR 7500)

£755 $1162 €1200 The Gs are fun (35x25cm-14x10in) mono.i.d.29.3.1981 pencil col chk. 26-Oct-2 Dr Lehr, Berlin #187/R
£972 $1536 €1400 Marginal somersaults (21x29cm-8x11in) s.i.d.7.5.91 W/C over pen. 26-Apr-3 Dr Lehr, Berlin #240/R
£972 $1536 €1400 Three musicians (21x29cm-8x11in) s.i.d.18.8.93 pen brush. 26-Apr-3 Dr Lehr, Berlin #241/R
£1026 $1590 €1600 Susanne (17x42cm-7x17in) s.i.d.18 8 75 biro col pen. 3-Dec-2 Lempertz, Koln #211/R est:1600
£1042 $1646 €1500 Figures (21x29cm-8x11in) s.i.d. pencil W/C. 26-Apr-3 Dr Lehr, Berlin #239/R est:900
£1064 $1723 €1500 Untitled (20x12cm-8x5in) s. col pen pencil. 24-May-3 Van Ham, Cologne #293/R est:1200
£1154 $1788 €1800 Ape concert (85x78cm-33x31in) s.i.d.9 9 70 pen viscose. 7-Dec-2 Ketterer, Hamburg #456/R est:600-700
£1218 $1888 €1900 Guardi (19x8cm-7x3in) s.i.d.20 7 86 W/C Indian ink wash over pencil. 7-Dec-2 Ketterer, Hamburg #455/R est:2000-2200
£1370 $2137 €2000 Evening greeting (40x27cm-16x11in) s.i.d.26.2.83 col pencil chk offsetlithograph verso. 11-Apr-3 Winterberg, Heidelberg #1170/R est:2650
£1392 $2158 €2200 Hair for Hopker (38x32cm-15x13in) i.d.23 4 66 pencil col pen board. 28-Sep-2 Ketterer, Hamburg #451/R est:4000-4500
£1603 $2484 €2500 Albertina Catalogue (25x17cm-10x7in) mono.i.d.20.4.82 pencil col chk. 6-Dec-2 Hauswedell & Nolte, Hamburg #177/R est:2000
£1884 $3090 €2600 Tessin (38x27cm-15x11in) s.i.d.12.9.72 col chk pencil. 28-May-3 Lempertz, Koln #200/R est:1500
£3237 $5309 €4500 87 times Pommery for 25.9.78 (21x34cm-8x13in) s.i.d. W/C pencil. 6-Jun-3 Ketterer, Munich #140/R est:5500-6500
£4203 $6893 €5800 Death and the girl (48x32cm-19x13in) mono.i. W/C over pencil. 31-May-3 Villa Grisebach, Berlin #374/R est:4500-5500
£4487 $6955 €7000 Lemmy's birthday (43x61cm-17x24in) s.i.d.29.7.91 W/C gouache. 6-Dec-2 Hauswedell & Nolte, Hamburg #180/R est:9000
£5063 $8000 €8000 No (32x20cm-13x8in) s.i.d.82 col chk pencil bodycol lit. 29-Nov-2 Villa Grisebach, Berlin #89/R est:8000-12000
£7246 $11884 €10000 Crispin de Passe after Jacques Bellange (49x32cm-19x13in) s.i.d.15 1 75 pencil col pen prov.lit. 31-May-3 Villa Grisebach, Berlin #375/R est:7000-9000
£7595 $12000 €12000 2. Advent (53x40cm-21x16in) is.i.d.7/12/80 pencil pen bodycol. 30-Nov-2 Villa Grisebach, Berlin #447/R est:12000-15000

JANSSEN, Ludovic (1888-1954) Belgian
£609 $944 €950 Jeune femme au chapeau rouge (45x34cm-18x13in) s. 9-Dec-2 Horta, Bruxelles #321

JANSSEN, Luplau (1869-1927) Danish
£347 $552 €521 Interior scene with mother and her two daughters (35x29cm-14x11in) s. 26-Feb-3 Kunsthallen, Copenhagen #532 (D.KR 3800)
£446 $696 €669 Winter's day with many figures on the ice rink (75x101cm-30x40in) s. 11-Nov-2 Rasmussen, Vejle #662/R (D.KR 5200)
£511 $807 €767 Shrove Monday (54x45cm-21x18in) s.d.1915 exhib. 2-Dec-2 Rasmussen, Copenhagen #1302/R (D.KR 6000)
£5049 $7978 €7574 With Imuk? - the teacher's field and sheep (173x222cm-68x87in) s.d.1897 d.23-7-97 verso exhib. 27-Nov-2 Falkkloos, Malmo #77689/R est:75000 (S.KR 72000)

JANSSEN, Peter (1844-1908) German
£405 $632 €600 Apple, top hat and bowler hat (85x90cm-33x35in) s.d.1970 s.i.d. stretcher. 28-Mar-3 Ketterer, Hamburg #396/R

JANSSENS, Abraham (circle) (1575-1632) Flemish
£8176 $12673 €13000 Young woman with pearls and parrot - Laszivia (103x79cm-41x31in) 2-Oct-2 Dorotheum, Vienna #159/R est:12000-16000

JANSSENS, Abraham (studio) (1575-1632) Flemish
£8228 $13000 €13000 Allegory of Happinass and Melancholy (90x82cm-35x32in) init. 27-Nov-2 Finarte, Milan #36/R

JANSSENS, Abraham (style) (1575-1632) Flemish
£6500 $10205 €9750 Allegory of winter (120x99cm-47x39in) prov.exhib.lit. 10-Dec-2 Sotheby's, Olympia #334/R est:7000-10000

JANSSENS, Hieronymus (1624-1693) Flemish
£8500 $13345 €12750 Elegant lady with two musicians in an interior (33x32cm-13x13in) indis sig, panel. 10-Dec-2 Bonhams, New Bond Street #183/R est:6000-8000

JANSSENS, Hieronymus (attrib) (1624-1693) Flemish
£10135 $15811 €15000 Departure of prodigal son (110x149cm-43x59in) prov. 27-Mar-3 Dorotheum, Vienna #218/R est:15000-20000
£21831 $36239 €31000 Rejouissance musicale devant un jardin (25x34cm-10x13in) copper. 16-Jun-3 Oger, Dumont, Paris #67/R est:15000-20000

JANSSENS, Jacques (19th C) Belgian
£377 $581 €600 Bords de la Meuse (29x43cm-11x17in) s.d.1882 verso panel. 22-Oct-2 Campo & Campo, Antwerp #139
£1172 $1876 €1700 Troupeau au paturage (34x44cm-13x17in) s.d.1873 verso. 17-Mar-3 Horta, Bruxelles #75 est:1800-2200

JANSSENS, René (1870-1936) Belgian
£475 $741 €750 Cabinet d'amateur (73x50cm-29x20in) s. exhib. 15-Oct-2 Vanderkindere, Brussels #71

JANSSENS, Victor Honore (1658-1736) Flemish
£3957 $6331 €5500 Death of Caesar (60x90cm-24x35in) s. 13-May-3 Sotheby's, Amsterdam #77/R est:6000-8000

JANSSON, Alfred (1863-1931) American/Swedish
£1429 $2200 €2144 Autumn landscape (56x46cm-22x18in) s. painted c.1910. 8-Sep-2 Treadway Gallery, Cincinnati #623/R est:2000-3000

JANSSON, Eugène (1862-1915) Swedish
£851 $1319 €1277 Fishermen by beach huts (31x36cm-12x14in) s. panel. 8-Dec-2 Uppsala Auktionskammare, Uppsala #151/R (S.KR 12000)
£14740 $23879 €21373 Summer evening, Aarsta bay (84x135cm-33x53in) s. prov.lit. 26-May-3 Bukowskis, Stockholm #94/R est:200000-250000 (S.KR 190000)
£21277 $32979 €31916 Gripsholm Palace in evening sun (33x43cm-13x17in) s. lit. 4-Dec-2 AB Stockholms Auktionsverk #1708/R est:175000-200000 (S.KR 300000)

JANSSON, Karl Emmanuel (1846-1874) Finnish
£7194 $11511 €10000 Interior, Jomala (27x34cm-11x13in) canvas on board. 17-May-3 Hagelstam, Helsinki #91/R est:12000

JANSSON, Rune (1918-) Swedish
£526 $820 €789 Land contour (59x118cm-23x46in) s.d.83. 6-Nov-2 AB Stockholms Auktionsverk #697/R (S.KR 7500)
£695 $1119 €1043 Start for individuals (22x73cm-9x29in) s.d.60. 7-May-3 AB Stockholms Auktionsverk #892/R (S.KR 9000)
£951 $1502 €1427 The sun (66x31cm-26x12in) s.d.60 lit. 28-Apr-3 Bukowskis, Stockholm #265/R (S.KR 12500)

JANSSON, Tove (1914-2001) Finnish
£1079 $1727 €1500 Woman (55x46cm-22x18in) s. 17-May-3 Hagelstam, Helsinki #192/R est:2000
£1392 $2200 €2200 View of the sea (28x35cm-11x14in) s.d.1948 canvas on board. 30-Nov-2 Hagelstam, Helsinki #149/R est:1000
£2089 $3300 €3300 From the Observatory Hill (38x46cm-15x18in) s.d.1944. 30-Nov-2 Hagelstam, Helsinki #147/R est:3500
£2109 $3353 €3100 Still life of butterfly, bowl and shell (52x61cm-20x24in) s.d.1945. 27-Feb-3 Hagelstam, Helsinki #838 est:4000
£2658 $4200 €4200 Window towards the sea, Bredskar (60x69cm-24x27in) s.d.1948. 30-Nov-2 Hagelstam, Helsinki #148/R est:4000
£3291 $5200 €5200 Self portrait (42x33cm-17x13in) s.d.45. 1-Dec-2 Bukowskis, Helsinki #322/R est:2500-3000
£4930 $7937 €7000 Still life of flowers in vase (61x81cm-24x32in) s.d.61. 10-May-3 Bukowskis, Helsinki #129/R est:4000-5000

Works on paper
£601 $986 €920 French coastal town (24x32cm-9x13in) s.d.38 W/C. 9-Feb-3 Bukowskis, Helsinki #265/R

JANSSON, Viktor (1886-1958) Finnish
Sculpture
£1392 $2200 €2200 Torso (47cm-19in) s. bronze. 1-Dec-2 Bukowskis, Helsinki #4/R est:1300-1500

JANSZ, Pieter (1612-1672) Dutch
Works on paper
£1656 $2583 €2600 Esther before Ahasuerus (28x19cm-11x7in) bears i.verso pen brown ink grey wash htd white prov. 5-Nov-2 Sotheby's, Amsterdam #33/R est:3500-4500
£2548 $3975 €4000 Allegorical portrait, probably Frederick Hendrick and Amalai van Solms (13x19cm-5x7in) pen brown ink grey wash prov. 5-Nov-2 Sotheby's, Amsterdam #35/R est:5000-7000

JANVIER, Alex (1935-) Canadian
£636 $1011 €954 Tricia's motocross (40x50cm-16x20in) s.i.d.1981 acrylic. 23-Mar-3 Hodgins, Calgary #98/R est:1200-1500 (C.D 1500)

Works on paper
£381 $606 €572 Eagle Valley (38x55cm-15x22in) s. gouache prov. 23-Mar-3 Hodgins, Calgary #58/R (C.D 900)
£508 $808 €762 Mineral hot springs (55x75cm-22x30in) s. gouache prov. 23-Mar-3 Hodgins, Calgary #109/R est:1000-1300 (C.D 1200)

JANZEN, Michael (?) Canadian?
£267 $437 €387 Alberta fields against foothills (30x36cm-12x14in) canvas on board. 1-Jun-3 Levis, Calgary #59/R (C.D 600)

JAPAJLARRI, Dinny (20th C) Australian
Works on paper
£319 $523 €463 Possum dreaming (107x76cm-42x30in) synthetic polymer linen. 3-Jun-3 Lawson Menzies, Sydney #800 (A.D 800)

JAPANESE SCHOOL
Prints
£9119 $14500 €13679 Oban Tate-e view of Mt. Fuji (25x38cm-10x15in) woodblock by Hokusai. 1-Mar-3 Thomaston Place, Thomaston #611

JAPANESE SCHOOL, 14th/15th C
Works on paper
£6579 $9803 €9869 Amida Raigo, la descente d'Amida (88x38cm-35x15in) i. col ink gold silk scroll prov. 26-Jun-2 Iegor de Saint Hippolyte, Montreal #30 (C.D 15000)

JAPANESE SCHOOL, 15th/16th C
Works on paper
£6000 $9480 €9000 Buddha lying down to die on a jewelled bed with other figures (139x136cm-55x54in) col ink gofun four silk panels. 13-Nov-2 Christie's, London #59/R est:6000-8000

JAPANESE SCHOOL, 18th C
Sculpture
£20144 $32230 €28000 Faucons en gres (32cm-13in) bronze ormolu mounts pair. 15-May-3 Christie's, Paris #425/R est:10000-15000

JAPANESE SCHOOL, 20th C
Sculpture
£9748 $15013 €15500 Kannon (167cm-66in) brown pat bronze enamel. 23-Oct-2 Piasa, Paris #347/R est:6000-8000

JAPY, Louis Aime (1840-1916) French
£415 $647 €623 Spring landscape with blossoming apple trees (19x27cm-7x11in) s. board. 6-Nov-2 Dobiaschofsky, Bern #714/R (S.FR 950)
£1397 $2180 €2096 River landscape with washerwoman (18x24cm-7x9in) s. panel prov. 9-Nov-2 Galerie Gloggner, Luzern #87/R est:1000-1200 (S.FR 3200)
£1500 $2430 €2250 Girl resting in pasture (17x32cm-7x13in) s. panel. 23-Jan-3 Christie's, Kensington #173/R est:800-1200
£1962 $3100 €3100 Vaches a la riviere (31x41cm-12x16in) s. 1-Dec-2 Peron, Melun #18
£2000 $3260 €2900 Les pommiers, an orchard in blossom with a farmhouse nearby (32x41cm-13x16in) s. panel. 17-Jul-3 Tennants, Leyburn #871/R est:1500-2000
£7372 $11647 €11500 River landscape (134x186cm-53x73in) s.d.1872. 16-Nov-2 Lempertz, Koln #1485/R est:5000
£17722 $28000 €26583 Springtime (134x185cm-53x73in) s.d.1879 exhib. 24-Apr-3 Sotheby's, New York #20/R est:40000-60000

JAQUES, Pierre (1913-) French
£694 $1118 €1006 Le pont de la gare sur le canal du Rhone a Sete (33x46cm-13x18in) s. painted 1957. 9-May-3 Dobiaschofsky, Bern #105/R (S.FR 1500)
£1019 $1640 €1478 L'etang de la tuilerie; Ferney Voltaire (50x61cm-20x24in) s. painted 1957. 9-May-3 Dobiaschofsky, Bern #107/R (S.FR 2200)

JAQUET, Jan Jozef (1822-1898) Belgian
Sculpture
£41667 $65417 €65000 Diane a l'enfant (230cm-91in) s. marble. 19-Nov-2 Servarts Themis, Bruxelles #100/R est:30000

JAQUILLARD, Daniele (20th C) French
£786 $1226 €1250 Chanteur de jazz (100x81cm-39x32in) s. acrylic mixed media. 9-Oct-2 Marc Kohn, Paris #130/R
£818 $1275 €1300 Cerf-volant (93x73cm-37x29in) s. acrylic mixed media. 9-Oct-2 Marc Kohn, Paris #129/R
£881 $1374 €1400 Apoll (61x50cm-24x20in) acrylic mixed media painted 2000. 9-Oct-2 Marc Kohn, Paris #134
£1321 $2060 €2100 Hibou (130x97cm-51x38in) acrylic mixed media. 9-Oct-2 Marc Kohn, Paris #131/R est:2300-3000
£1321 $2060 €2100 Sable et sang (120x120cm-47x47in) acrylic mixed media. 9-Oct-2 Marc Kohn, Paris #132/R est:2300-3000

JARDINES, Jose Maria (1862-?) Spanish
£541 $843 €800 Rural scene (35x51cm-14x20in) s. 25-Mar-3 Durán, Madrid #146/R
£1500 $2280 €2250 Paisaje con lago (35x26cm-14x10in) s. 3-Jul-2 Naón & Cia, Buenos Aires #110/R est:3000-4000
£2516 $3925 €4000 LOnely fisherman (50x65cm-20x26in) s. 23-Sep-2 Durán, Madrid #214/R

JARES, Jaroslav (1889-1967) Czechoslovakian
£327 $520 €491 Still life with fruit (40x60cm-16x24in) s. 8-Mar-3 Dorotheum, Prague #61/R est:15000-23000 (C.KR 15000)

JARL, Axel (1871-?) Danish
£287 $465 €416 Young female nude and man (119x195cm-47x77in) s. 24-May-3 Rasmussen, Havnen #2199 (D.KR 3000)

JARMAN, Derek (1942-) British?
£550 $858 €825 Figures beneath a pyramid (13x18cm-5x7in) s.d.1977 verso slate. 17-Sep-2 Bonhams, Knightsbridge #150/R

JARNEFELT, Eero (1863-1937) Finnish
£2405 $3800 €3800 Porkala (34x27cm-13x11in) s.d.1906 i.verso canvas on board. 30-Nov-2 Hagelstam, Helsinki #109/R est:4000
£4930 $7937 €7000 Woodland glade (24x37cm-9x15in) s.d.1886 board. 10-May-3 Bukowskis, Helsinki #93/R est:7000-8000
£5063 $8000 €8000 Autumn day (43x54cm-17x21in) s.d.1915. 1-Dec-2 Bukowskis, Helsinki #73/R est:8000-10000
£5380 $8500 €8500 Meadow (20x34cm-8x13in) s.d.1885 canvas on board. 30-Nov-2 Hagelstam, Helsinki #124/R est:8500
£6329 $10000 €10000 Wooded landscape with pine trees (66x52cm-26x20in) s.d.1928. 30-Nov-2 Hagelstam, Helsinki #108/R est:10000
£9155 $14739 €13000 Evening clouds (32x46cm-13x18in) s.d.1897 exhib.prov. 10-May-3 Bukowskis, Helsinki #100/R est:8000-10000
£9177 $14500 €14500 Coastal landscape, Tusby Trask (45x65cm-18x26in) s.d.1931. 1-Dec-2 Bukowskis, Helsinki #72/R est:14000-15000
£9209 $14734 €12800 Coastal landscape (45x64cm-18x25in) s.d.1905 exhib. 17-May-3 Hagelstam, Helsinki #86/R est:12000
Works on paper
£1046 $1715 €1600 Street scene (30x21cm-12x8in) s.i.d.05 W/C. 9-Feb-3 Bukowskis, Helsinki #268/R est:1500
£1079 $1727 €1500 Coastal landscape (39x28cm-15x11in) i. verso W/C. 17-May-3 Hagelstam, Helsinki #88/R est:1700
£1871 $3068 €2600 The Forum, Rome (39x30cm-15x12in) s.i.d.1925 mixed media. 5-Jun-3 Hagelstam, Helsinki #1007 est:850
£2353 $3859 €3600 Old pine tree (40x30cm-16x12in) s.i.d.1916 gouache. 9-Feb-3 Bukowskis, Helsinki #269/R est:2200
£2848 $4500 €4500 Fast running river (38x55cm-15x22in) s.d.1923 W/C gouache. 30-Nov-2 Hagelstam, Helsinki #123/R est:5000
£4810 $7600 €7600 Summer wind (39x47cm-15x19in) s.i.d.1924 W/C. 1-Dec-2 Bukowskis, Helsinki #74/R est:3500-4000

JARNEFELT, Laura (1904-1985) Finnish
Works on paper
£277 $426 €440 Birches on the shore (37x32cm-15x13in) s.d.1943 gouache. 27-Oct-2 Bukowskis, Helsinki #199/R

JAROSZYNSKA, Karin (1937-) South African
£1025 $1599 €1538 Warrior and horse (45x98cm-18x39in) s. exhib. 11-Nov-2 Stephan Welz, Johannesburg #583 est:6000-8000 (SA.R 16000)
Works on paper
£480 $750 €720 Lovers II (45x60cm-18x24in) s.d.83 mixed media prov. 11-Nov-2 Stephan Welz, Johannesburg #272 (SA.R 7500)

JAROSZYNSKI, Tadeusz (1933-) South African
£705 $1099 €1058 Figure in red (62x47cm-24x19in) s.indis.d. paper prov. 11-Nov-2 Stephan Welz, Johannesburg #225 (SA.R 11000)
£1333 $2146 €2000 Two women (89x116cm-35x46in) s.d.86 i.on strtcher prov. 12-May-3 Stephan Welz, Johannesburg #524/R est:7000-10000 (SA.R 15500)

JARVIS, Don (1923-2001) Canadian
£385 $612 €578 Red landscape theme (65x102cm-26x40in) s. s.i.d.1963 verso acrylic prov. 6-Mar-3 Heffel, Vancouver #23/R (C.D 900)
£411 $654 €596 Coast landscape (69x112cm-27x44in) s. s.i.d.1959 verso prov. 1-May-3 Heffel, Vancouver #52/R (C.D 950)
£556 $883 €834 October (114x91cm-45x36in) s. s.i.d.1960 verso acrylic board prov. 6-Mar-3 Heffel, Vancouver #22/R (C.D 1300)
£583 $933 €875 Beach fire (102x76cm-40x30in) s. s.i.d.1959 verso acrylic prov. 15-May-3 Heffel, Vancouver #182 est:1200-1500 (C.D 1300)

JARVIS, Henry C (1867-1955) British

Works on paper

£650 $1014 €975 Cottages at Blewbury, Oxfordshire. Cottages at Billinghurst, Sussex (19x28cm-7x11in) s. bears i. W/C two. 5-Nov-2 Bonhams, New Bond Street #140/R

JARVIS, John (1946-) American

Works on paper

£534 $850 €801 Western landscape with Indian and his mount (23x30cm-9x12in) s.d.1980 gouache. 7-Mar-3 Jackson's, Cedar Falls #730/R

£1145 $1900 €1660 Landscape with native American encampment (30x61cm-12x24in) s. W/C on board. 11-Jun-3 Boos Gallery, Michigan #357/R est:1200-1800

JARVIS, John Wesley (attrib) (1780-1840) American

£1452 $2250 €2178 Portrait of a gentleman. Portrait of a woman (91x71cm-36x28in) canvas on masonite pair. 29-Oct-2 Doyle, New York #27/R est:4000-6000

JASMIN, Andre (1922-) Canadian

£202 $329 €303 Untitled (105x45cm-41x18in) s.d.1964 s.d. verso isorel. 12-Feb-3 Iegor de Saint Hippolyte, Montreal #105 (C.D 500)

JASUSCH, Anton (1882-1965) Czechoslovakian

£819 $1269 €1229 Bankov (69x93cm-27x37in) painted c.1940. 1-Oct-2 SOGA, Bratislava #38/R est:65000 (SL.K 52000)

£866 $1343 €1299 Mengusovske Peaks (66x84cm-26x33in) 1-Oct-2 SOGA, Bratislava #39/R est:55000 (SL.K 55000)

£992 $1449 €1488 Prophetess (48x61cm-19x24in) board painted c.1960. 4-Jun-2 SOGA, Bratislava #40/R est:58000 (SL.K 63000)

£1575 $2237 €2363 Winter landscape (80x108cm-31x43in) painted 1920. 26-Mar-2 SOGA, Bratislava #69/R est:55000 (SL.K 100000)

JAUDON, Valerie (1945-) American

£633 $1000 €950 Position. s.i.d.1989 verso alkyd on canvas prov. 3-Apr-3 Boos Gallery, Michigan #290/R est:2000-3000

JAUGEY, Daniel (1929-) French

£255 $397 €400 Marine mediterraneenne (53x64cm-21x25in) 6-Nov-2 Gioffredo, Nice #22/R

JAUMOTTE, Gaston (1926-) Belgian

£390 $604 €620 Village de pecheurs dans le Westhoek a la panne (30x40cm-12x16in) s. s.i.verso panel. 5-Oct-2 De Vuyst, Lokeren #180

JAVOR, Pal (1880-1923) Hungarian

£500 $800 €750 Portrait of a elderly gentleman (71x61cm-28x24in) s. 15-Mar-3 Jeffery Burchard, Florida #68/R

JAWLENSKY, Alexej von (1864-1941) Russian

£10860 $18136 €15747 Meditation. Juli 1935 No 40 (17x13cm-7x5in) mono. s.i.1935 VII verso paper on board prov.exhib.lit. 24-Jun-3 Koller, Zurich #143/R est:30000-50000 (S.FR 24000)

£16026 $24840 €25000 Meditation: blue sound (18x13cm-7x5in) mono.d.36 i.verso paper on board prov.lit. 7-Dec-2 Van Ham, Cologne #267/R est:40000

£18269 $28317 €28500 Large meditation (25x17cm-10x7in) s.d. board. 7-Dec-2 Hauswedell & Nolte, Hamburg #762/R est:38000

£20290 $33275 €28000 Sea at Borkum (32x45cm-13x18in) s. i. verso board prov. 31-May-3 Villa Grisebach, Berlin #196/R est:30000-40000

£25641 $40000 €38462 Stilleben dahlien letzter sonnenstrahl (29x2cm-11x1in) init.i.d.36 i.verso oil on linen finish paper on cardboard. 5-Nov-2 Phillips, New York #124/R est:40000-50000

£25641 $40000 €38462 Dahlien mit rotem hintergrund (18x13cm-7x5in) init.i.d.1936 i.verso oil linen finish paper on cardbord prov.exh. 5-Nov-2 Phillips, New York #125/R est:40000-50000

£26282 $40737 €41000 Meditation: l'heure bleu et en moi (19x12cm-7x5in) mono.d. board. 7-Dec-2 Hauswedell & Nolte, Hamburg #761/R est:25000

£26415 $41208 €42000 Meditation (19x13cm-7x5in) init.d.35 s.i.d.verso oil on linen prov.exhib.lit. 9-Oct-2 Sotheby's, London #114/R est:40000-50000

£34532 $56633 €48000 Meditation (19x12cm-7x5in) mono.d. s.i.d.1935 IV verso linen paper on board prov. 6-Jun-3 Ketterer, Munich #75/R est:40000-50000

£34615 $53654 €54000 Large meditation: hope (26x19cm-10x7in) mono.d.36 paper on board. 4-Dec-2 Lempertz, Koln #793a/R est:40000-45000

£35443 $56000 €56000 Meditation: Siesta in summer (18x12cm-7x5in) mono.d.35 i.verso linen paper on cardboard prov.exhib.lit. 29-Nov-2 Villa Grisebach, Berlin #72/R est:40000-50000

£39855 $65362 €55000 Young girl (35x25cm-14x10in) board on masonite prov.exhib. 29-May-3 Lempertz, Koln #685/R est:60000-70000

£55128 $85449 €86000 Still life of apples (32x51cm-13x20in) s. board prov. 4-Dec-2 Lempertz, Koln #793/R est:40000-45000

£56962 $90000 €90000 Still life (15x27cm-6x11in) s. s.d.1931 verso cardboard prov. 29-Nov-2 Villa Grisebach, Berlin #21/R est:80000-90000

£60897 $95000 €91346 Zwei blaue Tassen und Apfel (34x36cm-13x14in) s. canvas on panel painted c.1904 prov.lit. 7-Nov-2 Christie's, Rockefeller NY #234/R est:70000-90000

£63291 $98734 €100000 Mystical head (26x16cm-10x6in) s.d.1917 verso board prov.exhib. 18-Oct-2 Dr Fritz Nagel, Stuttgart #538/R est:150000

£110000 $183700 €159500 Variation mit kirchturm - variation with church steeple (37x26cm-15x10in) init.d.1915 prov.exhib.lit. 24-Jun-3 Sotheby's, London #185/R est:120000-150000

£181159 $297101 €250000 Saviour's face: prayer (35x27cm-14x11in) mono. board prov.exhib.lit. 30-May-3 Villa Grisebach, Berlin #40/R est:250000-350000

£220000 $343200 €330000 Madchen mit weisser schurze - Girl with a white apron (68x54cm-27x21in) s.d.1906 cardboard prov.exhib.lit. 9-Oct-2 Sotheby's, London #12/R est:180000-250000

£220126 $343396 €350000 Landschaft, Murnau - Landscape, Murnau (32x44cm-13x17in) s. i.verso board painted c.1908 prov.exhib.lit. 8-Oct-2 Sotheby's, London #6/R est:240000-320000

£366460 $590000 €549690 Mysticher kopf das staunen - mystical head astonishment (40x31cm-16x12in) i.d.1917 i.verso board on panel prov.exhib.lit. 7-May-3 Sotheby's, New York #223/R est:250000-350000

£398734 $630000 €630000 Apples with purple jug and figure (50x54cm-20x21in) s. cardboard prov.lit. 29-Nov-2 Villa Grisebach, Berlin #24/R est:400000-600000

£400000 $652000 €600000 Blaue vase mit orangen (45x56cm-18x22in) init. painted c.1907. 3-Feb-3 Christie's, London #5/R est:250000-350000

£754717 $1177358 €1200000 Blauer shawl - Blue shawl (69x50cm-27x20in) s.d.1912 verso board prov.exhib.lit. 8-Oct-2 Sotheby's, London #7/R est:1300000-1800000

£1383648 $2158491 €2200000 Halbakt - Nude half figure (73x52cm-29x20in) board painted c.1912 prov.exhib.lit. 8-Oct-2 Sotheby's, London #13/R est:1400000-1800000

£1923077 $3000000 €2884616 Junges madchen mit den grunen Augen (53x49cm-21x19in) s.board painted c.1910 prov.exhib.lit. 6-Nov-2 Christie's, Rockefeller NY #29/R est:1200000-1600000

JAWLENSKY, Andreas (1902-1984) Polish

£3846 $5962 €6000 Bad Konig in the Odenwald (30x40cm-12x16in) s.i.d. s.i.d. verso board. 7-Dec-2 Hauswedell & Nolte, Hamburg #764/R est:7500

JAY, Florence (fl.1905-1920) British

£1400 $2212 €2100 Micky, a red setter in a landscape (51x66cm-20x26in) s. 28-Nov-2 Christie's, Kensington #357/R est:1000-1500

£1800 $2844 €2700 Beagle. Foxhound (35x46cm-14x18in) s. i.verso pair. 28-Nov-2 Christie's, Kensington #308/R est:2000-3000

JAY, Hamilton (fl.1875-1913) British

£950 $1492 €1425 Farmyard scene with milkmaid milking a cow and talking to a seated figure (44x64cm-17x25in) s.d.98. 21-Nov-2 Clevedon Sale Rooms #231/R

JAY, William Samuel (1843-1933) British

£720 $1174 €1044 Extensive landscape with cattle (38x61cm-15x24in) s.d.80. 16-Jul-3 Sotheby's, Olympia #67/R

JAZZAMOART (20th C) Mexican

£618 $989 €896 Nocturno de la mascara o que carajos somos (120x90cm-47x35in) s.d.1995. 15-May-3 Louis Morton, Mexico #6/R (M.P 10000)

JEAN, Marcel (1900-) French

Works on paper

£310 $518 €450 Nu au pied leve (24x32cm-9x13in) s.i.d.31chl W/C ink dr. 10-Jul-3 Artcurial Briest, Paris #59/R

£408 $649 €600 Ombres transparentes (32x45cm-13x18in) s. gouache panel on cardboard exec.1976. 24-Mar-3 Claude Boisgirard, Paris #94/R

JEAN, Philippe (1755-1802) British
Miniatures
£3500 $5495 €5250 Young gentleman in a blue coat (6cm-2xin) silver gilt frame oval. 10-Dec-2 Christie's, London #169/R est:2000-3000
£5000 $7850 €7500 Naval officer (7cm-3xin) gilt metal frame oval. 10-Dec-2 Christie's, London #175/R est:600-800

JEANES, Sigismond (1863-?) French
£272 $433 €400 Paysage aux coquelicots et au clocher (22x33cm-9x13in) s. panel. 24-Mar-3 Claude Boisgirard, Paris #41
£1206 $1953 €1700 Les belles montagnes (115x179cm-45x70in) s. i.verso panel. 26-May-3 Joron-Derem, Paris #64/R est:400-600

JEANMAIRE, Edouard (1847-1916) Swiss
£472 $746 €708 Cow grazing in la Joux Perret (58x40cm-23x16in) s.i.verso board. 29-Nov-2 Zofingen, Switzerland #2931 (S.FR 1100)
£850 $1309 €1275 Figure in a woodland, a la Foix Perret (76x61cm-30x24in) s. 3-Sep-2 Gorringes, Lewes #2292
£2273 $3500 €3410 Farmstead (37x58cm-15x23in) s.indis.i. s.i.d.1886 verso. 4-Sep-2 Christie's, Rockefeller NY #334/R est:3000-5000
£2347 $3850 €3403 Le Chasseron vu des hauteurs de Sommartel (44x61cm-17x24in) s.i.d.Aout 1985. 4-Jun-3 Fischer, Luzern #1242/R est:3000-4000 (S.FR 5000)

JEANNEAU, Fernand (20th C) French
£313 $509 €450 L'elle a Quimperle (31x40cm-12x16in) s. panel. 19-Jul-3 Thierry & Lannon, Brest #347

JEANNIN, Georges (1841-1925) French
£1397 $2180 €2096 Still life of flowers (46x55cm-18x22in) s.d.1902 prov. 9-Nov-2 Galerie Gloggner, Luzern #88/R est:1200-1500 (S.FR 3200)
£1400 $2282 €2030 Still life of peaches and grapes (49x60cm-19x24in) s.d.1903. 16-Jul-3 Sotheby's, Olympia #234/R est:1500-2500
£1603 $2532 €2500 Fleurs dans un vase (55x46cm-22x18in) s. 18-Nov-2 Tajan, Paris #126 est:3000-3800
£2800 $4452 €4200 Summer roses in a vase (55x48cm-22x19in) s.d.1919. 20-Mar-3 Christie's, Kensington #35/R est:3000-5000
£2842 $4405 €4263 Autumn flowers (50x65cm-20x26in) painted c.1890. 3-Dec-2 SOGA, Bratislava #163/R est:180000 (SL.K 180000)
£3378 $5270 €5000 Bouquet de fleurs sur entablement (65x81cm-26x32in) s. 28-Mar-3 Claude Aguttes, Neuilly #95/R
£7500 $12000 €11250 Still life with roses in a clay pot. Still life (64x79cm-25x31in) s. canvas on board pair. 14-May-3 Butterfields, San Francisco #1121/R est:6000-8000

JEANNIOT, Pierre Alexandre (1826-1892) French
£833 $1317 €1300 Chateau en ruines (81x111cm-32x44in) s.d.1852 exhib. 18-Nov-2 Sotheby's, Paris #67/R

JEANNIOT, Pierre Georges (1848-1934) French
£696 $1100 €1100 La prairie (40x54cm-16x21in) s. 1-Dec-2 Peron, Melun #36

JEANNOT, Sarah (1883-1958) French
£278 $447 €417 Bielersee with St Petersinsel (46x60cm-18x24in) s. i. stretcher. 7-May-3 Dobiaschofsky, Bern #3360 (S.FR 600)
£328 $511 €492 Portrait of Claudine Jeannot on park bench (48x66cm-19x26in) s.d.1911 i. verso board. 6-Nov-2 Dobiaschofsky, Bern #717/R (S.FR 750)
£699 $1090 €1049 Fillette d'Evolene (37x31cm-15x12in) s. board. 6-Nov-2 Dobiaschofsky, Bern #3437 (S.FR 1600)

JEAURAT, Edme (1688-1738) French
Works on paper
£1314 $2037 €2050 Angelique gravant son nom dans l'ecorce d'un arbre (28x25cm-11x10in) s. crayon chk. 4-Dec-2 Piasa, Paris #83/R

JEAURAT, Étienne (1699-1789) French
£6250 $9875 €9000 Erigone (71x89cm-28x35in) s.d.1763. 25-Apr-3 Beaussant & Lefèvre, Paris #18/R est:6000-8000
Works on paper
£333 $517 €520 Petit carrosse (27x36cm-11x14in) s.d.1765 W/C pen. 9-Dec-2 Thierry & Lannon, Brest #228

JEAURAT, Étienne (attrib) (1699-1789) French
£7801 $12092 €11702 Sitting room interior with couple (45x36cm-18x14in) 4-Dec-2 AB Stockholms Auktionsverk #1960/R est:60000-80000 (S.KR 110000)

JECT-KEY, David Wu (1890-1968) Chinese
£441 $700 €662 Rockport street view (45x52cm-18x20in) i. prov. 7-Mar-3 Skinner, Boston #514/R
£755 $1200 €1133 Back beach (51x87cm-20x34in) s. prov. 7-Mar-3 Skinner, Boston #494/R
£944 $1500 €1416 Summer haze (48x89cm-19x35in) s.i. prov. 7-Mar-3 Skinner, Boston #511/R est:1000-1500
£1006 $1600 €1509 Drawbridge (51x87cm-20x34in) s. prov. 7-Mar-3 Skinner, Boston #512/R est:800-1200
£1006 $1600 €1509 Seaside cottage (51x87cm-20x34in) s. prov. 7-Mar-3 Skinner, Boston #513/R est:800-1200

JEFFERSON, John (fl.1811-1815) British
£420 $655 €630 Portrait of a gentleman, half length (58x46cm-23x18in) s.d.1817. 9-Apr-3 Andrew Hartley, Ilkley #939

JEFFERSON, Joseph (1829-1905) American
£3226 $5000 €4839 Moonrise, Louisiana (51x76cm-20x30in) s.i. prov. 2-Nov-2 North East Auctions, Portsmouth #72/R est:5000-8000

JEFFERYS, Charles William (1869-1951) Canadian
Works on paper
£661 $1038 €992 Last exit (36x28cm-14x11in) i. s.verso W/C htd white. 24-Jul-2 Walker's, Ottawa #207/R est:600-800 (C.D 1600)

JEFFERYS, Jack (1896-1961) Belgian
£1923 $2981 €3000 Still life (54x65cm-21x26in) mono. 7-Dec-2 De Vuyst, Lokeren #162/R est:3000-4000

JEFFERYS, Marcel (1872-1924) Belgian
£540 $863 €750 Elegante a la mantille (48x60cm-19x24in) mono. 19-May-3 Horta, Bruxelles #68
£566 $872 €900 Bruyere (20x40cm-8x16in) s. cardboard. 22-Oct-2 Campo, Vlaamse Kaai #526
£5346 $8286 €8500 Pavots (48x60cm-19x24in) s. painted 1897 exhib. 5-Oct-2 De Vuyst, Lokeren #448/R est:8500-9500
Works on paper
£1258 $1950 €2000 Interior of the San Marco Bascilica in Venice (48x38cm-19x15in) mono. W/C pastel prov.exhib. 5-Oct-2 De Vuyst, Lokeren #181/R est:2000-2500

JEFFRIES, H (19th C) British?
£420 $638 €630 Two gun dogs in a woodland landscape (51x76cm-20x30in) s. 9-Jul-2 Capes Dunn, Manchester #762

JELBERT, Wendy (20th C) British
Works on paper
£300 $489 €450 Red geraniums (39x48cm-15x19in) s. W/C htd bodycol. 29-Jan-3 Hampton & Littlewood, Exeter #376/R

JELINEK, Franz A (1890-1977) Czechoslovakian
£454 $736 €658 Semi nude in room (59x40cm-23x16in) s. panel. 24-May-3 Dorotheum, Prague #41/R est:10000-15000 (C.KR 20000)
£536 $848 €804 Bouquet (95x126cm-37x50in) s. 30-Nov-2 Dorotheum, Prague #61/R (C.KR 26000)
£701 $1108 €1052 Female semi-nude with hat and fan (71x56cm-28x22in) s. 30-Nov-2 Dorotheum, Prague #62/R (C.KR 34000)

JELINEK, Josef (1871-1945) Czechoslovakian
£513 $795 €800 Summer pleasures (32x40cm-13x16in) s. 5-Dec-2 Schopman, Hamburg #578

JELINEK, Rudolf (1880-?) Austrian
£655 $1022 €983 Rabbi reading (26x20cm-10x8in) s. panel. 20-Nov-2 Fischer, Luzern #2154/R est:1500-1800 (S.FR 1500)
£994 $1600 €1491 Interior scene with figures (58x79cm-23x31in) s. 23-Feb-3 Butterfields, Los Angeles #7019 est:1500-2000

JELINKOVA-JIRASKOVA, Bozena (1880-1951) Czechoslovakian
£310 $483 €465 Vase with bouquet (55x47cm-22x19in) s. 12-Oct-2 Dorotheum, Prague #60 (C.KR 15000)

JELLETT, Mainie (1897-1944) Irish
Prints
£2264 $3532 €3600 Abstract (39x30cm-15x12in) s.d.1927 silkscreen gouache prov. 17-Sep-2 Whyte's, Dublin #210/R est:1000-2000
Works on paper
£408 $678 €580 Abstract composition (24x11cm-9x4in) pencil. 10-Jun-3 James Adam, Dublin #272/R
£414 $646 €650 Study for Achill horses (24x38cm-9x15in) pencil. 6-Nov-2 James Adam, Dublin #91/R
£437 $725 €620 Abstract composition (25x17cm-10x7in) pencil. 10-Jun-3 James Adam, Dublin #274/R

£599 $994 €850 Abstract composition (26x16cm-10x6in) pencil. 10-Jun-3 James Adam, Dublin #273/R
£845 $1403 €1200 Abstract composition (20x26cm-8x10in) pencil. 10-Jun-3 James Adam, Dublin #275/R est:700-1000
£1646 $2551 €2600 Abstract compostion (18x24cm-7x9in) W/C. 25-Sep-2 James Adam, Dublin #82/R est:2500-3500
£2051 $3221 €3200 Abstract with stepped composition (17x16cm-7x6in) gouache over pencil card prov. 19-Nov-2 Whyte's, Dublin #2/R est:1800-2000
£2397 $3764 €3500 Adam (23x8cm-9x3in) gouache prov. 15-Apr-3 De Veres Art Auctions, Dublin #274/R est:2500-3500
£2603 $4086 €3800 Abstract study (21x12cm-8x5in) gouache. 15-Apr-3 De Veres Art Auctions, Dublin #120/R est:3000-4000
£3221 $5187 €4800 Abstract composition (20x22cm-8x9in) gouache over pencil card prov. 18-Feb-3 Whyte's, Dublin #13/R est:2000-3000
£3562 $5592 €5200 Abstract composition (26x21cm-10x8in) gouache. 15-Apr-3 De Veres Art Auctions, Dublin #119/R est:5000-7000
£3767 $5914 €5500 Abstract composition (18x10cm-7x4in) s. gouache. 15-Apr-3 De Veres Art Auctions, Dublin #210/R est:4500-6500
£4795 $7527 €7000 Female nude (21x28cm-8x11in) s.d.28 gouache. 15-Apr-3 De Veres Art Auctions, Dublin #121/R est:5000-7000

JEMOLI, Achille (1878-1960) Italian
£374 $595 €550 Cottages in the mountains (19x27cm-7x11in) s. board. 18-Mar-3 Finarte, Milan #167/R

JENDRASSIK, Jeno (1860-1919) Hungarian
£4644 $7244 €6966 Melon harvest, 1897 (125x80cm-49x31in) s.d.1897. 11-Sep-2 Kieselbach, Budapest #34/R (H.F 1800000)

JENE, Edgar (1904-1984) Austrian
Works on paper
£364 $594 €550 Heads (37x31cm-15x12in) s.d.29 W/C. 28-Jan-3 Dorotheum, Vienna #23/R

JENKINS, Arthur H (1871-?) British
£440 $682 €660 Springtime (34x44cm-13x17in) s. canvasboard. 26-Sep-2 Mellors & Kirk, Nottingham #694/R

JENKINS, Blanche (attrib) (fl.1872-1915) British
£580 $934 €870 Head and shoulders portrait of a young lady holding a single rose (47x37cm-19x15in) 19-Feb-3 Rupert Toovey, Partridge Green #22

JENKINS, David C (?-1916) British
£1500 $2460 €2250 Sur la plage (25x35cm-10x14in) s. panel. 29-May-3 Christie's, Kensington #262/R est:1200-1800

JENKINS, F Lynn (1870-1927) American/British
Sculpture
£1600 $2496 €2320 Classical manner with nude seated on a rock with putti (27cm-11in) s.d.1914 bronze on green marble base. 27-Mar-3 Lane, Penzance #391/R est:800-1000

JENKINS, George Henry (1843-1914) British
£340 $558 €510 Sloe picking, Dartmoor (44x76cm-17x30in) s. 10-Feb-3 Robin Fenner, Tavistock #683
£426 $660 €639 Coastal landscape with boat and figures (58x92cm-23x36in) s. 8-Dec-2 Uppsala Auktionskammare, Uppsala #70/R (S.KR 6000)
£1400 $2212 €2100 After a storm near the lizard with lifeboats by a wreck in a moonlit stormy sea (45x75cm-18x30in) s. i. on stretcher. 7-Apr-3 David Duggleby, Scarborough #402/R est:1000-1500
Works on paper
£1000 $1550 €1500 Agamemnon, moored in the Thames (36x54cm-14x21in) init. i.verso W/C. 4-Oct-2 ELR Auctions, Sheffield #259/R est:1000-1200

JENKINS, J Lebrun (1876-1951) American
£409 $650 €614 Missouri landscape (61x91cm-24x36in) s. board painted c.1940. 2-Mar-3 Toomey, Oak Park #717/R

JENKINS, Paul (1923-) American
£1206 $2013 €1700 Phenomena au parira de l'avril, Saint Paul de Vence (26x38cm-10x15in) s. s.i.d.verso. 18-Jun-3 Pierre Berge, Paris #85/R est:2000-3000
£1603 $2500 €2405 Phenomena sun shade (122x162cm-48x64in) s.i.d.1985 verso acrylic prov. 5-Nov-2 Doyle, New York #45/R est:4000-6000
£1603 $2500 €2405 Phenomena yellow gold trace (102x67cm-40x26in) s. s.i.d.1967 stretcher acrylic. 5-Nov-2 Doyle, New York #46/R est:2000-3000
£1824 $2827 €2900 Phenomena man entering doorway (100x81cm-39x32in) s.d.23/08/84 acrylic. 30-Oct-2 Artcurial Briest, Paris #692/R est:1500-2000
£2006 $3250 €2909 Phenomena telltale (91x91cm-36x36in) s. s.i.d.1964 overlap i.stretcher prov. 21-May-3 Doyle, New York #38/R est:1500-2500
£2083 $3292 €3000 Phenomena reading the signs (191x142cm-75x56in) acrylic collage. 28-Apr-3 Cornette de St.Cyr, Paris #421 est:3000-4000
£2800 $4564 €4200 Phenomena red wing (65x100cm-26x39in) s. s.i.d.1961 verso prov. 3-Feb-3 Sotheby's, Olympia #171/R est:3000-4000
£2848 $4500 €4500 Phenomena Prisma Reach (72x114cm-28x45in) s. s.i.d.1988 verso acrylic. 26-Nov-2 Camard, Paris #127/R est:5500
£2872 $4480 €4308 Phenomena Venus de Saint-Paul de Vence (100x81cm-39x32in) s. acrylic painted 1984. 18-Sep-2 Kunsthallen, Copenhagen #248/R est:40000 (D.KR 34000)
Works on paper
£488 $800 €708 Alice frog (53x35cm-21x14in) init. W/C pen ink wash exec.c.1950. 5-Jun-3 Swann Galleries, New York #128/R
£943 $1500 €1415 Phenomena Rheims' plane (58x77cm-23x30in) s. i.d.1972 verso W/C. 4-Mar-3 Swann Galleries, New York #364/R est:3000-5000
£976 $1600 €1415 Phenomena taino eye (57x76cm-22x30in) s.i.d. W/C. 5-Jun-3 Swann Galleries, New York #129/R est:2000-3000
£1019 $1600 €1529 Untitled (42x33cm-17x13in) s. W/C prov. 19-Nov-2 Wright, Chicago #216/R est:1000-1500
£1783 $2800 €2675 Abstract composition (77x57cm-30x22in) s. W/C. 21-Nov-2 Swann Galleries, New York #88/R est:1500-2500
£3165 $5000 €5000 Phenomena King f Diamonds (110x79cm-43x31in) s. s.i.d.1985 verso W/C. 29-Nov-2 Farsetti, Prato #426/R est:5500

JENKINS, Reginald (20th C) British
£490 $804 €735 Shepherd with his flock on a wooded track (37x41cm-15x16in) indis.sig. board. 29-May-3 Christie's, Kensington #171/R

JENKINS, Waveney (20th C) British
Sculpture
£1200 $1968 €1800 Two swimming otters (26cm-10in) num.3/10 bronze marble base. 3-Jun-3 Sotheby's, Olympia #102/R est:1200-1800

JENKINS, Wilfred (fl.1875-1888) British
£720 $1123 €1080 Street scenes at moonlight (46x35cm-18x14in) s. pair. 26-Mar-3 Sotheby's, Olympia #77/R
£750 $1170 €1125 Foss-Gate, York (46x35cm-18x14in) s.d.85 i.verso. 10-Apr-3 Tennants, Leyburn #958
£820 $1272 €1230 Cossington Manor, near Lincoln (50x76cm-20x30in) s. i.verso. 3-Dec-2 Sotheby's, Olympia #165/R
£1050 $1638 €1523 Scarborough. Whitby, harbour scenes (7x14cm-3x6in) s. board pair. 27-Mar-3 Neales, Nottingham #1049 est:750-900
£1800 $2916 €2700 Art gallery, Edinburgh (41x61cm-16x24in) s. i.verso. 20-May-3 Sotheby's, Olympia #235/R est:1000-1500
£4500 $7110 €6525 Moonlit quayside scenes with illuminated shops (39x59cm-15x23in) s. pair. 28-Jul-3 David Duggleby, Scarborough #285/R est:5000-7000

JENKINS, Wilfred (attrib) (fl.1875-1888) British
£580 $905 €870 Moonlit harbour scene with figures and fishing boats, possibly at Whitby (61x91cm-24x36in) bears sig. 25-Mar-3 Bonhams, Leeds #652

JENKINS, William John (1912-1994) British
£660 $1056 €990 Picnic party (63x124cm-25x49in) s. panel sold with preliminary sketch. 11-Mar-3 David Duggleby, Scarborough #191/R
Works on paper
£370 $592 €555 View of York (30x48cm-12x19in) s.d.1931 W/C. 11-Mar-3 David Duggleby, Scarborough #173/R

JENKINSON, John (attrib) (fl.1790-1823) British
£1600 $2480 €2400 Estuary scene with fisherman and a man-o-war at anchor (46x63cm-18x25in) s. with work by Daniel Turner two. 3-Dec-2 Sotheby's, Olympia #14/R est:1000-1500

JENNER, Isaac Walter (1836-1901) Australian
£820 $1304 €1230 Stranded on the rocks (25x41cm-10x16in) s. 4-Mar-3 Bonhams, Knightsbridge #285/R
£2000 $3040 €3000 Troopships at Spithead (20x42cm-8x17in) mono. board. 15-Aug-2 Bonhams, New Bond Street #426/R est:2000-3000
£3500 $5425 €5250 Troopships loading at Spithead (20x41cm-8x16in) mono. board. 31-Oct-2 Christie's, Kensington #481/R est:3000-5000

JENNEY, Neil (1945-) American
£35937 $57500 €53906 Atmosphere (84x202cm-33x80in) i. panel painted 1988-91 prov. 14-May-3 Sotheby's, New York #373/R est:60000-80000
£56250 $90000 €84375 Angled wood and angled wood (149x194cm-59x76in) i. s.d.1969 stretcher acrylic pencil prov. 14-May-3 Sotheby's, New York #370/R est:120000-180000
£63291 $100000 €94937 Sawn and saw (99x156cm-39x61in) i. painted 1970 prov.exhib. 13-Nov-2 Sotheby's, New York #550/R est:80000-120000

JENNINGS, Alix (20th C) British
£750 $1185 €1125 King Charles Spaniels (63x76cm-25x30in) s.d.1948. 28-Nov-2 Christie's, Kensington #335/R

JENNINGS, Humphrey (1907-1950) British
£6507 $10216 €9500 Usine a parfums (23x31cm-9x12in) i.verso exhib. 15-Apr-3 Laurence Calmels, Paris #4202/R

JENNY, Arnold (1831-1881) Swiss
£568 $886 €852 Urnersee with Nauen (70x104cm-28x41in) s.d.1867 canvas on board. 20-Nov-2 Fischer, Luzern #2155/R (S.FR 1300)

JENSEN, Alfred (1903-1981) American
£4839 $7500 €7259 Magneto-optical study No.19 (51x51cm-20x20in) s.i.d.1974 verso prov. 26-Sep-2 Christie's, Rockefeller NY #734/R est:8000-12000
£19266 $32174 €27936 Pyramid study (70x90cm-28x35in) s.i. verso prov. 20-Jun-3 Kornfeld, Bern #74/R est:50000 (S.FR 42000)
£20253 $32000 €30380 King Yu's odd progression and King Yu's even progression (122x102cm-48x40in) s.i.d.1971 acrylic diptych prov. 14-Nov-2 Christie's, Rockefeller NY #171/R est:30000-40000

Works on paper
£4255 $6894 €6000 Hekatompedon Per 6 (127x101cm-50x40in) s.i.d.Dez/ 1-1965 gouache board prov. 24-May-3 Van Ham, Cologne #295/R est:8000

JENSEN, Alfred (1859-1935) Danish
£302 $471 €480 Sailing ship (25x16cm-10x6in) s.d.1906 panel lit. 20-Sep-2 Schloss Ahlden, Ahlden #1161/R
£306 $496 €444 Seascape off Kronborg (54x81cm-21x32in) s. 24-May-3 Rasmussen, Havnen #2141 (D.KR 3200)
£366 $578 €530 Sailing ship at dusk (53x80cm-21x31in) s.d.1924 canvas on panel. 5-Apr-3 Quittenbaum, Hamburg #33/R
£387 $624 €550 Gathering storm in the high seas (74x117cm-29x46in) s.d.1917 lit. 9-May-3 Schloss Ahlden, Ahlden #1408/R
£652 $1036 €978 Hamburg Harbour (60x100cm-24x39in) s. 10-Mar-3 Rasmussen, Vejle #497/R (D.KR 7000)
£680 $1082 €1000 Seascape (24x36cm-9x14in) s. board. 25-Feb-3 Dorotheum, Vienna #113
£943 $1472 €1500 Harbour scene (80x120cm-31x47in) s. lit. 20-Sep-2 Schloss Ahlden, Ahlden #1159/R est:1600
£1633 $2596 €2400 The two-master 'Marie' being loaded in harbour (25x37cm-10x15in) s.d.1891 bears i. stretcher. 28-Mar-3 Bolland & Marotz, Bremen #469/R est:1100
£5479 $8548 €8000 Passenger ship (80x215cm-31x85in) s.d.1903. 10-Apr-3 Schopman, Hamburg #709a est:9000

JENSEN, Alfred V (19/20th C) Danish
£255 $403 €383 Kronborg at night (70x100cm-28x39in) s. 2-Dec-2 Rasmussen, Copenhagen #1391/R (D.KR 3000)
£354 $563 €531 From Copenhagen's main railway station (24x33cm-9x13in) s. 5-Mar-3 Rasmussen, Copenhagen #1846/R (D.KR 3800)
£455 $729 €683 Christian X on horseback on the liberation of Southern Jylland (50x72cm-20x28in) s. 13-Jan-3 Rasmussen, Vejle #175/R (D.KR 5200)
£596 $941 €894 Fishing boat at sea, sunset (110x150cm-43x59in) s. 2-Dec-2 Rasmussen, Copenhagen #1381/R (D.KR 7000)
£718 $1163 €1041 Red roses on white farmhouse (44x60cm-17x24in) s. 26-May-3 Rasmussen, Copenhagen #1465/R (D.KR 7500)

JENSEN, Arup (1906-) Danish
£409 $650 €614 Havenpart (64x94cm-25x37in) 28-Feb-3 Douglas, South Deerfield #4
£549 $846 €824 Naval battle (70x100cm-28x39in) s. 26-Oct-2 Rasmussen, Havnen #3126 (D.KR 6500)

JENSEN, Axel P (1885-1972) Danish
£280 $448 €420 Landscape (82x80cm-32x31in) s. 13-Jan-3 Rasmussen, Vejle #286 (D.KR 3200)
£306 $496 €444 White farm (66x92cm-26x36in) s. 24-May-3 Rasmussen, Havnen #4135 (D.KR 3200)
£317 $503 €476 Cherry orchard near Vedbaek (67x81cm-26x32in) s.d.39. 10-Mar-3 Rasmussen, Vejle #578 (D.KR 3400)
£322 $499 €483 Winter landscape with farm (118x141cm-46x56in) s.d.35. 1-Oct-2 Rasmussen, Copenhagen #293 (D.KR 3800)
£335 $529 €503 Coastal road, Vedbaek (65x81cm-26x32in) s.d.24. 1-Apr-3 Rasmussen, Copenhagen #570 (D.KR 3600)
£621 $1005 €900 Still life of bowl of fruit and bouquet of flowers (80x70cm-31x28in) s.d.51. 25-May-3 Uppsala Auktionskammare, Uppsala #261/R (S.KR 8000)
£782 $1244 €1173 Thawing - landscape with young couple (97x123cm-38x48in) s.d.1910 exhib.lit. 10-Mar-3 Rasmussen, Vejle #615/R (D.KR 8400)

JENSEN, Berit (1956-) Danish
£286 $478 €415 From Titan to Texas (65x56cm-26x22in) s.d.26/05/83 verso. 17-Jun-3 Rasmussen, Copenhagen #156 (D.KR 3000)
£743 $1175 €1115 Massernes Pneumatik (195x130cm-77x51in) s.d.1995 verso exhib. 1-Apr-3 Rasmussen, Copenhagen #364/R (D.KR 8000)

Works on paper
£758 $1258 €1099 Morphology - development of illusions (180x188cm-71x74in) s.d.1986 verso mixed media. 12-Jun-3 Kunsthallen, Copenhagen #133 (D.KR 8000)

JENSEN, Bill (1945-) American
£7595 $12000 €11393 Divers ferry (91x61cm-36x24in) s.i.d.1981-82-83 verso linen prov.exhib. 13-Nov-2 Sotheby's, New York #604/R est:8000-10000

JENSEN, C A (1792-1870) Danish
£838 $1332 €1257 The Holy Family (46x36cm-18x14in) after Raphael exhib. 5-Mar-3 Rasmussen, Copenhagen #1660/R (D.KR 9000)

JENSEN, Carl (1887-1961) Danish
£279 $441 €419 Shadows on the wall (81x65cm-32x26in) init.d.60. 1-Apr-3 Rasmussen, Copenhagen #507 (D.KR 3000)
£1208 $1909 €1812 Musicians (62x90cm-24x35in) s.d.1917 prov. 1-Apr-3 Rasmussen, Copenhagen #12/R est:5000 (D.KR 13000)

JENSEN, Christian Albrecht (1792-1870) Danish
£3825 $6081 €5738 Portraits of Hans Staal and Anne Sophie Hagen (64x50cm-25x20in) one s.d.1820 pair prov. 5-May-3 Rasmussen, Vejle #418/R est:10000-15000 (D.KR 41000)
£6891 $10474 €10337 Portrait of Levin Jorgen Rohde wearing blue uniform (66x51cm-26x20in) s.d.1828 prov. 27-Aug-2 Rasmussen, Copenhagen #1413/R est:100000-150000 (D.KR 80000)

JENSEN, Edvard Michael (1822-1915) Danish
£309 $482 €464 Deer by woodland lake (18x27cm-7x11in) mono. 11-Nov-2 Rasmussen, Vejle #637/R (D.KR 3600)

JENSEN, Einar Herman (1915-1951) Danish
£298 $471 €447 Landscape with ploughed fields (126x154cm-50x61in) s.d.43. 30-Nov-2 Rasmussen, Havnen #2087 (D.KR 3500)
£360 $580 €540 Potato harvesting (65x92cm-26x36in) s.d.42. 22-Feb-3 Rasmussen, Havnen #2205 (D.KR 4000)

JENSEN, Finn Hjortskov (1936-) Danish
£283 $451 €425 Composition (100x130cm-39x51in) init.d.75 verso. 26-Feb-3 Kunsthallen, Copenhagen #100 (D.KR 3100)
£283 $451 €425 Evening (65x78cm-26x31in) init.d.76 verso. 26-Feb-3 Kunsthallen, Copenhagen #150 (D.KR 3100)

JENSEN, George (1878-?) American
£390 $600 €585 Landscape (28x38cm-11x15in) s. panel. 8-Sep-2 DeFina, Austinburg #109

JENSEN, H P (?) ?

Works on paper
£317 $507 €476 Ship's portrait of Helge from Troense (52x74cm-20x29in) s. gouache. 16-Mar-3 Hindemae, Ullerslev #553 (D.KR 3400)

JENSEN, Hans Christian (1836-1903) Danish
£280 $445 €420 Portrait of Jorgen Hansen, Bishop of Als and Aero (37x32cm-15x13in) s,. 5-May-3 Rasmussen, Vejle #415/R (D.KR 3000)
£1490 $2369 €2235 Portrait of Agnes Drake, married to William Wain (111x97cm-44x38in) 5-Mar-3 Rasmussen, Copenhagen #1736/R est:15000-20000 (D.KR 16000)

JENSEN, Herman (1893-1947) Danish
£439 $698 €659 Figures on verandah (52x61cm-20x24in) s. 26-Feb-3 Kunsthallen, Copenhagen #303 (D.KR 4800)

JENSEN, Holger J (1900-1966) Danish

£343 $535 €515 Still life of objects on table (82x91cm-32x36in) mono. 11-Nov-2 Rasmussen, Vejle #28/R (D.KR 4000)

£431 $668 €647 Nature morte (51x65cm-20x26in) mono.d.33. 4-Dec-2 Kunsthallen, Copenhagen #359/R (D.KR 5000)

£743 $1175 €1115 Still life of fruit (52x68cm-20x27in) mono.d.30. 1-Apr-3 Rasmussen, Copenhagen #522/R (D.KR 8000)

JENSEN, Holger W (1880-?) American/Danish

£408 $600 €612 Great Smokie Mountain of NC (43x48cm-17x19in) board. 23-Jun-2 Susanin's, Chicago #5108/R

JENSEN, J-L (1800-1856) Danish

£1351 $2108 €2027 Yellow marguerites (22x15cm-9x6in) s. panel. 22-Sep-2 Hindemae, Ullerslev #7214/R est:20000 (D.KR 16000)

JENSEN, Johan-Laurents (1800-1856) Danish

£394 $634 €591 White blossom on twig (14x20cm-6x8in) s. panel. 7-May-3 Dobiaschofsky, Bern #716/R (S.FR 850)

£1292 $2093 €1873 Pansies in a Greek vase (8x11cm-3x4in) s. panel. 26-May-3 Rasmussen, Copenhagen #1227/R est:6000-8000 (D.KR 13500)

£1560 $2418 €2340 Bridal crown (13x17cm-5x7in) s. panel. 3-Dec-2 Bukowskis, Stockholm #361/R est:30000-35000 (S.KR 22000)

£1741 $2785 €2612 Still life of game (40x50cm-16x20in) s.d.1843 panel prov. 17-Mar-3 Blomqvist, Oslo #308/R est:40000-50000 (N.KR 20000)

£1795 $2782 €2800 Sprig of carnations (19x14cm-7x6in) i. panel. 4-Dec-2 Neumeister, Munich #776/R est:2500

£1862 $2961 €2793 Pink roses (25x19cm-10x7in) s. panel prov. 5-Mar-3 Rasmussen, Copenhagen #1538/R est:30000 (D.KR 20000)

£2700 $4293 €4050 Pink roses (23x16cm-9x6in) s. 5-Mar-3 Rasmussen, Copenhagen #1537/R est:20000-25000 (D.KR 29000)

£2705 $4301 €4058 Still life of pink roses in bowl on stone ledge (11x14cm-4x6in) s. 5-May-3 Rasmussen, Vejle #585/R est:25000 (D.KR 29000)

£3275 $5109 €4913 Still life with roses and anemonies (16x23cm-6x9in) s.d.1838 panel prov. 9-Nov-2 Galerie Gloggner, Luzern #89/R est:8000-9000 (S.FR 7500)

£3403 $5478 €5105 Still life of peonies (25x19cm-10x7in) s. panel. 11-May-3 Hindemae, Ullerslev #194/R est:30000 (D.KR 36000)

£4655 $7402 €6983 Bridal garland of pink roses (24x32cm-9x13in) s.d.1852. 5-Mar-3 Rasmussen, Copenhagen #1535/R est:70000 (D.KR 50000)

£4655 $7402 €6983 Still life of grapes growing and melon, peaches and nuts on table (69x53cm-27x21in) s. 5-Mar-3 Rasmussen, Copenhagen #1539/R est:60000-80000 (D.KR 50000)

£4842 $7698 €7263 Still life of roses on woodland (26x37cm-10x15in) s.d.1852. 5-Mar-3 Rasmussen, Copenhagen #1554/R est:40000-50000 (D.KR 52000)

£5599 $8510 €8399 Bouquet of roses on ledge (23x30cm-9x12in) s.d.1841. 27-Aug-2 Rasmussen, Copenhagen #1404/R (D.KR 65000)

£11483 $18603 €16650 Pink roses in a tall glass (32x24cm-13x9in) s. panel. 26-May-3 Rasmussen, Copenhagen #1158/R est:100000 (D.KR 120000)

£15311 $24804 €22201 Bouquet of flowers in a glass (36x27cm-14x11in) s. panel. 26-May-3 Rasmussen, Copenhagen #1159/R est:100000 (D.KR 160000)

£17000 $28390 €25500 Potted forget-me-nots with red, pink and white roses (36x46cm-14x18in) s.d.1824 prov.exhib. 19-Jun-3 Christie's, London #75/R est:20000-30000

£48000 $78720 €72000 Opstilling med georginer - still life with dahlias (94x69cm-37x27in) s.d.1842 prov. 3-Jun-3 Sotheby's, London #226/R est:50000-70000

£80851 $127745 €121277 Hollyhocks and dahlias in garden (160x108cm-63x43in) s.d.53. 2-Dec-2 Rasmussen, Copenhagen #1174/R est:900000-1000000 (D.KR 950000)

Works on paper

£380 $600 €600 Still life of flowers. s.d.1832 brush over pencil. 29-Nov-2 Bassenge, Berlin #5939/R

JENSEN, Johan-Laurents (attrib) (1800-1856) Danish

£1831 $2948 €2600 Still life of flowers with roses (14x19cm-6x7in) panel lit. 9-May-3 Schloss Ahlden, Ahlden #1347/R est:2600

JENSEN, Johan-Laurents (school) (1800-1856) Danish

£415 $643 €660 Autumn flowers (44x36cm-17x14in) 2-Nov-2 Hans Stahl, Toestorf #75

JENSEN, Johannes (1818-1874) Danish

£302 $462 €453 Portrait of Bertel Thorvaldsen (39x32cm-15x13in) s. 24-Aug-2 Rasmussen, Havnen #2042/R (D.KR 3500)

JENSEN, K (19/20th C) ?

£629 $981 €1000 Seascape (50x70cm-20x28in) s. 9-Oct-2 Michael Zeller, Lindau #747/R

JENSEN, Karl (1851-1933) Danish

£596 $941 €894 Interior scene with Professor Carl Thomsen and his family (42x55cm-17x22in) init. 30-Nov-2 Rasmussen, Havnen #2231 (D.KR 7000)

£605 $968 €908 Summer landscape with farm (32x40cm-13x16in) init.d.1910 prov. 16-Mar-3 Hindemae, Ullerslev #391/R (D.KR 6500)

£762 $1219 €1143 Old Bispegaard in Odense (56x73cm-22x29in) init.d.1915 exhib. 13-Jan-3 Rasmussen, Vejle #19/R (D.KR 8700)

JENSEN, Louis (20th C) American

£455 $700 €683 Surf and boulders (64x76cm-25x30in) s.i. board painted c.1920. 8-Sep-2 Treadway Gallery, Cincinnati #566/R

JENSEN, Louis Isak Napolean (1858-1908) Danish

£287 $465 €416 Landscape from North Sjaelland with view of Kronborg (22x26cm-9x10in) s. panel. 24-May-3 Rasmussen, Havnen #2097 (D.KR 3000)

£560 $857 €840 Landscape from Koge (76x96cm-30x38in) s.d.1883. 24-Aug-2 Rasmussen, Havnen #2183/R (D.KR 6500)

JENSEN, Max (fl.1887) German

£432 $708 €600 Sailing ship off steep coast (50x100cm-20x39in) s. 5-Jun-3 Dorotheum, Salzburg #488/R

£552 $883 €800 Seascape (60x100cm-24x39in) s. 11-Mar-3 Dorotheum, Vienna #23/R

£597 $926 €950 Off Rugen (68x105cm-27x41in) s. canvas on board. 29-Oct-2 Dorotheum, Vienna #103/R

£1096 $1710 €1600 Stormy sea (65x106cm-26x42in) s. 10-Apr-3 Dorotheum, Vienna #147/R est:1600-1800

£1218 $1912 €1900 Stormy sea (110x181cm-43x71in) s. 10-Dec-2 Dorotheum, Vienna #261/R est:1400-1700

JENSEN, Niels (20th C) Danish

£274 $436 €411 Romantic picture (94x58cm-37x23in) s.d.56 verso exhib. 26-Feb-3 Kunsthallen, Copenhagen #24/R (D.KR 3000)

JENSEN, Simony (1864-1932) Danish

£263 $411 €395 Interior scene with grandmother (47x36cm-19x14in) s. 5-Aug-2 Rasmussen, Vejle #2320 (D.KR 3100)

£306 $496 €444 Interior scene with monks (43x53cm-17x21in) s. 24-May-3 Rasmussen, Havnen #2131 (D.KR 3200)

£345 $549 €518 Wooded landscape with women by lake (45x65cm-18x26in) s. 5-May-3 Rasmussen, Vejle #711/R (D.KR 3700)

£559 $906 €850 Monks in ashop (41x51cm-16x20in) s. 21-Jan-3 Durán, Madrid #698/R

£560 $851 €840 At the gentleman's club (44x46cm-17x18in) 29-Aug-2 Christie's, Kensington #8/R

£633 $981 €1000 Three monks eating (41x51cm-16x20in) s. 26-Sep-2 Neumeister, Munich #2748/R

JENSEN, Thomas (1831-1916) British

£290 $450 €435 Portrait of a gentleman, purportedly William Pewrry (69x56cm-27x22in) s.d.1881. 25-Sep-2 Doyle, New York #44/R

JENSEN, Ulf Valde (1945-) Norwegian

Works on paper

£1286 $2108 €1865 From California suite VII (110x162cm-43x64in) s. W/C pencil exhib. 2-Jun-3 Blomqvist, Oslo #208/R est:8000-10000 (N.KR 14000)

JENSEN, Vilhelm (19/20th C) Danish

£1633 $2596 €2400 Stormy sea (71x110cm-28x43in) s.d.1913. 25-Feb-3 Dorotheum, Vienna #73/R est:2800-3400

JENSEN-KLINT, Peder Vilhelm (1853-?) Danish

£314 $487 €500 Evening lake and woodland with distant castle (90x126cm-35x50in) s. i. stretcher verso. 2-Nov-2 Hans Stahl, Toestorf #58/R

JENSSEN, Olav Christopher (1954-) Norwegian

£2437 $3899 €3656 Untitled (70x90cm-28x35in) s.i.d.1989 exhib. 17-Mar-3 Blomqvist, Oslo #439/R est:25000-30000 (N.KR 28000)

£4152 $6561 €6228 Violet composition (50x70cm-20x28in) s.i.d.1989 exhib. 2-Dec-2 Blomqvist, Oslo #491/R est:25000-30000 (N.KR 48000)

£5536 $8747 €8304 Pale afternoon XII (50x70cm-20x28in) s.i.d.1989 exhib. 2-Dec-2 Blomqvist, Oslo #485/R est:30000-35000 (N.KR 64000)

£6527 $10444 €9791 The family No. VIII (245x165cm-96x65in) s.i.d.1989-90 verso exhib. 17-Mar-3 Blomqvist, Oslo #447/R est:120000-150000 (N.KR 75000)

£10467 $16538 €15701 The family (245x165cm-96x65in) s.i.d.1989-90 stretcher exhib. 2-Dec-2 Blomqvist, Oslo #478/R est:120000-150000 (N.KR 121000)

JENTSCH, Adolph (1888-1977) German
Works on paper
£499 $803 €749 Extensive landscape (18x34cm-7x13in) init.d.1956 W/C. 12-May-3 Stephan Welz, Johannesburg #114 est:3000-5000 (SA.R 5800)
£723 $1143 €1085 Bome, Suidwest Afrika (37x59cm-15x23in) init.d.1967 s.i.verso W/C. 1-Apr-3 Stephan Welz, Johannesburg #444/R est:6000-9000 (SA.R 9000)

JENTZSCH, Johannes Gabriel (1862-?) German
£705 $1093 €1100 Biedermeier figures in garden (94x120cm-37x47in) s. 5-Dec-2 Neumeister, Munich #2815

JENUFA, Waiti (20th C) New Zealander
£702 $1095 €1053 Yeild (60x110cm-24x43in) s. painted 2002. 27-Mar-3 International Art Centre, Auckland #206 (NZ.D 2000)

JEPSEN, Morten (1826-1903) Danish
£379 $629 €550 The old market with figures (53x70cm-21x28in) 12-Jun-3 Kunsthallen, Copenhagen #335/R (D.KR 4000)
£419 $666 €629 Entrance at the Sanen Fratri Monastery, Capri (24x30cm-9x12in) mono. 5-Mar-3 Rasmussen, Copenhagen #1687/R (D.KR 4500)

JEPSON, Keith (?) British?
£300 $468 €450 Windjammer in full sail (49x69cm-19x27in) s.d.1970. 9-Apr-3 Cheffins Grain & Comins, Cambridge #749

JEPSON, Kenneth (?) British?
£450 $684 €675 Pericles (50x76cm-20x30in) s.d.72. 15-Aug-2 Bonhams, New Bond Street #382
Works on paper
£500 $745 €750 Sea battle (53x74cm-21x29in) s.d.1976 W/C. 28-Jun-2 Chrystals Auctions, Isle of Man #155/R
£520 $775 €780 Mermaid and Loire (53x74cm-21x29in) s.d.1975 i.verso W/C. 28-Jun-2 Chrystals Auctions, Isle of Man #154

JEQUIER, Jules (1834-1898) Swiss
£1397 $2194 €2096 St Gingolph au Lac Leman (34x49cm-13x19in) s. prov. 25-Nov-2 Sotheby's, Zurich #10/R est:2500-3500 (S.FR 3200)

JERICHAU, Harald Adolf Nikolai (1851-1878) Danish
£420 $667 €630 Man on donkey by town wall of Babylon (25x35cm-10x14in) mono. 5-May-3 Rasmussen, Vejle #574/R (D.KR 4500)
£559 $899 €839 Sunset (17x28cm-7x11in) init. panel. 22-Feb-3 Rasmussen, Havnen #2117 (D.KR 6200)
£5912 $9223 €8868 Parthenon in Athens (40x54cm-16x21in) mono.i. prov. 23-Sep-2 Rasmussen, Vejle #63/R est:80000-100000 (D.KR 70000)

JERICHAU, Holger H (1861-1900) Danish
£279 $444 €419 Mountain landscape (33x43cm-13x17in) s.i.d.1893. 10-Mar-3 Rasmussen, Vejle #181 (D.KR 3000)
£383 $605 €575 Italian flower seller (23x16cm-9x6in) init. 2-Dec-2 Rasmussen, Copenhagen #1303/R (D.KR 4500)
£426 $672 €639 Mother and child by gate on the Italian Campagna (33x56cm-13x22in) s. 2-Dec-2 Rasmussen, Copenhagen #1548/R (D.KR 5000)
£466 $740 €699 Italian woman by mountain lake (67x47cm-26x19in) s. 5-Mar-3 Rasmussen, Copenhagen #1881/R (D.KR 5000)
£511 $807 €767 Girl on woodland path (40x75cm-16x30in) s. 2-Dec-2 Rasmussen, Copenhagen #1314/R (D.KR 6000)
£511 $807 €767 View from a boat in the Mediterranean (33x41cm-13x16in) s. 2-Dec-2 Rasmussen, Copenhagen #1415/R (D.KR 6000)
£515 $803 €773 View of the sea with sailing ship, fisherboy in foreground, Italy (23x37cm-9x15in) s. 11-Nov-2 Rasmussen, Vejle #594/R (D.KR 6000)
£555 $899 €805 From the Bay of Naples with fishermen (31x46cm-12x18in) s. 24-May-3 Rasmussen, Havnen #2206/R (D.KR 5800)
£652 $1036 €978 Southern town scene with bridge across river (17x36cm-7x14in) s. 5-Mar-3 Rasmussen, Copenhagen #1803/R (D.KR 7000)
£802 $1252 €1203 Summer's day in an Italian garden with fountain, villa in background (41x33cm-16x13in) s.i. 23-Sep-2 Rasmussen, Vejle #222/R (D.KR 9500)
£885 $1406 €1328 Field landscape with waterway (44x68cm-17x27in) s. 5-Mar-3 Rasmussen, Copenhagen #2056/R (D.KR 9500)
£1274 $1987 €2000 Fishermen off Naples beach (37x67cm-15x26in) s.i. 6-Nov-2 Vendue Huis, Gravenhage #524/R est:2000-3000
£1582 $2453 €2500 Vue de Banares (54x75cm-21x30in) s. 27-Sep-2 Rabourdin & Choppin de Janvry, Paris #12/R est:3000-3200
£1637 $2488 €2456 Coastal landscape with beached boats, Capri (32x47cm-13x19in) s. 27-Aug-2 Rasmussen, Copenhagen #1688/R est:6000-8000 (D.KR 19000)
£1702 $2689 €2553 Coastal landscape with sailing boats and fishermen mending nets on beach, Italy (71x112cm-28x44in) s. 30-Nov-2 Rasmussen, Havnen #2278/R est:20000-25000 (D.KR 20000)
£3158 $5116 €4737 View towards Sorento from Capri (71x112cm-28x44in) s. 21-May-3 Museumsbygningen, Copenhagen #64/R est:25000-30000 (D.KR 33000)

JERICHAU, Jens Adolf (1816-1883) Danish
Sculpture
£1064 $1681 €1596 The panther hunter (70cm-28in) pat.bronze st.f.Rasmussen. 26-Nov-2 Rasmussen, Copenhagen #2381/R est:10000-12000 (D.KR 12500)
Works on paper
£360 $562 €540 Woman in profile (30x23cm-12x9in) s. pencil. 11-Nov-2 Rasmussen, Vejle #458/R (D.KR 4200)

JERICHAU, Jens Adolf (1890-1916) Danish
£775 $1202 €1163 Landscape from Hesselo (28x36cm-11x14in) 4-Dec-2 Kunsthallen, Copenhagen #351/R (D.KR 9000)
£2198 $3385 €3297 Palm trees in the South of France (42x29cm-17x11in) painted 1915 lit. 23-Oct-2 Kunsthallen, Copenhagen #44/R est:25000 (D.KR 26000)
£3717 $5874 €5576 The school in Athen (55x81cm-22x32in) painted c.1914 after Raphael prov.lit. 1-Apr-3 Rasmussen, Copenhagen #32/R est:40000-50000 (D.KR 40000)
£8453 $13018 €12680 Landscape, Bormes (48x58cm-19x23in) s.d.1912 prov.exhib.lit. 23-Oct-2 Kunsthallen, Copenhagen #114/R est:125000 (D.KR 100000)

JERICHAU-BAUMANN, Elisabeth (1819-1881) Danish
£1436 $2240 €2154 Portrait of girl with hat and shawl (38x32cm-15x13in) i.verso. 23-Sep-2 Rasmussen, Vejle #157/R est:12000-15000 (D.KR 17000)
£3158 $5116 €4579 Mother and her child (57x47cm-22x19in) s/d/1852 oval. 26-May-3 Rasmussen, Copenhagen #1127/R est:30000-40000 (D.KR 33000)
£6374 $9688 €9561 Portrait of the young archaeologist Conrad Engelhardt (62x49cm-24x19in) 28-Aug-2 Museumsbygningen, Copenhagen #78/R est:75000 (D.KR 74000)
Works on paper
£383 $620 €555 Portrait of the actress Johanne-Luise Heiberg (8x6cm-3x2in) pen Indian ink. 26-May-3 Rasmussen, Copenhagen #1593/R (D.KR 4000)

JERICHAU-BAUMANN, Elisabeth (attrib) (1819-1881) Danish
£2264 $3487 €3600 Bachi-bouzouk (83x66cm-33x26in) 23-Oct-2 Rabourdin & Choppin de Janvry, Paris #154/R

JERKEN, Erik (1898-1947) Swedish
£305 $473 €458 View toward Gustav Adolf's square (62x73cm-24x29in) s.d.1936. 8-Dec-2 Uppsala Auktionskammare, Uppsala #289 (S.KR 4300)
£388 $628 €563 Stockholm river with fishermen by Palace (50x60cm-20x24in) s.i. 25-May-3 Uppsala Auktionskammare, Uppsala #265 (S.KR 5000)
£701 $1093 €1052 Interior scene with flowers (92x73cm-36x29in) s.i.d.1941 panel. 5-Nov-2 Bukowskis, Stockholm #51/R (S.KR 10000)

JERNBERG, August (1826-1896) Swedish
£2082 $3310 €3123 Basket of flowers (43x52cm-17x20in) s. 3-Mar-3 Lilla Bukowskis, Stockholm #369 est:10000-12000 (S.KR 28000)

JERNBERG, August (attrib) (1826-1896) Swedish
£270 $449 €392 From an inn (37x47cm-15x19in) canvas on panel. 16-Jun-3 Lilla Bukowskis, Stockholm #492 (S.KR 3500)

JERNBERG, Olof (1855-1935) Swedish
£506 $800 €800 Landscape with low horizon, trees and farm buildings (51x61cm-20x24in) s. 30-Nov-2 Berlinghof, Heidelberg #330/R
£685 $1068 €1000 Castle in the lower Rhine (61x48cm-24x19in) s. panel. 10-Apr-3 Van Ham, Cologne #1512

£5319 $8245 €7979 Harbour scene with vessels in evening sunshine, entrance to Gothenburg (78x131cm-31x52in) s. 4-Dec-2 AB Stockholms Auktionsverk #1728/R est:50000-60000 (S.KR 75000)

JERNDORFF, August (1846-1906) Danish
£276 $422 €414 Garden at Frederiksborg Palace (48x41cm-19x16in) init. 24-Aug-2 Rasmussen, Havnen #2189/R (D.KR 3200)
£388 $589 €582 Young nude woman getting up, man lying by her side (27x33cm-11x13in) exhib.prov. 27-Aug-2 Rasmussen, Copenhagen #1947/R (D.KR 4500)

JEROME (19th C) American
£287 $448 €431 1967 (46x77cm-18x30in) s. panel on paper. 10-Sep-2 Iegor de Saint Hippolyte, Montreal #49 (C.D 700)

JEROME, G (19th C) American
£3774 $6000 €5661 Tropical landscape (76x127cm-30x50in) s.d.1876. 7-Mar-3 Skinner, Boston #285/R est:2000-4000

JEROME, Jean Paul (20th C) Canadian
£193 $302 €290 Geometric abstraction (30x24cm-12x9in) s.d.27/11/87. 25-Mar-3 Iegor de Saint Hippolyte, Montreal #69 (C.D 450)

JERVAS, Charles (1675-1739) British
£3354 $5500 €4863 Portrait of a lady, a fountain beyond (127x102cm-50x40in) 4-Jun-3 Christie's, Rockefeller NY #166/R est:6000-8000
£5500 $9130 €8250 Portrait of the Hon Mary Digby in a maroon dress and blue wrap, holding a basket of oranges (128x103cm-50x41in) prov. 10-Jun-3 Christie's, London #27/R est:6000-8000
£5500 $9075 €7975 Portrait of a lady (115x99cm-45x39in) canvas on panel prov. 2-Jul-3 Sotheby's, Olympia #9/R est:2000-3000

JERVAS, Charles (attrib) (1675-1739) British
£2700 $4401 €4050 Portrait of two boys, possibly brothers (72x59cm-28x23in) 30-Jan-3 Lawrence, Crewkerne #689/R est:1200-1800
£9756 $16000 €14634 Portrait of a boy, full-length, in a red coat, a dog by his side, in a landscape (152x101cm-60x40in) prov. 30-May-3 Christie's, Rockefeller NY #47/R est:10000-15000

JERVAS, Charles (style) (1675-1739) British
£7800 $12090 €11700 Portrait of King George II (236x145cm-93x57in) 30-Sep-2 Lawrence, Crewkerne #131/R est:7000-10000

JERZY, Richard (20th C) American
£385 $600 €578 Nude (81x61cm-32x24in) 18-Oct-2 Du Mouchelle, Detroit #2357/R
£750 $1200 €1125 Michelle (41x28cm-16x11in) board. 16-May-3 Du Mouchelle, Detroit #2224/R

JESPERS, Floris (1889-1965) Belgian
£278 $442 €400 L'etable (28x35cm-11x14in) s. panel. 29-Apr-3 Campo, Vlaamse Kaai #169
£284 $474 €400 Still life with vegetables (16x21cm-6x8in) s. panel. 23-Jun-3 Bernaerts, Antwerp #189/R
£302 $496 €420 Vue de maison - view of a house (12x14cm-5x6in) s. board. 3-Jun-3 Christie's, Amsterdam #289/R
£313 $497 €450 Dandy. s.d.1949 paper panel. 29-Apr-3 Campo & Campo, Antwerp #158
£340 $541 €500 Landscape with farmhouse (42x60cm-17x24in) s. 24-Mar-3 Bernaerts, Antwerp #813/R
£382 $607 €550 Arbres (34x40cm-13x16in) s. 29-Apr-3 Campo & Campo, Antwerp #156
£442 $703 €650 African sunset (54x75cm-21x30in) s. 24-Mar-3 Bernaerts, Antwerp #812/R
£475 $741 €750 Embouchure de l'Escaut (39x50cm-15x20in) s. 15-Oct-2 Horta, Bruxelles #425
£510 $811 €750 Le Christ (124x85cm-49x33in) s. panel. 18-Mar-3 Galerie Moderne, Brussels #534/R
£556 $883 €800 Printemps (60x50cm-24x20in) s. painted c.1935. 29-Apr-3 Campo & Campo, Antwerp #162
£597 $920 €950 Femmes africaines au marche (47x25cm-19x10in) paper prov. 22-Oct-2 Campo & Campo, Antwerp #144
£683 $1094 €950 Scene africaine (33x50cm-13x20in) s. cardboard. 13-May-3 Vanderkindere, Brussels #170
£692 $1072 €1100 Fishing boats. Along the River Schelde (22x26cm-9x10in) s. exhib. two. 5-Oct-2 De Vuyst, Lokeren #185
£694 $1104 €1000 Paysage Ardennais (78x50cm-31x20in) s. 29-Apr-3 Campo & Campo, Antwerp #161/R
£709 $1184 €1000 Marche africain (60x50cm-24x20in) s. 18-Jun-3 Hotel des Ventes Mosan, Brussels #244
£755 $1162 €1200 L'Escaut a Hoboken (18x22cm-7x9in) s.d.1913 cardboard. 22-Oct-2 Campo, Vlaamse Kaai #535
£769 $1192 €1200 Interior (42x54cm-17x21in) s. paper. 7-Dec-2 De Vuyst, Lokeren #166
£833 $1325 €1200 Abstraction en bleu et rouge (46x56cm-18x22in) s. 29-Apr-3 Campo & Campo, Antwerp #157/R
£886 $1382 €1400 Port d'Anvers. Arc-en-ciel (21x25cm-8x10in) s. one s.verso cardboard pair. 15-Oct-2 Horta, Bruxelles #426
£943 $1462 €1500 Landscape with cows (51x70cm-20x28in) s. 5-Oct-2 De Vuyst, Lokeren #184/R est:1700-2000
£1034 $1655 €1500 African forest (34x53cm-13x21in) s.d.51 paper. 15-Mar-3 De Vuyst, Lokeren #167/R est:1600-1800
£1181 $1877 €1700 Deux Congolaises (82x54cm-32x21in) eglomise. 29-Apr-3 Campo, Vlaamse Kaai #165 est:1200-1500
£1295 $2124 €1800 Still life (120x60cm-47x24in) s. board. 3-Jun-3 Christie's, Amsterdam #296/R est:1800-2200
£1392 $2172 €2200 Antwerpen (36x46cm-14x18in) s.d.1912 panel. 21-Oct-2 Bernaerts, Antwerp #520/R est:2000-3000
£1439 $2302 €2000 Summer landscape (42x60cm-17x24in) s. 17-May-3 De Vuyst, Lokeren #217/R est:2000-2400
£1572 $2421 €2500 Vue sur l'Escaut (82x121cm-32x48in) s.d.1963 panel. 22-Oct-2 Campo & Campo, Antwerp #142
£1583 $2596 €2200 Seascape (41x59cm-16x23in) s. verre eglomise. 3-Jun-3 Christie's, Amsterdam #275/R est:2500-3500
£1667 $2650 €2400 Abstraction blanc-rouge (57x75cm-22x30in) s.d.1928. 29-Apr-3 Campo & Campo, Antwerp #155/R est:2000-3000
£2083 $3312 €3000 Corbeille de fruits et legumes (65x80cm-26x31in) s.d.1942 paper on panel. 29-Apr-3 Campo, Vlaamse Kaai #162 est:3000-3500
£2244 $3478 €3500 Fleurs sur fond vert (60x75cm-24x30in) s. board. 3-Dec-2 Christie's, Amsterdam #235/R est:3000-5000
£2381 $3786 €3500 Les femmes africaines (102x147cm-40x58in) s. 19-Mar-3 Hotel des Ventes Mosan, Brussels #234/R est:4200-5600
£3472 $5521 €5000 Porteuse Congolaise (88x106cm-35x42in) s. 29-Apr-3 Campo, Vlaamse Kaai #168/R est:4000-5000
£7595 $11772 €12000 Arlequin (44x26cm-17x10in) s. on glass. 24-Sep-2 Galerie Moderne, Brussels #892/R est:10000-15000
£15972 $25396 €23000 Jeune fille a la palette (95x75cm-37x30in) s.d.1928. 29-Apr-3 Campo, Vlaamse Kaai #158/R est:23000-30000
£15972 $25396 €23000 Congolaises (33x61cm-13x24in) s. cardboard. 29-Apr-3 Campo, Vlaamse Kaai #158a est:750-850
£17730 $29610 €25000 Scene de cirque (88x67cm-35x26in) s. glass painting. 23-Jun-3 Bernaerts, Antwerp #191/R est:25000-30000
£100000 $164000 €150000 Mascarade de clowns (93x107cm-37x42in) board prov.exhib. 5-Feb-3 Sotheby's, London #143/R est:120000

Works on paper
£277 $429 €440 Nude (14x8cm-6x3in) s.d.1940 chl dr. 5-Oct-2 De Vuyst, Lokeren #187
£409 $634 €650 Congolees Tafereel (24x34cm-9x13in) s. W/C exhib. 5-Oct-2 De Vuyst, Lokeren #186
£552 $883 €800 Beach by the sea (24x31cm-9x12in) s.d.13 W/C. 15-Mar-3 De Vuyst, Lokeren #168
£881 $1374 €1400 Congolaises (46x64cm-18x25in) 14-Oct-2 Amberes, Antwerp #165
£1111 $1767 €1600 Fils Paul et son tourne-disque (32x24cm-13x9in) s.d.1923 dr exhib. 29-Apr-3 Campo & Campo, Antwerp #159/R est:500-750
£1151 $1888 €1600 Paysage - dune landscape (12x16cm-5x6in) s. oil on plywood. 3-Jun-3 Christie's, Amsterdam #288/R est:700-900
£3103 $4966 €4500 Clown (46x40cm-18x16in) s. eglomise exec.c.1957 prov. 15-Mar-3 De Vuyst, Lokeren #477/R est:5000-6000

JESPERS, Oscar (1887-1970) Belgian

Sculpture
£1154 $1812 €1800 Femme au chignon (51cm-20in) s.verso stone. 10-Dec-2 Renaud, Paris #128
£2051 $3179 €3200 Head of a woman (17cm-7in) s. enamelled earthenware conceived 1933-34 exhib.lit. 3-Dec-2 Christie's, Amsterdam #46/R est:1500-2000
£13669 $22417 €19000 Juvenile - Wiegekind (43cm-17in) s.d.1930 limestone prov.exhib.lit. 3-Jun-3 Christie's, Amsterdam #165/R est:12000-16000

JESPERSEN, Henrik (1853-1936) Danish
£287 $443 €431 River landscape with mountains in background (56x58cm-22x23in) s. 26-Oct-2 Rasmussen, Havnen #2166/R (D.KR 3400)
£355 $547 €533 Lake with snow covered mountains in background (52x80cm-20x31in) s. 26-Oct-2 Rasmussen, Havnen #2167 (D.KR 4200)
£360 $580 €540 Heather on the heath (52x98cm-20x39in) s. 22-Feb-3 Rasmussen, Havnen #2020 (D.KR 4000)
£467 $729 €701 Mountain landscape with pergola and fountain in foreground (65x98cm-26x39in) s. 5-Aug-2 Rasmussen, Vejle #134/R (D.KR 5500)
£478 $775 €693 Summer's day in the park - Brahetrolleborg (62x99cm-24x39in) s. exhib. 26-May-3 Rasmussen, Copenhagen #1489/R (D.KR 5000)
£508 $808 €762 Atop the forest (64x99cm-25x39in) s. 18-Mar-3 Maynards, Vancouver #38/R (C.D 1200)
£725 $1145 €1088 Mountain landscape (105x110cm-41x43in) s.d.1913. 5-Apr-3 Rasmussen, Havnen #2008/R (D.KR 7800)
£811 $1305 €1217 Park with manor house in background (39x61cm-15x24in) s. 22-Feb-3 Rasmussen, Havnen #2139 (D.KR 9000)
£1892 $3046 €2838 Palace garden in bloom (78x127cm-31x50in) s. 22-Feb-3 Rasmussen, Havnen #2141/R est:5000 (D.KR 21000)

JESPERSEN, Knud (1879-1954) Danish
£785 $1271 €1138 Landscape with house and cows (108x122cm-43x48in) s. 24-May-3 Rasmussen, Havnen #4141 (D.KR 8200)

JESS (1923-) American
Works on paper
£7692 $12000 €11538 Untitled, tribute to Edward Kitson (57x84cm-22x33in) s.i. collage. 14-Oct-2 Butterfields, San Francisco #2104/R est:6000-8000

JESSARI, V (?) ?
£360 $547 €540 Young beauty wearing a scarf in her hair (25x18cm-10x7in) s. b. 4-Jul-2 Duke & Son, Dorchester #250

JESSEN, Carl Ludwig (1833-1917) Danish/German
£1034 $1583 €1551 Portrait of Auguste and Peter Owesen (102x76cm-40x30in) s.d.1865 pair. 24-Aug-2 Rasmussen, Havnen #2304/R est:10000-15000 (D.KR 12000)

JESSER, Frederick (1971-) American
£563 $900 €816 Bridge (152x122cm-60x48in) s.d.2001 verso acrylic latex India ink acrylic paper map. 13-May-3 Sotheby's, Tel Aviv #78/R
£610 $1000 €885 Unhurried imagination (122x122cm-48x48in) s.d.2002 acrylic ink printed fabric on wood. 28-May-3 Sotheby's, Amsterdam #161/R est:1200-1800

JESSUP, Frederick (1920-) Australian
£1071 $1682 €1607 Still life (40x94cm-16x37in) s.d.58. 25-Nov-2 Christie's, Melbourne #274/R est:3000-5000 (A.D 3000)

JETELOWA, Magdalena (1946-) ?
Works on paper
£256 $405 €400 Untitled (61x41cm-24x16in) mono. mixed media board. 14-Nov-2 Neumeister, Munich #815/R
£284 $460 €400 Time present and time past are both present in time future, (107x76cm-42x30in) soot. 24-May-3 Van Ham, Cologne #296/R

JETOT, Ernestine (19th C) French
£759 $1200 €1200 Musicienne orientale (97x110cm-38x43in) s. 28-Nov-2 Piasa, Paris #60

JETTEL, Eugen (1845-1901) Austrian
£1100 $1716 €1650 Tending the geese (30x47cm-12x19in) s. canvasboard. 10-Sep-2 Bonhams, Knightsbridge #150/R est:400-600
£4000 $6280 €6000 At the edge of a farm (45x65cm-18x26in) 19-Nov-2 Bonhams, New Bond Street #29/R est:2000-3000
£6329 $10000 €10000 View of the Seine near Montereau (46x65cm-18x26in) s.d.94. 28-Nov-2 Dorotheum, Vienna #144/R est:12000-16000
£7848 $12243 €11772 Landscape at sunset (55x71cm-22x28in) s.d.80 panel. 12-Oct-2 Dorotheum, Prague #28/R est:300000-450000 (C.KR 380000)

JETTMAR, Rudolf (1869-1939) Austrian
Works on paper
£252 $390 €400 Landscape with cloudy sky (43x31cm-17x12in) s.d.909 W/C. 1-Oct-2 Dorotheum, Vienna #325/R

JEUNE, Henry le (1820-1904) British
£1050 $1638 €1575 Blackberry gatherers (23x28cm-9x11in) prov. 15-Oct-2 Canterbury Auctions, UK #156/R
£8000 $12880 €12000 Thy will be done (29x24cm-11x9in) panel prov.exhib.lit. 20-Feb-3 Christie's, London #155/R est:10000
£10127 $16000 €15191 Bite (71x56cm-28x22in) mono.d.1875 canvas on panel. 23-Apr-3 Christie's, Rockefeller NY #137/R est:12000-18000
Works on paper
£800 $1296 €1200 Primroses (24x34cm-9x13in) mono.d.1870 W/C. 20-May-3 Sotheby's, Olympia #220/R
£5000 $7750 €7500 In thought (33x25cm-13x10in) mono.d.1868 W/C. 3-Dec-2 Sotheby's, Olympia #132/R est:4000-6000

JEUNE, James le (1910-1983) Irish
£1745 $2809 €2600 Carribean boys (51x41cm-20x16in) s. canvasboard. 18-Feb-3 Whyte's, Dublin #174/R est:3000-4000
£1800 $2880 €2700 Portrait of Lady Kilbrachan (76x65cm-30x26in) s. 15-May-3 Christie's, Kensington #143/R est:2000-3000
£3718 $5763 €5800 Young girl and boy at garden gate (25x35cm-10x14in) s. prov. 3-Dec-2 Bonhams & James Adam, Dublin #60/R est:3000-5000
£3846 $5962 €6000 At the races (29x45cm-11x18in) s. board prov. 3-Dec-2 Bonhams & James Adam, Dublin #57/R est:2800-3200

JEUNE, le (?) ?
£1039 $1579 €1600 Landscape with two figures. board. 2-Jul-2 Thomas Adams, Dublin #255

JEWELS, Mary (1886-1977) British
£4800 $8016 €6960 Mousehole Harbour (41x51cm-16x20in) s.d.1943 board prov. 19-Jun-3 Lane, Penzance #160/R est:5000-7000

JEWETT, William Smith (1812-1873) American
£1592 $2500 €2388 Portrait of a couple in a landscape with a valley beyond (76x64cm-30x25in) s.verso prov. 19-Nov-2 Butterfields, San Francisco #8011/R est:5000-7000

JEX, Garnet W (1895-1979) American
£3481 $5500 €5222 Under the arch, Key Bridge (51x61cm-20x24in) s. i.d.1932 verso prov. 24-Apr-3 Shannon's, Milford #208/R est:3000-5000

JIANG HANTING (1903-1963) Chinese
Works on paper
£1159 $1901 €1600 Lotus and insects (101x49cm-40x19in) s. seal Indian ink col hanging scroll. 30-May-3 Dr Fritz Nagel, Stuttgart #1195/R est:600-1000

JIANG JIA SHENG (1955-) Chinese
£314 $484 €500 Nude (100x100cm-39x39in) s. 22-Oct-2 Campo & Campo, Antwerp #149

JIANG PU (1708-1761) Chinese
Works on paper
£3108 $5128 €4507 Flowers, birds and insects (28x22cm-11x9in) one s. ink col eight. 6-Jul-3 Christie's, Hong Kong #452/R est:50000-60000 (HK.D 40000)

JIANG SHI GUO (1960-) Chinese
Works on paper
£442 $703 €650 Poisson en colere (68x68cm-27x27in) st.sig.d.2002 mixed media collage. 24-Mar-3 Coutau Begarie, Paris #332

JIANG TINGXI (attrib) (1669-1732) Chinese
£658 $980 €987 Paysage aux fleurs et oiseau (169x82cm-67x32in) st.i. paint silk laid on masonite. 26-Jun-2 Iegor de Saint Hippolyte, Montreal #56 (C.D 1500)

JIJE (20th C) French
Works on paper
£417 $688 €600 L'Angelus (24x32cm-9x13in) s. W/C ink crayon paper on board. 3-Jul-3 Christie's, Paris #34/R

JILOVSKY, Georg (1884-?) Czechoslovakian
£321 $506 €500 Flourishing meadows (68x78cm-27x31in) s. 18-Nov-2 Dorotheum, Linz #294/R

JIMENEZ Y ARANDA, Jose (1837-1903) Spanish
£5625 $9000 €8438 La lecture amusante (33x24cm-13x9in) s.i.d.1887 prov. panel. 14-May-3 Butterfields, San Francisco #1054/R est:6000-8000
£12000 $18600 €18000 Que calor hace!! (24x32cm-9x13in) s.d.1873 s.i. verso panel. 4-Dec-2 Christie's, London #1/R est:15000-20000
£27419 $43323 €42500 Scene from Don Quixote (55x79cm-22x31in) s.d.1868 lit. 18-Dec-2 Castellana, Madrid #16/R est:42000
£35484 $56065 €55000 Scene from Don Quixote (56x79cm-22x31in) s.d.1868 lit. 18-Dec-2 Castellana, Madrid #36/R est:55000
£54839 $86645 €85000 Lace sellers (56x72cm-22x28in) s.d.1869 i.verso lit. 18-Dec-2 Castellana, Madrid #14/R est:85000
Works on paper
£14000 $21980 €21000 Sketches for Don Quijote. one s. pen ink wash htd white set of 23. 19-Nov-2 Sotheby's, London #76/R est:4000-5000

JIMENEZ Y FERNANDEZ, Federico (1841-?) Spanish
£2830 $4415 €4500 Good mother (75x52cm-30x20in) s. 23-Sep-2 Durán, Madrid #225/R
£2830 $4415 €4500 Unexpected (40x75cm-16x30in) s. 23-Sep-2 Durán, Madrid #244/R

JIMENEZ Y MARTIN, Juan (1858-1901) Spanish
£2516 $3925 €4000 Story teller (28x35cm-11x14in) s. board. 23-Sep-2 Durán, Madrid #243/R
£3020 $4862 €4500 Story-teller (28x35cm-11x14in) s. board. 18-Feb-3 Durán, Madrid #216/R

JIMENEZ, Luis Alfonso (jnr) (1940-) American
Sculpture
£1603 $2500 €2405 Fiesta dancers (46x51x33cm-18x20x13in) s.d.86 num.2/6 fiberglass with wood base. 5-Nov-2 Doyle, New York #23/R est:2000-3000

JINDRA, Jaromir (1895-1984) Czechoslovakian
£431 $699 €625 Windows (68x25cm-27x10in) s.d.32. 24-May-3 Dorotheum, Prague #109/R est:12000-18000 (C.KR 19000)

JIRASEK, Alfred (1863-1931) Austrian
£256 $405 €400 River landscape (24x30cm-9x12in) s. board. 18-Nov-2 Dorotheum, Linz #295/R

JIRLOW, Lennart (1936-) Swedish
£3089 $4973 €4634 Exterior of restaurant (37x45cm-15x18in) s. 7-May-3 AB Stockholms Auktionsverk #897/R est:50000-60000 (S.KR 40000)
£7428 $11884 €10771 Coffee in the garden (81x65cm-32x26in) s. 18-May-3 Anders Antik, Landskrona #51 est:100000 (S.KR 95000)
£7605 $12015 €11408 In the garden, Provence (50x61cm-20x24in) s. 28-Apr-3 Bukowskis, Stockholm #297/R est:100000-125000 (S.KR 100000)
£9506 $15019 €14259 The auction (65x91cm-26x36in) s. 28-Apr-3 Bukowskis, Stockholm #288/R est:125000-150000 (S.KR 125000)
£14672 $23622 €22008 Picnic in the country (65x81cm-26x32in) s. 7-May-3 AB Stockholms Auktionsverk #753/R est:150000-200000 (S.KR 190000)
Works on paper
£618 $1025 €896 Lady wearing hat (32x21cm-13x8in) s. mixed media. 16-Jun-3 Lilla Bukowskis, Stockholm #242 (S.KR 8000)
£1121 $1749 €1682 Le Figaro (51x37cm-20x15in) s.i.d.29.10 mixed media on newspaper. 5-Nov-2 Bukowskis, Stockholm #137/R est:15000-18000 (S.KR 16000)
£1141 $1802 €1712 Le Figaro (52x37cm-20x15in) s.i.d.1990 hand col newspaper page. 28-Apr-3 Bukowskis, Stockholm #287/R est:15000-18000 (S.KR 15000)
£1313 $2114 €1970 The cook (21x11cm-8x4in) s. gouache on airmail envelope. 7-May-3 AB Stockholms Auktionsverk #738/R est:12000-15000 (S.KR 17000)

JIRSKI, P E (19th C) ?
Sculpture
£20382 $32000 €30573 Bathing woman with child (18cm-7in) s. marble raised marble pediment. 21-Nov-2 Sotheby's, New York #112/R est:15000-20000

JIVENS, H (?) ?
£520 $822 €780 Harvesting scene (71x92cm-28x36in) s. 12-Nov-2 Rosebery Fine Art, London #705

JOACHIM, Guy (1955-) Haitian
£202 $329 €303 Wounded man (39x39cm-15x15in) s.i. 12-Feb-3 Iegor de Saint Hippolyte, Montreal #106/R (C.D 500)

JOACHIM, Jean (1905-1990) French
Sculpture
£972 $1605 €1400 Le chat couche (11x15x8cm-4x6x3in) s.num.8/8 red brown pat bronze. 2-Jul-3 Artcurial Briest, Paris #47/R est:1500-2000
£1795 $2782 €2800 Canard (31x36x15cm-12x14x6in) s. num.1/8 brown pat bronze Cast Bodin. 7-Dec-2 Martinot & Savignat, Pontoise #80

JOANNIS, Alex (19th C) Canadian?
£410 $639 €615 Portrait de dame a la mantille (106x71cm-42x28in) s.d.1880. 10-Sep-2 Iegor de Saint Hippolyte, Montreal #63 (C.D 1000)

JOANOVITCH, Paul (1859-1957) Austrian
£8861 $14000 €14000 Girl with rye spinner (24x32cm-9x13in) s. panel. 28-Nov-2 Dorotheum, Vienna #36/R est:5000-6000

JOANS, Ted (1928-) American
Works on paper
£1096 $1721 €1600 White hair revolver is still loaded (33x24cm-13x9in) s. s.d.1963 verso assemblage oil on canvas. 15-Apr-3 Laurence Calmels, Paris #4220/R

JOBBINS, William H (fl.1872-1893) British
£772 $1282 €1119 It is time for a meal (41x57cm-16x22in) s.d.83. 16-Jun-3 Lilla Bukowskis, Stockholm #511 (S.KR 10000)

JOBERT, Fernand (19th C) French
Works on paper
£810 $1304 €1150 Lande printanniere au Belon (23x32cm-9x13in) mono. W/C. 11-May-3 Thierry & Lannon, Brest #88

JOBERT, Paul (1863-?) French
£1097 $1700 €1646 Sailing ship at sea (60x73cm-24x29in) s.i. 2-Oct-2 Christie's, Rockefeller NY #799/R est:2000-3000
£2075 $3196 €3300 Port de Philippeville (60x74cm-24x29in) s. i.verso lit. 23-Oct-2 Rabourdin & Choppin de Janvry, Paris #260/R

JOBLING, Isa (1850-1926) British
£390 $605 €585 Lincluden, from Nunholme (24x33cm-9x13in) s.d.22 i.verso. 24-Sep-2 Anderson & Garland, Newcastle #526/R

JOBLING, Robert (1841-1923) British
£780 $1303 €1131 Ships moored at North Shields harbour (29x44cm-11x17in) s. 17-Jun-3 Anderson & Garland, Newcastle #450/R
£850 $1292 €1275 Looking across the lake on a calm day (30x51cm-12x20in) s.d.1878. 29-Aug-2 Christie's, Kensington #44/R
£3000 $4560 €4500 Brig Pearl off the coast (82x123cm-32x48in) s. 15-Aug-2 Bonhams, New Bond Street #368/R est:2000-3000
£4000 $6480 €6000 Shipping off a jetty at dusk (30x51cm-12x20in) s.d.1873. 22-Jan-3 Bonhams, New Bond Street #382/R est:4000-6000
£4444 $7067 €6666 Launching the cable (34x52cm-13x20in) s.d.1884. 4-Mar-3 Dales, Durban #11 (SA.R 56000)
£6000 $9960 €9000 Yorkshire cobbles with figures on a beach (61x93cm-24x37in) s. 10-Jun-3 Bonhams, Leeds #199/R est:6000-8000
Works on paper
£600 $930 €900 North Shields ferry with ships in the harbour beyond (36x49cm-14x19in) s. W/C. 24-Sep-2 Anderson & Garland, Newcastle #340

JOBSON, John (1941-) British
£500 $800 €750 Tide pool, near Green Castle, Co Down (30x24cm-12x9in) mono. s.i.d.01 on backboard. 15-May-3 Christie's, Kensington #249/R
£550 $803 €825 Back road, Annaghmore (23x23cm-9x9in) s. board. 12-Jun-2 John Ross, Belfast #190
£1911 $2981 €3000 Farmyard (75x89cm-30x35in) init. board. 6-Nov-2 James Adam, Dublin #60/R est:2000-4000
£3767 $5914 €5500 Gaggle of geese (107x122cm-42x48in) s.d.02 canvas on board. 15-Apr-3 De Veres Art Auctions, Dublin #225/R est:6000-8000

JOCQUE, Willy (1900-1960) Belgian
£651 $1015 €950 Barge dans un canal (68x70cm-27x28in) s. canvas on panel. 14-Apr-3 Horta, Bruxelles #59

JODE, Hans de (attrib) (17th C) Dutch
£774 $1223 €1200 Mountainous landscape with bridge (36x47cm-14x19in) panel. 20-Dec-2 Tajan, Paris #91

JODE, Peeter de II (1606-?) Flemish
Works on paper
£380 $600 €600 Pope Innocent discovering the wounds of St Francis (11x18cm-4x7in) pen wash. 29-Nov-2 Bassenge, Berlin #5329

JODICE, Mimmo (1934-) Italian
Photographs
£9000 $13860 €13500 Atleti dalla villa dei papiri (97x160cm-38x63in) polyptych four black white photograph executed 2000. 22-Oct-2 Christie's, London #58/R est:9000-10000

JOENSEN-MIKINES, S (1906-1979) Danish
Works on paper
£521 $865 €755 Killing of whale (25x31cm-10x12in) s.d.42 Indian ink. 12-Jun-3 Kunsthallen, Copenhagen #261 (D.KR 5500)
£1073 $1706 €1610 Killing of the whale (33x47cm-13x19in) s.d.68 W/C. 29-Apr-3 Kunsthallen, Copenhagen #223/R (D.KR 11500)

JOENSEN-MIKINES, Samuel (1906-1979) Danish
£1501 $2341 €2252 Coastal landscape with cliffs, Faroe Islands (62x80cm-24x31in) s. 11-Nov-2 Rasmussen, Vejle #57/R est:15000-20000 (D.KR 17500)
£2479 $4139 €3595 Landscape with houses, Faroe Islands (73x87cm-29x34in) s.d.55. 17-Jun-3 Rasmussen, Copenhagen #82/R est:30000-40000 (D.KR 26000)

£2574 $4298 €3732 Jesus at Lake Genezareth (55x70cm-22x28in) s.d.49. 17-Jun-3 Rasmussen, Copenhagen #77/R est:25000-35000 (D.KR 27000)
£2756 $4189 €4134 Killing the whale (65x80cm-26x31in) s. 3-Sep-2 Museumsbygningen, Copenhagen #568/R est:30000-40000 (D.KR 32000)
£4647 $7342 €6971 Rural district with green hills in background (90x111cm-35x44in) s.d.60. 1-Apr-3 Rasmussen, Copenhagen #65/R est:50000 (D.KR 50000)
£4803 $7492 €7205 Killing of whales, Faroe Islands with figures and boats (85x100cm-33x39in) s.d.64. 11-Nov-2 Rasmussen, Vejle #65/R est:30000-50000 (D.KR 56000)
£4833 $7636 €7250 Bonfire on beach, Midsummer Night (100x125cm-39x49in) s.d.62. 1-Apr-3 Rasmussen, Copenhagen #68/R est:40000-50000 (D.KR 52000)
£6691 $10572 €10037 Green cliff formation (106x125cm-42x49in) s.d.1960. 1-Apr-3 Rasmussen, Copenhagen #86/R est:75000 (D.KR 72000)
£6856 $10900 €10284 Killing of whale (100x130cm-39x51in) s.d.42. 26-Feb-3 Kunsthallen, Copenhagen #270/R est:80000 (D.KR 75000)

JOFFE, Chantal (1969-) British
£380 $635 €551 Batman (10x10cm-4x4in) s.i.d.2000 verso card. 24-Jun-3 Sotheby's, Olympia #10/R
£720 $1202 €1044 Me and Mill (21x29cm-8x11in) s.i.d.April 2000 board. 24-Jun-3 Sotheby's, Olympia #9/R
£1058 $1639 €1650 Untitled (29x21cm-11x8in) s.d.1999 verso board. 4-Dec-2 Finarte, Milan #454/R

JOHANN, Hugo (1890-?) ?
£2193 $3421 €3290 Landscape with houses, 1921 (31x23cm-12x9in) W/C. 11-Sep-2 Kieselbach, Budapest #92/R (H.F 850000)
Works on paper
£538 $834 €780 Italian landscape with viaduct (23x29cm-9x11in) chl exhib. 9-Dec-2 Mu Terem Galeria, Budapest #31/R est:180000 (H.F 200000)
£914 $1417 €1325 Siena (31x22cm-12x9in) s.d.1921 chl exhib. 9-Dec-2 Mu Terem Galeria, Budapest #30/R est:180000 (H.F 340000)

JOHANNESEN, Nils Andreas (1844-1926) Norwegian
£565 $886 €848 Landscape with figures by waterfall (72x116cm-28x46in) s.i. 16-Dec-2 Lilla Bukowskis, Stockholm #5 (S.KR 8000)

JOHANNESSEN, Erik Harry (1902-1980) Norwegian
£664 $1082 €996 Ballad about the strange town (100x100cm-39x39in) s.d.1973. 17-Feb-3 Blomqvist, Lysaker #1089 (N.KR 7500)
£929 $1515 €1394 Landscape from Arles (54x59cm-21x23in) s.d.1960. 17-Feb-3 Blomqvist, Lysaker #1088/R (N.KR 10500)
£1044 $1671 €1566 Inspecting the tools (90x95cm-35x37in) s.d.1952 s.i.d.verso. 17-Mar-3 Blomqvist, Oslo #425/R (N.KR 12000)
£1218 $1950 €1827 Four women (65x81cm-26x32in) s. s.i.d.1960 verso. 17-Mar-3 Blomqvist, Oslo #429/R est:18000-22000 (N.KR 14000)
£1741 $2785 €2612 Home from fishing (80x94cm-31x37in) init. s.i.d.1955 verso panel. 17-Mar-3 Blomqvist, Oslo #428/R est:25000-30000 (N.KR 20000)
£2805 $4545 €4208 Longing (70x70cm-28x28in) init. s.i.d.1963 verso. 26-May-3 Grev Wedels Plass, Oslo #115/R est:40000 (N.KR 31000)
£3620 $5864 €5430 Old street scene with figures (81x65cm-32x26in) init. s.i.d.1947 verso panel. 26-May-3 Grev Wedels Plass, Oslo #114/R est:50000-70000 (N.KR 40000)
Works on paper
£1214 $1894 €1821 Figures in alley (59x47cm-23x19in) s.d.1948 pastel. 21-Oct-2 Blomqvist, Oslo #460/R est:14000-16000 (N.KR 14000)
£1327 $2097 €1991 Figures in alley (59x47cm-23x19in) s.d.1948 pastel. 28-Apr-3 Blomqvist, Oslo #350/R est:12000-15000 (N.KR 15000)

JOHANNESSEN, Jens (1934-) Norwegian
£1085 $1758 €1628 The steel sickle (31x31cm-12x12in) s. exhib. 27-Jan-3 Blomqvist, Lysaker #1102/R (N.KR 12000)
£2611 $4178 €3917 Composition with leaves (33x19cm-13x7in) init. i.d.1995 verso. 17-Mar-3 Blomqvist, Oslo #458/R est:40000-50000 (N.KR 30000)
£8651 $13668 €12977 Sky and sun (100x80cm-39x31in) s.d.68 exhib. 2-Dec-2 Blomqvist, Oslo #464/R est:80000-100000 (N.KR 100000)
£11246 $17768 €16869 Sign (100x80cm-39x31in) s.d.68 exhib. 2-Dec-2 Blomqvist, Oslo #497/R est:80000-100000 (N.KR 130000)
£26980 $43168 €40470 Pavilion (207x140cm-81x55in) init. lit. 17-Mar-3 Blomqvist, Oslo #441/R est:350000-450000 (N.KR 310000)
£260191 $405898 €390287 Collage journey (120x270cm-47x106in) init.d.74 triptych exhib.lit. 21-Oct-2 Blomqvist, Oslo #425/R est:2500000-2800000 (N.KR 3000000)
Works on paper
£796 $1298 €1194 Town with harbour (34x47cm-13x19in) s. W/C oval. 17-Feb-3 Blomqvist, Lysaker #1090 (N.KR 9000)

JOHANNESSEN, Johannes (1890-1981) Danish
£1144 $1910 €1659 Cubist landscape (68x73cm-27x29in) s.d.17. 17-Jun-3 Rasmussen, Copenhagen #164/R est:5000 (D.KR 12000)

JOHANNOT, Alfred (1800-1837) French
Works on paper
£285 $450 €450 Painting lesson (10x7cm-4x3in) s. W/C. 2-Dec-2 Rieunier, Paris #36
£4494 $7100 €7100 Francois I et Charles V (48x68cm-19x27in) s. W/C htd gouache. 2-Dec-2 Rieunier, Paris #37/R

JOHANNSEN, Albert (1890-1975) German
Works on paper
£270 $422 €400 Husum harbour slipway (32x44cm-13x17in) s. ochre prov. 28-Mar-3 Ketterer, Hamburg #45/R

JOHANNSEN, Theodor (1868-?) German
£417 $646 €650 Mark landscape (101x80cm-40x31in) s.d.1935 prov. 7-Dec-2 Ketterer, Hamburg #174/R

JOHANSEN, Axel (1872-1938) Danish
£279 $441 €419 From Copenhagen Canal (40x36cm-16x14in) s.d.1926. 5-Apr-3 Rasmussen, Havnen #2153 (D.KR 3000)
£297 $481 €431 From Copenhagen's Harbour (54x77cm-21x30in) s. 24-May-3 Rasmussen, Havnen #2003 (D.KR 3100)
£321 $495 €482 Canal view, Copenhagen (53x68cm-21x27in) s.d.1927. 26-Oct-2 Rasmussen, Havnen #2157 (D.KR 3800)
£500 $785 €750 Vessels at a Danish port (53x69cm-21x27in) s.d.1927. 16-Apr-3 Christie's, Kensington #589/R
£651 $1028 €977 Harbour scene (73x92cm-29x36in) mono. exhib. 1-Apr-3 Rasmussen, Copenhagen #43/R (D.KR 7000)
£2278 $3532 €3600 Market in Nurnberg (73x60cm-29x24in) s.d.1913. 28-Sep-2 Hans Stahl, Hamburg #21/R est:2400

JOHANSEN, Hans Lorentz (19th C) Danish
Works on paper
£603 $916 €905 Still life of roses, tulips and lilacs in vase with bluetit on ledge (49x38cm-19x15in) s.d.1858 gouache. 27-Aug-2 Rasmussen, Copenhagen #1796/R (D.KR 7000)

JOHANSEN, Svein (1946-) Norwegian
£1735 $2706 €2603 Winter journey XXIII (73x100cm-29x39in) s. i.verso. 21-Oct-2 Blomqvist, Oslo #416/R est:25000-30000 (N.KR 20000)
£2775 $4330 €4163 Building with arched opening (74x97cm-29x38in) s. s.verso. 21-Oct-2 Blomqvist, Oslo #441/R est:22000-26000 (N.KR 32000)

JOHANSEN, Svend (1890-1970) Danish
£429 $716 €622 Composition with three nude women and dog (163x130cm-64x51in) with sig.stretcher. 17-Jun-3 Rasmussen, Copenhagen #140/R (D.KR 4500)
£540 $859 €810 Town prospect with Gothic towers (39x67cm-15x26in) init. stage design. 4-Mar-3 Museumsbygningen, Copenhagen #469/R (D.KR 5800)
£2332 $3708 €3498 Still life of fruit on table (54x65cm-21x26in) init.i.d.24. 29-Apr-3 Kunsthallen, Copenhagen #234/R est:30000 (D.KR 25000)
£5338 $8915 €7740 Hojbro Plads with Kristiansborg (136x116cm-54x46in) exhib. 17-Jun-3 Rasmussen, Copenhagen #95/R est:60000-80000 (D.KR 56000)
£10223 $16152 €15335 Still life of fruit and jugs (110x81cm-43x32in) init.d.25 exhib. 1-Apr-3 Rasmussen, Copenhagen #18/R est:80000-100000 (D.KR 110000)
Works on paper
£355 $547 €533 Stage picture - Maybe we forget - at the New Theatre (46x64cm-18x25in) init. gouache exhib. 23-Oct-2 Kunsthallen, Copenhagen #333/R (D.KR 4200)
£447 $711 €671 Woodland (39x67cm-15x26in) init. i.verso W/C stage design exhib. 4-Mar-3 Museumsbygningen, Copenhagen #468/R (D.KR 4800)

JOHANSEN, Viggo (1851-1935) Danish
£298 $471 €447 Coastal landscape (40x52cm-16x20in) s. 27-Nov-2 Museumsbygningen, Copenhagen #51 (D.KR 3500)
£343 $542 €515 Coastal landscape (22x31cm-9x12in) init.d.75. 13-Nov-2 Kunsthallen, Copenhagen #5 (D.KR 4000)
£360 $580 €540 Botanical Garden, Copenhagen (56x41cm-22x16in) st.verso painted c.1925. 26-Feb-3 Museumsbygningen, Copenhagen #109 (D.KR 4000)

£388 $628 €563 Still life of flowers in green vase (47x41cm-19x16in) s.d.12.9.19. 25-May-3 Uppsala Auktionskammare, Uppsala #220/R (S.KR 5000)
£423 $651 €635 Still life of apples in bowl and dish (63x61cm-25x24in) s.d.1918. 26-Oct-2 Rasmussen, Havnen #2098 (D.KR 5000)
£474 $720 €711 Copenhagen's Harbour in winter (33x40cm-13x16in) s.d.1924. 27-Aug-2 Rasmussen, Copenhagen #1732/R (D.KR 5500)
£512 $814 €768 Door to garden at Hillerod, sunny day (46x39cm-18x15in) s.d.1934 exhib. 5-Mar-3 Rasmussen, Copenhagen #2035/R (D.KR 5500)
£596 $941 €894 Cloud study (44x67cm-17x26in) prov. 2-Dec-2 Rasmussen, Copenhagen #1221/R (D.KR 7000)
£596 $941 €894 Rowing boat at edge of sea (32x45cm-13x18in) s.i.d.1896. 2-Dec-2 Rasmussen, Copenhagen #1357/R (D.KR 7000)
£670 $1066 €1005 Interior scene with man (35x43cm-14x17in) s.i.d.1893. 10-Mar-3 Rasmussen, Vejle #71/R (D.KR 7200)
£681 $1076 €1022 In the country - ducks outside farm (63x84cm-25x33in) s.d.1894. 2-Dec-2 Rasmussen, Copenhagen #1755/R (D.KR 8000)
£807 $1259 €1211 Coastal landscape from Hornbaek (23x30cm-9x12in) s.i.d.75. 5-Aug-2 Rasmussen, Vejle #26/R (D.KR 9500)
£919 $1471 €1379 Thatched white farmhouse in Kastrup (40x61cm-16x24in) s.d.1895. 13-Jan-3 Rasmussen, Vejle #142/R (D.KR 10500)
£933 $1483 €1400 Coastal landscape, Skagen (26x33cm-10x13in) s.i.d.80 prov. 5-May-3 Rasmussen, Vejle #261/R (D.KR 10000)
£1277 $2017 €1916 Road past farm at sunset (53x50cm-21x20in) mono.d.1906. 2-Dec-2 Rasmussen, Copenhagen #1758/R est:15000 (D.KR 15000)
£1397 $2221 €2096 Academic gathering at Charlottenborg in 1904 (69x92cm-27x36in) s.d.Jan 1906 study. 5-Mar-3 Rasmussen, Copenhagen #2021/R est:15000-20000 (D.KR 15000)
£1545 $2441 €2318 Clear day in September at Skagen (45x66cm-18x26in) s.d.1912 exhib. 13-Nov-2 Kunsthallen, Copenhagen #76/R est:20000 (D.KR 18000)
£1637 $2488 €2456 Skagen Nordstrand with beached boats and dunes in background (44x70cm-17x28in) s.d.18.9.10 st.verso. 28-Aug-2 Museumsbygningen, Copenhagen #57/R est:20000-25000 (D.KR 19000)
£2500 $4175 €3625 Young girl knitting (58x4cm-23x2in) s. 8-Jul-3 Bonhams, Knightsbridge #94/R est:2500-3500
£7656 $12402 €11101 Children listening to grown-ups talking (72x95cm-28x37in) s.d.90 prov. 26-May-3 Rasmussen, Copenhagen #1486/R est:50000 (D.KR 80000)
£14468 $22860 €21702 Coastal landscape, Skagen (127x105cm-50x41in) s.i.d.90. 2-Dec-2 Rasmussen, Copenhagen #1111/R est:100000-150000 (D.KR 170000)
£18723 $29583 €28085 Beached boats on shore, low sun (42x84cm-17x33in) init.i.d.90 prov. 2-Dec-2 Rasmussen, Copenhagen #1112/R est:250000 (D.KR 220000)

Works on paper
£468 $740 €702 Women and children feeding geese at pond (45x60cm-18x24in) s.d.1900 pastel. 2-Dec-2 Rasmussen, Copenhagen #1825/R (D.KR 5500)

JOHANSEN, Viggo (attrib) (1851-1935) Danish
£886 $1409 €1329 Woman washing clothes in courtyard (50x42cm-20x17in) 5-May-3 Rasmussen, Vejle #653/R (D.KR 9500)

JOHANSON-THOR, Emil (1889-1958) Swedish
£262 $404 €393 The church by the sea (41x32cm-16x13in) s.d.1931 panel. 27-Oct-2 Anders Antik, Landskrona #2 (S.KR 3800)

JOHANSSON, Albert (1926-1998) Swedish
£666 $1039 €999 Fata Morgana (92x122cm-36x48in) s.d.1985 verso panel. 6-Nov-2 AB Stockholms Auktionsverk #700/R (S.KR 9500)
£847 $1330 €1271 Untitled (86x117cm-34x46in) 16-Dec-2 Lilla Bukowskis, Stockholm #75 (S.KR 12000)
£1472 $2296 €2208 Plav - abstract composition (58x51cm-23x20in) s.d.1959 verso panel. 6-Nov-2 AB Stockholms Auktionsverk #538/R est:8000-12000 (S.KR 21000)
£1612 $2514 €2418 Ra - composition (100x199cm-39x78in) s.d.jan 1959 verso panel. 6-Nov-2 AB Stockholms Auktionsverk #536/R est:30000-35000 (S.KR 23000)

Works on paper
£771 $1203 €1157 Walk at night (80x60cm-31x24in) s.d.1961 verso mixed media panel. 6-Nov-2 AB Stockholms Auktionsverk #766/R (S.KR 11000)
£1081 $1741 €1622 Boys choir (50x60cm-20x24in) s.d.1962 mixed media. 7-May-3 AB Stockholms Auktionsverk #777/R est:8000-10000 (S.KR 14000)
£1197 $1927 €1796 Gront Jaglosa I - green mask composition (60x75cm-24x30in) s.d.1965 mixed media. 7-May-3 AB Stockholms Auktionsverk #778/R est:8000-10000 (S.KR 15500)

JOHANSSON, Carl (1863-1944) Swedish
£319 $495 €479 Landscape with watercourse, Kallsjon (31x46cm-12x18in) s.d.20 panel. 8-Dec-2 Uppsala Auktionskammare, Uppsala #142 (S.KR 4500)
£412 $626 €618 Bay with boat houses (38x55cm-15x22in) s. 16-Aug-2 Lilla Bukowskis, Stockholm #162 (S.KR 6000)
£550 $902 €798 Summer landscape with fence and building (31x46cm-12x18in) s.i. 4-Jun-3 AB Stockholms Auktionsverk #2317/R (S.KR 7000)
£786 $1288 €1140 Summer landscape (50x76cm-20x30in) s.d.92. 4-Jun-3 AB Stockholms Auktionsverk #2173/R (S.KR 10000)
£864 $1417 €1253 Summer landscape, Ramsele (39x54cm-15x21in) s.indis.d. panel. 4-Jun-3 AB Stockholms Auktionsverk #2310/R (S.KR 11000)
£929 $1478 €1394 Sunset on the west coast (58x84cm-23x33in) s. 3-Mar-3 Lilla Bukowskis, Stockholm #335 (S.KR 12500)
£1206 $1869 €1809 Landscape with mountains (34x60cm-13x24in) s.d.84. 4-Dec-2 AB Stockholms Auktionsverk #1780/R est:12000-15000 (S.KR 17000)
£1296 $2126 €1879 Lake landscape, Bollnas (27x45cm-11x18in) s. panel. 4-Jun-3 AB Stockholms Auktionsverk #2163/R est:12000-15000 (S.KR 16500)
£2128 $3298 €3192 Winter landscape (52x78cm-20x31in) s.d.88. 4-Dec-2 AB Stockholms Auktionsverk #1584/R est:25000-30000 (S.KR 30000)
£2405 $3896 €3487 Boy fishing (64x113cm-25x44in) s.i.d.91. 26-May-3 Bukowskis, Stockholm #129/R est:20000-25000 (S.KR 31000)

JOHANSSON, Eric (1896-1979) German
Works on paper
£309 $497 €464 Spiral composition (31x23cm-12x9in) chl lit. 7-May-3 AB Stockholms Auktionsverk #904/R (S.KR 4000)

JOHANSSON, Helge (1886-1926) Swedish
£466 $728 €699 View from the ruin, Cagnes (60x46cm-24x18in) s.d.1923. 13-Sep-2 Lilla Bukowskis, Stockholm #670 (S.KR 6800)
£1141 $1802 €1712 Landscape from the hills near Port d'Orleans (60x73cm-24x29in) s.i.d.1924. 28-Apr-3 Bukowskis, Stockholm #27/R est:18000-20000 (S.KR 15000)

JOHANSSON, Johan (1879-1951) Swedish
£254 $399 €368 Untitled. prov. 15-Dec-2 Anders Antik, Landskrona #22 (S.KR 3600)

JOHANSSON, Lars (1945-) Swedish
£608 $961 €912 Standing figure (102x80cm-40x31in) s. 28-Apr-3 Bukowskis, Stockholm #958a/R (S.KR 8000)

JOHANSSON, Rune (1943-) Swedish
£241 $372 €362 Otter and dippers (60x73cm-24x29in) s.d.2000. 27-Oct-2 Anders Antik, Landskrona #284/R (S.KR 3500)
£248 $382 €372 Young fox with his catch (60x73cm-24x29in) s.d.1999. 27-Oct-2 Anders Antik, Landskrona #283/R (S.KR 3600)
£320 $509 €480 Still life (38x56cm-15x22in) init. 26-Feb-3 Kunsthallen, Copenhagen #306 (D.KR 3500)

JOHANSSON, Stefan (1876-1955) Swedish
Works on paper
£1800 $2808 €2700 Portrait of a girl (27x22cm-11x9in) W/C exec.c.1903. 17-Sep-2 Sotheby's, Olympia #286/R est:2000-3000
£2483 $4022 €3600 Landscape (30x40cm-12x16in) s. pastel exec.c.1900. 26-May-3 Bukowskis, Stockholm #118/R est:30000-40000 (S.KR 32000)
£2560 $4147 €3712 Study of lamp (23x16cm-9x6in) s. W/C canvas. 26-May-3 Bukowskis, Stockholm #117/R est:25000-30000 (S.KR 33000)

JOHANSSON, Sven-Erik (1925-) Swedish
Works on paper
£477 $753 €716 Composition (57x42cm-22x17in) s.d.1969 mixed media. 30-Nov-2 Goteborg Auktionsverk, Sweden #552/R (S.KR 6800)

JOHFRA (1919-) Dutch
£633 $1000 €950 Landscape with female nude (23x18cm-9x7in) s.d.1951 board. 3-Apr-3 Boos Gallery, Michigan #207/R
£695 $1119 €1043 De mistere van het sameneijn (24x18cm-9x7in) s.d.1957 panel. 7-May-3 AB Stockholms Auktionsverk #1109/R (S.KR 9000)

JOHN, Augustus (1878-1961) British

£4115 $6379 €6173 Woman in a purple dress and green hood (229x117cm-90x46in) prov. 3-Dec-2 Ritchie, Toronto #3023/R est:10000-15000 (C.D 10000)

£4800 $7440 €7200 Mask - Harry Melville (112x86cm-44x34in) s. exhib. 4-Dec-2 Christie's, Kensington #417/R est:4000-6000

£6500 $10075 €9750 Portrait of a boy (76x64cm-30x25in) s. 3-Dec-2 Bonhams, New Bond Street #21/R est:7000-10000

£7200 $11808 €10800 Portrait of Vivien, the artist's daughter (51x41cm-20x16in) prov. 6-Jun-3 Christie's, London #140/R est:6000-8000

£16000 $24960 €24000 Portrait of Dorelia, in a coloured headscarf by a tree (41x33cm-16x13in) 10-Apr-3 Tennants, Leyburn #1132/R est:6000-8000

£110000 $180400 €165000 Dorelia in a red dress (183x82cm-72x32in) painted c.1906 prov. 6-Jun-3 Christie's, London #138/R est:50000-80000

Works on paper

£380 $593 €570 Study for an allegorical composition (17x23cm-7x9in) pen ink wash prov. 15-Oct-2 Bonhams, Knightsbridge #158/R

£420 $693 €609 Standing female nude (41x22cm-16x9in) pen black ink. 3-Jul-3 Christie's, Kensington #250/R

£600 $954 €900 Three women (28x38cm-11x15in) s.i. pencil two. 26-Feb-3 Sotheby's, Olympia #57/R

£600 $954 €900 Gypsies (18x28cm-7x11in) pen ink. 26-Feb-3 Sotheby's, Olympia #62/R

£650 $1007 €975 Profile of the head of a bearded man (11x11cm-4x4in) s. sepia dr. 3-Dec-2 Bonhams, Knightsbridge #227/R

£650 $1034 €975 Soldier and cure conversing. Roman soldiers by a fire (16x24cm-6x9in) pen ink two. 26-Feb-3 Sotheby's, Olympia #58/R

£786 $1241 €1179 Two girls (31x25cm-12x10in) s. ink col wash. 26-Nov-2 Sotheby's, Melbourne #238 est:2200-2800 (A.D 2200)

£1100 $1716 €1650 Head of a woman (34x23cm-13x9in) s. pencil. 10-Apr-3 Tennants, Leyburn #912/R est:500-700

£1400 $2282 €2100 Composition, figures round a piano in an interior (33x23cm-13x9in) s. pen ink exhib. 30-Jan-3 Lawrence, Crewkerne #658/R est:1400-1800

£1500 $2355 €2250 Mulatto, study for an etching (10x9cm-4x4in) s. pencil executed c.1906 prov. 21-Nov-2 Christie's, London #120/R est:1500-2500

£1500 $2460 €2250 Sailor's return (39x43cm-15x17in) pen ink. 3-Jun-3 Sotheby's, Olympia #8/R est:1500-2000

£1800 $2826 €2700 Head of Ida (13x11cm-5x4in) pencil executed c.1900-05 prov. 21-Nov-2 Christie's, London #119/R est:2000-3000

£1800 $2808 €2700 Study of Dorelia standing in profile (32x19cm-13x7in) pencil. 10-Apr-3 Tennants, Leyburn #911 est:1000-1500

£1900 $3001 €2850 Three girls by a tree (13x21cm-5x8in) s. pen ink prov. 27-Nov-2 Sotheby's, Olympia #14/R est:600-800

£2000 $3280 €2900 Dorelia (30x23cm-12x9in) s. pencil W/C prov.exhib. 5-Jun-3 Christie's, London #197/R est:3000-5000

£2000 $3120 €3000 Studies of the artist's son Pyramus (23x24cm-9x9in) s. pencil. 10-Apr-3 Tennants, Leyburn #910/R est:2500-3500

£2013 $3242 €3000 Self portrait (19x30cm-7x12in) red chk prov. 18-Feb-3 Whyte's, Dublin #76/R est:3000-4000

£2200 $3608 €3190 Fur collar, portrait of Helen Georgiana Grant (35x25cm-14x10in) s. col chk executed c.1905 prov. 5-Jun-3 Christie's, London #198/R est:2500-3500

£2400 $3816 €3600 Male figure (30x35cm-12x14in) i. red conte. 26-Feb-3 Sotheby's, Olympia #60/R est:1000-1500

£3000 $4830 €4500 Dorelia (21x25cm-8x10in) s. black chk prov. 15-Jan-3 Cheffins Grain & Comins, Cambridge #397/R

£3500 $5600 €5250 Study for composition, Galway (24x35cm-9x14in) s. pencil exec.c.1915 prov. 15-May-3 Christie's, London #62/R est:3000

£3800 $5890 €5700 Dorelia (32x25cm-13x10in) s. pencil prov. 4-Dec-2 Christie's, Kensington #235/R est:1500-2000

£4000 $6680 €5800 Portrait of Romilly John (29x23cm-11x9in) s.d.1931 prov.exhib. 24-Jun-3 Bonhams, New Bond Street #32/R est:2000-3000

£4500 $7380 €6750 Tambimuttu (32x27cm-13x11in) s. black chk. 3-Jun-3 Sotheby's, Olympia #9/R est:4000-6000

£4600 $7222 €6900 Casper (35x21cm-14x8in) s. pencil executed c.1910. 21-Nov-2 Christie's, London #121/R est:5000-8000

£4600 $7176 €6900 Portrait of Aida Nettleship (27x22cm-11x9in) col chk. 10-Apr-3 Tennants, Leyburn #914/R est:6000-8000

£6000 $9420 €9000 Study of a female nude (41x27cm-16x11in) chl executed c.1898. 21-Nov-2 Christie's, London #122/R est:2500-3500

£7500 $11775 €11250 Fishergirl's at Equihen, Normandy (34x48cm-13x19in) s. pen ink wash executed 1907 prov.exhib.lit. 21-Nov-2 Christie's, London #118/R est:8000-12000

£7500 $11925 €11250 Portrait of a girl, possibly Ethel Nettleship (17x15cm-7x6in) red chk. 26-Feb-3 Sotheby's, Olympia #63/R est:3000-5000

£14000 $22960 €20300 Portrait of Iris Tree (37x28cm-15x11in) s.d.1914 pencil prov. 5-Jun-3 Christie's, London #199/R est:12000-16000

£18000 $29520 €26100 Dorelia with folded arms (34x16cm-13x6in) s. pencil prov.lit. 5-Jun-3 Christie's, London #196/R est:15000-20000

£55000 $86350 €82500 Head of Edie McNeill (34x23cm-13x9in) s. pencil executed c.1906. 21-Nov-2 Christie's, London #116/R est:40000-60000

JOHN, Augustus (attrib) (1878-1961) British

£383 $571 €575 Spanish maid (65x55cm-26x22in) i. painted 1954 prov. 27-Aug-2 Christie's, Melbourne #356/R est:1500-2500 (A.D 1000)

£10000 $15600 €15000 Portrait of the artist's son, Caspar, in a black hat (35x30cm-14x12in) 10-Apr-3 Tennants, Leyburn #1131/R est:10000-15000

Works on paper

£250 $385 €375 Portrait of a lady (36x25cm-14x10in) s. 8-Sep-2 Lots Road, London #344

JOHN, Edwin (1905-) British

Works on paper

£380 $635 €551 Still life with hyacinths and oranges on a table (36x34cm-14x13in) s. W/C double-sided. 19-Jun-3 Lane, Penzance #122

JOHN, Gwen (1876-1939) British

£54000 $83700 €81000 Portrait of a girl in grey (25x20cm-10x8in) painted 1910-20 prov.exhib.lit. 4-Dec-2 Sotheby's, London #44/R est:25000-35000

Works on paper

£300 $468 €450 Portrait of a young girl (23x18cm-9x7in) pencil dr. 11-Apr-3 Keys, Aylsham #249

£1000 $1550 €1500 Study of a plant (19x12cm-7x5in) s. pencil W/C prov. 3-Dec-2 Bonhams, New Bond Street #34/R est:1000-1500

£2516 $4000 €3774 Seated cat washing (17x14cm-7x6in) i. brush ink wash pencil executed c.1905. 3-Mar-3 Swann Galleries, New York #33/R est:3000-5000

£3500 $5460 €5250 Sleeping cats (12x16cm-5x6in) estate st. pencil W/C prov. 9-Oct-2 Woolley & Wallis, Salisbury #113/R est:800-1200

£3600 $5580 €5400 Boy wearing a cap (22x17cm-9x7in) st.sig. pencil prov.exhib.lit. 4-Dec-2 Sotheby's, London #23/R est:3000-5000

£12000 $18840 €18000 Portrait of lady reclining (19x25cm-7x10in) pencil grey wash executed c.1910. 21-Nov-2 Christie's, London #123/R est:8000-10000

JOHN, Marie (20th C) ?

Works on paper

£818 $1267 €1300 Voir au dela et savoir (60x60cm-24x24in) s. mixed media panel. 7-Oct-2 Claude Aguttes, Neuilly #80

JOHNS, Dora (?) British

£280 $468 €406 Old slip, Newlyn (53x48cm-21x19in) s. indis d. verso. 20-Jun-3 Keys, Aylsham #411

JOHNS, Jasper (1930-) American

£5696203 $9000000 €8544305 O through 9 (137x105cm-54x41in) s.d.61 verso prov.exhib. 13-Nov-2 Christie's, Rockefeller NY #44/R est:6000000-8000000

Prints

£1887 $3000 €2831 Ventriloquist (83x56cm-33x22in) s.d.num.34/70 lithograph. 2-May-3 Sotheby's, New York #485/R est:3000-5000

£1911 $3000 €2867 Sketch from untitled I (109x74cm-43x29in) s.d.num.34/50 col lithograph. 21-Nov-2 Swann Galleries, New York #91/R est:2500-3500

£2044 $3250 €3066 Black and white numerals number 2 (69x53cm-27x21in) s.d.1968 num.36/70 col lithograph. 3-May-3 Rachel Davis, Shaker Heights #373/R est:1500-2500

£2051 $3200 €3077 Sketch, from untitled II (93x66cm-37x26in) s.d.num.24/50 black grey lithograph. 5-Nov-2 Christie's, Rockefeller NY #417/R est:2000-3000

£2244 $3500 €3366 Souvenir (78x57cm-31x22in) s.d.num.50/50 col lithograph. 5-Nov-2 Christie's, Rockefeller NY #414/R est:2500-3500

£2244 $3500 €3366 Zone (112x74cm-44x29in) s.d.num.63/65 col lithograph. 5-Nov-2 Christie's, Rockefeller NY #415/R est:2000-3000

£2436 $3800 €3654 Voice 2 (50x66cm-20x26in) s.d.num.8/9 col lithograph edition of 41. 5-Nov-2 Christie's, Rockefeller NY #433/R est:5000-7000

£2516 $4000 €3774 Ale cans (12x21cm-5x8in) s.i.d.67-69 etching aquatint. 29-Apr-3 Christie's, Rockefeller NY #626/R est:2500-3500

£2516 $4000 €3774 Zone (91x55cm-36x22in) s.d.num.62/65 col lithograph. 29-Apr-3 Christie's, Rockefeller NY #627/R est:3000-4000

£2564 $4000 €3846 Critic smiles (64x51cm-25x20in) s.i.d.num.20/40 metallic paint lithograph. 5-Nov-2 Christie's, Rockefeller NY #410/R est:5000-6000

£2690 $4250 €4035 Untitled (86x62cm-34x24in) s.d.1982 num.55/77 etching. 22-Apr-3 Butterfields, San Francisco #2305/R est:5000-6000

£2800 $4620 €4060 Untitled (85x65cm-33x26in) s.d.num.16/66 col lithograph. 2-Jul-3 Christie's, London #258/R est:2000-3000

£2987 $4750 €4481 Flag (43x66cm-17x26in) s.num.225/300 col offset lithograph. 2-May-3 Sotheby's, New York #484/R est:3000-4000

£3145 $5000 €4718 Souvenir (67x54cm-26x21in) s.d.num.55/63 col lithograph. 29-Apr-3 Christie's, Rockefeller NY #629/R est:3000-5000

£3145 $5000 €4718 Evian (112x74cm-44x29in) s.d.num.43/64 col lithograph. 29-Apr-3 Christie's, Rockefeller NY #630/R est:5000-7000

£3165 $5000 €4748 Usuyuki (117x37cm-46x15in) s.d.1980 col lithograph. 22-Apr-3 Butterfields, San Francisco #2304/R est:6000-8000

£3200 $5280 €4640 Figure 8, from Black Numeral Series (71x55cm-28x22in) s.d.num.68/70 col lithograph. 2-Jul-3 Christie's, London #91/R est:3000-5000

£3205 $5000 €4808 Voice (50x64cm-20x25in) s.d.num.4/4 col lithograph three on one sheet. 5-Nov-2 Christie's, Rockefeller NY #432/R est:6000-8000
£3226 $5000 €4839 Savarin (116x76cm-46x30in) s. offset lithograph. 25-Sep-2 Christie's, Rockefeller NY #301/R est:7000-9000
£3459 $5500 €5189 Fool's house (104x51cm-41x20in) s.d.72 num.67/67 col lithograph. 29-Apr-3 Christie's, Rockefeller NY #628/R est:7000-9000
£3700 $5735 €5550 Fool's house (111x73cm-44x29in) s.d.1972 num.58/67 col lithograph. 5-Dec-2 Sotheby's, London #217/R est:4000-6000
£4487 $7000 €6731 Land's end (132x92cm-52x36in) s.d.num.62/70 lithograph. 5-Nov-2 Christie's, Rockefeller NY #424/R est:6000-8000
£4487 $7000 €6731 Two costumes (76x31cm-30x12in) s.d.num.26/49 col etching aquatint drypoint. 5-Nov-2 Christie's, Rockefeller NY #435/R est:5000-7000
£4800 $7920 €6960 Target with four faces (92x67cm-36x26in) s.num.24/100 col screenprint. 2-Jul-3 Christie's, London #92/R est:5000-7000
£5128 $8000 €7692 Two flags (121x92cm-48x36in) s.d.num.4/45 lithograph. 5-Nov-2 Christie's, Rockefeller NY #429/R est:6000-8000
£5449 $8500 €8174 Two flags (121x91cm-48x36in) s.d.num.6/13 lithograph. 5-Nov-2 Christie's, Rockefeller NY #428/R est:5000-8000
£5975 $9500 €8963 Target (34x34cm-13x13in) s.d.num.2/28 col lithograph prov. 29-Apr-3 Christie's, Rockefeller NY #624/R est:8000-10000
£5975 $9500 €8963 Two flags (101x78cm-40x31in) s.d.num.21/45 lithograph. 29-Apr-3 Christie's, Rockefeller NY #634/R est:6000-8000
£6000 $9300 €9000 Target with plaster casts (75x58cm-30x23in) s.d.1980 num.8/88 etching aquatint. 3-Dec-2 Christie's, London #138/R est:5000-7000
£6410 $10000 €9615 Target with four faces (105x75cm-41x30in) s.d.num.21/100 col screenprint. 5-Nov-2 Christie's, Rockefeller NY #411/R est:8000-12000
£6410 $10000 €9615 Cicada (89x66cm-35x26in) s.d.num.47/58 col lithograph. 5-Nov-2 Christie's, Rockefeller NY #430/R est:10000-15000
£6918 $11000 €10377 Periscope (86x62cm-34x24in) s.d.num.76/88 col etching aquatint. 29-Apr-3 Christie's, Rockefeller NY #636/R est:8000-10000
£7000 $11690 €10150 Untitled (25x25cm-10x10in) s. col silkscreen. 24-Jun-3 Sotheby's, Olympia #57/R est:2000-3000
£10692 $17000 €16038 Targets (87x64cm-34x25in) s.d.67-68 num.36/42 col lithograph. 29-Apr-3 Christie's, Rockefeller NY #625/R est:8000-12000
£10692 $17000 €16038 Target with four faces (86x62cm-34x24in) s.i.d.num.9/13 col intaglio three. 2-May-3 Sotheby's, New York #481/R est:15000-20000
£10897 $17000 €16346 Target with plaster casts (76x58cm-30x23in) s.d.num.74/88 col etching aquatint. 5-Nov-2 Christie's, Rockefeller NY #427/R est:18000-22000
£11321 $18000 €16982 Untitled (62x94cm-24x37in) s.d.num.11/53 col lithograph. 29-Apr-3 Christie's, Rockefeller NY #632/R est:20000-24000
£11538 $18000 €17307 Untitled (69x102cm-27x40in) s.d.num.4/53 col lithograph. 5-Nov-2 Christie's, Rockefeller NY #422/R est:25000-35000
£11950 $19000 €17925 Untitled (87x77cm-34x30in) s.d.77-80 num.AP 12/12 col lithograph. 29-Apr-3 Christie's, Rockefeller NY #633/R est:20000-24000
£12102 $19000 €18153 Flag (43x58cm-17x23in) s.i.d. lead relief multiple. 21-Nov-2 Swann Galleries, New York #90/R est:18000-22000
£12179 $18878 €19000 Fizzles - Foirades. Samuel Beckett (34x27cm-13x11in) s. col 33 W/C etchings 2 col lithographs. 6-Dec-2 Hauswedell & Nolte, Hamburg #208/R est:20000
£14000 $23100 €20300 Savarin (100x75cm-39x30in) s.d.77-81 num.20/60 col lithograph. 2-Jul-3 Christie's, London #261/R est:12000-18000
£14103 $22000 €21155 Celine (98x69cm-39x27in) s.d.77 num.2/4 lithograph. 5-Nov-2 Christie's, Rockefeller NY #423/R est:20000-25000
£24359 $38000 €36539 After untitled 1975 (77x76cm-30x30in) s.d.num.6/13 8/15 5/11 6/13 6/13 20/20 col lithograph set of six. 5-Nov-2 Christie's, Rockefeller NY #421/R est:25000-35000
£30128 $47000 €45192 Scent (80x120cm-31x47in) s.d.75-76 num.11/42 col lithograph linocut woodcut. 5-Nov-2 Christie's, Rockefeller NY #419/R est:50000-60000
£37736 $60000 €56604 False start I (45x35cm-18x14in) s.i.d.num.3/38 col lithograph. 2-May-3 Sotheby's, New York #480/R est:60000-80000
£141026 $220000 €211539 Flags (70x90cm-28x35in) s.d.num.56/65 col screenprint. 5-Nov-2 Christie's, Rockefeller NY #416/R est:200000-250000
£201258 $320000 €301887 Savarin (102x77cm-40x30in) s.d.num.4/4 col monotype lithographic base. 29-Apr-3 Christie's, Rockefeller NY #637/R est:300000-500000

Sculpture
£8333 $13000 €12500 Light bulb (99x43cm-39x17in) s.d.1969 num.35/60 lead relief. 5-Nov-2 Christie's, Rockefeller NY #412/R est:16000-20000

Works on paper
£1139241 $1800000 €1708862 Untitled (168x112cm-66x44in) s.d.1995 encaustic on canvas prov.exhib. 12-Nov-2 Sotheby's, New York #41/R est:2000000-3000000

JOHNS, Myfanwy (20th C) British
£300 $492 €450 Fragile thoughts (61x36cm-24x14in) s.d.1994. 7-Feb-3 Biddle & Webb, Birmingham #344

JOHNSEN, Hjalmar (1852-1901) Norwegian
£658 $1039 €987 Sailing vessel by coast (32x41cm-13x16in) s. mahogany panel. 17-Dec-2 Grev Wedels Plass, Oslo #159/R (N.KR 7500)
£5877 $9521 €8816 Steinkjaer (60x90cm-24x35in) s. 27-Jan-3 Blomqvist, Lysaker #1108/R est:25000-35000 (N.KR 65000)

JOHNSEN, Johann (1650-1705) Scandinavian

Works on paper
£5120 $8295 €7424 Flowers in vase. Landscape with cockatoos (12x10cm-5x4in) gouache pair exec.c.1700. 26-May-3 Bukowskis, Stockholm #482/R est:40000-50000 (S.KR 66000)

JOHNSON, A Hale (?) American
£938 $1500 €1407 Monhegan meadow (10x20cm-4x8in) board. 14-Mar-3 Douglas, South Deerfield #15
£1000 $1600 €1500 Grey barn (13x25cm-5x10in) board. 14-Mar-3 Douglas, South Deerfield #11
£1438 $2300 €2157 Near Squeaker Cove (18x38cm-7x15in) board. 14-Mar-3 Douglas, South Deerfield #10

JOHNSON, Basil (20th C) British

Works on paper
£360 $587 €540 West vale, view of a country house garden (51x141cm-20x56in) s.i.d.12 W/C triptych. 28-Jan-3 Bristol Auction Rooms #458/R

JOHNSON, C E (1832-1913) British
£573 $900 €860 Landscape with stream and figures (46x61cm-18x24in) s.d.1902. 22-Nov-2 Eldred, East Dennis #1014/R

JOHNSON, Candice (20th C) British?

Works on paper
£302 $483 €420 Between the love letters (60x60cm-24x24in) s. mixed media. 18-May-3 Neret-Minet, Paris #53/R
£324 $518 €450 The day we were together (60x44cm-24x17in) s. mixed media. 18-May-3 Neret-Minet, Paris #189
£324 $518 €450 Memories of the Piddle Family (60x60cm-24x24in) s. mixed media canvas. 18-May-3 Neret-Minet, Paris #121/R

JOHNSON, Captain John Willes (fl.1828-1841) British

Works on paper
£650 $1034 €975 Opium clipper Castle Huntly in the straits of Malacca (19x30cm-7x12in) W/C exhib. 29-Apr-3 Bonhams, New Bond Street #25/R

JOHNSON, Charles Edward (1832-1913) British
£2600 $3978 €3900 Grouse shoot (35x60cm-14x24in) s.d.1890. 22-Aug-2 Bonhams, Edinburgh #1059/R est:1000-1500

Works on paper
£400 $652 €600 Spate on the river (63x102cm-25x40in) s.d.1908 pencil W/C scratching out. 13-Feb-3 Mellors & Kirk, Nottingham #776

JOHNSON, Cyrus (1848-1925) British

Works on paper
£850 $1309 €1275 Interior scene with three figures (64x48cm-25x19in) s. 5-Sep-2 Clevedon Sale Rooms #147/R

JOHNSON, David (1827-1908) American
£1698 $2750 €2462 On the Esopus (10x15cm-4x6in) init. canvas on board prov. 21-May-3 Doyle, New York #95/R est:4000-6000
£6962 $11000 €10443 Near Burlington, Lake Champlain (20x33cm-8x13in) mono.d.1873 s.i.d.verso panel prov. 24-Apr-3 Shannon's, Milford #15/R est:10000-15000
£10313 $16500 €15470 Sketch at Georgetown, Conn, summer landscape (28x33cm-11x13in) mono.i. prov. 11-Jan-3 James Julia, Fairfield #30 est:12000-18000
£23457 $38000 €35186 At Larchmont Manor, Long Island Sound, New York (35x50cm-14x20in) init. s.i.verso panel prov.lit. 22-May-3 Christie's, Rockefeller NY #8/R est:25000-35000
£32468 $50000 €48702 Buck Mountain, Lake George, 1867 (76x127cm-30x50in) s. 24-Oct-2 Shannon's, Milford #38/R est:50000-70000

JOHNSON, Eastman (1824-1906) American
£6169 $9500 €9254 Lady playing a harp (46x51cm-18x20in) init. board on aluminium prov. 24-Oct-2 Shannon's, Milford #85/R est:8000-12000

£13924 $22000 €20886 Study for the counterfeiters (41x38cm-16x15in) mono. prov. 24-Apr-3 Shannon's, Milford #154/R est:15000-25000
£54839 $85000 €82259 Study for the wounded drummer boy (25x22cm-10x9in) init. board executed c.1871. 5-Dec-2 Christie's, Rockefeller NY #21/R est:60000-80000
£320988 $520000 €481482 Ojibwe encampment (25x57cm-10x22in) init. lit. 22-May-3 Christie's, Rockefeller NY #31/R est:250000-350000

Works on paper
£629 $1000 €944 Portrait of Mrs Jeremiah Chandler (22x16cm-9x6in) bears i. pencil gouache prov.lit. 5-Mar-3 Christie's, Rockefeller NY #94/R est:2000-3000

JOHNSON, Eastman (attrib) (1824-1906) American
Works on paper
£477 $750 €716 Portrait of Rufus (41x24cm-16x9in) i.verso crayon. 14-Dec-2 Weschler, Washington #665/R

JOHNSON, Edward Killingworth (1825-1923) British
Works on paper
£1400 $2170 €2100 Breton fisher girl (15x20cm-6x8in) s.d.1864 W/C htd bodycol. 3-Dec-2 Sotheby's, Olympia #68/R est:800-1200
£3200 $4992 €4800 Lady and her daughter looking at butterflies on sunflowers (69x48cm-27x19in) s.d.1881 W/C. 26-Mar-3 Woolley & Wallis, Salisbury #89/R est:1500-2500

JOHNSON, Ernest Borough (1867-1949) British
£279 $444 €419 Moor Park with two women seated with their children (28x37cm-11x15in) s.i.d.1941. 5-Mar-3 Rasmussen, Copenhagen #1893/R (D.KR 3000)
£1100 $1782 €1650 Bringing in the catch (36x35cm-14x14in) s.d.1908 canvas on panel. 23-Jan-3 Christie's, Kensington #230/R est:600-800

JOHNSON, F (19th C) American
£481 $750 €722 Two ships at sea (74x102cm-29x40in) s.indis.d.19. 14-Sep-2 Selkirks, St. Louis #198

JOHNSON, Frank Tenney (1874-1939) American
£5128 $8000 €7692 Little Colorado (30x41cm-12x16in) s. canvas on board painted c.1920 prov.lit. 9-Nov-2 Santa Fe Art, Santa Fe #105/R est:8000-12000
£9554 $15000 €14331 Exchange of gunfire (46x72cm-18x28in) s.d.1920 prov. 19-Nov-2 Butterfields, San Francisco #8086/R est:20000-30000
£51613 $80000 €77420 Return at night (61x76cm-24x30in) s.i.d.1936 prov. 29-Oct-2 John Moran, Pasadena #701 est:70000-90000
£54839 $85000 €82259 Reflection (61x77cm-24x30in) s.i.d.1936 prov.exhib. 5-Dec-2 Christie's, Rockefeller NY #187/R est:40000-60000
£67901 $110000 €101852 Voices in the night (71x91cm-28x36in) s. prov. 22-May-3 Christie's, Rockefeller NY #23/R est:120000-180000
£99359 $155000 €149039 Somewhere on the range (61x76cm-24x30in) prov.lit. 9-Nov-2 Santa Fe Art, Santa Fe #153/R est:180000-220000

Works on paper
£1146 $1800 €1719 Banjo player (32x24cm-13x9in) s.i.d.Feb 18-96 pencil. 19-Nov-2 Butterfields, San Francisco #8095/R est:2500-3500
£30864 $50000 €46296 Nocturne (67x42cm-26x17in) s.d.1915 W/C on board. 22-May-3 Christie's, Rockefeller NY #19/R est:50000-70000
£89744 $140000 €134616 Navajo shepherdess (74x51cm-29x20in) s.d.1914 W/C prov.lit. 9-Nov-2 Santa Fe Art, Santa Fe #149/R est:70000-90000

JOHNSON, Guy (1927-) American
£929 $1468 €1394 Land of plenty (56x86cm-22x34in) s. oil painted on print exhib.prov. 1-Apr-3 Rasmussen, Copenhagen #365/R (D.KR 10000)

JOHNSON, Harry (?) American?
£285 $450 €413 Landscape with trees and stream (28x23cm-11x9in) s. board. 5-Apr-3 DeFina, Austinburg #1322
£316 $500 €458 Landscape with trees and stream (28x23cm-11x9in) s. board. 5-Apr-3 DeFina, Austinburg #1323

JOHNSON, Harry John (1826-1884) British
£58000 $90480 €87000 Temple of Aphaea, Aegina, Greece (55x102cm-22x40in) 15-Oct-2 Sotheby's, London #32/R est:15000-20000

Works on paper
£320 $534 €464 Naples (21x51cm-8x20in) st.mono.i. pencil bodycol wash. 17-Jun-3 Bristol Auction Rooms #510/R
£460 $750 €690 Avignon, Villeneuve (24x38cm-9x15in) studio st.i.d.Sep 1853 W/C pencil and another by the same hand. 30-Jan-3 Lawrence, Crewkerne #627
£1500 $2340 €2250 View of the Acropolis (32x50cm-13x20in) i. W/C over pencil htd bodycol stopping out. 15-Oct-2 Sotheby's, London #26/R est:1500-2000

JOHNSON, Harvey W (1920-) American
£1347 $2250 €1953 Beans and a good yarn (51x64cm-20x25in) s.d.1969 canvasboard. 21-Jun-3 Selkirks, St. Louis #187/R est:3000-5000
£1712 $2500 €2568 Mexican Sol Silver (66x51cm-26x20in) 18-May-2 Altermann Galleries, Santa Fe #145/R
£1856 $3100 €2691 Chow time (61x76cm-24x30in) s.d.1970 canvasboard. 21-Jun-3 Selkirks, St. Louis #188/R est:4000-5000
£2055 $3000 €3083 Clyman saves Sublette (61x91cm-24x36in) 18-May-2 Altermann Galleries, Santa Fe #146/R
£3549 $5750 €5146 They wuz by here (51x76cm-20x30in) board. 23-May-3 Altermann Galleries, Santa Fe #24
£3846 $6000 €5769 Grub and gab (51x76cm-20x30in) 9-Nov-2 Altermann Galleries, Santa Fe #41

JOHNSON, Isaac (fl.1799-1816) British
Works on paper
£260 $429 €377 North view of Woodbridge Church, Suffolk (35x47cm-14x19in) i. monochrome W/C. 1-Jul-3 Bonhams, Norwich #58

JOHNSON, John William (19/20th C) American
£755 $1200 €1133 Protection, horse portrait (51x66cm-20x26in) s.i.d.1891. 29-Apr-3 Doyle, New York #24

JOHNSON, Kaare Espolin (1907-1994) Norwegian
Prints
£2182 $3425 €3273 Towards Lofoten (55x37cm-22x15in) s. num.37/75 handcol lithograph. 25-Nov-2 Blomqvist, Lysaker #1144/R est:20000-25000 (N.KR 25000)
£2632 $4158 €3948 Ship in heaven (67x48cm-26x19in) s.I.num.VIII/IX lithograph. 17-Dec-2 Grev Wedels Plass, Oslo #19/R est:20000-30000 (N.KR 30000)
£2705 $4247 €4058 Nordland's trumpet. s.num.58/100 lithograph. 25-Nov-2 Blomqvist, Lysaker #1143/R est:25000-30000 (N.KR 31000)
£3097 $5049 €4646 Petter Dass I (41x66cm-16x26in) s.d.1962 num.78/100 col lithograph. 17-Feb-3 Blomqvist, Lysaker #1096/R est:25000-30000 (N.KR 35000)
£3396 $5229 €5094 Spring evening - Fylgje (39x53cm-15x21in) s.num.71/100 lithograph executed 1961. 28-Oct-2 Blomqvist, Lysaker #1123/R est:25000-30000 (N.KR 40000)

Works on paper
£2418 $4038 €3506 Russian fantasy (33x42cm-13x17in) indis.sig. i.verso mixed media scraping out exec.c.1950. 18-Jun-3 Grev Wedels Plass, Oslo #36/R est:30000 (N.KR 28000)

JOHNSON, Keith (?) British
Works on paper
£350 $546 €525 Choppy day, wherry at Clippesby (36x51cm-14x20in) s. W/C. 11-Apr-3 Keys, Aylsham #399

JOHNSON, Ken (1950-) Australian
£1275 $2091 €1913 Hurricane ebb (53x92cm-21x36in) s. i.verso oil gouache pastel paper on board painted c.1990 prov. 4-Jun-3 Deutscher-Menzies, Melbourne #324/R est:2000-3000 (A.D 3200)
£1550 $2465 €2325 Omphaloi (50x75cm-20x30in) s. s.i.verso prov. 5-May-3 Sotheby's, Melbourne #214/R est:4000-6000 (A.D 4000)

Works on paper
£1594 $2614 €2391 Red cluster, central Australia (76x91cm-30x36in) s.d.92 s.i.d.92 verso synthetic polymer paint canvas prov. 4-Jun-3 Deutscher-Menzies, Melbourne #153/R est:4000-6000 (A.D 4000)

JOHNSON, Marshall (1850-1921) American
£252 $400 €378 Rough seas (22x29cm-9x11in) s. board. 7-Mar-3 Skinner, Boston #325/R
£1656 $2600 €2484 American bark (36x51cm-14x20in) s. 26-Jul-2 Eldred, East Dennis #543a/R est:2500-4500
£2516 $4000 €3774 Clipper ship under sail (91x74cm-36x29in) s. 1-Mar-3 North East Auctions, Portsmouth #706/R est:3000-5000
£3797 $6000 €5696 Near the lighthouse (38x64cm-15x25in) s. prov. 24-Apr-3 Shannon's, Milford #2/R est:3000-5000

JOHNSON, Matthew Franklin (1963-) Australian
£4563 $7575 €6616 Sea study (131x183cm-52x72in) s.i.d.2002 oil on linen after Gabo. 10-Jun-3 Shapiro, Sydney #35/R est:7000-9000 (A.D 11500)

JOHNSON, Maurice (1920-) British
£380 $593 €570 Harbour (57x76cm-22x30in) s. board. 15-Oct-2 Bonhams, Knightsbridge #258

JOHNSON, Michael (1938-) Australian
£1769 $2813 €2654 Little Wimmera (61x45cm-24x18in) s.i.d.1986-67 s.d.1986-87 verso. 4-Mar-3 Deutscher-Menzies, Melbourne #75/R est:3500-5500 (A.D 4600)
£7171 $11761 €10757 Cattai revisit (214x152cm-84x60in) s.d.1990 verso s.i.d.stretcher. 4-Jun-3 Deutscher-Menzies, Melbourne #75/R est:20000-25000 (A.D 18000)
£7857 $12257 €11786 Aubergine night (122x365cm-48x144in) s.i.d.1996/9 verso prov. 11-Nov-2 Deutscher-Menzies, Melbourne #28/R est:20000-30000 (A.D 22000)
£15000 $23400 €22500 Jarocin blue (213x152cm-84x60in) s.i.d.1989 verso. 11-Nov-2 Deutscher-Menzies, Melbourne #18/R est:25000-35000 (A.D 42000)
£16786 $26521 €25179 Jarocin I 1989 (244x212cm-96x83in) prov. 27-Nov-2 Deutscher-Menzies, Melbourne #53/R est:28000-36000 (A.D 47000)
£17143 $26914 €25715 Under and over (243x213cm-96x84in) s.i.d.1992 verso linen prov. 25-Nov-2 Christie's, Melbourne #66/R est:35000-45000 (A.D 48000)

JOHNSON, Neville (1911-1999) British
£1667 $2617 €2600 Dark head (17x21cm-7x8in) board. 19-Nov-2 Hamilton Osborne King, Dublin #553/R est:1400-1800

Works on paper
£244 $382 €380 Abstract (21x29cm-8x11in) s.d.1973 pen pencil. 19-Nov-2 Hamilton Osborne King, Dublin #564
£285 $448 €445 Abstract with reclining nude (83x40cm-33x16in) s.d.1972 pen collage. 19-Nov-2 Hamilton Osborne King, Dublin #554/R
£897 $1409 €1400 Standing figure (35x26cm-14x10in) s.d.1958 mixed media. 19-Nov-2 Hamilton Osborne King, Dublin #545/R
£1154 $1812 €1800 Head (27x34cm-11x13in) s. mixed media. 19-Nov-2 Hamilton Osborne King, Dublin #540 est:300-500
£8000 $12800 €12000 Lamp and 4 (63x77cm-25x30in) s. pencil pen black ink oil board. 15-May-3 Christie's, Kensington #244/R est:2000-3000

JOHNSON, P D (20th C) American
£1346 $2100 €2019 Boy outfishing man (71x56cm-28x22in) s. 9-Nov-2 Illustration House, New York #20/R est:2500-3500

JOHNSON, R (20th C) Australian
£1100 $1760 €1650 By the fireside (18x23cm-7x9in) s. canvasboard. 7-Jan-3 Bonhams, Knightsbridge #168/R est:800-1200

JOHNSON, Ray (1927-1995) American

Works on paper
£889 $1378 €1334 Arthur Cravan - cave man (28x24cm-11x9in) s.d.1979-82 collage. 1-Oct-2 Rasmussen, Copenhagen #164/R (D.KR 10500)
£1270 $1969 €1905 Buddha urinating (30x12cm-12x5in) s.d.1979 collage. 1-Oct-2 Rasmussen, Copenhagen #1654/R est:8000-12000 (D.KR 15000)
£1487 $2349 €2231 Mirojoan (35x19cm-14x7in) s.d.1979-86 collage. 1-Apr-3 Rasmussen, Copenhagen #346/R est:8000-10000 (D.KR 16000)

JOHNSON, Richard (19th C) Irish
£1852 $3000 €2778 Neon orange (130x114cm-51x45in) init.i. init.d.1992verso acrylic. 24-Jan-3 New Orleans Auction, New Orleans #1056/R est:2500-4000
£2222 $3600 €3333 Dorchester (137x157cm-54x62in) i.d.1980 verso acrylic. 24-Jan-3 New Orleans Auction, New Orleans #1057/R est:4000-7000

JOHNSON, Robert (1890-1964) Australian
£268 $415 €402 Biogola Bay (59x74cm-23x29in) s. 29-Oct-2 Lawson Menzies, Sydney #368 (A.D 750)
£356 $544 €534 Terraced Mountain, Undoolya (45x56cm-18x22in) s. board painted c.1967 prov. 26-Aug-2 Sotheby's, Paddington #616 est:2000-4000 (A.D 1000)
£840 $1327 €1260 Frankland range, Tasmania (55x65cm-22x26in) s. 1-Apr-3 Lawson Menzies, Sydney #407 (A.D 2200)
£923 $1468 €1385 New England country (44x53cm-17x21in) s. canvas on board. 4-Mar-3 Deutscher-Menzies, Melbourne #134/R (A.D 2400)
£1254 $1956 €1881 West coast, Auckland (44x54cm-17x21in) s.d.1949 board. 7-Nov-2 International Art Centre, Auckland #137/R est:4000-6000 (NZ.D 4000)
£1550 $2465 €2325 Limpinwood (43x53cm-17x21in) s.d.1929 i.verso. 5-May-3 Sotheby's, Melbourne #294/R est:4000-6000 (A.D 4000)
£1717 $2713 €2576 Lorne, Victoria (44x54cm-17x21in) s. i.verso canvas on board. 2-Apr-3 Christie's, Melbourne #63 est:3000-5000 (A.D 4500)
£1786 $2768 €2679 Eastwood, New South Wales (36x45cm-14x18in) s. board. 29-Oct-2 Lawson Menzies, Sydney #119 est:5500-7500 (A.D 5000)
£2490 $3910 €3735 Jugiong landscape (44x53cm-17x21in) s. canvas on board. 15-Apr-3 Lawson Menzies, Sydney #49/R est:3500-5000 (A.D 6500)

Works on paper
£1410 $2200 €2115 Flowering (99x81cm-39x32in) s. chl collage. 20-Sep-2 New Orleans Auction, New Orleans #1419/R est:1200-1800

JOHNSON, Robert Ward (20th C) American
£432 $700 €626 Nude torso (76x56cm-30x22in) s.d.1921. 24-May-3 Susanin's, Chicago #21

JOHNSON, Sidney Yates (fl.1901-1910) British
£280 $437 €420 Mooring the punt (49x75cm-19x30in) s.d.1914. 12-Sep-2 Bonhams, Edinburgh #316
£280 $448 €420 Lakeland landscape (25x36cm-10x14in) s.d.1909. 7-Jan-3 Bonhams, Knightsbridge #30
£340 $537 €493 Landscape with pond and haycart (25x36cm-10x14in) mono. board. 22-Jul-3 Gorringes, Lewes #1692
£350 $543 €525 By a Highland loch. On a shore (32x61cm-13x24in) s.d.1905 pair. 25-Sep-2 Hamptons Fine Art, Godalming #376
£360 $565 €540 Shepherd and flock in a woodland glade (89x69cm-35x27in) sig.d.1898. 12-Dec-2 Richardson & Smith, Whitby #425
£360 $601 €522 Playing in the woods (59x89cm-23x35in) s. 25-Jun-3 Cheffins, Cambridge #793
£400 $616 €600 Seascape with figure on a beach below cliffs (18x38cm-7x15in) mono. 5-Sep-2 Clevedon Sale Rooms #158/R
£450 $702 €675 Blossom time (44x30cm-17x12in) mono.d.1901. 13-Sep-2 Lyon & Turnbull, Edinburgh #11/R
£500 $785 €750 Highland river landscape (24x36cm-9x14in) mono.d.1916 pair. 25-Nov-2 Bonhams, Chester #951
£620 $992 €930 Riverscapes with maid on a footpath and cattle watering (30x61cm-12x24in) s.d.1905 pair. 11-Mar-3 Gorringes, Lewes #2389
£800 $1304 €1200 Rowing at Richmond Bridge (51x76cm-20x30in) s. 13-Feb-3 Christie's, Kensington #88/R
£1100 $1716 €1650 Coniston Old Man and Coniston lake (53x168cm-21x66in) s.d.1904. 10-Apr-3 Tennants, Leyburn #986/R est:900-1200

JOHNSON, Stanley Q (1939-) American

Sculpture
£1090 $1700 €1635 Eagle boy (109x56x79cm-43x22x31in) i. bronze prov. 9-Nov-2 Santa Fe Art, Santa Fe #248/R est:1500-2500
£1603 $2500 €2405 Buffalo attack (46x56cm-18x22in) d.1976 bronze. 18-Oct-2 Du Mouchelle, Detroit #2108/R est:2000-3000

JOHNSON, Thomas H (19th C) American

Photographs
£16667 $26000 €25001 Landscape and industrial views of the Delaware and Hudson Canal (30x41cm-12x16in) albumen 27. 21-Oct-2 Swann Galleries, New York #37/R est:40000-60000

JOHNSON, Tim (1947-) Australian
£1066 $1695 €1599 Untitled (91x61cm-36x24in) s.d.96 verso. 5-May-3 Sotheby's, Melbourne #264/R est:2500-3500 (A.D 2750)
£1120 $1803 €1680 At papunya (44x59cm-17x23in) s.d.1979 verso acrylic prov. 6-May-3 Christie's, Melbourne #323/R est:2800-3500 (A.D 2800)
£1220 $1927 €1769 Reflection (121x152cm-48x60in) s. i.d.1967 verso acrylic. 22-Jul-3 Lawson Menzies, Sydney #143/R est:3000-5000 (A.D 3000)
£2800 $4508 €4200 Landscape with Buddha's (152x61cm-60x24in) painted c.1990 prov. 6-May-3 Christie's, Melbourne #98/R est:8000-12000 (A.D 7000)

Works on paper
£4286 $6600 €6429 Yellow Buddha (152x183cm-60x72in) s. i.d.1993 verso synthetic polymer on canvas. 8-Sep-2 Sotheby's, Melbourne #47/R est:6000-8000 (A.D 12000)

JOHNSSON, Lasse (1899-1992) Swedish
£430 $696 €645 Gorgeous garden (75x62cm-30x24in) s.i.d.1928. 3-Feb-3 Lilla Bukowskis, Stockholm #26 (S.KR 6000)

JOHNSTON, Alexander (1815-1891) British
£360 $551 €540 Maiden (35x28cm-14x11in) bears sig i.verso. 22-Aug-2 Bonhams, Edinburgh #1000
£1500 $2385 €2250 Winning hand (29x40cm-11x16in) init. board. 6-Mar-3 Christie's, Kensington #597/R est:1500-2000

JOHNSTON, David (1946-) British

Works on paper
£550 $858 €825 Vicent Amazon Macaws (44x29cm-17x11in) i. pencil W/C. 27-Mar-3 Christie's, Kensington #539/R
£1100 $1716 €1650 Spix Macaws (66x50cm-26x20in) s.d.Feb 1993 pencil W/C. 27-Mar-3 Christie's, Kensington #537/R est:600-800
£1900 $2964 €2850 Blue headed Macaws (49x36cm-19x14in) s. pencil W/C bodycol. 27-Mar-3 Christie's, Kensington #541/R est:1000-1500

£2200 $3432 €3300 Lears Macaws (48x37cm-19x15in) s. pencil W/C bodycol. 27-Mar-3 Christie's, Kensington #540/R est:1000-1500

JOHNSTON, Frances-Anne (1910-1987) Canadian

£311 $510 €467 Books, wine and fruit (50x60cm-20x24in) s. canvasboard. 3-Jun-3 Joyner, Toronto #461 (C.D 700)
£453 $702 €680 Le dejeuner (30x40cm-12x16in) s. canvas on board prov. 3-Dec-2 Joyner, Toronto #449 est:400-600 (C.D 1100)

JOHNSTON, Frank Hans (1888-1949) Canadian

£685 $1083 €1028 Turkey hunter (15x11cm-6x4in) s.i.verso tempera on board prov. 14-Nov-2 Heffel, Vancouver #51/R est:2000-3000 (C.D 1700)
£1148 $1779 €1722 Son of September (41x51cm-16x20in) s. s.i.d.Sept 18/47 verso board prov. 24-Sep-2 Ritchie, Toronto #3150/R est:2500-3000 (C.D 2800)
£1550 $2433 €2325 Shadowed snow (25x30cm-10x12in) s.i. s.verso board prov. 24-Jul-2 Walker's, Ottawa #255/R est:3000-3500 (C.D 3750)
£1600 $2624 €2400 Near midland (25x30cm-10x12in) board. 3-Jun-3 Joyner, Toronto #488 est:1200-1500 (C.D 3600)
£1728 $2679 €2592 Landscape with big sky (39x41cm-15x16in) i.verso board prov. 3-Dec-2 Joyner, Toronto #139/R est:3000-4000 (C.D 4200)
£1778 $2916 €2667 Ottawa River Valley (17x22cm-7x9in) s. painted 1945 canvasboard. 3-Jun-3 Joyner, Toronto #218/R est:2000-3000 (C.D 4000)
£1867 $3061 €2801 Gray, October sky (15x20cm-6x8in) s. board. 3-Jun-3 Joyner, Toronto #301/R est:1500-2000 (C.D 4200)
£1867 $3061 €2801 Summer landscape (23x33cm-9x13in) s. panel. 3-Jun-3 Joyner, Toronto #397/R est:2500-3500 (C.D 4200)
£2016 $3185 €3024 Cool shadows of spring (30x40cm-12x16in) s.i. panel prov. 14-Nov-2 Heffel, Vancouver #162/R est:4000-5000 (C.D 5000)
£2058 $3189 €3087 Morning sun (30x40cm-12x16in) s. board. 3-Dec-2 Joyner, Toronto #256/R est:2500-3000 (C.D 5000)
£2133 $3499 €3200 September clouds, Georgian Bay (15x20cm-6x8in) s. board. 3-Jun-3 Joyner, Toronto #545 est:1200-1500 (C.D 4800)
£2242 $3587 €3363 Passing showers - lake of the woods (27x34cm-11x13in) s.i. s.verso panel prov. 15-May-3 Heffel, Vancouver #26/R est:4500-6500 (C.D 5000)
£2410 $3807 €3615 Afterglow, the Sturgeon River (51x61cm-20x24in) hardboard. 1-Dec-2 Levis, Calgary #50/R est:6000-8000 (C.D 6000)
£2469 $3827 €3704 Northern camp (40x50cm-16x20in) s. board. 3-Dec-2 Joyner, Toronto #227/R est:7000-9000 (C.D 6000)
£2667 $4373 €4001 August, near Parry Sounds (17x22cm-7x9in) s. board painted 1947. 3-Jun-3 Joyner, Toronto #430/R est:2000-3000 (C.D 6000)
£2893 $4541 €4340 Winter in Quebec (30x41cm-12x16in) s.i. s.verso board. 24-Jul-2 Walker's, Ottawa #421/R est:4000-5000 (C.D 7000)
£3292 $5103 €4938 House on the hill (50x60cm-20x24in) s. board. 3-Dec-2 Joyner, Toronto #20/R est:9000-12000 (C.D 8000)
£3292 $5103 €4938 Rhapsody (40x50cm-16x20in) s. board prov. 3-Dec-2 Joyner, Toronto #212/R est:7000-9000 (C.D 8000)
£3333 $5467 €5000 Split rail fence and glade (25x30cm-10x12in) s. board. 3-Jun-3 Joyner, Toronto #398/R est:2000-3000 (C.D 7500)
£3498 $5422 €5247 Spring sunshine (55x70cm-22x28in) s. prov. 3-Dec-2 Joyner, Toronto #49/R est:6000-8000 (C.D 8500)
£4260 $6816 €6390 Laughing Valley (51x41cm-20x16in) s. s.i.verso board prov. 15-May-3 Heffel, Vancouver #193/R est:10000-12000 (C.D 9500)
£4321 $6698 €6482 October snow at Georgian Bay, Ont (40x50cm-16x20in) s. board prov.exhib. 3-Dec-2 Joyner, Toronto #163/R est:6000-8000 (C.D 10500)
£4667 $7653 €7001 North wind, Algoma, 1919 (36x49cm-14x19in) s. tempera prov. 3-Jun-3 Joyner, Toronto #273/R est:6000-8000 (C.D 10500)
£4933 $7892 €7400 Penetang Road (30x39cm-12x15in) s.d.1929 i.verso board prov.exhib.lit. 15-May-3 Heffel, Vancouver #116/R est:8000-12000 (C.D 11000)
£5761 $8930 €8642 Winter waning (40x50cm-16x20in) s. board. 3-Dec-2 Joyner, Toronto #58a/R est:15000-20000 (C.D 14000)
£8065 $12742 €12098 Algoma, heavy morning mist (26x34cm-10x13in) s. s.i.d.1918 verso board. 14-Nov-2 Heffel, Vancouver #235/R est:10000-12000 (C.D 20000)
£8889 $14578 €12889 Prospector (65x100cm-26x39in) s.i. masonite. 9-Jun-3 Hodgins, Calgary #400/R est:12000-15000 (C.D 20000)
£13559 $21559 €20339 Ojibway canoe (75x90cm-30x35in) s.i. masonite. 23-Mar-3 Hodgins, Calgary #67/R est:12000-15000 (C.D 32000)
£67265 $107623 €100898 Midsummer - northern lake (102x82cm-40x32in) s.d.1922 prov. 15-May-3 Heffel, Vancouver #115/R est:90000-120000 (C.D 150000)

Works on paper

£913 $1424 €1523 Backyard of cottage at Victoria Beach (19x14cm-7x6in) d.1923 gouache paper board. 13-Apr-3 Levis, Calgary #66/R est:2800-3200 (C.D 2100)
£1411 $2230 €2117 Sketches for Lunette in entrance of New Robert Simpson Bldg. four s. one i. gouache set of five. 18-Nov-2 Sotheby's, Toronto #114/R est:3000-5000 (C.D 3500)
£3333 $5467 €5000 Water towers (26x35cm-10x14in) s. pastel exhib. 3-Jun-3 Joyner, Toronto #345/R est:2000-2500 (C.D 7500)

JOHNSTON, Frederic (1890-1953) American

£2259 $3750 €3276 To the naval orange (76x61cm-30x24in) s. i.verso prov. 11-Jun-3 Butterfields, San Francisco #4229/R est:3000-5000

JOHNSTONE, George Whitton (1849-1901) British

£2000 $3120 €3000 Leuchars church (52x78cm-20x31in) s.i. 14-Apr-3 Sotheby's, London #58/R est:2000-3000

JOHNSTONE, Gwyneth (?) British

£250 $390 €375 Norwich (34x52cm-13x20in) init. 9-Oct-2 Woolley & Wallis, Salisbury #326/R
£260 $406 €390 Pink vase of flowers (30x41cm-12x16in) s. 9-Oct-2 Woolley & Wallis, Salisbury #327/R
£500 $770 €750 Woman with geese (49x61cm-19x24in) s. board. 5-Sep-2 Christie's, Kensington #615

Works on paper

£420 $701 €609 Spanish landscape (15x23cm-6x9in) mixed media. 20-Jun-3 Keys, Aylsham #608
£650 $1073 €943 Spanish hills (27x36cm-11x14in) init. pencil gouache. 3-Jul-3 Christie's, Kensington #304/R

JOHNSTONE, Harry Inge (20th C) American

Works on paper

£214 $350 €310 Old Absinthe house, New Orleans (18x13cm-7x5in) s. pencil. 7-Jun-3 Neal Auction Company, New Orleans #367
£229 $375 €332 Bassa-Bassa shrimper's houses in Barataria (20x13cm-8x5in) s.i. pencil. 7-Jun-3 Neal Auction Company, New Orleans #404
£275 $450 €399 Cafe on the Place d'Armes (20x13cm-8x5in) s.i. pencil. 7-Jun-3 Neal Auction Company, New Orleans #366
£275 $450 €399 Performer's entrance (41x28cm-16x11in) s. W/C. 7-Jun-3 Neal Auction Company, New Orleans #407
£336 $550 €487 Slave quarters, Vieux Carre (23x18cm-9x7in) s.i. pencil. 7-Jun-3 Neal Auction Company, New Orleans #365

JOHNSTONE, Henry James (1835-1907) British

£2788 $4405 €4182 In the Thames Valley (38x30cm-15x12in) s.d.1880. 5-Apr-3 Rasmussen, Havnen #2015/R est:15000-20000 (D.KR 30000)
£3101 $4930 €4652 Billabong (32x50cm-13x20in) s.d.1876. 5-May-3 Sotheby's, Melbourne #308/R est:6000-8000 (A.D 8000)
£4007 $6332 €6011 Two figures boating on a river (29x19cm-11x7in) s. canvas on board. 2-Apr-3 Christie's, Melbourne #48/R est:4000-6000 (A.D 10500)
£7252 $11458 €10878 Valley of the Sturt, Craigieburn, South Australia (34x54cm-13x21in) s.d.1878 i.verso. 2-Apr-3 Christie's, Melbourne #37/R est:12000-18000 (A.D 19000)

Works on paper

£1073 $1684 €1610 Flower seller (27x20cm-11x8in) s. W/C. 15-Apr-3 Lawson Menzies, Sydney #63/R est:3000-4000 (A.D 2800)
£2300 $3634 €3335 Collecting mussels on the shore (23x18cm-9x7in) s. W/C. 23-Jul-3 Mallams, Oxford #188/R est:1200-1500
£2862 $4523 €4293 Girl collecting wood (26x17cm-10x7in) s. W/C. 2-Apr-3 Christie's, Melbourne #55/R est:3000-5000 (A.D 7500)

JOHNSTONE, John Young (1887-1930) Canadian

£1152 $1786 €1728 White farmhouse, summer (12x17cm-5x7in) panel. 3-Dec-2 Joyner, Toronto #12/R est:2000-3000 (C.D 2800)
£2058 $3189 €3087 Retour des champs (30x37cm-12x15in) s.d.1914 prov.exhib. 3-Dec-2 Joyner, Toronto #145/R est:4000-5000 (C.D 5000)
£2318 $3615 €3477 Old church, Pointe aux Trembles (12x18cm-5x7in) s. s.i.verso board. 25-Mar-3 Iegor de Saint Hippolyte, Montreal #71 (C.D 5400)
£4222 $6924 €6333 Old farmhouse, St. Joachim (21x30cm-8x12in) s. board prov. 3-Jun-3 Joyner, Toronto #21/R est:4000-5000 (C.D 9500)

JOHNSTONE, William (1897-1981) British

£400 $660 €580 Figures in motion (19x14cm-7x6in) s.d.1937. 3-Jul-3 Christie's, Kensington #712

JOINER, Harvey (1852-?) American

£613 $950 €920 Forest interior (15x10cm-6x4in) board prov. 25-Sep-2 Doyle, New York #45/R
£938 $1500 €1407 Sunlit forest path (20x41cm-8x16in) canvasboard. 15-Mar-3 Selkirks, St. Louis #322 est:300-500
£1442 $2250 €2163 Autumn landscape. 21-Sep-2 Harvey Clar, Oakland #1462
£2484 $4000 €3726 Tree lined country path in early morning light (25x51cm-10x20in) s. canvasboard. 19-Jan-3 Jeffery Burchard, Florida #24/R
£2690 $4250 €4035 Road home (25x51cm-10x20in) s. board. 16-Nov-2 Harvey Clar, Oakland #1393

JOINVILLE, Eliza (19th C) French
£1500 $2370 €2250 Allegory of summer. Allegory of winter (25x40cm-10x16in) s.d.76 panel pair. 14-Nov-2 Christie's, Kensington #244/R est:1500-2500

JOISTEN, Bernard (1962-) French
£3846 $6038 €6000 Sampling (201x80cm-79x31in) acrylic panel prov. 11-Dec-2 Artcurial Briest, Paris #760/R

JOISTEN, Hans Karl (20th C) German
£692 $1072 €1100 Wasserburg on the Bodensee (53x110cm-21x43in) s. 2-Nov-2 Hans Stahl, Toestorf #14/R

JOKI, Olli (1943-) Finnish
£327 $504 €520 Washerwomen (30x40cm-12x16in) s. 24-Oct-2 Hagelstam, Helsinki #951
£425 $697 €650 Coastal cliffs (20x30cm-8x12in) s. 9-Feb-3 Bukowskis, Helsinki #266/R
£453 $697 €720 Aaland (30x47cm-12x19in) s. 24-Oct-2 Hagelstam, Helsinki #950

JOLE, Jef van (1905-1961) Dutch
£833 $1375 €1200 Heath (62x110cm-24x43in) mono.d.33. 1-Jul-3 Christie's, Amsterdam #264/R

JOLE, Joseph Gerard van (1877-1919) Dutch
Works on paper
£340 $541 €500 Harderwijk (42x30cm-17x12in) s. W/C bodycol. 19-Mar-3 Neumeister, Munich #370/R

JOLI, Antonio (1700-1770) Italian
£2830 $4415 €4500 View of the Tiber (51x85cm-20x33in) i. 20-Sep-2 Semenzato, Venice #560
£52469 $85000 €78704 San Remy, Southern France, with ruins of a monumental arch and an early first century tomb (49x75cm-19x30in) init. prov.lit. 24-Jan-3 Christie's, Rockefeller NY #62/R est:30000-50000
£92593 $150000 €138890 Venice, the Bacino di San Marco looking east with the Punta della Dogana (67x101cm-26x40in) prov. 24-Jan-3 Christie's, Rockefeller NY #161/R est:150000-200000
£123457 $200000 €185186 Piazzetta and the Libreria di San Marco, Santa Maria della Salute beyond (88x96cm-35x38in) prov.lit. 24-Jan-3 Christie's, Rockefeller NY #165/R est:200000-300000
£420000 $659400 €630000 View of the Bay of Naples with the Royal Procession to Piedigrotta (50x76cm-20x30in) pair prov. 12-Dec-2 Sotheby's, London #60/R est:300000-500000
£500000 $790000 €750000 Thames looking towards the city. Thames looking towards Westminster (45x90cm-18x35in) pair. 28-Nov-2 Sotheby's, London #5/R est:500000-800000
£567901 $920000 €851852 Rome, view of the Tiber looking downstream with the castle and ponte sant' Angelo (88x125cm-35x49in) prov.lit. 24-Jan-3 Christie's, Rockefeller NY #166/R est:500000-700000

JOLI, Antonio (school) (1700-1770) Italian
£6090 $9561 €9500 View of harbour (70x90cm-28x35in) 10-Dec-2 Della Rocca, Turin #178/R est:10000

JOLIN, Edouard (1817-?) French
£1346 $2127 €2100 Scene tiree d'Hamlet de Shakespeare (147x112cm-58x44in) s. 18-Nov-2 Tajan, Paris #9 est:2400-3000

JOLIN, Einar (1890-1976) Swedish
£562 $877 €843 Officer on horseback (46x55cm-18x22in) s.d.1931. 13-Sep-2 Lilla Bukowskis, Stockholm #528 (S.KR 8200)
£621 $1005 €900 Portrait of young man (55x46cm-22x18in) s.d.44. 25-May-3 Uppsala Auktionskammare, Uppsala #238/R (S.KR 8000)
£823 $1284 €1235 Still life of flowers and jug (55x46cm-22x18in) s.d.1953. 13-Sep-2 Lilla Bukowskis, Stockholm #800 (S.KR 12000)
£1051 $1640 €1577 Venice (46x38cm-18x15in) s.d.1952. 6-Nov-2 AB Stockholms Auktionsverk #547/R est:25000-30000 (S.KR 15000)
£1197 $1987 €1736 View from Riddarholmen (26x28cm-10x11in) s.d.1954. 16-Jun-3 Lilla Bukowskis, Stockholm #53/R est:8000-10000 (S.KR 15500)
£1217 $1922 €1826 Interior scene with dog (63x50cm-25x20in) s.d.1948. 28-Apr-3 Bukowskis, Stockholm #18/R est:20000-25000 (S.KR 16000)
£1369 $2163 €2054 Still life of spring bouquet and censers (38x47cm-15x19in) s.d.1954. 28-Apr-3 Bukowskis, Stockholm #17/R est:20000-22000 (S.KR 18000)
£1561 $2483 €2342 Still life of flowers and shell (55x46cm-22x18in) s.d.1956. 3-Mar-3 Lilla Bukowskis, Stockholm #722 est:18000-20000 (S.KR 21000)
£1749 $2763 €2624 San Giorgio Maggiore, Venice (54x65cm-21x26in) s.d.1962. 28-Apr-3 Bukowskis, Stockholm #12/R est:25000-30000 (S.KR 23000)
£1822 $2842 €2733 Old town in spring (50x65cm-20x26in) s.d.1973. 6-Nov-2 AB Stockholms Auktionsverk #540/R est:25000-30000 (S.KR 26000)
£1822 $2842 €2733 Still life (33x41cm-13x16in) s.d.1972. 6-Nov-2 AB Stockholms Auktionsverk #601/R est:15000-20000 (S.KR 26000)
£2104 $3324 €3156 Seated woman (64x52cm-25x20in) s.d.1922. 27-Nov-2 Falkkloos, Malmo #77761/R est:40000 (S.KR 30000)
£2162 $3481 €3243 Portrait of lady (65x54cm-26x21in) s.d.1922. 7-May-3 AB Stockholms Auktionsverk #813/R est:20000-25000 (S.KR 28000)
£2172 $3389 €3258 Still life (55x46cm-22x18in) s. 6-Nov-2 AB Stockholms Auktionsverk #760/R est:20000-25000 (S.KR 31000)
£2327 $3770 €3374 Still life of flowers and fruit (65x54cm-26x21in) s.d.1944. 25-May-3 Uppsala Auktionskammare, Uppsala #244/R est:20000-25000 (S.KR 30000)
£2394 $3854 €3591 Landscape with stags (81x100cm-32x39in) s.d.1958. 7-May-3 AB Stockholms Auktionsverk #824/R est:15000-20000 (S.KR 31000)
£2453 $3826 €3680 Still life of flowers in vase (75x64cm-30x25in) s.d.1951. 6-Nov-2 AB Stockholms Auktionsverk #574/R est:40000-50000 (S.KR 35000)
£2453 $3826 €3680 Orientalist still life with roses (46x55cm-18x22in) s.d.1958. 5-Nov-2 Bukowskis, Stockholm #60/R est:20000-22000 (S.KR 35000)
£2586 $4085 €3879 Still life of flowers and shell (62x51cm-24x20in) s.d.1960. 28-Apr-3 Bukowskis, Stockholm #149/R est:20000-22000 (S.KR 34000)
£3224 $5029 €4836 View towards Skeppsbron, Stockholm (50x71cm-20x28in) s.d.1970. 5-Nov-2 Bukowskis, Stockholm #59/R est:25000-30000 (S.KR 46000)
£4205 $6559 €6308 The old town in winter (50x61cm-20x24in) s.d.1968. 6-Nov-2 AB Stockholms Auktionsverk #522/R est:25000-30000 (S.KR 60000)
£4345 $6778 €6518 View of Wisby (73x60cm-29x24in) s.i.d.1925 prov.exhib. 5-Nov-2 Bukowskis, Stockholm #90/R est:40000-50000 (S.KR 62000)
£4639 $7329 €6959 Sodermalm's market in winter (50x61cm-20x24in) s.d.1962. 28-Apr-3 Bukowskis, Stockholm #150/R est:30000-35000 (S.KR 61000)
£6237 $9730 €9356 Riddarholmen and Gamla Stan, winter scene from Stockholm (61x50cm-24x20in) s.d.1937. 6-Nov-2 AB Stockholms Auktionsverk #629/R est:50000-60000 (S.KR 89000)
£11913 $18584 €17870 View from Soder, Stockholm (62x42cm-24x17in) s.d.1916. 5-Nov-2 Bukowskis, Stockholm #93/R est:120000-140000 (S.KR 170000)
£11913 $18584 €17870 Strandvagen, Stockholm with figures and animals (30x100cm-12x39in) s.d.1939 exhib. 5-Nov-2 Bukowskis, Stockholm #120/R est:100000-125000 (S.KR 170000)
£14716 $22957 €22074 Model seated with dog and parrot (75x63cm-30x25in) s.d.1918. 5-Nov-2 Bukowskis, Stockholm #61/R est:150000-175000 (S.KR 210000)
£24527 $38262 €36791 Model wearing black fur coat (116x81cm-46x32in) s.d.1916. 5-Nov-2 Bukowskis, Stockholm #97/R est:250000-300000 (S.KR 350000)

Works on paper
£288 $449 €432 Garden view with dog resting (32x39cm-13x15in) s.d.1949 W/C. 13-Sep-2 Lilla Bukowskis, Stockholm #258 (S.KR 4200)
£342 $544 €513 Stags in the park at Gripsholm (34x48cm-13x19in) s.d.1952 W/C. 3-Mar-3 Lilla Bukowskis, Stockholm #384 (S.KR 4600)
£353 $554 €512 Woman. gouache prov. 15-Dec-2 Anders Antik, Landskrona #1158 (S.KR 5000)
£487 $789 €731 Lady in Venice (47x32cm-19x13in) s.d.1935 W/C. 3-Feb-3 Lilla Bukowskis, Stockholm #86 (S.KR 6800)
£582 $943 €844 Bathers (30x45cm-12x18in) s.i.d.23 W/C. 25-May-3 Uppsala Auktionskammare, Uppsala #240/R (S.KR 7500)
£582 $943 €844 Venetian waiter (20x15cm-8x6in) s.d.1935 gouache. 25-May-3 Uppsala Auktionskammare, Uppsala #241 (S.KR 7500)
£659 $1068 €956 Polar bears at Skansen, Stockholm (30x48cm-12x19in) s.d.23 W/C. 25-May-3 Uppsala Auktionskammare, Uppsala #243/R (S.KR 8500)
£701 $1093 €1052 Deer in woodland grove (38x56cm-15x22in) s.d.1940 mixed media. 6-Nov-2 AB Stockholms Auktionsverk #542/R (S.KR 10000)
£736 $1148 €1104 Ballerina (33x25cm-13x10in) s. W/C illustration. 5-Nov-2 Bukowskis, Stockholm #55/R (S.KR 10500)
£965 $1602 €1399 Landscape, Kastellholmen (37x56cm-15x22in) s.d.1942 W/C. 16-Jun-3 Lilla Bukowskis, Stockholm #77/R (S.KR 12500)

£1081 $1795 €1567 Cassis (30x44cm-12x17in) s.d.19 april 1928 W/C. 16-Jun-3 Lilla Bukowskis, Stockholm #977 (S.KR 14000)
£1121 $1749 €1682 View from Arild (34x50cm-13x20in) s.i.d.1938 W/C. 5-Nov-2 Bukowskis, Stockholm #3/R est:18000-20000 (S.KR 16000)
£1141 $1802 €1712 Tatiana Angelin in interior (49x30cm-19x12in) s.d.1923 W/C. 28-Apr-3 Bukowskis, Stockholm #30/R est:15000-20000 (S.KR 15000)
£1445 $2283 €2168 Lady in deck-chair (27x18cm-11x7in) s.d.1937 W/C. 28-Apr-3 Bukowskis, Stockholm #89a/R est:15000-20000 (S.KR 19000)
£1822 $2842 €2733 View of Monte Carlo (49x62cm-19x24in) s.i.d.April 1949 gouache. 5-Nov-2 Bukowskis, Stockholm #2/R est:20000-25000 (S.KR 26000)
£1852 $2889 €2778 Landscape from Snackgardsbaden, Gotland (34x50cm-13x20in) s.i.d.1932 W/C. 13-Sep-2 Lilla Bukowskis, Stockholm #257 est:5000 (S.KR 27000)
£2008 $3232 €3012 Lady with parasol - view from Venice (46x31cm-18x12in) s.d.1935 W/C. 7-May-3 AB Stockholms Auktionsverk #655/R est:8000-10000 (S.KR 26000)

JOLLAIN, Nicolas René (younger) (1732-1804) French
£7693 $12847 €11000 Venus et cupidon (39x54cm-15x21in) panel. 25-Jun-3 Tajan, Paris #72/R est:10000-12000

JOLLEY, Jerry (1911-) American
£250 $400 €363 Portrait of a woman (30x25cm-12x10in) s. 17-May-3 CRN Auctions, Cambridge #50

JOLLY, Andre (19/20th C) French
Works on paper
£352 $567 €500 La porteuse de fagots (11x11cm-4x4in) mono. gouache. 11-May-3 Thierry & Lannon, Brest #123
£669 $1077 €950 Paysage synthetique de Bretagne (13x17cm-5x7in) mono. W/C. 11-May-3 Thierry & Lannon, Brest #90 est:900-1000

JOLLY, Nicholas (1963-) British
£380 $631 €570 The Montebanks (150x177cm-59x70in) s. prov. 15-Jun-3 Lots Road, London #341

JOLY DE BEYNAC, René (1870-?) French
£353 $554 €550 Voici le Sabre (55x46cm-22x18in) s. 13-Dec-2 Piasa, Paris #146
£1531 $2480 €2220 Interior scene with ornaments on fireplace shelf (55x46cm-22x18in) s. 26-May-3 Rasmussen, Copenhagen #1424/R est:10000 (D.KR 16000)

JON-AND, John (1889-1941) Swedish
£1682 $2624 €2523 Flowers (100x70cm-39x28in) s. tempera cardboard. 6-Nov-2 AB Stockholms Auktionsverk #577/R est:30000-35000 (S.KR 24000)
£2008 $3333 €2912 Model (74x48cm-29x19in) s. 16-Jun-3 Lilla Bukowskis, Stockholm #154 est:10000-12000 (S.KR 26000)
£3089 $4973 €4634 Woman (73x56cm-29x22in) s. painted c.1915. 7-May-3 AB Stockholms Auktionsverk #748/R est:40000-50000 (S.KR 40000)
Works on paper
£309 $513 €448 In the garden (38x42cm-15x17in) s.d.18 chk. 16-Jun-3 Lilla Bukowskis, Stockholm #143 (S.KR 4000)
£309 $513 €448 In the arm-chair (21x15cm-8x6in) s.d.15 chl. 16-Jun-3 Lilla Bukowskis, Stockholm #144 (S.KR 4000)
£1236 $1989 €1854 Lovers (52x34cm-20x13in) s. i.verso mixed media panel. 7-May-3 AB Stockholms Auktionsverk #830/R est:10000-12000 (S.KR 16000)
£1977 $3124 €2966 Mother and child (32x25cm-13x10in) s.d.nov.21 W/C. 28-Apr-3 Bukowskis, Stockholm #50/R est:15000-18000 (S.KR 26000)

JONAS, Henri Charles (1878-1944) Dutch
£446 $696 €700 Chateau de Bouillion (63x42cm-25x17in) s. board. 6-Nov-2 Vendue Huis, Gravenhage #50

JONAS, John (20th C) British
£1800 $2808 €2700 The grey, Goodwood (66x91cm-26x36in) s. 6-Nov-2 Sotheby's, Olympia #105/R est:700-1000

JONAS, Josef (1805-1863) Austrian
£1761 $2730 €2800 Landscape with family returning home (46x61cm-18x24in) s.d.850. 29-Oct-2 Dorotheum, Vienna #13/R est:2600-3200

JONAS, Louis Paul (20th C) American
Sculpture
£9677 $15000 €14516 Standard poodles. i.d.1948 green pat. bronze pair. 4-Dec-2 Sotheby's, New York #93/R est:20000-30000

JONAS, Rudolf (1822-1888) German
£769 $1192 €1200 Sunlit mountain lake with figures, boats and buildings (73x98cm-29x39in) mono.i.d.81. 7-Dec-2 Hans Stahl, Hamburg #19/R

JONAS, Walter Hermann (1910-1979) Swiss
£417 $671 €626 Portrait of Dorian Gray (80x64cm-31x25in) s.d.36 panel. 7-May-3 Dobiaschofsky, Bern #718/R (S.FR 900)

JONCHERIE, Gabriele Germain (19th C) French
£774 $1223 €1200 Nature morte aux poissons (60x73cm-24x29in) s.d.1841. 19-Dec-2 Bondu, Paris #10

JONES OF BATH, William (fl.1764-1777) British
£1400 $2240 €2100 Still life of fruit on a ledge (32x41cm-13x16in) oil on white metal. 13-May-3 Bonhams, Knightsbridge #69/R est:1500-2000

JONES, A M (19th C) Irish
£1411 $2201 €2117 Irish colleen (70x58cm-28x23in) 7-Nov-2 International Art Centre, Auckland #171/R est:5000-10000 (NZ.D 4500)

JONES, Adrian (1845-1938) British
£700 $1106 €1050 Chestnut racehorse in a stable (27x37cm-11x15in) s.i.d.1899 panel. 28-Nov-2 Christie's, Kensington #138/R
£800 $1304 €1200 White stallion in a field (69x56cm-27x22in) s.d.1922. 28-Jan-3 Gorringes, Lewes #1594

JONES, Allen (1937-) British
£29000 $45530 €43500 Portrait - flower (122x122cm-48x48in) painted 1966 prov.exhib. 22-Nov-2 Christie's, London #108/R est:10000-15000
£61000 $100040 €91500 General and his girl (122x91cm-48x36in) acrylic painted 1961 exhib. 6-Jun-3 Christie's, London #71/R est:20000-30000
Sculpture
£2100 $3255 €3150 Acrobat (70cm-28in) s.num.IX/X painted plywood. 2-Oct-2 Christie's, Kensington #107/R est:700-900
£2400 $3960 €3480 Acrobat (89cm-35in) s.d.93 num.I/X painted wood. 3-Jul-3 Christie's, Kensington #591/R est:1000-1500
£32000 $52800 €46400 Green table (74x112x74cm-29x44x29in) fibreglass leather glass executed 1972. 3-Jul-3 Christie's, Kensington #592/R est:10000-15000
Works on paper
£380 $619 €551 Party games (31x17cm-12x7in) s.i.d.82 pencil ink brush. 15-Jul-3 Bonhams, Knightsbridge #172
£503 $775 €800 Embryo WDR (57x77cm-22x30in) s. mixed media. 22-Oct-2 Campo, Vlaamse Kaai #538/R
£650 $1073 €943 Alban berg (34x24cm-13x9in) s.d.80-81 pencil wax acrylic. 3-Jul-3 Christie's, Kensington #590/R
£700 $1078 €1050 Woman on trial (16x20cm-6x8in) s.i.d.79 pencil brush ink biro col crayon collage. 5-Sep-2 Christie's, Kensington #620/R
£962 $1490 €1500 Composition (26x13cm-10x5in) s.d.1963 verso wax chk biro board. 6-Dec-2 Hauswedell & Nolte, Hamburg #209/R est:2000
£1000 $1540 €1500 Red letter (27x23cm-11x9in) s.d.77/78 pencil W/C. 5-Sep-2 Christie's, Kensington #621/R est:600-800
£1200 $1860 €1800 Woman masked (18x21cm-7x8in) s.d.74 pen black ink W/C. 4-Dec-2 Christie's, Kensington #308/R est:800-1200
£1458 $2406 €2100 Scarlett O'Hara (58x78cm-23x31in) s.i.d.May 70 pencil col crayon. 1-Jul-3 Artcurial Briest, Paris #834/R est:1800-2200
£1800 $2862 €2700 Seated doll (54x38cm-21x15in) s.d.84 W/C. 26-Feb-3 Sotheby's, Olympia #392/R est:2000-3000
£2400 $3960 €3480 Island life (16x30cm-6x12in) s.d.87 pencil pen ink wax crayon. 3-Jul-3 Christie's, Kensington #593/R est:800-1200

JONES, Angus (1962-) Australian
Works on paper
£358 $588 €537 Head (91x61cm-36x24in) synthetic polymer paint board. 4-Jun-3 Deutscher-Menzies, Melbourne #345/R (A.D 900)

JONES, Arne (1914-1976) Swedish
Sculpture
£2453 $3826 €3680 Pirouette (104cm-41in) s.d.58 dark pat.bronze. 5-Nov-2 Bukowskis, Stockholm #153a/R est:35000-40000 (S.KR 35000)

JONES, Bob (1926-) American
Works on paper
£1863 $3000 €2795 Four young women watching through binoculars (48x38cm-19x15in) s. gouache lit. 10-May-3 Illustration House, New York #133/R est:2500-3500

JONES, Brian J (19/20th C) British
£494 $800 €716 Barges and other shipping before Greenwich hospital (51x61cm-20x24in) s.d.97. 29-Jul-3 Christie's, Rockefeller NY #177/R est:1000-1500
£800 $1296 €1200 America's Cup Jubilee Round the Island Race, Diligent II and Partridge (61x76cm-24x30in) s. 21-May-3 Christie's, Kensington #509/R
£950 $1539 €1425 Candida racing off Cowes (61x91cm-24x36in) s.d.02. 21-May-3 Christie's, Kensington #508/R
£1500 $2430 €2250 Britannia in a tacking duel off the Isle of Wight (76x102cm-30x40in) s. 21-May-3 Christie's, Kensington #510/R est:2000-4000
£4500 $6975 €6750 Vigilant and Britannia close-hauled in Mount's Bay off Penzance (76x102cm-30x40in) s. 31-Oct-2 Christie's, Kensington #411/R est:1500-2500
£4800 $7440 €7200 Shamrock V, Velsheda, Britannia and Astra off the Needles during the America's cup (76x102cm-30x40in) s. 31-Oct-2 Christie's, Kensington #410/R est:1200-1800

JONES, C M (19th C) British?
£6000 $9960 €8700 British barque Premier leaving Table Bay with panorama of Cape Town beyond (56x76cm-22x30in) s.i.d.1860. 12-Jun-3 Christie's, London #518/R est:1500-2500

JONES, Calvert Richard (1804-1877) British
Photographs
£4600 $7222 €6900 Lupton's Range, Eton College (18x16cm-7x6in) num.33 calotype negative two. 19-Nov-2 Christie's, Kensington #6/R est:5000-7000

JONES, Calvert Richard (attrib) (1804-1877) British
Works on paper
£250 $398 €375 Shipping in the Mediterranean (22x33cm-9x13in) mono.d.1844 W/C. 29-Apr-3 Bonhams, Knightsbridge #112a

JONES, Charles (1836-1892) British
£350 $585 €508 Sheep on a hillock overlooking the sea (43x58cm-17x23in) mono.d.80. 20-Jun-3 Keys, Aylsham #654
£820 $1296 €1230 Cattle and sheep in a rural landscape (24x40cm-9x16in) mono.d.82 panel. 2-Dec-2 Bonhams, Bath #84/R
£980 $1529 €1470 Sheep on a clifftop (18x23cm-7x9in) mono. s.d.1875 verso. 10-Apr-3 Bonhams, Edinburgh #112/R
£2321 $3668 €3482 Ponies at Llandedr Fair, North Wales (52x105cm-20x41in) mono. 18-Nov-2 Joel, Victoria #358/R est:10000-12000 (A.D 6500)
£2700 $4266 €4050 Sheep on a hillside (18x23cm-7x9in) mono. board. 2-Dec-2 Gorringes, Lewes #2738/R est:2000-3000
£2800 $4396 €4200 Sheep on moorland beside a river (40x56cm-16x22in) s.d.73 verso board. 20-Nov-2 Sotheby's, Olympia #50/R est:2000-3000
£2914 $4750 €4371 Favorite terrier (35x51cm-14x20in) mono. s.d.1870 verso. 11-Feb-3 Bonhams & Doyles, New York #131a est:3000-5000
£3901 $6319 €5500 Cows and sheep in the meadow (61x91cm-24x36in) mono. i.verso. 22-May-3 Dorotheum, Vienna #86/R est:8000-10000
£5400 $8748 €7830 Highland cattle in a mountainous landscape (53x96cm-21x38in) mono.d.73. 29-Jul-3 Henry Adams, Chichester #545/R est:3500-5000
£5800 $9164 €8700 Leafy lane with sheep (110x85cm-43x33in) mono.d.79. 2-Dec-2 Bonhams, Bath #101/R est:7000-10000
£5900 $9617 €8850 Highland cattle before a mountainous landscape (61x102cm-24x40in) mono.d.83. 11-Feb-3 Bonhams, Knowle #86/R est:6000-8000
£6500 $10855 €9425 Highland cattle and sheep, seen near loch Linnhie, NB (51x96cm-20x38in) mono.d.75. 17-Jun-3 Bonhams, New Bond Street #46/R est:4000-6000
£6800 $10676 €10200 On the South Coast, Beachy Head in the distance (30x51cm-12x20in) mono.d.90. 19-Nov-2 Bonhams, New Bond Street #132/R est:4000-6000
£7407 $11481 €11111 Highland sheep on an outcrop (56x95cm-22x37in) mono. d.1868 verso. 3-Dec-2 Ritchie, Toronto #3036/R est:15000-20000 (C.D 18000)
£7500 $11925 €11250 Sheep in a winter landscape (56x97cm-22x38in) mono.d.67 s.d.verso. 6-Mar-3 Christie's, Kensington #431/R est:5000-7000
£7500 $11925 €11250 Sheep in an extensive river landscape (61x107cm-24x42in) mono.d. verso. 27-Feb-3 Greenslade Hunt, Taunton #1297/R est:5000-8000
£7900 $12877 €11850 Inquisitive neighbours (56x96cm-22x38in) s.d.1877 verso. 11-Feb-3 Bonhams, Knowle #109 est:6000-8000
£8500 $13855 €12750 Sheep on a hillside overlooking an open vista (61x102cm-24x40in) mono.d.81. 11-Feb-3 Bonhams, Knowle #116/R est:6000-8000
£10800 $16524 €16200 Highland cattle and black faced sheep on a snowy mountainside (83x62cm-33x24in) mono.d.74 s.d.verso arched top. 22-Aug-2 Bonhams, Edinburgh #1135/R est:5000-7000
£14000 $23240 €21000 Morning visit (91x153cm-36x60in) mono.d.78 s.verso. 10-Jun-3 Christie's, London #150/R est:10000-15000
Photographs
£2273 $3500 €3410 Onion, Ailsa Graig (20x25cm-8x10in) init.i. photograph. 24-Oct-2 Sotheby's, New York #40/R est:4000-6000
£3165 $5000 €4748 Bean longpod (15x11cm-6x4in) init.verso gelatin silver print executed c.1900 prov. 24-Apr-3 Phillips, New York #10/R est:5000-7000

JONES, Charles (attrib) (1836-1892) British
£900 $1422 €1350 Cairns terrier (36x52cm-14x20in) i.d.1870 verso. 27-Nov-2 Hamptons Fine Art, Godalming #447

JONES, David (1895-1974) British
Works on paper
£2600 $4342 €3770 Queen (31x20cm-12x8in) pencil W/C wax crayon. 24-Jun-3 Bonhams, New Bond Street #110/R est:2000-2500
£9000 $14760 €13500 Dusk is growing (75x55cm-30x22in) s.i.d.47 pencil col chk W/C bodycol prov. 6-Jun-3 Christie's, London #89/R est:6000-8000
£11500 $17710 €17250 Town gardens, Brockley (56x38cm-22x15in) s.d.26 W/C. 5-Sep-2 Christie's, Kensington #577/R est:8000-12000
£14000 $22960 €21000 Portslade (62x49cm-24x19in) s.d.1929 pencil W/C bodycol exhib.lit. 6-Jun-3 Christie's, London #162/R est:8000-12000

JONES, Deborah (1921-) British
£270 $427 €392 Still life of a shelf with bottles, jugs and books (48x74cm-19x29in) s.d.1973. 22-Jul-3 Bristol Auction Rooms #374/R
£480 $758 €720 Cupboard, my doll collection (75x50cm-30x20in) s.d.1984. 7-Apr-3 David Duggleby, Scarborough #391/R
£732 $1200 €1098 Cupboard with perfume bottles (91x46cm-36x18in) s.d.MCMLXXIV. 5-Feb-3 Christie's, Rockefeller NY #15/R

JONES, Dorothy (20th C) American
£641 $1000 €962 Indian boy (30x23cm-12x9in) s. canvas on board prov. 9-Nov-2 Santa Fe Art, Santa Fe #29/R est:1000-3000

JONES, E van (20th C) British
£1000 $1580 €1500 Appledore, Devon (44x59cm-17x23in) s. i.on stretcher. 2-Dec-2 Bonhams, Bath #49/R est:1200-1400

JONES, Evan (20th C) New Zealander
Works on paper
£345 $538 €518 Sunday night (60x60cm-24x24in) s.d.2001 mixed media. 7-Nov-2 International Art Centre, Auckland #6/R est:1000-2000 (NZ.D 1100)

JONES, Francis Coates (1857-1932) American
£714 $1100 €1035 Flowers in an oriental vase (58x46cm-23x18in) s. 8-Sep-2 DeFina, Austinburg #64
Works on paper
£903 $1500 €1309 Figures on a city street (34x28cm-13x11in) s. pencil ink wash gouache prov. 11-Jun-3 Butterfields, San Francisco #4052/R est:3000-5000

JONES, Frank (1900-1969) American
Works on paper
£1282 $2000 €1923 Untitled (41x54cm-16x21in) s. col pencil. 20-Sep-2 Sloan, North Bethesda #342/R est:2000-3000

JONES, Fred Cecil (1891-1956) British
Works on paper
£600 $936 €900 West Yorkshire view (48x64cm-19x25in) s.i.d.1936 W/C. 25-Mar-3 Bonhams, Leeds #525/R

JONES, Frederick D (1914-) American
£1635 $2600 €2371 Mother and child. s. W/C exec.c.1950. 4-May-3 Treadway Gallery, Cincinnati #605/R est:2000-3000
Works on paper
£1132 $1800 €1698 Woman with flowers (58x10cm-23x4in) s. gouache gold silver paint painted c.1950. 2-Mar-3 Toomey, Oak Park #746/R est:1000-2000

JONES, Gaston Adolphe (1891-c.1960) Belgian
£291 $475 €440 Hommage a Henri Thiebaut (54x71cm-21x28in) s.d.1930. 17-Feb-3 Horta, Bruxelles #307

JONES, George (1786-1869) British
£650 $1027 €975 Duenna outwitted (76x63cm-30x25in) i. 14-Nov-2 Christie's, Kensington #167
Works on paper
£600 $936 €900 Cleopatra reclining in reverie, surrounded by attendants with Alexandria in the distance (43x56cm-17x22in) pencil red black chk. 27-Mar-3 Christie's, Kensington #189/R

JONES, H F (?) British?
£800 $1192 €1200 London to Brighton coach outside an inn. Cambridge to London coach (24x44cm-9x17in) s. board pair. 27-Jun-2 Greenslade Hunt, Taunton #746/R

JONES, Henry Wanton (1925-) Canadian
£741 $1148 €1112 Woman in the bathtub (30x25cm-12x10in) s.d.01 board. 3-Dec-2 Joyner, Toronto #113/R est:1800-2200 (C.D 1800)

JONES, Herbert H (19/20th C) ?
£605 $950 €908 Portrait of a horse Topper in his stall (41x51cm-16x20in) s.d.1909 s.i.d.verso. 23-Nov-2 Pook & Pook, Downington #275/R
£950 $1482 €1425 Chestnut hunt - Tempter (22x35cm-9x14in) s.i. sold with a pointer painting. 6-Nov-2 Sotheby's, Olympia #150/R est:400-600

JONES, Hugh Bolton (1848-1927) American
£5128 $8000 €7692 Landscape wih pond (58x74cm-23x29in) s. 22-Sep-2 Susanin's, Chicago #5030/R est:8000-12000
£6962 $11000 €10443 Old bridge (76x91cm-30x36in) 24-Apr-3 Shannon's, Milford #62/R est:12000-18000
£6962 $11000 €10443 Spring landscape with stream (76x91cm-30x36in) 24-Apr-3 Shannon's, Milford #61/R est:12000-18000
£15190 $24000 €22785 Summer day on the pond (64x76cm-25x30in) s. 24-Apr-3 Shannon's, Milford #20 est:18000-22000
£26582 $42000 €39873 Winter landscape (43x69cm-17x27in) s. prov. 24-Apr-3 Shannon's, Milford #119/R est:20000-30000

JONES, J Llewellyn (fl.1880-1924) Australian
£614 $933 €921 Sydney Harbour Ferry (18x27cm-7x11in) s. board. 19-Aug-2 Joel, Victoria #346 est:1500-2000 (A.D 1750)
£842 $1280 €1263 Tree and boatshed (14x24cm-6x9in) s. 19-Aug-2 Joel, Victoria #285 est:2000-3000 (A.D 2400)

JONES, Jack (1922-1993) British
£480 $773 €720 Fish supper (30x40cm-12x16in) s.d.65 canvasboard. 18-Feb-3 Bonhams, Knightsbridge #183/R
£580 $934 €870 Boats in a harbour (51x61cm-20x24in) s.d.91 canvasboard. 18-Feb-3 Bonhams, Knightsbridge #182/R
£650 $1047 €975 Street scene (40x50cm-16x20in) s.d.65. 18-Feb-3 Bonhams, Knightsbridge #181/R
£700 $1127 €1050 Street scene (40x50cm-16x20in) s.d.89. 18-Feb-3 Bonhams, Knightsbridge #185/R

JONES, Jeffrey (1944-) American
£4037 $6500 €6056 Several figures attacking boy warrior (38x33cm-15x13in) init. canvas on masonite. 10-May-3 Illustration House, New York #164/R est:5000-7500

JONES, Jessie Barrows (1865-1944) American
£240 $400 €348 Country river landscape (30x46cm-12x18in) s. canvasboard. 22-Jun-3 Jeffery Burchard, Florida #54a/R
Works on paper
£342 $550 €513 Brooklyn Bridge (25x33cm-10x13in) s. W/C prov. 15-Jan-3 Boos Gallery, Michigan #574/R

JONES, Jo (1894-1989) British
£360 $580 €540 Two seated figures. s. 18-Feb-3 Bonhams, Knightsbridge #141/R est:300-500

JONES, Joe (1909-1963) American
£427 $700 €619 Portrait of a lady with a hat (45x33cm-18x13in) s. canvasboard. 5-Jun-3 Swann Galleries, New York #131/R
£1887 $3000 €2831 Boat dock (30x50cm-12x20in) s. painted c.1955. 4-May-3 Treadway Gallery, Cincinnati #600/R est:4000-6000

JONES, Josiah Clinton (1848-1936) British
£380 $635 €551 Cottage in North Wales (34x52cm-13x20in) s. 23-Jun-3 Bonhams, Bath #150

JONES, Leon Foster (1871-1934) American
£5195 $8000 €7793 Summer day by the river (64x64cm-25x25in) s.d.09 prov.exhib. 24-Oct-2 Shannon's, Milford #50/R est:9000-12000

JONES, Leonard (19/20th C) British?
£250 $395 €363 Dutch fishing boats in an estuary (17x34cm-7x13in) 22-Jul-3 Sworder & Son, Bishops Stortford #350/R

JONES, Lois Mailou (1905-1988) American
£10191 $16000 €15287 Canal, Georgetown (50x61cm-20x24in) s.d.39 i.verso. 14-Dec-2 Weschler, Washington #681/R est:2000-3000
Works on paper
£3077 $4800 €4616 Haiti Symbol (49x60cm-19x24in) s.i. W/C prov. 20-Sep-2 Sloan, North Bethesda #364/R est:2000-3000
£3269 $5100 €4904 Rain at Port Au Prince, Haiti (44x60cm-17x24in) s.d.60 W/C. 20-Sep-2 Sloan, North Bethesda #363/R est:2000-3000

JONES, Louie Johnson (1856-?) British
£4500 $7020 €6750 Study of a horse in a stable (42x52cm-17x20in) s. 14-Apr-3 Hamilton Osborne King, Dublin #1481/R est:2000-3000

JONES, Louisa (19th C) British
Works on paper
£1850 $2942 €2775 View of Castle Cornet and the new breakwater (30x44cm-12x17in) s.d.1867 W/C oval. 20-Mar-3 Martel Maides, Guernsey #44/R est:1000-1200

JONES, Maude Raphael (fl.1889-1900) British
£900 $1503 €1305 No smoke without fire (39x32cm-15x13in) s.d.5.6.09 board. 26-Jun-3 Mellors & Kirk, Nottingham #864/R

JONES, Mildred C (1899-1991) American
£478 $750 €717 At the rink (63x76cm-25x30in) s. board. 22-Nov-2 Skinner, Boston #183/R

JONES, Paul (1921-1998) Australian
£290 $450 €435 Mt Oka (58x76cm-23x30in) s. canvasboard prov. 25-Sep-2 Doyle, New York #97a/R
£629 $1000 €944 Mt Oka (58x76cm-23x30in) s. board. 7-Mar-3 Skinner, Boston #434/R
Works on paper
£722 $1119 €1083 Camellia (30x41cm-12x16in) s.d.58 W/C. 3-Dec-2 Lawson Menzies, Sydney #406/R (A.D 2000)

JONES, Paul (19th C) British
£568 $886 €852 Two hunters resting (20x30cm-8x12in) s.d.78. 6-Nov-2 Dobiaschofsky, Bern #719/R (S.FR 1300)
£600 $978 €870 Terriers ratting (20x25cm-8x10in) s.d.1856. 17-Jul-3 Tennants, Leyburn #877
£611 $954 €917 Young woman with bull and dog (15x20cm-6x8in) s.d.1879 panel. 6-Nov-2 Dobiaschofsky, Bern #718 (S.FR 1400)
£700 $1106 €1050 Terriers rabbiting (20x25cm-8x10in) 28-Nov-2 Christie's, Kensington #287/R
£850 $1411 €1233 Terriers ratting (13x21cm-5x8in) s.d.1888 canvas on panel pair. 12-Jun-3 Christie's, Kensington #244/R
£1400 $2282 €2100 Man and three dogs by a tub. Man and three dogs in an interior (20x25cm-8x10in) s.d.1855 pair. 11-Feb-3 Bonhams, Knowle #119/R est:800-1200
£2000 $3320 €2900 Man's best friend (20x25cm-8x10in) s.d.1855 pair prov. 12-Jun-3 Christie's, Kensington #294/R est:2000-3000

JONES, Paul (attrib) (19th C) British
£420 $689 €609 Waiting for his master (20x25cm-8x10in) 6-Jun-3 Halls, Shrewsbury #828
£650 $1060 €943 Terriers ratting in a barn (18x23cm-7x9in) board. 17-Jul-3 Tennants, Leyburn #878

JONES, Pelham (20th C) British
Works on paper
£350 $553 €525 Cutty Sark under full sail (37x53cm-15x21in) s.d.1933 W/C. 27-Nov-2 Hamptons Fine Art, Godalming #293

JONES, Ray Howard (1903-1996) British
£400 $616 €600 Farm on the Gann. s.d.1968 board. 22-Oct-2 Peter Francis, Wales #55
£420 $655 €630 Three cliffs, The Gower (39x55cm-15x22in) s.d.1956. 11-Sep-2 Bonhams, Newport #334

JONES, Reginald (1857-1920) British
Works on paper
£500 $790 €750 Woodland pool (71x122cm-28x48in) s.d.1895 W/C. 18-Dec-2 Mallams, Oxford #580

JONES, Rev Calvert Richard (c.1804-1877) British
Works on paper
£400 $624 €600 Harriet of Limerick. Beached fishing vessel (7x10cm-3x4in) one i. one d.1835 pen ink W/C double-sided. 9-Oct-2 Woolley & Wallis, Salisbury #57/R
£480 $749 €720 HMS Pylades (17x23cm-7x9in) i.d.1835 pen ink W/C prov. 9-Oct-2 Woolley & Wallis, Salisbury #58/R

JONES, Richard (attrib) (19th C) British
£450 $711 €675 In the scent (25x36cm-10x14in) panel prov. 28-Nov-2 Christie's, Kensington #101

JONES, Robert (fl.1906-1940) British
£320 $531 €464 Evening sea III (33x23cm-13x9in) init. s.i.d.1999 verso board. 10-Jun-3 David Lay, Penzance #444

JONES, Robert Edmond (1887-1954) American
Works on paper
£1543 $2500 €2237 Mephisto Valse - Costume designs (30x25cm-12x10in) col chks pencil blk paper five. 21-May-3 Doyle, New York #24/R est:2000-3000

JONES, Robert Edmond Lee (1913-) American
£535 $850 €803 Trabajo (64x53cm-25x21in) board painted c.1940. 2-Mar-3 Toomey, Oak Park #772/R

JONES, Samuel John Egbert (fl.1820-1855) British
£1786 $2821 €2679 English river scene (61x91cm-24x36in) s.d.1851. 27-Nov-2 Deutscher-Menzies, Melbourne #268/R est:5000-7000 (A.D 5000)

JONES, Sara (1959-) British
Photographs
£5000 $8350 €7250 Wash house, France (150x150cm-59x59in) C-type print aluminium 5 in edition of 5 prov. 24-Jun-3 Sotheby's, Olympia #44/R est:2000-3000

JONES, Seth C (1853-1930) American
£234 $375 €339 Near Beckeney Hills (31x39cm-12x15in) s. board. 16-May-3 Skinner, Boston #251/R
£446 $700 €669 Salting the sheep (46x62cm-18x24in) s. 22-Nov-2 Skinner, Boston #237/R est:300-350

JONES, Wallis (19/20th C) British
£272 $425 €408 Riverbank reflection (46x36cm-18x14in) s.d.98. 20-Sep-2 Freeman, Philadelphia #87/R

JONES, William (c.1798-1860) British
£11000 $16720 €16500 Ferreting (65x91cm-26x36in) 28-Aug-2 Sotheby's, London #834/R est:12000-18000

JONES, van (20th C) ?
£900 $1395 €1350 Portrait of the artist eldest daughter (28x23cm-11x9in) board. 4-Dec-2 Christie's, Kensington #424/R

JONES-MADILL, Kate (20th C) New Zealander?
Works on paper
£386 $602 €579 Flowers on a kitchen table (55x74cm-22x29in) s. W/C. 27-Mar-3 International Art Centre, Auckland #176/R (NZ.D 1100)

JONG, Germ de (1886-1967) Dutch
£764 $1177 €1200 Dauphine, France (80x65cm-31x26in) s.d.1953 i.verso. 3-Sep-2 Christie's, Amsterdam #384
£833 $1375 €1200 Ameland (54x65cm-21x26in) s.i.d.1962. 1-Jul-3 Christie's, Amsterdam #409/R
£2866 $4414 €4500 Still life with lillies and gladioli (65x54cm-26x21in) s.d.1946. 3-Sep-2 Christie's, Amsterdam #368/R est:4500-5500
Works on paper
£625 $1013 €950 Winter in Heelsum (40x33cm-16x13in) s.i.d.1916 gouache pastel black chk. 21-Jan-3 Christie's, Amsterdam #400

JONG, Hens de (1927-) Dutch
£255 $397 €400 Policeman on horse (31x50cm-12x20in) s.d.62 i.verso. 5-Nov-2 Vendu Notarishuis, Rotterdam #129/R

JONGE, Johan Antonio de (1864-1927) Dutch
£2778 $4583 €4000 Figures in traditional dress in a sunlit street (40x46cm-16x18in) mono. canvas on plywood. 1-Jul-3 Christie's, Amsterdam #124/R est:3000-5000
Works on paper
£510 $795 €800 Mother with child (28x20cm-11x8in) studio st. W/C chl. 6-Nov-2 Vendue Huis, Gravenhage #111/R

JONGERE, M de (1912-1978) Dutch
£507 $791 €761 Harbour view (40x60cm-16x24in) s. 23-Sep-2 Rasmussen, Vejle #113/R (D.KR 6000)
Works on paper
£637 $994 €1000 Sea port (56x88cm-22x35in) s. W/C. 6-Nov-2 Vendue Huis, Gravenhage #651

JONGERE, Marinus de (1912-1978) Dutch
£381 $606 €572 Shipping scene (41x81cm-16x32in) s. 18-Mar-3 Maynards, Vancouver #48/R (C.D 900)
£622 $1033 €902 Shipping in a Dutch harbour (61x91cm-24x36in) s. 16-Jun-3 Waddingtons, Toronto #242/R est:1500-2000 (C.D 1400)
£669 $1077 €950 Dutch polder landscape (59x98cm-23x39in) s. 6-May-3 Vendu Notarishuis, Rotterdam #50
£696 $1086 €1100 Polder landscape with mill (59x59cm-23x23in) s. 21-Oct-2 Glerum, Amsterdam #67/R
£892 $1373 €1400 Cargo ship in Rotterdam Harbour (60x100cm-24x39in) s. 3-Sep-2 Christie's, Amsterdam #301
£922 $1494 €1300 Rotterdam harbour view (50x80cm-20x31in) s. 26-May-3 Glerum, Amsterdam #13
£1019 $1569 €1600 Cargo ship moored in Rotterdam Harbour (40x60cm-16x24in) s. 3-Sep-2 Christie's, Amsterdam #337/R est:1400-2200
£1268 $2041 €1800 Polder landscape with windmill (59x99cm-23x39in) s. 6-May-3 Vendu Notarishuis, Rotterdam #107/R est:1200-1600
£1582 $2468 €2500 View of Grouw (60x100cm-24x39in) s. 21-Oct-2 Glerum, Amsterdam #62/R est:500-700
£1650 $2574 €2393 Port of Rotterdam with shipping and barges (50x80cm-20x31in) s. 13-May-3 Holloways, Banbury #677/R est:1500-2000
£1690 $2721 €2400 Activity in Rotterdam harbour (49x79cm-19x31in) s. 6-May-3 Vendu Notarishuis, Rotterdam #85/R est:1500-2000
£1736 $2865 €2500 Extensive polder landscape, with a village in the distance (60x100cm-24x39in) s. 1-Jul-3 Christie's, Amsterdam #81/R est:1500-2000
£1783 $2746 €2800 Shipping in Waal Harbour, Rotterdam (60x100cm-24x39in) s. 3-Sep-2 Christie's, Amsterdam #334 est:1400-2200
£1783 $2782 €2800 View if harbour with haulier (58x98cm-23x39in) s. 5-Nov-2 Vendu Notarishuis, Rotterdam #8/R est:2000-2500
£1793 $2851 €2600 Harbour of Rotterdam (50x80cm-20x31in) s. 10-Mar-3 Sotheby's, Amsterdam #192/R est:1000-1500
£1911 $2981 €3000 Activity in a Rotterdam harbour (57x97cm-22x38in) s. 5-Nov-2 Vendu Notarishuis, Rotterdam #92 est:3000-4000
£1944 $3208 €2800 Daily activities at Rotterdam harbour (60x100cm-24x39in) s. 1-Jul-3 Christie's, Amsterdam #139/R est:1500-2000
Works on paper
£293 $457 €460 River scene with mill (14x39cm-6x15in) s. mixed media. 5-Nov-2 Vendu Notarishuis, Rotterdam #153
£414 $646 €650 Lake scene with mill (9x30cm-4x12in) s. W/C. 5-Nov-2 Vendu Notarishuis, Rotterdam #154
£446 $696 €700 Harbour view (22x63cm-9x25in) s. mixed media. 5-Nov-2 Vendu Notarishuis, Rotterdam #164
£513 $795 €800 Rotterdam Harbour (10x39cm-4x15in) s. W/C over chk. 7-Dec-2 Ketterer, Hamburg #52/R
£599 $964 €850 Harbour activity (38x58cm-15x23in) s. W/C. 6-May-3 Vendu Notarishuis, Rotterdam #25
£637 $994 €1000 Activity in Rotterdam harbour (48x99cm-19x39in) s. W/C. 5-Nov-2 Vendu Notarishuis, Rotterdam #165

JONGERS, Alphonse (1872-1945) American/French
£234 $367 €351 Study of a young woman (25x13cm-10x5in) s. board. 10-Dec-2 Pinneys, Montreal #207 (C.D 575)
Works on paper
£348 $540 €522 Portrait of F R Heaton (18x14cm-7x6in) s.i.d.97 ink dr prov. 24-Sep-2 Ritchie, Toronto #3055 (C.D 850)

JONGH, Gabriel de (1913-) South African?
£307 $479 €461 Cottage, Banhoek, Stellenbosch (60x90cm-24x35in) s. i.stretcher. 15-Oct-2 Stephan Welz, Johannesburg #484 est:4000-6000 (SA.R 5000)
£307 $479 €461 Cape farmhouse bathed in afternoon light (59x90cm-23x35in) s. 15-Oct-2 Stephan Welz, Johannesburg #485 est:4000-6000 (SA.R 5000)

£338	$527	€507	Landscape with Cape farmhouse (44x59cm-17x23in) s. board. 15-Oct-2 Stephan Welz, Johannesburg #480 est:2500-3500 (SA.R 5500)
£338	$527	€507	Cottage by the sea (60x90cm-24x35in) s. 15-Oct-2 Stephan Welz, Johannesburg #483 est:4000-6000 (SA.R 5500)
£386	$610	€579	Cottage in the mountains (45x60cm-18x24in) s. 1-Apr-3 Stephan Welz, Johannesburg #209 est:3500-5000 (SA.R 4800)
£443	$727	€665	Farmyard with wagon tracks (67x100cm-26x39in) s. 4-Feb-3 Dales, Durban #1 (SA.R 6000)
£443	$727	€665	Rondavel in Drakensberg (60x90cm-24x35in) s. 4-Feb-3 Dales, Durban #2 (SA.R 6000)
£443	$727	€665	Wagon tracks, gum trees and mountains (74x100cm-29x39in) s. 4-Feb-3 Dales, Durban #5 (SA.R 6000)
£491	$767	€737	Table Bay from Bloubergstrand (44x59cm-17x23in) s. 15-Oct-2 Stephan Welz, Johannesburg #482 est:3500-5000 (SA.R 8000)
£545	$849	€818	Extensive landscape (59x90cm-23x35in) s. 11-Nov-2 Stephan Welz, Johannesburg #604 (SA.R 8500)
£591	$969	€887	House, Winelands and mountains (90x150cm-35x59in) s. 4-Feb-3 Dales, Durban #3 (SA.R 8000)
£591	$969	€887	Rocky gorge with river (74x120cm-29x47in) s. 4-Feb-3 Dales, Durban #4 (SA.R 8000)
£614	$958	€921	Mounted crusaders (175x119cm-69x47in) s. 15-Oct-2 Stephan Welz, Johannesburg #481 est:3000-5000 (SA.R 10000)
£731	$1177	€1097	Coastal landscape with a lookout point (58x89cm-23x35in) s. 12-May-3 Stephan Welz, Johannesburg #79 est:5000-7000 (SA.R 8500)
£774	$1246	€1161	Diaz Beach, Cape Point (67x101cm-26x40in) s. i.on stretcher verso. 12-May-3 Stephan Welz, Johannesburg #216 est:4000-6000 (SA.R 9000)
£817	$1315	€1226	Mountainous landscape with a gorge and river with low cloud (74x120cm-29x47in) s. indid d.1984. 12-May-3 Stephan Welz, Johannesburg #159 est:5000-8000 (SA.R 9500)
£860	$1384	€1290	Meirings poort (67x100cm-26x39in) s. i.verso. 12-May-3 Stephan Welz, Johannesburg #302 est:6000-8000 (SA.R 10000)
£884	$1397	€1326	Cape cottage with mountains in the distance (90x120cm-35x47in) s.d.1974. 1-Apr-3 Stephan Welz, Johannesburg #474 est:6000-9000 (SA.R 11000)

JONGH, Oene Romkes de (1812-1896) Dutch

£1210	$1864	€1900	Houses along a treelined path (53x86cm-21x34in) s. 3-Sep-2 Christie's, Amsterdam #108/R est:1200-1600
£1656	$2583	€2600	Port (66x53cm-26x21in) s. 6-Nov-2 Vendue Huis, Gravenhage #387/R est:3000-5000
£1951	$3200	€2829	View of Rotterdam (67x54cm-26x21in) s. prov. 4-Jun-3 Christie's, Rockefeller NY #239/R est:3000-5000
£2055	$3226	€3000	Snowy street scene (67x55cm-26x22in) s. 15-Apr-3 Sotheby's, Amsterdam #32/R est:3000-5000
£3082	$4839	€4500	View of the Prinsengracht with the Westerkerk, Amsterdam (45x36cm-18x14in) s. 15-Apr-3 Sotheby's, Amsterdam #40/R est:4500-5500
£3099	$4989	€4400	Dutch town in winter (44x35cm-17x14in) s. lit. 9-May-3 Schloss Ahlden, Ahlden #1471/R est:4500
£3819	$6302	€5500	Dutch town on a sunny day in winter (67x54cm-26x21in) s. 1-Jul-3 Christie's, Amsterdam #20/R est:5000-7000

JONGH, Tinus de (1885-1942) Dutch

£500	$810	€750	Landscape with distant hills (58x71cm-23x28in) s. 23-Jan-3 Scarborough Perry Fine Arts, Hove #140/R
£545	$849	€818	Mountainous river landscape (23x28cm-9x11in) s. 11-Nov-2 Stephan Welz, Johannesburg #273 (SA.R 8500)
£547	$864	€821	Cape homestead in the mountains (45x60cm-18x24in) s. 1-Apr-3 Stephan Welz, Johannesburg #436 est:5000-8000 (SA.R 6800)
£577	$899	€866	Mountainous landscape (26x31cm-10x12in) s. 11-Nov-2 Stephan Welz, Johannesburg #602 (SA.R 9000)
£602	$969	€903	Cape Dutch House (23x32cm-9x13in) s. board. 12-May-3 Stephan Welz, Johannesburg #208 est:3000-5000 (SA.R 7000)
£614	$958	€921	Soft evening glow (30x48cm-12x19in) s. board. 15-Oct-2 Stephan Welz, Johannesburg #433 est:5000-8000 (SA.R 10000)
£705	$1099	€1058	Extensive mountainous landscape (24x29cm-9x11in) s. 11-Nov-2 Stephan Welz, Johannesburg #603 (SA.R 11000)
£739	$1211	€1109	View up river towards mountains (24x31cm-9x12in) s. 4-Feb-3 Dales, Durban #17 (SA.R 10000)
£774	$1246	€1161	Cottage in a mountainous landscape (30x24cm-12x9in) s. 12-May-3 Stephan Welz, Johannesburg #209 est:3000-5000 (SA.R 9000)
£965	$1524	€1448	Late afternoon glow (29x48cm-11x19in) s. 1-Apr-3 Stephan Welz, Johannesburg #437/R est:6000-9000 (SA.R 12000)
£1032	$1661	€1548	Cape cottage in a mountainous landscape (30x46cm-12x18in) s. board. 12-May-3 Stephan Welz, Johannesburg #212 est:4000-6000 (SA.R 12000)
£1204	$1938	€1806	Avenue of trees (44x62cm-17x24in) s. 12-May-3 Stephan Welz, Johannesburg #494/R est:10000-15000 (SA.R 14000)
£1634	$2630	€2451	Cape Dutch house (30x49cm-12x19in) s. 12-May-3 Stephan Welz, Johannesburg #492/R est:12000-18000 (SA.R 19000)
£2236	$3599	€3354	House in a moutainous landscape (65x99cm-26x39in) s.d.1934. 12-May-3 Stephan Welz, Johannesburg #493/R est:20000-30000 (SA.R 26000)

JONGH, Tinus de (attrib) (1885-1942) Dutch

£800	$1248	€1200	Groot Drakenstein, South Africa (68x101cm-27x40in) indis sig. i.verso board. 26-Mar-3 Sotheby's, Olympia #271/R

JONGHE, Gustave de (1829-1893) Belgian

£1987	$3238	€3000	Femme a l'eventail rouge (35x25cm-14x10in) s. panel painted c.1870. 16-Feb-3 Mercier & Cie, Lille #216/R est:3500-4000
£9677	$15000	€14516	Sunday morning (56x45cm-22x18in) s.d.1864 panel prov. 29-Oct-2 Sotheby's, New York #70/R est:18000-25000

JONGHE, Jan Baptiste de (1785-1844) Flemish

£1707	$2800	€2475	Deer in a wooded landscape (21x30cm-8x12in) s. panel. 4-Jun-3 Christie's, Rockefeller NY #236/R est:3000-5000

JONGKIND, Johan Barthold (1819-1891) Dutch

£4248	$6967	€6500	Bateaux au clair de lune dans un port hollandais (43x65cm-17x26in) s.indis.d. 9-Feb-3 Anaf, Lyon #147/R
£6338	$10521	€9000	Bord de mer a Sainte-Adresse (23x32cm-9x13in) s.i.d. lit. 11-Jun-3 Beaussant & Lefèvre, Paris #78/R est:5000-6000
£6707	$11000	€10061	Paysage en bleu (33x48cm-13x19in) s.d.1886 prov. 8-Feb-3 Neal Auction Company, New Orleans #108/R est:10000-15000
£10000	$16400	€15000	Paysage hollandais (19x26cm-7x10in) s.indis.d. panel prov. 5-Feb-3 Sotheby's, London #216/R est:10000
£10323	$16000	€15485	Sailboat moored on the bank of a stream with a windmill beyond (23x32cm-9x13in) s.d.1869 card on canvas. 30-Oct-2 Christie's, Rockefeller NY #135/R est:20000-30000
£17419	$27000	€26129	L'arrivee au port (24x31cm-9x12in) s.d.62 panel. 29-Oct-2 Sotheby's, New York #65/R est:30000-50000
£18000	$29520	€27000	Moulin a vent pres d'Overschie (33x54cm-13x21in) s.d.57 prov. 5-Feb-3 Sotheby's, London #217/R est:30000
£18590	$28814	€29000	Rotterdam at moonlight (34x42cm-13x17in) s.d.1868 prov.lit. 9-Dec-2 Beaussant & Lefèvre, Paris #63/R est:30000
£25633	$39731	€40500	Le vieux bassin du port entrepot de Bruxelles (25x33cm-10x13in) s.d.1874 lit. 29-Sep-2 Eric Pillon, Calais #151/R
£34000	$55760	€51000	Around Dordrecht (25x33cm-10x13in) s.d.1870 prov.exhib. 4-Feb-3 Christie's, London #201/R est:30000
£35971	$57554	€50000	Le vieux bassin du port, entrepot de Bruxelles (25x33cm-10x13in) s.d. lit. 18-May-3 Eric Pillon, Calais #19/R
Prints			
£2179	$3444	€3400	Soleil couchant - Port d'Anvers. etching. 14-Nov-2 Libert, Castor, Paris #106/R est:3000
Works on paper			
£258	$407	€387	Four men in a tavern, two playing board game (14x18cm-6x7in) pen ink W/C prov. 26-Nov-2 Hans Widmer, St Gallen #1211 (S.FR 600)
£601	$949	€902	Ships near the shore. Ships at the dock (9x18cm-4x7in) s. W/C two. 3-Apr-3 Heffel, Vancouver #49/R (C.D 1400)
£649	$1006	€974	Landscape with canal and windmill (22x33cm-9x13in) s. chl W/C. 24-Sep-2 Koller, Zurich #6528/R (S.FR 1500)
£693	$1074	€1040	Peasants with cows by river (20x30cm-8x12in) s.i.d.1884. 24-Sep-2 Koller, Zurich #6529/R (S.FR 1600)
£1104	$1800	€1656	Marie Bonnat, Marie Gravel, Joseph Barbier, Auguste Rabatel (11x23cm-4x9in) s.i.d.16 Aout 1877 W/C chl pen ink prov.exhib. 12-Feb-3 Sotheby's, New York #2/R est:1000-1500
£1122	$1772	€1750	Trois mats a quai (20x26cm-8x10in) s.d. comte crayon. 14-Nov-2 Credit Municipal, Paris #39/R est:1800-2300
£1300	$2119	€1950	Spring landscape (10x13cm-4x5in) s.d.5 oct 85 chl W/C. 3-Feb-3 Bonhams, New Bond Street #15/R est:600-800
£1389	$2208	€2000	Voilier pres de Honfleur (14x24cm-6x9in) studio st. dr. 29-Apr-3 Campo & Campo, Antwerp #165/R est:2500-3000
£1646	$2567	€2600	Mountainous landscape with figures near a village (16x26cm-6x10in) s.i. W/C. 21-Oct-2 Bernaerts, Antwerp #621/R est:2500-3000
£1918	$3011	€2800	Paysage du Nivernais (25x41cm-10x16in) with sig W/C chl. 15-Apr-3 Sotheby's, Amsterdam #142/R est:3000-5000
£1923	$3019	€3000	Attelages d'anes (15x23cm-6x9in) st.sig.d.1883 W/C chl double-sided lit. 15-Dec-2 Eric Pillon, Calais #80/R
£2014	$3223	€2800	Les troupeaux et leurs gardiens (13x34cm-5x13in) s.d W/C chl exhib. 18-May-3 Eric Pillon, Calais #16/R
£2200	$3410	€3300	Village de Nivernais (24x32cm-9x13in) st.sig.d.Sept 71 W/C pencil prov. 5-Dec-2 Christie's, Kensington #2/R est:2500-3500
£2436	$3824	€3800	Paysage (15x24cm-6x9in) st.sig.i.d.1881 W/C chl. 13-Dec-2 Piasa, Paris #150/R
£2620	$4087	€3930	Banks of the Seine in Paris (20x31cm-8x12in) i.d.51 W/C over pencil. 6-Nov-2 Dobiaschofsky, Bern #721/R est:7500 (S.FR 6000)
£3007	$4841	€4600	La Cote Sainte Andre (19x30cm-7x12in) s.i.d. W/C. 19-Jan-3 Feletin, Province #94
£3957	$6331	€5500	Petite maison a Flanc de Colline (14x23cm-6x9in) s. W/C lit. 18-May-3 Eric Pillon, Calais #18/R
£4706	$7576	€7200	Rotterdam (20x36cm-8x14in) s.i.d. W/C. 19-Jan-3 Feletin, Province #93

£5000 $7950 €7500 Blandin pres Chablons, Isere (28x44cm-11x17in) st.sig.i.d.4 Sept 1874 W/C over pencil exhib. 20-Mar-3 Sotheby's, Olympia #11/R est:6000-8000
£6013 $9380 €9500 Paysage (16x22cm-6x9in) s. W/C double-sided. 15-Sep-2 Feletin, Province #82/R
£6028 $10067 €8500 Bateaux a Anvers (19x34cm-7x13in) s.i.d.18 sept 66 W/C exhib.lit. 20-Jun-3 Piasa, Paris #1/R est:8000-10000
£15823 $25000 €25000 Effet de soleil au travers les nuages (21x28cm-8x11in) studio st. W/C. 29-Nov-2 Drouot Estimations, Paris #55/R est:3500

JONGKIND, Johan Barthold (attrib) (1819-1891) Dutch
Works on paper
£693 $1074 €1040 Canal landscape with mill and boat (21x31cm-8x12in) s. W/C. 24-Sep-2 Koller, Zurich #6527/R (S.FR 1600)
£1667 $2683 €2501 Dutch river landscape in the summer (21x28cm-8x11in) i.d.62 W/C over pencil. 7-May-3 Dobiaschofsky, Bern #719/R est:7000 (S.FR 3600)

JONK, Nic (1928-1994) Dutch
Sculpture
£1282 $2013 €2000 Dawn (21cm-8in) s.d.73 bronze. 25-Nov-2 Glerum, Amsterdam #326/R est:2000-4000
£1583 $2596 €2200 Centaur with woman (31cm-12in) s.d.1977 bronze prov. 3-Jun-3 Christie's, Amsterdam #174/R est:2000-3000
£9353 $15338 €13000 Nereide op Triton II (75cm-30in) s.d.1964 bronze prov.lit. 3-Jun-3 Christie's, Amsterdam #166/R est:8000-12000

JONNEAU, J (19/20th C) ?
£800 $1248 €1200 Portrait of a lady seated on a settee, holding a fan (125x84cm-49x33in) s.d.1894. 10-Sep-2 Bonhams, Knightsbridge #163/R

JONNEVOLD, Carl Henrik (1856-1930) American
£1763 $2750 €2645 Indian camp. 21-Sep-2 Harvey Clar, Oakland #1486

JONSON, Cornelis (1593-1664) Dutch
£2150 $3461 €3225 Portrait of a woman (73x61cm-29x24in) i. 12-May-3 Stephan Welz, Johannesburg #415/R est:10000-15000 (SA.R 25000)
£9146 $15000 €13719 Portrait of George Villiers, 1st Duke of Buckingham (77x63cm-30x25in) prov. 5-Feb-3 Christie's, Rockefeller NY #240/R est:8000-12000
£30000 $49800 €43500 Charles II as the Prince of Wales (25x20cm-10x8in) copper prov.lit. 16-Jun-3 Duke & Son, Dorchester #217/R

JONSON, Cornelis (attrib) (1593-1664) Dutch
£4800 $8016 €6960 Portrait of a gentleman, bust-length in black doublet and lawn collar (71x55cm-28x22in) init.d.1655 feigned oval. 9-Jul-3 Bonhams, New Bond Street #168/R est:2000-3000

JONSON, Cornelis (circle) (1593-1664) Dutch
£5000 $8350 €7250 Double portrait of a lady and gentleman, seated, she offering him a rose (114x147cm-45x58in) 11-Jul-3 Christie's, Kensington #55/R est:6000-8000

JONSON, Raymond (1891-1982) American
£1923 $3000 €2885 Oil no.7 (81x61cm-32x24in) s.d.1960 masonite panel prov.lit. 9-Nov-2 Santa Fe Art, Santa Fe #227/R est:4000-6000
£2410 $4000 €3495 Chromatic contrasts no 29 (61x80cm-24x31in) s. acrylic prov. 11-Jun-3 Butterfields, San Francisco #4143/R est:5000-7000

JONSON, Sven (1902-1981) Danish
£343 $522 €515 Evening in August (24x33cm-9x13in) s.d.43. 16-Aug-2 Lilla Bukowskis, Stockholm #344 (S.KR 5000)
£760 $1202 €1140 Autumn landscape (38x46cm-15x18in) s. 28-Apr-3 Bukowskis, Stockholm #133/R (S.KR 10000)
£1051 $1640 €1577 And life goes on (30x35cm-12x14in) s.d.38. 5-Nov-2 Bukowskis, Stockholm #123/R est:12000-15000 (S.KR 15000)
£1141 $1802 €1712 Night landscape (22x27cm-9x11in) s. 28-Apr-3 Bukowskis, Stockholm #132/R est:12000-15000 (S.KR 15000)
£1931 $3108 €2897 The view (30x35cm-12x14in) s.d.46. 7-May-3 AB Stockholms Auktionsverk #696/R est:25000-30000 (S.KR 25000)
£2453 $3826 €3680 Theme with variations (180x75cm-71x30in) s. exhib. 5-Nov-2 Bukowskis, Stockholm #243/R est:50000-60000 (S.KR 35000)
£3083 $4810 €4625 Violet plan (23x42cm-9x17in) s.d.31 canvas on panel. 5-Nov-2 Bukowskis, Stockholm #36/R est:50000-60000 (S.KR 44000)
£3118 $4926 €4677 The light night's horizon (39x46cm-15x18in) s. 28-Apr-3 Bukowskis, Stockholm #139/R est:30000-35000 (S.KR 41000)
£3644 $5685 €5466 Preludium (129x75cm-51x30in) s.d.48. 5-Nov-2 Bukowskis, Stockholm #244/R est:50000-55000 (S.KR 52000)
£7336 $11811 €11004 Clair obscur (65x80cm-26x31in) s. 7-May-3 AB Stockholms Auktionsverk #818/R est:80000-100000 (S.KR 95000)
£21293 $33643 €31940 Hurdlers (55x75cm-22x30in) s.d.29 prov. 28-Apr-3 Bukowskis, Stockholm #143/R est:250000-300000 (S.KR 280000)

JONSSON, Erik (1893-1950) Swedish
£673 $1064 €1010 Mid summer (100x120cm-39x47in) s.d.1934 prov. 27-Nov-2 Falkkloos, Malmo #77659/R (S.KR 9600)

JONSSON, Lars (1952-) Swedish
£494 $770 €741 Bird of prey (65x85cm-26x33in) s.d.80. 13-Sep-2 Lilla Bukowskis, Stockholm #384 (S.KR 7200)
Works on paper
£375 $600 €544 Chipmunk (30x40cm-12x16in) s.d.95 W/C graphite. 16-May-3 Skinner, Boston #135/R
£375 $600 €544 Wellfleet (29x39cm-11x15in) s.i.d.94 W/C. 16-May-3 Skinner, Boston #271/R

JONSSON, Theodor (1888-1966) Swedish
£301 $476 €452 Street scene with lamplight in winter (50x62cm-20x24in) s.d.1957 canvas on panel. 16-Nov-2 Crafoord, Lund #79/R (S.KR 4300)

JONXIS, Pieter Hendrik Lodewyk (1815-1852) Dutch
£2000 $3100 €3000 Frozen river (60x72cm-24x28in) s.d.1842. 3-Dec-2 Sotheby's, Olympia #225/R est:2000-3000
Works on paper
£380 $589 €600 River landscape with windmill (18x23cm-7x9in) s. W/C. 25-Sep-2 Neumeister, Munich #408/R

JONZEN, Basil (1913-1967) British
£350 $543 €525 On the quay (41x51cm-16x20in) s.d.39. 4-Dec-2 Christie's, Kensington #501

JONZEN, Karin (1914-1998) British
Sculpture
£7000 $10920 €10500 Seated female nude (49cm-19in) init. green pat. bronze. 27-Mar-3 Christie's, Kensington #451/R est:4000-6000

JOORS, Eugeen (1850-1910) Belgian
£409 $634 €650 Nature morte aux oranges (30x45cm-12x18in) s. 1-Oct-2 Palais de Beaux Arts, Brussels #492
£3797 $5924 €6000 Selling fish (94x130cm-37x51in) s.d.1888. 21-Oct-2 Bernaerts, Antwerp #182/R est:5000-6000

JOOS, Hildegard (1909-) Austrian
Works on paper
£298 $486 €450 Untitled (38x32cm-15x13in) pencil gouache. 28-Jan-3 Dorotheum, Vienna #282/R

JOOSTEN, Dirk Jan Hendrik (1818-1882) Dutch
£15723 $24214 €25000 Still life with flowers, lace and jewellery (65x50cm-26x20in) s. panel. 22-Oct-2 Sotheby's, Amsterdam #164/R est:15000-20000

JOOSTENS, Paul (1889-1960) Belgian
£481 $760 €750 Poezeloes (60x50cm-24x20in) 18-Nov-2 Bernaerts, Antwerp #418/R
£641 $1013 €1000 Un sejour en bocal (53x60cm-21x24in) s.d.51 panel. 18-Nov-2 Bernaerts, Antwerp #420/R
£1042 $1656 €1500 La scala (80x60cm-31x24in) s.d.1916. 29-Apr-3 Campo & Campo, Antwerp #169/R est:1600-1800
Works on paper
£764 $1215 €1100 Poezeloes (59x48cm-23x19in) W/C. 29-Apr-3 Campo, Vlaamse Kaai #171
£1132 $1743 €1800 Composition aux figures (76x71cm-30x28in) s. col dr. 22-Oct-2 Campo, Vlaamse Kaai #540

JOPLING, Louise (1843-1933) British
Works on paper
£2917 $4638 €4200 An anxious moment (76x76cm-30x30in) pastel dr. on canvas exhib. 29-Apr-3 Whyte's, Dublin #89/R est:2000-3000

JORDAENS, Hans III (1595-1643) Flemish
£1892 $2951 €2800 Adoration of the Magi (31x25cm-12x10in) panel. 26-Mar-3 Tajan, Paris #118
£1892 $2951 €2800 Christ in the Olive Grove (30x47cm-12x19in) panel. 26-Mar-3 Tajan, Paris #111/R est:4000
£4088 $6296 €6500 Laissez venir a moi les petits enfants (43x57cm-17x22in) s. copper. 25-Oct-2 Tajan, Paris #59/R est:6000-9000

JORDAENS, Hans III (attrib) (1595-1643) Flemish
£7643 $11924 €12000 Capture of Jericho by Joshua and the Israelites (69x86cm-27x34in) copper prov. 5-Nov-2 Sotheby's, Amsterdam #116/R est:12000-18000
£9000 $15030 €13050 Capriccio of a Renaissance town square with elegant figures (47x60cm-19x24in) panel painted with style Hendrick van Cleve III. 11-Jul-3 Christie's, Kensington #88/R est:6000-8000

JORDAENS, Jacob (1593-1678) Flemish
Works on paper
£2658 $4200 €4200 Deux putti (17x23cm-7x9in) col chk. 27-Nov-2 Christie's, Paris #5/R est:3000-5000
£50955 $79490 €80000 Merry company, allegory of integrity (21x30cm-8x12in) s.i.d.1668 May 10 pen brown ink W/C gouache col chk joined sheets. 5-Nov-2 Sotheby's, Amsterdam #25/R est:30000-40000

JORDAENS, Jacob (circle) (1593-1678) Flemish
£7000 $10990 €10500 Peasant family dining in an interior (102x141cm-40x56in) prov. 13-Dec-2 Christie's, Kensington #112/R est:5000-7000
£50676 $79054 €75000 Workshop of Vulcan (194x143cm-76x56in) prov. 27-Mar-3 Dorotheum, Vienna #386/R est:3000-5000

JORDAENS, Jacob (studio) (1593-1678) Flemish
£9615 $14615 €15000 Pillaging of Europe (73x105cm-29x41in) panel parquet. 11-Jul-2 Allgauer, Kempten #2530/R est:15000

JORDAN, Rudolf (1810-1887) German
£2469 $4000 €3704 Sailing class (43x53cm-17x21in) tin. 21-Jan-3 Christie's, Rockefeller NY #385/R
£2848 $4500 €4272 Sailor's wife with her sleeping baby (33x41cm-13x16in) mono.d.53. 5-Apr-3 Neal Auction Company, New Orleans #191/R est:5000-7000

JORDAN, Rudolf (attrib) (1810-1887) German
£288 $438 €450 Mother and children in hut by sea (30x23cm-12x9in) panel. 17-Aug-2 Hans Stahl, Toestorf #41/R

JORDE, Lars (1865-1939) Norwegian
£702 $1109 €1053 Landscape with farm (34x48cm-13x19in) s.d.87 panel. 17-Dec-2 Grev Wedels Plass, Oslo #160/R (N.KR 8000)
£1381 $2098 €2072 Landscape from Storekoll (41x46cm-16x18in) s.d.18 i.verso panel. 31-Aug-2 Grev Wedels Plass, Oslo #132/R est:20000-30000 (N.KR 16000)
£2168 $3382 €3252 Girls by bridge across water (60x70cm-24x28in) s.d.35. 21-Oct-2 Blomqvist, Oslo #360/R est:25000-30000 (N.KR 25000)
£5236 $8220 €7854 Summer's day - vase of flowers in window (84x91cm-33x36in) s.d.1930 s.i.stretcher. 21-Nov-2 Grev Wedels Plass, Oslo #35/R est:80000-100000 (N.KR 60000)

JORDENS, Jan (1883-1962) Dutch
£823 $1300 €1300 Taormina (30x24cm-12x9in) s. s.i.verso board. 26-Nov-2 Sotheby's, Amsterdam #16/R est:1300-1800
£3453 $5663 €4800 Untitled (80x61cm-31x24in) s.d.58 board prov. 3-Jun-3 Christie's, Amsterdam #260/R est:4000-6000

JORGENSEN, Aksel (1883-1957) Danish
£279 $441 €419 Standing woman seen from behind (31x42cm-12x17in) init. canvas on veneer. 1-Apr-3 Rasmussen, Copenhagen #600 (D.KR 3000)
£297 $470 €446 View of Copenhagen (45x62cm-18x24in) mono.d.1908. 5-Apr-3 Rasmussen, Havnen #2126 (D.KR 3200)
£297 $470 €446 Still life of beer mug and food (26x68cm-10x27in) s.d.1911. 5-Apr-3 Rasmussen, Havnen #4270 (D.KR 3200)
£651 $1028 €977 Women in Holmensgade 6 (54x53cm-21x21in) s. painted 1907-08. 1-Apr-3 Rasmussen, Copenhagen #44/R (D.KR 7000)
£701 $1121 €1052 Lady wearing red coat and hat (97x76cm-38x30in) 13-Jan-3 Rasmussen, Vejle #6/R (D.KR 8000)
£1397 $2221 €2096 Woman rolling cigar with the artist in background (80x65cm-31x26in) s.d.1916. 5-Mar-3 Rasmussen, Copenhagen #1949/R est:8000 (D.KR 15000)

JORGENSEN, Anita (1942-) Danish
£272 $430 €408 Green composition (131x120cm-52x47in) s.stretcher. 30-Nov-2 Rasmussen, Havnen #2119 (D.KR 3200)

JORGENSEN, Borge (1926-1998) Danish
Sculpture
£2323 $3671 €3485 Staning figure (116cm-46in) s.d.79 corten steel sold with black painted wood socle. 1-Apr-3 Rasmussen, Copenhagen #330/R est:20000-25000 (D.KR 25000)

JORGENSEN, Christian (1860-1935) American
Works on paper
£250 $410 €363 Monastery courtyard with well (38x28cm-15x11in) s. W/C. 29-May-3 Mallams, Cheltenham #338/R
£1506 $2500 €2184 Summer home, Annisquam, Massachusetts (27x37cm-11x15in) s.d.1916 pencil W/C. 11-Jun-3 Butterfields, San Francisco #4184/R est:3000-5000
£2388 $3750 €3582 Adobe ruins (25x38cm-10x15in) s.d.03 W/C paperboard prov. 19-Nov-2 Butterfields, San Francisco #8128/R est:3000-5000
£2866 $4500 €4299 Adobe archway (68x25cm-27x10in) s.d.03 W/C paperboard prov. 19-Nov-2 Butterfields, San Francisco #8127/R est:3000-5000
£3503 $5500 €5255 Adobe mission (25x38cm-10x15in) s.d.03 W/C paperboard prov. 19-Nov-2 Butterfields, San Francisco #8129/R est:3000-5000
£4459 $7000 €6689 Bridalveil Falls and El Capitan, Yosemite Valley (34x48cm-13x19in) s. W/C. 19-Nov-2 Butterfields, San Francisco #8130/R est:5000-7000

JORGENSEN, Erling (1905-1977) Danish
£301 $467 €452 Composition (41x58cm-16x23in) s.d.1960 verso. 4-Dec-2 Kunsthallen, Copenhagen #224/R (D.KR 3500)
£320 $509 €480 Composition (52x59cm-20x23in) s.i.d.1965 verso. 26-Feb-3 Kunsthallen, Copenhagen #61 (D.KR 3500)

JORGENSEN, H L (19/20th C) American
£316 $500 €474 Low tide, Gloucester, Mass (51x61cm-20x24in) 17-Nov-2 Jeffery Burchard, Florida #68a/R

JORGENSEN, Knut (1937-1991) Norwegian
£3806 $6014 €5709 Spanish night (46x60cm-18x24in) s.indis.d.19. prov.exhib.lit. i.stretcher. 2-Dec-2 Blomqvist, Oslo #450/R est:35000-40000 (N.KR 44000)
£4510 $7036 €6765 The egg (41x33cm-16x13in) s.d.1983 panel. 21-Oct-2 Blomqvist, Oslo #413/R est:40000-50000 (N.KR 52000)
Works on paper
£1393 $2228 €2090 Carmen (25x17cm-10x7in) s.d.1979 pencil W/C. 17-Mar-3 Blomqvist, Oslo #423/R est:18000-22000 (N.KR 16000)

JORGENSEN, Steffen (1940-) Danish
£267 $414 €401 Geometrical figures (48x62cm-19x24in) oil collage. 4-Dec-2 Kunsthallen, Copenhagen #288 (D.KR 3100)

JORGENSEN, Willer (20th C) Danish
£622 $1008 €902 Saeby river (80x120cm-31x47in) s. 24-May-3 Rasmussen, Havnen #2257 (D.KR 6500)
£2800 $4396 €4200 Snowy river landscape (100x126cm-39x50in) s. 21-Nov-2 Christie's, Kensington #122/R est:2500-3500
£5599 $8510 €8399 Winter afternoon with low sun in Charlottenlund Forest (90x141cm-35x56in) s.i.d.1935. 27-Aug-2 Rasmussen, Copenhagen #1924/R est:20000-30000 (D.KR 65000)

JORHAN, Wenzeslaus (attrib) (1695-1752) German?
Sculpture
£2466 $3871 €3600 The Risen Christ (73cm-29in) carved wood gilded. 16-Apr-3 Dorotheum, Salzburg #307/R est:4500-5500

JORI, Marcello (1951-) Italian
£359 $575 €550 Untitled (50x38cm-20x15in) s.verso acrylic canvas on board. 4-Jan-3 Meeting Art, Vercelli #323
£380 $592 €600 Geometry (40x55cm-16x22in) s. acrylic canvas on board. 14-Sep-2 Meeting Art, Vercelli #745
£417 $654 €650 Untitled (40x34cm-16x13in) s.verso acrylic canvas on board. 23-Nov-2 Meeting Art, Vercelli #256/R
£417 $654 €650 Untitled (38x50cm-15x20in) s. acrylic canvas on board. 23-Nov-2 Meeting Art, Vercelli #268/R
£743 $1159 €1100 Super heroes (84x112cm-33x44in) s.verso acrylic canvas on board. 26-Mar-3 Finarte Semenzato, Milan #136/R
£764 $1215 €1100 Untitled (50x70cm-20x28in) s. canvas on board. 1-May-3 Meeting Art, Vercelli #147
£799 $1270 €1150 Untitled (50x70cm-20x28in) s.verso canvas on board. 1-May-3 Meeting Art, Vercelli #399

JORIS, Pio (1843-1921) Italian
£949 $1500 €1500 Rome, church interior (20x13cm-8x5in) s. board. 26-Nov-2 Christie's, Rome #129/R
Works on paper
£288 $453 €450 Paysanne italienne (42x25cm-17x10in) s. W/C graphite. 10-Dec-2 Renaud, Paris #14

JORN, Asger (1914-1973) Danish

£3015 $4673 €4523 Composition (32x24cm-13x9in) s.d.71 acrylic paper on canvas. 4-Dec-2 Kunsthallen, Copenhagen #160/R est:40000 (D.KR 35000)
£3903 $6167 €5855 La fleur marrante (40x30cm-16x12in) s.d.55 cardboard on canvas prov. 1-Apr-3 Rasmussen, Copenhagen #130/R est:60000-80000 (D.KR 42000)
£4647 $7342 €6971 Aggenakker - hedgehog (17x24cm-7x9in) s. s.d.1949 verso cardboard prov.lit. 1-Apr-3 Rasmussen, Copenhagen #135/R est:40000 (D.KR 50000)
£7321 $11348 €10982 Araba (40x30cm-16x12in) s.d.47 plywood prov.lit. 4-Dec-2 Kunsthallen, Copenhagen #100/R est:100000 (D.KR 85000)
£7692 $12846 €11153 Composition with head (56x46cm-22x18in) s.d.61 gouache prov. 24-Jun-3 Koller, Zurich #170/R est:20000-35000 (S.FR 17000)
£7790 $12075 €11685 Le pirate Melancolique (66x50cm-26x20in) s.d.71 acrylic gouache paper on canvas prov. 1-Oct-2 Rasmussen, Copenhagen #78/R est:100000 (D.KR 92000)
£10000 $16400 €15000 Finnfinn the faineant (54x65cm-21x26in) s.stretcher prov.exhib.lit. 7-Feb-3 Sotheby's, London #245/R est:12000-15000
£11197 $17356 €16796 Fantasy animal, Suresnes (30x37cm-12x15in) masonite lit. 4-Dec-2 Kunsthallen, Copenhagen #75/R est:150000 (D.KR 130000)
£11348 $18383 €16000 Figura (42x30cm-17x12in) s. d.191169 verso paper on canvas prov. 26-May-3 Christie's, Milan #346/R est:15000-20000
£12950 $21237 €18000 Tale of Timid terror (41x33cm-16x13in) s.d.66 acrylic paper on canvas prov.exhib.lit. 3-Jun-3 Christie's, Amsterdam #338/R est:18000-22000
£14000 $22820 €21000 Untitled (48x36cm-19x14in) s.d.62 prov. 3-Feb-3 Sotheby's, Olympia #66/R est:10000-15000
£17257 $27439 €25886 Figure (38x29cm-15x11in) s.d.39 lit. 29-Apr-3 Kunsthallen, Copenhagen #40/R est:100000 (D.KR 185000)
£21169 $32811 €31754 Dream picture Number 20 - Old boy from Venus (55x45cm-22x18in) s.i. s.d.1955 verso exhib. 1-Oct-2 Rasmussen, Copenhagen #79/R est:250000 (D.KR 250000)
£21938 $34881 €32907 Fantasy animal (70x50cm-28x20in) s.d.49 prov.exhib.lit. 26-Feb-3 Kunsthallen, Copenhagen #26/R est:300000 (D.KR 240000)
£22000 $34100 €33000 Nice (68x91cm-27x36in) s.i.d.46 prov.lit. 5-Dec-2 Christie's, Kensington #175/R est:15000-20000
£25409 $39384 €38114 Composition (46x55cm-18x22in) s. lit. 4-Dec-2 Kunsthallen, Copenhagen #68/R est:350000 (D.KR 295000)
£27338 $44835 €38000 Personnage (70x50cm-28x20in) s.d.56 verso prov.lit. 3-Jun-3 Christie's, Amsterdam #339/R est:30000-40000
£30000 $46200 €45000 La Terre nouvelle (65x54cm-26x21in) s. s.i.d.58 verso prov.lit. 22-Oct-2 Sotheby's, London #448/R est:30000-40000
£35256 $54647 €55000 Underdeveloped insult (84x65cm-33x26in) s.d.Jorn 61 s.i.d.verso prov.lit. 3-Dec-2 Christie's, Amsterdam #314/R est:55000-75000
£51115 $80762 €76673 Dalarne (72x84cm-28x33in) s.d.46 exhib.prov. 1-Apr-3 Rasmussen, Copenhagen #112/R est:700000 (D.KR 550000)
£58000 $95120 €87000 Stormy weather (81x100cm-32x39in) s. s.i.d.71 verso prov.exhib.lit. 7-Feb-3 Sotheby's, London #244/R est:60000-80000
£67739 $104996 €101609 Didaska composition (67x52cm-26x20in) s.d.46 artist's board on masonite lit.prov. 1-Oct-2 Rasmussen, Copenhagen #70/R est:800000-1000000 (D.KR 800000)
£74488 $118436 €111732 Aus den Schatten (81x65cm-32x26in) s. d.68 verso lit. 10-Mar-3 Rasmussen, Vejle #769/R est:800000-1000000 (D.KR 800000)
£90613 $143169 €135920 The hot blonde (100x72cm-39x28in) s.d.64 s.i.d.1964 and 1968 verso exhib. 1-Apr-3 Rasmussen, Copenhagen #118/R est:1200000-1500000 (D.KR 975000)
£100000 $164000 €150000 Le bouc emissaire (97x132cm-38x52in) s. s.i.verso painted 1956 prov.exhib.lit. 5-Feb-3 Christie's, London #33/R est:120000-160000
£110000 $180400 €165000 No man's land (120x100cm-47x39in) s. painted 1958 prov.exhib.lit. 6-Feb-3 Sotheby's, London #19/R est:150000
£115000 $192050 €166750 L'appel aux sauvages (114x146cm-45x57in) s. s.i.d.57 verso prov.lit. 26-Jun-3 Sotheby's, London #234/R est:55000-65000
£141026 $218590 €220000 Emigrants (91x122cm-36x48in) s.d.53 board prov.exhib.lit. 3-Dec-2 Christie's, Amsterdam #316/R est:165000-200000
£155000 $238700 €232500 Noblesse oblige (137x119cm-54x47in) s.d.64 prov.exhib.lit. 22-Oct-2 Sotheby's, London #444/R est:70000-100000
£191956 $305210 €287934 Toy picture (72x100cm-28x39in) s.d.45 i.d.1944 verso prov.exhib.lit. 26-Feb-3 Kunsthallen, Copenhagen #57/R est:1500000 (D.KR 2100000)
£201097 $319744 €301646 Myr og Mo - composition (122x122cm-48x48in) s. i.verso plywood exhib.lit. 26-Feb-3 Kunsthallen, Copenhagen #17/R est:2000000 (D.KR 2200000)

Prints

£2067 $3204 €3101 The red earth (90x119cm-35x47in) s.d.53 col lithograph in two parts. 4-Dec-2 Kunsthallen, Copenhagen #508/R est:30000 (D.KR 24000)
£2412 $3738 €3618 Das offene Versteck (102x140cm-40x55in) s.d.70 num.32/85 col lithograph. 4-Dec-2 Kunsthallen, Copenhagen #456/R est:30000 (D.KR 28000)

Sculpture

£2635 $4111 €3900 Figure (19x12x10cm-7x5x4in) s. polychrome ceramic exhib. 26-Mar-3 Finarte Semenzato, Milan #183/R
£4054 $6324 €6000 Embrace (33x20x18cm-13x8x7in) polychrome terracotta lit. 26-Mar-3 Finarte Semenzato, Milan #182/R

Works on paper

£731 $1163 €1097 Composition (21x16cm-8x6in) s. Indian ink executed c.1942. 26-Feb-3 Kunsthallen, Copenhagen #41 (D.KR 8000)
£1952 $3084 €2928 Figure composition (24x30cm-9x12in) s.d.42, 15-1 pencil Indian ink. 1-Apr-3 Rasmussen, Copenhagen #226/R est:18000 (D.KR 21000)
£2881 $4552 €4322 Figure composition (30x22cm-12x9in) s.d.46 W/C prov. 1-Apr-3 Rasmussen, Copenhagen #105/R est:30000 (D.KR 31000)
£3108 $4941 €4662 Composition (24x32cm-9x13in) s.d.59 W/C. 26-Feb-3 Kunsthallen, Copenhagen #42/R est:35000 (D.KR 34000)
£3656 $5814 €5484 Mask composition (24x31cm-9x12in) s.i.d.1943 crayon. 26-Feb-3 Kunsthallen, Copenhagen #49/R est:45000 (D.KR 40000)
£4322 $6828 €6483 Fantasy animal (31x23cm-12x9in) s.d.50 W/C gouache crayon prov. 1-Apr-3 Rasmussen, Copenhagen #139/R est:60000 (D.KR 46500)
£4487 $6955 €7000 Untitled (30x35cm-12x14in) s.d.48 W/C ink. 3-Dec-2 Christie's, Amsterdam #312/R est:4000-6000
£4647 $7342 €6971 Composition (45x38cm-18x15in) s. gouache Indian ink executed c.1972 exhib. 1-Apr-3 Rasmussen, Copenhagen #132/R est:40000-50000 (D.KR 50000)
£4717 $7358 €7076 Composition (45x30cm-18x12in) s.d.63 W/C. 11-Nov-2 Rasmussen, Vejle #118/R est:30000-40000 (D.KR 55000)
£5068 $7905 €7602 Figure composition (31x38cm-12x15in) s. W/C. 18-Sep-2 Kunsthallen, Copenhagen #45/R est:75000 (D.KR 60000)
£5674 $9191 €8000 Untitled (52x62cm-20x24in) s.d.69 paper decollage prov. 20-May-3 Dorotheum, Vienna #47/R est:10000-16000
£7313 $11627 €10970 Composition (48x36cm-19x14in) s.d.72 W/C. 26-Feb-3 Kunsthallen, Copenhagen #58/R est:85000 (D.KR 80000)
£9294 $14684 €13941 Figure composition (71x51cm-28x20in) s.d.71 gouache Indian ink exhib. 1-Apr-3 Rasmussen, Copenhagen #119/R est:125000-150000 (D.KR 100000)
£10557 $16470 €15836 Composition (77x55cm-30x22in) s.d.61 gouache prov. 18-Sep-2 Kunsthallen, Copenhagen #71/R est:150000 (D.KR 125000)
£10688 $16887 €16032 Figure composition (76x56cm-30x22in) s.d.71 gouache Indian ink exhib.lit. 1-Apr-3 Rasmussen, Copenhagen #133/R est:125000-150000 (D.KR 115000)
£12000 $20040 €17400 Unique au monde (75x54cm-30x21in) s.d.62 gouache prov. 26-Jun-3 Sotheby's, London #232/R est:4000-6000
£13011 $20558 €19517 Green figure on red background (65x50cm-26x20in) s.d.67 mixed media. 1-Apr-3 Rasmussen, Copenhagen #121/R est:125000-150000 (D.KR 140000)

JORON, Maurice Paul (1883-1937) French

£577 $906 €900 Nu assis (32x41cm-13x16in) 15-Dec-2 Mercier & Cie, Lille #395a

JORRES, Carl (1872-1947) German

£316 $500 €500 Spring at Worpe (60x69cm-24x27in) s. board. 29-Nov-2 Bolland & Marotz, Bremen #532/R
£748 $1190 €1100 Spring day on the Worpe (65x78cm-26x31in) s. 28-Mar-3 Bolland & Marotz, Bremen #350/R

JORSTEDT, Kjell (1943-) Scandinavian

£1051 $1640 €1577 Restaurant interior (72x94cm-28x37in) s.d.1975. 5-Nov-2 Bukowskis, Stockholm #359/R est:8000-10000 (S.KR 15000)

JOS, Julien (?) ?

£3000 $4560 €4500 Harvesters picnicking (50x70cm-20x28in) s. 29-Aug-2 Christie's, Kensington #46/R est:3000-5000

JOSEPH, Albert (1868-1952) French

£528 $850 €750 Rochers dans la mer (53x46cm-21x18in) s. 11-May-3 Lombrail & Teucquam, Paris #175/R

JOSEPH, Julian (1882-1964) American

£570 $889 €900 Les enfants, gardiens d'oies (36x56cm-14x22in) s. 16-Sep-2 Horta, Bruxelles #389

JOSEPH, Lily Delissa (1864-1940) British

£250 $390 €375 National Gallery (69x91cm-27x36in) 17-Sep-2 Bonhams, Knightsbridge #62

JOSEPH, Ronald (1910-1992) American
£11250 $18000 €16313 Peeling green apples (76x60cm-30x24in) bears sig.verso canvasboard. 16-May-3 Skinner, Boston #360/R est:6000-8000

JOSEPHSON, Ernst (1851-1906) Swedish
£1702 $2638 €2553 Interior scene with country woman (41x32cm-16x13in) mono.i. exhib. 8-Dec-2 Uppsala Auktionskammare, Uppsala #103/R est:30000-40000 (S.KR 24000)
£41135 $63759 €61703 Old man and girl (43x36cm-17x14in) s. painted c.1888 panel prov.exhib.lit. 3-Dec-2 Bukowskis, Stockholm #99/R est:500000-700000 (S.KR 580000)

Works on paper
£315 $498 €473 Portrait of woman (18x12cm-7x5in) s.d.dec.13 1868 pencil exhib. 16-Nov-2 Crafoord, Lund #107/R (S.KR 4500)
£340 $564 €493 Study of male model (71x50cm-28x20in) s.d.Nov.1874 dr. 16-Jun-3 Lilla Bukowskis, Stockholm #375 (S.KR 4400)
£853 $1382 €1237 Jeanne d'Arc (32x18cm-13x7in) s. Indian ink. 26-May-3 Bukowskis, Stockholm #49/R (S.KR 11000)
£1552 $2514 €2250 Papageno (35x22cm-14x9in) s. Indian ink. 26-May-3 Bukowskis, Stockholm #52/R est:25000-30000 (S.KR 20000)
£1773 $2748 €2660 The artist by his easel (37x22cm-15x9in) s. Indian ink. 4-Dec-2 AB Stockholms Auktionsverk #1602/R est:20000-25000 (S.KR 25000)
£1844 $2858 €2766 Man with hat filling his pipe (21x13cm-8x5in) s. Indian ink. 3-Dec-2 Bukowskis, Stockholm #101/R est:30000-35000 (S.KR 26000)
£2327 $3770 €3374 Gothic Prince II (34x21cm-13x8in) s. Indian ink. 26-May-3 Bukowskis, Stockholm #47/R est:18000-20000 (S.KR 30000)
£2553 $3957 €3830 Warriors (36x22cm-14x9in) s. Indian ink. 4-Dec-2 AB Stockholms Auktionsverk #1601/R est:35000-40000 (S.KR 36000)
£2793 $4524 €4050 The old telephone exchange at Malmskillnads Street (22x38cm-9x15in) s. i.verso Indian ink. 26-May-3 Bukowskis, Stockholm #50/R est:40000-50000 (S.KR 36000)
£3404 $5277 €5106 Lady Macbeth (37x22cm-15x9in) s Indian ink prov.exhib.lit. 4-Dec-2 AB Stockholms Auktionsverk #1546/R est:25000-30000 (S.KR 48000)
£5319 $8245 €7979 Drawing from the time of sickness (48x60cm-19x24in) s. W/C. 3-Dec-2 Bukowskis, Stockholm #104/R est:100000-125000 (S.KR 75000)

JOSEPHSON, Ken (1932-) American
Photographs
£2025 $3200 €3038 Chicago (14x14cm-6x6in) s.i.d.1964 gelatin silver print prov. 25-Apr-3 Phillips, New York #258/R est:2000-3000
£2025 $3200 €3038 Untitled (28x36cm-11x14in) s.verso gelatin silver print prov. 25-Apr-3 Phillips, New York #154/R est:2000-3000
£2405 $3800 €3608 Chicago (12x17cm-5x7in) s.d.1964 num.64-5-10-1 gelatin silver print on board prov. 25-Apr-3 Phillips, New York #54/R est:2000-3000
£2405 $3800 €3608 Chicago (13x23cm-5x9in) i.num.63-2-2-8 gelatin silver print prov. 25-Apr-3 Phillips, New York #156/R est:2000-3000
£2532 $4000 €3798 Chicago (23x16cm-9x6in) i.d.1967 verso gelatin silver print prov. 25-Apr-3 Phillips, New York #155/R est:2000-3000
£6329 $10000 €9494 Chicago (15x23cm-6x9in) s.i.d.1961 num.61-35-50-28 gelatin silver print prov.lit. 25-Apr-3 Phillips, New York #46/R est:4000-6000

JOTTI, Carlo (1826-1905) Italian
£4255 $6894 €6000 Castello di Scipione vicino a Salsomaggio (43x57cm-17x22in) i. 22-May-3 Dorotheum, Vienna #11/R est:3000-4000
£6289 $9686 €10000 Lugano (23x40cm-9x16in) s. cardboard. 23-Oct-2 Finarte, Milan #104/R est:10000-12000

JOUANNE-HUGONET, Marthe (1871-?) French
£1613 $2548 €2500 Marchande de violettes a Paris (118x71cm-46x28in) s. 19-Dec-2 Claude Aguttes, Neuilly #73/R est:4000

JOUANT, Jules (19th C) French
Sculpture
£17000 $26520 €25500 Mask of Ludvig von Beethoven (65cm-26in) s.st.f.H Gonot brown pat bronze green marble base. 9-Apr-3 Sotheby's, London #210/R est:5000-7000

JOUAS, Edouard Etienne (19th C) French
£738 $1189 €1100 Cote rocheuse (56x81cm-22x32in) s. 23-Feb-3 Lesieur & Le Bars, Le Havre #79

JOUBERT, A (19th C) French
£574 $895 €861 Hamam (89x70cm-35x28in) s. 10-Sep-2 Iegor de Saint Hippolyte, Montreal #64 (C.D 1400)

JOUBERT, Léon (19th C) French
£4196 $7007 €6000 Bateau a vapeur sur riviere (86x127cm-34x50in) s. 25-Jun-3 Artcurial Briest, Paris #10/R est:3000-3500

JOUBIN, Georges (1888-1983) French
£541 $845 €850 La dormeuse (130x97cm-51x38in) s. panel exhib. 7-Nov-2 Claude Aguttes, Neuilly #53

JOUDERVILLE, Isaac de (1612-1645) Flemish
£6452 $10000 €9678 Portrait of a man with a white beard and turban (48x36cm-19x14in) panel prov.lit. 2-Oct-2 Christie's, Rockefeller NY #165/R est:12000-18000

JOUENNE, Michel (1933-) French
£669 $1077 €950 Le bouquet blanc (38x55cm-15x22in) s. 11-May-3 Thierry & Lannon, Brest #259
£759 $1177 €1200 Les chalutiers (27x35cm-11x14in) s. 29-Sep-2 Eric Pillon, Calais #274/R
£1603 $2516 €2500 Retour des pecheurs (50x65cm-20x26in) s. s.i.verso. 15-Dec-2 Thierry & Lannon, Brest #235
£1656 $2583 €2600 Retour de peche (46x61cm-18x24in) s. 10-Nov-2 Eric Pillon, Calais #175/R
£2414 $4031 €3500 La lac (100x100cm-39x39in) s. 9-Jul-3 Millon & Associes, Paris #198/R est:3500-5000
£3205 $5032 €5000 Petite ferme en Provence (73x100cm-29x39in) s. 15-Dec-2 Eric Pillon, Calais #226/R

JOUHAUD, Léon (c.1874-1950) French
£608 $949 €900 Sonia (12x9cm-5x4in) mono. s.i.d.1931 verso emaux polychrome copper plaque. 31-Mar-3 Pierre Berge, Paris #84/R
£676 $1054 €1000 Mondaines (8cm-3in circular) mono. s.i.d.1922 verso emaux polychrome copper plaque. 31-Mar-3 Pierre Berge, Paris #90/R
£676 $1054 €1000 Alice (12x6cm-5x2in) mono. si.d.1933 verso emaux polychrome copper plaque. 31-Mar-3 Pierre Berge, Paris #93/R
£676 $1054 €1000 La ravaudeuse (11x7cm-4x3in) mono. s.i.verso emaux polychrome copper plaque. 31-Mar-3 Pierre Berge, Paris #100/R
£676 $1054 €1000 L'eglise de Saint Germain de Confolens (11x7cm-4x3in) mono. s.i.d.verso emaux polychrome copper plaque. 31-Mar-3 Pierre Berge, Paris #102/R
£743 $1159 €1100 Les aveux (10cm-4in circular) s.i.d.1931 verso emaux polychrome copper plaque. 31-Mar-3 Pierre Berge, Paris #92/R
£743 $1159 €1100 Temps gris pres de Tarnac (13x10cm-5x4in) mono. s.i.d.1933 verso emaux polychrome copper plaque. 31-Mar-3 Pierre Berge, Paris #96/R
£811 $1265 €1200 Veronique (9x7cm-4x3in) mono. s.i.d.1931 verso emaux polychrome copper plaque. 31-Mar-3 Pierre Berge, Paris #85/R
£946 $1476 €1400 Le peignoir (18x8cm-7x3in) s.i.d.1925 verso emaux polychrome copper plaque. 31-Mar-3 Pierre Berge, Paris #88/R
£1014 $1581 €1500 Prehistoire (9x12cm-4x5in) mono. s.i.d.1930 verso emaux polychrome copper plaque. 31-Mar-3 Pierre Berge, Paris #80/R est:1000-1500
£1351 $2108 €2000 Premiers pas (14x11cm-6x4in) s.i.d.1927 verso emaux polychrome copper plaque. 31-Mar-3 Pierre Berge, Paris #91/R est:2000-3000
£1419 $2214 €2100 Le bas (14x11cm-6x4in) mono. s.i.d.1928 verso emaux polychrome copper plaque. 31-Mar-3 Pierre Berge, Paris #81/R est:1000-1500
£1757 $2741 €2600 Le printemps (11x14cm-4x6in) mono. s.i.d.1917 verso emaux polychrome copper plaque. 31-Mar-3 Pierre Berge, Paris #86/R est:2000-3000
£1892 $2951 €2800 La cuisine (14x8cm-6x3in) s.i.d.1934 verso emaux polychrome copper plaque. 31-Mar-3 Pierre Berge, Paris #94/R est:2000-3000
£2095 $3268 €3100 Enigme (12x6cm-5x2in) s.i.d.1931 emaux polychrome copper plaque. 31-Mar-3 Pierre Berge, Paris #82/R est:2000-3000
£2365 $3689 €3500 Le bistrot, pres de Royeres (12x9cm-5x4in) mono. emaux polychrome copper plaque. 31-Mar-3 Pierre Berge, Paris #101/R est:1800-2400
£2568 $4005 €3800 Le rapport (12x9cm-5x4in) mono. s.i.d.1947 verso emaux polychrome copper plaque. 31-Mar-3 Pierre Berge, Paris #97 est:2000-3000
£2838 $4427 €4200 La Lingere dans ma ru (14x11cm-6x4in) mono. emaux polychrome copper plaque. 31-Mar-3 Pierre Berge, Paris #98/R est:1000-1500
£3108 $4849 €4600 Chanteur des rues (14x11cm-6x4in) mono. s.i.d.1932 verso emaux polychrome copper plaque. 31-Mar-3 Pierre Berge, Paris #95/R est:1500-2000

£3243 $5059 €4800 La toilette (15x11cm-6x4in) s.i.d.1919 verso emaux polychrome copper plaque. 31-Mar-3 Pierre Berge, Paris #89/R est:1500-2000
£3378 $5270 €5000 Le bouquet de fleurs (14x12cm-6x5in) mono. s.i.d.1921 verso emaux polychrome copper plaque. 31-Mar-3 Pierre Berge, Paris #87/R est:2000-3000

JOUKOVSKI, Stanislav (1873-1944) Russian
£3718 $5763 €5800 Lakeshore with boats, trees and houses (49x64cm-19x25in) s.cyrillic. 7-Dec-2 Hans Stahl, Hamburg #73/R est:2500
£8000 $12560 €12000 Lynx in a winter landscape (60x73cm-24x29in) s.d.1937. 16-Apr-3 Christie's, Kensington #839

JOULIA, Elisabeth (1925-) French?
Sculpture
£2590 $4247 €3600 Deesse solaire. sandstone. 6-Jun-3 Rabourdin & Choppin de Janvry, Paris #106/R est:800-1000

JOULIN, Lucien (1842-?) French
£2388 $3750 €3582 Encounter in the garden (116x89cm-46x35in) s.d.1873 prov. 22-Nov-2 Skinner, Boston #46/R est:3500-5500

JOULLIN, Amadee (1862-1917) American
£2019 $3250 €3029 Sand dunes in a coastal (16x20cm-6x8in) s. canvas on canvas prov. 18-Feb-3 John Moran, Pasadena #60a est:2000-3000
£2388 $3750 €3582 Young American Indian girl painting a pot (51x66cm-20x26in) s. 19-Nov-2 Butterfields, San Francisco #8172/R est:4000-6000

JOURAVLOV, Mikael (1952-) Russian
£250 $380 €375 Fond farewell (64x46cm-25x18in) s.i. 13-Aug-2 Canterbury Auctions, UK #106
£316 $512 €480 La robe a pois blanc (46x33cm-18x13in) s. canvas on cardboard. 27-Jan-3 Millon & Associes, Paris #62

JOURDAIN, Roger Joseph (1845-1918) French
£3200 $4960 €4800 Feeding the swans (44x61cm-17x24in) s. 3-Dec-2 Sotheby's, Olympia #287/R est:800-1200

JOURDAN, Émile (1860-1931) French
£50320 $81016 €71455 Brigneau, le semaphore et les ramasseurs de goemon (89x78cm-35x31in) panel. 11-May-3 Thierry & Lannon, Brest #185a/R
£62821 $98628 €98000 Naufrage (81x100cm-32x39in) s.d.1914. 15-Dec-2 Thierry & Lannon, Brest #144/R est:120000

JOURDEUIL, Louis-Adrien (1849-1907) Russian/French
£535 $829 €850 Port d'Antibes (27x46cm-11x18in) s. 30-Oct-2 Coutau Begarie, Paris #88/R

JOURNIAC, Michel (1943-) French
Works on paper
£355 $574 €500 Icone (34x23cm-13x9in) mixed media. 23-May-3 Binoche, Paris #94

JOUVE, Paul (1880-1973) French
£1290 $2039 €2000 Tete de sanglier (17x24cm-7x9in) s. board. 17-Dec-2 Claude Aguttes, Neuilly #32/R est:1500-2000
£1652 $2561 €2478 Cervin apres l'orage (90x80cm-35x31in) s.i. painted c.1920. 7-Dec-2 Galerie du Rhone, Sion #509/R est:7000-9000 (S.FR 3800)
£3103 $4934 €4500 Deux cornacs sur un elephant (38x46cm-15x18in) s. panel. 9-Mar-3 Feletin, Province #97
£3237 $5180 €4500 Aigle royal, ailes ouvertes (60x120cm-24x47in) s. lit. 19-May-3 Tajan, Paris #49/R est:5000-7000
£4194 $6626 €6500 Tete de tigre (18x23cm-7x9in) s. board. 17-Dec-2 Claude Aguttes, Neuilly #31/R est:3000-3300
£5570 $8689 €8800 Tigre couche (37x53cm-15x21in) s. i.verso paper on board. 20-Oct-2 Galerie de Chartres, Chartres #349 est:8000-10000
Prints
£1923 $2981 €3000 Tigre buvant (41x53cm-16x21in) s. eau-forte. 9-Dec-2 Artcurial Briest, Paris #85/R
£2452 $3874 €3800 Lionne et ses petits (60x75cm-24x30in) s. lithograph. 17-Dec-2 Claude Aguttes, Neuilly #36/R est:3500-4000
£3108 $4849 €4600 Panthere noire (74x80cm-29x31in) s. lithograph. 28-Mar-3 Camard, Paris #140/R
£4276 $6799 €6200 Sanglier au ferme (32x50cm-13x20in) st.sig. col lithograph vellum. 10-Mar-3 Coutau Begarie, Paris #138
£5036 $8057 €7000 Panthere jouant avec un serpent (55x75cm-22x30in) s.i. eua forte leather lit. 19-May-3 Tajan, Paris #50/R est:4000-5000
Sculpture
£21519 $33354 €34000 Lion marchant (41x76cm-16x30in) s. col pat bronze exec.c.1920 Cast Alexis Rudier. 29-Sep-2 Eric Pillon, Calais #146/R
Works on paper
£348 $550 €550 Tiger (38x26cm-15x10in) s. chl dr. 29-Nov-2 Sigalas, Stuttgart #1096/R
£552 $877 €800 Cheval (31x48cm-12x19in) s. chl. 7-Mar-3 Rabourdin & Choppin de Janvry, Paris #2
£903 $1435 €1300 Le paon (18x38cm-7x15in) s.i. W/C gouache prov. 29-Apr-3 Artcurial Briest, Paris #62 est:1200-1500
£949 $1500 €1500 Deux aigles (33x28cm-13x11in) s. W/C Chinese ink. 26-Nov-2 Camard, Paris #77/R
£1076 $1776 €1550 Panthere allongee de profil. blue crayon. 2-Jul-3 Artcurial Briest, Paris #69/R est:1200-1500
£1154 $1812 €1800 Le chevalier et le cerf (23x40cm-9x16in) s. mixed media. 16-Dec-2 Chochon-Barre & Allardi, Paris #75 est:2000-2300
£2432 $3795 €3600 Lion devorant sa proie (18x24cm-7x9in) s. crayon Chinese ink stump dr. 25-Mar-3 Claude Aguttes, Neuilly #106/R
£2708 $4469 €3900 Panthere couchee (31x25cm-12x10in) s. crayon Indian ink estompe. 1-Jul-3 Claude Aguttes, Neuilly #140/R est:3000-3500
£2911 $4600 €4600 GRand dic (46x41cm-18x16in) s. gouache W/C chl dr. 26-Nov-2 Camard, Paris #76/R est:6500
£6738 $10915 €9500 Lionne (49x67cm-19x26in) s. mixed media board. 23-May-3 Camard, Paris #110/R est:6000-8000

JOUVENET, Jean Baptiste (1644-1717) French
£4483 $7172 €6500 Portrait presume de Francois d'Aubigne (92x74cm-36x29in) oval prov.exhib.lit. 11-Mar-3 Christie's, Paris #253/R
Works on paper
£699 $1000 €1049 Putti with garland (14x26cm-6x10in) pen ink wash pair. 23-Jan-3 Swann Galleries, New York #239/R est:1500-2500

JOUVENET, Jean Baptiste (attrib) (1644-1717) French
Works on paper
£1300 $2041 €1950 Adoration of the shepherds (14x9cm-6x4in) pen ink wash htd white. 11-Dec-2 Sotheby's, Olympia #86/R est:1200-1500

JOVINGE, Torsten (1898-1936) Swedish
£3504 $5466 €5256 Rosenbad - view from the Centre Palace, Stockholm (50x61cm-20x24in) prov. 6-Nov-2 AB Stockholms Auktionsverk #716/R est:60000-80000 (S.KR 50000)
£5256 $8199 €7884 Hill planted with vines - Menton (50x61cm-20x24in) painted 1930-1933 exhib. 6-Nov-2 AB Stockholms Auktionsverk #573/R est:100000-125000 (S.KR 75000)
£20322 $31703 €30483 Still life with black cup and teapot (33x41cm-13x16in) s. painted 1930-1933 exhib. 6-Nov-2 AB Stockholms Auktionsverk #578/R est:250000-300000 (S.KR 290000)
Works on paper
£695 $1119 €1043 Bridge - Vasterbron (34x23cm-13x9in) Indian ink wash. 7-May-3 AB Stockholms Auktionsverk #831/R (S.KR 9000)
£2383 $3717 €3575 View above the lock, Stockholm (43x39cm-17x15in) s.d.28 W/C. 6-Nov-2 AB Stockholms Auktionsverk #529/R est:30000-35000 (S.KR 34000)

JOWETT, F B (fl.1915-1938) British
£480 $730 €720 Boating on a tranquil stretch of the river (63x76cm-25x30in) s. 29-Aug-2 Christie's, Kensington #77

JOWETT, Frank B (fl.1915-1938) British
Works on paper
£270 $427 €405 Cambridgeshire village, possibly Houghton (42x57cm-17x22in) s. W/C over pencil. 27-Nov-2 Bonhams, Knowle #178

JOWETT, S (19th C) British
£360 $562 €540 Maid feeding duck before a cottage (51x41cm-20x16in) s. 23-Sep-2 Bonhams, Chester #980

JOY, George William (1844-1925) British
£11429 $18171 €16800 Jeune soldat au tambourin (180x107cm-71x42in) s. 22-Mar-3 Livinec, Gaudcheau & Jezequel, Rennes #54

JOY, John (1925-) Canadian
£1156 $1895 €1734 Gerrard Street East (70x90cm-28x35in) s.d.89 acrylic on board. 3-Jun-3 Joyner, Toronto #441/R est:2000-3000 (C.D 2600)

JOY, John Cantiloe (1806-1866) British
Works on paper
£320 $496 €480 Inshore squadron (18x26cm-7x10in) s. W/C prov. 31-Oct-2 Christie's, Kensington #319/R
£4000 $5720 €6000 Shipping off the Norfolk coast (16x23cm-6x9in) pencil W/C prov.lit. 22-Jan-3 Christie's, London #62/R est:3500

JOY, Thomas Musgrave (1812-1866) British
£29000 $46690 €43500 Charing Cross to Bank omnibus (76x63cm-30x25in) mono. prov.exhib.lit. 20-Feb-3 Christie's, London #320/R

JOY, William (1803-1867) British
£12000 $18600 €18000 Frigate anchored in the roadstead, another following her in (51x72cm-20x28in) s. 31-Oct-2 Christie's, Kensington #443/R est:5000-7000
Works on paper
£1450 $2422 €2103 Sailing boats in rough weather (23x30cm-9x12in) W/C. 20-Jun-3 Keys, Aylsham #629/R est:1500-2000
£1605 $2600 €2327 Making sail from the fleet anchorage at Spithead (32x48cm-13x19in) s. W/C. 29-Jul-3 Christie's, Rockefeller NY #106/R est:3000-5000
£1605 $2600 €2327 View from Sheerness, evening (19x28cm-7x11in) pencil W/C. 29-Jul-3 Christie's, Rockefeller NY #108/R est:3000-5000
£1700 $2584 €2550 Fisherfolk on a beach (14x22cm-6x9in) 15-Aug-2 Bonhams, New Bond Street #385/R est:1000-1500
£2000 $3300 €2900 Shipping (33x47cm-13x19in) s. W/C. 1-Jul-3 Bonhams, Norwich #67/R est:1500-2000
£2200 $3432 €3300 Frigate at anchor and other shipping (18x25cm-7x10in) s. W/C. 17-Oct-2 David Lay, Penzance #1219/R est:2000-2500
£2800 $4676 €4060 Danish Mediterranean merchantman in distress off a rocky coast (41x56cm-16x22in) W/C prov. 20-Jun-3 Keys, Aylsham #628 est:3000-4000
£3500 $5425 €5250 Men-o-war art Spithead (27x39cm-11x15in) s.d.1857 pencil W/C htd white. 31-Oct-2 Christie's, Kensington #316/R est:800-1200
£3500 $5670 €5250 Evening gun (27x35cm-11x14in) W/C. 21-May-3 Christie's, Kensington #409a/R est:3000-5000

JOY, William (attrib) (1803-1867) British
Works on paper
£600 $972 €900 Racing cutter of the Royal Thames yacht club passing astern of an anchored three decker (26x42cm-10x17in) W/C scratching out. 22-Jan-3 Bonhams, New Bond Street #305/R
£650 $1001 €975 Man-o'-war in a calm (25x38cm-10x15in) pencil W/C. 25-Oct-2 Gorringes, Lewes #883

JOY, William and John Cantiloe (19th C) British
Works on paper
£1400 $2170 €2100 Howling gale in the Channel (25x35cm-10x14in) s.d.1856 pencil W/C. 31-Oct-2 Christie's, Kensington #317/R est:700-900
£3800 $5928 €5700 Ships of the fleet preparing to sail (26x36cm-10x14in) s.d.1854 W/C. 15-Oct-2 Bearnes, Exeter #371/R est:2000-3000
£4800 $7776 €7200 Landing the tender (22x30cm-9x12in) W/C htd white. 22-Jan-3 Bonhams, New Bond Street #332a/R est:3500-5000

JOYA, Jose (1931-1995) Philippino
£6216 $10256 €9013 Tivali, Copenhagen (46x123cm-18x48in) s.d.1964 board. 6-Jul-3 Christie's, Hong Kong #44/R est:85000-100000 (HK.D 80000)

JOYANT, Jules Romain (1803-1854) French
£576 $921 €800 Vue de canal a Venise (18x13cm-7x5in) s. panel. 13-May-3 Palais de Beaux Arts, Brussels #345/R
Works on paper
£612 $973 €900 Arc de Triomphe (25x31cm-10x12in) mono. crayon. 24-Mar-3 Tajan, Paris #120
£633 $1000 €1000 Vue du Capitole (36x43cm-14x17in) mono. crayon. 28-Nov-2 Tajan, Paris #171
£949 $1500 €1500 Vue d'eglise italienne (52x38cm-20x15in) crayon W/C. 28-Nov-2 Tajan, Paris #172/R
£2215 $3500 €3500 Vue du Capitole sur le Forum (40x51cm-16x20in) crayon W/C. 28-Nov-2 Tajan, Paris #132/R

JOYCE, Ena (1925-) Australian
£558 $914 €837 Taking tea (62x49cm-24x19in) s. board painted c.1973. 4-Jun-3 Deutscher-Menzies, Melbourne #305/R (A.D 1400)

JOYCE, Marshall W (1912-1998) American
£265 $425 €398 Harbour business (36x46cm-14x18in) s. panel. 15-Mar-3 Eldred, East Dennis #123/R
Works on paper
£281 $450 €422 Harbour scene (23x36cm-9x14in) s. 15-Mar-3 Eldred, East Dennis #130/R
£312 $500 €452 Pen Berth cove, Cornwall (53x73cm-21x29in) s. i.verso W/C. 16-May-3 Skinner, Boston #359/R

JOZSA, Karoly (1872-?) Hungarian
£314 $491 €500 Young woman baring breast (59x46cm-23x18in) s. board. 9-Oct-2 Michael Zeller, Lindau #749/R

JU MING (1938-) Chinese
Sculpture
£9324 $15385 €13520 Taurine (31cm-12in) wood. 6-Jul-3 Christie's, Hong Kong #143/R est:150000-250000 (HK.D 120000)
£14763 $24359 €21406 Taiji, preparation for underarm strike (86cm-34in) edition of 11/20 bronze. 6-Jul-3 Christie's, Hong Kong #145/R est:150000-200000 (HK.D 190000)
£28455 $44959 €42683 Taichi (55x21x32cm-22x8x13in) s.d.1992 wood. 28-Apr-3 Sotheby's, Hong Kong #529/R est:300000-400000 (HK.D 350000)
£134615 $210000 €201923 Split taichi (289x220x150cm-114x87x59in) s. bronze. 27-Mar-3 Sotheby's, New York #120/R est:200000-300000

JUAN DE BORGONA (style) (16th C) Spanish
£8392 $14014 €12000 Saint Roch et Saint Sebastien (88x100cm-35x39in) panel. 25-Jun-3 Artcurial Briest, Paris #456/R est:6000-8000

JUAN DE FLANDES (attrib) (?-1519) Spanish
£15203 $23716 €22500 Saint-Augustin et l'ange (21x19cm-8x7in) panel. 28-Mar-3 Neret-Minet, Paris #26/R est:10000-15000

JUBELIN, Narelle (20th C) Australian
Works on paper
£903 $1399 €1355 Monuments (144x40cm-57x16in) i.verso pastel exec.c.1985. 3-Dec-2 Shapiro, Sydney #48 est:2500-3500 (A.D 2500)

JUBIEN, Antoine François Louis (1833-1909) French
£1282 $1987 €2000 Deux jeunes femmes au fleurs (150x60cm-59x24in) bears sig. 9-Dec-2 Horta, Bruxelles #183 est:2500-3500

JUDD, Donald (1928-1994) American
Prints
£1847 $2900 €2771 Untitled (29x35cm-11x14in) s.num.130 aquatint. 19-Nov-2 Wright, Chicago #219/R est:2000-3000
£4072 $6801 €5904 Untitled. s.i.d. woodcut cadmium red. 24-Jun-3 Koller, Zurich #429/R est:2800-3400 (S.FR 9000)
£4487 $7000 €6731 Untitled (52x64cm-20x25in) s.num.11/25 black woodcut cadmium red oilpaint frostlit vellum. 5-Nov-2 Christie's, Rockefeller NY #436/R est:5000-7000
£5975 $9500 €8963 Untitled (37x50cm-15x20in) s.d.num.17/25 red woodcut. 29-Apr-3 Christie's, Rockefeller NY #639/R est:5000-7000
£6918 $11000 €10377 Untitled (39x52cm-15x20in) s.d.num.6/25 red woodcut. 29-Apr-3 Christie's, Rockefeller NY #640/R est:5000-7000
£12579 $20000 €18869 Untitled (39x52cm-15x20in) s.d. one num.20/25 one num.12/25 red woodcut set of 2. 29-Apr-3 Christie's, Rockefeller NY #638/R est:10000-15000
£20126 $32000 €30189 Untitled (60x80cm-24x31in) s.num.5/25 verso col woodcut set of seven. 29-Apr-3 Christie's, Rockefeller NY #643/R est:15000-20000
Sculpture
£15000 $24600 €22500 Untitled (10x67x57cm-4x26x22in) galvanised iron one of 65 lit. 6-Feb-3 Christie's, London #696/R est:15000-22000
£22785 $36000 €34178 Untitled (15x105x15cm-6x41x6in) i. anodized aluminum prov.lit. 12-Nov-2 Phillips, New York #103/R est:20000-30000
£38000 $62320 €57000 Untitled - Lehni 85-3 (30x60x30cm-12x24x12in) st.sig.num.3 d.85 prov.exhib. 6-Feb-3 Christie's, London #701/R est:25000-35000
£45000 $73800 €67500 Untitled (15x69x61cm-6x27x24in) stainless steel amber pebbled plexiglas exec.1968 prov. 6-Feb-3 Sotheby's, London #10/R est:70000
£46875 $75000 €70313 Untitled - 92-6 ballantine (25x100x24cm-10x39x9in) American Douglas fir plywood amber plexiglas prov. 15-May-3 Christie's, Rockefeller NY #320/R est:60000-80000
£48000 $80160 €69600 Untitled - Lehni 85-046/100 (30x60x30cm-12x24x12in) pulverised aluminium executed 1985 prov. 27-Jun-3 Christie's, London #227/R est:40000-60000
£65000 $106600 €97500 Untitled (25x101x25cm-10x40x10in) s.d.86 num.21 verso aluminium plexiglass prov.exhib. 7-Feb-3 Sotheby's, London #151/R est:25000-35000
£70000 $114800 €105000 Untitled - Menziken 88-58 (25x100x25cm-10x39x10in) st.sig.num.58 d.88 aluminium blue plexiglas prov.exhib. 6-Feb-3 Christie's, London #698/R est:50000-70000
£70000 $114800 €105000 Untitled - Menziken 87-54 (25x102x25cm-10x40x10in) st.sig.num.54 d.87 aluminium yellow plexiglas prov.exhib. 6-Feb-3 Christie's, London #699/R est:50000-70000
£72785 $115000 €109178 Untitled - meter box (50x100x50cm-20x39x20in) stainless steel purple plexiglas st.f. executed 1977 prov. 12-Nov-2 Phillips, New York #108/R est:100000-150000

£75000 $120000 €112500 Untitled -89-42 ballantine (50x100x50cm-20x39x20in) American Douglas fir plywood two unit executed 1989 prov.exhib. 15-May-3 Christie's, Rockefeller NY #311/R est:70000-90000
£82278 $130000 €123417 Untitled (30x150x30cm-12x59x12in) sig.d.87-24 verso pulver on aluminum. 13-Nov-2 Sotheby's, New York #303/R est:70000-90000
£84375 $135000 €126563 Desk and chairs. mahogany executed 1989 prov. 15-May-3 Christie's, Rockefeller NY #304/R est:100000-150000
£88608 $140000 €132912 Untitled - menziken 86-26 (25x114x25cm-10x45x10in) st.d.num.26 aluminum red plexiglas executed 1986 prov. 14-Nov-2 Christie's, Rockefeller NY #367/R est:100000-150000
£102564 $160000 €153846 Untitled (25x178x25cm-10x70x10in) polished aluminum executed 1984 prov. 11-Nov-2 Phillips, New York #35/R est:100000-150000
£164557 $260000 €246836 Desk and chairs. s. mahogany executed 1988 prov. 14-Nov-2 Christie's, Rockefeller NY #368/R est:80000-120000
£165625 $265000 €248438 Untitled (100x100x50cm-39x39x20in) cor-ten steel plexiglass in two parts executed 1984 prov.lit. 15-May-3 Phillips, New York #32/R est:100000-150000
£175000 $280000 €262500 Untitled (13x102x23cm-5x40x9in) st.sig.d.87 anodized aluminium prov. 13-May-3 Sotheby's, New York #28/R est:300000-400000
£193750 $310000 €290625 Untitled (13x102x22cm-5x40x9in) aluminum executed 1985 prov.lit. 15-May-3 Phillips, New York #10/R est:350000-450000
£240506 $380000 €360759 Untitled (13x190x13cm-5x75x5in) st.d.74 num.16 purple anodized aluminum brass prov.lit. 13-Nov-2 Christie's, Rockefeller NY #70/R est:350000-450000
£281250 $450000 €421875 Untitled (13x65x22cm-5x26x9in) s.d.65 galvanized iron lacquer prov.lit. 14-May-3 Christie's, Rockefeller NY #31/R est:300000-400000
£362500 $580000 €543750 Untitled - progression (21x409x20cm-8x161x8in) clear anodized purple anodized aluminum executed 1970 prov.exhib. 15-May-3 Christie's, Rockefeller NY #309/R est:350000-450000
£468750 $750000 €703125 Untitled (15x69x61cm-6x27x24in) anodized aluminium in 10 parts exec.1978 prov.exhib. 14-May-3 Christie's, Rockefeller NY #34/R est:800000-1200000
£506329 $800000 €759494 Untitled (22x176x13cm-9x69x5in) st.sig.num.70-35 copper prov.lit. 12-Nov-2 Sotheby's, New York #30/R est:600000-800000
£822785 $1300000 €1234178 Untitled (305x68x61cm-120x27x24in) ten copper units executed 1969 prov.exhib.lit. 13-Nov-2 Christie's, Rockefeller NY #9/R est:900000-1200000
£822785 $1300000 €1234178 Untitled - bernstein 87-34 (457x102x79cm-180x40x31in) ten copper and clear plexiglas units executed 1987 prov. 13-Nov-2 Christie's, Rockefeller NY #24/R est:700000-900000

Works on paper
£3200 $5056 €4800 Untitled (33x48cm-13x19in) init.i.d.87 pencil prov.exhib. 3-Apr-3 Christie's, Kensington #238/R
£5000 $7700 €7500 Untitled (60x80cm-24x31in) pencil two executed 1990 prov. 23-Oct-2 Christie's, London #219/R est:4000-6000
£7595 $12000 €11393 Untitled - study for plywood (49x62cm-19x24in) s.d.72 pencil black ink prov. 13-Nov-2 Sotheby's, New York #299/R est:3000-5000
£14000 $23380 €20300 Untitled (57x77cm-22x30in) s.d.74 graphite five prov. 27-Jun-3 Christie's, London #226/R est:18000-25000
£17187 $27500 €25781 Untitled (63x79cm-25x31in) s.d.74 pencil prov. 14-May-3 Sotheby's, New York #218a/R est:12000-18000
£22152 $35000 €33228 Six untitled drawings (30x21cm-12x8in) s.d.76 s.verso pencil six sheets prov. 13-Nov-2 Sotheby's, New York #300/R est:25000-35000

JUDKIN, Rev Thomas James (1788-1871) British
£420 $647 €630 House in which Lord Byron lodged in Athens (27x20cm-11x8in) s. i.verso board. 22-Oct-2 Bonhams, Bath #179

JUDSON, C Chapel (1864-1946) American
£3822 $6000 €5733 Bouquet of roses (76x102cm-30x40in) s. i.d.1893 verso prov. 19-Nov-2 Butterfields, San Francisco #8151/R est:6000-8000

JUDSON, Jeannette Alexander (1912-) American
£610 $1000 €885 Zodiac no.2 (97x122cm-38x48in) s. acrylic prov. 1-Jun-3 Wright, Chicago #300/R est:2000-3000

JUDSON, William Lees (1842-1928) American
£500 $800 €750 Landscape (51x76cm-20x30in) s. 18-May-3 Butterfields, Los Angeles #7044
£3548 $5500 €5322 Girl in flower field (69x51cm-27x20in) s. 29-Oct-2 John Moran, Pasadena #711 est:7000-9000

JUDSON, William Lees (attrib) (1842-1928) American
£515 $803 €773 Thames River, London, Ontario (61x152cm-24x60in) 25-Mar-3 Ritchie, Toronto #55/R est:1500-2000 (C.D 1200)

JUEGEL, Johann Friedrich (18/19th C) German
Prints
£12751 $20528 €19000 Darstellung der koniglich preussischen cavallerie in 41 figuren (40x28cm-16x11in) 37 aquatint prov. 18-Feb-3 Sotheby's, Amsterdam #1007/R est:4000-6000
£14764 $23770 €22000 Konigl preussischen infanterie (40x25cm-16x10in) 48 hand col engravings. 18-Feb-3 Sotheby's, Amsterdam #1009/R est:5000-7000

JUEL, Jens (1745-1802) Danish
£8540 $13151 €12810 Portrait of Elizabeth Henriette Sophie Bernstorff (70x55cm-28x22in) s.d.1786 oval prov. 4-Sep-2 Kunsthallen, Copenhagen #32/R est:125000 (D.KR 100000)
£9328 $14832 €13992 Portrait of Sophie Magdalene, Countess von Knuth (75x59cm-30x23in) oval prov.lit. 5-May-3 Rasmussen, Vejle #408/R est:50000-100000 (D.KR 100000)
£12766 $20170 €19149 Portrait of Johan L Heining's first wife Margaretha Elisabeth (70x56cm-28x22in) oval painted c.1795-1800 prov. 2-Dec-2 Rasmussen, Copenhagen #1135/R est:150000-200000 (D.KR 150000)
£19139 $31005 €27752 View from Copenhagen, possibly near Fortunen (42x51cm-17x20in) 26-May-3 Rasmussen, Copenhagen #1179/R est:150000 (D.KR 200000)
£28085 $44374 €42128 Portraits of Henrik Even Moe and his wife Henriette Frederikke (69x54cm-27x21in) oval pair. 2-Dec-2 Rasmussen, Copenhagen #1175/R est:300000-400000 (D.KR 330000)
£39149 $61855 €58724 Johan Carl von Moller as 3 years old holding a whip (100x68cm-39x27in) exhib.prov. 2-Dec-2 Rasmussen, Copenhagen #1133/R est:600000-800000 (D.KR 460000)

Works on paper
£1053 $1705 €1527 Allegorical representation of the art of sculpture (15x20cm-6x8in) s.i. pencil wash exec.c.1764 exhib.prov. 26-May-3 Rasmussen, Copenhagen #1577/R (D.KR 11000)

JUEL, Jens (attrib) (1745-1802) Danish
£2200 $3454 €3300 Portrait of a gentleman seated at a table, holding a letter (79x63cm-31x25in) 13-Dec-2 Christie's, Kensington #155/R est:2500-3500

JUEL, Jens (circle) (1745-1802) Danish
£6000 $9300 €9000 Portrait of two girls standing embracing each other (78x64cm-31x25in) bears sig. oval. 30-Oct-2 Bonhams, New Bond Street #161/R est:6000-8000

JUELL, Tore (1942-) Norwegian
£333 $527 €500 Landscape, Krokheia (29x61cm-11x24in) s. s.i.d.1988 verso panel. 17-Dec-2 Grev Wedels Plass, Oslo #241/R (N.KR 3800)
£518 $865 €751 Evening at Jumfruland (40x61cm-16x24in) s. panel. 18-Jun-3 Grev Wedels Plass, Oslo #190 (N.KR 6000)

JUELL-GLEDITSCH, Rolf (1892-1984) Norwegian
£341 $532 €512 Landscape from Skarvange, Vaga (37x45cm-15x18in) s. panel. 23-Sep-2 Blomqvist, Lysaker #1056/R (N.KR 4000)

Works on paper
£372 $570 €558 Garden in Cagnes (43x48cm-17x19in) s. W/C executed 1921. 26-Aug-2 Blomqvist, Lysaker #1121 (N.KR 4300)

JUKAN, Nagasawa (19th C) Japanese
Sculpture
£22000 $34760 €33000 Flower seller with basket of flowers on his back (59cm-23in) s. ivory. 13-Nov-2 Christie's, London #111/R est:5000-7000

JULEN, Heinz (1964-) Swiss
Works on paper
£306 $480 €459 Panorama Schwarzsee (50x34cm-20x13in) s.d.1992 mixed media oil collage. 23-Nov-2 Burkhard, Luzern #90/R (S.FR 700)

JULES, Mervin (1912-) American
£503 $800 €755 Two musicians (46x30cm-18x12in) s. board painted c.1945. 2-Mar-3 Toomey, Oak Park #736/R

£701 $1100 €1052 Rehearsal (30x45cm-12x18in) s. i.verso board. 22-Nov-2 Skinner, Boston #186/R est:800-1200

JULIAN, Paul (?) ?
£219 $350 €329 Crowd of people (51x76cm-20x30in) s. board. 18-May-3 Butterfields, Los Angeles #7014

JULIANA Y ALBERT, Jose (1844-1890) Spanish
Works on paper
£321 $487 €500 Untitled (33x22cm-13x9in) s.i.d.1872 W/C. 28-Aug-2 Castellana, Madrid #3/R

JULIARD, Nicolas Jacques (1715-1790) French
£11034 $17655 €16000 Couples de pecheurs (16x21cm-6x8in) panel pair prov. 11-Mar-3 Christie's, Paris #422/R

JULIEN, Henri (1852-1908) Canadian
£1867 $3061 €2801 Les caricaturistes (34x25cm-13x10in) s.d.1900 panel prov. 3-Jun-3 Joyner, Toronto #383/R est:3000-4000 (C.D 4200)
Works on paper
£311 $510 €467 Soldier and frontiersman (29x24cm-11x9in) pencil. 3-Jun-3 Joyner, Toronto #506/R (C.D 700)
£656 $1016 €984 L'arrivee du courrier (29x23cm-11x9in) s. pencil ink wash. 24-Sep-2 Iegor de Saint Hippolyte, Montreal #54 (C.D 1600)

JULIEN, Jean (20th C) French
£302 $465 €480 Jardin du palais (60x42cm-24x17in) s. cardboard. 23-Oct-2 Rabourdin & Choppin de Janvry, Paris #226

JULIEN, Jean Antoine (1736-1799) French
Works on paper
£2986 $4748 €4300 Priamus at the feet of Achilles (31x39cm-12x15in) s.i.d.1776 pen wash paper on board prov. 5-May-3 Ketterer, Munich #335/R est:400-600

JULIEN, Jean Pierre (1888-?) French
Works on paper
£417 $654 €650 Baignade (38x46cm-15x18in) s. chl pastel. 20-Nov-2 Claude Boisgirard, Paris #16

JULIEN, Remy-Eugène (1797-1868) French
£769 $1199 €1154 Four monks joyously reading together (43x53cm-17x21in) s. 11-Nov-2 Stephan Welz, Johannesburg #51 (SA.R 12000)

JULIEN, René (1937-) Belgian
£1266 $1975 €2000 Violoniste (152x97cm-60x38in) s. 15-Oct-2 Horta, Bruxelles #113

JULIEN, Simon (attrib) (1735-1798) French
£6452 $10194 €10000 Entree du Christ a Jerusalem (32x64cm-13x25in) panel lit. 18-Dec-2 Piasa, Paris #88/R est:15000

JULIUS, Per (1951-) Swedish
Works on paper
£2042 $3350 €2961 Northern landscape in autumn colours (74x54cm-29x21in) s. W/C. 4-Jun-3 AB Stockholms Auktionsverk #2266/R est:15000-18000 (S.KR 26000)

JUMAIE, Saleh Al (1939-) Iraqi
£800 $1272 €1200 Abstract (35x36cm-14x14in) s. 30-Apr-3 Sotheby's, London #155/R

JUNCKER, Justus (1703-1767) German
£2739 $4246 €4109 Couple in kitchen (37x30cm-15x12in) s. panel. 9-Dec-2 Philippe Schuler, Zurich #3915/R est:8000-10000 (S.FR 6300)
£4000 $6280 €6000 Interior with a man seated before a table smoking a pipe (47x40cm-19x16in) s.d.1752. 10-Dec-2 Sotheby's, Olympia #396/R est:4000-6000
£4221 $6289 €6500 Old man at table smoking pipe (48x41cm-19x16in) s.d.1752. 26-Jun-2 Neumeister, Munich #640/R est:1800
£4730 $7378 €7000 Rhine river landscape (32x42cm-13x17in) s. panel prov. 27-Mar-3 Dorotheum, Vienna #239/R est:4000-6000
£8108 $12649 €12000 Scholar in study sharpening quill (44x34cm-17x13in) s. panel lit. 27-Mar-3 Dorotheum, Vienna #275/R est:15000-18000

JUNEMANN, Carl (19/20th C) ?
£300 $456 €450 Girl on a path aside fields of heather (39x56cm-15x22in) s. 29-Aug-2 Christie's, Kensington #64

JUNG, Claude (?) ?
£600 $972 €900 Still life of carnations (61x50cm-24x20in) s. board. 21-May-3 Bonhams, Knightsbridge #186a

JUNG, Frederic Charles (1865-1936) French
£769 $1208 €1200 Bouquet de fleurs (41x33cm-16x13in) d.89 panel. 15-Dec-2 Mercier & Cie, Lille #390a

JUNG, Myung (1949-) Korean
£449 $700 €674 Still life of glass of water and apples (20x25cm-8x10in) s. board. 29-Mar-3 Charlton Hall, Columbia #227/R

JUNG, Simonetta (20th C) ?
£468 $748 €650 Homo novus (70x90cm-28x35in) s. s.i.d.1975. 17-May-3 De Vuyst, Lokeren #221

JUNG, Theodore (1803-1865) French
Works on paper
£321 $503 €500 La casade de Wad-El-Raml, en dessous de la Casbah de Constantine (33x21cm-13x8in) s.d.1833 W/C. 16-Dec-2 Gros & Delettrez, Paris #237/R
£321 $503 €500 Vue de Santarem (22x38cm-9x15in) s.d.1833 W/C. 16-Dec-2 Gros & Delettrez, Paris #243
£321 $503 €500 Aqueduc en Algerie (20x32cm-8x13in) s.d.1835 W/C. 16-Dec-2 Gros & Delettrez, Paris #245
£340 $533 €530 Vue de Mazouna a Cap Koch (24x36cm-9x14in) s.d.1853 W/C. 16-Dec-2 Gros & Delettrez, Paris #242
£385 $604 €600 Vue do Pont sur le Wad-El-Raml a Constantine (32x21cm-13x8in) s.d.1833 W/C. 16-Dec-2 Gros & Delettrez, Paris #236/R
£423 $664 €660 Paysans arabes parmi les ruines (32x48cm-13x19in) s.d.1833 W/C. 16-Dec-2 Gros & Delettrez, Paris #244/R
£551 $866 €860 Vue presumee du port de Mers El Kebir (24x21cm-9x8in) s. W/C. 16-Dec-2 Gros & Delettrez, Paris #238/R
£1026 $1610 €1600 L'aqueduc sur le Wad-El-Raml, pres de Constantine (21x30cm-8x12in) s.d.1833 W/C. 16-Dec-2 Gros & Delettrez, Paris #239/R est:500-800
£5319 $8883 €7500 L'entree du jardin des Tuileries sous la neige (21x34cm-8x13in) s. W/C prov. 23-Jun-3 Beaussant & Lefèvre, Paris #300/R est:2500-3000

JUNG-ILSENHEIM, Franz Xaver (1883-1963) Austrian
£288 $453 €450 Summer in the alpine meadow (59x79cm-23x31in) s. oil mixed media fibreboard. 21-Nov-2 Dorotheum, Vienna #154/R
£962 $1510 €1500 Brown bear in rocky woodland (58x78cm-23x31in) s. oil mixed media fibreboard. 21-Nov-2 Dorotheum, Vienna #153/R est:800-1100
Works on paper
£288 $453 €450 View of Gaisbergspitze in Salzburg (19x29cm-7x11in) s.i. gouache. 21-Nov-2 Dorotheum, Vienna #413/R
£288 $472 €400 Stockalpe in Innergebirge Salzburg (46x63cm-18x25in) s.i. mixed media masonite. 5-Jun-3 Dorotheum, Salzburg #798/R
£513 $805 €800 Monk from Mt Casino on lookout to Mondsee (20x30cm-8x12in) mixed media. 21-Nov-2 Dorotheum, Vienna #424/R
£545 $855 €850 Lookout - the legend from Gastein (20x30cm-8x12in) mixed media. 21-Nov-2 Dorotheum, Vienna #423/R

JUNGBLUT, Johann (1860-1912) German
£252 $392 €400 Figure walking by wood in winter (60x80cm-24x31in) s. 21-Sep-2 Berlinghof, Heidelberg #129/R
£256 $390 €400 Lower Rhine landscape in evening sun (24x36cm-9x14in) s. panel. 17-Aug-2 Hans Stahl, Toestorf #42/R
£380 $600 €600 Autumnal forest landscape with running water (32x24cm-13x9in) s. 30-Nov-2 Berlinghof, Heidelberg #331
£392 $643 €600 Norwegian fjord landscape (24x36cm-9x14in) s. 29-Mar-3 Dannenberg, Berlin #606/R
£417 $654 €650 Autumnal lake landscape (18x29cm-7x11in) s. panel. 21-Nov-2 Van Ham, Cologne #1702
£475 $736 €750 Fishermen with punt lighting fire at river's edge (33x53cm-13x21in) s.i. 25-Sep-2 Neumeister, Munich #611/R
£690 $1090 €1000 Dutch winter landscape (18x26cm-7x10in) s. board. 5-Apr-3 Quittenbaum, Hamburg #34/R
£704 $1155 €1021 Wild boar in snowy wood (66x70cm-26x28in) s. 4-Jun-3 Fischer, Luzern #2197/R est:1800-2200 (S.FR 1500)
£986 $1587 €1400 Lower Rhine waters with village beyond (24x17cm-9x7in) s. panel. 7-May-3 Michael Zeller, Lindau #755/R
£1096 $1721 €1600 Landscape with birch trees by water (24x17cm-9x7in) s. bears d.08 paper on panel. 16-Apr-3 Dorotheum, Salzburg #90/R est:800-1200
£1233 $1923 €1800 Naero fjord in summer (64x59cm-25x23in) s. 10-Apr-3 Van Ham, Cologne #1513/R est:2500
£1266 $2000 €2000 Winter's evening on edge of village (60x90cm-24x35in) mono. i. stretcher lit. 29-Nov-2 Schloss Ahlden, Ahlden #1316/R est:2400

£1572 $2453 €2500 Winter landscape in moonlight (94x77cm-37x30in) s. 21-Sep-2 Bolland & Marotz, Bremen #505/R est:3200
£2516 $3874 €4000 Winter landscape with a figure on a frozen river (94x77cm-37x30in) s. 22-Oct-2 Sotheby's, Amsterdam #72/R est:4000-5000
£2837 $4397 €4256 Figures on the ice (80x119cm-31x47in) s. 4-Dec-2 AB Stockholms Auktionsverk #1915/R est:60000-80000 (S.KR 40000)
£2917 $4813 €4200 Walking home on a winters day at dusk (79x58cm-31x23in) s. 1-Jul-3 Christie's, Amsterdam #132/R est:3000-5000

JUNGE, Friedrich August (1781-1841) German
Miniatures
£4500 $7380 €6525 Mother and child (7cm-3xin) s.d.1821 gilt metal frame. 3-Jun-3 Christie's, London #182/R est:1500-2500
Works on paper
£355 $592 €500 Cafe a Top-Khaneh, Constantinople (14x24cm-6x9in) s.d.1837 pencil W/C prov. 23-Jun-3 Beaussant & Lefèvre, Paris #102

JUNGHANNS, Julius Paul (1876-1958) Austrian
£769 $1208 €1200 Peasant leading horses pulling cart (100x130cm-39x51in) s. panel. 23-Nov-2 Arnold, Frankfurt #768/R
£833 $1308 €1300 Church in Ehrwald in Tyrol (18x18cm-7x7in) s. board. 21-Nov-2 Van Ham, Cologne #1705/R
£1282 $2026 €2000 Horses at water trough (26x48cm-10x19in) s. 16-Nov-2 Lempertz, Koln #1490/R est:2000
£1410 $2186 €2200 Boy with goats (29x51cm-11x20in) s. 5-Dec-2 Dr Fritz Nagel, Stuttgart #668/R est:2500
£1667 $2617 €2600 Peasant with horse drawn cart on field track (40x50cm-16x20in) s. 21-Nov-2 Van Ham, Cologne #1706/R est:2400
£1974 $3197 €3000 Spring, goats and horse near a fence (30x40cm-12x16in) s. indis d.08. 21-Jan-3 Christie's, Amsterdam #96/R est:3000-5000
£2013 $3099 €3200 Horse drawn cart with figures near a farmhouse (22x28cm-9x11in) s. panel. 23-Oct-2 Christie's, Amsterdam #53/R est:3000-5000
£3082 $4808 €4500 Peasant with four horses pulling cart (40x60cm-16x24in) s. 10-Apr-3 Van Ham, Cologne #1514/R est:5800
£3846 $6038 €6000 Peasant with four horses pulling cart (43x77cm-17x30in) s. 21-Nov-2 Van Ham, Cologne #1704/R est:4500

JUNGHANNS, Julius Paul (attrib) (1876-1958) Austrian
£445 $695 €650 Peasant woman with two goats (30x39cm-12x15in) panel. 10-Apr-3 Van Ham, Cologne #1515

JUNGHEIM, Carl (1803-1886) German
£1250 $2063 €1800 Cowherds by a lake in an extensive mountain landscape (63x94cm-25x37in) s.d.1859. 1-Jul-3 Christie's, Amsterdam #26/R est:2000-3000

JUNGLER, J B (?) German?
£909 $1355 €1400 Musketeers at tavern entrance (10x12cm-4x5in) s.i. panel. 27-Jun-2 Neumeister, Munich #2759

JUNGMANN, Gottlob (18/19th C) American
Works on paper
£266 $425 €399 Heart surrounded by potted flowers and vines (33x38cm-13x15in) W/C printed taufschein. 17-May-3 Pook & Pook, Downington #92

JUNGMANN, Maarten Johannes Balthasar (1877-1964) Dutch
£605 $944 €950 Still life with flowers (69x72cm-27x28in) s. 5-Nov-2 Vendu Notarishuis, Rotterdam #155/R

JUNGMANN, Nico W (1872-1935) British/Dutch
£4800 $8016 €7200 Peasant boy of the land of Goes (38x28cm-15x11in) s. board. 18-Jun-3 Christie's, Kensington #133/R est:3000-5000
Works on paper
£400 $632 €580 Mare teerhuis (47x38cm-19x15in) s.i.d.1910 W/C. 22-Jul-3 Bonhams, Knightsbridge #71/R

JUNGNICKEL, Ludwig Heinrich (1881-1965) German
£2119 $3454 €3200 Breakers (33x46cm-13x18in) paper. 28-Jan-3 Dorotheum, Vienna #30/R est:3600-5000
£2270 $3677 €3200 Tree in bloom (39x49cm-15x19in) s.d.1907 gouache prov. 20-May-3 Dorotheum, Vienna #115/R est:3600-4500
£2500 $3950 €3600 Sea (35x56cm-14x22in) 24-Apr-3 Dorotheum, Vienna #71/R est:3600-5000
Prints
£2152 $3357 €3400 Chicken and cockerel (29x28cm-11x11in) s. col woodcut. 15-Oct-2 Dorotheum, Vienna #2/R est:2200-2400
Works on paper
£253 $395 €400 Cat (31x22cm-12x9in) chl. 15-Oct-2 Dorotheum, Vienna #73/R
£256 $405 €400 Cat with spoils (21x29cm-8x11in) s. chl. 12-Nov-2 Dorotheum, Vienna #96/R
£280 $468 €406 Rearing horse (28x34cm-11x13in) s. pencil W/C. 25-Jun-3 Cheffins, Cambridge #727/R
£316 $494 €500 Dachshund (20x28cm-8x11in) pastel chk. 15-Oct-2 Dorotheum, Vienna #72/R
£353 $557 €550 Dog (18x27cm-7x11in) st.sig chl W/C. 12-Nov-2 Dorotheum, Vienna #93/R
£377 $588 €550 Cat (23x32cm-9x13in) st.sig. chl. 8-Apr-3 Dorotheum, Vienna #68
£385 $596 €600 Cockerell (21x21cm-8x8in) s. chl W/C. 5-Dec-2 Dorotheum, Graz #115/R
£385 $604 €600 Lion in love (22x32cm-9x13in) i. chl. 20-Nov-2 Dorotheum, Klagenfurt #88
£481 $745 €750 Donkey study (21x30cm-8x12in) mono. chl W/C. 5-Dec-2 Dorotheum, Graz #113/R
£514 $801 €750 Sleeping cat (22x30cm-9x12in) st.sig. chl. 8-Apr-3 Dorotheum, Vienna #66
£568 $886 €852 Cat lying down (26x34cm-10x13in) chl. 20-Nov-2 Fischer, Luzern #2539/R (S.FR 1300)
£577 $912 €900 Tiger cat (22x29cm-9x11in) chl. 12-Nov-2 Dorotheum, Vienna #95/R
£590 $933 €850 Tiger cat (30x39cm-12x15in) st.sig. chl. 24-Apr-3 Dorotheum, Vienna #150/R
£601 $938 €950 Tiger head (23x26cm-9x10in) chl ochre. 15-Oct-2 Dorotheum, Vienna #54/R
£641 $994 €1000 Fox study (26x29cm-10x11in) mono. chl W/C. 5-Dec-2 Dorotheum, Graz #114/R
£641 $1013 €1000 Stallion (34x43cm-13x17in) s. chl. 12-Nov-2 Dorotheum, Vienna #46/R
£833 $1317 €1300 Spanish rider (36x29cm-14x11in) chl sold with another. 12-Nov-2 Dorotheum, Vienna #45/R
£903 $1435 €1300 Two gazelles (44x29cm-17x11in) s. chl. 29-Apr-3 Wiener Kunst Auktionen, Vienna #608/R
£962 $1519 €1500 Girls wearing harem pants (47x31cm-19x12in) s. chk W/C. 12-Nov-2 Dorotheum, Vienna #97/R est:1200-1600
£1111 $1756 €1600 Cat (24x31cm-9x12in) st.sig. chl W/C. 24-Apr-3 Dorotheum, Vienna #148/R est:1400-1800
£1181 $1865 €1700 Donkeys (29x40cm-11x16in) st.sig. chl W/C. 24-Apr-3 Dorotheum, Vienna #151/R est:1200-1600
£1250 $1975 €1800 Tiger's head (34x39cm-13x15in) st.sig. chl W/C. 24-Apr-3 Dorotheum, Vienna #149/R est:1800-2400
£2051 $3241 €3200 Deer in spring (48x62cm-19x24in) st.sig. i. chl W/C. 12-Nov-2 Dorotheum, Vienna #90/R est:2200-2800
£2083 $3292 €3000 Tiger cat (43x31cm-17x12in) s. chl W/C. 24-Apr-3 Dorotheum, Vienna #147/R est:2000-2800
£3819 $6035 €5500 Two donkeys (28x38cm-11x15in) s.i. chl W/C. 24-Apr-3 Dorotheum, Vienna #146/R est:1900-2600
£4348 $7130 €6000 Schonbrunn with Gloriette (42x42cm-17x17in) s. mixed media prov. 27-May-3 Wiener Kunst Auktionen, Vienna #68/R est:5000-10000

JUNGO, Jean Paul (1920-) Swiss
£926 $1491 €1389 Musique II (65x82cm-26x32in) s. i. verso. 7-May-3 Dobiaschofsky, Bern #724/R est:2500 (S.FR 2000)

JUNGSTEDT, Axel (attrib) (1859-1933) Swedish
£1030 $1565 €1545 Oscar II (115x90cm-45x35in) i.d.1907 verso. 16-Aug-2 Lilla Bukowskis, Stockholm #576 est:12000-15000 (S.KR 15000)

JUNGSTEDT, Kurt (1894-1963) Swedish
£573 $928 €860 Pile-driver (54x81cm-21x32in) s.d.55 verso. 3-Feb-3 Lilla Bukowskis, Stockholm #646 (S.KR 8000)
£1051 $1640 €1577 Scherzo (33x41cm-13x16in) s. prov.lit. 5-Nov-2 Bukowskis, Stockholm #201/R est:12000-15000 (S.KR 15000)
£1544 $2486 €2316 View from Stockholm (81x54cm-32x21in) s. 7-May-3 AB Stockholms Auktionsverk #734/R est:8000-10000 (S.KR 20000)
Works on paper
£270 $435 €405 Indian women in Fattipur Sikri (35x24cm-14x9in) s.d.15/2 34 W/C exhib. 7-May-3 AB Stockholms Auktionsverk #909/R (S.KR 3500)

JUNGWIRTH, Josef (1869-1950) Austrian
£340 $538 €510 Tulips in a green vase on table (79x63cm-31x25in) s. 2-Dec-2 Rasmussen, Copenhagen #1444/R (D.KR 4000)
£482 $800 €699 Landscape with nude female (140x64cm-55x25in) s. 11-Jun-3 Boos Gallery, Michigan #565/R
£1773 $2748 €2660 Views from Italy. s. five framed together twice. 8-Dec-2 Uppsala Auktionskammare, Uppsala #148/R est:12000-15000 (S.KR 25000)

JUNGWIRTH, Martha (1940-) Austrian
£4747 $7500 €7500 Sisters (195x100cm-77x39in) s.d.92 verso prov. 27-Nov-2 Dorotheum, Vienna #332/R est:8000-10000
Works on paper
£1250 $1987 €1800 Untitled (47x61cm-19x24in) s.d.71 col chks. 29-Apr-3 Wiener Kunst Auktionen, Vienna #484/R est:1500-2500

JUNIPER, Robert (1929-1983) Australian
£961 $1470 €1442 Bush shack (50x67cm-20x26in) s.d.70 i.verso board prov. 25-Aug-2 Sotheby's, Paddington #162/R est:2000-3000 (A.D 2700)
£1321 $2088 €1982 Screen of pines (50x61cm-20x24in) s.d.69. 18-Nov-2 Goodman, Sydney #81 est:2000-3000 (A.D 3700)
£1833 $3005 €2750 Hark at that (33x45cm-13x18in) s.d.92 oil synthetic polymer paint linen prov. 4-Jun-3 Deutscher-Menzies, Melbourne #339/R est:3000-5000 (A.D 4600)
£1916 $2854 €2874 Storm has passed (85x131cm-33x52in) s.d.70 canvas on board prov. 27-Aug-2 Christie's, Melbourne #304 est:4000-6000 (A.D 5000)
£5039 $8012 €7559 Sons of Gwalia (100x171cm-39x67in) s.d.79 i.verso prov. 5-May-3 Sotheby's, Melbourne #52/R est:12000 (A.D 13000)
£14000 $22540 €21000 Watcher at the window (183x183cm-72x72in) s.d.85 acrylic oil lit. 6-May-3 Christie's, Melbourne #14/R est:25000-35000 (A.D 35000)

JUNKER, Leo Helmholz (1882-?) American
£288 $450 €432 Landscape - Pelham Wood, New York (53x76cm-21x30in) s.d.1917. 20-Sep-2 Freeman, Philadelphia #130/R
£548 $850 €822 Moonlit garden (91x107cm-36x42in) s.d. board. 8-Dec-2 Toomey, Oak Park #676/R

JUNKEUN, Kim (19th C) Korean
Works on paper
£176101 $280000 €264152 Scenes of daily life (29x36cm-11x14in) forty-nine sealed ink col silk fifty lit. 24-Mar-3 Christie's, Rockefeller NY #321/R est:50000-70000

JUNTTILA, Einari (1901-1975) Finnish
£331 $543 €460 Vatikuru, Pallas (60x77cm-24x30in) s.d.71. 4-Jun-3 Bukowskis, Helsinki #311/R

JUNYENT SANS, Olegario (1876-1956) Spanish
£1842 $2984 €2800 Allegory of Bacchus (98x130cm-39x51in) oval. 21-Jan-3 Ansorena, Madrid #285/R

JUNYER MUNOZ, Joan (1904-) Spanish
£2075 $3238 €3300 Frida Khalo in red (130x97cm-51x38in) s.d.1932 i.verso. 17-Sep-2 Segre, Madrid #130/R

JUNYING WANG (1970-) Chinese
£2469 $3802 €3704 Portrait (75x61cm-30x24in) s. 22-Oct-2 Iegor de Saint Hippolyte, Montreal #122/R (C.D 6000)
£5081 $7978 €7622 Reflet (116x89cm-46x35in) 12-Dec-2 Iegor de Saint Hippolyte, Montreal #123 (C.D 12500)

JUPP, George Herbert (1869-?) British
Works on paper
£900 $1395 €1350 Game of cards (35x37cm-14x15in) s.i. W/C bodycol. 31-Oct-2 Christie's, Kensington #398/R

JURGENS, A (?) ?
£845 $1361 €1200 Brunnspark beach and Kalliolinna (55x45cm-22x18in) s. 10-May-3 Bukowskis, Helsinki #375/R

JURGENS, Grethe (1899-1981) German
Works on paper
£962 $1490 €1500 Mother with child (61x46cm-24x18in) s.d.1930 W/C. 7-Dec-2 Ketterer, Hamburg #276/R est:1700-1900

JURGENSSEN, Birgit (1949-) Austrian
Works on paper
£288 $456 €450 Put out the lights (84x84cm-33x33in) s.i.d.87 verso mixed media gauze. 12-Nov-2 Dorotheum, Vienna #256/R

JURRES, Johannes Hendricus (1875-1946) Dutch
£2229 $3433 €3500 Cavalrists resting (131x88cm-52x35in) s. 3-Sep-2 Christie's, Amsterdam #141/R est:3500-5000

JURY, Anne P (1907-1995) Irish
£380 $589 €570 Old farmstead, Whitepark, Co. Antrim (15x20cm-6x8in) s. canvas on board. 2-Oct-2 John Ross, Belfast #23
£380 $589 €570 Slieve Donard from Tyrella beach (15x20cm-6x8in) s. canvas on board. 2-Oct-2 John Ross, Belfast #24
£400 $636 €600 Rocks on the Antrim Coast (30x38cm-12x15in) s. 5-Mar-3 John Ross, Belfast #5
£420 $651 €630 Lough Inagh, Connemara (30x38cm-12x15in) s. canvasboard. 4-Dec-2 John Ross, Belfast #3
£450 $698 €675 In the Mournes, Co. Down (18x25cm-7x10in) s. canvas on board. 2-Oct-2 John Ross, Belfast #173
£458 $760 €650 Donkey (22x17cm-9x7in) s. i.d.1965 verso board. 10-Jun-3 James Adam, Dublin #17/R
£500 $795 €750 Baby Brogan (17x12cm-7x5in) s. canvas on board. 5-Mar-3 John Ross, Belfast #83
£650 $949 €975 Lightbody's cottage (25x36cm-10x14in) s.i.verso canvasboard. 12-Jun-2 John Ross, Belfast #74
£800 $1168 €1200 In the garden by the cottage (30x38cm-12x15in) s. canvas on board. 12-Jun-2 John Ross, Belfast #265
£800 $1240 €1200 Gypsies on the road to Achill Island (30x38cm-12x15in) s. canvas on board. 4-Dec-2 John Ross, Belfast #178
£900 $1395 €1350 Chip (50x40cm-20x16in) s. canvas on board. 4-Dec-2 John Ross, Belfast #50
£950 $1492 €1425 Mountainous landscape with two figures and a dog (30x40cm-12x16in) s. i.verso board. 21-Nov-2 Clevedon Sale Rooms #264/R
£1000 $1550 €1500 Lane beside the Wee Field, Donegal (35x56cm-14x22in) s. canvasboard. 4-Dec-2 John Ross, Belfast #201 est:800-1000
£1208 $1945 €1800 Slieve More, Achill Island (28x37cm-11x15in) s. i.verso canvasboard prov. 18-Feb-3 Whyte's, Dublin #2/R est:1800-2200
£1300 $1898 €1950 Magheravarty (25x33cm-10x13in) s. canvas on board. 12-Jun-2 John Ross, Belfast #215 est:800-1000
£1500 $2325 €2250 Still life, japonica (50x61cm-20x24in) s. 4-Dec-2 John Ross, Belfast #30 est:1000-1200

JUSELIUS, Erik (1891-1948) Finnish
£442 $703 €650 Boathouse, Eckero (30x37cm-12x15in) s.i.d.34. 24-Mar-3 Bukowskis, Helsinki #109/R
£588 $965 €900 Reflections (37x30cm-15x12in) s. 9-Feb-3 Bukowskis, Helsinki #267/R
£793 $1253 €1150 Geta (45x52cm-18x20in) s. 3-Apr-3 Hagelstam, Helsinki #846

JUSSEL, Eugen (1912-1997) Austrian
£1528 $2384 €2292 Frunt near Vals with Lenta and Zervreilerhorn (54x64cm-21x25in) s.d.35 i. verso. 6-Nov-2 Hans Widmer, St Gallen #140/R est:2500-4500 (S.FR 3500)
£3797 $5924 €6000 Snowy mountains (69x89cm-27x35in) oil tempera board. 15-Oct-2 Dorotheum, Vienna #123/R est:5000-6500

JUSTH, Andres (20th C) Spanish?
£256 $405 €400 Cadaques (50x61cm-20x24in) s. 19-Nov-2 Durán, Madrid #72/R

JUSTITZ, Alfred (1879-1934) Czechoslovakian
£2187 $3500 €3171 Still life with mums (65x54cm-26x21in) s. 16-May-3 Skinner, Boston #174/R est:700-900
£2888 $4564 €4332 Bouquet of yellow flowers in a vase (57x43cm-22x17in) s. plywood. 30-Nov-2 Dorotheum, Prague #111/R est:100000-200000 (C.KR 140000)

JUTSUM, Henry (1816-1869) British
£3200 $4864 €4800 Highland loch (88x150cm-35x59in) s.d.1871. 28-Aug-2 Sotheby's, London #880/R est:2000-3000
Works on paper
£500 $820 €750 Figures on a path at the edge of a wood (20x30cm-8x12in) s.i. W/C. 4-Feb-3 Bonhams, Leeds #228
£2400 $3936 €3600 Angler by a river (28x47cm-11x19in) s.d.1853 pencil W/C. 4-Feb-3 Bonhams, Leeds #229 est:600-800

JUTTNER, Brune (1880-?) Scandinavian
£261 $418 €400 Two fishing boats and horse and cart on the beach with figures (64x94cm-25x37in) s. lit. 10-Jan-3 Allgauer, Kempten #1637/R

JUTZ, Carl (elder) (1838-1916) German
£3145 $4843 €5000 Chicken in a yard (27x27cm-11x11in) s. paper on panel. 22-Oct-2 Sotheby's, Amsterdam #68/R est:8000-12000
£11538 $17885 €18000 Ducks by pond (13x16cm-5x6in) s. panel. 5-Dec-2 Dr Fritz Nagel, Stuttgart #669/R est:4500
£11538 $17885 €18000 Cock with chickens (13x16cm-5x6in) s. panel. 5-Dec-2 Dr Fritz Nagel, Stuttgart #670/R est:4500
£17949 $28359 €28000 Poultry yard (38x48cm-15x19in) s.d.99. 16-Nov-2 Lempertz, Koln #1491/R est:20000
£33333 $52667 €52000 Poultry yard (39x49cm-15x19in) s.d.02 prov. 16-Nov-2 Lempertz, Koln #1492/R est:50000

JUUEL, Andreas (1817-1868) Danish
£766 $1240 €1111 Watering the horse on a calm summer evening (25x33cm-10x13in) s. 26-May-3 Rasmussen, Copenhagen #1145/R (D.KR 8000)
Works on paper
£287 $465 €416 Prospect view of Augustenborg Palace (16x23cm-6x9in) s. W/C. 24-May-3 Rasmussen, Havnen #2034 (D.KR 3000)

JUUL, Ole (1852-1927) Norwegian
£504 $822 €756 Sunset over the ocean (22x34cm-9x13in) s. canvas on panel. 17-Feb-3 Blomqvist, Lysaker #1099 (N.KR 5700)
£526 $832 €789 Rocks covered by snow (80x99cm-31x39in) s. panel. 17-Dec-2 Grev Wedels Plass, Oslo #161/R (N.KR 6000)
£679 $1046 €1019 Boathouse and boats, Lofoten (35x57cm-14x22in) s. 28-Oct-2 Blomqvist, Lysaker #1124/R (N.KR 8000)
£1754 $2772 €2631 Fishing village (38x60cm-15x24in) s. 17-Dec-2 Grev Wedels Plass, Oslo #162/R est:15000-20000 (N.KR 20000)

JUVARRA, Filippo (attrib) (1676-1736) Italian
Works on paper
£811 $1265 €1200 Projects (49x32cm-19x13in) i. pen ink wash pair. 27-Mar-3 Maigret, Paris #16
£962 $1510 €1500 Capricio (17x20cm-7x8in) pen Chinese ink. 13-Dec-2 Pierre Berge, Paris #29

JUVELA, Lennu (1886-1979) Finnish
£302 $465 €480 In Paradise (47x56cm-19x22in) s.d.1915. 27-Oct-2 Bukowskis, Helsinki #197/R
£380 $592 €600 Flowers (46x44cm-18x17in) s.i.d.1914. 12-Sep-2 Hagelstam, Helsinki #1009
£384 $591 €610 Town (41x46cm-16x18in) s. 24-Oct-2 Hagelstam, Helsinki #936/R
£405 $632 €640 River landscape (35x45cm-14x18in) s.d.1910. 12-Sep-2 Hagelstam, Helsinki #984
£510 $811 €750 Fishermen (95x66cm-37x26in) s. 27-Feb-3 Hagelstam, Helsinki #1038

JUVENELL, Paul (elder) (1579-1643) German
£3514 $5481 €5200 Tribut de Cesar (97x132cm-38x52in) s.d.MDCXXX panel. 31-Mar-3 Ribeyre & Baron, Paris #14/R

KAAN-ALBEST, Julius von (1874-1942) German
£451 $713 €650 Church in Kaltern (55x41cm-22x16in) s.d.1924 board. 24-Apr-3 Dorotheum, Vienna #51/R

KABAKOV, Ilya (1933-) Russian
Works on paper
£7500 $12525 €10875 Untitled (20x27cm-8x11in) s. one d.70 one d.68 col pencil ink card two prov.exhib. 26-Jun-3 Sotheby's, London #127/R est:4000-6000

KABELL, Ludwig (1853-1902) Danish
£362 $550 €543 Calm foggy autumn morning (30x51cm-12x20in) s. 28-Aug-2 Museumsbygningen, Copenhagen #2 (D.KR 4200)
£397 $612 €596 Farm with view to the fjord (64x99cm-25x39in) s.d.1894. 26-Oct-2 Rasmussen, Havnen #2163/R (D.KR 4700)
£1021 $1614 €1532 Kalkovn woods near Holckenhavn, Nyborgfjord (74x123cm-29x48in) s.d.1899. 2-Dec-2 Rasmussen, Copenhagen #1477/R est:12000 (D.KR 12000)
£3546 $5745 €5000 Summers day (74x123cm-29x48in) s.d.1899 i.verso. 22-May-3 Dorotheum, Vienna #141/R est:4500-5000

KABREGU, Enzo Domestico (1906-1971) ?
£281 $450 €422 Going around (53x42cm-21x17in) s. oil pastel card. 5-Jan-3 Galleria Y Remates, Montevideo #53

KACZ, Endre Komaromi (1880-1969) Hungarian
£401 $625 €602 Young woman lounging on a daybed (69x56cm-27x22in) s. 14-Sep-2 Selkirks, St. Louis #733
£749 $1093 €1124 Interior with seated woman (81x61cm-32x24in) s. 17-Jun-2 Philippe Schuler, Zurich #4383/R (S.FR 1700)
£1034 $1571 €1551 Madame Butterfly in stitting-room with flowers (40x50cm-16x20in) s. 27-Aug-2 Rasmussen, Copenhagen #1961/R est:12000 (D.KR 12000)
£1154 $1812 €1800 Young woman thinking (80x60cm-31x24in) s. 15-Dec-2 Eric Pillon, Calais #57/R

KADAR, Bela (1877-1955) Hungarian
£284 $443 €426 Sitting nude (28x19cm-11x7in) s. tempera paper. 11-Sep-2 Kieselbach, Budapest #208/R (H.F 110000)
£538 $850 €850 Traveller in front of Hungarian farmhouse, with startled geese in foreground (80x70cm-31x28in) s.d.54. 29-Nov-2 Sigalas, Stuttgart #1097/R
£894 $1395 €1341 Theatre scene (45x28cm-18x11in) s. tempra. 11-Apr-3 Kieselbach, Budapest #62/R est:300000-320000 (H.F 320000)
£1892 $2951 €2800 Composition (62x48cm-24x19in) s. tempera paper. 26-Mar-3 Finarte Semenzato, Milan #94/R
£2017 $3126 €3026 Sunlit courtyard (69x96cm-27x38in) s. cardboard. 6-Dec-2 Kieselbach, Budapest #109/R (H.F 750000)
£3353 $5231 €5030 Models (34x44cm-13x17in) s. tempera. 11-Apr-3 Kieselbach, Budapest #192/R est:1200000 (H.F 1200000)
£4751 $7411 €6889 Bathers (72x96cm-28x38in) s. tempera paper. 12-Apr-3 Mu Terem Galeria, Budapest #30/R est:1600000 (H.F 1700000)
£5030 $7847 €7545 Seated nude (43x29cm-17x11in) s. tempera. 11-Apr-3 Kieselbach, Budapest #181/R est:1200000-1800000 (H.F 1800000)
£5160 $8049 €7740 Show (36x26cm-14x10in) s. W/C. 11-Sep-2 Kieselbach, Budapest #93/R (H.F 2000000)
£5500 $9020 €8250 Four women (85x59cm-33x23in) s. tempera on paper. 3-Jun-3 Sotheby's, London #117/R est:6000-8000
£6148 $9591 €9222 Girl with mandolin before blue background (71x50cm-28x20in) s. tempera. 11-Apr-3 Kieselbach, Budapest #186/R est:2000000-2200000 (H.F 2200000)
£6191 $9659 €9287 Horse composition with figures (28x42cm-11x17in) s. tempera paper. 11-Sep-2 Kieselbach, Budapest #163/R (H.F 2400000)
£6383 $10340 €9000 Arcadian scene (61x76cm-24x30in) s. prov. 20-May-3 Dorotheum, Vienna #121/R est:7000-12000
£6707 $10464 €10061 Meeting (28x42cm-11x17in) s. tempera. 11-Sep-2 Kieselbach, Budapest #116/R (H.F 2600000)
£8383 $13078 €12155 Carpet mending (59x41cm-23x16in) s. tempera. 12-Apr-3 Mu Terem Galeria, Budapest #102/R est:2000000 (H.F 3000000)
£8606 $13339 €12479 Evening in the garden (54x76cm-21x30in) s. tempera. 9-Dec-2 Mu Terem Galeria, Budapest #133/R est:950000 (H.F 3200000)
£9287 $14488 €13466 Ladies of the town (84x61cm-33x24in) s. tempera paper exhib. 13-Sep-2 Mu Terem Galeria, Budapest #94/R est:2500000 (H.F 3600000)
£11117 $17787 €16676 Still life of flowers with fruit (44x34cm-17x13in) s. tempera. 16-May-3 Kieselbach, Budapest #31/R (H.F 3800000)
£11295 $17507 €16943 Veiled woman with a mandolin (84x57cm-33x22in) s. tempera on paper. 6-Dec-2 Kieselbach, Budapest #159/R (H.F 4200000)
£11295 $17507 €16378 Village scene (30x47cm-12x19in) s. tempera. 9-Dec-2 Mu Terem Galeria, Budapest #78/R est:1400000 (H.F 4200000)
£11351 $17708 €17027 Village scene, 1924 (35x50cm-14x20in) s. tempera paper. 11-Sep-2 Kieselbach, Budapest #59/R (H.F 4400000)
£12908 $20008 €19362 Chat (55x37cm-22x15in) s. tempera on paper. 6-Dec-2 Kieselbach, Budapest #26/R (H.F 4800000)
£13164 $21063 €19746 Friends (101x72cm-40x28in) s. tempera paper. 16-May-3 Kieselbach, Budapest #39/R (H.F 4500000)
£13972 $21797 €20259 Veiled lady with still life (81x60cm-32x24in) s. tempera exhib. 12-Apr-3 Mu Terem Galeria, Budapest #220/R est:3000000 (H.F 5000000)
£17553 $28084 €26330 Chamber music (79x59cm-31x23in) s. tempera. 16-May-3 Kieselbach, Budapest #10/R (H.F 6000000)
£18058 $28171 €27087 Girl with string of blue pearls (56x38cm-22x15in) s. tempera paper. 11-Sep-2 Kieselbach, Budapest #211/R (H.F 7000000)
£20169 $31263 €30254 Girl with a guitar (103x7cm-41x3in) s. tempera. 6-Dec-2 Kieselbach, Budapest #154/R (H.F 7500000)
£20169 $31263 €29245 Portrait study in interior (55x34cm-22x13in) s. exhib.lit. 9-Dec-2 Mu Terem Galeria, Budapest #75/R est:4000000 (H.F 7500000)
£20638 $32196 €29925 Still life of flowers with glass and grapes (84x59cm-33x23in) s. tempera exhib. 13-Sep-2 Mu Terem Galeria, Budapest #72/R est:2500000 (H.F 8000000)

Works on paper
£244 $383 €366 Bathers in a clearing (15x23cm-6x9in) s. mixed media. 10-Dec-2 Pinneys, Montreal #33 (C.D 600)
£284 $460 €400 Men and dogs (18x24cm-7x9in) s. Indian ink. 24-May-3 Van Ham, Cologne #301/R
£488 $800 €708 Four women (28x23cm-11x9in) s. W/C. 1-Jun-3 Wright, Chicago #244/R
£761 $1217 €1142 Couple with a horse (35x21cm-14x8in) s. Indian ink. 16-May-3 Kieselbach, Budapest #11/R (H.F 260000)
£769 $1199 €1154 Three nudes bathing, one in a boat (17x22cm-7x9in) s. W/C. 11-Nov-2 Stephan Welz, Johannesburg #422 est:4000-6000 (SA.R 12000)
£950 $1482 €1378 Reclining nude. Mother with her child (22x30cm-9x12in) s. ink double-sided. 12-Apr-3 Mu Terem Galeria, Budapest #145/R est:300000 (H.F 340000)
£995 $1591 €1493 Women with jars (29x23cm-11x9in) s. Indian ink. 16-May-3 Kieselbach, Budapest #74/R (H.F 340000)
£1022 $1584 €1482 Dancers (30x21cm-12x8in) s. Indian ink. 9-Dec-2 Mu Terem Galeria, Budapest #209/R est:220000 (H.F 380000)
£1129 $1751 €1694 Composition (29x20cm-11x8in) s. mixed media. 6-Dec-2 Kieselbach, Budapest #79/R (H.F 420000)
£1537 $2398 €2229 Nude with dotted stole (63x45cm-25x18in) s. ink. 12-Apr-3 Mu Terem Galeria, Budapest #144/R est:380000 (H.F 550000)
£1724 $2759 €2500 Composition cubiste (14x10cm-6x4in) s. W/C. 12-Mar-3 Rabourdin & Choppin de Janvry, Paris #152/R
£1943 $3051 €2915 Nude (46x30cm-18x12in) W/C prov. 25-Nov-2 Germann, Zurich #137/R est:4500-5000 (S.FR 4450)
£2096 $3291 €3144 Untitled (30x43cm-12x17in) s. W/C study verso. 23-Nov-2 Burkhard, Luzern #179/R est:3000-4000 (S.FR 4800)
£2759 $4414 €4000 Composition cubiste (22x26cm-9x10in) s. W/C. 12-Mar-3 Rabourdin & Choppin de Janvry, Paris #154/R
£4808 $7452 €7500 Still life of fruit (45x28cm-18x11in) s. gouache prov. 7-Dec-2 Ketterer, Hamburg #272/R est:1800-2200
£4902 $7646 €7353 Mother with child (42x29cm-17x11in) s. pastel. 11-Sep-2 Kieselbach, Budapest #108/R (H.F 1900000)

£5161 $8000 €7742 Cubist interior with figures (58x78cm-23x31in) s. gouache executed 1929 prov. 26-Sep-2 Christie's, Rockefeller NY #616/R est:4000-6000
£6200 $9858 €9300 Le reve (60x41cm-24x16in) s. gouache. 20-Mar-3 Sotheby's, Olympia #213/R est:3000-5000
£15370 $23977 €23055 Girl in flowery hat (70x50cm-28x20in) s. mixed media. 11-Apr-3 Kieselbach, Budapest #9/R est:380000-1000000 (H.F 5500000)

KADAR, Geza (1878-1952) Hungarian
£1614 $2501 €2340 Winter in Nagybanya (47x57cm-19x22in) s. 9-Dec-2 Mu Terem Galeria, Budapest #66/R est:400000 (H.F 600000)
£2375 $3705 €3444 Flowers in the shadow of the stack (60x74cm-24x29in) s.d.1928. 12-Apr-3 Mu Terem Galeria, Budapest #89/R est:800000 (H.F 850000)
£5916 $9170 €8578 Snow-bounded haystacks (69x67cm-27x26in) s. 9-Dec-2 Mu Terem Galeria, Budapest #173/R est:650000 (H.F 2200000)

KADEN, Siegfried (20th C) German
£432 $691 €600 Last supper (157x156cm-62x61in) s.d. sackcloth. 15-May-3 Neumeister, Munich #466/R

KADERABEK, Josef (1915-) Czechoslovakian
£897 $1364 €1400 Still life with bread and jug (36x45cm-14x18in) s. lit. 11-Jul-2 Allgauer, Kempten #2532

KADISHMAN, Menashe (1932-) Israeli
£950 $1473 €1425 Head of a sheep (80x61cm-31x24in) s. acrylic. 3-Dec-2 Bonhams, Knightsbridge #277/R

KAEMMERER, Frederik Hendrik (1839-1902) Dutch
£526 $853 €800 Portrait of a lady (25x20cm-10x8in) s. canvas on board. 21-Jan-3 Christie's, Amsterdam #90
£5660 $8717 €9000 Flirtation (32x20cm-13x8in) s. 22-Oct-2 Sotheby's, Amsterdam #88/R est:9000-12000
£8219 $12904 €12000 Flirtation (46x33cm-18x13in) s. 15-Apr-3 Sotheby's, Amsterdam #66/R est:6000-8000
£77419 $120000 €116129 On the lookout (40x25cm-16x10in) s. 29-Oct-2 Sotheby's, New York #64/R est:60000-80000
£274194 $425000 €411291 Beach at Scheveningen, Holland (70x141cm-28x56in) s. prov.exhib.lit. 29-Oct-2 Sotheby's, New York #60/R est:300000-400000

KAEMMERER, Johan Hendrik (1894-1970) Dutch
£382 $630 €550 Peasant woman at work in late summer (25x45cm-10x18in) s. i.stretcher. 1-Jul-3 Christie's, Amsterdam #134
£625 $1031 €900 Setting out (50x90cm-20x35in) s. 1-Jul-3 Christie's, Amsterdam #83
£655 $1042 €950 Peasant woman near a farm in a polder landscape (50x80cm-20x31in) s. 10-Mar-3 Sotheby's, Amsterdam #218/R est:900-1200

KAERCHER, Amalie (19th C) German
£1538 $2415 €2400 Still life with lilies, pansies and other flowers (21x26cm-8x10in) s.d.1875. 23-Nov-2 Arnold, Frankfurt #772/R est:1600
£2000 $3260 €2900 Still life of flowers (20x26cm-8x10in) s.d.1875. 16-Jul-3 Sotheby's, Olympia #233/R est:2000-3000

KAESBACH, Rudolph (1873-?) German
Sculpture
£1026 $1610 €1600 Mountain goat. i. dark brown pat.bronze Cast.Berl Ernst. 21-Nov-2 Van Ham, Cologne #1225/R

KAGER, Erika von (1890-?) Swiss
£513 $800 €770 Still life (61x119cm-24x47in) 18-Oct-2 Du Mouchelle, Detroit #2115/R

KAGER, Johann Matthias (1575-1634) German
Works on paper
£811 $1265 €1200 Adoration of the shepherds (11x8cm-4x3in) s. pen ink wash prov. 26-Mar-3 Piasa, Paris #22/R
£856 $1336 €1250 Apotheosis of the Holy Trinity (46x27cm-18x11in) Indian ink wash over pencil squaring. 11-Apr-3 Winterberg, Heidelberg #103/R est:720

KAGIE, Jan (1885-1971) Dutch
£446 $696 €700 Still life with hat (68x89cm-27x35in) s. 6-Nov-2 Vendue Huis, Gravenhage #191/R

KAHAN, Louis (1905-2002) Australian
£430 $654 €645 Rocking in the sun (38x57cm-15x22in) s.d. board prov. 28-Aug-2 Deutscher-Menzies, Melbourne #367/R (A.D 1200)
Works on paper
£251 $381 €377 On the beach II (34x50cm-13x20in) s.i. pencil W/C. 28-Aug-2 Deutscher-Menzies, Melbourne #419 (A.D 700)
£321 $508 €482 Champ (47x33cm-19x13in) s.d.1971 pencil dr. 18-Nov-2 Joel, Victoria #236 est:1000-1200 (A.D 900)
£356 $544 €534 Tuning the guitar (36x53cm-14x21in) s.i.d.75 ink W/C prov. 25-Aug-2 Sotheby's, Paddington #235 est:500-800 (A.D 1000)
£357 $564 €536 Street corner (29x23cm-11x9in) s.d.58 W/C. 18-Nov-2 Joel, Victoria #333 est:800-1000 (A.D 1000)
£445 $681 €668 Girl with guitar (73x54cm-29x21in) s.i.d.66 mixed media on board prov. 25-Aug-2 Sotheby's, Paddington #248 est:500-800 (A.D 1250)
£500 $790 €750 Cannes (35x44cm-14x17in) s.i.d.69 ink wash. 18-Nov-2 Joel, Victoria #167 est:1000-1200 (A.D 1400)
£640 $1030 €928 Three dancers (54x35cm-21x14in) s.i.d.85 ink col wash. 12-May-3 Joel, Victoria #333 est:1000-1500 (A.D 1600)
£643 $1016 €965 Two nude figures (51x38cm-20x15in) s. ink wash. 18-Nov-2 Joel, Victoria #187 est:1000-1200 (A.D 1800)
£643 $1016 €965 Drawing life (54x74cm-21x29in) s.i. ink wash. 18-Nov-2 Joel, Victoria #297 est:1000-1200 (A.D 1800)
£1354 $2221 €2031 Three figures resting (51x70cm-20x28in) s.d.72 W/C pastel pen ink paper on board. 4-Jun-3 Deutscher-Menzies, Melbourne #354/R est:1000-2000 (A.D 3400)

KAHANA, Aharon (1905-1967) Israeli
£4747 $7500 €7121 Untitled (65x54cm-26x21in) s.d.63. 27-Apr-3 Sotheby's, Tel Aviv #71/R est:6000-8000

KAHLER, Carl (1855-?) Austrian
£5380 $8500 €8070 Interoir with artist sketching (97x137cm-38x54in) s. 24-Apr-3 Shannon's, Milford #155/R est:8000-12000

KAHLHAMER, Brad (1956-) American?
£10127 $16000 €15191 Little war pony (213x152cm-84x60in) s.i.d.1999 verso prov.exhib.lit. 12-Nov-2 Phillips, New York #187/R est:18000-25000
Works on paper
£633 $1000 €950 Rattler 7.53 (56x37cm-22x15in) init.d.98 ink gouache prov. 12-Nov-2 Phillips, New York #210/R est:1500-2000

KAHLO, Frida (1907-1954) Mexican
Works on paper
£1511 $2358 €2267 Carta autografa dirigida a las hermanas de Frida, Elenita y Tere (27x21cm-11x8in) s.d.21 de junio 1952 tinta. 17-Oct-2 Louis Morton, Mexico #62 est:6000-8000 (M.P 24000)
£42683 $70000 €64025 View of Central Park (27x20cm-11x8in) s.d.1932 W/C pencil prov. 28-May-3 Christie's, Rockefeller NY #20/R est:80000-120000

KAHN, Eric (1904-1979) German
£450 $707 €675 Portrait of Fred Orda as Valentine (91x71cm-36x28in) i.stretcher prov.exhib. 10-Dec-2 Rosebery Fine Art, London #621/R

KAHN, Wolf (1927-) American
£4808 $7500 €7212 Sugar maples (69x76cm-27x30in) s. prov. 5-Nov-2 Doyle, New York #60/R est:5000-7000
£4938 $8000 €7160 Tre Alberi (79x99cm-31x39in) prov.exhib. 21-May-3 Doyle, New York #55/R est:5000-7000
£8176 $13000 €12264 Black Brook (71x94cm-28x37in) s. 4-Mar-3 Christie's, Rockefeller NY #115/R est:12000-18000
£18868 $30000 €28302 Midsummer barn (132x153cm-52x60in) s. prov. 4-Mar-3 Christie's, Rockefeller NY #120/R est:20000-30000
£28302 $45000 €42453 Declivity (127x183cm-50x72in) init. painted 1968 prov. 4-Mar-3 Christie's, Rockefeller NY #123/R est:20000-30000
Works on paper
£387 $600 €581 Truck and horse trailers (30x45cm-12x18in) s. pastel prov. 3-Dec-2 Christie's, Rockefeller NY #603/R
£671 $1100 €973 Wearing red (33x38cm-13x15in) pastel prov. 1-Jun-3 Wright, Chicago #317/R est:1500-2000
£750 $1200 €1125 Landscape with house and barn (36x48cm-14x19in) s. pastel. 17-May-3 Pook & Pook, Downington #324/R est:1500-2000
£774 $1200 €1161 Stables (30x45cm-12x18in) s. pastel prov. 3-Dec-2 Christie's, Rockefeller NY #602/R
£1677 $2600 €2516 Bartlett Place (30x45cm-12x18in) s.d.1977 pastel prov. 3-Dec-2 Christie's, Rockefeller NY #604/R est:2500-3500
£1899 $3000 €2849 Venice (35x42cm-14x17in) s.i.d.58 pastel. 22-Apr-3 Butterfields, San Francisco #6068/R est:3000-5000

KAHRER, Max (1878-1937) Rumanian
£1218 $1924 €1900 Autumn in Schiessstattgraben (50x60cm-20x24in) s.d.1934 panel. 12-Nov-2 Dorotheum, Vienna #106/R est:1800-2200
£1392 $2200 €2200 Donau meadows near Klosterneuburg (92x92cm-36x36in) s. 26-Nov-2 Wiener Kunst Auktionen, Vienna #57/R est:2200-2800

£5369 $8643 €8000 Alpine village, South Tyrol. Kitchen garden (74x79cm-29x31in) s.d.1914 pair. 18-Feb-3 Sotheby's, Amsterdam #332/R est:6000-8000

KAIOKU, Nukina (1778-1863) Japanese
Works on paper
£1500 $2505 €2175 Autumn and Winter landscapes (132x42cm-52x17in) s. ink slight colour silk hanging scrolls pair. 18-Jun-3 Christie's, London #289/R est:1200-1800
£3019 $4800 €4529 Winter landscape (140x56cm-55x22in) s.d.1841 ink col silk hanging scroll. 24-Mar-3 Christie's, Rockefeller NY #43/R est:1000-1500

KAIPIAINEN, Birger (1915-1988) Finnish
Sculpture
£10638 $16489 €15957 Curlew (80x90cm-31x35in) s. metal pearls porcelain lit. 8-Dec-2 Uppsala Auktionskammare, Uppsala #860/R est:60000-80000 (S.KR 150000)

KAIRA, Alice (1913-) Finnish
£317 $519 €440 Flowers (46x27cm-18x11in) s.d.1968. 5-Jun-3 Hagelstam, Helsinki #971
£759 $1200 €1200 Donkey (38x46cm-15x18in) s.d.1981. 1-Dec-2 Bukowskis, Helsinki #323/R
£886 $1382 €1400 Eve (38x46cm-15x18in) s.d.1974. 12-Sep-2 Hagelstam, Helsinki #962
£1456 $2271 €2300 Visiting the photographer (46x38cm-18x15in) s.d.1974. 12-Sep-2 Hagelstam, Helsinki #961/R est:850
£2025 $3200 €3200 The kiss (27x35cm-11x14in) s.d.1977. 30-Nov-2 Hagelstam, Helsinki #164/R est:2000

KAISER, Eduard (1820-1895) Austrian
Works on paper
£704 $1134 €1000 Field Marshall Friedrich Xaver, Prince of Hohenzollern-Hechingen (30x25cm-12x10in) s.d.1842 gouache board. 7-May-3 Dorotheum, Vienna #317/R

KAISER, Ernst (1803-1865) German
£1100 $1793 €1650 Collecting hay (63x63cm-25x25in) s. 29-Jan-3 Sotheby's, Olympia #259/R est:800-1200

KAISER, Friedrich (1815-1889) German
£833 $1292 €1300 Prussian cavalry (18x26cm-7x10in) s. prov. two. 7-Dec-2 Ketterer, Hamburg #108/R
Works on paper
£513 $795 €800 House building in Charlottenburg (20x27cm-8x11in) s. brush dr over pencil. 4-Dec-2 Neumeister, Munich #522/R

KAISER, Leander (1947-) Austrian
£411 $642 €650 Room (67x46cm-26x18in) mono. paper. 15-Oct-2 Dorotheum, Vienna #202/R

KAISER, Richard (1868-1941) German
£255 $397 €400 Landscape with trees (56x72cm-22x28in) s. 6-Nov-2 Hugo Ruef, Munich #1164
£1603 $2340 €2500 Naturdenkmal... Laueninsel, Chiemsee (72x85cm-28x33in) s.i. 4-Jun-2 Karl & Faber, Munich #297a/R est:2500
£1646 $2551 €2600 Summer evening near Diessen (101x151cm-40x59in) s.i. 25-Sep-2 Neumeister, Munich #614/R est:2500

KAISER, Walter (1899-1973) German
£575 $943 €880 Hamburg - harbour landscape with bridge (23x31cm-9x12in) s. board lit. 8-Feb-3 Hans Stahl, Hamburg #131/R

KAISER, Wolfgang (20th C) German
£400 $628 €600 Two wire haired dachshund (15x20cm-6x8in) s. panel. 16-Dec-2 Bonhams, Bury St Edmunds #507

KAISER-HERBST, Carl (1858-1940) Austrian
£345 $552 €500 Viennese wood (15x24cm-6x9in) board on panel. 11-Mar-3 Dorotheum, Vienna #89/R
£364 $594 €550 On the Thames (33x56cm-13x22in) board. 28-Jan-3 Dorotheum, Vienna #11/R

KAISIN, Lucien (1901-1963) Belgian
£304 $474 €450 Vue sur un petit port (40x50cm-16x20in) s. 25-Mar-3 Campo & Campo, Antwerp #99
£478 $745 €750 Le port des deriveurs (60x70cm-24x28in) s. 11-Nov-2 Horta, Bruxelles #709
£828 $1308 €1200 Port de peche (60x70cm-24x28in) s. 2-Apr-3 Vanderkindere, Brussels #535

KAJLICK, Aurel (1901-1973) Czechoslovakian
Works on paper
£441 $684 €662 Woman from Piest'any (58x37cm-23x15in) pencil chl pastel. 1-Oct-2 SOGA, Bratislava #16/R est:20000 (SL.K 28000)
£772 $1196 €1158 Homecoming from field (61x84cm-24x33in) pastel exec.c.1930. 1-Oct-2 SOGA, Bratislava #15/R est:25000 (SL.K 49000)

KAKS, Olle (1941-) Swedish
£412 $642 €618 Ducks on river in winter (65x88cm-26x35in) s. 13-Sep-2 Lilla Bukowskis, Stockholm #550 (S.KR 6000)

KAKUSEI (19th C) Japanese
Sculpture
£6000 $10020 €8700 Boatman and four travellers in a boat (37cm-15in) s. ivory group. 18-Jun-3 Christie's, London #145/R est:2500-3000

KALB, Rudolf (19/20th C) German
£285 $441 €450 Bad Tolz street (70x10cm-28x4in) i. 27-Sep-2 Dr Fritz Nagel, Leipzig #3956/R
£500 $785 €750 Cattle grazing in pasture (90x109cm-35x43in) s. 16-Apr-3 Christie's, Kensington #686/R

KALCKREUTH, Karl Walter Leopold von (1855-1928) German
£1282 $1987 €2000 Girl in blue smock (59x49cm-23x19in) s.d.11 board. 4-Dec-2 Lempertz, Koln #797/R est:2500
£6410 $10128 €10000 Young woman with tea tray (103x87cm-41x34in) s.d.10 prov. 16-Nov-2 Lempertz, Koln #1493/R est:7000

KALCKREUTH, Patrick von (1892-1970) German
£385 $604 €600 Waves (68x98cm-27x39in) s. 21-Nov-2 Weidler, Nurnberg #4687/R
£411 $641 €600 Breaking waves in evening light (71x100cm-28x39in) s. 9-Apr-3 Neumeister, Munich #688
£449 $696 €700 Waves breaking on rocky coast (62x72cm-24x28in) s. lit. 6-Dec-2 Karlheinz Kaupp, Staufen #2241/R
£483 $743 €725 Seascape with large sailing vessel (70x100cm-28x39in) s. 27-Oct-2 Anders Antik, Landskrona #47/R (S.KR 7000)
£503 $785 €800 Surf at sunset (70x100cm-28x39in) s. lit. 20-Sep-2 Karlheinz Kaupp, Staufen #1924
£506 $800 €800 Ship in full sail on the high seas (72x101cm-28x40in) s. lit. 29-Nov-2 Schloss Ahlden, Ahlden #1252/R
£545 $855 €850 Breaking waves at dusk (81x121cm-32x48in) s. 23-Nov-2 Arnold, Frankfurt #773/R
£566 $883 €900 Seascape (70x100cm-28x39in) s. 21-Sep-2 Bolland & Marotz, Bremen #613/R
£704 $1134 €1000 Waves breaking on the beach (60x90cm-24x35in) s. lit. 9-May-3 Schloss Ahlden, Ahlden #1407/R
£833 $1308 €1300 Waves breaking on beach at dusk (70x100cm-28x39in) s. 23-Nov-2 Arnold, Frankfurt #774/R
£987 $1599 €1500 Surf at sunset (70x100cm-28x39in) s. 21-Jan-3 Christie's, Amsterdam #123 est:1500-2000
£1145 $1672 €1718 Surf (61x91cm-24x36in) s. 17-Jun-2 Philippe Schuler, Zurich #4382/R est:2000-2500 (S.FR 2600)

KALCKREUTH, Stanislas von (attrib) (1821-1894) German
£1583 $2596 €2200 Mountain lake in the morning with figures (30x55cm-12x22in) bears sig. 4-Jun-3 Reiss & Sohn, Konigstein #147/R est:3000

KALINITCHENKO, Jakoff Jakovievitch (1869-1938) Russian
£10128 $15395 €15800 Jeune fille a la lecture (84x53cm-33x21in) s.d.1894 prov. 16-Aug-2 Deauville, France #105/R est:22000
£20000 $32400 €30000 Lesson (84x52cm-33x20in) s.d.1894. 21-May-3 Sotheby's, London #74/R est:10000-15000

KALINOWSKI, Horst Egon (1924-) German
Works on paper
£818 $1267 €1300 Cerf-volant chinois (37x36cm-15x14in) s.d.59 i.d.59 verso collage mixed media panel. 5-Oct-2 De Vuyst, Lokeren #189/R
£870 $1426 €1200 Sepulcre Marin (64x49cm-25x19in) s.i.d.58 collage cloth board. 28-May-3 Lempertz, Koln #202/R

KALISH, Max (1891-1945) American
Sculpture
£1783 $2800 €2675 Standing female nude (41cm-16in) s.d.1930 brown pat bronze. 10-Dec-2 Doyle, New York #96/R est:4000-6000

KALKAR, Isidor (19/20th C) ?
£438 $701 €657 Landscape with thatched farm, girl and boy in cart (40x61cm-16x24in) init.i.d.Aug 75. 13-Jan-3 Rasmussen, Vejle #147/R (D.KR 5000)

KALLMORGEN, Friedrich (1856-1924) German
£4710 $7725 €6500 Peddler (26x35cm-10x14in) s.d.1893. 31-May-3 Villa Grisebach, Berlin #124/R est:3000-4000
£5063 $7848 €8000 Wet weather (45x61cm-18x24in) s. 28-Sep-2 Hans Stahl, Hamburg #155/R est:7000
£10067 $16207 €15000 Returning from the harvest (63x93cm-25x37in) s.d.91. 18-Feb-3 Sotheby's, Amsterdam #335/R est:4000-6000
£33554 $54022 €50000 Picking flowers (68x103cm-27x41in) s.d.1893 s.on stretcher. 18-Feb-3 Sotheby's, Amsterdam #494/R est:10000-15000

KALLOS, Paul (1928-) French
£805 $1297 €1200 Composition (116x89cm-46x35in) s.d.1958. 23-Feb-3 Mercier & Cie, Lille #124/R
£1689 $2635 €2500 Composition (195x114cm-77x45in) s.d.1989 acrylic. 28-Mar-3 Charbonneaux, Paris #97/R

KALLSTENIUS, Gottfried (1861-1943) Swedish
£343 $522 €515 Viking ship (55x70cm-22x28in) s.d.1923 panel. 16-Aug-2 Lilla Bukowskis, Stockholm #413 (S.KR 5000)
£583 $909 €875 Pine trees in the skerries (66x87cm-26x34in) s.d.36. 13-Sep-2 Lilla Bukowskis, Stockholm #394 (S.KR 8500)
£665 $1051 €998 Sunlit bay in the skerries (74x100cm-29x39in) s.d.28. 16-Nov-2 Crafoord, Lund #88/R (S.KR 9500)
£701 $1108 €1052 Pine trees on cliff in the skerries, afternoon sunshine (90x100cm-35x39in) s.d.25. 27-Nov-2 Falkkloos, Malmo #77836/R (S.KR 10000)
£851 $1319 €1277 Moonlit night, landscape from Klinte, Gotland (42x59cm-17x23in) s.d.1899 lit. 4-Dec-2 AB Stockholms Auktionsverk #1550/R (S.KR 12000)
£917 $1440 €1376 Coastal landscape with pine trees (73x100cm-29x39in) s.d.28. 16-Dec-2 Lilla Bukowskis, Stockholm #102 (S.KR 13000)
£993 $1539 €1490 Fisherman in boat, Stockholm's river (43x60cm-17x24in) s.d.87. 8-Dec-2 Uppsala Auktionskammare, Uppsala #113/R (S.KR 14000)
£2553 $3957 €3830 Cupid with man resting (50x201cm-20x79in) s.d.90 prov. 4-Dec-2 AB Stockholms Auktionsverk #1744/R est:10000-12000 (S.KR 36000)

KALMAKOFF, Nicolas (1873-1955) Russian
£10256 $15897 €16000 Danseuse couronnee (61x33cm-24x13in) s.d.1925 cardboard. 5-Dec-2 Gros & Delettrez, Paris #56/R est:5000
£16000 $25920 €24000 Gateway to dreams (140x96cm-55x38in) oil htd gold paint. 21-May-3 Sotheby's, London #213/R est:20000-30000
Works on paper
£20000 $31600 €30000 Astartee (74x55cm-29x22in) mono.d.1926 gouache paper on panel lit. 26-Nov-2 Christie's, Kensington #42/R est:6000-8000
£35000 $54950 €52500 Winged Goddess of Wine (100x69cm-39x27in) s. gouache htd gold silver executed c.1930. 20-Nov-2 Sotheby's, London #97/R est:30000-40000

KALMAN, Peter (1877-1948) Hungarian
£1761 $2747 €2800 Woman holding lute with other people at table (59x49cm-23x19in) s.d.1924 i. verso panel. 9-Oct-2 Michael Zeller, Lindau #750/R est:2500
£5844 $8708 €9000 Procession of young women and nuns (135x135cm-53x53in) s.d.1923 lit. 26-Jun-2 Neumeister, Munich #769/R est:3000

KALMYKOW, Grigory Odissejewitsch (1873-1942) Russian
£285 $444 €450 Moonlit night on lower Don (38x28cm-15x11in) s. board. 14-Sep-2 Weidler, Nurnberg #317/R
£7500 $11774 €11250 View of Kara Bay at sunset (33x50cm-13x20in) 20-Nov-2 Sotheby's, London #27/R est:8000-12000
£20000 $31400 €30000 The Black Sea coast by moonlight (83x121cm-33x48in) s. 20-Nov-2 Sotheby's, London #60/R est:22000-28000

KALO, E B (jnr) (?) American
£577 $900 €866 Impressionist landscape of hazy morning (51x41cm-20x16in) s. board. 18-Sep-2 Alderfer's, Hatfield #280/R

KALOGEROPOULOS, Leon (1928-) Greek
£2000 $3140 €3000 Elli (42x51cm-17x20in) s. canvas on board. 16-Dec-2 Sotheby's, Olympia #187/R est:2500-3500

KALTENMOSER, Karl (1853-1923) German
£316 $491 €500 Summer landscape (78x113cm-31x44in) s. 26-Sep-2 Neumeister, Munich #2750/R
£382 $596 €600 Landscape with lakeside village (60x90cm-24x35in) s. board. 6-Nov-2 Hugo Ruef, Munich #1165/R
£510 $795 €800 Farmstead on moorland (60x90cm-24x35in) s. board. 6-Nov-2 Hugo Ruef, Munich #1166

KALTENMOSER, Kaspar (1806-1867) German
£1878 $3080 €2723 Mother and child on terrace in Istria (29x23cm-11x9in) s.d.1866 panel prov. 4-Jun-3 Fischer, Luzern #1125/R est:6000-9000 (S.FR 4000)
£4255 $6723 €6383 Interior scene with grandfather playing violin and children dancing (68x96cm-27x38in) s.d.1864. 2-Dec-2 Rasmussen, Copenhagen #1720/R est:50000 (D.KR 50000)

KALTENMOSER, Max (1842-1887) German
£1879 $3026 €2800 Portrait of Maria Mancini (50x41cm-20x16in) s.i.verso prov. 18-Feb-3 Sotheby's, Amsterdam #853/R est:1200-1800

KALVODA, Alois (1875-1934) Czechoslovakian
£330 $522 €495 Lilacs (20x29cm-8x11in) s. cardboard. 30-Nov-2 Dorotheum, Prague #42 (C.KR 16000)
£590 $950 €885 River landscape with houses in distance (48x69cm-19x27in) s. fiberboard. 22-Feb-3 Brunk, Ashville #479/R
£817 $1324 €1226 Late winter landscape (36x50cm-14x20in) s. board. 24-May-3 Dorotheum, Prague #62/R est:30000-45000 (C.KR 36000)
£826 $1289 €1239 Landscape with fields (44x43cm-17x17in) s. 12-Oct-2 Dorotheum, Prague #47/R (C.KR 40000)

KAMEKE, Egon von (1881-1955) German
£705 $1093 €1100 Autumn day on Rugen (41x55cm-16x22in) prov. 4-Dec-2 Lempertz, Koln #798/R

KAMEKE, Otto von (1826-1899) German
£506 $800 €800 Coastal landscape in Swiss Alps, with figures (16x24cm-6x9in) s. board. 29-Nov-2 Bolland & Marotz, Bremen #718/R

KAMENEFF, Ljeff (1833-1886) Russian
£17123 $26712 €25000 Fishermen on the Volga by moonlight (57x92cm-22x36in) s.d.1863. 10-Apr-3 Van Ham, Cologne #1518/R est:12000

KAMIHIRA, Ben (1925-) American
£1078 $1800 €1563 Seated woman by a table (61x46cm-24x18in) s.d.1962 verso. 22-Jun-3 Freeman, Philadelphia #164/R est:1000-1500
£1484 $2300 €2226 Card players (61x89cm-24x35in) s. 8-Dec-2 Freeman, Philadelphia #150/R est:2500-4000

KAMIR-KAUFMAN, Léon (1872-1933) Polish
£1224 $1947 €1800 Paysage lacustre (32x41cm-13x16in) s.d. panel. 3-Mar-3 Claude Boisgirard, Paris #54 est:1100-1300

KAMKE, Ivar (1882-1936) Swedish
£305 $473 €458 Southern street scene, Sicily (66x51cm-26x20in) s.d.1933 prov. 8-Dec-2 Uppsala Auktionskammare, Uppsala #129 (S.KR 4300)
£3546 $5496 €5319 Models by water (50x61cm-20x24in) s. 4-Dec-2 AB Stockholms Auktionsverk #1793/R est:25000-30000 (S.KR 50000)

KAMLAH, Hans (1861-1908) German
£412 $626 €618 Landscape with farm (53x84cm-21x33in) s. 16-Aug-2 Lilla Bukowskis, Stockholm #257 (S.KR 6000)

KAMLANDER, Franz (1920-) Austrian
Works on paper
£309 $500 €464 Untitled - cow (15x21cm-6x8in) graphite col pencil prov. 27-Jan-3 Christie's, Rockefeller NY #116/R

KAMM, John Daniel (1702-?) British
Miniatures
£2200 $3454 €3300 Prince Charles Edward Stewart (6cm-2xin) s.d.1750 verso vellum. 10-Dec-2 Christie's, London #52/R est:1000-1500

KAMMERER, Robert (1870-1950) German
Works on paper
£326 $535 €450 Old school in Berlin - Zehlendorf (32x41cm-13x16in) s.d.1919 gouache board. 31-May-3 Villa Grisebach, Berlin #582/R

KAMPER, Anna (?) Dutch?
£2800 $4564 €4200 Venus and Adonis (114x97cm-45x38in) s.i.verso after Pieter Pauwel Rubens. 13-Feb-3 Christie's, Kensington #29/R est:1200-1800

KAMPF, Arthur (1864-1950) German
£417 $654 €650 Man wearing red coat (63x48cm-25x19in) s. 21-Nov-2 Van Ham, Cologne #1708
Works on paper
£255 $397 €400 Fisherwomen on beach (47x62cm-19x24in) s. chk. 6-Nov-2 Hugo Ruef, Munich #1389/R

KAMPF, Arthur (attrib) (1864-1950) German
£314 $491 €500 Circus act (42x35cm-17x14in) 23-Sep-2 Dr Fritz Nagel, Stuttgart #6986/R

KAMPF, Eugen (1861-1933) German
£573 $894 €900 Northern German landscape with windmill (50x32cm-20x13in) s. 6-Nov-2 Hugo Ruef, Munich #1167/R
£1096 $1710 €1600 Fishermen with ships in harbour (47x60cm-19x24in) s. 10-Apr-3 Van Ham, Cologne #1522/R est:1400
£1815 $2832 €2650 Extensive landscape on the lower Rhine with sheep by farmstead (52x34cm-20x13in) s.d.92. 10-Apr-3 Van Ham, Cologne #1521/R est:2300

KAMPF, Max (1912-1982) Swiss
£262 $411 €393 Untitled (28x21cm-11x8in) s.d.1965 oil chk. 25-Nov-2 Germann, Zurich #755 (S.FR 600)
£563 $924 €816 Landscape (26x26cm-10x10in) s. board. 4-Jun-3 Fischer, Luzern #2198/R (S.FR 1200)
£833 $1342 €1208 In refuge cellar (28x37cm-11x15in) s. board exhib.lit. 9-May-3 Dobiaschofsky, Bern #195/R (S.FR 1800)
£926 $1491 €1343 Indian (38x26cm-15x10in) s.d.77 i.verso board. 9-May-3 Dobiaschofsky, Bern #194/R (S.FR 2000)
£1157 $1863 €1678 Self portrait (49x44cm-19x17in) s. board exhib.lit. 9-May-3 Dobiaschofsky, Bern #196/R est:3500 (S.FR 2500)

KAMPLE, Peter (1934-) ?
£440 $687 €700 Composition a la pyramide (130x100cm-51x39in) s.d.1974. 8-Oct-2 Christie's, Paris #165/R

KAMPMAN, Jack (1914-1989) Danish
£279 $441 €419 Houses in hilly landscape, Faroe Islands (50x60cm-20x24in) s. 1-Apr-3 Rasmussen, Copenhagen #622 (D.KR 3000)
£299 $475 €449 Parish near the sea, Faroe Islands (38x46cm-15x18in) s. 29-Apr-3 Kunsthallen, Copenhagen #273 (D.KR 3200)
£300 $468 €450 Mother-Daughter (89x120cm-35x47in) s.d.64. 11-Nov-2 Rasmussen, Vejle #36 (D.KR 3500)
£320 $509 €480 Rural district by the sea, Faroe Islands (33x41cm-13x16in) s. 26-Feb-3 Kunsthallen, Copenhagen #308 (D.KR 3500)
£325 $514 €488 Houses by the sea (32x41cm-13x16in) s. 1-Apr-3 Rasmussen, Copenhagen #558 (D.KR 3500)
£325 $514 €488 Houses, Faroe Islands (33x41cm-13x16in) s. 1-Apr-3 Rasmussen, Copenhagen #557 (D.KR 3500)
£340 $538 €510 Rural area by water, Faroe Islands (64x80cm-25x31in) s. 27-Nov-2 Museumsbygningen, Copenhagen #672 (D.KR 4000)
£347 $552 €521 Rural district, Faroe Islands (33x41cm-13x16in) s. 26-Feb-3 Kunsthallen, Copenhagen #307 (D.KR 3800)
£428 $681 €642 Houses by the sea (39x46cm-15x18in) s. 10-Mar-3 Rasmussen, Vejle #601 (D.KR 4600)
£446 $705 €669 Houses by fjord (38x46cm-15x18in) s. 1-Apr-3 Rasmussen, Copenhagen #653 (D.KR 4800)
£508 $787 €762 Figures and houses by the sea (54x65cm-21x26in) s. 1-Oct-2 Rasmussen, Copenhagen #269 (D.KR 6000)
£1022 $1615 €1533 View of village by the sea, Faroe Islands (67x81cm-26x32in) s. painted c.1958. 1-Apr-3 Rasmussen, Copenhagen #572/R (D.KR 11000)

KAMPMANN, Utz (20th C) Swiss
Sculpture
£2201 $3390 €3500 Farbobjekt. s.d.1966 num.66/42 assemblage. 22-Oct-2 Campo, Vlaamse Kaai #541

KAMPPURI, Vaino (1891-1972) Finnish
£476 $757 €700 Village (32x37cm-13x15in) s. 24-Mar-3 Bukowskis, Helsinki #115/R
£483 $763 €700 Winter (30x40cm-12x16in) indis.sig. i. 3-Apr-3 Hagelstam, Helsinki #808
£544 $865 €800 Bridge (38x47cm-15x19in) i.verso. 24-Mar-3 Bukowskis, Helsinki #117/R
£552 $872 €800 Cottage (31x38cm-12x15in) s.d.1924. 3-Apr-3 Hagelstam, Helsinki #804/R
£634 $1020 €900 Still life of fish in a dish (46x38cm-18x15in) s.d.1927 board. 10-May-3 Bukowskis, Helsinki #140/R
£935 $1496 €1300 Still life of fruit and potted plant (46x42cm-18x17in) s.d.1925 board. 17-May-3 Hagelstam, Helsinki #141/R
£949 $1500 €1500 Cottage (38x46cm-15x18in) s. board. 30-Nov-2 Hagelstam, Helsinki #140/R est:2000
£1203 $1876 €1900 House by river (41x49cm-16x19in) s.d.35. 15-Sep-2 Bukowskis, Helsinki #211/R est:1500
£1582 $2500 €2500 Still life of flowers and fruit (63x79cm-25x31in) s. board exhib. 30-Nov-2 Hagelstam, Helsinki #139/R est:2000
£1830 $3001 €2800 Reading by the river (46x38cm-18x15in) s. 9-Feb-3 Bukowskis, Helsinki #271/R est:2000

KAMPS, Heinrich (1896-1954) German
£319 $517 €450 Fruit bowl against ornamental background (93x74cm-37x29in) mono. tempera paper lit. 24-May-3 Van Ham, Cologne #303/R

KAMROWSKI, Gerome (1914-) American
£2603 $4086 €3800 Preliminary growth (29x42cm-11x17in) s. i.verso exhib. 15-Apr-3 Laurence Calmels, Paris #4322/R est:6000
£5137 $8065 €7500 Female constellation (50x61cm-20x24in) s. i.verso oil mixed media exhib. 15-Apr-3 Laurence Calmels, Paris #4321/R est:6000

KANAGA, Consuelo (1894-1978) American?
Photographs
£2195 $3600 €3293 Portrait of Alice Rohrer (25x19cm-10x7in) s. silver print exec.c.1930. 10-Feb-3 Swann Galleries, New York #45/R est:4000-5000
£2215 $3500 €3323 Alice Rohrer (24x19cm-9x7in) s. gelatin silver print prov.exhib. 24-Apr-3 Phillips, New York #108/R est:4000-6000
£4545 $7000 €6818 She is a tree of life (34x26cm-13x10in) i.verso photograph lit. 22-Oct-2 Sotheby's, New York #194/R est:5000-8000

KANDELIN, Ole (1920-1947) Finnish
£1871 $2993 €2600 The red executioner (76x56cm-30x22in) s.d.1944 board exhib. 17-May-3 Hagelstam, Helsinki #198/R est:2800
Works on paper
£759 $1200 €1200 Abstract model (30x23cm-12x9in) s.d.46 pastel. 1-Dec-2 Bukowskis, Helsinki #324/R
£1266 $2000 €2000 The cyclist (23x30cm-9x12in) s.d.46 pastel. 1-Dec-2 Bukowskis, Helsinki #325/R est:1000-1300

KANDINSKY, Wassily (1866-1944) Russian
£70000 $114800 €105000 Waldrand (24x33cm-9x13in) canvas on board painted c.1903 prov.exhib.lit. 4-Feb-3 Christie's, London #265/R est:120000
£124224 $200000 €186336 Park von St. Cloud (24x33cm-9x13in) i.d.1906 verso board prov.exhib.lit. 8-May-3 Christie's, Rockefeller NY #174/R est:200000-300000
£128205 $198718 €200000 Kallmunz (24x33cm-9x13in) i.verso painted 1903 prov.exhib. 6-Dec-2 Ketterer, Munich #19/R est:200000-300000
£169811 $264906 €270000 Landschaft mit rosa wolke - Landscape with pink cloud (33x44cm-13x17in) s. s.i.verso board painted 1908 prov.lit. 8-Oct-2 Sotheby's, London #8/R est:300000-400000
£169811 $264906 €270000 Schweben uber fest - Hovering above firm (42x57cm-17x22in) mono.d.29 mono.d.verso board prov.exhib.lit. 8-Oct-2 Sotheby's, London #27/R est:300000-400000
£264151 $412075 €420000 Reiter und apfelpfluckern - Rider and woman picking apples (19x20cm-7x8in) oil on glass painted 1911 prov.exhib.lit. 8-Oct-2 Sotheby's, London #2/R est:180000-250000
£314465 $490566 €500000 Voisinage (60x92cm-24x36in) mono.d.39 mono.d.verso prov.exhib.lit. 8-Oct-2 Sotheby's, London #24/R est:450000-550000
Prints
£2390 $3728 €3800 Erste radierung fur die editions cahiers d'art (28x23cm-11x9in) s. drypoint. 9-Oct-2 Sotheby's, London #454/R est:4500-6500
£2577 $4200 €3866 Kleine welten IV (27x26cm-11x10in) s. col lithograph exec.1922. 13-Feb-3 Christie's, Rockefeller NY #74/R
£2885 $4500 €4328 Kleine Welten IX (30x27cm-12x11in) s. drypoint edition of 200. 5-Nov-2 Christie's, Rockefeller NY #166/R est:5000-7000
£3269 $5067 €5100 Bauhaus friends circle (20x24cm-8x9in) s.mono.d.32 drypoint etching prov. 7-Dec-2 Ketterer, Hamburg #211/R est:5000-7000
£3774 $6000 €5661 Kleine welten VIII (27x23cm-11x9in) s. woodcut edition of 200. 29-Apr-3 Christie's, Rockefeller NY #479/R est:5000-7000
£4500 $7425 €6525 Kleine welten V (31x23cm-12x9in) s. col woodcut. 2-Jul-3 Christie's, London #264/R est:5000-7000
£4717 $7500 €7076 Kleine welten III (27x23cm-11x9in) s. col lithograph edition of 200. 2-May-3 Sotheby's, New York #188/R est:10000-15000
£5128 $8000 €7692 Kleine Welten VI (35x31cm-14x12in) s. woodcut edition of 200. 5-Nov-2 Christie's, Rockefeller NY #165/R est:8000-12000
£5660 $9000 €8490 Kleine welten IV (27x56cm-11x22in) s. col lithograph edition of 200. 29-Apr-3 Christie's, Rockefeller NY #478/R est:9000-12000
£6500 $10075 €9750 Lithograph fur die vierte bauhausmappe (26x24cm-10x9in) s. col lithograph. 5-Dec-2 Sotheby's, London #139/R est:2500-3000
£6962 $11000 €11000 Blue lithograph (21x15cm-8x6in) s. col lithograph. 30-Nov-2 Villa Grisebach, Berlin #261/R est:5000-6000
£7292 $11521 €10500 Composition (30x24cm-12x9in) s. wood engraving. 26-Apr-3 Cornette de St.Cyr, Paris #16/R est:7000-8000
£8200 $12710 €12300 Lithographie no.1 (34x22cm-13x9in) s.d.1925 lithograph. 5-Dec-2 Sotheby's, London #137/R est:3500-4500
£8200 $12710 €12300 Lithograph no.II (35x19cm-14x7in) s.d.1925 num.44/50 lithograph. 5-Dec-2 Sotheby's, London #138/R est:3500-4500
£9500 $15675 €13775 Kleine welten IV (27x26cm-11x10in) s. col lithograph edition of 200. 1-Jul-3 Sotheby's, London #86/R est:6000-8000
£10897 $17000 €16346 Lithographie fur die Vierte Bauhausmappe (27x24cm-11x9in) s. col lithograph edition of 100. 7-Nov-2 Swann Galleries, New York #658/R est:20000-30000
£18310 $30394 €26000 Autumn (23x19cm-9x7in) s.i. col woodcut. 14-Jun-3 Hauswedell & Nolte, Hamburg #1271/R est:25000
£20126 $31396 €32000 Violett (34x27cm-13x11in) s.num.woii/50 col lithograph. 9-Oct-2 Sotheby's, London #451/R est:23000-30000

£20183 $33706 €29265 Kandinsky. Tone (28x28cm-11x11in) s.i. woodcut. 20-Jun-3 Kornfeld, Bern #76/R est:50000 (S.FR 44000)
£23188 $38029 €32000 Merry ascent (24x19cm-9x7in) s. i. verso col lithograph W/C. 29-May-3 Lempertz, Koln #689/R est:20000-25000
£44872 $69551 €70000 Levee de la lune (25x15cm-10x6in) s.i. col woodcut. 7-Dec-2 Hauswedell & Nolte, Hamburg #768/R est:80000

Works on paper

£10870 $16848 €16305 Composition (18x27cm-7x11in) mono.d.K41 pen exhib. 4-Dec-2 Koller, Zurich #121/R est:25000-40000 (S.FR 25000)
£13208 $20604 €21000 Ohne titel - Untitled (21x18cm-8x7in) mono.i.d.34 brush ink card prov.exhib. 9-Oct-2 Sotheby's, London #111/R est:30000-40000
£15101 $24312 €22500 Dessin 6 (37x30cm-15x12in) s.d.27 ink W/C prov. 23-Feb-3 Mercier & Cie, Lille #58/R est:30000
£21384 $33358 €34000 Untitled (17x16cm-7x6in) mono.i.d.1931 pen brush prov.exhib. 9-Oct-2 Sotheby's, London #112/R est:30000-40000
£25157 $39245 €40000 Zeichnung fur improvisation mit rot blauem ring - Improvisation with red and blue ring (33x21cm-13x8in) mono. pen brush ink executed 1913 prov.exhib.lit. 9-Oct-2 Sotheby's, London #106/R est:45000-65000
£30496 $47270 €45744 Composition (25x19cm-10x7in) mono.d.16 ink. 3-Dec-2 Bukowskis, Stockholm #193/R est:350000-400000 (S.KR 430000)
£100000 $167000 €150000 Komposition mit weissen formen (32x50cm-13x20in) mono.d.40 st.d.verso gouache prov.lit. 26-Jun-3 Christie's, London #414/R est:80000-120000
£157233 $245283 €250000 Haftend - Adhering (48x32cm-19x13in) mono.d.27 i.num.222.d. verso W/C gouache Indian ink prov.exhib.lit. 8-Oct-2 Sotheby's, London #20/R est:280000-350000
£157233 $245283 €250000 Braun um bunt - Brown around colourful (48x32cm-19x13in) mono.d.27 i.d.verso W/C gouache prov.exhib.lit. 8-Oct-2 Sotheby's, London #26/R est:280000-350000
£628931 $981132 €1000000 Schwarzes dreieck - Black triangle (30x40cm-12x16in) mono.d.23 mono.i.d.verso W/C pen Indian ink prov.exhib.lit. 8-Oct-2 Sotheby's, London #9/R est:800000-1000000

KANDIS, Chris (1966-) Australian

Works on paper

£286 $443 €429 Sydney harbour (59x100cm-23x39in) W/C. 29-Oct-2 Lawson Menzies, Sydney #367 (A.D 800)

KANDLER, Ludwig (1856-1927) German

£380 $593 €570 Lady playing a musical instrument in a landscape (140x99cm-55x39in) s. 8-Oct-2 Bonhams, Knightsbridge #248/R

KANE, Bob (1937-) American

Works on paper

£2070 $3250 €3105 Batman (102x76cm-40x30in) s.i.d.1973 black marker col chk board. 10-Dec-2 Doyle, New York #162/R est:4000-6000

KANE, Gil (20th C) American

Works on paper

£271 $425 €407 Lone Ranger and Tonto (36x51cm-14x20in) dr. 21-Nov-2 Shelley, Hendersonville #1188/R

KANE, John (1860-1934) American

£2800 $4340 €4200 English gothic - The Deviant (218x154cm-86x61in) s.i. s.i.d.1988 verso canvas on newspaper prov. 3-Dec-2 Bonhams, New Bond Street #123/R est:1000-1500

KANE, Paul (1810-1871) Canadian

£883534 $1395983 €1325301 Portrait of Maungwudaus (76x64cm-30x25in) d.1851. 1-Dec-2 Levis, Calgary #51/R est:2800000-3000000 (C.D 2200000)

KANELBA, Raymond (1897-1960) Polish

£1667 $2617 €2600 Peniche au bord de riviere (81x65cm-32x26in) s.d.1932 verso. 12-Dec-2 Rabourdin & Choppin de Janvry, Paris #64/R
£2270 $3790 €3200 Jeune fille au foulard (40x30cm-16x12in) s. 17-Jun-3 Claude Boisgirard, Paris #69/R est:3000-3500
£2270 $3790 €3200 Jeune garcon en bleu (33x24cm-13x9in) s.d. 17-Jun-3 Claude Boisgirard, Paris #70/R est:3000-3500
£2436 $3824 €3800 Nature morte a la lampe a petrole (91x57cm-36x22in) s.d.1929 verso. 12-Dec-2 Rabourdin & Choppin de Janvry, Paris #59
£2692 $4227 €4200 Fillette regardant dans un miroir (92x65cm-36x26in) s.d.1929 verso. 12-Dec-2 Rabourdin & Choppin de Janvry, Paris #21/R
£2878 $4719 €4000 La bretonne (61x38cm-24x15in) s. 3-Jun-3 Tajan, Paris #37 est:1000-1200
£4388 $7197 €6100 Scene a la campagne (50x65cm-20x26in) s.d.1958 verso. 3-Jun-3 Tajan, Paris #38 est:1000-1500

KANELLIS, Orestis (1910-1979) Greek

£3000 $4740 €4500 Girl sitting on the stairs (81x60cm-32x24in) painted 1954. 1-Apr-3 Bonhams, New Bond Street #71 est:3000-5000
£3000 $4740 €4500 In the foliage (97x130cm-38x51in) 1-Apr-3 Bonhams, New Bond Street #93 est:2000-3000

KANER, Sam (20th C) Danish?

£258 $401 €387 Mene Mene Tekel - our children's heritage (70x85cm-28x33in) s.d.67. 4-Dec-2 Kunsthallen, Copenhagen #242 (D.KR 3000)

KANERVA, Aino (1909-1991) Finnish

£392 $643 €600 Landscape with mountain (37x48cm-15x19in) s.d.48. 9-Feb-3 Bukowskis, Helsinki #272/R

Works on paper

£377 $581 €600 Bog-myrtle (37x56cm-15x22in) s.d.56 W/C. 27-Oct-2 Bukowskis, Helsinki #206/R
£377 $581 €600 Vuokatti (31x46cm-12x18in) s.d.49 W/C. 27-Oct-2 Bukowskis, Helsinki #207/R
£432 $708 €600 Pine tree (36x44cm-14x17in) s.d.1952 mixed media. 5-Jun-3 Hagelstam, Helsinki #912
£440 $678 €700 Flowers (50x66cm-20x26in) s.d.1974 W/C. 24-Oct-2 Hagelstam, Helsinki #867/R
£506 $800 €800 Lappviken, Helsinki (35x47cm-14x19in) s.d.48 W/C. 1-Dec-2 Bukowskis, Helsinki #77/R
£586 $926 €850 Bog myrtle (37x46cm-15x18in) s.d.1956 W/C. 3-Apr-3 Hagelstam, Helsinki #888/R
£786 $1219 €1250 Vetch (65x50cm-26x20in) s.d.76 W/C. 6-Oct-2 Bukowskis, Helsinki #202/R
£1392 $2200 €2200 Bog-myrtle (64x48cm-25x19in) s.d.23.6.78 W/C. 1-Dec-2 Bukowskis, Helsinki #76/R est:1000-1200

KANGRA SCHOOL (19th C) Indian

£7692 $12000 €11538 Scene from the Ramayana, battle between Rama's Allies and the Demon Army (20x30cm-8x12in) 27-Mar-3 Christie's, Rockefeller NY #215/R est:15000-20000

KANNEMANS, Christian Cornelis (1812-1884) Dutch

£2229 $3433 €3500 Sailing vessels near harbour entrance at dusk (37x50cm-15x20in) s.d.1854 panel. 3-Sep-2 Christie's, Amsterdam #300/R est:4000-6000
£2278 $3600 €3600 Paysage cotier par un temps orageux (33x44cm-13x17in) s. panel. 26-Nov-2 Palais de Beaux Arts, Brussels #194/R est:3500-5000
£4795 $7527 €7000 Boat trip (66x91cm-26x36in) s. 15-Apr-3 Sotheby's, Amsterdam #15/R est:8000-12000
£4861 $7729 €7000 Tallship on choppy water by a lighthouse (33x44cm-13x17in) s.d.1856 panel. 29-Apr-3 Christie's, Amsterdam #54/R est:6000-8000
£5000 $7850 €7500 Shipping off the coast (92x124cm-36x49in) s.d.1847. 16-Dec-2 Sotheby's, Olympia #80/R est:4000-6000
£5660 $8717 €9000 Shipping off the coast (57x74cm-22x29in) s. 22-Oct-2 Sotheby's, Amsterdam #155/R est:10000-15000

KANNIK, Frans (1949-) Danish

£297 $481 €431 Erotic figure composition (115x90cm-45x35in) s.d.1999. 24-May-3 Rasmussen, Havnen #4258/R (D.KR 3100)
£431 $698 €625 Erotic figure composition (90x115cm-35x45in) s.d.1999. 24-May-3 Rasmussen, Havnen #4257/R (D.KR 4500)
£1866 $2966 €2799 Figure composition (142x175cm-56x69in) s.d.1986 oil mixed media canvas. 29-Apr-3 Kunsthallen, Copenhagen #173/R est:25000 (D.KR 20000)

KANO SCHOOL (17th C) Japanese

Works on paper

£23899 $38000 €35849 Farming in the four seasons (145x35cm-57x14in) ink col six-panel screens pair. 24-Mar-3 Christie's, Rockefeller NY #80/R est:10000-15000
£88050 $140000 €132075 Horses in stables in spring and autumn (150x34cm-59x13in) ink col gold gold leaf six-panel screens pair. 24-Mar-3 Christie's, Rockefeller NY #79/R est:60000-80000

KANOLDT, Alexander (1881-1939) German

£26000 $40560 €39000 Stilleben VII - Still life VII (90x70cm-35x28in) s. s.i.d.1926 verso prov. 9-Oct-2 Sotheby's, London #41/R est:25000-35000

Works on paper

£641 $994 €1000 Red poppies (39x29cm-15x11in) s.d.20 W/C htd white lit. 6-Dec-2 Karlheinz Kaupp, Staufen #2314/R
£1250 $1975 €1800 Chiemsee landscape in winter (47x62cm-19x24in) s. W/C. 26-Apr-3 Dr Lehr, Berlin #261/R est:2500

KANOLDT, Edmund (1845-1904) German
Works on paper
£404 $630 €590 Hoffmann house in Bacharach (33x23cm-13x9in) mono.i.d.18.Septb.91 pencil. 11-Apr-3 Winterberg, Heidelberg #421/R

KANONY, Marie (20th C) French
Works on paper
£8278 $13493 €12500 Composition (146x114cm-57x45in) s.d.2000 verso mixed media canvas. 1-Feb-3 Claude Aguttes, Neuilly #176/R est:13000-14000
£9936 $15401 €15500 Untitled (190x175cm-75x69in) s. d.2000 verso mixed media on canvas prov.exhib. 7-Dec-2 Cornette de St.Cyr, Paris #132/R est:15000-20000

KANTERS, Hans (20th C) ?
£1603 $2484 €2500 Fantasy figures (39x60cm-15x24in) s. board. 3-Dec-2 Christie's, Amsterdam #174/R est:1500-2000
£3205 $5032 €5000 Upside down (32x52cm-13x20in) s.d.80 i.verso panel. 25-Nov-2 Glerum, Amsterdam #268/R est:5000-7000
£4103 $6441 €6400 Remorse (43x36cm-17x14in) s.d.81 i.verso panel lit. 25-Nov-2 Glerum, Amsterdam #266/R est:5000-7000

KANTOR, Morris (1896-1974) American
Works on paper
£366 $600 €531 Untitled abstraction (25x18cm-10x7in) s.d.22 pencil. 1-Jun-3 Wright, Chicago #152/R

KANTOR, Tadeus (1915-1990) Polish
£5532 $8574 €8298 Peinture - composition (82x100cm-32x39in) s. s.d.24/12/64 verso. 8-Dec-2 Uppsala Auktionskammare, Uppsala #251/R est:8000-10000 (S.KR 78000)

KAPELLER, Jean Joseph (1702-1790) French
Works on paper
£1266 $2000 €2000 Vue de port anime (21x32cm-8x13in) s.d.1779 verso gouache. 28-Nov-2 Tajan, Paris #57/R est:1000

KAPFHAMMER, Adolf (1867-c.1911) German
£269 $423 €420 Autumn day in the Alps (81x101cm-32x40in) s. 23-Nov-2 Arnold, Frankfurt #775

KAPINSKI, Alfons (1875-?) ?
£1200 $1944 €1800 Peonies in a yellow vase (80x70cm-31x28in) s. 23-Jan-3 Christie's, Kensington #190/R est:1000-1500

KAPLAN, Anatoli (1903-) Israeli/Russian
Works on paper
£311 $507 €470 Marriage (23x16cm-9x6in) s. gouache. 3-Feb-3 Cornette de St.Cyr, Paris #444

KAPLAN, Hubert (1940-) German
£685 $1068 €1000 Ducks in water (9x12cm-4x5in) s. panel. 9-Apr-3 Neumeister, Munich #692
£828 $1275 €1300 Winter landscape with farmstead and figures (13x18cm-5x7in) s. panel. 5-Sep-2 Arnold, Frankfurt #795/R
£955 $1490 €1500 Poultry under an elder bush with village in background (9x12cm-4x5in) s. panel. 7-Nov-2 Allgauer, Kempten #2848/R est:1500
£1056 $1701 €1500 Fish market on North Sea beach (15x30cm-6x12in) s. panel. 10-May-3 Hans Stahl, Toestorf #7/R est:2500
£1197 $1927 €1700 Winter landscape in evening sunshine (24x30cm-9x12in) s. panel. 10-May-3 Hans Stahl, Toestorf #8/R est:2500
£1223 $1907 €1835 Bavarian market scene (18x24cm-7x9in) s. canvas on panel prov. 9-Nov-2 Galerie Gloggner, Luzern #90/R est:3500-4000 (S.FR 2800)
£1301 $2030 €1900 Herder with cattle watering (20x40cm-8x16in) s.d.79 panel. 9-Apr-3 Neumeister, Munich #689/R est:900
£1507 $2351 €2200 Chiemsee in summer (15x30cm-6x12in) s. panel. 9-Apr-3 Neumeister, Munich #691/R est:1500
£1644 $2564 €2400 Horses in the paddock with Lower Alpine landscape in the distance (9x12cm-4x5in) s. canvas on panel lit. 10-Apr-3 Allgauer, Kempten #2824/R est:1600
£1747 $2725 €2621 Country market in winter (20x40cm-8x16in) s. canvas on panel prov. 9-Nov-2 Galerie Gloggner, Luzern #91/R est:4800-5500 (S.FR 4000)
£1923 $2923 €3000 Watermill with animals and figures and a view of a village (24x30cm-9x12in) s. canvas on panel lit. 11-Jul-2 Allgauer, Kempten #2536/R
£2260 $3526 €3300 Wood transport in winter (15x30cm-6x12in) s. panel. 9-Apr-3 Neumeister, Munich #690/R est:1200
£2564 $3897 €4000 View of a village with poultry and peacock at a pond (15x20cm-6x8in) s. canvas on panel. 11-Jul-2 Allgauer, Kempten #2538/R est:5000
£2721 $4327 €4000 Lively street in Garmisch in the spring (24x30cm-9x12in) s. panel. 20-Mar-3 Neumeister, Munich #2656/R est:2000
£3899 $6083 €6200 Alpine village with smithy and tavern (40x50cm-16x20in) s. 11-Oct-2 Winterberg, Heidelberg #1320/R est:6800

KAPOOR, Anish (1954-) British/Indian
Sculpture
£25000 $40000 €37500 Pot is gold (41x51x38cm-16x20x15in) pigment sculpture executed 1985 prov. 14-May-3 Sotheby's, New York #354/R est:35000-45000

Works on paper
£3200 $5248 €4800 Untitled (45x60cm-18x24in) s.d.1989 verso gouache pencil prov. 7-Feb-3 Sotheby's, London #282/R est:3000-4000
£4747 $7500 €7500 Untitled (57x76cm-22x30in) sand pigment executed 1987 prov. 26-Nov-2 Sotheby's, Amsterdam #272/R est:3000-4000
£6329 $10000 €9494 Untitled, AK21 (79x56cm-31x22in) gouache gesso pigment exec.1986 prov. 13-Nov-2 Sotheby's, New York #597/R est:8000-12000

KAPP, Edmond Xavier (1890-1978) British
£290 $447 €435 Still life of tulips and fruit (73x49cm-29x19in) s.d.54. 23-Oct-2 Hampton & Littlewood, Exeter #454
Works on paper
£340 $537 €493 Pianist at a concert grand piano (30x46cm-12x18in) s.d.57 mixed media. 22-Jul-3 Gorringes, Lewes #1586

KAPP, Gary (1942-) American
£6164 $9000 €9246 Nez Perce sunset (76x102cm-30x40in) 18-May-2 Altermann Galleries, Santa Fe #72/R

KAPPES, Alfred (1850-1894) American
£562 $900 €815 Clearing sand (35x50cm-14x20in) bears sig.verso. 16-May-3 Skinner, Boston #213/R

KAPPES, Karl (1861-1943) American
£390 $600 €585 Cavalier (81x66cm-32x26in) s. 8-Sep-2 DeFina, Austinburg #380a

KAPPIS, Albert (1836-1914) German
£308 $483 €480 Old oak in wood (42x27cm-17x11in) i. st.sig. verso paper on board. 21-Nov-2 Van Ham, Cologne #1711/R
£513 $805 €800 Pigs and poultry outside farmstead (21x31cm-8x12in) s. 21-Nov-2 Van Ham, Cologne #1710
£617 $919 €950 Evening landscape with haystacks (18x41cm-7x16in) s. canvas on board. 28-Jun-2 Sigalas, Stuttgart #816/R
£701 $1100 €1052 In the hay fields (43x61cm-17x24in) init. 10-Dec-2 Doyle, New York #178/R est:2000-3000
£755 $1177 €1200 Landscape (18x41cm-7x16in) s. canvas on board. 19-Sep-2 Dr Fritz Nagel, Stuttgart #951/R
£3526 $5571 €5500 Corn harvest (20x34cm-8x13in) s. panel. 16-Nov-2 Lempertz, Koln #1495/R est:3000
£10968 $16123 €17000 Bodensee shore (105x95cm-41x37in) s. 20-Jun-2 Dr Fritz Nagel, Stuttgart #778/R est:11000

KAPPIS, Albert (attrib) (1836-1914) German
£483 $768 €700 Fisherman with nets at shore (32x48cm-13x19in) board. 8-Mar-3 Arnold, Frankfurt #618/R

KAPRIELIAN, Yetvart (1959-) French
£769 $1200 €1154 Pont Croix le Halage (61x74cm-24x29in) s. 9-Oct-2 Doyle, New York #61
£1026 $1600 €1539 Port de Trouville (74x91cm-29x36in) s. i.verso. 9-Oct-2 Doyle, New York #62 est:2500-3000
£1076 $1700 €1614 Canal de Moret sur Loing (61x74cm-24x29in) s. s.i.verso. 2-Apr-3 Doyle, New York #44/R est:1200-1800

KAPUSTIN, Grigory (1865-1925) Russian
£10443 $16500 €16500 Beach at night (75x151cm-30x59in) s. 1-Dec-2 Bukowskis, Helsinki #254/R est:2000-3000

KARAKA, Emily (1952-) New Zealander
£281 $446 €422 Giraffes (85x62cm-33x24in) s. board. 25-Feb-3 Peter Webb, Auckland #185 (NZ.D 800)

KARAS, Alexander (20th C) Russian
£2100 $3276 €3150 Summer Idyll (65x53cm-26x21in) s. 6-Nov-2 Bonhams, Chester #505/R est:1200-1600

KARAS, Michael B (20th C) American
£353 $550 €530 11th hole, Doylestown Country Club (36x61cm-14x24in) s.d.78. 18-Sep-2 Alderfer's, Hatfield #347/R

KARASIN, Nikolai (1842-1908) Russian
Works on paper
£1013 $1600 €1600 Cossack (30x40cm-12x16in) s.d.1895 Indian ink. 1-Dec-2 Bukowskis, Helsinki #255/R est:1000-1500
£1100 $1738 €1650 Siam strand at a Palace exhibition (44x32cm-17x13in) s.d.93 gouache W/C panel on cardboard. 26-Nov-2 Christie's, Kensington #35/R est:700-900

KARCHER, Amalie (19th C) German
£1795 $2818 €2800 Still life of fruit (28x34cm-11x13in) s.d.1869. 21-Nov-2 Van Ham, Cologne #1707/R est:3000

KARDORFF, Konrad von (1877-1945) German
£1132 $1766 €1800 Farmstead with peasant woman in autumn sun (60x74cm-24x29in) bears si.d.08 panel. 21-Sep-2 Bolland & Marotz, Bremen #509/R
Works on paper
£942 $1545 €1300 Beer garden (18x25cm-7x10in) s.d.11 pastel chk. 29-May-3 Lempertz, Koln #690/R

KARFIOL, Bernard (1886-1952) American
£382 $600 €573 Two nudes in a landscape (41x30cm-16x12in) s. canvasboard. 10-Dec-2 Doyle, New York #144/R
£701 $1100 €1052 Spring landscape, 1949 (61x76cm-24x30in) s.i.on stretcher. 10-Dec-2 Doyle, New York #145/R est:2000-4000
£2315 $3750 €3357 Resting - Perkins Cove, Ogunquit (102x76cm-40x30in) s. i.stretcher prov. 21-May-3 Doyle, New York #136/R est:2000-3000

KARGEL, Axel (1896-1971) Swedish
£811 $1305 €1217 Vessel in Borgholm's Harbour (34x51cm-13x20in) s. painted c.1948 exhib. 7-May-3 AB Stockholms Auktionsverk #858/R (S.KR 10500)
£1313 $2179 €1904 House and tree (29x42cm-11x17in) s. panel. 16-Jun-3 Lilla Bukowskis, Stockholm #462 est:10000-12000 (S.KR 17000)
£1331 $2077 €1997 Cornfield, Oland (36x53cm-14x21in) s. painted 1965. 6-Nov-2 AB Stockholms Auktionsverk #531/R est:12000-15000 (S.KR 19000)
£1544 $2486 €2316 Boats on beach (27x44cm-11x17in) s.d.1969. 7-May-3 AB Stockholms Auktionsverk #729/R est:10000-12000 (S.KR 20000)
£1544 $2486 €2316 Houses by the sea (30x36cm-12x14in) s. d.1948 verso. 7-May-3 AB Stockholms Auktionsverk #871/R est:15000-18000 (S.KR 20000)
£1682 $2624 €2523 Coastal road, Oland (31x50cm-12x20in) s.d.1963 panel exhib. 6-Nov-2 AB Stockholms Auktionsverk #533/R est:10000-12000 (S.KR 24000)
£1776 $2859 €2664 Landscape with buildings, Oland (36x53cm-14x21in) s.i. panel. 7-May-3 AB Stockholms Auktionsverk #872/R est:18000-20000 (S.KR 23000)

KARLOVSKY, Bertalan de (1858-c.1938) Austrian
£620 $967 €930 Lady with mandolin (33x41cm-13x16in) s.i. 17-Sep-2 Rosebery Fine Art, London #592/R
£1285 $2005 €1863 Portrait of a lady in a hat (33x34cm-13x13in) s.i. 12-Apr-3 Mu Terem Galeria, Budapest #124/R est:250000 (H.F 460000)
£1418 $2070 €2127 Portrait of a woman (49x39cm-19x15in) wood. 4-Jun-2 SOGA, Bratislava #105/R est:90000 (SL.K 90000)
£18164 $28336 €27246 Woman in hat in red armchair (43x54cm-17x21in) s. 11-Apr-3 Kieselbach, Budapest #152/R est:4000000-6500000 (H.F 6500000)

KARLOWSKA, Stanislawa (1876-1952) Polish
£1000 $1540 €1500 Devon landscape (43x53cm-17x21in) prov. 5-Sep-2 Christie's, Kensington #543/R est:1500-2000

KARLSSON, C Goran (1944-) Swedish
£913 $1442 €1370 Untitled (58x45cm-23x18in) init.d.95 tempera. 28-Apr-3 Bukowskis, Stockholm #274/R (S.KR 12000)
£1331 $2103 €1997 Untitled (114x84cm-45x33in) init.d.99 tempera. 28-Apr-3 Bukowskis, Stockholm #273/R est:15000-20000 (S.KR 17500)
£4633 $7459 €6950 Semaphore (198x75cm-78x30in) init. oil tempera prov. 7-May-3 AB Stockholms Auktionsverk #807/R est:40000-50000 (S.KR 60000)

KARLSSON, Kent (1945-) Swedish
£281 $443 €422 Amalthea II (158x209cm-62x82in) init.d.82 verso oil mixed media textile. 30-Nov-2 Goteborg Auktionsverk, Sweden #554/R (S.KR 4000)

KARNEC, Jean Etienne (1875-1934) Austrian
£886 $1373 €1400 Le port (19x24cm-7x9in) s. panel. 29-Sep-2 Eric Pillon, Calais #18/R
£1108 $1717 €1750 Le port dans la ville (20x29cm-8x11in) s. panel. 29-Sep-2 Eric Pillon, Calais #16/R

KAROLY, Gerna (1867-1944) Hungarian
£616 $962 €900 Camel drover in Cairo (50x40cm-20x16in) s.indis.d. lit. 10-Apr-3 Allgauer, Kempten #2825/R
£833 $1308 €1300 Oriental street (80x60cm-31x24in) s. 23-Nov-2 Arnold, Frankfurt #776/R
£1923 $3019 €3000 Figures by mosque (50x40cm-20x16in) s. 10-Dec-2 Tajan, Paris #175/R est:3700
£2014 $3303 €2800 Scene animee a la mosquee Muhammad Ali au Caire (50x40cm-20x16in) s.i. 4-Jun-3 Tajan, Paris #274/R est:2700-3700

KARP, Leon (1903-1951) American
£802 $1300 €1203 Yellow apples (20x41cm-8x16in) s.i.verso painted 1949 prov.exhib. 24-Jan-3 Freeman, Philadelphia #153/R est:400-600
£1097 $1700 €1646 Still life with pumpkins (76x89cm-30x35in) s. exhib. 8-Dec-2 Freeman, Philadelphia #156/R est:1000-1500

KARPATHY, Eugène (1871-1950) French?
£897 $1391 €1400 Le debut de la fenaison (62x81cm-24x32in) s. 9-Dec-2 Horta, Bruxelles #417

KARPATHY, Janos (19/20th C) Hungarian
£512 $799 €768 Collecting water at the lake (58x78cm-23x31in) s. 11-Nov-2 Stephan Welz, Johannesburg #411 (SA.R 8000)

KARPATHY, Jeno (1871-?) Hungarian
£306 $487 €450 Bord de mer (59x79cm-23x31in) s. 18-Mar-3 Vanderkindere, Brussels #54
£544 $865 €800 Rocky coastline (92x123cm-36x48in) s. lit. 21-Mar-3 Auktionhaus Georg Rehm, Augsburg #8049

KARPINSKI, Alfons (1875-1961) Polish
£1986 $3316 €2800 Dimanche (58x54cm-23x21in) s.d. 17-Jun-3 Claude Boisgirard, Paris #72/R est:2000-2500

KARPOFF, Ivan (1898-1970) Russian
£417 $608 €650 Landscape with ship (40x50cm-16x20in) s. 5-Jun-2 Il Ponte, Milan #177
£417 $646 €650 Winter landscape (45x60cm-18x24in) s. board. 5-Dec-2 Stadion, Trieste #664/R
£481 $745 €750 Winter landscape (45x60cm-18x24in) s. board. 5-Dec-2 Stadion, Trieste #675/R
£548 $866 €850 Gamba de legn (50x69cm-20x27in) s. 18-Dec-2 Finarte, Milan #70
£774 $1223 €1200 Harvesters (50x70cm-20x28in) s. 18-Dec-2 Finarte, Milan #118

KARPPANEN, Matti (1873-1953) Finnish
£506 $790 €800 Pigeon (19x25cm-7x10in) s. 15-Sep-2 Bukowskis, Helsinki #214/R
£612 $973 €900 Seagull (25x35cm-10x14in) s.d.1942. 27-Feb-3 Hagelstam, Helsinki #918
£1290 $2039 €2000 Birds (23x27cm-9x11in) s.d.1952. 19-Dec-2 Hagelstam, Helsinki #804/R est:2000
£1424 $2222 €2250 Blackgrouse (76x65cm-30x26in) s.d.1944. 15-Sep-2 Bukowskis, Helsinki #215/R est:2200
£1691 $2705 €2350 Bullfinches on branch (48x34cm-19x13in) s.d.1940 board. 17-May-3 Hagelstam, Helsinki #121/R est:2000
£2057 $3188 €3086 Small birds on branch (35x30cm-14x12in) mono.d.1896 verso. 8-Dec-2 Uppsala Auktionskammare, Uppsala #46/R est:15000-20000 (S.KR 29000)
£2113 $3401 €3000 Small birds on branch (36x30cm-14x12in) s.d.1896 verso. 10-May-3 Bukowskis, Helsinki #94/R est:3000-3500
£2532 $4000 €4000 Waxwings on branches (36x32cm-14x13in) s.d.1895 verso. 1-Dec-2 Bukowskis, Helsinki #78/R est:2000-2500
£2662 $4259 €3700 Waxwings (34x41cm-13x16in) s.d.1897 verso. 17-May-3 Hagelstam, Helsinki #120/R est:4000

KARS, Georges (1882-1945) Czechoslovakian
£2690 $4303 €3900 Jeune femme orientale (65x54cm-26x21in) s. 12-Mar-3 Rabourdin & Choppin de Janvry, Paris #114/R
£3448 $5517 €5000 Strollers in the park (51x65cm-20x26in) st.sig. 12-Mar-3 Rabourdin & Choppin de Janvry, Paris #103/R
£5161 $8155 €8000 Portrait of woman (80x62cm-31x24in) s. 18-Dec-2 Digard, Paris #187/R
£7000 $11130 €10500 Nature morte (54x46cm-21x18in) s. 20-Mar-3 Sotheby's, Olympia #68/R est:4000-6000

Works on paper
£258 $408 €400 Nu feminin (56x43cm-22x17in) s. sanguine dr. 18-Dec-2 Digard, Paris #123
£321 $503 €500 Nude (52x41cm-20x16in) s.d.21 sanguine. 12-Dec-2 Rabourdin & Choppin de Janvry, Paris #122
£355 $561 €550 Monte-Carlo (36x28cm-14x11in) s.i. chl pastel. 18-Dec-2 Digard, Paris #178/R
£838 $1308 €1257 Boy in blue shirt (60x38cm-24x15in) s. mixed media. 11-Apr-3 Kieselbach, Budapest #138/R est:250000-300000 (H.F 300000)
£1224 $1947 €1800 Nu dans un fauteuil (47x33cm-19x13in) s. chl. 3-Mar-3 Claude Boisgirard, Paris #55/R est:1500-1800

KARS, Jiri (1882-1945) Czechoslovakian
£868 $1346 €1302 Woman with moon (52x35cm-20x14in) tempera paper. 3-Dec-2 SOGA, Bratislava #230/R (SL.K 55000)

KARSEN, Kaspar (1810-1896) Dutch
£3425 $5377 €5000 Figures on the quay of a town (15x21cm-6x8in) s. panel. 15-Apr-3 Sotheby's, Amsterdam #2/R est:3000-5000
£5556 $8833 €8000 Figures crossing a bridge in a Dutch town (32x41cm-13x16in) s. panel prov. 29-Apr-3 Christie's, Amsterdam #74/R est:7000-9000
£17949 $27821 €28000 Town view with cows wading in a river (56x99cm-22x39in) s. 3-Dec-2 Sotheby's, Amsterdam #19/R est:25000-30000
£26389 $41958 €38000 View of Katwijk village with a Groot Badhotel in the background (57x92cm-22x36in) s. prov.exhib. 29-Apr-3 Christie's, Amsterdam #184/R est:15000-20000

KARSH, Yousuf (1908-) Armenian
Photographs
£1948 $3000 €2922 Pablo Casals (50x40cm-20x16in) s. photograph. 24-Oct-2 Sotheby's, New York #121/R est:3000-5000
£2179 $3400 €3269 Albert Einstein (43x40cm-17x16in) s. silver. 21-Oct-2 Swann Galleries, New York #172/R est:4000-6000
£2516 $3899 €4000 Albert Einstein (28x27cm-11x11in) s. i. verso gelatin silver. 2-Nov-2 Lempertz, Koln #45/R est:2000
£2848 $4500 €4272 Muhammed Ali (60x51cm-24x20in) with sig.num.14/100 oversized gelatin silver print. 22-Apr-3 Butterfields, San Francisco #2459/R est:4000-6000
£3247 $5000 €4871 Albert Einstein (49x53cm-19x21in) s.num.14/100 photograph. 24-Oct-2 Sotheby's, New York #119/R est:5000-7000
£3427 $5415 €5141 Rt. Hon Sir Winston Churchill (23x19cm-9x7in) s.d.1967 black white silver gelatin print prov.lit. 18-Nov-2 Sotheby's, Toronto #144/R est:8000-10000 (C.D 8500)
£3537 $5800 €5306 Winston Churchill (47x38cm-19x15in) s. silver print exec.c.1970. 10-Feb-3 Swann Galleries, New York #63/R est:4000-6000
£3571 $5500 €5357 Ernest Hemingway (61x50cm-24x20in) s.num.14/100 photograph. 24-Oct-2 Sotheby's, New York #120/R est:4000-6000
£3846 $6000 €5769 Winston Churchill (50x40cm-20x16in) silver. 21-Oct-2 Swann Galleries, New York #171/R est:5000-6000

KARSKAYA, Ida (1905-1990) French
Works on paper
£577 $906 €900 Untitled (25x32cm-10x13in) s. w grattage. 10-Dec-2 Piasa, Paris #156

KARSSEN, Anton (1932-) Dutch
£1338 $2154 €1900 Children playing on the beach (28x38cm-11x15in) s. 7-May-3 Vendue Huis, Gravenhage #18/R est:1000-1200
£1620 $2608 €2300 Children playing on the beach (29x39cm-11x15in) s. 7-May-3 Vendue Huis, Gravenhage #19 est:1500-2000
£1656 $2583 €2600 Amusement on the ice (47x69cm-19x27in) s. 6-Nov-2 Vendue Huis, Gravenhage #419/R est:2500-3500

KARSTEN, Ludvig (1876-1926) Norwegian
£929 $1468 €1394 Self portrait (31x29cm-12x11in) s.verso painted c.1920. 1-Apr-3 Rasmussen, Copenhagen #54/R (D.KR 10000)
£2595 $4100 €3893 An artistic friend (44x42cm-17x17in) s.d.16 i.stretcher exhib. 2-Dec-2 Blomqvist, Oslo #370/R est:35000-45000 (N.KR 30000)
£2949 $4600 €4424 Three children (53x43cm-21x17in) canvas on panel prov. 21-Oct-2 Blomqvist, Oslo #362/R est:40000-50000 (N.KR 34000)
£4344 $7037 €6516 Portrait of Mrs Inger Magnussen (103x83cm-41x33in) s.d.21 exhib. 26-May-3 Grev Wedels Plass, Oslo #123/R est:40000-60000 (N.KR 48000)
£12216 $19180 €18324 Landscape from Skagen (36x42cm-14x17in) s.d.23 i.verso exhib. 21-Nov-2 Grev Wedels Plass, Oslo #82/R est:200000-300000 (N.KR 140000)
£13055 $20888 €19583 Mrs art-dealer Anna Grosell (189x90cm-74x35in) s.d.1912 exhib.lit. 17-Mar-3 Blomqvist, Oslo #380/R est:200000-250000 (N.KR 150000)
Works on paper
£508 $787 €762 Portrait of woman (27x20cm-11x8in) s.d.22 chl. 1-Oct-2 Rasmussen, Copenhagen #125/R (D.KR 6000)

KASATKIN, Nikolai Alexeievich (1859-1930) Russian
£3846 $6000 €5769 Russian cavalry (48x69cm-19x27in) 20-Sep-2 Du Mouchelle, Detroit #2022/R est:2500-3500
£8500 $14195 €12750 Addressing the troops (51x71cm-20x28in) s. 18-Jun-3 Christie's, Kensington #80/R est:4000-6000

KASEBIER, Gertrude (1852-1934) American
Photographs
£2273 $3500 €3410 Maynard White (24x12cm-9x5in) i.verso platinum print prov. 22-Oct-2 Sotheby's, New York #140/R est:5000-8000
£2760 $4250 €4140 F. Holland day, Newport (16x11cm-6x4in) mono.i. platinum print prov. 22-Oct-2 Sotheby's, New York #37/R est:6000-9000
£2760 $4250 €4140 Sunshine in the house - Clarence H White and family (20x19cm-8x7in) platinum print prov.lit. 22-Oct-2 Sotheby's, New York #142/R est:7000-10000
£5519 $8500 €8279 Frederick H Evans, London (13x16cm-5x6in) gum print prov. 22-Oct-2 Sotheby's, New York #36/R est:5000-7000
£6494 $10000 €9741 Silhouettes of a young boy (21x16cm-8x6in) gum prints executed c.1905 set of three. 22-Oct-2 Sotheby's, New York #147/R est:5000-7000

KASELITZ, Albert Friedrich (1821-1884) German
£2641 $4068 €4200 Un repas d'amis (52x72cm-20x28in) s. 25-Oct-2 Tajan, Paris #44/R est:3000-4000

KASIMIR, Luigi (1881-1962) Austrian
Works on paper
£1392 $2172 €2200 Salzburg (21x15cm-8x6in) s.d.1920 col pen. 15-Oct-2 Dorotheum, Vienna #53/R est:900-1600

KASIMIR, Robert (1914-) Austrian
£641 $1013 €1000 Karntnerstrasse, Adlmuller department store (36x29cm-14x11in) s.i. col pen. 12-Nov-2 Dorotheum, Vienna #181/R

KASPAR, Paul (1891-1953) Austrian
Works on paper
£612 $973 €900 Vienna (19x13cm-7x5in) s. W/C. 19-Mar-3 Dorotheum, Vienna #14/R
£743 $1159 €1100 Maria Theresienstrasse, Innsbruck (12x9cm-5x4in) s.d.1924 W/C. 28-Mar-3 Dorotheum, Vienna #330/R
£878 $1370 €1300 Summer's day in Grinzing (12x16cm-5x6in) s.d.1924 W/C. 28-Mar-3 Dorotheum, Vienna #341/R
£1132 $1755 €1800 Kartnerstrasse with view of Stephansdom (20x15cm-8x6in) s.d.908 W/C. 1-Oct-2 Dorotheum, Vienna #278/R
£1258 $1950 €2000 Flower stalls on Hohen Markt (20x15cm-8x6in) s.d.908 W/C. 1-Oct-2 Dorotheum, Vienna #277/R est:1600-1800

KASPARIDES, Edouard (1858-1926) Austrian
£3000 $5010 €4500 Archadian lake landscape (95x120cm-37x47in) 18-Jun-3 Christie's, Kensington #176/R est:3000-5000
£3797 $6000 €6000 Sunset (151x200cm-59x79in) 26-Nov-2 Wiener Kunst Auktionen, Vienna #74/R est:6000-10000

KASPER, Ludwig (1893-1945) German
Sculpture
£2394 $3975 €3400 Portrait bust of Ottilie Kasper (65x41x23cm-26x16x9in) marble cement. 14-Jun-3 Hauswedell & Nolte, Hamburg #1275/R est:3000

KASS, Joel (20th C) Israeli
£278 $442 €400 Couple avec fleur (80x100cm-31x39in) s.verso. 29-Apr-3 Campo & Campo, Antwerp #660
£278 $442 €400 Bonheur familial (88x115cm-35x45in) s.verso. 29-Apr-3 Campo & Campo, Antwerp #661
£313 $497 €450 Marriage juif (65x130cm-26x51in) mono. 29-Apr-3 Campo & Campo, Antwerp #655
£313 $497 €450 Marriage juif (65x130cm-26x51in) mono. 29-Apr-3 Campo & Campo, Antwerp #658
£486 $773 €700 Figure priant (80x100cm-31x39in) s. 29-Apr-3 Campo & Campo, Antwerp #659

KASSAK, Lajos (1887-1967) Hungarian
Works on paper
£2051 $3200 €3077 Untitled (30x23cm-12x9in) s. col paper newsprint collage gouache crayon exec.c.1920. 18-Sep-2 Swann Galleries, New York #34/R est:5000-8000

£3475 $5595 €5213 Geometric composition (62x48cm-24x19in) s. i.d.1923 verso gouache prov. 7-May-3 AB Stockholms Auktionsverk #1139/R est:50000-60000 (S.KR 45000)
£7029 $11528 €9700 Untitled (61x55cm-24x22in) s. W/C prov.exhib. 31-May-3 Villa Grisebach, Berlin #214/R est:7000-9000

KASSECKER, Paul (1903-) Austrian
£321 $497 €500 Still life of flowers (56x48cm-22x19in) s. panel. 5-Dec-2 Dorotheum, Graz #26

KASTEELE, Johanna Margaretha van de (1858-1951) Dutch
Works on paper
£955 $1490 €1500 Peonies (59x45cm-23x18in) s.indis.d. W/C prov. 6-Nov-2 Vendue Huis, Gravenhage #466/R est:2000-3000
£1401 $2186 €2200 Bouquet of peonies (67x47cm-26x19in) W/C prov. 6-Nov-2 Vendue Huis, Gravenhage #465/R est:2000-3000

KASTELIC, Ronald Victor (1964-) American
£1631 $2643 €2300 Cover girl II (70x100cm-28x39in) s.i.d.2002 verso. 20-May-3 Porro, Milan #33/R est:2500-2800

KASTLER, Hans (1931-) German
Sculpture
£962 $1404 €1500 Curious (52cm-20in) s.d.1991 bronze lit. 4-Jun-2 Karl & Faber, Munich #302/R est:3000

KASTNER, A (19/20th C) ?
£404 $614 €630 Vase with autumn flowers (33x46cm-13x18in) s. board. 11-Jul-2 Allgauer, Kempten #2542/R

KASYN, John (1926-) Canadian
£815 $1272 €1182 Old stucco (25x20cm-10x8in) s.i.d.69 board prov. 26-Mar-3 Walker's, Ottawa #229/R est:1500-2000 (C.D 1900)
£1233 $1973 €1850 Red house near Euclid Avenue (25x20cm-10x8in) s. s.i.verso board. 15-May-3 Heffel, Vancouver #159/R est:1800-2200 (C.D 2750)
£1422 $2332 €2133 Stucco house on bleecker (30x25cm-12x10in) s. board. 3-Jun-3 Joyner, Toronto #323/R est:2500-3500 (C.D 3200)
£1435 $2238 €2393 On Queen Street West (30x25cm-12x10in) s. board. 13-Apr-3 Levis, Calgary #67/R est:3000-3500 (C.D 3300)
£1511 $2478 €2267 Yellow stucco near Oak St. (25x20cm-10x8in) s. board. 3-Jun-3 Joyner, Toronto #404/R est:2000-2500 (C.D 3400)
£2016 $3185 €3024 Back yard with tree and weeds, Caroline St (16x36cm-6x14in) s.i.d.1974 s.verso board prov. 14-Nov-2 Heffel, Vancouver #114/R est:4500-5500 (C.D 5000)
£3556 $5831 €5334 In late afternoon, Ontario Street (41x56cm-16x22in) s. s.i.verso masonite. 27-May-3 Sotheby's, Toronto #124/R est:9000-12000 (C.D 8000)
£3831 $6052 €5747 Back yard on River Street (61x46cm-24x18in) s.i.verso board. 14-Nov-2 Heffel, Vancouver #132/R est:9000-11000 (C.D 9500)
£4444 $7289 €6666 Homewood Hall (46x61cm-18x24in) s. s.i.verso oil lucite on board prov. 27-May-3 Sotheby's, Toronto #126/R est:10000-12000 (C.D 10000)
£6996 $10844 €10494 Shanon St. Yard after the snow (75x70cm-30x28in) s. board. 3-Dec-2 Joyner, Toronto #106/R est:18000-22000 (C.D 17000)
£7661 $12105 €11492 Along Wellesley Street (51x71cm-20x28in) s.i.verso board. 14-Nov-2 Heffel, Vancouver #126/R est:12000-15000 (C.D 19000)
£10090 $16143 €15135 On McCaul Street before demolition (86x76cm-34x30in) s. s.i.verso board. 15-May-3 Heffel, Vancouver #158/R est:22500-27500 (C.D 22500)
Works on paper
£489 $802 €734 Dark winter's day, Jarvis Street (17x26cm-7x10in) s. W/C prov. 3-Jun-3 Joyner, Toronto #537 est:1000-1500 (C.D 1100)
£600 $954 €900 Rupert Valley Farm, Gatineau, Quebec (51x69cm-20x27in) s.i.verso W/C. 29-Apr-3 Bonhams, New Bond Street #183/R
£756 $1239 €1134 Lane to Spadina (18x26cm-7x10in) s. W/C prov. 3-Jun-3 Joyner, Toronto #342/R est:1000-1500 (C.D 1700)

KASZNAR, Jeno (1875-?) Czechoslovakian
£725 $1029 €1088 Autumn birches (96x142cm-38x56in) painted c.1920. 26-Mar-2 SOGA, Bratislava #124/R (SL.K 46000)

KAT, Anne-Pierre de (1881-1968) Belgian
£1250 $2025 €1900 Amsterdam canal (29x34cm-11x13in) s. i.verso. 21-Jan-3 Christie's, Amsterdam #291 est:1800-2200
£2158 $3540 €3000 Village near Brussels (90x100cm-35x39in) s.d.43. 3-Jun-3 Christie's, Amsterdam #277/R est:3000-5000
£2614 $4209 €4000 Fleuve anime (71x93cm-28x37in) s.d.1933. 20-Jan-3 Horta, Bruxelles #205/R est:5000-7000
£2621 $4193 €3800 Skater, Germaine Westerwoudt (92x65cm-36x26in) s.d.1934 exhib. 15-Mar-3 De Vuyst, Lokeren #545/R est:4000-5000
Works on paper
£303 $482 €440 Nu allonge (24x32cm-9x13in) s.d.1936 pencil. 4-Mar-3 Palais de Beaux Arts, Brussels #300

KAT, Otto Boudewijn de (1907-1995) Dutch
£791 $1298 €1100 Huizen in het bos - houses in a forest (25x34cm-10x13in) s. painted c.1937 prov.lit. 3-Jun-3 Christie's, Amsterdam #51/R est:1200-1600
£2222 $3667 €3200 Liege, Belgium (60x81cm-24x32in) s.d.62 prov. 1-Jul-3 Christie's, Amsterdam #413/R est:3000-5000
£2302 $3776 €3200 Interior (70x50cm-28x20in) s.d.93. 3-Jun-3 Christie's, Amsterdam #49/R est:3500-4500
£3077 $4831 €4800 French landscape (45x53cm-18x21in) s.d.35. 25-Nov-2 Glerum, Amsterdam #120/R est:1400-1600
Works on paper
£1210 $1864 €1900 Dorre bladeren (36x53cm-14x21in) s.d.46 W/C exhib. 3-Sep-2 Christie's, Amsterdam #351/R est:600-800

KATCHADOURIAN, Sarkis (20th C) Iranian
£4173 $6843 €5800 Marche au Caire (82x66cm-32x26in) s.i.d.1922. 4-Jun-3 Tajan, Paris #273/R est:6000-7000

KATEI, Taki (attrib) (1830-1901) Japanese
Works on paper
£276 $450 €414 Geese swimming (124x47cm-49x19in) bears sig. ink scroll. 16-Feb-3 Butterfields, San Francisco #2245

KATENHAUSEN, John N (20th C) American
£548 $850 €822 Portraot of a native American (61x46cm-24x18in) s. canvasboard painted c.1954 prov. 8-Dec-2 Toomey, Oak Park #710/R

KATER, Arie (1922-1972) Dutch
£382 $630 €550 Woman leaning on a bar (60x70cm-24x28in) s. 1-Jul-3 Christie's, Amsterdam #506/R
£417 $688 €600 Woman and cat (80x70cm-31x28in) s. 1-Jul-3 Christie's, Amsterdam #507
£590 $974 €850 Nude (60x50cm-24x20in) s. exhib. 1-Jul-3 Christie's, Amsterdam #505

KATHY, Roger (1934-1979) Belgian
£347 $559 €521 Le ciel vert (27x35cm-11x14in) s. 7-May-3 Dobiaschofsky, Bern #728/R (S.FR 750)
£371 $579 €557 Evening river landscape with bridge (65x81cm-26x32in) s. 6-Nov-2 Dobiaschofsky, Bern #724/R (S.FR 850)
£644 $1017 €966 Still life with bottles, candlestick and fruit (46x55cm-18x22in) s. 26-Nov-2 Hans Widmer, St Gallen #1214 est:1500-2800 (S.FR 1500)
£696 $1078 €1044 Harbour (45x81cm-18x32in) s. 9-Dec-2 Philippe Schuler, Zurich #3821 (S.FR 1600)
£739 $1153 €1109 Summer landscape (19x33cm-7x13in) s. 16-Sep-2 Philippe Schuler, Zurich #3378 (S.FR 1700)
Works on paper
£286 $418 €429 Village (20x46cm-8x18in) s. W/C over Indian ink. 17-Jun-2 Philippe Schuler, Zurich #4191 (S.FR 650)

KATO, Eizo (20th C) Japanese
Works on paper
£311 $510 €451 Tamura Temple, three steps pagoda (48x30cm-19x12in) s.i.d.1906 W/C. 9-Jun-3 Hodgins, Calgary #279/R (C.D 700)

KATONA, Nandor (1864-1932) Czechoslovakian
£315 $447 €473 High Tatras village (34x51cm-13x20in) tempera board painted c.1912. 26-Mar-2 SOGA, Bratislava #43/R (SL.K 20000)
£394 $575 €591 Pile of hay (25x34cm-10x13in) wood painted c.1910. 4-Jun-2 SOGA, Bratislava #34/R est:25000 (SL.K 25000)
£410 $636 €615 Woman by forest (26x12cm-10x5in) panel painted c.1910. 3-Dec-2 SOGA, Bratislava #26/R (SL.K 26000)
£473 $690 €710 At the river Vah (32x47cm-13x19in) board painted c.1920. 4-Jun-2 SOGA, Bratislava #33/R est:30000 (SL.K 30000)
£504 $736 €756 Boat (28x40cm-11x16in) plywood painted c.1910. 4-Jun-2 SOGA, Bratislava #32/R est:32000 (SL.K 32000)
£567 $879 €851 Road in forest (34x50cm-13x20in) wood painted c.1900. 1-Oct-2 SOGA, Bratislava #24/R est:28000 (SL.K 36000)
£599 $874 €899 Fire at river (30x51cm-12x20in) painted c.1910. 4-Jun-2 SOGA, Bratislava #31/R est:38000 (SL.K 38000)
£3308 $5127 €4962 Waterfall (230x161cm-91x63in) painted c.1900. 1-Oct-2 SOGA, Bratislava #23/R est:210000 (SL.K 210000)

KATUNARIC, Antonio (?) Czechoslovakian?
£567 $902 €851 Harbour (20x40cm-8x16in) s.d.98. 8-Mar-3 Dorotheum, Prague #148/R est:12000-18000 (C.KR 26000)

KATZ, Alex (1927-) American
£3800 $6346 €5510 Black brook no.2 (30x23cm-12x9in) s.d.89 prov. 27-Jun-3 Christie's, London #241/R est:4000-6000
£4167 $6500 €6251 Karalyn - study no.III (23x31cm-9x12in) masonite painted c.1976 prov. 5-Nov-2 Doyle, New York #53/R est:6000-8000
£4487 $7000 €6731 Girl on sofa (19x30cm-7x12in) masonite painted c.1974 prov. 5-Nov-2 Doyle, New York #54/R est:5000-7000
£5380 $8500 €8070 Harbor No.1 (23x30cm-9x12in) s.d.99 board prov. 13-Nov-2 Sotheby's, New York #273/R est:8000-12000
£6500 $10855 €9425 Purple wind (30x24cm-12x9in) s.d.95 prov. 27-Jun-3 Christie's, London #242/R est:5000-7000
£6790 $11000 €9846 Forsythia 2 (30x23cm-12x9in) s.d.97 board. 21-May-3 Doyle, New York #48/R est:8000-12000
£7500 $12000 €11250 Nude (20x41cm-8x16in) s.d.88 panel prov.exhib. 14-May-3 Sotheby's, New York #204/R est:8000-12000
£7595 $12000 €11393 Landscape - with trees (30x41cm-12x16in) s.d.81 i.on stretcher board prov. 13-Nov-2 Sotheby's, New York #274/R est:8000-12000
£11392 $18000 €17088 Hanging branch No.2 (41x18cm-16x7in) s.d.90 board prov. 13-Nov-2 Sotheby's, New York #269/R est:8000-12000
£13750 $22000 €20625 Madison Square Park (30x39cm-12x15in) s.d.64 masoniteprov. 15-May-3 Christie's, Rockefeller NY #148/R est:35000
£18987 $30000 €28481 Ada with red hat (38x61cm-15x24in) s.d.62 prov. 14-Nov-2 Christie's, Rockefeller NY #145/R est:30000-40000
£26250 $42000 €39375 Green reflections (122x152cm-48x60in) painted 1998 prov. 16-May-3 Phillips, New York #141/R est:40000-60000
£38750 $62000 €58125 Couple (86x183cm-34x72in) painted c.1997 prov. 15-May-3 Christie's, Rockefeller NY #149/R est:40000-60000
£56962 $90000 €85443 Kim (101x101cm-40x40in) painted 1990 prov. 14-Nov-2 Christie's, Rockefeller NY #174/R est:40000-60000
£88608 $140000 €132912 Ada in front of 4.P.M (152x183cm-60x72in) executed 1977 prov. 13-Nov-2 Sotheby's, New York #275/R est:80000-120000
£112500 $180000 €168750 Good afternoon (183x244cm-72x96in) painted 1974 prov.exhib. 14-May-3 Sotheby's, New York #203/R est:180000-250000
£118750 $190000 €178125 Bicycle rider (183x244cm-72x96in) painted 1982 prov. 15-May-3 Christie's, Rockefeller NY #175/R est:100000-150000
£128205 $200000 €192308 Ada Ada (152x306cm-60x120in) painted 1991 prov.exhib. 11-Nov-2 Phillips, New York #39/R est:250000-350000
Prints
£2201 $3500 €3302 Samantha (168x73cm-66x29in) s.num.PP 2/3 col screenprint. 29-Apr-3 Christie's, Rockefeller NY #646/R est:4000-6000
£2201 $3500 €3302 Ada and Alex (76x91cm-30x36in) s.num.61/75 col screenprint. 2-May-3 Sotheby's, New York #489/R est:2000-3000
£3459 $5500 €5189 Red band (139x92cm-55x36in) s.i. col screenprint. 29-Apr-3 Christie's, Rockefeller NY #645/R est:5000-7000
£5449 $8500 €8174 Red band (139x92cm-55x36in) s.num.59/60 col screenprint. 5-Nov-2 Christie's, Rockefeller NY #439/R est:4000-6000
£9434 $15000 €14151 Red coat (147x73cm-58x29in) s.num.PP 2/2 col screenprint. 2-May-3 Sotheby's, New York #488/R est:10000-15000
£10063 $16000 €15095 Anne (174x62cm-69x24in) s.num.PP 5/5 col screenprint cut aluminum. 2-May-3 Sotheby's, New York #490/R est:10000-15000
Sculpture
£4808 $7500 €7212 Ada (166cm-65in) s.num.73/75 cut aluminum col screenprint. 5-Nov-2 Christie's, Rockefeller NY #440/R est:6000-8000
Works on paper
£2315 $3750 €3357 Amanda II (38x53cm-15x21in) s.d.12 73 pencil prov. 21-May-3 Doyle, New York #49/R est:3000-5000

KATZMANN, J (20th C) Austrian
Works on paper
£1342 $2161 €2000 Panoramic view of a grand hunting lodge (24x91cm-9x36in) s.d.20/9/ 1918 W/C pencil. 18-Feb-3 Sotheby's, Amsterdam #284/R est:1200-1800

KAUBA, C (1865-1922) Austrian/American
Sculpture
£1006 $1550 €1600 Red indian (73cm-29in) i. col bronze stone socle. 22-Oct-2 Wiener Kunst Auktionen, Vienna #1060/R est:500-1000
£1258 $1937 €2000 Red Indian on horseback (44x39x24cm-17x15x9in) s. col bronze stone socle. 22-Oct-2 Wiener Kunst Auktionen, Vienna #1056/R est:300-1000

KAUBA, Carl (1865-1922) Austrian/American
Sculpture
£1069 $1668 €1700 Red Indian chief (60cm-24in) s. col bronze. 20-Sep-2 Schloss Ahlden, Ahlden #1692/R est:1650
£1266 $2000 €1899 Indian (23cm-9in) i. polychrome bronze. 3-Apr-3 Christie's, Rockefeller NY #140/R est:1500-2000
£1410 $2214 €2200 Cossack (35cm-14in) i. brown oliver green pat.bronze marble socle. 11-Dec-2 Dorotheum, Vienna #158/R est:1600-2400
£1646 $2551 €2600 Mountain a wild one (21cm-8in) lit. brown pat.bronze marble socle. 25-Sep-2 Neumeister, Munich #231/R est:1500
£2315 $3750 €3473 Indian on horseback roping a steer (28x15x30cm-11x6x12in) i. golden brown pat. bronze. 24-Jan-3 Freeman, Philadelphia #106/R est:5000-8000
£4276 $6500 €6414 Native American chief (28cm-11in) s.i. pat bronze amber marble base. 17-Aug-2 North East Auctions, Portsmouth #140/R est:5000-8000

KAUFFMANN, Angelica (1741-1807) Swiss
£18000 $29880 €27000 Diana preparing for hunting (19x15cm-7x6in) copper oval. 12-Jun-3 Sotheby's, London #96/R est:4000-6000
£20000 $31600 €30000 Phryne seducing the philosopher Zenokrates (43x47cm-17x19in) s.i.d.1794 prov.exhib.lit. 26-Nov-2 Christie's, London #41/R est:25000-35000
£20000 $31600 €30000 Egeria handing Numa Pompilius his shield (43x47cm-17x19in) s.i.d.1794 prov.exhib.lit. 26-Nov-2 Christie's, London #42/R est:25000-35000
£26000 $41080 €39000 Portrait of Louise Henrietta Campbell later Lady Scarlett (74x61cm-29x24in) 28-Nov-2 Sotheby's, London #167/R est:15000-20000
£450000 $747000 €675000 Portrait of Philip Tisdal with his wife and family (154x190cm-61x75in) s. prov.exhib.lit. 12-Jun-3 Sotheby's, London #8/R est:200000-300000
Works on paper
£49383 $80000 €74075 Portrait of Emma Hamilton (36x42cm-14x17in) i. chk prov.lit. 22-Jan-3 Christie's, Rockefeller NY #94/R est:30000

KAUFFMANN, Angelica (attrib) (1741-1807) Swiss
£8176 $12673 €13000 Penelope (30x25cm-12x10in) panel. 2-Oct-2 Dorotheum, Vienna #380/R est:8000-12000

KAUFFMANN, Hermann (elder) (1808-1889) German
£2793 $4524 €4050 Winter landscape with horses and carriage on town road in snowy weather (56x80cm-22x31in) s. prov. 25-May-3 Uppsala Auktionskammare, Uppsala #59/R est:40000-50000 (S.KR 36000)
£3879 $6284 €5625 Landscape with riders (44x57cm-17x22in) s. prov. 25-May-3 Uppsala Auktionskammare, Uppsala #60/R est:25000-30000 (S.KR 50000)
Works on paper
£253 $392 €400 Peasant smoking while horses drink (13x23cm-5x9in) s.d.1854 W/C over pencil. 25-Sep-2 Neumeister, Munich #410/R

KAUFFMANN, Hermann (younger) (1873-?) German
£2548 $3975 €4000 Taylor in workshop (27x18cm-11x7in) s.d.1896 panel. 6-Nov-2 Hugo Ruef, Munich #1169/R est:2500

KAUFFMANN, Hugo Wilhelm (1844-1915) German
£5063 $7848 €8000 Girl sitting at window playing with cat (15x12cm-6x5in) s.d.1903 panel. 25-Sep-2 Neumeister, Munich #617/R est:3500
£6757 $10541 €10000 Peasants in village tavern (24x20cm-9x8in) s.d.88 panel. 27-Mar-3 Dr Fritz Nagel, Stuttgart #821/R est:7500
£7843 $12549 €12000 Casualty is brought into the hut for the young woman (92x130cm-36x51in) s. panel lit. 10-Jan-3 Allgauer, Kempten #1641/R est:18000
£17904 $27930 €26856 Hunter with fox and girl (17x23cm-7x9in) s.d.91 panel lit. 20-Nov-2 Fischer, Luzern #1170/R est:25000-35000 (S.FR 41000)

KAUFMANN (19/20th C) ?
£886 $1373 €1400 Shepherdess with sheep in meadow (25x30cm-10x12in) s. board. 26-Sep-2 Neumeister, Munich #2754/R

KAUFMANN, Adolf (1848-1916) Austrian
£833 $1308 €1300 Scandinavian coast with ship in stormy seas (58x37cm-23x15in) s. panel. 21-Nov-2 Van Ham, Cologne #1714/R
£833 $1308 €1300 Fishing boat stranded on rocky coast (58x37cm-23x15in) s. panel. 21-Nov-2 Van Ham, Cologne #1715/R
£1923 $3019 €3000 Park landscape in autumn with shepherd and sheep (98x143cm-39x56in) s. 21-Nov-2 Dorotheum, Vienna #176/R est:4500-6000
£2143 $3193 €3300 Brittany (31x47cm-12x19in) s.i. panel. 26-Jun-2 Neumeister, Munich #770/R est:3500
£2278 $3600 €3600 Bunch of flowers (58x36cm-23x14in) board. 28-Nov-2 Dorotheum, Vienna #142/R est:3600-4000
£2375 $3705 €3563 Autumn forest (80x60cm-31x24in) s. 11-Apr-3 Kieselbach, Budapest #11/R est:450000-850000 (H.F 850000)
£2564 $4026 €4000 Farm in autumn (64x99cm-25x39in) s. 21-Nov-2 Dorotheum, Vienna #178/R est:5000-6500
£2600 $4108 €3770 Fishermen and boats in a harbour (74x112cm-29x44in) s. 23-Jul-3 Mallams, Oxford #245/R
£3546 $5745 €5000 Autumn woods with twig collectors (45x58cm-18x23in) s. 22-May-3 Dorotheum, Vienna #36/R est:3800-4200
£3797 $6000 €6000 Fishing in the North sea (80x125cm-31x49in) s.d.1882. 28-Nov-2 Dorotheum, Vienna #73/R est:6000-8000

£3797 $6000 €6000 Water landscape in autumn with grazing cows (72x44cm-28x17in) s.d.1894 panel. 28-Nov-2 Dorotheum, Vienna #218/R est:3800-4500
£4430 $7000 €7000 Resting in the beech-wood (90x74cm-35x29in) s. 28-Nov-2 Dorotheum, Vienna #123/R est:7500-9000
£15942 $26145 €22000 Park with autumn trees (131x200cm-52x79in) s.d.1900. 27-May-3 Wiener Kunst Auktionen, Vienna #39/R est:25000-40000

KAUFMANN, Ferdinand (1864-1942) German/American
£1000 $1600 €1500 Colourful landscape (29x36cm-11x14in) s. board. 18-May-3 Butterfields, Los Angeles #7000 est:1000-1500
£1138 $1900 €1650 Cloudy day, Rockport Harbor (30x41cm-12x16in) s. i.verso board prov. 17-Jun-3 John Moran, Pasadena #192 est:2500-3500
£1198 $2000 €1737 English prison ship on Ullagehaua River (38x30cm-15x12in) s. i.verso panel prov. 17-Jun-3 John Moran, Pasadena #190 est:2500-3500
£1347 $2250 €1953 Beach motif laguna beach, California (33x41cm-13x16in) s.d.39 i.verso prov. 17-Jun-3 John Moran, Pasadena #191 est:2500-3500
£1796 $3000 €2604 Landscape, Hollywood Hills (33x41cm-13x16in) s.d.8.39 board prov. 17-Jun-3 John Moran, Pasadena #52 est:3000-4000
£4491 $7500 €6512 Landscape - where the wild flowers are blooming in the foothills (64x76cm-25x30in) s. prov. 17-Jun-3 John Moran, Pasadena #51 est:9000-12000

KAUFMANN, Isidor (1853-1921) Austrian
£1154 $1823 €1800 Village square with rabbis (19x20cm-7x8in) study board. 16-Nov-2 Lempertz, Koln #1498/R est:2000
£6090 $9561 €9500 Fenetre ouverte sur synagogue (41x31cm-16x12in) s. panel. 12-Dec-2 Rabourdin & Choppin de Janvry, Paris #5/R
Works on paper
£5449 $8554 €8500 Rabbin priant (31x22cm-12x9in) s. W/C. 12-Dec-2 Rabourdin & Choppin de Janvry, Paris #8/R

KAUFMANN, Joseph Clemens (1867-1925) Swiss
£472 $746 €708 Procession in Luzerne village (22x33cm-9x13in) s.d.1891. 29-Nov-2 Zofingen, Switzerland #2937/R (S.FR 1100)
Works on paper
£262 $409 €393 Matterhorn in summer (63x47cm-25x19in) s.d.1919 pastel. 6-Nov-2 Dobiaschofsky, Bern #725/R (S.FR 600)

KAUFMANN, Karl (1843-1901) Austrian
£256 $397 €400 Spring landscape (47x26cm-19x10in) s. pseudonym B Lambert panel. 6-Dec-2 Michael Zeller, Lindau #802/R
£380 $600 €600 Moonlight on the Etsch (31x21cm-12x8in) s. i.verso panel. 29-Nov-2 Bolland & Marotz, Bremen #719
£481 $745 €750 View of Oriental city with wealthy figures (19x31cm-7x12in) s. lit. 7-Dec-2 Bergmann, Erlangen #809/R
£822 $1282 €1200 View of Amsterdam (74x100cm-29x39in) bears sig. i.verso. 10-Apr-3 Allgauer, Kempten #2827/R
£850 $1368 €1300 Vue d'Odessa animee (35x52cm-14x20in) s. panel. 20-Jan-3 Horta, Bruxelles #201
£886 $1373 €1400 Fishing boats at harbour quayside (31x54cm-12x21in) s. 25-Sep-2 Neumeister, Munich #619/R
£890 $1389 €1300 Spring landscape with trees (47x26cm-19x10in) s.pseudonym B Lambert. 10-Apr-3 Dorotheum, Vienna #130/R
£909 $1382 €1400 Italian coast (21x31cm-8x12in) s. panel. 6-Jul-2 Berlinghof, Heidelberg #216/R
£949 $1472 €1500 Market street in Istanbul (39x30cm-15x12in) s. panel. 25-Sep-2 Neumeister, Munich #618/R est:1400
£952 $1514 €1400 Old harbour town with fishing boats (71x98cm-28x39in) s.pseudonym F Gilbert canvas on board. 28-Mar-3 Bolland & Marotz, Bremen #471/R
£980 $1569 €1500 Dutch harbour scene with defence tower and silhouette of town (68x104cm-27x41in) s. canvas on canvas lit. 10-Jan-3 Allgauer, Kempten #1642/R est:1300
£1006 $1560 €1600 Rome with Engelsburg (18x32cm-7x13in) s.pseudonym panel. 29-Oct-2 Dorotheum, Vienna #246/R est:1500-1600
£1096 $1710 €1600 Fishing boats off the coast (31x47cm-12x19in) s.d.1889. 10-Apr-3 Schopman, Hamburg #711 est:550
£1132 $1766 €1800 Bruges (74x100cm-29x39in) s.pseudonym lit. 20-Sep-2 Schloss Ahlden, Ahlden #1119/R est:1800
£1489 $2309 €2234 Venetian scene (45x58cm-18x23in) s,. 3-Dec-2 Bukowskis, Stockholm #179/R est:15000-20000 (S.KR 21000)
£1529 $2385 €2400 Vue d'Odessa animee (35x52cm-14x20in) s. panel. 11-Nov-2 Horta, Bruxelles #44 est:2500-3500
£1635 $2535 €2600 Rome - view of Engelsburg and St Peter's from the Tiber (18x31cm-7x12in) s.pseudonym panel. 29-Oct-2 Dorotheum, Vienna #186/R est:2600-3000
£1667 $2617 €2600 Dutch harbour towns (26x53cm-10x21in) s.pseudonym two. 21-Nov-2 Van Ham, Cologne #1716/R est:2800
£1735 $2707 €2603 Canal in Venice (31x21cm-12x8in) s. panel. 28-Mar-3 Koller, Zurich #3157/R est:3500-4500 (S.FR 3800)
£1736 $2760 €2500 View of a harbour town at dusk (31x53cm-12x21in) s. 29-Apr-3 Christie's, Amsterdam #68/R est:3000-4000
£1736 $2760 €2500 Grand Canal with Santa Maria della Salute. River with monastery (47x26cm-19x10in) s. two. 29-Apr-3 Wiener Kunst Auktionen, Vienna #510/R est:2000-4000
£1816 $2834 €2633 View of Rome (26x20cm-10x8in) s. panel. 12-Apr-3 Mu Terem Galeria, Budapest #9/R est:600000 (H.F 650000)
£1859 $2881 €2900 St Maria della Salute in Venice. Engelsburg (18x31cm-7x12in) s.pseudonym H Carnier panel two. 5-Dec-2 Neumeister, Munich #2816/R est:1500
£1956 $3052 €2836 Venice (26x20cm-10x8in) s. panel. 12-Apr-3 Mu Terem Galeria, Budapest #10/R est:600000 (H.F 700000)
£2013 $3119 €3200 Steamer on Norwegian fjord (74x101cm-29x40in) s. 29-Oct-2 Dorotheum, Vienna #192/R est:3400-3600
£2055 $3205 €3083 San Giorgio Maggiore (31x47cm-12x19in) s. panel. 28-Mar-3 Koller, Zurich #3156/R est:4500-7000 (S.FR 4500)
£2055 $3226 €3000 Fjord landscape with houses (68x89cm-27x35in) s.pseudonym J Rollin. 16-Apr-3 Dorotheum, Salzburg #85/R est:2400-3200
£2191 $3527 €3287 Venetian scenes (30x51cm-12x20in) s. board pair. 7-May-3 Dunbar Sloane, Auckland #80/R est:1500-3000 (NZ.D 6200)
£2254 $3628 €3200 River landscape with cows on summer morning (52x79cm-20x31in) s.pseudonym. 7-May-3 Michael Zeller, Lindau #758/R est:2600
£2405 $3800 €3800 View of Amsterdam (68x105cm-27x41in) s.i.d.1880. 28-Nov-2 Dorotheum, Vienna #61/R est:6000-8000
£2500 $4100 €3750 Trading vessels on the Bosphorous at dusk, Istanbul (32x53cm-13x21in) s. set of three. 5-Jun-3 Christie's, Kensington #716/R est:1800-2200
£2532 $4000 €4000 Danzig with Krahntor (52x80cm-20x31in) bears sig. 29-Nov-2 Bassenge, Berlin #5943/R est:2800
£2800 $4312 €4200 El-Golea, Algeria (98x142cm-39x56in) with sig. 24-Oct-2 Christie's, Kensington #203/R est:1200-1800
£5634 $9239 €8169 Santa Maria della Salute and San Geremia (58x37cm-23x15in) s.d.1897 pair. 4-Jun-3 Fischer, Luzern #1159/R est:8000-12000 (S.FR 12000)
£5800 $9048 €8700 Riverside city (95x147cm-37x58in) bears another sig. 17-Sep-2 Sotheby's, Olympia #255/R est:5000-7000
£7862 $12186 €12500 View from Riva degli Schiavoni (96x141cm-38x56in) s.d.1896. 2-Oct-2 Dorotheum, Vienna #382/R est:14000-18000

KAUFMANN, Karl (attrib) (1843-1901) Austrian
£1000 $1580 €1500 Beirut (52x42cm-20x17in) with sig.d.1890 panel. 14-Nov-2 Christie's, Kensington #221/R est:1200-1800

KAUFMANN, Massimo (1963-) Italian
£1923 $2981 €3000 Now that I see you (120x100cm-47x39in) s.i.d.1993 verso. 4-Dec-2 Finarte, Milan #266

KAUFMANN, Wilhelm (1895-1975) Austrian
£475 $741 €750 Outing (60x80cm-24x31in) i. verso masonite. 15-Oct-2 Dorotheum, Vienna #126/R
£1154 $1823 €1800 Woman with parrot (53x41cm-21x16in) s. board. 12-Nov-2 Dorotheum, Vienna #160/R est:700-1100
£1667 $2633 €2600 Southern landscape (36x27cm-14x11in) s. canvas on board. 12-Nov-2 Dorotheum, Vienna #161/R est:700-1100
£1944 $3072 €2800 Gladioli and dahlias (70x90cm-28x35in) s. masonite. 24-Apr-3 Dorotheum, Vienna #181/R est:2800-3400
Works on paper
£481 $760 €750 Landscape with vineyards (48x62cm-19x24in) s. W/C gouache. 12-Nov-2 Dorotheum, Vienna #190/R

KAULA, Lee Lufkin (1865-1957) American
£5732 $9000 €8598 Portrait of Hathaway Stetson (122x77cm-48x30in) s.i. 22-Nov-2 Skinner, Boston #166/R est:18000-22000

KAULA, William J (1871-1952) American
£1274 $2000 €1911 Upright landscape (74x61cm-29x24in) 22-Nov-2 Skinner, Boston #270/R est:4000-6000
£2230 $3500 €3345 Hillside (26x33cm-10x13in) s. board. 22-Nov-2 Skinner, Boston #247/R
£2914 $4750 €4371 October landscape (53x66cm-21x26in) s. board. 2-Feb-3 Grogan, Boston #63 est:3000-5000
£3125 $5000 €4531 Danville Hills, Vermont (26x33cm-10x13in) s. i.verso canvasboard. 16-May-3 Skinner, Boston #207/R est:5000-7000

KAULBACH, Anton (1864-1930) German
£479 $748 €700 Portrait of Old Fritz (80x60cm-31x24in) s. 10-Apr-3 Van Ham, Cologne #1528
Works on paper
£316 $491 €500 Girl's portrait (44x44cm-17x17in) s. pastel. 25-Sep-2 Neumeister, Munich #411/R

KAULBACH, Friedrich August von (1850-1920) German
£742 $1158 €1113 Two King Charles spaniels (39x25cm-15x10in) s. panel oval. 6-Nov-2 Dobiaschofsky, Bern #726/R (S.FR 1700)

£1384 $2131 €2200 Portrait of smiling woman (70x66cm-28x26in) s. 28-Oct-2 Il Ponte, Milan #214/R
£2273 $3386 €3500 Female nude (53x36cm-21x14in) s. panel. 26-Jun-2 Neumeister, Munich #771/R est:2500

KAULBACH, Hermann (1846-1909) German
£822 $1282 €1200 In a Tyrolean back yard near Eppan (49x39cm-19x15in) mono.d.5.07 board. 10-Apr-3 Van Ham, Cologne #1529/R
£4551 $6918 €7100 Interior of barracks with soldier sharing his bread with children (41x30cm-16x12in) s.d.1871 panel lit. 11-Jul-2 Allgauer, Kempten #2545/R est:6300
£22436 $34776 €35000 Young mother sitting at the fireside feeding her two small girls (35x25cm-14x10in) s. panel. 4-Dec-2 Neumeister, Munich #777/R est:18000

KAULBACH, Wilhelm von (1805-1874) German
£699 $1090 €1049 Flower girl (31x15cm-12x6in) mono.d.1855 panel. 6-Nov-2 Dobiaschofsky, Bern #729/R (S.FR 1600)
£2516 $3925 €4000 Girl with grapes (102x83cm-40x33in) mono. 23-Sep-2 Wiener Kunst Auktionen, Vienna #70/R est:4000-9000

KAULUM, Haakon Jensen (1863-1933) Norwegian
£433 $662 €650 Seascape (40x52cm-16x20in) s. 26-Aug-2 Blomqvist, Lysaker #1210 (N.KR 5000)
£638 $989 €957 Harvesting women (33x32cm-13x13in) s.d.1887 pair. 4-Dec-2 AB Stockholms Auktionsverk #1899/R (S.KR 9000)

KAUS, Max (1891-1977) German
£2025 $3200 €3200 Bathers on beach (52x68cm-20x27in) s. s.i.d.50 verso tempera. 30-Nov-2 Villa Grisebach, Berlin #256/R est:3000-4000
£11594 $19014 €16000 Women in meadow (115x90cm-45x35in) s. s.i. verso prov. 29-May-3 Lempertz, Koln #691/R est:15000-20000

Prints
£4487 $6955 €7000 Female nude (65x49cm-26x19in) s.i.d. col lithograph. 7-Dec-2 Hauswedell & Nolte, Hamburg #775/R est:10000

Works on paper
£633 $1000 €1000 Coastal landscape (54x75cm-21x30in) s.d.53 gouache W/C. 29-Nov-2 Villa Grisebach, Berlin #701/R
£1197 $1987 €1700 Still life with blue jug and blue flowers (54x72cm-21x28in) s.d. W/C bodycol pencil col pen. 14-Jun-3 Hauswedell & Nolte, Hamburg #1276/R est:2500
£4114 $6500 €6500 Cityscape with bridge (39x47cm-15x19in) s.d.20 gouache over chk. 30-Nov-2 Villa Grisebach, Berlin #252/R est:5000-7000
£7278 $11500 €11500 Landscape with lake (36x44cm-14x17in) s.d.21 W/C. 30-Nov-2 Villa Grisebach, Berlin #250/R est:8000-10000

KAUW, Albrecht (attrib) (1621-1681) Swiss
£1643 $2695 €2382 Madonna and child with boy holding bowl of porridge (84x76cm-33x30in) mono. 4-Jun-3 Fischer, Luzern #1199/R est:4500-5500 (S.FR 3500)

KAUZMANN, Paul (1874-1951) German
£2740 $4274 €4000 Courtyard of Leipheim Castle in spring (54x61cm-21x24in) s.d.1932 lit. 10-Apr-3 Allgauer, Kempten #2828/R est:6500
£3774 $5887 €6000 View through open window (118x88cm-46x35in) s.d.1924. 9-Oct-2 Michael Zeller, Lindau #752/R est:4800

KAVAN, Frantisek (1866-1941) Czechoslovakian
£499 $809 €749 Mercy (16x25cm-6x10in) mono.i. paper. 24-May-3 Dorotheum, Prague #65/R est:20000-30000 (C.KR 22000)
£629 $981 €1000 Farmsteads in winter landscape (49x69cm-19x27in) s. canvas on board. 9-Oct-2 Michael Zeller, Lindau #753/R
£681 $1103 €1022 Shocks of wheat after storm (39x51cm-15x20in) s.i. i. verso board. 24-May-3 Dorotheum, Prague #66/R est:30000-45000 (C.KR 30000)
£785 $1249 €1178 Kost Castle (40x52cm-16x20in) s. 8-Mar-3 Dorotheum, Prague #55/R est:30000-45000 (C.KR 36000)
£829 $1318 €1244 Summer landscape with pathway (40x53cm-16x21in) s. board. 8-Mar-3 Dorotheum, Prague #43/R est:26000-37000 (C.KR 38000)
£873 $1387 €1310 Summer landscape (41x52cm-16x20in) s. board. 8-Mar-3 Dorotheum, Prague #41 est:20000-30000 (C.KR 40000)
£929 $1450 €1394 Early spring (34x49cm-13x19in) s. cardboard. 12-Oct-2 Dorotheum, Prague #56/R (C.KR 45000)
£982 $1561 €1473 Winter landscape (38x49cm-15x19in) s.i. board. 8-Mar-3 Dorotheum, Prague #51/R est:30000-45000 (C.KR 45000)
£1033 $1611 €1550 Summer landscape with Trosky (40x53cm-16x21in) indis.s.i. cardboard. 12-Oct-2 Dorotheum, Prague #54/R (C.KR 50000)
£1239 $1933 €1859 Scene from railroad (20x28cm-8x11in) s.i. paper on cardboard. 12-Oct-2 Dorotheum, Prague #51/R est:20000-30000 (C.KR 60000)

Works on paper
£268 $424 €402 Where Elba flows from its spring (19x27cm-7x11in) s.i.d.93 wash dr. 30-Nov-2 Dorotheum, Prague #176/R (C.KR 13000)

KAVLI, Arne Texnes (1878-1970) Norwegian
£524 $822 €786 Sunny landscape (16x18cm-6x7in) s. panel. 25-Nov-2 Blomqvist, Lysaker #1148 (N.KR 6000)
£611 $959 €917 Pine tree in snow (21x18cm-8x7in) s. panel. 25-Nov-2 Blomqvist, Lysaker #1147/R (N.KR 7000)
£1745 $2861 €2530 Regatta (17x26cm-7x10in) s. panel. 2-Jun-3 Blomqvist, Oslo #103/R est:8000-10000 (N.KR 19000)
£2163 $3417 €3245 Still life (48x60cm-19x24in) init. 2-Dec-2 Blomqvist, Oslo #423/R est:35000-45000 (N.KR 25000)
£2675 $4066 €4013 Aase (57x46cm-22x18in) s.i.d.1930. 31-Aug-2 Grev Wedels Plass, Oslo #133/R est:12000-15000 (N.KR 31000)
£2949 $4600 €4424 Coastal landscape from Ronnes (70x80cm-28x31in) s. exhib. 21-Oct-2 Blomqvist, Oslo #386/R est:40000-50000 (N.KR 34000)
£3109 $5192 €4508 View from Ronnes (58x68cm-23x27in) s. 18-Jun-3 Grev Wedels Plass, Oslo #191/R est:30000-40000 (N.KR 36000)
£3158 $4989 €4737 Summer landscape (34x40cm-13x16in) s. 17-Dec-2 Grev Wedels Plass, Oslo #244/R est:20000-30000 (N.KR 36000)
£3296 $5141 €4944 Flowering trees (50x44cm-20x17in) s.d.94. 21-Oct-2 Blomqvist, Oslo #371/R est:50000-60000 (N.KR 38000)
£3810 $5906 €5715 Seascape with sailing race (82x66cm-32x26in) s.d.24 i.stretcher prov. 1-Oct-2 Rasmussen, Copenhagen #128/R est:60000-75000 (D.KR 45000)
£7421 $12022 €11132 House with steps to garden (60x69cm-24x27in) s. panel. 26-May-3 Grev Wedels Plass, Oslo #110/R est:90000-100000 (N.KR 82000)
£8726 $13700 €13089 Small girl on bed with wine glass (94x74cm-37x29in) s.d.13. 21-Nov-2 Grev Wedels Plass, Oslo #39/R est:120000-150000 (N.KR 100000)
£9502 $15394 €14253 Woman and man on pier with sailing boats (30x43cm-12x17in) s. 26-May-3 Grev Wedels Plass, Oslo #49/R est:70000-90000 (N.KR 105000)
£15000 $24600 €22500 Sommerdag - summer's day (89x116cm-35x46in) s. 3-Jun-3 Sotheby's, London #220/R est:15000-20000
£16742 $27122 €25113 View towards the fjord, Ronnes (100x140cm-39x55in) s. 26-May-3 Grev Wedels Plass, Oslo #111/R est:120000-150000 (N.KR 185000)
£22624 $36652 €33936 On the steps (131x121cm-52x48in) s. exhib.lit. 26-May-3 Grev Wedels Plass, Oslo #20/R est:300000-400000 (N.KR 250000)
£27149 $43982 €40724 Open-air restaurant on the pier and sailing boats (117x178cm-46x70in) init.i.d.28. 26-May-3 Grev Wedels Plass, Oslo #82/R est:300000-400000 (N.KR 300000)

KAWAKUBO, Masano (19/20th C) Japanese

Works on paper
£356 $590 €516 Shinto Temple (32x47cm-13x19in) s. W/C. 16-Jun-3 Waddingtons, Toronto #338/R (C.D 800)

KAWARA, On (1933-) Japanese

Works on paper
£3478 $5704 €4800 Untitled - I am still alive (42x31cm-17x12in) s. verso paper collage. 28-May-3 Lempertz, Koln #204/R est:3000
£17722 $28000 €26583 Sept 27, 1986 - today series no.26 (25x33cm-10x13in) s. liquitex on canvas board box newspaper clipping executed 1986. 14-Nov-2 Christie's, Rockefeller NY #357/R est:25000-35000
£164557 $260000 €246836 July 12-18 1998 - Today series nos 18-24 (20x25cm-8x10in) s. liquitex on canvas seven units executed 1998 prov.exhib. 13-Nov-2 Christie's, Rockefeller NY #11/R est:250000-350000

KAY, Archibald (1860-1935) British
£680 $1129 €986 Highland river in Spate (45x60cm-18x24in) s. 13-Jun-3 Lyon & Turnbull, Edinburgh #73
£687 $1085 €1031 Cattle in a field (51x61cm-20x24in) s. prov. 3-Apr-3 Heffel, Vancouver #51/R (C.D 1600)
£1000 $1660 €1450 Punchbowl above Strathblane (34x45cm-13x18in) s. 13-Jun-3 Lyon & Turnbull, Edinburgh #34 est:600-900
£1800 $2790 €2700 Sheep on the woodland path above a loch (71x91cm-28x36in) s. 6-Dec-2 Lyon & Turnbull, Edinburgh #104/R est:2000-3000
£1800 $2790 €2700 Harvest time (39x55cm-15x22in) s. 5-Dec-2 Bonhams, Edinburgh #78 est:800-1200

Works on paper
£340 $568 €493 La rue des Pierres, Bruges (17x22cm-7x9in) W/C. 23-Jun-3 Bonhams, Bath #87
£680 $1061 €1020 Market scene, Italy (35x53cm-14x21in) s. W/C. 26-Mar-3 Sotheby's, Olympia #134/R

KAY, Dorothy (1886-1964) South African/Irish

£602 $969 €903 Tented night scene with figures (22x39cm-9x15in) s. board. 12-May-3 Stephan Welz, Johannesburg #320 est:6000-8000 (SA.R 7000)
£3686 $5749 €5529 Transkei, he said his name was Paulumbaan (81x51cm-32x20in) s.d.1947 board exhib. 15-Oct-2 Stephan Welz, Johannesburg #432/R est:40000-60000 (SA.R 60000)

Works on paper

£553 $862 €830 Pipe smoker (45x31cm-18x12in) s. chl gouache. 15-Oct-2 Stephan Welz, Johannesburg #431/R est:10000-15000 (SA.R 9000)

KAY, Hermann (1839-1902) German

£621 $1005 €900 Visiting the fortune teller (64x83cm-25x33in) s.d.74. 25-May-3 Uppsala Auktionskammare, Uppsala #91/R (S.KR 8000)

KAY, James (1858-1942) British

£380 $593 €570 Fishermen in a rocky cove (30x40cm-12x16in) s. 13-Sep-2 Lyon & Turnbull, Edinburgh #123/R
£800 $1248 €1200 Highland burn (60x51cm-24x20in) s. board. 13-Sep-2 Lyon & Turnbull, Edinburgh #45/R
£1000 $1550 €1500 On the Clyde (19x29cm-7x11in) bears sig.d.1890 canvas on board. 5-Dec-2 Bonhams, Edinburgh #9 est:1000-1500
£1000 $1550 €1500 Shepherd and his flock on a snowy hillside (29x44cm-11x17in) s. 5-Dec-2 Bonhams, Edinburgh #17 est:1000-1500
£1100 $1716 €1650 Buckhaven (16x26cm-6x10in) s. 17-Sep-2 Sotheby's, Olympia #41/R est:800-1200
£2000 $3120 €3000 Clyde near Bowling (62x75cm-24x30in) s. 10-Apr-3 Bonhams, Edinburgh #134/R est:2000-3000
£2600 $4030 €3900 Launch of battleship, river Clyde (71x91cm-28x36in) s. s.i.verso. 31-Oct-2 Christie's, London #102/R est:3000-5000
£2800 $4256 €4200 Roslin Chapel (51x60cm-20x24in) indis sig. board. 28-Aug-2 Sotheby's, London #1036/R est:2000-3000
£2800 $4368 €4200 The channel (63x76cm-25x30in) s. 17-Sep-2 Sotheby's, Olympia #42/R est:3000-4000
£3000 $4860 €4500 West highland harbour (56x75cm-22x30in) 23-May-3 Lyon & Turnbull, Edinburgh #91a est:3000-4000
£4000 $6200 €6000 Dutch fishing boats by moonlight (63x76cm-25x30in) s. 6-Dec-2 Lyon & Turnbull, Edinburgh #34/R est:4000-6000
£4500 $6975 €6750 Fisherman by a canal, Zeebrugge (50x60cm-20x24in) s. board. 6-Dec-2 Lyon & Turnbull, Edinburgh #63/R est:2500-4000
£6200 $10044 €9300 Lingering leaves (51x61cm-20x24in) s. exhib. 23-May-3 Lyon & Turnbull, Edinburgh #54/R est:2000-3000
£7500 $11400 €11250 Paris street scene (62x51cm-24x20in) s. 28-Aug-2 Sotheby's, London #1015/R est:8000-12000
£7800 $12090 €11700 Church square (76x63cm-30x25in) s. 6-Dec-2 Lyon & Turnbull, Edinburgh #53/R est:5000-7000

Works on paper

£480 $749 €720 In the forest of Klampenborg, Denmark (14x19cm-6x7in) s.i.indis.d.25 pastel. 18-Sep-2 Dreweatt Neate, Newbury #79/R
£500 $780 €750 Mending the nets (17x24cm-7x9in) s. gouache. 13-Sep-2 Lyon & Turnbull, Edinburgh #93/R
£1000 $1540 €1500 On the Clyde (20x29cm-8x11in) s. W/C prov. 23-Oct-2 Hamptons Fine Art, Godalming #51/R est:1000-1500
£1100 $1749 €1650 Head of Glen Fallock (25x35cm-10x14in) s. bodycol. 6-Mar-3 Christie's, Kensington #157/R est:600-800
£1400 $2142 €2100 Shipping on the Clyde (18x25cm-7x10in) W/C htd white scratching out. 22-Aug-2 Bonhams, Edinburgh #1146 est:600-800
£1400 $2184 €2100 Fisherfolk on the beach (47x59cm-19x23in) s. gouache. 10-Apr-3 Bonhams, Edinburgh #147 est:1200-1500
£1700 $2652 €2550 Ferryman's cottage. Three scenes at Portincaple (18x18cm-7x7in) col chk set of four. 14-Apr-3 Sotheby's, London #135/R est:1000-1500
£2500 $3900 €3750 Garlanded girl in profile (35x25cm-14x10in) s.d.1893 gouache. 17-Oct-2 Bonhams, Edinburgh #219 est:1000-1500
£4200 $6510 €6300 Red parasol (50x61cm-20x24in) s. W/C prov. 6-Dec-2 Lyon & Turnbull, Edinburgh #51/R est:3000-4000

KAY, Pamela (1939-) British

£580 $928 €870 Dusk, Grand Canal Venice (30x38cm-12x15in) mono. board. 14-Mar-3 Gardiner & Houlgate, Bath #35/R

KAY, Violet M (1914-1971) British

£800 $1248 €1200 Loch Golihead (71x91cm-28x36in) s. 17-Sep-2 Sotheby's, Olympia #68/R
£1050 $1691 €1575 Clovelly, Devon (60x50cm-24x20in) s. 15-Jan-3 James Thompson, Kirby Lonsdale #99

KAYAMA, Matazo (1927-) Japanese

Works on paper

£53459 $85000 €80189 Flock of birds in a winter forest (91x117cm-36x46in) s. ink col. 24-Mar-3 Christie's, Rockefeller NY #210/R est:50000-70000

KAYSER, Conrad (1880-?) German

£823 $1300 €1300 Black Forest landscape in early spring (95x74cm-37x29in) s.d.40. 29-Nov-2 Bolland & Marotz, Bremen #801/R est:1300

KAYSER-EICHBERG, Carl (1873-?) German

£2215 $3434 €3500 Shepherd talking to man on white horse in spring landscape (95x118cm-37x46in) s.d.08. 25-Sep-2 Neumeister, Munich #620/R est:1800

KAYYALI, Louai (1934-1978) Syrian

£10000 $15900 €15000 Little net restorer (77x98cm-30x39in) s.d.77 s.i.d.1977 verso oil pencil. 30-Apr-3 Sotheby's, London #143/R est:12000-15000
£10000 $15900 €15000 Sleeper (72x82cm-28x32in) s.d.1971 i.d.1971 verso. 30-Apr-3 Sotheby's, London #144/R est:12000-15000
£20000 $31800 €30000 Flower boy (94x74cm-37x29in) s.d.1975. 30-Apr-3 Sotheby's, London #145/R est:12000-15000

KAZENWADEL, Fred R (20th C) American/German

£348 $550 €522 Willows by lily pond (76x61cm-30x24in) init. 22-Apr-3 Arthur James, Florida #156

KAZOVSZKIJ, El (1950-) Hungarian

£413 $644 €620 Grail with egg (100x70cm-39x28in) s. paper. 11-Sep-2 Kieselbach, Budapest #120/R (H.F 160000)
£2794 $4359 €4191 Leaving Chimaera (100x80cm-39x31in) s.d.78. 11-Apr-3 Kieselbach, Budapest #161/R est:450000-1000000 (H.F 1000000)

KCHAOUDOFF, Jeantimir (20th C) ?

Works on paper

£324 $518 €450 La guerre etait enevitable (50x65cm-20x26in) s. Indian ink col crayon. 18-May-3 Neret-Minet, Paris #72

KCHO (1970-) Cuban

Works on paper

£6098 $10000 €9147 Propeler and tire balancing (156x220cm-61x87in) s.d.99 chl wash prov. 28-May-3 Christie's, Rockefeller NY #54/R est:12000-16000

KEANE, John (1954-) British

Works on paper

£550 $853 €825 Trickle down theory (61x56cm-24x22in) s.i.d.April 1992 PVA bodycol oil collage prov. 4-Dec-2 Christie's, Kensington #309/R

KEANE, William (19/20th C) American

£577 $900 €866 Coastal scene at sunset with sailing ships (41x66cm-16x26in) s. 20-Oct-2 Jeffery Burchard, Florida #72/R

KEARNE, Lindsay (19th C) British

£370 $577 €555 Tenby old harbour (33x48cm-13x19in) s.d.1886 i.verso. 11-Sep-2 Bonhams, Newport #228

KEATING, John (1889-?) British

Works on paper

£633 $981 €1000 Head of a man (40x29cm-16x11in) s. mixed media. 24-Sep-2 De Veres Art Auctions, Dublin #174 est:1000-1500

KEATING, Sean (1889-1978) Irish

£28000 $44800 €42000 Young girl before fireplace (101x91cm-40x36in) s. s.verso. 15-May-3 Christie's, London #81/R est:15000-25000
£86538 $134135 €135000 Unloading a turf boat, Aran (62x78cm-24x31in) s. canvas on board prov. 3-Dec-2 Bonhams & James Adam, Dublin #49/R est:70000-80000
£120000 $192000 €180000 Feast of Bridget (96x117cm-38x46in) s. s.i.verso exhib. 15-May-3 Christie's, London #82/R est:50000-80000

Works on paper

£962 $1490 €1500 Study of a young woman wearing a shawl (46x34cm-18x13in) s. pastel. 3-Dec-2 Bonhams & James Adam, Dublin #145/R est:1500-2500
£1006 $1570 €1600 Clouds over Inis Sheer (48x74cm-19x29in) s. crayon. 17-Sep-2 Thomas Adams, Dublin #2
£1081 $1686 €1600 Portrait of a boy (31x23cm-12x9in) s. pastel. 26-Mar-3 James Adam, Dublin #85/R est:1200-1500
£2101 $3446 €2900 Aran man (47x39cm-19x15in) chl. 28-May-3 Bonhams & James Adam, Dublin #162/R est:3000-5000
£2400 $3816 €3600 Couple (50x76cm-20x30in) s. pastel. 5-Mar-3 John Ross, Belfast #47 est:600-800
£3188 $5229 €4400 Study of an old man (43x32cm-17x13in) s. pastel. 28-May-3 Bonhams & James Adam, Dublin #163/R est:2500-3500
£4795 $7527 €7000 Fortune teller (55x68cm-22x27in) s. chl. 15-Apr-3 De Veres Art Auctions, Dublin #146/R est:5000-7000

KEATING, Tom (1917-1984) British
£320 $509 €480 Portrait of lady (41x51cm-16x20in) s. 29-Apr-3 Sworder & Son, Bishops Stortford #336/R
£760 $1224 €1140 Mother and child holding parasols in a wooded avenue (99x68cm-39x27in) s. 18-Feb-3 Bonhams, Knowle #228
Works on paper
£800 $1336 €1160 Dedham mill (33x51cm-13x20in) s.i. gouache. 25-Jun-3 Brightwells, Leominster #1024/R

KEATS, C J (?) British
Works on paper
£470 $734 €705 Village scene (29x49cm-11x19in) s. W/C. 7-Nov-2 International Art Centre, Auckland #177/R est:1500-2500 (NZ.D 1500)

KECK, H (19/20th C) ?
Sculpture
£1887 $2943 €3000 Your turn. pat.bronze ivory gilded lit. 14-Oct-2 Amberes, Antwerp #384/R

KECK, Otto (1873-1948) German
£288 $438 €450 Farmer's wife from Allgau in festive dress (47x38cm-19x15in) s.d.1925 lit. 11-Jul-2 Allgauer, Kempten #2547/R

KECK, Paul (1904-1973) German
£1301 $2030 €1900 Two skiers in old snow with view of High Ifen (27x33cm-11x13in) s. board lit. 10-Apr-3 Allgauer, Kempten #2830/R est:900

KEDL, Rudolf (1928-1991) Austrian?
Sculpture
£1013 $1580 €1600 Lovers (36cm-14in) s.d.1963 dark pat.bronze. 15-Oct-2 Dorotheum, Vienna #159/R est:2200-3600
£1582 $2453 €2500 Ptah (29cm-11in) s.d.1991 bronze. 24-Sep-2 Wiener Kunst Auktionen, Vienna #255/R est:2500-4000
£2848 $4500 €4500 Kneeling figure (45cm-18in) s.d.1961 gold brown pat.bronze. 27-Nov-2 Dorotheum, Vienna #256/R est:4500-6000

KEELING, David (1951-) Australian
£1720 $2615 €2580 Sign (59x59cm-23x23in) s. s.i.d.1989-90 verso wood panel. 28-Aug-2 Deutscher-Menzies, Melbourne #54/R est:4000-6000 (A.D 4800)
£3187 $5227 €4781 Diorama (101x76cm-40x30in) s.d.99 linen exhib. 4-Jun-3 Deutscher-Menzies, Melbourne #3/R est:7000-9000 (A.D 8000)
Works on paper
£1220 $1927 €1769 Untitled (50x30cm-20x12in) s.d.97 verso exhib. 22-Jul-3 Lawson Menzies, Sydney #15/R est:3000-5000 (A.D 3000)

KEELING, Michael (?-1820) British
£9375 $15000 €14063 Thomas Charlton Whitmore (49x40cm-19x16in) 14-Mar-3 Du Mouchelle, Detroit #2008/R est:10000-12000

KEENE, Caleb (1862-1954) Canadian
£262 $414 €393 Edge of the forest, Galt (37x30cm-15x12in) s. board. 14-Nov-2 Heffel, Vancouver #250/R (C.D 650)

KEENE, Charles Samuel (1823-1891) British
Works on paper
£300 $474 €450 Enemy (14x22cm-6x9in) init. sepia over pencil. 26-Nov-2 Bonhams, Knightsbridge #38/R

KEENE, Elmer (19/20th C) British
£340 $547 €510 Fisherman with beached fishing boats (51x69cm-20x27in) s. 19-Feb-3 Mallams, Oxford #466/R
£750 $1178 €1125 Winter landscape at sunset with figures, horses and a dog in the foreground (76x127cm-30x50in) s. 19-Nov-2 Bonhams, Leeds #238

KEENE, Paul F (1920-) American
£1282 $2000 €1923 After image (51x41cm-20x16in) s. 20-Sep-2 Freeman, Philadelphia #133/R est:600-1000
£2315 $3750 €3473 Abstract (46x25cm-18x10in) s. i.v. 24-Jan-3 Freeman, Philadelphia #152/R est:1000-1500

KEETMAN, Peter (1916-) German
Photographs
£1899 $3000 €3000 Children in snow (24x18cm-9x7in) s.d.1954 verso silver gelatin. 28-Nov-2 Villa Grisebach, Berlin #1250/R est:2800-3200
£2013 $3119 €3200 Stachus Munich (38x29cm-15x11in) s.i.d.1953 verso gelatin silver lit. 2-Nov-2 Lempertz, Koln #46/R est:3500
£2264 $3509 €3600 Munich, Auer Dult (31x24cm-12x9in) s.i.d.1965 verso gelatin silver. 2-Nov-2 Lempertz, Koln #47/R est:3000
£2466 $3847 €3600 Sparkling drops (29x38cm-11x15in) s.i.d. verso gelatin silver lit. 12-Apr-3 Lempertz, Koln #100/R est:2800
£2532 $4000 €3798 Garten stuhlr, Wendelstein (29x39cm-11x15in) s.i.d.1950 gelatin silver print prov.lit. 24-Apr-3 Phillips, New York #138/R est:4000-6000
£4545 $7000 €6818 Spiegelnde tropfen (29x38cm-11x15in) s.i.verso gelatin silver print board prov.lit. 25-Oct-2 Phillips, New York #105/R est:7000-10000

KEGELJAN, Franz (1847-1920) Belgian
£1772 $2800 €2800 Jeunes femmes dans les dunes (40x60cm-16x24in) s. 26-Nov-2 Palais de Beaux Arts, Brussels #335/R est:3000-4000

KEHNEY, G (?) ?
£270 $410 €405 Hunting figures on horseback riding through woods (48x79cm-19x31in) 28-Aug-2 Brightwells, Leominster #1097

KEHR, Karl (1866-1919) German
£265 $434 €405 Wiesen valley with Neideck ruins (73x98cm-29x39in) s.i.d.Nov 1907 panel. 6-Feb-3 Weidler, Nurnberg #7072
£865 $1341 €1350 Traveller on rain soaked field (60x49cm-24x19in) s.i. 7-Dec-2 Dannenberg, Berlin #694/R

KEIGA, Kwahara (attrib) (19th C) Japanese
Works on paper
£22785 $35316 €36000 Views of the island of Deshima, seen from the Bay of Nagasaki (17x37cm-7x15in) W/C pair. 24-Sep-2 Christie's, Amsterdam #159/R est:36000-42000

KEIL, Peter (1943-) German
£288 $456 €450 Untitled (68x56cm-27x22in) s.d.59 acrylic board. 12-Nov-2 Dorotheum, Vienna #203/R
£288 $460 €400 Figure with cigarette (74x79cm-29x31in) s. 14-May-3 Dorotheum, Linz #414/R
£316 $494 €500 Untitled (60x30cm-24x12in) s.d.75 i. verso acrylic panel. 15-Oct-2 Dorotheum, Vienna #215/R
£321 $506 €500 Figure composition (100x100cm-39x39in) s. acrylic. 18-Nov-2 Dorotheum, Linz #435/R
£380 $589 €600 Hildegard Knef - Hildchen (100x100cm-39x39in) s.i. s.i.d.1984 verso. 28-Sep-2 Ketterer, Hamburg #820/R
£432 $691 €600 Four heads (100x100cm-39x39in) s.d.82 acrylic. 14-May-3 Dorotheum, Linz #415/R
£506 $790 €800 Berlin youths (69x44cm-27x17in) s.i.d.59 verso acrylic panel. 15-Oct-2 Dorotheum, Vienna #176/R
£552 $883 €800 People (100x100cm-39x39in) s. 11-Mar-3 Dorotheum, Vienna #269/R
£861 $1403 €1300 Untitled (104x100cm-41x39in) s.d.89 acrylic. 28-Jan-3 Dorotheum, Vienna #258/R

KEIL, Robert (1905-1989) Austrian
£4430 $7000 €7000 Tuscan landscape (80x100cm-31x39in) s.d.52 exhib. 27-Nov-2 Dorotheum, Vienna #219/R est:5000-7000
Works on paper
£310 $497 €450 Vase with yellow chrysanthemums (66x48cm-26x19in) s.d.69 W/C. 11-Mar-3 Dorotheum, Vienna #156/R
£314 $487 €500 Flowers (66x48cm-26x19in) s.d.VIII.69 col pen. 30-Oct-2 Dorotheum, Vienna #127
£1377 $2258 €1900 Spring II (61x50cm-24x20in) s.d.62 i.d.II 62 verso W/C pastel chk. 28-May-3 Lempertz, Koln #206/R est:1800

KEINANEN, Sigfrid August (1841-1914) Finnish
£1266 $2000 €2000 Villa in Terijoki (21x33cm-8x13in) s.d.1890 panel. 30-Nov-2 Hagelstam, Helsinki #99/R est:2000
£2025 $3200 €3200 Rowing trip (33x44cm-13x17in) s.d.1891. 30-Nov-2 Hagelstam, Helsinki #98/R est:4000
£2595 $4100 €4100 Old country road (40x30cm-16x12in) s.d.1888. 1-Dec-2 Bukowskis, Helsinki #81/R est:4500-5000
£2848 $4500 €4500 Walking on village road in winter (36x86cm-14x34in) s. 1-Dec-2 Bukowskis, Helsinki #80/R est:6000-7000
£3291 $5200 €5200 With grandfather as teacher (40x30cm-16x12in) s.d.1884 board. 1-Dec-2 Bukowskis, Helsinki #79/R est:6000-8000
£4507 $7256 €6400 Sunny winter's day with man on sleigh pulled by horse (42x95cm-17x37in) s. 10-May-3 Bukowskis, Helsinki #125/R est:4000-5000

KEIRINCX, Alexander (1600-1652) Flemish
£2250 $3645 €3263 River landscape (12x10cm-5x4in) panel. 26-May-3 Bukowskis, Stockholm #445/R est:12000-15000 (S.KR 29000)
£9259 $15000 €13889 Wooded landscape with a stream and a stag (19x24cm-7x9in) panel prov. 24-Jan-3 Christie's, Rockefeller NY #40/R est:20000-30000

£13000 $20410 €19500 Landscape with pond by woods and figures on a track (39x49cm-15x19in) panel. 12-Dec-2 Sotheby's, London #133/R est:15000-20000

KEIRSBILCK, Jules van (1833-1896) Belgian

£2600 $4160 €3900 Rest from spinning (80x67cm-31x26in) s. 11-Mar-3 Bonhams, Knightsbridge #318c/R est:3000-5000

KEISERMANN, Franz (1765-1833) Swiss

Works on paper

£2405 $3800 €3800 View of Lanuvio (23x30cm-9x12in) s.i. W/C card. 26-Nov-2 Christie's, Rome #124/R est:5000
£3636 $5200 €5454 Italianate landscape (54x75cm-21x30in) s.i.d.1814 W/C. 23-Jan-3 Swann Galleries, New York #371/R est:6000-9000
£6087 $9435 €9131 Vue de Grotte des Syrinx et du Temple de la Sibille aTivoli (76x54cm-30x21in) s.i. W/C. 9-Dec-2 Philippe Schuler, Zurich #4167/R est:10000-14000 (S.FR 14000)
£7097 $10432 €11000 Temple of Paestum (66x103cm-26x41in) s.d.1810 W/C. 20-Jun-2 Dr Fritz Nagel, Stuttgart #668/R est:6000
£9091 $15182 €13000 Vue du ponte Lucano et du tombeau de la Famille Plautia (60x110cm-24x43in) s. pierre noire W/C prov. 25-Jun-3 Sotheby's, Paris #45/R est:10000-15000

KEITA, Seydou (1921-2001) African

Photographs

£2200 $3674 €3190 Untitled (40x54cm-16x21in) s.d.1998 black white photo. 24-Jun-3 Sotheby's, Olympia #141/R est:700-900
£3165 $5000 €4748 Man with flower (53x40cm-21x16in) s.d.1959/1998 gelatin silver print prov.lit. 22-Apr-3 Christie's, Rockefeller NY #99/R est:4000-6000
£3250 $5200 €4875 Untitled (51x41cm-20x16in) s.d.10.9.2001 gelatin silver print prov. 16-May-3 Phillips, New York #196/R est:3000-5000
£4114 $6500 €6171 Woman with baby (40x57cm-16x22in) s.i.d.1952-55/1995 gelatin silver print. 22-Apr-3 Christie's, Rockefeller NY #98/R est:6000-8000
£7143 $11000 €10715 Twins in European dress (119x165cm-47x65in) s. gelatin silver print exec.c.1957 prov.lit. 25-Oct-2 Phillips, New York #130/R est:12000-15000

KEITH, Elizabeth (1887-?) American

Works on paper

£1300 $2055 €1950 Moonlight, Hong Kong (30x38cm-12x15in) s.d.1924 W/C bodycol. 15-Nov-2 Sotheby's, London #18 est:800-1200

KEITH, William (1839-1911) American

£1625 $2600 €2438 Clearing in the forest (51x66cm-20x26in) s. style of Barbizon School prov. 15-Mar-3 Eldred, East Dennis #282/R est:4000-5000
£1911 $3000 €2867 Northern California landscape (51x41cm-20x16in) s. 14-Dec-2 Weschler, Washington #669/R est:3000-5000
£2707 $4250 €4061 Under the oak (51x76cm-20x30in) s.i. i.verso prov. 19-Nov-2 Butterfields, San Francisco #8155/R est:5000-7000
£2885 $4500 €4328 Figures among the oak trees. 21-Sep-2 Harvey Clar, Oakland #1507a
£3293 $5500 €4775 Figures in Barbazon landscape (41x71cm-16x28in) s.i. prov. 17-Jun-3 John Moran, Pasadena #98 est:5000-7500
£4217 $7000 €6115 Mt Shasta (37x61cm-15x24in) s. prov. 11-Jun-3 Butterfields, San Francisco #4174/R est:7000-10000
£4459 $7000 €6689 Sierra foothills (77x102cm-30x40in) s.i. 19-Nov-2 Butterfields, San Francisco #8134/R est:8000-12000
£4518 $7500 €6551 White water stream in a mountain landscape (46x31cm-18x12in) s. canvas on board prov. 11-Jun-3 Butterfields, San Francisco #4175/R est:7000-10000
£11180 $18000 €16770 Springtime, river landscape (20x26cm-8x10in) s. wood panel prov. 18-Feb-3 John Moran, Pasadena #65a est:12000-15000
£11613 $18000 €17420 Oak glade (56x46cm-22x18in) s. prov. 29-Oct-2 John Moran, Pasadena #626 est:7000-9000
£12821 $20000 €19232 Evening Sierras. 21-Sep-2 Harvey Clar, Oakland #1506
£37037 $60000 €55556 Yosemite Valley (62x87cm-24x34in) s. prov.exhib.lit. 22-May-3 Christie's, Rockefeller NY #29/R est:70000-90000

KEITH, William Castle (1864-1927) American

£1164 $1816 €1700 Woman reading in front of a window (24x15cm-9x6in) s. canvas on board. 14-Apr-3 Glerum, Amsterdam #80/R est:400-600

KEIUN (19th C) Japanese

Sculpture

£1578 $2477 €2367 Okimono of a monkey trainer (31cm-12in) s. wood ivory. 25-Nov-2 Stephan Welz, Johannesburg #173/R est:10000-15000 (SA.R 24000)

KEIZO, Morishita (1944-) Japanese

£347 $552 €500 Archipelagus (50x70cm-20x28in) s. acrylic tempera cardboard. 1-May-3 Meeting Art, Vercelli #153

KELDER, Toon (1894-1973) Dutch

£318 $497 €500 Self portrait (72x47cm-28x19in) s.d.33. 6-Nov-2 Vendue Huis, Gravenhage #167
£480 $758 €720 Figures on horses (61x49cm-24x19in) s. 14-Nov-2 Christie's, Kensington #255/R
£559 $900 €839 Still life of sunflowers (134x109cm-53x43in) s.d.29. 12-May-3 Stephan Welz, Johannesburg #433/R est:7000-10000 (SA.R 6500)
£1019 $1569 €1600 Portrait of a man smoking a cigarette (98x80cm-39x31in) s.d.26. 3-Sep-2 Christie's, Amsterdam #389/R est:1600-1800
£2014 $3304 €2800 Lamentation (41x35cm-16x14in) s. prov.exhib. 3-Jun-3 Christie's, Amsterdam #226/R est:2500-3500
£2532 $4000 €4000 Zittend Naakt (110x90cm-43x35in) s. exhib. 26-Nov-2 Sotheby's, Amsterdam #123/R est:4000-6000
£3597 $5899 €5000 Maripits in South Limburg (90x110cm-35x43in) s. 3-Jun-3 Christie's, Amsterdam #230/R est:5000-7000
£10256 $15897 €16000 Spaansche vrouw - Spanish woman (111x90cm-44x35in) s. painted c.1925 prov.exhib. 3-Dec-2 Christie's, Amsterdam #2/R est:4000-6000

Works on paper

£704 $1134 €1000 Portrait of the conductor Frits Coeberg van "Musica" (55x41cm-22x16in) s. W/C. 7-May-3 Vendue Huis, Gravenhage #199/R
£1083 $1689 €1700 Abstract composition (46x30cm-18x12in) s.d.50 gouache. 6-Nov-2 Vendue Huis, Gravenhage #230 est:2000-3000

KELETI, Gusztav (1834-1902) Hungarian

£1062 $1657 €1593 Forest lake (15x23cm-6x9in) panel. 11-Apr-3 Kieselbach, Budapest #16/R est:380000 (H.F 380000)

KELETY, Alexander (20th C) French

Sculpture

£1154 $1788 €1800 Chasseur poursuivant deux gazelles (50x95cm-20x37in) s. gilt silver pat bronze. 3-Dec-2 Sotheby's, Paris #114/R

KELLEN, Hendrika Wilhelmina van der (1846-1903) Dutch

£395 $639 €600 Birds of a feather hang together (42x35cm-17x14in) s. panel. 21-Jan-3 Christie's, Amsterdam #279
£461 $746 €700 Bouquet of roses (46x56cm-18x22in) s.d.VX. 21-Jan-3 Christie's, Amsterdam #283
£855 $1386 €1300 Still life with rhododendrons in a jug and books (68x78cm-27x31in) s. 21-Jan-3 Christie's, Amsterdam #7/R est:1300-1500

KELLER, A (?) ?

Sculpture

£1144 $1876 €1750 Dancing female nude (70cm-28in) s. brown pat.bronze marble socle. 29-Mar-3 Dannenberg, Berlin #209/R est:500

KELLER, Adolphe (20th C) Belgian

£345 $548 €500 Chenes et bouleaux (72x92cm-28x36in) s.d.1943. 4-Mar-3 Palais de Beaux Arts, Brussels #348
£479 $748 €700 Barque de peche a maree basse (45x55cm-18x22in) s. panel. 14-Apr-3 Horta, Bruxelles #372
£655 $1048 €950 Etang a Watermael Boitsfort (51x85cm-20x33in) s. 17-Mar-3 Horta, Bruxelles #70
£1727 $2763 €2400 Vue de canal avec peniches (100x120cm-39x47in) s. 13-May-3 Palais de Beaux Arts, Brussels #81/R est:2500-3750

KELLER, Albert von (1844-1920) Swiss

£873 $1362 €1310 Female nude dancing outdoors (41x25cm-16x10in) s. panel. 6-Nov-2 Dobiaschofsky, Bern #730/R (S.FR 2000)
£1282 $1987 €2000 Elegant lady in dark gown standing in front of a spinet (26x18cm-10x7in) s.d.1870 panel. 4-Dec-2 Neumeister, Munich #778/R est:800
£1646 $2551 €2600 Woman praying at wayside cross (18x14cm-7x6in) s. panel. 26-Sep-2 Neumeister, Munich #2755/R est:600
£1717 $2712 €2576 Piano teacher (20x40cm-8x16in) s. panel lit. 29-Nov-2 Zofingen, Switzerland #2939/R est:4500 (S.FR 4000)

KELLER, Alfred (1875-1945) Austrian

£324 $531 €450 Wachauer Donau landscape with Hoch-Arnsdorf (68x98cm-27x39in) s. 5-Jun-3 Dorotheum, Salzburg #526/R

KELLER, Arthur I (1866-1925) American

£2404 $3750 €3606 Man surprising couple in formal gardens (76x58cm-30x23in) s. canvasboard. 9-Nov-2 Illustration House, New York #181/R est:4000-6000

KELLER, Clyde Leon (1872-1962) American
£621 $1000 €932 Autumn gold, cows in wooded landscape (56x69cm-22x27in) i.d.1938 verso masonite. 18-Feb-3 John Moran, Pasadena #148
KELLER, Ferdinand (1842-1922) German
£1582 $2500 €2500 Water nymphe (27x17cm-11x7in) lit. 29-Nov-2 Schloss Ahlden, Ahlden #1181/R est:3800
£10000 $16400 €15000 Puttenfries musik - frieze with putti, music (82x185cm-32x73in) s.d.1882 prov.exhib.lit. 3-Jun-3 Sotheby's, London #8/R est:10000-15000
£12500 $19625 €18750 Beauty and butterfly (138x102cm-54x40in) s.d.1870 exhib.lit. 25-Nov-2 Christie's, Melbourne #138/R est:40000-50000 (A.D 35000)
KELLER, Friedrich von (1840-1914) German
£1290 $1897 €2000 Quarry (42x59cm-17x23in) s. 20-Jun-2 Dr Fritz Nagel, Stuttgart #781/R est:2500
£13836 $21585 €22000 Peasants on workshop (118x162cm-46x64in) s.i. prov. 19-Sep-2 Dr Fritz Nagel, Stuttgart #952/R est:22000
KELLER, Hans (1884-?) Swiss
£515 $814 €773 Horgen - Huttensee (59x78cm-23x31in) s.d. s.i. verso pavatex. 29-Nov-2 Falk & Falk, Zurich #502/R (S.FR 1200)
KELLER, Henry George (1870-1949) American
£2439 $4000 €3537 Three periods of art (76x64cm-30x25in) s. exhib. 30-May-3 Aspire, Cleveland #38/R est:5000-10000
Works on paper
£352 $550 €528 Entrance to the Giudecca Canal, Venice (48x30cm-19x12in) s.d. W/C exec.c.1901. 28-Mar-3 Aspire, Cleveland #58/R
£759 $1200 €1101 Caravan wagon (58x51cm-23x20in) s. W/C gouache. 5-Apr-3 DeFina, Austinburg #1301
£898 $1500 €1302 Circus scene (42x57cm-17x22in) mono. W/C. 22-Jun-3 Freeman, Philadelphia #97/R est:2000-3000
£3617 $5750 €5426 Vieux carre from Jackson Square (28x38cm-11x15in) i.verso W/C on board executed c.1850-69. 22-Mar-3 New Orleans Auction, New Orleans #1256/R est:4000-7000
£4790 $8000 €6946 Figures and umbrellas on beach (51x69cm-20x27in) mono. W/C gouache chl prov. 17-Jun-3 John Moran, Pasadena #84 est:3000-5000
KELLER, Joseph von (1811-1873) German
£366 $600 €549 Musicians counting their earnings (34x24cm-13x9in) s. panel prov. 5-Feb-3 Christie's, Rockefeller NY #289/R
KELLER, Terrence (1947-) Canadian
£201 $315 €302 Untitled (115x158cm-45x62in) s.d.1980 acrylic. 25-Nov-2 Hodgins, Calgary #190/R (C.D 500)
KELLER, Willi (1942-) Swiss
£1528 $2384 €2292 Cattle in Appenzell (34x55cm-13x22in) s.d.1974 board. 6-Nov-2 Hans Widmer, St Gallen #106/R est:3500-6500 (S.FR 3500)
£1528 $2384 €2292 Appenzell council (38x58cm-15x23in) s.d.1982 board. 6-Nov-2 Hans Widmer, St Gallen #107/R est:3500-6500 (S.FR 3500)
KELLER-REUTLINGEN, Paul Wilhelm (1854-1920) German
£897 $1399 €1346 View of houses with cattle grazing alongside a riverbank (30x47cm-12x19in) s. 11-Nov-2 Stephan Welz, Johannesburg #427/R (SA.R 14000)
£5696 $8829 €9000 Young peasant woman in meadow with white and red flowers (63x80cm-25x31in) s. 25-Sep-2 Neumeister, Munich #621/R est:6000
£9494 $15000 €14241 In the poppy field (63x80cm-25x31in) s. 24-Apr-3 Sotheby's, New York #97/R est:15000-20000
KELLEY, Mike (1954-) American
£3797 $6000 €5696 Wedged lump (102x81cm-40x32in) acrylic paper painted 1991 prov. 13-Nov-2 Sotheby's, New York #490/R est:6000-8000
£9494 $15000 €14241 Fabric of life (126x122cm-50x48in) i. acrylic on board prov. 22-Apr-3 Butterfields, San Francisco #6076/R est:15000-20000
Photographs
£4000 $6560 €6000 More tragic! More plangent! More purple! Rothko Chapel No.5 (76x61cm-30x24in) s.d.1996 num.3/5 verso col photo Museum board prov.exhib. 6-Feb-3 Christie's, London #708/R est:5000-7000
£9494 $15000 €14241 Color and form (124x213cm-49x84in) s. col coupler prints diptych executed 1999 prov.exhib.lit. 14-Nov-2 Christie's, Rockefeller NY #447/R est:20000-30000
Sculpture
£11392 $18000 €17088 Untitled (28x37x8cm-11x15x3in) sewn fabric stuffed animals exec.1990 prov. 13-Nov-2 Sotheby's, New York #475/R est:25000-35000
KELLEY, Ramon (1939-) American
Works on paper
£353 $550 €530 Antonio, Mazatlan, Mexico (30x23cm-12x9in) s. i.verso pastel prov. 9-Nov-2 Santa Fe Art, Santa Fe #254/R
KELLY, Cecil (1879-1954) New Zealander
£451 $722 €654 Govenors Bay, Banks Peninsula (39x50cm-15x20in) s. board. 13-May-3 Watson's, Christchurch #174/R (NZ.D 1250)
KELLY, Chapman (1932-) American
£1090 $1700 €1635 Arco de Tito, Roma (46x66cm-18x26in) s.d.57 s.i.d.57 verso prov. 12-Oct-2 Neal Auction Company, New Orleans #646/R est:2000-3000
£1154 $1800 €1731 Woman with flowers (51x76cm-20x30in) 19-Oct-2 David Dike, Dallas #132/R est:3000-4000
KELLY, David (1959-) Malawian
£500 $780 €750 Herd of African elephants on the Savanna (98x145cm-39x57in) d.94. 6-Aug-2 Outhwaite & Litherland, Liverpool #266
KELLY, Ellsworth (1923-) American
£750000 $1200000 €1125000 Green white (180x358cm-71x141in) init.d.1968 verso canvas on panel prov.exhib.lit. 14-May-3 Christie's, Rockefeller NY #36/R est:1200000-1600000
Prints
£2000 $3100 €3000 Blue - yellow-red (107x76cm-42x30in) s.num.13/75 col lithograph. 5-Dec-2 Sotheby's, London #218/R est:2500-3000
£2258 $3500 €3387 Saint Martin landscape (68x85cm-27x33in) s.num.11/12 col lithograph screenprint. 25-Sep-2 Christie's, Rockefeller NY #315/R est:1000-1500
£2673 $4250 €4010 Blue/white/red (108x76cm-43x30in) s.num.40/54 col lithograph. 2-May-3 Sotheby's, New York #491/R est:2500-3500
£2673 $4250 €4010 Magnolia (155x224cm-61x88in) s.i.d.1966 lithograph. 30-Apr-3 Doyle, New York #217/R est:1500-2000
£3459 $5500 €5189 Lemon (69x37cm-27x15in) s.num.23/75 lithograph. 29-Apr-3 Christie's, Rockefeller NY #648/R est:2500-3500
£3797 $6000 €5696 Color paper image (82x116cm-32x46in) s.num.15/21 hand col print paper pulp. 22-Apr-3 Butterfields, San Francisco #2310/R est:3000-5000
£4403 $7000 €6605 Coloured paper image XVIII, green square with dark gray (80x78cm-31x31in) s.num.18/22 col pressed paper pulp. 2-May-3 Sotheby's, New York #492/R est:7000-10000
£4430 $7000 €6645 Nine square (103x103cm-41x41in) s.num.40/44 col silkscreen lithograph. 22-Apr-3 Butterfields, San Francisco #2311/R est:10000-15000
£5806 $9000 €8709 Colored paper image XX (82x79cm-32x31in) s.num.10/22 col pressed paper. 25-Sep-2 Christie's, Rockefeller NY #314/R est:3000-4000
£7547 $12000 €11321 Dracena I. Dracena II (103x67cm-41x26in) s.num.AP 7/9 lithograph two. 29-Apr-3 Christie's, Rockefeller NY #650/R est:4000-6000
£9615 $15000 €14423 Nine squares (103x103cm-41x41in) s.num.10/44 col screenprint offset lithograph. 5-Nov-2 Christie's, Rockefeller NY #442/R est:10000-15000
£20570 $32500 €30855 Untitled - red and blue squares (56x85cm-22x33in) s. col pressed paper pulp executed 1976 prov. 13-Nov-2 Sotheby's, New York #307/R est:20000-30000
Sculpture
£202532 $320000 €303798 Diagonal curve XXI - EK790 (129x236x1cm-51x93x0in) stainless steel executed 1988 prov. 12-Nov-2 Sotheby's, New York #56/R est:400000-600000
£237500 $380000 €356250 Curve in relief III - EK561 (38x335x4cm-15x132x2in) painted aluminium exec.1978 prov.exhib.lit. 13-May-3 Sotheby's, New York #30/R est:300000-400000
Works on paper
£2243 $3500 €3365 Untitled (28x22cm-11x9in) s.i.d.31 October 1963 pen ink. 14-Oct-2 Butterfields, San Francisco #2053/R est:5000-7000
KELLY, Felix (1916-1994) New Zealander
£1200 $1860 €1800 P.S Eagle, Auckland (43x56cm-17x22in) s.d.52 board prov.exhib. 4-Dec-2 Christie's, Kensington #44/R est:1000-1500

£1300 $2145 €1885 Plush Manor, Dorchester (63x76cm-25x30in) s.d.84 board. 3-Jul-3 Christie's, Kensington #705a/R est:1200-1800
£1700 $2839 €2465 Alpine folly (36x46cm-14x18in) s. board prov. 24-Jun-3 Bonhams, New Bond Street #36/R est:1500-2000
£1800 $3006 €2610 The Lodge, Marble Arch (49x71cm-19x28in) s.d.65 board prov.exhib. 24-Jun-3 Bonhams, New Bond Street #34/R est:1200-1800
£16000 $26400 €23200 Nuns on the beach (56x71cm-22x28in) s.d.69 tempera on board prov. 3-Jul-3 Christie's, Kensington #705/R est:5000-7000

KELLY, Grace Veronica (1877-1950) American
£443 $700 €642 Two figures walking on the beach (74x94cm-29x37in) s. 5-Apr-3 DeFina, Austinburg #1305

KELLY, James Edward (1855-1933) American
Sculpture
£2229 $3500 €3344 Sheridan's ride (48cm-19in) s.i.d.79 green brown pat bronze 19/64. 10-Dec-2 Doyle, New York #98/R est:4000-6000

KELLY, John (1965-) Australian
£3393 $5259 €5090 Aerial view (40x30cm-16x12in) s.i.d.March 93 verso oval. 29-Oct-2 Lawson Menzies, Sydney #2/R est:7500-9500 (A.D 9500)
£3559 $5445 €5339 Zebra (35x40cm-14x16in) s.d.98. 25-Aug-2 Sotheby's, Paddington #135/R est:7000-10000 (A.D 10000)
£3915 $5989 €5873 Study for camouflage cow (25x40cm-10x16in) i.d.95 verso prov. 25-Aug-2 Sotheby's, Paddington #136/R est:5000-7000 (A.D 11000)
£4264 $6779 €6396 Untitled (137x91cm-54x36in) s.d.88. 5-May-3 Sotheby's, Melbourne #164/R est:12000-18000 (A.D 11000)
£4781 $7841 €6932 Study for man wearing a cow's head (50x25cm-20x10in) s.d.94 i.d.verso prov. 4-Jun-3 Deutscher-Menzies, Melbourne #1/R est:14000-18000 (A.D 12000)
£6202 $9860 €9303 Dobell's cow (26x44cm-10x17in) s.d.93 s.i.d.93 verso exhib. 5-May-3 Sotheby's, Melbourne #122/R est:15000-20000 (A.D 16000)
£6202 $9860 €9303 Untitled (75x91cm-30x36in) 5-May-3 Sotheby's, Melbourne #137/R est:12000-18000 (A.D 16000)
£7364 $11709 €11046 Arial view no 1 (123x78cm-48x31in) s.d.93 canvasboard oval prov. 5-May-3 Sotheby's, Melbourne #129/R est:18000-28000 (A.D 19000)
£7857 $12414 €11786 Looking in the dark (137x152cm-54x60in) painted 2000 prov.exhib. 26-Nov-2 Sotheby's, Melbourne #24/R est:25000-35000 (A.D 22000)
£9609 $14701 €14414 Labyrinth (91x136cm-36x54in) s.d.1996 i.verso. 25-Aug-2 Sotheby's, Paddington #36/R est:18000-25000 (A.D 27000)
£9690 $15407 €14535 Two heads (91x60cm-36x24in) s.d.93 i.verso. 5-May-3 Sotheby's, Melbourne #102/R est:12000-18000 (A.D 25000)
£9690 $15407 €14535 Dobell's cow. Mitchell bomber II (27x54cm-11x21in) s.d.93 exhib. two. 5-May-3 Sotheby's, Melbourne #153/R est:25000-30000 (A.D 25000)
£11923 $18957 €17885 Nine cows in a stack (35x71cm-14x28in) s.d.94 linen prov. 4-Mar-3 Deutscher-Menzies, Melbourne #16/R est:12000-18000 (A.D 31000)
£14235 $21779 €21353 Dobell's cows (90x120cm-35x47in) s.d.1992 board prov. 25-Aug-2 Sotheby's, Paddington #63/R est:40000-60000 (A.D 40000)
£14286 $22571 €21429 Cow depot waiting to be painted 1993 (78x87cm-31x34in) s.d.93 oil on linen prov. 27-Nov-2 Deutscher-Menzies, Melbourne #5/R est:18000-26000 (A.D 40000)
£16923 $26908 €25385 Heads and tales (112x183cm-44x72in) i.d.1997/98 verso prov. 4-Mar-3 Deutscher-Menzies, Melbourne #39/R est:25000-35000 (A.D 44000)
£19713 $29964 €29570 Upside down head II (56x91cm-22x36in) s.d.95 i.verso prov. 28-Aug-2 Deutscher-Menzies, Melbourne #55/R est:12000-18000 (A.D 55000)
£21352 $32669 €32028 Aerial view I (119x119cm-47x47in) panel prov.exhib. 25-Aug-2 Sotheby's, Paddington #24/R est:35000-45000 (A.D 60000)
£22093 $35128 €33140 Two cows and a windsock (37x65cm-15x26in) prov. 5-May-3 Sotheby's, Melbourne #141/R est:25000-35000 (A.D 57000)
£25000 $39500 €37500 Black and white composition (122x122cm-48x48in) s.d.95 oil on linen prov.exhib. 27-Nov-2 Deutscher-Menzies, Melbourne #37/R est:30000-40000 (A.D 70000)
£25000 $39500 €37500 Dobell's cow nocturne (75x121cm-30x48in) s.d.93 plywood on panel prov. 26-Nov-2 Sotheby's, Melbourne #8/R est:28000-38000 (A.D 70000)
£26786 $42321 €40179 Man lifting cow I (182x152cm-72x60in) s.d.94 s.i.d.verso oil on linen prov. 27-Nov-2 Deutscher-Menzies, Melbourne #19/R est:30000-40000 (A.D 75000)
£26882 $40860 €40323 Camouflaged cow (90x152cm-35x60in) i.d.1995/96 verso. 28-Aug-2 Deutscher-Menzies, Melbourne #28/R est:35000-40000 (A.D 75000)
£30000 $48300 €45000 Cow stack (167x122cm-66x48in) s.d.01 prov. 6-May-3 Christie's, Melbourne #18/R est:50000-80000 (A.D 75000)
£33915 $53924 €50873 Dobell's cow on trestles (110x166cm-43x65in) s.d.93 i.verso prov. 5-May-3 Sotheby's, Melbourne #109/R est:60000-80000 (A.D 87500)
£35714 $56429 €53571 Cow depot V (120x181cm-47x71in) s.d.94 panel prov. 26-Nov-2 Sotheby's, Melbourne #1/R est:50000-70000 (A.D 100000)
£35842 $54480 €53763 Stack (167x122cm-66x48in) i.d.1995 verso prov. 28-Aug-2 Deutscher-Menzies, Melbourne #1/R est:25000-35000 (A.D 100000)
Sculpture
£5385 $8562 €8078 Cow up a tree (24x18x12cm-9x7x5in) s.i.d.1998 oil on bronze edition 3/10. 4-Mar-3 Deutscher-Menzies, Melbourne #2/R est:10000-15000 (A.D 14000)
£5694 $8712 €8541 Cow (15cm-6in) s.d.95 painted bronze. 25-Aug-2 Sotheby's, Paddington #220/R est:5000-8000 (A.D 16000)
£6071 $9593 €9107 8 cow stacked 2000 (21x22x22cm-8x9x9in) oil bronze. 27-Nov-2 Deutscher-Menzies, Melbourne #2/R est:8000-12000 (A.D 17000)
£7857 $12414 €11786 Cow up a tree (57x57x36cm-22x22x14in) num.6/9 oil bronze. 27-Nov-2 Deutscher-Menzies, Melbourne #1/R est:10000-15000 (A.D 22000)
£8571 $13543 €12857 Cow on trestles (21x33x16cm-8x13x6in) bronze oil. 27-Nov-2 Deutscher-Menzies, Melbourne #35/R est:8000-12000 (A.D 24000)
£9231 $14677 €13847 Cow on a trestle (23x34x16cm-9x13x6in) s.d.96 oil on bronze. 4-Mar-3 Deutscher-Menzies, Melbourne #3/R est:12000-16000 (A.D 24000)
£9319 $14165 €13979 Two cow stacks (25x38x11cm-10x15x4in) bronze pair. 28-Aug-2 Deutscher-Menzies, Melbourne #2/R est:10000-15000 (A.D 26000)
£9562 $15681 €13865 Two cows on a trestle (30x48x15cm-12x19x6in) s.d.96 painted bronze. 4-Jun-3 Deutscher-Menzies, Melbourne #17/R est:28000-35000 (A.D 24000)
£48000 $77280 €72000 Three cows stacked (169x140x41cm-67x55x16in) incised oil painted bronze on steel base prov. 6-May-3 Christie's, Melbourne #50/R est:120000-150000 (A.D 120000)
Works on paper
£2789 $4573 €4044 Upside down cow (21x33cm-8x13in) s.d.01 W/C. 4-Jun-3 Deutscher-Menzies, Melbourne #152/R est:7000-9000 (A.D 7000)
£4781 $7841 €6932 Cow stack (37x26cm-15x10in) s.d.94 W/C gouache chk prov. 4-Jun-3 Deutscher-Menzies, Melbourne #13/R est:9000-12000 (A.D 12000)
£6513 $10226 €9770 Study for a cow stack 1994 (34x74cm-13x29in) s.d.94 gouache chk prov. 15-Apr-3 Lawson Menzies, Sydney #7/R est:7000-9000 (A.D 17000)
£8846 $14065 €13269 Two men lifting a cow (42x56cm-17x22in) s.d.95 i.verso W/C gouache pencil. 4-Mar-3 Deutscher-Menzies, Melbourne #17/R est:4500-6500 (A.D 23000)

KELLY, John (1932-) Irish
Works on paper
£372 $603 €525 Icarus Head (54x28cm-21x11in) s. W/C pencil. 20-May-3 Mealy's, Castlecomer #1317/R

KELLY, Lloyd (20th C) American
£574 $900 €861 Autumn tree (36x46cm-14x18in) s.d.1987. 22-Nov-2 Skinner, Boston #279/R est:1200-1800

KELLY, Paul (1968-) Irish
£1250 $1987 €1800 Cattle grazing, County Kerry (23x30cm-9x12in) s. i.d.2000 verso board. 29-Apr-3 Whyte's, Dublin #170/R est:1800-2200
£1282 $1987 €2000 Vegetable garden, Ardgillan (21x29cm-8x11in) s. board. 3-Dec-2 Bonhams & James Adam, Dublin #44/R est:1500-2000

KELLY, Philip (1950-) Irish
£350 $567 €525 La Faena (104x193cm-41x76in) s.i.d.93 verso. 21-Jan-3 Rosebery Fine Art, London #639
£371 $594 €538 Ecsena urbana (71x56cm-28x22in) s.d.1996 paper. 15-May-3 Louis Morton, Mexico #24b (M.P 6000)

KELLY, Richard Barrett Talbot (1896-1971) British
Works on paper
£300 $474 €435 Lapwing in flight (26x36cm-10x14in) mono.d.60 W/C. 22-Jul-3 Bonhams, Knightsbridge #12/R

£1000 $1580 €1500 Redshanks (117x130cm-46x51in) s. W/C. 28-Nov-2 Bonhams, Knightsbridge #48/R est:1200-1800

KELLY, Robert George Talbot (1861-1934) British
£700 $1113 €1050 Danger in the desert (26x46cm-10x18in) s.d.1897. 29-Apr-3 Bonhams, New Bond Street #111a
Works on paper
£280 $434 €420 Shepherd and his flock by a river (28x38cm-11x15in) s.d.1899 W/C. 24-Sep-2 Bonhams, Knightsbridge #158/R
£480 $773 €720 Desert scene with a woman carrying a water pot and sheep at a well (32x53cm-13x21in) s. W/C prov. 15-Jan-3 Cheffins Grain & Comins, Cambridge #390/R
£650 $1034 €975 Banks of the Nile (18x32cm-7x13in) s.d.1894 W/C. 29-Apr-3 Bonhams, New Bond Street #99a
£1900 $2964 €2850 Tombs of the Khalifs (54x94cm-21x37in) s.i.d.1888 W/C. 26-Mar-3 Sotheby's, Olympia #128/R est:1200-1800

KELLY, Robert W (1956-) American
Works on paper
£7092 $11489 €10000 Antiquary XXXIX (76x58cm-30x23in) s.i.d.2002 verso mixed media canvas. 20-May-3 Porro, Milan #34/R est:12000-12500

KELLY, Samuel Edward (fl.1920s) British
Works on paper
£980 $1529 €1470 Babbacombe from the East. Babbacombe from the west (27x37cm-11x15in) s. W/C pair. 8-Apr-3 Bearnes, Exeter #519
£1050 $1670 €1575 Babbacombe from the east. Babbacombe from the west (19x27cm-7x11in) s. W/C pair. 4-Mar-3 Bearnes, Exeter #371/R est:400-600

KELLY, Sir Gerald (1879-1972) British
£400 $640 €600 Eastern temple (27x35cm-11x14in) indis.i.verso board. 15-May-3 Christie's, Kensington #226/R
£500 $820 €750 La fontaine de Carpeaux, Paris (27x22cm-11x9in) i. panel exhib. 5-Jun-3 Christie's, Kensington #721/R
£700 $1120 €1050 Little golden pagoda, Taungdwingyi (35x26cm-14x10in) board. 15-May-3 Christie's, Kensington #225/R
£900 $1440 €1350 Taungdwingyi girls (35x27cm-14x11in) board painted 1908. 15-May-3 Christie's, Kensington #227/R
£2600 $4056 €3900 Loretta (62x48cm-24x19in) prov.exhib. 25-Mar-3 Bonhams, New Bond Street #13/R est:3000-5000
£4800 $7680 €7200 Portrait of Mrs Kelly (86x90cm-34x35in) s. 15-May-3 Christie's, Kensington #142/R est:2000-3000

KELPE, Paul (1902-) German
£1410 $2200 €2115 Abstract - femme a la toilet (66x38cm-26x15in) painted c.1981. 19-Oct-2 David Dike, Dallas #179/R est:2500-5000
£1442 $2250 €2163 Composition in the 1935 style (69x53cm-27x21in) painted c.1980. 19-Oct-2 David Dike, Dallas #184/R est:3000-6000
Works on paper
£1282 $2000 €1923 Untitled - collage (41x30cm-16x12in) paper board collage executed c.1949. 19-Oct-2 David Dike, Dallas #180/R est:3000-6000

KELSEY, Frank (fl.1887-1923) British
£1000 $1560 €1500 Sailing ships entering harbour, tugs in attendance (44x57cm-17x22in) s. i.verso. 25-Mar-3 Gildings, Market Harborough #402/R est:600-800
Works on paper
£420 $659 €630 Harbour scene (12x18cm-5x7in) init. W/C. 16-Dec-2 Sotheby's, Olympia #150/R
£460 $750 €690 Old church, West Looe, Cornwall (24x34cm-9x13in) s. W/C. 17-Feb-3 Bonhams, Bath #49
£500 $785 €750 Fishing boats in a harbour (24x34cm-9x13in) s. W/C. 16-Dec-2 Sotheby's, Olympia #151/R

KEMARRE, Josie Petrick (1953-) Australian
Works on paper
£1083 $1679 €1625 Bush tomato country (150x90cm-59x35in) i.verso synthetic polymer paint linen. 3-Dec-2 Shapiro, Sydney #193/R est:3000-5000 (A.D 3000)

KEMBLE, Herbert (1894-1986) New Zealander
£287 $451 €431 Nude on yellow background (105x91cm-41x36in) s. board. 15-Apr-3 Lawson Menzies, Sydney #194/R (A.D 750)

KEMENY, Nandor (1885-?) Hungarian
£652 $1036 €978 Grandmother reading to two small girls (100x70cm-39x28in) s. 5-Mar-3 Rasmussen, Copenhagen #1957/R (D.KR 7000)

KEMENY, Zoltan (1907-1965) Swiss
Sculpture
£5556 $9167 €8000 Nature, K42 (74x78x15cm-29x31x6in) s.verso demi-tubes on brass plaque prov.exhib.lit. 1-Jul-3 Artcurial Briest, Paris #492/R est:8000-10000

KEMM, Robert (fl.1874-1885) British
£1100 $1793 €1595 Mussel gatherers (51x61cm-20x24in) s. 16-Jul-3 Sotheby's, Olympia #118/R est:800-1200
£4800 $7920 €6960 Blessing before the fight (72x91cm-28x36in) s. 2-Jul-3 Sotheby's, Olympia #319/R est:4000-6000
£13000 $21710 €18850 Return from market (102x153cm-40x60in) s. 17-Jun-3 Bonhams, New Bond Street #64/R est:15000-20000

KEMP, Jeka (1876-1967) British
Works on paper
£440 $726 €638 Breton woman (61x63cm-24x25in) s. W/C. 1-Jul-3 Bearnes, Exeter #421/R

KEMP, Oliver (1887-1934) American
£474 $750 €711 High sign (64x51cm-25x20in) s. 3-Apr-3 Boos Gallery, Michigan #230/R
£4167 $6500 €6251 Elk chase (30x91cm-12x36in) s. en grisaille. 14-Sep-2 Weschler, Washington #631/R est:1500-2500
£7595 $12000 €11013 Long shot (91x61cm-36x24in) s. en grisaille. 26-Jul-3 Coeur d'Alene, Hayden #144/R est:10000-20000

KEMP, Roger (1908-1987) Australian
£964 $1523 €1446 Reorganisation of form (43x80cm-17x31in) prov. 18-Nov-2 Joel, Victoria #325 est:1200-1800 (A.D 2700)
£2191 $3593 €3287 Opus I (60x91cm-24x36in) s. enamel composition board. 4-Jun-3 Deutscher-Menzies, Melbourne #128/R est:6000-9000 (A.D 5500)
£4643 $7289 €6965 Untitled (71x100cm-28x39in) s. acrylic paper prov. 25-Nov-2 Christie's, Melbourne #427/R est:6000-9000 (A.D 13000)
Works on paper
£9286 $14671 €13929 Untitled (147x174cm-58x69in) s.i. synthetic polymer paper on canvas. 27-Nov-2 Deutscher-Menzies, Melbourne #26/R est:12000-18000 (A.D 26000)

KEMP-WELCH, Lucy (1869-1958) British
£9119 $14225 €13679 Logging team and horses at rest (49x59cm-19x23in) s. 17-Sep-2 Peter Webb, Auckland #188/R est:25000-35000 (NZ.D 30000)
Works on paper
£300 $492 €450 Gate (37x27cm-15x11in) s. W/C. 9-Feb-3 Lots Road, London #339
£500 $780 €750 Sheep grazing on a headland (14x25cm-6x10in) s.d.1900 W/C. 9-Oct-2 Woolley & Wallis, Salisbury #95/R
£700 $1092 €1050 Figures and horses with show jumping in distance (23x36cm-9x14in) s. 10-Sep-2 Louis Taylor, Stoke on Trent #1133
£700 $1078 €1050 Figures and horses with show jumping in distance (23x36cm-9x14in) s. W/C. 9-Sep-2 Louis Taylor, Stoke on Trent #1133/R
£2400 $3816 €3600 Calves in an orchard (23x33cm-9x13in) s. W/C. 30-Apr-3 Halls, Shrewsbury #218/R est:2000-3000

KEMP-WELCH, Lucy (attrib) (1869-1958) British
£540 $842 €810 Mares and foals in a field (55x76cm-22x30in) bears sig. 17-Oct-2 Lawrence, Crewkerne #501/R

KEMPER, Charles Jean (1913-1986) Dutch
Works on paper
£280 $437 €440 Port with trans-shipment (42x58cm-17x23in) s.d.61 W/C. 5-Nov-2 Vendu Notarishuis, Rotterdam #711

KEMPTER, Ernst (1891-1958) Swiss
£1485 $2316 €2228 Autumn (61x75cm-24x30in) s.d.20 i. stretcher. 6-Nov-2 Hans Widmer, St Gallen #49/R est:2000-4200 (S.FR 3400)

KENDALL, Donald (fl.1886-1927) British
Works on paper
£280 $434 €420 Road by the river (39x29cm-15x11in) s. pencil W/C htd white. 26-Sep-2 Mellors & Kirk, Nottingham #668

KENDALL, Helen King (1895-1965) American
£1026 $1600 €1539 Building in Taos (41x56cm-16x22in) 19-Oct-2 David Dike, Dallas #247/R est:1000-2000

KENDALL, O (20th C) New Zealander
Works on paper
£518 $793 €777 Army camp NZ Army Third Divison Solomon Island (25x38cm-10x15in) s.d. W/C. 21-Aug-2 Dunbar Sloane, Auckland #132 est:2000-3500 (NZ.D 1700)

KENDAM, Mona (20th C) ?
£800 $1264 €1200 Grand Canal, Venice (51x86cm-20x34in) s. 14-Nov-2 Christie's, Kensington #186/R

KENDE, Geza (1889-1952) American
£1076 $1667 €1560 Gallant scene (44x35cm-17x14in) s.d.1908. 9-Dec-2 Mu Terem Galeria, Budapest #48/R est:300000 (H.F 400000)

KENDE, Jacques Samu (1865-?) Hungarian
£1062 $1657 €1593 Autumn afternoon in the fields (40x53cm-16x21in) s.d.92 panel. 11-Apr-3 Kieselbach, Budapest #10/R est:180000-380000 (H.F 380000)

KENDERDINE, Augustus (1870-1947) Canadian
£683 $1079 €1025 Kilchum Castle, Loch Awe (36x30cm-14x12in) d.1921. 1-Dec-2 Levis, Calgary #52/R (C.D 1700)
£1807 $2837 €2711 North Sasketchewan River (55x40cm-22x16in) s.d.1923 prov. 25-Nov-2 Hodgins, Calgary #276/R est:5500-6000 (C.D 4500)

KENDRICK, James L (20th C) American
£305 $500 €442 Tugboat Independent (36x46cm-14x18in) s.d.1986. 7-Jun-3 Neal Auction Company, New Orleans #434
£336 $550 €487 Steamboat Sprague (36x46cm-14x18in) s.d.s.d.14 verso acrylic. 7-Jun-3 Neal Auction Company, New Orleans #433
£397 $650 €576 St. Charles streetcar (36x46cm-14x18in) s.d.1986 s.d.verso. 7-Jun-3 Neal Auction Company, New Orleans #435

KENDRICK, Sydney (1874-1955) British
£520 $822 €754 Elderly fisherman, daughter and granddaughter (67x49cm-26x19in) s. 22-Jul-3 Bristol Auction Rooms #418/R
£2000 $3240 €3000 Fireside scene, mother and child (102x76cm-40x30in) s. 21-May-3 James Thompson, Kirby Lonsdale #150/R
£3247 $5000 €4871 Elegant lady (86x65cm-34x26in) s. 4-Sep-2 Christie's, Rockefeller NY #312/R est:5000-7000

KENES, Marcel (1898-1960) Belgian
£321 $503 €500 Vase garni de fleurs (54x45cm-21x18in) s. panel. 19-Nov-2 Galerie Moderne, Brussels #311
£321 $503 €500 La femme en rouge (57x45cm-22x18in) s. 19-Nov-2 Galerie Moderne, Brussels #281/R
£353 $554 €550 Jardin (60x70cm-24x28in) s. 19-Nov-2 Galerie Moderne, Brussels #244
£353 $554 €550 Le toit noir (70x80cm-28x31in) s. 19-Nov-2 Galerie Moderne, Brussels #297

KENNEDY, C J (?) British
Works on paper
£1000 $1600 €1500 Malvern Hills - extensive landscape scene. s.d.1931 W/C pair. 3-Jan-3 Moore Allen & Innocent, Cirencester #751 est:1000-1500

KENNEDY, Cecil (1905-1997) British
£1400 $2282 €2030 Vignette of South African flowers (30x25cm-12x10in) s.i. 15-Jul-3 Bonhams, Knightsbridge #125/R est:1500-2000
£3200 $5344 €4640 Roses (49x39cm-19x15in) s. prov. 17-Jun-3 Bristol Auction Rooms #545/R est:2000-3000
£5000 $8250 €7250 Still life with roses and camellias (25x30cm-10x12in) s. 3-Jul-3 Christie's, Kensington #481/R est:5000-7000
£6000 $9420 €9000 Vase of anemones (51x41cm-20x16in) s. 22-Nov-2 Christie's, London #40/R est:7000-10000
£7500 $12225 €11250 Autumn flowers and small glass vase with roses and carnations on a table top (77x63cm-30x25in) s. 29-Jan-3 Dreweatt Neate, Newbury #153/R est:8000-9000
£12000 $18600 €18000 White irises, apples blossom and narcissi in a glass vase (66x50cm-26x20in) s. prov. 3-Dec-2 Bonhams, New Bond Street #14/R est:12000-15000
£12000 $18720 €18000 Magnolia (66x51cm-26x20in) s. prov. 27-Mar-3 Christie's, Kensington #530/R est:7000-10000
£12500 $20500 €18750 Camelias, freesias and forsythia in a vase (51x41cm-20x16in) s. 4-Feb-3 Bonhams, Leeds #398 est:5000-7000
£12500 $19500 €18750 Still life of flowers (51x41cm-20x16in) s. 25-Mar-3 Bonhams, New Bond Street #14/R est:6000-8000
£50000 $82000 €75000 Summer flowers (76x63cm-30x25in) s. 6-Jun-3 Christie's, London #53/R est:20000-30000
£57000 $88920 €85500 Summer group - still life of flowers (76x63cm-30x25in) prov.exhib. 9-Oct-2 Woolley & Wallis, Salisbury #336/R est:20000-30000

KENNEDY, Charles Napier (1852-1898) British
£800 $1304 €1200 Portrait of a colonel (57x32cm-22x13in) s.d.79. 29-Jan-3 Sotheby's, Olympia #76/R

KENNEDY, Mary (20th C) Canadian
£800 $1312 €1160 Field for the lazy gaze (160x170cm-63x67in) s.i.d.1996. 9-Jun-3 Hodgins, Calgary #108/R est:2000-2500 (C.D 1800)

KENNEDY, William (1860-1918) British
£850 $1343 €1275 Dragoons (30x38cm-12x15in) s. board. 12-Nov-2 Bonhams, Knightsbridge #280b/R

KENNETHSON, George (1910-1993) British
Sculpture
£2800 $4368 €4200 Reclining female form (28cm-11in) carved alabaster. 25-Mar-3 Bonhams, New Bond Street #111/R est:1500-2500

KENNEY, John Theodore Eardley (1911-1972) British
£920 $1454 €1380 Cottesmore hunt (51x76cm-20x30in) s.d.71. 27-Nov-2 Bonhams, Knowle #210
£2000 $3120 €3000 Over the stubble (53x74cm-21x29in) s.d.62 i.verso. 25-Mar-3 Gildings, Market Harborough #427/R est:1800-2400
£3250 $5070 €4875 Colonel Murray Smith, Wistow Church (69x93cm-27x37in) s. exhib. 25-Mar-3 Gildings, Market Harborough #426/R est:3000-4000

KENNINGTON, Eric (1888-1960) British
£400 $624 €600 Portrait of a gentleman, with a black tie (43x30cm-17x12in) prov. 18-Sep-2 Dreweatt Neate, Newbury #135
Works on paper
£700 $1092 €1050 Design for a mural (49x57cm-19x22in) i. gouache. 12-Sep-2 Sotheby's, Olympia #104/R

KENNINGTON, Thomas Benjamin (1856-1916) British
£300 $468 €450 Portrait of Anne Struthers (23x23cm-9x9in) board prov. 18-Sep-2 Dreweatt Neate, Newbury #131
£350 $546 €525 Robin Hood's Bay (26x36cm-10x14in) i.d.1892 canvasboard prov. 18-Sep-2 Dreweatt Neate, Newbury #134

KENNIS, Ignace Jacques Lucien (1888-1973) Belgian
£317 $510 €450 Old beggar in winter (95x90cm-37x35in) s. 12-May-3 Bernaerts, Antwerp #716

KENSETT, John Frederick (1816-1872) American
£6289 $10000 €9434 Brook in the Catskills (23x34cm-9x13in) init. prov. 5-Mar-3 Sotheby's, New York #13/R est:10000-15000
£24051 $38000 €36077 View in Italy (61x91cm-24x36in) init.d.1847 exhib. 24-Apr-3 Shannon's, Milford #81/R est:40000-60000
£33778 $56071 €48978 Beach at Newport (36x62cm-14x24in) init.i. prov. 16-Jun-3 Waddingtons, Toronto #12/R est:20000-30000 (C.D 76000)
£123457 $200000 €185186 Mountain lake (61x91cm-24x36in) init.d.66 prov. 22-May-3 Christie's, Rockefeller NY #7/R est:120000-180000
£309678 $480000 €464517 Sunset over Lake George (71x117cm-28x46in) mono.d.67 prov.exhib. 3-Dec-2 Phillips, New York #23/R est:600000-800000

KENSINGTON, C (?) ?
£833 $1300 €1250 English passenger steamer (53x76cm-21x30in) s. 28-Mar-3 Eldred, East Dennis #784/R

KENT, Leslie (1890-1980) British
£420 $664 €630 Brown Sea Island (39x49cm-15x19in) s. i.stretcher. 27-Nov-2 Sotheby's, Olympia #122/R
£800 $1248 €1200 Little harbour (35x45cm-14x18in) s. board. 12-Sep-2 Sotheby's, Olympia #109/R
£1050 $1712 €1575 St Ives harbour (25x33cm-10x13in) s. board. 13-Feb-3 David Lay, Penzance #53/R est:800-850

KENT, Rockwell (1882-1971) American
£46296 $75000 €69444 Sermilik fjord, Greenland (51x61cm-20x24in) s.i. indis d. canvas on panel prov. 21-May-3 Sotheby's, New York #176/R est:20000-30000
Prints
£1923 $3000 €2885 Lookout (20x15cm-8x6in) s. wood engraving edition of 120. 7-Nov-2 Swann Galleries, New York #659/R est:2000-3000
£3774 $6000 €5661 Lovers (43x66cm-17x26in) s.d.1928 wood engraving one of 100. 30-Apr-3 Doyle, New York #219/R est:1500-2000
Works on paper
£590 $950 €885 American eagle with flag and soldier soils our liberties (25x23cm-10x9in) estate st. pen ink chl exec.c.1940. 10-May-3 Illustration House, New York #150/R

£881 $1400 €1322 Parry Harbour (9x16cm-4x6in) s.i.d.Oct 19 graphite. 7-Mar-3 Skinner, Boston #435/R est:800-1200
£915 $1500 €1327 Two studies of a standing female nude (30x32cm-12x13in) estate st. pencil. 5-Jun-3 Swann Galleries, New York #146/R est:2000-3000
£976 $1600 €1415 Reclining figure with upstretched arms (15x11cm-6x4in) estate st. brush ink engraving wood block. 5-Jun-3 Swann Galleries, New York #142/R est:2000-3000
£976 $1600 €1415 Young man on a bed with a man holding a switch. Pocket watches (32x23cm-13x9in) estate st.i. pencil drs vellum two joined studies. 5-Jun-3 Swann Galleries, New York #147/R est:800-1200
£1220 $2000 €1769 Nude figure. Letter I. House at night. estate st. pen ink drs three sold with an engraving one exhib. 5-Jun-3 Swann Galleries, New York #148/R est:1500-2500
£1341 $2200 €1944 Embracing couple (17x14cm-7x6in) pen ink brush exec.c.1917. 5-Jun-3 Swann Galleries, New York #139/R est:1000-1500
£1463 $2400 €2121 Music play your merriest tune (14x8cm-6x3in) init.i.d.June 12th MCMXVII W/C over pencil card stock. 5-Jun-3 Swann Galleries, New York #140/R est:1000-1500
£1951 $3200 €2829 Creation of man (44x33cm-17x13in) s.i. gouache pencil. 5-Jun-3 Swann Galleries, New York #144/R est:4000-6000
£1951 $3200 €2829 Figure studies. one init. pencil pen ink 4 sold with 3 wood engravings. 5-Jun-3 Swann Galleries, New York #149/R est:3000-5000
£2195 $3600 €3183 St John's, New Foundland (8x12cm-3x5in) s.i.d. brush brown ink exhib. 5-Jun-3 Swann Galleries, New York #136/R est:1000-1500

KENT, William (1685-1748) British
Sculpture
£1220 $2000 €1769 Alder fly (41x38x140cm-16x15x55in) s. carved sugar maple prov. 1-Jun-3 Wright, Chicago #253/R est:2000-3000

KENTRIDGE, William (1955-) South African?
Works on paper
£688 $1107 €1032 Standard bank pound note (18x27cm-7x11in) s. chl. 12-May-3 Stephan Welz, Johannesburg #400 est:4000-6000 (SA.R 8000)
£5000 $8200 €7500 Untitled, self portrait (56x56cm-22x22in) s.d.92 chl gouache pastel prov. 7-Feb-3 Sotheby's, London #283/R est:5000-7000
£12658 $20000 €18987 Nandi viewing the landscape with theodolite (70x85cm-28x33in) s.d.93 chl col pastel executed 1983. 12-Nov-2 Phillips, New York #200/R est:20000-30000
£22152 $35000 €33228 Mine shaft (236x74cm-93x29in) s.d.91 chl col chk on four sheets prov. 12-Nov-2 Phillips, New York #154/R est:50000-70000

KENWORTHY, Jonathan (1943-) British
Works on paper
£475 $750 €713 Young dagadiri somal (20x15cm-8x6in) s. ink wash prov. 3-Apr-3 Christie's, Rockefeller NY #143/R

KENZLER, Carl (20th C) German
£517 $822 €750 Evening light on waves breaking on rocks (100x150cm-39x59in) s. 8-Mar-3 Arnold, Frankfurt #621/R
£578 $919 €850 Evening beach (70x100cm-28x39in) s. 28-Mar-3 Bolland & Marotz, Bremen #472/R
£845 $1403 €1200 Spring in winter forest in evening (80x120cm-31x47in) s. 14-Jun-3 Arnold, Frankfurt #781/R
£897 $1409 €1400 Snowy river bend in evening (95x115cm-37x45in) s. 23-Nov-2 Arnold, Frankfurt #777/R
£1026 $1590 €1600 Moor landscape (72x102cm-28x40in) s. 5-Dec-2 Schopman, Hamburg #579 est:1200

KEOWN, Wallace T (?) New Zealander
£289 $462 €419 Late Te Anau, Murchison Mountains (49x69cm-19x27in) s.d.76 board. 13-May-3 Watson's, Christchurch #169/R (NZ.D 800)

KEPES, Gyorgy (1906-2001) American/Hungarian
£1451 $2250 €2177 Bronze landscape (56x56cm-22x22in) oil sand. 29-Sep-2 Butterfields, Los Angeles #4425/R est:2500-3500
Works on paper
£750 $1200 €1088 Pearl (61x66cm-24x26in) s.d.1964 mixed media oil canvas. 16-May-3 Skinner, Boston #375/R

KERCKHOVE, Antoine Joseph van den (1849-?) Belgian
Sculpture
£1338 $2154 €1900 Bust of woman (70cm-28in) s. gold pat.bronze. 9-May-3 Schloss Ahlden, Ahlden #703/R est:1800

KERCKHOVE, Joseph van den (attrib) (1667-1724) Flemish
£680 $1082 €1000 Still life with dead gme (65x48cm-26x19in) s. panel. 21-Mar-3 Millon & Associes, Paris #10

KERG, Theo (1909-1993) Luxembourger
£755 $1177 €1200 Structure (65x50cm-26x20in) s. spray. 11-Oct-2 Winterberg, Heidelberg #1324/R
£828 $1316 €1200 Cette lumiere dehors (24x41cm-9x16in) s. s.i.verso. 5-Mar-3 Doutrebente, Paris #67
£1034 $1645 €1500 Laque (24x41cm-9x16in) s. s.i.verso paper on canvas. 5-Mar-3 Doutrebente, Paris #65/R est:400
£2069 $3290 €3000 Charm marin (46x55cm-18x22in) s. s.i.verso. 5-Mar-3 Doutrebente, Paris #66/R est:1000-1200
Works on paper
£331 $530 €480 Composition (16x20cm-6x8in) s. mixed media cardboard. 12-Mar-3 E & Eve, Paris #119

KERGEL, Carl Franz Ludwig (1814-1874) German
£1859 $2881 €2900 Snowy winter town (58x81cm-23x32in) s.d.1856 lit. 6-Dec-2 Karlheinz Kaupp, Staufen #2328/R est:2900

KERINEC, Roger (20th C) French
£1282 $2013 €2000 Chalutiers au mouillage (81x65cm-32x26in) s.d.81. 15-Dec-2 Thierry & Lannon, Brest #145
Works on paper
£317 $510 €450 Le port de Concarneau (27x40cm-11x16in) s.d.51 gouache. 11-May-3 Thierry & Lannon, Brest #124
£347 $566 €500 Barques au sec, le Fret (32x49cm-13x19in) s. W/C. 19-Jul-3 Thierry & Lannon, Brest #212
£1042 $1698 €1500 Les statices (73x53cm-29x21in) s.d.96 gouache. 19-Jul-3 Thierry & Lannon, Brest #270a est:1500-2000
£1090 $1711 €1700 Audierne (76x55cm-30x22in) s.d.80 gouache. 15-Dec-2 Thierry & Lannon, Brest #332
£1154 $1812 €1800 Port de Sauzon (76x55cm-30x22in) s.d.83 gouache. 15-Dec-2 Thierry & Lannon, Brest #84
£1282 $2013 €2000 Auray (55x75cm-22x30in) s.d.88 gouache. 15-Dec-2 Thierry & Lannon, Brest #85

KERKAM, Earl C (1890-1965) American
£2591 $4250 €3757 Self portrait no.2 (61x38cm-24x15in) board prov. 1-Jun-3 Wright, Chicago #234/R est:3000-4000

KERKHOVE, Fritz van de (19th C) Belgian
£411 $642 €650 Paysage lacustre. s.d.1873 panel. 10-Sep-2 Vanderkindere, Brussels #375

KERKOVIUS, Ida (1879-1970) German
£380 $600 €600 Figures and forms (20x27cm-8x11in) mono. chl. 27-Nov-2 Dr Fritz Nagel, Stuttgart #3091/R
£1887 $2943 €3000 Red reclining figure. Abstract composition (22x20cm-9x8in) init. board double-sided painted 1940 prov. 9-Oct-2 Sotheby's, London #391/R est:4500-6500
£2174 $3565 €3000 Colours in circle (24x18cm-9x7in) mono. board prov. 29-May-3 Lempertz, Koln #694/R est:3000-3500
£2848 $4500 €4500 Composition (32x45cm-13x18in) tempera pastel col chk graphite exhib.lit. 27-Nov-2 Dr Fritz Nagel, Stuttgart #3180/R est:6400
£3165 $5000 €5000 Annunciation (26x31cm-10x12in) mono. board. 27-Nov-2 Dr Fritz Nagel, Stuttgart #3051/R est:6000
£3261 $5348 €4500 Still life of yellow and violet (37x48cm-15x19in) mono. i. verso board prov.exhib. 29-May-3 Lempertz, Koln #693/R est:5000
£3481 $5500 €5500 Untitled (93x32cm-37x13in) i. pastel packing paper exhib. 27-Nov-2 Dr Fritz Nagel, Stuttgart #3183/R est:7000
£3797 $6000 €6000 Adoration - Christmas (26x31cm-10x12in) mono. board. 27-Nov-2 Dr Fritz Nagel, Stuttgart #3052/R est:6000
£3797 $6000 €6000 The spider (30x21cm-12x8in) mono. 27-Nov-2 Dr Fritz Nagel, Stuttgart #3172/R est:3600
£4088 $6377 €6500 Figural composition (18x22cm-7x9in) init. board painted 1960 prov. 9-Oct-2 Sotheby's, London #353/R est:9000-12000
£4231 $6177 €6600 Portrait of bearded man (50x36cm-20x14in) board. 4-Jun-2 Karl & Faber, Munich #304/R est:8000-9000
£8228 $13000 €13000 Mulatto (67x63cm-26x25in) mono. exhib.lit. 27-Nov-2 Dr Fritz Nagel, Stuttgart #3130/R est:16000
£8228 $13000 €13000 Dahlias on red background (63x67cm-25x26in) mono. s. verso prov. 30-Nov-2 Villa Grisebach, Berlin #305/R est:10000-12000
£8861 $14000 €14000 Still life (48x82cm-19x32in) mono. masonite. 27-Nov-2 Dr Fritz Nagel, Stuttgart #3065/R est:17000
£9420 $15449 €13000 Clouds (80x80cm-31x31in) mono.d.66 prov. 31-May-3 Villa Grisebach, Berlin #240/R est:15000-20000
£16352 $25509 €26000 Liegendes madchen - Reclining girl (33x53cm-13x21in) init. painted 1945 prov. 9-Oct-2 Sotheby's, London #367/R est:28000-35000
£18868 $29434 €30000 Waldlandschaft - Wooded landscape (47x62cm-19x24in) mono.d.61 prov.lit. 9-Oct-2 Sotheby's, London #351/R est:24000-28000

Sculpture

£8805 $13736 €14000 Glasfenster - Stained glass window (106x60cm-42x24in) executed 1951 prov.exhib. 9-Oct-2 Sotheby's, London #362/R est:20000-30000
£26415 $41208 €42000 Glasfenster - Stained glass window (73x65cm-29x26in) prov.exhib. 9-Oct-2 Sotheby's, London #363/R est:40000-50000

Works on paper

£252 $392 €400 Boats in bay (49x65cm-19x26in) mono. chk lit. 20-Sep-2 Karlheinz Kaupp, Staufen #2153
£253 $395 €400 Small format 222 (10x15cm-4x6in) col chk pencil. 18-Oct-2 Dr Fritz Nagel, Stuttgart #209/R
£253 $400 €400 Interior with three figures (11x15cm-4x6in) mono. col pen graphite. 27-Nov-2 Dr Fritz Nagel, Stuttgart #3119/R
£253 $400 €400 In the park (17x27cm-7x11in) mono. graphite exhib. 27-Nov-2 Dr Fritz Nagel, Stuttgart #3135/R
£253 $400 €400 Mountains in winter (21x29cm-8x11in) mono. chl. 27-Nov-2 Dr Fritz Nagel, Stuttgart #3137/R
£302 $496 €420 Landscape with figural composition (21x30cm-8x12in) mono. graphite wash chl. 4-Jun-3 Reiss & Sohn, Konigstein #419
£316 $500 €500 Going to church (17x24cm-7x9in) mono. col pen. 27-Nov-2 Dr Fritz Nagel, Stuttgart #3009/R
£385 $608 €600 Landscape (32x23cm-13x9in) mono. chk. 15-Nov-2 Reiss & Sohn, Konigstein #566/R
£504 $826 €700 Landscape (19x26cm-7x10in) wash chl. 4-Jun-3 Reiss & Sohn, Konigstein #418/R
£692 $1011 €1080 Flowers (20x17cm-8x7in) mono. pastel chk. 4-Jun-2 Karl & Faber, Munich #305
£709 $1149 €1000 Composition (27x19cm-11x7in) mono. W/C. 24-May-3 Van Ham, Cologne #308/R
£753 $1175 €1100 Two figures (12x15cm-5x6in) s. pastel prov. 11-Apr-3 Sigalas, Stuttgart #452
£881 $1374 €1400 Abstract composition with coloured areas (11x15cm-4x6in) mono. col chk graphite lit. 20-Sep-2 Schloss Ahlden, Ahlden #1311/R
£943 $1472 €1500 Stuttgart heights (36x25cm-14x10in) mono. pencil. 20-Sep-2 Sigalas, Stuttgart #1106/R est:1600
£973 $1567 €1450 Abstract figures (10x13cm-4x5in) mono. pastel. 21-Feb-3 Sigalas, Stuttgart #912/R est:1800
£1006 $1570 €1600 Composition (15x10cm-6x4in) init. pastel executed 1951 prov. 9-Oct-2 Sotheby's, London #388/R est:1200-1800
£1013 $1600 €1600 Interior with two figures (27x40cm-11x16in) mono. chl graphite lit. 27-Nov-2 Dr Fritz Nagel, Stuttgart #3148/R est:2100
£1076 $1700 €1700 On orange (26x39cm-10x15in) chl gouache exhib.lit. 27-Nov-2 Dr Fritz Nagel, Stuttgart #3118/R est:2100
£1241 $1961 €1800 Bathers in landscape (37x45cm-15x18in) mono.d.1962 col chk. 2-Apr-3 Dr Fritz Nagel, Stuttgart #9496/R est:2000
£1266 $2000 €2000 Untitled (60x52cm-24x20in) col chk W/C collage exhib. 27-Nov-2 Dr Fritz Nagel, Stuttgart #3110/R est:2700
£1282 $1987 €2000 Landscape with pond and fish (19x25cm-7x10in) mono. lit. pastel. 6-Dec-2 Karlheinz Kaupp, Staufen #2029/R est:1600
£1392 $2200 €2200 Untitled (59x39cm-23x15in) s. col chk gouache exhib. 27-Nov-2 Dr Fritz Nagel, Stuttgart #3081/R est:2800
£1519 $2400 €2400 Animal world (45x60cm-18x24in) mono. graphite chl exhib. 27-Nov-2 Dr Fritz Nagel, Stuttgart #3021/R est:3100
£1519 $2400 €2400 Three daytimes (30x21cm-12x8in) mono. col chk. 27-Nov-2 Dr Fritz Nagel, Stuttgart #3092/R est:2800
£1532 $2420 €2420 Summer (42x56cm-17x22in) mono. gouache. 27-Nov-2 Dr Fritz Nagel, Stuttgart #3111/R est:2600
£1646 $2600 €2600 To one another (36x44cm-14x17in) W/C exhib. 27-Nov-2 Dr Fritz Nagel, Stuttgart #3181/R est:4000
£1667 $2583 €2600 On green, two figures (25x19cm-10x7in) s.d.61 pastel lit. 6-Dec-2 Karlheinz Kaupp, Staufen #2317/R est:2600
£1887 $2943 €3000 Christmas Angel (12x15cm-5x6in) s.i. pastels executed 1950 prov. 9-Oct-2 Sotheby's, London #386/R est:3000-4000
£2276 $3596 €3300 Evening landscape with rowing boat (27x33cm-11x13in) mono. col chk. 2-Apr-3 Dr Fritz Nagel, Stuttgart #9495/R est:5000
£3038 $4800 €4800 Flower vase and flower basket (49x77cm-19x30in) mono. pastel velvet paper. 27-Nov-2 Dr Fritz Nagel, Stuttgart #3193/R est:5400
£3459 $5396 €5500 Christmas (13x14cm-5x6in) s.i. pastel paper on folded card executed 1943 prov. 9-Oct-2 Sotheby's, London #387/R est:3000-4000
£5346 $8340 €8500 Neckar landscape (40x65cm-16x26in) s.d.55 pastel prov. 9-Oct-2 Sotheby's, London #354/R est:12000-18000
£5975 $9321 €9500 Landscape on Lake Constance at Bodmann (50x69cm-20x27in) s.d.39 pastel paper on card prov. 9-Oct-2 Sotheby's, London #376/R est:10000-15000

KERMADEC, Eugène Nestor le (1899-1976) French

£741 $1200 €1074 Aqua Toffana (64x53cm-25x21in) s. i.stretcher prov. 21-May-3 Doyle, New York #3/R
£759 $1200 €1200 Autre tentative pour justifier les appelants (38x55cm-15x22in) s. acrylic. 2-Dec-2 Tajan, Paris #193
£1583 $2500 €2500 Essai de fragments rapides (92x73cm-36x29in) s. acrylic painted 1957. 2-Dec-2 Tajan, Paris #194 est:2000
£3205 $5032 €5000 Femme a la lanterne (65x50cm-26x20in) s. 11-Dec-2 Artcurial Briest, Paris #542/R
£5200 $8268 €7800 Le corset noir (73x51cm-29x20in) s. prov. 20-Mar-3 Sotheby's, Olympia #205/R est:4000-6000

Works on paper

£517 $864 €750 Les retours (24x32cm-9x13in) s. W/C pastel prov. 9-Jul-3 Cornette de St.Cyr, Paris #304/R
£573 $894 €900 Apostrophe (32x24cm-13x9in) s. W/C gouache exec.c.1973. 10-Nov-2 Eric Pillon, Calais #239/R
£1014 $1581 €1500 Mes entours (24x31cm-9x12in) s. gouache exec.1959. 26-Mar-3 Finarte Semenzato, Milan #85/R

KERMARREC, Joel (1939-) French

£621 $1037 €900 Composition fond rose (80x80cm-31x31in) s. s.d.verso. 9-Jul-3 Cornette de St.Cyr, Paris #305
£764 $1207 €1100 Decontraction (80x80cm-31x31in) s.i.d.verso. 28-Apr-3 Cornette de St.Cyr, Paris #431
£870 $1426 €1200 Untitled (116x89cm-46x35in) s.d.1969 verso acrylic prov. 27-May-3 Tajan, Paris #36/R est:1500-2000
£1139 $1766 €1800 Composition, fond bleu (100x100cm-39x39in) s.d.verso. 28-Sep-2 Cornette de St.Cyr, Paris #344 est:1200-1500
£1250 $1975 €1800 Composition fond rose (130x130cm-51x51in) s.d.verso. 28-Apr-3 Cornette de St.Cyr, Paris #429/R est:1500-2000

KERN, Anton (attrib) (1710-1747) German

£1603 $2484 €2500 Juno and Argus (24x16cm-9x6in) copper. 6-Dec-2 Rieunier, Bailly-Pommery, Mathias, Paris #32/R

KERN, Hermann (1839-1912) Hungarian

£968 $1500 €1452 Man drinking (46x30cm-18x12in) s. panel painted c.1870. 8-Dec-2 Toomey, Oak Park #629/R est:2000-3000
£1610 $2560 €2415 Cheers (41x30cm-16x12in) panel. 18-Mar-3 Maynards, Vancouver #27/R est:5000-7000 (C.D 3800)
£1689 $2635 €2500 Old man reading paper in peasant kitchen (50x33cm-20x13in) s.d.1909. 27-Mar-3 Dr Fritz Nagel, Stuttgart #822/R est:1500
£1812 $2971 €2500 A glass of wine (47x31cm-19x12in) s. 27-May-3 Wiener Kunst Auktionen, Vienna #14/R est:2500-6000
£1859 $2881 €2900 Violin player (53x42cm-21x17in) s.d.1882. 5-Dec-2 Stadion, Trieste #686/R
£1859 $2881 €2900 Player in interior (53x42cm-21x17in) s.d.1882. 5-Dec-2 Stadion, Trieste #687/R
£1935 $3000 €2903 Making the bouquet (43x30cm-17x12in) s. 2-Oct-2 Christie's, Rockefeller NY #783/R est:4000-6000
£2244 $3545 €3500 Feeding the canary (48x32cm-19x13in) s. 16-Nov-2 Lempertz, Koln #1501/R est:4000
£2244 $3545 €3500 Vegetable seller (48x32cm-19x13in) s.d.87. 16-Nov-2 Lempertz, Koln #1502/R est:4000
£2245 $3569 €3300 Old fiddle player counting takings at tavern table (47x31cm-19x12in) s. panel. 19-Mar-3 Neumeister, Munich #605/R est:2800
£2397 $3740 €3500 Kitchen maid (72x58cm-28x23in) s.d.1878 canvas on canvas lit. 10-Apr-3 Allgauer, Kempten #2831/R est:3500
£2679 $4341 €3885 The botanist having some refreshments (48x33cm-19x13in) s. panel. 26-May-3 Rasmussen, Copenhagen #1314/R est:25000 (D.KR 28000)
£3096 $4829 €4489 Visit (57x49cm-22x19in) s. 13-Sep-2 Mu Terem Galeria, Budapest #55/R est:800000 (H.F 1200000)
£3145 $4843 €5000 Man with turnips (48x31cm-19x12in) s.d.1904 mono.i.d. verso panel. 26-Oct-2 Quittenbaum, Hamburg #25/R est:6500
£3265 $5192 €4800 Taking a break after the hunt (47x31cm-19x12in) s.d.1904 panel. 28-Mar-3 Bolland & Marotz, Bremen #473/R est:4500
£3546 $5745 €5000 Bird lover (48x32cm-19x13in) s. 22-May-3 Dorotheum, Vienna #96/R est:5500-6500
£3546 $5745 €5000 Greengrocer (48x32cm-19x13in) s.d.87. 22-May-3 Dorotheum, Vienna #97/R est:5500-6500
£3901 $6319 €5500 A good drop (47x31cm-19x12in) s.i.d.1904 panel. 22-May-3 Dorotheum, Vienna #152/R est:5500-5800
£4000 $6360 €6000 Threading the eye of a needle (48x31cm-19x12in) s. panel. 20-Mar-3 Christie's, Kensington #178/R est:2000-3000
£4192 $6539 €6078 Mender of the old instrument (46x32cm-18x13in) s. 12-Apr-3 Mu Terem Galeria, Budapest #50/R est:1300000 (H.F 1500000)
£5660 $8717 €9000 Latest news (42x52cm-17x20in) s.d.1908. 22-Oct-2 Sotheby's, Amsterdam #69/R est:10000-15000
£6449 $10061 €9674 Bridegroom's farewell party, 1881 (83x135cm-33x53in) s. 11-Sep-2 Kieselbach, Budapest #206/R (H.F 2500000)

KERNAN, Joseph F (1878-1958) American

£348 $550 €522 Portrait of a black and white cat (48x43cm-19x17in) s. 30-Nov-2 Thomaston Place, Thomaston #216
£1731 $2700 €2597 Boy with snowball calling out, other boys and dog looking on (51x46cm-20x18in) s. 9-Nov-2 Illustration House, New York #6/R est:3500-5000
£8861 $14000 €12848 Fly fisherman (61x51cm-24x20in) s. prov.lit. 26-Jul-3 Coeur d'Alene, Hayden #29/R est:4000-6000

KERNBEIS, Franz (1935-) Austrian

Works on paper

£617 $1000 €926 Untitled (57x88cm-22x35in) s.d.1984 gouache crayon pair prov.exhib. 27-Jan-3 Christie's, Rockefeller NY #114/R est:600-800

KERNN-LARSEN, Rita (1904-1998) Danish

£410 $651 €615 Composition (27x35cm-11x14in) s. 10-Mar-3 Rasmussen, Vejle #697 (D.KR 4400)

£603 $935 €905 Composition (65x55cm-26x22in) init. 4-Dec-2 Kunsthallen, Copenhagen #51/R (D.KR 7000)
£760 $1186 €1140 Composition in green and yellow (61x46cm-24x18in) init. 18-Sep-2 Kunsthallen, Copenhagen #241a/R (D.KR 9000)
£1115 $1762 €1673 Found on the beach (46x55cm-18x22in) init. painted 1932-33 exhib. 1-Apr-3 Rasmussen, Copenhagen #237/R est:15000 (D.KR 12000)
£1115 $1762 €1673 Det genfundne - surrealistic composition (65x81cm-26x32in) init. exhib. 1-Apr-3 Rasmussen, Copenhagen #240/R est:6000-8000 (D.KR 12000)
£1162 $1836 €1743 Woman with cross (38x61cm-15x24in) init. painted c.1938. 1-Apr-3 Rasmussen, Copenhagen #239/R est:6000-8000 (D.KR 12500)
£1208 $1909 €1812 Easy life (25x33cm-10x13in) s. i.d.Xmas 1938 verso oil covered in sand cardboard prov. 1-Apr-3 Rasmussen, Copenhagen #155/R est:10000 (D.KR 13000)
£1208 $1909 €1812 Hand (54x75cm-21x30in) init. 1-Apr-3 Rasmussen, Copenhagen #279/R est:8000 (D.KR 13000)
£1394 $2203 €2091 Surrealistic figure composition (48x55cm-19x22in) init. painted c.1935 prov. 1-Apr-3 Rasmussen, Copenhagen #159/R est:10000 (D.KR 15000)
£1673 $2643 €2510 Poppy (75x53cm-30x21in) init. 1-Apr-3 Rasmussen, Copenhagen #275/R est:8000 (D.KR 18000)

KERNOFF, Harry Aaron (1900-1974) British
£1757 $2741 €2600 Mrs. Wolfe Briscoe (50x37cm-20x15in) s.d.64 board. 26-Mar-3 James Adam, Dublin #138/R est:1500-2000
£3544 $5175 €5600 Haystackers at Skerries with windmill in the background (6x8cm-2x3in) s.i.verso panel. 21-May-2 Thomas Adams, Dublin #342
£4795 $7527 €7000 Trees on the dodder (40x30cm-16x12in) s.d.52 i.verso board. 15-Apr-3 De Veres Art Auctions, Dublin #201/R est:7000-10000
£8108 $12649 €12000 O'Loughlin's off licence house in Dalkey (34x44cm-13x17in) s. i.verso board. 26-Mar-3 James Adam, Dublin #122/R est:12000-15000
£12179 $19122 €19000 Making hay at Renvyle, Connemara (36x48cm-14x19in) s.d.1936 panel. 19-Nov-2 Whyte's, Dublin #85/R est:15000-20000
£15823 $24525 €25000 James Larkin addressing a crowd at Bolands Mill, Dublin (38x50cm-15x20in) s. board sold with a woodcut by same hand. 25-Sep-2 James Adam, Dublin #39/R est:10000-15000
£15942 $26145 €22000 Metro, Paris (61x75cm-24x30in) s. s.i.d.1931 verso. 28-May-3 Bonhams & James Adam, Dublin #52/R est:25000-30000
£80000 $128000 €120000 Winetavern Street, juky morning, Dublin (71x81cm-28x32in) s.d.40 s.i.verso board prov. 16-May-3 Sotheby's, London #106/R est:30000-40000

Works on paper
£648 $1075 €920 Portrait of a boy (20x15cm-8x6in) s. pastel. 10-Jun-3 Thomas Adams, Dublin #363
£750 $1200 €1125 Portrait of Shiela Fitzpatrick (53x37cm-21x15in) s.d.28 chl pastel. 15-May-3 Christie's, Kensington #154/R
£823 $1275 €1300 Portrait of a young woman with red hair (49x38cm-19x15in) s. conte. 25-Sep-2 James Adam, Dublin #78/R est:800-1200
£1100 $1760 €1650 Self-portrait (37x24cm-15x9in) s. W/C. 15-May-3 Christie's, Kensington #156/R est:1000-1500
£1200 $1848 €1800 Time, space is curved (20x15cm-8x6in) s. i.verso gouache. 5-Sep-2 Christie's, Kensington #738/R est:1000-1500
£1474 $2285 €2300 Half length portrait of Kathleen Egan (49x37cm-19x15in) s. chl wash. 3-Dec-2 Bonhams & James Adam, Dublin #140/R est:1500-2000
£1667 $2750 €2400 Coloured boxes and dice (15x19cm-6x7in) s. mixed media pair. 7-Jul-3 Hamilton Osborne King, Dublin #218/R est:1600-2000
£1667 $2750 €2400 Coloured boxes (15x19cm-6x7in) s. mixed media pair prov. 7-Jul-3 Hamilton Osborne King, Dublin #220/R est:1500-2000
£1944 $3208 €2800 Bubbles (20x23cm-8x9in) s. mixed media prov. 7-Jul-3 Hamilton Osborne King, Dublin #221 est:1200-1600
£2609 $4278 €3600 Hell fire club (28x39cm-11x15in) s. W/C. 28-May-3 Bonhams & James Adam, Dublin #120/R est:2000-3000
£2642 $4121 €4200 Cottages, near Renvyle, Connemara (25x36cm-10x14in) s.d.1933 W/C. 17-Sep-2 Whyte's, Dublin #62/R est:4000-5000
£2949 $4571 €4600 Old Barn Enniskerry 1940 (23x33cm-9x13in) s. W/C. 3-Dec-2 Bonhams & James Adam, Dublin #133/R est:1200-1800
£5063 $7848 €8000 Whiskey connoiss (50x35cm-20x14in) s.d.48 pastel. 25-Sep-2 James Adam, Dublin #103/R est:8000-12000
£5878 $9170 €8700 Pepper canister church from Percy Place, Dublin (25x31cm-10x12in) s. W/C. 26-Mar-3 James Adam, Dublin #48/R est:8000-12000
£6731 $10433 €10500 On the Dublin Quays, Johnny Forty Coats (23x33cm-9x13in) s.d.1945 prov. 3-Dec-2 Bonhams & James Adam, Dublin #39/R est:8000-12000

KERNSTOCK, Karoly (1873-1940) Hungarian
£1258 $1962 €1887 Landscape by River Danube (55x68cm-22x27in) s. canvas on board. 11-Apr-3 Kieselbach, Budapest #112/R est:450000 (H.F 450000)
£1935 $3018 €2903 Hilly landscape (33x46cm-13x18in) s. board. 11-Sep-2 Kieselbach, Budapest #70/R (H.F 750000)
£2580 $4024 €3870 Dinner in Emmaus (102x108cm-40x43in) 11-Sep-2 Kieselbach, Budapest #186/R (H.F 1000000)
£4751 $7411 €7127 Boat in river (60x76cm-24x30in) s.d.20. 11-Apr-3 Kieselbach, Budapest #134/R est:500000 (H.F 1700000)
£7223 $11268 €10835 Grove in a sunny afternoon, 1904 (103x89cm-41x35in) s.d.1904. 11-Sep-2 Kieselbach, Budapest #176/R (H.F 2800000)

Works on paper
£1290 $2012 €1871 Standing male nude (34x19cm-13x7in) s.d.909 Indian ink. 13-Sep-2 Mu Terem Galeria, Budapest #98/R est:250000 (H.F 500000)
£1677 $2616 €2432 Horses at the waterfront (42x68cm-17x27in) s. W/C ink. 12-Apr-3 Mu Terem Galeria, Budapest #216/R est:420000 (H.F 600000)

KERR, Charles (1858-1907) British
£1100 $1749 €1650 Beach at Runswick (18x26cm-7x10in) indis i. panel. 6-Mar-3 Christie's, Kensington #477/R est:400-600

KERR, Elizabeth Lamorna (1904-1990) British
£300 $486 €450 Old Harbour Newlyn (26x33cm-10x13in) s. board. 23-May-3 Honiton Galleries, Honiton #718

KERR, George Cochrane (attrib) (c.1825-1907) British
£1300 $2028 €1950 Mounts Bay, Cornwall (76x127cm-30x50in) s. after J K Meadows. 15-Oct-2 Gorringes, Lewes #2297 est:1000-1200

KERR, Henry Wright (1857-1936) British
£450 $734 €675 Tramp (32x26cm-13x10in) 14-Feb-3 Lyon & Turnbull, Edinburgh #50
£1250 $2038 €1875 Study of a fisherman (37x29cm-15x11in) 14-Feb-3 Lyon & Turnbull, Edinburgh #72

Works on paper
£500 $820 €750 Proud Maisie (378x28cm-149x11in) mono. W/C. 7-Jun-3 Shapes, Edinburgh #437/R
£780 $1279 €1170 Winding, Holland (44x33cm-17x13in) s. W/C. 7-Jun-3 Shapes, Edinburgh #369/R
£2200 $3366 €3300 A guide track (29x24cm-11x9in) s.d.88 W/C. 22-Aug-2 Bonhams, Edinburgh #1132/R est:1000-1500

KERR, Illingsworth Holey (1905-1988) Canadian
£444 $729 €644 Banana carrier, St. Lucia (40x30cm-16x12in) mono.i.d.1980 canvas on board. 9-Jun-3 Hodgins, Calgary #410/R est:1200-1500 (C.D 1000)
£511 $838 €741 Windemer hills (30x41cm-12x16in) oil paper on board. 1-Jun-3 Levis, Calgary #63/R est:1500-2000 (C.D 1150)
£533 $875 €773 Cultis Lake, BC (30x41cm-12x16in) board. 1-Jun-3 Levis, Calgary #64/R est:1500-2000 (C.D 1200)
£602 $946 €903 Denali, Alaska (30x40cm-12x16in) s.i.d.1985 board prov. 25-Nov-2 Hodgins, Calgary #61/R (C.D 1500)
£602 $946 €903 Dam on Ralf's Ranch (40x50cm-16x20in) s.i.d.1988 board. 25-Nov-2 Hodgins, Calgary #302/R (C.D 1500)
£667 $1093 €967 Grey day, Kananaskis (30x41cm-12x16in) canvasboard. 1-Jun-3 Levis, Calgary #62/R est:1750-2250 (C.D 1500)
£756 $1239 €1096 Hill farm, California (30x40cm-12x16in) mono.i.d.1981 board. 9-Jun-3 Hodgins, Calgary #121/R est:1200-1500 (C.D 1700)
£766 $1210 €1149 Nanton, Alberta, spring (56x76cm-22x30in) mono.i.d.1986 prov. 14-Nov-2 Heffel, Vancouver #195 est:2000-2500 (C.D 1900)
£783 $1230 €1175 Beaver Dam, Upper Highwood (30x40cm-12x16in) s.i.d.1985 board. 25-Nov-2 Hodgins, Calgary #311/R est:1500-2000 (C.D 1950)
£843 $1333 €1265 Pinewoods, spring 1973 (30x41cm-12x16in) d.1973 plywood. 1-Dec-2 Levis, Calgary #53/R est:2000-2500 (C.D 2100)
£933 $1531 €1353 Salt river near Suguaro Lake, Arizona (30x40cm-12x16in) mono.i.d,1987 board two. 9-Jun-3 Hodgins, Calgary #34/R est:2400-3000 (C.D 2100)
£978 $1604 €1418 Ghost Lake (30x40cm-12x16in) mono.i.d.1981 board. 9-Jun-3 Hodgins, Calgary #277/R est:1500-2000 (C.D 2200)
£1111 $1822 €1611 Highland Qu'Appelle Valley Lumsden (41x51cm-16x20in) canvas on board. 1-Jun-3 Levis, Calgary #61/R est:2000-3000 (C.D 2500)
£1156 $1895 €1676 Kenell Hill Road, East of Craven, Sask (30x40cm-12x16in) mono.i.d.1981 board. 9-Jun-3 Hodgins, Calgary #344/R est:1500-2000 (C.D 2600)
£1186 $1886 €1779 Woods, Banff (40x30cm-16x12in) mono.i.d.1976 board. 23-Mar-3 Hodgins, Calgary #89/R est:1200-1500 (C.D 2800)
£1467 $2405 €2127 Eagle ride, October (45x60cm-18x24in) mono.i.d.1978. 9-Jun-3 Hodgins, Calgary #80/R est:2750-3250 (C.D 3300)
£1695 $2695 €2543 Late October (60x75cm-24x30in) mono.i.d.1977. 23-Mar-3 Hodgins, Calgary #17/R est:2750-3250 (C.D 4000)
£1707 $2680 €2561 Near Vancouver (25x30cm-10x12in) s.i.d.1945 board prov. 25-Nov-2 Hodgins, Calgary #68/R est:4000-4500 (C.D 4250)

£1907 $3032 €2861 Pat Majury's Place, Qu' Appelle Valley (30x40cm-12x16in) mono.i.d.1978 board. 23-Mar-3 Hodgins, Calgary #57/R est:2000-3000 (C.D 4500)
£2108 $3310 €3162 Gravel pits, Autumn (25x30cm-10x12in) s.i.d.1931 board. 25-Nov-2 Hodgins, Calgary #83/R est:5000-5500 (C.D 5250)
£2309 $3626 €3464 Ravine, Sasketchewan River hills (30x40cm-12x16in) s.i.d.1949 board. 25-Nov-2 Hodgins, Calgary #100/R est:4500-5000 (C.D 5750)
£3067 $5029 €4447 The Bow, night (45x60cm-18x24in) mono.i.d.1986. 9-Jun-3 Hodgins, Calgary #44/R est:3000-3500 (C.D 6900)
£3414 $5359 €5121 Ranch at Millarville (60x85cm-24x33in) s.i.d.1976. 25-Nov-2 Hodgins, Calgary #277/R est:7000-8000 (C.D 8500)
£3614 $5675 €5421 Fireweed, burn on Storm Mountain (90x120cm-35x47in) s.i.d.1982. 25-Nov-2 Hodgins, Calgary #373/R est:10000-12000 (C.D 9000)
£3815 $5990 €5723 Harvest pattern (135x180cm-53x71in) s.i.d.1988. 25-Nov-2 Hodgins, Calgary #136/R est:12000-15000 (C.D 9500)
£5111 $8382 €7411 Nanton, Alberta, spring (55x75cm-22x30in) mono.i.d.1986. 9-Jun-3 Hodgins, Calgary #265/R est:3500-4000 (C.D 11500)
£6889 $11298 €9989 Spring ice, Saskatchewan River (90x120cm-35x47in) mono.i.d.1963. 9-Jun-3 Hodgins, Calgary #349/R est:8000-10000 (C.D 15500)

Works on paper
£207 $322 €344 Old mine West of Drumheller (39x57cm-15x22in) s.i.d.1950 chl. 13-Apr-3 Levis, Calgary #481/R (C.D 475)
£289 $474 €419 California farm, June (36x51cm-14x20in) W/C. 1-Jun-3 Levis, Calgary #67/R (C.D 650)
£333 $547 €483 Young redwoods (51x36cm-20x14in) W/C. 1-Jun-3 Levis, Calgary #66/R (C.D 750)
£360 $573 €540 Qu' Appelle Valley, snowy day (28x35cm-11x14in) mono.i.d.1972 felt pen. 23-Mar-3 Hodgins, Calgary #54/R (C.D 850)
£489 $802 €709 Wreck beach (36x53cm-14x21in) mono. W/C. 9-Jun-3 Hodgins, Calgary #291/R est:1200-1500 (C.D 1100)
£803 $1261 €1205 Fraser delta (38x55cm-15x22in) s.i. W/C. 25-Nov-2 Hodgins, Calgary #116/R est:1000-1400 (C.D 2000)

KERR, Mary (1905-1982) Canadian
£360 $573 €540 Cut bank, forest reserve, Autumn (30x40cm-12x16in) s.i.d.1977 board. 23-Mar-3 Hodgins, Calgary #88/R (C.D 850)

KERR, Paul (20th C) Irish?
£423 $701 €600 Struggle (90x70cm-35x28in) s.d.03. 10-Jun-3 James Adam, Dublin #53/R
£458 $760 €650 Death of love (60x90cm-24x35in) s.d.2003 acrylic. 10-Jun-3 James Adam, Dublin #23/R

KERR, Tiko (1953-) Canadian?
£1082 $1721 €1569 Brave new world, City hall (102x76cm-40x30in) s. s.i.verso acrylic. 1-May-3 Heffel, Vancouver #54/R est:3000-4000 (C.D 2500)

KERR, Tom (1925-) Irish
£500 $730 €750 Foreshore, Strangford (30x41cm-12x16in) s. acrylic on board. 12-Jun-2 John Ross, Belfast #78
£800 $1168 €1200 Causeway coast path (36x51cm-14x20in) s.d.April 02 acrylic board. 12-Jun-2 John Ross, Belfast #143

Works on paper
£440 $682 €660 Kelly's coal boat (25x22cm-10x9in) s. W/C. 4-Dec-2 John Ross, Belfast #204
£500 $775 €750 Cottages in a stormy landscape (38x46cm-15x18in) s. W/C. 2-Oct-2 John Ross, Belfast #190
£650 $1034 €975 Horses on the beach (35x50cm-14x20in) s. W/C. 5-Mar-3 John Ross, Belfast #202

KERR, Vernon (?-1982) American
£342 $550 €513 Mendocino headlands (51x41cm-20x16in) s. i.verso masonite prov. 18-Feb-3 John Moran, Pasadena #158

KERR-LAWSON, James (1865-1939) British
£720 $1116 €1080 Mediterranean archway (29x20cm-11x8in) board. 3-Dec-2 Sotheby's, Olympia #204/R

KERR-LAWSON, James (attrib) (1865-1939) British
£480 $744 €720 Eastern European street scene with figures (44x35cm-17x14in) 1-Nov-2 Moore Allen & Innocent, Cirencester #443

KERRICX, Willem Ignatius (1682-1745) Flemish
£5072 $8319 €7000 Portrait de Saint Louis (160x120cm-63x47in) s. 27-May-3 Campo & Campo, Antwerp #118 est:200-300

KERSCHBAUMER, Anton (1885-1931) ?

Works on paper
£258 $407 €387 House on the Chiemsee (22x29cm-9x11in) s.d.21 W/C. 26-Nov-2 Hans Widmer, St Gallen #1219 (S.FR 600)
£258 $407 €387 Pianist at a grand piano and flute player (21x33cm-8x13in) s.d.21 pen ink wash. 26-Nov-2 Hans Widmer, St Gallen #1220 (S.FR 600)
£1410 $2186 €2200 Hallesches Tor station with bridge and church (68x57cm-27x22in) s.d.26 Indian ink brush W/C. 4-Dec-2 Lempertz, Koln #806/R est:3000

KERSCHENSTEINER, Walther (1887-?) German
£377 $588 €550 Elephant calf in the zoo (41x50cm-16x20in) s. board. 10-Apr-3 Van Ham, Cologne #1532

KERSEY, Laurie (20th C) American
£1656 $2750 €2401 Roses in a silver pitcher (50x61cm-20x24in) s. i. on stretcher. 11-Jun-3 Butterfields, San Francisco #4340/R est:3000-5000

KERSWILL, Roy (1925-) British
£4487 $7000 €6731 Before the white man (102x152cm-40x60in) 9-Nov-2 Altermann Galleries, Santa Fe #150

KERTESZ, Andre (1894-1985) American/Hungarian

Photographs
£1772 $2800 €2800 Distortion (28x38cm-11x15in) s. verso silver gelatin. 28-Nov-2 Villa Grisebach, Berlin #1253/R est:1000-1200
£1899 $3000 €2849 Carrefour, Blois (19x25cm-7x10in) s. gelatin silver print lit. 22-Apr-3 Christie's, Rockefeller NY #152/R est:2500-3500
£1911 $3000 €2867 Carrefour, Blois (41x51cm-16x20in) s.d.verso gelatin silver print. 21-Apr-3 Phillips, New York #7/R est:5000-7000
£1948 $3000 €2922 Long Island (25x17cm-10x7in) s.d.1962 photograph. 24-Oct-2 Sotheby's, New York #213/R est:2500-3500
£1963 $3200 €2945 Melancholic tulip (25x18cm-10x7in) s.d.1939 verso gelatin silver print. 12-Feb-3 Christie's, Rockefeller NY #234/R est:3500-4500
£2203 $3546 €3305 Melancholic tulip, New York (24x18cm-9x7in) silver print. 9-May-3 Waddingtons, Toronto #203/R est:5000-6000 (C.D 5000)
£2264 $3509 €3600 Winter garden (18x25cm-7x10in) s.d.1970 verso gelatin silver lit. 2-Nov-2 Lempertz, Koln #259/R est:2800
£2532 $4000 €4000 Tetes lumineuses pour le Theatre de Blatnere (17x18cm-7x7in) i. verso silver gelatin. 28-Nov-2 Villa Grisebach, Berlin #1255/R est:5000-7000
£2532 $4000 €3798 Self portrait, Paris (21x20cm-8x8in) s.d.1926 verso gelatin silver print prov.lit. 24-Apr-3 Phillips, New York #94/R est:4000-6000
£2532 $4000 €3798 September window, New York (35x23cm-14x9in) s.d.1970 verso gelatin silver print prov.lit. 25-Apr-3 Phillips, New York #331/R est:1500-2500
£2577 $4200 €3866 Shadow of the Eiffel Tower (27x34cm-11x13in) s. d.1929 verso gelatin silver print. 12-Feb-3 Christie's, Rockefeller NY #62/R est:3000-5000
£2597 $4000 €3896 Satiric dancer (35x27cm-14x11in) s.i.d.1926 photograph. 24-Oct-2 Sotheby's, New York #151/R est:3000-5000
£2597 $4000 €3896 Stairs of Montmartre (20x25cm-8x10in) s.d.1925 verso photograph. 24-Oct-2 Sotheby's, New York #154/R est:3000-5000
£2625 $4200 €3938 Martinique (27x34cm-11x13in) with sig.i.d.1972 verso silver print. 15-May-3 Swann Galleries, New York #385/R est:4000-6000
£2658 $4200 €3987 Buy, Long Island University. New York (35x25cm-14x10in) s.d.1962 verso gelatin silver print prov.lit. 25-Apr-3 Phillips, New York #261/R est:4000-6000
£2750 $4400 €4125 Chez mondrian (49x37cm-19x15in) silver print. 15-May-3 Swann Galleries, New York #384/R est:6000-9000
£2761 $4500 €4142 Alexander Calder, Paris (27x35cm-11x14in) estate st.verso gelatin silver print. 12-Feb-3 Christie's, Rockefeller NY #88/R est:2000-3000
£2763 $4476 €4200 Strip-tease forain (21x16cm-8x6in) st.sig.verso silver print exec.c.1930. 22-Jan-3 Millon & Associes, Paris #193/R est:3500
£2848 $4500 €4272 Place de la Concorde on a rainy day (25x20cm-10x8in) s.i.d.66 verso gelatin silver print lit. 22-Apr-3 Christie's, Rockefeller NY #53/R est:3000-5000
£2848 $4500 €4272 Jardin des Tuileries, Paris (24x20cm-9x8in) s.d.1980 gelatin silver print. 22-Apr-3 Christie's, Rockefeller NY #150/R est:5000-7000
£2848 $4500 €4272 Mondrian's pipe and glasses (27x35cm-11x14in) s.d.1926 photograph prov. 23-Apr-3 Sotheby's, New York #172/R est:5000-7000
£2922 $4500 €4383 Paris cafe (16x22cm-6x9in) s.d.Dec 5 1983 photograph prov. 22-Oct-2 Sotheby's, New York #81/R est:4000-6000
£3481 $5500 €5222 Chez Mondrian, Paris (25x19cm-10x7in) s.d.1926/1970 verso gelatin silver print. 22-Apr-3 Christie's, Rockefeller NY #151/R est:4000-6000

£3481 $5500 €5222 September 17 1967 (34x23cm-13x9in) s.d.1967 verso gelatin silver print prov. 25-Apr-3 Phillips, New York #161/R est:3000-5000
£3681 $6000 €5522 Underwater swimmer. Swimmer (18x24cm-7x9in) s.d.1917 gelatin silver print two. 12-Feb-3 Christie's, Rockefeller NY #65/R est:4000-6000
£5063 $8000 €7595 Fork, Paris (27x35cm-11x14in) s.d.1928 photograph prov. 23-Apr-3 Sotheby's, New York #174/R est:5000-7000
£5063 $8000 €7595 Chez Mondrian (50x37cm-20x15in) s.d.1926 oversized photograph. 23-Apr-3 Sotheby's, New York #176/R est:8000-12000
£5063 $8000 €7595 Homing ship, New York (35x27cm-14x11in) s.i.d.1944 verso gelatin silver print prov.lit. 25-Apr-3 Phillips, New York #329/R est:1500-2500
£5380 $8500 €8070 Washington Square, February 24 1966 (34x23cm-13x9in) s.d.1966 verso gelatin silver print prov. 25-Apr-3 Phillips, New York #264/R est:3000-5000
£6494 $10000 €9741 Esztergom, Hungary (5x4cm-2x2in) s.i.d.1916 verso gelatin silver contact print prov.lit. 25-Oct-2 Phillips, New York #6/R est:10000-15000
£8228 $13000 €12342 Washington Square, New York (35x23cm-14x9in) s.i.d.1954 verso gelatin silver print prov.lit. 25-Apr-3 Phillips, New York #260/R est:5000-7000
£10127 $16000 €15191 Washington Square (13x9cm-5x4in) s.d.1954 ferrotyped lit. 23-Apr-3 Sotheby's, New York #223/R est:7000-10000

KERTON, Sudjana (1922-1994) Indonesian
£116550 $192308 €168998 Indonesia, my country (200x292cm-79x115in) s.d.87 lit. 6-Jul-3 Christie's, Hong Kong #62/R est:700000-900000 (HK.D 1500000)

KERVAL, Laurent (20th C) French?
£1918 $2973 €3050 Gold mai (73x60cm-29x24in) s. acrylic. 7-Oct-2 Claude Aguttes, Neuilly #14 est:3350

KESERU, Ilona (1936-) Hungarian
£6191 $9659 €8977 We are going to Szentendre (180x60cm-71x24in) s.d.1979. 13-Sep-2 Mu Terem Galeria, Budapest #151/R est:1500000 (H.F 2400000)

KESSANLIS, Nikos (1930-) Greek
£633 $987 €1000 Composition (35x49cm-14x19in) s. 19-Oct-2 Semenzato, Venice #18/R
£9000 $14220 €13500 Il magnifico uccello (70x100cm-28x39in) 1-Apr-3 Bonhams, New Bond Street #111 est:4000-6000

KESSEL, Ferdinand van (1648-1696) Flemish
£16129 $25484 €25000 Repas des singes. Singes jouant aux cartes (16x21cm-6x8in) bears sig. copper pair. 18-Dec-2 Piasa, Paris #27/R est:15000

KESSEL, Ferdinand van (attrib) (1648-1696) Flemish
£3671 $5727 €5800 Le corps de garde (70x89cm-28x35in) prov. 20-Oct-2 Mercier & Cie, Lille #249/R est:6000-7000

KESSEL, Jan van (17th C) Flemish
£10127 $15696 €16000 Still life with monkey and basket of grapes and flowers (16x27cm-6x11in) s. copper. 25-Sep-2 Neumeister, Munich #494/R est:16000
£30000 $50100 €43500 Cartouche with flowers surrounding image of Virgin, Child and infant Saint John the Baptist (56x42cm-22x17in) copper. 10-Jul-3 Sotheby's, London #123/R est:15000-20000

KESSEL, Jan van (attrib) (17th C) Flemish
£577 $894 €900 Woodland clearing (54x43cm-21x17in) canvas on panel. 5-Dec-2 Dr Fritz Nagel, Stuttgart #617/R

KESSEL, Jan van I (1626-1679) Flemish
£5200 $8164 €7800 Still life of various fish and crustaceans on a beach, with boats beyond (12x17cm-5x7in) s. copper. 12-Dec-2 Sotheby's, London #163/R est:6000-8000
£58642 $95000 €87963 Concert of birds (18x24cm-7x9in) mono. copper pair. 24-Jan-3 Christie's, Rockefeller NY #69/R est:60000-80000

KESSEL, Jan van I (circle) (1626-1679) Flemish
£7000 $10990 €10500 Garden of Eden (26x35cm-10x14in) 13-Dec-2 Christie's, Kensington #44/R est:5000-7000

KESSEL, Jan van I and STALBEMPT, Adriaen van (17th C) Flemish
£314685 $525525 €450000 Les cinq sens (72x107cm-28x42in) i. panel prov. 25-Jun-3 Tajan, Paris #20/R est:450000-550000

KESSEL, Jan van II (1654-1708) Flemish
£7051 $11141 €11000 Cocks and turkeys fighting (16x22cm-6x9in) copper. 13-Nov-2 Marc Kohn, Paris #51/R
£7051 $11141 €11000 Rural scene (16x22cm-6x9in) copper. 13-Nov-2 Marc Kohn, Paris #52/R est:10000-12000
£12903 $20387 €20000 Sine narguant chien (16x22cm-6x9in) copper. 18-Dec-2 Tajan, Paris #23/R est:8000
£18710 $29561 €29000 Chien et chat se disputant (34x43cm-13x17in) panel. 18-Dec-2 Piasa, Paris #28/R est:45000
£20645 $32620 €32000 Still life with basket of grapes and other fruit (16x22cm-6x9in) copper. 18-Dec-2 Tajan, Paris #22/R est:20000
£28846 $44712 €45000 Nature morte a la coupe de fleurs (19x27cm-7x11in) copper. 5-Dec-2 Oger, Dumont, Paris #26/R est:40000

KESSEL, Jan van II (attrib) (1654-1708) Flemish
£7000 $10990 €10500 Still life with fawn, pigeon, jays and fruit (16x22cm-6x9in) copper. 11-Dec-2 Christie's, London #18/R est:10000-15000
£34000 $53040 €51000 Grapes, plums and other fruit in a bowl, lemons and other fruit on a ledge with a monkey and dog (16x22cm-6x9in) copper. 9-Apr-3 Christie's, London #2/R est:8000-12000

KESSEL, Jan van II (studio) (1654-1708) Flemish
£80000 $133600 €116000 To guinea pigs amongst fruit and vegetables and dish with roses. Monkey picking fruit on a table (16x22cm-6x9in) copper pair. 9-Jul-3 Bonhams, New Bond Street #2/R est:15000-20000

KESSEL, Jan van III (1641-1680) Flemish
£4459 $6955 €7000 Wooded landscape with a small river in the foreground (37x48cm-15x19in) bears sig prov.exhib.lit. 5-Nov-2 Sotheby's, Amsterdam #88/R est:8000-12000
£25641 $39744 €40000 Wooded river landscape with fishermen, hunter and travellers (95x120cm-37x47in) s.d.1661 prov.lit. 3-Dec-2 Sotheby's, Amsterdam #32/R est:40000-60000

KESSEL, van (17th C) Flemish
£18987 $30000 €30000 Porcelaines, verres, chaudran, fruits et autres objets sur table drapee (21x29cm-8x11in) copper. 27-Nov-2 Christie's, Paris #28/R est:30000-50000

KESSEL, van (circle) (17th C) Flemish
£23718 $37237 €37000 L'eau. Le feu. La terre. L'air (21x26cm-8x10in) copper set of four. 19-Nov-2 Vanderkindere, Brussels #160/R est:20000-30000

KESSELL, James E (20th C) British
£325 $517 €488 Winter landscape with chicken runs (54x56cm-21x22in) 27-Feb-3 Locke & England, Leamington Spa #162/R
£1200 $1860 €1800 Still life of fruit, teapot and decanter (70x62cm-28x24in) board. 26-Sep-2 Locke & England, Leamington Spa #298 est:1250-1500

KESSLER, Carl (1876-?) German
Works on paper
£769 $1192 €1200 Winter in St. Christoph at Arlberg (50x74cm-20x29in) s.i. W/C over pencil. 4-Dec-2 Neumeister, Munich #524/R

KESSLER, Joseph (1826-1887) Austrian
£1761 $2923 €2500 Still life of St Martin (24x35cm-9x14in) five. 11-Jun-3 Dorotheum, Vienna #459/R est:3000-5000

KESSLER, Stephan (1622-1700) Austrian
£8000 $12560 €12000 Horatius cocles fighting the estruscan forces (165x234cm-65x92in) 10-Dec-2 Sotheby's, Olympia #337/R est:4000-6000
£8500 $13345 €12750 Parting of the Red Sea (154x231cm-61x91in) 10-Dec-2 Sotheby's, Olympia #340/R est:6000-8000
£11000 $17270 €16500 Death of Cleopatra (156x229cm-61x90in) 10-Dec-2 Sotheby's, Olympia #338/R est:6000-8000
£12500 $19625 €18750 Mucius scaevola (168x237cm-66x93in) 10-Dec-2 Sotheby's, Olympia #336/R est:6000-8000
£14000 $21980 €21000 Prodigal son begging for food (166x241cm-65x95in) 10-Dec-2 Sotheby's, Olympia #339/R est:6000-8000

KESTELMAN, Morris (1905-1998) British
£900 $1404 €1350 Labourer working in the field (34x46cm-13x18in) s. board. 15-Oct-2 Bonhams, Knightsbridge #46/R

KESTING, Edmund (1892-1970) German
Photographs
£1887 $2925 €3000 Portrait of father and son (30x24cm-12x9in) i. verso gelatin silver. 2-Nov-2 Lempertz, Koln #50/R est:3000
£2264 $3509 €3600 Still life with plaice (29x40cm-11x16in) i.d.1951 verso gelatin silver. 2-Nov-2 Lempertz, Koln #264 est:3000
Works on paper
£570 $900 €900 Crescent moon by hill (44x62cm-17x24in) s. s.i.d.1942 verso gouache over pencil. 29-Nov-2 Villa Grisebach, Berlin #705/R
£2885 $4212 €4500 Scherzando (31x42cm-12x17in) s.i. mixed media. 4-Jun-2 Karl & Faber, Munich #306/R est:8000-9000

KESZLER, Johanna (1878-?) Austrian
£730 $1153 €1095 Portrait of a boy in tennis clothes (104x57cm-41x22in) s.d.1922. 29-Nov-2 Zofingen, Switzerland #2476/R (S.FR 1700)

KET, Dick (1902-1940) Dutch
Works on paper
£12821 $19872 €20000 Self portrait (21x15cm-8x6in) s.d.1926 pencil chk htd white prov.exhib.lit. 3-Dec-2 Christie's, Amsterdam #192/R est:6000-10000

KETELSLEGERS, Robert (1939-) Belgian
£364 $594 €550 Culte (70x60cm-28x24in) s. 17-Feb-3 Horta, Bruxelles #467

KETHULLE, Eugene de la (fl.1846) French
£6410 $9936 €10000 La traversee du gue dans la foret (134x180cm-53x71in) s.d.1851. 9-Dec-2 Horta, Bruxelles #184/R est:12500-18000

KETTEMANN, Erwin (1897-1971) German
£253 $395 €400 Winter landscape with alpine village (62x80cm-24x31in) s. 14-Sep-2 Weidler, Nurnberg #6508/R
£260 $387 €400 Oberammergau (16x12cm-6x5in) s.i. board. 27-Jun-2 Neumeister, Munich #2761
£273 $415 €420 Winter evening in Zillertal (57x78cm-22x31in) s. 5-Jul-2 Weidler, Nurnberg #8597/R
£278 $434 €440 Winter landscape in southern Tyrol (79x99cm-31x39in) s. 14-Sep-2 Weidler, Nurnberg #6526/R
£308 $481 €450 View of Berchtes Garden in winter (50x60cm-20x24in) s.i. lit. 10-Apr-3 Allgauer, Kempten #2832/R
£353 $554 €550 Early spring at the Serless peak near Innsbruck (70x100cm-28x39in) s. 21-Nov-2 Dorotheum, Vienna #165/R
£442 $703 €650 Dolomite landscape lit by the evening sun in winter (60x80cm-24x31in) s. i. verso. 28-Mar-3 Bolland & Marotz, Bremen #559/R
£448 $717 €650 Zugspitze covered in snow (92x120cm-36x47in) s. 11-Mar-3 Dorotheum, Vienna #120/R
£481 $745 €750 Reith near Kitzbuhl (61x80cm-24x31in) s.i. i. verso. 5-Dec-2 Neumeister, Munich #2817/R
£481 $745 €750 Valstal in winter (59x78cm-23x31in) s. 6-Dec-2 Weidler, Nurnberg #8837/R
£490 $784 €750 Mountain chapel in front of high mountain chain (70x100cm-28x39in) s.i. lit. 10-Jan-3 Allgauer, Kempten #1648/R
£510 $785 €800 Winter evening in Hirschbichl with Muhlsturzhorner (95x125cm-37x49in) s.i. 5-Sep-2 Arnold, Frankfurt #796/R
£541 $845 €850 Early spring in Watzmann (60x80cm-24x31in) s.i. lit. 7-Nov-2 Allgauer, Kempten #2852/R
£563 $907 €800 Winter morning in lofer, Austria (70x100cm-28x39in) s.i. i. verso. 7-May-3 Michael Zeller, Lindau #759/R
£759 $1206 €1100 Snowy alpine village by river (60x80cm-24x31in) s.i. 8-Mar-3 Arnold, Frankfurt #622/R
£818 $1275 €1300 Winter evening in Spielmannsau near Oberstdorf, Allgau (60x80cm-24x31in) s.i. i. stretcher lit. 20-Sep-2 Schloss Ahlden, Ahlden #1252/R
£1644 $2564 €2400 Early spring at the Serlesspitze near Innsbruck (60x80cm-24x31in) s.i. i.verso. 10-Apr-3 Allgauer, Kempten #2833/R est:600

KETTER, Clay (1961-) Swedish
£618 $995 €927 Surfacing - crystal (43x16cm-17x6in) s.d.94 verso wood panel prov. 7-May-3 AB Stockholms Auktionsverk #995/R (S.KR 8000)

KETTLE, Tilly (1735-1786) British
£2600 $4238 €3770 Portrait of a lady, half-length wearing a white and gold dress and pink cloak (73x62cm-29x24in) 21-Jul-3 Sotheby's, London #561/R est:2000-3000
£10000 $15900 €15000 Portrait of Lord Charles Spencer-Churchill (75x62cm-30x24in) 19-Mar-3 Sotheby's, London #41/R est:6000-8000
£10000 $16300 €14500 Portrait of George Rowley of Shropshire and Priory Hill, Cambridgeshire (75x62cm-30x24in) prov. 21-Jul-3 Sotheby's, London #337/R est:4000-6000

KETWEG, Isaac van (18th C) Dutch
Works on paper
£472 $731 €750 View of the Pauw-mill near Delft (22x33cm-9x13in) W/C. 4-Nov-2 Glerum, Amsterdam #84/R
£503 $780 €800 Bergse Plas near Hillegersberg in Rotterdam (24x34cm-9x13in) W/C. 4-Nov-2 Glerum, Amsterdam #83/R
£535 $829 €850 View of the Oostpoort in Delft (24x35cm-9x14in) W/C. 4-Nov-2 Glerum, Amsterdam #94/R

KEUDELL, Kurt von (1896-?) German
£340 $541 €500 Sunflowers (50x60cm-20x24in) s. panel. 28-Mar-3 Bolland & Marotz, Bremen #560

KEULEMANS, Johannes Gerardus (1842-1912) Dutch
Works on paper
£300 $486 €450 Swallows mobbing a cuckoo (65x49cm-26x19in) i.verso W/C. 21-May-3 Bonhams, Knightsbridge #98/R
£400 $632 €580 Wren chirruping (22x16cm-9x6in) init. W/C. 22-Jul-3 Bonhams, Knightsbridge #3/R
£450 $711 €653 Winter robin (31x20cm-12x8in) s. W/C bodycol. 22-Jul-3 Bonhams, Knightsbridge #4/R

KEULLER, Vital (1866-1945) Belgian
£274 $430 €400 Paysage avec vaches (30x50cm-12x20in) s. panel. 15-Apr-3 Galerie Moderne, Brussels #394
£296 $480 €450 Rocher des patriotes (30x50cm-12x20in) s. panel. 21-Jan-3 Galerie Moderne, Brussels #226
£448 $708 €650 L'estacade a Ostende (41x79cm-16x31in) s. cardboard. 2-Apr-3 Vanderkindere, Brussels #522/R
£552 $883 €800 View of forest with sheep herder and flock (54x79cm-21x31in) s.d.24 panel. 15-Mar-3 De Vuyst, Lokeren #172
£586 $926 €850 Coucher de soleil sur la mer (65x100cm-26x39in) s. 2-Apr-3 Vanderkindere, Brussels #526/R
£719 $1151 €1000 Ferme en Campine (42x64cm-17x25in) s.d.42. 19-May-3 Horta, Bruxelles #306
£1100 $1826 €1100 Riviere (80x100cm-31x39in) s.d.34 panel. 16-Jun-3 Horta, Bruxelles #117
Works on paper
£432 $691 €600 L'entree du troupeau de moutons au village (124x84cm-49x33in) s.d.1911 gouache. 19-May-3 Horta, Bruxelles #307

KEUN, Hendrik (1738-1788) Dutch
£11000 $18370 €15950 Singel, Amsterdam, with the Munttorren (36x48cm-14x19in) s. panel. 9-Jul-3 Christie's, London #53/R est:10000-15000

KEVER, Jacob Simon Hendrik (1854-1922) Dutch
£486 $802 €700 Flowers in an earthenware pot (31x42cm-12x17in) s. 1-Jul-3 Christie's, Amsterdam #101
£764 $1260 €1100 Summer flowers (65x55cm-26x22in) s. 1-Jul-3 Christie's, Amsterdam #145
£897 $1400 €1346 Still life with flowers in a green vase (56x61cm-22x24in) s. 18-Sep-2 Alderfer's, Hatfield #258/R
£1096 $1710 €1600 Interior with mother and her two children (22x32cm-9x13in) panel. 14-Apr-3 Glerum, Amsterdam #75/R est:1600-1800
£1100 $1716 €1650 Baby seated on a girls lap (45x35cm-18x14in) indis sig. panel. 8-Oct-2 Bonhams, Knightsbridge #199/R est:1200-1800
£2390 $3681 €3800 Motherly love (60x75cm-24x30in) s. 22-Oct-2 Sotheby's, Amsterdam #102/R est:4000-6000
£3438 $5500 €5157 Nap time (40x51cm-16x20in) s. 14-May-3 Butterfields, San Francisco #1059/R est:3000-5000
£5380 $8500 €8070 Still life with peonies (79x89cm-31x35in) s. prov. 24-Apr-3 Sotheby's, New York #150/R est:10000-15000
£6597 $10885 €9500 Suppertime, Laren (63x51cm-25x20in) s.d.84 prov.exhib. 1-Jul-3 Christie's, Amsterdam #110/R est:3000-5000
Works on paper
£1304 $2022 €1956 Little visitor (19x24cm-7x9in) s.d.1886 W/C. 9-Dec-2 Philippe Schuler, Zurich #4168/R est:700-900 (S.FR 3000)
£2013 $3099 €3200 Leisurely moment (48x30cm-19x12in) s.d. W/C. 22-Oct-2 Sotheby's, Amsterdam #112/R est:2000-3000

KEY, Adriaen Thomasz (1544-1590) Flemish
£12162 $18973 €18000 Portrait of gentleman in ruff (48x39cm-19x15in) panel. 27-Mar-3 Dorotheum, Vienna #196/R est:18000-25000
£26000 $40820 €39000 Portrait of a lady aged 31, in a black dress (49x38cm-19x15in) d.1573 panel prov.exhib. 10-Dec-2 Bonhams, New Bond Street #299/R est:10000-15000

KEY, Adriaen Thomasz (attrib) (1544-1590) Flemish
£5500 $8635 €8250 Portrait of a bearded man (51x39cm-20x15in) panel prov. 16-Dec-2 Sotheby's, London #35/R est:6000-8000
£7092 $10993 €10638 Portrait of young man wearing Spanish costume (39x31cm-15x12in) panel prov. 3-Dec-2 Bukowskis, Stockholm #427/R est:100000-125000 (S.KR 100000)

£22642 $35094 €36000 Portrait of 24-year old lady wearing a white bonnet (36x28cm-14x11in) d.1557 panel prov.exhib. 4-Nov-2 Glerum, Amsterdam #2/R est:5000-8000

KEY, Geoffrey (1946-) British
£380 $616 €551 Park lake, park scene with lake and trees (9x17cm-4x7in) s.d.1980. 29-Jul-3 Capes Dunn, Manchester #3/R
£500 $795 €750 Broughton (23x28cm-9x11in) s.i.d.5.3.70 paper. 18-Mar-3 Capes Dunn, Manchester #420
£550 $864 €825 Toilet of Venus (97x81cm-38x32in) s.d.65. 10-Dec-2 Capes Dunn, Manchester #717
£550 $875 €825 Industrial roofscape (20x28cm-8x11in) s.d.1971 board. 18-Mar-3 Capes Dunn, Manchester #423
£700 $1099 €1050 Dancers at the bar (51x61cm-20x24in) s.d.66. 10-Dec-2 Capes Dunn, Manchester #708
Works on paper
£280 $445 €420 Abstract figure study (48x58cm-19x23in) s.d.1966. 18-Mar-3 Capes Dunn, Manchester #432
£450 $729 €653 Head and hands (15x9cm-6x4in) s.d.79 W/C. 29-Jul-3 Capes Dunn, Manchester #4/R

KEY, John Ross (1837-1920) American
£2673 $4250 €4010 Colombian exposition (76x51cm-30x20in) s. painted c.1893. 4-May-3 Treadway Gallery, Cincinnati #526/R est:4000-6000

KEYLL, Johann (17th C) German
Works on paper
£1216 $1897 €1800 Interior with the Holy Family (30x39cm-12x15in) mono.d.1672 pen ink wash. 31-Mar-3 Piasa, Paris #27

KEYSER, Albert de (1829-1890) Belgian
£676 $1054 €1000 Retour a l'etable (56x79cm-22x31in) s. 25-Mar-3 Campo & Campo, Antwerp #51/R

KEYSER, Elisabeth (1851-1898) Swedish
Works on paper
£1650 $2705 €2393 Parisian lady (49x40cm-19x16in) s. pastel. 4-Jun-3 AB Stockholms Auktionsverk #2166/R est:12000-15000 (S.KR 21000)

KEYSER, Nicaise de (1813-1887) Flemish
£1019 $1590 €1600 L'Italienne (55x64cm-22x25in) s. s.i.verso. 11-Nov-2 Horta, Bruxelles #24 est:1500-2000
£92949 $145930 €145000 Les odalisques au collier de perles (172x130cm-68x51in) s.d.1854. 16-Dec-2 Gros & Delettrez, Paris #127/R est:65000-80000
Works on paper
£306 $487 €450 St Jacques de Compostelle (26x19cm-10x7in) s. W/C. 18-Mar-3 Campo, Vlaamse Kaai #42

KEYSER, Raoul de (1933-) Belgian
£18345 $29353 €25500 Traces II (150x121cm-59x48in) s.i.d.1973-1974 verso. 17-May-3 De Vuyst, Lokeren #492/R est:5000-7000

KEYSER, Thomas de (1596-1667) Dutch
£8917 $13911 €14000 The deposition (92x69cm-36x27in) s.1635 panel prov.lit. 6-Nov-2 Christie's, Amsterdam #72/R est:15000-20000
£24691 $40000 €37037 Portrait of a family group (86x60cm-34x24in) d.1634 panel prov.exhib.lit. 23-Jan-3 Sotheby's, New York #3/R est:40000-60000
£150000 $235500 €225000 Group portrait of three gentlemen (104x99cm-41x39in) init.d.1635 prov.exhib.lit. 11-Dec-2 Christie's, London #49/R est:100000-150000

KEYT, George (1901-1993) Indian
£3800 $5928 €5700 Radha and Krishna (43x64cm-17x25in) s.d.47 board prov. 17-Oct-2 Bonhams, Knightsbridge #549/R est:4000-6000
£8000 $12720 €12000 Dreaming in the sun (50x65cm-20x26in) s.d.36. 2-May-3 Christie's, Kensington #580/R est:1500-2000

KEZDI-KOVACS, Elmer (1898-?) Hungarian
£1677 $2616 €2516 Nudes outdoors, 1932 (92x73cm-36x29in) s.d.1932. 11-Sep-2 Kieselbach, Budapest #40/R (H.F 650000)

KHAETSCHER, J M (18th C) German
Miniatures
£1600 $2512 €2400 Jan Wellem (2cm-1xin) enamel on gold prov. 10-Dec-2 Christie's, London #4/R est:500-700

KHAKKAR, Bhupen (1934-) Indian
Works on paper
£450 $702 €675 Jaiselmar (21x25cm-8x10in) s. W/C. 17-Oct-2 Bonhams, Knightsbridge #637/R

KHAN, Ghulam Ali (19th C) Indian
Works on paper
£700 $1113 €1050 Portrait of Alamgur II (33x24cm-13x9in) i.d. gouache gold. 2-May-3 Christie's, Kensington #537/R
£700 $1113 €1050 Portrait of Raushan Akhtar (33x24cm-13x9in) i.d. gouache gold. 2-May-3 Christie's, Kensington #538/R

KHAN, Mir Khalan (18th C) Indian
Works on paper
£11000 $17160 €16500 European saint revered by devotees in a palace chapel (19x10cm-7x4in) s.i.verso gouache exec.c.1760. 17-Oct-2 Bonhams, Knightsbridge #158/R est:6000-8000

KHANINE, Alexandre (1955-) Russian
£276 $461 €400 Mon anniversaire (65x60cm-26x24in) s. 9-Jul-3 Millon & Associes, Paris #212d
£276 $461 €400 Allegorie d'automne (73x60cm-29x24in) s. 9-Jul-3 Millon & Associes, Paris #212f
£349 $565 €530 Pres du ruisseau (61x80cm-24x31in) s. 27-Jan-3 Millon & Associes, Paris #25
£352 $587 €510 Chambre rose (81x65cm-32x26in) s. 9-Jul-3 Millon & Associes, Paris #212a
£352 $587 €510 Asise sous la couverture a carreaux (80x80cm-31x31in) s. 9-Jul-3 Millon & Associes, Paris #212b/R
£359 $599 €520 Petite cour a la campagne (60x65cm-24x26in) s. 9-Jul-3 Millon & Associes, Paris #212c/R
£379 $633 €550 Sommeil du midi (89x117cm-35x46in) s. 9-Jul-3 Millon & Associes, Paris #212j
£395 $639 €600 Courantes vers le soleil (96x96cm-38x38in) s. 27-Jan-3 Millon & Associes, Paris #27
£395 $639 €600 Apollon et Psyche (80x100cm-31x39in) s. 27-Jan-3 Millon & Associes, Paris #28
£414 $691 €600 Peche des Amazones (89x116cm-35x46in) s. 9-Jul-3 Millon & Associes, Paris #212l
£483 $806 €700 Jeu dans l'eau (90x95cm-35x37in) s. 9-Jul-3 Millon & Associes, Paris #212h
£497 $829 €720 Lac a la steppe (120x190cm-47x75in) s. 9-Jul-3 Millon & Associes, Paris #212k/R

KHMELUK, Vassyl (1903-) Russian
£563 $935 €800 Automne (60x81cm-24x32in) s.d.59 panel. 11-Jun-3 Beaussant & Lefèvre, Paris #75

KHNOPFF, Fernand (1858-1921) Belgian
£8000 $13360 €12000 Paysage a fosset (13x17cm-5x7in) s. painted c.1890-95 prov.lit. 19-Jun-3 Christie's, London #78/R est:9000-12000
Works on paper
£4114 $6500 €6500 Jeune femme la tete legerement inclinee (18x13cm-7x5in) s.i.d.1918 chl prov. 26-Nov-2 Palais de Beaux Arts, Brussels #108/R est:3250-4500
£4828 $7724 €7000 Etude de femme (21x18cm-8x7in) mono. pencil dr exec.c.1908 exhib.lit. 15-Mar-3 De Vuyst, Lokeren #430/R est:8000-10000
£6013 $9500 €9500 Tete de femme a la couronne de laurier (14x9cm-6x4in) mono.d.1918 prov. 26-Nov-2 Palais de Beaux Arts, Brussels #107/R est:7500-10000
£90000 $147600 €135000 Encens (27x19cm-11x7in) s.i. chl col pencil exec.1917 prov.exhib.lit. 6-Feb-3 Christie's, London #406/R est:150000

KHOOR, Jozsef (19th C) ?
£1614 $2501 €2421 Romantic landscape with a shepherd (154x113cm-61x44in) s. 6-Dec-2 Kieselbach, Budapest #167/R (H.F 600000)

KHOURY, Michael (?) Canadian?
£309 $478 €464 Iris in a pitcher with lemons (35x27cm-14x11in) s. 3-Dec-2 Joyner, Toronto #470 (C.D 750)
£494 $765 €741 Still life with cineraria and fruit (45x60cm-18x24in) s. 3-Dec-2 Joyner, Toronto #238/R est:1200-1500 (C.D 1200)
£711 $1166 €1067 Still life with white pitcher (60x45cm-24x18in) s. 3-Jun-3 Joyner, Toronto #507 est:1200-1500 (C.D 1600)

KHUDOYAROV, Vasili Pavlovich (1831-1891) Russian
£34000 $53380 €51000 Woodland path (104x78cm-41x31in) s. 20-Nov-2 Sotheby's, London #23/R est:15000-20000

KIAERSKOU, F (1805-1891) Danish
£284 $472 €412 Prospect view from Jaegersborg Dyrehave (27x33cm-11x13in) s.d.1841 panel. 12-Jun-3 Kunsthallen, Copenhagen #336 (D.KR 3000)
£335 $543 €503 Frederiksdal's wood (35x48cm-14x19in) s. prov. 21-May-3 Museumsbygningen, Copenhagen #31/R (D.KR 3500)
£383 $594 €575 Landscape, Tyrol (31x42cm-12x17in) s. 28-Sep-2 Rasmussen, Havnen #2156/R (D.KR 4500)

£478 $775 €693 One afternoon after the rain - Skovpavillonen (34x47cm-13x19in) s.d.1878. 26-May-3 Rasmussen, Copenhagen #1521/R (D.KR 5000)
£478 $775 €693 Alpine landscape with houses by river (26x36cm-10x14in) panel. 26-May-3 Rasmussen, Copenhagen #1573/R (D.KR 5000)
£484 $770 €726 View across mountain landscape towards town (35x48cm-14x19in) s.d.1867. 10-Mar-3 Rasmussen, Vejle #174 (D.KR 5200)
£500 $765 €750 Fjord landscape with sailing boats (22x29cm-9x11in) init. 24-Aug-2 Rasmussen, Havnen #2001 (D.KR 5800)
£549 $856 €824 Landscape with mountain lake, Southern Tyrol (28x39cm-11x15in) i.verso. 23-Sep-2 Rasmussen, Vejle #244/R (D.KR 6500)
£581 $894 €872 Panorama landscape with heather hills (37x50cm-15x20in) 4-Sep-2 Kunsthallen, Copenhagen #80/R (D.KR 6800)
£605 $962 €908 Half-timbered house with watermill (19x27cm-7x11in) 5-Mar-3 Rasmussen, Copenhagen #1828/R (D.KR 6500)
£617 $963 €926 Family having a rest, evening (35x46cm-14x18in) init. exhib. 11-Nov-2 Rasmussen, Vejle #630/R (D.KR 7200)
£621 $950 €932 Fjord landscape with girl and cattle (51x71cm-20x28in) s. 24-Aug-2 Rasmussen, Havnen #2138/R (D.KR 7200)
£766 $1210 €1149 Landscape from Kullen after the storm (64x88cm-25x35in) s.indis.d.1883. 2-Dec-2 Rasmussen, Copenhagen #1232/R (D.KR 9000)
£766 $1240 €1111 Landscape, Guldoefaldet near Trollhettan (24x32cm-9x13in) s. 26-May-3 Rasmussen, Copenhagen #1308/R (D.KR 8000)
£876 $1401 €1314 Mountain landscape with house and woman hanging out clothes (25x35cm-10x14in) i.stretcher. 13-Jan-3 Rasmussen, Vejle #127/R (D.KR 10000)
£931 $1480 €1397 Part of Rosenborg Garden (37x47cm-15x19in) s.d.1859. 5-Mar-3 Rasmussen, Copenhagen #1767/R (D.KR 10000)
£1053 $1705 €1527 Tyrolean landscape (45x60cm-18x24in) s.d.1845. 24-May-3 Rasmussen, Havnen #2042/R (D.KR 11000)

KIAERSKOU, Frederik (1805-1891) Danish
£1787 $2824 €2681 Ruins at Koldinghus (35x44cm-14x17in) s.d.37 exhib.prov. 2-Dec-2 Rasmussen, Copenhagen #1245/R est:15000 (D.KR 21000)
£2089 $3237 €3300 Vue de Copenhague (38x51cm-15x20in) s.i.d. 27-Sep-2 Rabourdin & Choppin de Janvry, Paris #10/R est:4000-4500
£2425 $3856 €3638 Landscape from Tirsbaek Palace near Vejle (28x38cm-11x15in) s.d.1846 panel exhib. 5-May-3 Rasmussen, Vejle #388/R est:25000 (D.KR 26000)
£3254 $5271 €4718 Landscape from Dronningeborg near Randers (83x130cm-33x51in) s.d.1863. 24-May-3 Rasmussen, Havnen #2281/R est:20000 (D.KR 34000)

KIAERSKOU, Frederik (attrib) (1805-1891) Danish
£884 $1406 €1300 Mountain landscape in South Tyrol (28x39cm-11x15in) i.verso. 25-Feb-3 Dorotheum, Vienna #37/R

KIBEL, Wolf (1903-1938) Polish
Works on paper
£205 $320 €308 Trees (27x22cm-11x9in) s. W/C. 11-Nov-2 Stephan Welz, Johannesburg #598 (SA.R 3200)
£559 $900 €839 Red roofed house (21x24cm-8x9in) pastel. 12-May-3 Stephan Welz, Johannesburg #504/R est:7000-10000 (SA.R 6500)

KIBIGER, Julius (1903-) German
Works on paper
£288 $447 €450 Badenweiler (40x49cm-16x19in) s.i. lit. 6-Dec-2 Karlheinz Kaupp, Staufen #2061

KICCO (1969-) Italian
£347 $552 €500 Artificial paradise (40x40cm-16x16in) s.i.d.2002 verso paint silicon photograph plastic. 1-May-3 Meeting Art, Vercelli #394

KICK, Simon (1603-1652) Dutch
£8025 $13000 €12038 Rabbi reading (67x51cm-26x20in) s.d.1637 panel prov.lit. 24-Jan-3 Christie's, Rockefeller NY #53/R est:15000-20000

KICKERT, Conrad (1882-1965) Dutch
£382 $596 €600 Woman under a tree (49x59cm-19x23in) s. s.d.1923 verso. 6-Nov-2 Vendue Huis, Gravenhage #14/R
£461 $746 €700 Still life with fish and poultry (64x54cm-25x21in) s.d.1929 board. 21-Jan-3 Christie's, Amsterdam #399/R

KIDD, Richard (1917-) British
Works on paper
£500 $815 €750 Drawing 9/10 (67x96cm-26x38in) s.d.80 W/C pencil collage. 3-Feb-3 Sotheby's, Olympia #130/R

KIDD, William (1790-1863) British
£3000 $4560 €4500 Fair exchange (30x36cm-12x14in) indis sig. panel. 28-Aug-2 Sotheby's, London #821/R est:3000-4000
£13000 $20930 €19500 By the campfire (52x64cm-20x25in) s.prov.exhib. 20-Feb-3 Christie's, London #357/R est:12000

KIDMAN, Hilda Elizabeth (1891-?) British
£700 $1092 €1050 Still life of flowers in a vase (51x40cm-20x16in) s. 9-Oct-2 Woolley & Wallis, Salisbury #288/R

KIECHLE, Edgar O (1911-1960) American
Works on paper
£545 $850 €790 Gypsy's camp, Griffith Park (37x48cm-15x19in) s. W/C. 13-Apr-3 Butterfields, Los Angeles #7006

KIEFER, Anselm (1945-) German
£12903 $20000 €19355 Die Frauen du Antike (81x54cm-32x21in) i. init.verso oil gelatin silver print. 26-Sep-2 Christie's, Rockefeller NY #775/R est:20000-30000
£84375 $135000 €126563 Grane (187x257cm-74x101in) i. oil on burlap painted 1977 prov. 14-May-3 Sotheby's, New York #420/R est:70000-90000
£212500 $340000 €318750 Urd, werdandi, skuld (170x190cm-67x75in) i. s.d.1980 verso oil photograph burlap prov.exhib. 14-May-3 Christie's, Rockefeller NY #54/R est:350000-450000
£379747 $600000 €569621 Die funf torichten Jungfrauen - Five foolish Virgins (240x340cm-94x134in) i.on stretcher oil acrylic emulsion shellac straw mirror. 12-Nov-2 Sotheby's, New York #42/R est:700000-900000
£420000 $701400 €630000 The Ridge Way (134x228cm-53x90in) i. oil emulsion shellac straw burlap exc.1983 prov. 26-Jun-3 Christie's, London #27/R est:300000-400000
Photographs
£16774 $26000 €25161 Die Himmelspalaste (221x124cm-87x49in) sand on gelatin silver print executed 1997 prov.exhib. 26-Sep-2 Christie's, Rockefeller NY #778/R est:25000-35000
£23750 $38000 €35625 Sefer Hechalot (221x124cm-87x49in) i. sand on gelatin silver print executed 1997 prov. 15-May-3 Christie's, Rockefeller NY #356/R est:20000-30000
Works on paper
£19872 $30801 €31000 Wood (24x34cm-9x13in) s.i. verso gouache W/C prov. 3-Dec-2 Lempertz, Koln #223/R est:18000
£130000 $213200 €195000 Johannisnacht (132x244cm-52x96in) fern lead wire lead in glazed steel frame prov.exhib. 6-Feb-3 Christie's, London #714/R est:75000-100000

KIEKEBUSCH, Herman (1857-?) German
£316 $500 €500 Rowing boat on the Konigssee (60x90cm-24x35in) s. 29-Nov-2 Bolland & Marotz, Bremen #722/R

KIELBERG, Ole (1911-1985) Danish
£380 $586 €570 Cows in landscape (65x100cm-26x39in) init. painted 1964-65-66. 23-Oct-2 Kunsthallen, Copenhagen #100 (D.KR 4500)
£719 $1107 €1079 The road to Landstrup (75x100cm-30x39in) init. painted 1962-63-64. 23-Oct-2 Kunsthallen, Copenhagen #158/R (D.KR 8500)
£803 $1237 €1205 June landscape (54x73cm-21x29in) init. painted 1965-66. 23-Oct-2 Kunsthallen, Copenhagen #14 (D.KR 9500)

KIELDRUP, A E (1826-1869) Danish
£495 $798 €743 Fjord landscape with town (26x36cm-10x14in) s.verso. 22-Feb-3 Rasmussen, Havnen #2246 (D.KR 5500)
£517 $786 €776 Southern house and pergola (18x26cm-7x10in) init. 28-Aug-2 Museumsbygningen, Copenhagen #101/R (D.KR 6000)
£1955 $3109 €2933 View from Ermelunden towards Charlottenlund (50x68cm-20x27in) s. 5-Mar-3 Rasmussen, Copenhagen #1765/R est:12000-15000 (D.KR 21000)
£2102 $3363 €3153 Wooded landscape with footbridge across river (105x140cm-41x55in) s.d.1862. 13-Jan-3 Rasmussen, Vejle #27/R est:15000-20000 (D.KR 24000)

KIELDRUP, Anton Edvard (1826-1869) Danish
£361 $570 €542 Norwegian waterfall (21x29cm-8x11in) paper on panel. 13-Nov-2 Kunsthallen, Copenhagen #45/R (D.KR 4200)

KIELLAND, Else Christie (1903-1993) Norwegian
£256 $399 €384 Landscape from Jolster in Sogn (100x77cm-39x30in) s. painted 1927. 23-Sep-2 Blomqvist, Lysaker #1115 (N.KR 3000)
£349 $548 €524 Drying of fish (81x100cm-32x39in) s. panel. 25-Nov-2 Blomqvist, Lysaker #1150 (N.KR 4000)
£401 $630 €602 Man and boats (100x87cm-39x34in) s. 25-Nov-2 Blomqvist, Lysaker #1149 (N.KR 4600)

KIELLAND, Kitty (1843-1914) Norwegian
£1741 $2785 €2612 Woman on sofa knitting (29x30cm-11x12in) i.d.1885 verso panel. 17-Mar-3 Blomqvist, Oslo #321/R est:25000-30000 (N.KR 20000)
£8239 $12853 €12359 From Cernay-la-Ville (65x52cm-26x20in) i. stretcher painted 1887 prov.exhib.lit. 21-Oct-2 Blomqvist, Oslo #307/R est:80000-100000 (N.KR 95000)

KIELLERUP, Theodor Julius (1818-1850) Danish
£791 $1266 €1187 Deer at watering place, morning glow (73x104cm-29x41in) s.i.d.1849. 16-Mar-3 Hindemae, Ullerslev #349/R (D.KR 8500)

KIEN, Minagawa (1734-1807) Japanese
Works on paper
£17610 $28000 €26415 Landscape, sold with one by Yosa Buson and one by Ike Taiga (124x28cm-49x11in) s. ink col hanging scroll three. 24-Mar-3 Christie's, Rockefeller NY #18/R est:25000-30000

KIENER, Robert (1866-1945) Swiss
£349 $545 €524 View of Eiger, Monch and Jungfrau from Langenberg (61x91cm-24x36in) s. 6-Nov-2 Dobiaschofsky, Bern #3454 (S.FR 800)

KIENHOLZ, Edward (1927-1994) American
Sculpture
£75000 $120000 €112500 Future as afterthought (132x53x48cm-52x21x19in) s.d.62 dolls wood sheet metal prov.exhib.lit. 14-May-3 Christie's, Rockefeller NY #25/R est:70000-90000
Works on paper
£949 $1500 €1500 For 274.00 American Dollars (30x40cm-12x16in) s.d.74 W/C. 1-Dec-2 Bukowskis, Helsinki #386/R est:1000-1300

KIENHOLZ, Edward and Nancy (20th C) American
Sculpture
£9677 $15000 €14516 Fandango black (145x56x29cm-57x22x11in) s.i.d.1986 verso porcelain figurine horns burnt wood rods tar. 26-Sep-2 Christie's, Rockefeller NY #762/R est:8000-12000
£11212 $17491 €16818 Drawing for The Hoerengracht No.2 - Berlin West 1984 (164x85x16cm-65x33x6in) mixed media armature board exhib. 6-Nov-2 AB Stockholms Auktionsverk #821/R est:200000-250000 (S.KR 160000)

KIENMAYER, Franz (20th C) German
£294 $471 €450 Portrait of an elegant lady sitting in front of park landscape with coat of arms (110x90cm-43x35in) s.d.1943 lit. 10-Jan-3 Allgauer, Kempten #1649/R

KIERNER, Rudolf (1876-1941) Austrian
Works on paper
£743 $1159 €1100 Sievering (46x66cm-18x26in) s. mixed media board. 28-Mar-3 Dorotheum, Vienna #284/R

KIERULF, Frode (1889-1963) Danish
£286 $478 €415 Two dancers resting (70x58cm-28x23in) s.d.1918. 17-Jun-3 Rasmussen, Copenhagen #188 (D.KR 3000)

KIESEL, Conrad (1846-1921) German
£342 $534 €500 Portrait of a young lady with hat and flower basket (46x28cm-18x11in) s.i. canvas on canvas lit. 10-Apr-3 Allgauer, Kempten #2835/R
£6329 $10000 €9494 Flora (45x32cm-18x13in) s. panel prov. 23-Apr-3 Christie's, Rockefeller NY #133/R est:10000-15000
£75949 $120000 €113924 Mandolin player (106x134cm-42x53in) s. 23-Apr-3 Christie's, Rockefeller NY #16/R est:100000-150000

KIESLING, Ernst (1851-1929) German
£274 $427 €400 Tegernsee (60x90cm-24x35in) s.i.d.1920 board. 9-Apr-3 Neumeister, Munich #694/R

KIESLING, Ferdinand (1810-1882) German
£2308 $3577 €3600 Burg Eltz on summer's day (48x42cm-19x17in) s.d.1873. 6-Dec-2 Michael Zeller, Lindau #803/R est:2200

KIFF, Ken (1935-2001) British
£4200 $6930 €6090 Man climbing a ladder (61x50cm-24x20in) s. s.d.1979 verso board prov.exhib. 3-Jul-3 Christie's, Kensington #585/R est:1000-1500

KIHLE, Harald (1905-1997) Norwegian
£907 $1514 €1315 Snowfall over Ormeggen, Vinje (33x41cm-13x16in) s.d.55 s.i.d.1955 verso panel. 18-Jun-3 Grev Wedels Plass, Oslo #192 (N.KR 10500)
£1295 $2163 €1878 It's raining in Austbo (37x46cm-15x18in) s. s.i.d.1949 verso panel. 18-Jun-3 Grev Wedels Plass, Oslo #193/R est:30000 (N.KR 15000)
£2255 $3518 €3383 Seated nude from Middelfart's studio (34x27cm-13x11in) s.d.1966 i.verso panel. 21-Oct-2 Blomqvist, Oslo #391/R est:15000-18000 (N.KR 26000)
£3114 $4920 €4671 Green landscape (33x41cm-13x16in) s.d.69 panel. 2-Dec-2 Blomqvist, Oslo #434/R est:20000-25000 (N.KR 36000)

KIITSU, Suzuki (1796-1858) Japanese
Works on paper
£2642 $4200 €3963 Chrysanthemums by a stream (108x31cm-43x12in) s. ink col gold silk hanging scroll. 24-Mar-3 Christie's, Rockefeller NY #57/R est:8000-10000
£7547 $12000 €11321 Linden tree. Chinese milk vetch (95x39cm-37x15in) s. ink col gold silk hanging scrolls pair. 24-Mar-3 Christie's, Rockefeller NY #58/R est:15000-20000

KIJNO, Ladislas (1921-) French
£348 $540 €550 Visage (62x97cm-24x38in) s. acrylic paper. 28-Sep-2 Cornette de St.Cyr, Paris #353
£430 $702 €650 Icone pour Igor Strawinski (67x51cm-26x20in) s. s.i.d.30-10-98 verso acrylic crumpled paper. 31-Jan-3 Charbonneaux, Paris #113
£475 $736 €750 Mains (70x100cm-28x39in) s. acrylic collage paper. 28-Sep-2 Cornette de St.Cyr, Paris #352/R
£500 $790 €750 Untitled (83x55cm-33x22in) s. acrylic diffusion. 3-Apr-3 Christie's, Kensington #254/R
£506 $790 €800 Composition (20x13cm-8x5in) s. acrylic paper. 20-Oct-2 Charbonneaux, Paris #63 est:450-500
£550 $869 €825 Sur les traces de Gauguin (81x65cm-32x26in) s. s.i.d.1989 verso acrylic diffusion. 3-Apr-3 Christie's, Kensington #255/R
£552 $872 €800 Composition (93x72cm-37x28in) s. s.d.1968 verso. 4-Apr-3 Tajan, Paris #279
£552 $872 €800 Composition au fond gris (81x65cm-32x26in) s. 4-Apr-3 Tajan, Paris #278
£600 $948 €900 Fleurs de nuit (81x65cm-32x26in) s.d.89 s.i.d.verso acrylic diffusion. 3-Apr-3 Christie's, Kensington #253/R
£690 $1090 €1000 Untitled (121x85cm-48x33in) s. acrylic paper prov. 2-Apr-3 Christie's, Paris #27/R
£1054 $1677 €1550 Composition (95x46cm-37x18in) s. acrylic. 26-Feb-3 Artcurial Briest, Paris #528 est:1000-1200
£1076 $1700 €1700 Untitled (162x220cm-64x87in) s. panel in 4 parts painted 1969. 2-Dec-2 Tajan, Paris #209
£1103 $1743 €1600 Untitled (130x97cm-51x38in) s. prov. 2-Apr-3 Christie's, Paris #36/R
£1111 $1756 €1600 Composition (100x81cm-39x32in) ecritures blanches prov. 28-Apr-3 Cornette de St.Cyr, Paris #432 est:1500-2000
£1310 $2070 €1900 Composition bi-face (130x97cm-51x38in) s. painted 1970. 4-Apr-3 Tajan, Paris #275
£1379 $2179 €2000 Homage to Dmitrienko (104x67cm-41x26in) s.i.d.75 acrylic paper prov. 2-Apr-3 Christie's, Paris #25/R
£1811 $2971 €2500 Serie des retours de Tahiti (139x150cm-55x59in) s. s.i.d.1990 verso. 27-May-3 Tajan, Paris #73/R est:2500-3000
£1867 $2894 €2950 Cris et silence (162x130cm-64x51in) s. acrylic spray. 28-Sep-2 Cornette de St.Cyr, Paris #354 est:3000-4000
£2532 $4000 €4000 Tiki (132x104cm-52x41in) s. s.i.d.1990 verso. 27-Nov-2 Tajan, Paris #114/R
Works on paper
£314 $487 €500 Composition (28x27cm-11x11in) s. mixed media. 7-Oct-2 Claude Aguttes, Neuilly #280
£355 $574 €500 Composition abstraite (78x54cm-31x21in) s. mixed media crumpled paper. 26-May-3 Joron-Derem, Paris #53
£378 $585 €600 Sans titre (69x52cm-27x20in) s. creased paper. 4-Oct-2 Tajan, Paris #129
£532 $862 €750 Composition (48x37cm-19x15in) s. mixed media creased paper. 23-May-3 Binoche, Paris #71
£556 $878 €800 Composition (62x54cm-24x21in) s. mixed media prov. 27-Apr-3 Perrin, Versailles #16
£570 $883 €900 Hommage a Angela Davis (23x65cm-9x26in) s.i. mixed media. 28-Sep-2 Cornette de St.Cyr, Paris #355
£604 $972 €900 Composition (37x23cm-15x9in) s. mixed media prov. 23-Feb-3 Mercier & Cie, Lille #140
£629 $975 €1000 Composition (92x67cm-36x26in) s. mixed media. 30-Oct-2 Artcurial Briest, Paris #693
£671 $1081 €1000 Composition (33x24cm-13x9in) s. mixed media prov. 23-Feb-3 Mercier & Cie, Lille #141
£692 $1072 €1100 Tahiti (115x93cm-45x37in) s.i.d.90 W/C ink crumpled paper. 30-Oct-2 Artcurial Briest, Paris #698

£759 $1206 €1100 Icone pour un enfant perdu (55x46cm-22x18in) s. s.i.verso mixed media paper on canvas. 7-Mar-3 Claude Aguttes, Neuilly #10/R
£881 $1365 €1400 Tahiti (115x93cm-45x37in) s.i.d.90 W/C ink crumpled paper. 30-Oct-2 Artcurial Briest, Paris #697 est:1200-1800
£1132 $1755 €1800 Tahiti (115x93cm-45x37in) s.i.d.90 W/C ink crumpled paper. 30-Oct-2 Artcurial Briest, Paris #696 est:1200-1800
£1184 $1918 €1800 Sans titre (70x52cm-28x20in) s. crumpled paper. 22-Jan-3 Tajan, Paris #253/R est:2000-3000
£1479 $2455 €2100 Sans titre (104x74cm-41x29in) s. crumpled paper. 11-Jun-3 Beaussant & Lefèvre, Paris #77 est:1000
£1538 $2569 €2200 Composition (33x24cm-13x9in) s. gouache. 25-Jun-3 Claude Aguttes, Neuilly #104/R est:300-400
£2109 $3353 €3100 Composition (60x52cm-24x20in) s. gouache panel. 26-Feb-3 Artcurial Briest, Paris #527/R est:1000-1500
£3020 $4862 €4500 Expansion serielle I (193x163cm-76x64in) s. s.i.d.1961 verso collage on canvas. 23-Feb-3 Mercier & Cie, Lille #139

KIKOINE, Michel (1892-1968) Russian
£2400 $3720 €3600 Le port arabe (47x68cm-19x27in) s. board prov. 5-Dec-2 Christie's, Kensington #124/R est:1000-1500
£2483 $3972 €3600 Landscape (38x46cm-15x18in) s.d.1935. 12-Mar-3 Rabourdin & Choppin de Janvry, Paris #87/R
£2575 $4017 €3734 Woman by an open window (65x54cm-26x21in) s. prov. 26-Mar-3 Walker's, Ottawa #44/R est:6000-8000 (C.D 6000)
£2642 $4121 €4200 Bouquet sur un gueridon (37x72cm-15x28in) s. 9-Oct-2 Lombrail & Teucquam, Paris #6/R
£3526 $5535 €5500 Paysage d'Annay-sur-Serein (46x60cm-18x24in) s. painted c.1964. 24-Nov-2 Chayette & Cheval, Paris #276/R est:6000-7000
£4082 $6490 €6000 Paysage d'Israel, Safed (46x55cm-18x22in) s. painted c.1954. 26-Feb-3 Artcurial Briest, Paris #209/R est:4000-4500
£5000 $7850 €7800 Cap d'Antibes (81x65cm-32x26in) s. s.i.verso. 12-Dec-2 Rabourdin & Choppin de Janvry, Paris #84/R
£5068 $8058 €7450 Saltimbanque (46x27cm-18x11in) s. 26-Feb-3 Artcurial Briest, Paris #208/R est:4000-5000
£6122 $9735 €9000 Paysage des environs de Toulouse (60x41cm-24x16in) s. 3-Mar-3 Claude Boisgirard, Paris #57/R est:10000-12000
£6207 $9931 €9000 Still life with basket of fruit (46x55cm-18x22in) s. 12-Mar-3 Rabourdin & Choppin de Janvry, Paris #97/R

Works on paper
£833 $1308 €1300 Paysage (36x50cm-14x20in) s. mixed media. 12-Dec-2 Rabourdin & Choppin de Janvry, Paris #86
£1020 $1622 €1500 Paysage (31x46cm-12x18in) s. W/C gouache. 3-Mar-3 Claude Boisgirard, Paris #56 est:1500-2000
£1408 $2268 €2000 Still life of flowers (57x42cm-22x17in) s. W/C lit. 9-May-3 Schloss Ahlden, Ahlden #1558/R est:2100

KILANOWICZ, Grazyna (20th C) Polish
£285 $450 €450 Geisha (128x80cm-50x31in) s.d.1988. 29-Nov-2 Schloss Ahlden, Ahlden #1272/R

KILBOURNE, Samuel A (1836-1881) American
£1154 $1800 €1731 Trout hooked on a fly (25x46cm-10x18in) s. prov. 21-Sep-2 Pook & Pook, Downington #353/R est:1000-1500
£1205 $2000 €1747 Extensive landscape with three American Indians on a cliff (36x56cm-14x22in) s. prov. 11-Jun-3 Butterfields, San Francisco #4004/R est:4000-6000

KILBURNE, George Goodwin (1839-1924) British
£1800 $2808 €2700 Tally ho (23x43cm-9x17in) s.d.1900 panel. 10-Apr-3 Tennants, Leyburn #1050 est:2000-3000
£3556 $5902 €5156 Squire's story (59x81cm-23x32in) s. 16-Jun-3 Waddingtons, Toronto #174/R est:10000-15000 (C.D 8000)

Works on paper
£600 $936 €900 Children playing in the snow (10x7cm-4x3in) s. W/C htd white pair. 25-Mar-3 Bonhams, Knightsbridge #61/R
£650 $1021 €975 Playing chess. Young lady at the piano (15x18cm-6x7in) s. pencil W/C htd white two. 16-Apr-3 Christie's, Kensington #964
£800 $1248 €1200 Portrait of a seated lady (24x17cm-9x7in) s.d.1871 W/C htd white. 25-Mar-3 Bonhams, Knightsbridge #39/R
£1150 $1898 €1668 Bedtime story (17x23cm-7x9in) s. pencil W/C htd white. 3-Jul-3 Christie's, Kensington #34/R est:800-1200
£1200 $1956 €1740 Sunday (27x36cm-11x14in) s. W/C. 21-Jul-3 Bonhams, Bath #10/R est:1200-1800
£1300 $2028 €1950 Brother and sister (20x14cm-8x6in) s. W/C. 26-Mar-3 Hamptons Fine Art, Godalming #100/R est:1500-2500
£1510 $2295 €2265 By the bath (26x19cm-10x7in) s. W/C. 16-Aug-2 Lilla Bukowskis, Stockholm #435 est:8000 (S.KR 22000)
£1700 $2686 €2550 Rough morning (37x53cm-15x21in) s. W/C. 7-Apr-3 Bonhams, Bath #35/R est:2000-3000
£1800 $2808 €2700 Motherhood (35x24cm-14x9in) s. W/C. 5-Nov-2 Bonhams, New Bond Street #124/R est:2000-3000
£1800 $2880 €2700 Reluctant playmate (43x32cm-17x13in) s. W/C. 11-Mar-3 Bonhams, New Bond Street #88/R est:2000-3000
£2000 $3200 €3000 Health of the master (37x53cm-15x21in) s. i.verso W/C. 11-Mar-3 Bonhams, New Bond Street #89/R est:2000-3000
£2000 $3120 €3000 Gentleman and a lady in a drawing room (39x26cm-15x10in) s. pencil W/C. 27-Mar-3 Christie's, Kensington #32/R est:2000-3000
£2200 $3454 €3300 Lady and her dog looking into a fish pond (28x21cm-11x8in) s. pencil W/C scratching out. 21-Nov-2 Christie's, London #100/R est:2000-3000
£2500 $3875 €3750 Her portraits (24x34cm-9x13in) s. W/C. 29-Oct-2 Henry Adams, Chichester #444/R est:2500-3000
£2500 $3900 €3750 Reclining by the riverbank (16x21cm-6x8in) s. pencil W/C bodycol. 27-Mar-3 Christie's, Kensington #27/R est:1500-2000
£3800 $6004 €5700 Afternoon tea (37x53cm-15x21in) s.d.1897 W/C pencil. 2-Dec-2 Sotheby's, London #47/R est:3000-4000
£4000 $6640 €6000 Duet (24x34cm-9x13in) s. W/C. 12-Jun-3 Sotheby's, London #249/R est:2000-3000
£4500 $7065 €6750 Afternoon rest (18x23cm-7x9in) s.d.76 pencil W/C htd bodycol. 21-Nov-2 Christie's, London #102/R est:3000-5000

KILBURNE, George Goodwin (attrib) (1839-1924) British

Works on paper
£380 $604 €570 Hawkehurst, Kent (33x48cm-13x19in) W/C. 29-Apr-3 Gorringes, Lewes #2357

KILBURNE, George Goodwin (jnr) (1863-1938) British

Works on paper
£400 $624 €600 Coaching scene (23x33cm-9x13in) s. W/C. 6-Nov-2 Sotheby's, Olympia #67/R

KILGOUR, Jack Noel (1900-1987) Australian
£338 $538 €507 Nude with mirror (47x40cm-19x16in) s. 3-Mar-3 Lawson Menzies, Sydney #341 (A.D 900)

KILIMNICK, Karen (1962-) American
£4684 $7400 €7026 Bulemic, baby haircut (89x58cm-35x23in) d.2.28.92 acrylic wax pencil prov. 12-Nov-2 Phillips, New York #212/R est:5000-7000

KILLEEN, Richard (1946-) New Zealander
£2817 $4648 €4085 Fish business (63x86cm-25x34in) s.i.d.2000 acrylic gesso on aluminium 40 pieces. 1-Jul-3 Peter Webb, Auckland #13/R est:7000-9000 (NZ.D 8000)
£3647 $5690 €5471 Mixing vessel (100x117cm-39x46in) s.i.d.1988 acrylic on polystyrene on gesso. 17-Sep-2 Peter Webb, Auckland #82/R est:12000-18000 (NZ.D 12000)
£8333 $13000 €12500 Destruction of the circle part III (100x100cm-39x39in) acrylic collage aluminium exec.1990. 8-Apr-3 Peter Webb, Auckland #47/R est:12000-18000 (NZ.D 24000)
£13194 $20583 €19791 Three coloured blocks (90x91cm-35x36in) board painted c.1969 lit. 8-Apr-3 Peter Webb, Auckland #60/R est:25000-35000 (NZ.D 38000)
£19097 $29792 €28646 How may we learn? (210x400cm-83x157in) acrylic collage aluminium lit. 8-Apr-3 Peter Webb, Auckland #59/R est:50000-70000 (NZ.D 55000)

Works on paper
£485 $747 €728 From this place (28x38cm-11x15in) s.i.d.1993 mixed media. 4-Sep-2 Dunbar Sloane, Wellington #57 est:1800-2200 (NZ.D 1600)
£528 $824 €915 Still life (76x76cm-30x30in) s.d.1994 mixed media prov. 31-Mar-3 Goodman, Sydney #65 (A.D 1400)
£669 $1043 €1004 Tooth (47x30cm-19x12in) s.i.d.2000 ink on jeweller's tags. 17-Sep-2 Peter Webb, Auckland #109/R est:1000-2000 (NZ.D 2200)
£909 $1400 €1364 Time to change male institutionalised war (76x58cm-30x23in) s.i.d.19.6.86 W/C. 4-Sep-2 Dunbar Sloane, Wellington #53 est:3500-6000 (NZ.D 3000)

KILP, Friedrich Anton (1822-1872) German
£11950 $18522 €19000 Horses (73x94cm-29x37in) s. 2-Oct-2 Dorotheum, Vienna #232/R est:6000-9000

KILPACK, Sarah Louise (fl.1880-1909) British
£300 $474 €450 Cloudy weather on the sea coast (11x15cm-4x6in) s.i.verso board. 27-Nov-2 Bonhams, Brooks & Langlois, Jersey #154
£340 $554 €510 Battle Abbey (25x41cm-10x16in) s. board. 28-Jan-3 Gorringes, Lewes #1593
£420 $701 €609 Fishing boats under an evening sky (20x14cm-8x6in) s. 23-Jun-3 Bonhams, Bath #68
£460 $731 €690 Moonlit run ashore (23x49cm-9x19in) s. board. 4-Mar-3 Bearnes, Exeter #454/R
£480 $797 €696 Ship in distress off a rocky coastline (24x19cm-9x7in) s. 12-Jun-3 Martel Maides, Guernsey #37/R

£550 $847 €825 Two figures on a shore near a cliff fortification with distant shipping (21x29cm-8x11in) s. panel. 23-Oct-2 Hampton & Littlewood, Exeter #445
£550 $875 €825 Stormy coastal scene (27x20cm-11x8in) s. card. 20-Mar-3 Martel Maides, Guernsey #37/R
£580 $916 €870 Le Chateau de Rocquaine, Guernsey (11x19cm-4x7in) board. 27-Nov-2 Bonhams, Brooks & Langlois, Jersey #82/R
£650 $1014 €975 Shipping off St Michael's Mount (15x23cm-6x9in) s. card. 8-Apr-3 Bonhams, Knightsbridge #54/R
£700 $1106 €1050 Casquets lighthouse (9x16cm-4x6in) s. board. 27-Nov-2 Bonhams, Brooks & Langlois, Jersey #90/R
£700 $1120 €1050 Citadel, Plymouth (15x24cm-6x9in) s.i.verso board. 13-May-3 Bonhams, Knightsbridge #55/R
£800 $1264 €1200 Fisherfolk by the shore (22x35cm-9x14in) s. 28-Nov-2 Martel Maides, Guernsey #18/R
£800 $1248 €1200 Figures near a stream (29x23cm-11x9in) s. card oval. 26-Mar-3 Bonhams & Langlois, Jersey #149/R
£800 $1320 €1160 St. Michael's Mount (12x19cm-5x7in) s. board. 1-Jul-3 Bearnes, Exeter #456/R
£900 $1467 €1350 Garden scenes (25x20cm-10x8in) s. card pair. 29-Jan-3 Sotheby's, Olympia #66/R est:1000-1500
£920 $1454 €1380 Channel Island lighthouse, possibly la Corbiere. The Needles (12x18cm-5x7in) s. board pair. 14-Nov-2 Christie's, Kensington #245/R
£1050 $1628 €1575 Fishing boats on the shore with figures at sunset (29x46cm-11x18in) s. 1-Oct-2 Bristol Auction Rooms #490 est:400-600
£1150 $1817 €1725 Country lane with donkey and figures (14x10cm-6x4in) s. board. 27-Nov-2 Bonhams, Brooks & Langlois, Jersey #77/R est:600-800
£1200 $1896 €1800 Ships and figures at night (14x10cm-6x4in) s. card. 27-Nov-2 Bonhams, Brooks & Langlois, Jersey #74/R est:600-800
£1400 $2296 €2100 La Corbiere lighthouse, Jersey (10x15cm-4x6in) s. board pair. 7-Feb-3 Honiton Galleries, Honiton #286/R est:1400-1600
£1900 $3097 €2850 Watching the shipwreck from rocks. Rocky coastline. Strolling along the shoreline (13x20cm-5x8in) s. board three. 29-Jan-3 Dreweatt Neate, Newbury #148/R est:800-1200
£2000 $3160 €3000 Country church and figure at sunset (22x15cm-9x6in) s. board. 27-Nov-2 Bonhams, Brooks & Langlois, Jersey #73/R est:800-1200
£2100 $3360 €3150 Figure retrieving wreckage under a storm swept cliff (61x51cm-24x20in) s. 14-Mar-3 Gardiner & Houlgate, Bath #198/R est:300-600
£2700 $4266 €4050 Just come ashore at Portel (21x29cm-8x11in) s.i.verso board. 27-Nov-2 Bonhams, Brooks & Langlois, Jersey #86/R est:800-1200
£2800 $4536 €4200 Seaweed gathering, Guernsey. West Pier, Boulogne (23x31cm-9x12in) s. i.verso board pair. 21-May-3 Christie's, Kensington #619/R est:2000-3000

KILPACK, Sarah Louise (attrib) (fl.1880-1909) British
£400 $620 €600 Coming ashore, unloading the catch (74x61cm-29x24in) paper oval. 26-Sep-2 Lane, Penzance #269

KILPATRICK, Aaron Edward (1872-1953) American
£569 $950 €825 Coastal sand dunes (30x41cm-12x16in) s. masonite prov. 17-Jun-3 John Moran, Pasadena #195 est:1500-2000
£637 $1000 €956 House at Morro bay (30x41cm-12x16in) s. masonite. 19-Nov-2 Butterfields, San Francisco #8291/R
£1751 $2750 €2627 Summer landscape, San Luis Obispo. Autumn sycamore (46x61cm-18x24in) one s. canvas on board one s.d.24 i.stretcher pair prov. 19-Nov-2 Butterfields, San Francisco #8231/R est:3000-5000
£1911 $3000 €2867 Breaking waves. California coast (36x46cm-14x18in) s. painted c.1924 pair prov. 19-Nov-2 Butterfields, San Francisco #8232/R est:3000-5000
£2108 $3500 €3057 Morro mist (46x62cm-18x24in) s.d.1926. 11-Jun-3 Butterfields, San Francisco #4274/R est:3000-5000
£2258 $3500 €3387 Grey day (51x61cm-20x24in) s.d.1928 i.verso prov. 29-Oct-2 John Moran, Pasadena #782 est:2500-3500
£4777 $7500 €7166 By the bay (46x61cm-18x24in) s. i.verso prov. 19-Nov-2 Butterfields, San Francisco #8230/R est:4000-6000

KILPATRICK, Robert (fl.1935-1939) British
Works on paper
£260 $406 €390 Rural wooded landscape (41x49cm-16x19in) s. pencil W/C. 17-Oct-2 Christie's, Kensington #153

KILROE, Ora E C (20th C) British?
£700 $1162 €1015 St.Martin, bay hunter. Rathenesker, dark brown hunter held by groom (51x61cm-20x24in) s.i. canvasboard two. 12-Jun-3 Christie's, Kensington #77/R

KIM EN JOONG (20th C) ?
£2534 $3979 €3700 Homage to hope (120cm-47in circular) prov. 15-Apr-3 De Veres Art Auctions, Dublin #268/R est:3000-4000

KIMBERLY, Denison (1814-1863) American
£612 $973 €900 Portrait of a lady (26x18cm-10x7in) s. panel. 25-Feb-3 Dorotheum, Vienna #85/R

KIMMEL, Cornelis (1804-1877) British
£2381 $3690 €3572 Landscape with herders, cows and sheep (80x110cm-31x43in) s.d.1862. 24-Sep-2 Koller, Zurich #6536/R est:6000-8000 (S.FR 5500)

KIMPE, Reimond (1885-1970) Belgian
£3597 $5899 €5000 Family (66x50cm-26x20in) s. 3-Jun-3 Christie's, Amsterdam #306/R est:6000-8000
£5396 $8849 €7500 Mannequins (95x60cm-37x24in) s.d.58 prov. 3-Jun-3 Christie's, Amsterdam #307/R est:8000-12000

KIMPIL, Henri (19/20th C) ?
£3797 $6000 €6000 Changeurs (65x77cm-26x30in) s.indis.d. 1-Dec-2 Anaf, Lyon #101/R

KINCH, Agnete Helvig (1872-1956) Danish
£380 $586 €570 Work horses grazing, grey day in early spring (128x98cm-50x39in) init.d.1902 exhib. 26-Oct-2 Rasmussen, Havnen #2093 (D.KR 4500)

KINDBORG, Johan (1861-1907) Swedish
£556 $923 €806 Scene with riders (30x51cm-12x20in) s.d.92. 16-Jun-3 Lilla Bukowskis, Stockholm #340 (S.KR 7200)
£628 $1031 €911 Landscape with figures and house (28x42cm-11x17in) s.d.83. 4-Jun-3 AB Stockholms Auktionsverk #2202/R (S.KR 8000)
£851 $1319 €1277 Katarina Ostra Qvarngata - street scene (60x73cm-24x29in) s.indis.8. 3-Dec-2 Bukowskis, Stockholm #9/R (S.KR 12000)
£982 $1610 €1424 Lake landscape (41x31cm-16x12in) s.i.d.maj 84. 4-Jun-3 AB Stockholms Auktionsverk #2192/R (S.KR 12500)
£993 $1539 €1490 Katarina Ostra Qvarnsgata - street scene (43x53cm-17x21in) s.d.80. 3-Dec-2 Bukowskis, Stockholm #339a/R est:12000-15000 (S.KR 14000)

KINDER, Maria List (1902-) American
£956 $1500 €1434 North shore view (50x61cm-20x24in) s. 22-Nov-2 Skinner, Boston #353/R est:300-500

KINDERMANN, Adolf (1823-1892) German
£700 $1092 €1050 Mother with her children in an interior (59x48cm-23x19in) s. 10-Sep-2 Bonhams, Knightsbridge #202/R

KINDERMANS, Jean-Baptiste (c.1822-1876) Belgian
£3205 $4968 €5000 Bords de la Semois (94x139cm-37x55in) s.d.1868. 7-Dec-2 De Vuyst, Lokeren #513/R est:5000-6000

KINDT, Adele (1804-1884) Belgian
£1633 $2596 €2400 Portrait of Catherine of Medici and Ruggieri (66x58cm-26x23in) s.d.1835. 24-Mar-3 Bernaerts, Antwerp #258/R est:1250-1500
£2000 $3120 €3000 An attentive admierer (72x59cm-28x23in) s.d.1862. 10-Sep-2 Bonhams, Knightsbridge #33/R est:1200-1800
£3006 $4690 €4750 Le gouter (110x88cm-43x35in) s.d.1868. 10-Sep-2 Vanderkindere, Brussels #300/R est:3750-5000

KING GUSTAF III (1746-1792) Swedish
Works on paper
£1939 $3142 €2812 River and mountain landscape (24x32cm-9x13in) s.i.d.4 Juini 1763 Indian ink wash. 26-May-3 Bukowskis, Stockholm #485/R est:20000-25000 (S.KR 25000)

KING, Albert F (1854-1945) American
£2273 $3500 €3410 Western Pennsylvania river landscape with figure (56x91cm-22x36in) s. painted c.1898 lit. 8-Sep-2 Treadway Gallery, Cincinnati #524/R est:2000-3000

KING, Cecil (1881-1942) British
Works on paper
£320 $518 €480 View of Oporto, Portugal (17x26cm-7x10in) s. W/C. 20-May-3 Bonhams, Knightsbridge #132/R
£333 $543 €480 Revue navale Malta Nove (29x51cm-11x20in) s. W/C. 19-Jul-3 Thierry & Lannon, Brest #271
£353 $546 €550 Vaisseaux de haut bord (34x45cm-13x18in) s. W/C. 9-Dec-2 Thierry & Lannon, Brest #241

£380 $593 €570 Richmond Bridge (35x51cm-14x20in) s. pencil W/C. 17-Oct-2 Christie's, Kensington #51/R

KING, Cecil (1921-1986) Irish
£329 $510 €520 Abstract (18x18cm-7x7in) oil on card prov. 24-Sep-2 De Veres Art Auctions, Dublin #169
£850 $1360 €1275 Ringsend morning (42x44cm-17x17in) board exhib. 16-May-3 Sotheby's, London #140/R

KING, Dorothy (fl.1937-1940) British
£1150 $1806 €1725 Three figures (102x147cm-40x58in) s.d.51 s.i.verso. 15-Apr-3 Bonhams, Knowle #127/R est:800-1200

KING, Edith Louise Mary (1870-1962) South African
Works on paper
£241 $381 €362 Tropical vegetation (54x44cm-21x17in) s. W/C. 1-Apr-3 Stephan Welz, Johannesburg #163 est:3000-5000 (SA.R 3000)
£1075 $1730 €1613 Indigenous tree in a landscape (34x51cm-13x20in) s. chl W/C executed c.1950. 12-May-3 Stephan Welz, Johannesburg #577/R est:6000-9000 (SA.R 12500)

KING, Edward (1863-?) British
£270 $419 €405 Landscape with cattle (20x28cm-8x11in) board. 4-Dec-2 Neal & Fletcher, Woodbridge #266
£360 $562 €540 Town square (28x41cm-11x16in) s. board. 25-Mar-3 Bonhams, Leeds #639

KING, George W (1836-1922) American
£1019 $1600 €1529 Autumn in the Adirondacks (61x91cm-24x36in) s. 10-Dec-2 Doyle, New York #16/R est:3000-4000

KING, Gordon (?) British
£1000 $1550 €1500 Portrait of a seated girl (93x61cm-37x24in) s. 3-Dec-2 Bonhams, Knightsbridge #93/R est:1000-1500
Works on paper
£350 $571 €525 Two girls (38x25cm-15x10in) s. W/C. 13-Feb-3 David Lay, Penzance #10
£800 $1240 €1200 Young woman in a garden (53x68cm-21x27in) s. W/C. 3-Dec-2 Bonhams, Knightsbridge #94/R

KING, Haynes (1831-1904) British
£414 $637 €621 On the look-out (30x25cm-12x10in) s.d.1861. 27-Oct-2 Anders Antik, Landskrona #96/R (S.KR 6000)
£506 $800 €759 Portrait of a lady (28x23cm-11x9in) s. 16-Nov-2 New Orleans Auction, New Orleans #549
£13000 $20540 €19500 Homeless (91x71cm-36x28in) s.d.1872 exhib. 2-Dec-2 Sotheby's, London #96/R est:7000-9000
Works on paper
£2000 $3160 €3000 Pleasant reflections (59x44cm-23x17in) s.indis.d.188 W/C over pencil htd white. 27-Nov-2 Bonhams, Knowle #176 est:2000-3000

KING, Henry C (19th C) British
£920 $1536 €1334 Streatley Bridge, Streatley on Thames (41x61cm-16x24in) s.i.verso sold with a companion. 25-Jun-3 Bonhams, Bury St Edmunds #543/R

KING, Henry John Yeend (1855-1924) British
£343 $536 €497 Highland landscape with deer (46x35cm-18x14in) s. panel. 26-Mar-3 Walker's, Ottawa #68/R (C.D 800)
£400 $668 €580 River landscape with a wooden house beyond (26x34cm-10x13in) s. panel. 8-Jul-3 Bonhams, Knightsbridge #125/R
£520 $822 €780 Young lady reading a letter by a window, her dog by her side (25x20cm-10x8in) s. 2-Dec-2 Bonhams, Bath #147/R
£537 $843 €806 Deer at river's edge (46x36cm-18x14in) s. panel. 24-Jul-2 Walker's, Ottawa #28/R est:2000-2500 (C.D 1300)
£600 $942 €900 Feeding the ducks (25x36cm-10x14in) s. 16-Apr-3 Christie's, Kensington #673/R
£957 $1550 €1388 Young girl with dog in forest, autumn (41x33cm-16x13in) s. 26-May-3 Rasmussen, Copenhagen #1531 (D.KR 10000)
£1067 $1771 €1547 Girls near the garden (36x46cm-14x18in) s.d.1899 s.verso. 10-Jun-3 Ritchie, Toronto #62/R est:3000-5000 (C.D 2400)
£1397 $2221 €2096 Two young girls by river (51x76cm-20x30in) s. exhib. 10-Mar-3 Rasmussen, Vejle #541/R est:20000-30000 (D.KR 15000)
£1400 $2184 €2100 Path throught the woods (46x61cm-18x24in) s. 10-Sep-2 Bonhams, Knightsbridge #83/R est:1500-2000
£1422 $2361 €2062 Young lad near cottage at river's edge (46x61cm-18x24in) s. 10-Jun-3 Ritchie, Toronto #62a/R est:3000-5000 (C.D 3200)
£1700 $2771 €2550 Ferry (35x25cm-14x10in) s. panel. 29-Jan-3 Sotheby's, Olympia #160/R est:1000-2000
£1800 $2772 €2700 Woodland pool (37x55cm-15x22in) s. 5-Sep-2 Christie's, Kensington #176/R est:2200-2800
£2623 $4250 €3803 Gathering flowers (91x71cm-36x28in) s. indis.d.18.. 21-May-3 Doyle, New York #178/R est:4000-6000
£2985 $4896 €4328 By the river (61x92cm-24x36in) s. 4-Jun-3 AB Stockholms Auktionsverk #2448/R est:35000-40000 (S.KR 38000)
£3500 $5425 €5250 The goose girl (51x76cm-20x30in) s. 25-Sep-2 John Nicholson, Haslemere #1027/R est:3000-5000
£4435 $7008 €6653 Feeding the geese (51x77cm-20x30in) s. prov. 18-Nov-2 Waddingtons, Toronto #149/R est:8000-10000 (C.D 11000)
£4500 $7515 €6525 In the courtyard (61x51cm-24x20in) s. 17-Jun-3 Bonhams, New Bond Street #86/R est:5000-7000
£4721 $7365 €6845 At the village stream (61x91cm-24x36in) s. 26-Mar-3 Walker's, Ottawa #65/R est:10000-12000 (C.D 11000)
£4965 $8043 €7199 Girl by duck pond (92x72cm-36x28in) s. 26-May-3 Bukowskis, Stockholm #238/R est:40000-50000 (S.KR 64000)
£5161 $8000 €7742 Two ladies punting on the river (61x46cm-24x18in) s. 30-Oct-2 Christie's, Rockefeller NY #189/R est:10000-15000
£7500 $11925 €11250 Fishing village with boy by quayside (64x91cm-25x36in) s. 29-Apr-3 Gorringes, Lewes #2308
£8400 $13692 €12600 In the kitchen garden (51x76cm-20x30in) s.d.May 84 verso. 29-Jan-3 Sotheby's, Olympia #224/R est:6000-8000
£10473 $16967 €15186 Summer landscape with women at well (92x71cm-36x28in) s. 25-May-3 Uppsala Auktionskammare, Uppsala #94/R est:60000-80000 (S.KR 135000)
£11000 $17270 €16500 Tranquil moment (137x103cm-54x41in) s. 19-Nov-2 Bonhams, New Bond Street #138/R est:10000-15000
£11268 $16000 €16902 In the garden (102x76cm-40x30in) 8-Aug-1 Barridorf, Portland #91/R est:15000-25000
Works on paper
£250 $393 €375 Wild flowers (17x24cm-7x9in) W/C bodycol. 14-Dec-2 Lacy Scott, Bury St.Edmunds #440
£300 $492 €450 Young lovers driving geese beside a pond (29x21cm-11x8in) s. W/C. 3-Jun-3 Bearnes, Exeter #415
£450 $752 €653 Kitchen maid (53x35cm-21x14in) s. pencil W/C htd white. 26-Jun-3 Mellors & Kirk, Nottingham #833/R
£460 $731 €690 Spring river landscape (33x50cm-13x20in) s. W/C. 30-Apr-3 Hampton & Littlewood, Exeter #449/R
£470 $738 €705 Village scene with figures beside cottages (35x51cm-14x20in) s. pencil W/C htd white. 19-Nov-2 Bonhams, Leeds #43
£520 $868 €754 Village street scene with boys playing marbles by the brewery store (36x26cm-14x10in) s. W/C. 17-Jun-3 Anderson & Garland, Newcastle #302/R
£750 $1170 €1125 Cattle brazing. Pastoral scene (25x35cm-10x14in) s. W/C. 17-Sep-2 Sotheby's, Olympia #125/R

KING, Inge (1918-) Australian
Sculpture
£1053 $1600 €1580 Lovers (54cm-21in) init. bronze. 19-Aug-2 Joel, Victoria #223 est:3500-4500 (A.D 3000)
£10000 $16100 €15000 Balance of steel forms (207x43x119cm-81x17x47in) black painted steel executed 1971-72 prov. 6-May-3 Christie's, Melbourne #73/R est:25000-35000 (A.D 25000)
£16800 $27048 €25200 Euridice (210x45x31cm-83x18x12in) black painted steel executed 1965 prov.exhib.lit. 6-May-3 Christie's, Melbourne #71/R est:28000-35000 (A.D 42000)

KING, Jan (1945-) Australian
Sculpture
£1132 $1765 €1961 Dark beach (220x108x24cm-87x43x9in) painted steel prov. 31-Mar-3 Goodman, Sydney #171/R (A.D 3000)

KING, Jessie M (1875-1949) British
Works on paper
£950 $1473 €1425 Young woman sketching (23x19cm-9x7in) W/C exhib. 2-Nov-2 Shapes, Edinburgh #301
£2600 $4030 €3900 Sleeping angel (40x12cm-16x5in) s. pen ink W/C exhib. 2-Nov-2 Shapes, Edinburgh #300/R est:800-1200
£4000 $6200 €6000 Queen of the garden. Rembrance (31x26cm-12x10in) s. pen ink W/C two. 24-Sep-2 Bonhams, New Bond Street #18/R est:1000-1500

KING, John (20th C) British
£1200 $1968 €1800 Duke of Beaufort's Hunt (61x91cm-24x36in) s.i. 3-Jun-3 Bonhams, Knightsbridge #80/R est:800-1200

KING, John Baragwanath (1864-1939) British
£450 $711 €675 Fishing fleet sailing out (46x76cm-18x30in) indis sig. 14-Nov-2 Christie's, Kensington #9
Works on paper
£280 $437 €420 Casting the nets at sea (25x72cm-10x28in) s. W/C bodycol. 27-Mar-3 Christie's, Kensington #149/R
£300 $468 €450 Heuckaby bridge, Dartmoor (27x45cm-11x18in) s. W/C gouache exhib. 26-Mar-3 Woolley & Wallis, Salisbury #31/R

KING, Marcus (1891-1985) New Zealander
£351 $547 €527 Portrait of a lady (74x54cm-29x21in) s. canvasboard. 27-Mar-3 International Art Centre, Auckland #178/R (NZ.D 1000)
£491 $766 €737 River reflections (40x50cm-16x20in) s. canvasboard. 27-Mar-3 International Art Centre, Auckland #166/R (NZ.D 1400)

KING, Margaret (18th C) British
£350 $557 €525 Yachts in shipping lane (76x102cm-30x40in) s.verso. 18-Mar-3 Capes Dunn, Manchester #430

KING, Michel (1930-) French
£2215 $3566 €3300 La radoub (100x100cm-39x39in) s. 23-Feb-3 Lesieur & Le Bars, Le Havre #81/R

KING, Paul (1867-1947) American
£313 $500 €470 Fall landscape (18x23cm-7x9in) 11-Jan-3 James Julia, Fairfield #439
£500 $800 €725 Cedar Creek, Adirondacks (65x54cm-26x21in) s.i.verso. 16-May-3 Skinner, Boston #200/R
£943 $1500 €1415 Autumnal landscape with birches (41x30cm-16x12in) s. 1-Mar-3 North East Auctions, Portsmouth #693/R est:1000-2000
£1783 $2800 €2675 Golden autumn (52x62cm-20x24in) s. masonite prov. 14-Dec-2 Weschler, Washington #655/R est:2500-3500
£2373 $3750 €3560 Harbor scene (51x41cm-20x16in) s. 24-Apr-3 Shannon's, Milford #229/R est:3000-5000

KING, Peter (1928-1957) British
Sculpture
£1300 $2041 €1950 Elongated boat form (125x20x29cm-49x8x11in) black softwood prov. 10-Dec-2 Rosebery Fine Art, London #736/R est:200-300

KING, Robert (1936-) British
£1100 $1705 €1650 Sailing boats in an estuary by a yacht (28x41cm-11x16in) s. two. 4-Dec-2 Christie's, Kensington #544 est:200-300
£4500 $6975 €6750 Burnham over hill (61x91cm-24x36in) s. sold with three sailing scenes by same hand. 4-Dec-2 Christie's, Kensington #542/R est:800-1200

KING, Samuel (attrib) (17th C) British
£1600 $2608 €2320 Portrait of Lady Hoskyns and Portrait of of her sister (35x30cm-14x12in) i.stretcher pair prov. 21-Jul-3 Sotheby's, London #396 est:800-1200

KING, Tony (20th C) British
£318 $500 €477 Untitled (122x122cm-48x48in) i.d.75. 14-Dec-2 Weschler, Washington #603/R

KING, W Gunning (1859-1940) British
£550 $836 €825 Sussex cottage (48x58cm-19x23in) s.d.1929. 16-Aug-2 Keys, Aylsham #613

KING, Wallace S (20th C) ?
£200 $332 €290 Moorish courtyard (28x42cm-11x17in) s.d.1928 canvas on board. 10-Jun-3 Ritchie, Toronto #74/R (C.D 450)

KING, William (18/19th C) British
Works on paper
£1119 $1600 €1679 Ahouai-thevetia (45x29cm-18x11in) i. W/C. 22-Jan-3 Doyle, New York #69

KING-HARMAN, Ann Stafford (1919-1979) Irish
Works on paper
£577 $906 €900 From Cladderduuff Road, Connemara. Kylemore Lough, Connemara (28x51cm-11x20in) one i.d.1976 verso one s.i.d.1976 gouache board pair prov. 19-Nov-2 Whyte's, Dublin #142/R

KINGERLEE, John (1936-) Irish?
£342 $538 €500 Lovers (36x48cm-14x19in) s.d.62 s.i.verso. 15-Apr-3 De Veres Art Auctions, Dublin #24
£651 $1015 €950 Abstract (13x10cm-5x4in) mono.d.97 board. 8-Apr-3 James Adam, Dublin #35/R
£915 $1520 €1300 Turkish delight (51x41cm-20x16in) mono.d.84. 10-Jun-3 Thomas Adams, Dublin #344
£1139 $1766 €1800 Tree and figures - homage to Patrick Collins (70x46cm-28x18in) mono.d.78 i.d.verso. 24-Sep-2 De Veres Art Auctions, Dublin #83/R est:1500-2500
£2113 $3507 €3000 Landscape composition (52x39cm-20x15in) mono. board. 10-Jun-3 James Adam, Dublin #22/R est:1500-2500
£2200 $3520 €3300 To whom time belongs (49x29cm-19x11in) mono.d.88. 15-May-3 Christie's, Kensington #167/R est:800-1200
£2603 $4060 €3800 Abstract (37x40cm-15x16in) mono.d.97 board. 8-Apr-3 James Adam, Dublin #33/R est:500-700
£3288 $5129 €4800 Abstract (41x57cm-16x22in) mono.d.97 board. 8-Apr-3 James Adam, Dublin #34/R est:500-700

KINGMAN, Dong (1911-2000) American
Works on paper
£671 $1100 €1007 Laundry drying (56x41cm-22x16in) s. W/C prov. 5-Feb 3 Doyle, New York #59/R est:1000-2000
£1220 $2000 €1830 Waterfront at Okinawa (38x56cm-15x22in) s. W/C prov. 5-Feb-3 Doyle, New York #58/R est:1000-2000
£2388 $3750 €3582 Chicken house (37x55cm-15x22in) s. W/C prov. 19-Nov-2 Butterfields, San Francisco #8349/R est:3000-5000
£7831 $13000 €11355 From the opening credits of the film "Flower Drum Song" (28x59cm-11x23in) seven s. pencil W/C eight prov. 11-Jun-3 Butterfields, San Francisco #4301/R est:10000-15000

KINGMAN, Eduardo (1913-1997) Ecuadorian
Works on paper
£652 $1017 €978 Untitled - head with hands covering eyes (45x56cm-18x22in) s.d.1976 mixed media. 16-Sep-2 Philippe Schuler, Zurich #3038 (S.FR 1500)

KINGSBURY, Alan (1960-) British
£550 $847 €825 Summer holiday (56x41cm-22x16in) s. s.i.verso board sold with another by the same artist. 5-Sep-2 Christie's, Kensington #590

KINGSBURY, Edward R (1879-1940) American
£955 $1500 €1433 Summer landscape in sunlit morning with trees and hillside (51x61cm-20x24in) s. 19-Apr-3 James Julia, Fairfield #292/R est:800-1200

KINGSLEY, Harry (1914-) British
£320 $509 €480 Cigarettes, Hulme, Manchester. s.d.1946 board. 2-Mar-3 ELR Auctions, Sheffield #226

KINGSTON, H (19th C) British
£800 $1248 €1200 Spalding, Lincs (63x85cm-25x33in) s.d.1822. 10-Sep-2 Sworder & Son, Bishops Stortford #740/R

KINGSTON, Richard (1922-2003) British
£3904 $6129 €5700 Winter birds at 19 (46x38cm-18x15in) s. board. 15-Apr-3 De Veres Art Auctions, Dublin #245/R est:3500-4500
£4832 $7780 €7200 Water descent (46x81cm-18x32in) s. prov. 18-Feb-3 Whyte's, Dublin #42/R est:7000-9000
£5705 $9185 €8500 Shore (38x56cm-15x22in) s. i.verso board. 18-Feb-3 Whyte's, Dublin #58/R est:7000-9000
£7246 $11884 €10000 Waiting currachs (75x121cm-30x48in) s. board. 28-May-3 Bonhams & James Adam, Dublin #64/R est:10000-15000
£9028 $14354 €13000 Still November (76x122cm-30x48in) s. i.verso board. 29-Apr-3 Whyte's, Dublin #52/R est:12000-15000
£19565 $32087 €27000 Coastal landscape (90x121cm-35x48in) s. board prov.exhib. 28-May-3 Bonhams & James Adam, Dublin #65/R est:15000-25000

Works on paper
£356 $559 €520 View of buildings (18x17cm-7x7in) s. gouache prov. 15-Apr-3 De Veres Art Auctions, Dublin #26
£411 $641 €600 Abstract (26x21cm-10x8in) s. W/C. 8-Apr-3 James Adam, Dublin #127/R
£548 $855 €800 Bark study (22x33cm-9x13in) s. W/C. 8-Apr-3 James Adam, Dublin #178/R

KINGSTONE, Ian (20th C) New Zealander
£304 $474 €456 Friend in low places (46x45cm-18x18in) s. s.i.verso. 17-Sep-2 Peter Webb, Auckland #156/R est:1500-2500 (NZ.D 1000)
£313 $489 €470 Cast waltz (45x45cm-18x18in) s. 7-Nov-2 International Art Centre, Auckland #151/R est:900-1400 (NZ.D 1000)
£376 $587 €564 Room for hope (45x45cm-18x18in) s. s.i.verso. 5-Nov-2 Peter Webb, Auckland #91/R est:1200-1600 (NZ.D 1200)
£421 $657 €632 Blue angel (80x60cm-31x24in) s. canvasboard. 27-Mar-3 International Art Centre, Auckland #13/R (NZ.D 1200)
£470 $734 €705 The astonishment of Sergei Diachilev (120x79cm-47x31in) s. s.i.d.1997 verso board. 5-Nov-2 Peter Webb, Auckland #114/R est:1500-2500 (NZ.D 1500)

KINKADE, Thomas (20th C) American
£15663 $26000 €22711 Trail to Vista Point (76x61cm-30x24in) s.d.1984 canvas on panel prov. 11-Jun-3 Butterfields, San Francisco #4141/R est:30000-40000

KINLEY, Peter (1926-1988) British
£1000 $1650 €1450 Studio for seated nude n.2 (28x20cm-11x8in) s. board painted 1960 prov. 3-Jul-3 Christie's, Kensington #541/R est:800-1200
£1200 $1980 €1740 Study for flowers (26x18cm-10x7in) s. board prov. 3-Jul-3 Christie's, Kensington #646/R est:700-1000
Works on paper
£1300 $2145 €1885 Study for studio interior I (28x21cm-11x8in) s. pencil on board prov. 3-Jul-3 Christie's, Kensington #693/R est:800-1200

KINMANSSON, Lars Gustav (1822-1887) Swedish
£329 $514 €494 Lake landscape with figures in punt (80x125cm-31x49in) s.d.1867. 13-Sep-2 Lilla Bukowskis, Stockholm #60 (S.KR 4800)
£1479 $2381 €2100 Approaching rain (81x130cm-32x51in) s.d.1866. 10-May-3 Bukowskis, Helsinki #359/R est:1500-2000

KINNAIRD, Henry J (fl.1880-1908) British
£750 $1170 €1125 Haymaking near Sussex (20x30cm-8x12in) s. 17-Sep-2 Bonhams, Oxford #50
£750 $1170 €1125 Riverscape with cottage and ducks (43x66cm-17x26in) s. 15-Oct-2 Gorringes, Lewes #2256
£850 $1318 €1275 On the Thames near Pangbourne (41x61cm-16x24in) indis.sig. i.verso. 25-Sep-2 Hamptons Fine Art, Godalming #445/R
Works on paper
£340 $530 €510 Arundel Castle, Sussex (20x41cm-8x16in) s.i. W/C. 26-Mar-3 Hamptons Fine Art, Godalming #81
£400 $636 €600 Shepherd and flock on a lane (15x20cm-6x8in) s. W/C. 29-Apr-3 Gorringes, Lewes #2179
£550 $913 €798 Winchester with cattle watering in the foreground and the cathedral beyond (13x15cm-5x6in) s.i. W/C. 16-Jun-3 Duke & Son, Dorchester #141
£600 $936 €900 Cornfield (23x34cm-9x13in) s. pencil W/C htd white. 19-Sep-2 Christie's, Kensington #52/R
£650 $1014 €975 Thames near Goring (34x50cm-13x20in) s. W/C. 17-Sep-2 Sotheby's, Olympia #106/R
£700 $1092 €1050 Thames near Tilehurst (33x51cm-13x20in) s.i. W/C. 18-Sep-2 Dreweatt Neate, Newbury #15/R
£700 $1106 €1050 Thames near Pangbourne (19x40cm-7x16in) s.i. W/C htd white. 26-Nov-2 Bonhams, Knightsbridge #16/R
£800 $1248 €1200 Sussex cornfield (35x52cm-14x20in) s. W/C bodycol. 10-Apr-3 Tennants, Leyburn #847/R
£800 $1336 €1160 Cornfield near Arundel (25x35cm-10x14in) s.i. W/C htd bodycol. 24-Jun-3 Bonhams, Knightsbridge #41/R
£880 $1382 €1320 Arundel Castle, Sussex (19x40cm-7x16in) s.i. pencil W/C htd white. 19-Nov-2 Bonhams, Leeds #40/R
£900 $1422 €1350 Cattle watering in the meadows before Salisbury Cathedral (25x18cm-10x7in) s.i. W/C. 13-Nov-2 Halls, Shrewsbury #346/R
£950 $1549 €1378 View of Salisbury (28x19cm-11x7in) s.i. W/C htd white. 17-Jul-3 Tennants, Leyburn #728/R
£1000 $1520 €1500 Abingdon. Arundel Castle (33x52cm-13x20in) s.i. pencil W/C htd white pair. 4-Jul-2 Mellors & Kirk, Nottingham #816/R est:1000-1500
£1000 $1620 €1450 On the Itchen Hampshire (18x27cm-7x11in) s. W/C. 22-May-3 Wintertons, Lichfield #535/R est:1000-1500
£1200 $1956 €1740 River landscape with a view of Salisbury cathedral (34x25cm-13x10in) s.i. W/C bodycol. 17-Jul-3 Tennants, Leyburn #729/R est:600-800
£1244 $2066 €1804 Windsor Castle (42x63cm-17x25in) s.i. W/C. 16-Jun-3 Waddingtons, Toronto #91/R est:1500-2500 (C.D 2800)
£1350 $2201 €1958 Surrey cornfield with figures (31x54cm-12x21in) s.i. W/C htd gouache. 16-Jul-3 Rupert Toovey, Partridge Green #2/R est:400-600
£1800 $2808 €2700 Sussex lane. Country lane, Perth (35x27cm-14x11in) s.i. pencil W/C htd white pair. 19-Sep-2 Christie's, Kensington #47/R est:1500-2000
£1875 $3000 €2813 Old mill on the Thames (52x74cm-20x29in) s.i. pencil W/C gouache. 14-May-3 Butterfields, San Francisco #1172/R est:2000-3000
£3400 $5644 €5100 View near Arundel. View near Salisbury (18x27cm-7x11in) s.i. W/C bodycol pair. 12-Jun-3 Bonhams, New Bond Street #681/R est:1200-1800

KINNEAR, James (fl.1880-1917) British
£565 $892 €848 Sheep by a stream (44x53cm-17x21in) s. 18-Nov-2 Waddingtons, Toronto #179/R (C.D 1400)
Works on paper
£316 $492 €474 Landscape with figures on road (21x35cm-8x14in) s. W/C. 13-Sep-2 Lilla Bukowskis, Stockholm #326 (S.KR 4600)
£404 $638 €606 Woodland path through a pasture (49x74cm-19x29in) s.d.1913 W/C. 18-Nov-2 Waddingtons, Toronto #168/R (C.D 1000)
£429 $670 €622 Bakehouse close, Edinburgh (37x27cm-15x11in) s.d.1908 W/C bodycol. 26-Mar-3 Walker's, Ottawa #49/R est:900-1200 (C.D 1000)

KINNEY, Desmond (1934-) British
£493 $774 €720 Stooking corn (22x22cm-9x9in) s. acrylic board prov. 15-Apr-3 De Veres Art Auctions, Dublin #100

KINSELLA, James (1857-1923) American
Works on paper
£1389 $2250 €2014 Bullfinch State house, Boston (66x48cm-26x19in) s. W/C pencil. 21-May-3 Doyle, New York #111/R est:2000-3000

KINSEN, Mori (1888-1959) Japanese
£556 $917 €800 Indonesian landscape (61x112cm-24x44in) s. 1-Jul-3 Christie's, Amsterdam #300

KINSEY, Alberta (1875-1955) American
£446 $700 €669 Patio entry with arched doorway (41x30cm-16x12in) s. board. 22-Nov-2 Eldred, East Dennis #1135/R
£478 $775 €693 Green trees and bushes in pots in a backyard, Southern States (48x38cm-19x15in) s. 26-May-3 Rasmussen, Copenhagen #1558/R (D.KR 5000)
£478 $775 €693 Backyard in Southern States with shutters and doors (50x37cm-20x15in) s. 26-May-3 Rasmussen, Copenhagen #1559/R (D.KR 5000)
£766 $1240 €1111 White flowers in jug (46x40cm-18x16in) s. 26-May-3 Rasmussen, Copenhagen #1560/R (D.KR 8000)
£957 $1550 €1388 Graveyard in the Southern States (51x96cm-20x38in) s. 26-May-3 Rasmussen, Copenhagen #1562/R (D.KR 10000)
£957 $1550 €1388 Figures at market in Southern States (44x48cm-17x19in) s. 26-May-3 Rasmussen, Copenhagen #1563/R (D.KR 10000)
£957 $1550 €1388 Everyday life in a backyard in Southern States (56x63cm-22x25in) s. 26-May-3 Rasmussen, Copenhagen #1565/R (D.KR 10000)
£1037 $1700 €1504 French quarter courtyard (43x33cm-17x13in) s. 7-Jun-3 Neal Auction Company, New Orleans #398/R est:1200-1800
£1053 $1705 €1527 Two ladies strolling in garden in Southern States (48x56cm-19x22in) s. 26-May-3 Rasmussen, Copenhagen #1561/R (D.KR 11000)
£1282 $2000 €1923 French quarter courtyard (30x43cm-12x17in) s. board. 12-Oct-2 Neal Auction Company, New Orleans #637/R est:1200-1800
£1340 $2170 €1943 The French Quarter in New Orleans with characteristic iron balconies (54x48cm-21x19in) s. 26-May-3 Rasmussen, Copenhagen #1564/R est:10000-15000 (D.KR 14000)
£1341 $2200 €2012 Pirate's alley (36x28cm-14x11in) s. illustration board. 8-Feb-3 Neal Auction Company, New Orleans #381 est:1000-1500
£2222 $3600 €3333 Little theatre (51x41cm-20x16in) s. i.on stretcher verso prov. 24-Jan-3 New Orleans Auction, New Orleans #379/R est:2500-4000
£2452 $3800 €3678 French quarter courtyard (48x58cm-19x23in) s. 7-Dec-2 Neal Auction Company, New Orleans #481/R est:2500-3500

KINSLEY, Nelson Gray (1863-1945) German
£417 $654 €650 Forest clearing in evening (16cm-6in circular) s.d.1944 panel tondo. 23-Nov-2 Arnold, Frankfurt #779/R
£503 $800 €755 Winter landscape (56x66cm-22x26in) s.d.1935. 7-Mar-3 Jackson's, Cedar Falls #636/R
£719 $1180 €1000 Autumnal woodland (23x17cm-9x7in) s. canvas on board. 4-Jun-3 Reiss & Sohn, Konigstein #149/R
£719 $1180 €1000 Path through summer woodland (21x18cm-8x7in) s. canvas on board. 4-Jun-3 Reiss & Sohn, Konigstein #150/R

KINSON, François Joseph (1771-1839) Flemish
£1748 $2920 €2500 Portrait de jeune femme. Portrait d'homme a la veste noire (65x54cm-26x21in) one s. pair. 27-Jun-3 Piasa, Paris #99/R est:2500-3000
£7500 $12000 €11250 Portrait of a lady in a blue dress resting against a parapet (190x126cm-75x50in) s. 14-May-3 Butterfields, San Francisco #1104/R est:12000-18000

KINSON, François Joseph (attrib) (1771-1839) Flemish
£1026 $1610 €1600 Portrait de jeune femme a la robe rouge (61x49cm-24x19in) 14-Dec-2 Artcurial Briest, Paris #60/R

KINSON, François Joseph (circle) (1771-1839) Flemish
£10063 $15698 €16000 Portrait de Louis de Bourbon (115x90cm-45x35in) prov. 8-Oct-2 Christie's, Paris #26/R est:12000

KINZEL, Josef (1852-1925) Austrian
£1538 $2415 €2400 Portrait of a society woman (80x127cm-31x50in) s.d.82. 10-Dec-2 Dorotheum, Vienna #103/R est:2600-3000
£2201 $3390 €3500 Cigar smoker (21x26cm-8x10in) s. panel. 22-Oct-2 Wiener Kunst Auktionen, Vienna #1076/R est:1300-4000

£9494 $15000 €15000 Village politics (60x78cm-24x31in) s.i.d.1903. 28-Nov-2 Dorotheum, Vienna #59/R est:18000-22000
£14184 $22979 €20000 Friendly chat in a room (50x60cm-20x24in) s.i. 22-May-3 Dorotheum, Vienna #34/R est:10000-12000

KINZEL, Liesl (1886-1961) Austrian
Works on paper
£811 $1265 €1200 Farmstead in Spitz (29x23cm-11x9in) s.i. gouache. 28-Mar-3 Dorotheum, Vienna #305/R

KINZINGER, Edmund Daniel (1888-1963) German
£1282 $2000 €1923 Women in Taxco (46x36cm-18x14in) paper painted c.1936. 19-Oct-2 David Dike, Dallas #273/R est:1500-3000
Works on paper
£321 $500 €482 Taxco man and woman (23x28cm-9x11in) pencil. 19-Oct-2 David Dike, Dallas #40/R
£481 $750 €722 Young girl (30x23cm-12x9in) dr executed c.1936. 19-Oct-2 David Dike, Dallas #41/R
£769 $1200 €1154 Young Taxco woman (30x23cm-12x9in) chl executed c.1940. 19-Oct-2 David Dike, Dallas #84/R

KIOERBOE, Carl Fredrik (1799-1876) Swedish
£993 $1539 €1490 Dog standing in landscape (34x44cm-13x17in) s.indis.d. 4-Dec-2 AB Stockholms Auktionsverk #1674/R (S.KR 14000)
£1164 $1885 €1688 Fox hunting (55x46cm-22x18in) s. prov. 26-May-3 Bukowskis, Stockholm #102a/R est:15000-20000 (S.KR 15000)
£1702 $2638 €2553 King Karl XV on horseback (86x75cm-34x30in) 3-Dec-2 Bukowskis, Stockholm #418/R est:30000-35000 (S.KR 24000)
£1939 $3142 €2812 Two dogs (59x73cm-23x29in) s. 26-May-3 Bukowskis, Stockholm #102/R est:30000-35000 (S.KR 25000)

KIPLING, Frank E (?) British?
£267 $443 €387 Washing day on the farm (56x41cm-22x16in) s. i.verso board. 10-Jun-3 Ritchie, Toronto #77/R (C.D 600)

KIPPENBERGER, Martin (1953-1997) German
£13924 $22000 €22000 Copa V (91x76cm-36x30in) mono.d.86 acrylic silicon varnish cotton. 30-Nov-2 Villa Grisebach, Berlin #479/R est:15000-20000
£14000 $21560 €21000 Untitled (73x88cm-29x35in) s.d.94-95 verso oil collage on canvas prov. 22-Oct-2 Sotheby's, London #472/R est:20000-30000
£23438 $37500 €35157 Untitled (100x120cm-39x47in) init.d.84 oil screenprint prov. 14-May-3 Sotheby's, New York #399/R est:40000-60000
£29487 $45705 €46000 Proceeds mountain (90x75cm-35x30in) oil silicon prov. 3-Dec-2 Lempertz, Koln #227/R est:25000-30000
£85000 $139400 €127500 Frau mit viel zeit (75x90cm-30x35in) painted 1984 in 4 parts prov.exhib. 6-Feb-3 Sotheby's, London #42/R est:80000
£105000 $175350 €157500 We don't have problems with disco door-waiters (150x180cm-59x71in) oil silkscreen plexiglas silicon exc.1986 prov.exhib. 26-Jun-3 Christie's, London #42/R est:65000-85000
Sculpture
£1449 $2377 €2000 Per pastra ad astra (3x46x27cm-1x18x11in) s.i.d. macaroni wooden bead nylon thread box. 28-May-3 Lempertz, Koln #210/R est:2200
£1667 $2583 €2600 Reserve - I hold myself closed (46cm-18in) s.d.89 child's chair wood raffia sticky tape. 3-Dec-2 Lempertz, Koln #225/R est:2500
£10256 $15897 €16000 Don't wake up Daddy - Schreber (90x73x5cm-35x29x2in) wood varnish lit. two parts. 3-Dec-2 Lempertz, Koln #226/R est:18000-20000
£10870 $17826 €15000 No nati. s.d.87 drum book hot water bottle. 28-May-3 Lempertz, Koln #209/R est:12000
£17201 $26490 €27350 Crucified frog (130x110cm-51x43in) s.i.verso painted wood one of 5 exec.1990. 26-Oct-2 Cornette de St.Cyr, Paris #94/R est:12000
Works on paper
£1042 $1646 €1500 Self portrait (76x63cm-30x25in) mixed media. 24-Apr-3 Dorotheum, Vienna #260/R est:1500-1600
£2041 $3245 €3000 Momas meets Mamco (116x103cm-46x41in) s.d.80 frottage. 24-Mar-3 Cornette de St.Cyr, Paris #39/R
£3846 $5962 €6000 Hunky Dory - David Bowie - self portrait as David Bowie (31x31cm-12x12in) i.d. verso collage photo acrylic record sleeve. 3-Dec-2 Lempertz, Koln #228/R est:6000
£4354 $6922 €6400 Al dente (29x20cm-11x8in) mono.d.1989 col crayon graphite prov. 24-Mar-3 Cornette de St.Cyr, Paris #41/R
£4747 $7500 €7121 Tic-tac-toe (96x96cm-38x38in) nine elements black clear vinyl wood executed 1990 prov. 14-Nov-2 Christie's, Rockefeller NY #316/R est:15000-20000
£6000 $10020 €8700 Untitled, hotelserie (29x21cm-11x8in) init.d.95 ink felt tip pen correction fluid prov.exhib. 26-Jun-3 Sotheby's, London #267/R est:3000-4000
£6013 $9320 €9500 Heightened mortality through alcoholism and heroin addiction (65x64cm-26x25in) mono.d.1985 cloth silicon collage plastic. 28-Sep-2 Ketterer, Hamburg #840/R est:9500-11000

KIPPENBERGER, Martin and OEHLEN, Albert (20th C) German
Works on paper
£3671 $5800 €5800 Transit camp Neptune Kull (170x67cm-67x26in) lilo silk print collage board newspaper. 30-Nov-2 Villa Grisebach, Berlin #478/R est:5000-6000

KIPS, Alexander (1858-1910) German
£481 $745 €750 Villa d'Este park (41x28cm-16x11in) s.i.d.93 canvas on board. 6-Dec-2 Bassenge, Berlin #8261

KIPS, Erich (1869-?) German
£1572 $2452 €2358 Asiatic river scene (35x50cm-14x20in) s. panel. 6-Nov-2 Dobiaschofsky, Bern #731/R est:2500 (S.FR 3600)

KIRALL, Emmerich (20th C) Austrian
Works on paper
£252 $390 €400 Hanging out the washing (7x11cm-3x4in) s.i.d.1927. 1-Oct-2 Dorotheum, Vienna #280/R
£409 $634 €650 Old Vienna, Margarethenplatz (10x14cm-4x6in) s.i.d.1927 W/C. 1-Oct-2 Dorotheum, Vienna #281/R

KIRBY, John (1949-) British
£9200 $14260 €13800 Night watch (213x183cm-84x72in) s. i.d.1989 verso acrylic. 3-Dec-2 Bonhams, New Bond Street #127/R est:2000-3000

KIRCHBACH, F (1859-1912) German
£419 $616 €650 Still life with lobster and fish (70x120cm-28x47in) s. 24-Jun-2 Dr Fritz Nagel, Stuttgart #5900/R

KIRCHENPAUER, Gustav Heinrich (1808-1897) German
Works on paper
£1972 $3175 €2800 Classical villa in park (22x30cm-9x12in) W/C over pencil prov. 9-May-3 Schloss Ahlden, Ahlden #1982/R est:240

KIRCHER, Alexandre (1867-?) German
£1408 $2268 €2000 Constantinople harbour in the evening (66x50cm-26x20in) s. lit. 9-May-3 Schloss Ahlden, Ahlden #1394/R est:2200
£5414 $8500 €8121 New York harbour (60x151cm-24x59in) init.d.97. 20-Nov-2 Christie's, Los Angeles #39/R est:7000-9000

KIRCHMAYR, Tony (1887-1965) Austrian
£1060 $1727 €1600 Study of Steirhof-Endfelden in Wildschonau (49x70cm-19x28in) s.d.1919 board. 28-Jan-3 Dorotheum, Vienna #12/R est:1200-1600

KIRCHNER, Albert Emil (1813-1885) German
£7770 $12122 €11500 Sonnenburg near St Lorenzen in Pustertal in Tyrol (70x100cm-28x39in) s.d.1872. 26-Mar-3 Hugo Ruef, Munich #145/R est:4500
Works on paper
£321 $497 €500 Palazzo dei Turchi, Venice (38x52cm-15x20in) s.i.d.1847 pencil dr. 4-Dec-2 Neumeister, Munich #526/R

KIRCHNER, Ernst Ludwig (1880-1938) German
£759 $1177 €1200 Fortress (21x16cm-8x6in) pencil. 28-Sep-2 Ketterer, Hamburg #171/R
£13043 $21391 €18000 Two female nudes (49x38cm-19x15in) oil chk. 29-May-3 Lempertz, Koln #699/R est:20000-22000
£14388 $23597 €20000 Two female nudes in studio (36x39cm-14x15in) col oil crayon prov. 6-Jun-3 Ketterer, Munich #62/R est:20000-30000
£96330 $160872 €139679 Flowers in front of batik (75x60cm-30x24in) s.i.d.36 verso prov. 20-Jun-3 Kornfeld, Bern #80/R est:250000 (S.FR 210000)
£115385 $180000 €173078 Landschaft, weg mit baumen (35x41cm-14x16in) s. cardboard painted c.1906-07 prov.exhib.lit. 5-Nov-2 Phillips, New York #121/R est:180000-220000
£117241 $185241 €170000 Cowshed: alpine peasant milking (61x70cm-24x28in) prov.exhib. 2-Apr-3 Dr Fritz Nagel, Stuttgart #9497/R est:60000
£2000000 $3120000 €3000000 Rote akte - Red nudes (120x90cm-47x35in) init.d.1912 prov.exhib.lit. 9-Oct-2 Sotheby's, London #15/R est:2500000-3500000
Prints
£1899 $3000 €3000 Women dancing (15x9cm-6x4in) drypoint etching. 30-Nov-2 Bassenge, Berlin #6377/R est:3500
£2000 $3120 €3000 Der friseur (34x25cm-13x10in) etching aquatint. 10-Oct-2 Sotheby's, London #126/R est:2500-3000

£2051 $3179 €3200 Ruth seated (26x32cm-10x13in) lithograph. 7-Dec-2 Hauswedell & Nolte, Hamburg #787/R est:6000
£2115 $3342 €3300 Cycle race (25x31cm-10x12in) s.i. drypoint etching zinc pencil board. 14-Nov-2 Neumeister, Munich #592/R est:3000-4000
£2201 $3434 €3500 Old and young woman (33x24cm-13x9in) st.sig. woodcut. 11-Oct-2 Winterberg, Heidelberg #1333/R est:4500
£2400 $3744 €3600 Frau professor schaxel (44x39cm-17x15in) woodcut double-sided. 10-Oct-2 Sotheby's, London #138/R est:3000-4000
£2778 $4417 €4000 Harvesting (30x25cm-12x10in) s.i. drypoint. 5-May-3 Ketterer, Munich #887/R est:2000-3000
£3200 $4992 €4800 Frau mit katze. i. woodcut. 10-Oct-2 Sotheby's, London #129/R est:4000-6000
£3333 $5300 €4800 Amongst the larches (12x14cm-5x6in) s.i.d.18 ethcing. 5-May-3 Ketterer, Munich #888/R est:2000-3000
£4110 $6411 €6000 Head with lace collar (40x33cm-16x13in) s.i. lithograph. 11-Apr-3 Winterberg, Heidelberg #1215/R est:7800
£5556 $8833 €8000 Three bathers by Moritzburg Lake (18x20cm-7x8in) s. drypoint. 5-May-3 Ketterer, Munich #876/R est:3000-4000
£5903 $9385 €8500 Girl (32x27cm-13x11in) i. lithograph. 5-May-3 Ketterer, Munich #886/R est:5000-7000
£6250 $9938 €9000 Ships on the Elbe in the Ubigau shipyard (20x25cm-8x10in) s.d.07 drypoint aquatint. 5-May-3 Ketterer, Munich #880/R est:3000-4000
£6250 $9938 €9000 Portrait of Frau Bluth (42x32cm-17x13in) lithograph. 5-May-3 Ketterer, Munich #890/R est:2800-3400
£6757 $10541 €10000 Two naked girls playing (68x38cm-27x15in) s.i. woodcut. 28-Mar-3 Ketterer, Hamburg #409/R est:8000-12000
£6787 $11335 €9841 Stafelalp with Tinzenhorn and Altein (35x45cm-14x18in) woodcut double-sided. 24-Jun-3 Koller, Zurich #433/R est:15000-25000 (S.FR 15000)
£9028 $14354 €13000 Berlin dancer (25x20cm-10x8in) s. i. verso drypoint. 5-May-3 Ketterer, Munich #879/R est:1400-1800
£9353 $15338 €13000 Four dancers (32x42cm-13x17in) lithograph. 6-Jun-3 Ketterer, Munich #30/R est:14000-18000
£10550 $17619 €15298 Staberhof garden - house in park (32x42cm-13x17in) s.i. s.i. verso lithograph. 20-Jun-3 Kornfeld, Bern #84/R est:25000 (S.FR 23000)
£11538 $17885 €18000 Three nude women and reclining man (49x34cm-19x13in) s.i. woodcut. 7-Dec-2 Hauswedell & Nolte, Hamburg #792/R est:8000
£12385 $20683 €17958 Erna with wooden sculpture (42x31cm-17x12in) s.i. lithograph. 20-Jun-3 Kornfeld, Bern #82/R est:30000 (S.FR 27000)
£12500 $19875 €18000 Girl in bathtub (32x38cm-13x15in) i. lithograph. 5-May-3 Ketterer, Munich #877/R est:7000-9000
£14103 $21859 €22000 Head of Professor Graef (50x60cm-20x24in) s. lithograph board prov. 4-Dec-2 Lempertz, Koln #815/R est:25000-30000
£15000 $24750 €21750 Kopf Dr Bauer (50x35cm-20x14in) s.i.d. col woodcut prov.exhib. 1-Jul-3 Sotheby's, London #88/R est:15000-20000
£15596 $26046 €22614 Head of Mary Wigman (33x27cm-13x11in) s.i.d.26 col lithograph. 20-Jun-3 Kornfeld, Bern #90/R est:30000 (S.FR 34000)
£18116 $29710 €25000 Brandenburg Gate, Berlin (25x28cm-10x11in) s.i. drypoint prov.lit. 30-May-3 Villa Grisebach, Berlin #31/R est:25000-35000
£19231 $29808 €30000 Seated dancer (26x18cm-10x7in) s. col woodcut. 7-Dec-2 Hauswedell & Nolte, Hamburg #790/R est:30000
£20183 $33706 €29265 Nude girl (44x24cm-17x9in) s.i. woodcut. 20-Jun-3 Kornfeld, Bern #81/R est:50000 (S.FR 44000)
£25316 $40000 €40000 Head of Ludwig Schames (56x25cm-22x10in) s. woodcut. 30-Nov-2 Bassenge, Berlin #6375/R est:48000
£27523 $45963 €39908 Head of Henry van de Velde, light - Van de Velde as architect (50x40cm-20x16in) s.i. woodcut. 20-Jun-3 Kornfeld, Bern #87/R est:60000 (S.FR 60000)
£32609 $53478 €45000 Junkernboden (33x61cm-13x24in) s.i. woodcut prov. 30-May-3 Villa Grisebach, Berlin #30/R est:35000-45000
£57339 $95757 €83142 Head of Ludwig Schames (57x25cm-22x10in) s.i. i. verso woodcut. 20-Jun-3 Kornfeld, Bern #88/R est:125000 (S.FR 125000)
£65000 $105950 €97500 Jahresmappe V. Tanzerin mit gehobenem rock. Mit Schilf werfende badende. Drei badende im moritzburge (42x55cm-17x22in) set of four prints prov.lit. 3-Feb-3 Christie's, London #8/R est:70000-100000

Works on paper

£570 $900 €900 Peter in the clouds (21x16cm-8x6in) i. verso pencil. 29-Nov-2 Villa Grisebach, Berlin #709/R
£617 $900 €926 Figures at table (16x21cm-6x8in) pencil. 17-Jun-2 Philippe Schuler, Zurich #4040/R (S.FR 1400)
£641 $1000 €962 Artistengruppe (18x23cm-7x9in) pencil dr exec.c.1915. 19-Sep-2 Swann Galleries, New York #469/R
£759 $1200 €1200 Ice skater (22x17cm-9x7in) chk sketch verso. 29-Nov-2 Villa Grisebach, Berlin #708/R
£962 $1490 €1500 Wettiner Strasse - Dresden (14x11cm-6x4in) pencil. 7-Dec-2 Hauswedell & Nolte, Hamburg #778/R est:1800
£972 $1536 €1400 Reclining chair (16x21cm-6x8in) i. verso pencil lit. 24-Apr-3 Dorotheum, Vienna #70/R
£1139 $1800 €1800 Girl coming out of the water (21x17cm-8x7in) pencil exhib. 29-Nov-2 Villa Grisebach, Berlin #707/R est:1800-1900
£1154 $1800 €1731 Frauenportrait (21x16cm-8x6in) pencil dr. exec.c.1915. 19-Sep-2 Swann Galleries, New York #470/R est:2000-3000
£1282 $2000 €1923 Dame mit hut (22x17cm-9x7in) pencil dr. 19-Sep-2 Swann Galleries, New York #471/R est:2000-3000
£1329 $2100 €2100 Two bathers (11x18cm-4x7in) chk exhib.prov. 29-Nov-2 Villa Grisebach, Berlin #706/R est:750-850
£1389 $2208 €2000 Herdress (27x23cm-11x9in) s. chk prov. 5-May-3 Ketterer, Munich #882/R est:2000-3000
£1646 $2600 €2600 At the table (21x17cm-8x7in) pencil three. 27-Nov-2 Dorotheum, Vienna #23/R est:2500-2800
£1899 $3000 €3000 Standing female nude (23x16cm-9x6in) Indian ink prov.lit.exhib. 30-Nov-2 Villa Grisebach, Berlin #211/R est:3000-4000
£2025 $3139 €3200 Two people talking (21x16cm-8x6in) pencil. 28-Sep-2 Ketterer, Hamburg #170/R est:2800-3000
£2174 $3565 €3000 In the big garden, Dresden (15x21cm-6x8in) pen. 31-May-3 Villa Grisebach, Berlin #174/R est:3500-4500
£3077 $4769 €4800 Suburb (17x21cm-7x8in) wash chk dr exec.c.1910/12. 6-Dec-2 Ketterer, Munich #26/R est:4000-6000
£3333 $5300 €4800 Woman's head (20x16cm-8x6in) s.d. i.verso Indian ink prov. 5-May-3 Ketterer, Munich #883/R est:2000-3000
£4167 $6625 €6000 Woman's head (19x15cm-7x6in) s.d. i. verso pen ink. 5-May-3 Ketterer, Munich #885/R est:4000-6000
£4348 $7130 €6000 Corner of the Winter Garden, Berlin (20x17cm-8x7in) pencil lit.exhib. 31-May-3 Villa Grisebach, Berlin #173/R est:6000-8000
£4348 $7130 €6000 Mountain villae in winter, Davos (36x51cm-14x20in) col chk prov. 29-May-3 Lempertz, Koln #702/R est:7500
£5449 $8445 €8500 Girl seated (33x42cm-13x17in) i.verso chl dr cardboard exec.c.1907-10. 6-Dec-2 Ketterer, Munich #39/R est:12000-15000
£5769 $8942 €9000 Two bathers (50x31cm-20x12in) W/C exec.c.1909/10. 6-Dec-2 Ketterer, Munich #42/R est:10000-15000
£5797 $9507 €8000 Circus (27x34cm-11x13in) i. verso pencil prov. 31-May-3 Villa Grisebach, Berlin #175/R est:8000-10000
£5797 $9507 €8000 Bathers by Moritzburger lake (34x45cm-13x18in) pen brush. 31-May-3 Villa Grisebach, Berlin #177/R est:900-12000
£6250 $9938 €9000 Steamer and rowing boat (31x46cm-12x18in) s. i. verso pencil col oil crayon prov. 5-May-3 Ketterer, Munich #875/R est:4000-6000
£6329 $10000 €10000 Bent over nude (49x43cm-19x17in) Indian ink brush over pencil prov. 30-Nov-2 Villa Grisebach, Berlin #189/R est:12000-15000
£6329 $10000 €10000 Konigstein in the Taunus (43x49cm-17x19in) s. i. verso chk prov. 30-Nov-2 Villa Grisebach, Berlin #210/R est:9000-12000
£6410 $9936 €10000 Erna seated (47x31cm-19x12in) pencil dr exec.c.1913 double-sided. 6-Dec-2 Ketterer, Munich #40/R est:9000-12000
£6522 $10696 €9000 Sophiekirche Dresden (34x27cm-13x11in) s. i. verso pencil exhib.lit. 31-May-3 Villa Grisebach, Berlin #171/R est:6000-8000
£6646 $10500 €10500 Playing in circles (36x51cm-14x20in) s. Indian ink brush W/C over pencil prov. 30-Nov-2 Villa Grisebach, Berlin #215/R est:12500-17500
£7051 $10929 €11000 Nude standing (34x23cm-13x9in) pencil dr exec.c.1912/15. 6-Dec-2 Ketterer, Munich #46/R est:9000-12000
£7595 $12000 €12000 Two ladies in a park (9x8cm-4x3in) s. W/C over crayon cardboard prov. 29-Nov-2 Villa Grisebach, Berlin #18/R est:12000-15000
£8805 $13736 €14000 Sitzender weiblicher akt - Seated female nude (43x30cm-17x12in) s. pen ink executed 1916 prov. 9-Oct-2 Sotheby's, London #115/R est:20000-30000
£8974 $13910 €14000 Nude sitting on beach (37x45cm-15x18in) s. W/C pen graphite. 7-Dec-2 Hauswedell & Nolte, Hamburg #780/R est:15000
£9028 $14354 €13000 Seated female nude - Erna (47x32cm-19x13in) s. pencil. 5-May-3 Ketterer, Munich #881/R est:7000-9000
£9058 $14855 €12500 Mountain landscape from Davos (28x44cm-11x17in) W/C chl board. 29-May-3 Lempertz, Koln #701/R est:10000-12000
£9722 $15458 €14000 Two female nudes, standing (51x38cm-20x15in) oil crayon double-sided. 5-May-3 Ketterer, Munich #884/R est:9000-12000
£10145 $16638 €14000 Female nude (45x35cm-18x14in) s.d.1912 pencil wash prov. 31-May-3 Villa Grisebach, Berlin #176/R est:15000-20000
£10550 $17619 €15298 Erna, fixing stocking (53x39cm-21x15in) pencil. 20-Jun-3 Kornfeld, Bern #78/R est:25000 (S.FR 23000)
£13924 $22000 €22000 Portrait of Hardt's son (59x42cm-23x17in) s.d.14 chl prov. 29-Nov-2 Villa Grisebach, Berlin #25/R est:25000-30000
£14493 $23768 €20000 Woman in tub (50x34cm-20x13in) s. chl board prov. 31-May-3 Villa Grisebach, Berlin #192/R est:25000-35000
£16667 $25833 €26000 Fehrmarn beach (26x35cm-10x14in) W/C pencil. 7-Dec-2 Hauswedell & Nolte, Hamburg #779/R est:14000
£16901 $28056 €24000 Nude in studio (48x36cm-19x14in) carpenter's pencil. 14-Jun-3 Hauswedell & Nolte, Hamburg #1281/R est:20000
£20833 $33542 €31250 Two peasant women (36x43cm-14x17in) W/C over chk prov. 7-May-3 Dobiaschofsky, Bern #736/R est:60000 (S.FR 45000)
£21519 $34000 €34000 Seated woman in a blue corsett (56x36cm-22x14in) s.d.1913 W/C pencil double-sided prov. 29-Nov-2 Villa Grisebach, Berlin #28/R est:30000-40000
£44025 $68679 €70000 Kokotte auf der strasse - street girl. Artillerist, ein pferd besteignd (34x24cm-13x9in) s. gouache over monotype woodcut double-sided executed 1915 prov. 9-Oct-2 Sotheby's, London #123/R est:100000-150000
£59355 $93781 €92000 Sur la passerelle (33x43cm-13x17in) s.d.1905 W/C. 19-Dec-2 Delvaux, Paris #15/R est:35000
£76923 $119231 €120000 Sitzende Frau vor einem Ofen (67x1cm-26x0in) s. chk pastel exec.c.1913 prov. 4-Dec-2 Lempertz, Koln #19/R est:100000-120000
£90278 $143542 €130000 Franzi lying down by water (33x43cm-13x17in) s. gouache W/C chk. 5-May-3 Ketterer, Munich #878/R est:80000-120000

£403670 $674128 €585322 Two women in variety in Dresden (65x88cm-26x35in) s.d.05 col chk over pencil prov.exhib. 20-Jun-3 Kornfeld, Bern #77/R est:200000 (S.FR 880000)

KIRCHNER, Otto (1887-1960) German
£513 $805 €800 Monk at vespers (24x18cm-9x7in) s. panel. 21-Nov-2 Van Ham, Cologne #2053
£693 $1074 €1040 Old man writing letter (24x18cm-9x7in) s. 24-Sep-2 Koller, Zurich #6552/R (S.FR 1600)
£830 $1294 €1245 Monk tasting wine (24x18cm-9x7in) s. pavatex. 20-Nov-2 Fischer, Luzern #2163/R est:1200-1400 (S.FR 1900)
£1200 $1860 €1800 Old man reading a letter (18x13cm-7x5in) s.i. panel. 31-Oct-2 Duke & Son, Dorchester #223

KIRCHNER, Raphael (1867-1917) Austrian
Works on paper
£264 $425 €396 How do I love thee (41x33cm-16x13in) s.i. W/C pencil. 19-Feb-3 Doyle, New York #7

KIRCHNER-KRUSE, Agnes (1881-?) German
Works on paper
£411 $641 €600 Karden on the Mosel (45x59cm-18x23in) s. W/C. 10-Apr-3 Van Ham, Cologne #1536/R

KIRCHSBERG, Ernestine von (1857-1924) Austrian
£422 $616 €650 Still life with roses (39x33cm-15x13in) s. canvas on board. 15-Jun-2 Hans Stahl, Hamburg #34

KIRK, Frank C (1889-1963) American
£325 $500 €488 Amsterdam, Holland (18x15cm-7x6in) s. i.verso board. 9-Sep-2 Schrager Galleries, Milwaukee #1083/R
£629 $1000 €944 My lucubration (81x86cm-32x34in) s. exhib. 18-Mar-3 Doyle, New York #35/R

KIRK, Thomas (c.1765-1797) British
Works on paper
£360 $583 €540 Bathers in a classical landscape (14x11cm-6x4in) W/C oval. 21-Jan-3 Bonhams, Knightsbridge #66/R

KIRKE, Wilhelm (20th C) German
£528 $850 €750 Hens on country road (12x20cm-5x8in) s. panel. 9-May-3 Schloss Ahlden, Ahlden #1459/R

KIRKEBY, Per (1938-) Danish
£5720 $9552 €8294 Green composition (70x50cm-28x20in) i.d.1988 verso prov. 17-Jun-3 Rasmussen, Copenhagen #14/R est:40000-50000 (D.KR 60000)
£8696 $14261 €12000 Untitled (116x95cm-46x37in) s.d.1983 verso prov. 31-May-3 Villa Grisebach, Berlin #386/R est:10000-15000
£9294 $14684 €13941 Composition (122x60cm-48x24in) s.d.1982 verso masonite. 1-Apr-3 Rasmussen, Copenhagen #204/R est:125000-150000 (D.KR 100000)
£10223 $16152 €15335 Composition (122x60cm-48x24in) s.d.1982 verso masonite. 1-Apr-3 Rasmussen, Copenhagen #199/R est:125000-150000 (D.KR 110000)
£11563 $18038 €17345 Untitled (117x95cm-46x37in) s.d.1983 verso. 5-Nov-2 Bukowskis, Stockholm #400/R est:100000-120000 (S.KR 165000)
£18088 $28036 €27132 The beauty of the flat mountain - composition (102x203cm-40x80in) s.d.1976-77 verso plywood exhib.lit. 4-Dec-2 Kunsthallen, Copenhagen #28/R est:250000 (D.KR 210000)
£28789 $44623 €43184 Laeso - composition (160x160cm-63x63in) s.i.d.1997 verso lit.prov. 1-Oct-2 Rasmussen, Copenhagen #50/R est:350000-400000 (D.KR 340000)
£43478 $71304 €60000 Changes of the surface. s.i.d.1990 verso prov. 28-May-3 Lempertz, Koln #215/R est:50000-60000
Works on paper
£301 $467 €452 Monument (34x23cm-13x9in) s.d.68 W/C. 4-Dec-2 Kunsthallen, Copenhagen #8/R (D.KR 3500)
£345 $534 €518 Figure composition (31x22cm-12x9in) s.d.75 W/C. 4-Dec-2 Kunsthallen, Copenhagen #4/R (D.KR 4000)
£388 $601 €582 Landscape (23x25cm-9x10in) init.d.78 W/C. 4-Dec-2 Kunsthallen, Copenhagen #2/R (D.KR 4500)
£500 $774 €750 Portrait of woman (26x13cm-10x5in) s.d.75 W/C gouache. 4-Dec-2 Kunsthallen, Copenhagen #10/R (D.KR 5800)
£560 $868 €840 Model with red hair (38x28cm-15x11in) s.d.68 crayon. 4-Dec-2 Kunsthallen, Copenhagen #3/R (D.KR 6500)
£1371 $2180 €2057 Reclining model. Yellow and blue circles. Composition (41x29cm-16x11in) s.d.68 gouache W/C crayon three. 26-Feb-3 Kunsthallen, Copenhagen #146/R est:18000 (D.KR 15000)
£1723 $2670 €2585 Composition, Salzburg (56x42cm-22x17in) init.d.84 W/C. 4-Dec-2 Kunsthallen, Copenhagen #7/R est:20000 (D.KR 20000)
£1731 $2683 €2700 Untitled (100x65cm-39x26in) mono.d.2-8-91 bears i. chl gouache. 6-Dec-2 Hauswedell & Nolte, Hamburg #216/R est:3500
£1809 $2804 €2714 Interior scene with model (30x42cm-12x17in) s.d.1964 W/C. 4-Dec-2 Kunsthallen, Copenhagen #1/R est:12000 (D.KR 21000)
£2436 $3776 €3800 Untitled (57x99cm-22x39in) mono.i.d.92 94 pencil col chk W/C. 6-Dec-2 Hauswedell & Nolte, Hamburg #217/R est:4000

KIRKLEY, Caroline (18th C) British
£845 $1361 €1200 Landscape with farmhouse (6x9cm-2x4in) copper pair. 12-May-3 Bernaerts, Antwerp #213

KIRKPATRICK, Joseph (1872-c.1930) British
Works on paper
£740 $1214 €1110 Lady in summer garden (34x24cm-13x9in) s. W/C. 4-Jun-3 Bonhams, Chester #290

KIRKWOOD, H W (1854-1925) New Zealander
£274 $420 €411 Golden Bay, Nelson (13x21cm-5x8in) init. board. 21-Aug-2 Dunbar Sloane, Auckland #104 (NZ.D 900)
£274 $420 €411 Dusky Sounds, South Island (23x15cm-9x6in) init. board. 21-Aug-2 Dunbar Sloane, Auckland #107 (NZ.D 900)

KIRKWOOD, Henry William (1854-1925) New Zealander
£295 $460 €443 Twin peaks, Hampden, North Otago (60x85cm-24x33in) init. 6-Aug-2 Peter Webb, Auckland #231 est:1000-2000 (NZ.D 1000)
£310 $483 €465 River and mountains landscape (25x17cm-10x7in) s. board. 6-Aug-2 Peter Webb, Auckland #49/R est:1200-1800 (NZ.D 1050)
£316 $502 €474 Waimea, Nelson (15x24cm-6x9in) init. i.verso board. 25-Feb-3 Peter Webb, Auckland #117 (NZ.D 900)
£398 $625 €597 Summer beach scene with figures and a dinghy (13x28cm-5x11in) init. oil on card. 10-Dec-2 Peter Webb, Auckland #94/R est:1200-1800 (NZ.D 1250)
£406 $654 €609 Paratutu Hill, New Plymouth (18x29cm-7x11in) init. board. 7-May-3 Dunbar Sloane, Auckland #45/R (NZ.D 1150)
£596 $929 €894 Manawatu Stream (14x22cm-6x9in) s. board. 7-Nov-2 International Art Centre, Auckland #114/R est:1400-2500 (NZ.D 1900)
£596 $929 €894 Brighwater (19x29cm-7x11in) s. board. 7-Nov-2 International Art Centre, Auckland #158 est:1000-2000 (NZ.D 1900)

KIRMSE, Persis (fl.1929) British
Works on paper
£429 $700 €644 Golden retriever (23x18cm-9x7in) s. pastel. 11-Feb-3 Bonhams & Doyles, New York #199

KIRNER, Johann Baptist (1806-1866) German
£641 $936 €1000 Monk gathering alms (31x26cm-12x10in) s.d.1839. 4-Jun-2 Karl & Faber, Munich #98/R

KIRNER, Johann Baptist (attrib) (1806-1866) German
£346 $533 €550 Portrait of Henriette de Stael (68x55cm-27x22in) i. verso. 23-Oct-2 Neumeister, Munich #677/R

KIRNER, Lukas (1794-1851) German
£490 $784 €750 Portrait of a gentleman (46x33cm-18x13in) s.d.1818 canvas on canvas lit. 10-Jan-3 Allgauer, Kempten #1650/R

KIRNIG, Alois (1840-1911) Austrian
£1418 $2255 €2127 Landscape (29x53cm-11x21in) s.d.1910 canvas on board. 8-Mar-3 Dorotheum, Prague #6/R est:50000-75000 (C.KR 65000)
£1745 $2775 €2618 Alpine landscape (53x65cm-21x26in) s.d.187. 8-Mar-3 Dorotheum, Prague #62/R est:80000-120000 (C.KR 80000)
£1811 $2572 €2717 Inside the forest (70x101cm-28x40in) painted c.1875. 26-Mar-2 SOGA, Bratislava #206/R est:48000 (SL.K 115000)

KIROUAC, Louise Lecor (1939-) Canadian
£350 $542 €525 Encore sur la route beauce, QC (50x60cm-20x24in) s. acrylic. 3-Dec-2 Joyner, Toronto #308/R (C.D 850)
£582 $920 €873 Belle journee d'Avril QC (41x51cm-16x20in) acrylic. 1-Dec-2 Levis, Calgary #54/R (C.D 1450)
£667 $1093 €1001 Par une bella journee, QC (60x75cm-24x30in) s. 3-Jun-3 Joyner, Toronto #385/R est:2000-2500 (C.D 1500)
£723 $1135 €1085 Dans la vallee, Harrington, QC (60x75cm-24x30in) s.i. acrylic. 25-Nov-2 Hodgins, Calgary #273/R (C.D 1800)
£905 $1403 €1358 L'anse St. Jean, Saguenay, Lac St. Jean QC (75x90cm-30x35in) s. ca. 3-Dec-2 Joyner, Toronto #284/R est:2500-3500 (C.D 2200)

KIRSCHENBAUM, Jules (1930-) American
£4573 $7500 €6631 Day dream (41x30cm-16x12in) mono. tempera on masonite prov. 1-Jun-3 Wright, Chicago #207/R est:2000-3000

KIRSCHNEROVA, Marie Luisa (1852-1931) Czechoslovakian
£454 $736 €658 Country farm (25x35cm-10x14in) s. 24-May-3 Dorotheum, Prague #46/R est:20000-30000 (C.KR 20000)

KIRZINGER, Marianne (1770-1809) German
£1773 $2961 €2500 Don Juan, la statue du commandeur (51x39cm-20x15in) s.d.1780 panel. 18-Jun-3 Tajan, Paris #100 est:2500-3000
£1923 $3019 €3000 Susanna in the bath (44x35cm-17x14in) s.d.1790 panel. 21-Nov-2 Van Ham, Cologne #1387/R est:2500

KISCHKA, Isis (1908-1974) French
£250 $400 €363 Les oranges sur fond bleu (46x37cm-18x15in) s. s.i.d.1961-62 on the stretcher. 16-May-3 Skinner, Boston #181/R
£321 $500 €482 St. Tropez le village (28x36cm-11x14in) s. s.verso. 5-Nov-2 Arthur James, Florida #178

KISELEWSKI, Joseph (1901-1986) British
Sculpture
£20440 $32500 €30660 Sea horse (114cm-45in) i. greenish brown pat. prov.lit. 5-Mar-3 Sotheby's, New York #91/R est:25000-35000

KISELYOV, Sergei (1974-) Russian
£350 $543 €525 Joy of motherhood (47x35cm-19x14in) s. 8-Dec-2 John Nicholson, Haslemere #66
£350 $543 €525 Girl with a book (50x35cm-20x14in) s. 8-Dec-2 John Nicholson, Haslemere #88/R
£440 $687 €700 Roses (51x63cm-20x25in) 23-Sep-2 Durán, Madrid #705/R
£575 $891 €863 Near the blooming rose (46x61cm-18x24in) s. 8-Dec-2 John Nicholson, Haslemere #205
£800 $1240 €1200 At sea (55x38cm-22x15in) s. 8-Dec-2 John Nicholson, Haslemere #89/R

KISFALUDY-STROBL, Szigmond (1884-1975) Hungarian
Sculpture
£3765 $5836 €5459 Dancer (40cm-16in) s. bronze marble base. 9-Dec-2 Mu Terem Galeria, Budapest #8/R est:1000000 (H.F 1400000)
£8606 $13339 €12479 Curled up (28cm-11in) s. marble. 9-Dec-2 Mu Terem Galeria, Budapest #7/R est:1500000 (H.F 3200000)

KISHINEVSKY, Solomon Yakovlevich (1863-1941) Russian
Works on paper
£2000 $3240 €3000 Practicing his letters (48x62cm-19x24in) s. pastel. 21-May-3 Sotheby's, London #121/R est:3000-4000

KISLING, Moise (1891-1953) French
£9000 $13860 €13500 Portrait (40x32cm-16x13in) s.d.1930 prov.lit. 22-Oct-2 Sotheby's, London #238/R est:10000-15000
£9615 $15096 €15000 Paysage de Sanary (22x27cm-9x11in) s. 12-Dec-2 Rabourdin & Choppin de Janvry, Paris #90/R
£11000 $18370 €15950 Jeune fille (35x24cm-14x9in) s. painted 1925. 24-Jun-3 Sotheby's, London #210/R est:12000-15000
£11392 $18000 €18000 Fleurs (35x24cm-14x9in) s. painted 1938 lit. 27-Nov-2 Marc Kohn, Paris #21/R est:15000-20000
£16987 $26670 €26500 Paysage de Provence (54x66cm-21x26in) s. prov.lit. 10-Dec-2 Artcurial Briest, Paris #500/R
£17901 $25420 €29000 Vase de fleurs (35x24cm-14x9in) s. prov.lit. 16-Mar-3 Eric Pillon, Calais #115/R
£19876 $32000 €29814 Les deux bateaux (55x38cm-22x15in) s. painted 1917 prov.lit. 8-May-3 Christie's, Rockefeller NY #183/R est:30000-40000
£21192 $34543 €32000 Bouquet de fleurs (41x27cm-16x11in) s. 2-Feb-3 Muizon & Le Coent, Paris #54
£21739 $35000 €32609 Vase de fleurs (41x33cm-16x13in) s. 8-May-3 Christie's, Rockefeller NY #220/R est:40000-60000
£21739 $35000 €32609 Nu (73x61cm-29x24in) s.d.1917 s.i.d.verso. 8-May-3 Christie's, Rockefeller NY #204/R est:35000-45000
£21795 $34000 €32693 Vase de fleurs (56x38cm-22x15in) s. prov. 7-Nov-2 Christie's, Rockefeller NY #300/R est:40000-60000
£23006 $37500 €34509 Nu allonge (50x73cm-20x29in) s. painted 1920 prov.lit. 12-Feb-3 Sotheby's, New York #130/R est:40000-60000
£24000 $40080 €34800 Portrait de Madeleine Sologne (105x65cm-41x26in) s.d.1952 prov.lit. 25-Jun-3 Christie's, London #174/R est:25000-35000
£24359 $38000 €36539 Saint-Tropez (55x38cm-22x15in) s. painted 1918 prov.lit. 7-Nov-2 Christie's, Rockefeller NY #298/R est:30000-40000
£24845 $40000 €37268 Port de sanary (46x55cm-18x22in) s. painted 1929 lit. 8-May-3 Christie's, Rockefeller NY #194/R est:25000-35000
£25806 $40774 €40000 Buste nu (55x38cm-22x15in) s. painted c.1930 prov.lit. 18-Dec-2 Tajan, Paris #71/R est:45000-50000
£26000 $42640 €39000 Vase de fleurs (55x38cm-22x15in) s. painted 1928 prov.lit. 4-Feb-3 Christie's, London #278/R est:35000
£30220 $47143 €44725 Dahlias et mimosas (55x38cm-22x15in) s.d.1947 prov.lit. 26-Mar-3 Tajan, Paris #7/R
£30449 $47500 €45674 Portrait de Jeune femme au buste nu - Ingrid rouge (55x38cm-22x15in) s. painted 1937 prov. 6-Nov-2 Sotheby's, New York #339/R est:40000-60000
£32000 $53440 €46400 Nu au divan rouge (56x74cm-22x29in) s. painted 1925 prov.lit. 25-Jun-3 Christie's, London #180/R est:40000-60000
£32051 $50000 €48077 Bouquet de fleurs (56x38cm-22x15in) s. painted 1944 prov.lit. 7-Nov-2 Christie's, Rockefeller NY #296/R est:50000-70000
£32051 $50000 €48077 Portrait de femme (55x38cm-22x15in) s. prov. 7-Nov-2 Christie's, Rockefeller NY #313/R est:30000-40000
£35000 $58450 €50750 Fleurs (65x46cm-26x18in) s. painted 1928 prov.lit. 25-Jun-3 Christie's, London #168/R est:35000-45000
£37163 $57974 €55000 Mona Luisa (55x46cm-22x18in) s.d.1952 prov.lit. 26-Mar-3 Tajan, Paris #6/R
£263975 $425000 €395963 Grand bouquet de mimosas (95x130cm-37x51in) s.i.d.1942 prov. 8-May-3 Christie's, Rockefeller NY #207/R est:250000-350000
Works on paper
£468 $748 €650 Une allee dans le midi (28x22cm-11x9in) s.i.d.Juin 1948 col crayon graphite. 15-May-3 Christie's, Paris #329
£641 $1006 €1000 Portrait presume de Madame Toussaint (21x16cm-8x6in) s.i. crayon. 10-Dec-2 Renaud, Paris #53
£2973 $4638 €4400 Nu assis (59x44cm-23x17in) s.i.d.1922 pen. 26-Mar-3 Millon & Associes, Paris #40/R
£4487 $7090 €7000 Saint Tropez (44x55cm-17x22in) s. W/C gouache over pencil paper on board prov. 14-Nov-2 Neumeister, Munich #595/R est:7000-9000
£4487 $6821 €7000 Portrait de jeune fille (14x14cm-6x6in) s. gouache tempera lit. 16-Aug-2 Deauville, France #54/R est:9000

KISS, Karoly (1883-1953) Hungarian
£1285 $2005 €1863 Flourishing garden in Nagybanyan (54x59cm-21x23in) s. 12-Apr-3 Mu Terem Galeria, Budapest #88/R est:180000 (H.F 460000)

KISSACK, R A (?) ?
£1583 $2500 €2375 At the piano (51x61cm-20x24in) s. 24-Apr-3 Shannon's, Milford #29/R est:2500-3500

KISSONERGHIS, Ioannis (?-1963) Greek
£3000 $4740 €4500 Villa garden (29x45cm-11x18in) 1-Apr-3 Bonhams, New Bond Street #110 est:1000-1500

KISTENMACHER, Fritz (1889-?) German
£1299 $1896 €2000 North German landscape in early spring (84x96cm-33x38in) s.d.1924. 15-Jun-2 Hans Stahl, Hamburg #199/R

KITAJ, R B (1932-) American
£18000 $29520 €27000 Piccadilly (123x123cm-48x48in) s.i.d.1992 verso prov.exhib. 6-Feb-3 Christie's, London #659/R est:20000-30000
Works on paper
£7500 $12300 €11250 After soutine's only nude (77x57cm-30x22in) s. chl pastel executed 1997-200 prov. 6-Jun-3 Christie's, London #192/R est:8000-12000

KITCHELL, Hudson Mindell (1862-1944) American
£272 $425 €408 Luminist autumn landscape (30x43cm-12x17in) s. i.verso. 15-Oct-2 Winter Associates, Plainville #220
£446 $700 €669 Landscapes (20x30cm-8x12in) s. two. 22-Nov-2 Skinner, Boston #80/R
£457 $750 €686 Landscape with houses (20x30cm-8x12in) s. board. 9-Feb-3 William Jenack, New York #394
£898 $1500 €1302 Sunset landscape (23x36cm-9x14in) s. prov. 17-Jun-3 John Moran, Pasadena #175 est:1000-2000
£1355 $2100 €2033 Woodland stream (43x56cm-17x22in) s. painted c.1900. 8-Dec-2 Toomey, Oak Park #720/R est:1000-2000
£1613 $2500 €2420 Marsh with figure in a rowboat (43x56cm-17x22in) s. painted c.1900. 8-Dec-2 Toomey, Oak Park #690/R est:1000-2000
£1818 $2800 €2727 Autumn woods (64x76cm-25x30in) s. painted c.1900. 8-Sep-2 Treadway Gallery, Cincinnati #570/R est:3000-5000

KITE, Joseph Milner (1862-1946) British
£270 $422 €400 Paysage mediterraneen (23x32cm-9x13in) s. panel. 31-Mar-3 Rossini, Paris #50
£284 $443 €420 Le hameau (24x33cm-9x13in) s. cardboard. 31-Mar-3 Rossini, Paris #48
£320 $531 €480 Boats on a shoreline (24x33cm-9x13in) s. board. 10-Jun-3 Sworder & Son, Bishops Stortford #518/R
£400 $664 €600 Mediterranean fishing boats on a shore with figures (24x33cm-9x13in) s. board. 10-Jun-3 Sworder & Son, Bishops Stortford #519/R
£417 $679 €600 Rochefort en Terre, paysage a la riviere (13x16cm-5x6in) s.i.verso panel. 19-Jul-3 Thierry & Lannon, Brest #368
£507 $791 €750 Deux promeneurs sur le chemin en Bretagne (24x33cm-9x13in) s. cardboard. 31-Mar-3 Rossini, Paris #49/R
£547 $854 €810 Voiliers (24x34cm-9x13in) s. cardboard. 31-Mar-3 Rossini, Paris #47/R
£1034 $1571 €1551 Girl sewing in sunshine (61x50cm-24x20in) s.d.1890. 27-Aug-2 Rasmussen, Copenhagen #1681/R est:15000 (D.KR 12000)

Works on paper
£692 $1079 €1100 Sun on the sea (37x53cm-15x21in) mono.i. gouache W/C. 11-Oct-2 Binoche, Paris #121

KITT, Ferdinand (1897-1962) Austrian
£437 $681 €656 Landscape (59x79cm-23x31in) s. i. verso. 6-Nov-2 Dobiaschofsky, Bern #732/R (S.FR 1000)
£2431 $3865 €3500 Spring landscape in Salzkammergut (60x80cm-24x31in) s.d.1917 i. verso. 29-Apr-3 Wiener Kunst Auktionen, Vienna #632/R est:3500-7000
£4965 $8043 €7000 Blue vase of flowers (79x59cm-31x23in) s. 20-May-3 Dorotheum, Vienna #156/R est:7000-10000
Works on paper
£396 $633 €550 Composition (34x56cm-13x22in) s. W/C. 14-May-3 Dorotheum, Linz #463
£504 $826 €700 Salzkammergut landscape (31x42cm-12x17in) s. W/C. 5-Jun-3 Dorotheum, Salzburg #801/R
£612 $1003 €850 Salzkammergut landscape (29x43cm-11x17in) s. W/C. 5-Jun-3 Dorotheum, Salzburg #802/R

KITTELSEN, Theodor (1857-1914) Norwegian
£25339 $41050 €38009 The brook (68x90cm-27x35in) s.d.1897 s.i.d.verso exhib. 26-May-3 Grev Wedels Plass, Oslo #56/R est:200000-300000 (N.KR 280000)
Works on paper
£535 $851 €803 From Asbjornsen's fairytale - the boy who made himself into a lion (7x21cm-3x8in) s. pencil W/C. 3-Mar-3 Lilla Bukowskis, Stockholm #88 (S.KR 7200)
£597 $932 €896 The Devil and the bailiff (25x18cm-10x7in) pencil. 23-Sep-2 Blomqvist, Lysaker #1121/R (N.KR 7000)
£745 $1154 €1118 From Asbjornsen's fairy tale - Hvidebjorn King Valernon (20x18cm-8x7in) init. Indian ink W/C. 3-Dec-2 Bukowskis, Stockholm #264/R (S.KR 10500)
£769 $1200 €1154 Winter landscape (23x28cm-9x11in) s. 30-Mar-3 Simpson's, Houston #386
£1560 $2418 €2340 From Asbjornsen's fairy tale - The boy with the old cheese (29x19cm-11x7in) init. pencil W/C. 3-Dec-2 Bukowskis, Stockholm #268/R est:30000-40000 (S.KR 22000)
£2270 $3518 €3405 From Asbjornsen's fairy tale - Virgin Mary and the swallow (29x21cm-11x8in) init. pencil W/C. 3-Dec-2 Bukowskis, Stockholm #267/R est:40000-50000 (S.KR 32000)
£3050 $4727 €4575 From Asbjornsen's fairy tale - Hvidebjorn King Valernon (15x21cm-6x8in) init. mixed media. 3-Dec-2 Bukowskis, Stockholm #263/R est:20000-30000 (S.KR 43000)
£3054 $4795 €4581 Cat and squirrel (27x20cm-11x8in) s.d.93 pen. 21-Nov-2 Grev Wedels Plass, Oslo #93/R est:15000-20000 (N.KR 35000)
£3070 $4851 €4605 The lover in the woods (15x20cm-6x8in) init. i.verso pencil. 17-Dec-2 Grev Wedels Plass, Oslo #245/R est:25000-30000 (N.KR 35000)
£3167 $5131 €4751 The green knight (30x20cm-12x8in) init. s.i.verso wash chl paper on cardboard exhib. 26-May-3 Grev Wedels Plass, Oslo #54/R est:30000-40000 (N.KR 35000)
£3258 $5278 €4887 Consultation in the women's club (35x42cm-14x17in) s.i. Indian ink exhib. 26-May-3 Grev Wedels Plass, Oslo #55/R est:20000 (N.KR 36000)
£3333 $5167 €5000 From Asbjornsen's fairy tale - Fugl dam (29x20cm-11x8in) init. pencil W/C. 3-Dec-2 Bukowskis, Stockholm #266/R est:30000-40000 (S.KR 47000)
£3333 $5267 €5000 The parish clerk in our district (22x15cm-9x6in) init. s.i.verso pencil wash exhib. 17-Dec-2 Grev Wedels Plass, Oslo #246/R est:25000-30000 (N.KR 38000)
£3421 $5405 €5132 The parish clerk in our district (29x19cm-11x7in) init. s.i.verso pen wash exhib. 17-Dec-2 Grev Wedels Plass, Oslo #247/R est:25000-30000 (N.KR 39000)
£5702 $9009 €8553 Not driving and not riding (14x18cm-6x7in) init. s.i. pen wash exhib. 17-Dec-2 Grev Wedels Plass, Oslo #248/R est:25000-30000 (N.KR 65000)
£8865 $13741 €13298 Gnomes in the mine (44x33cm-17x13in) s.d.07 mixed media. 3-Dec-2 Bukowskis, Stockholm #262/R est:140000-150000 (S.KR 125000)
£113438 $178098 €170157 Bullfinch on twig with hoare frost - winter morning (52x38cm-20x15in) s.d.06 mixed media prov.exhib.lit. 21-Nov-2 Grev Wedels Plass, Oslo #92/R est:1300000-1500000 (N.KR 1300000)

KIVITS, Jos (1945-) Australian
£381 $583 €572 Country lane (59x74cm-23x29in) s. panel. 21-Aug-2 Dunbar Sloane, Auckland #88 est:2000-4000 (NZ.D 1250)
£389 $626 €584 Still life (23x29cm-9x11in) s. board. 7-May-3 Dunbar Sloane, Auckland #47a (NZ.D 1100)
£470 $734 €705 Pewter and brass (37x21cm-15x8in) s. panel. 7-Nov-2 International Art Centre, Auckland #153/R est:1500-2500 (NZ.D 1500)
£772 $1204 €1158 Dutch harbour scene (29x39cm-11x15in) s. panel. 27-Mar-3 International Art Centre, Auckland #156/R (NZ.D 2200)
£1069 $1689 €1604 Still life with fruit (51x41cm-20x16in) s. board. 1-Apr-3 Lawson Menzies, Sydney #543 (A.D 2800)
£1097 $1712 €1646 French still life (36x49cm-14x19in) s. panel. 7-Nov-2 International Art Centre, Auckland #154/R est:2500-3500 (NZ.D 3500)

KIYOCHIKA, Kobayashi (1847-1915) Japanese
Prints
£2564 $4000 €3846 Masts, shore at Miho (24x36cm-9x14in) s.d.1881 col print. 25-Mar-3 Christie's, Rockefeller NY #377/R est:3000-5000
£2564 $4000 €3846 Morning glories on bamboo stakes (25x36cm-10x14in) s.d.1879 col print. 25-Mar-3 Christie's, Rockefeller NY #378/R est:4000-6000

KIYOMASU, Torii III (1735-1785) Japanese
Prints
£1923 $3000 €2885 Actor Ichiyama Schichizo as Teruto no hime holding a blossoming branch (31x14cm-12x6in) col print. 25-Mar-3 Christie's, Rockefeller NY #6/R est:2000-2500

KIYONAGA, Torii (1752-1815) Japanese
Prints
£1923 $3000 €2885 Three actors under a willow tree (39x26cm-15x10in) s. print. 25-Mar-3 Christie's, Rockefeller NY #67/R est:3000-5000
£1923 $3000 €2885 Actors in an interior scene (37x25cm-15x10in) s. print. 25-Mar-3 Christie's, Rockefeller NY #68/R est:3000-3500

KJAER, Kirsten (20th C) Danish
£255 $398 €383 Landscape (74x67cm-29x26in) s. 5-Aug-2 Rasmussen, Vejle #2329 (D.KR 3000)
£1022 $1615 €1533 Girl from Limfjord (100x80cm-39x31in) s.d.1938 s.i.verso exhib. 1-Apr-3 Rasmussen, Copenhagen #526 (D.KR 11000)

KJAER, Lilly (20th C) Austrian
£345 $552 €500 Apparition (65x75cm-26x30in) s. 11-Mar-3 Dorotheum, Vienna #105/R

KJAERSGAARD, Soren (1935-) Danish
£568 $943 €824 Composition (100x120cm-39x47in) s.d.1990. 12-Jun-3 Kunsthallen, Copenhagen #120/R (D.KR 6000)

KJERNER, Esther (1873-1952) Swedish
£274 $428 €411 Late autumn by Solna Church (37x32cm-15x13in) s. canvas on panel prov. 13-Sep-2 Lilla Bukowskis, Stockholm #256 (S.KR 4000)
£278 $461 €403 Clump of trees (30x35cm-12x14in) s. canvas on panel prov. 16-Jun-3 Lilla Bukowskis, Stockholm #976 (S.KR 3600)
£402 $667 €583 Landscape, Valdemarsvik (38x42cm-15x17in) s.d.1943 canvas on panel prov. 16-Jun-3 Lilla Bukowskis, Stockholm #1150 (S.KR 5200)
£494 $820 €716 Landscape, Satuna, Uppland (33x37cm-13x15in) s.d.1941 canvas on panel prov. 16-Jun-3 Lilla Bukowskis, Stockholm #1151 (S.KR 6400)
£709 $1099 €1064 The porch in autumn (47x37cm-19x15in) s.i.d.1928 panel. 4-Dec-2 AB Stockholms Auktionsverk #1784/R (S.KR 10000)
£931 $1508 €1350 Still life of jug and apple (28x20cm-11x8in) s.indis.d. canvas on panel prov. 26-May-3 Bukowskis, Stockholm #22/R (S.KR 12000)
£1015 $1604 €1523 Still life of fruit and pot (34x40cm-13x16in) s. panel. 16-Nov-2 Crafoord, Lund #65/R est:12000 (S.KR 14500)
£1064 $1649 €1596 Still life of chrysanthemums (32x26cm-13x10in) s. panel. 4-Dec-2 AB Stockholms Auktionsverk #1711/R est:20000-25000 (S.KR 15000)
£1227 $1939 €1841 Still life of pomegranate (24x33cm-9x13in) s. panel. 27-Nov-2 Falkkloos, Malmo #77806/R est:12000 (S.KR 17500)
£1241 $1924 €1862 Flowers in black jug (57x53cm-22x21in) s. canvas on panel. 3-Dec-2 Bukowskis, Stockholm #24/R est:20000-25000 (S.KR 17500)
£1650 $2705 €2393 Still life of pomegranates (24x33cm-9x13in) s. panel. 4-Jun-3 AB Stockholms Auktionsverk #2124/R est:20000-25000 (S.KR 21000)
£1762 $2855 €2643 Still life of roses (40x33cm-16x13in) s. panel. 3-Feb-3 Lilla Bukowskis, Stockholm #951 est:15000-20000 (S.KR 24600)

£1915 $2968 €2873 Flowers (43x56cm-17x22in) s. 3-Dec-2 Bukowskis, Stockholm #25/R est:25000-30000 (S.KR 27000)

£1964 $3221 €2848 Still life of fruit (35x42cm-14x17in) s. panel. 4-Jun-3 AB Stockholms Auktionsverk #2088/R est:18000-20000 (S.KR 25000)

£2270 $3518 €3405 Still life of oranges and grapes on pewter dish (28x36cm-11x14in) s.d.1951. 4-Dec-2 AB Stockholms Auktionsverk #1547/R est:18000-20000 (S.KR 32000)

£2405 $3896 €3487 Still life of grapes and lemon (35x42cm-14x17in) s. canvas on panel. 26-May-3 Bukowskis, Stockholm #139/R est:25000-30000 (S.KR 31000)

Works on paper

£1418 $2199 €2127 Still life of lady's hat, gloves and parasol (37x59cm-15x23in) s. W/C. 4-Dec-2 AB Stockholms Auktionsverk #1575/R est:20000-25000 (S.KR 20000)

KLADNICKI, Taddeus (1904-1982) American/Polish

Works on paper

£446 $700 €669 Ashore. Beached Dory (36x54cm-14x21in) s. W/C two. 22-Nov-2 Skinner, Boston #382/R

KLAIBERG, Fritz (1921-) German

£480 $758 €720 Venice (60x77cm-24x30in) s. 14-Nov-2 Bonhams, Edinburgh #320

KLAPHECK, Konrad (1935-) German

£19178 $30110 €28000 Satisfacction of desires (68x80cm-27x31in) s. i.on stretcher prov.exhib.lit. 15-Apr-3 Laurence Calmels, Paris #4323/R est:20000

£23913 $39217 €33000 The missed rendezvous (100x80cm-39x31in) s. verso i.d. stretcher prov.exhib.lit. 30-May-3 Villa Grisebach, Berlin #77/R est:35000-45000

£25316 $40000 €40000 Chief ideologist (90x99cm-35x39in) s.i.d.65 prov. 29-Nov-2 Villa Grisebach, Berlin #88/R est:40000-50000

£25342 $39534 €37000 Liberte, amour, art (81x60cm-32x24in) s.d.64 prov.exhib.lit. 14-Apr-3 Laurence Calmels, Paris #4083/R est:22000

£32000 $52160 €48000 Demi-vierge (161x130cm-63x51in) s.i.d.72 prov.exhib. 3-Feb-3 Christie's, London #187/R est:45000

KLAPISH, Liliane (1933-) Israeli

£1450 $2290 €2175 Figures in landscape (27x35cm-11x14in) s.d.2001 acrylic oil pastel. 27-Apr-3 Sotheby's, Tel Aviv #98/R est:2500-3500

KLAR, Otto (1908-1994) South African

£276 $431 €414 Drakensberg mountains (48x58cm-19x23in) s. board. 15-Oct-2 Stephan Welz, Johannesburg #461/R est:4000-6000 (SA.R 4500)

£344 $554 €516 Chalet in an alpine landscape (20x25cm-8x10in) s. board. 12-May-3 Stephan Welz, Johannesburg #194 est:2000-4000 (SA.R 4000)

£461 $719 €692 African village (24x29cm-9x11in) s. board. 15-Oct-2 Stephan Welz, Johannesburg #459 est:3000-5000 (SA.R 7500)

£584 $910 €876 Landscape with cottages (14x43cm-6x17in) s. board. 15-Oct-2 Stephan Welz, Johannesburg #460 est:2500-3500 (SA.R 9500)

£769 $1199 €1154 Alpine landscape (70x70cm-28x28in) s.i. 11-Nov-2 Stephan Welz, Johannesburg #593/R (SA.R 12000)

£903 $1454 €1355 Extensive landscape with a dirt road and a fence (60x68cm-24x27in) s. board. 12-May-3 Stephan Welz, Johannesburg #581/R est:8000-12000 (SA.R 10500)

£961 $1499 €1442 Extensive Bushveld landscape (23x57cm-9x22in) s. board. 11-Nov-2 Stephan Welz, Johannesburg #550/R est:8000-12000 (SA.R 15000)

£1057 $1649 €1586 Still life of flowers in a blue vase (45x40cm-18x16in) s. board. 11-Nov-2 Stephan Welz, Johannesburg #529 est:5000-7000 (SA.R 16500)

£2752 $4430 €4128 Fiures outside fishermen's cottages (60x90cm-24x35in) s. board. 12-May-3 Stephan Welz, Johannesburg #471/R est:12000-18000 (SA.R 32000)

KLASEN, Peter (1935-) German

£1250 $1975 €1800 Camion bache rouge-bleu (43x38cm-17x15in) s.i.d.verso acrylic. 28-Apr-3 Cornette de St.Cyr, Paris #436/R est:2500-3000

£1282 $2013 €2000 Camion bache-vert-rouge (40x33cm-16x13in) s.i.verso acrylic. 15-Dec-2 Perrin, Versailles #104/R

£1293 $2055 €1900 Peril, serrage gris-jaune (61x48cm-24x19in) s.i. acrylic gouache collage cardboard. 24-Mar-3 Cornette de St.Cyr, Paris #67/R

£1736 $2760 €2500 Camion bache rouge-vert E78 (56x47cm-22x19in) s.i.d.2000 verso acrylic. 29-Apr-3 Artcurial Briest, Paris #396/R est:1800-2000

£1923 $2981 €3000 Verrou / F rouge (103x73cm-41x29in) s. s.i.d.1986 verso acrylic paper. 7-Dec-2 Cornette de St.Cyr, Paris #127/R

£1987 $3238 €3000 Flammable solid (55x46cm-22x18in) s.i.d.1994 verso acrylic. 3-Feb-3 Cornette de St.Cyr, Paris #457/R

£1987 $3238 €3000 Camion bache (41x33cm-16x13in) s.i. acrylic. 3-Feb-3 Cornette de St.Cyr, Paris #456/R

£2013 $3119 €3200 Nu/fond rouge 38 (55x46cm-22x18in) s.i.d.2000 verso acrylic collage prov. 30-Oct-2 Artcurial Briest, Paris #594/R est:2800-3300

£2308 $3577 €3600 Camion bache AR909/02 (41x33cm-16x13in) s.i.verso acrylic. 7-Dec-2 Cornette de St.Cyr, Paris #113/R est:3000

£2405 $3728 €3800 G29 (73x53cm-29x21in) s.d.verso acrylic. 28-Sep-2 Cornette de St.Cyr, Paris #359/R est:3500-4000

£2436 $3776 €3800 E.N.View ofI.E. (172x117cm-68x46in) s.d.1997 acrylic collage paper. 7-Dec-2 Cornette de St.Cyr, Paris #112/R est:3500

£3077 $4831 €4800 Panneau noir MK (81x116cm-32x46in) s.d.84 i.verso acrylic. 22-Nov-2 Millon & Associes, Paris #123/R

£3526 $5535 €5500 Manette fond bleu (75x50cm-30x20in) s.i.d.89 acrylic collage paper. 10-Dec-2 Piasa, Paris #158

£3846 $6038 €6000 High tension (89x116cm-35x46in) s.i.d.1975 verso acrylic prov. 15-Dec-2 Perrin, Versailles #113/R

£13889 $22083 €20000 Paranoiac lady version no 2 (150x60cm-59x24in) s.i.d.1968 verso acrylic. 29-Apr-3 Artcurial Briest, Paris #377/R est:12000-15000

Sculpture

£2319 $3803 €3200 Untitled (104x40cm-41x16in) s.d.1996 num.3/8 table painted wood collage. 27-May-3 Tajan, Paris #58/R est:1500-2000

Works on paper

£665 $1030 €1050 Manette/fond bleu 813 (38x32cm-15x13in) s. mixed media. 28-Sep-2 Cornette de St.Cyr, Paris #360

£818 $1267 €1300 Manette ouvert open (40x32cm-16x13in) s.i. gouache aerographe. 30-Oct-2 Artcurial Briest, Paris #699/R

£884 $1406 €1300 HB/Z.14 (40x32cm-16x13in) s.d.98 gouache collae cardboard. 24-Mar-3 Coutau Begarie, Paris #257/R

£4500 $7515 €6525 Mirage (22x16cm-9x6in) s.d.66 s.i.d.1966 verso pencil oil canvas. 24-Jun-3 Sotheby's, Olympia #106/R est:3000-5000

KLASHORST, Peter (1957-) Dutch?

£513 $805 €800 Reclining nude woman (80x104cm-31x41in) s.verso. 25-Nov-2 Glerum, Amsterdam #339/R

KLASSOVA, Zuzana (20th C) Czechoslovakian

Works on paper

£253 $392 €380 Nude (76x60cm-30x24in) pastel exec.2002. 3-Dec-2 SOGA, Bratislava #131/R (SL.K 16000)

KLAUKE, Jurgen (1943-) German

Photographs

£14384 $22438 €21000 Composition - man with pile of hats on head (215x125cm-85x49in) gelatin silver prov.lit. 12-Apr-3 Lempertz, Koln #249/R est:7000-9000

KLAUS, Christian (1843-1893) German

£833 $1317 €1300 Peasant kitchen (35x26cm-14x10in) s. panel. 16-Nov-2 Lempertz, Koln #1503/R

KLAUS, Reinhold (1881-1963) Austrian

Works on paper

£886 $1382 €1400 Waidhofen an der Ybbs (47x38cm-19x15in) s.d.1963 W/C. 15-Oct-2 Dorotheum, Vienna #167/R

£1013 $1580 €1600 Waidhfen an der Ybbs (69x49cm-27x19in) s.i.d.1950 W/C gouache. 15-Oct-2 Dorotheum, Vienna #122/R

KLAUSNER, R (?) ?

£1300 $2028 €1950 Close scrutiny (37x26cm-15x10in) s. panel. 10-Sep-2 Bonhams, Knightsbridge #169/R est:700-900

KLAUSNER, Ruth (?) ?

£573 $836 €860 Interior with woman reading (53x43cm-21x17in) s. panel. 17-Jun-2 Philippe Schuler, Zurich #7343 (S.FR 1300)

KLECZYNSKI, Bohdan (1851-1916) Polish

£7742 $12000 €11613 Waiting to depart (54x90cm-21x35in) s.d.1883 panel. 30-Oct-2 Christie's, Rockefeller NY #117/R est:15000-20000

£17000 $27880 €25500 Rescue (74x120cm-29x47in) s.i.d.86 prov. 3-Jun-3 Sotheby's, London #20/R est:8000-12000

KLEE, Felix (1907-1990) German

Works on paper

£513 $795 €800 Composition with red sun (31x33cm-12x13in) s.i.d.Juni 1923 W/C pen. 4-Dec-2 Lempertz, Koln #817/R

KLEE, Paul (1879-1940) Swiss

£35897	$55641	€56000	Beginning of a celebration (21x32cm-8x13in) s. tempera. 7-Dec-2 Hauswedell & Nolte, Hamburg #795/R est:45000
£75000	$125250	€108750	Das haus in der hohe - the house on high (49x63cm-19x25in) s.d.23.14 W/C brush ink prov.exhib.lit. 24-Jun-3 Sotheby's, London #252/R est:60000-80000
£384615	$596154	€600000	Pfeil und Trichter (22x14cm-9x6in) s.i.d.1920 oil ink dr prov.exhib. 4-Dec-2 Lempertz, Koln #26/R est:400000-600000
£512821	$800000	€769232	Schlangen-toterin (41x24cm-16x9in) s.i.d.1923 oil W/C pen pencil paper on mount prov.exhib.lit. 5-Nov-2 Sotheby's, New York #31/R est:700000-900000

Prints

£3205	$4968	€5000	The lofty side (14x7cm-6x3in) col lithograph. 7-Dec-2 Hauswedell & Nolte, Hamburg #797/R est:5000
£3774	$5887	€6000	Kleinwelt (14x10cm-6x4in) s.i.num.2/3 etching aquatint. 9-Oct-2 Sotheby's, London #456/R est:3500-4500
£4277	$6672	€6800	Die hexe mit dem kamm (40x28cm-16x11in) s. lithograph. 9-Oct-2 Sotheby's, London #457/R est:9500-12500
£4565	$7487	€6300	Garden of passion (10x15cm-4x6in) s.i. etching. 29-May-3 Lempertz, Koln #705/R est:4000
£5435	$8913	€7500	Cheerful side (10x14cm-4x6in) col lithograph board. 31-May-3 Villa Grisebach, Berlin #207/R est:7000-9000
£24359	$37756	€38000	Insecks (21x15cm-8x6in) i.d. col lithograph. 7-Dec-2 Hauswedell & Nolte, Hamburg #796/R est:8000
£29817	$49794	€43235	Tightrope walker (44x27cm-17x11in) s.i. col lithograph. 20-Jun-3 Kornfeld, Bern #100/R est:60000 (S.FR 65000)
£44025	$68679	€70000	Drohendes haupt (42x32cm-17x13in) s.i.d.1905 etching. 9-Oct-2 Sotheby's, London #455/R est:100000-130000

Works on paper

£3718	$5428	€5800	Mr Lune (23x17cm-9x7in) s.i. pen pencil. 4-Jun-2 Karl & Faber, Munich #307/R est:7000-8000
£8896	$14857	€12899	Harbour (22x27cm-9x11in) s. Indian ink prov. 24-Jun-3 Koller, Zurich #29/R est:20000-30000 (S.FR 19660)
£9155	$15197	€13000	Protector (15x8cm-6x3in) s.i.d. pen. 14-Jun-3 Hauswedell & Nolte, Hamburg #1288/R est:18000
£10256	$16000	€15384	Ordnung an Stelle von Gluck (35x46cm-14x18in) s.i.d.1929 pen ink paperboard prov. 14-Oct-2 Butterfields, San Francisco #2013/R est:20000-25000
£13380	$22211	€19000	Milbertshofen (10x25cm-4x10in) s. pencil. 14-Jun-3 Hauswedell & Nolte, Hamburg #1287/R est:15000
£14000	$22960	€21000	Hexendenkmal (28x22cm-11x9in) s.i.d.1922 pencil prov.lit. 6-Feb-3 Christie's, London #451/R est:18000
£15596	$26046	€22614	Sheep (18x28cm-7x11in) i.d.April 1908 Indian ink prov.exhib. 20-Jun-3 Kornfeld, Bern #92/R est:27500 (S.FR 34000)
£17391	$28000	€26087	Trotzdem geschmuckt (29x30cm-11x12in) s.i.d.1928 pen ink prov.exhib.lit. 8-May-3 Christie's, Rockefeller NY #103/R est:35000-45000
£17391	$28000	€26087	Familiares (30x45cm-12x18in) s.i.d.1927 pen ink prov.exhib.lit. 8-May-3 Christie's, Rockefeller NY #106/R est:35000-45000
£17890	$29876	€25941	Curves with foliage II (18x28cm-7x11in) s. W/C over pencil Indian ink writing paper prov. 20-Jun-3 Kornfeld, Bern #96/R est:40000 (S.FR 39000)
£19313	$30515	€28970	Untidy bed (21x29cm-8x11in) s.i.d.1938 crayon prov.lit. 3-Apr-3 Heffel, Vancouver #52/R est:40000-45000 (C.D 45000)
£20186	$32500	€30279	Stadtteil am hafen - quater near the harbour (30x46cm-12x18in) s. W/C executed 1929 prov.exhib.lit. 7-May-3 Sotheby's, New York #212/R est:30000-40000
£25641	$40000	€38462	Komposition (27x21cm-11x8in) d.1938 estate st.verso gouache prov.exhib. 5-Nov-2 Phillips, New York #131/R est:40000-60000
£30000	$50100	€43500	Krankes madchen - sick girl (32x21cm-13x8in) s. gouache executed 1937 prov.exhib. 24-Jun-3 Sotheby's, London #251/R est:35000-45000
£34161	$55000	€51242	Mutter U kind - mother and child (10x11cm-4x4in) s. i.d.1913 verso quill ink gouache prov.exhib.lit. 7-May-3 Sotheby's, New York #214/R est:35000-45000
£34404	$57454	€49886	Stick man (42x21cm-17x8in) s. paste prov.lit.exhib. 20-Jun-3 Kornfeld, Bern #99/R est:80000 (S.FR 75000)
£42000	$64680	€63000	Terzert von einer operetta - trio from an operetta (20x30cm-8x12in) s. W/C chl prov.exhib. 22-Oct-2 Sotheby's, London #225/R est:30000-40000
£46584	$75000	€69876	Dame im breiten hut - lady in a wide brimmed hat (26x40cm-10x16in) s. W/C oil paper on board executed 1931 prov.exhib.lit. 7-May-3 Sotheby's, New York #206/R est:60000-80000
£50322	$79510	€78000	Groupe d'arbres (31x47cm-12x19in) s. W/C chl paper on cardboard prov. 18-Dec-2 Tajan, Paris #52/R est:70000-80000
£70136	$117127	€101697	Swiss clown (29x20cm-11x8in) s.i.d. W/C wax chk ochre paper on board prov.exhib.lit. 24-Jun-3 Koller, Zurich #30/R est:160000-220000 (S.FR 155000)
£73718	$115000	€110577	Anmassung - arrogance (21x21cm-8x8in) s.i.d.1926 W/C pen ink paper on card prov.exhib.lit. 6-Nov-2 Sotheby's, New York #204/R est:140000-180000
£80745	$130000	€121118	Kl parklandschaft - small park landscape (13x11cm-5x4in) s.i.d.1914-16 W/C paper on card prov.exhib.lit. 7-May-3 Sotheby's, New York #207/R est:80000-120000
£84862	$141720	€123050	Double tower (23x29cm-9x11in) s. wax chk prov.exhib. 20-Jun-3 Kornfeld, Bern #98/R est:200000 (S.FR 185000)
£125000	$193750	€195000	Femme penchee en arriere (33x31cm-13x12in) s. W/C exec.1929 prov.exhib.lit. 9-Dec-2 Piasa, Paris #21/R est:300000-400000
£169872	$263301	€265000	Petit esprit du jardin (48x30cm-19x12in) s. W/C exec.1929 prov.exhib.lit. 9-Dec-2 Piasa, Paris #20/R est:400000-500000
£169872	$263301	€265000	White Easter I (41x27cm-16x11in) s. W/C oil. 7-Dec-2 Hauswedell & Nolte, Hamburg #794/R est:175000
£220000	$358600	€330000	Wasservogel-enten (23x19cm-9x7in) s.i.d.1919 chl W/C pen ink paper on mount prov.exhib.lit. 3-Feb-3 Christie's, London #29/R est:220000-280000
£256410	$400000	€384615	Hauptszene aus dem ballet der falsche schwur (48x31cm-19x12in) s.d.1922 W/C pencil paper on board prov.exhib.lit. 6-Nov-2 Christie's, Rockefeller NY #47/R est:500000-700000
£357798	$597523	€518807	Landscape in orange with brown colour rhythm (18x25cm-7x10in) s.i. W/C prov.exhib. 20-Jun-3 Kornfeld, Bern #94/R est:600000 (S.FR 780000)

KLEEF, Jan van (1901-1995) Dutch

£379	$603	€550	Frog (34x40cm-13x16in) s.d.81 panel. 10-Mar-3 Sotheby's, Amsterdam #357

KLEEHAAS, Theodor (1854-1929) German

£962	$1462	€1500	Flirting in the mountains (101x74cm-40x29in) s.i. 11-Jul-2 Allgauer, Kempten #2557/R
£1410	$2186	€2200	Small girl sitting with dog by mountain path (100x74cm-39x29in) s.i. 5-Dec-2 Dr Fritz Nagel, Stuttgart #672/R est:2000

KLEEMAN, Ron (1937-) American

£42500	$68000	€63750	Perfect vision (102x168cm-40x66in) painted 1989 prov.lit. 15-May-3 Christie's, Rockefeller NY #162/R est:70000-90000
£44304	$70000	€66456	Soho Saint 33 and 4 score (146x159cm-57x63in) s. i.d.Oct 1974 prov.exhib.lit. 14-Nov-2 Christie's, Rockefeller NY #166/R est:70000-90000

KLEEMANN, Johann Jakob (1739-1790) German

Works on paper

£5247	$8500	€7871	Interior of gallery (12x22cm-5x9in) gouache. 23-Jan-3 Sotheby's, New York #256/R est:8000

KLEEMANN, Nikolaus Moritz (?-1756) German

£638	$1027	€950	Portrait of Zacharias Handler (79x61cm-31x24in) i.d. 18-Feb-3 Sotheby's, Amsterdam #378/R est:800-1200

KLEEMEYER, Christian Ernst (18th C) German

Sculpture

£3521	$5669	€5000	Berlin Louis VI clock (55x40x16cm-22x16x6in) s. marble bronze. 10-May-3 Hans Stahl, Toestorf #454 est:3500

KLEIBER, Hans (1887-1967) American

£903	$1400	€1355	Cottonwoods on Tongue River (25x38cm-10x15in) s. oil on paper. 7-Dec-2 Selkirks, St. Louis #240/R est:1800-2400
£1899	$3000	€2754	Eaton's ranch (28x36cm-11x14in) s. board prov. 26-Jul-3 Coeur d'Alene, Hayden #16/R est:2000-4000

Works on paper

£339	$525	€509	Along the ditch on Tongue River (15x23cm-6x9in) s.i. W/C. 7-Dec-2 Selkirks, St. Louis #239
£1899	$3000	€2754	Tongue River (18x25cm-7x10in) s. W/C. 26-Jul-3 Coeur d'Alene, Hayden #41/R est:1500-2500
£2532	$4000	€3671	North of Hell Creek (25x36cm-10x14in) s. W/C prov. 26-Jul-3 Coeur d'Alene, Hayden #15/R est:2000-4000

KLEIN VON DIEPOLD, Julian (1868-1947) German

£7595	$12000	€12000	Summer landscape in Ostfriesland with windmill on the river (99x135cm-39x53in) s. 29-Nov-2 Bolland & Marotz, Bremen #723/R est:3600

KLEIN VON DIEPOLD, Maximilian (1873-1927) German

£897	$1409	€1400	Eifel landscape (60x81cm-24x32in) s. 21-Nov-2 Van Ham, Cologne #1720/R

KLEIN, Cesar (1876-1954) German

Works on paper

£870	$1426	€1200	Wind women (30x21cm-12x8in) s.d.1948 gouache board. 31-May-3 Villa Grisebach, Berlin #587/R

£1282 $1987 €2000 Seated female nude (35x43cm-14x17in) s. gouache. 4-Dec-2 Lempertz, Koln #819/R est:2200

KLEIN, Friedrich Franz (1898-1990) Dutch
£258 $379 €400 Portrait of a lady (105x85cm-41x33in) s. 24-Jun-2 Dr Fritz Nagel, Stuttgart #5914/R
£1529 $2385 €2400 Horses in the pasture (46x55cm-18x22in) s. 6-Nov-2 Vendue Huis, Gravenhage #93/R est:1500-2000

KLEIN, Herman Franz (20th C) ?
Works on paper
£2193 $3421 €3290 Views of bombing of Cologne, Germany (26x21cm-10x8in) s. pastel three. 27-Mar-3 International Art Centre, Auckland #161/R est:8000-12000 (NZ.D 6250)

KLEIN, Hugo (1866-1932) Austrian
£278 $447 €417 Four soldiers riding across battlefield near Sokal (95x150cm-37x59in) s.d.1917. 7-May-3 Dobiaschofsky, Bern #3370 (S.FR 600)

KLEIN, J (?) Dutch
£1014 $1581 €1500 Extensive landscape with grazing cows (41x60cm-16x24in) s. 27-Mar-3 Dr Fritz Nagel, Stuttgart #824/R est:2500

KLEIN, Johann Adam (1792-1875) German
£1899 $2943 €3000 Peasant family in horse drawn cart (35x29cm-14x11in) mono.d.1837 i. stretcher prov. 28-Sep-2 Ketterer, Hamburg #1/R est:3500-4000
£5000 $7600 €7800 Three cows in upper Bavarian landscape (17x19cm-7x7in) mono.d.1819 panel. 11-Jul-2 Hugo Ruef, Munich #721/R est:7800
£7051 $10718 €11000 Constantin Basilica in Rome (15x22cm-6x9in) s.d.1821 paper on board. 11-Jul-2 Hugo Ruef, Munich #720/R est:5200
Works on paper
£278 $440 €440 Carthorse (11x15cm-4x6in) d.2 Mai 1812 pencil. 29-Nov-2 Bassenge, Berlin #5952/R
£288 $456 €450 Seated male nude (18x25cm-7x10in) ochre. 16-Nov-2 Lempertz, Koln #1348
£333 $507 €520 Horse and cart (12x18cm-5x7in) d.1817 pencil. 11-Jul-2 Hugo Ruef, Munich #903
£486 $773 €700 Italian woman, man leaning on arms (11x11cm-4x4in) s.i.d. W/C over pencil pencil sketch double-sided. 5-May-3 Ketterer, Munich #303/R
£521 $829 €750 Two men in boat (13x16cm-5x6in) pencil. 5-May-3 Ketterer, Munich #301/R
£570 $900 €900 Peasant working (16x11cm-6x4in) s.d.1844 pencil W/C two. 29-Nov-2 Bassenge, Berlin #5950
£633 $1000 €1000 Viennese woman (15x12cm-6x5in) s.i.d.10.Dec. 1816 double-sided. 29-Nov-2 Bassenge, Berlin #5951/R
£696 $1100 €1100 Landscape with signpost (18x24cm-7x9in) Indian ink over pencil double-sided. 29-Nov-2 Bassenge, Berlin #5949
£1154 $1754 €1800 Mounted officer (12x10cm-5x4in) s.d.1815 W/C. 11-Jul-2 Hugo Ruef, Munich #904 est:1800

KLEIN, Johann Adam (attrib) (1792-1875) German
Works on paper
£382 $608 €550 Wolkenstein Castle in the Ennsthal, Steiermark (25x41cm-10x16in) i. i. verso pencil. 5-May-3 Ketterer, Munich #302/R
£486 $773 €700 Portrait of young man, possibly Johann Christian Erhard (11x7cm-4x3in) pencil. 5-May-3 Ketterer, Munich #304/R

KLEIN, Jozsef (1896-1945) Hungarian?
£894 $1395 €1296 Forest way in shadow (72x60cm-28x24in) s.d.920. 12-Apr-3 Mu Terem Galeria, Budapest #90/R est:180000 (H.F 320000)
£11295 $17507 €16378 Idyllic scene with ladies (110x140cm-43x55in) s.d.1918-19. 9-Dec-2 Mu Terem Galeria, Budapest #216/R est:3000000 (H.F 4200000)

KLEIN, Jurgen (1904-1978) German
Sculpture
£1346 $2087 €2100 Cordula (62cm-24in) brown bronze pat.bronze Cast.W Fussel Berlin prov. 4-Dec-2 Lempertz, Koln #821/R est:3000-4000

KLEIN, Medard P (1905-2002) American
£915 $1500 €1327 Inscape no.101 (41x23cm-16x9in) s. acrylic on board prov. 1-Jun-3 Wright, Chicago #170/R est:2000-3000
£1935 $3000 €2903 Arrangement (56x76cm-22x30in) s.d. board. 8-Dec-2 Toomey, Oak Park #828/R est:3000-5000
Works on paper
£244 $400 €354 Untitled (25x36cm-10x14in) s. pencil prov. 1-Jun-3 Wright, Chicago #167/R
£427 $700 €619 Untitled (36x28cm-14x11in) s. pencil prov. 1-Jun-3 Wright, Chicago #168/R
£488 $800 €708 Untitled (36x25cm-14x10in) s. pencil prov. 1-Jun-3 Wright, Chicago #165/R
£732 $1200 €1061 Untitled (25x25cm-10x10in) s. pencil prov. 1-Jun-3 Wright, Chicago #166/R est:500-700
£1083 $1700 €1625 Piacevole (19x12cm-7x5in) s. mixed media exec.c.1949. 19-Nov-2 Wright, Chicago #153/R est:2000-3000

KLEIN, Micha (1964-) Dutch
Prints
£5380 $8500 €8500 White chill (75x151cm-30x59in) s.i.d.1996 num.1/5 col print prov.exhib. 26-Nov-2 Sotheby's, Amsterdam #304/R est:4000-5000

KLEIN, Paul (1909-1993) French
£417 $654 €650 Camargue le soir (100x120cm-39x47in) s. d.1982 verso. 19-Nov-2 Vanderkindere, Brussels #154
£513 $805 €800 Les heureux (97x116cm-38x46in) s. d.1977 verso. 19-Nov-2 Vanderkindere, Brussels #537
£616 $962 €900 Les clowns (92x60cm-36x24in) s. 14-Apr-3 Horta, Bruxelles #61
£1146 $1789 €1800 La batteuse (95x120cm-37x47in) s. 11-Nov-2 Horta, Bruxelles #41 est:1500-2500
£1667 $2617 €2600 Le cirque (200x300cm-79x118in) s. i.d.1969 verso. 19-Nov-2 Vanderkindere, Brussels #536/R est:2000-3000
£8333 $13250 €12000 Untitled (114x243cm-45x96in) s. 5-May-3 Bernaerts, Antwerp #405/R

KLEIN, Wilhelm (1821-1897) German
£1370 $2137 €2000 Summer landscape (78x111cm-31x44in) s.d.1871. 10-Apr-3 Van Ham, Cologne #1540/R est:2200

KLEIN, William (1926-) American
Photographs
£1963 $3200 €2945 Smoke plus veil (36x25cm-14x10in) s.i.d.1958 verso gelatin silver print. 12-Feb-3 Christie's, Rockefeller NY #265/R est:2500-3500
£6013 $9500 €9020 New York (28x35cm-11x14in) s.i.d.1954 verso gelatin silver print prov.lit. 25-Apr-3 Phillips, New York #42/R est:10000-15000
£6329 $10000 €9494 Baseball cards, New York (26x36cm-10x14in) s.i.verso gelatin silver print prov.exhib.lit. 25-Apr-3 Phillips, New York #43/R est:10000-15000
£6962 $11000 €10443 Bride (28x35cm-11x14in) s.i. verso gelatin silver print prov. 25-Apr-3 Phillips, New York #41/R est:10000-15000

KLEIN, Yves (1928-1962) French
£17949 $27821 €28000 IKB - Mediterranean blue (21x17cm-8x7in) pigment prov. 3-Dec-2 Lempertz, Koln #239/R est:20000-30000
Sculpture
£1006 $1550 €1600 Monochrome (190x240cm-75x94in) num.5/300. 22-Oct-2 Campo, Vlaamse Kaai #542
£3269 $5067 €5100 Catalogue raisonne des editions et sculptures. num.59/440 book pigment gold leaves plexiglas exec.2000. 7-Dec-2 Cornette de St.Cyr, Paris #103/R
£5000 $7700 €7500 Pink table (37x125x100cm-15x49x39in) s.num.01a116 pigment in plexiglass table prov. 22-Oct-2 Sotheby's, London #356/R est:5000-7000
£6000 $9480 €9000 Table bleue (36x124x100cm-14x49x39in) glass plexiglas pigment aluminium. 3-Apr-3 Christie's, Kensington #278/R est:8000
£6200 $10168 €9300 Blue table (37x125x100cm-15x49x39in) pigment plexiglass prov. 7-Feb-3 Sotheby's, London #195/R est:6000-8000
£6800 $10540 €10200 Table bleue (36x124x100cm-14x49x39in) glass plexiglass blue pigment. 5-Dec-2 Christie's, Kensington #281/R est:5000-7000
£7000 $10780 €10500 Gold table (37x125x100cm-15x49x39in) s.num.01a115 gold leaf in plexiglass table. 22-Oct-2 Sotheby's, London #320/R est:6000-8000
£8000 $12320 €12000 Table rose (37x125x100cm-15x49x39in) glass plexiglas pink pigment. 23-Oct-2 Christie's, London #131/R est:8000-15000
£9050 $13937 €14390 Terre bleue (36cm-14in) pigment resin plaster one of 350 prov.lit. 26-Oct-2 Cornette de St.Cyr, Paris #35/R est:15000
£9677 $15000 €14516 Table bleu (37x125x100cm-15x49x39in) plexiglas glass blue pigment. 26-Sep-2 Christie's, Rockefeller NY #800/R est:8000-12000
£10000 $15400 €15000 Table bleue (36x124x100cm-14x49x39in) glass plexiglas blue pigment. 23-Oct-2 Christie's, London #128/R est:10000-15000
£13000 $20020 €19500 Blue table (37x125x100cm-15x49x39in) s.num.01a117 pigment in plexiglass table prov. 22-Oct-2 Sotheby's, London #321/R est:6000-8000
£13750 $22000 €20625 Venus of Alexandria (68x23x22cm-27x9x9in) plaster sculpture dry blue pigment resin executed 1962. 16-May-3 Phillips, New York #173/R est:25000-30000

£14000 $23380 €20300 Table bleue (36x124x100cm-14x49x39in) num.00A/111 glass plexiglas blue pigment. 27-Jun-3 Christie's, London #168/R est:8000-12000
£17000 $26860 €25500 Venus d'Alexandrie (67cm-26in) num.131/300 blue pigment plaster lit. 3-Apr-3 Christie's, Kensington #279/R est:12000-18000
£20000 $33400 €29000 La Venus d'Alexandrie (68cm-27in) num.28/300 dry blue pigment synthetic resin plaster executed 1961. 27-Jun-3 Christie's, London #171/R est:20000-30000
£23000 $38410 €33350 Victoire de samothrace (50x25x36cm-20x10x14in) num.23/175 dry blue pigment synthetic resin plaster prov. 27-Jun-3 Christie's, London #167/R est:24000-28000
£58742 $90463 €93400 SE 272 (48x18x15cm-19x7x6in) pigment resin sponge metal exec.1961 exhib.lit. 26-Oct-2 Cornette de St.Cyr, Paris #50/R est:90000

Works on paper
£1667 $2567 €2650 Enveloppe et timbre bleu (11x17cm-4x7in) mixed media. 26-Oct-2 Cornette de St.Cyr, Paris #37/R
£25000 $41750 €36250 Untitled (9x7cm-4x3in) s.d.57 verso pigment on wood prov. 27-Jun-3 Christie's, London #164/R est:25000-35000
£34810 $55000 €52215 IKB 150 (22x18cm-9x7in) pigment synthetic resin paper on board executed c.1959 prov.lit. 13-Nov-2 Sotheby's, New York #293/R est:40000-60000
£85443 $135000 €128165 IKB 134 (22x36cm-9x14in) s.overlap s.verso pigment synthetic resin line on panel lit. 13-Nov-2 Sotheby's, New York #308/R est:100000-150000
£180000 $295200 €270000 Ant 159 (107x74cm-42x29in) s.d.1960 pigment paper on canvas prov. 6-Feb-3 Sotheby's, London #29/R est:250000
£2937500 $4700000 €4406250 Re 2 (135x121cm-53x48in) sponges pigment synthetic resin board exec.1958 prov.exhib.lit. 14-May-3 Christie's, Rockefeller NY #39/R est:3000000-4000000

KLEINEH, Oskar (1846-1919) Finnish
£1020 $1622 €1500 Evening in the skerries (25x32cm-10x13in) oil sketch prov. 27-Feb-3 Hagelstam, Helsinki #950 est:2000
£1384 $2131 €2200 Fjord landscape (22x31cm-9x12in) 27-Oct-2 Bukowskis, Helsinki #214/R est:2200
£3741 $5986 €5200 Sunset at sea (22x29cm-9x11in) s. board. 17-May-3 Hagelstam, Helsinki #98/R est:5000
£4795 $7527 €7000 Steamer, sailing ship and rowing boat off Finnish coast (38x61cm-15x24in) s.d.1883. 16-Apr-3 Dorotheum, Salzburg #151/R est:9000-14000
£5063 $8000 €8000 Mediterranean, Gibraltar (20x32cm-8x13in) s. canvas on board executed c.1880. 30-Nov-2 Hagelstam, Helsinki #133/R est:8000
£6187 $9899 €8600 Summer's day by the coast (10x18cm-4x7in) s. panel. 17-May-3 Hagelstam, Helsinki #97/R est:5000
£9810 $15500 €15500 Moonlight at sea (22x39cm-9x15in) s. 1-Dec-2 Bukowskis, Helsinki #85/R est:8000-9000
£10759 $17000 €17000 Calm day at sea (122x38cm-48x15in) s. board. 1-Dec-2 Bukowskis, Helsinki #86/R est:9000-11000
£14085 $22676 €20000 Steam boat in rough seas (60x76cm-24x30in) s. 10-May-3 Bukowskis, Helsinki #148/R est:20000-25000
£25949 $41000 €41000 Sailing in Porkala Skerries (46x39cm-18x15in) s. 1-Dec-2 Bukowskis, Helsinki #83/R est:33000-35000
£28169 $45352 €40000 Seascape with boats in a calm (43x75cm-17x30in) s. 10-May-3 Bukowskis, Helsinki #106/R est:30000-35000

KLEINERT, Eduard Vaclav (20th C) American
£255 $400 €383 Chicago shacks (81x71cm-32x28in) s. s.d.July 15 1931 verso. 23-Nov-2 Jackson's, Cedar Falls #105/R

KLEINHOLZ, Frank (1901-?) American
£266 $425 €399 Embracing couple. s. painted c.1950. 12-Jan-3 William Jenack, New York #391

KLEINSCHMIDT, Paul (1883-1949) German
£21127 $35070 €30000 Bar - blonde woman (150x61cm-59x24in) mono.d.38 Juli. 14-Jun-3 Hauswedell & Nolte, Hamburg #1290/R est:40000

KLEINTJES, Jan (1872-1955) Dutch
£563 $907 €800 Portrait of an elegant lady (134x90cm-53x35in) s.d.1908 i.verso. 7-May-3 Vendue Huis, Gravenhage #559

KLEISS-HERZIG, Yvonne (1895-1968) French
£1151 $1887 €1600 Le cafe de la perruche (46x38cm-18x15in) s. 4-Jun-3 Tajan, Paris #278/R est:1200-1500

KLEITSCH, Joseph (1885-1931) American
£7784 $13000 €11287 Kittens (49x65cm-19x26in) s. painted c.1914. 18-Jun-3 Christie's, Los Angeles #107/R est:12000-18000
£30573 $48000 €45860 Old Laguna, foot of Anita Street (34x45cm-13x18in) s. i.verso board prov. 20-Nov-2 Christie's, Los Angeles #44/R est:20000-30000
£65868 $110000 €95509 Interrupted hand (61x80cm-24x31in) s.i.d.1911. 18-Jun-3 Christie's, Los Angeles #41/R est:20000-30000

Works on paper
£2903 $4500 €4355 Old mission (33x38cm-13x15in) s. mixed media prov. 29-Oct-2 John Moran, Pasadena #763 est:4000-6000

KLEIVAN, Nina (1960-) Danish
£550 $853 €825 Compositions with riders (70x86cm-28x34in) s.d.1990 pair prov. 1-Oct-2 Rasmussen, Copenhagen #150 (D.KR 6500)

KLELL, Eduard (20th C) Austrian
£468 $767 €650 Impression of autumn with view of Rhein valley (25x21cm-10x8in) s.d.89 i.verso panel. 5-Jun-3 Dorotheum, Salzburg #734/R

KLEMM, Walther (1883-1957) German
£606 $939 €909 Horse drawn cart (68x105cm-27x41in) s. 24-Sep-2 Koller, Zurich #6730 (S.FR 1400)

KLEMMER, Robert (1938-1971) Austrian
£1042 $1646 €1500 Circus Klemmer (110x80cm-43x31in) s.i.d.1968. 24-Apr-3 Dorotheum, Vienna #193/R est:1500-2200
£2162 $3373 €3200 I (91x95cm-36x37in) s.i.d.69 panel. 25-Mar-3 Wiener Kunst Auktionen, Vienna #24/R est:3000-5500

KLENGEL, Johan Christian (1751-1824) German
£1090 $1689 €1700 Wooded landscape with young herdsman and cattle on edge of a path (55x75cm-22x30in) 4-Dec-2 Neumeister, Munich #784/R est:1100

Works on paper
£382 $608 €550 In the pasture (14x20cm-6x8in) s. pen wash. 5-May-3 Ketterer, Munich #307/R

KLENGEL, Johan Christian (attrib) (1751-1824) German

Works on paper
£411 $638 €650 Rochsburg on the Zwickauer Mulde near Lunzenau. i.d.9. Aug. 18 chk wash. 27-Sep-2 Venator & Hansten, Koln #1003

KLENZE, Leo von (1784-1864) German
£344156 $512792 €530000 Roman Forum (73x99cm-29x39in) mono.d.40 prov.lit. 26-Jun-2 Neumeister, Munich #773/R est:11000

KLEPINSKI, Johann (1872-?) Polish
£943 $1472 €1500 Boys bathing in lake (55x65cm-22x26in) s. lit. 20-Sep-2 Karlheinz Kaupp, Staufen #1836 est:1000

KLEPPER, Frank (1890-1955) American
£513 $800 €770 Landscape (28x36cm-11x14in) board. 19-Oct-2 David Dike, Dallas #324/R
£1763 $2750 €2645 Windmill Gruge Holland (71x71cm-28x28in) 19-Oct-2 David Dike, Dallas #120/R est:3000-6000

Works on paper
£288 $450 €432 Shipbuilding (38x46cm-15x18in) W/C. 19-Oct-2 David Dike, Dallas #112/R
£414 $650 €621 Galloping horse (39x46cm-15x18in) s. W/C paper on board. 14-Dec-2 Weschler, Washington #654/R

KLERK, Michel de (1884-1923) Dutch

Works on paper
£1871 $3068 €2600 In the forest (32x24cm-13x9in) s. black red chk prov. 3-Jun-3 Christie's, Amsterdam #40/R est:800-1200

KLERX, Zilia (fl.c.1900) Dutch
£353 $546 €550 Composition au panier de framboises (28x50cm-11x20in) s. 9-Dec-2 Horta, Bruxelles #450

KLESTOVA, Irene (?) ?
£600 $978 €900 Roses (24x18cm-9x7in) s. board sold with another similar. 13-Feb-3 Christie's, Kensington #245/R
£850 $1335 €1275 Roses (24x19cm-9x7in) s. board. 16-Apr-3 Christie's, Kensington #881/R

KLETT, Walter (1897-1966) American
£353 $550 €530 Courtly woman eyeing statue of Pan (71x76cm-28x30in) s.d.1924. 9-Nov-2 Illustration House, New York #89/R

KLEVER, Julius Sergius von (1850-1924) Russian

£3234 $5110 €4851 Getreideernte - corn harvest must be brought indoors (101x50cm-40x20in) s.d.1905 exhib. 2-Dec-2 Rasmussen, Copenhagen #1254/R est:20000 (D.KR 38000)
£4808 $7452 €7500 Twig collector in snow-covered winter forest (73x99cm-29x39in) s. canvas on canvas. 4-Dec-2 Neumeister, Munich #785/R est:6000
£5200 $8424 €7800 Frozen river (78x62cm-31x24in) s.d.1881. 21-May-3 Sotheby's, London #73/R est:6000-8000
£7000 $11410 €10500 Sunset over the cemetery (171x142cm-67x56in) s.d.1890. 13-Feb-3 Christie's, Kensington #165/R est:1000-1500
£8333 $13250 €12000 Winter, snow covered farms at dusk (32x40cm-13x16in) s. 29-Apr-3 Christie's, Amsterdam #91/R est:10000-15000
£13000 $21060 €19500 Summer bridge (49x73cm-19x29in) s.d.1915. 21-May-3 Sotheby's, London #63/R est:12000-15000
£14557 $23000 €23000 Sunset (53x78cm-21x31in) s.d.1882. 1-Dec-2 Bukowskis, Helsinki #256/R est:10000-12000
£15823 $25000 €25000 On the path (107x72cm-42x28in) s.d.1896. 1-Dec-2 Bukowskis, Helsinki #257/R est:10000-12000
£20408 $32449 €30000 Sunset in winter wood (131x86cm-52x34in) s.d.1904 one of pair. 19-Mar-3 Neumeister, Munich #606/R est:30000
£20408 $32449 €30000 Evening sun on birches along track in winter (131x86cm-52x34in) s.d.1904 one of pair. 19-Mar-3 Neumeister, Munich #607/R est:30000
£22000 $34540 €33000 Forest at sunset (132x90cm-52x35in) s.d.1883. 20-Nov-2 Sotheby's, London #18/R est:25000-35000
£22000 $34540 €33000 Strolling along the riverbank (54x81cm-21x32in) s.i.d.1918 prov. 20-Nov-2 Sotheby's, London #45/R est:10000-15000
£22152 $35000 €33228 Winter landscape (45x67cm-18x26in) s.d.1893. 24-Apr-3 Sotheby's, New York #113/R est:18000-25000
£28481 $45000 €42722 Cottage by a stream (61x81cm-24x32in) s. 24-Apr-3 Sotheby's, New York #114/R est:12000-18000
£34000 $55080 €51000 Hamlet well (75x101cm-30x40in) s. prov. 21-May-3 Sotheby's, London #26/R est:25000-35000
£37500 $60000 €56250 View of a garden with s swan pond, possibly Pavl ousk Park (108x133cm-43x52in) s.d.1878. 14-May-3 Butterfields, San Francisco #1100/R est:10000-150000

KLEVER, Julius Sergius von (attrib) (1850-1924) Russian

£2000 $3240 €3000 Homeward bound through the snow (67x31cm-26x12in) bears sig. 21-May-3 Sotheby's, London #75/R est:2000-3000

KLEVER, Juri (1879-?) Russian

£1054 $1677 €1550 Flowers in vase (53x34cm-21x13in) s.d.1916. 24-Mar-3 Bukowskis, Helsinki #378/R est:400
£2177 $3461 €3200 Still life (67x80cm-26x31in) s.d.1908. 24-Mar-3 Bukowskis, Helsinki #377/R est:600

KLEVER, Yuli Yulievich (younger) (1882-1942) Russian

£6500 $10530 €9750 Still life with berries and plums (38x46cm-15x18in) s.d.1915. 21-May-3 Sotheby's, London #35/R est:4000-6000

KLEY, Heinrich (1863-1945) German

Works on paper

£295 $457 €460 Boats on beach - Winter in Heist sur Mer (18x34cm-7x13in) s.i. Indian ink htd white board. 7-Dec-2 Ketterer, Hamburg #34/R
£346 $550 €519 Trojan horse (28x25cm-11x10in) s. pen ink W/C. 3-May-3 Rachel Davis, Shaker Heights #113/R
£471 $750 €707 Devilish creature (20x38cm-8x15in) s. gouache pen ink. 3-May-3 Rachel Davis, Shaker Heights #112/R
£503 $800 €755 Racing devil (23x38cm-9x15in) s. gouache pen ink. 3-May-3 Rachel Davis, Shaker Heights #111/R
£601 $932 €950 Jumble sale. Dance floor (23x29cm-9x11in) s.i.d.1918 Indian ink two. 25-Sep-2 Neumeister, Munich #413/R

KLEYN, Lodewyk Johannes (1817-1897) Dutch

£1392 $2158 €2200 Dutch river landscape (15x23cm-6x9in) s. panel. 27-Sep-2 Karrenbauer, Konstanz #1643 est:2000
£2083 $3312 €3000 Journey at dawn (26x33cm-10x13in) s. panel. 29-Apr-3 Christie's, Amsterdam #3/R est:3000-5000
£4140 $6500 €6210 Dutch canal scene (25x33cm-10x13in) panel. 13-Dec-2 Du Mouchelle, Detroit #2083/R est:8000-12000
£4403 $6780 €7000 Wood gatherers in a winter landscape (23x36cm-9x14in) s. panel. 22-Oct-2 Sotheby's, Amsterdam #7/R est:7000-9000
£7500 $11925 €11250 Frozen winter landscape (26x35cm-10x14in) s. panel. 20-Mar-3 Christie's, Kensington #145/R est:4000-6000
£7639 $12146 €11000 Numerous figures and a koek en zopie on the ice (27x37cm-11x15in) s. panel. 29-Apr-3 Christie's, Amsterdam #9/R est:6000-8000
£7643 $11924 €12000 Trekvliet, The Hague (33x51cm-13x20in) s. panel. 6-Nov-2 Vendue Huis, Gravenhage #399/R est:10000-15000
£9032 $14000 €13548 Shipping in a Dutch harbour (39x53cm-15x21in) s. panel. 30-Oct-2 Christie's, Rockefeller NY #112/R est:15000-20000
£12579 $19371 €20000 Skaters on a frozen river near a Koek en zopie (49x72cm-19x28in) s. 22-Oct-2 Sotheby's, Amsterdam #169/R est:25000-35000
£13699 $21507 €20000 Skaters on a frozen river near a koek en zopie (49x72cm-19x28in) s. 15-Apr-3 Sotheby's, Amsterdam #202/R est:20000-25000
£17722 $27646 €28000 Extensive landscape with skaters and figures (90x120cm-35x47in) s. prov. 21-Oct-2 Glerum, Amsterdam #57/R est:10000-20000

KLEYN, Reinhardt Willem (1828-1889) Dutch

£1268 $2041 €1800 Bride in wedding dress (35x27cm-14x11in) s.d.1887 panel. 6-May-3 Vendu Notarishuis, Rotterdam #59/R est:1500-2000

KLIE, Zoltan (1897-?) Swiss?

£903 $1409 €1355 Young woman with bouquet (60x80cm-24x31in) s. 11-Sep-2 Kieselbach, Budapest #38/R (H.F 350000)
£914 $1417 €1325 Nagymaros (50x61cm-20x24in) s. i.verso. 9-Dec-2 Mu Terem Galeria, Budapest #189/R est:320000 (H.F 340000)
£2236 $3487 €3354 Nudes in open air (50x61cm-20x24in) 11-Apr-3 Kieselbach, Budapest #102/R est:350000-800000 (H.F 800000)
£3870 $6037 €5612 Nude in the studio at Balaton (86x67cm-34x26in) s. 13-Sep-2 Mu Terem Galeria, Budapest #65/R est:900000 (H.F 1500000)
£16769 $26159 €24315 Edge of the woods (75x100cm-30x39in) s.d.934 exhib.lit. 13-Sep-2 Mu Terem Galeria, Budapest #80/R est:2500000 (H.F 6500000)

KLIEN, Erika Giovanna (1900-1957) German

Works on paper

£2899 $4754 €4000 Petersdorf, Neustiftgasse (9x15cm-4x6in) s.i. black chk. 27-May-3 Wiener Kunst Auktionen, Vienna #102/R est:4000-7000
£2899 $4754 €4000 Petersdorf, Hochstrasse (16x8cm-6x3in) s.i. black chk. 27-May-3 Wiener Kunst Auktionen, Vienna #103/R est:4000-7000
£4317 $7079 €6000 Crystal study (31x31cm-12x12in) s.i. chk pencil peramine lit. 6-Jun-3 Ketterer, Munich #60/R est:6000-8000
£6013 $9500 €9500 Nude (32x10cm-13x4in) s.i.d.1923 col pen. 27-Nov-2 Dorotheum, Vienna #154/R est:2800-3400

KLIMEK, Ludwig (1912-1992) Polish

£892 $1391 €1400 Nu assis (46x38cm-18x15in) s. 10-Nov-2 Eric Pillon, Calais #270/R

KLIMENCO, Philip Philipovich (1862-?) Russian

Works on paper

£776 $1257 €1125 View of bay with sailing boats (21x39cm-8x15in) s.d.1913 W/C. 25-May-3 Uppsala Auktionskammare, Uppsala #140/R (S.KR 10000)

KLIMKOVITS, Ignac (1800-1853) Czechoslovakian

£1418 $2070 €2127 Coronation of St Steven (67x36cm-26x14in) painted c.1840. 4-Jun-2 SOGA, Bratislava #23/R est:90000 (SL.K 90000)

KLIMO, Alojz (1922-) Czechoslovakian

£395 $612 €593 Two squares (70x49cm-28x19in) tempera painted 1987. 3-Dec-2 SOGA, Bratislava #279/R (SL.K 25000)

KLIMSCH, Eugen (1839-1896) German

Works on paper

£287 $447 €450 Madonna with child and putti playing music (21x14cm-8x6in) wash pencil. 6-Nov-2 Hugo Ruef, Munich #1390/R

KLIMSCH, Fritz (1870-1960) German

Sculpture

£1456 $2300 €2300 Standing female nude (15x6x4cm-6x2x2in) mono. gold pat.bronze Cast.H Noack Berlin. 30-Nov-2 Bassenge, Berlin #6381/R est:2400
£2405 $3728 €3800 Seated - siesta (24x17x19cm-9x7x7in) dark brown pat.bronze. 28-Sep-2 Ketterer, Hamburg #405/R est:3800-4800
£2483 $3948 €3600 Siesta (25cm-10in) mono. bronze Cast.Strassacker, Sussen. 8-Mar-3 Arnold, Frankfurt #236/R est:3000
£3261 $5348 €4500 Little Neriedes (45cm-18in) mono. verso bronze lit. 29-May-3 Lempertz, Koln #712/R est:4200
£3270 $5036 €5200 Siesta (24x21x17cm-9x8x7in) mono. black brown pat.bronze. 26-Oct-2 Dr Lehr, Berlin #224/R est:5500
£5449 $8446 €8500 Girl wearing turban (30cm-12in) mono. dark bronze pat.bronze Cast.H.Noack Berlin. 4-Dec-2 Lempertz, Koln #822/R est:8000-10000
£6522 $10696 €9000 Female figure laying down wreath (74x57cm-29x22in) s. bronze relief prov. 29-May-3 Lempertz, Koln #711/R est:8000
£9615 $14904 €15000 Dreamer (50cm-20in) mono. bronze exec.1935 prov.lit. 7-Dec-2 Van Ham, Cologne #282/R est:18000
£10145 $16638 €14000 Small female figure (49cm-19in) mono. Cast.H.Noack Berlin. 31-May-3 Villa Grisebach, Berlin #274/R est:12000-14000
£14103 $21859 €22000 Nude (47x100cm-19x39in) s. dark pat.bronze lit. 6-Dec-2 Karlheinz Kaupp, Staufen #876/R est:12000

£22152 $35000 €35000 Spring (180cm-71in) s. brown pat.bronze Cast.H.Noack Berlin. 30-Nov-2 Villa Grisebach, Berlin #339/R est:35000-40000

KLIMSCH, Hans Paul (1868-1917) German

£423 $701 €600 Two long-tailed monkeys (35x45cm-14x18in) s. board. 14-Jun-3 Arnold, Frankfurt #783/R

KLIMT, Gustav (1862-1918) Austrian

£77419 $120000 €116129 Akt mit gespreitzen beinen - nude with spread legs (57x37cm-22x15in) i.verso panel prov.lit. 4-Nov-2 Phillips, New York #5/R est:70000-90000

Works on paper

£1439 $2360 €2000 Children's heads (44x31cm-17x12in) s. black chk executed c.1901. 3-Jun-3 Christie's, Amsterdam #22a/R est:2000-3000

£4088 $6500 €6132 Standing female nude (48x27cm-19x11in) st.sig. col pencil exec.1902 prov.lit. 27-Feb-3 Christie's, Rockefeller NY #25/R est:10000

£5208 $8229 €7500 Nude study (45x31cm-18x12in) pencil board. 26-Apr-3 Dr Lehr, Berlin #277/R est:4500

£5435 $8913 €7500 Two female nudes (44x31cm-17x12in) ochre. 29-May-3 Lempertz, Koln #714/R est:9000

£6410 $10064 €10000 Pregnant woman in profile (44x30cm-17x12in) pencil lit. 21-Nov-2 Finarte, Rome #181/R est:10000-12000

£7500 $11850 €11850 Study for Jurisprudence (44x31cm-17x12in) chk prov. 30-Nov-2 Villa Grisebach, Berlin #108/R est:10000-12000

£8000 $13360 €12000 Paar (29x45cm-11x18in) s. pencil executed c.1902 prov. 26-Jun-3 Christie's, London #367/R est:8000-12000

£8025 $13000 €12038 Seated woman holding her head in her hands (45x31cm-18x12in) chk prov.lit. 22-Jan-3 Christie's, Rockefeller NY #129/R est:8000

£8333 $13083 €13000 Reclining nude (37x56cm-15x22in) Indian ink lit. 25-Nov-2 Hassfurther, Vienna #18/R est:10000-12000

£8500 $13090 €12750 Sitzend von vorne - seated nude (56x37cm-22x15in) pencil executed c.1912 lit. 22-Oct-2 Sotheby's, London #212/R est:6000-8000

£9615 $14904 €15000 Portrait of Hermine Gallia (45x32cm-18x13in) chk prov. 4-Dec-2 Lempertz, Koln #823a/R est:15000

£10000 $16400 €15000 Standing nude (44x31cm-17x12in) pencil exec.1902 prov.exhib.lit. 6-Feb-3 Christie's, London #409/R est:12000

£10127 $16000 €16000 Bent over nude (55x37cm-22x15in) pencil prov.lit.exhib. 30-Nov-2 Villa Grisebach, Berlin #109/R est:20000-30000

£11111 $17667 €16000 Seated female nude (44x30cm-17x12in) pencil. 5-May-3 Ketterer, Munich #891/R est:4000-6000

£12258 $19000 €18387 Geneigter mannerkopf nach links (57x37cm-22x15in) i.verso pencil executed 1917-18 prov.exhib.lit. 4-Nov-2 Phillips, New York #2/R est:18000-22000

£13000 $21320 €19500 Love scene (35x55cm-14x22in) st.sig. pencil prov.exhib.lit. 6-Feb-3 Christie's, London #407/R est:20000

£13406 $21986 €18500 Reclining friends, towards the right, with the back of front one showing (35x50cm-14x20in) pencil exec.1904 lit. 27-May-3 Hassfurther, Vienna #16/R est:10000-14000

£13924 $22000 €22000 Portrait of Magda Mautner of Markhof (55x35cm-22x14in) pencil packing paper prov. 26-Nov-2 Wiener Kunst Auktionen, Vienna #80/R est:22000-28000

£14907 $24000 €22361 Stehender akt von vorne (50x32cm-20x13in) pencil executed 1916-17 prov.exhib.lit. 8-May-3 Christie's, Rockefeller NY #123/R est:25000-35000

£16000 $26720 €24000 Frau nachs links (56x37cm-22x15in) s. pen ink prov.lit. 26-Jun-3 Christie's, London #366/R est:10000-15000

£18065 $28000 €27098 Sitzende dame in profil nach rechts - profile of a seated woman from the right (56x37cm-22x15in) i.verso red pencil prov.exhib.lit. 4-Nov-2 Phillips, New York #8/R est:30000-40000

£18440 $29872 €26000 Nude leaning over (55x37cm-22x15in) pencil. 20-May-3 Dorotheum, Vienna #4/R est:20000-30000

£20000 $33400 €30000 Aufgestutzt Liegende, links Wiederholung (37x56cm-15x22in) st. verso col.crayons prov.lit. 26-Jun-3 Christie's, London #368/R est:20000-30000

£20253 $32000 €32000 Standing figure (45x31cm-18x12in) pencil exhib.lit. 27-Nov-2 Dorotheum, Vienna #5/R est:25000-28000

£21000 $35070 €30450 Stehender akt - standing nude (44x31cm-17x12in) init. black crayon executed c.1901-02 prov.exhib.lit. 24-Jun-3 Sotheby's, London #262/R est:15000-20000

£23226 $36000 €34839 Studie fur das bildnis der pelzkragen - painting the fur collar (57x37cm-22x15in) i.verso pencil executed 1916 prov.lit. 4-Nov-2 Phillips, New York #10/R est:35000-45000

£23602 $38000 €35403 Madchenakt mit langen haaren und nach vorn gebeugtem oberkorper (56x37cm-22x15in) pencil executed c.1907 prov.exhib.lit. 8-May-3 Christie's, Rockefeller NY #124/R est:40000-60000

£29032 $45000 €43548 Brustbild eines madchens - Portrait of a girl (47x30cm-19x12in) i.verso chl executed 1898 prov.lit. 4-Nov-2 Phillips, New York #3/R est:50000-70000

£35484 $55000 €53226 Brustbild eines madchens mit langen harren von vorne - portrait of a girl with long hair (44x32cm-17x13in) i.verso chl red panel white chk prov.exhib.lit. 4-Nov-2 Phillips, New York #7/R est:40000-60000

£36111 $57417 €52000 Seated female nude (52x34cm-20x13in) pencil white traces redchk. 5-May-3 Ketterer, Munich #892/R est:8000-12000

£38710 $60000 €58065 Liegender Halbakt - reclining nude (56x37cm-22x15in) i.verso pencil executed c.1917-18prov.exhib.lit. 4-Nov-2 Phillips, New York #1/R est:80000-120000

£45161 $70000 €67742 Akt eines greises mit vorgehaltenen handen - nude old man with heads and hands (45x32cm-18x13in) i.verso chl executed c.1900-07 prov.exhib.lit. 4-Nov-2 Phillips, New York #6/R est:15000-20000

£50000 $83500 €75000 Zwei liegende Frauenakte (37x57cm-15x22in) st. pen ink red crayon exec c.1913 prov.lit. 26-Jun-3 Christie's, London #369/R est:50000-70000

£51613 $80000 €77420 Liegender halbakt nach rechts - reclining nude (37x56cm-15x22in) i. pencil htd red blue pencil executed 1914-15 prov.lit. 4-Nov-2 Phillips, New York #4/R est:80000-120000

£67742 $105000 €101613 Kauernder halbakt nach links - crouching nude from left (37x56cm-15x22in) s. i.verso pencil prov.exhib.lit. 4-Nov-2 Phillips, New York #9/R est:90000-120000

KLINE, Franz (1910-1962) American

£11976 $20000 €17365 Untitled (21x29cm-8x11in) s. acrylic on board. 22-Jun-3 Freeman, Philadelphia #138/R est:12000-18000

£18750 $30000 €28125 Study (27x20cm-11x8in) s.d.53 verso oil paper on paperboard prov. 14-May-3 Sotheby's, New York #114/R est:30000-40000

£28000 $45920 €42000 Untitled (25x17cm-10x7in) paper painted c.1958 prov. 6-Feb-3 Sotheby's, London #7/R est:35000

£41139 $65000 €61709 Untitled (28x22cm-11x9in) s.d.57 oil paper collage prov. 14-Nov-2 Christie's, Rockefeller NY #121/R est:30000-40000

£59375 $95000 €89063 Lehigh V Span (26x42cm-10x17in) s.i. oil ink wash paper on board painted c.1959 prov. 14-May-3 Sotheby's, New York #109/R est:80000-120000

£406250 $650000 €609375 Painting 1 (71x51cm-28x20in) exec.1954 prov.exhib. 13-May-3 Sotheby's, New York #20/R est:500000-700000

£593750 $950000 €890625 Sawyer (208x168cm-82x66in) s.d.59 verso prov.exhib. 13-May-3 Sotheby's, New York #25/R est:1200000-1800000

£2594937 $4100000 €3892406 Ninth Street (152x198cm-60x78in) s. painted 1951 prov.exhib.lit. 12-Nov-2 Sotheby's, New York #13/R est:4000000-6000000

Prints

£4403 $7000 €6605 Untitled (21x37cm-8x15in) s.i. etching aquatint sold with etched poem. 2-May-3 Sotheby's, New York #493/R est:2500-3500

Works on paper

£7500 $12000 €11250 Untitled (46x53cm-18x21in) s.d.50 ink prov. 15-May-3 Christie's, Rockefeller NY #104/R est:18000-22000

£9375 $15000 €14063 Cat (13x12cm-5x5in) brush ink crayon executed c.1947 prov. 14-May-3 Sotheby's, New York #119/R est:15000-20000

£26582 $42000 €39873 Study for cupola - final state (27x36cm-11x14in) s.d.60 brush ink oil ballpoint pen on two sheets exhib.lit. 14-Nov-2 Christie's, Rockefeller NY #122/R est:40000-60000

KLING, Wendell (20th C) American

Works on paper

£621 $1000 €932 Seated woman beseeches man in interior (48x36cm-19x14in) s. gouache. 20-Feb-3 Illustration House, New York #91/R est:1500-2000

KLINGER, E (20th C) German

£287 $465 €416 Poultry in the orchard (55x67cm-22x26in) s.indis.d. 26-May-3 Rasmussen, Copenhagen #1390/R (D.KR 3000)

KLINGER, Max (1857-1920) German

Sculpture

£4600 $7176 €6900 Bathing woman (66cm-26in) mono.i. green pat bronze marble base. 5-Nov-2 Sotheby's, London #198/R est:5000-7000

Works on paper

£449 $710 €710 Sketch (49x32cm-19x13in) s. pen bodycol. 29-Nov-2 Bassenge, Berlin #5956

£1282 $1987 €2000 Self portrait (29x19cm-11x7in) mono.i.d. 7-Dec-2 Hauswedell & Nolte, Hamburg #804/R est:2500

£1351 $2176 €2027 Marthe in Goethe's Faust (14x11cm-6x4in) s. pencil pen Indian ink prov. 26-Feb-3 Museumsbygningen, Copenhagen #65/R est:4000-6000 (D.KR 15000)

£1410 $2228 €2200 Portrait of woman (65x39cm-26x15in) s.d.1913 pencil wash. 15-Nov-2 Reiss & Sohn, Konigstein #309/R est:3000

£1644 $2581 €2400 Two nude studies (43x28cm-17x11in) s.d.83 pencil htd brush prov. 16-Apr-3 Dorotheum, Salzburg #183/R est:1600-2000

£2096 $3250 €3144 Anatomie (18x16cm-7x6in) s.i. pencil black ink prov.exhib. 29-Oct-2 Sotheby's, New York #107/R est:1500-2000
£3354 $5300 €5300 Portrait of young woman (64x49cm-25x19in) mono.d.27.8.10 col chks htd white. 29-Nov-2 Bassenge, Berlin #5955/R est:3000
£8633 $14158 €12000 Portrait study (76x71cm-30x28in) mono.i. col chk lit. 6-Jun-3 Ketterer, Munich #53/R est:12000-15000

KLINGMAN, Eric Lee (1979-) American
£1220 $2000 €1769 Bohmen vanning (137x155cm-54x61in) s.verso. 28-May-3 Sotheby's, Amsterdam #180/R est:1800-2200
£1375 $2200 €1994 Untitled - parameters (76x137cm-30x54in) s.verso. 13-May-3 Sotheby's, Tel Aviv #66/R est:1800-2200
£2438 $3900 €3535 Untitled - stretched (140x256cm-55x101in) s.verso. 13-May-3 Sotheby's, Tel Aviv #67/R est:2900-3200
£2874 $4800 €4167 Untitled - suspense (157x86cm-62x34in) s.verso. 25-Jun-3 Sotheby's, Moscow #240/R est:2200-2800
£4268 $7000 €6189 Nicole (112x178cm-44x70in) s.verso. 28-May-3 Sotheby's, Amsterdam #181/R est:2500-3000

KLINGSBOGL, Hermann (1874-1943) Austrian
£309 $500 €464 Charming still life (30x36cm-12x14in) s. 23-Jan-3 Aspire, Cleveland #17

KLINGSHIRN, Richard (1941-) German
£629 $969 €1000 Tulips (80x90cm-31x35in) s. acrylic. 26-Oct-2 Quittenbaum, Hamburg #160/R

KLINGSTEDT, Carl Gustave (attrib) (1657-1734) Swedish
Miniatures
£745 $1154 €1118 Gallant scene with monk and nun (6x8cm-2x3in) grisaille rec. gilded bronze frame. 3-Dec-2 Bukowskis, Stockholm #1197/R (S.KR 10500)

KLINKAN, Alfred (1950-) Austrian
£448 $717 €650 Angel and devil (100x70cm-39x28in) acrylic gouache paper on canvas. 11-Mar-3 Dorotheum, Vienna #238/R
£5380 $8500 €8500 Snowman (160cm-63xin) paper on canvas. 27-Nov-2 Dorotheum, Vienna #296/R est:9000-12000

KLINKENBERG, Johannes Christiaan Karel (1852-1924) Dutch
£1842 $2984 €2800 Houses along a canal (54x36cm-21x14in) s. 21-Jan-3 Christie's, Amsterdam #221/R est:2000-3000
£1911 $2981 €3000 View of town with boats (21x35cm-8x14in) s. 6-Nov-2 Vendue Huis, Gravenhage #566/R est:5000-6000
£2397 $3764 €3500 View of the Koppelpoort (32x52cm-13x20in) s. prov. 15-Apr-3 Sotheby's, Amsterdam #129/R est:4000-6000
£17123 $26884 €25000 View of the Binnenpoort, Culemborg (48x39cm-19x15in) s. 15-Apr-3 Sotheby's, Amsterdam #215/R est:20000-30000
£17610 $27119 €28000 View of Amsterdam (25x36cm-10x14in) s. panel prov. 22-Oct-2 Sotheby's, Amsterdam #151/R est:15000-20000
£24359 $37756 €38000 View of Hoorn with the Hoofdtoren (47x39cm-19x15in) s. 3-Dec-2 Sotheby's, Amsterdam #7/R est:30000-40000
£28302 $43585 €45000 De Bierksde, The Hague (40x47cm-16x19in) s. prov.exhib.lit. 23-Oct-2 Christie's, Amsterdam #114/R est:40000-60000
£34591 $53270 €55000 View of the Leuvehaven, Rotterdam (40x54cm-16x21in) s. 22-Oct-2 Sotheby's, Amsterdam #132/R est:40000-60000
£45139 $71771 €65000 View of the Magere Brug over the river Amstel, Amsterdam (39x53cm-15x21in) s. 29-Apr-3 Christie's, Amsterdam #193/R est:50000-70000

Works on paper
£700 $1092 €1050 Dogana and St. Maria della salute, Grand Canel, Venice (23x33cm-9x13in) s. W/C. 5-Nov-2 Bonhams, New Bond Street #2/R
£2778 $4417 €4000 View on a draw bridge (24x34cm-9x13in) s. pencil W/C htd white. 29-Apr-3 Christie's, Amsterdam #75/R est:5000-7000
£4777 $7452 €7500 View of Amsterdam in winter with Luther church (34x51cm-13x20in) s. W/C. 6-Nov-2 Vendue Huis, Gravenhage #567/R est:8000-10000

KLINT, Hilma af (1862-1944) Swedish
£1571 $2577 €2278 Winter landscape with farm (21x30cm-8x12in) s.d.91. 4-Jun-3 AB Stockholms Auktionsverk #2235/R est:20000-25000 (S.KR 20000)
£12766 $19787 €19149 Park scene with buildings and children playing, Stockholm (44x56cm-17x22in) s.d.89. 4-Dec-2 AB Stockholms Auktionsverk #1632/R est:80000-100000 (S.KR 180000)

KLIPPEL, Robert (1920-2001) Australian
Sculpture
£1145 $1809 €1983 Untitled (35cm-14in) init. wood. 1-Apr-3 Goodman, Sydney #55/R est:2500-5000 (A.D 3000)
£3065 $4812 €4598 No.923 (49x27x9cm-19x11x4in) painted wood prov. 15-Apr-3 Lawson Menzies, Sydney #1/R est:6000-10000 (A.D 8000)
£3815 $6028 €6609 Wooden assemblage (130cm-51in) wood. 1-Apr-3 Goodman, Sydney #52/R est:8000-16000 (A.D 10000)
£6429 $10029 €9644 No 694 (163x52x48cm-64x20x19in) wood assemblage exhib.lit. 11-Nov-2 Deutscher-Menzies, Melbourne #66/R est:20000-25000 (A.D 18000)
£6429 $10029 €9644 No 781 (142x48x48cm-56x19x19in) wood assemblage exhib.lit. 11-Nov-2 Deutscher-Menzies, Melbourne #107/R est:20000-25000 (A.D 18000)
£13571 $21171 €20357 No 437 (139x30x20cm-55x12x8in) i.d.1982 num.4/6 bronze lit. 11-Nov-2 Deutscher-Menzies, Melbourne #88/R est:30000-40000 (A.D 38000)
£16429 $25629 €24644 No 778 (187x73x91cm-74x29x36in) init.i.d. wood assemblage exhib.lit. 11-Nov-2 Deutscher-Menzies, Melbourne #25/R est:40000-60000 (A.D 46000)
£24806 $39442 €37209 Opus; metal construction (113cm-44in) welded metal exec.c.1958-59 prov.exhib. 5-May-3 Sotheby's, Melbourne #112/R est:20000-30000 (A.D 64000)
£27758 $42470 €41637 Sentinel (170cm-67in) init. grey pat. bronze. 26-Aug-2 Sotheby's, Paddington #530/R est:30000-50000 (A.D 78000)

Works on paper
£308 $489 €462 Untitled (31x22cm-12x9in) s.d.91 gouache collage. 4-Mar-3 Deutscher-Menzies, Melbourne #265/R (A.D 800)
£476 $790 €812 Untitled (8x12cm-3x5in) init.d.86 W/C. 10-Jun-3 Shapiro, Sydney #99 est:1000-1500 (A.D 1200)
£956 $1568 €1434 Abstract (37x44cm-15x17in) init.d.3/78 W/C collage. 4-Jun-3 Deutscher-Menzies, Melbourne #129/R (A.D 2400)

KLITSCH, Peter (1934-) Austrian
£633 $987 €1000 Rider in idealised landscape (44x61cm-17x24in) mono.d.77 masonite. 15-Oct-2 Dorotheum, Vienna #187/R

KLITZ, Anthony Robert (1917-) British
£260 $406 €390 Salisbury Cathedral (61x51cm-24x20in) s. 26-Mar-3 Woolley & Wallis, Salisbury #179/R

KLITZ, Tony (1917-2000) Irish/British
£633 $981 €1000 Along the liffey quays (46x36cm-18x14in) s. 24-Sep-2 De Veres Art Auctions, Dublin #121 est:800-1200
£641 $1006 €1000 Canal, Dublin (30x41cm-12x16in) s. 19-Nov-2 Whyte's, Dublin #227
£1282 $2013 €2000 Horse race (51x61cm-20x24in) s. 19-Nov-2 Whyte's, Dublin #225/R est:1500-1800
£1301 $2043 €1900 Along the Liffey with view of the four courts (48x99cm-19x39in) s. 15-Apr-3 De Veres Art Auctions, Dublin #15/R est:2000-3000
£1384 $2158 €2200 Merchant's Arch, Dublin (46x36cm-18x14in) s. i.d.1999 verso prov. 17-Sep-2 Whyte's, Dublin #2/R est:1500-2000
£1795 $2818 €2800 O'Connell Street, Dublin (36x46cm-14x18in) s.i. prov. 19-Nov-2 Whyte's, Dublin #6/R est:2000-2500
£1944 $3092 €2800 O'Connell Bridge, Dublin (51x102cm-20x40in) s. 29-Apr-3 Whyte's, Dublin #204/R est:2500-3500
£2642 $4121 €4200 Liffey, Dublin (51x102cm-20x40in) s. studio st.i.d.1977 verso. 17-Sep-2 Whyte's, Dublin #191/R est:2500-3500
£14765 $23772 €22000 Dublin's Liffey bridges (51x102cm-20x40in) s. ten prov. 18-Feb-3 Whyte's, Dublin #135/R est:20000-30000

KLIUN, Ivan (1873-1943) Russian
£11392 $17772 €18000 Composition (20x14cm-8x6in) s.d.1922 panel prov. 18-Oct-2 Dr Fritz Nagel, Stuttgart #547/R est:9000

KLODIC, Paolo (1887-1961) Italian
£284 $460 €400 Marina, Alessandretta (34x47cm-13x19in) s.d.22 board. 22-May-3 Stadion, Trieste #248

Works on paper
£780 $1264 €1100 Marina (70x100cm-28x39in) s.d.61 pastel. 22-May-3 Stadion, Trieste #333/R

KLODT VON JURGENSBURG, Michael (1832-1902) Russian
£8451 $13606 €12000 Moment of silence (35x26cm-14x10in) s.d.1891 panel. 10-May-3 Bukowskis, Helsinki #413/R est:7000-9000

Works on paper
£6827 $11060 €9899 Orthodox nun (48x25cm-19x10in) s.d.1892 W/C prov. 26-May-3 Bukowskis, Stockholm #255/R est:10000-12000 (S.KR 88000)

KLODT, Nikolai Aleksandrovich (1865-1918) Russian
£601 $938 €950 Morning sun (58x90cm-23x35in) s.d.1912. 15-Sep-2 Bukowskis, Helsinki #338/R

KLOMBEEK, Johann Bernard (1815-1893) Dutch
£21918 $34411 €32000 Figures on a path in a snow covered landscape (41x54cm-16x21in) s.d.1843. 15-Apr-3 Sotheby's, Amsterdam #159/R est:25000-35000
£47222 $75083 €68000 Travelers resting on a forest path in a wooded valley (63x83cm-25x33in) s.d.1849 panel prov. 29-Apr-3 Christie's, Amsterdam #207/R est:70000-90000

KLOMBEEK, Johann Bernard (attrib) (1815-1893) Dutch
£1117 $1777 €1676 Winter landscape with figures skating on frozen canal, Holland (47x70cm-19x28in) indis.sig. panel. 10-Mar-3 Rasmussen, Vejle #388/R est:12000-15000 (D.KR 12000)

KLOMBEEK, Johann Bernard and VERBOECKHOVEN, Eugène (19th C) Dutch
£51572 $79421 €82000 Hunters in the snow (92x123cm-36x48in) s.d.1869 prov. 22-Oct-2 Sotheby's, Amsterdam #175/R est:60000-80000

KLOOS, Cornelis (1895-1976) Dutch
Works on paper
£637 $994 €1000 Harem scene (58x39cm-23x15in) s.d.1952. 6-Nov-2 Vendue Huis, Gravenhage #166/R
£764 $1192 €1200 Circus interior (59x69cm-23x27in) s. W/C. 5-Nov-2 Vendu Notarishuis, Rotterdam #106/R

KLOSS, Gene (1903-) American
Prints
£1667 $2600 €2501 Noonday shadows (18x20cm-7x8in) s.i. etching prov.lit. 9-Nov-2 Santa Fe Art, Santa Fe #97/R est:3000-4000
£2244 $3500 €3366 Old mine of the mountains (36x25cm-14x10in) s.i. drypoint quatint prov.lit. 9-Nov-2 Santa Fe Art, Santa Fe #99/R est:4000-5000
£2404 $3750 €3606 Processional - Taos 1948 (23x36cm-9x14in) s.i. drypoint on paper prov.lit. 9-Nov-2 Santa Fe Art, Santa Fe #50/R est:3500-4500
£2724 $4250 €4086 Summer evening in New Mexico (23x30cm-9x12in) s.i. aquatint etching prov.lit. 9-Nov-2 Santa Fe Art, Santa Fe #98/R est:5500-7500
£5769 $9000 €8654 Penitente fires (36x48cm-14x19in) s.i. drypoint aquatint edition of 50. 14-Oct-2 Butterfields, San Francisco #1024/R est:2000-3000
Works on paper
£2564 $4000 €3846 Early lamp light (51x71cm-20x28in) W/C. 9-Nov-2 Altermann Galleries, Santa Fe #9

KLOSSOWSKI, Erich (1875-?) German
£900 $1386 €1350 Paysage, Provence (62x80cm-24x31in) prov. 24-Oct-2 Christie's, Kensington #188/R est:1000-1500
£1154 $1685 €1800 Provencal landscape with donkey cart (60x75cm-24x30in) s. 4-Jun-2 Karl & Faber, Munich #311/R est:3500

KLOTZ, Lenz (1925-) Swiss
£2037 $3280 €2954 Graded lines (60x70cm-24x28in) s.d.87. 9-May-3 Dobiaschofsky, Bern #275/R est:4000 (S.FR 4400)
Works on paper
£1296 $2087 €1879 Picture-sheet (51x66cm-20x26in) s.d.65 pencil dr. 9-May-3 Dobiaschofsky, Bern #256/R est:2700 (S.FR 2800)

KLOTZ, Matthias (1748-1821) German
Works on paper
£2324 $3742 €3300 Quattro ritratti di fanciulli (21x16cm-8x6in) two s. blk pencil htd white oval four. 12-May-3 Sotheby's, Milan #71/R est:2000-3000

KLUCIK, Peter (1953-) Czechoslovakian
£788 $1150 €1182 Virgin forest (120x90cm-47x35in) 4-Jun-2 SOGA, Bratislava #272/R est:48000 (SL.K 50000)

KLUGE, Constantine (1912-) French
£318 $497 €500 Place avec fontaine (55x46cm-22x18in) s. 6-Nov-2 Claude Boisgirard, Paris #26
£400 $632 €600 L'Institut (61x81cm-24x32in) s. 7-Apr-3 Bonhams, Bath #54/R
£796 $1242 €1250 Pommiers en fleurs (60x73cm-24x29in) s. 6-Nov-2 Claude Boisgirard, Paris #27/R
£823 $1300 €1300 Parisian scene (39x61cm-15x24in) s. 29-Nov-2 Schloss Ahlden, Ahlden #1348/R
£1226 $1900 €1839 Place de la Concorde (54x65cm-21x26in) s. 2-Oct-2 Christie's, Rockefeller NY #765/R est:2500-3500
£1582 $2500 €2373 Paris street at night (51x61cm-20x24in) s. 17-Nov-2 CRN Auctions, Cambridge #7/R
£1700 $2635 €2550 Le quai du Louvre (61x74cm-24x29in) s. 5-Dec-2 Christie's, Kensington #77/R est:1500-2000
£7097 $11000 €10646 L' Avenue Marceau (74x91cm-29x36in) s. i.on stretcher prov. 16-Jul-2 Arthur James, Florida #103
£9032 $14000 €13548 Le Pont Neuf (114x196cm-45x77in) s. i.on stretcher prov. 16-Jul-2 Arthur James, Florida #104

KLUGE, Gustav (1947-) German
£6500 $10595 €9750 Franziskus, Vianney (191x230cm-75x91in) init.i.verso painted 1987 prov.exhib. 3-Feb-3 Sotheby's, Olympia #183/R est:4000-6000

KLUMB, Andre (1925-) French
£496 $804 €700 Fleurs (73x60cm-29x24in) s. 26-May-3 Joron-Derem, Paris #56

KLUSKA, Johann (1904-c.1973) German
£321 $497 €500 Still life with carp and vegetables (45x49cm-18x19in) s.d.1933. 7-Dec-2 Van Ham, Cologne #285/R

KLUYVER, Pieter Lodewijk Francisco (1816-1900) Dutch
£855 $1386 €1300 Hunter walking on a forest path (29x21cm-11x8in) s. panel. 21-Jan-3 Christie's, Amsterdam #18/R est:1000-1500
£1401 $2158 €2200 Winter landscape with traveller on a path (27x26cm-11x10in) s. panel. 3-Sep-2 Christie's, Amsterdam #119/R est:2000-3000
£2431 $4010 €3500 Woodgatherers on a frozen river (75x64cm-30x25in) s. 1-Jul-3 Christie's, Amsterdam #12/R est:3000-5000

KLYN, Willem (1892-1961) Dutch
£526 $853 €800 View of Ransdorp (68x72cm-27x28in) s.d.1943. 21-Jan-3 Christie's, Amsterdam #294

KMELUCK, Wassyl (1903-) ?
£1218 $1912 €1900 Girl in red dress (55x38cm-22x15in) s.d.48 prov. 12-Dec-2 Rabourdin & Choppin de Janvry, Paris #163/R est:2200
£1552 $2483 €2250 Petit Bar-mitzvah (73x50cm-29x20in) s. 12-Mar-3 Rabourdin & Choppin de Janvry, Paris #78/R

KMETTY, Janos (1889-1975) Hungarian
£1479 $2293 €2219 Houses with red roofs (43x35cm-17x14in) s. 6-Dec-2 Kieselbach, Budapest #172/R (H.F 550000)
£3227 $5002 €4841 View of Szentendre (45x60cm-18x24in) s. canvas on cardboard. 6-Dec-2 Kieselbach, Budapest #177/R (H.F 1200000)
£4841 $7503 €7262 Summer afternoon in Szentendre (50x70cm-20x28in) s. cardboard. 6-Dec-2 Kieselbach, Budapest #145/R (H.F 1800000)
£6707 $10462 €9725 Still life with apple and jug (32x44cm-13x17in) s. board prov.exhib. 12-Apr-3 Mu Terem Galeria, Budapest #21/R est:1500000 (H.F 2400000)
£7825 $12206 €11346 Painter resting (46x59cm-18x23in) s. 12-Apr-3 Mu Terem Galeria, Budapest #202/R est:1800000 (H.F 2800000)
£10219 $15840 €15329 Plan of the fresco (60x87cm-24x34in) s. cardboard. 6-Dec-2 Kieselbach, Budapest #80/R (H.F 3800000)
£21941 $35105 €32912 Hilly landscape with rays of light and houses (67x77cm-26x30in) s. 16-May-3 Kieselbach, Budapest #38/R (H.F 7500000)
Works on paper
£1816 $2834 €2633 Roots of Szentendre (39x49cm-15x19in) s. pastel. 12-Apr-3 Mu Terem Galeria, Budapest #194/R est:500000 (H.F 650000)

KMIT, Michael (1910-1981) Russian
£364 $571 €546 Self portrait (33x23cm-13x9in) board. 15-Apr-3 Lawson Menzies, Sydney #158/R (A.D 950)
£571 $886 €857 Still life with squash (41x52cm-16x20in) s. i.verso board. 29-Oct-2 Lawson Menzies, Sydney #11/R (A.D 1600)
£902 $1435 €1353 Cogito ergo sum (86x54cm-34x21in) s.d.1954 board. 3-Mar-3 Lawson Menzies, Sydney #411 est:2500-3500 (A.D 2400)
£1912 $3136 €2868 Mardi gras at Luna Park (59x89cm-23x35in) s.d.67 board. 4-Jun-3 Deutscher-Menzies, Melbourne #355/R est:3000-5000 (A.D 4800)
Works on paper
£645 $981 €968 Cassandra (63x34cm-25x13in) s.d.79 synthetic polymer paint board. 28-Aug-2 Deutscher-Menzies, Melbourne #364/R (A.D 1800)

KNAB, Ferdinand (1834-1902) German
£1013 $1570 €1600 Landscape with water near Rome at sunset (85x65cm-33x26in) s.d. 25-Sep-2 Neumeister, Munich #624/R est:1200
£1732 $2684 €2598 Landscape in evening (81x67cm-32x26in) s.d.1884. 24-Sep-2 Koller, Zurich #6557/R est:5000-8000 (S.FR 4000)

KNAPP, Charles W (1822-1900) American

£290 $450 €435 Sea at Agua Quieta, Mexico (20x25cm-8x10in) s. i.verso board. 7-Dec-2 Neal Auction Company, New Orleans #474
£1786 $2750 €2679 View of Bear Mountain (46x81cm-18x32in) s. 24-Oct-2 Shannon's, Milford #222/R est:2500-3500
£1935 $3000 €2903 View of a forest clearing and brook (36x56cm-14x22in) s. 2-Nov-2 North East Auctions, Portsmouth #50/R est:3000-4000
£2188 $3500 €3282 Rocky brook within wooded clearing (56x36cm-22x14in) s. 16-May-3 York Town, York #1013 est:2700-3200

KNAPP, F V (?) ?

£2158 $3453 €3000 Flower still life (40x30cm-16x12in) s. panel two. 17-May-3 Lempertz, Koln #1417/R est:5000

KNAPP, N Woodbury (?) American

£685 $1000 €1028 Pines (48x33cm-19x13in) s.d.15 canvasboard. 3-Nov-1 North East Auctions, Portsmouth #232/R

KNAPTON, George (attrib) (1698-1778) British

£2250 $3600 €3263 Portrait of Richard Fitzwilliam, the 7th viscount (76x64cm-30x25in) i. 17-May-3 New Orleans Auction, New Orleans #1065/R est:3000-5000
£5000 $8300 €7500 Portrait of Margaret, Lady Conyers (74x62cm-29x24in) prov. 12-Jun-3 Sotheby's, London #64/R est:6000-8000

KNAPTON, George (circle) (1698-1778) British

£21000 $33180 €31500 Portrait of Eleanor Savage wearing pink silk dress (77x63cm-30x25in) i. prov. 26-Nov-2 Christie's, London #25/R est:3000-5000

KNAUPP, Werner (1936-) German

Works on paper

£345 $545 €500 Vulcano (81x100cm-32x39in) s.i.d. verso biro canvas on masonite prov. 2-Apr-3 Dr Fritz Nagel, Stuttgart #9127/R
£347 $549 €500 Head 23.7.79 (54x74cm-21x29in) s.d.23.7.79 gouache. 26-Apr-3 Dr Lehr, Berlin #280/R

KNAUS, Ludwig (1829-1910) German

£5031 $7748 €8000 Der spaziergang (34x28cm-13x11in) s.d.1850 prov. 23-Oct-2 Christie's, Amsterdam #92/R est:8000-12000

Works on paper

£443 $700 €700 African (47x28cm-19x11in) s.d.1870 chl htd white lit. 29-Nov-2 Schloss Ahlden, Ahlden #1190/R

KNEBEL, Franz (jnr) (1809-1877) Swiss

£2690 $4250 €4035 Roman square with figures by a fountain (25x38cm-10x15in) s.d.1864. 18-Nov-2 Winter Associates, Plainville #175/R
£40559 $67734 €58000 Vue de Rome (110x180cm-43x71in) s. 27-Jun-3 Claude Aguttes, Neuilly #24/R est:30000-40000

KNECHT, Fred E (1934-) Swiss

£437 $638 €656 Untitled (100x70cm-39x28in) s. 4-Jun-2 Germann, Zurich #782 (S.FR 1000)
£437 $638 €656 Untitled - Station Road, Zurich (70x100cm-28x39in) s. 4-Jun-2 Germann, Zurich #783/R (S.FR 1000)

KNEE, Howard (1899-?) Irish

Works on paper

£356 $556 €520 Dunmore East, Co Waterford (26x37cm-10x15in) s. W/C. 8-Apr-3 James Adam, Dublin #45/R

KNEIPP, Georg (1793-1862) German

£2060 $3193 €3090 Still life with flowers, fruit and bird's nest (53x42cm-21x17in) s.d.1829 panel. 3-Oct-2 Koller, Zurich #3124/R est:5000-7000 (S.FR 4800)
£3185 $4904 €5000 Still life with grapes on a forest ground. Still life with grapes by a pond (58x45cm-23x18in) one s.d.1840 one s. panel pair. 3-Sep-2 Christie's, Amsterdam #114/R est:6000-8000

KNELL, Adolphus (fl.1860-1890) British

£320 $534 €464 Seascape with shipping, figures in rowing boat (28x36cm-11x14in) s. 20-Jun-3 Keys, Aylsham #670
£400 $620 €600 Shipping becalmed at dusk (15x23cm-6x9in) s. board. 31-Oct-2 Christie's, Kensington #535
£750 $1140 €1125 Fishermen casting nets, three masted vessels beyond (15x19cm-6x7in) s. board. 15-Aug-2 Bonhams, New Bond Street #305
£750 $1170 €1125 Shipping in a swell off a coast (32x46cm-13x18in) s. board. 26-Mar-3 Hamptons Fine Art, Godalming #195/R
£2800 $4340 €4200 Merchantman and other shipping running in to port at dusk (48x62cm-19x24in) s. board. 31-Oct-2 Christie's, Kensington #532/R est:1000-1500
£4500 $7155 €6750 Fishing and other boats off the coast (48x74cm-19x29in) s. pair. 19-Mar-3 John Nicholson, Haslemere #1202/R est:5000-7500

KNELL, William Adolphus (1805-1875) British

£850 $1386 €1233 Moonlit harbour (25x46cm-10x18in) s. 16-Jul-3 Sotheby's, Olympia #13/R
£1056 $1701 €1500 Ships by moonlight (22x30cm-9x12in) s. board. 10-May-3 Hans Stahl, Toestorf #82/R est:1500
£1100 $1705 €1650 Shipping at sunset. Ship becalmed on a moonlit sea (13cm-5in circular) s. board pair. 26-Sep-2 Mellors & Kirk, Nottingham #674/R est:800-1200
£1300 $2015 €1950 Shipping at sunset. Shipping by moonlight (12x30cm-5x12in) s. panel pair. 26-Sep-2 Mellors & Kirk, Nottingham #673/R est:800-1200
£1550 $2418 €2248 Fleet at anchor (12x22cm-5x9in) s.d.1878. 27-Mar-3 Neales, Nottingham #1062/R est:800-1200
£1600 $2656 €2320 Shipping, dawn (20x30cm-8x12in) s. 10-Jun-3 David Lay, Penzance #376/R est:2000-2400
£2400 $3768 €3600 Hay barge. Shipping by moonlight (12x30cm-5x12in) s. panel pair. 16-Dec-2 Sotheby's, Olympia #45/R est:2000-3000
£2700 $4509 €3915 Leaving port (55x72cm-22x28in) 18-Jun-3 Sotheby's, Olympia #59/R est:2000-3000

Works on paper

£850 $1352 €1275 Close hauled RYS cutter (28x39cm-11x15in) i.verso W/C. 26-Feb-3 Cheffins Grain & Comins, Cambridge #488/R
£880 $1390 €1320 Sailing vessels. Fishing boats in a squall (23x46cm-9x18in) s. W/C pair. 18-Dec-2 Mallams, Oxford #527/R

KNELL, William Adolphus (attrib) (1805-1875) British

£1600 $2432 €2400 Fishing off the Fort Perch Rock, Liverpool. Running into Ramsgate (50x60cm-20x24in) pair. 15-Aug-2 Bonhams, New Bond Street #315/R est:1200-1800
£3200 $5216 €4640 Ship at sea (45x61cm-18x24in) 16-Jul-3 Sotheby's, Olympia #24/R est:1000-1500

Works on paper

£1000 $1590 €1500 Shipping at Spithead in choppy seas (22x34cm-9x13in) i.mount W/C. 29-Apr-3 Rowley Fine Art, Newmarket #426/R est:500-700

KNELL, William Callcott (19th C) British

£360 $576 €540 Fishing boats off Brixham (19x39cm-7x15in) s. i.d.1872 verso. 13-May-3 Bonhams, Knightsbridge #144/R
£440 $700 €660 Morning vessels of the (21x40cm-8x16in) s. d.1877 verso. 29-Apr-3 Sworder & Son, Bishops Stortford #371/R
£650 $1086 €943 Evening off the Dutch coast (19x39cm-7x15in) s.d.1871 s.i.d.verso. 26-Jun-3 Mellors & Kirk, Nottingham #908/R
£900 $1395 €1350 In the Channel (46x82cm-18x32in) 31-Oct-2 Christie's, Kensington #546/R
£1236 $2051 €1792 Summer's morning on the French coast (30x56cm-12x22in) s. indis.d.verso. 16-Jun-3 Lilla Bukowskis, Stockholm #714 est:8000-10000 (S.KR 16000)
£1400 $2240 €2100 Paddle steamer and fishing boats in choppy seas (30x50cm-12x20in) one s.d.1859 pair. 11-Mar-3 David Duggleby, Scarborough #255/R est:1200-1800
£1500 $2430 €2250 Salvaging the wreck (46x81cm-18x32in) s.d.1876. 21-May-3 Christie's, Kensington #600/R est:1500-2000
£1500 $2505 €2175 Fishing boats in heavy seas off port (31x61cm-12x24in) s.d.1873. 18-Jun-3 Sotheby's, Olympia #58/R est:1500-2000
£3000 $4650 €4500 Fishing boats in close quarters off the coast (61x91cm-24x36in) s.d.1858. 31-Oct-2 Christie's, Kensington #552/R est:1200-1800

Works on paper

£550 $891 €825 Ships of the Blue Squadron lying in Spithead (26x45cm-10x18in) s.d.1854 pencil W/C. 21-May-3 Christie's, Kensington #435/R
£600 $954 €900 Calm breeze (33x49cm-13x19in) W/C. 4-Mar-3 Bonhams, Knightsbridge #234/R

KNELL, William Callcott (attrib) (19th C) British

£6400 $10688 €9280 Fishing boats paying out a drift net (74x129cm-29x51in) bears sig d.1853. 17-Jun-3 Anderson & Garland, Newcastle #451/R est:2000-3500

KNELLER (17/18th C) British

£2400 $3744 €3600 Portrait of a lady of the Needham Family (76x62cm-30x24in) feigned oval. 14-Apr-3 Hamilton Osborne King, Dublin #1490/R est:1000-1500

KNELLER, Sir Godfrey (1646-1723) British
£5389 $9000 €7814 Portrait of Tatianna (127x102cm-50x40in) i.verso prov. 21-Jun-3 Charlton Hall, Columbia #220/R est:5000-8000
£13000 $20670 €19500 Portrait of a lady, wearing satin gown and a green cloak, with a dog at her feet (175x109cm-69x43in) 19-Mar-3 Sotheby's, London #39/R est:8000-12000
£13141 $20500 €19712 Sir Charles Sedley (127x102cm-50x40in) s. prov. 28-Mar-3 Aspire, Cleveland #7/R est:20000-30000

KNELLER, Sir Godfrey (attrib) (1646-1723) British
£3045 $4780 €4750 First Viscount of Folkestone (77x63cm-30x25in) 19-Nov-2 Castellana, Madrid #46/R est:5000
£4043 $6266 €6065 Portrait of a nobleman (100x125cm-39x49in) 4-Dec-2 AB Stockholms Auktionsverk #1992/R est:70000-80000 (S.KR 57000)
Works on paper
£2174 $3565 €3000 Portrait de jeune enfant (17x12cm-7x5in) sanguine prov. 27-May-3 Palais de Beaux Arts, Brussels #459/R est:2300-3000

KNELLER, Sir Godfrey (circle) (1646-1723) British
£8500 $13260 €12750 Portrait of King George I, seated in garter robes (225x141cm-89x56in) prov. 7-Nov-2 Christie's, Kensington #13/R est:5000-8000
£8500 $13940 €12750 Portrait of a boy, with a greyhound (124x99cm-49x39in) prov. 29-May-3 Christie's, Kensington #23/R est:2000-3000

KNELLER, Sir Godfrey (school) (1646-1723) British
£5449 $8500 €8174 Portrait of a lady in blue satin dress seated with a book (124x102cm-49x40in) i.on stretcher prov. 20-Sep-2 New Orleans Auction, New Orleans #1020/R est:5000-8000
£7000 $10920 €10500 Portrait of Lucy Sambrook (127x102cm-50x40in) prov. 9-Oct-2 Woolley & Wallis, Salisbury #337/R est:1500-2500

KNELLER, Sir Godfrey (studio) (1646-1723) British
£755 $1162 €1200 Portrait presume de Charles III (14x11cm-6x4in) copper oval. 25-Oct-2 Tajan, Paris #168/R
£5200 $8632 €7800 Portrait of Sophia Colston in a white dress (76x63cm-30x25in) 10-Jun-3 Christie's, London #20/R est:3000-5000
£7800 $12324 €11700 Portrait of two ladies (182x149cm-72x59in) 28-Nov-2 Sotheby's, London #165/R est:3000-4000
£8000 $13040 €11600 Portrait of the Hon Lucy Sherard, Duchess of Rutland (124x102cm-49x40in) 21-Jul-3 Sotheby's, London #4/R est:3000-5000
£11218 $17500 €16827 Mrs fisher of Packington, Warrick (127x102cm-50x40in) prov. 28-Mar-3 Aspire, Cleveland #8/R est:10000-15000

KNEWSTUB, Walter John (1831-1906) British
Works on paper
£900 $1404 €1350 Portrait of a child (26x21cm-10x8in) mono. W/C gum arabic prov. 26-Mar-3 Sotheby's, Olympia #151/R

KNGWARREYE, Emily (c.1916-1996) Australian
£2299 $3609 €3449 Yam 1995 (60x46cm-24x18in) acrylic. 15-Apr-3 Lawson Menzies, Sydney #113/R est:7000-10000 (A.D 6000)
£6897 $10828 €10346 Yam dreaming (193x116cm-76x46in) s.verso acrylic. 15-Apr-3 Lawson Menzies, Sydney #97/R est:16000-25000 (A.D 18000)
Works on paper
£843 $1323 €1265 Awelye (76x56cm-30x22in) synthetic polymer on paper. 15-Apr-3 Lawson Menzies, Sydney #114/R est:2000-3000 (A.D 2200)
£2094 $3245 €3141 Yam dreaming (93x62cm-37x24in) synthetic polymer paint linen prov. 3-Dec-2 Shapiro, Sydney #200/R est:6000-9000 (A.D 5800)
£4215 $6280 €6323 Yam country (151x91cm-59x36in) synthetic polymer paint on canvas executed 1993 prov. 27-Aug-2 Christie's, Melbourne #212/R est:8000-12000 (A.D 11000)
£5081 $8029 €7367 Untitled 1994 (135x180cm-53x71in) polyvinylacetate on canvas. 22-Jul-3 Lawson Menzies, Sydney #54/R est:15000-25000 (A.D 12500)
£5957 $9233 €8936 Yam country (121x91cm-48x36in) i.verso synthetic polymer paint canvas prov. 3-Dec-2 Shapiro, Sydney #150/R est:18000-25000 (A.D 16500)
£15278 $23681 €22917 Anatye, bush potato (151x90cm-59x35in) s.i.verso synthetic polymer paint canvas prov. 3-Dec-2 Shapiro, Sydney #167/R est:50000-70000 (A.D 42320)
£17625 $26261 €26438 Untitled (150x90cm-59x35in) s.i.verso synthetic polymer paint on canvas prov. 27-Aug-2 Christie's, Melbourne #87/R est:25000-35000 (A.D 46000)
£50000 $77000 €75000 Muna everything (214x121cm-84x48in) s.i. synthetic polymer executed 1991 prov. 8-Sep-2 Sotheby's, Melbourne #17/R est:120000-180000 (A.D 140000)

KNGWARREYE, Tommy Jones (20th C) Australian
£575 $902 €863 Wallaby dreaming 2000 (91x90cm-36x35in) s.verso acrylic on linen. 15-Apr-3 Lawson Menzies, Sydney #105/R est:1700-2200 (A.D 1500)

KNIE, Rolf (jnr) (1949-) Swiss
Works on paper
£348 $539 €522 Untitled - clowns (24x32cm-9x13in) s.d.1987 mixed media. 9-Dec-2 Philippe Schuler, Zurich #3564 (S.FR 800)

KNIEP, Christoph Heinrich (1755-1825) German
Works on paper
£2000 $3120 €3000 Arcadian landscape with a tomb, women in classical dress and sheep in the foreground (61x81cm-24x32in) s. pen ink. 9-Apr-3 Bonhams, New Bond Street #124 est:450-600

KNIGHT, A Roland (19th C) British
£300 $456 €450 Hooked trout (18x13cm-7x5in) s. 14-Aug-2 Andrew Hartley, Ilkley #671
£360 $572 €540 River landscape with salmon (30x45cm-12x18in) s. 6-Mar-3 Clevedon Sale Rooms #116
£880 $1399 €1320 Hooked salmon on the Teign (42x55cm-17x22in) s. board. 4-Mar-3 Bearnes, Exeter #430/R
£900 $1494 €1305 Hooked pike. Pike on a line (13x17cm-5x7in) s. board two. 12-Jun-3 Christie's, Kensington #168/R
£1400 $2212 €2100 Pike coming to the gaff (41x56cm-16x22in) indis sig. 28-Nov-2 Christie's, Kensington #5/R est:1500-2000

KNIGHT, Charles (19/20th C) British
Works on paper
£300 $471 €450 View of Chartres Cathedral (30x44cm-12x17in) s. W/C over pencil. 15-Apr-3 Bonhams, Knowle #91
£380 $604 €570 Rocky shore and open sea (25x36cm-10x14in) s. W/C. 29-Apr-3 Gorringes, Lewes #2181
£500 $795 €750 Thunderclouds (28x36cm-11x14in) s. W/C. 29-Apr-3 Gorringes, Lewes #2182
£1100 $1749 €1650 Chancellors Ridge, Glencoe (41x64cm-16x25in) s. W/C exhib. 29-Apr-3 Gorringes, Lewes #2085
£1200 $1908 €1800 Mousehole, Cornwall (25x38cm-10x15in) W/C. 29-Apr-3 Gorringes, Lewes #2086
£1200 $1908 €1800 Long pool on the Lyn (38x53cm-15x21in) s. W/C exhib. 29-Apr-3 Gorringes, Lewes #2087

KNIGHT, Charles Parsons (1829-1897) British
£629 $969 €1000 Fishing fleet off coast (51x76cm-20x30in) s. 26-Oct-2 Quittenbaum, Hamburg #26/R
£1338 $2154 €1900 Stormy seascape with boat (27x35cm-11x14in) s. board. 7-May-3 Michael Zeller, Lindau #762/R est:1200
Works on paper
£500 $790 €750 St Govens, Pembrokeshire (32x49cm-13x19in) init.i.d.53 W/C htd bodycol. 26-Nov-2 Bonhams, Knightsbridge #53/R

KNIGHT, Charles Robert (1874-1953) American
Sculpture
£1818 $2800 €2727 Seated puma (17cm-7in) s.num.Q281 green pat bronze st.f.Gorham Co. 4-Sep-2 Christie's, Rockefeller NY #354/R est:2000-3000

KNIGHT, Dame Laura (1877-1970) British
£4600 $7130 €6900 Portrait of a young woman (152x124cm-60x49in) s. 26-Sep-2 Lane, Penzance #205/R est:4000-5000
Works on paper
£260 $408 €390 All hail, Perdita! (20x16cm-8x6in) s.i. pen ink. 10-Dec-2 Cheffins Grain & Comins, Cambridge #346/R
£260 $419 €390 Portrait of Joe Craston (23x14cm-9x6in) s. red chk. 15-Jan-3 Cheffins Grain & Comins, Cambridge #409/R
£300 $483 €450 Circus dwarves (26x20cm-10x8in) s. pencil W/C. 15-Jan-3 Cheffins Grain & Comins, Cambridge #396/R
£300 $501 €435 Between performances (30x40cm-12x16in) pencil col chk prov. 26-Jun-3 Mellors & Kirk, Nottingham #843
£320 $496 €480 Sketch for a ballerina (33x21cm-13x8in) init. pencil. 24-Sep-2 Bonhams, Knightsbridge #173/R
£320 $496 €480 Head of a horse (30x23cm-12x9in) s. pencil. 3-Dec-2 Bonhams, Knightsbridge #223/R
£320 $502 €480 Skaters (35x24cm-14x9in) s. chl. 10-Dec-2 Lane, Penzance #47
£400 $668 €580 Romanies, hay bluff (19x22cm-7x9in) s.i.d.1922 ink W/C. 19-Jun-3 Lane, Penzance #187
£420 $689 €630 Circus juggler (23x15cm-9x6in) s. chl. prov. 5-Jun-3 Amersham Auction Rooms, UK #212

£450 $711 €675 Acrobats. Elephant (35x25cm-14x10in) s. black chk double-sided. 2-Dec-2 Bonhams, Bath #43
£500 $785 €750 Actors (26x36cm-10x14in) init. indis i. chl dr. 15-Apr-3 Bonhams, Knightsbridge #13/R
£520 $816 €780 Standing figure of a semi nude woman (43x25cm-17x10in) s. ink dr. 10-Dec-2 Lane, Penzance #218
£520 $863 €780 View of Spanish dancers (29x24cm-11x9in) s.29 etching aquatint. 10-Jun-3 Sworder & Son, Bishops Stortford #537/R
£600 $966 €900 Magenta (34x25cm-13x10in) s.i. chl. 14-Jan-3 Bonhams, Knightsbridge #207/R
£620 $1011 €930 Ballerina (33x23cm-13x9in) s. pencil dr. 14-Feb-3 Keys, Aylsham #468/R
£650 $1034 €975 Flannigan and Allen (28x20cm-11x8in) s. chl. 6-Mar-3 Scarborough Perry Fine Arts, Hove #533
£680 $1081 €1020 Four circus horses with decorative bridles and feathered head-dresses (21x18cm-8x7in) s. black chalk. 19-Mar-3 Rupert Toovey, Partridge Green #192/R
£700 $1092 €1050 Seated figures in a cloak (34x24cm-13x9in) s. chl. 15-Oct-2 Bonhams, Knightsbridge #127/R
£720 $1123 €1080 Chorus The Angels Bethlehem (30x24cm-12x9in) init.i. conte prov. 25-Mar-3 Bonhams, New Bond Street #34/R
£750 $1170 €1125 Study of Ballerina. Dancing study (33x23cm-13x9in) s. init.verso chl double-sided. 20-Sep-2 Richardson & Smith, Whitby #95
£750 $1163 €1125 Ringmaster (36x26cm-14x10in) s. pencil. 3-Dec-2 Bonhams, Knightsbridge #225/R
£800 $1264 €1200 Carmo's Circus, Southsea (19x14cm-7x6in) s.i.d.1929 pencil crayon. 27-Nov-2 Sotheby's, Olympia #21/R
£800 $1248 €1200 Backstage at the Old Vic - The Richards (36x24cm-14x9in) s.i. chl. 25-Mar-3 Bonhams, New Bond Street #38/R
£850 $1343 €1275 Circus ring (26x35cm-10x14in) s. pencil. 27-Nov-2 Sotheby's, Olympia #15/R
£900 $1404 €1350 Portrait of Ella Napper standing (33x23cm-13x9in) pencil. 17-Sep-2 Bonhams, Knightsbridge #265/R
£950 $1473 €1425 Circus ring (35x51cm-14x20in) s. pencil. 3-Dec-2 Bonhams, Knightsbridge #226/R
£1000 $1590 €1500 Dancing couples (28x20cm-11x8in) s.i.d.1925 W/C pencil prov. 19-Mar-3 John Nicholson, Haslemere #1085/R est:500-1000
£1100 $1716 €1650 Flannagan and Allen (28x20cm-11x8in) s.i. chl. 27-Mar-3 Christie's, Kensington #253/R est:500-700
£1200 $1848 €1800 At the circus (34x23cm-13x9in) s. crayon. 5-Sep-2 Christie's, Kensington #524/R est:1200-1800
£1200 $1872 €1800 Portrait of Francis Jack Chown, 2nd lieut, in Royal Flying Corps (35x24cm-14x9in) init. pencil. 25-Mar-3 Bonhams, New Bond Street #36/R est:1500-2000
£1374 $2171 €2061 Carmos circus, Hampstead Heath (14x34cm-6x13in) s. W/C pasteboard. 7-Apr-3 Shapiro, Sydney #420/R est:3000-5000 (A.D 3600)
£1400 $2310 €2030 Portrait of Joe Craxton (23x14cm-9x6in) s.i. red chalk prov. 3-Jul-3 Christie's, Kensington #247/R est:700-1000
£1500 $2460 €2250 Ballet scenes (33x21cm-13x8in) one s.i. one init.i. pencil pair. 3-Jun-3 Sotheby's, Olympia #19/R est:1500-2000
£2400 $3792 €3600 Ready for entree (36x26cm-14x10in) s. pencil crayon. 27-Nov-2 Sotheby's, Olympia #20/R est:700-900
£3800 $5890 €5700 Dovecote (101x67cm-40x26in) s.d.1957 chl W/C exhib. 3-Dec-2 Bonhams, New Bond Street #29/R est:4000-6000
£4000 $6360 €6000 Jo Maxmason in his dressing room (36x46cm-14x18in) i.d.46 crayon W/C. 26-Feb-3 Sotheby's, Olympia #178/R est:2000-3000
£4400 $6864 €6600 Dressing room (51x38cm-20x15in) s. pastel W/C. 12-Sep-2 Sotheby's, Olympia #44/R est:2500-3500
£4400 $6864 €6600 Tattenhan Corner (39x51cm-15x20in) s.d.1935 W/C exhib. 26-Mar-3 Hamptons Fine Art, Godalming #55/R est:1500-2500
£5000 $7800 €7500 Waiting in the wings (37x27cm-15x11in) s.d.1920 pencil W/C gouache prov. 18-Sep-2 Dreweatt Neate, Newbury #60/R est:1500-2000
£5800 $9570 €8410 Portrait of Juanita (35x25cm-14x10in) s.i. pastel. 3-Jul-3 Christie's, Kensington #244/R est:2000-3000
£8500 $13175 €12750 Looking in the mirror (56x38cm-22x15in) s. W/C over gouache pencil. 3-Dec-2 Bonhams, New Bond Street #27/R est:3000-5000
£8500 $13855 €12325 Fantail pigeons, bees, goat with kids, and life guards (25x35cm-10x14in) all s. pencil chl. six. 21-Jul-3 Sotheby's, London #548/R est:4000-6000
£8800 $13640 €13200 Before the performance (56x38cm-22x15in) s.d.1960 chl col wash. 3-Dec-2 Bonhams, New Bond Street #28/R est:3000-5000
£80000 $131200 €116000 On the cliffs (74x53cm-29x21in) s. W/C gouache prov. 4-Jun-3 Sotheby's, London #5/R est:30000-50000

KNIGHT, Daniel Ridgway (1839-1924) American

£22152 $35000 €35000 Sharing secrets (65x54cm-26x21in) s.i. 27-Nov-2 Blanchet, Paris #42/R
£48387 $75000 €72581 Beneath the apple tree (77x63cm-30x25in) s.i. prov. 29-Oct-2 Sotheby's, New York #127/R est:100000-150000
£51613 $80000 €77420 Resting in the garden (61x51cm-24x20in) s.i. 29-Oct-2 Sotheby's, New York #129/R est:80000-120000
£70968 $110000 €106452 Woman with a watering can by the river (56x65cm-22x26in) s.i. 30-Oct-2 Christie's, Rockefeller NY #56/R est:120000-160000
£89172 $140000 €133758 Marie (81x65cm-32x26in) s.i. 20-Nov-2 Christie's, Los Angeles #41/R est:120000-180000
£90323 $140000 €135485 Maid in her garden (83x67cm-33x26in) s. prov. 4-Dec-2 Sotheby's, New York #31/R est:80000-120000
£94937 $150000 €142406 Tying up the hollyhocks (92x73cm-36x29in) s. indis d. painted c.1885. 23-Apr-3 Christie's, Rockefeller NY #46/R est:150000-250000
£116129 $180000 €174194 Maria and Madeleine fishing (66x82cm-26x32in) s.i. 29-Oct-2 Sotheby's, New York #126/R est:150000-200000

Works on paper

£2800 $4368 €4200 Peasant girl leaning on a rake (35x26cm-14x10in) s.d.1881 W/C. 9-Oct-2 Woolley & Wallis, Salisbury #139/R est:800-1200

KNIGHT, Edward Loxton (1905-) British

£320 $496 €480 In the Chilterns (26x44cm-10x17in) s. tempera on board. 3-Dec-2 Bonhams, Knightsbridge #165/R
£750 $1163 €1125 Downs over Seaford (40x64cm-16x25in) s. tempera on board. 3-Dec-2 Bonhams, Knightsbridge #164/R
£900 $1395 €1350 View of St. Tropez (58x74cm-23x29in) s. tempera on board. 3-Dec-2 Bonhams, Knightsbridge #99

Works on paper

£300 $456 €450 Mediterranean landscape (50x75cm-20x30in) s. gouache. 4-Jul-2 Mellors & Kirk, Nottingham #803
£350 $546 €525 Parkland landscape (49x74cm-19x29in) s. W/C htd bodycol. 12-Sep-2 Sotheby's, Olympia #106/R

KNIGHT, Edwin H (20th C) British?

£600 $948 €900 Cracker a chestnut hunter in a paddock. Belinda a brown hunter in a paddock (41x46cm-16x18in) s.d.1938 pair. 28-Nov-2 Christie's, Kensington #152/R

KNIGHT, Ellis Cordelia (1757-1837) British

Works on paper

£550 $869 €825 Palace at Capodimonte, Naples (34x48cm-13x19in) i. i.verso pen ink W/C over pencil. 28-Nov-2 Sotheby's, London #240/R
£650 $1027 €975 Church of San Giovanni in Laterano Rome (33x51cm-13x20in) i. W/C over pencil. 28-Nov-2 Sotheby's, London #237/R
£650 $1027 €975 Chigi palace and church at Ariccia (24x36cm-9x14in) i.verso pen ink wash. 28-Nov-2 Sotheby's, London #239/R
£650 $1027 €975 Temple of peace and church of Santa Francesca Romana seen from the Palatine Hill, Rome (32x48cm-13x19in) i. pen ink W/C over pencil. 28-Nov-2 Sotheby's, London #242/R
£780 $1287 €1131 View near Posilippo (36x52cm-14x20in) one i. pencil ink W/C two. 2-Jul-3 Sotheby's, Olympia #246/R
£900 $1423 €1350 Figure sketching ruins in the Roman campagna (46x61cm-18x24in) pen ink W/C over pencil. 28-Nov-2 Sotheby's, London #241/R est:500-700
£1100 $1737 €1650 Terme di Tito, Rome (33x51cm-13x20in) i. pen ink W/C over pencil. 28-Nov-2 Sotheby's, London #238/R est:600-800

KNIGHT, Ernest (20th C) British?

£217 $339 €363 Brixham light (41x51cm-16x20in) s. i.verso. 13-Apr-3 Levis, Calgary #485/R (C.D 500)

KNIGHT, George (19th C) British

£550 $919 €798 Off Whitby (39x65cm-15x26in) s.i. 19-Jun-3 Lane, Penzance #412
£650 $1014 €975 Shipping in open sea (53x76cm-21x30in) s. 10-Sep-2 Bonhams, Knightsbridge #226/R
£850 $1352 €1275 Off the coast. Bracing wind (23x31cm-9x12in) s. pair. 4-Mar-3 Bonhams, Knightsbridge #288/R
£1100 $1749 €1650 Shipping off the coast (20x30cm-8x12in) s. pair. 4-Mar-3 Bonhams, Knightsbridge #290/R est:500-800

KNIGHT, Gwen (19/20th C) New Zealander

£316 $502 €474 Spring moon (32x39cm-13x15in) s. s.i.verso. 25-Feb-3 Peter Webb, Auckland #135 (NZ.D 900)

KNIGHT, Harold (1874-1961) British

£900 $1404 €1350 Portrait of H J Mitchel, President of ICI 1936-38 (124x101cm-49x40in) s. 12-Sep-2 Sotheby's, Olympia #231/R
£950 $1482 €1425 Portrait of Mrs Johnson, Laura's mother (51x41cm-20x16in) s. i.verso. 26-Mar-3 Woolley & Wallis, Salisbury #219/R
£1800 $2790 €2700 By the hearth (40x30cm-16x12in) s. 3-Dec-2 Bonhams, New Bond Street #13/R est:2000-3000
£1800 $2808 €2700 Iranian girl (35x31cm-14x12in) 27-Mar-3 Christie's, Kensington #415/R est:2000-3000
£9000 $14760 €13500 Portrait of Dame Laura Knight sketching (46x46cm-18x18in) s. prov.exhib. 6-Jun-3 Christie's, London #44/R est:10000-15000

KNIGHT, John Baverstock (1788-1859) British

Works on paper

£250 $393 €375 Grange Bridge, looking down Borrowdale, along the River Derwent (28x43cm-11x17in) pencil W/C. 16-Apr-3 Christie's, Kensington #1016

KNIGHT, John Buxton (1843-1908) British
£380 $589 €570 Rural landscape with sheep (32x50cm-13x20in) s. 4-Oct-2 ELR Auctions, Sheffield #295/R
£500 $780 €750 Waterside, Knaresborough (59x48cm-23x19in) s. 10-Apr-3 Tennants, Leyburn #1001/R
£750 $1170 €1125 Figures outside a thatched cottage (76x66cm-30x26in) s. 8-Oct-2 Bonhams, Knightsbridge #80/R
£900 $1404 €1350 View on the river Nidd, with figures near a windmill (61x92cm-24x36in) s. 10-Apr-3 Tennants, Leyburn #1000/R
Works on paper
£250 $390 €375 Fishing village (17x24cm-7x9in) s. pencil W/C htd bodycol. 17-Oct-2 Christie's, Kensington #176
£280 $434 €420 Figures punting in a river landscape (43x69cm-17x27in) s.d.92 W/C. 4-Oct-2 Mallams, Oxford #506
£380 $619 €570 Coastal scene, with cottages, between St Margarets Bay and Kingsdown (37x59cm-15x23in) s.d.93 W/C. 30-Jan-3 Lawrence, Crewkerne #634/R
£500 $780 €750 Tuillerires gardens, Paris (48x70cm-19x28in) s.d.1902 W/C pen ink. 17-Oct-2 Christie's, Kensington #175
£500 $820 €750 Going to the beach, Brighton (35x58cm-14x23in) s.d.93 pencil W/C scratching out. 5-Jun-3 Christie's, Kensington #966/R
£600 $936 €900 Wide Vale of the Trent (55x61cm-22x24in) mixed media board exhib. 26-Mar-3 Hamptons Fine Art, Godalming #102

KNIGHT, John Prescott (1803-1881) British
£1700 $2771 €2465 Portrait of of the Rev. George Lock (89x68cm-35x27in) prov.exhib. 21-Jul-3 Sotheby's, London #341 est:1000-1500

KNIGHT, John Prescott (attrib) (1803-1881) British
£680 $1136 €986 Study of a donkey (33x25cm-13x10in) 20-Jun-3 Keys, Aylsham #709

KNIGHT, Joseph (1837-1909) British
£500 $815 €750 Snowdonia (49x65cm-19x26in) s.d.83. 29-Jan-3 Sotheby's, Olympia #194/R
£500 $815 €750 Estuary scene with sheep (30x41cm-12x16in) s.d.96 board. 28-Jan-3 Rogers Jones, Clwyd #129/R
Works on paper
£600 $942 €900 Summertime (60x46cm-24x18in) s.d.82 gouache. 20-Nov-2 Sotheby's, Olympia #36/R
£1700 $2601 €2550 Lone piper (31x21cm-12x8in) s.d.1867 gouache. 22-Aug-2 Bonhams, Edinburgh #1148 est:800-1200

KNIGHT, Louis Aston (1873-1948) American
£1258 $2000 €1887 Garden on the Riviera (56x46cm-22x18in) s. 1-Mar-3 North East Auctions, Portsmouth #770/R est:1500-2500
£1290 $2000 €1935 Lion of St Mark, Venice (55x46cm-22x18in) s.i. board. 3-Dec-2 Christie's, Rockefeller NY #588/R est:2000-4000
£1677 $2600 €2516 Arch of Titus, the Form, Rome (55x46cm-22x18in) s.i. board. 3-Dec-2 Christie's, Rockefeller NY #590/R est:4000-6000
£2000 $3160 €3000 La Seine a Vernon (46x55cm-18x22in) s.i. 3-Apr-3 Christie's, Kensington #43/R
£4221 $6500 €6332 Covered bridge, Wallingford, Connecticut (25x33cm-10x13in) s.i. board prov. 4-Sep-2 Christie's, Rockefeller NY #343/R est:3000-5000
£6452 $10000 €9355 French country landscapes (46x53cm-18x21in) pair. 7-Dec-2 South Bay, Long Island #134a/R
£6918 $11000 €10377 Below the mills (81x65cm-32x26in) s.i. 4-Mar-3 Christie's, Rockefeller NY #44/R est:10000-15000
£6918 $11000 €10377 Quiet river view with a house on the banks (51x69cm-20x27in) s.i. 5-May-3 Butterfields, San Francisco #94/R est:15000-20000
£8966 $14345 €13000 La Risle a Beaumont le Roger (66x81cm-26x32in) s.i. 12-Mar-3 E & Eve, Paris #106/R est:6000-8000
£12346 $20000 €17902 Summer garden (89x117cm-35x46in) s. 21-May-3 Doyle, New York #102/R est:35000-45000
£18710 $29000 €28065 View of a chateaux (67x83cm-26x33in) s.i. 29-Oct-2 Sotheby's, New York #125/R est:30000-50000

KNIGHT, William Henry (1823-1863) British
£600 $936 €870 Crossing the Northampton race course in a November fog (33x38cm-13x15in) s. i.d.1894 verso. 27-Mar-3 Lane, Penzance #328/R
£1500 $2340 €2250 Stacking the bricks (21x36cm-8x14in) s.d.1860 panel. 26-Mar-3 Woolley & Wallis, Salisbury #223/R est:500-700
£7000 $11060 €10500 Peace versus war, a troublesome neighbour (25x30cm-10x12in) s.d.1862 s.i.d.verso panel. 2-Dec-2 Sotheby's, London #21/R est:7000-10000

KNIKKER, Aris (1887-1962) Dutch
£282 $454 €400 Polder canal (13x25cm-5x10in) s. panel. 6-May-3 Vendu Notarishuis, Rotterdam #70
£304 $474 €480 Polder landscape with woman and child on a path (24x43cm-9x17in) s. panel. 21-Oct-2 Glerum, Amsterdam #30
£362 $586 €550 Peasant woman by a farm at dusk (23x36cm-9x14in) s. 21-Jan-3 Christie's, Amsterdam #169
£382 $630 €550 Cows by the waterside (20x26cm-8x10in) s. board. 1-Jul-3 Christie's, Amsterdam #170
£528 $850 €750 Ducks (46x72cm-18x28in) s. 7-May-3 Vendue Huis, Gravenhage #40/R
£625 $1013 €950 Shepherd tending to his flock at dusk (40x60cm-16x24in) s. 21-Jan-3 Christie's, Amsterdam #164
£694 $1146 €1000 Polder landscape with flowers in bloom (18x14cm-7x6in) s. canvas on board. 1-Jul-3 Christie's, Amsterdam #165
£845 $1361 €1200 Veere harbour with houses (44x33cm-17x13in) s. 7-May-3 Vendue Huis, Gravenhage #118/R

KNIKKER, Jan (jnr) (1911-1990) Dutch
£260 $379 €400 Ducks on the water (17x21cm-7x8in) s. panel. 19-Jun-2 Vendue Huis, Gravenhage #270/R
£266 $415 €420 Farmer ploughing (24x30cm-9x12in) s. 21-Oct-2 Glerum, Amsterdam #216
£318 $497 €500 City canal (49x39cm-19x15in) s. 5-Nov-2 Vendu Notarishuis, Rotterdam #219/R
£422 $616 €650 Polder landscape with water mill (23x29cm-9x11in) s. 19-Jun-2 Vendue Huis, Gravenhage #269
£445 $695 €650 Leuvehaven of Rotterdam (38x48cm-15x19in) s. 14-Apr-3 Glerum, Amsterdam #56/R
£486 $802 €700 Fishermen in the surroundings of Loosduinen (24x30cm-9x12in) s. 1-Jul-3 Christie's, Amsterdam #123/R
£487 $711 €750 Polder lake with anglers in reed bed (39x59cm-15x23in) s. 19-Jun-2 Vendue Huis, Gravenhage #272
£582 $908 €850 View of Delfzijl (40x80cm-16x31in) s. 14-Apr-3 Glerum, Amsterdam #115/R
£649 $948 €1000 View of Dromedaris in Enkhuizen (18x26cm-7x10in) s. panel. 19-Jun-2 Vendue Huis, Gravenhage #268/R
£844 $1232 €1300 View of Zierikzee (49x69cm-19x27in) s. 19-Jun-2 Vendue Huis, Gravenhage #271
£1111 $1833 €1600 River landscape in summer (50x71cm-20x28in) s. 1-Jul-3 Christie's, Amsterdam #149 est:1200-1600
£1197 $1927 €1700 River scene near a town with many ships and figures (59x79cm-23x31in) s. 6-May-3 Vendu Notarishuis, Rotterdam #183/R est:1200-1600

KNIKKER, Jan (snr) (1889-1957) Dutch
£266 $415 €420 View of a mill and canal with a village in the background (39x50cm-15x20in) s. 21-Oct-2 Glerum, Amsterdam #65/R
£316 $494 €500 Farm in the summer (33x48cm-13x19in) s. 21-Oct-2 Glerum, Amsterdam #168/R
£347 $573 €500 Angler in a polder landscape (27x45cm-11x18in) s. 1-Jul-3 Christie's, Amsterdam #97
£417 $688 €600 Figures at work in a polder landscape (25x45cm-10x18in) s. 1-Jul-3 Christie's, Amsterdam #116
£478 $745 €750 Sun over calm seas (50x71cm-20x28in) s. lit. 7-Nov-2 Allgauer, Kempten #2867/R
£510 $795 €800 Koningswinter am Rhein, Drachenfels (45x65cm-18x26in) s. 6-Nov-2 Vendue Huis, Gravenhage #48
£592 $959 €900 Farm under blossomtrees (24x30cm-9x12in) s. plywood. 21-Jan-3 Christie's, Amsterdam #263
£605 $944 €950 Port in The Hague (23x32cm-9x13in) s. panel. 6-Nov-2 Vendue Huis, Gravenhage #20/R

KNIP, Henri (1819-1897) Dutch
£974 $1422 €1500 Landscape with watermill (75x100cm-30x39in) i. lit. 14-Jun-2 Auktionhaus Georg Rehm, Augsburg #8074/R est:1800
Works on paper
£1026 $1621 €1600 Moselle landscape with small chapel and ruins (50x70cm-20x28in) s. gouache. 16-Nov-2 Lempertz, Koln #1351/R est:1600
£1026 $1621 €1600 Koblenz with Ehrenbreitstein castle (50x70cm-20x28in) s. gouache. 16-Nov-2 Lempertz, Koln #1352/R est:1600
£2000 $3340 €2900 Rhine view with a church and ruined castle on a hill possibly Oberwesel (69x70cm-27x28in) bears sig. gouache. 9-Jul-3 Sotheby's, London #71/R est:2000-3000

KNIP, Henri (attrib) (1819-1897) Dutch
Works on paper
£3200 $5344 €4640 View to church of Sta Maria Dell'Assunzione and Palazzo Chigi at Ariccia (45x65cm-18x26in) gouache. 9-Jul-3 Sotheby's, London #76/R est:1800-2500

KNIP, Henriette G (1783-1842) Dutch
£6751 $10463 €10127 Flowers in ceramic vase (36x27cm-14x11in) mono. pair. 3-Oct-2 Koller, Zurich #3127/R est:16000-22000 (S.FR 15730)

KNIP, Josephus Augustus (1777-1847) Dutch
£4403 $6780 €7000 Flock of a sheep in a stable (55x73cm-22x29in) s.d.1827 exhib. 23-Oct-2 Christie's, Amsterdam #15/R est:5000-7000
Works on paper
£1151 $1842 €1600 Mountainous landscape (33x44cm-13x17in) graphite W/C gouache. 15-May-3 Christie's, Paris #515/R est:2000-3000

£2055 $3205 €3000 Wooded landscape in Duitsland with three figures by a waterfall (51x74cm-20x29in) W/C. 14-Apr-3 Glerum, Amsterdam #10/R est:2500-3000

KNIP, Josephus Augustus (attrib) (1777-1847) Dutch
Works on paper
£2420 $3727 €3800 View of Roman Campagna, pilgrims beneath an arch (60x85cm-24x33in) bodycol. 3-Sep-2 Christie's, Amsterdam #89/R est:2000-3000

KNIP, M (20th C) Dutch?
£669 $1077 €950 Pig slaughter (25x31cm-10x12in) s. 7-May-3 Vendue Huis, Gravenhage #44

KNIP, Nicolaas Frederik (18/19th C) Dutch
£10563 $17007 €15000 Pastoral landscape (54x71cm-21x28in) s. 7-May-3 Vendue Huis, Gravenhage #342/R est:15000-20000

KNIP, Willem (1883-1967) Dutch
£333 $547 €510 Dutch coastal town (22x16cm-9x6in) s. panel lit. 8-Feb-3 Hans Stahl, Hamburg #56/R
£345 $548 €500 Town in France (58x48cm-23x19in) s. 10-Mar-3 Sotheby's, Amsterdam #354
£494 $760 €741 Flat bottom boat on Zwiderzee (40x50cm-16x20in) 26-Oct-2 Heffel, Vancouver #24 (C.D 1200)
£494 $760 €741 View of village in winter (24x35cm-9x14in) board. 26-Oct-2 Heffel, Vancouver #26 (C.D 1200)
£1029 $1584 €1544 House on canal (50x85cm-20x33in) 26-Oct-2 Heffel, Vancouver #25 est:1200-1600 (C.D 2500)
£1146 $1789 €1800 Fishing place (48x78cm-19x31in) s. 6-Nov-2 Vendue Huis, Gravenhage #132 est:2000-3000

KNIPSCHILD, Robert (1927-) American
£477 $750 €716 New England, three views (127x66cm-50x26in) s. i.d.1966 on stretcher. 14-Dec-2 Weschler, Washington #739/R

KNIZEK, Emanuel (1889-?) Czechoslovakian
£660 $1043 €990 Boys playing (81x67cm-32x26in) s.i.d.1922. 30-Nov-2 Dorotheum, Prague #56/R (C.KR 32000)

KNOBLOCH, Josef Rolf (1891-1964) Czechoslovakian
£538 $834 €850 Autumn near Dachau (50x62cm-20x24in) s.i. 26-Sep-2 Neumeister, Munich #2762
£578 $919 €850 Pre-alpine landscape (60x81cm-24x32in) s.i. 20-Mar-3 Neumeister, Munich #2663/R

KNOCHL, Hans (1850-?) Czechoslovakian
£700 $1141 €1050 Young girl sitting by a tree with a book (32x27cm-13x11in) s.i. panel. 12-Feb-3 Bonhams, Knightsbridge #86

KNOEBEL, Imi (1940-) German
£1923 $2981 €3000 Untitled (98x69cm-39x27in) s.d.80 Imi 82 acrylic varnish transparent paper. 3-Dec-2 Lempertz, Koln #245/R est:4000
£1923 $2981 €3000 Untitled (98x68cm-39x27in) s.i. collage acrylic board. 3-Dec-2 Lempertz, Koln #247/R est:3500
£3205 $4968 €5000 Untitled (98x68cm-39x27in) s.d.81 acrylic varnish transparent foil on board. 3-Dec-2 Lempertz, Koln #246/R est:4000
£3333 $5467 €4600 Child's star (74x84cm-29x33in) s.i.d.89 verso acrylic panel. 28-May-3 Lempertz, Koln #221/R est:4500
£4487 $6955 €7000 Large coloured collage (119x100cm-47x39in) s.d.1988 acrylic acrylic-glass over collage col paper on board. 6-Dec-2 Ketterer, Munich #212/R est:7000-9000
£18354 $29000 €27531 Grace Kelly (248x168cm-98x66in) init.d.89 verso acrylic wood prov. 13-Nov-2 Sotheby's, New York #477/R est:20000-30000
£28846 $44712 €45000 Grace Kelly (250x170cm-98x67in) s.d.1990 verso acrylic wood prov. 6-Dec-2 Ketterer, Munich #215/R est:45000-55000
Sculpture
£2899 $4754 €4000 Seven sided (47x51x5cm-19x20x2in) s.d.75 87 wood. 28-May-3 Lempertz, Koln #219/R est:3600
£12500 $20000 €18750 Meissen (230x48x14cm-91x19x6in) s.d.1981 verso oil bassed house paint acrylic aluminum steel. 16-May-3 Phillips, New York #132/R est:15000-20000

KNOFF, Anne-Lise (1937-) Norwegian
£696 $1114 €1044 Symbol (100x80cm-39x31in) s.d.76 exhib. 17-Mar-3 Blomqvist, Oslo #462/R (N.KR 8000)

KNOFF, Johan (1935-) Norwegian
£349 $548 €524 Memory from Arles, Night cafe (85x110cm-33x43in) s. 25-Nov-2 Blomqvist, Lysaker #1158 (N.KR 4000)
£393 $616 €590 Bill's bar, New York (81x100cm-32x39in) s. 25-Nov-2 Blomqvist, Lysaker #1157 (N.KR 4500)
£649 $994 €974 The tea garden (105x135cm-41x53in) s. painted 1996. 26-Aug-2 Blomqvist, Lysaker #1218/R (N.KR 7500)
£864 $1442 €1253 A bar in Rome II (92x161cm-36x63in) s.d.84 i.verso oil collage. 18-Jun-3 Grev Wedels Plass, Oslo #196/R (N.KR 10000)

KNOKE, Albert (1896-?) German
£340 $541 €500 Steamer entering Hamburg harbour (75x90cm-30x35in) s. 28-Mar-3 Bolland & Marotz, Bremen #561/R

KNOLLYS, Eardley (1902-1991) British
£360 $565 €540 Landscape at Gassin (51x35cm-20x14in) painted c.1953 prov. 15-Apr-3 Bonhams, Knightsbridge #217/R

KNOOP, August (1856-1900) German
£409 $610 €630 Musketeers drinking (21x16cm-8x6in) s.i. panel. 27-Jun-2 Neumeister, Munich #2766
£1572 $2453 €2500 Entertaining the clergyman (59x80cm-23x31in) s. 23-Sep-2 Wiener Kunst Auktionen, Vienna #47/R est:1800-3500
£3481 $5500 €5222 Interior with figures (43x56cm-17x22in) s.d.1904. 3-Apr-3 Boos Gallery, Michigan #261/R est:6000-8000

KNOPF, Herman (1870-1928) Austrian
£2848 $4500 €4500 In a dream while reading (91x75cm-36x30in) s.i. lit. 29-Nov-2 Schloss Ahlden, Ahlden #1268/R est:5500

KNOPF, Nellie A (1875-1962) American
£377 $600 €566 White chapel (20x16cm-8x6in) s. board painted c.1940. 4-May-3 Treadway Gallery, Cincinnati #547/R

KNOPFF, Fernand (1858-1921) Belgian
Works on paper
£6369 $9936 €10000 Etude de femme (18x12cm-7x5in) pencil dr prov. 11-Nov-2 Horta, Bruxelles #169 est:10000-12000

KNOPPEL, Arvid (1893-1970) Swedish
Sculpture
£1435 $2325 €2081 Bison ox (36x44cm-14x17in) s. dark pat.bronze. 26-May-3 Bukowskis, Stockholm #293/R est:20000-25000 (S.KR 18500)
£2837 $4397 €4256 Venus kneeling on shell (58cm-23in) s.d.26 dark pat.bronze st.f.Meyers. 4-Dec-2 AB Stockholms Auktionsverk #1819/R est:12000-15000 (S.KR 40000)
£24113 $37376 €36170 Brown bear (82cm-32in) s. green pat.bronze st.f.Bergman. 3-Dec-2 Bukowskis, Stockholm #63/R est:80000-100000 (S.KR 340000)

KNORR, Karen (1954-) ?
Photographs
£1935 $3000 €2903 Genius of the place, connoisseurs (88x88cm-35x35in) s.num.3/5 verso cibachrome print. 3-Dec-2 Christie's, Rockefeller NY #663/R est:2000-3000

KNOWELDEN, Martin (20th C) ?
Works on paper
£497 $790 €720 Fuligule milouinan (33x46cm-13x18in) pencil W/C. 10-Mar-3 Coutau Begarie, Paris #234/R

KNOWLES, Davidson (fl.1879-1902) British
£520 $811 €780 Interior scene with a young lady seated at a piano (35x46cm-14x18in) s. panel. 25-Mar-3 Bonhams, Leeds #654
£1600 $2608 €2400 Sheikh of the Sudan (23x16cm-9x6in) s.d. board. 29-Jan-3 Sotheby's, Olympia #128/R est:800-1200

KNOWLES, Dorothy (1927-) Canadian
£763 $1198 €1145 Grey water (53x75cm-21x30in) s.i.d.1982 acrylic. 25-Nov-2 Hodgins, Calgary #88/R est:2500-3000 (C.D 1900)
£3111 $5102 €4667 Field with roses (95x176cm-37x69in) s.d.76 acrylic. 3-Jun-3 Joyner, Toronto #69/R est:4000-5000 (C.D 7000)
£3704 $5741 €5556 Weeds on the lake shore (189x119cm-74x47in) i.d.83 verso acrylic. 3-Dec-2 Joyner, Toronto #184/R est:10000-12000 (C.D 9000)
Works on paper
£181 $285 €272 Foothills (18x25cm-7x10in) d.1973 W/C. 1-Dec-2 Levis, Calgary #316/R (C.D 450)
£484 $765 €726 South saskatchewan (56x76cm-22x30in) s.d.1979 s.i.verso W/C. 14-Nov-2 Heffel, Vancouver #53 est:1500-2000 (C.D 1200)
£609 $950 €1015 Untitled - view of the lake (55x74cm-22x29in) s. indis d. W/C. 13-Apr-3 Levis, Calgary #68a/R est:1500-2000 (C.D 1400)

KNOWLES, Elizabeth McGillivray (1886-1929) Canadian
£400 $656 €600 Livestock grazing at dusk (16x14cm-6x6in) s. canvas on board. 3-Jun-3 Joyner, Toronto #540 est:500-700 (C.D 900)
£412 $638 €618 Old pines (41x29cm-16x11in) s.d.1906 panel exhib. 3-Dec-2 Joyner, Toronto #428 est:1000-1500 (C.D 1000)
£766 $1210 €1149 Rooster and chickens in the barn (23x11cm-9x4in) s. canvas on board. 14-Nov-2 Heffel, Vancouver #52 est:1200-1500 (C.D 1900)

KNOWLES, Farquhar McGillivray (1859-1932) Canadian
£578 $948 €867 Crashing surf (25x30cm-10x12in) s. canvas on board. 3-Jun-3 Joyner, Toronto #442/R est:1500-1800 (C.D 1300)
£685 $1083 €1028 Brittany girl (25x20cm-10x8in) board painted 1897 prov. 14-Nov-2 Heffel, Vancouver #183/R est:1200-1500 (C.D 1700)
£1333 $2187 €2000 Nude female bather, moonlight (40x30cm-16x12in) s. canvas on board. 3-Jun-3 Joyner, Toronto #355/R est:1200-1500 (C.D 3000)
£5645 $8919 €8468 Fisher folk of Perce, Quebec. Ships in harbour (8x11cm-3x4in) one s.d.25 one oil one W/C two prov.exhib. 18-Nov-2 Sotheby's, Toronto #1/R est:3000-3500 (C.D 14000)

Works on paper
£451 $699 €677 HMS Foudroyant (35x53cm-14x21in) s.d.1892 W/C prov. 24-Sep-2 Ritchie, Toronto #3088/R (C.D 1100)

KNOWLES, Fred J (1874-?) British
£700 $1078 €1050 Two girls crossing a stream (50x35cm-20x14in) s. 22-Oct-2 Sworder & Son, Bishops Stortford #656/R
£1600 $2608 €2320 Horses in a stream (51x76cm-20x30in) s. 16-Jul-3 Sotheby's, Olympia #135/R est:800-1200
£2400 $3744 €3600 Feeding the calves (61x86cm-24x34in) s. 17-Sep-2 Sotheby's, Olympia #165/R est:2000-3000
£2600 $4134 €3900 View at Poynton, Cheshire (46x61cm-18x24in) s. 30-Apr-3 Halls, Shrewsbury #295/R est:3000-4000

Works on paper
£280 $445 €420 Draught horses and logs (25x36cm-10x14in) s. W/C. 30-Apr-3 Halls, Shrewsbury #211
£300 $468 €450 Breezy day (30x33cm-12x13in) s. i.verso W/C. 18-Oct-2 Keys, Aylsham #658/R
£360 $565 €540 Llanrhaiadr, North Wales (34x50cm-13x20in) s. pencil W/C. 19-Nov-2 Bonhams, Leeds #46
£370 $581 €555 Snow scene in Flintshire (32x43cm-13x17in) s. pencil W/C. 19-Nov-2 Bonhams, Leeds #47
£380 $623 €570 Good Morning (38x41cm-15x16in) s. W/C. 4-Jun-3 Bonhams, Chester #291
£420 $659 €630 Village scene with a milkmaid and two calves (25x35cm-10x14in) s. pencil W/C. 19-Nov-2 Bonhams, Leeds #48
£420 $668 €630 On the river Ryder (49x76cm-19x30in) s. W/C. 27-Feb-3 Bonhams, Chester #357
£520 $811 €754 Feeding the chickens (13x10cm-5x4in) s. W/C htd white. 27-Mar-3 Neales, Nottingham #936
£720 $1130 €1080 Resting, Llanrhaiadr (43x30cm-17x12in) s.i. pencil W/C. 19-Nov-2 Bonhams, Leeds #45
£1200 $1908 €1800 Dairy maid with cattle on a moorland path (30x48cm-12x19in) s. W/C. 30-Apr-3 Halls, Shrewsbury #212/R est:800-1200

KNOWLES, George Sheridan (1863-1931) British
£550 $852 €825 Portrait of Vera Florence Rowe (78x65cm-31x26in) prov. 3-Dec-2 Sotheby's, Olympia #56/R
£11500 $19090 €17250 Summer pleasure on the river (76x103cm-30x41in) s.d.1908. 12-Jun-3 Sotheby's, London #266/R est:7000-9000

Works on paper
£356 $590 €516 Legend of Queen Elizabeth of Hungary (49x34cm-19x13in) s. W/C. 16-Jun-3 Waddingtons, Toronto #92/R (C.D 800)
£380 $600 €570 Portrait of a young girl, in 17thC dress (25x18cm-10x7in) s.d.92 W/C. 27-Nov-2 Hamptons Fine Art, Godalming #224

KNOX, Archibald (1864-1933) British

Works on paper
£600 $930 €900 Windmill at Dhowin (25x36cm-10x14in) i. W/C. 6-Dec-2 Chrystals Auctions, Isle of Man #220
£1100 $1705 €1650 Trees in a landscape (43x56cm-17x22in) W/C. 6-Dec-2 Chrystals Auctions, Isle of Man #155 est:800-1200
£1400 $2086 €2100 Rowing boat and anvil (43x56cm-17x22in) W/C. 28-Jun-2 Chrystals Auctions, Isle of Man #187 est:1200-1800
£1700 $2635 €2550 Farm behind the trees (43x56cm-17x22in) W/C. 6-Dec-2 Chrystals Auctions, Isle of Man #154 est:1200-1800
£1900 $2945 €2850 Trees in a landscape (43x56cm-17x22in) W/C. 6-Dec-2 Chrystals Auctions, Isle of Man #196 est:2000-3000
£3000 $5010 €4350 Landscape (42x56cm-17x22in) W/C. 26-Jun-3 Mellors & Kirk, Nottingham #809/R est:800-1200

KNOX, Cynthia Maree (1940-) New Zealander?
£433 $693 €628 Canty Uni students waiting (91x49cm-36x19in) s.d.61 board. 13-May-3 Watson's, Christchurch #63/R (NZ.D 1200)

KNOX, George James (1810-1897) British

Works on paper
£350 $546 €525 Coastal dwelling with vessels (20x41cm-8x16in) s. W/C. 20-Sep-2 Richardson & Smith, Whitby #185
£2050 $3260 €3075 Prince Albert's statue and St Peter Port, Guernsey (17x38cm-7x15in) s. W/C. 20-Mar-3 Martel Maides, Guernsey #35/R est:500-700

KNOX, James (1866-1942) American
£1198 $2000 €1737 Winter (63x76cm-25x30in) s. canvas on masonite prov.exhib. 18-Jun-3 Christie's, Los Angeles #42/R est:3000-5000

KNOX, John (attrib) (1778-1845) British
£6500 $10206 €9750 Looking south east through Nant Francon Valley (81x111cm-32x44in) prov. 20-Nov-2 Sotheby's, Olympia #47/R est:4000-6000

KNOX, Mary Mann (20th C) American

Works on paper
£284 $475 €412 Coastal village with sailing vessels (28x53cm-11x21in) s.d.1921 W/C. 21-Jun-3 Charlton Hall, Columbia #543/R

KNOX, Susan Ricker (1875-1959) American
£597 $950 €896 Immigrants (41x51cm-16x20in) s. board. 7-Mar-3 Skinner, Boston #597/R
£5696 $9000 €8544 Young girl is the artist's favorite model, Hazel Moulton of Kittery, Maine. painted c.1916. 24-Apr-3 Shannon's, Milford #32/R est:10000-15000

KNOX, W D (1880-1945) Australian
£2884 $4586 €4326 Little dock, Melbourne (35x45cm-14x18in) s. 4-Mar-3 Deutscher-Menzies, Melbourne #147/R est:5000-7000 (A.D 7500)

KNOX, Wilfred (1884-1966) British
£723 $1143 €1085 Red jacket off Rio (48x74cm-19x29in) s.d.1947 i.verso canvas on board. 1-Apr-3 Stephan Welz, Johannesburg #416/R est:10000-15000 (SA.R 9000)

Works on paper
£550 $869 €825 Clipper and other sailing vessels at sea. Days of sail (25x36cm-10x14in) gouache pair. 13-Nov-2 Halls, Shrewsbury #330/R
£600 $942 €900 Fishing boats off a coastline (37x54cm-15x21in) s.d.1914 W/C bodycol. 21-Nov-2 Tennants, Leyburn #655/R
£903 $1454 €1355 Three views of Venice with gondolas (24x35cm-9x14in) s. W/C three. 12-May-3 Stephan Welz, Johannesburg #427 est:6000-8000 (SA.R 10500)

KNOX, William (1862-1925) British
£400 $624 €600 Dittisham on the Dart (45x61cm-18x24in) s. i.overlap. 17-Sep-2 Sotheby's, Olympia #186/R

Works on paper
£320 $499 €480 Figures in the desert approaching a town (28x49cm-11x19in) s. W/C. 26-Mar-3 Woolley & Wallis, Salisbury #25/R
£346 $550 €519 Covered bridge, Venice (38x28cm-15x11in) s. W/C. 18-Mar-3 Doyle, New York #37/R
£400 $624 €600 Gondolas on the Rialto (29x48cm-11x19in) s. W/C. 26-Mar-3 Woolley & Wallis, Salisbury #24/R

KNOX, William Dunn (1880-1945) Australian
£1491 $2267 €2237 Panorama from Arthur's Seat, Dromana, Vic (44x54cm-17x21in) s. 19-Aug-2 Joel, Victoria #140/R est:2500-3500 (A.D 4250)
£1520 $2447 €2280 Towards the Dandenongs (29x43cm-11x17in) s. canvas on board painted c.1916 prov. 6-May-3 Christie's, Melbourne #277 est:3000-5000 (A.D 3800)
£1520 $2447 €2280 Tasmanian schooner in little dock, Melbourne (23x31cm-9x12in) s. board prov. 6-May-3 Christie's, Melbourne #369 est:2000-3000 (A.D 3800)
£1779 $2722 €2669 Christmas Hills (41x54cm-16x21in) s. board. 25-Aug-2 Sotheby's, Paddington #219 est:5000-8000 (A.D 5000)
£1908 $3015 €2862 Summers day, looking from Olinda (33x44cm-13x17in) s. canvas on board. 2-Apr-3 Christie's, Melbourne #46/R est:3000-5000 (A.D 5000)
£3200 $5152 €4640 Moonrise (58x73cm-23x29in) s. 12-May-3 Joel, Victoria #319/R est:8000-10000 (A.D 8000)

KNUDSEN, Borge L (1911-1994) Danish

£304 $469 €456 Still life of jug, lemons and newspaper (62x75cm-24x30in) s.d.39 verso. 23-Oct-2 Kunsthallen, Copenhagen #10/R (D.KR 3600)
£498 $806 €722 Still life of flowers, music and pipe by window (85x97cm-33x38in) init. 24-May-3 Rasmussen, Havnen #4159 (D.KR 5200)
£860 $1393 €1290 Portrait of my pipe (156x180cm-61x71in) s.d.1942. 3-Feb-3 Lilla Bukowskis, Stockholm #83 (S.KR 12000)

KNUDSEN, Christian (1945-) Canadian
Works on paper
£407 $638 €611 Painting 15.5/40/21 (38x96cm-15x38in) s. i. verso mixed media. 12-Dec-2 Iegor de Saint Hippolyte, Montreal #41 (C.D 1000)

KNUDSEN, Hans (1865-1947) Danish
£517 $786 €776 Village street with thatched houses in winter (112x165cm-44x65in) s.d.05. 28-Aug-2 Museumsbygningen, Copenhagen #55/R (D.KR 6000)

KNUDSEN, Leif (1928-1975) Swedish
£982 $1551 €1473 Dark concert (115x135cm-45x53in) s.d.52. 30-Nov-2 Goteborg Auktionsverk, Sweden #556/R (S.KR 14000)

KNUDSEN, Peder (1868-1944) Danish
£335 $529 €503 Harbour scene with fishing boats from Nexo, Bornholm (96x72cm-38x28in) s. 17-Nov-2 Hindemae, Ullerslev #7223/R (D.KR 3900)
£422 $659 €633 Coastal landscape with dunes (76x120cm-30x47in) s. 23-Sep-2 Rasmussen, Vejle #122/R (D.KR 5000)
£448 $686 €672 Seascape (115x155cm-45x61in) s.d.1941. 24-Aug-2 Rasmussen, Havnen #2136 (D.KR 5200)
£549 $846 €824 Coastal landscape with cliffs, Bornholm (74x96cm-29x38in) s. 26-Oct-2 Rasmussen, Havnen #2027 (D.KR 6500)
£657 $1051 €986 Winter landscape (87x80cm-34x31in) s. 13-Jan-3 Rasmussen, Vejle #116/R (D.KR 7500)

KNUDSON, Robert L (1929-) American
£301 $500 €436 Symphony of the season (61x66cm-24x26in) s. masonite. 14-Jun-3 Jackson's, Cedar Falls #420/R

KNUPFER, Benes (1848-1910) Czechoslovakian
£203 $319 €305 Portrait of a woman (41x32cm-16x13in) init. 10-Dec-2 Pinneys, Montreal #92 (C.D 500)
£1547 $2445 €2321 Nymphs (46x36cm-18x14in) canvas on canvas. 30-Nov-2 Dorotheum, Prague #17/R est:60000-90000 (C.KR 75000)
£1986 $3078 €2979 Water-nymphs and Centaurs (60x100cm-24x39in) s. 3-Dec-2 Bukowskis, Stockholm #177/R est:25000-30000 (S.KR 28000)
£4472 $7020 €6708 Two nymphs in a sunlit glade (96x62cm-38x24in) s.d.1884. 10-Dec-2 Pinneys, Montreal #58 est:14000-18000 (C.D 11000)
£5200 $8476 €7800 Embrace (164x150cm-65x59in) s. 29-Jan-3 Sotheby's, Olympia #345/R est:3000-5000

KNUTSEN, Edwin B (1901-) American
£471 $750 €707 Late fall farmyard (61x81cm-24x32in) s.d.1940. 7-Mar-3 Jackson's, Cedar Falls #643/R

KNUTSON, Johan (1816-1899) Finnish
£654 $1014 €1040 Boat on beach (27x34cm-11x13in) s. 6-Oct-2 Bukowskis, Helsinki #207/R
£654 $1072 €1000 Coastal landscape (17x26cm-7x10in) s. 9-Feb-3 Bukowskis, Helsinki #275/R
£1127 $1814 €1600 Coastal landscape (25x40cm-10x16in) s. 10-May-3 Bukowskis, Helsinki #101/R est:1600-1800
£1582 $2468 €2500 Farm (32x57cm-13x22in) s. 12-Sep-2 Hagelstam, Helsinki #966/R est:2500
£1901 $3061 €2700 Imatra - landscape with rapids (30x54cm-12x21in) s. 10-May-3 Bukowskis, Helsinki #92/R est:2500-2800
£20886 $33000 €33000 View from Southern harbour towards Brunnsparken (36x56cm-14x22in) s. lit. 1-Dec-2 Bukowskis, Helsinki #87/R est:8000-10000

KNUTTEL, Graham (1954-) Irish
£1150 $1679 €1725 Rabbit (53cm-21in circular) s. oil on pottery plate. 12-Jun-2 John Ross, Belfast #269 est:1200-1500
£1156 $1688 €1850 Still life (52x61cm-20x24in) s. acrylic. 14-May-2 Thomas Adams, Dublin #381
£1188 $1734 €1900 Sheep grazing under blue sky (51x76cm-20x30in) s. acrylic. 14-May-2 Thomas Adams, Dublin #399
£1275 $2053 €1900 Peaches, aubergine and watermelon (41x30cm-16x12in) s. prov. 18-Feb-3 Whyte's, Dublin #233/R est:1500-2000
£1392 $2158 €2200 Still life with pears (47x62cm-19x24in) s. 24-Sep-2 De Veres Art Auctions, Dublin #108a est:2000-3000
£1400 $2226 €2100 Girl in a green dress (71x56cm-28x22in) s. 5-Mar-3 John Ross, Belfast #204 est:1200-1500
£1438 $2244 €2100 Still life with artichoke and tomatoes (59x48cm-23x19in) s. 8-Apr-3 James Adam, Dublin #181/R est:1000-1500
£1447 $2257 €2300 Punch (51x41cm-20x16in) s. 17-Sep-2 Whyte's, Dublin #215 est:2000-3000
£1644 $2564 €2400 Still life with aubergines on a plate (59x59cm-23x23in) s. 8-Apr-3 James Adam, Dublin #180/R est:1800-2200
£1849 $2885 €2700 Still life with plums and yellow bowl (59x74cm-23x29in) s. board. 8-Apr-3 James Adam, Dublin #182/R est:1000-1500
£2000 $3200 €3000 Artichoke (61x61cm-24x24in) s.d.88 oil collage board. 15-May-3 Christie's, Kensington #242/R est:1500-2000
£2179 $3422 €3400 Punch as shepherd (36x25cm-14x10in) s. 19-Nov-2 Whyte's, Dublin #237/R est:1500-2000
£2192 $3419 €3200 Two male figures seated in a cafe (87x88cm-34x35in) s. 8-Apr-3 James Adam, Dublin #124/R est:1500-2000
£2215 $3434 €3500 Cristal (55x71cm-22x28in) s. prov. 24-Sep-2 De Veres Art Auctions, Dublin #11 est:3000-5000
£2300 $3680 €3450 Still life with fish, lemons and spring onions (61x61cm-24x24in) s.d.88 oil collage board. 15-May-3 Christie's, Kensington #241/R est:1500-2000
£2500 $3975 €3600 Mr Punch (41x41cm-16x16in) s. 29-Apr-3 Whyte's, Dublin #233/R est:2500-3500
£2778 $4417 €4000 Punch releasing doves (51x61cm-20x24in) s. prov. 29-Apr-3 Whyte's, Dublin #222/R est:2500-3000
£3500 $5600 €5250 Portrait of a man and woman (51x61cm-20x24in) s. pair. 16-May-3 Sotheby's, London #132/R est:2500-3500
£3624 $5835 €5400 Recumbent nude with cat (91x183cm-36x72in) s. prov. 18-Feb-3 Whyte's, Dublin #173/R est:5000-7000
£3774 $5887 €6000 My girl (71x56cm-28x22in) s. 17-Sep-2 Whyte's, Dublin #183/R est:4000-6000
£4167 $6625 €6000 Still life with watermelon slices (97x97cm-38x38in) s. 29-Apr-3 Whyte's, Dublin #156/R est:6000-7000
£5000 $7950 €7200 Titanic (122x91cm-48x36in) s. 29-Apr-3 Whyte's, Dublin #229/R est:5000-6000
£6918 $10792 €11000 Up to no good (122x91cm-48x36in) s. 17-Sep-2 Whyte's, Dublin #181/R est:7000-9000
Works on paper
£1900 $3040 €2850 Artichoke (61x61cm-24x24in) s. collage board. 15-May-3 Christie's, Kensington #240/R est:1500-2000

KOBAYASHI, Milton (1950-) American
£1169 $1800 €1754 Flowers (30x20cm-12x8in) 25-Oct-2 Morris & Whiteside, Hilton Head Island #7

KOBELI, Eli (1932-1999) South African?
Works on paper
£192 $300 €288 Happy girls (45x67cm-18x26in) s.i. mixed media. 11-Nov-2 Stephan Welz, Johannesburg #269 (SA.R 3000)
£387 $623 €581 Township Street scene with children at play (60x90cm-24x35in) s. mixed media on board. 12-May-3 Stephan Welz, Johannesburg #221 est:5000-7000 (SA.R 4500)
£1118 $1800 €1677 Township Street scene (90x120cm-35x47in) s.d.1/76 mixed media on board. 12-May-3 Stephan Welz, Johannesburg #498/R est:10000-15000 (SA.R 13000)

KOBELKA, T (19th C) ?
£1258 $1950 €2000 Attersee (42x58cm-17x23in) s.d.68 i. verso one of pair. 29-Oct-2 Dorotheum, Vienna #26/R est:2000-2500
£1258 $1950 €2000 Ramsau (42x58cm-17x23in) s.d.68 i. verso one of pair. 29-Oct-2 Dorotheum, Vienna #27/R est:2000-2500

KOBELL, Ferdinand (1740-1799) German
Works on paper
£514 $801 €750 Wolfsbrunnen in Heidelberg (20x23cm-8x9in) i. wash brush sepia over pencil. 11-Apr-3 Winterberg, Heidelberg #256/R
£576 $921 €800 River landscape with herdsmen (10x13cm-4x5in) d.1791 sepia brush pencil. 17-May-3 Lempertz, Koln #1234/R

KOBELL, Ferdinand (attrib) (1740-1799) German
Works on paper
£764 $1215 €1100 Trees in rocky landscape with stream (13x18cm-5x7in) pen wash. 5-May-3 Ketterer, Munich #274/R

KOBELL, Franz (1749-1822) German
Works on paper
£274 $427 €400 Cattle drinking (11x16cm-4x6in) pen. 11-Apr-3 Winterberg, Heidelberg #269
£377 $589 €600 Trees in mountain landscape with travellers by water (16x22cm-6x9in) pencil. 11-Oct-2 Winterberg, Heidelberg #408
£472 $736 €750 Mountain landscape with water and girl with goats (19x25cm-7x10in) i. verso pen over pencil. 11-Oct-2 Winterberg, Heidelberg #406
£579 $903 €920 Landscape with trees (15x22cm-6x9in) pen. 11-Oct-2 Winterberg, Heidelberg #405

£719 $1122 €1050 Pre-alpine landscape with trees and houses (17x22cm-7x9in) sepia brush. 11-Apr-3 Winterberg, Heidelberg #268/R
£753 $1175 €1100 Isar shore (18x21cm-7x8in) sepia brush. 11-Apr-3 Winterberg, Heidelberg #265/R
£755 $1177 €1200 Fields by the Isaa (17x21cm-7x8in) wash brush. 11-Oct-2 Winterberg, Heidelberg #403
£788 $1229 €1150 House on the Isar (18x21cm-7x8in) sepia brush. 11-Apr-3 Winterberg, Heidelberg #264/R
£818 $1275 €1300 Bank of the Isar (15x20cm-6x8in) wash brush. 11-Oct-2 Winterberg, Heidelberg #404
£822 $1282 €1200 Farmstead on the banks of the Isar (18x21cm-7x8in) sepia brush. 11-Apr-3 Winterberg, Heidelberg #267/R
£881 $1374 €1400 Peasant with horse by fence (18x22cm-7x9in) wash brush. 11-Oct-2 Winterberg, Heidelberg #401/R
£890 $1389 €1300 Farmstead on Isar shore (18x21cm-7x8in) sepia brush. 11-Apr-3 Winterberg, Heidelberg #266/R
£943 $1472 €1500 House by the Isar (16x22cm-6x9in) wash pen. 11-Oct-2 Winterberg, Heidelberg #402
£1027 $1603 €1500 Farmstead in trees (16x20cm-6x8in) sepia brush. 11-Apr-3 Winterberg, Heidelberg #263/R
£1069 $1668 €1700 Wooded landscape with path (18x21cm-7x8in) wash brush. 11-Oct-2 Winterberg, Heidelberg #400/R
£1154 $1685 €1800 Moonlit landscape with twofigures (13x21cm-5x8in) s.d.1814 pen wash. 4-Jun-2 Karl & Faber, Munich #27/R est:1500
£1667 $2433 €2600 Landscape with classical ruins and female figures by water (15x21cm-6x8in) s.d.1817 pen wash. 4-Jun-2 Karl & Faber, Munich #28/R est:1800
£12179 $18878 €19000 Landscape studies and sketches (19x23cm-7x9in) Indian ink 188 in album prov.lit. 7-Dec-2 Ketterer, Hamburg #67/R est:6000-7000

KOBELL, Franz (attrib) (1749-1822) German
£483 $763 €700 Landscape (13x21cm-5x8in) wash Indian ink brush. 5-Apr-3 Quittenbaum, Hamburg #38/R
£800 $1336 €1160 Cattle watering. Cattle by ruins (35x49cm-14x19in) pair. 8-Jul-3 Bonhams, Knightsbridge #78/R
Works on paper
£2405 $3728 €3800 Pasticcio of the Colosseum, Rome (34x47cm-13x19in) i. pen W/C paper on board. 27-Sep-2 Venator & Hansten, Koln #1008 est:1800

KOBELL, Hendrik (1751-1779) Dutch
£2793 $4441 €4190 Seascape - harbour scene with many sailing vessels (37x52cm-15x20in) s.d.1778. 10-Mar-3 Rasmussen, Vejle #359/R est:30000 (D.KR 30000)

KOBELL, Jan (1756-1833) Dutch
£1000 $1600 €1500 Cattle and sheep in a landscape (25x33cm-10x13in) s. panel. 13-Mar-3 Duke & Son, Dorchester #275/R est:800-1500

KOBELL, Jan Baptist (1778-1814) Dutch
£3526 $5465 €5500 Berger et troupeau (25x35cm-10x14in) 6-Dec-2 Maigret, Paris #125
Works on paper
£900 $1395 €1350 Wooded landscape with barn, grazing cows and figures (32x40cm-13x16in) s. black chk prov. 30-Oct-2 Bonhams, New Bond Street #220/R

KOBELL, Jan III (1800-1838) Dutch
Works on paper
£321 $497 €500 Horse at the food basket in the stall (19x16cm-7x6in) s. W/C. 4-Dec-2 Neumeister, Munich #528

KOBELL, Wilhelm von (1766-1855) German
Works on paper
£396 $633 €550 Sketches of Hussars (17x27cm-7x11in) pencil htd white. 13-May-3 Hartung & Hartung, Munich #4057/R
£1042 $1656 €1500 Sheep (13x18cm-5x7in) pencil double-sided. 5-May-3 Ketterer, Munich #306/R
£3885 $6216 €5400 The meeting (38x50cm-15x20in) W/C prov. 17-May-3 Lempertz, Koln #1305/R est:8000

KOBERLING, Bernd (1938-) German
Works on paper
£316 $500 €500 Untitled (40x53cm-16x21in) s.d.88 W/C. 29-Nov-2 Villa Grisebach, Berlin #717/R
£362 $594 €500 Block lava (29x21cm-11x8in) s.d.82 Indian ink chk W/C. 31-May-3 Villa Grisebach, Berlin #857/R

KOBINGER, Hans (1892-1974) Austrian
Works on paper
£420 $651 €655 Still life of flowers (65x49cm-26x19in) s.d.1967, 24.XII W/C. 5-Dec-2 Schopman, Hamburg #581

KOBKE, Christen (1810-1848) Danish
£1866 $2966 €2799 Study of dark clouds above hilly landscape (8x19cm-3x7in) 5-May-3 Rasmussen, Vejle #331/R est:20000 (D.KR 20000)
£9569 $15502 €13875 A peacock against white background (25x35cm-10x14in) i.d.4 Juli 1839 exhib.prov. 26-May-3 Rasmussen, Copenhagen #1141/R est:100000 (D.KR 100000)
£37244 $59218 €55866 Portrait of Peter Petersen, the artist's uncle (31x23cm-12x9in) painted c.1845 exhib.prov. 5-Mar-3 Rasmussen, Copenhagen #1548/R est:300000-400000 (D.KR 400000)
Works on paper
£766 $1240 €1111 Studies of a female model (21x19cm-8x7in) s. pencil exec.c.1833 prov. 26-May-3 Rasmussen, Copenhagen #1578/R (D.KR 8000)
£1396 $2248 €2094 Medal engraver Krohn (19x11cm-7x4in) pencil. 26-Feb-3 Museumsbygningen, Copenhagen #78/R est:2500 (D.KR 15500)
£3441 $5368 €5162 Portrait of Thorvaldsen (27x22cm-11x9in) s.d.5 Marts 1831 pencil. 5-Aug-2 Rasmussen, Vejle #253/R est:5000-10000 (D.KR 40500)

KOBOLD, Johann Werner (attrib) (?-1803) German
£541 $843 €800 Portrait of Philippine Auguste Amalie von Brandenburg-Schwedt (60x49cm-24x19in) 27-Mar-3 Dr Fritz Nagel, Stuttgart #770/R
£566 $883 €900 Portrait of Philippine Auguste Amalie von Brandenburg-Schwedt (60x49cm-24x19in) 19-Sep-2 Dr Fritz Nagel, Stuttgart #883/R
£692 $1079 €1100 Portrait of Landgraf Friedrich II von Hessen (60x49cm-24x19in) one of pair. 19-Sep-2 Dr Fritz Nagel, Stuttgart #882/R

KOCH, Carl Friedrich (1856-?) German
£701 $1093 €1100 Nude washing in morning (46x60cm-18x24in) s. board lit. 8-Nov-2 Auktionhaus Georg Rehm, Augsburg #8086

KOCH, François (19/20th C) Austrian
£1333 $2146 €2000 Bushveld landscape with road (108x149cm-43x59in) s.d.90. 12-May-3 Stephan Welz, Johannesburg #146 est:2000-4000 (SA.R 15500)
£23734 $37500 €34414 Approaching winter (91x119cm-36x47in) s. 26-Jul-3 Coeur d'Alene, Hayden #156/R est:15000-25000

KOCH, Friedrich (1859-?) German
Works on paper
£466 $750 €699 Street scene in turn of the century Vienna (46x33cm-18x13in) s.d. pen ink gouache. 10-May-3 Illustration House, New York #157/R

KOCH, G (?) German
£513 $779 €800 Cows and sheep in extensive meadow landscape (60x90cm-24x35in) s. 11-Jul-2 Hugo Ruef, Munich #725

KOCH, Georg (1857-1926) German
£1761 $2747 €2800 Horse dealer (71x107cm-28x42in) s. 19-Sep-2 Dr Fritz Nagel, Stuttgart #953/R est:1500
£1923 $3038 €3000 Fox hunt (58x70cm-23x28in) mono.d.91. 16-Nov-2 Lempertz, Koln #1509/R est:3000

KOCH, H (19th C) German
£1027 $1603 €1500 Still life with fruit and wine glass (37x50cm-15x20in) s.i. board. 9-Apr-3 Neumeister, Munich #695/R est:800

KOCH, Helen C (1895-?) American
£909 $1400 €1364 St Louis Brewery, Budweiser (61x51cm-24x20in) s. board painted c.1940. 8-Sep-2 Treadway Gallery, Cincinnati #707/R

KOCH, John (1909-1978) American
£342 $500 €513 Portrait of Mrs Elizabeth W Proud (53x38cm-21x15in) s.d.1949. 3-Nov-1 North East Auctions, Portsmouth #575
£6289 $10000 €9434 Double portrait (102x76cm-40x30in) s. executed c.1955 prov. 4-Mar-3 Christie's, Rockefeller NY #103/R est:6000-8000

KOCH, Josef Anton (1768-1839) Austrian
£17483 $29196 €25000 Paysage d'Italie (62x83cm-24x33in) mono. 27-Jun-3 Claude Aguttes, Neuilly #23/R est:20000-30000

KOCH, Josef Anton (attrib) (1768-1839) Austrian
Works on paper
£1667 $2650 €2400 The flood (19x22cm-7x9in) pen. 5-May-3 Ketterer, Munich #276/R est:1500-2000

KOCH, Julius (1882-1952) German
£372 $580 €550 Bodensee (60x80cm-24x31in) s. 28-Mar-3 Karrenbauer, Konstanz #1755
£388 $601 €605 Girl with long hair sitting by water (65x49cm-26x19in) s. lit. 6-Dec-2 Karlheinz Kaupp, Staufen #2323/R

KOCH, Ludwig (1866-1934) Austrian
£4126 $6519 €6189 Horse-race (110x120cm-43x47in) s.d.1920. 30-Nov-2 Dorotheum, Prague #58/R est:120000-180000 (C.KR 200000)
Works on paper
£1034 $1655 €1500 Proud horse and rider (70x60cm-28x24in) s.d.1912 mixed media. 11-Mar-3 Dorotheum, Vienna #12/R est:1800-2600
£1500 $2370 €2250 Breaking the defence (29x29cm-11x11in) s. W/C htd gouache. 28-Nov-2 Bonhams, Knightsbridge #58/R est:1500-2000

KOCH, Martin (20th C) American
£260 $434 €377 Cape Bonetebok in a valley (70x91cm-28x36in) s.d.97. 17-Jun-3 Rosebery Fine Art, London #591/R
£550 $919 €798 Oryx on a plain with mountains in the distance. Wild dogs in river landscape (75x120cm-30x47in) s.d.95 two. 17-Jun-3 Rosebery Fine Art, London #592/R
£1281 $1999 €1922 Mountainous landscape with impala (99x300cm-39x118in) s.d.91. 11-Nov-2 Stephan Welz, Johannesburg #601/R est:7000-10000 (SA.R 20000)

KOCH, Robert (1971-) South African
£705 $1099 €1058 Extensive landscape with elephants (99x300cm-39x118in) s.d.92. 11-Nov-2 Stephan Welz, Johannesburg #600 (SA.R 11000)

KOCHANOWSKY, Roman (1856-1945) Polish
£481 $702 €750 Monlit winter landscape (20x26cm-8x10in) s. board. 4-Jun-2 Karl & Faber, Munich #312
£503 $825 €770 Landscape with figures under trees (14x19cm-6x7in) s. panel. 8-Feb-3 Hans Stahl, Hamburg #29/R

KOCHERSCHEIDT, Kurt (1943-1992) Austrian
£2342 $3630 €3700 Teilchengleich (62x81cm-24x32in) s.i.d.82 paper. 24-Sep-2 Wiener Kunst Auktionen, Vienna #237/R est:3500-5000
Works on paper
£397 $648 €600 Southern cross (35x50cm-14x20in) s.i.d.72 pencil col pencil. 28-Jan-3 Dorotheum, Vienna #246/R

KOCHL, Alois (1951-) Austrian
Works on paper
£321 $503 €500 Composition (26x35cm-10x14in) s.d.87 mixed media. 20-Nov-2 Dorotheum, Klagenfurt #50

KOCK, Franz (1886-1975) German
£3846 $5962 €6000 Hilly landscape with Mariatrost Basilica (24x35cm-9x14in) s. board. 5-Dec-2 Dorotheum, Graz #29/R est:600

KOCKE, Hugo Wilhelm Georg (1874-1956) German
£519 $774 €800 Neustadt/Holstein (46x66cm-18x26in) s. board. 27-Jun-2 Neumeister, Munich #2768/R

KODAT, Bela (1908-1986) Hungarian
£327 $523 €500 Horse in the paddock with approaching storm (60x80cm-24x31in) s. 10-Jan-3 Allgauer, Kempten #1656/R

KODRA, Ibrahim (1918-) Middle Eastern
£353 $554 €550 Player (46x38cm-18x15in) s.i.verso. 19-Nov-2 Finarte, Milan #76
£510 $811 €750 Player (46x38cm-18x15in) s. s.i.verso. 1-Mar-3 Meeting Art, Vercelli #696
£949 $1481 €1500 Totem (70x50cm-28x20in) s.d.1995. 14-Sep-2 Meeting Art, Vercelli #917/R
£949 $1481 €1500 Padua cathedral (50x70cm-20x28in) s. s.i.d.1949-50 verso. 14-Sep-2 Meeting Art, Vercelli #963/R
£962 $1510 €1500 Bergamo Alta (60x80cm-24x31in) s.d.1965. 23-Nov-2 Meeting Art, Vercelli #478/R
Works on paper
£348 $543 €550 Milan Duomo (50x70cm-20x28in) s. s.i.d.1988 verso mixed media paper on canvas. 14-Sep-2 Meeting Art, Vercelli #783/R

KOECHL, Manfred (1956-) Austrian
£397 $648 €600 Two heads (44x35cm-17x14in) s.d.98 oil-stick acrylic. 28-Jan-3 Dorotheum, Vienna #313/R
£411 $642 €650 Heads in bright blue (42x34cm-17x13in) s. oilstick acrylic. 15-Oct-2 Dorotheum, Vienna #276/R
£432 $708 €600 Still life with flowers and fruit (48x63cm-19x25in) s.d.86 oil mixed media paper. 5-Jun-3 Dorotheum, Salzburg #659/R
£497 $810 €750 Two heads (42x34cm-17x13in) s. oil-stick acrylic. 28-Jan-3 Dorotheum, Vienna #312/R
£506 $790 €800 Heads on dark blue (42x34cm-17x13in) s. oilstick acrylic. 15-Oct-2 Dorotheum, Vienna #279/R

KOECHLIN, Alfred Eugene (1845-1878) French
£282 $437 €440 Sunset (20x27cm-8x11in) mono. paper on canvas. 7-Dec-2 De Vuyst, Lokeren #171/R
£321 $497 €500 Washer-woman by a river (17x24cm-7x9in) mono. 7-Dec-2 De Vuyst, Lokeren #170/R

KOEFOED, H C (1849-1921) Danish
£293 $448 €440 Young couple (95x69cm-37x27in) mono.d.85. 24-Aug-2 Rasmussen, Havnen #2147 (D.KR 3400)

KOEHLER, Henry (1927-) American
£6000 $9480 €9000 Gates at Kempton Park (41x61cm-16x24in) s. s.i.d.1971 verso. 27-Nov-2 Christie's, London #54/R
Works on paper
£605 $944 €950 In the paddock (48x61cm-19x24in) s. mixed media. 6-Nov-2 James Adam, Dublin #116/R
£1646 $2600 €2469 Blue and green on the ball (42x60cm-17x24in) s. W/C crayon prov. 3-Apr-3 Christie's, Rockefeller NY #186/R est:3000-5000

KOEHLER, Paul R (c.1866-1909) American
Works on paper
£272 $425 €408 Snowy river landscape at dusk (41x60cm-16x24in) s. gouache. 12-Apr-3 Weschler, Washington #558/R
£342 $500 €513 Grazing cattle in a field (51x76cm-20x30in) s. pastel prov. 3-Nov-1 North East Auctions, Portsmouth #1010/R

KOEK-KOEK, Stephen Roberto (1887-1934) Argentinian
£288 $450 €432 Dusk (12x26cm-5x10in) s. board. 10-Oct-2 Galleria Y Remates, Montevideo #3/R
£372 $580 €558 Procesion (14x28cm-6x11in) s. board. 30-Jul-2 Galleria Y Remates, Montevideo #28/R
£1063 $1700 €1595 Dusk in El Recodo (51x60cm-20x24in) s. board. 5-Jan-3 Galleria Y Remates, Montevideo #88/R
£1274 $2000 €1911 Allies at dusk, World War II (80x106cm-31x42in) s. 19-Nov-2 Galleria Y Remates, Montevideo #127/R

KOEKKOEK, Barend Cornelis (1803-1862) Dutch
£1146 $1800 €1719 Farmer with cows (18x23cm-7x9in) s. panel. 14-Dec-2 CRN Auctions, Cambridge #88/R
£4225 $7014 €6000 Vast hilly landscape with farmer on his way and town in background (13x17cm-5x7in) s. panel. 14-Jun-3 Arnold, Frankfurt #785/R est:3000
£13889 $22083 €20000 View of a park with figures (37x45cm-15x18in) s. oil paper on canvas prov. 29-Apr-3 Christie's, Amsterdam #189/R est:15000-20000
£27000 $42390 €40500 Figures and cattle on a rocky woodland path (23x18cm-9x7in) s.d.1849 panel. 19-Nov-2 Bonhams, New Bond Street #14/R est:20000-40000
£38462 $60769 €60000 Wooded landscape with hunters and walkers (33x41cm-13x16in) s.d.1851 panel prov.lit. 16-Nov-2 Lempertz, Koln #1510/R est:40000-45000
£43548 $67500 €65322 Forest in winter (19x16cm-7x6in) s.d.1842 panel prov.lit. 29-Oct-2 Sotheby's, New York #32/R est:20000-30000
£53459 $82327 €85000 Een Heuvelachtig landschap waarin eene Burgtruine en een rivier in de agtergrond (29x40cm-11x16in) s.d.1854 panel prov.exhib.lit. 23-Oct-2 Christie's, Amsterdam #120/R est:90000-120000
£60127 $95000 €90191 Figure walking a dog on a path in winter landscape (37x51cm-15x20in) s.d.1836 panel prov. 23-Apr-3 Christie's, Rockefeller NY #20/R est:120000-160000
£157233 $242138 €250000 Skaters with a horse drawn sledge on a frozen river (37x46cm-15x18in) s.d.1837 panel prov.exhib.lit. 22-Oct-2 Sotheby's, Amsterdam #146/R est:270000-300000
£207547 $319623 €330000 Travellers on a country road in a wooded river landscape (72x100cm-28x39in) s.d.1852 panel prov.exhib.lit. 22-Oct-2 Sotheby's, Amsterdam #140/R est:350000-500000
Works on paper
£1258 $1937 €2000 Harvesters resting near a shed (16x21cm-6x8in) init. pencil pen ink wash exhib. 23-Oct-2 Christie's, Amsterdam #75/R est:2000-3000

£2830 $4358 €4500 Soldiers resting by a forest (24x32cm-9x13in) s.d.1830 pencil pen ink grey wash exhib.lit. 23-Oct-2 Christie's, Amsterdam #68/R est:4000-6000
£3333 $5500 €4800 Cottage by a stream (11x15cm-4x6in) s. pen black ink W/C. 1-Jul-3 Christie's, Amsterdam #18 est:1500-2000

KOEKKOEK, Barend Cornelis (attrib) (1803-1862) Dutch
£4500 $7289 €6525 Landscape with man and cattle on village road (33x48cm-13x19in) bears sig.indis.d.183. panel prov. 25-May-3 Uppsala Auktionskammare, Uppsala #62/R est:40000-50000 (S.KR 58000)

KOEKKOEK, Gerard (1871-1956) Dutch
£2763 $4476 €4200 Haybarge in a stiff breeze (19x24cm-7x9in) s.d.1893 panel. 21-Jan-3 Christie's, Amsterdam #12/R est:2200-2800
£5660 $8717 €9000 Katwijker bomschuiten in open water (81x58cm-32x23in) s.d.1897. 23-Oct-2 Christie's, Amsterdam #18/R est:3000-5000

KOEKKOEK, H (1815-1882) Dutch
£545 $855 €850 Lookout post (10x15cm-4x6in) s. panel. 19-Nov-2 Hamilton Osborne King, Dublin #404
£5223 $8148 €8200 Le dechargement du scheldeboot sur la glace (24x34cm-9x13in) s. 11-Nov-2 Horta, Bruxelles #228 est:4000-6000

KOEKKOEK, Hendrik Barend (1849-1909) Dutch
£2100 $3339 €3150 Winter and summer figures in a landscape with sheep (18x28cm-7x11in) s. pair. 19-Mar-3 John Nicholson, Haslemere #1170/R est:1800-2500
£2201 $3390 €3500 Peasant woman on a forest path, in summer. In winter (20x25cm-8x10in) s. pair. 22-Oct-2 Sotheby's, Amsterdam #50/R est:4000-6000
£2300 $3565 €3450 Winter. Summer (18x28cm-7x11in) s. s.i.verso pair. 29-Oct-2 Gorringes, Lewes #1301/R est:1000-1500
£2800 $4424 €4200 Figures on a tack through a wood (75x62cm-30x24in) s. s.i.verso. 2-Dec-2 Bonhams, Bath #115/R est:2500-3500
£4200 $7014 €6090 Woman at well with sheep in a wooded landscape. Travellers resting beneath a tree with sheep (58x79cm-23x31in) s. pair. 25-Jun-3 Cheffins, Cambridge #788 est:4000-6000
£6164 $9678 €9000 Women gathering wood in a winter landscape (76x64cm-30x25in) s. 15-Apr-3 Sotheby's, Amsterdam #73/R est:4000-6000
£7143 $11286 €10715 Wood gatherers in a winter forest (102x75cm-40x30in) s. 26-Nov-2 Sotheby's, Melbourne #197/R est:20000-30000 (A.D 20000)

KOEKKOEK, Hendrik Pieter (1843-1890) Dutch
£320 $496 €480 Woman on a country path (36x51cm-14x20in) s. panel. 26-Sep-2 Lane, Penzance #151
£2500 $4000 €3625 Travellers on a country lane (29x41cm-11x16in) s.d.1869 panel. 16-May-3 Skinner, Boston #31/R est:2500-3000
£3500 $5565 €5250 Wood gatherers (30x45cm-12x18in) s. 20-Mar-3 Christie's, Kensington #143/R est:4000-6000
£11000 $17270 €16500 Summer landscape with figures netting at a stream (91x117cm-36x46in) s. 19-Nov-2 Bonhams, New Bond Street #13/R est:10000-15000

Works on paper
£318 $497 €500 Summer day with children playing (40x25cm-16x10in) s. W/C. 6-Nov-2 Vendue Huis, Gravenhage #449/R

KOEKKOEK, Hermanus (1815-1882) Dutch
£6707 $11000 €9725 Shipwreck off the coast (38x58cm-15x23in) s. 7-Jun-3 Neal Auction Company, New Orleans #150/R est:12000-18000
£6944 $11042 €10000 Fishermen on a jetty with sailing vessels approaching (23x31cm-9x12in) s.d.1858 panel. 29-Apr-3 Christie's, Amsterdam #182/R est:10000-15000
£12057 $19532 €17000 Fishermen on the beach (10x15cm-4x6in) s. panel. 22-May-3 Dorotheum, Vienna #51/R est:5000-6000
£12579 $19371 €20000 Calm, fishing vessels at anchor in a river estuary (32x43cm-13x17in) s.d.1833 panel. 23-Oct-2 Christie's, Amsterdam #131/R est:15000-20000
£13309 $21295 €18500 River landscape (33x43cm-13x17in) mono. panel prov. 17-May-3 Lempertz, Koln #1418/R est:20000
£17610 $27119 €28000 Sailing vessels off the Dutch Coast (40x54cm-16x21in) s.d.1836 panel. 22-Oct-2 Sotheby's, Amsterdam #176/R est:25000-35000
£20548 $32260 €30000 Sailing vessels in choppy waters (40x54cm-16x21in) s. panel prov. 15-Apr-3 Sotheby's, Amsterdam #152/R est:15000-20000
£26027 $40863 €38000 Shipwreck near the coast (57x100cm-22x39in) s. 15-Apr-3 Sotheby's, Amsterdam #172/R est:12000-15000
£30000 $47100 €45000 On the Scheldt (38x58cm-15x23in) s.d.1864 prov. 19-Nov-2 Sotheby's, London #137/R est:15000-20000
£31250 $49687 €45000 Shipping in a breeze with figures in the foreground (37x58cm-15x23in) s. 29-Apr-3 Christie's, Amsterdam #201/R est:50000-70000
£35000 $54250 €52500 Shipping on a calm (39x55cm-15x22in) s.d.1852. 4-Dec-2 Christie's, London #28/R est:30000-40000
£37000 $60680 €55500 Bringing in the catch (36x58cm-14x23in) s. prov. 3-Jun-3 Sotheby's, London #149/R est:15000-25000
£45000 $73800 €67500 Provisoning a tall ship at anchor (38x58cm-15x23in) s. prov. 3-Jun-3 Sotheby's, London #148/R est:15000-25000

Works on paper
£242 $382 €363 Dutch river view with windmills (29x18cm-11x7in) s. W/C. 18-Nov-2 Waddingtons, Toronto #189/R (C.D 600)

KOEKKOEK, Hermanus (attrib) (19th C) Dutch
£1900 $3078 €2850 Shipping and barges off the Dutch coast (45x61cm-18x24in) s. 23-May-3 Lyon & Turnbull, Edinburgh #78 est:1000-1500

Works on paper
£851 $1421 €1200 Navires pres d'un cote Hollandaise (27x40cm-11x16in) s. graphite W/C vellum exec.c.1850. 18-Jun-3 Charbonneaux, Paris #7/R

KOEKKOEK, Hermanus (jnr) (1836-1909) Dutch
£758 $1206 €1100 View of a boat in a harbour near a town (45x35cm-18x14in) s. 10-Mar-3 Sotheby's, Amsterdam #115
£2105 $3411 €3200 View of a Dutch town along a river (61x92cm-24x36in) s. 21-Jan-3 Christie's, Amsterdam #133/R est:3000-5000
£2222 $3533 €3200 Picnic in the dunes (30x43cm-12x17in) s. 29-Apr-3 Christie's, Amsterdam #81/R est:2500-3500
£3333 $5500 €4800 Setting out from the harbour (46x61cm-18x24in) s. 1-Jul-3 Christie's, Amsterdam #93/R est:5000-7000
£4777 $7357 €7500 Sailing barges setting out for sea (64x81cm-25x32in) s. 3-Sep-2 Christie's, Amsterdam #281/R est:3000-4000
£10432 $16691 €14500 Entree du port animee (55x88cm-22x35in) s. 13-May-3 Vanderkindere, Brussels #35/R est:8000-10000

Works on paper
£311 $516 €451 Rotterdam, Holland (36x53cm-14x21in) s.i.verso W/C. 10-Jun-3 Ritchie, Toronto #141/R (C.D 700)
£479 $748 €700 View of a wooden mill near Haarlem (35x52cm-14x20in) bears sig. W/C. 14-Apr-3 Glerum, Amsterdam #45/R
£479 $748 €700 View of a town and a river (35x52cm-14x20in) bears sig. W/C. 14-Apr-3 Glerum, Amsterdam #47/R

KOEKKOEK, Hermanus Willem (1867-1929) Dutch
£7639 $12146 €11000 Troop of horse artillery, gele rijders (27x21cm-11x8in) s. panel. 29-Apr-3 Christie's, Amsterdam #8/R est:1500-2500

KOEKKOEK, J H B (1840-1912) Dutch
£382 $589 €600 Den waterval , a rapid flow (42x66cm-17x26in) s. 3-Sep-2 Christie's, Amsterdam #116
£2866 $4414 €4500 Fishermen at work on the English coast (37x59cm-15x23in) s.d.1890. 3-Sep-2 Christie's, Amsterdam #322 est:5000-7000

KOEKKOEK, Jan Hermanus (1778-1851) Dutch
£2979 $4617 €4469 Vessels in high seas (30x38cm-12x15in) s. panel prov. 4-Dec-2 AB Stockholms Auktionsverk #1889/R est:40000-50000 (S.KR 42000)
£3000 $4860 €4500 Caught in a stiff breeze (46x57cm-18x22in) 21-May-3 Christie's, Kensington #661/R est:2000-4000

KOEKKOEK, Jan Hermanus Barend (1840-1912) Dutch
£1282 $2000 €1923 Untitled (28x36cm-11x14in) board. 30-Mar-3 Susanin's, Chicago #6049/R est:3000-5000
£2222 $3533 €3200 Setting out on choppy waters (11x16cm-4x6in) s. panel. 29-Apr-3 Christie's, Amsterdam #55/R est:3500-4500
£3846 $6038 €6000 Shipwreck off English coast (34x52cm-13x20in) s. 21-Nov-2 Van Ham, Cologne #1728/R est:2000
£4392 $6851 €6500 Sailing ships off coast (36x54cm-14x21in) s. 27-Mar-3 Dr Fritz Nagel, Stuttgart #825/R est:2800
£7006 $10930 €11000 Fishing couple on the beach (24x41cm-9x16in) s. panel. 6-Nov-2 Vendue Huis, Gravenhage #414/R est:12000-15000
£10063 $15497 €16000 Shipping on the river Maas near Rotterdam (25x42cm-10x17in) s. panel. 22-Oct-2 Sotheby's, Amsterdam #28/R est:6000-8000
£12324 $19842 €17500 River view (36x58cm-14x23in) s.d.1889. 7-May-3 Vendue Huis, Gravenhage #388/R est:22000-25000
£23973 $37637 €35000 Harbours of Hoorn (38x59cm-15x23in) s.d.1861. 15-Apr-3 Sotheby's, Amsterdam #160/R est:8000-12000

Works on paper
£400 $648 €600 Dutch barque Cornelia off a fleet anchorage (22x32cm-9x13in) init. pencil pen brown ink W/C. 21-May-3 Christie's, Kensington #415/R

KOEKKOEK, Marinus Adrianus I (1807-1870) Dutch
£886 $1373 €1400 Fishing boat at harbour entry (20x27cm-8x11in) s. 24-Sep-2 Galerie Moderne, Brussels #939/R

£1172 $1852 €1700 Vaches en foret (42x38cm-17x15in) s. 2-Apr-3 Vanderkindere, Brussels #518/R est:750-1000
£6000 $9840 €9000 Wooded landscape with cottage and cattle watering (25x32cm-10x13in) s.d.1849 panel. 4-Feb-3 Sworder & Son, Bishops Stortford #122/R est:4000-5000
£6289 $9686 €10000 Figures conversing on a sandy track at the edge of a forest (34x46cm-13x18in) s. indis d.1854 panel. 23-Oct-2 Christie's, Amsterdam #39/R est:7000-9000
£6500 $10855 €9750 Wooded landscape with peasants on a country road (47x62cm-19x24in) s.d.1864 prov. 18-Jun-3 Christie's, Kensington #46/R est:7000-9000
£11806 $18771 €17000 Travelers in a wooded river landscape (44x55cm-17x22in) s.d.1853. 29-Apr-3 Christie's, Amsterdam #188/R est:15000-20000
£34911 $56555 €50621 Pastoral landscape with figures and cattle (90x114cm-35x45in) s. prov. 26-May-3 Bukowskis, Stockholm #258/R est:70000-80000 (S.KR 450000)
£41667 $66250 €60000 Extensive river landscape with figure unloading a stone transport (49x66cm-19x26in) s.d.1854. 29-Apr-3 Christie's, Amsterdam #183/R est:25000-35000

KOEKKOEK, Marinus Adrianus I (attrib) (1807-1870) Dutch
£694 $1097 €1000 Landscape with shepherd and cattle (24x29cm-9x11in) panel. 23-Apr-3 Rabourdin & Choppin de Janvry, Paris #64/R
£2759 $4359 €4000 Winter evening landscape with ice skaters (55x68cm-22x27in) bears s. 5-Apr-3 Hans Stahl, Hamburg #36 est:4500

KOEKKOEK, Marinus Adrianus II (1873-1944) Dutch
£582 $908 €850 Hens and a cock near a brick wall (18x25cm-7x10in) s. panel. 14-Apr-3 Glerum, Amsterdam #38/R
Works on paper
£272 $433 €400 Paysanne en promenade (22x34cm-9x13in) s. W/C. 19-Mar-3 Hotel des Ventes Mosan, Brussels #272/R

KOEKKOEK, Willem (1839-1895) Dutch
£9500 $14724 €14250 Dutch town houses (16x23cm-6x9in) s. panel. 3-Dec-2 Sotheby's, Olympia #224/R est:3000-5000
£25316 $40000 €37974 Dutch street with figures by an inn (54x69cm-21x27in) s. prov. 23-Apr-3 Christie's, Rockefeller NY #19/R est:50000-70000
£45000 $70650 €67500 Dutch street with church tower (54x70cm-21x28in) s. prov. 19-Nov-2 Sotheby's, London #138/R est:35000-45000
£48000 $76320 €72000 Figures conversing in a Dutch town (54x70cm-21x28in) s. 18-Mar-3 Bonhams, New Bond Street #15/R est:40000-60000
£65000 $102050 €97500 Street in Vianen, Holland (54x70cm-21x28in) s. prov. 19-Nov-2 Sotheby's, London #139/R est:40000-60000
£79861 $126979 €115000 Winter, daily activities on a sunny day in Oudewater (62x75cm-24x30in) s. prov. 29-Apr-3 Christie's, Amsterdam #209/R est:45000-55000
£115000 $178250 €172500 Town in summer (84x124cm-33x49in) s. prov. 4-Dec-2 Christie's, London #45/R est:100000-150000
£120000 $186000 €180000 Dutch town in summer (86x124cm-34x49in) s. prov. 4-Dec-2 Christie's, London #41/R est:50000-70000
Works on paper
£1572 $2421 €2500 View in a Dutch village (21x27cm-8x11in) init. pencil W/C htd white. 23-Oct-2 Christie's, Amsterdam #71/R est:1500-2000

KOELEWYN, Job (1962-) Dutch
Sculpture
£1139 $1800 €1800 Farewell spakenburg (60cm-24in) laundry basket blankets and paste executed 1994 prov.lit. 26-Nov-2 Sotheby's, Amsterdam #312/R est:1800-2500

KOELMAN, Johan Daniel (1831-1857) Dutch
£2083 $3312 €3000 Peasant girl and cattle resting in a landscape (32x46cm-13x18in) s.d.51 panel. 29-Apr-3 Christie's, Amsterdam #44/R est:2500-3500
£8500 $13515 €12750 Summer landscape with cattle grazing (97x147cm-38x58in) s.d.53. 20-Mar-3 Christie's, Kensington #160/R est:5000-7000

KOEMPOECZI-BALOGH, Endre (1911-1977) Hungarian
£400 $628 €600 Peonies (61x76cm-24x30in) s. 16-Apr-3 Christie's, Kensington #880/R
£480 $768 €720 Still life of summer flowers in a copper bowl (60x80cm-24x31in) s. 11-Mar-3 Bonhams, Knightsbridge #30

KOENIGER, Walter (1881-1945) American
£1707 $2800 €2561 First snow (51x61cm-20x24in) 5-Feb-3 Doyle, New York #34/R est:2000-3000
£1763 $2750 €2645 Winter landscape with creek (36x36cm-14x14in) s. canvasboard. 18-Sep-2 Alderfer's, Hatfield #372/R est:800-1200
£2000 $3200 €2900 Stream in winter, possibly a Woodstock, New York view (46x55cm-18x22in) s. 16-May-3 Skinner, Boston #264/R est:2500-3500
£3165 $5000 €4748 Mountain landscape in winter (61x76cm-24x30in) s. board. 24-Apr-3 Shannon's, Milford #207/R est:4000-6000
£3906 $6250 €5859 Sunlit winter scene (76x76cm-30x30in) s. 11-Jan-3 James Julia, Fairfield #78 est:5000-7000
£5346 $8500 €8019 Distant hills, winter (89x94cm-35x37in) s.d.28. 4-Mar-3 Christie's, Rockefeller NY #60/R est:6000-8000

KOERLE, Pancraz (1823-1875) German
£1096 $1710 €1600 Elegant woman in rococo castle (41x27cm-16x11in) s. panel. 10-Apr-3 Van Ham, Cologne #1547
£1500 $2505 €2250 Serving the refreshments (53x43cm-21x17in) s.d.1866. 18-Jun-3 Christie's, Kensington #94/R est:2000-3000

KOERNER, Ernst Karl Eugen (1846-1927) German
£2500 $3900 €3750 View of the Dolmabhce Palace, Constantinople (34x52cm-13x20in) s.d.1923. 15-Oct-2 Sotheby's, London #90/R est:3000-5000
£8500 $14195 €12750 Egyptian ruins beside the Nile (100x150cm-39x59in) s.d.1892-99. 18-Jun-3 Christie's, Kensington #181/R est:6000-8000
£12179 $19122 €19000 View of Constantinople over Bosphorus (101x151cm-40x59in) s.d.1916. 21-Nov-2 Van Ham, Cologne #1729/R est:8000
£40541 $63243 €60000 Vue de la Corne d'Or (101x150cm-40x59in) s.d.1916. 28-Mar-3 Claude Aguttes, Neuilly #184/R est:80000
£45000 $70200 €67500 View across the Golden Horn, Constantinople (84x126cm-33x50in) s.d.1913 exhib. 15-Oct-2 Sotheby's, London #80/R est:20000-30000

KOERNER, W H D (1878-1938) American
£25316 $40000 €36708 Rocky mountain house (71x102cm-28x40in) s. prov.exhib.lit. 26-Jul-3 Coeur d'Alene, Hayden #130/R est:25000-35000
£30063 $47500 €43591 Once in the saddle (71x102cm-28x40in) s.d.1925 prov.exhib. 26-Jul-3 Coeur d'Alene, Hayden #131/R est:25000-35000

KOERNER, William Henry Dethlef (1878-1938) American
£1592 $2500 €2388 Mother and child at the port of embarkment (41x46cm-16x18in) s. painted c.1920 prov. 19-Nov-2 Butterfields, San Francisco #8061/R est:3000-5000
£19108 $30000 €28662 I apologize, sure (61x91cm-24x36in) s.d.1918 i.verso prov.lit. 20-Nov-2 Christie's, Los Angeles #71/R est:30000-50000

KOESTER, Alexander (1864-1932) German
£5346 $8286 €8500 Park landscape with figures (66x49cm-26x19in) s. sketch verso board. 29-Oct-2 Dorotheum, Vienna #128/R est:4000-5000
£9677 $14226 €15000 Ducks on water on sultry afternoon (45x76cm-18x30in) s. 20-Jun-2 Dr Fritz Nagel, Stuttgart #787/R
£11613 $17071 €18000 Still life with roses (32x55cm-13x22in) oval prov.lit. 20-Jun-2 Dr Fritz Nagel, Stuttgart #786/R est:18500
£13974 $21799 €20961 Ducks on pond (54x82cm-21x32in) s. 6-Nov-2 Dobiaschofsky, Bern #734/R est:36000 (S.FR 32000)
£17000 $26690 €25500 Elf enten - eleven ducks (52x69cm-20x27in) s. exhib.lit. 19-Nov-2 Sotheby's, London #171/R est:18000-22000
£17000 $28390 €25500 Weisse enten am fluss (46x77cm-18x30in) s. 19-Jun-3 Christie's, London #69/R est:10000-15000
£30216 $48345 €42000 Eight ducks resting (58x96cm-23x38in) s. 17-May-3 Lempertz, Koln #1419/R est:40000-50000
£34810 $55000 €52215 Ducks on a pond (56x76cm-22x30in) s. 23-Apr-3 Christie's, Rockefeller NY #6/R est:50000-70000
£42918 $66524 €64377 Ducks by shore (48x82cm-19x32in) s. prov. 3-Oct-2 Koller, Zurich #3104/R est:100000-150000 (S.FR 100000)
£50955 $78471 €80000 23 ducks on pond (98x170cm-39x67in) s. 5-Sep-2 Arnold, Frankfurt #798/R
Works on paper
£322 $502 €470 Eight ducks on shore (8x13cm-3x5in) pencil. 11-Apr-3 Winterberg, Heidelberg #1232
£410 $636 €640 Eight ducks walking along bank (8x15cm-3x6in) pencil paper on board prov. 7-Dec-2 Ketterer, Hamburg #152/R
£436 $676 €680 Seven ducks in reeds (10x17cm-4x7in) pencil paper on board prov. 7-Dec-2 Ketterer, Hamburg #151/R

KOESTER, Christian Philipp (1784-1851) German
£4545 $6909 €7000 Self portrait (55x50cm-22x20in) i. verso. 6-Jul-2 Berlinghof, Heidelberg #217/R est:5500

KOETS, Roelof (elder) (1592-1655) Dutch
£12162 $18973 €18000 Still life with wine glasses and nuts in Ming dish (56x68cm-22x27in) panel. 27-Mar-3 Dorotheum, Vienna #149/R est:18000-22000

KOETS, Roelof (elder-attrib) (1592-1655) Dutch
£124127 $201086 €179984 Still life of fruit and dead birds (56x108cm-22x43in) panel prov. 25-May-3 Uppsala Auktionskammare, Uppsala #7/R est:80000-100000 (S.KR 1600000)

KOETS, Roelof (elder-circle) (1592-1655) Dutch
£18244 $28460 €27000 Still life of fruit and tools on table (43x71cm-17x28in) panel. 26-Mar-3 Tajan, Paris #134/R est:30000

KOGAN, Anna (1902-1974) Russian
£37681 $61797 €52000 Syuprematist architectural composition (75x102cm-30x40in) bears i. verso prov.exhib.lit. 29-May-3 Lempertz, Koln #686/R est:60000-65000

KOGAN, Moissey (1879-1942) Russian
Sculpture
£1268 $2104 €1800 Two nude women (13x7x1cm-5x3x0in) bronze relief. 14-Jun-3 Hauswedell & Nolte, Hamburg #1295/R est:1000
Works on paper
£285 $450 €450 Two seated female nudes (14x10cm-6x4in) mono. ochre. 30-Nov-2 Bassenge, Berlin #6384/R

KOGAN, Nina (1887-1942) Russian
Works on paper
£544 $865 €800 Suprematist composition (21x14cm-8x6in) mono.cyrillic gouache collage. 28-Mar-3 Bolland & Marotz, Bremen #652/R
£559 $888 €839 Geometric composition (20x14cm-8x6in) mixed media. 10-Mar-3 Rasmussen, Vejle #655 (D.KR 6000)
£612 $973 €900 Suprematist composition (30x20cm-12x8in) gouache. 28-Mar-3 Bolland & Marotz, Bremen #651/R
£637 $994 €956 Composition (27x20cm-11x8in) s. mixed media. 5-Aug-2 Rasmussen, Vejle #314/R (D.KR 7500)
£2048 $3257 €3072 Geometric composition (26x20cm-10x8in) s. mixed media. 10-Mar-3 Rasmussen, Vejle #665 est:4000 (D.KR 22000)
£3205 $5032 €5000 Composition (41x31cm-16x12in) mono.verso W/C crayon. 12-Dec-2 Rabourdin & Choppin de Janvry, Paris #172/R est:6000

KOGL, B (1892-1969) German
£419 $616 €650 Two cats (12x11cm-5x4in) s. 24-Jun-2 Dr Fritz Nagel, Stuttgart #5943/R

KOGL, Benedict (1892-1969) German
£405 $632 €600 Black and white kitten (11x8cm-4x3in) s. panel. 26-Mar-3 Hugo Ruef, Munich #147
£475 $741 €750 Two kittens (23x16cm-9x6in) s. 14-Sep-2 Weidler, Nurnberg #301/R
£573 $894 €900 Cat with kittens (12x16cm-5x6in) s. panel. 6-Nov-2 Hugo Ruef, Munich #1173/R
£676 $1054 €1000 Kittens playing (12x15cm-5x6in) s. panel. 27-Mar-3 Dr Fritz Nagel, Stuttgart #823/R
£774 $1138 €1200 Young cats watching beetle (18x24cm-7x9in) s. 20-Jun-2 Dr Fritz Nagel, Stuttgart #782/R
£774 $1138 €1200 Kittens watching butterfly (18x24cm-7x9in) s. 20-Jun-2 Dr Fritz Nagel, Stuttgart #783/R
£774 $1138 €1200 Kittens playing in basket (18x24cm-7x9in) s. panel. 20-Jun-2 Dr Fritz Nagel, Stuttgart #784/R
£816 $1298 €1200 Three kittens (19x24cm-7x9in) s. board. 20-Mar-3 Neumeister, Munich #2665/R
£962 $1490 €1500 Three young cats on the meadow (18x24cm-7x9in) s. panel lit. 7-Dec-2 Bergmann, Erlangen #817/R est:1300
£1013 $1580 €1600 Three kittens (17x23cm-7x9in) s. panel lit. 14-Sep-2 Bergmann, Erlangen #755/R
£1497 $2380 €2200 Five kittens with butterflies (18x24cm-7x9in) s. panel. 19-Mar-3 Neumeister, Munich #610/R est:1200

KOGLER, Peter (1959-) Austrian
£694 $1146 €1000 Ant (90x60cm-35x24in) s.i.d.91 verso acrylic screenprint. 1-Jul-3 Artcurial Briest, Paris #870/R
£3191 $5170 €4500 Eye and brain (90x90cm-35x35in) s.i.d.88 acrylic. 20-May-3 Dorotheum, Vienna #86/R est:4500-6000
£3378 $5270 €5000 Untitled (113x113cm-44x44in) s.d.96 verso acrylic. 25-Mar-3 Wiener Kunst Auktionen, Vienna #41/R est:5500-8000

KOHEN, Linda (1924-) Italian/Brazilian
£288 $453 €450 Untitled (42x53cm-17x21in) s. cardboard. 16-Dec-2 Castellana, Madrid #941/R
£414 $662 €600 Still life (43x52cm-17x20in) s. cardboard. 11-Mar-3 Castellana, Madrid #60/R

KOHL, Hans (1897-1990) German
£601 $938 €950 Three male nudes (100x110cm-39x43in) board lit. 14-Sep-2 Bergmann, Erlangen #769/R

KOHL, Thomas (1960-) German
£725 $1188 €1000 Seascape (20x44cm-8x17in) s.i.d.1994 verso panel prov.exhib. 28-May-3 Lempertz, Koln #229/R
£962 $1490 €1500 Liv (50x70cm-20x28in) s.i.d.1992 prov.lit. 3-Dec-2 Lempertz, Koln #249/R est:2000

KOHL, Wilhelm (19th C) German
Works on paper
£480 $744 €720 Portrait of a boy (70x56cm-28x22in) d.1872 s.verso pastel. 3-Nov-2 Lots Road, London #336

KOHLER, Alfred (1916-1983) German
Works on paper
£1139 $1777 €1800 Forest interior (51x78cm-20x31in) mono.d.1963 W/C. 18-Oct-2 Dr Fritz Nagel, Stuttgart #560/R est:2800

KOHLER, Auguste (1881-1964) German
£409 $638 €650 Circus (50x60cm-20x24in) i. 23-Sep-2 Dr Fritz Nagel, Stuttgart #6982/R

KOHLER, Florian (1935-) German
£962 $1490 €1500 Untitled (50x60cm-20x24in) s.d.56. 3-Dec-2 Christie's, Amsterdam #169/R est:1500-2500
£962 $1490 €1500 Zuruck ins Dunkel (50x60cm-20x24in) s.i.d.63. 3-Dec-2 Christie's, Amsterdam #171/R est:1500-2000

KOHLER, Gustav (1859-?) German
£300 $462 €450 Portrait of a Bavarian gentleman (18x14cm-7x6in) s.i. panel. 24-Oct-2 Christie's, Kensington #175/R

KOHLER, Hans Georg (1962-) Norwegian?
Works on paper
£597 $932 €896 Passage from life to life (65x48cm-26x19in) s. gouache ink executed 1990. 23-Sep-2 Blomqvist, Lysaker #1122 (N.KR 7000)

KOHLHOFF, Walter (1906-1981) German
£346 $533 €550 Red railway bridge (25x36cm-10x14in) s.d.1938 egg tempera board. 26-Oct-2 Dr Lehr, Berlin #233/R
£347 $549 €500 Untitled (47x63cm-19x25in) s. egg tempera panel. 26-Apr-3 Dr Lehr, Berlin #282/R
£535 $823 €850 Cityscape (57x74cm-22x29in) s.d.1975 egg tempera masonite. 26-Oct-2 Dr Lehr, Berlin #234/R
£694 $1097 €1000 Untitled (54x74cm-21x29in) s.d.1974 egg tempera panel. 26-Apr-3 Dr Lehr, Berlin #281/R
£696 $1100 €1100 Trees by canal (73x109cm-29x43in) s.d.57 egg tempera board. 30-Nov-2 Bassenge, Berlin #6388/R
Works on paper
£316 $500 €500 Underpass in winter (47x69cm-19x27in) s.d.78 bodycol egg tempera board. 30-Nov-2 Bassenge, Berlin #6391
£380 $600 €600 Northern harbour (47x63cm-19x25in) s.d.76 bodycol egg tempera board. 30-Nov-2 Bassenge, Berlin #6390

KOHLHOFF, Wilhelm (1893-1971) German
£1635 $2551 €2600 Three workshop students (60x49cm-24x19in) s. board on panel. 21-Sep-2 Bolland & Marotz, Bremen #736/R est:3000
£6522 $10696 €9000 Street, Paris (79x100cm-31x39in) s.d.30 i. verso panel. 31-May-3 Villa Grisebach, Berlin #272/R est:9000-12000
Works on paper
£385 $596 €600 Female nude sitting on edge of bed (54x40cm-21x16in) s. W/C lit. 6-Dec-2 Karlheinz Kaupp, Staufen #2316/R
£755 $1162 €1200 Figure assise (38x29cm-15x11in) s.d.1918 pastel. 22-Oct-2 Campo, Vlaamse Kaai #543/R

KOHLMANN, Ejnar (1888-1968) Finnish
£290 $459 €450 Bullfinches (47x40cm-19x16in) s.d.1952. 19-Dec-2 Hagelstam, Helsinki #813/R
£313 $498 €460 Black cocks in winter landscape (41x33cm-16x13in) s. 24-Mar-3 Bukowskis, Helsinki #129/R
£314 $484 €500 Swans (24x33cm-9x13in) s.d.1954. 27-Oct-2 Bukowskis, Helsinki #215/R
£348 $543 €550 Coastal landscape (90x60cm-35x24in) s. 12-Sep-2 Hagelstam, Helsinki #856
£408 $649 €600 Pheasants in woodland glade (61x81cm-24x32in) s,. 24-Mar-3 Bukowskis, Helsinki #130/R
£456 $711 €720 Mallards (49x66cm-19x26in) s. 15-Sep-2 Bukowskis, Helsinki #218/R
£458 $750 €700 Capercaillies crooning (61x50cm-24x20in) s. 9-Feb-3 Bukowskis, Helsinki #278/R
£520 $828 €780 Cranes (50x61cm-20x24in) s. 2-Mar-3 Uppsala Auktionskammare, Uppsala #135 (S.KR 7000)
£556 $911 €850 Birds in marshy landscape (60x82cm-24x32in) s. 9-Feb-3 Bukowskis, Helsinki #276/R
£556 $911 €850 Ducks on the ice (50x61cm-20x24in) s. 9-Feb-3 Bukowskis, Helsinki #279/R
£558 $887 €820 Stags watering (69x85cm-27x33in) s.d.1954. 24-Mar-3 Bukowskis, Helsinki #126/R
£588 $965 €900 Pair of capercaillies (60x80cm-24x31in) s. 9-Feb-3 Bukowskis, Helsinki #277/R
£633 $987 €1000 Winter landscape with capercaillies (60x81cm-24x32in) s. 15-Sep-2 Bukowskis, Helsinki #219/R

KOHLMEYER, Ida (1912-1997) American

£1384 $2200 €2076 Tangential no.3 (30x61cm-12x24in) s. s.i.verso masonite. 22-Mar-3 New Orleans Auction, New Orleans #1064/R est:1200-1800
£1806 $2800 €2709 Abstraction (30x25cm-12x10in) s. indis d. 7-Dec-2 Neal Auction Company, New Orleans #501/R est:3000-5000
£2125 $3400 €3081 Untitled abstract (122x91cm-48x36in) s. masonite. 17-May-3 New Orleans Auction, New Orleans #953/R est:3000-5000
£2516 $4000 €3774 Magnolia (89x97cm-35x38in) s. s.i.d.November 25 1968 verso. 22-Mar-3 New Orleans Auction, New Orleans #1065/R est:4500-7000

Works on paper

£267 $425 €401 Cluster series - grid of squares (15x18cm-6x7in) init.d.1979 mixed media silkscreen. 22-Mar-3 New Orleans Auction, New Orleans #1067
£458 $750 €664 Still life of a vase of flowers (15x20cm-6x8in) s. W/C tempera. 7-Jun-3 Neal Auction Company, New Orleans #418
£503 $800 €755 Cluster series - square within square (15x18cm-6x7in) init.d.1979 mixed media silkscreen. 22-Mar-3 New Orleans Auction, New Orleans #1066
£1125 $1800 €1631 Blow up drawing no.1 (81x48cm-32x19in) s.d.1978 mixed media. 17-May-3 New Orleans Auction, New Orleans #954/R est:1000-1500
£2405 $3800 €3608 Geometric composition (41x64cm-16x25in) s.d.1982 pastel. 5-Apr-3 Neal Auction Company, New Orleans #366/R est:4000-6000
£11321 $18000 €16982 Synthesis 84-1 (102x152cm-40x60in) mixed media. 22-Mar-3 New Orleans Auction, New Orleans #1063/R est:25000-40000

KOHLSCHEIN, Hans (1879-?) German

£252 $392 €400 Cannons firing in battle (21x34cm-8x13in) s. canvas on board. 9-Oct-2 Michael Zeller, Lindau #765/R
£317 $510 €450 Two peasants with horses (54x69cm-21x27in) s. 7-May-3 Michael Zeller, Lindau #766/R

KOHLUND, Ekkehard (1887-1976) Swiss

£699 $1104 €1049 Peaceful meadow (35x58cm-14x23in) s. mono.i. verso pavatex. 14-Nov-2 Stuker, Bern #339 est:600-800 (S.FR 1600)

KOHNHOLZ, Johann Wilhelm Julius (1839-1925) German

£432 $696 €648 Mountain lake (81x113cm-32x44in) s. 22-Feb-3 Rasmussen, Havnen #2354/R (D.KR 4800)
£1021 $1614 €1532 Mountain lake with rowing boat, Southern Germany, evening (83x116cm-33x46in) s. 30-Nov-2 Rasmussen, Havnen #2238 est:4000-6000 (D.KR 12000)
£3493 $5449 €5100 Paysage de montagnes au coucher du soleil (107x96cm-42x38in) s. 8-Apr-3 Gioffredo, Nice #56/R

KOHRL, Ludwig (1858-1927) German

£316 $494 €500 Moine buvant (27x21cm-11x8in) s. panel. 15-Oct-2 Vanderkindere, Brussels #68
£350 $532 €525 Tyrolean pipe smoker (27x21cm-11x8in) s. panel. 29-Aug-2 Christie's, Kensington #83/R

KOIDL, Leopold (1916-) Austrian

£374 $595 €550 Cottage in the mountains (99x69cm-39x27in) init. cardboard. 1-Mar-3 Stadion, Trieste #136

KOISTINEN, Unto (1917-1994) Finnish

£683 $1094 €950 Nude (45x60cm-18x24in) s.d.1961 paper. 17-May-3 Hagelstam, Helsinki #168/R
£719 $1151 €1000 Nude (12x9cm-5x4in) s.d.1976 board. 17-May-3 Hagelstam, Helsinki #167/R
£719 $1180 €1000 Woman (18x13cm-7x5in) s.d.1965. 5-Jun-3 Hagelstam, Helsinki #967/R
£755 $1239 €1050 Woman (18x13cm-7x5in) s.d.1965. 5-Jun-3 Hagelstam, Helsinki #968/R
£791 $1298 €1100 Crucifixion (13x22cm-5x9in) s.d.1965. 5-Jun-3 Hagelstam, Helsinki #969/R
£935 $1534 €1300 The strength of a wife. s.d.73. 4-Jun-3 Bukowskis, Helsinki #324/R
£949 $1500 €1500 Mother and child (11x10cm-4x4in) s.d.1976 board. 30-Nov-2 Hagelstam, Helsinki #162/R est:1500
£1007 $1652 €1400 Family (13x13cm-5x5in) s.d.1971. 5-Jun-3 Hagelstam, Helsinki #966/R
£1456 $2300 €2300 The lace collar (22x19cm-9x7in) s.d.1985 board. 1-Dec-2 Bukowskis, Helsinki #93/R est:2000-2500
£1646 $2567 €2600 God-daughter (17x15cm-7x6in) s.d.1984. 12-Sep-2 Hagelstam, Helsinki #819/R est:2200
£1667 $2567 €2650 Tanja (16x20cm-6x8in) s.d.1985. 24-Oct-2 Hagelstam, Helsinki #853 est:2800
£1871 $2993 €2600 Nude (21x17cm-8x7in) s.d.1980. 17-May-3 Hagelstam, Helsinki #170/R est:2500
£1899 $3000 €3000 Old theme a la Decamerone (23x27cm-9x11in) s.d.1969 board exhib. 1-Dec-2 Bukowskis, Helsinki #92/R est:3000-3500
£2215 $3500 €3500 Woman with thick hair (23x18cm-9x7in) s.d.1981 board. 30-Nov-2 Hagelstam, Helsinki #161/R est:2800
£2785 $4400 €4400 In deep thoughts (22x18cm-9x7in) s.d.1977 board. 1-Dec-2 Bukowskis, Helsinki #91/R est:3000-3500
£2911 $4600 €4600 Young woman (37x26cm-15x10in) s.d.1982 board. 30-Nov-2 Hagelstam, Helsinki #160/R est:5000
£3741 $5986 €5200 Young female (36x27cm-14x11in) s. board. 17-May-3 Hagelstam, Helsinki #169/R est:5000
£3924 $6200 €6200 Female nude (74x65cm-29x26in) s. exhib. 1-Dec-2 Bukowskis, Helsinki #90/R est:7000-7500
£5102 $8112 €7500 Brudnabbar (63x51cm-25x20in) s.d.1980. 27-Feb-3 Hagelstam, Helsinki #937 est:8000

Works on paper

£491 $755 €780 Woman (63x45cm-25x18in) s.d.1962 mixed media. 24-Oct-2 Hagelstam, Helsinki #862
£604 $930 €960 Mother and child (45x40cm-18x16in) s.d.1978 wash. 24-Oct-2 Hagelstam, Helsinki #1046
£1056 $1701 €1500 Woman resting (51x39cm-20x15in) s.d.1976 Indian ink wash. 10-May-3 Bukowskis, Helsinki #135/R est:1500-1800

KOIVISTO, Aukusti (1886-1962) Finnish

£264 $409 €420 Landscape from Lapland (50x69cm-20x27in) s.d.1941. 6-Oct-2 Bukowskis, Helsinki #208/R

KOIVU, Rudolf (1890-1946) Finnish

£361 $571 €560 Beach landscape (38x53cm-15x21in) s. 19-Dec-2 Hagelstam, Helsinki #883

Works on paper

£252 $387 €400 On the way to church at Christmas (15x26cm-6x10in) W/C. 24-Oct-2 Hagelstam, Helsinki #881
£252 $387 €400 Joulutouhu - 1935 (31x24cm-12x9in) mixed media original to cover picture. 24-Oct-2 Hagelstam, Helsinki #893
£252 $387 €400 Kotiliesi (29x22cm-11x9in) s. W/C original to cover picture. 24-Oct-2 Hagelstam, Helsinki #894
£252 $387 €400 Pieni joulupukki - 1935 (22x15cm-9x6in) s. mixed media original to cover picture. 24-Oct-2 Hagelstam, Helsinki #898
£258 $408 €400 From the south (15x28cm-6x11in) W/C. 19-Dec-2 Hagelstam, Helsinki #885
£264 $407 €420 Pastelliliituja (13x13cm-5x5in) mixed media original to lid of box. 24-Oct-2 Hagelstam, Helsinki #886
£264 $407 €420 Kotiliesi (29x22cm-11x9in) mixed media original to cover picture. 24-Oct-2 Hagelstam, Helsinki #889
£264 $407 €420 Joulutouhu - 1932 (31x22cm-12x9in) s. mixed media original to cover picture. 24-Oct-2 Hagelstam, Helsinki #891
£327 $504 €520 Frost II (13x32cm-5x13in) s. mixed media. 24-Oct-2 Hagelstam, Helsinki #879/R
£365 $562 €580 At the front (24x18cm-9x7in) s.d.1940 mixed media. 24-Oct-2 Hagelstam, Helsinki #877
£374 $591 €580 On the beach (27x23cm-11x9in) s.d.1930 W/C. 19-Dec-2 Hagelstam, Helsinki #897/R
£390 $601 €620 Joulutouhu (36x25cm-14x10in) mixed media original to cover picture. 24-Oct-2 Hagelstam, Helsinki #890
£415 $639 €660 Returning home (26x20cm-10x8in) s.d.1940 mixed media. 24-Oct-2 Hagelstam, Helsinki #878
£422 $671 €620 Children (10x21cm-4x8in) s. mixed media. 27-Feb-3 Hagelstam, Helsinki #828/R
£422 $671 €620 Child (7x20cm-3x8in) s. mixed media. 27-Feb-3 Hagelstam, Helsinki #829/R
£453 $697 €720 Troll (30x23cm-12x9in) s. W/C. 24-Oct-2 Hagelstam, Helsinki #882
£581 $917 €900 Wood (43x31cm-17x12in) s. W/C. 19-Dec-2 Hagelstam, Helsinki #884
£786 $1211 €1250 Soldiers skiing (27x19cm-11x7in) s.d.1940 mixed media. 24-Oct-2 Hagelstam, Helsinki #876/R

KOKEN, Paul (1853-?) German

£1013 $1600 €1600 Summer's day in Ottersdorf harbour (45x31cm-18x12in) s.i.d.Juni 86 canvas on board lit. 29-Nov-2 Schloss Ahlden, Ahlden #1256/R est:1400
£1509 $2355 €2400 Church in winter landscape (64x96cm-25x38in) s.i. lit. 20-Sep-2 Schloss Ahlden, Ahlden #1131/R est:2400

KOKINE, Mikhail (1921-) Russian

£658 $1066 €1000 Garden (73x54cm-29x21in) s. 21-Jan-3 Durán, Madrid #727/R

KOKO-MICOLETZKY, Friedrich (1887-1981) Austrian

£833 $1292 €1300 High mountains on winter's day (60x80cm-24x31in) s.i. 6-Dec-2 Michael Zeller, Lindau #810/R
£5484 $8500 €8226 Die jungfrau im alpengau, Schweiz (41x61cm-16x24in) s. 2-Nov-2 North East Auctions, Portsmouth #36/R

KOKOSCHKA, Oskar (1886-1980) Austrian

£12805 $21000 €18567 Untitled - self portrait (30x23cm-12x9in) s. prov.exhib. 1-Jun-3 Wright, Chicago #100/R est:20000-25000

Prints

£2158 $3453 €3000 Summer flowers in glass jug (59x48cm-23x19in) s. num.70/150 col lithograph. 15-May-3 Neumeister, Munich #289/R est:2000-2200
£2848 $4500 €4500 Summer flowers with roses (55x49cm-22x19in) s.i. col lithograph. 27-Nov-2 Dorotheum, Vienna #253/R est:2800-3000
£3546 $5745 €5000 Helene Ritscher (66x57cm-26x22in) s. lithograph. 20-May-3 Dorotheum, Vienna #125/R est:5000-5500

Works on paper

£283 $439 €450 Sphinge (18x24cm-7x9in) mono.i.d.60 blue ink dr. 30-Oct-2 Artcurial Briest, Paris #282
£405 $632 €608 Bacchus boy (11x8cm-4x3in) i. verso Indian ink. 18-Sep-2 Kunsthallen, Copenhagen #96/R (D.KR 4800)
£616 $954 €924 Drawing (15x10cm-6x4in) pen Indian ink dr exec.1936. 3-Dec-2 SOGA, Bratislava #197/R (SL.K 39000)
£845 $1403 €1200 Ex Libris Frau Olga Marx (10x9cm-4x4in) mono.d. gouache pencil. 14-Jun-3 Hauswedell & Nolte, Hamburg #1296/R
£1258 $1950 €2000 L'art abstrait (21x16cm-8x6in) s.i.d.58 col crayon dr. 30-Oct-2 Artcurial Briest, Paris #281 est:1900-2500
£2536 $4159 €3500 Nevin - beach with figure (19x28cm-7x11in) s.d.43 col pen. 31-May-3 Villa Grisebach, Berlin #596/R est:2500-3000
£2848 $4500 €4500 Girl walking (68x51cm-27x20in) s. Indian ink prov.lit. 30-Nov-2 Villa Grisebach, Berlin #208/R est:5000-6000
£3623 $5942 €5000 Girl's head (38x28cm-15x11in) s.d.44 col chks prov. 31-May-3 Villa Grisebach, Berlin #287/R est:4000-5000
£3797 $6000 €6000 Seated nude (56x44cm-22x17in) s. ochre prov. 30-Nov-2 Villa Grisebach, Berlin #209/R est:8000-12000
£3797 $6000 €6000 Portrait of Roswitha Haftmann (59x42cm-23x17in) s.d.5.10.75 chk prov.lit. 30-Nov-2 Villa Grisebach, Berlin #328/R est:7000-8000
£3822 $6000 €5733 Portrait (56x43cm-22x17in) init. indis i.d.53 gouache. 22-Nov-2 Skinner, Boston #395/R est:8000-12000
£5000 $7750 €7500 Der krebs (30x36cm-12x14in) s. W/C htd white. 5-Dec-2 Christie's, Kensington #142/R est:5000-7000
£7595 $12000 €12000 Girl seated (66x45cm-26x18in) s. chk exhib.prov. 27-Nov-2 Dorotheum, Vienna #13/R est:12000-15000
£8861 $14000 €14000 Portrait of Ezra Pound (57x46cm-22x18in) i. chk lit. 30-Nov-2 Villa Grisebach, Berlin #327/R est:8000-10000
£9000 $13950 €13500 Stehendes madchen (68x47cm-27x19in) s. pen ink executed c.1919 prov.exhib.lit. 5-Dec-2 Christie's, Kensington #116/R est:10000-15000
£11111 $17667 €16000 Nude boy, seated (23x26cm-9x10in) mono. pencil chl. 5-May-3 Ketterer, Munich #897/R est:4000-6000
£13043 $21391 €18000 Flowers (63x50cm-25x20in) s.d.1945 W/C bodycol prov.exhib. 31-May-3 Villa Grisebach, Berlin #289/R est:10000-15000
£15094 $23547 €24000 Mannlicher ark - Male nude (45x31cm-18x12in) init. pencil double-sided. 9-Oct-2 Sotheby's, London #116/R est:9000-12000
£16456 $26000 €26000 Minona (40x25cm-16x10in) s.d.44 col pen study verso prov. 27-Nov-2 Dorotheum, Vienna #33/R est:26000-32000
£20833 $32917 €32500 Flowers (66x48cm-26x19in) s.d.1971 W/C prov. 14-Nov-2 Neumeister, Munich #601/R est:45000-50000
£20833 $32917 €32500 Still life of flowers (51x44cm-20x17in) s.d.1970 W/C prov. 14-Nov-2 Neumeister, Munich #602/R est:45000-50000
£88608 $140000 €140000 Standing woman. Figure (41x26cm-16x10in) s. init.verso pencil double-sided. 26-Nov-2 Sotheby's, Amsterdam #100/R est:4000-6000

KOLAR, Jiri (1914-) Czechoslovakian

£574 $931 €810 Untitled (31x23cm-12x9in) mono.d.64 verso collage board. 24-May-3 Van Ham, Cologne #332/R

Works on paper

£278 $441 €400 OH (30x48cm-12x19in) s.d.91 verso collage decoupage. 29-Apr-3 Artcurial Briest, Paris #644
£1088 $1731 €1600 Assomption terrestre (40x55cm-16x22in) s.i.d.1980-82 collage panel. 24-Mar-3 Cornette de St.Cyr, Paris #171/R
£1088 $1731 €1600 Little homage to Mondrian (55x40cm-22x16in) s.d.1981-82 collage panel. 24-Mar-3 Cornette de St.Cyr, Paris #170/R

KOLARE, Nils (1930-) Swedish

£281 $443 €422 Geometric composition (170x72cm-67x28in) s. acrylic. 30-Nov-2 Goteborg Auktionsverk, Sweden #560/R (S.KR 4000)
£596 $929 €894 Composition (70x80cm-28x31in) s. 6-Nov-2 AB Stockholms Auktionsverk #926/R (S.KR 8500)
£734 $1181 €1101 Untitled (80x80cm-31x31in) s.d.81 acrylic. 7-May-3 AB Stockholms Auktionsverk #1012/R (S.KR 9500)

KOLB, Alexander Khristoforovich (19th C) Russian

Works on paper

£17000 $27540 €25500 Interior of the Uspensky Cathedral Moscow (48x39cm-19x15in) s.d.1855 W/C htd white on card. 21-May-3 Sotheby's, London #10/R est:6000-8000

KOLB, Hans (1877-1951) German?

£368 $582 €552 Woman seated in deck chair (74x65cm-29x26in) s. 17-Dec-2 Grev Wedels Plass, Oslo #163 (N.KR 4200)

KOLBE, Georg (1877-1947) German

Sculpture

£4516 $7000 €6774 Nu (42cm-17in) init. gold pat. bronze i.f.H.Noack prov. 26-Sep-2 Christie's, Rockefeller NY #611/R est:8000-10000
£4531 $7250 €6797 Kauernde (28cm-11in) mono.num.7 bronze. 15-Mar-3 Selkirks, St. Louis #600/R est:6000-8000
£5797 $9507 €8000 Portrait mask of Mechtilde Lichnowsky (31cm-12in) mono. iron marble socle prov. 31-May-3 Villa Grisebach, Berlin #258/R est:4000-5000
£8333 $13167 €13000 Looking back (70cm-28in) mono. brown pat.bronze. 14-Nov-2 Neumeister, Munich #603/R est:16000-18000
£8750 $14000 €12688 Standing nude (43cm-17in) mono.i.d.1912 gold brown pat bronze st.f.H Noack. 17-May-3 Selkirks, St. Louis #256/R est:10000-15000
£9615 $15000 €14423 Kniende (54cm-21in) mono. brown pat. bronze st.f.Noack conceived 1926 lit. 7-Nov-2 Christie's, Rockefeller NY #271/R est:30000-40000
£11538 $18000 €17307 Traum (36cm-14in) mono. red brown pat. bronze st.f.Noack cast 1922 prov.lit. 7-Nov-2 Christie's, Rockefeller NY #270/R est:25000-35000
£12579 $20000 €18869 Kneeling woman (54cm-21in) mono.st.f.Noack brown pat bronze lit. 27-Feb-3 Christie's, Rockefeller NY #26/R est:22000
£13043 $21391 €18000 Announcement - Victoria (33cm-13in) mono.verso brown green pat.bronze Cast.H.Noack Berlin. 31-May-3 Villa Grisebach, Berlin #286/R est:18000-24000
£13462 $20865 €21000 Crouching figure (28cm-11in) mono. dark pat.bronze Cast.HNoack Berlin lit. 4-Dec-2 Lempertz, Koln #826/R est:20000
£25362 $41594 €35000 Seated figure (28cm-11in) mono. yellow pat.bronze Cast.H.Noack Berlin prov. 30-May-3 Villa Grisebach, Berlin #19/R est:25000-35000
£30769 $47692 €48000 Design for fountain figure (85cm-33in) mono. dark pat bronze prov.exhib.lit. 4-Dec-2 Lempertz, Koln #13/R est:40000-45000
£36232 $59420 €50000 Allegro (72cm-28in) mono.i. brown pat.bronze Cast.H.Noack Berlin Friedenau prov.exhib. 30-May-3 Villa Grisebach, Berlin #58/R est:50000-70000
£51282 $80000 €76923 Die sturzende (38x46x34cm-15x18x13in) init. brown pat. bronze st.f.H Noack prov.lit. 5-Nov-2 Phillips, New York #122/R est:20000-30000
£70000 $109200 €105000 Badende - Bathing woman (71cm-28in) init. bronze st.f.H Noack prov.lit. 9-Oct-2 Sotheby's, London #29/R est:70000-90000

Works on paper

£1795 $2836 €2800 Embrace (42x22cm-17x9in) mono. wash sepia prov. 14-Nov-2 Neumeister, Munich #604/R est:3000-3500
£1875 $3000 €2719 Nude female (25x28cm-10x11in) mono. sepia dr. 17-May-3 Selkirks, St. Louis #257/R est:3500-4500
£9615 $14904 €15000 Kneeling female nude (39x25cm-15x10in) mono. wash brush. 7-Dec-2 Hauswedell & Nolte, Hamburg #816/R est:15000

KOLDEWAY, Bernard Marie (1859-1898) Dutch

£2548 $3975 €4000 Shell fisherman on the beach (83x106cm-33x42in) s. 6-Nov-2 Vendue Huis, Gravenhage #564/R est:3000-4000

KOLEAN, Peter (20th C) American?

£296 $450 €444 Lily pond, spring vacation (28x36cm-11x14in) s. s.i.verso board. 15-Aug-2 Doyle, New York #56

KOLESNIKOFF, Sergei (1889-?) Russian

£2390 $3728 €3800 Bare trees in sunny winter landscape (49x59cm-19x23in) s. 9-Oct-2 Michael Zeller, Lindau #766/R est:2800

Works on paper

£2222 $3511 €3200 Winter landscape (50x66cm-20x26in) s. gouache. 24-Apr-3 Dorotheum, Vienna #49/R est:1500-2000

KOLESNIKOFF, Stepan (1879-1955) Russian

£6000 $9720 €9000 Thaw (50x59cm-20x23in) s. 21-May-3 Sotheby's, London #83/R est:6000-8000

KOLESNIKOV, Ivan Feodorovich (1887-1929) Russian

£2817 $4535 €4000 Night in the city (18x30cm-7x12in) s.d.1922 board. 10-May-3 Bukowskis, Helsinki #382/R est:1500-2000

KOLIG, Anton (1886-1950) Austrian

Works on paper

£1410 $2214 €2200 Reclining male nude (47x35cm-19x14in) mono. pencil transparent paper. 20-Nov-2 Dorotheum, Klagenfurt #89 est:1300
£9420 $15449 €13000 Reclining nude (51x73cm-20x29in) mono. W/C tempera oil board. 29-May-3 Lempertz, Koln #722/R est:4000-5000

KOLITZ, Louis (1845-1914) German
£2230 $3478 €3300 England's battle in the colonies (115x170cm-45x67in) s. lit. 28-Mar-3 Karrenbauer, Konstanz #1756/R est:2500

KOLJONEN, Veli (?) Finnish
£494 $770 €780 Frosty day in Lapland (75x90cm-30x35in) s.d.81. 15-Sep-2 Bukowskis, Helsinki #221/R

KOLLAR, Jozef (1899-1982) Czechoslovakian
£315 $460 €473 Poplars (49x41cm-19x16in) wood painted c.1940. 4-Jun-2 SOGA, Bratislava #234/R est:16000 (SL.K 20000)
£378 $552 €567 Autumn in Banska Stiavnica (50x65cm-20x26in) board. 4-Jun-2 SOGA, Bratislava #233/R est:22000 (SL.K 24000)
£599 $850 €899 Stiavnica village in winter (53x73cm-21x29in) board painted c.1950. 26-Mar-2 SOGA, Bratislava #231/R (SL.K 38000)
£662 $966 €993 View of Banska Stiavnica town (58x47cm-23x19in) 4-Jun-2 SOGA, Bratislava #232/R est:32000 (SL.K 42000)

KOLLE, C A (1827-1872) Danish
£392 $623 €588 Couple walking along the jetty (18x24cm-7x9in) 5-May-3 Rasmussen, Vejle #380/R (D.KR 4200)
£517 $786 €776 Ducks by edge of water (27x40cm-11x16in) 27-Aug-2 Rasmussen, Copenhagen #1828/R (D.KR 6000)
£1281 $1973 €1922 Landscape with steep cliff by coast (30x35cm-12x14in) s. prov. 4-Sep-2 Kunsthallen, Copenhagen #34/R est:20000 (D.KR 15000)

KOLLER, Ben-Ami (1948-) French?
Works on paper
£288 $460 €400 Sans titre (28x53cm-11x21in) s. pigment pastel pierre noire. 18-May-3 Neret-Minet, Paris #182
£298 $486 €450 Still life (56x71cm-22x28in) s. chl crayon. 3-Feb-3 Cornette de St.Cyr, Paris #458

KOLLER, Julius (1939-) Czechoslovakian
£473 $671 €710 Summer landscape near Moravany village (50x72cm-20x28in) painted 1963. 26-Mar-2 SOGA, Bratislava #281/R (SL.K 30000)
Works on paper
£583 $828 €875 New cultural situation - UFO (61x100cm-24x39in) latex spray board exec.1988. 26-Mar-2 SOGA, Bratislava #280/R (SL.K 37000)
£929 $1320 €1394 Game (60x75cm-24x30in) latex textile exec.1968. 26-Mar-2 SOGA, Bratislava #279/R est:38000 (SL.K 59000)

KOLLER, Konrad (1916-2001) Austrian
Works on paper
£288 $453 €450 Church day, Villach (45x40cm-18x16in) mono.d.21.10.82 Indian ink. 20-Nov-2 Dorotheum, Klagenfurt #90

KOLLER, Oskar (20th C) German?
Works on paper
£577 $906 €900 Trees (28x38cm-11x15in) s.d.1983 W/C. 21-Nov-2 Weidler, Nurnberg #7020/R
£719 $1179 €1100 The boy (28x38cm-11x15in) s.d.1986. 6-Feb-3 Weidler, Nurnberg #7000/R est:1100

KOLLER, Rudolf (1828-1905) Swiss
£513 $805 €800 Mountainous landscape with lake (32x51cm-13x20in) 16-Dec-2 Pandolfini, Florence #72
£652 $1017 €978 Nature study with rocks (31x46cm-12x18in) s.d.1870. 16-Sep-2 Philippe Schuler, Zurich #3379 (S.FR 1500)
£1116 $1763 €1674 Cow herd on the alpine meadow (36x50cm-14x20in) mono.d.1867. 29-Nov-2 Zofingen, Switzerland #2947 est:3500 (S.FR 2600)
£3620 $6045 €5249 Two girls from Haslital (60x51cm-24x20in) mono.d.60. 24-Jun-3 Koller, Zurich #8/R est:8000-12000 (S.FR 8000)
£7042 $11549 €10211 Cows, ducks and dog by Zurichhorn (59x88cm-23x35in) s.d.1876. 4-Jun-3 Fischer, Luzern #1219/R est:15000-18000 (S.FR 15000)
£22831 $35616 €34247 Cows by the Zurichhorn (114x173cm-45x68in) s.d.1882 prov. 28-Mar-3 Koller, Zurich #3113/R est:35000-45000 (S.FR 50000)
£39450 $65881 €57203 Cowherd with cow with women cutting flax in Meiringen (45x61cm-18x24in) s.i.d.1867 lit.exhib. 20-Jun-3 Kornfeld, Bern #101/R est:60000 (S.FR 86000)
Works on paper
£708 $1146 €1253 Bearded man (43x28cm-17x11in) mono. pencil. 26-May-3 Sotheby's, Zurich #10/R est:1500-2000 (S.FR 1500)
£1584 $2645 €2297 Study of cow (37x48cm-15x19in) mono. chl. 24-Jun-3 Koller, Zurich #9/R est:2500-3500 (S.FR 3500)

KOLLER, Rudolf (attrib) (1828-1905) Swiss
£1645 $2550 €2468 Wooded landscape with fox by river (54x78cm-21x31in) i.d.1851. 24-Sep-2 Koller, Zurich #6639/R est:4000-7000 (S.FR 3800)

KOLLER-PINELL, Broncia (1863-1934) Austrian
£1793 $2869 €2600 Grace (26x40cm-10x16in) board lit.prov. 11-Mar-3 Dorotheum, Vienna #2/R est:2600-3600
£7092 $11489 €10000 Still life with parrot in cage (102x83cm-40x33in) s.d.1927 exhib. 20-May-3 Dorotheum, Vienna #137/R est:10000-13000

KOLLIKER, David (1807-1875) Swiss
£969 $1415 €1454 Mountain landscapes (42x32cm-17x13in) canvas on board pair. 17-Jun-2 Philippe Schuler, Zurich #4274/R (S.FR 2200)
Works on paper
£892 $1463 €1293 Zuich with Weid and Hongg (23x34cm-9x13in) s. gouache. 4-Jun-3 Fischer, Luzern #2722/R est:1500-1800 (S.FR 1900)

KOLLMANN, Carl Ivanovich (1788-1846) Russian
Works on paper
£800 $1264 €1200 Russian peasants (19x27cm-7x11in) d.1838 pencil W/C. 26-Nov-2 Christie's, Kensington #12/R
£811 $1265 €1200 Paysage avec russes dechargant un bloc de glace (23x31cm-9x12in) s.i. graphite pen ink W/C htd white. 27-Mar-3 Christie's, Paris #167/R
£1000 $1570 €1500 St Petersburg itinerants (16x23cm-6x9in) d.1846 pencil W/C. 20-Nov-2 Sotheby's, London #11/R est:1000-1500
£1700 $2754 €2550 Roadside scenes (20x28cm-8x11in) s.i.d.1812 W/C ink two. 21-May-3 Sotheby's, London #8/R est:1700-2200

KOLLWITZ, Kathe (1867-1945) German
Prints
£1887 $3000 €2831 Ruf des Todes (38x38cm-15x15in) s.i.num.68/100 lithograph. 2-May-3 Sotheby's, New York #193/R est:2500-3500
£1923 $2981 €3000 Trampled (24x20cm-9x8in) s.i. etching. 7-Dec-2 Hauswedell & Nolte, Hamburg #826/R est:1500
£1944 $3092 €2800 Mother with child in arms (20x13cm-8x5in) s.i. etching drypoint. 5-May-3 Ketterer, Munich #619/R est:1200-1500
£1944 $3092 €2800 Young mother with new born (28x28cm-11x11in) s.i. lithograph. 5-May-3 Ketterer, Munich #709/R est:1800-2200
£2013 $3140 €3200 Brustbild einer arbeiterfrau mit blauem (50x37cm-20x15in) s. col lithograph. 9-Oct-2 Sotheby's, London #466/R est:4500-6500
£2013 $3140 €3200 Stehende mutter, Ihr bublein futternd (19x15cm-7x6in) s. etching aquatint. 9-Oct-2 Sotheby's, London #475/R est:3500-4500
£2014 $3202 €2900 Listeners (22x19cm-9x7in) s. lithograph. 5-May-3 Ketterer, Munich #714/R est:1200-1500
£2025 $3200 €3200 Child's head (13x10cm-5x4in) s. lithograph. 30-Nov-2 Bassenge, Berlin #6418/R est:2400
£2075 $3238 €3300 Ein Weberaufstand, Weberzug (31x45cm-12x18in) s. etching. 9-Oct-2 Sotheby's, London #477/R est:2000-2500
£2083 $3312 €3000 Death and woman encapsulating child (23x28cm-9x11in) s. num.27/50 etching prov. 5-May-3 Ketterer, Munich #629/R est:2000-2500
£2083 $3312 €3000 Self portrait (14x10cm-6x4in) s. etching. 5-May-3 Ketterer, Munich #630/R est:1200-1400
£2083 $3312 €3000 Anti alcohol week (33x40cm-13x16in) s. lithograph. 5-May-3 Ketterer, Munich #663/R est:1200-1500
£2083 $3312 €3000 Infant death (37x28cm-15x11in) s.i. woodcut. 5-May-3 Ketterer, Munich #699/R est:3200-3600
£2083 $3312 €3000 Self portrait (32x30cm-13x12in) s. transfer lithograph. 5-May-3 Ketterer, Munich #716/R est:2500-3000
£2174 $3565 €3000 Maria and Elisabeth (37x34cm-15x13in) s. woodcut. 31-May-3 Villa Grisebach, Berlin #156/R est:3000-4000
£2174 $3565 €3000 Sharpening (30x29cm-12x11in) s. etching aquatint vernis mou. 31-May-3 Villa Grisebach, Berlin #605/R est:1800-2400
£2201 $3434 €3500 Brot (31x28cm-12x11in) s. lithograph. 9-Oct-2 Sotheby's, London #459/R est:2500-3000
£2201 $3434 €3500 Bauernkrieg die gefangenen (32x42cm-13x17in) s.i. etching aquatint. 9-Oct-2 Sotheby's, London #469/R est:2000-2500
£2243 $3500 €3365 Zwei Schwatzende Frauen mit Zwei Kindern (46x36cm-18x14in) s. lithograph. 14-Oct-2 Butterfields, San Francisco #1130/R est:3000-5000
£2292 $3644 €3300 Praying girl (20x15cm-8x6in) s. aquatint. 5-May-3 Ketterer, Munich #547/R est:1500-2000
£2292 $3644 €3300 Death (22x18cm-9x7in) s.i. lithograph prov. 5-May-3 Ketterer, Munich #558/R est:1500-1800
£2292 $3644 €3300 The end (25x31cm-10x12in) s. aquatint emery. 5-May-3 Ketterer, Munich #561/R est:1500-1800
£2292 $3644 €3300 Suburb (23x18cm-9x7in) s. algraph from aluminium plate. 5-May-3 Ketterer, Munich #572/R est:2500-3500
£2292 $3644 €3300 Killed in action (41x38cm-16x15in) s.i. lithograph. 5-May-3 Ketterer, Munich #654/R est:2400-2600
£2292 $3644 €3300 Self portrait (15x11cm-6x4in) s. num.3/50 woodcut. 5-May-3 Ketterer, Munich #690/R est:1800-2200
£2292 $3644 €3300 Mother and child (21x14cm-8x6in) s. lithograph prov. 5-May-3 Ketterer, Munich #703/R est:1100-1400

£2292 $3644 €3300 Self portrait (32x30cm-13x12in) s.i.d. transfer lithograph. 5-May-3 Ketterer, Munich #717/R est:2200-2500
£2292 $3644 €3300 Sleeping with child (30x36cm-12x14in) s. woodcut. 5-May-3 Ketterer, Munich #719/R est:2500-3500
£2292 $3644 €3300 Self portrait (32x30cm-13x12in) s.d. transfer lithograph. 5-May-3 Ketterer, Munich #746/R est:2500-2800
£2361 $3754 €3400 The crushed - poor family (23x19cm-9x7in) s. aquatint drypoint. 5-May-3 Ketterer, Munich #568/R est:1400-1800
£2431 $3865 €3500 Sharpening (30x30cm-12x12in) s.i. etching aquatint transfer. 5-May-3 Ketterer, Munich #596/R est:800-1200
£2431 $3865 €3500 Sacrifice (37x40cm-15x16in) s. woodcut prov. 5-May-3 Ketterer, Munich #669/R est:3000-3500
£2431 $3865 €3500 The last one - old man with noose (30x12cm-12x5in) s. woodcut lit. 5-May-3 Ketterer, Munich #696/R est:1000-1200
£2431 $3865 €3500 Mother give up your surplus! (34x31cm-13x12in) s. lithograph. 5-May-3 Ketterer, Munich #710/R est:2000-2500
£2431 $3865 €3500 Standing woman feeding child (20x15cm-8x6in) s.i. etching prov. 5-May-3 Ketterer, Munich #730/R est:2200-2500
£2639 $4196 €3800 Peasants pulling plough followed by woman (36x50cm-14x20in) s.i.d. lithograph prov. 5-May-3 Ketterer, Munich #576/R est:1800-2000
£2639 $4196 €3800 Death and woman encapsulating child (23x28cm-9x11in) s. etching prov. 5-May-3 Ketterer, Munich #628/R est:2500
£2639 $4196 €3800 Parents (35x42cm-14x17in) s.i. woodcut. 5-May-3 Ketterer, Munich #672/R est:2000-2500
£2639 $4196 €3800 Self portrait (29x22cm-11x9in) s. lithograph. 5-May-3 Ketterer, Munich #688/R est:3000-3500
£2639 $4196 €3800 Self portrait (21x30cm-8x12in) s. woodcut prov. 5-May-3 Ketterer, Munich #692/R est:2800-3000
£2639 $4196 €3800 Head of child (14x10cm-6x4in) s. lithograph. 5-May-3 Ketterer, Munich #701/R est:1200-1500
£2639 $4196 €3800 Death seizing woman (51x37cm-20x15in) s.d. lithograph. 5-May-3 Ketterer, Munich #738/R est:2400-2600
£2642 $4121 €4200 Tod, ruf des todes (38x40cm-15x16in) s. lithograph. 9-Oct-2 Sotheby's, London #462/R est:3000-4000
£2692 $4173 €4200 The end (24x31cm-9x12in) s.i. i. verso etching aquatint emery. 7-Dec-2 Hauswedell & Nolte, Hamburg #825/R est:4000
£2778 $4417 €4000 Advice (30x18cm-12x7in) s. etching drypoint. 5-May-3 Ketterer, Munich #553/R est:600-800
£2778 $4417 €4000 Weavers (21x29cm-8x11in) etching. 5-May-3 Ketterer, Munich #555/R est:1800-2200
£2778 $4417 €4000 Inspiration (56x30cm-22x12in) s.i. etching transfer. 5-May-3 Ketterer, Munich #599/R est:3000-3500
£2778 $4417 €4000 Poster (69x48cm-27x19in) s. lithograph prov. 5-May-3 Ketterer, Munich #601/R est:5000-7000
£2778 $4417 €4000 Death and woman (45x45cm-18x18in) s. etching transfer prov. 5-May-3 Ketterer, Munich #613/R est:2500-2800
£2778 $4417 €4000 Memorial sheet for Lark Liebknecht (35x50cm-14x20in) s.i. woodcut prov. 5-May-3 Ketterer, Munich #644/R est:2500-3000
£2778 $4417 €4000 Sleeping with child (30x36cm-12x14in) s. woodcut. 5-May-3 Ketterer, Munich #718/R est:2000-2500
£2778 $4417 €4000 Mary and Elisabeth (37x34cm-15x13in) s. woodcut. 5-May-3 Ketterer, Munich #721/R est:4000-4500
£2986 $4748 €4300 Young couple (30x32cm-12x13in) s.i. etching transfer. 5-May-3 Ketterer, Munich #586/R est:2000-3000
£2986 $4748 €4300 Death and woman encapsulating child (23x28cm-9x11in) s. etching prov. 5-May-3 Ketterer, Munich #627/R est:2500-3000
£2986 $4748 €4300 The widow (26x26cm-10x10in) s.i. etching prov. 5-May-3 Ketterer, Munich #635/R est:2000-2400
£2986 $4748 €4300 Self portrait (27x23cm-11x9in) s. transfer lithograph. 5-May-3 Ketterer, Munich #636/R est:1800-2200
£3019 $4709 €4800 Bauernkrieg, beim dengeln (30x30cm-12x12in) etching aquatint in brown. 9-Oct-2 Sotheby's, London #461/R est:2000-3000
£3019 $4709 €4800 Maria und Elisabeth (40x46cm-16x18in) s. woodcut. 9-Oct-2 Sotheby's, London #484/R est:4000-5500
£3125 $4969 €4500 Self portrait at table (18x13cm-7x5in) s. aquatint drypoint. 5-May-3 Ketterer, Munich #550/R est:1800-2200
£3125 $4969 €4500 Scene from Germinal (24x53cm-9x21in) s.i. etching drypoint prov. 5-May-3 Ketterer, Munich #552/R est:2200-2500
£3125 $4969 €4500 Working class woman in profile (45x33cm-18x13in) s. lithograph. 5-May-3 Ketterer, Munich #580/R est:1600-1800
£3125 $4969 €4500 Young couple (29x31cm-11x12in) s.i. etching transfer prov. 5-May-3 Ketterer, Munich #587/R est:1800-2200
£3125 $4969 €4500 Self portrait (15x15cm-6x6in) s. woodcut. 5-May-3 Ketterer, Munich #664/R est:2500-3000
£3125 $4969 €4500 Volunteers (35x50cm-14x20in) s.i. woodcut prov. 5-May-3 Ketterer, Munich #670/R est:2500-3000
£3125 $4969 €4500 City shelter (42x56cm-17x22in) s. lithograph. 5-May-3 Ketterer, Munich #708/R est:3000-3500
£3145 $4906 €5000 Selbstbildnis (21x30cm-8x12in) s. woodcut. 9-Oct-2 Sotheby's, London #474/R est:3000-5000
£3191 $5170 €4500 Mother's pride (22x31cm-9x12in) s. lithograph. 24-May-3 Van Ham, Cologne #336/R est:5000
£3205 $4968 €5000 Maria and Elizabeth (36x35cm-14x14in) s. woodcut. 7-Dec-2 Hauswedell & Nolte, Hamburg #841/R est:5000
£3333 $5300 €4800 Mother (44x58cm-17x23in) s. lithograph. 5-May-3 Ketterer, Munich #638/R est:3000-4000
£3333 $5300 €4800 Self portrait (21x26cm-8x10in) s.i. etching. 5-May-3 Ketterer, Munich #656/R est:2200-2500
£3333 $5300 €4800 Germany's children are starving! (43x69cm-17x27in) s. lithograph. 5-May-3 Ketterer, Munich #684/R est:2000-2500
£3333 $5300 €4800 City shelter (44x55cm-17x22in) s. lithograph. 5-May-3 Ketterer, Munich #707/R est:3500-4000
£3472 $5521 €5000 The crushed - corpse and naked woman at stake (24x62cm-9x24in) s.i. aquatint drypoint. 5-May-3 Ketterer, Munich #566/R est:800-1200
£3472 $5521 €5000 Break out (52x60cm-20x24in) s.d. etching aquatint transfer. 5-May-3 Ketterer, Munich #578/R est:1200-1500
£3472 $5521 €5000 Ploughing (32x45cm-13x18in) s. aquatint transfer. 5-May-3 Ketterer, Munich #603/R est:2000-2500
£3472 $5521 €5000 Armed figures in chamber (50x33cm-20x13in) s. aquatint transfer prov. 5-May-3 Ketterer, Munich #605/R est:2200-2600
£3472 $5521 €5000 Self portrait with hand on brow (15x14cm-6x6in) s.i. etching. 5-May-3 Ketterer, Munich #617/R est:1800-2200
£3472 $5521 €5000 Memorial sheet for Karl Liebknecht (34x38cm-13x15in) s.i. etching roulette. 5-May-3 Ketterer, Munich #643/R est:2200-2500
£3472 $5521 €5000 Self portrait (21x26cm-8x10in) s.i. etching prov. 5-May-3 Ketterer, Munich #658/R est:3000-4000
£3472 $5521 €5000 Self portrait (21x18cm-8x7in) s. lithograph. 5-May-3 Ketterer, Munich #731/R est:1500-1800
£3478 $5704 €4800 Mother (44x58cm-17x23in) s. lithograph. 31-May-3 Villa Grisebach, Berlin #159/R est:4000-5000
£3590 $5564 €5600 Mother's joy (22x31cm-9x12in) s. lithograph. 7-Dec-2 Hauswedell & Nolte, Hamburg #843/R est:4000
£3750 $5963 €5400 Working class woman in profile (45x33cm-18x13in) s. lithograph. 5-May-3 Ketterer, Munich #579/R est:1800-2200
£3819 $6073 €5500 Sharpening (29x30cm-11x12in) i. etching aquatint transfer. 5-May-3 Ketterer, Munich #597/R est:500-700
£3819 $6073 €5500 Lonely man (32x26cm-13x10in) s. lithograph prov. 5-May-3 Ketterer, Munich #631/R est:2000-3000
£3819 $6073 €5500 Woman with sleeping child (39x33cm-15x13in) s. lithograph. 5-May-3 Ketterer, Munich #713/R est:3500-4000
£3819 $6073 €5500 Two women with two children chatting (30x26cm-12x10in) s. lithograph. 5-May-3 Ketterer, Munich #722/R est:4500-5500
£3873 $6430 €5500 Mother (44x58cm-17x23in) s. lithograph. 14-Jun-3 Hauswedell & Nolte, Hamburg #1311/R est:5000
£4088 $6500 €6132 Tod, Frau und Kind (39x39cm-15x15in) s.i. brown etching aquatint drypoint sandpaper. 2-May-3 Sotheby's, New York #191/R est:8000-12000
£4167 $6625 €6000 Woman hiding mouth with hand (39x24cm-15x9in) transfer lithograph prov. 5-May-3 Ketterer, Munich #594/R est:3000-3500
£4167 $6625 €6000 Mother's joy (21x32cm-8x13in) s. lithograph. 5-May-3 Ketterer, Munich #728/R est:5500-6500
£4167 $6625 €6000 Call of death (37x38cm-15x15in) s.i. lithograph. 5-May-3 Ketterer, Munich #747/R est:2000-2500
£4487 $6955 €7000 City shelter (47x55cm-19x22in) s. lithograph. 7-Dec-2 Hauswedell & Nolte, Hamburg #840/R est:8000
£4507 $7482 €6400 City shelter (42x56cm-17x22in) s. lithograph. 14-Jun-3 Hauswedell & Nolte, Hamburg #1321/R est:8000
£4514 $7177 €6500 Advice (27x17cm-11x7in) s.i. lithograph. 5-May-3 Ketterer, Munich #559/R est:1200-1500
£4514 $7177 €6500 Inspiration (55x29cm-22x11in) bears sig.i. etching transfer prov. 5-May-3 Ketterer, Munich #598/R est:4000-6000
£4514 $7177 €6500 Hunger (59x43cm-23x17in) s.i. woodcut. 5-May-3 Ketterer, Munich #698/R est:2500-3000
£4514 $7177 €6500 Mother with child (36x21cm-14x8in) s. lithograph. 5-May-3 Ketterer, Munich #727/R est:3500-4000
£4861 $7729 €7000 Carmagnole (59x41cm-23x16in) s. etching aquatint drypoint prov. 5-May-3 Ketterer, Munich #569/R est:3000-4000
£4861 $7729 €7000 Mother pressing new born to her face (40x36cm-16x14in) s. lithograph prov. 5-May-3 Ketterer, Munich #705/R est:3000-4000
£4861 $7729 €7000 Visit to the children's hospital (27x34cm-11x13in) s. lithograph. 5-May-3 Ketterer, Munich #706/R est:3500-4500
£4861 $7729 €7000 Women chatting (22x20cm-9x8in) s.i. etching aquatint board prov. 5-May-3 Ketterer, Munich #723/R est:5000-6000
£4930 $8183 €7000 Out of work (36x30cm-14x12in) s.i. woodcut. 14-Jun-3 Hauswedell & Nolte, Hamburg #1318/R est:4000
£5031 $7849 €8000 Arbeiterfrau mit schlafendem jungen (39x30cm-15x12in) s. lithograph. 9-Oct-2 Sotheby's, London #471/R est:6000-8000
£5031 $7849 €8000 Mutter mit jungen (38x20cm-15x8in) s. lithograph. 9-Oct-2 Sotheby's, London #481/R est:5500-7000
£5069 $8060 €7300 Germany's children are starving! (41x29cm-16x11in) s. lithograph. 5-May-3 Ketterer, Munich #683/R est:2000-2500
£5208 $8281 €7500 Female nude holding stick (27x22cm-11x9in) s. algraph prov. 5-May-3 Ketterer, Munich #571/R est:3000-3500
£5208 $8281 €7500 Death, woman and child (41x41cm-16x16in) s.i. etching transfer prov. 5-May-3 Ketterer, Munich #620/R est:2000-2500
£5208 $8281 €7500 Mother (34x40cm-13x16in) s. num.74/100 woodcut. 5-May-3 Ketterer, Munich #676/R est:2000-3000
£5208 $8281 €7500 Prisoners listening to music (34x34cm-13x13in) s. lithograph prov. 5-May-3 Ketterer, Munich #695/R est:5000-5500
£5208 $8281 €7500 Unemployed (36x30cm-14x12in) s.i. woodcut. 5-May-3 Ketterer, Munich #697/R est:2400-2800
£5556 $8833 €8000 Head of working woman (30x24cm-12x9in) s. transfer lithograph. 5-May-3 Ketterer, Munich #593/R est:5000-7000
£5797 $9507 €8000 Visit to the children's hospital (27x33cm-11x13in) s. lithograph. 31-May-3 Villa Grisebach, Berlin #158/R est:6000-8000
£5903 $9385 €8500 Bread (31x28cm-12x11in) s.i. lithograph prov. 5-May-3 Ketterer, Munich #685/R est:3500-3800
£6250 $9938 €9000 Uprising (30x32cm-12x13in) s. aquatint drypoint board prov. 5-May-3 Ketterer, Munich #564/R est:1800-2000
£6250 $9938 €9000 Peasants pulling plough followed by woman (37x51cm-15x20in) s.i.d. lithograph chk col pencil prov. 5-May-3 Ketterer, Munich #577/R est:3500-4000
£6250 $9938 €9000 Seated woman with hand on face (48x41cm-19x16in) s. lithograph prov. 5-May-3 Ketterer, Munich #687/R est:5000-7000
£6458 $10269 €9300 Woman resting chin in hand (37x26cm-15x10in) s. transfer lithograph prov. 5-May-3 Ketterer, Munich #592/R est:6000-8000

£6597 $10490 €9500 Carmagnole (57x41cm-22x16in) s. etching aquatint drypoint prov. 5-May-3 Ketterer, Munich #570/R est:3000-4000
£6944 $11042 €10000 Armed gathering in cave (37x23cm-15x9in) s.d. col lithograph prov. 5-May-3 Ketterer, Munich #575/R est:2000-3000
£7639 $12146 €11000 Parents (39x52cm-15x20in) s. lithograph prov. 5-May-3 Ketterer, Munich #648/R est:3000-4000
£7639 $12146 €11000 The widow I (37x22cm-15x9in) s. num.74/100 woodcut. 5-May-3 Ketterer, Munich #673/R est:2000-2500
£7639 $12146 €11000 Girl carrying child (19x15cm-7x6in) s. woodcut opaque white prov. 5-May-3 Ketterer, Munich #678/R est:900-1300
£7639 $12146 €11000 Empty pot (36x30cm-14x12in) s.i. woodcut prov. 5-May-3 Ketterer, Munich #691/R est:1300-1500
£8333 $13250 €12000 Ploughing (31x45cm-12x18in) s.i. aquatint opaque white chk pencil prov. 5-May-3 Ketterer, Munich #602/R est:6000-8000
£8333 $13250 €12000 Death, woman and child (41x40cm-16x16in) s.i. etching transfer pencil ink prov. 5-May-3 Ketterer, Munich #622/R est:2500-3500
£8861 $14000 €14000 Woman with dead child (42x49cm-17x19in) s. etching drypoint. 30-Nov-2 Bassenge, Berlin #6413/R est:6000
£9174 $15321 €13302 Mother with child in arms (27x22cm-11x9in) s.i. etching Indian ink pencil. 20-Jun-3 Kornfeld, Bern #107/R est:25000 (S.FR 20000)
£9174 $15321 €13302 Self portrait (22x10cm-9x4in) s.i. etching drypoint vernis mou. 20-Jun-3 Kornfeld, Bern #108/R est:20000 (S.FR 20000)
£9722 $15458 €14000 Woman with arms crossed (55x42cm-22x17in) s. col lithograph board prov. 5-May-3 Ketterer, Munich #595/R est:20000-30000
£9722 $15458 €14000 Two dead (19x27cm-7x11in) s.i. woodcut prov. 5-May-3 Ketterer, Munich #645/R est:8000-10000
£9722 $15458 €14000 Parents (35x43cm-14x17in) s. num.43/100 woodcut. 5-May-3 Ketterer, Munich #671/R est:3000-3500
£10417 $16563 €15000 Working class woman wearing blue shawl (36x25cm-14x10in) s.i. col lithograph prov. 5-May-3 Ketterer, Munich #582/R est:4000-5000
£10417 $16563 €15000 Battlefield (41x52cm-16x20in) s.i. etching aquatint transfer board prov. 5-May-3 Ketterer, Munich #608/R est:3000-4000
£10417 $16563 €15000 Mother (35x40cm-14x16in) s.i. woodcut prov. 5-May-3 Ketterer, Munich #675/R est:4000-6000
£11111 $17667 €16000 Uprising (28x30cm-11x12in) s. verso aquatint drypoint pencil col pencil opaque white prov. 5-May-3 Ketterer, Munich #565/R est:2500-3000
£11111 $17667 €16000 Self portrait (15x17cm-6x7in) s.i. woodcut prov. 5-May-3 Ketterer, Munich #665/R est:2200-2500
£11927 $19917 €17294 Man ploughing (31x45cm-12x18in) s.i. etching Indian ink chl bodycol. 20-Jun-3 Kornfeld, Bern #106/R est:20000 (S.FR 26000)
£12500 $19875 €18000 Parents (37x45cm-15x18in) s.i. woodcut prov. 5-May-3 Ketterer, Munich #668/R est:4000-4500
£12500 $19875 €18000 Self portrait (22x30cm-9x12in) s.i. woodcut prov. 5-May-3 Ketterer, Munich #693/R est:3000-3500
£13194 $20979 €19000 Mother at dead child's bedside (22x27cm-9x11in) s.i. etching ink prov. 5-May-3 Ketterer, Munich #625/R est:4500-5500
£13194 $20979 €19000 Woman with child going to death (50x40cm-20x16in) s.i.s.i. woodcut opaque white prov. 5-May-3 Ketterer, Munich #682/R est:6000-8000
£15278 $24292 €22000 Fight in tavern - Germinal (34x53cm-13x21in) s. etching prov. 5-May-3 Ketterer, Munich #588/R est:12000-15000
£16667 $26500 €24000 Death and woman encapsulating child (23x28cm-9x11in) s.i. etching prov. 5-May-3 Ketterer, Munich #626/R est:2500-3000
£18056 $28708 €26000 Woman with dead child (42x49cm-17x19in) s. etching transfer prov. 5-May-3 Ketterer, Munich #585/R est:6000-8000
£25694 $40854 €37000 The survivors (56x69cm-22x27in) s. lithograph prov. 5-May-3 Ketterer, Munich #679/R est:6000-8000
£27778 $44167 €40000 Mother (24x32cm-9x13in) s.i. etching aquatint opaque white ink prov. 5-May-3 Ketterer, Munich #637/R est:3500-4500
£28440 $47495 €41238 Mother and dead son (22x33cm-9x13in) s.d.03 etching drypoint vernis mou paste. 20-Jun-3 Kornfeld, Bern #105/R est:35000 (S.FR 62000)
£30556 $48583 €44000 The widow (26x26cm-10x10in) s.i. etching pencil opaque white. 5-May-3 Ketterer, Munich #634/R est:2500-3000
£30556 $48583 €44000 Seed for the planing must not be ground (37x39cm-15x15in) s. lithograph prov. 5-May-3 Ketterer, Munich #748/R est:20000-30000
£31944 $50792 €46000 Men ploughing watched by woman (46x59cm-18x23in) s. aquatint transfer opaque white W/C prov. 5-May-3 Ketterer, Munich #600/R est:10000-15000
£33333 $53000 €48000 Death tearing child away from mother (24x34cm-9x13in) s. etching roulette ink opaque white pencil prov. 5-May-3 Ketterer, Munich #624/R est:4000-5000
£70513 $110000 €105770 Sellbstbildnis en fac (49x33cm-19x13in) s.i.d. col lithograph prov. 14-Oct-2 Butterfields, San Francisco #1128/R est:80000-100000
£93750 $149063 €135000 Self portrait (45x33cm-18x13in) s. col lithograph board prov. 5-May-3 Ketterer, Munich #589/R est:40000-60000

Sculpture

£8451 $14028 €12000 The complaint (26x26x10cm-10x10x4in) bronze. 14-Jun-3 Hauswedell & Nolte, Hamburg #1307/R est:15000
£9494 $15000 €15000 Wives of soldiers waving goodbye, 2nd version (32cm-13in) s. st.f.H Noack verso brown pat zinc exec.1937 prov. 29-Nov-2 Villa Grisebach, Berlin #62/R est:15000-20000
£9494 $15000 €15000 Children (19cm-7in) s. brown pat.bronze. 30-Nov-2 Villa Grisebach, Berlin #203/R est:15000-20000
£9615 $14904 €15000 Rest in the peace of his hands (34x31x8cm-13x12x3in) s. bronze. 7-Dec-2 Hauswedell & Nolte, Hamburg #820/R est:15000
£12579 $19623 €20000 Kindergruppe - group of children (19cm-7in) zinc conceived 1937-38 prov.exhib.lit. 9-Oct-2 Sotheby's, London #198/R est:7500-10000
£14493 $23768 €20000 Complaint (26x25x10cm-10x10x4in) s. brown pat.bronze relief Cast.H.Noack Berlin. 31-May-3 Villa Grisebach, Berlin #157/R est:10000-12000
£14907 $24000 €22361 Ruht im frieden seiner hande - rest in the peace of his hand (35x32cm-14x13in) i.brown pat. bronze i.f.H Hoack conceived 1935-36 lit. 7-May-3 Sotheby's, New York #213/R est:12000-18000
£18841 $30899 €26000 Woman with child on lap (40cm-16in) s. dark brown pat.bronze prov. 31-May-3 Villa Grisebach, Berlin #160/R est:22000-25000

Works on paper

£2083 $3312 €3000 Unemployment (45x55cm-18x22in) s. aquatint transfer prov. 5-May-3 Ketterer, Munich #612/R est:1800-2200
£2292 $3644 €3300 Man holding child (40x28cm-16x11in) chk. 5-May-3 Ketterer, Munich #542/R est:3500-4000
£2431 $3865 €3500 Boy pulling plough (17x36cm-7x14in) s.d. chlk pencil opaque white prov. 5-May-3 Ketterer, Munich #515/R est:3500-4500
£2431 $3865 €3500 Peasant woman seated on stool with goat (23x29cm-9x11in) s. pencil prov. 5-May-3 Ketterer, Munich #516/R est:7000-9000
£2778 $4417 €4000 Studies of man with child (47x54cm-19x21in) s. litho crayon. 5-May-3 Ketterer, Munich #541/R est:7000-9000
£3333 $5300 €4800 Two studies of baby's head (34x26cm-13x10in) s. chl. 5-May-3 Ketterer, Munich #533/R est:4000-5000
£3472 $5521 €5000 Seated man wearing hat (29x23cm-11x9in) s.i. pencil prov. 5-May-3 Ketterer, Munich #505/R est:4000-4500
£3472 $5521 €5000 Standing man in hat (38x16cm-15x6in) s. chk prov. 5-May-3 Ketterer, Munich #522/R est:4500-5000
£3472 $5521 €5000 Crouching female nude (63x48cm-25x19in) s. chl sketch verso. 5-May-3 Ketterer, Munich #528/R est:8000-10000
£3472 $5521 €5000 Seated female nude (39x28cm-15x11in) s. chl. 5-May-3 Ketterer, Munich #529/R est:7000-9000
£3472 $5521 €5000 Child at sick mother's bedside (18x24cm-7x9in) litho crayon exhib. 5-May-3 Ketterer, Munich #535/R est:6000-7000
£4403 $6868 €7000 Girl holding a baby (19x16cm-7x6in) init. pen ink executed c.1920 prov.exhib.lit. 9-Oct-2 Sotheby's, London #200/R est:4500-5500
£4514 $7177 €6500 Seated old man with beard (55x38cm-22x15in) s. chl. 5-May-3 Ketterer, Munich #540/R est:5000-5500
£5208 $8281 €7500 Hunger (20x16cm-8x6in) s.d. Indian ink prov. 5-May-3 Ketterer, Munich #534/R est:5500-6000
£5696 $9000 €9000 Death, woman and child (63x48cm-25x19in) s. chl exec.1910 prov.exhib. 29-Nov-2 Villa Grisebach, Berlin #63/R est:9000-12000
£5903 $9385 €8500 Laughing woman (38x18cm-15x7in) chalk pencil htd white prov. 5-May-3 Ketterer, Munich #511/R est:10000-12000
£5903 $9385 €8500 Seated figure wrapped in blanket (42x45cm-17x18in) s. chl. 5-May-3 Ketterer, Munich #526/R est:6000-8000
£5903 $9385 €8500 Two children eating (15x16cm-6x6in) s. crayon chl prov.lit. 5-May-3 Ketterer, Munich #537/R est:4500-5000
£6597 $10490 €9500 Mother breastfeeding baby (40x31cm-16x12in) s. chl studies verso. 5-May-3 Ketterer, Munich #509/R est:5000-6000
£6597 $10490 €9500 Julen - hug (42x34cm-17x13in) s. chl prov.lit. 5-May-3 Ketterer, Munich #524/R est:7000-9000
£6944 $11042 €10000 Seated boy (28x17cm-11x7in) s.init. pencil. 5-May-3 Ketterer, Munich #517/R est:8000-10000
£6944 $11042 €10000 Three studies of woman complaining (54x42cm-21x17in) s.mono. chl exhib.lit. 5-May-3 Ketterer, Munich #518/R est:8000-10000
£6944 $11042 €10000 Child sleeping on mother's lap (33x45cm-13x18in) s. chl pencil. 5-May-3 Ketterer, Munich #519/R est:6000-8000
£6944 $11042 €10000 Two studies of shackled peasant (46x40cm-18x16in) s. chl pencil. 5-May-3 Ketterer, Munich #523/R est:4000-6000
£7547 $11774 €12000 An einem tisch sitzender mann, arme und kopf aufgelegt schlafend - man seated at a table (23x31cm-9x12in) s. chl executed 1904 prov.exhib.lit. 9-Oct-2 Sotheby's, London #202/R est:9000-12000
£7639 $12146 €11000 Two men wrestling (12x14cm-5x6in) s. Indian ink W/C board. 5-May-3 Ketterer, Munich #502/R est:3500-3800
£8228 $13000 €13000 The time will come (38x47cm-15x19in) s.i. pencil prov. 30-Nov-2 Villa Grisebach, Berlin #155/R est:12500-15000
£8333 $13250 €12000 Hand studies (18x29cm-7x11in) s. Indian ink lit. 5-May-3 Ketterer, Munich #504/R est:4000-5000
£8333 $13250 €12000 Female nude (38x41cm-15x16in) s. chl chk exhib. 5-May-3 Ketterer, Munich #512/R est:4000-4500
£8333 $13250 €12000 Mother, hugging child (22x23cm-9x9in) s. litho crayon. 5-May-3 Ketterer, Munich #536/R est:10000-12000

£9434 $14717 €15000 Familie - family (44x49cm-17x19in) s. chl prov.exhib.lit. 9-Oct-2 Sotheby's, London #192/R est:9000-12000
£9722 $15458 €14000 Study of seated figure with hand (17x14cm-7x6in) s. Indian ink. 5-May-3 Ketterer, Munich #503/R est:1400-1800
£9722 $15458 €14000 Noose - Bound man with noose (30x33cm-12x13in) s. chl lit.prov. 5-May-3 Ketterer, Munich #539/R est:7000-9000
£10321 $17236 €14965 Death tearing a child from its mother (48x41cm-19x16in) s. chl prov. 20-Jun-3 Kornfeld, Bern #103/R est:25000 (S.FR 22500)
£10692 $16679 €17000 Besuch im kinderkrankenhaus - visit to the children's hospital (36x30cm-14x12in) s.i. pencil executed 1926 prov.lit. 9-Oct-2 Sotheby's, London #201/R est:9000-12000
£11468 $19151 €16629 Child drinking at table (30x22cm-12x9in) s. chl prov. 20-Jun-3 Kornfeld, Bern #104/R est:15000 (S.FR 25000)
£11806 $18771 €17000 Four men in pub (29x32cm-11x13in) brush pen Indian ink wash paper on board lit.prov. 5-May-3 Ketterer, Munich #506/R est:10000-15000
£11950 $18642 €19000 Mother with child in her arms (59x42cm-23x17in) s. chl executed 1919 prov.exhib.lit. 9-Oct-2 Sotheby's, London #193/R est:28000-35000
£12579 $19623 €20000 Leidendes volk - suffering people (63x48cm-25x19in) s.i. chl executed 1918 prov.exhib.lit. 9-Oct-2 Sotheby's, London #194/R est:30000-40000
£12579 $19623 €20000 Kopf-und handestudien - study of head and hands (42x39cm-17x15in) s. chl executed 1906 prov.exhib.lit. 9-Oct-2 Sotheby's, London #204/R est:4500-5500
£13194 $20979 €19000 Woman with dead child (30x42cm-12x17in) s. chk chl chk exhib.prov. 5-May-3 Ketterer, Munich #513/R est:15000-18000
£13194 $20979 €19000 Figures in interior fighting (32x49cm-13x19in) s.d. chl pastel prov. 5-May-3 Ketterer, Munich #514/R est:12000-14000
£13194 $20979 €19000 Mother sitting next to sleeping child (35x46cm-14x18in) s. litho crayon prov.lit. 5-May-3 Ketterer, Munich #538/R est:15000-18000
£13208 $20604 €21000 Der agitationsrendner - public speaker inciting the crowd (51x38cm-20x15in) s. chl executed 1926 prov.exhib.lit. 9-Oct-2 Sotheby's, London #195/R est:30000-40000
£13208 $20604 €21000 Tod mit frau im schoss - death with woman in its lap (45x59cm-18x23in) s. chl brown chk executed 1921 prov.exhib.lit. 9-Oct-2 Sotheby's, London #203/R est:30000-40000
£13889 $22083 €20000 The fate of women - Martyrdom of the woman (38x30cm-15x12in) s. Indian ink brush studies verso. 5-May-3 Ketterer, Munich #501/R est:4000-6000
£15094 $23547 €24000 Stehender arbeiter - standing worker (64x48cm-25x19in) s. chl executed c.1904-06 prov.exhib.lit. 9-Oct-2 Sotheby's, London #196/R est:9000-12000
£16667 $26500 €24000 Couple with child (48x39cm-19x15in) s. chk prov. 5-May-3 Ketterer, Munich #530/R est:20000-22000
£17361 $27604 €25000 Two figures with arms around each other (41x42cm-16x17in) chl. 5-May-3 Ketterer, Munich #520/R est:4000-6000
£17610 $27472 €28000 Knabenakt - young male nude (63x48cm-25x19in) s. chl executed c.1910 prov.lit. 9-Oct-2 Sotheby's, London #197/R est:20000-30000
£18750 $29812 €27000 Winter (50x23cm-20x9in) s.i.d. crayon chl prov.lit. 5-May-3 Ketterer, Munich #543/R est:8000-12000
£20833 $33125 €30000 Couple (38x31cm-15x12in) s. chl prov. 5-May-3 Ketterer, Munich #531/R est:20000-25000
£22222 $35333 €32000 Figures by candlelight (29x40cm-11x16in) W/C Indian ink gouache chl prov. 5-May-3 Ketterer, Munich #507/R est:30000-35000
£22936 $38303 €33257 Woman sewing by lamplight (25x23cm-10x9in) s. pencil pen chk W/C brush prov.exhib. 20-Jun-3 Kornfeld, Bern #102/R est:50000 (S.FR 50000)
£25000 $39750 €36000 Study for 'Fallen version 1' (39x29cm-15x11in) s. drawing with litho crayon over pencil prov. 5-May-3 Ketterer, Munich #532/R est:8000-12000
£25694 $40854 €37000 Farewell (39x44cm-15x17in) s. chl prov. 5-May-3 Ketterer, Munich #527/R est:12000-14000
£26389 $41958 €38000 Strike breakers (45x47cm-18x19in) s. chk chl over pencil wash htd white chk. 5-May-3 Ketterer, Munich #525/R est:10000-12000
£27778 $44167 €40000 Sketch (50x41cm-20x16in) s.i. Indian ink pencil wash prov.exhib. 5-May-3 Ketterer, Munich #500/R est:15000-18000
£34722 $55208 €50000 Self portrait (35x28cm-14x11in) s. chl pencil lit. 5-May-3 Ketterer, Munich #521/R est:30000-40000
£36111 $57417 €52000 Gretchen (24x18cm-9x7in) s.i. pencil over chalk prov. 5-May-3 Ketterer, Munich #510/R est:15000-18000
£37736 $58868 €60000 Selbstbilnis en face - Self portrait en face (38x44cm-15x17in) s.i.d.1923 chl prov.exhib.lit. 9-Oct-2 Sotheby's, London #191/R est:30000-40000

KOLLWITZ, Kathe (after) (1867-1945) German
Sculpture
£5346 $8340 €8500 Pieta (39cm-15in) i. bronze conceived 1937-38 prov.exhib.lit. 9-Oct-2 Sotheby's, London #199/R est:10000-15000
£13836 $21585 €22000 Die klage - sorrow in memory of Barlach's death in 1938 (27cm-11in) i. bronze conceived 1938-40 prov.exhib.lit. 9-Oct-2 Sotheby's, London #205/R est:7500-10000

KOLNER, August (1812-1906) American
Works on paper
£7692 $12000 €11538 Pottsville, Pennsylvania, from the northeast (28x64cm-11x25in) s.i.d.1853 W/C ink prov. 21-Sep-2 Pook & Pook, Downington #114/R est:8000-12000

KOLOANE, David (1938-) South African
Works on paper
£310 $498 €465 Howling at the moon (30x41cm-12x16in) s. indid d. gouache. 12-May-3 Stephan Welz, Johannesburg #387 est:1800-2400 (SA.R 3600)

KOLODKO, Oleg (1973-) Russian
£436 $702 €650 Harem (60x45cm-24x18in) 18-Feb-3 Durán, Madrid #673/R

KOLOSVARY, Kamillo (20th C) Hungarian?
£380 $631 €551 Polo match (51x61cm-20x24in) s. 12-Jun-3 Christie's, Kensington #112/R

KOLOSVARY, Sigismund (1899-1983) Hungarian
£276 $460 €400 Composition (73x60cm-29x24in) s.d.74. 10-Jul-3 Artcurial Briest, Paris #314
£284 $460 €400 Composition (19x24cm-7x9in) s.d. 23-May-3 Binoche, Paris #73
£440 $708 €660 Matterhorn (102x80cm-40x31in) s. bears d. 7-May-3 Dobiaschofsky, Bern #746/R (S.FR 950)
£671 $1081 €1000 Composition in blue and grey (73x92cm-29x36in) s.d.1959. 23-Feb-3 Mercier & Cie, Lille #115
£738 $1189 €1100 Composition in pink and black (118x60cm-46x24in) s.d.1957 s.d.verso. 23-Feb-3 Mercier & Cie, Lille #114
£1677 $2616 €2516 Opening forms, 1976 (82x101cm-32x40in) s.d.1976. 11-Sep-2 Kieselbach, Budapest #123/R (H.F 650000)
£1816 $2834 €2724 Landscape (97x129cm-38x51in) s.d.64-65. 11-Apr-3 Kieselbach, Budapest #160/R est:650000 (H.F 650000)

KOLOZSVARY, Lajos (1871-1937) Hungarian
£1310 $2044 €1965 Kitchen interior (73x100cm-29x39in) s. 6-Nov-2 Dobiaschofsky, Bern #740/R est:3300 (S.FR 3000)

KOLSTO, Frederik (1860-1945) Norwegian
£658 $1039 €987 Interior (59x75cm-23x30in) s. 17-Dec-2 Grev Wedels Plass, Oslo #164/R (N.KR 7500)
£690 $1097 €1000 Sunny afternoon (73x54cm-29x21in) s.d.96. 10-Mar-3 Sotheby's, Amsterdam #126 est:1000-1500
£828 $1316 €1200 View of a landscape (27x44cm-11x17in) s.d.96. 10-Mar-3 Sotheby's, Amsterdam #125/R est:1000-1500
£2336 $3690 €3504 Farm under the mountains (44x67cm-17x26in) s.d.97 i.verso. 2-Dec-2 Blomqvist, Oslo #301/R est:18000-22000 (N.KR 27000)
£5061 $7946 €7592 Rowing boats in a bay (53x65cm-21x26in) s.d.86. 21-Nov-2 Grev Wedels Plass, Oslo #24/R est:40000-60000 (N.KR 58000)
£7788 $12304 €11682 Afternoon - interior scene with woman reading (60x53cm-24x21in) s.d.86 i.stretcher lit. 28-Apr-3 Blomqvist, Oslo #306/R est:80000-100000 (N.KR 88000)
£12397 $20331 €17976 Visiting grandfather (60x52cm-24x20in) s.d.85 lit. 2-Jun-3 Blomqvist, Oslo #152/R est:150000-200000 (N.KR 135000)

KOMAN, Ion (1954-) Balkan
Works on paper
£321 $503 €500 Composition (100x130cm-39x51in) s.d.1998 mixed media on canvas. 23-Nov-2 Meeting Art, Vercelli #74

KOMET (1943-) ?
£450 $734 €680 Paysage pour oublier (100x100cm-39x39in) s.verso painted 1983. 3-Feb-3 Cornette de St.Cyr, Paris #461

KOMLOSY, Irma (1850-?) Austrian
£629 $975 €1000 Roses on woodland floor (13x20cm-5x8in) s. panel. 29-Oct-2 Dorotheum, Vienna #101/R

KOMPANEK, Vladimir (1927-) Czechoslovakian
£284 $439 €426 Game in snow (25x30cm-10x12in) plywood painted c.1980. 1-Oct-2 SOGA, Bratislava #280/R est:22000 (SL.K 18000)

£583 $828 €875 Unos III (30x24cm-12x9in) panel painted 1983. 26-Mar-2 SOGA, Bratislava #266/R (SL.K 37000)
£914 $1297 €1371 Silent winter (34x48cm-13x19in) board painted 1980. 26-Mar-2 SOGA, Bratislava #264/R est:47000 (SL.K 58000)
£1166 $1655 €1749 Whitsuntide mask (80x55cm-31x22in) board painted 1981. 26-Mar-2 SOGA, Bratislava #265/R est:40000 (SL.K 74000)

Works on paper
£315 $460 €473 Entry (37x53cm-15x21in) ink. 4-Jun-2 SOGA, Bratislava #282/R est:18000 (SL.K 20000)

KONCHALOVSKY, Piotr Petrovich (1876-1956) Russian
£16000 $25760 €24000 Santa Apostoli, Venice (79x61cm-31x24in) s. s.i.verso. 14-Jan-3 Bonhams, Knightsbridge #21/R est:3000-5000
£45000 $70650 €67500 Lilacs in the dacha (153x200cm-60x79in) s. s.i.d.1949 verso. 20-Nov-2 Sotheby's, London #92/R est:40000-60000
£50000 $78500 €75000 Tree in blossom (74x62cm-29x24in) s. s.d.1927 verso exhib. 20-Nov-2 Sotheby's, London #87/R est:25000-35000
£70000 $109900 €105000 Autumn landscape (80x88cm-31x35in) s.d.23 s.i.d.1923 verso exhib. 20-Nov-2 Sotheby's, London #77/R est:30000-40000
£100000 $157000 €150000 Peter and Paul church in Pskov (71x89cm-28x35in) s. s.i.d.1925 verso. 20-Nov-2 Sotheby's, London #91/R est:40000-60000
£150000 $243000 €225000 Sainted Apostles Bridge, Venice (80x61cm-31x24in) s. s.i.verso prov.lit. 21-May-3 Sotheby's, London #192/R est:60000-80000

KONDOR, Bela (1931-1972) Hungarian
£12899 $20122 €19349 Bride and bridegroom, 1960 (36x27cm-14x11in) s.d.1960 goldleaf board. 11-Sep-2 Kieselbach, Budapest #114/R (H.F 5000000)
£92872 $144880 €134664 Launch of the Artificial Cricket (46x30cm-18x12in) s.d.58 oil gold cardboard. 13-Sep-2 Mu Terem Galeria, Budapest #112/R est:5500000 (H.F 36000000)

KONDOS, Gregory (20th C) American
£2070 $3250 €3105 Mediterranean sea coast (25x28cm-10x11in) s.d.63 prov. 19-Nov-2 Butterfields, San Francisco #8335/R est:3000-5000

KONECNY, Josef (1907-) Czechoslovakian
£541 $845 €850 Still life of flowers (23x18cm-9x7in) s. board. 6-Nov-2 Hugo Ruef, Munich #1176/R
£608 $949 €900 Summer flowers in ceramic jug (46x36cm-18x14in) s. panel. 27-Mar-3 Dr Fritz Nagel, Stuttgart #827/R
£1899 $3000 €2849 Floral still life (140x99cm-55x39in) s. 3-Apr-3 Boos Gallery, Michigan #273/R est:6000-8000

KONEK, Ida (1856-?) Hungarian
£548 $855 €800 Girl with blossom on twigs (54x42cm-21x17in) s. 10-Apr-3 Dorotheum, Vienna #69/R

KONIG, Franz Niklaus (attrib) (1765-1832) Swiss
£524 $817 €786 Portrait of girl in white dress (49x37cm-19x15in) prov. 6-Nov-2 Dobiaschofsky, Bern #741/R (S.FR 1200)

KONIG, Friedrich (1857-1941) Austrian
£1736 $2760 €2500 Landscape in lower Austria (67x99cm-26x39in) s. 29-Apr-3 Wiener Kunst Auktionen, Vienna #630/R est:2500-5000

KONIG, Fritz (1924-) German

Sculpture
£2532 $4000 €4000 Group (15cm-6in) s. black brown pat.bronze. 30-Nov-2 Villa Grisebach, Berlin #415/R est:4000-6000
£6159 $10101 €8500 Horse between bars (79cm-31in) s.d.59 black pat.bronze. 31-May-3 Villa Grisebach, Berlin #325/R est:9000-12000
£49275 $80812 €68000 Call-sign IV (238cm-94in) s. bronze stone socle prov. 30-May-3 Villa Grisebach, Berlin #74/R est:35000-45000

KONIG, G (20th C) German
£1156 $1839 €1700 Winter landscape with ice skaters (80x100cm-31x39in) s. 28-Mar-3 Bolland & Marotz, Bremen #562/R est:1100

KONIG, Hugo (1856-1899) German
£570 $900 €900 Reading in the evening (40x32cm-16x13in) s. lit. 29-Nov-2 Schloss Ahlden, Ahlden #1424/R

KONIG, Leo von (1871-1944) German
£692 $1079 €1100 Europa on bull (37x46cm-15x18in) s. panel. 9-Oct-2 Michael Zeller, Lindau #762/R

KONIJNENBURG, Willem A van (1868-1943) Dutch

Works on paper
£255 $392 €400 Pieta (42x28cm-17x11in) mono. black chk pastel. 3-Sep-2 Christie's, Amsterdam #387
£414 $658 €600 Two horsemen passing a group of monks (60x48cm-24x19in) s.d.1940 chk. 10-Mar-3 Sotheby's, Amsterdam #360/R
£426 $689 €600 File of figures with town in background (59x71cm-23x28in) mono. chl chk. 26-May-3 Glerum, Amsterdam #127

KONINCK, Andries de (17th C) Dutch
£22000 $34320 €33000 Still life of lobster, pie and various fruits in blue and white bowls and on pewter plates (113x159cm-44x63in) 10-Apr-3 Sotheby's, London #52/R est:8000-12000

KONINCK, Edmond de (1839-1883) Belgian
£696 $1086 €1100 Composition aux fleurs et aux fruits sur entablement (60x44cm-24x17in) s.d.1869 oval. 16-Sep-2 Horta, Bruxelles #460

KONINCK, Kerstiaen de (elder) (fl.1580-1630) Flemish
£21622 $33730 €32000 Mountainous landscape with travellers (67x104cm-26x41in) panel. 26-Mar-3 Tajan, Paris #119/R est:45000

KONINCK, Philips de (1619-1688) Dutch
£60000 $94200 €90000 Landscape with the goldweigher's field, Haarlem beyond (30x45cm-12x18in) panel prov.exhib.lit. 12-Dec-2 Sotheby's, London #22/R est:60000-80000

KONINCK, Salomon (1609-1656) Dutch
£40000 $62800 €60000 Philosopher (114x85cm-45x33in) panel prov. 11-Dec-2 Christie's, London #45/R est:30000-50000

KONINCK, Salomon (attrib) (1609-1656) Dutch
£9220 $14291 €13830 Jesus and the salesman (65x85cm-26x33in) 4-Dec-2 AB Stockholms Auktionsverk #2018/R est:60000-80000 (S.KR 130000)

KONING, Edzard (1869-1954) Dutch
£660 $1023 €990 Pastoral scene with lily pond (23x30cm-9x12in) init. board. 4-Oct-2 Mallams, Oxford #524/R
£700 $1134 €1050 Pond in a pastoral landscape (24x32cm-9x13in) init. panel. 23-Jan-3 Christie's, Kensington #260/R

KONING, Roeland (1898-1985) Dutch
£420 $676 €630 Apple orchard (51x72cm-20x28in) s.indis.d. board. 14-Jan-3 Bonhams, Knightsbridge #183/R
£955 $1490 €1500 Portrait of a lady (109x78cm-43x31in) s.d.1930. 6-Nov-2 Vendue Huis, Gravenhage #107/R est:2000-3000

Works on paper
£300 $483 €450 Egmond aan Zee (44x61cm-17x24in) s.d.1925 pastel. 14-Jan-3 Bonhams, Knightsbridge #158

KONINGH, Arie Ketting de (1815-1867) Dutch
£1457 $2375 €2200 Trois chiens attendant l'heure de chasse (36x29cm-14x11in) s. panel. 17-Feb-3 Horta, Bruxelles #210

KONINGH, Leendert de (elder) (1777-1849) Dutch
£2817 $4535 €4000 Cows by water (40x47cm-16x19in) s. panel lit. 9-May-3 Schloss Ahlden, Ahlden #1432/R est:3500

KONINGH, Sophie de (1807-1870) Dutch

Works on paper
£345 $548 €500 Cattle in a landscape (42x54cm-17x21in) s. W/C. 10-Mar-3 Sotheby's, Amsterdam #123

KONIS, Ben (1939-) American

Works on paper
£390 $600 €585 Head study (23x30cm-9x12in) pastel. 25-Oct-2 Morris & Whiteside, Hilton Head Island #176

KONJOVIC, Milan (1898-1983) Yugoslavian
£3927 $6243 €5891 Still life with candlestick (60x72cm-24x28in) s.d.928 board. 8-Mar-3 Dorotheum, Prague #150/R est:30000-45000 (C.KR 180000)

Works on paper
£1418 $2255 €2127 Chair with pierrot (70x50cm-28x20in) mono.d.1922 W/C. 8-Mar-3 Dorotheum, Prague #241/R est:20000-30000 (C.KR 65000)

KONNEL, Stanyik (19th C) Austrian
£8000 $13360 €12000 Danae (124x207cm-49x81in) 18-Jun-3 Christie's, Kensington #118/R est:8000-12000

KONO, Micao (1900-1979) Japanese
£3712 $5790 €5568 Femme et Arlequin (92x65cm-36x26in) s.d.XX-XI. 6-Nov-2 Dobiaschofsky, Bern #742/R est:8000 (S.FR 8500)

KONOK, Tamas (1930-) Hungarian
Works on paper
£371 $583 €557 Untitled (34x27cm-13x11in) mixed media. 23-Nov-2 Burkhard, Luzern #92/R (S.FR 850)

KONOPA, Rudolf (1864-1938) Austrian
£769 $1215 €1200 Calm water (40x52cm-16x20in) s. 12-Nov-2 Dorotheum, Vienna #40/R

KONOW, Jurgen von (1915-1959) Swedish
£2471 $3978 €3707 Tegelbacken, Stockholm (58x64cm-23x25in) s.d.1943 panel. 7-May-3 AB Stockholms Auktionsverk #834/R est:10000-12000 (S.KR 32000)

KONSTANTIN-HANSEN, Elise (1858-1946) Danish
£439 $685 €659 Kitchen interior with dog (43x33cm-17x13in) init.i.d.1881. 23-Sep-2 Rasmussen, Vejle #32/R (D.KR 5200)
£1914 $3100 €2775 Starlings on branch of horse chestnut in spring (47x60cm-19x24in) init. 26-May-3 Rasmussen, Copenhagen #1392/R est:20000 (D.KR 20000)
Works on paper
£466 $740 €699 View towards Acropolis (35x52cm-14x20in) i. W/C executed c.1895. 5-Mar-3 Rasmussen, Copenhagen #2075/R (D.KR 5000)

KONTI, Isidore (1862-1938) Austrian/American
Sculpture
£2548 $4000 €3822 Pushing men, pair of bookends (15cm-6in) s. st. red brown pat bronze. 10-Dec-2 Doyle, New York #100/R est:1000-1500

KONTOGIANNOPOULOU, Leda (1971-) Greek
£305 $500 €442 Interior II (35x35cm-14x14in) s.d.2002 verso. 28-May-3 Sotheby's, Amsterdam #109/R
£305 $500 €442 Interior III (40x25cm-16x10in) s.d.2002 verso. 28-May-3 Sotheby's, Amsterdam #110/R
£938 $1500 €1360 Untitled 2 (99x170cm-39x67in) s.d.2000 verso. 13-May-3 Sotheby's, Tel Aviv #10/R est:1200-1800
£1125 $1800 €1631 Interior IV (50x25cm-20x10in) s.d.2001 verso. 13-May-3 Sotheby's, Tel Aviv #9/R est:800-1000

KONTULY, Bela (1904-1983) Belgian?
£650 $1053 €975 Vase of daisies, bowl of pears, grapes and peppers and a jug (61x91cm-24x36in) s. 23-Jan-3 Christie's, Kensington #185
£7021 $11234 €10532 White, dressed girl with a clown (80x80cm-31x31in) s. 16-May-3 Kieselbach, Budapest #69/R (H.F 2400000)

KONTULY, Bela (attrib) (1904-1983) Belgian?
£1213 $1722 €1820 Still life (80x60cm-31x24in) painted c.1960. 26-Mar-2 SOGA, Bratislava #137/R est:35000 (SL.K 77000)

KOOL, Catharina (1860-1933) Dutch
£2016 $3185 €3024 Preparing a meal (80x61cm-31x24in) s. canvas on masonite. 18-Nov-2 Waddingtons, Toronto #194/R est:700-900 (C.D 5000)

KOOL, Willem (1608-1666) Dutch
£4500 $7020 €6750 Figures and boats on a beach (40x50cm-16x20in) mono. panel prov.lit. 10-Apr-3 Christie's, Kensington #44/R est:5000-7000
£7097 $11213 €11000 Seashore scene (40x60cm-16x24in) panel. 18-Dec-2 Tajan, Paris #16/R est:12000

KOONING, Willem de (1904-1997) American/Dutch
£13478 $20891 €20217 Untitled (58x74cm-23x29in) newspaper prov. 4-Dec-2 Koller, Zurich #172/R est:35000-45000 (S.FR 31000)
£21875 $35000 €32813 Untitled (74x58cm-29x23in) s.i. newsprint on canvas prov. 15-May-3 Christie's, Rockefeller NY #189/R est:30000-50000
£23438 $37500 €35157 Untitled (48x60cm-19x24in) painted c.1965 prov. 14-May-3 Sotheby's, New York #127/R est:40000-60000
£25000 $40000 €37500 Seated woman (69x27cm-27x11in) s. oil gouache painted 1963-65 prov. 14-May-3 Sotheby's, New York #128/R est:40000-60000
£34014 $54082 €50000 Untitled (57x73cm-22x29in) s. paper on cardboard. 24-Mar-3 Cornette de St.Cyr, Paris #11/R est:70000
£94937 $150000 €142406 Untitled woman (60x48cm-24x19in) oil on paper executed 1955 prov. 13-Nov-2 Sotheby's, New York #212/R est:200000-250000
£101266 $160000 €151899 L'orage (58x73cm-23x29in) s.i.d.1963 oil paper on masonite prov.exhib.lit. 14-Nov-2 Christie's, Rockefeller NY #130/R est:120000-180000
£118750 $190000 €178125 Untitled - woman (61x76cm-24x30in) s. oil on paper painted c.1966 prov. 14-May-3 Sotheby's, New York #115/R est:120000-180000
£168750 $270000 €253125 Untitled 18 (76x105cm-30x41in) s.verso oil paper on canvas painted 1977 prov. 14-May-3 Sotheby's, New York #159/R est:200000-300000
£187500 $300000 €281250 Untitled (109x76cm-43x30in) s. oil paper on canvas painted 1968 prov. 15-May-3 Phillips, New York #27/R est:300000-400000
£325000 $520000 €487500 Untitled (105x76cm-41x30in) s. paper on canvas painted 1977 prov.exhib. 15-May-3 Christie's, Rockefeller NY #170/R est:250000-350000
£512821 $800000 €769232 Untitled (174x197cm-69x78in) painted 1971 prov. 11-Nov-2 Phillips, New York #15/R est:900000-1200000
£1062500 $1700000 €1593750 Untitled V (177x203cm-70x80in) s.verso prov.exhib. 13-May-3 Sotheby's, New York #21/R est:2000000-3000000
£1265823 $2000000 €1898735 Untitled VIII (150x140cm-59x55in) s.verso painted 1976 prov.exhib.lit. 12-Nov-2 Sotheby's, New York #18/R est:2000000-3000000
£1455696 $2300000 €2183544 Woman (41x39cm-16x15in) s. enamel chl paper on board painted 1947 prov.exhib.lit. 12-Nov-2 Sotheby's, New York #6/R est:3000000-4000000
£7594937 $12000000 €11392406 Orestes (61x92cm-24x36in) s. s.verso enamel paper collage board painted 1947. 12-Nov-2 Sotheby's, New York #11/R est:8000000-10000000
Prints
£1887 $3000 €2831 Landscape at Stanton Street (64x48cm-25x19in) s.i.d.1971 lithograph. 1-May-3 Swann Galleries, New York #474/R est:3000-5000
£1935 $3000 €2903 Woman with a corset and long hair (94x76cm-37x30in) s.d.70 num.34/61 lithograph. 25-Sep-2 Christie's, Rockefeller NY #320/R est:2000-3000
£2281 $3605 €3422 Minnie Mouse (69x53cm-27x21in) s.num.49/60 lithograph lit. 28-Apr-3 Bukowskis, Stockholm #446/R est:25000-35000 (S.KR 30000)
£2357 $3725 €3536 Landscape at Stanton Street (65x48cm-26x19in) s.num.29/60 lithograph lit. 28-Apr-3 Bukowskis, Stockholm #447/R est:30000-35000 (S.KR 31000)
£3226 $5000 €4839 Man and big blond (62x77cm-24x30in) s.num.68/150 col offset lithograph. 25-Sep-2 Christie's, Rockefeller NY #322/R est:6000-8000
£8974 $14000 €13461 Man and the big blonde (65x77cm-26x30in) s.num.133/150 col offset lithograph. 5-Nov-2 Christie's, Rockefeller NY #444/R est:6000-8000
Sculpture
£99359 $155000 €149039 Head no.3 (46x25x28cm-18x10x11in) bronze cast 1973 prov.exhib.lit. 11-Nov-2 Phillips, New York #21/R est:250000-350000
Works on paper
£4114 $6500 €6171 Untitled - owl (25x20cm-10x8in) s. chl executed c.1970 prov. 13-Nov-2 Sotheby's, New York #224/R est:7000-9000
£18000 $30060 €26100 Untitled (35x28cm-14x11in) graphite executed 1975 prov. 27-Jun-3 Christie's, London #201/R est:20000-30000
£18987 $30000 €28481 Untitled (60x47cm-24x19in) s.i. gouache chl paper on canvas executed c.1965-70 prov. 13-Nov-2 Sotheby's, New York #227/R est:40000-60000
£21250 $34000 €31875 Woman - better late then never (60x48cm-24x19in) s.i. brush black ink executed c.1969 prov. 16-May-3 Phillips, New York #167/R est:35000-45000
£53797 $85000 €80696 Woman (47x43cm-19x17in) s.d.54 pencil on vellum prov. 14-Nov-2 Christie's, Rockefeller NY #128/R est:60000-80000
£103125 $165000 €154688 Woman (33x25cm-13x10in) s.i. graphite prov.lit. 15-May-3 Christie's, Rockefeller NY #116/R est:100000-150000
£2151899 $3400000 €3227849 Woman (52x36cm-20x14in) s. pastel graphite executed 1952. 12-Nov-2 Sotheby's, New York #12/R est:4000000-6000000

KOONS, Jeff (1955-) American
£44304 $70000 €66456 I assume you drink Martell (114x152cm-45x60in) executed 1986 prov.exhib.lit. 14-Nov-2 Christie's, Rockefeller NY #388/R est:80000-120000
£151899 $240000 €227849 Puppy (305x427cm-120x168in) oil ink on canvas painted 1992 prov.exhib. 12-Nov-2 Sotheby's, New York #59/R est:300000-400000
£270000 $442800 €405000 Cracked egg (325x252cm-128x99in) painted 1995-97 prov.lit. 5-Feb-3 Christie's, London #13/R est:260000-350000
Photographs
£183544 $290000 €275316 Wolfman - close up (229x152cm-90x60in) s.d.91 on overlap silkscreen ink on canvas prov.exhib.lit. 13-Nov-2 Christie's, Rockefeller NY #4/R est:250000-350000

Sculpture

£23750 $38000 €35625 Donkey (61x46x1cm-24x18x0in) s.d.1997 num.6/10 stainless steel prov. 14-May-3 Sotheby's, New York #336/R est:18000-25000

£23750 $38000 €35625 Untitled (61x46cm-24x18in) s.d.1997 num.50 stainless steel mirror prov. 16-May-3 Phillips, New York #106/R est:12000-16000

£150000 $240000 €225000 Hippo, dark pink (211x150x4cm-83x59x2in) s.d.1999 verso crystal glass steel prov.exhib. 14-May-3 Christie's, Rockefeller NY #51/R est:200000-300000

£227848 $360000 €341772 Wishing well (221x142x20cm-87x56x8in) s. d.1988 num.3/3 verso gilded wood mirror executed 1988 prov.exhib. 12-Nov-2 Sotheby's, New York #61/R est:300000-400000

£641026 $1000000 €961539 Buster Keaton (167x127x67cm-66x50x26in) i.d.88 polychrome prov.exhib.lit. 11-Nov-2 Phillips, New York #32/R est:1000000-1500000

£1185898 $1850000 €1778847 Self portrait (95x52x37cm-37x20x15in) marble executed 1991 prov.exhib.lit. 11-Nov-2 Phillips, New York #10/R est:1500000-2000000

KOOP, Gustave (19th C) Swiss

Works on paper

£1092 $1725 €1638 Beckenried on Vierwaldstadter See (32x44cm-13x17in) i. verso gouache. 14-Nov-2 Stuker, Bern #9200 est:2000-2500 (S.FR 2500)

KOOPER, Ary Cornelis (1855-1921) Dutch

£387 $624 €550 Cattle resting (11x18cm-4x7in) s. board. 6-May-3 Vendu Notarishuis, Rotterdam #84

KOORNSTRA, Metten (1912-1978) Dutch

£694 $1146 €1000 Mother and child in a street (29x39cm-11x15in) mono.d.65 board prov. 1-Jul-3 Christie's, Amsterdam #382

£955 $1490 €1500 Landscape with figures (29x39cm-11x15in) mono.d.65 board. 5-Nov-2 Vendu Notarishuis, Rotterdam #133/R est:500-700

£986 $1587 €1400 Ball tent (25x35cm-10x14in) mono.d.66 board. 7-May-3 Vendue Huis, Gravenhage #550/R

£1223 $2006 €1700 Still life with drawing and flowers in a vase (29x39cm-11x15in) mono.d.71 board prov. 3-Jun-3 Christie's, Amsterdam #63/R est:1200-1600

KOPALLIK, Franz (1860-?) Austrian

Works on paper

£503 $780 €800 Landscape with farmstead on track (36x48cm-14x19in) s. W/C. 1-Oct-2 Dorotheum, Vienna #340/R

KOPCKE, Arthur (1928-1977) Danish

£1487 $2349 €2231 Kopcke-Reading-Work-Piece (100x100cm-39x39in) s. painted 1965 exhib. 1-Apr-3 Rasmussen, Copenhagen #291/R est:12000-15000 (D.KR 16000)

Works on paper

£415 $643 €623 Partial connections (38x27cm-15x11in) s.d.73 mixed media partly on glass. 1-Oct-2 Rasmussen, Copenhagen #172/R (D.KR 4900)

£422 $659 €633 Composition (45x38cm-18x15in) s.d.74 mixed media. 18-Sep-2 Kunsthallen, Copenhagen #157 (D.KR 5000)

£883 $1395 €1325 Treatment of a canvas and Action piece (70x100cm-28x39in) s.d.65 chess picture puzzle prov. 1-Apr-3 Rasmussen, Copenhagen #288/R (D.KR 9500)

KOPECKY, Bohdan (1928-) Czechoslovakian

£636 $1030 €922 Forgotten Vetrna No 2 (100x65cm-39x26in) s.d.1971. 24-May-3 Dorotheum, Prague #132/R est:20000-30000 (C.KR 28000)

KOPMAN, Benjamin (1887-1965) American

£755 $1200 €1133 Street scene, Bronx, New York (61x81cm-24x32in) s.d.53 i.d.verso. 18-Mar-3 Doyle, New York #36/R

KOPONEN, Erkki (1899-1996) Finnish

£276 $436 €400 Town (46x55cm-18x22in) s.d.1951. 3-Apr-3 Hagelstam, Helsinki #968

£302 $496 €420 Seated woman (42x27cm-17x11in) s.d.50. 4-Jun-3 Bukowskis, Helsinki #330/R

£440 $678 €700 Three circles (90x140cm-35x55in) s.d.1992. 27-Oct-2 Bukowskis, Helsinki #222/R

£586 $926 €850 Helsinki (38x55cm-15x22in) s.d.1946. 3-Apr-3 Hagelstam, Helsinki #967/R

KOPP, Dieter (1939-) German

Works on paper

£256 $403 €400 Landscape by Strohl Fern Villa (50x70cm-20x28in) s. W/C. 21-Nov-2 Finarte, Rome #124

KOPPAY, Joszi Arpad Baron von Dretoma (1859-?) Hungarian

£704 $1134 €1000 Erzherzog, Crown Prince Franz Ferdinand (70x100cm-28x39in) s. board. 7-May-3 Dorotheum, Vienna #302/R

£1690 $2721 €2400 Erzherzog, Crown Prince Franz Ferdinand (97x58cm-38x23in) bears sig. 7-May-3 Dorotheum, Vienna #300/R est:2800-5000

Works on paper

£775 $1247 €1100 Maria Anna von Braganza (74x59cm-29x23in) s. pastel board. 7-May-3 Dorotheum, Vienna #312/R

£986 $1587 €1400 Crown Princess Stephanie with daughter (99x73cm-39x29in) s. pastel sketch board. 7-May-3 Dorotheum, Vienna #307/R

£1268 $2041 €1800 Erzherzogin Isabella (69x46cm-27x18in) s. pastel sketch board. 7-May-3 Dorotheum, Vienna #309/R est:1200-1800

£1408 $2268 €2000 Sophie Herzogin von Hohenberg (94x75cm-37x30in) s. pastel sketch. 7-May-3 Dorotheum, Vienna #301/R est:1200-1800

£1972 $3175 €2800 Princess Windischgratz Metternich (100x76cm-39x30in) s. pastel board. 7-May-3 Dorotheum, Vienna #310/R est:1200-1800

£4577 $7370 €6500 Queen Elisabeth of Austria (98x70cm-39x28in) pastel board. 7-May-3 Dorotheum, Vienna #299/R est:2500-4000

KOPPEN, Theodor (1828-1903) German

£456 $706 €720 Panorama of a blue bay on the Cote d'Azur (18x33cm-7x13in) i. verso board. 28-Sep-2 Hans Stahl, Hamburg #78/R

£479 $748 €700 Rowing boat in the surf (55x75cm-22x30in) s.d.1893. 10-Apr-3 Van Ham, Cologne #1546

KOPPENOL, Cornelis (1865-1946) Dutch

£318 $497 €500 Interior with lady (39x49cm-15x19in) s. 6-Nov-2 Vendue Huis, Gravenhage #96

KOPS, Franz (1846-1896) German

£3000 $4680 €4500 Card players (132x150cm-52x59in) s.d.1888. 17-Sep-2 Sotheby's, Olympia #270/R est:3000-5000

KOPS, Jean Baptiste Charles (attrib) (1824-?) Flemish

£1600 $2560 €2400 Wayside chat (59x73cm-23x29in) panel. 13-May-3 Bonhams, Knightsbridge #306/R est:1200-1800

KORAB, Karl (1937-) Austrian

£759 $1214 €1100 Untitled (30x38cm-12x15in) s.d.94 gouache collage. 11-Mar-3 Dorotheum, Vienna #287/R

£3378 $5270 €5000 Projekt Petra 01 (120x100cm-47x39in) s.i.d.1976 verso. 25-Mar-3 Wiener Kunst Auktionen, Vienna #19/R est:7000-12000

Works on paper

£283 $439 €450 Untitled (35x46cm-14x18in) s.d.80 chk. 30-Oct-2 Dorotheum, Vienna #136

£464 $756 €700 On village edge (34x46cm-13x18in) s.d.85 verso chl. 28-Jan-3 Dorotheum, Vienna #264

£464 $756 €700 Houses in Waldviertel (47x62cm-19x24in) s.d.2000 black crayon. 28-Jan-3 Dorotheum, Vienna #314/R

£563 $918 €850 Landscape (23x16cm-9x6in) s.d.99 mixed media. 28-Jan-3 Dorotheum, Vienna #310/R

£828 $1324 €1200 Untitled (50x65cm-20x26in) s.d.61 collage. 11-Mar-3 Dorotheum, Vienna #168/R

£897 $1418 €1400 Still life (37x50cm-15x20in) s.d.77 gouache W/C. 12-Nov-2 Dorotheum, Vienna #234/R

£962 $1519 €1500 Houses (36x48cm-14x19in) s. mixed media. 12-Nov-2 Dorotheum, Vienna #251/R est:1300-1800

£1090 $1722 €1700 Landscape (40x57cm-16x22in) s.d.93 mixed media collage. 12-Nov-2 Dorotheum, Vienna #283/R est:1400-1800

£1899 $2943 €3000 Landscape (70x100cm-28x39in) s.d.91 mixed media collage. 24-Sep-2 Wiener Kunst Auktionen, Vienna #258/R est:3000-5000

KORBER, Adolf (20th C) ?

£454 $736 €681 Landscape with Kokorin Castle (75x66cm-30x26in) s. 24-May-3 Dorotheum, Prague #30/R est:20000-30000 (C.KR 20000)

£2072 $3295 €3108 Garden flowers (85x100cm-33x39in) s. 8-Mar-3 Dorotheum, Prague #95/R est:60000-90000 (C.KR 95000)

KORDA, Vincent (1897-1979) Hungarian

£352 $567 €500 Bord de mer, les grands arbres (54x72cm-21x28in) s. 11-May-3 Thierry & Lannon, Brest #260

£1935 $3018 €2903 Still life of jug (65x50cm-26x20in) s. canvas on canvasboard. 11-Sep-2 Kieselbach, Budapest #95/R (H.F 750000)

£5000 $8200 €7500 In the garden (80x59cm-31x23in) s.d. prov. 3-Jun-3 Sotheby's, London #113/R est:4000-6000

KORDER, Walter (1891-1962) American

£745 $1200 €1118 Post office scene (51x61cm-20x24in) s.d.1955. 20-Feb-3 Illustration House, New York #92/R est:1000-1500

£932 $1500 €1398 Victorian interior with organ (64x76cm-25x30in) s.d. 10-May-3 Illustration House, New York #64/R est:2000-3000

£1090 $1700 €1635 Ice cream freeze and bowl on summer porch (76x64cm-30x25in) s. 9-Nov-2 Illustration House, New York #24/R est:2000-3000

KOREC, Karl Johann (1937-) Austrian
Works on paper
£319 $517 €450 The female being Frau B - cleaner (11x30cm-4x12in) s.d.20.1.1972 pen Indian ink W/C. 20-May-3 Dorotheum, Vienna #246/R
£319 $517 €450 Chriestie Ro as gypsy girl (21x30cm-8x12in) s.d.1972 pen Indian ink W/C. 20-May-3 Dorotheum, Vienna #253/R
£494 $800 €741 Untitled (31x22cm-12x9in) s.d.1980 ink W/C pair prov. 27-Jan-3 Christie's, Rockefeller NY #119/R

KORECKI, Victor (1890-1980) Polish
£353 $550 €530 Winter landscape with road between trees (51x61cm-20x24in) 11-Apr-3 Du Mouchelle, Detroit #2306/R
£510 $795 €800 Winter in the East (25x35cm-10x14in) s. board. 6-Nov-2 Hugo Ruef, Munich #1177
£686 $1070 €1029 Rowing boat on calm water at sunset (50x62cm-20x24in) s. 11-Nov-2 Rasmussen, Vejle #618/R (D.KR 8000)

KOREN, Shlomo (1932-) Israeli
Works on paper
£1282 $1987 €2000 Hiroglyfen (159x99cm-63x39in) s.d.64 mixed media on canvas. 3-Dec-2 Christie's, Amsterdam #100/R est:1200-1600

KORETSKY, Viktor Borisowitch (1909-) Russian
£641 $1006 €1000 Winter landscape. s. 16-Dec-2 Bernaerts, Antwerp #840

KORLIND, Einar Nielsen (1884-1975) Danish?
£317 $495 €476 Rocky coast, Bornholm (79x110cm-31x43in) s.d.35. 11-Nov-2 Rasmussen, Vejle #58/R (D.KR 3700)

KORN, Johan Philip (1728-1796) Swedish
£2121 $3478 €3075 Coastal landscape with fishermen and wooden building (39x59cm-15x23in) init. s.d.1777 verso. 4-Jun-3 AB Stockholms Auktionsverk #2244/R est:25000-30000 (S.KR 27000)

KORN, Johan Philip (attrib) (1728-1796) Swedish
£1178 $1932 €1708 Landscape with fishermen in boats (23x33cm-9x13in) panel pair. 4-Jun-3 AB Stockholms Auktionsverk #2243/R est:20000-25000 (S.KR 15000)

KORNBECK, J (19/20th C) German
£818 $1275 €1300 Washerwoman by farmstead (28x35cm-11x14in) 23-Sep-2 Dr Fritz Nagel, Stuttgart #6957/R

KORNBECK, Julius (1839-1920) German
£270 $422 €400 Summer landscape (63x80cm-25x31in) i. verso. 31-Mar-3 Dr Fritz Nagel, Stuttgart #7058/R

KORNBECK, Peter (1837-1894) Danish
£1532 $2466 €2298 Venetian canal scene (35x25cm-14x10in) s. 22-Feb-3 Rasmussen, Havnen #2359/R est:12000-15000 (D.KR 17000)
£2105 $3411 €3052 The monastery walkway, San Joan de Los Reyes in Toledo (81x60cm-32x24in) s.d.1879. 24-May-3 Rasmussen, Havnen #2252/R est:20000-30000 (D.KR 22000)
£2883 $4641 €4325 Italian town scene with figures on square (37x56cm-15x22in) s.d.1886. 22-Feb-3 Rasmussen, Havnen #2029/R est:18000-20000 (D.KR 32000)
£3445 $5237 €5168 Sacristy at the convent Monastero Maggiore in Mailand (72x98cm-28x39in) s.d.1872 exhib. 27-Aug-2 Rasmussen, Copenhagen #1504/R est:40000-50000 (D.KR 40000)

KORNER, Erich (1866-?) German
£417 $646 €650 Portrait of nobleman in armour (92x72cm-36x28in) i. verso after van Dyck. 5-Dec-2 Neumeister, Munich #2825

KORNERUP, Valdemar (1865-1924) Danish
£431 $655 €647 Cottage interior with woman knitting socks (53x57cm-21x22in) s.d.1920. 27-Aug-2 Rasmussen, Copenhagen #1911/R (D.KR 5000)
£478 $775 €693 Woman in garden with flowers (38x46cm-15x18in) s.d.1915 panel. 26-May-3 Rasmussen, Copenhagen #1238 (D.KR 5000)

KORNISS, Dezso (1908-1984) Hungarian
£1237 $1917 €1794 Calligraphy (22x44cm-9x17in) s.d.63 oil collage canvas on paper. 9-Dec-2 Mu Terem Galeria, Budapest #94/R est:440000 (H.F 460000)
£3074 $4795 €4457 Calligraphy (75x105cm-30x41in) s.d.959 paper. 12-Apr-3 Mu Terem Galeria, Budapest #110/R est:460000 (H.F 1100000)
£11178 $17437 €16767 Angel (88x43cm-35x17in) 11-Apr-3 Kieselbach, Budapest #162/R est:2500000-4000000 (H.F 4000000)

KOROVINE (19/20th C) Russian
Works on paper
£548 $866 €850 Getting ready for a party (20x25cm-8x10in) s. W/C. 19-Dec-2 Hagelstam, Helsinki #920/R

KOROVINE, A G (1928-) Russian
£288 $460 €400 Vue de Beaumont-sur-Oise (54x65cm-21x26in) s. s.i.verso. 14-May-3 Blanchet, Paris #141/R

KOROVINE, Alexei Konstantinovitch (1897-1950) Russian
£31441 $49048 €47162 Porte de St Denis at night (81x65cm-32x26in) s.i. 6-Nov-2 Dobiaschofsky, Bern #744/R est:8000 (S.FR 72000)
Works on paper
£483 $806 €700 Parc aux sculptures (20x26cm-8x10in) s.d.36 W/C gouache. 10-Jul-3 Artcurial Briest, Paris #222
£552 $922 €800 Jardins du palais (23x31cm-9x12in) s.d.36 W/C gouache. 10-Jul-3 Artcurial Briest, Paris #223

KOROVINE, Constantin (1861-1939) Russian
£1064 $1777 €1500 Roses et tulipes dans un vase vert (60x43cm-24x17in) s. paper. 17-Jun-3 Claude Boisgirard, Paris #76 est:1500-1800
£1341 $2200 €2012 Paris evening street scene (18x23cm-7x9in) s. board. 8-Feb-3 Neal Auction Company, New Orleans #436/R est:3000-4000
£2327 $3770 €3374 Landscape study, winter (13x17cm-5x7in) s. panel prov. 25-May-3 Uppsala Auktionskammare, Uppsala #130/R est:15000-20000 (S.KR 30000)
£3000 $4860 €4500 Bivouac on the forest edge (33x41cm-13x16in) s.i. oil on card. 21-May-3 Sotheby's, London #109/R est:3000-5000
£3041 $4743 €4500 Paris (48x63cm-19x25in) s. 26-Mar-3 Hugo Ruef, Munich #282/R est:4500
£3200 $5024 €4800 Promenading in Paris by night (8x18cm-3x7in) s.i.d.1905 panel. 20-Nov-2 Sotheby's, London #110/R est:2000-3000
£3500 $5494 €5250 Gathering fruit (12x18cm-5x7in) s. board. 20-Nov-2 Sotheby's, London #112 est:4000-6000
£4000 $6280 €6000 Parisian street scene (33x41cm-13x16in) s. i.d.1927 verso board. 20-Nov-2 Sotheby's, London #114a est:4000-6000
£4304 $6800 €6800 Tour Saint-Jacques (41x33cm-16x13in) s.i. cardboard. 29-Nov-2 Drouot Estimations, Paris #73/R
£6000 $9420 €9000 Parisian boulevard at night (15x31cm-6x12in) s.i.indis.d. board. 20-Nov-2 Sotheby's, London #88/R est:6000-8000
£6329 $10000 €10000 Fete au village, Russie (41x33cm-16x13in) s. cardboard. 29-Nov-2 Drouot Estimations, Paris #75/R est:4000
£6329 $10000 €10000 View of Paris (40x32cm-16x13in) s. panel. 29-Nov-2 Drouot Estimations, Paris #91 est:6500
£6709 $10600 €10600 Rue de Paris (41x33cm-16x13in) s.i. cardboard. 29-Nov-2 Drouot Estimations, Paris #74/R est:3000
£7000 $10990 €10500 By the Dacha (33x41cm-13x16in) board. 20-Nov-2 Sotheby's, London #111/R est:7000-9000
£8000 $12560 €12000 Russia (31x41cm-12x16in) s.i. board. 20-Nov-2 Sotheby's, London #113/R est:10000-15000
£8276 $13241 €12000 Boulevard de nuit (12x16cm-5x6in) s. panel. 12-Mar-3 Libert, Castor, Paris #128 est:1000-1200
£14000 $21980 €21000 Troika dashing through the snow (32x40cm-13x16in) s. 20-Nov-2 Sotheby's, London #114/R est:3000-5000
£20000 $32400 €30000 View of the Arc de Triomphe, Paris (43x33cm-17x13in) s. board. 21-May-3 Sotheby's, London #110/R est:18000-25000
£24000 $38880 €36000 Paris street scene by night (41x48cm-16x19in) s.i. board. 21-May-3 Sotheby's, London #113/R est:6000-8000
£28000 $43960 €42000 Paris by night (32x40cm-13x16in) s.i. board. 20-Nov-2 Sotheby's, London #109/R est:10000-15000
£38000 $59660 €57000 On the frozen lake (65x81cm-26x32in) s. i.verso. 20-Nov-2 Sotheby's, London #89/R est:20000-30000
£50000 $81000 €75000 Apples in the garden (89x66cm-35x26in) s.d.1920 prov. 21-May-3 Sotheby's, London #131/R est:50000-70000
£77580 $125679 €112491 Street scene from Paris with many figures (84x65cm-33x26in) s. indis.i.d.1922 verso prov. 25-May-3 Uppsala Auktionskammare, Uppsala #129/R est:300000-400000 (S.KR 1000000)
£85337 $138247 €123739 Interior scene with lady wearing red dress (86x65cm-34x26in) s. prov. 25-May-3 Uppsala Auktionskammare, Uppsala #128/R est:300000-400000 (S.KR 1100000)
£110000 $172700 €165000 Quayside in the South of France (59x80cm-23x31in) s.d.1923. 20-Nov-2 Sotheby's, London #90/R est:20000-30000
Works on paper
£1026 $1600 €1539 Set design for a wooded seaside landscape. Set sketches (34x44cm-13x17in) s.i.d. i.verso gouache pen ink double-sided. 18-Sep-2 Swann Galleries, New York #26/R est:3000-5000

£2400 $3888 €3600 Costume designs for a peasant from Prince Igor and middle Eastern princess (38x26cm-15x10in) s. W/C over pencil two. 21-May-3 Sotheby's, London #167/R est:800-1200
£4000 $6480 €6000 Costume designs for Prince Igor (32x20cm-13x8in) i. Indian ink pencil gouache crayon. 21-May-3 Sotheby's, London #140/R est:2500-3500
£7000 $11340 €10500 Easter celebrations by the village church (40x33cm-16x13in) s.i. mixed media on board. 21-May-3 Sotheby's, London #108/R est:6000-8000

KORSAKOFF-GALSTON, Alexandra (1884-1969) American/Russian
£810 $1344 €1150 Reverently to Paul Klee (76x51cm-30x20in) s.i.d.1955 board. 14-Jun-3 Hauswedell & Nolte, Hamburg #1323/R

KORTE, Henricus Gerardus de (20th C) Dutch
£350 $567 €525 Before the beach huts, a sunny day (24x30cm-9x12in) s. board. 23-Jan-3 Christie's, Kensington #263
£775 $1247 €1100 Farmer's wife with corn bundle (68x88cm-27x35in) s. 7-May-3 Vendue Huis, Gravenhage #148/R

KORTHALS, Johannes (1916-) Dutch
£278 $458 €400 Towngate (60x50cm-24x20in) s. 1-Jul-3 Christie's, Amsterdam #175
£701 $1093 €1100 Market day (39x29cm-15x11in) s. 6-Nov-2 Vendue Huis, Gravenhage #42/R
£955 $1490 €1500 Amsterdam canal (59x49cm-23x19in) s. 6-Nov-2 Vendue Huis, Gravenhage #44/R est:1000-1200
£966 $1535 €1400 Street scene, Paris (40x50cm-16x20in) s. 10-Mar-3 Sotheby's, Amsterdam #226 est:1000-1500
£1019 $1590 €1600 City view with moored boats (58x78cm-23x31in) s. 6-Nov-2 Vendue Huis, Gravenhage #43/R est:1500-2500
£1655 $2632 €2400 View of a canal in winter, Amsterdam (50x60cm-20x24in) s. 10-Mar-3 Sotheby's, Amsterdam #225/R est:1500-2000
£2414 $3837 €3500 Rue St. Antoine (60x80cm-24x31in) s. 10-Mar-3 Sotheby's, Amsterdam #221/R est:1200-1800
Works on paper
£828 $1316 €1200 Porte St. Denis, Paris (44x52cm-17x20in) s.i. W/C. 10-Mar-3 Sotheby's, Amsterdam #223/R est:600-900

KORTHAUS, Carl A (1879-1956) German
£261 $429 €400 Lower alpine landscape with heaps of corn (83x86cm-33x34in) s. 5-Feb-3 Neumeister, Munich #740/R

KORTMAN, Johan E (1858-1923) Finnish
£1511 $2417 €2100 Rapids (36x67cm-14x26in) s.d.1902. 17-May-3 Hagelstam, Helsinki #145/R est:1000

KORTOKRAKS, Rudolf (1923-) German
£863 $1416 €1200 View of Salzburg in winter from Maria Plain (50x70cm-20x28in) s. 5-Jun-3 Dorotheum, Salzburg #643/R

KORYO DYNASTY (13th C) Korean
Works on paper
£157233 $250000 €227988 Visualization of the Hwaom Pure Land (131x58cm-52x23in) ink colour gold silk hanging scroll exhib.prov. 24-Mar-3 Christie's, Rockefeller NY #314/R est:250000-350000

KORYUSAI, Isoda (fl.c.1766-1788) Japanese
Prints
£2564 $4000 €3846 Courtesan Kikunoe of the Wakamatsuya before a mirror (38x26cm-15x10in) s. print prov. 25-Mar-3 Christie's, Rockefeller NY #13/R est:4000-5000

KORZENDORFER, Konstantin (1871-?) Czechoslovakian
£550 $858 €825 Portrait of a mother and daughter seated in a landscape (96x75cm-38x30in) s.d.1910. 8-Apr-3 Bonhams, Knightsbridge #145/R

KOS, Gojmir Anton (1896-1970) Yugoslavian
£4679 $7253 €7300 Transparences on the Carso (53x38cm-21x15in) s.d.60. 5-Dec-2 Stadion, Trieste #696/R est:7000

KOSA, Emil (jnr) (1903-1968) American
£683 $1100 €1025 Some dogs are like some people (102x76cm-40x30in) s.i. s.verso. 23-Feb-3 Butterfields, Los Angeles #7013
£1048 $1750 €1520 Lady Godiva (102x76cm-40x30in) s. i.on stretcher. 17-Jun-3 John Moran, Pasadena #133 est:2500-3500
£1647 $2750 €2388 Tuning up (76x127cm-30x50in) s. i.verso. 17-Jun-3 John Moran, Pasadena #132 est:4000-6000
£3106 $5000 €4659 Distance is relative (64x81cm-25x32in) estate st. i.stretcher. 18-Feb-3 John Moran, Pasadena #147b est:6000-8000
£3822 $6000 €5733 Time's passage (61x86cm-24x34in) s. i.stretcher. 19-Nov-2 Butterfields, San Francisco #8302/R est:6000-8000
£4140 $6500 €6210 Historic hills (63x91cm-25x36in) s. i.stretcher. 19-Nov-2 Butterfields, San Francisco #8301/R est:6000-8000
£4487 $7000 €6731 Kiss of gold (61x76cm-24x30in) s. masonite prov. 14-Sep-2 Weschler, Washington #633/R est:5000-7000
£4819 $8000 €6988 Eagle's nest (27x36cm-11x14in) s. i.verso canvasboard. 11-Jun-3 Butterfields, San Francisco #4278/R est:5000-7000
£5161 $8000 €7742 House in California coastal (61x91cm-24x36in) s. prov. 29-Oct-2 John Moran, Pasadena #625 est:7000-9000
£5422 $9000 €7862 Western gold (61x91cm-24x36in) s. i.verso masonite. 11-Jun-3 Butterfields, San Francisco #4279/R est:5000-7000
£5732 $9000 €8598 Day's end (76x102cm-30x40in) s. i.verso. 19-Nov-2 Butterfields, San Francisco #8300/R est:7000-10000
£5901 $9500 €8852 White dove of Tucson (76x102cm-30x40in) s. i.stretcher prov. 18-Feb-3 John Moran, Pasadena #147a est:10000-15000
£6129 $9500 €9194 Sheep herder's cottage (61x81cm-24x32in) s. i.verso masonite prov. 29-Oct-2 John Moran, Pasadena #625a est:5000-7000
£6369 $10000 €9554 Chatsworth Manor (76x91cm-30x36in) s. i.verso masonite prov.exhib. 19-Nov-2 Butterfields, San Francisco #8303/R est:10000-15000
£12102 $19000 €18153 Meeting place (61x91cm-24x36in) s. i.stretcher masonite. 19-Nov-2 Butterfields, San Francisco #8299/R est:12000-15000
Works on paper
£641 $1000 €962 Cemetery (36x55cm-14x22in) s. W/C. 13-Apr-3 Butterfields, Los Angeles #7023
£2258 $3500 €3387 Coastal, rocks and waves (51x71cm-20x28in) s. W/C prov. 29-Oct-2 John Moran, Pasadena #681 est:4500-6000
£3226 $5000 €4839 Cityscape, Taxco, Mexico (51x71cm-20x28in) s. W/C prov. 29-Oct-2 John Moran, Pasadena #682 est:4500-6000
£3892 $6500 €5643 Horses and barns in summer landscape (36x56cm-14x22in) s. W/C. 17-Jun-3 John Moran, Pasadena #82 est:3000-4000

KOSA, Emil (snr) (1876-1955) American
£1398 $2250 €2097 Floral still life, roses (58x71cm-23x28in) s. canvas on canvas prov. 18-Feb-3 John Moran, Pasadena #142 est:1500-2000
£1656 $2750 €2401 Flowers and two birds (114x86cm-45x34in) s. prov. 11-Jun-3 Butterfields, San Francisco #4312/R est:3000-5000
£1796 $3000 €2604 Chrysanthemums (71x58cm-28x23in) s. prov. 17-Jun-3 John Moran, Pasadena #145 est:2000-3000

KOSHIN, Kano (17/18th C) Japanese
Works on paper
£4403 $7000 €6605 Tiger and dragon (150x324cm-59x128in) s. ink six-panel screens pair. 24-Mar-3 Christie's, Rockefeller NY #82/R est:10000-15000

KOSKULL, Anders Gustaf (1831-1904) Swedish
£857 $1337 €1286 Church collection (73x82cm-29x32in) s. 13-Sep-2 Lilla Bukowskis, Stockholm #207 (S.KR 12500)

KOSLER, Franz Xavier (1864-?) Austrian
£2000 $3340 €3000 Portrait of Egyptian man, head and shoulders, in dark red coat (63x50cm-25x20in) s. 18-Jun-3 Christie's, Kensington #189/R est:2000-3000
£3200 $5024 €4800 Portrait of a Arab man (68x50cm-27x20in) s. 21-Nov-2 Christie's, Kensington #200/R est:2000-3000
£3262 $5057 €4893 Le beautee africiane en blanc (80x62cm-31x24in) s.d.1884. 8-Dec-2 Uppsala Auktionskammare, Uppsala #90/R est:30000-40000 (S.KR 46000)
£9494 $15000 €15000 Fortune-teller (58x70cm-23x28in) s. 28-Nov-2 Dorotheum, Vienna #92/R est:15000-18000

KOSNICK-KLOSS, Jeanne (1892-1955) German
Works on paper
£312 $496 €450 Composition (29x19cm-11x7in) mono. pastel. 29-Apr-3 Artcurial Briest, Paris #120
£312 $496 €450 Composition (17x10cm-7x4in) s. gouache. 29-Apr-3 Artcurial Briest, Paris #121
£818 $1267 €1300 Composition (40x29cm-16x11in) mono. W/C. 30-Oct-2 Artcurial Briest, Paris #30
£962 $1490 €1500 Geometric composition (50x33cm-20x13in) mono. pastel velour paper. 4-Dec-2 Lempertz, Koln #834/R est:2000

KOSONEN, Erkki (1902-1966) Finnish
£432 $708 €600 Still life (100x80cm-39x31in) s. 5-Jun-3 Hagelstam, Helsinki #833

KOSSAK, Carol (19/20th C) Hungarian
£3205 $5032 €5000 Retour du Marche a Fes (59x49cm-23x19in) s. i.d.1935 verso. 16-Dec-2 Gros & Delettrez, Paris #328/R est:3500-4000

KOSSAK, Jerzy (1890-1963) Polish
£828 $1300 €1242 Russian patrol attacking Austrian officers (50x65cm-20x26in) s.i.d.1916 panel prov. 14-Dec-2 Weschler, Washington #635/R est:1500-2500
£1100 $1837 €1595 Round-up (53x78cm-21x31in) s.d.1907 s.i.verso board. 8-Jul-3 Bonhams, Knightsbridge #234/R est:1200-1800
£1229 $1916 €1844 Napoleon in the snow (36x49cm-14x19in) s.d.1930 board. 15-Oct-2 Stephan Welz, Johannesburg #394/R est:4000-6000 (SA.R 20000)
£1282 $1987 €2000 Soldiers on horseback in snow-covered woodland (49x69cm-19x27in) s.d.1940 chipboard lit. 7-Dec-2 Bergmann, Erlangen #825/R est:2700
£3355 $5301 €5200 Charge de cavalerie (60x91cm-24x36in) s.d.1930. 19-Dec-2 Delvaux, Paris #51/R
£3472 $5590 €5208 Soldiers resting (71x99cm-28x39in) s.d.1935 panel. 7-May-3 Dobiaschofsky, Bern #747/R est:7500 (S.FR 7500)

KOSSAK, Woiciech von (1857-1942) Polish
£581 $900 €842 Polish naval semaphores (51x41cm-20x16in) 7-Dec-2 South Bay, Long Island #57
£1229 $1916 €1844 Two horses in the snow (39x47cm-15x19in) s.d.1925 canvasboard. 15-Oct-2 Stephan Welz, Johannesburg #387/R est:7000-10000 (SA.R 20000)
£1410 $2228 €2200 Kaiser Wilhelm II (50x40cm-20x16in) s. panel. 16-Nov-2 Lempertz, Koln #1511/R est:2000
£1783 $2782 €2800 Soldat a cheval au bord de riviere (42x31cm-17x12in) s.d. paper. 6-Nov-2 Claude Boisgirard, Paris #28 est:2500-3000

KOSSOFF, Léon (1926-) British
£16312 $26426 €23000 Self portrait II (56x51cm-22x20in) panel prov.exhib. 24-May-3 Van Ham, Cologne #340/R est:15000
£23000 $38410 €33350 Self portrait (28x23cm-11x9in) s.d.1971 verso prov. 26-Jun-3 Sotheby's, London #228/R est:12000-15000
Works on paper
£1000 $1650 €1450 Figures around a table (16x20cm-6x8in) felt tip. 3-Jul-3 Christie's, Kensington #547/R est:1000-1500
£6500 $10660 €9750 Street in Willesden, summer (42x58cm-17x23in) s.i.d.85 chl. 6-Jun-3 Christie's, London #195/R est:5000-8000
£17000 $27880 €25500 Children's swimming pool (35x50cm-14x20in) s. chl oil executed 1969. 6-Jun-3 Christie's, London #193/R est:7000-10000

KOSSOFF, Léon (attrib) (1926-) British
£875 $1400 €1313 Untitled (48x40cm-19x16in) bears sig board. 16-Mar-3 Butterfields, San Francisco #1079 est:300-500

KOSTABI, Mark (1961-) American
£719 $1150 €1100 SSSSS (25x20cm-10x8in) s.d.2002 s.i.d.verso. 4-Jan-3 Meeting Art, Vercelli #596
£972 $1546 €1400 Inescapable stress (25x35cm-10x14in) s.d.2002. 1-May-3 Meeting Art, Vercelli #20
£972 $1546 €1400 Immersion (28x28cm-11x11in) s.d.2002. 1-May-3 Meeting Art, Vercelli #176
£1218 $1912 €1900 Out off the blue (46x30cm-18x12in) s.d.2002 oval. 23-Nov-2 Meeting Art, Vercelli #259/R
£1348 $2183 €1900 Trifecta (61x45cm-24x18in) s.d.1995 s.i.d.2-11-95 verso. 26-May-3 Christie's, Milan #136/R est:1800-2200
£1565 $2488 €2300 New woman (60x46cm-24x18in) s.d.1997. 1-Mar-3 Meeting Art, Vercelli #344
£1569 $2510 €2400 Sustain (60cm-24in circular) s.d.2002. 4-Jan-3 Meeting Art, Vercelli #82
£1701 $2704 €2500 Cat flowers (76x102cm-30x40in) s.d.1991 lit. 1-Mar-3 Meeting Art, Vercelli #653
£1736 $2760 €2500 Both (46x61cm-18x24in) s.d.2001. 1-May-3 Meeting Art, Vercelli #208
£1772 $2765 €2800 Untitled (100x70cm-39x28in) 18-Oct-2 Dr Fritz Nagel, Stuttgart #553/R est:3000
£2014 $3202 €2900 Icarus (81x41cm-32x16in) s.d.2001 lit. 1-May-3 Meeting Art, Vercelli #462
£2372 $3724 €3700 Touch and go (76x102cm-30x40in) s.d.1996. 23-Nov-2 Meeting Art, Vercelli #344/R
£3056 $4858 €4400 Frequent flyer (122x122cm-48x48in) s.i.d.1990 verso. 1-May-3 Meeting Art, Vercelli #442

KOSTABI, Paul (1962-) American
£577 $906 €900 Untitled (61x46cm-24x18in) s. s.d.2002 verso. 23-Nov-2 Meeting Art, Vercelli #304

KOSTER, A (?) ?
£2837 $4397 €4256 Portraits of dog - one lying down, one sitting (22x28cm-9x11in) s. panel pair. 4-Dec-2 AB Stockholms Auktionsverk #1927/R est:20000-25000 (S.KR 40000)

KOSTER, Antonie L (1859-1937) Dutch
£552 $877 €800 Bloembollenvelden (30x40cm-12x16in) s. canvas on board. 10-Mar-3 Sotheby's, Amsterdam #134
£764 $1177 €1200 Flower transport (31x41cm-12x16in) s. 3-Sep-2 Christie's, Amsterdam #235

KOSTER, Antonius Henricus (1913-1990) Dutch
£255 $397 €400 Activity in Rotterdam harbour (37x52cm-15x20in) s. panel. 5-Nov-2 Vendu Notarishuis, Rotterdam #249
£256 $403 €400 Reclining dog (80x65cm-31x26in) s.d.59. 25-Nov-2 Glerum, Amsterdam #163
£282 $454 €400 Little house in Nieuwkoop in the evening (20x25cm-8x10in) s. board. 6-May-3 Vendu Notarishuis, Rotterdam #154
£296 $476 €420 Nieuwkoop in the evening (25x20cm-10x8in) s. board. 6-May-3 Vendu Notarishuis, Rotterdam #174
£382 $596 €600 Small house on the water (23x18cm-9x7in) s. board. 5-Nov-2 Vendu Notarishuis, Rotterdam #248
£387 $624 €550 Polder landscape (79x99cm-31x39in) s. board. 6-May-3 Vendu Notarishuis, Rotterdam #26/R
£387 $624 €550 Still life with cyclamen and fruit (75x60cm-30x24in) s. panel. 6-May-3 Vendu Notarishuis, Rotterdam #163
£423 $680 €600 Wooden boat on the beach (49x69cm-19x27in) s. 7-May-3 Vendue Huis, Gravenhage #20
£437 $703 €620 Nieuwkoop in winter (11x29cm-4x11in) s. board. 6-May-3 Vendu Notarishuis, Rotterdam #173/R
£446 $696 €700 Houses by the river in the evening (16x44cm-6x17in) s. panel. 5-Nov-2 Vendu Notarishuis, Rotterdam #226
£541 $845 €850 Winter landscape with river in the evening (48x68cm-19x27in) s. 5-Nov-2 Vendu Notarishuis, Rotterdam #250/R
£669 $1077 €950 Various still life (60x100cm-24x39in) s. panel. 6-May-3 Vendu Notarishuis, Rotterdam #175
£1197 $1927 €1700 View of Vier Leeuwenbrug in Rotterdam in winter (43x63cm-17x25in) s. board. 6-May-3 Vendu Notarishuis, Rotterdam #17/R est:1000-1500

KOSTER, Eduard (1883-1910) German
£408 $649 €600 Flooded fields near Worpswede (37x45cm-15x18in) s. board. 28-Mar-3 Bolland & Marotz, Bremen #351/R

KOSTER, Everhardus (1817-1892) Dutch
£4430 $6867 €7000 Arrival of a V.O.C. ship in an African harbour (72x57cm-28x22in) s. 24-Sep-2 Christie's, Amsterdam #143/R est:7000-9000
£4717 $7264 €7500 Sailing barges on the IJ, Amsterdam beyond (81x101cm-32x40in) s. 23-Oct-2 Christie's, Amsterdam #13/R est:8000-12000
£4861 $8021 €7000 Glorious salute (36x50cm-14x20in) s. panel. 1-Jul-3 Christie's, Amsterdam #24/R est:3000-5000
£6289 $9686 €10000 Waterslootpoort ar Delft at sunset, with the Prinsenhof in the distance (58x76cm-23x30in) s.d.47 prov. 23-Oct-2 Christie's, Amsterdam #103/R est:12000-16000
£15723 $24214 €25000 Regatta on the IJ, Amsterdam (41x62cm-16x24in) s. panel. 23-Oct-2 Christie's, Amsterdam #119/R est:15000-20000
Works on paper
£318 $497 €500 View of Schevening (16x22cm-6x9in) s. W/C. 6-Nov-2 Vendue Huis, Gravenhage #413

KOSTER, Jo (1869-1944) Dutch
£1313 $1916 €2100 Field of corn (43x63cm-17x25in) s. 14-May-2 Thomas Adams, Dublin #395
£7692 $11923 €12000 Cornfield (42x63cm-17x25in) s.d.1914. 3-Dec-2 Christie's, Amsterdam #214/R est:8000-12000

KOSTER, Karl Georg (1812-1893) German
£353 $554 €550 Lively stream in the mountains (25x22cm-10x9in) s. panel. 21-Nov-2 Van Ham, Cologne #1730/R
£769 $1192 €1200 Tyrolean landscape (70x90cm-28x35in) s.d.1877. 5-Dec-2 Schopman, Hamburg #526

KOSTER, Paul (1855-1946) German
£1139 $1766 €1800 Mountain hut by stream (94x111cm-37x44in) s. i. stretcher. 25-Sep-2 Neumeister, Munich #626/R est:1500
£2721 $4327 €4000 Alpine hut in mountain valley (94x111cm-37x44in) s. 25-Feb-3 Dorotheum, Vienna #147/R est:4000-4400

KOSTERSITZ, Carl von (19/20th C) Austrian?
£5674 $9191 €8000 Reger ship transport in Venice harbour (226x123cm-89x48in) mono.d.1892 i.verso. 22-May-3 Dorotheum, Vienna #50/R est:3000-3400

KOSTKA, Joseph (1846-1927) Polish
£1039 $1600 €1559 Lovebirds (48x36cm-19x14in) s.d.1913 prov. 24-Oct-2 Shannon's, Milford #175/R est:1200-1800

KOSTKA, Jozef (1912-1997) Czechoslovakian
Works on paper
£299 $464 €449 Reclining nude (21x32cm-8x13in) red chk exec.c.1960. 1-Oct-2 SOGA, Bratislava #91/R est:12000 (SL.K 19000)

KOSUTH, Joseph (1945-) American
Photographs
£5500 $8470 €8250 Untitled - art as idea as idea (105x105cm-41x41in) photostat mounted on board executed 1967 prov. 23-Oct-2 Christie's, London #165/R est:6000-8000
Prints
£12000 $19680 €18000 Art as idea as idea (76x91cm-30x36in) photostat board prov. 7-Feb-3 Sotheby's, London #134/R est:4000-6000
Sculpture
£9000 $15030 €13050 C.S - difficulty in understanding now lies elsewhere (17x225cm-7x89in) neon photographic paper executed 1988 prov. 27-Jun-3 Christie's, London #229/R est:10000-15000
£28481 $44146 €45000 One and three plants. installation of a plant photo. 28-Sep-2 Cornette de St.Cyr, Paris #361a est:50000-60000
Works on paper
£20000 $33400 €29000 Art as idea as idea (115x115cm-45x45in) photostat board. 26-Jun-3 Sotheby's, London #126/R est:5000-7000

KOSVANEC, Vlastimil (1887-?) Czechoslovakian
£536 $848 €804 Summer afternoon (70x100cm-28x39in) s. 30-Nov-2 Dorotheum, Prague #86 (C.KR 26000)
£578 $913 €867 Summer afternoon (70x90cm-28x35in) s. 30-Nov-2 Dorotheum, Prague #123 (C.KR 28000)
£636 $1030 €954 Sunday (70x100cm-28x39in) s. 24-May-3 Dorotheum, Prague #87/R est:26000-37000 (C.KR 28000)

KOSZEGI-FANGH, Dezsdo (1876-?) Hungarian
Works on paper
£278 $447 €403 Summer village (51x41cm-20x16in) s.d.1917 gouache. 7-May-3 Dobiaschofsky, Bern #3379 (S.FR 600)

KOSZKOL, Jeno (1868-1935) Hungarian
Works on paper
£1341 $2092 €1944 Gondoliers in Venice (68x48cm-27x19in) s. W/C paper on board. 12-Apr-3 Mu Terem Galeria, Budapest #123/R est:250000 (H.F 480000)
£2555 $3960 €3705 Gondoliers on the Grand Canal (68x100cm-27x39in) s. W/C. 9-Dec-2 Mu Terem Galeria, Budapest #55/R est:300000 (H.F 950000)

KOSZTA, Jozsef (1864-1949) Hungarian
£8771 $13683 €12718 Windmill (39x47cm-15x19in) s. 13-Sep-2 Mu Terem Galeria, Budapest #145/R est:2200000 (H.F 3400000)
£11178 $17437 €16208 Geraniums (47x39cm-19x15in) s. 12-Apr-3 Mu Terem Galeria, Budapest #165/R est:2600000 (H.F 4000000)
£11295 $17507 €16943 Purple lilacs (50x45cm-20x18in) s. 6-Dec-2 Kieselbach, Budapest #34/R (H.F 4200000)
£12383 $19317 €18575 Landscape with windmill (49x59cm-19x23in) s. 11-Sep-2 Kieselbach, Budapest #180/R (H.F 4800000)
£14791 $22926 €21447 Still life of lilac (49x35cm-19x14in) s. lit. 9-Dec-2 Mu Terem Galeria, Budapest #127/R est:2400000 (H.F 5500000)
£16767 $26156 €24312 Still life with lilacs (47x34cm-19x13in) s. paperboard. 12-Apr-3 Mu Terem Galeria, Budapest #219/R est:3000000 (H.F 6000000)
£16769 $26159 €24315 Parisian shop window (52x45cm-20x18in) s. lit. 13-Sep-2 Mu Terem Galeria, Budapest #18/R est:2600000 (H.F 6500000)
£20169 $31263 €29245 In the cornfield in the second half of the 1910s (73x52cm-29x20in) s. 9-Dec-2 Mu Terem Galeria, Budapest #144/R est:4000000 (H.F 7500000)

KOSZTOLANYI, Gyula (1868-1945) Hungarian
£4000 $6560 €6000 Village at dusk. Figures in a landscape. Sunlit village (62x46cm-24x18in) s. board three exhib. 3-Jun-3 Sotheby's, London #108/R est:5000-7000

KOTEI, Fukui (19th C) Japanese
Works on paper
£469 $750 €704 Tigers attacking dragon (178x274cm-70x108in) W/C silk. 15-Mar-3 Selkirks, St. Louis #412/R

KOTHE, Fritz (1916-) German
£316 $500 €500 Eva (21x25cm-8x10in) mono.d.1970 i. verso. 29-Nov-2 Villa Grisebach, Berlin #742/R
£316 $500 €500 Esther (25x21cm-10x8in) mono.d.1970 i. verso. 29-Nov-2 Villa Grisebach, Berlin #745/R
£411 $650 €650 Cathy (25x21cm-10x8in) mono.d.1970 i. verso. 29-Nov-2 Villa Grisebach, Berlin #743/R
£487 $770 €770 Belly button (27x21cm-11x8in) mono.d.1969. 29-Nov-2 Villa Grisebach, Berlin #741/R
£633 $1000 €1000 Susan (27x21cm-11x8in) mono.d.1968 i. stretcher. 29-Nov-2 Villa Grisebach, Berlin #740/R
£823 $1300 €1300 Ulla (25x21cm-10x8in) mono.d.1970 i. verso. 29-Nov-2 Villa Grisebach, Berlin #744/R est:500-600
£3333 $5467 €4600 Toblerone (100x69cm-39x27in) mono.d.1965 s.i.d. verso acrylic prov. 28-May-3 Lempertz, Koln #226/R est:4400

KOTIK, Jan (1916-) Czechoslovakian
£1032 $1630 €1548 Werewolf (41x50cm-16x20in) s.d.56 hardboard. 30-Nov-2 Dorotheum, Prague #97/R (C.KR 50000)
£1362 $2207 €2043 Nude (24x33cm-9x13in) s.d.45. 24-May-3 Dorotheum, Prague #130/R est:40000-60000 (C.KR 60000)
£3507 $5542 €5261 Woman at aquarium (116x90cm-46x35in) s.d.52. 30-Nov-2 Dorotheum, Prague #94/R est:60000-90000 (C.KR 170000)

KOTIK, Pravoslav (1889-1970) Czechoslovakian
£7092 $11489 €10000 Man, woman and houses (61x81cm-24x32in) s.d.46. 20-May-3 Dorotheum, Vienna #28/R est:12000-15000
Works on paper
£413 $644 €620 Sitting girl (29x14cm-11x6in) s.d.40 W/C. 12-Oct-2 Dorotheum, Prague #270/R (C.KR 20000)
£2065 $3222 €3098 In the gallery (26x20cm-10x8in) s.d.42 W/C. 12-Oct-2 Dorotheum, Prague #269/R est:12000-18000 (C.KR 100000)

KOTLER, Martin (20th C) American
£503 $800 €755 Navy yard, White Building series (51x61cm-20x24in) s.d.85. 7-Mar-3 Skinner, Boston #614/R

KOTSCHENREITER, G (?) ?
£1887 $2906 €3000 Woman whispering in man's ear (41x29cm-16x11in) s. 22-Oct-2 Wiener Kunst Auktionen, Vienna #1104/R est:1000-1500

KOTSCHENREITER, Hugo (1854-1908) German
£563 $935 €800 Amusing pipe smoker (29x22cm-11x9in) s.d.1894. 14-Jun-3 Arnold, Frankfurt #788/R
£590 $939 €850 Tiroler charakterkopf (25x18cm-10x7in) s.d.880 panel prov. 29-Apr-3 Christie's, Amsterdam #60/R
£620 $1011 €930 Pipe smoker (29x22cm-11x9in) s.d.1902. 29-Jan-3 Sotheby's, Olympia #267/R

KOUNELAKIS, Nicholaos (1829-1869) Greek
£110000 $170500 €165000 Evening prayer (105x69cm-41x27in) s. prov.exhib. 2-Oct-2 Sotheby's, London #27/R est:100000-150000

KOUNELLIS, Jannis (1936-) Greek
£14063 $22500 €21095 Untitled (69x99cm-27x39in) enamel on panel painted 1963 prov.exhib. 14-May-3 Sotheby's, New York #219/R est:18000-22000
Sculpture
£31646 $50000 €47469 Untitled (200x262x13cm-79x103x5in) steel lead wood in two parts executed 1989 prov.exhib. 13-Nov-2 Sotheby's, New York #111/R est:60000-80000
£40000 $62400 €60000 Untitled (200x180x27cm-79x71x11in) iron burlap and beam executed 1989. 21-Oct-2 Sotheby's, London #40/R est:40000-60000
Works on paper
£16000 $26240 €24000 Segnali (70x100cm-28x39in) gouache prov. 6-Feb-3 Christie's, London #638/R est:12000-15000
£25316 $40000 €37974 Untitled (272x152cm-107x60in) brush China ink paper on canvas painted c.1980 prov. 12-Nov-2 Phillips, New York #106/R est:40000-60000

KOUPETZIAN, Aram (1928-) Russian
£379 $603 €550 Violin (60x50cm-24x20in) s. oil collage. 10-Mar-3 Millon & Associes, Paris #113
£414 $658 €600 Serenade (60x78cm-24x31in) s. oil collage. 10-Mar-3 Millon & Associes, Paris #114
£414 $658 €600 Music (61x50cm-24x20in) s. oil collage. 10-Mar-3 Millon & Associes, Paris #115/R
£450 $684 €675 Still life with violin (46x61cm-18x24in) s. 14-Jul-2 John Nicholson, Haslemere #181
£811 $1265 €1200 Composition with violins (60x78cm-24x31in) s. 25-Mar-3 Durán, Madrid #738/R
£1053 $1705 €1600 Composition with violins (60x40cm-24x16in) s. 21-Jan-3 Durán, Madrid #730/R

KOURA, Bernard (1923-) French
£272 $433 €400 Vue de saint-Cenery dans l'Orne (62x96cm-24x38in) s. 21-Mar-3 Rieunier, Bailly-Pommery, Mathias, Paris #141

KOUSNETZOFF, Constantin (1863-1936) Russian
£705 $1107 €1100 Paysage vallonne (65x81cm-26x32in) s. 15-Dec-2 Thierry & Lannon, Brest #394
£1064 $1777 €1500 Maisons au bord de mer (60x74cm-24x29in) s. panel. 17-Jun-3 Claude Boisgirard, Paris #77 est:1500-1800
£1410 $2214 €2200 Paysage de Bretagne (61x73cm-24x29in) s. panel. 15-Dec-2 Eric Pillon, Calais #120/R

KOUWENHOVEN, Jakob van (1777-1825) Dutch
£1655 $2632 €2400 Cattle in an extensive landscape (51x65cm-20x26in) s. panel. 10-Mar-3 Sotheby's, Amsterdam #18 est:2000-3000

KOVACS, Ildiko (1962-) Australian?
£516 $856 €858 Untitled (51x64cm-20x25in) s.d.1997 verso oil paper on board two. 10-Jun-3 Shapiro, Sydney #53a est:1500-2500 (A.D 1300)

KOVACS, Mihaly (1818-1892) Hungarian
£1772 $2800 €2800 Woman with vine (93x67cm-37x26in) 26-Nov-2 Wiener Kunst Auktionen, Vienna #126/R est:1500-3000
£4386 $6842 €6579 Self portrait, 1852 (37x35cm-15x14in) s.d.1852. 11-Sep-2 Kieselbach, Budapest #177/R (H.F 1700000)

KOVACS, Zoltan (1883-1952) Austrian
£833 $1308 €1300 Water carrier in Capri (57x35cm-22x14in) s.d.1889. 21-Nov-2 Dorotheum, Vienna #241/R

KOWALCZEWSKI, Paul Ludwig (1865-1910) German
Sculpture
£1034 $1645 €1500 David (53cm-21in) s. marble. 8-Mar-3 Arnold, Frankfurt #241/R

KOWALCZYK, Izabela (1975-) Polish
£479 $800 €695 Dialogue 1 (12x130cm-5x51in) s.d.2001 verso oil acrylic sand. 25-Jun-3 Sotheby's, Moscow #226/R
£479 $800 €695 Dialogue 4 (116x141cm-46x56in) s.d.2001 verso. 25-Jun-3 Sotheby's, Moscow #227/R

KOWALEWSKY, Pawel Ossipovitch (1843-1903) Russian
£4487 $7000 €6731 Russian soldiers (25x51cm-10x20in) panel. 20-Sep-2 Du Mouchelle, Detroit #2014/R est:2500-3500
£4815 $6837 €7800 Charge des cavaliers (42x77cm-17x30in) s.d.1887. 16-Mar-3 Eric Pillon, Calais #63/R
£13621 $22066 €19750 Horses on pasture (35x54cm-14x21in) s.cyrillic. 24-May-3 Dorotheum, Prague #45/R est:30000-50000 (C.KR 600000)
Works on paper
£823 $1300 €1300 Soldiers (19x12cm-7x5in) s. sepia ink. 1-Dec-2 Bukowskis, Helsinki #260/R

KOWALSKI, Ivan Ivanovitch (20th C) Russian
£510 $795 €800 Paysage russe (27x35cm-11x14in) s.d.1906. 10-Nov-2 Eric Pillon, Calais #66/R

KOWALSKI, Ludwig Peter (1891-1967) German
Works on paper
£347 $549 €500 Still life of flowers (46x74cm-18x29in) mono.d.1961 s.i.d. verso W/C board. 26-Apr-3 Dr Lehr, Berlin #287/R
£483 $763 €700 Female nude (60x40cm-24x16in) bears sig. W/C Indian ink. 2-Apr-3 Dr Fritz Nagel, Stuttgart #9131/R

KOWALSKI, Piotr (1927-) ?
Sculpture
£1042 $1719 €1500 X,Y,Z (63x63x63cm-25x25x25in) metal neon plexiglas electric wire. 1-Jul-3 Artcurial Briest, Paris #833/R est:1500-2000

KOWALSKY, Leopold Franz (1856-1931) Russian/French
£3919 $6114 €5800 Allegory of Love (110x180cm-43x71in) s. oval. 28-Mar-3 Delvaux, Paris #26 est:8000

KOWARSKI, Felicjan (1890-1948) Polish
£900 $1422 €1350 Odessa (32x53cm-13x21in) s. 14-Nov-2 Christie's, Kensington #222/R

KOZLOWSKI, Jaroslaw (1910-1983) Polish
£244 $400 €366 Horses racing (33x53cm-13x21in) s. 31-May-3 Harvey Clar, Oakland #1136

KOZMAN, Myron (1916-2002) American
£943 $1500 €1415 Triller (38x46cm-15x18in) s.d. board. 4-May-3 Treadway Gallery, Cincinnati #641/R est:2000-3000
£943 $1500 €1415 Urban view (38x46cm-15x18in) s.d. board. 4-May-3 Treadway Gallery, Cincinnati #642/R est:2000-3000
£1006 $1600 €1509 Composition (41x30cm-16x12in) s. i.verso board painted c.1960. 2-Mar-3 Toomey, Oak Park #771/R est:2000-3000
£1132 $1800 €1698 Composition (36x28cm-14x11in) s. i.verso board painted c.1960. 2-Mar-3 Toomey, Oak Park #769/R est:2000-3000

KRABBE, Hendrik Maarten (1868-1931) Dutch
£296 $476 €420 Wood gatherers (48x37cm-19x15in) s. 6-May-3 Vendu Notarishuis, Rotterdam #112/R
£1887 $2906 €3000 In the artist's studio (50x38cm-20x15in) s.d.95. 22-Oct-2 Sotheby's, Amsterdam #115/R est:3000-5000

KRABBE, Marie (1837-1918) Danish
£687 $1085 €1031 Bouquet of fuchsia, jasmin and pansies (25x32cm-10x13in) init.d.1870. 13-Nov-2 Kunsthallen, Copenhagen #119 (D.KR 8000)

KRACHKOVSKY, Iosef Evstafevich (1854-1899) Russian
£12000 $19440 €18000 View of Yalta (106x131cm-42x52in) s. 21-May-3 Sotheby's, London #86/R est:15000-20000

KRACIK, Fedor Antonin (1888-?) Czechoslovakian
Works on paper
£268 $415 €402 Village (42x59cm-17x23in) pastel board exec.c.1930. 1-Oct-2 SOGA, Bratislava #215/R est:15000 (SL.K 17000)

KRACKER, Johann Lucas (attrib) (1717-1779) Czechoslovakian
£5405 $8432 €8000 Christ among the doctors (75x45cm-30x18in) prov. 27-Mar-3 Dorotheum, Vienna #258/R est:8500-12000

KRAEMER, Nathalie (1891-1943) French
£7891 $12547 €11600 Le penseur (81x60cm-32x24in) s. 3-Mar-3 Claude Boisgirard, Paris #61/R est:6000-8000

KRAEMER, Peter (19/20th C) German
Works on paper
£633 $1000 €1000 Bavarian farmer sitting at a table smelling a cigar with a grim look (22x17cm-9x7in) s.i. W/C. 29-Nov-2 Sigalas, Stuttgart #1099/R
£823 $1275 €1300 Peasant with currency note (22x17cm-9x7in) s. W/C over pencil htd white. 25-Sep-2 Neumeister, Munich #415/R
£1088 $1731 €1600 The bad loser (18x15cm-7x6in) s.i. W/C htd white. 19-Mar-3 Neumeister, Munich #377 est:900
£1224 $1947 €1800 Peasant smoking (21x17cm-8x7in) s.i. W/C over pencil htd white. 19-Mar-3 Neumeister, Munich #376 est:1000
£1474 $2285 €2300 Farmers playing cards (20x99cm-8x39in) s. W/C htd white two in same frame. 4-Dec-2 Neumeister, Munich #529/R est:1800

KRAEMER, Peter (jnr) (1857-1941) German
£769 $1192 €1200 Flute player standing in front of a music desk (16x11cm-6x4in) s.d.1888 panel. 4-Dec-2 Neumeister, Munich #787
Works on paper
£816 $1298 €1200 Peasant with pipe (20x16cm-8x6in) s.i. W/C htd white. 20-Mar-3 Neumeister, Munich #2498/R

KRAFFT, Barbara (1764-1825) Austrian
£2848 $4500 €4500 Flute player (18x14cm-7x6in) s. copper. 26-Nov-2 Wiener Kunst Auktionen, Vienna #1/R est:2500-10000

KRAFFT, Carl R (1884-1938) American
£955 $1500 €1433 Autumn landscape with figures (64x76cm-25x30in) s. 20-Nov-2 Boos Gallery, Michigan #413/R est:800-1200
£1274 $2000 €1911 Lacy trees (64x76cm-25x30in) s. 22-Nov-2 Skinner, Boston #293/R est:4000-6000
£1419 $2200 €2129 Autumn song (61x69cm-24x27in) s. painted c.1934. 8-Dec-2 Toomey, Oak Park #684/R est:2000-3000
£2903 $4500 €4355 Along the river (76x102cm-30x40in) s.d. 8-Dec-2 Toomey, Oak Park #650/R est:6000-8000

KRAFFT, David von (1655-1724) Swedish
£3546 $5496 €5319 Portrait of Baron Bernhard von Liewen (145x120cm-57x47in) 4-Dec-2 AB Stockholms Auktionsverk #1692/R est:30000-40000 (S.KR 50000)
£8156 $12642 €12234 Portrait of Count Ture Gabriel Bielke (84x67cm-33x26in) i.verso. 4-Dec-2 AB Stockholms Auktionsverk #1700/R est:30000-40000 (S.KR 115000)

KRAFFT, David von (studio) (1655-1724) Swedish
£7758 $12568 €11249 King Karl XII (92x75cm-36x30in) oval. 26-May-3 Bukowskis, Stockholm #351/R est:100000-150000 (S.KR 100000)

KRAFFT, Per (elder) (1724-1793) Swedish
£1646 $2600 €2600 Johan Chrysotomus Martineau (69x54cm-27x21in) painted c.1770 lit. 1-Dec-2 Bukowskis, Helsinki #261/R est:3000-4000
£1646 $2600 €2600 Portrait of Ulrika Antoinetta Reyron (64x52cm-25x20in) s.d.1787 oval lit. 1-Dec-2 Bukowskis, Helsinki #262/R est:3000-4000
£49645 $76950 €74468 Portrait of the young Crown Prince Gustav IV Adolf in interior (193x129cm-76x51in) painted 1785-1787 prov.lit. 4-Dec-2 AB Stockholms Auktionsverk #1702/R est:700000-900000 (S.KR 700000)

KRAFT, Frederik (1823-1854) Danish
£766 $1210 €1149 Landscape from Lyngbyso with view towards Frederiksdal, morning (47x57cm-19x22in) s.d.1843. 2-Dec-2 Rasmussen, Copenhagen #1258/R (D.KR 9000)
£8613 $13092 €12920 September evening near Dyrehaven (110x157cm-43x62in) s.d.1854 exhib. 27-Aug-2 Rasmussen, Copenhagen #1408/R est:100000 (D.KR 100000)

KRAG, Helene Wilhelmine (19th C) Danish
£525 $841 €788 Landscape with Sorterup Church (37x48cm-15x19in) s.verso. 13-Jan-3 Rasmussen, Vejle #144/R (D.KR 6000)

KRAGH, Ejnar R (1903-1981) Danish
£1117 $1777 €1676 Children playing (225x137cm-89x54in) s.d.46. 10-Mar-3 Rasmussen, Vejle #627 est:12000 (D.KR 12000)

KRAGH-PEDERSEN, Hjalmar (1883-?) Danish
£316 $491 €500 Nurnberg canal (53x37cm-21x15in) s. i. verso. 28-Sep-2 Hans Stahl, Hamburg #115
£458 $737 €650 Nurnberg canal (55x41cm-22x16in) s. 10-May-3 Hans Stahl, Toestorf #13/R
£566 $877 €900 Canal in Nurnberg (52x41cm-20x16in) s. i. verso. 2-Nov-2 Hans Stahl, Toestorf #16/R

KRAIKE, Jane (20th C) American
£599 $1000 €869 Wrestlers (51x89cm-20x35in) s.d.1940. 17-Jun-3 John Moran, Pasadena #155 est:1500-2500

KRAITZ, Ulla (1936-) Swedish?
£280 $437 €420 Untitled - collage (709x64cm-279x25in) s.d.91 oil paper. 6-Nov-2 AB Stockholms Auktionsverk #854/R (S.KR 4000)

KRAL, Josef (1859-1910) Czechoslovakian
£454 $736 €681 Meadow with red poppies (32x27cm-13x11in) s. board. 24-May-3 Dorotheum, Prague #64/R est:18000-30000 (C.KR 20000)
£863 $1398 €1295 Hamburg (15x25cm-6x10in) s.i.d.1907 board. 24-May-3 Dorotheum, Prague #63/R est:20000-30000 (C.KR 38000)
£1033 $1611 €1550 Brook (26x34cm-10x13in) s.d.04 cardboard. 12-Oct-2 Dorotheum, Prague #53/R (C.KR 50000)
£1200 $1908 €1800 Night city (34x42cm-13x17in) s. board. 8-Mar-3 Dorotheum, Prague #70/R est:26000-40000 (C.KR 55000)

KRAMER, Cornelis Groenewoud (1918-) Dutch
£599 $964 €850 Dyke house (39x49cm-15x19in) init. s.i.verso. 7-May-3 Vendue Huis, Gravenhage #534

KRAMER, Jacob (1892-1962) British
£550 $858 €825 Still life of marigolds in a brown vase (41x30cm-16x12in) s. 25-Mar-3 Bonhams, Leeds #563/R

Works on paper
£300 $501 €435 Portrait of a lady (29x23cm-11x9in) s. pastel. 17-Jun-3 Bonhams, Knightsbridge #83
£300 $468 €435 Gypsy girl - artist's sister Sarah (33x20cm-13x8in) s. chl. 27-Mar-3 Lane, Penzance #147
£300 $492 €435 Gypsy (40x28cm-16x11in) s. chl. 5-Jun-3 Morphets, Harrogate #378
£320 $496 €480 Head of a woman (35x28cm-14x11in) s. chl conte. 1-Oct-2 Bonhams, Leeds #257
£400 $668 €580 Portrait of a young girl (28x26cm-11x10in) s.i.d.1926 pastel exhib. 17-Jun-3 Bonhams, Knightsbridge #82
£650 $1014 €975 Portrait of a lady in a shawl (53x39cm-21x15in) s.d.1916 chl. 27-Mar-3 Christie's, Kensington #267/R
£720 $1130 €1080 Two figures (46x27cm-18x11in) s.d.1921 pastel prov. 15-Apr-3 Bonhams, Knightsbridge #212/R
£750 $1238 €1088 Gypsy girl, the artist's sister, Sarah (33x20cm-13x8in) s. chl prov. 3-Jul-3 Christie's, Kensington #255/R
£820 $1271 €1230 Peasant woman (62x46cm-24x18in) s.d.1916 chl. 1-Oct-2 Bonhams, Leeds #258/R

KRAMER, Jacob (attrib) (1892-1962) British
£2421 $3849 €3632 Lady wearing red hat (79x62cm-31x24in) indis.sig. 5-Mar-3 Rasmussen, Copenhagen #1734/R est:7000-10000 (D.KR 26000)

KRAMER, Johann Victor (1861-1949) Austrian
£1258 $1950 €2000 Cupid carving his bow, after Parmigianino (67x32cm-26x13in) s. verso panel. 2-Oct-2 Dorotheum, Vienna #422/R est:2200-2600
£2329 $3633 €3400 Portrait of Oriental man (45x36cm-18x14in) s.i.d.1899. 10-Apr-3 Dorotheum, Vienna #73/R est:2200-2600

KRANZ, Kurt (1910-1997) German

Works on paper
£655 $1028 €983 Untitled (56x78cm-22x31in) s.d.1972 W/C prov. 25-Nov-2 Germann, Zurich #756 est:1000-1500 (S.FR 1500)
£1538 $2385 €2400 Untitled (66x49cm-26x19in) s.d.1936-37 collage splash technique. 7-Dec-2 Van Ham, Cologne #290/R est:1500

KRASIN, Konstantin (1928-) Russian
£400 $608 €600 Grapes gathering (50x34cm-20x13in) s. board. 14-Jul-2 John Nicholson, Haslemere #230/R

KRASNER, Lee (1908-1984) American
£106250 $170000 €159375 Uncial (173x216cm-68x85in) s.d.67 prov.exhib.lit. 14-May-3 Sotheby's, New York #132/R est:100000-150000

KRASNOFF, Nicholas (20th C) Russian

Works on paper
£900 $1431 €1350 Grand Harbour from St. Francis de Paul Bay (15x23cm-6x9in) s.i. W/C. 29-Apr-3 Bonhams, New Bond Street #139/R
£1300 $2067 €1950 Morning light, Valletta street, Malta (35x25cm-14x10in) s.i.d.1922 W/C. 29-Apr-3 Bonhams, New Bond Street #168/R est:1000-1500

KRASNY, Yuri (1925-) Russian

Works on paper
£2000 $3240 €3000 Watching the card players (43x39cm-17x15in) s.d.78 gouache. 21-May-3 Sotheby's, London #227/R est:2500-3500

KRASSNIG, Reinhold Ludwig (1898-?) Austrian
£3103 $4966 €4500 Still life (100x80cm-39x31in) mono.d.31 exhib.prov. 11-Mar-3 Dorotheum, Vienna #63/R est:2600-3400

KRASSNUSCHKINA, Jelisaweta Sacharowna (1858-?) Russian
£1702 $2689 €2553 Man with horse in snow storm (50x75cm-20x30in) s.d.1887. 2-Dec-2 Rasmussen, Copenhagen #1562/R est:15000 (D.KR 20000)

KRASULIN, Valery (1950-) Russian
£550 $853 €825 Wintry evening on the Italian Boulevard, Paris (50x61cm-20x24in) s. 8-Dec-2 John Nicholson, Haslemere #67/R

KRASULIN, Victor (1950-) Russian
£493 $799 €750 Paris, by the Madeleine (46x55cm-18x22in) s. 21-Jan-3 Durán, Madrid #731/R
£570 $918 €850 By Place de la Concorde, Paris (46x55cm-18x22in) s. 18-Feb-3 Durán, Madrid #674/R
£815 $1313 €1215 Chatting (61x50cm-24x20in) s. 18-Feb-3 Durán, Madrid #675/R

KRATSCHOWSKI, Jossif (1854-1914) Russian
£7500 $11774 €11250 View across an Italian lake (54x73cm-21x29in) s.d.1906. 20-Nov-2 Sotheby's, London #72/R est:4000-6000

KRATZER, Hans (19/20th C) German
£417 $633 €650 Church concert (67x56cm-26x22in) s. 11-Jul-2 Hugo Ruef, Munich #729/R
£528 $850 €750 Coming to a decision (51x61cm-20x24in) s. lit. 9-May-3 Schloss Ahlden, Ahlden #1474/R

KRAUGERUD, Ragnar (1909-1987) Norwegian
£345 $525 €518 Woman with portrait of man (69x62cm-27x24in) init. paper on panel. 31-Aug-2 Grev Wedels Plass, Oslo #56 (N.KR 4000)
£358 $559 €537 Landscape (60x73cm-24x29in) s. panel. 23-Sep-2 Blomqvist, Lysaker #1134/R (N.KR 4200)
£393 $616 €590 Southern town (29x41cm-11x16in) s. panel. 25-Nov-2 Blomqvist, Lysaker #1165/R (N.KR 4500)
£1327 $2097 €1991 Green landscape (90x100cm-35x39in) init. 28-Apr-3 Blomqvist, Oslo #384/R est:18000-22000 (N.KR 15000)
£1735 $2706 €2603 Figures in landscape (85x100cm-33x39in) init. s.verso. 21-Oct-2 Blomqvist, Oslo #407/R est:25000-30000 (N.KR 20000)
£2832 $4474 €4248 Study (72x100cm-28x39in) init. panel exhib. 28-Apr-3 Blomqvist, Oslo #381/R est:40000-50000 (N.KR 32000)

KRAUL, Fritz (1862-1935) German
£1586 $2521 €2379 Interior scene with woman setting table (46x58cm-18x23in) s.d.1915. 5-May-3 Rasmussen, Vejle #655/R est:20000 (D.KR 17000)

KRAUPA, Wenzel (19/20th C) Austrian
£380 $589 €600 Smugglers resting at night (65x54cm-26x21in) s.d.1850 i. verso. 26-Sep-2 Neumeister, Munich #2770/R

KRAUSE WICHMANN, Eduard (1864-?) German
£759 $1200 €1200 Stettin harbour (96x150cm-38x59in) s. 29-Nov-2 Bolland & Marotz, Bremen #725/R
£784 $1286 €1200 Stettin harbour (116x100cm-46x39in) s. 8-Feb-3 Hans Stahl, Hamburg #98/R est:1600

KRAUSE, Emil (1871-1945) Danish
£1034 $1571 €1551 Landscape from Myggenaes, Faroe Islands (63x85cm-25x33in) init. 27-Aug-2 Rasmussen, Copenhagen #1840/R est:5000-7000 (D.KR 12000)

KRAUSE, Emil A (fl.1891-1914) British
Works on paper
£380 $578 €570 Over the river Tyne (7x12cm-3x5in) s.i. W/C prov. 15-Aug-2 Bonhams, New Bond Street #231
£400 $632 €580 Morning at Derwentwater (48x74cm-19x29in) s.d. 24-Jul-3 John Nicholson, Haslemere #1032
£550 $858 €825 Castle on the coast of Scotland (34x51cm-13x20in) s. pencil W/C htd white. 19-Sep-2 Christie's, Kensington #79
£580 $969 €841 Southampton water. Off the Bar Liverpool (17x24cm-7x9in) s.i. W/C pair. 24-Jun-3 Bearnes, Exeter #473
£650 $1086 €943 Derwentwater. Bassenthwaite (33x50cm-13x20in) s. W/C pair. 24-Jun-3 Bonhams, Knightsbridge #59/R
£1300 $2132 €1885 Conway, estuary scene at low tide (51x71cm-20x28in) s.d.1903 W/C. 3-Jun-3 Capes Dunn, Manchester #43/R

KRAUSE, Franz Emil (1836-1900) German
£528 $830 €792 Fishing boats leaving the harbour (56x91cm-22x36in) s. 10-Dec-2 Pinneys, Montreal #35 (C.D 1300)
£2270 $3518 €3405 After the shipwreck (76x113cm-30x44in) s.d.74. 3-Dec-2 Bukowskis, Stockholm #236/R est:30000-35000 (S.KR 32000)

KRAUSE, Franz Emil (attrib) (1836-1900) German
£1135 $1771 €1703 HMS Temerair (30x46cm-12x18in) i.d.84 i. verso. 6-Nov-2 Dobiaschofsky, Bern #745/R est:2400 (S.FR 2600)

KRAUSE, H Max (19th C) British?
£30000 $48600 €43500 Custom House, Dublin (100x151cm-39x59in) s. 21-May-3 Outhwaite & Litherland, Liverpool #199/R

KRAUSE, Hans (1864-?) German
£316 $500 €474 Man and woman with dog (51x41cm-20x16in) s. 16-Nov-2 New Orleans Auction, New Orleans #964

KRAUSE, Heinrich (1885-1985) Austrian
£662 $1079 €1000 Still life with cactus and lemons (37x50cm-15x20in) s. paper. 28-Jan-3 Dorotheum, Vienna #84/R
£662 $1079 €1000 Lilies on a red background (63x47cm-25x19in) s. 28-Jan-3 Dorotheum, Vienna #89/R
£962 $1519 €1500 Still life with pot plant and lemons (51x45cm-20x18in) s. prov. 12-Nov-2 Dorotheum, Vienna #124/R est:1700-2200
£1076 $1678 €1700 Vase with tulips and lily (62x47cm-24x19in) s. board. 15-Oct-2 Dorotheum, Vienna #61/R est:1600-2400
Works on paper
£2532 $3949 €4000 River trip (38x44cm-15x17in) s. 15-Oct-2 Dorotheum, Vienna #81/R est:1300-1800

KRAUSE, M (19/20th C) ?
£800 $1248 €1200 Unloading timber, Hull Docks (49x39cm-19x15in) s.d.1900. 6-Nov-2 Bonhams, Chester #508

KRAUSE, Wilhelm August (1803-1864) German
£1370 $2137 €2000 Romantic lake landscape (43x59cm-17x23in) s.d.1840. 10-Apr-3 Van Ham, Cologne #1552/R est:2500
£1948 $2903 €3000 River landscape (35x42cm-14x17in) s.d.1855 oval. 26-Jun-2 Neumeister, Munich #777/R est:2000

KRAUSKOPF, Bruno (1892-1960) German
£1519 $2354 €2400 Self portrait (63x48cm-25x19in) s. oil tempera wash sepia Indian ink. 28-Sep-2 Hans Stahl, Hamburg #105/R est:2500
£3623 $5942 €5000 Elisabeth Bergner as St Johanna (65x55cm-26x22in) s. 31-May-3 Villa Grisebach, Berlin #270/R est:5000-7000
£4167 $6458 €6500 Flowers in the garden (65x50cm-26x20in) s. exec.c.1923-26. 6-Dec-2 Ketterer, Munich #80/R est:7000-9000
£4167 $6458 €6500 On the Hudson, New York (61x90cm-24x35in) s. 4-Dec-2 Lempertz, Koln #838/R est:7200
£4348 $7130 €6000 Still life with chrysanthemums and cyclamen (100x80cm-39x31in) s. 31-May-3 Villa Grisebach, Berlin #279/R est:6000-8000
Works on paper
£377 $589 €600 Oriental street scene (34x45cm-13x18in) s. mixed media. 21-Sep-2 Dannenberg, Berlin #575/R
£552 $850 €828 Burning sun (54x39cm-21x15in) s. W/C gouache executed 1941. 28-Oct-2 Blomqvist, Lysaker #1165/R (N.KR 6500)

KRAUSKOPF, Bruno (attrib) (1892-1960) German
£552 $872 €800 Old city roof tops (49x32cm-19x13in) s. mixed media board. 5-Apr-3 Hans Stahl, Hamburg #77/R

KRAUSZ, Simon Andreas (1760-1825) Dutch
£352 $567 €500 Farmer's wife with watering cows (31x37cm-12x15in) s. panel. 7-May-3 Vendue Huis, Gravenhage #332

KRAWAGNER, Peter (1937-) German
£1325 $2159 €2000 On the Worther lake (100x81cm-39x32in) tempera. 28-Jan-3 Dorotheum, Vienna #171/R est:2000-2800
£3205 $5032 €5000 Landscape (120x140cm-47x55in) s.d.78. 20-Nov-2 Dorotheum, Klagenfurt #11 est:3000
Works on paper
£504 $826 €700 Landscape in Istrien (50x35cm-20x14in) s.d.74 mixed media. 5-Jun-3 Dorotheum, Salzburg #885/R

KRAWIEC, Walter (1889-?) American
£719 $1200 €1043 Cage wagon (51x89cm-20x35in) s. exhib. 21-Jun-3 Selkirks, St. Louis #166/R est:1000-1500

KRAY, Wilhelm (1828-1889) German
£1747 $2725 €2621 Le reve du pecheur (74x121cm-29x48in) s. 6-Nov-2 Dobiaschofsky, Bern #746/R est:4600 (S.FR 4000)
£3200 $5024 €4800 Children on the Italian coast with a basket of grapes, Capri beyond (42x71cm-17x28in) s.i. 16-Apr-3 Christie's, Kensington #770/R est:3000-5000

KREBS, Friederich (19th C) American
Works on paper
£621 $1000 €932 Certificate of baptism for Johannes Gobel with elaborate surround (33x41cm-13x16in) W/C. 22-Feb-3 Pook & Pook, Downington #316/R

KREBS, Walter (1900-1965) Swiss
£324 $522 €486 Oriental scene with sailing boats (72x63cm-28x25in) s. 7-May-3 Dobiaschofsky, Bern #748 (S.FR 700)
£324 $522 €486 Sailing boat on the Nile (63x72cm-25x28in) s.d.57 paper. 7-May-3 Dobiaschofsky, Bern #750/R (S.FR 700)
Works on paper
£324 $522 €486 Bedouins in desert (72x63cm-28x25in) s. gouache. 7-May-3 Dobiaschofsky, Bern #749/R (S.FR 700)
£324 $522 €486 Mountains (71x83cm-28x33in) s.d.38 mixed media. 7-May-3 Dobiaschofsky, Bern #3385 (S.FR 700)

KREGTEN, Fedor van (1871-1937) Dutch
£348 $543 €550 Farm with calves in foreground (59x79cm-23x31in) s. 21-Oct-2 Glerum, Amsterdam #172/R
£483 $764 €725 On the Maas (41x56cm-16x22in) s. 18-Nov-2 Waddingtons, Toronto #190a/R (C.D 1200)
£530 $864 €800 Caravane dans le desert (30x40cm-12x16in) s. 17-Feb-3 Horta, Bruxelles #426
£582 $908 €850 Wooded landscape with two calves (65x88cm-26x35in) s. 14-Apr-3 Glerum, Amsterdam #51/R
£625 $1013 €950 Calves in a pasture (40x60cm-16x24in) s. 21-Jan-3 Christie's, Amsterdam #149
£690 $1097 €1000 Cows near the waterside (60x89cm-24x35in) s. 10-Mar-3 Sotheby's, Amsterdam #144 est:1000-1500
£701 $1093 €1100 Cows at the pond (40x60cm-16x24in) s. lit. 7-Nov-2 Allgauer, Kempten #2873/R
£704 $1134 €1000 Landscape with two calves (38x58cm-15x23in) s. 6-May-3 Vendu Notarishuis, Rotterdam #181
£1274 $2000 €1911 Cattle drinking riverbank (144x104cm-57x41in) prov. 10-Dec-2 Peter Webb, Auckland #140/R est:3000-5000 (NZ.D 4000)

KREHBIEL, Albert H (20th C) American
Works on paper
£503 $800 €755 Stream and fallen trees (23x28cm-9x11in) s. i.verso pastel. 7-Mar-3 Skinner, Boston #450/R

KREHM, William P (1901-1968) American
£1282 $2000 €1923 Barn and the eucalyptus. 21-Sep-2 Harvey Clar, Oakland #1546

KREIDOLF, Ernst Konrad Theophil (1863-1956) Swiss
£786 $1226 €1179 Mother and two children following deer (61x80cm-24x31in) s. canvas on board. 6-Nov-2 Hans Widmer, St Gallen #110/R est:2000-4500 (S.FR 1800)
£1921 $2997 €2882 Baldr, the old Germanic god of light (75x99cm-30x39in) s.d.1922. 8-Nov-2 Dobiaschofsky, Bern #186/R est:5000 (S.FR 4400)
Works on paper
£322 $509 €483 Two clouds (25x17cm-10x7in) s.d.1932 W/C gouache. 26-Nov-2 Hans Widmer, St Gallen #1228 (S.FR 750)
£393 $613 €590 Dream of the green Henry (19x12cm-7x5in) mono. W/C ink. 8-Nov-2 Dobiaschofsky, Bern #187/R (S.FR 900)
£394 $634 €571 Still life (24x15cm-9x6in) s. gouache. 7-May-3 Dobiaschofsky, Bern #1702 (S.FR 850)
£1135 $1771 €1703 Winterthur (24x33cm-9x13in) s.d.1922 col pen paper on board. 6-Nov-2 Hans Widmer, St Gallen #111/R est:1200-2800 (S.FR 2600)
£2402 $3747 €3603 View from Oberwinterthur (24x32cm-9x13in) s. gouache. 8-Nov-2 Dobiaschofsky, Bern #188/R est:4000 (S.FR 5500)

KREIENBUHL, Jurg (1932-) Swiss
£472 $746 €708 Harbour region (16x23cm-6x9in) s.d.1969 dispersion masonite. 29-Nov-2 Zofingen, Switzerland #2949/R (S.FR 1100)

KREISEL, Alexander (1901-1953) American
£390 $600 €585 Urban scene (64x76cm-25x30in) s. painted c.1940. 8-Sep-2 Treadway Gallery, Cincinnati #686/R

KREITMAYER, Johann Baptist (19th C) German
£568 $903 €835 Medieval city with canals (49x62cm-19x24in) s.d.1873 lit. 21-Mar-3 Auktionhaus Georg Rehm, Augsburg #8048/R
£779 $1161 €1200 Burg Trausnitz near Landshut (46x39cm-18x15in) s.d.1850. 26-Jun-2 Neumeister, Munich #778

KREJCAR, Anton (1923-) Austrian
Works on paper
£268 $432 €400 In the garden (25x21cm-10x8in) s.d.1954 pencil. 18-Feb-3 Dorotheum, Vienna #103
£276 $441 €400 Passion picture (20x17cm-8x7in) s.i.d.1956 pen Indian ink W/C. 11-Mar-3 Dorotheum, Vienna #132/R
£345 $552 €500 Horse (35x23cm-14x9in) s.d.1955 pen Indian ink W/C. 11-Mar-3 Dorotheum, Vienna #131/R
£369 $594 €550 Susanna bathing (29x19cm-11x7in) s.d.1954 s.i.d. verso pen brush Indian ink W/C. 18-Feb-3 Dorotheum, Vienna #102
£397 $648 €600 Flute player (21x34cm-8x13in) s.d.1966 col pencil. 28-Jan-3 Dorotheum, Vienna #173/R
£530 $864 €800 Long shadows (21x27cm-8x11in) s.d.50 pen ink W/C. 28-Jan-3 Dorotheum, Vienna #135/R
£833 $1317 €1200 Bathers (25x54cm-10x21in) s.d.1972/74 col pen wash. 24-Apr-3 Dorotheum, Vienna #217/R
£861 $1403 €1300 Window (22x28cm-9x11in) s.d.1962 mixed media board. 28-Jan-3 Dorotheum, Vienna #174/R

KRELING, Wilhelm (1855-?) German
£3671 $5800 €5800 Couple in castle room (49x32cm-19x13in) s. panel lit. 29-Nov-2 Schloss Ahlden, Ahlden #1185/R est:4800

KREMEGNE, Pinchus (1890-1981) Russian
£769 $1208 €1200 Enfant pres de la coupe de fruits (55x38cm-22x15in) s. 15-Dec-2 Lombrail & Teucquam, Paris #21/R
£922 $1540 €1300 Portrait de femme (45x65cm-18x26in) s. cardboard prov. 17-Jun-3 Claude Boisgirard, Paris #82
£993 $1658 €1400 Nature morte aux fruits (27x35cm-11x14in) s. 20-Jun-3 Piasa, Paris #173 est:1200-1500
£1241 $1986 €1800 Fish (38x53cm-15x21in) s. 12-Mar-3 Rabourdin & Choppin de Janvry, Paris #131/R
£1419 $2214 €2100 Nature morte aux poires (33x41cm-13x16in) s. painted c.1960. 30-Mar-3 Anaf, Lyon #158/R
£1583 $2500 €2500 Assiette de fruits (50x61cm-20x24in) s. 2-Dec-2 Tajan, Paris #117/R
£1596 $2618 €2314 Roses in ceramic jug (46x38cm-18x15in) s. 4-Jun-3 Fischer, Luzern #1169/R est:3500-4500 (S.FR 3400)
£1795 $2818 €2800 Interior (50x61cm-20x24in) s. painted 1953. 12-Dec-2 Rabourdin & Choppin de Janvry, Paris #58/R
£1911 $2981 €3000 Fleurs et fruits (35x44cm-14x17in) s. canvas on panel. 7-Nov-2 Claude Aguttes, Neuilly #57/R est:3000-3500
£2013 $3119 €3200 Nature morte au bouquet de fleurs (65x46cm-26x18in) s. 30-Oct-2 Artcurial Briest, Paris #34/R est:4000-4500
£2482 $4145 €3500 Vue de Ceret (31x45cm-12x18in) s. prov. 23-Jun-3 Claude Boisgirard, Paris #91/R est:3000-3500
£2603 $4086 €3800 Paysage de Ceret (46x55cm-18x22in) s. 21-Apr-3 Rabourdin & Choppin de Janvry, Paris #121/R est:2500-3000
£2734 $4483 €3800 An orchard (65x81cm-26x32in) s. prov. 3-Jun-3 Christie's, Amsterdam #46/R est:2000-3000
£2756 $4328 €4300 Faubourgs de la ville (61x58cm-24x23in) s. 15-Dec-2 Eric Pillon, Calais #245/R
£2857 $4543 €4200 L'atelier (50x61cm-20x24in) s. 26-Feb-3 Artcurial Briest, Paris #213/R est:3500-4000
£2979 $4974 €4200 Nature morte au violon (73x60cm-29x24in) s. prov. 17-Jun-3 Claude Boisgirard, Paris #83/R est:4500-5000
£4167 $6542 €6500 Figures au bord de lac (73x60cm-29x24in) s. 12-Dec-2 Rabourdin & Choppin de Janvry, Paris #56/R
Works on paper
£355 $592 €500 Homme face a son destin (34x26cm-13x10in) s. W/C. 17-Jun-3 Claude Boisgirard, Paris #80

KREMP, Erminio (20th C) Italian
£1048 $1635 €1572 Southern Italian beach (30x61cm-12x24in) s.i. 6-Nov-2 Dobiaschofsky, Bern #748/R est:1200 (S.FR 2400)
£1135 $1771 €1703 Southern Italian coast in evening (54x98cm-21x39in) s.i. i. stretcher. 6-Nov-2 Dobiaschofsky, Bern #747/R est:1800 (S.FR 2600)
£1217 $1887 €1826 Coastal landscape near Palermo (70x130cm-28x51in) s.i.d.07. 9-Dec-2 Philippe Schuler, Zurich #3947 est:1100-1400 (S.FR 2800)

KRENEK, Carl (1880-1948) Austrian
£493 $818 €700 May - the lovers (16x11cm-6x4in) tempera htd egg white. 14-Jun-3 Hauswedell & Nolte, Hamburg #1325/R

KRENN, Edmund (1846-1902) Austrian
Works on paper
£629 $975 €1000 Kohlmarkt (50x64cm-20x25in) s.d.1890 w/C. 1-Oct-2 Dorotheum, Vienna #247/R

KRENZ, Alfred (1899-1980) South African
£1025 $1599 €1538 Still life with flowers in a vase (75x54cm-30x21in) s.d.1964 board. 11-Nov-2 Stephan Welz, Johannesburg #526/R est:10000-15000 (SA.R 16000)
£1089 $1699 €1634 Magnolias in a vase (60x74cm-24x29in) s.d.1964 board. 11-Nov-2 Stephan Welz, Johannesburg #519/R est:8000-12000 (SA.R 17000)

KREPP, Friedrich (19th C) Austrian
£1195 $1852 €1900 Portrait of peasant woman (66x52cm-26x20in) s. oval. 29-Oct-2 Dorotheum, Vienna #125/R est:1800-2000

KRESENISA, J G (18th C) French
£2500 $3950 €3750 Fridrich Philipp d'Alezenheim (80x64cm-31x25in) s.i.d.1753 verso. 7-Apr-3 Bonhams, Bath #74/R est:800-1200

KRESENISA, J G (attrib) (18th C) French
£920 $1454 €1380 Lady wearing a white tulle gown (80x63cm-31x25in) 7-Apr-3 Bonhams, Bath #75

KRESS, Annick (20th C) French
Works on paper
£324 $518 €450 Sans titre (80x80cm-31x31in) s. mixed media canvas. 18-May-3 Neret-Minet, Paris #88

KRETSCHMER, Karl (20th C) German
Sculpture
£3000 $4740 €4500 Diana (45cm-18in) s. gilt bronze. 14-Nov-2 Christie's, Kensington #198/R est:2000-3000

KRETSCHMER, Robert (1818-1872) German
Works on paper
£709 $1100 €1064 Field mouse (8x14cm-3x6in) indis i.d. pencil W/C. 29-Oct-2 Sotheby's, New York #109/R est:200-300

KRETZ, Anne (20th C) ?
£396 $633 €550 Le defi (80x80cm-31x31in) mono. 18-May-3 Neret-Minet, Paris #194

KRETZSCHMAR, Bernhard (1889-1972) German
£13889 $21944 €20000 Dresden old town - Bruhlsche Terrasse (75x115cm-30x45in) mono. bears d. 26-Apr-3 Dr Lehr, Berlin #290/R est:20000
Works on paper
£705 $1093 €1100 Sunflowers (42x52cm-17x20in) mono.d.25 W/C pencil. 7-Dec-2 Van Ham, Cologne #291/R

KRETZSCHMER, Johann Hermann (1811-1890) German
£2183 $3406 €3275 Portrait of Wilhelm von Guerard as a boy (104x86cm-41x34in) s. 20-Nov-2 Fischer, Luzern #1145/R est:6000-8000 (S.FR 5000)
£7547 $11623 €12000 Oriental man sitting down holding gun and pipe (182x157cm-72x62in) s.d.1845. 22-Oct-2 Wiener Kunst Auktionen, Vienna #1074/R est:3000-11000

KRETZSCHMER, Johann Hermann (attrib) (1811-1890) German
£472 $726 €750 Boy smoking (69x47cm-27x19in) s. 22-Oct-2 Wiener Kunst Auktionen, Vienna #1093/R

KREUGER, Nils (1858-1930) Swedish
£903 $1482 €1309 Trees by road (24x34cm-9x13in) s.d.1919 panel exhib.lit. 4-Jun-3 AB Stockholms Auktionsverk #2125/R (S.KR 11500)
£1280 $2074 €1856 Ducks on the march (20x26cm-8x10in) s.d.1884 panel lit. 26-May-3 Bukowskis, Stockholm #4/R est:10000-12000 (S.KR 16500)
£1312 $2034 €1968 Harbour scene with steam ship (15x22cm-6x9in) panel. 4-Dec-2 AB Stockholms Auktionsverk #1598/R est:20000-25000 (S.KR 18500)
£3413 $5530 €4949 Summer landscape with cattle grazing (14x34cm-6x13in) s. 26-May-3 Bukowskis, Stockholm #36/R est:20000-25000 (S.KR 44000)
£3972 $6156 €5958 Horses grazing at Alvaret (44x55cm-17x22in) s.d.1904 panel. 3-Dec-2 Bukowskis, Stockholm #4/R est:35000-40000 (S.KR 56000)
£4000 $6560 €6000 Sommer - summer (56x45cm-22x18in) s.d.1884 panel prov. 3-Jun-3 Sotheby's, London #252/R est:5000-7000
£5674 $8794 €8511 Landscape with geese, Morbylanga, Oland (45x76cm-18x30in) s.i.d.85 exhib.lit. 4-Dec-2 AB Stockholms Auktionsverk #1600/R est:80000-100000 (S.KR 80000)
£7092 $10993 €10638 Evening stroll (55x46cm-22x18in) s. 3-Dec-2 Bukowskis, Stockholm #148/R est:60000-80000 (S.KR 100000)
£10638 $16489 €15957 Sailing at twilight, Varberg (56x100cm-22x39in) s.d.1903 prov. 3-Dec-2 Bukowskis, Stockholm #147/R est:100000-150000 (S.KR 150000)
£13475 $20887 €20213 Spring morning - park scene with trees and buildings (107x86cm-42x34in) s. lit. 4-Dec-2 AB Stockholms Auktionsverk #1743/R est:200000-250000 (S.KR 190000)
£14740 $23879 €21373 Horses in evening sunshine (121x193cm-48x76in) s.d.1919 exhib. 26-May-3 Bukowskis, Stockholm #167/R est:100000-125000 (S.KR 190000)
£30851 $47819 €46277 Autumn evening, Hogalidsbergen (49x61cm-19x24in) s.d.1917 panel prov.lit. 3-Dec-2 Bukowskis, Stockholm #340/R est:300000-350000 (S.KR 435000)

KREUL, Johann Friedrich Karl (1804-1867) German
Works on paper
£3165 $4905 €5000 Portraits of man and woman. s. pastel oval two. 27-Sep-2 Weidler, Nurnberg #8702/R est:7000

KREUL, Johann Lorenz (attrib) (1765-1840) German
Works on paper
£1342 $2161 €2000 Portrait of Philipp Saint Andre (34x28cm-13x11in) s. pastel. 18-Feb-3 Sotheby's, Amsterdam #451/R est:2000-3000
£5897 $9318 €9200 Karl August Freiherr von Hardenberg (58x46cm-23x18in) pastel prov. 16-Nov-2 Lempertz, Koln #1253/R est:7000

KREUTZ, Heinz (1923-) German
£538 $850 €850 Wishy washy (26x39cm-10x15in) s.d.12.2.1996 oil chk paper. 30-Nov-2 Arnold, Frankfurt #327/R
£2692 $4173 €4200 Little hymn (38x41cm-15x16in) s.i.d.1956 masonite. 3-Dec-2 Lempertz, Koln #252/R est:2200
£6069 $9589 €8800 Composition (70x97cm-28x38in) s.d.1959. 5-Apr-3 Quittenbaum, Hamburg #150/R est:7500

KREUZBERGER, Karl (1916-1990) Austrian
Works on paper
£310 $497 €450 Geological (56x74cm-22x29in) mono.i.d.69 verso W/C. 11-Mar-3 Dorotheum, Vienna #212/R

KREUZER, Konrad (1810-1861) Austrian
£1667 $2617 €2600 View of area near Graz (23x34cm-9x13in) lit. 10-Dec-2 Dorotheum, Vienna #32 est:2600-3000

KREUZER, Konrad (attrib) (1810-1861) Austrian
£1667 $2583 €2600 Vineyards in the southern Steiermark (34x42cm-13x17in) 5-Dec-2 Dorotheum, Graz #30/R est:1800

KREYDER, Alexis (1839-1912) French
£1498 $2187 €2247 Still life with basket and red cherrie (32x50cm-13x20in) s. 17-Jun-2 Philippe Schuler, Zurich #4349/R est:2000-2500 (S.FR 3400)
£2600 $4238 €3900 Basket of cherries (32x50cm-13x20in) s. 29-Jan-3 Sotheby's, Olympia #310/R est:1500-2000
£7006 $11000 €10509 Peonies (122x100cm-48x39in) s.d.1903 exhib. 21-Nov-2 Sotheby's, New York #225/R est:12000-15000
£7770 $12122 €11500 Corbeille de raisins (75x94cm-30x37in) s. 28-Mar-3 Claude Aguttes, Neuilly #93/R est:15000

KRICHELDORF, Carl (1863-?) German
£312 $464 €480 Girl with peasant woman (70x85cm-28x33in) s.i. 27-Jun-2 Neumeister, Munich #2772

KRICHELDORF, Carl (attrib) (1863-?) German
£769 $1192 €1200 Three old card players at a table in the tavern (58x71cm-23x28in) canvas on canvas. 4-Dec-2 Neumeister, Munich #788/R

KRICHELDORF, Hermann (1867-1949) German
£943 $1472 €1500 Sunlit flowers (64x52cm-25x20in) s.d.1924 panel. 9-Oct-2 Michael Zeller, Lindau #772/R

KRICKE, Norbert (1922-1984) German
Sculpture
£4115 $6337 €6173 Sans titre (27cm-11in) iron prov. 22-Oct-2 Iegor de Saint Hippolyte, Montreal #50/R (C.D 10000)
£7194 $11799 €10000 Sculpture (22x53cm-9x21in) s.d. steel wire prov. 6-Jun-3 Ketterer, Munich #143/R est:10000-15000
£7372 $11426 €11500 Untitled (22x47x28cm-9x19x11in) steel. 6-Dec-2 Hauswedell & Nolte, Hamburg #225/R est:15000
Works on paper
£385 $596 €600 Untitled (20x1cm-8x0in) mono.d.1974 felt pen. 6-Dec-2 Hauswedell & Nolte, Hamburg #227/R
£449 $696 €700 Untitled (16x1cm-6x0in) mono.d.1974 feltpen. 6-Dec-2 Hauswedell & Nolte, Hamburg #226/R
£513 $795 €800 Untitled (15x20cm-6x8in) mono.d.1975 feltpen. 6-Dec-2 Hauswedell & Nolte, Hamburg #229/R
£577 $894 €900 Untitled (19x23cm-7x9in) mono.d.1974 feltpen. 6-Dec-2 Hauswedell & Nolte, Hamburg #228/R
£797 $1307 €1100 Untitled (61x43cm-24x17in) mono.d.74 Indian ink board prov. 28-May-3 Lempertz, Koln #236/R

KRIEBEL, Anton Maria Ludwig (1823-1890) German
£11950 $18642 €19000 Portrait of young girl (171x103cm-67x41in) s.i.d.1870 prov. 19-Sep-2 Dr Fritz Nagel, Stuttgart #955/R est:5600

KRIEF, Menahem (1928-) ?
£1154 $1812 €1800 Houppah (81x65cm-32x26in) s. acrylic. 12-Dec-2 Rabourdin & Choppin de Janvry, Paris #183/R

KRIEGHOFF, Cornelius (1815-1872) Canadian
£3111 $5102 €4667 Portrait of Colonel J.F. Turnbull (71x61cm-28x24in) s.d.1855 prov.lit. 3-Jun-3 Joyner, Toronto #292/R est:10000-12000 (C.D 7000)
£3498 $5422 €5247 Mother and child (31x24cm-12x9in) s.d.1843 board prov.lit. 3-Dec-2 Joyner, Toronto #265/R est:4000-6000 (C.D 8500)
£8468 $13379 €12702 Moccasin seller (28x23cm-11x9in) s.d.1867 prov.lit. 18-Nov-2 Sotheby's, Toronto #87/R est:15000-20000 (C.D 21000)
£10700 $16584 €16050 Lorette Indian on a hunt, Quebec (26x22cm-10x9in) s. oval prov. 3-Dec-2 Joyner, Toronto #99/R est:15000-20000 (C.D 26000)
£10887 $17202 €16331 Indian hunter (29x24cm-11x9in) s. prov.lit. 18-Nov-2 Sotheby's, Toronto #88/R est:15000-20000 (C.D 27000)
£14574 $23318 €21861 Indian hunter (28x23cm-11x9in) s. prov.lit. 15-May-3 Heffel, Vancouver #136/R est:20000-25000 (C.D 32500)
£18145 $28669 €27218 Bears in the woods (36x46cm-14x18in) s.i.d.1859 prov.exhib.lit. 18-Nov-2 Sotheby's, Toronto #89/R est:50000-60000 (C.D 45000)
£18145 $28669 €27218 Running the rapids (33x46cm-13x18in) s. prov.lit. 14-Nov-2 Heffel, Vancouver #48/R est:50000-70000 (C.D 45000)
£19058 $30493 €28587 Spearing salmon by torchlight (23x27cm-9x11in) s. board prov. 15-May-3 Heffel, Vancouver #55/R est:30000-40000 (C.D 42500)
£22177 $35040 €33266 Pioneer homestead (43x70cm-17x28in) s. prov. 18-Nov-2 Sotheby's, Toronto #152/R est:60000-80000 (C.D 55000)

£22177 $35040 €33266 Indian family by the river in winter (33x56cm-13x22in) s.verso prov.lit. 18-Nov-2 Sotheby's, Toronto #153/R est:60000-80000 (C.D 55000)
£24194 $38226 €36291 Sleighs racing in front of the Citadel, Quebec (22x33cm-9x13in) s. prov.lit. 14-Nov-2 Heffel, Vancouver #47/R est:60000-80000 (C.D 60000)
£24444 $40089 €36666 Habitants in a blizzard (33x46cm-13x18in) s.i. prov.lit. 27-May-3 Sotheby's, Toronto #75/R est:60000-80000 (C.D 55000)
£24691 $38272 €37037 Shooting the rapids (30x44cm-12x17in) s.d.1861 oval lit. 3-Dec-2 Joyner, Toronto #41/R est:60000-80000 (C.D 60000)
£106667 $174933 €160001 Preparing for the trip to town (36x55cm-14x22in) s.d.1865 prov. 3-Jun-3 Joyner, Toronto #26/R est:175000-225000 (C.D 240000)

KRIEGHOFF, Cornelius (attrib) (1815-1872) Canadian
£1807 $3000 €2620 Winter's day (42x66cm-17x26in) s. prov. 11-Jun-3 Butterfields, San Francisco #4013/R est:4000-6000
£3226 $5097 €4839 Habitant family with horse and sleigh (33x43cm-13x17in) bears sig prov. 18-Nov-2 Sotheby's, Toronto #9/R est:3000-5000 (C.D 8000)
£4839 $7645 €7259 Winter sleigh scene (36x53cm-14x21in) bears sig prov. 18-Nov-2 Sotheby's, Toronto #10/R est:10000-12000 (C.D 12000)

KRIEHUBER, Josef (1800-1876) Austrian
Miniatures
£2800 $4592 €4060 Lothae Freiherr Pratobevera von Wiesborn as a young boy (29x23cm-11x9in) s.d.1862 W/C pencil on card rec. prov. 3-Jun-3 Christie's, London #239/R est:1000-1500
Works on paper
£577 $894 €900 Portrait of a man's head from the right (10x9cm-4x4in) red ochre dr. 4-Dec-2 Neumeister, Munich #531/R
£676 $1054 €1000 Portrait of Erzherzog Franz Carl in uniform (25x17cm-10x7in) s.d.851 W/C. 28-Mar-3 Dorotheum, Vienna #212/R
£692 $1072 €1100 Portrait of man looking over shoulder (13x11cm-5x4in) s.d.836 W/C pencil. 1-Oct-2 Dorotheum, Vienna #374/R est:1000-1100
£878 $1370 €1300 Portrait of young blonde woman (26x20cm-10x8in) s.d.871 W/C oval. 28-Mar-3 Dorotheum, Vienna #213/R
£2516 $3899 €4000 Portrait of two boys on couch (22x26cm-9x10in) s.d.834 W/C. 1-Oct-2 Dorotheum, Vienna #370/R est:1800-2500

KRIG, Anton Otto (1896-1942) American
£390 $600 €585 Desert giants. s. painted c.1930. 8-Sep-2 Treadway Gallery, Cincinnati #591/R

KRIGE, François (1913-1994) South African
£243 $380 €365 Metal worker (33x42cm-13x17in) s.d.80 chl. 11-Nov-2 Stephan Welz, Johannesburg #585 (SA.R 3800)
£512 $799 €768 Proteas in a blue vase (34x29cm-13x11in) s.d.92. 11-Nov-2 Stephan Welz, Johannesburg #520/R (SA.R 8000)
£769 $1199 €1154 Cape carnival (48x42cm-19x17in) s. board on masonite. 11-Nov-2 Stephan Welz, Johannesburg #512/R (SA.R 12000)
£860 $1342 €1290 Seascape (44x59cm-17x23in) s. board. 15-Oct-2 Stephan Welz, Johannesburg #478/R est:15000-20000 (SA.R 14000)
£1843 $2875 €2765 Coon carnival (50x35cm-20x14in) s. card. 15-Oct-2 Stephan Welz, Johannesburg #479/R est:20000-30000 (SA.R 30000)
£2580 $4153 €3870 Paternoster (34x44cm-13x17in) init. s.i.verso board exhib. 12-May-3 Stephan Welz, Johannesburg #459/R est:10000-15000 (SA.R 30000)
£3203 $4997 €4805 Poppies in a blue vase (52x44cm-20x17in) s. 11-Nov-2 Stephan Welz, Johannesburg #528/R est:40000-60000 (SA.R 50000)
£6086 $9494 €9129 Artist's garden and house, Montagu (54x62cm-21x24in) s.d.89. 11-Nov-2 Stephan Welz, Johannesburg #530/R est:70000-90000 (SA.R 95000)

KRIKI (1965-) French
£927 $1511 €1400 Cosmonaute (162x130cm-64x51in) s.d.1995 acrylic. 3-Feb-3 Cornette de St.Cyr, Paris #464
£1875 $2963 €2700 Sweet sexy lady (162x114cm-64x45in) s.d. s.i.d.verso acrylic. 28-Apr-3 Cornette de St.Cyr, Paris #440/R est:3000-4000
£2153 $3401 €3100 La vente aux encheres (162x130cm-64x51in) s.d. i.verso acrylic. 28-Apr-3 Cornette de St.Cyr, Paris #439/R est:3000-4000
£2381 $3786 €3500 Teuf (113x146cm-44x57in) s.d.1992 acrylic. 24-Mar-3 Cornette de St.Cyr, Paris #144/R
£2595 $4022 €4100 Eurotunnel (130x195cm-51x77in) acrylic prov. 28-Sep-2 Cornette de St.Cyr, Paris #365/R est:2000-3000
Sculpture
£1081 $1686 €1600 Prostituee (190x100cm-75x39in) s.d.91 painted resin one of 8. 28-Mar-3 Charbonneaux, Paris #158/R

KRIKI and TURPAULT, Alain (20th C) French
£347 $573 €500 14 Juillet 96 (100x100cm-39x39in) s. acrylic photo. 1-Jul-3 Artcurial Briest, Paris #857/R

KRILLE, Jean (20th C) ?
£662 $1079 €1000 Landscape (50x70cm-20x28in) s. panel. 28-Jan-3 Dorotheum, Vienna #203/R

KRIMMEL, Johann Ludwig (1787-1821) American/German
£6452 $10000 €9678 Study for German funeral (21x29cm-8x11in) panel prov.exhib.lit. 8-Dec-2 Freeman, Philadelphia #100/R est:10000-15000
£12903 $20000 €19355 Study for village tavern (21x29cm-8x11in) panel prov.exhib.lit. 8-Dec-2 Freeman, Philadelphia #99/R est:20000-30000

KRINGER, Manuel (?) ?
Works on paper
£460 $731 €690 Fetish dance in Gabon (23x31cm-9x12in) s.i. pen brown ink. 18-Mar-3 Rosebery Fine Art, London #871

KRINNER, Michaela (1915-) German
£1139 $1777 €1800 Dolls (35x27cm-14x11in) s.d.1993 panel. 18-Oct-2 Dr Fritz Nagel, Stuttgart #545/R est:2500
£1583 $2596 €2200 Still life with fruit and jug (45x60cm-18x24in) s.d.68 board. 5-Jun-3 Dorotheum, Salzburg #582/R est:3000-4000

KRINS, Ernest (1820-1899) Belgian
£497 $810 €750 Ramasseur de bois (18x37cm-7x15in) s. panel. 17-Feb-3 Horta, Bruxelles #301

KRIPPENDORF, William (1910-) American
£1242 $2000 €1863 Still life with fruit on a table (74x91cm-29x36in) s. masonite. 23-Feb-3 Butterfields, Los Angeles #7014 est:2000-3000

KRISCHKE, Franz (1885-1960) Austrian
£355 $557 €533 Still life with pink and red roses in a vase, books and clock (56x50cm-22x20in) s. panel. 10-Dec-2 Rosebery Fine Art, London #576/R
£366 $600 €549 Assembled still life with clock, oil lamp, vase, cup and saucer (61x51cm-24x20in) s. 5-Feb-3 Doyle, New York #35/R
£861 $1395 €1248 Still life of clock, books and flowers in vase (55x48cm-22x19in) s. panel. 26-May-3 Rasmussen, Copenhagen #1229/R (D.KR 9000)
£1027 $1603 €1500 Still life with clock, globe, cup and saucer (54x49cm-21x19in) s. panel. 10-Apr-3 Dorotheum, Vienna #142/R est:1800-2000

KRISTO, Bela de (1920-) ?
£1274 $1987 €2000 Nature morte au flacon et a la guitare (63x59cm-25x23in) s. panel. 7-Nov-2 Chochon-Barre & Allardi, Paris #173/R

KRIVOS, Rudolf (1933-) Czechoslovakian
Works on paper
£583 $828 €875 Woman in armchair (61x40cm-24x16in) pastel exec.1959. 26-Mar-2 SOGA, Bratislava #273/R (SL.K 37000)

KRIZAN, Ludovit (1900-1979) Czechoslovakian
Works on paper
£395 $612 €593 Still life of autumn (45x68cm-18x27in) pastel exec.1962. 3-Dec-2 SOGA, Bratislava #7/R (SL.K 25000)

KRIZEK, Jan (1919-1985) Czechoslovakian
Sculpture
£5137 $8065 €7500 Untitled (18x17cm-7x7in) carved wood. 15-Apr-3 Laurence Calmels, Paris #4219/R est:2500
£6164 $9678 €9000 Untitled (18x17cm-7x7in) carved wood. 15-Apr-3 Laurence Calmels, Paris #4218/R est:2500

KRIZSAN, Janos (1866-1948) Hungarian
£1806 $2817 €2709 Early spring in Felsobanya (100x120cm-39x47in) s. 11-Sep-2 Kieselbach, Budapest #79/R (H.F 700000)

KROCK, Hendrik (1671-1738) German
Works on paper
£348 $550 €550 Bacchus assis (41x28cm-16x11in) i. col chk. 27-Nov-2 Christie's, Paris #295/R

KROGH, Charlotte Sofie von (1827-1914) Danish
£527 $822 €791 Still life of fruit and berries in bowl (37x48cm-15x19in) panel. 5-Aug-2 Rasmussen, Vejle #165/R (D.KR 6200)

KROHA, Ladislav (20th C) ?
£276 $439 €400 Composition (17x36cm-7x14in) s. panel. 10-Mar-3 Sotheby's, Amsterdam #331

KROHG, Christian (1852-1925) Norwegian
£2142 $3405 €3213 Bay with boat house (31x40cm-12x16in) init.d.81. 5-Mar-3 Rasmussen, Copenhagen #2039/R est:15000 (D.KR 23000)
£2389 $3775 €3584 Outside the house, possibly at Brekkesto (51x62cm-20x24in) s. painted c.1913. 28-Apr-3 Blomqvist, Oslo #302/R est:20000-25000 (N.KR 27000)
£3982 $6451 €5973 Pilot at the helm (28x46cm-11x18in) s. 26-May-3 Grev Wedels Plass, Oslo #9/R est:40000-60000 (N.KR 44000)
£4072 $6597 €6108 On the lookout (57x45cm-22x18in) s. i.stretcher. 26-May-3 Grev Wedels Plass, Oslo #10/R est:50000-70000 (N.KR 45000)
£4152 $6561 €6228 Lady dressed in black (48x72cm-19x28in) s. 2-Dec-2 Blomqvist, Oslo #343/R est:35000-45000 (N.KR 48000)
£4152 $6561 €6228 Red barn (65x80cm-26x31in) exhib. 2-Dec-2 Blomqvist, Oslo #347/R est:30000-40000 (N.KR 48000)
£4525 $7330 €6788 Marie Krohg making paper animals for Per (55x45cm-22x18in) s. lit. 26-May-3 Grev Wedels Plass, Oslo #36/R est:50000-70000 (N.KR 50000)
£4525 $7330 €6788 His portrait - Albertine (53x51cm-21x20in) s. i.d.1885-86 stretcher lit. 26-May-3 Grev Wedels Plass, Oslo #37/R est:50000-70000 (N.KR 50000)
£4706 $7624 €7059 Portrait of young lady (37x32cm-15x13in) s. paper on cardboard. 26-May-3 Grev Wedels Plass, Oslo #38/R est:40000-60000 (N.KR 52000)
£5510 $9036 €7990 At the helm (50x60cm-20x24in) s. 2-Jun-3 Blomqvist, Oslo #88/R est:80000-100000 (N.KR 60000)
£9362 $14791 €14043 Portrait of fisherboy at Skagen Osterstrand (26x41cm-10x16in) init. 27-Nov-2 Museumsbygningen, Copenhagen #80/R est:75000-100000 (D.KR 110000)
£15000 $24600 €22500 Ong kvinne pa en bank - young woman on a bench (59x57cm-23x22in) s. prov. 3-Jun-3 Sotheby's, London #238/R est:15000-20000
£15666 $25065 €23499 Eye witnesses (55x66cm-22x26in) s. lit. 17-Mar-3 Blomqvist, Oslo #371/R est:150000-200000 (N.KR 180000)
£40140 $63019 €60210 From Gonnegate 19 - figures at table in garden (72x99cm-28x39in) s. lit. 21-Nov-2 Grev Wedels Plass, Oslo #56/R est:500000 (N.KR 460000)

KROHG, Christian (attrib) (1852-1925) Norwegian
£2104 $3324 €3156 Woman by chair (49x69cm-19x27in) 30-Nov-2 Goteborg Auktionsverk, Sweden #187/R est:25000 (S.KR 30000)
£6520 $10692 €9454 Sailor at the helm (37x53cm-15x21in) s. 2-Jun-3 Blomqvist, Oslo #99/R est:80000-90000 (N.KR 71000)

KROHG, Per (1889-1965) Norwegian
£289 $469 €434 Solstice (19x26cm-7x10in) panel prov. 27-Jan-3 Blomqvist, Lysaker #1132/R (N.KR 3200)
£522 $793 €783 Seamen's pub (35x43cm-14x17in) s.d.1925 panel. 16-Aug-2 Lilla Bukowskis, Stockholm #313 (S.KR 7600)
£611 $959 €917 Summer haze (31x40cm-12x16in) s. panel. 25-Nov-2 Blomqvist, Lysaker #1167 (N.KR 7000)
£859 $1392 €1289 Woodland scene (81x65cm-32x26in) s. prov. 27-Jan-3 Blomqvist, Lysaker #1131 (N.KR 9500)
£1390 $2238 €2085 Sailors in Toulon (36x45cm-14x18in) s.d.1927 panel prov. 7-May-3 AB Stockholms Auktionsverk #1122/R est:20000-25000 (S.KR 18000)
£1837 $3012 €2664 Woman with jug on her head (46x38cm-18x15in) s.d.mai 1920 panel. 2-Jun-3 Blomqvist, Oslo #200/R est:30000-35000 (N.KR 20000)
£2453 $3826 €3680 North African town scene (33x40cm-13x16in) s.d.24 panel prov. 6-Nov-2 AB Stockholms Auktionsverk #936/R est:10000-12000 (S.KR 35000)
£2611 $4178 €3917 Lady wearing black hat (35x26cm-14x10in) s. panel. 17-Mar-3 Blomqvist, Oslo #322/R est:20000-25000 (N.KR 30000)
£31223 $48708 €46835 Lucy (92x72cm-36x28in) s.d.1911 s.i.verso lit. 21-Oct-2 Blomqvist, Oslo #363/R est:300000-400000 (N.KR 360000)

KROHN, Pietro (1840-1905) Danish
£1053 $1705 €1580 Woman chatting to her pet starling (39x31cm-15x12in) init.d.71 exhib. 21-May-3 Museumsbygningen, Copenhagen #15/R (D.KR 11000)

KROHN, Pietro (attrib) (1840-1905) Danish
£364 $589 €528 Interior scene with woman seated in chair (40x26cm-16x10in) 24-May-3 Rasmussen, Havnen #2157/R (D.KR 3800)

KROHN, Xan (1882-1959) Norwegian
£273 $426 €410 Madonna and Child (45x35cm-18x14in) s. 23-Sep-2 Blomqvist, Lysaker #1136/R (N.KR 3200)

KROJER, Tom (1942-) Danish
£259 $396 €389 Composition (144x97cm-57x38in) s.d.c.1983 acrylic. 24-Aug-2 Rasmussen, Havnen #2327 (D.KR 3000)
£266 $431 €399 Venice (70x65cm-28x26in) s.d.1984. 25-Jan-3 Rasmussen, Havnen #2126 (D.KR 3000)
£423 $656 €635 The man in the mirror (100x87cm-39x34in) s.d.88 prov. 1-Oct-2 Rasmussen, Copenhagen #235/R (D.KR 5000)

KROKFORS, Kristian (1952-) Finnish
Works on paper
£388 $637 €540 Park (58x38cm-23x15in) s. mixed media. 5-Jun-3 Hagelstam, Helsinki #961

KROKHALEU, Piotr (1919-1997) Russian
£380 $592 €600 Landscape (73x119cm-29x47in) s.verso. 14-Sep-2 Meeting Art, Vercelli #482
£411 $642 €650 Boy at the seaside (110x72cm-43x28in) s.verso. 14-Sep-2 Meeting Art, Vercelli #437

KROL, Gerard Cornelis (1882-1950) Dutch
£458 $737 €650 Activity on the river (35x47cm-14x19in) s.d.1915 cardboard. 6-May-3 Vendu Notarishuis, Rotterdam #103

KROLL, Leon (1884-1974) American
£625 $1000 €938 Portrait of a young girl in an interior (76x61cm-30x24in) s. 18-May-3 Jeffery Burchard, Florida #64/R
£1274 $2000 €1911 Spring landscape with cottage (23x30cm-9x12in) s. indis d. canvasboard. 14-Dec-2 Weschler, Washington #706/R est:1000-1500
£4088 $6500 €6132 Village lane (39x46cm-15x18in) s.d.1920. 5-Mar-3 Sotheby's, New York #66/R est:8000-12000
£5346 $8500 €8019 Study for conversation (37x49cm-15x19in) s.i.d.1940 lit. 5-Mar-3 Sotheby's, New York #93/R est:8000-12000
£7643 $12000 €11465 Study of Queenborough Bridge, 1913 (20x28cm-8x11in) s. board prov. 10-Dec-2 Doyle, New York #135/R est:2500-3500
£8280 $13000 €12420 View of the New York City skyline from New Jersey (21x28cm-8x11in) s.d.1916 board exhib. 14-Dec-2 Weschler, Washington #703/R est:2000-3000
£8917 $14000 €13376 Rolling landscape with view of a village (66x81cm-26x32in) s.d.1915. 14-Dec-2 Weschler, Washington #704/R est:20000-30000
£8917 $14000 €13376 Young Robert Rogers playing the piano (66x74cm-26x29in) 14-Dec-2 Weschler, Washington #705/R est:7000-9000
£15484 $24000 €23226 Marble quarry at Gloucester (66x81cm-26x32in) s. prov. 5-Dec-2 Christie's, Rockefeller NY #98/R est:20000-30000
£42254 $60000 €63381 Rockport quarries (117x132cm-46x52in) 8-Aug-1 Barridorf, Portland #70/R est:60000-90000
Works on paper
£573 $900 €860 Sleeping nude (30x50cm-12x20in) s. conte crayon. 14-Dec-2 Weschler, Washington #701/R est:400-600

KROLL-ROBERTS, Peggi (1954-) American
£2208 $3400 €3312 Full day at the beach (61x76cm-24x30in) 25-Oct-2 Morris & Whiteside, Hilton Head Island #77 est:3000-3500
£2857 $4400 €4286 Waterproof mascara (46x61cm-18x24in) 25-Oct-2 Morris & Whiteside, Hilton Head Island #76 est:2500-3000

KROMJONG, Paul (1903-) Dutch
£318 $497 €500 Book (70x86cm-28x34in) s. exhib. 6-Nov-2 Vendue Huis, Gravenhage #168

KRON, Adolf (1884-1962) Swiss
£349 $545 €524 Village in the Alps (115x115cm-45x45in) s. 6-Nov-2 Dobiaschofsky, Bern #3472/R (S.FR 800)
£480 $759 €720 Extensive landscape with trees in storm (97x119cm-38x47in) s. 14-Nov-2 Stuker, Bern #347 (S.FR 1100)

KRON, Paul (1869-1936) French
£371 $579 €557 Colourful flowers in blue vase (73x60cm-29x24in) s. 6-Nov-2 Dobiaschofsky, Bern #749/R (S.FR 850)
£376 $616 €545 Cattle in meadow (50x65cm-20x26in) s. 4-Jun-3 Fischer, Luzern #2209/R (S.FR 800)
£376 $616 €545 Interior with geranium (50x65cm-20x26in) s. 4-Jun-3 Fischer, Luzern #2210/R (S.FR 800)

KRONBERG, Julius (1850-1921) Swedish
Works on paper
£323 $510 €485 Green spring landscape (33x21cm-13x8in) s.d.86 gouache. 30-Nov-2 Goteborg Auktionsverk, Sweden #216/R (S.KR 4600)

KRONBERG, Louis (1872-1965) American
£1037 $1700 €1556 Preparing for the dance (76x64cm-30x25in) s. init.d.May 2 1944 stretcher. 5-Feb-3 Doyle, New York #19/R est:2500-3500

£4430 $7000 €6645 Before the ballet (64x51cm-25x20in) s.i. s.i.d.1913 verso. 24-Apr-3 Shannon's, Milford #27/R est:5000-7000

Works on paper

£1644 $2400 €2466 Ballet girl (66x48cm-26x19in) s.d.1914 pastel. 3-Nov-1 North East Auctions, Portsmouth #272/R

KRONBERGER, Carl (1841-1921) Austrian

£1701 $2704 €2500 Reverend with wine glass (17x13cm-7x5in) s. panel. 19-Mar-3 Neumeister, Munich #616 est:2300

£1905 $3029 €2800 Old soldier wearing hat and reading newspaper (27x22cm-11x9in) s. panel. 19-Mar-3 Neumeister, Munich #615/R est:2700

£2200 $3498 €3300 Bavarian lady reading the bible (18x13cm-7x5in) s. panel. 18-Mar-3 Bonhams, New Bond Street #23/R est:1500-2000

KRONENBERG, Fritz (20th C) German?

£1282 $1872 €2000 Garden (50x73cm-20x29in) s.d.38. 4-Jun-2 Karl & Faber, Munich #320/R est:4000

Works on paper

£563 $935 €800 Still life with artichokes (34x53cm-13x21in) s.d. W/C chk pencil. 14-Jun-3 Hauswedell & Nolte, Hamburg #1326/R

KRONER (19/20th C) German

£1218 $1912 €1900 Deer in autumn wood (80x106cm-31x42in) s. 23-Nov-2 Arnold, Frankfurt #780/R est:600

KRONER, Christian (1838-1911) German

£609 $956 €950 Deer in clearing (35x26cm-14x10in) s.d.87. 21-Nov-2 Van Ham, Cologne #1736/R

£1410 $2228 €2200 Deer in wooded landscape (85x64cm-33x25in) s.d.1897. 15-Nov-2 Reiss & Sohn, Konigstein #61/R est:2000

£1646 $2600 €2600 Herd of deer in Teutoburg forest (80x60cm-31x24in) s.d.85. 29-Nov-2 Bolland & Marotz, Bremen #726/R est:2800

£1781 $2778 €2600 Deer in autumnal wood (88x126cm-35x50in) s.d.91. 10-Apr-3 Van Ham, Cologne #1554/R est:2500

£3944 $6349 €5600 Deer in clearing (85x64cm-33x25in) s.i.d.97 lit. 9-May-3 Schloss Ahlden, Ahlden #1418/R est:4500

KROPFF, Joop (1892-1979) Dutch

£296 $476 €420 Polder landscape with farm (33x43cm-13x17in) s. 6-May-3 Vendu Notarishuis, Rotterdam #221/R

£352 $567 €500 Flowers in a vase (36x29cm-14x11in) s. 7-May-3 Vendue Huis, Gravenhage #197/R

£400 $636 €580 View of a landscape (13x20cm-5x8in) s. panel. 10-Mar-3 Sotheby's, Amsterdam #190

£423 $680 €600 Farm (35x50cm-14x20in) s. 7-May-3 Vendue Huis, Gravenhage #195

£458 $737 €650 View of The Hague (90x70cm-35x28in) s.d.26. 7-May-3 Vendue Huis, Gravenhage #196

£461 $746 €700 Woodcutters at work (30x50cm-12x20in) s. 21-Jan-3 Christie's, Amsterdam #159

£724 $1151 €1050 View of Dordrecht (72x81cm-28x32in) s. canvas on triplex. 10-Mar-3 Sotheby's, Amsterdam #188/R est:1300-1600

£1310 $2083 €1900 View of Dordrecht (31x37cm-12x15in) s. panel. 10-Mar-3 Sotheby's, Amsterdam #189 est:900-1200

KROTOV, Youri (1964-) Russian

£700 $1085 €1050 Young girl playing by the sea (47x40cm-19x16in) s. 8-Dec-2 John Nicholson, Haslemere #97/R

£700 $1085 €1050 Artist painting etudes (50x61cm-20x24in) s. 8-Dec-2 John Nicholson, Haslemere #99/R

£900 $1395 €1350 Sunny day (65x54cm-26x21in) s. 8-Dec-2 John Nicholson, Haslemere #96/R

£1100 $1705 €1650 Little flower girl (55x38cm-22x15in) s. 8-Dec-2 John Nicholson, Haslemere #95/R

£1500 $2325 €2250 Star of Cberet (61x38cm-24x15in) s. 8-Dec-2 John Nicholson, Haslemere #98/R

£1600 $2480 €2400 Near the blooming rose (55x38cm-22x15in) s. 29-Sep-2 John Nicholson, Haslemere #70/R

£1800 $2790 €2700 Getting ready to the feast (61x46cm-24x18in) s. 29-Sep-2 John Nicholson, Haslemere #67/R

£3000 $4650 €4500 On the terrace of an old house (61x50cm-24x20in) s. 29-Sep-2 John Nicholson, Haslemere #68/R

KROUTHEN, Johan (1858-1932) Swedish

£957 $1484 €1436 Summer landscape with cattle resting (37x51cm-15x20in) s. 3-Dec-2 Bukowskis, Stockholm #378/R est:15000-18000 (S.KR 13500)

£1429 $2371 €2072 Landscape with red cottage and appletree in blossom (30x40cm-12x16in) s. cardboard. 16-Jun-3 Lilla Bukowskis, Stockholm #560 est:12000-15000 (S.KR 18500)

£1571 $2577 €2278 View of Norrkoping - twilight (57x73cm-22x29in) s.d.1914. 4-Jun-3 AB Stockholms Auktionsverk #2095/R est:20000-25000 (S.KR 20000)

£2661 $4204 €3992 Summer landscape with haystooks, chickens, ducks and pigeons (64x50cm-25x20in) s.d.1924. 16-Nov-2 Crafoord, Lund #78/R est:30000 (S.KR 38000)

£2695 $4177 €4043 Spring landscape with apple blossom (50x75cm-20x30in) s. 3-Dec-2 Bukowskis, Stockholm #121/R est:30000-35000 (S.KR 38000)

£2766 $4287 €4149 Autumn landscape with chickens feeding by rhododendrons (73x125cm-29x49in) s.d.1912. 3-Dec-2 Bukowskis, Stockholm #120/R est:55000-60000 (S.KR 39000)

£2793 $4524 €4050 Summer landscape with brook (40x60cm-16x24in) s.d.1912. 26-May-3 Bukowskis, Stockholm #196/R est:20000-25000 (S.KR 36000)

£2979 $4617 €4469 Summer landscape with cattle and milkmaid (50x75cm-20x30in) s.d.1910. 3-Dec-2 Bukowskis, Stockholm #380/R est:35000-40000 (S.KR 42000)

£3546 $5496 €5319 Summer landscape (70x100cm-28x39in) s.d.1924. 3-Dec-2 Bukowskis, Stockholm #379/R est:40000-45000 (S.KR 50000)

£3771 $6184 €5468 Summer landscape with cattle (80x110cm-31x43in) s.d.1918. 4-Jun-3 AB Stockholms Auktionsverk #2255/R est:50000-60000 (S.KR 48000)

£3830 $5936 €5745 Farm yard with cherry tree in blossom (50x75cm-20x30in) s.d.1915. 4-Dec-2 AB Stockholms Auktionsverk #1662/R est:30000-40000 (S.KR 54000)

£3879 $6284 €5625 Village road with sunshine and fruit trees in blossom (60x90cm-24x35in) s. 25-May-3 Uppsala Auktionskammare, Uppsala #171/R est:30000-40000 (S.KR 50000)

£3879 $6284 €5625 Summer landscape (50x75cm-20x30in) s.d.1913. 26-May-3 Bukowskis, Stockholm #169/R est:25000-30000 (S.KR 50000)

£4113 $6376 €6170 Sunny farmyard with chickens feeding (76x104cm-30x41in) s.d.1906. 3-Dec-2 Bukowskis, Stockholm #119/R est:40000-45000 (S.KR 58000)

£4500 $7289 €6525 Summer landscape (50x73cm-20x29in) s. 26-May-3 Bukowskis, Stockholm #195/R est:30000-35000 (S.KR 58000)

£4556 $7472 €6606 Summer landscape with cottage by lake (70x100cm-28x39in) s.d.1923. 4-Jun-3 AB Stockholms Auktionsverk #2096/R est:40000-50000 (S.KR 58000)

£4655 $7541 €6750 The sunflower (78x110cm-31x43in) s.d.1919. 26-May-3 Bukowskis, Stockholm #172/R est:80000-100000 (S.KR 60000)

£4965 $7695 €7448 Bay in summer (36x44cm-14x17in) s.d.1901. 3-Dec-2 Bukowskis, Stockholm #312/R est:60000-70000 (S.KR 70000)

Works on paper

£2979 $4617 €4469 On mother's arms (87x73cm-34x29in) pastel paper on canvas. 3-Dec-2 Bukowskis, Stockholm #276/R est:25000-30000 (S.KR 42000)

KROYER, Peder Severin (1851-1909) Danish

£2412 $3666 €3618 Sunset over Skagen Strand (22x27cm-9x11in) init. panel. 27-Aug-2 Rasmussen, Copenhagen #1466/R est:25000-35000 (D.KR 28000)

£3731 $5933 €5597 Coastal landscape with houses at edge of water (28x57cm-11x22in) s.i. panel. 5-May-3 Rasmussen, Vejle #252/R est:50000 (D.KR 40000)

£4737 $7201 €7106 Shot hares in field (49x79cm-19x31in) s. study exhib.prov. 27-Aug-2 Rasmussen, Copenhagen #1482/R est:75000-100000 (D.KR 55000)

£4842 $7698 €7263 Fisherman with pipe (22x19cm-9x7in) init.i.d.74 prov. 5-Mar-3 Rasmussen, Copenhagen #1514/R est:30000 (D.KR 52000)

£10242 $16285 €15363 Evening landscape by the antique theatre in Taormina (32x43cm-13x17in) s.i.d.1901 panel. 5-Mar-3 Rasmussen, Copenhagen #1575/R est:150000-175000 (D.KR 110000)

£14833 $24029 €21508 Skagen fisherman Lars Gaihede. Breakers (30x24cm-12x9in) init.i.d.88 double-sided. 26-May-3 Rasmussen, Copenhagen #1163/R est:75000 (D.KR 155000)

£23830 $37651 €35745 Cloud study - sunset over Skagen Town (33x43cm-13x17in) init.d.18 juni 99 panel prov. 2-Dec-2 Rasmussen, Copenhagen #1115/R est:300000-400000 (D.KR 280000)

£59574 $94128 €89361 Skagen's hunters (33x44cm-13x17in) study panel exhib.prov. 2-Dec-2 Rasmussen, Copenhagen #1116/R est:700000-1000000 (D.KR 700000)

£221277 $349617 €331916 Spring sunshine, Skagen Plantage - woman dressed in white with flowers in her hand (75x54cm-30x21in) init.i.d.1909 prov. 2-Dec-2 Rasmussen, Copenhagen #1120/R est:2500000-3500000 (D.KR 2600000)

Prints

£2584 $3928 €3876 Edvard Grieg accompanying Mrs Nina Grieg's song (37x47cm-15x19in) s.d.30 Oktober 1900 etching. 27-Aug-2 Rasmussen, Copenhagen #2188/R est:8000-10000 (D.KR 30000)

Sculpture
£2213 $3496 €3320 Portrait bust of Holger Drachmann (190cm-75in) s.d.82 pat.plaster incl. wood socle. 2-Dec-2 Rasmussen, Copenhagen #1641/R est:10000-15000 (D.KR 26000)
Works on paper
£901 $1450 €1352 Italian boy (17x10cm-7x4in) mono.d.1880 wash pe. 26-Feb-3 Museumsbygningen, Copenhagen #79/R (D.KR 10000)

KROYER, Peder Severin (attrib) (1851-1909) Danish
£4167 $6625 €6000 Auto-portrait presume (50x40cm-20x16in) init. 30-Apr-3 Tajan, Paris #141/R
Works on paper
£345 $524 €518 Portrait study of Otto Bentzon (10x15cm-4x6in) pencil. 28-Aug-2 Museumsbygningen, Copenhagen #62/R (D.KR 4000)
£775 $1178 €1163 Portrait of the artist Deyrolle (15x11cm-6x4in) s.i.d.79 pencil. 28-Aug-2 Museumsbygningen, Copenhagen #60/R (D.KR 9000)
£1164 $1851 €1746 Portrait of the artist Frants Henningsen (16x13cm-6x5in) init.d.Dec.74 W/C pencil. 5-Mar-3 Rasmussen, Copenhagen #2089/R est:10000 (D.KR 12500)
£1378 $2095 €2067 Midday scene (13x22cm-5x9in) init. pencil. 27-Aug-2 Rasmussen, Copenhagen #1982/R est:10000-15000 (D.KR 16000)

KRUCHEN, Medardus (1877-1957) German
£1346 $2087 €2100 Still life with cherries, coffee jug and open book (55x69cm-22x27in) s. i. stretcher. 4-Dec-2 Lempertz, Koln #840/R est:2000

KRUGER, Elizabeth (1955-) Australian
£3386 $5554 €4910 Bent screen, bent tree (154x72cm-61x28in) s.i.d.1990 verso panel prov.exhib. 4-Jun-3 Deutscher-Menzies, Melbourne #98/R est:7500-9500 (A.D 8500)

KRUGER, Erna (1883-?) German
£316 $500 €500 Winter evening mountain valley (71x100cm-28x39in) s. lit. 29-Nov-2 Schloss Ahlden, Ahlden #1292/R

KRUGER, Eugen (1832-1876) German
£705 $1093 €1100 Hay harvest (60x82cm-24x32in) s.d.1865. 5-Dec-2 Schopman, Hamburg #637

KRUGER, Franz (1797-1857) German
Works on paper
£1295 $2072 €1800 Portrait of man wearing decorations (28x24cm-11x9in) i. verso Indian ink brush htd white. 17-May-3 Lempertz, Koln #1309/R est:1600

KRUGER, Franz (attrib) (1797-1857) German
Works on paper
£253 $392 €400 Portrait of King Friedrich Wilhelm IV von Preussen (42x32cm-17x13in) i. verso chk pencil board. 27-Sep-2 Venator & Hansten, Koln #1304
£1090 $1689 €1700 Berlin under lime trees with six horse coach in front of opera house (12x46cm-5x18in) W/C over pencil. 4-Dec-2 Neumeister, Munich #533/R est:800

KRUGER, Richard (1880-?) American
£346 $550 €519 Autumn (61x71cm-24x28in) s. painted c.1915. 2-Mar-3 Toomey, Oak Park #676/R
£483 $764 €725 Arizona moonlight (63x77cm-25x30in) s. i.stretcher. 18-Nov-2 Waddingtons, Toronto #10a/R (C.D 1200)

KRUIJFF, Cornelis de (1771-1854) Dutch
£890 $1389 €1300 Brothel interior (12x17cm-5x7in) metal prov. 14-Apr-3 Glerum, Amsterdam #6/R

KRUIZINGA, Dirk (1895-?) Dutch
£461 $746 €700 Still life with strawberries and forget-me-nots (35x45cm-14x18in) s. 21-Jan-3 Christie's, Amsterdam #395

KRULL, Germaine (1897-1985) Czechoslovakian
Photographs
£1923 $3038 €3000 Etude de mains (22x16cm-9x6in) st. i.num.verso gelatin silver print exec.c.1938. 16-Nov-2 Christie's, Paris #304/R est:2500-3500
£3797 $6000 €5696 La tour Eiffel, Paris constructivisme (22x16cm-9x6in) i. ferrotyped executed c.1928. 23-Apr-3 Sotheby's, New York #191/R est:7000-10000

KRUMBHOLZ, Ferdinand (1810-1878) Austrian
£11613 $18348 €18000 Portrait of the Marquis of Seran's son (140x106cm-55x42in) s.d.1841 prov.exhib. 18-Dec-2 Renaud, Paris #41/R est:10000

KRUMLINDE, Olof (1856-1945) Swedish
£505 $798 €758 Autumn landscape (60x73cm-24x29in) s. 27-Nov-2 Falkkloos, Malmo #77597/R (S.KR 7200)
£517 $797 €776 Coastal landscape with figure and fishing hut (63x84cm-25x33in) s. 27-Oct-2 Anders Antik, Landskrona #302 (S.KR 7500)
£775 $1178 €1163 Gardening in front of farm (48x76cm-19x30in) s. 27-Aug-2 Rasmussen, Copenhagen #1899/R (D.KR 9000)
£912 $1440 €1368 Boy and girl on country road (41x55cm-16x22in) s. prov.exhib. 27-Nov-2 Falkkloos, Malmo #77827/R (S.KR 13000)
£965 $1506 €1399 Reading in the park (84x129cm-33x51in) s. prov. 26-Mar-3 Walker's, Ottawa #35/R est:2500-3500 (C.D 2250)
£995 $1551 €1493 Landscape with woman walking (50x73cm-20x29in) s. 13-Sep-2 Lilla Bukowskis, Stockholm #62 (S.KR 14500)
£1332 $2105 €1998 Man and dog with woman picking vegetables by farm (48x75cm-19x30in) s. 27-Nov-2 Falkkloos, Malmo #77819/R est:25000 (S.KR 19000)

KRUMMACHER, Karl (1867-1955) German
£578 $919 €850 Landscape with farmstead (48x61cm-19x24in) board on canvas. 28-Mar-3 Bolland & Marotz, Bremen #353/R
£2177 $3461 €3200 Moor landscape near Worpswede in summer (64x82cm-25x32in) s. board. 28-Mar-3 Bolland & Marotz, Bremen #352/R est:2200
Works on paper
£380 $600 €600 Farm girl working (29x22cm-11x9in) s. W/C chl. 29-Nov-2 Bolland & Marotz, Bremen #535

KRUMPER, Hans (1570-1634) German
Works on paper
£5556 $8833 €8000 God the Father in clouds (13x14cm-5x6in) pen wash. 5-May-3 Ketterer, Munich #207/R est:800-1000

KRUPA-KRUPINSKY, Emil (1872-1924) German
£390 $592 €600 Night time dance of the Bacchanten (52x65cm-20x26in) s.d.1922. 5-Jul-2 Weidler, Nurnberg #8607

KRUSE, H (19th C) Dutch
Works on paper
£377 $588 €550 Woman's portrait (31x25cm-12x10in) s. W/C. 9-Apr-3 Neumeister, Munich #534/R

KRUSE, Max (1854-1942) German
Sculpture
£1154 $1823 €1800 Marathon's messenger (53cm-21in) s. pat bronze. 16-Nov-2 Farsetti, Prato #243/R

KRUSEMAN, Cornelis (1797-1857) Dutch
£1172 $1864 €1700 Portrait of a lady as one of the Vestal Virgins (66x52cm-26x20in) s. 10-Mar-3 Sotheby's, Amsterdam #99/R est:1500-2000

KRUSEMAN, Frederik Marianus (1817-1882) Dutch
£1401 $2186 €2200 Winter (18x22cm-7x9in) s. indis.d. panel. 6-Nov-2 Vendue Huis, Gravenhage #421 est:1500-2000
£15000 $23250 €22500 Winter landscape with figures on a frozen river (51x66cm-20x26in) indis sig. panel. 4-Dec-2 Christie's, London #43/R est:15000-20000
£22000 $34100 €33000 Winter landscape with figures (59x82cm-23x32in) s. panel prov.lit. 4-Dec-2 Christie's, London #44/R est:25000-35000
£27211 $43265 €40000 Enjoying the ice outside old Dutch town (41x56cm-16x22in) s.d.1855 panel. 28-Mar-3 Bolland & Marotz, Bremen #477/R est:16000

KRUSEMAN, Jan Adam (1804-1862) Dutch
£4140 $6459 €6500 Portrait of Bishop van Heemskerk. Wife of Bishop van Heemskerk (71x57cm-28x22in) s.d.1828 two. 6-Nov-2 Vendue Huis, Gravenhage #480/R est:2000-3000
£5346 $8233 €8500 Portrait of Diederich Janssen Eyken Sluyters (82x66cm-32x26in) s.d.1831 lit. 23-Oct-2 Christie's, Amsterdam #42/R est:5000-7000

KRUSEMAN, Jan Theodor (1835-1895) Dutch
£506 $790 €800 La mer a Scheveningen (25x46cm-10x18in) s. 10-Sep-2 Vanderkindere, Brussels #389

KRUSHENICK, Nicholas (1929-) American
£1310 $1913 €1965 Penetration (131x114cm-52x45in) s.i.d.1963 verso acrylic prov.exhib. 4-Jun-2 Germann, Zurich #95/R est:4000-6000 (S.FR 3000)

KRUSI, Hans (1920-1995) Swiss
£343 $542 €515 Figures in front of pinewoods (37x31cm-15x12in) mono. acrylic. 26-Nov-2 Hans Widmer, St Gallen #1459 (S.FR 800)
£415 $606 €623 Untitled (34x22cm-13x9in) mono.d.1981 mixed media. 4-Jun-2 Germann, Zurich #785 (S.FR 950)
£515 $814 €773 Bathing at the fishpond (40x34cm-16x13in) mono. acrylic. 26-Nov-2 Hans Widmer, St Gallen #1458/R (S.FR 1200)
£655 $1022 €983 People in park (35x25cm-14x10in) s.d.1980 acrylic paper. 6-Nov-2 Dobiaschofsky, Bern #750/R (S.FR 1500)
Works on paper
£1048 $1635 €1572 Two people sitting at two tables (25x35cm-10x14in) mono.d.81 mixed media collage. 6-Nov-2 Hans Widmer, St Gallen #145/R est:1200-2400 (S.FR 2400)
£1528 $2460 €2216 Mountain pasture parade in yellow (29x39cm-11x15in) mono.d.1978 mixed media. 9-May-3 Dobiaschofsky, Bern #261/R est:2000 (S.FR 3300)

KRUSMANN, Gero (?) ?
£550 $897 €825 Family group, mother with three children peeling apples (48x58cm-19x23in) s. 28-Jan-3 Henry Adams, Chichester #433/R

KRUTZER, B (19th C) ?
£321 $500 €482 Mountain landscape with stream and figures (51x71cm-20x28in) s. 1-Aug-2 Eldred, East Dennis #377t/R

KRUYF, Cornelis de (1774-1828) Dutch
Works on paper
£276 $439 €400 Pastorie to soest (45x55cm-18x22in) s. W/C. 10-Mar-3 Sotheby's, Amsterdam #39

KRUYS, Cornelis (?-1702) Dutch
£25943 $42028 €37617 Still life of fruit, roses, glasses and jug (91x120cm-36x47in) bears i. prov.lit. 24-May-3 Galerie Gloggner, Luzern #78/R est:18000-25000 (S.FR 55000)

KRUYSEN, Antoon (1898-1977) Dutch
£283 $439 €450 Figures sur le port (50x61cm-20x24in) s. s.d.1957 verso. 6-Oct-2 Livinec, Gaudcheau & Jezequel, Rennes #40
£290 $461 €420 Citrons (27x36cm-11x14in) s. 4-Mar-3 Livinec, Gaudcheau & Jezequel, Rennes #109
£345 $548 €500 Bouquet de fleurs (46x33cm-18x13in) s.d.64. 4-Mar-3 Livinec, Gaudcheau & Jezequel, Rennes #110
£377 $585 €600 Figure in landscape (46x55cm-18x22in) s.d.70. 6-Oct-2 Livinec, Gaudcheau & Jezequel, Rennes #36
£377 $585 €600 Bord de cote rocheuse (46x55cm-18x22in) s.d.66. 6-Oct-2 Livinec, Gaudcheau & Jezequel, Rennes #37/R
£379 $603 €550 Bateau de peche (61x74cm-24x29in) s. 4-Mar-3 Livinec, Gaudcheau & Jezequel, Rennes #107
£414 $658 €600 Chateau dominant le port (46x55cm-18x22in) s. 4-Mar-3 Livinec, Gaudcheau & Jezequel, Rennes #106
£421 $669 €610 Nature morte aux fruits (38x46cm-15x18in) s.d.60. 4-Mar-3 Livinec, Gaudcheau & Jezequel, Rennes #112
£517 $822 €750 Pecheur au filet (81x65cm-32x26in) s. 4-Mar-3 Livinec, Gaudcheau & Jezequel, Rennes #116
£552 $877 €800 Roulotte (61x50cm-24x20in) s.d.60. 4-Mar-3 Livinec, Gaudcheau & Jezequel, Rennes #114
£556 $917 €800 Peasant with wheelbarrow in a landscape (38x46cm-15x18in) 1-Jul-3 Christie's, Amsterdam #402/R
£566 $899 €820 Le port de la Rochelle (46x56cm-18x22in) s.d.74. 4-Mar-3 Livinec, Gaudcheau & Jezequel, Rennes #111
£586 $932 €850 Bateau de peche en mer (61x72cm-24x28in) s. 4-Mar-3 Livinec, Gaudcheau & Jezequel, Rennes #115
£634 $1009 €920 Village (46x55cm-18x22in) s. 4-Mar-3 Livinec, Gaudcheau & Jezequel, Rennes #113
£660 $1024 €1050 Bateaux et poisson (46x55cm-18x22in) s. 6-Oct-2 Livinec, Gaudcheau & Jezequel, Rennes #39
£723 $1121 €1150 Rousse (55x46cm-22x18in) s.d.68. 6-Oct-2 Livinec, Gaudcheau & Jezequel, Rennes #38
£1379 $2193 €2000 Paysage Provencal (51x61cm-20x24in) s. 4-Mar-3 Livinec, Gaudcheau & Jezequel, Rennes #118/R
£1447 $2345 €2200 Still life with a pipe, a bottle and eggs (61x50cm-24x20in) s.d.28. 21-Jan-3 Christie's, Amsterdam #368/R est:800-1200
£1517 $2412 €2200 La Cathedrale de Chartres (55x46cm-22x18in) s. 4-Mar-3 Livinec, Gaudcheau & Jezequel, Rennes #117/R
£2138 $3314 €3400 Fenetre sur Chartres (61x50cm-24x20in) s. i.d.67 verso. 6-Oct-2 Livinec, Gaudcheau & Jezequel, Rennes #41

KRUYSEN, Johannes (1874-1938) Dutch
£395 $639 €600 In the kitchen (53x60cm-21x24in) s. board. 21-Jan-3 Christie's, Amsterdam #459
£1316 $2132 €2000 Portrait of a farmer (63x46cm-25x18in) board. 21-Jan-3 Christie's, Amsterdam #457 est:800-1200

KRYGER, Henk (1914-1979) Dutch
£268 $417 €420 Sower (91x69cm-36x27in) s.d.1940. 5-Nov-2 Vendu Notarishuis, Rotterdam #74
£268 $417 €420 Girl with rabbit (85x60cm-33x24in) s.d.1943. 5-Nov-2 Vendu Notarishuis, Rotterdam #77
£637 $994 €1000 Three girls (43x50cm-17x20in) s.d.1948. 5-Nov-2 Vendu Notarishuis, Rotterdam #83/R
£701 $1093 €1100 Two fishermen (108x92cm-43x36in) s.d.1942. 5-Nov-2 Vendu Notarishuis, Rotterdam #80/R
£2803 $4372 €4400 Loving couple (94x69cm-37x27in) s.d.1936. 5-Nov-2 Vendu Notarishuis, Rotterdam #75/R est:400-500
Works on paper
£280 $437 €440 Loving couple (45x45cm-18x18in) s.d.1946 mixed media. 5-Nov-2 Vendu Notarishuis, Rotterdam #82

KRYSTALLIS, Andreas (1901-1951) Greek
£4500 $7110 €6750 Piraiki, Piraeus (45x55cm-18x22in) 1-Apr-3 Bonhams, New Bond Street #57 est:3500-4500

KUBA, Ludvik (1863-1956) Czechoslovakian
£478 $745 €750 Reines-marguerites (42x38cm-17x15in) s. cardboard. 6-Nov-2 Claude Boisgirard, Paris #29/R
£620 $967 €930 Market by Mostar (30x30cm-12x12in) s. plywood. 12-Oct-2 Dorotheum, Prague #64 est:26000-40000 (C.KR 30000)
£1033 $1611 €1550 Mountain scene with small church (29x23cm-11x9in) s. cardboard. 12-Oct-2 Dorotheum, Prague #72/R (C.KR 50000)
£3924 $6121 €5886 Still life with a mortar (49x42cm-19x17in) s.d.1944 exhib.lit. 12-Oct-2 Dorotheum, Prague #66/R est:100000-150000 (C.KR 190000)

KUBALL, Mischa (1959-) German
£1087 $1783 €1500 Double volume I (138x44cm-54x17in) s.i.d. verso panel exhib. 28-May-3 Lempertz, Koln #239/R est:1900

KUBANYI, Lajos (1855-1912) Hungarian
£592 $917 €888 Galloping with the cart (98x75cm-39x30in) s. 6-Dec-2 Kieselbach, Budapest #98/R (H.F 220000)

KUBICEK, Juro (1906-1970) German
£503 $775 €800 Painted desert (62x170cm-24x67in) mono.d.1949 s.i. verso. 26-Oct-2 Dr Lehr, Berlin #258/R

KUBIERSCHKY, Erich (1854-1944) German
£440 $687 €700 Village on canal (60x44cm-24x17in) s.d.1887. 19-Sep-2 Dr Fritz Nagel, Stuttgart #956/R

KUBIK, Kamil (1930-) American
Works on paper
£380 $616 €570 Central Park, New York (63x48cm-25x19in) s. black col chk exhib. 21-Jan-3 Rosebery Fine Art, London #560

KUBIN, Alfred (1877-1959) Austrian
£13208 $20604 €21000 Buddhistischer monch - Buddhist monk (36x29cm-14x11in) s.d.05 tempera gouache prov.exhib. 9-Oct-2 Sotheby's, London #146/R est:30000-40000
£26415 $41208 €42000 Der basilisk - Basilisk (25x36cm-10x14in) s.i. col paste distemper executed 1905 prov. 9-Oct-2 Sotheby's, London #152/R est:28000-35000
Works on paper
£321 $506 €500 Figures (29x22cm-11x9in) mono. i. verso. 18-Nov-2 Dorotheum, Linz #486
£353 $546 €550 Head studies (15x9cm-6x4in) pencil double-sided. 7-Dec-2 Hauswedell & Nolte, Hamburg #847/R
£513 $795 €800 Sketch (30x27cm-12x11in) pencil. 4-Dec-2 Lempertz, Koln #845/R
£612 $1003 €850 In anticipation (19x24cm-7x9in) st.sig.verso pencil dr. 5-Jun-3 Dorotheum, Salzburg #747
£629 $981 €1000 Basilisk (33x20cm-13x8in) mono.i. pencil executed c.1928 prov. 9-Oct-2 Sotheby's, London #161/R est:1500-2000
£648 $1044 €972 Woman's head (22x16cm-9x6in) s. Indian ink. 7-May-3 Dobiaschofsky, Bern #1706/R (S.FR 1400)
£755 $1177 €1200 Rubezahl (33x40cm-13x16in) s. pencil executed c.1937 prov. 9-Oct-2 Sotheby's, London #160/R est:2000-3000
£1410 $2228 €2200 Spirit of the Sudeten mountains (19x13cm-7x5in) s. pen Indian ink. 12-Nov-2 Dorotheum, Vienna #88/R est:1800-2400

£1844 $2987 €2600 St Sebastian (17x11cm-7x4in) s.i. pen Indian ink. 20-May-3 Dorotheum, Vienna #139/R est:3000-4000
£1887 $2943 €3000 Death as a gardener (39x31cm-15x12in) s. pen brush ink W/C executed c.1930 prov. 9-Oct-2 Sotheby's, London #142/R est:4500-6500
£1887 $2943 €3000 LAO-TSE (24x13cm-9x5in) s.i. pen brush ink executed c.1923 prov.exhib. 9-Oct-2 Sotheby's, London #154/R est:4500-6500
£1887 $2943 €3000 Galopp - gallop (20x33cm-8x13in) s. pen brush ink W/C executed 1939-40 prov. 9-Oct-2 Sotheby's, London #155/R est:4500-6500
£2174 $3565 €3000 Till Eulenspiegel (26x39cm-10x15in) s.i.d.38 pen prov. 31-May-3 Villa Grisebach, Berlin #130/R est:3000-4000
£2201 $3434 €3500 Friedrich Huch's new dreams II, collapsing castle (36x26cm-14x10in) s.i. pen brush ink illustration executed 1921 prov.exhib. 9-Oct-2 Sotheby's, London #148/R est:5000-7000
£2590 $4247 €3600 Sleigh ride across ice (17x13cm-7x5in) s. pen over pencil chk. 4-Jun-3 Reiss & Sohn, Konigstein #433/R est:1000
£2639 $4196 €3800 Farmstead (23x36cm-9x14in) s. Indian ink W/C. 29-Apr-3 Wiener Kunst Auktionen, Vienna #603/R est:3000-5000
£2642 $4121 €4200 Bull on the alpine pastures of Lofer (36x26cm-14x10in) s. pen brush ink W/C executed c.1922-23 prov. 9-Oct-2 Sotheby's, London #159/R est:6000-9000
£3378 $5270 €5000 Battle scene (36x30cm-14x12in) s.d.1948 Indian ink W/C. 25-Mar-3 Wiener Kunst Auktionen, Vienna #141/R est:5000-10000
£4487 $7045 €7000 Herdress (39x30cm-15x12in) s.i.d.1935 W/C pen. 25-Nov-2 Hassfurther, Vienna #50/R est:2500-3500
£5282 $8768 €7500 Indians (23x31cm-9x12in) s. Indian ink. 14-Jun-3 Hauswedell & Nolte, Hamburg #1327/R est:10000
£6090 $9439 €9500 Canal scene (29x31cm-11x12in) s. wash Indian ink paper on board. 4-Dec-2 Lempertz, Koln #842/R est:4000-6000
£6604 $10302 €10500 Eihorn im walde - Unicorn in the forest (24x36cm-9x14in) s. i.verso gouache W/C prov.exhib. 9-Oct-2 Sotheby's, London #139/R est:15000-20000
£14744 $22853 €23000 The old king (39x32cm-15x13in) s.i. wash sprayed Indian ink pencil prov. 4-Dec-2 Lempertz, Koln #841/R est:14000-16000
£21384 $33358 €34000 Die poesie der landstrasse - poetry of the country road (31x40cm-12x16in) s.i. pen ink W/C executed c.1912-15 prov.exhib. 9-Oct-2 Sotheby's, London #145/R est:30000-40000
£25157 $39245 €40000 Am grund liegender wels - Catfish lying on the bottom (25x36cm-10x14in) s. col paste distemper W/C executed c.1905-06 prov.exhib. 9-Oct-2 Sotheby's, London #140/R est:20000-30000
£119497 $186415 €190000 Der prinz - prince (26x24cm-10x9in) s.i. pen ink wash pastel executed c.1903-04 prov.exhib. 9-Oct-2 Sotheby's, London #144/R est:45000-55000
£176101 $274717 €280000 Seegespent - sea monster (38x30cm-15x12in) s.i. pen ink wash pastel executed c.1901-02 prov.exhib.lit. 9-Oct-2 Sotheby's, London #138/R est:40000-50000

KUBIN, Alfred (attrib) (1877-1959) Austrian
£769 $1192 €1200 Figure sitting on back of chair (51x41cm-20x16in) s.d.29 panel lit. 6-Dec-2 Karlheinz Kaupp, Staufen #2295

KUBLER, Ludwig (19th C) Austrian
£755 $1208 €1133 Stable with two horses (31x39cm-12x15in) s. 17-Mar-3 Philippe Schuler, Zurich #4624/R (S.FR 1600)
£802 $1283 €1203 Two horses and dog in stable (31x39cm-12x15in) s. 17-Mar-3 Philippe Schuler, Zurich #4623/R (S.FR 1700)
£1239 $1933 €1859 Mare with foal (53x66cm-21x26in) s. canvas on canvas. 12-Oct-2 Dorotheum, Prague #19/R est:60000-90000 (C.KR 60000)

KUCHARSKI, Alexander (attrib) (1741-1819) Polish
£17021 $27574 €24000 Portrait de Marie Antoinette au temple (24x18cm-9x7in) 21-May-3 Piasa, Paris #368/R est:3000-4000

KUCHENMEISTER, Rainer (1926-) German
Works on paper
£481 $745 €750 Composition (82x59cm-32x23in) mono.i.d.3.62 col chk wax chk board. 7-Dec-2 Ketterer, Hamburg #408/R

KUCHLER, Albert (1803-1886) Danish
£1722 $2790 €2497 Napoleon on Elba looking out to sea. prov. 26-May-3 Rasmussen, Copenhagen #1198/R est:15000-25000 (D.KR 18000)
£13966 $22207 €20949 An older girl teaching two younger girls to pray with rosary (69x80cm-27x31in) s.i.d.1836 prov.exhib. 10-Mar-3 Rasmussen, Vejle #186/R est:150000-175000 (D.KR 150000)

KUCHLER, Hans (1929-2001) German
Works on paper
£279 $441 €419 Flying machine (60x47cm-24x19in) s. W/C col pencil pencil. 29-Nov-2 Zofingen, Switzerland #2954 (S.FR 650)

KUCHLER, Rudolf (1867-?) Austrian
Sculpture
£2900 $4524 €4350 Coup de main (37x28cm-15x11in) s. brown pat bronze lit. 9-Apr-3 Sotheby's, London #199/R est:1500-2000

KUCHLIN, Jacob (1820-1885) Swiss
Works on paper
£343 $542 €515 Rheinfall (50x72cm-20x28in) s.d.1889 gouache htd white. 29-Nov-2 Falk & Falk, Zurich #429/R (S.FR 800)

KUCHUMOV, Fedor (19/20th C) Russian
Works on paper
£1200 $1944 €1800 Evening on the Volga (21x32cm-8x13in) s. indis d. gouache. 21-May-3 Sotheby's, London #78/R est:2000-3000

KUCZYNSKA, Maria (1948-) Australian/Polish
Sculpture
£1964 $3064 €2946 Warrior (62x19x17cm-24x7x7in) init.d.98 bronze. 11-Nov-2 Deutscher-Menzies, Melbourne #54/R est:6000-9000 (A.D 5500)

KUDLAC, Frantisek (1909-) Czechoslovakian
£284 $414 €426 Woman with a cat (41x30cm-16x12in) tempera board painted c.1970. 4-Jun-2 SOGA, Bratislava #242/R est:18000 (SL.K 18000)

KUDO, Tetsumi (1935-) Japanese
Sculpture
£2973 $4638 €4400 Meditation between memory and future (48x49x24cm-19x19x9in) s. cage mixed media prov. 28-Mar-3 Charbonneaux, Paris #101/R
£8333 $13750 €12000 Paradise (50x31x29cm-20x12x11in) s.i.d.80 mixed media cage prov. 1-Jul-3 Artcurial Briest, Paris #537a/R est:10000-15000

KUDRYASHOV, Oleg (1932-) Russian
Works on paper
£700 $1134 €1050 Untitled composition. mixed media in perspex box. 20-May-3 Bonhams, Knightsbridge #120/R

KUEHL, Gotthardt Johann (1850-1915) German
£966 $1526 €1400 Still life with mirror (55x44cm-22x17in) s. masonite. 2-Apr-3 Dr Fritz Nagel, Stuttgart #9132/R
£1583 $2596 €2200 Farmer calling (20x16cm-8x6in) s. panel. 5-Jun-3 Dorotheum, Salzburg #615/R est:3000-4000
£1757 $2741 €2600 Elegant scene, possibly in Dresden (19x12cm-7x5in) panel. 27-Mar-3 Dr Fritz Nagel, Stuttgart #828/R est:1900
£3247 $4838 €5000 Travemunde - houses on Marktstrasse (24x17cm-9x7in) s.i. panel. 26-Jun-2 Neumeister, Munich #779/R est:2000
£4088 $6296 €6500 Sonntag Nachmittag (76x64cm-30x25in) s. prov. 23-Oct-2 Christie's, Amsterdam #21/R est:3000-5000
£4487 $7045 €7000 Catharinen Church, Hamburg (98x57cm-39x22in) s. panel. 23-Nov-2 Arnold, Frankfurt #783/R est:2000
£9000 $14760 €13500 Interieur (22x14cm-9x6in) s. panel prov. 3-Jun-3 Sotheby's, London #59/R est:2000-3000
£10256 $16205 €16000 Franciscan church in Uberlingen (130x100cm-51x39in) s. 16-Nov-2 Lempertz, Koln #1514/R est:18000
Works on paper
£2692 $4227 €4200 Two women sewing by fire (32x40cm-13x16in) s. W/C. 23-Nov-2 Arnold, Frankfurt #782/R est:2000

KUEHNE, Max (1880-c.1968) American
£250 $400 €375 Farmstead (28x38cm-11x15in) s. canvas on board. 11-Jan-3 James Julia, Fairfield #303a
£344 $550 €516 Sound of pounding surf. s. 12-Jan-3 William Jenack, New York #249
£488 $800 €732 Beach (61x76cm-24x30in) s. 9-Feb-3 William Jenack, New York #391
£577 $900 €866 Seagulls over the ocean (56x91cm-22x36in) s. masonite prov. 12-Apr-3 Weschler, Washington #574/R est:1000-1500
£625 $1000 €938 Rooftops overlooking harbor (33x38cm-13x15in) s. board. 11-Jan-3 James Julia, Fairfield #304 est:1500-2500
£813 $1300 €1220 Vase of chrysanthemums (61x46cm-24x18in) s. 11-Jan-3 James Julia, Fairfield #303 est:1250-1500
£833 $1300 €1250 Spanish harbour town (61x76cm-24x30in) s. prov. 12-Apr-3 Weschler, Washington #575/R est:1500-2500
£955 $1500 €1433 Crest of the wave (66x81cm-26x32in) s. s.i.d.1919 on stretcher prov. 14-Dec-2 Weschler, Washington #688/R est:1000-1500
£1026 $1600 €1539 Roses (61x51cm-24x20in) s. i.d.1951 verso prov. 12-Apr-3 Weschler, Washington #573/R est:1200-1800
£1529 $2400 €2294 Aleazare at Segovia (66x81cm-26x32in) s.i. s.d.1917 verso prov. 14-Dec-2 Weschler, Washington #687/R est:3000-5000

£1899 $3000 €2849 Studio interior (33x48cm-13x19in) s. board prov. 24-Apr-3 Shannon's, Milford #147/R est:3000-5000
£2160 $3500 €3132 Rooftops, Palma Mallorca (15x20cm-6x8in) s.i.d.1922 verso panel. 21-May-3 Doyle, New York #97/R est:2000-3000
£2215 $3500 €3323 Ocean and surf (46x56cm-18x22in) s. canvasboard prov. 24-Apr-3 Shannon's, Milford #220/R est:2000-3000
£3185 $5000 €4778 Parisian street scene (61x51cm-24x20in) s. masonite prov. 14-Dec-2 Weschler, Washington #686/R est:1500-2500
£4194 $6500 €6291 View from the window (76x61cm-30x24in) estate st. board painted c.1925. 8-Dec-2 Toomey, Oak Park #666/R est:8000-12000
£4430 $7000 €6645 View from the studio window (20x30cm-8x12in) s. oil paperboard prov. 24-Apr-3 Shannon's, Milford #145/R est:4000-6000
£6329 $10000 €9494 Flowers in a vase (61x76cm-24x30in) s. prov. 24-Apr-3 Shannon's, Milford #139/R est:8000-12000
£6329 $10000 €9494 Floral (64x76cm-25x30in) s. prov. 24-Apr-3 Shannon's, Milford #146/R est:10000-15000
£7792 $12000 €11688 Summer flowers (69x84cm-27x33in) s. panel prov. 24-Oct-2 Shannon's, Milford #78/R est:12000-18000

KUGLMAYER, Max (1863-?) German
£346 $550 €519 Alpine farm scene (15x30cm-6x12in) s.i.d.1911 panel. 5-Mar-3 Doyle, New York #39/R

KUHFUSS, Paul (1883-1960) German
£694 $1097 €1000 Ships at Dunmare (35x41cm-14x16in) s. board. 26-Apr-3 Dr Lehr, Berlin #299/R
£1831 $2948 €2600 Coastal scene with nets drying (50x60cm-20x24in) s. panel lit. 9-May-3 Schloss Ahlden, Ahlden #1544/R est:1400

Works on paper
£580 $951 €800 Flowers in vase (62x50cm-24x20in) s. gouache. 31-May-3 Villa Grisebach, Berlin #613/R
£704 $1134 €1000 Mending nets (50x65cm-20x26in) s. W/C lit. 9-May-3 Schloss Ahlden, Ahlden #1541/R

KUHLBRANDT, Ernst (1891-?) Austrian

Works on paper
£250 $415 €363 Mare and pointer in a landscape (27x36cm-11x14in) s.i.d.49 pencil W/C htd white. 12-Jun-3 Christie's, Kensington #50/R

KUHLING, Wilhelm (1823-1886) German
£962 $1519 €1500 Over the Venetian roofs (33x41cm-13x16in) s.d.81. 16-Nov-2 Lempertz, Koln #1515/R est:1300

KUHLMANN-REHER, Emil (1876-1957) German
£268 $417 €420 Pipe smoking gentleman with tin utensils (48x37cm-19x15in) s.i. lit. 7-Nov-2 Allgauer, Kempten #2874/R
£2800 $4564 €4200 Good story (79x98cm-31x39in) s.i. 29-Jan-3 Sotheby's, Olympia #301/R est:2000-3000

KUHLSTRUNK, Franz (1861-1944) Austrian
£641 $1006 €1000 Gosau lake with view of Dachstein (51x40cm-20x16in) s.indis.i.d.25. 21-Nov-2 Dorotheum, Vienna #196/R
£641 $1013 €1000 Gosausee with Dachstein (79x63cm-31x25in) s. 18-Nov-2 Dorotheum, Linz #308/R
£897 $1409 €1400 Salzburg area (48x65cm-19x26in) s.indis.d. 21-Nov-2 Dorotheum, Vienna #194/R
£1026 $1610 €1600 Country chapel with mountain range in background (44x58cm-17x23in) s.d.31. 21-Nov-2 Dorotheum, Vienna #195/R est:1300-1800
£1410 $2214 €2200 Mountain valley. s. fibreboard. 21-Nov-2 Dorotheum, Vienna #147/R est:1400-2000

Works on paper
£324 $531 €450 Old mill in autumn woods (29x22cm-11x9in) s. W/C bodycol. 5-Jun-3 Dorotheum, Salzburg #796/R

KUHN, Bob (1920-) American
£9589 $14000 €14384 Nary a wiggle (30x51cm-12x20in) acrylic. 18-May-2 Altermann Galleries, Santa Fe #228/R
£10616 $15500 €15924 Desert scrim (36x20cm-14x8in) acrylic. 18-May-2 Altermann Galleries, Santa Fe #213/R
£31646 $50000 €45887 In Dakota territory (61x91cm-24x36in) s. acrylic on board. 26-Jul-3 Coeur d'Alene, Hayden #85/R est:30000-40000

Works on paper
£1266 $2000 €1899 Very big elephant (41x58cm-16x23in) s.i.d.81 chl prov. 3-Apr-3 Christie's, Rockefeller NY #175/R est:1000-1500
£2405 $3800 €3608 Crouched beside a gored boy, hunter had barely time to snatch up his rifle (30x60cm-12x24in) s. gouache chl board. 3-Apr-3 Christie's, Rockefeller NY #180/R est:1500-2500

KUHN, Friedrich (1926-1972) Swiss
£2009 $2933 €3014 Inferno (45x40cm-18x16in) s.d.1966 i. verso panel lit. 4-Jun-2 Germann, Zurich #84/R est:5000-7000 (S.FR 4600)
£6438 $10172 €9657 Drummer girl (65x54cm-26x21in) s.d.56 prov.exhib.lit. 28-Nov-2 Christie's, Zurich #98/R est:15000-18000 (S.FR 15000)

Photographs
£5519 $8500 €8279 Sommer - man in the mountains (39x29cm-15x11in) gum pigment print lit. 24-Oct-2 Sotheby's, New York #66/R est:7000-10000

Works on paper
£306 $446 €459 Untitled (35x53cm-14x21in) feltpen. 4-Jun-2 Germann, Zurich #787 (S.FR 700)
£348 $539 €522 In the ring (17x20cm-7x8in) s. Indian ink. 9-Dec-2 Philippe Schuler, Zurich #3569 (S.FR 800)
£609 $943 €914 Untitled composition (38x30cm-15x12in) s.d.1957 Indian ink. 9-Dec-2 Philippe Schuler, Zurich #3565/R (S.FR 1400)

KUHN, Hans (1905-1992) German
£1887 $2906 €3000 Early light (90x120cm-35x47in) varnish panel. 26-Oct-2 Dr Lehr, Berlin #260/R est:2000
£1899 $3000 €3000 Untitled (60x80cm-24x31in) s.d.72 oil sand. 30-Nov-2 Villa Grisebach, Berlin #416/R est:3000-4000

KUHN, Heinrich (1866-1944) German

Photographs
£2700 $4374 €4050 Wanderer with a cloud (20x28cm-8x11in) bromoil transfer print on Japanese tissue exec.c.1914 lit. 22-May-3 Sotheby's, London #57/R est:3000-5000
£3247 $5000 €4871 Die brise - the breeze (29x23cm-11x9in) s. bromoil print. 24-Oct-2 Sotheby's, New York #67/R est:4000-6000
£3800 $6156 €5700 Carafe, glass and peach (24x30cm-9x12in) photogravure exec.c.1911 lit. 22-May-3 Sotheby's, London #54/R est:2000-3000
£3800 $6156 €5700 Nude study, scene from behind (30x24cm-12x9in) i.verso silver print exec.c.1920. 22-May-3 Sotheby's, London #55/R est:1500-2000

KUHN, Walt (1877-1949) American
£3185 $5000 €4778 Half length portrait of a woman in pink dress (61x51cm-24x20in) s.d.1944. 19-Apr-3 James Julia, Fairfield #190/R est:4000-6000
£22754 $38000 €32993 Eye opener (61x86cm-24x34in) s.d.06 prov.lit. 18-Jun-3 Christie's, Los Angeles #40/R est:25000-35000
£225806 $350000 €338709 Chorus captain (102x76cm-40x30in) s.d.1935 prov.exhib.lit. 3-Dec-2 Phillips, New York #66/R est:150000-250000

KUHNERT, Wilhelm (1865-1926) German
£1000 $1560 €1500 African landscape (40x65cm-16x26in) s.i.d.24.7.05 board. 17-Sep-2 Bonhams, Knightsbridge #127/R est:1000-1500
£7742 $12000 €11613 Common waterbuck (42x53cm-17x21in) s.i.d.2.8.05 canvas on board. 30-Oct-2 Christie's, Rockefeller NY #126/R est:15000-20000
£7742 $12000 €11613 African buffalo (37x66cm-15x26in) s. s.i.verso. 30-Oct-2 Christie's, Rockefeller NY #127/R est:15000-20000

Works on paper
£435 $713 €600 Mealtime (20x28cm-8x11in) s.i.d.12.6.05 pencil col pen. 31-May-3 Villa Grisebach, Berlin #614/R
£696 $1100 €1100 Tree root (28x39cm-11x15in) s.i.d.1911 chk pencil. 29-Nov-2 Bassenge, Berlin #5971
£1745 $2809 €2600 Lions with zebra carcass being disturbed by vultures (18x27cm-7x11in) s. col drawing. 21-Feb-3 Sigalas, Stuttgart #955/R est:2950
£2025 $3200 €3200 Grey coloured group of five lions drinking (19x35cm-7x14in) s. pencil dr. 29-Nov-2 Sigalas, Stuttgart #1100/R est:3800
£2848 $4500 €4500 Elephant bull grips a hunter with his trunk and lifts him into the air (28x18cm-11x7in) s. black white W/C. 29-Nov-2 Sigalas, Stuttgart #1103/R est:5800
£3038 $4800 €4800 Lion attacks a herd of goats and grasps an animal (25x36cm-10x14in) s. W/C. 29-Nov-2 Sigalas, Stuttgart #1102/R est:6900

KUHSTOSS, Paul (1870-1898) Belgian
£647 $1036 €900 Paysage (59x97cm-23x38in) s. 13-May-3 Vanderkindere, Brussels #66
£3448 $5517 €5000 Pecheurs de crevettes sur la plage devant la barque de peche (98x165cm-39x65in) 17-Mar-3 Amberes, Antwerp #225/R

KUITCA, Guillermo (1961-) Argentinian
£25478 $40000 €38217 Enfance du Christ (198x198cm-78x78in) s.i.d.1999 acrylic prov.lit. 19-Nov-2 Sotheby's, New York #140/R

Works on paper
£28662 $45000 €42993 Come thick night (102x122cm-40x48in) s.d.1995 i.verso pastel muslin prov.exhib.lit. 20-Nov-2 Christie's, Rockefeller NY #52/R est:40000-60000

KUJASALO, Matti (1946-) Finnish
£264 $409 €420 Black/white composition (35x35cm-14x14in) s.d.76 acrylic. 6-Oct-2 Bukowskis, Helsinki #210/R
£294 $482 €450 Black-white composition (40x65cm-16x26in) s.d.86 verso acrylic. 9-Feb-3 Bukowskis, Helsinki #282/R
£463 $746 €695 Untitled (40x40cm-16x16in) s.d.25.6 2001 canvas on panel. 7-May-3 AB Stockholms Auktionsverk #964/R (S.KR 6000)
£915 $1474 €1300 Composition (125x125cm-49x49in) s.d.80 board exhib. 10-May-3 Bukowskis, Helsinki #251/R
£1007 $1612 €1400 Untitled (168x42cm-66x17in) s.d.1977 verso acrylic canvas on board. 17-May-3 Hagelstam, Helsinki #187/R
£3354 $5300 €5300 Composition (141x141cm-56x56in) s.d.82 board. 1-Dec-2 Bukowskis, Helsinki #328/R est:1200-1500
Sculpture
£1127 $1814 €1600 Construction (58x139cm-23x55in) s.d.89 num.1/2 metal. 10-May-3 Bukowskis, Helsinki #206/R est:1000-1200
Works on paper
£1266 $2000 €2000 Composition (124x25cm-49x10in) s.d.1980 mixed media in five parts. 30-Nov-2 Hagelstam, Helsinki #181/R est:2500
£1266 $2000 €2000 Composition (200x72cm-79x28in) s.d.1978 mixed media. 30-Nov-2 Hagelstam, Helsinki #182/R est:2000

KUKLA, Reinhold (1877-1965) Austrian
£552 $883 €800 Winter scene (46x57cm-18x22in) s. 11-Mar-3 Dorotheum, Vienna #36/R

KUKUK, Willy (1875-1943) German
£490 $784 €750 View of Sollereck near Oberstdorf (60x70cm-24x28in) s. lit. 10-Jan-3 Allgauer, Kempten #1669

KULHAVY, Bohus Zaboj (1937-) Czechoslovakian
£600 $930 €900 Hard years (149x100cm-59x39in) painted c.1965. 3-Dec-2 SOGA, Bratislava #262/R (SL.K 38000)

KULLE, Jakob (1838-1898) Swedish
£1560 $2418 €2340 Confidential chat (38x29cm-15x11in) s.d.1876. 3-Dec-2 Bukowskis, Stockholm #175/R est:15000-20000 (S.KR 22000)

KULLRICH, Gustav (19th/20th C) German
£279 $441 €419 Waldsee in the sunshine (51x63cm-20x25in) 29-Nov-2 Zofingen, Switzerland #2479 (S.FR 650)

KULMALA, George Arthur (1896-1940) Canadian
£363 $573 €545 Lambton Heights (23x28cm-9x11in) s.d.1924 s.i.verso board prov. 14-Nov-2 Heffel, Vancouver #254/R est:750-1000 (C.D 900)
£565 $892 €848 Early morning walk (22x27cm-9x11in) s.d.1924 board prov. 14-Nov-2 Heffel, Vancouver #257/R est:750-1000 (C.D 1400)
£605 $950 €908 Winter landscape with yellow house (36x30cm-14x12in) s. 19-Apr-3 James Julia, Fairfield #457/R
£1475 $2302 €2213 Paysage (25x30cm-10x12in) s. panel exhib. 10-Sep-2 Iegor de Saint Hippolyte, Montreal #67 (C.D 3600)

KULOVESI, Erkki (1895-1971) Finnish
£621 $981 €900 Washerwomen (100x82cm-39x32in) s.d.1953. 3-Apr-3 Hagelstam, Helsinki #1046

KUMALO, Sidney (1935-) South African
Sculpture
£2251 $3556 €3377 Seated Zulu maiden (83cm-33in) bronze. 1-Apr-3 Stephan Welz, Johannesburg #522/R est:30000-40000 (SA.R 28000)
£2562 $3997 €3843 Reclining figure (20cm-8in) s.num.5/5 bronze. 11-Nov-2 Stephan Welz, Johannesburg #566/R est:15000-20000 (SA.R 40000)

KUMAR, Ram (1924-) Indian
£7770 $12821 €11267 Bananas series (91x91cm-36x36in) s.i.d.02. 6-Jul-3 Christie's, Hong Kong #86/R est:90000-120000 (HK.D 100000)
£46620 $76923 €67599 Untitled (110x60cm-43x24in) s.d.57 board. 6-Jul-3 Christie's, Hong Kong #85/R est:140000-180000 (HK.D 600000)

KUMMER, Karl Robert (1810-1889) German
£949 $1500 €1500 Clouds over landscape (15x30cm-6x12in) paper. 29-Nov-2 Bassenge, Berlin #5977 est:600
£1013 $1600 €1600 Cies island near Vigo in Spain (26x39cm-10x15in) board. 29-Nov-2 Bassenge, Berlin #5976/R est:1500

KUMMER, Karl Robert (attrib) (1810-1889) German
£605 $944 €950 Gosau lake with view of Dachstein mountains (43x52cm-17x20in) board lit. 7-Nov-2 Allgauer, Kempten #2875/R

KUMPF, Gottfried (1930-) Austrian
£7595 $12000 €12000 Munich before the Olympiade (65x70cm-26x28in) s.d.71 acrylic board. 27-Nov-2 Dorotheum, Vienna #262/R est:17000-22000
£14184 $22979 €20000 Salzburg - Mirabell garden with fortress beyond (50x64cm-20x25in) s.d.67 masonite prov. 20-May-3 Dorotheum, Vienna #206/R est:20000-28000

KUNA, Henri (1885-?) Polish
Sculpture
£4131 $6444 €6197 Torso of a woman (85cm-33in) s.i.d.1933 bronze. 12-Oct-2 Dorotheum, Prague #292/R est:80000-120000 (C.KR 200000)

KUNDIG, Reinhold (1888-1984) Swiss
£352 $525 €528 Hilly landscape with trees (50x61cm-20x24in) s. 25-Jun-2 Koller, Zurich #6649 (S.FR 800)
£435 $674 €653 Melting snow (21x28cm-8x11in) s. 9-Dec-2 Philippe Schuler, Zurich #3823 (S.FR 1000)
£609 $943 €914 Summer (53x65cm-21x26in) s. 9-Dec-2 Philippe Schuler, Zurich #3824 (S.FR 1400)
£630 $983 €945 Interior with still life (60x69cm-24x27in) s. 16-Sep-2 Philippe Schuler, Zurich #3384/R (S.FR 1450)
£739 $1153 €1109 The last snow (60x73cm-24x29in) s. 16-Sep-2 Philippe Schuler, Zurich #3383 (S.FR 1700)
£837 $1222 €1256 Spring landscape with fruit trees in bloom (40x47cm-16x19in) s. 17-Jun-2 Philippe Schuler, Zurich #4277 (S.FR 1900)
£849 $1358 €1274 Landscape near Hirzel with Glarnisch (50x65cm-20x26in) s.d. 17-Mar-3 Philippe Schuler, Zurich #4533 (S.FR 1800)
£849 $1358 €1274 Early spring (74x100cm-29x39in) s.d. 17-Mar-3 Philippe Schuler, Zurich #4534 (S.FR 1800)
£1223 $1920 €1835 Still life with dahlias (54x46cm-21x18in) s. 25-Nov-2 Sotheby's, Zurich #133/R est:2800-3500 (S.FR 2800)
£1604 $2566 €2406 Mallow in garden (60x73cm-24x29in) s. 17-Mar-3 Philippe Schuler, Zurich #4535/R est:3000-3500 (S.FR 3400)
£2533 $3951 €3800 Moor landscape (65x81cm-26x32in) s.d.45. 6-Nov-2 Hans Widmer, St Gallen #45/R est:2000-4500 (S.FR 5800)

KUNERT, Ove (20th C) ?
£2328 $3701 €3492 Duet playing for dancing at Tisvilde Beach Hotel (114x133cm-45x52in) s.d.1922. 5-Mar-3 Rasmussen, Copenhagen #1931/R est:25000 (D.KR 25000)

KUNFFY, Lajos (1869-1962) Hungarian
£293 $468 €440 Evening lights on the river Danube (18x27cm-7x11in) panel. 16-May-3 Kieselbach, Budapest #2/R (H.F 100000)
£380 $608 €570 Lights by the river Danube (18x24cm-7x9in) panel. 16-May-3 Kieselbach, Budapest #14/R (H.F 130000)
£410 $655 €615 Lovers in the park (27x18cm-11x7in) panel. 16-May-3 Kieselbach, Budapest #34/R (H.F 140000)
£468 $749 €702 Tunis (22x15cm-9x6in) panel. 16-May-3 Kieselbach, Budapest #5/R (H.F 160000)
£615 $959 €892 Flower still life (60x50cm-24x20in) s.d.1955. 12-Apr-3 Mu Terem Galeria, Budapest #25/R est:180000 (H.F 220000)
£968 $1501 €1452 Still life of flowers (55x47cm-22x19in) s. 6-Dec-2 Kieselbach, Budapest #28/R (H.F 360000)
£3354 $5232 €5031 Girl in red dress (92x76cm-36x30in) s. 11-Sep-2 Kieselbach, Budapest #5/R (H.F 1300000)

KUNIMASA, Utagawa (1773-1810) Japanese
Prints
£3205 $5000 €4808 Actor Ichikawa Danjuro VI holding a sword in a night scene (36x24cm-14x9in) s. print prov. 25-Mar-3 Christie's, Rockefeller NY #27/R est:3000-4000
£3205 $5000 €4808 Portrait of the actor Ichikawa Danjuro VI (21x19cm-8x7in) s. print prov. 25-Mar-3 Christie's, Rockefeller NY #126/R est:5000-6000

KUNINAGA, Utagawa (?-1829) Japanese
Prints
£3205 $5000 €4808 Pyramids of Egypt (25x38cm-10x15in) s. print. 25-Mar-3 Christie's, Rockefeller NY #109/R est:5000-7000
£3205 $5000 €4808 Tomb of King Mausolus, Asia (25x38cm-10x15in) s. print. 25-Mar-3 Christie's, Rockefeller NY #110/R est:5000-7000

KUNISADA, Utagawa (1786-1864) Japanese
Prints
£1923 $3000 €2885 Head portrait of actor Kataoka Nizaemon (37x25cm-15x10in) s. lacquer col print. 25-Mar-3 Christie's, Rockefeller NY #271/R est:3000-3500
£1923 $3000 €2885 Head portrait of actor Onoe Kikujiro (39x27cm-15x11in) s. col print. 25-Mar-3 Christie's, Rockefeller NY #272/R est:3000-3500
£1923 $3000 €2885 Baho of the five Tiger Generals (52x22cm-20x9in) s. col print. 25-Mar-3 Christie's, Rockefeller NY #275/R est:3000-3500

£1923 $3000 €2885 Choun of the five Tiger Generals (52x23cm-20x9in) s. col print. 25-Mar-3 Christie's, Rockefeller NY #277/R est:3000-3500
£2692 $4200 €4038 Head portrait of actor Ichikawa Danzo (39x26cm-15x10in) s. col on col print. 25-Mar-3 Christie's, Rockefeller NY #270/R est:3000-3500
£3846 $6000 €5769 Kanshojo (35x25cm-14x10in) s. col print. 25-Mar-3 Christie's, Rockefeller NY #268/R est:6000-8000

KUNITSUGU, Utagawa (1800-1861) Japanese
£1583 $2532 €2200 Femme marchand sous la neige (66x37cm-26x15in) st.sig. silk. 15-May-3 Christie's, Paris #33/R est:2000-3000

KUNITZBERGER, Hanns (1955-) Austrian
£3901 $6319 €5500 Wing (140x180cm-55x71in) mono.i.d.92 verso. 20-May-3 Dorotheum, Vienna #289/R est:6000-9000

KUNIYOSHI (19th C) Japanese
Prints
£1987 $3120 €3100 Scene of Koso life. s. print. 16-Dec-2 Beaussant & Lefèvre, Paris #213/R

KUNIYOSHI, Ichiyusai (1797-1861) Japanese
Prints
£5449 $8500 €8174 Walking through snow at Tsukahara on Sado Island (25x38cm-10x15in) s. col print. 25-Mar-3 Christie's, Rockefeller NY #306/R est:8000-12000
£9615 $15000 €14423 Mongaki Shonin enacting his penance below a waterfall (35x25cm-14x10in) s. col print triptych. 25-Mar-3 Christie's, Rockefeller NY #316/R est:15000-20000

KUNIYOSHI, Yasuo (1893-1953) American
£44586 $70000 €66879 Nude dressing at a window (51x41cm-20x16in) s. prov. 14-Dec-2 Weschler, Washington #709/R est:15000-25000
Photographs
£2658 $4200 €3987 Snow scene from 14th Street Studio, Overking Union Square (17x22cm-7x9in) i.verso gelatin silver print prov.exhib. 25-Apr-3 Phillips, New York #20/R est:2500-3500
Prints
£2358 $3750 €3537 Dancing (29x26cm-11x10in) s.d.num.9/30 lithograph. 2-May-3 Sotheby's, New York #19/R est:6000-8000
Works on paper
£1465 $2300 €2198 View from Brooklyn (11x8cm-4x3in) s.d.1921 ink prov. 19-Nov-2 Wright, Chicago #112/R est:2500-3000

KUNNAS, Waino (1896-1929) Finnish
Works on paper
£759 $1185 €1200 Clown (34x30cm-13x12in) s.d.1926 W/C exhib. 12-Sep-2 Hagelstam, Helsinki #979

KUNSTLER, Anna (19th C) Austrian?
£833 $1308 €1300 Still life of flowers with fruit and bird (45x36cm-18x14in) s.d.1853. 10-Dec-2 Dorotheum, Vienna #235/R
£833 $1308 €1300 Still life of flowers with fruit and bird (45x36cm-18x14in) s.d.1853. 10-Dec-2 Dorotheum, Vienna #255

KUNTZ, Ludwig Joseph (1803-1876) German
£409 $638 €650 Peasant house by lake (27x35cm-11x14in) s.d.1843. 11-Oct-2 Winterberg, Heidelberg #616/R

KUNZ, Emma (1892-1963) Swiss?
£1135 $1783 €1703 Untitled (89x99cm-35x39in) col pen graph paper. 25-Nov-2 Germann, Zurich #98/R est:3000-3500 (S.FR 2600)
Works on paper
£1135 $1783 €1703 Untitled (103x99cm-41x39in) col pen graph paper. 25-Nov-2 Germann, Zurich #99/R est:3000-5000 (S.FR 2600)

KUNZ, Ludwig Adam (1857-1929) Austrian
£818 $1275 €1300 Still life with figs, cherries and wine glass (50x65cm-20x26in) s. 21-Sep-2 Bolland & Marotz, Bremen #508/R
£1667 $2617 €2600 Still life with flowers lobster, dead game and silverware (110x171cm-43x67in) 23-Nov-2 Arnold, Frankfurt #786/R est:2000
£2041 $3245 €3000 Still life with fruit on plate, glass dish and wine glass (50x66cm-20x26in) s. 19-Mar-3 Neumeister, Munich #619/R est:2500
£2051 $3221 €3200 Nature morte aux fruits (126x101cm-50x40in) s. 19-Nov-2 Vanderkindere, Brussels #22/R est:2000-3000

KUNZ, Paul (1890-1959) Swiss
Sculpture
£1389 $2236 €2084 Woman's torso (97cm-38in) s. pat.bronze Cast.C Herzig Ligerz. 7-May-3 Dobiaschofsky, Bern #2335/R est:2500 (S.FR 3000)

KUNZEL, Gero (1962-) German
£417 $658 €600 Female nude wearing earrings (66x25cm-26x10in) s. s.d.1988 verso masonite. 26-Apr-3 Dr Lehr, Berlin #306
£417 $658 €600 Self portrait (53x38cm-21x15in) s.d.1989 masonite. 26-Apr-3 Dr Lehr, Berlin #307/R

KUO PO-CHUAN (1901-1974) Chinese
£32634 $53846 €47319 Nude on the chair (44x36cm-17x14in) s.d.58 paperboard. 6-Jul-3 Christie's, Hong Kong #144/R est:450000-550000 (HK.D 420000)

KUPCZYNSKI, Zbigniew (1930-) Canadian?
Works on paper
£217 $339 €363 Untitled - Girl with violin (75x60cm-30x24in) s. pastel prov. 13-Apr-3 Levis, Calgary #488/R (C.D 500)

KUPELWIESER, Leopold (1796-1862) Austrian
£2848 $4500 €4500 Portrait of Kaiser Franz I of Austria in Field Marshall's uniform (23x18cm-9x7in) board oval prov.lit. 28-Nov-2 Dorotheum, Vienna #146/R est:4000-5000

KUPER, Yuri (1940-) ?
£4490 $7139 €6600 La malle (200x200cm-79x79in) prov. 26-Feb-3 Artcurial Briest, Paris #532 est:3000-9000
Sculpture
£4430 $7000 €7000 Chaise et scie (90x61x43cm-35x24x17in) s. num.1/6 grey pat bronze Cast Godard lit. 26-Nov-2 Camard, Paris #161/R est:7600
£5190 $8200 €8200 Chaise et tube (90x34x43cm-35x13x17in) s. num.HC1/2 pat bronze Cat Godard lit. 26-Nov-2 Camard, Paris #154/R est:9000
£5696 $9000 €9000 Escabeau (85x82x44cm-33x32x17in) s. num.1/3 green pat bronze Cast Godard l. 26-Nov-2 Camard, Paris #162/R est:10700
£6646 $10500 €10500 Table cheval (98x58x77cm-39x23x30in) s. num.2/6 grey pat bronze Cast Godard lit. 26-Nov-2 Camard, Paris #155/R est:12500

KUPESIC, Rajka (1952-) Canadian
£382 $599 €573 Beautious (33x23cm-13x9in) s.i. pastel paper. 25-Nov-2 Hodgins, Calgary #336/R (C.D 950)

KUPETZKI, Johann (1667-1740) German
£11321 $17547 €18000 Portrait of Baroness Huldenberg with lapdog (116x95cm-46x37in) 2-Oct-2 Dorotheum, Vienna #195/R est:11000-16000

KUPETZKI, Johann (attrib) (1667-1740) German
£670 $1053 €972 Portrait of man. 15-Dec-2 Anders Antik, Landskrona #215 (S.KR 9500)
£4540 $7355 €6583 Portrait of a man (77x61cm-30x24in) 24-May-3 Dorotheum, Prague #3/R est:200000-300000 (C.KR 200000)
£6800 $10676 €10200 Portrait of a man reading a book within a garland of flowers (128x100cm-50x39in) lit. 10-Dec-2 Sotheby's, Olympia #395/R est:4000-6000
£15000 $25050 €21750 Portrait of a man said to be Prince Alexander Benedikt Stanislaus Sobieski (118x89cm-46x35in) prov.exhib.lit. 10-Jul-3 Sotheby's, London #202/R est:8000-12000

KUPETZKI, Johann (circle) (1667-1740) German
£6329 $10000 €10000 Portrait o writer (134x97cm-53x38in) 2-Dec-2 Finarte, Milan #165/R est:9000

KUPFER, Walter (1876-1938) Swiss
£657 $1078 €953 Village of St Moritz (53x96cm-21x38in) s. 4-Jun-3 Fischer, Luzern #2211/R (S.FR 1400)
£657 $1078 €953 St Moritz Bad in the autumn (60x96cm-24x38in) s. 4-Jun-3 Fischer, Luzern #2212/R (S.FR 1400)

KUPFERMAN, Moshe (1926-) Israeli
£769 $1208 €1200 Untitled (50x65cm-20x26in) s.d.88 oil graphite. 12-Dec-2 Rabourdin & Choppin de Janvry, Paris #92/R
£4286 $6770 €6429 Untitled (99x100cm-39x39in) s.d.72 s.d.verso. 27-Apr-3 Sotheby's, Tel Aviv #83/R est:6000-8000
£4430 $7000 €6645 Untitled (100x81cm-39x32in) s. s.d.1999 verso. 27-Apr-3 Sotheby's, Tel Aviv #82/R est:8000-12000

Works on paper

£633 $1000 €950 Untitled (57x76cm-22x30in) s.d.84 W/C graphite. 27-Apr-3 Sotheby's, Tel Aviv #84/R est:1500-2000
£633 $1000 €950 Untitled (56x76cm-22x30in) s.d.87 W/C graphite. 27-Apr-3 Sotheby's, Tel Aviv #85/R est:1500-2000
£1203 $1900 €1805 Untitled (75x104cm-30x41in) s.d.86 W/C graphite. 27-Apr-3 Sotheby's, Tel Aviv #86/R est:2200-2800

KUPFERSTEIN, Imre (?-1944) Hungarian?

£2487 $3979 €3731 Still life from the window with view to the tennis court (68x91cm-27x36in) s. canvas on cardboard. 16-May-3 Kieselbach, Budapest #55/R (H.F 850000)

KUPKA, Frank (1871-1957) Czechoslovakian

£56410 $87436 €88000 Vibrante 2 (74x74cm-29x29in) s.d.53 s.i.d.verso exhib.lit. 9-Dec-2 Piasa, Paris #47/R est:50000-60000

Works on paper

£567 $948 €800 Kupka (27x21cm-11x8in) bears i. bears sig.verso. 18-Jun-3 Pierre Berge, Paris #114/R
£600 $978 €900 Study of a dog and a donkey (33x23cm-13x9in) st.sig. pencil prov. 3-Feb-3 Bonhams, New Bond Street #17/R
£601 $950 €950 Female nude studies (17x36cm-7x14in) s. pencil. 30-Nov-2 Bassenge, Berlin #6429/R
£1181 $1677 €1772 Torso of a nude (20x11cm-8x4in) pencil exec.c.1906-1910. 26-Mar-2 SOGA, Bratislava #221/R est:45000 (SL.K 75000)
£1266 $2000 €2000 Vive Kruger (24x31cm-9x12in) s. W/C Indian ink. 26-Nov-2 Wiener Kunst Auktionen, Vienna #83/R est:2000-4000
£1603 $2516 €2500 Untitled (31x34cm-12x13in) s. pastel. 15-Dec-2 Perrin, Versailles #53/R
£1678 $2803 €2400 Tete de femme (38x34cm-15x13in) s.i. pastel. 26-Jun-3 Tajan, Paris #155 est:2500-3000
£2308 $3623 €3600 Composition abstraite (11x10cm-4x4in) s. crayon W/C. 10-Dec-2 Renaud, Paris #46/R
£2414 $4031 €3500 Composition abstraite (14x23cm-6x9in) s. white gouache exec.c.1920. 10-Jul-3 Artcurial Briest, Paris #80/R est:3500-4000
£2600 $4134 €3900 Composition (15x24cm-6x9in) s. black white gouache exec.c.1920. 20-Mar-3 Sotheby's, Olympia #85/R est:2000-3000
£3205 $5032 €5000 Composition abstraite (17x13cm-7x5in) s. W/C. 10-Dec-2 Renaud, Paris #47/R
£3265 $5192 €4800 Etude pour contrastes gothiques (19x22cm-7x9in) st.sig. pastel exec.c.1915-1920. 26-Feb-3 Artcurial Briest, Paris #94/R est:4000-5000
£3394 $5667 €4921 Composition (27x22cm-11x9in) s. W/C. 24-Jun-3 Koller, Zurich #130/R est:2800-4000 (S.FR 7500)
£5449 $8554 €8500 Paysage de bord de mer (31x54cm-12x21in) s. W/C gouache. 10-Dec-2 Renaud, Paris #45/R est:3000
£8176 $13000 €12264 Studies (21x21cm-8x8in) s.i.d.1911 W/C chl pair prov. 27-Feb-3 Christie's, Rockefeller NY #31/R est:15000
£8462 $13285 €13200 Composition abstraite (22x26cm-9x10in) s. W/C ink wash. 11-Dec-2 Artcurial Briest, Paris #537/R
£14085 $23380 €20000 Machinism (22x32cm-9x13in) s. gouache over pencil. 14-Jun-3 Hauswedell & Nolte, Hamburg #1330/R est:20000
£26000 $43420 €39000 Cercles descendant (30x28cm-12x11in) st.sig. gouache collage pencil exec c.1931-35 prov.exhib. 26-Jun-3 Christie's, London #396/R est:7000-10000

KUPPERS, Friedrich (19th C) German?

£2245 $3569 €3300 Young peasant woman with child on knee (96x88cm-38x35in) s. panel. 19-Mar-3 Neumeister, Munich #617/R est:1500

KUPRIN, Aleksandr Vasilievich (1880-1960) Russian

Works on paper

£2000 $3160 €3000 Boats in Crimea (28x22cm-11x9in) s. W/C. 26-Nov-2 Christie's, Kensington #31/R est:500-700

KURELEK, William (1927-1977) Canadian

£8000 $13120 €12000 Cleaning the cow barn in winter (51x61cm-20x24in) s.d.1961 mixed media on masonite prov.exhib. 27-May-3 Sotheby's, Toronto #7/R est:20000-30000 (C.D 18000)
£8696 $13565 €14500 Mendelsohn in Canadian winter (91x66cm-36x26in) init.d.1967 board prov. 13-Apr-3 Levis, Calgary #71/R est:25000-35000 (C.D 20000)
£13333 $21867 €20000 Harvesting with horses in Saskatchewan - summer (22x79cm-9x31in) init.d.66 board. 3-Jun-3 Joyner, Toronto #129/R est:15000-20000 (C.D 30000)
£15111 $24782 €22667 Autumn (49x61cm-19x24in) init.d.65 board. 3-Jun-3 Joyner, Toronto #155/R est:10000-15000 (C.D 34000)

Works on paper

£2146 $3348 €3219 Fallen boy in a hayrake (49x35cm-19x14in) s. mixed media on board. 25-Mar-3 Ritchie, Toronto #137/R est:5000-7000 (C.D 5000)
£3629 $5734 €5444 B.C seen through sunglasses (32x79cm-13x31in) mono.i.d.1973 mixed media on masonite pair prov.exhib. 18-Nov-2 Sotheby's, Toronto #33/R est:6000-8000 (C.D 9000)
£3629 $5734 €5444 Fallen boy in a hay rake (49x36cm-19x14in) s. mixed media on board prov.lit. 18-Nov-2 Sotheby's, Toronto #184/R est:7000-9000 (C.D 9000)
£4000 $6560 €6000 Winter colds (39x39cm-15x15in) init.d.67 mixed media on board. 3-Jun-3 Joyner, Toronto #39/R est:10000-15000 (C.D 9000)
£6222 $10204 €9333 Abandoned Ukrainian Pioneer House (50x62cm-20x24in) init.d.1964 mixed media on board. 3-Jun-3 Joyner, Toronto #106/R est:8000-12000 (C.D 14000)
£7792 $12390 €11298 Baseball at home, Renfrew County (23x27cm-9x11in) init. s.i.d.1976 verso mixed media board prov. 1-May-3 Heffel, Vancouver #55/R est:7000-9000 (C.D 18000)
£8000 $13120 €12000 Mission to Moscow (36x7cm-14x3in) init.d.73 mixed media on board. 3-Jun-3 Joyner, Toronto #91/R est:20000-25000 (C.D 18000)
£9274 $14653 €13911 Indian summer on the Humber (61x122cm-24x48in) mono. mixed media on masonite sold with a book prov.exhib.lit. 18-Nov-2 Sotheby's, Toronto #37/R est:35000-45000 (C.D 23000)
£12444 $20409 €18666 Retired sea captain, Newfoundland (60x60cm-24x24in) init.d.76 mixed media prov.lit. 3-Jun-3 Joyner, Toronto #73/R est:20000-30000 (C.D 28000)
£13992 $21687 €20988 Divine symphony of forest, rock and snow (72x120cm-28x47in) init.d.74 mixed media on board prov.exhib.lit. 3-Dec-2 Joyner, Toronto #110/R est:20000-30000 (C.D 34000)
£15254 $24254 €22881 And arctic nature sings (60x60cm-24x24in) init.i.d.1975 mixed media on board prov. 23-Mar-3 Hodgins, Calgary #83/R est:18000-24000 (C.D 36000)
£17778 $29156 €26667 Suburban church (63x77cm-25x30in) mono.d.65 mixed media on masonite prov.exhib. 27-May-3 Sotheby's, Toronto #90/R est:40000-60000 (C.D 40000)
£20444 $33529 €30666 Swiftness did i sue (119x119cm-47x47in) init. mixed media board prov. 3-Jun-3 Joyner, Toronto #53/R est:45000-50000 (C.D 46000)
£102881 $159465 €154322 Reminiscences of youth (120x145cm-47x57in) s.d.68 mixed media on board. 3-Dec-2 Joyner, Toronto #44/R est:250000-300000 (C.D 250000)

KURFISS, Gottlieb (20th C) ?

£1202 $1899 €1803 In the circus arena (77x36cm-30x14in) s.i.verso hessian. 29-Nov-2 Zofingen, Switzerland #2952 est:1500 (S.FR 2800)

KURLAND, Justine (1969-) American?

Photographs

£2000 $3200 €3000 Sheep wranglers (76x102cm-30x40in) satin finished UV laminated c-print executed 2001 prov. 16-May-3 Phillips, New York #213/R est:4000-6000

KURODA, Aki (1944-) ?

Works on paper

£503 $780 €800 Aria mezzo voce VII (76x108cm-30x43in) s.i. W/C prov. 30-Oct-2 Artcurial Briest, Paris #700

KURON, Herbert (1888-?) German

£390 $569 €600 View over meadow to German wheat hillock (35x45cm-14x18in) s. i.verso board. 15-Jun-2 Hans Stahl, Hamburg #35/R

KURPERSHOEK, Theo (1914-1998) Dutch

£694 $1146 €1000 Eysden Zuid Limburg Zinkwitfabriek (18x24cm-7x9in) s.d.77 s.i.d.verso canvas on plywood prov. 1-Jul-3 Christie's, Amsterdam #411/R
£833 $1375 €1200 Summer, Belgium (18x24cm-7x9in) s.d.82 s.i.d.verso canvas on plywood prov. 1-Jul-3 Christie's, Amsterdam #417/R
£2917 $4813 €4200 Rowers on the river Amstel, Amsterdam (50x60cm-20x24in) s.d.53. 1-Jul-3 Christie's, Amsterdam #350/R est:2500-3500

Works on paper

£390 $632 €550 Flowers in a vase on a small table (60x39cm-24x15in) s. mixed media. 26-May-3 Glerum, Amsterdam #71/R

KURSCHNER, Henning (1941-) German

£316 $500 €500 Untitled (68x32cm-27x13in) s.i.d.1990 verso acrylic. 29-Nov-2 Villa Grisebach, Berlin #756/R

KURTEN, Stefan (1963-) German
£320 $500 €480 Darker (41x30cm-16x12in) s.i.d.2001 verso oil metallic paint prov. 14-Oct-2 Butterfields, San Francisco #2119/R est:2500-3500

KURTH, Damian (20th C) New Zealander
£421 $657 €632 Two pm (61x46cm-24x18in) s.verso. 27-Mar-3 International Art Centre, Auckland #14/R (NZ.D 1200)

KURZ, Erwin (1857-1931) German
Sculpture
£1918 $2992 €2800 Head of girl with hair in bun (50x36x5cm-20x14x2in) i. marble relief. 11-Apr-3 Winterberg, Heidelberg #651/R est:3500

KURZ, Rudolph Friedrich (1818-1871) Swiss
£452 $750 €655 Marsh at dusk (41x64cm-16x25in) s. 14-Jun-3 Jackson's, Cedar Falls #377/R

KURZWEIL, Maximilian (1867-1916) Austrian
Works on paper
£385 $608 €600 Horse and cart (29x47cm-11x19in) s.d.1903 pastel chk. 12-Nov-2 Dorotheum, Vienna #12/R

KUSAMA, Yayoi (1929-) Japanese
£637 $1000 €956 Face (28x20cm-11x8in) s.d.1953 i.d.verso oil wash paper. 20-Nov-2 Boos Gallery, Michigan #425/R
£1829 $2872 €2744 Chaussure rayee verte et maron (18x33cm-7x13in) s.d.1965. 12-Dec-2 Iegor de Saint Hippolyte, Montreal #42 (C.D 4500)
£1829 $2872 €2744 Chaussure rayee verte et marron (18x31cm-7x12in) s.d.1965. 12-Dec-2 Iegor de Saint Hippolyte, Montreal #43 (C.D 4500)
£6329 $10000 €9494 Infinity - yellow dots (117x94cm-46x37in) s.i.d.1996 verso acrylic on canvas prov.exhib. 12-Nov-2 Phillips, New York #201/R est:15000-20000
£8974 $14090 €14000 Untitled (70x80cm-28x31in) s.d.1967 verso acrylic. 25-Nov-2 Glerum, Amsterdam #302/R est:14000-18000
£20000 $30800 €30000 Infinity nets (91x116cm-36x46in) s.i.d.1998 verso acrylic on canvas prov. 22-Oct-2 Sotheby's, London #322/R est:20000-30000
£123418 $195000 €185127 No.G (101x129cm-40x51in) s. i.d.1959 verso. 13-Nov-2 Sotheby's, New York #320/R est:60000-80000
Sculpture
£4500 $7515 €6525 Silver shoe (16x29x9cm-6x11x4in) s.d.1976 spray paint shoe stuffed fabric. 24-Jun-3 Sotheby's, Olympia #101/R est:1500-2000
£6013 $9500 €9020 Yellow dots (69x61x10cm-27x24x4in) acrylic on papier mache wood prov. 13-Nov-2 Sotheby's, New York #318/R est:10000-15000
Works on paper
£1282 $2013 €2000 Flower petal 2 (30x26cm-12x10in) s.d.1954 pastel. 25-Nov-2 Glerum, Amsterdam #278 est:2000-3000
£1667 $2617 €2600 Moon 1 (20x28cm-8x11in) s.d.1962 verso pastel. 25-Nov-2 Glerum, Amsterdam #277/R est:2500-3500
£2051 $3221 €3200 Ground 6 (25x19cm-10x7in) s.d.1952 verso pastel. 25-Nov-2 Glerum, Amsterdam #281/R est:2500-3500

KUSCHEL, Max (1862-?) German
£449 $655 €700 Woman wearing green hairband (51x40cm-20x16in) s. 4-Jun-2 Karl & Faber, Munich #325

KUSTNER, Carl (1861-1934) German
£274 $427 €400 View over water to a village with trees behind (33x37cm-13x15in) s.i. canvas on board lit. 10-Apr-3 Allgauer, Kempten #2852/R
£316 $491 €500 Willow trees on river bank in early spring (50x60cm-20x24in) 26-Sep-2 Neumeister, Munich #2771

KUSTODIEV, Boris (1878-1927) Russian
£5352 $8617 €7600 Meditating (25x20cm-10x8in) s. board. 10-May-3 Bukowskis, Helsinki #402/R est:7000-9000
£750000 $1215000 €1125000 Belle - krasavitsa (78x102cm-31x40in) s.d.1919. 21-May-3 Sotheby's, London #136/R est:250000-350000
Works on paper
£3000 $4860 €4500 Young girl arranging flowers (28x19cm-11x7in) s.d.1918 pencil. 21-May-3 Sotheby's, London #101/R est:2000-3000

KUTSCHA, Paul (1872-?) Czechoslovakian
£408 $649 €600 Boats tied up by windmill (50x70cm-20x28in) s. 28-Mar-3 Bolland & Marotz, Bremen #480/R
£429 $626 €660 View of a small town with church and flowering garden in foreground (23x35cm-9x14in) s. i.verso cardboard. 15-Jun-2 Hans Stahl, Hamburg #36/R
£1965 $3066 €2948 Asiatic temple at dusk (95x135cm-37x53in) s. 6-Nov-2 Dobiaschofsky, Bern #751/R est:4000 (S.FR 4500)

KUTTERER, August (1898-1954) German
£1370 $2137 €2000 Entrance to Forchheim (52x65cm-20x26in) s. i. stretcher. 11-Apr-3 Winterberg, Heidelberg #1272/R est:1380

KUUSI, Helmi (1913-2000) Finnish
£276 $436 €400 Madonna (46x38cm-18x15in) s. 3-Apr-3 Hagelstam, Helsinki #961
£408 $649 €600 Still life of books on table (46x55cm-18x22in) s. 24-Mar-3 Bukowskis, Helsinki #134/R
£423 $680 €600 Still life (92x65cm-36x26in) s.d.1951. 10-May-3 Bukowskis, Helsinki #145/R
£517 $817 €750 Landscape (54x65cm-21x26in) s.d.1946. 3-Apr-3 Hagelstam, Helsinki #969/R
£523 $858 €800 Flowers on chair (62x54cm-24x21in) s.d.1950. 9-Feb-3 Bukowskis, Helsinki #283/R

KUWASSEG, Charles Euphrasie (1838-1904) French
£641 $994 €1000 Village anime (21x16cm-8x6in) s. cardboard. 9-Dec-2 Horta, Bruxelles #395
£1300 $2028 €1950 Figures on a woodland path (46x38cm-18x15in) s. indis d. 26-Mar-3 Sotheby's, Olympia #207/R est:800-1200
£1900 $3097 €2850 Beach boats threatened by heavy seas (28x41cm-11x16in) with sig.d.1856 panel. 29-Jan-3 Sotheby's, Olympia #249/R est:1000-2000
£2585 $4110 €3800 Personnages au bord d'un lac de montagne (41x57cm-16x22in) s. 2-Mar-3 Lombrail & Teucquam, Paris #155/R
£2703 $4216 €4000 Ville de montagne (35x27cm-14x11in) s.panel. 28-Mar-3 Claude Aguttes, Neuilly #35/R
£2866 $4471 €4500 Bord de riviere anime (39x61cm-15x24in) s.d.1900. 8-Nov-2 Pierre Berge, Paris #17/R
£3025 $4750 €4538 Afternoon on the river (30x51cm-12x20in) s. 22-Nov-2 Skinner, Boston #12/R est:5000-7000
£3165 $5000 €4748 Continental city canal scene (30x46cm-12x18in) s.d.1873. 3-Apr-3 Boos Gallery, Michigan #275/R est:10000-15000
£3548 $5606 €5500 Maison au bord del'eau (24x19cm-9x7in) s. panel. 19-Dec-2 Claude Aguttes, Neuilly #26/R
£3548 $5606 €5500 Maison au bord de l'eau (24x19cm-9x7in) s.d.1861 panel. 19-Dec-2 Claude Aguttes, Neuilly #27/R
£3800 $5890 €5700 Vilvorde, Belguim (32x51cm-13x20in) s.d.1879. 3-Dec-2 Sotheby's, Olympia #221/R est:3000-4000
£5200 $8476 €7800 Mountain villages (32x24cm-13x9in) s. two. 29-Jan-3 Sotheby's, Olympia #317/R est:3000-4000
£5500 $8635 €8250 Harbour in the calm. Harbour in rough seas (46x38cm-18x15in) s. pair. 21-Nov-2 Christie's, Kensington #10/R est:6000-8000
£7000 $11130 €10500 Mountainside villages (33x25cm-13x10in) s.d.1870 panel pair prov. 18-Mar-3 Bonhams, New Bond Street #124/R est:3000-5000
£7051 $10929 €11000 Ports (37x46cm-15x18in) s.d.56 pair. 5-Dec-2 Gros & Delettrez, Paris #14/R est:8400
£15484 $24000 €23226 Alpine village (58x100cm-23x39in) s.d.1878. 30-Oct-2 Christie's, Rockefeller NY #210/R est:15000-20000
Works on paper
£1081 $1686 €1600 Plage. Escalier. Barque. Voiliers. s.d.1892 W/C dr htd gouache set of 4. 27-Mar-3 Maigret, Paris #269

KUWASSEG, Charles Euphrasie (attrib) (1838-1904) French
£385 $585 €600 City with stream (18x35cm-7x14in) panel. 11-Jul-2 Hugo Ruef, Munich #732
£600 $954 €900 Sailing vessels in a harbour (21x39cm-8x15in) panel. 4-Mar-3 Bearnes, Exeter #453/R

KUWASSEG, Josef (1799-1854) Austrian
Works on paper
£886 $1400 €1400 Tobelbad near Graz (18x26cm-7x10in) s. WC. 26-Nov-2 Wiener Kunst Auktionen, Vienna #142/R

KUWAYAMA, Tadaaki (1932-) Japanese
£1522 $2374 €2283 Yellow, white and red with chrome (151x72cm-59x28in) s.d.68 acrylic prov. 16-Sep-2 Philippe Schuler, Zurich #6467 est:2500-3000 (S.FR 3500)

KUYCK, Frans van (1852-1915) Belgian
£428 $693 €650 Sportsman with his dog (35x64cm-14x25in) s.d.1883 panel. 21-Jan-3 Christie's, Amsterdam #108
£4459 $6955 €7000 Retour des champs (100x75cm-39x30in) s.d.1882. 11-Nov-2 Horta, Bruxelles #185/R est:8700-14000

KUYCK, Jean Louis van (1821-1871) Flemish
£4110 $6452 €6000 Surprise homecoming (62x69cm-24x27in) s.d.1851 panel. 15-Apr-3 Sotheby's, Amsterdam #76/R est:4000-6000
£4800 $7584 €7200 Barn interior with a plough team returning from the fields (43x60cm-17x24in) s.d.1864. 7-Apr-3 Bonhams, Bath #133/R est:2000-3000

KUYK, Gijsbert Buitendijk (1805-1884) Dutch
£1019 $1590 €1600 Musicians company (80x67cm-31x26in) s.d.1846. 6-Nov-2 Vendue Huis, Gravenhage #474a est:1000-1500

KUYPERS, Cornelis (1864-1932) Dutch
£417 $688 €600 Daily activities on a river (32x51cm-13x20in) canvas on board. 1-Jul-3 Christie's, Amsterdam #209
£590 $974 €850 Willows by a stream in summer (20x49cm-8x19in) canvas on board. 1-Jul-3 Christie's, Amsterdam #205
£590 $974 €850 Houses in Heelsum, Gelderland (33x43cm-13x17in) s. canvas on board sold with another by the same hand. 1-Jul-3 Christie's, Amsterdam #211
£625 $1031 €900 Kitchen garden (36x46cm-14x18in) s.d.1894 canvas on board sold with another by the same hand. 1-Jul-3 Christie's, Amsterdam #210
£660 $1089 €950 Summer, landscape with a bridge (28x44cm-11x17in) s. canvas on board sold with another by the same hand. 1-Jul-3 Christie's, Amsterdam #207/R
£694 $1146 €1000 Birch in sunlight (52x23cm-20x9in) s. canvas on board sold with another by the same hand. 1-Jul-3 Christie's, Amsterdam #208
£764 $1260 €1100 Trees in spring (40x29cm-16x11in) init. canvas on board sold with another by the same hand. 1-Jul-3 Christie's, Amsterdam #201/R
£833 $1375 €1200 Villagers conversing (47x26cm-19x10in) s. canvas on board. 1-Jul-3 Christie's, Amsterdam #204
£855 $1386 €1300 Peaceful polder landscape (24x43cm-9x17in) s. 21-Jan-3 Christie's, Amsterdam #224 est:1000-1500
£892 $1391 €1400 Winter farmyard with free-range chickens (42x74cm-17x29in) s. 6-Nov-2 Vendue Huis, Gravenhage #32/R
£966 $1535 €1400 Feeding the chickens (17x32cm-7x13in) s. canvas on board. 10-Mar-3 Sotheby's, Amsterdam #224/R est:800-1200
£1042 $1719 €1500 Evening, moonlit polder landscape (59x98cm-23x39in) s. 1-Jul-3 Christie's, Amsterdam #206/R est:1000-1500
£1667 $2750 €2400 Autumn, cows grazing (42x107cm-17x42in) s. 1-Jul-3 Christie's, Amsterdam #199/R est:1000-1500

KUYPERS, Dirk (1733-1796) Dutch
Works on paper
£1235 $2000 €1853 Travellers on mountainous road (28x41cm-11x16in) s.d.1776 wash prov.exhib. 21-Jan-3 Sotheby's, New York #152/R

KUYT, Herman (1893-1978) Dutch
£276 $439 €400 Beach scene (26x33cm-10x13in) s.d.10 board. 10-Mar-3 Sotheby's, Amsterdam #366
£1899 $3000 €3000 Still life (60x80cm-24x31in) lit. 26-Nov-2 Sotheby's, Amsterdam #18/R est:3000-5000

KUYTEN, Harrie (1883-1952) Dutch
£3546 $5745 €5000 Prater alley in Vienna (69x55cm-27x22in) s. 26-May-3 Glerum, Amsterdam #10/R est:2000-3000

KUZNETSOV, Pavel (1878-1968) Russian
Works on paper
£1538 $2400 €2307 Village scene (40x28cm-16x11in) s. col pastel stock exec.c.1912. 18-Sep-2 Swann Galleries, New York #27/R est:3000-5000

KVAPIL, Charles (1884-1958) Belgian
£408 $649 €600 Route en borde de riviere (21x27cm-8x11in) s. cardboard. 26-Feb-3 Artcurial Briest, Paris #268
£443 $691 €700 Au bord de la riviere (37x46cm-15x18in) s. masonite prov. 18-Oct-2 Dr Fritz Nagel, Stuttgart #559/R
£566 $877 €900 Paysage de Morbihan (26x35cm-10x14in) s.d.1926 panel. 30-Oct-2 Coutau Begarie, Paris #98/R
£692 $1072 €1100 Nu assis dans le jardin (73x60cm-29x24in) s. 1-Oct-2 Palais de Beaux Arts, Brussels #496
£986 $1568 €1450 Nu (25x35cm-10x14in) s.d.1926 panel. 28-Feb-3 Joron-Derem, Paris #38
£1060 $1727 €1600 Female nude (33x24cm-13x9in) s. 28-Jan-3 Dorotheum, Vienna #31/R est:1400-1800
£1195 $1852 €1900 Le pot jaune (62x80cm-24x31in) s.d.1927. 4-Oct-2 Tajan, Paris #134 est:1200-1500
£1290 $2039 €2000 Dahlias au vase bleu (73x60cm-29x24in) s. 19-Dec-2 Claude Aguttes, Neuilly #166/R
£1565 $2488 €2300 Nu a la riviere (46x55cm-18x22in) s. 3-Mar-3 Claude Boisgirard, Paris #62 est:2500-3000
£1831 $2948 €2600 Azalee rose (74x61cm-29x24in) s.d.1941. 12-May-3 Lesieur & Le Bars, Le Havre #50/R
£1899 $3000 €3000 Still life with flowers (65x50cm-26x20in) s.d.1941. 26-Nov-2 Sotheby's, Amsterdam #96/R est:3800-4500
£2436 $3824 €3800 Bouquet de tulipes (50x65cm-20x26in) s. 12-Dec-2 Rabourdin & Choppin de Janvry, Paris #47/R
£2535 $4208 €3600 Deux baigneuses dans un paysage (65x54cm-26x21in) s.d. 15-Jun-3 Anaf, Lyon #123/R est:3000-4000
£3086 $4383 €5000 Grand vase de tournesols (100x72cm-39x28in) s. 16-Mar-3 Eric Pillon, Calais #139/R
£3172 $5076 €4600 Bouquet de fleurs sur une table (91x60cm-36x24in) s. 12-Mar-3 Libert, Castor, Paris #129/R est:2000-3000
Works on paper
£576 $921 €800 Bouquet d'anemones (43x31cm-17x12in) s. W/C graphite. 15-May-3 Christie's, Paris #320/R

KVIUM, Michael (1955-) Danish
£929 $1468 €1394 Composition (38x60cm-15x24in) s.d.89 verso prov. 1-Apr-3 Rasmussen, Copenhagen #307/R est:8000 (D.KR 10000)
£3316 $5140 €4974 Twisted painting I (200x200cm-79x79in) s.d.96 verso. 4-Dec-2 Kunsthallen, Copenhagen #113/R est:50000 (D.KR 38500)
£3316 $5140 €4974 Twisted painting II (200x200cm-79x79in) s.i.d.96 verso. 4-Dec-2 Kunsthallen, Copenhagen #114/R est:50000 (D.KR 38500)
£3980 $6169 €5970 Waiting picture wearing heavy hat (110x110cm-43x43in) s.d.94 verso prov. 1-Oct-2 Rasmussen, Copenhagen #51/R est:50000 (D.KR 47000)
£6482 $10826 €9399 The looser's back (160x175cm-63x69in) s.d.93 verso prov. 17-Jun-3 Rasmussen, Copenhagen #27/R est:75000 (D.KR 68000)
Works on paper
£836 $1322 €1254 Figure composition (29x40cm-11x16in) W/C Indian ink chk pencil. 1-Apr-3 Rasmussen, Copenhagen #278/R (D.KR 9000)

KWADYK-VERBEEK, Margarethe (1902-) Dutch
£701 $1093 €1100 Still life with letter and kitchen utensils (64x44cm-25x17in) mono. 6-Nov-2 Vendue Huis, Gravenhage #131/R

KWIATKOWSKI, Jean (1896-1971) Polish
£1529 $2385 €2400 Bord de riviere (55x46cm-22x18in) s.d.1958. 5-Nov-2 Tajan, Paris #50/R

KWONG-SANG (19th C) Chinese
£1645 $2500 €2468 China trade portrait of British ship, Vimeira (64x89cm-25x35in) s.d.1894. 17-Aug-2 North East Auctions, Portsmouth #567/R

KYHN, Vilhelm (1819-1903) Danish
£280 $437 €420 Summer landscape near Hellebaek beach (22x32cm-9x13in) mono. 5-Aug-2 Rasmussen, Vejle #2164/R (D.KR 3300)
£354 $564 €531 Coastal landscape, evening (38x36cm-15x14in) 5-May-3 Rasmussen, Vejle #287 (D.KR 3800)
£478 $775 €693 Father and children picking flowers in vicarage garden (31x48cm-12x19in) i. stretcher. 26-May-3 Rasmussen, Copenhagen #1239 (D.KR 5000)
£523 $841 €785 Coastal landscape, evening (19x28cm-7x11in) init. panel. 22-Feb-3 Rasmussen, Havnen #2064 (D.KR 5800)
£524 $817 €786 Landscape with figures (30x38cm-12x15in) init. 23-Sep-2 Rasmussen, Vejle #65/R (D.KR 6200)
£548 $872 €822 September landscape (32x40cm-13x16in) init.i.d.9/9. 26-Feb-3 Kunsthallen, Copenhagen #529 (D.KR 6000)
£553 $874 €830 Landscape from Rold Woods (40x53cm-16x21in) 2-Dec-2 Rasmussen, Copenhagen #1239/R (D.KR 6500)
£560 $851 €840 Hammershus Palace ruin (24x35cm-9x14in) mono.i. 27-Aug-2 Rasmussen, Copenhagen #1848/R (D.KR 6500)
£566 $883 €849 By Horsen's fjord, cloudy day (38x50cm-15x20in) s.d.08 exhib. 11-Nov-2 Rasmussen, Vejle #644/R (D.KR 6600)
£596 $924 €894 Scene from a village (38x50cm-15x20in) s.d.1907. 28-Sep-2 Rasmussen, Havnen #2082/R (D.KR 7000)
£745 $1184 €1118 Landscape with tall trees by lake (41x51cm-16x20in) init. 10-Mar-3 Rasmussen, Vejle #292/R (D.KR 8000)
£851 $1345 €1277 View from Mariager Fjord (22x30cm-9x12in) prov. 2-Dec-2 Rasmussen, Copenhagen #1363/R (D.KR 10000)
£856 $1378 €1284 Study of a thicket (17x15cm-7x6in) init.d.65 paper on canvas. 26-Feb-3 Museumsbygningen, Copenhagen #29/R (D.KR 9500)
£861 $1309 €1292 Hvidore Palace at Strandvejen in summer (35x44cm-14x17in) mono. prov. 27-Aug-2 Rasmussen, Copenhagen #1869/R (D.KR 10000)
£931 $1480 €1397 Summer landscape with fields, Vester Bisholt near Horsens (36x50cm-14x20in) mono.d.84 exhib.prov. 5-Mar-3 Rasmussen, Copenhagen #1908/R (D.KR 10000)
£1095 $1751 €1643 View across fields (24x31cm-9x12in) mono.indis.d. 13-Jan-3 Rasmussen, Vejle #24/R est:10000 (D.KR 12500)
£1095 $1751 €1643 Winter landscape with faggot gatherer and large trees (24x34cm-9x13in) indis.i.verso. 13-Jan-3 Rasmussen, Vejle #122/R est:4000 (D.KR 12500)
£1257 $1999 €1886 Norwegian mountain landscape (19x31cm-7x12in) i.d.22/7-73. 5-Mar-3 Rasmussen, Copenhagen #1906/R est:12000 (D.KR 13500)
£1288 $2034 €1932 Summer's day in garden with Sara Gyrithe Kyhn walking by lake. prov. 13-Nov-2 Kunsthallen, Copenhagen #96/R est:15000 (D.KR 15000)
£1340 $2170 €1943 The beach at Hellebaek (22x31cm-9x12in) mono. prov. 26-May-3 Rasmussen, Copenhagen #1511/R est:10000-15000 (D.KR 14000)

£1723 $2618 €2585 Dogroses in flower by waterway (47x59cm-19x23in) mono. 27-Aug-2 Rasmussen, Copenhagen #1418/R est:25000 (D.KR 20000)
£1769 $2813 €2654 Manager's house near Gisselfeld (27x37cm-11x15in) mono. 5-Mar-3 Rasmussen, Copenhagen #2066/R est:15000 (D.KR 19000)
£1914 $3100 €2775 Summer landscape by the fjord (18x28cm-7x11in) mono.d.49. 26-May-3 Rasmussen, Copenhagen #1528/R est:8000 (D.KR 20000)
£1926 $3082 €2889 Summer landscape with peasant girl driving cows (41x53cm-16x21in) mono. exhib. 13-Jan-3 Rasmussen, Vejle #25/R est:25000 (D.KR 22000)
£2010 $3256 €2915 Seated nude model (27x28cm-11x11in) 26-May-3 Rasmussen, Copenhagen #1516/R est:20000 (D.KR 21000)
£2392 $3876 €3468 Landscape with hedge and hills (37x50cm-15x20in) s.d.1899 prov. 26-May-3 Rasmussen, Copenhagen #1101/R est:20000-25000 (D.KR 25000)
£2412 $3666 €3618 English landscape with woman walking (31x42cm-12x17in) mono.d.maj 44. 28-Aug-2 Museumsbygningen, Copenhagen #17/R est:30000 (D.KR 28000)
£2553 $4034 €3830 Tall beech trees in forest (45x33cm-18x13in) mono. 2-Dec-2 Rasmussen, Copenhagen #1132/R est:30000-40000 (D.KR 30000)

KYHN, Vilhelm (attrib) (1819-1903) Danish
£452 $664 €700 View of sea through trees (38x50cm-15x20in) bears sig. 20-Jun-2 Dr Fritz Nagel, Stuttgart #788/R
£882 $1420 €1323 Model study (27x28cm-11x11in) panel exhib. 19-Jan-3 Hindemae, Ullerslev #7317/R (D.KR 10000)

KYLBERG, Carl (1878-1952) Danish
£2943 $4591 €4415 Ruth (46x38cm-18x15in) s. 5-Nov-2 Bukowskis, Stockholm #20/R est:20000-25000 (S.KR 42000)
£3802 $6008 €5703 Summer rain (23x29cm-9x11in) canvas on board exhib.lit. 28-Apr-3 Bukowskis, Stockholm #205b/R est:60000-80000 (S.KR 50000)
£9310 $15081 €13500 Figures in landscape (84x96cm-33x38in) s. 25-May-3 Uppsala Auktionskammare, Uppsala #268/R est:150000-200000 (S.KR 120000)
£10512 $16398 €15768 Wearing dressing gown (57x48cm-22x19in) init. prov.lit. 5-Nov-2 Bukowskis, Stockholm #100/R est:150000-200000 (S.KR 150000)
£16468 $25690 €24702 Green sail and setting sun (45x53cm-18x21in) init. s.verso. 5-Nov-2 Bukowskis, Stockholm #187/R est:200000-250000 (S.KR 235000)
£17761 $28595 €26642 Coucher du soleil - sunset (57x69cm-22x27in) s. 7-May-3 AB Stockholms Auktionsverk #669/R est:250000-300000 (S.KR 230000)
£22053 $34844 €33080 The day going to rest (63x77cm-25x30in) init. prov.exhib. 28-Apr-3 Bukowskis, Stockholm #197/R est:275000-300000 (S.KR 290000)
£209125 $330418 €313688 The Flying Dutchman III (93x111cm-37x44in) init. painted 1946-50 prov.exhib.lit. 28-Apr-3 Bukowskis, Stockholm #105/R est:1500000-2000000 (S.KR 2750000)

Works on paper
£1191 $1858 €1787 Figure by water (19x25cm-7x10in) s. i.verso W/C. 5-Nov-2 Bukowskis, Stockholm #21/R est:20000-25000 (S.KR 17000)
£6027 $9402 €9041 Self portrait (89x51cm-35x20in) s.d.03 gouache prov.lit. 5-Nov-2 Bukowskis, Stockholm #22/R est:40000-60000 (S.KR 86000)

KYODEN, Santo (1761-1816) Japanese
Works on paper
£2013 $3200 €3020 Enlightenment. s. ink col hanging scroll sold with one by O Haritsu. 24-Mar-3 Christie's, Rockefeller NY #30/R est:2000-3000

KYOSHO, Tachihara (1785-1840) Japanese
Works on paper
£2013 $3200 €3020 Chinese scholar in a pine forest (127x45cm-50x18in) s.d.1837 ink col hanging scroll. 24-Mar-3 Christie's, Rockefeller NY #47/R est:1500-2000
£3019 $4800 €4529 Shoki on horseback (100x31cm-39x12in) s. ink col silk hanging scroll and another scroll prov. 24-Mar-3 Christie's, Rockefeller NY #46/R est:2000-3000

KYOSHO, Tachihara (attrib) (1785-1840) Japanese
Works on paper
£250 $400 €375 Mountain landscape (129x50cm-51x20in) bears sig hanging scroll ink on silk. 16-Mar-3 Butterfields, San Francisco #1205

KYYHKYNEN, Juho (1875-1909) Finnish
£1054 $1677 €1550 Girl from Lapland (51x33cm-20x13in) 24-Mar-3 Bukowskis, Helsinki #137/R est:250
Works on paper
£377 $581 €600 Laplanders (14x16cm-6x6in) s.d.1900 mixed media. 27-Oct-2 Bukowskis, Helsinki #226/R

LAABS, Hans (1915-) Polish
£319 $505 €460 Breaking waves (21x30cm-8x12in) s.d. acrylic over pencil paper. 26-Apr-3 Dr Lehr, Berlin #309/R
£347 $549 €500 Beach flags (40x50cm-16x20in) s.d. s.i. verso acrylic chk panel. 26-Apr-3 Dr Lehr, Berlin #310/R
£833 $1317 €1200 Snow bird (80x100cm-31x39in) s.d. s.i.d.verso acrylic. 26-Apr-3 Dr Lehr, Berlin #308/R
£2319 $3803 €3200 Blue to the fore (60x79cm-24x31in) s.d.58 s.i. verso panel. 31-May-3 Villa Grisebach, Berlin #333/R est:2500-3500
Works on paper
£616 $1010 €850 Couple in the rain (31x46cm-12x18in) s.d.86 gouache pencil. 31-May-3 Villa Grisebach, Berlin #862/R
£818 $1259 €1300 Five heads (15x32cm-6x13in) s.d.1952 mixed media. 26-Oct-2 Dr Lehr, Berlin #265/R

LAAGER, Ken (1953-) American
£5063 $8000 €7341 Captain Lewis and the grizzly (46x76cm-18x30in) s. 26-Jul-3 Coeur d'Alene, Hayden #77/R est:12000-18000

LAAN, Gerard van der (1844-1915) Dutch
£328 $521 €475 Sailing vessel at calm seas (9x13cm-4x5in) init. panel. 10-Mar-3 Sotheby's, Amsterdam #153

LAANEN, Jasper van der (1592-1626) Flemish
£6081 $9486 €9000 John the Evangelist on patmos (25x18cm-10x7in) copper. 27-Mar-3 Dorotheum, Vienna #155/R est:9000-12000

LAAR, Jan Hendrik van de (1807-1874) Dutch
£1422 $2361 €2062 Visit to the artist's studio (58x48cm-23x19in) s. panel. 16-Jun-3 Waddingtons, Toronto #246/R est:3000-5000 (C.D 3200)
£2621 $4167 €3800 Letter (54x43cm-21x17in) s. panel. 10-Mar-3 Sotheby's, Amsterdam #89 est:2000-3000

LABARRE, Raoul (1902-1987) Belgian
£1056 $1701 €1500 Town square with figures (72x91cm-28x36in) s.d.48. 7-May-3 Vendue Huis, Gravenhage #143/R est:1500-2000

LABHARDT, Emanuel (1810-1874) Swiss
Works on paper
£2138 $3314 €3400 Bern (43x56cm-17x22in) s.i. W/C gouache. 1-Oct-2 Dorotheum, Vienna #216/R est:4000-4500

LABIOS, A (?) ?
£324 $525 €486 Girl in petticoats (41x30cm-16x12in) 24-Jan-3 Douglas, South Deerfield #3

LABISSE, Felix (1905-1982) French
£1655 $2615 €2400 Delires d'anemones (60x73cm-24x29in) s. s.i.d.1962 verso prov.lit. 4-Apr-3 Tajan, Paris #229
£2025 $3200 €3200 Albandar (46x38cm-18x15in) s.d.1976 verso. 26-Nov-2 Palais de Beaux Arts, Brussels #113 est:2000-3000
£3404 $5515 €4800 Libidoscaphes dans la baie de Rio (88x115cm-35x45in) s. s.i.d. verso exhib.lit. 24-May-3 Van Ham, Cologne #346/R est:5700
£4000 $6520 €6000 Conversation Ancestrale 1928 (59x72cm-23x28in) s. canvas on board prov.exhib.lit. 3-Feb-3 Bonhams, New Bond Street #60/R est:1000-2000
£4403 $6824 €7000 Messaline (81x60cm-32x24in) s. s.i.d.1972 verso prov.exhib.lit. 5-Oct-2 De Vuyst, Lokeren #577/R est:7000-8000
£5200 $8008 €7800 Les praques (73x60cm-29x24in) s. i.verso prov.exhib.lit. 23-Oct-2 Sotheby's, Olympia #784/R est:3000-5000
£7595 $12000 €12000 La papesse Jeanne (73x50cm-29x20in) s.d.1970 verso. 26-Nov-2 Palais de Beaux Arts, Brussels #337/R est:8700-11000
£8228 $13000 €13000 Cotyto, Perfica, Volupie (130x97cm-51x38in) s.d.1963 verso exhib. 26-Nov-2 Palais de Beaux Arts, Brussels #114/R est:8700-12000
Works on paper
£258 $408 €400 Derriere le miroir (23x16cm-9x6in) i.verso gouache black ink. 17-Dec-2 Rossini, Paris #36
£314 $525 €450 Le chateau dans les nuages (30x23cm-12x9in) s. ink dr. 26-Jun-3 Tajan, Paris #159

£719 $1151 €1000 Les graces (63x50cm-25x20in) s. gouache. 13-May-3 Vanderkindere, Brussels #233
£1538 $2415 €2400 Untitled (35x25cm-14x10in) s. gouache prov. 24-Nov-2 Laurence Calmels, Paris #169/R
£1974 $3197 €3000 Le taureau (49x32cm-19x13in) s. gouache ink. 22-Jan-3 Tajan, Paris #215/R est:2400-3000

LABITTE, Eugène-Leon (1858-1937) French
£521 $849 €750 Jeune Bretonne en costume de Pont-Aven (26x21cm-10x8in) s. panel. 19-Jul-3 Thierry & Lannon, Brest #352
£550 $858 €825 Young farmhand (40x32cm-16x13in) s. 13-Sep-2 Lyon & Turnbull, Edinburgh #52/R
£833 $1358 €1200 Le jeune pecheur (34x27cm-13x11in) s. 19-Jul-3 Thierry & Lannon, Brest #353
£1014 $1581 €1500 Ramasseurs de goemon a Concarneau (37x53cm-15x21in) s. i.verso cardboard. 28-Mar-3 Charbonneaux, Paris #102/R
£2958 $4762 €4200 Scene de fenaison en Bretagne (60x73cm-24x29in) s. 11-May-3 Thierry & Lannon, Brest #189/R est:5000-6000

LABLAIS, Michel (20th C) ?
£850 $1352 €1275 Owl (83x63cm-33x25in) s.d.55 board. 4-Mar-3 Bearnes, Exeter #443/R
£1250 $1988 €1875 Mother and child (97x68cm-38x27in) s.d.54 s.verso. 4-Mar-3 Bearnes, Exeter #441/R est:800-1200

LABOR, Charles (1813-1900) ?
£205 $320 €308 La mare aux grenouilles (55x37cm-22x15in) s.d.72 s.i.verso panel. 10-Sep-2 Iegor de Saint Hippolyte, Montreal #68 (C.D 500)

LABORDE, Charles L Theodore (?-1818) French?
Works on paper
£7000 $10850 €10500 Vue de Faubourg de la Lapa et la Montagne du Corcovado, Rio Janerio. Harbour and city (39x55cm-15x22in) i. pencil two sold with six W/C by same hand. 26-Sep-2 Christie's, London #29/R est:6000-8000

LABORNE, Edme Émile (1837-1913) French
Works on paper
£570 $900 €900 Famille de bucherons en foret (53x37cm-21x15in) s. pastel. 1-Dec-2 Peron, Melun #67

LABOULAYE, Paul de (1902-1961) French
£800 $1272 €1200 Paysage (22x41cm-9x16in) s. panel pair prov. 20-Mar-3 Sotheby's, Olympia #30/R

LABOUREUR, Jean Émile (1877-1943) French
Prints
£2767 $4400 €4151 Ernest Garcon de restaurant (44x27cm-17x11in) s.num.9/20 col woodcut. 1-May-3 Swann Galleries, New York #478/R est:6000-9000
£3451 $5728 €4900 Le cafe du commerce (31x24cm-12x9in) s.num. engraving vellum edition of 39. 12-Jun-3 Piasa, Paris #92/R
Works on paper
£629 $975 €1000 Heure du bain (21x15cm-8x6in) s.i. pen Chinese ink dr. 30-Oct-2 Coutau Begarie, Paris #11

LABROUCHE, Pierre (fl.1905-1921) French
Works on paper
£972 $1585 €1400 Le port de Douarnenez (54x58cm-21x23in) s. wash. 19-Jul-3 Thierry & Lannon, Brest #406

LABRUZZI, Carlo (1748-1818) Italian
Works on paper
£350 $574 €525 Long bridge over the River Calore (20x29cm-8x11in) pencil W/C prov. 5-Jun-3 Christie's, Kensington #950
£550 $902 €825 Tivoli, a view of Tivoli from the countryside with figures in the foreground (30x40cm-12x16in) s.i.d.1783 ink wash. 3-Jun-3 Bonhams, Oxford #45/R
£1622 $2530 €2400 View of Castel Gandolfo (43x51cm-17x20in) pen ink wash. 26-Mar-3 Piasa, Paris #20/R
£3774 $5811 €6000 Tivoli, waterfall (58x46cm-23x18in) W/C tempera lit. 23-Oct-2 Finarte, Rome #429/R

LABRUZZI, Pietro (1739-1805) Italian
£18590 $28814 €29000 Portrait of Hermann Boerhaaven (76x61cm-30x24in) i.d. i. verso prov. 5-Dec-2 Dr Fritz Nagel, Stuttgart #618/R est:1500

LACASSE, Joseph (1894-1975) Belgian
£1139 $1766 €1800 Untitled (55x38cm-22x15in) s. s.d.1969 verso. 28-Sep-2 Ketterer, Hamburg #501/R est:1500-1600
£4348 $7130 €6000 Composition abstraite (81x65cm-32x26in) s.d.1954 prov. 29-May-3 Lempertz, Koln #738/R est:7000
Works on paper
£256 $403 €400 Composition (19x16cm-7x6in) mono.d.1937 gouache. 15-Dec-2 Perrin, Versailles #2/R

LACAZE, Germaine (1908-1994) French
£552 $921 €800 Harmonie bleue (33x24cm-13x9in) s. lit. 9-Jul-3 Millon & Associes, Paris #200/R
£690 $1152 €1000 Plate-forme, autobus (55x46cm-22x18in) s. s.d.1932 verso lit. 9-Jul-3 Millon & Associes, Paris #201a
£759 $1206 €1100 Nature morte aux figues et mirabelles (27x46cm-11x18in) s. s.i.d.1971 verso lit. 10-Mar-3 Millon & Associes, Paris #28
£759 $1206 €1100 Printemps, vallee du Morin (60x30cm-24x12in) s. s.i.d.1962 verso lit. 10-Mar-3 Millon & Associes, Paris #30
£759 $1267 €1100 La bruine, square du Bon-Marche (33x24cm-13x9in) s. lit. 9-Jul-3 Millon & Associes, Paris #201/R
£769 $1208 €1200 Rue de Paris (60x30cm-24x12in) 22-Nov-2 Millon & Associes, Paris #105
£1034 $1645 €1500 Fleurs du jardin et bigarreaux (92x73cm-36x29in) s. s.i.d.1992 verso lit. 10-Mar-3 Millon & Associes, Paris #32
£1034 $1645 €1500 Roses de Noel (48x38cm-19x15in) s. s.i.d.1992 verso lit. 10-Mar-3 Millon & Associes, Paris #29
£1282 $2013 €2000 Hommage a Francois Couperin (116x89cm-46x35in) s. painted 1976 exhib.lit. 22-Nov-2 Millon & Associes, Paris #110/R
£1724 $2741 €2500 Nature morte aux orchidees (97x130cm-38x51in) s. s.d.1988 verso lit. 10-Mar-3 Millon & Associes, Paris #35
£1731 $2717 €2700 Modele a l'atelier (116x89cm-46x35in) s. lit. 22-Nov-2 Millon & Associes, Paris #109
£1731 $2717 €2700 Coin d'atelier au chat (92x73cm-36x29in) s. painted 1991 lit. 22-Nov-2 Millon & Associes, Paris #108/R
£2069 $3290 €3000 Juliette (146x114cm-57x45in) s. s.i.d.1957 verso lit. 10-Mar-3 Millon & Associes, Paris #38/R
£2244 $3522 €3500 Automnale a Villeneuve-le-Comte (116x89cm-46x35in) s. painted 1968 exhib.lit. 22-Nov-2 Millon & Associes, Paris #111/R
£5172 $8224 €7500 Automne (100x81cm-39x32in) s. s.i.d.1963 verso lit. 10-Mar-3 Millon & Associes, Paris #33/R
Works on paper
£552 $877 €800 Boulevard des Italiens (47x30cm-19x12in) s.i.d.1934 gouache. 10-Mar-3 Millon & Associes, Paris #27

LACAZE, Pierre (1816-1884) Swiss
£1258 $1937 €2000 Paysage anime au bord du Nil (45x78cm-18x31in) s.i.d.1877. 23-Oct-2 Rabourdin & Choppin de Janvry, Paris #225

LACCATARIS, Demeter (1798-1864) Hungarian
£4034 $6253 €6051 Joy of meeting again (83x64cm-33x25in) s. 6-Dec-2 Kieselbach, Budapest #133/R (H.F 1500000)

LACH, Andreas (1817-1882) Austrian
£3930 $6131 €5895 Still life of fruit (68x54cm-27x21in) s.d.78. 6-Nov-2 Dobiaschofsky, Bern #754/R est:11000 (S.FR 9000)

LACH, Fritz (1868-1933) Austrian
Works on paper
£633 $1000 €1000 Mondsee (40x46cm-16x18in) s.i.d.1925 W/C. 28-Nov-2 Dorotheum, Vienna #127/R est:2000-2500
£1007 $1612 €1400 Oberwolz (31x42cm-12x17in) s.i.d.1919 W/C. 14-May-3 Dorotheum, Linz #462/R

LACHAISE, Eugene A (1857-1925) American
£8500 $13940 €12750 Danse Japonaise (124x166cm-49x65in) s.d.1889 prov. 3-Jun-3 Sotheby's, London #163/R est:6000-8000

LACHAISE, Gaston (1882-1935) American/French
Sculpture
£11950 $19000 €17925 Woman in chair (33cm-13in) i. brown pat. bronze lit. 4-Mar-3 Christie's, Rockefeller NY #80/R est:10000-15000
£18902 $31000 €27408 Untitled - woman reclined (20x20x48cm-8x8x19in) bronze prov. 1-Jun-3 Wright, Chicago #108/R est:20000-30000
£20968 $32500 €31452 Classic torso (26cm-10in) reddish pat. bronze prov. 4-Dec-2 Sotheby's, New York #96/R est:20000-30000
£92593 $150000 €138890 Equestrienne (27cm-11in) i. greenish gold pat. bronze conceived 1918 prov.exhib.lit. 21-May-3 Sotheby's, New York #38/R est:150000-200000
£111111 $180000 €166667 Peacocks (56x142cm-22x56in) i. dark brown pat. bronze i.f.Roman cast 1922 prov.lit. 21-May-3 Sotheby's, New York #5/R est:250000-350000
£111111 $180000 €166667 Penguin (29cm-11in) polychrome red brown pat. bronze executed c.1925 prov.exhib.lit. 21-May-3 Sotheby's, New York #31/R est:75000-100000
Works on paper
£710 $1100 €1065 Nude with veil (61x43cm-24x17in) s. pencil. 3-Dec-2 Christie's, Rockefeller NY #611/R

£774 $1200 €1161 Standing female nude (29x22cm-11x9in) s. pencil. 3-Dec-2 Christie's, Rockefeller NY #610/R
£1032 $1600 €1548 Standing nude (25x18cm-10x7in) s. pencil exhib. 25-Sep-2 Doyle, New York #47/R est:1200-1600
£2006 $3250 €3009 Nude torso (48x33cm-19x13in) s. pencil prov.exhib. 21-May-3 Sotheby's, New York #100/R est:4000-6000

LACHAT, Joseph (1908-1991) Swiss
£417 $671 €626 A. Portrait au chevalet (64x40cm-25x16in) mono.i. verso panel. 7-May-3 Dobiaschofsky, Bern #3392 (S.FR 900)
£429 $678 €644 Dream (100x110cm-39x43in) i.d.1962. 29-Nov-2 Zofingen, Switzerland #2958 (S.FR 1000)

LACHENWITZ, F Sigmund (1820-1868) German
£4430 $7000 €7000 Dog trainer (42x54cm-17x21in) s. 28-Nov-2 Dorotheum, Vienna #100/R est:8000-8500

LACHER, Georg (1809-1882) German
£286 $426 €440 Holy Family with angels and Infant St John (30x27cm-12x11in) s.mono.d.1831. 27-Jun-2 Neumeister, Munich #2774

LACHEVRE, Bernard (?) ?
£268 $432 €400 Paquebot sur une mer formee (60x78cm-24x31in) s. cardboard. 23-Feb-3 Lesieur & Le Bars, Le Havre #83

LACHMAN, Harry (1886-1974) American/French
£429 $700 €644 Fleet in harbour (20x15cm-8x6in) s. board. 2-Feb-3 Grogan, Boston #26
£994 $1600 €1491 Village in winter landscape (33x41cm-13x16in) s.d.14 board prov. 18-Feb-3 John Moran, Pasadena #90 est:2000-3000
£2201 $3500 €3302 Chemain a moret (46x56cm-18x22in) s. i.on stretcher prov. 5-Mar-3 Christie's, Rockefeller NY #84/R est:3000-5000
£3896 $6000 €5844 Seine at Meudon (61x81cm-24x32in) s. painted c.1915. 8-Sep-2 Treadway Gallery, Cincinnati #625/R est:6000-8000

LACHNIT, Max (1900-1972) German
£566 $872 €900 Abstract composition (24x45cm-9x18in) panel. 26-Oct-2 Dr Lehr, Berlin #267/R

LACHNIT, Wilhelm (1899-1962) German
£2013 $3099 €3200 Mountain landscape with figures and horse (35x51cm-14x20in) s.d.1938 panel. 26-Oct-2 Dr Lehr, Berlin #268/R est:2000

LACHOWICZ, Rachel (1964-) American?
Works on paper
£5063 $8000 €7595 Color chart No.1 (121x119cm-48x47in) eye shadow in aluminum pans on panel executed 1993 prov.exhib. 14-Nov-2 Christie's, Rockefeller NY #348/R est:10000-15000

LACHTROPIUS, Nicolaes (17th C) Dutch
£18519 $30000 €27779 Roses, peonies and other flowers in a glass bowl, with a silk drapery (73x59cm-29x23in) prov. 24-Jan-3 Christie's, Rockefeller NY #142/R est:15000-20000

LACINA, Josef (1899-?) Czechoslovakian
£788 $1150 €1182 Bathing (121x100cm-48x39in) painted c.1935. 4-Jun-2 SOGA, Bratislava #190/R est:28000 (SL.K 50000)
£4114 $6500 €6500 Skier (126x142cm-50x56in) 27-Nov-2 Dorotheum, Vienna #178/R est:6000-8500

LACOMA, Francisco Jose Pablo (1784-1849) Spanish
£1731 $2735 €2700 Portrait of gentleman (87x66cm-34x26in) 14-Nov-2 Arte, Seville #211/R

LACOMBE, Georges (1868-1916) French
Works on paper
£780 $1264 €1100 Pont d'Albi (29x43cm-11x17in) st. graphite col crayon. 21-May-3 Cornette de St.Cyr, Paris #1/R
£1525 $2470 €2150 Etude pour le marche breton (43x30cm-17x12in) st. graphite prov. 21-May-3 Cornette de St.Cyr, Paris #2/R est:1500-2000

LACOSTE, Charles (1870-1959) French
£1831 $3039 €2600 Fougeres et pins (55x35cm-22x14in) s.d. 11-Jun-3 Beaussant & Lefèvre, Paris #82/R est:2000-2500
£2113 $3507 €3000 Chemin au bord de l'eau (54x65cm-21x26in) s.d. 11-Jun-3 Beaussant & Lefèvre, Paris #83/R est:3000-4000
£3205 $5032 €5000 Les toits (29x35cm-11x14in) s.d.1905. 11-Dec-2 Maigret, Paris #126 est:3500-4500
£21935 $34658 €34000 Rue Rousselet (34x18cm-13x7in) s.d.1905 cardboard exhib. 18-Dec-2 Ferri, Paris #82/R est:9000

LACOSTE, Eugène (19th C) French
Works on paper
£340 $541 €500 Etudes de costumes (23x13cm-9x5in) W/C. 21-Mar-3 Rieunier, Bailly-Pommery, Mathias, Paris #103
£476 $757 €700 Etude de costumes (23x13cm-9x5in) W/C. 21-Mar-3 Rieunier, Bailly-Pommery, Mathias, Paris #104

LACOURT, L (?) ?
£993 $1539 €1490 Interior scene with gentleman reading poems to two young ladies (50x40cm-20x16in) 8-Dec-2 Uppsala Auktionskammare, Uppsala #97/R (S.KR 14000)

LACROIX DE MARSEILLE, Charles François (1720-c.1782) French
£13000 $20280 €19500 Coastal landscape at sunset (15x23cm-6x9in) s.d.1767 copper. 10-Apr-3 Sotheby's, London #99/R est:15000
£15172 $24276 €22000 Cascatelle animee (62x53cm-24x21in) s.d.1770 oval. 14-Mar-3 Libert, Castor, Paris #35/R
£22785 $36000 €36000 Trois pecheurs sur des rochers (55x38cm-22x15in) s.d.1771. 27-Nov-2 Christie's, Paris #39/R est:30000-50000
£46897 $74097 €68000 View of the Vesuvius at night (51x76cm-20x30in) s.d.1767 prov.exhib.lit. 3-Apr-3 Porro, Milan #38/R est:90000
£75949 $120000 €120000 Tempete. Temps calme (48x62cm-19x24in) s.d.1760 pair. 27-Nov-2 Christie's, Paris #49/R est:80000-120000
£76923 $119231 €120000 Vue fantaisiste autour de phare mediterraneen (51x62cm-20x24in) s.i.d.1755. 6-Dec-2 Maigret, Paris #100/R est:20000-30000
£284810 $444304 €450000 Vue de port mediterraneen au lever du jour. Vue de port mediterraneen au crepuscule (104x145cm-41x57in) s.d.1774 pair. 20-Oct-2 Anaf, Lyon #164/R

LACROIX DE MARSEILLE, Charles François (attrib) (1720-c.1782) French
£638 $1034 €900 Naufrage pres des cotes (22x33cm-9x13in) bears mono. 23-May-3 Beaussant & Lefèvre, Paris #36/R
£1461 $2250 €2192 Figures along the shore (61x82cm-24x32in) prov.exhib. 23-Oct-2 Doyle, New York #60/R est:2500-3500
£5068 $7905 €7500 Fishermen in stormy sea off rocky coastline (164x94cm-65x37in) 27-Mar-3 Dorotheum, Vienna #80/R est:8000-12000

LACROIX DE MARSEILLE, Charles François (style) (1720-c.1782) French
£7143 $11000 €10715 Fisher folk at harbour (64x95cm-25x37in) 23-Oct-2 Doyle, New York #95/R est:6000-8000

LACROIX, Gaspard Jean (1810-1878) French
£345 $548 €500 Coucher de soleil (68x99cm-27x39in) 5-Mar-3 Doutrebente, Paris #43
£1103 $1754 €1600 Scene bucolique (95x128cm-37x50in) s.d. 5-Mar-3 Doutrebente, Paris #42/R est:1500-1800

LACROIX, H (19th C) ?
£976 $1600 €1415 Returning from fishing (56x69cm-22x27in) s. 4-Jun-3 Doyle, New York #36 est:1000-1500

LACROIX, Paul (fl.1858-1869) French?
£4747 $7500 €7121 Still life with apples and grapes (20x28cm-8x11in) s.d.1863 panel. 24-Apr-3 Shannon's, Milford #113/R est:8000-12000

LACROIX, Tristan (19th C) French
£1667 $2633 €2600 Sous-bois (248x200cm-98x79in) s.d.1889. 17-Nov-2 Herbette, Doullens #48/R

LACROIX-BAVARD, Pierre Gabriel (1875-1950) French
Works on paper
£355 $592 €500 Trois canards (49x65cm-19x26in) s.i. gouache. 20-Jun-3 Piasa, Paris #170
£638 $1066 €900 Porc-epic (58x95cm-23x37in) s. gouache. 20-Jun-3 Piasa, Paris #171

LACY, Charles J de (1860-1936) British
£2600 $4212 €3900 Greenwich Reach (61x107cm-24x42in) s. 22-Jan-3 Bonhams, New Bond Street #367/R est:2000-3000
£2800 $4676 €4060 Shipping on the Thames at sunset with St. Pauls in the distance (61x107cm-24x42in) s. 18-Jun-3 Sotheby's, Olympia #85/R est:3000-5000
Works on paper
£350 $532 €525 HMS Warspite (46x33cm-18x13in) s.i. W/C. 14-Aug-2 Andrew Hartley, Ilkley #581
£489 $812 €709 Ran aground (36x28cm-14x11in) s. W/C on board. 10-Jun-3 Ritchie, Toronto #8/R est:600-800 (C.D 1100)

LACY, Ernest (20th C) American
Works on paper
£297 $475 €446 Secert sharer (102x66cm-40x26in) s.i.d.1959 W/C pastel. 16-Mar-3 Butterfields, San Francisco #1091

LADA, Josef (1887-1957) Czechoslovakian
£2724 $4413 €4086 Pig slaughtering (24x22cm-9x9in) s. ink W/C. 24-May-3 Dorotheum, Prague #159/R est:28000-45000 (C.KR 120000)
Works on paper
£330 $515 €495 Chalupa (18x28cm-7x11in) s.d.1935 Indian ink dr W/C. 12-Oct-2 Dorotheum, Prague #260 (C.KR 16000)
£349 $555 €524 Collision with airplane (12x20cm-5x8in) mono. ink white lead. 8-Mar-3 Dorotheum, Prague #294/R est:8000-12000 (C.KR 16000)
£363 $588 €545 Good soldier Svejk (26x15cm-10x6in) ink white lead. 24-May-3 Dorotheum, Prague #157/R est:10000-15000 (C.KR 16000)
£436 $694 €654 Gamblers (13x20cm-5x8in) s. col pen. 8-Mar-3 Dorotheum, Prague #293/R est:18000-27000 (C.KR 20000)
£499 $809 €749 Cullies (7x12cm-3x5in) mono. ink W/C. 24-May-3 Dorotheum, Prague #158/R est:10000-15000 (C.KR 22000)
£578 $902 €867 Beer drinking (8x13cm-3x5in) mono. Indian ink dr W/C. 12-Oct-2 Dorotheum, Prague #176 (C.KR 28000)
£636 $1030 €954 Traffic offence (27x19cm-11x7in) mono. ink white lead. 24-May-3 Dorotheum, Prague #160/R est:12000-20000 (C.KR 28000)
£654 $1041 €981 Courting (13x17cm-5x7in) s. col ink. 8-Mar-3 Dorotheum, Prague #292/R est:18000-27000 (C.KR 30000)
£661 $1031 €992 Conversation (15x11cm-6x4in) s. Indian ink dr whitewash. 12-Oct-2 Dorotheum, Prague #271 (C.KR 32000)
£661 $1031 €992 Conversation about soccer (24x18cm-9x7in) mono. Indian ink dr whitewash. 12-Oct-2 Dorotheum, Prague #272/R (C.KR 32000)
£982 $1561 €1473 Bureaucratic mare (12x15cm-5x6in) s. col ink. 8-Mar-3 Dorotheum, Prague #291/R est:18000-27000 (C.KR 45000)
£1022 $1655 €1533 Bartosh, Bartosh! (14x14cm-6x6in) s. ink W/C. 24-May-3 Dorotheum, Prague #155/R est:20000-30000 (C.KR 45000)
£1362 $2207 €2043 Goat climbs a birch tree (14x14cm-6x6in) s. ink W/C. 24-May-3 Dorotheum, Prague #156/R est:20000-30000 (C.KR 60000)
£7853 $12487 €11780 Night watchman (25x39cm-10x15in) s.d.46 gouache. 8-Mar-3 Dorotheum, Prague #175/R est:200000-300000 (C.KR 360000)

LADAGE, Gerardus Johannes (1878-1932) Dutch
Works on paper
£641 $994 €1000 Oosterhout (62x51cm-24x20in) s. W/C prov. 3-Dec-2 Christie's, Amsterdam #25/R est:900-1200
£2436 $3776 €3800 Symphonie no.9 (72x53cm-28x21in) s. W/C prov. 3-Dec-2 Christie's, Amsterdam #23/R est:2500-3500

LADAS, Anneliese (1941-) German
£648 $1043 €920 Spring landscape with alpine lake (18x33cm-7x13in) s. board. 7-May-3 Michael Zeller, Lindau #773/R

LADBROOKE, Henry (1800-1870) British
£1900 $3135 €2755 Cattle and sheep (51x61cm-20x24in) 1-Jul-3 Bonhams, Norwich #234/R est:2000-3000

LADBROOKE, Henry (attrib) (1800-1870) British
£1700 $2669 €2550 Hay wagon. Gathering faggots (48x56cm-19x22in) pair. 13-Dec-2 Keys, Aylsham #720/R est:1500-2000

LADBROOKE, John Berney (1803-1879) British
£750 $1238 €1088 Woodman (38x23cm-15x9in) 1-Jul-3 Bonhams, Norwich #249/R
£1200 $1908 €1800 Cottage in a woodland landscape (51x77cm-20x30in) mono.d.1878. 5-Mar-3 Bonhams, Bury St Edmunds #351/R est:1200-1800
£1500 $2445 €2250 Landscape (51x66cm-20x26in) 13-Feb-3 David Lay, Penzance #21/R est:1500-2500
£7000 $11060 €10500 Wooded landscape with cottages and figure resting (46x61cm-18x24in) mono.d.1807 exhib. 26-Nov-2 Christie's, London #75/R est:7000-10000

LADBROOKE, John Berney (attrib) (1803-1879) British
£750 $1245 €1088 Wooded landscape with a figure on a track beside a windmill (28x33cm-11x13in) panel. 16-Jun-3 Duke & Son, Dorchester #214/R
£1000 $1550 €1500 Thatched cottage in a woodland (71x92cm-28x36in) 30-Sep-2 Bonhams, Ipswich #499 est:1200-1800

LADD, Laura D Stroud (1863-1943) American
£3548 $5500 €5322 Harbour scene (46x51cm-18x20in) s. board. 8-Dec-2 Freeman, Philadelphia #153/R est:3000-5000

LADELL, Edward (1821-1886) British
£2800 $4340 €4200 Mallard still life (51x41cm-20x16in) mono.d.1860 s.i.d.verso. 3-Dec-2 Sotheby's, Olympia #153/R est:3000-5000
£5000 $7850 €7500 Still life of fruit (25x30cm-10x12in) mono.d.60 i.verso panel prov. 19-Nov-2 Bonhams, Leeds #173 est:5000-8000
£24000 $37920 €36000 Plums and other fruit in tazza and on ledge with bird's nest (35x30cm-14x12in) mono. 26-Nov-2 Christie's, London #132/R est:25000-35000
£35000 $57400 €52500 Still life of roses, fruit and bird's nest on a table by a window (43x35cm-17x14in) mono. 4-Feb-3 Sworder & Son, Bishops Stortford #112/R est:20000-30000

LADELL, Ellen (fl.1886-1898) British
£610 $969 €915 Hunting still life with birds and butterfly (25x30cm-10x12in) s. 3-Mar-3 Lilla Bukowskis, Stockholm #601 (S.KR 8200)
£2000 $3140 €3000 Stil life of fruit (25x30cm-10x12in) mono. prov. 19-Nov-2 Bonhams, Leeds #174/R est:2000-3000

LADUREAU, Pierre (1882-1975) French
£641 $994 €1000 Hiver (60x73cm-24x29in) s. 9-Dec-2 Beaussant & Lefèvre, Paris #64/R

LADWIG, Roland (1935-) German?
£256 $397 €400 Outer court of a country property, with roof (50x57cm-20x22in) s.d.76 s.indis.i.d.76. 7-Dec-2 Dannenberg, Berlin #700/R

LAEMAN, Gabrielle (?) Belgian?
£506 $790 €800 Vase chinois fleuri de glaieuls (100x80cm-39x31in) s. 16-Sep-2 Horta, Bruxelles #6

LAER, Pieter van (attrib) (c.1582-c.1642) Dutch
£4965 $7695 €7448 Market scene (76x93cm-30x37in) 4-Dec-2 AB Stockholms Auktionsverk #1944/R est:80000-100000 (S.KR 70000)

LAER, Pieter van (circle) (c.1582-c.1642) Dutch
£20000 $31400 €30000 Greyhound (22x26cm-9x10in) canvas on panel. 13-Dec-2 Christie's, Kensington #60/R est:3000-5000

LAERMANS, Eugène (1864-1940) Belgian
£10692 $16572 €17000 Rayons mourants (76x105cm-30x41in) s. painted 1912 prov.exhib.lit. 5-Oct-2 De Vuyst, Lokeren #445/R est:15000-17000
£12414 $19862 €18000 Le repos des paysans (99x58cm-39x23in) 17-Mar-3 Amberes, Antwerp #226/R
£15603 $26057 €22000 Les deportes (83x140cm-33x55in) s.d.1916 exhib. 17-Jun-3 Palais de Beaux Arts, Brussels #590/R est:15000-20000
£25899 $41439 €36000 Haymaking (75x100cm-30x39in) s.d.1921 prov.lit. 17-May-3 De Vuyst, Lokeren #453/R
Works on paper
£353 $554 €550 Homme a la pelle (25x17cm-10x7in) dr. 10-Dec-2 Campo, Vlaamse Kaai #285
£833 $1308 €1300 Couple. s.d.1919 chl. 19-Nov-2 Galerie Moderne, Brussels #154/R
£943 $1462 €1500 Farmer seen from behind (46x28cm-18x11in) s. black chk pencil dr exhib. 5-Oct-2 De Vuyst, Lokeren #199/R est:1200-1400
£5396 $8633 €7500 Rest day (48x70cm-19x28in) s.d.1916 W/C chl dr lit. 17-May-3 De Vuyst, Lokeren #454/R est:8000-9000
£5396 $8633 €7500 Family walk (49x70cm-19x28in) s.d.1916 W/C chl dr lit. 17-May-3 De Vuyst, Lokeren #455/R est:8000-9000
£15385 $23846 €24000 L'aveugle (100x66cm-39x26in) s.d.1903 W/C pastel black chk prov.lit. 7-Dec-2 De Vuyst, Lokeren #432/R est:8000-14000

LAESSOE, Augusta (1851-1926) Danish?
£378 $609 €567 Branches of apple blossom (27x34cm-11x13in) init.d.1907 panel. 11-May-3 Hindemae, Ullerslev #202/R (D.KR 4000)

LAESSOE, Thorald (1816-1878) Danish
£342 $526 €513 Seascape with vessels in morning haze (9x19cm-4x7in) cardboard. 4-Sep-2 Kunsthallen, Copenhagen #31a (D.KR 4000)
£468 $740 €702 Bay of Naples with Vesuvius in background (24x32cm-9x13in) i.stretcher. 2-Dec-2 Rasmussen, Copenhagen #1585/R (D.KR 5500)
£686 $1070 €1029 Cliffs in Capri (32x29cm-13x11in) 11-Nov-2 Rasmussen, Vejle #673/R (D.KR 8000)
£1306 $2076 €1959 Fox earth (30x22cm-12x9in) init. 5-May-3 Rasmussen, Vejle #704/R est:1500-2000 (D.KR 14000)
£2793 $4496 €4190 Roman ruin and woman (24x31cm-9x12in) s.i.d.1852. 22-Feb-3 Rasmussen, Havnen #2112/R est:8000-10000 (D.KR 31000)
£4664 $7416 €6996 View of Villa Borghese in Rome, Raphael's studio in foreground (38x51cm-15x20in) s.d.30.Mai 1875. 29-Apr-3 Kunsthallen, Copenhagen #535/R est:50000 (D.KR 50000)
Works on paper
£364 $589 €546 Wooded landscape, Italy (16x16cm-6x6in) s.d.1829 pencil W/C. 21-May-3 Museumsbygningen, Copenhagen #22 (D.KR 3800)
£468 $740 €702 Villa Borghese (22x26cm-9x10in) mono.i. W/C. 30-Nov-2 Rasmussen, Havnen #2176 (D.KR 5500)
£1034 $1571 €1551 The manor house Borreby near Skaeldsor seen from south west (24x34cm-9x13in) s. W/C pen prov. 28-Aug-2 Museumsbygningen, Copenhagen #51/R est:12000-15000 (D.KR 12000)

LAESSOE, Thorald (attrib) (1816-1878) Danish
£687 $1085 €1031 Gravel-pit (11x30cm-4x12in) sketch cardboard. 13-Nov-2 Kunsthallen, Copenhagen #41/R (D.KR 8000)
£947 $1440 €1421 Mountain landscape with bay, Italy (26x34cm-10x13in) 27-Aug-2 Rasmussen, Copenhagen #1718/R (D.KR 11000)

LAET, Alois de (1869-1949) Belgian
£1806 $2871 €2600 La disparition de Kallo (120x180cm-47x71in) s. 29-Apr-3 Campo & Campo, Antwerp #64/R est:2000-2500

LAEZZA, Giuseppe (?-1905) Italian
£1761 $2712 €2800 Marine in Naples (25x46cm-10x18in) s. 23-Oct-2 Finarte, Milan #24/R
£3234 $5110 €4851 Figures on the coast in Carraciolo, Naples (20x39cm-8x15in) s. i.verso panel. 2-Dec-2 Rasmussen, Copenhagen #1604/R est:25000 (D.KR 38000)
£4596 $7261 €6894 Children on pier by harbour, Naples (20x39cm-8x15in) s. i.verso panel. 2-Dec-2 Rasmussen, Copenhagen #1603/R est:25000 (D.KR 54000)
Works on paper
£588 $965 €900 Boy fishing on Capri beach (27x47cm-11x19in) s. W/C lit. 8-Feb-3 Hans Stahl, Hamburg #79/R

LAFAGE, Raymond (1656-1690) French
Works on paper
£650 $1086 €943 Classical figures studies (26x22cm-10x9in) ben brown ink traces blk chk double-sided. 9-Jul-3 Sotheby's, London #134/R
£1081 $1686 €1600 Figures conversant a l'ombre d'un arbre (34x26cm-13x10in) i. pen ink over crayon. 27-Mar-3 Maigret, Paris #66/R
£6500 $10855 €9425 Judgement of Solomon (43x57cm-17x22in) s. i.verso black chk ink pen wash. 8-Jul-3 Christie's, London #62/R est:4000-6000

LAFARGE, John (1835-1910) American
£191358 $310000 €287037 Roses in a shallow bowl (34x62cm-13x24in) s. painted c.1879 prov.exhib.lit. 21-May-3 Sotheby's, New York #48/R est:300000-500000
Works on paper
£7547 $12000 €11321 Study of trees in moonlight, Honolulu, Hawaii (20x26cm-8x10in) W/C gouache executed 1890 prov.lit. 5-Mar-3 Sotheby's, New York #59/R est:12000-18000
£12258 $19000 €18387 Great statue of amida Buddha at Kamakura (25x25cm-10x10in) i.d.1856 W/C prov.exhib. 2-Nov-2 North East Auctions, Portsmouth #23/R est:15000-25000

LAFFON, Carmen (1934-) Spanish
£24359 $38487 €38000 Homage to D Manuel Gonzalez Santos (53x65cm-21x26in) s.i.d.1965. 14-Nov-2 Arte, Seville #459/R est:36000

LAFITTE, Louis (1770-1828) French
Works on paper
£473 $738 €700 Portrait de Mademoiselle Emilie Bigiottini (43x29cm-17x11in) s.i. graphite. 27-Mar-3 Christie's, Paris #111/R

LAFON, Jean (1886-1973) French
£349 $545 €524 Moonlit fishing boat ready to sail (60x73cm-24x29in) s. 6-Nov-2 Dobiaschofsky, Bern #3452 (S.FR 800)

LAFOND, Simon Daniel (1763-1831) Swiss
Works on paper
£385 $604 €600 Cow herds in high alpine valley in Switzerland (49x43cm-19x17in) s. W/C. 21-Nov-2 Van Ham, Cologne #1388

LAFONTAINE, Christopher de (18th C) ?
£420 $701 €609 Portrait of Francis Brown Esq of Greatford Hall, Lincolnshire (74x62cm-29x24in) painted 1731. 25-Jun-3 Cheffins, Cambridge #756/R

LAFONTAINE, Marie Jo (1950-) Belgian
Photographs
£4000 $6160 €6000 Schoneres kann nicht sein und werden (126x252cm-50x99in) s.d.1991 s.i.d.verso col photograph mounted on aluminium. 23-Oct-2 Christie's, London #239/R est:4000-6000

LAFOSSE, Charles de (1636-1716) French
Works on paper
£1772 $2800 €2800 Dieu le Pere entoure d'anges (22x23cm-9x9in) cold chk. 27-Nov-2 Christie's, Paris #145/R est:3000-5000
£3974 $6160 €6200 Etude de femme en pied (40x18cm-16x7in) crayon. 4-Dec-2 Piasa, Paris #49/R
£5128 $7949 €8000 Etude de femme en pied (40x18cm-16x7in) crayon. 4-Dec-2 Piasa, Paris #50/R
£21154 $32788 €33000 Deux etudes de femmes assises (23x35cm-9x14in) i. crayon double-sided. 4-Dec-2 Piasa, Paris #51/R est:10000

LAFRENSEN, Nicolas (younger) (1737-1807) Swedish
Miniatures
£2500 $3925 €3750 Melanie le Doulceur wearing a white dress (5cm-2in) s. oval. 10-Dec-2 Christie's, London #78/R est:1500-2500
Works on paper
£3879 $6284 €5625 Karl Erik Wadenstierna and both his wives - Jacobina and Fredrika (9x7cm-4x3in) gouache oval three prov.lit. 26-May-3 Bukowskis, Stockholm #486/R est:60000 (S.KR 50000)

LAFRENSEN, Nicolas (younger-attrib) (1737-1807) Swedish
Works on paper
£405 $632 €600 Spectateurs dans le hall de la Comedie Francaise (16x28cm-6x11in) W/C gouache over crayon. 26-Mar-3 Piasa, Paris #73

LAFUENTE, Ramiro (19th C) Spanish
£535 $834 €850 Landscape (60x100cm-24x39in) s. 23-Sep-2 Durán, Madrid #67/R
£1103 $1754 €1600 Rural path (60x100cm-24x39in) s.d.1986. 4-Mar-3 Ansorena, Madrid #150/R
£1742 $2752 €2700 Madrid seen from Manzanares (51x156cm-20x61in) s.d.1893. 18-Dec-2 Ansorena, Madrid #66/R

LAFUGIE, Lea (1890-1972) ?
Works on paper
£1160 $1786 €1740 Musicians, woman and child (49x38cm-19x15in) one s.i. one s. W/C two prov. 27-Oct-2 Christie's, Hong Kong #45/R est:18000-28000 (HK.D 14000)

LAGAGE, Pierre (1911-1977) French
£596 $972 €900 Composition (50x65cm-20x26in) s.d.1963 paper prov. 3-Feb-3 Cornette de St.Cyr, Paris #466
£600 $948 €900 Composition (65x49cm-26x19in) s.d.67 card. 3-Apr-3 Christie's, Kensington #219/R
£600 $948 €900 Composition (65x49cm-26x19in) s.d.65 card. 3-Apr-3 Christie's, Kensington #224/R
£600 $948 €900 Composition (65x49cm-26x19in) s.d.68 card. 3-Apr-3 Christie's, Kensington #229
£700 $1085 €1050 Composition (65x49cm-26x19in) s.d.68 card two. 5-Dec-2 Christie's, Kensington #199/R
£700 $1085 €1050 Composition (65x49cm-26x19in) s.d.67 card two. 5-Dec-2 Christie's, Kensington #200/R
£1282 $2013 €2000 Composition (41x54cm-16x21in) s.d. paper. 16-Dec-2 Charbonneaux, Paris #265 est:1200-1500
£4038 $6340 €6300 Scenes enfantines (81x65cm-32x26in) cardboard set of 6. 15-Dec-2 Mercier & Cie, Lille #413/R est:7000
Works on paper
£600 $930 €900 Composition (65x49cm-26x19in) s.d.65 card two. 5-Dec-2 Christie's, Kensington #198/R

LAGAR, Celso (1891-1966) Spanish
£2564 $4026 €4000 Port de Honfleur (19x25cm-7x10in) s. i.d.1919 verso panel. 15-Dec-2 Eric Pillon, Calais #191/R
£5862 $9262 €8500 Village covered in snow (27x19cm-11x7in) s. cardboard. 7-Apr-3 Castellana, Madrid #429/R
£9615 $14904 €15000 Collation. s. 4-Dec-2 Pierre Berge, Paris #143/R
£10323 $16310 €16000 Sacalay path (48x55cm-19x22in) s. i.verso lit. 18-Dec-2 Castellana, Madrid #42/R
£10323 $16310 €16000 Circus people in winter (47x55cm-19x22in) s. lit. 18-Dec-2 Castellana, Madrid #55/R est:9000
£11639 $18506 €17459 Spanish town scene with view of the sea (65x80cm-26x31in) s. 10-Mar-3 Rasmussen, Vejle #600/R est:50000-75000 (D.KR 125000)
Works on paper
£272 $430 €425 Nudes (22x22cm-9x9in) ink dr. 19-Nov-2 Durán, Madrid #649/R
£346 $540 €550 Modele de dos, bras tendu en avant (15x11cm-6x4in) s. W/C. 10-Oct-2 Ribeyre & Baron, Paris #50
£362 $564 €575 Clwn (23x16cm-9x6in) s.d.1945 pencil dr. 17-Sep-2 Segre, Madrid #135/R
£411 $641 €600 Female nude (23x29cm-9x11in) s.d.1936 pencil dr. 8-Apr-3 Ansorena, Madrid #696/R

£513 $810 €800 Village and animals (18x23cm-7x9in) s. W/C. 13-Nov-2 Ansorena, Madrid #196/R
£870 $1400 €1305 Circus clown with bear (25x41cm-10x16in) s. W/C gouache htd white paper on card. 19-Feb-3 Doyle, New York #24
£903 $1435 €1300 Femme en bleu (28x15cm-11x6in) s.i.d.1913 ink W/C dr cardboard. 29-Apr-3 Artcurial Briest, Paris #41 est:250-300
£968 $1529 €1500 Circus scene (32x22cm-13x9in) s. wax crayon dr. 18-Dec-2 Ansorena, Madrid #970/R
£1039 $1517 €1600 Cubist woman (26x20cm-10x8in) s. W/C. 17-Jun-2 Ansorena, Madrid #24/R

LAGATTA, John (1894-1977) American
£1553 $2500 €2330 Wedding scene (79x41cm-31x16in) s. oil chl board. 10-May-3 Illustration House, New York #99/R est:3000-5000

LAGERBERG, Brita (1878-1952) Swedish
£287 $465 €416 Young boy and a Scottie dog (61x82cm-24x32in) s. 26-May-3 Rasmussen, Copenhagen #1440/R (D.KR 3000)

LAGERSTAM, Berndt (1868-1930) Finnish
£360 $590 €500 River (60x50cm-24x20in) s. 5-Jun-3 Hagelstam, Helsinki #952
£373 $601 €530 Kymmene, Kuusankoski (45x60cm-18x24in) s.d.1921. 10-May-3 Bukowskis, Helsinki #76/R
£612 $1003 €850 Naked woman on beach (37x46cm-15x18in) s. 4-Jun-3 Bukowskis, Helsinki #333/R
£949 $1500 €1500 From the view point (61x29cm-24x11in) s.d.97. 1-Dec-2 Bukowskis, Helsinki #96/R est:1500-1800

LAGERSTEDT, Georg (1892-1982) Swedish
£274 $438 €397 Cafe Bobino, Calle Coude del Asalta, Barcelona (49x60cm-19x24in) s.i.d.1920 verso. 18-May-3 Anders Antik, Landskrona #1 (S.KR 3500)
£274 $438 €397 Gymnasts (90x69cm-35x27in) s.d.1922. 18-May-3 Anders Antik, Landskrona #3 (S.KR 3500)
£328 $525 €476 Street in small French town (46x60cm-18x24in) s. 18-May-3 Anders Antik, Landskrona #2 (S.KR 4200)

LAGLENNE, Jean Francis (1899-1962) French
£270 $422 €400 Vase empire (60x46cm-24x18in) s. 26-Mar-3 Millon & Associes, Paris #112

LAGNEAU, Nicolas (16/17th C) French
Works on paper
£2517 $3600 €3776 Portrait of a bearded man (28x23cm-11x9in) black red chk. 23-Jan-3 Swann Galleries, New York #231/R est:3000-5000

LAGO RIVERA, Antonio (1916-1990) Spanish
£1216 $1897 €1800 Couple (35x28cm-14x11in) s.d.1981 board. 25-Mar-3 Durán, Madrid #132/R
£2069 $3290 €3000 Apples (38x46cm-15x18in) s.d.1986. 4-Mar-3 Ansorena, Madrid #16/R
£2482 $4021 €3500 Desnudos (73x60cm-29x24in) s.d.9-1984 exhib. 20-May-3 Segre, Madrid #140/R est:3500
£2552 $4057 €3700 Landscape (61x50cm-24x20in) s.d.1976. 4-Mar-3 Ansorena, Madrid #373/R
Works on paper
£256 $405 €400 Woman in blue (16x12cm-6x5in) s.d.1980 W/C. 19-Nov-2 Durán, Madrid #124/R
£290 $459 €450 Orange landscape (16x23cm-6x9in) s.d.1980 W/C. 17-Dec-2 Durán, Madrid #103/R

LAGOOR, Jan van (attrib) (17th C) Dutch
£14013 $21860 €22000 Extensive wooded landscape with houses (72x88cm-28x35in) prov.exhib.lit. 5-Nov-2 Sotheby's, Amsterdam #86/R est:20000-30000

LAGORIO, Lev Feliksovich (1827-1905) Russian
£10000 $15800 €15000 Heavy seas in the Black Sea (44x76cm-17x30in) s. 26-Nov-2 Christie's, Kensington #29/R est:4000-6000
Works on paper
£485 $722 €728 Rider on coast at night (21cm-8in circular) s.cyrillic d.1853 pencil on gouache grisaille. 25-Jun-2 Koller, Zurich #6727 (S.FR 1100)

LAGORIO, Maria (1893-1979) Polish
£900 $1413 €1350 Portrait of a fisherman (100x81cm-39x32in) s. 10-Dec-2 Rosebery Fine Art, London #670/R

LAGOSSE, Paulette (?) French
Prints
£4138 $6579 €6000 Chiens au chenil (29x39cm-11x15in) col engraving. 10-Mar-3 Coutau Begarie, Paris #89
Works on paper
£2897 $4606 €4200 Cavaliers, veneurs et meute (18x24cm-7x9in) W/C ink pair. 10-Mar-3 Coutau Begarie, Paris #103

LAGOUTTE, Claude (1935-) French
£764 $1207 €1100 Oleron (267x64cm-105x25in) s.i.d. painting on stitched canvas painted c.1983. 28-Apr-3 Cornette de St.Cyr, Paris #446

LAGRANGE, Andre (1889-?) French
£696 $1079 €1100 Bord de mer (52x72cm-20x28in) s. isorel. 28-Sep-2 Cornette de St.Cyr, Paris #167

LAGRANGE, Jacques (1917-1995) French
£1274 $1987 €2000 Village (54x65cm-21x26in) s. 10-Nov-2 Eric Pillon, Calais #245/R
Works on paper
£387 $612 €600 Paysage (50x65cm-20x26in) s.d.56 W/C prov. 18-Dec-2 Digard, Paris #74
£578 $919 €850 Composition (49x63cm-19x25in) s.d.48 W/C gouache. 26-Feb-3 Artcurial Briest, Paris #316

LAGRENEE, Anthelme François (1774-1832) French
Miniatures
£6500 $10530 €9750 Portrait of a lady, probably Empress Alexandra Feodorovna (6cm-2in) en grisaille prov. 22-May-3 Bonhams, New Bond Street #32/R est:600-800

LAGRENEE, Jean Jacques (1739-1821) French
Works on paper
£743 $1159 €1100 Bapteme du Christ (20x29cm-8x11in) i. pen ink crayon. 31-Mar-3 Piasa, Paris #45
£9929 $16582 €14000 Etude pur une figure de Chronos. Etude de trois femmes (42x53cm-17x21in) pierre noire sanguine double-sided. 23-Jun-3 Beaussant & Lefèvre, Paris #271/R est:12000-15000

LAGRENEE, Jean Jacques (attrib) (1739-1821) French
£6452 $10194 €10000 Trois nymphes et l'Amour. Venus, Mars et l'Amour (69x57cm-27x22in) panel pair. 18-Dec-2 Piasa, Paris #85/R est:15000
£9091 $15182 €13000 Charles et Ubalde allant chercher Renaud retenu dans le Palais d'Armide (60x73cm-24x29in) 25-Jun-3 Tajan, Paris #64/R est:8000-12000

LAGRENEE, Louis Jean François (1725-1805) French
£1132 $1743 €1800 La fidelite (13x17cm-5x7in) panel board. 25-Oct-2 Tajan, Paris #121 est:2000-3000
£4196 $7007 €6000 Sainte Marie-Madeleine (46x37cm-18x15in) prov.exhib.lit. 25-Jun-3 Tajan, Paris #62/R est:4000-6000
£9459 $14757 €14000 Education de la Vierge (43x34cm-17x13in) prov.exhib.lit. 26-Mar-3 Tajan, Paris #88/R est:15000

LAGRENEE, Louis Jean François (attrib) (1725-1805) French
£20000 $31800 €29000 Mercurius and Cupid. Nymphs and Love (70x60cm-28x24in) board pair. 4-Mar-3 Ansorena, Madrid #56/R est:25000

LAGRU, Dominique (1873-1960) French
£621 $981 €900 Halte (26x34cm-10x13in) s.i.d.1952. 4-Apr-3 Tajan, Paris #70
£896 $1416 €1300 Auberge de la Route Bleue (37x45cm-15x18in) s.d.1956. 4-Apr-3 Tajan, Paris #69/R

LAHARRAGUE, Carlos (1936-) Spanish
£453 $697 €720 Hydrangeas (33x40cm-13x16in) s. 28-Oct-2 Segre, Madrid #255/R

LAHEY, Frances Vida (1882-1968) Australian
£645 $980 €968 Still life, capsicums (28x51cm-11x20in) canvas on board exhib.lit. 28-Aug-2 Deutscher-Menzies, Melbourne #343/R (A.D 1800)
Works on paper
£2873 $4281 €4310 White vase (70x60cm-28x24in) s. W/C prov.exhib.lit. 27-Aug-2 Christie's, Melbourne #326/R est:7000-10000 (A.D 7500)

LAHNER, Émile (1893-1980) French
£755 $1170 €1200 Paysage mediterraneen (38x46cm-15x18in) s.d.1929 mono.verso. 30-Oct-2 Artcurial Briest, Paris #313

LAHS, Curt (1893-1958) German
£417 $658 €600 Southern window (14x33cm-6x13in) s. 26-Apr-3 Dr Lehr, Berlin #313/R

£440 $678 €700 Still life (31x24cm-12x9in) s.d.1930. 26-Oct-2 Dr Lehr, Berlin #270/R
£755 $1162 €1200 Abstract landscape (50x65cm-20x26in) s. panel. 26-Oct-2 Dr Lehr, Berlin #271/R
Works on paper
£1923 $2981 €3000 Seated figure (34x46cm-13x18in) s. W/C pen prov. 4-Dec-2 Lempertz, Koln #849/R est:2000

LAHUERTA, Genaro (1905-1985) Spanish
£818 $1275 €1300 Landscape (14x24cm-6x9in) s. board exhib. 23-Sep-2 Durán, Madrid #64/R
£5862 $9321 €8500 Rocky landscape (38x61cm-15x24in) s. 4-Mar-3 Ansorena, Madrid #217/R
Works on paper
£1226 $1937 €1900 The Seine in Paris (23x32cm-9x13in) s. W/C. 18-Dec-2 Ansorena, Madrid #241/R

LAI FONG (fl.1890-1910) Chinese
£1200 $1944 €1800 Four masted barque, Milton Stuart at sea (25x41cm-10x16in) s.i.indis.d.189. 21-May-3 Christie's, Kensington #567/R est:300-500
£4321 $7000 €6482 Sailing in choppy waters (66x91cm-26x36in) s.d.1896. 21-Jan-3 Christie's, Rockefeller NY #363/R
£4938 $8000 €7407 Four-masted sailing ship of County of Peebles (25x41cm-10x16in) s.d.1900. 21-Jan-3 Christie's, Rockefeller NY #361/R
£5556 $9000 €8334 The Lynton (66x89cm-26x35in) s.d.1887. 21-Jan-3 Christie's, Rockefeller NY #357/R
£6579 $10000 €9869 Sailing ship, Gleneright, in Chinese waters (66x91cm-26x36in) s.d.1893. 17-Aug-2 North East Auctions, Portsmouth #925/R est:10000-15000

LAIB, Wolfgang (1950-) German
Sculpture
£15625 $25000 €23438 Sealing wax house (20x106x16cm-8x42x6in) sealing wax wood rice executed 1987 prov. 15-May-3 Christie's, Rockefeller NY #358/R est:12000-18000
£28000 $45920 €42000 Reishaus, rice house (16x101x17cm-6x40x7in) marble rice prov.exhib. 7-Feb-3 Sotheby's, London #154/R est:8000-12000

LAIDLAY, William James (1846-1912) British
£267 $443 €387 Sailboats nearing a marshland (43x61cm-17x24in) s. 16-Jun-3 Waddingtons, Toronto #106/R (C.D 600)
£496 $770 €744 Woman and sheep in evening sunshine (72x114cm-28x45in) s. s.d.1891 verso. 8-Dec-2 Uppsala Auktionskammare, Uppsala #65/R (S.KR 7000)
£550 $902 €825 After the storm (63x86cm-25x34in) s. 5-Jun-3 Christie's, Kensington #755

LAIDMAN, Ida F (fl.1905-1935) British
£280 $456 €420 Still life of roses in a vase (51x41cm-20x16in) s. 28-Jan-3 Gorringes, Lewes #1706

L'AIN, Girod de (1926-) French?
£641 $1000 €962 Le tricot (64x53cm-25x21in) s. 18-Sep-2 Alderfer's, Hatfield #317/R

LAINE, Olavi (1922-) Finnish
£271 $428 €420 Landscape (60x74cm-24x29in) s. 19-Dec-2 Hagelstam, Helsinki #929
£286 $454 €420 Pine trees on beach (60x54cm-24x21in) s. 27-Feb-3 Hagelstam, Helsinki #914
£299 $476 €440 Winter (50x60cm-20x24in) s. 27-Feb-3 Hagelstam, Helsinki #856
£314 $484 €500 Nude (80x65cm-31x26in) s. 24-Oct-2 Hagelstam, Helsinki #937
£317 $519 €440 Harbour (55x65cm-22x26in) s. 5-Jun-3 Hagelstam, Helsinki #900
£327 $536 €500 Two beggars (100x73cm-39x29in) s.d.71. 9-Feb-3 Bukowskis, Helsinki #284/R
£374 $595 €550 Woman with waterjug (117x65cm-46x26in) s. 27-Feb-3 Hagelstam, Helsinki #855
£392 $643 €600 Winter in town (54x73cm-21x29in) s. 9-Feb-3 Bukowskis, Helsinki #285/R

LAING, Annie Rose (1869-1946) British
£6000 $9120 €9000 Blue ribbon (56x47cm-22x19in) s. 28-Aug-2 Sotheby's, London #913/R est:6000-8000
£16000 $24800 €24000 After dinner (51x61cm-20x24in) s. exhib. 31-Oct-2 Christie's, London #121/R est:15000-20000

LAING, Frank (1862-?) British
£645 $1019 €968 Haystacks (30x46cm-12x18in) s. 18-Nov-2 Waddingtons, Toronto #92/R (C.D 1600)

LAING, James Garden (1852-1915) British
Works on paper
£300 $468 €450 Peterborough (24x34cm-9x13in) s. W/C. 28-Mar-3 Bonhams, Edinburgh #157
£360 $558 €540 Glasgow Cathedral (35x25cm-14x10in) s. W/C. 5-Oct-2 Shapes, Edinburgh #258
£500 $780 €750 Dieppe (23x15cm-9x6in) s. W/C. 15-Oct-2 Gorringes, Lewes #2108/R

LAING, Tomson (fl.1890-1904) British
£560 $874 €840 At the tavern door (24x19cm-9x7in) s. 17-Oct-2 Bonhams, Edinburgh #211
£600 $978 €870 Snowy landscape with highland cattle (35x45cm-14x18in) s. 16-Jul-3 Sotheby's, Olympia #73/R
£900 $1404 €1350 Kelp gathering (30x60cm-12x24in) s. 17-Oct-2 Bonhams, Edinburgh #224/R

LAINS, Jornson (19/20th C) Scandinavian
£480 $749 €720 Plough team on a country lane (19x35cm-7x14in) s. panel. 7-Nov-2 Bonhams, Cornwall #832

LAIRESSE, Gerard de (1641-1711) Flemish
£20863 $33381 €29000 Resting by the spring (77x690cm-30x272in) s. prov. 17-May-3 Lempertz, Koln #1069/R est:35000-40000
£22000 $36740 €31900 Allegorical portrait of a family (121x174cm-48x69in) 9-Jul-3 Bonhams, New Bond Street #26/R est:15000-25000

LAIRESSE, Gerard de (attrib) (1641-1711) Flemish
£3200 $5344 €4640 Apelles painting (76x99cm-30x39in) prov. 11-Jul-3 Christie's, Kensington #114/R est:3000-4000
£14000 $23380 €20300 Marcus Curtius Dentatus leaping into the chasm (52x46cm-20x18in) oak panel prov. 10-Jul-3 Sotheby's, London #129/R est:12000-16000

LAIT, Edward (fl.1865-1869) British
Works on paper
£280 $434 €420 Country scene with thatched cottage, woman and dog by a stream (36x23cm-14x9in) s.d.1868 W/C. 4-Nov-2 Brightwells, Leominster #1266/R

LAIT, Edward Beecham (19th C) British
Works on paper
£550 $886 €825 Walkers by a cottage. Walkers passing sheep on a track (12x32cm-5x13in) s. W/C pair. 15-Jan-3 Cheffins Grain & Comins, Cambridge #369/R

LAITILA, Atte (1893-1972) Finnish
£360 $590 €500 Model (50x38cm-20x15in) s. 4-Jun-3 Bukowskis, Helsinki #335/R
£493 $794 €700 Summer idyll (63x123cm-25x48in) s. board. 10-May-3 Bukowskis, Helsinki #123/R
£1259 $2014 €1750 Baltic herring market (81x66cm-32x26in) s.d.1940. 17-May-3 Hagelstam, Helsinki #203/R est:1500

LAJOIE, Noel (1927-) Canadian
Works on paper
£363 $592 €545 Untitled (21x28cm-8x11in) s.d.5/9/54 ink W/C. 12-Feb-3 Iegor de Saint Hippolyte, Montreal #111 (C.D 900)

LAJOUE, Jacques de (1687-1761) French
£2658 $4200 €4200 Guitariste (25x12cm-10x5in) panel prov. 27-Nov-2 Christie's, Paris #46/R

LAJOUE, Jacques de (attrib) (1687-1761) French
Works on paper
£250 $388 €375 Scene Galante (18x9cm-7x4in) W/C over pen ink prov. 9-Dec-2 Bonhams, New Bond Street #17

LAKE, Albert (1903-1990) American
£1923 $3000 €2885 Lily lodge (91x76cm-36x30in) 19-Oct-2 David Dike, Dallas #295/R est:2000-4000
£2468 $3850 €3702 Danilova (132x132cm-52x52in) 19-Oct-2 David Dike, Dallas #309/R est:3000-6000

LAKHOVSKY, Arnold Borisovich (1880-1937) Russian
£1447 $2257 €2300 Baltic farmstead with children playing (50x68cm-20x27in) s.cyrillicd.1925 panel. 21-Sep-2 Bolland & Marotz, Bremen #620/R est:2000
£1500 $2370 €2250 Landscape (50x61cm-20x24in) s. 26-Nov-2 Christie's, Kensington #23/R est:1500-2500

LALANNE, Claude (20th C) French
Sculpture
£10000 $16400 €15000 La dormeuse (34x38x28cm-13x15x11in) init.d.94 num.1/1 bronze copper prov. 7-Feb-3 Sotheby's, London #211/R est:10000-15000

LALANNE, François-Xavier (1924-) French
Sculpture
£6897 $11034 €10000 Sheep (89x100cm-35x39in) s.num.34/250 bronze stone. 15-Mar-3 De Vuyst, Lokeren #498/R est:7500-10000
£6897 $11034 €10000 Sheep (89x100cm-35x39in) s.num.32/250 bronze stone. 15-Mar-3 De Vuyst, Lokeren #499/R est:7500-10000
£7692 $12077 €12000 Bison americain (35x36x11cm-14x14x4in) mono.num.7/8 brown pat bronze exec.1983 lit. 11-Dec-2 Artcurial Briest, Paris #738a/R est:12000
£9655 $15448 €14000 Sheep (87x93cm-34x37in) s.num.238/250 bronze stone. 15-Mar-3 De Vuyst, Lokeren #500/R est:7500-10000
£11500 $18860 €17250 Sea turtle II (32x94x62cm-13x37x24in) init.num.4/8 copper plants wheels prov. 7-Feb-3 Sotheby's, London #212/R est:12000-15000

LALAUZE, Alphonse (1872-?) French
Works on paper
£6282 $9863 €9800 Rencontre (54x44cm-21x17in) s.d.1909 W/C. 16-Dec-2 Rabourdin & Choppin de Janvry, Paris #54/R est:13000

LALIBERTE, Alfred (1878-1953) Canadian
£215 $335 €323 Self portrait (51x41cm-20x16in) i.verso. 25-Mar-3 Ritchie, Toronto #130/R (C.D 500)
Sculpture
£1210 $1911 €1815 Portrait of Charles Tulley (43cm-17in) s.d.1938 bronze prov. 18-Nov-2 Sotheby's, Toronto #17/R est:4000-5000 (C.D 3000)
£1754 $2614 €2631 L'homme et la pierre (37x57cm-15x22in) s.i. bronze. 26-Jun-2 Iegor de Saint Hippolyte, Montreal #57b (C.D 4000)
£2305 $3572 €3458 L'etoile tombee (17cm-7in) s. bronze. 3-Dec-2 Joyner, Toronto #217/R est:2000-3000 (C.D 5600)

LALIQUE, Suzanne (1899-?) French
£651 $1022 €950 Nature morte aux journaux (65x54cm-26x21in) s.d.1930. 15-Apr-3 Galerie Moderne, Brussels #402/R

LALL, Oscar de (1903-1971) Canadian
£305 $479 €458 Paysage d'automne (51x66cm-20x26in) s. 10-Dec-2 Pinneys, Montreal #12 (C.D 750)
£447 $702 €671 Rue St Paul, Montreal (30x41cm-12x16in) s. board. 10-Dec-2 Pinneys, Montreal #174 (C.D 1100)

LALLEMAND, Georges (1575-1635) French
Works on paper
£9877 $16000 €14816 Supper at Emmaus. Right-hand pilgrim (22x29cm-9x11in) chk pen ink wash htd white double-sided. 22-Jan-3 Christie's, Rockefeller NY #60/R est:12000

LALLEMAND, Jean Baptiste (1710-1805) French
£4403 $6780 €7000 Baigneuses pres d'une fontaine antique (64x53cm-25x21in) 25-Oct-2 Tajan, Paris #136/R est:4000-6000
£8392 $14014 €12000 Port mediterraneen avec paysans sur le rivage (72x90cm-28x35in) s. 25-Jun-3 Tajan, Paris #68/R est:12000-18000
Works on paper
£507 $791 €750 Etudes de figures (14x18cm-6x7in) crayon wash. 26-Mar-3 Piasa, Paris #70
£541 $843 €800 Paysage italien (26x44cm-10x17in) pen ink wash. 26-Mar-3 Piasa, Paris #67
£638 $1066 €900 Quatre esquisses d'Orientaux en differentes postures (21x16cm-8x6in) pen black ink grey wash. 19-Jun-3 Piasa, Paris #96
£1216 $1897 €1800 Halte des pelerins (31x48cm-12x19in) W/C gouache wash over crayon. 26-Mar-3 Piasa, Paris #58/R

L'ALLEMAND, Siegmund (1840-1910) Austrian
Works on paper
£818 $1267 €1300 Storming of the Konigshugel from Oversee (41x61cm-16x24in) s.d.1864 W/C. 1-Oct-2 Dorotheum, Vienna #194/R est:2200-2900

LALOUE, Auguste (19th C) French
£1410 $2228 €2200 Dans l'atelier (56x81cm-22x32in) s.d.99. 18-Nov-2 Tajan, Paris #166 est:2400-2600

LALOUX, Victor Alexandre Frederic (circle) (1850-1937) French
Works on paper
£8805 $14000 €13208 Architectural fantasy (59x197cm-23x78in) s.i. pencil W/C. 5-Mar-3 Christie's, Rockefeller NY #66/R est:8000-12000

LALOY, Yves (1928-) French
£2740 $4301 €4000 Barques a maree basse (38x61cm-15x24in) s. 15-Apr-3 Laurence Calmels, Paris #4326/R est:1200
£3562 $5592 €5200 Untitled (22x27cm-9x11in) 15-Apr-3 Laurence Calmels, Paris #4327/R est:2000
£8219 $12904 €12000 Untitled (65x92cm-26x36in) lit. 15-Apr-3 Laurence Calmels, Paris #4324/R est:2000
£10959 $17205 €16000 Untitled (89x130cm-35x51in) 15-Apr-3 Laurence Calmels, Paris #4325/R est:4000
£54795 $85479 €80000 Les petits pois sont verts, les petits poissons rouges (60x92cm-24x36in) exhib.lit. 14-Apr-3 Laurence Calmels, Paris #4005/R

LALUHA, Milan (1930-) Czechoslovakian
£583 $851 €875 Apples (34x43cm-13x17in) board painted c.1955-57. 4-Jun-2 SOGA, Bratislava #285/R est:25000 (SL.K 37000)
£1026 $1591 €1539 Hay maker (41x61cm-16x24in) painted c.1968. 3-Dec-2 SOGA, Bratislava #286/R est:35000 (SL.K 65000)

LAM QUA (attrib) (19th C) Chinese
£4321 $7000 €6482 Portrait of ship's captain (40x35cm-16x14in) prov. 21-Jan-3 Christie's, Rockefeller NY #354/R

LAM, Wilfredo (1902-1982) Cuban
£9615 $15096 €15000 Figure (30x40cm-12x16in) s.d.1967. 19-Nov-2 Finarte, Milan #211/R est:13000-15000
£14103 $22141 €22000 Totem (50x60cm-20x24in) s.d.1974. 23-Nov-2 Meeting Art, Vercelli #118/R
£18987 $30000 €30000 Totem (50x40cm-20x16in) s.d.1965. 30-Nov-2 Farsetti, Prato #711/R est:32000
£28846 $42115 €45000 Totem (73x60cm-29x24in) s.d.1963 prov.lit. 5-Jun-2 Il Ponte, Milan #134/R est:30000-40000
£35897 $56359 €56000 Untitled (50x70cm-20x28in) s.d.1964 prov. 24-Nov-2 Laurence Calmels, Paris #170/R est:40000
£42683 $70000 €61890 Mascara (72x60cm-28x24in) s.d.1940 prov.exhib.lit. 27-May-3 Sotheby's, New York #23
£47468 $75000 €75000 Untitled (54x80cm-21x31in) s.d.1959. 30-Nov-2 Farsetti, Prato #710/R est:90000
£69000 $106260 €103500 La colombe moire (70x130cm-28x51in) s.d.59 s.i.d.verso oil on jute prov.exhib.lit. 22-Oct-2 Sotheby's, London #379/R est:80000-100000
£89172 $140000 €133758 Warrior (73x84cm-29x33in) s.d.1948 prov.exhib.lit. 20-Nov-2 Christie's, Rockefeller NY #22/R est:130000-160000
£89172 $140000 €133758 Composition (161x130cm-63x51in) s.d.1963 prov.lit. 19-Nov-2 Sotheby's, New York #33/R est:200000
£91463 $150000 €132621 Sans titre (127x110cm-50x43in) s.d.1964 prov.exhib.lit. 27-May-3 Sotheby's, New York #24
£150685 $235068 €220000 Roi-mangue (65x77cm-26x30in) s.d.1944. 14-Apr-3 Laurence Calmels, Paris #4049/R est:150000
Sculpture
£2013 $3200 €3020 Pajaro de oro. Pajaro de plateado (23cm-9in) i. metal two. 3-Mar-3 Swann Galleries, New York #75/R est:3000-5000
Works on paper
£2516 $4000 €3774 Figural pieces (37x46cm-15x18in) s. mixed media three. 7-Mar-3 Skinner, Boston #635/R est:2000-4000
£3846 $6000 €5769 Untitled (49x63cm-19x25in) s.d.1957 ink. 14-Oct-2 Butterfields, San Francisco #2136/R est:7000-9000
£4166 $6500 €6249 Untitled (63x49cm-25x19in) s.d.57 ink. 14-Oct-2 Butterfields, San Francisco #2137/R est:7000-9000
£5128 $8051 €8000 Totem (70x50cm-28x20in) s.d.1970 pastel paper on cardboard. 23-Nov-2 Meeting Art, Vercelli #111/R
£5319 $8617 €7500 Personaje (30x22cm-12x9in) s.d.14-2-1941 ink sketch. 20-May-3 Segre, Madrid #123/R est:7500
£6000 $9840 €8700 L'Oiseau, study of exotic bird (57x75cm-22x30in) s.d.1958 pastel. 5-Jun-3 Morphets, Harrogate #377/R est:6000-8000
£6289 $9811 €10000 Peasant woman (60x50cm-24x20in) s.d.1927 pencil dr exhib.lit. 17-Sep-2 Segre, Madrid #152/R est:11500
£7000 $11690 €10150 Oiseau bleu (66x48cm-26x19in) s.d.1968 s.i.d. verso pastel prov. 27-Jun-3 Christie's, London #110/R est:8000-12000
£8411 $13457 €12196 Les oisseaux (57x42cm-22x17in) s.d.1953 pastel chl. 15-May-3 Louis Morton, Mexico #100/R est:140000-150000 (M.P 136000)
£9756 $16000 €14146 Sin titulo (72x52cm-28x20in) s.d.62 mixed media paper on canvas prov. 27-May-3 Sotheby's, New York #75
£12025 $19000 €19000 Totem (63x48cm-25x19in) s.d.1958 W/C chl. 29-Nov-2 Farsetti, Prato #550/R est:21000

£17123 $26884 €25000 Untitled (16x16cm-6x6in) W/C. 15-Apr-3 Laurence Calmels, Paris #4331/R est:15000
£28767 $45164 €42000 Untitled (51x62cm-20x24in) s.i.d.1946 ink prov. 15-Apr-3 Laurence Calmels, Paris #4329/R est:40000
£146341 $240000 €219512 Sin titulo (98x72cm-39x28in) gouache paper on canvas exec.c.1937 prov.lit. 28-May-3 Christie's, Rockefeller NY #27/R est:150000-200000
£157534 $247329 €230000 Attendu (106x84cm-42x33in) s.d.42 i.verso crayon as. prov.exhib.lit. 15-Apr-3 Laurence Calmels, Paris #4330/R est:150000
£226027 $354863 €330000 Untitled (64x97cm-25x38in) s.i.d.1944 mixed media prov.lit. 15-Apr-3 Laurence Calmels, Paris #4332/R est:150000

LAM, Wilfredo and LEBEL, Jean Jacques (20th C) Cuban/French
Works on paper
£10274 $16130 €15000 Untitled (50x65cm-20x26in) s. col crayon exec.1959 prov. 15-Apr-3 Laurence Calmels, Paris #4333/R est:15000

LAMAS, Menchu (1954-) Spanish
£2830 $4358 €4500 Untitled (195x97cm-77x38in) s.d.1987 verso oil mixed media prov.lit. 28-Oct-2 Segre, Madrid #157/R

LAMASURE, Edwin (jnr) (1866-1916) American
Works on paper
£705 $1100 €1058 Twilight (65x63cm-26x25in) s. W/C. 20-Sep-2 Sloan, North Bethesda #355/R est:500-700

LAMAY, Art (20th C) American
Works on paper
£2025 $3200 €3038 Great blue heron (86x62cm-34x24in) s. W/C gouache on board. 3-Apr-3 Christie's, Rockefeller NY #229/R est:1500-2500

LAMAZARES, Anton (1954-) Spanish
£6038 $9298 €9600 Macarea (126x122cm-50x48in) s.d.1981-82 oil mixed media cardboard prov.exhib. 28-Oct-2 Segre, Madrid #156/R est:9600
Works on paper
£631 $984 €947 XEUX (114x73cm-45x29in) mixed media panel. 6-Nov-2 AB Stockholms Auktionsverk #843/R (S.KR 9000)
£833 $1292 €1300 Mecias (70x50cm-28x20in) s. mixed media exec.1984 prov. 7-Dec-2 De Vuyst, Lokeren #178

LAMB, Charles Vincent (1893-1965) Irish
£1096 $1721 €1600 Sheep at Dooagh, Achill (45x59cm-18x23in) s. canvasboard. 15-Apr-3 De Veres Art Auctions, Dublin #86/R est:1000-1500
£2051 $3179 €3200 Soft day at Rostrevor (26x35cm-10x14in) s. board. 3-Dec-2 Bonhams & James Adam, Dublin #31/R est:3000-5000
£2516 $3925 €4000 Summer day on road to Maam Cross (27x36cm-11x14in) s. i.d.1938 verso panel. 17-Sep-2 Whyte's, Dublin #61/R est:4000-5000
£2685 $4322 €4000 In the village of Carraroe (25x36cm-10x14in) s. i.verso panel. 18-Feb-3 Whyte's, Dublin #80/R est:4000-5000
£2770 $4322 €4100 Day in winter (32x40cm-13x16in) s. board exhib. 26-Mar-3 James Adam, Dublin #126/R est:2000-3000
£3145 $4906 €5000 Break in the clouds, west of Ireland (32x39cm-13x15in) s. board prov. 17-Sep-2 Whyte's, Dublin #134/R est:5000-7000
£3165 $4905 €5000 Blossomed furze, Connemara (27x36cm-11x14in) s. board prov. 24-Sep-2 De Veres Art Auctions, Dublin #126/R est:5000-7000
£3333 $5167 €5200 West of Ireland landscape with cottages (29x39cm-11x15in) board. 3-Dec-2 Bonhams & James Adam, Dublin #30/R est:4000-6000
£3378 $5270 €5000 Connemara river landscape (23x33cm-9x13in) s. board. 26-Mar-3 James Adam, Dublin #45/R est:4000-6000
£3611 $5742 €5200 Innishmaan (33x41cm-13x16in) s. board. 29-Apr-3 Whyte's, Dublin #106/R est:6000-8000
£4054 $6324 €6000 Coastal inlet (24x29cm-9x11in) s. board. 26-Mar-3 James Adam, Dublin #113/R est:4000-6000
£6164 $9678 €9000 West of Ireland coastal landscape with cottage (32x40cm-13x16in) s. board. 15-Apr-3 De Veres Art Auctions, Dublin #228/R est:6000-8000

LAMB, F Mortimer (1861-1936) American
£886 $1400 €1329 Sunlight on woodland boulder (91x66cm-36x26in) s.d.1904. 17-Nov-2 CRN Auctions, Cambridge #37/R

LAMB, Henry (1883-1960) British
£300 $495 €435 Breton woman working (51x41cm-20x16in) oil crayon prov. 3-Jul-3 Christie's, Kensington #404
£1100 $1705 €1650 Square at Aallon (30x40cm-12x16in) s.d.27 canvasboard exhib. 3-Dec-2 Bonhams, New Bond Street #3/R est:1200-1800
£1400 $2254 €2100 Autumn flowers (51x41cm-20x16in) s.d.30 board. 18-Feb-3 Bonhams, Knightsbridge #202/R est:1500-2000
£2800 $4452 €4200 Felicia (61x51cm-24x20in) exhib. 26-Feb-3 Sotheby's, Olympia #223/R est:3000-5000
£16000 $26240 €24000 Portrait of Stephen Tomlin (86x69cm-34x27in) s.d.32 prov.exhib.lit. 6-Jun-3 Christie's, London #23/R est:10000-15000
Works on paper
£260 $419 €390 Portrait of a soldier (26x18cm-10x7in) s. pencil. 15-Jan-3 Cheffins Grain & Comins, Cambridge #398/R
£550 $908 €798 Harwich Dock 1940 (24x32cm-9x13in) pencil W/C ink prov. 3-Jul-3 Christie's, Kensington #445
£650 $1066 €975 Gola islander I (21x13cm-8x5in) pencil executed 1913 prov. 6-Jun-3 Christie's, London #80/R

LAMB, John (?-1909) British
£649 $1025 €974 Untitled, military portrait (128x102cm-50x40in) s.d.1885 prov. 7-Apr-3 Shapiro, Sydney #496 (A.D 1700)

LAMBA, Jacqueline (1910-1993) American
Works on paper
£1380 $2304 €2000 Sans titre (47x62cm-19x24in) s.d.70 ink wash ink dr. 10-Jul-3 Artcurial Briest, Paris #316 est:1000-1200

LAMBDIN, George Cochran (1830-1896) American
£1437 $2300 €2084 Blossoms (41x30cm-16x12in) s.d.1864 i.verso panel. 16-May-3 Skinner, Boston #81/R est:1000-1500
£2400 $3768 €3600 Study of roses (39x32cm-15x13in) s.d.79. 16-Apr-3 Christie's, Kensington #878/R est:2000-4000
£7792 $12000 €11688 Goldfish (36x28cm-14x11in) s.d.59 i.verso. 27-Oct-2 Grogan, Boston #31 est:3000-5000
£14194 $22000 €21291 Courtship (58x46cm-23x18in) s.d.1864-65 prov. 5-Dec-2 Christie's, Rockefeller NY #22/R est:20000-30000

LAMBDIN, James Reid (1807-1889) American
£373 $600 €560 Portrait of a lady (51x43cm-20x17in) s. 15-Jan-3 Boos Gallery, Michigan #654/R

LAMBEAUX, Jef (1852-1908) Belgian
Sculpture
£962 $1510 €1500 Le baiser (60x65cm-24x26in) s. green pat bronze. 10-Dec-2 Vanderkindere, Brussels #415/R est:1500-2000
£1013 $1580 €1600 Faucheur (77cm-30in) s. green pat bronze. 16-Sep-2 Horta, Bruxelles #140
£1076 $1678 €1700 Woman's bust (54cm-21in) s. brown pat bronze. 21-Oct-2 Bernaerts, Antwerp #122/R est:2000-2500
£1139 $1777 €1800 Semeur (77cm-30in) s. green pat bronze. 16-Sep-2 Horta, Bruxelles #142
£1154 $1788 €1800 Faune et muse (59cm-23in) s. col pat bronze. 9-Dec-2 Horta, Bruxelles #83/R est:2000-3000
£1218 $1888 €1900 Danseuse aux raisins (61cm-24in) s. green pat bronze. 9-Dec-2 Horta, Bruxelles #84 est:1500-2000
£1408 $2268 €2000 Bust of a bacchante (61cm-24in) s. yellow pat bronze socle. 12-May-3 Bernaerts, Antwerp #61 est:2000-3000
£1572 $2421 €2500 Baiser (57cm-22in) s. bronze. 22-Oct-2 Campo & Campo, Antwerp #159/R
£1583 $2532 €2200 Nu allonge lisant (55x70x33cm-22x28x13in) marble. 13-May-3 Palais de Beaux Arts, Brussels #89/R est:2000-3000
£1899 $3000 €3000 Le baiser (57x62x24cm-22x24x9in) bronze. 26-Nov-2 Palais de Beaux Arts, Brussels #339/R est:3000-4000
£2446 $3914 €3400 Couple (74x45x33cm-29x18x13in) s. pat bronze Cast Usine Vojave Ste Ane lit. 13-May-3 Palais de Beaux Arts, Brussels #88/R est:3500-4500
£2483 $3972 €3600 Chasseur d'aigle (87x64cm-34x25in) s. dark brown pat bronze iron base. 15-Mar-3 De Vuyst, Lokeren #180/R est:4000-5000
£3165 $5000 €5000 Wrestlers (68x82cm-27x32in) s. verso. 27-Nov-2 Wiener Kunst Auktionen, Vienna #558/R est:5000-8000
£4029 $6446 €5600 Cain et Abel (93x93x50cm-37x37x20in) s. pat bronze Cast G Paternotte. 13-May-3 Palais de Beaux Arts, Brussels #94/R est:4750-6000
£15278 $24292 €22000 Centaure entoure de nus (105x84x70cm-41x33x28in) s. bronze Cast Nationale des Bronzes. 29-Apr-3 Campo, Vlaamse Kaai #182/R est:23000-28000

LAMBERT, Andre (20th C) French
Works on paper
£263 $415 €410 Aux postes de manoeuvre (44x60cm-17x24in) W/C. 12-Nov-2 Thierry & Lannon, Brest #67/R

LAMBERT, C (?) ?
£1100 $1716 €1650 The old mill at Aber. N. Wales. Autumn near Newcastle, Emlin. S. Wales (51x76cm-20x30in) s. pair. 15-Oct-2 Gorringes, Lewes #2330/R est:1000-1500

LAMBERT, Camille Nicholas (1876-?) Belgian
£1290 $2039 €2000 Carnaval (18x33cm-7x13in) s. panel. 17-Dec-2 Rossini, Paris #100/R
£3205 $4968 €5000 Portrait de famille (95x124cm-37x49in) s. 9-Dec-2 Horta, Bruxelles #139/R est:5000-7000
£5319 $8883 €7500 Jeune femme dans le jardin fleuri (54x68cm-21x27in) s. 17-Jun-3 Palais de Beaux Arts, Brussels #605/R est:7500-10000

LAMBERT, Eugène (1825-1900) French
£920 $1500 €1380 Les chiens de repos (65x54cm-26x21in) s. 11-Feb-3 Bonhams & Doyles, New York #152/R est:3000-5000
£3038 $4739 €4800 Interior with playing kittens (34x26cm-13x10in) s. 21-Oct-2 Bernaerts, Antwerp #86/R est:750-1000

LAMBERT, George (circle) (1700-1765) British
£19000 $31540 €28500 Extensive wooded river landscape with figures on a path and a drover with his cattle (95x110cm-37x43in) 12-Jun-3 Sotheby's, London #105/R est:8000-12000

LAMBERT, George Washington (1873-1930) Australian
£681 $1035 €1022 Blue Mountains, open air study (25x35cm-10x14in) s.d.1922 wood panel. 27-Aug-2 Goodman, Sydney #98 (A.D 1900)
£2857 $4514 €4286 Pig rooter, standing female (35x53cm-14x21in) s.d.1910 prov.exhib.lit. 17-Nov-2 Sotheby's, Paddington #58/R est:12000-18000 (A.D 8000)

Works on paper
£357 $561 €536 She trips across the street (23x16cm-9x6in) s.d.1900 gouache ink. 25-Nov-2 Christie's, Melbourne #346/R (A.D 1000)
£714 $1121 €1071 No assets, at an at home (17x24cm-7x9in) s.i. gouache. 25-Nov-2 Christie's, Melbourne #248/R (A.D 2000)
£720 $1159 €1080 Portrait of a gentleman (27x19cm-11x7in) s. pencil. 6-May-3 Christie's, Melbourne #305 est:2000-3000 (A.D 1800)

LAMBERT, Ray (1889-1969) French
Works on paper
£286 $454 €420 Lion de profil (20x25cm-8x10in) st.sig. crayon. 27-Feb-3 Chochon-Barre & Allardi, Paris #217/R
£306 $487 €450 Tete de lion (25x20cm-10x8in) st.sig. crayon. 27-Feb-3 Chochon-Barre & Allardi, Paris #203

LAMBERT, Ronald (1923-1995) Australian
£854 $1307 €1281 Marat sade (120x90cm-47x35in) painted c.1960 prov. 26-Aug-2 Sotheby's, Paddington #681 est:1000-2000 (A.D 2400)

LAMBERT, Ted R (1905-1960) American
£4430 $7000 €6424 Mt. McKinley from the Susitna country (25x30cm-10x12in) s.d.1940 board prov. 26-Jul-3 Coeur d'Alene, Hayden #62/R est:10000-15000

LAMBERT, Terence (1951-) British
Works on paper
£800 $1312 €1200 Red grouse in a highland landscape (45x65cm-18x26in) s. W/C. 3-Jun-3 Bonhams, Knightsbridge #25/R

LAMBERT-RUCKI, Jean (1888-1967) French
£2721 $4327 €4000 Profils dans la ville (40x50cm-16x20in) s.d.1922 cardboard. 21-Mar-3 Rieunier, Bailly-Pommery, Mathias, Paris #118/R
£3481 $5396 €5500 L'accordeoniste (73x54cm-29x21in) s. cardboard on canvas. 28-Sep-2 Cornette de St.Cyr, Paris #168/R est:6000-8000
£5102 $8112 €7500 Femme aux amphores (73x54cm-29x21in) s.d.1919 cardboard. 24-Mar-3 Digard, Paris #39/R
£8148 $11570 €13200 Passant dans la ville (50x61cm-20x24in) s. painteda. 16-Mar-3 Eric Pillon, Calais #268/R
£8562 $13442 €12500 La rencontre (51x73cm-20x29in) s.d.1926 i.verso. 21-Apr-3 Rabourdin & Choppin de Janvry, Paris #207/R est:6000-7000
£9554 $14904 €15000 Figures dans la ville (43x32cm-17x13in) s. panel. 10-Nov-2 Eric Pillon, Calais #220/R

Sculpture
£1209 $1983 €1850 Christ (90x80cm-35x31in) s. bronze wooden cross. 7-Feb-3 Oger, Dumont, Paris #157/R
£2878 $4604 €4000 Petit roi mage (30cm-12in) s. num.1/8 polychrome pat.bronze. 19-May-3 Tajan, Paris #u/R est:4000-5000
£3957 $6331 €5500 Masque aux yeux bleus (9x6cm-4x2in) s. num.II/IV polychrome pat.bronze. 19-May-3 Tajan, Paris #a/R est:2500-3000
£4317 $6907 €6000 L'ombre et l'ane. s. num.1/8 polychrome pat.bronze lit. 19-May-3 Tajan, Paris #y/R est:6000-8000
£4375 $7000 €6344 Umbrella man (41cm-16in) welded iron exec.c.1950. 16-May-3 Skinner, Boston #367/R est:6000-8000
£6329 $10000 €10000 Double masque (14cm-6in) s.d.1922 lit. 26-Nov-2 Tajan, Paris #79/R est:8000-10000
£6475 $10360 €9000 La famille (36x18x9cm-14x7x4in) s. polychrome pat.bronze lit. 19-May-3 Tajan, Paris #n/R est:10000-12000
£7914 $12663 €11000 Taureau de profil (63x60x15cm-25x24x6in) s. polychrome pat.bronze lit. 19-May-3 Tajan, Paris #t/R est:12000-15000
£7914 $12663 €11000 Le combat (61x12x29cm-24x5x11in) s. num.I/IV polychrome pat.bronze. 19-May-3 Tajan, Paris #x/R est:12000-15000
£7968 $12749 €11075 Oiseau et son petit (153x24x24cm-60x9x9in) s. num.I/IV polychrome pat.bronze. 19-May-3 Tajan, Paris #o/R est:12000-15000
£20144 $32231 €28000 Le boeuf derriere la haie (123x84cm-48x33in) s. polychrome pat.bronze lit. 19-May-3 Tajan, Paris #d/R est:30000-35000
£28000 $46760 €40600 La lune (230cm-91in) painted plaster on wooden base. 27-Jun-3 Christie's, London #109/R est:10000-15000

Works on paper
£278 $458 €400 Agneau pascal (60x53cm-24x21in) bears studio st. chl. 2-Jul-3 Artcurial Briest, Paris #94/R
£350 $547 €550 Anneau de Saturne (21x13cm-8x5in) crayon Chinese ink htd silver dr prov. 6-Nov-2 Tajan, Paris #7/R
£755 $1170 €1200 La jambe de bois (44x21cm-17x8in) s.d. graphite dr. 4-Oct-2 Tajan, Paris #136
£2258 $3568 €3500 Fenetres (67x24cm-26x9in) s.d.31 pastel prov. 18-Dec-2 Digard, Paris #189/R

LAMBERTI, Lamberto (1925-) Italian
£272 $433 €400 Snowfall (60x80cm-24x31in) s. masonite painted 1996. 1-Mar-3 Meeting Art, Vercelli #454
£417 $663 €600 Composition with fruit (60x80cm-24x31in) s. 1-May-3 Meeting Art, Vercelli #116
£476 $757 €700 Still life (80x60cm-31x24in) s. s.i.verso masonite painted 1990. 1-Mar-3 Meeting Art, Vercelli #507
£506 $790 €800 Interior (100x70cm-39x28in) s. s.i.d.1988 verso. 14-Sep-2 Meeting Art, Vercelli #492
£590 $939 €850 Two friends (100x120cm-39x47in) s. 1-May-3 Meeting Art, Vercelli #329
£694 $1104 €1000 Intimacy (150x100cm-59x39in) s. painted 1990 lit. 1-May-3 Meeting Art, Vercelli #576
£817 $1307 €1250 White houses (120x140cm-47x55in) s. s.i.verso. 4-Jan-3 Meeting Art, Vercelli #722
£915 $1464 €1400 Landscape (100x120cm-39x47in) s. painted 1990 lit. 4-Jan-3 Meeting Art, Vercelli #504
£962 $1510 €1500 Model (150x120cm-59x47in) s. painted 1990. 23-Nov-2 Meeting Art, Vercelli #143/R
£1190 $1893 €1750 Nap (120x140cm-47x55in) s. s.verso. 1-Mar-3 Meeting Art, Vercelli #499
£1635 $2566 €2550 Sticky day (120x200cm-47x79in) s. s.i.d.1990 verso exhib. 23-Nov-2 Meeting Art, Vercelli #220/R

LAMBILLOTTE, George (1915-) Belgian
£446 $700 €669 Leisurely afternoon (46x56cm-18x22in) s. 23-Nov-2 Jackson's, Cedar Falls #32/R

LAMBINET, Émile (1815-1877) French
£1698 $2632 €2700 Paysage de Normandie (43x65cm-17x26in) 29-Oct-2 Artcurial Briest, Paris #57/R est:2000
£3418 $5400 €5400 La vie a la ferme (33x47cm-13x19in) s.d.1876. 1-Dec-2 Peron, Melun #41

LAMBOURNE, Nigel (1919-) British
Works on paper
£280 $451 €420 Standing woman (66x50cm-26x20in) s. chl. 14-Jan-3 Bonhams, Knightsbridge #37

LAMBRE, Sylvain (1889-1958) Belgian
£280 $437 €440 Promeneur au coucher du soleil (60x70cm-24x28in) s. 11-Nov-2 Horta, Bruxelles #692

LAMBRECHTS, Jan Baptist (1680-1731) Flemish
£1226 $1937 €1900 Vegetable seller (32x27cm-13x11in) 20-Dec-2 Tajan, Paris #78
£1400 $2170 €2100 Family sitting around a table outside a house (39x49cm-15x19in) 30-Oct-2 Bonhams, New Bond Street #25/R est:1000-2000

LAMBRECHTS, Jan Baptist (attrib) (1680-1731) Flemish
£1923 $2981 €3000 Figures at tables outside (41x33cm-16x13in) i. verso prov. 5-Dec-2 Dr Fritz Nagel, Stuttgart #619/R est:5000

LAMBRICHS, Edmond Alfonse Charles (1830-1887) Belgian
£504 $806 €700 Femme au miroir (70x50cm-28x20in) s. 13-May-3 Vanderkindere, Brussels #248
£959 $1496 €1400 Still life of summer flowers and fruit on table (70x95cm-28x37in) s. board. 10-Apr-3 Van Ham, Cologne #1559

LAMBRON DES PILTIERES, Albert (1836-?) French
£800 $1248 €1200 Gentleman gardener in 18th Century dress (20x13cm-8x5in) s. 26-Mar-3 Hamptons Fine Art, Godalming #138/R
£1739 $2800 €3000 Portrait of a harlequin (46x38cm-18x15in) s. 9-May-3 Eldred, East Dennis #765/R
£37975 $60000 €56963 Young widow (216x126cm-85x50in) s.d.1869. 24-Apr-3 Sotheby's, New York #83/R est:70000-90000

L'AMBROSIO, Alberto (?) Italian
£1500 $2325 €2250 Holy Family (137x104cm-54x41in) i. after Raphael prov. 31-Oct-2 Duke & Son, Dorchester #224/R est:500-1000

LAMEN, Christoffel Jacobsz van der (c.1606-1651) Flemish
£11000 $17270 €16500 Elegant company at table on a terrace (51x79cm-20x31in) with sig. panel prov. 13-Dec-2 Christie's, Kensington #31/R est:7000-10000
£15000 $23550 €22500 Elegant company drinking and conversing on a terrace (74x102cm-29x40in) copper prov.exhib. 12-Dec-2 Sotheby's, London #140/R est:15000-20000

LAMEN, Christoffel Jacobsz van der (attrib) (c.1606-1651) Flemish
£1206 $1869 €1809 Allegory of one of the five senses (50x40cm-20x16in) panel. 4-Dec-2 AB Stockholms Auktionsverk #1940/R est:18000-20000 (S.KR 17000)

LAMERS, Kiki (1964-) Dutch
£4487 $6955 €7000 Woman bathing (125x125cm-49x49in) s.d.1992 on stretcher acrylic. 3-Dec-2 Christie's, Amsterdam #309/R est:4000-6000

LAMI, Alphonse (1822-1867) French
Sculpture
£1367 $2187 €1900 Buste de Michel Chevalier (55x27cm-22x11in) s. white Carrare marble. 16-May-3 Beaussant & Lefèvre, Paris #46/R est:750

LAMI, Eugène Louis (1800-1890) French
£256 $405 €400 Proclamation de Louis Philippe (16x20cm-6x8in) s.d.30 i.verso exhib. 15-Nov-2 Beaussant & Lefèvre, Paris #74
Works on paper
£304 $474 €450 Frere et soeur (31x23cm-12x9in) s.d.1834 pen Chinese ink W/C wash. 31-Mar-3 Piasa, Paris #93
£633 $1000 €1000 Etudes de soldats (17x23cm-7x9in) s. W/C gouache over crayon. 28-Nov-2 Tajan, Paris #163/R
£696 $1086 €1100 Les grands escaliers (36x38cm-14x15in) sketch canvas. 20-Oct-2 Galerie de Chartres, Chartres #109
£759 $1200 €1200 La Dame du Lac, d'apres Walter Scott (28x22cm-11x9in) s. col chk W/C prov.exhib.lit. 27-Nov-2 Christie's, Paris #249/R
£780 $1303 €1100 Officier a cheval (27x22cm-11x9in) s.d.1820 W/C gouache black crayon. 19-Jun-3 Piasa, Paris #161/R
£851 $1421 €1200 Officier Prussien, hussard (16x11cm-6x4in) s. W/C gouache black crayon. 19-Jun-3 Piasa, Paris #162
£993 $1658 €1400 Le jeune homme endormi (13x18cm-5x7in) mono.d.1887 W/C. 23-Jun-3 Beaussant & Lefèvre, Paris #292/R
£1139 $1800 €1709 Fete a Venise, le bucentaure devsnt l'Eglide de La Salute (28x45cm-11x18in) init.d.1866 pencil W/C gouache prov. 24-Apr-3 Sotheby's, New York #172/R
£1290 $2000 €1935 Wedding festivities of Louis XVI and Marie Antoinette at the Royal Theatre, Versailles (14x28cm-6x11in) init.d.1855 pencil W/C gouache prov. 29-Oct-2 Sotheby's, New York #47/R est:4000-6000
£1399 $2000 €2099 Carmosine (10x16cm-4x6in) W/C exhib. 23-Jan-3 Swann Galleries, New York #306/R est:2000-3000
£2051 $3221 €3200 Scene galante (21x41cm-8x16in) s.d.1875 gouache. 13-Dec-2 Pierre Berge, Paris #48/R
£2258 $3500 €3387 Military leaders on horseback (28x18cm-11x7in) init.d.81 one init.d.1881 W/C gouache two prov. 29-Oct-2 Sotheby's, New York #49/R est:7000-9000
£2411 $4027 €3400 Il faut au'une porte soit ouverte ou fermee (10x14cm-4x6in) W/C prov. 23-Jun-3 Beaussant & Lefèvre, Paris #291/R est:2000-2500
£2848 $4500 €4500 Etude de hussard a cheval (25x20cm-10x8in) W/C over crayon. 28-Nov-2 Tajan, Paris #169/R
£5443 $8654 €8000 Cavalier et amazone (13x20cm-5x8in) mono. W/C htd gouache over crayon. 24-Mar-3 Tajan, Paris #42/R
£22451 $35697 €33000 Reception officielle aux Tuileries (35x51cm-14x20in) s.d. W/C gouache over crayon lit. 24-Mar-3 Tajan, Paris #43/R est:35000

LAMI, Eugène Louis (attrib) (1800-1890) French
Works on paper
£1100 $1704 €1650 French imperial cavalry (27x40cm-11x16in) bears sig. W/C body col. 3-Dec-2 Sotheby's, Olympia #294/R est:400-600

LAMIS, Leroy (1925-) American
Sculpture
£967 $1500 €1451 Construction no 86 (71x13x13cm-28x5x5in) acrylic polymer. 29-Sep-2 Butterfields, Los Angeles #4426/R est:900-1200

LAMMERS, Wilhelm Albertus (1857-1913) Dutch
£268 $417 €420 Poultry in the farmyard (20x28cm-8x11in) s. board. 5-Nov-2 Vendu Notarishuis, Rotterdam #42/R

LAMMERVO, Marko (1970-) Finnish
£314 $484 €500 White tailed eagle (59x60cm-23x24in) s. 27-Oct-2 Bukowskis, Helsinki #227/R
£544 $865 €800 Gerfalcon (60x80cm-24x31in) s. 24-Mar-3 Bukowskis, Helsinki #143/R
£576 $944 €800 Ducklings (50x60cm-20x24in) s. 4-Jun-3 Bukowskis, Helsinki #336/R

LAMMI, Ilkka (1976-2000) Finnish
£2817 $4535 €4000 Girl on beach (40x41cm-16x16in) s.d.99 board. 10-May-3 Bukowskis, Helsinki #254/R est:2000-2500
£6962 $11000 €11000 Nude (120x105cm-47x41in) 1-Dec-2 Bukowskis, Helsinki #329/R est:2500-3000
£13380 $21542 €19000 In my world (130x110cm-51x43in) s.d.2000. 10-May-3 Bukowskis, Helsinki #209/R est:12000-15000

LAMOND, William B (1857-1924) British
£380 $581 €570 Ruined castle on the coast (18x31cm-7x12in) s. canvas on board. 22-Aug-2 Bonhams, Edinburgh #1089
£800 $1248 €1200 Fisherman's cottage (35x53cm-14x21in) s. 26-Mar-3 Sotheby's, Olympia #68/R
£3000 $4560 €4500 Tending sheep. Crossing the bridge (33x25cm-13x10in) s.d.97 pair. 28-Aug-2 Sotheby's, London #893/R est:2000-3000
£4800 $7632 €7200 Firin bannocks (51x61cm-20x24in) s. 6-Mar-3 Christie's, Kensington #132/R est:2000-3000

LAMORE, François (1952-) American
Works on paper
£282 $468 €400 Couple (100x100cm-39x39in) s.i.d.verso mixed media. 18-Jun-3 Anaf, Lyon #52/R

LAMORINIERE, Jean Pierre François (1828-1911) Belgian
£255 $397 €400 Wooded landscape with shepherdess (22x26cm-9x10in) s. 6-Nov-2 Vendue Huis, Gravenhage #453
£538 $839 €850 Woodview near the water (25x15cm-10x6in) s. panel. 21-Oct-2 Bernaerts, Antwerp #2/R
£972 $1546 €1400 Paysage de montagne (23x40cm-9x16in) mono.d.1870 panel. 29-Apr-3 Campo, Vlaamse Kaai #183
£7000 $11690 €10150 Figures conversing beside a river (101x142cm-40x56in) s.d.1852. 17-Jun-3 Bonhams, New Bond Street #2/R est:8000-12000

LAMOTTE, Emmanuel (?) French
£256 $403 €400 Honfleur (50x65cm-20x26in) s. 24-Nov-2 Lesieur & Le Bars, Le Havre #86

LAMPI, Johann Baptist (18/19th C) Italian
£13043 $21391 €18000 Duchess Bauffy in the house of the Duke Wilczek-Traun. prov. 27-May-3 Wiener Kunst Auktionen, Vienna #16/R est:7000-14000

LAMPI, Johann Baptist (elder) (1751-1830) Italian
£3176 $4954 €4700 Portrait of lady in red dress and white undergarment (21x18cm-8x7in) lit. 27-Mar-3 Dorotheum, Vienna #420/R est:4700-6000
£6983 $11103 €10475 Lady wearing pink dress with blue scarf around her waist (80x62cm-31x24in) s. prov. 5-Mar-3 Rasmussen, Copenhagen #1646/R est:50000 (D.KR 75000)
£12676 $20408 €18000 King Franz I of Austria and Queen Maria Ludovika (100x75cm-39x30in) two prov. 7-May-3 Dorotheum, Vienna #39/R est:15000-20000

LAMPI, Vilho (1898-1936) Finnish
£1329 $2100 €2100 The old cart (20x28cm-8x11in) s.d.30 board. 1-Dec-2 Bukowskis, Helsinki #97/R

LAMPISUO, Antti (1926-) Finnish
£388 $637 €540 Still life (100x85cm-39x33in) s. 5-Jun-3 Hagelstam, Helsinki #829
£784 $1286 €1200 Sunflowers (105x90cm-41x35in) s.d.69. 9-Feb-3 Bukowskis, Helsinki #287/R

LAMPIT, Ronald (1906-) British
£1000 $1590 €1500 Spring and winter (33x46cm-13x18in) s. board pair. 29-Apr-3 Gorringes, Lewes #2102
£1100 $1749 €1650 Summer and Autumn (43x38cm-17x15in) s. board pair. 29-Apr-3 Gorringes, Lewes #2101

LAMPLOUGH, Augustus Osborne (1877-1930) British
Works on paper
£372 $584 €558 Street in Cairo, Egypt (30x20cm-12x8in) s.d.99 W/C. 24-Jul-2 Walker's, Ottawa #12/R (C.D 900)

£400	$636	€600	Desert scene with figures on camels, dow on a river (25x64cm-10x25in) s.d.1914 W/C. 30-Apr-3 Brightwells, Leominster #920/R
£450	$743	€653	Figures seated outside a mosque (25x32cm-10x13in) s.indis.d. pencil W/C. 3-Jul-3 Christie's, Kensington #161/R
£580	$922	€870	Desert temple (25x36cm-10x14in) s. W/C. 29-Apr-3 Bonhams, Knightsbridge #178/R
£650	$1034	€975	Desert track with figures (38x49cm-15x19in) s.d.1906 W/C. 29-Apr-3 Bonhams, Knightsbridge #183/R
£700	$1092	€1050	Dhows moored off the shore (23x35cm-9x14in) s. W/C over pencil htd bodycol. 15-Oct-2 Sotheby's, London #215/R
£700	$1113	€1050	On the upper Nile (22x60cm-9x24in) s.i. W/C. 29-Apr-3 Bonhams, Knightsbridge #180/R
£700	$1113	€1050	Sunset at the Pyramids (24x62cm-9x24in) s.i. W/C. 29-Apr-3 Bonhams, New Bond Street #116a
£720	$1145	€1080	After glow at Luxor (22x59cm-9x23in) s. W/C. 29-Apr-3 Bonhams, Knightsbridge #181/R
£750	$1193	€1125	Dawn in the desert (24x63cm-9x25in) s. W/C. 29-Apr-3 Bonhams, New Bond Street #124/R
£800	$1272	€1200	Camels crossing the desert (21x60cm-8x24in) s. W/C. 29-Apr-3 Bonhams, Knightsbridge #182/R
£800	$1272	€1200	On the Nile (23x60cm-9x24in) s. W/C. 29-Apr-3 Bonhams, New Bond Street #119/R
£880	$1399	€1320	Nile afterglow (22x60cm-9x24in) s.i. W/C. 29-Apr-3 Bonhams, Knightsbridge #179/R
£900	$1431	€1350	Crossing the Wadi (25x63cm-10x25in) s. W/C. 29-Apr-3 Bonhams, New Bond Street #123/R
£900	$1431	€1350	Temple on the banks of the Nile (23x61cm-9x24in) s. W/C. 29-Apr-3 Bonhams, New Bond Street #120/R
£1000	$1590	€1500	Encounter on the banks of the Nile (24x61cm-9x24in) s. W/C. 29-Apr-3 Bonhams, New Bond Street #121/R est:800-1200
£1100	$1749	€1650	Pyramids at Giza (23x60cm-9x24in) s. W/C. 29-Apr-3 Bonhams, New Bond Street #122/R est:800-1200
£1200	$1908	€1800	Nile at Kitchener's Island, Aswan (39x76cm-15x30in) s. W/C. 29-Apr-3 Bonhams, New Bond Street #118/R est:1200-1800
£1300	$2028	€1950	Warrior on a camel crossing the desert. Arabs crossing the desert (22x60cm-9x24in) s. W/C over pencil htd bodycol pair. 15-Oct-2 Sotheby's, London #218/R est:1500-2000
£1800	$2808	€2700	View of the interior of the Temple of Medinet-Habou, Thebes (51x73cm-20x29in) s. indis.i. W/C over pencil htd bodycol. 15-Oct-2 Sotheby's, London #216/R est:2000-3000
£1800	$2862	€2700	Noonday heat. On the Nile (24x61cm-9x24in) s. W/C pair. 29-Apr-3 Bonhams, New Bond Street #116/R est:1600-2000
£3500	$5460	€5250	Dhow on the Nile at Cairo (64x97cm-25x38in) s. W/C over pencil htd bodycol. 15-Oct-2 Sotheby's, London #214/R est:4000-6000

LAMPRECHT, Anton (1901-1984) German

£683	$1094	€950	City in winter (50x40cm-20x16in) s. panel double-sided. 15-May-3 Neumeister, Munich #303/R
£1410	$2214	€2200	House on Chiemsee (55x71cm-22x28in) 21-Nov-2 Dorotheum, Vienna #293/R est:3800-4500

LAMSWEERDE, Inez van (1963-) Dutch?

Photographs

£2564	$3974	€4000	Jessica 83-63-93 (50x50cm-20x20in) s.i.d.1992 num.2/5 verso c-print within perspex. 3-Dec-2 Christie's, Amsterdam #394/R est:3500-5500
£3846	$5962	€6000	Cola twins (50x90cm-20x35in) s.i.d.1990 num.1/5 c-print within perspex prov. 3-Dec-2 Christie's, Amsterdam #395/R est:5500-6500

LAN-BAR, David (1912-1987) Israeli

£270	$435	€405	Still life (74x55cm-29x22in) s.d.47. 18-Feb-3 Bonhams, Knightsbridge #154
£374	$595	€550	Portrait de femme (73x50cm-29x20in) s.d.15.V.52. 26-Feb-3 Artcurial Briest, Paris #214

LANARO, Dino (1909-) Italian

£475	$741	€750	Autumn (65x100cm-26x39in) s.d.1960 cardboard on canvas. 14-Sep-2 Meeting Art, Vercelli #888/R

LANCASTER, Alfred Dobree (?-1909) British

£7000	$11690	€10150	Classical beauty (125x82cm-49x32in) s.d.1880. 17-Jun-3 Bonhams, New Bond Street #87/R est:8000-12000

LANCASTER, Osbert (1908-1986) British

Works on paper

£280	$431	€420	All things bright and beautiful (25x13cm-10x5in) s.i. pen ink crayon. 22-Oct-2 Bonhams, Knightsbridge #182/R

LANCASTER, Percy (1878-1951) British

£560	$907	€840	Harvest scene (24x30cm-9x12in) board. 21-May-3 James Thompson, Kirby Lonsdale #251
£1000	$1590	€1500	View on the River Lune (51x76cm-20x30in) s.d.1936 canvasboard. 30-Apr-3 Halls, Shrewsbury #270/R est:800-1200
£1200	$1956	€1800	Harvest in Ribblesdale (48x60cm-19x24in) s.d.24. 28-Jan-3 Henry Adams, Chichester #428/R est:1500-2500

Works on paper

£250	$415	€375	Pastoralle in Surrey (23x32cm-9x13in) s. W/C. 10-Jun-3 Bonhams, Leeds #84
£320	$509	€480	Haymaking landscape (34x49cm-13x19in) s. W/C. 27-Feb-3 Bonhams, Chester #344
£380	$593	€570	Girl with blue bow (30x21cm-12x8in) mono. W/C. 18-Sep-2 James Thompson, Kirby Lonsdale #100
£391	$610	€653	Haying time, Corriston (34x51cm-13x20in) s. W/C prov. 13-Apr-3 Levis, Calgary #211/R est:800-1000 (C.D 900)
£400	$624	€600	Lakeland landscape with Langdale Pike (34x49cm-13x19in) s. W/C. 18-Sep-2 James Thompson, Kirby Lonsdale #46
£420	$659	€630	Breton figures at a cathedral doorway (34x40cm-13x16in) s. W/C. 19-Nov-2 James Thompson, Kirby Lonsdale #78
£550	$853	€825	Dutch scenes (22x33cm-9x13in) mono. W/C pair. 24-Sep-2 Anderson & Garland, Newcastle #266/R
£580	$905	€870	Continental street market (35x18cm-14x7in) s. W/C. 6-Nov-2 Bonhams, Chester #309
£1000	$1570	€1500	Landscape with haytimers (22x36cm-9x14in) s. W/C. 19-Nov-2 James Thompson, Kirby Lonsdale #65

LANCASTER, Richard Hume (1773-1853) British

£7000	$10850	€10500	Bustling quays and foreshore at Old Dover Harbour (54x76cm-21x30in) 31-Oct-2 Christie's, Kensington #451/R est:1500-2000

LANCE, George (1802-1864) British

£1250	$2063	€1813	Still life of fruit, goblet and knife on a carved wooden table (14x10cm-6x4in) board prov. 1-Jul-3 Bonhams, Norwich #213/R est:700-1000
£2482	$3848	€3723	Still life of fruit (50x61cm-20x24in) bears sig.d.1846. 3-Dec-2 Bukowskis, Stockholm #517/R est:35000-40000 (S.KR 35000)
£5800	$9454	€8700	Still life study of sliced melon, grapes and other fruit with autumnal leaves (58cm-23in circular) s.d.1863. 11-Feb-3 Fellows & Sons, Birmingham #60/R est:2000-3000
£8200	$13202	€12300	Monkey in a market (30x25cm-12x10in) s.d.1858 i.verso prov. 20-Feb-3 Christie's, London #72/R

LANCE, George (attrib) (1802-1864) British

£542	$900	€786	Still life with fruit (33x48cm-13x19in) s. 14-Jun-3 Jackson's, Cedar Falls #220/R

LANCELEY, Colin (1938-) Australian

£10163	$16057	€14736	Pelican dusk - Werri Lagoon 2000 (179x197cm-70x78in) init. s.i.verso wood on canvas exhib. 22-Jul-3 Lawson Menzies, Sydney #41/R est:30000-40000 (A.D 25000)

Sculpture

£4215	$6617	€6323	Seeds of discontent (255cm-100in) s.d.1973 oil carved wood on canavs prov.exhib. 15-Apr-3 Lawson Menzies, Sydney #45/R est:15000-25000 (A.D 11000)

Works on paper

£581	$918	€872	Kingdom of the snail (78x112cm-31x44in) s.d.1988 ink pastel W/C. 27-Nov-2 Deutscher-Menzies, Melbourne #194/R est:2000-3000 (A.D 1625)
£1434	$2179	€2151	Coming up for air (110x112cm-43x44in) s.d.74 mixed media. 27-Aug-2 Goodman, Sydney #114 est:4000-6000 (A.D 4000)

LANCERAY, Eugène Alexandro (1848-1886) Russian

Sculpture

£1000	$1570	€1500	Cossacks in combat (52cm-20in) i. cast iron i.f.Kasli. 21-Nov-2 Sotheby's, Olympia #209/R est:1000-1500
£1139	$1777	€1800	Ordonnance d'Yvan (15x15cm-6x6in) s. pat bronze. 15-Oct-2 Horta, Bruxelles #168
£1223	$1957	€1700	Cosaque a cheval (27cm-11in) s. brown pat bronze. 19-May-3 Horta, Bruxelles #150/R est:2000-3000
£2244	$3410	€3500	Le baiser au cavalier (43cm-17in) s.st.f. brown pat bronze. 10-Jul-2 Rabourdin & Choppin de Janvry, Paris #52/R est:3800-4000
£2468	$3900	€3900	Mongolian rider with horse having a rest (31x45cm-12x18in) i. pat bronze stone base exec.c.1880. 29-Nov-2 Bolland & Marotz, Bremen #476/R est:1100
£2700	$4266	€4050	Young boy on a mule driving two pack mules (22cm-9in) s. bronze. 27-Nov-2 Bonhams, Brooks & Langlois, Jersey #45/R est:1500-2000
£2973	$4638	€4400	Horses pulling sledge (54cm-21in) s.cyrillic brown pat.bronze Cast.Shtange N. 27-Mar-3 Dr Fritz Nagel, Stuttgart #989/R est:1450
£3774	$6000	€5661	Mounted warriors (26x27cm-10x11in) s. st.f.Chopin black marble base. 30-Apr-3 Sotheby's, New York #9/R est:6000-9000

£7628 $11976 €11900 Prise de guerre (67x48cm-26x19in) s. brown pat bronze. 22-Nov-2 Millon & Associes, Paris #147/R est:12000-15000
£8387 $13000 €12581 Svyatoslav (53cm-21in) s.i.d.brown pat. bronze. 16-Jul-2 Arthur James, Florida #120
£18000 $28260 €27000 Prince Svetoslav mounted on horseback (54x53cm-21x21in) s.d.1886 gilt bronze. 21-Nov-2 Sotheby's, Olympia #215/R est:22000-28000

LANCEROTTO, Egisto (1848-1916) Italian
£5484 $8500 €8226 Portrait of a distinguished Italian gentleman (124x76cm-49x30in) s.d.1886. 30-Oct-2 Christie's, Rockefeller NY #121/R est:10000-15000
£8000 $12560 €12000 Hand of cards (150x74cm-59x29in) s. 19-Nov-2 Sotheby's, London #195/R est:10000-15000

LANCHARD, A (19th C) French
£1204 $1938 €1806 Female nude outside (100x81cm-39x32in) s. 7-May-3 Dobiaschofsky, Bern #763/R est:1600 (S.FR 2600)

LANCKOW, Ludwig (19th C) German
£645 $1044 €968 Evening (67x95cm-26x37in) s.d.1875. 3-Feb-3 Lilla Bukowskis, Stockholm #542 (S.KR 9000)

LANCRET, Nicolas (1690-1743) French
£18000 $28260 €27000 Fete galante (30x41cm-12x16in) prov. 12-Dec-2 Sotheby's, London #227/R est:20000-30000
Works on paper
£650 $1007 €975 Study of a young man standing seen from behind (21x12cm-8x5in) red chk. 9-Dec-2 Bonhams, New Bond Street #76/R
£2381 $3786 €3500 Etudes de mains et de pieds (18x29cm-7x11in) crayon chk. 24-Mar-3 Tajan, Paris #96/R
£2517 $3600 €3776 Man playing a guitar (20x12cm-8x5in) red chk. 23-Jan-3 Swann Galleries, New York #246/R est:3000-5000
£2721 $4327 €4000 Femme assise a l'eventail (24x23cm-9x9in) crayon chk. 24-Mar-3 Tajan, Paris #98/R
£4422 $7031 €6500 Femme debout (22x12cm-9x5in) sanguine. 24-Mar-3 Tajan, Paris #30/R

LANCRET, Nicolas (attrib) (1690-1743) French
Works on paper
£1000 $1600 €1500 Study of a seated man. Italianate landscape (17x21cm-7x8in) red black chk double-sided. 14-May-3 Doyle, New York #31 est:1200-1800

LANCRET, Nicolas (circle) (1690-1743) French
£35000 $58450 €50750 Elegant company dancing before an arbour (124x112cm-49x44in) 11-Jul-3 Christie's, Kensington #185/R est:10000-15000

LANDA, Hubert (1870-1938) German
Works on paper
£304 $474 €450 Women on steps (29x41cm-11x16in) s.d.3.6.1918 W/C. 28-Mar-3 Dorotheum, Vienna #276/R
£314 $487 €500 Village landscape (25x45cm-10x18in) s.d.1907 gouache board. 1-Oct-2 Dorotheum, Vienna #335/R

LANDALUZE, Victor Patricio (1828-1889) Cuban/Spanish
£7547 $11623 €12000 Getting ready for the party (30x24cm-12x9in) s. board. 22-Oct-2 Durán, Madrid #269/R est:12000
£15287 $24000 €22931 Meeting (35x20cm-14x8in) s. painted c.1875 prov. 20-Nov-2 Christie's, Rockefeller NY #66/R

LANDAU, Zygmunt (1898-1962) Polish
£1554 $2424 €2300 Portrait of woman (65x46cm-26x18in) s. 26-Mar-3 Millon & Associes, Paris #142/R est:1800
£1724 $2759 €2500 Portrait presume de la fille de l'artiste (65x54cm-26x21in) s. masonite. 12-Mar-3 Rabourdin & Choppin de Janvry, Paris #111/R
£1905 $3029 €2800 La marchande de violettes (81x65cm-32x26in) s. 3-Mar-3 Claude Boisgirard, Paris #64/R est:3000-4000
Works on paper
£250 $390 €375 Portrait of a lady in a blue dress (68x48cm-27x19in) s.d.1959 col chk W/C. 17-Sep-2 Rosebery Fine Art, London #602/R
£550 $858 €825 Study of a female nude (61x41cm-24x16in) s. W/C crayon. 26-Mar-3 Woolley & Wallis, Salisbury #6/R
£1852 $2630 €3000 Portrait of Isabelle (64x47cm-25x19in) s. pastel. 16-Mar-3 Eric Pillon, Calais #161/R

LANDELLE, Charles Zacharie (1812-1908) French
£385 $600 €578 Village street scene. 21-Sep-2 Harvey Clar, Oakland #1422
£3219 $5086 €4829 Portrait of a young lady in Oriental costume (60x50cm-24x20in) s. 29-Nov-2 Zofingen, Switzerland #2482/R est:6000 (S.FR 7500)
£5240 $8175 €7860 Portrait of oriental woman (73x670cm-29x264in) s. 6-Nov-2 Dobiaschofsky, Bern #758/R est:14000 (S.FR 12000)
£6803 $10816 €10000 La belle Orientale en bleu (61x51cm-24x20in) s. 24-Mar-3 Rabourdin & Choppin de Janvry, Paris #75/R est:6000-8000
£12079 $19448 €18000 Portrait of a Basque boy and girl (61x50cm-24x20in) s.d.1856 pair prov. 18-Feb-3 Sotheby's, Amsterdam #449/R est:10000-15000

LANDENBERGER, Christian (1862-1927) German
£548 $806 €850 Boys bathing in evening (40x58cm-16x23in) 20-Jun-2 Dr Fritz Nagel, Stuttgart #790/R
£641 $994 €1000 Naked boy (57x40cm-22x16in) s. canvas on board lit. 5-Dec-2 Dr Fritz Nagel, Stuttgart #673/R
£1509 $2355 €2400 Young girl with apple (70x55cm-28x22in) 19-Sep-2 Dr Fritz Nagel, Stuttgart #961/R est:1000
£2264 $3532 €3600 Girl dancing with children (68x90cm-27x35in) s. 19-Sep-2 Dr Fritz Nagel, Stuttgart #959/R est:1400
Works on paper
£310 $490 €450 Young man with violin (57x41cm-22x16in) s.d. chl htd white. 2-Apr-3 Dr Fritz Nagel, Stuttgart #9133/R

LANDER, Cyril George (1892-1983) Australian
Works on paper
£1429 $2243 €2144 Hay Street, Perth (37x50cm-15x20in) s. W/C gouache. 25-Nov-2 Christie's, Melbourne #304 est:4000-6000 (A.D 4000)

LANDER, John St Helier (1869-1944) British
£472 $750 €708 Sir F H Thornton (91x71cm-36x28in) s.i.d.1907. 5-Mar-3 Christie's, Rockefeller NY #76/R
£2000 $3260 €3000 Portrait of Major Romer in uniform (121x90cm-48x35in) s.d.1938. 12-Feb-3 Bonhams, Knightsbridge #256/R est:2000-3000
£2700 $4320 €4050 View in the Vallee Des Vaux, Jersey (73x93cm-29x37in) s.d.1934. 19-May-3 Robin Fenner, Tavistock #318/R est:3000-4000

LANDER, John St Helier (attrib) (1869-1944) British
£320 $499 €480 Portrait of an old woman with a red headscarf holding a basket (35x24cm-14x9in) indis.mono. board. 26-Mar-3 Bonhams & Langlois, Jersey #165/R

LANDER, Mark (1955-) New Zealander
Works on paper
£295 $460 €443 Pouring jug (140x105cm-55x41in) ws.i.d.18.2.98 clay pigment. 6-Aug-2 Peter Webb, Auckland #12/R est:2000-3000 (NZ.D 1000)

LANDI, Angelo (1879-1944) Italian
£302 $465 €480 Figure at door (16x10cm-6x4in) s. cardboard. 28-Oct-2 Il Ponte, Milan #337

LANDI, Bruno (1941-) Italian
£261 $418 €400 Knight (50x30cm-20x12in) s. painted 2001. 4-Jan-3 Meeting Art, Vercelli #519
£294 $471 €450 Small nude (60x30cm-24x12in) s. s.i.verso. 4-Jan-3 Meeting Art, Vercelli #743
£316 $494 €500 Still life (60x50cm-24x20in) s. painted 2001 lit. 14-Sep-2 Meeting Art, Vercelli #866/R
£359 $575 €550 Knight (60x30cm-24x12in) s. painted 2001. 4-Jan-3 Meeting Art, Vercelli #493
£392 $627 €600 Still life with guitar (43x64cm-17x25in) s. cardboard. 4-Jan-3 Meeting Art, Vercelli #50
£442 $703 €650 Green plant (60x30cm-24x12in) s. 1-Mar-3 Meeting Art, Vercelli #553
£443 $691 €700 Blue dress (70x50cm-28x20in) s. s.verso painted 2001. 14-Sep-2 Meeting Art, Vercelli #894/R
£475 $741 €750 Detail of the Last Super (60x70cm-24x28in) s.i.d.2001 verso. 14-Sep-2 Meeting Art, Vercelli #195
£475 $741 €750 Maternity (70x70cm-28x28in) s. painted 2001. 14-Sep-2 Meeting Art, Vercelli #280
£475 $741 €750 Adam (60x60cm-24x24in) s. s.i.d.2001 verso. 14-Sep-2 Meeting Art, Vercelli #330/R
£475 $741 €750 Woman and horse (60x50cm-24x20in) s. s.i.verso painted 2001 lit. 14-Sep-2 Meeting Art, Vercelli #385/R
£475 $741 €750 Night scene (70x50cm-28x20in) s. s.i.d.2001 verso. 14-Sep-2 Meeting Art, Vercelli #415
£475 $741 €750 Night serenade (70x70cm-28x28in) s. s.i.verso painted 2001. 14-Sep-2 Meeting Art, Vercelli #903/R
£481 $755 €750 Homage to Modigliani (50x40cm-20x16in) s. 23-Nov-2 Meeting Art, Vercelli #135
£490 $784 €750 Rider (70x70cm-28x28in) s. s.verso. 4-Jan-3 Meeting Art, Vercelli #712
£510 $811 €750 Figures (80x60cm-31x24in) s. s.i.verso. 1-Mar-3 Meeting Art, Vercelli #509
£510 $811 €750 Three Graces (70x70cm-28x28in) s. painted 2002. 1-Mar-3 Meeting Art, Vercelli #741

£521 $828 €750 Girl with fruit bowl (80x50cm-31x20in) s. s.verso. 1-May-3 Meeting Art, Vercelli #102
£521 $828 €750 Sculpture and guitar (70x70cm-28x28in) s. painted 2002. 1-May-3 Meeting Art, Vercelli #288
£521 $828 €750 Srenade to the moon (70x70cm-28x28in) s. painted 2003. 1-May-3 Meeting Art, Vercelli #515
£523 $837 €800 Guitar player (70x70cm-28x28in) s. painted 2002. 4-Jan-3 Meeting Art, Vercelli #204
£556 $889 €850 White rose (70x60cm-28x24in) s. s.i.verso. 4-Jan-3 Meeting Art, Vercelli #208
£590 $939 €850 Nude (60x30cm-24x12in) s. painted 2001. 1-May-3 Meeting Art, Vercelli #101
£590 $939 €850 Pierrot in love (50x30cm-20x12in) s. s.i.verso. 1-May-3 Meeting Art, Vercelli #87
£633 $987 €1000 Painter and model (100x70cm-39x28in) s. s.i.d.2001 verso. 14-Sep-2 Meeting Art, Vercelli #360/R
£633 $987 €1000 Gift (70x50cm-28x20in) s. s.verso painted 2001. 14-Sep-2 Meeting Art, Vercelli #859/R
£633 $987 €1000 Woman with necklace (100x70cm-39x28in) s. s.i.d.2001 verso. 14-Sep-2 Meeting Art, Vercelli #954/R
£654 $1046 €1000 Woman and apple (100x70cm-39x28in) s. s.i.verso painted 2001. 4-Jan-3 Meeting Art, Vercelli #516
£694 $1104 €1000 Coral necklace (100x80cm-39x31in) s. painted 2003 lit. 1-May-3 Meeting Art, Vercelli #505
£729 $1159 €1050 Ascending knight (50x90cm-20x35in) s. painted 2001. 1-May-3 Meeting Art, Vercelli #265
£784 $1255 €1200 Oedipus and the sphynx (100x70cm-39x28in) s. painted 2000. 4-Jan-3 Meeting Art, Vercelli #70
£886 $1382 €1400 Red rose (100x70cm-39x28in) s. s.i.verso painted 2001. 14-Sep-2 Meeting Art, Vercelli #245/R
£1042 $1656 €1500 Hector and Andromaca (100x120cm-39x47in) s. painted 2003 lit. 1-May-3 Meeting Art, Vercelli #330

LANDI, Gaspar (1756-1830) Italian
£45455 $75909 €65000 Portrait de Jean Abraham Andre Poupart (235x164cm-93x65in) s.d.1804. 27-Jun-3 Piasa, Paris #98/R est:30000-40000

LANDI, Ricardo Verdugo (1871-1930) Spanish
£272 $430 €425 Seascape (9x14cm-4x6in) s. cardboard. 19-Nov-2 Durán, Madrid #602/R
Works on paper
£336 $540 €500 By Seth temple (13x16cm-5x6in) s. gouache. 18-Feb-3 Durán, Madrid #39/R

LANDINI, Andrea (1847-1912) Italian
£4200 $6678 €6300 Red rose (61x46cm-24x18in) s. 20-Mar-3 Christie's, Kensington #54/R est:3000-5000
£11111 $17667 €16000 Cardinals eating (38x54cm-15x21in) s. 30-Apr-3 Tajan, Paris #131/R est:15000
£13305 $20755 €19292 Cardinal with pigeons (46x38cm-18x15in) s.i. 26-Mar-3 Walker's, Ottawa #33/R est:25000-30000 (C.D 31000)
£13500 $22005 €20250 Tucking in (33x24cm-13x9in) s. 29-Jan-3 Sotheby's, Olympia #303/R est:7000-9000
£19500 $31785 €29250 Patience (35x27cm-14x11in) s. 29-Jan-3 Sotheby's, Olympia #332/R est:8000-12000
£24000 $40080 €36000 Cardinal's pleasure (45x37cm-18x15in) s. 19-Jun-3 Christie's, London #50/R est:25000-35000

LANDIS, John (1805-1851) American?
£5280 $8500 €7920 Portrait of George Washington (30x25cm-12x10in) s. 16-Jan-3 Christie's, Rockefeller NY #337/R est:2000-3000

LANDKROON, Piet (1907-) Dutch
£256 $403 €400 Mediterranean landscape with a village (60x80cm-24x31in) s. 25-Nov-2 Glerum, Amsterdam #172

LANDOLT, Karl (1925-) Swiss
Works on paper
£330 $528 €495 Hilly landscape with flowers and farmsteads (37x54cm-15x21in) s.d. W/C. 17-Mar-3 Philippe Schuler, Zurich #4348 (S.FR 700)

LANDOLT, Salomon (1741-1818) Swiss
Works on paper
£485 $707 €728 Cossack patrol (13x16cm-5x6in) mono.d.1789 verso gouache. 17-Jun-2 Philippe Schuler, Zurich #4805 (S.FR 1100)

LANDON, Charles Paul (1760-1826) French
£5128 $8051 €8000 Portrait de femme a la colonne (63x54cm-25x21in) s.d.1798. 13-Dec-2 Pierre Berge, Paris #59/R est:12000
£13000 $21710 €18850 Portrait of a lady, wearing a yellow dress and holding a basket of fruit (60x50cm-24x20in) s.d.1794 paper on canvas. 10-Jul-3 Sotheby's, London #205/R est:6000-8000

LANDOWSKI, Paul Maximilien (1875-1961) French
Sculpture
£2837 $4738 €4000 Tete de jeune homme (58x50x60cm-23x20x24in) limestone. 20-Jun-3 Rieunier, Paris #40/R est:5000-6000
£5192 $8152 €8100 Herakles et la biche au pied d'airain (58x59cm-23x23in) s.d.1922 silver pat bronze Cast Barbedienne. 15-Dec-2 Eric Pillon, Calais #156/R
£18590 $29186 €29000 Heros (16x45x48cm-6x18x19in) brown pat bronze Cast Compagnie des Artistes exec.c.1925. 16-Dec-2 Rabourdin & Choppin de Janvry, Paris #76/R est:32000

LANDRE, Louise Amelie (1852-?) French
£348 $539 €522 Young girl in kitchen (46x37cm-18x15in) s. panel. 9-Dec-2 Philippe Schuler, Zurich #8658 (S.FR 800)

LANDSEER, Charles (1799-1879) British
£280 $454 €420 Mr B taking from Pamela the letter she had been writing to her parents (27x20cm-11x8in) s. board. 23-Jan-3 Christie's, Kensington #99
£2000 $3080 €3000 First steps (55x76cm-22x30in) s.d.1840. 5-Sep-2 Christie's, Kensington #287/R est:2000-3000
£115000 $185150 €172500 Return of the dove to the Ark (137x184cm-54x72in) prov.exhib.lit. 20-Feb-3 Christie's, London #220/R est:70000
Works on paper
£360 $576 €540 Portrait of Bessie Maud, three and a half years (30x20cm-12x8in) pastel. 11-Mar-3 Gorringes, Lewes #2521

LANDSEER, Sir Edwin (1802-1873) British
£420 $647 €630 Three women (20x25cm-8x10in) card prov. 8-Sep-2 Lots Road, London #351
£3800 $6346 €5510 Head of a young woman (30x26cm-12x10in) 26-Jun-3 Mellors & Kirk, Nottingham #889/R est:800-1200
£9000 $14580 €13500 River scene, with otter eating a fish (20x25cm-8x10in) board prov. 22-May-3 Christie's, London #28/R est:4000-6000
£11000 $17050 €16500 Spearing salmon by torchlight (35x45cm-14x18in) board prov. 31-Oct-2 Christie's, London #57/R est:5000-8000
£1150000 $1851500 €1725000 Scene in Chillingham Park, portrait of Lord Ossulston or death of the wild bull (225x225cm-89x89in) prov.exhib.lit. 19-Feb-3 Christie's, London #6/R est:800000-1200000
Works on paper
£450 $716 €675 Cottage and ruins, Richmond (19x32cm-7x13in) i. pencil. 19-Mar-3 Sotheby's, London #130
£1300 $2067 €1950 Study of a kneeling woman (17x11cm-7x4in) pen ink wash over pencil. 19-Mar-3 Sotheby's, London #129/R est:600-800
£1472 $2400 €2208 Head of a mastiff (10x20cm-4x8in) pen ink prov. 11-Feb-3 Bonhams & Doyles, New York #78/R est:600-800
£2300 $3703 €3450 Scottish deerhound (17x24cm-7x9in) pencil chl htd white. 15-Jan-3 Cheffins Grain & Comins, Cambridge #363/R
£3800 $6232 €5510 Blackgame (31x47cm-12x19in) col chk prov.exhib. 5-Jun-3 Christie's, London #115/R est:4000-6000
£6135 $10000 €9203 Running spaniel (10x20cm-4x8in) pen ink prov. 11-Feb-3 Bonhams & Doyles, New York #77/R est:2000-3000
£11000 $17050 €16500 Two hounds with a dead stag (34x48cm-13x19in) col chk prov. 31-Oct-2 Christie's, London #58/R est:12000-18000
£18987 $30000 €28481 Stags in a snowdrift (34x49cm-13x19in) col chks prov.exhib. 3-Apr-3 Christie's, Rockefeller NY #174/R est:15000-25000

LANDSEER, Sir Edwin (attrib) (1802-1873) British
£3354 $5300 €5300 Red deer in mountain forest (80x100cm-31x39in) canvas on canvas lit. 29-Nov-2 Sigalas, Stuttgart #1109/R est:5900
£6000 $9960 €9000 Dog sitting by a tree in a landscape (47x36cm-19x14in) 12-Jun-3 Sotheby's, London #92/R est:6000-8000
£14000 $22120 €21000 Sleeping dog (27x32cm-11x13in) prov.exhib. 26-Nov-2 Christie's, London #65/R est:15000-25000

LANDSINGER, Sigmund (1855-?) Yugoslavian
Works on paper
£338 $527 €500 Sleeping cupid (27x24cm-11x9in) mono. pencil paper on board. 28-Mar-3 Dorotheum, Vienna #98/R

LANDSTROM, Bjorn (1917-2002) Finnish
£415 $660 €610 Aabo Palace (50x40cm-20x16in) s.d.1940. 27-Feb-3 Hagelstam, Helsinki #1002
Works on paper
£302 $496 €420 African dream (30x46cm-12x18in) s.d.1987 gouache. 5-Jun-3 Hagelstam, Helsinki #877
£317 $519 €440 Tree in blossom (46x46cm-18x18in) s.d.1987 gouache. 5-Jun-3 Hagelstam, Helsinki #875
£345 $553 €480 Lemmikainen at Tuonela (42x29cm-17x11in) gouache. 17-May-3 Hagelstam, Helsinki #69/R
£360 $576 €500 Kullervo (23x28cm-9x11in) gouache. 17-May-3 Hagelstam, Helsinki #64/R
£374 $614 €520 The poor tree, Oscar Wilde (34x28cm-13x11in) s. gouache prov. 5-Jun-3 Hagelstam, Helsinki #867/R
£374 $614 €520 Antero Vipunen (34x50cm-13x20in) s.d.1987 gouache. 5-Jun-3 Hagelstam, Helsinki #872

£403 $661 €560 The beast (25x28cm-10x11in) s. gouache. 5-Jun-3 Hagelstam, Helsinki #869/R
£414 $654 €600 Magpie (78x53cm-31x21in) s.d.1972 graphite. 3-Apr-3 Hagelstam, Helsinki #910
£432 $691 €600 Lemminkainen and the giant snake (26x61cm-10x24in) gouache. 17-May-3 Hagelstam, Helsinki #63/R
£432 $691 €600 Ilmatar and the dawn of creation (52x29cm-20x11in) gouache. 17-May-3 Hagelstam, Helsinki #70/R
£453 $697 €720 Fairy tale illustration (22x25cm-9x10in) s.d.43 gouache. 27-Oct-2 Bukowskis, Helsinki #228/R
£460 $755 €640 The beauty and the beast (34x27cm-13x11in) s. gouache. 5-Jun-3 Hagelstam, Helsinki #868
£504 $806 €700 Vaina virgin's boat poem (19x60cm-7x24in) gouache. 17-May-3 Hagelstam, Helsinki #62/R
£532 $852 €740 Vaina virgin walking at Pohjola beach (16x29cm-6x11in) gouache. 17-May-3 Hagelstam, Helsinki #66/R
£532 $852 €740 Ilmaris hostess and cow being changed to a bear (23x29cm-9x11in) gouache. 17-May-3 Hagelstam, Helsinki #73/R
£561 $898 €780 Lemminkainen departing for Pohjola (42x29cm-17x11in) gouache. 17-May-3 Hagelstam, Helsinki #67/R
£633 $1013 €880 The Virgin cage (28x29cm-11x11in) gouache. 17-May-3 Hagelstam, Helsinki #74/R
£691 $1105 €960 Sampo smithy (41x29cm-16x11in) gouache. 17-May-3 Hagelstam, Helsinki #71/R
£719 $1151 €1000 Ilmarinen and the pike (42x29cm-17x11in) gouache. 17-May-3 Hagelstam, Helsinki #68/R
£863 $1381 €1200 Vaina virgin go courting (42x29cm-17x11in) gouache. 17-May-3 Hagelstam, Helsinki #72/R

LANDT, Frants (1885-1976) Danish
£254 $391 €381 Fresh day in the sunshine off Hveen (58x82cm-23x32in) s.d.1950. 26-Oct-2 Rasmussen, Havnen #3127 (D.KR 3000)
£257 $401 €386 Seascape with sailing vessels (71x100cm-28x39in) s. 11-Nov-2 Rasmussen, Vejle #2098 (D.KR 3000)
£293 $448 €440 Seascape with fishing boats (66x92cm-26x36in) s.d.1931. 24-Aug-2 Rasmussen, Havnen #2177 (D.KR 3400)
£354 $563 €531 Seascape with sailing vessels (51x73cm-20x29in) s.d.1947. 10-Mar-3 Rasmussen, Vejle #436 (D.KR 3800)
£362 $554 €543 Seascape with sailing and steam boats (56x83cm-22x33in) s.d.1932. 24-Aug-2 Rasmussen, Havnen #2242 (D.KR 4200)
£383 $620 €555 The Royal Yacht and man-o-war at Greenland (43x57cm-17x22in) s.i.d.1952. 26-May-3 Rasmussen, Copenhagen #1361/R (D.KR 4000)
£391 $622 €587 Vessels at entrance to Copenhagen (65x96cm-26x38in) s.d.1926. 10-Mar-3 Rasmussen, Vejle #438 (D.KR 4200)
£467 $729 €701 Seascape with boats off Kullen (70x110cm-28x43in) s.d.1939. 5-Aug-2 Rasmussen, Vejle #56/R (D.KR 5500)
£497 $800 €746 Seascape with three masted ship (66x91cm-26x36in) s. i.verso. 22-Feb-3 Brunk, Ashville #665/R
£547 $880 €821 Seascape with three master schooner (45x68cm-18x27in) s. 19-Jan-3 Hindemae, Ullerslev #7449/R (D.KR 6200)
£639 $990 €959 Seascape with sailing ship at Oresund (65x94cm-26x37in) s.d.1929. 28-Sep-2 Rasmussen, Havnen #2002/R (D.KR 7500)
£800 $1216 €1200 Danish vessel being towed out from a continental harbour (56x81cm-22x32in) s. 15-Aug-2 Bonhams, New Bond Street #322/R
£900 $1503 €1305 Tall ships off the coast (69x108cm-27x43in) s.d.1939. 18-Jun-3 Sotheby's, Olympia #105/R

LANDUYT, Charles Joseph van (1854-1934) Belgian
£317 $508 €460 Fillette uouant dans les pres (50x35cm-20x14in) s. 17-Mar-3 Horta, Bruxelles #99
£317 $508 €460 Marine au coucher du soleil (33x47cm-13x19in) s. canvas on panel. 17-Mar-3 Horta, Bruxelles #100
£655 $1048 €950 Fenaison devant la ferme (35x55cm-14x22in) s. sold with another. 17-Mar-3 Horta, Bruxelles #98
£3034 $4855 €4400 Les joueurs de quilles devant une ferme (107x143cm-42x56in) s. 17-Mar-3 Horta, Bruxelles #96/R est:3500-4500

LANDUYT, Octave (1922-) Belgian
£382 $607 €550 Organe (50x60cm-20x24in) s. paper. 29-Apr-3 Campo, Vlaamse Kaai #184

Works on paper
£540 $863 €750 Om zich te bevredigen (50x68cm-20x27in) s. mixed media. 13-May-3 Palais de Beaux Arts, Brussels #273
£566 $877 €900 Protege (44x32cm-17x13in) s. Indian ink gouache exec.1979 exhib.lit. 5-Oct-2 De Vuyst, Lokeren #209
£4483 $7172 €6500 Aanfewezen lichaamsbloei (130x100cm-51x39in) s. pastel canvas prov.lit. 15-Mar-3 De Vuyst, Lokeren #490/R est:7500-10000

LANDWEHR-PRAGENAU, Ottokar von (1905-) Austrian
£321 $506 €500 Rijeka (80x120cm-31x47in) s. panel. 18-Nov-2 Dorotheum, Linz #311/R

LANE, F R (?) ?
£636 $967 €980 Portrait of a bearded gent (89x69cm-35x27in) s. 2-Jul-2 Thomas Adams, Dublin #404

LANE, Joseph (1900-) American
£409 $650 €614 Spring flowers (30x36cm-12x14in) s. painted c.1930. 4-May-3 Treadway Gallery, Cincinnati #532/R

LANE, Leonard C (c.1910-1978) Canadian?
£1811 $2807 €2717 Prospect, N.S (50x65cm-20x26in) s. 3-Dec-2 Joyner, Toronto #330/R est:2000-3000 (C.D 4400)

LANE, Lois (1948-) American
£1220 $2000 €1769 Untitled no.11 (244x183cm-96x72in) acrylic gesso on canvas prov.exhib. 1-Jun-3 Wright, Chicago #347/R est:2000-3000

LANE, Martella Cone (1875-1962) American
£256 $400 €384 California mountain scene (41x61cm-16x24in) board. 19-Oct-2 David Dike, Dallas #367/R

LANE, Samuel (1780-1859) British
£66000 $104940 €99000 Portrait of Captain Sir Philip Bowes Vere Broke (240x147cm-94x58in) prov.exhib.lit. 19-Mar-3 Sotheby's, London #9/R est:20000-30000

LANE, Tony (1949-) New Zealander
£526 $837 €789 Iris (120x177cm-47x70in) 25-Feb-3 Peter Webb, Auckland #35 est:1500-3000 (NZ.D 1500)
£1408 $2324 €2042 Two elements (76x47cm-30x19in) i. s.d.1990 verso oil metal. 1-Jul-3 Peter Webb, Auckland #40/R est:4000-6000 (NZ.D 4000)
£2465 $4067 €3574 Dolorossa (60x100cm-24x39in) init.i.d.1993 oil silver leaf. 1-Jul-3 Peter Webb, Auckland #39/R est:8000-12000 (NZ.D 7000)
£2548 $4000 €3822 Suspension of gravity (97x37cm-38x15in) i. s.d.1991 verso oil schlag metal gesso panel. 10-Dec-2 Peter Webb, Auckland #51/R est:6000-9000 (NZ.D 8000)

Works on paper
£298 $465 €447 Night moves (47x62cm-19x24in) pastel. 5-Nov-2 Peter Webb, Auckland #15/R (NZ.D 950)

LANEUVILLE, Jean Louis (c.1748-1826) French
£14839 $23445 €23000 Portrait de Louis Legendre (105x82cm-41x32in) exhib. 18-Dec-2 Piasa, Paris #93/R est:15000

LANEUVILLE, Jean Louis (attrib) (c.1748-1826) French
£5461 $8465 €8192 Portrait d'un jeune homme (46x37cm-18x15in) prov. 4-Dec-2 AB Stockholms Auktionsverk #2005/R est:50000-60000 (S.KR 77000)

LANFANT DE METZ (1814-1892) French
£600 $948 €900 Story of war (15x23cm-6x9in) indis.sig. 12-Nov-2 Bonhams, Knightsbridge #269/R
£2278 $3554 €3600 Enfants ecoutant de la musique (7x12cm-3x5in) s. panel. 20-Oct-2 Mercier & Cie, Lille #312/R est:3500-4000

LANFANT DE METZ, François Louis (1814-1892) French
£1859 $2919 €2900 Deux fillettes (16x9cm-6x4in) s. panel. 15-Dec-2 Eric Pillon, Calais #42/R
£1973 $3137 €2900 Enfant jouant avec des poissons rouges (22x16cm-9x6in) s. 21-Mar-3 Rieunier, Bailly-Pommery, Mathias, Paris #91/R
£2431 $3865 €3500 Petit chapardeur (16x9cm-6x4in) s. cardboard. 30-Apr-3 Tajan, Paris #3/R
£4295 $6528 €6700 Scene villageoise (26x16cm-10x6in) s. panel. 16-Aug-2 Deauville, France #78/R est:7000

LANFRANCO, Giovanni (1582-1647) Italian

Works on paper
£1399 $2000 €2099 Sailors in a boat on a stormy sea with a vision of a Saint (31x29cm-12x11in) pen ink wash htd white. 23-Jan-3 Swann Galleries, New York #62/R est:1500-2500

LANG, Albert (1847-1933) German
£681 $1076 €1022 Mountain landscape from the Alps with wanderers by watermill (74x103cm-29x41in) s. 2-Dec-2 Rasmussen, Copenhagen #1543/R (D.KR 8000)
£1096 $1721 €1600 Travellers on track from village in evening (105x77cm-41x30in) s.d.89. 16-Apr-3 Dorotheum, Salzburg #146/R est:1400-2200
£1438 $2358 €2200 In meadow land (62x49cm-24x19in) s.d.72 panel. 5-Feb-3 Neumeister, Munich #746/R est:1000

Works on paper
£302 $471 €480 Woodland near Landshut (35x44cm-14x17in) s.i.d.1911 chl wash htd bodycol. 11-Oct-2 Winterberg, Heidelberg #617

LANG, Ernest Friedrich Carl (18th C) German

Works on paper
£1400 $2338 €2030 Waxwing on a perch (29x21cm-11x8in) s. gouache vellum. 9-Jul-3 Sotheby's, London #124/R est:1400-1800

LANG, Ernst (?) ?
£354 $562 €520 Chiemsee with Frauenchiemsee island (18x24cm-7x9in) s. panel. 28-Mar-3 Bolland & Marotz, Bremen #1258/R

LANG, Hans (1898-1971) Austrian
£345 $545 €500 Trees in meadow in Swabia (65x80cm-26x31in) s. bears d. 2-Apr-3 Dr Fritz Nagel, Stuttgart #9134/R

LANG, Leon (20th C) French
£385 $604 €600 Jeune femme a la corbeille de fruits (118x150cm-46x59in) 25-Nov-2 Rieunier, Bailly-Pommery, Mathias, Paris #11

LANG, Philippe (?) French
Works on paper
£481 $755 €750 Port de peche en Bretagne (39x60cm-15x24in) s. W/C. 15-Dec-2 Thierry & Lannon, Brest #335

LANG, Richard (1861-?) German
£793 $1181 €1190 Shrimp fishermen in Venice (13x26cm-5x10in) s.i. panel. 25-Jun-2 Koller, Zurich #6460 (S.FR 1800)

LANG, Steven (1944-) American
£1234 $1900 €1851 Warrior's drum (30x23cm-12x9in) 25-Oct-2 Morris & Whiteside, Hilton Head Island #51 est:2000-2500
£2485 $4025 €3603 Pecunni hunter (51x41cm-20x16in) 23-May-3 Altermann Galleries, Santa Fe #60

LANGASKENS, Maurice (1884-1946) Belgian
£377 $585 €600 La lecture (31x51cm-12x20in) s.d.2 sept 1915. 1-Oct-2 Palais de Beaux Arts, Brussels #498
£440 $734 €620 Tetes d'enfants (25x19cm-10x7in) s.d.31 juillet 1929 canvas laid down. 17-Jun-3 Palais de Beaux Arts, Brussels #593
£1096 $1710 €1600 Homme en meditation sur fond d'or (51x34cm-20x13in) s. panel. 14-Apr-3 Horta, Bruxelles #239 est:1000-1500
£1176 $1894 €1800 La forge (51x57cm-20x22in) s. 20-Jan-3 Horta, Bruxelles #180 est:2000-3000
£1266 $1975 €2000 Marin dans son interieur (39x48cm-15x19in) s. 16-Sep-2 Horta, Bruxelles #24
£2158 $3453 €3000 L'accueil (64x74cm-25x29in) s. 13-May-3 Palais de Beaux Arts, Brussels #90/R est:3000-5000
£2302 $3683 €3200 Fortune teller (42x53cm-17x21in) s. 17-May-3 De Vuyst, Lokeren #230/R est:2400-3000
Works on paper
£540 $863 €750 Kwiebe-Kwiebus (63x48cm-25x19in) s. W/C. 13-May-3 Palais de Beaux Arts, Brussels #275/R

LANGDALE, Marmaduke A (?-1905) British
£250 $393 €375 Trumps Mill, Surrey (51x76cm-20x30in) s.d.1880 i.verso. 16-Apr-3 Christie's, Kensington #609

LANGDON, Beatrice (1898-1986) British
£280 $442 €420 The lone cottage near Ingleborough, Yorks (28x39cm-11x15in) board. 27-Nov-2 Peter Wilson, Nantwich #42

LANGE, Andde (20th C) American
£236 $375 €354 Parrots (61x91cm-24x36in) s. 7-Mar-3 Jackson's, Cedar Falls #862/R

LANGE, Dorothea (1895-1965) American
Photographs
£4000 $6480 €6000 Filipinos cutting lettuce, Salinas, California (37x36cm-15x14in) num.38263 164 verso gelatin silver print prov. 21-May-3 Christie's, London #163/R est:2000-3000
£22727 $35000 €34091 White angel bread line, San Francisco (34x28cm-13x11in) s.i.verso gelatin silver print board exec.c.1940 prov.lit. 25-Oct-2 Phillips, New York #13/R est:35000-45000
Works on paper
£7143 $11000 €10715 Migrant mother (24x19cm-9x7in) i.num.RA9058-C photograph lit. 24-Oct-2 Sotheby's, New York #101/R est:5000-7000

LANGE, Dorothea and PETERSEN, Rolf (20th C) American
Photographs
£2051 $3200 €3077 Migrant mother, Nipomo, California (23x18cm-9x7in) i. verso silver. 21-Oct-2 Swann Galleries, New York #187/R est:3000-4000

LANGE, E (19/20th C) ?
£2174 $3500 €3261 Summer. Spring (38x25cm-15x10in) s. panel pair. 19-Feb-3 Doyle, New York #69 est:2000-3000

LANGE, Frederik (1870-1941) Danish
£732 $1200 €1061 Woman sewing beside a window (48x38cm-19x15in) s. indis i. 4-Jun-3 Doyle, New York #67 est:1000-1500

LANGE, Johann (18/19th C) German
£479 $748 €700 Mountain river (38x47cm-15x19in) mono.d. 10-Apr-3 Van Ham, Cologne #1560

LANGE, Johann Gustav (1811-1887) German
£432 $696 €648 Winter landscape with figure in moonlight (95x77cm-37x30in) s. 22-Feb-3 Rasmussen, Havnen #2142/R (D.KR 4800)

LANGE, Jorgen (1886-1959) Danish
£266 $431 €399 Boy getting dressed after a swim in the river (128x160cm-50x63in) s.d.1921. 25-Jan-3 Rasmussen, Havnen #2100 (D.KR 3000)

LANGE, Joseph (1751-1831) Austrian
£287 $465 €416 Nobleman at writing desk (60x48cm-24x19in) 26-May-3 Rasmussen, Copenhagen #1296/R (D.KR 3000)

LANGE, Julius (1817-1878) German
£705 $1107 €1100 Landscape with rainbow (30x47cm-12x19in) s.indis.d. canvas on canvas. 21-Nov-2 Dorotheum, Vienna #124/R est:2200-3000
£1400 $2282 €2100 Mountain lake scene (84x116cm-33x46in) s. 11-Feb-3 Bonhams, Knowle #70 est:1500-2500
£4367 $6812 €6551 Mountain landscape with stream and herder (70x92cm-28x36in) s.d.63 prov. 20-Nov-2 Fischer, Luzern #1180/R est:12000-14000 (S.FR 10000)

LANGE, Karl Ernst (1887-) German
£1103 $1743 €1600 Still life of flowers (98x87cm-39x34in) 5-Apr-3 Dr Fritz Nagel, Leipzig #4053/R est:2000

LANGE, Niels Erik (1890-1919) Danish
£296 $459 €444 Landscape with mill (68x58cm-27x23in) s.d.1919. 1-Oct-2 Rasmussen, Copenhagen #338 (D.KR 3500)
£334 $557 €484 View from a village (35x36cm-14x14in) s.d.15. 17-Jun-3 Rasmussen, Copenhagen #80/R (D.KR 3500)

LANGE, Otto (1879-1944) German
£589 $931 €884 Still life of sculpture and model doll (55x43cm-22x17in) s. 27-Nov-2 Falkkloos, Malmo #77813/R (S.KR 8400)
£629 $969 €1000 Woodland stream (34x40cm-13x16in) s. panel. 26-Oct-2 Dr Lehr, Berlin #273/R
£1013 $1600 €1600 Village street with figures (45x53cm-18x21in) s. board. 29-Nov-2 Sigalas, Stuttgart #1239 est:1800
Works on paper
£576 $921 €800 Still life with apples and pears (37x52cm-15x20in) s. W/C. 13-May-3 Hartung & Hartung, Munich #2576/R
£590 $933 €850 Cinqueterre (34x45cm-13x18in) s. W/C over monotype. 26-Apr-3 Dr Lehr, Berlin #318/R
£1026 $1590 €1600 Atrani (34x45cm-13x18in) s. W/C over monotype. 7-Dec-2 Hauswedell & Nolte, Hamburg #854/R est:1800

LANGE, Thomas (20th C) German
Works on paper
£440 $678 €700 Farewell (120x150cm-47x59in) s.i.d.1984 mixed media collage paper on panel. 26-Oct-2 Dr Lehr, Berlin #279/R

LANGE, Willi Otto Max (1876-1950) German
£342 $534 €500 Hamburg harbour (51x58cm-20x23in) s. 10-Apr-3 Schopman, Hamburg #713

LANGENBACH, Clara Emma (1871-?) American
£287 $450 €431 Gathering autumn leaves (23x30cm-9x12in) s. i.verso panel exhib. 23-Nov-2 Jackson's, Cedar Falls #327/R

LANGENDYK, Dirk (1748-1805) Dutch
£8280 $12917 €13000 Cavalry battle scene in a hilly landscape with troops retreating (41x48cm-16x19in) s.d.1781 panel. 5-Nov-2 Sotheby's, Amsterdam #241/R est:10000-15000
Works on paper
£255 $397 €400 Ruins of Bergen op Zoom after the Napoleonic bombardment (11x17cm-4x7in) s.d.1799 pen brown ink grey wash. 5-Nov-2 Sotheby's, Amsterdam #132/R
£405 $632 €600 Marchande de fleurs (22x17cm-9x7in) s. W/C. 31-Mar-3 Ribeyre & Baron, Paris #29
£764 $1192 €1200 Battle scene (22x31cm-9x12in) s.d.1799 pen brown ink grey wash black chk. 5-Nov-2 Sotheby's, Amsterdam #130/R

£816 $1298 €1200 Ship battle (12x18cm-5x7in) s.d.1799 pen ink wash. 24-Mar-3 Tajan, Paris #27
£1689 $2635 €2500 Battle field (12x18cm-5x7in) s.d.1796 pen ink wash pair. 27-Mar-3 Christie's, Paris #152/R

LANGENDYK, Jan Anthonie (1780-1818) Dutch
Works on paper
£1401 $2186 €2200 Winter scene, with soldiers and gun carriage approaching a farm (21x33cm-8x13in) s.d.1816 pen brown ink W/C over black chk prov. 5-Nov-2 Sotheby's, Amsterdam #121/R est:2000-3000
£1529 $2385 €2400 Covered cheese market on the edge of a town square (26x31cm-10x12in) pen black ink grey wash W/C. 5-Nov-2 Sotheby's, Amsterdam #123/R est:2500-3500
£6500 $10855 €9425 View of Gibraltar (34x53cm-13x21in) s. W/C traces blk chk. 9-Jul-3 Sotheby's, London #69/R est:3000-5000

LANGENEGGER, Johannes (1879-1951) Swiss?
£4148 $6472 €6222 Procession of cattle in Alpstein landscape (37x68cm-15x27in) paper on board lit. 6-Nov-2 Hans Widmer, St Gallen #57/R est:8000-14000 (S.FR 9500)
£7075 $11462 €12524 Farmstead (44x58cm-17x23in) board. 26-May-3 Sotheby's, Zurich #69/R est:10000-12000 (S.FR 15000)

LANGENHOVE, J van (1920-1986) Belgian
£1139 $1777 €1800 Still life with flowers and Kanton vase (130x96cm-51x38in) s. 21-Oct-2 Bernaerts, Antwerp #115/R est:1000-1500

LANGER, Karel (1878-1947) Czechoslovakian
£327 $520 €491 Fruit picking in Dalmatia (17x29cm-7x11in) s. board. 8-Mar-3 Dorotheum, Prague #48/R est:10000-15000 (C.KR 15000)
£414 $659 €621 Dalmatian motif (19x28cm-7x11in) s. canvas on board. 8-Mar-3 Dorotheum, Prague #47/R est:15000-23000 (C.KR 19000)
£620 $967 €930 Sea by Dubrovnik (60x84cm-24x33in) s. 12-Oct-2 Dorotheum, Prague #52/R (C.KR 30000)
£698 $1110 €1047 Sea at Dubrovnik (60x84cm-24x33in) s. 8-Mar-3 Dorotheum, Prague #40/R est:30000-45000 (C.KR 32000)

LANGER, Robert von (1783-1846) German
Works on paper
£264 $409 €420 Roman soldiers threatening citizens (31x44cm-12x17in) s.d.1898 W/C over pencil. 4-Oct-2 Paul Kieffer, Pforzhiem #9481/R

LANGER, Viggo (1860-1942) Danish
£242 $382 €363 Ducks and farm buildings on the river bank (37x49cm-15x19in) s.d.1930 s.i.stretcher. 18-Nov-2 Waddingtons, Toronto #186/R (C.D 600)
£258 $393 €387 Autumn landscape with crooked tree (83x66cm-33x26in) s.i.d.Oktbr.1894. 27-Aug-2 Rasmussen, Copenhagen #1916/R (D.KR 3000)
£270 $417 €405 Winter landscape from Lellinge (47x63cm-19x25in) s.d.1918. 26-Oct-2 Rasmussen, Havnen #2026 (D.KR 3200)
£270 $435 €405 Spring landscape with farm (55x63cm-22x25in) s. 22-Feb-3 Rasmussen, Havnen #2172 (D.KR 3000)
£280 $448 €420 Coastal landscape with sailing ship (61x69cm-24x27in) s.d.aug.1909. 13-Jan-3 Rasmussen, Vejle #2020 (D.KR 3200)
£288 $455 €432 Terraces with flowers, Menton (42x35cm-17x14in) s.d.1933. 5-Apr-3 Rasmussen, Havnen #2152 (D.KR 3100)
£297 $470 €446 Coastal landscape with houses and bathers (39x51cm-15x20in) s. 5-Apr-3 Rasmussen, Havnen #2033 (D.KR 3200)
£355 $553 €533 Autumn scene by farmhouse (37x50cm-15x20in) s.d.9/8 1934. 23-Sep-2 Rasmussen, Vejle #76/R (D.KR 4200)
£361 $570 €542 Kronborg seen from the coast of North Sjaelland (32x88cm-13x35in) s.d.1906. 13-Nov-2 Kunsthallen, Copenhagen #2/R (D.KR 4200)
£372 $592 €558 Angler by river (33x53cm-13x21in) s.i.d.1881. 10-Mar-3 Rasmussen, Vejle #305/R (D.KR 4000)
£414 $646 €650 Farmstead with geese (48x65cm-19x26in) s. 6-Nov-2 Hugo Ruef, Munich #1190/R
£423 $651 €635 Winter landscape from Kirkeskoven near Sollerod (46x62cm-18x24in) s.d.1917. 26-Oct-2 Rasmussen, Havnen #2054 (D.KR 5000)
£426 $672 €639 Figures by the old railway station (35x42cm-14x17in) s.d.1902. 2-Dec-2 Rasmussen, Copenhagen #1227/R (D.KR 5000)
£431 $698 €625 The beach north of Kronborg (32x58cm-13x23in) s. 26-May-3 Rasmussen, Copenhagen #1365/R (D.KR 4500)
£497 $800 €746 Blossoming trees in spring. s. 16-Jan-3 Skinner, Bolton #910/R
£592 $923 €888 Sitting room interior (64x82cm-25x32in) s.d.1914. 11-Aug-2 Hindemae, Ullerslev #7380/R (D.KR 7000)
£603 $916 €905 Pompeii, view from Albergo de Sole (48x62cm-19x24in) s.i.d.1899. 27-Aug-2 Rasmussen, Copenhagen #1657/R (D.KR 7000)
£696 $1100 €1100 Gadevang on summer evening (35x50cm-14x20in) s.d.1929 i. verso lit. 29-Nov-2 Schloss Ahlden, Ahlden #1341/R
£822 $1282 €1200 Mountain landscape with Pont St Louis near Menton (80x68cm-31x27in) s.d.1932. 10-Apr-3 Dorotheum, Vienna #198/R
£1039 $1517 €1600 Coast at evening time (47x73cm-19x29in) s.d.1913. 15-Jun-2 Hans Stahl, Hamburg #150/R
£1090 $1689 €1700 Spring landscape near Menton (34x47cm-13x19in) s.d.1914. 6-Dec-2 Michael Zeller, Lindau #820/R
£3445 $5581 €4995 Landscape from Dyrehaven (106x146cm-42x57in) s.d.1912. 26-May-3 Rasmussen, Copenhagen #1497/R est:25000 (D.KR 36000)

LANGERER, Freddie (1899-1948) Dutch
£513 $805 €800 Reclining woman surrounded by deer and dog (35x46cm-14x18in) prov. 25-Nov-2 Glerum, Amsterdam #122
£694 $1146 €1000 Resting girl (45x55cm-18x22in) s. s.i.stretcher prov. 1-Jul-3 Christie's, Amsterdam #351/R

LANGEROCK, Henri (1830-1915) Belgian
£261 $429 €400 Amoureux dans un sous-bois (39x29cm-15x11in) s. cardboard prov. 7-Feb-3 Oger, Dumont, Paris #102
£669 $1077 €950 Autumn landscape with fisherman at sunset (32x40cm-13x16in) s. panel. 12-May-3 Bernaerts, Antwerp #32/R
£861 $1309 €1292 Provincial landscape with farm, waterway and woman walking (35x60cm-14x24in) s. panel. 27-Aug-2 Rasmussen, Copenhagen #1673/R (D.KR 10000)
£1325 $2159 €2000 Promenade au parc (66x46cm-26x18in) s. 17-Feb-3 Horta, Bruxelles #144
Works on paper
£655 $1048 €950 Le retour du cavalier - orientaliste (30x47cm-12x19in) s. W/C. 17-Mar-3 Horta, Bruxelles #69

LANGETTI, Giovanni Battista (1625-1676) Italian
£20126 $31195 €32000 The death of Archimedes (71x91cm-28x36in) prov. 2-Oct-2 Dorotheum, Vienna #2/R est:8000-10000

LANGETTI, Giovanni Battista (attrib) (1625-1676) Italian
£2270 $3790 €3200 Un philosophe antique (115x94cm-45x37in) 23-Jun-3 Beaussant & Lefèvre, Paris #243/R est:4000-5000
£31000 $51770 €44950 Death of Cato (103x115cm-41x45in) with sig. canvas on board. 11-Jul-3 Christie's, Kensington #219/R est:7000-10000

LANGEVIN, Claude (1942-) Canadian
£262 $414 €393 De retour, St. Calixte (25x30cm-10x12in) s.d.1981 i.verso prov. 14-Nov-2 Heffel, Vancouver #89 (C.D 650)
£279 $435 €405 Cabin by the stream (61x51cm-24x20in) s. 26-Mar-3 Walker's, Ottawa #451/R (C.D 650)
£494 $765 €741 Dernieres lueurs (20x40cm-8x16in) s. 3-Dec-2 Joyner, Toronto #473 est:700-900 (C.D 1200)
£739 $1153 €1233 Soir de grands vents (51x61cm-20x24in) s. s.i.verso prov. 13-Apr-3 Levis, Calgary #73/R est:2000-2500 (C.D 1700)
£741 $1148 €1112 Promenade (50x60cm-20x24in) s. 3-Dec-2 Joyner, Toronto #298/R est:1800-2200 (C.D 1800)
£889 $1458 €1334 En Grande conference (60x75cm-24x30in) s. 3-Jun-3 Joyner, Toronto #329/R est:2000-2500 (C.D 2000)
£905 $1403 €1358 Derniere lueur du jour (60x75cm-24x30in) s. 3-Dec-2 Joyner, Toronto #305/R est:2000-3000 (C.D 2200)
£1022 $1676 €1482 Laurentides (60x50cm-24x20in) s.i. 9-Jun-3 Hodgins, Calgary #45/R est:1500-2000 (C.D 2300)
£1084 $1713 €1626 Devant l'Etable (41x51cm-16x20in) 1-Dec-2 Levis, Calgary #57/R est:1600-2000 (C.D 2700)
£1165 $1829 €1748 Deux erables (50x60cm-20x24in) s.i. acrylic. 25-Nov-2 Hodgins, Calgary #148/R est:2000-2400 (C.D 2900)
£1245 $1967 €1868 Debut d'automne (76x61cm-30x24in) 1-Dec-2 Levis, Calgary #56/R est:2200-2600 (C.D 3100)
£1317 $2041 €1976 Enfin de retour (60x75cm-24x30in) s. 3-Dec-2 Joyner, Toronto #233/R est:3000-4000 (C.D 3200)
£1399 $2169 €2099 Signe du printemps (75x100cm-30x39in) s. 3-Dec-2 Joyner, Toronto #246/R est:3000-4000 (C.D 3400)
£1696 $2645 €2828 Milieu Octobre (76x102cm-30x40in) s. s.i.verso. 13-Apr-3 Levis, Calgary #72/R est:3500-4000 (C.D 3900)

LANGEWEG, Ger (1891-1970) Dutch
£496 $804 €700 Hen (56x68cm-22x27in) s. i.verso exhib. 26-May-3 Glerum, Amsterdam #32/R

LANGHAMMER, Carl (1868-?) German
£284 $460 €426 Sheep grazing in meadow (48x35cm-19x14in) s. 25-Jan-3 Rasmussen, Havnen #2281 (D.KR 3200)

LANGKER, Sir Erik (1898-1982) Australian
£395 $627 €593 Landscape (39x49cm-15x19in) canvas on board. 23-Mar-3 Goodman, Sydney #106 (A.D 1050)
£502 $763 €753 Poppies (51x55cm-20x22in) s. canvasboard. 28-Aug-2 Deutscher-Menzies, Melbourne #410/R (A.D 1400)
£717 $1176 €1040 The spit (24x35cm-9x14in) s. board. 3-Jun-3 Lawson Menzies, Sydney #759 (A.D 1800)
£912 $1387 €1368 Towards twilight (58x73cm-23x29in) s. 19-Aug-2 Joel, Victoria #294 est:2000-2500 (A.D 2600)

LANGLACE, Jean Baptiste Gabriel (1786-1864) French
£3049 $5000 €4421 Vue du Petit Bellevue de St Cloud, nr Vallerienne (33x46cm-13x18in) s.d.1818 prov. 4-Jun-3 Christie's, Rockefeller NY #250/R est:6000-8000

LANGLAIS, Xavier de (1906-1975) French
£252 $390 €400 Jeune femme rousse lisant (65x54cm-26x21in) s.d.65 panel. 6-Oct-2 Livinec, Gaudcheau & Jezequel, Rennes #49

LANGLANDS and BELL (20th C) British
Works on paper
£4000 $6560 €6000 Highpoint (76x258cm-30x102in) MDF wood glass lacquer prov.exhib. 7-Feb-3 Sotheby's, London #108/R est:4000-6000

LANGLANDS, George Nasmyth (?-1940) British
£440 $722 €638 Lauder moor, figure on horseback (22x32cm-9x13in) s.d.1914 board. 7-Jun-3 Shapes, Edinburgh #418/R

LANGLET, Alexander (1870-1953) Swedish
£252 $399 €378 Carolean with horse in snowstorm (50x65cm-20x26in) s.d.35. 30-Nov-2 Goteborg Auktionsverk, Sweden #157/R (S.KR 3600)
£281 $443 €422 Carolean on horseback in snowstorm (38x30cm-15x12in) s.d.39. 30-Nov-2 Goteborg Auktionsverk, Sweden #158/R (S.KR 4000)
£330 $534 €495 Horses grazing (62x92cm-24x36in) s.d.15. 3-Feb-3 Lilla Bukowskis, Stockholm #512 (S.KR 4600)
£409 $643 €614 Carolean in snowy landscape (40x31cm-16x12in) s. 16-Dec-2 Lilla Bukowskis, Stockholm #430 (S.KR 5800)

LANGLEY, Edward M (1870-1949) American
£531 $850 €770 Mist on hills, Coochella Valley (53x71cm-21x28in) s.d.26. 17-May-3 CRN Auctions, Cambridge #17

LANGLEY, Walter (1852-1922) British
£650 $1021 €975 Highland cattle in a mountainous landscape (41x61cm-16x24in) s. 16-Apr-3 Christie's, Kensington #619/R
£25000 $38750 €37500 Washing day (71x99cm-28x39in) s.d.1892 prov.exhib.lit. 26-Sep-2 Lane, Penzance #350/R est:25000-30000
Works on paper
£740 $1169 €1110 Farm well (18x26cm-7x10in) s.d.76 W/C. 7-Apr-3 Bonhams, Bath #33/R
£1500 $2340 €2250 Dutch maiden (33x23cm-13x9in) s. i.verso W/C. 17-Oct-2 David Lay, Penzance #1447/R est:2000-3000
£1800 $2808 €2700 Portrait of Miss Low (11x10cm-4x4in) mono. bears i.verso W/C. 5-Nov-2 Bonhams, New Bond Street #164a/R est:1200-1800
£3500 $5845 €5075 Fisherman reading a newspaper (19x24cm-7x9in) s.d.1884 Indian ink. 19-Jun-3 Lane, Penzance #90/R est:2000-2500
£3600 $5580 €5400 Figures before cottages at Paul village near Penzance (38x56cm-15x22in) s. W/C. 26-Sep-2 Lane, Penzance #195/R est:3500-4500
£3800 $5890 €5700 Dutch girl (37x26cm-15x10in) W/C. 3-Dec-2 Bonhams, New Bond Street #9/R est:4000-6000
£3800 $6346 €5510 Old harbour Newlyn (22x15cm-9x6in) s. W/C. 19-Jun-3 Lane, Penzance #285/R est:3000-4000
£5000 $8150 €7500 In thought (34x20cm-13x8in) s.d.92 W/C. 29-Jan-3 Sotheby's, Olympia #226/R est:2000-3000
£5500 $8525 €8250 Granny takes a nap (38x29cm-15x11in) s. W/C. 3-Dec-2 Bonhams, New Bond Street #10/R est:5000-8000
£7000 $10920 €10500 Old fishwife (22x14cm-9x6in) s. W/C pencil prov. 25-Mar-3 Bonhams, New Bond Street #7/R est:7000-10000
£8500 $13175 €12750 Country walk, women with baskets (112x203cm-44x80in) s.d.1884 W/C. 26-Sep-2 Lane, Penzance #370/R est:10000-15000
£10000 $15600 €15000 Fishwife beside the hearth (26x35cm-10x14in) s. W/C prov. 25-Mar-3 Bonhams, New Bond Street #6/R est:10000-15000
£10000 $15600 €14500 Waiting for the return - young woman with knitting at the harbour wall (34x46cm-13x18in) s.d.1892 W/C. 27-Mar-3 Lane, Penzance #80/R est:9000-11000
£13500 $20925 €20250 Cornish maiden (33x24cm-13x9in) s. W/C. 3-Dec-2 Bonhams, New Bond Street #1/R est:4000-6000
£15000 $23250 €22500 Cornish fisherman (74x56cm-29x22in) s. W/C. 26-Sep-2 Lane, Penzance #360/R est:15000-20000
£15000 $23400 €21750 Their task being ended with declining day, homeward the weary peasants (42x61cm-17x24in) s. painted c.1880 W/C prov.lit. 27-Mar-3 Lane, Penzance #100/R est:15000-20000
£27000 $41850 €40500 Newlyn fishwives (31x47cm-12x19in) s.i. W/C bodycol scratching out. 3-Dec-2 Bonhams, New Bond Street #4/R est:12000-18000

LANGLEY, William (fl.1880-1920) British
£270 $419 €405 Seascape with sand dunes in foreground (38x58cm-15x23in) s. 4-Nov-2 Brightwells, Leominster #1201/R
£280 $434 €420 Daily toil (34x24cm-13x9in) canvas on panel. 26-Sep-2 Mellors & Kirk, Nottingham #690
£280 $468 €406 Morning in the Welsh hill (49x74cm-19x29in) s. 26-Jun-3 Mellors & Kirk, Nottingham #863
£350 $532 €525 Misty morning (51x71cm-20x28in) s. 29-Aug-2 Christie's, Kensington #235/R
£350 $557 €525 Highland scene with drover and cattle (76x51cm-30x20in) s. 7-Mar-3 Biddle & Webb, Birmingham #108
£380 $589 €570 Coastal scene with grassy sand dunes to foreground (48x74cm-19x29in) s. 6-Dec-2 Biddle & Webb, Birmingham #406
£400 $648 €600 Cattle watering at dusk in a Highland landscape (41x61cm-16x24in) s. 23-Jan-3 Christie's, Kensington #213/R
£450 $734 €675 Near Shoreham (51x76cm-20x30in) s. i.verso. 12-Feb-3 Bonhams, Knightsbridge #202/R
£460 $750 €690 Rural landscape with figures, lake and cottage (50x75cm-20x30in) s. 17-Feb-3 Bonhams, Bath #30
£600 $936 €900 Cattle watering in a lake landscape (51x76cm-20x30in) s. 7-Nov-2 Christie's, Kensington #107/R
£750 $1245 €1088 Highland cattle watering (51x76cm-20x30in) s. 12-Jun-3 Gorringes, Lewes #1748
£1000 $1560 €1500 Highland cattle watering in a mountain stream (30x50cm-12x20in) s. pair. 13-Sep-2 Lyon & Turnbull, Edinburgh #119/R est:400-600
£1125 $1643 €1800 Cattle grazing in mountain landscape (28x39cm-11x15in) s. 14-May-2 Thomas Adams, Dublin #366

LANGLOIS, Chris (1969-) Australian
£1971 $2996 €2957 Three sunrises no 7 (171x150cm-67x59in) s.i.d.1995 verso prov.exhib. 28-Aug-2 Deutscher-Menzies, Melbourne #6/R est:6000-8000 (A.D 5500)
£2500 $3925 €3750 Rain no 21 (170x120cm-67x47in) s.i.d.1996 verso linen prov.exhib. 25-Nov-2 Christie's, Melbourne #238/R est:6000-8000 (A.D 7000)

LANGLOIS, J (19th C) British
£270 $424 €405 Terriers ratting (24x34cm-9x13in) s. 29-Jul-2 David Duggleby, Scarborough #435
£1646 $2567 €2600 Terriers rabbiting (29x69cm-11x27in) 30-Jul-2 Hamilton Osborne King, Dublin #125/R est:1400-1800
£3200 $5056 €4800 Spaniels by a river (76x127cm-30x50in) with sig. 28-Nov-2 Christie's, Kensington #352/R est:3000-5000

LANGLOIS, Mark W (fl.1862-1873) British
£500 $825 €725 Reading the letter (25x30cm-10x12in) s. 2-Jul-3 Sotheby's, Olympia #322/R
£605 $956 €908 Interesting customer (53x43cm-21x17in) s. i.stretcher. 18-Nov-2 Waddingtons, Toronto #107/R (C.D 1500)
£641 $1000 €962 Birds' nest (51x41cm-20x16in) s. 9-Oct-2 Doyle, New York #63
£700 $1078 €1050 Bad loser (60x51cm-24x20in) init. 5-Sep-2 Christie's, Kensington #271/R
£750 $1223 €1088 Feeding the rabbit (53x43cm-21x17in) s. 17-Jul-3 Thomson, Roddick & Medcalf, Carlisle #120/R
£893 $1411 €1340 Breakfast party (53x43cm-21x17in) s. s.i.on stretcher pair. 26-Nov-2 Sotheby's, Melbourne #216/R est:3000-5000 (A.D 2500)
£900 $1431 €1350 Fireside musical gathering (75x61cm-30x24in) s. 27-Feb-3 Bonhams, Chester #468/R
£900 $1404 €1350 Politicians. Rustic melody (20x26cm-8x10in) s. on s.i.verso panel pair. 26-Mar-3 Sotheby's, Olympia #155/R
£920 $1417 €1380 School room (55x43cm-22x17in) s. 23-Oct-2 Hamptons Fine Art, Godalming #168/R
£1027 $1613 €1500 Children playing (53x43cm-21x17in) s. 16-Apr-3 Dorotheum, Salzburg #97/R est:2000-2800
£1800 $2772 €2700 Compulsory service. Little soldier (53x43cm-21x17in) s. pair. 5-Sep-2 Christie's, Kensington #269/R est:2000-3000
Works on paper
£400 $628 €600 Rejected suitor (36x51cm-14x20in) s.d.1879 W/C. 13-Dec-2 Keys, Aylsham #573/R

LANGLOIS, Mark W (attrib) (fl.1862-1873) British
£500 $775 €750 Young boys smoking observed by grandmother. 25-Sep-2 Brightwells, Leominster #936/R

LANGLOIS, Paul (1858-1906) French
£478 $775 €693 Grandmother reading aloud to her grandchildren (53x43cm-21x17in) indis sig. i.verso. 26-May-3 Rasmussen, Copenhagen #1301 (D.KR 5000)

LANGMAID, Rowland (1897-1956) British
Works on paper
£300 $486 €450 Orion in a seaway (23x34cm-9x13in) s.i. pencil W/C. 21-May-3 Christie's, Kensington #384/R
£700 $1134 €1050 St Paul's from Bankside (18x13cm-7x5in) s.i. W/C. 21-May-3 Christie's, Kensington #481/R
£2200 $3564 €3300 Shipping in the Pool of London (20x34cm-8x13in) pencil W/C. 21-May-3 Christie's, Kensington #482/R est:800-1200

LANGSTAFFE, John (?) British
£417 $650 €626 Medmanham Abbey, on the Thames. 21-Sep-2 Harvey Clar, Oakland #1428

LANNEAU, Patrick (1951-) French
£420 $701 €600 Composition, Nice (93x115cm-37x45in) s.verso. 25-Jun-3 Claude Aguttes, Neuilly #174/R

LANNES, Mario (1900-1983) Italian
£238 $379 €350 Flowers (45x35cm-18x14in) s. cardboard. 1-Mar-3 Stadion, Trieste #334
£442 $703 €650 Driadi (71x61cm-28x24in) cardboard. 1-Mar-3 Stadion, Trieste #554
£544 $865 €800 Extensive landscape (72x102cm-28x40in) s. cardboard. 1-Mar-3 Stadion, Trieste #551

LANOE, Alphonse (1926-) Swiss
£1092 $1703 €1638 Fleurs et desserts (30x26cm-12x10in) s. pavatex. 20-Nov-2 Fischer, Luzern #1115/R est:2800-3200 (S.FR 2500)
Works on paper
£262 $409 €393 Circus tent (21x30cm-8x12in) s.d.78 mixed media. 20-Nov-2 Fischer, Luzern #2651/R (S.FR 600)

LANOOY, Chris (1881-1948) Dutch
£5380 $8500 €8500 Boomgaard (49x60cm-19x24in) s. 26-Nov-2 Sotheby's, Amsterdam #1/R est:3500-4500

LANSAC, François-Emile de (1803-1890) French
£2201 $3434 €3500 Brown horse (82x99cm-32x39in) s.d.1859 lit. 20-Sep-2 Schloss Ahlden, Ahlden #1231/R est:3500

LANSDOWNE, James Fenwick (1937-) Canadian
Works on paper
£2466 $3946 €3699 Ducks. Pair of mallard ducks (63x71cm-25x28in) s. W/C pair prov. 15-May-3 Heffel, Vancouver #142/R est:4000-5000 (C.D 5500)

LANSIL, Walter Franklin (1846-1925) American
£1132 $1800 €1698 Venice (20x31cm-8x12in) s. i.d.1889 verso. 7-Mar-3 Skinner, Boston #339/R est:1000-1500
£1875 $3000 €2719 The Meuse at Dortrecht, Holland (29x154cm-11x61in) s. s.i.d.1915 verso. 16-May-3 Skinner, Boston #356/R est:3000-5000
Works on paper
£457 $750 €686 Venetian fishing boats (38x56cm-15x22in) s. W/C paper on board. 5-Feb-3 Doyle, New York #21/R

LANSKOY, Andre (1902-1976) French/Russian
£833 $1325 €1200 Composition vert (12x22cm-5x9in) s. prov. 29-Apr-3 Artcurial Briest, Paris #646
£1301 $2030 €1900 Abstract composition with geometric shapes (27x21cm-11x8in) s. tempera. 11-Apr-3 Winterberg, Heidelberg #1277/R est:2400
£1424 $2250 €2136 Abstract modernist table top with still life (53x64cm-21x25in) s. 26-Apr-3 Jeffery Burchard, Florida #84
£1736 $2760 €2500 Bouquet de fleurs (73x60cm-29x24in) s.d. mono.verso painted c.1935-1937. 29-Apr-3 Artcurial Briest, Paris #262/R est:2500-3000
£1923 $3019 €3000 Nature morte (33x46cm-13x18in) s. 24-Nov-2 Laurence Calmels, Paris #176/R
£2297 $3584 €3400 Composition (29x40cm-11x16in) s.d.1974 card on canvas. 26-Mar-3 Finarte Semenzato, Milan #86/R
£2564 $4026 €4000 Interior (54x65cm-21x26in) s. painted 1932. 10-Dec-2 Piasa, Paris #142/R
£2568 $4005 €3800 Nature morte (46x55cm-18x22in) s. 26-Mar-3 Millon & Associes, Paris #143/R
£2885 $4529 €4500 Paysage (60x81cm-24x32in) s. painted 1929 prov. 10-Dec-2 Piasa, Paris #250
£2885 $4529 €4500 Hiver (13x24cm-5x9in) init. painted 1944 prov.exhib. 10-Dec-2 Piasa, Paris #254
£3165 $4905 €5000 Still life (60x81cm-24x32in) s. prov. 28-Sep-2 Ketterer, Hamburg #144/R est:5000-6000
£3205 $5032 €5000 Violettes perdues (33x41cm-13x16in) s. painted 1953 prov. 10-Dec-2 Piasa, Paris #249
£3205 $5032 €5000 Secrets d'automne (22x27cm-9x11in) init. i.d.50 verso prov. 10-Dec-2 Piasa, Paris #252/R
£3526 $5535 €5500 Signe de vie (22x27cm-9x11in) init. i.d.50 verso prov. 10-Dec-2 Piasa, Paris #253
£4200 $6636 €6300 Composition (46x54cm-18x21in) s. 3-Apr-3 Christie's, Kensington #216/R
£4304 $6800 €6800 Composition (50x65cm-20x26in) s. 2-Dec-2 Tajan, Paris #214
£4403 $6824 €7000 Composition (54x65cm-21x26in) s. 30-Oct-2 Artcurial Briest, Paris #434/R est:7000-8000
£4808 $7500 €7212 Untitled (81x54cm-32x21in) s.d.70. 20-Sep-2 Sloan, North Bethesda #371/R est:7000-9000
£5063 $8000 €8000 On se raccroche aux reves (81x65cm-32x26in) s. s.i.d.61 verso. 27-Nov-2 Blanchet, Paris #128/R
£5128 $8051 €8000 Par la fenetre du voisin (54x73cm-21x29in) s. i.d.61 verso. 24-Nov-2 Laurence Calmels, Paris #177/R
£5500 $8470 €8250 Untitled (100x65cm-39x26in) s. s.d.13 Avril 70 verso. 22-Oct-2 Sotheby's, London #434/R est:6000-8000
£5792 $9324 €8688 Sans titre (50x61cm-20x24in) s. 7-May-3 AB Stockholms Auktionsverk #1106/R est:80000-100000 (S.KR 75000)
£6369 $9936 €10000 Soeur de la violette (60x73cm-24x29in) s. painted 1957 prov. 7-Nov-2 Chochon-Barre & Allardi, Paris #177/R est:6500
£6410 $9936 €10000 Composition (66x47cm-26x19in) s. s.verso. 7-Dec-2 Cornette de St.Cyr, Paris #85/R est:12000
£6475 $10360 €9000 Composition (73x60cm-29x24in) s. s.d.55 lit. 17-May-3 De Vuyst, Lokeren #488/R est:9000-10000
£6711 $10805 €10000 Composition vitrail (54x65cm-21x26in) painted c.1950. 23-Feb-3 Mercier & Cie, Lille #116/R
£7051 $11071 €11000 Composition en long (50x81cm-20x32in) s. painted 1945. 10-Dec-2 Piasa, Paris #135/R est:12000
£7051 $11071 €11000 Derriere la foret (60x81cm-24x32in) s. painted 1946 prov.exhib. 10-Dec-2 Piasa, Paris #248/R
£7051 $10929 €11000 Untitled (60x73cm-24x29in) s. painted c.1963 prov. 6-Dec-2 Ketterer, Munich #152/R est:10000-12000
£7436 $11674 €11600 Composition (81x54cm-32x21in) s. 15-Dec-2 Eric Pillon, Calais #272/R
£7586 $12138 €11000 La recherche de l'objet (73x100cm-29x39in) s. i.d.67 verso. 12-Mar-3 Libert, Castor, Paris #131/R est:8000-10000
£7718 $12426 €11500 Composition vitrail (65x50cm-26x20in) s. painted c.1950. 23-Feb-3 Mercier & Cie, Lille #117/R est:11000
£7843 $12549 €12000 Composition (54x65cm-21x26in) s. 4-Jan-3 Meeting Art, Vercelli #627
£8974 $14090 €14000 Larmes du mage (81x65cm-32x26in) s. i.d.1962 verso prov. 15-Dec-2 Perrin, Versailles #68/R est:10000
£8974 $14090 €14000 Paysage (65x92cm-26x36in) s. painted 1923 prov.exhib. 10-Dec-2 Piasa, Paris #256 est:1500
£9864 $15684 €14500 Ivresse d'un rendez-vous (81x60cm-32x24in) s. i.d.60 verso. 3-Mar-3 Marc Kohn, Paris #15/R
£9929 $16085 €14000 Impasse sans images (60x73cm-24x29in) s. i.verso prov. 26-May-3 Christie's, Milan #323/R est:8000-10000
£10069 $15910 €14500 La soeur de la violette (60x73cm-24x29in) s. i.verso prov. 27-Apr-3 Perrin, Versailles #37/R est:12000-15000
£10403 $16748 €15500 Spirales desesperees (81x100cm-32x39in) s. i.d.1964 verso. 23-Feb-3 Mercier & Cie, Lille #79
£10897 $17109 €17000 Sous le poids de Shakespeare (100x73cm-39x29in) s. i.d.61 verso. 10-Dec-2 Piasa, Paris #136/R est:9000
£11655 $18647 €16200 Il etait une fois (73x92cm-29x36in) s. i.d.verso. 14-May-3 Blanchet, Paris #186/R est:15000-20000
£12179 $19122 €19000 Proposition de combat (73x100cm-29x39in) s. i.d.58 verso prov. 10-Dec-2 Piasa, Paris #251/R est:12000
£12422 $20000 €18633 Peregrination of a poppy (60x72cm-24x28in) s. painted 1961 prov. 7-May-3 Sotheby's, New York #313/R est:12000-18000
£12821 $20128 €20000 Inscrit sur la neige (73x60cm-29x24in) s. i.d.56 verso prov. 10-Dec-2 Piasa, Paris #257/R est:8000
£12821 $20128 €20000 Untitled (99x65cm-39x26in) s. d.1971 verso. 24-Nov-2 Laurence Calmels, Paris #173/R est:12000
£13669 $21871 €19000 Le vol du papillon bleu (73x92cm-29x36in) s. i.d.verso. 14-May-3 Blanchet, Paris #182/R est:15000-20000
£14744 $23147 €23000 Hommage a Georges de la Tour (65x81cm-26x32in) s. i.verso prov.exhib.lit. 10-Dec-2 Piasa, Paris #255/R est:7000
£16000 $24640 €24000 La souscription pour une attaque (194x95cm-76x37in) s. i.d.67 verso exhib. 22-Oct-2 Sotheby's, London #409/R est:18000-25000
£16129 $25484 €25000 Composition (73x100cm-29x39in) s. painted c.1960. 19-Dec-2 Ruellan, Paris #120/R est:22000
£19231 $30192 €30000 Elan pathetique (81x116cm-32x46in) s. i.d.1950 verso exhib. 10-Dec-2 Piasa, Paris #242/R est:22000
£22000 $36740 €31900 Sons et intervalles (95x143cm-37x56in) s.d.65 i.d.65 verso prov. 26-Jun-3 Sotheby's, London #187/R est:8000-12000
£24000 $40080 €34800 Partage de la nuit (81x116cm-32x46in) s. i.verso painted 1947-48 prov. 27-Jun-3 Christie's, London #115/R est:15000-20000
£26923 $41731 €42000 Chemin de feu (81x116cm-32x46in) s. i.d.1945-49 verso. 9-Dec-2 Piasa, Paris #56/R est:15000-20000
£26923 $42269 €42000 Oublie sous la neige (113x145cm-44x57in) s. painted 1951. 10-Dec-2 Piasa, Paris #133/R est:30000
£28846 $45288 €45000 Sonate norvegienne (81x116cm-32x46in) s. painted 1946. 10-Dec-2 Piasa, Paris #134/R est:20000
£28846 $45288 €45000 Magie violette (195x97cm-77x38in) s. i.d.61 verso prov.exhib. 10-Dec-2 Piasa, Paris #247/R est:35000
£29787 $49745 €42000 Affectueusement a Paolo Ucello (97x195cm-38x77in) s. prov.exhib. 20-Jun-3 Piasa, Paris #26/R est:20000-25000
£31056 $50000 €46584 Objets sur la neige (81x116cm-32x46in) s. painted 1944 prov.exhib.lit. 7-May-3 Sotheby's, New York #359/R est:10000-15000
£32051 $50321 €50000 Calendrier des jours heureux (114x146cm-45x57in) s. i.d.1955 verso prov.exhib.lit. 10-Dec-2 Piasa, Paris #244/R est:30000
£35256 $55353 €55000 Plus pres de la terre (146x97cm-57x38in) s. i.d.60 verso prov. 10-Dec-2 Piasa, Paris #240/R est:30000
£35256 $55353 €55000 Composition noire (130x97cm-51x38in) s. painted 1946 prov.exhib.lit. 10-Dec-2 Piasa, Paris #241/R est:30000
£39744 $62397 €62000 Mois de juillet (97x146cm-38x57in) s. i.d.57 verso. 10-Dec-2 Piasa, Paris #132/R est:30000
£40000 $66800 €58000 Composition jaune (195x97cm-77x38in) s. painted 1960 prov. 27-Jun-3 Christie's, London #130/R est:18000-25000
£44872 $70449 €70000 Feu souterrain (97x195cm-38x77in) s. i.d.60 verso prov.exhib. 10-Dec-2 Piasa, Paris #243/R est:35000
£46154 $71538 €72000 Obstacle dans l'obscurite (96x195cm-38x77in) s. i.d.1959 verso. 9-Dec-2 Piasa, Paris #55/R est:30000-40000

£48077 $74519 €75000 Un, black background (130x400cm-51x157in) s. 9-Dec-2 Piasa, Paris #49/R est:30000-40000
£52564 $81474 €82000 Contre attaque (97x195cm-38x77in) s. i.d.59 verso. 9-Dec-2 Piasa, Paris #54/R est:30000-40000
£54487 $84455 €85000 Protection (145x96cm-57x38in) s. i.d.58 verso exhib. 9-Dec-2 Piasa, Paris #53/R est:30000-40000
£54487 $85545 €85000 Nuits de mai (130x400cm-51x157in) s. painted 1961 prov.exhib. 10-Dec-2 Piasa, Paris #246/R est:40000
£68000 $113560 €98600 Voyage indirect (96x195cm-38x77in) s. i.verso painted 1958 prov. 27-Jun-3 Christie's, London #114/R est:15000-20000
£83333 $130833 €130000 Sang des papillons (140x260cm-55x102in) s. painted 1961 prov.exhib. 10-Dec-2 Piasa, Paris #245/R est:40000
£102564 $158974 €160000 Untitled (140x260cm-55x102in) s. 9-Dec-2 Piasa, Paris #48/R est:30000-40000

Works on paper

£506 $790 €800 Baigneues (50x65cm-20x26in) gouache exec.c.1925. 20-Oct-2 Mercier & Cie, Lille #351
£592 $959 €900 Sans titre (64x50cm-25x20in) s. chl dr. 22-Jan-3 Tajan, Paris #244
£612 $973 €900 Composition (31x24cm-12x9in) gouache. 18-Mar-3 Galerie Moderne, Brussels #520/R
£654 $1027 €1020 Untitled (47x62cm-19x24in) s. gouache exec.c.1925 pair. 24-Nov-2 Chayette & Cheval, Paris #222
£1382 $2238 €2100 Composition (21x34cm-8x13in) s. gouache. 22-Jan-3 Tajan, Paris #243/R est:2500-3000
£1603 $2516 €2500 Composition (25x32cm-10x13in) init. chl. 10-Dec-2 Piasa, Paris #408
£1862 $2942 €2700 Composition (53x39cm-21x15in) s. gouache. 4-Apr-3 Tajan, Paris #256/R
£2051 $3221 €3200 Sourires d'un souris (24x31cm-9x12in) s. gouache exec.1958. 10-Dec-2 Piasa, Paris #137/R
£2075 $3217 €3300 Composition (106x73cm-42x29in) s. chl chk. 30-Oct-2 Artcurial Briest, Paris #703/R est:1800-2300
£2308 $3623 €3600 Composition (74x54cm-29x21in) s. gouache. 15-Dec-2 Perrin, Versailles #48/R
£2436 $3824 €3800 Papiers colles (49x32cm-19x13in) s. collage exec.1959. 10-Dec-2 Piasa, Paris #140/R
£2548 $3975 €4000 Composition sur fond noir (48x64cm-19x25in) s. gouache. 7-Nov-2 Chochon-Barre & Allardi, Paris #176/R
£2564 $4026 €4000 Orientation vers la pelouse (25x32cm-10x13in) s. gouache prov. 10-Dec-2 Piasa, Paris #412 est:1500
£2692 $4227 €4200 Composition sur fond noir (49x64cm-19x25in) st.sig.verso gouache. 24-Nov-2 Laurence Calmels, Paris #171/R
£2814 $4446 €4221 Untitled (50x32cm-20x13in) s. gouache prov. 28-Apr-3 Bukowskis, Stockholm #328/R est:25000-30000 (S.KR 37000)
£2885 $4529 €4500 Landau (50x61cm-20x24in) mosaoic. 10-Dec-2 Piasa, Paris #141/R est:2000
£2885 $4529 €4500 Composition (45x33cm-18x13in) s. collage gouache prov. 10-Dec-2 Piasa, Paris #411 est:1000
£2890 $4566 €4335 Untitled (64x49cm-25x19in) s. gouache. 28-Apr-3 Bukowskis, Stockholm #329/R est:22000-25000 (S.KR 38000)
£3057 $4799 €4586 Composition sur fond noir (60x47cm-24x19in) s. gouache prov. 25-Nov-2 Germann, Zurich #20/R est:8000-12000 (S.FR 7000)
£3129 $4976 €4600 Composition (27x22cm-11x9in) s. gouache. 26-Feb-3 Artcurial Briest, Paris #457/R est:2300-2700
£3462 $5435 €5400 Untitled (48x63cm-19x25in) s. gouache. 24-Nov-2 Laurence Calmels, Paris #175/R est:6000
£3526 $5535 €5500 Composition (75x106cm-30x42in) s. sanguine exec.1947 prov. 10-Dec-2 Piasa, Paris #406/R
£3546 $5922 €5000 Composition abstraite, fond noir (66x50cm-26x20in) s. gouache prov. 20-Jun-3 Piasa, Paris #27/R est:5000-6000
£3974 $6240 €6200 Composition sur fond noir (48x63cm-19x25in) s. gouache. 24-Nov-2 Laurence Calmels, Paris #172/R
£3974 $6240 €6200 Composition sur fond noir (64x25cm-25x10in) s. gouache. 24-Nov-2 Laurence Calmels, Paris #174/R est:6000
£4167 $6583 €6000 Composition (49x62cm-19x24in) s. gouache. 27-Apr-3 Perrin, Versailles #19/R est:7000-8000
£4400 $7348 €6380 Untitled (107x75cm-42x30in) s. chl crayon prov.exhib. 26-Jun-3 Sotheby's, London #186/R est:4000-6000
£4487 $7045 €7000 Composition (64x23cm-25x9in) s. chl. 10-Dec-2 Piasa, Paris #138/R
£4487 $7045 €7000 Separation limitee (25x65cm-10x26in) s. gouache exec.1959 prov. 10-Dec-2 Piasa, Paris #410 est:3000
£4487 $7045 €7000 Composition (75x110cm-30x43in) collage gouache exec.1961 prov. 10-Dec-2 Piasa, Paris #407/R est:4000
£4487 $7045 €7000 Composition (16x50cm-6x20in) s. gouache. 10-Dec-2 Piasa, Paris #415 est:1500
£5128 $8051 €8000 Composition (108x74cm-43x29in) s. chl exec.1947 prov. 10-Dec-2 Piasa, Paris #405/R est:3000
£5769 $9058 €9000 Composition (100x65cm-39x26in) s. collage gouache exec.1959 prov. 10-Dec-2 Piasa, Paris #409/R
£5769 $9058 €9000 Fragment d'une ville (104x75cm-41x30in) s. collage gouache exec.1961 prov. 10-Dec-2 Piasa, Paris #413 est:3500
£7051 $11071 €11000 Composition (63x48cm-25x19in) s. gouache. 10-Dec-2 Piasa, Paris #414 est:3500
£9048 $14386 €13300 Fete (100x146cm-39x57in) s. gouache exec.1960. 3-Mar-3 Marc Kohn, Paris #22/R
£10256 $16103 €16000 Papiers colles (102x74cm-40x29in) collage. 10-Dec-2 Piasa, Paris #139/R est:3500

LANSKOY, Ivan Ivanovitch (1845-?) Russian

£535 $834 €850 Mother with child on river shore (37x47cm-15x19in) s. 21-Sep-2 Dannenberg, Berlin #579/R

LANSON, Alfred Desire (1851-1898) French

Sculpture

£8500 $13260 €12750 Jason and the golden fleece (100cm-39in) s.st.f.Susse brown green pat bronze lit. 5-Nov-2 Sotheby's, London #144/R est:7000-10000

LANSYER, Emmanuel (1835-1893) French

£3797 $6000 €6000 Elegantes pres de Cernay, matin d'Avril (127x175cm-50x69in) s.d.75 i.verso. 1-Dec-2 Peron, Melun #49

LANTARA, Simon Mathurin (attrib) (1729-1778) French

£494 $800 €741 Paysage (18x28cm-7x11in) panel prov. 24-Jan-3 Freeman, Philadelphia #246/R
£516 $815 €800 Paysage de riviere au soleil couchant (23x30cm-9x12in) 18-Dec-2 Piasa, Paris #82
£1600 $2480 €2400 Italianate landscape with fishermen (16x24cm-6x9in) panel. 31-Oct-2 Sotheby's, Olympia #164/R est:1500-2000

Works on paper

£878 $1370 €1300 Orage (28x33cm-11x13in) crayon dr htd gouache. 31-Mar-3 Ribeyre & Baron, Paris #33a/R

LANTOINE, Fernand (1876-c.1955) French

£2432 $3795 €3600 Marche a Marrakech (38x46cm-15x18in) s. canvas on masonite. 28-Mar-3 Claude Aguttes, Neuilly #218/R
£3137 $5051 €4800 La corrida (130x130cm-51x51in) s. 20-Jan-3 Horta, Bruxelles #92 est:2000-3000

LANYON, Andrew (1947-) British

£260 $406 €390 Sitting duck (23x15cm-9x6in) s. i.d.1979 verso paper. 16-Oct-2 David Lay, Penzance #262/R

LANYON, Ellen (1926-) American

£272 $400 €408 Episode I (178x183cm-70x72in) s.d.66-67 acrylic. 23-Jun-2 Susanin's, Chicago #5128/R

LANYON, Peter (1918-1964) British

£3000 $4710 €4500 Landscape with a path (32x41cm-13x16in) s.d.1939 i.verso board. 10-Dec-2 Lane, Penzance #20/R est:3000-3500
£3800 $5928 €5700 Market, Bruges (33x41cm-13x16in) s. panel exhib. 16-Oct-2 David Lay, Penzance #301 est:1500-2500
£12000 $18720 €18000 North coast (28x23cm-11x9in) s.d.1948 board. 16-Oct-2 David Lay, Penzance #275/R est:4000-6000

Works on paper

£1100 $1716 €1650 Roman fort (40x50cm-16x20in) s.i.d.1957 conte. 25-Mar-3 Bonhams, New Bond Street #106/R est:1200-1800
£1800 $2772 €2700 Old Cornish tin mine (32x22cm-13x9in) gouache prov. 5-Sep-2 Christie's, Kensington #700/R est:2000-3000
£1900 $2964 €2850 Standing female nude (71x54cm-28x21in) s.d.54 chl. 25-Mar-3 Bonhams, New Bond Street #107/R est:1000-1500
£2200 $3432 €3300 Newlyn Harbour (28x33cm-11x13in) s.indisd.57 pen ink. 16-Oct-2 David Lay, Penzance #226/R est:2000-3000
£2600 $4342 €3770 Untitled, San Gimignano (35x25cm-14x10in) s.d.64 pencil W/C collage prov. 24-Jun-3 Bonhams, New Bond Street #111/R est:2500-4000
£2800 $4340 €4200 Texan highway (49x34cm-19x13in) s.d.63 s.i.d.1963 verso black crayon gouache prov. 4-Dec-2 Christie's, Kensington #363/R est:3000-5000
£10000 $15600 €15000 Coastguard (76x53cm-30x21in) s.d.1958 s.i.d.verso gouache. 16-Oct-2 David Lay, Penzance #347/R est:8000-12000
£10500 $16380 €15750 Still life with pitcher (43x61cm-17x24in) s. i.d.1951 verso mixed media. 16-Oct-2 David Lay, Penzance #241/R est:8000-12000
£22000 $34540 €33000 Collage guitar (55x75cm-22x30in) s. i.d.63 verso collage brush ink pencil bodycol oil prov. 22-Nov-2 Christie's, London #97/R est:20000-30000

LANZA, Giovanni (1827-1889) Italian

Works on paper

£380 $600 €600 Meeting (32x50cm-13x20in) s. W/C. 2-Dec-2 Rieunier, Paris #21
£1392 $2200 €2200 Naples seen from Posillipo. Fishermen (19x27cm-7x11in) s. one W/C card one oil cardboard two. 26-Nov-2 Christie's, Rome #236/R
£1800 $2808 €2700 Temples at Paestum, Italy (41x76cm-16x30in) s. W/C. 5-Nov-2 Bonhams, New Bond Street #7/R est:1200-1800
£3400 $5270 €5100 Sorento coast (45x74cm-18x29in) s. W/C. 3-Dec-2 Sotheby's, Olympia #280/R est:1000-1500

LANZA, L G (?) Italian
Works on paper
£2700 $4266 €4050 On the Italian coast, possibly near Capri (44x66cm-17x26in) s. W/C card. 27-Nov-2 Hamptons Fine Art, Godalming #202 est:280-350

LANZA, Luigi (19th C) Italian
£500 $800 €750 View of the Grand Canal, Venice (36x53cm-14x21in) s. 18-May-3 Jeffery Burchard, Florida #32a/R
£602 $969 €903 Grand Canal with Santa Maria della Salute (59x80cm-23x31in) s.d.1934. 7-May-3 Dobiaschofsky, Bern #766/R (S.FR 1300)
£620 $1016 €899 Venetian Vedute (36x53cm-14x21in) s. i. verso. 4-Jun-3 Fischer, Luzern #1086/R (S.FR 1320)
£1038 $1619 €1650 Venice (29x20cm-11x8in) s. panel. 9-Oct-2 Michael Zeller, Lindau #782/R
£2000 $3120 €3000 Gondolas on the Grand Canal, Venice (54x36cm-21x14in) s. 17-Oct-2 Lawrence, Crewkerne #479 est:1000-1500

LANZA, Luigi (attrib) (19th C) Italian
£1088 $1731 €1600 Venice (30x40cm-12x16in) s. panel. 20-Mar-3 Neumeister, Munich #2676 est:150

LANZA, Vicenzo (1822-1902) Italian
Works on paper
£6500 $10140 €9750 View of the Theseum, the Acropolis beyond (34x53cm-13x21in) s. W/C over pencil htd bodycol. 15-Oct-2 Sotheby's, London #5/R est:7000-10000

LANZIROTI, Antonio Giovanni (1839-?) Italian
Sculpture
£1987 $3238 €3000 Young woman seated on rock (38cm-15in) s.i. black pat bronze marble base. 31-Jan-3 Rabourdin & Choppin de Janvry, Paris #157/R

LAOKOON (?) ?
Sculpture
£6918 $10792 €11000 Figure with snake (170cm-67in) bronze. 23-Sep-2 Wiener Kunst Auktionen, Vienna #82/R est:5000-10000

LAPAGLIA, Anthony (20th C) American?
Works on paper
£290 $475 €421 Untitled, abstract composition (33x46cm-13x18in) s.d. W/C over pencil exhib. 5-Jun-3 Swann Galleries, New York #157/R

LAPAYESE BRUNA, Jose (1899-1982) Spanish
£673 $1063 €1050 White houses (65x81cm-26x32in) s.d.973 mixed media board. 13-Nov-2 Ansorena, Madrid #56/R
£897 $1418 €1400 Fish (110x150cm-43x59in) s. s.i.verso board. 13-Nov-2 Ansorena, Madrid #283/R
£1623 $2370 €2500 After the bath (89x67cm-35x26in) s. board. 17-Jun-2 Ansorena, Madrid #342/R

LAPAYESE, Teresa (1966-) Spanish
£252 $392 €400 Still life with lemons (22x46cm-9x18in) s. 17-Sep-2 Segre, Madrid #230/R

LAPCHINE, Georges (c.1880-1940) Russian
£1923 $3019 €3000 Village sous la neige (54x73cm-21x29in) s.d.1930. 16-Dec-2 Rabourdin & Choppin de Janvry, Paris #6/R
£1935 $3058 €3000 Neige en sous-bois (81x100cm-32x39in) s. 19-Dec-2 Claude Aguttes, Neuilly #185/R
£3038 $4709 €4800 Le petit moulin (60x92cm-24x36in) s. 29-Sep-2 Eric Pillon, Calais #162/R
£3200 $5184 €4800 Winter landscape (50x61cm-20x24in) s. 21-May-3 Sotheby's, London #84/R est:2000-3000
£3205 $5032 €5000 Eglise pres du parc (100x155cm-39x61in) s. 15-Dec-2 Eric Pillon, Calais #162/R

LAPEGUE (20th C) French?
Sculpture
£1800 $2880 €2700 Figural group with female warrior (56cm-22in) bronze. 15-May-3 Christie's, Kensington #353/R est:2000-3000

LAPEYRE, Victoria (19/20th C) French?
£437 $690 €656 Still life of flowers (65x54cm-26x21in) s. 14-Nov-2 Stuker, Bern #351/R (S.FR 1000)

LAPICQUE, Charles (1898-1988) French
£903 $1435 €1300 Composition (64x48cm-25x19in) s. acrylic paper. 29-Apr-3 Artcurial Briest, Paris #299 est:1200-1500
£1111 $1766 €1600 Calvaire Breton (55x42cm-22x17in) s.d.48 paper lit. 29-Apr-3 Artcurial Briest, Paris #297 est:1200-1500
£1348 $2250 €1900 Paysage (50x65cm-20x26in) s. acrylic paper. 18-Jun-3 Pierre Berge, Paris #125/R est:2000-2500
£2564 $4026 €4000 Jeune femme vetue d'ecossais (73x60cm-29x24in) s. s.i.d.1944 masonite prov.exhib. 10-Dec-2 Piasa, Paris #434
£2662 $4233 €3835 Aphrodite (56x33cm-22x13in) s. s.i.d.1964 verso. 29-Apr-3 Artcurial Briest, Paris #301/R est:4500-6000
£2917 $4638 €4200 Figure armee (100x65cm-39x26in) s.d.50 paper on canvas prov. 29-Apr-3 Artcurial Briest, Paris #303 est:1800-2200
£3084 $4502 €4626 Monastere en Castille (65x54cm-26x21in) s. s.i.d.1973 verso prov. 17-Jun-2 Philippe Schuler, Zurich #4385/R est:8000-12000 (S.FR 7000)
£3205 $5032 €5000 Portrait de jeune homme (55x33cm-22x13in) s. s.i.d.1944 verso prov. 10-Dec-2 Piasa, Paris #438 est:3000
£3524 $5145 €5286 Mere et enfant (55x33cm-22x13in) s.d.47 lit.exhib.prov. 17-Jun-2 Philippe Schuler, Zurich #4384/R est:10000-14000 (S.FR 8000)
£3526 $5535 €5500 Orage en mer (65x92cm-26x36in) s.d.87 acrylic. 24-Nov-2 Laurence Calmels, Paris #179/R
£3548 $5500 €5322 Avant l'orage (60x73cm-24x29in) s. s.i.d.1978 verso acrylic prov. 26-Sep-2 Christie's, Rockefeller NY #622/R est:7000-9000
£3901 $6514 €5500 Lumieres a Venise (147x37cm-58x15in) s.d. paper on canvas. 18-Jun-3 Pierre Berge, Paris #127/R est:5000-6000
£4487 $7045 €7000 Portrait d'homme (54x65cm-21x26in) s. s.i.d.1944 verso lit. 10-Dec-2 Piasa, Paris #130/R
£4514 $7178 €6500 Hippolyte (65x54cm-26x21in) s.d.71 s.i.d.1971 verso lit. 29-Apr-3 Artcurial Briest, Paris #298/R est:6000-7500
£4723 $7509 €6800 Le messager (55x46cm-22x18in) s.d.47 s.i.d.1947 verso prov.exhib. 29-Apr-3 Artcurial Briest, Paris #304/R est:3800-5000
£4839 $7645 €7500 Ferme (38x61cm-15x24in) s. s.i.verso prov. 18-Dec-2 Digard, Paris #53/R est:9000
£5128 $8051 €8000 Ker (60x92cm-24x36in) s.d.47 s.i.d.1947 verso prov.exhib.lit. 10-Dec-2 Piasa, Paris #448/R est:8000
£5208 $8281 €7500 La peche miraculeuse (33x46cm-13x18in) s. s.i.d.1978 verso acrylic. 29-Apr-3 Artcurial Briest, Paris #296/R est:6000-7500
£5449 $8554 €8500 Deux figures mangeant une pomme (50x61cm-20x24in) s.d.45 s.i.d.verso prov.lit. 10-Dec-2 Piasa, Paris #441/R est:4500
£5769 $9058 €9000 Mere et fils sur la falaise (65x81cm-26x32in) s. s.i.d.1944 verso prov.exhib.lit. 10-Dec-2 Piasa, Paris #433 est:6000
£5769 $9058 €9000 Jeune femme aux regates (73x54cm-29x21in) s. s.i.d.1944 verso exhib.lit. 10-Dec-2 Piasa, Paris #437 est:6000
£6383 $10660 €9000 La route de Nagpour (33x25cm-13x10in) s.d. paper on canvas. 18-Jun-3 Pierre Berge, Paris #130/R est:9000-10000
£6410 $10064 €10000 Baiser dans la banlieue (73x60cm-29x24in) s.i.d.1944 verso prov.exhib.lit. 10-Dec-2 Piasa, Paris #436 est:6000
£6410 $10064 €10000 Pauvre dans la banlieue (65x54cm-26x21in) s.d.45 s.i.d.verso prov. 10-Dec-2 Piasa, Paris #440/R est:6000
£6410 $10064 €10000 Croises devant Chypre (65x92cm-26x36in) s.d.46 s.i.d.verso prov.exhib.lit. 10-Dec-2 Piasa, Paris #447/R est:8000
£6410 $10064 €10000 Danse guerriere (92x73cm-36x29in) s.d.45 s.i.d.1945 verso ppel. 10-Dec-2 Piasa, Paris #443/R est:6000
£6688 $10433 €10500 Monastere en Castille (54x65cm-21x26in) s. painted 1973. 10-Nov-2 Eric Pillon, Calais #229/R
£7051 $11071 €11000 Rendez-vous d'Aix-en-Provence (116x89cm-46x35in) s. s.i.verso acrylic. 24-Nov-2 Laurence Calmels, Paris #178/R est:30000
£7692 $12077 €12000 Calvaire de saint-Norgan (65x92cm-26x36in) s.d.45 s.i.d.verso prov.lit. 10-Dec-2 Piasa, Paris #442/R est:6000
£8333 $13083 €13000 Adieu (73x50cm-29x20in) s. s.i.d.1944 verso prov.lit. 10-Dec-2 Piasa, Paris #431/R est:7000
£8333 $13083 €13000 Aniversaire (81x100cm-32x39in) s.d.45 s.i.d.verso prov.lit. 10-Dec-2 Piasa, Paris #439 est:7000
£8654 $13587 €13500 Pecheurs a la ligne (73x54cm-29x21in) s. s.i.d.1944 verso prov.exhib. 10-Dec-2 Piasa, Paris #432/R est:6000
£8974 $14090 €14000 Rencotre dans la campagne (60x73cm-24x29in) s. s.i.d.1944 verso prov.exhib. 10-Dec-2 Piasa, Paris #435/R est:4000
£9028 $14896 €13000 Sur les bords du Guadalquivir (65x81cm-26x32in) s.d.78 s.i.d.1978 verso acrylic exhib. 2-Jul-3 Artcurial Briest, Paris #718/R est:10000-12000
£10191 $15898 €16000 Avant l'orage (60x73cm-24x29in) s. i.d.1978 verso acrylic. 10-Nov-2 Eric Pillon, Calais #214/R
£12766 $20681 €18000 Avant le depart (130x97cm-51x38in) s.d. 23-May-3 Binoche, Paris #65/R est:20000-25000
£12821 $20128 €20000 Homme au bord de l'eau (73x50cm-29x20in) s. s.i.d.1944 verso prov.exhib.lit. 10-Dec-2 Piasa, Paris #430/R est:7000
£13000 $20020 €19500 Nuit sur la lagune (38x55cm-15x22in) s.d.55 s.i.d.1955 s.i.d.verso prov.exhib. 22-Oct-2 Sotheby's, London #402/R est:15000-20000
£13000 $20020 €19500 Quai a Venise (38x57cm-15x22in) s.d.55 oil paper on panel prov.exhib. 22-Oct-2 Sotheby's, London #428/R est:15000-20000
£14744 $23147 €23000 Ker a la meule (65x81cm-26x32in) s.d.47 s.i.d.1947 prov.exhib.lit. 10-Dec-2 Piasa, Paris #449/R est:8000
£15278 $25208 €22000 Nuit sur la lagune (33x46cm-13x18in) s.d.55 s.i.d.1955 verso lit. 2-Jul-3 Artcurial Briest, Paris #719/R est:18000-25000
£16667 $25833 €26000 Embarcadere (65x81cm-26x32in) s.d.45 s.i.d.verso exhib.lit. 9-Dec-2 Piasa, Paris #50/R est:15000-20000
£18000 $27720 €27000 Croiseur au mouillage de St. Marc la Nuit (54x81cm-21x32in) s.d.55 s.i.d.verso. 22-Oct-2 Sotheby's, London #410/R est:20000-30000
£22069 $35310 €32000 Le paddock (116x89cm-46x35in) s.d.50. 12-Mar-3 Libert, Castor, Paris #132/R est:20000-30000

£26950 $45007 €38000 Les regates (73x100cm-29x39in) s.d. s.i.d.verso exhib.lit. 18-Jun-3 Pierre Berge, Paris #138/R est:40000-50000
Works on paper
£290 $459 €450 Remous (27x21cm-11x8in) s.d.46 brush ink lit. 19-Dec-2 Ruellan, Paris #114/R
£323 $510 €500 Rome (27x21cm-11x8in) s.d.57 W/C lit. 19-Dec-2 Ruellan, Paris #112/R
£323 $510 €500 Chypre (27x21cm-11x8in) s.d.46 brush ink lit. 19-Dec-2 Ruellan, Paris #116/R
£340 $541 €500 Le Calvaire de Kerembzel (27x21cm-11x8in) d.47 wash. 18-Mar-3 Galerie Moderne, Brussels #504
£346 $536 €550 Paysage (25x33cm-10x13in) s.d. gouache. 4-Oct-2 Tajan, Paris #138
£347 $549 €500 Visages (65x50cm-26x20in) s. pastel. 28-Apr-3 Cornette de St.Cyr, Paris #270
£380 $592 €600 Sans titre (27x21cm-11x8in) s.d.1946 gouache ink. 20-Oct-2 Claude Boisgirard, Paris #74/R
£380 $592 €600 Deux personnages (24x31cm-9x12in) s. pastel pencil. 20-Oct-2 Claude Boisgirard, Paris #78
£417 $688 €600 Personnage (48x31cm-19x12in) s. graphite col wax pastel dr. 1-Jul-3 Artcurial Briest, Paris #798
£451 $713 €650 Deux personnages (65x50cm-26x20in) s.d. chl pastel. 28-Apr-3 Cornette de St.Cyr, Paris #269
£472 $731 €750 Le rois lear (40x32cm-16x13in) s. wax pastel prov. 30-Oct-2 Artcurial Briest, Paris #285
£1348 $2250 €1900 Destroyers en manoeuvre (28x43cm-11x17in) s.d. col ink tracing paper. 18-Jun-3 Pierre Berge, Paris #120/R est:2000-2500
£1348 $2250 €1900 Figure (35x27cm-14x11in) s. col ink. 18-Jun-3 Pierre Berge, Paris #123/R est:2000-2500
£1795 $2818 €2800 Bord de mer (45x55cm-18x22in) s.d.52 wash lit. 10-Dec-2 Piasa, Paris #131/R
£1800 $2772 €2700 Untitled (50x65cm-20x26in) s.d.45 pastel pencil prov. 22-Oct-2 Sotheby's, London #419/R est:2000-3000
£1800 $2772 €2700 Untitled (49x65cm-19x26in) s.d.45 pastel pencil prov. 22-Oct-2 Sotheby's, London #420/R est:2000-3000
£1923 $3019 €3000 Entrevue (57x45cm-22x18in) s.d.45 pastel lit. 10-Dec-2 Piasa, Paris #446
£2244 $3522 €3500 Echauffouree (50x65cm-20x26in) s.d.45 chl col chk lit. 10-Dec-2 Piasa, Paris #445
£2564 $4026 €4000 Match (62x48cm-24x19in) s.d.45 col chk lit. 10-Dec-2 Piasa, Paris #444/R est:700
£3472 $5486 €5000 Henri III (63x37cm-25x15in) s.d. gouache oil prov. 27-Apr-3 Perrin, Versailles #60/R est:4500-5000

LAPIDOTH, Maurits Constantin (1868-1930) Dutch
£382 $596 €600 Milk carrier (37x46cm-15x18in) s. panel. 6-Nov-2 Vendue Huis, Gravenhage #489/R

LAPIERRE-RENOUARD, Paul Marie (1854-?) French
£838 $1332 €1257 Wild flowers in vase on table (81x65cm-32x26in) s. 5-Mar-3 Rasmussen, Copenhagen #2024/R (D.KR 9000)

LAPINE, Andreas Christian Gottfried (1868-1952) Canadian
£222 $364 €333 Laurentian autumn (30x40cm-12x16in) s. canvas on board. 3-Jun-3 Joyner, Toronto #408/R (C.D 500)
£1070 $1658 €1605 Sand pit (32x42cm-13x17in) s. prov. 3-Dec-2 Joyner, Toronto #289/R est:2500-3000 (C.D 2600)
£2444 $4009 €3666 Upland road (63x76cm-25x30in) s. masonite prov. 27-May-3 Sotheby's, Toronto #97/R est:4000-6000 (C.D 5500)

LAPINI, Cesare (1848-?) Italian
Sculpture
£3100 $5053 €4650 Young girl embroidering, seated on a chair (58cm-23in) s. alabaster. 11-Feb-3 Sotheby's, Olympia #339/R est:2000-3000
£8228 $13000 €12342 Sopresa (112cm-44in) i.d.1883 marble on dark green marble pedestal. 24-Apr-3 Christie's, Rockefeller NY #219/R est:12000-18000
£8861 $14000 €13292 Figure of Flora (94cm-37in) i. marble. 24-Apr-3 Christie's, Rockefeller NY #184/R est:6000-8000
£15625 $25000 €23438 Psyche, thinly clad woman with wings (114cm-45in) s. marble floral base octagonal foot. 4-Jan-3 Brunk, Ashville #350/R est:15000-25000
£15823 $25000 €23735 Seated girl sewing (70cm-28in) i. marble on a pink marble pedestal. 24-Apr-3 Christie's, Rockefeller NY #263/R est:10000-15000

LAPIRA (attrib) (?) Italian
Works on paper
£3521 $5845 €5000 Napoli dal Carmine. Napoli dal Campio (45x65cm-18x26in) one d.1853 i.verso gouache pair. 15-Jun-3 Anaf, Lyon #127/R est:5000-6000

LAPIS, Gaetano (studio) (1706-1758) Rumanian
£11000 $17270 €16500 Armida restrained by Rinaldo (119x168cm-47x66in) 13-Dec-2 Christie's, Kensington #249/R est:7000-10000

LAPITO, Louis Auguste (1803-1874) French
£7595 $12000 €12000 Enfants jouant a la source, hauteurs de Franchard, Fontainebleau (63x93cm-25x37in) s.d.1858. 1-Dec-2 Peron, Melun #53

LAPORTE, Émile Henri (1841-1919) French
£15000 $23700 €22500 Broken necklace (91x116cm-36x46in) s.d.77 canvas on board. 18-Nov-2 Joel, Victoria #356/R est:45000-55000 (A.D 42000)

LAPORTE, G (?) ?
Sculpture
£2113 $3507 €3000 Jeune fille a l'oiseau (103cm-41in) s. brown pat bronze. 11-Jun-3 Beaussant & Lefèvre, Paris #228/R est:3800-4000

LAPORTE, George Henry (1799-1873) German
£3572 $5500 €5358 Fourth Light Dragoons trooper with a carriage horse outside stables (63x86cm-25x34in) 4-Sep-2 Christie's, Rockefeller NY #376/R est:4000-6000

LAPORTE, George Henry (attrib) (1799-1873) German
£2000 $3200 €3000 After a long run (61x74cm-24x29in) Bears sig. d.1863. 15-May-3 Lawrence, Crewkerne #940/R est:2000-2500

LAPORTE, Georges (1926-2000) French
£446 $714 €620 Barques sur la plage (32x21cm-13x8in) s. paper. 18-May-3 Eric Pillon, Calais #222/R
£763 $1220 €1060 Vase de fleurs (18x12cm-7x5in) s. oil gouache. 18-May-3 Eric Pillon, Calais #220/R
£793 $1158 €1190 Souvenir de Guiberon (33x41cm-13x16in) s. s. verso s.i. stretcher. 17-Jun-2 Philippe Schuler, Zurich #4386/R (S.FR 1800)
£828 $1308 €1200 Rue (73x92cm-29x36in) s.d.68. 4-Apr-3 Tajan, Paris #247/R
£849 $1358 €1274 Winter landscape with farmstead (38x55cm-15x22in) s. s. verso. 17-Mar-3 Philippe Schuler, Zurich #4644/R (S.FR 1800)
£1007 $1621 €1500 Lagoon (22x25cm-9x10in) s. i.verso. 23-Feb-3 Mercier & Cie, Lille #101
£1216 $1897 €1800 Ile de Sein (50x65cm-20x26in) s. i.verso. 28-Mar-3 Delvaux, Paris #58
£1522 $2374 €2283 Les bords de la Saone en hiver (97x145cm-38x57in) s. prov. 16-Sep-2 Philippe Schuler, Zurich #3515/R est:3500-4500 (S.FR 3500)

LAPORTE, John (1761-1839) British
Works on paper
£352 $585 €500 Paysage de la campagne Anglaise (34x50cm-13x20in) W/C prov. 13-Jun-3 Rossini, Paris #75/R
£1350 $2214 €2025 Sheep and donkeys in a wooded landscape (48x63cm-19x25in) bodycol. 4-Feb-3 Bonhams, Leeds #283 est:600-800
£1900 $2944 €2850 Figures on a track. Cattle grazing (29x37cm-11x15in) s. gouache pair. 3-Dec-2 Sotheby's, Olympia #33/R est:1500-2000
£3000 $4290 €4500 Distant view of Edinburgh (16x23cm-6x9in) i. W/C bodycol prov.lit. 22-Jan-3 Christie's, London #48/R est:3000

LAPORTE, John (attrib) (1761-1839) British
Works on paper
£850 $1403 €1233 River in Cumberland. Keswick lake (53x80cm-21x31in) i.verso W/C over pencil two. 2-Jul-3 Sotheby's, Olympia #206/R

LAPORTE-BLAIRSY, Leo (1865-1923) French
Sculpture
£3165 $5000 €5000 Fee au coffret (43cm-17in) s. biscuit de Sevres lit. 27-Nov-2 Camard, Paris #163/R

LAPOSTOLET, Charles (1824-1890) French
£700 $1120 €1050 River view with factories (36x66cm-14x26in) s. panel. 13-May-3 Bonhams, Knightsbridge #274/R
£3219 $4989 €4829 Rouen (39x56cm-15x22in) s. 3-Oct-2 Koller, Zurich #3121/R est:6000-8000 (S.FR 7500)
£4200 $6846 €6090 On the banks of the Seine (38x46cm-15x18in) s. 16-Jul-3 Sotheby's, Olympia #175/R est:2000-3000
Works on paper
£405 $628 €640 Harbour (20x28cm-8x11in) chk W/C. 25-Sep-2 Neumeister, Munich #416/R

LAPOUJADE, Robert (1921-) French
£256 $403 €400 Paysage du Maroc (33x46cm-13x18in) s.d. i.verso. 16-Dec-2 Charbonneaux, Paris #266
£348 $550 €550 Coteau de Bernex (44x76cm-17x30in) s. 27-Nov-2 Blanchet, Paris #95

LAPPART, Jean Yves (20th C) French

£486 $792 €700 Embarquement sur le port de Douarnenez (38x46cm-15x18in) s. 19-Jul-3 Thierry & Lannon, Brest #213

LAPRADE, Pierre (1875-1932) French

£641 $1006 €1000 Statue dans un parc (60x71cm-24x28in) s. 13-Dec-2 Piasa, Paris #155
£1389 $2292 €2000 Fleurs des champs dans un verre (41x33cm-16x13in) s. 1-Jul-3 Claude Aguttes, Neuilly #107/R est:2500-3000

LARA, Edwina (19th C) British

£400 $608 €600 Hauling the nets (40x61cm-16x24in) s. 15-Aug-2 Bonhams, New Bond Street #329
£1100 $1837 €1595 Fishing boats in rough seas (39x60cm-15x24in) s. pair. 18-Jun-3 Sotheby's, Olympia #68/R est:1200-1800

LARA, Ernest (1870-?) British

£1350 $2093 €2025 Farm labourers, in busy farmyard scene (24x44cm-9x17in) s. 29-Oct-2 Henry Adams, Chichester #599/R est:1500-2000

LARA, Georgina (fl.1862-1871) British

£650 $1086 €943 Figures in a country hamlet (20x38cm-8x15in) 8-Jul-3 Bonhams, Knightsbridge #149/R
£720 $1174 €1080 Country folk outside a village inn (20x33cm-8x13in) 29-Jan-3 Hampton & Littlewood, Exeter #400/R
£1650 $2607 €2475 Busy village scene (50x75cm-20x30in) 2-Dec-2 Bonhams, Bath #96/R est:2000-3000
£1700 $2635 €2550 Outside the Crown Inn (30x50cm-12x20in) s. 1-Oct-2 Bristol Auction Rooms #473/R est:250-350
£2000 $3280 €3000 Midday (30x51cm-12x20in) canvas on board. 29-May-3 Christie's, Kensington #253/R est:2000-3000
£2300 $3588 €3450 Livestock in farmyard (35x53cm-14x21in) with sig. 26-Mar-3 Sotheby's, Olympia #48/R est:1000-1500
£3000 $4710 €4500 Welcome reward. Friends at the stile (23x30cm-9x12in) s.d.70 pair prov. 16-Apr-3 Christie's, Kensington #661/R est:3000-5000
£3200 $4992 €4800 Figures outside a tavern (25x35cm-10x14in) two. 8-Oct-2 Bonhams, Knightsbridge #272/R est:2000-3000
£3600 $5940 €5220 Busy farmstead with figures, covered wagon, horses watering and poultry (20x38cm-8x15in) pair. 3-Jul-3 Duke & Son, Dorchester #268/R est:1500-2500
£7000 $10990 €10500 Village scene (51x76cm-20x30in) s. 19-Nov-2 Bonhams, New Bond Street #74/R est:4000-6000

LARA, Georgina (attrib) (fl.1862-1871) British

£410 $668 €615 Figures on a country track (19x37cm-7x15in) 28-Jan-3 Bristol Auction Rooms #547
£1350 $2133 €2025 Busy village street scene with figures, horse and cart (35x58cm-14x23in) pair. 2-Dec-2 Bonhams, Bath #166/R est:1500-2500

LARCHE, Raoul (1860-1912) French
Sculpture

£1006 $1570 €1600 Filette. brown pat.bronze Cast.Siot Decauville, Paris. 14-Oct-2 Amberes, Antwerp #386
£1500 $2340 €2250 Christ before the doctors (52cm-20in) s.i. brown pat bronze st.f.Colin. 9-Apr-3 Sotheby's, London #196/R est:1500-2000
£4000 $6200 €6000 Young warrior (90cm-35in) s.st.f.Siot golden brown pat bronze square base. 29-Oct-2 Bonhams, New Bond Street #167/R est:5000-6000
£5405 $8432 €8000 Loie Fuller (34cm-13in) s.st.f.Siot-Decauville gilt pat bronze lit. 26-Mar-3 Rossini, Paris #181/R est:10000
£9295 $14593 €14500 Danse (45cm-18in) st.f.Siot Decauville num.J136 gilt pat bronze lit. 10-Dec-2 Renaud, Paris #132/R est:18000
£9873 $15401 €15500 Loie Fuller (33cm-13in) s.st.f.Siot-Decauville gilt pat bronze lit. 8-Nov-2 Camard, Paris #132/R
£16667 $26167 €26000 Allegorie du Temps (75cm-30in) st.f.Siot Decauville gilt pat bronze. 10-Dec-2 Renaud, Paris #133/R est:30000
£18750 $29812 €27000 Loie Fuller (45cm-18in) s.num.H751 gold bronze st.f.Siot Decauville lit. 30-Apr-3 Camard, Paris #81/R est:20000-22000

LARCHER, Jules (1849-1920) French

£53797 $85000 €80696 Tazza of peaches, fruit in a bowl and bottles on draped table. Bottles of champagne, bread on table (92x73cm-36x29in) s.d.1889 pair prov. 23-Apr-3 Christie's, Rockefeller NY #4/R est:70000-90000

LARDERA, Berto (1911-) French
Sculpture

£10256 $16103 €16000 Composition (64x60x32cm-25x24x13in) welded iron. 11-Dec-2 Artcurial Briest, Paris #708/R est:15000

LARESCHE, Auguste (19th C) French
Photographs

£5769 $9115 €9000 Chapelle au Puy (33x26cm-13x10in) salt print exec.c.1850. 13-Nov-2 Beaussant & Lefèvre, Paris #102/R est:3000-3800

LARGILLIERE, Nicolas de (1656-1746) French

£49383 $80000 €74075 Portrait of Mlle, Jeanne de Gagne Perrigny (81x65cm-32x26in) prov. 23-Jan-3 Sotheby's, New York #93a/R est:60000-80000

LARGILLIERE, Nicolas de (attrib) (1656-1746) French

£4930 $8183 €7000 Portrait d'homme en cuirasse (83x66cm-33x26in) oval painted with studio. 16-Jun-3 Oger, Dumont, Paris #74/R est:6000-8000
£20000 $31200 €30000 Venus and Adonis (83x64cm-33x25in) 9-Apr-3 Christie's, London #81/R est:15000-20000

LARGILLIERE, Nicolas de (circle) (1656-1746) French

£7092 $11844 €10000 Portrait de femme en buste (81x62cm-32x24in) oval. 20-Jun-3 Rieunier, Paris #22/R est:10000
£14085 $23099 €20423 Portrait of young man (200x128cm-79x50in) 4-Jun-3 Fischer, Luzern #1033/R est:12000-15000 (S.FR 30000)

LARGILLIERE, Nicolas de (studio) (1656-1746) French

£8392 $14014 €12000 Portrait d'un gentilhomme a la lavalliere brodee (90x74cm-35x29in) painted oval. 25-Jun-3 Tajan, Paris #54/R est:12000-15000

LARIONOV, Igor (1967-) Russian

£450 $698 €675 White embroidering (46x61cm-18x24in) s. 8-Dec-2 John Nicholson, Haslemere #147/R
£550 $853 €825 Early evening (50x61cm-20x24in) s. 8-Dec-2 John Nicholson, Haslemere #148/R

LARIONOV, Mikhail (1881-1964) Russian

£3219 $5086 €4829 Boulevard venus (34x25cm-13x10in) s.verso cardboard painted c.1909 prov. 3-Apr-3 Heffel, Vancouver #54/R est:7000-10000 (C.D 7500)
£9000 $14130 €13500 Two water-carriers (49x37cm-19x15in) init. s.i.d.1930 verso board. 20-Nov-2 Sotheby's, London #127/R est:6000-8000
£16667 $25833 €26000 Female nude (81x46cm-32x18in) mono. s.verso i. stretcher. 4-Dec-2 Lempertz, Koln #850/R est:7000
£25000 $40500 €37500 Walking the dogs (77x72cm-30x28in) init. i.verso. 21-May-3 Sotheby's, London #205/R est:25000-35000
£45000 $70650 €67500 Still life of fruit (30x40cm-12x16in) init. board. 20-Nov-2 Sotheby's, London #138/R est:15000-20000

Works on paper

£266 $412 €420 Jeune homme assis (13x9cm-5x4in) mono. ink. 28-Sep-2 Cornette de St.Cyr, Paris #170
£476 $757 €700 Marine (22x39cm-9x15in) s. ink dr. 26-Feb-3 Artcurial Briest, Paris #82
£1282 $2000 €1923 Men bathing (16x11cm-6x4in) init.d.24 pen ink. 19-Sep-2 Swann Galleries, New York #506/R est:1500-2500
£1400 $2282 €2100 Portrait of Serge Diaghilev (27x21cm-11x8in) init.d.June 915 pencil. 3-Feb-3 Bonhams, New Bond Street #51/R est:700-1000
£2431 $4010 €3500 Portrait de Serge de Diaghilev (19x12cm-7x5in) init. graphite dr double-sided. 2-Jul-3 Artcurial Briest, Paris #690/R est:2500-3500

LARIONOV, Mikhail (attrib) (1881-1964) Russian
Works on paper

£699 $1090 €1049 Abstract composition (22x16cm-9x6in) mixed media. 20-Nov-2 Fischer, Luzern #2577/R est:1500-1800 (S.FR 1600)

LARIVE-GODEFROY, Pierre Louis de (1735-1817) Swiss

£5479 $8548 €8000 La conduite du troupeau en bord de lac. bears sig. 14-Apr-3 Horta, Bruxelles #218/R est:11000-12000

Works on paper

£393 $621 €590 Resting pack donkey with figures (15x13cm-6x5in) s. sepia W/C. 14-Nov-2 Stuker, Bern #9606 (S.FR 900)

LARIVIERE, Charles Philippe Auguste de (1798-1876) French
Works on paper

£14527 $22662 €21500 Vues de Rome et Pompei. crayon wash gouache album. 26-Mar-3 Piasa, Paris #118/R

LARKEN, Diarmud (1918-1989) Irish

£306 $477 €480 Green field with distant mountains (38x49cm-15x19in) s. board. 6-Nov-2 James Adam, Dublin #14/R
£318 $497 €500 Hedgerow (37x49cm-15x19in) s. board. 6-Nov-2 James Adam, Dublin #12/R
£445 $695 €650 Fisherman and boats in harbour (21x28cm-8x11in) s. board. 8-Apr-3 James Adam, Dublin #143/R
£548 $860 €800 Coastal landscape (38x51cm-15x20in) s. 15-Apr-3 De Veres Art Auctions, Dublin #22

LARMIER, Pierre Philibert (attrib) (1752-1807) French
Sculpture
£9615 $14904 €15000 Projet de fronton (14x30x5cm-6x12x2in) terracotta relief lit. 9-Dec-2 Rabourdin & Choppin de Janvry, Paris #49/R est:3700

LAROCHE, C (?) ?
£430 $688 €624 Brook in landscape (50x81cm-20x32in) s. 18-May-3 Anders Antik, Landskrona #106 (S.KR 5500)

LAROCHE, Ernesto (1879-1940) Uruguayan
£656 $1050 €984 Landscape and carts (28x16cm-11x6in) s.d.78 board. 5-Jan-3 Galleria Y Remates, Montevideo #45/R

LAROSE, Ludger (1868-1915) Canadian
£1066 $1662 €1599 Femme de profil (65x54cm-26x21in) s.d.1888 after H. Flandrin. 10-Sep-2 Iegor de Saint Hippolyte, Montreal #69/R (C.D 2600)
£1220 $1915 €1830 Vue du quai de la Malbaie (25x40cm-10x16in) s.d.1895 panel. 12-Dec-2 Iegor de Saint Hippolyte, Montreal #58 (C.D 3000)
£1423 $2234 €2135 Deux ananas (31x39cm-12x15in) s.i. s.d.mai 1893 verso. 12-Dec-2 Iegor de Saint Hippolyte, Montreal #51 (C.D 3500)
£1423 $2234 €2135 Plat de noix piquees (24x33cm-9x13in) s.d.1900 s.d. verso panel. 12-Dec-2 Iegor de Saint Hippolyte, Montreal #52 (C.D 3500)
£2033 $3191 €3050 Panier d'oignons, 1899 (35x46cm-14x18in) s. 12-Dec-2 Iegor de Saint Hippolyte, Montreal #54 (C.D 5000)
£3455 $5425 €5183 Moise frappant le rocher, 1896 (59x99cm-23x39in) s. 12-Dec-2 Iegor de Saint Hippolyte, Montreal #53 (C.D 8500)
£6301 $9892 €9452 Coin de Serre Logan (82x66cm-32x26in) s.d.1900. 12-Dec-2 Iegor de Saint Hippolyte, Montreal #57 (C.D 15500)
£16260 $25528 €24390 Deux paniers de poires (49x65cm-19x26in) s. 12-Dec-2 Iegor de Saint Hippolyte, Montreal #59 (C.D 40000)

LAROT, Dina (1943-) Austrian
Works on paper
£283 $436 €450 Woman smoking (63x44cm-25x17in) s.d.1984 W/C board. 22-Oct-2 Wiener Kunst Auktionen, Vienna #1133/R
£283 $436 €450 Woman with bare breast smoking (63x44cm-25x17in) s.d.1984 W/C board. 22-Oct-2 Wiener Kunst Auktionen, Vienna #1134/R
£472 $726 €750 Woman in blue dress smoking (63x44cm-25x17in) s.d.1984 W/C board. 22-Oct-2 Wiener Kunst Auktionen, Vienna #1136/R
£472 $726 €750 Seated girl taking cigarette from case (63x44cm-25x17in) s.d.1984 W/C board. 22-Oct-2 Wiener Kunst Auktionen, Vienna #1135/R

LARPENTEUR, J D (19th C) French
£528 $850 €792 Cows resting in a landscape (38x61cm-15x24in) s. masonite prov. 18-Feb-3 John Moran, Pasadena #154

LARRAVIDE, Manuel (1871-1910) Uruguayan
£833 $1300 €1250 Vapores transatlanticos (73x100cm-29x39in) s. 30-Jul-2 Galleria Y Remates, Montevideo #42/R

LARRAZ, Julio (1944-) Cuban
£3774 $5849 €6000 Study for Sinforosa (30x41cm-12x16in) s.d.76 s.d.verso. 7-Oct-2 Ansorena, Madrid #89/R est:6000
£5096 $8000 €7644 Ojeda's monkey (30x41cm-12x16in) s.d.1977 prov. 19-Nov-2 Sotheby's, New York #99/R
£5921 $9592 €9000 Stuady (30x41cm-12x16in) s.d.76 exhib. 21-Jan-3 Durán, Madrid #142/R
£44586 $70000 €66879 Gramma (126x149cm-50x59in) s.d.90 prov.lit. 19-Nov-2 Sotheby's, New York #35/R est:80000
£48780 $80000 €70731 Millennium voyager (130x160cm-51x63in) s.d.97 s.i.d.verso prov. 27-May-3 Sotheby's, New York #31

LARSEN, Adolph (1856-1942) Danish
£392 $623 €588 Summer landscape in evening, Denmark (31x42cm-12x17in) s.d.1914. 5-May-3 Rasmussen, Vejle #685/R (D.KR 4200)
£403 $637 €605 Winter landscape at sunset (26x37cm-10x15in) s.d.1929. 13-Nov-2 Kunsthallen, Copenhagen #17 (D.KR 4700)
£6029 $9165 €9044 View of Frederiksberg Avenue (49x65cm-19x26in) s. 27-Aug-2 Rasmussen, Copenhagen #1502/R est:15000 (D.KR 70000)

LARSEN, Alfred (1860-1946) Danish
£288 $450 €432 Harbour scene (69x89cm-27x35in) 28-Mar-3 Douglas, South Deerfield #2
£311 $500 €467 Woman emerging from gate onto dirt lane with 3 chickens in front of her (69x46cm-27x18in) s. 21-Feb-3 York Town, York #1073
£818 $1300 €1227 Winter village scene (69x97cm-27x38in) 3-May-3 Van Blarcom, South Natick #214/R

LARSEN, Emanuel (1823-1859) Danish
£861 $1309 €1292 Landscape from Scheweningen, Holland (31x35cm-12x14in) s. 27-Aug-2 Rasmussen, Copenhagen #1746/R (D.KR 10000)
£963 $1541 €1445 View of Marseilles (23x34cm-9x13in) i.d.1853. 13-Jan-3 Rasmussen, Vejle #57/R (D.KR 11000)

LARSEN, Hugo Valdemar (1875-1950) Danish
£681 $1076 €1022 Young woman wearing black Charleston dress (121x87cm-48x34in) s.d.1924. 2-Dec-2 Rasmussen, Copenhagen #1797/R (D.KR 8000)
£3445 $5237 €5168 Harbour scene at St Thomas with women dressed in white (35x47cm-14x19in) s.i.d.05. 27-Aug-2 Rasmussen, Copenhagen #1472/R est:40000-50000 (D.KR 40000)

LARSEN, Johannes (1867-1961) Danish
£468 $740 €702 White-headed eagle in flight above American coast (28x44cm-11x17in) mono.d.1907 pencil W/C. 2-Dec-2 Rasmussen, Copenhagen #1832/R (D.KR 5500)
£652 $1036 €978 Birds in flight over the meadow (52x66cm-20x26in) mono.d.1910. 10-Mar-3 Rasmussen, Vejle #611/R (D.KR 7000)
£794 $1278 €1191 Nude portrait of Alhed Larsen (62x47cm-24x19in) study. 19-Jan-3 Hindemae, Ullerslev #7511/R (D.KR 9000)
£803 $1237 €1205 Henne Church (57x71cm-22x28in) mono.d.1920. 23-Oct-2 Kunsthallen, Copenhagen #365/R (D.KR 9500)
£888 $1367 €1332 Wild spring flowers (36x47cm-14x19in) mono.d.1910. 23-Oct-2 Kunsthallen, Copenhagen #2/R (D.KR 10500)
£1106 $1748 €1659 Stags (49x66cm-19x26in) mono.d.1910 exhib.prov. 2-Dec-2 Rasmussen, Copenhagen #1475/R est:10000 (D.KR 13000)
£1954 $3048 €2931 Mossy landscape with ducks in flight at sunset (52x59cm-20x23in) mono. 5-Aug-2 Rasmussen, Vejle #101/R est:30000 (D.KR 23000)
£2383 $3980 €3455 Mallards in flight, Wedellsborg (48x57cm-19x22in) mono.d.1912. 17-Jun-3 Rasmussen, Copenhagen #67/R est:15000-20000 (D.KR 25000)
£4198 $6674 €6297 Coastal landscape with eider ducks (40x51cm-16x20in) mono.d.1913. 5-May-3 Rasmussen, Vejle #39/R est:30000 (D.KR 45000)
£8511 $13447 €12767 Geese in flight over the heath (95x132cm-37x52in) mono.d.1922. 2-Dec-2 Rasmussen, Copenhagen #1117/R est:50000-70000 (D.KR 100000)

Works on paper
£502 $793 €753 Coastal landscape (46x61cm-18x24in) mono. Indian ink W/C. 5-Apr-3 Rasmussen, Havnen #4186 (D.KR 5400)
£887 $1383 €1331 Ducks in flight over meadow (22x16cm-9x6in) mono.d.1921 pen W/C sold with book. 23-Sep-2 Rasmussen, Vejle #195/R (D.KR 10500)

LARSEN, Karl (1897-1977) Danish
£304 $469 €456 Still life (29x35cm-11x14in) s.d.1966. 23-Oct-2 Kunsthallen, Copenhagen #99 (D.KR 3600)
£334 $557 €484 Still life of fruit, flowers and bottle (65x55cm-26x22in) init. 17-Jun-3 Rasmussen, Copenhagen #196/R (D.KR 3500)
£347 $552 €521 Still life of oranges (38x46cm-15x18in) init.d.26. 26-Feb-3 Kunsthallen, Copenhagen #320 (D.KR 3800)
£651 $1028 €977 View from Nyhavn with newspaper stall in foreground (97x130cm-38x51in) init.d.38. 1-Apr-3 Rasmussen, Copenhagen #579/R (D.KR 7000)
£667 $1114 €967 Village street with trees (82x113cm-32x44in) init.d.30 prov. 17-Jun-3 Rasmussen, Copenhagen #155/R (D.KR 7000)
£845 $1302 €1268 Nature morte (27x43cm-11x17in) s. cardboard painted c.1920. 23-Oct-2 Kunsthallen, Copenhagen #86/R (D.KR 10000)
£931 $1480 €1397 Still life of red potted plant. Portrait sketch (60x50cm-24x20in) init.d.1919 double-sided. 10-Mar-3 Rasmussen, Vejle #568/R (D.KR 10000)
£1525 $2547 €2211 Lady at the art gallery (43x32cm-17x13in) s.d.1918 prov. 17-Jun-3 Rasmussen, Copenhagen #74/R est:18000 (D.KR 16000)

LARSEN, Knud (1865-1922) Danish
£1292 $1964 €1938 Two fisherwomen on beach in windy weather (54x70cm-21x28in) s.d.1912-13. 27-Aug-2 Rasmussen, Copenhagen #1485/R est:20000-25000 (D.KR 15000)
£2793 $4441 €4190 Interior scene with young girl sewing (69x53cm-27x21in) mono.d.1916. 10-Mar-3 Rasmussen, Vejle #22/R est:30000 (D.KR 30000)
£4588 $7157 €6882 Woman seated in garden with drawing pad in front of flowers in container (48x62cm-19x24in) s.d.1914. 5-Aug-2 Rasmussen, Vejle #17/R est:60000-80000 (D.KR 54000)
£9569 $15502 €13875 Young lady artist drawing flowers in the sunshine (47x62cm-19x24in) s.d.1914. 26-May-3 Rasmussen, Copenhagen #1160/R est:100000 (D.KR 100000)

LARSEN, Lars (1876-1955) Norwegian
£702 $1109 €1053 Two women in farmyard (61x83cm-24x33in) s.d.1927. 17-Dec-2 Grev Wedels Plass, Oslo #253/R (N.KR 8000)

LARSEN, Oscar (1882-1972) Austrian
£828 $1324 €1200 Flight from Egypt (57x78cm-22x31in) s.d.1959. 11-Mar-3 Dorotheum, Vienna #116/R
Works on paper
£321 $498 €482 Moses and the burning bush (67x95cm-26x37in) s.d.1973 W/C. 29-Oct-2 Lawson Menzies, Sydney #527 (A.D 900)
£621 $993 €900 Flight of the Israelites from Egypt (70x98cm-28x39in) s.d.1922 mixed media board. 11-Mar-3 Dorotheum, Vienna #43/R
£1090 $1722 €1700 Festival in the Venice Lagoon (72x99cm-28x39in) s. bears d.19 mixed media board. 12-Nov-2 Dorotheum, Vienna #27/R est:2000-2800

LARSEN, Peter Julius (1818-1852) Danish
£426 $672 €639 Interior scene with boy blowing bubbles (40x36cm-16x14in) s. 2-Dec-2 Rasmussen, Copenhagen #1531/R (D.KR 5000)

LARSSEN, Ansgar (1897-1967) Norwegian
£1730 $2734 €2595 Burning sea tangle (62x70cm-24x28in) s. i.verso panel. 2-Dec-2 Blomqvist, Oslo #374/R est:20000-25000 (N.KR 20000)

LARSSEN, Johan (1853-1920) Norwegian
£652 $1036 €978 Busy traffic at sea, calm summer's day off Norwegian coast (65x54cm-26x21in) s/d/81. 10-Mar-3 Rasmussen, Vejle #428/R (D.KR 7000)

LARSSON, Bo (1945-) Swedish
£847 $1330 €1271 View from Plintsberg towards Tallberg (43x59cm-17x23in) init.d.96. 16-Dec-2 Lilla Bukowskis, Stockholm #335 (S.KR 12000)
£3644 $5685 €5466 The lock, Stockholm (47x55cm-19x22in) init.d.74. 5-Nov-2 Bukowskis, Stockholm #135/R est:30000-35000 (S.KR 52000)

LARSSON, Carl (1853-1919) Swedish
£4690 $7222 €7035 Portrait of Louise Magnus, nee Furstenberg (61x50cm-24x20in) mono.d.1903 lit. 27-Oct-2 Anders Antik, Landskrona #147/R est:80000-100000 (S.KR 68000)
£15711 $25766 €22781 Goekgutten - real name is Gustaf Haglund, who sold fish to the farms (50x75cm-20x30in) init.d.1910 study lit. 4-Jun-3 AB Stockholms Auktionsverk #2332/R est:200000-250000 (S.KR 200000)
£60000 $98400 €90000 Portratt av Dora Lamm - Portrait of Dora Lamm (50x35cm-20x14in) init. canvas on board prov.exhib.lit. 3-Jun-3 Sotheby's, London #205/R est:60000-80000
£155000 $254200 €232500 Karin i Grez, Hostmotiv - Karin in Grez, autumn scene (143x83cm-56x33in) s.i.d.1884 prov.exhib.lit. 3-Jun-3 Sotheby's, London #240/R est:120000-180000
£226950 $351773 €340425 Midwinter sacrifice (123x199cm-48x78in) s.i. prov.exhib.lit. 4-Dec-2 AB Stockholms Auktionsverk #1657/R est:2000000-2500000 (S.KR 3200000)
Works on paper
£349 $566 €506 Boy reading (7x11cm-3x4in) mono. Indian ink. 25-May-3 Uppsala Auktionskammare, Uppsala #115 (S.KR 4500)
£967 $1567 €1451 Necken (61x50cm-24x20in) s.i. Indian ink pencil sketch. 3-Feb-3 Lilla Bukowskis, Stockholm #792 (S.KR 13500)
£2553 $3957 €3830 Rococo model (60x46cm-24x18in) init. chl exhib. 4-Dec-2 AB Stockholms Auktionsverk #1755/R est:12000-14000 (S.KR 36000)
£34043 $52766 €51065 Boy on the road to Grez (44x64cm-17x25in) s.i.d.1884 W/C exhib.lit. 4-Dec-2 AB Stockholms Auktionsverk #1747/R est:475000-500000 (S.KR 480000)
£38000 $62320 €57000 Portrait av august Strindbergs Dotter Anne-Marie - Portrait of August Strindberg's daughter Anne (63x47cm-25x19in) init.i.d.1905 W/C black crayon prov.exhib.lit. 3-Jun-3 Sotheby's, London #204/R est:30000-50000
£184603 $302749 €267674 Parterre (65x57cm-26x22in) s. W/C prov.exhib.lit. 4-Jun-3 AB Stockholms Auktionsverk #2258/R est:2500000-3000000 (S.KR 2350000)
£240000 $393600 €360000 Skalorna - playing scales (36x53cm-14x21in) mono.i. pen ink W/C htd bodycol prov.exhib.lit. 3-Jun-3 Sotheby's, London #211/R est:200000-300000
£512025 $829480 €742436 Near Loing, Grez-sur-Loing (46x65cm-18x26in) s. W/C exhib.lit. 26-May-3 Bukowskis, Stockholm #46/R est:3000000-3500000 (S.KR 6600000)

LARSSON, E (?) Swedish
£423 $665 €613 Battle scene. 15-Dec-2 Anders Antik, Landskrona #1025 (S.KR 6000)

LARSSON, Marcus (1825-1864) Swedish
£669 $1064 €1004 Sunset of coastal landscape with cliffs (26x36cm-10x14in) s.d.1854 canvas on panel. 3-Mar-3 Lilla Bukowskis, Stockholm #550 (S.KR 9000)
£993 $1539 €1490 Spear fishing in moonlight (49x69cm-19x27in) s.d.1860. 3-Dec-2 Bukowskis, Stockholm #367/R est:20000-25000 (S.KR 14000)
£1115 $1773 €1673 Ship by rocky coast (29x40cm-11x16in) s. 3-Mar-3 Lilla Bukowskis, Stockholm #157 est:15000-20000 (S.KR 15000)

LARSSON, Marcus (attrib) (1825-1864) Swedish
£993 $1539 €1490 Vessel on fire (55x74cm-22x29in) panel. 8-Dec-2 Uppsala Auktionskammare, Uppsala #56/R (S.KR 14000)

LARSSON, Ola (1863-1939) Swedish
£258 $407 €387 Still life of azaleas (43x33cm-17x13in) s. 13-Nov-2 Kunsthallen, Copenhagen #70/R (D.KR 3000)

LARTER, Richard (1929-) Australian
£2169 $3297 €3254 Untitled (91x60cm-36x24in) s.d.1970 composition board. 28-Aug-2 Deutscher-Menzies, Melbourne #191/R est:6000-8000 (A.D 6050)
£4457 $7087 €6686 Stare (131x81cm-52x32in) 5-May-3 Sotheby's, Melbourne #243/R est:8000-12000 (A.D 11500)
£5357 $8464 €8036 Epicycloidal sliding shifts (178x147cm-70x58in) s. prov.exhib. 27-Nov-2 Deutscher-Menzies, Melbourne #124/R est:7000-10000 (A.D 15000)
£7504 $11931 €11256 Heroine no jinx but gone (180x112cm-71x44in) s.d.1976 i.verso prov. 4-Mar-3 Deutscher-Menzies, Melbourne #31/R est:15000-20000 (A.D 19510)
Works on paper
£582 $885 €873 Untitled, Soapbox Corner, Hyde Park, London (75x55cm-30x22in) init.d.59 crayon pencil. 28-Aug-2 Deutscher-Menzies, Melbourne #198/R (A.D 1625)
£1275 $2091 €1913 Storm clouds gathering (106x84cm-42x33in) init.d.10 99 i.d.verso synthetic polymer paint gesso canvas prov. 4-Jun-3 Deutscher-Menzies, Melbourne #351/R est:3000-5000 (A.D 3200)
£1964 $3084 €2946 Offset no 4 (178x103cm-70x41in) init.d.1986 s.i.d.March 1986 verso synthetic polymer paint prov. 25-Nov-2 Christie's, Melbourne #221/R est:6000-8000 (A.D 5500)
£5179 $8494 €7769 Untitled (192x128cm-76x50in) synthetic polymer paint canvas exhib. 4-Jun-3 Deutscher-Menzies, Melbourne #21/R est:15000-20000 (A.D 13000)

LARTIGUE, Dany (1921-) French
£481 $755 €750 Femme au bouquet de fleurs (100x81cm-39x32in) s. 15-Dec-2 Eric Pillon, Calais #222/R

LARTIGUE, Jacques Henri (1894-1986) French
Photographs
£2273 $3500 €3410 Zissou and Madeleine Thibault, Rouzat (23x35cm-9x14in) mono. photograph. 24-Oct-2 Sotheby's, New York #146/R est:3000-5000
£12025 $19000 €18038 Au bois (13x9cm-5x4in) i.d.1913 i.verso gelatin silver print prov. 24-Apr-3 Phillips, New York #12/R est:18000-22000

LARUE, Lucien de (1925-) French
£769 $1200 €1154 French village scene (46x53cm-18x21in) s. 22-Sep-2 Susanin's, Chicago #5164/R est:300-400

LARUS, Eliane (1944-) French
£561 $898 €780 Un beau dimanche (36x55cm-14x22in) s. acrylic torn paper. 18-May-3 Neret-Minet, Paris #59/R
£1086 $1738 €1510 Scene du rue a la maison qui fume (70x70cm-28x28in) s. acrylic wood. 18-May-3 Neret-Minet, Paris #103/R est:1950-2200
Works on paper
£370 $526 €600 Portrait (55x46cm-22x18in) s. mixed media panel. 16-Mar-3 Eric Pillon, Calais #250/R
£446 $714 €620 Enfants Indiens au chien (22x17cm-9x7in) s. Indian ink sugar. 18-May-3 Neret-Minet, Paris #172

LARWILL, David (1956-) Australian
£488 $771 €708 Bungendore (29x26cm-11x10in) oil gouache on paper prov. 22-Jul-3 Lawson Menzies, Sydney #49/R est:800-1200 (A.D 1200)

£732 $1156 €1061 Explorer (25x18cm-10x7in) s.i.d.2001 oil gouache on paper prov. 22-Jul-3 Lawson Menzies, Sydney #45/R est:1200-1800 (A.D 1800)

£976 $1541 €1415 Dance (25x18cm-10x7in) s.i.d.2001 oil gouache on paper prov. 22-Jul-3 Lawson Menzies, Sydney #44/R est:1200-1800 (A.D 2400)

£1138 $1798 €1650 Painted up IV 1999 (56x45cm-22x18in) init.d.99 s.i.d.verso prov. 22-Jul-3 Lawson Menzies, Sydney #43/R est:3000-5000 (A.D 2800)

£1138 $1798 €1650 Two heads (22x30cm-9x12in) init.d.93 oil gouache collage on paper prov. 22-Jul-3 Lawson Menzies, Sydney #47/R est:1200-1800 (A.D 2800)

£1545 $2441 €2240 This way (37x27cm-15x11in) s.i.d.14.4.93 oil acrylic gouache on paper prov. 22-Jul-3 Lawson Menzies, Sydney #48/R est:1200-1800 (A.D 3800)

£1626 $2569 €2358 Bungendore (56x66cm-22x26in) s. i.d.1989 verso prov. 22-Jul-3 Lawson Menzies, Sydney #50/R est:4000-6000 (A.D 4000)

£2236 $3533 €3242 On the hop (68x50cm-27x20in) s.i.d.1993 oil gouache collage prov. 22-Jul-3 Lawson Menzies, Sydney #7/R est:2500-5000 (A.D 5500)

£4615 $7338 €6923 Ubu roi (237x182cm-93x72in) 4-Mar-3 Deutscher-Menzies, Melbourne #191/R est:14000-18000 (A.D 12000)

£4643 $7196 €6965 Fish tale (134x117cm-53x46in) s.97 s.d.1998 verso acrylic. 29-Oct-2 Lawson Menzies, Sydney #45/R est:10000-15000 (A.D 13000)

£7143 $11143 €10715 Bush walk (152x121cm-60x48in) s.i.d.2000 verso. 11-Nov-2 Deutscher-Menzies, Melbourne #40/R est:15000-20000 (A.D 20000)

£7570 $12414 €11355 Your guess (91x106cm-36x42in) init.d.95 prov.exhib. 4-Jun-3 Deutscher-Menzies, Melbourne #14/R est:12000-16000 (A.D 19000)

£7679 $12132 €11519 Tom tom club 1999 (184x152cm-72x60in) i.d.99. 18-Nov-2 Goodman, Sydney #149/R est:20000-30000 (A.D 21500)

£8337 $13256 €12506 Red rum (184x143cm-72x56in) s.d.1983 verso. 4-Mar-3 Deutscher-Menzies, Melbourne #114/R est:22000-30000 (A.D 21680)

£13415 $21195 €19452 What a month (182x214cm-72x84in) init.d.95 s.i.d.verso prov. 22-Jul-3 Lawson Menzies, Sydney #46/R est:20000-30000 (A.D 33000)

Works on paper

£6375 $10454 €9563 Greenpeace warrior I (120x89cm-47x35in) synthetic polymer paint linen prov. 4-Jun-3 Deutscher-Menzies, Melbourne #105/R est:14000-18000 (A.D 16000)

£15714 $24829 €23571 FNQ - North Queensland (182x243cm-72x96in) s.d.1988 verso oil synthetic polymer paint diptych. 27-Nov-2 Deutscher-Menzies, Melbourne #15/R est:28000-35000 (A.D 44000)

LARWIN, Johann (1873-1938) Austrian

£683 $1094 €950 Portrait of an Indian man (50x36cm-20x14in) s.d.1916 board. 14-May-3 Dorotheum, Linz #357/R

£1563 $2500 €2345 Portrait of a gentleman, in a theater (121x107cm-48x42in) s.d.1912. 14-May-3 Butterfields, San Francisco #1087/R est:3000-5000

LASAR, C (19th C) French

£335 $533 €503 Vessels in the horizon (39x62cm-15x24in) s.d.91. 10-Mar-3 Rasmussen, Vejle #476/R (D.KR 3600)

LASCAUX, Elie (1888-1969) French

£700 $1092 €1050 Eglise de Bretevenez (69x56cm-27x22in) s. i.verso. 18-Oct-2 Keys, Aylsham #461

LASEK, Eva (1953-) Polish

£261 $418 €400 Bird on a flower branch with snail (20x25cm-8x10in) s. panel lit. 10-Jan-3 Allgauer, Kempten #1676/R

LASH, Lee (20th C) American

£497 $800 €746 Plein aire landscape (30x41cm-12x16in) s. canvasboard. 19-Jan-3 Jeffery Burchard, Florida #24a/R

LASIBILLE, Madeleine (1879-?) French

£1560 $2418 €2340 Le plat de moules (66x81cm-26x32in) s. 4-Dec-2 AB Stockholms Auktionsverk #1879/R est:15000-20000 (S.KR 22000)

LASKE, Oskar (1874-1951) Austrian

£13924 $22000 €22000 Vienna, Prater (39x32cm-15x13in) s.d.1943. 27-Nov-2 Dorotheum, Vienna #192/R est:22000-26000

£68104 $110329 €102156 Ship of fools (130x158cm-51x62in) s.i. tempera. 24-May-3 Dorotheum, Prague #57/R est:900000-2000000 (C.KR 3000000)

Works on paper

£486 $768 €700 Innsbruck (29x21cm-11x8in) s.i. pencil Indian ink. 24-Apr-3 Dorotheum, Vienna #66/R

£506 $800 €800 Jealous Estremadurer (33x22cm-13x9in) s.d.1941 W/C over pencil board. 30-Nov-2 Bassenge, Berlin #6437/R

£662 $1079 €1000 Portrait of a man in profile (14x10cm-6x4in) s. pencil W/C. 28-Jan-3 Dorotheum, Vienna #20/R

£694 $1097 €1000 Main square in Steyr (30x21cm-12x8in) s.i. ink. 24-Apr-3 Dorotheum, Vienna #67/R

£943 $1453 €1500 Church (16x10cm-6x4in) s.mono.i. gouache over pencil. 26-Oct-2 Quittenbaum, Hamburg #111/R est:1500

£1389 $2194 €2000 Street in Kairouan (36x50cm-14x20in) s.d.1913 W/C gouache. 24-Apr-3 Dorotheum, Vienna #26/R est:2400-3400

£1795 $2818 €2800 The Three Kings (20x14cm-8x6in) s.i. W/C bodycol. 25-Nov-2 Hassfurther, Vienna #52 est:1000-1500

£1795 $2836 €2800 St Francis of Assissi (41x48cm-16x19in) s.i. gouache W/C. 12-Nov-2 Dorotheum, Vienna #65/R est:1500-2000

£2119 $3454 €3200 Salzkammergut lake (34x50cm-13x20in) s.d.1941 W/C gouache. 28-Jan-3 Dorotheum, Vienna #82/R est:3800-5000

£2536 $4159 €3500 Stork warehouse (42x53cm-17x21in) s.i. gouache. 27-May-3 Hassfurther, Vienna #47 est:4000-6000

£2848 $4500 €4500 Lofer (35x42cm-14x17in) s.i.d.41 gouache board prov. 27-Nov-2 Dorotheum, Vienna #194/R est:4500-5500

£3165 $5000 €5000 Old harbour of Marseilles (60x44cm-24x17in) s. gouache board prov. 27-Nov-2 Dorotheum, Vienna #153/R est:7000-10000

£3797 $6000 €6000 Grundlsee (49x35cm-19x14in) s.d.47 gouache prov. 27-Nov-2 Dorotheum, Vienna #189/R est:5000-7000

£4710 $7725 €6500 Renovating St Stephen's Cathedral (48x35cm-19x14in) s. W/C. 27-May-3 Wiener Kunst Auktionen, Vienna #70/R est:6000-12000

£4965 $8043 €7000 Spring in Schonbrunn (40x50cm-16x20in) s.i.d.33 gouache. 20-May-3 Dorotheum, Vienna #160/R est:6000-9000

£5128 $8051 €8000 Ghent (36x50cm-14x20in) s. W/C bodycol. 25-Nov-2 Hassfurther, Vienna #51/R est:8000-9000

£5380 $8500 €8500 Altausee - fete day (41x32cm-16x13in) s.i. W/C gouache. 27-Nov-2 Dorotheum, Vienna #172/R est:8500-10000

£6738 $10915 €9500 Grinzing (36x48cm-14x19in) s.i.d.34 gouache paper. 20-May-3 Dorotheum, Vienna #159/R est:6000-9000

£8108 $12649 €12000 Dubrovnik (52x42cm-20x17in) s.i. W/C. 25-Mar-3 Wiener Kunst Auktionen, Vienna #142/R est:8000-15000

LASKE, Oskar and KOBINGER, Hans (20th C) Austrian

Works on paper

£385 $608 €600 In the kitchen (25x35cm-10x14in) s.d.18.8.1947 pencil W/C. 12-Nov-2 Dorotheum, Vienna #157/R

LASKER, Jonathan (1948-) American

£23438 $37500 €35157 Supreme ideals (203x152cm-80x60in) s.d.1990 verso oil on linen prov. 14-May-3 Sotheby's, New York #440/R est:30000-40000

£25316 $40000 €37974 Double play (193x254cm-76x100in) s.d.1987 verso prov. 12-Nov-2 Phillips, New York #151/R est:50000-70000

£41139 $65000 €61709 Object of love (198x274cm-78x108in) painted 1991 prov.exhib. 13-Nov-2 Sotheby's, New York #581/R est:30000-40000

Works on paper

£1282 $2026 €2000 Untitled (75x55cm-30x22in) pencil paper on board. 14-Nov-2 Neumeister, Munich #828/R est:1200-1500

LASKER-SCHULER, Else (1876-1945) German

Works on paper

£8228 $13000 €13000 Schah (18x12cm-7x5in) i. pen Indian ink brush col pencil double-sided prov.lit. 29-Nov-2 Villa Grisebach, Berlin #26/R est:8000-10000

LASNE, Jean (1911-1940) French

Works on paper

£1216 $1897 €1800 Nature morte au verre de liqueur (28x37cm-11x15in) s.d.38 chl exhib.lit. 26-Mar-3 Piasa, Paris #139

£1351 $2108 €2000 Homme dans son lit (22x37cm-9x15in) graphite exhib.lit. 26-Mar-3 Piasa, Paris #140

£2027 $3162 €3000 Portrait du docteur Pierre Chatourne (63x48cm-25x19in) chl exhib.lit. 26-Mar-3 Piasa, Paris #138

£2905 $4532 €4300 Nus mythologiques (24x43cm-9x17in) gouache exhib.lit. 26-Mar-3 Piasa, Paris #137

LASSALLE, Emile (1813-1871) French

£2099 $3400 €3149 Maiden on a wooded path with a playful dog (104x76cm-41x30in) s. 24-Jan-3 New Orleans Auction, New Orleans #190/R est:3500-5000

LASSEN, Aksel M (1870-1946) Danish

£377 $585 €600 Deer in snowy winter landscape (16x24cm-6x9in) s. panel. 29-Oct-2 Dorotheum, Vienna #104/R

LASSEN, Hans August (1857-1938) German
£1026 $1621 €1600 Gathering of men (79x59cm-31x23in) s.d.1907. 18-Nov-2 Dorotheum, Linz #312/R est:1200-1500
£1026 $1621 €1600 Wine tasting. Old men playing chess (24x36cm-9x14in) s.d.1886 two. 16-Nov-2 Lempertz, Koln #1518 est:500
£1218 $1851 €1900 Gathering of men in the wine cellar (42x70cm-17x28in) s.i.d.1901 lit. 11-Jul-2 Allgauer, Kempten #2587/R

LASSENCE, Paul de (1886-1962) Belgian
£352 $567 €500 Le pont fleuri a Quimperle (38x46cm-15x18in) s. panel. 11-May-3 Thierry & Lannon, Brest #371

LASSNIG, Maria (1919-) Austrian
£17391 $28522 €24000 Red anger (72x65cm-28x26in) i.d.1984 verso exhib.lit. 28-May-3 Lempertz, Koln #243/R est:25000-30000
£19231 $29808 €30000 Truth is bought with blood (85x65cm-33x26in) s.d.1984 verso. 3-Dec-2 Lempertz, Koln #258/R est:40000-50000
Works on paper
£1410 $2186 €2200 Seat (45x60cm-18x24in) s.d.1971 pencil. 3-Dec-2 Lempertz, Koln #259/R est:2000
£1560 $2528 €2200 Looking (31x44cm-12x17in) s.i.d.1949 pencil. 20-May-3 Dorotheum, Vienna #187/R est:2200-3200
£3125 $4938 €4500 Hairy (40x57cm-16x22in) s.d.15.Feb.1990 i. verso pencil W/C. 24-Apr-3 Dorotheum, Vienna #275/R est:5000-6500
£3165 $4905 €5000 Mountain folk (43x61cm-17x24in) s.i.d.1981 w/C exhib.lit. 24-Sep-2 Wiener Kunst Auktionen, Vienna #243/R est:5000-8000
£3481 $5396 €5500 Alpine plant woman (42x61cm-17x24in) s.d.1982 W/C. 24-Sep-2 Wiener Kunst Auktionen, Vienna #244/R est:5000-7500
£4348 $7130 €6000 Fly von Beutelstroke family tree (61x43cm-24x17in) i.d.1979 W/C pencil exhib. 28-May-3 Lempertz, Koln #244/R est:6000
£5769 $9058 €9000 Untitled (43x61cm-17x24in) s.d.1951 W/C oil double-sided. 25-Nov-2 Hassfurther, Vienna #53/R est:5000-7000

LASSONDE, Omer (1903-1980) American
£1069 $1700 €1604 Valley and the hill (61x67cm-24x26in) s. board prov. 7-Mar-3 Skinner, Boston #408/R est:3000-5000

LASTMAN, Pieter (1583-1633) Dutch
£19753 $32000 €29630 Judgement of Midas (84x100cm-33x39in) panel prov.exhib. 24-Jan-3 Christie's, Rockefeller NY #11/R est:30000-50000

LASTRA, Ramon (?) Spanish
Works on paper
£481 $760 €750 Santiago covered in snow (68x96cm-27x38in) s.i. W/C. 19-Nov-2 Durán, Madrid #17/R

LASZENKO, Aleksander (attrib) (1883-1944) Polish
£1034 $1634 €1500 Female nude in landscape (50x54cm-20x21in) bears sig. board on panel. 5-Apr-3 Hans Stahl, Hamburg #63/R est:1500

LASZLO DE LOMBOS, Philip Alexius de (1869-1937) British
£400 $620 €600 Knoydart (14x25cm-6x10in) s.i.d.1916 board. 5-Dec-2 Bonhams, Edinburgh #11
£886 $1400 €1400 Portrait of a lady with yellow hat (40x30cm-16x12in) s.i.indis.d. board. 28-Nov-2 Dorotheum, Vienna #50/R est:1800-2400
£4088 $6377 €6500 Portrait of the young Dona Maria del Rosario Silva de Guturbay (92x47cm-36x19in) s.i.d.1904 i.verso. 23-Sep-2 Durán, Madrid #206/R
Works on paper
£580 $922 €870 Portrait of a lady (42x35cm-17x14in) s. pastel. 26-Feb-3 Cheffins Grain & Comins, Cambridge #546/R

LASZLO DE LOMBOS, Philip Alexius de (attrib) (1869-1937) British
£850 $1377 €1275 Study of a beaded man (70x50cm-28x20in) indis i.d.1913 board. 20-May-3 Bonhams, Knightsbridge #20/R

LASZLO, Fulop (20th C) Hungarian
£1537 $2398 €2229 Breathing a prayer (62x34cm-24x13in) s.d.90. 12-Apr-3 Mu Terem Galeria, Budapest #127/R est:400000 (H.F 550000)
£4128 $6439 €6192 Still life of lfowers, 1937 (50x40cm-20x16in) s.d.1937 canvas on canvasboard. 11-Sep-2 Kieselbach, Budapest #170/R (H.F 1600000)
£18058 $28171 €26184 Double portrait of Elizabeth and Stephanie (140x110cm-55x43in) s.d.1896 prov.lit. 13-Sep-2 Mu Terem Galeria, Budapest #121/R est:1500000 (H.F 7000000)

LATAPIE, Louis (1891-1972) French
£409 $634 €650 Le taureau (50x65cm-20x26in) s. paper. 4-Oct-2 Tajan, Paris #140
£596 $972 €900 Jeune femme assise, mains croisees (51x35cm-20x14in) s. 31-Jan-3 Charbonneaux, Paris #116
£949 $1481 €1500 Modele dans l'atelier (104x75cm-41x30in) s. paper on canvas. 20-Oct-2 Chayette & Cheval, Paris #103/R
£1346 $2113 €2100 Boat (50x65cm-20x26in) s. 15-Dec-2 Mercier & Cie, Lille #411/R
£1667 $2650 €2400 Nature morte au fruit (81x100cm-32x39in) s. s.d.1947 verso. 29-Apr-3 Artcurial Briest, Paris #313 est:2000-2500
£2917 $4608 €4200 Nature morte aux bouteilles (59x92cm-23x36in) s. 25-Apr-3 Piasa, Paris #195/R
£38000 $63080 €55100 Le clown (101x65cm-40x26in) s. s.i.d.1920 verso exhib. 12-Jun-3 Christie's, London #207/R est:5000-7000
Works on paper
£304 $474 €450 Gare (50x32cm-20x13in) s. W/C gouache paper on canvas. 26-Mar-3 Millon & Associes, Paris #41
£316 $500 €500 Femme attablee (31x23cm-12x9in) s. chl pastel dr. 26-Nov-2 Camard, Paris #69

LATASTER, Ger (1920-) Dutch
Works on paper
£382 $596 €600 Abstract composition (48x68cm-19x27in) s.d.72 W/C. 6-Nov-2 Vendue Huis, Gravenhage #154
£1304 $2139 €1800 Untitled (74x108cm-29x43in) s.d.64 gouache. 28-May-3 Lempertz, Koln #245/R est:1500

LATHAM, Barbara (1896-1976) American
Works on paper
£1603 $2500 €2405 Irises (43x33cm-17x13in) s. W/C prov.lit. 9-Nov-2 Santa Fe Art, Santa Fe #181/R est:2000-3000

LATHAM, Molly M (c.1900-1987) British
Works on paper
£1100 $1749 €1650 Foxhunter (64x76cm-25x30in) s.d.1952. 29-Apr-3 Gorringes, Lewes #2315

LATHANGUE, Henry Herbert (1859-1929) British
£3822 $6000 €5733 At the well (85x60cm-33x24in) s. 22-Nov-2 Skinner, Boston #33/R est:1500-2500
£600000 $966000 €900000 Leaving home (179x150cm-70x59in) s.d.89-90 prov.exhib.lit. 19-Feb-3 Christie's, London #19/R est:300000-500000

LATHROP, Sobrina P (20th C) American
£479 $800 €695 Yosemite Falls, California (66x30cm-26x12in) s. i.d.1913 verso. 17-Jun-3 John Moran, Pasadena #33

LATHROP, William Langson (1859-1938) American
£2096 $3500 €3039 Trees by a river (30x36cm-12x14in) init. 22-Jun-3 Freeman, Philadelphia #145/R est:3000-5000

LATIMER, Lorenzo Palmer (1857-1941) American
Works on paper
£353 $550 €530 Forest scene. s. W/C. 19-Oct-2 Harvey Clar, Oakland #1410
£528 $850 €792 Rocky outcrop (13x23cm-5x9in) s. W/C prov. 18-Feb-3 John Moran, Pasadena #86a
£710 $1100 €1065 Winter landscape (23x30cm-9x12in) s. pastel. 29-Oct-2 John Moran, Pasadena #609

LATINCA, Elsa (20th C) ?
£365 $562 €580 Poppies, cornflower and daisies in glass vase (33x47cm-13x19in) s. 24-Oct-2 Hagelstam, Helsinki #859

LATOIX, Gaspard (fl.1882-1903) British
£1625 $2599 €2356 Bargemen (52x68cm-20x27in) s. 13-May-3 Watson's, Christchurch #80/R est:2000-6000 (NZ.D 4500)
Works on paper
£3526 $5500 €5289 Bronco rider (64x79cm-25x31in) s. W/C prov. 9-Nov-2 Santa Fe Art, Santa Fe #73/R est:2000-3000

LATORRE VIEDMA, Rafael (1872-1960) Spanish
£342 $534 €500 Sancho Panza (116x59cm-46x23in) s. 8-Apr-3 Ansorena, Madrid #138/R

LATOUCHE, Gaston de (1854-1913) French
£2158 $3453 €3000 Les cygnes a Versailles (57x48cm-22x19in) s.d.1887 panel. 13-May-3 Vanderkindere, Brussels #246/R est:3000-5000
£5102 $8112 €7500 Dans les coulisses (78x81cm-31x32in) s.d.1890. 18-Mar-3 Vanderkindere, Brussels #60/R est:7500-10000
£7693 $12847 €11000 Jeux d'eau (226x207cm-89x81in) s.i.d.1902 exhib. 25-Jun-3 Tajan, Paris #10/R est:12000-15000
£8917 $14000 €13376 Grand Fountain, Versailles (131x122cm-52x48in) s. exhib. 21-Nov-2 Sotheby's, New York #265/R est:15000-20000
£9677 $15290 €15000 Dejeuner sur l'herbe (121x121cm-48x48in) s.prov. 18-Dec-2 Tajan, Paris #1/R est:15000-20000

Works on paper
£517 $822 €750 Scene galante (29x18cm-11x7in) s. pastel. 4-Mar-3 Livinec, Gaudcheau & Jezequel, Rennes #90
£2600 $4238 €3770 L'etreinte (46x42cm-18x17in) s. W/C gouache exhib. 16-Jul-3 Sotheby's, Olympia #236/R est:1500-2000

LATOUR, Joseph Pierre Tancrede (1807-1865) French
Works on paper
£608 $949 €900 Ardeche a l'Argentiere (24x36cm-9x14in) i. graphite dr. 26-Mar-3 Rieunier, Paris #32/R

LATOUR, Maurice Quentin de (1704-1788) French
Works on paper
£87413 $145979 €125000 Autoportrait a l'oeil de boeuf (58x49cm-23x19in) pastel prov. 25-Jun-3 Sotheby's, Paris #29/R est:100000-150000

LATOUR, Tony de (20th C) New Zealander
£316 $493 €474 Fifty eight A (9x9cm-4x4in) s.d.1997 board. 27-Mar-3 International Art Centre, Auckland #28/R (NZ.D 900)

LAUB, Ernst C C (1838-1867) Danish
£272 $424 €408 Portrait of small girl (41x34cm-16x13in) with sig.verso. 5-Aug-2 Rasmussen, Vejle #227 (D.KR 3200)

LAUBIES, René (1924-) French
£516 $815 €800 Composition (40x34cm-16x13in) s.d.59 exhib. 18-Dec-2 Digard, Paris #44

L'AUBINIERE (?) Canadian
£1200 $1920 €1800 Near Barbizon. Cernay la ville le matin (20x28cm-8x11in) s. board pair. 13-May-3 Bonhams, Knightsbridge #147/R est:700-1000

L'AUBINIERE, Georgina M de (1848-1930) British
£500 $825 €725 Valley of Peace - afternoon. Montmorency Falls, near Quebec, Canada (50x34cm-20x13in) s.i.verso board two. 1-Jul-3 Bearnes, Exeter #523/R
Works on paper
£380 $627 €551 Reedy pool, Hampstead (17x24cm-7x9in) s.d.1878 i.verso W/C. 1-Jul-3 Bearnes, Exeter #476/R
£889 $1458 €1289 Figures on a woodland path (57x38cm-22x15in) s.d.1879 W/C. 9-Jun-3 Hodgins, Calgary #114/R est:2000-3000 (C.D 2000)
£1111 $1822 €1667 Girl in a field. River scene with steamboat (34x24cm-13x9in) s.d.1884 one d.1887 W/C pair prov. 27-May-3 Sotheby's, Toronto #34/R est:3000-3500 (C.D 2500)
£1550 $2465 €2325 Evening by the river. Afternoon in the woods (24x35cm-9x14in) s.d.1880 i.verso W/C pair. 4-Mar-3 Bearnes, Exeter #372/R est:300-500

LAUBSER, Maggie (1886-1973) South African
£723 $1143 €1085 Portrait of Arnold (43x32cm-17x13in) s.d.22 card. 1-Apr-3 Stephan Welz, Johannesburg #442/R est:9000-12000 (SA.R 9000)
£3203 $4997 €4805 Flamingoes, houses and people in a hilly landscape (49x42cm-19x17in) s. board. 11-Nov-2 Stephan Welz, Johannesburg #498/R est:20000-30000 (SA.R 50000)
£3215 $5080 €4823 Magnolia (52x39cm-20x15in) s. i.verso board. 1-Apr-3 Stephan Welz, Johannesburg #443/R est:40000-60000 (SA.R 40000)
£4484 $6996 €6726 Portrait of a woman with a pink headscarf (44x35cm-17x14in) s.d.22 board exhib. 11-Nov-2 Stephan Welz, Johannesburg #503/R est:20000-30000 (SA.R 70000)
£4729 $7614 €7094 Lnadscape with pigs (29x37cm-11x15in) s. indis d. board lit. 12-May-3 Stephan Welz, Johannesburg #458/R est:40000-60000 (SA.R 55000)
£4729 $7614 €7094 Landscape with person (34x43cm-13x17in) s.d.30 i.d.verso paper on board prov.exhib. 12-May-3 Stephan Welz, Johannesburg #461/R est:50000-70000 (SA.R 55000)
£4914 $7666 €7371 Malay woman holding a duck (44x34cm-17x13in) s. board. 15-Oct-2 Stephan Welz, Johannesburg #434/R est:40000-60000 (SA.R 80000)
£4987 $8029 €7481 Portrait of a Hottentot woman (47x37cm-19x15in) s.d.29 board exhib. 12-May-3 Stephan Welz, Johannesburg #455/R est:30000-50000 (SA.R 58000)
£8598 $13844 €12897 Still life od Saint Joseph Lilies and irises (59x44cm-23x17in) s. board. 12-May-3 Stephan Welz, Johannesburg #569/R est:30000-40000 (SA.R 100000)
£10318 $16612 €15477 Extensive landscape with a view of a willow tree, birds and a house in the distance (39x49cm-15x19in) s. board. 12-May-3 Stephan Welz, Johannesburg #487/R est:120000-140000 (SA.R 120000)
Works on paper
£1281 $1999 €1922 Two swans (41x36cm-16x14in) bears sig. gouache over chl. 11-Nov-2 Stephan Welz, Johannesburg #497 est:8000-12000 (SA.R 20000)
£2236 $3599 €3354 Man wearing a hat with a feather (53x38cm-21x15in) s. chl. 12-May-3 Stephan Welz, Johannesburg #530/R est:25000-35000 (SA.R 26000)
£3611 $5814 €5417 Swanm fish and flowers (49x36cm-19x14in) s. chl gouache. 12-May-3 Stephan Welz, Johannesburg #486/R est:10000-15000 (SA.R 42000)

LAUCHERT, Richard (1823-1869) German
Works on paper
£310 $490 €450 Portrait d'un gentilhomme (37x30cm-15x12in) s.d.1845 pencil dr. 2-Apr-3 Vanderkindere, Brussels #33

LAUDER, Charles James (1841-1920) British
£350 $546 €525 Doge's Palace (36x54cm-14x21in) s.i. 26-Mar-3 Sotheby's, Olympia #161/R
£1600 $2624 €2400 Shipping on the Clyde (51x30cm-20x12in) s.d.80. 29-May-3 Christie's, Kensington #189/R est:1000-1500
Works on paper
£400 $624 €600 At the Palazzo Dario, Venice (25x20cm-10x8in) s. W/C. 17-Oct-2 Bonhams, Edinburgh #178
£700 $1092 €1050 From canal house, Bowling (33x51cm-13x20in) s. W/C. 14-Apr-3 Sotheby's, London #85/R
£2100 $3318 €3150 Strand, London (21x33cm-8x13in) s. W/C htd bodycol. 7-Apr-3 Bonhams, Bath #30/R est:1000-1500
£4000 $6200 €6000 Princes Street, Edinburgh from Waterloo Place (33x51cm-13x20in) s.i. W/C lit. 6-Dec-2 Lyon & Turnbull, Edinburgh #94/R est:2000-3000

LAUDER, Robert Scott (1803-1869) British
£1900 $3135 €2755 Lady and her Knight errant. Gentleman in his library (63x48cm-25x19in) millboard two. 2-Jul-3 Sotheby's, Olympia #120/R est:2000-3000

LAUDY, Jean (1877-1956) Belgian
£252 $390 €400 Autoportrait (35x26cm-14x10in) s. panel. 1-Oct-2 Palais de Beaux Arts, Brussels #499
£451 $718 €650 Nu (45x64cm-18x25in) s. 29-Apr-3 Campo, Vlaamse Kaai #185
£540 $863 €750 L'etang du chateau (50x60cm-20x24in) s. panel. 19-May-3 Horta, Bruxelles #48
£545 $845 €850 Scene de chasse a courre (18x23cm-7x9in) s.d.1899. 9-Dec-2 Horta, Bruxelles #28
£577 $894 €900 Les levres rouges (65x50cm-26x20in) s. i.verso cardboard. 9-Dec-2 Horta, Bruxelles #27
£1392 $2172 €2200 Vase fleuri de roses (56x44cm-22x17in) s. panel. 16-Sep-2 Horta, Bruxelles #415
£1439 $2302 €2000 Importante composition florale (76x100cm-30x39in) s. 19-May-3 Horta, Bruxelles #47 est:2000-3000
£1509 $2340 €2400 Bouquet de fleurs sur une table (81x101cm-32x40in) s. 1-Oct-2 Palais de Beaux Arts, Brussels #500/R est:2000-3000
£2345 $3752 €3400 Bouquet (55x38cm-22x15in) s.d.1925 prov.exhib. 15-Mar-3 De Vuyst, Lokeren #182/R est:2600-2800
£5128 $8051 €8000 Still life of roses in vase and apples on plate (72x91cm-28x36in) s. 21-Nov-2 Van Ham, Cologne #1741/R est:3200
Works on paper
£442 $703 €650 Torse de femme nue (39x28cm-15x11in) pastel. 19-Mar-3 Hotel des Ventes Mosan, Brussels #258

LAUER, Josef (1818-1881) Austrian
£3030 $4697 €4545 Flowers in basket (64x47cm-25x19in) s. panel. 24-Sep-2 Koller, Zurich #6555/R est:3500-5500 (S.FR 7000)
£7483 $11898 €11000 Roses by basket with bird (50x63cm-20x25in) s. 19-Mar-3 Neumeister, Munich #621/R est:8000
£31646 $50000 €50000 Still life with rose branches on bank of the stream (50x63cm-20x25in) s. 28-Nov-2 Dorotheum, Vienna #136/R est:26000-30000
Works on paper
£4054 $6324 €6000 Still life (60x48cm-24x19in) s.d.1843 W/C. 28-Mar-3 Dorotheum, Vienna #228/R est:6000-7000

LAUFFER, Lance Ray (20th C) American
£1935 $3000 €2903 Peaches (61x46cm-24x18in) s.d.1979 s.i.d.verso board. 8-Dec-2 Freeman, Philadelphia #193/R est:800-1200

LAUGE, Achille (1861-1944) French

£1923 $2981 €3000 Portrait de Pierre Lauge, fils de l'artiste (35x30cm-14x12in) st.sig. panel en grisaille. 4-Dec-2 Pierre Berge, Paris #49/R
£8621 $13707 €12500 Portrait de fillette (46x38cm-18x15in) s.d. 5-Mar-3 Doutrebente, Paris #47/R est:3000-4000
£9177 $14500 €14500 Bouquet de roses (55x38cm-22x15in) s.d.1918. 2-Dec-2 Tajan, Paris #51/R
£13287 $22189 €19000 Collioure (55x73cm-22x29in) s.d.27 prov. 26-Jun-3 Tajan, Paris #244 est:12000-15000
£14724 $24000 €22086 La route de Cailhau (54x73cm-21x29in) s.d.09 prov.exhib. 12-Feb-3 Sotheby's, New York #16/R est:20000-30000
£15500 $25885 €22475 Arbres en fleur (50x72cm-20x28in) s. panel prov. 24-Jun-3 Sotheby's, London #116/R est:15000-20000
£16667 $27833 €23500 Allee d'arbres en automne (54x73cm-21x29in) s.d. lit. 23-Jun-3 Claude Boisgirard, Paris #92/R est:18000-20000
£44872 $70000 €67308 Route de campagne (22x40cm-9x16in) s.d.92 prov. 6-Nov-2 Sotheby's, New York #123a/R est:75000-100000

Works on paper

£288 $447 €450 Homme debout (24x16cm-9x6in) st.sig.chl htd chk. 4-Dec-2 Pierre Berge, Paris #65
£333 $517 €520 Femme debout (24x16cm-9x6in) st.sig. chl htd chk. 4-Dec-2 Pierre Berge, Paris #80
£449 $696 €700 Etude de moissonneurs (24x15cm-9x6in) st.sig. chl htd chk. 4-Dec-2 Pierre Berge, Paris #45
£481 $745 €750 Etude de moissonneurs (16x24cm-6x9in) st.sig. chl htd chk. 4-Dec-2 Pierre Berge, Paris #30/R
£574 $896 €850 Route (25x37cm-10x15in) pen ink prov. 31-Mar-3 Piasa, Paris #107
£609 $944 €950 Femme assise (16x22cm-6x9in) st.sig. chl htd chk. 4-Dec-2 Pierre Berge, Paris #37/R
£641 $994 €1000 Femme assise (24x15cm-9x6in) st.sig. chl htd chk. 4-Dec-2 Pierre Berge, Paris #26
£839 $1401 €1200 Route pres d'une foret (38x52cm-15x20in) s. pastel. 26-Jun-3 Tajan, Paris #134
£2115 $3279 €3300 Portrait de femme (45x34cm-18x13in) s.d.1893 chl htd chk. 4-Dec-2 Pierre Berge, Paris #54/R

LAUGEE, Desire (1823-1896) French

£31646 $50000 €47469 Laundress (125x79cm-49x31in) s.d.1882 exhib. 24-Apr-3 Sotheby's, New York #98/R est:30000-40000

LAUNAY, J de (?) ?

£1538 $2415 €2400 Courtisane et buste (64x43cm-25x17in) 16-Dec-2 Amberes, Antwerp #255

LAUNOIS, Jean (1898-1942) French

Works on paper

£245 $409 €350 Le grenier (35x40cm-14x16in) s. ink wash. 26-Jun-3 Tajan, Paris #9
£2848 $4500 €4500 Attente (46x61cm-18x24in) s. gouache. 28-Nov-2 Piasa, Paris #53/R

LAUPHEIMER, Anton (1848-1927) German

£851 $1345 €1277 On the way to church (79x61cm-31x24in) s. 2-Dec-2 Rasmussen, Copenhagen #1538/R (D.KR 10000)

LAUR, Marie Yvonne (1879-1943) French

£4255 $6596 €6383 La chatte et ses chatons (65x81cm-26x32in) s. panel. 4-Dec-2 AB Stockholms Auktionsverk #1877/R est:25000-30000 (S.KR 60000)

LAUREL, Pierre (?) French

Sculpture

£1700 $2720 €2550 Farandole (55cm-22in) i. green pat. bronze. 15-May-3 Christie's, Kensington #414/R est:1200-1500

LAUREN, Per Ake (1879-1951) Finnish

£252 $387 €400 Boiling the pot (46x38cm-18x15in) s.d.35. 27-Oct-2 Bukowskis, Helsinki #230/R
£449 $714 €660 Anti-clockwise (24x32cm-9x13in) s.d.24. 24-Mar-3 Bukowskis, Helsinki #147/R

LAURENCE, Janet Lister (1949-) Australian

£1643 $2563 €2465 Marsh fire seed (167x122cm-66x48in) s.i.d.1992 verso pigments oil canvas wood diptych. 11-Nov-2 Deutscher-Menzies, Melbourne #49/R est:4000-6000 (A.D 4600)

LAURENCE, Sydney Mortimer (1865-1940) American

£6024 $10000 €8735 Mendenhall Valley (41x51cm-16x20in) s. 11-Jun-3 Butterfields, San Francisco #4117/R est:15000-25000
£7595 $12000 €11013 Mountain landscape (41x51cm-16x20in) s. canvas on board. 26-Jul-3 Coeur d'Alene, Hayden #158/R est:15000-25000
£10127 $16000 €14684 Halibut longliner (41x51cm-16x20in) s. canvas on board prov. 26-Jul-3 Coeur d'Alene, Hayden #197/R est:20000-30000
£11392 $18000 €16518 Early snow (38x51cm-15x20in) s. 26-Jul-3 Coeur d'Alene, Hayden #98/R est:20000-30000
£12658 $20000 €18354 Mt. McKinley (61x46cm-24x18in) s. canvas on board. 26-Jul-3 Coeur d'Alene, Hayden #157/R est:15000-25000
£12903 $20000 €19355 Food cache, Mount McKinley (51x41cm-20x16in) s. prov. 5-Dec-2 Christie's, Rockefeller NY #151/R est:25000-35000
£17405 $27500 €25237 Mt. Mckinley (51x38cm-20x15in) s. 26-Jul-3 Coeur d'Alene, Hayden #97/R est:20000-30000
£31080 $49000 €45066 Welcome light along the trail (91x102cm-36x40in) s. prov.exhib.lit. 26-Jul-3 Coeur d'Alene, Hayden #52/R est:60000-90000

Works on paper

£518 $850 €751 Boats at dusk (35x16cm-14x6in) s. W/C. 5-Jun-3 Swann Galleries, New York #158/R

LAURENCIN, Marie (1885-1956) French

£791 $1266 €1100 Jeune fille a la guitaire (18x12cm-7x5in) st.sig. graphite double-sided. 14-May-3 Blanchet, Paris #105
£4783 $7413 €7175 Still life (29x23cm-11x9in) s. board prov.lit. 4-Dec-2 Koller, Zurich #112/R est:7000-9000 (S.FR 11000)
£5031 $8000 €7547 Portrait de madame Cole Porter (33x24cm-13x9in) s. masonite on board prov. 27-Feb-3 Christie's, Rockefeller NY #53/R est:18000
£12587 $21021 €18000 Portrait de Mlle Brigitte Sourdel (60x50cm-24x20in) s. painted c.1923 prov.lit. 30-Jun-3 Pierre Berge, Paris #52/R est:18000-20000
£16026 $25000 €24039 Jeune femme au echarpe jaune (41x33cm-16x13in) s. 14-Oct-2 Butterfields, San Francisco #2009/R est:30000-50000
£17949 $28000 €26924 Portrait de femme (41x33cm-16x13in) s. prov. 7-Nov-2 Christie's, Rockefeller NY #351/R est:35000-45000
£18000 $30060 €26100 Pivoines dans un vase blanc (46x38cm-18x15in) init. prov.lit. 25-Jun-3 Christie's, London #170/R est:15000-20000
£20513 $32000 €30770 Manola (46x38cm-18x15in) s.d.1925 prov.exhib.lit. 7-Nov-2 Christie's, Rockefeller NY #301/R est:40000-60000
£22000 $36080 €33000 Tete pensive (41x33cm-16x13in) s. prov. 5-Feb-3 Sotheby's, London #270/R est:25000
£23602 $38000 €35403 Le chapeau a plumes (41x34cm-16x13in) s. prov.lit. 8-May-3 Christie's, Rockefeller NY #187/R est:40000-60000
£24000 $40080 €34800 Acrobates (46x38cm-18x15in) s. prov.lit. 25-Jun-3 Christie's, London #127/R est:30000-40000
£24325 $37947 €36000 Jeune femme a la mantille (41x36cm-16x14in) s. prov. 26-Mar-3 Tajan, Paris #35/R
£27950 $45000 €41925 Buste de jeune femme (46x38cm-18x15in) s. prov.lit. 7-May-3 Sotheby's, New York #386/R est:40000-60000
£30000 $49200 €45000 Madame Suzanne Girod (65x54cm-26x21in) s.d.1923 prov.exhib.lit. 4-Feb-3 Christie's, London #335/R est:30000
£32051 $50000 €48077 Femme a la guitare (35x27cm-14x11in) s. 7-Nov-2 Christie's, Rockefeller NY #295/R est:50000-70000
£45000 $73350 €67500 Portrait of Mia Bergmann (92x73cm-36x29in) s. 3-Feb-3 Bonhams, New Bond Street #40/R est:50000-80000
£45000 $75150 €65250 Jeune femme a l'etole mauve (24x33cm-9x13in) s. 25-Jun-3 Christie's, London #158/R est:45000-55000
£48000 $78720 €72000 Jeune fille au collier de perles (33x24cm-13x9in) s. canvas on board prov. 4-Feb-3 Christie's, London #256/R est:60000
£89744 $140000 €134616 Jeune femme au caniche (91x62cm-36x24in) s. painted 1925 prov.exhib.lit. 7-Nov-2 Christie's, Rockefeller NY #282/R est:150000-200000
£90062 $145000 €135093 Clowns ou saltimbanques (92x74cm-36x29in) s.d.1929 prov.exhib.lit. 7-May-3 Sotheby's, New York #358/R est:180000-250000
£96154 $150000 €144231 Trois jeunes filles (81x65cm-32x26in) s.d.1929 prov.lit. 7-Nov-2 Christie's, Rockefeller NY #289/R est:150000-200000

Works on paper

£563 $900 €845 Untitled (33x25cm-13x10in) s. graphic pencil. 10-Jan-3 Du Mouchelle, Detroit #2067/R
£633 $981 €1000 Etude de chats (12x13cm-5x5in) s.d. graphite prov. 28-Sep-2 Cornette de St.Cyr, Paris #171
£694 $1146 €1000 Jeune femme au chapeau de plumes (40x26cm-16x10in) black crayon chl. 1-Jul-3 Claude Aguttes, Neuilly #106/R
£780 $1303 €1100 La lecture (21x16cm-8x6in) blk crayon. 20-Jun-3 Piasa, Paris #86/R est:4000-6000
£1301 $2043 €1900 Portrait de jeune fille (29x20cm-11x8in) s. col crayon pencil exec.c.1940. 21-Apr-3 Rabourdin & Choppin de Janvry, Paris #137/R est:2000-2200
£1378 $2164 €2150 Etude pour 'Ile de France' (16x24cm-6x9in) crayon dr. 11-Dec-2 Artcurial Briest, Paris #521a/R
£1538 $2400 €2307 Jeune fille assise (26x17cm-10x7in) s. pencil exec.c.1940. 19-Sep-2 Swann Galleries, New York #510/R est:2000-3000
£1800 $2772 €2700 Etude de danseuse (22x17cm-9x7in) s. pen ink sold with two others by the same artist. 23-Oct-2 Sotheby's, Olympia #666/R est:1800-2500
£2158 $3453 €3000 Les danseuses (24x31cm-9x12in) init. graphite dr. 18-May-3 Eric Pillon, Calais #81/R
£2518 $4029 €3500 Fillette jouant a la corde a sauter (12x10cm-5x4in) W/C. 18-May-3 Eric Pillon, Calais #72/R
£2800 $4312 €4200 Femme au noeud (36x26cm-14x10in) s. col crayon pencil prov. 23-Oct-2 Sotheby's, Olympia #680/R est:2000-3000
£3500 $5390 €5250 Jeune fille au foulard rouge (24x19cm-9x7in) s.d.1940 pencil col crayon prov. 23-Oct-2 Sotheby's, Olympia #679/R est:2000-3000

£3654 $5773 €5700 Head and shoulder study (18x14cm-7x6in) s. W/C. 12-Nov-2 Mealy's, Castlecomer #1041/R

£4348 $6739 €6522 Petite fille a la rose (37x28cm-15x11in) s.d.28 pencil col pen. 4-Dec-2 Koller, Zurich #153/R est:4500-6000 (S.FR 10000)

£4403 $7000 €6605 Jeune elegante au chale (26x21cm-10x8in) s.i.d.1928 col pencil graphite prov.lit. 27-Feb-3 Christie's, Rockefeller NY #48/R est:6000

£6481 $9204 €10500 Portrait de jeune fille au turban (31x23cm-12x9in) s. col crayon dr. 16-Mar-3 Eric Pillon, Calais #125/R

£7000 $10850 €10500 Quatre nymphes (28x24cm-11x9in) W/C prov. 5-Dec-2 Christie's, Kensington #106/R est:6000-8000

£7194 $11511 €10000 Jeune elegante au chale (25x19cm-10x7in) s.d. col crayon lit. 18-May-3 Eric Pillon, Calais #80/R

£10000 $16400 €15000 Dans son beau jardin (23x15cm-9x6in) W/C exec.1931 set of 5. 6-Feb-3 Christie's, London #426/R est:15000

£10843 $18000 €15722 Mother and daughter (33x25cm-13x10in) W/C. 13-Jun-3 Du Mouchelle, Detroit #2023/R est:4000-7000

£12238 $20437 €17500 Jeunes filles au voile bleu (43x35cm-17x14in) s. W/C prov. 26-Jun-3 Tajan, Paris #110/R est:15000-20000

£13376 $20866 €21000 Portrait de jeune fille au foulard rose (25x29cm-10x11in) s. W/C. 10-Nov-2 Eric Pillon, Calais #25/R

£15528 $25000 €23292 Les deux amies sur la terrasse et le jeune page (35x44cm-14x17in) s. W/C prov. 7-May-3 Sotheby's, New York #390/R est:25000-35000

£57692 $90000 €86538 Jeune femme a la guitare (55x46cm-22x18in) s. prov. 5-Nov-2 Phillips, New York #119/R est:90000-120000

LAURENS, Henri (1885-1954) French

Sculpture

£25000 $41750 €36250 La petite sirene (28cm-11in) mono.num.5/6 bronze st.f.C. Valsuani prov.lit. 24-Jun-3 Sotheby's, London #160/R est:28000-35000

£39437 $65466 €56000 Femme accroupie a la draperie (34cm-13in) mono.num.2 terracotta edition of 8 prov.lit. 12-Jun-3 Tajan, Paris #25/R est:60000-80000

£41825 $66084 €62738 Femme couchee (15x36cm-6x14in) mono.num.VI terracotta executed 1928 prov. 28-Apr-3 Bukowskis, Stockholm #303/R est:350000-400000 (S.KR 550000)

£46000 $76820 €66700 Le petit boxeur (43cm-17in) i.num.5/6 bronze conceived 1920 prov.exhib.lit. 24-Jun-3 Sotheby's, London #152/R est:45000-60000

£48000 $80160 €69600 Femme debout a la draperie au bras leve (38cm-15in) mono.num.5/6 bronze conceived 1928 prov.exhib.lit. 24-Jun-3 Sotheby's, London #181/R est:30000-40000

£52000 $85280 €78000 Ondine (46cm-18in) mono.st.f.Valsuani num.1/6 bronze prov.lit. 5-Feb-3 Sotheby's, London #171/R est:80000

£52000 $86840 €75400 Metamorphose (9x22x8cm-4x9x3in) mono.num.V/V verso lead brown pat bronze conceived 1940 prov. 24-Jun-3 Christie's, London #25/R est:18000-25000

£62179 $97000 €93269 Femme couchee (30cm-12in) mono.num.6/8 brown pat. bronze i.f.Valsuani conceived 1921 prov. 7-Nov-2 Christie's, Rockefeller NY #304/R est:100000-150000

£75000 $125250 €108750 Femme a l'eventail (40x32x11cm-16x13x4in) mono. terracotta one of seven prov.lit. 24-Jun-3 Christie's, London #18/R est:20000-30000

£80000 $133600 €116000 Le petit adieu (22x25x22cm-9x10x9in) mono.num.6/6 terracotta one of seven prov. 24-Jun-3 Christie's, London #4/R est:25000-35000

£105769 $163942 €165000 Flora (27cm-11in) mono. num.1 terracotta exec.1939 lit. 9-Dec-2 Piasa, Paris #12/R est:100000-150000

£705128 $1100000 €1057692 Le matin (118cm-46in) init.num.5/6 brown pat. bronze f.Valsuani executed 1944. 5-Nov-2 Sotheby's, New York #29/R est:1300000-1600000

Works on paper

£1863 $3000 €2795 Femme allongee (12x16cm-5x6in) mono. pencil prov. 7-May-3 Sotheby's, New York #353a/R est:3000-5000

£3224 $5029 €4836 Deux tetes (33x25cm-13x10in) init. pencil crayon. 6-Nov-2 AB Stockholms Auktionsverk #927/R est:40000-50000 (S.KR 46000)

£3333 $5400 €4700 Femme assise (28x33cm-11x13in) mono. graphite prov. 21-May-3 Cornette de St.Cyr, Paris #65/R est:5000-6000

£4167 $6542 €6500 Nu recroqueville (45x56cm-18x22in) init. graphite dr prov. 10-Dec-2 Piasa, Paris #323/R

£4808 $7548 €7500 Nu (45x56cm-18x22in) init. graphite dr prov. 10-Dec-2 Piasa, Paris #321/R est:12000

£5128 $7949 €8000 Nu se tenant les cuisses (45x56cm-18x22in) mono. crayon dr. 9-Dec-2 Piasa, Paris #16/R

£5128 $7949 €8000 Couple enlace (45x56cm-18x22in) mono. crayon dr. 9-Dec-2 Piasa, Paris #19/R est:10000-12000

£5128 $7949 €8000 Nu assis, bras croises (55x45cm-22x18in) mono. crayon dr. 9-Dec-2 Piasa, Paris #18/R est:10000-12000

£5449 $8554 €8500 Nu allonge (44x56cm-17x22in) init. graphite dr. 10-Dec-2 Piasa, Paris #322/R

£6090 $9561 €9500 Nu assis (45x56cm-18x22in) init. graphite dr prov. 10-Dec-2 Piasa, Paris #324/R est:10000

£6410 $10064 €10000 Femme allongee (45x56cm-18x22in) init. graphite dr prov. 10-Dec-2 Piasa, Paris #319/R est:15000

£9615 $14904 €15000 Nu accoude, jambes croisees (44x56cm-17x22in) mono. crayon dr. 9-Dec-2 Piasa, Paris #17/R est:10000-12000

£17000 $28390 €24650 Femme a la corbeille (56x45cm-22x18in) mono. W/C pencil cardboard prov. 24-Jun-3 Christie's, London #24/R est:4000-6000

£21023 $32796 €31535 Composition - cover illustration for Konstrevy 1952 (29x22cm-11x9in) init. gouache collage lit. 6-Nov-2 AB Stockholms Auktionsverk #929/R est:150000-200000 (S.KR 300000)

£22000 $36740 €31900 Femme a la corbeille (56x45cm-22x18in) mono. W/C pencil cardboard prov. 24-Jun-3 Christie's, London #23/R est:4000-6000

LAURENS, Jean Paul (1838-1921) French

£1319 $2085 €1900 Etude pour scene merovingienne (41x25cm-16x10in) 25-Apr-3 Piasa, Paris #116/R est:1200

£1700 $2669 €2550 Treaty of Venice (49x76cm-19x30in) s. panel. 21-Nov-2 Christie's, Kensington #177/R est:2000-3000

£7911 $12342 €12500 Le savant (66x52cm-26x20in) s. 15-Oct-2 Regis & Thiollet, Argentuil #189

LAURENS, Jules Joseph Augustin (1825-1901) French

£12658 $19747 €20000 A la porte d'une ville d'Asie Mineure (102x83cm-40x33in) s. lit. 20-Oct-2 Anaf, Lyon #188/R

Works on paper

£426 $711 €600 Portrait de Vely-Bek, Radkhan. s.i. chl prov. 23-Jun-3 Beaussant & Lefèvre, Paris #78

LAURENS, Paul Albert (1870-1934) French

£609 $950 €914 Elegant ladies in a garden (36x25cm-14x10in) one on canvasboard one on panel pair. 20-Sep-2 Sloan, North Bethesda #439/R

LAURENT, Ernest Joseph (1859-1929) French

£6918 $10723 €11000 Vase de fleurs devant la glace (55x46cm-22x18in) s.i.d.06. 30-Oct-2 Coutau Begarie, Paris #107/R est:10000-12000

Works on paper

£586 $932 €850 Portrait de famille (40x30cm-16x12in) st.mono. dr. 4-Mar-3 Livinec, Gaudcheau & Jezequel, Rennes #22/R

LAURENT, Jean (1906-) French

£380 $593 €570 Fishing boats off coast (30x40cm-12x16in) s. panel. 10-Nov-2 Lots Road, London #351

£420 $655 €630 View of a three masted sailing ship (61x91cm-24x36in) 10-Sep-2 Sworder & Son, Bishops Stortford #723/R

£473 $761 €710 Clipper in full sail (60x90cm-24x35in) s. 12-May-3 Stephan Welz, Johannesburg #56 est:4000-6000 (SA.R 5500)

£800 $1336 €1160 Man of war in a stormy sea (120x90cm-47x35in) s. 25-Jun-3 Cheffins, Cambridge #826

LAURENT, Jean Antoine (1763-1832) French

£13580 $22000 €20370 Three sisters (60x49cm-24x19in) s.d.1824 exhib. 23-Jan-3 Sotheby's, New York #224/R est:35000

Miniatures

£4000 $6280 €6000 Young lady holding a olive branch (18x13cm-7x5in) init. rec exhib.lit. 10-Dec-2 Christie's, London #96/R est:4000-6000

LAURENT, Jean Antoine (attrib) (1763-1832) French

£5346 $8233 €8500 Portrait des enfants de la famille de Vogue (49x62cm-19x24in) pair. 25-Oct-2 Tajan, Paris #155/R est:4000-5000

LAURENT, Jean Émile (1906-) French

£828 $1349 €1250 Place Djema El Fna (60x48cm-24x19in) s. 3-Feb-3 Cornette de St.Cyr, Paris #469

LAURENT, John Louis (1921-) American

£881 $1400 €1322 From Sewall's Bride (71x122cm-28x48in) masonite. 1-Mar-3 Thomaston Place, Thomaston #37

LAURENT, Marie Pauline (1805-1860) French

£15000 $23250 €22500 Mother with her child having his palm read by an old peasant lady (86x72cm-34x28in) s.d.1834. 1-Oct-2 Christie's, London #81/R est:15000-20000

LAURENT, Robert (1890-1970) American

Sculpture

£2166 $3400 €3249 Eve (57cm-22in) s. walnut wood prov. 14-Dec-2 Weschler, Washington #699/R est:1000-1500

Works on paper
£335 $550 €486 Reclining nude (18x44cm-7x17in) s. pencil. 5-Jun-3 Swann Galleries, New York #159/R

LAURENT-DESROUSSEAUX, Henry Alphonse Louis (1862-1906) French
£2404 $3750 €3606 First communion (91x74cm-36x29in) s. exhib. 9-Oct-2 Doyle, New York #64/R est:4000-6000

LAURENTI, Cesare (attrib) (1854-1937) Italian
£1677 $2650 €2600 Peasant woman (32x21cm-13x8in) bears sig. board. 18-Dec-2 Finarte, Milan #139/R

LAURENTY, L (19th C) French
£800 $1216 €1200 Waiting for the fishermans return (65x92cm-26x36in) s. 29-Aug-2 Christie's, Kensington #236/R

LAURET, Emmanuel Joseph (1809-1882) French
£10897 $17109 €17000 Panorama de Constantine (48x60cm-19x24in) s.d.1853 lit. 16-Dec-2 Gros & Delettrez, Paris #111/R est:9000-12000

LAURET, François (1820-1868) French
£1282 $2013 €2000 Jeune femme au harem (17x14cm-7x6in) s.d.1853 panel. 10-Dec-2 Tajan, Paris #188/R

LAURET, Richard (20th C) French?
Sculpture
£1727 $2832 €2400 Untitled. resin wood leather exec.c.90. 6-Jun-3 Rabourdin & Choppin de Janvry, Paris #42/R est:1800-2000

LAUREUS, Alexander (1783-1823) Swedish
£943 $1546 €1367 Cow-shed (34x40cm-13x16in) lit. 4-Jun-3 AB Stockholms Auktionsverk #2503/R est:15000-20000 (S.KR 12000)
£949 $1500 €1500 Farewell (16x21cm-6x8in) 1-Dec-2 Bukowskis, Helsinki #100/R est:1800-2000
£1120 $1702 €1680 Kitchen maid with candle and basket of vegetables (22x17cm-9x7in) s.i.d.1815 panel. 27-Aug-2 Rasmussen, Copenhagen #1566/R est:8000-10000 (D.KR 13000)
£2152 $3400 €3400 Girl with candle (20x17cm-8x7in) s.i.d.1815 panel. 1-Dec-2 Bukowskis, Helsinki #99/R est:2500-3000
£5027 $8245 €7289 Portrait of Governor J A von Gerdten (60x50cm-24x20in) prov.exhib.lit. 4-Jun-3 AB Stockholms Auktionsverk #2501/R est:30000-35000 (S.KR 64000)
Works on paper
£627 $1029 €960 From Vincennes (21x28cm-8x11in) s.i.d.1 Junii 1819 wash. 9-Feb-3 Bukowskis, Helsinki #290/R

LAUREYS, Armand (1867-?) Belgian
£396 $633 €550 Chez l'antiquaire (65x47cm-26x19in) s. 13-May-3 Galerie Moderne, Brussels #344

LAURGE, Franz (20th C) French
£368 $600 €552 Portrait of Grace (51x69cm-20x27in) s. 2-Feb-3 Simpson's, Houston #202

LAURI, Filippo (1623-1694) Italian
£1773 $2961 €2500 Le portement de croix (34x47cm-13x19in) 18-Jun-3 Tajan, Paris #29/R est:3000-4000
£2027 $3162 €3000 Jugement de Midas (13x22cm-5x9in) copper. 26-Mar-3 Tajan, Paris #12
£64865 $101189 €96000 L'enlevement d'Orithye par Boree (135x116cm-53x46in) 25-Mar-3 Chochon-Barre & Allardi, Paris #22/R

LAURI, Filippo (attrib) (1623-1694) Italian
£1700 $2720 €2550 Scene from the Old Testament with a putto above (33x30cm-13x12in) 13-Mar-3 Duke & Son, Dorchester #280/R est:300-500

LAURI, Filippo (circle) (1623-1694) Italian
£10671 $17500 €16007 Academic male nude studies (18x10cm-7x4in) paper on panel eight prov. 30-May-3 Christie's, Rockefeller NY #36/R est:6000-8000

LAURIA, Giuseppe (1940-) Italian
£278 $442 €400 Untitled (40x30cm-16x12in) s. painted 1998. 1-May-3 Meeting Art, Vercelli #366
£513 $795 €800 Garden (50x40cm-20x16in) s. 4-Dec-2 Finarte, Milan #542/R

LAURIN, Gabriel (20th C) French
Works on paper
£839 $1325 €1300 Les ponchettes (31x40cm-12x16in) s.i. chl dr exec.c.1933. 17-Dec-2 Claude Boisgirard, Paris #28

LAURIOL, M (19/20th C) French
£745 $1184 €1118 Woman seen from behind, sewing (65x48cm-26x19in) s. 5-Mar-3 Rasmussen, Copenhagen #2032/R (D.KR 8000)

LAURITZ, Jack (20th C) American
£353 $550 €530 Mountains (36x41cm-14x16in) s. board. 29-Mar-3 Charlton Hall, Columbia #642/R

LAURITZ, Paul (1889-1975) American
£469 $750 €704 Seventeen Mile Drive-Carmel (69x94cm-27x37in) s. board. 11-Jan-3 Harvey Clar, Oakland #1210
£497 $800 €746 Winter landscape (76x102cm-30x40in) s. 18-Feb-3 John Moran, Pasadena #187
£833 $1300 €1250 Stormy skies (51x64cm-20x25in) s. board. 29-Mar-3 Charlton Hall, Columbia #355 est:2000-3000
£1592 $2500 €2388 Spring time, California (64x76cm-25x30in) s. 10-Dec-2 Doyle, New York #118/R est:2500-3500
£1911 $3000 €2867 Mountain landscape with trees (61x86cm-24x34in) s. canvas on board prov. 19-Nov-2 Butterfields, San Francisco #8290/R est:4000-6000
£2756 $4300 €4134 Morning light Grand Canyon Arizona (61x86cm-24x34in) 9-Nov-2 Altermann Galleries, Santa Fe #185
£3065 $4750 €4598 Figure and dog sled team in nocturnal Alaska (48x36cm-19x14in) s. 29-Oct-2 John Moran, Pasadena #629 est:5000-7500
£3892 $6500 €5643 Autumn day (71x81cm-28x32in) s. i.on stretcher. 18-Jun-3 Christie's, Los Angeles #60/R est:8000-12000
£5090 $8500 €7381 Sierra landscape (81x91cm-32x36in) s. 18-Jun-3 Christie's, Los Angeles #52/R est:10000-15000
£8280 $13000 €12420 Arroyo Seco (89x129cm-35x51in) s. canvas on masonite painted c.1925 prov. 19-Nov-2 Butterfields, San Francisco #8282/R est:12000-15000
£9554 $15000 €14331 Summer splendour (71x81cm-28x32in) s. 19-Nov-2 Butterfields, San Francisco #8203/R est:12000-16000

LAUSEN, Uwe (1941-1970) ?
£1266 $2000 €2000 Landscape composition (100x100cm-39x39in) painted 1963 exhib. 29-Nov-2 Bolland & Marotz, Bremen #887/R est:2700
Works on paper
£1646 $2551 €2600 Untitled (44x27cm-17x11in) s.d.1965 W/C col chk pencil. 28-Sep-2 Ketterer, Hamburg #420/R est:3000-3500

LAUTERWASSER, Siegfried (1913-2000) German
Photographs
£1887 $2925 €3000 Reflections in water (40x30cm-16x12in) gelatin silver. 2-Nov-2 Lempertz, Koln #58/R est:2000

LAUTH, Robert (1896-1985) German
£453 $706 €720 Pfalz landscape - Niederkirchen with Peterskopf (49x60cm-19x24in) s. s.i. verso panel. 11-Oct-2 Winterberg, Heidelberg #1401

LAUTOUR, Tony de (20th C) New Zealander
£2170 $3364 €3255 New World (95x90cm-37x35in) s.d.2001. 4-Dec-2 Dunbar Sloane, Auckland #33/R est:3000-5000 (NZ.D 6750)

LAUVRAY, Abel (1870-1950) French
£2564 $4026 €4000 Campagne provencale (60x81cm-24x32in) s. lit. 22-Nov-2 Millon & Associes, Paris #69

LAUWERS, Balthasar (attrib) (c.1570-1645) Flemish
£32099 $52000 €48149 Wooded river landscape (21x29cm-8x11in) bears sig. copper. 23-Jan-3 Sotheby's, New York #130/R est:40000
£49383 $80000 €74075 Wooded landscape with animals and huntsmen (21x29cm-8x11in) copper. 23-Jan-3 Sotheby's, New York #131/R est:40000

LAUX, August (1847-1921) American
£1875 $3000 €2813 Strawberries and hydrangeas (25x36cm-10x14in) s. 15-Mar-3 Eldred, East Dennis #277/R est:4000-5000
£2250 $3600 €3375 Still life with pineapple, strawberries and peaches (30x41cm-12x16in) s. 15-Mar-3 Eldred, East Dennis #276/R est:5000-6000
£2259 $3750 €3276 Still life of strawberries. board. 13-Jun-3 Du Mouchelle, Detroit #2034/R est:4000-5000
£2532 $4000 €3798 Still life with pineapple, orange and nuts (25x36cm-10x14in) s. 24-Apr-3 Shannon's, Milford #111/R est:4000-6000
£3896 $6000 €5844 Apples in a tin pan (25x36cm-10x14in) s. prov. 24-Oct-2 Shannon's, Milford #55/R est:8000-12000

LAUZERO, Albert (1909-) French
£648 $920 €1050 Village du Mesnil Amelot (54x73cm-21x29in) s. 16-Mar-3 Eric Pillon, Calais #221/R

LAVAGNA, Francesco (18th C) Italian
£1500 $2355 €2250 Rose, peonies and other flowers in a brozen vase on a stone ledge (64x49cm-25x19in) 10-Dec-2 Bonhams, New Bond Street #84/R est:2000-3000

LAVAGNA, Francesco (circle) (18th C) Italian
£8500 $13260 €12750 Landscape garden with urns, platters, ewers of mixed flowers and melons (71x91cm-28x36in) prov. 10-Apr-3 Christie's, Kensington #299/R est:6000-8000

LAVAGNA, Giuseppe (1684-1724) Italian
£3200 $4992 €4800 Flowers, porcelain dishes and melon in an ornamental garden (48x64cm-19x25in) 10-Apr-3 Tennants, Leyburn #1080/R est:3000-4000

LAVAGNINO, Pier Luigi (1933-) Italian
Works on paper
£354 $562 €520 Rocks (48x66cm-19x26in) s.d.1972 W/C. 1-Mar-3 Meeting Art, Vercelli #583

LAVAL, Fernand (1886-1966) French
£355 $592 €500 Rue a Montmartre (60x73cm-24x29in) s.d. 23-Jun-3 Delvaux, Paris #172

LAVALLE, John (1896-?) American
Works on paper
£283 $450 €425 Swimming lesson at Mulanda Rock (53x71cm-21x28in) s. W/C exec.c.1961. 2-Mar-3 Toomey, Oak Park #696/R

LAVALLEE, Geeraert de (attrib) (17th C) Flemish
£2365 $3689 €3500 Agar et l'ange (38x54cm-15x21in) copper. 28-Mar-3 Piasa, Paris #24/R

LAVALLEY, Alexandre Claude Louis (1862-1927) French
£476 $742 €714 Female nude seated (22x16cm-9x6in) s. 5-Aug-2 Rasmussen, Vejle #74/R (D.KR 5600)

LAVAULT, Albert Tibule Furcy de (19th C) French
£1321 $2100 €1982 Still life with pink roses (73x51cm-29x20in) s. 7-Mar-3 Skinner, Boston #262/R est:700-900
£3600 $6012 €5400 Pink roses in a glass vase (74x51cm-29x20in) s. 18-Jun-3 Christie's, Kensington #29/R est:2000-3000
£5096 $8000 €7644 Still life with roses and plums (105x85cm-41x33in) s. 21-Nov-2 Sotheby's, New York #224/R est:10000-15000
£6500 $10205 €9750 Summer flowers and fruit on a stone ledge (100x151cm-39x59in) s.d.1878. 21-Nov-2 Christie's, Kensington #92/R est:6000-8000

LAVENSON, Alma R (1897-1989) American
Photographs
£3247 $5000 €4871 Church at Taos (18x25cm-7x10in) s. photograph. 24-Oct-2 Sotheby's, New York #132/R est:5000-7000

LAVENSTEIN, Cyril (1891-?) British
Works on paper
£270 $424 €405 Long Jan, Middleburg (39x31cm-15x12in) s.d.1930 i.verso W/C over pencil. 15-Apr-3 Bonhams, Knowle #70

LAVERY, Sir John (1856-1941) British
£3500 $5600 €5250 Countess of Oxford and Asquith, study for Their Majesties' Court (50x40cm-20x16in) s.i. canvasboard prov.exhib. 15-May-3 Christie's, Kensington #146/R est:4000-6000
£3800 $6080 €5700 Study for portrait of lady Diana Cooper (35x45cm-14x18in) canvasboard prov. 16-May-3 Sotheby's, London #71/R est:4000-6000
£4000 $6360 €6000 Portrait of Arabella, Duchess of Marlborough (36x25cm-14x10in) s. board. 29-Apr-3 Gorringes, Lewes #2176
£4500 $7200 €6750 Portrait of Katherine Fitz Gerald (61x51cm-24x20in) canvasboard prov. 16-May-3 Sotheby's, London #67/R est:5000-7000
£4965 $8043 €7199 Portrait of lady (51x40cm-20x16in) s.d.1891. 26-May-3 Bukowskis, Stockholm #234/R est:40000-50000 (S.KR 64000)
£8000 $12800 €12000 Faust (76x50cm-30x20in) s.d.1881 s.i.d.1881 verso. 15-May-3 Christie's, Kensington #147/R est:6000-8000
£8000 $12800 €12000 On the banks of the Tiber (12x20cm-5x8in) s.d.95 board prov. 16-May-3 Sotheby's, London #38/R est:8000-12000
£10000 $15600 €15000 Street in Tangiers (23x27cm-9x11in) s. canvas on board painted c.1892 prov. 15-Oct-2 Sotheby's, London #231/R est:10000-15000
£15000 $24000 €22500 Lady Diana Cooper (45x35cm-18x14in) prov. 16-May-3 Sotheby's, London #69/R est:15000-20000
£16000 $25600 €24000 Moonlight, Tetuan Morocco (36x63cm-14x25in) s. s.i.d.1911 verso prov.exhib.lit. 16-May-3 Sotheby's, London #55/R est:20000-30000
£18000 $28800 €27000 Evening at the bar, entrance to harbour (25x35cm-10x14in) s. i.indis d.verso canvas on panel. 16-May-3 Sotheby's, London #60/R est:20000-30000
£21622 $33730 €32000 Pious reflections (52x30cm-20x12in) s.d.1880 prov.exhib.lit. 26-Mar-3 James Adam, Dublin #84/R est:25000-35000
£22000 $35200 €33000 Esther (46x37cm-18x15in) mono. s.i.verso. 16-May-3 Sotheby's, London #50/R est:8000-12000
£28000 $44800 €42000 Two ladies talking on a sofa (25x35cm-10x14in) s.i.d.1912 canvas on board. 15-May-3 Christie's, London #52/R est:30000-50000
£28986 $47536 €40000 Eileen at Dieppe (17x35cm-7x14in) s.i.d.October 1905 canvasboard. 28-May-3 Bonhams & James Adam, Dublin #105a/R est:30000-40000
£29487 $45705 €46000 Tangier from the Hotel Continental (46x35cm-18x14in) s. 3-Dec-2 Bonhams & James Adam, Dublin #35/R est:40000-60000
£35256 $54647 €55000 Flamingo pool at the Japanese Gardens, Kildare (51x61cm-20x24in) s. board. 3-Dec-2 Bonhams & James Adam, Dublin #62/R est:60000-80000
£40000 $64000 €60000 Coast of Kerry (51x61cm-20x24in) s. s.i.d.1924 verso prov. 15-May-3 Christie's, London #53/R est:20000-30000
£44872 $69551 €70000 Glendalough, Ireland 1924 (51x61cm-20x24in) s. s.i.d.1924 verso canvasboard. 3-Dec-2 Bonhams & James Adam, Dublin #77/R est:50000-70000
£55000 $88000 €82500 Portrait of the honorable Diana Janet Darling (37x26cm-15x10in) s.d.1905 canvas on panel prov.lit. 16-May-3 Sotheby's, London #56/R est:15000-20000
£57971 $95072 €80000 Jaixquibel, mountain in Spain (64x77cm-25x30in) s. s.i.d.1917 verso canvasboard prov. 28-May-3 Bonhams & James Adam, Dublin #89/R est:80000-120000
£60000 $98400 €90000 Early morning, Bay of Tunis (51x61cm-20x24in) s. s.i.d.1919 verso. 6-Jun-3 Christie's, London #48/R est:30000-50000
£95541 $150000 €143312 Beach - evening, Tangier Bay (25x30cm-10x12in) s. s.d.1920 verso prov.exhib. 10-Dec-2 Doyle, New York #227/R est:80000-120000
£110000 $170500 €165000 Golf links, North Berwick (63x76cm-25x30in) s. s.i.d.1921 verso. 31-Oct-2 Christie's, London #157/R est:150000-200000
£118000 $182900 €177000 Golf course, North Berwick (61x76cm-24x30in) s. i.verso prov.exhib.lit. 5-Dec-2 Bonhams, Edinburgh #112/R est:100000-150000
£145000 $232000 €217500 Portrait of Mrs Charles Baker (188x91cm-74x36in) s. s.i.verso lit. 16-May-3 Sotheby's, London #74/R est:100000-150000
£220000 $352000 €330000 Spanish coast from Tangier (76x63cm-30x25in) s. s.i.d.1920 verso prov. 15-May-3 Christie's, London #51/R est:150000-250000
£432258 $682968 €670000 La lecture - Reading (64x82cm-25x32in) s. painted c.1914 prov. 18-Dec-2 Tajan, Paris #4/R

LAVES, Werner (1903-1972) German
£411 $650 €650 Le Bassin de Cavenage, Marseille (80x125cm-31x49in) s.d.1962 i. verso. 30-Nov-2 Arnold, Frankfurt #340/R
£506 $800 €800 Cityscape (80x115cm-31x45in) 29-Nov-2 Villa Grisebach, Berlin #757/R

LAVIE, Raffi (1937-) Israeli
£5380 $8500 €8070 Untitled (89x89cm-35x35in) s.d.62 oil graphite. 27-Apr-3 Sotheby's, Tel Aviv #72/R est:6000-8000

LAVIEILLE, Eugène (1820-1889) French
£400 $636 €600 Village in the dunes (29x40cm-11x16in) s.i. on stretcher. 18-Mar-3 Rosebery Fine Art, London #801/R
£1474 $2285 €2300 Bord de Seine (15x25cm-6x10in) s. s.i.verso panel. 9-Dec-2 Beaussant & Lefèvre, Paris #66/R
£1899 $2962 €3000 A travers champs (41x27cm-16x11in) s.d. s.i.d.verso. 20-Oct-2 Mercier & Cie, Lille #307/R est:3500-4000

LAVIER, Bertrand (1949-) French
£23145 $35643 €36800 Painting (59x72cm-23x28in) acrylic painted 1983 prov. 26-Oct-2 Cornette de St.Cyr, Paris #139/R est:15000

LAVILLE, Henri (1916-) French
£349 $545 €524 Female nude on bed (54x46cm-21x18in) s. panel. 6-Nov-2 Dobiaschofsky, Bern #3489 (S.FR 800)
£500 $785 €750 Female nude sitting on a bed (54x46cm-21x18in) s. board. 16-Apr-3 Christie's, Kensington #857

LAVILLE, Joy (1923-) British
£10366 $17000 €15549 Terminal beach (135x160cm-53x63in) s. acrylic prov. 28-May-3 Christie's, Rockefeller NY #153/R est:15000-20000
Works on paper
£1259 $1965 €1889 Florero rosa (39x19cm-15x7in) s.d.1970 pastel prov. 17-Oct-2 Louis Morton, Mexico #151/R est:24000-28000 (M.P 20000)

LAVOINE, L P Robert (1916-1999) French
£385 $604 €600 Marais a Honfleur (54x65cm-21x26in) s. 24-Nov-2 Lesieur & Le Bars, Le Havre #91
£385 $604 €600 Village sous la neige (54x65cm-21x26in) s. 24-Nov-2 Lesieur & Le Bars, Le Havre #90
£449 $696 €700 Paris, Montmartre, rue du Mont-Cenis (54x65cm-21x26in) s.i. s.i.verso. 9-Dec-2 Beaussant & Lefèvre, Paris #67
£529 $836 €820 Paris vu de la Butte Montmartre (63x80cm-25x31in) s.i.d. cardboard. 17-Dec-2 Rossini, Paris #105/R
£563 $907 €800 Le bourg de Villier (49x63cm-19x25in) s.i. panel. 11-May-3 Thierry & Lannon, Brest #261
£570 $918 €850 Le port de Honfleur a maree basse (51x65cm-20x26in) s. 23-Feb-3 Lesieur & Le Bars, Le Havre #84
£772 $1096 €1250 Montmartre, Lapin Agile (51x61cm-20x24in) s. 16-Mar-3 Eric Pillon, Calais #215/R
Works on paper
£353 $554 €550 Plage de Cancale (31x46cm-12x18in) s. gouache. 24-Nov-2 Lesieur & Le Bars, Le Havre #89
£385 $604 €600 Chaumieres a Quiberon (33x47cm-13x19in) s. W/C. 24-Nov-2 Lesieur & Le Bars, Le Havre #88
£497 $770 €790 La roulotte (32x46cm-13x18in) s. W/C. 3-Nov-2 Feletin, Province #74

LAVONEN, Ahti (1928-1970) Finnish
£381 $625 €530 Composition (35x24cm-14x9in) s. 5-Jun-3 Hagelstam, Helsinki #894
Works on paper
£317 $519 €440 Untitled (60x70cm-24x28in) s. Indian ink. 5-Jun-3 Hagelstam, Helsinki #826
£331 $523 €480 Der zerbrochene Krug (67x55cm-26x22in) s. mixed media. 3-Apr-3 Hagelstam, Helsinki #909/R

LAVRENKO, Boris (1920-) Russian
£921 $1492 €1400 Wakening (130x140cm-51x55in) s. s.i.verso painted 1984. 21-Jan-3 Christie's, Amsterdam #423/R est:800-1200

LAVROFF, Georges (1895-?) Russian
Sculpture
£1088 $1731 €1600 Art Deco group of fox with pheasant (55x35cm-22x14in) s. brown pat.bronze gilt marble socle. 24-Mar-3 Bernaerts, Antwerp #26/R est:700-850
£1111 $1833 €1600 Fennec couche (8x12x12cm-3x5x5in) s. silver pat bronze exec.c.1925-30 Cast Marcel Guillemard. 2-Jul-3 Artcurial Briest, Paris #48/R est:1500-2000

LAW, Andrew (attrib) (19/20th C) British
£850 $1326 €1275 Portrait of a lady in a green dress (169x102cm-67x40in) board. 7-Nov-2 Christie's, Kensington #68/R

LAW, Charles Anthony (1916-) Canadian
£205 $318 €308 Late afternoon, winter (33x40cm-13x16in) s. panel. 24-Sep-2 Ritchie, Toronto #3181b (C.D 500)
£304 $475 €508 Melville Cove, Halifax, Nova Scotia (34x40cm-13x16in) s. s.i.d.1991 verso board prov. 13-Apr-3 Levis, Calgary #492/R (C.D 700)
£410 $639 €615 Paysage d'hiver (33x40cm-13x16in) s. panel. 10-Sep-2 Iegor de Saint Hippolyte, Montreal #77 (C.D 1000)
£1235 $1914 €1853 Reflection - Prince Christian Sound, Greenland (60x75cm-24x30in) s. painted February 1989. 3-Dec-2 Joyner, Toronto #206/R est:1000-1500 (C.D 3000)

LAW, David (1831-1901) British
Works on paper
£320 $499 €480 Riverbank at eventide (16x33cm-6x13in) s.i.d.1859 pencil W/C. 19-Sep-2 Christie's, Kensington #83

LAW, Denys (1907-1981) British
£280 $434 €420 Sunlight and shade (41x51cm-16x20in) s. board. 25-Sep-2 Hamptons Fine Art, Godalming #462
£300 $474 €450 Wooded landscape with bluebells and a stream (61x77cm-24x30in) board. 26-Nov-2 Bonhams, Ipswich #345
£300 $468 €450 Woodland stream with waterfall (38x46cm-15x18in) s. 11-Apr-3 Keys, Aylsham #297
£330 $511 €495 Stream at Lamorna (48x61cm-19x24in) s. board. 26-Sep-2 Lane, Penzance #102/R
£420 $701 €609 South east wind, Lamorna (40x50cm-16x20in) s. board. 25-Jun-3 Bonhams, Bury St Edmunds #570
£450 $702 €675 Lamorna stream (41x48cm-16x19in) s. 17-Oct-2 David Lay, Penzance #1223
£480 $782 €720 Lamorna cottage (46x56cm-18x22in) s. 13-Feb-3 David Lay, Penzance #51
£780 $1303 €1131 Lamorna (49x60cm-19x24in) s. board. 19-Jun-3 Lane, Penzance #215/R

LAWES, Harold (fl.1890`s) British
Works on paper
£300 $468 €450 Near Barmouth, North Wales (24x34cm-9x13in) s.i. W/C. 25-Mar-3 Bonhams, Knightsbridge #16/R
£333 $550 €480 Island stream with sheep (48x73cm-19x29in) s. W/C. 7-Jul-3 Hamilton Osborne King, Dublin #198/R
£346 $550 €519 Highland landscape with sheep along a stream (117x193cm-46x76in) s. W/C. 7-Mar-3 Jackson's, Cedar Falls #532/R
£400 $624 €600 Ann Hathaway's cottage (36x25cm-14x10in) s.i. W/C. 18-Oct-2 Keys, Aylsham #648/R
£400 $664 €580 Stratford on Avon. Ullswater, Cumberland (25x36cm-10x14in) s.i. W/C pair. 16-Jun-3 Waddingtons, Toronto #47/R est:800-1200 (C.D 900)
£515 $803 €747 Kentshire cottage (25x37cm-10x15in) s.i. W/C. 26-Mar-3 Walker's, Ottawa #50/R est:700-900 (C.D 1200)
£515 $803 €747 Sutton, Oxford (25x37cm-10x15in) s.i. W/C. 26-Mar-3 Walker's, Ottawa #51/R est:700-900 (C.D 1200)
£550 $897 €798 Lakeland landscape with sheep in the foreground (24x51cm-9x20in) s. W/C htd white. 17-Jul-3 Tennants, Leyburn #735
£750 $1215 €1125 Devonshire cottage (36x25cm-14x10in) s. W/C. 21-May-3 Bonhams, Knightsbridge #134/R
£900 $1476 €1350 On the coast of Devon, sheep grazing. Killarney, cattle watering (22x51cm-9x20in) s. one d.1891 W/C pair. 2-Jun-3 David Duggleby, Scarborough #261/R

LAWLER, Louise (1947-) American
Photographs
£6000 $10020 €8700 Combien our ce chapeau (71x81cm-28x32in) st.sig.d.1987 num.3/5 verso black white photo 3 parts prov.lit. 26-Jun-3 Sotheby's, London #280/R est:6000-8000
£10000 $16000 €15000 Scene (121x179cm-48x70in) s.d.1990 num.2/5 cibachrome print prov. 15-May-3 Christie's, Rockefeller NY #365/R est:10000-15000
£15823 $25000 €23735 Gold Jackie (71x69cm-28x27in) s.d.1993 c-print one of 5 prov. 13-Nov-2 Sotheby's, New York #493/R est:15000-20000

LAWLESS, Carl (1894-1934) American
£2019 $3250 €3029 Wooded forest interior (38x38cm-15x15in) s. 18-Feb-3 John Moran, Pasadena #18 est:1000-2000

LAWLEY, Douglas (1906-1971) Canadian
£472 $736 €684 Winter, Baie St. Paul (51x61cm-20x24in) s. board. 26-Mar-3 Walker's, Ottawa #214/R est:1000-1500 (C.D 1100)
£800 $1312 €1200 Caleche, Sherbrooke St. West (20x25cm-8x10in) s. canvas on board. 3-Jun-3 Joyner, Toronto #574 est:1500-1800 (C.D 1800)
£978 $1604 €1467 La visite (50x60cm-20x24in) s. board exhib. 3-Jun-3 Joyner, Toronto #192/R est:2500-3000 (C.D 2200)
£1317 $2041 €1976 Sable island ponies (20x25cm-8x10in) s. board two. 3-Dec-2 Joyner, Toronto #245/R est:3000-4000 (C.D 3200)
£1600 $2624 €2400 Logging, Les Eboulements (62x80cm-24x31in) s. prov. 3-Jun-3 Joyner, Toronto #173/R est:3500-4500 (C.D 3600)

LAWLOR, Adrian (1899-1969) Australian
£1077 $1712 €1616 Still life (49x35cm-19x14in) s. card. 4-Mar-3 Deutscher-Menzies, Melbourne #246/R est:3000-4000 (A.D 2800)

LAWMAN, Jasper Holman (1825-1906) American
£1235 $2000 €1853 Portrait of a lady in a black lace dress (122x81cm-48x32in) s.d.1882. 24-Jan-3 New Orleans Auction, New Orleans #466 est:2500-4000

LAWRENCE, Alfred Kingsley (1893-1975) British
£900 $1404 €1350 Allegory (57x88cm-22x35in) prov. 27-Mar-3 Christie's, Kensington #427/R

LAWRENCE, George Feather (1901-1981) Australian
£246 $385 €369 River scene (27x32cm-11x13in) s. board. 21-Oct-2 Australian Art Auctions, Sydney #104 (A.D 700)
£287 $451 €431 House at Northwood (25x30cm-10x12in) s. board. 15-Apr-3 Lawson Menzies, Sydney #243/R (A.D 750)
£305 $482 €458 Hyde Park at night (26x37cm-10x15in) s.d.67 board. 7-Apr-3 Australian Art Auctions, Sydney #171 (A.D 800)

£423 $659 €635 North Ryde (41x51cm-16x20in) s. board. 21-Oct-2 Australian Art Auctions, Sydney #51 (A.D 1200)
£575 $902 €863 Campbell Street, Sydney (40x50cm-16x20in) s. board. 15-Apr-3 Lawson Menzies, Sydney #244/R est:1000-1500 (A.D 1500)
£681 $1035 €1022 Harbour from Woolwich (29x37cm-11x15in) s.indis.d.59 board. 27-Aug-2 Goodman, Sydney #85 (A.D 1900)
£786 $1241 €1179 Notre Dame (47x59cm-19x23in) s.d.76 board. 18-Nov-2 Goodman, Sydney #85 (A.D 2200)
£929 $1467 €1394 Burdekin River (50x75cm-20x30in) s.d.69 board. 17-Nov-2 Sotheby's, Paddington #70/R est:3000-5000 (A.D 2600)
£1071 $1693 €1607 Old house, Appin (42x57cm-17x22in) s.d.69 board. 17-Nov-2 Sotheby's, Paddington #62 est:1500-3000 (A.D 3000)
£1071 $1693 €1607 Nambucca (55x81cm-22x32in) s.d.64 i.verso board. 17-Nov-2 Sotheby's, Paddington #69/R est:3000-5000 (A.D 3000)
£1240 $1972 €1860 Hilltop near Orange (59x76cm-23x30in) s.d.73 i.verso board prov. 5-May-3 Sotheby's, Melbourne #8/R (A.D 3200)
£1357 $2157 €2036 Dockside Newcastle (60x75cm-24x30in) s.d.71 board prov. 5-May-3 Sotheby's, Melbourne #7/R est:5000 (A.D 3500)
£1423 $2178 €2135 Timber yards, Blackwattle Bay (64x85cm-25x33in) s.d.62 i.verso board prov. 25-Aug-2 Sotheby's, Paddington #123/R est:4000-6000 (A.D 4000)
£1550 $2465 €2325 White house (40x55cm-16x22in) s. board prov. 5-May-3 Sotheby's, Melbourne #56/R (A.D 4000)
£1829 $2891 €2652 Paddington (50x61cm-20x24in) s.d.45 board. 22-Jul-3 Lawson Menzies, Sydney #154/R est:6000-8000 (A.D 4500)
£3053 $4824 €4580 Winter landscape, Bathurst (34x44cm-13x17in) s.d.65 board prov. 2-Apr-3 Christie's, Melbourne #56/R est:2000-3000 (A.D 8000)

LAWRENCE, Jacob (1917-2000) American
£33951 $55000 €50927 Courtyard library (28x37cm-11x15in) s.d.66 tempera gouache on board prov.lit. 21-May-3 Sotheby's, New York #111/R est:40000-60000
£179012 $290000 €268518 Ten fugitives (62x93cm-24x37in) s.d.67 egg tempera on gessoed board prov.exhib.lit. 21-May-3 Sotheby's, New York #15/R est:200000-300000

Prints
£2404 $3750 €3606 New York in transit II (51x102cm-20x40in) s.d.num.17/50 col silkscreen. 14-Oct-2 Butterfields, San Francisco #1298/R est:3500-4500
£22642 $36000 €33963 Eight passages (66x102cm-26x40in) s.num.22/22 col screenprints portfolio. 1-May-3 Swann Galleries, New York #481/R est:25000-35000

LAWRENCE, John (1933-) British
Works on paper
£2200 $3630 €3190 Bigwig leading Hazel and others away from ditch. Black rabbit. Bigwig (18x18cm-7x7in) s. pencil pen black ink W/C htd white sold with book. 3-Jul-3 Christie's, Kensington #236/R est:2000-3000

LAWRENCE, Joseph (?) British
£300 $477 €450 Bay hunter in a stable (34x44cm-13x17in) s.d.1838. 6-Mar-3 Christie's, Kensington #524y/R

LAWRENCE, Samuel (19th C) British
£11613 $18000 €17420 Portrait of Lord Charles Stewart (48x37cm-19x15in) millboard prov. 2-Oct-2 Christie's, Rockefeller NY #166/R est:20000-30000

LAWRENCE, Sir Thomas (1769-1830) British
£550 $902 €825 Chestnut hunter in a stable (43x58cm-17x23in) s.d.1841. 3-Jun-3 Bonhams, Knightsbridge #56/R
£8000 $13280 €12000 Portrait of Anne, Lady Romilly in a white dress (76x63cm-30x25in) painted oval prov.lit. 10-Jun-3 Christie's, London #40/R est:10000-15000
£9375 $15000 €14063 Mrs John William of Gwersylt (76x63cm-30x25in) prov.exhib.lit. 14-May-3 Doyle, New York #104/R est:12000-18000
£16352 $25509 €26000 Portrait of William Robertson (128x102cm-50x40in) prov.exhib.lit. 8-Oct-2 Christie's, Paris #27/R est:50000
£180000 $280800 €270000 Portrait of Lady Georgiana Agar-Ellis, with her son Henry (129x104cm-51x41in) exhib.lit. 26-Mar-3 Woolley & Wallis, Salisbury #218/R est:40000-60000

Works on paper
£1000 $1650 €1450 Portrait of Eleanor Carne, bust-length, in a white dress (30x25cm-12x10in) pastel oval. 3-Jul-3 Christie's, Kensington #1/R est:800-1200
£2800 $4452 €4200 Portrait of Laurence Sullivan as a child (42x31cm-17x12in) s. pastel oval. 19-Mar-3 Sotheby's, London #117/R est:3000-4000
£3000 $4800 €4500 Bust length portrait of Elizabeth, Lady Templeton, wearing blue dress (24x19cm-9x7in) pastel pencil htd white oval prov. 15-May-3 Lawrence, Crewkerne #818/R est:1200-1800
£47000 $73790 €70500 Portrait of a lady, probably Mrs James Denham (46x31cm-18x12in) init.d.1789 pencil black red chk lit. 21-Nov-2 Christie's, London #10/R est:7000-10000

LAWRENCE, Sir Thomas (attrib) (1769-1830) British
£3165 $5000 €4748 Portrait of Thomas Hutchinson (74x61cm-29x24in) 18-Nov-2 Schrager Galleries, Milwaukee #1293
£13250 $20670 €19875 Portrait of a gentleman, probably the Hon Gerald Valerian Wellesley (90x70cm-35x28in) prov. 17-Oct-2 Lawrence, Crewkerne #471/R

Works on paper
£350 $550 €525 Portrait of a young girl, Miss Hinde (23x20cm-9x8in) pencil red crayon. 16-Apr-3 Christie's, Kensington #958
£567 $919 €800 Portrait of young woman wearing hat with large feather (11x15cm-4x6in) s. pencil. 21-May-3 Piasa, Paris #183

LAWRENCE, Sir Thomas (studio) (1769-1830) British
£34000 $53720 €51000 Portrait of King George IV in Garter robes, crown on table (281x203cm-111x80in) 26-Nov-2 Christie's, London #47/R est:20000-30000
£55000 $86900 €82500 Portrait of Arthur Wellesley, 1st Duke of Wellington (242x157cm-95x62in) prov.lit. 26-Nov-2 Christie's, London #46/R est:25000-40000

LAWRENCE, William Hurd (1866-1938) American
£590 $950 €885 Well wishers seeing off woman at train, older man waiting off to side (43x28cm-17x11in) s.d. 10-May-3 Illustration House, New York #156/R
£1104 $1700 €1656 Autumn in the mountains (81x61cm-32x24in) s. painted c.1900. 8-Sep-2 Treadway Gallery, Cincinnati #574/R est:1000-2000

LAWRENSON, Edward Louis (1868-1940) British
Works on paper
£1667 $2650 €2400 In Sussex. Kingston Down, Sussex. Fleeting clouds. Blackboys, Sussex. Blue jar (29x42cm-11x17in) s.i. W/C set of five prov.exhib. 29-Apr-3 Whyte's, Dublin #75/R est:2000-3000

LAWRIE, Alexander (1828-1917) American
£9615 $15000 €14423 Woodland interior, Adirondacks (30x25cm-12x10in) s. panel prov. 12-Apr-3 Weschler, Washington #565/R est:15000-20000
£12739 $20000 €19109 Autumn river landscape (20x32cm-8x13in) s. panel. 14-Dec-2 Weschler, Washington #656/R est:500-700

LAWRIE, Hamish (1919-1987) British
£320 $531 €464 Archway to a courtyard (59x40cm-23x16in) s. board. 13-Jun-3 Lyon & Turnbull, Edinburgh #49
£390 $612 €585 An avenue (40x63cm-16x25in) 17-Apr-3 Bonhams, Edinburgh #384
£780 $1225 €1170 Continental street (69x57cm-27x22in) 17-Apr-3 Bonhams, Edinburgh #385

LAWSON, A (?) ?
£968 $1500 €1404 Folky circus scene (74x89cm-29x35in) 7-Dec-2 South Bay, Long Island #236/R

LAWSON, Cecil Gordon (1851-1882) British
£600 $936 €900 Meadow scene (28x43cm-11x17in) i.on stretcher. 18-Sep-2 Cheffins Grain & Comins, Cambridge #531/R

LAWSON, Constance B (fl.1880-1903) British
Works on paper
£380 $600 €570 Still life of lilacs in a jug (45x34cm-18x13in) s.d.1907 W/C. 26-Nov-2 Bonhams, Knightsbridge #244/R

LAWSON, Ernest (1873-1939) American
£629 $1000 €944 Portrait of a cat (29x23cm-11x9in) init. prov. 5-Mar-3 Christie's, Rockefeller NY #98/R est:2000-3000
£755 $1200 €1133 Still life with Chinese pot (30x41cm-12x16in) init. prov. 5-Mar-3 Christie's, Rockefeller NY #104/R est:2500-3500
£2516 $4000 €3774 Still life with apples (23x37cm-9x15in) prov.exhib. 4-Mar-3 Christie's, Rockefeller NY #69/R est:4000-6000
£2656 $4250 €3984 Sunset landscape (20x25cm-8x10in) s. board. 11-Jan-3 James Julia, Fairfield #170 est:4000-6000
£3145 $5000 €4718 Farm on the hill (30x37cm-12x15in) s. oil ink prov. 7-Mar-3 Skinner, Boston #380/R est:6000-8000
£5346 $8500 €8019 Trees and rocks (20x25cm-8x10in) s. board on panel prov.exhib. 4-Mar-3 Christie's, Rockefeller NY #62/R est:8000-12000

£6918 $11000 €10377 Red house, Sounds Beach (20x25cm-8x10in) s. board on panel prov.exhib. 4-Mar-3 Christie's, Rockefeller NY #54/R est:10000-15000
£11305 $17750 €16958 Florida landscape with central water surrounded by tropical vegetation (61x76cm-24x30in) s. prov. 19-Apr-3 James Julia, Fairfield #154/R est:6000-8000
£11976 $20000 €17365 Haystacks mountains, Norfolk, Connecticut (41x51cm-16x20in) s. i.verso prov. 18-Jun-3 Christie's, Los Angeles #18/R est:20000-30000
£12102 $19000 €18153 Norfolk meadows (51x64cm-20x25in) s. i.verso. 10-Dec-2 Doyle, New York #94/R est:20000-30000
£15484 $24000 €23226 Playtime (20x25cm-8x10in) s. board prov.exhib. 5-Dec-2 Christie's, Rockefeller NY #90/R est:25000-35000
£35484 $55000 €53226 Stream by the farm (51x61cm-20x24in) s. prov.lit. 3-Dec-2 Phillips, New York #63/R est:70000-90000
£41935 $65000 €62903 Winter, Connecticut (63x76cm-25x30in) s. exhib. 5-Dec-2 Christie's, Rockefeller NY #74/R est:70000-100000
£92593 $150000 €138890 Cos cob in winter (51x71cm-20x28in) s. prov. 22-May-3 Christie's, Rockefeller NY #62/R est:120000-180000
£129630 $210000 €194445 Spuyten Duyvil Creek (63x76cm-25x30in) s. painted c.1914 prov.lit. 21-May-3 Sotheby's, New York #68/R est:150000-200000

LAWSON, Fred (1888-1968) British
Works on paper
£250 $415 €375 Haybarn and stacks in a field (23x34cm-9x13in) s.d.1919 W/C. 10-Jun-3 Bonhams, Leeds #72
£250 $408 €363 Dwellings on a hillside with figures beyond (28x38cm-11x15in) s. W/C. 17-Jul-3 Richardson & Smith, Whitby #526
£280 $440 €420 Winter landscape (33x41cm-13x16in) s. W/C. 21-Nov-2 Tennants, Leyburn #639
£300 $471 €450 Ledsham church, Yorkshire (37x45cm-15x18in) s.i.d.Oct 1958 W/C over pencil. 21-Nov-2 Tennants, Leyburn #638
£300 $489 €435 Figure on a horse drawn cart entering Castle Bolton (29x39cm-11x15in) s. pencil W/C. 17-Jul-3 Tennants, Leyburn #743
£320 $499 €480 Landscape study (26x36cm-10x14in) s. pen ink W/C. 10-Apr-3 Tennants, Leyburn #865
£360 $565 €540 Barrels by a river (27x38cm-11x15in) s.d.1912 W/C. 21-Nov-2 Tennants, Leyburn #640
£380 $597 €570 Yorkshire landscape (27x38cm-11x15in) s. W/C. 21-Nov-2 Tennants, Leyburn #641
£750 $1223 €1088 High street, Northallerton (27x37cm-11x15in) s.i.d.1949 W/C. 17-Jul-3 Tennants, Leyburn #746
£2400 $3912 €3480 Market place at Leyburn with a fairground and figures, motor vehicles nearby (31x36cm-12x14in) s. pencil W/C. 17-Jul-3 Tennants, Leyburn #744/R est:600-800

LAWSON, George Anderson (1832-1904) British
Sculpture
£1600 $2432 €2400 Robert Burns (24cm-9in) s.d.1891 dark golden brown pat. 28-Aug-2 Sotheby's, London #826/R est:1000-1500

LAY, Cecil Howard (1885-1956) British
£550 $858 €825 Ipswich Park. Day out (54x74cm-21x29in) s.d.31 board pair. 17-Sep-2 Bonhams, Knightsbridge #268/R

LAY, Trevor (20th C) British
£300 $462 €450 Study of a spitfire in flight and bomber aircraft below (48x61cm-19x24in) s.d.1987. 6-Sep-2 Biddle & Webb, Birmingham #259
£310 $477 €465 Hawker Hart (71x91cm-28x36in) init.d.88. 6-Sep-2 Biddle & Webb, Birmingham #255

LAYCOCK, Brent R (1947-) Canadian
£975 $1550 €1463 Windswept ridge (59x89cm-23x35in) s.i.d.1997 acrylic. 23-Mar-3 Hodgins, Calgary #21/R est:1500-2000 (C.D 2300)
Works on paper
£489 $802 €709 Tulips and white iris (35x54cm-14x21in) s. W/C prov. 9-Jun-3 Hodgins, Calgary #69/R est:900-1200 (C.D 1100)
£636 $1011 €954 Bow River Valley (59x85cm-23x33in) s.d.1977 W/C. 23-Mar-3 Hodgins, Calgary #74/R est:900-1200 (C.D 1500)

LAYNE, Bill (20th C) American
Works on paper
£2244 $3500 €3366 Spaniel tries to steal beach blanket from dressing beauty (53x43cm-21x17in) c. W/C airbrushed. 9-Nov-2 Illustration House, New York #139/R est:3000-4000

LAYS, Jean Pierre (1825-1887) French
£15094 $23547 €24000 Allegory of autumn with head of a woman surrounded by grapes (120x80cm-47x31in) s.d.1868. 20-Sep-2 Millon & Associes, Paris #330/R est:30000-45000

LAZERGES, Jean Raymond Hippolyte (1817-1887) French
£962 $1490 €1500 Descente de Croix (40x38cm-16x15in) s.d.1861 panel. 5-Dec-2 Gros & Delettrez, Paris #76
£1571 $2577 €2278 Girl on swing and boy pushing (50x36cm-20x14in) s. 4-Jun-3 AB Stockholms Auktionsverk #2413/R est:15000-20000 (S.KR 20000)

LAZZARINI, Gregorio (1655-1730) Italian
£20690 $32897 €30000 Artemisia (112x89cm-44x35in) 9-Mar-3 Semenzato, Venice #42/R
£20690 $32897 €30000 Cleopatra (112x89cm-44x35in) 9-Mar-3 Semenzato, Venice #41/R

LAZZARINI, Gregorio (attrib) (1655-1730) Italian
£6790 $11000 €10185 Portrait of Saint Joseph (46x39cm-18x15in) prov. 23-Jan-3 Sotheby's, New York #192a/R est:12000

LAZZARINI, Pietro (1842-1918) Italian
Sculpture
£6135 $10000 €8896 Young girl (104cm-41in) d.1887 marble. 18-Jul-3 Du Mouchelle, Detroit #5/R est:4000-6000

LAZZELL, Blanche (1878-1956) American
£8280 $13000 €12420 Still life with jug and oranges (46x41cm-18x16in) s.d.1918 i.verso. 10-Dec-2 Doyle, New York #150/R est:5000-7000
Works on paper
£1218 $1900 €1827 Untitled, houses by docks. Dunes in October (14x21cm-6x8in) s. one d.1936 one d.1943 chl tracing paper pair. 14-Oct-2 Butterfields, San Francisco #1031/R est:1200-1800
£6962 $11000 €10443 Abstract still life of bottles and fruit (48x38cm-19x15in) s.d.1944 W/C gouache. 26-Apr-3 Thomaston Place, Thomaston #549

LAZZERINI, Giuseppe (1831-1895) Italian
Sculpture
£25316 $40000 €37974 Young maiden threading a garland (127cm-50in) i. marble on pedestal. 24-Apr-3 Christie's, Rockefeller NY #295/R est:40000-60000

LE PHO (1907-2001) Vietnamese
£1250 $2000 €1875 Dans le jardin (64x41cm-25x16in) s. 11-Jan-3 Susanin's, Chicago #5015/R est:1500-2000
£1943 $3205 €2817 Flowers (118x70cm-46x28in) s. prov. 6-Jul-3 Christie's, Hong Kong #32/R est:22000-45000 (HK.D 25000)
£2051 $3200 €3077 Fleurs (64x46cm-25x18in) s. 22-Sep-2 Susanin's, Chicago #5006/R est:800-1200
£2800 $4312 €4200 Fleurs dans un vase (46x33cm-18x13in) s.i. 23-Oct-2 Sotheby's, Olympia #641/R est:2000-3000
£4662 $7692 €6760 Pivoines et iris (72x48cm-28x19in) s. silk on board painted c.1958 prov.exhib. 6-Jul-3 Christie's, Hong Kong #33/R est:60000-80000 (HK.D 60000)
£5200 $8008 €7800 Bouquet de fleurs (92x65cm-36x26in) s.i. 23-Oct-2 Sotheby's, Olympia #640/R est:4500-5500
£5385 $8293 €8078 La maternite - motherhood (32x23cm-13x9in) s. oil silk on board. 27-Oct-2 Christie's, Hong Kong #58/R est:40000-60000 (HK.D 65000)
£5385 $8293 €8078 Bouquet de fleurs - bouquet of flowers (81x54cm-32x21in) s. oil ink silk on panel painted c.1958. 27-Oct-2 Christie's, Hong Kong #59/R est:80000-100000 (HK.D 65000)
£6993 $11538 €10140 Bouquet jaune (105x76cm-41x30in) s. 6-Jul-3 Christie's, Hong Kong #36/R est:85000-100000 (HK.D 90000)
£9000 $13860 €13500 Nature morte aux fleurs et pommes (92x60cm-36x24in) s.i. silk on card. 23-Oct-2 Sotheby's, Olympia #642/R est:4500-5500
£9324 $15385 €13520 Mother and child (82x101cm-32x40in) s. 6-Jul-3 Christie's, Hong Kong #34/R est:80000-120000 (HK.D 120000)
£16352 $26000 €24528 Deux filles dans le jardin (114x147cm-45x58in) s. prov. 27-Feb-3 Christie's, Rockefeller NY #86/R est:18000
£24855 $38277 €37283 Lady in the garden (81x100cm-32x39in) s. 27-Oct-2 Christie's, Hong Kong #60/R est:65000-85000 (HK.D 300000)
£40000 $63600 €58000 Jeune femme assise sur une terrasse lissant une meche de cheveux (85x69cm-33x27in) s. polychrome silk. 5-Mar-3 Doutrebente, Paris #64/R est:20000-30000
£40404 $66667 €58586 Women and child in the garden (128x161cm-50x63in) s. 6-Jul-3 Christie's, Hong Kong #31/R est:280000-320000 (HK.D 520000)

LE THI LUU (1911-1988) Vietnamese
£3453 $5663 €4800 Femme et enfant (30x25cm-12x10in) s.d.59 lit. 6-Jun-3 Piasa, Paris #360/R est:6000-8000

LE-TAN, Pierre (1950-) French
Works on paper
£845 $1318 €1250 La rue (18x23cm-7x9in) init. W/C pen. 31-Mar-3 Pierre Berge, Paris #59/R

LEA, Frank (1904-) American
£2244 $3500 €3366 Woman applying lipstick watched by portrait of disapproving ancestor (61x66cm-24x26in) S. 9-Nov-2 Illustration House, New York #102/R est:3500-4500

LEA, Tom (1907-2001) American
£2244 $3500 €3366 Cross on hill (36x25cm-14x10in) board. 19-Oct-2 David Dike, Dallas #224a est:4000-8000
£9615 $15000 €14423 New country (66x76cm-26x30in) 19-Oct-2 David Dike, Dallas #219/R est:100000-150000
£10256 $16000 €15384 Indian woman (71x51cm-28x20in) board painted c.1928. 19-Oct-2 David Dike, Dallas #267/R est:20000-30000
Works on paper
£3045 $4750 €4568 Spanish soldier (51x51cm-20x20in) ink wash. 19-Oct-2 David Dike, Dallas #222/R est:4000-8000
£4808 $7500 €7212 Study for a lead steer (30x20cm-12x8in) s.d.1941 crayon. 29-Mar-3 Charlton Hall, Columbia #226/R est:8000-12000

LEACH, Bernard (1887-?) British
Works on paper
£450 $702 €675 Two figures sheltering under an umbrella under a rain cloud (8x8cm-3x3in) ink wash dr circular. 16-Oct-2 David Lay, Penzance #98/R
£520 $811 €780 Japanese figures planting rice and figure cutting bamboo (18x13cm-7x5in) init. ink wash dr. 16-Oct-2 David Lay, Penzance #96
£550 $858 €825 Two figures in a small boat on a lake (13x15cm-5x6in) init.d.35 ink dr. 16-Oct-2 David Lay, Penzance #97
£600 $936 €900 Eight chambered climbing Japanese kiln within a landscape (10x18cm-4x7in) i. ink wash dr. 16-Oct-2 David Lay, Penzance #99/R

LEACH-JONES, Alun (1937-) Australian
£2330 $3541 €3495 Celtic ritual (122x113cm-48x44in) s.d. s.i.d.verso prov.exhib. 28-Aug-2 Deutscher-Menzies, Melbourne #336/R est:3000-4000 (A.D 6500)
Sculpture
£1047 $1623 €1571 Untitled (33x17x11cm-13x7x4in) s.d.1993 black pat bronze prov. 3-Dec-2 Shapiro, Sydney #86/R est:2500-3500 (A.D 2900)
Works on paper
£1964 $3064 €2946 Instruments for a solitary navigator IV (122x137cm-48x54in) s.d.91 verso synthetic polymer paint canvas. 11-Nov-2 Deutscher-Menzies, Melbourne #35/R est:6000-8000 (A.D 5500)

LEADER, Benjamin Eastlake (?-1916) British
£500 $780 €750 Sand dunes. Heath land (20x28cm-8x11in) s. panel pair. 26-Mar-3 Hamptons Fine Art, Godalming #119
£540 $842 €810 West Country landscape (76x102cm-30x40in) init. 17-Sep-2 Sotheby's, Olympia #210/R
£1400 $2184 €2100 Newlyn harbour (30x41cm-12x16in) 17-Sep-2 Sotheby's, Olympia #207/R est:1000-1500

LEADER, Benjamin Williams (1831-1923) British
£650 $1014 €975 Flood on the Llugwy, N Wales (20x30cm-8x12in) s.d.1886 i.verso. 8-Apr-3 Bonhams, Knightsbridge #205/R
£650 $1060 €943 On the Llugwy, near Capel Curig (27x36cm-11x14in) s.d.1908 prov. 16-Jul-3 Sotheby's, Olympia #66/R
£800 $1272 €1200 In Spetchley Park, Worcestershire (20x24cm-8x9in) s. i.verso board. 6-Mar-3 Christie's, Kensington #481/R
£950 $1511 €1425 Llyn Llydaw with Snowden beyond (41x61cm-16x24in) s.i.d.1871 board. 30-Apr-3 Halls, Shrewsbury #310/R
£1000 $1560 €1500 On the Llugwy, N Wales (31x42cm-12x17in) s.d.1908 board. 17-Sep-2 Bonhams, Oxford #40/R est:1000-1200
£1000 $1550 €1500 Weir on a river (42x51cm-17x20in) s. panel. 25-Sep-2 Hamptons Fine Art, Godalming #374/R est:1500-2000
£1200 $1872 €1800 Figures and pine trees in an open landscape (25x20cm-10x8in) s.d.1907. 15-Oct-2 Gorringes, Lewes #2107/R
£1200 $1896 €1800 Cascading river in a wooded valley at sunset, near Betws Y Coed (25x20cm-10x8in) s. panel. 26-Nov-2 Bonhams, Oxford #73/R est:1200-1800
£1800 $2880 €2700 River landscape (35x46cm-14x18in) s. board. 13-May-3 Bonhams, Knightsbridge #102/R est:2000-3000
£2000 $2860 €3000 Evening on the Welsh borders (40x61cm-16x24in) s.d.1889. 28-Feb-2 Greenslade Hunt, Taunton #427/R est:1500-2500
£2000 $3260 €3000 Sand dunes (41x61cm-16x24in) s.d.1920. 29-Jan-3 Sotheby's, Olympia #112/R est:800-1200
£2177 $3461 €3200 Landscape from Ben Vorlich (23x35cm-9x14in) s.d.1858 exhib.prov. 27-Feb-3 Hagelstam, Helsinki #869 est:700
£2308 $3600 €3462 Village smithy (33x43cm-13x17in) s.d.1914. 30-Mar-3 Susanin's, Chicago #6051/R est:3000-5000
£2800 $4452 €4200 Bodiam Castle, Sussex (46x76cm-18x30in) s.d.1894 i.on stretcher prov. 6-Mar-3 Christie's, Kensington #479/R est:3000-5000
£2800 $4396 €4200 On the river Meavy, South Devon (35x45cm-14x18in) s.d.1877 s.i.verso board. 15-Apr-3 Bonhams, Knowle #137/R est:3000-5000
£2800 $4648 €4200 An estuary scene (20x35cm-8x14in) s.d.1895 indis sig.verso board. 10-Jun-3 Christie's, London #90/R est:3000-5000
£3000 $4920 €4500 Cattle watering, Derwentwater (51x76cm-20x30in) s.d.1868. 29-May-3 Christie's, Kensington #106/R est:4000-6000
£3500 $5810 €5250 On the Severn (26x41cm-10x16in) s.d.1895 i.verso board. 10-Jun-3 Christie's, London #91/R est:4000-6000
£3892 $6150 €5838 Farmer returning home (55x69cm-22x27in) s.d.1902. 15-Nov-2 Naón & Cia, Buenos Aires #114/R
£4573 $7500 €6631 Travellers resting by a river in a mountainous landscape (60x107cm-24x42in) s.d.1896. 4-Jun-3 Christie's, Rockefeller NY #252/R est:8000-12000
£6000 $9540 €9000 Quiet pool on the Llugwy, Wales (29x41cm-11x16in) init. board on panel. 6-Mar-3 Christie's, Kensington #480/R est:2500-3500
£8800 $13904 €13200 Morning - Ullswater (41x61cm-16x24in) s.d.1869 i.verso board. 13-Nov-2 Halls, Shrewsbury #422/R est:5000-7000
£9000 $14220 €13500 Far from the maddening crowd (51x76cm-20x30in) s.d.1877. 26-Nov-2 Christie's, London #117/R est:10000-15000
£10000 $15800 €15000 Hayfield, Whittington, Worcester (45x91cm-18x36in) s.d.1890 s.i.verso prov. 27-Nov-2 Deutscher-Menzies, Melbourne #265c/R est:20000-30000 (A.D 28000)
£13000 $20670 €19500 Haymaking, Whittingdon, Worcester (52x76cm-20x30in) s. 18-Mar-3 Bonhams, New Bond Street #95/R est:10000-15000
£14000 $22260 €21000 An old manor house (51x69cm-20x27in) s.d.1871 prov. 18-Mar-3 Bonhams, New Bond Street #94/R est:6000-8000
£17419 $27000 €26129 Sunshine after rain (82x123cm-32x48in) s. prov. 29-Oct-2 Sotheby's, New York #148/R est:30000-40000
£25000 $39500 €37500 Blue bells (36x46cm-14x18in) s.d.1858 i.d.verso board. 2-Dec-2 Sotheby's, London #6/R est:12000-18000
£25000 $39500 €37500 An old Worcestershire manor house (69x112cm-27x44in) s.d.1893 prov. 2-Dec-2 Sotheby's, London #9/R est:15000-20000

LEADER, Benjamin Williams (attrib) (1831-1923) British
Works on paper
£450 $752 €653 View of Sussex (36x53cm-14x21in) W/C. 20-Jun-3 Keys, Aylsham #501/R

LEADER, Charles (19th C) British
£400 $668 €580 Vale of llangollen, n Wales (40x61cm-16x24in) s. 24-Jun-3 Bonhams, Knowle #95
£540 $842 €810 Scottish loch and mountain landscape with cattle watering (48x74cm-19x29in) s. 11-Apr-3 Keys, Aylsham #690
£1100 $1716 €1650 On the river Severn at Kempsey, near Worcester (58x89cm-23x35in) s. 9-Oct-2 Andrew Hartley, Ilkley #721/R

LEAKE, John Travis (1810-1880) Australian
Works on paper
£1938 $3081 €2907 View on the Derwent. Hegley Flats. River landscape (12x21cm-5x8in) W/C prov. six. 5-May-3 Sotheby's, Melbourne #286/R est:1000-2000 (A.D 5000)

LEAKEY, James (1775-1865) British
£585 $900 €878 Portrait of a gentleman, seated holding a note (23x18cm-9x7in) s. panel prov. 4-Sep-2 Christie's, Rockefeller NY #229/R est:2000-3000
Miniatures
£4000 $6560 €5800 Lieutenant Colonel W George Collier in uniform (8cm-3in) gilt metal frame oval prov.exhib. 3-Jun-3 Christie's, London #176/R est:3000-5000

LEANDRE, Charles (1862-1930) French
Works on paper
£222 $350 €350 Portrait caricature de Francisque Sarcey (30x24cm-12x9in) crayon W/C. 28-Nov-2 Tajan, Paris #187
£2254 $3741 €3200 La lecture (44x57cm-17x22in) s.d. col crayon dr. 11-Jun-3 Beaussant & Lefèvre, Paris #92 est:250-300

LEAR, Edward (1812-1888) British
£52000 $80600 €78000 Parnassus ans lake Copais (33x54cm-13x21in) s.d.1856 i.d.verso prov. 2-Oct-2 Sotheby's, London #1/R est:25000-35000
£110000 $170500 €165000 Ioannina (65x129cm-26x51in) mono.d.1864 i.d.verso prov.exhib. 2-Oct-2 Sotheby's, London #5/R est:60000-80000

Works on paper

£420 $697 €609 San Marino (8x10cm-3x4in) i.d.May 8 1867 ink W/C. 12-Jun-3 Gorringes, Lewes #1632

£700 $1105 €1050 Birds of paradise (22x17cm-9x7in) s. pencil W/C htd gold. 28-Nov-2 Sotheby's, London #274/R

£700 $1105 €1050 Bird of paradise (17x22cm-7x9in) s. pencil W/C htd gold. 28-Nov-2 Sotheby's, London #275/R

£750 $1238 €1088 Aqueduct of Claudia, the Roman Campagna, Italy (17x42cm-7x17in) i. pen ink over pencil. 2-Jul-3 Sotheby's, Olympia #258/R

£1000 $1540 €1500 Figures in Eastern dress by a boat (16x25cm-6x10in) s.d.Oct 1837 pencil sold with another by the same hand. 22-Oct-2 Bonhams, Knightsbridge #42/R est:800-1200

£1000 $1550 €1500 Landscape with ruin on a hilltop (25x41cm-10x16in) d.16 May pen sepia ink over pencil. 30-Sep-2 Bonhams, Ipswich #306/R est:1000-1500

£1500 $2490 €2250 Italian landscape (24x37cm-9x15in) s.d.1840 pencil prov. 12-Jun-3 Bonhams, New Bond Street #615/R est:1200-1800

£1500 $2490 €2175 Konitza, Albania (13x18cm-5x7in) i.d.16 April 1857 ink W/C. 12-Jun-3 Gorringes, Lewes #1631 est:1500-2000

£1900 $3040 €2850 Mount Voltine from near Minervino (28x46cm-11x18in) i.d.Spet 22 1847. 11-Mar-3 Gorringes, Lewes #2285/R est:1500-2000

£1900 $3154 €2850 Near Ain Howara, Sinai Peninsula (20x40cm-8x16in) i.d.19 January 1849 pen ink. 12-Jun-3 Bonhams, New Bond Street #613/R est:1500-2000

£2300 $3588 €3450 Wady Wadan (8x23cm-3x9in) i.d.1899 W/C ink. 15-Oct-2 Gorringes, Lewes #2332/R est:1200-1800

£2600 $4056 €3900 Nice (23x34cm-9x13in) i.d.1865 W/C brown ink. 15-Oct-2 Bearnes, Exeter #355/R est:1000-1500

£3500 $5740 €5075 Saint Hospice, on the Riviera France (17x53cm-7x21in) i.d.1864 pencil ink W/C htd white prov. 5-Jun-3 Christie's, London #154/R est:3000-5000

£3800 $5928 €5700 Purple mountain Youder - mount Olympus, Thessaly, Greece (34x54cm-13x21in) i. pen ink wash over pencil. 15-Oct-2 Sotheby's, London #37/R est:2000-3000

£3800 $6232 €5510 Buon Ricovero, Rome (8x14cm-3x6in) s.i.d.1844 pen ink W/C. 5-Jun-3 Christie's, London #160/R est:3000-4000

£3800 $6232 €5510 Crescenza, Rome (8x14cm-3x6in) s.i.d.1844 pen ink W/C htd white. 5-Jun-3 Christie's, London #161/R est:3000-4000

£4800 $7872 €7200 Mount Oeta and Thermopylae from near Lamia (25x45cm-10x18in) i.d.26 June 1848 pencil pen ink W/C htd white prov. 6-Jun-3 Christie's, London #94/R est:4000-6000

£5000 $7850 €7500 Topolia, Crete (35x50cm-14x20in) i.d.28-29 April 1864 pencil pen ink W/C htd white. 21-Nov-2 Christie's, London #69/R est:3000-5000

£5600 $8848 €8400 Palaiokastritsa, Corfu (16x25cm-6x10in) s. W/C over pencil htd bodycol. 28-Nov-2 Sotheby's, London #330/R est:2000-3000

£6000 $9420 €9000 Zante, Greece (16x26cm-6x10in) mono. W/C htd bodycol prov. 21-Nov-2 Christie's, London #70/R est:5000-8000

£6000 $9840 €8700 Arkodyllus, Corfu (13x23cm-5x9in) i. pencil black chk ink W/C prov. 5-Jun-3 Christie's, London #153/R est:3000-5000

£7200 $11376 €10800 View of Florence from San Miniato (16x25cm-6x10in) s. W/C over pencil htd bodycol. 28-Nov-2 Sotheby's, London #329/R est:3000-5000

£7500 $10725 €11250 Edfu at sunset (15x23cm-6x9in) i.d.1854 pencil W/C prov.exhib.lit. 22-Jan-3 Christie's, London #70/R est:12000

£8000 $11440 €12000 Moonlit dhows on the Nile (10x20cm-4x8in) mono. pencil W/C htd white prov.exhib.lit. 22-Jan-3 Christie's, London #69/R est:8000

£9000 $12870 €13500 Pinetum at Ravenna (10x20cm-4x8in) mono.i.d.1884 pencil pen ink W/C gum prov.exhib.lit. 22-Jan-3 Christie's, London #68/R est:8000

£9000 $14760 €13050 Doge's Palace, Venice (29x48cm-11x19in) s.i.d.Nov 16 1865 pencil pen ink W/C. 5-Jun-3 Christie's, London #165/R est:5000-8000

£11000 $17270 €16500 Parnassus (48x70cm-19x28in) s.i.d.1851 pencil pen ink W/C bodycol prov.exhib. 21-Nov-2 Christie's, London #67/R est:12000-18000

£11000 $18040 €15950 View of Jerusalem (15x31cm-6x12in) mono.i.d.1865 pencil W/C squared for transfer prov. 5-Jun-3 Christie's, London #156/R est:12000-18000

£14000 $21980 €21000 Constantinople from Ayoub (27x45cm-11x18in) s.d.1850 pen brown ink W/C over pencil. 16-Dec-2 Sotheby's, London #73/R est:10000-15000

£15000 $24900 €22500 Dhows on the Nile at Gebel Sheikh Abou Fodde, Egypt (17x37cm-7x15in) mono.i. W/C over pencil htd bodycol prov. 12-Jun-3 Sotheby's, London #163/R est:4000-6000

£18000 $28260 €27000 Kasr-es said, Egypt (31x50cm-12x20in) i.d.28 Feb 1854 pencil pen ink W/C. 21-Nov-2 Christie's, London #66/R est:15000-25000

£22000 $34540 €33000 Grand Canal looking towards the Rialto Bridge, Venice (35x50cm-14x20in) i.d.13 November 1865 pen brown ink W/C over pencil prov. 16-Dec-2 Sotheby's, London #72/R est:10000-15000

£30000 $49200 €43500 Garf Hassan Rocks, Malta (16x25cm-6x10in) s.d.1866 pencil pen ink W/C htd white prov. 5-Jun-3 Christie's, London #155/R est:7000-10000

LEAR, Edward (attrib) (1812-1888) British

Works on paper

£550 $897 €825 My tall dark pines that plumed the craggy edge, Bavella, Corsica (35x55cm-14x22in) wash W/C. 29-Jan-3 Sotheby's, Olympia #51/R

£1250 $1950 €1875 Continental landscape with house and distant hills (22x33cm-9x13in) i. pen ink W/C. 26-Mar-3 Woolley & Wallis, Salisbury #16/R est:1200-1800

LEAR, John (20th C) American

Works on paper

£247 $400 €371 Rural landscape (28x43cm-11x17in) s. W/C. 24-Jan-3 Freeman, Philadelphia #121/R

£385 $600 €578 Shade (20x18cm-8x7in) s.i.verso ink W/C arched top. 20-Sep-2 Freeman, Philadelphia #24/R

£1451 $2250 €2177 Worker's circus (56x76cm-22x30in) s. W/C gouache. 29-Oct-2 Sotheby's, New York #271/R est:1500-2000

LEASON, Percival Alexander (1889-1959) Australian

Works on paper

£351 $533 €527 Unusual encounter (21x9cm-8x4in) s. W/C. 19-Aug-2 Joel, Victoria #227/R est:1000-1500 (A.D 1000)

LEAVER, Charles (19th C) British

£800 $1280 €1200 Near Lyndhurst, Hampshire (51x77cm-20x30in) 11-Mar-3 Bonhams, Knightsbridge #207/R

LEAVER, Noel Harry (1889-1951) British

Works on paper

£300 $465 €450 Watermill by a bridge in a wooded landscape (37x51cm-15x20in) s. pencil W/C htd bodycol. 4-Dec-2 Christie's, Kensington #20

£400 $608 €600 Tunisian street scene with figures (15x23cm-6x9in) s. W/C. 16-Aug-2 Keys, Aylsham #577

£400 $636 €600 Old Dutch village (18x27cm-7x11in) s. W/C. 5-Mar-3 Bonhams, Bury St Edmunds #324

£520 $811 €780 Mauresa, Spain (37x26cm-15x10in) s. W/C. 13-Sep-2 Lyon & Turnbull, Edinburgh #127/R

£750 $1185 €1125 Eastern street scene with mosque and figures (18x25cm-7x10in) s. 29-Nov-2 Dee Atkinson & Harrison, Driffield #870/R

£750 $1193 €1125 Figures on a bridge leading to a village (26x34cm-10x13in) s. W/C. 5-Mar-3 Bonhams, Bury St Edmunds #327/R

£850 $1318 €1275 After rain, Surrey Common (26x36cm-10x14in) s. W/C. 24-Sep-2 Anderson & Garland, Newcastle #358/R

£920 $1490 €1380 Erpingham Gate, Norwich (50x35cm-20x14in) s. W/C. 20-May-3 Sotheby's, Olympia #238/R

£950 $1511 €1425 Trading on the street (18x26cm-7x10in) s. bodycol. 29-Apr-3 Bonhams, Knightsbridge #1/R

£1000 $1550 €1500 City gateway (26x37cm-10x15in) s. W/C. 3-Dec-2 Sotheby's, Olympia #124/R est:1000-1500

£1000 $1550 €1500 Arab gateway (27x37cm-11x15in) s. W/C. 3-Dec-2 Sotheby's, Olympia #125/R est:1000-1500

£1000 $1620 €1500 Lincoln Cathedral (35x50cm-14x20in) s. W/C. 20-May-3 Sotheby's, Olympia #270/R est:1000-1500

£1020 $1581 €1530 Monks Bar, York (25x17cm-10x7in) s. W/C. 2-Oct-2 Bonhams, Knowle #46 est:400-600

£1024 $1700 €1485 Continental mountain landscape (46x56cm-18x22in) W/C prov. 11-Jun-3 Boos Gallery, Michigan #500/R est:3000-5000

£1050 $1628 €1575 Yorkshire Dales (26x36cm-10x14in) s. W/C. 24-Sep-2 Anderson & Garland, Newcastle #356/R est:400-600

£1200 $1908 €1800 Moorish gateway (26x36cm-10x14in) s. W/C. 5-Mar-3 Bonhams, Bury St Edmunds #323/R est:1200-1800

£1258 $2000 €1887 Piazza Bassano (35x26cm-14x10in) s. W/C. 7-Mar-3 Skinner, Boston #224/R est:1500-2000

£1300 $2015 €1950 Bolton Abbey, Yorkshire (26x36cm-10x14in) s. W/C. 24-Sep-2 Anderson & Garland, Newcastle #355/R est:600-900

£1300 $2028 €1950 Street in Morocco (27x36cm-11x14in) s. W/C. 10-Apr-3 Bonhams, Edinburgh #104/R est:1000-1500

£1300 $2067 €1950 Extensive rural landscape (18x25cm-7x10in) s. W/C. 29-Apr-3 Henry Adams, Chichester #226 est:300-500

£1400 $2184 €2100 Approach to a mosque, Algiers (28x38cm-11x15in) s. i.verso pencil W/C htd bodycol. 17-Oct-2 Christie's, Kensington #117/R est:700-1000

£1400 $2198 €2100 High bridge, Knaresborough (28x37cm-11x15in) s.i. W/C. 21-Nov-2 Tennants, Leyburn #632 est:600-800

£1450 $2248 €2175 Blarney Castle, Ireland (26x36cm-10x14in) s. W/C. 24-Sep-2 Anderson & Garland, Newcastle #357/R est:600-900
£1500 $2460 €2175 Horse Guards by moonlight (25x37cm-10x15in) s. W/C prov. 1-Jun-3 Lots Road, London #331/R est:800-1200
£1600 $2480 €2400 Spires of Lichfield (44x27cm-17x11in) s. W/C. 2-Nov-2 Shapes, Edinburgh #303/R est:400-600
£1800 $2826 €2700 Eastern street scene with figures beside buildings and mosques nearby (35x51cm-14x20in) s. pencil W/C. 19-Nov-2 Bonhams, Leeds #38/R est:2000-3000
£1800 $2826 €2700 Figures beside an eastern gateway (35x51cm-14x20in) s. pencil W/C. 19-Nov-2 Bonhams, Leeds #39/R est:2000-3000
£1900 $2983 €2850 Moroccan mosque (25x35cm-10x14in) s. W/C. 19-Nov-2 James Thompson, Kirby Lonsdale #100
£2000 $3040 €3000 Eastern market (36x50cm-14x20in) s. pencil W/C htd white. 4-Jul-2 Mellors & Kirk, Nottingham #798/R est:2000-3000
£2000 $3040 €3000 Ancient Tunis (36x50cm-14x20in) s. pencil W/C htd white. 4-Jul-2 Mellors & Kirk, Nottingham #799/R est:2000-3000
£2000 $3140 €3000 Lincoln cathedral (35x51cm-14x20in) s. pencil W/C. 19-Nov-2 Bonhams, Leeds #37/R est:2000-2500
£2100 $3339 €3150 Boats at anchor, Peel Harbour, Isle of Man (24x34cm-9x13in) s. W/C. 5-Mar-3 Bonhams, Bury St Edmunds #328/R est:800-1200
£2484 $4000 €3726 Tombs of the Caliphs, Cairo. Temples of the Benares. Tobacco fields, Turkey (38x28cm-15x11in) s. pencil W/C board three. 19-Feb-3 Doyle, New York #15/R est:4000-6000
£2500 $3925 €3750 Whitby (25x36cm-10x14in) s. pencil W/C. 19-Nov-2 Bonhams, Leeds #35/R est:2500-3000
£2600 $4056 €3900 Algerian mosque (37x26cm-15x10in) s. W/C. 13-Sep-2 Lyon & Turnbull, Edinburgh #14/R est:500-800
£2700 $4374 €3915 An Algerian Mosque (14x20cm-6x8in) s. i.verso W/C. 29-Jul-3 Capes Dunn, Manchester #26/R
£2900 $4756 €4350 Street scene in Northern France. Spanish archway (37x27cm-15x11in) s. W/C pair. 4-Jun-3 Bonhams, Chester #330/R est:2000-3000
£2970 $4750 €4455 Chateau, Menthon, St Bernard. Old bridge, Chartres (44x28cm-17x11in) s. i.verso pencil W/C board pair. 14-May-3 Butterfields, San Francisco #1177/R est:2500-3500

LEAVITT, Edward C (1842-1904) American

£2065 $3200 €3098 Cluster of grapes with leaves (51x61cm-20x24in) s. lit. 2-Nov-2 North East Auctions, Portsmouth #56/R
£3822 $6000 €5733 Still life with fruit and a silver compote (51x76cm-20x30in) s.d.1893. 22-Nov-2 Skinner, Boston #103/R est:1500-3000

LEBADANG (1922-) French/Vietnamese

£1442 $2250 €2163 Untitled (95x74cm-37x29in) s. 14-Oct-2 Butterfields, San Francisco #2037/R est:3000-5000

LEBAS, Gabriel-Hippolyte (1812-1880) French

Works on paper

£270 $422 €400 Bord de riviere (12x14cm-5x6in) s. W/C prov. 26-Mar-3 Rieunier, Paris #34
£475 $750 €750 Paysage au crepuscule (28x45cm-11x18in) s. W/C gouache. 28-Nov-2 Tajan, Paris #180
£567 $948 €800 Deux releves d'architecture a Caprarola (48x28cm-19x11in) s. 23-Jun-3 Beaussant & Lefèvre, Paris #295/R
£696 $1100 €1100 Figures sur des rochers au bord de la mer (27x18cm-11x7in) s. W/C htd gouache. 28-Nov-2 Tajan, Paris #155/R

LEBASQUE, Henri (1865-1937) French

£1013 $1570 €1600 Etude de nus. Etude femme (33x43cm-13x17in) s. paper double-sided. 27-Sep-2 Rabourdin & Choppin de Janvry, Paris #48 est:1500-1600
£5473 $8538 €8100 Bord de Seine (14x21cm-6x8in) s. s.verso cardboard on canvas. 28-Mar-3 Neret-Minet, Paris #7/R
£11000 $17050 €16500 Madame Lebasque et sa fille Martha au promenade, Montevrain (36x26cm-14x10in) panel. 5-Dec-2 Christie's, Kensington #54/R est:6000-8000
£11000 $17490 €16500 Femme et enfants a la campagne (35x26cm-14x10in) s. painted c.1912-13. 20-Mar-3 Sotheby's, Olympia #51/R est:7000-9000
£11801 $19000 €17702 Mere et enfant devant la portail (30x23cm-12x9in) s.i. verso panel painted c.1912 prov. 7-May-3 Sotheby's, New York #399/R est:15000-20000
£12000 $18960 €18000 Nature morte aux peches (46x55cm-18x22in) s. 3-Apr-3 Christie's, Kensington #46/R
£12252 $19970 €18500 Les baigneurs (33x41cm-13x16in) s. prov. 2-Feb-3 Muizon & Le Coent, Paris #50
£12422 $20000 €18633 Baigneurs a Saint Tropez (33x41cm-13x16in) s. painted c.1925-30 exhib. 7-May-3 Sotheby's, New York #380/R est:20000-25000
£12975 $20241 €20500 Baignarde a Saint Jean de Mont (33x54cm-13x21in) s. canvas on board prov. 31-Jul-2 Tajan, Paris #37/R est:15000-18000
£13000 $21710 €18850 La rue pavoisee (38x46cm-15x18in) s. 25-Jun-3 Christie's, London #130/R est:8000-12000
£13878 $21789 €21650 Voiliers sur la Marne (24x31cm-9x12in) s. paper lit. 11-Dec-2 Artcurial Briest, Paris #512/R
£15385 $24000 €23078 Baignade a Saint Jean de Mont (33x55cm-13x22in) s. canvas on card prov. 6-Nov-2 Sotheby's, New York #333/R est:30000-40000
£16026 $25160 €25000 Bouquet de fleurs dans un interieur (60x70cm-24x28in) s. 13-Dec-2 Piasa, Paris #17/R est:30000
£19231 $30000 €28847 Vase de dalhias avec livre sur la table (65x55cm-26x22in) s. prov. 7-Nov-2 Christie's, Rockefeller NY #265/R est:30000-40000
£19231 $30000 €28847 Portrait de Marthe Lebasque (53x36cm-21x14in) s.d.1917 prov. 7-Nov-2 Christie's, Rockefeller NY #266/R est:40000-60000
£20915 $34301 €32000 Jeune femme au jardin dans le fauteuil vert (55x46cm-22x18in) s.d.1910. 9-Feb-3 Anaf, Lyon #151/R est:40000
£23077 $38538 €33000 La lecon de piano (46x33cm-18x13in) s. i.indis.d.1911 verso. 27-Jun-3 Claude Aguttes, Neuilly #96/R est:30000-40000
£24476 $40874 €35000 Femme a sa coiffure dans un fauteuil (55x46cm-22x18in) s. lit. 30-Jun-3 Artcurial Briest, Paris #72/R est:30000-40000
£27244 $42500 €40866 La robe rose (49x61cm-19x24in) s. prov. 6-Nov-2 Sotheby's, New York #172/R est:35000-45000
£29814 $48000 €44721 Bouquet de fleurs sur la cheminee (60x65cm-24x26in) s. painted c.1920 exhib. 8-May-3 Christie's, Rockefeller NY #203/R est:30000-40000
£34839 $55046 €54000 Nu au miroir (49x44cm-19x17in) s. prov. 18-Dec-2 Tajan, Paris #65/R est:30000
£35000 $57400 €52500 Parc Monceau (26x35cm-10x14in) s. panel painted c.1900 prov. 4-Feb-3 Christie's, London #235/R est:35000
£35000 $57400 €52500 Nono au chapeau rose (56x46cm-22x18in) st.sig. 4-Feb-3 Christie's, London #291/R est:40000
£36538 $56635 €57000 Nu sur la plage (65x54cm-26x21in) s. paper on canvas prov. 9-Dec-2 Beaussant & Lefèvre, Paris #68/R est:45000
£38000 $63460 €55100 Village au bord de la riviere (51x74cm-20x29in) s. prov. 24-Jun-3 Sotheby's, London #138/R est:40000-50000
£38462 $60000 €57693 L'enfant au bonnet ou la curiosite (50x61cm-20x24in) s. painted c.1913-14 prov. 6-Nov-2 Sotheby's, New York #154/R est:40000-60000
£42000 $68880 €63000 Parc de Saint-Cloud (26x35cm-10x14in) s. panel painted c.1900 prov. 4-Feb-3 Christie's, London #232/R est:30000
£45000 $75150 €65250 Femme assise dans un paysage (50x61cm-20x24in) s. prov.lit. 25-Jun-3 Christie's, London #115/R est:18000-24000
£50000 $82000 €75000 Deux fillettes dans un paysage (60x81cm-24x32in) s. painted c.1907 prov. 5-Feb-3 Sotheby's, London #229/R est:70000
£74534 $120000 €111801 La terrasse au Pradet (55x65cm-22x26in) s. painted c.1923 prov.exhib.lit. 7-May-3 Sotheby's, New York #161/R est:100000-150000
£76129 $120284 €118000 Femme nue allongee (73x100cm-29x39in) s. 18-Dec-2 Ferri, Paris #85/R est:100000
£83916 $140140 €120000 Nu sur une peau de panthere (60x92cm-24x36in) s. lit. 30-Jun-3 Artcurial Briest, Paris #81a/R est:120000-150000
£105590 $170000 €158385 Madame lebasque et sa fille au bord de la marne (73x116cm-29x46in) s. painted c.1899 prov. 8-May-3 Christie's, Rockefeller NY #162/R est:150000-200000
£109028 $172264 €157000 Sainte-Maxime, lecture au jardin (65x81cm-26x32in) s. lit. 23-Apr-3 Rabourdin & Choppin de Janvry, Paris #32/R

Works on paper

£379 $634 €550 Nu au sofa (27x23cm-11x9in) s.i. graphite dr paper on cardboard. 10-Jul-3 Artcurial Briest, Paris #29
£420 $701 €600 L'entree du village (10x12cm-4x5in) s. W/C black crayon. 26-Jun-3 Tajan, Paris #148/R
£451 $718 €650 Petite fille au chapeau de soleil (33x15cm-13x6in) s. Indian ink wash dr. 29-Apr-3 Artcurial Briest, Paris #8
£513 $795 €800 Standing female nude (32x14cm-13x6in) s. lit. 6-Dec-2 Karlheinz Kaupp, Staufen #2379
£539 $900 €782 Sleeping nude (14x19cm-6x7in) s. W/C over pencil. 22-Jun-3 Freeman, Philadelphia #57/R
£539 $900 €782 Seated lady (20x51cm-8x20in) s. W/C over pencil. 22-Jun-3 Freeman, Philadelphia #59/R
£597 $950 €896 Nue (37x27cm-15x11in) s. pencil paper on board. 27-Feb-3 Christie's, Rockefeller NY #50/R
£646 $1028 €950 Les roches rouges. Femme dans un paysage (31x46cm-12x18in) st.sig. W/C pencil graphite double-sided. 26-Feb-3 Artcurial Briest, Paris #28
£896 $1497 €1300 Nu assis au peignoir rouge et vert (28x21cm-11x8in) s. W/C pencil. 10-Jul-3 Artcurial Briest, Paris #30/R est:1200-1500
£1000 $1550 €1500 Les baigneuses (26x20cm-10x8in) s. pencil W/C. 5-Dec-2 Christie's, Kensington #55/R est:1000-1500
£1006 $1600 €1509 Vue en village (28x39cm-11x15in) s. W/C pencil. 27-Feb-3 Christie's, Rockefeller NY #64/R
£1111 $1766 €1600 Le cannet, jeune fille lisant sur un banc (24x22cm-9x9in) s. W/C pencil. 29-Apr-3 Artcurial Briest, Paris #14/R est:1800-2500
£1119 $1868 €1600 Femme et enfant sur la plage (10x17cm-4x7in) bears sig. W/C. 26-Jun-3 Tajan, Paris #147/R est:700-800
£1259 $2102 €1800 Sur la plage (17x23cm-7x9in) bears sig. W/C. 26-Jun-3 Tajan, Paris #144/R est:2000-3000
£1351 $2108 €2000 Paysage de Provence (20x28cm-8x11in) s. W/C. 25-Mar-3 Chochon-Barre & Allardi, Paris #154 est:2000-2200
£1389 $2209 €2000 Enfant a la plage (12x21cm-5x8in) s. W/C pencil. 29-Apr-3 Artcurial Briest, Paris #11/R est:2500-3500
£1399 $2336 €2000 Nus debout (26x19cm-10x7in) s. pencil W/C prov. 26-Jun-3 Tajan, Paris #145/R est:2000-2200

£1447 $2242 €2300 Femme a la guirlande (56x42cm-22x17in) s. gouache ink exec.c.1913 prov.lit. 30-Oct-2 Artcurial Briest, Paris #210/R est:2500-3500
£1500 $2310 €2250 Nu allonge (25x34cm-10x13in) s. W/C pencil. 23-Oct-2 Sotheby's, Olympia #661/R est:1800-2500
£1728 $2454 €2800 Jeune garcon au cerf volant (24x16cm-9x6in) s. W/C prov. 16-Mar-3 Eric Pillon, Calais #124/R
£2069 $3310 €3000 Femme allongee jouant avec son collier (38x53cm-15x21in) s. W/C gouache. 12-Mar-3 Libert, Castor, Paris #133 est:1800-2500
£2357 $3676 €3700 Voiliers au soleil couchant (23x31cm-9x12in) s. W/C. 7-Nov-2 Claude Aguttes, Neuilly #59/R est:3000-4000
£2837 $4596 €4000 Scene de plage (26x20cm-10x8in) s. W/C graphite. 21-May-3 Cornette de St.Cyr, Paris #17/R est:3000-4000
£4645 $7339 €7200 Jeune femme au hamac (38x50cm-15x20in) s. W/C. 19-Dec-2 Bondu, Paris #13/R
£5245 $8759 €7500 Champ dans le midi (27x31cm-11x12in) s. W/C gouache. 26-Jun-3 Tajan, Paris #143/R est:7500-10500
£7453 $12000 €11180 Dans le jardin (23x37cm-9x15in) s. W/C pencil paper on card prov. 7-May-3 Sotheby's, New York #388/R est:8000-12000
£16000 $26720 €24000 Femme a la mandoline. Femme lisant dans un jardin. L'eglise Sainte-Catherine (24x21cm-9x8in) s. W/C chl exec c.1923-25 three prov. 26-Jun-3 Christie's, London #375/R est:8000-12000

LEBDUSKA, Lawrence (1894-1966) American
£286 $450 €429 Two white cranes in a wheatfield (39x30cm-15x12in) s.d.64 panel. 14-Dec-2 Weschler, Washington #728/R

LEBEDEV, Vladimir V (1891-1967) Russian
£17000 $26690 €25500 Portrait of the artist's wife (55x47cm-22x19in) init.d.43. 20-Nov-2 Sotheby's, London #128/R est:20000-30000
Works on paper
£565 $876 €848 Couple bourgeois (30x26cm-12x10in) ink pochoir W/C exec.c.1925 prov. 7-Dec-2 Galerie du Rhone, Sion #143/R (S.FR 1300)
£609 $943 €914 Le fardeau (29x28cm-11x11in) ink pochoir W/C exec.c.1925 prov. 7-Dec-2 Galerie du Rhone, Sion #145/R (S.FR 1400)
£609 $943 €914 Piano-bar (27x17cm-11x7in) ink pochoir W/C exec.c.1925 prov. 7-Dec-2 Galerie du Rhone, Sion #147/R (S.FR 1400)
£670 $1066 €1005 Revolution's animal (32x22cm-13x9in) mono. pastel. 10-Mar-3 Rasmussen, Vejle #702 (D.KR 7200)
£696 $1078 €1044 Remontrances (30x26cm-12x10in) ink pochoir W/C exec.c.1925 prov. 7-Dec-2 Galerie du Rhone, Sion #148/R (S.FR 1600)
£739 $1146 €1109 Les amoureux (27x23cm-11x9in) ink pochoir W/C exec.c.1925pr. 7-Dec-2 Galerie du Rhone, Sion #146/R (S.FR 1700)
£957 $1483 €1436 Couple (28x24cm-11x9in) ink pochoir W/C exec.c.1925 prov. 7-Dec-2 Galerie du Rhone, Sion #142/R est:700-900 (S.FR 2200)
£1130 $1752 €1695 Joueur de balalaika (33x24cm-13x9in) ink pochor W/C exec.c.1925 prov. 7-Dec-2 Galerie du Rhone, Sion #144/R est:700-900 (S.FR 2600)
£1268 $2104 €1800 Figural compositions (22x17cm-9x7in) pen stamps three. 14-Jun-3 Hauswedell & Nolte, Hamburg #1341/R est:1500

LEBEDEV, Vladimir V (attrib) (1891-1967) Russian
Works on paper
£949 $1500 €1500 Landscape with man and sickle (42x29cm-17x11in) indis.mono. gouache. 29-Nov-2 Bolland & Marotz, Bremen #888/R est:1600

LEBEDJEV, Klawdij (1852-1916) Russian
£45000 $72900 €67500 Princess and the fool (40x32cm-16x13in) s.d.1892. 21-May-3 Sotheby's, London #41/R est:5000-7000
Works on paper
£1400 $2268 €2100 Ancient Rus (40x32cm-16x13in) s.d. W/C. 21-May-3 Sotheby's, London #38/R est:1200-1800

LEBEL, Jean Jacques (1936-) French
£5479 $8603 €8000 Iceberg de poche (42x24cm-17x9in) s.i.d.1955 panel prov.exhib. 15-Apr-3 Laurence Calmels, Paris #4335/R est:2000

LEBENSTEIN, Jan (1930-1999) Polish/French
£2837 $4738 €4000 Deux figures (81x65cm-32x26in) s.d. 18-Jun-3 Charbonneaux, Paris #96/R est:3000-4000
£7447 $12436 €10500 Figure totemique (180x65cm-71x26in) s. 18-Jun-3 Charbonneaux, Paris #95 est:6000-8000
£8511 $14213 €12000 Figure masque (180x67cm-71x26in) s.d. 18-Jun-3 Charbonneaux, Paris #94/R est:8000-10000
Works on paper
£1156 $1839 €1700 Personnage (56x27cm-22x11in) ink wash W/C. 26-Feb-3 Artcurial Briest, Paris #533 est:1000-1200
£2518 $4029 €3500 Untitled (100x50cm-39x20in) mixed media panel. 18-May-3 Charbonneaux, Paris #166b

LEBLANC, Julien (19th C) French
£680 $1082 €1000 Piqueux et chevaux en main (19x24cm-7x9in) s.d.1872. 24-Mar-3 Fraysse & Associes, Paris #50/R

LEBLANC, Lee (1913-1983) American
£1519 $2400 €2279 Through the birch - mallards (61x81cm-24x32in) s. prov. 3-Apr-3 Christie's, Rockefeller NY #209/R est:2000-3000
£3896 $6000 €5844 Wood duck (56x76cm-22x30in) 25-Oct-2 Morris & Whiteside, Hilton Head Island #66 est:5000-7000

LEBLANC, Walter (1932-1986) Belgian
£1528 $2414 €2200 Guitare (47x56cm-19x22in) cardboard. 28-Apr-3 Amberes, Antwerp #299
£4167 $6625 €6000 Bateaux (94x126cm-37x50in) s.d.1954 panel lit. 29-Apr-3 Campo & Campo, Antwerp #177/R est:5000-7500
Works on paper
£764 $1215 €1100 Bateaux (37x27cm-15x11in) s.d.1955 mixed media lit. 29-Apr-3 Campo & Campo, Antwerp #178/R
£1449 $2377 €2000 Torsions PF 0 27 (28x28cm-11x11in) s.i. verso polyvinyl prov.exhib. 28-May-3 Lempertz, Koln #246/R est:2000

LEBON, Charles (1906-1957) Belgian
£277 $429 €440 Demeure de Lupke (45x38cm-18x15in) s.1924 s.i.verso board. 5-Oct-2 De Vuyst, Lokeren #211
£694 $1104 €1000 Le domaine (70x94cm-28x37in) s. 29-Apr-3 Campo, Vlaamse Kaai #187/R
£1006 $1560 €1600 Evening (75x150cm-30x59in) s.d.1927. 5-Oct-2 De Vuyst, Lokeren #210 est:1700-2000

LEBON, Léon G (1846-?) Belgian
£1087 $1783 €1500 Abres pres de l'etang (40x57cm-16x22in) s. 27-May-3 Campo & Campo, Antwerp #122 est:1250-1350

LEBOURG, Albert (1849-1928) French
£1000 $1580 €1500 Cheminee (16x22cm-6x9in) studio st. panel. 3-Apr-3 Christie's, Kensington #41/R
£1008 $1593 €1512 Fishing boats at sunset (13x23cm-5x9in) s. panel prov. 18-Nov-2 Waddingtons, Toronto #236/R est:3000-5000 (C.D 2500)
£1026 $1559 €1600 Pecheur et son chien a quai (21x30cm-8x12in) panel lit. 16-Aug-2 Deauville, France #131/R
£1026 $1590 €1600 November day on the banks of the Seine, Paris (20x28cm-8x11in) s. board lit. 6-Dec-2 Karlheinz Kaupp, Staufen #2252 est:2000
£1154 $1754 €1800 Soleil couchant a Chaloux Moulineux (21x30cm-8x12in) s. panel lit. 16-Aug-2 Deauville, France #130/R
£1965 $3105 €2948 Seine landscape with ships (23x40cm-9x16in) s. 14-Nov-2 Stuker, Bern #357 est:8000-12000 (S.FR 4500)
£1965 $3105 €2948 Seine landscape (27x41cm-11x16in) s. 14-Nov-2 Stuker, Bern #358 est:8000-12000 (S.FR 4500)
£2826 $4409 €4239 Paris - view of Pont Mari (23x33cm-9x13in) s. panel prov. 16-Sep-2 Philippe Schuler, Zurich #3485/R est:6000-8000 (S.FR 6500)
£2838 $4485 €4257 Seine shore with bridge (38x55cm-15x22in) s. 14-Nov-2 Stuker, Bern #359/R est:8000-12000 (S.FR 6500)
£3275 $5175 €4913 Seine by the Louvre (40x32cm-16x13in) s. 14-Nov-2 Stuker, Bern #354/R est:10000-15000 (S.FR 7500)
£4487 $7090 €7000 Le village de Montfort-sur-Risle (46x56cm-18x22in) s. prov.lit. 18-Nov-2 Tajan, Paris #139/R est:7500-9000
£5000 $7600 €7800 Paris, l'Ecluse de la Monnaie et le Pont-Neuf (38x61cm-15x24in) s. prov. 16-Aug-2 Deauville, France #112/R est:12000
£5190 $8044 €8200 Champs apres la moisson (35x65cm-14x26in) s. lit. 29-Sep-2 Eric Pillon, Calais #176/R
£5660 $9000 €8490 Pont Boieldieu, Rouen (49x65cm-19x26in) s. 27-Feb-3 Christie's, Rockefeller NY #12/R
£6962 $10861 €11000 Bateau-dragueur sur la Seine (51x73cm-20x29in) s. 18-Oct-2 Rabourdin & Choppin de Janvry, Paris #30/R est:8000
£7042 $11690 €10000 Rouen (50x73cm-20x29in) s.i. 11-Jun-3 Beaussant & Lefèvre, Paris #90/R est:12000-15000
£7097 $11000 €10646 Les bords du lac de Geneve a Saint-Gingolph, en hiver (61x80cm-24x31in) s. prov.exhib.lit. 26-Sep-2 Christie's, Rockefeller NY #518/R est:15000-20000
£7693 $12847 €11000 Vue de la Seine (33x55cm-13x22in) s. prov. 26-Jun-3 Tajan, Paris #242/R est:9000-12000
£8544 $13244 €13500 Bord de riviere a l'automne (46x61cm-18x24in) s. 29-Sep-2 Eric Pillon, Calais #147/R
£8633 $14158 €12000 Paris, les quais de Bercy, peniches a quai, hiver (40x65cm-16x26in) s. 5-Jun-3 Fraysse & Associes, Paris #17/R est:10000-12000
£9000 $13860 €13500 Le viex pont de sevres (31x47cm-12x19in) s.d.1877 prov.lit. 22-Oct-2 Sotheby's, London #111/R est:8000-12000
£9091 $15182 €13000 Paysage (35x65cm-14x26in) s. prov. 26-Jun-3 Tajan, Paris #240/R est:18000-20000
£9500 $15580 €14250 La Seine a POrt-Marly (50x73cm-20x29in) s. lit. 5-Feb-3 Sotheby's, London #120/R
£10791 $17266 €15000 Peniche et barque sur la riviere (46x62cm-18x24in) s. 18-May-3 Eric Pillon, Calais #39/R
£12000 $19680 €18000 Valle de la Seine en aval de Paris (46x65cm-18x26in) s.d.1895 prov. 5-Feb-3 Sotheby's, London #119/R est:18000
£12500 $19500 €18500 Dieppe, les falaises (40x65cm-16x26in) s.i. 25-Mar-3 Chochon-Barre & Allardi, Paris #155/R est:19000-20000
£13000 $20670 €19500 Ornans (50x65cm-20x26in) s.i.d.1899 exhib. 20-Mar-3 Sotheby's, Olympia #36/R est:8000-12000

£13514 $21081 €20000 La Seine a Rouen (46x75cm-18x30in) s.i.d.1916 prov.lit. 26-Mar-3 Millon & Associes, Paris #69/R
£15385 $23846 €24000 Bac a la Bouille (61x86cm-24x34in) s.i.d.1907 exhib. 9-Dec-2 Beaussant & Lefèvre, Paris #72/R est:25000
£16000 $26240 €24000 Embouchure de la Seine (47x73cm-19x29in) s.d.1893 lit. 4-Feb-3 Christie's, London #209/R
£16561 $25834 €26000 Bords du lac de Geneve sous la neige (61x80cm-24x31in) s. lit. 10-Nov-2 Eric Pillon, Calais #52/R

Prints

£10432 $16691 €14500 Rouen, le pont Boildieu (49x65cm-19x26in) s. 18-May-3 Eric Pillon, Calais #28/R

Works on paper

£321 $503 €500 Bateaux a quai (19x30cm-7x12in) s.d.70 ink dr. 11-Dec-2 Maigret, Paris #106
£392 $611 €580 Riviere au pont et aux arbres (33x48cm-13x19in) s. black ink wash. 31-Mar-3 Rossini, Paris #53
£541 $843 €800 Barques a la bouille (14x23cm-6x9in) s. W/C. 26-Mar-3 Millon & Associes, Paris #28/R
£566 $883 €900 L'arc de triomphe du Caroussel (12x19cm-5x7in) s. chl. 10-Oct-2 Ribeyre & Baron, Paris #39
£673 $1023 €1050 Vue de Dieppe (30x45cm-12x18in) s.i.d.1872 verso chl dr. 16-Aug-2 Deauville, France #32/R
£705 $1072 €1100 Attelage (20x29cm-8x11in) s. chl dr prov. 16-Aug-2 Deauville, France #33/R
£764 $1192 €1200 Chemin anime aux environs de Rouen (51x35cm-20x14in) s. W/C. 11-Nov-2 Horta, Bruxelles #662
£833 $1267 €1300 Poules a Hondouville (31x21cm-12x8in) init.i. W/C. 16-Aug-2 Deauville, France #19/R
£1026 $1559 €1600 Paysage en bord de Seine (23x14cm-9x6in) studio st. W/C double-sided. 16-Aug-2 Deauville, France #23/R
£1154 $1812 €1800 View of Rouen (39x60cm-15x24in) s. graphite dr. 15-Dec-2 Lombrail & Teucquam, Paris #9/R
£1859 $2919 €2900 Pont des Invalides (28x44cm-11x17in) s. sepia ink wash prov. 21-Nov-2 Neret-Minet, Paris #25/R

LEBOURG, Charles Auguste (1829-1906) French

Sculpture

£1500 $2445 €2250 Dancing bagpiper (44cm-17in) s. reddish brown pat. bronze. 13-Feb-3 Mellors & Kirk, Nottingham #890/R est:1000-1400

LEBRET, Frans (1820-1909) Dutch

£1321 $2100 €1982 In the pasture (23x32cm-9x13in) s. panel. 7-Mar-3 Skinner, Boston #234/R est:1000-1500
£2900 $4640 €4350 Watering place (81x99cm-32x39in) s.d.1860. 13-May-3 Bonhams, Knightsbridge #99/R est:3000-5000
£4500 $7065 €6750 Sheep in a meadow (71x60cm-28x24in) s. 21-Nov-2 Christie's, Kensington #107/R est:2500-3500

LEBRUN, Charles (attrib) (1619-1690) French

£6115 $10029 €8500 Portrait de l'architecte Charles Perrault (11x8cm-4x3in) copper. 5-Jun-3 Fraysse & Associes, Paris #8/R est:1500-2000

LEBRUN, Christopher (1951-) British

£3000 $5010 €4350 Clearing (266x254cm-105x100in) lit. 24-Jun-3 Sotheby's, Olympia #114/R est:3000-4000
£5500 $8470 €8250 Untitled (212x151cm-83x59in) s.d.28.2.1982 verso prov. 22-Oct-2 Sotheby's, London #452/R est:6000-8000
£5800 $9512 €8700 Garden Hook II (180x110cm-71x43in) s. i.d.88 and 14.6.89 verso prov. 7-Feb-3 Sotheby's, London #279/R est:4000-6000

LEBRUN, Henriette Perrard (19th C) French

£577 $894 €900 Portrait assis (73x92cm-29x36in) s. 8-Dec-2 Feletin, Province #111

LEBRUN, Marcel (19/20th C) French?

£7643 $12000 €11465 Walk on Sunday (65x100cm-26x39in) s.d.1897. 21-Nov-2 Sotheby's, New York #228/R est:15000-20000

LEBRUN, Rico (1900-1964) American/Italian

£385 $600 €578 Seated female nude (58x53cm-23x21in) s. panel. 1-Aug-2 Eldred, East Dennis #112/R

LEBSCHE, Karl-August (1800-1877) Polish

£915 $1474 €1300 People walking in idealised landscape (52x64cm-20x25in) mono.d.1875 lit. 9-May-3 Schloss Ahlden, Ahlden #1401/R

Works on paper

£462 $674 €720 Village with church (21x29cm-8x11in) s.i.d.1866 W/C pen over pencil. 4-Jun-2 Karl & Faber, Munich #104

LEBZELTER, Martin (circle) (1492-1520) Swiss

Sculpture

£19500 $30420 €29250 Mourning Virgin (98cm-39in) polychrome wood exec.c.1500-1510 prov.exhib.lit. 9-Apr-3 Sotheby's, London #11/R est:12000-18000

LECHNER, Ferdinand (1855-?) German

Works on paper

£253 $392 €400 Italian Alps (52x74cm-20x29in) s. i. verso gouache. 25-Sep-2 Neumeister, Munich #418/R

LECK, Bart van der (1876-1958) Dutch

£107914 $176978 €150000 Girl playing the flute with goat (70x100cm-28x39in) init. painted c.1944-45 prov.exhib.lit. 3-Jun-3 Christie's, Amsterdam #249/R est:150000-200000
£126582 $200000 €200000 Olifant (32x38cm-13x15in) init.d.24 prov.exhib.lit. 26-Nov-2 Sotheby's, Amsterdam #112/R est:150000-250000

Works on paper

£1410 $2186 €2200 Arums in a glass jar (49x45cm-19x18in) pen ink sketch executed c.1927 prov. 3-Dec-2 Christie's, Amsterdam #9/R est:2500-3500
£4367 $6856 €6551 Untitled (19x19cm-7x7in) W/C gouache prov.exhib. 23-Nov-2 Burkhard, Luzern #44/R est:6000-8000 (S.FR 10000)

LECLAIRE, Victor (1830-1885) French

£4054 $6324 €6000 Roseraie devant le chateau (130x188cm-51x74in) s. 28-Mar-3 Delvaux, Paris #5/R est:8000

LECLERC, Sebastien (elder) (1637-1714) French

Works on paper

£1361 $2164 €2000 Cene (18x23cm-7x9in) sanguine wash gouache over crayon. 24-Mar-3 Tajan, Paris #80/R

LECLERC, Sebastien (elder-attrib) (1637-1714) French

Works on paper

£696 $1100 €1100 Destruction d'une ville antique avec des personnages dansant (19x35cm-7x14in) black chk pen ink grey wash. 27-Nov-2 Christie's, Paris #143/R

LECLERCQ, F (19th C) French

Sculpture

£2848 $4443 €4500 Winged putti (45cm-18in) s.d.1780 verso white marble. 19-Oct-2 Semenzato, Venice #224/R

LECLERCQ, Victor (1896-1944) Belgian

£411 $641 €600 Impression au Pays Noir (60x68cm-24x27in) s. 14-Apr-3 Horta, Bruxelles #393

LECLERE, Theodore (19th C) French

£480 $749 €720 Still life with fruit, green jug and basket (32x46cm-13x18in) s.d.1887. 20-Nov-2 Fischer, Luzern #2170/R (S.FR 1100)

LECOMTE DU NOUY, Jean Jules Antoine (1842-1923) French

£355 $592 €500 Tete de jeune homme, d'apres un maitre Italien (13x9cm-5x4in) s. 23-Jun-3 Beaussant & Lefèvre, Paris #120
£355 $592 €500 Etude pour un portrait de femme (35x29cm-14x11in) s. 23-Jun-3 Beaussant & Lefèvre, Paris #127
£567 $948 €800 Tete de Christ (33x24cm-13x9in) s. 23-Jun-3 Beaussant & Lefèvre, Paris #122
£5745 $9594 €8100 Vue de Paris sous la neige (30x44cm-12x17in) s. i.d.1871 verso. 23-Jun-3 Beaussant & Lefèvre, Paris #119/R est:300-500

Works on paper

£1014 $1581 €1500 Vues de la Corne d'Or (11x19cm-4x7in) s.i. gouache pair. 28-Mar-3 Claude Aguttes, Neuilly #117/R

LECOMTE DU NOUY, Jean Jules Antoine (after) (1842-1923) French

Sculpture

£4221 $6500 €6332 Semi draped maiden seated by a cistern (43cm-17in) i. silvered bronze. 28-Oct-2 Butterfields, San Francisco #3180/R est:4000-6000

LECOMTE DU NOUY, Jean Jules Antoine (attrib) (1842-1923) French

£709 $1184 €1000 Egypte, route de Choubra au Caire (15x45cm-6x18in) i.d.1865 verso. 23-Jun-3 Beaussant & Lefèvre, Paris #137/R
£709 $1184 €1000 France, le Mont-Pilat et les trois dents vus de Malleval, Loire (21x31cm-8x12in) i.verso. 23-Jun-3 Beaussant & Lefèvre, Paris #138
£851 $1421 €1200 Venise, vue prise des jardins publics (13x32cm-5x13in) i.d.1873 verso. 23-Jun-3 Beaussant & Lefèvre, Paris #133

£1064 $1777 €1500 Egypte, vue de Choubra, pres du Caire (15x41cm-6x16in) i.d.1865 verso. 23-Jun-3 Beaussant & Lefèvre, Paris #134/R est:200-300
£1064 $1777 €1500 Egypte, vue du sphinx et des pyramides (16x29cm-6x11in) i.d.1865 verso. 23-Jun-3 Beaussant & Lefèvre, Paris #135/R est:300-400
£1064 $1777 €1500 France, la Grande Place, Malleval, Loire (22x30cm-9x12in) 23-Jun-3 Beaussant & Lefèvre, Paris #139 est:200-300
£1064 $1777 €1500 Venise, quartier de San Giovanni et Paolo (27x18cm-11x7in) i.d.1873 verso. 23-Jun-3 Beaussant & Lefèvre, Paris #143 est:300-400
£1773 $2961 €2500 France, les Alpes et le Dauphines vus du Mont-Pelat, Loire (21x31cm-8x12in) i.verso. 23-Jun-3 Beaussant & Lefèvre, Paris #136 est:200-300
£1773 $2961 €2500 Egypte, vue des pyramides de Gizeh (13x28cm-5x11in) i.verso. 23-Jun-3 Beaussant & Lefèvre, Paris #141 est:300-400
£1844 $3079 €2600 Mont du Fleschhorn, Simplon (15x34cm-6x13in) i.d.1872 verso. 23-Jun-3 Beaussant & Lefèvre, Paris #144 est:200-300
£1986 $3316 €2800 Venise, l'eglise San Giovanni et Paolo (27x11cm-11x4in) i.d.1873 verso. 23-Jun-3 Beaussant & Lefèvre, Paris #140 est:300-400
£1986 $3316 €2800 France, vue de Malleval, Loire (28x22cm-11x9in) i.d.1870 verso. 23-Jun-3 Beaussant & Lefèvre, Paris #142 est:200-300

LECOMTE, Émile (1866-1938) Belgian
£641 $994 €1000 Source a Nivelles (100x80cm-39x31in) s. 9-Dec-2 Horta, Bruxelles #371
£705 $1093 €1100 Cloitre (51x71cm-20x28in) s. 9-Dec-2 Horta, Bruxelles #370
£863 $1381 €1200 Baigneuses (67x70cm-26x28in) s. 13-May-3 Vanderkindere, Brussels #97
£897 $1409 €1400 Woodland stream in summer (39x55cm-15x22in) s. 21-Nov-2 Van Ham, Cologne #1742

LECOMTE, Hippolyte (attrib) (1781-1857) French
£1321 $2034 €2100 Campement de la grand armee en Espagne (49x61cm-19x24in) 25-Oct-2 Tajan, Paris #147 est:1200-1500

LECOMTE, Paul (1842-1920) French
£494 $701 €800 Charrette attelee (47x60cm-19x24in) s. 16-Mar-3 Eric Pillon, Calais #96/R
£962 $1519 €1500 Arbres et rocher au bord de la mer (38x61cm-15x24in) s. 18-Nov-2 Sotheby's, Paris #77/R
£962 $1519 €1500 Barriere de Kerlagadic (38x55cm-15x22in) s. 18-Nov-2 Sotheby's, Paris #80/R
£962 $1519 €1500 Port Sauzon (32x46cm-13x18in) bears sig. 18-Nov-2 Sotheby's, Paris #85/R
£976 $1600 €1464 Vue d'un Navire sur la plage (31x46cm-12x18in) s. 5-Feb-3 Christie's, Rockefeller NY #210/R est:1000-1500
£1026 $1621 €1600 Barque echouee (38x55cm-15x22in) s. 18-Nov-2 Sotheby's, Paris #79/R
£1026 $1621 €1600 Arbre et trou (32x46cm-13x18in) s. 18-Nov-2 Sotheby's, Paris #84/R
£1282 $2026 €2000 Bord de mer a Concarneau (38x55cm-15x22in) s. 18-Nov-2 Sotheby's, Paris #76/R
£1316 $2132 €2000 Paysage vallonne avec personages aupres d'un Lac (37x59cm-15x23in) s. 21-Jan-3 Christie's, Amsterdam #94/R est:2000-3000
£1410 $2228 €2200 Carriole sur route (37x55cm-15x22in) s. 18-Nov-2 Sotheby's, Paris #75/R
£1410 $2228 €2200 Paris, quai de Bercy (29x40cm-11x16in) bears sig. 18-Nov-2 Sotheby's, Paris #88/R
£1538 $2431 €2400 View of Saint-Malo (25x40cm-10x16in) s. 18-Nov-2 Sotheby's, Paris #87/R
£1603 $2532 €2500 Pont a Mannetout-sur-Cher (38x55cm-15x22in) s. cardboard. 18-Nov-2 Sotheby's, Paris #74/R
£1603 $2532 €2500 Pont-Neuf a Paris (32x52cm-13x20in) bears sig. 18-Nov-2 Sotheby's, Paris #86/R
£1667 $2633 €2600 Deux femmes assises sur la plage (27x35cm-11x14in) bears s ig. cardboard. 18-Nov-2 Sotheby's, Paris #83/R
£1795 $2836 €2800 Au bord de la mer (26x34cm-10x13in) s. 18-Nov-2 Sotheby's, Paris #82/R
£1795 $2836 €2800 Promenade au bord de la mer (34x64cm-13x25in) s. 18-Nov-2 Sotheby's, Paris #89/R
Works on paper
£372 $580 €550 Kerlagaden, la ferme Sainte Anne (26x37cm-10x15in) s. W/C. 31-Mar-3 Rossini, Paris #21
£574 $896 €850 Fresnay-sur-Sarthe (21x28cm-8x11in) s. W/C. 31-Mar-3 Rossini, Paris #20/R
£577 $894 €900 Paysanne dans un paysage d'automne (36x54cm-14x21in) s. W/C over crayon. 4-Dec-2 Piasa, Paris #168
£641 $994 €1000 Rue de village (29x23cm-11x9in) s. W/C over crayon. 4-Dec-2 Piasa, Paris #167/R

LECOMTE, Paul Émile (1877-1950) French
£393 $621 €590 Small river landscape (16x21cm-6x8in) s. panel. 14-Nov-2 Stuker, Bern #362 (S.FR 900)
£764 $1245 €1100 Paysage a l'arbre mort (46x38cm-18x15in) s. panel. 19-Jul-3 Thierry & Lannon, Brest #142
£1058 $1608 €1650 Patio (46x37cm-18x15in) s. panel. 16-Aug-2 Deauville, France #132/R
£1203 $1900 €1900 Petit canal a Venise (24x27cm-9x11in) s. panel. 27-Nov-2 Blanchet, Paris #17/R
£1389 $2264 €2000 Ile d'Yeu (33x41cm-13x16in) s. panel. 19-Jul-3 Thierry & Lannon, Brest #141/R est:1100-1200
£1549 $2494 €2200 Paysage mediterraneen (38x46cm-15x18in) s. 11-May-3 Thierry & Lannon, Brest #194/R est:2300-2500
£2244 $3522 €3500 Moulin en bord de riviere (70x140cm-28x55in) s. 15-Dec-2 Eric Pillon, Calais #98/R
£2423 $3610 €3635 French market (65x54cm-26x21in) s. prov. 25-Jun-2 Koller, Zurich #6650 est:600-800 (S.FR 5500)
£3354 $5500 €4863 Farm along river (61x81cm-24x32in) s. 4-Jun-3 Doyle, New York #68 est:2000-3000
Works on paper
£545 $828 €850 Bord de mer (28x38cm-11x15in) s. W/C. 16-Aug-2 Deauville, France #64/R
£705 $1072 €1100 Jardin en Afrique du Nord (28x39cm-11x15in) s. W/C. 16-Aug-2 Deauville, France #62/R
£833 $1267 €1300 Maison du pecheur (50x61cm-20x24in) s. W/C. 16-Aug-2 Deauville, France #63/R

LECOMTE-VERNET, Charles Émile (1821-1900) French
£383 $543 €620 Nu au rocher. 17-Mar-2 Galerie de Chartres, Chartres #117
£32258 $50000 €48387 Tambourine player (116x77cm-46x30in) s.d.1868 prov.exhib. 30-Oct-2 Christie's, Rockefeller NY #81/R est:60000-80000

LECOQUE, Alois (1891-1981) Czechoslovakian
£353 $550 €530 Paris (30x41cm-12x16in) s.d.75 s.i.d.verso board. 5-Nov-2 Arthur James, Florida #179
£2258 $3500 €3387 Terase palma Mallorca (46x61cm-18x24in) s. i.verso. 26-Sep-2 Christie's, Rockefeller NY #586/R est:2000-4000

LECOR, Paul Tex (1930-) Canadian
£460 $717 €690 Premiere place, Lac Mistassimi (35x46cm-14x18in) s. i.d.83 verso. 30-Jul-2 Iegor de Saint Hippolyte, Montreal #85 (C.D 1140)
£609 $950 €1015 Village Greenville (61x76cm-24x30in) s. i.d.1981 verso. 13-Apr-3 Levis, Calgary #74/R est:1500-2000 (C.D 1400)
£782 $1212 €1173 Figures in a tavern (92x65cm-36x26in) s. board. 3-Dec-2 Joyner, Toronto #464 est:1000-1500 (C.D 1900)

LECOSSOIS, Victor (1897-1976) Belgian
£340 $541 €500 Gasthof de Vink (50x60cm-20x24in) s. 18-Mar-3 Campo, Vlaamse Kaai #130

LECOURT, Raymond (1882-1946) French
£387 $624 €550 Le peintre a son chevalet (33x46cm-13x18in) s. panel. 12-May-3 Lesieur & Le Bars, Le Havre #56
£680 $1082 €1000 Peasant ploughing (80x117cm-31x46in) s.d.23 aout 1901. 28-Mar-3 Bolland & Marotz, Bremen #484a
£775 $1247 €1100 Les paturages (33x41cm-13x16in) s.d.1920. 12-May-3 Lesieur & Le Bars, Le Havre #55/R
£1477 $2377 €2200 Scene de labours (37x61cm-15x24in) s. panel. 23-Feb-3 Lesieur & Le Bars, Le Havre #86
£1549 $2494 €2200 Les labours (52x71cm-20x28in) s. 12-May-3 Lesieur & Le Bars, Le Havre #54
£1972 $3175 €2800 Gardienne de vaches pres de la mare (80x116cm-31x46in) s.d.1913. 12-May-3 Lesieur & Le Bars, Le Havre #53/R

LECOURTIER, Prosper (1855-1924) French
Sculpture
£1280 $2100 €1856 La fantasia Arabe (89x76x25cm-35x30x10in) with sig. bronze. 7-Jun-3 Neal Auction Company, New Orleans #74/R est:2500-3500
£1400 $2184 €2100 Lion on a rocky outcrop (30x25x140cm-12x10x55in) s.d.1898 num.64 green pat bronze. 9-Apr-3 Sotheby's, London #117/R est:1500-2000
£3656 $5814 €5484 La fantasia arabe (82x74cm-32x29in) s. pat.bronze gun missing. 25-Feb-3 Rasmussen, Copenhagen #863/R est:40000 (D.KR 40000)

LECOURTIER, Prosper (attrib) (1855-1924) French
Sculpture
£962 $1500 €1443 Grey hounds (38x38cm-15x15in) s. bronze. 22-Sep-2 Susanin's, Chicago #5050/R est:2000-4000

LECURIEUX (fl.1555-1581) French
Works on paper
£37037 $60000 €55556 Portrait of bearded man wearing slashed doublet (33x22cm-13x9in) black red chk. 22-Jan-3 Christie's, Rockefeller NY #58/R est:20000-30000

LEDELI, Moritz (1856-1920) Czechoslovakian
Works on paper
£314 $487 €500 Coach and horses on avenue (22x39cm-9x15in) s. w/C. 1-Oct-2 Dorotheum, Vienna #267/R
£377 $585 €600 Card players and horse-drawn carriage (30x45cm-12x18in) s. Indian ink W/C. 1-Oct-2 Dorotheum, Vienna #334/R

LEDERLE, Karl (20th C) German
Works on paper
£570 $900 €900 Winter's day in the Black Forest (96x67cm-38x26in) s.d.1920 W/C. 29-Nov-2 Schloss Ahlden, Ahlden #1294/R

LEDOUX, Jeanne Philiberte (attrib) (1767-1840) French
£2600 $4056 €3900 Portrait of a young girl (48x41cm-19x16in) panel oval. 9-Apr-3 Bonhams, New Bond Street #40/R est:3000-5000
Miniatures
£1200 $1872 €1800 Gentleman wearing dark grey coat brown waistcoat with black trim (6cm-2in circular) gold frame glazed reverse. 5-Nov-2 Bonhams, New Bond Street #43/R est:1200-1500

LEDRAY, Charles (1960-) American
Sculpture
£3226 $5000 €4839 Spiral stairs (21x13x18cm-8x5x7in) s.d.97 velveteen covered wood metal two elements. 26-Sep-2 Christie's, Rockefeller NY #870/R est:5000-7000

LEDUC, Arthur Jacques (1848-1918) French
Sculpture
£961 $1519 €1500 Deux chiens de chasse (42x22x36cm-17x9x14in) s. bronze Cast Thiebault. 18-Nov-2 Tajan, Paris #80 est:1500-1800
£4400 $6996 €6600 After the chores (54x64cm-21x25in) s.d. bronze st.f. 29-Apr-3 Sotheby's, Olympia #141/R est:4000-6000

LEDUC, Charles (1831-1911) French
£3000 $4860 €4500 French regatta with racing cutter approaching the finishing line (58x84cm-23x33in) s.anchor device. 21-May-3 Christie's, Kensington #489/R est:2000-3000

LEDUC, Charles (attrib) (1831-1911) French
£4600 $7452 €6900 S.S. Cognac (43x73cm-17x29in) s. 21-Jan-3 Bonhams, New Bond Street #223/R est:1000-1500

LEDUC, Fernand (1916-) Canadian
£1895 $2994 €2843 Untitled (90x71cm-35x28in) s.d.69 prov. 18-Nov-2 Sotheby's, Toronto #177/R est:5000-8000 (C.D 4700)

LEDUC, Ozias (1864-1955) Canadian
Works on paper
£206 $321 €309 Study of a Saint (22x15cm-9x6in) s. graphite. 25-Mar-3 Ritchie, Toronto #147/R (C.D 480)
£278 $456 €417 Crucifixion (23x19cm-9x7in) s. pencil prov. 6-Feb-3 Heffel, Vancouver #031/R (C.D 700)
£343 $536 €515 Study of St. Joseph (14x7cm-6x3in) init. i.verso graphite. 25-Mar-3 Ritchie, Toronto #148/R (C.D 800)

LEDUC, Paul (1876-1943) Belgian
£481 $755 €750 Paysage (25x34cm-10x13in) s. i.verso. 19-Nov-2 Vanderkindere, Brussels #102
£540 $863 €750 Vase de chrysanthemes (106x53cm-42x21in) s.d.1898. 13-May-3 Vanderkindere, Brussels #95
£1373 $2210 €2100 Le porche de l'Abbaye de Furnes (45x60cm-18x24in) s. 14-Jan-3 Vanderkindere, Brussels #21/R est:1500-2500
£2041 $3245 €3000 Pont sur la Semois (34x45cm-13x18in) s.d.1930 panel. 18-Mar-3 Galerie Moderne, Brussels #524/R est:3000-4000
£2329 $3633 €3400 Vue de Cap Martin (34x40cm-13x16in) s. canvas on panel. 14-Apr-3 Horta, Bruxelles #84/R est:3500-4500
£2590 $4144 €3600 La Chapelle de la Bonne Mere at St-Tropez (45x60cm-18x24in) s.d.1939 verso. 13-May-3 Vanderkindere, Brussels #80/R est:2500-3500
£2675 $4173 €4200 Soir a Sospel, France (80x60cm-31x24in) s. 11-Nov-2 Horta, Bruxelles #171/R est:5000-7500
£3526 $5465 €5500 Traversee du village sous le neige (70x80cm-28x31in) s.d.1917. 9-Dec-2 Horta, Bruxelles #163/R est:6000-8000
£4795 $7479 €7000 Saint Tropez (37x45cm-15x18in) s. 14-Apr-3 Horta, Bruxelles #83/R est:6000-8000
£5031 $7799 €8000 Venice canal (80x60cm-31x24in) s. s.i.verso. 5-Oct-2 De Vuyst, Lokeren #547/R est:8500-10000
£12179 $18878 €19000 Vue a Martigues (60x80cm-24x31in) s. 7-Dec-2 De Vuyst, Lokeren #455/R est:15000-17000

LEE FOONG (19th C) Chinese
£6908 $10500 €10362 American ship, Vancouver (64x97cm-25x38in) i.verso. 17-Aug-2 North East Auctions, Portsmouth #962/R est:9000-15000

LEE MAN FONG (1913-1988) Chinese
£18648 $30769 €27040 Two buffaloes by the river with a boy resting under a tree (113x51cm-44x20in) s. board. 6-Jul-3 Christie's, Hong Kong #55/R est:100000-200000 (HK.D 240000)
£24087 $39744 €34926 Fruit seller (96x70cm-38x28in) s.d.1955. 6-Jul-3 Christie's, Hong Kong #57/R est:130000-180000 (HK.D 310000)
£26418 $43590 €38306 Two rabbits (410x50cm-161x20in) s. board. 6-Jul-3 Christie's, Hong Kong #56/R est:100000-200000 (HK.D 340000)

LEE, Bertha Stringer (1873-1937) American
£2410 $4000 €3495 Monterey Bay, Pacific Grove (56x71cm-22x28in) s. board. 11-Jun-3 Butterfields, San Francisco #4214/R est:3000-5000

LEE, Dick (1923-2001) British
£1950 $3218 €2828 Peach tree at Ingleville. Garden at Ingleville (183x153cm-72x60in) s. pair. 1-Jul-3 Bonhams, Norwich #357/R est:2000-3000

LEE, Doris (1905-1983) American
£4268 $7000 €6189 Strawberry pickers (43x66cm-17x26in) prov.lit. 1-Jun-3 Wright, Chicago #221/R est:6000-8000

LEE, Frederick Richard (1798-1879) British
£650 $1060 €975 The valley (25x36cm-10x14in) s.verso board. 29-Jan-3 Sotheby's, Olympia #31/R
£850 $1292 €1275 Figures resting before farm buildings in landscape (48x66cm-19x26in) s.d.1856. 16-Aug-2 Keys, Aylsham #619/R
£1161 $1800 €1742 Landscape with man and child fishing (46x61cm-18x24in) s. 28-Sep-2 Charlton Hall, Columbia #534/R est:1000-1500
£1548 $2400 €2322 Figures overlooking a river (46x61cm-18x24in) s. 28-Sep-2 Charlton Hall, Columbia #533/R est:1000-1500
£2000 $3180 €3000 Figure by a river in a wooded river landscape (76x91cm-30x36in) prov. 6-Mar-3 Christie's, Kensington #438/R est:2000-3000
£7500 $11625 €11250 Scottish wooded river landscape with anglers on the rocks (70x91cm-28x36in) s.d.1862 prov. 31-Oct-2 Christie's, London #16/R est:5000-8000
£14000 $23240 €21000 Sketch of the new bridge built by Lord Lynedoch. Saw mill. Swiss Bridge. Angler on a bridge (25x35cm-10x14in) s.d.1838 board set of four. 10-Jun-3 Christie's, London #67/R est:15000-20000

LEE, Frederick Richard and COOPER, Thomas Sidney (19th C) British
£943 $1472 €1500 River landscape with trees (54x64cm-21x25in) s. 19-Sep-2 Dr Fritz Nagel, Stuttgart #962/R est:2500

LEE, George (fl.1923-1933) British
£360 $587 €540 Truro Cathedral (55x70cm-22x28in) s. 17-Feb-3 Bonhams, Bath #202

LEE, Laura (1867-1954) American
Works on paper
£779 $1200 €1169 Haystacks (15x23cm-6x9in) s.d.1904 W/C. 27-Oct-2 Grogan, Boston #80 est:300-500

LEE, Lindy (1954-) Australian
£2786 $4290 €4179 Philanthropic encounter with posterity (194x150cm-76x59in) s.d.1993 verso oil wax on linen. 8-Sep-2 Sotheby's, Melbourne #33/R est:8000-12000 (A.D 7800)

LEE, Nikki S (1970-) American
Photographs
£2500 $4000 €3750 Punk project (55x72cm-22x28in) s.i.d.1997 num. fugiflex print mounted on foamcore prov.exhib.lit. 14-May-3 Sotheby's, New York #330/R est:4000-6000
£2690 $4250 €4035 Hispanic project (102x76cm-40x30in) fujiflex print exec.1998 one of 3 prov.exhib.lit. 13-Nov-2 Sotheby's, New York #428/R est:4000-6000

LEE, Phillip (19/20th C) Australian
£464 $720 €696 Landscape with blue mountains (30x45cm-12x18in) s. board. 29-Oct-2 Lawson Menzies, Sydney #22/R (A.D 1300)
£1214 $1882 €1821 Coogee beach (26x40cm-10x16in) s.d.1891 board. 29-Oct-2 Lawson Menzies, Sydney #54/R est:1500-2000 (A.D 3400)

LEE, Russell (1903-1986) American
Photographs
£1899 $3000 €2849 Soda fountain, Corpus Christi, Texas (25x33cm-10x13in) s.num.163 verso gelatin silver print prov. 25-Apr-3 Phillips, New York #86/R est:2000-3000
£3671 $5800 €5507 Storage tanks at refinery, Texas (25x33cm-10x13in) s.verso gelatin silver print prov. 25-Apr-3 Phillips, New York #139/R est:2000-3000

LEE, Terry (1935-) British
£500 $820 €750 Summer flowers in a glass vase on a garden table (81x71cm-32x28in) s.d.90. 5-Jun-3 Christie's, Kensington #786/R
£570 $935 €855 Flower study (86x75cm-34x30in) s.d.89. 5-Jun-3 Christie's, Kensington #785/R

LEE-HANKEY, W (1869-1952) British
Works on paper
£325 $527 €488 River landscape (19x31cm-7x12in) s. W/C. 21-May-3 James Thompson, Kirby Lonsdale #109

LEE-HANKEY, William (1869-1952) British
£1511 $2508 €2191 Woman and child by the harbour, St Tropez (23x30cm-9x12in) s. panel. 16-Jun-3 Waddingtons, Toronto #146/R est:3000-4000 (C.D 3400)
£1700 $2771 €2550 Portrait of a young lady in 1930's dress (91x71cm-36x28in) s. 28-Jan-3 Gorringes, Lewes #1601/R est:2000-3000
£1793 $2761 €2690 Interior scene with woman seated holding baby (35x30cm-14x12in) s. panel. 27-Oct-2 Anders Antik, Landskrona #167/R est:25000-30000 (S.KR 26000)
£1956 $3246 €2836 Boats in a harbour, St. Tropez (23x30cm-9x12in) s. panel. 16-Jun-3 Waddingtons, Toronto #145/R est:3000-4000 (C.D 4400)
£2800 $4340 €4200 White roads of Sussex (52x61cm-20x24in) s. s.i.on overlap prov. 3-Dec-2 Bonhams, New Bond Street #20/R est:3000-5000
£3556 $5902 €5156 St. Ives, Cornwall (30x36cm-12x14in) s. 16-Jun-3 Waddingtons, Toronto #154/R est:4000-6000 (C.D 8000)
£3797 $6000 €5696 Crockery stall (64x76cm-25x30in) s. 3-Apr-3 Boos Gallery, Michigan #228/R est:8000-10000
£4000 $6280 €6000 Mentone from the sea wall (30x35cm-12x14in) s. s.i. on overlap prov. 22-Nov-2 Christie's, London #18/R est:5000-8000
£6000 $9420 €9000 Ferry, Concarneau (51x61cm-20x24in) s. s.i.on overlap prov. 22-Nov-2 Christie's, London #20/R est:7000-10000
£6500 $10075 €9750 Low tide, Concarneau (61x75cm-24x30in) s. prov. 3-Nov-2 Lots Road, London #345/R est:5000-7000
£8000 $12560 €12000 Boats in a harbour, Cornwall (63x76cm-25x30in) s. prov. 22-Nov-2 Christie's, London #19/R est:8000-12000
£8000 $12560 €12000 Mill in the meadows (63x76cm-25x30in) s. prov. 22-Nov-2 Christie's, London #81/R est:10000-15000
£45000 $71100 €67500 Goose girl (170x114cm-67x45in) s. 27-Nov-2 Christie's, London #28/R est:40000-60000
Works on paper
£300 $465 €450 St. Ives Harbour (20x30cm-8x12in) s. W/C. 3-Dec-2 Bonhams, Knightsbridge #204/R
£380 $593 €570 On the Schveldt (30x34cm-12x13in) s. W/C pencil. 26-Mar-3 Woolley & Wallis, Salisbury #45/R
£500 $780 €750 Parisian street scene (22x27cm-9x11in) s.i.d.1949 pencil W/C htd white over pencil. 7-Nov-2 Bonhams, Cornwall #780
£550 $858 €825 By the docks (25x35cm-10x14in) s. W/C. 15-Oct-2 Bonhams, Knightsbridge #131/R
£900 $1404 €1350 La place nationale, Dieppe (26x35cm-10x14in) s.i.d.1947 W/C. 15-Oct-2 Bonhams, Knightsbridge #220/R
£1000 $1670 €1450 Village market (34x24cm-13x9in) s. W/C. 17-Jun-3 Bonhams, Knightsbridge #129/R est:1000-1500
£1300 $2002 €1950 French fishing village (25x38cm-10x15in) s.d.1900 W/C. 23-Oct-2 Hamptons Fine Art, Godalming #43/R est:500-700
£1400 $2128 €2100 Alms houses, Bruges (36x25cm-14x10in) s. W/C. 14-Aug-2 Andrew Hartley, Ilkley #605/R est:500-800
£1400 $2184 €2100 At the table (35x45cm-14x18in) s. W/C. 25-Mar-3 Bonhams, New Bond Street #5/R est:1500-2000
£1600 $2640 €2320 Tea time (26x36cm-10x14in) s.i. pencil W/C. 3-Jul-3 Christie's, Kensington #254/R est:1500-2000
£1778 $2951 €2578 Young girl with baby in a wheelbarrow by river (13x10cm-5x4in) mono. W/C. 16-Jun-3 Waddingtons, Toronto #98/R est:4000-5000 (C.D 4000)

LEE-JOHNSON, Eric (1908-1993) New Zealander
£1562 $2437 €2343 Maori motif (29cm-11in circular) wood prov. after photograph by Theo Schoon. 8-Apr-3 Peter Webb, Auckland #20/R est:2000-3000 (NZ.D 4500)
Works on paper
£351 $547 €527 Cottage at Mahurangi (32x28cm-13x11in) s.d.1957 W/C ink. 27-Mar-3 International Art Centre, Auckland #153/R (NZ.D 1000)
£707 $1138 €1061 Northland cottage (38x56cm-15x22in) s.d.68. 7-May-3 Dunbar Sloane, Auckland #52/R (NZ.D 2000)
£2432 $3793 €3648 Tiki and manaia (50x56cm-20x22in) s.d.1947 W/C. 17-Sep-2 Peter Webb, Auckland #125/R est:12000-18000 (NZ.D 8000)

LEE-SMITH, Hughie (1915-1999) American
£701 $1100 €1052 Desolate landscape (41x51cm-16x20in) 13-Dec-2 Du Mouchelle, Detroit #2112/R est:500-700
£949 $1500 €1424 Sunrise over Lake Erie (30x41cm-12x16in) s. 3-Apr-3 Boos Gallery, Michigan #265/R est:3000-5000
£2031 $3250 €3047 Figure on seashore (11x15cm-4x6in) masonite. 14-Mar-3 Du Mouchelle, Detroit #2116/R est:2500-3000
Works on paper
£1000 $1600 €1500 Couple by sea (8x19cm-3x7in) W/C. 14-Mar-3 Du Mouchelle, Detroit #2115/R est:500-1000

LEEB-LUNDBERG, Gustav Leo Valdemar (1880-1927) Swedish
£502 $833 €728 Female nude (65x44cm-26x17in) 16-Jun-3 Lilla Bukowskis, Stockholm #151 (S.KR 6500)

LEECH, William John (1881-1968) Irish
£5000 $7750 €7500 Fossils (25x36cm-10x14in) s. board. 2-Oct-2 John Ross, Belfast #157 est:6000-7000
£15000 $24000 €22500 Street in Concarneau (17x22cm-7x9in) s. canvas on board. 16-May-3 Sotheby's, London #59/R est:10000-15000
£16000 $25600 €24000 Little boats, Nice (19x24cm-7x9in) s. s.i.verso board. 16-May-3 Sotheby's, London #68/R est:8000-12000
£19231 $29808 €30000 Peasant girl, Concarneau (43x35cm-17x14in) s. i.verso. 3-Dec-2 Bonhams & James Adam, Dublin #34/R est:15000-18000
£28986 $47536 €40000 Farm yard (33x50cm-13x20in) s. board prov. 28-May-3 Bonhams & James Adam, Dublin #128/R est:30000-40000
£44872 $70449 €70000 Margurites (46x38cm-18x15in) s. prov. 19-Nov-2 Whyte's, Dublin #58/R est:35000-45000
£76923 $119231 €120000 Boats moored under a bridge (60x73cm-24x29in) s. prov. 3-Dec-2 Bonhams & James Adam, Dublin #71/R est:80000-120000
Works on paper
£5137 $8065 €7500 Artist in his studio (56x40cm-22x16in) s. W/C. 15-Apr-3 De Veres Art Auctions, Dublin #213/R est:8000-12000
£12658 $19620 €20000 Portrait of Elizabeth (53x36cm-21x14in) s. W/C prov.exhib. 24-Sep-2 De Veres Art Auctions, Dublin #35/R est:20000-30000

LEEKE, Ferdinand (1859-1923) German
£510 $795 €800 Siegfried with ring (80x60cm-31x24in) s. 6-Nov-2 Hugo Ruef, Munich #1191

LEEMANS, Johannes (1633-1688) Dutch
£22000 $34540 €33000 Still life of implements of the chase hanging against wooden panels (106x145cm-42x57in) s.d.1674 trompe l'oeil prov. 16-Dec-2 Sotheby's, London #41/R est:20000-30000

LEEMANS, T (18th C) British
£20833 $30000 €31250 First rater firing the morning gun (100x125cm-39x49in) 15-Jan-3 Christie's, Rockefeller NY #144/R est:40000

LEEMPOELS, Jef (1867-1935) Belgian
£769 $1192 €1200 L'heure du Rosaire (45x37cm-18x15in) s. s.i.verso. 9-Dec-2 Horta, Bruxelles #116
£833 $1267 €1300 Nature morte aux roses (30x48cm-12x19in) s. 27-Aug-2 Galerie Moderne, Brussels #264
£1154 $1788 €1800 Au cabaret (80x65cm-31x26in) s. s.i.verso. 9-Dec-2 Horta, Bruxelles #115 est:2000-3000
£2553 $4136 €3600 Roses in a vase (36x47cm-14x19in) s. s.i.verso. 22-May-3 Dorotheum, Vienna #195/R est:3000-3500
£3165 $4937 €5000 Titie et son chien (140x124cm-55x49in) s. 15-Oct-2 Horta, Bruxelles #134/R est:8000-12000

LEEMPUTTEN, Cornelis van (1841-1902) Belgian
£256 $397 €400 Interieur de l'etable (25x35cm-10x14in) s. panel. 3-Dec-2 Campo & Campo, Antwerp #314
£448 $717 €650 In the field (21x32cm-8x13in) s. canvas on panel. 15-Mar-3 De Vuyst, Lokeren #344
£479 $748 €700 Sheep in the dunes (26x33cm-10x13in) s. panel. 10-Apr-3 Schopman, Hamburg #582
£503 $810 €750 Berger et moutons (22x29cm-9x11in) panel. 18-Feb-3 Galerie Moderne, Brussels #289/R
£577 $906 €900 Le berger et ses moutons (35x22cm-14x9in) s. 11-Dec-2 Hotel des Ventes Mosan, Brussels #232a
£1389 $2250 €2014 Shepherd with his flock (30x41cm-12x16in) s.d.68 panel. 21-May-3 Doyle, New York #183/R est:3000-5000
£1646 $2600 €2600 Idyllic landscape (22x33cm-9x13in) s.d.1861 panel. 28-Nov-2 Dorotheum, Vienna #44/R est:3000-3200
£4200 $6594 €6300 Landscape and poultry in a landscape (30x51cm-12x20in) s.d.64 panel exhib. 21-Nov-2 Christie's, Kensington #105/R est:4000-6000
£5000 $8200 €7500 Shepherd boys with their flock (74x102cm-29x40in) s.d.1869 prov. 3-Jun-3 Sotheby's, London #153/R est:6000-8000

£10897 $16891 €17000 Old shepherd with flock (76x102cm-30x40in) s.d.1880. 6-Dec-2 Michael Zeller, Lindau #823/R est:7500

LEEMPUTTEN, Frans van (1850-1914) Belgian
£417 $663 €600 Moutons (18x24cm-7x9in) s. panel. 29-Apr-3 Campo, Vlaamse Kaai #327
£443 $691 €700 Moutons sur fond de paysage (17x24cm-7x9in) s. panel. 15-Oct-2 Horta, Bruxelles #71
£966 $1545 €1400 Cheval attele (19x24cm-7x9in) mono.d.81 panel exhib. 15-Mar-3 De Vuyst, Lokeren #346/R
£3671 $5727 €5800 Charrette a cheval et gardienne de moutons (70x45cm-28x18in) s.d.1889. 15-Oct-2 Horta, Bruxelles #70

LEEMPUTTEN, J L van (19th C) Belgian
£692 $1079 €1100 Bergere et son troupeau (99x79cm-39x31in) panel. 14-Oct-2 Amberes, Antwerp #217

LEEMPUTTEN, Jean Baptiste Leopold van (1831-1924) Belgian
£5036 $8058 €7000 Shepherd in the snow (55x70cm-22x28in) s. 17-May-3 De Vuyst, Lokeren #531/R est:8000-9000

LEEMPUTTEN, Jef Louis van (1865-1948) Belgian
£310 $497 €450 Chat aux aguets (9x14cm-4x6in) panel. 17-Mar-3 Amberes, Antwerp #278
£321 $497 €500 Femme dans un sous-bois (26x37cm-10x15in) s. panel. 3-Dec-2 Campo & Campo, Antwerp #319
£326 $535 €450 Le retour du champ (70x103cm-28x41in) s. 27-May-3 Campo & Campo, Antwerp #250
£362 $594 €500 Poules et coq (19x24cm-7x9in) s. panel. 27-May-3 Campo, Vlaamse Kaai #243
£439 $685 €650 Rentree du paysan avec sa charette (26x41cm-10x16in) s. panel. 25-Mar-3 Campo & Campo, Antwerp #231/R
£449 $696 €700 Berger avec ses moutons (23x34cm-9x13in) s. 3-Dec-2 Campo & Campo, Antwerp #317
£490 $789 €750 Bergere et son troupeau (24x36cm-9x14in) s. 20-Jan-3 Horta, Bruxelles #358
£558 $870 €809 Shepherd and flock (24x36cm-9x14in) s. s.i.verso. 26-Mar-3 Walker's, Ottawa #4/R est:800-1200 (C.D 1300)
£590 $939 €850 Berger et son troupeau dans un paysage (38x49cm-15x19in) s. 29-Apr-3 Campo, Vlaamse Kaai #328
£705 $1100 €1058 Roosters in a farmyard (23x36cm-9x14in) s. 28-Mar-3 Eldred, East Dennis #699/R
£705 $1100 €1058 Roosters and hens near a water trough (23x36cm-9x14in) s. 28-Mar-3 Eldred, East Dennis #700/R
£1088 $1731 €1600 Soldier with horse (70x63cm-28x25in) s.d.97. 24-Mar-3 Bernaerts, Antwerp #122/R est:1200-1500
£2065 $3200 €3098 Plower on a dirt road (80x110cm-31x43in) s.d.1896. 2-Oct-2 Christie's, Rockefeller NY #794/R est:2000-3000
Works on paper
£443 $691 €700 Batterij gaat in stelling (48x78cm-19x31in) s.d.1916 pastel. 21-Oct-2 Bernaerts, Antwerp #187/R

LEEN, Willem van (1753-1825) Dutch
£7000 $10990 €10500 Still life with fruit in a bowl, and a snail on a stone ledge (41x31cm-16x12in) s. panel prov. 12-Dec-2 Sotheby's, London #214/R est:7000-10000

LEENE, J van de (1887-1962) Belgian
£704 $1134 €1000 Anemones in a vase (59x64cm-23x25in) s. 7-May-3 Vendue Huis, Gravenhage #153/R

LEENE, Jules van de (1887-1962) Belgian
£705 $1093 €1100 Soir aux docks d'Anvers (52x66cm-20x26in) s. i.verso cardboard. 9-Dec-2 Horta, Bruxelles #374
Works on paper
£324 $518 €450 Ruelle animee en Flandres (56x47cm-22x19in) s.i. W/C executed 1910-1915. 13-May-3 Vanderkindere, Brussels #116
£1172 $1864 €1700 Moored boats in the harbour (51x64cm-20x25in) s. W/C. 10-Mar-3 Sotheby's, Amsterdam #202/R est:500-700

LEENHOUWERS, Carl (20th C) ?
£2600 $4134 €3900 Still life with fruit and tropical fish (64x76cm-25x30in) board. 30-Apr-3 Halls, Shrewsbury #318/R est:3000-4000

LEEPIN, Robert (1884-1967) ?
£257 $401 €386 Nordby Harbour, Fano (65x81cm-26x32in) s. 11-Nov-2 Rasmussen, Vejle #62/R (D.KR 3000)

LEES, Charles (attrib) (1800-1880) British
£1442 $2264 €2250 Family (64x76cm-25x30in) 19-Nov-2 Castellana, Madrid #68/R

LEES, Derwent (1885-1931) British
Works on paper
£251 $381 €377 Portrait of Ethelreda (45x34cm-18x13in) pencil prov.lit. 28-Aug-2 Deutscher-Menzies, Melbourne #421/R (A.D 700)
£1300 $2119 €1950 Angeles, Pyrenees (24x35cm-9x14in) s.i.d.1910 W/C pen ink prov.exhib. 30-Jan-3 Lawrence, Crewkerne #671/R est:500-700
£1500 $2505 €2175 Angeles, Pyrenees (24x34cm-9x13in) s.i.d.1910 pen ink W/C prov.exhib. 24-Jun-3 Bonhams, New Bond Street #38/R est:1000-1500

LEES, Stephen (1954-) Australian
£376 $598 €564 Over the fence (99x108cm-39x43in) painted 1985 prov. 23-Mar-3 Goodman, Sydney #27 (A.D 1000)

LEESER, Till (1949-) German
Photographs
£2278 $3600 €3600 Forum Hotel, Berlin Alexanderplatz (100x75cm-39x30in) s.i.d.2002 verso col lambda print. 28-Nov-2 Villa Grisebach, Berlin #1285/R est:1800-2200

LEEUW, Alexis de (fl.1848-1883) Belgian
£1000 $1640 €1500 Loggers in a winter landscape (76x127cm-30x50in) s. 29-May-3 Christie's, Kensington #162/R est:500-700
£1905 $3029 €2800 Winter landscape with lumberjacks at work (77x126cm-30x50in) s. 24-Mar-3 Bernaerts, Antwerp #63/R est:3000-4000
£1976 $3102 €2964 Winter landscape with figures and horses (60x94cm-24x37in) s. 16-Dec-2 Lilla Bukowskis, Stockholm #1006 est:20000-22000 (S.KR 28000)
£2200 $3476 €3300 Figures skating in a winter landscape (26x35cm-10x14in) s. 12-Nov-2 Bonhams, Knightsbridge #300/R est:1000-1500

LEEUWEN, Henk van (1890-1972) Dutch
£310 $493 €450 Flower still life (80x80cm-31x31in) s. 10-Mar-3 Sotheby's, Amsterdam #252
£320 $499 €480 Dutch canal scene with church, houses and bridge (39x59cm-15x23in) s. 16-Oct-2 Mervyn Carey, Tenterden #161
£475 $741 €750 View of southern harbour (50x60cm-20x24in) s.i. 21-Oct-2 Glerum, Amsterdam #26
£526 $853 €800 Girl with a lute in an interior (50x35cm-20x14in) s. 21-Jan-3 Christie's, Amsterdam #201
£704 $1134 €1000 Summer landscape with farm behind shed (39x59cm-15x23in) s. 7-May-3 Vendue Huis, Gravenhage #87/R
£780 $1240 €1170 Winter scene at dusk, with church in background (71x94cm-28x37in) s. 19-Mar-3 Brightwells, Leominster #1160
£1552 $2467 €2250 Plough team (85x130cm-33x51in) s. 10-Mar-3 Sotheby's, Amsterdam #285/R est:2500-3500

LEEWENS, Will (1923-1987) Dutch
£353 $554 €550 Abstract composition (60x80cm-24x31in) s.verso. 25-Nov-2 Glerum, Amsterdam #334/R
£2692 $4173 €4200 Still life (50x41cm-20x16in) s.d.43. 3-Dec-2 Christie's, Amsterdam #26/R est:1800-2200

LEFCORT, Allison (20th C) American
£1220 $2000 €1830 Portrait of Barbara Streisand (122x122cm-48x48in) s.indis.i. 5-Feb-3 Christie's, Rockefeller NY #21/R est:800-1200

LEFEBRE, Wilhelm (1873-1974) German
£287 $441 €450 Boat by Rententurm (34x25cm-13x10in) s. panel. 5-Sep-2 Arnold, Frankfurt #804/R

LEFEBURE, J (1930-) Canadian
£365 $569 €548 Plongee no 3 (130x88cm-51x35in) s.d.60 s.i.d.verso. 25-Mar-3 Iegor de Saint Hippolyte, Montreal #82 (C.D 850)

LEFEBVRE, Jules Joseph (1836-1911) French
£1389 $2250 €2014 Woman in profile (30x23cm-12x9in) s. panel. 21-May-3 Doyle, New York #207/R est:4000-6000
£1646 $2600 €2469 Young girl in profile (39x26cm-15x10in) s. panel. 1-Apr-3 Christie's, Rockefeller NY #189/R est:3500-4500

LEFEBVRE, Valentin (attrib) (c.1642-1680) Flemish
Works on paper
£284 $474 €400 Le sacrifice d'Isaac (22x30cm-9x12in) brown wash prov. 23-Jun-3 Beaussant & Lefèvre, Paris #187

LEFEVRE, Adolphe (1834-1868) French
£700 $1092 €1050 In the studio (16x12cm-6x5in) s.d.1862 panel. 8-Oct-2 Bonhams, Knightsbridge #229/R
£949 $1481 €1500 Les gitans dans les ruines (61x48cm-24x19in) s. 20-Oct-2 Mercier & Cie, Lille #280 est:1500-2500

LEFEVRE, Edouard (19th C) French
Works on paper
£577 $906 €900 Haut de la rue Norvins a Montmartre (17x24cm-7x9in) s.d.1875 W/C. 13-Dec-2 Piasa, Paris #156

LEFEVRE, L (?) ?
£1447 $2257 €2300 Summer flowers in ceramic jug (65x45cm-26x18in) s. 19-Sep-2 Dr Fritz Nagel, Stuttgart #963/R est:2500

LEFEVRE, Robert Jacques François (1755-1830) French
£769 $1192 €1200 Junon supplie par Cupidon (32x23cm-13x9in) s.d.1829. 6-Dec-2 Rieunier, Bailly-Pommery, Mathias, Paris #50/R
£6757 $10541 €10000 Portrait de l'acteur Francois Joseph Talma (74x60cm-29x24in) s.d.1820 prov.lit. 26-Mar-3 Peschetau-Badin Godeau & Leroy, Paris #84/R est:12000
£24648 $40915 €35000 Portrait de Madame d'Arbelles et de son fils (200x147cm-79x58in) s.d. 16-Jun-3 Claude Aguttes, Neuilly #32/R est:45000

LEFFEL, David (1931-) American
£2397 $3500 €3596 Still life (30x51cm-12x20in) 18-May-2 Altermann Galleries, Santa Fe #243/R
£2922 $4500 €4383 Orange and glass (28x23cm-11x9in) 25-Oct-2 Morris & Whiteside, Hilton Head Island #127 est:5000-7000

LEFIRVRE, Abel (19th C) French
£2885 $4500 €4328 Sun dappled farmhouse (67x96cm-26x38in) s.d.Septembre 93. 12-Apr-3 Weschler, Washington #530/R est:1000-1500

LEFKOVITZ, Sylvia (1924-) Canadian
£288 $444 €432 Mexican still life (30x61cm-12x24in) s.d.1958 prov. 22-Oct-2 Iegor de Saint Hippolyte, Montreal #53 (C.D 700)

LEFLER, Franz (attrib) (1831-1898) Czechoslovakian
£4717 $7358 €7500 Allegory of autumn (110x500cm-43x197in) 23-Sep-2 Wiener Kunst Auktionen, Vienna #64/R est:4000-9000

LEFLOT, Alys (?) Belgian?
£759 $1177 €1200 Nu debout (100x70cm-39x28in) s. 24-Sep-2 Galerie Moderne, Brussels #898

LEFORT, Agnes (1891-1973) Canadian
£247 $380 €371 Deux saules (31x40cm-12x16in) s. i.d.verso canvas on cardboard. 22-Oct-2 Iegor de Saint Hippolyte, Montreal #54 (C.D 600)

LEFRANC, Jean (?) French?
£2857 $4543 €4200 Vue de la Seine (28x23cm-11x9in) s. 28-Feb-3 Joron-Derem, Paris #43

LEFRANC, Jules (1887-1972) French
£510 $795 €800 Sacre Coeur (40x29cm-16x11in) s. panel. 5-Nov-2 Tajan, Paris #101/R
£1380 $2180 €2000 Zumaya, harbour and church (24x33cm-9x13in) s. s.i.verso panel prov.exhib.lit. 4-Apr-3 Tajan, Paris #41/R
£2207 $3487 €3200 Bastingage (34x27cm-13x11in) s.d.1925. 4-Apr-3 Tajan, Paris #38/R
£2207 $3487 €3200 Marais salants (19x24cm-7x9in) s. s.i.verso. 4-Apr-3 Tajan, Paris #90/R

LEFRANC, Roland (1931-2000) French
£256 $425 €371 Ete (23x28cm-9x11in) s. 11-Jun-3 Boos Gallery, Michigan #348/R
£1275 $2053 €1900 Marine a Courseulles (60x73cm-24x29in) s. 23-Feb-3 Lesieur & Le Bars, Le Havre #87/R
£1392 $2172 €2200 Le port de Doelan (60x75cm-24x30in) s. i.d.1972 verso. 15-Sep-2 Etude Bailleul, Bayeux #126/R
£1408 $2268 €2000 Les tournesols (81x60cm-32x24in) s. d.1974 verso. 12-May-3 Lesieur & Le Bars, Le Havre #57b
£1603 $2516 €2500 Brasseurs de pommes (48x62cm-19x24in) s. 24-Nov-2 Lesieur & Le Bars, Le Havre #96/R
£2183 $3515 €3100 Le parasol rouge (34x46cm-13x18in) s. 12-May-3 Lesieur & Le Bars, Le Havre #57/R

LEGA, Giovanni (?) Italian
£823 $1300 €1235 Still life with fruit (36x48cm-14x19in) s.verso. 17-Nov-2 CRN Auctions, Cambridge #45/R
£1013 $1600 €1520 Fishing boats return (36x56cm-14x22in) s. stretcher. 17-Nov-2 CRN Auctions, Cambridge #44/R

LEGA, Silvestro (1826-1895) Italian
£1384 $2131 €2200 Mother and daughter in the garden (13x18cm-5x7in) s. board. 28-Oct-2 Il Ponte, Milan #274/R
£3774 $5811 €6000 Portrait of Fattori resting (11x22cm-4x9in) init. i.verso cardboard. 28-Oct-2 Il Ponte, Milan #256/R
£30968 $48929 €48000 Young peasant woman (25x15cm-10x6in) i.verso board lit. 18-Dec-2 Finarte, Milan #94/R est:60000
£38406 $62986 €53000 Campagna con figura femminile (26x55cm-10x22in) s. panel lit. 27-May-3 Finarte, Milan #75/R est:38000-44000

LEGA, Silvestro (attrib) (1826-1895) Italian
£5346 $8233 €8500 Mother and child (33x42cm-13x17in) s. board. 28-Oct-2 Il Ponte, Milan #231/R est:9000

LEGAE, Ezrom (1938-1999) South African
Works on paper
£192 $300 €288 Dog licking its leg (91x58cm-36x23in) s.d.67 pencil chl. 11-Nov-2 Stephan Welz, Johannesburg #248 (SA.R 3000)
£243 $380 €365 Anguished man (91x59cm-36x23in) s.d.67 pencil chl. 11-Nov-2 Stephan Welz, Johannesburg #233 (SA.R 3800)
£480 $750 €720 Seated pregnant woman (91x58cm-36x23in) s.d.67 pencil chl. 11-Nov-2 Stephan Welz, Johannesburg #268 (SA.R 7500)

LEGANGER, Nicolay Tysland (1832-1894) American
£411 $650 €617 Afternoon at Tamworth (69x79cm-27x31in) s. s.i.d.1903 verso. 26-Apr-3 Susanin's, Chicago #5009
£897 $1400 €1346 Boy fishing in mountainous landscape (53x43cm-21x17in) s. 28-Mar-3 Eldred, East Dennis #563/R est:500-1000
£909 $1400 €1364 Coastal view with cliffs (66x107cm-26x42in) s. 27-Oct-2 Grogan, Boston #62 est:2000-3000
£21605 $35000 €32408 Near Pearl point, Lake George (76x128cm-30x50in) s.i.on stretcher painted c.1881 prov.exhib. 21-May-3 Sotheby's, New York #194/R est:30000-50000

LEGARES, Josep Olivet (1885-1956) Spanish
£524 $765 €786 Recolta de Heno (25x36cm-10x14in) s. panel. 4-Jun-2 Germann, Zurich #791 (S.FR 1200)

LEGASPI, Cesar (1917-1994) Philippino
£9114 $14035 €13671 Abstract (117x60cm-46x24in) s.d.76 board. 27-Oct-2 Christie's, Hong Kong #73/R est:135000-180000 (HK.D 110000)

LEGENDRE, Guy (?) French
£256 $397 €400 Honfleur (33x41cm-13x16in) s. 8-Dec-2 Feletin, Province #177

LEGENVRE (18/19th C) ?
£400 $644 €580 Portrait of a Bourgeois woman (63x54cm-25x21in) s.d.1832. 12-May-3 Joel, Victoria #366/R est:1500-2000 (A.D 1000)

LEGER, Fernand (1881-1955) French
£1384 $2145 €2200 Composition aux pommes et fleurs. lit. 7-Oct-2 Claude Aguttes, Neuilly #216/R
£14194 $22426 €22000 Nature morte sur fond gris (35x24cm-14x9in) s.d.1939 cardboard prov. 19-Dec-2 Ruellan, Paris #89/R est:30000
£16564 $27000 €24846 Visage a la main (44x31cm-17x12in) init.d.53 s.i.d.verso painted ceramic prov.lit. 12-Feb-3 Sotheby's, New York #118/R est:20000-25000
£50000 $83500 €72500 La fermiere (65x50cm-26x20in) init.d.52 gouache brush ink over pencil prov.lit. 24-Jun-3 Sotheby's, London #250/R est:50000-70000
£60000 $98400 €90000 Nature morte (65x54cm-26x21in) s.d.28 s.i.d.verso prov.exhib.lit. 4-Feb-3 Christie's, London #351/R est:150000
£70513 $110000 €105770 Composition abstraite (46x27cm-18x11in) s.d.31 prov.exhib.lit. 7-Nov-2 Christie's, Rockefeller NY #309/R est:70000-90000
£96154 $150962 €150000 Fer a cheval (50x40cm-20x16in) s.d.44 prov.exhib.lit. 10-Dec-2 Piasa, Paris #211/R est:150000
£96273 $155000 €144410 Folies (33x46cm-13x18in) s.d.29 s.i.d.verso prov.lit. 7-May-3 Sotheby's, New York #354/R est:120000-180000
£113924 $180000 €180000 Composition (145x88cm-57x35in) painted 1938 lit. 30-Nov-2 Farsetti, Prato #715/R est:220000
£134615 $211346 €210000 Papillon rouge (54x65cm-21x26in) s.d.37 s.i.d.verso prov.exhib.lit. 10-Dec-2 Piasa, Paris #212/R est:350000
£140000 $233800 €203000 Composition a la fleur (45x38cm-18x15in) s.d.31 canvasboard prov.lit. 25-Jun-3 Christie's, London #198/R est:80000-120000
£150000 $246000 €225000 Composition au couteau (65x54cm-26x21in) s. painted 1947 prov.exhib.lit. 4-Feb-3 Christie's, London #356/R est:220000
£160839 $268601 €230000 Rose et figure (54x65cm-21x26in) s.d.31 prov.exhib.lit. 30-Jun-3 Artcurial Briest, Paris #60/R
£161491 $260000 €242237 La theiere rouge (50x65cm-20x26in) s.d.52 s.i.d.verso prov. 7-May-3 Sotheby's, New York #350/R est:180000-250000
£172414 $272414 €250000 Composition jaune et noir (65x54cm-26x21in) s.d.29 s.i.d.verso lit. 2-Apr-3 Christie's, Paris #4/R est:90000-105000
£200000 $328000 €300000 Composition circulaire (65x50cm-26x20in) s.d.28 prov.exhib.lit. 4-Feb-3 Sotheby's, London #52/R est:300000
£211538 $330000 €317307 Composition (46x55cm-18x22in) s.d.24 prov.exhib. 6-Nov-2 Sotheby's, New York #252/R est:250000-350000
£250000 $390000 €375000 Composition avec figure (65x92cm-26x36in) s.d.30 s.i.d.verso prov.exhib.lit. 6-Nov-2 Sotheby's, New York #298/R est:225000-325000

£280000 $467600 €406000 Paysage au coq rouge (65x92cm-26x36in) s.d.37 s.i.d.1937 verso prov.exhib.lit. 24-Jun-3 Christie's, London #76/R est:250000-350000
£310559 $500000 €465839 Etoile rouge (130x89cm-51x35in) s.d.38 prov.exhib.lit. 6-May-3 Sotheby's, New York #32/R est:500000-700000
£372671 $600000 €559007 Papillons (129x89cm-51x35in) s.d.37 prov.exhib.lit. 7-May-3 Christie's, Rockefeller NY #29/R est:600000-800000
£380000 $619400 €570000 Femme au chat (65x92cm-26x36in) s.d.1955 s.i.d.verso prov. 3-Feb-3 Christie's, London #83/R est:600000
£550000 $902000 €825000 Jeune fille tenant une poupee (91x73cm-36x29in) s.d.37-38 i.d.verso prov.exhib.lit. 4-Feb-3 Sotheby's, London #54/R est:700000
£700000 $1148000 €1050000 Sujet mecanique (65x46cm-26x18in) s.d.20 i.verso prov.lit. 4-Feb-3 Sotheby's, London #39/R est:1200000
£794872 $1232051 €1240000 Composition a l'escalier (65x92cm-26x36in) s.d.25 s.i.d.verso prov.exhib.lit. 9-Dec-2 Piasa, Paris #24/R est:1000000-1300000
£1128205 $1748718 €1760000 Disque rouge (65x56cm-26x22in) s.d.19 exhib.lit. 9-Dec-2 Piasa, Paris #22/R est:1400000-1600000
£1282051 $2000000 €1923077 Composition les trois soeurs (128x96cm-50x38in) s.d.1950-51 i.d. prov.exhib.lit. 5-Nov-2 Sotheby's, New York #62/R est:2000000-3000000
£1410257 $2185898 €2200000 Marie l'acrobate (97x130cm-38x51in) s.d.33 s.i.d.verso exhib.lit. 9-Dec-2 Piasa, Paris #23/R est:2000000-2500000
£1987180 $3100000 €2980770 Les femmes a la toilette (92x73cm-36x29in) s.d.20 s.i.d.verso prov.exhib.lit. 6-Nov-2 Christie's, Rockefeller NY #46/R est:3500000-4500000
£3205128 $5000000 €4807692 Les deux acrobates (89x58cm-35x23in) s. s.i.d.1918 verso prov.exhib.lit. 6-Nov-2 Christie's, Rockefeller NY #41/R est:6000000-8000000

Prints

£1923 $2981 €3000 La parade (35x45cm-14x18in) s. col lithograph. 7-Dec-2 Hauswedell & Nolte, Hamburg #859/R est:3000
£2138 $3400 €3207 Composition aux deux personnages (29x24cm-11x9in) s. lithograph. 1-May-3 Swann Galleries, New York #482/R est:4000-6000
£2436 $3776 €3800 La colombe (41x33cm-16x13in) s. col lithograph. 7-Dec-2 Hauswedell & Nolte, Hamburg #858/R est:3800
£2500 $3925 €3750 Les constructeurs (75x55cm-30x22in) s.num.58/75 col aquatint screenprint. 17-Apr-3 Christie's, Kensington #280/R est:1800-2200
£2658 $4200 €4200 Enfant a l'accordeon (56x76cm-22x30in) num.72/75 col aquatint. 29-Nov-2 Drouot Estimations, Paris #24
£2830 $4500 €4245 Visage aux deux mains sur fond orange (46x33cm-18x13in) col glazed terre de faience plaque edition of 250. 2-May-3 Sotheby's, New York #198/R est:5000-7000
£3521 $5845 €5000 Les constructeurs (44x59cm-17x23in) s. col lithograph. 14-Jun-3 Hauswedell & Nolte, Hamburg #1343/R est:4800
£4167 $6500 €6251 Composition aux deux personnages (29x24cm-11x9in) s. lithograph edition of 125. 7-Nov-2 Swann Galleries, New York #673/R est:4000-6000
£14465 $23000 €21698 Cirque (43x33cm-17x13in) s.num.190 col lithograph 34 illuminations 22 book. 2-May-3 Sotheby's, New York #196/R est:15000-20000

Sculpture

£6918 $11000 €10377 Fleur qui marche au coeur rouge (61cm-24in) painted glazed ceramic prov.lit. 27-Feb-3 Christie's, Rockefeller NY #74/R est:6000
£7500 $11550 €11250 La mere et l'enfant (27x17cm-11x7in) s. num.3/20 verso painted glazed ceramic tile lit. 23-Oct-2 Sotheby's, Olympia #753/R est:7000-8000
£9655 $15352 €14000 Visage cache (45x37x3cm-18x15x1in) st.f.Valsuani num.5/8 pat bronze. 7-Mar-3 Claude Aguttes, Neuilly #11/R est:8000
£15000 $25050 €21750 La tete de cheval (48x40x6cm-19x16x2in) init.d.53 num.28 painted ceramic relief lit. 25-Jun-3 Christie's, London #224/R est:15000-20000
£22013 $34340 €35000 Les algues - bleu et jaune No 2 (49x36cm-19x14in) s.init.i.d.52 enamelled ceramic prov. 10-Oct-2 Ribeyre & Baron, Paris #69/R est:18000-20000
£115385 $180000 €173078 Femmes au perroquet (78x116cm-31x46in) s.d.53 five partially glazed ceramic edtions prov. 6-Nov-2 Sotheby's, New York #286/R est:300000-400000

Works on paper

£994 $1600 €1491 Three entangled figures (23x18cm-9x7in) gouache W/C. 9-May-3 Douglas, South Deerfield #12
£2083 $3437 €3000 Echafaudages (22x27cm-9x11in) i. W/C crayon exec.c.1936-37 prov. 2-Jul-3 Artcurial Briest, Paris #695/R est:4000-6000
£2848 $4500 €4500 Le pauvre songe, peut-etre un soir, m'attend ou je boirai tranquille (30x24cm-12x9in) mono. Indian ink. 27-Nov-2 Dorotheum, Vienna #20/R est:4500-4800
£5180 $8288 €7200 Projet de decor pour bolivar (24x31cm-9x12in) gouache prov. 18-May-3 Eric Pillon, Calais #265/R
£5385 $8454 €8400 Creation du monde (34x12cm-13x5in) ink wash htd gouache. 11-Dec-2 Artcurial Briest, Paris #536/R
£5769 $9058 €9000 Dessin de guerre (15x11cm-6x4in) mono.i. ink dr. 11-Dec-2 Artcurial Briest, Paris #535/R
£5797 $9507 €8000 Sketch for ballet (22x27cm-9x11in) gouache pencil board double-sided prov. 31-May-3 Villa Grisebach, Berlin #317/R est:8000-10000
£5882 $9824 €8529 Verdun / Les soldats en deplacement (12x21cm-5x8in) s. pen prov. 24-Jun-3 Koller, Zurich #156/R est:2000-3000 (S.FR 13000)
£6500 $10010 €9750 Composition au tournesol (29x24cm-11x9in) init.d.53 brush ink W/C pencil paper on canvas prov. 23-Oct-2 Sotheby's, Olympia #694/R est:7000-9000
£7500 $11550 €11250 Paix et pardon, Madeleine dans les Rochers (27x21cm-11x8in) st.init.i. gouache W/C brush ink. 23-Oct-2 Sotheby's, Olympia #696/R est:8000-12000
£7500 $11625 €11250 Projet pour le mur a l'escalier (24x28cm-9x11in) i. pencil gouache executed 1939-41 prov. 5-Dec-2 Christie's, Kensington #146/R est:8000-12000
£7566 $12256 €11500 Composition (20x15cm-8x6in) ink dr prov. 22-Jan-3 Tajan, Paris #226/R est:12000-15000
£9000 $14312 €13500 Paix et pardon (27x21cm-11x8in) st.init.i. gouache W/C brush ink. 20-Mar-3 Sotheby's, Olympia #88/R est:7000-9000
£9615 $15096 €15000 Composition a la selle (30x22cm-12x9in) init.d.45 Chinese ink prov.exhib.lit. 10-Dec-2 Piasa, Paris #317/R est:15000
£9677 $15290 €15000 Composition a la mappemonde (27x21cm-11x8in) init.d.46 gouache ink prov. 20-Dec-2 Ribeyre & Baron, Paris #48/R est:15000
£9677 $15290 €15000 Composition (43x49cm-17x19in) mono. gouache exec.c.1950 prov. 19-Dec-2 Ruellan, Paris #91/R est:25000
£9712 $15540 €13500 Les deux vaches (44x33cm-17x13in) init.i.d. gouache W/C prov. 18-May-3 Eric Pillon, Calais #271/R
£10000 $16700 €15000 Hissage de forme mobile (14x9cm-6x4in) init.i. pen ink exec 1916 prov.exhib.lit. 26-Jun-3 Christie's, London #395/R est:10000-15000
£10000 $16700 €15000 Le chapeau sur la chaise (32x25cm-13x10in) init.d.50 brush blk.ink chl. prov. 26-Jun-3 Christie's, London #408/R est:10000-15000
£10730 $16953 €16095 Rockefeller stairway mural commission (23x27cm-9x11in) gouache paper laid down board prov. 3-Apr-3 Heffel, Vancouver #55/R est:30000-35000 (C.D 25000)
£11000 $18370 €15950 Deauville (24x32cm-9x13in) init.d.Aout 50 brush ink gouache W/C over pencil prov. 24-Jun-3 Sotheby's, London #267/R est:12000-15000
£11538 $18115 €18000 Roue brisee (30x22cm-12x9in) init.d.45 Chinese ink prov. 10-Dec-2 Piasa, Paris #318/R est:15000
£14103 $22000 €21155 Le tournesol (49x41cm-19x16in) init.d.51 gouache prov. 6-Nov-2 Sotheby's, New York #309/R est:20000-30000
£15468 $24748 €21500 Frise de poissons (20x110cm-8x43in) s. gouache ink. 16-May-3 Lombrail & Teucquam, Paris #127/R
£15823 $25000 €25000 Etude pour les constructeurs (28x22cm-11x9in) s.i.d.48 gouache crayon over pencil paper on paper prov. 29-Nov-2 Villa Grisebach, Berlin #70/R est:25000-30000
£16149 $26000 €24224 Fleur (27x22cm-11x9in) init.d.50 W/C gouache paper on canvas prov. 7-May-3 Sotheby's, New York #318/R est:20000-30000
£16667 $26333 €24000 Etude pour une sculpture (49x32cm-19x13in) mono. ink gouache. 27-Apr-3 Perrin, Versailles #44/R est:25000-30000
£17500 $29225 €25375 Dessin aux mains (31x49cm-12x19in) init.d.51 pencil brush ink wash prov.exhib. 24-Jun-3 Sotheby's, London #277/R est:18000-25000
£20000 $32800 €30000 Charmeuse d'oiseaux (32x37cm-13x15in) i. gouache ink over pencil prov. 5-Feb-3 Sotheby's, London #179/R est:35000
£20000 $32800 €30000 Tournesol (36x28cm-14x11in) init.d.51 gouache pencil prov. 6-Feb-3 Christie's, London #472/R est:24000
£21000 $32340 €31500 Le tournesol (63x48cm-25x19in) init.d.50 brush ink gouache over pencil. 22-Oct-2 Sotheby's, London #180/R est:18000-25000
£22436 $35224 €35000 Baigneuses sur la plage (38x50cm-15x20in) init.d.42 Chinese ink dr prov. 10-Dec-2 Piasa, Paris #313/R est:30000
£24000 $40080 €34800 Le perroquet (27x21cm-11x8in) gouache W/C India ink pencil prov. 24-Jun-3 Christie's, London #19/R est:8000-12000
£25000 $41750 €36250 Les musiciens (42x32cm-17x13in) W/C pen ink pencil prov. 24-Jun-3 Christie's, London #11/R est:18000-24000
£27097 $42813 €42000 Portrait de femme (61x47cm-24x19in) init.d.1952 W/C dr prov. 19-Dec-2 Ruellan, Paris #90/R est:40000
£27586 $46069 €40000 L'ouvrier constructeur (64x50cm-25x20in) mono. gouache ink prov. 9-Jul-3 Cornette de St.Cyr, Paris #176/R est:50000-60000
£28000 $46760 €40600 Le combattant - etude pour fortune (25x18cm-10x7in) init.d.39 W/C gouache pen ink prov. 24-Jun-3 Sotheby's, London #249/R est:30000-40000
£30000 $50100 €43500 Cirque (45x63cm-18x25in) init.i. W/C India ink prov. 24-Jun-3 Christie's, London #7/R est:20000-30000

£30769 $48308 €48000 Fleur et disque polychrome (29x36cm-11x14in) init.d.45 gouache prov. 10-Dec-2 Piasa, Paris #316/R est:35000

£32000 $52480 €48000 Etoile jaune (40x56cm-16x22in) gouache exec.1937-38 prov. 6-Feb-3 Christie's, London #507/R est:50000

£32051 $50321 €50000 Plongeurs (37x38cm-15x15in) s.i.d.42 Chinese ink gouache. 10-Dec-2 Piasa, Paris #314/R est:15000

£34000 $52360 €51000 Etude pour femme a genoux (37x26cm-15x10in) init.d.21 pencil prov.exhib. 22-Oct-2 Sotheby's, London #138/R est:20000-30000

£35000 $58450 €52500 Le jongleur (19x24cm-7x9in) init. gouache ink paper on canvas exec 1954 prov.exhib. 26-Jun-3 Christie's, London #436/R est:40000-60000

£35000 $58450 €50750 L'homme a la canne (30x38cm-12x15in) gouache India ink pencil prov. 24-Jun-3 Christie's, London #16/R est:18000-24000

£35849 $55925 €57000 Nature morte aux pommes et pichet devant la fenetre (40x57cm-16x22in) i. gouache ink. 9-Oct-2 Lombrail & Teucquam, Paris #11/R

£37179 $58372 €58000 Femme a la rose (54x43cm-21x17in) st.init. gouache prov. 24-Nov-2 Laurence Calmels, Paris #180/R est:25000

£38000 $63460 €57000 Nature morte aux pommes sur fond bleu (69x50cm-27x20in) init. gouache exec 1938 prov. 26-Jun-3 Christie's, London #437/R est:35000-45000

£39744 $62397 €62000 Nature morte au pichet (25x34cm-10x13in) init.i.d.48-49 gouache. 10-Dec-2 Piasa, Paris #315/R est:40000

£40373 $65000 €60560 Nature morte aux pommes et pichet devant la fenetre (70x87cm-28x34in) s.i. gouache brush ink prov. 7-May-3 Sotheby's, New York #334/R est:70000-90000

£41667 $65000 €62501 La creation du monde (48x64cm-19x25in) gouache ink wash paper on board executed c.1923 prov.exhib. 6-Nov-2 Sotheby's, New York #212/R est:60000-80000

£57692 $90577 €90000 Acrobates (63x48cm-25x19in) init.d.1938 Chinese ink. 10-Dec-2 Piasa, Paris #312/R

£65000 $108550 €97500 Composition (33x25cm-13x10in) init.d.1924 pencil prov.exhib.lit. 26-Jun-3 Christie's, London #397/R est:40000-60000

£68000 $113560 €98600 Composition a la branche noire (64x49cm-25x19in) init. s.i.verso gouache brush ink wash over pencil executed 1938. 24-Jun-3 Sotheby's, London #254/R est:60000-80000

£70000 $107800 €105000 Etude pour l'escalier (35x29cm-14x11in) init.d.20 brush ink over pencil prov.exhib. 22-Oct-2 Sotheby's, London #139/R est:40000-60000

£75000 $125250 €108750 L'acrobate (38x30cm-15x12in) init.d.47 W/C black ink gouache over pencil prov.exhib. 24-Jun-3 Christie's, London #20/R est:20000-30000

£85000 $141950 €123250 Je ne te demande pas si ta grand-mere fait du velo (37x28cm-15x11in) init.i. gouache W/C black ink pencil prov. 24-Jun-3 Christie's, London #14/R est:25000-35000

£90000 $150300 €130500 Buste de femme (31x25cm-12x10in) init.d.31 pencil prov. 24-Jun-3 Christie's, London #5/R est:30000-40000

£96774 $152903 €150000 Arbre dans la ville (30x23cm-12x9in) init.d.21 gouache prov. 19-Dec-2 Bondu, Paris #12/R est:90000-120000

£102564 $160000 €153846 Personnage dans un interieur (43x30cm-17x12in) init.d.20 W/C panel prov.exhib. 7-Nov-2 Christie's, Rockefeller NY #134/R est:140000-180000

£102564 $160000 €153846 La belle equipe (36x55cm-14x22in) init.d.44 gouache brush India ink pencil paper on canvas prov. 7-Nov-2 Christie's, Rockefeller NY #142/R est:150000-200000

£165000 $275550 €247500 La grande parade (55x69cm-22x27in) init.d.53 gouache ink prov.exhib. 26-Jun-3 Christie's, London #435/R est:150000-200000

£236025 $380000 €354038 Composition aux deux perroquets (152x190cm-60x75in) gouache brush ink chl paper on canvas executed c.1935 prov.exhib. 8-May-3 Christie's, Rockefeller NY #129/R est:380000-450000

£280000 $467600 €406000 La lecture (25x32cm-10x13in) pencil exec.c.1923 prov. 24-Jun-3 Christie's, London #31/R est:120000-180000

LEGGE, Arthur J (1859-1942) British

Works on paper

£650 $1066 €975 Tinker's camp (48x71cm-19x28in) s.d.93 pencil W/C scratching out. 5-Jun-3 Christie's, Kensington #964

LEGGE, Frederick (1841-1918) Australian

£560 $902 €812 Resting cattle (59x89cm-23x35in) s. 12-May-3 Joel, Victoria #313 est:2000-3000 (A.D 1400)

LEGGETT, Alexander (1848-1884) British

£255 $424 €370 Sorting the day's catch (22x29cm-9x11in) oil over graphite on board prov. 10-Jun-3 Ritchie, Toronto #53/R (C.D 575)

LEGILLON, Jean François (1739-1797) Flemish

Works on paper

£500 $785 €750 Views of the Ramparts of Fribourg (25x37cm-10x15in) s.i. brown ink. 11-Dec-2 Sotheby's, Olympia #225/R

LEGORA, Giovanni Cappa (1887-1970) Italian

£516 $815 €800 Santa Caterina del Sasso (15x25cm-6x10in) s. board. 18-Dec-2 Finarte, Milan #205

£1304 $2139 €1800 Casolare di montagna (34x44cm-13x17in) s. 27-May-3 Finarte, Milan #23/R est:1000-1200

£6289 $9686 €10000 Lake Maggiore (100x133cm-39x52in) s.d.1915 double-sided. 23-Oct-2 Finarte, Milan #47/R est:5000-6000

LEGOUT-GERARD, Fernand (1856-1924) French

£704 $1134 €1000 Interieur d'eglise (46x55cm-18x22in) st. c.1911. 11-May-3 Thierry & Lannon, Brest #374

£1497 $2380 €2200 Harbour in evening (33x56cm-13x22in) s. 19-Mar-3 Neumeister, Munich #623/R est:1200

£1931 $3225 €2800 Echoppes et rues animees dans la vieille ville (21x27cm-8x11in) s. panel. 10-Jul-3 Artcurial Briest, Paris #135/R est:3000-4000

£2821 $4428 €4400 View of Concarneau (18x27cm-7x11in) s. panel. 10-Dec-2 Renaud, Paris #16/R

£2885 $4529 €4500 Soir d'ete au Cabelou (21x27cm-8x11in) s. 15-Dec-2 Thierry & Lannon, Brest #149

£4148 $6472 €6222 Le port de Concarneau (54x65cm-21x26in) s. 20-Nov-2 Fischer, Luzern #1081/R est:4500-5500 (S.FR 9500)

£4196 $7007 €6000 Quai anime en Bretagne (35x27cm-14x11in) s. 26-Jun-3 Tajan, Paris #259/R est:6000-7000

£4722 $7697 €6800 Venise, gondoles sur le Grand Canal (54x65cm-21x26in) s. 19-Jul-3 Thierry & Lannon, Brest #144/R est:7000-8000

£5000 $8150 €7250 Marche a Concarneau, market scene with figures and children (22x27cm-9x11in) s.i. panel. 17-Jul-3 Tennants, Leyburn #872/R est:1500-2000

£5192 $8152 €8100 Retour des pecheurs (22x27cm-9x11in) s. 15-Dec-2 Thierry & Lannon, Brest #150

£5200 $8060 €7800 Market at Quimper (17x27cm-7x11in) s.i. i.verso board. 3-Dec-2 Sotheby's, Olympia #289/R est:2500-3500

£5800 $8990 €8700 Concarneau (32x24cm-13x9in) s. board. 3-Dec-2 Sotheby's, Olympia #291/R est:4000-6000

£6500 $10205 €9750 St. Mark's Square, Venice (54x63cm-21x25in) s. 21-Nov-2 Christie's, Kensington #167/R est:4000-6000

£15493 $24944 €22000 Le marche de Pont Aven (46x55cm-18x22in) s. 11-May-3 Thierry & Lannon, Brest #196/R est:12000-15000

£16456 $26000 €24684 Pecheurs a Concarneau (54x65cm-21x26in) s. 24-Apr-3 Sotheby's, New York #95a/R est:15000-20000

Works on paper

£278 $453 €400 Etude de Bretonnes (18x12cm-7x5in) s. chl. 19-Jul-3 Thierry & Lannon, Brest #38

£278 $453 €400 Sardiniers a la Digue (21x29cm-8x11in) studio st. crayon. 19-Jul-3 Thierry & Lannon, Brest #42

£333 $543 €480 Paysanne aux paniers (21x15cm-8x6in) s. graphite. 19-Jul-3 Thierry & Lannon, Brest #39

£417 $679 €600 Concarneau (11x18cm-4x7in) s. crayon. 19-Jul-3 Thierry & Lannon, Brest #41

£451 $736 €650 Marine, retour de peche (23x29cm-9x11in) s. chl. 19-Jul-3 Thierry & Lannon, Brest #40

£634 $1020 €900 Jeune femme a l'epaule denudee (40x28cm-16x11in) s. chl chk. 11-May-3 Thierry & Lannon, Brest #67

£769 $1208 €1200 Marche sur place Terre au Duc (45x52cm-18x20in) s. chl. 15-Dec-2 Thierry & Lannon, Brest #300

LEGOUT-GERARD, Fernand (attrib) (1856-1924) French

£755 $1162 €1200 Vue sur la baie (27x35cm-11x14in) s. panel. 22-Oct-2 Campo, Vlaamse Kaai #184

LEGRAND, Louis Auguste Mathieu (1863-1951) French

£602 $969 €903 Old woman and child (29x37cm-11x15in) s.d.1887 panel. 12-May-3 Stephan Welz, Johannesburg #425/R est:7000-10000 (SA.R 7000)

Works on paper

£609 $944 €950 Etude de nu feminin (31x52cm-12x20in) i. chl stump sanguine. 4-Dec-2 Piasa, Paris #170

LEGRAND, Nicolas (1817-1883) ?

£566 $883 €900 Young woman with child by church door (60x47cm-24x19in) s.d.1847 panel. 19-Sep-2 Dr Fritz Nagel, Stuttgart #964/R

LEGRAND, Paul Emmanuel (1860-?) French

£1250 $2012 €1875 Seated female nude (145x80cm-57x31in) s.d.1881. 7-May-3 Dobiaschofsky, Bern #775/R est:2000 (S.FR 2700)

LEGRAS, Auguste J F (1864-1915) Dutch

£1389 $2292 €2000 Oriental market at Chardaia (85x112cm-33x44in) s. 1-Jul-3 Christie's, Amsterdam #156/R est:2000-3000

LEGROS, Alphonse (1837-1911) French

£2800 $4396 €4200 Religious procession (51x68cm-20x27in) s. 21-Nov-2 Christie's, Kensington #141/R est:3000-5000

Works on paper
£700 $1148 €1050 Wooded river landscape (28x44cm-11x17in) init. pen ink brown wash. 5-Jun-3 Christie's, Kensington #930
£1500 $2385 €2250 Portrait of Alice Knewstub (38x28cm-15x11in) s. red chk sold with to lithograph portraits. 26-Feb-3 Sotheby's, Olympia #1/R est:700-1000

LEGUAY, Charles Étienne (1762-1846) French
Miniatures
£4000 $6560 €5800 Violinist Pierre Baillot in a brown coat (7cm-3in) s. gilt bronze frame. 3-Jun-3 Christie's, London #125/R est:3000-4000
Works on paper
£380 $600 €600 Allegory (29x20cm-11x8in) crayon stump. 28-Nov-2 Tajan, Paris #73
£633 $1000 €1000 Portrait de femme en pied (25x19cm-10x7in) s. crayon. 28-Nov-2 Tajan, Paris #70/R

LEGUAY, Charles Étienne (attrib) (1762-1846) French
Miniatures
£26000 $40820 €39000 The artist's second wife Marie Victoire Jaquotot (20x14cm-8x6in) gilt wood frame rec exhib.lit. 10-Dec-2 Christie's, London #173/R est:4000-6000

LEGUEULT, Raymond (1898-1971) French
£1233 $1936 €1800 Paysage (51x62cm-20x24in) s.i.d.1928. 21-Apr-3 Rabourdin & Choppin de Janvry, Paris #77/R est:1800-2000
£4194 $6500 €6291 Emilienne au chapeau (81x100cm-32x39in) s.d.62 s.d.verso prov.exhib. 26-Sep-2 Christie's, Rockefeller NY #578/R est:8000-10000
Works on paper
£1051 $1639 €1650 Jeunes filles sur la plage (42x54cm-17x21in) s.d.1958 W/C. 10-Nov-2 Eric Pillon, Calais #116/R
£5128 $8051 €8000 Interieur au gueridon (42x54cm-17x21in) s. W/C prov. 10-Dec-2 Piasa, Paris #450/R est:2000
£6090 $9561 €9500 Acrobate (42x54cm-17x21in) s. W/C prov. 10-Dec-2 Piasa, Paris #451/R est:2000

LEHAR, Jean (1925-) French
£637 $1000 €956 At the dock (91x122cm-36x48in) s. 22-Nov-2 Skinner, Boston #388/R est:2000-4000

LEHEUTRE, Gustave (1861-?) French
£2885 $4471 €4500 Soir de neige a Montmartre (49x73cm-19x29in) s.d.93 prov.exhib. 4-Dec-2 Lempertz, Koln #852/R est:5000-6000

LEHMAN, Anne (20th C) American
£267 $425 €401 Arizona (102x76cm-40x30in) painted c.1950. 2-Mar-3 Toomey, Oak Park #799/R
£535 $850 €803 On the shore (102x76cm-40x30in) s. painted c.1950. 2-Mar-3 Toomey, Oak Park #811/R

LEHMAN, Carl Peter (1794-1876) Swedish
£1003 $1625 €1505 Mountain landscape with waterfall (82x98cm-32x39in) s.d.1870. 3-Feb-3 Lilla Bukowskis, Stockholm #523 (S.KR 14000)

LEHMAN, Irving (1900-1983) American
£419 $650 €629 Blue dawn (61x76cm-24x30in) s. board painted c.1950. 8-Dec-2 Toomey, Oak Park #826/R
£578 $925 €867 Boat regatta (46x61cm-18x24in) s. masonite. 11-Jan-3 James Julia, Fairfield #371 est:1000-1500

LEHMANN, Alfred (1899-1979) German
£379 $599 €550 Figural composition (64x36cm-25x14in) s. masonite. 2-Apr-3 Dr Fritz Nagel, Stuttgart #9135/R

LEHMANN, Edvard (1815-1892) Danish
£372 $573 €558 Portrait of young girl (21x17cm-8x7in) init. panel. 26-Oct-2 Rasmussen, Havnen #2115/R (D.KR 4400)

LEHMANN, Gustav (20th C) ?
£316 $491 €500 Misty river (45x44cm-18x17in) s.d.08. 26-Sep-2 Neumeister, Munich #2778/R

LEHMANN, Henri (1814-1882) French
Works on paper
£1290 $2000 €1935 Studies of a reclining nude (29x41cm-11x16in) i.19 Oct pencil htd white ink prov. 29-Oct-2 Sotheby's, New York #22/R est:1000-1500

LEHMANN, Henriette (1862-?) German
£380 $600 €600 Bunch of autumn flowers with marguerites (100x70cm-39x28in) s.d.1925. 29-Nov-2 Bolland & Marotz, Bremen #730/R

LEHMANN, Kurt (1905-) German
Sculpture
£2179 $3378 €3400 Female figure (40cm-16in) mono. brown pat.bronze Cast.Barth Berlin prov.lit. 6-Dec-2 Karlheinz Kaupp, Staufen #859/R est:3400
£4088 $6377 €6500 Grape eater (23x23cm-9x9in) mono. pat.bronze Cast.Barth Rinteln. 20-Sep-2 Karlheinz Kaupp, Staufen #973/R est:100

LEHMANN, Olga (fl.1932-1933) British
Works on paper
£450 $738 €675 Capriccio (26x33cm-10x13in) s. W/C gouache. 3-Jun-3 Sotheby's, Olympia #14/R

LEHMANN, Rudolf (1819-1905) German
£650 $1014 €975 Sifting the grain (47x34cm-19x13in) s.i. 26-Mar-3 Sotheby's, Olympia #234/R

LEHMANN, Wilhelm Ludwig (1861-1932) Swiss
£321 $503 €500 Rocks on the Rhein (26x36cm-10x14in) s. i.d.1919 verso canvas on board. 21-Nov-2 Dorotheum, Vienna #200/R
£328 $511 €492 Lake Bernina (45x65cm-18x26in) s. i. verso canvas on board. 6-Nov-2 Dobiaschofsky, Bern #767/R (S.FR 750)
£705 $1029 €1058 Extensive summer landscape (73x100cm-29x39in) s.d.1907. 17-Jun-2 Philippe Schuler, Zurich #7424 (S.FR 1600)

LEHMANN, Willy (?) German?
£449 $696 €700 Still life with apples (46x57cm-18x22in) i. 9-Dec-2 Dr Fritz Nagel, Stuttgart #6904/R

LEHMANN-DUMONT, Karl (19/20th C) German
£338 $527 €500 Woman wearing turban (49x30cm-19x12in) s. board. 26-Mar-3 Hugo Ruef, Munich #162

LEHMANN-FAHRWASSER, Georg (1887-) German
£1258 $1950 €2000 Village street in Wyk on Fohr (58x65cm-23x26in) s. 2-Nov-2 Hans Stahl, Toestorf #78/R est:350

LEHMANN-LEONHARD, Wilhelm (1877-1954) German
£528 $850 €750 Inn keeper with two men drinking at table (40x49cm-16x19in) s.i. 7-May-3 Michael Zeller, Lindau #778/R

LEHMBRUCK, Wilhelm (1881-1919) German
£13043 $21391 €18000 Woman's portrait (57x74cm-22x29in) s. oil chk board prov. 29-May-3 Lempertz, Koln #746/R est:15000-20000
Sculpture
£3819 $6073 €5500 Small figure in thought (53x16x17cm-21x6x7in) i. dark brown pat.bronze Cast.H Pelargus. 5-May-3 Ketterer, Munich #902/R est:4000-6000
£15942 $26145 €22000 Girl resting her leg (63cm-25in) s.i. brown pat.bronze Cast.N.Noack Berlin Friedenau prov.exhib. 30-May-3 Villa Grisebach, Berlin #10/R est:20000-30000
£17266 $28317 €24000 Seated girl (28x44x16cm-11x17x6in) i. blackish brown pat.bronze prov.lit. 6-Jun-3 Ketterer, Munich #52/R est:18000-24000
£57971 $95072 €80000 Small female torso - Hagener torso (70cm-28in) s. verso stone prov.exhib. 29-May-3 Lempertz, Koln #745/R est:80000-100000
£141304 $231739 €195000 Bust of kneeling woman - inclined female head (49cm-19in) s. verso glazed terracotta exhib. 30-May-3 Villa Grisebach, Berlin #15/R est:120000-150000
£170000 $265200 €255000 Kleiner weiblicher torso - Small female torso (70cm-28in) cast stone executed c.1911 prov.exhib.lit. 9-Oct-2 Sotheby's, London #16/R est:50000-70000
Works on paper
£2986 $4748 €4300 Girl's head (24x23cm-9x9in) chk prov. 5-May-3 Ketterer, Munich #899/R est:500-800
£3311 $5397 €5000 Entwined couple (30x22cm-12x9in) s.d.1913 chl W/C. 14-Feb-3 Paul Kieffer, Pforzhiem #7175/R est:7500
£4855 $7962 €6700 Female nude (48x31cm-19x12in) s.d.1912 col chk. 29-May-3 Lempertz, Koln #747/R est:2500

LEHMDEN, Anton (1929-) Austrian
£3481 $5500 €5500 Large stone (34x44cm-13x17in) s.d.1984-85 panel. 27-Nov-2 Dorotheum, Vienna #265/R est:6000-9000

Works on paper

£1844	$2987	€2600	Birds flying over landscape (19x12cm-7x5in) s.d.1971 W/C. 20-May-3 Dorotheum, Vienna #216/R est:2400-3200
£2083	$3312	€3000	Reeds (37x54cm-15x21in) s.d.1999-2000 W/C. 29-Apr-3 Wiener Kunst Auktionen, Vienna #445/R est:3000-5000

LEHNERT, Hildegard (1857-?) German

£352	$567	€500	Still life with hortensia (90x75cm-35x30in) s. lit. 9-May-3 Schloss Ahlden, Ahlden #1506/R

LEHTO, Nikolai (1905-1994) Finnish

£284	$449	€440	Girl (18x13cm-7x5in) s. 19-Dec-2 Hagelstam, Helsinki #901
£297	$469	€460	Woman (18x16cm-7x6in) s. 19-Dec-2 Hagelstam, Helsinki #902/R
£301	$493	€460	Boy (20x15cm-8x6in) s.d.80. 9-Feb-3 Bukowskis, Helsinki #291/R
£317	$510	€450	Figure on the roof (29x23cm-11x9in) s.d.82 board. 10-May-3 Bukowskis, Helsinki #127/R
£386	$602	€610	The Holy Family (27x40cm-11x16in) S.D.82. 15-Sep-2 Bukowskis, Helsinki #225/R
£387	$612	€600	The Devil's ravine (26x30cm-10x12in) s. 19-Dec-2 Hagelstam, Helsinki #801
£408	$649	€600	Red lips (22x18cm-9x7in) s.d.82. 24-Mar-3 Bukowskis, Helsinki #151/R
£440	$678	€700	By the gate (39x26cm-15x10in) s.d.1971. 24-Oct-2 Hagelstam, Helsinki #863/R
£503	$775	€800	Midsummer dance (37x47cm-15x19in) s.d.1956. 24-Oct-2 Hagelstam, Helsinki #934/R
£704	$1134	€1000	Madonna and Child (43x28cm-17x11in) s.d.68 board. 10-May-3 Bukowskis, Helsinki #126/R
£759	$1200	€1200	Morning (20x17cm-8x7in) s.d.70 board. 1-Dec-2 Bukowskis, Helsinki #102/R

LEIBL, Wilhelm (1844-1900) German

£1282	$1987	€2000	Room in a country house with garden view (22x19cm-9x7in) s. panel. 4-Dec-2 Neumeister, Munich #801/R est:2200
£2597	$3870	€4000	Old peasant woman (46x37cm-18x15in) board prov. 26-Jun-2 Neumeister, Munich #784/R est:1200
£4870	$7256	€7500	Peasant girl (35x38cm-14x15in) prov.lit. 26-Jun-2 Neumeister, Munich #783/R est:2000

LEIBMANN, J M (19th C) German?

£577	$906	€900	Music lesson (37x40cm-15x16in) s.d.1841. 23-Nov-2 Arnold, Frankfurt #787/R

LEIBOVITZ, Annie (1949-) American

Photographs

£3896	$6000	€5844	John Lennon and Yoko Ono (38x38cm-15x15in) s.i.d.1980 num.8/30 photograph. 24-Oct-2 Sotheby's, New York #230/R est:6000-8000

LEICKERT, Charles (1818-1907) Belgian

£4577	$7370	€6500	Ships on calm water (29x42cm-11x17in) s. 7-May-3 Vendue Huis, Gravenhage #382/R est:5000-7000
£4610	$7468	€6500	At the city gate (17x14cm-7x6in) s. panel. 22-May-3 Dorotheum, Vienna #54/R est:6500-8000
£4808	$7452	€7500	River landscape in Holland with rowing boat, sailing boat and windmill (37x50cm-15x20in) s. 4-Dec-2 Neumeister, Munich #803/R est:7500
£5500	$8745	€8250	Dutch estuary (25x33cm-10x13in) s. board. 20-Mar-3 Christie's, Kensington #146/R est:3000-5000
£5696	$8886	€9000	Dutch city with figures in a snow-covered street (21x16cm-8x6in) s. panel. 21-Oct-2 Glerum, Amsterdam #55/R est:8000-10000
£5975	$9201	€9500	Figures skating on a frozen waterway on a windy day (14x20cm-6x8in) s. panel. 23-Oct-2 Christie's, Amsterdam #2/R est:7000-9000
£6000	$9540	€9000	Skaters on a frozen river beside a village (25x33cm-10x13in) s. panel prov. 18-Mar-3 Bonhams, New Bond Street #16/R est:6000-8000
£6289	$9686	€10000	Figures on a frozen river, with windmill beyond (40x59cm-16x23in) s. 23-Oct-2 Christie's, Amsterdam #122/R est:12000-16000
£7556	$12391	€10956	Summer canal scene (21x29cm-8x11in) s. panel. 9-Jun-3 Hodgins, Calgary #377/R est:10000-14000 (C.D 17000)
£7595	$11772	€12000	Moonlit Dutch beach (49x65cm-19x26in) s. 28-Sep-2 Hans Stahl, Hamburg #62/R est:12000
£7914	$12662	€11000	Vue de village Hollandais avec pecheurs et lavandieres (42x51cm-17x20in) s. 13-May-3 Palais de Beaux Arts, Brussels #96/R est:10000-15000
£8805	$13560	€14000	Winter landscape with figures on the ice (25x32cm-10x13in) s. panel. 22-Oct-2 Sotheby's, Amsterdam #144/R est:15000-20000
£9000	$15030	€13500	Villages gathered at the beach (46x61cm-18x24in) s. indis d. 18-Jun-3 Christie's, Kensington #43/R est:9000-12000
£9028	$14354	€13000	Skaters on a frozen river (19x25cm-7x10in) s. panel. 29-Apr-3 Christie's, Amsterdam #47/R est:7000-9000
£10063	$15497	€16000	Skaters in a winter landscape at dusk (24x46cm-9x18in) s. 22-Oct-2 Sotheby's, Amsterdam #26/R est:12000-15000
£10063	$15497	€16000	Fisherfolk on the beach (32x50cm-13x20in) s. panel. 22-Oct-2 Sotheby's, Amsterdam #173/R est:16000-20000
£10063	$15497	€16000	Street scene with villagers by a market stall (31x25cm-12x10in) s. panel. 22-Oct-2 Sotheby's, Amsterdam #179/R est:15000-20000
£11321	$17434	€18000	Fishermen on a beach at sunset (37x54cm-15x21in) s. 23-Oct-2 Christie's, Amsterdam #102/R est:20000-30000
£12000	$18840	€18000	View of a town, evening (38x54cm-15x21in) s.d.53 prov. 19-Nov-2 Sotheby's, London #146/R est:10000-15000
£13836	$21308	€22000	River landscape with figures on a country road (28x40cm-11x16in) s. panel. 22-Oct-2 Sotheby's, Amsterdam #161/R est:15000-20000
£14194	$22426	€22000	Bateaux et pecheurs a maree basse (26x36cm-10x14in) s.d.1854 panel. 19-Dec-2 Claude Aguttes, Neuilly #28/R est:20000
£15068	$23658	€22000	Villagers in the street of a Dutch town (36x42cm-14x17in) s. panel. 15-Apr-3 Sotheby's, Amsterdam #200/R est:20000-30000
£15723	$25000	€23585	Skaters on the river Amstel (61x99cm-24x39in) s. canvas on masonite painted c.1870. 4-May-3 Treadway Gallery, Cincinnati #480/R est:30000-50000
£18182	$30364	€26000	Vue de ville (30x22cm-12x9in) s. panel. 25-Jun-3 Artcurial Briest, Paris #528/R est:8000-10000
£19178	$30110	€28000	Skaters by a koek en zopie, mills in the distance (46x64cm-18x25in) s. 15-Apr-3 Sotheby's, Amsterdam #173/R est:30000-50000
£20755	$31962	€33000	Town view with villages in a boat on a canal (28x22cm-11x9in) s. panel. 22-Oct-2 Sotheby's, Amsterdam #168/R est:25000-35000
£21384	$32931	€34000	Villagers in the streets of a wintry town (27x21cm-11x8in) s. panel. 22-Oct-2 Sotheby's, Amsterdam #135/R est:20000-30000
£27097	$42000	€40646	Skaters on a frozen lake by the ruins of a castle (58x73cm-23x29in) s.d.63 prov. 30-Oct-2 Christie's, Rockefeller NY #3/R est:40000-60000
£34247	$53767	€50000	Skaters on the ice near a Koek en Zopie (65x101cm-26x40in) s.d.87. 15-Apr-3 Sotheby's, Amsterdam #154/R est:50000-70000
£50314	$77484	€80000	Winter landscape with skaters, Haarlem in the distance (62x100cm-24x39in) s. 22-Oct-2 Sotheby's, Amsterdam #139/R est:80000-120000

Works on paper

£1410	$2214	€2200	Amsterdam (33x23cm-13x9in) s. W/C. 21-Nov-2 Van Ham, Cologne #1744/R est:3000
£2466	$3871	€3600	View of the Jewish quarter (42x32cm-17x13in) s. W/C htd white. 15-Apr-3 Sotheby's, Amsterdam #46/R est:4000-6000

LEICKERT, Charles (attrib) (1818-1907) Belgian

£2500	$3925	€3750	Skaters in a winter landscape (28x44cm-11x17in) s. panel prov. 21-Nov-2 Christie's, Kensington #99/R est:3000-5000
£3145	$4906	€5000	Dutch town in winter (45x37cm-18x15in) s. prov. 19-Sep-2 Dr Fritz Nagel, Stuttgart #965/R est:8000
£8511	$13787	€12000	Paysages fluviaux (26x52cm-10x20in) panel pair. 26-May-3 Amberes, Antwerp #47

LEICKERT, Charles (circle) (1818-1907) Belgian

£10000	$16200	€15000	Skaters in a winter landscape (56x72cm-22x28in) s. panel. 23-Jan-3 Christie's, Kensington #102/R est:3000-4000

LEICKERT, Charles (style) (1818-1907) Belgian

£5200	$8476	€7800	Figures skating on a lake with a windmill (23x33cm-9x13in) bears sig board. 29-Jan-3 Sotheby's, Olympia #250/R est:1000-2000

LEIDL, Anton (1900-) German

£260	$379	€400	Still life on window ledge with Madonna and books (32x61cm-13x24in) s.d.45 panel. 14-Jun-2 Auktionhaus Georg Rehm, Augsburg #8082/R

LEIDNER, Bernard (20th C) French

£685	$1075	€1000	Joueurs de polo (120x120cm-47x47in) s.d.91. 21-Apr-3 Rabourdin & Choppin de Janvry, Paris #201

LEIER, Grant (1956-) American

£239	$373	€399	Troublemaker at the K.D Laing concert (38x25cm-15x10in).d.1990 s.i.d.verso ac. b. 13-Apr-3 Levis, Calgary #314/R (C.D 550)
£402	$627	€670	Martinis fireside (76x76cm-30x30in) s. s.i.d.1999 verso acrylic prov. 13-Apr-3 Levis, Calgary #313 est:800-1000 (C.D 925)

Works on paper

£283	$441	€471	Tis the season to be jolly (57x65cm-22x26in) s.d.1984 mixed media board prov. 13-Apr-3 Levis, Calgary #312/R (C.D 650)

LEIGH, Conrad Heighton (1883-?) British
Works on paper
£350 $571 €525 Graciosa and Persinette (34x22cm-13x9in) s. s.i.verso pencil W/C. 29-Jan-3 Dreweatt Neate, Newbury #104/R

LEIGH, William R (1866-1955) American
£4221 $6500 €6332 Blue hills (33x43cm-13x17in) s. canvasboard. 24-Oct-2 Shannon's, Milford #237/R est:4000-6000
£7547 $12000 €11321 Sunset (20x10cm-8x4in) s. board prov. 4-Mar-3 Christie's, Rockefeller NY #63/R est:7000-10000
£9434 $15000 €14151 Hopi water carrier (34x28cm-13x11in) s.d.1914 canvasboard prov. 5-Mar-3 Sotheby's, New York #147/R est:15000-20000
£15823 $25000 €22943 Zebra country (41x56cm-16x22in) s. board. 26-Jul-3 Coeur d'Alene, Hayden #121/R est:20000-30000
£18987 $30000 €27531 Serengeti Plains (41x56cm-16x22in) s. board prov. 26-Jul-3 Coeur d'Alene, Hayden #122/R est:20000-30000
£32051 $50000 €48077 Papago weaving grain basket (46x51cm-18x20in) 9-Nov-2 Altermann Galleries, Santa Fe #112
£60127 $95000 €87184 Grand Canyon (69x84cm-27x33in) s.d.1910 prov.exhib. 26-Jul-3 Coeur d'Alene, Hayden #51/R est:40000-60000
£68493 $100000 €102740 Sioux family escaping from Wounded Knee (56x71cm-22x28in) 18-May-2 Altermann Galleries, Santa Fe #43/R
£78767 $115000 €118151 The old family mare (102x152cm-40x60in) 18-May-2 Altermann Galleries, Santa Fe #44/R
£83871 $130000 €125807 Wild Texas steer (71x56cm-28x22in) s. indis d. prov. 5-Dec-2 Christie's, Rockefeller NY #178/R est:100000-150000
£90323 $140000 €135485 Navajo scout (61x46cm-24x18in) s.i.d.1915 prov.exhib. 5-Dec-2 Christie's, Rockefeller NY #180/R est:70000-100000
£96774 $150000 €145161 Looking for sheep (56x71cm-22x28in) s.d.1941 prov.exhib. 5-Dec-2 Christie's, Rockefeller NY #181/R est:100000-150000
Works on paper
£1752 $2750 €2628 Study for the buffalo drive (41x36cm-16x14in) s.i. pencil. 10-Dec-2 Doyle, New York #126/R est:4000-6000
£1911 $3000 €2867 Study for the best on the bunch (64x43cm-25x17in) s.i. pencil. 10-Dec-2 Doyle, New York #127/R est:4000-6000
£5414 $8500 €8121 Indian shooting arrow, study for the buffalo hunt (43x28cm-17x11in) s. pencil. 10-Dec-2 Doyle, New York #124/R est:10000-15000
£5732 $9000 €8598 Buffalo study for the buffalo hunt (36x43cm-14x17in) s. pencil. 10-Dec-2 Doyle, New York #125/R est:10000-15000

LEIGH-PEMBERTON, John (1911-) British
£400 $656 €600 Life on the wall, March (32x42cm-13x17in) s.d.58 board. 3-Jun-3 Sotheby's, Olympia #136/R
£550 $869 €825 Admiring the view (111x84cm-44x33in) s.d.48 canvas on board. 27-Nov-2 Sotheby's, Olympia #79/R
£1500 $2325 €2250 Fairground (113x121cm-44x48in) s.d.1936. 26-Sep-2 Mellors & Kirk, Nottingham #728/R est:1000-1500
Works on paper
£600 $984 €900 Derby day (32x42cm-13x17in) s.d.46 gouache on fabric. 3-Jun-3 Bonhams, Knightsbridge #61/R

LEIGHTON, Alfred Crocker (1901-1965) British
£2754 $4379 €4131 Early morning, Lake Louise (40x50cm-16x20in) s. 23-Mar-3 Hodgins, Calgary #34/R est:4000-6000 (C.D 6500)
£6992 $11117 €10488 Wolverine Plateau (60x75cm-24x30in) s.i. 23-Mar-3 Hodgins, Calgary #53/R est:8000-11000 (C.D 16500)
Works on paper
£341 $536 €512 Old Hastings, East Hill from the beach (20x28cm-8x11in) s.i. W/C. 25-Nov-2 Hodgins, Calgary #183/R (C.D 850)
£356 $583 €516 Study for sunlit peaks (20x25cm-8x10in) W/C pencil. 9-Jun-3 Hodgins, Calgary #346/R (C.D 800)
£422 $692 €612 Village in winter (23x29cm-9x11in) s.d.1956 W/C. 9-Jun-3 Hodgins, Calgary #111/R est:1000-1400 (C.D 950)
£440 $682 €660 Sawback Range, Banff (25x33cm-10x13in) s. W/C htd white. 4-Oct-2 Mallams, Oxford #474/R
£445 $707 €668 Millarville District (20x26cm-8x10in) s. pastel. 23-Mar-3 Hodgins, Calgary #121/R est:750-1000 (C.D 1050)
£551 $876 €827 Near Millarville (18x25cm-7x10in) s. W/C. 23-Mar-3 Hodgins, Calgary #113/R est:750-1000 (C.D 1300)
£800 $1312 €1160 Bit of old Calgary (21x29cm-8x11in) s.i.d.1933 W/C. 9-Jun-3 Hodgins, Calgary #4/R est:900-1100 (C.D 1800)
£1422 $2332 €2062 Sunlit Peaks (33x42cm-13x17in) s. W/C. 9-Jun-3 Hodgins, Calgary #347/R est:3500-4000 (C.D 3200)

LEIGHTON, Edmund Blair (1853-1922) British
£1500 $2340 €2250 Cut off with a shilling (13x18cm-5x7in) panel. 7-Nov-2 Christie's, Kensington #233/R est:800-1200
£2400 $3768 €3600 Medieval beauty (25x20cm-10x8in) init. panel. 19-Nov-2 Bonhams, New Bond Street #76/R est:1000-2000
£380000 $600400 €570000 Little Prince likely in time to bless a Royal Throne (178x144cm-70x57in) s. s.i.verso prov. 27-Nov-2 Christie's, London #11/R est:200000-300000

LEIGHTON, Kathryn Woodman (1876-1952) American
£937 $1500 €1406 Portrait of Pawnee Bill (77x64cm-30x25in) s. prov. 16-Mar-3 Butterfields, San Francisco #1042 est:2000-3000
£1056 $1700 €1584 Glacier park, mountain landscape (46x61cm-18x24in) i. 18-Feb-3 John Moran, Pasadena #116 est:2000-3000
£1774 $2750 €2661 Banff, Lake Louise (53x61cm-21x24in) s. masonite. 29-Oct-2 John Moran, Pasadena #704 est:2000-3000
£7186 $12000 €10420 Laguna Bay from Arch Beach (61x46cm-24x18in) s. i.d.1924 verso prov. 17-Jun-3 John Moran, Pasadena #43 est:5000-7000

LEIGHTON, Lord Frederic (1830-1896) British
£2258 $3500 €3387 Sketch near Cairo (10x17cm-4x7in) panel. 29-Oct-2 Sotheby's, New York #152/R est:6000-8000
£12000 $19920 €18000 Interior of a mosque of Mimbar of the Great Mosque at Damascus (31x24cm-12x9in) prov.lit. 10-Jun-3 Christie's, London #112/R est:12000-18000
£28000 $44240 €42000 Interior of St. Mark's, Venice (30x48cm-12x19in) canvas on board prov.exhib.lit. 27-Nov-2 Christie's, London #2/R est:30000-50000
£55000 $91300 €82500 Letty (30x25cm-12x10in) prov.exhib.lit. 12-Jun-3 Sotheby's, London #212/R est:60000-80000
£100000 $161000 €150000 Portrait of Ida, Adrian and Frederic marryat (130x91cm-51x36in) oval prov.exhib. 20-Feb-3 Christie's, London #292/R est:150000
£101266 $160000 €151899 Phoebe (60x53cm-24x21in) prov.exhib.lit. 24-Apr-3 Sotheby's, New York #1/R est:70000-90000
Sculpture
£8200 $12710 €12300 The sluggard, naked man with upheld flexing arms (92cm-36in) s.i. golden brown pat bronze square base. 29-Oct-2 Bonhams, New Bond Street #151/R est:7000-10000
£9032 $14000 €13548 Sluggard (52cm-20in) s.i. green pat. bronze prov.exhib.lit. 29-Oct-2 Sotheby's, New York #247/R est:10000-15000
£27419 $42500 €41129 Athlete struggling with a python (52cm-20in) s.d.1877 copper brown pat. bronze prov.exhib.lit. 29-Oct-2 Sotheby's, New York #248/R est:20000-30000
£40000 $64400 €60000 Study for athlete wrestling with python (24cm-9in) i.d.1895 plaster prov.exhib. 20-Feb-3 Christie's, London #150/R est:12000
£400000 $644000 €600000 Athlete wrestling with a python (178cm-70in) white marble on rectangular wooden and marble base prov.exhib.lit. 19-Feb-3 Christie's, London #28/R est:600000-800000
Works on paper
£3000 $4650 €4500 Study of a young boy (30x46cm-12x18in) pencil prov. 4-Dec-2 Christie's, Kensington #129/R est:2000-3000
£5500 $9020 €7975 Study of figures embracing (23x15cm-9x6in) i. black white chk prov.exhib. 5-Jun-3 Christie's, London #118/R est:3000-5000

LEIGHTON, Scott (1849-1898) American
£839 $1300 €1259 Roosters in barnyard (33x30cm-13x12in) s. i.verso. 29-Sep-2 Provenance, Pittstown #246

LEIMANIS, Andris (1938-) Canadian
£823 $1276 €1235 Sunny spring day in Montreal (67x100cm-26x39in) s. prov. 3-Dec-2 Joyner, Toronto #292/R est:1800-2200 (C.D 2000)

LEIPOLD, Karl (1864-1943) German
£755 $1170 €1200 Northern German fishing harbour with windmill and village (80x79cm-31x31in) 2-Nov-2 Hans Stahl, Toestorf #79/R

LEIRO, Francisco (1957-) Spanish
Sculpture
£2830 $4358 €4500 Reclining figure (54x31x22cm-21x12x9in) s.d.1989 wood exhib.lit. 28-Oct-2 Segre, Madrid #155/R est:5400

LEISNER, Vilhelm (1837-1910) Danish
£456 $725 €684 Wooded landscape (63x79cm-25x31in) s.d.Jan.1887. 10-Mar-3 Rasmussen, Vejle #288/R (D.KR 4900)

LEISSLER, Friedrich (1862-1926) German
£417 $654 €650 The broken pipe (64x40cm-25x16in) s.i.d.86. 23-Nov-2 Arnold, Frankfurt #789/R

LEISTEN, Jacobus (1844-1918) German
£408 $649 €600 Monks drinking at table (24x31cm-9x12in) s.d.1885 board. 20-Mar-3 Neumeister, Munich #2677/R

LEISTIKOW, Walter (1865-1908) Russian
£9494 $15000 €15000 Sunlit wood (74x93cm-29x37in) s. prov.exhib. 30-Nov-2 Villa Grisebach, Berlin #129/R est:20000-30000
£11538 $17885 €18000 Forest lake (54x71cm-21x28in) bears sig. 4-Dec-2 Lempertz, Koln #856/R est:18000-20000
£33544 $53000 €53000 Lake Grunewald (81x100cm-32x39in) s. painted c.1900 prov. 29-Nov-2 Villa Grisebach, Berlin #11/R est:50000-60000

Works on paper

£1282 $1987 €2000 Swedish coastal landscape (31x48cm-12x19in) W/C gouache board prov.lit. 7-Dec-2 Ketterer, Hamburg #137/R est:2200-2500
£4277 $6586 €6800 Mark lake (43x52cm-17x20in) s. gouache board. 26-Oct-2 Dr Lehr, Berlin #281/R est:9000
£4348 $7130 €6000 Evening (31x48cm-12x19in) s. s.i. verso gouache paper on board. 31-May-3 Villa Grisebach, Berlin #121/R est:7000-9000

LEITCH, Richard Principal (?-1882) British
Works on paper
£550 $847 €825 House at a lake side (37x53cm-15x21in) s.i.d.1878 W/C. 23-Oct-2 Hamptons Fine Art, Godalming #53/R

LEITCH, William Leighton (1804-1883) British
Works on paper
£260 $434 €377 Italian terrace with a woman standing on a flight of steps (23x33cm-9x13in) mono. W/C. 23-Jun-3 Bonhams, Bath #73
£380 $593 €570 Castle on a loch (13x22cm-5x9in) s.d.1876 W/C. 10-Apr-3 Bonhams, Edinburgh #145
£400 $624 €600 Eildon Hills (13x22cm-5x9in) s.d.1876 W/C. 10-Apr-3 Bonhams, Edinburgh #144
£410 $672 €615 Wooded landscape (30x44cm-12x17in) init.d.1845 W/C. 4-Feb-3 Bonhams, Leeds #260
£420 $655 €630 Windmill (7x11cm-3x4in) init. W/C prov. 18-Sep-2 Dreweatt Neate, Newbury #98
£480 $749 €720 Birks of Inverary (27x42cm-11x17in) s.d.1874 W/C. 10-Apr-3 Bonhams, Edinburgh #105/R
£520 $853 €780 Italian hilltop town (24x35cm-9x14in) mono. W/C. 4-Feb-3 Bonhams, Leeds #259
£700 $1155 €1015 Figures on a track in a mountainous landscape (23x39cm-9x15in) s.d.1859 pencil W/C htd bodycol. 3-Jul-3 Christie's, Kensington #112/R
£850 $1326 €1275 On the Tweed. Drumlanrig (21x32cm-8x13in) mono. pencil W/C pair. 27-Mar-3 Christie's, Kensington #76/R
£1000 $1540 €1500 Highland landscape at dusk (67x100cm-26x39in) indis.i. W/C. 22-Oct-2 Bonhams, Knightsbridge #46/R est:800-1200
£1000 $1530 €1500 Prospect of Dumbarton Rock from the town (17x27cm-7x11in) bears studio st. W/C htd white over pencil. 22-Aug-2 Bonhams, Edinburgh #1058/R est:1000-1500
£1000 $1580 €1500 Highland cattle and sheep below a ruined castle (32x57cm-13x22in) s. W/C. 26-Nov-2 Bonhams, Knightsbridge #23/R est:1000-1500
£1100 $1760 €1650 Figures by a tower in the Roman campagna (19x32cm-7x13in) s.d.1870 W/C. 11-Mar-3 Bonhams, New Bond Street #50/R est:800-1200
£2200 $3344 €3300 Bass Rock (37x59cm-15x23in) indis sid.d.1876 W/C scratching out exhib. 28-Aug-2 Sotheby's, London #868/R est:1500-2000
£3000 $4770 €4500 Bethlehem - evening after harvest (22x32cm-9x13in) i. W/C over pencil bodycol prov.exhib. 19-Mar-3 Sotheby's, London #217/R est:2000-3000
£6000 $8580 €9000 Parkland view at dusk (21x34cm-8x13in) st.sig. pencil W/C prov.lit. 22-Jan-3 Christie's, London #47/R est:5000

LEITCH, William Leighton (attrib) (1804-1883) British
Works on paper
£310 $484 €465 Highland croft in extensive landscape (33x53cm-13x21in) W/C. 11-Apr-3 Keys, Aylsham #401/R
£400 $632 €600 Capriccio of figures at a harbour side with trees beyond (24x34cm-9x13in) bears sig. W/C prov. 27-Nov-2 Hamptons Fine Art, Godalming #302/R
£520 $858 €754 Bolzano (35x51cm-14x20in) W/C. 2-Jul-3 Sotheby's, Olympia #248/R
£920 $1435 €1380 Marines rowing over to a warship, possibly on the Thames (11x19cm-4x7in) W/C laid down. 10-Apr-3 Bonhams, Edinburgh #146

LEITGEB, Franz (?) ?
£300 $465 €450 Floral still life with fruit (33x29cm-13x11in) s. panel. 6-Oct-2 Lots Road, London #342
£700 $1106 €1015 Portraits of Tyrolean gentlemen (25x20cm-10x8in) s. board pair. 22-Jul-3 Gorringes, Lewes #1711

LEITH-ROSS, Harry (1886-1973) American
£1899 $3000 €2849 Pinto Hills (20x28cm-8x11in) s. canvasboard. 24-Apr-3 Shannon's, Milford #179/R est:3000-5000

LEITNER, Thomas (1876-1948) Austrian
£605 $950 €908 Late afternoon light (30x43cm-12x17in) s.d.1920. 23-Nov-2 Jackson's, Cedar Falls #27/R
£649 $968 €1000 Ostsee coast near Heiligendamm (36x58cm-14x23in) i.d.1913 i. verso panel. 26-Jun-2 Neumeister, Munich #785/R
£671 $1081 €1000 Bridge near Mitterndorf (70x90cm-28x35in) s.d.1912 prov.exhib. 18-Feb-3 Sotheby's, Amsterdam #291/R est:800-1200
£1090 $1722 €1700 Dalmatian coast (54x90cm-21x35in) s.d.1908. 12-Nov-2 Dorotheum, Vienna #5/R est:1700-2400
£1238 $1956 €1857 Winter landscape (73x100cm-29x39in) s.d.1907. 30-Nov-2 Dorotheum, Prague #15/R est:60000-90000 (C.KR 60000)
£1517 $2428 €2200 Landscape with trees (100x110cm-39x43in) s.d.1922 prov. 11-Mar-3 Dorotheum, Vienna #34/R est:2600-3600

LEITNER-GRUNDBERG, Rudolf (1955-) Austrian
£2069 $3310 €3000 Wounded deer by tear lake (168x186cm-66x73in) 11-Mar-3 Dorotheum, Vienna #283/R est:6000-9000

LEIVA, Nicolas (1958-) Argentinian
Sculpture
£12739 $20000 €19109 Flowers (41x240x2cm-16x94x1in) yellow clay glass exec.2000 prov. 20-Nov-2 Christie's, Rockefeller NY #64/R est:20000-25000

LEJEUNE, Eugène (1818-1897) French
£8000 $13360 €12000 Feeding time (52x63cm-20x25in) s. 18-Jun-3 Christie's, Kensington #89/R est:8000-12000

LEK, Hans van der (1936-2001) Dutch
£414 $646 €650 Still life (99x37cm-39x15in) mono. 5-Nov-2 Vendu Notarishuis, Rotterdam #123/R

LEK, Karel (1929-) British
Works on paper
£480 $749 €720 Mother, child and pram (13x16cm-5x6in) s. crayon pastel. 11-Sep-2 Bonhams, Newport #372

LEKGOTHO, Simon (1929-1985) South African
£416 $650 €624 Divination objects with a calabash (54x43cm-21x17in) s.d.64 canvasboard. 11-Nov-2 Stephan Welz, Johannesburg #578/R (SA.R 6500)
£921 $1437 €1382 Still life with calabash (61x44cm-24x17in) s.d.65 canvas on board. 15-Oct-2 Stephan Welz, Johannesburg #502/R est:7000-10000 (SA.R 15000)

LEKINFF, Linda (1949-) French
£833 $1300 €1250 Le fleur grise (81x99cm-32x39in) 11-Apr-3 Du Mouchelle, Detroit #90/R est:1800-2200

LELEE, Leopold (1872-1947) French
Works on paper
£437 $681 €656 Deux Arlesiennes pres du theatre antique d'Arles (31x36cm-12x14in) s. W/C over pencil. 6-Nov-2 Dobiaschofsky, Bern #769/R (S.FR 1000)

LELEUX, Armand-Hubert-Simon (1818-1885) French
£4268 $7000 €6402 Connoisseur's visit (81x65cm-32x26in) s. prov. 5-Feb-3 Christie's, Rockefeller NY #183/R est:4000-6000

LELIE, Adriaen de (1755-1820) Dutch
£510 $795 €800 Christ on the cross (282x215cm-111x85in) s.d.1820 prov. 5-Nov-2 Sotheby's, Amsterdam #123/R
£1769 $2812 €2600 Amoureux (49x39cm-19x15in) s. 18-Mar-3 Campo, Vlaamse Kaai #44/R est:4500-5500

LELIENBERGH, Cornelis van (1626-c.1676) Dutch
£6918 $10723 €11000 Still life of game birds (58x49cm-23x19in) mono.d.1672. 2-Oct-2 Dorotheum, Vienna #147/R est:10000-15000
£16667 $26333 €26000 Hunting still life (137x11cm-54x4in) canvas on panel prov. 16-Nov-2 Lempertz, Koln #1048/R est:15000

LELLI, Giovan Battista (1828-1887) Italian
£629 $969 €1000 View of farm with peasants and animals (21x36cm-8x14in) s. 28-Oct-2 Il Ponte, Milan #299

LELLOUCHE, Jules (1903-1963) French
£566 $872 €900 Marine (16x22cm-6x9in) s. s.i.verso cardboard. 23-Oct-2 Rabourdin & Choppin de Janvry, Paris #255/R
£1295 $2124 €1800 Nu au drap jaune (46x65cm-18x26in) s. 4-Jun-3 Tajan, Paris #303/R est:1800-2000
£1361 $2163 €2000 Ruelle dans la medina (31x23cm-12x9in) s.d.1921 cardboard prov. 24-Mar-3 Rabourdin & Choppin de Janvry, Paris #210/R est:1000-1500

LELOIR, Alexandre Louis (1843-1884) French
£1887 $3000 €2831 At the balcony (37x28cm-15x11in) s. panel. 7-Mar-3 Skinner, Boston #251/R est:3000-5000
Works on paper
£1100 $1749 €1650 Chance meeting with a fortune teller (30x80cm-12x31in) s. W/C shaped as a fan. 20-Mar-3 Christie's, Kensington #107/R est:1000-1500

LELOIR, Maurice (1853-1940) French
£443 $687 €700 La halte du cavalier (24x32cm-9x13in) s. panel. 29-Sep-2 Eric Pillon, Calais #36/R
£1497 $2380 €2200 Young woman making flower garden (71x60cm-28x24in) s. 19-Mar-3 Neumeister, Munich #624/R est:1200

LELONG, Corinne (20th C) French
Works on paper
£511 $817 €710 La taille (90x90cm-35x35in) mono. mixed media canvas. 18-May-3 Neret-Minet, Paris #128

LELONG, Paul (19th C) French
£353 $554 €550 Recolte du goemon (22x27cm-9x11in) s. panel. 15-Dec-2 Thierry & Lannon, Brest #398
Works on paper
£2436 $3849 €3800 Nature morte au perroquet et nature morte au livre (15x20cm-6x8in) gouache pair. 15-Nov-2 Drouot Estimations, Paris #61/R est:3000-4500
£2564 $4026 €4000 Natures mortes (15x20cm-6x8in) s. gouache pair. 14-Dec-2 Artcurial Briest, Paris #10/R

LELONG, Pierre (?-1645) French
£316 $500 €500 A la piscine (46x55cm-18x22in) s. 27-Nov-2 Blanchet, Paris #79
£320 $499 €480 Le rue Mauffetard (48x56cm-19x22in) s. exhib. 9-Oct-2 Woolley & Wallis, Salisbury #285/R

LELONG, René (19th C) French?
£1392 $2200 €2200 Elegant couple (65x35cm-26x14in) s. cardboard. 26-Nov-2 Christie's, Rome #26/R
£9032 $14000 €13548 Sarah Bernhardt at the Paris opera (49x36cm-19x14in) s. canvas on board. 29-Oct-2 Sotheby's, New York #91/R est:15000-20000
Works on paper
£962 $1490 €1500 Propagande electorale (37x52cm-15x20in) s. chl htd white. 6-Dec-2 Rieunier, Bailly-Pommery, Mathias, Paris #71/R

LELU, Pierre (1741-1810) French
Works on paper
£285 $450 €450 Soldats jouant aux des dans un interieur (38x30cm-15x12in) pen black ink brown wash gouache. 27-Nov-2 Christie's, Paris #174/R
£507 $800 €800 Traite des chevres (22x44cm-9x17in) pen ink wash crayon. 28-Nov-2 Tajan, Paris #76

LELY, Sir Peter (1618-1680) British
£1258 $2000 €1887 Portrait of a distinguished gentleman (76x61cm-30x24in) painted c.1670. 2-Mar-3 Toomey, Oak Park #598/R est:3000-5000
£3659 $6000 €5489 Portrait of Elizabeth Howard, Countess of Peterborough, bust-length (76x63cm-30x25in) i. 30-May-3 Christie's, Rockefeller NY #45/R est:8000-12000
£12000 $18960 €18000 Portrait of Elizabeth Countess of Cork (114x91cm-45x36in) 28-Nov-2 Sotheby's, London #150/R est:10000-15000
£26000 $41080 €39000 Portrait of Henry Fitzroy, Earl of Euston, 1st Duke of Grafton (126x103cm-50x41in) unlined canvas. 26-Nov-2 Christie's, London #6a/R est:30000-50000
£800000 $1328000 €1200000 Chesterfield portrait, two boys, probably Philip Stanhope and brother Charles (117x171cm-46x67in) 12-Jun-3 Sotheby's, London #10/R est:400000-600000

LELY, Sir Peter (circle) (1618-1680) British
£5200 $8060 €7800 Half length portrait of a lady in a blue dress trimmed with ermine (35x28cm-14x11in) prov. 6-Dec-2 Lyon & Turnbull, Edinburgh #21/R est:4000-6000
£11000 $16940 €16500 Portrait of Isabella Chicheley, nee Lawson (127x102cm-50x40in) 5-Sep-2 Christie's, Kensington #15/R est:6000-8000

LELY, Sir Peter (studio) (1618-1680) British
£8000 $13280 €12000 Portrait of Princess Isabella, seated with garland of flowers in her hair, in an landscape (126x102cm-50x40in) i. prov. 10-Jun-3 Christie's, London #7/R est:7000-10000
£11000 $17380 €16500 Portrait of lady, possibly Louise de Kerouaille by tree (126x102cm-50x40in) prov.exhib. 26-Nov-2 Christie's, London #7/R est:8000-12000

LEMAIRE, F (?) ?
£500 $795 €725 Portrait of a lady half length (35x25cm-14x10in) panel. 29-Apr-3 Henry Adams, Chichester #281

LEMAIRE, Fernand (19th C) French
£253 $395 €400 La cuillere aux roses (75x100cm-30x39in) s. painted c.1900. 10-Sep-2 Vanderkindere, Brussels #406

LEMAIRE, Hector Joseph (1846-?) French
Sculpture
£1195 $1864 €1900 Judith (64cm-25in) s.i.d.1873 dark brown pat.bronze. 20-Sep-2 Schloss Ahlden, Ahlden #637/R est:2400

LEMAIRE, Jean (1598-1659) French
£30488 $50000 €45732 Figures amongst classical architectural ruins (80x101cm-31x40in) prov.lit. 30-May-3 Christie's, Rockefeller NY #57/R est:60000-80000

LEMAIRE, Louis Marie (1824-1910) French
£993 $1539 €1490 Still life of roses (46x38cm-18x15in) s. 4-Dec-2 AB Stockholms Auktionsverk #1866/R (S.KR 14000)
£1800 $2934 €2700 Still life of roses (73x59cm-29x23in) s. 29-Jan-3 Sotheby's, Olympia #304/R est:2000-3000
£11465 $18000 €17198 Lilacs and peonies with porcelain vase in the garden (138x115cm-54x45in) s. exhib. 21-Nov-2 Sotheby's, New York #223/R est:20000-30000

LEMAIRE, Madeleine (1845-1928) French
Works on paper
£709 $1120 €1064 Vase of flowers (52x37cm-20x15in) s. 15-Nov-2 Naón & Cia, Buenos Aires #129/R
£900 $1395 €1350 Roses in a basket (55x77cm-22x30in) s. W/C. 24-Sep-2 Bonhams, Knightsbridge #22/R
£962 $1510 €1500 Kiss (50x34cm-20x13in) s.d.1887 W/C. 13-Dec-2 Piasa, Paris #159

LEMAIRE, Pierre (attrib) (1612-1688) French
£9434 $14623 €15000 Mythological scene, Roman solider with fishermen (72x93cm-28x37in) s. 2-Oct-2 Dorotheum, Vienna #251/R est:15000-20000

LEMAITRE, Albert (1886-1975) Belgian
£284 $474 €400 Vue sur les champs (58x69cm-23x27in) s. panel. 18-Jun-3 Hotel des Ventes Mosan, Brussels #211

LEMAITRE, Andre (1909-1995) French
£890 $1398 €1300 Voiliers, le soir a maree haute (40x56cm-16x22in) s. panel. 21-Apr-3 Rabourdin & Choppin de Janvry, Paris #142
£1027 $1613 €1500 Le port de Granville le soir (39x42cm-15x17in) s. s.i.d.verso. 21-Apr-3 Rabourdin & Choppin de Janvry, Paris #140 est:1200-1400
£1336 $2097 €1950 Nature morte (60x72cm-24x28in) s. 21-Apr-3 Rabourdin & Choppin de Janvry, Paris #141/R est:2200-2500
£1646 $2567 €2600 Le vase de fleurs (55x46cm-22x18in) s. isorel. 15-Sep-2 Etude Bailleul, Bayeux #136/R
Works on paper
£304 $474 €480 Le pot de fleurs (64x49cm-25x19in) s.d.1974 W/C. 15-Sep-2 Etude Bailleul, Bayeux #137/R

LEMAITRE, E G (19th C) French
Sculpture
£2700 $4185 €4050 Au coup de fusil - two alert pointers (27x44cm-11x17in) s. bronze executed c.1890. 3-Dec-2 Sworder & Son, Bishops Stortford #428/R est:1200-1500

LEMAITRE, Eglantine (19th C) French
Sculpture
£1200 $1848 €1800 Hound (26x35cm-10x14in) s. bronze. 5-Sep-2 Sotheby's, Olympia #139/R est:1200-1800

LEMAITRE, Maurice (1929-) French

£311 $500 €467 Coastal scene with figures and boats at low tide (48x33cm-19x13in) s. 19-Jan-3 Jeffery Burchard, Florida #76a/R
£331 $533 €470 Village provencal (22x27cm-9x11in) s. 12-May-3 Lesieur & Le Bars, Le Havre #58/R
£570 $889 €900 Paysage (45x63cm-18x25in) s. 20-Oct-2 Chayette & Cheval, Paris #113
£943 $1472 €1500 Paysage a Clairmarais (27x35cm-11x14in) s. panel. 9-Oct-2 Lombrail & Teucquam, Paris #7/R
£955 $1490 €1500 Pommiers au printemps a Saint-Augustin (27x35cm-11x14in) s. i.verso. 10-Nov-2 Eric Pillon, Calais #113/R
£1000 $1600 €1450 Le Lay aux Moutiers (33x46cm-13x18in) s. i.verso. 16-May-3 Skinner, Boston #341/R est:3000-5000
£1216 $1897 €1800 Montigny-sur-Long (54x81cm-21x32in) 28-Mar-3 Claude Aguttes, Neuilly #81/R
£1218 $1912 €1900 Au bord du Chera Savonnieres (27x35cm-11x14in) s. panel. 15-Dec-2 Lombrail & Teucquam, Paris #12/R
£1234 $1875 €1900 Coin de marais a Ecourt Saint-Quentin (33x46cm-13x18in) s. 7-Jul-2 Lombrail & Teucquam, Paris #58/R
£1258 $1962 €2000 Paysage a Marnay (38x55cm-15x22in) s. 9-Oct-2 Lombrail & Teucquam, Paris #5/R
£1268 $2041 €1800 Les bords de l'Yerres a Bernay (46x61cm-18x24in) s. 11-May-3 Lombrail & Teucquam, Paris #237/R
£1474 $2315 €2300 Hortillonnages, Amienss (38x55cm-15x22in) s. 15-Dec-2 Lombrail & Teucquam, Paris #11/R
£1625 $2600 €2356 Coquelicots a Vezilly (46x65cm-18x26in) s. i.verso. 16-May-3 Skinner, Boston #330/R est:4000-6000
£1667 $2617 €2600 Chemin dans le marais a Ecourt Saint-Quentin (46x61cm-18x24in) s. 15-Dec-2 Lombrail & Teucquam, Paris #10/R
£2323 $3670 €3600 Paysage printanier (60x73cm-24x29in) s. 19-Dec-2 Claude Aguttes, Neuilly #184/R

LEMAITRE, Nathanael (1831-1897) French

£880 $1416 €1276 Part of bank of Lake Geneva (46x80cm-18x31in) s. 9-May-3 Dobiaschofsky, Bern #50/R (S.FR 1900)
£2066 $3388 €2996 Aletsch glacier (35x51cm-14x20in) s. 4-Jun-3 Fischer, Luzern #1237/R est:3000-3500 (S.FR 4400)

LEMAN, Robert (1799-1863) British
Works on paper

£260 $406 €390 River landscape with figures working in the fields (25x46cm-10x18in) W/C bodycol over pencil. 10-Apr-3 Tennants, Leyburn #841

LEMAN, Robert (attrib) (1799-1863) British
Works on paper

£380 $589 €570 Heron on the riverbank (29x41cm-11x16in) W/C. 30-Sep-2 Bonhams, Ipswich #303

LEMARCHAND, David (attrib) (1674-1726) French
Sculpture

£15493 $25718 €22000 Venus (25cm-10in) ivory wood socle. 16-Jun-3 Anaf, Lyon #55/R est:25000-28000

LEMASLE, Louis Nicolas (1788-1870) French

£2302 $3776 €3200 Portrait du roi Louis Philippe (48x39cm-19x15in) i. panel. 5-Jun-3 Fraysse & Associes, Paris #16 est:3000-5000

LEMATTE, Jacques François Fernand (1850-?) French

£704 $1134 €1000 Portrait de jeune garcon (23x15cm-9x6in) s. 11-May-3 Thierry & Lannon, Brest #376

LEMCHEN, Lisen (?) Swedish

£461 $715 €692 Still life of flowers (39x56cm-15x22in) s. panel. 8-Dec-2 Uppsala Auktionskammare, Uppsala #163 (S.KR 6500)

LEMEUNIER, Basile (1852-?) French

£645 $1019 €1000 Scene galante (25x32cm-10x13in) s. 18-Dec-2 Ferri, Paris #87/R
£1603 $2532 €2500 Partie de plage a Maree Basse (57x80cm-22x31in) s. 18-Nov-2 Tajan, Paris #199/R est:1500-2400
£6323 $9990 €9800 Elegante au chapeau (46x32cm-18x13in) s.i.d.1901. 18-Dec-2 Ferri, Paris #86/R est:10000
£6452 $10194 €10000 Elegante au balcon (55x36cm-22x14in) s. 19-Dec-2 Claude Aguttes, Neuilly #67/R est:12000

LEMIEUX, Clement (1946-) Canadian
Sculpture

£978 $1604 €1467 Two par 2 danes, les amoureux (76cm-30in) s. painted wood granite base. 3-Jun-3 Joyner, Toronto #330/R est:1500-2000 (C.D 2200)

LEMIEUX, Jean Paul (1904-1990) Canadian

£2222 $3644 €3333 Ile aux coudres (31x39cm-12x15in) s.d.32 panel on masonite prov. 27-May-3 Sotheby's, Toronto #11/R est:5000-7000 (C.D 5000)
£5333 $8747 €8000 Woman in yellow (29x23cm-11x9in) s. oil on paper. 3-Jun-3 Joyner, Toronto #10/R est:10000-12000 (C.D 12000)
£5778 $9476 €8667 La riviere (46x107cm-18x42in) s.d.54 prov.exhib.lit. 27-May-3 Sotheby's, Toronto #10/R est:8000-10000 (C.D 13000)
£7819 $12119 €11729 Femme en noir (50x37cm-20x15in) s.d.52 board prov. 3-Dec-2 Joyner, Toronto #96/R est:15000-20000 (C.D 19000)
£14113 $22298 €21170 Glaces au bord de la mer (69x110cm-27x43in) s.d.1962 prov.exhib.lit. 18-Nov-2 Sotheby's, Toronto #50/R est:40000-50000 (C.D 35000)
£15695 $25112 €23543 Novembre (51x126cm-20x50in) s.d.1962 prov. 15-May-3 Heffel, Vancouver #186/R est:30000-40000 (C.D 35000)
£16889 $27698 €25334 House in a forest (54x129cm-21x51in) s.d.64 prov. 3-Jun-3 Joyner, Toronto #87/R est:40000-50000 (C.D 38000)
£19153 $30262 €28730 La tuque bleu (36x46cm-14x18in) s.i.d.1975 prov. 14-Nov-2 Heffel, Vancouver #45/R est:50000-60000 (C.D 47500)
£20576 $31893 €30864 Train station (62x75cm-24x30in) s. 3-Dec-2 Joyner, Toronto #100/R est:75000-100000 (C.D 50000)
£26210 $41411 €39315 Promenade nocturne (41x51cm-16x20in) s. 14-Nov-2 Heffel, Vancouver #106/R est:35000-45000 (C.D 65000)
£40323 $63710 €60485 Printemps (76x56cm-30x22in) s.d.1968 i.verso prov. 14-Nov-2 Heffel, Vancouver #64/R est:60000-80000 (C.D 100000)
£53333 $87467 €80000 Une famile (172x107cm-68x42in) s.d.66 prov.exhib.lit. 3-Jun-3 Joyner, Toronto #58/R est:125000-175000 (C.D 120000)

Works on paper

£2319 $3664 €3479 Petite Poule D'eau Portage-des-pres (23x30cm-9x12in) s.i. indis d. ink wash pencil prov.lit. 18-Nov-2 Sotheby's, Toronto #163/R est:3000-4000 (C.D 5750)
£3333 $5467 €5000 La missionaire Anglicane (59x47cm-23x19in) s.i. ink. 3-Jun-3 Joyner, Toronto #151/R est:10000-15000 (C.D 7500)

LEMIRE, Charles Gabriel (1741-1827) French
Sculpture

£1972 $3273 €2800 Amour enfant mettant une corde a son arc (41x26x12cm-16x10x5in) s. green brown pat bronze. 11-Jun-3 Cornette de St.Cyr, Paris #218/R est:3000-3500

LEMKE, Johann Philip (attrib) (1631-1711) German

£2553 $3957 €3830 Battle scene (33x50cm-13x20in) 3-Dec-2 Bukowskis, Stockholm #394/R est:15000-18000 (S.KR 36000)
£3169 $5261 €4500 Camp with resting and card playing soldiers (44x60cm-17x24in) mono. panel prov. 11-Jun-3 Dorotheum, Vienna #138/R est:5000-7000
£5499 $9018 €7974 Preparation for battle - soldiers and horses (77x133cm-30x52in) 4-Jun-3 AB Stockholms Auktionsverk #2246/R est:35000-40000 (S.KR 70000)

LEMMEN, Georges (1865-1916) Belgian

£5975 $9261 €9500 Nu a l'eventail (46x55cm-18x22in) board lit. 5-Oct-2 De Vuyst, Lokeren #541/R est:8000-9000
£7194 $11799 €10000 Paysage sous la neige - landscape in winter (31x40cm-12x16in) i. panel exhib. 3-Jun-3 Christie's, Amsterdam #267/R est:12000-16000
£8333 $13083 €13000 Nu de dos (38x46cm-15x18in) s.d.1913 cardboard. 10-Dec-2 Vanderkindere, Brussels #65/R est:7500-10000
£12500 $19625 €19500 Jeune femme assise au chapeau (71x60cm-28x24in) mono.d.1908. 10-Dec-2 Vanderkindere, Brussels #45/R est:8000-12000

Works on paper

£1600 $2464 €2400 La couture, Madame Lemmen, Pierre et Jacques (15x19cm-6x7in) st.mono.d.aout 1904 pen ink pencil W/C col crayon. 23-Oct-2 Sotheby's, Olympia #677/R est:1500-2000
£5396 $8633 €7500 Woman seated (36x33cm-14x13in) black chk, oil, W/C pastel board lit. 17-May-3 De Vuyst, Lokeren #547/R est:5500-6000
£6774 $10500 €10161 Portrait du Julie et Madame Lemmen (34x24cm-13x9in) d.jeudi 8 janv.91 graphite chl exhib. 3-Dec-2 Christie's, Rockefeller NY #40/R est:500-700

LEMMEN, Georges (attrib) (1865-1916) Belgian
Prints

£1923 $3019 €3000 Jeune femme au chapeau assise (36x33cm-14x13in) engraving htd W/C exhib. 10-Dec-2 Vanderkindere, Brussels #28 est:500-750

LEMMENS, Theophile Victor Émile (1821-1867) French

£1218 $1900 €1827 Hound in pursuit of ducks (18x23cm-7x9in) s. panel. 20-Sep-2 Freeman, Philadelphia #115/R est:600-1000

LEMMERS, Georges (1871-1944) Belgian
£443 $691 €700 Chemin mediterraneen anime (33x43cm-13x17in) s. 16-Sep-2 Horta, Bruxelles #148
£890 $1398 €1300 L'arcade (100x73cm-39x29in) s. 15-Apr-3 Galerie Moderne, Brussels #334
£1013 $1580 €1600 Arcade (101x73cm-40x29in) s. 16-Sep-2 Horta, Bruxelles #146
£1042 $1656 €1500 Nature morte aux roses (55x66cm-22x26in) s. 29-Apr-3 Campo & Campo, Antwerp #181/R est:1800-2200
£1203 $1876 €1900 Tournant de riviere a Aurillac (73x101cm-29x40in) s. s.i.verso. 16-Sep-2 Horta, Bruxelles #147

LEMOINE, Charles (1839-?) French
Sculpture
£6600 $10296 €9900 Psyche (84cm-33in) s. white marble lit. 9-Apr-3 Sotheby's, London #86/R est:5000-7000

LEMOINE, Elisabeth (attrib) (18th C) French
£4054 $6324 €6000 Portrait de jeune femme au noeud rouge (64x53cm-25x21in) oval. 26-Mar-3 Tajan, Paris #78/R

LEMOINE, Jacques (1751-1824) French
Miniatures
£2400 $3888 €3600 Lady wearing pale blue dress (6cm-2in) i. 22-May-3 Bonhams, New Bond Street #56/R est:800-1200
£4000 $6560 €5800 Mother with her child at her breast (6cm-2in circular) gilt metal frame lit. 3-Jun-3 Christie's, London #106/R est:4000-6000
Works on paper
£1139 $1800 €1800 Portrait d'homme. Portrait de femme (13cm-5in circular) pierre noire stump chk pair. 28-Nov-2 Tajan, Paris #64/R

LEMOINE, Marie Victoire (attrib) (1754-1820) French
£3097 $4893 €4800 Portrait d'homme en habit rouge. Portrait de jeune femme a la coiffure ornee de lilas (70x56cm-28x22in) pair oval. 19-Dec-2 Delvaux, Paris #96/R
£3205 $4968 €5000 Esquisse pour portrait de Madame de Cosse (54x52cm-21x20in) oval prov. 4-Dec-2 Libert, Castor, Paris #51/R
£5449 $8446 €8500 Portrait de femme peintre (58x48cm-23x19in) panel. 6-Dec-2 Rieunier, Bailly-Pommery, Mathias, Paris #44/R

LEMON, Arthur (1850-1912) British
£900 $1395 €1350 Nude boy wearing a wide brimmed hat seated on a beach. Study of a cow (13x18cm-5x7in) one s.verso panel two exhib. 31-Oct-2 Duke & Son, Dorchester #291/R

LEMONNIER, Anicet Charles Gabriel (attrib) (1743-1824) French
£4000 $6240 €6000 Mercury delivering Peace to the victims of war (61x50cm-24x20in) 10-Apr-3 Christie's, Kensington #196/R est:4000-6000

LEMONNIER, Eugene (19th C) French?
Works on paper
£979 $1635 €1400 Femme et enfant pleurant (109x75cm-43x30in) s.d.1877 pastel. 25-Jun-3 Artcurial Briest, Paris #516/R est:2000-2500

LEMORDANT, Jean Julien (1882-1968) French
£278 $440 €440 Puits (26x21cm-10x8in) i. cardboard. 1-Dec-2 Livinec, Gaudcheau & Jezequel, Rennes #79/R
£962 $1510 €1500 Nu au peignoir rouge (58x47cm-23x19in) s. 15-Dec-2 Thierry & Lannon, Brest #152
£2658 $4438 €3800 La criee (46x38cm-18x15in) s. cardboard prov. 26-Jun-3 Tajan, Paris #67/R est:3800-4000
£3544 $5494 €5600 Marche Breton (33x41cm-13x16in) s.d.1902 panel. 29-Sep-2 Eric Pillon, Calais #191/R
Works on paper
£1319 $2151 €1900 Danse Bretonne (36x45cm-14x18in) s. gouache chl. 19-Jul-3 Thierry & Lannon, Brest #277 est:500-600

LEMOS, Luis (1954-) French?
Works on paper
£316 $500 €500 La punk aux cheveux bleus (140x110cm-55x43in) s.d.1990 s.i.d. verso mixed media. 30-Nov-2 Arnold, Frankfurt #342/R

LEMOS, Pedro Joseph (1882-1954) American
Works on paper
£994 $1600 €1491 Cypress in Monterey coastal (25x23cm-10x9in) s. pastel board prov. 18-Feb-3 John Moran, Pasadena #5 est:1000-1500

LEMOYNE, François (1688-1737) French
Works on paper
£3475 $5804 €4900 Trois etudes de mains et d'avant bras (18x23cm-7x9in) col crayon. 19-Jun-3 Piasa, Paris #100/R est:3000

LEMOYNE, François (style) (1688-1737) French
£26923 $41731 €42000 Mythological figures (70x83cm-28x33in) board set of 4 prov. 4-Dec-2 Christie's, Rome #436/R est:12000-18000

LEMOYNE, Jean Baptiste (younger) (1704-1778) French
Sculpture
£6081 $9486 €9000 Bust of elegant woman, possibly Mme Devandeuil (63cm-25in) s. bears d.1770 terracotta marble socle. 27-Mar-3 Dr Fritz Nagel, Stuttgart #987/R est:8000
£16026 $24840 €25000 Portrait de Ange-Jacques Gabriel (68x50x29cm-27x20x11in) terracotta marble base lit. 9-Dec-2 Rabourdin & Choppin de Janvry, Paris #10/R est:60000
£224359 $347756 €350000 Portrait du Baron Jean Francois de Fontette (61x37x30cm-24x15x12in) terracotta marble base prov.exhib.lit. 9-Dec-2 Rabourdin & Choppin de Janvry, Paris #12/R est:90000
Works on paper
£1582 $2468 €2500 Portrait de jeune fille (32x24cm-13x9in) bears sig. pierre noire sanguine htd pastel prov. 18-Oct-2 Rabourdin & Choppin de Janvry, Paris #77/R

LEMOYNE, Jean Baptiste (younger-attrib) (1704-1778) French
Sculpture
£2885 $4471 €4500 Portrait de Crebillon (48x28x22cm-19x11x9in) terracotta marble base lit. 9-Dec-2 Rabourdin & Choppin de Janvry, Paris #13/R

LEMOYNE, Serge (1941-) Canadian
£407 $638 €611 Untitled (66x50cm-26x20in) s. spray acrylic. 12-Dec-2 Iegor de Saint Hippolyte, Montreal #61 (C.D 1000)
£877 $1307 €1316 Sans titre (40x41cm-16x16in) isorel. 26-Jun-2 Iegor de Saint Hippolyte, Montreal #59 (C.D 2000)
£988 $1521 €1482 Janvier 62 (61x40cm-24x16in) s.i.d.verso isorel. 22-Oct-2 Iegor de Saint Hippolyte, Montreal #57 (C.D 2400)

LEMPICKA, Tamara de (1898-1980) Polish
£20186 $32500 €30279 Etude d'apres Botticelli (23x30cm-9x12in) s. canvasboard painted c.1950 prov.exhib.lit. 7-May-3 Sotheby's, New York #384/R est:35000-45000
£21384 $34000 €32076 Deux madones (27x35cm-11x14in) painted 1954 exhib.lit. 27-Feb-3 Christie's, Rockefeller NY #70/R est:35000
£22973 $35839 €34000 Tete de femme slave (46x38cm-18x15in) s. painted c.1925 exhib.lit. 26-Mar-3 Tajan, Paris #40/R
£30864 $43827 €50000 Raisins abstraits (86x106cm-34x42in) s. lit. 16-Mar-3 Eric Pillon, Calais #270/R
Works on paper
£1837 $2920 €2700 Etude academique (44x27cm-17x11in) studio st. col crayon dr. 26-Feb-3 Artcurial Briest, Paris #50 est:300-400
£2109 $3353 €3100 Nu pensif (28x44cm-11x17in) st.sig. sanguine dr. 26-Feb-3 Artcurial Briest, Paris #49 est:600-800

LENAGHAN, Brenda (1941-) British
£650 $1014 €975 Girl with peonies (29x29cm-11x11in) s. board. 17-Oct-2 Bonhams, Edinburgh #31/R
£740 $1169 €1110 Girl and peonies (74x74cm-29x29in) s. board. 5-Apr-3 Shapes, Edinburgh #318
£1200 $1824 €1800 Girls on beach (60x60cm-24x24in) s.d.83 board exhib. 28-Aug-2 Sotheby's, London #1030/R est:1500-2000
£1450 $2262 €2175 Girl in the amazing turban (75x75cm-30x30in) s.d.87 board. 17-Oct-2 Bonhams, Edinburgh #39 est:700-1000

LENAIL, Marie Joseph Ernest (19th C) French
Works on paper
£833 $1292 €1300 Chevaux dans un prairie (22x34cm-9x13in) s.d.1890 W/C. 4-Dec-2 Libert, Castor, Paris #35/R

LENAIN, Mathieu (studio) (1607-1677) French
£14000 $21980 €21000 Two men playing cards, with onlookers (108x145cm-43x57in) 10-Dec-2 Bonhams, New Bond Street #287/R est:8000-12000

LENARDI, Giovan Battista (1656-1704) Italian
£33537 $55000 €50306 Assumption of the Virgin with Saint Nicholas of Myra and Anne (256x169cm-101x67in) prov.lit. 29-May-3 Sotheby's, New York #55/R est:60000-80000

LENBACH, Franz von (1836-1904) German

£1429 $2129 €2200 Gabriel von Seidl (92x74cm-36x29in) s.d.1895. 26-Jun-2 Neumeister, Munich #787/R est:800

£2055 $3205 €3000 Piggy back (101x74cm-40x29in) bears sig. board on panel lit. 10-Apr-3 Van Ham, Cologne #1562/R est:3200

£2229 $3478 €3500 Portrait of Maxime Elliot - actress (105x75cm-41x30in) 6-Nov-2 Hugo Ruef, Munich #1194/R est:3800

£2899 $4754 €4000 Maria Principessa Bandini (56x44cm-22x17in) board. 31-May-3 Villa Grisebach, Berlin #109/R est:4000-6000

£3205 $4968 €5000 Maria Grafin Donhoff, later Princess of Bulow (61x47cm-24x19in) s. painted c.1873. 6-Dec-2 Ketterer, Munich #16/R est:5000-7000

£3425 $5377 €5000 Portrait of young woman (57x49cm-22x19in) s.d.1901 board. 16-Apr-3 Dorotheum, Salzburg #106/R est:6000-9000

£3774 $5887 €6000 Portrait of young woman in sailor dress and feather in hat (41cm-16in circular) s. prov.lit. 20-Sep-2 Karlheinz Kaupp, Staufen #1936/R est:5500

£3797 $6000 €6000 Marion of Lenbach, full-length portrait of artist's daughter (65x85cm-26x33in) s.d.1900. 28-Nov-2 Dorotheum, Vienna #3/R est:8000-12000

£5442 $8653 €8000 Marion Lenbach with cat (78x65cm-31x26in) s.d.1899 panel. 19-Mar-3 Neumeister, Munich #626/R est:9000

£5732 $8943 €9000 Portrait of Furstin Bulow-Minghetti (67x52cm-26x20in) i. verso. 6-Nov-2 Hugo Ruef, Munich #1193/R est:5000

£5797 $9507 €8000 Otto Furst von Bismarck in uniform (41x35cm-16x14in) s.d.1891 panel prov.lit. 31-May-3 Villa Grisebach, Berlin #111/R est:8000-10000

£8442 $12578 €13000 Marion Lenbach (94x71cm-37x28in) s. board. 26-Jun-2 Neumeister, Munich #786/R est:10000

Works on paper

£443 $687 €700 Portrait of young woman (35x31cm-14x12in) col chk. 25-Sep-2 Neumeister, Munich #420/R

£1096 $1710 €1644 Portrait of artist's sister (31x29cm-12x11in) pencil. 28-Mar-3 Koller, Zurich #3124/R est:3000-5000 (S.FR 2400)

£1232 $2020 €1700 Sons of Prince Ludwig von Bayern - study (54x66cm-21x26in) pastel over pencil board prov.exhib. 31-May-3 Villa Grisebach, Berlin #110/R est:2500-3500

£1304 $2022 €1956 Portrait of young woman (70x59cm-28x23in) pastel chk board. 9-Dec-2 Philippe Schuler, Zurich #4170 est:2600-3000 (S.FR 3000)

£1698 $2750 €2462 Portrait of Eleanor Duse and Marion Lenbach (23x20cm-9x8in) s. pastel pencil board. 21-May-3 Doyle, New York #200/R est:2000-3000

£3846 $5962 €6000 Portrait of young woman with red hair (83x67cm-33x26in) s. pastel htd white pencil board. 5-Dec-2 Dr Fritz Nagel, Stuttgart #675/R est:2500

LENBACH, Franz von (attrib) (1836-1904) German

£629 $969 €1000 Portrait of William I of Germany (94x69cm-37x27in) prov. 28-Oct-2 Il Ponte, Milan #252

£4167 $6583 €6500 Portrait of Chancellor Otto Furst von Bismarck (111x89cm-44x35in) prov. 16-Nov-2 Lempertz, Koln #1522/R est:4000

LENDORFF, Hans (1863-1946) Swiss

£437 $681 €656 Portrait of young girl with flower (61x46cm-24x18in) s. 6-Nov-2 Dobiaschofsky, Bern #3494/R (S.FR 1000)

LENGO Y MARTINEZ, Horacio (1840-1890) Spanish

£3846 $6077 €6000 Hungry meeting (65x54cm-26x21in) s. 14-Nov-2 Arte, Seville #358/R

LENHUSEN, A (19th C) ?

£1277 $2017 €1916 Young female nude on leopard skin in the jungle (51x89cm-20x35in) s.d.1886. 2-Dec-2 Rasmussen, Copenhagen #1724/R est:20000 (D.KR 15000)

LENK, Franz (1898-1968) German

£738 $1189 €1100 Bodensee (38x49cm-15x19in) s. panel. 21-Feb-3 Sigalas, Stuttgart #922/R est:980

£2436 $3556 €3800 Dunes (51x59cm-20x23in) s.d.1926 panel. 4-Jun-2 Karl & Faber, Munich #331/R est:4000

£2821 $4456 €4400 Still life with tulips and glass (67x37cm-26x15in) mono.d.1965 canvas on panel. 14-Nov-2 Neumeister, Munich #611/R est:1000-1200

£2949 $4659 €4600 Still life with flowers and shell (67x37cm-26x15in) mono.d.1965 panel. 14-Nov-2 Neumeister, Munich #612/R est:1000-1200

£5696 $9000 €9000 House on the Po (53x73cm-21x29in) mono.d.1950 oil egg tempera canvas on panel exhib.lit. 30-Nov-2 Villa Grisebach, Berlin #285/R est:9000-12000

£8861 $14000 €14000 Flowering cactus on window sill (61x42cm-24x17in) mono.d.1948 panel. 30-Nov-2 Villa Grisebach, Berlin #287/R est:9000-12000

£11392 $18000 €18000 Factory beneath rainbow (58x68cm-23x27in) s.d.1926 exhib.lit. 30-Nov-2 Villa Grisebach, Berlin #290a/R est:18000-24000

£14000 $21840 €21000 Hauser mit baum - Houses with a tree (40x34cm-16x13in) s.d.1927 panel exhib. 9-Oct-2 Sotheby's, London #42/R est:15000-20000

Works on paper

£443 $700 €700 Flowers (27x24cm-11x9in) s.d.1928 W/C. 27-Nov-2 Dorotheum, Vienna #18/R

£704 $1169 €1000 Landscape (47x32cm-19x13in) s.d. W/C. 14-Jun-3 Hauswedell & Nolte, Hamburg #1346/R

£851 $1379 €1200 Thuringen landscape near Orlamunde (33x49cm-13x19in) s.d.1935 i. verso W/C board prov. 24-May-3 Van Ham, Cologne #353/R

£1282 $1987 €2000 Tuscan fortress (34x50cm-13x20in) mono.d.1949 W/C. 4-Dec-2 Lempertz, Koln #858/R est:1500

£2101 $3446 €2900 Wartburg (46x65cm-18x26in) s.d.1939 i. verso W/C pen. 29-May-3 Lempertz, Koln #748/R est:2000

LENK, Thomas (1933-) German

Sculpture

£1474 $2285 €2300 Untitled (26x46x18cm-10x18x7in) s.d.70 aluminium. 3-Dec-2 Lempertz, Koln #261/R est:2300

LENKIEWICZ (1941-2002) British/Jewish

Works on paper

£500 $790 €750 Portrait of a young man (30x20cm-12x8in) s. pencil dr. 25-Apr-3 Rendalls, Ashburton #1533

£640 $1011 €960 Portrait of a dog (25x20cm-10x8in) s. pencil dr. 25-Apr-3 Rendalls, Ashburton #1547

£1350 $2133 €2025 Portrait of a tramp (33x18cm-13x7in) s. W/C. 25-Apr-3 Rendalls, Ashburton #1575 est:800-1200

LENKIEWICZ, R O (1941-2002) British/Jewish

£2100 $3318 €3150 Portrait of Reuben (38x33cm-15x13in) s. card. 25-Apr-3 Rendalls, Ashburton #1619 est:2500-3000

£4100 $6478 €6150 Painter with Karen Ciambriello (41x30cm-16x12in) s.verso. 25-Apr-3 Rendalls, Ashburton #1629 est:4000-5000

£4100 $6478 €6150 Woman with jealous lover - study of jealousy theme (33x48cm-13x19in) s. acrylic paper. 25-Apr-3 Rendalls, Ashburton #1618 est:3000-4000

£4500 $7110 €6750 Study of Bianca Ciambriello (23x18cm-9x7in) s.verso board. 25-Apr-3 Rendalls, Ashburton #1621 est:3500-4500

£4600 $7268 €6900 Study of Lisa (48x23cm-19x9in) s.verso. 25-Apr-3 Rendalls, Ashburton #1637 est:4500-5500

£5000 $7900 €7500 Study of Lisa Stokes (41x28cm-16x11in) s.verso board. 25-Apr-3 Rendalls, Ashburton #1635 est:5500-6500

£5700 $9006 €8550 Painter with Patti Avery (46x36cm-18x14in) s. i.verso. 25-Apr-3 Rendalls, Ashburton #1640 est:6000-7000

£5800 $9164 €8700 Study of the painter (86x69cm-34x27in) s.verso. 25-Apr-3 Rendalls, Ashburton #1631 est:4500-5500

£6000 $9480 €9000 Portrait of Ord (41x114cm-16x45in) s.verso board. 25-Apr-3 Rendalls, Ashburton #1633 est:6000-8000

£6100 $9638 €9150 Portrait of a girl in a red dress (51x102cm-20x40in) s.i.verso. 25-Apr-3 Rendalls, Ashburton #1627 est:5500-6000

£6200 $9796 €9300 Painter with Greenie (58x53cm-23x21in) s.verso board. 25-Apr-3 Rendalls, Ashburton #1649 est:10000-12000

£6400 $10112 €9600 Painter with women project 18 (61x58cm-24x23in) s.i.verso board. 25-Apr-3 Rendalls, Ashburton #1647 est:6000-8000

£7500 $11850 €11250 Self portrait (51x94cm-20x37in) s.d.69 board. 25-Apr-3 Rendalls, Ashburton #1646 est:8000-10000

£7600 $12008 €11400 Jealousy theme (66x84cm-26x33in) acrylic wood. 25-Apr-3 Rendalls, Ashburton #1639 est:6000-8000

£10200 $16116 €15300 Study of Lisa Stokes (61x58cm-24x23in) s.i.verso. 25-Apr-3 Rendalls, Ashburton #1652 est:11000-13000

£15000 $23700 €22500 Portrait of Gemma Hennigan (91x91cm-36x36in) s.verso. 25-Apr-3 Rendalls, Ashburton #1660 est:16000-20000

Works on paper

£1300 $2054 €1950 Study of Lindsay Seers (28x18cm-11x7in) i.d.1990 W/C. 25-Apr-3 Rendalls, Ashburton #1580a est:1200-1500

£1500 $2370 €2250 Anna at the house (23x20cm-9x8in) s.i. W/C. 25-Apr-3 Rendalls, Ashburton #1580b est:1200-1500

£1550 $2449 €2325 Boats at the Barbican, Plymouth (28x36cm-11x14in) s.d.70 W/C. 25-Apr-3 Rendalls, Ashburton #1606 est:1000-1500

£2200 $3476 €3300 Self portrait wearing green (23x18cm-9x7in) s. W/C. 25-Apr-3 Rendalls, Ashburton #1607 est:1800-2200

£2300 $3634 €3450 Stove at the end of the long room (30x28cm-12x11in) s. W/C. 25-Apr-3 Rendalls, Ashburton #1595 est:1500-2000

£4000 $6320 €6000 Lovers (15x18cm-6x7in) s.d.1971 W/C. 25-Apr-3 Rendalls, Ashburton #1620 est:2500-3000

LENKIEWICZ, Robert O (1941-2002) British/Jewish

£1500 $2355 €2250 Portrait of a young boy (24x25cm-9x10in) s.verso board. 10-Dec-2 Lane, Penzance #64 est:1500-2000

£2900 $4611 €4350 Diogenese on the Barbican (33x43cm-13x17in) s. board. 4-Mar-3 Bearnes, Exeter #444/R est:2000-3000
£4000 $6280 €6000 Girl with blond hair (48x23cm-19x9in) s.i.verso. 10-Dec-2 Lane, Penzance #170/R est:5000-6000
£4000 $6680 €5800 Study of Frank - project gossip on the Barbican (28x38cm-11x15in) s. i.on stretcher. 19-Jun-3 Lane, Penzance #10/R est:3000-5000
£4400 $6864 €6380 Last self portrait (57x55cm-22x22in) s.i.verso. 27-Mar-3 Lane, Penzance #55/R est:4000-6000
£5000 $7850 €7500 Study of Rachel with painter (60x60cm-24x24in) s.i.verso board. 10-Dec-2 Lane, Penzance #35/R est:4000-5000
£6200 $9672 €9300 Seated woman (53x43cm-21x17in) board. 17-Oct-2 David Lay, Penzance #1554/R est:2500-3000
£13000 $20410 €19500 Self portrait of the artist with a painting of Gustave Carbe (122x76cm-48x30in) s. 10-Dec-2 Lane, Penzance #115/R est:20000-30000

Works on paper
£420 $655 €609 Head and shoulder portrait of a young boy (37x25cm-15x10in) s. pencil. 27-Mar-3 Lane, Penzance #346
£420 $701 €609 Chess players, Loft Hampstead (25x33cm-10x13in) s. ink dr. executed c.1965. 19-Jun-3 Lane, Penzance #238
£680 $1068 €1020 Embrace (28x38cm-11x15in) W/C. 25-Nov-2 Bonhams, Chester #895
£720 $1130 €1080 Standing man (25x16cm-10x6in) pencil dr. 25-Nov-2 Bonhams, Chester #897
£1000 $1570 €1500 LOvers (20x27cm-8x11in) W/C. 25-Nov-2 Bonhams, Chester #896
£1200 $1944 €1800 Portrait of seated gentleman with cigarette (35x39cm-14x15in) s.d.73 W/C. 20-May-3 Bonhams, Knightsbridge #10/R est:300-500
£1800 $2916 €2700 Cockney Jim listening to Wagner (38x26cm-15x10in) s.i.d.73 W/C four sold two other. 20-May-3 Bonhams, Knightsbridge #35 est:300-500
£2250 $3758 €3263 Country landscape with walled yard and the naked figures of the artist and young woman (39x57cm-15x22in) s. W/C. 19-Jun-3 Lane, Penzance #447 est:3000-4000
£2500 $3925 €3750 Woman in red shawl (38x31cm-15x12in) s. mixed media. 10-Dec-2 Lane, Penzance #270/R est:3500-4000

LENKIEWICZ, Robert O (attrib) (1941-2002) British/Jewish
£2800 $4424 €4060 Orgasm (36x18cm-14x7in) acrylic paper. 25-Apr-3 Rendalls, Ashburton #1611 est:1500-2000
£6100 $9638 €8845 Portrait of Mary with two candles (51x36cm-20x14in) board. 25-Apr-3 Rendalls, Ashburton #1638 est:6000-8000

LENNON, Ciaran (20th C) Irish?
£1389 $2208 €2000 Tinker tune on 4 (119x99cm-47x39in) s.d.1969. 29-Apr-3 Whyte's, Dublin #57/R est:3000-4000

LENOIR, Albert (1801-1891) French
Works on paper
£946 $1476 €1400 Vues d'Athenes: Tour des Vents, Eglise de Saint-Eleftherios (28x41cm-11x16in) s. graphite wash W/C pair. 27-Mar-3 Christie's, Paris #132/R

LENOIR, Charles Amable (1861-1940) French
£7372 $11574 €11500 Naissance de Venus (42x80cm-17x31in) s. 15-Dec-2 Eric Pillon, Calais #64/R

LENOIR, Maurice (20th C) French
£845 $1403 €1200 Temps gris sur le marche (41x32cm-16x13in) s. panel. 11-Jun-3 Beaussant & Lefèvre, Paris #84/R

LENORDEZ, Pierre (19th C) French
Sculpture
£1401 $2186 €2200 Jument el licol (30x40cm-12x16in) s.st. brown pat bronze. 11-Nov-2 Horta, Bruxelles #56/R est:2500-3500
£1500 $2340 €2250 Standing mare (25x33cm-10x13in) s.i. brown pat bronze. 5-Nov-2 Sotheby's, London #93/R est:1500-2000

LENS, Bernard III (1682-1740) British
Miniatures
£1800 $2808 €2700 Lady thought to be Mary Queen of Scots wearing black dress (5cm-2in) mono.i. set in lid of silver gilt snuff box. 5-Nov-2 Bonhams, New Bond Street #27/R est:700-900

LENS, Johannes Jacobus (1746-1814) Flemish
£3873 $6430 €5500 Portrait of Emperor Leopold II (33x44cm-13x17in) prov. 11-Jun-3 Dorotheum, Vienna #133/R est:5000-7000

LENTDECKER, Emile de (?) Belgian?
£308 $484 €450 La Lys en hiver (50x75cm-20x30in) s. 15-Apr-3 Galerie Moderne, Brussels #381

LENTINE, John (1930-) American
£297 $475 €446 Beach umbrellas (41x51cm-16x20in) s. i.verso. 8-Jan-3 Doyle, New York #55/R

LENTNER, Josef Friedrich (1814-1852) German
Works on paper
£629 $975 €1000 Hallstattersee (21x27cm-8x11in) s. W/C. 1-Oct-2 Dorotheum, Vienna #210/R

LENTULOV, Aristarkh (1882-1943) Russian
Works on paper
£3623 $5942 €5000 Le monastere (51x33cm-20x13in) s.cyrillic i.d.1917 W/C chk over pencil prov. 29-May-3 Lempertz, Koln #749/R est:5000-6000
£18590 $28814 €29000 Sketch for the curtain for Prometheus (32x33cm-13x13in) gouache board prov.lit. 4-Dec-2 Lempertz, Koln #859/R est:7000-8000

LEOEL, Jean Claude (1954-) French
£1152 $1774 €1728 Oceanondiniah, l'ange feminin sur les ondes du petit ocean (60x60cm-24x24in) monosided tainted polystyrene. 22-Oct-2 Iegor de Saint Hippolyte, Montreal #59/R (C.D 2800)

LEON Y ESCOSURA, Ignacio de (1834-1901) Spanish
£2673 $4170 €4250 Playing music (18x12cm-7x5in) s. board. 23-Sep-2 Durán, Madrid #222/R

LEON, Carlos (1948-) Spanish
£1391 $2267 €2100 Mirror, black garden (215x220cm-85x87in) painted 1983 exhib.lit. 11-Feb-3 Segre, Madrid #258/R

LEON, Jose de (1958-) Spanish?
£710 $1121 €1100 Secret buttons (123x80cm-48x31in) s.d.1993 s.i.d.verso board. 17-Dec-2 Segre, Madrid #192/R

LEONARD, Agathan (1841-?) French
Sculpture
£4500 $7020 €6750 Bust of cupid (53cm-21in) s. white marble. 9-Apr-3 Sotheby's, London #85/R est:5000-7000
£4500 $7020 €6750 Bust of a woman (61cm-24in) s. white marble lit. 9-Apr-3 Sotheby's, London #92/R est:4000-6000
£7372 $11574 €11500 Danseuse a l'echarpe (60cm-24in) s. gilt pat bronze. 10-Dec-2 Renaud, Paris #130/R

LEONARD, Jos (20th C) Swiss?
Works on paper
£1389 $2208 €2000 Composition (31x24cm-12x9in) s.d.1922 ink dr. 29-Apr-3 Campo, Vlaamse Kaai #190 est:1600-2000

LEONARD, Julia I (19/20th C) American
£1774 $2750 €2661 Pink roses on table top (41x76cm-16x30in) s. prov. 29-Oct-2 John Moran, Pasadena #700 est:1000-1500

LEONARD, Maurice (1899-?) French
£863 $1381 €1200 Retour de peche (60x73cm-24x29in) s.d.1930 verso. 16-May-3 Lombrail & Teucquam, Paris #245

LEONARD, Patrick (1918-) British
£856 $1336 €1250 Mother and daughter on evening walk at Red Island, Skerries (38x29cm-15x11in) s. board. 8-Apr-3 James Adam, Dublin #129/R
£962 $1510 €1500 Donkeys resting (46x61cm-18x24in) s. board. 19-Nov-2 Whyte's, Dublin #117/R est:1500-2000
£1132 $1766 €1800 Home from school (25x36cm-10x14in) s. board. 17-Sep-2 Whyte's, Dublin #1 est:1500-2000
£1389 $2208 €2000 Watchman's hut (41x51cm-16x20in) s. i.verso board. 29-Apr-3 Whyte's, Dublin #201/R est:1500-2500
£1486 $2319 €2200 Harbour scene with boats in stormy seas (37x47cm-15x19in) s. board. 26-Mar-3 James Adam, Dublin #65/R est:1500-1800
£1667 $2650 €2400 Waiting for the bus at Burgh Quay, Dublin (41x51cm-16x20in) s. verso board. 29-Apr-3 Whyte's, Dublin #159/R est:3000-4000
£1667 $2650 €2400 Landscape with roadsign to Dublin (72x57cm-28x22in) s. board. 29-Apr-3 Whyte's, Dublin #200/R est:2000-3000
£1689 $2635 €2500 Running in - trawler at Loughshinney with a view of Lambay (40x50cm-16x20in) s. board. 26-Mar-3 James Adam, Dublin #67/R est:1500-2000

£1745 $2809 €2600 Gresham wedding (51x56cm-20x22in) s. i.verso panel. 18-Feb-3 Whyte's, Dublin #121/R est:4000-6000
£2027 $3162 €3000 Loughshinney Harbour - return of the boats (25x35cm-10x14in) s.d.1952 i.verso board. 26-Mar-3 James Adam, Dublin #66/R est:1000-1500
£2264 $3532 €3600 Country lane, midday, Rush, County Dublin (69x51cm-27x20in) s. i.verso board. 17-Sep-2 Whyte's, Dublin #152/R est:3000-4000
£2564 $4026 €4000 Mother and child by seaside (51x61cm-20x24in) s. board. 19-Nov-2 Whyte's, Dublin #111/R est:3000-4000
£5897 $9141 €9200 Unloading a trawler at Loughshinney Harbour. Portrait of a woman (58x71cm-23x28in) s. double-sided. 3-Dec-2 Bonhams & James Adam, Dublin #48/R est:8000-12000

LEONARDI, Eduard (1828-1905) German
£2179 $3378 €3400 Forest thicket in autumn colours with heron at the water (62x47cm-24x19in) i.d.1888 verso. 4-Dec-2 Neumeister, Munich #804/R est:1000

LEONARDO DA VINCI (after) (1452-1519) Italian
£22000 $36740 €31900 Mona Lisa (81x57cm-32x22in) panel prov.exhib. 10-Jul-3 Sotheby's, London #158/R est:15000-20000
Sculpture
£19753 $32000 €29630 Rearing stallion (16cm-6in) red brown pat bronze lit. 23-Jan-3 Sotheby's, New York #195/R est:12000

LEONARDO DA VINCI (style) (1452-1519) Italian
£7000 $10920 €10500 Saint John the Baptist in landscape (103x73cm-41x29in) panel prov.lit. 10-Apr-3 Sotheby's, London #21/R

LEONARDO, Paolo (1973-) Italian
Works on paper
£833 $1292 €1300 Untitled (140x100cm-55x39in) s.i.d.2001 verso mixed media poster on canvas exhib. 4-Dec-2 Finarte, Milan #507/R

LEONCILLO (1915-1968) Italian
Sculpture
£3205 $4679 €5000 Composition (27x20x20cm-11x8x8in) terracotta. 5-Jun-2 Il Ponte, Milan #129/R
£8219 $12822 €12000 Saint Sebastian (54x16x15cm-21x6x6in) s. gres enamel exhib. 10-Apr-3 Finarte Semenzato, Rome #221/R est:14000
Works on paper
£1218 $1912 €1900 Untitled (45x54cm-18x21in) collage tempera cardboard. 20-Nov-2 Pandolfini, Florence #121/R

LEONE, Romolo (19th C) French
£260 $411 €390 Continental street scene after a shower of rain (21x29cm-8x11in) s. board. 18-Nov-2 Bonhams, Bath #577
£1266 $2000 €2000 Farms (100x140cm-39x55in) s. 26-Nov-2 Christie's, Rome #60

LEONESSA, Enrico della (1865-1921) Italian
£5442 $8653 €8000 Market in Rome (42x47cm-17x19in) s.d.1912. 18-Mar-3 Finarte, Milan #97/R

LEONI, Ottavio (1587-1630) Italian
Works on paper
£2848 $4500 €4500 Portrait de gentilhomme de profil (23x16cm-9x6in) i. crayon chk prov.exhib. 28-Nov-2 Tajan, Paris #4/R est:3000-3500

LEOPOLD-LEVY (1882-1966) French
£283 $439 €450 La ciotat, cytaris (35x22cm-14x9in) s. 30-Oct-2 Artcurial Briest, Paris #37
£302 $468 €480 Chemin des oiseaux, la ciotat (38x46cm-15x18in) 30-Oct-2 Artcurial Briest, Paris #39
£440 $682 €700 Ciel blanc (54x47cm-21x19in) s. 30-Oct-2 Artcurial Briest, Paris #36/R

LEPAGE, Celine (1882-1928) French
Sculpture
£57555 $92088 €80000 Femme nue aux antilopes (105x139cm-41x55in) s.d.1926 pat.bronze gilt. 19-May-3 Tajan, Paris #24/R est:35000-40000

LEPAGE, Paul (1869-1958) Belgian
£481 $745 €750 Bord de Semois (35x50cm-14x20in) s. 9-Dec-2 Horta, Bruxelles #10

LEPAPE, George (1887-1971) French
£1099 $1692 €1649 Portrait - girl holding mask (33x30cm-13x12in) s. cardboard. 23-Oct-2 Kunsthallen, Copenhagen #430/R est:15000 (D.KR 13000)
£3846 $6038 €6000 Peche (86x46cm-34x18in) s.d.1935 panel exhib. 20-Nov-2 Claude Boisgirard, Paris #39/R

LEPAULLE, François Gabriel (1804-1886) French
£4872 $7551 €7600 Portrait du prince Demidoff (45x35cm-18x14in) 4-Dec-2 Libert, Castor, Paris #58/R est:8000

LEPCKE, Ferdinand (1866-1909) German
Sculpture
£1013 $1600 €1600 Girl carrying water, kissing her worshipper (59cm-23in) i. bronze Cast Martin Pilting. 29-Nov-2 Bolland & Marotz, Bremen #477/R est:1500
£1361 $2163 €2000 Kiss (60cm-24in) i. wood. 28-Mar-3 Bolland & Marotz, Bremen #868/R est:2400

LEPEINTRE, Mathias (1763-1845) French
Miniatures
£1150 $1886 €1668 Young lady seated in a wooden chair holding two pansies (8cm-3in) s.d.1803 gilt metal. 3-Jun-3 Christie's, London #198 est:600-800

LEPERE, Auguste (1849-1918) French
Prints
£2692 $4227 €4200 Le bassin des Tuileries (22x33cm-9x13in) s.i. woodcut. 22-Nov-2 Tajan, Paris #338/R est:3000
£3333 $5267 €5200 On va gouter. s.i. col engraving. 13-Nov-2 Piasa, Paris #228/R est:2500-3000
£4167 $6583 €6500 Lames deferlent. s.i. col engraving. 13-Nov-2 Piasa, Paris #229/R
Works on paper
£245 $409 €350 Rue a Marseille (41x28cm-16x11in) s.i. chl dr. 26-Jun-3 Tajan, Paris #133

LEPESQUEUR, Hyacinthe Florentin (19th C) French
£1538 $2415 €2400 Scene de plage animee (15x21cm-6x8in) s. panel. 19-Nov-2 Servarts Themis, Bruxelles #131/R

LEPET DE DONAY, François (18th C) French
Works on paper
£475 $750 €750 Projet de grille ornee de medaillons figurant St Pierre et St Paul (29x66cm-11x26in) s.d.1779 pen ink col wash. 27-Nov-2 Christie's, Paris #185/R

LEPETIT, Alfred (1841-1909) French
Works on paper
£321 $503 €500 Mere Gaud (62x46cm-24x18in) s.i.d.1890 W/C. 15-Dec-2 Eric Pillon, Calais #131/R
£321 $503 €500 Saint-Brieuc, marchande de poissons (62x46cm-24x18in) s.i. W/C. 15-Dec-2 Eric Pillon, Calais #130/R

LEPETIT, Alfred Marie (1876-1953) French
£256 $403 €400 Barques de peche en Bretagne (27x41cm-11x16in) s. panel. 24-Nov-2 Lesieur & Le Bars, Le Havre #98

LEPIC, Ludovic Napoleon (1839-1890) French
£1132 $1755 €1800 Bateaux de peche a Berck (27x46cm-11x18in) s. 30-Oct-2 Coutau Begarie, Paris #89/R

LEPICIE, Michel Nicolas Bernard (1735-1784) French
Works on paper
£1361 $2164 €2000 Academie d'homme a mi-corps (21x36cm-8x14in) crayon stump chk. 24-Mar-3 Tajan, Paris #97/R
£2532 $4000 €4000 Study (45x37cm-18x15in) i. sanguine. 28-Nov-2 Tajan, Paris #74/R
£2838 $4427 €4200 Jeune homme assis (29x23cm-11x9in) s. crayon stump sanguine. 27-Mar-3 Maigret, Paris #21/R
£3061 $4867 €4500 Diseuse de bonne aventure (22x36cm-9x14in) s. graphitepen ink wash lit. 28-Feb-3 Joron-Derem, Paris #10/R

LEPIDIS, Clement (1920-1997) French
£1233 $1936 €1800 Graffiti (38x55cm-15x22in) s. i.d.54 verso. 15-Apr-3 Laurence Calmels, Paris #4340/R

LEPIE, Ferdinand (1824-1883) Czechoslovakian
£548 $860 €800 Dachstein and Gosausee (26x52cm-10x20in) s. i. verso. 16-Apr-3 Dorotheum, Salzburg #98/R
£1507 $2351 €2200 Gmunden with Orth Castle beyond (26x52cm-10x20in) s. 10-Apr-3 Dorotheum, Vienna #143/R est:2000-2500
£2837 $4596 €4000 View over Naples (68x105cm-27x41in) s. 22-May-3 Dorotheum, Vienna #145/R est:4000-4500
£3057 $4769 €4800 Chateau sur fond de paysage montagneux (74x100cm-29x39in) s.d.1844. 11-Nov-2 Horta, Bruxelles #131/R est:5000-7500
£3145 $4874 €5000 Konigssee on summer's day (134x180cm-53x71in) s. 29-Oct-2 Dorotheum, Vienna #132/R est:5000-6000

LEPINARD, Paul (20th C) Swiss
£365 $576 €548 Landscape around Lake Geneva (24x33cm-9x13in) s.d.1934. 29-Nov-2 Zofingen, Switzerland #2969 (S.FR 850)
£370 $596 €555 Printemps a Paudex (24x32cm-9x13in) s.d.1935 i. verso canvas on board. 7-May-3 Dobiaschofsky, Bern #779 (S.FR 800)
£509 $820 €764 Morning - Dezaley (23x33cm-9x13in) s.d.1934 i. verso. 7-May-3 Dobiaschofsky, Bern #778/R (S.FR 1100)
£699 $1090 €1049 Part of the shore of Lake Geneva near Pully (39x55cm-15x22in) s.d.1938. 8-Nov-2 Dobiaschofsky, Bern #74/R (S.FR 1600)

LEPINE, Stanislas (1835-1892) French
£417 $650 €626 Landscape river scene. 21-Sep-2 Harvey Clar, Oakland #1415
£2436 $3824 €3800 Portrait d'homme (22x18cm-9x7in) s.i.d.1898 canvas on cardboard. 16-Dec-2 Rabourdin & Choppin de Janvry, Paris #36/R
£3500 $5705 €5075 La foret de Fontainebleau (23x30cm-9x12in) s.i. 17-Jul-3 Tennants, Leyburn #865/R est:5000-7000
£8917 $13911 €14000 Coteaux de Sannois (14x23cm-6x9in) s. panel prov.lit. 7-Nov-2 Chochon-Barre & Allardi, Paris #181/R est:9000
£10759 $17000 €16139 La Seine a la Garenne Saint Denis (21x32cm-8x13in) s. painted c.1877-81 prov. 23-Apr-3 Christie's, Rockefeller NY #58/R est:18000-25000
£130000 $213200 €195000 La Seine a la Garenne Saint-Denis (78x150cm-31x59in) s. prov.lit. 4-Feb-3 Christie's, London #204/R est:100000

L'EPLATTENIER, Charles (1874-1946) Swiss
£961 $1518 €1442 Wooded landscape (110x110cm-43x43in) s.d.1906. 14-Nov-2 Stuker, Bern #348/R est:2000-3000 (S.FR 2200)
£1528 $2460 €2216 Zinnias (73x55cm-29x22in) s.i.d.1945 verso. 9-May-3 Dobiaschofsky, Bern #135/R est:4000 (S.FR 3300)
£1887 $3057 €3339 Still life with peonies (103x69cm-41x27in) s.d.1920 s.i.d. verso board. 26-May-3 Sotheby's, Zurich #115/R est:4000-6000 (S.FR 4000)
£2315 $3727 €3357 Le bec du Chasseron pres de Ste-Croix (42x87cm-17x34in) s.d.1911. 9-May-3 Dobiaschofsky, Bern #95/R est:5500 (S.FR 5000)
£3009 $4845 €4363 Plateau in the Jura (60x110cm-24x43in) s.d.1922. 9-May-3 Dobiaschofsky, Bern #97/R est:5500 (S.FR 6500)
£3472 $5590 €5034 Doubs; contre jour (60x73cm-24x29in) s.d.1941 i.verso board. 9-May-3 Dobiaschofsky, Bern #98/R est:5000 (S.FR 7500)
£8333 $13417 €12083 Roche de l'Echo-Soleil (88x115cm-35x45in) s.i.d.1945 verso. 9-May-3 Dobiaschofsky, Bern #94/R est:20000 (S.FR 18000)
£9607 $14987 €14411 Lumiere du soir (115x115cm-45x45in) s.d.1942 i.verso. 8-Nov-2 Dobiaschofsky, Bern #94/R est:15000 (S.FR 22000)

Works on paper
£304 $472 €456 Jeune fille a la harpe (59x34cm-23x13in) s.d.06 chl. 7-Dec-2 Galerie du Rhone, Sion #402 (S.FR 700)
£648 $1044 €972 Soldier at swearing in (62x25cm-24x10in) s.d.1916 W/C over chl pencil. 7-May-3 Dobiaschofsky, Bern #758 (S.FR 1400)

LEPOITTEVIN, Eugène (1806-1870) French
£2564 $3974 €4000 Arrivee des bateaux devant les falaises en Normandie (71x92cm-28x36in) s. 6-Dec-2 Millon & Associes, Paris #73/R
£22785 $35544 €36000 Pecheurs halant un bateau a terre, vue prise a Port-en-Bessin (146x260cm-57x102in) s.d. exhib. 20-Oct-2 Mercier & Cie, Lille #303/R est:35000-40000

LEPOITTEVIN, Louis (1847-1909) French
£699 $1090 €1049 River landscape in summer (46x65cm-18x26in) s. 6-Nov-2 Dobiaschofsky, Bern #772/R (S.FR 1600)
£2436 $3824 €3800 Bergere gardant son troupeau (65x92cm-26x36in) s. 15-Dec-2 Mercier & Cie, Lille #348/R est:6000

LEPPIEN, Jean (1910-1991) German
£405 $632 €600 Untitled (35x27cm-14x11in) init.verso acrylic. 26-Mar-3 Finarte Semenzato, Milan #97
£633 $987 €1000 Composition (55x45cm-22x18in) s. init.d.1959 verso fresco. 19-Oct-2 Semenzato, Venice #12/R
£680 $1082 €1000 Boreal (35x27cm-14x11in) s. 1-Mar-3 Meeting Art, Vercelli #382
£1497 $2380 €2200 Composition (55x46cm-22x18in) s. painted 1959. 1-Mar-3 Meeting Art, Vercelli #657
£1538 $2415 €2400 9/58 VI (46x55cm-18x22in) s. init.i.verso. 24-Nov-2 Laurence Calmels, Paris #182/R
£1667 $2617 €2600 6/57 XLVIII (54x65cm-21x26in) s.d.57 init.i.d.verso. 24-Nov-2 Laurence Calmels, Paris #183/R
£1905 $3029 €2800 Composition (92x73cm-36x29in) s.d.LXVI. 24-Mar-3 Claude Boisgirard, Paris #108/R
£1923 $3019 €3000 7/72 XXIX (70x70cm-28x28in) init.i.verso. 24-Nov-2 Laurence Calmels, Paris #184/R
£2183 $3188 €3275 Composition (94x56cm-37x22in) s. mono.d.1969 verso acrylic. 4-Jun-2 Germann, Zurich #71/R est:5500-6500 (S.FR 5000)
£2244 $3522 €3500 8/60 LVII (73x60cm-29x24in) s. init.i.verso. 24-Nov-2 Laurence Calmels, Paris #185/R
£8974 $14090 €14000 1/51 I. s.d.51 cardboard prov.exhib. 24-Nov-2 Laurence Calmels, Paris #181/R est:6000

Works on paper
£541 $843 €800 Composition (42x31cm-17x12in) s.d.1950 wax crayon. 26-Mar-3 Finarte Semenzato, Milan #91/R
£1474 $2315 €2300 Composition LXVII (41x29cm-16x11in) s. pastel prov. 15-Dec-2 Perrin, Versailles #22/R

LEPRECHT, F (19th C) French?
£1474 $2388 €2137 Portrait of woman draped in pink and white (98x72cm-39x28in) s. 25-May-3 Uppsala Auktionskammare, Uppsala #66/R est:10000-12000 (S.KR 19000)

LEPRI, Stanislao (1905-1980) Italian

Works on paper
£759 $1214 €1100 Gerard Albouy dans son magasin (27x21cm-11x8in) s. ink. 12-Mar-3 Libert, Castor, Paris #134

LEPRIN, Marcel (1891-1933) French
£1418 $2369 €2000 Nature morte au lievre (45x65cm-18x26in) s. exhib. 20-Jun-3 Piasa, Paris #123 est:2000-3000
£2482 $4145 €3500 L'Eglise de Poissy (73x60cm-29x24in) s. exhib. 20-Jun-3 Piasa, Paris #125 est:4000-6000
£2837 $4738 €4000 Rue a Saint Servan (46x55cm-18x22in) s. 20-Jun-3 Piasa, Paris #122/R est:4000-6000
£4430 $6867 €7000 Vase de fleurs sur un gueridon (65x54cm-26x21in) s. 29-Sep-2 Eric Pillon, Calais #209/R
£6962 $10791 €11000 La corrida (50x65cm-20x26in) s. 29-Sep-2 Eric Pillon, Calais #202/R
£7092 $11844 €10000 L'estocade (54x73cm-21x29in) s. exhib.lit. 20-Jun-3 Piasa, Paris #124/R est:8000-10000
£7912 $12500 €12500 Moulin (63x90cm-25x35in) s. 2-Dec-2 Tajan, Paris #77
£8516 $13455 €13200 Eglise Saint-Victor a Marseille (50x65cm-20x26in) s. 19-Dec-2 Claude Aguttes, Neuilly #213/R est:10000
£9241 $14323 €14600 Paris, la Seine et Notre Dame (46x55cm-18x22in) s. 29-Sep-2 Eric Pillon, Calais #207/R

LEPRINCE, Jean Baptiste (1734-1781) French

Works on paper
£709 $1107 €1050 Tete de vieillard de profil (14x10cm-6x4in) chk prov. 27-Mar-3 Christie's, Paris #206/R
£1497 $2380 €2200 Peintre et figures dans un parc (16x20cm-6x8in) pen ink wash. 24-Mar-3 Tajan, Paris #114/R
£3565 $5526 €5348 Jeune aristocrate russe a la cape de fourrure (25x20cm-10x8in) pencil sanguine paper on cardboard prov. 7-Dec-2 Galerie du Rhone, Sion #502/R est:2500-3000 (S.FR 8200)
£4200 $7014 €6090 View of a Russian Village (24x45cm-9x18in) red chk. 9-Jul-3 Sotheby's, London #75/R est:3000-4000
£4321 $7000 €6482 Russian peasant (29x18cm-11x7in) chk. 21-Jan-3 Sotheby's, New York #87/R

LEPRINCE, Jean Baptiste (attrib) (1734-1781) French
£14190 $22136 €21000 Marchand de rue (29x33cm-11x13in) panel. 26-Mar-3 Tajan, Paris #69/R

LEQUEU, Jean Jacques (1757-1825) French

Works on paper
£5586 $8938 €8100 Frise bacchique (18x41cm-7x16in) s.i. pen black ink brown wash after Clodion. 12-Mar-3 E & Eve, Paris #27/R est:2500-3500

LERAY, Philippe (1944-) French

Works on paper
£828 $1316 €1200 Les elephants (24x31cm-9x12in) pencil pair. 10-Mar-3 Coutau Begarie, Paris #127

LERBERGHE, Karel van (1899-1953) Dutch
£285 $444 €450 Paysage enneige (65x80cm-26x31in) s. panel. 15-Oct-2 Vanderkindere, Brussels #79

LERCHE, Vincent Stoltenberg (1837-1892) Norwegian
£2655 $4195 €3983 The town gate (37x47cm-15x19in) s.d.1870 exhib. 28-Apr-3 Blomqvist, Oslo #311/R est:35000-45000 (N.KR 30000)

£5934 $9316 €8901 Interior from a Gothic church (35x45cm-14x18in) s/d/65. 21-Nov-2 Grev Wedels Plass, Oslo #53/R est:40000-60000 (N.KR 68000)

LERFELDT, Hans Henrik (1946-1990) Danish
£515 $803 €773 Magic figures (27x22cm-11x9in) s.d.74 verso. 11-Nov-2 Rasmussen, Vejle #136/R (D.KR 6000)
Works on paper
£466 $742 €699 Moment of devotion (23x17cm-9x7in) W/C pencil study lit. 29-Apr-3 Kunsthallen, Copenhagen #95/R (D.KR 5000)

LERGAARD, Niels (1893-1982) Danish
£2651 $4215 €3977 Figure by the sea (60x80cm-24x31in) init.d.52 prov. 26-Feb-3 Kunsthallen, Copenhagen #291/R est:20000 (D.KR 29000)
£3381 $5207 €5072 Landscape at dawn, Bornholm (95x125cm-37x49in) s.d.1951 exhib. 23-Oct-2 Kunsthallen, Copenhagen #62/R est:50000 (D.KR 40000)
£3813 $6368 €5529 Road through Korpenland, Bornholm (95x125cm-37x49in) s.d.50 exhib.prov. 17-Jun-3 Rasmussen, Copenhagen #65/R est:50000-75000 (D.KR 40000)
£3918 $6229 €5877 Towards the sea, Bornholm (50x65cm-20x26in) s. 29-Apr-3 Kunsthallen, Copenhagen #235/R est:25000 (D.KR 42000)
£5112 $8076 €7668 Church by the sea, Gudhjem (85x100cm-33x39in) init.d.39. 1-Apr-3 Rasmussen, Copenhagen #66/R est:60000-80000 (D.KR 55000)

LERICHE (attrib) (18/19th C) ?
£1268 $2104 €1800 Bouquet of flowers (41x32cm-16x13in) paper on card lit. 11-Jun-3 Dorotheum, Vienna #185/R est:1500-2500

LERICHE, Dany (20th C) French?
Photographs
£2564 $4026 €4000 Florence (125x125cm-49x49in) col photograph one of 6 exec.1996. 15-Dec-2 Perrin, Versailles #163/R est:3800

LERIN, Lars (20th C) ?
£575 $896 €863 Cold cars (66x73cm-26x29in) s.d.77. 5-Nov-2 Bukowskis, Stockholm #358/R (S.KR 8200)

LERIUS, Joseph Henri François van (1823-1876) Belgian
£1042 $1656 €1500 Jeune couple (62x50cm-24x20in) s.d.1859 panel pair. 30-Apr-3 Tajan, Paris #13

LERMITE, Jean Pierre (1920-1977) French
Works on paper
£5556 $8944 €8056 Nochturne a Bois d'Amont / Vallee des Rousses (41x100cm-16x39in) s.d.57 i.verso wax canvas lit. 9-May-3 Dobiaschofsky, Bern #136/R est:12000 (S.FR 12000)

LERNIA, Francesco di (1966-) Italian
£2553 $4136 €3600 Hombre (100x115cm-39x45in) s.i.d.1999 verso. 20-May-3 Porro, Milan #16/R est:3500-3700

LEROUGE, J (?) ?
£525 $841 €788 Nature morte (80x138cm-31x54in) s. 13-Jan-3 Rasmussen, Vejle #48/R (D.KR 6000)

LEROUX, Andre (1911-) French
£570 $900 €900 Bouquet de pivoines (61x50cm-24x20in) s. 26-Nov-2 Camard, Paris #116
Works on paper
£380 $623 €570 Study of the Belvedere torso (61x49cm-24x19in) s.d.1928 chl chk htd white. 5-Jun-3 Christie's, Kensington #850

LEROUX, Auguste (1871-1954) French
£446 $696 €700 Jeune bretonne (65x44cm-26x17in) s. paper. 7-Nov-2 Chochon-Barre & Allardi, Paris #183/R
£563 $907 €800 Femme a l'ombrelle sur la plage (18x24cm-7x9in) s. panel. 11-May-3 Lombrail & Teucquam, Paris #235/R
£563 $907 €800 Fete foraine (15x23cm-6x9in) s. panel. 11-May-3 Lombrail & Teucquam, Paris #236/R
£951 $1531 €1350 Ballerine ajustant son chausson (27x22cm-11x9in) s. panel. 11-May-3 Lombrail & Teucquam, Paris #232/R

LEROUX, Gaston (1854-1942) French
Sculpture
£1795 $2782 €2800 Rebecca (74cm-29in) s. brown pat.bronze. 5-Dec-2 Dr Fritz Nagel, Stuttgart #783/R est:2900
£1935 $3058 €3000 Jeune porteuse d'eau Rebecca (73cm-29in) pat bronze. 17-Dec-2 Palais de Beaux Arts, Brussels #838 est:2250-3500

LEROUX, Georges (1877-1957) French
£629 $981 €1000 Jeune peintre a son chevalet (46x38cm-18x15in) s.i. 8-Oct-2 Christie's, Paris #35/R

LEROUX, Henri (1872-1942) Belgian
£360 $576 €500 Vase de fleurs sur une table (60x50cm-24x20in) s.d.36. 13-May-3 Palais de Beaux Arts, Brussels #277
£385 $604 €600 Le bain du bebe (50x50cm-20x20in) s.d.1937. 19-Nov-2 Vanderkindere, Brussels #437
£448 $717 €650 La preparation du bain de bebe (50x50cm-20x20in) s.d.37. 17-Mar-3 Horta, Bruxelles #49
£448 $717 €650 La table du petit dejeuner (60x50cm-24x20in) s. 17-Mar-3 Horta, Bruxelles #46
£517 $828 €750 Interieur fleuri (70x60cm-28x24in) s.d.39. 17-Mar-3 Horta, Bruxelles #47
£637 $994 €1000 Petit dejeuner au jardin (50x40cm-20x16in) s.d.38. 11-Nov-2 Horta, Bruxelles #698
£683 $1094 €950 Paysage d'ete (60x48cm-24x19in) s. 17-May-3 De Vuyst, Lokeren #237/R
£3966 $6345 €5750 Vue de parc Leopold, Bruxelles (70x70cm-28x28in) s.d.16 s.i.d.1916 verso. 15-Mar-3 De Vuyst, Lokeren #538/R est:5000-6500

LEROUX, Louis (19th C) French
£641 $1000 €962 River landscape (23x41cm-9x16in) init. panel. 9-Oct-2 Doyle, New York #65

LEROUX, Louis Hector (1829-1900) French
£2188 $3500 €3282 Vestel Virgin (86x50cm-34x20in) s. 14-May-3 Butterfields, San Francisco #1129/R est:4000-6000

LEROUX-DEVIN, Jean Michel (20th C) French
£256 $403 €400 Totem (90x90cm-35x35in) s. 15-Dec-2 Thierry & Lannon, Brest #238

LEROY, Camille (1905-1995) French?
£769 $1208 €1200 Patio de la villa Abdel-Tif (46x33cm-18x13in) s. i.verso panel. 16-Dec-2 Gros & Delettrez, Paris #359

LEROY, Eugène (1910-2000) French
£1410 $2186 €2200 Untitled - female nude (63x47cm-25x19in) s.d.78 chk chl board prov. 3-Dec-2 Lempertz, Koln #262/R est:2000
£7383 $11886 €11000 Vue de foret (81x60cm-32x24in) s. 23-Feb-3 Mercier & Cie, Lille #105/R
£18345 $29353 €25500 Self portrait (130x162cm-51x64in) s.d.69 prov. 17-May-3 De Vuyst, Lokeren #495/R
Works on paper
£302 $486 €450 Landscape (71x26cm-28x10in) s.d.62 crayon dr. 23-Feb-3 Mercier & Cie, Lille #91
£972 $1604 €1400 Personnage feminin (88x61cm-35x24in) s.i.d.82 chl prov. 1-Jul-3 Artcurial Briest, Paris #807/R
£1463 $2326 €2150 Sans titre (65x50cm-26x20in) s.d.93 chl prov.exhib. 26-Feb-3 Artcurial Briest, Paris #535/R est:1500-2000

LEROY, Jean Francois (20th C) French?
Sculpture
£1410 $2158 €2200 Chevauux en accolade (27x20cm-11x8in) num.2/8 brown pat bronze. 23-Aug-2 Deauville, France #289/R

LEROY, Joseph Francois (1768-1829) French
Miniatures
£2600 $4004 €3900 Claire de Maille holding a brown dog (7cm-3in circular) s. gilt metal frame exec.c.1800. 24-Oct-2 Sotheby's, Olympia #47/R est:1400-1800

LEROY, Jules (1856-1921) French
£887 $1480 €1250 Jeunes chats (27x22cm-11x9in) s. 18-Jun-3 Pierre Berge, Paris #150/R
£896 $1416 €1300 Chatons dans un panier (33x41cm-13x16in) s. 4-Apr-3 Tajan, Paris #143/R
£950 $1549 €1378 An unexpected guest (16x22cm-6x9in) s. panel. 16-Jul-3 Sotheby's, Olympia #242/R
£1100 $1672 €1650 Cat with a bowl of milk (21x15cm-8x6in) s. panel. 29-Aug-2 Christie's, Kensington #198/R est:700-1000
£1433 $2250 €2150 Three cats playing on a desk with a map, eyeglasses and books (48x64cm-19x25in) i.verso. 23-Nov-2 Pook & Pook, Downington #292/R est:3000-5000
£1613 $2548 €2420 Kitten and rabbit family (20x25cm-8x10in) s. panel. 18-Nov-2 Waddingtons, Toronto #242/R est:4000-6000 (C.D 4000)
£1935 $3000 €2903 Kittens (25x33cm-10x13in) s.d.1909 panel. 7-Dec-2 Neal Auction Company, New Orleans #94/R est:3000-5000

£2083 $3437 €3000 Chacun son tour, patience (38x46cm-15x18in) s. init.i.verso. 1-Jul-3 Christie's, Amsterdam #567 est:3000-5000
£2580 $4153 €3870 Cat and kittens on a chair (34x26cm-13x10in) s.d.1899. 12-May-3 Stephan Welz, Johannesburg #424/R est:20000-30000 (SA.R 30000)
£2848 $4500 €4500 Jeux de chatons dans le salon (46x37cm-18x15in) s. panel. 1-Dec-2 Peron, Melun #47

LEROY, Patrick (1948-) French
£370 $526 €600 Elegantes sous les arbres pres du lac (72x59cm-28x23in) s. panel. 16-Mar-3 Eric Pillon, Calais #254/R
£417 $654 €650 Composition (77x64cm-30x25in) s.panel. 15-Dec-2 Eric Pillon, Calais #271/R
£432 $691 €600 Composition (63x49cm-25x19in) s. panel. 18-May-3 Eric Pillon, Calais #228/R
£899 $1439 €1250 Composition (80x64cm-31x25in) s. panel. 18-May-3 Eric Pillon, Calais #260/R

LEROY, Paul Alexandre Alfred (1860-1942) French
£2564 $4026 €4000 Jeune femme au turban ainsi qu'un paysage (41x26cm-16x10in) panel ceramic tile. 16-Dec-2 Gros & Delettrez, Paris #324/R est:3000-5000

LEROY, Pierre Jean Baptiste (1784-1862) Belgian
£949 $1481 €1500 Dangerous liaisons (45x53cm-18x21in) s.d.1836. 21-Oct-2 Bernaerts, Antwerp #84/R est:1400-1600

LEROY, Sebastien (fl.1798-1832) French
Works on paper
£6000 $9300 €9000 Port Jackson (30x38cm-12x15in) s. wash sold with engraving. 26-Sep-2 Christie's, London #92/R est:2000-3000

LEROY, Sebastien (attrib) (fl.1798-1832) French
Works on paper
£3200 $4960 €4800 Nouvelle Hollande, Port Jackson (23x30cm-9x12in) pencil two and sold with three engraving after Nicolas Martin Pet. 26-Sep-2 Christie's, London #94/R est:3000-5000

LEROY-SAINT-AUBERT (1852-1907) French
£390 $651 €550 Mas en bord de mer (45x81cm-18x32in) s. 23-Jun-3 Delvaux, Paris #190

LERPA, Nes (1942-) Danish
£457 $727 €686 Composition (100x135cm-39x53in) s. acrylic. 26-Feb-3 Kunsthallen, Copenhagen #149 (D.KR 5000)

LESAGE, Augustin (1876-1954) French
£27778 $45000 €41667 Composition symbolique (127x95cm-50x37in) s.d.1928 oil graphite exhib. 27-Jan-3 Christie's, Rockefeller NY #40/R est:45000-55000

LESCOURT, Henri (1925-) French
£316 $500 €500 Duck pond (20x25cm-8x10in) s. panel. 29-Nov-2 Schloss Ahlden, Ahlden #1309/R
£348 $550 €550 Ducks by pond (20x25cm-8x10in) s. panel. 29-Nov-2 Schloss Ahlden, Ahlden #1307/R

LESIEUR, P (1922-) French
£1162 $1871 €1650 Composition au pichet (50x50cm-20x20in) s. 11-May-3 Thierry & Lannon, Brest #377 est:150-200

LESIEUR, Pierre (1922-) French
£1592 $2484 €2500 Plage (54x54cm-21x21in) s. 10-Nov-2 Eric Pillon, Calais #228/R
£1592 $2484 €2500 Plage (54x54cm-21x21in) s. 10-Nov-2 Eric Pillon, Calais #227/R

LESLIE, Alfred (1927-) American
£10692 $17000 €16038 No 25 (184x199cm-72x78in) s.i.d.1959 exhib. 7-Mar-3 Skinner, Boston #642/R est:15000-25000

LESLIE, C (19th C) British
£340 $524 €510 Mountainous landscape scene with figures (30x61cm-12x24in) s. 6-Sep-2 Biddle & Webb, Birmingham #52

LESLIE, Charles (1835-1890) British
£280 $448 €420 Moonlit lake view (31x62cm-12x24in) s.d.1872. 13-May-3 Bonhams, Knightsbridge #54/R
£288 $447 €432 Loch landscape (30x61cm-12x24in) bears sig. 3-Dec-2 Ritchie, Toronto #3037/R (C.D 700)
£300 $468 €450 Loch landscape with anglers (30x61cm-12x24in) mono. pair. 6-Nov-2 Bonhams, Chester #527
£305 $482 €458 Lyn Penarth, North Wales (92x46cm-36x18in) 7-Apr-3 Shapiro, Sydney #499 (A.D 800)
£323 $510 €485 Ben Ledi and Loch Venechar (38x69cm-15x27in) s.d.1872 s.i.d.stretcher. 18-Nov-2 Waddingtons, Toronto #90/R (C.D 800)
£350 $574 €525 Across the loch (30x61cm-12x24in) s. 29-May-3 Christie's, Kensington #92
£420 $655 €630 Loch Kintrea, Perthshire (31x61cm-12x24in) s.d.81. 10-Apr-3 Tennants, Leyburn #979
£450 $720 €675 Highland loch landscape (34x59cm-13x23in) s. 11-Mar-3 Bonhams, Knightsbridge #100/R
£513 $800 €770 Scottish highlands with view of a loch (76x127cm-30x50in) s.d.1878. 12-Apr-3 Weschler, Washington #512/R
£524 $828 €786 Shepherd and flock by a loch (46x81cm-18x32in) s.d.1884. 18-Nov-2 Waddingtons, Toronto #105/R (C.D 1300)
£550 $891 €825 Moonlight on the Cambrian coast. Sunset over the Cambrian mountains (30x61cm-12x24in) s.d.1882 one i.stretcher pair. 23-Jan-3 Christie's, Kensington #217
£580 $899 €870 Loch Dhulich, Perthshire (31x61cm-12x24in) s.d.1881. 7-Dec-2 Shapes, Edinburgh #394
£701 $1108 €1052 Mountain landscape with lake, Helwellyn (31x61cm-12x24in) s.d.1876. 27-Nov-2 Falkkloos, Malmo #77826/R (S.KR 10000)
£1900 $2983 €2850 Morning flight (76x127cm-30x50in) s.d.1886. 16-Dec-2 Bonhams, Bury St Edmunds #528/R est:1800-2500
£2000 $3140 €3000 Highland loch scenes (30x61cm-12x24in) s.d.1877 two. 21-Nov-2 Tennants, Leyburn #801/R est:800-1200

LESLIE, Charles (attrib) (19th C) British
£600 $978 €870 Summer, Crummuck Water. Snow on the Grampians (29x59cm-11x23in) i. pair. 16-Jul-3 Anthemion, Cardiff #942

LESLIE, Charles Robert (1794-1859) British
£400 $624 €600 Ernest discussion (61x48cm-24x19in) 26-Mar-3 Hamptons Fine Art, Godalming #215
£400 $656 €600 Consecration of Saint Nicholas (51x34cm-20x13in) i. verso board after Paolo Caliari IL Verinese. 5-Jun-3 Christie's, Kensington #650
£3774 $6000 €5661 Secret messenger (119x104cm-47x41in) s. 5-Mar-3 Christie's, Rockefeller NY #62/R est:2500-3500
£12000 $19320 €18000 Sancho Panza in the apartment of the duchess (61x76cm-24x30in) s.d.1857 prov.exhib.lit. 20-Feb-3 Christie's, London #78/R est:20000

LESLIE, George Dunlop (1835-1921) British
£35000 $58100 €52500 Matilda - Dante Purgatorio, Canto (51x93cm-20x37in) mono.d.1859 i.verso prov.exhib.lit. 10-Jun-3 Christie's, London #103/R est:40000-60000
£135000 $217350 €202500 Five o'clock (84x112cm-33x44in) prov.exhib.lit. 20-Feb-3 Christie's, London #268/R est:80000
£400000 $632000 €600000 Pot-pourri (99x99cm-39x39in) prov.exhib.lit. 27-Nov-2 Christie's, London #13/R est:400000-600000

LESLIE, George Dunlop (attrib) (1835-1921) British
£2000 $3280 €3000 Portrait of John Philip Kemble holding the skull of Yorrick (122x110cm-48x43in) after Sir Thomas Lawrence. 29-May-3 Christie's, Kensington #53 est:2500-3500

LESLIE, Peter (1877-?) British
£400 $628 €600 Reapers (39x59cm-15x23in) s. 15-Dec-2 Lots Road, London #354

LESNE, Camille (20th C) French
£286 $450 €429 Le tubort le phare (23x33cm-9x13in) s. panel prov. 14-Dec-2 Weschler, Washington #612/R

LESNIEWICZ, Horst (1926-) German
£340 $541 €500 The shuffle (43x58cm-17x23in) s. i. verso. 28-Mar-3 Bolland & Marotz, Bremen #661/R

LESPINASSE, Louis Nicolas de (1734-1808) French
Works on paper
£55556 $90000 €83334 Reception of an ambassador. Presentation o ambassador (25x39cm-10x15in) s.d.1790 pencil ink pen W/C bodycol htd white pair. 22-Jan-3 Christie's, Rockefeller NY #70/R est:160000

LESREL, Adolphe Alexandre (1839-1929) French
£1800 $2826 €2700 Game of chess (50x57cm-20x22in) s.d.1880. 21-Nov-2 Christie's, Kensington #67/R est:2000-3000
£2033 $3253 €2948 Couple flirting (66x52cm-26x20in) s.d.1891. 18-May-3 Anders Antik, Landskrona #149 est:60000 (S.KR 26000)
£12500 $20000 €18750 Art connoisseurs (58x48cm-23x19in) s.d.1896 panel. 14-May-3 Butterfields, San Francisco #1114/R est:15000-20000

£13924 $22000 €20886 Portrait (56x45cm-22x18in) s. panel. 24-Apr-3 Sotheby's, New York #137/R est:18000-25000

LESSI, Tito (1858-1917) Italian
£3926 $6163 €5889 Chestnut seller (69x48cm-27x19in) s.d.1886. 24-Jul-2 Walker's, Ottawa #37/R est:3000-4000 (C.D 9500)

LESSIEUX, Ernest Louis (1848-1925) French
£2100 $3256 €3150 Views of Cap Martin. Monaco (25x34cm-10x13in) s. board with another work by G Charpentier three. 3-Dec-2 Sotheby's, Olympia #279/R est:2000-3000

Works on paper
£481 $760 €750 To the chapel (28x38cm-11x15in) s. W/C. 13-Nov-2 Ansorena, Madrid #204/R
£980 $1528 €1450 Porteuse d'eau (34x23cm-13x9in) s. W/C. 26-Mar-3 Rieunier, Paris #12/R
£1600 $2496 €2400 Monaco from Cap Martin, Provence (29x46cm-11x18in) s. i.verso W/C. 5-Nov-2 Bonhams, New Bond Street #12/R est:1000-1500

LESSING, Karl Friedrich (1808-1880) German
£881 $1313 €1322 Wounded soldier and burning ruins in wooded landscape (51x68cm-20x27in) mono. 25-Jun-2 Koller, Zurich #6455 (S.FR 2000)

LESSING, Karl Friedrich (attrib) (1808-1880) German
£2013 $3242 €3000 Hermit (33x24cm-13x9in) init. prov. 18-Feb-3 Sotheby's, Amsterdam #326/R est:3750-4500

LESSING, Konrad Ludwig (1852-1916) German
£962 $1510 €1500 Barge near Bad Honnef am Rhein (48x64cm-19x25in) s. 21-Nov-2 Van Ham, Cologne #1748/R est:1500
£2255 $3563 €3383 Mountain landscape with church (68x118cm-27x46in) s. 2-Dec-2 Rasmussen, Copenhagen #1595/R est:30000 (D.KR 26500)
£2302 $3683 €3200 Eifel landscape with Ulmener Maar (68x82cm-27x32in) s. 17-May-3 Lempertz, Koln #1425/R est:4000

LESSORE, John (1939-) British
£380 $593 €570 Block of flats in Lambeth (30x40cm-12x16in) board prov. 15-Oct-2 Bonhams, Knightsbridge #217/R

LESSORE, Jules (1849-1892) French/British
Works on paper
£280 $468 €406 Shipping in an estuary (17x24cm-7x9in) s. W/C rubbing out. 23-Jun-3 Bonhams, Bath #81
£440 $695 €660 Fishing boats, Shoreham (50x34cm-20x13in) s. W/C bodycol. 26-Nov-2 Bonhams, Knightsbridge #204/R
£550 $858 €825 Venetian backwater (50x34cm-20x13in) s. W/C bodycol. 25-Mar-3 Bonhams, Knightsbridge #57/R

LESSORE, Therese (1884-1945) French
£900 $1404 €1350 Lady at the theatre (61x51cm-24x20in) s.d.1918 prov. 25-Mar-3 Bonhams, New Bond Street #32/R
£950 $1482 €1425 Street scene (63x66cm-25x26in) s.d.40 prov. 25-Mar-3 Bonhams, New Bond Street #29/R
£2800 $4368 €4200 Upper circle (45x61cm-18x24in) indis sig.d.1918 prov. 25-Mar-3 Bonhams, New Bond Street #31/R est:2500-3500

LESSORE, Therese (attrib) (1884-1945) French
Works on paper
£1100 $1749 €1650 Old Cafe Royal. Riding at Blackfriars (16x23cm-6x9in) red ink W/C pair. 26-Feb-3 Sotheby's, Olympia #137/R est:800-1200

LESTER, Adrienne (19/20th C) British
£950 $1416 €1425 Firm friends (18x28cm-7x11in) s. board. 28-Jun-2 Chrystals Auctions, Isle of Man #139
£1000 $1550 €1500 Two kittens on a wall watching a butterfly (49x67cm-19x26in) s. 2-Oct-2 George Kidner, Lymington #158/R

LESTER, Kerrie (1953-) Australian
£407 $642 €590 Heading home (25x30cm-10x12in) s. 22-Jul-3 Lawson Menzies, Sydney #147/R est:900-1100 (A.D 1000)
£488 $771 €708 In a hurry home (25x30cm-10x12in) s. 22-Jul-3 Lawson Menzies, Sydney #146/R est:900-1100 (A.D 1200)
£1916 $3008 €2874 Waiting 2000 (84x102cm-33x40in) s. oil on cavas handstitched fishing reels. 15-Apr-3 Lawson Menzies, Sydney #93/R est:4000-6000 (A.D 5000)
£2846 $4496 €4127 Away with the pixies (122x152cm-48x60in) s. 22-Jul-3 Lawson Menzies, Sydney #145/R est:8000-10000 (A.D 7000)

Works on paper
£1916 $3008 €2874 Hidden (74x83cm-29x33in) s. mixed media handstitched. 15-Apr-3 Lawson Menzies, Sydney #94/R est:3500-6500 (A.D 5000)

LESTER, William Lewis (1910-1991) American
Works on paper
£353 $550 €530 Abstract (61x46cm-24x18in) W/C. 19-Oct-2 David Dike, Dallas #16/R

LESUEUR, Augustine Camille (fl.1847-1850) French
£1034 $1645 €1500 Jeune femme au bonnet de dentelles (88x70cm-35x28in) s. 5-Mar-3 Doutrebente, Paris #48/R est:1000-1300

LESUEUR, Pierre Étienne (18th C) French
£3549 $5607 €5500 Presentation de l'esclave. Denicheur d'oiseau (17x20cm-7x8in) s.d.1796 panel pair. 20-Dec-2 Tajan, Paris #132/R est:7000
£15385 $24154 €24000 Depart pour Cythere (181x140cm-71x55in) s.d.1753 prov. 16-Dec-2 Rabourdin & Choppin de Janvry, Paris #182/R est:32000

LESUEUR, Pierre II (1663-1698) French
Works on paper
£886 $1400 €1400 Joseph asleep in his workshop (56x37cm-22x15in) pen htd white. 29-Nov-2 Bassenge, Berlin #5522/R

LESUR, Henri Victor (1863-1900) French
£1719 $2750 €2579 Romantic dalliance (55x45cm-22x18in) s. panel. 14-May-3 Butterfields, San Francisco #1117/R est:3000-5000
£3226 $5097 €4839 Parisian flower market (65x53cm-26x21in) s. panel. 18-Nov-2 Waddingtons, Toronto #247/R est:8000-12000 (C.D 8000)
£3416 $5500 €5124 Flower seller (41x33cm-16x13in) s. board. 19-Jan-3 Jeffery Burchard, Florida #93/R
£9032 $14000 €13548 Promenade in the gardens (49x61cm-19x24in) s. panel. 30-Oct-2 Christie's, Rockefeller NY #177/R est:12000-16000

LETELLIER, Pierre (1928-2000) French
£959 $1505 €1400 Barques pres de Camerone (54x82cm-21x32in) s. 21-Apr-3 Rabourdin & Choppin de Janvry, Paris #165

Works on paper
£728 $1135 €1150 Danseuse cu Crazy (65x50cm-26x20in) s. chl wash. 15-Sep-2 Etude Bailleul, Bayeux #159/R

LETENDRE, Rita (1928-) Canadian
£610 $957 €915 Enigme (50x50cm-20x20in) s.d.62 s.i.d. verso. 12-Dec-2 Iegor de Saint Hippolyte, Montreal #62 (C.D 1500)
£844 $1385 €1266 Ma-a-ta (180x104cm-71x41in) s.i.d.80 verso acrylic. 3-Jun-3 Joyner, Toronto #411/R est:2000-3000 (C.D 1900)

Works on paper
£288 $444 €432 Sans titre (32x39cm-13x15in) s.d. gouache. 22-Oct-2 Iegor de Saint Hippolyte, Montreal #60 (C.D 700)
£489 $802 €709 Sans Titre no.5 (23x30cm-9x12in) gouache. 1-Jun-3 Levis, Calgary #72 est:1200-1500 (C.D 1100)

LETERREUX, Gervaix (1930-) French
£316 $494 €500 Chaumieres a Pennedepie (38x46cm-15x18in) s. 15-Sep-2 Etude Bailleul, Bayeux #111/R
£423 $680 €600 Honfleur (38x46cm-15x18in) s. 12-May-3 Lesieur & Le Bars, Le Havre #60

LETH, Harald (1899-1986) Danish
£287 $465 €416 Field landscape (30x36cm-12x14in) with sig. verso. 24-May-3 Rasmussen, Havnen #4391 (D.KR 3000)
£719 $1107 €1079 Winter landscape (34x46cm-13x18in) init. 23-Oct-2 Kunsthallen, Copenhagen #27/R (D.KR 8500)

LETHBRIDGE, Julian (1947-) American
Works on paper
£1139 $1800 €1709 Pair (67x51cm-26x20in) graphite exec.1984-86. 13-Nov-2 Sotheby's, New York #572/R

LETHBRIDGE, Walter Stephens (1771-1831) British
£400 $628 €600 Edwin and Angelina (20x12cm-8x5in) s.i.verso oil on ivory. 16-Apr-3 Christie's, Kensington #508/R

LETHBRIDGE, Walter Stephens (attrib) (1771-1831) British
Miniatures
£1600 $2480 €2400 Officer, possibly of the Militia or Volunteers (7cm-3in) gold frame oval. 1-Oct-2 Bonhams, New Bond Street #215/R est:500-700

LETHIERE, Guillaume-Guillon (1760-1832) French
Works on paper
£8108 $12649 €12000 Portrait de Paul Joseph Notre (19x15cm-7x6in) pierre noire htd white. 27-Mar-3 Maigret, Paris #107/R est:5000

LETO, Antonino (1844-1913) Italian
£3117 $4800 €4676 Fishermen in the Bay of Naples by the Palazzo Sant'Anna (25x39cm-10x15in) s. 4-Sep-2 Christie's, Rockefeller NY #335/R est:3000-5000
£34810 $55000 €55000 Day in the countryside (61x111cm-24x44in) s. lit. 26-Nov-2 Christie's, Rome #285/R est:70000

LETOURNEAU, Edouard (1851-1907) French
£2885 $4529 €4500 Jeune femme du harem cueillant des roses (41x27cm-16x11in) s. 16-Dec-2 Gros & Delettrez, Paris #156/R est:2000-3000

LETSIA, Louis (19/20th C) ?
£845 $1386 €1225 Sunflowers and phlox in Chinese vase (70x50cm-28x20in) s. 4-Jun-3 Fischer, Luzern #2221/R est:1800-2200 (S.FR 1800)
£1033 $1694 €1498 Roses in Delft vase (36x27cm-14x11in) s. board. 4-Jun-3 Fischer, Luzern #2220/R est:1600-1800 (S.FR 2200)

LETT-HAINES, Arthur (1894-1978) British
£550 $853 €825 Landscape with cattle (46x38cm-18x15in) s. 4-Dec-2 Neal & Fletcher, Woodbridge #242
Works on paper
£1200 $1872 €1800 Strand at Luz Lagos (25x35cm-10x14in) s.d.1965 W/C chl. 15-Oct-2 Bonhams, Knightsbridge #123/R est:1200-1800

LETTERINI, Bartolomeo (18th C) Italian
£4054 $6324 €6000 Raising of Lazarus (85x136cm-33x54in) s.d. prov. 27-Mar-3 Dorotheum, Vienna #49/R est:6000-10000

LETTNER, Franz (1909-1998) Austrian
£1079 $1770 €1500 Orphische Welt (34x60cm-13x24in) s.d.68 paper. 5-Jun-3 Dorotheum, Salzburg #541/R est:2000-2600

LEU, August Wilhelm (1819-1897) German
£288 $447 €450 Paddle-steamer and sailing boat on a fjord (17x27cm-7x11in) s. board. 7-Dec-2 Dannenberg, Berlin #702/R
£1892 $2951 €2800 Morning sun on mountain lake (37x49cm-15x19in) s.d.48. 27-Mar-3 Dr Fritz Nagel, Stuttgart #829/R est:2800
£3200 $5024 €4800 In the shadow of the Alps (90x126cm-35x50in) s.d.1860. 16-Apr-3 Christie's, Kensington #731/R est:4000-6000

LEU, Ernst (1913-) Swiss
£408 $644 €612 Apple blossom branch on the studio table (80x65cm-31x26in) s.i. 29-Nov-2 Zofingen, Switzerland #2961 (S.FR 950)

LEU, Hans (younger-attrib) (1490-1531) Swiss
£5595 $9343 €8000 Seigneurs rencontrant un Saint Ermite devant une forteresse (69x82cm-27x32in) panel four boards. 25-Jun-3 Tajan, Paris #17/R est:8000-10000

LEU, Oscar (1864-1942) German
£252 $387 €400 Summer landscape (61x80cm-24x31in) s.i. 23-Oct-2 Neumeister, Munich #695/R
£329 $513 €480 Running steam in forest (69x52cm-27x20in) s. 10-Apr-3 Allgauer, Kempten #2873/R
£380 $589 €600 Still water in evening light (59x48cm-23x19in) s. canvas on board. 25-Sep-2 Neumeister, Munich #632/R
£380 $600 €600 Group of oak trees in Upper Bavaria (63x53cm-25x21in) s. board. 29-Nov-2 Bolland & Marotz, Bremen #732/R
£458 $750 €700 Summer landscape with chapel (70x100cm-28x39in) i. 5-Feb-3 Neumeister, Munich #750/R
£573 $883 €900 Summer landscape with pond and farmstead (86x96cm-34x38in) s. 5-Sep-2 Arnold, Frankfurt #806/R

LEU, Otto (1855-1922) German
£253 $392 €400 Reiteralm in Ramsau (47x63cm-19x25in) i. verso board. 26-Sep-2 Neumeister, Munich #2780/R
£274 $427 €400 Les Dents de Midi (61x42cm-24x17in) s. bears d. i. verso. 9-Apr-3 Neumeister, Munich #702/R

LEUENBERGER, Werner Otto (1932-) Swiss
£556 $894 €806 Untitled (93x79cm-37x31in) mono.d.62. 9-May-3 Dobiaschofsky, Bern #273/R (S.FR 1200)

LEUPIN, Hans W (1920-) Swiss
£385 $596 €600 Isolated courtyard (40x40cm-16x16in) mono. lit. 6-Dec-2 Karlheinz Kaupp, Staufen #2376/R

LEUPPI, Leo Peter (1893-1972) Swiss
£408 $644 €612 Peddler couple with calico printer in Kratten coming home from Silsersee (35x37cm-14x15in) s.d.1924. 29-Nov-2 Zofingen, Switzerland #2963 (S.FR 950)
£2264 $3668 €3283 Blancheur filete (74x110cm-29x43in) s.i.d.1960 verso string oil exhib. 26-May-3 Sotheby's, Zurich #147/R est:2500-4500 (S.FR 4800)
£4292 $6781 €6438 Variation I (65x53cm-26x21in) s.d.37 prov.exhib. 26-Nov-2 Phillips, Zurich #86/R est:9000-12000 (S.FR 10000)
£5365 $8476 €8048 Untitled (60x53cm-24x21in) s.d.47 prov.exhib. 26-Nov-2 Phillips, Zurich #87/R est:9000-12000 (S.FR 12500)
£9871 $15597 €14807 Still life with guitar (57x45cm-22x18in) s.d.1931. 28-Nov-2 Christie's, Zurich #95/R est:6000-8000 (S.FR 23000)
Works on paper
£858 $1356 €1287 Game and law II (48x81cm-19x32in) s.i.d.54 mixed media. 28-Nov-2 Christie's, Zurich #94/R (S.FR 2000)
£1389 $2236 €2014 Playful forms (46x60cm-18x24in) s.d.54 gouache. 9-May-3 Dobiaschofsky, Bern #277/R est:3800 (S.FR 3000)
£1502 $2373 €2253 Winter (31x26cm-12x10in) s.d.39 W/C prov. 26-Nov-2 Phillips, Zurich #84/R est:3500-4500 (S.FR 3500)
£3774 $6113 €5472 Composition III (53x53cm-21x21in) s.d.1944 collage oil exhib. 26-May-3 Sotheby's, Zurich #143/R est:4000-6000 (S.FR 8000)

LEURS, Johannes Karel (1865-1938) Dutch
£987 $1599 €1500 Dinkel by Denekamp (35x52cm-14x20in) s. cardboard. 21-Jan-3 Christie's, Amsterdam #166 est:800-1200
£1240 $1946 €1860 Cattle at waters edge (48x74cm-19x29in) s. 24-Jul-2 Walker's, Ottawa #9/R est:4000-4500 (C.D 3000)
£1842 $2984 €2800 Shepherd with his flock resting on the heath (57x73cm-22x29in) s. 21-Jan-3 Christie's, Amsterdam #146/R est:1500-2000

LEUSCHNER, Franz (20th C) German
£3077 $4831 €4800 West African forest - Togo (86x128cm-34x50in) s.d.1925. 21-Nov-2 Van Ham, Cologne #1750/R est:4000

LEUSDEN, Willem van (1886-?) Dutch
£1250 $2025 €1900 De Grote market, Groningen (40x50cm-16x20in) s. 21-Jan-3 Christie's, Amsterdam #321/R est:500-700

LEUTENEZ, Richard (1884-1963) Belgian
£331 $540 €500 Arrivee de la peniche (59x81cm-23x32in) s. 17-Feb-3 Horta, Bruxelles #460

LEUTERITZ, Franz Wilhelm (1817-1902) German
£687 $1085 €1031 Steam ship Rorschach at a landing place in a Bodensee village (30x36cm-12x14in) s.d.1867. 29-Nov-2 Zofingen, Switzerland #2488/R (S.FR 1600)
£4808 $7452 €7500 Elb valley with view of Konigstein fortress and Lilienstein (58x81cm-23x32in) s.d.1878. 6-Dec-2 Ketterer, Munich #6/R est:8000-9000

LEUTZE, Emanuel Gottlieb (1816-1868) American/German
£19231 $30385 €30000 Tasso and the two Leonoras (82x65cm-32x26in) s.d.59 prov. 16-Nov-2 Lempertz, Koln #1523/R est:35000

LEUTZE, Emanuel Gottlieb (attrib) (1816-1868) American/German
£1538 $2400 €2307 Portrait of Marquis de Lafayette (105x74cm-41x29in) masonite panel prov. 12-Apr-3 Freeman, Philadelphia #197/R est:1500-2500
£2404 $3750 €3606 Portrait of George Washington (117x80cm-46x31in) masonite prov. 12-Apr-3 Freeman, Philadelphia #195/R est:1500-2500
£3526 $5500 €5289 Portrait of Andrew Jackson (106x76cm-42x30in) masonite. 12-Apr-3 Freeman, Philadelphia #196/R est:2500-3500

LEVANON, Mordechai (1901-1968) Israeli
Works on paper
£346 $550 €519 City on a hill (69x48cm-27x19in) s. mixed media gouache. 7-Mar-3 Skinner, Boston #542/R
£1778 $2951 €2578 Boy with violin (71x49cm-28x19in) s.d.63 gouache. 16-Jun-3 Waddingtons, Toronto #320/R est:1500-2000 (C.D 4000)

LEVASSEUR, Henri (1853-1934) French
£380 $600 €600 Fete au village (38x46cm-15x18in) s.d.55 panel. 27-Nov-2 Blanchet, Paris #46
Sculpture
£1282 $1987 €2000 L'improvisation (78cm-31in) s. brown pat bronze. 9-Dec-2 Horta, Bruxelles #132/R est:3000-3700
£2215 $3500 €3323 Apres le Combat (79cm-31in) s. num.3337 bronze brown pat. 22-Apr-3 Arthur James, Florida #391
£3200 $4928 €4800 Gloire au travail (74cm-29in) s. bronze. 5-Sep-2 Sotheby's, Olympia #115/R est:2000-3000

LEVASTI, Filli (1883-1966) Italian
£1603 $2516 €2500 Women on terrace (20x20cm-8x8in) s. board. 16-Dec-2 Pandolfini, Florence #242
£1667 $2633 €2600 Fashion boutique (99x116cm-39x46in) 15-Nov-2 Farsetti, Prato #596/R

LEVAVASSEUR, Henri (?) French
£411 $642 €650 Vase de fleurs (45x38cm-18x15in) s. d.1962 verso panel. 15-Sep-2 Etude Bailleul, Bayeux #174/R
£481 $750 €760 Le vieux moulin (27x35cm-11x14in) s. cardboard. 15-Sep-2 Etude Bailleul, Bayeux #173/R
£519 $810 €820 Scene familiale (45x38cm-18x15in) s. d.1959 verso panel. 15-Sep-2 Etude Bailleul, Bayeux #175/R

LEVCHENKO, Petr Alekseevich (1859-1917) Russian
£1119 $1869 €1600 Ferme Ukrainienne (19x32cm-7x13in) s. panel. 27-Jun-3 Claude Aguttes, Neuilly #61/R est:3000-4000

LEVE, Andre (20th C) French
£1266 $2000 €2000 Portrait of young woman (81x65cm-32x26in) s. 30-Nov-2 Bassenge, Berlin #6987 est:600

LEVEE, John (1924-) American
£944 $1500 €1416 Abstract (201x170cm-79x67in) s.d.58 s.d.February 1 1958 verso. 7-Mar-3 Skinner, Boston #641/R est:3000-5000
£993 $1658 €1400 February II (170x130cm-67x51in) s.d.61 i.verso. 20-Jun-3 Piasa, Paris #199/R
£993 $1658 €1400 Octobre 1 (205x87cm-81x34in) s.i.d.1963 verso. 20-Jun-3 Piasa, Paris #200/R
£993 $1658 €1400 Octobre 2 (203x87cm-80x34in) s.i.d.1963 verso. 20-Jun-3 Piasa, Paris #201/R
£1042 $1646 €1500 Composition (195x195cm-77x77in) s.d. 27-Apr-3 Perrin, Versailles #20 est:1500-2000
£1844 $3079 €2600 Sans titre (100x123cm-39x48in) s.d.56. 20-Jun-3 Piasa, Paris #202 est:1500-2000

Works on paper
£341 $532 €512 Abstract composition - December III (54x40cm-21x16in) s. mixed media canvas. 23-Sep-2 Blomqvist, Lysaker #1141 (N.KR 4000)
£1572 $2437 €2500 Composition (195x128cm-77x50in) s.d.54. 30-Oct-2 Artcurial Briest, Paris #706 est:800-1000

LEVEE, Madelaine (19th C) French
£1000 $1620 €1500 Still life of roses in blue vase (61x51cm-24x20in) s. 20-May-3 Sotheby's, Olympia #409/R est:1000-1500

LEVEQUE, Auguste (1866-1921) Belgian
£972 $1546 €1400 Modele dans l'atelier (71x40cm-28x16in) s. 30-Apr-3 Tajan, Paris #145/R
£1096 $1710 €1600 Allegorie de la reussite (60x86cm-24x34in) s. 14-Apr-3 Horta, Bruxelles #56 est:1500-2000

LEVER, Richard Hayley (1876-1958) American
£723 $1200 €1048 Pear and apple (23x29cm-9x11in) paperboard. 11-Jun-3 Butterfields, San Francisco #4043/R
£818 $1300 €1227 Hillside landscape with distant river (26x31cm-10x12in) canvasboard. 7-Mar-3 Skinner, Boston #414/R est:2000-4000
£892 $1400 €1338 Green Mountains (26x31cm-10x12in) s.d.1933 verso board. 22-Nov-2 Skinner, Boston #240/R est:800-1200
£903 $1400 €1355 Still life with peppers (46x61cm-18x24in) s. prov. 25-Sep-2 Doyle, New York #52/R
£1026 $1600 €1539 Self portrait. s.i.d.1942 board. 19-Oct-2 Harvey Clar, Oakland #1427
£1049 $1700 €1521 Still life with grapes (36x61cm-14x24in) s. 21-May-3 Doyle, New York #120/R est:2000-3000
£1563 $2500 €2345 Drawbridge, Westchester, New York (25x30cm-10x12in) s. board. 11-Jan-3 James Julia, Fairfield #132 est:2500-3000
£1573 $2500 €2360 Fishing boats, Cornwall, England (46x61cm-18x24in) s. i.verso. 7-Mar-3 Skinner, Boston #540/R est:3500-4500
£1613 $2500 €2420 Fishing boats, Cornwall 1908 (46x61cm-18x24in) s. i.d.1908 stretcher. 25-Sep-2 Doyle, New York #48/R est:1000-1500
£1750 $2800 €2538 New England cottage (51x61cm-20x24in) prov. 16-May-3 Skinner, Boston #233/R est:800-1200
£1807 $3000 €2620 Canal locks, Devon, England (41x51cm-16x20in) s.i. 11-Jun-3 Butterfields, San Francisco #4064/R est:3000-5000
£2117 $3325 €3176 Coastal landscape of Stoney Creek, Connecticut with rowboat and trees (33x41cm-13x16in) s. s.i.verso board. 19-Apr-3 James Julia, Fairfield #155/R est:3500-4500
£2215 $3500 €3323 Bridge over Thames River, London (15x23cm-6x9in) s. i.d.verso prov. 24-Apr-3 Shannon's, Milford #24/R est:2000-3000
£2273 $3500 €3410 Artist's dining room (76x102cm-30x40in) s. canvas on plywood prov. 24-Oct-2 Shannon's, Milford #159/R est:5000-7000
£2548 $4000 €3822 Canal with tugboat (30x41cm-12x16in) s. canvasboard prov. 20-Nov-2 Christie's, Los Angeles #68/R est:5000-7000
£2903 $4500 €4355 Grand Mannan, Canada (61x91cm-24x36in) s. i.stretcher. 25-Sep-2 Doyle, New York #50/R est:3000-5000
£3086 $5000 €4475 Twin trees. Silvermine, Connecticut (30x41cm-12x16in) s. i.verso canvas on masonite other panel two. 21-May-3 Doyle, New York #121/R est:3000-5000
£3145 $5000 €4718 Seascape (26x36cm-10x14in) s. canvasboard. 7-Mar-3 Skinner, Boston #399/R est:1200-1800
£3226 $5000 €4839 Sea mist in the dock, Exmouth 1913 (41x51cm-16x20in) s.d.1913 i.verso. 25-Sep-2 Doyle, New York #51/R est:2000-3000
£3226 $5000 €4839 Gloucester, Mass 1913 (33x41cm-13x16in) s. i.d.1913 stretcher. 25-Sep-2 Doyle, New York #53/R est:2500-3500
£3813 $6100 €5720 Grand Manan Island (61x91cm-24x36in) s. 11-Jan-3 James Julia, Fairfield #131 est:6000-8000
£3963 $6500 €5746 Hocktown, New Jersey (61x91cm-24x36in) s. s.i.verso linen canvas. 5-Jun-3 Swann Galleries, New York #162/R est:3000-5000
£4194 $6500 €6291 Sailboats. Fishing boats. fishing boat. Gloucester (23x30cm-9x12in) three s. one s.d.1904. 25-Sep-2 Doyle, New York #49/R est:2500-3500
£5096 $8000 €7644 Rocks and surf, Gloucester, Massachusetts, 1913 (51x61cm-20x24in) s. canvas on board prov. 10-Dec-2 Doyle, New York #73/R est:8000-10000
£5247 $8500 €7608 New York from the Queensborough Bridge (30x46cm-12x18in) i.verso board. 21-May-3 Doyle, New York #118/R est:5000-7000
£5346 $8500 €8019 Evening, Nantucket, Mass (41x50cm-16x20in) s.i. canvas on board prov. 5-Mar-3 Sotheby's, New York #43/R est:12000-18000
£5732 $9000 €8598 Fishing under the bridge (61x74cm-24x29in) s. i.verso panel. 10-Dec-2 Doyle, New York #72/R est:15000-20000
£6289 $10000 €9434 Seascape (77x102cm-30x40in) s.d.1941 prov. 5-Mar-3 Sotheby's, New York #88/R est:12000-18000
£6369 $10000 €9554 Chowder boats, Gloucester, Massachusetts, 1912 (51x61cm-20x24in) s. 10-Dec-2 Doyle, New York #70/R est:5000-7000
£6369 $10000 €9554 Gloucester, fish drying yard, 1913 (76x91cm-30x36in) s.i. 10-Dec-2 Doyle, New York #74/R est:6000-8000
£7317 $12000 €10610 Fishing boats, Rockport harbour (51x61cm-20x24in) s. particle board painted c.1925. 5-Jun-3 Swann Galleries, New York #163/R est:3000-5000
£7547 $12000 €11321 Landscape and pond, Woodstock, Catskills, NY (41x51cm-16x20in) s. prov. 5-Mar-3 Sotheby's, New York #65/R est:12000-18000
£8280 $13000 €12420 Gloucester, Massachusetts, 1913 (51x61cm-20x24in) s. 10-Dec-2 Doyle, New York #76/R est:4000-6000
£8917 $14000 €13376 Rocks with autumn foliage by the ocean (51x61cm-20x24in) s. 10-Dec-2 Doyle, New York #75/R est:5000-7000
£10828 $17000 €16242 Nantucket, Massachusetts, 1913 (51x61cm-20x24in) s. 10-Dec-2 Doyle, New York #66/R est:8000-10000
£14198 $23000 €20587 Day liner (61x76cm-24x30in) s. masonite. 21-May-3 Doyle, New York #117/R est:18000-24000
£34810 $55000 €52215 Bathing beach, Gloucester (64x76cm-25x30in) s. s.i.verso prov. 24-Apr-3 Shannon's, Milford #26/R est:40000-60000

Works on paper
£457 $750 €663 Self portrait (12x13cm-5x5in) s.i. pencil. 5-Jun-3 Swann Galleries, New York #160/R
£1258 $2000 €1887 Central Park, New York (36x47cm-14x19in) s.i. W/C. 7-Mar-3 Skinner, Boston #620/R est:3500-5500
£1419 $2200 €2129 Boat house, Marblehead (33x53cm-13x21in) s.i. W/C. 2-Nov-2 North East Auctions, Portsmouth #40/R est:1000-1500
£2500 $3800 €3750 Boston Yacht Club, Marblehead, Massachusetts (38x51cm-15x20in) s.i.d.1925 W/C graphite. 17-Aug-2 North East Auctions, Portsmouth #1097/R

LEVERD, Edouard (20th C) French
Works on paper
£1736 $2830 €2500 Lavandiere au moulin d'Ascoet a Pont l'Abbe (34x64cm-13x25in) s. W/C gouache. 19-Jul-3 Thierry & Lannon, Brest #94 est:1200-1500

LEVERD, René (1872-1938) French
Works on paper
£405 $632 €600 Quai des Celestins (37x27cm-15x11in) s.i. W/C. 30-Mar-3 Anaf, Lyon #392

LEVESON-MEARES, Sandra (1944-) Australian
£480 $773 €696 Untitled (120x243cm-47x96in) s.d.89. 12-May-3 Joel, Victoria #346 est:1500-2000 (A.D 1200)
£643 $1003 €965 Gorge, landscape (100x108cm-39x43in) s.d.86 board. 11-Nov-2 Deutscher-Menzies, Melbourne #146/R (A.D 1800)

LEVI, Basil (1878-1954) Russian
£252 $390 €400 River landscape (61x50cm-24x20in) s.d.1951. 6-Oct-2 Bukowskis, Helsinki #340/R
£261 $429 €400 Prince Eugen's Waldemarsudde (63x80cm-25x31in) s. 9-Feb-3 Bukowskis, Helsinki #417/R
£272 $433 €400 Winter (81x67cm-32x26in) 24-Mar-3 Bukowskis, Helsinki #386/R

LEVI, Basil (attrib) (1878-1954) Russian
£567 $902 €851 Forest (50x36cm-20x14in) i. board. 8-Mar-3 Dorotheum, Prague #156/R est:26000-37000 (C.KR 26000)

LEVI, Carlo (1902-1975) Italian
£1582 $2468 €2500 In the vineyard (50x65cm-20x26in) s. s.i.verso. 14-Sep-2 Meeting Art, Vercelli #960/R
£1677 $2650 €2600 Still life of fruit (50x70cm-20x28in) s. s.d.73 verso prov. 18-Dec-2 Christie's, Rome #217
£1874 $2943 €2925 Shells (52x70cm-20x28in) s. 10-Dec-2 Della Rocca, Turin #351/R
£2405 $3752 €3800 Lovers (69x53cm-27x21in) painted 1963. 15-Oct-2 Babuino, Rome #351/R
£2740 $4274 €4000 Trinita' dei Monti, Rome (20x25cm-8x10in) s. s.d.1947 verso. 10-Apr-3 Finarte Semenzato, Rome #173/R
£5479 $8548 €8000 Garden (50x60cm-20x24in) s. s.verso. 10-Apr-3 Finarte Semenzato, Rome #241/R
£6452 $10194 €10000 Reclining female nude (72x101cm-28x40in) s. d.34 verso prov. 18-Dec-2 Christie's, Rome #220/R
£11613 $18348 €18000 Alassio beach (60x50cm-24x20in) s.d.1927 board prov. 18-Dec-2 Christie's, Rome #216/R
Works on paper
£541 $843 €800 Maternity (70x50cm-28x20in) s.d.1970 wax crayon cardboard. 26-Mar-3 Finarte Semenzato, Milan #45/R

LEVI, Clemente Pugliese (1855-1936) Italian
£1156 $1839 €1700 Mountainous landscape (27x40cm-11x16in) s. board. 1-Mar-3 Meeting Art, Vercelli #109
£1667 $2433 €2600 Moonlight (78x64cm-31x25in) s. 5-Jun-2 Il Ponte, Milan #255
£2041 $3245 €3000 Angry (37x27cm-15x11in) s.d.1918 board. 1-Mar-3 Meeting Art, Vercelli #251

LEVI-STRAUSS, Raymond Urbain Elie (20th C) French
£680 $1082 €1000 Chemin vers la plage (61x46cm-24x18in) s. 24-Mar-3 Coutau Begarie, Paris #212

LEVIER, Charles (1920-) French
£252 $400 €378 Country road (54x63cm-21x25in) s. board. 7-Mar-3 Skinner, Boston #518/R
£427 $700 €619 Boats at the quay (76x102cm-30x40in) s. prov. 4-Jun-3 Doyle, New York #69
£444 $701 €666 Boats by the cafe (38x76cm-15x30in) s. board. 18-Nov-2 Waddingtons, Toronto #231/R (C.D 1100)
£472 $731 €750 Carnaval (76x100cm-30x39in) s. 3-Nov-2 Feletin, Province #130
£472 $731 €750 Lanvit (100x81cm-39x32in) s. 3-Nov-2 Feletin, Province #132
£500 $800 €750 Fleurs (102x76cm-40x30in) s. s.i.verso. 16-Mar-3 Butterfields, San Francisco #1078
£570 $900 €855 Boats at the quai (76x102cm-30x40in) s. prov. 2-Apr-3 Doyle, New York #48/R
£597 $950 €896 On the beach (61x76cm-24x30in) s. i.verso. 7-Mar-3 Skinner, Boston #520/R
£613 $950 €920 Provence II (51x127cm-20x50in) s. s.i.verso. 7-Dec-2 Neal Auction Company, New Orleans #940 est:1200-1800
£710 $1100 €1065 Village in Corsica (74x102cm-29x40in) s. s.i.verso. 7-Dec-2 South Bay, Long Island #65/R
£764 $1200 €1146 Still life on veranda (102x76cm-40x30in) 13-Dec-2 Du Mouchelle, Detroit #2191/R est:1500-2000
£828 $1300 €1242 Sete (51x127cm-20x50in) s. 22-Nov-2 Skinner, Boston #318/R est:700-900
£1258 $2000 €1887 Fleurs dans un port (76x101cm-30x40in) s. i.verso. 7-Mar-3 Skinner, Boston #516/R est:800-1200
Works on paper
£312 $500 €452 Floral still life (72x53cm-28x21in) s. W/C. 16-May-3 Skinner, Boston #191/R
£344 $550 €499 Still life with flowers before an open landscape (53x74cm-21x29in) s. W/C. 16-May-3 Skinner, Boston #193/R

LEVIEUX, Henri (19/20th C) French
£621 $1000 €932 Vagabond. Peniches (25x41cm-10x16in) s. panel pair. 19-Feb-3 Doyle, New York #66
£968 $1500 €1452 Cobblers in an interior (46x64cm-18x25in) s. 7-Dec-2 Selkirks, St. Louis #762 est:1500-1800

LEVIEUX, Reynaud (attrib) (c.1625-1690) French
£9038 $14281 €14100 Bouquet de fleurs sur entablement (115x88cm-45x35in) 13-Nov-2 Marc Kohn, Paris #54/R est:15000-18000
£10577 $16606 €16500 Nature morte au perroquet et aux Cavaliers King charles (127x104cm-50x41in) 20-Nov-2 Libert, Castor, Paris #32/R est:18000-20000

LEVIGNE, Theodore (1848-1912) French
£759 $1185 €1200 La lecture (46x38cm-18x15in) s. 10-Sep-2 Vanderkindere, Brussels #366
£1824 $2846 €2700 Retour sous la neige (48x65cm-19x26in) s. 30-Mar-3 Anaf, Lyon #394
£3165 $4905 €5000 La partie de campagne (80x100cm-31x39in) s. 27-Sep-2 Rabourdin & Choppin de Janvry, Paris #170/R est:5700-6000
£3243 $5059 €4800 Chiens de meute (73x92cm-29x36in) s. 30-Mar-3 Anaf, Lyon #393

LEVILLAIN, Ferdinand (1837-1905) French
Sculpture
£1800 $2934 €2610 Classical market scene (14x57cm-6x22in) s. bronze relief. 15-Jul-3 Sotheby's, Olympia #65/R est:1200-1800

LEVIN, Joseph (1894-1979) Russian
£345 $552 €500 Composition (80x60cm-31x24in) s. 12-Mar-3 Rabourdin & Choppin de Janvry, Paris #3
£345 $552 €500 Composition (61x50cm-24x20in) s.d.67. 12-Mar-3 Rabourdin & Choppin de Janvry, Paris #8/R
£414 $662 €600 Composition (92x73cm-36x29in) s. 12-Mar-3 Rabourdin & Choppin de Janvry, Paris #9/R
£483 $772 €700 Composition (89x76cm-35x30in) s. 12-Mar-3 Rabourdin & Choppin de Janvry, Paris #5/R
£655 $1048 €950 Composition (120x56cm-47x22in) s. 12-Mar-3 Rabourdin & Choppin de Janvry, Paris #15/R
£1241 $1986 €1800 Composition (65x46cm-26x18in) s. 12-Mar-3 Rabourdin & Choppin de Janvry, Paris #1/R
£1310 $2097 €1900 Composition (65x46cm-26x18in) s. 12-Mar-3 Rabourdin & Choppin de Janvry, Paris #13/R
£1379 $2207 €2000 Composition (87x66cm-34x26in) s. 12-Mar-3 Rabourdin & Choppin de Janvry, Paris #14/R

LEVIN, Julo (1901-1943) ?
£1261 $1967 €1892 Two cows in meadow (101x72cm-40x28in) masonite prov.exhib. 16-Sep-2 Philippe Schuler, Zurich #3516/R est:3000-5000 (S.FR 2900)

LEVIN, Phoebus (19th C) German
£1079 $1727 €1500 Bouquet (47x37cm-19x15in) s.d.1857 board. 17-May-3 De Vuyst, Lokeren #238/R est:1500-1700

LEVINE, Ben (20th C) American
£800 $1264 €1200 Late summer, Herefordshire (30x39cm-12x15in) init. s.i.verso board prov. 27-Nov-2 Sotheby's, Olympia #139/R

LEVINE, David (20th C) American
Works on paper
£967 $1500 €1451 In bed (29x40cm-11x16in) pencil pastel prov.exhib. 29-Oct-2 Sotheby's, New York #273/R est:800-1200
£1032 $1600 €1548 Workshop (36x51cm-14x20in) W/C gouache prov. 29-Oct-2 Sotheby's, New York #274/R est:1500-2000

LEVINE, Jack (1915-) American
£490 $813 €711 Calling the hounds (61x91cm-24x36in) s. 12-Jun-3 Christie's, Kensington #32/R
£500 $830 €725 Looking for a scent (61x91cm-24x36in) s. 12-Jun-3 Christie's, Kensington #33/R
£1000 $1560 €1500 Girl in violet robe (24x11cm-9x4in) s. i.d.1940 verso canvasboard prov. 17-Sep-2 Rosebery Fine Art, London #531/R est:400-600
£16975 $27500 €25463 Oh moon of Alabama (102x89cm-40x35in) s. painted 1972 prov.exhib.lit. 21-May-3 Sotheby's, New York #91/R est:40000-60000
Works on paper
£488 $800 €708 Horse study (44x76cm-17x30in) s. chl W/C. 5-Jun-3 Swann Galleries, New York #165/R
£1402 $2300 €2033 Passing comrade (47x54cm-19x21in) s. brush ink. 5-Jun-3 Swann Galleries, New York #166/R est:3000-5000

LEVINE, Sherrie (1947-) American
Photographs
£2658 $4200 €3987 Untitled (74x11cm-29x4in) photograph after Walker Evans negative executed 1989 prov. 12-Nov-2 Phillips, New York #241/R est:3000-4000
£4114 $6500 €6171 Untitled (50x40cm-20x16in) s.d.1989 black/white photograph prov.exhib. 13-Nov-2 Sotheby's, New York #505/R
£15823 $25000 €23735 Untitled (51x41cm-20x16in) s.d.1990 gelatin silver print prov. 14-Nov-2 Christie's, Rockefeller NY #448/R est:12000-18000
Works on paper
£6250 $10000 €9375 Untitled - thin stripe no.7 (61x51cm-24x20in) casein on mahogany executed 1986 prov.lit. 14-May-3 Sotheby's, New York #434/R est:10000-15000

LEVINSEN, Sophus (1869-1943) French
£490 $789 €750 Nature morte aux fruits (50x65cm-20x26in) s. 14-Jan-3 Vanderkindere, Brussels #48
£638 $1027 €950 Nature morte aux fleurs et aux fruits (40x50cm-16x20in) s. panel. 18-Feb-3 Vanderkindere, Brussels #54

LEVINSTEIN, Leon (1913-1988) ?
Photographs
£1948 $3000 €2922 Coney Island (33x33cm-13x13in) s.st.i.d.1958 num.36 verso gelatin silver print board prov.lit. 25-Oct-2 Phillips, New York #117/R est:3000-4000
£2215 $3500 €3323 Untitled (35x24cm-14x9in) st.verso gelatin silver print prov. 24-Apr-3 Phillips, New York #39/R est:4000-6000
£4870 $7500 €7305 Handball players, Houston Street, New York (34x28cm-13x11in) s.verso gelatin silver print board prov.lit. 25-Oct-2 Phillips, New York #40/R est:3000-4000

LEVINTHAL, David (1949-) American?
Photographs
£2147 $3500 €3221 Untitled (51x61cm-20x24in) s.num.3/4 polacolor print. 12-Feb-3 Christie's, Rockefeller NY #121/R est:3000-5000
£2187 $3500 €3281 Terminator (76x56cm-30x22in) s.i.d.1995 c-print prov. 14-May-3 Sotheby's, New York #307/R est:4000-6000
£3750 $6000 €5625 Untitled - from the desire series (81x56cm-32x22in) s.d.1990 num.1/5 c-print ceramic figure prov.exhib. 14-May-3 Sotheby's, New York #310/R est:5000-7000
£5000 $8000 €7500 Untitled - from the desire series (81x56cm-32x22in) s.d.1990 num.2/5 verso c-print on aluminum prov. 14-May-3 Sotheby's, New York #309/R est:4000-6000
£12025 $19000 €18038 Untitled - American beauties (51x61cm-20x24in) polaroid prints three executed 1989 prov. 13-Nov-2 Sotheby's, New York #137/R est:12000-18000

LEVIS, Giuseppe Augusto (1873-1926) Italian
£769 $1208 €1200 Winter lake (31x44cm-12x17in) s. board. 10-Dec-2 Della Rocca, Turin #257/R

LEVIS, Maurice (1860-1940) French
£1129 $1784 €1694 Le deversoir (43x61cm-17x24in) s.d.04 s.i.stretcher. 18-Nov-2 Waddingtons, Toronto #233/R est:2000-2500 (C.D 2800)
£1197 $1927 €1700 River landscape in spring with old mill (23x33cm-9x13in) s. panel. 7-May-3 Michael Zeller, Lindau #780/R est:600
£1500 $2505 €2250 Le Vieux moulin. Aux bords du cher (10x15cm-4x6in) s. panel pair. 18-Jun-3 Christie's, Kensington #4/R est:1800-2200
£1772 $2747 €2800 Carthago (34x48cm-13x19in) s.i.d.92. 25-Sep-2 Neumeister, Munich #634/R est:1800
£1900 $3173 €2755 On the banks of the river (47x66cm-19x26in) s.d.88. 17-Jun-3 Bonhams, New Bond Street #113/R est:1500-2500
£2000 $3140 €3000 Saint Dye sur Loire (24x33cm-9x13in) s. paper on panel. 21-Nov-2 Christie's, Kensington #5/R est:2000-3000
£3500 $5565 €5250 Ruins at Chauvigny (51x76cm-20x30in) s. 18-Mar-3 Bonhams, New Bond Street #120/R est:3000-5000
£3800 $6042 €5700 Les peupliers de la Char. Un barrage sur la riviere (16x22cm-6x9in) s. indis i.verso panel pair prov. 18-Mar-3 Bonhams, New Bond Street #122/R est:3000-5000
£4500 $7155 €6750 Saint Leonard. La Seine a la frette (24x35cm-9x14in) s. pair prov. 20-Mar-3 Christie's, Kensington #14/R est:3000-5000
£8974 $13910 €14000 Echoppe de chaudronnier arabe a Constantine (130x82cm-51x32in) s.i.d.86 i.verso. 9-Dec-2 Beaussant & Lefèvre, Paris #17/R est:5000
Works on paper
£245 $409 €350 Village (22x30cm-9x12in) s. chl W/C. 26-Jun-3 Tajan, Paris #53

LEVITAN, Isaac Ilyitch (1860-1900) Russian
£28000 $43400 €42000 Wooded river landscape with silver birches (71x94cm-28x37in) s. board. 4-Dec-2 Christie's, London #94/R est:15000-20000

LEVITOKYS, D (?) ?
£533 $831 €800 Elegante (67x55cm-26x22in) s. 10-Sep-2 Iegor de Saint Hippolyte, Montreal #74 (C.D 1300)

LEVITT, Helen (1918-) American
Photographs
£2152 $3400 €3228 New York (27x18cm-11x7in) s.verso gelatin silver print prov.lit. 25-Apr-3 Phillips, New York #96/R est:5000-7000
£2215 $3500 €3323 Untitled (24x36cm-9x14in) s.i.d.1972 verso dye transfer print prov.lit. 24-Apr-3 Phillips, New York #173/R est:3000-5000
£2405 $3800 €3608 New York (28x21cm-11x8in) s. verso gelatin silver print prov. 25-Apr-3 Phillips, New York #88/R est:8000-12000
£3038 $4800 €4557 New York (19x26cm-7x10in) s.verso gelatin silver print prov. 25-Apr-3 Phillips, New York #97/R est:6000-8000
£3165 $5000 €4748 New York (25x17cm-10x7in) s. verso gelatin silver print prov.lit. 25-Apr-3 Phillips, New York #89/R est:8000-12000
£4747 $7500 €7121 New York (19x28cm-7x11in) s.i. verso gelatin silver print lit. 25-Apr-3 Phillips, New York #27/R est:22000-28000

LEVITZKY, Dimitri (attrib) (1735-1822) Russian
£26000 $42120 €39000 Portrait of Grand Duchess Alexandra Pavlovna in childhood (67x48cm-26x19in) 21-May-3 Sotheby's, London #6/R est:15000-20000

LEVORATI, Ernesto (19th C) Italian
Works on paper
£285 $444 €450 Portrait of young Venetian girl (29x20cm-11x8in) s.d.1884 W/C. 16-Oct-2 Dorotheum, Vienna #20
£690 $1097 €1000 Femme au chale a pois (28x22cm-11x9in) s.d.1882 W/C. 6-Mar-3 Artcurial Briest, Paris #13

LEVY, Alexander (1881-1947) American
£4747 $7500 €7121 Suppertime (122x122cm-48x48in) s. prov. 24-Apr-3 Shannon's, Milford #98/R est:5000-7000

LEVY, Alphonse (1843-1918) French
£1603 $2516 €2500 Rabbin (32x24cm-13x9in) s. cardboard. 12-Dec-2 Rabourdin & Choppin de Janvry, Paris #53/R
£4487 $7045 €7000 Cacherisation (65x49cm-26x19in) s. 12-Dec-2 Rabourdin & Choppin de Janvry, Paris #32/R
Works on paper
£641 $1006 €1000 La declaration (54x40cm-21x16in) s. chl. 24-Nov-2 Chayette & Cheval, Paris #237b
£641 $1006 €1000 Portrait de Bar A Wolff (59x44cm-23x17in) s. chl. 24-Nov-2 Chayette & Cheval, Paris #237d
£769 $1208 €1200 Meditation dans le cimetiere (35x43cm-14x17in) s. mixed media. 24-Nov-2 Chayette & Cheval, Paris #237a/R
£962 $1510 €1500 Le marche aux chevaux (53x40cm-21x16in) s. chl. 24-Nov-2 Chayette & Cheval, Paris #237c

LEVY, Charles-Octave (?-1899) French
Sculpture
£3500 $5460 €5250 Farm labourer (80cm-31in) s.i.num.3668 brown pat bronze lit. 5-Nov-2 Sotheby's, London #203/R est:3000-5000

LEVY, Émile (1826-1890) French
£14194 $22000 €21291 Young mother feeding her baby (112x70cm-44x28in) s.d.1881 exhib.lit. 29-Oct-2 Sotheby's, New York #41/R est:15000-20000
Works on paper
£811 $1265 €1200 Italian landscapes (18x34cm-7x13in) one d.1853 crayon chk pair. 26-Mar-3 Piasa, Paris #106/R

LEVY, Henri (?) French?
£1474 $2241 €2300 Ariane a Naxos (47x47cm-19x19in) s. 10-Jul-2 Rabourdin & Choppin de Janvry, Paris #22/R est:2700-2900

LEVY, Lazar (20th C) French
£943 $1453 €1500 Femme dans les souks (33x24cm-13x9in) s. panel. 23-Oct-2 Rabourdin & Choppin de Janvry, Paris #228/R
£1006 $1550 €1600 Scene de rue animeee (24x19cm-9x7in) s. canvas on board. 23-Oct-2 Rabourdin & Choppin de Janvry, Paris #230
£1132 $1743 €1800 Dans les souks (33x24cm-13x9in) s. panel. 23-Oct-2 Rabourdin & Choppin de Janvry, Paris #229
£1156 $1839 €1700 Scene de marche (24x33cm-9x13in) s. cardboard. 24-Mar-3 Rabourdin & Choppin de Janvry, Paris #181/R est:1700-2000

LEVY, Lucien (19th C) French
Works on paper
£3500 $5705 €5075 Portrait of a young lady wearing a choker (41x30cm-16x12in) pastel. 17-Jul-3 Tennants, Leyburn #757a/R est:200-300

LEVY, Moses (1885-1968) Italian
£2123 $3312 €3100 On the beach (14x18cm-6x7in) s. cardboard painted 1920. 10-Apr-3 Finarte Semenzato, Rome #157
£2800 $4340 €4200 Beach at Livorno (10x12cm-4x5in) s. card. 5-Dec-2 Christie's, Kensington #84/R est:1200-1800
£5102 $8112 €7500 Le marchand de ballons (54x44cm-21x17in) s.d.1950 cardboard prov. 24-Mar-3 Rabourdin & Choppin de Janvry, Paris #144/R est:7500-8500
£5442 $8653 €8000 Chevaux devant la porte rose (46x33cm-18x13in) s.d.1940 prov. 24-Mar-3 Rabourdin & Choppin de Janvry, Paris #143/R est:7500-8500
Works on paper
£544 $865 €800 Scene de cafe. Promenade dans le jardin. s. pencil col crayon one d.1957 one d.1959 two in one mount prov. 24-Mar-3 Rabourdin & Choppin de Janvry, Paris #140/R

£1020 $1622 €1500 Scene de jardin (22x30cm-9x12in) s. col crayon prov. 24-Mar-3 Rabourdin & Choppin de Janvry, Paris #141/R est:1800-2000

LEVY, Rudolf (1875-1943) German

£15000 $24600 €22500 Marseille harbour (74x94cm-29x37in) s. painted 1926 prov.exhib.lit. 4-Feb-3 Christie's, London #271/R est:12000

LEVY-DHURMER, Lucien (1865-1953) French

£897 $1391 €1400 Daphne in a storm before the transformation (30x20cm-12x8in) mono.d.1912. 7-Dec-2 Hans Stahl, Hamburg #59/R
£14000 $21700 €21000 La fantaisie orientale (88x200cm-35x79in) s.d.1921. 4-Dec-2 Christie's, London #98/R est:12000-18000

Works on paper

£4167 $6458 €6500 Diane dans la tourmente (84x61cm-33x24in) s. pastel. 3-Dec-2 Sotheby's, Paris #6/R
£45570 $72000 €72000 Bourrasque (37x61cm-15x24in) s. pastel. 26-Nov-2 Camard, Paris #50/R est:38000

LEWANDOWSKI, Edmund D (1914-) American

£1842 $2800 €2763 Precision abstract (152x178cm-60x70in) s.d.1972. 18-Aug-2 Jeffery Burchard, Florida #96/R

LEWERS, Margo (1908-1978) Australian

£345 $541 €518 Surrounded (26x25cm-10x10in) s. acrylic on board. 15-Apr-3 Lawson Menzies, Sydney #235/R (A.D 900)
£429 $673 €644 Abstract (36x27cm-14x11in) s. paper on board. 25-Nov-2 Christie's, Melbourne #413/R (A.D 1200)
£613 $962 €920 Annotation (39x36cm-15x14in) s. acrylic on board. 15-Apr-3 Lawson Menzies, Sydney #232/R est:1000-1500 (A.D 1600)
£1071 $1779 €1826 Fusion (84x129cm-33x51in) s. i.verso hardboard. 10-Jun-3 Shapiro, Sydney #3 est:3000-5000 (A.D 2700)
£2778 $4611 €4733 Abstraction (39x39cm-15x15in) s. i.verso panel. 10-Jun-3 Shapiro, Sydney #2/R est:2000-4000 (A.D 7000)
£3214 $5046 €4821 Three ideas of spring (121x172cm-48x68in) s. i.stretcher board prov. 25-Nov-2 Christie's, Melbourne #53/R est:9000-12000 (A.D 9000)

Works on paper

£1032 $1713 €1757 Abstract in blue and brown (80x59cm-31x23in) s. i.verso W/C on board. 10-Jun-3 Shapiro, Sydney #4 est:1000-2000 (A.D 2600)

LEWICKI, Walter V (20th C) Canadian?

£222 $364 €322 Untitled - landscape with flowers (69x61cm-27x24in) 1-Jun-3 Levis, Calgary #73/R (C.D 500)

LEWIN, Stephen (fl.1890-1910) British

£600 $924 €900 Still life of daffodils in an Oriental vase, with a mandolin on a table (91x77cm-36x30in) s. 23-Oct-2 Hamptons Fine Art, Godalming #185/R
£850 $1326 €1275 Dr Johnston in his study (36x30cm-14x12in) s.d.1899. 8-Oct-2 Bonhams, Knightsbridge #34/R est:400-600
£1200 $1896 €1800 In the artist's studio (53x69cm-21x27in) s. 12-Nov-2 Bonhams, Knightsbridge #191/R est:1200-1800

LEWIS, A (?) British

£500 $795 €750 Loch landscape with highland cattle (51x76cm-20x30in) s. 27-Feb-3 Bonhams, Chester #369

LEWIS, Betsy (18/19th C) American

Works on paper

£637 $1000 €956 Hearts, houses, birds and overall floral decoration (18x15cm-7x6in) d.1801 W/C. 23-Nov-2 Pook & Pook, Downington #52/R

LEWIS, Charles (attrib) (1753-1795) British

£1650 $2541 €2475 Fruits in a wicker basket (42x47cm-17x19in) 5-Sep-2 Christie's, Kensington #331/R est:1000-1500

LEWIS, Charles James (1830-1892) British

£1300 $2119 €1950 Children at play (39x54cm-15x21in) s. 29-Jan-3 Sotheby's, Olympia #202/R est:1000-1500
£1400 $2184 €2100 Summer's breeze (24x32cm-9x13in) s.d.1873 canvas on panel. 7-Nov-2 Christie's, Kensington #167/R est:800-1200

Works on paper

£1500 $2430 €2250 Fishing village in Sussex (58x110cm-23x43in) s. W/C. 21-May-3 James Thompson, Kirby Lonsdale #224/R

LEWIS, Edmonia (1843-?) American

Sculpture

£70000 $109200 €105000 Night, two sleeping children (64x50x39cm-25x20x15in) s.i.d.1870 white marble. 9-Apr-3 Sotheby's, London #88/R est:20000-30000

LEWIS, Edmund Darch (1835-1910) American

£1835 $2900 €2753 New England landscape, summer day with river, figure and cottage (38x58cm-15x23in) s.d.1879. 18-Nov-2 Winter Associates, Plainville #100/R
£1946 $3250 €2822 Ladies at rest by a river (46x63cm-18x25in) s. indis d. 22-Jun-3 Freeman, Philadelphia #88/R est:2000-3000
£1987 $3100 €2981 Old mill (61x79cm-24x31in) s. 1-Aug-2 Eldred, East Dennis #797/R est:1500-2500
£2258 $3500 €3387 Derasago Falls (67x94cm-26x37in) s.d.1892. 8-Dec-2 Freeman, Philadelphia #102/R est:2500-4000
£2609 $4200 €3914 River scene in summer with herd and house on left bank and sailboat (74x127cm-29x50in) s.d.1886. 22-Feb-3 Pook & Pook, Downington #315/R est:5500-6500
£2724 $4250 €4086 Mill pond (38x69cm-15x27in) s.i.d.1868. 21-Sep-2 Pook & Pook, Downington #406/R est:5000-5500
£3065 $4750 €4598 Panoramic landscape of mountains and river, with figures and houses (76x127cm-30x50in) s. 2-Nov-2 North East Auctions, Portsmouth #55/R est:2500-4500
£3293 $5500 €4775 Old mill (76x127cm-30x50in) s.d.1880. 22-Jun-3 Freeman, Philadelphia #79/R est:5000-8000
£4194 $6500 €6291 Sailboats in an estuary (76x127cm-30x50in) s.d.1884. 8-Dec-2 Freeman, Philadelphia #101/R est:3000-5000
£4630 $7500 €6945 Camping out on Lake George (175x104cm-69x41in) s.i.d.1871. 23-Jan-3 Aspire, Cleveland #11 est:5000-8000
£4839 $7500 €7259 Nebraska Notch (91x152cm-36x60in) s.i.d.1875. 8-Dec-2 Freeman, Philadelphia #98/R est:5000-8000
£5380 $8500 €8070 Cows watering by the river (61x107cm-24x42in) s.d.1879. 24-Apr-3 Shannon's, Milford #116/R est:7000-9000
£9091 $14000 €13637 Valley of Washington (76x127cm-30x50in) s.d.1876 i.verso. 24-Oct-2 Shannon's, Milford #4/R est:9000-12000
£9740 $15000 €14610 Looking up the Hudson from West Point (76x127cm-30x50in) s.d.1876 i.verso. 24-Oct-2 Shannon's, Milford #5/R est:9000-12000

Works on paper

£247 $400 €371 Ducks on a lake (23x48cm-9x19in) s.d.1888 W/C. 24-Jan-3 Freeman, Philadelphia #137/R
£256 $400 €384 Seascape with sandy shoreline (23x48cm-9x19in) s.indis.d.18 W/C. 18-Sep-2 Alderfer's, Hatfield #357/R
£283 $450 €425 Sailing (22x49cm-9x19in) s.d.1886 W/C graphite. 7-Mar-3 Skinner, Boston #328/R
£305 $500 €442 Coastal scene with sailboats (32x49cm-13x19in) s.d. W/C. 5-Jun-3 Swann Galleries, New York #167/R
£350 $575 €508 Shoreline view with schooners and men in a dory (30x61cm-12x24in) W/C gouache. 31-May-3 Van Blarcom, South Natick #18/R
£535 $850 €803 Narragansett Bay (24x52cm-9x20in) s.d.1885 W/C gouache. 7-Mar-3 Skinner, Boston #491/R
£705 $1100 €1058 Seascape with sailboats at sea (23x51cm-9x20in) s.d.1901 W/C. 18-Sep-2 Alderfer's, Hatfield #383/R
£774 $1200 €1161 Coastal scene with sailing vessels (46x71cm-18x28in) s.d. W/C prov. 8-Dec-2 Toomey, Oak Park #692/R
£833 $1300 €1250 Coastal view (23x50cm-9x20in) s.d.1893 W/C gouache. 20-Sep-2 Sloan, North Bethesda #351/R est:700-1000
£944 $1500 €1416 Watching, possibly the New Bedford Coast (39x69cm-15x27in) s.d.1883 W/C. 7-Mar-3 Skinner, Boston #330/R est:2500-3500
£958 $1600 €1389 Waiting for the light (56x86cm-22x34in) s.i. indis d. W/C gouache. 22-Jun-3 Freeman, Philadelphia #91/R est:1500-2500
£974 $1500 €1461 Point Judith, Rhode Island (46x71cm-18x28in) s.d.1883 W/C gouache prov. 24-Oct-2 Shannon's, Milford #23/R est:2500-3500
£1032 $1600 €1548 Entrance to East Passage, Narragansett Bay, Rhode Island (22x50cm-9x20in) s.d.1901 i.verso W/C gouache prov. 8-Dec-2 Freeman, Philadelphia #116/R est:800-1200
£1032 $1600 €1548 Ships leaving rowboats (24x51cm-9x20in) s.d.1895 W/C gouache prov. 8-Dec-2 Freeman, Philadelphia #117/R est:800-1200
£2893 $4600 €4340 Rhode Island coastline (23x51cm-9x20in) s.d.1905 W/C. 1-Mar-3 North East Auctions, Portsmouth #724/R

LEWIS, Edmund Darch (attrib) (1835-1910) American

£3226 $5000 €4839 Waterfall in a tropical landscape, sunset (76x127cm-30x50in) 8-Dec-2 Freeman, Philadelphia #178/R est:3000-5000

LEWIS, Edward Morland (1903-1943) British

£2600 $4108 €3900 Wharf (26x18cm-10x7in) s. board exhib. 27-Nov-2 Sotheby's, Olympia #52/R est:1500-2000

LEWIS, Frederick (19/20th C) British

£755 $1200 €1133 Forgotten (46x38cm-18x15in) init.d.1883 i.d.1883 verso. 5-Mar-3 Doyle, New York #40/R
£968 $1500 €1452 Maggie (41x43cm-16x17in) s.d.verso. 8-Dec-2 Toomey, Oak Park #662/R est:1000-2000

LEWIS, H (19th C) ?
£246 $384 €369 Nature morte a l'aquarium (39x61cm-15x24in) s. 10-Sep-2 Iegor de Saint Hippolyte, Montreal #75/R (C.D 600)

LEWIS, Harry Emerson (1892-1958) American
£510 $795 €800 Canal in a French landscape (43x52cm-17x20in) init. 6-Nov-2 James Adam, Dublin #26/R
£1613 $2500 €2420 Peg's place (64x76cm-25x30in) s. prov.exhib. 29-Oct-2 John Moran, Pasadena #728 est:2000-3000
£2096 $3500 €3039 Industrial, salt mine (51x61cm-20x24in) s. board exhib. 17-Jun-3 John Moran, Pasadena #96 est:2000-3000
Works on paper
£903 $1400 €1355 Powell St cable car turnaround at Market St (25x33cm-10x13in) s. W/C. 29-Oct-2 John Moran, Pasadena #792 est:900-1400

LEWIS, J (?) ?
£417 $650 €626 River town with docked sailboats and distant bridge (51x76cm-20x30in) s. 14-Sep-2 Selkirks, St. Louis #199

LEWIS, James (20th C) American
£1199 $1750 €1799 Still life of fruit (20x25cm-8x10in) s.d.1982 artist board pair. 3-Nov-1 North East Auctions, Portsmouth #247/R

LEWIS, James Otto (1799-1858) American
£823 $1300 €1235 Hudson Valley School scene of river viewed from above a hillside (48x76cm-19x30in) s. 26-Apr-3 Thomaston Place, Thomaston #142

LEWIS, John (circle) (18th C) British
£5500 $8634 €8250 Portrait of Robert Wynne (125x100cm-49x39in) 20-Nov-2 Sotheby's, Olympia #56/R est:3000-5000

LEWIS, John Frederick (1805-1876) British
Works on paper
£420 $676 €630 Pisa June 24 (10x13cm-4x5in) pencil dr htd white prov. 19-Feb-3 Mallams, Oxford #382/R
£1582 $2500 €2373 Portrait of a young woman (36x27cm-14x11in) mono.d.1835 pencil W/C htd white prov.exhib. 24-Apr-3 Sotheby's, New York #180/R est:5000-7000
£2667 $4427 €3867 Spanish girl at a window (33x27cm-13x11in) s.d.1835 W/C prov. 16-Jun-3 Waddingtons, Toronto #99/R est:6000-8000 (C.D 6000)
£6000 $8580 €9000 Interior of Chapterhouse, Toledo cathedral (18x25cm-7x10in) pencil W/C gum prov.exhib.lit. 22-Jan-3 Christie's, London #67/R est:8000
£7600 $12008 €11400 Valley of the Lynn, Devon (22x29cm-9x11in) s. W/C over pencil htd bodycol prov. 28-Nov-2 Sotheby's, London #258/R est:4000-6000
£14000 $21840 €21000 An Eastern girl (33x24cm-13x9in) init.d.May 13 18 W/C chl gouache exhib. 26-Mar-3 Sotheby's, Olympia #35/R est:3000-4000

LEWIS, Lennard (1826-1913) British
Works on paper
£649 $968 €1000 Rocky coastline with fishing boats (24x54cm-9x21in) s.d.45 W/C two. 26-Jun-2 Neumeister, Munich #589/R

LEWIS, Lexden (20th C) New Zealander
Works on paper
£276 $392 €414 Young lady and roses (64x89cm-25x35in) s. W/C. 20-Mar-2 Watson's, Christchurch #33/R est:1000-3500 (NZ.D 900)

LEWIS, Margaret Sarah (1907-) American
Works on paper
£337 $525 €506 Street scene with man and woman shoveling snow on the sidewalk (76x53cm-30x21in) s. pastel. 8-Nov-2 York Town, York #689

LEWIS, Martin (1881-1962) American
Prints
£2308 $3600 €3462 Night in New York (21x23cm-8x9in) s. etching edition of 135. 7-Nov-2 Swann Galleries, New York #684/R est:4000-6000
£2532 $4000 €3798 Night in New York (22x23cm-9x9in) s. etching. 22-Apr-3 Butterfields, San Francisco #2034/R est:3000-5000
£2893 $4600 €4340 Great shadow (26x17cm-10x7in) s. drypoint. 1-May-3 Swann Galleries, New York #485/R est:4000-6000
£2893 $4600 €4340 Building a babylon, Tudor City, NY (33x21cm-13x8in) s.i. drypoint. 1-May-3 Swann Galleries, New York #498/R est:4000-6000
£2987 $4750 €4481 Corner shadows (53x56cm-21x22in) s.d.1929 drypoint one of 242. 30-Apr-3 Doyle, New York #226/R est:4000-6000
£3019 $4800 €4529 Charleston practice - lunch hour (20x25cm-8x10in) s.i. etching. 1-May-3 Swann Galleries, New York #486/R est:6000-9000
£3097 $4800 €4646 Chance meeting (39x27cm-15x11in) s. drypoint. 25-Sep-2 Christie's, Rockefeller NY #24/R est:4000-6000
£3270 $5200 €4905 Shadows on the ramp (23x27cm-9x11in) s. drypoint. 1-May-3 Swann Galleries, New York #487/R est:4000-6000
£4088 $6500 €6132 Arch, midnight (20x29cm-8x11in) s.i. drypoint. 1-May-3 Swann Galleries, New York #492/R est:4000-6000
£4717 $7500 €7076 Tree Manhattan (33x25cm-13x10in) s.i. drypoint. 1-May-3 Swann Galleries, New York #495/R est:5000-8000
£4839 $7500 €7259 Morning on the river (22x15cm-9x6in) s. mezzotint. 25-Sep-2 Christie's, Rockefeller NY #22/R est:6500-8500
£5031 $8000 €7547 Chance meeting (26x19cm-10x7in) s. drypoint. 1-May-3 Swann Galleries, New York #499/R est:7000-10000
£5660 $9000 €8490 Chance meeting (26x19cm-10x7in) s. drypoint edition of 105. 2-May-3 Sotheby's, New York #35/R est:6000-8000
£5975 $9500 €8963 Rain on Murray Hill (22x30cm-9x12in) s. drypoint edition of 110. 29-Apr-3 Christie's, Rockefeller NY #429/R est:9000-12000
£6918 $11000 €10377 Spring night, Greenwich Village (25x31cm-10x12in) s.i. drypoint. 1-May-3 Swann Galleries, New York #493/R est:6000-9000
£7547 $12000 €11321 Winter on White Street (28x17cm-11x7in) s.i. drypoint. 1-May-3 Swann Galleries, New York #497/R est:4000-6000
£8176 $13000 €12264 Quarter of nine, Saturday's children (25x33cm-10x13in) s.i. drypoint. 1-May-3 Swann Galleries, New York #490/R est:10000-15000
£8805 $14000 €13208 Rain on Murray Hill (20x30cm-8x12in) s.i. drypoint. 1-May-3 Swann Galleries, New York #489/R est:10000-15000
£12579 $20000 €18869 Shadow dance (24x28cm-9x11in) s.i. drypoint. 1-May-3 Swann Galleries, New York #494/R est:10000-15000
£13836 $22000 €20754 Relics (30x26cm-12x10in) s.i. drypoint. 1-May-3 Swann Galleries, New York #488/R est:18000-22000
£13836 $22000 €20754 Subway steps (35x21cm-14x8in) s.i. drypoint. 1-May-3 Swann Galleries, New York #496/R est:8000-12000
Works on paper
£259 $425 €376 Young woman standing in profile (20x4cm-8x2in) bears another sig. brush ink wash over pencil. 5-Jun-3 Swann Galleries, New York #168/R

LEWIS, Maud (1903-1970) Canadian
£1289 $2114 €1934 Loading hay wagon (29x32cm-11x13in) s. board prov. 3-Jun-3 Joyner, Toronto #270/R est:3000-4000 (C.D 2900)
£1333 $2187 €2000 Winter landscape (30x36cm-12x14in) s. board prov. 27-May-3 Sotheby's, Toronto #44/R est:3000-4000 (C.D 3000)
£1411 $2230 €2117 Team of oxen hauling load of hay (30x36cm-12x14in) s. board painted c.1965-70 prov. 18-Nov-2 Sotheby's, Toronto #22/R est:3000-4000 (C.D 3500)
£1411 $2230 €2117 Trian crossing (20x25cm-8x10in) s. board. 14-Nov-2 Heffel, Vancouver #13/R est:4000-5000 (C.D 3500)
£1613 $2548 €2420 Pair of oxen hauling logs (30x36cm-12x14in) s. board painted c.1965-70 prov. 18-Nov-2 Sotheby's, Toronto #21/R est:3000-4000 (C.D 4000)
£1667 $2733 €2417 Oxen team in winter (29x34cm-11x13in) s. board. 9-Jun-3 Hodgins, Calgary #372/R est:4000-5000 (C.D 3750)
£1778 $2916 €2578 Sleigh in winter landscape (30x29cm-12x11in) s. board. 9-Jun-3 Hodgins, Calgary #131/R est:4000-5000 (C.D 4000)
£2000 $3280 €2900 Oxen team and tulips (28x29cm-11x11in) s. board. 9-Jun-3 Hodgins, Calgary #373/R est:4000-5000 (C.D 4500)
£2000 $3280 €3000 House and ox cart by the river (30x37cm-12x15in) s. board prov. 27-May-3 Sotheby's, Toronto #47/R est:3000-4000 (C.D 4500)
£2000 $3280 €2900 Three black kittens (30x29cm-12x11in) board. 9-Jun-3 Hodgins, Calgary #132/R est:4500-5500 (C.D 4500)
£2111 $3463 €3167 Pair of oxen. White dog (30x36cm-12x14in) s. board two prov. 27-May-3 Sotheby's, Toronto #45/R est:5000-7000 (C.D 4750)
£2309 $3626 €3464 Covered bridge in winter (29x34cm-11x13in) s. board painted c.1966 exhib. 25-Nov-2 Hodgins, Calgary #36/R est:4000-4500 (C.D 5750)
£2419 $3823 €3629 Horse hauling logs (30x36cm-12x14in) s. board painted 1965-70 prov. 18-Nov-2 Sotheby's, Toronto #117/R est:2500-3000 (C.D 6000)
£2621 $4141 €3932 Covered bridge in winter (30x41cm-12x16in) s. masonite painted c.1965-70 prov. 18-Nov-2 Sotheby's, Toronto #23/R est:3000-5000 (C.D 6500)
£3111 $5102 €4667 By the sea. Pumpkin cart (23x31cm-9x12in) s. board two prov. 27-May-3 Sotheby's, Toronto #43/R est:4000-6000 (C.D 7000)

LEWIS, Neville (1895-1972) South African
£461 $719 €692 Pondo head (34x24cm-13x9in) s. i.verso panel. 15-Oct-2 Stephan Welz, Johannesburg #436 est:3000-5000 (SA.R 7500)
£688 $1107 €1032 Hilly landscape (23x33cm-9x13in) board prov. 12-May-3 Stephan Welz, Johannesburg #133 est:2000-4000 (SA.R 8000)

£1025 $1599 €1538 Head of a man, wearing a blue hat (39x29cm-15x11in) s. 11-Nov-2 Stephan Welz, Johannesburg #508/R est:6000-8000 (SA.R 16000)
£1806 $2907 €2709 Seated Zulu woman (34x23cm-13x9in) s. panel. 12-May-3 Stephan Welz, Johannesburg #545/R est:15000-18000 (SA.R 21000)

LEWIS, Percy Wyndham (1882-1957) British
Works on paper
£2200 $3498 €3300 Pensive woman (49x32cm-19x13in) s.d.1921 W/C pen ink. 26-Feb-3 Sotheby's, Olympia #183/R est:1500-2000
£2200 $3498 €3300 Eleusis, Morning (31x24cm-12x9in) s. i.verso pen ink W/C. 26-Feb-3 Sotheby's, Olympia #185/R est:1500-2000
£3600 $5724 €5400 Seated figure (22x20cm-9x8in) init.d.1925 pen ink W/C. 26-Feb-3 Sotheby's, Olympia #184/R est:2000-3000
£8500 $13515 €12750 Madge Pulsford (37x47cm-15x19in) s. pencil. 26-Feb-3 Sotheby's, Olympia #79/R est:2000-3000

LEWIS, Thomas E (1909-1979) American
£1290 $2000 €1935 Consuela (56x46cm-22x18in) s. i.verso painted c.1935 prov. 8-Dec-2 Toomey, Oak Park #791/R est:2000-3000

LEWIS-BROWN, John (1829-1890) British
£3205 $4968 €5000 L'equipage (30x55cm-12x22in) 8-Dec-2 Teitgen, Nancy #89/R

LEWITSKA, Sophie (1882-1937) Polish?
£2229 $3478 €3500 Eglise romaine derriere les arbres (54x73cm-21x29in) s. 6-Nov-2 Claude Boisgirard, Paris #30/R est:4000-5000
£3265 $5192 €4800 Le chapeau de paille et les hortensias (73x60cm-29x24in) s. 3-Mar-3 Claude Boisgirard, Paris #67/R est:4500-5500

LEWITT, Sol (1928-) American
£3205 $4968 €5000 Triangle with left side torn off (41x48cm-16x19in) s.i.d.1995 card. 4-Dec-2 Finarte, Milan #448/R
£3846 $5962 €6000 Composition (28x28cm-11x11in) s.d.1994 tempera paper. 4-Dec-2 Finarte, Milan #579/R est:4500
Prints
£1807 $3000 €2711 Forms derived from a cube of colour (51x132cm-20x52in) s.num.20 screenprint prov. 11-Jun-3 Phillips, New York #361/R est:4000-6000
£2200 $3630 €3190 Horizontal colour bands and vertical colour bands, I and II (45x89cm-18x35in) s.num.14/30 col etching aquatint two. 1-Jul-3 Sotheby's, London #198/R est:2500-3000
£2229 $3500 €3344 Untitled, 8 versions of intersecting colour lines (36x17cm-14x7in) s.num.21 woodcut set of four exec.c.1982. 19-Nov-2 Wright, Chicago #209/R est:3500-4500
£3077 $4800 €4616 Brushstrokes in different colors in two direction (122x76cm-48x30in) s.d.1994 etching aquatint. 20-Sep-2 New Orleans Auction, New Orleans #1409/R est:3000-5000
£4777 $7500 €7166 Stars, 5 pointed (137x137cm-54x54in) relief prints 13 of edition of 15 thirty six sheets. 21-Nov-2 Swann Galleries, New York #108/R est:8000-12000
£6918 $11000 €10377 Eight cubic rectangles (176x59cm-69x23in) s.num.18/50 col aquatint two sheets. 2-May-3 Sotheby's, New York #495/R est:6000-8000
Sculpture
£1800 $2790 €2700 Pyramid (38cm-15in) s.num.6/12 painted aluminium executed 1989. 5-Dec-2 Christie's, Kensington #277/R est:2000-3000
£2246 $3684 €3100 Cube without a cube (20x20x20cm-8x8x8in) s.i. wood. 28-May-3 Lempertz, Koln #250/R est:3000
£2754 $4516 €3800 Pyramide (39x22cm-15x9in) s. num.6/12 inside aluminium paint prov. 27-May-3 Tajan, Paris #38/R est:4500-5500
£4167 $6542 €6500 Untitled (16x16x16cm-6x6x6in) s.d.84 painted metal. 11-Dec-2 Artcurial Briest, Paris #747/R
£6500 $10270 €9750 Three cubes. s.d.84 baked enamel metal prov. 3-Apr-3 Christie's, Kensington #245/R
£14000 $23380 €20300 Cube (20x39x20cm-8x15x8in) painted wood prov. 26-Jun-3 Sotheby's, London #140/R est:5000-7000
£25000 $41750 €36250 Folding screen (182x386cm-72x152in) s.d.1989 col ink wash double-sided five panels prov. 26-Jun-3 Sotheby's, London #142/R est:12000-18000
£37975 $60000 €56963 5 open geometric forms (145x142x30cm-57x56x12in) s.d.1979 wood paint white in six parts exhib. 13-Nov-2 Sotheby's, New York #311/R est:70000-90000
£53797 $85000 €80696 Incomplete cube 10-2 (105x105x105cm-41x41x41in) enamel on aluminum executed 1975 prov. 14-Nov-2 Christie's, Rockefeller NY #363/R est:40000-60000
Works on paper
£692 $1072 €1100 Composition (35x28cm-14x11in) s.d.91 gouache prov. 30-Oct-2 Artcurial Briest, Paris #709
£692 $1072 €1100 Composition (35x28cm-14x11in) s.d.91 gouache prov. 30-Oct-2 Artcurial Briest, Paris #710
£692 $1072 €1100 Composition (31x23cm-12x9in) s.d.92 gouache prov. 30-Oct-2 Artcurial Briest, Paris #712
£692 $1072 €1100 Composition (31x23cm-12x9in) s.d.92 gouache prov. 30-Oct-2 Artcurial Briest, Paris #713
£818 $1267 €1300 Composition (35x28cm-14x11in) s.d.91 gouache prov. 30-Oct-2 Artcurial Briest, Paris #708
£1069 $1657 €1700 Composition (35x26cm-14x10in) s.d.91 gouache prov. 30-Oct-2 Artcurial Briest, Paris #711 est:900-1200
£1154 $1800 €1731 Study for 46 piece series (28x23cm-11x9in) s.d.1967 ink exhib.prov. 20-Sep-2 New Orleans Auction, New Orleans #1410/R est:2000-4000
£1154 $1800 €1731 Study for 46 piece series (23x28cm-9x11in) s.d.1967 ink. 20-Sep-2 New Orleans Auction, New Orleans #1411/R est:2000-4000
£1154 $1788 €1800 Untitled (31x20cm-12x8in) s.d.92 gouache prov. 3-Dec-2 Christie's, Amsterdam #295/R est:1800-2200
£1219 $1852 €1829 Abstract (32x25cm-13x10in) s.d.98 gouache. 28-Aug-2 Deutscher-Menzies, Melbourne #293/R est:4000-5000 (A.D 3400)
£1258 $1950 €2000 Sans titre (32x23cm-13x9in) s.d.94 gouache prov. 30-Oct-2 Artcurial Briest, Paris #707 est:900-1200
£1319 $2177 €1900 Sans titre no 12 (30x22cm-12x9in) s. Indian ink crayon prov.lit. 1-Jul-3 Artcurial Briest, Paris #819/R est:400-600
£2452 $3874 €3800 R492 (31cm-12in circular) s.i.d.75 prov. cut coffee filter. 18-Dec-2 Christie's, Rome #63/R
£2837 $4738 €4000 Variation on a cube (77x57cm-30x22in) s.d. gouache. 18-Jun-3 Charbonneaux, Paris #77/R est:3000-4000
£2950 $4927 €4278 Untitled (56x56cm-22x22in) pencil gouache card. 24-Jun-3 Sotheby's, Olympia #67/R est:3000-4000
£3500 $5530 €5250 Form derived from a cube (48x48cm-19x19in) s.d.84 pencil W/C prov. 3-Apr-3 Christie's, Kensington #246/R
£3500 $5530 €5250 Pyramids (28x51cm-11x20in) s.d.86 pencil W/C prov. 3-Apr-3 Christie's, Kensington #250/R
£3548 $5500 €5322 Two incomplete open cube drawings (34x34cm-13x13in) s.d.74 graphite pen ink prov. 26-Sep-2 Christie's, Rockefeller NY #780/R est:2000-4000
£3800 $5890 €5700 Untitled (28x28cm-11x11in) s.d.93 W/C bodycol on card prov. 5-Dec-2 Christie's, Kensington #254/R est:2000-3000
£4200 $7014 €6090 Untitled (56x56cm-22x22in) s.d.1984 pencil W/C prov. 27-Jun-3 Christie's, London #224/R est:4000-6000
£4250 $6800 €6375 Untitled (24x24cm-9x9in) s.d.99 gouache two prov. 16-May-3 Phillips, New York #183/R est:6000-8000
£4500 $7515 €6525 Untitled (56x56cm-22x22in) s.d.1984 pencil W/C prov. 27-Jun-3 Christie's, London #225/R est:4000-6000
£5200 $8476 €7800 Irregular horizontal bands of equal width starting at bottom (56x75cm-22x30in) s.d.91 gouache prov. 3-Feb-3 Sotheby's, Olympia #47/R est:5000-7000
£5500 $9020 €8250 Untitled (76x56cm-30x22in) s.d.90 gouache pencil prov. 7-Feb-3 Sotheby's, London #140/R est:3000-4000
£6701 $10654 €9850 Uneven vertical bands of colour V (57x75cm-22x30in) s.d.1988 gouache pencil prov. 26-Feb-3 Artcurial Briest, Paris #370/R est:5000-6000
£7595 $12000 €11393 Straight yellow lines in four directions (45x45cm-18x18in) s.d.February 20.1971 ink pencil prov. 13-Nov-2 Sotheby's, New York #304/R est:10000-15000
£8228 $13000 €12342 Arcs from one corner. Parallel horizontal lines (29x29cm-11x11in) s.d.Sept 3 1973 one s.i.d.Oct 25.1972 ink two. 13-Nov-2 Sotheby's, New York #301/R est:7000-9000
£15625 $25000 €23438 Parallel curved lines (153x150cm-60x59in) s. verso gouache executed 2000 prov.exhib. 14-May-3 Sotheby's, New York #218b/R est:25000-35000
£20000 $33400 €29000 Lines in all directions (152x152cm-60x60in) s.d.93 gouache prov. 26-Jun-3 Sotheby's, London #141/R est:18000-25000
£28481 $45000 €42722 Not straight brushstrokes in all directions (152x152cm-60x60in) s.d.1994 gouache prov. 13-Nov-2 Sotheby's, New York #302/R est:25000-35000

LEWITT, Vivienne Shark (1956-) Australian
£1429 $2229 €2144 Cat (81x81cm-32x32in) s.i.d.1996 verso. 11-Nov-2 Deutscher-Menzies, Melbourne #15/R est:4000-6000 (A.D 4000)
£1938 $3081 €2907 Farewell my lovely (89x190cm-35x75in) s.i.d.1984 panel in two parts. 5-May-3 Sotheby's, Melbourne #187/R est:4000-6000 (A.D 5000)
£3750 $5775 €5625 Marvellous Melbourne (45x61cm-18x24in) s.d.91 i.verso. 8-Sep-2 Sotheby's, Melbourne #31/R est:4000-6000 (A.D 10500)

LEWY, James (19th C) American
£428 $650 €642 Still life of five peaches (43x51cm-17x20in) s. canvas on board. 30-Aug-2 Thomaston Place, Thomaston #96

LEWY, Kurt (1898-1963) Belgian
Works on paper
£265 $432 €400 Composition (48x67cm-19x26in) mono.d.1952 W/C. 17-Feb-3 Horta, Bruxelles #465
£347 $552 €500 Composition (31x41cm-12x16in) mono. W/C. 29-Apr-3 Campo, Vlaamse Kaai #191

LEY, Hans Christian Clausen (1828-1875) Danish
£1435 $2325 €2081 Gnome orchestra playing to dance (62x56cm-24x22in) init. 26-May-3 Rasmussen, Copenhagen #1449/R est:25000 (D.KR 15000)
£1550 $2357 €2325 Cigar shop in Ostergade (55x46cm-22x18in) s.d.1867 prov. 27-Aug-2 Rasmussen, Copenhagen #1500/R est:10000-15000 (D.KR 18000)

LEY, Sophie (1859-1918) German
£1410 $2186 €2200 Bodensee landscape near Bodman in the evening (33x54cm-13x21in) s. 6-Dec-2 Michael Zeller, Lindau #825/R
£1972 $3175 €2800 Loaded punt on Untersee (33x53cm-13x21in) s.d.80. 7-May-3 Michael Zeller, Lindau #781/R est:1800

LEYAOUANC, Alain (1940-) French
£1079 $1770 €1500 Projet pour une oeuvre realisee pour l'entree du palais B Aabda (200x200cm-79x79in) exec.c.80. 6-Jun-3 Rabourdin & Choppin de Janvry, Paris #76/R est:1500-2000

LEYBOLD, Eduard Friedrich (1798-1847) German
£2308 $3623 €3600 Portrait of a lady and gentleman in front of a landscape (129x105cm-51x41in) s.i.d.1838. 21-Nov-2 Dorotheum, Vienna #86/R est:5200-6500
Works on paper
£314 $487 €500 Portrait of Anna v Martens (17x13cm-7x5in) s.d.1840 W/C board. 1-Oct-2 Dorotheum, Vienna #358/R

LEYDE, Kurt (1881-?) German
£786 $1226 €1179 Three Indian children eating fruit (65x73cm-26x29in) s.i.d.1927. 6-Nov-2 Dobiaschofsky, Bern #777/R (S.FR 1800)
£961 $1499 €1442 Young Indian woman with two children (65x73cm-26x29in) s.i.d.1927. 6-Nov-2 Dobiaschofsky, Bern #776/R (S.FR 2200)

LEYDE, Otto (1835-1897) German
£280 $456 €420 Portrait of a Scotsman, in a tartan cloak (36x32cm-14x13in) s.d.3/53. 29-Jan-3 Hampton & Littlewood, Exeter #389/R
£1229 $1954 €1844 Children on a beach (20x25cm-8x10in) s. 18-Mar-3 Maynards, Vancouver #18/R est:2500-3500 (C.D 2900)
Works on paper
£250 $390 €375 Corner of a hayfield (36x26cm-14x10in) s. pencil W/C htd white scratching out. 17-Oct-2 Christie's, Kensington #69

LEYDEN, Ernest van (1892-1969) Dutch
Works on paper
£818 $1259 €1300 Composition (35x50cm-14x20in) s.d.1960 mixed media collage. 22-Oct-2 Campo & Campo, Antwerp #305/R
£881 $1356 €1400 Composition (40x50cm-16x20in) s.d.1961 mixed media collage. 22-Oct-2 Campo & Campo, Antwerp #304/R
£2482 $4145 €3500 Lolita (130x195cm-51x77in) s.i.d. mixed media. 18-Jun-3 Pierre Berge, Paris #100 est:2000-3000

LEYDEN, Jan van (17th C) Dutch
£14085 $23380 €20000 Portuguese and Dutch three masted sailing ship at anchor in calm weather (59x83cm-23x33in) 11-Jun-3 Dorotheum, Vienna #62/R est:20000-25000

LEYDEN, Lucas van (1494-1538) Dutch
Prints
£1887 $3000 €2831 Samson and Delilah (28x20cm-11x8in) engraving executed c.1507. 1-May-3 Swann Galleries, New York #191/R est:4000-6000
£2949 $4600 €4424 Young man with a skull (16x15cm-6x6in) engraving exec.c.1519. 6-Nov-2 Swann Galleries, New York #42/R est:2000-3000
£3038 $4800 €4800 Golgathat (29x41cm-11x16in) copperplate. 29-Nov-2 Bassenge, Berlin #5351/R est:3000
£4808 $7500 €7212 David playing the harp before Saul (26x19cm-10x7in) engraving exec.c.1508. 6-Nov-2 Swann Galleries, New York #39/R est:10000-15000

LEYDENFROST, Alexander (1888-1961) American?
Works on paper
£577 $900 €866 Prisoners of war rescued in icy fjord (43x41cm-17x16in) s. chl W/C en grisaille. 9-Nov-2 Illustration House, New York #31/R

LEYEN, Helene van der (1874-?) German
£1019 $1590 €1600 Woman with violin (135x75cm-53x30in) s.d.1874. 6-Nov-2 Hugo Ruef, Munich #1195/R est:400

LEYENDECKER, Frank Xavier (1877-1924) American
£19876 $32000 €29814 Football tackle (74x61cm-29x24in) s. painted c.1910 prov. 10-May-3 Illustration House, New York #141/R est:4000-6000

LEYENDECKER, Joseph (1810-1867) German
£4819 $8000 €6988 House of Kuppenheimer (66x54cm-26x21in) prov. 11-Jun-3 Butterfields, San Francisco #4052a/R est:3000-5000

LEYENDECKER, Joseph C (1874-1951) American
£2484 $4000 €3726 Boy must finish rug beating before playing baseball (36x28cm-14x11in) 20-Feb-3 Illustration House, New York #99/R est:2000-3000
£3106 $5000 €4659 Head of man wearing striped tie (23x15cm-9x6in) chl. 10-May-3 Illustration House, New York #78/R est:6000-8000
£4487 $7000 €6731 Couple hailing cab after a costume party (56x48cm-22x19in) 9-Nov-2 Illustration House, New York #14/R est:6000-9000
£4808 $7500 €7212 Young Dutch girl holding tulips (48x28cm-19x11in) 9-Nov-2 Illustration House, New York #13/R est:7500-10000
£51282 $80000 €76923 Man with Thanksgiving turkey accosted by hunting dogs (81x61cm-32x24in) s. prov. 9-Nov-2 Illustration House, New York #12/R est:60000-80000

LEYENDECKER, Paul Joseph (1842-?) French
£1216 $1897 €1800 Jeune femme au bal (22x16cm-9x6in) s. 30-Mar-3 Anaf, Lyon #184/R
£4800 $7440 €7200 Gift box (34x26cm-13x10in) s.d.1871 prov. 3-Nov-2 Lots Road, London #359 est:2000-3000

LEYES, Daniel (20th C) South American?
£256 $400 €384 constructivo (48x60cm-19x24in) s. 30-Jul-2 Galleria Y Remates, Montevideo #107/R

LEYMAN, A (1856-1933) British
Works on paper
£640 $992 €960 A 19th century street market (54x36cm-21x14in) s. W/C. 24-Sep-2 Anderson & Garland, Newcastle #360

LEYMAN, Alfred (1856-1933) British
Works on paper
£300 $456 €450 West Country street scene (53x36cm-21x14in) s. W/C. 14-Aug-2 Andrew Hartley, Ilkley #595
£440 $686 €660 Clovelly, Devon (54x37cm-21x15in) s. W/C exhib. 18-Sep-2 Cheffins Grain & Comins, Cambridge #462
£460 $759 €667 House that moved, Exeter (37x54cm-15x21in) s.d.1904 W/C. 1-Jul-3 Bearnes, Exeter #474/R
£480 $744 €720 Guildhall, Exeter (54x36cm-21x14in) s. W/C. 2-Oct-2 George Kidner, Lymington #118/R
£500 $800 €725 House that moved, Exeter. Cathedral Close, Exeter (37x26cm-15x10in) s. one d.99 W/C pair. 19-May-3 Bearnes, Exeter #238/R
£1700 $2703 €2550 Rural scene with thatched cottages and figures (36x54cm-14x21in) s. W/C pair. 6-Mar-3 Clevedon Sale Rooms #119 est:500-750

LEYS, Baron H (1815-1869) Belgian
£1361 $2163 €2000 En priere (47x38cm-19x15in) s. 18-Mar-3 Campo, Vlaamse Kaai #135/R est:2500-3000

LEYS, Baron Hendrik (1815-1869) Belgian
£993 $1619 €1500 Coeur de l'eglise Saint-Paul (32x26cm-13x10in) s.d.1839 panel. 17-Feb-3 Horta, Bruxelles #96
£1918 $2992 €2800 Conversation au bord des ruines (34x26cm-13x10in) s.d.1845 panel. 14-Apr-3 Horta, Bruxelles #150 est:3000-4000
£3262 $5448 €4600 Preparing the wedding dress (50x39cm-20x15in) s.d.1856 panel. 23-Jun-3 Bernaerts, Antwerp #107/R est:4000-5000
£5862 $9379 €8500 La furie espagnole a Anvers (53x64cm-21x25in) s.d. 17-Mar-3 Horta, Bruxelles #139 est:10000-15000

LEYS, Baron Hendrik (attrib) (1815-1869) Belgian
£748 $1190 €1100 Les armateurs presidant un embarquement (46x63cm-18x25in) s. 18-Mar-3 Campo, Vlaamse Kaai #136
£4483 $7172 €6500 Le ministeriel devant le rempart de la ville (61x79cm-24x31in) panel. 17-Mar-3 Amberes, Antwerp #230/R

LEYSING, Piet (1885-1933) German
£513 $795 €800 Interior with pair reading a newspaper (62x55cm-24x22in) s. plywood. 7-Dec-2 Van Ham, Cologne #299

LHERMITTE, Georges (20th C) French?
£513 $805 €800 Pardon en Bretagne a Saint-Cornely (27x34cm-11x13in) s. panel. 15-Dec-2 Eric Pillon, Calais #115/R

LHERMITTE, Léon (1844-1925) French
£106452 $165000 €159678 Le reveil du Faucheur (78x101cm-31x40in) s.d.1899 prov.exhib.lit. 30-Oct-2 Christie's, Rockefeller NY #26/R est:100000-150000
£145570 $230000 €218355 Little goose girl of Mezy (160x85cm-63x33in) s.d.1892 prov.exhib.lit. 24-Apr-3 Sotheby's, New York #35/R est:200000-300000

Works on paper
£516 $815 €800 Etude pour l'aieule de Grand (32x24cm-13x9in) s. pen black ink exec.c.1879-1883 lit. 17-Dec-2 Rossini, Paris #40a
£774 $1200 €1161 Portrait of Charles Drouet (30x13cm-12x5in) s.i.d.1885 chl prov.exhib.lit. 29-Oct-2 Sotheby's, New York #79/R est:1500-2000
£1613 $2500 €2420 Study of a Breton fisherman kneeling (47x30cm-19x12in) pencil white chk prov.exhib.lit. 29-Oct-2 Sotheby's, New York #80/R est:5000-7000
£1613 $2500 €2420 Study of a Breton fisherman standing (44x33cm-17x13in) pencil prov.exhib.lit. 29-Oct-2 Sotheby's, New York #81/R est:5000-7000
£1646 $2600 €2469 Portrait d'Amedee Julien (54x49cm-21x19in) init. pencil chl prov.lit. 24-Apr-3 Sotheby's, New York #183/R est:2000-3000
£4200 $6972 €6300 Lavandienes Bretonnes (43x36cm-17x14in) s. pastel. 12-Jun-3 Bonhams, New Bond Street #612/R est:4500-6000
£6452 $10000 €9678 Chevaux, vus de dos (32x35cm-13x14in) init. pastel prov.lit. 29-Oct-2 Sotheby's, New York #82/R est:5000-7000
£8584 $13391 €12447 La famille en moisson (34x41cm-13x16in) s.i. pastel executed 1908 prov.exhib. 26-Mar-3 Walker's, Ottawa #27/R est:15000-20000 (C.D 20000)
£10000 $15500 €15000 Washerwomen (48x66cm-19x26in) s. pastel. 6-Dec-2 Lyon & Turnbull, Edinburgh #110/R est:7000-10000
£12258 $19000 €18387 Sorting the catch (66x47cm-26x19in) init. chl lit. 29-Oct-2 Sotheby's, New York #77/R est:15000-20000
£13000 $20410 €19500 Au lavoir (49x60cm-19x24in) s. pastel chl paper on canvas executed 1901 prov.lit. 19-Nov-2 Sotheby's, London #159/R est:12000-18000
£15190 $24000 €22785 Famille de pecheurs (42x50cm-17x20in) s. pastel paper on canvas executed 1921 prov.lit. 23-Apr-3 Christie's, Rockefeller NY #59/R est:18000-25000
£17419 $27000 €26129 Baignade a Mont-Saint-Pere (31x49cm-12x19in) s. indis i.verso chl prov. 29-Oct-2 Sotheby's, New York #76/R est:18000-25000
£22581 $35000 €33872 Feeding the bady (27x22cm-11x9in) s.d.88 pencil chl. 30-Oct-2 Christie's, Rockefeller NY #138/R est:15000-20000
£35484 $55000 €53226 Avril (82x108cm-32x43in) s. pastel paper on canvas executed 1911 prov.exhib.lit. 30-Oct-2 Christie's, Rockefeller NY #13/R est:70000-90000

L'HOEST, Engelbert (1919-) Dutch

Works on paper
£290 $461 €420 Composition (55x37cm-22x15in) s.d.55 gouache. 10-Mar-3 Sotheby's, Amsterdam #367

LHOMME, Modeste Jean (1883-1946) Belgian
£284 $474 €400 Meule dans un champs (29x42cm-11x17in) s. i.verso board. 18-Jun-3 Hotel des Ventes Mosan, Brussels #213
£411 $642 €650 Sur la route de Stoumont (81x116cm-32x46in) s.d.1935. 16-Sep-2 Horta, Bruxelles #279

LHOTAK, Kamil (1912-1990) Czechoslovakian
£3709 $5897 €5564 Two advertising botts at race course (20x29cm-8x11in) s. i. verso. 8-Mar-3 Dorotheum, Prague #121/R est:100000-150000 (C.KR 170000)

Works on paper
£289 $451 €434 Aeroplane (15x19cm-6x7in) s.d.1960 Indian ink dr W/C. 12-Oct-2 Dorotheum, Prague #245/R (C.KR 14000)
£414 $659 €621 Fairytale illustration (24x18cm-9x7in) s. mixed media. 8-Mar-3 Dorotheum, Prague #210/R est:8000-12000 (C.KR 19000)
£524 $832 €786 Yellow tent (19x12cm-7x5in) s. col ink. 8-Mar-3 Dorotheum, Prague #212/R est:15000-23000 (C.KR 24000)
£742 $1179 €1113 Yellow airship (10x11cm-4x4in) s.d.53 col pencil. 8-Mar-3 Dorotheum, Prague #211/R est:15000-23000 (C.KR 34000)

LHOTE, Andre (1885-1962) French
£3103 $5027 €4499 Nature morte aux fruits (23x17cm-9x7in) s. panel. 25-May-3 Uppsala Auktionskammare, Uppsala #236/R est:25000-30000 (S.KR 40000)
£3165 $5000 €4748 Landscape (46x61cm-18x24in) s. prov. 24-Apr-3 Shannon's, Milford #82/R est:7000-9000
£3400 $5542 €5100 Paysage a le meule de foin (38x45cm-15x18in) s.i. 3-Feb-3 Bonhams, New Bond Street #33/R est:3000-5000
£3793 $5993 €5500 Composition de fruits et lat (33x55cm-13x22in) s. 4-Apr-3 Tajan, Paris #189/R
£4423 $6944 €6900 Bord de riviere (17x27cm-7x11in) s. panel painted c.1930 lit. 15-Dec-2 Eric Pillon, Calais #155/R
£4430 $7000 €7000 Landscape (33x55cm-13x22in) s. 26-Nov-2 Sotheby's, Amsterdam #91/R est:7000-10000
£4546 $7591 €6500 Nu assis (33x22cm-13x9in) s. 26-Jun-3 Tajan, Paris #267/R est:4500-5000
£5000 $7900 €7500 Paysage (29x46cm-11x18in) s. board. 3-Apr-3 Christie's, Kensington #104/R
£5806 $9174 €9000 Nature morte aux pichets (65x46cm-26x18in) s. panel prov. 18-Dec-2 Digard, Paris #63/R
£6154 $9538 €9600 Femme tricotant (27x22cm-11x9in) s. 6-Dec-2 Rieunier, Bailly-Pommery, Mathias, Paris #87/R
£6500 $10010 €9750 L'etude (46x15cm-18x6in) s. 23-Oct-2 Sotheby's, Olympia #657/R est:6000-8000
£7000 $10780 €10500 Nu assis (41x33cm-16x13in) s.i.d.1930 panel prov. 22-Oct-2 Sotheby's, London #239/R est:6000-8000
£7547 $12000 €11321 Nu couche (16x37cm-6x15in) s. board prov.exhib. 27-Feb-3 Christie's, Rockefeller NY #118/R est:8000
£8974 $14090 €14000 Bouquet de fleurs (45x55cm-18x22in) s.d.1911. 13-Dec-2 Piasa, Paris #25/R est:15000
£9615 $15096 €15000 Nu dans un paysage (38x46cm-15x18in) s. 22-Nov-2 Millon & Associes, Paris #90/R est:8000-10000
£10231 $17086 €14835 Portrait of a woman (54x45cm-21x18in) s. 24-Jun-3 Koller, Zurich #113/R est:18000-25000 (S.FR 22610)
£11000 $18370 €15950 Paysage a contre-jour (50x64cm-20x25in) s. prov. 24-Jun-3 Sotheby's, London #151/R est:8000-12000
£11806 $19479 €17000 Nu feminin (35x54cm-14x21in) s. painted c.1929 prov. 2-Jul-3 Artcurial Briest, Paris #669/R est:18000-22000
£15544 $24715 €22850 La table d'offrande (73x60cm-29x24in) s. 26-Feb-3 Artcurial Briest, Paris #296/R est:9000-12000
£16026 $25160 €25000 Aux environs de Boissierette (100x65cm-39x26in) s. painted c.1920 lit. 10-Dec-2 Artcurial Briest, Paris #493/R est:25000-35000
£16084 $26860 €23000 Maisons et pins a Arachon (54x65cm-21x26in) s.d.37 prov.lit. 30-Jun-3 Artcurial Briest, Paris #56/R est:24000-28000
£16456 $26000 €26000 Modele dans l'atelier (72x50cm-28x20in) s. s.verso. 1-Dec-2 Anaf, Lyon #116/R
£17000 $27880 €25500 Nu (38x46cm-15x18in) s. 5-Feb-3 Sotheby's, London #273/R est:15000
£17000 $28390 €24650 Leda et le cygne dans un sous-bois (116x81cm-46x32in) s. oil paper on canvas painted c.1930. 25-Jun-3 Christie's, London #207/R est:20000-30000
£18631 $29437 €27947 Femme aux cypres (80x115cm-31x45in) s.d.32. 28-Apr-3 Bukowskis, Stockholm #319/R est:250000-300000 (S.KR 245000)
£22436 $35000 €33654 Fete de famille (81x117cm-32x46in) s. oil on burlap. 6-Nov-2 Sotheby's, New York #331/R est:40000-60000

Works on paper
£263 $427 €400 Portrait presume de Carla Alardi (33x21cm-13x8in) mono. pencil dr. 22-Jan-3 Tajan, Paris #135
£431 $686 €647 Untitled (27x21cm-11x8in) s.d.1914 W/C prov. 3-Mar-3 Lilla Bukowskis, Stockholm #12 (S.KR 5800)
£443 $700 €700 Nu assis (30x23cm-12x9in) s. graphite. 27-Nov-2 Blanchet, Paris #81/R
£481 $750 €722 Study of chrysanthemums (58x46cm-23x18in) chl gouache. 20-Sep-2 New Orleans Auction, New Orleans #53/R
£504 $806 €700 Nu au lever du lit (26x20cm-10x8in) s. pen Indian ink. 14-May-3 Blanchet, Paris #117
£538 $850 €850 Nu allonge (15x27cm-6x11in) s. chl. 27-Nov-2 Blanchet, Paris #78/R
£676 $1054 €1000 Personnage, femme assise (26x17cm-10x7in) mono. graphite. 25-Mar-3 Chochon-Barre & Allardi, Paris #159
£694 $1097 €1000 Baigneuses (19x26cm-7x10in) s. pen dr. 25-Apr-3 Piasa, Paris #129
£922 $1494 €1300 Sous bois (30x22cm-12x9in) s. pastel. 21-May-3 Cornette de St.Cyr, Paris #27/R
£962 $1490 €1500 Untitled (30x23cm-12x9in) s. W/C. 7-Dec-2 Van Ham, Cologne #300/R est:2500
£993 $1609 €1400 Paysage (19x30cm-7x12in) st.sig. graphite. 21-May-3 Cornette de St.Cyr, Paris #21/R
£1090 $1689 €1700 Female nude (15x20cm-6x8in) s. Indian ink. 7-Dec-2 Ketterer, Hamburg #290/R est:700-800
£1241 $2073 €1800 Nu au miroir (14x10cm-6x4in) s. W/C pencil. 10-Jul-3 Artcurial Briest, Paris #75 est:1000-1200
£1259 $2102 €1800 Femme assise dans un fauteuil (17x13cm-7x5in) s. crayon dr prov. 27-Jun-3 Claude Aguttes, Neuilly #92/R est:1000-1500
£1316 $2132 €2000 Etude du nu, assis (60x45cm-24x18in) s. black crayon chl dr. 22-Jan-3 Tajan, Paris #139/R est:1800-2400
£1316 $2132 €2000 Nu debout (64x44cm-25x17in) s. black crayon chl. 22-Jan-3 Tajan, Paris #140/R est:1200-1500
£1316 $2132 €2000 Nu assis de dos (60x44cm-24x17in) s. black crayon chl. 22-Jan-3 Tajan, Paris #141/R est:1200-1500
£1329 $2219 €1900 Le village dr Rochemaure (24x35cm-9x14in) s. pen dr. 26-Jun-3 Tajan, Paris #70/R est:2000-2500
£1521 $2403 €2282 French landscape (30x47cm-12x19in) s. W/C. 28-Apr-3 Bukowskis, Stockholm #321/R est:20000-25000 (S.KR 20000)
£1899 $2962 €3000 Vallon dans le Midi (38x58cm-15x23in) s.d.29 W/C. 31-Jul-2 Tajan, Paris #33/R est:3000-4600

£2014 $3223 €2800 Paysage (23x28cm-9x11in) s. W/C. 14-May-3 Blanchet, Paris #116/R est:2800-3200
£2051 $3241 €3200 Paysage (26x33cm-10x13in) s. gouache canvas on cardboard. 15-Nov-2 Laurence Calmels, Paris #12a/R
£2207 $3487 €3200 Bord de Mediterranee (28x39cm-11x15in) s. W/C. 4-Apr-3 Tajan, Paris #190/R
£2270 $3677 €3200 Venise (11x15cm-4x6in) s. W/C. 21-May-3 Cornette de St.Cyr, Paris #20/R est:2500-3000
£2308 $3623 €3600 Nature morte sur table (31x40cm-12x16in) s. gouache. 22-Nov-2 Millon & Associes, Paris #30/R
£2632 $4264 €4000 St Tropez et la rade (18x27cm-7x11in) s. Indian ink. 22-Jan-3 Tajan, Paris #132/R est:4000-5000
£2632 $4264 €4000 Tartanes dans le port de St Tropez devant Senequier (18x27cm-7x11in) s.i. Indian ink pen. 22-Jan-3 Tajan, Paris #133/R est:4000-5000
£2653 $4218 €3900 Cadiere d'Azur (28x38cm-11x15in) s. gouache. 24-Mar-3 Coutau Begarie, Paris #183/R
£2675 $4173 €4200 Paysage de Provence (37x56cm-15x22in) s.d.1929 W/C. 10-Nov-2 Eric Pillon, Calais #80
£2763 $4476 €4200 Etude de nu cubiste (42x30cm-17x12in) s. W/C gouache. 22-Jan-3 Tajan, Paris #138 est:2400-3000
£3169 $5102 €4500 Nu allonge (32x50cm-13x20in) s. pastel. 11-May-3 Thierry & Lannon, Brest #69 est:4800-5000
£3237 $5180 €4500 Bord de mer (29x38cm-11x15in) s. W/C gouache. 18-May-3 Eric Pillon, Calais #235/R
£3346 $5287 €5019 Martiniquaise (71x55cm-28x22in) s. pastel prov. 28-Apr-3 Bukowskis, Stockholm #317/R est:20000-25000 (S.KR 44000)
£3459 $5500 €5189 Nature morte (31x47cm-12x19in) s. gouache over chl. 27-Feb-3 Christie's, Rockefeller NY #33/R
£3473 $5521 €5000 Paysage de la drome (28x42cm-11x17in) s. W/C. 29-Apr-3 Artcurial Briest, Paris #127/R est:5000-6000
£3608 $5592 €5700 Le port de Bordeaux (35x54cm-14x21in) s.i.d.1917 W/C. 29-Sep-2 Eric Pillon, Calais #235/R
£4000 $6160 €6000 Buste de femme (31x24cm-12x9in) s. gouache executed 1920 prov. 22-Oct-2 Sotheby's, London #233/R est:5000-7000
£4082 $6490 €6000 Baigneuse dans un sous-bois (27x38cm-11x15in) s. gouache. 26-Feb-3 Artcurial Briest, Paris #86/R est:4500-5500
£4483 $7172 €6500 Paysage du midi (36x56cm-14x22in) s.d.32 W/C graphite. 12-Mar-3 Libert, Castor, Paris #136/R est:2000-2500
£4487 $7045 €7000 Arbre (30x40cm-12x16in) s. W/C. 13-Dec-2 Piasa, Paris #256/R
£5500 $8745 €8250 France, paradis du vin (112x70cm-44x28in) s.i. W/C gouache pencil. 20-Mar-3 Sotheby's, Olympia #165/R est:3000-4000
£6000 $9540 €9000 In vino veritas (112x70cm-44x28in) s.i. W/C gouache pencil. 20-Mar-3 Sotheby's, Olympia #164/R est:3000-4000

LHOTE, Andre (attrib) (1885-1962) French
Works on paper
£273 $425 €410 Academic head study (56x41cm-22x16in) chl. 20-Sep-2 New Orleans Auction, New Orleans #1034/R

LI CHAOSHI (1893-1971) Chinese
Works on paper
£6216 $10256 €9013 New born (34x44cm-13x17in) s. pastel. 6-Jul-3 Christie's, Hong Kong #163/R est:100000-150000 (HK.D 80000)

LI KERAN (1907-1989) Chinese
Works on paper
£3885 $6410 €5633 Herding under the shade of willow (65x39cm-26x15in) s. col ink scroll. 6-Jul-3 Christie's, Hong Kong #226/R est:30000-40000 (HK.D 50000)
£50407 $79642 €75611 Freshness after a shower (68x45cm-27x18in) s.i.d.1985 ink col. 28-Apr-3 Sotheby's, Hong Kong #656/R est:450000-650000 (HK.D 620000)
£52846 $83496 €79269 Spring mountains shrouded in mist (69x46cm-27x18in) s.i.d.1984 ink col prov. 28-Apr-3 Sotheby's, Hong Kong #587/R est:40000-60000 (HK.D 650000)
£56911 $89919 €85367 Herdboy in different seasons (68x45cm-27x18in) s. one i.d.1988 one i.d.1989 one i. ink col scroll 4 exhib. 28-Apr-3 Sotheby's, Hong Kong #611/R est:250000-300000 (HK.D 700000)

LI WEI (1970-) Chinese
Prints
£2270 $3677 €3200 Li Wei falls to earth (70x130cm-28x51in) performance photograph. 20-May-3 Porro, Milan #57/R est:2500-2700

LIA, Anne Marie (20th C) French
Works on paper
£432 $691 €600 Sans titre (60x60cm-24x24in) s. mixed media. 18-May-3 Neret-Minet, Paris #118

LIAN XI (1816-1884) Chinese
Works on paper
£797 $1307 €1100 Bamboo (121x60cm-48x24in) s. seal Indian ink. 30-May-3 Dr Fritz Nagel, Stuttgart #1139/R

LIAN, Laura (1952-) British
Sculpture
£2800 $4452 €4200 John Lennon (46x60cm-18x24in) bronze one of 25. 10-Mar-3 Christie's, London #2

LIAUSU, Camille (1894-1975) French
£345 $576 €500 Nature morte aux pommes, poires et raisins (49x76cm-19x30in) s. panel. 10-Jul-3 Artcurial Briest, Paris #192
£345 $576 €500 Saint Paul de Coubressac (50x65cm-20x26in) s. 10-Jul-3 Artcurial Briest, Paris #196
£483 $806 €700 Couple assis dans un paysage (55x38cm-22x15in) s. 10-Jul-3 Artcurial Briest, Paris #199
£621 $1037 €900 Pere et enfant assis devant le pont (42x57cm-17x22in) 10-Jul-3 Artcurial Briest, Paris #189
£1103 $1842 €1600 Marocaine (146x90cm-57x35in) s. isorel panel. 10-Jul-3 Artcurial Briest, Paris #198/R est:2000-3000
£2414 $4031 €3500 Jeune femme assise au chapeau et au bouquet de fleurs (81x100cm-32x39in) s. 10-Jul-3 Artcurial Briest, Paris #183/R est:4000-5000

LIBAL, Frantisek (1896-1974) Czechoslovakian
£371 $590 €557 Steamship in harbour (39x50cm-15x20in) s. board. 8-Mar-3 Dorotheum, Prague #117/R est:10000-15000 (C.KR 17000)

LIBENSKY, Stanislav (1921-2002) Czechoslovakian
£413 $644 €620 Allegory of earth (64x96cm-25x38in) s.d.45 tempera cardboard. 12-Oct-2 Dorotheum, Prague #230/R (C.KR 20000)

LIBERATORE, Fausto Maria (1923-) Italian
£324 $506 €480 Models (30x40cm-12x16in) s. board. 28-Mar-3 Farsetti, Prato #517/R
£513 $810 €800 Figures (35x50cm-14x20in) s. 15-Nov-2 Farsetti, Prato #42

LIBERI, Pietro (1614-1687) Italian
£43210 $70000 €64815 Angel playing the violin (136x89cm-54x35in) 23-Jan-3 Sotheby's, New York #51/R est:40000-60000
£60000 $93600 €90000 Venus being bound bt two putti (103x112cm-41x44in) prov. 9-Apr-3 Christie's, London #115/R est:15000-20000
£160494 $260000 €240741 Finding of Moses (46x64cm-18x25in) oil paper on canvas prov.exhib.lit. 23-Jan-3 Sotheby's, New York #67/R est:50000-70000

LIBERICH, Nicolai Ivanovich (after) (1828-1883) Russian
Sculpture
£5208 $7500 €7812 Bear (59cm-23in) i. bronze. 15-Jan-3 Christie's, Rockefeller NY #248/R est:3000

LIBERMAN, Alexander (1912-) American
£297 $475 €446 Erg I (152x244cm-60x96in) s.d.77 acrylic. 16-Mar-3 Butterfields, San Francisco #1076

LIBERT, Amalie Betzy (1862-1927) Danish
£861 $1395 €1248 Still life of fruit and earthenware jug on table (51x64cm-20x25in) s.d.77-78. 26-May-3 Rasmussen, Copenhagen #1248/R (D.KR 9000)

LIBERT, Georg Emil (1820-1908) Danish
£301 $458 €452 View of a lake, ruin in background (57x95cm-22x37in) init. 27-Aug-2 Rasmussen, Copenhagen #1531 (D.KR 3500)
£420 $667 €630 Wooded landscape with figures in boat on lake at moonlight (41x52cm-16x20in) indis.init. 5-May-3 Rasmussen, Vejle #697/R (D.KR 4500)
£502 $793 €753 Landscape from Hardanger Fjord (45x63cm-18x25in) s. 5-Apr-3 Rasmussen, Havnen #2194 (D.KR 5400)
£511 $807 €767 Ruin in moonlight (44x31cm-17x12in) s.d.1901. 2-Dec-2 Rasmussen, Copenhagen #1224/R (D.KR 6000)
£574 $896 €861 Mountain landscape with fast running river (39x58cm-15x23in) s.d.78 i.stretcher. 23-Sep-2 Rasmussen, Vejle #241/R (D.KR 6800)
£637 $994 €956 Archipelago (26x40cm-10x16in) s.d.1900. 5-Aug-2 Rasmussen, Vejle #50/R (D.KR 7500)
£732 $1113 €1098 Landscape from Kildesoen, Jaegersborg Dyrehave (36x51cm-14x20in) s.d.90. 27-Aug-2 Rasmussen, Copenhagen #1887/R (D.KR 8500)

£853 $1382 €1237 Mountain landscape from Odd in Hardanger, Norway (40x59cm-16x23in) mono.d.83. 25-May-3 Uppsala Auktionskammare, Uppsala #97/R (S.KR 11000)
£963 $1541 €1445 Landscape from Gudvangen in Sogn, Norway (78x63cm-31x25in) s.d.1900. 13-Jan-3 Rasmussen, Vejle #88/R (D.KR 11000)
£1191 $1883 €1787 View from Himmelbjerget with Silkeborg (18x26cm-7x10in) s.d.68 i.verso. 27-Nov-2 Museumsbygningen, Copenhagen #2/R est:6000 (D.KR 14000)
£5517 $8828 €8000 Quietude (66x90cm-26x35in) s.d.67. 15-Mar-3 De Vuyst, Lokeren #188/R est:6500-7500

LIBERT, Georg Emil (attrib) (1820-1908) Danish
£377 $585 €600 Fishermen in bay (26x35cm-10x14in) i. verso. 29-Oct-2 Dorotheum, Vienna #280/R

LIBERTE, Jean (1896-1965) American/Italian
£316 $500 €474 Rocks and sea, moonlight (66x81cm-26x32in) s. board. 30-Nov-2 Thomaston Place, Thomaston #208

LIBERTS, Ludolfs (1895-1945) Russian
£633 $987 €1000 Interior of Stephansdom in Vienna (65x47cm-26x19in) s. board. 16-Oct-2 Dorotheum, Vienna #9

LIBONEAS, Albin (20th C) Italian
£321 $497 €500 Battle (35x50cm-14x20in) s.d.1928. 5-Dec-2 Stadion, Trieste #827/R

LIBUDA, Walter (1950-) German
Works on paper
£1154 $1788 €1800 The fall (50x91cm-20x36in) s.i.d.1986 mixed media W/C Indian ink col pen prov. 7-Dec-2 Ketterer, Hamburg #691/R est:1800-2000

LICATA, Cavalier Antonio (1810-1892) Italian
£1282 $1987 €2000 Portrait of Enrico Accinni (79x58cm-31x23in) s.d.86. 4-Dec-2 Finarte, Rome #766

LICATA, Riccardo (1929-) Italian
£298 $483 €420 Composition rosa (13x17cm-5x7in) s.d.64 tempera paper. 22-May-3 Stadion, Trieste #366/R
£481 $755 €750 Blue, red and yellow (20x30cm-8x12in) s.d.1999 tempera paper. 23-Nov-2 Meeting Art, Vercelli #41/R
£510 $811 €750 Changing blue (30x20cm-12x8in) s.d.1999 tempera paper. 1-Mar-3 Meeting Art, Vercelli #319
£590 $939 €850 Copper III (22cm-9in circular) s.d.1996 enamel copper lit. 1-May-3 Meeting Art, Vercelli #177
£641 $1006 €1000 Composition (30x40cm-12x16in) s.d.1977 egg tempera card. 23-Nov-2 Meeting Art, Vercelli #38/R
£1020 $1622 €1500 Composition (45x64cm-18x25in) s. paper. 1-Mar-3 Meeting Art, Vercelli #342
£1111 $1767 €1600 Composition (57x38cm-22x15in) s. tempera paper. 1-May-3 Meeting Art, Vercelli #477
£1307 $2092 €2000 Untitled (33x40cm-13x16in) s. painted 2002. 4-Jan-3 Meeting Art, Vercelli #390
£1799 $2878 €2500 Composition (100x100cm-39x39in) s. 16-May-3 Lombrail & Teucquam, Paris #181/R
£2041 $3245 €3000 Composition (50x70cm-20x28in) s.d.1988. 1-Mar-3 Meeting Art, Vercelli #654
£2308 $3623 €3600 Love of charity and compassion (100x100cm-39x39in) oil acrylic paper painted 1998 exhib.lit. 23-Nov-2 Meeting Art, Vercelli #105/R
£2614 $4183 €4000 Composition (80x100cm-31x39in) s.d.1983 egg tempera. 4-Jan-3 Meeting Art, Vercelli #613
Sculpture
£962 $1510 €1500 Mitto (74x28cm-29x11in) s. wood. 23-Nov-2 Meeting Art, Vercelli #318/R
£1250 $1987 €1800 Icarus (158x116x28cm-62x46x11in) s. polychrome wood. 1-May-3 Meeting Art, Vercelli #448
Works on paper
£261 $418 €400 Tifeo AB (23x16cm-9x6in) s.d.1999 pencil pastel. 4-Jan-3 Meeting Art, Vercelli #541
£385 $604 €600 Gradual blue (27x24cm-11x9in) s.d.1992 pastel. 19-Nov-2 Finarte, Milan #159
£496 $804 €700 Composition (34x48cm-13x19in) s.d. mixed media. 23-May-3 Binoche, Paris #79
£521 $828 €750 Composition (31x21cm-12x8in) s.d.1999 mixed media card. 1-May-3 Meeting Art, Vercelli #25
£680 $1082 €1000 Madonna of Balance (50x30cm-20x12in) s.i.d.1998 wax crayon. 1-Mar-3 Meeting Art, Vercelli #582
£709 $1149 €1000 Composition bleue (48x34cm-19x13in) s.d. mixed media. 23-May-3 Binoche, Paris #80
£769 $1192 €1200 Untitled (48x64cm-19x25in) s.d.1959 mixed media paper on canvas. 4-Dec-2 Finarte, Milan #263/R
£922 $1494 €1300 Composition (64x51cm-25x20in) s.d. mixed media cardboard. 23-May-3 Binoche, Paris #78
£1020 $1622 €1500 Music for violins (25x35cm-10x14in) s.d.2002 mixed media on canvas. 1-Mar-3 Meeting Art, Vercelli #619
£1154 $1812 €1800 Untitled (40x50cm-16x20in) s. mixed media on canvas. 23-Nov-2 Meeting Art, Vercelli #43/R
£2292 $3644 €3300 Composition (100x75cm-39x30in) s. mixed media paper on canvas. 1-May-3 Meeting Art, Vercelli #220

LICHTENBERGER, Hans Reinhold (1876-1941) German
Works on paper
£256 $397 €400 Couple dining in restaurant (27x29cm-11x11in) s. W/C bodycol. 5-Dec-2 Neumeister, Munich #2669

LICHTENHELD, Wilhelm (1817-1891) German
£486 $773 €700 Clair de lune sur la riviere (40x32cm-16x13in) s. 30-Apr-3 Tajan, Paris #60
£582 $908 €850 Moonlit mountain lake (10x25cm-4x10in) mono. panel. 11-Apr-3 Winterberg, Heidelberg #469

LICHTENSTEIN, Roy (1923-1997) American
£126582 $200000 €189873 Eccentric scientist (91x91cm-36x36in) enamelled steel painted 1964 prov.lit. 14-Nov-2 Christie's, Rockefeller NY #136/R est:80000-120000
£284810 $450000 €427215 Mirror no.7 (91cm-36in circular) s.d.71 verso oil magna on canvas prov. 12-Nov-2 Sotheby's, New York #47/R est:450000-550000
£288462 $450000 €432693 Yellow abstraction (122x335cm-48x132in) s.d.1968 oil magna on canvas in four parts prov.lit. 11-Nov-2 Phillips, New York #18/R est:300000-400000
£297468 $470000 €446202 Gas station attendant - yellow man (61x41cm-24x16in) mono. oil pencil on canvas prov.exhib. 13-Nov-2 Sotheby's, New York #243/R est:400000-600000
£384615 $600000 €576923 Head with monocle (91x76cm-36x30in) s.d.1980 prov.exhib. 11-Nov-2 Phillips, New York #16/R est:700000-900000
£437500 $700000 €656250 Landscape with seated figure (178x267cm-70x105in) s.d.96 verso oil magna prov.lit. 13-May-3 Sotheby's, New York #38/R est:500000-700000
£656250 $1050000 €984375 Reflections, mystical painting (142x190cm-56x75in) s.d.89 verso oil magna prov.exhib.lit. 14-May-3 Christie's, Rockefeller NY #45/R est:800000-1200000
£750000 $1200000 €1125000 Reflections on Jessica Helms (157x123cm-62x48in) s.d.90 verso oil magna prov.exhib. 13-May-3 Sotheby's, New York #16/R est:800000-1200000
£875000 $1400000 €1312500 Stretcher frame with vertical bars (91x173cm-36x68in) s.d.68 verso oil magna prov.exhib.lit. 14-May-3 Christie's, Rockefeller NY #14/R est:1500000-2000000
£1202532 $1900000 €1803798 Reclining bather (152x229cm-60x90in) s.d.77 verso oil magna on canvas prov.exhib. 12-Nov-2 Sotheby's, New York #43/R est:1800000-2500000
£2784810 $4400000 €4177215 Step-on can with leg (81x132cm-32x52in) s.d.61 oil on canvas in two parts. 12-Nov-2 Sotheby's, New York #35/R est:2000000-3000000
£4113924 $6500000 €6170886 Happy tears (96x96cm-38x38in) s.d.64 verso magna on canvas prov.exhib.lit. 13-Nov-2 Christie's, Rockefeller NY #30/R est:5000000-7000000
Prints
£1807 $3000 €2711 Painting fragment (83x60cm-33x24in) s.d.83 col lithograph edition of 100. 11-Jun-3 Phillips, New York #539 est:4000-6000
£1887 $3000 €2831 Still life with lobster (81x78cm-32x31in) s.d.num.A/P 12/14 col lithograph screenprint. 2-May-3 Sotheby's, New York #502/R est:4000-6000
£1887 $3000 €2831 American Indian theme IV (72x71cm-28x28in) s.i.d.1980 col woodcut lithograph. 1-May-3 Swann Galleries, New York #505/R est:2500-3500
£2000 $3100 €3000 Indian with pony (43x26cm-17x10in) i. woodcut. 5-Dec-2 Sotheby's, London #220/R est:2000-2500
£2027 $3162 €3000 Inaugural print (51x76cm-20x30in) s.i.d.77 col serigraph lit. 28-Mar-3 Farsetti, Prato #325/R
£2051 $3179 €3200 Paris review (105x65cm-41x26in) s.num.74/150 col screenprint. 3-Dec-2 Christie's, Amsterdam #486/R est:3000-4000
£2051 $3179 €3200 Sunrise (47x62cm-19x24in) s. col lithograph exec.1965. 7-Dec-2 Van Ham, Cologne #301/R est:3800
£2057 $3250 €3086 American Indian theme I (62x61cm-24x24in) s.d.1980 num.34/50 col woodcut. 12-Nov-2 Doyle, New York #284/R est:2000-3000

£2057 $3250 €3086 American Indian theme III (67x49cm-26x19in) s.d.1980 num.3/50 col woodcut. 12-Nov-2 Doyle, New York #285/R est:2000-3000
£2083 $3292 €3000 Liberte (76x96cm-30x38in) s.num.58/75 col serigraph. 26-Apr-3 Cornette de St.Cyr, Paris #109/R est:3000-4000
£2138 $3400 €3207 Haystack no.7 (35x60cm-14x24in) s.d.1969 num.35/100 relief print. 1-May-3 Swann Galleries, New York #504/R est:2500-3500
£2200 $3432 €3300 Apple and lemon (58x88cm-23x35in) s.d.1983 num.48/60 col woodcut. 10-Oct-2 Sotheby's, London #268/R est:1500-2000
£2201 $3500 €3302 Crak (50x72cm-20x28in) s. col offset lithograph. 2-May-3 Sotheby's, New York #496/R est:3500-4500
£2201 $3500 €3302 American Indian theme I (62x61cm-24x24in) s.d.num.AP 14 col woodcut. 2-May-3 Sotheby's, New York #503/R est:3000-4000
£2258 $3500 €3387 Girl/spray can (41x28cm-16x11in) s. two col lithographs framed as one. 25-Sep-2 Christie's, Rockefeller NY #328/R est:1500-2500
£2319 $3803 €3200 The Solomon R Guggenheim Museum poster (59x59cm-23x23in) s.d.1969 col serigraph. 28-May-3 Lempertz, Koln #253/R est:3000-4000
£2331 $3800 €3497 Foot and hand (44x55cm-17x22in) s.d.1964 num.151/300 offset col lithograph. 13-Feb-3 Christie's, Rockefeller NY #295/R
£2361 $3754 €3400 Foot and hand (44x54cm-17x21in) s.d.64 num.141/300 col offset lithograph. 29-Apr-3 Artcurial Briest, Paris #410/R est:2800-3200
£2436 $3800 €3654 American Indian theme II (82x95cm-32x37in) s.d.num.10 col woodcut. 5-Nov-2 Christie's, Rockefeller NY #452/R est:3500-4500
£2436 $3800 €3654 Dancing figures (64x57cm-25x22in) s.num.7/32 soft ground aquatint engraving. 5-Nov-2 Christie's, Rockefeller NY #453/R est:3500-4500
£2500 $4125 €3625 Inaugural print (41x66cm-16x26in) s.d.num.87/100 col silkscreen. 1-Jul-3 Sotheby's, London #200/R est:2500-3000
£2500 $4125 €3625 Sunrise (44x59cm-17x23in) s. col offset lithograph. 2-Jul-3 Christie's, London #97/R est:1500-2000
£2516 $4000 €3774 Untitled, II (22x22cm-9x9in) s.d.80 num.6/8 col etching. 2-May-3 Sotheby's, New York #505/R est:2500-3500
£2548 $4000 €3822 Bicentennial print (64x46cm-25x18in) s.d.num.115/200 col lithograph screenprint. 21-Nov-2 Swann Galleries, New York #111/R est:4000-6000
£2642 $4200 €3963 Red apple and yellow apple (71x94cm-28x37in) s.d.num.30/60 col woodcut. 2-May-3 Sotheby's, New York #507/R est:4000-5000
£2721 $4327 €4000 Liberte (83x102cm-33x40in) d.1991 serigraphie vellum. 18-Mar-3 Galerie Moderne, Brussels #570/R est:4000-6000
£2733 $4263 €4100 Modern head number 1 (51x32cm-20x13in) s.num.19/100 col woodcut lit. 5-Nov-2 Bukowskis, Stockholm #577/R est:50000-70000 (S.KR 39000)
£2761 $4500 €4142 Painting on blue and yellow wall (120x80cm-47x31in) s.d.1984 woodcut col lithograph. 13-Feb-3 Christie's, Rockefeller NY #299/R
£2830 $4500 €4245 Two figures with teepee (25x22cm-10x9in) s.d.num.20/32 col soft ground etching aquatint engraving. 29-Apr-3 Christie's, Rockefeller NY #670/R est:3000-4000
£2830 $4500 €4245 Imperfect print for BAM (137x66cm-54x26in) s.d.num.63/75 col woodcut screenprint. 29-Apr-3 Christie's, Rockefeller NY #671/R est:4000-6000
£2830 $4500 €4245 Sandwich and soda (48x58cm-19x23in) col screenprint clear plastic edition of 500. 2-May-3 Sotheby's, New York #497/R est:2500-3500
£2830 $4500 €4245 Study of hands (80x83cm-31x33in) s.d.num.73/100 col lithograph screenprint. 2-May-3 Sotheby's, New York #506/R est:3000-4000
£3019 $4800 €4529 Pyramids (29x89cm-11x35in) s.d.num.75/101 col lithograph. 29-Apr-3 Christie's, Rockefeller NY #658/R est:3000-4000
£3019 $4800 €4529 Modern print (61x61cm-24x24in) s.d.num.98/200 col lithograph screenprint. 29-Apr-3 Christie's, Rockefeller NY #661/R est:4000-6000
£3145 $5000 €4718 Foot and hand (43x53cm-17x21in) s.d.num.251/300 col offset lithograph. 29-Apr-3 Christie's, Rockefeller NY #655/R est:2000-4000
£3145 $5000 €4718 Explosion (56x43cm-22x17in) s.i. col lithograph. 29-Apr-3 Christie's, Rockefeller NY #657/R est:4000-6000
£3145 $5000 €4718 Still life with pitcher and flowers (77x115cm-30x45in) s.d.num.59/100 col lithograph screenprint. 29-Apr-3 Christie's, Rockefeller NY #664/R est:4000-6000
£3185 $5000 €4778 Rain forest (65x55cm-26x22in) s.i.d.1992 col screenprint. 21-Nov-2 Swann Galleries, New York #112/R est:5000-8000
£3190 $5200 €4785 Mao (68x51cm-27x20in) s.d.1971 col lithograph. 13-Feb-3 Christie's, Rockefeller NY #297/R
£3374 $5500 €5061 Shipboard (69x51cm-27x20in) s. offset col lithograph. 13-Feb-3 Christie's, Rockefeller NY #296/R
£3459 $5500 €5189 Solomon R Guggenheim Museum poster (73x73cm-29x29in) s.d.num.194/250 col screenprint. 2-May-3 Sotheby's, New York #498/R est:3000-4000
£3510 $5721 €5300 Industry in the arts (68x50cm-27x20in) s. num.144/250 col serigraph. 3-Feb-3 Cornette de St.Cyr, Paris #154/R est:6000
£3525 $5500 €5288 At the beach (66x107cm-26x42in) s.d.num.37/38 col lithograph. 14-Oct-2 Butterfields, San Francisco #1300/R est:6000-8000
£3526 $5500 €5289 Industry and the arts (43x48cm-17x19in) s.d.num.132/250 col screenprint. 5-Nov-2 Christie's, Rockefeller NY #448/R est:3000-4000
£3600 $5940 €5220 Still life with red jar (39x33cm-15x13in) s.i.d.num.50/50 col silkscreen. 1-Jul-3 Sotheby's, London #203/R est:2000-2500
£3681 $6000 €5522 Still life with pitcher and flowers (94x132cm-37x52in) s.d.1974 lithograph col screenprint. 13-Feb-3 Christie's, Rockefeller NY #298/R
£3774 $6000 €5661 Reflections on brushstrokes (128x165cm-50x65in) s.d.num.11/16 col lithograph screenprint woodcut PVC collage. 2-May-3 Sotheby's, New York #510/R est:7000-9000
£3800 $6270 €5510 Reflections on brushstrokes (128x17cm-50x7in) s.d.num.30/68 lithograph screenprint woodcut mixed media. 2-Jul-3 Christie's, London #98/R est:4000-6000
£3871 $6000 €5807 Ten Dollar Bill (48x62cm-19x24in) s.d.1956/79 num.11/25 lithograph. 25-Sep-2 Christie's, Rockefeller NY #327/R est:3000-4000
£3903 $6167 €5855 Crying girl (45x61cm-18x24in) s. col lithograph. 1-Apr-3 Rasmussen, Copenhagen #438/R est:20000-25000 (D.KR 42000)
£4088 $6500 €6132 Still life with figurine (99x77cm-39x30in) s.d.num.59/100 col lithograph screenprint. 29-Apr-3 Christie's, Rockefeller NY #662/R est:4000-6000
£4088 $6500 €6132 Still life with lobster (82x79cm-32x31in) s.d.num.59/100 col lithograph screenprint. 29-Apr-3 Christie's, Rockefeller NY #663/R est:6000-8000
£4487 $7000 €6731 Still life with lobster (99x95cm-39x37in) s.d.num.21/100 col lithograph screenprint. 5-Nov-2 Christie's, Rockefeller NY #450/R est:6000-8000
£4514 $7132 €6500 Salute to aviation (116x62cm-46x24in) s.num.64/135 col serigraph lit. 26-Apr-3 Cornette de St.Cyr, Paris #100/R est:5000-6000
£4514 $7448 €6500 Shipboard girl (69x51cm-27x20in) s. col screenprint. 2-Jul-3 Artcurial Briest, Paris #92/R est:6500-7000
£4717 $7500 €7076 Imperfect diptych (122x213cm-48x84in) s.d.num.AP 6/14 col woodcut screenprint collage. 29-Apr-3 Christie's, Rockefeller NY #676/R est:9000-12000
£4808 $7500 €7212 Still life with windmill (91x114cm-36x45in) s.d.num.21/100 col lithograph screenprint debossing. 5-Nov-2 Christie's, Rockefeller NY #451/R est:6000-8000
£4908 $8000 €7362 Reflections on brushstrokes (145x180cm-57x71in) s.i.d. lithograph woodcut screenprint. 13-Feb-3 Christie's, Rockefeller NY #300/R
£5031 $8000 €7547 Bright light (47x54cm-19x21in) s.d.num.PP II col lithograph. 29-Apr-3 Christie's, Rockefeller NY #669/R est:6000-8000
£5031 $8000 €7547 Imperfect diptych (98x207cm-39x81in) s.d.num.AP 6/14 col woodcut screenprint collage. 29-Apr-3 Christie's, Rockefeller NY #672/R est:8000-10000
£5031 $8000 €7547 Reflections on brushstrokes (128x166cm-50x65in) s.d.num.27/68 col lithograph screenprint woodcut collage. 29-Apr-3 Christie's, Rockefeller NY #677/R est:7000-9000
£5031 $8000 €7547 Reflections on hair (126x99cm-50x39in) s.d.num.10/16 col lithograph screenprint woodcut. 2-May-3 Sotheby's, New York #509/R est:7000-9000
£5128 $8000 €7692 Bedroom (145x200cm-57x79in) s.d.num.16/60 col woodcut silkscreen. 14-Oct-2 Butterfields, San Francisco #1302/R est:6000-8000
£5128 $8000 €7692 Reflections on brushtrokes (145x180cm-57x71in) s.d.num.15/16 col lithograph screenprint woodcut collage. 5-Nov-2 Christie's, Rockefeller NY #455/R est:7000-9000
£5346 $8500 €8019 Still life with portrait (97x73cm-38x29in) s.d.num.59/100 col lithograph screenprint debossing. 29-Apr-3 Christie's, Rockefeller NY #665/R est:5000-7000
£5449 $8500 €8174 Shipboard girl (33x49cm-13x19in) s. offset col lithograph. 7-Nov-2 Swann Galleries, New York #690/R est:5000-8000
£5660 $9000 €8490 Huh (101x71cm-40x28in) s.d.num.1/100 col screenprint. 29-Apr-3 Christie's, Rockefeller NY #668/R est:5000-7000

£5660 $9000 €8490 Imperfect (149x218cm-59x86in) s.d.num.17/45 col woodcut screenprint collage. 29-Apr-3 Christie's, Rockefeller NY #675/R est:9000-12000
£5975 $9500 €8963 Still life with windmill (75x97cm-30x38in) s.d.num.59/100 col lithograph screenprint debossing. 29-Apr-3 Christie's, Rockefeller NY #666/R est:7000-9000
£5975 $9500 €8963 Imperfect (104x236cm-41x93in) s.d.num.AP 6/14 col woodcut screenprint collage. 29-Apr-3 Christie's, Rockefeller NY #673/R est:12000-16000
£5975 $9500 €8963 Imperfect (122x217cm-48x85in) s.d.num.AP 6/14 col woodcut screenprint collage. 29-Apr-3 Christie's, Rockefeller NY #674/R est:9000-12000
£6000 $9300 €9000 Crak! (49x69cm-19x27in) s.d.1963-4 num.236/300 col offset lithograph. 3-Dec-2 Christie's, London #142/R est:2000-3000
£6000 $9300 €9000 I love Liberty (82x54cm-32x21in) s.num.209/250 col silkscreen. 5-Dec-2 Sotheby's, London #221/R est:3000-5000
£6159 $10101 €8500 Crying girl (44x59cm-17x23in) s. col offset lithograph. 28-May-3 Lempertz, Koln #251/R est:800-10000
£6289 $10000 €9434 Reflections on Minerva (90x113cm-35x44in) s.d.num.1/68 col lithograph screenprint relief. 2-May-3 Sotheby's, New York #511/R est:12000-15000
£6918 $11000 €10377 CRAK (47x69cm-19x27in) s. col offset lithograph. 29-Apr-3 Christie's, Rockefeller NY #654/R est:5000-7000
£7000 $11550 €10150 Crying girl (44x59cm-17x23in) s. col offset lithograph. 1-Jul-3 Sotheby's, London #202/R est:6000-8000
£7014 $11082 €10100 Shipboard girl (68x50cm-27x20in) s. col offset lithograph lit. 26-Apr-3 Cornette de St.Cyr, Paris #101/R est:6000-8000
£7547 $12000 €11321 Landscape with boats (71x147cm-28x58in) s.d.num.44/60 col lithograph screenprint. 2-May-3 Sotheby's, New York #517/R est:10000-15000
£7800 $12168 €11700 Crak! (47x69cm-19x27in) s. offset lithograph. 10-Oct-2 Sotheby's, London #266/R est:3000-4000
£8805 $14000 €13208 Two nudes, state I (105x89cm-41x35in) s.i.d.num.1/10 col relief. 2-May-3 Sotheby's, New York #516/R est:12000-15000
£9500 $15675 €13775 Shipboard girl (66x49cm-26x19in) s. col offset lithograph. 2-Jul-3 Christie's, London #269/R est:3000-5000
£9615 $15000 €14423 Nude reading (78x92cm-31x36in) s.d.num.6/60 col relief print. 5-Nov-2 Christie's, Rockefeller NY #456/R est:10000-15000
£10000 $16500 €14500 Wall paper with blue floor interior (274x105cm-108x41in) s.d.num.36/300 col silkscreen set of five panels. 1-Jul-3 Sotheby's, London #201/R est:4000-6000
£10063 $16000 €15095 Nude with yellow pillow (117x94cm-46x37in) s.d.num.60/60 col relief. 2-May-3 Sotheby's, New York #515/R est:12000-15000
£10127 $16000 €16000 Crying girl (43x59cm-17x23in) s. col offset lithograph. 30-Nov-2 Villa Grisebach, Berlin #432/R est:12000-14000
£10256 $16000 €15384 Thinking nude (107x158cm-42x62in) s.d.num.3/40 col relief print. 5-Nov-2 Christie's, Rockefeller NY #457/R est:12000-18000
£10692 $17000 €16038 Roommates (147x115cm-58x45in) s.d.num.38/40 col relief. 29-Apr-3 Christie's, Rockefeller NY #678/R est:15000-20000
£11321 $18000 €16982 Reflections on girl (98x123cm-39x48in) s.d.num.57/68 col lithograph screenprint relief collage. 2-May-3 Sotheby's, New York #513/R est:15000-20000
£11950 $19000 €17925 Roommates (146x114cm-57x45in) s.d.num.6/40 col relief. 2-May-3 Sotheby's, New York #514/R est:15000-18000
£12821 $20000 €19232 Reflections on crash (150x190cm-59x75in) s.d.num.11/68 col lithograph screenprint collage. 5-Nov-2 Christie's, Rockefeller NY #454/R est:20000-30000
£14423 $22500 €21635 Reflections on crash (136x176cm-54x69in) s.d.num.1/68 col lithograph silkscreen collage. 14-Oct-2 Butterfields, San Francisco #1301/R est:20000-30000
£14493 $23768 €20000 Sweet dreams baby! (90x65cm-35x26in) s.d. col serigraph. 28-May-3 Lempertz, Koln #252/R est:12000-14000
£16352 $26000 €24528 Reflections on the scream (108x150cm-43x59in) s.d.num.AP 11/16 col lithograph screenprint woodcut collage. 2-May-3 Sotheby's, New York #512/R est:20000-30000
£17000 $28050 €24650 Nude with blue hair (130x80cm-51x31in) s.d.num.20/40 col relief print. 2-Jul-3 Christie's, London #270/R est:10000-15000
£23899 $38000 €35849 Sweet dream, baby (90x65cm-35x26in) s.num.106/200 col screenprint. 2-May-3 Sotheby's, New York #499/R est:30000-40000
£25000 $40000 €37500 Water lilies blue lily pads (110x98cm-43x39in) screenprint stainless steel executed 1992 prov.lit. 14-May-3 Sotheby's, New York #244/R est:22000-28000
£25157 $40000 €37736 Brushstroke figures series (150x104cm-59x41in) s.d.num.13/60 lithograph woodcut screenprint collage 7 portfolio. 2-May-3 Sotheby's, New York #508/R est:35000-45000

Sculpture

£7547 $12000 €11321 Modern head relief (61x45x2cm-24x18x1in) s.d.num.35/100 verso brass relief. 29-Apr-3 Christie's, Rockefeller NY #660/R est:12000-18000
£7547 $12000 €11321 Modern head relief (61x45x2cm-24x18x1in) s.d.num.40/100 brass relief. 2-May-3 Sotheby's, New York #500/R est:15000-20000
£11218 $17500 €16827 Modern head relief (61x45x2cm-24x18x1in) s.d.num.85/100 bas relief. 5-Nov-2 Christie's, Rockefeller NY #449/R est:10000-15000
£36709 $58000 €55064 Brushstroke IV (173x76x21cm-68x30x8in) s.i.num.8/10 verso wall relief acrylic lacquer enamel prov. 14-Nov-2 Christie's, Rockefeller NY #163/R est:70000-90000
£37975 $60000 €56963 Bushstroke III (163x69x30cm-64x27x12in) s.verso acrylic cherry wood executed 1987 prov.lit. 13-Nov-2 Sotheby's, New York #252/R est:50000-70000
£177215 $280000 €265823 Brushstorke head II (76x30x46cm-30x12x18in) painted bronze executed 1987 prov.exhib. 13-Nov-2 Sotheby's, New York #282/R est:200000-250000

Works on paper

£2436 $3849 €3800 Paysage (33x63cm-13x25in) s.i. cardboard collage on plastic. 15-Nov-2 Laurence Calmels, Paris #9/R
£3503 $5500 €5255 Wallpaper with blue floor interior (102x200cm-40x79in) one s.d.num.52 screenprint five parts. 19-Nov-2 Wright, Chicago #239/R est:4000-5000
£18750 $30000 €28125 Entablature (71x104cm-28x41in) s.d.1971 verso pencil prov. 14-May-3 Sotheby's, New York #201a/R est:25000-35000
£28846 $45000 €43269 Study for eccentric scientist (15x15cm-6x6in) init. pencil col pencil board prov.exhib. 14-Oct-2 Butterfields, San Francisco #2052/R est:45000-65000
£53797 $85000 €80696 Nude sunbathing (25x26cm-10x10in) s.d.95 verso graphite col pencil prov. 14-Nov-2 Christie's, Rockefeller NY #188/R est:40000-60000

LICINI, James (1937-) Swiss

Sculpture

£1135 $1783 €1703 Hook (32x39cm-13x15in) mono.d.1995 iron. 23-Nov-2 Burkhard, Luzern #25/R est:2000-2500 (S.FR 2600)
£1572 $2295 €2358 Untitled (58x16x11cm-23x6x4in) mono.d.1993 iron. 4-Jun-2 Germann, Zurich #91/R est:2000-3000 (S.FR 3600)

LICINI, Osvaldo (1894-1958) Italian

£22436 $32756 €35000 Landscape (21x31cm-8x12in) prov. 5-Jun-2 Il Ponte, Milan #91/R est:30000-40000
£28481 $45000 €45000 Fantasy flower (18x24cm-7x9in) canvas on cardboard painted 1957. 30-Nov-2 Farsetti, Prato #704/R est:55000

Works on paper

£1844 $2987 €2600 Missili (15x21cm-6x8in) pencil prov.exhib. 26-May-3 Christie's, Milan #67/R est:2500-3000
£3401 $5408 €5000 Untitled (20x26cm-8x10in) pencil. 1-Mar-3 Meeting Art, Vercelli #719

LIDBERG, Sven (1929-1985) Swedish

£266 $421 €399 End of the day (32x24cm-13x9in) s. panel. 30-Nov-2 Goteborg Auktionsverk, Sweden #569/R (S.KR 3800)
£603 $934 €905 Street scene with cafe, Copenhagen (33x24cm-13x9in) s. panel exhib. 8-Dec-2 Uppsala Auktionskammare, Uppsala #301 (S.KR 8500)

LIDDELL, J D (19th C) British

Works on paper

£330 $538 €495 Sheilds Harbour a coastal view (28x18cm-11x7in) s. pencil W/C. 15-Feb-3 Jim Railton, Durham #1519

LIDDELL, T Hodgson (1860-1925) British

£500 $780 €750 Brig O'Turk, Pethshire (51x76cm-20x30in) s.d.1882 i.verso. 7-Nov-2 Christie's, Kensington #146/R

LIDDERDALE, Charles Sillem (1831-1895) British

£500 $795 €750 Love letter (61x51cm-24x20in) init.d.79. 6-Mar-3 Christie's, Kensington #550/R
£850 $1326 €1275 Portrait of a lady (57x43cm-22x17in) mono. 26-Mar-3 Sotheby's, Olympia #75/R
£860 $1428 €1290 Portrait of gypsy girl with fruit in a rural landscape (43x33cm-17x13in) 10-Jun-3 Lawrences, Bletchingley #1521/R
£1400 $2282 €2100 Meditation (18x26cm-7x10in) init. 12-Feb-3 Andrew Hartley, Ilkley #842/R est:1000-1500
£1719 $2750 €2579 Springtime (53x43cm-21x17in) mono. canvas on board. 14-May-3 Butterfields, San Francisco #1149/R est:3000-5000
£2317 $3800 €3360 Model (53x43cm-21x17in) exhib. 30-May-3 Aspire, Cleveland #28/R est:3000-6000
£2700 $4185 €4050 Portrait of a girl (48x40cm-19x16in) mono.board. 3-Dec-2 Sworder & Son, Bishops Stortford #948/R est:800-1200
£4400 $6864 €6600 Young beauty (52x42cm-20x17in) mono. 6-Nov-2 Bonhams, Chester #533/R est:2500-3500

£5800 $9338 €8700 Study of young woman's head (28x25cm-11x10in) paper prov.exhib. 20-Feb-3 Christie's, London #162/R
£14000 $22540 €21000 Scottish vigil (49x79cm-19x31in) init.d.70 i.verso prov.exhib. 20-Feb-3 Christie's, London #63/R est:15000

Works on paper
£260 $416 €390 Portrait of a young lady (46x38cm-18x15in) mono.d.1883 W/C. 11-Mar-3 Gorringes, Lewes #2392

LIDDERDALE, Charles Sillem (attrib) (1831-1895) British
£450 $702 €675 In thought (36x24cm-14x9in) 26-Mar-3 Sotheby's, Olympia #73/R
£4100 $6601 €6150 Portrait of a young woman wearing a red cape (88x73cm-35x29in) 18-Feb-3 Rowley Fine Art, Newmarket #373/R est:3000-5000

LIDY, Matthias (1954-) Austrian
£411 $642 €650 Never enough (70x50cm-28x20in) s.i.d.3/01 acrylic. 15-Oct-2 Dorotheum, Vienna #272/R

LIE, Jonas (1880-1940) American
£3503 $5500 €5255 Misty forest clearing (66x89cm-26x35in) s.d.08 prov. 14-Dec-2 Weschler, Washington #679/R est:6000-8000
£7229 $12000 €10482 Rockbound coast (76x114cm-30x45in) s. prov. 11-Jun-3 Butterfields, San Francisco #4070/R est:12000-15000

LIE, Robert (1899-1980) American
£478 $750 €717 Portrait of a full rigged ship (64x76cm-25x30in) s. 26-Jul-2 Eldred, East Dennis #620/R

LIE-GJEMRE, Johan (1900-1993) Norwegian
£346 $530 €519 Landscape with animals (99x116cm-39x46in) s. painted 1934 exhib. 26-Aug-2 Blomqvist, Lysaker #1237 (N.KR 4000)
£382 $588 €573 Landscape with cattle grazing (97x116cm-38x46in) s. exhib. 28-Oct-2 Blomqvist, Lysaker #1174 (N.KR 4500)
£384 $599 €576 Landscape, Hallingskarvet (101x135cm-40x53in) 23-Sep-2 Blomqvist, Lysaker #1142 (N.KR 4500)
£504 $822 €756 April 1945 (65x80cm-26x31in) s. panel. 17-Feb-3 Blomqvist, Lysaker #1117 (N.KR 5700)

LIE-JORGENSEN, Thorbjorn (1900-1961) Norwegian
£327 $534 €491 By the sea (46x55cm-18x22in) s.d.1949 panel. 17-Feb-3 Blomqvist, Lysaker #1118 (N.KR 3700)

LIEBER, August (1828-1850) German

Works on paper
£352 $585 €500 Italian landscape (41x55cm-16x22in) s. chk wash. 12-Jun-3 Hauswedell & Nolte, Hamburg #368/R

LIEBERMANN, Ernst (1869-1960) German
£321 $503 €500 Schambach valley (35x30cm-14x12in) s. i.d.1923 verso panel. 23-Nov-2 Arnold, Frankfurt #792/R
£385 $596 €600 From my garden (30x39cm-12x15in) s.i.d.Juli 1949 panel lit. 6-Dec-2 Karlheinz Kaupp, Staufen #2209/R
£705 $1093 €1100 Le fumeur au chapeau buse (70x60cm-28x24in) s. panel. 9-Dec-2 Horta, Bruxelles #181
£818 $1275 €1300 Autumnal landscape with angler in punt (47x103cm-19x41in) s.d.1905 lit. 20-Sep-2 Karlheinz Kaupp, Staufen #2088/R
£912 $1423 €1350 Female nude in landscape (80x100cm-31x39in) s.i. 27-Mar-3 Dr Fritz Nagel, Stuttgart #834/R
£1410 $2214 €2200 Female nude in studio (70x70cm-28x28in) s.d.1911. 21-Nov-2 Van Ham, Cologne #1752/R est:1200
£1781 $2778 €2600 Children's time (75x66cm-30x26in) s.d.1917. 10-Apr-3 Van Ham, Cologne #1571/R est:2800

LIEBERMANN, Ferdinand (1883-1941) German

Sculpture
£1622 $2530 €2400 Female nude (79cm-31in) s. pat.bronze. 26-Mar-3 Hugo Ruef, Munich #1512/R est:2400

LIEBERMANN, Max (1847-1935) German
£823 $1275 €1300 Landscape (13x20cm-5x8in) s. oil chk. 28-Sep-2 Ketterer, Hamburg #55/R
£1295 $2124 €1800 Artist and model (15x18cm-6x7in) s. pencil. 5-Jun-3 Dorotheum, Salzburg #743/R est:2800-3200
£12658 $20000 €20000 Portraits of Johann Georg Wolde and Adele Wolde (112x92cm-44x36in) s.d.1907 s.d.1910 prov.exhib.lit. two. 30-Nov-2 Villa Grisebach, Berlin #130/R est:20000-30000
£12821 $19872 €20000 Portrait of Felix Benjamin (98x75cm-39x30in) s. 4-Dec-2 Lempertz, Koln #860/R est:25000-28000
£17000 $27880 €25500 Worker in the field (37x47cm-15x19in) panel painted c.1874 prov.lit. 4-Feb-3 Christie's, London #205/R est:12000
£18987 $30000 €30000 Peasant with horse drawn plough - study for mural (34x58cm-13x23in) s.d.97 board prov. 30-Nov-2 Villa Grisebach, Berlin #125/R est:30000-40000
£21739 $35652 €30000 Dutch farmstead - landscape near Laren (34x49cm-13x19in) s. paper on board prov.lit. 31-May-3 Villa Grisebach, Berlin #119/R est:30000-40000
£49275 $80812 €68000 Alley in Tiergarten with strollers, cab and tram (21x27cm-8x11in) s. panel prov. 30-May-3 Villa Grisebach, Berlin #6/R est:40000-60000
£72464 $118841 €100000 Wannsee garden (32x41cm-13x16in) s. panel. 30-May-3 Villa Grisebach, Berlin #5/R est:80000-100000
£72464 $118841 €100000 Avenue in the Tiergarten (35x45cm-14x18in) s. prov. 29-May-3 Lempertz, Koln #753/R est:130000-140000
£80128 $125000 €120192 Beach scene (33x38cm-13x15in) s. canvasboard. 15-Oct-2 Winter Associates, Plainville #50 est:100000-200000
£88607 $140000 €140000 Garden bench under the chestnut tree in the garden at Wannsee (40x50cm-16x20in) s. panel prov.lit. 29-Nov-2 Villa Grisebach, Berlin #16/R est:90000-120000
£99359 $156987 €155000 Garden cafe on the Wannsee (37x47cm-15x19in) s. 14-Nov-2 Neumeister, Munich #615/R est:40000-50000
£123188 $202029 €170000 Hunter in the dunes (50x68cm-20x27in) s. prov.lit. 29-May-3 Lempertz, Koln #752/R est:180000-200000
£128205 $198718 €200000 Youths on the beach (64x91cm-25x36in) s.d.1903 prov.exhib.lit. 4-Dec-2 Lempertz, Koln #18/R est:200000-220000
£130000 $202800 €195000 Der kunstler in seinem atelier in Wannsee - Artist in his studio in Wannsee (42x54cm-17x21in) s. painted 1932 prov.exhib.lit. 9-Oct-2 Sotheby's, London #6/R est:140000-180000
£300000 $468000 €450000 Konzert in der oper - Concert at the opera (52x75cm-20x30in) s. painted c.1923 prov.exhib.lit. 9-Oct-2 Sotheby's, London #5/R est:300000-500000
£869565 $1400000 €1304348 My house in Wannsee, garden (70x90cm-28x35in) s. painted 1926 prov. 6-May-3 Sotheby's, New York #6/R est:950000

Prints
£2431 $3865 €3500 Jewish quarter in Amsterdam (31x22cm-12x9in) s. num.16/30 etching. 5-May-3 Ketterer, Munich #912/R est:1200-1800
£3169 $5261 €4500 Uhlenhorst ferry post (32x43cm-13x17in) s. etching drypoint. 14-Jun-3 Hauswedell & Nolte, Hamburg #1352/R est:5000

Works on paper
£280 $437 €440 Peasant carving stick (10x15cm-4x6in) s. chl pencil. 5-Nov-2 Hartung & Hartung, Munich #2154/R
£347 $552 €500 Bauernhaus mit den Sonnenblumen (24x34cm-9x13in) s. gouache panel. 29-Apr-3 Campo & Campo, Antwerp #193/R
£577 $894 €900 Horse market (9x12cm-4x5in) s. pen. 7-Dec-2 Hauswedell & Nolte, Hamburg #864/R
£725 $1188 €1000 Riders in wood (11x18cm-4x7in) pencil. 31-May-3 Villa Grisebach, Berlin #620/R
£725 $1188 €1000 Figures strolling (11x18cm-4x7in) pencil. 31-May-3 Villa Grisebach, Berlin #621/R
£797 $1307 €1100 Field workers (14x20cm-6x8in) s. chk bodycol study verso. 31-May-3 Villa Grisebach, Berlin #618/R
£797 $1307 €1100 Figures walking in Tiergarten (11x18cm-4x7in) pencil. 31-May-3 Villa Grisebach, Berlin #622/R
£935 $1496 €1300 Man's portrait (79x58cm-31x23in) s.d. pastel chk. 15-May-3 Neumeister, Munich #305/R
£1014 $1664 €1400 Figures strolling in Tiergarten (11x18cm-4x7in) pencil. 31-May-3 Villa Grisebach, Berlin #623/R est:800-1200
£1026 $1600 €1539 Skizzen von die Dunen, die Niederlande (27x36cm-11x14in) s. black chk htd white exec.c.1905-10. 18-Sep-2 Swann Galleries, New York #19/R est:1500-2500
£1181 $1877 €1700 Woman sewing (33x19cm-13x7in) s. chl sketch verso. 5-May-3 Ketterer, Munich #904/R est:800-1200
£1258 $1962 €2000 Walker (14x11cm-6x4in) s. pen ink prov. 9-Oct-2 Sotheby's, London #184/R est:3000-4000
£1295 $2124 €1800 Samson and Delila (25x33cm-10x13in) i. pencil dr. 5-Jun-3 Dorotheum, Salzburg #742/R est:2000-2600
£1582 $2500 €2500 Seated Dutch woman (34x28cm-13x11in) s. pencil. 30-Nov-2 Villa Grisebach, Berlin #126/R est:2500-3500
£1603 $2532 €2500 Woman hanging out washing (24x37cm-9x15in) s. pencil. 15-Nov-2 Reiss & Sohn, Konigstein #609/R est:4000
£2083 $3312 €3000 Cafe garden (11x16cm-4x6in) pencil board. 5-May-3 Ketterer, Munich #910/R est:900-1200
£2292 $3644 €3300 Study for 'Old men's house in Amsterdam' (26x20cm-10x8in) s. pencil paper on board. 5-May-3 Ketterer, Munich #903/R est:800-1200
£2390 $3800 €3585 Self-portrait (22x14cm-9x6in) s. pencil prov. 27-Feb-3 Christie's, Rockefeller NY #21/R
£2899 $4754 €4000 Boys bathing (27x36cm-11x14in) s.i. chk htd white. 31-May-3 Villa Grisebach, Berlin #122/R est:3000-3500
£3043 $4991 €4200 Dune landscape with building (30x46cm-12x18in) s. chk htd white. 31-May-3 Villa Grisebach, Berlin #126/R est:2500-3500
£3987 $6300 €6300 Zandvoort Customs Post (25x31cm-10x12in) chk htd white. 30-Nov-2 Bassenge, Berlin #6446/R est:4000
£4430 $7000 €7000 Roofs and trees - study (10x10cm-4x4in) s. gouache. 30-Nov-2 Villa Grisebach, Berlin #114/R est:7000-9000
£5435 $8913 €7500 Ropewalk in Katwijk (30x21cm-12x8in) s. chl htd white prov. 29-May-3 Lempertz, Koln #754/R est:7500
£7639 $12146 €11000 Mother and child (24x17cm-9x7in) s. chl study verso. 5-May-3 Ketterer, Munich #907/R est:2000-3000

£7639 $12146 €11000 Boys bathing (26x34cm-10x13in) s. chl W/C htd white. 5-May-3 Ketterer, Munich #909/R est:9000-12000

£7971 $13072 €11000 Tennis players on beach (10x17cm-4x7in) s. pastel chk over pencil prov. 29-May-3 Lempertz, Koln #755/R est:2000-3000

£9494 $15000 €15000 Beach scene (12x20cm-5x8in) s. pastel prov. 29-Nov-2 Villa Grisebach, Berlin #9/R est:15000-20000

£13291 $21000 €21000 Garden cafe in Wannsee (13x22cm-5x9in) s. pastel pencil prov. 29-Nov-2 Villa Grisebach, Berlin #10/R est:20000-30000

£20513 $31795 €32000 Wannsee garden (22x28cm-9x11in) s. pastel. 4-Dec-2 Lempertz, Koln #861/R est:15000-20000

£24823 $40213 €35000 Boys swimming (31x48cm-12x19in) s. gouache. 20-May-3 Dorotheum, Vienna #2/R est:35000-45000

£25000 $41000 €37500 Study (24x36cm-9x14in) s. pen ink prov. 5-Feb-3 Sotheby's, London #209/R est:15000

£25725 $42188 €35500 Garden of the Villa Oppenheim, Wannsee (23x30cm-9x12in) s. pastel prov. 30-May-3 Villa Grisebach, Berlin #8/R est:14000-18000

£55000 $89650 €82500 Tennisspielernnen am meer (32x48cm-13x19in) s. W/C chl executed c.1901 prov.exhib. 3-Feb-3 Christie's, London #2/R est:35000-45000

LIEBICH, Curt (1868-?) German

£1384 $2158 €2200 Black Forest house (51x40cm-20x16in) s.d.19. 19-Sep-2 Dr Fritz Nagel, Stuttgart #957/R

£4398 $7081 €6597 Children playing in front of bakehouse (31x35cm-12x14in) s.d.09. 7-May-3 Dobiaschofsky, Bern #785/R est:1800 (S.FR 9500)

LIEBSCHER, Karl (1851-1906) Czechoslovakian

£2837 $4596 €4000 Picture of Karlsbad (40x50cm-16x20in) s.d.1888. 22-May-3 Dorotheum, Vienna #169/R est:4500-5500

LIEDER, Franz (1780-1859) Austrian

Miniatures

£2000 $3340 €2900 Lady with a white veil and lace ruff (14cm-6in) s.d.1818 card gilt metal bezel rec. giltwood frame oval. 25-Jun-3 Sotheby's, Olympia #37/R est:1500-2000

Works on paper

£634 $1020 €900 Portrait of elegant man in uniform (24x20cm-9x8in) s.d.1826 W/C oval. 7-May-3 Michael Zeller, Lindau #784/R

LIEGI, Ulvi (1860-1939) Italian

£3654 $5737 €5700 Landscape with shepherd (21x33cm-8x13in) s. board prov. 16-Dec-2 Pandolfini, Florence #323/R

£6013 $9500 €9500 Wheat amongst olive trees (9x21cm-4x8in) init. board. 26-Nov-2 Christie's, Rome #185/R est:10000-12000

£8013 $12660 €12500 Livorno harbour (32x22cm-13x9in) s. cardboard. 15-Nov-2 Farsetti, Prato #558/R est:8000

£9797 $15284 €14500 Settignano (21x32cm-8x13in) s. board. 28-Mar-3 Farsetti, Prato #725/R est:18000

£9797 $15284 €14500 Landscape in Arcetri (19x29cm-7x11in) s. board. 28-Mar-3 Farsetti, Prato #737/R est:18000

£33333 $52667 €52000 Saint Margaret's in Montici (44x69cm-17x27in) s.d.1900 lit. 15-Nov-2 Farsetti, Prato #556/R est:30000-33000

LIENDER, Jacobus van (1696-1759) Flemish

Works on paper

£1656 $2583 €2600 Wooded landscape with hunter shooting duck (13x20cm-5x8in) pen brown ink W/C. 5-Nov-2 Sotheby's, Amsterdam #162/R est:2800-3500

£1783 $2782 €2800 Mountainous wooded landscape with waterfall, seated figure and tomb (13x22cm-5x9in) s. pen brown ink W/C. 5-Nov-2 Sotheby's, Amsterdam #134/R est:3000-5000

LIENDER, Paul van (1731-1797) Dutch

Works on paper

£276 $439 €400 Landscape with peasants on a country road and other resting (18x25cm-7x10in) pen ink grey wash over black chk. 10-Mar-3 Sotheby's, Amsterdam #46

£276 $436 €400 Village with farmstead, church, trees and figures. s.d.1781 verso chk W/C. 4-Apr-3 Venator & Hansten, Koln #1540

LIENDER, Pieter Jan van (attrib) (1727-1779) Dutch

Works on paper

£828 $1275 €1300 View of Oudeschans, Amsterdam with Montelbaanstoren to the right (23x37cm-9x15in) i.verso black chk pen grey ink brown grey wash. 3-Sep-2 Christie's, Amsterdam #84/R

LIER, Adolf (1826-1882) German

£629 $981 €1000 Peasant ploughing (16x20cm-6x8in) s. paper on panel. 11-Oct-2 Winterberg, Heidelberg #630/R

£714 $1064 €1100 Boy and cows on forest path (28x30cm-11x12in) mono. paper on canvas. 26-Jun-2 Neumeister, Munich #791

£755 $1177 €1200 Cattle in landscape (24x35cm-9x14in) board. 11-Oct-2 Winterberg, Heidelberg #631/R

£755 $1208 €1133 Sunset over shore landscape (19x32cm-7x13in) panel prov. 17-Mar-3 Philippe Schuler, Zurich #4626/R (S.FR 1600)

£884 $1406 €1300 Landscape with pond (24x19cm-9x7in) s. 25-Feb-3 Dorotheum, Vienna #84/R

£1154 $1788 €1800 Stormy landscape with shepherd and flock at the bank of a lake (31x50cm-12x20in) s. canvas on canvas lit. 4-Dec-2 Neumeister, Munich #808/R est:2000

£2397 $3740 €3500 Harvest time (59x88cm-23x35in) s. 11-Apr-3 Winterberg, Heidelberg #470/R est:4800

£3038 $4739 €4800 Lake on summer evening (44x94cm-17x37in) s. 14-Sep-2 Weidler, Nurnberg #303/R est:4800

£3165 $4905 €5000 Coastal landscape at dusk (65x127cm-26x50in) s. 25-Sep-2 Neumeister, Munich #636/R est:6500

£5195 $7740 €8000 Corn harvest (18x25cm-7x10in) s. panel. 26-Jun-2 Neumeister, Munich #790/R est:1500

LIES, Jozef H (1821-1865) Belgian

£5256 $8147 €8200 Alchimiste (50x63cm-20x25in) s.d.58 panel. 5-Dec-2 Gros & Delettrez, Paris #82 est:4600

LIESEGANG, Helmut (1858-1945) German

£540 $863 €750 Flowers in bloom in front of farmstead (25x28cm-10x11in) s. board. 17-May-3 Lempertz, Koln #1427

£759 $1200 €1200 Sunny village church in spring (56x60cm-22x24in) s. 29-Nov-2 Sigalas, Stuttgart #1242/R

£962 $1510 €1500 Fishing boats on Dutch canal (109x95cm-43x37in) s. 21-Nov-2 Van Ham, Cologne #1754 est:2200

£1282 $2026 €2000 Flock of sheep on tree lined track (43x53cm-17x21in) s. panel. 16-Nov-2 Lempertz, Koln #1525/R est:2500

£1923 $3019 €3000 Village idyll (38x27cm-15x11in) s. panel. 21-Nov-2 Van Ham, Cologne #1753/R est:2500

£1923 $3038 €3000 Market place in Flemish town (48x58cm-19x23in) s. 16-Nov-2 Lempertz, Koln #1526/R est:3500

LIESKE, Karl (attrib) (1816-1878) German

£545 $855 €850 Alpine landscape (26x22cm-10x9in) mono. 21-Nov-2 Van Ham, Cologne #1755

LIESLER, Josef (1912-) Czechoslovakian?

Works on paper

£371 $587 €557 Still life with apples (55x49cm-22x19in) s.d.59 mixed media cardboard. 30-Nov-2 Dorotheum, Prague #155 (C.KR 18000)

LIETZMANN, Hans (1872-?) German

£272 $433 €400 Italian mountain village in the evening (36x45cm-14x18in) s.d.1929 double-sided. 28-Mar-3 Bolland & Marotz, Bremen #489

LIEVENS, Jan (attrib) (1607-1674) Dutch

£1549 $2447 €2400 Portrait of bearded man (63x57cm-25x22in) 20-Dec-2 Tajan, Paris #59/R est:4000

LIEVIN, Jacques (1850-?) French

£2581 $4077 €4000 Trois-mats au port (33x46cm-13x18in) s. 18-Dec-2 Ferri, Paris #88/R

LIEW, Jerry (fl.1980s) Australian

£357 $568 €536 Second time around (134x204cm-53x80in) prov. 23-Mar-3 Goodman, Sydney #30/R (A.D 950)

LIGARE, David (attrib) (1945-) American

Works on paper

£396 $650 €594 December 21st 1967 (48x43cm-19x17in) s. W/C prov. 9-Feb-3 William Jenack, New York #191

LIGERON, Rene (1880-?) French

£1100 $1837 €1650 Paris from the banks of the Seine (11x16cm-4x6in) s. panel. 18-Jun-3 Christie's, Kensington #14/R est:800-1200

LIGNIER, James Camille (fl.1880-1914) French

£719 $1179 €1100 By the sea (16x22cm-6x9in) s.i. 9-Feb-3 Bukowskis, Helsinki #418/R

LIGON, Glenn (1960-) American

£3871 $6000 €5807 Study for white series (84x63cm-33x25in) oilstick painted 1996 prov. 26-Sep-2 Christie's, Rockefeller NY #830/R est:6000-8000

LIGOZZI, Jacopo (attrib) (1547-1632) Italian
Works on paper
£16892 $26351 €25000 Christ soutenu par les anges (35x22cm-14x9in) i. pen ink htd white prov.exhib. 27-Mar-3 Christie's, Paris #6/R

LIGTELIJN, Evert Jan (1893-1977) Dutch
£449 $704 €700 Flying ducks (60x50cm-24x20in) s. 25-Nov-2 Glerum, Amsterdam #66
£510 $785 €800 De Hooiberg, Aruba - man on a donkey on a rocky shore (50x60cm-20x24in) st.sig.i. plywood exhib. 3-Sep-2 Christie's, Amsterdam #215/R
£1118 $1812 €1700 View on the River Vecht near Weesp (25x40cm-10x16in) s.i.d.20.8.33 plywood prov. 21-Jan-3 Christie's, Amsterdam #299/R est:1000-1500
£1250 $2063 €1800 Reading to the children (80x100cm-31x39in) s.d.1929. 1-Jul-3 Christie's, Amsterdam #117/R est:1800-2200

LIHL, Heinrich (1690-1756) German
£1208 $1945 €1800 Hunting still life with three bittern hanging and a woodcock on a table (77x52cm-30x20in) prov. 18-Feb-3 Sotheby's, Amsterdam #937/R est:2500-3500
£1745 $2809 €2600 Hunting still life with a godwit (46x36cm-18x14in) 18-Feb-3 Sotheby's, Amsterdam #939/R est:2000-3000
£2148 $3458 €3200 Hunting still life with a lark and two other birds (45x30cm-18x12in) 18-Feb-3 Sotheby's, Amsterdam #942/R est:2000-3000
£2685 $4322 €4000 Hunting still life with woodcock, a hoopoe and other birds (54x38cm-21x15in) 18-Feb-3 Sotheby's, Amsterdam #936/R est:1500-2000
£3600 $6012 €5220 Still life of two hung ducks (75x85cm-30x33in) i.d.1749. 8-Jul-3 Sotheby's, Olympia #469/R est:1500-2000
£3691 $5942 €5500 Hunting still life with a snipe (42x40cm-17x16in) i.d.1748. 18-Feb-3 Sotheby's, Amsterdam #935/R est:2000-3000
£3691 $5942 €5500 Hunting still life with a snipe (42x41cm-17x16in) i.d.1742. 18-Feb-3 Sotheby's, Amsterdam #941/R est:2000-3000

LILANGA DI NYAMA, Georges (1944-) African
£437 $681 €656 Composition (30x60cm-12x24in) cycling paint masonite prov. 20-Nov-2 Fischer, Luzern #2172/R (S.FR 1000)
£1921 $2997 €2882 Composition (60x60cm-24x24in) cycle paint masonite prov. 20-Nov-2 Fischer, Luzern #1137/R est:3000-3600 (S.FR 4400)

LILIO, Andrea (1555-1610) Italian
Works on paper
£1392 $2200 €2200 St Jean l'Evangeliste assis sur des nuages (14x12cm-6x5in) black chk pen brown ink brown wash. 27-Nov-2 Christie's, Paris #40/R est:2000-3000

LILJEBLADH, Birgitta (1924-) Swedish
£295 $478 €428 Landscape in Bohuslan (65x50cm-26x20in) s.d.58. 25-May-3 Uppsala Auktionskammare, Uppsala #316 (S.KR 3800)
£315 $511 €473 Tallulah (62x54cm-24x21in) s.d.80 canvas on panel. 3-Feb-3 Lilla Bukowskis, Stockholm #263 (S.KR 4400)
£325 $510 €488 Figure (46x50cm-18x20in) s.d.66 panel. 16-Dec-2 Lilla Bukowskis, Stockholm #47 (S.KR 4600)
£339 $532 €509 Flowers (39x44cm-15x17in) s.d.65 canvas on panel. 16-Dec-2 Lilla Bukowskis, Stockholm #48 (S.KR 4800)
£367 $576 €551 Orange blossom (60x60cm-24x24in) s.d.1955 canvas on panel. 16-Dec-2 Lilla Bukowskis, Stockholm #217 (S.KR 5200)
£401 $650 €602 Wild roses in blue jug (70x65cm-28x26in) s.d.60 canvas on board. 3-Feb-3 Lilla Bukowskis, Stockholm #20 (S.KR 5600)
£430 $676 €645 Flowers (45x55cm-18x22in) s.d.1965. 16-Dec-2 Lilla Bukowskis, Stockholm #46 (S.KR 6100)
£466 $731 €699 Garden (67x58cm-26x23in) s.d.1953. 16-Dec-2 Lilla Bukowskis, Stockholm #215 (S.KR 6600)
£631 $997 €947 Still life of jug, knife and apple (58x72cm-23x28in) s.d.1954. 30-Nov-2 Goteborg Auktionsverk, Sweden #571/R (S.KR 9000)

LILJEFORS, Bruno (1860-1939) Swedish
£638 $989 €957 Coastal cliffs (18x32cm-7x13in) panel. 8-Dec-2 Uppsala Auktionskammare, Uppsala #174 (S.KR 9000)
£652 $991 €978 Landscape with church (31x48cm-12x19in) s. 16-Aug-2 Lilla Bukowskis, Stockholm #491 (S.KR 9500)
£811 $1346 €1176 Study of model bathing (28x43cm-11x17in) s.i.d.1906 canvas on panel. 16-Jun-3 Lilla Bukowskis, Stockholm #543 (S.KR 10500)
£965 $1602 €1399 Spring landscape, boggy field study (20x29cm-8x11in) s. panel. 16-Jun-3 Lilla Bukowskis, Stockholm #302 (S.KR 12500)
£1647 $2504 €2471 Landscape with fence (50x68cm-20x27in) st.verso. 16-Aug-2 Lilla Bukowskis, Stockholm #158 est:30000 (S.KR 24000)
£1647 $2504 €2471 Mountain slope, Norrland (50x72cm-20x28in) s.d.91 exhib. 16-Aug-2 Lilla Bukowskis, Stockholm #690 est:30000-35000 (S.KR 24000)
£1702 $2638 €2553 Study of fox (25x34cm-10x13in) canvas on panel. 3-Dec-2 Bukowskis, Stockholm #113/R est:30000-35000 (S.KR 24000)
£1707 $2765 €2475 The artist's wife Signe (26x21cm-10x8in) s. panel oval prov. 25-May-3 Uppsala Auktionskammare, Uppsala #127/R est:25000-30000 (S.KR 22000)
£1807 $2963 €2620 Landscape with waterway and cattle grazing (50x65cm-20x26in) stamped verso. 4-Jun-3 AB Stockholms Auktionsverk #2094/R est:25000-30000 (S.KR 23000)
£1835 $2881 €2753 Female mallard swimming (22x28cm-9x11in) st.verso panel. 16-Dec-2 Lilla Bukowskis, Stockholm #875 est:15000-18000 (S.KR 26000)
£2317 $3846 €3360 Mountain slope, Norrland (50x70cm-20x28in) s.d.91. 16-Jun-3 Lilla Bukowskis, Stockholm #1002 est:35000-40000 (S.KR 30000)
£2837 $4397 €4256 Eiderducks in flight (75x95cm-30x37in) sketch. 4-Dec-2 AB Stockholms Auktionsverk #1651/R est:50000-60000 (S.KR 40000)
£3271 $5201 €4907 Ducks in flight (68x100cm-27x39in) stamped verso. 3-Mar-3 Lilla Bukowskis, Stockholm #165 est:40000-50000 (S.KR 44000)
£4034 $6535 €5849 Twilight landscape with family of foxes (18x24cm-7x9in) s.d.81 panel. 26-May-3 Bukowskis, Stockholm #53/R est:70000-80000 (S.KR 52000)
£4255 $6596 €6383 Winter landscape with hunter and dog (52x43cm-20x17in) init. prov. 4-Dec-2 AB Stockholms Auktionsverk #1774/R est:50000-60000 (S.KR 60000)
£4479 $7435 €6495 Winter landscape with hare (35x50cm-14x20in) s. 16-Jun-3 Lilla Bukowskis, Stockholm #954 est:50000 (S.KR 58000)
£4965 $8043 €7199 Pair of mallards (50x80cm-20x31in) s.d.1920 prov. 26-May-3 Bukowskis, Stockholm #53a/R est:100000-125000 (S.KR 64000)
£5106 $7915 €7659 Fox in snowy landscape (58x84cm-23x33in) s.d.1931. 3-Dec-2 Bukowskis, Stockholm #355/R est:100000-125000 (S.KR 72000)
£5275 $8546 €7649 Fox by den (60x80cm-24x31in) s.d.1918. 25-May-3 Uppsala Auktionskammare, Uppsala #179/R est:80000-100000 (S.KR 68000)
£5390 $8355 €8085 Leaping hare (52x74cm-20x29in) s.d.1928. 3-Dec-2 Bukowskis, Stockholm #205/R est:100000-150000 (S.KR 76000)
£5741 $9300 €8324 Fox in snowy landscape (35x50cm-14x20in) s. 26-May-3 Bukowskis, Stockholm #113/R est:80000-100000 (S.KR 74000)
£6028 $9344 €9042 Dogs hunting fox (60x80cm-24x31in) s.d.1918. 4-Dec-2 AB Stockholms Auktionsverk #1573/R est:50000-60000 (S.KR 85000)
£6051 $9803 €8774 Winter landscape with fox and blackgrouse (35x51cm-14x20in) s.d.1933. 26-May-3 Bukowskis, Stockholm #61/R est:80000-100000 (S.KR 78000)
£6383 $9894 €9575 Seagull on rocks (100x60cm-39x24in) init. prov. 4-Dec-2 AB Stockholms Auktionsverk #1726/R est:100000-125000 (S.KR 90000)
£6383 $9894 €9575 Autumn landscape with elk (35x50cm-14x20in) s. 4-Dec-2 AB Stockholms Auktionsverk #1731/R est:50000-60000 (S.KR 90000)
£7092 $10993 €10638 Boy in artist's studio (46x35cm-18x14in) s.i.d.82 canvas on panel. 3-Dec-2 Bukowskis, Stockholm #29/R est:100000-125000 (S.KR 100000)
£7092 $10993 €10638 Wild geese in flight over the marshes (70x100cm-28x39in) s.d.1926. 4-Dec-2 AB Stockholms Auktionsverk #1652/R est:125000-150000 (S.KR 100000)
£7801 $12092 €11702 Fox and hounds in winter landscape (35x50cm-14x20in) s. 3-Dec-2 Bukowskis, Stockholm #108/R est:80000-100000 (S.KR 110000)
£7801 $12092 €11702 Swans in flight over water (35x50cm-14x20in) s. 4-Dec-2 AB Stockholms Auktionsverk #1572/R est:100000-125000 (S.KR 110000)
£8511 $13191 €12767 Winter landscape with fox and blackgrouse (35x50cm-14x20in) s. 4-Dec-2 AB Stockholms Auktionsverk #1773/R est:100000-125000 (S.KR 120000)
£8534 $13825 €12374 Summer landscape with hare by fence (65x90cm-26x35in) s.d.1926. 26-May-3 Bukowskis, Stockholm #60/R est:100000-125000 (S.KR 110000)
£8652 $13411 €12978 Fox hunting birds (35x50cm-14x20in) s. 3-Dec-2 Bukowskis, Stockholm #107/R est:120000-140000 (S.KR 122000)
£8652 $13411 €12978 Blackgrouse in snow (58x83cm-23x33in) s.d.1928. 3-Dec-2 Bukowskis, Stockholm #354/R est:120000-140000 (S.KR 122000)
£9310 $15081 €13500 Geese in wet landscape (62x84cm-24x33in) s.d.1929. 26-May-3 Bukowskis, Stockholm #114/R est:150000-175000 (S.KR 120000)
£9427 $15460 €13669 Winter landscape with hare (35x50cm-14x20in) s. 4-Jun-3 AB Stockholms Auktionsverk #2319/R est:120000-150000 (S.KR 120000)

£9574 $14840 €14361 Winter landscape with dogs and hunter holding dead fox (65x80cm-26x31in) s.d.1924. 8-Dec-2 Uppsala Auktionskammare, Uppsala #173/R est:150000-200000 (S.KR 135000)
£9929 $15390 €14894 Mallards by frozen watercourse (60x90cm-24x35in) s.d.1918. 3-Dec-2 Bukowskis, Stockholm #204/R est:150000-175000 (S.KR 140000)
£9955 $16127 €14933 Winter landscape with hare (55x80cm-22x31in) s.d.1922. 26-May-3 Grev Wedels Plass, Oslo #71/R est:100000-150000 (N.KR 110000)
£10861 $17595 €15748 Summer landscape with fox in forest (70x100cm-28x39in) s. 25-May-3 Uppsala Auktionskammare, Uppsala #174/R est:120000-140000 (S.KR 140000)
£11702 $18138 €17553 Winter landscape with fox by fence (70x99cm-28x39in) s.d.1938. 3-Dec-2 Bukowskis, Stockholm #106/R est:150000-175000 (S.KR 165000)
£12413 $20109 €17999 Harriers and fox (100x140cm-39x55in) s.d.1929 exhib. 26-May-3 Bukowskis, Stockholm #112/R est:175000-200000 (S.KR 160000)
£12766 $19787 €19149 Coastal landscape with mallards in flight (70x100cm-28x39in) s.d.1910. 4-Dec-2 AB Stockholms Auktionsverk #1720/R est:175000-200000 (S.KR 180000)
£13475 $20887 €20213 Mallards (70x120cm-28x47in) s.d.1931. 3-Dec-2 Bukowskis, Stockholm #211/R est:200000-225000 (S.KR 190000)
£15248 $23635 €22872 Mallards by reeds (80x100cm-31x39in) s.d.1897. 3-Dec-2 Bukowskis, Stockholm #212/R est:250000-300000 (S.KR 215000)
£16889 $27698 €24489 Wooded landscape with elk (100x75cm-39x30in) s.d.1929. 4-Jun-3 AB Stockholms Auktionsverk #2190/R est:225000-250000 (S.KR 215000)
£17730 $27482 €26595 Retrieving (61x75cm-24x30in) s.d.1924. 3-Dec-2 Bukowskis, Stockholm #353/R est:120000-140000 (S.KR 250000)
£19149 $29681 €28724 Blackgrouse in winter landscape (70x100cm-28x39in) s.d.1915. 4-Dec-2 AB Stockholms Auktionsverk #1713/R est:200000-300000 (S.KR 270000)
£19395 $31420 €28123 Winter fox in landscape (165x200cm-65x79in) s.d.1916. 26-May-3 Bukowskis, Stockholm #54/R est:250000-300000 (S.KR 250000)
£21334 $34562 €30934 Female mallard and chicks (52x92cm-20x36in) s.d.1905. 26-May-3 Bukowskis, Stockholm #62/R est:225000-250000 (S.KR 275000)
£24352 $39937 €35310 Sparrows among thorns (17x26cm-7x10in) s.d.86 panel prov. 4-Jun-3 AB Stockholms Auktionsverk #2148/R est:300000-350000 (S.KR 310000)
£24823 $38475 €37235 Landscape with swans in flight (93x163cm-37x64in) s.d.1918 prov. 4-Dec-2 AB Stockholms Auktionsverk #1656/R est:300000-350000 (S.KR 350000)
£26241 $40674 €39362 Long-tailed ducks (76x180cm-30x71in) s.d.1913 exhib. 3-Dec-2 Bukowskis, Stockholm #114/R est:300000-350000 (S.KR 370000)
£28369 $43972 €42554 Hunter with harriers (120x178cm-47x70in) s.d.1915. 3-Dec-2 Bukowskis, Stockholm #109/R est:400000-500000 (S.KR 400000)
£29078 $45071 €43617 Men playing cricket - summer in Visby (148x72cm-58x28in) s.d.88. 4-Dec-2 AB Stockholms Auktionsverk #1789/R est:300000-400000 (S.KR 410000)
£30063 $47500 €43591 Golden eagle attacking a hare (163x198cm-64x78in) s. 26-Jul-3 Coeur d'Alene, Hayden #191/R est:60000-90000
£34752 $53865 €52128 Capercaillies displaying (50x36cm-20x14in) s.d.c.1885 lit. 3-Dec-2 Bukowskis, Stockholm #207/R est:500000-600000 (S.KR 490000)
£50427 $81691 €73119 Swans in flight (78x151cm-31x59in) s.d.1910 exhib.prov. 26-May-3 Bukowskis, Stockholm #116/R est:700000-800000 (S.KR 650000)
£58916 $96622 €85428 Peasant hunter in snowy landscape (43x33cm-17x13in) s.d.90 exhib. 4-Jun-3 AB Stockholms Auktionsverk #2276/R est:850000-900000 (S.KR 750000)
£287234 $445213 €430851 Goshawk and collar-dove (121x77cm-48x30in) s.d.85 prov. 3-Dec-2 Bukowskis, Stockholm #105/R (S.KR 4050000)

Sculpture

£1596 $2473 €2394 Working-day (15cm-6in) s. green pat.bronze st.f.O Meyers. 3-Dec-2 Bukowskis, Stockholm #70/R est:18000-20000 (S.KR 22500)

Works on paper

£268 $426 €402 Seagull seen through Lulles telescope (19x13cm-7x5in) mono.i.d.18 april 1900 dr. 2-Mar-3 Uppsala Auktionskammare, Uppsala #213 (S.KR 3600)
£587 $974 €851 Small birds (3x7cm-1x3in) s.d.15 nov 86 Indian ink. 16-Jun-3 Lilla Bukowskis, Stockholm #344 (S.KR 7600)
£1059 $1662 €1589 Mountain landscape with flock of reindeer (12x15cm-5x6in) s. gouache W/C. 16-Dec-2 Lilla Bukowskis, Stockholm #4/R est:20000-25000 (S.KR 15000)
£1257 $2061 €1823 Winter landscape with soldiers (43x38cm-17x15in) s.d.1902 Indian ink wash. 4-Jun-3 AB Stockholms Auktionsverk #2344/R est:10000-12000 (S.KR 16000)
£1614 $2518 €2421 Bird and bee (29x22cm-11x9in) s. W/C. 5-Aug-2 Rasmussen, Vejle #117/R est:15000-20000 (D.KR 19000)
£5499 $9018 €7974 Winter landscape with hunter and dogs (30x48cm-12x19in) s.d.91 W/C. 4-Jun-3 AB Stockholms Auktionsverk #2228/R est:70000-80000 (S.KR 70000)
£9929 $15390 €14894 Studies of duck (34x20cm-13x8in) s. W/C. 3-Dec-2 Bukowskis, Stockholm #299/R est:80000-100000 (S.KR 140000)
£15516 $25136 €22498 Partridge by nest (37x51cm-15x20in) s.d.94 Indian ink W/C. 26-May-3 Bukowskis, Stockholm #58/R est:125000-150000 (S.KR 200000)
£26950 $41773 €40425 Jeppe (50x35cm-20x14in) s.d.86 Indian ink. 3-Dec-2 Bukowskis, Stockholm #208/R est:225000-250000 (S.KR 380000)

LILJEFORS, Lindorm (1909-1985) Swedish

£384 $584 €576 Wooded landscape with hare (41x57cm-16x22in) s.d.79 panel. 16-Aug-2 Lilla Bukowskis, Stockholm #34 (S.KR 5600)
£384 $584 €576 Ducks in flight (40x56cm-16x22in) s.d.80 panel. 16-Aug-2 Lilla Bukowskis, Stockholm #36 (S.KR 5600)
£405 $616 €608 Pair of golden-eyes (45x44cm-18x17in) acrylic canvas on panel exhib. 16-Aug-2 Lilla Bukowskis, Stockholm #914 (S.KR 5900)
£412 $626 €618 Hole in the ice (33x41cm-13x16in) s.d.60 panel. 16-Aug-2 Lilla Bukowskis, Stockholm #131 (S.KR 6000)
£453 $689 €680 Dog by red cottage (46x56cm-18x22in) s.d.39 panel. 16-Aug-2 Lilla Bukowskis, Stockholm #35 (S.KR 6600)
£456 $720 €684 Winter landscape with fox (27x35cm-11x14in) s.d.69. 30-Nov-2 Goteborg Auktionsverk, Sweden #159/R (S.KR 6500)
£466 $731 €699 Ducks (33x45cm-13x18in) s. panel. 16-Dec-2 Lilla Bukowskis, Stockholm #429 (S.KR 6600)
£511 $837 €741 Wooded landscape with elk cow (41x56cm-16x22in) s.d.60 panel. 4-Jun-3 AB Stockholms Auktionsverk #2143/R (S.KR 6500)
£522 $820 €783 Bear walking (41x37cm-16x15in) s.i.d.62 panel. 16-Dec-2 Lilla Bukowskis, Stockholm #755 (S.KR 7400)
£621 $1005 €900 Fox and mallard (33x45cm-13x18in) s.d.81 panel. 25-May-3 Uppsala Auktionskammare, Uppsala #185 (S.KR 8000)
£621 $1005 €900 Blackcocks (46x54cm-18x21in) s.d.41 panel. 25-May-3 Uppsala Auktionskammare, Uppsala #194/R (S.KR 8000)
£630 $996 €945 Spring landscape with magpies (46x54cm-18x21in) s.d.43 panel. 16-Nov-2 Crafoord, Lund #33/R (S.KR 9000)
£723 $1185 €1048 Ducks in flight (46x55cm-18x22in) s.d.50 panel. 4-Jun-3 AB Stockholms Auktionsverk #2093/R (S.KR 9200)
£737 $1194 €1069 Landscape with birds (60x73cm-24x29in) s.d.46 panel. 25-May-3 Uppsala Auktionskammare, Uppsala #195/R (S.KR 9500)
£776 $1257 €1125 Landscape with deer (47x55cm-19x22in) s.d.59 panel. 25-May-3 Uppsala Auktionskammare, Uppsala #187/R (S.KR 10000)
£812 $1274 €1218 Winter by the sea (34x50cm-13x20in) s.i.d.81 panel. 16-Dec-2 Lilla Bukowskis, Stockholm #754 (S.KR 11500)
£1021 $1675 €1480 Winter landscape with fox in sunshine (60x73cm-24x29in) s.d.45 panel. 4-Jun-3 AB Stockholms Auktionsverk #2103/R (S.KR 13000)
£1064 $1649 €1596 Pheasant shoot (46x55cm-18x22in) s.d.57 panel. 8-Dec-2 Uppsala Auktionskammare, Uppsala #184/R est:10000-12000 (S.KR 15000)
£1277 $1979 €1916 Sunny early spring landscape with magpies on top of oak tree (51x36cm-20x14in) s.d.41. 4-Dec-2 AB Stockholms Auktionsverk #1583/R est:20000-25000 (S.KR 18000)
£1348 $2089 €2022 Red-backed shrike in evening sunshine (56x46cm-22x18in) s.d.52 panel. 8-Dec-2 Uppsala Auktionskammare, Uppsala #185/R est:6000-8000 (S.KR 19000)
£3901 $6046 €5852 Wooded landscape with elks and elkhounds (90x120cm-35x47in) s.d.41. 4-Dec-2 AB Stockholms Auktionsverk #1597/R est:30000-40000 (S.KR 55000)

LILJELUND, Arvid (1844-1899) Finnish

£7042 $11338 €10000 Cottage interior (34x43cm-13x17in) s. 10-May-3 Bukowskis, Helsinki #164/R est:10000-12000

LILLONI, Umberto (1898-1980) Italian

£3797 $5924 €6000 Portrait of lady (56x46cm-22x18in) s.d.1921. 14-Sep-2 Meeting Art, Vercelli #977/R
£3819 $6073 €5500 Spring (20x30cm-8x12in) s. painted 1976 lit. 1-May-3 Meeting Art, Vercelli #352
£3851 $6008 €5700 Autumn on the Generoso (30x40cm-12x16in) s. painted 1968. 28-Mar-3 Farsetti, Prato #351/R
£4167 $6458 €6500 Lake Maggiore (40x50cm-16x20in) s. painted 1968. 4-Dec-2 Finarte, Milan #296/R est:6000
£6536 $10458 €10000 Costanza lake (50x70cm-20x28in) s. s.i.d.1968 verso. 4-Jan-3 Meeting Art, Vercelli #526 est:10000

£9615 $15096 €15000 Bardonecchia (70x100cm-28x39in) s.i.d.1951. 23-Nov-2 Meeting Art, Vercelli #248/R est:15000
£10759 $16785 €17000 Landscape by lake (60x80cm-24x31in) s. board painted 1946. 14-Sep-2 Meeting Art, Vercelli #988/R

LILLYWHITE, Raphael (1891-1958) American
£943 $1500 €1415 Cowboys (46x61cm-18x24in) s. canvasboard. 5-Mar-3 Sotheby's, New York #160/R est:3000-5000

LIMBACH, Russell (1904-1971) American
Works on paper
£288 $470 €418 Tenement City view (25x36cm-10x14in) W/C. 30-May-3 Aspire, Cleveland #140/R

LIMBORCH, Michiel D van (attrib) (fl.1647-1675) Dutch
£2819 $4538 €4200 Musical party in an interior (42x55cm-17x22in) bears sig panel prov.lit. 18-Feb-3 Sotheby's, Amsterdam #211/R est:4000-6000

LIMES AMBROS, Luis (1922-) Spanish
Works on paper
£323 $510 €500 Amused boy (42x33cm-17x13in) s.d.97 pastel s.i.d.verso. 17-Dec-2 Durán, Madrid #91/R

LIMNELL, Per Emanuel (1764-1861) Swedish
Works on paper
£393 $644 €570 Olof Skotkonung and Tony Lagman at Uppsala Court (47x58cm-19x23in) i. verso Indian ink wash W/C. 4-Jun-3 AB Stockholms Auktionsverk #2212/R (S.KR 5000)

LIMOUSE, Roger (1894-1990) French
£637 $994 €1000 Orientales (37x45cm-15x18in) panel. 10-Nov-2 Eric Pillon, Calais #196/R
£980 $1608 €1500 Nature morte a la pipe (55x65cm-22x26in) s. painted c.1930. 9-Feb-3 Anaf, Lyon #179
£3800 $6042 €5700 Contre-jour, nature morte (117x89cm-46x35in) s.d.33 s.i.d.1933 verso. 20-Mar-3 Sotheby's, Olympia #33/R est:1600-2000
£6575 $10323 €9600 Le port de Sanary (73x94cm-29x37in) s.d. 21-Apr-3 Rabourdin & Choppin de Janvry, Paris #155/R est:10000-12000

LIN FENGMIAN (1900-1991) Chinese
£271950 $448718 €394328 Bountiful catch (78x78cm-31x31in) s.d.1960 prov.exhib. 6-Jul-3 Christie's, Hong Kong #131/R est:2400000-3000000 (HK.D 3500000)

Works on paper
£625 $1044 €906 Approaching a mountain temple (32x32cm-13x13in) s. W/C. 17-Jun-3 Waddingtons, Toronto #1715/R est:1500-2000 (C.D 1400)
£1339 $2237 €1942 Riverside pavilion (39x47cm-15x19in) s. W/C. 17-Jun-3 Waddingtons, Toronto #1716/R est:3000-4000 (C.D 3000)
£2232 $3728 €3236 Cormorant fishing (62x66cm-24x26in) s. W/C. 17-Jun-3 Waddingtons, Toronto #1718/R est:5000-7500 (C.D 5000)
£2455 $4100 €3560 Riverside willows (56x66cm-22x26in) s. W/C. 17-Jun-3 Waddingtons, Toronto #1717/R est:6000-9000 (C.D 5500)
£2679 $4473 €3885 Park pavilion (60x67cm-24x26in) s. W/C. 17-Jun-3 Waddingtons, Toronto #1721/R est:6000-9000 (C.D 6000)
£3500 $5460 €5250 Teo Beijing opera figures performing the sword dance (53x43cm-21x17in) ink W/C. 10-Sep-2 Bonhams, New Bond Street #191/R est:3000-4000
£3571 $5964 €5178 Village in mountains (66x66cm-26x26in) s. W/C. 17-Jun-3 Waddingtons, Toronto #1719/R est:7500-10000 (C.D 8000)
£4274 $7051 €6197 Opera figures (33x32cm-13x13in) s. ink scroll two. 6-Jul-3 Christie's, Hong Kong #376/R est:40000-50000 (HK.D 55000)
£4878 $7707 €7317 Lady with lotus (32x32cm-13x13in) s. ink col. 28-Apr-3 Sotheby's, Hong Kong #504/R est:60000-80000 (HK.D 60000)
£4878 $7707 €7317 Hair dressing (33x33cm-13x13in) s. ink col. 28-Apr-3 Sotheby's, Hong Kong #505/R est:60000-80000 (HK.D 60000)
£5691 $8992 €8537 Wild goose (32x32cm-13x13in) s. ink col. 28-Apr-3 Sotheby's, Hong Kong #506/R est:70000-90000 (HK.D 70000)
£6027 $10065 €8739 Beijing opera actors (64x64cm-25x25in) s. W/C. 17-Jun-3 Waddingtons, Toronto #1720/R est:7500-10000 (C.D 13500)
£6993 $11538 €10140 Farm house (69x69cm-27x27in) s. ink scroll. 6-Jul-3 Christie's, Hong Kong #229/R est:100000-120000 (HK.D 90000)
£6993 $11538 €10140 Fishing pond (37x64cm-15x25in) s. ink scroll. 6-Jul-3 Christie's, Hong Kong #323/R est:65000-80000 (HK.D 90000)
£7770 $12821 €11267 Snowscape (66x66cm-26x26in) s. ink scroll. 6-Jul-3 Christie's, Hong Kong #227/R est:60000-80000 (HK.D 100000)
£9324 $15385 €13520 Still life (67x68cm-26x27in) s. ink scroll prov. 6-Jul-3 Christie's, Hong Kong #373/R est:100000-120000 (HK.D 120000)
£10101 $16667 €14646 Forest (66x67cm-26x26in) s. ink scroll prov. 6-Jul-3 Christie's, Hong Kong #374/R est:100000-120000 (HK.D 130000)
£10878 $17949 €15773 Summer (66x67cm-26x26in) s. ink scroll. 6-Jul-3 Christie's, Hong Kong #228/R est:100000-120000 (HK.D 140000)
£10878 $17949 €15773 Fisherman (66x66cm-26x26in) s. ink scroll. 6-Jul-3 Christie's, Hong Kong #320/R est:120000-150000 (HK.D 140000)
£10878 $17949 €15773 Geese and reed (57x67cm-22x26in) s. ink scroll. 6-Jul-3 Christie's, Hong Kong #322/R est:150000-200000 (HK.D 140000)
£12195 $19268 €18293 Egrets (48x68cm-19x27in) s.d.1977 ink col. 28-Apr-3 Sotheby's, Hong Kong #507/R est:150000-200000 (HK.D 150000)
£14763 $24359 €21406 Egrets (66x67cm-26x26in) s. ink scroll. 6-Jul-3 Christie's, Hong Kong #321/R est:120000-180000 (HK.D 190000)
£15447 $24407 €23171 Still life (66x66cm-26x26in) s. ink col. 28-Apr-3 Sotheby's, Hong Kong #509/R est:120000-150000 (HK.D 190000)
£15540 $25641 €22533 Opera figures (66x67cm-26x26in) s. ink scroll. 6-Jul-3 Christie's, Hong Kong #230/R est:120000-160000 (HK.D 200000)
£15540 $25641 €22533 Nude (40x49cm-16x19in) s. ink scroll lit. 6-Jul-3 Christie's, Hong Kong #326/R est:150000-200000 (HK.D 200000)
£15540 $25641 €22533 Ladies (33x32cm-13x13in) s. ink scroll set of four. 6-Jul-3 Christie's, Hong Kong #377/R est:80000-100000 (HK.D 200000)
£18648 $30769 €27040 Steel foundry (79x78cm-31x31in) s. ink scroll. 6-Jul-3 Christie's, Hong Kong #231/R est:200000-250000 (HK.D 240000)
£20202 $33333 €29293 Cherry blossom and birds (54x60cm-21x24in) s. ink scroll. 6-Jul-3 Christie's, Hong Kong #324/R est:150000-200000 (HK.D 260000)
£20325 $32114 €30488 Hydrangea (68x69cm-27x27in) s.d.1977 ink col. 28-Apr-3 Sotheby's, Hong Kong #510/R est:250000-300000 (HK.D 250000)
£23310 $38462 €33800 Sampans storm (64x64cm-25x25in) s. ink scroll. 6-Jul-3 Christie's, Hong Kong #232/R est:200000-250000 (HK.D 300000)
£23577 $37252 €35366 Garden view (34x34cm-13x13in) s.i. ink col. 28-Apr-3 Sotheby's, Hong Kong #508/R est:120000-180000 (HK.D 290000)
£26418 $43590 €38306 Still life (66x64cm-26x25in) s. ink scroll. 6-Jul-3 Christie's, Hong Kong #327/R est:200000-250000 (HK.D 340000)
£34965 $57692 €50699 Village woman. s. ink scroll set of five various sizes prov. 6-Jul-3 Christie's, Hong Kong #375/R est:100000-150000 (HK.D 450000)

LIN FENGMIAN and TANG YUN (20th C) Chinese
Works on paper
£4662 $7692 €6760 Landscape, bamboo (18x48cm-7x19in) s.i. ink fan. 6-Jul-3 Christie's, Hong Kong #357/R est:35000-45000 (HK.D 60000)

LIN HUKUI (1945-) Chinese
Works on paper
£3497 $5769 €5071 Goldfish (50x93cm-20x37in) s.i. ink scroll. 6-Jul-3 Christie's, Hong Kong #337/R est:50000-70000 (HK.D 45000)

LIN JIYOU (1918-1984) Chinese
Works on paper
£362 $594 €500 Ram (77x83cm-30x33in) i. seal Indian ink col hanging scroll. 30-May-3 Dr Fritz Nagel, Stuttgart #1160/R
£797 $1307 €1100 Two rabbits (68x45cm-27x18in) i. seal Indian ink col hanging scroll. 30-May-3 Dr Fritz Nagel, Stuttgart #1161/R

LIN LIANG (c.1416-1480) Chinese
Works on paper
£9324 $15385 €13520 Ducks in the shade of willow trees (139x81cm-55x32in) s. ink silk hanging scroll exhib.lit. 6-Jul-3 Christie's, Hong Kong #419/R est:150000-250000 (HK.D 120000)

LIN XIMING (1926-) Chinese
Works on paper
£362 $594 €500 Shore with boats (60x85cm-24x33in) i.d.1985 seals Indian ink col. 30-May-3 Dr Fritz Nagel, Stuttgart #1190/R

LIN YUAN (1913-1991) Chinese
Works on paper
£550 $858 €825 Snow clouds (235x127cm-93x50in) i. ink after Shenren. 10-Sep-2 Bonhams, New Bond Street #175

LIN, Richard (1933-) British
£2300 $3588 €3450 Heatwave 71 (63x63cm-25x25in) oil collage on canvas prov. 27-Mar-3 Christie's, Kensington #668/R est:1500-2000

LINAAE, Paul (1791-1866) Norwegian
£1047 $1644 €1571 Entrance to Langesund (37x52cm-15x20in) 25-Nov-2 Blomqvist, Lysaker #1171/R (N.KR 12000)

LINCE, Marcel de (1886-?) Belgian
£321 $503 €500 Vue de Venise (20x24cm-8x9in) s. cardboard. 11-Dec-2 Hotel des Ventes Mosan, Brussels #273

LINCK, Walter (1903-1975) Swiss
Sculpture
£11354 $17825 €17031 L'oiseau II (117cm-46in) mono. num.3/6 steel iron prov. 25-Nov-2 Sotheby's, Zurich #166/R est:10000-15000 (S.FR 26000)

LINCOLN, Joe (19/20th C) American
Sculpture
£5185 $8400 €7518 Ducks. i. painted carvings exec.c.1920 two. 22-May-3 Sotheby's, New York #743
£5926 $9600 €8593 Ducks. painted carvings exec.c.1920 three. 22-May-3 Sotheby's, New York #745
£7407 $12000 €10740 Ducks. painted carvings exec.c.1930 three. 22-May-3 Sotheby's, New York #746
£8148 $13200 €11815 Ducks. painted carvings exec.c.1930 three. 22-May-3 Sotheby's, New York #744

LINCOLN, Kevin (1941-) Australian
£478 $784 €717 Untitled (83x76cm-33x30in) s.d.76 d.19-20 Nov 76 verso. 4-Jun-3 Deutscher-Menzies, Melbourne #347 (A.D 1200)
£932 $1416 €1398 Bowl (71x56cm-28x22in) s. i.d.17 October 1980 verso. 28-Aug-2 Deutscher-Menzies, Melbourne #390/R est:1500-2000 (A.D 2600)
£1077 $1712 €1616 Still life, grey (96x96cm-38x38in) s. s.i.d.1/11/96 verso prov. 4-Mar-3 Deutscher-Menzies, Melbourne #224/R est:3000-5000 (A.D 2800)
£1143 $1806 €1715 Vessels (61x91cm-24x36in) s. 27-Nov-2 Deutscher-Menzies, Melbourne #161/R est:1500-2500 (A.D 3200)

LIND, A (19/20th C) ?
£3597 $5755 €5000 Captain's painting of the frigate Arvio (30x46cm-12x18in) s.i.d.1895. 17-May-3 Hagelstam, Helsinki #76/R est:2000

LIND, Andreas (1815-1885) Norwegian
Works on paper
£4591 $7530 €6657 Ship's portrait - Freya of Thjome (48x75cm-19x30in) s.i.d.1880 W/C pencil gouache. 2-Jun-3 Blomqvist, Oslo #64/R est:20000-25000 (N.KR 50000)

LIND, Lone (?) Danish?
£410 $651 €615 Elephant (120x100cm-47x39in) s. 10-Mar-3 Rasmussen, Vejle #626 (D.KR 4400)

LIND, Yrsa (1948-) Danish
£429 $669 €644 Composition with divine woman (85x54cm-33x21in) init. 11-Nov-2 Rasmussen, Vejle #147/R (D.KR 5000)
£493 $769 €740 Japanese female figures (100x70cm-39x28in) 5-Aug-2 Rasmussen, Vejle #353/R (D.KR 5800)
£515 $803 €773 Composition with Japanese women (120x38cm-47x15in) s. masonite pair. 11-Nov-2 Rasmussen, Vejle #146/R (D.KR 6000)
£527 $822 €791 Japanese female figure (100x70cm-39x28in) s.d.2001. 5-Aug-2 Rasmussen, Vejle #352/R (D.KR 6200)
£652 $1036 €978 Oriental woman surrounded by flowering fruit trees (80x110cm-31x43in) s. 10-Mar-3 Rasmussen, Vejle #649/R (D.KR 7000)
£746 $1187 €1119 Two Oriental women (110x80cm-43x31in) s. two. 5-May-3 Rasmussen, Vejle #81/R (D.KR 8000)

LINDAU, Dietrich Wilhelm (1799-1862) German
£11565 $18388 €17000 Cattle before the Porta S Paolo and Cestius - Pyramid in Rome (95x125cm-37x49in) s. bears d.1841. 19-Mar-3 Neumeister, Munich #628/R est:2500

LINDAUER, Gottfried (1839-1926) New Zealander
£4573 $6997 €6860 Maori Chief Te Mahunga (76x60cm-30x24in) s.d. prov. 21-Aug-2 Dunbar Sloane, Auckland #33/R est:15000-40000 (NZ.D 15000)
£6316 $9853 €9474 Nireaha Tamaki (68x56cm-27x22in) prov. 27-Mar-3 International Art Centre, Auckland #82/R est:15000-25000 (NZ.D 18000)
£12539 $19561 €18809 Ana rupene and Huria (85x66cm-33x26in) s. 7-Nov-2 International Art Centre, Auckland #75/R est:40000-60000 (NZ.D 40000)

LINDBERG DE GEER, Marianne (1946-) Swedish
£2733 $4263 €4100 Girl and boy (155x153cm-61x60in) init.d.1990 verso. 6-Nov-2 AB Stockholms Auktionsverk #875/R est:20000-25000 (S.KR 39000)

Works on paper
£911 $1421 €1367 Rabbit tales - study in postcoital depression (75x55cm-30x22in) s.verso crayon executed 1998 prov. 6-Nov-2 AB Stockholms Auktionsverk #924/R est:8000-10000 (S.KR 13000)
£1141 $1802 €1712 Rabbit tales - study in postcoital depression (86x66cm-34x26in) crayon prov. 28-Apr-3 Bukowskis, Stockholm #938/R est:6000-8000 (S.KR 15000)

LINDBERG, Alf (1905-1990) Swedish
£372 $587 €558 View from Berzelii street towards Lorensberg's Circus (55x59cm-22x23in) s. 30-Nov-2 Goteborg Auktionsverk, Sweden #572/R (S.KR 5300)
£716 $1160 €1074 Landscape with house (61x85cm-24x33in) s. painted c.1940. 3-Feb-3 Lilla Bukowskis, Stockholm #240 (S.KR 10000)
£877 $1385 €1316 View across rooftops (70x88cm-28x35in) s. 27-Nov-2 Falkkloos, Malmo #77662/R (S.KR 12500)
£1467 $2362 €2201 Interior scene with drapery (99x80cm-39x31in) s. exhib.prov. 7-May-3 AB Stockholms Auktionsverk #852/R est:20000-25000 (S.KR 19000)
£2102 $3280 €3153 Two figures (142x135cm-56x53in) s. painted 1979 lit. 6-Nov-2 AB Stockholms Auktionsverk #707/R est:30000-35000 (S.KR 30000)

LINDBERG, Gustaf (1852-1932) Swedish
Sculpture
£1939 $3142 €2812 Misty (89cm-35in) s. dark pat.bronze. 26-May-3 Bukowskis, Stockholm #298/R est:20000-25000 (S.KR 25000)

LINDBERG, Harald (1901-1976) Swedish
£1051 $1640 €1577 On the skerries, July (25x64cm-10x25in) s. panel. 5-Nov-2 Bukowskis, Stockholm #182/R est:15000-18000 (S.KR 15000)
£3504 $5466 €5256 Gleaming July (54x73cm-21x29in) s.d.1969 exhib. 5-Nov-2 Bukowskis, Stockholm #184/R est:30000-35000 (S.KR 50000)
£5886 $9183 €8829 On guard at twilight (130x190cm-51x75in) s.d.65 exhib.lit. 5-Nov-2 Bukowskis, Stockholm #179/R est:100000-120000 (S.KR 84000)

Works on paper
£535 $835 €803 Breakers (46x56cm-18x22in) s. panel mixed media. 13-Sep-2 Lilla Bukowskis, Stockholm #174 (S.KR 7800)

LINDBERG, Maria (1958-) Swedish
£1051 $1640 €1577 From in front (122x110cm-48x43in) s.d.91 verso varnish panel. 6-Nov-2 AB Stockholms Auktionsverk #796/R est:10000-12000 (S.KR 15000)
£1313 $2114 €1970 Untitled (122x109cm-48x43in) s.d.1991 verso varnish panel. 7-May-3 AB Stockholms Auktionsverk #950/R est:10000-12000 (S.KR 17000)
£1467 $2362 €2201 I'm leaving (80x61cm-31x24in) s.d.95 verso varnish acrylic panel prov. 7-May-3 AB Stockholms Auktionsverk #1061/R est:12000-15000 (S.KR 19000)
£2662 $4205 €3993 Dead girl in arm-chair (105x93cm-41x37in) s.d.91 verso varnish panel prov.lit. 28-Apr-3 Bukowskis, Stockholm #934/R est:15000-20000 (S.KR 35000)

LINDBERGH, Peter (1944-) ?
Photographs
£2532 $4000 €4000 Models for Vogue USA, Brooklyn (33x26cm-13x10in) s.i.d.1991 verso silver gelatin lit.exhib. 28-Nov-2 Villa Grisebach, Berlin #1295/R est:4000-6000

LINDBLOM, Sivert (1931-) Swedish
Sculpture
£1051 $1640 €1577 Untitled (35cm-14in) init.d.1986 num.1/6 pat.bronze st.f.Bergman cire perdue. 6-Nov-2 AB Stockholms Auktionsverk #871/R est:20000-30000 (S.KR 15000)
£2662 $4205 €3993 Figure (182cm-72in) s.d.1968 varnished gold plastic exhib.lit. 28-Apr-3 Bukowskis, Stockholm #975/R est:18000-20000 (S.KR 35000)

LINDE, Jan van der (1864-1945) Dutch
£331 $527 €480 Vroege morgen (72x56cm-28x22in) s.i. 10-Mar-3 Sotheby's, Amsterdam #152
£921 $1492 €1400 Shipping on the Zuiderzee (70x100cm-28x39in) s. 21-Jan-3 Christie's, Amsterdam #266 est:600-800

£1019 $1590 €1600 Grand church and neighbourhood of Dordrecht (46x38cm-18x15in) s. 5-Nov-2 Vendu Notarishuis, Rotterdam #282/R est:800-1000
£1646 $2600 €2600 Dutch canal landscape with windmill (100x115cm-39x45in) s. 28-Nov-2 Dorotheum, Vienna #56/R est:4500-5000

LINDE, Ossip L (1880-1940) American
£1750 $2800 €2538 Market day, Venice (53x65cm-21x26in) s. 16-May-3 Skinner, Boston #350/R est:1000-1500

LINDEBERG, Linda (20th C) American
Works on paper
£255 $400 €383 Provincetown (19x24cm-7x9in) W/C. 19-Nov-2 Wright, Chicago #181/R

LINDEBURG, H P (1854-1932) Danish
£270 $422 €405 Christian VIII's room at Rosenborg (36x32cm-14x13in) s. prov. 23-Sep-2 Rasmussen, Vejle #161/R (D.KR 3200)
£1839 $2942 €2759 Young girl at her morning toilet (65x83cm-26x33in) s.d.87. 13-Jan-3 Rasmussen, Vejle #9/R est:25000 (D.KR 21000)
£5263 $8526 €7631 Old Vind preaching for Christian IV (110x193cm-43x76in) s.d.1885 exhib. 26-May-3 Rasmussen, Copenhagen #1204/R est:30000-50000 (D.KR 55000)

LINDELL, Lage (1920-1980) Swedish
£418 $661 €627 Untitled (5x17cm-2x7in) init. sketch paper. 28-Apr-3 Bukowskis, Stockholm #246a/R (S.KR 5500)
£1822 $2842 €2733 Abstraction (45x65cm-18x26in) init. canvas on canvas. 5-Nov-2 Bukowskis, Stockholm #266/R est:20000-25000 (S.KR 26000)
£2281 $3605 €3422 Landscape, Herrvik (37x52cm-15x20in) s. panel. 28-Apr-3 Bukowskis, Stockholm #252/R est:30000-40000 (S.KR 30000)
£2943 $4591 €4415 Untitled composition (75x130cm-30x51in) init. painting collage linen exhib. 6-Nov-2 AB Stockholms Auktionsverk #537/R est:50000-60000 (S.KR 42000)
£3861 $6216 €5792 Town scene (67x97cm-26x38in) init. 7-May-3 AB Stockholms Auktionsverk #932/R est:40000-50000 (S.KR 50000)
£5046 $7871 €7569 From the farmyard (38x115cm-15x45in) init. canvas on canvas painted c.1945-47 prov. 5-Nov-2 Bukowskis, Stockholm #264/R est:100000-125000 (S.KR 72000)
£13900 $22378 €20850 Herrvik - landscape from Gotland (100x131cm-39x52in) init. painted c.1962-64. 7-May-3 AB Stockholms Auktionsverk #922/R est:60000-80000 (S.KR 180000)
Works on paper
£635 $997 €953 Composition in blue, yellow and black (27x18cm-11x7in) s. gouache. 16-Dec-2 Lilla Bukowskis, Stockholm #908 (S.KR 9000)
£700 $1105 €1050 Composition (17x12cm-7x5in) s.d.1952 gouache. 28-Apr-3 Bukowskis, Stockholm #254/R (S.KR 9200)
£771 $1203 €1157 Figure composition (38x46cm-15x18in) s. gouache pencil cardboard. 5-Nov-2 Bukowskis, Stockholm #267/R (S.KR 11000)
£772 $1243 €1158 The wanderer (19x39cm-7x15in) s.d.47 pastel. 7-May-3 AB Stockholms Auktionsverk #926/R (S.KR 10000)
£853 $1382 €1237 Composition with figures (37x43cm-15x17in) s. mixed media. 25-May-3 Uppsala Auktionskammare, Uppsala #319/R (S.KR 11000)
£1141 $1802 €1712 Composition (37x44cm-15x17in) s. W/C. 28-Apr-3 Bukowskis, Stockholm #253/R est:15000-20000 (S.KR 15000)

LINDEMANN, Kai (1931-) Danish
£257 $401 €386 Composition (45x35cm-18x14in) s.d.1968 verso. 11-Nov-2 Rasmussen, Vejle #110/R (D.KR 3000)
£326 $519 €489 Composition (81x60cm-32x24in) s.d.63. 29-Apr-3 Kunsthallen, Copenhagen #94 (D.KR 3500)
£559 $888 €839 View across Venice (60x73cm-24x29in) s. d.90/96 verso. 10-Mar-3 Rasmussen, Vejle #720/R (D.KR 6000)
£604 $954 €906 Landscape, South of France (55x46cm-22x18in) s. s.i.d.95 verso. 1-Apr-3 Rasmussen, Copenhagen #391 (D.KR 6500)
£620 $1035 €899 Portrait of standing female nude (130x97cm-51x38in) s. s.d.85 verso. 17-Jun-3 Rasmussen, Copenhagen #222/R (D.KR 6500)
£633 $988 €950 Yellow facade (45x50cm-18x20in) s.i.d.77 verso. 18-Sep-2 Kunsthallen, Copenhagen #263/R (D.KR 7500)
£710 $1179 €1030 Composition (116x89cm-46x35in) s.d.70 verso. 12-Jun-3 Kunsthallen, Copenhagen #98/R (D.KR 7500)
£929 $1468 €1394 Landscape, South of France (73x92cm-29x36in) s. s.i.d.93 verso. 1-Apr-3 Rasmussen, Copenhagen #371/R (D.KR 10000)
£1478 $2468 €2143 Landscape from South of France (97x130cm-38x51in) s. s.i.d.93 verso prov. 17-Jun-3 Rasmussen, Copenhagen #130/R est:12000 (D.KR 15500)
£2323 $3671 €3485 Havana (162x130cm-64x51in) s. s.i.d.94 verso. 1-Apr-3 Rasmussen, Copenhagen #327/R est:25000 (D.KR 25000)
Works on paper
£521 $865 €755 Gable picture (120x160cm-47x63in) s. W/C paper on canvas. 12-Jun-3 Kunsthallen, Copenhagen #79/R (D.KR 5500)

LINDEMANN-FROMMEL, Karl (1819-1891) German
£2830 $4415 €4500 Italian coast with fishing boat (36x77cm-14x30in) s.i.d.1876 prov. 19-Sep-2 Dr Fritz Nagel, Stuttgart #958/R est:2000
Works on paper
£634 $1052 €900 Isola Bella in Lago Maggiore (11x16cm-4x6in) i.d. verso brush sepia over pen. 12-Jun-3 Hauswedell & Nolte, Hamburg #369/R
£2405 $3800 €3800 View of Castelgandolfo with Albano Lake (52x43cm-20x17in) s.i.d.1864 W/C card. 26-Nov-2 Christie's, Rome #128/R

LINDEMANN-FROMMEL, Karl (attrib) (1819-1891) German
£696 $1100 €1100 View of Lanuvio (28x42cm-11x17in) i. cardboard. 26-Nov-2 Christie's, Rome #23

LINDENAU, Martin (20th C) French
£1457 $2375 €2200 Le port de Saint Tropez (60x73cm-24x29in) s.i. i.verso. 16-Feb-3 Mercier & Cie, Lille #277/R est:2500-3000

LINDENEG, Thor (1941-) Danish
£836 $1322 €1254 Surrealistic composition (121x80cm-48x31in) s.d.84 panel. 1-Apr-3 Rasmussen, Copenhagen #368/R (D.KR 9000)

LINDENMUTH, Tod (1885-1976) American
£1063 $1700 €1595 Spring New England landscape (58x79cm-23x31in) s. 11-Jan-3 James Julia, Fairfield #438 est:1000-2000

LINDENSCHMIT, Wilhelm (elder) (1806-1848) German
£1154 $1812 €1800 Death of the Duke Luidpolt from Bavaria in the Pressburg battle (26x35cm-10x14in) board. 10-Dec-2 Dorotheum, Vienna #185/R est:2000-2400

LINDER, Johan Anders (1783-1877) Swedish
£1296 $2126 €1879 Gustavian interior with women working (56x42cm-22x17in) s.d.1832. 4-Jun-3 AB Stockholms Auktionsverk #2253/R est:10000-12000 (S.KR 16500)

LINDER, Philippe Jacques (19th C) French
Works on paper
£850 $1385 €1275 Fashionable ladies with their pets (37x27cm-15x11in) s. W/C pair. 29-Jan-3 Sotheby's, Olympia #265/R est:600-800

LINDEROS, Bengt Arne (1929-1989) Swedish
£351 $554 €527 Landscape composition (60x70cm-24x28in) init. acrylic. 30-Nov-2 Goteborg Auktionsverk, Sweden #574/R (S.KR 5000)

LINDFORS, Anton (1890-1943) Finnish
£281 $461 €430 River through woodland (50x41cm-20x16in) s.d.24. 9-Feb-3 Bukowskis, Helsinki #292/R
£288 $472 €400 Fjord landscape (32x45cm-13x18in) s.d.1934. 5-Jun-3 Hagelstam, Helsinki #920
£444 $729 €680 The last snow (49x34cm-19x13in) s.d.1916. 9-Feb-3 Bukowskis, Helsinki #293/R

LINDGREN, Emil (1866-1940) Swedish
£247 $388 €358 Reclining woman. 15-Dec-2 Anders Antik, Landskrona #433 (S.KR 3500)
£310 $503 €450 Kalle Andersson and his wife seated at table outside, Grisslehamn (68x88cm-27x35in) s.i.d.1924. 25-May-3 Uppsala Auktionskammare, Uppsala #178 (S.KR 4000)

LINDH, Bror (1877-1941) Swedish
£2837 $4397 €4256 Marsh marigold (100x105cm-39x41in) s. 4-Dec-2 AB Stockholms Auktionsverk #1788/R est:40000-50000 (S.KR 40000)
£3103 $5027 €4499 Summer twilight with silver birch copse (103x136cm-41x54in) s. 26-May-3 Bukowskis, Stockholm #120/R est:40000-50000 (S.KR 40000)
£3688 $5716 €5532 Cottages below snow covered pines (91x100cm-36x39in) s. 3-Dec-2 Bukowskis, Stockholm #76/R est:40000-50000 (S.KR 52000)

LINDH, Bror (attrib) (1877-1941) Swedish
£596 $942 €894 Landscape with cloud formations (62x77cm-24x30in) 30-Nov-2 Goteborg Auktionsverk, Sweden #133/R (S.KR 8500)

LINDH, Johan (1793-1865) Finnish
£1582 $2500 €2500 Portrait of lady (65x52cm-26x20in) 30-Nov-2 Hagelstam, Helsinki #131/R est:2500

£1871 $2993 €2600 Portrait of Erik Gustaf Ehrstrom (35x28cm-14x11in) after B A Godenhjelm painted c.1852 lit. 17-May-3 Hagelstam, Helsinki #93/R est:1500

LINDH, Johan (attrib) (1793-1865) Finnish
£345 $524 €518 Portrait of R Studenger (70x58cm-28x23in) i.d.1844 verso. 28-Aug-2 Museumsbygningen, Copenhagen #49 (D.KR 4000)

LINDHEIN, M de (19th C) ?
£1103 $1743 €1600 La Chartreuse pres de Bruun (21x31cm-8x12in) i.d.verso. 2-Apr-3 Vanderkindere, Brussels #320/R est:300-400

LINDHOLM, Berndt (1841-1914) Finnish
£638 $989 €957 Wooded landscape with pile of large stones (20x33cm-8x13in) mono.d.66 panel. 8-Dec-2 Uppsala Auktionskammare, Uppsala #119/R (S.KR 9000)
£638 $989 €957 Wooded landscape with pile of large stones (20x35cm-8x14in) s.d.1866 panel. 8-Dec-2 Uppsala Auktionskammare, Uppsala #118/R (S.KR 9000)
£1939 $3142 €2812 From Skarvik - Hisingen (19x35cm-7x14in) s. canvas on cardboard. 26-May-3 Bukowskis, Stockholm #270/R est:18000-20000 (S.KR 25000)
£1961 $3216 €3000 Stones in the wood (20x34cm-8x13in) s.d.juli 66. 9-Feb-3 Bukowskis, Helsinki #294/R est:1700
£2199 $3408 €3299 Seascape with breakers, stormy weather (37x54cm-15x21in) s. 8-Dec-2 Uppsala Auktionskammare, Uppsala #117/R est:40000-50000 (S.KR 31000)
£2270 $3518 €3405 Coastal landscape with sailing boat in moonlight (15x25cm-6x10in) s. panel. 4-Dec-2 AB Stockholms Auktionsverk #1911/R est:15000-20000 (S.KR 32000)
£2270 $3518 €3405 Road to town (15x23cm-6x9in) s.d.92 panel. 4-Dec-2 AB Stockholms Auktionsverk #1912/R est:15000-20000 (S.KR 32000)
£2435 $3994 €3531 Coastal landscape (34x55cm-13x22in) s. panel. 4-Jun-3 AB Stockholms Auktionsverk #2436/R est:22000-25000 (S.KR 31000)
£2514 $4123 €3645 Cliffs and ocean (30x43cm-12x17in) s.d.1901. 4-Jun-3 AB Stockholms Auktionsverk #2470/R est:20000-30000 (S.KR 32000)
£3268 $5359 €5000 Foaming rapids (16x24cm-6x9in) s.d.91. 9-Feb-3 Bukowskis, Helsinki #295/R est:5000
£4112 $6661 €5962 Fishing village (23x50cm-9x20in) s.d.1893. 25-May-3 Uppsala Auktionskammare, Uppsala #86/R est:40000-50000 (S.KR 53000)
£6329 $10000 €10000 Coastal breakers (47x58cm-19x23in) s. 1-Dec-2 Bukowskis, Helsinki #114/R est:10000-12000
£6803 $10816 €10000 Coastal landscape with cliffs (32x41cm-13x16in) s. 24-Mar-3 Bukowskis, Helsinki #160/R est:6000
£9155 $14739 €13000 Fisherman's croft (47x70cm-19x28in) s.d.1901. 10-May-3 Bukowskis, Helsinki #53/R est:15000-20000
£9574 $14840 €14361 Breakers against rocky coast (62x96cm-24x38in) s. 4-Dec-2 AB Stockholms Auktionsverk #1914/R est:100000-125000 (S.KR 135000)
£9804 $16078 €15000 Market day (22x31cm-9x12in) s.d.1879. 9-Feb-3 Bukowskis, Helsinki #295a/R est:13000
£11392 $18000 €18000 Traffic at sea (30x51cm-12x20in) s.d.77. 1-Dec-2 Bukowskis, Helsinki #112/R est:20000-25000
£11511 $18417 €16000 Girl in the woods (70x46cm-28x18in) s. 17-May-3 Hagelstam, Helsinki #107/R est:18000
£12025 $19000 €19000 Mountain slope (64x95cm-25x37in) s. 30-Nov-2 Hagelstam, Helsinki #97/R est:12000
£12658 $20000 €20000 Fishermen on beach (47x70cm-19x28in) s.d.88. 1-Dec-2 Bukowskis, Helsinki #109/R est:22000-25000
£13924 $22000 €22000 Boy fishing (45x65cm-18x26in) s.i.d.1871. 1-Dec-2 Bukowskis, Helsinki #111/R est:22000-24000
£17089 $27000 €27000 Summer evening by the coast (47x70cm-19x28in) s. 1-Dec-2 Bukowskis, Helsinki #110/R est:25000-28000
£56962 $90000 €90000 Sunlight in the forest (113x150cm-44x59in) s.d.1886 exhib. 1-Dec-2 Bukowskis, Helsinki #106/R est:90000-100000
Works on paper
£1224 $1947 €1800 Waterfall (41x33cm-16x13in) s. W/C. 27-Feb-3 Hagelstam, Helsinki #824/R est:2400

LINDHOLM, Lorenz August (1819-1854) Swedish
£1414 $2319 €2050 Feeding the chickens (50x38cm-20x15in) s.d.1844. 4-Jun-3 AB Stockholms Auktionsverk #2187/R est:10000-15000 (S.KR 18000)

LINDI (1904-1991) Swiss
£463 $745 €671 Oriental woman with veil (55x38cm-22x15in) s. i.d.1932 verso. 9-May-3 Dobiaschofsky, Bern #244/R (S.FR 1000)
Works on paper
£283 $453 €425 Three clowns (20x25cm-8x10in) s.d.1958 mixed media board. 17-Mar-3 Philippe Schuler, Zurich #4353 (S.FR 600)

LINDIN, Carl Olof Eric (1869-1942) American/Swedish
£1125 $1800 €1631 Nantucket beach (20x26cm-8x10in) s. board exhib. 16-May-3 Skinner, Boston #290/R est:800-1200
£1650 $2706 €2475 Young woman sketching on the banks of the Seine (32x21cm-13x8in) s.d.95 board. 10-Feb-3 David Duggleby, Scarborough #590/R est:400-600

LINDKVIST, Jonas (1889-1955) Swedish
£349 $542 €524 Uppsala meadow (72x91cm-28x36in) s.d.42 panel. 29-Sep-2 Uppsala Auktionskammare, Uppsala #22 (S.KR 5000)

LINDLAR, Johann Wilhelm (1816-1896) German
£359 $590 €550 High mountain valley in summer (61x102cm-24x40in) s. 8-Feb-3 Hans Stahl, Hamburg #57
£808 $1276 €1212 Alpine landscape (18x25cm-7x10in) s. 17-Nov-2 Koller, Geneva #1308 (S.FR 1850)

LINDMAN, Axel (1848-1930) Swedish
£864 $1417 €1253 Breakers, Marstrand (37x52cm-15x20in) s. exhib.prov. 4-Jun-3 AB Stockholms Auktionsverk #2260/R (S.KR 11000)
£2113 $3401 €3000 Winter landscape with stream (64x84cm-25x33in) s.d.1912. 10-May-3 Bukowskis, Helsinki #368/R est:1500-2000
£2357 $3865 €3418 Woman sitting in summer meadow (27x26cm-11x10in) panel. 4-Jun-3 AB Stockholms Auktionsverk #2230/R est:30000-40000 (S.KR 30000)

LINDMAN, Marjatta (1935-) Finnish
£272 $433 €400 Bush in flower (110x92cm-43x36in) s.d.70-71. 24-Mar-3 Bukowskis, Helsinki #161/R

LINDNER, Ernest (1897-1988) Canadian
Works on paper
£1156 $1895 €1676 Emma Lake shoreline (38x26cm-15x10in) s.d.1940 W/C. 9-Jun-3 Hodgins, Calgary #275/R est:2500-3000 (C.D 2600)
£2218 $3504 €3327 Toadstool and fungi (37x56cm-15x22in) s. s.i.d.1964 verso W/C prov. 18-Nov-2 Sotheby's, Toronto #46/R est:6000-8000 (C.D 5500)

LINDNER, Peter Moffat (1854-1949) British
£1600 $2480 €2400 Sunset over the harbour (130x155cm-51x61in) s. 26-Sep-2 Lane, Penzance #368 est:1500-1700
Works on paper
£480 $739 €720 Approach to Dordrecht (25x36cm-10x14in) s. W/C. 3-Sep-2 Gorringes, Lewes #2237
£650 $1021 €975 Evening glow, Venice (26x36cm-10x14in) s. W/C over pencil. 21-Nov-2 Tennants, Leyburn #656

LINDNEUX, Robert (1871-1970) American
£291 $475 €437 Porcupine (64x46cm-25x18in) s.d.1928. 16-Feb-3 Butterfields, San Francisco #2080
£291 $475 €437 Wawona tunnel tree (61x56cm-24x22in) s.d.1926-1958. 16-Feb-3 Butterfields, San Francisco #2085

LINDOE, Luke (1913-2001) Canadian
£890 $1415 €1335 Camp (40x50cm-16x20in) s.i.d.1951 board. 23-Mar-3 Hodgins, Calgary #120/R est:1200-1500 (C.D 2100)
Works on paper
£222 $364 €322 Winter in red and black (30x45cm-12x18in) s.d. col ink. 9-Jun-3 Hodgins, Calgary #447/R (C.D 500)

LINDROOS, Thor (1930-) Finnish
£881 $1356 €1400 Gaasoren (88x105cm-35x41in) s.d.1986. 24-Oct-2 Hagelstam, Helsinki #917

LINDSAY, Lady Elizabeth Keith (fl.1800-1840s) Irish
£480 $749 €720 Portrait of Charles Robert Lindsay (77x64cm-30x25in) i.d.1802 verso. 18-Sep-2 Cheffins Grain & Comins, Cambridge #535/R

LINDSAY, Norman Alfred Williams (1879-1969) Australian
£2299 $3609 €3449 On the headlands (40x32cm-16x13in) s. 15-Apr-3 Lawson Menzies, Sydney #51/R est:6000-7000 (A.D 6000)
£2550 $4182 €3698 Balinese girl (29x24cm-11x9in) s. board. 3-Jun-3 Lawson Menzies, Sydney #983 est:6000-10000 (A.D 6400)
£10000 $15900 €15000 Gossip (34x29cm-13x11in) s. i.verso canvas on board. 4-Mar-3 Deutscher-Menzies, Melbourne #144/R est:20000-30000 (A.D 26000)
£10400 $16744 €15600 Dancer (23x18cm-9x7in) s. canvas on board. 6-May-3 Christie's, Melbourne #61/R est:20000-25000 (A.D 26000)
£11905 $19762 €20283 Necklace (54x43cm-21x17in) s. board. 10-Jun-3 Shapiro, Sydney #15/R est:30000-50000 (A.D 30000)
£13571 $21443 €20357 Rose (36x30cm-14x12in) s. canvasboard. 26-Nov-2 Sotheby's, Melbourne #28/R est:28000-38000 (A.D 38000)

£13953 $22186 €20930 Procession (22x41cm-9x16in) s. i.verso canvasboard prov. 5-May-3 Sotheby's, Melbourne #118/R est:15000-20000 (A.D 36000)
£16429 $25957 €24644 Rose (54x45cm-21x18in) s. canvas on board prov. 17-Nov-2 Sotheby's, Paddington #38/R est:25000-35000 (A.D 46000)
£21270 $35308 €36250 In the woods (62x48cm-24x19in) s. 10-Jun-3 Shapiro, Sydney #21/R est:80000-120000 (A.D 53600)
£22000 $35420 €33000 Green drape (58x50cm-23x20in) s. canvas on board. 6-May-3 Christie's, Melbourne #79/R est:55000-65000 (A.D 55000)
£34286 $54171 €51429 Court napping (77x61cm-30x24in) s. prov. 26-Nov-2 Sotheby's, Melbourne #55/R est:80000-120000 (A.D 96000)
£42146 $62797 €63219 Party - Urs Graf entertains (67x100cm-26x39in) s. painted 1945 prov.exhib. 27-Aug-2 Christie's, Melbourne #76/R est:120000-150000 (A.D 110000)
£48000 $77280 €72000 Veronica (78x54cm-31x21in) s. i.verso. 6-May-3 Christie's, Melbourne #40/R est:95000-115000 (A.D 120000)
£85714 $134571 €128571 Seventies (80x64cm-31x25in) s. prov.lit. 25-Nov-2 Christie's, Melbourne #30/R est:120000-180000 (A.D 240000)
£100000 $157000 €150000 Spring's innocence (65x90cm-26x35in) s.d.1937 prov.lit. 25-Nov-2 Christie's, Melbourne #16/R est:180000-250000 (A.D 280000)

Prints

£1607 $2523 €2411 Life in the temple (30x35cm-12x14in) s.i.num.26/35 etching prov.exhib. 25-Nov-2 Christie's, Melbourne #246/R est:3000-5000 (A.D 4500)
£1643 $2595 €2465 Love on Earth (35x29cm-14x11in) s.d.num.11./55 etching engraving. 27-Nov-2 Deutscher-Menzies, Melbourne #285/R est:2500-3500 (A.D 4600)
£1786 $2804 €2679 Walpurgis (29x31cm-11x12in) s.i.num.7/40 etching prov. 25-Nov-2 Christie's, Melbourne #243/R est:3000-5000 (A.D 5000)
£1786 $2804 €2679 Unknown seas (36x28cm-14x11in) s.i.num.36/55 etching prov.exhib. 25-Nov-2 Christie's, Melbourne #301/R est:2500-3500 (A.D 5000)
£1786 $2804 €2679 To the refined spirit (25x30cm-10x12in) s.i.num.15/25 etching. 25-Nov-2 Christie's, Melbourne #344/R est:3000-5000 (A.D 5000)
£1792 $2724 €2688 Toilet (16x14cm-6x6in) s.num.23/45 etching aquatint engraving. 27-Aug-2 Goodman, Sydney #122/R est:5000-7000 (A.D 5000)
£1923 $3057 €2885 Virginity (38x29cm-15x11in) s.i.d.num.40/50 etching engraving soft ground stipple lit. 4-Mar-3 Deutscher-Menzies, Melbourne #292/R est:3000-5000 (A.D 5000)
£1964 $3084 €2946 She arrives (24x22cm-9x9in) s.i.num.8/25 etching. 25-Nov-2 Christie's, Melbourne #276/R est:3000-5000 (A.D 5500)
£1964 $3084 €2946 Hyperborea (34x29cm-13x11in) s.i.num.47/55 etching prov.exhib. 25-Nov-2 Christie's, Melbourne #343/R est:3000-5000 (A.D 5500)
£2107 $3308 €3161 Ragged poet (34x27cm-13x11in) s.d.1964 num.37/55 etching. 15-Apr-3 Lawson Menzies, Sydney #271/R est:4500-7500 (A.D 5500)
£2321 $3644 €3482 Ragged poet (35x27cm-14x11in) s.i.num.6/55 etching exhib. 25-Nov-2 Christie's, Melbourne #341/R est:3000-5000 (A.D 6500)
£2500 $3925 €3750 Innocents (35x30cm-14x12in) s.i.num.5/55 etching prov.exhib. 25-Nov-2 Christie's, Melbourne #338/R est:3000-5000 (A.D 7000)
£2542 $3863 €3813 Love on earth (35x29cm-14x11in) s.d.1925 num.41/55 etching engraving stipple lit. 27-Aug-2 Goodman, Sydney #115/R est:5000-8000 (A.D 7090)
£3214 $5079 €4821 C sharp minor quartet (37x29cm-15x11in) s.d.1927 num.20/55 etching. 18-Nov-2 Goodman, Sydney #155 est:9000-12000 (A.D 9000)
£3393 $5327 €5090 Where life ascends (35x29cm-14x11in) s.i.num.14/45 etching prov.exhib. 25-Nov-2 Christie's, Melbourne #299/R est:3000-5000 (A.D 9500)
£3455 $5460 €5010 In vain the Christian (52x70cm-20x28in) s.i. engraving executed c.1928. 22-Jul-3 Lawson Menzies, Sydney #87/R est:7000-9000 (A.D 8500)
£4286 $6729 €6429 Visitors to hell (32x45cm-13x18in) s.i.num.9/25 etching. 25-Nov-2 Christie's, Melbourne #339/R est:3000-5000 (A.D 12000)

Works on paper

£393 $621 €590 Lord Bishop O' witches pool (22x24cm-9x9in) s. ink. 26-Nov-2 Sotheby's, Melbourne #161 est:1200-1800 (A.D 1100)
£429 $664 €644 Family life of British Prime Minister Asquith (35x30cm-14x12in) s. ink cardboard. 29-Oct-2 Lawson Menzies, Sydney #206 (A.D 1200)
£448 $681 €672 Welcome (22x17cm-9x7in) pencil exec.c.1935. 27-Aug-2 Goodman, Sydney #29 (A.D 1250)
£502 $763 €753 Sorcerer's apprentice (18x17cm-7x7in) pencil exec.c.1928. 27-Aug-2 Goodman, Sydney #92 (A.D 1400)
£516 $856 €879 At the blow hole, Kiama (29x22cm-11x9in) s. i.verso ink. 10-Jun-3 Shapiro, Sydney #16 est:700-900 (A.D 1300)
£635 $1054 €1082 Untitled (32x34cm-13x13in) s. i.verso ink. 10-Jun-3 Shapiro, Sydney #17 est:1000-1500 (A.D 1600)
£678 $1065 €1017 Galahad Jones (30x21cm-12x8in) s. W/C prov. 25-Nov-2 Christie's, Melbourne #297/R (A.D 1900)
£680 $1095 €986 In the dog house (29x32cm-11x13in) s. pen ink. 12-May-3 Joel, Victoria #232 est:1000-1500 (A.D 1700)
£692 $1101 €1038 Mr Bandparts and Robert (22x27cm-9x11in) s.i. pen ink chl. 4-Mar-3 Deutscher-Menzies, Melbourne #230/R (A.D 1800)
£732 $1156 €1061 Celebration of Suffragettes 1908 (21x15cm-8x6in) s. ink. 22-Jul-3 Lawson Menzies, Sydney #210/R est:300-500 (A.D 1800)
£840 $1327 €1260 Afternoon ride (13x23cm-5x9in) pen ink pencil exec.c.1928 prov. 7-Apr-3 Shapiro, Sydney #452 (A.D 2200)
£873 $1449 €1488 Afternoon ride (13x23cm-5x9in) pencil ink executed c.1928. 10-Jun-3 Shapiro, Sydney #12 est:2200-2600 (A.D 2200)
£929 $1458 €1394 Bear hug (18x17cm-7x7in) s. ink prov. 25-Nov-2 Christie's, Melbourne #275/R est:2000-3000 (A.D 2600)
£996 $1564 €1494 Illustration to James Odmond's A journalist and two bears (21x25cm-8x10in) s. pen ink. 15-Apr-3 Lawson Menzies, Sydney #140/R est:2500-3000 (A.D 2600)
£1068 $1633 €1602 Onlookers (31x24cm-12x9in) s. ink. 25-Aug-2 Sotheby's, Paddington #158 est:2000-4000 (A.D 3000)
£1071 $1682 €1607 Nude study (30x17cm-12x7in) pencil. 25-Nov-2 Christie's, Melbourne #417/R est:3000-4000 (A.D 3000)
£1073 $1684 €1610 Male model in dressing gown 2 (28x14cm-11x6in) pencil executed c.1935. 15-Apr-3 Lawson Menzies, Sydney #126/R est:2000-3000 (A.D 2800)
£1073 $1684 €1610 Rita (25x16cm-10x6in) init. pencil. 15-Apr-3 Lawson Menzies, Sydney #143/R est:2500-3500 (A.D 2800)
£1200 $1932 €1740 Angel and nymph (28x27cm-11x11in) s. conte. 12-May-3 Joel, Victoria #256/R est:2000-2500 (A.D 3000)
£1219 $1852 €1829 League of nations (40x30cm-16x12in) s. pen ink. 28-Aug-2 Deutscher-Menzies, Melbourne #310/R est:1500-2000 (A.D 3400)
£1240 $1972 €1860 Study of two nudes (35x22cm-14x9in) init. pencil. 5-May-3 Sotheby's, Melbourne #364 est:1500-2500 (A.D 3200)
£1461 $2324 €2192 Quartilla (33x25cm-13x10in) s. pen ink. 4-Mar-3 Deutscher-Menzies, Melbourne #229/R est:3000-4000 (A.D 3800)
£1500 $2370 €2250 Warrior (46x34cm-18x13in) s. ink. 26-Nov-2 Sotheby's, Melbourne #123 est:2800-3800 (A.D 4200)
£1680 $2705 €2520 Model (28x21cm-11x8in) init. pencil. 6-May-3 Christie's, Melbourne #217 est:4000-6000 (A.D 4200)
£1833 $3005 €2750 Portrait of Frances (38x25cm-15x10in) init. pencil prov. 4-Jun-3 Deutscher-Menzies, Melbourne #315/R est:4000-6000 (A.D 4600)
£1908 $3015 €2862 Untitled, female nude (37x30cm-15x12in) s.i. pen ink pencil. 7-Apr-3 Shapiro, Sydney #447/R est:4000-6000 (A.D 5000)
£3011 $4576 €4517 Shirley (41x24cm-16x9in) init. pencil. 27-Aug-2 Goodman, Sydney #124 est:3000-6000 (A.D 8400)
£3203 $4900 €4805 Bathers (29x24cm-11x9in) s.i. W/C prov. 25-Aug-2 Sotheby's, Paddington #243 est:6000-10000 (A.D 9000)
£4643 $7335 €6965 Victim (44x53cm-17x21in) s.d.1924 W/C. 27-Nov-2 Deutscher-Menzies, Melbourne #50/R est:15000-20000 (A.D 13000)
£4660 $7082 €6990 Marmalade cat (37x37cm-15x15in) s.d.1935 W/C. 28-Aug-2 Deutscher-Menzies, Melbourne #64/R est:10000-15000 (A.D 13000)
£5536 $8691 €8304 Casanova (36x25cm-14x10in) s. gouache exec.c.1905 prov. 25-Nov-2 Christie's, Melbourne #242/R est:3000-5000 (A.D 15500)
£5536 $8525 €8304 Dancers (23x23cm-9x9in) s.d.1917 W/C prov. 3-Sep-2 Shapiro, Sydney #350/R est:15000-20000 (A.D 15500)
£5714 $9029 €8571 Goths (32x42cm-13x17in) s. i.verso W/C. 27-Nov-2 Deutscher-Menzies, Melbourne #49/R est:18000-24000 (A.D 16000)
£6107 $9649 €9161 Seated nude (33x25cm-13x10in) s. W/C. 2-Apr-3 Christie's, Melbourne #62/R est:8000-12000 (A.D 16000)
£7143 $11214 €10715 Night begins (44x37cm-17x15in) s. W/C prov. 25-Nov-2 Christie's, Melbourne #85/R est:20000-30000 (A.D 20000)
£7886 $11986 €11829 My army, o, my army (25x20cm-10x8in) s. W/C lit. 28-Aug-2 Deutscher-Menzies, Melbourne #16/R est:20000-25000 (A.D 22000)
£8800 $14168 €13200 Guests to the castle (43x33cm-17x13in) s. i.verso W/C prov. 6-May-3 Christie's, Melbourne #54/R est:18000-25000 (A.D 22000)
£9286 $14671 €13929 At the ball (42x34cm-17x13in) s.d.1940 W/C. 26-Nov-2 Sotheby's, Melbourne #7/R est:25000-35000 (A.D 26000)
£9964 $15246 €14946 Harlequin (50x33cm-20x13in) s.d.1929 W/C. 25-Aug-2 Sotheby's, Paddington #51/R est:28000-38000 (A.D 28000)
£10000 $15500 €15000 Youth (49x36cm-19x14in) s. W/C. 29-Oct-2 Lawson Menzies, Sydney #59/R est:35000-45000 (A.D 28000)
£10119 $16798 €17262 Untitled (45x38cm-18x15in) s. i.verso canvas on board. 10-Jun-3 Shapiro, Sydney #13 est:40000-60000 (A.D 25500)
£10714 $16929 €16071 Ship wreck with sirens (41x51cm-16x20in) s. W/C. 18-Nov-2 Goodman, Sydney #153/R est:28000-48000 (A.D 30000)
£10853 $17256 €16280 Reclining nude (35x39cm-14x15in) s. W/C. 5-May-3 Sotheby's, Melbourne #108/R est:20000-25000 (A.D 28000)
£11494 $17126 €17241 Visitors (42x40cm-17x16in) s.d.1920 W/C. 27-Aug-2 Christie's, Melbourne #18/R est:30000-40000 (A.D 30000)
£12000 $19320 €18000 Sultana's fortune (43x34cm-17x13in) s. W/C. 6-May-3 Christie's, Melbourne #103/R est:30000-40000 (A.D 30000)
£15000 $23700 €22500 Kiss (30x23cm-12x9in) s. W/C. 26-Nov-2 Sotheby's, Melbourne #6/R est:18000-28000 (A.D 42000)

£16071 $25232 €24107 My devil for yours (45x36cm-18x14in) s.d.1933 W/C. 25-Nov-2 Christie's, Melbourne #13/R est:30000-40000 (A.D 45000)
£16279 $25884 €24419 Book of destiny (44x63cm-17x25in) s. i.verso W/C card. 5-May-3 Sotheby's, Melbourne #120/R est:35000-55000 (A.D 42000)
£16786 $26521 €25179 Ladies who wait (41x36cm-16x14in) s. W/C. 26-Nov-2 Sotheby's, Melbourne #18/R est:25000-35000 (A.D 47000)
£16794 $26534 €25191 Demon's desire (52x47cm-20x19in) s. W/C. 2-Apr-3 Christie's, Melbourne #1/R est:20000-30000 (A.D 44000)
£17204 $26151 €25806 That maid (46x41cm-18x16in) s.d.1930 W/C. 27-Aug-2 Goodman, Sydney #136/R est:40000-60000 (A.D 48000)
£20000 $32200 €30000 High constable's wife (46x35cm-18x14in) s.d.58 W/C. 6-May-3 Christie's, Melbourne #35/R est:35000-40000 (A.D 50000)
£21429 $33857 €32144 To the witches carnival (46x34cm-18x13in) s. i.verso W/C. 27-Nov-2 Deutscher-Menzies, Melbourne #51/R est:55000-70000 (A.D 60000)
£22000 $35420 €33000 Satyr and two nymphs (38x38cm-15x15in) s. W/C prov. 6-May-3 Christie's, Melbourne #20/R est:45000-65000 (A.D 55000)
£24038 $38221 €36057 Our lost Olympus (49x48cm-19x19in) s.d.1931 i.verso W/C prov. 4-Mar-3 Deutscher-Menzies, Melbourne #47/R est:75000-95000 (A.D 62500)
£24107 $38089 €36161 Benevolence (38x30cm-15x12in) s. W/C. 27-Nov-2 Deutscher-Menzies, Melbourne #20/R est:38000-45000 (A.D 67500)
£25801 $39475 €38702 Indian fantasy (59x49cm-23x19in) s.d.1954 W/C prov. 25-Aug-2 Sotheby's, Paddington #71/R est:55000-75000 (A.D 72500)
£28000 $45080 €42000 Orgy (48x42cm-19x17in) s.d.1932 W/C prov. 6-May-3 Christie's, Melbourne #24/R est:60000-80000 (A.D 70000)
£30000 $48300 €45000 Merchandise (66x55cm-26x22in) s.d.1941 W/C prov. 6-May-3 Christie's, Melbourne #5/R est:60000-80000 (A.D 75000)
£32558 $51767 €48837 Maidens in a spring garden (57x79cm-22x31in) s. W/C paper on board. 5-May-3 Sotheby's, Melbourne #166/R est:70000-90000 (A.D 84000)
£50188 $76286 €75282 Blue hat (61x53cm-24x21in) s.d.48 W/C lit. 28-Aug-2 Deutscher-Menzies, Melbourne #17/R est:60000-80000 (A.D 140025)
£51971 $78996 €77957 East and West (52x72cm-20x28in) s.d.1934 i.verso W/C prov. 28-Aug-2 Deutscher-Menzies, Melbourne #21/R est:55000-75000 (A.D 145000)

LINDSAY, Percy (1870-1952) Australian
£534 $844 €801 Sackville Reach (30x43cm-12x17in) board sold with two others by the same artist prov. 7-Apr-3 Shapiro, Sydney #427 (A.D 1400)
£750 $1155 €1125 Cattle crossing (21x31cm-8x12in) s. board. 7-Sep-2 Goodman, Sydney #225 est:250-450 (A.D 2100)
£6071 $9593 €9107 Near ballarat (24x47cm-9x19in) s.d.94 board. 17-Nov-2 Sotheby's, Paddington #77/R est:6000-10000 (A.D 17000)
£6870 $10855 €10305 Prospector at the minehead (35x26cm-14x10in) s.d.17. 2-Apr-3 Christie's, Melbourne #35/R est:3000-4000 (A.D 18000)

LINDSAY, Raymond (1904-1960) Australian
£305 $463 €458 Still life (57x45cm-22x18in) s. board. 27-Aug-2 Goodman, Sydney #235 (A.D 850)

LINDSAY, Sir Daryl Ernest (1889-1976) Australian
£232 $367 €348 Portrait of Lorand Andahazy (32x25cm-13x10in) s.i.d.38 conte. 27-Nov-2 Deutscher-Menzies, Melbourne #244/R (A.D 650)
£285 $436 €428 Five hundred miles to go (41x76cm-16x30in) s.d.1960 prov. 26-Aug-2 Sotheby's, Paddington #737 (A.D 800)
£534 $817 €801 Drover's team (38x66cm-15x26in) s.d.60 prov. 26-Aug-2 Sotheby's, Paddington #574 est:1500-3000 (A.D 1500)

LINDSAY, Sir Lionel (1874-1961) Australian
£249 $381 €374 Red gums (23x29cm-9x11in) s. i.verso canvas on pulpboard prov. 26-Aug-2 Sotheby's, Paddington #642 (A.D 700)
£783 $1198 €1175 Neutral Bay, Sydney (23x30cm-9x12in) s. i.verso oil on pulpboard painted 1912 prov. 26-Aug-2 Sotheby's, Paddington #600 est:1000-2000 (A.D 2200)

Works on paper
£320 $515 €464 Ruined shrine, Delhi (27x38cm-11x15in) s. W/C. 12-May-3 Joel, Victoria #316 (A.D 800)
£339 $536 €509 Old Herald Building (25x17cm-10x7in) s. ink prov. 17-Nov-2 Sotheby's, Paddington #53/R (A.D 950)
£357 $564 €536 Arab street scene (26x37cm-10x15in) s. W/C. 18-Nov-2 Joel, Victoria #208 est:1000-2000 (A.D 1000)
£1536 $2380 €2304 Raglan Street Wharf, Mosman (24x28cm-9x11in) s.d.1906 W/C. 29-Oct-2 Lawson Menzies, Sydney #160/R est:1800-2400 (A.D 4300)

LINDSELL, Edith Margaret (19th C) British
£500 $835 €725 Waterfall (44x34cm-17x13in) s.d.verso i.stretcher sold with a companion. 25-Jun-3 Bonhams, Bury St Edmunds #563

LINDSTROM, Arvid Mauritz (1849-1923) Swedish
£750 $1170 €1125 Autumnal river landscape (35x71cm-14x28in) s. 10-Sep-2 Bonhams, Knightsbridge #275/R
£851 $1319 €1277 Lake landscape (36x72cm-14x28in) s. 4-Dec-2 AB Stockholms Auktionsverk #1661/R (S.KR 12000)
£1277 $1979 €1916 Mountain birches from Snasahogarna (75x128cm-30x50in) s. 3-Dec-2 Bukowskis, Stockholm #302/R est:20000-25000 (S.KR 18000)
£1348 $2089 €2022 Autumn landscape with lake (36x65cm-14x26in) s. 4-Dec-2 AB Stockholms Auktionsverk #1594/R est:10000-12000 (S.KR 19000)
£1519 $2400 €2400 Elks in forest (75x127cm-30x50in) s. 1-Dec-2 Bukowskis, Helsinki #264/R est:2000-2500

LINDSTROM, Bengt (1925-) Swedish
£382 $603 €550 Sans titre (52x38cm-20x15in) s. acrylic. 28-Apr-3 Cornette de St.Cyr, Paris #451
£521 $828 €750 Figures (76x56cm-30x22in) s. acrylic panel. 29-Apr-3 Campo & Campo, Antwerp #194
£763 $1213 €1145 Composition with head (112x147cm-44x58in) s. 18-Mar-3 Maynards, Vancouver #42/R (C.D 1800)
£776 $1219 €1164 Tete Iaponc (61x38cm-24x15in) s. exhib. 16-Dec-2 Lilla Bukowskis, Stockholm #717 (S.KR 11000)
£851 $1319 €1277 Composition with heads (55x75cm-22x30in) s. 8-Dec-2 Uppsala Auktionskammare, Uppsala #272/R (S.KR 12000)
£881 $1365 €1400 Composition (120x80cm-47x31in) s. acrylic paper on panel. 5-Oct-2 De Vuyst, Lokeren #217/R
£953 $1592 €1382 Composition (125x80cm-49x31in) s. 17-Jun-3 Rasmussen, Copenhagen #202/R (D.KR 10000)
£993 $1539 €1490 Archipelago in summer (100x140cm-39x55in) s.d.1913. 4-Dec-2 AB Stockholms Auktionsverk #1772/R (S.KR 14000)
£1164 $1885 €1688 Composition in yellow with figures (46x38cm-18x15in) s. 25-May-3 Uppsala Auktionskammare, Uppsala #321/R est:15000-18000 (S.KR 15000)
£1172 $1876 €1700 Composition with three figures (53x74cm-21x29in) s. acrylic paper. 15-Mar-3 De Vuyst, Lokeren #189/R est:1800-2200
£1241 $2011 €1799 Composition in red and blue with female figure (46x38cm-18x15in) s. 25-May-3 Uppsala Auktionskammare, Uppsala #320/R est:16000-18000 (S.KR 16000)
£1290 $2039 €2000 Composition avec animal (65x54cm-26x21in) s. 17-Dec-2 Palais de Beaux Arts, Brussels #559/R est:2000-3000
£1367 $2187 €1900 Visages (77x57cm-30x22in) s.d.1974 acrylic paper laid on canvas. 18-May-3 Charbonneaux, Paris #175 est:1500-2000
£1411 $2216 €2117 The frightened (47x38cm-19x15in) s. 16-Dec-2 Lilla Bukowskis, Stockholm #562/R est:12000-15000 (S.KR 20000)
£1436 $2240 €2154 Personnage (72x60cm-28x24in) s. prov. 18-Sep-2 Kunsthallen, Copenhagen #27/R est:15000 (D.KR 17000)
£1622 $2611 €2433 The artist's dogs (33x40cm-13x16in) s. 7-May-3 AB Stockholms Auktionsverk #891/R est:10000-15000 (S.KR 21000)
£1753 $2770 €2630 White figure (66x54cm-26x21in) s/. 30-Nov-2 Goteborg Auktionsverk, Sweden #576/R est:20000 (S.KR 25000)
£1923 $2981 €3000 Tete verte (33x41cm-13x16in) s. acrylic. 7-Dec-2 Cornette de St.Cyr, Paris #91/R
£2008 $3232 €3012 Head (65x54cm-26x21in) s. 7-May-3 AB Stockholms Auktionsverk #894/R est:18000-20000 (S.KR 26000)
£2051 $3179 €3200 Petite fille aux yeux bleus (55x46cm-22x18in) s. acrylic. 7-Dec-2 Cornette de St.Cyr, Paris #89/R
£2102 $3280 €3153 Wild animal (38x46cm-15x18in) s. 6-Nov-2 AB Stockholms Auktionsverk #566/R est:20000-25000 (S.KR 30000)
£2158 $3453 €3000 Composition with animal (65x54cm-26x21in) s. 17-May-3 De Vuyst, Lokeren #579/R est:2800-3300
£2172 $3389 €3258 Eagle - the watch (38x46cm-15x18in) s. 6-Nov-2 AB Stockholms Auktionsverk #567/R est:20000-25000 (S.KR 31000)
£2465 $3968 €3500 Portrait (106x71cm-42x28in) s. acrylic paper c.1988. 11-May-3 Thierry & Lannon, Brest #267/R est:3600-4000
£2471 $3978 €3707 Abstract composition (74x60cm-29x24in) s. 7-May-3 AB Stockholms Auktionsverk #896/R est:40000-50000 (S.KR 32000)
£2523 $3936 €3785 Woman with salamander (100x81cm-39x32in) s. 5-Nov-2 Bukowskis, Stockholm #258/R est:15000-18000 (S.KR 36000)
£2663 $4154 €3995 Mythological gods (60x73cm-24x29in) 6-Nov-2 AB Stockholms Auktionsverk #701/R est:25000-30000 (S.KR 38000)
£2774 $4383 €4300 Personnage a la bouteille (55x46cm-22x18in) s. 19-Dec-2 Delvaux, Paris #49/R
£2821 $4428 €4400 Eteinte (50x61cm-20x24in) s. 23-Nov-2 Meeting Art, Vercelli #348/R
£2848 $4500 €4500 Untitled (65x81cm-26x32in) s. prov. 27-Nov-2 Tajan, Paris #5/R
£2973 $4638 €4400 Untitled (55x65cm-22x26in) s. 26-Mar-3 Finarte Semenzato, Milan #380/R
£3038 $4800 €4800 Le regard intense (100x84cm-39x33in) s. i.verso. 26-Nov-2 Sotheby's, Amsterdam #48/R est:2500-3500
£3050 $5093 €4300 Figure bleu rouge jaune (46x55cm-18x22in) s.d. 18-Jun-3 Charbonneaux, Paris #93/R est:4000-5000
£3097 $4893 €4800 Figure rouge (162x130cm-64x51in) s.i.verso. 17-Dec-2 Palais de Beaux Arts, Brussels #568/R est:5000-7500
£3121 $5055 €4400 Folla (38x46cm-15x18in) s. prov. 26-May-3 Christie's, Milan #322/R est:4000-6000
£3270 $5167 €4905 Green figure (100x80cm-39x31in) s/. 28-Apr-3 Bukowskis, Stockholm #282/R est:40000-50000 (S.KR 43000)
£3398 $5470 €5097 Figures in red and yellow (100x81cm-39x32in) s. 7-May-3 AB Stockholms Auktionsverk #895/R est:30000-35000 (S.KR 44000)
£3544 $5600 €5600 Figures (92x73cm-36x29in) s. 26-Nov-2 Palais de Beaux Arts, Brussels #269/R est:5000-7000
£3673 $5841 €5400 Sans titre (105x74cm-41x29in) s. acrylic paper on panel. 26-Feb-3 Artcurial Briest, Paris #537/R est:2500-3000

£3707 $5968 €5561 The bird Phoenix (65x54cm-26x21in) s. 7-May-3 AB Stockholms Auktionsverk #893/R est:25000-30000 (S.KR 48000)
£4167 $6458 €6500 Head (100x73cm-39x29in) s. painted c.1970. 7-Dec-2 De Vuyst, Lokeren #568/R est:7000-9000
£5326 $8308 €7989 The big party (130x163cm-51x64in) s. 5-Nov-2 Bukowskis, Stockholm #259/R est:40000-60000 (S.KR 76000)
£6038 $9298 €9600 Figure (91x73cm-36x29in) s.d. 26-Oct-2 Cornette de St.Cyr, Paris #31/R
£6792 $10460 €10800 Personnage (129x97cm-51x38in) s.d. acrylic. 26-Oct-2 Cornette de St.Cyr, Paris #32/R est:6000
£6803 $10816 €10000 Imaginary figure (130x97cm-51x38in) s. 1-Mar-3 Meeting Art, Vercelli #429 est:10000
£7051 $11071 €11000 Capture (202x202cm-80x80in) s. painted 1984. 11-Dec-2 Artcurial Briest, Paris #715/R
£7383 $11886 €11000 Personnage (81x65cm-32x26in) s. 23-Feb-3 Mercier & Cie, Lille #132/R est:12000

Sculpture

£1544 $2486 €2316 Head - composition (27cm-11in) init. sterling silver incl.black wood socle. 7-May-3 AB Stockholms Auktionsverk #781/R est:4000-5000 (S.KR 20000)
£1667 $2567 €2650 Tete (70x68x26cm-28x27x10in) s. num.13/20 painted resin. 26-Oct-2 Cornette de St.Cyr, Paris #33/R

Works on paper

£903 $1427 €1400 Composition (75x105cm-30x41in) s. ink paper on panel. 19-Dec-2 Ruellan, Paris #155
£1784 $2837 €2676 Woman smoking (146x113cm-57x44in) s. mixed media paper on canvas. 3-Mar-3 Lilla Bukowskis, Stockholm #96 est:15000-20000 (S.KR 24000)
£1887 $2906 €3000 Composition (105x75cm-41x30in) s. mixed media. 22-Oct-2 Campo, Vlaamse Kaai #546/R
£1887 $2906 €3000 Excuse (105x75cm-41x30in) s. gouache exec.1980. 26-Oct-2 Cornette de St.Cyr, Paris #29/R

LINDSTROM, Eleonora (1852-1930) Swedish

£881 $1356 €1400 Fairies playing (90x150cm-35x59in) s. i.d.1879 verso after August Malmstrom. 27-Oct-2 Bukowskis, Helsinki #324/R

LINDSTROM, Fritz (1874-1962) Swedish

£1773 $2748 €2660 Landscape (46x60cm-18x24in) s.d.1906. 4-Dec-2 AB Stockholms Auktionsverk #1579/R est:18000-20000 (S.KR 25000)

LINDSTROM, Matt (1890-1975) Canadian

£185 $290 €278 Early spring (30x40cm-12x16in) s. board. 25-Nov-2 Hodgins, Calgary #141/R (C.D 460)
£241 $378 €362 Sunrise in the mountains (50x65cm-20x26in) s.i. 25-Nov-2 Hodgins, Calgary #291/R (C.D 600)

LINDSTROM, Rikard (1882-1943) Swedish

£248 $385 €372 Skiers (72x92cm-28x36in) s.d.1926. 8-Dec-2 Uppsala Auktionskammare, Uppsala #140 (S.KR 3500)
£310 $503 €450 Riddarholmen (47x61cm-19x24in) s. panel. 25-May-3 Uppsala Auktionskammare, Uppsala #175 (S.KR 4000)
£409 $650 €614 View from the artist's window, Copenhagen (22x22cm-9x9in) panel prov. 3-Mar-3 Lilla Bukowskis, Stockholm #392 (S.KR 5500)
£494 $765 €741 Schooner in a good wind (91x102cm-36x40in) s.d.1926 board. 3-Dec-2 Ritchie, Toronto #3105/R est:1500-2000 (C.D 1200)
£618 $1025 €896 Vessel at anchor (90x70cm-35x28in) s.d.1942 panel. 16-Jun-3 Lilla Bukowskis, Stockholm #92 (S.KR 8000)
£1064 $1649 €1596 Houses, Fiskebackskil (63x100cm-25x39in) s.d.1941. 3-Dec-2 Bukowskis, Stockholm #131/R est:20000-25000 (S.KR 15000)

LINDSTROM, Sven Otto (1883-1932) Scandinavian

Works on paper

£719 $1179 €1100 Sailing boats (70x99cm-28x39in) s.d.1917 gouache. 9-Feb-3 Bukowskis, Helsinki #419/R

LINELLI, Aide (19th C) ?

£1000 $1600 €1500 Portrait of a boy and his two sisters holding an open book (89x71cm-35x28in) s. oval. 17-May-3 Pook & Pook, Downington #394/R est:2500-3500

LINER, Carl (1914-1997) Swiss

£386 $610 €579 Three ladies (15x22cm-6x9in) s.d.50 panel. 26-Nov-2 Hans Widmer, St Gallen #1245 (S.FR 900)
£509 $820 €738 Summer harbour (34x48cm-13x19in) s.d.1947 col chk gouache. 7-May-3 Dobiaschofsky, Bern #788/R (S.FR 1100)
£655 $1028 €983 Coastal landscape (34x49cm-13x19in) s.d.1955 paper on panel. 25-Nov-2 Germann, Zurich #58/R est:2000-3000 (S.FR 1500)
£866 $1342 €1299 Peasant woman wearing headscarf (40x40cm-16x16in) s. 24-Sep-2 Koller, Zurich #6679/R (S.FR 2000)
£873 $1362 €1310 Grey brown composition (46x38cm-18x15in) s. 6-Nov-2 Hans Widmer, St Gallen #3/R est:2400-4000 (S.FR 2000)
£944 $1492 €1416 Tunis (32x49cm-13x19in) s. W/C prov. 28-Nov-2 Christie's, Zurich #106/R (S.FR 2200)
£996 $1573 €1494 Composition in dark red and black (74x51cm-29x20in) s.d.61 paper. 26-Nov-2 Hans Widmer, St Gallen #2320 est:1500-4200 (S.FR 2320)
£1073 $1695 €1610 Small composition in green, yellow, blue and black (34x26cm-13x10in) s.d.69 panel. 26-Nov-2 Hans Widmer, St Gallen #1253 est:1500-3200 (S.FR 2500)
£1223 $1907 €1835 Corsica (44x55cm-17x22in) s.d.52 i. verso board. 6-Nov-2 Hans Widmer, St Gallen #69/R est:2500-4000 (S.FR 2800)
£1304 $2022 €1956 Composition (54x45cm-21x18in) s. 9-Dec-2 Philippe Schuler, Zurich #3826 est:2000-3000 (S.FR 3000)
£1335 $2109 €2003 Woman on the Nile (33x46cm-13x18in) s.d.37 oil over chl panel. 26-Nov-2 Hans Widmer, St Gallen #1238/R est:3000-4800 (S.FR 3110)
£1397 $2180 €2096 Figures under tree in bay, Corsica (40x60cm-16x24in) s.d.49 board. 6-Nov-2 Hans Widmer, St Gallen #6/R est:3500-6000 (S.FR 3200)
£1397 $2180 €2096 Trees in winter landscape (35x49cm-14x19in) s.d.54 oil chl board. 6-Nov-2 Hans Widmer, St Gallen #71/R est:3000-5500 (S.FR 3200)
£1397 $2180 €2096 Sailing boat on beach (42x50cm-17x20in) s. 20-Nov-2 Fischer, Luzern #1286/R est:2500-3000 (S.FR 3200)
£1502 $2373 €2253 Composition in ochre and black on blue background (73x50cm-29x20in) s.d.70. 26-Nov-2 Hans Widmer, St Gallen #1240/R est:3000-5500 (S.FR 3500)
£1545 $2441 €2318 Still life with fishes (22x33cm-9x13in) s.d.54 board prov. 28-Nov-2 Christie's, Zurich #107/R est:3000-4000 (S.FR 3600)
£1582 $2468 €2500 Composition (100x81cm-39x32in) s.d.1970 lit. 20-Oct-2 Charbonneaux, Paris #139 est:2500-3000
£1747 $2725 €2621 Hilly landscape in Appenzell with farmstead (38x54cm-15x21in) s. board. 6-Nov-2 Hans Widmer, St Gallen #72/R est:4000-6500 (S.FR 4000)
£1747 $2742 €2621 Mediterranean village (51x66cm-20x26in) s.d.1954 paper on panel. 25-Nov-2 Germann, Zurich #62/R est:2500-3500 (S.FR 4000)
£1948 $3019 €2922 Landscape with tree (46x54cm-18x21in) s. panel. 24-Sep-2 Koller, Zurich #6676/R est:6000-8000 (S.FR 4500)
£1965 $3066 €2948 Blue, red, white, black composition (90x61cm-35x24in) s.d.59 board. 6-Nov-2 Hans Widmer, St Gallen #7/R est:4000-6800 (S.FR 4500)
£2096 $3270 €3144 Blue yellow black composition (146x60cm-57x24in) s. 6-Nov-2 Hans Widmer, St Gallen #4/R est:3500-6000 (S.FR 4800)
£2183 $3406 €3275 Ochre, green, black composition (65x50cm-26x20in) s.d.64 board. 6-Nov-2 Hans Widmer, St Gallen #68/R est:4000-6000 (S.FR 5000)
£2183 $3406 €3275 Olive, ochre, grey composition (91x62cm-36x24in) s.d.58. 6-Nov-2 Hans Widmer, St Gallen #130/R est:5000-9000 (S.FR 5000)
£2183 $3428 €3275 Composition (116x88cm-46x35in) s.d.1964. 25-Nov-2 Germann, Zurich #60/R est:6000-8000 (S.FR 5000)
£2271 $3542 €3407 Woman carrying water, Corsica (65x50cm-26x20in) s.d.56. 6-Nov-2 Hans Widmer, St Gallen #5/R est:4000-6500 (S.FR 5200)
£2304 $3595 €3456 Untitled (80x40cm-31x16in) s.d.1964. 16-Sep-2 Philippe Schuler, Zurich #3387 est:2500-3000 (S.FR 5300)
£2445 $3815 €3668 Yellow, blue, black composition (61x50cm-24x20in) s.d.66 board. 6-Nov-2 Hans Widmer, St Gallen #144/R est:3000-5500 (S.FR 5600)
£2620 $4087 €3930 Ships in Rhein harbour (73x100cm-29x39in) s.d.55. 8-Nov-2 Dobiaschofsky, Bern #182/R est:6500 (S.FR 6000)
£2838 $4428 €4257 Neckertal landscape (54x73cm-21x29in) s.d.1946. 6-Nov-2 Hans Widmer, St Gallen #29/R est:4000-7500 (S.FR 6500)
£2838 $4428 €4257 Dark red, grey blue, black composition (89x116cm-35x46in) s.d.59. 6-Nov-2 Hans Widmer, St Gallen #70/R est:4000-8500 (S.FR 6500)
£3057 $4799 €4586 Abstract (100x81cm-39x32in) s.d.1961. 25-Nov-2 Germann, Zurich #59/R est:5500-7500 (S.FR 7000)
£3493 $5450 €5240 Mountain lake (65x85cm-26x33in) s.d.43. 6-Nov-2 Hans Widmer, St Gallen #8/R est:8000-12000 (S.FR 8000)
£3493 $5450 €5240 Red, grey, brown composition (96x146cm-38x57in) s.d.60. 6-Nov-2 Hans Widmer, St Gallen #67/R est:8000-12000 (S.FR 8000)
£3712 $5828 €5568 Gorge (81x65cm-32x26in) s. 25-Nov-2 Sotheby's, Zurich #135/R est:5000-7000 (S.FR 8500)
£3718 $5763 €5800 Composition in blue/yellow/white (80x129cm-31x51in) s.d.1970. 7-Dec-2 Ketterer, Hamburg #593/R est:2500-3500
£4348 $6783 €6522 Summer near Weissbad (60x73cm-24x29in) s.d.1959. 16-Sep-2 Philippe Schuler, Zurich #3386/R est:5000-6000 (S.FR 10000)
£5000 $7800 €7500 Glandenstein near Weissbad (73x92cm-29x36in) s.d.1952. 16-Sep-2 Philippe Schuler, Zurich #3385/R est:7000-9000 (S.FR 11500)
£5022 $7834 €7533 Appenzell landscape with Santis (60x81cm-24x32in) s. 6-Nov-2 Hans Widmer, St Gallen #28/R est:10000-15000 (S.FR 11500)
£5150 $8137 €7725 Corsica (89x116cm-35x46in) s.d.54 prov. 28-Nov-2 Christie's, Zurich #108/R est:10000-15000 (S.FR 12000)
£6987 $10969 €10481 Egyptian stone quarry (101x150cm-40x59in) s.d.1937. 25-Nov-2 Sotheby's, Zurich #75/R est:8000-12000 (S.FR 16000)

£7391 $11457 €11087 Alpstein (81x100cm-32x39in) s. 9-Dec-2 Philippe Schuler, Zurich #3825/R est:8000-12000 (S.FR 17000)

£7860 $12262 €11790 Rocca d'Orcia, Italy (81x100cm-32x39in) s.d.56 i.d. stretcher. 6-Nov-2 Hans Widmer, St Gallen #46/R est:15000-22000 (S.FR 18000)

£11588 $18309 €17382 Samtisersee (73x54cm-29x21in) s. prov. 28-Nov-2 Christie's, Zurich #109/R est:6000-8000 (S.FR 27000)

Works on paper

£408 $644 €612 Three women (16x24cm-6x9in) s.d.1951 gouache. 29-Nov-2 Zofingen, Switzerland #2966 (S.FR 950)

£452 $756 €655 Mountain landscape (24x31cm-9x12in) s. gouache. 24-Jun-3 Koller, Zurich #63/R (S.FR 1000)

£472 $746 €708 Church (34x23cm-13x9in) s.d.50 chl gouache. 26-Nov-2 Hans Widmer, St Gallen #1249 (S.FR 1100)

£553 $857 €830 Composition (33x25cm-13x10in) s.d.21 gouache. 4-Dec-2 Koller, Zurich #184/R est:1600-2400 (S.FR 1270)

£562 $888 €843 On the Weissbach (33x40cm-13x16in) s. W/C over chl. 26-Nov-2 Hans Widmer, St Gallen #1239/R (S.FR 1310)

£565 $882 €848 Rear view of girl in traditional costume (34x27cm-13x11in) s.d.1935 W/C pencil. 16-Sep-2 Philippe Schuler, Zurich #3212 (S.FR 1300)

£601 $949 €902 Harbour for boats on the Corsican coast (34x49cm-13x19in) s.d.54 ink tempera. 26-Nov-2 Hans Widmer, St Gallen #1248 (S.FR 1400)

£601 $949 €902 Ship in Corsican harbour (22x33cm-9x13in) s.d.1954 chl gouache col chk. 26-Nov-2 Hans Widmer, St Gallen #1254 (S.FR 1400)

£611 $960 €917 Southern landscape (31x40cm-12x16in) s. W/C. 25-Nov-2 Germann, Zurich #61 (S.FR 1400)

£655 $1028 €983 Spanish coast (32x48cm-13x19in) s. gouache. 25-Nov-2 Germann, Zurich #57 est:1000-1500 (S.FR 1500)

£696 $1078 €1044 Corsican landscape (30x45cm-12x18in) s.d.1950 W/C over pencil. 9-Dec-2 Philippe Schuler, Zurich #3576 (S.FR 1600)

£696 $1078 €1044 Corsican landscape (30x46cm-12x18in) s.d.1950 mixed media. 9-Dec-2 Philippe Schuler, Zurich #3577/R (S.FR 1600)

£699 $1097 €1049 Mountain landscape (28x38cm-11x15in) s. gouache. 25-Nov-2 Germann, Zurich #762 est:1000-1500 (S.FR 1600)

£793 $1158 €1190 Lac de St Remy (28x41cm-11x16in) s.i. gouache. 17-Jun-2 Philippe Schuler, Zurich #4199/R (S.FR 1800)

£858 $1356 €1287 Antibes (31x42cm-12x17in) s.i. W/C prov. 28-Nov-2 Christie's, Zurich #105/R (S.FR 2000)

£1013 $1580 €1600 Composition (72x51cm-28x20in) s.d.1964 cardboard exhib. 20-Oct-2 Charbonneaux, Paris #67/R est:1200-1500

LINER, Carl August (1871-1946) Swiss

£1174 $1925 €1702 Portrait of an officer (59x43cm-23x17in) s.d.95. 4-Jun-3 Fischer, Luzern #1245/R est:2500-3500 (S.FR 2500)

£3219 $5086 €4829 Woman with sickle, Terracina (30x10cm-12x4in) s.d.92. 26-Nov-2 Phillips, Zurich #25/R est:7500-8500 (S.FR 7500)

£17467 $27249 €26201 Appenzell landscape with river (70x100cm-28x39in) s.d.1921 exhib. 6-Nov-2 Hans Widmer, St Gallen #26/R est:40000-60000 (S.FR 40000)

£19313 $30515 €28970 Young herdsman (70x100cm-28x39in) s. painted 1927. 26-Nov-2 Phillips, Zurich #23/R est:45000-55000 (S.FR 45000)

£48035 $70131 €72053 Terracina (44x60cm-17x24in) s.i.d.1898. 4-Jun-2 Germann, Zurich #75/R est:12000-16000 (S.FR 110000)

Works on paper

£786 $1226 €1179 Peasant scene (26x47cm-10x19in) pencil. 6-Nov-2 Hans Widmer, St Gallen #27/R (S.FR 1800)

£1073 $1695 €1610 Oasis in Algiers (24x36cm-9x14in) s.d.48 gouache. 26-Nov-2 Phillips, Zurich #26/R est:2500-3500 (S.FR 2500)

£1717 $2712 €2576 View of Rhein valley (32x47cm-13x19in) s.d.56 W/C. 26-Nov-2 Phillips, Zurich #27/R est:2800-3500 (S.FR 4000)

LINES, Frederick Thomas (19th C) British

Works on paper

£1800 $2808 €2700 Portrait of a country gentleman (86x53cm-34x21in) W/C sold with art society book. 5-Nov-2 Bonhams, New Bond Street #67/R est:2000-3000

LINES, Henry H (1800-1889) British

£360 $558 €540 Wooded landscape with figures (18x23cm-7x9in) s.i.verso board. 26-Sep-2 Mellors & Kirk, Nottingham #679

Works on paper

£320 $522 €480 Cottages at Clevendon (25x35cm-10x14in) s. W/C over pencil. 11-Feb-3 Bonhams, Knowle #22

LINGELBACH, Johannes (1622-1674) Dutch

£4000 $6280 €6000 Extensive landscape with haymakers (35x29cm-14x11in) init. canvas on panel prov. 13-Dec-2 Christie's, Kensington #140/R est:2500-3500

£11321 $17547 €18000 Resting hunting party outside palace gate (53x65cm-21x26in) s. prov. 2-Oct-2 Dorotheum, Vienna #213/R est:15000-22000

£14000 $23380 €20300 Figures and tradesmen near a fountain in Roman Square (68x65cm-27x26in) s. prov. 10-Jul-3 Sotheby's, London #140/R est:8000-12000

Works on paper

£2500 $4175 €3625 Orientals and seamen on a Mediterranean Quay (18x28cm-7x11in) s. point of brush wash over pen brown ink prov.exhib. 9-Jul-3 Sotheby's, London #97/R est:1800-2200

LINGELBACH, Johannes (attrib) (1622-1674) Dutch

£17308 $27173 €27000 Travellers in harbour scene (57x67cm-22x26in) i. 21-Nov-2 Van Ham, Cologne #1390/R est:8000

LINGENFELDER, Daniel (1862-1910) German

£276 $450 €414 Fishing boats on a beach at sunset (51x79cm-20x31in) s. 2-Feb-3 Simpson's, Houston #169

LINGNER, Otto (1856-?) German

£1870 $2917 €2805 Reclining female nude (82x128cm-32x50in) s. 16-Sep-2 Philippe Schuler, Zurich #3486/R est:3000-5000 (S.FR 4300)

£2500 $3950 €3750 Woman undressing (96x68cm-38x27in) s. 14-Nov-2 Christie's, Kensington #22/R est:1000-1500

LINGUET, Henri (fl.1881-1914) French

£335 $543 €486 Village in Southern France (27x35cm-11x14in) s. panel. 26-May-3 Rasmussen, Copenhagen #1408/R (D.KR 3500)

LINK, O Winston (1914-2001) American

Photographs

£1948 $3000 €2922 Policeman, Weldon Painter patrols the main street of Stanley, Virginia (40x49cm-16x19in) s.d.1998 photograph. 24-Oct-2 Sotheby's, New York #232/R est:3000-5000

£2761 $4500 €4142 Hotshot, East bound, laeger, west (39x49cm-15x19in) s.d.1956/1996 gelatin silver print. 12-Feb-3 Christie's, Rockefeller NY #191/R est:4000-6000

£2848 $4500 €4272 Swimming pool, Welch, Virginia (40x49cm-16x19in) s. two gelatin silver print prov. 25-Apr-3 Phillips, New York #250/R est:2500-3500

£3291 $5200 €4937 Main line Main Street, Norfolk, West Virginia (40x49cm-16x19in) s. 2 gelatin silver print prov.lit. 25-Apr-3 Phillips, New York #248/R est:2500-3500

£3896 $6000 €5844 Hot shot Eastbound, Iager, West Virginia (39x49cm-15x19in) s.d.1957 photograph. 24-Oct-2 Sotheby's, New York #231/R est:6000-9000

£4114 $6500 €6171 Hot shot Eastbound, Iager, West Virginia (39x49cm-15x19in) s.d.1957 photograph. 23-Apr-3 Sotheby's, New York #33/R est:6000-9000

£4430 $7000 €6645 Hot shot east bound, laeger, West Virginia (40x49cm-16x19in) s. gelatin silver print prov. 22-Apr-3 Christie's, Rockefeller NY #43/R est:5000-7000

£8861 $14000 €13292 Hot shot eastbound, West Virginia (39x49cm-15x19in) s. 2 gelatin silver print executed c.1956 prov.lit. 25-Apr-3 Phillips, New York #247 est:4000-6000

LINKLATER, Barrie (1931-) British

£3400 $5508 €5100 Mares and their foals (60x96cm-24x38in) s. 20-May-3 Sotheby's, Olympia #158/R est:2000-3000

LINNELL, John (1792-1882) British

£250 $390 €375 Portrait of Robert B Walker (13x11cm-5x4in) i.verso prov. 18-Sep-2 Cheffins Grain & Comins, Cambridge #533

£1000 $1670 €1450 Dusty road (17x23cm-7x9in) s.d.1868 board. 17-Jun-3 Bonhams, New Bond Street #38/R est:1000-1500

£1511 $2508 €2191 Portrait of Alexander Milford Sutherland (77x63cm-30x25in) s.d.1840 exhib. 16-Jun-3 Waddingtons, Toronto #140/R est:3000-3500 (C.D 3400)

£2700 $4482 €4050 Surrey glade (27x34cm-11x13in) s. panel prov. 10-Jun-3 Sworder & Son, Bishops Stortford #532/R est:2000-3000

£2800 $4536 €4060 Wooded landscape with shepherd and shepherdess and sheep (14x11cm-6x4in) panel. 29-Jul-3 Capes Dunn, Manchester #20/R

£3500 $5530 €5250 Portrait of Mrs Henry Stephen seated in landscape (26x21cm-10x8in) s.d.1830 i.d.1829 verso panel prov.lit. 26-Nov-2 Christie's, London #49/R est:4000-6000

£3800 $6004 €5700 Wooded landscape with herdsmen and cattle (20x14cm-8x6in) s.d.1828 panel. 26-Nov-2 Christie's, London #72/R est:2500-3500

£5938 $9500 €8907 View of the windmill at Reigate Heath with a figure and sheep (79x110cm-31x43in) s.d.1878. 14-May-3 Butterfields, San Francisco #1141/R est:5000-7000

£7000 $11620 €10500 Portraits of Robert and Jane Ogle aged five and three (21x16cm-8x6in) s. panel pair prov. 12-Jun-3 Sotheby's, London #81/R est:8000-12000

£8500 $13430 €12750 Kensington gravel pits (14x23cm-6x9in) panel prov. 26-Nov-2 Christie's, London #71/R est:2000-3000

£150000 $241500 €225000 Return of Ulysses (124x185cm-49x73in) s.i.d.1848 prov.exhib.lit. 19-Feb-3 Christie's, London #4/R est:80000-120000

Miniatures

£2000 $3120 €3000 Lady Elizabeth Belgrave wearing decollete burgundy and white dress (10cm-4in) s.d.1820 gilt frame ormolu slip rec. prov.lit. 5-Nov-2 Bonhams, New Bond Street #145/R est:1200-1800

Works on paper

£250 $390 €375 Study of a young child (28x21cm-11x8in) s. pencil. 27-Mar-3 Christie's, Kensington #19

£620 $1023 €899 Hillside (38x51cm-15x20in) blk chk wash. 2-Jul-3 Sotheby's, Olympia #225/R

£1000 $1640 €1450 Woodcutters, Bray Wood, Windsor (15x18cm-6x7in) init.i. pencil htd white prov.exhib. 5-Jun-3 Christie's, London #49/R est:1200-1800

£1100 $1727 €1650 Reverend Edward Bury (25x15cm-10x6in) s.i. pencil htd white prov. 21-Nov-2 Christie's, London #33/R est:1200-1800

£2400 $3936 €3480 Dolwyddelan Valley, North Wales (19x25cm-7x10in) s.i.d.1813 pencil W/C. 5-Jun-3 Christie's, London #76/R est:1500-2000

£3000 $4710 €4500 Finchley Commom (23x33cm-9x13in) s.i.d.1805 black white chk prov.exhib. 21-Nov-2 Christie's, London #30/R est:4000-6000

£5500 $9020 €7975 Extensive landscape in North Wales (25x37cm-10x15in) s.i.d.1813 pencil W/C prov.exhib. 5-Jun-3 Christie's, London #75/R est:2000-3000

£9000 $14760 €13050 Resting woodcutters, Bray Wood, Windsor (16x27cm-6x11in) s.d.1827 pencil ink W/C gum arabic htd bodycol prov.exhib. 5-Jun-3 Christie's, London #78/R est:7000-10000

£11000 $18040 €15950 Rooks Hill, Kent (29x35cm-11x14in) s.d.1828 pencil pen ink W/C prov. 5-Jun-3 Christie's, London #92/R est:4000-6000

LINNELL, John (attrib) (1792-1882) British

£260 $403 €390 Harvesters in a field (17x25cm-7x10in) board. 24-Sep-2 Anderson & Garland, Newcastle #519

LINNELL, William (1826-1910) British

£833 $1300 €1250 Shepherds and their flock at rest (69x99cm-27x39in) s.d.1874. 9-Oct-2 Doyle, New York #66

£5000 $8300 €7500 Goat herds in the Apennines (67x115cm-26x45in) s.i.d.1864 prov. 12-Jun-3 Sotheby's, London #273/R est:3000-5000

LINNIG, Ben (1860-1929) Belgian

£417 $654 €650 Le forgeron de cuivre (82x110cm-32x43in) 25-Nov-2 Amberes, Antwerp #176

LINNIG, Egidius (1821-1860) Belgian

£2041 $3245 €3000 Marine (65x84cm-26x33in) s. 18-Mar-3 Galerie Moderne, Brussels #580/R est:4000-6000

LINNIG, Willem (younger) (1842-1890) Belgian

£449 $696 €700 Vieille femme (18x16cm-7x6in) s. panel. 3-Dec-2 Campo & Campo, Antwerp #186/R

£4167 $6458 €6500 Chez la diseuse de bonne aventure (100x75cm-39x30in) s. panel. 3-Dec-2 Campo & Campo, Antwerp #187/R est:8000-12000

Works on paper

£1633 $2596 €2400 Elegant woman (100x74cm-39x29in) mixed media. 24-Mar-3 Bernaerts, Antwerp #821/R est:2500-3500

LINNOVAARA, Juhani (1934-) Finnish

£3165 $5000 €5000 Mystic landscape (73x75cm-29x30in) s. 30-Nov-2 Hagelstam, Helsinki #165/R est:5000

Works on paper

£345 $545 €500 Toledo (44x60cm-17x24in) s.d.1964 Indian ink wash. 3-Apr-3 Hagelstam, Helsinki #891/R

£949 $1481 €1500 Marshes (60x80cm-24x31in) s.d.1965 gouache. 12-Sep-2 Hagelstam, Helsinki #838 est:2000

£1942 $3108 €2700 Figure (71x51cm-28x20in) s.d.1974 gouache. 17-May-3 Hagelstam, Helsinki #202/R est:3000

LINNQVIST, Hilding (1891-1984) Swedish

£913 $1442 €1370 Market stalls (37x46cm-15x18in) init. panel exhib. 28-Apr-3 Bukowskis, Stockholm #170/R (S.KR 12000)

£1078 $1714 €1617 Black tureen (55x45cm-22x18in) mono. d.1953 verso panel. 3-Mar-3 Lilla Bukowskis, Stockholm #18 est:15000-20000 (S.KR 14500)

£2433 $3845 €3650 Still life of jug and fruit (74x92cm-29x36in) mono. 28-Apr-3 Bukowskis, Stockholm #180b/R est:40000-60000 (S.KR 32000)

£2663 $4154 €3995 Still life of figs (20x26cm-8x10in) s.d.1921 panel. 6-Nov-2 AB Stockholms Auktionsverk #641/R est:30000-35000 (S.KR 38000)

£3422 $5407 €5133 Architecture and children playing III, Piazzetta degli Leoncini (84x106cm-33x42in) init. exhib. 28-Apr-3 Bukowskis, Stockholm #211/R est:50000-70000 (S.KR 45000)

£7008 $10932 €10512 Still life of flowers and butterflies (152x150cm-60x59in) mono. 6-Nov-2 AB Stockholms Auktionsverk #640/R est:125000-150000 (S.KR 100000)

£7104 $11438 €10656 Making of the chalkstone quay, Luxor I (97x58cm-38x23in) mono. exhib. 7-May-3 AB Stockholms Auktionsverk #658/R est:60000-70000 (S.KR 92000)

£9125 $14418 €13688 View towards Soder across Reimersholme, Stockholm (59x93cm-23x37in) init. panel. 28-Apr-3 Bukowskis, Stockholm #84/R est:125000-150000 (S.KR 120000)

£20849 $33568 €31274 The harbour in Ancona (34x55cm-13x22in) mono. s.d.1922 verso panel prov.exhib.lit. 7-May-3 AB Stockholms Auktionsverk #752/R est:200000-250000 (S.KR 270000)

£25228 $39355 €37842 View over Karlbergs Palace, Stockholm (28x21cm-11x8in) i.verso sketch of boy verso canvas on cardboard. 5-Nov-2 Bukowskis, Stockholm #9/R est:300000-400000 (S.KR 360000)

Works on paper

£491 $765 €737 Woman with leopard (43x30cm-17x12in) init. Indian ink. 5-Nov-2 Bukowskis, Stockholm #8/R (S.KR 7000)

£561 $875 €842 The Britania on Stockholm's river (24x35cm-9x14in) init. W/C exhib. 6-Nov-2 AB Stockholms Auktionsverk #686/R (S.KR 8000)

£596 $929 €894 Cedar by Lake Garda (75x51cm-30x20in) mono.d.1968 mixed media. 6-Nov-2 AB Stockholms Auktionsverk #649/R (S.KR 8500)

£1191 $1858 €1787 Oriental figures (78x28cm-31x11in) mono. W/C. 6-Nov-2 AB Stockholms Auktionsverk #684/R est:20000-25000 (S.KR 17000)

£2934 $4724 €4401 Still life of daffodils (51x38cm-20x15in) mono. W/C. 7-May-3 AB Stockholms Auktionsverk #657/R est:30000-35000 (S.KR 38000)

LINO, Gustave (1893-1961) ?

£833 $1308 €1300 Le port d'Alger (13x24cm-5x9in) s. panel. 16-Dec-2 Gros & Delettrez, Paris #302/R

£993 $1619 €1500 Venise (73x51cm-29x20in) s. 31-Jan-3 Charbonneaux, Paris #122/R est:2500-3000

£3061 $4867 €4500 Le souk des moutons (45x55cm-18x22in) s. panel. 24-Mar-3 Rabourdin & Choppin de Janvry, Paris #62/R est:4000-4500

£3270 $5036 €5200 Port d'Alger (65x54cm-26x21in) s. 23-Oct-2 Rabourdin & Choppin de Janvry, Paris #205/R

LINS, Adolf (1856-1927) German

£560 $902 €812 Winter sky (38x32cm-15x13in) s. canvasboard. 12-May-3 Joel, Victoria #360 est:1000-1500 (A.D 1400)

£1410 $2214 €2200 Melting snows (54x35cm-21x14in) s. panel. 21-Nov-2 Van Ham, Cologne #1756 est:2200

£4452 $6945 €6500 Ducks and hens by water in spring (69x56cm-27x22in) s. 10-Apr-3 Van Ham, Cologne #1573/R est:5800

£4717 $7358 €7500 Wild geese on pond (125x190cm-49x75in) s. 19-Sep-2 Dr Fritz Nagel, Stuttgart #966/R est:9800

LINSLEY, W (?) ?

£550 $858 €825 View of St. Paul's from the Thames (28x20cm-11x8in) s. board. 10-Sep-2 Bonhams, Knightsbridge #92a

LINT, Giacomo van (1723-1790) Italian

£16667 $27000 €25001 View of Piazza colonna (35x45cm-14x18in) 23-Jan-3 Sotheby's, New York #157/R est:20000

LINT, Giacomo van (studio) (1723-1790) Italian

£11000 $18370 €15950 The Campidoglio, Rome (62x74cm-24x29in) 9-Jul-3 Bonhams, New Bond Street #16/R est:6000-8000

LINT, Hendrik van (1684-1763) Flemish

£6289 $9748 €10000 View of Roman Campagna (46x37cm-18x15in) 2-Oct-2 Dorotheum, Vienna #68/R est:10000-15000

£104938 $170000 €157407 Rome, the Colosseum with the Arch of Constantine, from the Orto of the Frati di Santa (39x72cm-15x28in) prov. 24-Jan-3 Christie's, Rockefeller NY #57/R est:120000-180000

LINT, Hendrik van (attrib) (1684-1763) Flemish
£12000 $20040 €17400 Classical landscape with the nymph Egeria mourning for Numa (95x74cm-37x29in) after Claude Gellee. 10-Jul-3 Sotheby's, London #212/R est:10000-15000

LINT, Hendrik van (style) (1684-1763) Flemish
£7000 $10850 €10500 Classical landscape with figures conversing on a hilltop near a temple, coastal town beyond (117x162cm-46x64in) 30-Oct-2 Christie's, Kensington #59/R est:7000-10000
£7000 $10990 €10500 Extensive landscape with peasants and a donkey on a track (37x59cm-15x23in) 10-Dec-2 Bonhams, New Bond Street #221/R est:7000-10000
£32000 $50240 €48000 Southern landscapes with figures at a fountain, and beside an urn (48x65cm-19x26in) oval pair prov. 12-Dec-2 Sotheby's, London #224/R est:12000-18000

LINT, Louis van (1909-1986) Belgian
£1572 $2421 €2500 Composition (74x145cm-29x57in) s.d.1960 exhib. 22-Oct-2 Campo, Vlaamse Kaai #654/R
£7051 $10929 €11000 Abstracr composition (100x130cm-39x51in) s. painted c.1949-51. 3-Dec-2 Christie's, Amsterdam #282/R est:9000-12000
£20645 $32619 €32000 La symphonie en rouge (150x200cm-59x79in) s.d.49 exhib. 17-Dec-2 Palais de Beaux Arts, Brussels #633/R est:11500-15000
Works on paper
£256 $397 €400 Composition (19x15cm-7x6in) s. W/C exec.1965 lit. 7-Dec-2 De Vuyst, Lokeren #362
£881 $1365 €1400 Interior with man (61x41cm-24x16in) s.d.61 W/C pastel pencil. 5-Oct-2 De Vuyst, Lokeren #380

LINT, Peter van (1609-1690) Flemish
£12903 $20387 €20000 Flore (119x93cm-47x37in) 18-Dec-2 Piasa, Paris #71/R est:30000

LINT, Peter van (attrib) (1609-1690) Flemish
£23226 $36696 €36000 Moise sauve des eaux. Bethsabee au bain (96x145cm-38x57in) pair. 18-Dec-2 Tajan, Paris #33/R est:15000

LINTON, Frank Benton (1871-1943) American
£5519 $8500 €8279 Portrait of Ruth St Denis (244x142cm-96x56in) s.d.1918 canvas on board. 8-Sep-2 Treadway Gallery, Cincinnati #626/R est:7000-9000

LINTON, Richard (1935-) Australian
£1300 $2093 €1885 Bay steamers Hygeia and courier at Mornington Pier (29x53cm-11x21in) s.d.74 board. 12-May-3 Joel, Victoria #278 est:1000-1500 (A.D 3250)

LINTON, Sir James Dromgole (1840-1916) British
£764 $1192 €1200 Portrait of musician (40x30cm-16x12in) mono. i.verso panel. 7-Nov-2 Chochon-Barre & Allardi, Paris #3/R
Works on paper
£260 $411 €377 Alice Bridgnorth SS (46x34cm-18x13in) s.d.1885 W/C. 22-Jul-3 Bonhams, Knightsbridge #208/R
£450 $752 €653 Final touch (34x47cm-13x19in) init.d.08 W/C. 24-Jun-3 Bonhams, Knightsbridge #78/R
£800 $1288 €1160 Trial scene, the merchant of Venice (37x51cm-15x20in) init. W/C. 12-May-3 Joel, Victoria #409 est:2000-3000 (A.D 2000)
£2200 $3542 €3300 Page (34x21cm-13x8in) mono. pencil W/C htd white gum arabic prov. 20-Feb-3 Christie's, London #71/R

LINTON, William (1791-1876) British
£350 $553 €508 Portrait of a polo pony before a marquee (38x48cm-15x19in) 24-Jul-3 John Nicholson, Haslemere #1199
£800 $1256 €1200 View of an Italian hilltop town (24x33cm-9x13in) mono. paper on canvas. 19-Nov-2 Bonhams, New Bond Street #47/R
£1600 $2512 €2400 Venice, St. Simeone Piccolo (25x34cm-10x13in) mono. paper on panel. 19-Nov-2 Bonhams, New Bond Street #46/R est:1000-1500
£2800 $4452 €4200 View of Osmington Bay, Dorset (24x32cm-9x13in) oil on paper. 19-Mar-3 Sotheby's, London #83/R est:2000-3000
£8000 $13280 €12000 View of Broad Oak Printwork, near Accrington, Lancashire, with Broad Oak House beyond (65x91cm-26x36in) 10-Jun-3 Christie's, London #68/R est:8000-12000

LINTON, William Evans (1878-?) British
£1200 $1872 €1800 Midday (84x112cm-33x44in) s. exhib. 26-Mar-3 Hamptons Fine Art, Godalming #169/R est:1000-1500
£3200 $4960 €4800 End of the day (49x79cm-19x31in) s.i. 4-Dec-2 Outhwaite & Litherland, Liverpool #330/R

LINTOTT, Edward Bernard (1875-1951) British
£1122 $1750 €1683 Still life with yellow roses (64x71cm-25x28in) s. 11-Aug-2 Thomaston Place, Thomaston #35

LINTOTT, Henry John (1877-1965) British
£750 $1223 €1125 Figures in a forest (77x103cm-30x41in) 14-Feb-3 Lyon & Turnbull, Edinburgh #89
£5200 $8424 €7800 Green dress (182x91cm-72x36in) 23-May-3 Lyon & Turnbull, Edinburgh #46/R est:3000-5000

LINTURI, Into (1902-1989) Finnish
£403 $661 €560 Town scene (41x34cm-16x13in) s.d.1932. 4-Jun-3 Bukowskis, Helsinki #346/R

LINUS, Axel (1885-1980) American
£755 $1200 €1133 Landscape with lake (25x33cm-10x13in) s. canvas on board. 2-Mar-3 Toomey, Oak Park #659/R

LION, Alexander (1823-1852) Belgian
£828 $1292 €1300 Dentelliere dans un interieur flamand (38x32cm-15x13in) s. 11-Nov-2 Horta, Bruxelles #677

LION, C (?) ?
£606 $939 €909 Woman by bridge (65x49cm-26x19in) s. 24-Sep-2 Koller, Zurich #6755 (S.FR 1400)

LIONE, Andrea di (1596-1675) Italian
Works on paper
£12162 $18973 €18000 Three men on elephants carrying trophies (27x34cm-11x13in) i. chk wash. 27-Mar-3 Christie's, Paris #29/R est:30000

LIONE, Andrea di (attrib) (1596-1675) Italian
£72000 $120240 €104400 Study of the head of an old man crowned with laurel, probably a poet (42x42cm-17x17in) round laid onto square relining canvas. 10-Jul-3 Sotheby's, London #171/R est:6000-8000

LIONEL, Percy (?) British
£1500 $2445 €2250 Wherry on the Norfolk Broads (46x79cm-18x31in) s. 14-Feb-3 Keys, Aylsham #646/R est:300-400

LIOT, Paul (1855-1902) French
£6500 $10335 €9750 Harbour (81x130cm-32x51in) s. 20-Mar-3 Christie's, Kensington #82/R est:7000-10000

LIOTARD, Jean-Étienne (1702-1789) Swiss
Works on paper
£2078 $3221 €3117 Children playing music (45x36cm-18x14in) pastel pair. 24-Sep-2 Koller, Zurich #6471 est:5000-8000 (S.FR 4800)

LIPCHITZ, Jacques (1891-1973) French
Prints
£3205 $5000 €4808 Danseuse (18x14cm-7x6in) s.i. aquantint exec.c.1940. 7-Nov-2 Swann Galleries, New York #691/R est:2500-3500
£4717 $7500 €7076 Danseuse (18x14cm-7x6in) s.i. aquatint. 1-May-3 Swann Galleries, New York #506/R est:6000-9000
Sculpture
£4294 $7000 €6441 Woman on elbow (23cm-9in) num.5/7 brown pat. bronze st.f.Modern Art prov.lit. 12-Feb-3 Sotheby's, New York #90/R est:8000-12000
£4403 $7000 €6605 Portrait de Freddy Homburger (45cm-18in) s. brown pat bronze prov.exhib.lit. 27-Feb-3 Christie's, Rockefeller NY #46/R est:4000
£5346 $8500 €8019 Birth of the muses I (13cm-5in) s.verso green brown pat bronze lit. 27-Feb-3 Christie's, Rockefeller NY #1/R
£27950 $45000 €41925 Ploumanach (78cm-31in) i.num.4/7 green pat. bronze cast 1961 prov.exhib.lit. 7-May-3 Sotheby's, New York #356/R est:60000-80000
£68323 $110000 €102485 Homme a la mandoline (43cm-17in) i.num.3/7 brown pat. bronze prov.lit. 7-May-3 Sotheby's, New York #195/R est:120000-180000
£288462 $450000 €432693 Arlequin a l'accordeon (66cm-26in) i.num.4/7 dark green pat. bronze f.Modren Art conceived 1919. 5-Nov-2 Sotheby's, New York #26/R est:400000-600000
£341615 $550000 €512423 Danseuse (62cm-24in) s. brown pat bronze prov.exhib. 6-May-3 Sotheby's, New York #34/R est:350000-450000
£357143 $575000 €535715 Baigneuse (72cm-28in) s.st.f.Valsuani brown pat bronze prov.exhib.lit. 6-May-3 Sotheby's, New York #27/R est:600000-800000

Works on paper
£1049 $1752 €1500 Animaux meles (25x18cm-10x7in) chl pencil dr. 26-Jun-3 Tajan, Paris #96/R est:1500-1800
£3133 $5200 €4700 Study for benediction I (61x46cm-24x18in) s. gouache chk exec.c.1941 prov.exhib. 11-Jun-3 Phillips, New York #302/R est:15000-20000

LIPCHYTZ, Samuel (20th C) French
Sculpture
£1300 $2054 €1950 Dancing girl with a bird (45cm-18in) s. bronze. 14-Nov-2 Christie's, Kensington #239/R est:1500-2000

LIPOT, Herman (1884-1972) Hungarian
£272 $425 €408 Nude figures in repose (18x23cm-7x9in) s. board. 18-Sep-2 Alderfer's, Hatfield #268/R
£586 $938 €850 Bathers (39x71cm-15x28in) s. 12-Mar-3 Rabourdin & Choppin de Janvry, Paris #83/R

LIPP, Kilian (1953-) German
£548 $855 €800 View of Gailenberg (40x80cm-16x31in) s. s.d.98 verso lit. 10-Apr-3 Allgauer, Kempten #2875/R

LIPPENS, Piet (1890-1981) Belgian
£360 $576 €500 Campement de gitans (50x60cm-20x24in) s. 13-May-3 Palais de Beaux Arts, Brussels #279

LIPPI, Fra Filippo (1406-1469) Italian
£116129 $183484 €180000 Madonna and Child with Saint Lucy, Saint lawrence and Saint Catherine (79x45cm-31x18in) tempera board lit. 19-Dec-2 Semenzato, Venice #26/R est:220000

LIPPI, Lorenzo (attrib) (1606-1665) Italian
£28000 $46760 €40600 Triumph of David (88x106cm-35x42in) prov.lit. 11-Jul-3 Christie's, Kensington #217/R est:7000-10000

LIPPINCOTT, William H (1849-1920) American
£1946 $3250 €2822 Helena (66x55cm-26x22in) s.d.1883 panel. 22-Jun-3 Freeman, Philadelphia #78/R est:3000-5000

LIPPISCH, Franz (1859-1941) German
£603 $940 €880 Evening in the Albanian mountains (60x82cm-24x32in) s. i. verso. 10-Apr-3 Schopman, Hamburg #643/R

LIPPMANN, Karl Friedrich (1858-?) German
£458 $760 €650 Forest worker resting (40x85cm-16x33in) s. 14-Jun-3 Arnold, Frankfurt #797/R

LIPPS, Richard (1857-1926) German
£1538 $2338 €2400 Italian landscape with elegant figures (92x63cm-36x25in) s. 17-Aug-2 Hans Stahl, Toestorf #14/R est:2200

LIPSCOMBE, Guy (fl.1908-1937) British
£680 $1068 €1020 Pretty young lady seated on a white garden bench in a walled garden (58x48cm-23x19in) s. 13-Dec-2 Keys, Aylsham #646/R

LIPSZIC, S (20th C) ?
Sculpture
£3312 $5167 €5200 Femme au collier (24x33cm-9x13in) s. ivory pat bronze marble base. 6-Nov-2 Tajan, Paris #12/R

LIPTAK, Frantisek (1962-) Czechoslovakian
£614 $897 €921 Strange family (80x80cm-31x31in) 4-Jun-2 SOGA, Bratislava #274/R est:35000 (SL.K 39000)

LISA, Mario (1908-1992) Italian
£331 $523 €480 View of the Vittoriale (17x23cm-7x9in) s. cardboard. 1-Apr-3 Babuino, Rome #350/R
£897 $1417 €1300 Views of the Forum (30x22cm-12x9in) one s. cardboard set of 3. 1-Apr-3 Babuino, Rome #355/R

LISAERT, Pieter IV (1595-c.1629) Flemish
£8633 $13813 €12000 The annunciation (30x24cm-12x9in) oil gold copper. 13-May-3 Sotheby's, Amsterdam #30/R est:4000-6000

LISCHKA, Karl (1907-1994) Austrian
Works on paper
£521 $823 €750 Secrets of the street at night (55x39cm-22x15in) i. verso col chk prov. 24-Apr-3 Dorotheum, Vienna #77/R
£1181 $1865 €1700 Viennese street in the evening (44x32cm-17x13in) i. verso pencil prov. 24-Apr-3 Dorotheum, Vienna #76/R est:800-1100

LISCHKE, Emmy (1860-1919) German
£642 $1001 €950 White roses in vase (72x75cm-28x30in) s. panel. 26-Mar-3 Hugo Ruef, Munich #164

LISIO, Arnaldo de (1869-1949) Italian
Works on paper
£705 $1093 €1100 Reclining cat (50x67cm-20x26in) s. pastel. 4-Dec-2 Neumeister, Munich #536/R

LISMER, Arthur (1885-1969) Canadian
£2444 $4009 €3666 Rocky shore (31x41cm-12x16in) s. s.d.64 verso panel prov. 27-May-3 Sotheby's, Toronto #194/R est:5000-7000 (C.D 5500)
£3614 $5711 €5421 Beach cornucopi (30x38cm-12x15in) d.1960 woodboard. 1-Dec-2 Levis, Calgary #58/R est:10000-12000 (C.D 9000)
£3629 $5734 €5444 Logs and sea shells on the beach (27x41cm-11x16in) s.d.1960 s.d.verso panel prov. 14-Nov-2 Heffel, Vancouver #98/R est:8000-10000 (C.D 9000)
£4435 $7008 €6653 Rural landscape (23x28cm-9x11in) s.d.1922 board prov. 18-Nov-2 Sotheby's, Toronto #86/R est:8000-10000 (C.D 11000)
£4933 $7892 €7400 BC forest (28x41cm-11x16in) s.d.1959 i.verso panel prov.exhib. 15-May-3 Heffel, Vancouver #27/R est:7000-9000 (C.D 11000)
£5217 $8139 €8700 Untitled - Roots and undergrowth (31x41cm-12x16in) s.d.1959 board. 13-Apr-3 Levis, Calgary #75a/R est:14000-18000 (C.D 12000)
£5652 $8817 €9425 Great tree, Vancouver Island (46x36cm-18x14in) s.d.1964 canvasboard prov. 13-Apr-3 Levis, Calgary #75/R est:14000-18000 (C.D 13000)
£6855 $10831 €10283 Northern landscape (23x30cm-9x12in) s.verso panel prov. 14-Nov-2 Heffel, Vancouver #91/R est:10000-15000 (C.D 17000)
£7407 $11481 €11111 Rocky cliff by the shore (40x30cm-16x12in) s. panel double-sided. 3-Dec-2 Joyner, Toronto #158/R est:7000-9000 (C.D 18000)
£8230 $12757 €12345 Georgian Bay, near Manitou Dock (31x44cm-12x17in) s.d.Aug 12. 3-Dec-2 Joyner, Toronto #67/R est:10000-15000 (C.D 20000)
£20000 $32800 €29000 Island Lake Superior - morning Lake Superior (33x40cm-13x16in) s.i.d.1927 panel. 9-Jun-3 Hodgins, Calgary #60/R est:15000-20000 (C.D 45000)
£22634 $35082 €33951 Rocky channel (45x54cm-18x21in) s.d.35 board. 3-Dec-2 Joyner, Toronto #19/R est:20000-30000 (C.D 55000)
£30242 $47782 €45363 Newfoundland (53x66cm-21x26in) s.d.1945 i.d.verso prov.exhib. 14-Nov-2 Heffel, Vancouver #2/R est:40000-60000 (C.D 75000)

Works on paper
£261 $410 €392 Barn at night (14x11cm-6x4in) init. ink. 25-Nov-2 Hodgins, Calgary #339/R (C.D 650)
£322 $502 €483 Tangle west coast (29x36cm-11x14in) init. i.verso ink drybrush sold with a W/C by Lois Darroch. 25-Mar-3 Ritchie, Toronto #53/R (C.D 750)
£413 $649 €620 French soldier, study of an old man (23x18cm-9x7in) s. ink wash chk prov. 24-Jul-2 Walker's, Ottawa #417/R est:1000-1500 (C.D 1000)
£413 $644 €689 Untitled - Skunk cabbage study (18x22cm-7x9in) s. ink prov. 13-Apr-3 Levis, Calgary #77 est:1000-1200 (C.D 950)
£478 $746 €798 Untitled - beach scene (30x38cm-12x15in) s. ink double-sided prov. 13-Apr-3 Levis, Calgary #76/R est:1200-1500 (C.D 1100)
£606 $964 €879 Vancouver Island (20x28cm-8x11in) estate seal verso chl pastel prov. 1-May-3 Heffel, Vancouver #57/R (C.D 1400)
£615 $959 €923 Personnage pensif (46x45cm-18x18in) s.i.d.28/62 W/C chl. 10-Sep-2 Iegor de Saint Hippolyte, Montreal #76 (C.D 1500)
£2419 $3823 €3629 Rocks and pines, Georgian Bay (39x58cm-15x23in) s. gouache cardboard prov. 18-Nov-2 Sotheby's, Toronto #48/R est:3000-4000 (C.D 6000)

LISMONDE, Jules (1908-2001) Belgian
Works on paper
£302 $486 €450 L'entree du parc. s. chl. 18-Feb-3 Galerie Moderne, Brussels #244/R
£360 $576 €500 View of Vatican City (48x62cm-19x24in) s.d.54 chl pastel. 17-May-3 De Vuyst, Lokeren #242

LISSA, Chr (19th C) ?
£882 $1447 €1350 Twig collectors in autumn woods (69x47cm-27x19in) s. 5-Feb-3 Neumeister, Munich #751/R
£882 $1447 €1350 Twig collectors in autumnal beech woods (69x47cm-27x19in) s. 5-Feb-3 Neumeister, Munich #752

LISSE, Dirck van der (attrib) (?-1669) Dutch

£2453 $3826 €3900 Jeunes femmes et troupeau dans un paysage (37x30cm-15x12in) panel. 10-Oct-2 Ribeyre & Baron, Paris #17/R est:3800-4500
£2749 $4509 €3986 Nymphs dancing and faun playing music (51x75cm-20x30in) 4-Jun-3 AB Stockholms Auktionsverk #2594/R est:60000-80000 (S.KR 35000)

LISSITZKY, El (1890-1941) Russian
Prints
£8696 $14261 €12000 Fighting pen (39x31cm-15x12in) s. col lithograph lit. 29-May-3 Lempertz, Koln #759/R est:12000-14000
£100000 $163000 €150000 Die plastische gestaltung der elektro-mechanischen (53x44cm-21x17in) s.num.59 col lithograph set of ten lit. 3-Feb-3 Christie's, London #35/R est:100000-150000
Works on paper
£15190 $24000 €24000 Cover design (27x18cm-11x7in) mono. w/C over pencil prov. 30-Nov-2 Villa Grisebach, Berlin #260/R est:20000-25000

LIST, Georg Nikolaus (17th C) German
£608 $949 €900 Portrait of Thomas Widenmann (89x70cm-35x28in) i.d.35 16.83 prov.lit. 27-Mar-3 Dr Fritz Nagel, Stuttgart #771/R

LIST, Herbert (1903-1974) German
Photographs
£1899 $3000 €3000 Knock out, Paris (34x25cm-13x10in) s.i. silver gelatin lit.exhib. 28-Nov-2 Villa Grisebach, Berlin #1297/R est:3000-4000
£2078 $3200 €3117 Stairway to heaven (39x28cm-15x11in) s.i.d.verso gelatin silver print prov.lit. 25-Oct-2 Phillips, New York #100/R est:4000-6000
£2278 $3600 €3417 Flaschen im sand (17x30cm-7x12in) i.verso gelatin silver print. 24-Apr-3 Phillips, New York #150/R est:3500-4500
£2848 $4500 €4272 Christian Berard, Paris (28x22cm-11x9in) i.verso gelatin silver print prov.lit. 24-Apr-3 Phillips, New York #33/R est:5000-7000

LIST, J (?) ?
£2603 $4060 €3800 Putti and children in an allegory of the seasons (101x250cm-40x98in) s. four. 9-Apr-3 Neumeister, Munich #706/R est:1200

LISTER, Edward d'Arcy (1911-) British
£600 $954 €900 Flowers in a jug (51x38cm-20x15in) exhib. 26-Feb-3 Sotheby's, Olympia #259/R

LISTER, Kenneth (20th C) British
£480 $749 €720 Portrait of Winston Churchill (45x35cm-18x14in) i.on stretcher. 15-Oct-2 Bonhams, Knightsbridge #188d

LISTER, William Lister (1859-1943) Australian
£241 $381 €362 Coastal scene (34x59cm-13x23in) s. 18-Nov-2 Goodman, Sydney #15 (A.D 675)
Works on paper
£226 $359 €339 Coastal landscape (28x45cm-11x18in) s. W/C prov. 23-Mar-3 Goodman, Sydney #31 (A.D 600)
£250 $395 €375 Tall trees (49x32cm-19x13in) s. W/C. 18-Nov-2 Goodman, Sydney #22 (A.D 700)
£345 $541 €518 River scene with boat (32x48cm-13x19in) s. W/C. 15-Apr-3 Lawson Menzies, Sydney #133/R est:1000-2000 (A.D 900)
£351 $533 €527 Pulpit Rock, Blue Mountains (32x49cm-13x19in) s. W/C. 19-Aug-2 Joel, Victoria #221 est:1200-1400 (A.D 1000)
£367 $583 €551 Coastal landscape (45x60cm-18x24in) s. W/C. 3-Mar-3 Lawson Menzies, Sydney #334 (A.D 975)
£421 $662 €632 River scene (27x54cm-11x21in) s. W/C. 15-Apr-3 Lawson Menzies, Sydney #208/R est:1200-1800 (A.D 1100)
£464 $715 €696 Distant ship (23x81cm-9x32in) s. W/C. 3-Sep-2 Shapiro, Sydney #370 est:1400-1800 (A.D 1300)
£536 $842 €804 Village scene (36x54cm-14x21in) s. W/C. 15-Apr-3 Lawson Menzies, Sydney #134/R est:1500-2500 (A.D 1400)
£766 $1203 €1149 Sydney Harbour (33x48cm-13x19in) s. W/C. 15-Apr-3 Lawson Menzies, Sydney #132/R est:2000-3000 (A.D 2000)

LISZEWSKI, Christian Friedrich Reinhold (attrib) (1725-1794) German
Works on paper
£345 $524 €518 Portrait of Maria Elisabeth Link (50x40cm-20x16in) i.verso gouache. 28-Aug-2 Museumsbygningen, Copenhagen #105/R (D.KR 4000)

LISZTAY, Jozsef (?) Hungarian
£1032 $1610 €1496 Church under the mountain, Nagybanya (60x49cm-24x19in) s. 13-Sep-2 Mu Terem Galeria, Budapest #166/R est:250000 (H.F 400000)

LITKOW, A (19th C) ?
£1341 $2200 €1944 Horse carts (41x69cm-16x27in) s. 4-Jun-3 Doyle, New York #70 est:1500-2500

LITO, G (?) ?
£860 $1428 €1290 Tavern scene with figures merry-making. s. 10-Jun-3 Lawrences, Bletchingley #1385

LITOVTCHENKO, Alexander Dmitrievitch (1835-1890) Russian
£1266 $2000 €1899 Wooded landscape (41x60cm-16x24in) s.d.1874. 1-Apr-3 Christie's, Rockefeller NY #206/R est:3000-5000

LITSCHAUER, Karl Joseph (1830-1871) Austrian
£849 $1325 €1350 Composition (66x84cm-26x33in) s. 21-Sep-2 Bolland & Marotz, Bremen #515/R

LITTECZKY, Endre (1880-1953) Hungarian
£430 $667 €624 Farmyard (35x32cm-14x13in) s. card. 9-Dec-2 Mu Terem Galeria, Budapest #60/R est:150000 (H.F 160000)
£439 $684 €637 Street in a small town (48x50cm-19x20in) s. 13-Sep-2 Mu Terem Galeria, Budapest #36/R est:140000 (H.F 170000)
£671 $1046 €973 On the sunlit courtyard of Nagybanya (47x66cm-19x26in) s.d.1920 cardboard. 13-Sep-2 Mu Terem Galeria, Budapest #35/R est:180000 (H.F 260000)
£1237 $1917 €1794 Shady road (61x81cm-24x32in) s. 9-Dec-2 Mu Terem Galeria, Budapest #62/R est:280000 (H.F 460000)

LITTLE, James (fl.1880-1910) British
Works on paper
£980 $1529 €1470 Boulevard des Italiens, Paris (26x38cm-10x15in) s.i. W/C laid down. 17-Oct-2 Bonhams, Edinburgh #230

LITTLE, John C (1928-) Canadian
£820 $1270 €1230 Ave Ste Genevieve, Parc des Gouveneurs, in spring sunshine (20x25cm-8x10in) s.i.d.94 i.verso prov. 24-Sep-2 Ritchie, Toronto #3159/R est:900-1200 (C.D 2000)
£1202 $1875 €1803 Kids skating, Charlevoix county (21x28cm-8x11in) s. i.verso canvasboard. 25-Mar-3 Ritchie, Toronto #93/R est:1200-1500 (C.D 2800)
£1333 $2187 €2000 Une journee estivale, Rue Logan a Plessis, Montreal (30x40cm-12x16in) s. prov. 3-Jun-3 Joyner, Toronto #115/R est:3000-4000 (C.D 3000)
£1440 $2218 €2160 Rue Christophe-Colomb coin Victoria, Quebec (30x40cm-12x16in) s. 22-Oct-2 Iegor de Saint Hippolyte, Montreal #62 (C.D 3500)
£1609 $2510 €2333 Patinoire Rue du college, Montreal (30x41cm-12x16in) s.i.d.69. 26-Mar-3 Walker's, Ottawa #215/R est:3000-4000 (C.D 3750)
£2000 $3280 €3000 Rue St. Dominique - La Gauchetiere, Montreal (40x50cm-16x20in) s. 3-Jun-3 Joyner, Toronto #166/R est:4000-5000 (C.D 4500)
£2273 $3568 €3410 Rue Latourelle, Quebec (30x41cm-12x16in) s.i.d.65 s.verso canvasboard prov. 24-Jul-2 Walker's, Ottawa #217/R est:2000-2500 (C.D 5500)
£2400 $3936 €3600 Summer night, St. Louis Square, Montreal (22x30cm-9x12in) s. board painted 1964. 3-Jun-3 Joyner, Toronto #191/R est:3000-5000 (C.D 5400)
£2469 $3827 €3704 St. Pauls, Montreal (30x40cm-12x16in) s.i.d.June 10 63 canvasboard. 3-Dec-2 Joyner, Toronto #57/R est:3000-4000 (C.D 6000)
£3414 $5359 €5121 Rue Laval vers Duluth, Montreal (60x75cm-24x30in) s.i.d.1977 prov. 25-Nov-2 Hodgins, Calgary #107/R est:6500-8500 (C.D 8500)
£3556 $5831 €5334 Jeune fille qui porte un manteau, Rue Kerouac, Quebec (69x76cm-27x30in) s. s.i.d.76 on stretcher verso prov. 27-May-3 Sotheby's, Toronto #117/R est:5000-7000 (C.D 8000)
£4000 $6560 €6000 Tavern at 8.00 A.M (61x76cm-24x30in) s.d.56 masonite prov. 27-May-3 Sotheby's, Toronto #115/R est:7000-9000 (C.D 9000)
£4435 $7008 €6653 Christmas day (55x75cm-22x30in) s. i.verso board exhib. 14-Nov-2 Heffel, Vancouver #141/R est:9000-12000 (C.D 11000)
£6222 $10204 €9333 Sunday, Sherbrooke St. W at Stanley, Montreal (61x76cm-24x30in) s. s.i.d.64 verso prov. 27-May-3 Sotheby's, Toronto #128/R est:7000-9000 (C.D 14000)
£12097 $19113 €18146 Bonsecours market (115x279cm-45x110in) s.d.1953 prov. 18-Nov-2 Sotheby's, Toronto #71/R est:40000-50000 (C.D 30000)
Works on paper
£1317 $2041 €1976 At dock in New York Harbour (51x66cm-20x26in) s. W/C ink. 3-Dec-2 Joyner, Toronto #275/R est:1000-1500 (C.D 3200)

LITTLE, Robert (1854-1944) British

Works on paper

£650 $1014 €975 On the river (26x17cm-10x7in) s. pencil W/C. 27-Mar-3 Christie's, Kensington #35/R

LITTLEJOHN, William (1929-) British

£290 $473 €435 Still life with dark harbour (11x52cm-4x20in) 14-Feb-3 Lyon & Turnbull, Edinburgh #5

£900 $1458 €1350 Green thought 1971 (146x230cm-57x91in) exhib. 23-Jan-3 Christie's, Kensington #275/R

Works on paper

£450 $702 €675 Still life of fish (59x83cm-23x33in) s.d.1985 gouache. 28-Mar-3 Bonhams, Edinburgh #173

£500 $780 €750 Still life with fruit (33x54cm-13x21in) s.d.82 W/C collage. 10-Apr-3 Bonhams, Edinburgh #41

£580 $905 €870 Fish and blue screen (47x58cm-19x23in) s.d.1990 W/C collage. 10-Apr-3 Bonhams, Edinburgh #10/R

£650 $1053 €975 Sun dragon (39x178cm-15x70in) pencil oil canvasboard. 23-Jan-3 Christie's, Kensington #285/R

LITTLEWOOD, Edward (20th C) British

£1500 $2280 €2250 Norfolk wooded landscape with loggers resting beneath oak trees (56x86cm-22x34in) s.d.1882. 16-Aug-2 Keys, Aylsham #655

LITTROW, Leo von (1860-1914) Austrian

£685 $1068 €1000 Abbazia beach, IX, 886 (33x46cm-13x18in) s.i. verso. 10-Apr-3 Dorotheum, Vienna #25/R

£4392 $6851 €6500 Istria (40x60cm-16x24in) mono. board. 25-Mar-3 Wiener Kunst Auktionen, Vienna #124/R est:5000-10000

£5500 $8635 €8250 Sunny day on the Amalfi coast (50x38cm-20x15in) s. panel prov. 21-Nov-2 Christie's, Kensington #131/R est:2000-3000

£7092 $11489 €10000 Coastal landscape in bloom (37x55cm-15x22in) mono. 22-May-3 Dorotheum, Vienna #137/R est:10000-15000

LIU BOSHU (1935-) Chinese

Works on paper

£870 $1426 €1200 Three horses at watering place (129x68cm-51x27in) s.d.1984 seals Indian ink col hanging scroll. 30-May-3 Dr Fritz Nagel, Stuttgart #1267/R

LIU DU (16/17th C) Chinese

Works on paper

£27195 $44872 €39433 Landscape of Tiantai Shan (28x531cm-11x209in) s. ink silk handscroll. 6-Jul-3 Christie's, Hong Kong #426/R est:400000-500000 (HK.D 350000)

LIU HAISHU (1896-1994) Chinese

Works on paper

£7770 $12821 €11267 Winter landscape (177x94cm-70x37in) s.i. ink scroll. 6-Jul-3 Christie's, Hong Kong #269/R est:100000-150000 (HK.D 100000)

LIU MAOSHAN (1942-) Chinese

Works on paper

£6216 $10256 €9013 Water village (96x90cm-38x35in) s.i. ink scroll. 6-Jul-3 Christie's, Hong Kong #277/R est:80000-90000 (HK.D 80000)

LIU XUN (1958-) Chinese

Works on paper

£8943 $14130 €13415 Hazy view of the river bank (59x183cm-23x72in) s. ink col. 28-Apr-3 Sotheby's, Hong Kong #530/R est:45000-65000 (HK.D 110000)

LIU YE (1964-) Chinese

£15540 $25641 €22533 Spirit of the sea (118x138cm-46x54in) s. 6-Jul-3 Christie's, Hong Kong #112/R est:150000-250000 (HK.D 200000)

LIU YONG (1719-1805) Chinese

Works on paper

£2846 $4496 €4269 Xingshu (13x125cm-5x49in) s.i. ink handscroll. 28-Apr-3 Sotheby's, Hong Kong #651/R est:40000-60000 (HK.D 35000)

LIVACHE, Rene Victor (1831-1909) French

£5036 $8259 €7000 Prince Nubien tenant un vase a parfum (92x74cm-36x29in) s.d.1896. 4-Jun-3 Tajan, Paris #284/R est:3500-4000

LIVEMONT, Privat (1861-1936) Belgian

£409 $630 €650 Still life (60x75cm-24x30in) s.d.1934. 22-Oct-2 Campo & Campo, Antwerp #164

£701 $1093 €1100 Vase fleuri de dahlias (60x72cm-24x28in) s.i.d.1933. 11-Nov-2 Horta, Bruxelles #39

£822 $1290 €1200 Nature morte aux fleurs et a la statuette chinoise (60x75cm-24x30in) s.d.1934. 15-Apr-3 Galerie Moderne, Brussels #350/R

Works on paper

£248 $353 €400 Bacchanale chinoise (22x27cm-9x11in) crayon W/C. 20-Mar-2 Chayette & Cheval, Paris #74

£275 $442 €420 Buveuse de the au kimono (30x17cm-12x7in) s.d.1892 W/C. 20-Jan-3 Horta, Bruxelles #383

£11000 $18260 €11000 Untitled (57x35cm-22x14in) s.d.1900 drawing W/C. 16-Jun-3 Horta, Bruxelles #112/R est:10000-12000

LIVENS, H (19th C) British?

£580 $951 €870 Female nude reclining on a gilt settee (50x60cm-20x24in) s. 7-Jun-3 Shapes, Edinburgh #381/R

LIVENS, Henry (19th C) British

£550 $891 €825 Plums, apples, grapes and a peach on a mossy bank (51x61cm-20x24in) s.d.1878. 23-Jan-3 Christie's, Kensington #178

LIVESAY, Frances (fl.1880-1914) British

Works on paper

£570 $883 €900 Cottage interior (35x52cm-14x20in) init.d.1875 W/C. 24-Sep-2 De Veres Art Auctions, Dublin #115/R

LIVINGS, Henry (?) ?

£2000 $3100 €3000 Evening in the Highlands (76x102cm-30x40in) 3-Dec-2 Sotheby's, Olympia #161/R est:1000-1500

LIZARD, Kate (19th C) Continental

Sculpture

£1377 $2300 €1997 Shepherd boy (32x51cm-13x20in) i. brown pat. bronze. 22-Jun-3 Freeman, Philadelphia #73/R est:2000-3000

LIZCANO Y ESTEBAN, Angel (1846-1929) Spanish

£426 $711 €600 Portrait de jeune femme (39x28cm-15x11in) s.d.1881 panel. 18-Jun-3 Hotel des Ventes Mosan, Brussels #170

£2987 $4601 €4750 Kids playing in the street (37x53cm-15x21in) s.d.74. 22-Oct-2 Durán, Madrid #240/R

£3226 $5097 €5000 Scarry moment (63x53cm-25x21in) s.d.1897. 17-Dec-2 Durán, Madrid #199/R

£3846 $6077 €6000 Dance (52x33cm-20x13in) s. 14-Nov-2 Arte, Seville #333/R

£14516 $22935 €22500 May Cross (90x140cm-35x55in) s.d.1896. 17-Dec-2 Durán, Madrid #231/R est:6000

LJOSNE, Halvdan (1929-) Norwegian

Works on paper

£973 $1587 €1460 Photo stone (49x60cm-19x24in) s.d.1968 collage. 17-Feb-3 Blomqvist, Lysaker #1119 (N.KR 11000)

LJUBA (1934-) Yugoslavian

£791 $1266 €1100 Impressions d'ete (45x89cm-18x35in) s.d.1989 verso. 16-May-3 Lombrail & Teucquam, Paris #200/R

£1013 $1600 €1600 Corps nuage (55x46cm-22x18in) s.i.d.1981 verso. 2-Dec-2 Tajan, Paris #239

£1032 $1631 €1600 La dimension mythique, Paris (55x46cm-22x18in) s.i. i.d.verso. 17-Dec-2 Rossini, Paris #106/R

£1241 $1961 €1800 Still life (38x46cm-15x18in) s.i.d.1969 verso. 4-Apr-3 Tajan, Paris #263/R

£1393 $2200 €2200 Miroirs et fantomes (54x82cm-21x32in) s. i.d.verso. 2-Dec-2 Tajan, Paris #238

£1887 $2925 €3000 Hommage a JH Fussli (146x101cm-57x40in) s.i.d.1981 i.verso. 30-Oct-2 Artcurial Briest, Paris #715 est:3000-3800

£2405 $3800 €3800 Cite desoleil (65x92cm-26x36in) s.i.d.1981. 2-Dec-2 Tajan, Paris #240

£2532 $4000 €4000 Multiplication de bizarre (131x98cm-52x39in) s.i.d.1964 verso. 2-Dec-2 Tajan, Paris #241

£7609 $12479 €10500 Barrage devant l'eternite (162x130cm-64x51in) s.i.d.1977 verso prov. 27-May-3 Tajan, Paris #53/R est:10000-12000

Works on paper

£833 $1308 €1300 Homage to Rita Renoir (98x77cm-39x30in) s.d.1976 ink wash. 15-Dec-2 Perrin, Versailles #80/R

LJUNGBERG, Sven (1913-) Swedish

£2943 $4591 €4415 Ljungby railway station (60x74cm-24x29in) s. 6-Nov-2 AB Stockholms Auktionsverk #580/R est:15000-20000 (S.KR 42000)

LJUNGBERG-COSMATOS, Birgitta (1940-) Swedish
Works on paper
£280 $437 €420 Living bond - Catena vivente (60x60cm-24x24in) mixed media executed 1970 exhib. 6-Nov-2 AB Stockholms Auktionsverk #922/R (S.KR 4000)

LJUNGGREN, Reinhold (1920-) Swedish
£280 $433 €420 By river's edge (24x33cm-9x13in) s. panel. 29-Sep-2 Uppsala Auktionskammare, Uppsala #191 (S.KR 4000)

LLACER, Teresa (1932-) Spanish
£440 $687 €700 Mountains in Catalunia (50x61cm-20x24in) s.i.d.97. 8-Oct-2 Ansorena, Madrid #593/R

LLANECES, Jose (1863-1919) Spanish
£692 $1079 €1100 Portrait of boy in profile (48x43cm-19x17in) s. 23-Sep-2 Durán, Madrid #671/R
£4645 $7339 €7200 Sword fighter (113x78cm-44x31in) s. 18-Dec-2 Ansorena, Madrid #158/R est:7000
£12579 $19623 €20000 Satyrical book (99x138cm-39x54in) s. 23-Sep-2 Durán, Madrid #211/R est:19000
Works on paper
£3459 $5396 €5500 Playing dices (43x48cm-17x19in) s. W/C. 23-Sep-2 Durán, Madrid #255/R

LLANOS Y VALDES, Sebastian de (?-1668) Spanish
£10000 $15600 €15000 Heads of Saint Paul, John the Baptist and James the great on platters on a draped ledge (108x133cm-43x52in) prov. 9-Apr-3 Christie's, London #83/R est:10000-15000

LLEDO, Guillermo (20th C) Spanish
£1210 $1900 €1815 Urban scene (65x95cm-26x37in) s.d.74 acrylic ink cardboard prov. 20-Nov-2 Christie's, Rockefeller NY #100/R

LLEWELLYN, Sir William (1858-1941) British
£650 $1066 €975 Redcastle, the Beauly Firth (58x91cm-23x36in) s. board. 5-Jun-3 Christie's, Kensington #734
£6000 $9540 €9000 Portrait of a lady (152x102cm-60x40in) s.d.1899. 19-Mar-3 Sotheby's, London #278/R est:6000-8000
£70968 $110000 €106452 Arranging flowers (75x96cm-30x38in) s. prov. 30-Oct-2 Christie's, Rockefeller NY #55/R est:120000-160000

LLEWELLYN, Sir William (attrib) (1858-1941) British
£700 $1148 €1050 Mushroom gatherers (46x61cm-18x24in) s.d.1895. 29-May-3 Christie's, Kensington #256/R

LLEWELLYN-ROBERTS, C A (20th C) British
£13500 $21465 €20250 Pisces, Cancer, Scorpio and Libra (47x36cm-19x14in) brass panel. 27-Feb-3 Sotheby's, Olympia #163/R est:5000-8000

LLONA, Ramiro (1947-) Peruvian
£4459 $7000 €6689 Volcano land (173x275cm-68x108in) s.i.d.83 oil acrylic prov.lit. 19-Nov-2 Sotheby's, New York #128/R est:15000

LLOP MARQUES, Francesc (1873-1970) Spanish
£274 $433 €425 Landscape (38x46cm-15x18in) s. 17-Dec-2 Durán, Madrid #602/R

LLORENZ POY, Vicente (1937-) Spanish
£4110 $6411 €6000 Hug (116x73cm-46x29in) s. 8-Apr-3 Ansorena, Madrid #215/R est:6000
£10063 $15597 €16000 Resting (150x200cm-59x79in) s.d.1975. 7-Oct-2 Ansorena, Madrid #88/R est:7000

LLOYD, Henry Grant (1829-1904) Australian
Works on paper
£788 $1198 €1182 Sydney from near Vaucluse (30x42cm-12x17in) s.i.d.1859 W/C. 28-Aug-2 Deutscher-Menzies, Melbourne #327/R (A.D 2200)

LLOYD, James (1905-1974) British
£1200 $1896 €1800 Town by a river (52x37cm-20x15in) s. gouache W/C. 27-Nov-2 Sotheby's, Olympia #147/R est:600-800
Works on paper
£600 $984 €900 Waterfall (52x37cm-20x15in) s. ink gouache. 3-Jun-3 Sotheby's, Olympia #113/R
£800 $1320 €1160 Birds feeding (37x52cm-15x20in) s. W/C bodycol prov. 3-Jul-3 Christie's, Kensington #637/R
£1200 $1980 €1740 Lady with a doll. Portrait of a lady. Lady in blue (24x34cm-9x13in) s. gouache set of three. 3-Jul-3 Christie's, Kensington #537/R est:1500-2000
£2400 $3696 €3600 Patting the horses (51x35cm-20x14in) s.d.58 gouache. 5-Sep-2 Christie's, Kensington #626/R est:800-1200

LLOYD, Llewelyn (1879-1950) Italian
£4747 $7500 €7500 Landscape at dawn (15x23cm-6x9in) s.d.1907 board. 26-Nov-2 Christie's, Rome #199/R est:6000-8000

LLOYD, Norman (1897-1985) Australian
£251 $381 €377 On Middle Harbour Heights (25x28cm-10x11in) s. board. 27-Aug-2 Goodman, Sydney #59 (A.D 700)
£320 $515 €480 Figures on a path (76x64cm-30x25in) s. 14-Jan-3 Bonhams, Knightsbridge #43
£500 $820 €750 Sunlit landscape (44x53cm-17x21in) s. 3-Jun-3 Sotheby's, Olympia #94/R
£571 $903 €857 On a summer day (18x47cm-7x19in) s.d.20 board. 18-Nov-2 Goodman, Sydney #14 (A.D 1600)
£1400 $2254 €2030 Sydney Harbour (25x59cm-10x23in) s. board painted c.1925. 12-May-3 Joel, Victoria #341 est:4500-5500 (A.D 3500)
Works on paper
£223 $353 €323 Venetian scene (31x39cm-12x15in) s. pastel. 22-Jul-3 Lawson Menzies, Sydney #155/R (A.D 550)

LLOYD, R Malcolm (fl.1879-1907) British
Works on paper
£280 $442 €420 Early morning, low tide (25x36cm-10x14in) s. W/C. 26-Nov-2 Bonhams, Knightsbridge #162b
£280 $442 €420 Barges on the Thames (24x43cm-9x17in) s. W/C. 27-Nov-2 Hamptons Fine Art, Godalming #239
£480 $778 €720 Low tide in the harbour (32x51cm-13x20in) s.d.1881 pencil W/C bodycol. 21-May-3 Christie's, Kensington #456/R
£530 $827 €795 Entrance to Gorleston Harbour (33x50cm-13x20in) s.d.1891 W/C. 11-Nov-2 Trembath Welch, Great Dunmow #444
£550 $891 €825 Congestion at the harbour mouth (11x18cm-4x7in) s. pencil W/C. 21-May-3 Christie's, Kensington #465/R
£600 $954 €900 Fishing vessels off the coast, north Wales (11x19cm-4x7in) s. W/C bodycol. 5-Mar-3 Bonhams, Bury St Edmunds #268/R
£2000 $3340 €2900 Fishing boats on the shore with Caernarvon Castle beyond (12x18cm-5x7in) s.i.verso W/C sold with 3 similar by the same hand. 25-Jun-3 Bonhams, Bury St Edmunds #495/R est:1200-1800

LLOYD, Robert (1969-) British
£1000 $1620 €1500 M.V Crofter at the Spithead Review, 1953 (65x100cm-26x39in) s.d.2000 board. 21-Jan-3 Bonhams, New Bond Street #188/R est:200-300
£1200 $1944 €1800 M.V Centurion rounding Cape Horn (67x98cm-26x39in) s.d.1998 board. 21-Jan-3 Bonhams, New Bond Street #189/R est:300-400
Works on paper
£350 $567 €525 Inkosi passing a fishing vessel (45x70cm-18x28in) s. gouache. 21-Jan-3 Bonhams, New Bond Street #171/R
£850 $1377 €1275 M.V Herdsman and Interpreter in Liverpool Docks (45x70cm-18x28in) s.d.May 1996 gouache. 21-Jan-3 Bonhams, New Bond Street #173/R
£1000 $1620 €1500 M.V Custodian in the Suez Canal (74x107cm-29x42in) s.d.1999 gouache. 21-Jan-3 Bonhams, New Bond Street #172/R est:300-400

LLOYD, T Ivester (1873-1942) British
£600 $984 €900 Huntsman and hounds. Fox hounds crossing a brook (18x24cm-7x9in) s. panel pair. 4-Jun-3 Bonhams, Chester #412
£900 $1422 €1350 Beagle (41x51cm-16x20in) s. 28-Nov-2 Christie's, Kensington #309/R
£950 $1587 €1378 Gone to ground (38x53cm-15x21in) s. board prov.exhib. 25-Jun-3 Cheffins, Cambridge #798/R
£1300 $2028 €1950 Crossing the river. Chase. By a riverbank (26x33cm-10x13in) s. board three. 26-Mar-3 Hamptons Fine Art, Godalming #220 est:1500-2500
Works on paper
£260 $434 €377 Thief (23x33cm-9x13in) s. W/C. 25-Jun-3 Cheffins, Cambridge #729
£300 $474 €450 On the scent (22x33cm-9x13in) s. W/C. 28-Nov-2 Christie's, Kensington #88/R
£800 $1264 €1200 Fox in snow (24x42cm-9x17in) s. W/C bodycol. 28-Nov-2 Christie's, Kensington #53/R

LLOYD, Thomas James (1849-1910) British
£350 $553 €525 An angler on a river bank (25x35cm-10x14in) s.d.77. 28-Nov-2 Christie's, Kensington #8
£650 $1060 €975 Bringing home the flock (40x90cm-16x35in) 14-Feb-3 Lyon & Turnbull, Edinburgh #60

Works on paper
£820 $1279 €1230 Winter ploughing near Bosham, Sussex (28x69cm-11x27in) s.d.1903 W/C. 26-Mar-3 Sotheby's, Olympia #129/R
£861 $1334 €1292 Summer evening (29x70cm-11x28in) s.d.1905 W/C. 24-Sep-2 Iegor de Saint Hippolyte, Montreal #199 (C.D 2100)
£2700 $4212 €4050 Otter hunting near Bolton Abbey (41x102cm-16x40in) s.d.1910 W/C. 26-Mar-3 Hamptons Fine Art, Godalming #92 est:2000-4000

LLOYD, W Stuart (fl.1875-1929) British
£2400 $3912 €3480 Richmond Castle, angler and his family in the foreground (51x76cm-20x30in) s.i. prov. 17-Jul-3 Tennants, Leyburn #845/R est:2500-3500
Works on paper
£300 $474 €450 Mountainous river landscape (89x64cm-35x25in) s.d.1880 W/C. 13-Nov-2 Halls, Shrewsbury #369
£400 $648 €600 Feeding ducks (17x30cm-7x12in) s. W/C bodycol. 21-May-3 Bonhams, Knightsbridge #32/R
£580 $940 €841 River landscape with figures and churches (33x48cm-13x19in) W/C pair. 31-Jul-3 Scarborough Perry Fine Arts, Hove #854
£600 $930 €900 Ducks and figures at the village pond (36x75cm-14x30in) s.d.1910 W/C. 1-Oct-2 Bristol Auction Rooms #396
£600 $978 €900 Fishing boats off Dover (24x54cm-9x21in) s. W/C. 29-Jan-3 Sotheby's, Olympia #171/R
£640 $1018 €960 River landscape with fishing and boats before the Ferry Hotel (26x37cm-10x15in) s. W/C. 27-Feb-3 Bonhams, Chester #395
£650 $1027 €975 Figures in a punt, stone arched bridge over the river with church steeple in distance (28x64cm-11x25in) s. W/C. 18-Dec-2 John Nicholson, Haslemere #1138/R
£750 $1155 €1125 River side (29x58cm-11x23in) s. W/C. 23-Oct-2 Hamptons Fine Art, Godalming #48/R
£750 $1155 €1125 Sunny morning, Fordwich (23x68cm-9x27in) s.d.1904 W/C. 23-Oct-2 Hamptons Fine Art, Godalming #49/R
£800 $1296 €1200 Springtime, Newport, Isle of Wight (19x60cm-7x24in) s.d.1901 W/C. 21-May-3 Bonhams, Knightsbridge #19/R
£975 $1482 €1463 Down by the Old Mill stream. Ford on the Arum (48x74cm-19x29in) s. W/C pair. 14-Aug-2 Andrew Hartley, Ilkley #546
£1300 $2119 €1950 In the silver woods, Shere. Purple heather (65x39cm-26x15in) s. one i. W/C htd white pair. 11-Feb-3 Fellows & Sons, Birmingham #133/R est:800-1200
£1400 $2184 €2100 Windsor Castle from the river (30x91cm-12x36in) s.d.1902 W/C. 13-Sep-2 Lyon & Turnbull, Edinburgh #42/R est:700-1000
£1450 $2262 €2175 Ferry point (39x65cm-15x26in) s.d.1900 W/C. 26-Mar-3 Hamptons Fine Art, Godalming #37/R est:600-800
£1653 $2595 €2480 View of Lincoln from the river (33x91cm-13x36in) s. W/C prov. 24-Jul-2 Walker's, Ottawa #17/R est:3000-4000 (C.D 4000)
£2400 $3768 €3600 Fishermen returning with the catch (76x127cm-30x50in) s. W/C. 16-Dec-2 Sotheby's, Olympia #140/R est:2000-3000

LLOYD, Wyndham (1909-) British
£620 $967 €899 Bridge at Polperro (51x61cm-20x24in) s. 27-Mar-3 Lane, Penzance #226

LLULL, Jose Pinelo (1861-1922) Spanish
£10323 $16310 €16000 Getting warm on a cold morning (87x145cm-34x57in) s.d.98. 17-Dec-2 Durán, Madrid #227/R est:9500

LO A NJOE, Guillaume Theodor (1937-) Dutch
£567 $919 €800 Composition (51x60cm-20x24in) s. s.d.92 verso. 26-May-3 Glerum, Amsterdam #278/R

LOAN, Dorothy van (1904-1999) American
£839 $1300 €1259 Sewing circle (51x46cm-20x18in) s. exhib. 8-Dec-2 Freeman, Philadelphia #183/R
£1290 $2000 €1935 Figures along the beach (76x91cm-30x36in) s. 8-Dec-2 Freeman, Philadelphia #113/R est:1500-2500
£1497 $2500 €2171 Bathers at Wissahickon 1931 (91x86cm-36x34in) s. 22-Jun-3 Freeman, Philadelphia #121/R est:2500-4000

LOARTE, Alejandro de (circle) (17th C) Spanish
£15000 $23550 €22500 Kitchen still life with chickens, hare, cauliflower, cardoon and utensils (145x138cm-57x54in) 12-Dec-2 Sotheby's, London #211/R est:15000-20000

LOB, Kurt Leopold (1926-) Dutch/German
£2014 $3304 €2800 Koud buffet in Salzburg (101x61cm-40x24in) s.d.74 s.i.d.verso. 3-Jun-3 Christie's, Amsterdam #386/R est:1500-2000

LOBANOFF, Serguei Ivanovitch (1887-1943) Russian
£1959 $3057 €2900 Traineau sous la neige poursuivi par les loups (55x68cm-22x27in) s. 25-Mar-3 Chochon-Barre & Allardi, Paris #160/R est:3300-3500

LOBANOFF, Serguei Ivanovitch (attrib) (1887-1943) Russian
£952 $1514 €1400 River landscape with sailing ships (38x52cm-15x20in) s. 19-Mar-3 Neumeister, Munich #631 est:1000
£3401 $5408 €5000 Ships tied up at river's edge (52x76cm-20x30in) s.d.1934. 19-Mar-3 Neumeister, Munich #630/R est:1500

LOBERG, Gunnar (1893-1950) Swedish
£595 $946 €893 Boy fishing (47x55cm-19x22in) s.d.1948 verso panel. 2-Mar-3 Uppsala Auktionskammare, Uppsala #3 (S.KR 8000)

LOBINGIER, Elizabeth Miller (1889-1973) American
£250 $400 €363 Wingaersheek Beach, Gloucester, MA (30x41cm-12x16in) s. board. 17-May-3 CRN Auctions, Cambridge #44

LOBISSER, Switbert (1878-1943) Austrian
£4483 $7172 €6500 Spring (49x61cm-19x24in) s.d.1919. 11-Mar-3 Dorotheum, Vienna #11/R est:6000-8000

LOBLEY, James (1829-1888) British
£4800 $7488 €7200 Lace maker (34x41cm-13x16in) s. panel. 26-Mar-3 Sotheby's, Olympia #38/R est:1500-2500

LOBLEY, John Hodgson (1878-?) British
£620 $1011 €930 Still life of summer flowers (71x56cm-28x22in) 17-Feb-3 Bonhams, Bath #4

LOBO, Balthazar (1910-1993) Spanish
Sculpture
£4194 $6626 €6500 Femme et centaure (13x16x10cm-5x6x4in) s.st.f.Susse num.5/8 black pat bronze lit. 17-Dec-2 Segre, Madrid #139/R
£4810 $7600 €7600 Seated woman holding her knee (32x47cm-13x19in) s. num.1/8 brown green pat bronze Cast Susse lit. 26-Nov-2 Camard, Paris #106/R est:10000
£35000 $58450 €50750 Le repos (51cm-20in) s.num.3/4 green pat. bronze st.f.Fonderia Art Bonvicini. 25-Jun-3 Christie's, London #201/R est:25000-35000
£42000 $68880 €63000 Face au miroir (60cm-24in) s.st.f.Susse num.7/8 green brown pat bronze. 4-Feb-3 Christie's, London #357/R est:24000
£52000 $86840 €75400 Face au vent (200cm-79in) s.num.1/6 green pat. bronze st.f.Susse lit. 25-Jun-3 Christie's, London #182/R est:30000-40000
Works on paper
£968 $1529 €1500 Peasant (50x32cm-20x13in) s.pencil dr. 17-Dec-2 Segre, Madrid #109/R
£972 $1546 €1400 Personnages (49x64cm-19x25in) s.d.1972 wax crayon col crayon dr. 29-Apr-3 Artcurial Briest, Paris #284 est:1500-2000

LOBRICHON, Timoleon Marie (1831-1914) French
£2318 $3778 €3500 Portrait d'une jeune fille (58x44cm-23x17in) s. 2-Feb-3 Muizon & Le Coent, Paris #30
£6000 $9540 €9000 Young teacher (34x53cm-13x21in) s.d.1868. 20-Mar-3 Christie's, Kensington #96/R est:6000-8000

LOCATELLI, Andrea (1693-1741) Italian
£1021 $1675 €1480 Landscape (48x57cm-19x22in) 4-Jun-3 AB Stockholms Auktionsverk #2564/R (S.KR 13000)
£4808 $7452 €7500 Landscape with shepherds (48x61cm-19x24in) 4-Dec-2 Christie's, Rome #450
£20000 $31400 €30000 Classical river landscape with fishermen and woman by a bank (54x41cm-21x16in) prov. 12-Dec-2 Sotheby's, London #225/R est:20000-30000
£28205 $43718 €44000 Landscape in Lazio with figures and tower (73x96cm-29x38in) 4-Dec-2 Christie's, Rome #459/R est:15000-25000

LOCATELLI, Andrea (circle) (1693-1741) Italian
£4194 $6500 €6291 Wooded landscape with a bacchanal (91x126cm-36x50in) 2-Oct-2 Christie's, Rockefeller NY #142/R est:6000-8000
£7200 $12024 €10440 Peasants sheep-shearing in an Italinate landscape (61x47cm-24x19in) oval. 9-Jul-3 Bonhams, New Bond Street #98/R est:3000-5000

LOCATELLI, Andrea (style) (1693-1741) Italian
£5000 $7750 €7500 Travellers playing dice in landscape (49x64cm-19x25in) 31-Oct-2 Sotheby's, Olympia #137/R est:2000-3000

LOCATELLI, Armando (19/20th C) Italian
£1549 $2494 €2200 Venetian canal with bridge (24x33cm-9x13in) s. i. verso panel. 7-May-3 Michael Zeller, Lindau #785/R est:1100

LOCATELLI, Giovan Francesco (1810-1882) Italian
£1635 $2535 €2600 Venetian woman with mask and fan (85x70cm-33x28in) s.d.1848. 29-Oct-2 Dorotheum, Vienna #138/R est:1800-2200

LOCATELLI, Luigi (?) Italian
£629 $969 €1000 Portrait of lady (59x48cm-23x19in) s.d.1928. 28-Oct-2 Il Ponte, Milan #330

LOCATELLI, Pietro (1634-1710) Italian
Works on paper
£2963 $4800 €4445 Head of prelate (29x22cm-11x9in) chk. 22-Jan-3 Christie's, Rockefeller NY #28/R est:5000

LOCATELLI, Romualdo (1905-1943) Italian
£283 $436 €450 Dead game (34x23cm-13x9in) init. cardboard. 28-Oct-2 Il Ponte, Milan #319
£1887 $2906 €3000 Boy riding donkey (98x70cm-39x28in) s. 23-Oct-2 Finarte, Milan #110/R
£82850 $127589 €124275 Portrait of a young girl (100x60cm-39x24in) s.d.1939. 27-Oct-2 Christie's, Hong Kong #28/R est:900000-1400000 (HK.D 1000000)

LOCATTI-SARRI, Bruna (1930-) American/Italian
£516 $800 €774 Water lilies, Genoa (79x58cm-31x23in) s. 28-Sep-2 Charlton Hall, Columbia #171

LOCCI, Bruno (1937-) Italian
£316 $494 €500 On hold (50x70cm-20x28in) s.i. masonite painted 2001. 14-Sep-2 Meeting Art, Vercelli #405/R
£347 $552 €500 Still image (50x70cm-20x28in) s.i. verso masonite. 1-May-3 Meeting Art, Vercelli #149
£347 $552 €500 Still image (50x70cm-20x28in) s.i.verso masonite painted 2001. 1-May-3 Meeting Art, Vercelli #397
£458 $732 €700 Stop (50x70cm-20x28in) s.i. masonite painted 2001. 4-Jan-3 Meeting Art, Vercelli #381

LOCHER, Carl (1851-1915) Danish
£288 $464 €432 Coastal landscape (27x47cm-11x19in) s.d.1897. 22-Feb-3 Rasmussen, Havnen #2240 (D.KR 3200)
£637 $994 €956 Dune landscape with road to the house (18x39cm-7x15in) init.d.96. 5-Aug-2 Rasmussen, Vejle #193/R (D.KR 7500)
£775 $1178 €1163 Coastal landscape with view across the sea (20x30cm-8x12in) s. 27-Aug-2 Rasmussen, Copenhagen #1643 (D.KR 9000)
£852 $1415 €1235 Seascape with small sailing boats off the coast (33x42cm-13x17in) init.d.1878. 12-Jun-3 Kunsthallen, Copenhagen #344/R (D.KR 9000)
£1083 $1700 €1625 Meeresufer mit seglern - sunset sail (47x60cm-19x24in) s. 22-Nov-2 Skinner, Boston #116/R est:1000-1500
£1120 $1702 €1680 Midsummer's Night, Skagen Harbour (31x42cm-12x17in) s.d.82. 27-Aug-2 Rasmussen, Copenhagen #1742/R est:8000-10000 (D.KR 13000)
£1182 $1891 €1773 Vessels saluting the Queen's birthday (42x57cm-17x22in) s.i.d.94. 13-Jan-3 Rasmussen, Vejle #70/R est:15000 (D.KR 13500)
£1397 $2235 €2096 Sailing ship off coast, crew on the way to the shore (28x50cm-11x20in) init.d.95. 16-Mar-3 Hindemae, Ullerslev #544/R est:15000 (D.KR 15000)
£1435 $2325 €2081 Danish fleet celebrating the Queen's birthday (42x56cm-17x22in) s.i.d.94. 26-May-3 Rasmussen, Copenhagen #1356/R est:15000 (D.KR 15000)
£1679 $2670 €2519 Beached boats at Skagen Strand (39x63cm-15x25in) s.i.d.1877. 5-May-3 Rasmussen, Vejle #264/R est:20000-30000 (D.KR 18000)
£1691 $2689 €2537 Sailing vessel off Kullen (26x48cm-10x19in) s. 26-Feb-3 Kunsthallen, Copenhagen #553/R est:12000 (D.KR 18500)
£1772 $2818 €2658 The life-boat going out (48x68cm-19x27in) s,. 5-May-3 Rasmussen, Vejle #265/R est:15000-20000 (D.KR 19000)
£1955 $3109 €2933 Evening, December, Skagen (27x34cm-11x13in) s.i.d.1908 panel. 5-Mar-3 Rasmussen, Copenhagen #2017/R est:10000 (D.KR 21000)
£2573 $4014 €3860 Seascape with the frigate Jylland in high seas (50x74cm-20x29in) s. 11-Nov-2 Rasmussen, Vejle #612/R est:30000 (D.KR 30000)
£3445 $5478 €5168 Seascape with fishing boats (42x64cm-17x25in) s. 5-Mar-3 Rasmussen, Copenhagen #1966/R est:20000 (D.KR 37000)
£3724 $5922 €5586 Coastal landscape with fishing boat going out to sea (80x135cm-31x53in) s.i.d.92. 5-Mar-3 Rasmussen, Copenhagen #1520/R est:50000-75000 (D.KR 40000)
£5236 $8169 €7854 Coastal landscape from Skagen with fishermen coming ashore (105x174cm-41x69in) s.i.d.1896. 23-Sep-2 Rasmussen, Vejle #106/R est:60000-80000 (D.KR 62000)

LOCHER, Gottfried (1730-1795) Swiss
Works on paper
£429 $665 €644 Interior with peasant family (21x17cm-8x7in) s.d.1776 W/C over sepia pen. 3-Oct-2 Koller, Zurich #3280 (S.FR 1000)

LOCHER, Jens (1825-1869) Danish
£279 $447 €419 Coastal landscape (27x36cm-11x14in) init.d.8/4/ 60 panel. 16-Mar-3 Hindemae, Ullerslev #529/R (D.KR 3000)

LOCHHEAD, John (1866-1921) British
£1100 $1705 €1650 In the farmyard (24x34cm-9x13in) s.d.97 board. 5-Dec-2 Bonhams, Edinburgh #72 est:800-1200
£1646 $2551 €2469 Day by the river (76x127cm-30x50in) s. 3-Dec-2 Ritchie, Toronto #3043/R est:2000-4000 (C.D 4000)

LOCHHEAD, Kenneth (1926-) Canadian
£2415 $3840 €3623 Filtered light (40x60cm-16x24in) s.i.d.1994 board. 23-Mar-3 Hodgins, Calgary #60/R est:3000-4000 (C.D 5700)

LOCHORE, Brad (1960-) New Zealander
£1282 $2013 €2000 Shadow 40 (100x100cm-39x39in) s.verso painted 1994 prov. 11-Dec-2 Artcurial Briest, Paris #775/R
£2500 $3875 €3750 Cloude no.5 (170x130cm-67x51in) painted 1997. 5-Dec-2 Christie's, Kensington #256/R est:3000-5000
£3000 $4920 €4500 Shadow no 25 (250x200cm-98x79in) init.d.1993 verso prov. 7-Feb-3 Sotheby's, London #114/R est:3000-4000

LOCHRIE, Elizabeth Davey (1890-1976) American
£750 $1200 €1125 Winter harvest (30x41cm-12x16in) s. 11-Jan-3 James Julia, Fairfield #358 est:1200-1800

LOCK, Freida (1902-1962) South African
£1505 $2423 €2258 Yachts moored in a bay (39x49cm-15x19in) s. 12-May-3 Stephan Welz, Johannesburg #446/R est:12000-18000 (SA.R 17500)
£4356 $6796 €6534 District Six street scene (43x51cm-17x20in) s.d.44. 11-Nov-2 Stephan Welz, Johannesburg #540/R est:40000-60000 (SA.R 68000)
Works on paper
£1290 $2077 €1935 Rooftops with pidgeons (44x56cm-17x22in) s. chl gouache on board. 12-May-3 Stephan Welz, Johannesburg #456/R est:7000-10000 (SA.R 15000)

LOCKER, Edward Hawke (attrib) (1777-1849) British
Works on paper
£280 $465 €406 Winchester Cathedral (18x25cm-7x10in) i.d.1803 verso W/C. 16-Jun-3 Duke & Son, Dorchester #200

LOCKER, John (19th C) British
£449 $700 €674 Peasant life (91x71cm-36x28in) s.indis.d. 9-Oct-2 Doyle, New York #67

LOCKERBY, Mabel I (1887-?) Canadian
£1794 $2870 €2691 Untitled - shade tree (56x76cm-22x30in) s.d.1950 canvasboard. 15-May-3 Heffel, Vancouver #25/R est:4000-4500 (C.D 4000)

LOCKHART, Sharon (1964-) American
Photographs
£18354 $29000 €27531 Untitled (124x165cm-49x65in) s.d.1998 num.6/6 two col coupler prints prov.exhib.lit. 14-Nov-2 Christie's, Rockefeller NY #475/R est:18000-22000

LOCKLEY, H J (fl.1887-1920) British
Works on paper
£290 $452 €435 Wintry countryside scene with farmer and his sheep (49x31cm-19x12in) s.d.03 W/C. 31-Jul-2 Bonhams, Knowle #255

LOCKROY, Eugene (?) ?
£380 $623 €570 Wooded landscape with figure (72x45cm-28x18in) s. 4-Feb-3 Sworder & Son, Bishops Stortford #95/R

LOCKWOOD, John Ward (1894-1963) American
Works on paper
£597 $950 €896 Still life with cherries (43x56cm-17x22in) s. W/C exec.c.1930. 2-Mar-3 Toomey, Oak Park #759/R
£1474 $2300 €2211 Andrew Dasburg in a duck blind (41x58cm-16x23in) s. i.verso W/C executed c.1930. 9-Nov-2 Santa Fe Art, Santa Fe #221/R est:4000-7000

LOCKWOOD, Lucy (20th C) British
£1650 $2574 €2475 On the road to the quarry (81x135cm-32x53in) s. 17-Sep-2 Bonhams, Oxford #28 est:1000-1500

LODDER, Captain Charles A (fl.1880-1885) British
£400 $656 €600 Largs, the mouth of the Findhorn (53x107cm-21x42in) i.verso. 29-May-3 Christie's, Kensington #196/R
£1400 $2198 €2100 Estuary scene with man-o-war at anchor and hay barge (30x35cm-12x14in) s.d.1871. 16-Dec-2 Sotheby's, Olympia #32/R est:500-700

Works on paper
£320 $522 €464 Harbour scene (24x34cm-9x13in) s. W/C. 17-Jul-3 Tennants, Leyburn #707
£650 $1007 €975 Manning the yards of H.M.S Defiant in harbour of the Queens birthday (33x47cm-13x19in) s.d.1869 W/C htd white. 31-Oct-2 Christie's, Kensington #320/R

LODDER, Captain James (fl.1885) British
£600 $930 €900 Small steamboat plying the Clyde (14x22cm-6x9in) mono.d.1885 board. 31-Oct-2 Christie's, Kensington #506/R

LODEIZEN, Johannes (1892-1980) Dutch
£284 $460 €400 Willows in the evening (48x63cm-19x25in) mono.d.29. 26-May-3 Glerum, Amsterdam #11/R
£321 $503 €500 French street (68x48cm-27x19in) s. 25-Nov-2 Glerum, Amsterdam #129/R
£816 $1321 €1150 Walkers on the path between trees on the edge of a river (90x80cm-35x31in) s.d.52. 26-May-3 Glerum, Amsterdam #9/R

LODER OF BATH, Edwin (1827-1885) British
£720 $1123 €1080 Terriers ratting (23x30cm-9x12in) s. pair. 6-Nov-2 Sotheby's, Olympia #151/R
£750 $1230 €1088 Greyhound and a beagle in a stable (24x29cm-9x11in) s.d.1845. 9-Jun-3 Bonhams, Bath #91/R
£800 $1328 €1160 Head of a terrier (13x15cm-5x6in) s. board. 12-Jun-3 Christie's, Kensington #229/R

LODER OF BATH, James (1784-1860) British
£8000 $12720 €12000 Tricolour cavalier king Charles spaniel (48x63cm-19x25in) s. 19-Mar-3 Sotheby's, London #110/R est:8000-12000

LODGE, George Edward (1860-1954) British
£700 $1092 €1050 Elverol (26x41cm-10x16in) s. canvasboard two. 26-Mar-3 Sotheby's, Olympia #67/R
£1500 $2445 €2250 Eagle perched on a rocky outcrop (28x42cm-11x17in) s. 28-Jan-3 Henry Adams, Chichester #471/R est:1000-1500
£2150 $3440 €3225 Partridges in a winter landscape (36x51cm-14x20in) s. sold with a book. 14-Mar-3 Gardiner & Houlgate, Bath #62/R est:2000-2500
£2400 $3984 €3480 Jay on a branch (47x36cm-19x14in) s. canvasboard prov. 12-Jun-3 Christie's, Kensington #138/R est:1800-2200
£5000 $7900 €7500 Mallards at the water's edge (61x91cm-24x36in) s.d.1907. 28-Nov-2 Christie's, Kensington #22/R est:4000-6000

Works on paper
£316 $500 €474 Two common blood pheasants (38x51cm-15x20in) s. W/C gouache prov.exhib. 3-Apr-3 Christie's, Rockefeller NY #212/R
£316 $500 €474 Blood pheasant in the snow (50x37cm-20x15in) s.i.d.Sep 7 1909 W/C gouache on board prov.exhib. 3-Apr-3 Christie's, Rockefeller NY #213/R
£411 $650 €617 Cock and hen in a landscape (36x51cm-14x20in) s. W/C gouache prov.exhib. 3-Apr-3 Christie's, Rockefeller NY #222/R
£580 $905 €841 Edge of the woods (11x15cm-4x6in) s. W/C htd white. 27-Mar-3 Neales, Nottingham #905/R
£620 $967 €899 Early autumn (13x18cm-5x7in) s. W/C. 27-Mar-3 Neales, Nottingham #904
£650 $1079 €943 Grouse rising (30x49cm-12x19in) s. bodycol monochrome prov. 12-Jun-3 Christie's, Kensington #140/R
£680 $1102 €1020 Greenland Gyr falcon (38x25cm-15x10in) s. W/C bodycol. 23-May-3 Lyon & Turnbull, Edinburgh #87a
£750 $1170 €1088 Pheasants on a wooded hillside (14x21cm-6x8in) s.d.1950 W/C bodycol. 27-Mar-3 Neales, Nottingham #906
£1100 $1793 €1650 Falcon (42x31cm-17x12in) s. W/C htd bodycol. 29-Jan-3 Sotheby's, Olympia #184/R est:600-800
£1646 $2600 €2469 Red grouse in flight. Ptarmigan in flight (22x37cm-9x15in) s. W/C gouache pair prov. 3-Apr-3 Christie's, Rockefeller NY #191/R est:3000-5000
£2000 $3100 €3000 Immature Greenland Gyr falcon (70x52cm-28x20in) s. W/C bodycol prov. 3-Dec-2 Sotheby's, Olympia #200/R est:2000-3000
£2500 $3800 €3750 Greenland falcon (66x50cm-26x20in) s. W/C. 28-Aug-2 Sotheby's, London #849/R est:2500-3000

LODI, Ermenegildo (17th C) Italian
Works on paper
£300 $471 €450 Father time (7x10cm-3x4in) i. black chk pen brown wash. 13-Dec-2 Christie's, Kensington #286/R
£3200 $5344 €4640 Assumption of the virgin (52x38cm-20x15in) pen brown ink wash. 9-Jul-3 Sotheby's, London #39/R est:1500-2000

LODOLA, Marco (1955-) Italian
£253 $395 €400 Face (41x31cm-16x12in) s.d.1996 verso perspex. 14-Sep-2 Meeting Art, Vercelli #748
£380 $592 €600 Cat (54x68cm-21x27in) s. acrylic collage. 14-Sep-2 Meeting Art, Vercelli #780/R
£411 $642 €650 Dancers (81x40cm-32x16in) s.i.d.1988 verso perspex enamel. 14-Sep-2 Meeting Art, Vercelli #90
£411 $642 €650 Flamenco dancers (88x92cm-35x36in) s. acrylic collage. 14-Sep-2 Meeting Art, Vercelli #110/R
£443 $691 €700 Dancers (80x60cm-31x24in) s. acrylic collage. 14-Sep-2 Meeting Art, Vercelli #295/R
£458 $732 €700 Rose (80x60cm-31x24in) s. acrylic collage. 4-Jan-3 Meeting Art, Vercelli #435
£486 $773 €700 Dancer (93x53cm-37x21in) s. oil collage. 1-May-3 Meeting Art, Vercelli #224
£538 $839 €850 Confessions (88x97cm-35x38in) s. acrylic collage. 14-Sep-2 Meeting Art, Vercelli #395/R
£538 $839 €850 Wedding photo (94x83cm-37x33in) s. acrylic collage. 14-Sep-2 Meeting Art, Vercelli #496/R
£556 $883 €800 Dancers (120x120cm-47x47in) s.d.2000v. oil enamel collage. 1-May-3 Meeting Art, Vercelli #39
£588 $941 €900 House of stars (83x70cm-33x28in) s.i.d.1999 verso perspex. 4-Jan-3 Meeting Art, Vercelli #684
£654 $1046 €1000 Disco (160x60cm-63x24in) s.i.d.2000 verso perspex. 4-Jan-3 Meeting Art, Vercelli #91
£769 $1208 €1200 Race (60x105cm-24x41in) s.i.d.2001 verso perspex. 23-Nov-2 Meeting Art, Vercelli #313/R
£833 $1308 €1300 Gossips (95x102cm-37x40in) s.i.d.2000 verso perspex. 23-Nov-2 Meeting Art, Vercelli #99/R
£833 $1325 €1200 Three dimensions (100x150cm-39x59in) s. oil collage. 1-May-3 Meeting Art, Vercelli #200
£833 $1325 €1200 Dancing figures (150x100cm-59x39in) s. oil collage. 1-May-3 Meeting Art, Vercelli #459
£980 $1569 €1500 Musical (120x85cm-47x33in) s.i.d.2000 verso perspex enamel. 4-Jan-3 Meeting Art, Vercelli #483
£1076 $1678 €1700 Cabaret (100x150cm-39x59in) s. acrylic collage. 14-Sep-2 Meeting Art, Vercelli #831/R
£1090 $1711 €1700 Musical (140x105cm-55x41in) s.i.d.1999 verso plastic. 19-Nov-2 Finarte, Milan #47/R
£1224 $1947 €1800 Knights (90x135cm-35x53in) s.i.d.2002 verso perspex. 1-Mar-3 Meeting Art, Vercelli #420
£1224 $1947 €1800 Scooters (125x100cm-49x39in) s.i.d.2001 perspex. 1-Mar-3 Meeting Art, Vercelli #630
£1266 $1975 €2000 Musical note (100x95cm-39x37in) s.i.d.2002 perspex neon. 14-Sep-2 Meeting Art, Vercelli #764/R
£1373 $2196 €2100 Wasp (80x100cm-31x39in) s.d.2002 verso perspex. 4-Jan-3 Meeting Art, Vercelli #330
£2692 $4227 €4200 Musical (105x160cm-41x63in) s.i.d. enamel perspex. 19-Nov-2 Finarte, Milan #124/R

Sculpture
£897 $1391 €1400 Dancers (110x65cm-43x26in) s.i.d.2000 verso plastic. 4-Dec-2 Finarte, Milan #573/R
£1806 $2871 €2600 Little mouse (103x94x12cm-41x37x5in) s.i.d.2002 perspex neon light. 1-May-3 Meeting Art, Vercelli #415

Works on paper
£327 $523 €500 Putti (60x80cm-24x31in) s.d.2002 verso collage mixed media on canvas. 4-Jan-3 Meeting Art, Vercelli #36
£327 $523 €500 Venus and the shell (80x60cm-31x24in) s. mixed media collage on canvas. 4-Jan-3 Meeting Art, Vercelli #119
£645 $1019 €1000 Hollywood revue 1929 (110x89cm-43x35in) s.i.d.1991 perspex enamel prov.exhib. 18-Dec-2 Christie's, Rome #98/R

LODSTROM, Georg (1915-1972) Swedish
£1612 $2514 €2418 Stockholm in winter, view from Fjellgatan (70x79cm-28x31in) s.d.65. 6-Nov-2 AB Stockholms Auktionsverk #598/R est:10000-15000 (S.KR 23000)

LOEB, Louis (1866-1909) American
£6918 $11000 €10377 Green apple (59x38cm-23x15in) s. prov.exhib. 5-Mar-3 Christie's, Rockefeller NY #103/R est:3000-5000

LOEBER, Lou (1894-1983) Dutch
£2532 $4000 €4000 Schuitenvoerder II (28x28cm-11x11in) s. i.d.1929 verso board. 26-Nov-2 Sotheby's, Amsterdam #111/R est:3200-3500
£2829 $4413 €4902 Man bij de Kachel I (85x66cm-33x26in) init.i.d.46 oil wood prov. 31-Mar-3 Goodman, Sydney #192/R (A.D 7500)
£3846 $5962 €6000 Wervelend landschap (56x56cm-22x22in) s.d.61 s.i.d.verso board. 3-Dec-2 Christie's, Amsterdam #139/R est:4000-6000
£8861 $14000 €14000 Zeeland (35x54cm-14x21in) init.d.23 s.i.d.verso canvasboard exhib. 26-Nov-2 Sotheby's, Amsterdam #107/R est:7000-9000

Works on paper
£1702 $2757 €2400 Abstract of a village in the mountains (50x50cm-20x20in) init.d.23 gouache. 26-May-3 Glerum, Amsterdam #160/R est:1500-2000

LOEDING, Harmen (1637-1673) Dutch
£20000 $31400 €30000 Still life of oranges, wine glass, crabs, and peeled lemon on a plate (45x37cm-18x15in) panel. 12-Dec-2 Sotheby's, London #156/R est:8000-12000

LOEF, Jacob Geritsz (1607-1675) Dutch
£4459 $6955 €7000 Christ on the sea of Galilee (45x76cm-18x30in) mono. panel prov.exhib.lit. 5-Nov-2 Sotheby's, Amsterdam #25/R est:8000-12000
£4459 $6955 €7000 Dutch man-of-war and other ships in stormy seas (59x85cm-23x33in) mono. panel prov.lit. 5-Nov-2 Sotheby's, Amsterdam #226/R est:7000-9000

LOEFFLER, Gisella (1900-) American/Austrian
Works on paper
£2083 $3250 €3125 Untitled (46x46cm-18x18in) s. gouache on board prov.lit. 9-Nov-2 Santa Fe Art, Santa Fe #78/R est:3500-5000

LOEMANS, Alexander François (c.1816-1898) American/French
£1258 $2000 €1887 Majestic landscapes (18x25cm-7x10in) one s. paper on board two. 5-Mar-3 Doyle, New York #42/R est:800-1200
£2066 $3244 €3099 Activity in a mountain gorge (56x91cm-22x36in) s. 24-Jul-2 Walker's, Ottawa #241/R est:2500-3000 (C.D 5000)

LOENEN, Cor van (1942-) Dutch
£313 $516 €450 Poppy field (80x100cm-31x39in) s. board prov. 1-Jul-3 Christie's, Amsterdam #337/R
£417 $688 €600 Landscape with dunes (85x100cm-33x39in) s. board. 1-Jul-3 Christie's, Amsterdam #346
£417 $688 €600 Rough landscape with wild flowers near Holthe, Drente (80x100cm-31x39in) s. board prov. 1-Jul-3 Christie's, Amsterdam #347
£694 $1146 €1000 Mound village Oostum (90x110cm-35x43in) s. i.stretcher prov. 1-Jul-3 Christie's, Amsterdam #335/R

LOESCHIN, Herman (?-1872) German
£445 $695 €650 Fast ride (21x30cm-8x12in) panel. 10-Apr-3 Dorotheum, Vienna #8

LOEW, Michael (1907-1985) American
£12676 $18000 €19014 Red, yellow, and blue (102x127cm-40x50in) 8-Aug-1 Barridorf, Portland #80/R est:6000-9000

LOFDAHL, Eva (1953-) Swedish
£849 $1368 €1274 Composition (58x58cm-23x23in) s.d.86 verso. 7-May-3 AB Stockholms Auktionsverk #1006/R (S.KR 11000)
Sculpture
£911 $1421 €1367 Untitled (64x64x22cm-25x25x9in) s. panel executed 1987-88 prov. 5-Nov-2 Bukowskis, Stockholm #471/R est:8000-10000 (S.KR 13000)
Works on paper
£911 $1421 €1367 Untitled (60x60cm-24x24in) s.d.86 verso mixed media canvas. 6-Nov-2 AB Stockholms Auktionsverk #893/R est:8000-12000 (S.KR 13000)

LOFFLER, August (1822-1866) German
Works on paper
£281 $438 €410 St George (38x31cm-15x12in) s.d. pencil. 11-Apr-3 Winterberg, Heidelberg #472

LOFFLER, August (attrib) (1822-1866) German
£962 $1490 €1500 Landscape with rainbow (18x22cm-7x9in) canvas on canvas prov. 4-Dec-2 Neumeister, Munich #809/R est:1200
£2041 $3245 €3000 Olevano (63x85cm-25x33in) mono.d.1859. 19-Mar-3 Neumeister, Munich #632/R est:4000

LOFFLER, Bertold (1874-1960) Austrian
Works on paper
£313 $494 €450 Durnstein (45x31cm-18x12in) mono.d.20.Aug.1909 chk. 24-Apr-3 Dorotheum, Vienna #7/R

LOFFLER, Emma (1843-1929) Danish
£1775 $2734 €2663 Water-lilies on woodland lake (73x66cm-29x26in) s.d.1882. 26-Oct-2 Rasmussen, Havnen #2085/R est:15000 (D.KR 21000)

LOFFLER, Franz Karl (1875-1955) German
£316 $491 €500 Wasserburg - Bodensee (19x22cm-7x9in) s. i. verso board. 27-Sep-2 Karrenbauer, Konstanz #1650
£943 $1472 €1500 Wasserburg on summer evening (31x43cm-12x17in) s. panel. 9-Oct-2 Michael Zeller, Lindau #786/R

LOFFLER, Hugo (1859-1935) German
£4000 $6360 €6000 Belshazzar's feast (114x214cm-45x84in) 20-Mar-3 Christie's, Kensington #193/R est:4000-6000

LOFFLER, Richard (1956-) American
Sculpture
£1090 $1700 €1635 Muffin (36x10x18cm-14x4x7in) num.3/10 bronze. 9-Aug-2 Altermann Galleries, Santa Fe #1/R
£1859 $2900 €2789 Timber lake grizzly (8x43x51cm-3x17x20in) num.14/40 bronze. 9-Aug-2 Altermann Galleries, Santa Fe #2/R

LOFFREDO, Silvio (1920-) Italian
£256 $403 €400 Three figures (100x70cm-39x28in) s. 19-Nov-2 Finarte, Milan #108
£443 $691 €700 Landscape (80x60cm-31x24in) s.d.1961. 19-Oct-2 Semenzato, Venice #145

LOGAN, Maurice (1886-1977) American
£1911 $3000 €2867 Farm in autumn (25x34cm-10x13in) s. paper on board prov. 19-Nov-2 Butterfields, San Francisco #8253/R est:3000-5000
£3226 $5000 €4839 Near Castroville, Salinas area (48x69cm-19x27in) s. canvasboard prov. 29-Oct-2 John Moran, Pasadena #665 est:6000-8000
Works on paper
£261 $425 €392 Fishermen on the shore of the bay (29x43cm-11x17in) s.i. W/C. 16-Feb-3 Butterfields, San Francisco #2101
£452 $700 €678 House in landscape (33x48cm-13x19in) s. W/C. 29-Oct-2 John Moran, Pasadena #686c
£1380 $2250 €2070 Fishing ships at the Monterey Wharf. Tree shaded home (40x53cm-16x21in) s. pencil W/C double-sided prov. 16-Feb-3 Butterfields, San Francisco #2102 est:2500-3500

LOGELAIN, Henri (1889-1968) Belgian
£256 $405 €400 City near the water with mountains in the background (38x64cm-15x25in) s. panel. 18-Nov-2 Bernaerts, Antwerp #335/R
£417 $654 €650 Nature morte aux poissons (27x36cm-11x14in) s. panel. 10-Dec-2 Campo, Vlaamse Kaai #307
£769 $1192 €1200 Vue de la Grand-Place de Bruxelles (26x35cm-10x14in) s. panel. 9-Dec-2 Horta, Bruxelles #426
£1154 $1812 €1800 Village Ardennais (85x100cm-33x39in) s. 10-Dec-2 Campo, Vlaamse Kaai #306/R est:2000-3000
Works on paper
£2949 $4629 €4600 Autoportrait (40x29cm-16x11in) s.d.1917 W/C. 19-Nov-2 Vanderkindere, Brussels #96 est:300-500

LOGSDAIL, William (1859-1944) British
£1923 $3019 €3000 Interior with figure (67x54cm-26x21in) s.d.1880. 21-Nov-2 Weidler, Nurnberg #6758/R
£2600 $4290 €3770 Near Menton (35x25cm-14x10in) s.d.91 board. 2-Jul-3 Sotheby's, Olympia #345/R est:3000-4000
£7000 $10780 €10500 Fishing in the Laguna, Venice (36x20cm-14x8in) s. board. 5-Sep-2 Christie's, Kensington #236/R est:3000-5000

LOHAN, Mary (20th C) Irish?
£886 $1373 €1400 Green rust plant (46x41cm-18x16in) s. oil on card prov. 24-Sep-2 De Veres Art Auctions, Dublin #105/R est:1000-1500

LOHMAN, Joseph (1884-1960) Dutch
£637 $994 €1000 Still life with apples, green flask and a white bowl (40x41cm-16x16in) s. panel. 5-Nov-2 Vendu Notarishuis, Rotterdam #109/R

LOHMANN, Adolf (1928-) German
£873 $1362 €1310 Ducks on pond (40x60cm-16x24in) s. panel. 6-Nov-2 Dobiaschofsky, Bern #782/R (S.FR 2000)

LOHMANN, Mogens (1918-1985) Danish
£326 $519 €489 Composition III (46x42cm-18x17in) s.d.1968 verso. 29-Apr-3 Kunsthallen, Copenhagen #39/R (D.KR 3500)

LOHR, August (1843-1919) German
£4367 $6900 €6551 Landscape (59x104cm-23x41in) s.d.1906. 28-Nov-2 Louis Morton, Mexico #271/R est:100000 (M.P 70000)
£16463 $27000 €23871 Popocatepetl (59x103cm-23x41in) s.d.1916 prov.exhib. 27-May-3 Sotheby's, New York #139

LOHR, Emil Ludwig (1809-1876) German
Works on paper
£260 $434 €377 Austrian landscape, German possibly of Bad Gastein (51x36cm-20x14in) W/C. 11-Jul-3 Bracketts, Tunbridge Wells #826/R

LOHSE, Richard Paul (1902-1988) Swiss
£7725 $12206 €11588 Three vertical groups with orange and red in centre (48x48cm-19x19in) s.i.d.1952/74 verso acrylic prov. 26-Nov-2 Phillips, Zurich #96/R est:10000-15000 (S.FR 18000)
£8297 $13026 €12446 Two complementary contrasts with red corners, sketch B (48x48cm-19x19in) s. verso s.i.d. stretcher acrylic prov.lit. 25-Nov-2 Germann, Zurich #24/R est:15000-20000 (S.FR 19000)
£8584 $13562 €12876 Horizontal permeation of magenta, blue-green and yellow through blue. s.I.d.1955 acrylic. 26-Nov-2 Phillips, Zurich #97/R est:15000-20000 (S.FR 20000)

LOIR, Luigi (1845-1916) French
£1258 $1937 €2000 Landscape (24x51cm-9x20in) s. board. 22-Oct-2 Durán, Madrid #239/R
£2536 $4159 €3500 Bateaux sur la Seine, Paris (9x14cm-4x6in) s. cardboard. 27-May-3 Artcurial Briest, Paris #151/R est:2500-3000
£2899 $4754 €4000 Boulevard Rochechouart, le soir (9x14cm-4x6in) s. cardboard. 27-May-3 Artcurial Briest, Paris #154/R est:2500-3000
£3261 $5348 €4500 Grand boulevards animes, le soir (9x14cm-4x6in) s. cardboard. 27-May-3 Artcurial Briest, Paris #156/R est:2500-3000
£3500 $5495 €5250 Still life with flowers (41x21cm-16x8in) s.i. 21-Nov-2 Christie's, Kensington #79/R est:4000-6000
£3551 $5823 €4900 Boulevard Bonne Nouvelle, le soir (9x14cm-4x6in) s. cardboard. 27-May-3 Artcurial Briest, Paris #152/R est:2500-3000
£3623 $5942 €5000 Foire aux pains d'epice, le soir (14x9cm-6x4in) s. cardboard. 27-May-3 Artcurial Briest, Paris #153/R est:2200-2800
£3986 $6536 €5500 Pres du Pont Saint Michel, les quais animes le soir (9x14cm-4x6in) s. cardboard. 27-May-3 Artcurial Briest, Paris #155/R est:2500-3000
£15484 $24000 €23226 Bustling day (24x35cm-9x14in) s. panel. 29-Oct-2 Sotheby's, New York #97/R est:18000-25000
£19504 $30230 €29256 View from Montmartre (56x47cm-22x19in) s. 3-Dec-2 Bukowskis, Stockholm #319/R est:100000-125000 (S.KR 275000)
£37975 $60000 €56963 Effect of snow (57x77cm-22x30in) s. prov.exhib. 24-Apr-3 Sotheby's, New York #3/R est:60000-80000
Works on paper
£709 $1100 €1064 Figures at a railway station (5x17cm-2x7in) s. black wash chk gouache. 29-Oct-2 Sotheby's, New York #87/R est:800-1200
£972 $1536 €1400 Marche aux fleurs (8x13cm-3x5in) s. W/C prov. 25-Apr-3 Piasa, Paris #124/R
£1296 $1841 €2100 Paris, quais de la Seine (16x11cm-6x4in) s. chl htd gouache dr. 16-Mar-3 Eric Pillon, Calais #18/R
£2754 $4516 €3800 Le pavillon Lefevre-Utile a l'Exposition Universelle de Paris en 1900 (20x28cm-8x11in) s. gouache. 27-May-3 Artcurial Briest, Paris #157/R est:1000-1500
£3718 $5837 €5800 Boulogne-sur-Mer (44x59cm-17x23in) s.i. W/C. 16-Dec-2 Rabourdin & Choppin de Janvry, Paris #116/R
£4321 $7000 €6265 Place de la Concorde (18x30cm-7x12in) s. gouache over pencil. 21-May-3 Doyle, New York #215/R est:5000-7000
£7609 $12478 €10500 Le patinage au bois de Boulogne (27x54cm-11x21in) s. W/C gouache cardboard exec.c.1903. 27-May-3 Artcurial Briest, Paris #74/R est:7000-9000

LOIR, Luigi (attrib) (1845-1916) French
£1800 $2934 €2700 Parisian boulevard (38x55cm-15x22in) 13-Feb-3 Christie's, Kensington #133/R est:2000-3000

LOIR, Marianne (c.1715-1769) French
£8387 $13252 €13000 Portrait presume de Madame de Seran (80x64cm-31x25in) 18-Dec-2 Renaud, Paris #30/R est:6000

LOIR, Marianne (attrib) (c.1715-1769) French
£2885 $4471 €4500 Portrait de jeune femme assise (142x113cm-56x44in) 4-Dec-2 Libert, Castor, Paris #50/R

LOIR, Nicolas (attrib) (1624-1679) French
£1698 $2615 €2700 La vierge a l'enfant et le petit Saint Jean Baptiste (40x33cm-16x13in) oval. 25-Oct-2 Tajan, Paris #102 est:1500-2400

LOISEAU, Gustave (1865-1935) French
£3600 $5724 €5400 La rue (35x26cm-14x10in) s. 20-Mar-3 Sotheby's, Olympia #46/R est:4000-6000
£13000 $20670 €19500 Maisons au bord de la riviere (27x41cm-11x16in) s. painted c.1890 prov. 20-Mar-3 Sotheby's, Olympia #37/R est:7000-9000
£14500 $24215 €21025 Les Barques echouees dans un port (28x34cm-11x13in) s. painted c.1913 prov. 24-Jun-3 Sotheby's, London #130/R est:12000-16000
£16667 $26000 €25001 Maison au bord de la mer (46x55cm-18x22in) s. 6-Nov-2 Sotheby's, New York #156/R est:25000-30000
£19231 $30000 €28847 Beynac en Dordogne (50x61cm-20x24in) s. 12-Apr-3 Weschler, Washington #534/R est:40000-60000
£19620 $31000 €31000 View of Saint-Cyr de Vandreuil (46x55cm-18x22in) s.d.1921. 29-Nov-2 Drouot Estimations, Paris #92/R est:32000
£20513 $32000 €30770 Petite ferme dans le Calvados (50x61cm-20x24in) s. i.on stretcher prov. 7-Nov-2 Christie's, Rockefeller NY #229/R est:30000-40000
£25478 $40000 €38217 Saint Cry Du Vaudreuil, November (24x32cm-9x13in) s. 10-Dec-2 Doyle, New York #234/R est:20000-30000
£28000 $45920 €42000 Entree du village de Mortain sous la neige (46x55cm-18x22in) s. 4-Feb-3 Christie's, London #227/R
£28481 $44146 €45000 Vue de Fecamp (54x65cm-21x26in) s. i.d.1925 verso prov. 28-Sep-2 Christie's, Paris #30/R est:30000-40000
£30769 $48308 €48000 Port (60x72cm-24x28in) s. prov. 10-Dec-2 Pierre Berge, Paris #19/R est:50000
£31056 $50000 €46584 La neige a Mortain (54x73cm-21x29in) s. indis d. 7-May-3 Sotheby's, New York #164/R est:50000-70000
£31690 $52606 €45000 Le pont suspendu a Triel (60x81cm-24x32in) s. lit. 12-Jun-3 Tajan, Paris #17/R est:45000-60000
£33775 $55053 €51000 Bord de l'Oise (50x61cm-20x24in) s. 2-Feb-3 Muizon & Le Coent, Paris #43
£34161 $55000 €51242 Les pres de Saint-Cyr (60x81cm-24x32in) s. painted c.1895. 8-May-3 Christie's, Rockefeller NY #177/R est:40000-60000
£40373 $65000 €60560 Vue de Saint Cyr du Vau Dreuil (46x55cm-18x22in) s.d.1921 prov. 7-May-3 Sotheby's, New York #154/R est:50000-60000
£41026 $64410 €64000 Paris, animation rue de Clignancourt (55x46cm-22x18in) s. prov. 15-Dec-2 Thierry & Lannon, Brest #163/R est:80000
£41667 $65000 €62501 Chaumiere, le vaudreuil (46x55cm-18x22in) s. painted 1903 prov. 6-Nov-2 Sotheby's, New York #141/R est:60000-80000
£44872 $70000 €67308 La cathedrale d'auxerre (66x55cm-26x22in) s.d.1907 prov. 6-Nov-2 Sotheby's, New York #142/R est:80000-120000
£46584 $75000 €69876 Bords de riviere, Normandie (66x81cm-26x32in) s. painted c.1918 prov. 7-May-3 Sotheby's, New York #171/R est:60000-80000
£57692 $90000 €86538 Les berges de la Seine en ete Tournedos-Sur-Seine (60x81cm-24x32in) s.d.99 prov.exhib. 6-Nov-2 Sotheby's, New York #146/R est:80000-120000
£60000 $100200 €87000 Bords de l'eure (92x73cm-36x29in) s. painted c.1920 prov. 24-Jun-3 Sotheby's, London #128/R est:60000-80000
£60897 $95000 €91346 Place de l'etoile (60x90cm-24x35in) s. painted 1930 prov. 6-Nov-2 Sotheby's, New York #176/R est:90000-120000
£64935 $94805 €100000 La Seine a Port Marly. 11-Jun-2 Thierry & Lannon, Brest #108a
£77640 $125000 €116460 Bords de l'Eure (65x81cm-26x32in) s. prov. 8-May-3 Christie's, Rockefeller NY #170/R est:90000-120000
£105590 $170000 €158385 Brouillard sur L'Eure (73x92cm-29x36in) s.d.1904 prov. 7-May-3 Sotheby's, New York #150/R est:100000-120000

LOISEAU, Jacques (1920-) French
£655 $1042 €950 Causses aux Baux (38x46cm-15x18in) s. 10-Mar-3 Millon & Associes, Paris #228

LOIZOU, Renos (20th C) ?
£950 $1482 €1425 Didymogenes (63x53cm-25x21in) s. painted 1990 prov. 27-Mar-3 Christie's, Kensington #597/R
£1400 $2184 €2100 Palm trees in a landscape (124x114cm-49x45in) s.d.86 oil paper on canvas prov. 27-Mar-3 Christie's, Kensington #593/R est:800-1200

LOJACONO, Francesco (1841-1915) Italian
£9058 $14855 €12500 Marina con scogliera (46x88cm-18x35in) s. 27-May-3 Finarte, Milan #65/R est:12000-15000
£13768 $22580 €19000 Paesaggio siciliano (63x96cm-25x38in) canvas on panel. 27-May-3 Finarte, Milan #73/R est:14000-16000
£17949 $26205 €28000 View of Palermo harbour (46x75cm-18x30in) 5-Jun-2 Il Ponte, Milan #269/R est:12000-15000
£28623 $46942 €39500 Dopo la pioggia (46x96cm-18x38in) s. 27-May-3 Finarte, Milan #81/R est:15000-18000
£30072 $49319 €41500 Golfo di Palermo con barche e pescatori (48x96cm-19x38in) s. 27-May-3 Finarte, Milan #66/R est:22000-24000

LOJACONO, Francesco (attrib) (1841-1915) Italian
£12000 $18600 €18000 Extensive continental landscape with girl, lamb and shepherd (47x95cm-19x37in) s. 4-Dec-2 Outhwaite & Litherland, Liverpool #315/R

LOKHORST, Dirk Pieter van (1848-?) Dutch
£1026 $1621 €1600 Landscape with goats grazing (13x27cm-5x11in) s. board. 16-Nov-2 Lempertz, Koln #1528 est:1600
£1887 $2906 €3000 Homeward bound (56x89cm-22x35in) s. 23-Oct-2 Christie's, Amsterdam #67/R est:4000-6000

LOKHORST, Dirk van (1818-1893) Dutch
Works on paper
£347 $573 €500 In the stable (23x33cm-9x13in) s. col ink W/C. 1-Jul-3 Christie's, Amsterdam #559

LOKHORST, Dirk van (attrib) (1818-1893) Dutch
£692 $1079 €1100 Herdswoman with cows in ford (34x48cm-13x19in) s. panel. 21-Sep-2 Bolland & Marotz, Bremen #516/R

LOKHORST, Jan van (1837-1874) Dutch
£4828 $7724 €7000 Small fisherman (47x68cm-19x27in) s.d.1872. 15-Mar-3 De Vuyst, Lokeren #508/R est:6500-7500

LOKKE, Karl (1870-1943) Norwegian
£454 $712 €681 Old alpine farm (37x66cm-15x26in) s. 25-Nov-2 Blomqvist, Lysaker #1179/R (N.KR 5200)
£454 $712 €681 Winter landscape (76x106cm-30x42in) s. 25-Nov-2 Blomqvist, Lysaker #1180 (N.KR 5200)

LOLEK, Stanislav (1873-1936) Czechoslovakian
£567 $902 €851 Kingfisher (48x70cm-19x28in) s. board. 8-Mar-3 Dorotheum, Prague #52/R est:18000-27000 (C.KR 26000)

LOMAKIN, Oleg (1924-) Russian
£600 $930 €900 Katherine (61x50cm-24x20in) s. 8-Dec-2 John Nicholson, Haslemere #199/R
£900 $1395 €1350 Evening light (65x54cm-26x21in) s. 8-Dec-2 John Nicholson, Haslemere #198/R
£1439 $2360 €2000 Woman sewing (80x59cm-31x23in) s. s.i.verso prov. 3-Jun-3 Christie's, Amsterdam #31/R est:2000-3000

LOMAS, J L (fl.1862-1874) British
£1050 $1523 €1575 Country girl feeding chickens (58x43cm-23x17in) s. 3-May-2 Biddle & Webb, Birmingham #320/R est:1000-2000

LOMAX, John Arthur (1857-1923) British
£620 $1004 €899 Cottage interior with a young girl and man in front of an open fire (29x39cm-11x15in) s.d.1884 panel. 23-May-3 Bracketts, Tunbridge Wells #981/R
£1067 $1771 €1547 Repairing the doll (64x76cm-25x30in) s.d.1880. 16-Jun-3 Waddingtons, Toronto #164/R est:3000-5000 (C.D 2400)
£1400 $2184 €2100 Elegant gentleman study in a library (41x30cm-16x12in) s. canvas on panel. 6-Nov-2 Bonhams, Chester #431/R est:500-700
Works on paper
£280 $456 €420 Interior scene with alchemist seated before an experiment (23x32cm-9x13in) mono.i. W/C. 11-Feb-3 Fellows & Sons, Birmingham #127/R
£1200 $1956 €1800 Huntsman feeding his dog (23x34cm-9x13in) s. pencil W/C prov. 13-Feb-3 Christie's, Kensington #95/R est:1500-1800

LOMBARD SCHOOL (?) Italian
£11006 $16950 €17500 Still lives with fruit and birds (24x36cm-9x14in) board pair. 28-Oct-2 Il Ponte, Milan #76/R est:3000

LOMBARD SCHOOL (15th C) Italian
£40123 $65000 €60185 Flagellation (42x34cm-17x13in) tempera panel. 23-Jan-3 Sotheby's, New York #58/R est:30000-40000

LOMBARD SCHOOL (16th C) Italian
£8966 $14166 €13000 Saint Ambrogio (100x50cm-39x20in) tempera board. 5-Apr-3 Finarte Semenzato, Milan #134/R est:6000
Works on paper
£9400 $14758 €14100 Study of a head (36x31cm-14x12in) black chk on joined sheets. 11-Dec-2 Sotheby's, Olympia #11/R est:1500-2000

LOMBARD SCHOOL (17th C) Italian
£5379 $8553 €7800 Still life with peaches, figs aand grapes (50x62cm-20x24in) Sotheby's, 5-Mar-3 Sotheby's, Milan #200
£6289 $9748 €10000 Three Life's Carers (115x117cm-45x46in) 29-Oct-2 Finarte, Milan #481/R est:4000-6000
£7986 $12698 €11500 Annunciation (157x81cm-62x32in) 3-May-3 Finarte, Venice #135/R est:12000
£8500 $13260 €12750 Garland of tulips, lilies and other flowers surrounding a medallion of the Virgin and Child (47x35cm-19x14in) panel. 10-Apr-3 Christie's, Kensington #233/R est:5000-8000
£9177 $14225 €14500 Allegorie des cinq sens (70x92cm-28x36in) 27-Sep-2 Rabourdin & Choppin de Janvry, Paris #163/R est:12000-17000
£9459 $14757 €14000 Armourer's workshop (90cm-35in) prov. 27-Mar-3 Dorotheum, Vienna #370/R est:6000-8000
£15190 $24000 €24000 Saint Augustin and Saint Ambrogio (99x127cm-39x50in) 2-Dec-2 Finarte, Milan #119/R est:22000

LOMBARD, Lambert (1506-1566) Flemish
Works on paper
£316 $500 €500 Allegorie de Rome assise sur un trone entouree de richesses (10x11cm-4x4in) i. pen brown ink. 27-Nov-2 Christie's, Paris #1/R

LOMBARD, Lambert (attrib) (1506-1566) Flemish
£17901 $29000 €26852 Descent of the Holy Spirit at Pentecost (100x198cm-39x78in) d.1558 panel prov. 23-Jan-3 Sotheby's, New York #192/R est:50000

LOMBARDELLI, Giovanni Battista (1532-1592) Italian
Works on paper
£839 $1200 €1259 Moses striking the rock (18x29cm-7x11in) pen ink blue wash. 23-Jan-3 Swann Galleries, New York #40/R est:1500-2500

LOMBARDI, Giovanni Battista (1823-c.1880) Italian
Sculpture
£3185 $5000 €4778 Veiled girl (67cm-26in) s. marble. 21-Nov-2 Sotheby's, New York #114/R est:5000-7000
£38217 $60000 €57326 Flight from the destruction of Pompeii (15cm-6in) s.d.1878 marble raised marble plinth prov. 21-Nov-2 Sotheby's, New York #125/R est:50000-70000

LOMBARDO, Federico (1970-) Italian
£1418 $2298 €2000 Untitled (170x80cm-67x31in) s.d.2001 verso. 20-May-3 Porro, Milan #36/R est:3300-3500

LOMI, Giovanni (1889-1969) Italian
£1020 $1622 €1500 Figures in the park (16x23cm-6x9in) s. board. 1-Mar-3 Meeting Art, Vercelli #97
£1081 $1686 €1600 Pasture in the mountains (17x23cm-7x9in) s. board. 28-Mar-3 Farsetti, Prato #410/R
£1419 $2243 €2200 Light effects (19x29cm-7x11in) s. board. 18-Dec-2 Finarte, Milan #40/R
£1824 $2846 €2700 Sunset (22x30cm-9x12in) s. board. 28-Mar-3 Farsetti, Prato #439/R
£1935 $3058 €3000 On the cliffs (19x29cm-7x11in) s. board. 18-Dec-2 Finarte, Milan #39 est:2500
£2162 $3373 €3200 Afternoon (25x29cm-10x11in) s. board. 28-Mar-3 Farsetti, Prato #525/R
£2372 $3724 €3700 Shepherds in the mountains (30x39cm-12x15in) s. s.i.verso board. 16-Dec-2 Pandolfini, Florence #325/R

LOMI, Massimo (1953-) Italian
£327 $523 €500 Travelling philosophy (73x52cm-29x20in) s.i.d.1998 tempera board. 4-Jan-3 Meeting Art, Vercelli #423
£348 $543 €550 Wooden budgies (67x69cm-26x27in) s.d.1999 tempera board. 14-Sep-2 Meeting Art, Vercelli #425
£348 $543 €550 Livorno, Villa Morazzana (43x88cm-17x35in) s.i. tempera board painted 1999. 14-Sep-2 Meeting Art, Vercelli #878/R
£451 $718 €650 Autumn effects (63x75cm-25x30in) s.i. tempera board painted 2002. 1-May-3 Meeting Art, Vercelli #583
£556 $889 €850 Trip (46x84cm-18x33in) s.d.2001 tempera board lit. 4-Jan-3 Meeting Art, Vercelli #173

LONBLAD, Emilia (1865-1946) Swedish
£279 $430 €419 Head of girl (26x21cm-10x8in) panel. 23-Oct-2 Kunsthallen, Copenhagen #422 (D.KR 3300)
£1178 $1932 €1708 Lilly - daughter of the shoemaker (50x41cm-20x16in) s. 4-Jun-3 AB Stockholms Auktionsverk #2204/R est:18000-20000 (S.KR 15000)

LONCHAMP, P (?) French
£300 $468 €450 14th July celebrations (53x72cm-21x28in) s.d.54. 17-Sep-2 Bonhams, Knightsbridge #15/R

LONDONIO, Francesco (1723-1783) Italian
£545 $845 €850 Little goat (23x29cm-9x11in) canvas on board. 4-Dec-2 Christie's, Rome #383
Works on paper
£1600 $2512 €2400 Seated woman with birds (23x20cm-9x8in) s. black chk wash htd white prov. 11-Dec-2 Sotheby's, Olympia #184/R est:1800-2200

LONDOT, Léon (1878-1953) Belgian
£633 $987 €1000 Les pots bleus. s. 10-Sep-2 Vanderkindere, Brussels #298
£1060 $1727 €1600 Barques de peche (61x54cm-24x21in) s. 17-Feb-3 Horta, Bruxelles #97

Works on paper
£348 $543 €550 Vue de la fontaine (72x53cm-28x21in) s.d.1909 mixed media. 16-Sep-2 Horta, Bruxelles #462

LONG, Andrew (fl.1843-1847) British
Works on paper
£320 $515 €480 Old Whitby (12x17cm-5x7in) s. W/C. 15-Jan-3 Cheffins Grain & Comins, Cambridge #377/R

LONG, Benjamin (20th C) Canadian
£244 $401 €354 Five angles (60x50cm-24x20in) s. 9-Jun-3 Hodgins, Calgary #212/R (C.D 550)

LONG, Edwin (1829-1891) British
£280 $437 €420 St Thomas of Villaneuve (40x26cm-16x10in) mono.i.d.1857 after Murillo. 8-Apr-3 Bonhams, Knightsbridge #306/R
£650 $1034 €975 Study of a boy (38x28cm-15x11in) init. prov. 6-Mar-3 Christie's, Kensington #612/R
£2600 $4238 €3770 Portraits of William Angerstein and his wife Mrs Angerstein (137x102cm-54x40in) s. pair prov.exhib. 21-Jul-3 Sotheby's, London #172/R est:4000-6000
£3400 $5406 €5100 Porcelain factory (90x127cm-35x50in) mono. 6-Mar-3 Christie's, Kensington #611/R est:800-1200
£9000 $14490 €13500 Study of head of Arab girl (35x30cm-14x12in) mono. canvas on board oval prov.exhib. 20-Feb-3 Christie's, London #161/R est:7000
£9000 $15030 €13050 Anthem (128x101cm-50x40in) mono.i. 17-Jun-3 Bonhams, New Bond Street #65/R est:6000-8000
£26000 $41080 €39000 Phyllis (129x94cm-51x37in) mono.d.1881 prov.lit. 26-Nov-2 Christie's, London #168/R est:25000-35000
£35000 $56350 €52500 Easter vigil (131x206cm-52x81in) s. prov.exhib.lit. 20-Feb-3 Christie's, London #160/R est:30000
£66456 $105000 €105000 Priestess (149x99cm-59x39in) init.d.1889 lit.prov. 30-Nov-2 Hagelstam, Helsinki #38/R est:120000
Works on paper
£750 $1193 €1125 Head study of an Arab (44x33cm-17x13in) mono.i.d.73 W/C. 29-Apr-3 Bonhams, New Bond Street #101/R

LONG, Leonard (1911-) Australian
£272 $414 €408 Shadowed ridge, Woodhill Mountain, Berry NSW (29x60cm-11x24in) s.d.74 canvasboard. 27-Aug-2 Goodman, Sydney #26 (A.D 760)
£286 $443 €429 Murray river near Jinjellie (60x95cm-24x37in) s.d.1978 board. 29-Oct-2 Lawson Menzies, Sydney #443 (A.D 800)

LONG, Lieutenant (19th C) ?
£6731 $10568 €10500 Halte de cavaliers (40x65cm-16x26in) s. pair. 10-Dec-2 Tajan, Paris #190/R

LONG, Marion (1882-1970) Canadian
£184 $286 €276 Still life (27x21cm-11x8in) s. panel. 24-Sep-2 Ritchie, Toronto #3191 (C.D 450)
£711 $1166 €1067 Marigolds (56x62cm-22x24in) s. exhib. 3-Jun-3 Joyner, Toronto #373/R est:800-1200 (C.D 1600)

LONG, Richard (1945-) British
Sculpture
£7595 $12000 €11393 Burnt driftwood ring Bristol (203x203cm-80x80in) charred wood executed 1986 prov. 13-Nov-2 Sotheby's, New York #141/R est:15000-20000

LONG, Sydney (1871-1955) Australian
£1068 $1633 €1602 Bell tower at Courreges, Belgium (52x29cm-20x11in) s.d.1912 prov. 25-Aug-2 Sotheby's, Paddington #120 est:3000-5000 (A.D 3000)
£1290 $1961 €1935 Newport, near Sydney, view from Bungan Castle (32x61cm-13x24in) s. academy board. 28-Aug-2 Deutscher-Menzies, Melbourne #316/R est:4000-6000 (A.D 3600)
£1786 $2821 €2679 Evening glow (37x44cm-15x17in) s. board. 18-Nov-2 Joel, Victoria #298/R est:6000-8000 (A.D 5000)
£2151 $3269 €3227 Narrabeen Lake (46x61cm-18x24in) s.d.1944. 28-Aug-2 Deutscher-Menzies, Melbourne #235/R est:7000-9000 (A.D 6000)
£2214 $3498 €3321 Boyd's boat shed, Collaroy (34x57cm-13x22in) with sig. board. 2-Apr-3 Christie's, Melbourne #36/R est:2000-3000 (A.D 5800)
£5694 $8712 €8541 Yellow flowers in a field (39x28cm-15x11in) s. panel painted c.1910 prov. 26-Aug-2 Sotheby's, Paddington #524/R est:18000-20000 (A.D 16000)
Works on paper
£325 $514 €471 Homestead (12x25cm-5x10in) s. W/C gouache. 22-Jul-3 Lawson Menzies, Sydney #212/R (A.D 800)
£571 $903 €857 Cattle drinking (22x28cm-9x11in) s.d.1915 W/C. 18-Nov-2 Joel, Victoria #178 est:2000-2500 (A.D 1600)
£1071 $1682 €1607 Flamingos (17x37cm-7x15in) s. W/C. 25-Nov-2 Christie's, Melbourne #347/R est:3000-5000 (A.D 3000)
£1680 $2705 €2520 Bush track (30x40cm-12x16in) s.d.1910 W/C. 6-May-3 Christie's, Melbourne #274/R est:2500-3000 (A.D 4200)
£1916 $3008 €2874 Passing storm (43x34cm-17x13in) s. W/C sold with two etchings. 15-Apr-3 Lawson Menzies, Sydney #207/R est:5500-6500 (A.D 5000)
£2289 $3617 €3966 Pink flamingos (33x59cm-13x23in) s. W/C. 1-Apr-3 Goodman, Sydney #60g/R est:6000-9000 (A.D 6000)
£2299 $3425 €3449 Trees and figures (23x16cm-9x6in) s.d.1910 W/C. 27-Aug-2 Christie's, Melbourne #255 est:6000-8000 (A.D 6000)
£2643 $4149 €3965 Flamingoes (32x60cm-13x24in) s. W/C. 25-Nov-2 Christie's, Melbourne #422/R est:6000-8000 (A.D 7400)
£4643 $7336 €6965 Moonrise (48x65cm-19x26in) s.d.1910 W/C prov. 17-Nov-2 Sotheby's, Paddington #17/R est:18000-28000 (A.D 13000)
£8397 $13267 €12596 Six flamingos (31x55cm-12x22in) s.d.1907 W/C. 2-Apr-3 Christie's, Melbourne #15/R est:6000-10000 (A.D 22000)
£13846 $22015 €20769 Solitary ramble (34x26cm-13x10in) s.d.1908 W/C lit. 4-Mar-3 Deutscher-Menzies, Melbourne #137/R est:38000-45000 (A.D 36000)

LONG, Ted (1933-) American
£513 $800 €744 Lone eagle (46x36cm-18x14in) s. board. 13-Apr-3 Butterfields, Los Angeles #7004

LONGA, Louis Anselme (1809-1869) French
£252 $390 €400 Portrait de femme a la robe verte (40x32cm-16x13in) s.d.1839. 29-Oct-2 Artcurial Briest, Paris #58/R

LONGARETTI, Trento (1916-) Italian
£408 $649 €600 Travellers in Old Russia (10x23cm-4x9in) s. board painted 1997. 1-Mar-3 Meeting Art, Vercelli #737
£490 $784 €750 Still life (15x20cm-6x8in) s. canvas on board. 4-Jan-3 Meeting Art, Vercelli #497
£510 $811 €750 Maternity (18x12cm-7x5in) s. board. 1-Mar-3 Meeting Art, Vercelli #443
£545 $855 €850 Mother in blue (20x10cm-8x4in) s. board. 23-Nov-2 Meeting Art, Vercelli #465/R
£769 $1208 €1200 Red and blue flowers (30x20cm-12x8in) s. 23-Nov-2 Meeting Art, Vercelli #386/R
£868 $1380 €1250 Boy with flag (24x18cm-9x7in) s. board. 1-May-3 Meeting Art, Vercelli #95
£1042 $1656 €1500 Family in blue background (20x30cm-8x12in) s. s.i.verso. 1-May-3 Meeting Art, Vercelli #292
£1293 $2055 €1900 Hill and travellers (20x30cm-8x12in) s. painted 1980. 1-Mar-3 Meeting Art, Vercelli #747
£1458 $2319 €2100 Musician and boy (30x20cm-12x8in) s. 1-May-3 Meeting Art, Vercelli #548
£3268 $5229 €5000 Sunny landscape with moon (50x70cm-20x28in) s. painted 1982. 4-Jan-3 Meeting Art, Vercelli #525
£4167 $6542 €6500 Woman (72x45cm-28x18in) s.d.1939. 19-Nov-2 Finarte, Milan #285/R est:2800
Works on paper
£321 $503 €500 Figure (43x35cm-17x14in) s. wash. 23-Nov-2 Meeting Art, Vercelli #390/R
£327 $523 €500 Travellers (40x30cm-16x12in) s. wash. 4-Jan-3 Meeting Art, Vercelli #128
£327 $523 €500 Girl with flowers (36x25cm-14x10in) s. W/C. 4-Jan-3 Meeting Art, Vercelli #176
£327 $523 €500 Beggar and boy with bird (49x37cm-19x15in) s. wash. 4-Jan-3 Meeting Art, Vercelli #719
£408 $649 €600 Sailing boat (20x30cm-8x12in) s. W/C paper on canvas. 1-Mar-3 Meeting Art, Vercelli #452
£442 $703 €650 Old man and boy (34x24cm-13x9in) s. W/C. 1-Mar-3 Meeting Art, Vercelli #731
£493 $818 €700 Maternita (50x35cm-20x14in) s. pencil W/C. 10-Jun-3 Finarte Semenzato, Milan #183/R
£641 $1006 €1000 Man in red with boy (46x31cm-18x12in) s. 23-Nov-2 Meeting Art, Vercelli #418/R

LONGBOTTOM, Malcolm Richard (20th C) British
Works on paper
£320 $499 €480 Quick tea break, boats moored on an estuary (32x52cm-13x20in) s. W/C exhib. 10-Sep-2 David Duggleby, Scarborough #177

LONGHI, Alessandro (1733-1813) Italian
£40141 $64627 €57000 Portrait of Francesco Grimani (51x33cm-20x13in) exhib.lit. 11-May-3 Finarte, Venice #5/R est:80000-90000
£41549 $66894 €59000 Portrait of Francesco Grimani (51x32cm-20x13in) exhib.lit. 11-May-3 Finarte, Venice #3/R est:80000-90000

LONGHI, Luca (1507-1580) Italian
£13924 $22000 €22000 Holy Family with Saint John (82x67cm-32x26in) board prov. 27-Nov-2 Finarte, Milan #124/R est:18000-22000

£29688 $47500 €44532 Adoration of the shepherds (86x73cm-34x29in) s. 14-May-3 Butterfields, San Francisco #1006/R est:25000-35000

LONGHI, Pietro (1702-1785) Italian
£49296 $79366 €70000 Portrait of gentleman in green coat (81x65cm-32x26in) exhib.lit. 11-May-3 Finarte, Venice #6/R est:100000-120000
£120423 $193880 €171000 The Grimanis' tutor (55x38cm-22x15in) prov.exhib.lit. 11-May-3 Finarte, Venice #9/R est:250000-280000

LONGHI, Pietro (circle) (1702-1785) Italian
£13580 $22000 €20370 La Lezione di ballo. La dichiarazione (74x56cm-29x22in) pair. 23-Jan-3 Sotheby's, New York #50/R est:20000-30000

LONGLEY, Sarah (20th C) Irish?
£506 $785 €800 Hanging leaves (36x29cm-14x11in) s.d.2001 board. 24-Sep-2 De Veres Art Auctions, Dublin #68d est:800-1200

LONGO, Robert (1953-) American
£1701 $2704 €2500 White cross with black edge (55x75cm-22x30in) s.i.d.1991 acrylic paper prov. 24-Mar-3 Cornette de St.Cyr, Paris #86/R
£1803 $2866 €2650 White cross on white (55x75cm-22x30in) s.d.1991 acrylic paper prov. 24-Mar-3 Cornette de St.Cyr, Paris #88/R
£2041 $3245 €3000 Black cross on white (55x75cm-22x30in) s.d.1991 acrylic paper prov. 24-Mar-3 Cornette de St.Cyr, Paris #87/R
£2431 $3865 €3500 Study for black flag (71x104cm-28x41in) s.i.d.90 acrylic paper prov.exhib. 29-Apr-3 Artcurial Briest, Paris #460/R est:4000-6000

Prints
£1763 $2750 €2645 Raphael (117x76cm-46x30in) s.d.num.54/120 col lithograph. 14-Oct-2 Butterfields, San Francisco #1308/R est:2000-3000
£3000 $4950 €4350 Cindy (152x51cm-60x20in) s.d.num.22/38 lithograph. 2-Jul-3 Christie's, London #271/R est:2000-3000
£11321 $18000 €16982 Men in the cities (172x99cm-68x39in) s.d. five num.8/38 one num.10/28 black lithograph six. 2-May-3 Sotheby's, New York #522/R est:22000-28000

Works on paper
£6875 $11000 €10313 Golden children stone (244x122cm-96x48in) chl graphite executed c.1982-83 prov. 16-May-3 Phillips, New York #229/R est:4000-6000
£6962 $11000 €10443 Untitled (122x122cm-48x48in) chl pencil exec.1981 prov.exhib. 13-Nov-2 Sotheby's, New York #570/R est:10000-15000

LONGOBARDI, Nino (1953-) Italian

Works on paper
£280 $437 €420 Untitled (47x36cm-19x14in) s.d.1983 pencil oil prov. 5-Nov-2 Bukowskis, Stockholm #432/R (S.KR 4000)
£725 $1188 €1000 Untitled (30x50cm-12x20in) s.d.1987 verso collage expresso pot acrylic plaster canvas. 28-May-3 Lempertz, Koln #255/R

LONGONI, Baldassare (1876-1956) Italian
£884 $1406 €1300 Lake landscape with trees (15x22cm-6x9in) s. board. 18-Mar-3 Finarte, Milan #14/R
£4000 $6320 €6200 Como lake (50x69cm-20x27in) s. 18-Dec-2 Finarte, Milan #169/R est:7000

LONGONI, Emilio (1859-1933) Italian
£4062 $6500 €5890 Interior genre scene (70x46cm-28x18in) s. 16-May-3 Skinner, Boston #17/R est:1500-2200
£7862 $12107 €12500 On the Bernina (34x42cm-13x17in) s. board painted c.1904 lit. 23-Oct-2 Finarte, Milan #62/R est:13000-15000

LONGPRE, Paul de (1855-1911) American/French
£2200 $3674 €3190 Studies of pink roses and butterflies (39x51cm-15x20in) s. canvas on board. 9-Jul-3 George Kidner, Lymington #163/R est:500-700
£3200 $5344 €4640 Studies of pink roses and dragonflies (39x51cm-15x20in) s. canvas on board. 9-Jul-3 George Kidner, Lymington #164/R est:500-700
£3600 $6012 €5220 Studies of red roses and insects (39x51cm-15x20in) s. canvas on board. 9-Jul-3 George Kidner, Lymington #165/R est:500-700
£3600 $6012 €5220 Studies of yellow roses and insects (39x51cm-15x20in) s. canvas on board. 9-Jul-3 George Kidner, Lymington #166/R est:500-700
£7143 $11000 €10715 Roses and French lilacs (58x74cm-23x29in) s. prov. 24-Oct-2 Shannon's, Milford #56/R est:9000-12000

Works on paper
£994 $1600 €1491 Floral still life (18x20cm-7x8in) s. W/C. 18-Feb-3 John Moran, Pasadena #87 est:1200-1600
£4491 $7500 €6512 Yellow and pink roses in glazed ceramic bowl (48x64cm-19x25in) s.d.1898 W/C. 17-Jun-3 John Moran, Pasadena #83a est:9000-12000
£13014 $19000 €19521 Spring floral spray with lilacs and roses (94x69cm-37x27in) s.d.1881 W/C gouache. 3-Nov-1 North East Auctions, Portsmouth #1054/R est:9000-12000

LONGPRE, Raoul de (1859-?) French

Works on paper
£710 $1100 €1065 Lilacs (68x49cm-27x19in) s. gouache paper on board. 3-Dec-2 Christie's, Rockefeller NY #593/R
£1457 $2375 €2200 Brassee de lilas (64x50cm-25x20in) s. W/C oval. 31-Jan-3 Rabourdin & Choppin de Janvry, Paris #102/R
£1497 $2500 €2171 White lilacs and cherry blossoms (48x69cm-19x27in) s. gouache W/C prov. 17-Jun-3 John Moran, Pasadena #118 est:3500-5000
£1532 $2421 €2298 Yellow roses with lilacs (53x36cm-21x14in) s. W/C gouache. 18-Nov-2 Waddingtons, Toronto #20a/R est:1000-1500 (C.D 3800)
£1700 $2720 €2550 Roses and lilacs (53x73cm-21x29in) s. gouache. 11-Mar-3 Bonhams, New Bond Street #117/R est:1500-2000
£3300 $5445 €4785 Still life of flowers (53x71cm-21x28in) s. bodycol. 3-Jul-3 Duke & Son, Dorchester #143/R est:2000-4000
£3915 $6500 €5677 Fresh-cut lilacs (53x72cm-21x28in) s. gouache paper on board. 11-Jun-3 Butterfields, San Francisco #4146/R est:6000-8000
£4600 $7176 €6900 Still life with roses and lilies (52x71cm-20x28in) s. gouache. 9-Oct-2 Woolley & Wallis, Salisbury #183c/R est:200-400

LONGPRE, Raoul de (attrib) (1859-?) French
£806 $1274 €1209 Pink and white roses with lilacs (74x61cm-29x24in) 18-Nov-2 Waddingtons, Toronto #20/R est:3000-4000 (C.D 2000)

LONGSTAFF, Sir John (1861-1941) Australian
£286 $451 €429 Portrait of Mrs R C Broomfield (65x48cm-26x19in) s.d.90 i.verso prov.exhib.lit. 17-Nov-2 Sotheby's, Paddington #80 (A.D 800)

LONGSTAFF, William (1879-1953) Australian
£828 $1316 €1200 Cour de ferme animee de personnages (71x91cm-28x36in) s. 4-Mar-3 Livinec, Gaudcheau & Jezequel, Rennes #124

LONGSTAFFE, Edgar (1849-1912) British
£280 $437 €420 Llyn Peris, Llanderis, North Wales (30x50cm-12x20in) init. 11-Sep-2 Bonhams, Newport #230
£370 $577 €555 Highland river and mountain landscape with cattle watering (38x56cm-15x22in) mono.d.1888. 18-Oct-2 Keys, Aylsham #715
£500 $790 €750 Highland landscape with figures fishing in the foreground (27x42cm-11x17in) mono.d.1891. 12-Nov-2 Bonhams, Knightsbridge #239
£1300 $2042 €1950 Waterfall on the River Hepste, South Wales (61x51cm-24x20in) mono.d.1882. 20-Nov-2 Sotheby's, Olympia #37/R est:800-1200

LONGUEVILLE, James (1942-) British
£320 $502 €480 Winter landscape (41x61cm-16x24in) s. board. 25-Nov-2 Bonhams, Chester #968

LONHOLDT, Sigurd V (1910-) Danish
£338 $527 €507 Portrait of woman (90x75cm-35x30in) mono. 22-Sep-2 Hindemae, Ullerslev #7628/R (D.KR 4000)

LONN, George (20th C) Canadian
£400 $656 €600 Dogsledding (40x55cm-16x22in) s.d.76. 3-Jun-3 Joyner, Toronto #426/R est:800-1200 (C.D 900)

LONNBERG, William (1887-1949) Finnish
£379 $599 €550 Landscape (34x46cm-13x18in) s. 3-Apr-3 Hagelstam, Helsinki #994
£408 $649 €600 Still life (46x55cm-18x22in) s. 24-Mar-3 Bukowskis, Helsinki #167/R
£1007 $1612 €1400 Helsingfors seen from the sea, Brunnsparken (16x22cm-6x9in) s. board painted c.1915. 17-May-3 Hagelstam, Helsinki #144/R

LONNEUX, D (19th C) French
£1875 $3000 €2813 Still life with roses, tulips and an iris in a vase (61x51cm-24x20in) s. 14-May-3 Butterfields, San Francisco #1124/R est:3000-5000

LONNGREN, Carl Ewald (1839-1902) Swedish
£2535 $4082 €3600 View from Kolmarden (66x85cm-26x33in) s.d.1883. 10-May-3 Bukowskis, Helsinki #367/R est:1500-1800

LONSDALE, James (1777-1839) British
£4200 $6804 €6300 Portrait of Rear-Admiral William Dashwood and of his wife Louisa Henrietta (76x63cm-30x25in) pair. 21-May-3 Christie's, Kensington #554/R est:3000-5000

LONZA, Antonio (1846-1918) Italian

£1250 $2050 €1875 Artist's studio (45x53cm-18x21in) s. 5-Jun-3 Christie's, Kensington #600/R est:1000-1500

LONZA, Antonio (attrib) (1846-1918) Italian

£943 $1509 €1415 Pumpkin seller (26x37cm-10x15in) s. board. 17-Mar-3 Philippe Schuler, Zurich #4627/R (S.FR 2000)

LOO, Amedee van (1719-1795) French

£6081 $9487 €9000 Portrait d'homme a la veste rouge (100x79cm-39x31in) 26-Mar-3 Tajan, Paris #65/R est:12000

LOO, Carle van (1705-1765) French

£4268 $7000 €6402 Head of a lady (41x32cm-16x13in) s. oval. 5-Feb-3 Christie's, Rockefeller NY #311/R est:7000-10000

Works on paper

£1058 $1661 €1650 Homme debout et accoude (56x34cm-22x13in) s.i. sanguine. 13-Dec-2 Rossini, Paris #137/R

£1419 $2214 €2100 Academie d'homme (53x38cm-21x15in) i/ sanguine wash. 27-Mar-3 Maigret, Paris #83/R

£2027 $3162 €3000 Academie d'homme (36x41cm-14x16in) i. sanguine. 27-Mar-3 Maigret, Paris #82/R

£2161 $3500 €3242 Prisoner with soldiers (32x27cm-13x11in) s. chk. 22-Jan-3 Christie's, Rockefeller NY #67/R

£2564 $4026 €4000 Mariage de la Vierge (45x35cm-18x14in) sanguine. 13-Dec-2 Pierre Berge, Paris #25/R

£2692 $4173 €4200 Personnage religieux drape (32x18cm-13x7in) crayon chk prov.exhib. 4-Dec-2 Piasa, Paris #70/R

£18243 $28459 €27000 Allegory of Painting (75x59cm-30x23in) pastel oval. 27-Mar-3 Christie's, Paris #97/R est:50000

LOO, Carle van (attrib) (1705-1765) French

Works on paper

£800 $1336 €1160 Standing figure in oriental costume holding a sword (52x24cm-20x9in) red chk corners rounded. 9-Jul-3 Sotheby's, London #135/R

LOO, Carle van (style) (1705-1765) French

£12102 $18879 €19000 Elegant company near a fountain in a park landscape (88x138cm-35x54in) bears sig d.1770. 5-Nov-2 Sotheby's, Amsterdam #325/R est:8000-12000

LOO, Frans van (1708-1732) Flemish

£972 $1536 €1400 Berger et bergere dans un paysage (222x103cm-87x41in) 28-Apr-3 Amberes, Antwerp #327

Works on paper

£647 $1036 €900 Vue d'interieur (27x35cm-11x14in) s.d.1876 W/C two. 13-May-3 Vanderkindere, Brussels #67

LOO, Jacob van (1614-1670) Dutch

£13000 $20410 €19500 Landscape with nymph and satyrs (74x60cm-29x24in) panel. 12-Dec-2 Sotheby's, London #179/R est:8000-12000

LOO, Jean Baptiste van (1684-1745) French

£20980 $35036 €30000 Une bergere courtisee par un pelerin de St Jacques de Compostelle (110x143cm-43x56in) s. 25-Jun-3 Tajan, Paris #61/R est:9000-12000

LOO, Jean Baptiste van (attrib) (1684-1745) French

£2000 $3300 €2900 Portrait of a gentleman possibly Peter Abraham Luard (105x86cm-41x34in) 2-Jul-3 Sotheby's, Olympia #31/R est:2000-3000

£3082 $4808 €4500 Moses in front of the burning bush (72x91cm-28x36in) i.d.1714. 10-Apr-3 Van Ham, Cologne #1237/R est:5000

£6000 $9900 €8700 Portrait of Francis Greville, 1st Earl of Warwick (126x100cm-50x39in) prov. 2-Jul-3 Sotheby's, Olympia #8/R est:6000-8000

LOO, Jules Cesar Denis van (1743-1821) French

£2709 $4281 €4200 Paysage au pont de pierres (60x87cm-24x34in) s.d.1808. 20-Dec-2 Tajan, Paris #143/R est:6000

£14865 $23189 €22000 Passage du Grand Saint-Bernard par le troupes franciases (59x73cm-23x29in) 30-Mar-3 Anaf, Lyon #409/R

LOO, Jules Cesar Denis van (circle) (1743-1821) French

£9000 $14130 €13500 View of Granada with a waterseller and other figures (69x91cm-27x36in) prov. 10-Dec-2 Sotheby's, Olympia #408/R est:4000-6000

LOO, Louis-Michel van (1707-1771) French

£6452 $10194 €10000 Portrait de dame au noeud rose (65x54cm-26x21in) 18-Dec-2 Tajan, Paris #44/R est:6000

£7000 $11690 €10150 Portrait of Mademoiselle Genevieve de Malboisiere 1746-66 (92x73cm-36x29in) indis.s.d.765. 10-Jul-3 Sotheby's, London #200/R est:8000-12000

£8000 $13360 €11600 Portrait of Francoise Laurette Randon de Malboisere (92x73cm-36x29in) prov. 10-Jul-3 Sotheby's, London #201/R est:7000-9000

£30000 $47100 €45000 Portrait of Chevalier Jacques d'Heusy d'Agimont (137x103cm-54x41in) prov.lit. 10-Dec-2 Bonhams, New Bond Street #313/R est:40000-60000

LOO, Louis-Michel van (attrib) (1707-1771) French

£3097 $4893 €4800 Portrait de magistrat (82x67cm-32x26in) 20-Dec-2 Tajan, Paris #128/R est:3000

£3819 $6035 €5500 Portrait de Francois Piquefeu de longpre (92x73cm-36x29in) prov. 25-Apr-3 Beaussant & Lefèvre, Paris #21/R

£4514 $7132 €6500 Portrait de Francoise Laurette Randon de Malboissiere (92x73cm-36x29in) prov. 25-Apr-3 Beaussant & Lefèvre, Paris #20/R

LOO, Louis-Michel van (style) (1707-1771) French

£10737 $17287 €16000 Portrait of Louis XV, King of France (233x180cm-92x71in) 18-Feb-3 Sotheby's, Amsterdam #777a/R est:7000-10000

LOO, Marten van der (1880-1920) Belgian

£503 $810 €750 Farm (80x100cm-31x39in) s.d.1909. 24-Feb-3 Bernaerts, Antwerp #13/R

LOOBY, Keith (1940-) Australian

£2640 $4119 €4575 Watching me watching you (169x183cm-67x72in) board prov. 31-Mar-3 Goodman, Sydney #149/R (A.D 7000)

£7921 $12357 €13724 Letter to artmaster (122x152cm-48x60in) s. prov. 31-Mar-3 Goodman, Sydney #160/R (A.D 21000)

Works on paper

£268 $423 €402 Last sign (48x67cm-19x26in) s. pastel. 27-Nov-2 Deutscher-Menzies, Melbourne #191/R (A.D 750)

£283 $442 €491 Like an unknown face (20x28cm-8x11in) s.i.verso col pencil prov. 31-Mar-3 Goodman, Sydney #77 (A.D 750)

£302 $471 €524 Untitled (20x28cm-8x11in) pen ink prov. 31-Mar-3 Goodman, Sydney #59 (A.D 800)

£438 $718 €657 Fertility corroboree (55x70cm-22x28in) s. i.verso felt tip pen ink paper on board exhib.lit. 4-Jun-3 Deutscher-Menzies, Melbourne #321/R (A.D 1100)

£466 $676 €699 Many wise men (45x18cm-18x7in) mixed media. 10-Dec-1 Goodman, Sydney #413 (A.D 1300)

£607 $941 €911 Bondi (72x108cm-28x43in) i.d.52 verso mixed media. 29-Oct-2 Lawson Menzies, Sydney #441 (A.D 1700)

LOOMIS, Andrew (1892-1959) American

£2484 $4000 €3726 Mourning mother and two children in church (102x76cm-40x30in) s. 19-Feb-3 Illustration House, New York #216/R est:5000-9000

£2640 $4250 €3960 Naval officer and family walk down aisle of church (91x71cm-36x28in) s. 19-Feb-3 Illustration House, New York #218/R est:4000-8000

£3416 $5500 €5124 Family in church paying tithe to church (102x81cm-40x32in) s. 19-Feb-3 Illustration House, New York #217/R est:3000-6000

£3846 $6000 €5769 Young girl mailing letter to Santa Claus (102x71cm-40x28in) s. 9-Nov-2 Illustration House, New York #106/R est:6000-9000

£6090 $9500 €9135 Young service people standing with mother at church services (91x64cm-36x25in) s. 9-Nov-2 Illustration House, New York #28/R est:3000-4000

LOOMIS, Charles Russell (19th C) American

Works on paper

£395 $600 €593 Sailboat off the Connecticut shore (38x53cm-15x21in) s. W/C. 17-Aug-2 North East Auctions, Portsmouth #72

LOOP, Leota Williams (1893-1961) American

£1883 $2900 €2825 Heavenly blue morning glories (64x76cm-25x30in) s.i. painted c.1944 exhib. 8-Sep-2 Treadway Gallery, Cincinnati #559/R est:2000-4000

£4088 $6500 €6132 Flower garden (36x43cm-14x17in) s. painted c.1930. 2-Mar-3 Toomey, Oak Park #551/R est:4000-6000

LOOS, Friedrich (attrib) (1797-1890) Austrian

£446 $696 €700 Olive trees by sea (27x38cm-11x15in) board. 6-Nov-2 Hugo Ruef, Munich #1196/R

£513 $795 €800 River landscape in the Lower Alps with peasant on rising path (30x40cm-12x16in) canvas on canvas. 4-Dec-2 Neumeister, Munich #810

£1635 $2551 €2600 Oak trees near Bremen (28x39cm-11x15in) board on board. 21-Sep-2 Bolland & Marotz, Bremen #518/R est:670

LOOS, John F (19th C) Belgian
£1361 $2163 €2000 Trois-mats Gateside (60x91cm-24x36in) s.i.d.1893. 21-Mar-3 Rieunier, Bailly-Pommery, Mathias, Paris #112/R
£5519 $8500 €8279 Ship Emma Ives, Captain J Waters (51x76cm-20x30in) s.i.d.1872. 27-Oct-2 Grogan, Boston #68 est:6000-9000
£7895 $12000 €11843 American schooner, Melville Bryant (53x76cm-21x30in) s.d.1875. 17-Aug-2 North East Auctions, Portsmouth #666/R est:12000-15000
£13158 $20000 €19737 American bark, Jenny Pitts (64x89cm-25x35in) s.d.1865. 17-Aug-2 North East Auctions, Portsmouth #667/R est:20000-30000

LOOSCHEN, Hans (1859-1923) German
£833 $1317 €1300 Woman in chair (40x35cm-16x14in) s. 14-Nov-2 Neumeister, Munich #622/R
£886 $1373 €1400 Lively dancing at Karneval (95x83cm-37x33in) s. 25-Sep-2 Neumeister, Munich #639/R

LOOSCHEN, Reent (1893-1945) German
£506 $785 €800 Ducks on pond (50x60cm-20x24in) s. i. verso board. 28-Sep-2 Hans Stahl, Hamburg #116/R

LOOSE, Basile de (1809-1885) Dutch
£1064 $1777 €1500 Deux jeunes freres (74x61cm-29x24in) s.d.1860 oval pair. 17-Jun-3 Palais de Beaux Arts, Brussels #534 est:100-150
£2885 $4529 €4500 Fatherly advice (92x79cm-36x31in) s. bears i.d. 23-Nov-2 Arnold, Frankfurt #795/R est:8000
£26000 $40820 €39000 Newly weds (101x122cm-40x48in) s.d.1875. 19-Nov-2 Sotheby's, London #132/R est:22000-28000
£30345 $48552 €44000 Waterpret; les pompiers volontaires (96x83cm-38x33in) s.i. painted 1883 exhib.lit. 15-Mar-3 De Vuyst, Lokeren #410/R

LOOSE, Basile de (attrib) (1809-1885) Dutch
£6164 $9616 €9000 Children in kitchen (50x45cm-20x18in) panel. 10-Apr-3 Schopman, Hamburg #583 est:4500

LOOTEN, Jan (1618-1681) Dutch
£5755 $9209 €8000 Wooded landscape at dawn with a stag hunt (64x72cm-25x28in) 14-May-3 Christie's, Amsterdam #128/R est:4000-6000

LOOTEN, Jan (attrib) (1618-1681) Dutch
£1200 $2004 €1740 River landscape with travelers by a cascade (60x70cm-24x28in) 11-Jul-3 Christie's, Kensington #126/R est:1500-2500

LOOTEN, Jan (circle) (1618-1681) Dutch
£10897 $17109 €17000 Paysage anime (139x210cm-55x83in) 19-Nov-2 Vanderkindere, Brussels #20/R est:7000-12000

LOOY, Jacobus van (1855-1930) Dutch
£6289 $9686 €10000 Acrobatique (44x50cm-17x20in) s. exhib.lit. 23-Oct-2 Christie's, Amsterdam #159/R est:12000-16000
£16667 $26500 €24000 Clematis tegen hekwerk - flowering clematis (42x47cm-17x19in) init. prov.exhib.lit. 29-Apr-3 Christie's, Amsterdam #177/R est:9000-12000

LOOY, Jan van (1882-1971) Belgian
£285 $444 €450 Estuaire a Dunkerque (34x46cm-13x18in) s.d.57. 16-Sep-2 Horta, Bruxelles #351

LOOY, van (19/20th C) ?
£316 $494 €500 Debardeuse assise (52x39cm-20x15in) 16-Sep-2 Amberes, Antwerp #265

LOOYMANS, Romain (1864-1914) Belgian
£1087 $1783 €1500 La couture (46x60cm-18x24in) s. 27-May-3 Campo & Campo, Antwerp #127 est:750-1000

LOPEZ CASADO, Luis (?) Spanish?
£439 $685 €650 Deposition (66x115cm-26x45in) s. board. 25-Mar-3 Durán, Madrid #21/R

LOPEZ DE PLANO, Eduardo (1840-1885) Spanish
£801 $1266 €1250 Portrait of elderly man (75x61cm-30x24in) s.i.d.1884. 13-Nov-2 Ansorena, Madrid #91/R

LOPEZ GARCIA, Antonio (1936-) Spanish
£28000 $43120 €42000 Josefina in the rocking chair (75x71cm-30x28in) s.d.54 panel lit. 22-Oct-2 Sotheby's, London #374/R est:25000-35000
Works on paper
£58621 $93207 €85000 Mother and son (22x31cm-9x12in) s.d.1961 mixed media dr lit. 4-Mar-3 Ansorena, Madrid #231/R est:80000

LOPEZ GARCIA, Ezequiel (1940-) Spanish
£316 $494 €500 Untitled (29x50cm-11x20in) s. s.verso. 14-Sep-2 Meeting Art, Vercelli #884/R
£437 $696 €630 Confidences (30x40cm-12x16in) s. board. 1-May-3 Meeting Art, Vercelli #106

LOPEZ MEZQUITA, Jose Maria (1883-1954) Spanish
£642 $1001 €950 Alhambra interior (21x15cm-8x6in) s. board painted c.1900. 25-Mar-3 Durán, Madrid #172/R

LOPEZ MEZQUITA, Jose Maria (attrib) (1883-1954) Spanish
£437 $681 €656 Mosque (16x10cm-6x4in) s. panel. 6-Nov-2 Dobiaschofsky, Bern #784/R (S.FR 1000)

LOPEZ MURIAS, Isidoro (20th C) Spanish
£321 $506 €500 Canete (50x65cm-20x26in) s. 19-Nov-2 Durán, Madrid #104/R

LOPEZ NAGUIL, Gregorio (1894-1953) Argentinian
£943 $1472 €1500 Landscape in Minorca (53x59cm-21x23in) s.d.1950 cardboard. 8-Oct-2 Ansorena, Madrid #445/R
£1184 $1918 €1800 Tree in Majorca (33x39cm-13x15in) s. canvas on cardboard. 21-Jan-3 Ansorena, Madrid #64/R

LOPEZ RAMON, Ramon (1905-1989) Spanish
£409 $630 €650 Cathedral, Barcelona (73x60cm-29x24in) s. s.i.verso. 22-Oct-2 Durán, Madrid #209/R
£833 $1317 €1300 Harbour (65x54cm-26x21in) s. 19-Nov-2 Durán, Madrid #141/R

LOPEZ RUIZ, Antonio (1935-) Spanish
£818 $1275 €1300 Seascape (37x25cm-15x10in) s. cardboard. 23-Sep-2 Durán, Madrid #590/R

LOPEZ TAJES, Agustin (20th C) Spanish
£355 $561 €550 Burgos cathedral (41x27cm-16x11in) s.d.2002 s.i.d.verso board. 17-Dec-2 Durán, Madrid #657/R

LOPEZ TORRES, Antonio (1902-1987) Spanish
£4110 $6411 €6000 Two women in the fields (27x24cm-11x9in) s.d.1947 s.i.verso exhib. 8-Apr-3 Ansorena, Madrid #216/R est:6000
£15385 $24308 €24000 Landscape with kids and donkey (90x74cm-35x29in) board. 13-Nov-2 Ansorena, Madrid #117/R est:24000
£16438 $25644 €24000 Landscape with cart and two donkeys (59x48cm-23x19in) s. exhib. 8-Apr-3 Ansorena, Madrid #230/R est:24000

LOPEZ Y PORTANA, Vicente (1772-1850) Spanish
£500 $785 €750 Portrait of an elderly lady, head and shoulders (48x36cm-19x14in) i. oval. 16-Apr-3 Christie's, Kensington #647
£25000 $41500 €36250 Portrait of a gentleman (106x82cm-42x32in) s.d.1840. 12-Jun-3 Christie's, London #208/R est:10000-15000

LOPEZ Y PORTANA, Vicente (attrib) (1772-1850) Spanish
£1689 $2635 €2500 Study of bearded man (57x48cm-22x19in) panel. 26-Mar-3 Tajan, Paris #16

LOPEZ Y TURRALDE, Jose Maria (1942-) Peruvian
£1027 $1603 €1500 Composition in red (33x33cm-13x13in) s.d.1973 verso board. 8-Apr-3 Ansorena, Madrid #281/R

LOPEZ, Carlos (20th C) Cuban
£542 $900 €786 Untitled (25x30cm-10x12in) board. 13-Jun-3 Du Mouchelle, Detroit #2279/R

LOPEZ, E (19th C) ?
£320 $499 €480 Ballet dancer in an interior (44x28cm-17x11in) s. panel. 17-Sep-2 Rosebery Fine Art, London #518

LOPEZ, Gasparo (1650-1732) Italian
£2064 $3262 €3200 Still life with bouquet (25x18cm-10x7in) 20-Dec-2 Tajan, Paris #24/R
£6792 $10596 €10800 Still life with flowers in landscape (88x116cm-35x46in) two. 22-Sep-2 Semenzato, Venice #121/R est:8000-11000
£6800 $11356 €9860 Classical garden with flowers in a stone urn before a column (24x34cm-9x13in) copper. 8-Jul-3 Sotheby's, Olympia #476/R est:7000-10000
£8633 $13813 €12000 Still life with flowers in silver vase and other flowers in garden setting (48x76cm-19x30in) 13-May-3 Sotheby's, Amsterdam #80/R est:10000-15000

LOPEZ, M (19/20th C) ?
£2100 $3339 €3150 Sevilla, Moorish interior (67x54cm-26x21in) s. 18-Mar-3 Sworder & Son, Bishops Stortford #409/R est:300-500

LOPEZ, Noel (20th C) Mexican
Works on paper
£402 $643 €583 Mano negra (43x30cm-17x12in) s.d.2002 mixed media. 15-May-3 Louis Morton, Mexico #164/R (M.P 6500)

LOPEZ-CABRERA, Ricardo (1866-1950) Spanish
£329 $533 €500 Landscape (11x21cm-4x8in) s. cardboard. 21-Jan-3 Durán, Madrid #25/R
£1150 $1829 €1668 Riverside town (49x74cm-19x29in) s. 26-Feb-3 John Bellman, Billingshurst #1809 est:200-300
£1316 $2132 €2000 By the fire (56x66cm-22x26in) s. 21-Jan-3 Durán, Madrid #144/R
£1935 $3058 €3000 Seville market (26x37cm-10x15in) s. board. 18-Dec-2 Ansorena, Madrid #378/R
£8966 $14255 €13000 Spinning (112x86cm-44x34in) s. 4-Mar-3 Ansorena, Madrid #177/R

LOPEZ-CURVAL, Catherine (1954-) French
£347 $549 €500 Le baiser dans la rue (20x20cm-8x8in) s.d. s.i.d.verso panel. 27-Apr-3 Perrin, Versailles #150/R

LOPPE, Gabriel (1825-1913) French
£420 $672 €630 Alpine landscape (12x21cm-5x8in) s. board. 7-Jan-3 Bonhams, Knightsbridge #285b/R
£613 $981 €920 Winter landscape with hunter and dog (24x32cm-9x13in) s. board. 17-Mar-3 Philippe Schuler, Zurich #8650 (S.FR 1300)

LOQUEYSSIE, Emile (1793-1863) German
Miniatures
£2800 $4396 €4200 Young lady in a off the shoulder black dressy (16x10cm-6x4in) s.d.1838 gilt metal mount rec. 10-Dec-2 Christie's, London #251/R est:800-1200

LORAINE, Nevison Arthur (fl.1889-1908) British
£400 $616 €600 Bodmin Moor with cattle watering in the foreground (73x99cm-29x39in) s.verso. 22-Oct-2 Bonhams, Bath #228

LORAN, Erle (1905-1999) American
£566 $900 €849 Beach forms (51x137cm-20x54in) s.d.1954. 8-Mar-3 Harvey Clar, Oakland #1189
£828 $1300 €1242 Drying the nets. Coastal driftwood (69x96cm-27x38in) s.d.48 double-sided. 19-Nov-2 Butterfields, San Francisco #8352/R est:3000-5000
£1198 $2000 €1737 House by the canal (48x64cm-19x25in) s.d.41. 17-Jun-3 John Moran, Pasadena #38 est:1800-2500
£1205 $2000 €1747 Navajo country (60x91cm-24x36in) s.d.47 masonite prov. 11-Jun-3 Butterfields, San Francisco #4308/R est:3000-5000
Works on paper
£440 $700 €638 Ancient roots. s.d.1949 W/C. 3-May-3 Harvey Clar, Oakland #1199

LORANGE, A (1833-1875) Danish
£511 $807 €767 Italian street scene (23x44cm-9x17in) mono. 2-Dec-2 Rasmussen, Copenhagen #1511 (D.KR 6000)

LORCA DI CORCIA, Philip (1953-) American
Photographs
£2761 $4500 €4142 Untitled (64x96cm-25x38in) s.verso col coupler print. 12-Feb-3 Christie's, Rockefeller NY #119/R est:6000-8000
£6013 $9500 €9020 New York (76x101cm-30x40in) s. prov. 14-Nov-2 Christie's, Rockefeller NY #486/R est:12000-18000

LORCA, Federico Garcia (1899-1936) Spanish
Works on paper
£3846 $6077 €6000 Drawing for altar (21x15cm-8x6in) ink dr. 14-Nov-2 Arte, Seville #424/R

LORCK, Karl Julius (1829-1882) Norwegian
£6440 $10305 €9660 Rookie sailor (56x43cm-22x17in) s.d.62. 17-Mar-3 Blomqvist, Oslo #340/R est:80000-100000 (N.KR 74000)
£11504 $18177 €17256 Grandmother telling a story (70x85cm-28x33in) s. 28-Apr-3 Blomqvist, Oslo #312/R est:100000-120000 (N.KR 130000)
£11709 $18265 €17564 Showing the lobster to children (66x81cm-26x32in) s.d.67 lit. 21-Oct-2 Blomqvist, Oslo #337/R est:150000-200000 (N.KR 135000)

LORD, Elyse Ashe (fl.1915-1939) British
Works on paper
£500 $825 €725 Tachibana (34x47cm-13x19in) s. pencil W/C bodycol. 3-Jul-3 Christie's, Kensington #216/R

LORD, Harriet (1879-1958) American
£414 $650 €621 Bluebirds perched atop a hollyhock (15x10cm-6x4in) s. 22-Nov-2 Skinner, Boston #101/R

LORENTSON, Waldemar (1899-1982) Swedish
£430 $688 €624 Fisherman coming to his boat (16x40cm-6x16in) s. 18-May-3 Anders Antik, Landskrona #148 (S.KR 5500)
£587 $952 €881 Fisherman going to his boat (27x35cm-11x14in) s. panel. 3-Feb-3 Lilla Bukowskis, Stockholm #634 (S.KR 8200)
£674 $1044 €1011 Alvaret I - man and woman talking by stone wall (16x41cm-6x16in) s. d.1953 verso panel. 8-Dec-2 Uppsala Auktionskammare, Uppsala #248/R (S.KR 9500)
£927 $1492 €1391 Element by the sea (47x48cm-19x19in) s. d.1958 verso panel. 7-May-3 AB Stockholms Auktionsverk #666/R (S.KR 12000)
£931 $1508 €1350 Theme - La Criadas (15x8cm-6x3in) s. panel. 25-May-3 Uppsala Auktionskammare, Uppsala #307/R (S.KR 12000)
£2008 $3232 €3012 From something to something (27x37cm-11x15in) s.d.45. 7-May-3 AB Stockholms Auktionsverk #651/R est:12000-15000 (S.KR 26000)
£2129 $3364 €3194 Summer afternoon (12x29cm-5x11in) s. d.1974 verso panel. 28-Apr-3 Bukowskis, Stockholm #183a/R est:15000-18000 (S.KR 28000)
£2586 $4085 €3879 Patch of the sea (22x28cm-9x11in) s. panel. 28-Apr-3 Bukowskis, Stockholm #44/R est:25000-30000 (S.KR 34000)
£3475 $5595 €5213 Bornholms visit (28x55cm-11x22in) s. panel. 7-May-3 AB Stockholms Auktionsverk #760/R est:40000-50000 (S.KR 45000)
£7224 $11414 €10836 The boathouse (34x33cm-13x13in) s. panel painted c.1920. 28-Apr-3 Bukowskis, Stockholm #126/R est:40000-50000 (S.KR 95000)
£35521 $57189 €53282 Cafe - young couple at table (41x32cm-16x13in) s.d.34 panel prov.exhib.lit. 7-May-3 AB Stockholms Auktionsverk #688/R est:250000-300000 (S.KR 460000)
£37066 $59676 €55599 Restaurante Lavigne - Montparnasse, Paris (60x50cm-24x20in) s.i.d.1924 prov.lit. 7-May-3 AB Stockholms Auktionsverk #742/R est:250000-300000 (S.KR 480000)
Works on paper
£2129 $3364 €3194 Balcony (14x9cm-6x4in) s. gouache W/C prov. 28-Apr-3 Bukowskis, Stockholm #43/R est:20000-25000 (S.KR 28000)

LORENTZEN, C A (1746-1828) Danish
£426 $672 €639 The German monk Atterbach in his workshop (86x61cm-34x24in) s.d.1818. 2-Dec-2 Rasmussen, Copenhagen #1749/R (D.KR 5000)
£931 $1480 €1397 Portrait of Frederikke Juliane Louise Wedell-Wedelsborg (81x66cm-32x26in) oval. 5-Mar-3 Rasmussen, Copenhagen #1647/R (D.KR 10000)
£1722 $2790 €2497 Cabinet minister Marcus Gjoe Rosenkrantz (71x57cm-28x22in) s.d.1801 oval. 26-May-3 Rasmussen, Copenhagen #1249/R est:20000 (D.KR 18000)

LORENTZEN, Christian August (attrib) (1746-1828) Danish
£388 $589 €582 The men of the village going to war (32x43cm-13x17in) 27-Aug-2 Rasmussen, Copenhagen #1576/R (D.KR 4500)

LORENTZEN, Mogens (1892-1953) Danish
£274 $436 €411 From the garden at Lindenborg Inn (68x63cm-27x25in) init. 26-Feb-3 Kunsthallen, Copenhagen #324 (D.KR 3000)

LORENZ, Richard (1858-1915) German
£158228 $250000 €229431 Sunset on the prairie (81x127cm-32x50in) s. prov.exhib. 26-Jul-3 Coeur d'Alene, Hayden #147/R est:75000-125000

LORENZ, Willi (1901-1981) German
£556 $889 €850 Wild boar resting on the forest edge (60x80cm-24x31in) s. lit. 10-Jan-3 Allgauer, Kempten #1681/R
£582 $908 €850 Boars fleeing through undergrowth (60x80cm-24x31in) s. 10-Apr-3 Van Ham, Cologne #1578
£833 $1308 €1300 Wild boar racing through wood (61x92cm-24x36in) s. 21-Nov-2 Van Ham, Cologne #1761/R
£1026 $1610 €1600 Deer in forest clearing (60x80cm-24x31in) s. 21-Nov-2 Van Ham, Cologne #1760/R est:1800

LORENZ-MUROWANA, Ernst Hugo (1872-?) German
£475 $750 €750 Fishermen on the beach in the evening (36x48cm-14x19in) s. 29-Nov-2 Bolland & Marotz, Bremen #736/R
£548 $855 €800 Berlin, cathedral at night (80x102cm-31x40in) s. 10-Apr-3 Schopman, Hamburg #644
£563 $935 €800 Berlin Cathedral with Friedrichsbrucke at night (36x51cm-14x20in) s. 14-Jun-3 Arnold, Frankfurt #799/R

LORENZETTI, Carlo (1858-1945) Italian
£510 $811 €750 Fruit and vegetables (47x64cm-19x25in) s. cardboard. 1-Mar-3 Meeting Art, Vercelli #35

LORENZETTI, Pietro (attrib) (?-1348) Italian
£43210 $70000 €64815 Madonna and Child (77x55cm-30x22in) gold ground tempera panel. 23-Jan-3 Sotheby's, New York #59/R est:80000-120000

LORENZI (?) Italian
Sculpture
£1100 $1738 €1650 Female figure (15cm-6in) cold painted bronze ivory. 14-Nov-2 Christie's, Kensington #298/R
£1300 $2054 €1950 Female figure (28cm-11in) cold painted bronze. 14-Nov-2 Christie's, Kensington #304/R est:1500-2000
£1800 $2844 €2700 Female figure (27cm-11in) s. bronze. 14-Nov-2 Christie's, Kensington #277/R est:600-800

LORENZI, Stoldo di Gino (attrib) (1534-1583) Italian
Sculpture
£38000 $59660 €57000 Fountain figure of a boy astride a dolphin (75cm-30in) white marble lit. 10-Dec-2 Sotheby's, London #107/R est:20000-25000

LORENZL, J (1892-1950) Austrian
Sculpture
£962 $1519 €1500 Dancer (39cm-15in) i. verso pat.bronze onyx socle. 16-Nov-2 Quittenbaum, Munich #670/R est:1100
£1086 $1694 €1629 Female nude figure (30cm-12in) s. pat.bronze onyx socle. 5-Nov-2 Bukowskis, Stockholm #1419/R est:5000-7000 (S.KR 15500)
£1200 $1920 €1800 Female figure (36cm-14in) s. cold pat. bronze. 15-May-3 Christie's, Kensington #399/R est:1000-1500
£1300 $2054 €1950 Figure of a nude woman sitting on a book (31cm-12in) s. bronze. 14-Nov-2 Christie's, Kensington #230/R est:1000-1500
£1900 $3040 €2850 Girl dancer (38cm-15in) s. cold pat. bronze. 15-May-3 Christie's, Kensington #397/R est:1200-1500
£4800 $7680 €7200 Nude female dancer (48cm-19in) s. cold pat. bronze. 15-May-3 Christie's, Kensington #394/R est:2500-3000
£5000 $7900 €7500 Female nude (55cm-22in) s. bronze. 14-Nov-2 Christie's, Kensington #233/R est:3000-4000

LORENZL, Josef (1892-1950) Austrian
Sculpture
£1064 $1723 €1500 Dancing female nude (35cm-14in) i. pat.bronze onyx socle. 21-May-3 Dorotheum, Vienna #247/R est:2200-3000
£3797 $6000 €6000 Dancer (28cm-11in) i. metal pat.bronze ivory marble socle. 26-Nov-2 Dorotheum, Vienna #326/R est:3000-4500

LORENZO, Antonio (1932-) Spanish
£957 $1550 €1388 Mother and child playing in sunshine in drawing room (79x59cm-31x23in) s. 26-May-3 Rasmussen, Copenhagen #1504/R (D.KR 10000)

LORIA, Vincenzo (1850-?) Italian
Works on paper
£260 $406 €390 Bay of Naples (43x79cm-17x31in) s. W/C. 7-Nov-2 Mallams, Cheltenham #365

LORIEN, Ellen (1925-) Dutch
£290 $461 €420 Ze kwamen uit de regenboog (43x54cm-17x21in) s.d.1976 board. 10-Mar-3 Sotheby's, Amsterdam #347

LORIMER, Thomas W (1941-) American
£719 $1200 €1043 Native American encampment (20x46cm-8x18in) s. 21-Jun-3 Selkirks, St. Louis #178/R est:1500-2000

LORIMY DELAROZIERE, S (20th C) French?
£2014 $3303 €2800 Jeune Marocaine aux tatouages (40x54cm-16x21in) s.i.d.1950 panel. 4-Jun-3 Tajan, Paris #286/R est:2000-2200

LORIN, Georges (1870-?) French
£400 $652 €600 French farmhouse (58x78cm-23x31in) s. board. 2-Feb-3 Lots Road, London #344/R

LORINCZ, Julius (1910-1980) Czechoslovakian
£568 $881 €852 Bouquet (90x68cm-35x27in) painted c.1960. 3-Dec-2 SOGA, Bratislava #78/R (SL.K 36000)
£599 $928 €899 Alert (35x27cm-14x11in) plywood. 1-Oct-2 SOGA, Bratislava #89/R est:38000 (SL.K 38000)
£882 $1252 €1323 Troubles I (61x50cm-24x20in) painted 1934-36. 26-Mar-2 SOGA, Bratislava #98/R est:39000 (SL.K 56000)

LORING, W (?) ?
£1000 $1590 €1450 Junk at sea near Hong Kong (51x102cm-20x40in) s. 29-Apr-3 Gorringes, Lewes #2024

LORIOT, Bernard (1925-) French
£458 $737 €650 Nature morte aux fleurs et ombrelles chinoises (55x46cm-22x18in) s. 12-May-3 Lesieur & Le Bars, Le Havre #63
£612 $978 €850 Vue de Honfleur (22x27cm-9x11in) s. pair. 13-May-3 Vanderkindere, Brussels #84
£641 $1006 €1000 Drague dans le bassin du Havre (65x81cm-26x32in) s. 24-Nov-2 Lesieur & Le Bars, Le Havre #103/R
£845 $1361 €1200 Eglise Saint Ouen a Rouen (81x65cm-32x26in) s. 12-May-3 Lesieur & Le Bars, Le Havre #62/R
Works on paper
£282 $454 €400 Honfleur (20x30cm-8x12in) s. W/C. 12-May-3 Lesieur & Le Bars, Le Havre #64
£417 $654 €650 Honfleur (38x52cm-15x20in) s. W/C. 24-Nov-2 Lesieur & Le Bars, Le Havre #102
£470 $756 €700 Honfleur (38x52cm-15x20in) s. W/C. 23-Feb-3 Lesieur & Le Bars, Le Havre #96

LORIS (20th C) ?
£1795 $2818 €2800 Nu (60x73cm-24x29in) s. 22-Nov-2 Millon & Associes, Paris #125
£1987 $3120 €3100 Astrid (162x130cm-64x51in) s. 22-Nov-2 Millon & Associes, Paris #124/R

LORJOU, Bernard (1908-1986) French
£513 $810 €800 Cathedrale (67x100cm-26x39in) s. paper on canvas. 14-Nov-2 Credit Municipal, Paris #52
£625 $987 €900 Deux personnages (38x46cm-15x18in) acrylic paper laid down. 28-Apr-3 Cornette de St.Cyr, Paris #274/R
£972 $1546 €1400 Nature morte (50x55cm-20x22in) s.d.53 prov. 29-Apr-3 Artcurial Briest, Paris #272 est:900-1200
£1181 $1865 €1700 Picador (60x73cm-24x29in) s. acrylic. 28-Apr-3 Cornette de St.Cyr, Paris #275/R est:1000-1200
£2038 $3180 €3200 Sabot (38x55cm-15x22in) s. 10-Nov-2 Eric Pillon, Calais #209/R
£2069 $3269 €3000 Maternity (161x130cm-63x51in) s. acrylic. 4-Apr-3 Tajan, Paris #239/R
£2522 $3909 €3783 Fleurs dans un vase vert (90x71cm-35x28in) s. 4-Dec-2 Koller, Zurich #182/R est:6000-9000 (S.FR 5800)
£3365 $5216 €5250 Picador a la pique rouge (151x135cm-59x53in) s. acrylic painted 1975 prov. 7-Dec-2 Cornette de St.Cyr, Paris #70/R
£3448 $5517 €5000 Cathedrale (100x67cm-39x26in) s.d.1959. 12-Mar-3 E & Eve, Paris #110/R est:4500-5500
£3546 $5745 €5000 Village dans un paysage (73x100cm-29x39in) s. 23-May-3 Binoche, Paris #59/R est:5000-6000
£4487 $7045 €7000 Bouquet sur fond rouge (73x54cm-29x21in) s. 22-Nov-2 Millon & Associes, Paris #103/R
£5031 $8000 €7547 Vase de fleurs (73x91cm-29x36in) s.d.56. 27-Feb-3 Christie's, Rockefeller NY #123/R est:6000
£5432 $7714 €8800 Grand bouquet de fleurs (2x73cm-1x29in) s. 16-Mar-3 Eric Pillon, Calais #259/R
£5924 $9241 €9300 Vase de fleurs (67x57cm-26x22in) s. 10-Nov-2 Eric Pillon, Calais #203/R
£6369 $9936 €10000 Vase de fleurs (65x50cm-26x20in) s. 10-Nov-2 Eric Pillon, Calais #202/R
£7325 $11427 €11500 Vase de tournesols (131x97cm-52x38in) s. 10-Nov-2 Eric Pillon, Calais #216/R
Works on paper
£256 $405 €400 Bouquet de fleurs (63x49cm-25x19in) s. gouache ink collage. 14-Nov-2 Credit Municipal, Paris #49
£442 $703 €650 Lion (37x54cm-15x21in) felt-tip pen. 28-Feb-3 Joron-Derem, Paris #39

LORME, Anthonie de (1610-1673) Dutch
£185185 $300000 €277778 Interior of the Protestant church at night with elegant figures (118x151cm-46x59in) s.i.d.1645 panel. 24-Jan-3 Christie's, Rockefeller NY #39/R est:100000-150000

LORRAIN, Robert le (1666-1743) French
Sculpture
£25641 $39744 €40000 Fleuve (28x38x15cm-11x15x6in) mono.verso terracotta lit. 9-Dec-2 Rabourdin & Choppin de Janvry, Paris #6/R est:37500

LORTEL, Leberecht (c.1818-1901) French
£317 $500 €500 Mountainous landscape (31x19cm-12x7in) s. cardboard. 2-Dec-2 Tajan, Paris #7

LORTEL, Leberecht (attrib) (c.1818-1901) French
Works on paper
£587 $910 €881 La vallee de Chamonix (31x48cm-12x19in) W/C. 7-Dec-2 Galerie du Rhone, Sion #303/R (S.FR 1350)

LORTHIOIR, Pierre (20th C) French
£317 $504 €460 Chalutier au sec (72x53cm-28x21in) s. 10-Mar-3 Thierry & Lannon, Brest #179

LORY, Gabriel Ludwig (1763-1840) Swiss
Works on paper
£300 $498 €435 Stag on an escarpment with a hill top town and a range of mountains beyond (23x30cm-9x12in) s. W/C bodycol. 16-Jun-3 Duke & Son, Dorchester #124

LORY, Matthias Gabriel (1784-1846) Swiss
Works on paper
£833 $1342 €1208 View of the domes of Bergamo (31x23cm-12x9in) s. i.verso W/C. 9-May-3 Dobiaschofsky, Bern #21/R (S.FR 1800)
£2222 $3578 €3222 View of Tells chapel on the Urner Lake (44x68cm-17x27in) s. W/C. 9-May-3 Dobiaschofsky, Bern #26/R est:3500 (S.FR 4800)

LORY, Matthias Gabriel (attrib) (1784-1846) Swiss
£705 $1029 €1058 Interlaken (47x37cm-19x15in) i. verso paper on board canvas. 17-Jun-2 Philippe Schuler, Zurich #4281/R (S.FR 1600)

LOS, Waldemar (1849-1888) Polish
£1582 $2453 €2500 Out riding (20x24cm-8x9in) s.i. canvas on panel. 25-Sep-2 Neumeister, Munich #640/R est:1200

LOSSOW, Heinrich (1843-1897) German
£943 $1509 €1415 In front of the mirror (36x30cm-14x12in) s. 17-Mar-3 Philippe Schuler, Zurich #4628/R (S.FR 2000)

LOTBINIERE, Marie Foucher (19th C) Canadian
Works on paper
£976 $1532 €1464 Vase francais (44x36cm-17x14in) s.i. W/C prov.exhib. 10-Dec-2 Pinneys, Montreal #163 est:900-1200 (C.D 2400)

LOTH, Johann Karl (1632-1698) German
£2759 $4359 €4000 Saint Sebastian (49x40cm-19x16in) 5-Apr-3 Finarte Semenzato, Milan #58/R est:4000
£8176 $12673 €13000 Blind Isaac deceived by his wife Rebecca into blessing Jacob instead of Esau (98x124cm-39x49in) 2-Oct-2 Dorotheum, Vienna #261/R est:13000-16000
£13924 $21582 €22000 Lot and his daughters (136x180cm-54x71in) prov. 25-Sep-2 Neumeister, Munich #495/R est:15000
Works on paper
£4500 $7515 €6525 Adoration of the golden calf (52x42cm-20x17in) pen brown ink htd white prov. 9-Jul-3 Sotheby's, London #40/R est:5000-7000
£20833 $33125 €30000 Jupiter and Ganymed (15x19cm-6x7in) s.d.1670 pen htd white. 5-May-3 Ketterer, Munich #237/R est:1200-1400

LOTH, Johann Karl (attrib) (1632-1698) German
£2432 $3795 €3600 Nymph and Satyr (72x98cm-28x39in) 27-Mar-3 Dorotheum, Vienna #417/R est:3600-5000
£10127 $16000 €16000 Holy Sebastian with angels (139x93cm-55x37in) canvas on canvas. 29-Nov-2 Bolland & Marotz, Bremen #657/R est:7600

LOTH, Johann Karl (circle) (1632-1698) German
£8333 $12917 €13000 Samson and Delilah (110x98cm-43x39in) prov. 5-Dec-2 Dr Fritz Nagel, Stuttgart #621/R est:3500

LOTIRON, Robert (1886-1966) French
£440 $682 €700 Bouquet de fleurs (36x27cm-14x11in) s. panel. 30-Oct-2 Artcurial Briest, Paris #315
£524 $817 €786 Paysage- Montmartre (41x33cm-16x13in) s.d.22 prov. 6-Nov-2 Dobiaschofsky, Bern #787/R (S.FR 1200)
£566 $877 €900 La promenade (27x47cm-11x19in) s. 30-Oct-2 Artcurial Briest, Paris #316
£777 $1212 €1150 View of Fontainebleau (50x61cm-20x24in) 28-Mar-3 Claude Aguttes, Neuilly #112/R
£828 $1292 €1300 Hiver, peniches et bateau - lavoir a quai (27x35cm-11x14in) s.d.24. 7-Nov-2 Claude Aguttes, Neuilly #61
£839 $1325 €1300 Pre a Saint-Jacques de Bergerac (27x41cm-11x16in) s. prov. 19-Dec-2 Claude Aguttes, Neuilly #190/R
£946 $1476 €1400 Les quais et Notre-Dame de Paris (33x46cm-13x18in) s. 31-Mar-3 Rossini, Paris #67
£949 $1500 €1500 Rue de Nice (35x27cm-14x11in) s.d.1922. 2-Dec-2 Tajan, Paris #163
£949 $1500 €1500 Place de village animee (29x27cm-11x11in) s. 2-Dec-2 Tajan, Paris #162
£1959 $3271 €2840 Paris, sabliere au bord des quais (41x33cm-16x13in) s. 10-Jul-3 Artcurial Briest, Paris #159/R est:1800-2200

LOTT, Frederick Tully (fl.1852-1879) British
Works on paper
£600 $990 €870 Devil's bridge, near Aberyswyth, North Wales (37x25cm-15x10in) s.d.1866 pencil W/C gum arabic scratching out. 3-Jul-3 Christie's, Kensington #78/R

LOTTER, Heinrich (1875-1941) German
Works on paper
£379 $599 €550 Insel Reichenau (24x20cm-9x8in) s. W/C. 5-Apr-3 Geble, Radolfzell #750/R
£379 $599 €550 Garden in bloom (20x17cm-8x7in) s. W/C pencil. 5-Apr-3 Geble, Radolfzell #751

LOTTIER, Louis (1815-1892) French
£2710 $4281 €4200 Marine au soleil couchant, Liban (29x45cm-11x18in) s. 19-Dec-2 Claude Aguttes, Neuilly #122a/R

LOTTO, Lorenzo (attrib) (1480-1556) Italian
£15854 $26000 €23781 Portrait of a councillor (72x66cm-28x26in) transferred from panel prov.exhib.lit. 29-May-3 Sotheby's, New York #123/R est:8000-12000

LOTZ, Karl (1833-1904) Hungarian
£503 $785 €755 Horses (11x19cm-4x7in) tempera. 11-Apr-3 Kieselbach, Budapest #7/R (H.F 180000)
£2064 $3220 €3096 Nude (30x6cm-12x2in) board. 11-Sep-2 Kieselbach, Budapest #54/R (H.F 800000)
£2193 $3421 €3290 Mother with child (38x63cm-15x25in) s. 11-Sep-2 Kieselbach, Budapest #88/R (H.F 850000)
£2794 $4359 €4191 Bacchante (30x32cm-12x13in) s. panel. 11-Apr-3 Kieselbach, Budapest #8/R est:350000-1000000 (H.F 1000000)
£3765 $5836 €5648 Storm (16x24cm-6x9in) s. oil paper on cardboard. 6-Dec-2 Kieselbach, Budapest #119/R (H.F 1400000)
£4386 $6842 €6360 Portrait of a girl (40x40cm-16x16in) s. 13-Sep-2 Mu Terem Galeria, Budapest #119/R est:1000000 (H.F 1700000)
£5309 $8283 €7698 Summer on the farm (22x34cm-9x13in) s. 12-Apr-3 Mu Terem Galeria, Budapest #136/R est:1500000 (H.F 1900000)
£16767 $26156 €24312 Lotz Komelia (20x54cm-8x21in) s. board prov. 12-Apr-3 Mu Terem Galeria, Budapest #137/R est:2500000 (H.F 6000000)

LOTZ, Mathilde (1858-1923) American
£2147 $3500 €3221 Portrait of a dog (56x46cm-22x18in) s.indis.i.d.1884. 16-Feb-3 Butterfields, San Francisco #2076 est:2000-3000

LOUBCHANSKY, Marcelle (1917-) French
£374 $595 €550 Composition (43x58cm-17x23in) s.d.1961. 24-Mar-3 Claude Boisgirard, Paris #157
£3425 $5377 €5000 Bethsabee (130x81cm-51x32in) s.i.d.1956 verso. 15-Apr-3 Laurence Calmels, Paris #4339/R

LOUBERE, J (19th C) French
£1020 $1622 €1500 Jeunes enfants a la fontaine (128x55cm-50x22in) s.i. 21-Mar-3 Rieunier, Bailly-Pommery, Mathias, Paris #109/R

LOUCHE, Constant (19/20th C) French
£1154 $1812 €1800 Mausolee au bord de l'Oued (42x123cm-17x48in) s. 10-Dec-2 Tajan, Paris #193/R

LOUDEN, Albert (1943-) British
£750 $1223 €1088 Forward to London (91x61cm-36x24in) s.d. i.verso. 15-Jul-3 Bonhams, Knightsbridge #56/R
Works on paper
£845 $1361 €1200 Couple in park (48x37cm-19x15in) s. W/C pastel. 10-May-3 Bukowskis, Helsinki #286/R

LOUDERBACK, Walt (1887-1941) American
£7962 $12500 €11943 Western street scene (61x99cm-24x39in) s. 23-Nov-2 Pook & Pook, Downington #209/R est:3000-4000

LOUDON, Margery (20th C) British
£500 $780 €750 Greenhouse interior (110x110cm-43x43in) s.d.78. 10-Apr-3 Bonhams, Edinburgh #25

LOUDON, Terence (fl.1921-1940) British
£450 $684 €675 Mixed bunch (61x51cm-24x20in) 29-Aug-2 Christie's, Kensington #71/R

LOUEDIN, Bernard (1938-) French
£346 $536 €550 Bord de mer (33x41cm-13x16in) s. 6-Oct-2 Livinec, Gaudcheau & Jezequel, Rennes #25
£506 $800 €800 Vanite aux montres de gousset (19x24cm-7x9in) s. 1-Dec-2 Livinec, Gaudcheau & Jezequel, Rennes #50/R

LOUGHEED, Robert Elmer (1910-1982) Canadian
£1290 $2103 €1935 Kerr's Team La Chute (20x15cm-8x6in) s. i. verso board. 12-Feb-3 Iegor de Saint Hippolyte, Montreal #127/R (C.D 3200)
£1506 $2500 €2184 Kerr's team "La Chute" (20x25cm-8x10in) s. i.verso board. 11-Jun-3 Butterfields, San Francisco #4135/R est:3000-5000
£2026 $3160 €3039 Southwest shade (30x41cm-12x16in) s. i.verso masonite panel prov.lit. 9-Nov-2 Santa Fe Art, Santa Fe #179/R est:4000-6000
£3526 $5500 €5289 In the valley of the Rio Chama (30x61cm-12x24in) 9-Nov-2 Altermann Galleries, Santa Fe #119
£3846 $6000 €5769 Trailing the konvone (30x61cm-12x24in) 9-Nov-2 Altermann Galleries, Santa Fe #116
£3846 $6000 €5769 In the village of Galisteo (30x61cm-12x24in) s. i.verso oil masonite panel prov.lit. 9-Nov-2 Santa Fe Art, Santa Fe #22/R est:9000-12000
£4969 $8050 €7205 Spring below the Jemez (30x61cm-12x24in) board. 23-May-3 Altermann Galleries, Santa Fe #14
£4969 $8050 €7205 Early snows (25x51cm-10x20in) board. 23-May-3 Altermann Galleries, Santa Fe #15
£5063 $8000 €7341 On the Santa Fe trail (30x61cm-12x24in) s. board exhib. 26-Jul-3 Coeur d'Alene, Hayden #19/R est:6000-9000
£9615 $15000 €14423 Scouting deep in snow country (30x61cm-12x24in) 9-Nov-2 Altermann Galleries, Santa Fe #118

LOUIS, Morris (1912-1962) American
£56250 $90000 €84375 Number 43 (223x29cm-88x11in) magna on canvas painted 1962 prov.exhib.lit. 14-May-3 Sotheby's, New York #149/R est:80000-120000
£65625 $105000 €98438 Number 1-37 (203x30cm-80x12in) acrylic painted 1962 prov.lit. 15-May-3 Christie's, Rockefeller NY #135/R est:80000-120000
£120253 $190000 €180380 Number 4 (234x83cm-92x33in) s. verso magna on canvas prov.exhib.lit. 13-Nov-2 Sotheby's, New York #220/R est:150000-200000
£125000 $200000 €187500 Seven bronze (225x321cm-89x126in) acrylic painted 1958 prov.exhib.lit. 14-May-3 Christie's, Rockefeller NY #12/R est:200000-300000
£949367 $1500000 €1424051 Untitled (251x359cm-99x141in) acrylic painted 1959-60 prov.exhib.lit. 13-Nov-2 Christie's, Rockefeller NY #21/R est:700000-900000

LOUKASIEVITCH, Soufandmich (?-1842) Polish
£2949 $4600 €4424 Family before an open window (46x37cm-18x15in) s. panel. 9-Nov-2 Sloan, North Bethesda #554/R est:5000-7000

LOUKOTA, Josef (1879-1967) Czechoslovakian
£1755 $2739 €2633 Nude girl by window (90x64cm-35x25in) s. 12-Oct-2 Dorotheum, Prague #62/R est:50000-75000 (C.KR 85000)

LOUND, Thomas (1802-1861) British
£4200 $6678 €6300 Fishermen near the jetty, Great Yarmouth (31x54cm-12x21in) exhib. 19-Mar-3 Sotheby's, London #70/R est:4000-6000

LOUND, Thomas (attrib) (1802-1861) British
Works on paper
£1600 $2544 €2400 Labourer at lunch in a cornfield near Herne Bay, Kent (40x64cm-16x25in) bears sig i.verso W/C over pencil htd bodycol. 19-Mar-3 Sotheby's, London #196/R est:800-1200

LOUP, Arnold (1882-1972) Swiss
£529 $772 €794 Weiningen in summer (71x98cm-28x39in) s.d.1907 i. verso. 17-Jun-2 Philippe Schuler, Zurich #7426 (S.FR 1200)

LOUPPE, Leo (1869-?) French
£769 $1192 €1200 Iris in vase with roses (96x69cm-38x27in) s. board. 6-Dec-2 Michael Zeller, Lindau #829/R

LOUREIRO, Arthur Jose de Souza (1853-1932) Portuguese
£853 $1356 €1280 Black panther (34x25cm-13x10in) canvasboard prov.exhib. 5-May-3 Sotheby's, Melbourne #351 (A.D 2200)

LOUSTAL, Jacques (1956-) French
Works on paper
£694 $1146 €1000 Les poissons des Mers du Sud (36x64cm-14x25in) s. gouache pastel ink. 3-Jul-3 Christie's, Paris #55/R

LOUSTAU, Marie Euphrosine (1831-?) French
£1000 $1630 €1500 Still life of fruit and flowers (46x55cm-18x22in) s. 29-Jan-3 Sotheby's, Olympia #309/R est:1000-1500

LOUSTAUNAU, Louis Auguste Georges (1846-1898) French
£2564 $4026 €4000 Scene galante devant un four a pain (67x92cm-26x36in) s.d.1874. 25-Nov-2 Rieunier, Bailly-Pommery, Mathias, Paris #5/R
£11613 $18000 €17420 Morning read (55x78cm-22x31in) s. 30-Oct-2 Christie's, Rockefeller NY #152/R est:18000-25000

LOUTHERBOURG, Jacques Philippe de II (1740-1812) French
Works on paper
£377 $585 €600 Berger et troupeau (26x36cm-10x14in) s. pen wash. 29-Oct-2 Artcurial Briest, Paris #14
£541 $843 €800 Mountainous landscape (17cm-7in circular) s. gouache. 27-Mar-3 Christie's, Paris #147/R
£1892 $2951 €2800 Bull and cows (25x42cm-10x17in) chk prov. 27-Mar-3 Christie's, Paris #148/R

LOUTHERBOURG, Jacques Philippe de II (attrib) (1740-1812) French
£1500 $2355 €2250 Stormy landscape with herdsman on a rocky path (25x30cm-10x12in) 13-Dec-2 Christie's, Kensington #156/R est:2500-3500
£4839 $7645 €7259 Embarking troops, French Revolutionary Wars (126x109cm-50x43in) 18-Nov-2 Waddingtons, Toronto #246/R est:10000-15000 (C.D 12000)
£7000 $11130 €10500 Landscape with herdsmen and animals (32x40cm-13x16in) pair. 19-Mar-3 Sotheby's, London #79/R est:2500-4000

LOUTHERBOURG, Jacques Philippe de II (style) (1740-1812) French
£7000 $11060 €10500 Stagecoach on the Dover Road (83x114cm-33x45in) bears sig. 28-Nov-2 Sotheby's, London #126/R est:3000-5000

LOUTREUIL, Maurice (1885-1925) French
£4577 $7599 €6500 Femme au hamac (72x128cm-28x50in) s. 11-Jun-3 Beaussant & Lefèvre, Paris #70/R est:3000-4000
Works on paper
£352 $585 €500 Nu agenouille (29x38cm-11x15in) bears st.sig. W/C black crayon. 11-Jun-3 Beaussant & Lefèvre, Paris #71
£563 $935 €800 Au cafe (23x31cm-9x12in) s. ink htd W/C dr. 11-Jun-3 Beaussant & Lefèvre, Paris #72/R

LOUVRIER, Maurice (1878-1954) French
£1987 $3021 €3100 Marche de Rouen (33x41cm-13x16in) s. cardboard double-sided. 16-Aug-2 Deauville, France #83/R
£3846 $6077 €6000 Marche Rue de l'Epicerie (81x66cm-32x26in) s. 17-Nov-2 Herbette, Doullens #47/R est:3000

LOUYOT, Edmond (1861-1909) German
£903 $1328 €1400 St Margherita (140x126cm-55x50in) s. i. verso. 20-Jun-2 Dr Fritz Nagel, Stuttgart #792/R
£3145 $4843 €5000 Little beggar (81x61cm-32x24in) s. exhib. 22-Oct-2 Sotheby's, Amsterdam #73/R est:6000-8000
£5822 $9140 €8500 Volendam girl (9x68cm-4x27in) s. 15-Apr-3 Sotheby's, Amsterdam #86/R est:8000-12000

LOVATI, Augusto (1816-?) Italian
£705 $1107 €1100 Section of coast near Capri (20x27cm-8x11in) s. wood. 21-Nov-2 Dorotheum, Vienna #181/R
£3846 $6038 €6000 View of rocky coast in front of Capri (50x89cm-20x35in) s. 21-Nov-2 Dorotheum, Vienna #180/R est:2200-3000

LOVE, Ralph (1907-) American
£321 $500 €482 Reynold's Peak (23x28cm-9x11in) s. i.verso canvas on board prov. 9-Nov-2 Santa Fe Art, Santa Fe #63/R

LOVEJOY, Rupert (1885-1975) American
£1171 $1850 €1757 Fall reflection (46x56cm-18x22in) s. board. 26-Apr-3 Jeffery Burchard, Florida #38a est:1000-2000

LOVELL, Charles Edward (fl.1890-1895) British
£950 $1530 €1425 True companion; young boy with dog (53x38cm-21x15in) s.d.1893. 19-Feb-3 Mallams, Oxford #452/R

LOVELL, Katharine Adams (1877-1965) American
£288 $450 €432 Bit of Maine (36x46cm-14x18in) s. board. 1-Aug-2 Eldred, East Dennis #937d

LOVELL, Tom (1909-1997) American
£1097 $1700 €1646 Study for Viking ships (18x28cm-7x11in) 20-Jul-2 Altermann Galleries, Santa Fe #19/R est:2000-2500
£1226 $1900 €1839 New Mexico summer landscape (20x25cm-8x10in) 20-Jul-2 Altermann Galleries, Santa Fe #50/R est:2000-3000
£1290 $2000 €1935 New Mexico winter landscape (15x25cm-6x10in) s. 20-Jul-2 Altermann Galleries, Santa Fe #49/R est:2000-3000

£1935 $3000 €2903 Boy and girl riding white horse (51x76cm-20x30in) 20-Jul-2 Altermann Galleries, Santa Fe #10/R est:4500-5500
£2000 $3100 €3000 Study for Indian with owl (30x23cm-12x9in) 20-Jul-2 Altermann Galleries, Santa Fe #40/R est:3000-4000
£2244 $3500 €3366 Physician and patients in colonial India (66x114cm-26x45in) 9-Nov-2 Altermann Galleries, Santa Fe #142
£2564 $4000 €3846 Summer to remember (66x99cm-26x39in) 9-Nov-2 Altermann Galleries, Santa Fe #143
£2774 $4300 €4161 The beach (56x86cm-22x34in) illustration. 20-Jul-2 Altermann Galleries, Santa Fe #8/R est:5000-7000
£2795 $4500 €4193 Couple ascending staircase watched by policeman (91x66cm-36x26in) s.d. 10-May-3 Illustration House, New York #107/R est:6000-8000
£3526 $5500 €5289 Man enters Liberia, surprising woman as other man lights up (41x58cm-16x23in) s. panel. 9-Nov-2 Illustration House, New York #160/R est:7000-10000
£4194 $6500 €6291 Study for White man's eyes (15x28cm-6x11in) s. 20-Jul-2 Altermann Galleries, Santa Fe #47/R est:7000-9000
£4516 $7000 €6774 Study for Surrender at Appomattox (13x20cm-5x8in) 20-Jul-2 Altermann Galleries, Santa Fe #22/R est:7000-9000
£4839 $7500 €7259 Study for Mr Bodmer's music box (23x20cm-9x8in) s. 20-Jul-2 Altermann Galleries, Santa Fe #24/R est:7000-9000
£5137 $7500 €7706 Study for Surrender at Appamatox (13x20cm-5x8in) 18-May-2 Altermann Galleries, Santa Fe #22/R
£6516 $10100 €9774 Abraham Lincoln and Mary Todd (61x61cm-24x24in) 20-Jul-2 Altermann Galleries, Santa Fe #12/R est:3000-4000
£26899 $42500 €39004 Tumbleweed serenade (41x71cm-16x28in) s. board prov. 26-Jul-3 Coeur d'Alene, Hayden #141/R est:30000-50000
£35714 $55000 €53571 Even trade (51x76cm-20x30in) 25-Oct-2 Morris & Whiteside, Hilton Head Island #24 est:55000-60000
£38710 $60000 €58065 Battle of the Crater (89x58cm-35x23in) s. 20-Jul-2 Altermann Galleries, Santa Fe #14/R est:70000-90000
£74194 $115000 €111291 The Grandfather (97x81cm-38x32in) s.d.1991. 20-Jul-2 Altermann Galleries, Santa Fe #26/R est:100000-120000

Works on paper

£435 $700 €653 Indian brave with camera (28x20cm-11x8in) s. brush ink. 20-Feb-3 Illustration House, New York #103/R
£581 $900 €872 The Jap helmet (25x25cm-10x10in) chl. 20-Jul-2 Altermann Galleries, Santa Fe #5/R
£645 $1000 €968 Ex Dick Feminine (23x18cm-9x7in) chl executed 1930. 20-Jul-2 Altermann Galleries, Santa Fe #3/R
£852 $1380 €1235 Boys and the frog (18x41cm-7x16in) chl. 23-May-3 Altermann Galleries, Santa Fe #108
£968 $1500 €1452 Shadow illustrations (30x20cm-12x8in) ink. 20-Jul-2 Altermann Galleries, Santa Fe #4/R est:1000-1500
£968 $1500 €1452 Male - female (15x18cm-6x7in) gouache. 20-Jul-2 Altermann Galleries, Santa Fe #9/R est:2000-2500
£1032 $1600 €1548 Study for Indian head (15x13cm-6x5in) chl. 20-Jul-2 Altermann Galleries, Santa Fe #33/R est:1000-1200
£1097 $1700 €1646 World War II battle (23x38cm-9x15in) W/C study. 20-Jul-2 Altermann Galleries, Santa Fe #7/R est:1500-2000
£1097 $1700 €1646 Study for Trading at Bulgar (28x41cm-11x16in) pastel. 20-Jul-2 Altermann Galleries, Santa Fe #15/R est:3000-4000
£1097 $1700 €1646 Study for Coming ashore (15x25cm-6x10in) pastel. 20-Jul-2 Altermann Galleries, Santa Fe #21/R est:1800-2400
£1290 $2000 €1935 Study for Civil War in the Gulf of Mexico - after Appomattox (28x30cm-11x12in) chl. 20-Jul-2 Altermann Galleries, Santa Fe #23/R est:2000-2500
£1355 $2100 €2033 Study for Viking trading on the Volgar river (28x41cm-11x16in) chl. 20-Jul-2 Altermann Galleries, Santa Fe #16/R est:2500-3000
£1355 $2100 €2033 Study for Alexander welcomed back (18x36cm-7x14in) s. mixed media. 20-Jul-2 Altermann Galleries, Santa Fe #17/R est:1800-2400
£1355 $2100 €2033 Study for Ship landing in Asia. Landing in Asia (25x25cm-10x10in) pastel double-sided. 20-Jul-2 Altermann Galleries, Santa Fe #18/R est:2000-3000
£1370 $2000 €2055 Study for The Viking funeral (18x36cm-7x14in) pastel. 18-May-2 Altermann Galleries, Santa Fe #21/R
£1494 $2300 €2241 Blackfoot Indian with capote (25x20cm-10x8in) chl. 25-Oct-2 Morris & Whiteside, Hilton Head Island #27 est:2500-3500
£1548 $2400 €2322 Study for Two Indians check campfire (28x20cm-11x8in) chl. 20-Jul-2 Altermann Galleries, Santa Fe #29/R est:1500-2000
£1548 $2400 €2322 Study for The cemetery (36x43cm-14x17in) s. chl. 20-Jul-2 Altermann Galleries, Santa Fe #39/R est:3000-4000
£1613 $2500 €2420 Rifle range (20x28cm-8x11in) W/C. 20-Jul-2 Altermann Galleries, Santa Fe #6/R est:1200-1750
£1633 $2645 €2368 Fire in the buffalo grass study (25x18cm-10x7in) chl. 23-May-3 Altermann Galleries, Santa Fe #106
£1677 $2600 €2516 Study for The swivel gun (46x30cm-18x12in) s. chl. 20-Jul-2 Altermann Galleries, Santa Fe #44/R est:3000-4000
£1742 $2700 €2613 Study for The scarecrow (28x20cm-11x8in) s. chl. 20-Jul-2 Altermann Galleries, Santa Fe #27/R est:1500-2000
£1742 $2700 €2613 Virginia driver (28x25cm-11x10in) s. gouache. 20-Jul-2 Altermann Galleries, Santa Fe #51/R est:2000-3000
£1935 $3000 €2903 Bless this house (43x66cm-17x26in) gouache. 20-Jul-2 Altermann Galleries, Santa Fe #13/R est:3500-4000
£1935 $3000 €2903 The lost canteen (36x46cm-14x18in) s. chl. 20-Jul-2 Altermann Galleries, Santa Fe #36/R est:3000-3500
£1935 $3000 €2903 Study for Lone cowboy (8x13cm-3x5in) W/C. 20-Jul-2 Altermann Galleries, Santa Fe #37/R est:2000-3000
£2000 $3100 €3000 Study for Abandoned dreams (25x43cm-10x17in) s. chl. 20-Jul-2 Altermann Galleries, Santa Fe #38/R est:3000-3500
£2000 $3100 €3000 Study for Indian with owl (36x30cm-14x12in) s. chl. 20-Jul-2 Altermann Galleries, Santa Fe #41/R est:2000-2500
£2179 $3400 €3269 Dragging the fire line study II (18x25cm-7x10in) pastel. 9-Nov-2 Altermann Galleries, Santa Fe #140
£2452 $3800 €3678 Study for Bad face strategy (13x23cm-5x9in) pastel. 20-Jul-2 Altermann Galleries, Santa Fe #34/R est:3000-5000
£2581 $4000 €3872 More than meets the eye (38x38cm-15x15in) s. chl. 20-Jul-2 Altermann Galleries, Santa Fe #46/R est:2500-3500
£2710 $4200 €4065 Sarcee Blackfoot (46x33cm-18x13in) s.d.1982 chl. 20-Jul-2 Altermann Galleries, Santa Fe #32/R est:3000-3500
£3032 $4700 €4548 Study for The horse raid (58x48cm-23x19in) s. chl. 20-Jul-2 Altermann Galleries, Santa Fe #28/R est:4000-6000
£3032 $4700 €4548 Study for The new water hole (61x102cm-24x40in) s. chl. 20-Jul-2 Altermann Galleries, Santa Fe #31/R est:7000-10000
£3097 $4800 €4646 Study for The new neighbours (61x91cm-24x36in) s. chl. 20-Jul-2 Altermann Galleries, Santa Fe #30/R est:8000-10000
£3161 $4900 €4742 Study for Lincoln (28x20cm-11x8in) chl W/C. 20-Jul-2 Altermann Galleries, Santa Fe #11/R est:2000-2500
£4452 $6900 €6678 Study for Chiricahua scout (41x30cm-16x12in) s.d.1992 chl. 20-Jul-2 Altermann Galleries, Santa Fe #42/R est:3000-3500
£5137 $7500 €7706 The wheel soakers (61x102cm-24x40in) chl. 18-May-2 Altermann Galleries, Santa Fe #20/R
£5484 $8500 €8226 Study for the Grandfather (97x81cm-38x32in) chl. 20-Jul-2 Altermann Galleries, Santa Fe #25/R est:8000-12000
£5696 $9000 €8259 Lost rag doll (61x91cm-24x36in) s.d.1989 chl. 26-Jul-3 Coeur d'Alene, Hayden #105/R est:10000-15000
£6452 $10000 €9678 Study for Fires on the Oregon Trail (86x71cm-34x28in) s. chl. 20-Jul-2 Altermann Galleries, Santa Fe #43/R est:8000-10000
£7051 $11000 €10577 Watering horses (66x91cm-26x36in) chl. 9-Nov-2 Altermann Galleries, Santa Fe #138
£7692 $12000 €11538 Fire in the buffalo grass (38x28cm-15x11in) pastel. 9-Nov-2 Altermann Galleries, Santa Fe #139
£9032 $14000 €13548 Study for Invitation to trade (122x91cm-48x36in) chl. 20-Jul-2 Altermann Galleries, Santa Fe #2/R est:10000-15000

LOVELL-SMITH, Colin (1894-1961) New Zealander

£760 $1185 €1140 Waiharakeke, Kaikoura (34x44cm-13x17in) s.i. s.d.1939 verso board. 17-Sep-2 Peter Webb, Auckland #166/R est:2000-3000 (NZ.D 2500)

LOVELL-SMITH, Rata (1900-1969) New Zealander

£226 $320 €339 Ngapara (44x54cm-17x21in) s. 21-Nov-1 Watson's, Christchurch #102/R (NZ.D 775)
£307 $491 €445 Black mountain, Northern Queensland, near Cairnes (45x45cm-18x18in) s. board. 13-May-3 Watson's, Christchurch #2/R (NZ.D 850)
£337 $479 €506 Magnolia on table cloth (41x48cm-16x19in) s. prov. 20-Mar-2 Watson's, Christchurch #19/R est:450-800 (NZ.D 1100)
£361 $578 €523 Flour mill near Hampden, North Otago (39x25cm-15x10in) s. board. 13-May-3 Watson's, Christchurch #46/R (NZ.D 1000)
£436 $619 €654 Onawe, Akaroa (44x50cm-17x20in) s. board prov. 21-Nov-1 Watson's, Christchurch #3/R (NZ.D 1500)
£441 $648 €662 Between storms Mt. Grey (34x46cm-13x18in) s. board. 19-Jun-2 Watson's, Christchurch #54/R est:300-1000 (NZ.D 1350)
£446 $700 €669 Two Thumb Range, South Canterbury (34x44cm-13x17in) s. board. 10-Dec-2 Peter Webb, Auckland #72/R est:800-1200 (NZ.D 1400)
£767 $1196 €1151 Coastal landscape (28x43cm-11x17in) s. 6-Aug-2 Peter Webb, Auckland #51/R est:1000-2000 (NZ.D 2600)
£940 $1467 €1410 Southern landscape (40x46cm-16x18in) s. canvasboard. 7-Nov-2 International Art Centre, Auckland #32/R est:2800-4000 (NZ.D 3000)

LOVEN, Frank W (1869-1941) American

£1563 $2500 €2345 Scenery of winter (30x41cm-12x16in) s. s.i.verso canvas on board. 15-Mar-3 Jeffery Burchard, Florida #78/R

LOVERING, Ida R (fl.1881-1903) British

£1400 $2170 €2100 Merle, daughter of h Gordon Tidey (86x74cm-34x29in) s. prov.exhib. 26-Sep-2 Lane, Penzance #237 est:1500-1700

LOVEROFF, Frederick Nicholas (1894-1959) Canadian

£1345 $2152 €2018 Across the lake (22x27cm-9x11in) panel. 15-May-3 Heffel, Vancouver #222/R est:2000-2500 (C.D 3000)
£1623 $2581 €2353 Old mill, near Sherbrooke (20x25cm-8x10in) s. i.verso panel painted c.1926 prov. 1-May-3 Heffel, Vancouver #58/R est:1000-1500 (C.D 3750)
£1630 $2543 €2719 Untitled - Autumn forest (27x22cm-11x9in) s. oil paper board prov. 13-Apr-3 Levis, Calgary #79/R est:4000-4500 (C.D 3750)

LOVESEY, Roderick (1944-) British
£1975 $3200 €2864 Engagement between the H.M.S Guerriere and U.S.S Constitution (89x120cm-35x47in) s. 29-Jul-3 Christie's, Rockefeller NY #181/R est:1000-2000

LOVET-LORSKI, Boris (1894-1973) Russian/American
Sculpture
£1656 $2583 €2600 Portrait of lady (28x20cm-11x8in) s. slate. 8-Nov-2 Camard, Paris #134
£3871 $6000 €5807 Venus (65cm-26in) carved plaster pencil executed c.1925. 6-Dec-2 Sotheby's, New York #163/R est:6000-9000
£4717 $7500 €7076 Torso (41cm-16in) i. black pat. bronze prov.lit. 4-Mar-3 Christie's, Rockefeller NY #83/R est:10000-15000
£18519 $30000 €27779 Stallion (49cm-19in) i. brown pat. bronze prov. 21-May-3 Sotheby's, New York #73/R est:20000-30000
£18519 $30000 €27779 Stallion (49cm-19in) i. brown pat. bronze prov. 21-May-3 Sotheby's, New York #74/R est:20000-30000
£24699 $41000 €37049 Torso (91cm-36in) s. gilt bronze exec.c.1935 prov.lit. 11-Jun-3 Phillips, New York #468/R est:18000-24000

LOVETT, Brigadier General A C (fl.1899-1901) British
Works on paper
£580 $905 €870 Governor's bodyguard, Bombay (37x52cm-15x20in) W/C. 25-Mar-3 Bonhams, Knightsbridge #14/R

LOVEWELL, Rominer (1853-1932) American
Works on paper
£252 $400 €378 HS Bishop, outward bound, off Thatcher's Island (15x49cm-6x19in) s. i.verso W/C gouache. 7-Mar-3 Skinner, Boston #337/R

LOVMAND, Christine Marie (1803-1872) Danish
£1474 $2388 €2137 Still life of with bunches of grapes (37x31cm-15x12in) init. 26-May-3 Bukowskis, Stockholm #473/R est:15000-20000 (S.KR 19000)

LOW, Bet (1924-) British
Works on paper
£950 $1482 €1425 Moonrise, Northern Isle (45x47cm-18x19in) s. W/C. 14-Apr-3 Sotheby's, London #177/R

LOW, Charles (fl.1870-1902) British
Works on paper
£2400 $3840 €3600 Milking times (27x38cm-11x15in) s. W/C. 11-Mar-3 Bonhams, New Bond Street #76/R est:1200-1800

LOW, Fritzi (1891-1975) Austrian
Works on paper
£506 $800 €800 Pepi in her room (29x22cm-11x9in) mono.d.1934 pencil. 30-Nov-2 Bassenge, Berlin #6466
£506 $800 €800 Market (30x21cm-12x8in) mono.d.1935 pencil. 30-Nov-2 Bassenge, Berlin #6467
£576 $910 €910 Street at night (29x29cm-11x11in) mono.d.1930. 30-Nov-2 Bassenge, Berlin #6465

LOW, Will Hicock (1853-1932) American
£385 $600 €578 Children feeding hay to a horse. s. 9-Nov-2 Sloan, North Bethesda #547/R
£594 $950 €861 Female harvester in a field at dusk (46x53cm-18x21in) s.d. board. 17-May-3 Selkirks, St. Louis #371/R
£1250 $2000 €1813 Personification of education and work (52x26cm-20x10in) s.d.1879. 16-May-3 Skinner, Boston #91/R est:700-900

LOWCOCK, Charles Frederick (fl.1878-1922) British
£620 $973 €930 Cottage interiors (25x30cm-10x12in) pair. 10-Dec-2 Capes Dunn, Manchester #866
£725 $1182 €1088 Cottage interior with figures at a table (9x11cm-4x4in) s. board. 12-Feb-3 Andrew Hartley, Ilkley #961
£760 $1239 €1140 Cottage interior with woman and children (9x11cm-4x4in) s. board. 12-Feb-3 Andrew Hartley, Ilkley #962
£2500 $3900 €3750 Lady with a fan (46x20cm-18x8in) s. board. 17-Sep-2 Sotheby's, Olympia #160/R est:2500-3500
£2800 $4564 €4200 Bather (46x21cm-18x8in) s. panel. 29-Jan-3 Sotheby's, Olympia #215/R est:2000-3000

LOWCOCK, Charles Frederick (attrib) (fl.1878-1922) British
£1300 $2119 €1885 Elegantly dressed girl standing on a marble balcony (46x20cm-18x8in) bears sig.i. panel. 17-Jul-3 Tennants, Leyburn #916 est:700-1000

LOWE, Robin (1959-) American
£2000 $3260 €3000 Blow you up (125x82cm-49x32in) init. i.d.1996 verso oil on aluminium prov. 3-Feb-3 Sotheby's, Olympia #18/R est:2000-3000
£2600 $4238 €3900 B-1 (56x42cm-22x17in) init. i.d.1986 verso oil on aluminium prov. 3-Feb-3 Sotheby's, Olympia #17/R est:2000-3000

LOWELL, Milton H (1848-1927) American
£1635 $2600 €2453 Lowell house beside a duck pond (41x51cm-16x20in) s. 7-Mar-3 Skinner, Boston #439/R est:1000-1500

LOWENSBERG, Verena (1912-1986) Swiss
£2402 $3507 €3603 Untitled (20x41cm-8x16in) s.d.1976/77 verso prov. 4-Jun-2 Germann, Zurich #115/R est:3000-5000 (S.FR 5500)

LOWER BAVARIAN SCHOOL (18th C) German
Sculpture
£9740 $14513 €15000 Maria Immaculata (132cm-52in) painted wood prov.lit. 26-Jun-2 Neumeister, Munich #21/R est:5000

LOWER RHINE SCHOOL, German
£3750 $6000 €5625 Christ before Pharisees, and the crucifixion (38x107cm-15x42in) monogramist panel prov.exhib. 14-May-3 Doyle, New York #79/R est:8000-12000

LOWERY, R (20th C) American
Sculpture
£1401 $2200 €2102 Figural group of four puppies (10x18cm-4x7in) s.num.22/200 green pat. bronze. 14-Dec-2 Charlton Hall, Columbia #330/R est:1000-1500

LOWITH, Wilhelm (1861-1932) Austrian
£2397 $3740 €3500 Reception in Rococo room (45x35cm-18x14in) s. panel. 10-Apr-3 Van Ham, Cologne #1575/R est:4300
£4487 $7045 €7000 Private study (25x17cm-10x7in) s. panel. 21-Nov-2 Van Ham, Cologne #1758/R est:900

LOWNDES, Alan (1921-1978) British
£800 $1336 €1160 Sleeping semi nude (49x75cm-19x30in) s.d.1952 board. 19-Jun-3 Lane, Penzance #163
£1600 $2544 €2400 Leyland Street (40x30cm-16x12in) s.d.1961 i.verso board. 26-Feb-3 Sotheby's, Olympia #264/R est:1000-1500
£2100 $3276 €3045 Red boat (40x51cm-16x20in) s.d.1962 board. 13-May-3 Holloways, Banbury #664 est:100-150
£3900 $6162 €5850 Stockport, street scene with lamp-post (51x42cm-20x17in) s.d.1953 board. 28-Nov-2 Morphets, Harrogate #555/R est:2000-3000
£4800 $7920 €6960 Figures in a street (51x41cm-20x16in) s. 3-Jul-3 Christie's, Kensington #550/R est:800-1200
£7000 $11480 €10150 March fair (86x76cm-34x30in) s.d.1960 i.d.1960 verso board prov. 4-Jun-3 Sotheby's, London #64/R est:4000-6000
£7500 $12300 €10875 High Street, Stockport (73x59cm-29x23in) s.d.1958 i.verso board prov. 4-Jun-3 Sotheby's, London #65/R est:3000-5000
£7500 $12300 €10875 The power and the glory II (56x71cm-22x28in) s.d.1959 i.verso board prov.exhib. 4-Jun-3 Sotheby's, London #66/R est:3000-5000

LOWRY, L S (1887-1976) British
Prints
£2400 $3720 €3600 Village on a hill (94x61cm-37x24in) s.num.75 black beige lithograph. 24-Sep-2 Bonhams, New Bond Street #97 est:1500-2000

LOWRY, Laurence Stephen (1887-1976) British
£22000 $36740 €31900 Head of an old man (39x29cm-15x11in) s. board prov.exhib. 24-Jun-3 Bonhams, New Bond Street #58/R est:18000-25000
£32000 $49920 €48000 Children playing (12x17cm-5x7in) s.d.1959 panel prov. 25-Mar-3 Bonhams, New Bond Street #97/R est:18000-25000
£45000 $70650 €67500 House on the moor, Heathcliff's House (51x61cm-20x24in) s.d.1950 prov.exhib.lit. 22-Nov-2 Christie's, London #59/R est:30000-50000
£48000 $75360 €72000 Lancashire street (22x28cm-9x11in) s.d.1951 panel prov.exhib. 22-Nov-2 Christie's, London #54/R est:50000-80000
£135000 $209250 €202500 Election (51x40cm-20x16in) board painted 1945 prov. 4-Dec-2 Sotheby's, London #61/R est:100000-150000
£170000 $278800 €246500 We two (53x43cm-21x17in) s.d.1943 board prov.lit. 4-Jun-3 Sotheby's, London #63/R est:60000-80000
£300000 $471000 €450000 Beach scene, Lancashire (46x61cm-18x24in) s.d.1945 prov. 22-Nov-2 Christie's, London #55/R est:300000-500000
£310000 $486700 €465000 White shop (61x51cm-24x20in) s.d.1951 prov. 16-Dec-2 Sotheby's, London #88/R est:200000-300000

Works on paper

£1250 $1938 €1875 Figures and dog (18x13cm-7x5in) pen ink dr prov. 1-Oct-2 Capes Dunn, Manchester #719/R
£1800 $2844 €2700 Portrait of a man (38x28cm-15x11in) s.i. pencil executed c.1918. 27-Nov-2 Sotheby's, Olympia #33/R est:2000-3000
£2100 $3444 €3045 Large seated dog and small man wearing a trilby (13x13cm-5x5in) init.d.1974 ballpoint pen cafe paper napkin. 3-Jun-3 Capes Dunn, Manchester #36/R
£3200 $5280 €4640 On the Mersey, Liverpool (24x32cm-9x13in) s.d.1962 pen ink prov. 3-Jul-3 Christie's, Kensington #654/R est:1500-2000
£4800 $7440 €7200 Man drinking tea (13x10cm-5x4in) s.d.1920 pencil. 4-Dec-2 Christie's, Kensington #253/R est:1000-1500
£5500 $8525 €8250 Self portrait (24x34cm-9x13in) s.d.1970 s.i.d.verso pencil felt tip pen prov. 4-Dec-2 Christie's, Kensington #251/R est:3000-5000
£5500 $9020 €8250 Church at Rockcliffe (16x20cm-6x8in) s.d.1963 pencil prov.lit. 6-Jun-3 Christie's, London #147/R est:3000-5000
£7000 $10990 €10500 Figures in a street (9x19cm-4x7in) s.d.71 blue black biro prov. 21-Nov-2 Tennants, Leyburn #704 est:1000-1500
£7500 $11775 €11250 Tanker entering the Tyne (25x35cm-10x14in) s.i.d.1963 pencil prov.exhib. 21-Nov-2 Christie's, London #141/R est:8000-12000
£8000 $12560 €12000 People with dogs (13x9cm-5x4in) s.d.1966 pencil. 21-Nov-2 Christie's, London #145/R est:6000-8000
£10000 $15600 €15000 Timber boat entering the Tyne (25x35cm-10x14in) s.d.1965 pencil prov. 25-Mar-3 Bonhams, New Bond Street #96/R est:5000-7000
£11000 $17270 €16500 Crowded beach, Sandsend (29x40cm-11x16in) s.d.1945 pencil prov.exhib.lit. 21-Nov-2 Christie's, London #142/R est:12000-18000
£11000 $17270 €16500 Group of figures (20x20cm-8x8in) s.d.1936 pencil prov. 21-Nov-2 Christie's, London #146/R est:5000-8000
£12000 $19320 €18000 Fishing village, Londondery (25x34cm-10x13in) s.d.1961 graphite prov.exhib. 6-May-3 Christie's, Melbourne #41/R est:30000-40000 (A.D 30000)
£13500 $20925 €20250 Our street (24x19cm-9x7in) init.d.1953 pencil prov. 3-Dec-2 Bonhams, New Bond Street #86/R est:3000-5000
£14000 $21840 €21000 Street in Maryport (24x34cm-9x13in) s. s.i.d.17 September 1966 pencil prov. 27-Mar-3 Christie's, Kensington #536/R est:7000-10000
£15000 $23550 €22500 Lytham promenade (30x40cm-12x16in) s.d.1944 pencil prov.lit. 21-Nov-2 Christie's, London #139/R est:15000-20000
£17000 $26690 €25500 Hulme Place, Salford (25x35cm-10x14in) s.d.1926 pencil prov. 21-Nov-2 Christie's, London #144/R est:12000-18000
£18000 $29520 €27000 Four young people (44x34cm-17x13in) s.d.1966 pencil ball point pen prov.exhib. 6-Jun-3 Christie's, London #149/R est:20000-30000
£22000 $34540 €33000 Steep street (34x25cm-13x10in) s.d.63 pencil prov. 21-Nov-2 Christie's, London #138/R est:15000-20000
£22000 $34540 €33000 Group of people (34x24cm-13x9in) s.d.1968 pencil prov.exhib. 21-Nov-2 Christie's, London #143/R est:10000-15000
£22000 $36080 €33000 Open air meeting (25x34cm-10x13in) pencil executed c.1921 prov. 6-Jun-3 Christie's, London #146/R est:15000-20000
£30000 $47100 €45000 Street scene (27x37cm-11x15in) s.d.1956 pencil black crayon W/C prov.lit. 21-Nov-2 Christie's, London #137/R est:30000-40000
£32000 $50240 €48000 Fishing boats at Lytham (41x49cm-16x19in) s.d.1915 i.verso pencil pastel prov.exhib.lit. 21-Nov-2 Christie's, London #140/R est:25000-35000
£34000 $53380 €51000 Piccadilly, Manchester (27x37cm-11x15in) s.d.1930 s.i.d.verso pencil prov. 21-Nov-2 Christie's, London #136/R est:30000-50000
£40000 $62000 €60000 Street in Cwm, South Wales (46x25cm-18x10in) s.d.1960 prov. 3-Dec-2 Bonhams, New Bond Street #87/R est:40000-60000

LOWRY, Laurence Stephen (after) (1887-1976) British

Prints

£5000 $8350 €7250 Going to the match (53x69cm-21x27in) s. col reproduction print. 24-Jun-3 Capes Dunn, Manchester #822/R
£5700 $8835 €8550 Going to the match (55x69cm-22x27in) s. print. 1-Oct-2 Bonhams, Leeds #220/R est:2000-3000

LOWRY, Laurence Stephen (attrib) (1887-1976) British

Works on paper

£420 $668 €630 Prestatyn, North Wales (18x20cm-7x8in) bears sig.d.1970 pencil dr. 18-Mar-3 Capes Dunn, Manchester #440

LOWRY, Laurence Stephen and RILEY, Harold (20th C) British

Works on paper

£1500 $2460 €2250 Sad dog (28x27cm-11x11in) s.d.67 pencil init. 4-Jun-3 Bonhams, Chester #316/R est:1500-2000

LOWTHER, Nellie A (19/20th C) British

£300 $477 €450 Portrait of Ellsa Locke (59x49cm-23x19in) s.d.94. 4-Mar-3 Bearnes, Exeter #436/R

LOXTON PEACOCK, Clarisse (1928-) British/Hungarian

£250 $390 €375 Studio table (63x76cm-25x30in) s.d.60. 17-Sep-2 Bonhams, Knightsbridge #267/R
£685 $1075 €1000 Lily (103x51cm-41x20in) s. board prov.exhib. 15-Apr-3 De Veres Art Auctions, Dublin #80/R est:1000-1500

LOXTON, John S (1903-1971) Australian

£261 $384 €392 Country road between Hotitika and Longford (62x74cm-24x29in) s. board prov. 19-Jun-2 Watson's, Christchurch #36/R (NZ.D 800)
£278 $408 €417 Sheep country, North Canterbury (50x59cm-20x23in) s. prov. 19-Jun-2 Watson's, Christchurch #51/R (NZ.D 850)
£278 $408 €417 Autumn at Alexandra (49x59cm-19x23in) s. board prov. 19-Jun-2 Watson's, Christchurch #67/R (NZ.D 850)
£389 $626 €584 Coastal landscape with rough seas (39x49cm-15x19in) s. 7-May-3 Dunbar Sloane, Auckland #48/R (NZ.D 1100)
£436 $619 €654 Snow scene (49x59cm-19x23in) s. board prov. 21-Nov-1 Watson's, Christchurch #69/R (NZ.D 1500)
£440 $708 €638 Eildon Lake, near Howqua (50x60cm-20x24in) s. 12-May-3 Joel, Victoria #281 est:1000-1500 (A.D 1100)
£478 $697 €717 Pioneer cottage, Arrowtown (49x60cm-19x24in) s. 12-Sep-1 Watson's, Christchurch #46 est:400-1000 (NZ.D 1600)
£555 $816 €833 Reflection at Redcliffs (49x59cm-19x23in) s. board prov. 19-Jun-2 Watson's, Christchurch #19/R est:1100-1400 (NZ.D 1700)
£597 $872 €896 Evening at Kailkoura (49x60cm-19x24in) s. 12-Sep-1 Watson's, Christchurch #17/R est:400-1400 (NZ.D 2000)
£597 $872 €896 Yachting redcliffs, Christchurch (63x75cm-25x30in) s. 12-Sep-1 Watson's, Christchurch #60/R est:900-1500 (NZ.D 2000)
£600 $966 €870 Self portrait (74x61cm-29x24in) board. 12-May-3 Joel, Victoria #386 est:1000-1500 (A.D 1500)
£627 $915 €941 Boatshed interior, Port Chalmer, Otago (49x59cm-19x23in) s. 12-Sep-1 Watson's, Christchurch #18/R est:600-1600 (NZ.D 2100)
£632 $960 €948 Sunset, Mordialloc Creek (61x74cm-24x29in) s. board. 19-Aug-2 Joel, Victoria #220/R est:1400-1800 (A.D 1800)
£945 $1341 €1418 Rhododendrons (73x65cm-29x26in) s. board prov. 21-Nov-1 Watson's, Christchurch #21/R est:4000-8000 (NZ.D 3250)

Works on paper

£276 $392 €414 Shipyard in Melbourne (32x43cm-13x17in) s. W/C prov. 21-Nov-1 Watson's, Christchurch #13/R (NZ.D 950)
£537 $784 €806 Dunedin coastline (51x71cm-20x28in) W/C. 12-Sep-1 Watson's, Christchurch #19 est:500-1500 (NZ.D 1800)
£651 $970 €977 September in the mountains (45x52cm-18x20in) s. W/C. 27-Aug-2 Christie's, Melbourne #182/R est:1500-2500 (A.D 1700)

LOYBOS, Jan Sebastiaen (17th C) Flemish

£10322 $16309 €16000 Village celebrations in a park (73x92cm-29x36in) s. 18-Dec-2 Tajan, Paris #34/R est:12000-15000

LOYE, Charles Auguste (1841-1905) French

Works on paper

£474 $720 €711 Arab on horseback (36x25cm-14x10in) s. pencil W/C. 27-Aug-2 Rasmussen, Copenhagen #1979/R (D.KR 5500)
£1020 $1622 €1500 Chef Arabe a cheval (36x24cm-14x9in) s. W/C. 24-Mar-3 Rabourdin & Choppin de Janvry, Paris #229/R est:1800-2000

LOYS, Christian (20th C) French

£315 $526 €450 Maternite a l'atelier (55x46cm-22x18in) s. 25-Jun-3 Claude Aguttes, Neuilly #42

LOYSEN, Arthur P (20th C) American

£248 $400 €372 New England winter landscape with villages (51x61cm-20x24in) s. board. 19-Jan-3 Jeffery Burchard, Florida #132a/R

LOZANO SANCHIS, Francisco (1912-2000) Spanish

£1858 $2899 €2750 Landscape (23x33cm-9x13in) s.d.79 s.d.verso. 25-Mar-3 Durán, Madrid #90/R
£2013 $3099 €3200 Dunes (14x20cm-6x8in) s. s.verso board. 28-Oct-2 Segre, Madrid #115/R
£3871 $6116 €6000 Landscape in Saler (27x41cm-11x16in) s.d.75 verso. 18-Dec-2 Ansorena, Madrid #180/R
£4027 $6483 €6000 Peasant man seen from the back (77x70cm-30x28in) s.d.1943. 18-Feb-3 Durán, Madrid #230/R
£4054 $6324 €6000 Mediterranean landscape (38x46cm-15x18in) s. s.i.d.88 verso. 25-Mar-3 Durán, Madrid #188/R
£4088 $6296 €6500 Landscape with dunes (27x35cm-11x14in) s. s.verso. 28-Oct-2 Segre, Madrid #116/R
£4167 $6542 €6500 Arrozal (27x35cm-11x14in) s.d.1967 board. 16-Dec-2 Castellana, Madrid #406/R
£13014 $20301 €19000 Villena Castle (65x93cm-26x37in) s. 8-Apr-3 Ansorena, Madrid #227/R

£20548 $32055 €30000 Landscape near Valencia (65x81cm-26x32in) s. 8-Apr-3 Ansorena, Madrid #232/R est:21000

LOZANO SIDRO, Adolfo (1874-?) Spanish
Works on paper
£419 $663 €650 Etiquette (28x20cm-11x8in) s.d.1932 W/C gouache. 17-Dec-2 Segre, Madrid #110/R

LOZANO, Margarita (1936-) Colombian
£5183 $8500 €7515 Paisaje tropical con lluvia de oro y platanar (105x119cm-41x47in) s. painted c.1998 prov.lit. 27-May-3 Sotheby's, New York #151

LOZOWICK, Louis (1892-1973) American
£14493 $23768 €20000 Untitled (92x61cm-36x24in) s. exhib. 29-May-3 Lempertz, Koln #760/R est:25000-28000
Prints
£1923 $3000 €2885 Construction (41x16cm-16x6in) s.d.1930 lithograph edition of 25. 7-Nov-2 Swann Galleries, New York #693/R est:3000-5000
£2051 $3200 €3077 Queensborough Bridge (34x19cm-13x7in) s.d.1930 num.17/50 lithograph. 7-Nov-2 Swann Galleries, New York #694/R est:2000-3000
£2201 $3500 €3302 Derricks and men, riding the girder (33x22cm-13x9in) s.d.num.9/15 lithograph. 2-May-3 Sotheby's, New York #36/R est:4000-6000
£2215 $3500 €3323 Mural study, lower Manhattan (36x20cm-14x8in) s.d.1926 lithograph. 24-Apr-3 Shannon's, Milford #92/R est:3000-5000
£3165 $5000 €4748 57th Street (38x19cm-15x7in) s.i.d.1929 lithograph one of 40. 12-Nov-2 Doyle, New York #287/R est:6000-8000
£5031 $8000 €7547 Hanover Square (38x23cm-15x9in) s.d. lithograph. 29-Apr-3 Christie's, Rockefeller NY #433/R est:4000-6000

LU DEZHI (1585-?) Chinese
Works on paper
£3497 $5769 €5071 Bamboo and rock (126x58cm-50x23in) s. ink hanging scroll. 6-Jul-3 Christie's, Hong Kong #477/R est:50000-70000 (HK.D 45000)

LU HUI (1851-1920) Chinese
Works on paper
£580 $951 €800 Monkey on red mapletree (198x50cm-78x20in) s. seals Indian ink col silk. 30-May-3 Dr Fritz Nagel, Stuttgart #1173/R

LU SHOUKUN (1919-1975) Chinese
Works on paper
£4065 $6423 €6098 Lonely boat (47x45cm-19x18in) s.d.1963 ink col hanging scroll. 28-Apr-3 Sotheby's, Hong Kong #523/R est:30000-40000 (HK.D 50000)

LU YANSHAO (1909-1993) Chinese
Works on paper
£2101 $3446 €2900 Resting beside the river (68x44cm-27x17in) i.d.1986 seals Indian ink col hanging scroll. 30-May-3 Dr Fritz Nagel, Stuttgart #1285/R est:500-800
£2246 $3684 €3100 Mountain landscape at the west lake (89x34cm-35x13in) i.d.1984 seals Indian ink col hanging scroll. 30-May-3 Dr Fritz Nagel, Stuttgart #1286/R est:500-800
£4065 $6423 €6098 Reservoir at the Lei canal (46x33cm-18x13in) s.i.d.January 1962 ink col. 28-Apr-3 Sotheby's, Hong Kong #588/R est:500000-700000 (HK.D 50000)
£4065 $6423 €6098 Crafts moored by the Dongting lake (24x67cm-9x26in) s.i.d.1963 ink col. 28-Apr-3 Sotheby's, Hong Kong #595/R est:450000-650000 (HK.D 50000)
£7724 $12203 €11586 Scholar under a pine tree (106x44cm-42x17in) s.i.d.1942 ink hanging scroll. 28-Apr-3 Sotheby's, Hong Kong #645/R est:70000-90000 (HK.D 95000)
£8537 $13488 €12806 Pines by the river (84x38cm-33x15in) s.i.d.1989 ink col hanging scroll silk. 28-Apr-3 Sotheby's, Hong Kong #646/R est:80000-120000 (HK.D 105000)
£9756 $15415 €14634 Rushing stream (88x44cm-35x17in) s.i. ink col hanging scroll. 28-Apr-3 Sotheby's, Hong Kong #581/R est:70000-90000 (HK.D 120000)
£20202 $33333 €29293 Country scenes (22x32cm-9x13in) ink scroll set of 12. 6-Jul-3 Christie's, Hong Kong #311/R est:150000-200000 (HK.D 260000)
£21756 $35897 €31546 City scenes (23x33cm-9x13in) ink scroll set of 12. 6-Jul-3 Christie's, Hong Kong #310/R est:150000-200000 (HK.D 280000)
£27642 $43675 €41463 Tumultuous waves (17x68cm-7x27in) s.i. ink col. 28-Apr-3 Sotheby's, Hong Kong #583/R est:150000-200000 (HK.D 340000)
£39024 $61659 €58536 Poetic landscape (24x33cm-9x13in) i. eleven s. ink col twelve leaves album. 28-Apr-3 Sotheby's, Hong Kong #598/R est:200000-300000 (HK.D 480000)
£62160 $102564 €90132 Landscape with calligraphy (198x111cm-78x44in) s.i. ink scroll three. 6-Jul-3 Christie's, Hong Kong #312/R est:450000-500000 (HK.D 800000)

LU YIFEI (1908-) Chinese
Works on paper
£1626 $2569 €2439 Flowers and insect (18x50cm-7x20in) s.i.d.1943 i.verso ink col folding fan. 28-Apr-3 Sotheby's, Hong Kong #560/R est:15000-20000 (HK.D 20000)
£2033 $3211 €3050 Goose (19x56cm-7x22in) s.i.d.1939 ink col handscroll. 28-Apr-3 Sotheby's, Hong Kong #569/R est:25000-35000 (HK.D 25000)

LUBBERS, Adriaan (1892-1954) Dutch
£1911 $3000 €2867 Still life with christusdoorn (39x31cm-15x12in) s.d.1942 i.verso. 10-Dec-2 Doyle, New York #220/R est:3000-4000
£3957 $6489 €5500 View of Zetdam (86x91cm-34x36in) s.d.1940 prov. 3-Jun-3 Christie's, Amsterdam #19/R est:3000-5000
£9554 $15000 €14331 View of Positano (39x49cm-15x19in) s.d.1925. 10-Dec-2 Doyle, New York #219/R est:15000-20000

LUBBERS, Holger (1850-1931) Danish
£265 $426 €398 Large waves at sea (21x38cm-8x15in) s. 19-Jan-3 Hindemae, Ullerslev #7491/R (D.KR 3000)
£270 $422 €405 Seascape with sailing vessels off coast (27x38cm-11x15in) s. 23-Sep-2 Rasmussen, Vejle #102/R (D.KR 3200)
£279 $444 €419 Fishing boats and fishermen on beach (20x26cm-8x10in) mono. 10-Mar-3 Rasmussen, Vejle #52 (D.KR 3000)
£287 $465 €416 Seascape with vessels at Sundet (26x40cm-10x16in) s.d.1920. 26-May-3 Rasmussen, Copenhagen #1381/R (D.KR 3000)
£343 $535 €515 Seascape with sailing vessel (21x28cm-8x11in) s.d.1918. 11-Nov-2 Rasmussen, Vejle #603/R (D.KR 4000)
£360 $562 €540 Seascape with boats (30x39cm-12x15in) s.d.1923. 11-Nov-2 Rasmussen, Vejle #619/R (D.KR 4200)
£402 $651 €583 Seascape with three master in evening sunshine (23x35cm-9x14in) s.d.1922. 26-May-3 Rasmussen, Copenhagen #1354 (D.KR 4200)
£467 $729 €701 Entrance to Aarhus with the frigate Jylland (14x22cm-6x9in) s. panel. 5-Aug-2 Rasmussen, Vejle #43/R (D.KR 5500)
£512 $814 €768 Coastal landscape with breakwater, North Sjaelland (37x63cm-15x25in) s. exhib. 5-Mar-3 Rasmussen, Copenhagen #1962/R (D.KR 5500)
£517 $791 €776 Coastal landscape with fishermen and beached boats (52x81cm-20x32in) s.d.1903. 24-Aug-2 Rasmussen, Havnen #2025 (D.KR 6000)
£531 $844 €797 Seascape with steamer and sailing vessels (50x44cm-20x17in) s. 10-Mar-3 Rasmussen, Vejle #426/R (D.KR 5700)
£553 $874 €830 Seascape (34x60cm-13x24in) s. 30-Nov-2 Rasmussen, Havnen #2059/R (D.KR 6500)
£563 $907 €800 Sailing ship at dusk (19x26cm-7x10in) s. lit. 9-May-3 Schloss Ahlden, Ahlden #1355/R
£596 $941 €894 Fisherman at edge of sea (52x36cm-20x14in) s.d.1914. 2-Dec-2 Rasmussen, Copenhagen #1346/R (D.KR 7000)
£681 $1076 €1022 Fishermen pulling in nets, Agger (17x26cm-7x10in) s.d.1914. 2-Dec-2 Rasmussen, Copenhagen #1386/R (D.KR 8000)
£766 $1210 €1149 Seascape with vessels (66x95cm-26x37in) s.d.1892. 2-Dec-2 Rasmussen, Copenhagen #1372/R (D.KR 9000)
£766 $1210 €1149 Vessels in Mesina Straight, Etna in background (77x97cm-30x38in) s. exhib. 2-Dec-2 Rasmussen, Copenhagen #1377/R (D.KR 9000)
£766 $1240 €1111 Jetty with woman and two men in rowing boat (78x63cm-31x25in) s.d.1923. 26-May-3 Rasmussen, Copenhagen #1397/R (D.KR 8000)
£845 $1318 €1268 Coastal landscape with breakers, Jylland (39x60cm-15x24in) s. 23-Sep-2 Rasmussen, Vejle #121/R (D.KR 10000)
£976 $1542 €1464 Seascape with many ship (83x108cm-33x43in) s. 5-Apr-3 Rasmussen, Havnen #2109/R (D.KR 10500)
£1378 $2095 €2067 Landing the day's catch (75x104cm-30x41in) s. 27-Aug-2 Rasmussen, Copenhagen #1759/R est:25000 (D.KR 16000)
£1522 $2343 €2283 Coastal landscape with fishermen (53x79cm-21x31in) s. 26-Oct-2 Rasmussen, Havnen #3102/R est:15000-20000 (D.KR 18000)

£1531 $2480 €2220 Vessels being towed in Sundet (83x102cm-33x40in) s. 26-May-3 Rasmussen, Copenhagen #1355/R est:12000-15000 (D.KR 16000)
£1576 $2522 €2364 Seascape with sailing ship and motor boat (119x79cm-47x31in) s.d.1900. 13-Jan-3 Rasmussen, Vejle #72/R est:20000 (D.KR 18000)
£2573 $4014 €3860 Landing the catch - fishermen and beached boats (75x103cm-30x41in) s. 11-Nov-2 Rasmussen, Vejle #616/R est:30000-40000 (D.KR 30000)
£3166 $5034 €4749 Busy trafic in Copenhagen Harbour (77x106cm-30x42in) s.d.1927. 5-Mar-3 Rasmussen, Copenhagen #1990/R est:30000 (D.KR 34000)
£7321 $11128 €10982 Prawn fishermen in North Sjaelland (75x105cm-30x41in) s.d.1905. 27-Aug-2 Rasmussen, Copenhagen #1470/R est:75000 (D.KR 85000)

Works on paper
£1274 $2000 €1911 Brooklyn Bridge 1927. Lower Manhattan. Horse and cart, 1926 (18x15cm-7x6in) s.d.1926-27 chl set of three. 10-Dec-2 Doyle, New York #223/R est:2000-3000

LUBECK, Gerald Louis (1942-) American
£531 $850 €797 Kitchen items (10x15cm-4x6in) board. 14-Mar-3 Douglas, South Deerfield #6
£594 $950 €891 Landscape with hills and houses (10x15cm-4x6in) board. 14-Mar-3 Douglas, South Deerfield #1
£625 $1000 €938 Landscape with red barn (13x18cm-5x7in) board. 14-Mar-3 Douglas, South Deerfield #8
£1313 $2100 €1970 Natural enemies (28x38cm-11x15in) board. 14-Mar-3 Douglas, South Deerfield #7

LUBIENIECKI, Christofel (1660-1728) Polish
£16463 $27000 €24695 Schoonmaster chastising two boys (58x49cm-23x19in) s.indis d. prov. 29-May-3 Sotheby's, New York #65a/R est:15000-20000

LUBITCH, Ossip (1896-1986) French
£1274 $1987 €2000 Quai du Point du jour (33x41cm-13x16in) s. 6-Nov-2 Claude Boisgirard, Paris #31/R est:1500-1800
£1274 $1987 €2000 Nature morte a l'echarpe bleue (50x61cm-20x24in) s. 6-Nov-2 Claude Boisgirard, Paris #32/R est:2500-3000

Works on paper
£629 $975 €1000 Portrait du musicien Mihalovici (60x45cm-24x18in) s. gouache. 30-Oct-2 Artcurial Briest, Paris #43

LUBOWSKI, Edmund (20th C) ?
£380 $600 €600 Wnetrze II - interior (100x120cm-39x47in) s.d.1976 i. verso. 30-Nov-2 Arnold, Frankfurt #349/R

LUCANDER, Anitra (1918-2000) Finnish
£1197 $1927 €1700 Still life (33x41cm-13x16in) s. 10-May-3 Bukowskis, Helsinki #226/R est:2500-3000
£1799 $2878 €2500 Landscape (48x57cm-19x22in) s. 17-May-3 Hagelstam, Helsinki #185/R est:2500
£2254 $3628 €3200 Winter (58x65cm-23x26in) s. 10-May-3 Bukowskis, Helsinki #242/R est:4000-5000
£2446 $3914 €3400 Still life (38x46cm-15x18in) s. painted c.1960. 17-May-3 Hagelstam, Helsinki #184/R est:1500
£2911 $4600 €4600 Still life of fruit (38x46cm-15x18in) s. 1-Dec-2 Bukowskis, Helsinki #331/R est:5000-6000
£4173 $6676 €5800 Interior (72x91cm-28x36in) s.d.1955. 17-May-3 Hagelstam, Helsinki #183/R est:6000
£5899 $9439 €8200 Laurel tree (108x108cm-43x43in) s. 17-May-3 Hagelstam, Helsinki #182/R est:5000

LUCANO, Pietro (1878-1972) Italian
£248 $402 €350 Villa a Lignano (39x49cm-15x19in) s. board. 22-May-3 Stadion, Trieste #384/R
£321 $497 €500 Church in the grove (51x39cm-20x15in) s. s.i.verso cardboard. 5-Dec-2 Stadion, Trieste #856/R
£461 $747 €650 Giochi in giardino (34x45cm-13x18in) s. faesite. 22-May-3 Stadion, Trieste #396/R
£638 $1034 €900 Giorno di festa (33x43cm-13x17in) s. s.i.verso board. 22-May-3 Stadion, Trieste #400/R

LUCAS Y PADILLA, Eugenio (attrib) (1824-1870) Spanish
£1538 $2415 €2400 Witches (24x32cm-9x13in) bears sig. panel. 16-Dec-2 Raboudin & Choppin de Janvry, Paris #163/R

LUCAS Y VILLAAMIL, Eugenio (1858-1918) Spanish
£1887 $2943 €3000 Woman (30x12cm-12x5in) s. board. 23-Sep-2 Durán, Madrid #131/R
£2903 $4587 €4500 Preparing the party (24x35cm-9x14in) s. board. 17-Dec-2 Durán, Madrid #223/R
£3188 $5133 €4750 Historical scene (43x52cm-17x20in) s. 18-Feb-3 Durán, Madrid #217a/R
£5000 $8350 €7500 La posada (33x60cm-13x24in) s. panel. 18-Jun-3 Christie's, Kensington #173/R est:4000-6000
£5034 $8104 €7500 What wonderful flowers! (36x54cm-14x21in) s. 18-Feb-3 Durán, Madrid #217/R
£6000 $9420 €9000 Drinks in the salon (35x23cm-14x9in) s. panel. 21-Nov-2 Christie's, Kensington #182/R est:6000-8000
£7000 $10990 €10500 Marriage (33x21cm-13x8in) s. panel. 21-Nov-2 Christie's, Kensington #181/R est:7000-10000
£9868 $15987 €15000 Scene from Goya (50x60cm-20x24in) s. 21-Jan-3 Durán, Madrid #162/R est:13000

Works on paper
£881 $1356 €1400 Goya and his figures (23x23cm-9x9in) s. mixed media cardboard. 22-Oct-2 Durán, Madrid #156/R

LUCAS, Albert Durer (1828-1918) British
£380 $597 €570 Scotch heather and deer grass (19x15cm-7x6in) s.i.d.77 board. 16-Apr-3 Christie's, Kensington #884
£446 $700 €669 Summer (20x25cm-8x10in) s.d.1866 i.verso. 22-Nov-2 Skinner, Boston #22/R
£480 $802 €696 Still life of strawberries and currants (25x19cm-10x7in) s.d.1871. 23-Jun-3 Bonhams, Bath #72
£1150 $1817 €1725 Bell heather in a landscape. figures resting beyond a view to Baddesley Church in the distance (26x20cm-10x8in) s.d.1870 board. 7-Apr-3 Bonhams, Bath #118/R est:1200-1800
£1300 $2119 €1885 Still life with heather and feather (25x21cm-10x8in) s.d.1870 board. 16-Jul-3 Sotheby's, Olympia #56/R est:1500-2000
£1800 $3006 €2610 Courtship - practical. Matrimony - practical (25x20cm-10x8in) s. one s.i.d.1869 two. 17-Jun-3 Bonhams, New Bond Street #50/R est:2000-3000
£2017 $3268 €2925 Heather and grasshopper (20x15cm-8x6in) s.d.1893 panel. 26-May-3 Bukowskis, Stockholm #228/R est:12000-15000 (S.KR 26000)
£2948 $4776 €4275 Heather and peacock butterfly (20x15cm-8x6in) s.d.1893 panel. 26-May-3 Bukowskis, Stockholm #229/R est:15000-20000 (S.KR 38000)

Works on paper
£280 $437 €420 Carmody children. s.d.1850 W/C. 10-Sep-2 Sworder & Son, Bishops Stortford #727/R

LUCAS, Albert Pike (1862-1945) American
£1019 $1600 €1529 Twilight (50x61cm-20x24in) s. 22-Nov-2 Skinner, Boston #221/R est:700-900

LUCAS, August Georg Friedrich (1803-1863) German
£5256 $8305 €8200 Feldberg in the Black Forest (28x39cm-11x15in) mono.d.18 AL 56 verso paper. 16-Nov-2 Lempertz, Koln #1530/R est:1000

LUCAS, David (1802-1881) British

Prints
£2000 $3100 €3000 English landscape. mezzotint after John Constable. 5-Dec-2 Sotheby's, London #91/R est:3500-4500
£3200 $4960 €4800 Salisbury Cathedral (18x25cm-7x10in) mezzotint two after John Constable. 5-Dec-2 Sotheby's, London #90/R est:1500-2000

LUCAS, Fred (1946-) American
£1796 $3000 €2604 Running the gauntlet (48x64cm-19x25in) s. 21-Jun-3 Selkirks, St. Louis #183/R est:4000-5000

LUCAS, George (19th C) British
£375 $600 €544 Pool (25x36cm-10x14in) s. 17-May-3 CRN Auctions, Cambridge #56

LUCAS, H F L (c.1848-1943) British
£1100 $1716 €1595 Starlight, i liver chestnut thoroughbred in a stable interior (50x66cm-20x26in) i.d.1885 verso. 28-Mar-3 ELR Auctions, Sheffield #229/R est:700-1000

LUCAS, Henry Frederick Lucas (c.1848-1943) British
£1125 $1800 €1688 Eva (51x66cm-20x26in) s.d. i.verso. 15-Mar-3 Selkirks, St. Louis #83/R est:1500-2000
£1200 $1896 €1800 Mrs R Burns on the Doctor, with Sparklet by her side, near Ranksborough Gorse (35x46cm-14x18in) s. i.verso. 28-Nov-2 Christie's, Kensington #158/R est:1500-2500
£1500 $2370 €2250 Saddle chestnut polo pony in a stable (28x37cm-11x15in) s.d.1900 i.verso. 28-Nov-2 Christie's, Kensington #163/R est:600-800
£1800 $2844 €2700 Charmer, chestnut polo pony in a stable (28x37cm-11x15in) s.i.d.98 i.verso. 28-Nov-2 Christie's, Kensington #161/R est:800-1200

£2200 $3476 €3300 Chestnut hunter in a stable (46x61cm-18x24in) s.d.1886 indis i.verso. 28-Nov-2 Christie's, Kensington #168/R est:1500-2000

LUCAS, John Seymour (1849-1923) British
£260 $406 €390 Soldier with musket looking from castle window (35x29cm-14x11in) s.d.1875. 10-Sep-2 Bonhams, Knightsbridge #12
£450 $702 €675 Interior scene (47x60cm-19x24in) mono.i.d.1883. 10-Sep-2 Bonhams, Knightsbridge #131/R
£506 $800 €759 Love letter (36x28cm-14x11in) s.d.1884. 16-Nov-2 New Orleans Auction, New Orleans #548
£650 $1034 €975 Duet (41x32cm-16x13in) s. 6-Mar-3 Christie's, Kensington #544/R
£650 $1086 €943 Off duty (45x35cm-18x14in) s.d.1887. 23-Jun-3 Bonhams, Bath #198
Works on paper
£4700 $7849 €6815 Tailor (49x39cm-19x15in) s.d.1877 W/C. 17-Jun-3 Anderson & Garland, Newcastle #303/R est:1500-2500

LUCAS, John Seymour (attrib) (1849-1923) British
£550 $858 €825 Theatrical study of a young man in highland dress (56x41cm-22x16in) 10-Apr-3 Tennants, Leyburn #1117/R

LUCAS, John Templeton (1836-1880) British
£650 $1079 €943 Piccolo player (50x40cm-20x16in) s.d.1875. 13-Jun-3 Lyon & Turnbull, Edinburgh #133

LUCAS, Nicus (20th C) ?
£544 $865 €800 Marylin (50x49cm-20x19in) s.d.2000 verso acrylic. 24-Mar-3 Cornette de St.Cyr, Paris #158/R

LUCAS, Sarah (1962-) British
£13125 $21000 €19688 Black and white bunny no.2 (122x91cm-48x36in) black white photograph exexuted 1997 prov. 16-May-3 Phillips, New York #126/R est:15000-20000
Photographs
£9494 $15000 €14241 Law (122x91cm-48x36in) col coupler print executed 2000 prov. 14-Nov-2 Christie's, Rockefeller NY #481/R est:15000-20000
£14000 $22960 €21000 Supersensible (122x180cm-48x71in) gelatin silver print num.five of six prov.lit. 6-Feb-3 Christie's, London #731/R est:8000-12000
Sculpture
£1830 $2946 €2800 Untitled (18x16cm-7x6in) s.d.1999 crashed boxes. 20-Jan-3 Cornette de St.Cyr, Paris #358
£4800 $8016 €6960 Self portrait mobile (110cm-43in) s.d.1993 verso cut out col photos thread wire prov. 26-Jun-3 Sotheby's, London #102/R est:4000-6000
Works on paper
£3000 $5010 €4350 Untitled (22x17cm-9x7in) pencil five envelope prov.lit. 26-Jun-3 Sotheby's, London #101/R est:3000-4000

LUCAS, W (19/20th C) ?
£503 $800 €755 Parthia (51x61cm-20x24in) s.d.1960. 1-Mar-3 Susanin's, Chicago #5050

LUCAS, Wilhelm (1884-1918) German
£1346 $2127 €2100 Village cemetery (80x120cm-31x47in) s.d.05. 16-Nov-2 Lempertz, Koln #1529/R est:3000
£6090 $9439 €9500 Marien square in Munich with view of old town hall and figures (105x81cm-41x32in) i. 4-Dec-2 Neumeister, Munich #811/R est:2500

LUCAS-ROBIQUET, Marie Aimee (1858-1959) French
£4038 $6260 €6300 Fillette assise dans un champ (51x63cm-20x25in) 8-Dec-2 Teitgen, Nancy #92/R
£34810 $55000 €52215 Young girl with wildflowers (53x64cm-21x25in) s. 24-Apr-3 Sotheby's, New York #8/R est:25000-35000
£35507 $58232 €49000 Tahadat et Khadidja (102x77cm-40x30in) s. painted c.1914. 27-May-3 Artcurial Briest, Paris #106/R est:60000-70000

LUCASSEN, Reinier (1939-) Dutch
£3526 $5465 €5500 Still life with melon and knife (28x35cm-11x14in) s.d.76 verso exhib. 3-Dec-2 Christie's, Amsterdam #334/R est:3000-5000
£3526 $5465 €5500 Croba (40x30cm-16x12in) init.i.d.80. 3-Dec-2 Christie's, Amsterdam #348/R est:3000-5000
£6410 $9936 €10000 Water (180x120cm-71x47in) s.d.67 acrylic two objects painted with Jan Dibbets Ger van Elk. 3-Dec-2 Christie's, Amsterdam #342/R est:12000-16000
£8974 $13910 €14000 Landschap - landscape (160x160cm-63x63in) s.d.67 verso acrylic on two joint canvases exhib. 3-Dec-2 Christie's, Amsterdam #339/R est:20000-30000
£8974 $13910 €14000 Bruidspaar - bridal couple (140x100cm-55x39in) s.d.65 s.d.verso prov. 3-Dec-2 Christie's, Amsterdam #346/R est:15000-20000
£16026 $24840 €25000 De hoed - the head (160x80cm-63x31in) s.d.67 verso. 3-Dec-2 Christie's, Amsterdam #343/R est:20000-30000
£22436 $34776 €35000 Interieur met gezicht naar buiten (140x130cm-55x51in) s.d.70-71 s.i.d.on stretcher prov.exhib.lit. 3-Dec-2 Christie's, Amsterdam #336/R est:20000-30000
Works on paper
£321 $497 €500 Het baasji (16x15cm-6x6in) init.i.d.76 pencil. 3-Dec-2 Christie's, Amsterdam #345/R
£353 $546 €550 Onmacht symmetries (40x33cm-16x13in) s.i.d.982 brush pen ink. 3-Dec-2 Christie's, Amsterdam #145/R
£719 $1180 €1000 Espana? (29x21cm-11x8in) init.d.983 pencil wax crayons ink. 3-Jun-3 Christie's, Amsterdam #140/R est:1000-1500

LUCATELLO, Albino (1927-1984) Italian
£538 $839 €850 Land at night (66x95cm-26x37in) s.d.verso. 19-Oct-2 Semenzato, Venice #44/R

LUCCHESI, Bruno (1926-) American
Sculpture
£1220 $2000 €1769 Nursing mother (74x61x119cm-29x24x47in) vaselite epoxy prov. 1-Jun-3 Wright, Chicago #258/R est:4000-5000

LUCCHINI, Cesare (1941-) Swiss
£1747 $2742 €2621 Composition (180x100cm-71x39in) s.d.1989 prov. 25-Nov-2 Germann, Zurich #120/R est:3500-4500 (S.FR 4000)

LUCE, Frederic (1896-1974) French
£366 $600 €549 Afternoon on the Seine (38x56cm-15x22in) s. 5-Feb-3 Doyle, New York #46/R
£3871 $6116 €6000 Voilier sur la greve (38x46cm-15x18in) s. panel. 17-Dec-2 Gioffredo, Nice #5/R

LUCE, Maximilien (1858-1941) French
£811 $1265 €1200 Trois etudes de mains, deux tenant des cartes (16x22cm-6x9in) s. cardboard. 26-Mar-3 Piasa, Paris #126
£818 $1267 €1300 Moulineux, enfant (16x23cm-6x9in) s. bears sig.i.verso cardboard lit. 30-Oct-2 Artcurial Briest, Paris #192
£850 $1368 €1300 Le modele a moustache (40x32cm-16x13in) s. 19-Jan-3 Feletin, Province #88
£1090 $1711 €1700 Riviere sous bois (24x16cm-9x6in) s. panel. 11-Dec-2 Maigret, Paris #116 est:2300-2500
£1108 $1750 €1750 Marine (18x25cm-7x10in) s. cardboard. 27-Nov-2 Lemoine & Ferrando, Paris #101/R est:3000-3500
£1195 $1852 €1900 Baignade au Lac des Settons (30x21cm-12x8in) s. cardboard lit. 30-Oct-2 Artcurial Briest, Paris #191 est:1500-2000
£1401 $2186 €2200 Environs de Rolleboise (19x39cm-7x15in) s. s.i.d.1926 verso panel. 7-Nov-2 Chochon-Barre & Allardi, Paris #188
£1414 $2361 €2050 La baignade (33x50cm-13x20in) s. paper on canvas. 9-Jul-3 Cornette de St.Cyr, Paris #178/R est:3000-4000
£1795 $2782 €2800 Pecheurs sur le port d'Honfleur (25x28cm-10x11in) s. panel. 4-Dec-2 Pierre Berge, Paris #145/R
£1950 $3022 €3100 Le retour de l'enfant prodigue (54x72cm-21x28in) s. 4-Oct-2 Tajan, Paris #156 est:1800-2000
£2115 $3215 €3300 Voiliers au large d'Honfleur (16x27cm-6x11in) studio st. panel prov.lit. 16-Aug-2 Deauville, France #119/R
£2158 $3453 €3000 Les plongeurs (31x24cm-12x9in) s. paper on canvas. 18-May-3 Eric Pillon, Calais #127/R
£2174 $3565 €3000 La plage du Treport (16x23cm-6x9in) s.i. board. 29-May-3 Lempertz, Koln #761/R est:3000-3500
£2244 $3410 €3500 Baignade a Rolleboise (22x28cm-9x11in) s. s.verso panel prov.lit. 16-Aug-2 Deauville, France #120/R
£2405 $3800 €3800 Rolleboise (21x38cm-8x15in) s. lit. 27-Nov-2 Blanchet, Paris #40/R
£2420 $3776 €3800 Voiliers a la sortie du port (19x31cm-7x12in) s. 10-Nov-2 Eric Pillon, Calais #49/R
£2447 $4087 €3500 Promeneurs au bord du lac (25x32cm-10x13in) s. paper on canvas prov. 30-Jun-3 Pierre Berge, Paris #48/R est:2000-3000
£2593 $3681 €4200 Bateaux sur la greve (18x28cm-7x11in) s. panel. 16-Mar-3 Eric Pillon, Calais #131/R
£2619 $4164 €3850 Les vagues au large de parame (34x46cm-13x18in) st.sig. paper lit. 26-Feb-3 Artcurial Briest, Paris #257/R est:3000-4000
£2703 $4216 €4000 Regates a Triel (22x34cm-9x13in) s. panel painted c.1925. 30-Mar-3 Anaf, Lyon #186/R
£2821 $4456 €4400 Rolleboise, le repas sur les berges (40x52cm-16x20in) st.sig. paper on canvas lit. 14-Nov-2 Credit Municipal, Paris #57/R
£2866 $4471 €4500 Rolleboise, femme dans la cour (26x35cm-10x14in) s. panel. 10-Nov-2 Eric Pillon, Calais #31/R
£3067 $5000 €4601 Vue du milieu de la cote de Rolleboise (33x45cm-13x18in) st.sig. oil paper on board. 12-Feb-3 Sotheby's, New York #20/R est:7000-9000
£3145 $5000 €4718 Mers-les-Bains, plage (31x39cm-12x15in) s. paper painted 1920 prov.lit. 27-Feb-3 Christie's, Rockefeller NY #116/R est:7000
£3291 $5200 €5200 Bord de riviere (20x35cm-8x14in) panel. 2-Dec-2 Tajan, Paris #64
£3312 $5167 €5200 Baignade (28x38cm-11x15in) st.sig. panel. 10-Nov-2 Eric Pillon, Calais #19/R

£3473 $5521 €5000 Honfleur, barques de peche et voiliers sortant du port (12x51cm-5x20in) s. cardboard lit. 29-Apr-3 Artcurial Briest, Paris #162/R est:3000-4000
£3500 $5390 €5250 Deux enfants sur la plage (18x26cm-7x10in) s. board. 23-Oct-2 Sotheby's, Olympia #650/R est:4000-6000
£3648 $5654 €5800 Environ d'Arcyt, le chemin (33x46cm-13x18in) s.d.1905 paper on cardboard lit. 30-Oct-2 Artcurial Briest, Paris #321/R est:10000-12000
£3718 $5763 €5800 Portrait de Louis Givort (42x36cm-17x14in) st.sig. panel painted c.1905 lit. 4-Dec-2 Pierre Berge, Paris #144/R
£3718 $5763 €5800 Remorqueur et peniche a Rolleboise (41x54cm-16x21in) st.sig. paper on canvas. 6-Dec-2 Rieunier, Bailly-Pommery, Mathias, Paris #98/R
£3800 $5890 €5700 Rolleboise, bouquet d'arbres au bord de l'eau (21x27cm-8x11in) s. board. 5-Dec-2 Christie's, Kensington #53/R est:1500-2000
£3899 $6005 €6200 Baigneurs pres de grand arbre (73x54cm-29x21in) s. 27-Oct-2 Muizon & Le Coent, Paris #48/R
£3947 $6394 €6000 Projet d'affiche pour Mevisto a la Scala, la folie de Pierrot (51x25cm-20x10in) paper on canvas prov.lit. 22-Jan-3 Tajan, Paris #49/R est:3000-3500
£4167 $6875 €6000 Maison a flanc de coteau (20x28cm-8x11in) s.d.1905 cardboard. 2-Jul-3 Artcurial Briest, Paris #638/R est:7000-9000
£4231 $6642 €6600 Ouvriers (31x26cm-12x10in) s. cardboard lit. 11-Dec-2 Artcurial Briest, Paris #525/R
£4516 $7000 €6774 Vue de Treport (20x25cm-8x10in) s. paper painted c.1910 prov. 8-Dec-2 Toomey, Oak Park #755/R est:10000-12000
£4865 $7589 €7200 Pecheurs et voilier (30x38cm-12x15in) s. prov. 25-Mar-3 Chochon-Barre & Allardi, Paris #161/R est:6500-7000
£5000 $7700 €7500 Rolleboise, le jardin (28x38cm-11x15in) st.sig. prov. 22-Oct-2 Sotheby's, London #207/R est:5000-7000
£5430 $9068 €7874 Les peniches a Rolleboise (27x40cm-11x16in) s. prov. 24-Jun-3 Koller, Zurich #107/R est:18000-30000 (S.FR 12000)
£5521 $9000 €8282 Environs d'arcy, le chemin (33x46cm-13x18in) s.d.1905 oil paper on board. 12-Feb-3 Sotheby's, New York #12/R est:12000-18000
£5521 $9000 €8282 La rouche-guyon, bord de riviere construction du pont (38x61cm-15x24in) s. prov.lit. 12-Feb-3 Sotheby's, New York #27/R est:8000-12000
£5696 $9000 €9000 Paysage d'Ile de France (38x55cm-15x22in) s. painted c.1905 lit. 27-Nov-2 Lemoine & Ferrando, Paris #102/R est:12000-15000
£6452 $10000 €9678 Echafaudages et affiches (80x60cm-31x24in) s. painted c.1912. 26-Sep-2 Christie's, Rockefeller NY #529/R est:12000-16000
£6500 $10010 €9750 Le vert galant (50x65cm-20x26in) s. s.i.d.1926 stretcher prov.exhib.lit. 23-Oct-2 Sotheby's, Olympia #624/R est:7000-9000
£6755 $11011 €10200 Bord de mer (25x40cm-10x16in) s. cardboard on panel. 2-Feb-3 Muizon & Le Coent, Paris #42
£6790 $9642 €11000 Dans le Jardin du Luxembourg (31x40cm-12x16in) s. paper on panel lit. 16-Mar-3 Eric Pillon, Calais #116/R
£8387 $13251 €13000 Pont des Arts a Paris (38x46cm-15x18in) st.sig. prov. 18-Dec-2 Tajan, Paris #33/R est:8000-10000
£9000 $14670 €13500 Paris, ouvriers et travailleurs sur les quais de la Seine (60x73cm-24x29in) s. board lit. 3-Feb-3 Bonhams, New Bond Street #12/R est:10000-15000
£9434 $14623 €15000 Rolleboise (54x65cm-21x26in) s. lit. 30-Oct-2 Artcurial Briest, Paris #186/R est:12000-16000
£9938 $16000 €14907 Vase de fleurs (64x50cm-25x20in) s.d.1907. 7-May-3 Sotheby's, New York #403/R est:15000-20000
£10759 $16677 €17000 Les quais de la Seine (27x37cm-11x15in) s. paper on canvas painted c.1900 prov.lit. 28-Sep-2 Christie's, Paris #5/R est:9000-12000
£10802 $15340 €17500 Village francais (26x40cm-10x16in) s.d.1903 canvas on cardboard. 17-Mar-2 Galerie de Chartres, Chartres #146
£11152 $17621 €16728 Les Debardeurs (100x80cm-39x31in) s.d.1909 prov.lit. 1-Apr-3 Rasmussen, Copenhagen #53/R est:75000-100000 (D.KR 120000)
£12000 $19680 €18000 Saint-Tropez (52x67cm-20x26in) s. board painted c.1900 prov.exhib.lit. 4-Feb-3 Christie's, London #220/R
£13000 $21710 €18850 Promenade en bateau (51x66cm-20x26in) s. paper on canvas prov. 24-Jun-3 Sotheby's, London #137/R est:15000-20000
£16149 $26000 €24224 Accolay, la cure (51x61cm-20x24in) s.d.1905 lit. 8-May-3 Christie's, Rockefeller NY #156/R est:30000-40000
£16352 $26000 €24528 Nature morte avec deux vases de fleurs (45x35cm-18x14in) s. board on masonite. 27-Feb-3 Christie's, Rockefeller NY #95/R est:20000
£20833 $32500 €31250 Rolleboise, un dimanche au bord de l'eau (89x130cm-35x51in) s.d.1922 prov.lit. 6-Nov-2 Sotheby's, New York #186/R est:30000-40000
£24038 $37500 €36057 Orleans, vue du pont Georges V et de la Cathedrale Saint Croix (38x46cm-15x18in) s.d.1905 prov. 6-Nov-2 Sotheby's, New York #144/R est:35000-40000
£28846 $45000 €43269 Rolleboise, le restaurant Cyrano (60x81cm-24x32in) s. painted 1939 prov. 6-Nov-2 Sotheby's, New York #187/R est:15000-20000
£32051 $50000 €48077 Catherdrale Sainte Croix, rue de la place de la bascule a Orleans (46x38cm-18x15in) s.d.1905 prov.exhib. 6-Nov-2 Sotheby's, New York #166/R est:30000-40000
£33654 $52500 €50481 Les meules, plaine d'essoyes (46x55cm-18x22in) s.d.97 i.verso. 6-Nov-2 Sotheby's, New York #165/R est:35000-45000
£44872 $70000 €67308 Les bords de la cure (51x68cm-20x27in) s. board painted c.1906-08. 6-Nov-2 Sotheby's, New York #162/R est:50000-70000
£65000 $106600 €97500 Rue Reaumur (65x50cm-26x20in) s.d.96 prov.lit. 4-Feb-3 Christie's, London #231/R est:70000
£65000 $108550 €94250 Four d'usines a Couillet (60x73cm-24x29in) s.d.1903 lit. 25-Jun-3 Christie's, London #141/R est:45000-55000
£90000 $147600 €135000 La Sambre, Marchiennes (54x73cm-21x29in) s.d.99 prov.exhib.lit. 4-Feb-3 Christie's, London #240/R est:70000
£156028 $252766 €220000 La sainte chapelle et le Quai des Orfevres (73x60cm-29x24in) st.sig. painted c.1900 prov. 21-May-3 Cornette de St.Cyr, Paris #34/R est:180000-220000
£210000 $344400 €315000 Pont de l'Archeveche (59x70cm-23x28in) s.d.96 prov. 4-Feb-3 Sotheby's, London #15/R est:350000
£250000 $390000 €375000 Le quai cinti, le jour (46x55cm-18x22in) s.d.96 prov. 6-Nov-2 Sotheby's, New York #147/R est:250000-350000
£340000 $557600 €510000 Bords de Seine a Herblay, coucher de soleil (50x65cm-20x26in) s. painted c.1889 prov.exhib.lit. 5-Feb-3 Sotheby's, London #125/R est:180000
£352564 $550000 €528846 Notre Dame (86x81cm-34x32in) s.d.1900-01 prov.exhib.lit. 5-Nov-2 Sotheby's, New York #3/R est:400000-600000

Works on paper

£276 $436 €400 Dejeuner de l'enfant (27x20cm-11x8in) s. chl dr. 4-Apr-3 Tajan, Paris #159
£276 $441 €400 Rue dans un village (26x21cm-10x8in) s. chl. 12-Mar-3 Libert, Castor, Paris #138
£278 $439 €400 Berger et son troupeau (9x13cm-4x5in) s. pen dr. 25-Apr-3 Piasa, Paris #136/R
£296 $480 €450 Usine a Charleroi (11x18cm-4x7in) s. pencil dr. 22-Jan-3 Tajan, Paris #52/R
£338 $561 €480 Homme assis (31x18cm-12x7in) s. black crayon dr. 11-Jun-3 Beaussant & Lefèvre, Paris #88
£382 $596 €600 La Seine a Rolleboise (11x16cm-4x6in) s. Chinese ink. 7-Nov-2 Chochon-Barre & Allardi, Paris #187
£420 $701 €600 Baignade a Rolleboise (15x25cm-6x10in) s. ink dr. 26-Jun-3 Tajan, Paris #68/R
£424 $669 €610 Ermenonville (12x17cm-5x7in) s.i. chl wash dr. 25-Apr-3 Piasa, Paris #137/R
£428 $693 €650 Remorqueur (14x20cm-6x8in) s.i. pencil dr. 22-Jan-3 Tajan, Paris #51
£475 $736 €750 Paris, les quais de Seine (19x27cm-7x11in) s. chl dr. 29-Sep-2 Eric Pillon, Calais #159/R
£481 $750 €722 Woman at an easel (22x102cm-9x40in) s. pencil. 19-Sep-2 Swann Galleries, New York #539/R
£764 $1215 €1100 Jeune paysanne (30x23cm-12x9in) st.sig. chl dr. 29-Apr-3 Artcurial Briest, Paris #7
£833 $1308 €1300 Paysage (23x33cm-9x13in) s.d.1908 pastel pencil. 11-Dec-2 Maigret, Paris #146
£1000 $1580 €1500 Workers (25x21cm-10x8in) s. pencil pair. 3-Apr-3 Christie's, Kensington #14/R
£1108 $1717 €1750 Paris, scene animee devant le grand magasin (23x28cm-9x11in) s. W/C. 29-Sep-2 Eric Pillon, Calais #158/R
£1277 $2068 €1800 Paysage (28x32cm-11x13in) st.sig. paper on canvas prov. 21-May-3 Cornette de St.Cyr, Paris #29/R est:2000-2500
£1290 $2039 €2000 POrt de Dieppe (31x47cm-12x19in) s.i.d.1922 ink chl wash. 18-Dec-2 Ferri, Paris #90/R
£1800 $2772 €2700 Camaret, flotille de peche (23x30cm-9x12in) s. chl pastel prov.lit. 23-Oct-2 Sotheby's, Olympia #603/R est:2000-3000
£1852 $2630 €3000 Vallon (22x32cm-9x13in) s.d.1908 pastel. 16-Mar-3 Eric Pillon, Calais #128/R
£1986 $3217 €2800 Les barques (27x38cm-11x15in) s. paper on canvas. 21-May-3 Cornette de St.Cyr, Paris #30/R est:3000-4000
£3191 $5170 €4500 Maison au bord de la riviere (46x38cm-18x15in) s. 21-May-3 Cornette de St.Cyr, Paris #28/R est:4500-5000
£3289 $5329 €5000 Le bras du fleuve (26x36cm-10x14in) s. pastel. 22-Jan-3 Tajan, Paris #58 est:4000
£12000 $19680 €18000 Nu penche (33x40cm-13x16in) s.d.89 pastel prov.lit. 6-Feb-3 Christie's, London #418/R est:12000

LUCEBERT (1924-1994) Dutch

£823 $1300 €1300 Untitled (49x64cm-19x25in) s.d.78 VII 29 oil gouache col crayon. 26-Nov-2 Sotheby's, Amsterdam #39/R est:800-1200
£1295 $2124 €1800 Het vismaal (48x67cm-19x26in) s.d.79.XI.27 acrylic board prov. 3-Jun-3 Christie's, Amsterdam #128/R est:2000-3000
£1439 $2360 €2000 Dwarf (69x48cm-27x19in) s.d.79.XII.22 acrylic W/C. 3-Jun-3 Christie's, Amsterdam #121/R est:1500-2000
£1646 $2600 €2600 Knox and Helen (40x80cm-16x31in) s.d.81. 1-Dec-2 Bukowskis, Helsinki #387/R est:2500-3000
£1736 $2760 €2500 Personnages abstraites (76x94cm-30x37in) s.d.1986 paper. 29-Apr-3 Campo & Campo, Antwerp #196/R est:3000-3500
£2158 $3540 €3000 Girl (69x99cm-27x39in) s.i.d.72 oil on paper prov. 3-Jun-3 Christie's, Amsterdam #130/R est:3500-4500
£3205 $4968 €5000 Magisch dubbelportret (89x129cm-35x51in) s.d.79 s.verso acrylic. 3-Dec-2 Christie's, Amsterdam #265/R est:5000-7000
£5449 $8446 €8500 Coloquio bajo el cipres (49x79cm-19x31in) s.d.74 prov. 3-Dec-2 Christie's, Amsterdam #263/R est:5000-7000
£5449 $8446 €8500 Rythm-a-ring (101x121cm-40x48in) s.d.86 s.i.d. 3-Dec-2 Christie's, Amsterdam #266/R est:8000-12000

£8974 $13910 €14000 Jongen - boy (100x80cm-39x31in) s.d.64 i.verso prov. 3-Dec-2 Christie's, Amsterdam #275/R est:10000-15000

£10256 $15897 €16000 Madman (130x100cm-51x39in) s.d.66 s.i.d.verso prov. 3-Dec-2 Christie's, Amsterdam #271/R est:13000-16000

£22436 $34776 €35000 De vreugde Van Janus (200x150cm-79x59in) s. d.63/17 prov.exhib. 3-Dec-2 Christie's, Amsterdam #272/R est:35000-55000

Works on paper

£274 $430 €400 Composition. s. mixed media. 15-Apr-3 Galerie Moderne, Brussels #142

£278 $458 €400 Head (26x28cm-10x11in) s.d.81.I.14 brush black ink. 1-Jul-3 Christie's, Amsterdam #422

£282 $437 €440 Composition (26x21cm-10x8in) s.d.25 Indian ink dr exec.1975. 7-Dec-2 De Vuyst, Lokeren #202

£313 $516 €450 Untitled (27x21cm-11x8in) s.d.81.XII.6 brush black ink W/C black chk. 1-Jul-3 Christie's, Amsterdam #423

£362 $586 €550 Study of a woman (27x27cm-11x11in) pencil executed c.1949 prov. 21-Jan-3 Christie's, Amsterdam #451

£379 $587 €569 Figure composition (32x24cm-13x9in) s.d.23.IX.88 Indian ink. 4-Dec-2 Kunsthallen, Copenhagen #64a (D.KR 4400)

£462 $725 €720 Two figures (26x20cm-10x8in) s.d.63 Indian ink. 25-Nov-2 Glerum, Amsterdam #338/R

£513 $805 €800 Untitled (31x22cm-12x9in) s.d.1988 ink W/C col crayon. 15-Dec-2 Perrin, Versailles #7/R

£576 $944 €800 Untitled (23x34cm-9x13in) s.i.d.72 pen ink. 3-Jun-3 Christie's, Amsterdam #123/R

£1013 $1580 €1600 Composition (33x23cm-13x9in) s.d.77 mixed media. 21-Oct-2 Bernaerts, Antwerp #644/R est:1000-1250

£1026 $1590 €1600 Kruisdrager (26x20cm-10x8in) s.i.d. brush ink prov. 3-Dec-2 Christie's, Amsterdam #124/R est:1500-2000

£1151 $1842 €1600 Composition (42x56cm-17x22in) s.d.74 W/C Indian ink. 17-May-3 De Vuyst, Lokeren #245/R est:1500-2000

£1295 $2124 €1800 Hij bekijkt de bloemen (21x32cm-8x13in) s.d.51 pen red ink prov.exhib. 3-Jun-3 Christie's, Amsterdam #116/R est:1800-2200

£1783 $2782 €2800 Reclining nude (19x29cm-7x11in) s.d.45 pastel. 6-Nov-2 Vendue Huis, Gravenhage #155/R est:1500-2000

£2014 $3304 €2800 Animal (48x73cm-19x29in) s.i.d.61 chl crayons gouache W/C. 3-Jun-3 Christie's, Amsterdam #122/R est:2200-3200

£2244 $3478 €3500 Untitled (69x51cm-27x20in) s. gouache. 3-Dec-2 Christie's, Amsterdam #114/R est:3500-4500

£2405 $3800 €3800 Het grote examen (78x52cm-31x20in) indis i. gouache prov. 26-Nov-2 Sotheby's, Amsterdam #42/R est:3000-4000

£3526 $5465 €5500 Untitled (41x24cm-16x9in) s.d.48 pen ink gouache. 3-Dec-2 Christie's, Amsterdam #125/R est:4000-6000

LUCIANI, Ascanio (attrib) (1621-1706) Italian

£8000 $12560 €12000 Capriccio of Roman ruins with herder and other figures (50x63cm-20x25in) pair. 13-Dec-2 Christie's, Kensington #259/R est:12000-18000

LUCIONI, Luigi (1900-1988) American

£1187 $1900 €1721 Lake Champlain (24x32cm-9x13in) s.d.1935 board. 16-May-3 Skinner, Boston #222/R est:3000-5000

£2201 $3500 €3302 Vermont classic (61x51cm-24x20in) s.d.27 panel exhib. 1-Mar-3 North East Auctions, Portsmouth #735/R est:1500-2500

£4717 $7500 €7076 Spring thaw, Vermont (61x41cm-24x16in) s.d.28 board prov. 7-Mar-3 Skinner, Boston #428/R est:8000-12000

£18519 $30000 €27779 Design for color (51x69cm-20x27in) s.d.1944 prov.exhib.lit. 21-May-3 Sotheby's, New York #110/R est:20000-30000

£24691 $40000 €37037 Still life by the window sill (46x41cm-18x16in) s.d.1933 prov.exhib. 21-May-3 Sotheby's, New York #109/R est:20000-30000

LUCKEROTH, Jupp (1919-1993) German

£513 $795 €800 10-9-73 (90x49cm-35x19in) s.i.verso sand painted 1973. 7-Dec-2 Van Ham, Cologne #306/R

LUCKHARDT, Karl (1886-1970) German

£414 $638 €650 Resting on village outskirts (21x40cm-8x16in) s. panel. 5-Sep-2 Arnold, Frankfurt #808/R

£759 $1206 €1100 Sommershausen blacksmiths (40x60cm-16x24in) s. i. verso. 8-Mar-3 Arnold, Frankfurt #636/R

£966 $1535 €1400 Horse drawn cart before old bridge in Frankfurt am Main (109x177cm-43x70in) s. 8-Mar-3 Arnold, Frankfurt #635/R

Works on paper

£353 $557 €550 Budingen gateway (29x41cm-11x16in) s. W/C chk. 15-Nov-2 Reiss & Sohn, Konigstein #323/R

LUCKNER, Heinrich Alexander Graf von (1891-1970) German

£3169 $5261 €4500 In the dunes (96x80cm-38x31in) s.d. 14-Jun-3 Hauswedell & Nolte, Hamburg #1359/R est:4000

Works on paper

£380 $631 €540 Portrait of woman (62x45cm-24x18in) mono. gouache. 14-Jun-3 Hauswedell & Nolte, Hamburg #1360/R

LUCOP, Thomas (19th C) British?

£1200 $1824 €1800 Fishing fleet by moonlight (50x66cm-20x26in) s. 15-Aug-2 Bonhams, New Bond Street #312/R est:1000-1500

LUDBY, Max (1858-1943) British

Works on paper

£380 $619 €551 Gleaners (52x39cm-20x15in) s.d.1901 W/C. 16-Jul-3 Sotheby's, Olympia #107/R

£415 $690 €602 Old town hall, High Street, Guilford (56x38cm-22x15in) s. W/C prov. 16-Jun-3 Waddingtons, Toronto #88/R est:1000-1500 (C.D 935)

LUDDECKE, H (20th C) German?

£1026 $1497 €1600 Doll (150x150cm-59x59in) mono.d.82 acrylic pavatex. 4-Jun-2 Karl & Faber, Munich #338/R

£1538 $2246 €2400 Summer (150x150cm-59x59in) mono.d.86 acrylic pavatex. 4-Jun-2 Karl & Faber, Munich #339/R est:2000

LUDEKENS, Fred (1900-1982) American

Works on paper

£1013 $1600 €1520 Cape buffalo (32x43cm-13x17in) s. W/C gouache on board prov. 3-Apr-3 Christie's, Rockefeller NY #181/R est:1000-1500

LUDERS, Hermann (1836-1908) German

£261 $429 €400 Coffee house in Istanbul (30x43cm-12x17in) s.i.d.1902 tempera. 29-Mar-3 Dannenberg, Berlin #613/R

LUDLOW, Henry Stephen (1861-?) British

Works on paper

£260 $421 €390 Experienced hand (32x25cm-13x10in) s.d.1912 W/C. 21-May-3 Bonhams, Knightsbridge #137

£6200 $9858 €9300 Study of a young lady golfer playing a tee shot (58x41cm-23x16in) W/C. 18-Mar-3 Lawrences, Bletchingley #1196 est:3000-5000

LUDLOW, R Fulton (20th C) American

£375 $600 €563 Brooklyn Bridge (51x76cm-20x30in) s. 12-Jan-3 William Jenack, New York #386

LUDOVICI, A (jnr) (1852-1932) British

Works on paper

£380 $578 €570 Hyde Park's Rotton Row (28x36cm-11x14in) init. W/C. 14-Aug-2 Andrew Hartley, Ilkley #590

LUDOVICI, Albert (1820-1894) British

Works on paper

£1100 $1716 €1650 Crowd on the harbour (24x34cm-9x13in) s. W/C. 17-Sep-2 Sotheby's, Olympia #135/R est:800-1200

LUDOVICI, Albert (attrib) (1820-1894) British

£450 $734 €653 Bride (31x26cm-12x10in) mono. 17-Jul-3 Tennants, Leyburn #924

LUDOVICI, Albert (jnr) (1852-1932) British

£1400 $2212 €2100 Knitting (20x15cm-8x6in) s. panel. 7-Apr-3 Bonhams, Bath #128/R est:800-1200

£2500 $4075 €3625 Bad loser (76x102cm-30x40in) s.d.1876. 16-Jul-3 Sotheby's, Olympia #81/R est:2500-3500

£3000 $4680 €4500 Return from the hunt (26x30cm-10x12in) s. panel. 6-Nov-2 Sotheby's, Olympia #81/R est:1000-2000

£3800 $5890 €5700 In the park (45x61cm-18x24in) s. 3-Dec-2 Sotheby's, Olympia #196/R est:2000-3000

LUDUENA, Jorge (1927-) Argentinian

£336 $540 €500 Still life (30x29cm-12x11in) s.d.70. 18-Feb-3 Durán, Madrid #98/R

£629 $981 €1000 Still life of fruit and vase (40x60cm-16x24in) s.d.71 board. 8-Oct-2 Ansorena, Madrid #623/R

LUDWIG, Ernst (?) German

£270 $422 €400 Monks drinking (68x98cm-27x39in) s. 25-Mar-3 Durán, Madrid #1295/R

LUDWIG, Heinrich (1829-1897) German

Works on paper

£365 $565 €548 Romantic landscape (40x49cm-16x19in) s. wash pen. 3-Oct-2 Koller, Zurich #3065/R (S.FR 850)

LUDWIG, Louis (20th C) Belgian?

£753 $1175 €1100 Meadow landscape with cows and farmstead (52x76cm-20x30in) s. 10-Apr-3 Van Ham, Cologne #1581

LUEDERS, Jimmy (1927-1994) American
£353 $550 €530 Thinking no thing (99x152cm-39x60in) s. exhib. 20-Sep-2 Freeman, Philadelphia #95/R
£659 $1100 €956 Flowers study 1 (102cm76cm-40x30in) s. exhib. 22-Jun-3 Freeman, Philadelphia #165/R est:1000-1500
£1935 $3000 €2903 Landscape (168x163cm-66x64in) s.i. prov. 8-Dec-2 Freeman, Philadelphia #188/R est:3000-5000
£2581 $4000 €3872 Zinias on a pink tablecloth (152x152cm-60x60in) s.i. s.stetcher. 8-Dec-2 Freeman, Philadelphia #189/R est:3000-5000

LUEGER, Michael (1804-1883) German
£753 $1175 €1100 Starnberg Lake with farm, figures and cows (28x40cm-11x16in) mono. panel lit. 10-Apr-3 Allgauer, Kempten #2880/R

LUGAR, R (18/19th C) British?
Works on paper
£360 $562 €540 Gosfield Hall, Essex (27x44cm-11x17in) s.d.1809 W/C prov. 18-Sep-2 Cheffins Grain & Comins, Cambridge #490

LUGARDON, Albert (1827-1909) French
£563 $924 €816 Cow in barn (31x42cm-12x17in) canvas on panel. 4-Jun-3 Fischer, Luzern #2228/R (S.FR 1200)
£957 $1483 €1436 La Ruinette vue de Chanrion Valais (38x55cm-15x22in) s. i.verso cardboard exhib. 7-Dec-2 Galerie du Rhone, Sion #331/R est:2000-3000 (S.FR 2200)
£1057 $1544 €1586 Black horse and dog (46x58cm-18x23in) s. board. 17-Jun-2 Philippe Schuler, Zurich #4282/R (S.FR 2400)
£1389 $2236 €2014 Cattle grazing in the evening (60x86cm-24x34in) s.d.1872. 9-May-3 Dobiaschofsky, Bern #13/R est:4000 (S.FR 3000)
£3478 $5391 €5217 Troupeau au bord d'un lac de montagne (56x81cm-22x32in) s.d.1880 prov. 7-Dec-2 Galerie du Rhone, Sion #456/R est:4000-6000 (S.FR 8000)

LUGARDON, Jean-Leonard (1801-1884) Swiss
£1478 $2291 €2217 Repos des chevriers (38x50cm-15x20in) s. prov. 7-Dec-2 Galerie du Rhone, Sion #455/R est:3000-4000 (S.FR 3400)

LUGER, Alfons (1869-1945) Austrian
£1772 $2765 €2800 Rappenlochschlucht, Dornbirn (64x50cm-25x20in) s.d.1923. 15-Oct-2 Dorotheum, Vienna #52/R est:2600-3600
£2152 $3357 €3400 Staufenspitze, Dornbirn, Oberdof (64x50cm-25x20in) s.d.1923. 15-Oct-2 Dorotheum, Vienna #51/R est:2600-3600

LUGERTH, Ferdinand (fl.1885-1915) ?
Sculpture
£1006 $1570 €1600 Deer (60cm-24in) i. bronze. 23-Sep-2 Dr Fritz Nagel, Stuttgart #8052/R est:800

LUGO, Emil (1840-1902) German
£704 $1134 €1000 Procession of children (44x59cm-17x23in) board. 10-May-3 Berlinghof, Heidelberg #271
£779 $1161 €1200 Country idyll with figures (56x89cm-22x35in) s.d.1894. 26-Jun-2 Neumeister, Munich #794/R
£1258 $1962 €2000 Peasant woman resting in landscape (21x33cm-8x13in) s.d.1860. 11-Oct-2 Winterberg, Heidelberg #638/R est:1800
£1282 $1987 €2000 Sabiner mountains with shepherdess and her sons, sheep and goat (48x38cm-19x15in) s.d.1875. 4-Dec-2 Neumeister, Munich #812/R est:1100
£3247 $4838 €5000 Egeria in the Campagna (56x84cm-22x33in) s.d.1876. 26-Jun-2 Neumeister, Munich #793/R est:1600
Works on paper
£609 $889 €950 Zahring ruins with Freiburg beyond (36x47cm-14x19in) s. W/C over pencil. 4-Jun-2 Karl & Faber, Munich #108

LUGRIS GONZALEZ, Urbano (1908-1973) Spanish
£8553 $13855 €13000 Landscape (50x60cm-20x24in) s. board. 21-Jan-3 Durán, Madrid #160/R est:10000

LUIGGI, P (19/20th C) Italian?
£1187 $1947 €1650 Le port a maree basse (32x53cm-13x21in) s. panel. 4-Jun-3 Marc Kohn, Paris #7/R est:1500-2500

LUIGI, Mario de (1908-1978) Italian
£1489 $2413 €2100 G R 207 (41x41cm-16x16in) s.verso prov. 26-May-3 Christie's, Milan #363/R est:1000-1500
£2903 $4587 €4500 Untitled (100x100cm-39x39in) board prov.exhib. 18-Dec-2 Christie's, Rome #263/R

LUIGINI, Ferdinand-Jean (1870-1943) French
£346 $550 €519 At the fountain (19x24cm-7x9in) s. panel. 7-Mar-3 Skinner, Boston #535/R
£535 $850 €803 Paris street scene (16x18cm-6x7in) s.i. board. 7-Mar-3 Skinner, Boston #533/R

LUINI, Aurelio (attrib) (1530-1593) Italian
Works on paper
£1700 $2669 €2550 Lamentation (28x27cm-11x11in) black chk. 11-Dec-2 Sotheby's, Olympia #9/R est:1400-1600

LUINI, Bernardino (circle) (1475-1532) Italian
£5172 $8276 €7500 Woman (44x36cm-17x14in) board. 17-Mar-3 Pandolfini, Florence #686/R

LUINI, Bernardino (style) (1475-1532) Italian
£20690 $32690 €30000 Madonna and Child with Saint John (52x57cm-20x22in) board. 5-Apr-3 Finarte Semenzato, Milan #137/R est:8000

LUKA, Madeleine (1900-1989) French
£270 $422 €400 Amoureux (55x46cm-22x18in) s. 26-Mar-3 Millon & Associes, Paris #126
£493 $799 €750 Milking time (65x81cm-26x32in) s. painted c.1929. 21-Jan-3 Christie's, Amsterdam #410
£1935 $3058 €3000 Jeune femme aux fleurs (117x89cm-46x35in) s.d.1942 exhib. 18-Dec-2 Digard, Paris #128/R

LUKE, Alexandra (1901-1967) Canadian
Works on paper
£256 $397 €384 Composition (45x30cm-18x12in) W/C ink prov. 24-Sep-2 Ritchie, Toronto #3166/R (C.D 625)
£667 $1093 €1001 Abstraction (44x30cm-17x12in) W/C ink executed c.1955. 3-Jun-3 Joyner, Toronto #403/R est:1500-2000 (C.D 1500)

LUKE, John (1906-1975) British
£6500 $10400 €9750 Girl's head (32x27cm-13x11in) tempera exhib. 15-May-3 Christie's, London #65/R est:10000
£10145 $16638 €14000 Still life, potted geranium (57x37cm-22x15in) s.d.1935 board exhib. 28-May-3 Bonhams & James Adam, Dublin #155/R est:5000-7000

LUKER, William (jnr) (1867-1951) British
£550 $902 €825 Cattle in a pasture (24x42cm-9x17in) mono.d.May 16 1894 board. 29-May-3 Christie's, Kensington #170/R
£1800 $2808 €2700 Marshes, Burham. The Downs, Lewes (24x42cm-9x17in) init. one d.September 1890 one d.September 1885 panel pair. 10-Apr-3 Tennants, Leyburn #993 est:1500-2000
Works on paper
£440 $678 €700 Horse (22x35cm-9x14in) s. pastel dr. 28-Oct-2 Segre, Madrid #36/R

LUKER, William (1828-1905) British
£420 $655 €630 Cattle grazing near Bramshot (12x22cm-5x9in) i.d.Sep 3rd 1870. 17-Sep-2 Sotheby's, Olympia #150/R
£450 $702 €675 Cattle and drover in landscape (24x42cm-9x17in) mono.d.1894 board. 7-Nov-2 Bonhams, Cornwall #831/R
£620 $992 €930 Hunter standing in stable (61x76cm-24x30in) s.d.1848. 8-Jan-3 Brightwells, Leominster #1048
£3100 $5022 €4495 Forest of deer (60x90cm-24x35in) s.d.1872. 21-May-3 Edgar Horn, Eastbourne #261/R est:2500-3500
£3268 $5261 €5000 Troupeau s'abreuvant dans un cours d'eau sur fond de paysage (93x150cm-37x59in) s. 20-Jan-3 Horta, Bruxelles #198 est:6200-8700
£4000 $6080 €6000 Deer in the New Forest (111x90cm-44x35in) s.d.1881. 28-Aug-2 Sotheby's, London #807/R est:4000-6000

LUKITS, Theodore Nikolai (1897-1992) American
£3012 $5000 €4367 Grand Canyon (46x61cm-18x24in) s. i.verso board. 11-Jun-3 Butterfields, San Francisco #4330/R est:5000-7000

LUKOVSKII, V (19th C) Russian
£1800 $2844 €2700 Forge in winter (44x61cm-17x24in) s. 26-Nov-2 Christie's, Kensington #11/R est:1500-2500

LUKOWSKY, Wladimir (1916-) Russian?
£455 $719 €660 Horse drawn sleigh in the snow (49x69cm-19x27in) s. cyrillic. 5-Apr-3 Hans Stahl, Hamburg #65/R

LUKS, George (1867-1933) American
£1644 $2400 €2466 Cossack (28x18cm-11x7in) s.d.03 academy board. 3-Nov-1 North East Auctions, Portsmouth #278
£67901 $110000 €101852 Brooklyn Bridge (36x48cm-14x19in) s.d.1916 verso prov.exhib.lit. 21-May-3 Sotheby's, New York #67/R est:50000-75000

Works on paper
£274 $450 €397 Meeting outside a church (37x34cm-15x13in) s. pen ink card stock. 5-Jun-3 Swann Galleries, New York #170/R
£325 $500 €488 Landscape with house (20x26cm-8x10in) s. pencil. 4-Sep-2 Christie's, Rockefeller NY #367/R
£4695 $7700 €6808 Couple in a cafe (20x26cm-8x10in) s. brush crayon. 5-Jun-3 Swann Galleries, New York #171/R est:5000-8000

LULAG, W (20th C) German?
£529 $772 €794 Riverside town (41x27cm-16x11in) s. panel. 17-Jun-2 Philippe Schuler, Zurich #7347 (S.FR 1200)

LUM, Bertha Boynton (1879-1954) American
Prints
£2096 $3500 €3039 Spider woman (97x61cm-38x24in) s.d.31 col woodcut prov. 17-Jun-3 John Moran, Pasadena #225 est:3000-5000

LUMINAIS, Evariste-Vital (1822-1896) French
£300 $456 €450 On the scent (52x44cm-20x17in) s. paper on canvas. 29-Aug-2 Christie's, Kensington #72
£380 $597 €570 Boy with two hunting dogs in a landscape (52x44cm-20x17in) s. i.verso. 10-Dec-2 Rosebery Fine Art, London #553
£1090 $1689 €1700 Chassea cour dans le sous-bois (22x37cm-9x15in) s. 5-Dec-2 Gros & Delettrez, Paris #26
£1731 $2683 €2700 Etude pour Bourse de Commerce (64x32cm-25x13in) s. 9-Dec-2 Beaussant & Lefèvre, Paris #73/R
£2051 $3221 €3200 Scene de bataille (73x92cm-29x36in) s. 13-Dec-2 Piasa, Paris #171/R

LUMNITZER, Paul (1861-?) Polish
£1258 $1962 €2000 March sun (66x80cm-26x31in) s.d.1906. 11-Oct-2 Winterberg, Heidelberg #1430 est:850

LUNA Y NOVICIO, Juan (1857-1900) Philippino
£497100 $765534 €745650 Parisian life (57x79cm-22x31in) s.i.d.1892 prov.lit. 27-Oct-2 Christie's, Hong Kong #62/R est:1800000-2000000 (HK.D 6000000)

LUNA, Charles de (19th C) French
Works on paper
£220 $350 €330 Out for a walk (69x97cm-27x38in) s.d.1859 W/C. 7-Mar-3 Jackson's, Cedar Falls #528/R

LUND, Aage (1892-1972) Danish
£466 $740 €699 Holiday maker, Hollose - girl with bouquet of flowers (50x54cm-20x21in) s. 5-Mar-3 Rasmussen, Copenhagen #1919/R (D.KR 5000)
£511 $807 €767 Green, lush garden with lady seated on bench in shade (97x77cm-38x30in) s/d/1936. 2-Dec-2 Rasmussen, Copenhagen #1783/R (D.KR 6000)

LUND, Anker Niels (1840-1922) Danish
£633 $981 €1000 A look into the future (73x88cm-29x35in) s. 25-Sep-2 Neumeister, Munich #64/R

LUND, Bjarne (1896-1931) Norwegian
£254 $394 €381 Taming the horse (59x73cm-23x29in) s. 1-Oct-2 Rasmussen, Copenhagen #340/R (D.KR 3000)

LUND, Carl Emil (1855-1928) Danish
£330 $525 €495 Landscape with sheep. s. 22-Mar-3 Fallon, Copake #171/R
£596 $941 €894 Woodland lake with six figures (37x54cm-15x21in) s. 27-Nov-2 Museumsbygningen, Copenhagen #62 (D.KR 7000)
£978 $1554 €1467 Interior scene with girl knitting (71x64cm-28x25in) s. 5-Mar-3 Rasmussen, Copenhagen #1951/R (D.KR 10500)
£1117 $1777 €1676 Children and women at Dyrehaven, summer (54x37cm-21x15in) s. 5-Mar-3 Rasmussen, Copenhagen #2057/R est:12000 (D.KR 12000)

LUND, F C (1826-1901) Danish
£1622 $2611 €2433 From Frederiksborg Palace (64x56cm-25x22in) s.i.d.1887. 22-Feb-3 Rasmussen, Havnen #2004/R est:20000 (D.KR 18000)

LUND, Frederik Christian (1826-1901) Danish
£1286 $2007 €1929 Monastery interior with monks (140x115cm-55x45in) s.d.1880. 11-Nov-2 Rasmussen, Vejle #597/R est:20000-30000 (D.KR 15000)
£1862 $2961 €2793 Two monks chatting (127x113cm-50x44in) s.d.1880. 5-Mar-3 Rasmussen, Copenhagen #1780/R est:25000 (D.KR 20000)
£2723 $4303 €4085 Farmers and citizens wearing national costumes in a procession (22x127cm-9x50in) study. 2-Dec-2 Rasmussen, Copenhagen #1268/R est:30000-50000 (D.KR 32000)
Works on paper
£3200 $5248 €4800 Forum Romanum, Forum Romanum (51x79cm-20x31in) s.i.d.1884 W/C. 3-Jun-3 Sotheby's, London #270/R est:1500-2000

LUND, Hans (19/20th C) ?
£448 $686 €672 From an Italian loggia with woman (71x101cm-28x40in) s. 24-Aug-2 Rasmussen, Havnen #2274/R (D.KR 5200)

LUND, Henrik (1879-1935) Norwegian
£1298 $2050 €1947 Woman wearing hat (100x85cm-39x33in) s.d.16. 2-Dec-2 Blomqvist, Oslo #380/R est:20000-30000 (N.KR 15000)
£2163 $3417 €3245 Portrait of Carl Burchardt (100x85cm-39x33in) s.d.14 lit. 2-Dec-2 Blomqvist, Oslo #369/R est:30000-40000 (N.KR 25000)

LUND, J C (?) ?
Works on paper
£340 $541 €510 Crossing the stream (20x38cm-8x15in) s. 19-Mar-3 James Thompson, Kirby Lonsdale #97

LUND, Jane (1939-) American
Works on paper
£625 $1000 €906 Untitled (87x55cm-34x22in) s.d.71 pastel. 16-May-3 Skinner, Boston #366/R

LUND, Jens Martin Victor (1871-1924) Danish
£517 $786 €776 Statue in a Parisian park (65x54cm-26x21in) s.i.d.1909. 27-Aug-2 Rasmussen, Copenhagen #1680/R (D.KR 6000)

LUND, Johan Ludvig (1777-1867) Danish
£4255 $6596 €6383 Young woman at her toilet (35x27cm-14x11in) s. panel prov. 3-Dec-2 Bukowskis, Stockholm #519/R est:25000-30000 (S.KR 60000)

LUNDAHL, Amelie (1850-1914) Finnish
£2848 $4500 €4500 Lake landscape from Kangasala (52x71cm-20x28in) s. 30-Nov-2 Hagelstam, Helsinki #101/R est:8500
£5380 $8500 €8500 Palace ruins (28x42cm-11x17in) s. board. 1-Dec-2 Bukowskis, Helsinki #116/R est:8500-10000
£21127 $34014 €30000 Evening stroll by Nasijarvi (68x80cm-27x31in) s. 10-May-3 Bukowskis, Helsinki #37/R est:30000-40000
Works on paper
£17722 $28000 €28000 Little flower girl (60x48cm-24x19in) s.d.1889 pastel. 1-Dec-2 Bukowskis, Helsinki #115/R est:20000-25000
£19014 $30613 €27000 Portrait of a beautiful lady (62x48cm-24x19in) s. pastel executed 1880s exhib.lit. 10-May-3 Bukowskis, Helsinki #124/R est:17000-20000

LUNDAHL, Fanny (1853-1918) Finnish
£372 $603 €558 Bouquet of roses on ledge (52x45cm-20x18in) s.i.d.1878 porcelain. 25-Jan-3 Rasmussen, Havnen #2118 (D.KR 4200)

LUNDAHL, Nadine (1958-) Finnish
£2254 $3628 €3200 Still life of strawberries (20x30cm-8x12in) s. board. 10-May-3 Bukowskis, Helsinki #105/R est:1500-1800

LUNDBERG, Gustaf (1695-1786) Swedish
Works on paper
£1915 $2968 €2873 Countess Fredrika de la Garde (47x38cm-19x15in) pastel. 3-Dec-2 Bukowskis, Stockholm #535/R est:30000-35000 (S.KR 27000)
£2057 $3188 €3086 Portrait of young lady wearing pale blue and white dress (65x49cm-26x19in) pastel. 3-Dec-2 Bukowskis, Stockholm #529/R est:35000-40000 (S.KR 29000)
£6028 $9344 €9042 Portrait of Beata Falker, nee Rosen wearing yellow dress (65x50cm-26x20in) pastel lit. 4-Dec-2 AB Stockholms Auktionsverk #1610/R est:60000-80000 (S.KR 85000)
£6206 $10054 €8999 Anthony de Geer and his wife Ulrika Charlotta (67x53cm-26x21in) pastel pair prov.lit. 26-May-3 Bukowskis, Stockholm #481/R est:100000-125000 (S.KR 80000)

LUNDBERG, Gustaf (attrib) (1695-1786) Swedish
Works on paper
£4478 $7343 €6493 Portrait of Isak Georg de Besche (65x50cm-26x20in) pastel. 4-Jun-3 AB Stockholms Auktionsverk #2242/R est:70000-80000 (S.KR 57000)

LUNDBERG, Lars-Gosta (1938-) Swedish
£491 $765 €737 Earth (85x60cm-33x24in) s.d.1989 panel. 6-Nov-2 AB Stockholms Auktionsverk #851/R (S.KR 7000)

LUNDBERG, Sture (1900-1930) Swedish
£1931 $3108 €2897 Fish market (73x58cm-29x23in) prov. 7-May-3 AB Stockholms Auktionsverk #732/R est:25000-30000 (S.KR 25000)
Works on paper
£502 $808 €753 Positano (26x37cm-10x15in) s.d.1924 pencil prov. 7-May-3 AB Stockholms Auktionsverk #829/R (S.KR 6500)

LUNDBOHM, Sixten (1895-1982) Swedish
£275 $432 €413 Southern town scene (34x42cm-13x17in) s. panel. 16-Dec-2 Lilla Bukowskis, Stockholm #356 (S.KR 3900)
£281 $443 €422 Landscape (65x82cm-26x32in) s. 30-Nov-2 Goteborg Auktionsverk, Sweden #577/R (S.KR 4000)
£329 $514 €494 Nordingraa (67x73cm-26x29in) s. s.d.1943 verso prov. 13-Sep-2 Lilla Bukowskis, Stockholm #427 (S.KR 4800)
£521 $813 €782 Landscape (46x60cm-18x24in) s. panel. 13-Sep-2 Lilla Bukowskis, Stockholm #827 (S.KR 7600)
£658 $1027 €987 Coliseum (50x70cm-20x28in) s. prov. 13-Sep-2 Lilla Bukowskis, Stockholm #432 (S.KR 9600)
£892 $1356 €1338 The church, Quimperle, Brittany (60x74cm-24x29in) s. exhib. 16-Aug-2 Lilla Bukowskis, Stockholm #144 (S.KR 13000)
£1699 $2735 €2549 Composition (133x94cm-52x37in) s. 7-May-3 AB Stockholms Auktionsverk #763/R est:25000-30000 (S.KR 22000)
Works on paper
£282 $443 €423 Kollonad (19x29cm-7x11in) s. W/C. 16-Dec-2 Lilla Bukowskis, Stockholm #162 (S.KR 4000)

LUNDBORG, Florence (1871-1949) American
£3915 $6500 €5677 Hills beyond the garden (216x107cm-85x42in) s. prov. 11-Jun-3 Butterfields, San Francisco #4093/R est:3000-5000

LUNDBYE, J T (1818-1848) Danish
Works on paper
£315 $508 €473 Four legs (7x16cm-3x6in) pencil prov. 26-Feb-3 Museumsbygningen, Copenhagen #77 (D.KR 3500)
£378 $609 €567 From a stable (9x15cm-4x6in) pen. 26-Feb-3 Museumsbygningen, Copenhagen #72 (D.KR 4200)
£378 $609 €567 Head of a dog (22x21cm-9x8in) pencil study. 26-Feb-3 Museumsbygningen, Copenhagen #93 (D.KR 4200)
£486 $783 €729 Woman with faggots in forest (9x12cm-4x5in) study pen. 26-Feb-3 Museumsbygningen, Copenhagen #81 (D.KR 5400)
£495 $798 €743 Horses and donkey from a travelling diary (22x18cm-9x7in) i. pen studies. 26-Feb-3 Museumsbygningen, Copenhagen #111 (D.KR 5500)
£766 $1233 €1149 Landscape, Ulstrup 6 June 1847 (19x24cm-7x9in) mono. wash pen W/C. 26-Feb-3 Museumsbygningen, Copenhagen #106 (D.KR 8500)
£991 $1595 €1487 Self portrait (17x14cm-7x6in) i. pencil. 26-Feb-3 Museumsbygningen, Copenhagen #66/R (D.KR 11000)

LUNDBYE, Johan Thomas (1818-1848) Danish
£1452 $2236 €2178 From a gravel pit, possibly Fredericksvaerk (21x29cm-8x11in) painted c.1838. 4-Sep-2 Kunsthallen, Copenhagen #8/R est:15000 (D.KR 17000)
£2553 $4034 €3830 Part of Hobjerg at Frederiksvaerk, Oct 1839 (16x27cm-6x11in) init. exhib.prov. 2-Dec-2 Rasmussen, Copenhagen #1131/R est:25000-35000 (D.KR 30000)
£4255 $6723 €6383 Portrait of the sculptor Jens Adolf Jerichau (24x19cm-9x7in) s.d.martz 1837 exhib.prov. 2-Dec-2 Rasmussen, Copenhagen #1277/R est:80000-100000 (D.KR 50000)
£9138 $14621 €13707 Stag lying down and doe standing (20x28cm-8x11in) mono. s.i.d.1836 stretcher. 17-Mar-3 Blomqvist, Oslo #307/R est:18000-20000 (N.KR 105000)
£14894 $23532 €22341 The Fountain at Loggia dei Mercanti in Florence (25x34cm-10x13in) mono.d.46 exhib.prov. 2-Dec-2 Rasmussen, Copenhagen #1148/R est:200000-250000 (D.KR 175000)
£46555 $74022 €69833 From Mollebakken near Kallundborg - landscape with windmills (37x55cm-15x22in) mono.d.47 exhib.prov. 5-Mar-3 Rasmussen, Copenhagen #1546/R est:500000-700000 (D.KR 500000)
£52632 $85263 €78948 Winter landscape without snow, view from Julebaeks Bridge (60x93cm-24x37in) mono.d.48 prov.lit. 21-May-3 Museumsbygningen, Copenhagen #35/R est:600000-800000 (D.KR 550000)
Works on paper
£431 $655 €647 Study of stags (16x20cm-6x8in) d.1838 pencil. 27-Aug-2 Rasmussen, Copenhagen #1989/R (D.KR 5000)
£511 $807 €767 Studies of stags (19x24cm-7x9in) s.d.Febr 36 pencil prov. 2-Dec-2 Rasmussen, Copenhagen #1857/R (D.KR 6000)
£766 $1210 €1149 Gnome patting horse on the muzzle (10x9cm-4x4in) i. pen. 27-Nov-2 Museumsbygningen, Copenhagen #90/R (D.KR 9000)
£861 $1395 €1248 Study of head of calf. Donkey and head of swan (15x13cm-6x5in) s. one d.1842 one d.1847 pen pencil sold with dr by T Laessoe. 26-May-3 Rasmussen, Copenhagen #1580/R (D.KR 9000)
£1024 $1628 €1536 Italian from Ciociaria area standing (25x17cm-10x7in) d.6 Dec 45 W/C pen. 5-Mar-3 Rasmussen, Copenhagen #2160/R (D.KR 11000)
£1544 $2408 €2316 Farmer from Refsnaes (23x16cm-9x6in) mono.i.d.19 juny 47 pen W/C exhib.prov. 11-Nov-2 Rasmussen, Vejle #459/R est:6000 (D.KR 18000)
£1973 $3077 €2960 Landscape from Gurreso (12x18cm-5x7in) i.d.30 juny 1840 pen W/C exhib.prov. 11-Nov-2 Rasmussen, Vejle #464/R est:3000 (D.KR 23000)
£2196 $3426 €3294 Winter in the country (18x24cm-7x9in) i.d.1848 pen prov.exhib.lit. 23-Sep-2 Rasmussen, Vejle #75/R est:15000-20000 (D.KR 26000)
£2213 $3496 €3320 Study of a cat (21x16cm-8x6in) mono.d.45 W/C pencil. 2-Dec-2 Rasmussen, Copenhagen #1858/R est:10000-15000 (D.KR 26000)
£2679 $4341 €3885 Coastal landscape from Refsnaes (11x19cm-4x7in) i.d.Juni 1842 W/C. 26-May-3 Rasmussen, Copenhagen #1576/R est:8000 (D.KR 28000)

LUNDBYE, Johan Thomas (attrib) (1818-1848) Danish
Works on paper
£2723 $4303 €4085 Portrait of Johannes Ewald (17x10cm-7x4in) i. pencil. 2-Dec-2 Rasmussen, Copenhagen #1845/R est:12000-15000 (D.KR 32000)

LUNDE, Anders (1809-1886) Danish
£1401 $2242 €2102 Landscape view towards Copenhagen (32x48cm-13x19in) s. panel. 13-Jan-3 Rasmussen, Vejle #23/R est:20000 (D.KR 16000)
£2584 $3928 €3876 Glade surrounded by large trees (33x50cm-13x20in) s. 27-Aug-2 Rasmussen, Copenhagen #1425/R est:30000 (D.KR 30000)
£3717 $5874 €5576 From Tivoli in Rome (44x32cm-17x13in) mono.i. paper on canvas. 5-Apr-3 Rasmussen, Havnen #2151/R est:8000-10000 (D.KR 40000)

LUNDE, Jardar (1909-) Norwegian
£1388 $2165 €2082 Fishing at Lofoten (198x125cm-78x49in) s.d.58 panel. 21-Oct-2 Blomqvist, Oslo #396/R est:12000-16000 (N.KR 16000)

LUNDEBY, Alf (1870-1961) Norwegian
£489 $767 €734 Bridge near Mysusaeter (32x41cm-13x16in) s. panel. 25-Nov-2 Blomqvist, Lysaker #1176 (N.KR 5600)
£524 $822 €786 Still life of flowers (35x27cm-14x11in) s. panel. 25-Nov-2 Blomqvist, Lysaker #1175/R (N.KR 6000)
£541 $849 €812 From Taormina (32x41cm-13x16in) s. panel. 25-Nov-2 Blomqvist, Lysaker #1177/R (N.KR 6200)
£7504 $11782 €11256 The railway station at Lillehammer (54x65cm-21x26in) s.d.1938. 21-Nov-2 Grev Wedels Plass, Oslo #36/R est:40000 (N.KR 86000)

LUNDEGARD, Justus (1860-1924) Swedish
£254 $399 €381 Landscape from Arild, Skane (61x40cm-24x16in) s,. 16-Dec-2 Lilla Bukowskis, Stockholm #124 (S.KR 3600)
£276 $425 €414 Interior scene with old thoughtful woman reading (38x28cm-15x11in) s.d.1895 panel. 27-Oct-2 Anders Antik, Landskrona #252/R (S.KR 4000)
£281 $450 €407 Arilds Pinier in morning light (46x66cm-18x26in) s. 18-May-3 Anders Antik, Landskrona #137 (S.KR 3600)
£634 $1020 €900 Sailing (75x99cm-30x39in) s. 10-May-3 Bukowskis, Helsinki #371/R
£1560 $2418 €2340 Farm by pond, Skaane (66x99cm-26x39in) s.d.1882. 3-Dec-2 Bukowskis, Stockholm #297/R est:30000-35000 (S.KR 22000)
£2017 $3268 €2925 Time for reading (39x29cm-15x11in) s.d.95 cardboard. 26-May-3 Bukowskis, Stockholm #166/R est:20000-25000 (S.KR 26000)

£5431 $8798 €7875 Winter landscape, France (112x190cm-44x75in) s.i.d.1898. 26-May-3 Bukowskis, Stockholm #44/R est:80000-100000 (S.KR 70000)

LUNDENS, Gerrit (1622-1677) Dutch
£5449 $8446 €8500 Peasant's meal with woman cooking by pan (52x62cm-20x24in) s. canvas on canvas lit. 4-Dec-2 Neumeister, Munich #612/R est:5000

LUNDGREN, Egron Sillif (1815-1875) Swedish
£1707 $2765 €2475 Spanish party (36x46cm-14x18in) s.d.1851. 26-May-3 Bukowskis, Stockholm #192/R est:15000-20000 (S.KR 22000)
Works on paper
£324 $538 €470 Girl on donkey (21x18cm-8x7in) s. W/C. 16-Jun-3 Lilla Bukowskis, Stockholm #657 (S.KR 4200)
£340 $564 €493 Young Spanish women (22x14cm-9x6in) s. W/C. 16-Jun-3 Lilla Bukowskis, Stockholm #659 (S.KR 4400)
£427 $691 €619 Romantic meeting on bridge in Venice (47x32cm-19x13in) wash htd white prov. 25-May-3 Uppsala Auktionskammare, Uppsala #103/R (S.KR 5500)
£631 $984 €947 Court, Kaiserbach, Lucknow (18x26cm-7x10in) W/C. 13-Sep-2 Lilla Bukowskis, Stockholm #387 (S.KR 9200)
£780 $1209 €1170 Temple interior with choir boys (51x76cm-20x30in) s. W/C exhib. 4-Dec-2 AB Stockholms Auktionsverk #1633/R (S.KR 11000)
£1086 $1760 €1575 Young Oriental beauty (42x32cm-17x13in) mono. mixed media oval. 25-May-3 Uppsala Auktionskammare, Uppsala #104/R (S.KR 14000)
£1164 $1885 €1688 Hindu of rank on horseback (50x33cm-20x13in) W/C exec.c.1858-59 prov. 26-May-3 Bukowskis, Stockholm #191/R est:20000-25000 (S.KR 15000)

LUNDGREN, Tyra (1897-1979) Swedish
Works on paper
£432 $718 €626 Still life of vase and pink flowers (38x30cm-15x12in) s. W/C cardboard. 16-Jun-3 Lilla Bukowskis, Stockholm #141 (S.KR 5600)

LUNDH, Theodor (1812-1896) Swedish
£290 $446 €435 Still life of ducks (63x32cm-25x13in) 27-Oct-2 Anders Antik, Landskrona #238/R (S.KR 4200)
£535 $814 €803 Still life of dead birds (53x38cm-21x15in) s.d.1877. 16-Aug-2 Lilla Bukowskis, Stockholm #865 (S.KR 7800)
£563 $907 €800 Still life of birds (30x36cm-12x14in) s. oval. 10-May-3 Bukowskis, Helsinki #364/R
£567 $879 €851 Still life with jay (49x40cm-19x16in) s.d.84. 3-Dec-2 Bukowskis, Stockholm #366/R (S.KR 8000)
£603 $953 €905 Collar dove (54x43cm-21x17in) s.d.1880. 27-Nov-2 Falkkloos, Malmo #77809/R (S.KR 8600)
£621 $1005 €900 Still life of with bullfinches and glass (45x36cm-18x14in) s.d.46. 26-May-3 Bukowskis, Stockholm #137/R (S.KR 8000)
£1064 $1649 €1596 Still life of dead birds hanging (47x35cm-19x14in) s.d.96 panel. 4-Dec-2 AB Stockholms Auktionsverk #1678/R est:20000-25000 (S.KR 15000)
£1064 $1649 €1596 Gustav II Adolf on horseback (105x87cm-41x34in) s.d.1867. 4-Dec-2 AB Stockholms Auktionsverk #1683/R est:15000-18000 (S.KR 15000)

LUNDIN, Bengt (1924-) Swedish
Sculpture
£1752 $2733 €2628 Vessel (55cm-22in) painted wood. 6-Nov-2 AB Stockholms Auktionsverk #753/R est:25000-30000 (S.KR 25000)

LUNDQUIST, Evert (1904-1994) Swedish
£423 $665 €635 And also a little house (20x15cm-8x6in) s. canvas on panel. 16-Dec-2 Lilla Bukowskis, Stockholm #158 (S.KR 6000)
£453 $689 €680 Girl wearing yellow hat (54x41cm-21x16in) s.d.54 s.verso canvas on canvas. 16-Aug-2 Lilla Bukowskis, Stockholm #652 (S.KR 6600)
£562 $877 €843 Pine tree (33x29cm-13x11in) s. panel. 13-Sep-2 Lilla Bukowskis, Stockholm #744 (S.KR 8200)
£567 $879 €851 Landscape (38x42cm-15x17in) mono. s.verso. 8-Dec-2 Uppsala Auktionskammare, Uppsala #226/R (S.KR 8000)
£596 $929 €894 Mountain top (21x28cm-8x11in) init. 5-Nov-2 Bukowskis, Stockholm #84/R (S.KR 8500)
£692 $1086 €1038 Birds (36x28cm-14x11in) s. 16-Dec-2 Lilla Bukowskis, Stockholm #252 (S.KR 9800)
£876 $1367 €1314 Portrait (46x42cm-18x17in) s. verso. 6-Nov-2 AB Stockholms Auktionsverk #693/R (S.KR 12500)
£913 $1442 €1370 From the garden (22x20cm-9x8in) s.d.61 verso. 28-Apr-3 Bukowskis, Stockholm #224/R (S.KR 12000)
£995 $1513 €1493 Artist still life (26x47cm-10x19in) i.verso. 16-Aug-2 Lilla Bukowskis, Stockholm #591 est:12000-15000 (S.KR 14500)
£1051 $1640 €1577 Man in profile (29x23cm-11x9in) init. s.d.1953 verso canvas on panel. 5-Nov-2 Bukowskis, Stockholm #85/R est:15000-20000 (S.KR 15000)
£1121 $1749 €1682 Figures at table (55x46cm-22x18in) s. 6-Nov-2 AB Stockholms Auktionsverk #692/R est:20000-25000 (S.KR 16000)
£1331 $2077 €1997 Standing model (73x60cm-29x24in) s.i. s.i.d.33 verso prov. 5-Nov-2 Bukowskis, Stockholm #222/R est:15000-20000 (S.KR 19000)
£1544 $2486 €2316 The model (46x38cm-18x15in) s.d.1950 verso. 7-May-3 AB Stockholms Auktionsverk #867/R est:20000-25000 (S.KR 20000)
£1544 $2486 €2316 Still life of fruit (55x96cm-22x38in) s.d.1952 verso. 7-May-3 AB Stockholms Auktionsverk #868/R est:20000-25000 (S.KR 20000)
£1752 $2733 €2628 Woman in landscape (55x46cm-22x18in) init. s.verso. 5-Nov-2 Bukowskis, Stockholm #86/R est:25000-30000 (S.KR 25000)
£1822 $2842 €2733 The jug II (27x35cm-11x14in) init.verso. 5-Nov-2 Bukowskis, Stockholm #87/R est:20000-25000 (S.KR 26000)
£2281 $3605 €3422 Resting (60x55cm-24x22in) init. s.d.1961 verso exhib. 28-Apr-3 Bukowskis, Stockholm #227/R est:40000-50000 (S.KR 30000)
£3224 $5029 €4836 The mountain pass (89x117cm-35x46in) s. i.d.1943 verso. 5-Nov-2 Bukowskis, Stockholm #114/R est:60000-80000 (S.KR 46000)
£3784 $6092 €5676 Motljuset - woman seated with reflecting light (100x89cm-39x35in) s. 7-May-3 AB Stockholms Auktionsverk #866/R est:60000-80000 (S.KR 49000)
£7008 $10932 €10512 Reclining model (76x102cm-30x40in) s.verso. 5-Nov-2 Bukowskis, Stockholm #127/R est:130000-150000 (S.KR 100000)
£10512 $16398 €15768 Red woman (90x99cm-35x39in) init. s.verso. 5-Nov-2 Bukowskis, Stockholm #89/R est:100000-150000 (S.KR 150000)
£11787 $18624 €17681 Harbour Street (111x83cm-44x33in) s. exhib.lit. 28-Apr-3 Bukowskis, Stockholm #223/R est:100000-125000 (S.KR 155000)
£12548 $19825 €18822 The urn (116x90cm-46x35in) s.d.1961 verso exhib.lit. 28-Apr-3 Bukowskis, Stockholm #216/R est:175000-200000 (S.KR 165000)
£14015 $21864 €21023 The jug (116x105cm-46x41in) init. s.d.1978 verso prov. 6-Nov-2 AB Stockholms Auktionsverk #695/R est:300000-350000 (S.KR 200000)
£19392 $30639 €29088 Clay pipe (101x82cm-40x32in) init. s.d.1975 verso. 28-Apr-3 Bukowskis, Stockholm #229/R est:200000-250000 (S.KR 255000)
£23166 $37297 €34749 The chair (118x104cm-46x41in) s.d.1955 verso prov. 7-May-3 AB Stockholms Auktionsverk #860/R est:250000-300000 (S.KR 300000)

LUNDQVIST, Anders (1803-1853) Swedish
£1047 $1697 €1518 Antique figure scene (35x38cm-14x15in) 26-May-3 Bukowskis, Stockholm #366/R (S.KR 13500)

LUNDSTROM, Knut (1892-1945) Swedish
£2394 $3854 €3591 Abstract composition (35x24cm-14x9in) s.i. panel. 7-May-3 AB Stockholms Auktionsverk #759/R est:30000-40000 (S.KR 31000)

LUNDSTROM, Kurt (?) Swedish
£776 $1219 €1125 Untitled. prov. 15-Dec-2 Anders Antik, Landskrona #1128 (S.KR 11000)

LUNDSTROM, Vilhelm (1893-1950) Danish
£2332 $3708 €3498 Cavalry battle after Rubens (60x75cm-24x30in) s.on stretcher painted c.1917-18 exhib.lit. 29-Apr-3 Kunsthallen, Copenhagen #230/R est:20000 (D.KR 25000)
£3631 $5774 €5447 Still life of jugs, pots and fruit on table (75x90cm-30x35in) 10-Mar-3 Rasmussen, Vejle #576/R est:30000 (D.KR 39000)
£6506 $10279 €9759 Still life of white cloth, bowl with two eggs and books (60x73cm-24x29in) init. painted c.1922 prov.exhib.lit. 1-Apr-3 Rasmussen, Copenhagen #17/R est:40000-60000 (D.KR 70000)
£6593 $10154 €9890 Still life of orange and dark purple jug (65x50cm-26x20in) init. verso painted 1943/44. 23-Oct-2 Kunsthallen, Copenhagen #51/R est:75000 (D.KR 78000)
£12257 $18876 €18386 Still life of white bowl, green bottle, jug and watering can (81x100cm-32x39in) init. painted 1924 lit. 23-Oct-2 Kunsthallen, Copenhagen #94/R est:150000 (D.KR 145000)
£21375 $33773 €32063 Seated model (120x90cm-47x35in) init.d.43 verso prov.exhib.lit. 1-Apr-3 Rasmussen, Copenhagen #24/R est:250000 (D.KR 230000)

Works on paper
£254 $394 €381 Saint Martin of Tours (24x15cm-9x6in) pencil prov. 1-Oct-2 Rasmussen, Copenhagen #477/R (D.KR 3000)
£271 $420 €407 Seated nude model (41x26cm-16x10in) pencil prov. 1-Oct-2 Rasmussen, Copenhagen #444 (D.KR 3200)
£271 $420 €407 Standing model with shawl (35x26cm-14x10in) pencil lit.prov. 1-Oct-2 Rasmussen, Copenhagen #451/R (D.KR 3200)
£271 $420 €407 Standing model with hands on her back (44x28cm-17x11in) pencil prov. 1-Oct-2 Rasmussen, Copenhagen #468 (D.KR 3200)
£279 $433 €419 Seated model (41x26cm-16x10in) pencil prov. 1-Oct-2 Rasmussen, Copenhagen #443 (D.KR 3300)
£288 $446 €432 Nude model seen from behind (33x23cm-13x9in) pencil prov. 1-Oct-2 Rasmussen, Copenhagen #462 (D.KR 3400)
£288 $446 €432 Reclining nude model (17x33cm-7x13in) pencil prov. 1-Oct-2 Rasmussen, Copenhagen #464 (D.KR 3400)
£296 $459 €444 Park scene (31x24cm-12x9in) mono. W/C exhib. 1-Oct-2 Rasmussen, Copenhagen #446 (D.KR 3500)
£296 $459 €444 Reclining nude model (18x38cm-7x15in) mono. pencil prov. 1-Oct-2 Rasmussen, Copenhagen #465 (D.KR 3500)
£305 $472 €458 Reclining nude model (25x40cm-10x16in) pencil prov. 1-Oct-2 Rasmussen, Copenhagen #450 (D.KR 3600)
£339 $525 €509 Nude model sitting on her hands (41x26cm-16x10in) pencil prov. 1-Oct-2 Rasmussen, Copenhagen #439/R (D.KR 4000)
£339 $525 €509 Standing nude model (42x20cm-17x8in) pencil prov. 1-Oct-2 Rasmussen, Copenhagen #466/R (D.KR 4000)
£355 $547 €533 Model (40x26cm-16x10in) init. sketch pencil prov. 23-Oct-2 Kunsthallen, Copenhagen #52 (D.KR 4200)
£440 $682 €660 Seated model with legs crossed (32x18cm-13x7in) pencil prov. 1-Oct-2 Rasmussen, Copenhagen #459/R (D.KR 5200)
£466 $722 €699 Seated nude model (41x26cm-16x10in) pencil prov. 1-Oct-2 Rasmussen, Copenhagen #442/R (D.KR 5500)
£508 $787 €762 Nude model seen from behind (24x17cm-9x7in) pencil prov. 1-Oct-2 Rasmussen, Copenhagen #473/R (D.KR 6000)

LUNEBURG, W (?) ?
£559 $888 €839 Still life of flowers in vase and objects on table (126x90cm-50x35in) s. 10-Mar-3 Rasmussen, Vejle #553/R (D.KR 6000)

LUNGKWITZ, Hermann (1813-1890) German
£1538 $2400 €2307 Watzmann near Salzberg (25x30cm-10x12in) paper. 19-Oct-2 David Dike, Dallas #14/R est:3000-4000
Works on paper
£769 $1200 €1154 Langden hei bolzen (25x38cm-10x15in) pencil executed c.1845. 19-Oct-2 David Dike, Dallas #76/R

LUNI, T Hansen (19th C) ?
Works on paper
£400 $636 €600 Quayside scene (64x94cm-25x37in) s. W/C. 2-Mar-3 Lots Road, London #353

LUNN, Agnes (1850-1941) Danish
£280 $445 €420 Black and white cow in field (50x60cm-20x24in) s.i.d.Aug.87 exhib. 5-May-3 Rasmussen, Vejle #603/R (D.KR 3000)

LUNN, Augustus (1905-1986) British
£500 $785 €750 Still life with potted plant (41x35cm-16x14in) s. 15-Apr-3 Bonhams, Knightsbridge #5/R
Works on paper
£300 $495 €435 Surreal landscape (47x65cm-19x26in) s.indis.d. W/C bodycol. 3-Jul-3 Christie's, Kensington #306/R
£420 $685 €630 Abstract (47x64cm-19x25in) s.indis.d.45 gouache. 30-Jan-3 Lawrence, Crewkerne #667/R

LUNS, Huib (1881-1942) Dutch
Works on paper
£255 $397 €400 Sketch of a woodcut of birds of prey. s. s.d.1914 verso chl oil. 6-Nov-2 Vendue Huis, Gravenhage #118/R

LUNSTADT, K (19th C) ?
£1728 $2662 €2592 Bateau a vapeur dans un fjord (84x125cm-33x49in) s.d.85. 22-Oct-2 Iegor de Saint Hippolyte, Montreal #64/R (C.D 4200)

LUNT, Wilmot (20th C) British
Works on paper
£500 $775 €750 Old Whitby (67x47cm-26x19in) s. W/C. 25-Sep-2 Peter Wilson, Nantwich #141/R

LUNTZ, Adolf (1875-1924) German
£417 $680 €630 Spring in Ruppur (36x48cm-14x19in) s.d. i. verso. 14-Feb-3 Paul Kieffer, Pforzhiem #7179/R

LUNY, Thomas (1759-1837) British
£1600 $2592 €2400 English frigate with pilot jack, running into port ahead of the storm (30x42cm-12x17in) s.d.1836 panel. 21-May-3 Christie's, Kensington #374/R est:1500-2500
£2000 $3260 €2900 On the Dart (30x39cm-12x15in) s. i.d.1825. 21-Jul-3 Bonhams, Bath #65/R est:800-1200
£2500 $3925 €3750 Fisherman landing the catch (38x50cm-15x20in) s. 16-Dec-2 Sotheby's, Olympia #19/R est:2500-3500
£3200 $5184 €4800 Passengers disembarking from the Dart ferry (25x36cm-10x14in) s.d.1825 panel. 21-May-3 Christie's, Kensington #536/R est:3000-5000
£3704 $6000 €5556 Fisherfolk on the Devonshire coast (25x28cm-10x11in) s.d.1834 board. 21-Jan-3 Christie's, Rockefeller NY #370/R
£3800 $5890 €5700 Frigate hove to offshore waiting for the pilot (28x39cm-11x15in) s.d.1825 panel. 31-Oct-2 Christie's, Kensington #437/R est:2000-4000
£3800 $6156 €5700 Hauling in the nets (30x41cm-12x16in) s.d.1831 panel. 22-Jan-3 Bonhams, New Bond Street #375/R est:3000-5000
£4000 $6200 €6000 Harbour at Teignmouth (29x39cm-11x15in) canvas on board. 31-Oct-2 Christie's, Kensington #436/R est:2000-4000
£4114 $6459 €6171 Hauling in the nets (50x68cm-20x27in) s.d.1832. 25-Nov-2 Peter Webb, Auckland #29/R est:14000-18000 (NZ.D 13000)
£5000 $8100 €7500 Unloading the catch (25x36cm-10x14in) s.d.1836 i.d.verso panel. 22-Jan-3 Bonhams, New Bond Street #388/R est:4000-6000
£6000 $9720 €9000 First Rate ship of the line arriving off a Naval port with other vessels (72x104cm-28x41in) s. 21-May-3 Christie's, Kensington #539/R est:10000-15000
£6500 $10530 €9750 Coastal landscapes with fisherfolk (31x41cm-12x16in) one s.d.1831 indis.i.verso one s.d.1832 panel pair prov. 21-May-3 Christie's, Kensington #537/R est:4000-6000
£6800 $10744 €10200 Dutch barges in open seas (30x40cm-12x16in) s. panel. 28-Nov-2 Sotheby's, London #101/R est:4000-6000
£12000 $18600 €18000 Bombardment of Algiers, 27 August 1816 (61x86cm-24x34in) s.d.1816. 31-Oct-2 Christie's, Kensington #440/R est:20000-30000
£16000 $25280 €24000 British frigate of the Blockading Squadron patrolling at Brest (86x130cm-34x51in) s.d.1830. 26-Nov-2 Christie's, London #61/R est:20000-30000
£18500 $29045 €27750 Flagship under attack at the battle of the Saintes, 12 April 1782 (83x133cm-33x52in) s. 16-Dec-2 Sotheby's, Olympia #20/R est:15000-20000
£23000 $34960 €34500 Battle of the Saintes (61x86cm-24x34in) s.d.1834. 15-Aug-2 Bonhams, New Bond Street #390/R est:15000-20000
£26000 $41340 €39000 Action between the H.M.S Shannon and the U.S.S Chesapeake (43x58cm-17x23in) prov. 19-Mar-3 Sotheby's, London #8/R est:8000-12000

LUNY, Thomas (attrib) (1759-1837) British
£759 $1200 €1139 Shipping in Plymouth Sound. prov. 1-Dec-2 Susanin's, Chicago #5134/R
£2200 $3454 €3300 Dutch barge off the coast (23x31cm-9x12in) board. 16-Dec-2 Sotheby's, Olympia #17/R est:1000-1500

LUO ZHONGLI (1948-) Chinese
£10101 $16667 €14646 Shepherd girl (63x79cm-25x31in) s.d.1990. 6-Jul-3 Christie's, Hong Kong #115/R est:60000-80000 (HK.D 130000)

LUOSTARINEN, Leena (1949-) Finnish
£2405 $3800 €3800 Bathers (147x175cm-58x69in) s.d.82. 1-Dec-2 Bukowskis, Helsinki #332/R est:3000-4000
Works on paper
£477 $782 €730 Flowers (63x48cm-25x19in) s.d.1999 mixed media. 9-Feb-3 Bukowskis, Helsinki #300/R

LUPERTZ, Markus (1941-) Czechoslovakian
£1418 $2298 €2000 Untitled (53x45cm-21x18in) s. tempera paper. 24-May-3 Van Ham, Cologne #363/R est:2500
£4000 $6520 €6000 Wutende vase (97x87cm-38x34in) mono.i.verso board prov. 3-Feb-3 Sotheby's, Olympia #165/R est:4000-6000
£9500 $14630 €14250 Untitled (200x150cm-79x59in) oil cardboard collage on canvas painted 1980 prov. 22-Oct-2 Sotheby's, London #455/R est:10000-15000
£12658 $20000 €20000 Composition (100x80cm-39x31in) s.i. verso. 27-Nov-2 Dorotheum, Vienna #106/R est:15000-20000
£23000 $38410 €33350 Zwischenraumgespenster, heute (200x162cm-79x64in) init.verso prov. 26-Jun-3 Sotheby's, London #255/R est:10000-15000
£35000 $53900 €52500 Soldat III - dithyrambisch (130x160cm-51x63in) acrylic executed 1972 prov. 22-Oct-2 Sotheby's, London #333/R est:40000-60000
Prints
£1923 $3019 €3000 Clitunno (200x120cm-79x47in) s. linocut one of 20 prov. 15-Dec-2 Perrin, Versailles #131/R

Works on paper
£461 $747 €650 Untitled (21x15cm-8x6in) st.sig. chl pencil biro. 24-May-3 Van Ham, Cologne #364/R
£545 $845 €850 Untitled (30x21cm-12x8in) bears sig. pastel crayon W/C board. 7-Dec-2 Van Ham, Cologne #311/R
£603 $977 €850 Untitled (30x21cm-12x8in) st.sig. ink gouache. 24-May-3 Van Ham, Cologne #365/R
£833 $1292 €1300 Football (38x64cm-15x25in) s. mixed media. 7-Dec-2 Van Ham, Cologne #310/R
£1026 $1590 €1600 Untitled (16x12cm-6x5in) mono. wash oil chk prov. 3-Dec-2 Lempertz, Koln #271/R est:1500
£1200 $1860 €1800 Manner ohne frauen, Parsifal (46x38cm-18x15in) mono. brush ink wax crayon executed 1997 prov. 5-Dec-2 Christie's, Kensington #245/R est:1200-1800
£1899 $3000 €3000 Five ravens (60x85cm-24x33in) mono. chl col pastel chk pen wash prov. 30-Nov-2 Villa Grisebach, Berlin #460/R est:3500-4000
£2014 $3223 €2800 Weight lifter (60x50cm-24x20in) s. oil col chk pencil prov. 15-May-3 Neumeister, Munich #722/R est:2500-3000
£2025 $3200 €3200 Untitled (67x48cm-26x19in) mono. chl chk. 27-Nov-2 Dorotheum, Vienna #110/R est:2500-3500
£2278 $3600 €3600 Untitled (60x85cm-24x33in) mono. gouache col wax pastel chks pen prov. 30-Nov-2 Villa Grisebach, Berlin #458/R est:3500-4000
£5000 $7750 €7800 English person (97x72cm-38x28in) s. gouache oil chk wrapping paper prov. 7-Dec-2 Ketterer, Hamburg #680/R est:8000-10000
£6410 $9936 €10000 Olevano (49x67cm-19x26in) s.i. pastel chk. 3-Dec-2 Lempertz, Koln #272/R est:9000

LUPI, Miguel Angelo (1823-1883) Portuguese
£6289 $9811 €10000 Gallant scene (45x32cm-18x13in) s.i.d.1881. 23-Sep-2 Durán, Madrid #236/R est:3500

LUPIANEZ Y CARRASCO, Jose (1864-1933) Spanish
£370 $577 €540 View of Madrid (19x24cm-7x9in) s. board. 8-Apr-3 Ansorena, Madrid #186/R
£616 $962 €900 Retiro Park (16x24cm-6x9in) s. cardboard. 8-Apr-3 Ansorena, Madrid #30/R
£1026 $1621 €1600 Landscape with trees (81x36cm-32x14in) s. 13-Nov-2 Ansorena, Madrid #279/R
Works on paper
£325 $529 €490 Pardo (25x16cm-10x6in) s.i.d.1899 W/C. 11-Feb-3 Segre, Madrid #8/R

LUPLAU, Marie (1848-1925) Danish
£354 $564 €531 The coachman cutting the grass at Kokkedal (56x32cm-22x13in) s.i.d.96. 5-May-3 Rasmussen, Vejle #727/R (D.KR 3800)
£378 $609 €567 Farm with thatched roof and women in front garden (42x59cm-17x23in) s.d.1880. 22-Feb-3 Rasmussen, Havnen #2081/R (D.KR 4200)

LUPO, Alessandro (1876-1953) Italian
£1474 $2315 €2300 Alpine stream (44x31cm-17x12in) s. board. 10-Dec-2 Della Rocca, Turin #388/R

LUPPEN, Frans van (1838-1899) Belgian
£417 $663 €600 Marine (90x50cm-35x20in) s. 29-Apr-3 Campo, Vlaamse Kaai #331
£540 $896 €540 La valle de Josaphat (48x90cm-19x35in) s. 16-Jun-3 Horta, Bruxelles #304

LUPPEN, Gerard Josef Adrian van (1834-1891) Belgian
£284 $460 €400 Vacher dans un paysage montagneux (38x24cm-15x9in) panel. 26-May-3 Amberes, Antwerp #91
£331 $540 €500 Village dans les Ardennes (40x32cm-16x13in) 17-Feb-3 Amberes, Antwerp #247
£601 $938 €950 Vue de Petit Modave (34x40cm-13x16in) s. 15-Oct-2 Horta, Bruxelles #252

LUPTON, Nevil Oliver (1828-?) British
£680 $1061 €1020 Three ducks on a stream (32x25cm-13x10in) mono. 10-Sep-2 Sworder & Son, Bishops Stortford #781/R

LURCAT, Jean (1892-1966) French
£5319 $8883 €7500 Marseille (82x116cm-32x46in) s.d.26 prov.exhib.lit. 20-Jun-3 Piasa, Paris #191/R est:8000-12000
£6993 $11678 €10000 Paysage de Philippeville (60x81cm-24x32in) s.d. 30-Jun-3 Pierre Berge, Paris #51/R est:10000-12000
£10559 $17000 €15839 Naissance du voilier (101x152cm-40x60in) s.d.31 prov.exhib.lit. 7-May-3 Sotheby's, New York #361/R est:20000-30000
Works on paper
£333 $530 €480 Coq (21x14cm-8x6in) s.d.1955 col dr. 29-Apr-3 Campo & Campo, Antwerp #691
£617 $877 €1000 Paysage (24x32cm-9x13in) s. gouache. 16-Mar-3 Eric Pillon, Calais #253/R
£720 $1174 €1080 Chateau au ciel etoile (58x44cm-23x17in) s. gouache executed 1949 exhib.lit. 3-Feb-3 Bonhams, New Bond Street #65/R
£730 $1153 €1095 Sunday in the countryside (22x31cm-9x12in) s.d.1916 pencil dr. 29-Nov-2 Zofingen, Switzerland #2493/R (S.FR 1700)
£800 $1264 €1200 Mythological scene (30x46cm-12x18in) s. gouache. 3-Apr-3 Christie's, Kensington #133/R
£873 $1362 €1310 Surrealist composition (38x56cm-15x22in) s.d.33 gouache. 6-Nov-2 Dobiaschofsky, Bern #790/R (S.FR 2000)
£1139 $1777 €1800 Marine (32x40cm-13x16in) s.d.1931 gouache. 20-Oct-2 Claude Boisgirard, Paris #28 est:1800-2000
£1200 $1956 €1800 Nature mote au poisson (41x69cm-16x27in) s. pencil gouache exhib. 3-Feb-3 Bonhams, New Bond Street #63/R est:500-800
£1611 $2593 €2400 Le Jugement de Paris. s. gouache. 18-Feb-3 Galerie Moderne, Brussels #246/R est:2000-3000
£2800 $4340 €4200 L'arlequin (32x23cm-13x9in) s. gouache executed 1944. 5-Dec-2 Christie's, Kensington #101/R est:3000-4000

LURCAT, Rossane (20th C) French
Works on paper
£19310 $30897 €28000 Tete de femme (56x45cm-22x18in) s.d.1911 crayon pastel. 13-Mar-3 Artcurial Briest, Paris #57

LURZER-ZECHENTHALL, Rudolf von (1875-1936) Austrian
£833 $1308 €1300 Cairo - Grabmoschee des Kait Bey with figures (100x75cm-39x30in) 21-Nov-2 Dorotheum, Vienna #232/R
£1218 $1912 €1900 Sailing ships on the Nile (100x75cm-39x30in) 21-Nov-2 Dorotheum, Vienna #233/R est:1500-1800
£1795 $2818 €2800 Interior of Egyptian temple with figures (75x100cm-30x39in) 21-Nov-2 Dorotheum, Vienna #234/R est:1500-1800

LUSCHER, Jean Jacques (1884-1955) Swiss
£258 $407 €387 Cow in the dunes (65x84cm-26x33in) s.d.33 s.i.verso. 26-Nov-2 Hans Widmer, St Gallen #1269 (S.FR 600)

LUSCOMBE, Henry A (1820-?) British
£400 $636 €600 Wreck (30x47cm-12x19in) s. board. 4-Mar-3 Bonhams, Knightsbridge #296/R
£630 $977 €945 HM vessel under pirate attack (50x75cm-20x30in) 4-Oct-2 Moore Allen & Innocent, Cirencester #595

LUSK, Doris (1916-1990) New Zealander
£672 $981 €1008 Bridge, central Otago (76x112cm-30x44in) s.d.1985. 12-Sep-1 Watson's, Christchurch #12/R est:28000-38000 (NZ.D 2250)
£2821 $4401 €4232 Art student (52x42cm-20x17in) s.d.1966 board. 7-Nov-2 International Art Centre, Auckland #86/R est:12000-18000 (NZ.D 9000)
£6716 $9806 €10074 Nelson landscape, near Onekaka (35x55cm-14x22in) s.d.1965 board. 12-Sep-1 Watson's, Christchurch #10/R est:20000-30000 (NZ.D 22500)
Works on paper
£796 $1250 €1194 South Island West Coast landscape (27x37cm-11x15in) s.d.1959 ink W/C prov. 10-Dec-2 Peter Webb, Auckland #73/R est:3000-4000 (NZ.D 2500)
£1492 $2179 €2238 Village in the mountains, Otago (27x37cm-11x15in) s.d.1962 W/C. 12-Sep-1 Watson's, Christchurch #79 est:5500-10000 (NZ.D 5000)

LUSSANET, Paul de (1940-) Dutch
£1410 $2186 €2200 Portrait d'une femme vampire (93x73cm-37x29in) s.d.65 s.i.d.verso. 3-Dec-2 Christie's, Amsterdam #349/R est:2000-3000

LUSSENBURGH, Johannes (1889-1975) Dutch
£972 $1604 €1400 Harbour of Elburg (40x60cm-16x24in) s. 1-Jul-3 Christie's, Amsterdam #377

LUSSI, Otto (1883-1942) Swiss
£349 $510 €524 Pan with onions and leek (38x55cm-15x22in) s. lit. 4-Jun-2 Germann, Zurich #796 (S.FR 800)

LUSSO, Paola (1962-) Italian
Works on paper
£327 $523 €500 King and queen (135x80cm-53x31in) s. fresco tempera board. 4-Jan-3 Meeting Art, Vercelli #577
£340 $541 €500 Obstacle overcome (135x75cm-53x30in) s. fresco board exec.2000. 1-Mar-3 Meeting Art, Vercelli #330

LUSTIG, Otto (?) ?
£279 $444 €419 Seascape with the frigate Jylland off Kronborg (22x39cm-9x15in) s. 10-Mar-3 Rasmussen, Vejle #434/R (D.KR 3000)

LUSTY, Otto (19th C) ?
£4610 $7468 €6500 Yacht of the Russian Czar, "Zidona" (64x95cm-25x37in) s. 22-May-3 Dorotheum, Vienna #198/R est:4500-5000

LUSURIER, Catherine (attrib) (1753-1781) French
£1958 $3270 €2800 Portrait d'homme (97x78cm-38x31in) oval. 25-Jun-3 Artcurial Briest, Paris #487/R est:3000-3500

LUTHER, Adolf (1912-1990) German
£1702 $2757 €2400 Material picture (60x50cm-24x20in) i. verso chk oil pigment panel. 24-May-3 Van Ham, Cologne #367/R est:3000

Sculpture
£1795 $2782 €2800 Lens. s.d.75 mirror glass. 3-Dec-2 Lempertz, Koln #277/R est:2800

Works on paper
£1731 $2683 €2700 Material picture in red (29x125cm-11x49in) chalk oil board. 7-Dec-2 Van Ham, Cologne #313/R est:3800

LUTHI, Ernest (1906-1983) Canadian
£304 $475 €508 Bridge across Salem Creek, Geenfields (30x41cm-12x16in) s.i. i.d.1976 verso canvasboard. 13-Apr-3 Levis, Calgary #80/R (C.D 700)

LUTHI, Urs (1947-) Swiss
£1747 $2550 €2621 Selfportrait from the series on devotion (30x40cm-12x16in) s.i.d.1985 verso acrylic. 4-Jun-2 Germann, Zurich #83/R est:2600-3000 (S.FR 4000)

LUTHY, Emil (1890-1966) Swiss?
£830 $1311 €1245 Woman on sun terrace (39x28cm-15x11in) 14-Nov-2 Stuker, Bern #375 est:2200-2600 (S.FR 1900)

LUTHY, J (19th C) Swiss
£1762 $2626 €2643 Portraits of Mr and Mrs Holzhalb (66x51cm-26x20in) s.d.1890 pair. 25-Jun-2 Koller, Zurich #6575 est:700-1000 (S.FR 4000)

LUTHY, Johannes (1803-1873) Swiss
£1810 $3023 €2625 Portrait, probably of artist's father holding brush (99x79cm-39x31in) s.d.1882 prov. 24-Jun-3 Koller, Zurich #4/R est:2500-3500 (S.FR 4000)
£1900 $3174 €2755 Self portrait holding drawing pen and glasses (91x72cm-36x28in) prov. 24-Jun-3 Koller, Zurich #3/R est:3000-5000 (S.FR 4200)

LUTHY, Oskar Wilhelm (1882-1945) Swiss
£437 $681 €656 Madonna with child (80x59cm-31x23in) s.d.44 board. 6-Nov-2 Dobiaschofsky, Bern #793 (S.FR 1000)
£1373 $2170 €2060 Rose branch (41x35cm-16x14in) s.d.1933 board. 29-Nov-2 Zofingen, Switzerland #2967/R est:1500 (S.FR 3200)
£1545 $2441 €2318 Roses in glass (53x46cm-21x18in) s. board. 29-Nov-2 Zofingen, Switzerland #2968 est:2000 (S.FR 3600)

LUTI, Benedetto (1666-1724) Italian
£21605 $35000 €32408 Head of Saint John (49x40cm-19x16in) copper oval. 23-Jan-3 Sotheby's, New York #111a/R est:40000-60000

LUTI, Benedetto (attrib) (1666-1724) Italian
£1793 $2869 €2600 Baptism of Christ (98x83cm-39x33in) 17-Mar-3 Pandolfini, Florence #543/R est:2500-3000

Works on paper
£633 $1000 €1000 Jael and Sisera (10x13cm-4x5in) pen wash ochre double-sided. 29-Nov-2 Bassenge, Berlin #5361
£3797 $6000 €6000 Tete d'homme barbu (26x20cm-10x8in) crayon chk. 28-Nov-2 Tajan, Paris #32/R

LUTICHER, Fernand (19th C) ?
£559 $888 €839 Shepherdess with sheep (35x65cm-14x26in) s. 5-Mar-3 Rasmussen, Copenhagen #1888/R (D.KR 6000)

LUTKEN, Mathias (1841-1905) Danish
£315 $508 €473 Seascape with vessel in rough seas (42x62cm-17x24in) s.d.1881. 22-Feb-3 Rasmussen, Havnen #2080/R (D.KR 3500)

LUTSCHER, Fernand (19th C) French
£281 $443 €422 Wooded landscape with hunter, dog and old woman (65x49cm-26x19in) s. 30-Nov-2 Goteborg Auktionsverk, Sweden #191/R (S.KR 4000)

LUTTER, Vera (20th C) ?

Photographs
£4841 $7600 €7262 Pepsi Cola, small vent (65x34cm-26x13in) gelatin silver print. 21-Apr-3 Phillips, New York #42/R est:4000-6000

LUTTERELL, Edward (1650-1710) British

Works on paper
£1600 $2656 €2400 Portrait of a cardinal (31x22cm-12x9in) pastel. 12-Jun-3 Sotheby's, London #112/R est:1000-1500

LUTTEROTH, Ascan (1842-1923) German
£338 $527 €500 Praying at wayside cross (28x40cm-11x16in) s.i. i. verso board. 26-Mar-3 Hugo Ruef, Munich #166
£816 $1298 €1200 Lake near Ratzeburg (39x58cm-15x23in) s. i.d.1898 verso canvas on board. 19-Mar-3 Neumeister, Munich #635/R est:2000
£1351 $2108 €2000 Southern landscape with peasants (75x64cm-30x25in) s. 27-Mar-3 Dr Fritz Nagel, Stuttgart #833/R est:1500
£1379 $2179 €2000 Spring on the Luthe (65x100cm-26x39in) s. 5-Apr-3 Hans Stahl, Hamburg #134/R est:1800
£1667 $2583 €2600 Capri (46x27cm-18x11in) s.i. 5-Dec-2 Schopman, Hamburg #527 est:3200
£2628 $4074 €4100 View of Menton across bay (42x66cm-17x26in) s. canvas on board. 7-Dec-2 Hans Stahl, Hamburg #129/R est:3000
£2800 $4676 €4200 Anacapri (63x47cm-25x19in) s. i.verso. 18-Jun-3 Christie's, Kensington #154/R est:2200-2500
£6000 $9780 €8700 Picnic on the riverbank (75x110cm-30x43in) s. 16-Jul-3 Sotheby's, Olympia #193/R est:5000-7000

Works on paper
£325 $474 €500 Rocky bay near San Terenzo (46x32cm-18x13in) s.i. W/C. 15-Jun-2 Hans Stahl, Hamburg #200/R
£650 $1066 €975 Coastal landscape with figures, a monastery and sailing boats in the distance (65x99cm-26x39in) s. W/C htd white. 4-Feb-3 Sworder & Son, Bishops Stortford #118/R

LUTTICHUYS, Isaak (1616-1673) Dutch
£11000 $17160 €16500 Portrait of a lady in a black dress (70x53cm-28x21in) s.d.1665 panel. 9-Apr-3 Bonhams, New Bond Street #104/R est:4000-6000

LUTTNER, Vera (1960-) American

Photographs
£25316 $40000 €37974 View of Cleveland Flats, V crittenden Court Apartments (141x254cm-56x100in) gelatin silver pin hole negative executed 1997 prov. 14-Nov-2 Christie's, Rockefeller NY #439/R est:20000-30000

LUTYENS, Frederick M (1860-1924) British
£620 $986 €930 Portrait of Beatrice Lutyens, niece of the artist, head and shoulders (61x51cm-24x20in) s. 27-Feb-3 Bonhams, Chester #375

LUTZ, Anton (20th C) ?
£3205 $5064 €5000 Attersee (56x64cm-22x25in) s. panel. 18-Nov-2 Dorotheum, Linz #320/R est:10000-12000
£3797 $6000 €6000 Seated female nude (55x37cm-22x15in) s.d.56 masonite. 27-Nov-2 Dorotheum, Vienna #197/R est:7000-9000
£3846 $6077 €6000 Harbour in Grado II (54x63cm-21x25in) s.d.60 panel. 18-Nov-2 Dorotheum, Linz #319/R est:9000-10000

LUTZ, Dan (1906-1978) American

Works on paper
£484 $750 €726 Shacks on the river (41x51cm-16x20in) s. W/C prov. 29-Oct-2 John Moran, Pasadena #687

LUTZ, Rudolf (1895-1955) German

Works on paper
£278 $439 €400 Composition (23x32cm-9x13in) mono.i. chl. 26-Apr-3 Dr Lehr, Berlin #328/R

LUVONI, Luigi (1859-1904) Italian
£442 $703 €650 Labour in the fields (70x85cm-28x33in) s. 1-Mar-3 Meeting Art, Vercelli #183

LUX, Adrian (1938-) Hungarian
£318 $497 €500 Watermill in romantic mountain valley (60x50cm-24x20in) s. lit. 7-Nov-2 Allgauer, Kempten #2890/R

LUYKEN, Jan (1649-1712) Dutch
Works on paper
£541 $843 €800 Fire (10x15cm-4x6in) i. pen ink wash. 26-Mar-3 Piasa, Paris #28
£1019 $1590 €1600 Roman battle scene (11x15cm-4x6in) pen brown ink wash prov. 5-Nov-2 Sotheby's, Amsterdam #199/R est:700-1000

LUYKEN, Jan (attrib) (1649-1712) Dutch
Works on paper
£2315 $3750 €3473 Audience watching performance (11x13cm-4x5in) pen ink wash chk. 21-Jan-3 Sotheby's, New York #165/R

LUYKX, Christiaan (1623-c.1653) Flemish
£16000 $24960 €24000 Still life of garland of flowers with Madonna and Child (65x49cm-26x19in) panel prov. 10-Apr-3 Sotheby's, London #54/R est:20000

LUYT, Arie Marthinus (1879-1951) Dutch
£1529 $2385 €2400 Still life of flowers (90x120cm-35x47in) s.i.d.08. 6-Nov-2 Vendue Huis, Gravenhage #485/R est:2000-3000

LUYT, Arie Marthinus (attrib) (1879-1951) Dutch
£1923 $3019 €3000 Still life of fruit with birds in park landscape (139x111cm-55x44in) s.d.1918. 21-Nov-2 Van Ham, Cologne #1766/R est:3200

LUYTEN, Henri (1859-1945) Belgian
£759 $1185 €1200 Still life with flowers (79x59cm-31x23in) s. 21-Oct-2 Bernaerts, Antwerp #113/R
£949 $1500 €1500 Chemin de campagne au coucher du soleil avec promeneur (40x62cm-16x24in) s. panel. 26-Nov-2 Palais de Beaux Arts, Brussels #343/R est:1000-1500
£1835 $2863 €2900 Etang aux canards (80x64cm-31x25in) s. 16-Sep-2 Horta, Bruxelles #459 est:1500-2000
£3797 $5924 €6000 Shepherd and his flock (100x149cm-39x59in) s. 21-Oct-2 Bernaerts, Antwerp #506/R est:3000-4000

LUZA, Raul (20th C) Mexican
£566 $900 €849 Woman and children (64x79cm-25x31in) indis.sig. painted c.1970. 2-Mar-3 Toomey, Oak Park #637/R

LUZURIAGA, Juan Ramon (1938-) Spanish
£582 $896 €925 Oven smoke (55x46cm-22x18in) s. s.i.d.1977. 22-Oct-2 Durán, Madrid #131/R
£677 $1070 €1050 Saint Anthony's church (73x60cm-29x24in) s.i.d.1974 verso. 18-Dec-2 Ansorena, Madrid #389
£755 $1177 €1200 Carmen (81x65cm-32x26in) s.d.1974 s.i.d.verso. 17-Sep-2 Segre, Madrid #207/R
£828 $1316 €1200 Rubber house (81x65cm-32x26in) s. s.i.d.1974 verso. 4-Mar-3 Ansorena, Madrid #214/R
£833 $1317 €1300 Boat (65x54cm-26x21in) s. s.i.d.1977 verso. 19-Nov-2 Durán, Madrid #208/R
£856 $1336 €1250 Boat (73x60cm-29x24in) s. s.i.d.1977. 8-Apr-3 Ansorena, Madrid #22/R
£878 $1370 €1300 Old boat (65x81cm-26x32in) s. s.i.d.1977 verso. 25-Mar-3 Durán, Madrid #129/R
£966 $1526 €1400 F. with umbrellas (73x92cm-29x36in) s.d.1974 s.i.d.verso. 1-Apr-3 Segre, Madrid #352/R
£1007 $1621 €1500 Seascape (92x73cm-36x29in) s. s.i.d.1978 verso. 18-Feb-3 Durán, Madrid #150/R

LVOV, Piotr Ivanovich (1882-1944) Russian
£860 $1341 €1350 Lake covered in snow (46x55cm-18x22in) s. 10-Nov-2 Eric Pillon, Calais #62/R
£949 $1472 €1500 Paysage de neige au soleil couchant (46x55cm-18x22in) s. 29-Sep-2 Eric Pillon, Calais #161/R
£1923 $3019 €3000 Swans on the lake (50x65cm-20x26in) s. 15-Dec-2 Eric Pillon, Calais #175/R

LYALL, Laura Adeline (1860-1930) Canadian
£1556 $2551 €2334 Young girl in cream (66x46cm-26x18in) s.d.1909 prov. 27-May-3 Sotheby's, Toronto #35/R est:4000-6000 (C.D 3500)
£6612 $10380 €9918 Portrait of Mary Scott Fry (53x36cm-21x14in) s.d.1928 prov.exhib. 24-Jul-2 Walker's, Ottawa #213/R est:3500-4000 (C.D 16000)
Works on paper
£1333 $2187 €2000 Forest nymph at dawn (22x47cm-9x19in) s.d.1902 W/C. 3-Jun-3 Joyner, Toronto #19/R est:3000-4000 (C.D 3000)
£2469 $3827 €3704 Girl with garland (41x27cm-16x11in) W/C. 3-Dec-2 Joyner, Toronto #79/R est:10000-15000 (C.D 6000)

LYBAERT, Theodore (19th C) ?
£1389 $2209 €2000 Tambour (65x38cm-26x15in) s. 30-Apr-3 Tajan, Paris #120/R est:2400-3000

LYBAERT, Theophile Marie Françoise (1848-1927) Belgian
£2484 $3999 €3800 Jeune chamelier au bord de la mer (53x78cm-21x31in) s. 20-Jan-3 Horta, Bruxelles #46 est:1500-2000

LYCETT, Joseph (1774-1828) British
Works on paper
£10000 $15800 €15000 Sydney from Parramatta Road (41x54cm 16x21in) W/C lit. 17 Nov 2 Sotheby's, Paddington #10/R est:30000 50000 (A.D 28000)

LYDEN, Edvin (1879-1956) Finnish
£503 $775 €800 Apple-tree (40x52cm-16x20in) s. 24-Oct-2 Hagelstam, Helsinki #933
£3481 $5500 €5500 Summer night (27x44cm-11x17in) s.d.1925 board. 1-Dec-2 Bukowskis, Helsinki #333/R est:2000-2500

LYDIS, Mariette (1890-1970) Austrian
£894 $1457 €1350 Portrait of Montherlant (53x43cm-21x17in) s.d.1950. 3-Feb-3 Cornette de St.Cyr, Paris #316/R
£1549 $2494 €2200 Enfant de cirque (61x49cm-24x19in) panel lit. 9-May-3 Schloss Ahlden, Ahlden #1555/R est:2600
Works on paper
£833 $1308 €1300 Hermine (29x46cm-11x18in) s.d.1930 crayon Chinese ink htd W/C. 20-Nov-2 Claude Boisgirard, Paris #18/R

LYLE, Thomas Byron (fl.1880-1890) British
£750 $1178 €1125 Young girl seated on a park bench wearing a brown dress and bonnet (46x33cm-18x13in) s.i.d.82. 19-Nov-2 Bonhams, Leeds #200

LYMAN, John Goodwin (1886-1967) Canadian
£288 $447 €432 Airplane (16x23cm-6x9in) s. oil on paper painted c.1912. 3-Dec-2 Joyner, Toronto #316/R (C.D 700)
£3863 $6026 €5795 Lake Massawippi, the coming storm (40x51cm-16x20in) s. 25-Mar-3 Iegor de Saint Hippolyte, Montreal #83/R (C.D 9000)
£5333 $8747 €8000 Portrait of Marcelle (100x70cm-39x28in) s. painted c.1935 prov.exhib.lit. 3-Jun-3 Joyner, Toronto #40/R est:15000-20000 (C.D 12000)
£6667 $10933 €10001 Quarrying by the roadside, St. Jovite (38x55cm-15x22in) s.i.d.1934 masonite prov.exhib. 27-May-3 Sotheby's, Toronto #1/R est:10000-15000 (C.D 15000)
Works on paper
£1564 $2424 €2346 Le liseur et les sirenes, 1949 (29x44cm-11x17in) s. W/C prov. 3-Dec-2 Joyner, Toronto #119/R est:4000-5000 (C.D 3800)

LYMAN, Stephen (1957-1996) American
£7595 $12000 €11013 Quiet rain (69x46cm-27x18in) s. acrylic on board prov.lit. 26-Jul-3 Coeur d'Alene, Hayden #35/R est:10000-15000
£8861 $14000 €12848 New territories (38x76cm-15x30in) s. acrylic prov. 26-Jul-3 Coeur d'Alene, Hayden #74/R est:6000-12000
£8861 $14000 €12848 Golden sanctuary (66x56cm-26x22in) s. acrylic on board prov. 26-Jul-3 Coeur d'Alene, Hayden #155/R est:10000-15000
£18987 $30000 €27531 High creek crossing (66x183cm-26x72in) s. acrylic prov.lit. 26-Jul-3 Coeur d'Alene, Hayden #207/R est:30000-50000

LYMBURNER, Francis (1916-1972) Australian
£1073 $1684 €1610 Harvest queen (45x60cm-18x24in) s. canvas on board. 15-Apr-3 Lawson Menzies, Sydney #173/R est:2500-3000 (A.D 2800)
£1107 $1749 €1661 Sewing machine (51x76cm-20x30in) s. 27-Nov-2 Deutscher-Menzies, Melbourne #209/R est:2500-4000 (A.D 3100)
£1214 $1919 €1821 Ship and mermaid hotel (54x61cm-21x24in) 17-Nov-2 Sotheby's, Paddington #47/R est:5000-8000 (A.D 3400)
£1220 $1927 €1769 Mother and children at the beech. Figures (55x35cm-22x14in) double-sided. 22-Jul-3 Lawson Menzies, Sydney #151/R est:3500-5500 (A.D 3000)
£1500 $2370 €2250 Jude (36x26cm-14x10in) s. board. 17-Nov-2 Sotheby's, Paddington #81/R est:2000-4000 (A.D 4200)
£1779 $2722 €2669 Palette table (75x49cm-30x19in) s. i.verso prov. 25-Aug-2 Sotheby's, Paddington #151/R est:3000-5000 (A.D 5000)
£1938 $3081 €2907 Summer day (54x84cm-21x33in) s. board prov. 5-May-3 Sotheby's, Melbourne #313/R est:5000-8000 (A.D 5000)
Works on paper
£430 $654 €645 Showgirl (52x40cm-20x16in) s. ink wash W/C exhib. 27-Aug-2 Goodman, Sydney #69 (A.D 1200)

LYNAS-GRAY, J A (1869-?) British
Works on paper
£280 $426 €420 Wooded scene with sheep in the distance (20x18cm-8x7in) s.d.1923 W/C. 4-Jul-2 Duke & Son, Dorchester #40

LYNAS-GRAY, John Abernethy (1869-?) British
Works on paper
£320 $496 €480 Figures outside a coastal cottage (24x34cm-9x13in) s.d.1916 W/C. 3-Dec-2 Sworder & Son, Bishops Stortford #950/R
£500 $810 €750 Near Henley in Arden (17x25cm-7x10in) s.d.1917 W/C. 21-Jan-3 Bonhams, Knightsbridge #258/R

LYNCH, Albert (1851-?) Peruvian
£4610 $7145 €6915 Lady reading against red background (62x50cm-24x20in) s. 4-Dec-2 AB Stockholms Auktionsverk #1845/R est:18000-20000 (S.KR 65000)
£6500 $10206 €9750 Beauty (46x33cm-18x13in) s. 19-Nov-2 Sotheby's, London #170/R est:6000-8000
£7500 $12525 €11250 Quiet read (61x50cm-24x20in) s. 18-Jun-3 Christie's, Kensington #127/R est:7000-9000
Works on paper
£471 $772 €720 Femme se penchant sur homme allonge dans une charrette (18x27cm-7x11in) s. W/C gouache crayon. 7-Feb-3 Piasa, Paris #192
£1341 $2200 €2012 Portrait of an elegant woman (117x89cm-46x35in) s. pastel on canvas. 5-Feb-3 Doyle, New York #68/R est:1000-1500

LYNCH, Padraig (1940-) Irish
£395 $616 €620 Cottage in woodland (30x25cm-12x10in) s. 6-Nov-2 James Adam, Dublin #5/R
£2464 $4041 €3400 Evening sun, Skerries, 1987 (46x61cm-18x24in) s. 28-May-3 Bonhams & James Adam, Dublin #96/R est:3000-4000

LYNCKER, Ernst (1883-?) German
Works on paper
£256 $390 €400 Femme au chapeau bleu (36x25cm-14x10in) st.sig. W/C. 10-Jul-2 Rabourdin & Choppin de Janvry, Paris #2
£256 $390 €400 Elegante a l'eventail (42x30cm-17x12in) st.sig. W/C. 10-Jul-2 Rabourdin & Choppin de Janvry, Paris #4
£256 $390 €400 Les deux amies (46x29cm-18x11in) st.sig. W/C. 10-Jul-2 Rabourdin & Choppin de Janvry, Paris #5/R
£256 $390 €400 Tenue de soiree dans la loge de theatre (48x31cm-19x12in) s.d.16 mars 1927 W/C. 10-Jul-2 Rabourdin & Choppin de Janvry, Paris #8
£256 $390 €400 Elegante au chapeau jaune (49x33cm-19x13in) s.d.1928 W/C. 10-Jul-2 Rabourdin & Choppin de Janvry, Paris #9
£353 $536 €550 Couple en tenue de soiree (48x30cm-19x12in) s.d.1927 chl pencil W/C. 10-Jul-2 Rabourdin & Choppin de Janvry, Paris #10/R

LYNDE, Raymond (?) British?
£15337 $25000 €23006 Proud mother (51x76cm-20x30in) s. 11-Feb-3 Bonhams & Doyles, New York #106/R est:25000-35000

LYNDSAY, Roy (20th C) Irish?
£1338 $2221 €1900 Off Tory Island (52x62cm-20x24in) s. 10-Jun-3 James Adam, Dublin #195/R est:2000-3000
£2027 $3162 €3000 Beach (38x98cm-15x39in) s. 26-Mar-3 James Adam, Dublin #94/R est:4000-6000

LYNE, Michael (1912-1989) British
£560 $913 €840 Eton College hounds - study of five beagles (30x50cm-12x20in) s.i.d.1936 pair. 17-Feb-3 Bonhams, Bath #34
£1200 $1992 €1740 In full gallop (41x76cm-16x30in) s. 12-Jun-3 Christie's, Kensington #109/R est:300-500
£1528 $2200 €2292 Home and dry (102x127cm-40x50in) s. prov. 15-Jan-3 Christie's, Rockefeller NY #172/R
£1800 $2844 €2700 Stalking black corries (71x91cm-28x36in) s. 13-Nov-2 Halls, Shrewsbury #419/R est:1800-2200
Works on paper
£260 $413 €390 An otter study (19x24cm-7x9in) s. pencil. 7-Mar-3 Tennants, Leyburn #106
£280 $445 €420 Heavy horse showing (16x19cm-6x7in) s. pencil. 7-Mar-3 Tennants, Leyburn #107
£320 $522 €480 Partners in crime (20x23cm-8x9in) s. chl pastel. 12-Feb-3 Bonhams, Knightsbridge #131/R
£345 $552 €500 Black and white terrier (23x25cm-9x10in) s. pastel. 12-Mar-3 James Adam, Dublin #143
£480 $778 €720 Steeplechasing (21x32cm-8x13in) s. pastel. 21-Jan-3 Bonhams, Knightsbridge #248/R
£650 $1079 €943 Jack Russell terrier (25x35cm-10x14in) s. pencil W/C htd white. 12-Jun-3 Christie's, Kensington #248/R
£1800 $2988 €2610 Mendip hunt near wells (42x58cm-17x23in) s. W/C bodycol prov. 12-Jun-3 Christie's, Kensington #26/R est:2000-3000

LYNEN, Amedee (1852-1938) Belgian
Works on paper
£272 $433 €400 Sur le quai (22x25cm-9x10in) s. W/C. 18-Mar-3 Campo, Vlaamse Kaai #143
£304 $474 €480 Jeune femme nuue au bord de l'eau (25x19cm-10x7in) s.d.87 mixed media. 16-Sep-2 Horta, Bruxelles #308
£719 $1151 €1000 Charretier buvant une chope (27x34cm-11x13in) s.d.1937 pen W/C dr. 19-May-3 Horta, Bruxelles #416

LYNEN, Armand (20th C) Belgian
£253 $395 €400 Les iris (55x43cm-22x17in) s. 15-Oct-2 Vanderkindere, Brussels #42

LYNGBO, Christen (1871-1968) Danish
£442 $689 €663 Heath landscape with small lake and two lapwings (40x67cm-16x26in) s. 5-Aug-2 Rasmussen, Vejle #192/R (D.KR 5200)
£578 $920 €867 View towards Blabjerg (43x60cm-17x24in) s.d.1917. 5-May-3 Rasmussen, Vejle #705/R (D.KR 6200)

LYNN, Elwyn Augustus (1917-1997) Australian
£575 $902 €863 Channel (36x46cm-14x18in) s.i.d.June 1991 oil collage on canvas. 15-Apr-3 Lawson Menzies, Sydney #238/R est:1500-3000 (A.D 1500)
£920 $1444 €1380 Fire on ice (25x38cm-10x15in) s.d.58 board prov. 15-Apr-3 Lawson Menzies, Sydney #118/R est:2500-3000 (A.D 2400)
£1357 $2131 €2036 Last tide (76x102cm-30x40in) s.i.d.Feb 1965 oil wood hessian rice paper. 25-Nov-2 Christie's, Melbourne #383/R est:3000-5000 (A.D 3800)
£1440 $2318 €2160 Nike (122x152cm-48x60in) s. i.d.1963 verso oil collage on canvas. 6-May-3 Christie's, Melbourne #204 est:6500-8500 (A.D 3600)
£2777 $4222 €4166 Trois nuages (150x150cm-59x59in) s.i.d.1983 verso oil mixed media. 28-Aug-2 Deutscher-Menzies, Melbourne #361/R est:4500-6500 (A.D 7750)
£2857 $4743 €4868 Miners huts (122x122cm-48x48in) s.i.verso exhib. 10-Jun-3 Shapiro, Sydney #33/R est:8000-12000 (A.D 7200)
£2873 $4281 €4310 Last tide (76x102cm-30x40in) s.d.Feb 1965 oil wood hessian rice paper on canvas. 27-Aug-2 Christie's, Melbourne #156/R est:3000-5000 (A.D 7500)
Works on paper
£529 $835 €767 Monkstone (32x50cm-13x20in) s.i.verso mixed media. 22-Jul-3 Lawson Menzies, Sydney #175/R est:1500-3000 (A.D 1300)
£843 $1323 €1265 Heroes on both sides (67x76cm-26x30in) s.i.d.6.8.81 mixed media on canvas. 15-Apr-3 Lawson Menzies, Sydney #263/R est:2200-2800 (A.D 2200)
£894 $1413 €1296 Arboreal (44x51cm-17x20in) s.d.1968 verso mixed media on ply. 22-Jul-3 Lawson Menzies, Sydney #170/R est:2500-3500 (A.D 2200)
£1922 $2940 €2883 Lascaux (103x76cm-41x30in) d.1962 verso mixed media on canvas prov.exhib. 26-Aug-2 Sotheby's, Paddington #578 est:1700-2000 (A.D 5400)
£2183 $3623 €3719 Silver murrumbidgee (103x154cm-41x61in) s.i.d.1991 mixed media paper on canvas. 10-Jun-3 Shapiro, Sydney #46/R est:5000-7000 (A.D 5500)

LYNN, John (fl.1826-1838) British
£2900 $4553 €4350 Topsail schooner off the coast (51x69cm-20x27in) 16-Dec-2 Sotheby's, Olympia #21/R est:1000-1500
£11321 $18000 €16982 East Indian Madagascar off Berry Head (53x81cm-21x32in) s. 30-Apr-3 Sotheby's, New York #574/R est:20000-30000

LYNN, John (attrib) (fl.1826-1838) British
£645 $1000 €968 Sailing vessels in stormy seas (46x61cm-18x24in) painted c.1852. 8-Dec-2 Toomey, Oak Park #652/R

LYNTON, H S (19/20th C) British
£380 $585 €570 Street scene in Cairo (48x74cm-19x29in) s.d.1866 i.d.verso. 5-Sep-2 Amersham Auction Rooms, UK #298/R

LYON SCHOOL (19th C) French
Works on paper
£18000 $30060 €26100 Three studies of loaves (20x29cm-8x11in) i. black chk W/C htd white. 8-Jul-3 Christie's, London #88/R est:3000-5000

LYON, Andrew (?) British
Works on paper
£340 $558 €510 Bradda Head, Port Erin, Isle of Man (29x44cm-11x17in) s.d.83 W/C. 4-Jun-3 Bonhams, Chester #299

LYON, Danny (1942-) American
Photographs
£3165 $5000 €4748 Crossing the Ohio River from Kentucky (22x33cm-9x13in) s.i. verso gelatin silver print prov.lit. 25-Apr-3 Phillips, New York #53/R est:3000-5000

LYON, Dustin (20th C) American
£868 $1450 €1259 Evening camp (64x91cm-25x36in) s. 21-Jun-3 Selkirks, St. Louis #179/R est:2000-3000
£1916 $3200 €2778 Evening campfire (61x76cm-24x30in) s. 21-Jun-3 Selkirks, St. Louis #180/R est:3000-4000
£2395 $4000 €3473 Songs to the morning (122x91cm-48x36in) s. 21-Jun-3 Selkirks, St. Louis #181/R est:5000-6000

LYON, Harold (1930-) Canadian
£602 $952 €903 Desert roundup (41x51cm-16x20in) 1-Dec-2 Levis, Calgary #60/R (C.D 1500)
£826 $1289 €1378 Ridge riders (46x61cm-18x24in) s. i.verso prov. 13-Apr-3 Levis, Calgary #81/R est:2000-3000 (C.D 1900)
£1245 $1967 €1868 Morning (61x91cm-24x36in) 1-Dec-2 Levis, Calgary #59/R est:2500-3000 (C.D 3100)
£1356 $2156 €2034 Packing it in (50x90cm-20x35in) s.i. 23-Mar-3 Hodgins, Calgary #29/R est:2000-3000 (C.D 3200)

LYON, John Howard (?-1921) British
£280 $456 €420 Rocky river torrent (50x60cm-20x24in) s. 17-Feb-3 Bonhams, Bath #148
£1100 $1793 €1650 Deer in the highlands (51x76cm-20x30in) s. 29-Jan-3 Sotheby's, Olympia #238/R est:600-800

LYON, Thomas Bonar (1873-1955) British
£400 $652 €600 Grenans Castle, Ayr (30cm-12in) 14-Feb-3 Lyon & Turnbull, Edinburgh #27
£580 $887 €870 Tam O'Shanter Inn, Ary (41x53cm-16x21in) s. canvas on board. 22-Aug-2 Bonhams, Edinburgh #950
£680 $1040 €1020 Holmston Farm (19x24cm-7x9in) s. 22-Aug-2 Bonhams, Edinburgh #1136
£720 $1195 €1044 Street trading, Bruges (25x30cm-10x12in) s. indis.i.verso panel. 10-Jun-3 David Lay, Penzance #81
£920 $1408 €1380 Yachts at Tarbert, Loch Fyne (19x24cm-7x9in) s. board. 22-Aug-2 Bonhams, Edinburgh #998
£1300 $2028 €1950 Fishing harbour (51x61cm-20x24in) s. 10-Apr-3 Bonhams, Edinburgh #114 est:800-1000
£1500 $2475 €2175 Golden boats, Dunure, Ayrshire (46x61cm-18x24in) s. s.i.verso. 3-Jul-3 Christie's, Kensington #448/R est:500-800
£2300 $3588 €3450 Fairground (19x24cm-7x9in) s. panel. 10-Apr-3 Bonhams, Edinburgh #124 est:300-500

LYONCOURT, Baron Hubard de (fl.1869-1883) British
£300 $477 €450 Beauregard Farm, Sark (16x30cm-6x12in) i.verso board painted 1872. 20-Mar-3 Martel Maides, Guernsey #31/R

LYONGRUN, Arnold (1871-?) German
£276 $427 €430 Fully rigged sailing ship (70x100cm-28x39in) s. i. verso. 7-Dec-2 Ketterer, Hamburg #39/R
£403 $648 €600 Peasant woman making butter inside (38x46cm-15x18in) s. 21-Feb-3 Sigalas, Stuttgart #957/R

LYRE, Adolphe la (1850-1935) French
£288 $453 €450 Desire (33x41cm-13x16in) s.d.1930 panel. 15-Dec-2 Mercier & Cie, Lille #346
£380 $589 €600 Portrait de femme devant la mer (47x56cm-19x22in) s. 29-Sep-2 Eric Pillon, Calais #89/R
£1266 $2000 €1899 Temptress with tambourine (61x51cm-24x20in) s. panel. 16-Nov-2 New Orleans Auction, New Orleans #334/R est:2500-4000

LYTH, Harald (1937-) Swedish
Works on paper
£1467 $2362 €2201 Untitled (65x40cm-26x16in) s. W/C collage. 7-May-3 AB Stockholms Auktionsverk #1015/R est:20000-25000 (S.KR 19000)

LYTLE, Ralph Arthur (1882-1959) American
£366 $600 €549 California landscape (61x91cm-24x36in) 9-Feb-3 William Jenack, New York #240

LYTRAS, Nicolas (1883-1927) Greek
£95000 $147250 €142500 In the garden (104x72cm-41x28in) s. 2-Oct-2 Sotheby's, London #30/R est:100000-150000

LYTRAS, Nicolas (attrib) (1883-1927) Greek
£6000 $9480 €9000 Seate boy (57x40cm-22x16in) 1-Apr-3 Bonhams, New Bond Street #51 est:8000-12000

LYTTLETON, W (17/18th C) British
Works on paper
£2700 $4266 €3915 View of Fort MacDonald Ceylon (18x33cm-7x13in) W/C sold with a brooch and letter. 22-Jul-3 Gorringes, Lewes #1730 est:1500-2000

LYTZEN, N A (1826-1890) Danish
£263 $420 €395 Portrait of dog (36x26cm-14x10in) i.verso. 13-Jan-3 Rasmussen, Vejle #29/R (D.KR 3000)
£271 $434 €407 Portrait of dog (22x20cm-9x8in) s. 13-Jan-3 Rasmussen, Vejle #30/R (D.KR 3100)
£328 $501 €492 Curious cat (13x18cm-5x7in) panel. 24-Aug-2 Rasmussen, Havnen #2011 (D.KR 3800)

LYYTIKAINEN, Olli (1949-1987) Finnish
Works on paper
£3291 $5200 €5200 Agony (23x31cm-9x12in) s.d.1977 W/C exhib. 1-Dec-2 Bukowskis, Helsinki #334/R est:1000-1200

MA JIN (1900-1971) Chinese
Works on paper
£1399 $2308 €2029 Landscapes (18x49cm-7x19in) s.i. ink fan. 6-Jul-3 Christie's, Hong Kong #282/R est:20000-25000 (HK.D 18000)
£5439 $8974 €7887 Horse (106x59cm-42x23in) s. ink scroll. 6-Jul-3 Christie's, Hong Kong #281/R est:35000-45000 (HK.D 70000)
£9324 $15385 €13520 Goats (129x66cm-51x26in) s.i. ink scroll. 6-Jul-3 Christie's, Hong Kong #282a/R est:120000-150000 (HK.D 120000)

MAAR, Dora (1909-1997) French
£344 $561 €520 Paysage (33x41cm-13x16in) prov. 3-Feb-3 Cornette de St.Cyr, Paris #319
£405 $632 €600 Arbres (54x68cm-21x27in) 26-Mar-3 Millon & Associes, Paris #127
£464 $756 €700 Paysage (46x38cm-18x15in) init.verso prov. 3-Feb-3 Cornette de St.Cyr, Paris #318
£507 $791 €750 Effets de lumiere (38x55cm-15x22in) init.verso. 26-Mar-3 Millon & Associes, Paris #128
£1060 $1727 €1600 Paysage (130x97cm-51x38in) s. prov. 3-Feb-3 Cornette de St.Cyr, Paris #317
£1603 $2532 €2500 Allegory of Religion (66x82cm-26x32in) s. 13-Nov-2 Ansorena, Madrid #169/R
Photographs
£1899 $3000 €2849 Headstand, Barcelona (28x24cm-11x9in) estate st. verso ferrotyped prov. 23-Apr-3 Sotheby's, New York #166/R est:3000-5000
£4000 $6480 €6000 Nude in a doorway (30x24cm-12x9in) st.verso silver print exec.c.1938 sold with Beaute magazine prov. 22-May-3 Sotheby's, London #76/R est:3000-4000
£7595 $12000 €11393 Assia en masque blanc suspendue a un Anneau (34x14cm-13x6in) i.verso gelatin silver print mounted on board executed c.1934. 24-Apr-3 Phillips, New York #21/R est:8000-12000

MAAREL, Marinus van der (1857-1921) Dutch
£586 $932 €850 Misdienaar (36x18cm-14x7in) s. panel. 10-Mar-3 Sotheby's, Amsterdam #185 est:400-600

MAARNI, Elvi (1907-) Finnish
£1532 $2512 €2221 Figures (37x29cm-15x11in) s. 4-Jun-3 AB Stockholms Auktionsverk #2483/R est:10000-12000 (S.KR 19500)
Works on paper
£324 $531 €450 Fruit (20x29cm-8x11in) s. mixed media. 5-Jun-3 Hagelstam, Helsinki #905
£475 $779 €660 Park avenue (25x17cm-10x7in) s. chl. 5-Jun-3 Hagelstam, Helsinki #906
£563 $907 €800 Spring is coming (40x28cm-16x11in) s. chl. 10-May-3 Bukowskis, Helsinki #109/R
£576 $944 €800 Girl and flower (38x28cm-15x11in) s. chl. 5-Jun-3 Hagelstam, Helsinki #927/R
£784 $1286 €1200 Solitary pine (23x18cm-9x7in) s. crayon. 9-Feb-3 Bukowskis, Helsinki #301/R
£935 $1534 €1300 Woman sewing (30x22cm-12x9in) s.d.1953 chl. 5-Jun-3 Hagelstam, Helsinki #903
£986 $1587 €1400 Playing (28x25cm-11x10in) s. mixed media. 10-May-3 Bukowskis, Helsinki #173/R
£1076 $1700 €1700 Autumn in the town (24x18cm-9x7in) s. crayon. 1-Dec-2 Bukowskis, Helsinki #117/R est:1200-1500
£1151 $1888 €1600 Woman and child (60x43cm-24x17in) s. mixed media. 5-Jun-3 Hagelstam, Helsinki #904/R est:1500

£1197 $1927 €1700 Sisters (22x20cm-9x8in) s. pastel. 10-May-3 Bukowskis, Helsinki #110/R est:1200-1500
£1408 $2268 €2000 The road (27x23cm-11x9in) s. pastel. 10-May-3 Bukowskis, Helsinki #119/R est:1200-1500
£1901 $3061 €2700 Girl playing the violin (43x34cm-17x13in) s. pastel. 10-May-3 Bukowskis, Helsinki #118/R est:2200-2500
£2065 $3262 €3200 Flowers (25x18cm-10x7in) s. pastel. 19-Dec-2 Hagelstam, Helsinki #871 est:1500

MAAS, Dirck (1659-1717) Dutch
£4459 $6955 €7000 Sportsmen resting in an open field in mountainous wooded landscape (47x62cm-19x24in) indis sig. 5-Nov-2 Sotheby's, Amsterdam #287/R est:7000-9000
£4573 $7500 €6860 Cossacks on horseback asking a hermit for directions (56x73cm-22x29in) s. prov. 30-May-3 Christie's, Rockefeller NY #9/R est:6000-8000
£11000 $17050 €16500 Frogs, butterflies and snails amid undergrowth near a wall, an Italianate garden (41x50cm-16x20in) s.d.1683 prov. 30-Oct-2 Christie's, Kensington #60/R est:6000-8000

MAAS, Dirck (attrib) (1659-1717) Dutch
Works on paper
£323 $510 €485 On the chase (24x22cm-9x9in) W/C en grisaille laid paper. 18-Nov-2 Waddingtons, Toronto #191/R (C.D 800)

MAAS, Ernst (1904-1971) Swiss
£730 $1153 €1095 November day in Auressio (34x53cm-13x21in) s.i.verso. 29-Nov-2 Zofingen, Switzerland #2970/R est:2200 (S.FR 1700)

MAAS, Harry (1906-1982) Dutch
£417 $688 €600 Portrait of a lady in a red dress (100x80cm-39x31in) s. 1-Jul-3 Christie's, Amsterdam #307/R
£609 $956 €950 Together by the stove (88x68cm-35x27in) s.d.1973. 25-Nov-2 Glerum, Amsterdam #198/R
£897 $1409 €1400 Young woman sitting in the nude (64x45cm-25x18in) s.d.1969. 25-Nov-2 Glerum, Amsterdam #203/R
£2394 $3855 €3400 Putting on stockings (100x75cm-39x30in) s.d.1975. 7-May-3 Vendue Huis, Gravenhage #545/R est:3000-5000

MAAS, Paul (1890-1962) Belgian
£345 $552 €500 Orange woman (65x50cm-26x20in) paper on canvas painted 1957 prov.exhib.lit. 15-Mar-3 De Vuyst, Lokeren #195
£818 $1259 €1300 Nu mauve et jaune (51x67cm-20x26in) s. paper. 22-Oct-2 Campo, Vlaamse Kaai #548/R
£1528 $2429 €2200 Parc avec palmiers (50x65cm-20x26in) s. panel. 29-Apr-3 Campo & Campo, Antwerp #202/R est:2400-2800

MAASS, David (20th C) American
£3974 $6200 €5961 Canvasback ducks in flight by shore's edge (91x61cm-36x24in) s. artist board. 8-Nov-2 York Town, York #483
£4747 $7500 €6883 With the wind (61x91cm-24x36in) s. 26-Jul-3 Coeur d'Alene, Hayden #154/R est:8000-12000

MAASS, Johann Gottfried (19th C) German
£2405 $3800 €3800 Karlsbad, Berlin (23x29cm-9x11in) mono.d.1840. 29-Nov-2 Bassenge, Berlin #5986/R est:2800

MAATEN, Jacob Jan van der (1820-1879) Dutch
£510 $795 €800 Figures and church court at the foot of the hill (11x16cm-4x6in) init. 6-Nov-2 Vendue Huis, Gravenhage #411/R

MAATSCH, Thilo (1900-1983) German
£696 $1100 €1100 Schmale maske (29x22cm-11x9in) s. s.verso board painted c.1926 prov. 26-Nov-2 Sotheby's, Amsterdam #298/R est:1000-1500

MABEE, Audrey (20th C) Canadian
£1017 $1617 €1526 There's a birthday in town (75x120cm-30x47in) s.i. 23-Mar-3 Hodgins, Calgary #23/R est:1000-1500 (C.D 2400)

McADAM, Walter (1866-1935) British
£550 $902 €825 Hillside road, Majorca (34x44cm-13x17in) canvasboard. 5-Jun-3 Christie's, Kensington #713/R
£700 $1092 €1050 Highland cottage (28x17cm-11x7in) s. panel pair. 28-Mar-3 Bonhams, Edinburgh #148
£1100 $1716 €1650 Winter landscape (61x91cm-24x36in) s. 17-Sep-2 Sotheby's, Olympia #37/R est:700-900
£1200 $1836 €1800 Loch Awe (34x44cm-13x17in) s. board. 22-Aug-2 Bonhams, Edinburgh #1159 est:600-900
£1600 $2496 €2400 Frosty evening (45x61cm-18x24in) s. 17-Sep-2 Sotheby's, Olympia #43/R est:1000-1500
Works on paper
£580 $899 €870 Snowy street scene (49x74cm-19x29in) s. W/C gouache. 5-Dec-2 Bonhams, Edinburgh #52

McAFEE, Ila Mae (1897-1995) American
£1364 $2100 €2046 Taos pueblo (15x10cm-6x4in) s. canvasboard painted c.1940. 8-Sep-2 Treadway Gallery, Cincinnati #603/R est:3000-5000
£3846 $6000 €5769 Animation (56x66cm-22x26in) s.i.verso canvas on board prov.lit. 9-Nov-2 Santa Fe Art, Santa Fe #116/R est:10000-15000
Works on paper
£513 $800 €770 Horses in abstract landscape (30x43cm-12x17in) s. W/C prov.lit. 9-Nov-2 Santa Fe Art, Santa Fe #223/R

MACAIONE, Tommy (1907-1992) American
£2949 $4600 €4424 Northern New Mexico landscape (46x122cm-18x48in) 9-Nov-2 Altermann Galleries, Santa Fe #186

McALLISTER, Therese (20th C) Irish
£1449 $2377 €2000 Fruit in dish (31x38cm-12x15in) s. s.i.verso board. 28-May-3 Bonhams & James Adam, Dublin #74/R est:2500-3500
£2432 $3795 €3600 Still life with green apples (22x48cm-9x19in) s. board. 26-Mar-3 James Adam, Dublin #111/R est:2500-3500

MACALLUM, Hamilton (1841-1896) British
£1800 $2826 €2700 Scilly anchorage (41x71cm-16x28in) s.d.86 i.verso. 16-Apr-3 Christie's, Kensington #916/R est:2000-3000
£5000 $7950 €7500 Lobster fishermen leaving harbour (41x71cm-16x28in) s.d. prov. 6-Mar-3 Christie's, Kensington #120/R est:5000-7000
Works on paper
£400 $624 €600 East wind in the Kyles of Bute (24x47cm-9x19in) s.d.1872 W/C. 17-Sep-2 Sotheby's, Olympia #36/R

McALPINE, William (attrib) (19th C) British
£2000 $3040 €3000 Battle of Trafalgar - late in the day (78x124cm-31x49in) 15-Aug-2 Bonhams, New Bond Street #301/R est:2000-3000

MACARA, Andrew (1944-) British
£300 $468 €450 White house, Zante (41x51cm-16x20in) s.d.1999. 27-Mar-3 Christie's, Kensington #466
£300 $471 €450 Boy fishing, canal de midi, France (40x50cm-16x20in) s.d.2000. 15-Apr-3 Bonhams, Knightsbridge #37/R
£500 $795 €750 Palombaggia, Corsica (39x48cm-15x19in) s.i.on stretcher verso. 26-Feb-3 Sotheby's, Olympia #251/R
£550 $858 €825 Beach shower (35x46cm-14x18in) s.d.1999. 27-Mar-3 Christie's, Kensington #510/R
£550 $858 €825 Sunbathers on a beach (46x36cm-18x14in) s. with another by same hand two. 26-Mar-3 Hamptons Fine Art, Godalming #151
£600 $984 €900 Cartwheel by the sea, Spain (40x53cm-16x21in) s. i.stretcher. 3-Jun-3 Sotheby's, Olympia #192/R
£680 $1074 €1020 Cricket on the beach, Isle of Wight (29x39cm-11x15in) s.d.1999 i.stretcher. 27-Nov-2 Sotheby's, Olympia #117/R
£1000 $1640 €1500 Pontaillac, Royan (51x60cm-20x24in) s. i.d.July 1991 verso. 3-Jun-3 Sotheby's, Olympia #176/R est:1000-1500
£1700 $2652 €2550 Sailboats, Isle of Wight (63x76cm-25x30in) s.d.1999. 27-Mar-3 Christie's, Kensington #519/R est:600-800
£2000 $3160 €3000 Beach cafe, Majorca (101x133cm-40x52in) s.d.1989 prov. 27-Nov-2 Sotheby's, Olympia #300/R est:2000-3000
£2000 $3300 €2900 Poole, Dorset (63x76cm-25x30in) s.d.2000 i.verso. 3-Jul-3 Christie's, Kensington #703/R est:800-1200
£4000 $6320 €6000 Winstead Park (102x137cm-40x54in) s.d.1990 i.d.verso prov. 27-Nov-2 Sotheby's, Olympia #298/R est:2000-3000

McARDLE, Montrose P (19th C) American
£254 $425 €368 River landscape (51x61cm-20x24in) s. 21-Jun-3 Selkirks, St. Louis #158

MACARTHUR, Blanche (fl.1870-1903) British
£997 $1535 €1496 Young woman (28x23cm-11x9in) s.d.1874. 23-Oct-2 Dunbar Sloane, Wellington #1217 (NZ.D 3200)

MACARTHUR, Charles M (fl.1860-1892) British
Works on paper
£452 $714 €700 Landscape with two figures (24x48cm-9x19in) s. W/C. 18-Dec-2 Ansorena, Madrid #248/R
£452 $714 €700 Landscape with bells (24x49cm-9x19in) s. W/C. 18-Dec-2 Ansorena, Madrid #247/R

MACARTHUR, Lindsay G (fl.1886-1940) British
£1502 $2373 €2253 Figure in a landscape (81x100cm-32x39in) s.d.1888. 3-Apr-3 Heffel, Vancouver #61/R est:700-900 (C.D 3500)

McAULEY, Charles (1910-1999) British
£704 $1169 €1000 View of the Mournes from above hilltown (17x24cm-7x9in) s. board. 10-Jun-3 James Adam, Dublin #15/R est:1000-1500
£800 $1240 €1200 River Dun, Antrim (38x68cm-15x27in) s. 4-Dec-2 John Ross, Belfast #270
£850 $1241 €1275 Feeding chickens in the glens (23x33cm-9x13in) s. board. 12-Jun-2 John Ross, Belfast #242

£	$	€	Details
£1000	$1550	€1500	Cattle grazing in the Glens (25x36cm-10x14in) s. 2-Oct-2 John Ross, Belfast #55 est:800-1000
£1180	$1865	€1770	Fishing boats (30x38cm-12x15in) s. board prov. 3-Apr-3 Heffel, Vancouver #62/R est:1000-1200 (C.D 2750)
£1282	$2013	€2000	Croagh Patrick, County Mayo (38x55cm-15x22in) s. i.verso board. 19-Nov-2 Whyte's, Dublin #200/R est:2000-3000
£1300	$2067	€1950	Cattle grazing in the glens (40x61cm-16x24in) s. 5-Mar-3 John Ross, Belfast #39 est:1400-1600
£1400	$2170	€2100	Glens men (25x36cm-10x14in) s. board. 2-Oct-2 John Ross, Belfast #139 est:1500-1800
£1410	$2214	€2200	Coastal road with cottage and hills (47x64cm-19x25in) s. 19-Nov-2 Whyte's, Dublin #197/R est:3000-4000
£1500	$2190	€2250	Sunset, Antrim Coast (46x61cm-18x24in) s. 12-Jun-2 John Ross, Belfast #51 est:1600-1800
£1500	$2325	€2250	Cushendall (30x40cm-12x16in) s. 4-Dec-2 John Ross, Belfast #81 est:1200-1400
£1600	$2336	€2400	River Dall, Co. Antrim (46x56cm-18x22in) s. board. 12-Jun-2 John Ross, Belfast #68 est:1750-2000
£1700	$2635	€2550	Beached rowing boat, Co. Antrim coast (41x66cm-16x26in) s. 2-Oct-2 John Ross, Belfast #58 est:1750-2000
£1700	$2703	€2550	Near Tievebulliah, County Antrim (30x40cm-12x16in) s. 5-Mar-3 John Ross, Belfast #8 est:1800-2000
£1700	$2703	€2550	Fishing boats at Red Bay (40x56cm-16x22in) s. 5-Mar-3 John Ross, Belfast #210 est:1500-1800
£1800	$2790	€2700	Road in the Glens towards Murlough Bay (40x61cm-16x24in) s. board. 4-Dec-2 John Ross, Belfast #42 est:1800-2000
£1850	$2868	€2775	River in the mountains (46x91cm-18x36in) s. 2-Oct-2 John Ross, Belfast #46 est:2000-2200
£2100	$3255	€3150	Mending nets, Co. Antrim (30x41cm-12x16in) s. board. 2-Oct-2 John Ross, Belfast #83 est:1800-2000
£2100	$3339	€3150	Cattle grazing near Red Bay, County Antrim (40x61cm-16x24in) s. 5-Mar-3 John Ross, Belfast #123 est:1500-2000
£2100	$3255	€3150	Digging potatoes in the glens (35x28cm-14x11in) board. 4-Dec-2 John Ross, Belfast #59 est:2500-2800
£2200	$3410	€3300	Out fishing near Red Bay (46x56cm-18x22in) s. 2-Oct-2 John Ross, Belfast #70 est:2200-2500
£2400	$3720	€3600	Returning with the catch, Red Bay (39x48cm-15x19in) s. board. 4-Dec-2 John Ross, Belfast #35 est:2500-3000
£2900	$4495	€4350	Antrim coast (61x76cm-24x30in) s. 4-Dec-2 John Ross, Belfast #142 est:3000-3500
£3100	$4805	€4650	Bringing in the nets, Cushendall (39x48cm-15x19in) s. board. 4-Dec-2 John Ross, Belfast #27 est:2500-3000
£10800	$16740	€16200	Picking potatoes in the glens (56x63cm-22x25in) s. board. 4-Dec-2 John Ross, Belfast #167 est:5000-6000

McAULIFFE, James J (1848-1921) American

£	$	€	Details
£531	$850	€770	Morning light, harbour (28x46cm-11x18in) s. 16-May-3 Skinner, Boston #101/R

MACAVOY, Edouard (1905-1991) French

£	$	€	Details
£1418	$2369	€2000	Vicenza (50x65cm-20x26in) s.d.89 s.i.d. verso. 20-Jun-3 Piasa, Paris #215 est:2000-3000

Works on paper

£	$	€	Details
£503	$780	€800	L'arlequin au repos (21x15cm-8x6in) s.d.58 gouache sold with W/C by Gabriel Dauchot. 30-Oct-2 Artcurial Briest, Paris #271

MACBETH, Robert Walker (1848-1910) British

£	$	€	Details
£55000	$88550	€82500	Sedge cutting in Wicken Fen, early morning (99x199cm-39x78in) init.d.1878 prov.exhib.lit. 20-Feb-3 Christie's, London #56/R est:50000

McBEY, James (1883-1959) British

Works on paper

£	$	€	Details
£400	$624	€600	Stonemasons at work (42x30cm-17x12in) s.d. W/C pen ink. 17-Sep-2 Bonhams, Sevenoaks #236
£440	$691	€660	Les beaux (31x48cm-12x19in) s.i.d.22nd September 1932 pen ink W/C. 16-Dec-2 Bonhams, Bury St Edmunds #408
£580	$905	€870	Loch Kinardochy (29x49cm-11x19in) s.d.13 July 1929 W/C pen with a W/C by Stirling Maxwell of Pollok. 17-Oct-2 Lawrence, Crewkerne #434/R
£740	$1177	€1110	Venice (27x38cm-11x15in) s.i.d.1925 W/C. 4-Mar-3 Bearnes, Exeter #334/R
£800	$1224	€1200	Concord (24x38cm-9x15in) s.i.d.22nd August 1940 black ink W/C. 22-Aug-2 Bonhams, Edinburgh #1012/R
£800	$1304	€1200	Grey day, Venice (25x26cm-10x10in) s.d.1925 W/C. 30-Jan-3 Locke & England, Leamington Spa #214
£950	$1539	€1378	Greenhithe, Kent, children on a quayside (23x41cm-9x16in) s.i.d.1928 W/C. 23-May-3 Bracketts, Tunbridge Wells #954/R
£1024	$1700	€1485	Harbour with sailboats (25x41cm-10x16in) W/C. 13-Jun-3 Du Mouchelle, Detroit #2189/R est:800-1500
£1250	$2050	€1875	Fountain of Neptune, Versailles (24x39cm-9x15in) s.i.d.1923 pen ink W/C. 4-Feb-3 Bonhams, Leeds #282 est:500-700
£1325	$2200	€1921	Venice (20x41cm-8x16in) W/C. 13-Jun-3 Du Mouchelle, Detroit #2190/R est:800-1500
£1350	$2106	€2025	Wash day, Douarnenez (27x45cm-11x18in) s.i.d.August 11th 1931 ink W/C. 17-Oct-2 Bonhams, Edinburgh #262/R est:1200-1800
£1600	$2496	€2400	Children by the harbour, Greenhithe (24x40cm-9x16in) s.i.d.July 1928 ink W/C. 17-Oct-2 Bonhams, Edinburgh #260/R est:1200-1800
£3600	$5616	€5400	Fountain of Neptune, Versailles (24x39cm-9x15in) s.i.d.1923 pen ink prov. 14-Apr-3 Sotheby's, London #149/R est:3000-5000

MacBRIDE, Alexander (1859-1955) British

Works on paper

£	$	€	Details
£550	$902	€825	Heat of the day, Amberley, Sussex (23x33cm-9x13in) s. W/C. 5-Feb-3 John Nicholson, Haslemere #1010

MACBRYDE, Robert (1913-1966) British

£	$	€	Details
£6500	$10660	€9425	Sliced cucumbers in a dish (56x40cm-22x16in) s. painted c.1949 prov.lit. 4-Jun-3 Sotheby's, London #27/R est:4000-6000

McBURNEY, James Edwin (1868-1955) American

£	$	€	Details
£414	$650	€621	Dawn, the summit, Colorado 1923 (56x46cm-22x18in) s. 10-Dec-2 Doyle, New York #119/R

McCABE, Claudia Jean (20th C) Canadian

£	$	€	Details
£696	$1085	€1160	Gassipers - Landra and Mattie (76x91cm-30x36in) s. i.d.2002 verso. 13-Apr-3 Levis, Calgary #84/R est:1000-1200 (C.D 1600)

MACCABE, Gladys (1918-) Irish

£	$	€	Details
£300	$477	€450	Narrow Water Castle, County Down (15x20cm-6x8in) s. board. 5-Mar-3 John Ross, Belfast #85
£300	$465	€450	Country Down lake (28x40cm-11x16in) s. board. 4-Dec-2 John Ross, Belfast #13
£500	$775	€750	Dark pool by the Lagan (41x61cm-16x24in) s. board. 2-Oct-2 John Ross, Belfast #66
£500	$795	€750	Donegal cottages (20x28cm-8x11in) s. board. 5-Mar-3 John Ross, Belfast #246
£550	$853	€825	Connemara cottages (30x46cm-12x18in) s. board. 2-Oct-2 John Ross, Belfast #246
£886	$1373	€1400	Brother and sister (37x30cm-15x12in) s. board. 25-Sep-2 James Adam, Dublin #104/R est:1500-2000
£900	$1395	€1350	Footballer (36x25cm-14x10in) s. board. 2-Oct-2 John Ross, Belfast #27
£1197	$1987	€1700	Flowers and apples (60x44cm-24x17in) s. board. 10-Jun-3 James Adam, Dublin #252/R est:1200-1500
£1200	$1908	€1800	Graduation day, Queens University Belfast (58x58cm-23x23in) s. board. 5-Mar-3 John Ross, Belfast #134 est:1200-1400
£1300	$2080	€1950	Seated clown (34x24cm-13x9in) board. 15-May-3 Christie's, Kensington #163/R est:1500-2500
£1400	$2226	€2100	Musical clown (61x50cm-24x20in) s. board. 5-Mar-3 John Ross, Belfast #68 est:1000-1200
£1543	$2191	€2500	At the ball (51x58cm-20x23in) s. 29-Mar-2 Woodwards, Cork #163
£1600	$2480	€2400	Jockeys and trainers (22x30cm-9x12in) s. board. 26-Sep-2 Mellors & Kirk, Nottingham #730/R est:600-800
£1611	$2593	€2400	Belfast street (32x46cm-13x18in) s. board. 18-Feb-3 Whyte's, Dublin #219/R est:1500-2000
£1620	$2689	€2300	Musical clown (61x51cm-24x20in) s. board. 10-Jun-3 James Adam, Dublin #5/R est:2500-3000
£1745	$2809	€2600	Artistic corner (27x25cm-11x10in) s. board. 18-Feb-3 Whyte's, Dublin #138/R est:2000-3000
£1761	$2747	€2800	Juggling clown (51x41cm-20x16in) s. board. 17-Sep-2 Whyte's, Dublin #182 est:2500-3000
£1944	$3092	€2800	Clown with banjo (51x41cm-20x16in) s. board. 29-Apr-3 Whyte's, Dublin #221/R est:2500-3500
£1957	$3209	€2700	Before the race (28x39cm-11x15in) s. board. 28-May-3 Bonhams & James Adam, Dublin #73/R est:1200-1800
£2000	$2920	€3000	Quiet glass of wine (25x36cm-10x14in) s. board. 12-Jun-2 John Ross, Belfast #134 est:1500-1800
£2278	$3532	€3600	Gypsy encampment (41x50cm-16x20in) s. board prov. 24-Sep-2 De Veres Art Auctions, Dublin #76/R est:2000-3000
£2390	$3728	€3800	Market day (30x41cm-12x16in) s. i.verso board. 17-Sep-2 Whyte's, Dublin #3 est:4000-5000
£2431	$3865	€3500	Juggling clown (51x41cm-20x16in) s. board. 29-Apr-3 Whyte's, Dublin #223/R est:2500-3000
£2550	$4106	€3800	At the races (24x34cm-9x13in) s. board. 18-Feb-3 Whyte's, Dublin #168/R est:3000-4000
£2564	$4026	€4000	Horse fair (41x51cm-16x20in) s. board. 19-Nov-2 Whyte's, Dublin #115/R est:4000-5000
£2600	$4030	€3900	Merry-go-round in the park (38x61cm-15x24in) s. board. 2-Oct-2 John Ross, Belfast #131 est:2800-3000
£2642	$4121	€4200	Going to mass (41x51cm-16x20in) s. board. 17-Sep-2 Whyte's, Dublin #177/R est:4000-5000
£2685	$4322	€4000	Bric-a-brac stall, outdoor market (41x51cm-16x20in) s. board. 18-Feb-3 Whyte's, Dublin #166/R est:5000-7000
£2700	$4185	€4050	China stall at the market (40x50cm-16x20in) s. board. 4-Dec-2 John Ross, Belfast #131 est:1500-2000
£2703	$4216	€4000	Before the hunt, Co. Down (43x59cm-17x23in) s. i.verso board. 26-Mar-3 James Adam, Dublin #123/R est:3500-4500
£2778	$4417	€4000	Gypsy encampment (30x36cm-12x14in) s. board. 29-Apr-3 Whyte's, Dublin #151/R est:4000-5000
£2900	$4234	€4350	Fruit and veg stall (41x51cm-16x20in) s. board. 12-Jun-2 John Ross, Belfast #71 est:2750-3000
£2917	$4638	€4200	Farm scene (25x36cm-10x14in) s. board prov. 29-Apr-3 Whyte's, Dublin #9/R est:4000-5000
£3165	$4620	€5000	Halt on market day (45x65cm-18x26in) s. card. 21-May-2 Thomas Adams, Dublin #360

£3205 $5032 €5000 At the horse sale (41x51cm-16x20in) s. board. 19-Nov-2 Whyte's, Dublin #8/R est:5000-6000
£3205 $4968 €5000 Punch and Judy (50x60cm-20x24in) s. board. 3-Dec-2 Bonhams & James Adam, Dublin #102/R est:3000-5000
£3333 $5167 €5200 Sunday morning in the west (49x59cm-19x23in) s. board. 3-Dec-2 Bonhams & James Adam, Dublin #101/R est:3000-5000
£3333 $5500 €4800 Before the race at Down Royal (31x50cm-12x20in) s. board. 7-Jul-3 Hamilton Osborne King, Dublin #209/R
£3356 $5403 €5000 Bandstand (41x51cm-16x20in) s. board. 18-Feb-3 Whyte's, Dublin #123/R est:4000-5000
£3459 $5396 €5500 At the ball (41x51cm-16x20in) s. board. 17-Sep-2 Whyte's, Dublin #168 est:4500-5500
£3590 $5636 €5600 Gypsies gathering (41x51cm-16x20in) s. board. 19-Nov-2 Whyte's, Dublin #234/R est:4000-5000
£4027 $6483 €6000 At the ball (41x51cm-16x20in) s. board. 18-Feb-3 Whyte's, Dublin #220/R est:5000-7000
£4088 $6377 €6500 Studying the form, down royal (38x60cm-15x24in) s. board. 17-Sep-2 Whyte's, Dublin #164/R est:5000-6000
£4295 $6915 €6400 Flower seller (41x51cm-16x20in) s. board prov. 18-Feb-3 Whyte's, Dublin #170/R est:5000-7000
£4487 $7045 €7000 Carousel at the village fair (41x56cm-16x22in) s. board. 19-Nov-2 Whyte's, Dublin #232/R est:4000-6000
£4936 $7749 €7700 Restaurant interior (41x51cm-16x20in) s. board. 19-Nov-2 Whyte's, Dublin #123/R est:4000-6000

Works on paper

£315 $492 €460 Dublin Street (25x34cm-10x13in) s. monochrome wash. 8-Apr-3 James Adam, Dublin #174/R
£347 $573 €500 Italian sketches (17x25cm-7x10in) s.i. chl wax pencil set of three prov. 7-Jul-3 Hamilton Osborne King, Dublin #206
£486 $802 €700 Rhine at Utrecht (22x34cm-9x13in) s. col wash over Indian ink. 7-Jul-3 Hamilton Osborne King, Dublin #208
£590 $974 €850 Puerto de la Cruz (25x33cm-10x13in) s. col wash over Indian ink prov. 7-Jul-3 Hamilton Osborne King, Dublin #207
£641 $1013 €1000 Before the start (10x15cm-4x6in) W/C. 12-Nov-2 Mealy's, Castlecomer #1251/R
£750 $1095 €1125 Street worker (20x28cm-8x11in) s. pen ink W/C. 12-Jun-2 John Ross, Belfast #7
£1000 $1550 €1500 Horses and children on the sand (20x61cm-8x24in) s. mixed media. 4-Dec-2 John Ross, Belfast #147 est:900-1000
£3826 $6159 €5700 At the lammas fair (46x61cm-18x24in) s. gouache board. 18-Feb-3 Whyte's, Dublin #120/R est:5000-7000

McCAHON, Colin (1930-1977) New Zealander

£10030 $15647 €15045 North Otago landscape (28x76cm-11x30in) acrylic on paper exhib. 17-Sep-2 Peter Webb, Auckland #86/R est:20000-30000 (NZ.D 33000)
£20463 $31308 €30695 Otago landscape (54x43cm-21x17in) s.d.1964 board prov. 26-Aug-2 Sotheby's, Paddington #531/R est:40000-60000 (A.D 57500)
£24116 $37379 €36174 Comet FII (92x62cm-36x24in) s.d.74 hessian. 4-Dec-2 Dunbar Sloane, Auckland #13/R est:90000-130000 (NZ.D 75000)
£26882 $40860 €40323 North Otago landscape (55x81cm-22x32in) s.i.d.67 polyvinyl acetate composition board prov.exhib. 28-Aug-2 Deutscher-Menzies, Melbourne #25/R est:65000-75000 (A.D 75000)
£27778 $43333 €41667 Northland landscape (77x67cm-30x26in) s.d.1956 s.i.verso prov. 8-Apr-3 Peter Webb, Auckland #50/R est:90000-120000 (NZ.D 80000)
£29880 $49004 €44820 Landscape, Titirangi (47x56cm-19x22in) s.d.Dec 56 composition board prov.lit. 4-Jun-3 Deutscher-Menzies, Melbourne #32/R est:80000-100000 (A.D 75000)
£52083 $81250 €78125 North Otago 7 (92x121cm-36x48in) s.i.d.1967 pva board exhib. 8-Apr-3 Peter Webb, Auckland #49/R est:150000-200000 (NZ.D 150000)
£100694 $157083 €151041 Noughts and crosses VI, series 2 (110x72cm-43x28in) s.i.d.1976 acrylic paper exhib. 8-Apr-3 Peter Webb, Auckland #53/R est:200000-250000 (NZ.D 290000)
£211806 $330417 €317709 No 2 (120x90cm-47x35in) s.d.1965 pva hardboard prov.exhib.lit. 8-Apr-3 Peter Webb, Auckland #54/R est:650000-850000 (NZ.D 610000)

Works on paper

£2390 $3920 €3585 Fog and sea, Miriwai (29x22cm-11x9in) s.i.d.73 pencil prov.exhib. 4-Jun-3 Deutscher-Menzies, Melbourne #182/R est:5000-7000 (A.D 6000)
£3819 $5958 €5729 Landscape Pangatotara (19x25cm-7x10in) s.d.1943 s.i.verso pen black ink W/C htd bodycol over pencil prov. 8-Apr-3 Peter Webb, Auckland #30/R est:10000-15000 (NZ.D 11000)
£10526 $16421 €15789 Flower (57x44cm-22x17in) s.d.1970 water-based crayon. 27-Mar-3 International Art Centre, Auckland #21/R est:34000-40000 (NZ.D 30000)
£33451 $55194 €48504 Poem of Kaipara flat (100x67cm-39x26in) s.i.d.1971 W/C waterbase crayon. 1-Jul-3 Peter Webb, Auckland #26/R est:100000-150000 (NZ.D 95000)
£35211 $58099 €51056 Evening Muriwai (101x67cm-40x26in) s.i.d.1971 W/C waterbase crayon prov. 1-Jul-3 Peter Webb, Auckland #25/R est:100000-150000 (NZ.D 100000)

McCAIG, Norman J (1929-2001) Irish

£520 $806 €780 Water reflection, South of France (40x30cm-16x12in) s. board. 4-Dec-2 John Ross, Belfast #157
£600 $876 €900 Beach (25x30cm-10x12in) s. board. 12-Jun-2 John Ross, Belfast #82
£823 $1275 €1300 Lough Currane, lower lake Kerry (31x26cm-12x10in) s. canvasboard. 24-Sep-2 De Veres Art Auctions, Dublin #16 est:1000-1500
£900 $1431 €1350 Wintrer sky (33x91cm-13x36in) s. board. 5-Mar-3 John Ross, Belfast #31
£949 $1472 €1500 Hauling in the nets (25x30cm-10x12in) s. canvasboard. 25-Sep-2 James Adam, Dublin #19 est:1500-2000
£1000 $1460 €1500 Letterfrack, Co. Galway (25x30cm-10x12in) s. board. 12-Jun-2 John Ross, Belfast #317 est:500-600
£1013 $1570 €1600 Duck pond, St. Stephen's Green (25x30cm-10x12in) s. board. 25-Sep-2 James Adam, Dublin #11 est:1000-1500
£1103 $1754 €1600 Fishing boats, Dingle (20x25cm-8x10in) s. board. 4-Mar-3 Mealy's, Castlecomer #1227/R est:1400-1600
£1146 $1789 €1800 Figures on the Strand (30x25cm-12x10in) s. 6-Nov-2 James Adam, Dublin #34/R est:1500-2000
£1200 $1860 €1800 Feeding ducks, Botanic Park, Belfast (35x45cm-14x18in) s. board. 4-Dec-2 John Ross, Belfast #1 est:1200-1400
£1233 $1936 €1800 Pastoral scene (39x50cm-15x20in) s. board. 15-Apr-3 De Veres Art Auctions, Dublin #46/R est:1800-2200
£1233 $1923 €1800 On the grand canal (31x40cm-12x16in) s. 8-Apr-3 James Adam, Dublin #168/R est:1500-2000
£1300 $1898 €1950 Lobstermen, Arranmore (30x25cm-12x10in) s. board. 12-Jun-2 John Ross, Belfast #307 est:800-1000
£1301 $2030 €1900 Fishermen morning, Los Boiches, Spain (26x30cm-10x12in) s. board. 8-Apr-3 James Adam, Dublin #167 est:1000-1500
£1329 $2060 €2100 Evening calm, River Shannon (31x41cm-12x16in) s. board. 24-Sep-2 De Veres Art Auctions, Dublin #161/R est:2000-3000
£1338 $2221 €1900 Muskish mountain, Donegal (25x30cm-10x12in) s. 10-Jun-3 James Adam, Dublin #258/R est:2000-2500
£1351 $2108 €2000 Children on the strand (29x24cm-11x9in) s. 26-Mar-3 James Adam, Dublin #124/R est:2000-3000
£1364 $2073 €2100 Hay stacks (30x41cm-12x16in) s. board painted c.1982. 2-Jul-2 Thomas Adams, Dublin #380a
£1400 $2044 €2100 Cornfields, Cellbridge (30x41cm-12x16in) s.d.verso board. 12-Jun-2 John Ross, Belfast #38 est:1000-1200
£1400 $2170 €2100 Bluebell time (50x40cm-20x16in) s. board. 4-Dec-2 John Ross, Belfast #25 est:1500-1800
£1474 $2315 €2300 Sketrick Island, County Down (33x91cm-13x36in) s. board. 19-Nov-2 Whyte's, Dublin #83/R est:2500-3500
£1500 $2190 €2250 Lobster boat, Cushendun (41x51cm-16x20in) s. board. 12-Jun-2 John Ross, Belfast #1
£1538 $2415 €2400 Path to the lake (36x91cm-14x36in) s. board. 19-Nov-2 Whyte's, Dublin #107/R est:3000-4000
£1538 $2385 €2400 John O the Rock's, Cushendun (25x30cm-10x12in) s. board. 3-Dec-2 Bonhams & James Adam, Dublin #147 est:2000-3000
£1635 $2551 €2600 Bluebell time (41x51cm-16x20in) s. canvasboard. 17-Sep-2 Whyte's, Dublin #222 est:2000-3000
£1667 $2617 €2600 Evening on the Shannon (41x51cm-16x20in) s. i.verso canvasboard. 19-Nov-2 Whyte's, Dublin #194 est:2500-3500
£1667 $2617 €2600 Lough Finn, Connemara (36x46cm-14x18in) s. i.verso canvasboard. 19-Nov-2 Whyte's, Dublin #199/R est:2500-3500
£1709 $2649 €2700 Picnic, Vale of Avoca (40x30cm-16x12in) s. board. 25-Sep-2 James Adam, Dublin #3/R est:2500-3500
£1745 $2809 €2600 Fishing on the Moy (30x41cm-12x16in) s. i.verso canvasboard. 18-Feb-3 Whyte's, Dublin #160/R est:2500-3500
£1800 $2862 €2700 Muckish mountain, Donegal (40x50cm-16x20in) s. 5-Mar-3 John Ross, Belfast #1 est:1500-1800
£1800 $2790 €2700 Lobster fisherman, Cushendan (45x35cm-18x14in) s. board. 4-Dec-2 John Ross, Belfast #266 est:1250-1500
£1806 $2871 €2600 In the Rosses, Donegal (41x51cm-16x20in) s. i.verso. 29-Apr-3 Whyte's, Dublin #168/R est:2500-3500
£1887 $2943 €3000 Cattle grazing by the sea (46x61cm-18x24in) s. 17-Sep-2 Whyte's, Dublin #5/R est:3000-5000
£1900 $2945 €2850 Afternoon tea (51x41cm-20x16in) s. board. 2-Oct-2 John Ross, Belfast #1 est:1500-1800
£1923 $3019 €3000 Moored boat on Lough Erne (61x46cm-24x18in) s. board. 19-Nov-2 Whyte's, Dublin #195 est:3500-4500
£1923 $2981 €3000 Roundstone Harbour, Galway (32x27cm-13x11in) s. board. 3-Dec-2 Bonhams & James Adam, Dublin #53/R est:2000-3000
£2013 $3140 €3200 Blue stack mountains (41x122cm-16x48in) s. board. 17-Sep-2 Whyte's, Dublin #9/R est:2000-3000
£2025 $3139 €3200 In the park, St Stephen's Green, Dublin (35x46cm-14x18in) s. board. 25-Sep-2 James Adam, Dublin #87/R est:2500-3500
£2051 $3221 €3200 Hillsborough Lake (41x51cm-16x20in) s. canvasboard. 19-Nov-2 Whyte's, Dublin #202 est:2000-3000
£2083 $3312 €3000 Fishing on the Moy (41x81cm-16x32in) s. board prov. 29-Apr-3 Whyte's, Dublin #169/R est:3000-4000
£2150 $3333 €3225 Fishing boats at Ballycotton (35x45cm-14x18in) s. board. 4-Dec-2 John Ross, Belfast #143 est:2000-2200
£2244 $3478 €3500 Children on the Lagan (35x44cm-14x17in) s. board. 3-Dec-2 Bonhams & James Adam, Dublin #54/R est:2500-3500
£2282 $3674 €3400 Cattle grazing, river Lagan (41x51cm-16x20in) s. i.verso canvasboard. 18-Feb-3 Whyte's, Dublin #134/R est:3500-4500

£2361 $3754 €3400 Fishing boats at sunset (39x29cm-15x11in) s. canvasboard. 29-Apr-3 Whyte's, Dublin #207/R est:2500-3500
£2416 $3890 €3600 Young couple boating (46x36cm-18x14in) s. acrylic canvasboard. 18-Feb-3 Whyte's, Dublin #212/R est:2000-3000
£2468 $3826 €3900 Peat bog, Connemara (25x30cm-10x12in) s.i.verso board. 25-Sep-2 James Adam, Dublin #42 est:2500-3000
£2500 $3975 €3600 Fairhead, County Antrim (36x91cm-14x36in) s. board. 29-Apr-3 Whyte's, Dublin #116/R est:3000-4000
£2685 $4322 €4000 Autumn (46x56cm-18x22in) s. i.verso. 18-Feb-3 Whyte's, Dublin #152/R est:3000-4000
£2692 $4173 €4200 Bather, Red Bay, Cushendun (35x45cm-14x18in) s. board. 3-Dec-2 Bonhams & James Adam, Dublin #52/R est:3000-4000
£2767 $4317 €4400 Joyce's country (61x91cm-24x36in) s. i.verso. 17-Sep-2 Whyte's, Dublin #138/R est:4000-5000
£2819 $4538 €4200 Landscape with view of cottages over water (36x91cm-14x36in) s. board. 18-Feb-3 Whyte's, Dublin #144/R est:3500-4500
£2885 $4529 €4500 Path through the fields, Kells (41x51cm-16x20in) s. canvasboard. 19-Nov-2 Whyte's, Dublin #4/R est:3500-4500
£3019 $4709 €4800 Lough Inagh, Recess, Connemara (61x91cm-24x36in) s. i.verso. 17-Sep-2 Whyte's, Dublin #135/R est:4500-5500
£3077 $4831 €4800 Road to Puckaun, near Nenagh, County Tipperary (51x76cm-20x30in) s. i.verso canvasboard. 19-Nov-2 Whyte's, Dublin #191/R est:5000-6000
£3087 $4970 €4600 Stroll on Brittas Beach, Co Wicklow (41x51cm-16x20in) s. i.d.1999 verso canvasboard. 18-Feb-3 Whyte's, Dublin #159/R est:3000-4000
£3165 $4905 €5000 Autumn leaves on St. Stephen's Green (50x76cm-20x30in) s. 25-Sep-2 James Adam, Dublin #98/R est:3000-4000
£3194 $5079 €4600 Sand dunes near Newcastle (41x51cm-16x20in) s. i.verso canvasboard. 29-Apr-3 Whyte's, Dublin #167/R est:2500-3500
£3356 $5403 €5000 Boats moored at Cashel Pier, Connemara (46x61cm-18x24in) s. canvasboard. 18-Feb-3 Whyte's, Dublin #150/R est:4000-5000
£3526 $5535 €5500 Ballynahinch River, Connemara (61x91cm-24x36in) s. 19-Nov-2 Whyte's, Dublin #102/R est:4000-5000
£3544 $5494 €5600 Lobster boat, Cushendun (41x51cm-16x20in) s. board. 25-Sep-2 James Adam, Dublin #110/R est:4000-5000
£3654 $5737 €5700 Barges on the Lagan (51x61cm-20x24in) s. i.verso board. 19-Nov-2 Whyte's, Dublin #78/R est:6000-8000
£3846 $5962 €6000 On Killiney strand (40x50cm-16x20in) s. board. 3-Dec-2 Bonhams & James Adam, Dublin #51/R est:3000-4000
£3924 $6082 €6200 Picnic (35x46cm-14x18in) s.i.verso canvasboard exhib. 25-Sep-2 James Adam, Dublin #74a/R est:4000-5000
£4054 $6324 €6000 Cottages, Cunningburn, Co. Down (61x91cm-24x36in) s. 26-Mar-3 James Adam, Dublin #90/R est:5000-8000

McCAIN, Buck (20th C) American
Sculpture
£1846 $2990 €2677 Invocation (53cm-21in) green pat. bronze. 23-May-3 Altermann Galleries, Santa Fe #116
Works on paper
£426 $690 €618 Prayer to the healing spirit (33x28cm-13x11in) mixed media. 23-May-3 Altermann Galleries, Santa Fe #115

McCALL, Charles (1907-1989) British
£260 $421 €390 Backwater on the Marne (46x35cm-18x14in) s.d.1976 board. 20-May-3 Sotheby's, Olympia #142/R
£270 $440 €405 Pont des Arts, Paris (21x26cm-8x10in) s.d.1972 board. 17-Feb-3 Bonhams, Bath #175
£550 $891 €825 Letter (26x21cm-10x8in) s.d.78 board. 20-May-3 Sotheby's, Olympia #128/R
£550 $891 €825 Indian shawl (32x21cm-13x8in) s.d.1975 board. 20-May-3 Sotheby's, Olympia #134/R
£600 $972 €900 Girl at mirror (20x15cm-8x6in) s.d.1979 board. 20-May-3 Sotheby's, Olympia #135/R
£600 $972 €900 Nurse (32x21cm-13x8in) s.d.1977 board. 20-May-3 Sotheby's, Olympia #136/R
£650 $1053 €975 Girl in front of mantepiece (21x17cm-8x7in) s.d.1978 s.i.verso board. 20-May-3 Sotheby's, Olympia #133/R
£850 $1318 €1275 Busy evening (56x43cm-22x17in) s.d.50 prov. 4-Dec-2 Christie's, Kensington #401/R

McCALLUM, Andrew (1821-1902) British
£1800 $2880 €2700 Russet winter at the feet of spring (57x101cm-22x40in) s.d.1886. 13-May-3 Bonhams, Knightsbridge #308/R est:2000-3000
£3400 $5304 €5100 Sunset with a distant view of Rome (116x167cm-46x66in) s.d.1865. 10-Sep-2 Bonhams, Knightsbridge #235/R est:2000-3000
£12000 $18960 €18000 Sunset over a forest (93x139cm-37x55in) s.d.1890. 26-Nov-2 Christie's, London #129/R est:8000-12000
Works on paper
£1300 $2027 €1950 Street urchins before Roman ruins. Figures resting by Roman ruins (48x59cm-19x23in) one s.i.d.1880 pencil W/C pair. 19-Sep-2 Christie's, Kensington #90/R est:1000-1500

McCANN, Gerald Patrick (1916-) American
£542 $900 €786 Western figures on horseback (46x61cm-18x24in) s. 11-Jun-3 Boos Gallery, Michigan #553/R est:1800-2200
Works on paper
£304 $475 €456 Portrait of a mountain man in winter landscape (30x48cm-12x19in) s. W/C. 29-Mar-3 Charlton Hall, Columbia #648/R
£577 $900 €866 Portrait of a mountain man and native Americans (33x48cm-13x19in) s. W/C. 29-Mar-3 Charlton Hall, Columbia #649

McCARA, Don (20th C) New Zealander
Works on paper
£251 $391 €377 Drydock, Lyttleton (54x35cm-21x14in) s. W/C. 7-Nov-2 International Art Centre, Auckland #203 (NZ.D 800)

MACCARI, Cesare (1840-1919) Italian
£3548 $5500 €5322 Model (32x24cm-13x9in) s.i. panel prov.exhib. 29-Oct-2 Sotheby's, New York #15/R est:8000-12000

MACCARI, Mino (1898-1989) Italian
£481 $760 €750 Head of girl (14x16cm-6x6in) s. cardboard. 15-Nov-2 Farsetti, Prato #435
£816 $1298 €1200 Cadet (25x28cm-10x11in) s. s.verso mixed media linoleum on canvas. 1-Mar-3 Meeting Art, Vercelli #535
£1216 $1897 €1800 Intruder (23x17cm-9x7in) s.i. board. 28-Mar-3 Farsetti, Prato #635/R
£1233 $1923 €1800 Twins (25x20cm-10x8in) s. cardboard on canvas. 10-Apr-3 Finarte Semenzato, Rome #139/R
£1373 $2196 €2100 Night scene (25x35cm-10x14in) s. card on canvas. 4-Jan-3 Meeting Art, Vercelli #496
£1389 $2208 €2000 Untitled (25x35cm-10x14in) s. painted 1981. 1-May-3 Meeting Art, Vercelli #64
£1400 $2212 €2100 Two women (39x20cm-15x8in) s. canvas on board painted 1968 prov. 3-Apr-3 Christie's, Kensington #75/R
£1644 $2564 €2400 Conversation (43x62cm-17x24in) s. tempera paper. 10-Apr-3 Finarte Semenzato, Rome #198
£1667 $2583 €2600 Napoleon (22x18cm-9x7in) board painted 1950 double-sided. 4-Dec-2 Finarte, Milan #290/R
£1712 $2671 €2500 Hurray for the newly weds! (43x62cm-17x24in) s. tempera paper. 10-Apr-3 Finarte Semenzato, Rome #197
£1806 $2854 €2800 Figures (50x40cm-20x16in) s. 18-Dec-2 Christie's, Rome #155
£1905 $3029 €2800 Saturnia's Baths (30x40cm-12x16in) s. board. 1-Mar-3 Meeting Art, Vercelli #754
£1923 $3038 €3000 Girl (50x40cm-20x16in) s. i.verso. 15-Nov-2 Farsetti, Prato #484/R
£1923 $3038 €3000 Girls in the countryside (40x50cm-16x20in) s. 15-Nov-2 Farsetti, Prato #591/R
£1986 $3217 €2800 Figure (40x31cm-16x12in) s. cardboard on canvas prov. 26-May-3 Christie's, Milan #45/R est:2500-3000
£2258 $3568 €3500 Figures (42x56cm-17x22in) s. tempera card. 18-Dec-2 Christie's, Rome #40/R
£2500 $3900 €3700 Figures (40x50cm-16x20in) s. canvas on cardboard. 28-Mar-3 Farsetti, Prato #530/R
£2614 $4183 €4000 Meeting (33x23cm-13x9in) s. cardboard. 4-Jan-3 Meeting Art, Vercelli #89
£2903 $4587 €4500 Gineceo (40x50cm-16x20in) s.d.52 s.d.verso. 18-Dec-2 Christie's, Rome #273/R
£3077 $4831 €4800 Meeting (40x30cm-16x12in) s.d.1955 cardboard on canvas. 23-Nov-2 Meeting Art, Vercelli #228/R
£3481 $5430 €5500 Courtship (40x55cm-16x22in) s. board. 14-Sep-2 Meeting Art, Vercelli #968/R
£3846 $5962 €6000 Friends (55x36cm-22x14in) board. 4-Dec-2 Finarte, Milan #288/R est:5000
£6597 $10490 €9500 Dancers (50x70cm-20x28in) s. 1-May-3 Meeting Art, Vercelli #573 est:8000
Works on paper
£256 $374 €400 Blue figure with hood (28x22cm-11x9in) mixed media. 5-Jun-2 Il Ponte, Milan #10
£290 $459 €450 Sticky (69x99cm-27x39in) s.i. chl card. 18-Dec-2 Christie's, Rome #30
£304 $474 €450 Woman in profile (28x26cm-11x10in) s.d.1964 wax crayon. 28-Mar-3 Farsetti, Prato #299
£338 $527 €500 Free exit (24x34cm-9x13in) s. gouache. 26-Mar-3 Finarte Semenzato, Milan #39/R
£345 $552 €500 Dairy (18x30cm-7x12in) s.i. pen on napkin. 11-Mar-3 Babuino, Rome #388/R
£439 $685 €650 Woman smoking (28x26cm-11x10in) s. wax crayon. 28-Mar-3 Farsetti, Prato #37
£481 $702 €750 Figures (23x30cm-9x12in) mixed media. 5-Jun-2 Il Ponte, Milan #73
£571 $901 €890 Faces (15x20cm-6x8in) pastel board. 12-Nov-2 Babuino, Rome #35/R
£578 $919 €850 Seated figure (33x24cm-13x9in) s. W/C paper on canvas. 1-Mar-3 Meeting Art, Vercelli #548
£759 $1214 €1100 Caricature (17x11cm-7x4in) s. pencil pen. 11-Mar-3 Babuino, Rome #129/R
£843 $1349 €1290 Little mermaid (50x70cm-20x28in) s. mixed media paper on canvas lit. 4-Jan-3 Meeting Art, Vercelli #699
£962 $1490 €1500 Meeting. Anything but a left opening. Three figures (25x37cm-10x15in) s.d.1960 W/C. 4-Dec-2 Finarte, Milan #210
£1154 $1812 €1800 Fighters (23x32cm-9x13in) s. ink sold with Chinese ink by Giuseppe Migneco. 21-Nov-2 Finarte, Rome #189
£1667 $2650 €2400 Girl in profile (40x30cm-16x12in) s. mixed media card. 1-May-3 Meeting Art, Vercelli #84

McCARTER, Henry Benbridge (1864-1942) American
£1138 $1900 €1650 Female nude (41x25cm-16x10in) prov. 22-Jun-3 Freeman, Philadelphia #163/R est:1500-2500
£2246 $3750 €3257 Gwentlands Park, Newham on Severn (81x102cm-32x40in) s. s.i.verso exhib. 22-Jun-3 Freeman, Philadelphia #120/R est:4000-6000

McCART, John (?) British?
£268 $417 €420 Portrait of Francis Stuart and cat (80x44cm-31x17in) s. acrylic board. 6-Nov-2 James Adam, Dublin #104/R
£287 $447 €450 Portrait of young Samuel Beckett (80x44cm-31x17in) s. acrylic board. 6-Nov-2 James Adam, Dublin #110/R
Works on paper
£350 $511 €525 James Joyce with Nora (76x41cm-30x16in) s.d.2000 verso mixed media. 12-Jun-2 John Ross, Belfast #283

McCARTHY, Brian (20th C) Irish
£1761 $2747 €2800 Fantail pigeons (25x51cm-10x20in) s. 17-Sep-2 Whyte's, Dublin #184 est:2000-2500

McCARTHY, Doris Jean (1910-) Canadian
£711 $1166 €1067 Rural dam in winter (29x34cm-11x13in) init.i.d.1989 panel. 3-Jun-3 Joyner, Toronto #321/R est:2000-2500 (C.D 1600)
£978 $1604 €1467 Autumn in Haliburton (29x34cm-11x13in) s.i.verso panel. 3-Jun-3 Joyner, Toronto #320/R est:2000-2500 (C.D 2200)
£8263 $13138 €12395 Ice floes, Broughton Island (90x120cm-35x47in) s. prov. 23-Mar-3 Hodgins, Calgary #82/R est:8000-10000 (C.D 19500)
Works on paper
£412 $638 €618 Fish store near Salvage, NFLD (36x51cm-14x20in) s. W/C. 3-Dec-2 Joyner, Toronto #381 est:1200-1500 (C.D 1000)
£924 $1450 €1386 Ice floe (36x54cm-14x21in) s. W/C. 25-Nov-2 Hodgins, Calgary #318/R est:1000-1250 (C.D 2300)
£988 $1531 €1482 Brixham Harbour (74x54cm-29x21in) s. W/C. 3-Dec-2 Joyner, Toronto #339/R est:800-1200 (C.D 2400)
£1152 $1786 €1728 Broughton flows towards pyramid (54x72cm-21x28in) s. W/C prov. 3-Dec-2 Joyner, Toronto #278/R est:1500-2000 (C.D 2800)
£2119 $3369 €3179 Broughton village in late light (55x75cm-22x30in) W/C prov. 23-Mar-3 Hodgins, Calgary #94/R est:2500-3000 (C.D 5000)

McCARTHY, Frank (1924-) American
£3194 $5175 €4631 Looking for something (30x38cm-12x15in) 23-May-3 Altermann Galleries, Santa Fe #27
£4795 $7000 €7193 Shoot out (41x74cm-16x29in) 18-May-2 Altermann Galleries, Santa Fe #115/R
£9434 $15000 €14151 In the pass (76x56cm-30x22in) s.i. prov. 5-Mar-3 Sotheby's, New York #153/R est:15000-25000
£12329 $18000 €18494 Cheyenne scout (46x76cm-18x30in) 18-May-2 Altermann Galleries, Santa Fe #8/R
£13462 $21000 €20193 Apaches (46x61cm-18x24in) 9-Nov-2 Altermann Galleries, Santa Fe #147
£15068 $22000 €22602 Kiowa on the Southern Plains (51x102cm-20x40in) 18-May-2 Altermann Galleries, Santa Fe #9/R
£15385 $24000 €23078 Hostile threat (71x76cm-28x30in) 9-Nov-2 Altermann Galleries, Santa Fe #146
£21795 $34000 €32693 Circle - Sioux (61x91cm-24x36in) 9-Nov-2 Altermann Galleries, Santa Fe #148
£22152 $35000 €32120 In search of new grass (51x61cm-20x24in) s. board prov. 26-Jul-3 Coeur d'Alene, Hayden #208/R est:15000-25000
£23549 $38150 €34146 To the Rendezvous (61x102cm-24x40in) 23-May-3 Altermann Galleries, Santa Fe #26
Works on paper
£1118 $1800 €1677 Hero with pistol, nude woman and sinister man in fez (43x36cm-17x14in) s. casein. 10-May-3 Illustration House, New York #130/R est:2000-3000

McCARTHY, J (?) American?
£6579 $10000 €9869 American bark, Kennebec, passing Ramsgate (61x91cm-24x36in) s.i. 17-Aug-2 North East Auctions, Portsmouth #949/R

McCARTHY, Justin (1892-1977) American
£915 $1500 €1327 Dorothy Osborne, Phyllis Lane and Amy Ford (48x61cm-19x24in) s.i. tempera pen ink paper on card stock. 5-Jun-3 Swann Galleries, New York #172/R est:2000-3000
£1656 $2600 €2484 Helsinki regatta (64x64cm-25x25in) s.i. board. 14-Dec-2 Charlton Hall, Columbia #461/R est:1500-2000
£3395 $5500 €5093 Jesus in the desert (59x90cm-23x35in) s. masonite prov. 27-Jan-3 Christie's, Rockefeller NY #19/R est:5000-7000

McCARTHY, Maeve (20th C) Irish
£685 $1075 €1000 Oisin Roche (92x71cm-36x28in) s. exhib. 15-Apr-3 De Veres Art Auctions, Dublin #100e est:1000-2000

McCARTHY, Paul (1945-) American
Photographs
£6329 $10000 €9494 Pinnochip pipenose householddilema. video tape executed 1994 prov.exhib.lit. 12-Nov-2 Phillips, New York #195/R est:15000-20000
£17500 $28000 €26250 Saloon action (52x52cm-20x20in) s. seven cibachrome prov.exhib. 16-May-3 Phillips, New York #134/R est:35000-45000
Works on paper
£2246 $3684 €3100 Untitled - Bavarian kick (61x45cm-24x18in) s.i. verso feltpen. 28-May-3 Lempertz, Koln #274/R est:2800
£3913 $6417 €5400 Untitled - the garden (45x60cm-18x24in) s.i. verso feltpen. 28-May-3 Lempertz, Koln #275/R est:3000

MACCARTHY, Sean (?) Irish?
Works on paper
£432 $614 €700 Christy ring (61x41cm-24x16in) s.d. chl. 29-Mar-2 Woodwards, Cork #173/R

McCAW, Dan (1942-) American
£1753 $2700 €2630 Lazy day (41x36cm-16x14in) 25-Oct-2 Morris & Whiteside, Hilton Head Island #78 est:3000-4000
£1883 $2900 €2825 First summer (41x36cm-16x14in) 25-Oct-2 Morris & Whiteside, Hilton Head Island #79 est:3000-5000
£2922 $4500 €4383 Day dreaming (41x36cm-16x14in) 25-Oct-2 Morris & Whiteside, Hilton Head Island #6 est:3000-4000

McCAW, Terence (1913-1979) South African
£360 $562 €540 Ruined Italianate town (64x80cm-25x31in) s.d.51. 17-Sep-2 Rosebery Fine Art, London #523/R
£362 $572 €543 Still life of flowers in a vase (38x43cm-15x17in) s.d.58 canvasboard. 1-Apr-3 Stephan Welz, Johannesburg #470 est:5000-8000 (SA.R 4500)
£416 $650 €624 Farm at Irene (24x35cm-9x14in) s.d.41 i.verso canvas on board. 11-Nov-2 Stephan Welz, Johannesburg #466 (SA.R 6500)
£545 $849 €818 Italian landscape (36x56cm-14x22in) s.d.46 i.d.4 March verso paper on board. 11-Nov-2 Stephan Welz, Johannesburg #464 (SA.R 8500)
£577 $899 €866 Fishing boats on the beach (49x59cm-19x23in) s.d.75 board. 11-Nov-2 Stephan Welz, Johannesburg #495/R (SA.R 9000)
£602 $969 €903 Man wearing a blue blanket (43x33cm-17x13in) s.d.54 canvasboard. 12-May-3 Stephan Welz, Johannesburg #534/R est:7000-10000 (SA.R 7000)
£737 $1149 €1106 Back street, Elim (35x45cm-14x18in) s.d.49 i.verso canvas on board. 11-Nov-2 Stephan Welz, Johannesburg #467/R (SA.R 11500)
£740 $1168 €1110 Still life with flowers (75x60cm-30x24in) s.d.69 canvas on board. 1-Apr-3 Stephan Welz, Johannesburg #472/R est:8000-12000 (SA.R 9200)
£769 $1199 €1154 Still life with lamp, jug, flowers and fruit (48x38cm-19x15in) s.d.54 canvasboard. 11-Nov-2 Stephan Welz, Johannesburg #522/R (SA.R 12000)
£1153 $1799 €1730 Still life of flowers (59x49cm-23x19in) s. canvasboard. 11-Nov-2 Stephan Welz, Johannesburg #525/R est:6000-9000 (SA.R 18000)
£1217 $1899 €1826 Hout Bay (39x50cm-15x20in) s.d.56 s.i.verso. 11-Nov-2 Stephan Welz, Johannesburg #465/R est:9000-12000 (SA.R 19000)
£1281 $1999 €1922 Still life with fruit and bottle of wine (49x60cm-19x24in) s.d.71 canvas on board. 11-Nov-2 Stephan Welz, Johannesburg #470/R est:8000-12000 (SA.R 20000)
£1290 $2077 €1935 Waterfront with figures (46x66cm-18x26in) s.d.57. 12-May-3 Stephan Welz, Johannesburg #517/R est:8000-12000 (SA.R 15000)
£1367 $2159 €2051 Italian villa (75x100cm-30x39in) s. 1-Apr-3 Stephan Welz, Johannesburg #471/R est:7000-10000 (SA.R 17000)
£1720 $2769 €2580 Street scene, Paarl (60x75cm-24x30in) s. canvas on board. 12-May-3 Stephan Welz, Johannesburg #495/R est:10000-15000 (SA.R 20000)
£1768 $2794 €2652 Liesbeeck Canal (70x100cm-28x39in) s.d.47. 1-Apr-3 Stephan Welz, Johannesburg #473/R est:8000-12000 (SA.R 22000)
£1892 $3046 €2838 Street scene in the Malay quarter (49x39cm-19x15in) s. canvasboard. 12-May-3 Stephan Welz, Johannesburg #491/R est:8000-12000 (SA.R 22000)
£1892 $3046 €2838 Indian market, Diagonal Street, Johannesburg (60x70cm-24x28in) s.d.43. 12-May-3 Stephan Welz, Johannesburg #499/R est:18000-24000 (SA.R 22000)
£2064 $3322 €3096 Old mill at Mamre, Cape (60x75cm-24x30in) s. canvas on board. 12-May-3 Stephan Welz, Johannesburg #490/R est:12000-16000 (SA.R 24000)

£2150 $3354 €3225 Yacht club, Cape Town (63x82cm-25x32in) s.d.46 i.verso. 15-Oct-2 Stephan Welz, Johannesburg #473/R est:25000-35000 (SA.R 35000)
£2236 $3599 €3354 Fishermen at Hout Bay (60x75cm-24x30in) s. canvas on board. 12-May-3 Stephan Welz, Johannesburg #470/R est:16000-20000 (SA.R 26000)
£2408 $3876 €3612 Looking down Long street Cape Town, from the Malay quarter (75x60cm-30x24in) s. i.verso canvasboard. 12-May-3 Stephan Welz, Johannesburg #496/R est:12000-16000 (SA.R 28000)
£2580 $4153 €3870 Street scene with figures in the Malay quarter (59x91cm-23x36in) s. indis d. canvas on board. 12-May-3 Stephan Welz, Johannesburg #497/R est:18000-24000 (SA.R 30000)

Works on paper
£184 $287 €276 Temple of Venus, Baalbek (59x49cm-23x19in) s.i.d.71 W/C pastel. 15-Oct-2 Stephan Welz, Johannesburg #192 est:1600-2000 (SA.R 3000)

MACCIO, Romulo (1931-) Argentinian
£2188 $3325 €3282 Sin titulo (30x30cm-12x12in) s. pair. 3-Jul-2 Naón & Cia, Buenos Aires #38 est:3000-3500
£2642 $4068 €4200 Untitled (100x81cm-39x32in) s. acrylic prov. 28-Oct-2 Segre, Madrid #178/R est:4200

McCLARY, Louise (1958-) British
Works on paper
£300 $498 €435 Untitled (56x76cm-22x30in) s.d.1994/95 verso pastel. 10-Jun-3 David Lay, Penzance #288

McCLELLAND, Robert John (1906-) American
Works on paper
£465 $730 €698 Large stone house with four chimneys on a late fall day (33x41cm-13x16in) s. W/C. 19-Apr-3 James Julia, Fairfield #372/R

McCLOSKEY, William J (1859-1941) American
£103226 $160000 €154839 Lady apples in overturned basket (23x30cm-9x12in) s. board prov.exhib. 5-Dec-2 Christie's, Rockefeller NY #43/R est:300000-500000

McCLOY, Samuel (1831-1904) British
£1384 $2158 €2200 Couple with a dog (25x20cm-10x8in) s.d.1864 prov. 17-Sep-2 Whyte's, Dublin #120/R est:3000-4000
Works on paper
£3000 $4770 €4500 They spread the frugal board (35x50cm-14x20in) s. W/C. 5-Mar-3 John Ross, Belfast #127 est:2000-2500
£3623 $5942 €5000 Stupid book (37x47cm-15x19in) s. W/C. 28-May-3 Bonhams & James Adam, Dublin #40/R est:5000-7000

McCLURE, Daphne (?) British
£600 $942 €900 Open window (39x43cm-15x17in) s. 10-Dec-2 Lane, Penzance #15/R
£1000 $1550 €1500 White boat (104x71cm-41x28in) s. board. 26-Sep-2 Lane, Penzance #126 est:600-700
Works on paper
£260 $406 €390 Fox on the mount (51x51cm-20x20in) s. i.verso mixed media. 17-Oct-2 David Lay, Penzance #1407

McCLURE, David (1926-1998) British
£2000 $3120 €3000 Flowers in a black jug (42x33cm-17x13in) s. panel. 17-Oct-2 Bonhams, Edinburgh #4/R est:1000-1500
£2200 $3432 €3300 Puberty (75x100cm-30x39in) s. 17-Oct-2 Bonhams, Edinburgh #105/R est:2500-3500
£3000 $4590 €4500 Nude figure with flowers (64x78cm-25x31in) s.d.63 s.i.d.verso. 22-Aug-2 Bonhams, Edinburgh #961/R est:1500-2000
£3000 $4770 €4500 Paola, owl and doll (63x76cm-25x30in) s.d.62 s.d.verso. 6-Mar-3 Christie's, Kensington #247/R est:3000-5000
£3400 $5304 €5100 Monsieur Braque's bird flies in (70x90cm-28x35in) s. s.i.verso board. 17-Oct-2 Bonhams, Edinburgh #46/R est:3000-5000
£4200 $6384 €6300 Numinous chalice (63x76cm-25x30in) s. s.i.verso. 28-Aug-2 Sotheby's, London #1045/R est:3000-5000
£4800 $7296 €7200 Flowers in a landscape (76x63cm-30x25in) s. s.i.d.1962 verso. 28-Aug-2 Sotheby's, London #1034/R est:4000-6000
£8000 $12160 €12000 The sofa - 3rd version (73x101cm-29x40in) s. s.i.d.1973 verso. 28-Aug-2 Sotheby's, London #1021/R est:4000-6000
Works on paper
£700 $1092 €1050 Toledo (35x39cm-14x15in) s.i. gouache pencil. 17-Oct-2 Bonhams, Edinburgh #38
£1250 $1950 €1875 Houses in Cadaques, Spain (34x43cm-13x17in) s.d.52 s.i.verso W/C. 17-Oct-2 Bonhams, Edinburgh #72 est:400-600

MACCO, Georg (1863-1933) German
£473 $738 €700 Acropolis (21x33cm-8x13in) s. board. 26-Mar-3 Hugo Ruef, Munich #171
£750 $1162 €1125 Shepherds resting in the shade of a tree (36x55cm-14x22in) s.d.1910. 3-Dec-2 Sotheby's, Olympia #236/R
£755 $1170 €1200 Winter in Tyrolean mountains (33x46cm-13x18in) s.d.1902. 29-Oct-2 Dorotheum, Vienna #112/R
£955 $1471 €1500 Harbour of Beyrouth, Libanon (21x32cm-8x13in) s. 3-Sep-2 Christie's, Amsterdam #145 est:1500-2000
£1026 $1610 €1600 Village in Swiss alpine valley (56x68cm-22x27in) s.d.1924. 21-Nov-2 Van Ham, Cologne #1768/R est:1500
£1304 $2073 €1956 From Jerusalem with view towards Omar Mosque (64x79cm-25x31in) s.d.1929. 5-Mar-3 Rasmussen, Copenhagen #1797/R est:15000 (D.KR 14000)
£1408 $2310 €2042 Oriental market (47x66cm-19x26in) s. 4-Jun-3 Fischer, Luzern #1153/R est:2500-3500 (S.FR 3000)
£1656 $2699 €2500 Vue de place italienne (65x49cm-26x19in) s. 31-Jan-3 Rabourdin & Choppin de Janvry, Paris #90/R
£2000 $3160 €3000 View of the Acropolis (42x60cm-17x24in) 1-Apr-3 Bonhams, New Bond Street #8 est:2000-3000
£2075 $3196 €3300 Rue animee au Caire (53x39cm-21x15in) s.d.1909. 23-Oct-2 Rabourdin & Choppin de Janvry, Paris #116/R
£2821 $4428 €4400 View of the Garden of Gethsemane, Jerusalem (49x109cm-19x43in) s.d.1930. 21-Nov-2 Van Ham, Cologne #1767/R est:1800
£3145 $4843 €5000 Scene de rue au Caire (76x55cm-30x22in) s.i.d. 23-Oct-2 Rabourdin & Choppin de Janvry, Paris #117/R
Works on paper
£510 $811 €750 Jerusalem (33x47cm-13x19in) s.i. gouache. 19-Mar-3 Neumeister, Munich #379

McCOLLUM, Allan (1944-) American
£6962 $11000 €10443 Plaster surrogates. s.d.1985 verso enamel hydrostone in 15 parts prov. 13-Nov-2 Sotheby's, New York #541/R est:7000-10000
£12025 $19000 €18038 64 plaster surrogates. s.d.1987 num.1-64 enamel on plaster prov. 14-Nov-2 Christie's, Rockefeller NY #387/R est:20000-30000
£16250 $26000 €24375 120 plaster surrogates. s.d.1988 enamel on cast hydrocal prov. 15-May-3 Christie's, Rockefeller NY #359/R est:25000-35000
Works on paper
£6463 $10276 €9500 Collection. s.d.1988-90 verso graphite board set of 15 prov. 24-Mar-3 Cornette de St.Cyr, Paris #108/R

McCOLVIN, John (?) British?
£1800 $2790 €2700 Woman fetching water. Emptying the nets (41x51cm-16x20in) s. pair. 3-Dec-2 Sotheby's, Olympia #167/R est:1500-2000

McCOMB, Leonard (1930-) British
Works on paper
£360 $583 €540 Chess players (29x37cm-11x15in) s.d.18 October 1985 pen ink. 20-May-3 Bonhams, Knightsbridge #176/R

McCONAHA, Lawrence (1894-?) American
£267 $425 €401 Autumn wooded landscape (46x56cm-18x22in) s. board painted c.1930. 2-Mar-3 Toomey, Oak Park #720/R
£452 $700 €678 Summer clouds (41x51cm-16x20in) s. board painted c.1935. 8-Dec-2 Toomey, Oak Park #733/R

McCONNELL, George (1852-1929) American
£409 $650 €614 Mountainous landscape with stream (20x46cm-8x18in) s. canvasboard. 7-Mar-3 Jackson's, Cedar Falls #752/R
£526 $800 €789 Still life of two baskets of strawberries one tipped over (38x61cm-15x24in) s. board. 30-Aug-2 Thomaston Place, Thomaston #97

MACCORD, Charles William (1852-1923) American
£446 $700 €669 Misty morning (30x41cm-12x16in) s.d.1906. 14-Dec-2 Charlton Hall, Columbia #496/R

McCORD, George (1848-1909) American
£1090 $1700 €1635 Landscape with fisherman on a lake (30x46cm-12x18in) s. 21-Sep-2 Pook & Pook, Downington #289/R est:2000-3000
£1282 $2000 €1923 Sunset over a rough ocean, with sailboat and cliffs (66x51cm-26x20in) 21-Sep-2 Pook & Pook, Downington #456/R est:3000-4000
£1299 $2000 €1949 Venice (41x64cm-16x25in) s. painted c.1895. 8-Sep-2 Treadway Gallery, Cincinnati #573/R est:2500-4500
£1806 $2800 €2709 Sunset (20x15cm-8x6in) s. board painted c.1860 prov. 3-Dec-2 Phillips, New York #2/R
£2848 $4500 €4272 New York Harbor (76x64cm-30x25in) s. prov. 24-Apr-3 Shannon's, Milford #190/R est:4000-6000
£3247 $5000 €4871 River at dusk (51x76cm-20x30in) s. prov. 24-Oct-2 Shannon's, Milford #185/R est:3000-5000
£3481 $5500 €5222 Autumn trees (76x64cm-30x25in) s. 24-Apr-3 Shannon's, Milford #197/R est:4000-6000
£5063 $8000 €7595 River in a mountain landscape (30x46cm-12x18in) s. 24-Apr-3 Shannon's, Milford #43/R est:5000-7000

£7547 $12000 €11321 Along the lakeshore at dusk (51x76cm-20x30in) s. 4-Mar-3 Christie's, Rockefeller NY #4/R est:15000-25000

Works on paper

£688 $1100 €1032 Fall fisherman (28x28cm-11x11in) s. W/C. 11-Jan-3 James Julia, Fairfield #550 est:1000-2000

McCORMACK, Selma (19/20th C) British?

£300 $465 €450 Dressing room (30x41cm-12x16in) s.d.02 acrylic on board. 2-Oct-2 John Ross, Belfast #248
£350 $511 €525 Summer evening (69x28cm-27x11in) s.d.01 acrylic on paper. 12-Jun-2 John Ross, Belfast #60
£350 $511 €525 Figure in a landscape (56x33cm-22x13in) s.d.01 acrylic. 12-Jun-2 John Ross, Belfast #284
£380 $604 €570 Boathouse door (30x20cm-12x8in) s.d.01 acrylic on paper. 5-Mar-3 John Ross, Belfast #52
£400 $620 €600 Drawing by numbers (51x58cm-20x23in) s.d.02 acrylic on board. 2-Oct-2 John Ross, Belfast #198
£400 $620 €600 Farewell (50x33cm-20x13in) s.d.02 acrylic on paper. 4-Dec-2 John Ross, Belfast #206

Sculpture

£1100 $1705 €1650 Dancer (26cm-10in) s. cast bronze. 4-Dec-2 John Ross, Belfast #240 est:1200-1300
£1200 $1860 €1800 Second star to the left (38cm-15in) s. bronze. 2-Oct-2 John Ross, Belfast #240 est:1200-1400
£1600 $2336 €2400 Dancer (51cm-20in) s.num.5/7 bronze. 12-Jun-2 John Ross, Belfast #272 est:1800-2000
£1900 $3021 €2850 Mother and child dancing (30cm-12in) s. cast bronze. 5-Mar-3 John Ross, Belfast #220 est:1700-1800

Works on paper

£340 $527 €510 Still life, nude (33x22cm-13x9in) chl. 4-Dec-2 John Ross, Belfast #268

McCORMACK, Thomas Arthur (1883-1973) New Zealander

Works on paper

£909 $1400 €1364 Kaikoura Coast (57x70cm-22x28in) s. W/C. 4-Sep-2 Dunbar Sloane, Wellington #4/R est:1000-2000 (NZ.D 3000)
£1125 $1754 €1688 Morning light (31x39cm-12x15in) s. W/C. 17-Sep-2 Peter Webb, Auckland #79/R est:2000-3000 (NZ.D 3700)

McCORMICK, Arthur David (1860-1943) British

£596 $941 €894 Ploughing scene (25x35cm-10x14in) s. panel. 30-Nov-2 Rasmussen, Havnen #2038/R (D.KR 7000)
£1100 $1782 €1650 Pirate's tribunal (46x61cm-18x24in) s.d.1900. 23-Jan-3 Christie's, Kensington #29/R est:500-700
£1500 $2280 €2250 Piratas en un iterior de taberna (76x56cm-30x22in) 3-Jul-2 Naón & Cia, Buenos Aires #6/R est:2000-3000
£1500 $2340 €2250 Sir Francis Drake at Cadiz (75x59cm-30x23in) s. canvas on board. 7-Nov-2 Christie's, Kensington #241/R est:1500-2000
£8500 $13855 €12325 Drake and the ransom of San Domingo (189x277cm-74x109in) s.d.21.22 exhib. 17-Jul-3 Tennants, Leyburn #926/R est:10000-15000
£19000 $28880 €28500 Sailor from HMS Invincible reading on a quayside (174x100cm-69x39in) prov. 15-Aug-2 Bonhams, New Bond Street #450/R est:7000-10000

McCORMICK, Arthur David (attrib) (1860-1943) British

£550 $858 €825 Guitar player (69x66cm-27x26in) 26-Mar-3 Hamptons Fine Art, Godalming #234

MACCORMICK, W A (?) New Zealander

£376 $587 €564 Sailing on Lake Rotorua (60x75cm-24x30in) s. 7-Nov-2 International Art Centre, Auckland #196 est:1400-2000 (NZ.D 1200)

McCOUCH, Gordon Mallet (1885-1956) American

Works on paper

£472 $764 €684 Tessin harbour landscape (33x47cm-13x19in) s.d.49 pastel chk prov. 24-May-3 Galerie Gloggner, Luzern #82/R (S.FR 1000)

McCOY, Wilton Guy (1902-1986) American

£1000 $1600 €1450 Desert flowers. Desert Bouquet, Andreas Canyon, near Palm Springs, California (21x26cm-8x10in) s. i.verso canvas and canvas-board two. 16-May-3 Skinner, Boston #240/R est:600-800
£1013 $1600 €1520 Desert landscape (46x61cm-18x24in) s. i.stretcher. 16-Nov-2 New Orleans Auction, New Orleans #1119/R est:1800-2500
£1032 $1600 €1548 Smoke tree (30x41cm-12x16in) s. i.verso board. 20-Jul-2 New Orleans Auction, New Orleans #799/R est:1800-2500

McCRACKEN, Francis (1879-1959) British

£704 $1162 €1021 Toledo landscape (46x55cm-18x22in) i.on stretcher. 1-Jul-3 Peter Webb, Auckland #69/R est:4000-6000 (NZ.D 2000)
£3873 $6391 €5616 Fishing boats drying their sails, Concarneau (46x54cm-18x21in) with sig. prov. 1-Jul-3 Peter Webb, Auckland #68/R est:18000-26000 (NZ.D 11000)
£4225 $6972 €6126 Picture book (59x44cm-23x17in) s. s.i.verso prov. 1-Jul-3 Peter Webb, Auckland #67/R est:18000-25000 (NZ.D 12000)

Works on paper

£2508 $3912 €3762 Pont de Nuef, Paris. French study (49x61cm-19x24in) s. gouache double-sided. 7-Nov-2 International Art Centre, Auckland #106/R est:7000-10000 (NZ.D 8000)

McCRACKEN, John (1934-) American

Sculpture

£1218 $1888 €1900 Untitled - Pink block (28x30x22cm-11x12x9in) s.d.1968 fibreglass. 6-Dec-2 Hauswedell & Nolte, Hamburg #257/R est:1500
£6962 $11000 €10443 Magenta beam (20x152x28cm-8x60x11in) s. i.d.87 verso polyester resin fiberglas plywood prov. 13-Nov-2 Sotheby's, New York #125/R est:10000-15000
£13750 $22000 €20625 Plane, red plank (309x46x4cm-122x18x2in) s.i.d.1988-93 polyester resin fiberglass on plywood prov. 14-May-3 Sotheby's, New York #304/R est:12000-18000
£14375 $23000 €21563 Diamond, black plank (295x44x4cm-116x17x2in) s.i.d.88-93 polyester resin fiberglas on plywood prov. 14-May-3 Sotheby's, New York #305/R est:12000-18000

McCRADY, John (1911-1968) American

£4808 $7500 €7212 West of Denver (41x51cm-16x20in) s. multi-stage. 12-Oct-2 Neal Auction Company, New Orleans #640/R est:8000-12000
£5380 $8500 €8070 A M (25x41cm-10x16in) s.i. carbon acrylic prov. 5-Apr-3 Neal Auction Company, New Orleans #338/R est:10000-15000

McCRAIG, Norman (20th C) Irish

£1835 $2845 €2900 Fishing, Cushendun Bay (25x30cm-10x12in) s.i.verso board. 25-Sep-2 James Adam, Dublin #49a est:2500-3000

McCROSSAN, Mary (?-1934) British

£850 $1335 €1275 Harbour scene. Boats (64x76cm-25x30in) s.i.on stretcher double-sided. 21-Nov-2 Tennants, Leyburn #763

McCUBBIN, Frederick (1855-1917) Australian

£7280 $10847 €10920 Hammersmith Bridge (24x34cm-9x13in) s.d.1947 board prov. 27-Aug-2 Christie's, Melbourne #80/R est:12000-15000 (A.D 19000)
£8541 $13068 €12812 Trees in a landscape (17x34cm-7x13in) s. i.verso board painted c.1911 prov. 26-Aug-2 Sotheby's, Paddington #566/R est:10000-12000 (A.D 24000)
£11450 $18092 €17175 Sheep grazing near a wooded landscape (34x24cm-13x9in) s.d.1908 prov. 2-Apr-3 Christie's, Melbourne #33/R est:20000-30000 (A.D 30000)
£13546 $22215 €20319 Flinders Street Railway Station (25x35cm-10x14in) s. canvasboard painted c.1911-12 prov.exhib. 4-Jun-3 Deutscher-Menzies, Melbourne #35/R est:40000-50000 (A.D 34000)
£14947 $22868 €22421 Sunny glade (32x48cm-13x19in) s. prov. 25-Aug-2 Sotheby's, Paddington #13/R est:50000-70000 (A.D 42000)
£20714 $32729 €31071 Artist's camp (36x51cm-14x20in) prov. 17-Nov-2 Sotheby's, Paddington #18/R est:60000-80000 (A.D 58000)
£27481 $43420 €41222 Figure on a hillside in a summer landscape (27x57cm-11x22in) s.d.1907. 2-Apr-3 Christie's, Melbourne #7/R est:50000-70000 (A.D 72000)
£46263 $70783 €69395 At Macedon (52x61cm-20x24in) s.d.1913 prov. 26-Aug-2 Sotheby's, Paddington #523/R est:100000-150000 (A.D 130000)
£64000 $103040 €96000 Mount Macedon (50x75cm-20x30in) s. painted c.1910 exhib. 6-May-3 Christie's, Melbourne #93/R est:180000-250000 (A.D 160000)

McCUBBIN, Louis (1890-1952) Australian

£440 $708 €638 Exhibition gardens (59x49cm-23x19in) s. 12-May-3 Joel, Victoria #242 est:1000-1500 (A.D 1100)
£1085 $1726 €1628 Bridges over the Yarra (39x53cm-15x21in) s. board. 5-May-3 Sotheby's, Melbourne #270/R est:1400-1800 (A.D 2800)
£1628 $2588 €2442 Towards the Yarra (59x49cm-23x19in) board. 5-May-3 Sotheby's, Melbourne #285/R est:3000-4000 (A.D 4200)

McCULLOCH, Hamilton (19th C) British

£780 $1287 €1131 Crossing the river (61x102cm-24x40in) s. indis.d. canvas on board. 2-Jul-3 Sotheby's, Olympia #331/R

McCULLOCH, Horatio (1805-1867) British
£800 $1248 €1200 Panoramic view of a loch, deer in a wooded landscape in the foreground (60x96cm-24x38in) s. 13-Sep-2 Lyon & Turnbull, Edinburgh #75/R
£1700 $2652 €2550 Bothwell Castle (40x30cm-16x12in) s. 13-Sep-2 Lyon & Turnbull, Edinburgh #18/R est:600-800
£1700 $2635 €2550 Wooded landscape with distant castle (30x46cm-12x18in) s.d.1859. 6-Dec-2 Lyon & Turnbull, Edinburgh #5/R est:1000-1500
£2500 $3900 €3750 Loch Leven (21x31cm-8x12in) s. i.verso panel. 14-Apr-3 Sotheby's, London #49/R est:2500-3000
£4800 $7296 €7200 Kilchurn Castle, Loch Awe (41x61cm-16x24in) s. prov. 28-Aug-2 Sotheby's, London #802/R est:3000-5000
£5000 $7750 €7500 View of Loch Fad, Isle of Bute, with Arran in the distance (56x77cm-22x30in) s. prov. 31-Oct-2 Christie's, London #21/R est:6000-10000
£12000 $18600 €18000 Mid-Lothian landscape with Edinburgh in the distance (91x137cm-36x54in) s. 31-Oct-2 Christie's, London #19/R est:12000-18000
£14000 $21700 €21000 After Culloden (91x127cm-36x50in) 31-Oct-2 Christie's, London #20/R est:15000-20000

McCULLOCH, Horatio (attrib) (1805-1867) British
£1000 $1560 €1500 Landscape with distant castle and washer woman (45x60cm-18x24in) 28-Mar-3 Bonhams, Edinburgh #138
£1000 $1640 €1500 Boys on a rocky ledge at sunset (42x31cm-17x12in) panel. 29-May-3 Christie's, Kensington #75/R est:1000-1500
£1400 $2184 €2100 Shepherd and flock in a highland landscape (70x91cm-28x36in) indis s.d. 28-Mar-3 Bonhams, Edinburgh #137/R est:2000-3000

MACCULLOCH, James (?-1915) British
Works on paper
£300 $468 €450 Entrance to Glen Sannox, Arran (20x36cm-8x14in) s. W/C. 17-Oct-2 Bonhams, Edinburgh #192

MACCULLOCH, Ross (20th C) Canadian
£932 $1482 €1398 Eventide sailor (60x75cm-24x30in) s.i. board. 23-Mar-3 Hodgins, Calgary #46/R est:600-900 (C.D 2200)

McCULLOUGH, Geraldine (20th C) American
Sculpture
£2110 $3250 €3165 Icarus (168x61x61cm-66x24x24in) metal various materials exec.c.1950. 8-Sep-2 Treadway Gallery, Cincinnati #765/R est:3000-5000

McDERMOTT and McGOUGH (20th C) American
£4861 $8021 €7000 Silhouette portraits of MacDermott and MacGough (64x92cm-25x36in) s. diptych prov.exhib. 3-Jul-3 Christie's, Paris #29/R est:7000-9000
Photographs
£2468 $3800 €3702 Model before the world (42x30cm-17x12in) i.verso palladium print 1 of 3 prov. 25-Oct-2 Phillips, New York #177/R est:4000-6000

McDERMOTT, John R (1919-1977) American
Works on paper
£3526 $5500 €5289 Man carrying unconscious woman along deserted street (33x30cm-13x12in) s. gouache. 9-Nov-2 Illustration House, New York #144/R est:6000-8000

McDERMOTT, Sean (20th C) Irish
£667 $1107 €967 Michael Collins (91x81cm-36x32in) s. 16-Jun-3 Waddingtons, Toronto #190/R est:2000-3000 (C.D 1500)

MACDIARMID, Douglas (1922-) New Zealander
£424 $653 €636 Recreation ground (31x37cm-12x15in) s.d.1947 board. 4-Sep-2 Dunbar Sloane, Wellington #150 est:1500-2500 (NZ.D 1400)
£788 $1213 €1182 Reclining nude (36x48cm-14x19in) s. board. 4-Sep-2 Dunbar Sloane, Wellington #149 est:600-1200 (NZ.D 2600)
£848 $1307 €1272 Untitled - abstract (38x26cm-15x10in) s. board. 4-Sep-2 Dunbar Sloane, Wellington #50/R est:2500-3500 (NZ.D 2800)
Works on paper
£303 $467 €455 Papa Cliff and pool with Maoir children (37x22cm-15x9in) s. W/C. 4-Sep-2 Dunbar Sloane, Wellington #151 est:800-1200 (NZ.D 1000)
£727 $1120 €1091 Helen Hitchings on a sunny afternoon (37x30cm-15x12in) s. W/C. 4-Sep-2 Dunbar Sloane, Wellington #152 est:1500-2500 (NZ.D 2400)

MACDONALD, A M (?) British
£1600 $2496 €2400 Young seamstress (40x30cm-16x12in) s.d.1884. 13-Sep-2 Lyon & Turnbull, Edinburgh #73/R est:300-500

MACDONALD, Alistair K (fl.1898-1947) British
Works on paper
£350 $578 €508 Walk in the winter sunset (34x32cm-13x13in) s.d.04 pencil pen black ink pastel bodycol. 3-Jul-3 Christie's, Kensington #213/R

MacDONALD, Arthur (fl.1897-1940) British
£1350 $2106 €2025 East Neuk harbour (22x30cm-9x12in) s. board. 17-Oct-2 Bonhams, Edinburgh #236 est:250-350

MACDONALD, Grant (1944-) American
£1859 $2900 €2789 Taos bouquet (30x48cm-12x19in) 9-Aug-2 Altermann Galleries, Santa Fe #24/R
£2051 $3200 €3077 Flower market in Paris (23x30cm-9x12in) 9-Aug-2 Altermann Galleries, Santa Fe #3/R
£2051 $3200 €3077 Early autumn (41x30cm-16x12in) 9-Aug-2 Altermann Galleries, Santa Fe #8/R
£2051 $3200 €3077 Palais Royale (23x30cm-9x12in) 9-Aug-2 Altermann Galleries, Santa Fe #16/R
£2244 $3500 €3366 Cotton woods on the Rio Grande (51x41cm-20x16in) 9-Aug-2 Altermann Galleries, Santa Fe #7/R
£2244 $3500 €3366 Hollyhocks (51x41cm-20x16in) 9-Aug-2 Altermann Galleries, Santa Fe #9/R
£2244 $3500 €3366 Notre Dame in Paris (51x41cm-20x16in) 9-Aug-2 Altermann Galleries, Santa Fe #14/R
£2244 $3500 €3366 September 2001 (41x51cm-16x20in) 9-Aug-2 Altermann Galleries, Santa Fe #20/R
£2628 $4100 €3942 October in Paris (46x61cm-18x24in) 9-Aug-2 Altermann Galleries, Santa Fe #15/R
£2628 $4100 €3942 Sandia at sundown (46x61cm-18x24in) 9-Aug-2 Altermann Galleries, Santa Fe #18/R
£2628 $4100 €3942 Sunshine on the Rio Grande (46x61cm-18x24in) 9-Aug-2 Altermann Galleries, Santa Fe #23/R
£2885 $4500 €4328 Lunch in Paris (61x46cm-24x18in) 9-Aug-2 Altermann Galleries, Santa Fe #12/R
£2885 $4500 €4328 Aspen trail (61x51cm-24x20in) 9-Aug-2 Altermann Galleries, Santa Fe #6/R
£2885 $4500 €4328 In Monet's Garden (61x51cm-24x20in) 9-Aug-2 Altermann Galleries, Santa Fe #10/R
£3123 $5060 €4528 Ducks on the water at sunset (48x64cm-19x25in) acrylic. 23-May-3 Altermann Galleries, Santa Fe #222
£3910 $6100 €5865 Lilacs (61x76cm-24x30in) 9-Aug-2 Altermann Galleries, Santa Fe #11/R
£4167 $6500 €6251 St Francis Cathedral (64x76cm-25x30in) 9-Aug-2 Altermann Galleries, Santa Fe #21/R
£4178 $6100 €6267 Cottonwoods on the Rio Grande (51x41cm-20x16in) 18-May-2 Altermann Galleries, Santa Fe #208/R
£4551 $7100 €6827 Rainy day at Givernu (61x91cm-24x36in) 9-Aug-2 Altermann Galleries, Santa Fe #17/R
£4551 $7100 €6827 Sunset over Mt Taylor (61x91cm-24x36in) 9-Aug-2 Altermann Galleries, Santa Fe #22/R
£5705 $8900 €8558 Aspen (76x102cm-30x40in) 9-Aug-2 Altermann Galleries, Santa Fe #5/R
£5705 $8900 €8558 Nature's laughter (102x76cm-40x30in) 9-Aug-2 Altermann Galleries, Santa Fe #13/R
£5705 $8900 €8558 Tesuque cotton woods (76x102cm-30x40in) 9-Aug-2 Altermann Galleries, Santa Fe #25/R
£5705 $8900 €8558 Winter in New Mexico (76x102cm-30x40in) 9-Aug-2 Altermann Galleries, Santa Fe #26/R
£12179 $19000 €18269 View from the portal (102x152cm-40x60in) 9-Aug-2 Altermann Galleries, Santa Fe #4/R
£12179 $19000 €18269 Sandia at sunset (102x152cm-40x60in) 9-Aug-2 Altermann Galleries, Santa Fe #19/R
£12685 $20550 €18393 Winter's tale (102x152cm-40x60in) 23-May-3 Altermann Galleries, Santa Fe #190

MACDONALD, Grant Kenneth (1909-) Canadian
£453 $702 €680 Promenade (50x62cm-20x24in) s.d.68 board prov. 3-Dec-2 Joyner, Toronto #270/R est:1500-2000 (C.D 1100)

MACDONALD, James Edward Hervey (1873-1932) Canadian
£1778 $2916 €2667 Summer fields (24x27cm-9x11in) board prov. 27-May-3 Sotheby's, Toronto #6/R est:3000-5000 (C.D 4000)
£3111 $5102 €4667 Barbados (22x27cm-9x11in) init.d.1.7.32 board prov.lit. 27-May-3 Sotheby's, Toronto #218/R est:7000-9000 (C.D 7000)
£3247 $5162 €4708 Memory of Point Amour Light, Straits of Bel Isle (19x25cm-7x10in) s. s.i.verso canvas on board prov. 1-May-3 Heffel, Vancouver #59/R est:6000-8000 (C.D 7500)
£3704 $5741 €5556 Lake O'Hara with cathedral MT. 8 miles up the trail (11x13cm-4x5in) s.i.verso board lit. 3-Dec-2 Joyner, Toronto #3/R est:5000-7000 (C.D 9000)
£4260 $6816 €6390 Barbados (20x25cm-8x10in) s.d.1932 panel prov.lit. 15-May-3 Heffel, Vancouver #94/R est:7000-9000 (C.D 9500)

£5350 $8292 €8025 Summer day, York Mill (21x26cm-8x10in) init. panel prov. 3-Dec-2 Joyner, Toronto #152/R est:10000-12000 (C.D 13000)
£5372 $8434 €8058 Low tide, Petite Riviere (20x25cm-8x10in) s.i.d.22 s.d.verso board prov. 24-Jul-2 Walker's, Ottawa #218/R est:14000-18000 (C.D 13000)
£6048 $9556 €9072 Fisherman's bay (21x27cm-8x11in) init.d.22 s.i.verso board prov.lit. 18-Nov-2 Sotheby's, Toronto #100/R est:7000-9000 (C.D 15000)
£6222 $10204 €9333 Atlantic shore, Nova Scotia, 1922 (21x26cm-8x10in) s. board prov. 3-Jun-3 Joyner, Toronto #178/R est:7000-9000 (C.D 14000)
£6222 $10204 €9333 Stream in winter (16x23cm-6x9in) init.d.12 board. 3-Jun-3 Joyner, Toronto #316/R est:3000-5000 (C.D 14000)
£6222 $10204 €9333 Winter hillside (15x23cm-6x9in) i.verso board. 3-Jun-3 Joyner, Toronto #354/R est:3000-5000 (C.D 14000)
£8072 $12915 €12108 High tide (22x27cm-9x11in) s.i.d.1931-32 verso panel prov.exhib. 15-May-3 Heffel, Vancouver #126/R est:20000-25000 (C.D 18000)
£8444 $13849 €12666 Edge of the field (21x26cm-8x10in) s. board. 3-Jun-3 Joyner, Toronto #364/R est:6000-8000 (C.D 19000)
£13105 $20706 €19658 Rocks on Mcleans Island (22x27cm-9x11in) s.d.September 28 1931 s.d.verso panel prov. 14-Nov-2 Heffel, Vancouver #10/R est:25000-30000 (C.D 32500)
£13333 $21867 €20000 Mount Owen, from Lake Mcarthur (22x27cm-9x11in) s. s.i.verso board prov. 27-May-3 Sotheby's, Toronto #18/R est:18000-20000 (C.D 30000)
£26667 $43733 €40001 Morning light, Lake O'Hara, Rocky Mountains (21x26cm-8x10in) board painted c.1929 lit. 3-Jun-3 Joyner, Toronto #55/R est:40000-50000 (C.D 60000)

Works on paper
£258 $402 €374 Cathedral mountain (13x8cm-5x3in) s.i.d.28 graphite dr. lit. 26-Mar-3 Walker's, Ottawa #447/R (C.D 600)
£281 $447 €407 Willows, Humber Valley (23x19cm-9x7in) i.d.Aug 08 graphite dr prov. 1-May-3 Heffel, Vancouver #60/R (C.D 650)

MACDONALD, James W G (1897-1960) Canadian
£1556 $2551 €2334 Lake Ontario (30x15cm-12x6in) s.i.d.July 1960 canvasboard prov. 27-May-3 Sotheby's, Toronto #219/R est:3000-5000 (C.D 3500)
£12097 $19113 €18146 Wave (102x82cm-40x32in) s.d.39 i.verso prov. 18-Nov-2 Sotheby's, Toronto #72/R est:10000-15000 (C.D 30000)

MACDONALD, John Blake (1829-1901) British
£980 $1529 €1470 Young shepherd (51x41cm-20x16in) s. 10-Apr-3 Bonhams, Edinburgh #120
£1000 $1560 €1500 Mother and child (42x53cm-17x21in) s. exhib. 17-Sep-2 Sotheby's, Olympia #11/R est:1000-1500
£1500 $2280 €2250 Veteran's return (75x62cm-30x24in) bears sig. 28-Aug-2 Sotheby's, London #895/R est:1500-2000

McDONALD, Jon (20th C) American
£472 $750 €708 Southwest figure of a woman (102x81cm-40x32in) s. acrylic painted c.1980. 2-Mar-3 Toomey, Oak Park #700/R

MACDONALD, Lawrence (1799-1878) British
Sculpture
£5200 $8684 €7540 Bust of a young girl (51cm-20in) s.d.1841 white marble. 8-Jul-3 Sotheby's, London #179/R est:3000-4000

MACDONALD, Manly Edward (1889-1971) Canadian
£389 $603 €584 Portrait of a man with pipe (26x21cm-10x8in) s. board prov. 24-Sep-2 Ritchie, Toronto #3130/R (C.D 950)
£390 $619 €566 Elms and hay stacks (30x41cm-12x16in) s. prov. 1-May-3 Heffel, Vancouver #62/R (C.D 900)
£617 $957 €926 Birches by the lake (29x29cm-11x11in) s. board prov. 3-Dec-2 Joyner, Toronto #373 est:1200-1500 (C.D 1500)
£658 $1021 €987 Lake through a break in the trees (30x40cm-12x16in) s.d.70 canvasboard. 3-Dec-2 Joyner, Toronto #446 est:1000-1500 (C.D 1600)
£717 $1148 €1076 Cherry Street, Toronto (22x27cm-9x11in) s.i.verso panel painted c.1930-35 prov. 15-May-3 Heffel, Vancouver #171/R est:1000-1500 (C.D 1600)
£736 $1170 €1067 Long Reach, Ontario (41x51cm-16x20in) s. canvasboard prov. 1-May-3 Heffel, Vancouver #63/R (C.D 1700)
£741 $1148 €1112 Corner of the pasture (30x40cm-12x16in) s. board prov. 3-Dec-2 Joyner, Toronto #358 est:1500-2000 (C.D 1800)
£773 $1205 €1160 Winter landscape (30x40cm-12x16in) s. i.verso canvasboard. 25-Mar-3 Ritchie, Toronto #81/R est:2000-2500 (C.D 1800)
£823 $1308 €1193 On the way to Glenora (30x41cm-12x16in) s. canvasboard prov. 1-May-3 Heffel, Vancouver #64/R est:1000-1500 (C.D 1900)
£897 $1435 €1346 The Ward, looking south (30x41cm-12x16in) s. canvasboard prov. 15-May-3 Heffel, Vancouver #164/R est:1000-1500 (C.D 2000)
£1022 $1676 €1482 In Kingston Harbour (30x35cm-12x14in) s. board. 9-Jun-3 Hodgins, Calgary #428/R est:1500-2000 (C.D 2300)
£1111 $1722 €1667 Apple blossoms, Bay of Quinte (30x40cm-12x16in) s. board. 3-Dec-2 Joyner, Toronto #386/R est:1000-1500 (C.D 2700)
£1152 $1786 €1728 Sand carts (32x40cm-13x16in) s. panel. 3-Dec-2 Joyner, Toronto #429 est:1500-2000 (C.D 2800)
£1159 $1808 €1681 Old mill (30x41cm-12x16in) s. canvasboard prov. 26-Mar-3 Walker's, Ottawa #265/R est:3000-4000 (C.D 2700)
£1333 $2187 €2000 Wilket Creek (30x41cm-12x16in) s. canvasboard prov. 27-May-3 Sotheby's, Toronto #103/R est:3000-4000 (C.D 3000)
£1345 $2152 €2018 Winter in Hastings county (51x66cm-20x26in) s. prov. 15-May-3 Heffel, Vancouver #167/R est:2500-3500 (C.D 3000)
£1440 $2233 €2160 Haymaking (40x50cm-16x20in) s. 3-Dec-2 Joyner, Toronto #222/R est:3000-4000 (C.D 3500)
£1457 $2332 €2186 Fishing in the bay (61x81cm-24x32in) s. prov. 15-May-3 Heffel, Vancouver #211/R est:3000-4000 (C.D 3250)
£1646 $2551 €2469 Autumn river reflection (50x65cm-20x26in) s. 3-Dec-2 Joyner, Toronto #261/R est:3000-4000 (C.D 4000)
£1646 $2551 €2469 Yellow house and barn in winter (30x40cm-12x16in) s. canvas on board. 3-Dec-2 Joyner, Toronto #354 est:1000-1500 (C.D 4000)
£1728 $2679 €2592 Spring break up (50x65cm-20x26in) s. 3-Dec-2 Joyner, Toronto #15/R est:3000-4000 (C.D 4200)
£2222 $3644 €3333 Winter landscape with barn (40x50cm-16x20in) s. board. 3-Jun-3 Joyner, Toronto #63/R est:4000-5000 (C.D 5000)
£2667 $4373 €4001 Horse drawn sleigh outside a village (50x65cm-20x26in) s. 3-Jun-3 Joyner, Toronto #43/R est:5000-7000 (C.D 6000)
£2667 $4373 €4001 Nain street of a village in winter (30x40cm-12x16in) s. canvasboard. 3-Jun-3 Joyner, Toronto #158/R est:3000-4000 (C.D 6000)
£3111 $5102 €4667 Village scene with horses and sleighs (30x40cm-12x16in) s. canvasboard. 3-Jun-3 Joyner, Toronto #241/R est:3000-4000 (C.D 7000)
£4000 $6560 €6000 Toronto from the island (41x51cm-16x20in) s. canvasboard. 27-May-3 Sotheby's, Toronto #220/R est:4000-6000 (C.D 9000)
£4889 $8018 €7334 Village of Lonsdale, Ontario - old mill and Salmon River (60x80cm-24x31in) s. 3-Jun-3 Joyner, Toronto #1/R est:7000-9000 (C.D 11000)

MACDONALD, Murray (fl.1889-1910) British
£360 $565 €540 On the Tummel (19x29cm-7x11in) 17-Apr-3 Bonhams, Edinburgh #348
£380 $597 €570 Paps of Glencoe (20x30cm-8x12in) 17-Apr-3 Bonhams, Edinburgh #345
£520 $816 €780 Fishing, Loch Doon (19x29cm-7x11in) 17-Apr-3 Bonhams, Edinburgh #346
£660 $1036 €990 Cattle, Loch Eck (20x30cm-8x12in) 17-Apr-3 Bonhams, Edinburgh #347
£760 $1178 €1140 Dornoch (34x50cm-13x20in) s.d.1900 s.i.verso W/C board. 5-Dec-2 Bonhams, Edinburgh #109

MACDONALD, Richard (20th C) British
Sculpture
£1796 $3000 €2604 White face, half-life (81cm-32in) s. bronze 33 of 90. 21-Jun-3 Susanin's, Chicago #5004/R est:700-1000

MACDONALD, Thomas Reid (1908-) Canadian
£266 $413 €399 Georgian bay (16x22cm-6x9in) init.d.50 i.verso panel prov. 24-Sep-2 Ritchie, Toronto #3153/R (C.D 650)
£730 $1138 €1059 Rocks and Monhegan (66x81cm-26x32in) s.d.1975 prov. 26-Mar-3 Walker's, Ottawa #409/R est:600-800 (C.D 1700)

MACDONALD, Thoreau (1901-) Canadian
£369 $572 €554 Lake Ontario in winter. Lake and sky (27x35cm-11x14in) i.verso board pair. 24-Sep-2 Ritchie, Toronto #3177a (C.D 900)

MACDONALD, W Alister (fl.1893-1910) British
Works on paper
£480 $749 €720 Westminster (9x12cm-4x5in) init. pencil W/C. 19-Sep-2 Christie's, Kensington #178
£1216 $1897 €1800 Palermo beach with Monte Pellegrino (24x34cm-9x13in) s.mono.d.1908 W/C. 28-Mar-3 Dorotheum, Vienna #240/R est:1400-1600
£3200 $5312 €4800 Thames at Westminster Bridge. Thames at Bankside (23x38cm-9x15in) s.d.1912-14 W/C. 12-Jun-3 Bonhams, New Bond Street #654/R est:1500-2000

MACDONALD, William (fl.1884-1938) British
£1000 $1560 €1500 Hillside village in the Ronda (56x46cm-22x18in) s. 14-Apr-3 Sotheby's, London #162/R est:1000-1500
£1000 $1560 €1500 Snow on the hills, Ronda (45x56cm-18x22in) s. 14-Apr-3 Sotheby's, London #159/R est:1000-1500
£4500 $6975 €6750 Still life with Chinese wallpaper (56x46cm-22x18in) s. 31-Oct-2 Christie's, London #119/R est:3000-5000

MACDONALD, William Purcell (1863-?) American
£1069 $1700 €1604 Country picnic (132x160cm-52x63in) s. painted c.1920. 2-Mar-3 Toomey, Oak Park #711/R est:1500-2000

MACDONALD-WRIGHT, Stanton (1890-1973) American
Works on paper
£915 $1500 €1327 Standing nude (71x46cm-28x18in) s. graphite prov. 1-Jun-3 Wright, Chicago #193/R est:2000-3000
£6918 $11000 €10377 Cubistic still life (58x40cm-23x16in) s.d.45 W/C prov.exhib. 5-Mar-3 Sotheby's, New York #67/R est:4000-6000

McDONNELL, Hector (1947-) British
£1300 $2145 €1885 Man leaving a pub (35x46cm-14x18in) s.i.d.80 board exhib. 3-Jul-3 Christie's, Kensington #465/R est:1000-1500
£5517 $8717 €8000 Quays near Christ Church (153x127cm-60x50in) i. verso prov.exhib. 2-Apr-3 Dr Fritz Nagel, Stuttgart #9508/R est:8000

McDONNELL, Vincent (20th C) British?
Works on paper
£300 $465 €450 Yellow Yeats (20x15cm-8x6in) s.d.2002 mixed media. 2-Oct-2 John Ross, Belfast #234

McDOUGAL, John (fl.1877-1941) British
Works on paper
£600 $948 €900 Coastal view with sailing boats racing in the distance (29x51cm-11x20in) s.d.1892 W/C htd white. 26-Nov-2 Bonhams, Knightsbridge #34/R
£680 $1061 €1020 Old cottages at Camaes Bay (20x25cm-8x10in) s.d.1916 W/C. 6-Nov-2 Bonhams, Chester #322

MACDOUGALD, Reza (20th C) Irish
£1027 $1603 €1500 O'Connell Street (100x150cm-39x59in) s. painted 2002. 8-Apr-3 James Adam, Dublin #120/R est:1500-2500

MacDOUGALL, Allan (fl.1840-1889) British
£1000 $1640 €1500 Across the loch (46x63cm-18x25in) s. 29-May-3 Christie's, Kensington #96/R est:1200-1800

McDOUGALL, Walt (20th C) American
Works on paper
£1366 $2200 €2049 Goings on Noah's ark (36x56cm-14x22in) s. pen ink four. 20-Feb-3 Illustration House, New York #113/R est:2500-3500

McDUFF, Frederick H (1931-) American
£2548 $4000 €3822 On the beach (34x45cm-13x18in) s. board. 22-Nov-2 Skinner, Boston #361/R est:1500-2500

MACE, John Edmund (1889-?) British
£250 $390 €375 Norfolk river landscape with figures in punt and cattle in a meadow (48x79cm-19x31in) mono. 18-Oct-2 Keys, Aylsham #727
Works on paper
£450 $693 €675 Torquay harbour (30x44cm-12x17in) s. W/C. 5-Sep-2 Christie's, Kensington #527

MACEGAN, Darius J (1856-1939) Irish
£348 $543 €550 Portrait of John Wright of Parsonstown (45x36cm-18x14in) s. i.verso. 15-Oct-2 Mealy's, Castlecomer #423
£694 $1104 €1000 Stable gossip (38x30cm-15x12in) s.d.1906 canvas on board prov.exhib. 29-Apr-3 Whyte's, Dublin #187/R est:1000-1500

McELCHERAN, William (1927-1999) Canadian
Sculpture
£1564 $2424 €2346 Man with muse (29cm-11in) init.d.89 num.5/9 bronze. 3-Dec-2 Joyner, Toronto #90/R est:4000-5000 (C.D 3800)
£3111 $5102 €4667 Donning his overcoat (46cm-18in) bronze prov. 3-Jun-3 Joyner, Toronto #348/R est:4000-6000 (C.D 7000)
£4839 $7645 €7259 Accountant (75cm-30in) init.d.96 num.8/9 bronze prov.lit. 18-Nov-2 Sotheby's, Toronto #189/R est:12000-15000 (C.D 12000)
£6222 $10204 €9333 Determined (72cm-28in) s.d.95 bronze. 3-Jun-3 Joyner, Toronto #89/R est:10000-15000 (C.D 14000)
£6278 $10045 €9417 Inspired (75x27x41cm-30x11x16in) s.d.1995 brown pat. bronze prov. 15-May-3 Heffel, Vancouver #86/R est:12000-16000 (C.D 14000)
£6452 $10194 €9678 Satisfied (76x28x28cm-30x11x11in) s.d.1996 num.7/9 bronze prov. 14-Nov-2 Heffel, Vancouver #57/R est:10000-15000 (C.D 16000)
£8230 $12757 €12345 Flat out (61x100cm-24x39in) s.d.91 num.1/9 bronze. 3-Dec-2 Joyner, Toronto #60/R est:10000-15000 (C.D 20000)

McENTAGGART, Brett (1939-) Irish?
£443 $687 €700 Pine trees at the scalp (50x35cm-20x14in) s. board. 25-Sep-2 James Adam, Dublin #34

McENTEE, Jervis (1828-1891) American
£4430 $7000 €6645 Falling leaves (46x30cm-18x12in) mono. i.d.1879 verso board. 24-Apr-3 Shannon's, Milford #42/R est:8000-12000
£5484 $8500 €8226 Bass rocks (20x33cm-8x13in) mono.d.72 prov.exhib. 3-Dec-2 Phillips, New York #26/R est:8000-12000
£24193 $37500 €36290 Skating party (41x36cm-16x14in) s.d.1872 prov.exhib. 4-Dec-2 Sotheby's, New York #129/R est:25000-35000
£24691 $40000 €37037 Gathering Christmas finery at Roundout, New Jersey (30x50cm-12x20in) mono.d.1877 board prov. 22-May-3 Christie's, Rockefeller NY #16/R est:30000-50000
£70968 $110000 €106452 Gathering firewood (41x72cm-16x28in) init.d.1866 prov. 5-Dec-2 Christie's, Rockefeller NY #5/R est:40000-60000

McEVOY, Ambrose (1878-1927) British
£400 $640 €600 Portrait of a lady (52x40cm-20x16in) 15-May-3 Christie's, Kensington #152/R
£1000 $1580 €1500 Self Portrait (77x52cm-30x20in) 27-Nov-2 Sotheby's, Olympia #96/R est:1000-1500
Works on paper
£260 $403 €390 Seated gentleman with two ladies (33x27cm-13x11in) pencil. 1-Oct-2 Bonhams, Leeds #259
£260 $403 €390 Seated gentleman with two ladies (33x27cm-13x11in) pencil. 1-Oct-2 Bonhams, Leeds #256
£300 $465 €450 Cloudy landscape (18x25cm-7x10in) studio st. pencil W/C. 4-Dec-2 Christie's, Kensington #240
£500 $780 €750 Priscilla, portrait of a young lady (44x33cm-17x13in) pen ink W/C. 10-Apr-3 Tennants, Leyburn #915/R
£550 $853 €825 Mother and child (48x31cm-19x12in) W/C. 4-Dec-2 Christie's, Kensington #234/R
£600 $954 €900 Birdcage (48x33cm-19x13in) pen ink wash. 26-Feb-3 Sotheby's, Olympia #56/R

McEVOY, William (fl.1858-1880) Irish
£570 $883 €900 Young girl with terrier dog in western landscape (30x44cm-12x17in) s.d.1862. 25-Sep-2 James Adam, Dublin #37
£577 $906 €900 Landscape with river and bridge (32x27cm-13x11in) s.d.1873 board. 19-Nov-2 Whyte's, Dublin #211/R

McEWAN, Tom (1846-1914) British
£320 $525 €480 Somebody's coming (40x29cm-16x11in) s.d.85. 2-Jun-3 David Duggleby, Scarborough #332
£500 $815 €750 Bath time (19x13cm-7x5in) init. panel. 29-Jan-3 Hampton & Littlewood, Exeter #394/R
£550 $858 €825 Old woman with a creel (51x33cm-20x13in) init. 17-Oct-2 Bonhams, Edinburgh #222
£1200 $1956 €1740 Posy (31x26cm-12x10in) s. s.i.verso. 16-Jul-3 Sotheby's, Olympia #77/R est:1200-1800
£2000 $3100 €3000 Good read (32x22cm-13x9in) s. 6-Dec-2 Lyon & Turnbull, Edinburgh #95 est:800-1200
£2100 $3255 €3150 News from the far west (48x59cm-19x23in) s.d.1885 canvas on board. 3-Dec-2 Sworder & Son, Bishops Stortford #943/R est:1200-1500
Works on paper
£420 $685 €630 Shelling peas (25x22cm-10x9in) s. pencil W/C. 13-Feb-3 Mellors & Kirk, Nottingham #790

McEWEN, Jean (1923-1999) Canadian
£407 $638 €611 Marie traversant le feu des signes (30x30cm-12x12in) s. s.d.69 verso prov. 12-Dec-2 Iegor de Saint Hippolyte, Montreal #65 (C.D 1000)
£978 $1604 €1467 Midi, temps jaune (30x27cm-12x11in) s. acrylic prov. 3-Jun-3 Joyner, Toronto #102/R est:1500-2000 (C.D 2200)
£5333 $8747 €8000 Printemps jaune (36x36cm-14x14in) i.d.1978 set of three prov. 27-May-3 Sotheby's, Toronto #86/R est:4000-6000 (C.D 12000)
£6667 $10933 €10001 Les jardins d'aube (180x180cm-71x71in) s.d.76. 3-Jun-3 Joyner, Toronto #85/R est:8000-12000 (C.D 15000)
£6667 $10933 €10001 Eligie de criblee de bleu no.4 (183x183cm-72x72in) s. i.d.86 verso acrylic prov. 27-May-3 Sotheby's, Toronto #88/R est:15000-20000 (C.D 15000)
£7556 $12391 €11334 Cyclades no.3 (127x127cm-50x50in) i.on stretcher prov.exhib. 27-May-3 Sotheby's, Toronto #189/R est:12000-15000 (C.D 17000)
£7895 $11763 €11843 Das Lied Underende (188x188cm-74x74in) s.i. 26-Jun-2 Iegor de Saint Hippolyte, Montreal #64/R (C.D 18000)
Works on paper
£325 $511 €488 Sans titre (21x28cm-8x11in) s.d.57 ink W/C. 12-Dec-2 Iegor de Saint Hippolyte, Montreal #64 (C.D 800)
£370 $574 €555 Untitled (42x55cm-17x22in) s.d.56 W/C. 3-Dec-2 Joyner, Toronto #258/R (C.D 900)

£1422 $2332 €2133 Untitled (85x120cm-33x47in) s.d.55 W/C. 3-Jun-3 Joyner, Toronto #222/R est:2000-3000 (C.D 3200)

McFADYEN, Jock (1950-) British
£280 $454 €420 Letter (178x137cm-70x54in) 20-May-3 Bonhams, Knightsbridge #92

McFADYEN, Ron (1943-) Canadian
£889 $1458 €1289 Prairie mansion (120x90cm-47x35in) s.i.d.2002. 9-Jun-3 Hodgins, Calgary #143/R est:1200-1600 (C.D 2000)

McFARLANE, Duncan (fl.1834-1871) British
£2800 $4536 €4200 Belfast colonial clipper, possibly the Slieve Donard, approaching Liverpool (37x65cm-15x26in) board lit. 21-May-3 Christie's, Kensington #578/R est:3000-5000
£11184 $17000 €16776 The Quebec, off Perch Rock (61x91cm-24x36in) s.d.1854. 17-Aug-2 North East Auctions, Portsmouth #859/R est:15000-25000

McFARLANE, Shona (?) New Zealander
Works on paper
£758 $1167 €1137 Queenstown (50x60cm-20x24in) s. W/C. 4-Sep-2 Dunbar Sloane, Wellington #72 est:1500-2500 (NZ.D 2500)
£930 $1321 €1395 Hibiscus in the mad tin cow container (66x54cm-26x21in) s. W/C prov. 21-Nov-1 Watson's, Christchurch #23/R est:2000-5000 (NZ.D 3200)

MACFARLANE, Stewart (1953-) Australian
£1964 $3064 €2946 Beach (122x152cm-48x60in) s.d.93 s.i.d.1993 verso. 11-Nov-2 Deutscher-Menzies, Melbourne #94/R est:3000-4000 (A.D 5500)
£2490 $3710 €3735 Vanquishers (152x183cm-60x72in) s.d.1999 s.i.d.on stretcher. 27-Aug-2 Christie's, Melbourne #241/R est:4000-6000 (A.D 6500)
£2596 $4128 €3894 Listen (121x152cm-48x60in) s.d.2000 s.i.d.verso exhib. 4-Mar-3 Deutscher-Menzies, Melbourne #55/R est:4500-6500 (A.D 6750)

McFAYDEN, Jock (1950-) British
Works on paper
£850 $1352 €1275 Reconstructors II (75x56cm-30x22in) s.i.d.91 gouache. 6-Mar-3 Christie's, Kensington #264/R

McFAYDEN, Ron (20th C) Canadian?
£489 $802 €734 Barnstomier (90x120cm-35x47in) s. acrylic. 3-Jun-3 Joyner, Toronto #400/R est:800-1200 (C.D 1100)

McFEE, Henry Lee (1886-1953) American
£3822 $6000 €5733 The plant (41x30cm-16x12in) s. canvasboard prov.exhib. 19-Nov-2 Butterfields, San Francisco #8343/R est:3000-5000

McGARY, Dave (1958-) American
Sculpture
£1775 $2875 €2574 Gift of the sunbird (53cm-21in) bronze. 23-May-3 Altermann Galleries, Santa Fe #119

McGEE, Barry (1966-) American
£29375 $47000 €44063 Untitled. panel board set of six painted 1996-97 prov. 15-May-3 Phillips, New York #41/R est:20000-30000

MACGEORGE, Norman (1872-1952) Australian
£250 $395 €375 Anglesea (34x42cm-13x17in) s. board. 18-Nov-2 Joel, Victoria #164 (A.D 700)

MacGEORGE, William Stewart (1861-1931) British
£250 $390 €375 In the Italian lakes (28x44cm-11x17in) s. 13-Sep-2 Lyon & Turnbull, Edinburgh #134/R
£3333 $5533 €4833 In the glen (51x61cm-20x24in) s.i.verso exhib. 10-Jun-3 Ritchie, Toronto #66/R est:3000-5000 (C.D 7500)
£6000 $9300 €9000 Gondolas on a Venetian backwater (23x31cm-9x12in) s. board prov. 31-Oct-2 Christie's, London #93a/R est:5000-8000
£6000 $9300 €9000 Gondolas on a Venetian backwater (23x31cm-9x12in) s. board prov. 31-Oct-2 Christie's, London #93a est:5000-8000
£17000 $26350 €25500 Children amongst spring blossom (84x89cm-33x35in) s. 31-Oct-2 Christie's, London #94/R est:15000-20000

McGERE, Charles (20th C) British
£520 $811 €780 River Dart below Totnes (24x35cm-9x14in) s. board exhib. 9-Oct-2 Woolley & Wallis, Salisbury #346/R

McGHIE, John (1867-1952) British
£600 $918 €900 Faggot gatherers (25x35cm-10x14in) s. 22-Aug-2 Bonhams, Edinburgh #993
£600 $936 €900 Italian girl (52x42cm-20x17in) s.d.1890. 13-Sep-2 Lyon & Turnbull, Edinburgh #109/R
£780 $1217 €1170 SS Stronsa leaving Aberdeen (30x45cm-12x18in) s.i.stretcher. 17-Oct-2 Bonhams, Edinburgh #145
£2600 $4056 €3900 Iona (71x91cm-28x36in) s. prov. 14-Apr-3 Sotheby's, London #118/R est:1500-2500
£3000 $4890 €4500 Mussel girl (51x66cm-20x26in) s. 28-Jan-3 Gorringes, Lewes #1787/R est:3000-4000
£7400 $11544 €11100 Fisher family, East Neuk (70x90cm-28x35in) s. 10-Apr-3 Bonhams, Edinburgh #170/R est:3000-5000

McGILL, Donald (1875-1962) British
Works on paper
£400 $620 €600 Why do you want to go to the zoo now Aunt Emily's here (27x17cm-11x7in) s. pencil W/C bodycol. 4-Dec-2 Christie's, Kensington #163/R
£420 $697 €630 I ain't good but I'm clean ! (19x13cm-7x5in) s.i.verso W/C bodycol. 12-Jun-3 Bonhams, New Bond Street #712
£500 $830 €750 What twins again Mrs Lovejoy ! (23x18cm-9x7in) s.i. W/C bodycol. 12-Jun-3 Bonhams, New Bond Street #709/R
£750 $1245 €1125 So these are your dear twins ! (13x26cm-5x10in) s. i.verso W/C bodycol two. 12-Jun-3 Bonhams, New Bond Street #710/R
£750 $1245 €1125 I'm after new business (11x228cm-4x90in) s. i.verso W/C sold with two others. 12-Jun-3 Bonhams, New Bond Street #711/R
£850 $1318 €1275 Do you keep stationary, Miss (24x18cm-9x7in) s. i.verso pencil W/C htd bodycoy. 4-Dec-2 Christie's, Kensington #161

McGILL, Leona (1892-1981) American
£705 $1100 €1058 Roses (51x46cm-20x18in) 19-Oct-2 David Dike, Dallas #157/R

McGILLIVRAY, Florence Helena (1864-1938) Canadian
£207 $322 €344 Meutone, Italy (30x41cm-12x16in) s. s.i.verso canvasboard. 13-Apr-3 Levis, Calgary #508 (C.D 475)
£372 $584 €558 Beach activity (23x15cm-9x6in) s. canvasboard sold with sketch book. 24-Jul-2 Walker's, Ottawa #409/R (C.D 900)
£622 $1020 €933 On the Labrador coast (29x34cm-11x13in) s. board. 3-Jun-3 Joyner, Toronto #530 est:1500-2000 (C.D 1400)
£1653 $2595 €2480 Caribbean market (46x56cm-18x22in) s. canvasboard prov. 24-Jul-2 Walker's, Ottawa #408/R est:4000-4500 (C.D 4000)

MACGILLIVRAY, James Pittendrigh (1856-1938) British
£3200 $5152 €4800 King Lear in the storm (61x51cm-24x20in) s.d.1881 prov.exhib. 20-Feb-3 Christie's, London #214/R

MACGILVARY, Norwood Hodge (1874-1950) American
£2373 $3750 €3560 Strolling (41x51cm-16x20in) s. 17-Nov-2 CRN Auctions, Cambridge #41/R

MACGINNIS, Robert E (1926-) American
£1553 $2500 €2330 Smoking woman standing at open door (33x20cm-13x8in) s. tempera. 10-May-3 Illustration House, New York #127/R est:3000-5000
£1875 $3000 €2813 Standing nude (51x33cm-20x13in) tempera panel. 10-Jan-3 Du Mouchelle, Detroit #1029/R est:2000-3000
£4167 $6500 €6251 Woman with cigarette and martini seated on ornate chair (25x18cm-10x7in) s. tempera. 9-Nov-2 Illustration House, New York #142/R est:3000-4500
£4658 $7500 €6987 Woman in orange bikini and dressing gown on a couch (41x41cm-16x16in) s. tempera. 10-May-3 Illustration House, New York #126/R est:3500-5000

McGLASHAN, Archibald A (1888-1980) British
£300 $501 €435 Apples on a plate (25x30cm-10x12in) s. board prov. 17-Jun-3 Bonhams, Knightsbridge #47

McGLYNN, Thomas A (1878-1966) American
£3614 $6000 €5240 Carmel River (51x62cm-20x24in) s. masonite prov. 11-Jun-3 Butterfields, San Francisco #4218/R est:4000-6000

McGONIGAL, Maurice (1900-1979) British
£962 $1490 €1500 Phoenix Park (30x39cm-12x15in) board exhib. 3-Dec-2 Bonhams & James Adam, Dublin #123/R est:1000-1500
£1757 $2741 €2600 Flower piece (43x53cm-17x21in) s. s.i.d.1977verso board prov. 26-Mar-3 James Adam, Dublin #133/R est:2000-3000
£2051 $3221 €3200 Gorteen, Co Donegal (30x39cm-12x15in) s. panel. 19-Nov-2 Whyte's, Dublin #110/R est:3000-4000
£2658 $4120 €4200 Green boat, Bray Harbour, Co. Wicklow (20x41cm-8x16in) s. board prov. 25-Sep-2 James Adam, Dublin #73/R est:4000-6000
£4110 $6452 €6000 Trees at Faul, Connemara (29x60cm-11x24in) s. i.d.1970 verso canvasboard. 15-Apr-3 De Veres Art Auctions, Dublin #173/R est:5000-7000

£4200 $6720 €6300 Tinker's site (25x50cm-10x20in) s. board prov. 16-May-3 Sotheby's, London #112/R est:2500-3500

£4487 $6955 €7000 Roundstone, Connemara (33x45cm-13x18in) s. board. 3-Dec-2 Bonhams & James Adam, Dublin #142/R est:5000-7000

£4710 $7725 €6500 O'Flaherty's cottage, Aran (41x51cm-16x20in) s. board. 28-May-3 Bonhams & James Adam, Dublin #45/R est:6000-8000

£7047 $11346 €10500 Dun Laoghaire from Dalkey Hill (11x15cm-4x6in) s. i.verso panel. 18-Feb-3 Whyte's, Dublin #28/R est:8000-10000

£7292 $11594 €10500 Early morning, Mannin Bay (51x76cm-20x30in) s. board. 29-Apr-3 Whyte's, Dublin #25/R est:8000-10000

£9434 $14717 €15000 Ballyconneely (61x102cm-24x40in) s. i.verso prov. 17-Sep-2 Whyte's, Dublin #21/R est:15000-20000

£22785 $35316 €36000 Harvest of the sea (76x92cm-30x36in) s. prov. 24-Sep-2 De Veres Art Auctions, Dublin #98/R est:18000-22000

McGORAN, Kieran (1932-1990) British

Works on paper

£450 $698 €675 Park bench, Botanic gardens (25x30cm-10x12in) pastel. 4-Dec-2 John Ross, Belfast #7

£700 $1085 €1050 Paper boys (33x22cm-13x9in) s. chl. 4-Dec-2 John Ross, Belfast #138

£800 $1168 €1200 Winter on the Lagan (46x61cm-18x24in) s. pastel. 12-Jun-2 John Ross, Belfast #105

£1200 $1860 €1800 Four shawlies (40x61cm-16x24in) s. pastel. 4-Dec-2 John Ross, Belfast #264 est:1000-1200

£1400 $2170 €2100 Mending nets, Ardglass (50x40cm-20x16in) s. pastel. 4-Dec-2 John Ross, Belfast #33 est:800-1000

McGOURTY, Gerard (1954-) British

£1197 $1987 €1700 Still life (90x90cm-35x35in) s. board. 10-Jun-3 James Adam, Dublin #80/R est:2000-3000

McGRATH, Jean (20th C) American

£968 $1500 €1452 Still life with flowers and apples (51x61cm-20x24in) s. 8-Dec-2 Freeman, Philadelphia #163/R est:3000-5000

MACGREGOR, Harry (fl.1894-1934) British

£280 $437 €420 Mill stream (30x41cm-12x16in) s. board. 13-Sep-2 Lyon & Turnbull, Edinburgh #57/R

£319 $500 €479 Landscape with trees (61x42cm-24x17in) s.d.1905. 22-Nov-2 Skinner, Boston #309/R

£350 $543 €525 River landscape (61x51cm-24x20in) s. 31-Oct-2 Duke & Son, Dorchester #275/R

£420 $668 €630 On the coast (35x51cm-14x20in) s. canvas on panel. 6-Mar-3 Christie's, Kensington #139/R

£800 $1248 €1200 Galloway river (49x60cm-19x24in) s. canvasboard. 17-Oct-2 Bonhams, Edinburgh #194

£1100 $1683 €1650 Woodland, Kirkcudbright (62x52cm-24x20in) s.d.1902. 22-Aug-2 Bonhams, Edinburgh #1117 est:1200-1800

MACGREGOR, J Duncan (jnr) (1907-) American

£346 $550 €519 Co-Panse, dog portrait (56x76cm-22x30in) s.i.d.40. 18-Mar-3 Doyle, New York #42/R

MACGREGOR, Jessie (?-1919) British

£1300 $2016 €1950 New pet (76x102cm-30x40in) s.d.1875. 3-Dec-2 Sotheby's, Olympia #137/R est:300-500

McGREGOR, John (20th C) British

£320 $499 €480 Country road (56x39cm-22x15in) init. board. 17-Sep-2 Bonhams, Knightsbridge #28/R

McGREGOR, Robert (1848-1922) British

£280 $456 €420 Grandchild (29x21cm-11x8in) s. board. 17-Feb-3 Bonhams, Bath #152/R

£300 $486 €435 Lady with parasol in her garden (20x28cm-8x11in) s. panel. 1-Aug-3 Dee Atkinson & Harrison, Driffield #643

£1300 $2028 €1950 Bullock cart (25x35cm-10x14in) s. board prov. 17-Sep-2 Sotheby's, Olympia #38/R est:800-1200

£1700 $2652 €2550 Home from market (21x16cm-8x6in) s. panel. 10-Apr-3 Bonhams, Edinburgh #110/R est:1500-2000

£1900 $2964 €2850 Potato pickers (12x17cm-5x7in) init. 17-Oct-2 Bonhams, Edinburgh #205/R est:1000-1500

£2435 $3994 €3531 Woman and two children (61x46cm-24x18in) s. 4-Jun-3 AB Stockholms Auktionsverk #2451/R est:15000-18000 (S.KR 31000)

£6711 $10805 €10000 Angelus (56x43cm-22x17in) s. prov. 18-Feb-3 Whyte's, Dublin #104/R est:10000-12000

£8000 $12400 €12000 Shrimping (142x102cm-56x40in) s. prov. 31-Oct-2 Christie's, London #103/R est:5000-8000

McGREW, Ralph Brownell (1916-1994) American

£1491 $2415 €2162 In the mouth of box canyon (38x46cm-15x18in) 23-May-3 Altermann Galleries, Santa Fe #192

£1603 $2500 €2405 Valley vespers (41x51cm-16x20in) 9-Nov-2 Altermann Galleries, Santa Fe #194

£1918 $2800 €2877 Under the flying clouds (43x36cm-17x14in) 18-May-2 Altermann Galleries, Santa Fe #30/R

£2343 $3795 €3397 Desert forms (51x61cm-20x24in) board. 23-May-3 Altermann Galleries, Santa Fe #193/R

£3205 $5000 €4808 Jimmie Yazzie (36x25cm-14x10in) 9-Nov-2 Altermann Galleries, Santa Fe #156

£3205 $5000 €4808 Canyon wall June (41x51cm-16x20in) 9-Nov-2 Altermann Galleries, Santa Fe #196

£3846 $6000 €5769 Hills of home (76x102cm-30x40in) 9-Nov-2 Altermann Galleries, Santa Fe #195

£5205 $7600 €7808 Lure of the Canyon (71x91cm-28x36in) 18-May-2 Altermann Galleries, Santa Fe #31/R

£8333 $13000 €12500 Jimmie yellow shirt (51x41cm-20x16in) 9-Nov-2 Altermann Galleries, Santa Fe #157

£8974 $14000 €13461 Siyah Naz Navajo (43x33cm-17x13in) 9-Nov-2 Altermann Galleries, Santa Fe #154

£9228 $14950 €13381 Little girl big land (25x36cm-10x14in) board. 23-May-3 Altermann Galleries, Santa Fe #150

£20548 $30000 €30822 By the Canyon (56x66cm-22x26in) 18-May-2 Altermann Galleries, Santa Fe #33/R

£21795 $34000 €32693 Hasti in cowshirt (46x61cm-18x24in) 9-Nov-2 Altermann Galleries, Santa Fe #155

McGUINNESS, Norah (1903-1980) British

£2778 $4417 €4000 Beached boat (44x56cm-17x22in) s. prov. 29-Apr-3 Whyte's, Dublin #105/R est:4000-6000

£3826 $6159 €5700 Shells and stones (36x51cm-14x20in) init. i.verso prov.exhib. 18-Feb-3 Whyte's, Dublin #50/R est:6000-8000

£6410 $9936 €10000 Landscape (36x51cm-14x20in) prov.exhib. 3-Dec-2 Bonhams & James Adam, Dublin #119/R est:10000-15000

£8333 $13250 €12000 First snow (38x51cm-15x20in) s. prov.exhib. 29-Apr-3 Whyte's, Dublin #29/R est:8000-10000

£10256 $16103 €16000 Two stones and a bird (48x74cm-19x29in) s.d.55. 19-Nov-2 Hamilton Osborne King, Dublin #555/R est:6000-8000

£10811 $16865 €16000 Cobweb (64x44cm-25x17in) s. 26-Mar-3 James Adam, Dublin #96/R est:16000-20000

£13356 $20969 €19500 Gossips at Herbert Park (31x41cm-12x16in) s.d.1958 prov. 15-Apr-3 De Veres Art Auctions, Dublin #254/R est:10000-15000

£26582 $41203 €42000 On the road to Roundstone (81x109cm-32x43in) s. prov. 24-Sep-2 De Veres Art Auctions, Dublin #73/R est:25000-35000

Works on paper

£272 $430 €425 Greetings from Templeogue (25x33cm-10x13in) s.i. W/C pen ink. 12-Nov-2 Mealy's, Castlecomer #1248/R

£560 $896 €840 Claddy River, Co. Donegal (24x35cm-9x14in) s. W/C. 11-Mar-3 David Duggleby, Scarborough #147

£822 $1290 €1200 Pattern of rushes (13x18cm-5x7in) init. one i. col chk two. 15-Apr-3 De Veres Art Auctions, Dublin #51 est:800-1200

£828 $1316 €1200 Mayo (26x33cm-10x13in) s. W/C crayon exhib. 4-Mar-3 Mealy's, Castlecomer #1228/R

£900 $1395 €1350 Pond and rush (20x30cm-8x12in) mixed media. 2-Oct-2 John Ross, Belfast #16

£1154 $1788 €1800 Near Callary (19x28cm-7x11in) init.i. col crayon. 3-Dec-2 Bonhams & James Adam, Dublin #73/R est:2000-3000

£1800 $2808 €2700 Clady river, Co. Donegal (23x33cm-9x13in) s. W/C. 11-Apr-3 Keys, Aylsham #475/R est:350-450

£1892 $2951 €2800 First cutting (25x33cm-10x13in) s.i.verso pen ink W/C. 26-Mar-3 James Adam, Dublin #47/R est:3000-4000

£2051 $3221 €3200 St Declan's well (31x40cm-12x16in) gouache. 19-Nov-2 Hamilton Osborne King, Dublin #546/R est:3000-5000

£2848 $4415 €4500 Sussex landscape (31x47cm-12x19in) s. gouache prov. 24-Sep-2 De Veres Art Auctions, Dublin #118 est:4000-5000

£2899 $4754 €4000 Still life with fruit and flowers (55x31cm-22x12in) s. W/C. 28-May-3 Bonhams & James Adam, Dublin #80/R est:3000-4000

£3077 $4831 €4800 Landscape. init.i. waxed chk four framed as one. 19-Nov-2 Hamilton Osborne King, Dublin #462/R est:5000-7000

£3200 $5120 €4800 Fahan, Co Donegal (25x37cm-10x15in) init. gouache W/C executed 1945 prov. 16-May-3 Sotheby's, London #97/R est:3000-5000

£5031 $7849 €8000 Deserted cottage (38x55cm-15x22in) s.d.1971 W/C gouache exhib. 17-Sep-2 Whyte's, Dublin #68/R est:4000-5000

£7534 $11829 €11000 Gandon's custom house from across the Liffey (35x50cm-14x20in) s.d.1940 gouache. 15-Apr-3 De Veres Art Auctions, Dublin #166/R est:9000-12000

£8861 $13734 €14000 Liffey wall (40x55cm-16x22in) s. gouache prov. 25-Sep-2 James Adam, Dublin #51/R est:10000-15000

McGUINNESS, Tom (?) British

Works on paper

£580 $911 €870 Miners near a pit head. Three miners on a track (10x11cm-4x4in) s.d.91 pen ink two. 21-Nov-2 Tennants, Leyburn #703/R

McGUINNESS, William Bingham (1849-1928) British

Works on paper

£217 $339 €363 Distant view of Lough Eske, Co. Donegal (25x36cm-10x14in) s.i.d.1912 W/C prov. 13-Apr-3 Levis, Calgary #212/R (C.D 500)

£300 $480 €450 Old house at Vitre, Brittany (22x27cm-9x11in) s.i.verso pencil W/C. 15-May-3 Christie's, Kensington #124/R

£320 $509 €480 Farmstead, Donegal (17x22cm-7x9in) s. W/C. 5-Mar-3 John Ross, Belfast #132

£400 $664 €580 At Sittleworth, Sussex (39x29cm-15x11in) s. W/C prov. 16-Jun-3 Waddingtons, Toronto #189/R est:1200-1500 (C.D 900)

£443 $718 €625 Continental fishing harbour (16x23cm-6x9in) init.i.d.1880 W/C. 20-May-3 Mealy's, Castlecomer #1314/R

£449 $737 €620 Fisherman by a mountain river (24x36cm-9x14in) s. W/C. 28-May-3 Bonhams & James Adam, Dublin #84/R
£500 $795 €750 Gathering seaweed, West of Ireland (25x35cm-10x14in) s. W/C. 5-Mar-3 John Ross, Belfast #180
£500 $795 €750 Dutch canal (35x25cm-14x10in) s. W/C. 5-Mar-3 John Ross, Belfast #198
£550 $869 €825 Flower market in Continental street scene (36x25cm-14x10in) s. W/C. 13-Nov-2 Halls, Shrewsbury #333/R
£597 $932 €950 West coast of Ireland (34x51cm-13x20in) s. W/C htd white. 17-Sep-2 Whyte's, Dublin #112/R
£620 $967 €930 Shore at Laide, Rosshire (48x69cm-19x27in) s.d.1887 W/C. 15-Oct-2 Bearnes, Exeter #357
£630 $989 €920 Continental town (39x26cm-15x10in) s. W/C htd white. 15-Apr-3 De Veres Art Auctions, Dublin #175/R
£797 $1307 €1100 Near Loch Maree, Scotland (28x45cm-11x18in) s. W/C. 28-May-3 Bonhams & James Adam, Dublin #38/R est:600-800
£805 $1297 €1200 Coastal landscape with sailing boats (24x37cm-9x15in) s. W/C htd white. 18-Feb-3 Whyte's, Dublin #90/R
£897 $1409 €1400 Coastal inlet (28x46cm-11x18in) s. W/C htd white prov. 19-Nov-2 Whyte's, Dublin #212/R est:1500-2000
£940 $1513 €1400 Thatched cottages with cattle. Grey day, Ballychulish (19x27cm-7x11in) one s. i.verso one init. W/C over pencil prov. pair. 18-Feb-3 Whyte's, Dublin #86/R
£950 $1387 €1425 Barges on the canal (25x36cm-10x14in) s. W/C. 12-Jun-2 John Ross, Belfast #28
£1284 $2003 €1900 Continental street scene (36x26cm-14x10in) s. W/C. 26-Mar-3 James Adam, Dublin #21/R est:800-1200
£1389 $2208 €2000 Continental town and castle (58x41cm-23x16in) s.d.1880 W/C htd white. 29-Apr-3 Whyte's, Dublin #185/R est:2500-3000
£1400 $2044 €2100 Eton College (33x51cm-13x20in) s. W/C. 12-Jun-2 John Ross, Belfast #153 est:900-1200

McGUIRE, Edward (1932-1986) Irish
£5128 $7949 €8000 Seabird I (51x40cm-20x16in) init.d.1977 board prov. 3-Dec-2 Bonhams & James Adam, Dublin #117/R est:6000-10000

MACH, David (1956-) British
Sculpture
£3819 $6302 €5500 Body (76cm-30in) s.i.d.98 verso hangers soldered metal prov. 3-Jul-3 Christie's, Paris #110/R est:5000-7000

MACHARD, Jules Louis (1839-1900) French
Works on paper
£780 $1303 €1100 Modele de dos (60x45cm-24x18in) s.i.d. pastel. 23-Jun-3 Delvaux, Paris #98

MACHERA, Ferdinand (1776-1843) French
Miniatures
£2400 $3768 €3600 Young girl in a white dress (6cm-2in) s.d.1809 gold frame oval. 10-Dec-2 Christie's, London #275/R est:1000-1500

MACHERET, Anne (20th C) French
£1119 $1869 €1600 Homme a la pipe (81x65cm-32x26in) panel. 25-Jun-3 Claude Aguttes, Neuilly #294 est:1600-1700

MACHETANZ, Fred (1908-2002) American
£2215 $3500 €3212 Out on the chain (46x61cm-18x24in) s.d.1964 board. 26-Jul-3 Coeur d'Alene, Hayden #215/R est:5000-10000
£3593 $6000 €5210 Whaling dance (56x71cm-22x28in) s.d.1962 i.verso. 22-Jun-3 Freeman, Philadelphia #135/R est:4000-6000

McIAN, Robert Ronald (1803-1856) British
£900 $1404 €1350 Peat gatherers (44x56cm-17x22in) s. 26-Mar-3 Sotheby's, Olympia #49/R

MACIEL, Leonel (1939-) Mexican
£1385 $2161 €2078 Tropico y elegancia (110x110cm-43x43in) s.d.1972. 17-Oct-2 Louis Morton, Mexico #4a est:12000-30000 (M.P 22000)

McILFATRICK, Hugh (?) Irish
£350 $557 €525 Cottage near Muckish mountains (50x76cm-20x30in) s. board. 5-Mar-3 John Ross, Belfast #64
£360 $526 €540 Away up the Glen by the River Dun (51x76cm-20x30in) s. board. 12-Jun-2 John Ross, Belfast #41
£380 $604 €570 Cottage by the sea, Donegal (30x46cm-12x18in) s. board. 5-Mar-3 John Ross, Belfast #137

McINNES, Robert (1801-1886) British
£3200 $5024 €4800 Feast day (35x57cm-14x22in) s.d.1845. 19-Nov-2 Bonhams, New Bond Street #78/R est:2000-3000

McINNES, Violet (1892-1971) Australian
£458 $724 €687 Little Dutch girl (24x29cm-9x11in) s. prov. 2-Apr-3 Christie's, Melbourne #30 est:800-1200 (A.D 1200)
£571 $903 €857 Magnolias in a Chinese vase (61x56cm-24x22in) s. 27-Nov-2 Deutscher-Menzies, Melbourne #62/R est:1200-1500 (A.D 1600)

McINNES, William Beckwith (1889-1939) Australian
£460 $685 €690 View from the hill (34x24cm-13x9in) s. 27-Aug-2 Christie's, Melbourne #256 est:1000-1500 (A.D 1200)
£1000 $1610 €1450 St. Ives, England 1912 (34x47cm-13x19in) s. 12-May-3 Joel, Victoria #305 est:4000-6000 (A.D 2500)
£2400 $3864 €3480 Still life with blue and white jar (61x73cm-24x29in) s. 12-May-3 Joel, Victoria #235/R est:3000-5000 (A.D 6000)
£4643 $7336 €6965 Farm scene with haystacks (18x62cm-7x24in) s. board prov. 17-Nov-2 Sotheby's, Paddington #67/R est:12000-18000 (A.D 13000)

MACINNIS, Charles (20th C) British
£540 $875 €810 Untitled (76x126cm-30x50in) bears sig. 23-Jan-3 Bonhams, Edinburgh #331

McINNIS, Robert (1942-) Canadian
£241 $378 €362 Dark days and hope, Ted Raftery (25x50cm-10x20in) s.i.d.1982. 25-Nov-2 Hodgins, Calgary #200/R (C.D 600)
£244 $401 €354 Dry and dusty (40x30cm-16x12in) s.i.d.1979. 9-Jun-3 Hodgins, Calgary #411/R (C.D 550)
£256 $419 €371 Prairie Road (30x40cm-12x16in) s.i.d.1978 board. 9-Jun-3 Hodgins, Calgary #345/R (C.D 575)
£261 $407 €435 Later winter, Prairie (102x122cm-40x48in) s.d.1977 s.i.d.verso. 13-Apr-3 Levis, Calgary #509 (C.D 600)
£267 $437 €387 Rain road west (30x40cm-12x16in) s.i.d.1981. 9-Jun-3 Hodgins, Calgary #105/R (C.D 600)
£326 $509 €544 Riding crop (61x51cm-24x20in) s.d.1981 s.i.d.verso. 13-Apr-3 Levis, Calgary #511/R (C.D 750)
£847 $1347 €1271 Crows at Hobbema (60x75cm-24x30in) s.i.d.1979. 23-Mar-3 Hodgins, Calgary #15/R est:1500-2000 (C.D 2000)
£1004 $1576 €1506 Prairie at night (50x60cm-20x24in) s.i.d.1993. 25-Nov-2 Hodgins, Calgary #99/R est:1500-2000 (C.D 2500)

MACINTIRE, Kenneth Stevens (1891-1979) American
£613 $950 €920 Summer landscape (76x91cm-30x36in) artist board prov. 28-Sep-2 Charlton Hall, Columbia #550/R
£625 $1000 €938 Siamese cat in still life (61x66cm-24x26in) s. 11-Jan-3 James Julia, Fairfield #503 est:1000-2000

MACINTOSH, John Macintosh (1847-1913) British
£250 $390 €375 Wood gatherers (37x44cm-15x17in) s. board. 6-Nov-2 Bonhams, Chester #437
Works on paper
£260 $406 €390 Girl and sheep on a country lane (53x36cm-21x14in) W/C. 6-Nov-2 Bonhams, Chester #438

McINTOSH, Pleasant Ray (1897-?) American
£597 $950 €896 Sunny day (41x49cm-16x19in) s. canvasboard. 7-Mar-3 Skinner, Boston #418/R

McINTYRE, Donald (1923-) British
£300 $465 €450 Pale evening winter (24x34cm-9x13in) mono. board. 5-Dec-2 Ambrose, Loughton #830
£400 $652 €600 Figures on the beach at Scarborough (41x48cm-16x19in) init. 14-Feb-3 Keys, Aylsham #883
£450 $702 €675 Shrub, Anglesey (50x62cm-20x24in) s. paper. 17-Sep-2 Bonhams, Knightsbridge #117/R
£500 $780 €750 Storm at St. Bride's Bay (24x34cm-9x13in) 11-Sep-2 Bonhams, Newport #356
£510 $852 €740 Cottage on hillside (46x70cm-18x28in) s. board. 24-Jun-3 Bonhams, Knowle #75
£600 $954 €900 Winter road, Anglesey (35x50cm-14x20in) init. board. 19-Mar-3 Anthemion, Cardiff #414/R
£600 $954 €900 Interior scene with a child in the foreground (35x25cm-14x10in) init. 19-Mar-3 Anthemion, Cardiff #415/R
£660 $1036 €990 Music (25x35cm-10x14in) init. i.verso. 20-Nov-2 Anthemion, Cardiff #572/R
£720 $1123 €1080 Evening sea (50x60cm-20x24in) s. board. 11-Sep-2 Bonhams, Newport #354/R
£800 $1240 €1200 Snow scene of an Irish mountainous river landscape (59x120cm-23x47in) board. 5-Dec-2 Ambrose, Loughton #829
£1000 $1560 €1500 White boats, Bunowen (30x40cm-12x16in) s. board. 12-Sep-2 Sotheby's, Olympia #118/R est:500-700
£1000 $1560 €1500 Anchorage (42x54cm-17x21in) s. board. 11-Sep-2 Bonhams, Newport #353 est:1000-1200
£1000 $1640 €1500 Porthscatho no 4 (53x66cm-21x26in) s. s.i.d.1979 verso board. 4-Feb-3 Sworder & Son, Bishops Stortford #119/R est:400-600
£1100 $1726 €1650 Port Enyon (49x75cm-19x30in) s. board. 20-Nov-2 Sotheby's, Olympia #66/R est:300-400
£1100 $1749 €1650 Aberdaron (35x50cm-14x20in) init. 19-Mar-3 Anthemion, Cardiff #413/R est:1000-1500
£1150 $1794 €1725 Cliffs, Solva no.2 (50x61cm-20x24in) s. 11-Sep-2 Bonhams, Newport #355/R est:600-800
£1200 $1872 €1800 Haford II (102x64cm-40x25in) s. board. 17-Sep-2 Bonhams, Knightsbridge #116/R est:1200-1800
£1200 $1872 €1800 Looking at Eilan Chalbha (53x78cm-21x31in) s. i.verso acrylic board. 17-Oct-2 Bonhams, Edinburgh #45/R est:1200-1500

£1300 $2028 €1950 Connemara coast (26x31cm-10x12in) init. s.i.stretcher. 12-Sep-2 Sotheby's, Olympia #125/R est:1200-1800
£1300 $2015 €1950 On the Broads (40x51cm-16x20in) s. board. 30-Sep-2 Bonhams, Ipswich #370/R est:1500-2000
£1300 $2028 €1950 Shore Road, Bally, Conneely Bay (30x77cm-12x30in) s. exhib. 26-Mar-3 Woolley & Wallis, Salisbury #229/R est:750-1000
£1300 $2132 €1950 Picnic on the rocks (29x39cm-11x15in) init. board. 3-Jun-3 Sotheby's, Olympia #194/R est:800-1200
£1500 $2369 €2250 Harbour scene (60x50cm-24x20in) s. board. 27-Nov-2 Sotheby's, Olympia #299/R est:1000-1500
£1500 $2340 €2250 Across the shore (61x122cm-24x48in) s. board. 27-Mar-3 Christie's, Kensington #614/R est:1500-2000
£1500 $2490 €2175 White fishing boat (18x23cm-7x9in) s. i.verso board. 10-Jun-3 David Lay, Penzance #56/R est:1500-1800
£1550 $2418 €2325 Cottage, Nebo (49x75cm-19x30in) s. board. 11-Sep-2 Bonhams, Newport #359/R est:1000-1500
£1600 $2512 €2400 Welsh village (50x60cm-20x24in) s. board. 20-Nov-2 Sotheby's, Olympia #72/R est:1000-1500
£1700 $2703 €2550 Skye from Arisaig (40x51cm-16x20in) s. s.i.verso. 26-Feb-3 Sotheby's, Olympia #326/R est:1800-2500
£1800 $2844 €2700 Boat shed (49x59cm-19x23in) s. board. 27-Nov-2 Sotheby's, Olympia #302/R est:1000-1500
£1800 $2898 €2700 Dark sea, Anglesey (70x163cm-28x64in) s. board prov. 14-Jan-3 Bonhams, Knightsbridge #209/R est:1500-2000
£2000 $3120 €3000 Winter sea - Briach lwyd, Porth y Post (60x152cm-24x60in) s. board. 11-Sep-2 Bonhams, Newport #357/R est:2000-3000
£2500 $3900 €3750 Island of storms (51x76cm-20x30in) s. board. 17-Sep-2 Bonhams, Knightsbridge #119/R est:2500-3500
£2600 $4134 €3900 Looking at Eileen Chalbha (56x91cm-22x36in) s. board. 26-Feb-3 Sotheby's, Olympia #262/R est:2500-3500
£3200 $5248 €4800 Mediterranean village (71x76cm-28x30in) s. canvas on board. 3-Jun-3 Sotheby's, Olympia #210/R est:2000-3000
£5000 $8200 €7500 Donkey cart, Connemara (63x101cm-25x40in) s. board prov. 3-Jun-3 Sotheby's, Olympia #209/R est:4000-6000

Works on paper
£400 $624 €600 Dry stone wall and farmhouse (28x41cm-11x16in) s. W/C bodycol over pencil chl. 11-Sep-2 Bonhams, Newport #260

McINTYRE, Hugh (1943-) British
£580 $899 €870 Camino do mar ajuda (61x51cm-24x20in) s.d.95 exhib. 4-Dec-2 Christie's, Kensington #419

MACINTYRE, James (1926-) British
Works on paper
£760 $1110 €1140 Turf digging (30x23cm-12x9in) s. gouache on board. 12-Jun-2 John Ross, Belfast #168
£950 $1387 €1425 Returning with the milk pail (56x46cm-22x18in) s.d.86 W/C. 12-Jun-2 John Ross, Belfast #80
£1000 $1460 €1500 Wary Collie (36x46cm-14x18in) s.d.99 W/C. 12-Jun-2 John Ross, Belfast #103 est:1000-1200
£1000 $1460 €1500 William James Stewart's farm (41x51cm-16x20in) s. W/C. 12-Jun-2 John Ross, Belfast #139 est:1000-1200
£1000 $1590 €1500 Fisherman's dogs, Roundstone, Connemara (43x53cm-17x21in) s.d.97 W/C. 5-Mar-3 John Ross, Belfast #116 est:1000-1400
£1200 $1908 €1800 Visiting boat from Ayrshire (40x50cm-16x20in) s.d.90 W/C. 5-Mar-3 John Ross, Belfast #74 est:1200-1400

MACINTYRE, James (1880-c.1950) British
Works on paper
£490 $764 €735 Clyde (26x37cm-10x15in) s. pencil W/C. 10-Apr-3 Bonhams, Edinburgh #87/R

McINTYRE, Jean Douglas (1889-1967) British
£310 $518 €450 Richmond Bridge (30x46cm-12x18in) init. 11-Jul-3 Bracketts, Tunbridge Wells #841/R

McINTYRE, Joseph Wrightson (fl.1866-1888) British
£880 $1408 €1320 Last gleam on the River Avon (76x127cm-30x50in) mono.d.72. 14-Mar-3 Gardiner & Houlgate, Bath #221/R
£1538 $2400 €2307 Solitary monk reading in a forest (61x107cm-24x42in) s.d.1889. 12-Apr-3 Weschler, Washington #505/R est:1000-1500
£2200 $3432 €3300 Ebbing tide, St. Abb's Head (77x128cm-30x50in) s.d.1882 s.i.d.verso. 6-Nov-2 Bonhams, Chester #432/R est:1500-1800

McINTYRE, Peter (1910-1995) New Zealander
£1215 $1896 €1823 Waikanae landscape (49x59cm-19x23in) s. tempera paper. 8-Apr-3 Peter Webb, Auckland #162/R est:4000-5000 (NZ.D 3500)
£1254 $1956 €1881 Sentinels (26x41cm-10x16in) s. board. 7-Nov-2 International Art Centre, Auckland #69/R est:4000-7000 (NZ.D 4000)
£1372 $2099 €2058 Rangitiki River (40x43cm-16x17in) s. board. 21-Aug-2 Dunbar Sloane, Auckland #130/R est:5000-7000 (NZ.D 4500)
£1970 $3033 €2955 Rangitikei River (59x74cm-23x29in) s. canvas on board. 4-Sep-2 Dunbar Sloane, Wellington #51/R est:3000-5000 (NZ.D 6500)
£2038 $3179 €3057 Gum tree, Havelock North (38x48cm-15x19in) s. board. 7-Nov-2 International Art Centre, Auckland #103/R est:7000-10000 (NZ.D 6500)
£2105 $3284 €3158 Gum tree with Te Mata Peak beyond (40x50cm-16x20in) s. board. 27-Mar-3 International Art Centre, Auckland #65/R est:6000-10000 (NZ.D 6000)
£2121 $3267 €3182 Hong Kong girl (59x49cm-23x19in) s. 4-Sep-2 Dunbar Sloane, Wellington #17/R est:2000-4000 (NZ.D 7000)
£2251 $3489 €3377 Upper Wanganui, King country (49x59cm-19x23in) s. board. 4-Dec-2 Dunbar Sloane, Auckland #23/R est:10000-15000 (NZ.D 7000)
£2326 $3302 €3489 Wellington from Tinakori Hill (50x75cm-20x30in) s. prov. 21-Nov-1 Watson's, Christchurch #62/R (NZ.D 8000)
£2807 $4379 €4211 Winter trees (56x75cm-22x30in) s. board. 27-Mar-3 International Art Centre, Auckland #81/R est:8000-12000 (NZ.D 8000)
£2866 $4500 €4299 Farm scene at branding time (42x72cm-17x28in) s. board painted c.1955. 10-Dec-2 Peter Webb, Auckland #54/R est:12000-18000 (NZ.D 9000)
£5145 $7974 €7718 National Orchestra rehearsal (54x74cm-21x29in) s.i.verso board. 4-Dec-2 Dunbar Sloane, Auckland #6/R est:15000-25000 (NZ.D 16000)
£5263 $8211 €7895 Wenderholm (60x78cm-24x31in) s. canvasboard. 27-Mar-3 International Art Centre, Auckland #60/R est:14000-20000 (NZ.D 15000)
£5486 $8558 €8229 Fisherman's son (91x70cm-36x28in) s. canvasboard. 7-Nov-2 International Art Centre, Auckland #56/R est:18000-28000 (NZ.D 17500)
£5614 $8758 €8421 Sun and shadow, Rangitikei River (50x60cm-20x24in) s. board. 27-Mar-3 International Art Centre, Auckland #72/R est:15000-20000 (NZ.D 16000)
£5643 $8803 €8465 Skippers Road near Queenstown (70x90cm-28x35in) s. 7-Nov-2 International Art Centre, Auckland #68/R est:20000-30000 (NZ.D 18000)
£12158 $18967 €18237 King Country landscape with drover and dogs (61x76cm-24x30in) s. board prov. 17-Sep-2 Peter Webb, Auckland #100/R est:25000-35000 (NZ.D 40000)

Works on paper
£224 $327 €336 Fishing sketch, Taupo (24x36cm-9x14in) s. W/C. 12-Sep-1 Watson's, Christchurch #152 (NZ.D 750)
£526 $837 €789 Beach at Haena (39x37cm-15x15in) s. ink dr. 25-Feb-3 Peter Webb, Auckland #71/R est:1500-2500 (NZ.D 1500)
£762 $1166 €1143 Sheep study (53x70cm-21x28in) W/C. 21-Aug-2 Dunbar Sloane, Auckland #26/R est:3000-6000 (NZ.D 2500)
£884 $1415 €1282 Waikato No 2 (52x70cm-20x28in) W/C. 13-May-3 Watson's, Christchurch #51/R (NZ.D 2450)
£993 $1588 €1440 Fiji boy fishing (52x73cm-20x29in) W/C. 13-May-3 Watson's, Christchurch #27/R (NZ.D 2750)
£1143 $1749 €1715 Auckland city with town hall (51x71cm-20x28in) W/C. 21-Aug-2 Dunbar Sloane, Auckland #25/R est:3000-5000 (NZ.D 3750)
£1818 $2800 €2727 World War II - portrait, possibly Keith Elliott (62x43cm-24x17in) s. chl. 4-Sep-2 Dunbar Sloane, Wellington #62/R est:6000-8000 (NZ.D 6000)
£1881 $2934 €2822 Aratiatia rapids (46x60cm-18x24in) s. W/C. 7-Nov-2 International Art Centre, Auckland #156/R est:6000-9000 (NZ.D 6000)
£2424 $3733 €3636 R troop of the Long Range Dessert group patrolling around the Kufra Oasis, Egypt (40x48cm-16x19in) s. pencil pen. 4-Sep-2 Dunbar Sloane, Wellington #16/R est:4000-8000 (NZ.D 8000)
£3647 $5690 €5471 View of the Rangitiki (71x54cm-28x21in) s. ink W/C. 17-Sep-2 Peter Webb, Auckland #150/R est:12000-18000 (NZ.D 12000)
£4514 $7042 €6771 Lake Rotoiti (53x70cm-21x28in) s. W/C. 8-Apr-3 Peter Webb, Auckland #154/R est:8000-12000 (NZ.D 13000)
£4577 $7553 €6637 Rural landscape , Te Taheke, Lake Rotoiti District (51x71cm-20x28in) s. W/C. 1-Jul-3 Peter Webb, Auckland #76/R est:8000-12000 (NZ.D 13000)

McINTYRE, Simon (?) ?
£193 $307 €290 Boat yard (31x21cm-12x8in) s. acrylic pastel dr. 25-Feb-3 Peter Webb, Auckland #22 (NZ.D 550)

MACK, Heinz (1931-) German
Sculpture
£3000 $4650 €4500 Tur, durch die nur Engel gehen (170x99cm-67x39in) i.num.2 verso aluminium wood. 5-Dec-2 Christie's, Kensington #279/R est:4000-6000
£3623 $5942 €5000 Silver rotor (62x64x19cm-24x25x7in) s.i.d.65 verso glass alluminium prov. 28-May-3 Lempertz, Koln #266/R est:5000-6000

Works on paper
£1603 $2484 €2500 Untitled (78x106cm-31x42in) s.d.82 pastel. 7-Dec-2 Van Ham, Cologne #316/R est:2800
£3546 $5745 €5000 Silveron black (80x100cm-31x39in) s.i.d.63 verso painted aluminium mesh sheet on canvas exhib. 24-May-3 Van Ham, Cologne #368/R est:10000

MACK, Leal (1892-1962) American
£1452 $2250 €2178 Wash day (41x51cm-16x20in) s. 29-Oct-2 John Moran, Pasadena #715a est:2000-3000

McKAY, F H (?) ?
£449 $700 €674 Village scene (61x91cm-24x36in) painted c.1940. 20-Sep-2 Du Mouchelle, Detroit #1110/R
£503 $800 €755 Road to the cove (61x91cm-24x36in) s.i. on stretcher. 5-Mar-3 Doyle, New York #44/R
£701 $1100 €1052 New England coastal village with harbour, ships and cottages (76x61cm-30x24in) s. 19-Apr-3 James Julia, Fairfield #205/R

MACKAY, Florence (fl.1890-1920) British
Works on paper
£260 $426 €390 Feeding geese at the cottage door (22x15cm-9x6in) s.d.1920 W/C. 4-Jun-3 Bonhams, Chester #308

MACKAY, James M (19/20th C) British
Works on paper
£650 $1021 €975 Fishing from the riverbank (16x23cm-6x9in) s. pencil W/C htd white. 16-Apr-3 Christie's, Kensington #1074

MACKAY, Patty Aberigh (fl.1904-1906) British
Works on paper
£520 $811 €780 Portrait of a girl in an apron (63x41cm-25x16in) st. W/C. 26-Mar-3 Woolley & Wallis, Salisbury #12/R

MACKAY, Thomas (19/20th C) British
Works on paper
£310 $484 €465 Young maid and her cat at the cottage door (19x16cm-7x6in) s.d.98 W/C. 23-Sep-2 Bonhams, Chester #892
£360 $562 €540 Woman on a lane (16x24cm-6x9in) s. W/C. 6-Nov-2 Bonhams, Chester #340
£900 $1404 €1350 Cottage garden with woman gathering flowers (15x24cm-6x9in) s.d.1904 W/C. 6-Nov-2 Bonhams, Chester #324
£1800 $2880 €2700 At the ferry, Hampton Lucy, Warwickshire (22x32cm-9x13in) s.d.1898 W/C. 11-Mar-3 Bonhams, New Bond Street #122/R est:800-1200

McKAY, Thomas Hope (fl.1900-1930) British
£311 $516 €451 Children at a brook (30x41cm-12x16in) s. 16-Jun-3 Waddingtons, Toronto #201/R (C.D 700)

McKAY, William Darling (1844-1924) British
£400 $652 €600 Wall over the moor (29x39cm-11x15in) 14-Feb-3 Lyon & Turnbull, Edinburgh #67
£740 $1154 €1110 Figures on a deserted beach at sunset (53x75cm-21x30in) init. 13-Sep-2 Lyon & Turnbull, Edinburgh #108/R
£1000 $1560 €1500 Chippie (33x27cm-13x11in) s.i.d.1854 board. 6-Nov-2 Sotheby's, Olympia #162/R est:600-900
£5000 $7750 €7500 Feeding the fowl (60x84cm-24x33in) init. 31-Oct-2 Christie's, London #87/R est:4000-6000
£5500 $8415 €8250 Prospect of Dumbarton from the south bank of the Clyde (77x109cm-30x43in) init. 22-Aug-2 Bonhams, Edinburgh #1077/R est:1200-1800

MACKE, August (1887-1914) German
£5380 $8500 €8500 Woman sewing II (32x25cm-13x10in) i. verso pencil exhib. 30-Nov-2 Villa Grisebach, Berlin #136/R est:7000-9000
£54348 $89130 €75000 Portrait study of Elisabeth Gerhardt (42x33cm-17x13in) board prov.exhib. 30-May-3 Villa Grisebach, Berlin #12/R est:80000-100000
£280000 $459200 €420000 Girl on balcony (79x48cm-31x19in) s.d.1910 s.i.d.on stretcher prov.exhib.lit. 4-Feb-3 Sotheby's, London #26/R est:400000
£817610 $1275472 €1300000 Sonnenuntergang nach dem regen - Sunset after rain, figures in the park (45x64cm-18x25in) s. i.d.1914 verso board prov.exhib.lit. 8-Oct-2 Sotheby's, London #5/R est:1600000-2400000
£1132075 $1766038 €1800000 Waldspaziergang - Forest walk (81x105cm-32x41in) s.i. i.num.8 verso painted 1913 prov.exhib.lit. 8-Oct-2 Sotheby's, London #16/R est:2500000-3000000
£2515723 $3924528 €4000000 Zwei frauen vor dem hutladen - Two women in front of a hat shop (56x42cm-22x17in) s.d.1913 prov.exhib.lit. 8-Oct-2 Sotheby's, London #10/R est:2250000-3000000
Works on paper
£1384 $2158 €2200 Abstract forms XVIII (17x10cm-7x4in) pencil col pen sketch lit. 20-Sep-2 Karlheinz Kaupp, Staufen #2189/R est:2800
£2642 $4121 €4200 Parisian street scene (32x24cm-13x9in) pencil col crayon paper on card executed 1907 prov.exhib.lit. 9-Oct-2 Sotheby's, London #131/R est:6000-9000
£3145 $4906 €5000 Blossoming tree. Wood in spring (23x28cm-9x11in) s.d.07 pen ink pencil double-sided prov.exhib.lit. 9-Oct-2 Sotheby's, London #130/R est:4500-6500
£3169 $5261 €4500 Walking Pierrot (12x4cm-5x2in) Indian ink. 14-Jun-3 Hauswedell & Nolte, Hamburg #1362/R est:4500
£4403 $6868 €7000 Madchen mit krug - Girls with a jug (18x17cm-7x7in) i.d.1912 pencil wash prov.exhib.lit. 9-Oct-2 Sotheby's, London #122/R est:10000-15000
£5634 $9352 €8000 Girls bathing in stream (21x33cm-8x13in) Indian ink brush. 14-Jun-3 Hauswedell & Nolte, Hamburg #1363/R est:12000
£6604 $10302 €10500 Frau bei der kirche - Woman near a church (35x34cm-14x13in) chl executed 1910 prov.exhib.lit. 9-Oct-2 Sotheby's, London #101/R est:15000-20000
£8696 $14261 €12000 Couple in southern park (10x16cm-4x6in) bears i. pencil prov. 29-May-3 Lempertz, Koln #763/R est:14000-15000
£8805 $13736 €14000 Malvolio (26x24cm-10x9in) i. gouache W/C executed 1907-08 prov.exhib.lit. 9-Oct-2 Sotheby's, London #132/R est:20000-30000
£11000 $18040 €16500 Street scene at night (11x8cm-4x3in) pencil col ink exec.1912 prov.exhib.lit. 6-Feb-3 Christie's, London #454/R est:6000
£12579 $19623 €20000 Klagende - Grieving women (27x32cm-11x13in) st.verso chl wash executed 1912 prov.exhib.lit. 9-Oct-2 Sotheby's, London #110/R est:15000-20000
£25641 $39744 €40000 Woman in car (26x31cm-10x12in) pencil. 7-Dec-2 Hauswedell & Nolte, Hamburg #875/R est:24000
£28986 $47536 €40000 Abstract composition with woman (31x40cm-12x16in) paper collage prov.exhib. 29-May-3 Lempertz, Koln #765/R est:22000-25000
£34591 $53962 €55000 Durchblick auf die gasse - View into an alleyway (29x34cm-11x13in) chl executed 1914 prov.exhib.lit. 9-Oct-2 Sotheby's, London #108/R est:80000-120000
£48000 $78240 €72000 Begegnung (17x11cm-7x4in) st.verso pencil executed 1913 prov.exhib.lit. 3-Feb-3 Christie's, London #1/R est:35000-45000
£144928 $237681 €200000 Yellow sail (25x16cm-10x6in) W/C over pencil prov.exhib.lit. 29-May-3 Lempertz, Koln #764/R est:130000-150000
£172662 $283165 €240000 Two men with woman - small (18x13cm-7x5in) i. W/C pencil prov.lit. 6-Jun-3 Ketterer, Munich #37/R est:150000-200000
£283019 $441509 €450000 In der tempelhalle - In the temple hall (26x21cm-10x8in) st.verso W/C on card executed 1914 prov.exhib. 8-Oct-2 Sotheby's, London #1/R est:400000-600000
£283019 $441509 €450000 Modegeschaft im laubengang - Fashion shop in a leafy street (45x57cm-18x22in) st.verso W/C pencil on card executed 1913 prov.exhib.lit. 8-Oct-2 Sotheby's, London #11/R est:400000-600000

McKEEVER, Ian (1946-) British
£1950 $3179 €2925 Fossils VII (220x170cm-87x67in) oil acrylic photo exhib. 1-Feb-3 Shapes, Edinburgh #314/R est:2000-3000

MACKELDEY, Karl Bernhard (1826-1890) German
Works on paper
£1069 $1647 €1700 View of Catania and the Etna (37x52cm-15x20in) s. W/C. 23-Oct-2 Finarte, Milan #13/R

McKELL, James (1885-1956) American
£955 $1500 €1433 Stagecoach being held up by several Indians on horseback (61x81cm-24x32in) s. board. 19-Apr-3 James Julia, Fairfield #286/R est:800-1200

McKELVEY, Frank (1895-1974) Irish
£340 $527 €510 Portrait of Ernest Young (76x89cm-30x35in) s. 4-Dec-2 John Ross, Belfast #222
£1736 $2760 €2500 Vase of chrysanthemum (41x36cm-16x14in) s. painted c.1922. 29-Apr-3 Whyte's, Dublin #102/R est:3000-4000
£2300 $3358 €3450 Gathering flowers (13x18cm-5x7in) s. board. 12-Jun-2 John Ross, Belfast #25 est:2000-2500
£2300 $3358 €3450 Old farm, Donegal (25x36cm-10x14in) s. 12-Jun-2 John Ross, Belfast #149/R est:2600-2800
£3600 $5724 €5400 Irish coastal scene (37x49cm-15x19in) s. prov. 26-Feb-3 Sotheby's, Olympia #234/R est:4000-6000
£5000 $7300 €7500 September evening, Buaghey Hrad, Co. Donegal (33x46cm-13x18in) s. board. 12-Jun-2 John Ross, Belfast #181 est:4000-5000
£5000 $7750 €7500 Cattle grazing in a misty landscape (51x66cm-20x26in) s. 2-Oct-2 John Ross, Belfast #143 est:6000-8000
£5000 $7750 €7500 Autumn morning, Antrim coast (40x50cm-16x20in) s. 4-Dec-2 John Ross, Belfast #172 est:5000-6000
£5405 $8432 €8000 Children on a beach (23x39cm-9x15in) s. 26-Mar-3 James Adam, Dublin #104/R est:8000-12000
£5960 $9715 €9000 River meandering through a landscape (15x19cm-6x7in) s. 29-Jan-3 Woodwards, Cork #194
£10000 $15500 €15000 Rain above Bryansford, in the Mournes (51x69cm-20x27in) s. 2-Oct-2 John Ross, Belfast #154 est:10000-11000

£11000 $17600 €16500 Marble strand, Co Donegal (30x43cm-12x17in) s. panel pair. 16-May-3 Sotheby's, London #110/R est:6000-8000
£14744 $22853 €23000 Marble strand, Co Donegal (50x68cm-20x27in) s. 3-Dec-2 Bonhams & James Adam, Dublin #127/R est:25000-30000
£20500 $31775 €30750 Stroll in the park, St. Stephens Green, Dublin (33x43cm-13x17in) s. 2-Oct-2 John Ross, Belfast #158 est:15000-18000
£25000 $39750 €36000 Hay making (38x48cm-15x19in) s. 29-Apr-3 Whyte's, Dublin #78/R est:30000-40000
£70000 $112000 €105000 Children on the banks of the Lagan (46x61cm-18x24in) s. 16-May-3 Sotheby's, London #86/R est:40000-60000
Works on paper
£795 $1295 €1200 Donegal landscape (5x8cm-2x3in) s. 29-Jan-3 Woodwards, Cork #198
£943 $1472 €1500 Claudy River, near Bunbeg, County Donegal (25x37cm-10x15in) s. W/C. 17-Sep-2 Whyte's, Dublin #130 est:2000-3000
£1100 $1749 €1650 Quinton Castle, Quinton Bay, Strangford Peninsula (25x35cm-10x14in) s. W/C. 5-Mar-3 John Ross, Belfast #144 est:1500-1800
£1410 $2214 €2200 Blackrock Castle (24x30cm-9x12in) s.d.1914 W/C prov. 19-Nov-2 Whyte's, Dublin #100/R est:2500-3500
£2200 $3498 €3300 Irish cottages (28x38cm-11x15in) s. W/C. 4-Mar-3 Bearnes, Exeter #402/R est:1200-1800
£4000 $6400 €6000 Port Na Blath, Co Donegal (35x51cm-14x20in) s. W/C. 16-May-3 Sotheby's, London #98/R est:4000-6000

MACKENDRICK, Lilian (1906-1987) American
£3503 $5500 €5255 Spring blooms (61x183cm-24x72in) s.verso triptych. 10-Dec-2 Doyle, New York #105/R est:2000-4000

McKENNA, Noel Vincent Joseph (1956-) Australian
Works on paper
£757 $1241 €1136 Chess players, Central Park, New York (27x35cm-11x14in) i.verso W/C bodycol chl exhib. 4-Jun-3 Deutscher-Menzies, Melbourne #103/R (A.D 1900)

McKENNA, Stephen (1939-) Irish?
£900 $1449 €1350 Two oranges (50x40cm-20x16in) s. d.1993 verso. 14-Jan-3 Bonhams, Knightsbridge #188
£1250 $1987 €1800 Surreal composition with optic nerves (91x76cm-36x30in) d.1967 verso. 29-Apr-3 Whyte's, Dublin #145/R est:2000-3000

MACKENNAL, Sir Edgar Bertram (1863-1931) Australian
Sculpture
£1429 $2257 €2144 Victoria (57cm-22in) i. bronze. 27-Nov-2 Deutscher-Menzies, Melbourne #79/R est:4000-6000 (A.D 4000)
£2857 $4514 €4286 Salome (29cm-11in) i. bronze executed c.1896. 27-Nov-2 Deutscher-Menzies, Melbourne #78/R est:8000-12000 (A.D 8000)
£5000 $7900 €7500 Untitled - female figure (57cm-22in) i. bronze cast c.1980. 27-Nov-2 Deutscher-Menzies, Melbourne #80/R est:10000-15000 (A.D 14000)
£5000 $7800 €7500 Madonna (31cm-12in) i. bronze on grey marble plinth prov. 8-Apr-3 Christie's, Melbourne #293/R est:12000-15000 (A.D 13000)
£5357 $8464 €8036 Diana wounded (36cm-14in) i. bronze. 27-Nov-2 Deutscher-Menzies, Melbourne #77/R est:15000-20000 (A.D 15000)
£5769 $9000 €8654 Fame, winged female figure holding a trumpet (50cm-20in) i. bronze. 8-Apr-3 Christie's, Melbourne #294/R est:15000-20000 (A.D 15000)

MACKENSEN, Fritz (1866-?) German
£601 $950 €950 Portrait of a man from Worpswede (79x60cm-31x24in) s.d.1925. 29-Nov-2 Bolland & Marotz, Bremen #536/R
£2857 $4171 €4400 Fruit garden and cottage near Worpswede (37x49cm-15x19in) s. cardboard. 15-Jun-2 Hans Stahl, Hamburg #152/R est:3200

MACKENZIE, Alexander (1850-1890) British
£6500 $10465 €9750 Out of tune (51x76cm-20x30in) s.d.1886 prov.exhib. 20-Feb-3 Christie's, London #340/R

MACKENZIE, Alexander (1923-2002) British
£512 $799 €768 Rocks Godrevy (37x73cm-15x29in) s.verso panel painted 1959. 23-Sep-2 Blomqvist, Lysaker #1148 (N.KR 6000)
£7000 $11480 €10150 Painting, Rocks, Godrevy (37x72cm-15x28in) s.i.verso board laid down painted 1959 prov. 4-Jun-3 Sotheby's, London #74/R est:4000-6000
£8000 $13120 €12000 Brown, grey March 63 (55x52cm-22x20in) s.i.d.63 verso board exhib. 6-Jun-3 Christie's, London #189/R est:4000-6000
Works on paper
£400 $624 €600 Hydra Saronic Gulf (28x23cm-11x9in) s.i.d.1994 pencil. 16-Oct-2 David Lay, Penzance #291/R
£500 $785 €750 AM above Litton, Yorkshire Dales (47x61cm-19x24in) s.d.1977 pencil on board. 10-Dec-2 Lane, Penzance #101
£580 $905 €870 Untitled (28x33cm-11x13in) init.d.1963 mixed media. 17-Oct-2 David Lay, Penzance #1388
£600 $942 €900 Abstract landscape (32x75cm-13x30in) s.i.d.July 92 chl pastel. 15-Apr-3 Bonhams, Knightsbridge #201/R
£1100 $1716 €1650 Mullion Cove (23x33cm-9x13in) s.i.d.92/93 mixed media. 16-Oct-2 David Lay, Penzance #267/R est:500-800

MACKENZIE, Frederick (1787-1854) British
Works on paper
£700 $1155 €1015 Rivaulx Abbey, Yorkshire (29x22cm-11x9in) s. pen blk ink W/C over pencil htd bodycol gum arabic prov. 2-Jul-3 Sotheby's, Olympia #203/R

MACKENZIE, Hugh Seaforth (1928-) Canadian
£218 $358 €327 Don (22x29cm-9x11in) s.d.1968 acrylic board. 6-Feb-3 Heffel, Vancouver #033/R (C.D 550)

MACKENZIE, J Hamilton (1875-1926) British
£3000 $4680 €4500 Venetian bridge (30x40cm-12x16in) s. 10-Apr-3 Bonhams, Edinburgh #89/R est:500-700
Works on paper
£450 $734 €653 Shepherd and his flock (33x49cm-13x19in) s. W/C. 16-Jul-3 Sotheby's, Olympia #47/R

MACKENZIE, Kenneth (1884-1899) British
£1200 $1908 €1800 Farmstead. Fishing village (36x61cm-14x24in) s.d.1888 two. 6-Mar-3 Christie's, Kensington #114/R est:700-1000

MACKENZIE, Marie Henrie (1878-1961) Dutch
£316 $494 €500 Street with houses and a mill (20x30cm-8x12in) s. board. 21-Oct-2 Glerum, Amsterdam #75
£347 $573 €500 View on the outskirts of a village (22x30cm-9x12in) s. board. 1-Jul-3 Christie's, Amsterdam #228
£348 $543 €550 View of houses (20x30cm-8x12in) s. board. 21-Oct-2 Glerum, Amsterdam #95
£417 $688 €600 Benne de laatste mooje (37x30cm-15x12in) s. i.verso cardboard prov. 1-Jul-3 Christie's, Amsterdam #229
£1944 $3208 €2800 Old Damrak, Amsterdam (41x59cm-16x23in) s. s.i.verso cardboard. 1-Jul-3 Christie's, Amsterdam #224 est:1800-2200
£1974 $3197 €3000 Girl with an orange umbrella (54x36cm-21x14in) s. board prov. 21-Jan-3 Christie's, Amsterdam #271 est:600-800
£2740 $4274 €4000 Kolkje in Amsterdam (70x50cm-28x20in) s. prov. 14-Apr-3 Glerum, Amsterdam #108/R est:3000-5000
£3618 $5862 €5500 Grimnessesluis, Amsterdam (63x76cm-25x30in) s. cardboard. 21-Jan-3 Christie's, Amsterdam #306/R est:3000-5000
£4514 $7448 €6500 Women on the Lijnbaansgracht, Amsterdam (50x70cm-20x28in) s. s.i.verso. 1-Jul-3 Christie's, Amsterdam #231/R est:5000-7000
£8553 $13855 €13000 Nieuwezijds Voorburgwal, Amsterdam, at night (101x70cm-40x28in) s. exhib. 21-Jan-3 Christie's, Amsterdam #307/R est:8000-12000

MACKENZIE, Marie Henrie (attrib) (1878-1961) Dutch
£3151 $4915 €4600 Snow-covered Amsterdam canal (47x59cm-19x23in) s. panel. 14-Apr-3 Glerum, Amsterdam #123/R est:2500-3000

McKENZIE, Queenie (c.1930-1998) Australian
Works on paper
£4301 $6667 €6452 Argyle diamond mine (160x90cm-63x35in) init.i.d. verso natural pigments prov. 3-Dec-2 Shapiro, Sydney #197/R est:15000-25000 (A.D 11900)

McKENZIE, Robert Tait (1867-1938) American
Sculpture
£4222 $6924 €6333 Boy scout (41cm-16in) s.d.1915 bronze. 3-Jun-3 Joyner, Toronto #211/R est:8000-10000 (C.D 9500)

MACKENZIE, Roderick D (1865-1941) American
£1090 $1700 €1635 Pouring slag, clouds of smoke, steel mill near Birmingham, Alabama (56x69cm-22x27in) s. canvasboard exhib. 12-Oct-2 Neal Auction Company, New Orleans #638/R est:3000-5000
£1553 $2500 €2330 Panoramic mountainous landscape (43x64cm-17x25in) s. i.verso. 15-Jan-3 Boos Gallery, Michigan #587/R est:5000-7000

MACKEPRANG, A (1833-1911) Danish
£255 $398 €383 Hare in fight with a crow (43x34cm-17x13in) mono. 5-Aug-2 Rasmussen, Vejle #2186 (D.KR 3000)
£397 $620 €596 Stag at the edge of wood (69x59cm-27x23in) s.verso. 11-Aug-2 Hindemae, Ullerslev #7387/R (D.KR 4700)
£466 $740 €699 An angry fox (40x36cm-16x14in) mono.d.1873. 5-Mar-3 Rasmussen, Copenhagen #1862/R (D.KR 5000)

£766 $1210 €1149 Gundog in rowing boat watching fishing rod (42x31cm-17x12in) s. panel. 2-Dec-2 Rasmussen, Copenhagen #1327/R (D.KR 9000)

£978 $1554 €1467 Stag on a hazy autumn day in Dyrehaven (108x84cm-43x33in) exhib. 10-Mar-3 Rasmussen, Vejle #143/R (D.KR 10500)

£1182 $1845 €1773 Woodland scene with stags (53x90cm-21x35in) mono.d.1910. 23-Sep-2 Rasmussen, Vejle #205/R est:15000 (D.KR 14000)

£1268 $1953 €1902 Stag by water (108x85cm-43x33in) mono. 26-Oct-2 Rasmussen, Havnen #2043/R est:15000-20000 (D.KR 15000)

£1679 $2670 €2519 Ducks in flight over woodland lake (53x90cm-21x35in) mono. exhib. 5-May-3 Rasmussen, Vejle #607/R est:20000 (D.KR 18000)

£3015 $4582 €4523 Cattle grazing by the fjord (77x115cm-30x45in) mono. 27-Aug-2 Rasmussen, Copenhagen #1469/R est:40000-50000 (D.KR 35000)

MACKEPRANG, Adolf (1833-1911) Danish

£1769 $2813 €2654 Two friends - two pugs seated on red sofa (71x50cm-28x20in) mono.d.88. 5-Mar-3 Rasmussen, Copenhagen #1559/R est:15000-20000 (D.KR 19000)

£2553 $4034 €3830 Horses by fence (81x60cm-32x24in) mono. 2-Dec-2 Rasmussen, Copenhagen #1340/R est:30000 (D.KR 30000)

MACKEPRANG, Adolf (attrib) (1833-1911) Danish

Works on paper

£859 $1400 €1289 Maltese terriers on a chair (58x46cm-23x18in) mono.d.1888 W/C. 11-Feb-3 Bonhams & Doyles, New York #146/R est:1000-1500

MACKETANZ, Ferdinand (1902-) Polish

Works on paper

£288 $438 €450 Mother and child reading book (24x16cm-9x6in) s. W/C Indian ink. 31-Aug-2 Geble, Radolfzell #690/R

McKEWAN, David Hall (c.1816-1875) British

Works on paper

£350 $557 €525 Highland landscape (53x74cm-21x29in) s. W/C htd white. 29-Apr-3 Bonhams, Knightsbridge #76/R

£500 $835 €725 Bout Mill, Eskdale, Cumbria, showery weather (53x77cm-21x30in) s.d.1862 W/C. 17-Jun-3 Anderson & Garland, Newcastle #187/R

£600 $978 €900 Near Ludlow (29x44cm-11x17in) W/C. 29-Jan-3 Sotheby's, Olympia #118/R

£2000 $3260 €3000 Ludford Bridge, Ludlow (29x44cm-11x17in) W/C. 29-Jan-3 Sotheby's, Olympia #123/R est:600-800

MACKEY, Haydn Reynolds (1883-?) British

£250 $405 €363 Portrait of Sybil Ayres (55x32cm-22x13in) s. canvasboard. 25-May-3 Lots Road, London #334

£280 $454 €406 Nymphs and satyrs (58x48cm-23x19in) canvasboard. 25-May-3 Lots Road, London #333

MACKIE, Charles H (1862-1920) British

£400 $664 €580 Cattle on a country road (40x46cm-16x18in) s. 13-Jun-3 Lyon & Turnbull, Edinburgh #77

£720 $1188 €1044 Moonlit harbour front (44x59cm-17x23in) s. 1-Jul-3 Bearnes, Exeter #491/R

£1698 $2750 €2462 Child in grass (15x23cm-6x9in) s.d.86 canvas on board prov. 21-May-3 Doyle, New York #182/R est:1000-1500

Works on paper

£260 $416 €390 Whitby pier (18x26cm-7x10in) W/C. 11-Mar-3 David Duggleby, Scarborough #53

MACKIE, John (1953-) British

£550 $858 €825 Rivesaltes, France (34x41cm-13x16in) s. i.verso. 10-Apr-3 Tennants, Leyburn #1137

£2200 $3454 €3300 Towards Grimaud, France (70x80cm-28x31in) s. 21-Nov-2 Tennants, Leyburn #864 est:1500-2000

MACKIE, Kathleen Isabella (1899-1996) Irish?

Works on paper

£500 $800 €750 Kilary Bay, Co Galway. Haystack (13x18cm-5x7in) init. bodycol two. 15-May-3 Christie's, Kensington #197/R

£500 $800 €750 Cottages near Delphi, Co Mayo. Delphi Lodge, Co Mayo (13x18cm-5x7in) init. bodycol. 15-May-3 Christie's, Kensington #200/R

MACKINLAY, Duncan (fl.1880-1891) British

£290 $481 €421 Village back street (54x38cm-21x15in) s. 13-Jun-3 Lyon & Turnbull, Edinburgh #33

MACKINLAY, Miguel (1895-1958) Spanish

£400 $668 €580 Laurie and Theresa, the artist's daughters (61x51cm-24x20in) s. 17-Jun-3 Bonhams, Knightsbridge #167/R

MACKINNON, Aileen Robertson (1901-?) British

Works on paper

£550 $858 €825 Studies of a French bulldog (35x53cm-14x21in) s. pastel. 9-Apr-3 Cheffins Grain & Comins, Cambridge #620

MACKINNON, Finlay (fl.1891-1930) British

Works on paper

£350 $546 €525 Fisherman on the Ewe (54x70cm-21x28in) W/C. 12-Sep-2 Bonhams, Edinburgh #307a

MACKINNON, Sine (1901-1997) Irish

£1100 $1716 €1650 Montrouge, Paris (46x61cm-18x24in) s. 26-Mar-3 Woolley & Wallis, Salisbury #211/R est:1000-1500

£2500 $4000 €3750 Daffodils and honesty - honesty among the flowers (66x48cm-26x19in) board prov. 16-May-3 Sotheby's, London #95/R est:2000-3000

£4800 $7680 €7200 Composition, fleurs (78x48cm-31x19in) s. prov. 16-May-3 Sotheby's, London #92/R est:3000-5000

McKINSTRY, Cherith (1928-) British

£300 $477 €450 Irish Coast (40x56cm-16x22in) s.verso. 5-Mar-3 John Ross, Belfast #193

£1195 $1864 €1900 Ben Bulben (41x51cm-16x20in) s. exhib. 17-Sep-2 Whyte's, Dublin #146/R est:1200-1500

MACKINTOSH, Charles Rennie (1868-1928) British

Works on paper

£18000 $28260 €27000 Wild pansy and wood violet (25x19cm-10x7in) i.d.May 1910 W/C over pencil prov. 16-Dec-2 Sotheby's, London #82/R est:20000-30000

MACKINTOSH, Dwight (1906-1999) American

Works on paper

£926 $1500 €1389 Untitled (36x74cm-14x29in) felt pen executed 1989 prov.exhib. 27-Jan-3 Christie's, Rockefeller NY #78/R est:2000-3000

£1728 $2800 €2592 Untitled - four figures (65x67cm-26x26in) W/C felt pen pencil prov. 27-Jan-3 Christie's, Rockefeller NY #79/R est:3000-4000

MACKINTOSH, Jessie (1893-1957) Australian

£398 $653 €577 Tree rhythm (34x44cm-13x17in) s. canvas on board prov. 4-Jun-3 Deutscher-Menzies, Melbourne #385/R (A.D 1000)

MACKLEY, Evan (1940-) Australian

£536 $846 €804 Lazy days 2000 (69x79cm-27x31in) s. 18-Nov-2 Joel, Victoria #195 est:2500-3000 (A.D 1500)

MACKLIN, Thomas Eyre (1867-1943) British

£380 $635 €551 Old cottages near Winchfield, Hants (26x32cm-10x13in) s.d.1937 i.verso. 9-Jul-3 Edgar Horn, Eastbourne #306/R

MACKLOT, Camille (20th C) French

£503 $785 €800 Hunting still life with dead game birds (71x55cm-28x22in) s.d.1911. 11-Oct-2 Winterberg, Heidelberg #1432/R

MACKNIGHT, Dodge (1860-1950) American

Works on paper

£959 $1400 €1439 Coastline (26x49cm-10x19in) s. W/C. 10-May-2 Skinner, Boston #226/R est:800-1200

£1083 $1700 €1625 View of the Spanish countryside (37x53cm-15x21in) s.i.d.1920 W/C. 14-Dec-2 Weschler, Washington #673/R est:2000-3000

McKNIGHT, Thomas (?) ?

£1241 $1961 €1800 Sagg pond, Long Island (56x66cm-22x26in) s. 4-Apr-3 Tajan, Paris #57

McKOY, Grainger (20th C) American

Sculpture

£6962 $11000 €10443 Wilson's snipe. grass round wood base sold with a carved envelope bird feather. 3-Apr-3 Christie's, Rockefeller NY #257/R est:5000-8000

MACKRILL, Martyn (1961-) British
Works on paper
£900 $1368 €1350 Sunset at Gravesend, a brigantine under tow (38x54cm-15x21in) s.d.89 W/C htd white. 15-Aug-2 Bonhams, New Bond Street #293/R

McLAREN, C (?) British
£565 $892 €848 Chickens and roosters in a barn. King of the roost (20x25cm-8x10in) init. s.stretcher pair prov. 18-Nov-2 Waddingtons, Toronto #82/R (C.D 1400)

MACLAREN, John Stewart (1860-c.1930) British
£620 $961 €930 Arab girl seated amongst fruit and basket of eggs (76x56cm-30x22in) s.d.1897. 25-Sep-2 Brightwells, Leominster #927/R

MACLAREN, Norman (1914-1987) Canadian
£267 $412 €401 Poires flottantes (51x25cm-20x10in) s. 22-Oct-2 Iegor de Saint Hippolyte, Montreal #67 (C.D 650)

McLAREN, Peter (20th C) British
£1600 $2496 €2400 Cyclist (186x202cm-73x80in) s.verso board. 17-Oct-2 Bonhams, Edinburgh #101 est:800-1200
£6500 $10075 €9750 Figure in car (104x102cm-41x40in) s.i.d.89 verso board prov. 31-Oct-2 Christie's, London #206/R est:5000-8000
Works on paper
£260 $406 €390 Fairground scene (34x42cm-13x17in) s. ink W/C. 10-Apr-3 Bonhams, Edinburgh #26
£280 $437 €420 Fairground (34x52cm-13x20in) ink gouache. 10-Apr-3 Bonhams, Edinburgh #42
£280 $437 €420 At the fairground (36x53cm-14x21in) ink W/C gouache. 10-Apr-3 Bonhams, Edinburgh #52

MACLAREN, Walter (fl.1869-1893) British
£1050 $1754 €1523 An girl from Capri (22x17cm-9x7in) s.i.d.78. 23-Jun-3 Bonhams, Bath #123/R est:500-700

McLARNON, Samuel (?) British?
£320 $496 €480 Near Glenarm (41x61cm-16x24in) s. 2-Oct-2 John Ross, Belfast #264
£360 $558 €540 River Dunn (41x76cm-16x30in) s. 2-Oct-2 John Ross, Belfast #79
£360 $572 €540 Newlands (40x76cm-16x30in) s. 5-Mar-3 John Ross, Belfast #97

McLAUGHLIN, Isabel (1903-) Canadian
£1008 $1593 €1512 Mood (69x91cm-27x36in) s.d.1961 prov.exhib. 18-Nov-2 Sotheby's, Toronto #68/R est:3500-4000 (C.D 2500)

McLEA, Duncan Fraser (1841-1916) British
£260 $424 €390 Evening outside a harbour (13x28cm-5x11in) s. 17-Feb-3 Bonhams, Bath #68

McLEAN, Bruce (1942-) British
£611 $960 €917 Lady pipe smoker (64x67cm-25x26in) s.i. acrylic. 25-Nov-2 Germann, Zurich #767 (S.FR 1400)

McLEAN, George E (1939-) Canadian
Works on paper
£870 $1357 €1450 Untitled - Rocky mountain goat (74x55cm-29x22in) s. gouache. 13-Apr-3 Levis, Calgary #85/R est:2500-3000 (C.D 2000)

McLEAN, Jack Lee (1924-) Canadian
£1042 $1594 €1563 Family affair (61x102cm-24x40in) board. 24-Aug-2 Heffel, Vancouver #14 est:3000-5000 (C.D 2500)

MACLEAN, Thomas Nelson (1845-1894) British
Sculpture
£10000 $16100 €15000 Spring festival (73cm-29in) bronze prov.exhib.lit. 20-Feb-3 Christie's, London #152/R est:10000

McLEAN, Thomas Wesley (1881-1951) Canadian
Works on paper
£184 $286 €276 Northern Lakeshore (23x24cm-9x9in) s. W/C. 24-Sep-2 Ritchie, Toronto #3106/R (C.D 450)
£322 $502 €483 Hay canoes (20x27cm-8x11in) s.i.verso W/C. 25-Mar-3 Ritchie, Toronto #66/R (C.D 750)
£356 $583 €516 Grain elevators, Kenora (23x26cm-9x10in) s.i. W/C. 9-Jun-3 Hodgins, Calgary #50/R (C.D 800)

MACLEAN, William Lacy (1860-1940) American
£478 $750 €717 Into the woods, an autumn landscape (25x30cm-10x12in) s.i. masonite. 22-Nov-2 Skinner, Boston #275/R

MACLEAY, Kenneth (1802-1878) British
Works on paper
£750 $1170 €1125 Inverlochy Castle and Fort William (17x51cm-7x20in) s.i.d.1845 W/C double-sided two sheets. 10-Apr-3 Bonhams, Edinburgh #107/R

MACLEAY, Kenneth (attrib) (1802-1878) British
£1000 $1560 €1500 Lady campbell and her son Archibaid (75x62cm-30x24in) 28-Mar-3 Bonhams, Edinburgh #128/R est:1500-2000

MACLEAY, McNeil (19th C) British
£1000 $1560 €1500 Waterfall (40x61cm-16x24in) s.d.1866. 14-Apr-3 Sotheby's, London #33/R est:1000-1500
£3200 $4992 €4800 Fishing at the loch (71x91cm-28x36in) s. 14-Apr-3 Sotheby's, London #29/R est:2500-3000
£3400 $5168 €5100 View near Stirling Castle (46x76cm-18x30in) s.d.1866 canvas on panel. 28-Aug-2 Sotheby's, London #871/R est:2000-3000

MACLEISH, Norman (1890-1975) American
£779 $1200 €1169 Country winter (61x51cm-24x20in) s.d.1936. 8-Sep-2 Treadway Gallery, Cincinnati #706/R

MACLEOD, Euan (1956-) New Zealander
£682 $1050 €1023 Smoking man (51x38cm-20x15in) s. i.d.11/97 verso. 4-Sep-2 Dunbar Sloane, Wellington #15/R est:1500-2500 (NZ.D 2250)
£961 $1529 €1442 Snow job (38x51cm-15x20in) s.i.d.9/99 verso. 4-Mar-3 Deutscher-Menzies, Melbourne #228/R (A.D 2500)
£2351 $3668 €3527 Elevated figure (135x182cm-53x72in) s.verso. 7-Nov-2 International Art Centre, Auckland #11/R est:8000-14000 (NZ.D 7500)

MACLEOD, Pegi Nichol (1904-1949) Canadian
£1794 $2870 €2691 Children lay anywhere (61x56cm-24x22in) s. board double-sided painted c.1937 prov. 15-May-3 Heffel, Vancouver #230/R est:2750-3250 (C.D 4000)
Works on paper
£700 $1084 €1050 Red door (34x24cm-13x9in) W/C pencil prov. 3-Dec-2 Joyner, Toronto #272/R est:1500-2000 (C.D 1700)

McLEOD, William (1811-1892) American
£2179 $3400 €3269 Ye Old Mill. The Ford, Rock Creek Park (30x41cm-12x16in) one s. pair. 14-Sep-2 Weschler, Washington #604/R est:2000-3000

MACLEOD, William Douglas (1892-1963) British
£510 $800 €765 Fallen rider with his faithful horse (33x28cm-13x11in) s.d.1881. 23-Nov-2 Jackson's, Cedar Falls #113/R

MACLET, Elisee (1881-1962) French
£452 $714 €700 Rue Berthon a Passy (14x18cm-6x7in) s. i.verso cardboard. 18-Dec-2 Ferri, Paris #91
£586 $932 €850 Maison dans la clairiere (38x46cm-15x18in) s. 9-Mar-3 Feletin, Province #91
£1122 $1761 €1750 Navire a quai (45x54cm-18x21in) s. cardboard. 22-Nov-2 Millon & Associes, Paris #76
£1258 $1950 €2000 Bouquet (60x80cm-24x31in) s. 7-Oct-2 Claude Aguttes, Neuilly #192
£1282 $2013 €2000 Coin de rue a Montmartre (55x38cm-22x15in) s. cardboard. 13-Dec-2 Piasa, Paris #257/R
£1419 $2200 €2129 Seascape (53x74cm-21x29in) 7-Dec-2 South Bay, Long Island #154/R
£1510 $2340 €2400 Le pont Royal (47x62cm-19x24in) s. cardboard. 4-Oct-2 Tajan, Paris #159 est:2500-3000
£1538 $2400 €2307 Rue St. Vincent (27x35cm-11x14in) s. i.on stretcher. 20-Sep-2 Sloan, North Bethesda #370/R est:2000-3000
£1554 $2424 €2300 La bergerie de Gabrielle d'Estree, ru du Mont Cenis (33x41cm-13x16in) s. i.verso. 31-Mar-3 Rossini, Paris #65/R
£1572 $2484 €2358 Sacre Coeur (55x38cm-22x15in) s. 14-Nov-2 Stuker, Bern #378 est:500-700 (S.FR 3600)
£1605 $2279 €2600 Paris, Passy (15x20cm-6x8in) s. panel. 16-Mar-3 Eric Pillon, Calais #237/R
£1656 $2583 €2600 Vase de fleurs (36x46cm-14x18in) s. panel. 10-Nov-2 Eric Pillon, Calais #130/R
£1761 $2923 €2500 Montmartre, rue Saint-Rustique (38x29cm-15x11in) s. cardboard. 11-Jun-3 Beaussant & Lefèvre, Paris #91/R est:1200
£1803 $2866 €2650 Coin de Paris (46x55cm-18x22in) s. cardboard. 26-Feb-3 Artcurial Briest, Paris #282/R est:2200-3000
£1921 $3036 €2882 Sacre Coeur (65x49cm-26x19in) s. 14-Nov-2 Stuker, Bern #377/R est:800-1200 (S.FR 4400)
£2270 $3790 €3200 Paris - L'eglise Saint Marcel (61x45cm-24x18in) s. board. 20-Jun-3 Piasa, Paris #154/R est:2000-3000
£2449 $3894 €3600 Montmartre (54x65cm-21x26in) s. 26-Feb-3 Artcurial Briest, Paris #283/R est:3000-4500

£	$	€	Description
£2611	$4074	€4100	Vue de Bures-sur-Yvette (35x27cm-14x11in) s. 10-Nov-2 Eric Pillon, Calais #124/R
£2642	$4094	€4200	Rue de Montmartre (61x45cm-24x18in) s.d.24 cardboard. 30-Oct-2 Artcurial Briest, Paris #318 est:2000-3000
£3038	$4800	€4800	Paris, bateaux-lavoir sur la Seine (65x50cm-26x20in) s. cardboard. 2-Dec-2 Tajan, Paris #157/R
£3057	$4769	€4800	Paris, Montmartre sous la neige (27x35cm-11x14in) s. 10-Nov-2 Eric Pillon, Calais #122/R
£3165	$5000	€5000	Rue a Montmartre (61x45cm-24x18in) s. cardboard. 2-Dec-2 Tajan, Paris #158/R
£3205	$5032	€5000	Vue du Sacre-Coeur (55x46cm-22x18in) s. 22-Nov-2 Millon & Associes, Paris #77/R
£3333	$5233	€5200	Paris, place Pigalle (46x55cm-18x22in) s. 11-Dec-2 Maigret, Paris #107/R est:1800-2000
£3526	$5465	€5500	Vue de Montmartre (38x45cm-15x18in) s. panel. 5-Dec-2 Gros & Delettrez, Paris #98
£3526	$5535	€5500	Paris, Montmartre au Moulin de La Galette (46x55cm-18x22in) s. 11-Dec-2 Maigret, Paris #109/R est:2000-2500
£4459	$6955	€7000	Paris, la Seine et Notre-Dame (46x55cm-18x22in) s. 10-Nov-2 Eric Pillon, Calais #121/R
£4698	$7564	€7000	Le moulin de la Galette sous la neige (46x55cm-18x22in) s. 23-Feb-3 Lesieur & Le Bars, Le Havre #98/R
£4904	$7651	€7700	Paris, Montmartre, Rue de l'Abreuvoir (46x50cm-18x20in) s. 10-Nov-2 Eric Pillon, Calais #123/R
Works on paper			
£324	$518	€450	Cinq mats a Dieppe (23x30cm-9x12in) s.i. W/C. 14-May-3 Blanchet, Paris #119
£331	$540	€500	Vue de port (11x18cm-4x7in) s. W/C Indian ink. 16-Feb-3 Mercier & Cie, Lille #263
£340	$541	€500	Auto-portrait au chevalet (29x21cm-11x8in) s. W/C exec.c.1910. 24-Mar-3 Coutau Begarie, Paris #158
£350	$584	€500	Navires en mer (23x28cm-9x11in) s. W/C. 26-Jun-3 Tajan, Paris #76
£401	$570	€650	Petit port de peche (9x14cm-4x6in) s. W/C. 16-Mar-3 Eric Pillon, Calais #186/R
£432	$691	€600	Le Seine a Paris (26x35cm-10x14in) s. W/C. 14-May-3 Blanchet, Paris #118/R
£476	$757	€700	Maison rose sous la neige (27x33cm-11x13in) s. gouache. 26-Feb-3 Artcurial Briest, Paris #284
£526	$799	€820	Tour Solidor (30x48cm-12x19in) s.i. W/C. 17-Aug-2 Livinec, Gaudcheau & Jezequel, Rennes #41
£886	$1400	€1400	Place a Paris (37x48cm-15x19in) s. W/C. 29-Nov-2 Drouot Estimations, Paris #39
£1014	$1581	€1500	Montmartre (35x29cm-14x11in) s. W/C. 28-Mar-3 Charbonneaux, Paris #109/R
£1720	$2683	€2700	Moulin a Montmartre (35x27cm-14x11in) s. gouache oil. 10-Nov-2 Eric Pillon, Calais #125/R

MACLIAMMOIR, Michael (1899-1978) Irish

£	$	€	Description
Works on paper			
£633	$981	€1000	Oriental lady standing on a bridge at moonlight (16x23cm-6x9in) s. W/C. 25-Sep-2 James Adam, Dublin #100/R
£2416	$3890	€3600	An allegory (33x24cm-13x9in) s.d.1918 W/C pen ink prov. 18-Feb-3 Whyte's, Dublin #15/R est:2000-3000

MACLISE, Daniel (1806-1870) British/Irish

£	$	€	Description
£1800	$2772	€2700	Faraway thoughts (33x27cm-13x11in) s. board prov. 5-Sep-2 Christie's, Kensington #325/R est:1500-2000
£280000	$450800	€420000	Wrestling scene in As you like it' (129x177cm-51x70in) s.d.1854 exhib.lit. 19-Feb-3 Christie's, London #38/R est:300000-500000
£300000	$474000	€450000	Robin Hood (183x366cm-72x144in) s.d.1839 prov.exhib.lit. 28-Nov-2 Sotheby's, London #20/R est:300000-400000
Works on paper			
£360	$558	€540	Biblical scene (33x30cm-13x12in) s. mixed media. 4-Dec-2 John Ross, Belfast #210
£5500	$7865	€8250	Writing lesson (12x11cm-5x4in) pencil W/C prov.exhib.lit. 22-Jan-3 Christie's, London #13/R est:3500
£14500	$23345	€21750	Play scene in Hamlet (35x64cm-14x25in) pencil W/C htd bodycol gum arabic arched top prov.exhib.lit. 20-Feb-3 Christie's, London #81/R est:25000

MACLISE, Daniel (attrib) (1806-1870) British/Irish

£	$	€	Description
£350	$546	€525	Portrait of a gentleman, thought to be William Ewart Gladstone (38x33cm-15x13in) prov. 7-Nov-2 Christie's, Kensington #60/R

McLOY, Samuel (1831-1904) British

£	$	€	Description
Works on paper			
£2650	$4134	€3975	Stupid book (36x46cm-14x18in) s. W/C. 15-Oct-2 Bearnes, Exeter #391/R est:900-1100

McMAHON, Bettina (1930-) Australian

£	$	€	Description
Works on paper			
£602	$956	€903	Giraffes, Western Plain Zoo (124x110cm-49x43in) s. gouache. 3-Mar-3 Lawson Menzies, Sydney #467 est:1000-1700 (A.D 1600)

McMAHON, Brett (1967-) Australian

£	$	€	Description
£433	$671	€650	Corner (46x61cm-18x24in) s.d.98 s.i.d.1998 verso. 3-Dec-2 Shapiro, Sydney #121 (A.D 1200)

McMANUS, James Goodwin (1882-1958) American

£	$	€	Description
£510	$800	€765	New England pastoral scene with small hillside and cows (64x76cm-25x30in) s.d.1947. 19-Apr-3 James Julia, Fairfield #393/R
£629	$1000	€944	River view (63x76cm-25x30in) s.d.1947. 7-Mar-3 Skinner, Boston #387/R

McMASTER, James (1856-1913) British

£	$	€	Description
Works on paper			
£550	$858	€825	On the Yorkshire coast (40x60cm-16x24in) s.i. W/C htd white. 17-Oct-2 Bonhams, Edinburgh #190
£580	$905	€870	Harbour, Dunure (24x34cm-9x13in) s.i. W/C. 13-Sep-2 Lyon & Turnbull, Edinburgh #130/R
£1900	$2964	€2850	Fisher's haven (40x60cm-16x24in) s.i. W/C. 13-Sep-2 Lyon & Turnbull, Edinburgh #139/R est:400-600

MACMIADHACHAIN, Padraig (1929-) Irish

£	$	€	Description
£250	$400	€375	Inigma in Co Mayo (25x30cm-10x12in) s. s.i. on overlay. 15-May-3 Christie's, Kensington #246/R
£600	$948	€900	Wind below the sea (43x119cm-17x47in) s. acrylic. 18-Dec-2 Mallams, Oxford #641/R
£650	$1040	€975	Toy fishing boat (26x30cm-10x12in) s. s.i. on stretcher. 15-May-3 Christie's, Kensington #248/R
£1027	$1613	€1500	She picked the stars from the argentine ice cream (48x60cm-19x24in) s.i.verso. 15-Apr-3 De Veres Art Auctions, Dublin #100j
Works on paper			
£528	$877	€750	Chapel on headland (22x22cm-9x9in) s. mixed media prov. 10-Jun-3 James Adam, Dublin #72/R

MACMILLAN, Sheila (1928-) British

£	$	€	Description
£520	$863	€754	Winter trees (40x40cm-16x16in) s. board. 13-Jun-3 Lyon & Turnbull, Edinburgh #111
£580	$905	€870	Grey and white still life (54x44cm-21x17in) 13-Sep-2 Lyon & Turnbull, Edinburgh #49/R

McMINN, William Kimmins (fl.1854-1880) British

£	$	€	Description
£2800	$4536	€4200	Three masted barque Orkney Lass off the waterfront at Liverpool (61x94cm-24x37in) 21-May-3 Christie's, Kensington #574/R est:3000-5000

McMINN, William Kimmins (attrib) (fl.1854-1880) British

£	$	€	Description
£2500	$4050	€3750	Barque Orkney Lass in two position off the Liverpool waterfront (58x92cm-23x36in) 21-Jan-3 Bonhams, New Bond Street #232/R est:3000-5000

MACMONNIES, Frederick William (1863-1937) American

£	$	€	Description
£25806	$40000	€38709	Marjorie and Berthe feed their pet rooster Coco (53x57cm-21x22in) painted c.1903 prov.lit. 4-Dec-2 Sotheby's, New York #24/R est:25000-35000
Sculpture			
£5660	$9000	€8490	Bacchante and infant faun (85cm-33in) i. brown pat. bronze. 4-Mar-3 Christie's, Rockefeller NY #37/R est:6000-8000
£6329	$10000	€9494	Dancing nude Bacchante and baby (84x30cm-33x12in) s.d.1894 pat. bronze. 16-Nov-2 New Orleans Auction, New Orleans #1125/R est:8000-12000
£9740	$15000	€14610	Bacchante and infant fawn (89cm-35in) s.i.d.1894 brown pat. bronze. 24-Oct-2 Shannon's, Milford #32/R est:7000-9000
£10968	$17000	€16452	Young faun with heron (70cm-28in) s.i. golden brown pat. bronze lit. 29-Oct-2 Sotheby's, New York #260/R est:10000-15000
£11728	$19000	€17592	Young faun with heron (69cm-27in) i. golden brown pat. bronze prov.lit. 21-May-3 Sotheby's, New York #182/R est:10000-15000
£17500	$28000	€25375	Pan of Rohallion (96cm-38in) s.i.d.1890 verso bronze prov. 16-May-3 Skinner, Boston #167/R est:12000-18000

MACNAB, Iain (1890-1967) British

£	$	€	Description
Works on paper			
£500	$780	€750	Standing nude. Nude (56x39cm-22x15in) s. chl two. 27-Mar-3 Christie's, Kensington #291

MACNAB, Peter (?-1900) British

£	$	€	Description
£280	$437	€420	Low tide with shrimper (45x35cm-18x14in) s. 13-Sep-2 Lyon & Turnbull, Edinburgh #53/R

McNALLY, M J (1874-1943) Australian
Works on paper
£358 $545 €537 Lady on a sunlit path (30x37cm-12x15in) s.d.1929 W/C. 28-Aug-2 Deutscher-Menzies, Melbourne #413/R (A.D 1000)

McNALLY, Matthew James (1874-1943) Australian
£717 $1090 €1076 By the sea (24x34cm-9x13in) s.d.1914. 27-Aug-2 Goodman, Sydney #178 (A.D 2000)
Works on paper
£325 $514 €471 Near Camden (29x39cm-11x15in) s.d.1939 W/C on fabric. 22-Jul-3 Lawson Menzies, Sydney #163/R (A.D 800)
£382 $603 €573 Big gums (26x23cm-10x9in) s.d.19 W/C pencil. 2-Apr-3 Christie's, Melbourne #47 est:1000-1500 (A.D 1000)

McNAUGHTON, Elizabeth Florence Baskerville (1906-) American
Works on paper
£870 $1400 €1305 Polynesian woman in a floral interior (20x30cm-8x12in) s.d.1981 mixed media board prov. 18-Feb-3 John Moran, Pasadena #80 est:1500-2000

MACNAUGHTON, John H (?) Canadian?
Works on paper
£3111 $5102 €4667 Sleighing scenes (20x32cm-8x13in) s. W/C pair. 3-Jun-3 Joyner, Toronto #142/R est:8000-12000 (C.D 7000)

MACNEE, Robert Russell (1880-1952) British
£260 $411 €390 Seascape (28x53cm-11x21in) s. 19-Dec-2 Bonhams, Edinburgh #320
£496 $779 €744 Seascape under blue sky (41x61cm-16x24in) s.d.31. 24-Jul-2 Walker's, Ottawa #18/R est:2000-3000 (C.D 1200)
£644 $1004 €934 Abernethy, Scotland (46x56cm-18x22in) s.d.96. 26-Mar-3 Walker's, Ottawa #67a/R est:1500-2000 (C.D 1500)
£1000 $1570 €1500 Two hens (23x28cm-9x11in) s. 13-Dec-2 Keys, Aylsham #722 est:1000-1500
£1900 $2964 €2850 In the farm yard (36x46cm-14x18in) s.d.19. 14-Apr-3 Sotheby's, London #155/R est:1200-1800
£2000 $3080 €3000 Harvesting (25x36cm-10x14in) s. board. 5-Sep-2 Christie's, Kensington #210/R est:2500-3500
£2400 $3744 €3600 Feeding poultry (34x44cm-13x17in) s.d.33. 10-Apr-3 Bonhams, Edinburgh #133/R est:1500-2000
£2500 $4050 €3625 Farmyard scene with a woman feeding chickens (22x18cm-9x7in) s. indis d. 29-Jul-3 Capes Dunn, Manchester #21/R
£3400 $5576 €5100 Poultry feeding outside a stone cottage (37x53cm-15x21in) s. board. 2-Jun-3 David Duggleby, Scarborough #334/R est:2000-3000

McNEELY, Perry (1886-1966) American
£649 $1000 €974 Owens Valley, California (61x76cm-24x30in) s. painted c.1940. 8-Sep-2 Treadway Gallery, Cincinnati #593/R
£2707 $4250 €4061 Cloudburst over desert mountains (46x56cm-18x22in) s.i. canvas on board. 19-Nov-2 Butterfields, San Francisco #8313/R est:4000-6000

MACNEIL, Carol Brooks (1871-1944) American
Sculpture
£1761 $2800 €2642 Cloudy day (32cm-13in) i. painted plaster prov.lit. 4-Mar-3 Christie's, Rockefeller NY #53/R est:4000-6000

McNEIL, George (1908-1995) American
£3045 $4750 €4568 Surprise 2 (152x190cm-60x75in) s.d.82 i.verso. 14-Oct-2 Butterfields, San Francisco #2113/R est:4000-6000

McNEILL, Paul (1961-) New Zealander
£283 $442 €491 Alby (122x122cm-48x48in) s.d.1993 verso prov. 31-Mar-3 Goodman, Sydney #13/R (A.D 750)

McNICOL, Ian (fl.1928-1938) British
£1500 $2340 €2250 Scottish coastal landscape (46x58cm-18x23in) s.d.1951. 17-Sep-2 Sotheby's, Olympia #58/R est:1500-2000

McNICOLL, Helen Galloway (1879-1915) Canadian
£13105 $20706 €19658 Tea time (61x76cm-24x30in) s. prov.exhib. 18-Nov-2 Sotheby's, Toronto #32/R est:30000-40000 (C.D 32500)
£32258 $50968 €48387 On the beach (41x46cm-16x18in) s. prov.exhib.lit. 18-Nov-2 Sotheby's, Toronto #54/R est:30000-40000 (C.D 80000)

MACOUN, Gustav (1892-1934) Czechoslovakian
£536 $848 €804 Coal market square in Prague (49x59cm-19x23in) s. cardboard. 30-Nov-2 Dorotheum, Prague #72/R (C.KR 26000)
£578 $913 €867 Landscape with lake and figures (43x60cm-17x24in) s.d.1925 cardboard. 30-Nov-2 Dorotheum, Prague #57/R (C.KR 28000)
£681 $1103 €1022 Winter landscape in Cesky Raj (100x112cm-39x44in) s.d.1918 board. 24-May-3 Dorotheum, Prague #76/R est:30000-45000 (C.KR 30000)
£1135 $1793 €1703 Landscape below mountains (145x165cm-57x65in) s.indis.d. 30-Nov-2 Dorotheum, Prague #107/R est:50000-75000 (C.KR 55000)

McPHAIL, Roger (1953-) British
Works on paper
£280 $442 €420 Kingfisher watching the water (35x22cm-14x9in) s. W/C htd white. 27-Nov-2 Bonhams, Knowle #189
£280 $442 €420 Kingfisher diving (34x22cm-13x9in) s. W/C. 27-Nov-2 Bonhams, Knowle #190
£300 $468 €450 Reluctant gun dog (34x25cm-13x10in) s. W/C. 6-Nov-2 Sotheby's, Olympia #160/R
£350 $553 €525 Startled roebuck (47x35cm-19x14in) s.d.76 W/C prov. 28-Nov-2 Christie's, Kensington #54/R
£550 $913 €798 Lapwings mobbing up a fox (42x53cm-17x21in) s. pencil W/C htd white prov. 12-Jun-3 Christie's, Kensington #150/R
£600 $936 €900 Grouse attaching a peregrine falcon (33x45cm-13x18in) s. W/C bodycol. 18-Sep-2 Dreweatt Neate, Newbury #5
£600 $996 €870 Bullfinches (23x33cm-9x13in) s. W/C prov. 12-Jun-3 Christie's, Kensington #149/R
£1100 $1716 €1650 Woodcock upon a forest floor (36x45cm-14x18in) s. W/C bodycol. 18-Sep-2 Dreweatt Neate, Newbury #6 est:2000-3000

McPHEE, Charles C (1910-) New Zealander
£281 $446 €422 Marera (88x68cm-35x27in) s.i. oil on velvet. 25-Feb-3 Peter Webb, Auckland #183 (NZ.D 800)

McPHERSON (?) ?
Works on paper
£460 $727 €690 At noon-day (24x38cm-9x15in) s. W/C. 27-Nov-2 Hamptons Fine Art, Godalming #109

McPHERSON, Donald (1920-1986) British
£651 $1015 €950 Coastal landscape (63x76cm-25x30in) s. 8-Apr-3 James Adam, Dublin #93/R

McPHERSON, Donald (fl.1924-1934) British
£280 $437 €420 Coastal landscape (66x76cm-26x30in) s. 9-Oct-2 Woolley & Wallis, Salisbury #342/R

MACPHERSON, Earl (1910-1993) American
Works on paper
£344 $550 €499 Seated nude female with gloves holding cards (51x33cm-20x13in) s. pastel. 17-May-3 Selkirks, St. Louis #374/R

MACPHERSON, John (fl.1865-1884) British
Works on paper
£360 $562 €540 Homewood bound (22x43cm-9x17in) s. W/C. 9-Oct-2 Woolley & Wallis, Salisbury #107/R
£740 $1177 €1110 Cattle resting in a summer landscape, near Dorking, Surrey (28x42cm-11x17in) s. W/C. 4-Mar-3 Bearnes, Exeter #400/R

MacPHERSON, Neil (1954-) British
£360 $587 €540 Portrait of a man in landscape (37x28cm-15x11in) s. board. 3-Feb-3 Sotheby's, Olympia #140/R

MACPHERSON, Robert (1811-1872) British
Photographs
£3200 $5184 €4800 Valley of the Anio (31x40cm-12x16in) st.i. albumen print card oval exec.c.1857. 22-May-3 Sotheby's, London #4/R est:1500-2000

McPHERSON, William (1905-1972) British
£550 $853 €825 Swimmer, Arran from Skelmore (43x66cm-17x26in) s.d.27 board. 6-Dec-2 Lyon & Turnbull, Edinburgh #56

MACQUEEN, Kenneth (1897-1960) Australian
Works on paper
£773 $1221 €1121 Untitled - darling downs (36x40cm-14x16in) s.d.1926 W/C. 22-Jul-3 Lawson Menzies, Sydney #164/R est:2500-3500 (A.D 1900)

£1071 $1682 €1607 South coast, New South Wales (30x39cm-12x15in) s.d.33 W/C. 25-Nov-2 Christie's, Melbourne #209/R est:2000-3000 (A.D 3000)

£1228 $1867 €1842 Arboretum (36x44cm-14x17in) s. W/C. 19-Aug-2 Joel, Victoria #308/R est:4000-6000 (A.D 3500)

£1354 $2221 €2031 Queensland beach scene (31x40cm-12x16in) s. W/C. 4-Jun-3 Deutscher-Menzies, Melbourne #150/R est:3500-5500 (A.D 3400)

£1530 $2341 €2295 Waterhole (40x53cm-16x21in) s. W/C pencil executed c.1958 prov. 26-Aug-2 Sotheby's, Paddington #714/R est:4000-6000 (A.D 4300)

MACQUEEN, Mary McCartney (1912-1994) Australian

£286 $451 €429 Still life with guitar (15x23cm-6x9in) canvas on board painted c.1947. 27-Nov-2 Deutscher-Menzies, Melbourne #224/R (A.D 800)

Works on paper

£338 $517 €507 Jetty, San Remo (40x53cm-16x21in) s.i.d.58 W/C gouache prov. 26-Aug-2 Sotheby's, Paddington #776 est:300-500 (A.D 950)

£400 $644 €580 Sketch for Aboriginal still life (26x31cm-10x12in) s. gouache. 12-May-3 Joel, Victoria #231/R est:800-1200 (A.D 1000)

MACQUOID, Thomas (1820-1912) British

Works on paper

£620 $961 €930 Rome, Palace of the Caesars. At Florence, Torne Vecchio (24x16cm-9x6in) i. verso W/C over pencil htd white pair. 2-Oct-2 Bonhams, Knowle #18

£850 $1420 €1233 Figures by a fountain in an Italian piazza (54x41cm-21x16in) s.d.1890 W/C. 24-Jun-3 Bonhams, Knightsbridge #51/R

£1650 $2574 €2475 Mosque, Cordova. San Domenico, Granada (44x34cm-17x13in) s.i. one d.1855 one d.1859 W/C pair. 15-Oct-2 Bearnes, Exeter #422/R est:400-600

MACRAE, Elmer (1875-1953) American

Works on paper

£3006 $4750 €4509 Mother and child (56x41cm-22x16in) s. pastel canvas on board. 24-Apr-3 Shannon's, Milford #194/R est:2000-3000

MACREAU, Michel (1935-) French

£1899 $3000 €3000 Etude pour crucifie (200x138cm-79x54in) s.d.1961. 2-Dec-2 Tajan, Paris #202

Works on paper

£884 $1406 €1300 Portrait (56x13cm-22x5in) s.d.1987 verso pigment panel. 24-Mar-3 Cornette de St.Cyr, Paris #25/R

McRICKARD, James P (1872-1947) American

£416 $650 €624 Mountains near New Milford, Ct (51x61cm-20x24in) s. i.stretcher. 12-Oct-2 Neal Auction Company, New Orleans #1420

MACRIS, Constantin Georges (1917-1984) French/Egyptian

£270 $422 €400 Paysage (60x73cm-24x29in) s. mono.d.verso. 31-Mar-3 Rossini, Paris #110

MACRUM, George (1888-?) American

£641 $1000 €962 Valley of the Dordogne (36x46cm-14x18in) s. s.i.verso board prov. 18-Sep-2 Boos Gallery, Michigan #190/R

McSWEENEY, Sean (1935-) Irish

£685 $1075 €1000 Bogland waters (24x14cm-9x6in) s.d.1987 s.i.verso board. 15-Apr-3 De Veres Art Auctions, Dublin #134/R est:1000-1500

£753 $1183 €1100 The white road (22x16cm-9x6in) s. i.verso. 15-Apr-3 De Veres Art Auctions, Dublin #133/R est:1000-1500

£1043 $1669 €1450 Coastal landscape (18x25cm-7x10in) s. board. 13-May-3 Thomas Adams, Dublin #363

£1218 $1912 €1900 Trees in the corner of the garden, Luglass (36x46cm-14x18in) s. i.verso prov. 19-Nov-2 Whyte's, Dublin #166/R est:2000-3000

£1266 $1962 €2000 Shoreline shapes (13x36cm-5x14in) s.d.82 i.verso prov. 24-Sep-2 De Veres Art Auctions, Dublin #87 est:1500-2000

£1384 $2158 €2200 White thorn tree (25x18cm-10x7in) s.d.1983 i.verso board prov. 17-Sep-2 Whyte's, Dublin #25/R est:2000-3000

£1391 $2267 €2100 Fields, Sligo (29x23cm-11x9in) s. 29-Jan-3 Woodwards, Cork #185

£1392 $2158 €2200 Evening bogland (13x36cm-5x14in) s.d.87 i.verso board. 24-Sep-2 De Veres Art Auctions, Dublin #19/R est:2000-3000

£1410 $2214 €2200 Emigrants (30x46cm-12x18in) s.d.1964 board prov. 19-Nov-2 Whyte's, Dublin #170/R est:2000-3000

£1582 $2453 €2500 Wetland (26x34cm-10x13in) s.d.2000 s.i.verso. 24-Sep-2 De Veres Art Auctions, Dublin #93/R est:2500-3500

£1899 $2943 €3000 Bogland (18x26cm-7x10in) s.i.verso board. 24-Sep-2 De Veres Art Auctions, Dublin #171/R est:1500-2500

£2025 $3139 €3200 Sligo bogland (26x36cm-10x14in) s.d.89 i.verso b/. 24-Sep-2 De Veres Art Auctions, Dublin #63/R est:2500-3500

£2138 $3336 €3400 PJ's Lugglass, County Wicklow (25x36cm-10x14in) s.d.1984 board prov.exhib. 17-Sep-2 Whyte's, Dublin #17/R est:3000-4000

£2740 $4301 €4000 Landscape with trees (51x59cm-20x23in) s. 15-Apr-3 De Veres Art Auctions, Dublin #144/R est:3000-4000

£2821 $4428 €4400 Above the lake (61x81cm-24x32in) s.d.1989 s.i.verso board prov. 19-Nov-2 Whyte's, Dublin #24/R est:5000-6000

£3481 $5396 €5500 Wetland (61x81cm-24x32in) s.d.00 i.verso. 24-Sep-2 De Veres Art Auctions, Dublin #27/R est:6000-8000

£3611 $5742 €5200 Bogland fire (25x36cm-10x14in) s.d.1988 board exhib. 29-Apr-3 Whyte's, Dublin #12/R est:3000-4000

£4161 $6699 €6200 Shoreline Cloonagh (36x46cm-14x18in) s.d.1990 s.i.verso board exhib. 18-Feb-3 Whyte's, Dublin #39/R est:3000-4000

£4873 $7554 €7700 Pools ath na Beith Eoige (61x137cm-24x54in) s.i.d.86 verso triptych. 24-Sep-2 De Veres Art Auctions, Dublin #144 est:5000-7000

£5616 $8818 €8200 Dried up bog (59x79cm-23x31in) s.d.88 s.i.d.verso board. 15-Apr-3 De Veres Art Auctions, Dublin #3273/R est:5000-7000

£5772 $9293 €8600 Beach (51x71cm-20x28in) s.d.1963 board exhib. 18-Feb-3 Whyte's, Dublin #54/R est:3000-4000

Works on paper

£769 $1208 €1200 Seafield, Sligo. Overgrown garden (15x20cm-6x8in) s. crayon wash pair. 19-Nov-2 Hamilton Osborne King, Dublin #470

McSWINEY, Eugène (1866-?) British

£2070 $3002 €3250 Lovers by a river (40x60cm-16x24in) 29-May-2 Woodwards, Cork #210

MacTAGGART, Sir William (1903-1981) British

£2000 $3280 €3000 Near Drumnadrochit (30x34cm-12x13in) s. board. 3-Jun-3 Sotheby's, Olympia #123/R est:800-1200

£2200 $3608 €3300 Glimpse of Loch Tay (28x49cm-11x19in) board prov. 3-Jun-3 Sotheby's, Olympia #125/R est:800-1200

£2300 $3519 €3450 Glimpse of Loch Tay (30x50cm-12x20in) s. board. 22-Aug-2 Bonhams, Edinburgh #1037/R est:2500-4000

£2400 $3888 €3600 October at Gullane (40x50cm-16x20in) s.d.69 board exhib. 23-May-3 Lyon & Turnbull, Edinburgh #57/R est:2000-3000

£3200 $5184 €4800 September sunshine (17x25cm-7x10in) s.d.65 board. 23-May-3 Lyon & Turnbull, Edinburgh #10/R est:1200-1800

£3500 $5425 €5250 Gnarled trees (71x91cm-28x36in) s.indis.d. painted c.1951-52 exhib. 31-Oct-2 Christie's, London #160/R est:4000-6000

£3500 $5670 €5250 Silver sea (17x25cm-7x10in) s. board. 23-May-3 Lyon & Turnbull, Edinburgh #9/R est:1200-1800

£3800 $5890 €5700 Deserted Highland Loch (37x49cm-15x19in) s. board. 6-Dec-2 Lyon & Turnbull, Edinburgh #45/R est:1500-2000

£3800 $6232 €5700 Winter evening, east Salton (31x51cm-12x20in) s. board prov. 3-Jun-3 Sotheby's, Olympia #124/R est:1000-1500

£4200 $6426 €6300 Golden harvest (18x25cm-7x10in) s.d.71 board exhib. 22-Aug-2 Bonhams, Edinburgh #1171/R est:1500-2000

£4500 $6885 €6750 Urquhart Castle, Loch Ness (39x50cm-15x20in) s. indis d. panel. 22-Aug-2 Bonhams, Edinburgh #1126/R est:4000-6000

£5400 $8262 €8100 Taarbek (30x72cm-12x28in) s. board. 22-Aug-2 Bonhams, Edinburgh #959/R est:5000-7000

£10000 $16200 €15000 Still life of apples and roses (48x38cm-19x15in) s. board. 23-May-3 Lyon & Turnbull, Edinburgh #36/R est:6000-8000

Works on paper

£520 $811 €780 Hillside (21x27cm-8x11in) s. conte. 17-Oct-2 Bonhams, Edinburgh #96

McTAGGART, William (1835-1910) British

£1800 $2808 €2700 Picking flowers (39x29cm-15x11in) s.d.1876. 14-Apr-3 Sotheby's, London #70/R est:2000-3000

£7000 $10850 €10500 Homeward bound (33x25cm-13x10in) s.indis.d. panel exhib.lit. 31-Oct-2 Christie's, London #95/R est:7000-10000

£8000 $12480 €12000 Among the bents (32x47cm-13x19in) s.d.1902. 10-Apr-3 Bonhams, Edinburgh #135/R est:7000-10000

£10000 $15500 €15000 Soldiers return (29x34cm-11x13in) s. prov.lit. 6-Dec-2 Lyon & Turnbull, Edinburgh #29/R est:10000-15000

£11000 $17710 €16500 Fisher boy (45x32cm-18x13in) s.d.1870 prov.exhib.lit. 20-Feb-3 Christie's, London #223/R est:18000

£16000 $24800 €24000 Watching the boat (77x56cm-30x22in) s. prov.lit. 6-Dec-2 Lyon & Turnbull, Edinburgh #82/R est:6000-8000

£22000 $33440 €33000 Going to sea (46x39cm-18x15in) mono.d.1866 s.i.verso panel prov.exhib.lit. 28-Aug-2 Sotheby's, London #1055/R est:15000-20000

Works on paper

£5000 $7800 €7500 Playing in the hay (25x35cm-10x14in) s. W/C. 14-Apr-3 Sotheby's, London #73/R est:3000-5000

£5200 $8060 €7800 Where St Columba landed (34x53cm-13x21in) s.d.1904 W/C prov.exhib.lit. 6-Dec-2 Lyon & Turnbull, Edinburgh #3/R est:2000-3000

£7000 $10920 €10500 Bringing home the catch (30x52cm-12x20in) W/C. 14-Apr-3 Sotheby's, London #74/R est:3000-5000

MACULLUM, Hamilton (19/20th C) British
Works on paper
£390 $632 €585 Gathering seaweed (41x33cm-16x13in) i. s.verso W/C. 21-Jan-3 Bonhams, Knightsbridge #236/R

McVEY, Leza (20th C) American
Sculpture
£15484 $24000 €23226 Stoppered bottle (19cm-7in) sig. stoneware lit. 8-Dec-2 Wright, Chicago #188/R est:15000-20000

McVITTIE, Robert (1935-) Canadian
£1091 $1789 €1637 Morning watch (51x76cm-20x30in) s. s.i.verso. 6-Feb-3 Heffel, Vancouver #035/R est:1500-2000 (C.D 2750)

McWHANNELL, Richard (1952-) New Zealander
£775 $1278 €1124 Federal Street, morning (27x31cm-11x12in) s.verso hardboard prov. 1-Jul-3 Peter Webb, Auckland #59/R est:2500-3500 (NZ.D 2200)
£1736 $2708 €2604 Portrait of Sappho Banks (38x30cm-15x12in) s.i.d.1995. 8-Apr-3 Peter Webb, Auckland #71/R est:5000-7000 (NZ.D 5000)

MACWHIRTER, Agnes Eliza (1837-?) British
£560 $874 €840 Quiet stream in Arran (31x44cm-12x17in) s.i.stretcher. 17-Oct-2 Lawrence, Crewkerne #491/R

MacWHIRTER, John (1839-1911) British
£800 $1304 €1160 First bud of May (53x43cm-21x17in) s. 17-Jul-3 Thomson, Roddick & Medcalf, Carlisle #20/R
£1000 $1600 €1500 Young girl returning from the forest with sheep and forage (74x46cm-29x18in) s. i.stretcher. 15-Mar-3 Eldred, East Dennis #76/R est:3000-3500
£1250 $2000 €1813 Autumn by the river (46x61cm-18x24in) s. 17-May-3 New Orleans Auction, New Orleans #1076/R est:2000-4000
£1300 $2028 €1950 Over the sea (74x47cm-29x19in) s. 17-Sep-2 Sotheby's, Olympia #10/R est:400-600
£1401 $2200 €2102 Into the woods (51x76cm-20x30in) s. 22-Nov-2 Skinner, Boston #16/R est:3500-4500
£1473 $2327 €2210 The Shepherds Bridge, Arran (51x76cm-20x30in) s. exhib. 27-Nov-2 Falkkloos, Malmo #77871/R est:12000 (S.KR 21000)
£2000 $3120 €3000 Casting on the loch (28x44cm-11x17in) s. 14-Apr-3 Sotheby's, London #31/R est:2000-3000
£2146 $3391 €3219 Gatherers (71x91cm-28x36in) s. 3-Apr-3 Heffel, Vancouver #57/R est:7000-9000 (C.D 5000)
£3000 $4860 €4500 Woodland path (45x35cm-18x14in) mono. i.verso. 23-May-3 Lyon & Turnbull, Edinburgh #8/R est:3000-4000
£4500 $7245 €6750 Silver birches (81x171cm-32x67in) s. canvas on panel prov.exhib.lit. 20-Feb-3 Christie's, London #277/R
£7500 $11400 €11250 Land of the mountain and flood (192x214cm-76x84in) s.i. s.on stretcher. 28-Aug-2 Sotheby's, London #921/R est:3000-5000
£12000 $19320 €18000 Track of the hurricane (152x215cm-60x85in) s. prov.exhib.lit. 20-Feb-3 Christie's, London #360/R est:20000
Works on paper
£330 $515 €495 Italian lake (22x14cm-9x6in) s. W/C. 15-Oct-2 Bearnes, Exeter #377
£800 $1272 €1200 Highland salmon river (36x51cm-14x20in) s. W/C. 19-Mar-3 John Nicholson, Haslemere #1086/R
£1200 $1992 €1800 On the Italians lakes. Village in Furka Pass, Switzerland (24x33cm-9x13in) mono. W/C two. 12-Jun-3 Bonhams, New Bond Street #680/R est:1500-2000

MACWHITE, Paula (20th C) Irish
£685 $1075 €1000 By the fireside (54x65cm-21x26in) s. exhib. 15-Apr-3 De Veres Art Auctions, Dublin #89/R est:1200-1600

McWILLIAM, F E (1909-1992) British
Sculpture
£3500 $5425 €5250 Seated woman (26cm-10in) init.num.1/3 dark brown pat. 4-Dec-2 Christie's, Kensington #499/R est:1500-2000

McWILLIAM, Frederick Edward (1909-1992) British
Sculpture
£1500 $2325 €2250 Lazarus and his sister (42cm-17in) init. resin. 4-Dec-2 Christie's, Kensington #503/R est:1000-1500
£3734 $5788 €5900 Flat figure (33cm-13in) s.num.2/5 bronze. 24-Sep-2 De Veres Art Auctions, Dublin #134/R est:5000-7000
£6000 $9360 €9000 Pianist (44cm-17in) init. green brown pat. bronze prov. 25-Mar-3 Bonhams, New Bond Street #128/R est:2000-3000
£14000 $22400 €21000 Man and wife (18cm-7in) dark brown pat bronze sold with marble base prov. 15-May-3 Christie's, Kensington #245/R est:6000-8000
Works on paper
£2416 $3890 €3600 Women of Belfast (28x39cm-11x15in) s.d.1974 pen ink wash prov. 18-Feb-3 Whyte's, Dublin #34/R est:3000-4000

McWILLIAMS, Joe (1938-) Irish
Works on paper
£400 $584 €600 Carson (30x30cm-12x12in) s.d.85 mixed media. 12-Jun-2 John Ross, Belfast #296
£400 $584 €600 Head study, Carson (30x30cm-12x12in) s.d.85 mixed media. 12-Jun-2 John Ross, Belfast #297

MAD-JAROVA, Antoinette (1937-) Bulgarian
£3613 $5708 €5600 Synergie (50x61cm-20x24in) s. 17-Dec-2 Rossini, Paris #110/R

MADARASZ, Adelina Katona (1871-1962) Hungarian
£450 $711 €675 Peonies in a vase on a draped ledge (73x100cm-29x39in) s. 14-Nov-2 Christie's, Kensington #23

MADDEN, John McIntosh (1856-1922) New Zealander
£424 $661 €636 Lyttleton Harbour (16x24cm-6x9in) s. s.i.verso board. 5-Nov-2 Peter Webb, Auckland #75 est:1500-2500 (NZ.D 1350)
£505 $809 €732 Valley of the dart (29x34cm-11x13in) s. board oval. 13-May-3 Watson's, Christchurch #49/R (NZ.D 1400)

MADDEN, Orval Clinton (1892-1971) Canadian
£324 $516 €470 Buttermilk Falls, Haliburton (42x51cm-17x20in) s. board. 1-May-3 Heffel, Vancouver #65/R (C.D 750)

MADDOCK, Bea (1934-) Australian
£4781 $7841 €6932 Figure with a crucifixion (162x122cm-64x48in) s.d.68 i.verso composition board. 4-Jun-3 Deutscher-Menzies, Melbourne #181/R est:9000-12000 (A.D 12000)

MADDOX, Alan (1948-2000) New Zealander
£764 $1200 €1146 Cross (41x34cm-16x13in) oil acrylic on paper. 10-Dec-2 Peter Webb, Auckland #65/R est:2000-3000 (NZ.D 2400)
£796 $1250 €1194 Butterflies (49x39cm-19x15in) oil on card. 10-Dec-2 Peter Webb, Auckland #66/R est:3000-5000 (NZ.D 2500)
£954 $1536 €1431 X Series (30x41cm-12x16in) init.d.10/84 enamel paper. 7-May-3 Dunbar Sloane, Auckland #72/R (NZ.D 2700)
£1053 $1642 €1580 Blues, yellow, white (43x26cm-17x10in) 27-Mar-3 International Art Centre, Auckland #27/R est:2500-3500 (NZ.D 3000)
£1060 $1707 €1590 Untitled painted door (198x76cm-78x30in) oil on wooden door. 7-May-3 Dunbar Sloane, Auckland #82/R (NZ.D 3000)
£1176 $1834 €1764 Untitled (43x35cm-17x14in) s.d.1994 oil on paper. 7-Nov-2 International Art Centre, Auckland #8/R est:2500-3500 (NZ.D 3750)
£1286 $1994 €1929 Untitled (121x91cm-48x36in) acrylic. 4-Dec-2 Dunbar Sloane, Auckland #52/R est:4000-6000 (NZ.D 4000)
£2993 $4938 €4340 Schule (120x80cm-47x31in) init.d.11.1984 acrylic on paper. 1-Jul-3 Peter Webb, Auckland #72/R est:6000-8000 (NZ.D 8500)
£3448 $5379 €5172 Light as a feather little bird (90x91cm-35x36in) s. d.1/2/00. 7-Nov-2 International Art Centre, Auckland #29/R est:10000-15000 (NZ.D 11000)
£3472 $5417 €5208 Grid (156x128cm-61x50in) acrylic hessian. 8-Apr-3 Peter Webb, Auckland #64/R est:15000-25000 (NZ.D 10000)
£3659 $5598 €5489 Untitled (127x146cm-50x57in) init.d.79 oil on loose canvas. 21-Aug-2 Dunbar Sloane, Auckland #15/R est:8000-16000 (NZ.D 12000)
£3822 $6000 €5733 Loose grid (122x122cm-48x48in) 10-Dec-2 Peter Webb, Auckland #64/R est:10000-15000 (NZ.D 12000)
£4167 $6500 €6251 Grid (122x122cm-48x48in) 8-Apr-3 Peter Webb, Auckland #65/R est:10000-15000 (NZ.D 12000)
£7042 $11620 €10211 Grid (167x167cm-66x66in) 1-Jul-3 Peter Webb, Auckland #29/R est:15000-25000 (NZ.D 20000)
£9507 $15687 €13785 Untitled - abstract (120x115cm-47x45in) oil collage on board prov. 1-Jul-3 Peter Webb, Auckland #30/R est:18000-25000 (NZ.D 27000)
Works on paper
£446 $700 €669 Abstract (24x20cm-9x8in) mixed media. 10-Dec-2 Peter Webb, Auckland #69/R est:1500-2500 (NZ.D 1400)
£601 $967 €902 Untitled (41x34cm-16x13in) W/C acrylic. 7-May-3 Dunbar Sloane, Auckland #100 (NZ.D 1700)
£632 $985 €948 Cross grid (40x57cm-16x22in) s.d.1983 W/C. 27-Mar-3 International Art Centre, Auckland #25/R (NZ.D 1800)
£702 $1095 €1053 To an aisle of blue scoria (38x49cm-15x19in) s.d.1993 W/C. 27-Mar-3 International Art Centre, Auckland #201/R (NZ.D 2000)
£965 $1505 €1448 Dear Peter (31x45cm-12x18in) s. mixed media prov. 27-Mar-3 International Art Centre, Auckland #30/R (NZ.D 2750)
£1088 $1729 €1632 Loose abstract (61x49cm-24x19in) init.d.1982 mixed media. 25-Feb-3 Peter Webb, Auckland #6/R est:1500-2500 (NZ.D 3100)

MADDOX, Conroy (1912-) British

£4200 $6636 €6300 Playgrounds of Salpetreier (97x76cm-38x30in) s.d.75 s.i.d.1975 verso prov. 27-Nov-2 Sotheby's, Olympia #294/R est:3000-5000

Works on paper

£350 $574 €525 Personage en ciel (29x20cm-11x8in) s.d.54 gouache. 3-Jun-3 Sotheby's, Olympia #296/R
£500 $775 €750 Bird trap (38x56cm-15x22in) s.d.41 W/C bodycol. 4-Dec-2 Christie's, Kensington #353/R
£550 $853 €825 Surreal composition (35x50cm-14x20in) s.d.40 W/C htd white. 4-Dec-2 Christie's, Kensington #352/R
£550 $902 €825 Magnetic creatures (35x31cm-14x12in) s.d.39 gouache. 3-Jun-3 Sotheby's, Olympia #298/R
£700 $1141 €1015 Storehouse of illusions (40x29cm-16x11in) s.d.61 gouache. 15-Jul-3 Bonhams, Knightsbridge #145/R
£750 $1230 €1125 Ancient beemaster's farewell (37x26cm-15x10in) s.d.69 ink gouache. 3-Jun-3 Sotheby's, Olympia #297/R

MADELAIN, Gustave (1867-1944) French

£355 $550 €533 Rampe du pont Louviers (25x38cm-10x15in) s. panel prov. 16-Jul-2 Arthur James, Florida #371
£529 $788 €794 Impasse pers (45x37cm-18x15in) s.i. 25-Jun-2 Koller, Zurich #6656 (S.FR 1200)
£823 $1284 €1300 Quai de la Seine a Notre Dame (61x49cm-24x19in) s. 20-Oct-2 Claude Boisgirard, Paris #20
£962 $1500 €1443 Bassin de St. Nazaire (33x41cm-13x16in) s. i.verso panel prov. 5-Nov-2 Arthur James, Florida #161
£1154 $1800 €1731 Le parc Notre Dame (46x56cm-18x22in) s. i.stretcher prov. 5-Nov-2 Arthur James, Florida #162
£1161 $1800 €1742 Nature morte en la coupe de fruits (46x64cm-18x25in) s.i.verso board prov. 16-Jul-2 Arthur James, Florida #50
£1290 $2000 €1935 Tours a semur en euxois (51x71cm-20x28in) s. board prov. 16-Jul-2 Arthur James, Florida #100
£1538 $2400 €2307 Vue d'autun (46x61cm-18x24in) s. prov. 5-Nov-2 Arthur James, Florida #159
£1614 $2502 €2550 La Seine a Rouen (33x45cm-13x18in) s. panel. 29-Sep-2 Eric Pillon, Calais #131/R
£2857 $4543 €4200 Paris, Notre-Dame, les quais sous la pluie (73x92cm-29x36in) s.d.1933. 26-Feb-3 Artcurial Briest, Paris #259/R est:3800-4500

MADELINE, Paul (1863-1920) French

£962 $1500 €1443 Industrial harbour scene (30x41cm-12x16in) s. 18-Sep-2 Alderfer's, Hatfield #293 est:200-400
£1582 $2453 €2500 Poste de commandement sur les pentes de l'hartmann (33x43cm-13x17in) s.i.d.mai 1917 paper on canvas. 29-Sep-2 Eric Pillon, Calais #173/R
£3228 $5003 €5100 Maison dans la vallee (65x81cm-26x32in) s. 29-Sep-2 Eric Pillon, Calais #142/R
£3544 $5494 €5600 Cabane a l'oree du bois (38x46cm-15x18in) s.d.1918. 29-Sep-2 Eric Pillon, Calais #172/R
£3671 $5800 €5800 Promenade en barque sur la Creuse (65x81cm-26x32in) studio st. prov. 2-Dec-2 Tajan, Paris #24/R
£4304 $6800 €6800 Port de La Rochelle (55x46cm-22x18in) st.sig. 26-Nov-2 Camard, Paris #43/R est:9000
£4861 $7729 €7000 Village en bord de riviere (46x55cm-18x22in) s. painted c.1918. 29-Apr-3 Artcurial Briest, Paris #164/R est:7500-8500
£5696 $8829 €9000 La cote rocheuse (46x35cm-18x14in) s. 29-Sep-2 Eric Pillon, Calais #148/R
£5769 $9000 €8654 Rue en Bretagne (65x53cm-26x21in) s. prov. 12-Apr-3 Weschler, Washington #531/R est:7000-9000

Works on paper

£8219 $12904 €12000 Valee de la Ceuse (82x100cm-32x39in) s. pastel. 21-Apr-3 Rabourdin & Choppin de Janvry, Paris #71/R est:13000-15000

MADERSON, Arthur (1942-) British

£823 $1275 €1300 Point of sunset (36x36cm-14x14in) s. board. 25-Sep-2 James Adam, Dublin #35/R
£959 $1496 €1400 Study of River Shelane, near Cappoquinn (44x52cm-17x20in) s. board. 8-Apr-3 James Adam, Dublin #19/R
£1141 $1837 €1700 September evening near Cappoquin (27x18cm-11x7in) s. s.i.verso oil pastel board. 18-Feb-3 Whyte's, Dublin #218/R est:1000-1200
£1795 $2818 €2800 Fishing from the shadows (122x81cm-48x32in) s. i.verso panel. 19-Nov-2 Whyte's, Dublin #116/R est:3000-4000
£1879 $3026 €2800 Stepping out at Tallow Fair (60x44cm-24x17in) s. s.i.d.1992 verso board. 18-Feb-3 Whyte's, Dublin #163/R est:2000-2500
£2013 $3140 €3200 Horse fair (84x114cm-33x45in) s. board. 17-Sep-2 Whyte's, Dublin #169/R est:3500-4500
£2013 $3242 €3000 Figure at market stall (91x61cm-36x24in) s. oil pastel board. 18-Feb-3 Whyte's, Dublin #217/R est:2000-3000
£2516 $3925 €4000 Dusk, Cappoquin fair (80x118cm-31x46in) s. s.i.verso panel. 17-Sep-2 Whyte's, Dublin #185/R est:4000-5000
£3270 $5102 €5200 Evening study by the pool (117x79cm-46x31in) s. s.i.verso panel. 17-Sep-2 Whyte's, Dublin #157/R est:4000-5000
£3590 $5636 €5600 Autumn evening tallow horse fair (81x122cm-32x48in) s. s.i.verso panel. 19-Nov-2 Whyte's, Dublin #224/R est:3000-4000

Works on paper

£1899 $2943 €3000 Dusk, Le Vigan, South of France (108x78cm-43x31in) mixed media. 25-Sep-2 James Adam, Dublin #143/R est:3000-5000
£2254 $3741 €3200 Evening practice (79x79cm-31x31in) s. mixed media. 10-Jun-3 James Adam, Dublin #158/R est:2000-3000
£2746 $4559 €3900 Market day, Le Vigan (79x107cm-31x42in) s. mixed media. 10-Jun-3 James Adam, Dublin #238/R est:3000-5000
£4167 $6625 €6000 Top the falls, cirque de Navecelles, Midi, France (112x79cm-44x31in) s. mixed media. 29-Apr-3 Whyte's, Dublin #166/R est:4000-5000
£4306 $6846 €6200 Bridge at St. Jean du gard, Midi, France (79x112cm-31x44in) s. mixed media. 29-Apr-3 Whyte's, Dublin #165/R est:4000-5000
£7971 $13072 €11000 Sunday morning (117x117cm-46x46in) s.i.verso mixed media. 28-May-3 Bonhams & James Adam, Dublin #91/R est:4000-6000

MADGE, Donald James (1920-) South African

£256 $400 €384 Street scene, District Six (58x73cm-23x29in) s. board. 11-Nov-2 Stephan Welz, Johannesburg #221 (SA.R 4000)
£269 $420 €404 Waenhuiskrans (29x60cm-11x24in) s. board. 11-Nov-2 Stephan Welz, Johannesburg #463 (SA.R 4200)
£288 $450 €432 Extensive landscape with farmhouse (72x112cm-28x44in) s.d.56. 11-Nov-2 Stephan Welz, Johannesburg #281 (SA.R 4500)
£361 $581 €542 Night street scene in District Six (38x45cm-15x18in) s. board. 12-May-3 Stephan Welz, Johannesburg #220 est:2000-3000 (SA.R 4200)
£585 $941 €878 Cape farmstead with figures (47x74cm-19x29in) s. canvas on board. 12-May-3 Stephan Welz, Johannesburg #213 est:3000-5000 (SA.R 6800)

MADGWICK, Clive (1934-) British

£250 $393 €375 Partridges in winter landscape (39x29cm-15x11in) 14-Dec-2 Lacy Scott, Bury St.Edmunds #481
£250 $393 €375 Pheasants in winter landscape (39x29cm-15x11in) 14-Dec-2 Lacy Scott, Bury St.Edmunds #482
£280 $437 €420 Spring cattle grazing within an autumn landscape (10x20cm-4x8in) board. 21-Sep-2 Lacy Scott, Bury St.Edmunds #370
£290 $455 €435 Boating river scene with bridge, cottage and figures (60x90cm-24x35in) 14-Dec-2 Lacy Scott, Bury St.Edmunds #483/R
£420 $651 €630 Cub hunting (35x55cm-14x22in) s. 30-Sep-2 Bonhams, Ipswich #518a

MADIGAN, Rosemary (1926-) Australian

Sculpture

£8214 $12650 €12321 Reclining nude (50cm-20in) bronze executed 1993 prov. 8-Sep-2 Sotheby's, Melbourne #39/R est:4000-6000 (A.D 23000)

MADIOL, Adrien Jean (1845-1892) Dutch

£1379 $2207 €2000 Les bonnes nouvelles (57x47cm-22x19in) s.d.1877. 17-Mar-3 Horta, Bruxelles #191 est:3000-4000

MADLENER, Jorg (attrib) (1939-) Belgian/German

£252 $387 €400 Rond point (100x73cm-39x29in) mono.1963. 22-Oct-2 Campo, Vlaamse Kaai #550

MADLENER, Josef (1881-1967) German

£1146 $1789 €1800 Christ risen (71x55cm-28x22in) s.d.1942. 7-Nov-2 Allgauer, Kempten #2892/R est:1800
£3694 $5763 €5800 Evening crib scene (55x49cm-22x19in) s. lit. 7-Nov-2 Allgauer, Kempten #2891/R est:2500

MADOU, Jean Baptiste (1796-1877) Belgian

£2800 $4396 €4200 Two gentlemen reading a letter (32x25cm-13x10in) s.d.1861 prov. 21-Nov-2 Christie's, Kensington #68/R est:2000-3000
£4430 $6911 €7000 Scene du rue (28x26cm-11x10in) s.d.1869. 16-Oct-2 Hotel des Ventes Mosan, Brussels #157/R est:7800-8200
£14388 $23022 €20000 Les boudeurs (26x32cm-10x13in) s.d.1862 panel. 19-May-3 Horta, Bruxelles #108/R est:12000-18000

Works on paper

£331 $529 €460 Esquisse d'apres nature (27x44cm-11x17in) pencil. 19-May-3 Horta, Bruxelles #109
£705 $1135 €1050 Homme assis (40x31cm-16x12in) mono. chl saguine. 18-Feb-3 Vanderkindere, Brussels #33
£759 $1199 €1100 Etude de personnages (30x36cm-12x14in) mono.d:1872 pencil dr. 2-Apr-3 Vanderkindere, Brussels #1/R
£897 $1409 €1400 L'arrestation (29x26cm-11x10in) s.d.1873 chl htd W/C. 10-Dec-2 Vanderkindere, Brussels #8 est:600-800
£1511 $2417 €2100 La lecon de musique (28x45cm-11x18in) mono.d.1853 chl htd white gouache. 13-May-3 Vanderkindere, Brussels #55/R est:1500-2500
£1745 $2809 €2600 Marchande de cerises (36x29cm-14x11in) s.d.1874 chl wash htd gouache. 18-Feb-3 Vanderkindere, Brussels #13/R
£1793 $2833 €2600 Etude de personnages (36x29cm-14x11in) mono.d.1872 pencil dr. 2-Apr-3 Vanderkindere, Brussels #2/R est:400-600
£3333 $5233 €5200 Etude de personnages d'apres nature (27x44cm-11x17in) s.d.1838 and 1840 verso pierre noire grey ink wash set of 4. 19-Nov-2 Vanderkindere, Brussels #100/R est:2500-4000

£3448 $5517 €5000 Musicians (31x41cm-12x16in) mono.d.1845 black chk W/C gouache exhib.prov. 15-Mar-3 De Vuyst, Lokeren #504/R est:5000-6000

MADOUX, Alfred (19th C) Belgian
£272 $433 €400 Berger et son troupeau (40x60cm-16x24in) s. 18-Mar-3 Campo, Vlaamse Kaai #146

MADRASSI, Luca (1848-1919) Italian
Sculpture
£1474 $2315 €2300 Source (56cm-22in) s. lead lit. 20-Nov-2 Claude Boisgirard, Paris #104/R
£1795 $2818 €2800 Diane chasseresse assise avec son chien (68cm-27in) s. brown pat bronze. 19-Nov-2 Vanderkindere, Brussels #138/R est:2500-3500

MADRAZO DE OCHOA, Federico de (1875-1934) Spanish
£5098 $8361 €7800 Woman in profile (52x45cm-20x18in) 5-Feb-3 Arte, Seville #770/R

MADRAZO Y GARRETA, Raimundo de (1841-1920) Spanish
£9032 $14000 €13548 Portrait of a lady (82x65cm-32x26in) s. indis i. prov. 29-Oct-2 Sotheby's, New York #14/R est:20000-30000
£17419 $27000 €26129 Portrait of a lady in pink ribbons (41x32cm-16x13in) s. panel. 29-Oct-2 Sotheby's, New York #67/R est:30000-40000
£41096 $64110 €60000 Mask (89x69cm-35x27in) s. 8-Apr-3 Ansorena, Madrid #115/R est:60000
£48387 $75000 €72581 Preparing for the costume ball (58x41cm-23x16in) s. panel exhib. 30-Oct-2 Christie's, Rockefeller NY #68/R est:50000-70000
£64516 $100000 €96774 Portrait of Aline leaning on a sofa (67x35cm-26x14in) s. panel prov. 30-Oct-2 Christie's, Rockefeller NY #65/R est:70000-90000
Works on paper
£3973 $6197 €5800 Portrait of lady (62x50cm-24x20in) s. pastel on canvas. 8-Apr-3 Ansorena, Madrid #119/R
£11132 $17143 €17700 Portrait of lady (60x40cm-24x16in) s. pastel dr. 28-Oct-2 Segre, Madrid #91/R est:12000

MADRAZO Y KUNTZ, don Federigo de (1815-1894) Spanish
£5921 $9592 €9000 Portrait of man (44x34cm-17x13in) lit. 21-Jan-3 Ansorena, Madrid #180/R est:9000
Works on paper
£314 $491 €500 Portrait of gentleman (28x24cm-11x9in) pencil dr. 17-Sep-2 Segre, Madrid #17/R
£535 $834 €850 Portrait of boy (29x23cm-11x9in) s.d.1835 pencil dr. 17-Sep-2 Segre, Madrid #3/R
£658 $1066 €1000 Portrait of M Fernz y Camaro (22x17cm-9x7in) s.i. chl dr. 21-Jan-3 Ansorena, Madrid #794/R
£1484 $2300 €2226 Portrait of a man gentleman (24x20cm-9x8in) s.i. pencil ink prov. 29-Oct-2 Sotheby's, New York #115/R est:2000-3000

MADRIGALI, Olynthe (20th C) ?
£638 $1034 €900 Port Tunisien (33x40cm-13x16in) s. panel. 23-May-3 Camard, Paris #63/R
£9554 $14904 €15000 Villefranche-sur-Mer (166x248cm-65x98in) s. 6-Nov-2 Gioffredo, Nice #10/R

MADRITSCH, Karl (1908-1986) Swiss
£349 $545 €524 Barn in landscape (32x40cm-13x16in) s. board. 20-Nov-2 Fischer, Luzern #2175/R (S.FR 800)
£609 $950 €914 Circus scene (51x34cm-20x13in) s. 16-Sep-2 Philippe Schuler, Zurich #3213/R (S.FR 1400)

MADSEN, A P (1822-1911) Danish
£345 $549 €518 Horse in field (35x45cm-14x18in) init. 5-May-3 Rasmussen, Vejle #604/R (D.KR 3700)
£490 $764 €735 Dog (20x25cm-8x10in) mono.d.1860. 23-Sep-2 Rasmussen, Vejle #209/R (D.KR 5800)
£503 $799 €755 Landscape with sheep (24x32cm-9x13in) s.d.1879. 10-Mar-3 Rasmussen, Vejle #544 (D.KR 5400)
£708 $1125 €1062 Landscape with sheep (41x55cm-16x22in) s.d.1889. 10-Mar-3 Rasmussen, Vejle #147/R (D.KR 7600)

MADSEN, Andreas Peter (1822-1911) Danish
£464 $732 €696 Landscape with shepherd resting (21x30cm-8x12in) s.d.1852 panel. 13-Nov-2 Kunsthallen, Copenhagen #46/R (D.KR 5400)

MADYOL, Jacques (1871-1950) Belgian
£514 $801 €750 Choux rouges a Coxyde (50x65cm-20x26in) s.i.d.1929 verso. 14-Apr-3 Horta, Bruxelles #348
£861 $1403 €1300 Fier petit joueur de tennis (77x61cm-30x24in) s.d.1895. 17-Feb-3 Horta, Bruxelles #94/R
£1111 $1833 €1600 Leading the sheep past the mill (107x117cm-42x46in) s.d.1903. 1-Jul-3 Christie's, Amsterdam #168/R est:1500-2000
Works on paper
£1519 $2370 €2400 Repos des chameliers (46x64cm-18x25in) s. mixed media. 16-Sep-2 Horta, Bruxelles #69

MAECKELBERGHE, Margo (1932-) British
£600 $936 €900 Landscape (61x107cm-24x42in) s.i.d.1964 board. 17-Oct-2 David Lay, Penzance #1539
£1500 $2355 €2250 Bisected yellow - West Penwith landscape Cornwall (58x118cm-23x46in) s.d.1971 board. 10-Dec-2 Lane, Penzance #89 est:1500-1800

MAEHLE, Ole (1904-1990) Norwegian
£366 $575 €549 Apple blossom time (46x59cm-18x23in) s. 25-Nov-2 Blomqvist, Lysaker #1198 (N.KR 4200)

MAEHLY, Otto (1869-1953) Swiss
£371 $579 €557 Val d'Entremont et Grand Combin (49x65cm-19x26in) s.d.1902. 6-Nov-2 Dobiaschofsky, Bern #796/R (S.FR 850)

MAENPAA, Arvid (1899-1976) Finnish
£275 $450 €420 Dancing on the bridge (13x25cm-5x10in) s. acrylic. 9-Feb-3 Bukowskis, Helsinki #316/R
£513 $800 €810 Horse and cart (7x10cm-3x4in) s. 15-Sep-2 Bukowskis, Helsinki #242/R
£552 $872 €800 Ring dance (7x16cm-3x6in) s.d.1948. 3-Apr-3 Hagelstam, Helsinki #1047
£728 $1135 €1150 The musician (8x12cm-3x5in) s.d.46. 15-Sep-2 Bukowskis, Helsinki #243/R
£897 $1417 €1300 Markkinahattuja (14x22cm-6x9in) s.d.1962. 3-Apr-3 Hagelstam, Helsinki #829/R

MAENTEL, Jacob (1763-1863) American
Works on paper
£198630 $290000 €297945 Portrait of a gentleman, seated in a Federal interior (58x41cm-23x16in) W/C prov.lit. 3-Nov-1 North East Auctions, Portsmouth #762/R est:80000-120000

MAENTEL, Jacob (attrib) (1763-1863) American
Works on paper
£318 $500 €477 Portrait of a gentleman (10x8cm-4x3in) W/C prov. 23-Nov-2 Pook & Pook, Downington #51/R
£892 $1400 €1338 Man in a top hat holding a cane (20x10cm-8x4in) W/C prov. 23-Nov-2 Pook & Pook, Downington #50/R est:1500-2000

MAERTELAERE, Edmond de (1876-1938) Belgian
£1218 $1888 €1900 Still life with white roses (58x51cm-23x20in) s. 7-Dec-2 De Vuyst, Lokeren #91/R est:1000-1500

MAERTENS, Medard (1875-c.1940) Belgian
£313 $497 €450 Nature morte (50x65cm-20x26in) s. 29-Apr-3 Campo & Campo, Antwerp #698
£313 $497 €450 Hiver en ville (39x26cm-15x10in) s. 29-Apr-3 Campo & Campo, Antwerp #699
£321 $497 €500 Boats on the lake (65x80cm-26x31in) s. 7-Dec-2 De Vuyst, Lokeren #205
£556 $883 €800 Dans le bois (60x73cm-24x29in) s. 29-Apr-3 Campo & Campo, Antwerp #696
£616 $968 €900 L'Abbaye de la Cambre (60x70cm-24x28in) s. 15-Apr-3 Galerie Moderne, Brussels #252
£1806 $2871 €2600 Vue de village (70x60cm-28x24in) s. 29-Apr-3 Campo & Campo, Antwerp #697

MAERZ, K (19th C) German
£1026 $1559 €1600 Trip up into the mountains - young herder with cows and sheep (68x87cm-27x34in) s.i.d.1875. 31-Aug-2 Geble, Radolfzell #648/R

MAES, Eugène Remy (1849-1931) Belgian
£3291 $5134 €5200 Cock and chicken on the haystack (35x45cm-14x18in) s. 21-Oct-2 Bernaerts, Antwerp #131/R est:1250-1500
£9000 $15030 €13500 In the farm yard (95x126cm-37x50in) s. 19-Jun-3 Christie's, London #54/R est:10000-15000

MAES, Godfried (1649-1700) Flemish
£1316 $2132 €2000 Saint Jean (150x100cm-59x39in) s. 21-Jan-3 Galerie Moderne, Brussels #188 est:4000-6000
Works on paper
£420 $600 €630 Creation of Adam (18x22cm-7x9in) pen ink. 23-Jan-3 Swann Galleries, New York #207/R

£1911 $2981 €3000 Alpheus and Arethusa (18x23cm-7x9in) bears i.mount brush black ink grey wash prov. 5-Nov-2 Sotheby's, Amsterdam #157/R est:4000-6000
£2166 $3378 €3400 Ascalaphus transformed into an owl (17x23cm-7x9in) bears i.mount brush black ink grey wash prov. 5-Nov-2 Sotheby's, Amsterdam #156/R est:4000-6000

MAES, Jacques (1905-1968) Belgian
£382 $607 €550 Fillettes jouant (38x46cm-15x18in) s. panel. 29-Apr-3 Campo & Campo, Antwerp #204
£513 $795 €800 Interior (50x60cm-20x24in) s.d.51. 7-Dec-2 De Vuyst, Lokeren #206
£514 $807 €750 Nature morte aux prunes (65x80cm-26x31in) s. 15-Apr-3 Galerie Moderne, Brussels #373/R

MAES, Jan Baptist Lodewyck (1794-1856) Flemish
£7547 $11623 €12000 Love letter (96x72cm-38x28in) s.d.1837. 23-Oct-2 Christie's, Amsterdam #109/R est:15000-20000
£12000 $19200 €18000 Letter to the bride, group of figures in an interior (76x102cm-30x40in) s.d.1854. 13-Mar-3 Duke & Son, Dorchester #290/R est:10000-15000

MAES, Nicolaes (1632-1693) Dutch
£3957 $6331 €5500 Portrait of a lady in a black dress (46x35cm-18x14in) indis sig. 14-May-3 Christie's, Amsterdam #119/R est:3000-5000
£4292 $6652 €6438 Portrait of young girl with flower garland (48x56cm-19x22in) s. 3-Oct-2 Koller, Zurich #3025/R est:12000-16000 (S.FR 10000)
£8000 $12560 €12000 Portrait of Rochus van der Does (107x91cm-42x36in) s.d.1675 prov.lit. 11-Dec-2 Christie's, London #51/R
£13605 $21633 €20000 Portrait of Catrina Pels (64x53cm-25x21in) i.verso. 21-Mar-3 Millon & Associes, Paris #15/R est:10500
£29000 $48430 €42050 Portrait of a gentleman, three-quarter length with brown tunic and red cloak (55x46cm-22x18in) s.d.1676 prov.lit. 10-Jul-3 Sotheby's, London #135/R est:15000-20000
£32000 $53440 €46400 Portrait of a young man, full length, with bow and arrow, spaniel and hare (69x57cm-27x22in) s.d.1673 prov.exhib.lit. 10-Jul-3 Sotheby's, London #136/R est:30000-40000
£60000 $94200 €90000 Portrait of a gentleman, in a landscape with a tethered horse beyond (114x92cm-45x36in) s.d.1669 prov.exhib.lit. 12-Dec-2 Sotheby's, London #36/R est:80000-120000
£300000 $471000 €450000 Interior with young girl eating curds and infant in cradle (32x26cm-13x10in) s. panel prov.exhib.lit. 11-Dec-2 Christie's, London #52/R est:250000-350000

Works on paper
£15432 $25000 €23148 Portrait of seated boy (12x10cm-5x4in) chk prov. 22-Jan-3 Christie's, Rockefeller NY #90/R est:8000

MAES, Nicolaes (attrib) (1632-1693) Dutch
£2800 $4368 €4200 Portrait of Cleric (38x31cm-15x12in) panel painted oval prov. 8-Apr-3 Sotheby's, Olympia #141/R est:1000-2000

MAES, Nicolaes (studio) (1632-1693) Dutch
£5915 $9820 €8400 Portrait de jeune garcon en chasseur (77x59cm-30x23in) 15-Jun-3 Anaf, Lyon #149/R est:6000-7000

MAES, Nicolaes (style) (1632-1693) Dutch
£15000 $23400 €22500 Portrait of a young girl, said to be Elizabeth Marco, in a landscape (117x97cm-46x38in) prov. 14-Apr-3 Hamilton Osborne King, Dublin #1510/R est:6000-10000

MAESTOSI, F (19th C) Italian
£8861 $14000 €13292 Sala di Saturno, Palazzo Pitti, Florence (90x115cm-35x45in) s. 23-Apr-3 Christie's, Rockefeller NY #102/R est:10000-15000

MAESTRI, Michelangelo (?-1812) Italian
Works on paper
£426 $711 €600 Amor lento (31x39cm-12x15in) s. gouache after Raphael. 19-Jun-3 Piasa, Paris #34/R
£900 $1403 €1350 Head of Pompey delivered to Caesar (42x31cm-17x12in) init.d.1817 bodycol. 19-Sep-2 Christie's, Kensington #129/R est:800-1200
£1800 $2880 €2700 Trionfo di Bacco. Trionfo di Sileno (40x55cm-16x22in) i. gouache pair. 11-Mar-3 Bonhams, New Bond Street #2/R est:2000-3000
£8000 $12560 €12000 The six hours of the night (45x34cm-18x13in) i. gouache set of six after Raphael. 11-Dec-2 Sotheby's, Olympia #297/R est:8000-10000

MAESTRI, Michelangelo (attrib) (?-1812) Italian
Works on paper
£513 $795 €800 Allegory of Autumn (41x31cm-16x12in) gouache. 4-Dec-2 Piasa, Paris #23

MAETZEL-JOHANNSEN, Dorothea (1886-1930) German
Works on paper
£316 $491 €500 Woman resting (17x20cm-7x8in) mono.d.1919 W/C carpenter's pencil. 28-Sep-2 Ketterer, Hamburg #89/R
£316 $491 €500 Two nudes - dance study (20x15cm-8x6in) mono.d.1919 W/C pencil. 28-Sep-2 Ketterer, Hamburg #90/R
£466 $727 €680 Mother with children (17x22cm-7x9in) mono.d. W/C Indian ink double-sided. 11-Apr-3 Winterberg, Heidelberg #1314

MAEXMONTAN, Lydia (1856-?) Finnish
£272 $433 €400 Lillvik (25x41cm-10x16in) s.d.1902. 24-Mar-3 Bukowskis, Helsinki #168/R

MAEYER, Lod de (1903-1981) Belgian
£475 $750 €750 La moisson (90x105cm-35x41in) s. 26-Nov-2 Palais de Beaux Arts, Brussels #302
£1042 $1656 €1500 Vue de village ensoleille (46x60cm-18x24in) s. 29-Apr-3 Campo & Campo, Antwerp #75/R est:900-1300

MAEYER, Marcel (1920-) Belgian
£2374 $3799 €3300 Booth (160x95cm-63x37in) s. 17-May-3 De Vuyst, Lokeren #247/R est:2600-3000

MAEZTU, Gustavo de (1887-1947) Spanish
Works on paper
£2581 $4077 €4000 Farm (27x35cm-11x14in) s. pastel. 18-Dec-2 Ansorena, Madrid #371/R

MAFAI, Mario (1902-1965) Italian
£7692 $12077 €12000 Still life with six carnations (40x50cm-16x20in) s. s.i.d.1955 verso. 21-Nov-2 Finarte, Rome #292/R est:12000
£8219 $12822 €12000 Portrait of Lina (38x29cm-15x11in) s. board painted 1930. 10-Apr-3 Finarte Semenzato, Rome #167/R
£17419 $27523 €27000 Still life with bottles (60x70cm-24x28in) s. prov. 18-Dec-2 Christie's, Rome #232/R

Works on paper
£2462 $3939 €3570 Peppers (28x40cm-11x16in) s.d.1946 pastel cardboard. 11-Mar-3 Babuino, Rome #143/R

MAFFEI, Alessandro (c.1780-1859) Italian
Works on paper
£700 $1091 €1050 Via di Citta, Siena (22x28cm-9x11in) s. pencil pen ink W/C. 19-Sep-2 Christie's, Kensington #122

MAFFEI, Dario (19th C) Italian
£375 $600 €563 Knights escorting a lady through a sunset landscape (41x56cm-16x22in) s. 15-Mar-3 Eldred, East Dennis #409/R

MAFFEI, Francesco (1620-1660) Italian
£10127 $16000 €16000 Historical scene (81x271cm-32x107in) 27-Nov-2 Finarte, Milan #59/R est:18000-22000
£25000 $39000 €37500 Saints Dominic and Catherine before Madonna and Child (39x44cm-15x17in) 10-Apr-3 Sotheby's, London #82/R est:15000
£67170 $104785 €106800 Soldiers before monarch (73x83cm-29x33in) 22-Sep-2 Semenzato, Venice #305/R

MAFLI, Walter (1915-) Swiss
£261 $404 €392 Grandvaux (33x42cm-13x17in) s. i.verso cardboard. 7-Dec-2 Galerie du Rhone, Sion #406 (S.FR 600)
£368 $570 €552 Landscape in winter at dusk (43x35cm-17x14in) i. board. 24-Sep-2 Koller, Zurich #6657 (S.FR 850)
£417 $671 €626 Neuenburgersee shore (50x61cm-20x24in) s. 7-May-3 Dobiaschofsky, Bern #802/R (S.FR 900)
£469 $770 €680 Portrait of a girl (46x38cm-18x15in) s. 4-Jun-3 Fischer, Luzern #2230/R (S.FR 1000)
£472 $746 €708 Part of the old city covered in snow in Fribourg (46x56cm-18x22in) s.d.1964. 29-Nov-2 Zofingen, Switzerland #2971 (S.FR 1100)
£786 $1234 €1179 Untitled (122x50cm-48x20in) s.d.1958 board. 25-Nov-2 Germann, Zurich #764 est:2000-2500 (S.FR 1800)
£866 $1342 €1299 House in the Jura (81x100cm-32x39in) s. 24-Sep-2 Koller, Zurich #6658/R (S.FR 2000)
£892 $1463 €1293 Sailing ships in harbour (50x122cm-20x48in) s. pavatex. 4-Jun-3 Fischer, Luzern #2232/R est:1500-1700 (S.FR 1900)

£957 $1483 €1436 New York, composition (100x100cm-39x39in) s.d.65 acrylic prov. 7-Dec-2 Galerie du Rhone, Sion #497/R est:3000-5000 (S.FR 2200)

MAGANZA, Giovanni Battista (elder-attrib) (1513-1586) Italian
Works on paper
£709 $1184 €1000 Scene de l'Ancien Testament (15x20cm-6x8in) pen brown ink brown wash. 19-Jun-3 Piasa, Paris #29/R

MAGAZZINI, Salvatore (1955-) Italian
£278 $444 €425 Tizwit (40x50cm-16x20in) s. s.i.verso board. 4-Jan-3 Meeting Art, Vercelli #695
£288 $453 €450 Houses in Sicily (30x40cm-12x16in) s. board. 23-Nov-2 Meeting Art, Vercelli #377
£316 $494 €500 Still life with landscape (50x70cm-20x28in) s. card. 14-Sep-2 Meeting Art, Vercelli #248
£316 $494 €500 Tuscan seascape (50x70cm-20x28in) s. board. 14-Sep-2 Meeting Art, Vercelli #302
£321 $503 €500 Houses in Tunisia (50x70cm-20x28in) s. board. 23-Nov-2 Meeting Art, Vercelli #433/R
£327 $523 €500 Tuscan seascape (50x70cm-20x28in) s. s.i.verso board. 4-Jan-3 Meeting Art, Vercelli #222
£327 $523 €500 Leather shops (70x50cm-28x20in) s.i.verso paper on canvas. 4-Jan-3 Meeting Art, Vercelli #438
£347 $552 €500 Venice (50x70cm-20x28in) s. board. 1-May-3 Meeting Art, Vercelli #58
£347 $552 €500 Jemaa El Ena (50x70cm-20x28in) s. s.i.verso cardboard on canvas. 1-May-3 Meeting Art, Vercelli #362
£359 $575 €550 Marrakech (40x60cm-16x24in) s. s.i.verso board. 4-Jan-3 Meeting Art, Vercelli #488
£380 $592 €600 Tunis (50x70cm-20x28in) s. s.i.verso board. 14-Sep-2 Meeting Art, Vercelli #710/R
£382 $607 €550 Tunis (50x70cm-20x28in) s. board. 1-May-3 Meeting Art, Vercelli #61
£382 $607 €550 Distributor (50x70cm-20x28in) s. s.i.verso board. 1-May-3 Meeting Art, Vercelli #495
£425 $680 €650 Tunis (50x70cm-20x28in) s. s.i.verso board. 4-Jan-3 Meeting Art, Vercelli #704
£443 $691 €700 Marrakech (50x70cm-20x28in) s. board. 14-Sep-2 Meeting Art, Vercelli #890/R
£490 $784 €750 Jemaa El Fna (60x80cm-24x31in) s. s.i.verso board. 4-Jan-3 Meeting Art, Vercelli #510
£510 $811 €750 Marrakech (40x60cm-16x24in) s. board. 1-Mar-3 Meeting Art, Vercelli #536
£510 $811 €750 Meknes (60x70cm-24x28in) s. board. 1-Mar-3 Meeting Art, Vercelli #769
£556 $889 €850 Sharm el Sheik (60x80cm-24x31in) s. s.i.verso board. 4-Jan-3 Meeting Art, Vercelli #372
£577 $906 €900 Venice (50x70cm-20x28in) s. s.i.verso board. 23-Nov-2 Meeting Art, Vercelli #202/R
£641 $1006 €1000 Marrakech (70x100cm-28x39in) s. s.i.verso board. 23-Nov-2 Meeting Art, Vercelli #320
£654 $1046 €1000 Jemaa El Fna (70x100cm-28x39in) s. board lit. 4-Jan-3 Meeting Art, Vercelli #524
£694 $1104 €1000 Marrakech (70x100cm-28x39in) s. s.i.verso board. 1-May-3 Meeting Art, Vercelli #344
£694 $1104 €1000 Marrakech (70x100cm-28x39in) s. board. 1-May-3 Meeting Art, Vercelli #535

MAGERER, H (20th C) ?
£1244 $1767 €1866 Collecting crabs (92x64cm-36x25in) painted c.1870. 26-Mar-2 SOGA, Bratislava #146/R est:65000 (SL.K 79000)

MAGGI, Cesare (1881-1961) Italian
£3741 $5949 €5500 Beach in Liguria (30x40cm-12x16in) s.d.1913 board. 1-Mar-3 Meeting Art, Vercelli #61
£8652 $14017 €12200 Grande veduta del Cervino (70x100cm-28x39in) s. 22-May-3 Stadion, Trieste #266/R est:12000-15000
£14194 $22426 €22000 Winter mountainous landscape (70x100cm-28x39in) s. 18-Dec-2 Finarte, Milan #46/R est:25000
£17610 $27119 €28000 Sunset on the Monviso (71x101cm-28x40in) s.d.1924. 23-Oct-2 Finarte, Milan #171/R
£21739 $35652 €30000 Tramonto sul Monte Bianco (101x100cm-40x39in) s.d.911. 27-May-3 Finarte, Milan #57/R est:32000-35000
£21769 $34612 €32000 Gressoney Valley, Mount Rosa (100x141cm-39x56in) s. 18-Mar-3 Finarte, Milan #89/R
£25362 $41594 €35000 Il Cervino (100x140cm-39x55in) s. 27-May-3 Finarte, Milan #82/R est:30000-34000

MAGGI, Gianpietro (1934-) Italian
£281 $450 €430 Lights and colours in Portofino (40x60cm-16x24in) s. s.i.verso. 4-Jan-3 Meeting Art, Vercelli #680

MAGGIONE, Piero (1931-1995) Italian
£719 $1150 €1100 Brianza (40x50cm-16x20in) s. board. 4-Jan-3 Meeting Art, Vercelli #475
£764 $1215 €1100 Lyrical (59x47cm-23x19in) s. board. 1-May-3 Meeting Art, Vercelli #151
£833 $1325 €1200 Composition (79x62cm-31x24in) s. 1-May-3 Meeting Art, Vercelli #444

MAGGIORANI, Luigi (19th C) Italian
Works on paper
£162 $253 €243 Portrait of gypsy girl with tambourine (54x37cm-21x15in) s. W/C. 6-Aug-2 Peter Webb, Auckland #10/R (NZ.D 550)

MAGGIS, Paolo (1978-) Italian
Works on paper
£1064 $1723 €1500 Per una volta tanto (110x130cm-43x51in) s.i.d.2002 verso mixed media canvas. 20-May-3 Porro, Milan #37/R est:1600-1800

MAGGS, John Charles (1819-1896) British
£680 $1061 €1020 Horse and dog in a stable (46x64cm-18x25in) s.d.1850. 8-Oct-2 Bonhams, Knightsbridge #139/R
£700 $1092 €1050 Oxford to London coach outside an inn in winter (33x66cm-13x26in) s.i.d.1878. 6-Nov-2 Sotheby's, Olympia #56/R
£750 $1245 €1088 Grey with a terrier in a stable (44x63cm-17x25in) s.d.1850 canvas on board. 12-Jun-3 Christie's, Kensington #68/R
£1600 $2544 €2400 Coaching in wind. Rain (46x76cm-18x30in) s.d.1882 pair. 6-Mar-3 Christie's, Kensington #588/R est:1500-2000
£1850 $2923 €2775 Bath to London coach passing a hunt. Bath to London coach at full speed (35x65cm-14x26in) s.i.d.1883 pair. 7-Apr-3 Bonhams, Bath #106/R est:2000-3000
£2201 $3500 €3302 London-Brighton royal mail coach (50x75cm-20x30in) s. prov. 5-Mar-3 Christie's, Rockefeller NY #69/R est:2500-3500
£2600 $4108 €3900 Norwich to London coach in the courtyard of the New Inn (36x66cm-14x26in) s. 13-Nov-2 Halls, Shrewsbury #421/R est:3000-4000

MAGNASCO, Alessandro (1667-1749) Italian
£21605 $35000 €32408 Two monks praying in a landscape (96x77cm-38x30in) prov.lit. 24-Jan-3 Christie's, Rockefeller NY #154/R est:30000-50000
£26000 $40820 €39000 Landscape with monks in prayer (93x71cm-37x28in) prov.lit. 16-Dec-2 Sotheby's, London #36/R est:12000-18000
£61538 $95385 €96000 Mediterranean coastline (110x165cm-43x65in) prov.lit. 4-Dec-2 Christie's, Rome #485/R est:55000-70000
£65385 $101346 €102000 Storm scene with monks and other figures (110x167cm-43x66in) prov.lit. 4-Dec-2 Christie's, Rome #486/R est:55000-70000
Works on paper
£1081 $1686 €1600 Saint Jerome in the desert (15x13cm-6x5in) chk wash prov. 27-Mar-3 Christie's, Paris #23/R

MAGNASCO, Alessandro (attrib) (1667-1749) Italian
£938 $1500 €1407 Landscape with waterfall (68x53cm-27x21in) prov. 14-May-3 Doyle, New York #69 est:3000-4000

MAGNASCO, Alessandro and PERUZZINI, Anton Francesco (17/18th C) Italian
£5000 $7800 €7500 Mountainous river landscape with figures at rest before a town (96x73cm-38x29in) 10-Apr-3 Christie's, Kensington #296/R est:6000-8000

MAGNE, Desire Alfred (1855-1936) French
£1206 $1869 €1809 Still life of flowers (65x92cm-26x36in) s. 4-Dec-2 AB Stockholms Auktionsverk #1865/R est:18000-20000 (S.KR 17000)

MAGNELLI, Alberto (1888-1971) Italian
£7742 $12232 €12000 Red house (52x62cm-20x24in) s.d.924 s.i.d.verso exhib. 18-Dec-2 Christie's, Rome #254/R
£11348 $18383 €16000 Sur fond gris n.12 (41x33cm-16x13in) s.d.63 s.i.d.verso prov. 26-May-3 Christie's, Milan #369/R est:15000-20000
£17722 $28000 €28000 Pierre numero special (53x47cm-21x19in) s.d.32 s.i.d.verso exhib.lit. 30-Nov-2 Farsetti, Prato #705/R est:30000
£18581 $28986 €27872 Rivalites (73x60cm-29x24in) s.d.53 exhib. 18-Sep-2 Kunsthallen, Copenhagen #16/R est:125000 (D.KR 220000)
£27823 $44239 €40900 Peinture (55x46cm-22x18in) s. exhib.lit. 26-Feb-3 Artcurial Briest, Paris #299/R est:18000-22000
£31034 $49034 €45000 Intersections 7 (146x97cm-57x38in) s.d.65 i.d.verso prov.exhib.lit. 2-Apr-3 Christie's, Paris #21/R est:55000
£31250 $51562 €45000 Construction precise (100x81cm-39x32in) s.d.68 s.i.d.verso prov.exhib.lit. 1-Jul-3 Artcurial Briest, Paris #787c/R est:40000-50000
Works on paper
£2069 $3269 €3000 Untitled (41x31cm-16x12in) s. ink felt-tip pen crayon prov. 2-Apr-3 Christie's, Paris #15/R
£2411 $3906 €3400 Composition (13x22cm-5x9in) s.d.64 collage board prov. 26-May-3 Christie's, Milan #72/R est:3000-4000
£3513 $5550 €5480 Composition (63x50cm-25x20in) W/C. 12-Nov-2 Babuino, Rome #80/R
£4028 $6404 €5800 Composition (32x25cm-13x10in) s.d.44 gouache black pencil cardboard lit. 29-Apr-3 Artcurial Briest, Paris #552/R est:2200-2500

£6552 $10352 €9500 Untitled (45x45cm-18x18in) s.d.63 collage cardboard paper prov.exhib. 2-Apr-3 Christie's, Paris #14/R est:7500
£8974 $14090 €14000 Untitled (49x64cm-19x25in) s. gouache chl W/C. 24-Nov-2 Laurence Calmels, Paris #186/R est:7000

MAGNI, Claude (20th C) ?
£302 $468 €480 Composition (60x73cm-24x29in) s. 7-Oct-2 Claude Aguttes, Neuilly #107

MAGNI, Giuseppe (1869-1956) Italian
£1310 $2097 €1900 Jeune fille au broc a eau (31x44cm-12x17in) s. panel. 17-Mar-3 Horta, Bruxelles #208 est:1800-2200
£6000 $10020 €9000 Amusing chapter (51x63cm-20x25in) s. panel. 18-Jun-3 Christie's, Kensington #163/R est:5000-7000

MAGNI, Pietro (1816-1877) Italian
Sculpture
£2070 $3250 €3105 Bust of a woman (75cm-30in) s. marble exec.c.1871. 21-Nov-2 Sotheby's, New York #113/R est:3000-5000

MAGNUS, Camille (1850-?) French
£637 $994 €1000 Fagoteuse dans un paysage (38x55cm-15x22in) s. 11-Nov-2 Horta, Bruxelles #661

MAGNUS, Emma (1856-1936) British
£450 $711 €675 Portia, portrait, this band cloth give here no jot of blood, merchant of Venice (104x71cm-41x28in) s.d.March 1885. 18-Dec-2 John Nicholson, Haslemere #1272/R

MAGNUSSON, Gustaf (1890-1957) Swedish
£388 $609 €563 Boys. prov. 15-Dec-2 Anders Antik, Landskrona #34 (S.KR 5500)

MAGNY, S T (?) ?
Works on paper
£288 $421 €450 Yellow sails (27x35cm-11x14in) pastel. 5-Jun-2 Il Ponte, Milan #191

MAGRATH, William (1838-1918) British
Works on paper
£500 $815 €750 Roman figures near a temple overlooking a bay (33x66cm-13x26in) s. W/C. 11-Feb-3 Gorringes, Lewes #886
£550 $897 €825 Gathering peat (46x76cm-18x30in) W/C. 11-Feb-3 Gorringes, Lewes #885

MAGRITTE, René (1898-1967) Belgian
£55000 $89650 €82500 Shell in the form of an ear (19x24cm-7x9in) s. gouache prov.exhib.lit. 3-Feb-3 Christie's, London #174/R est:60000
£110000 $180400 €165000 Parfum de l'abime (47x33cm-19x13in) s.painted 1928 lit. 4-Feb-3 Christie's, London #323/R est:150000
£160000 $260800 €240000 Echo (55x45cm-22x18in) s. s.i.d.1944 verso prov.exhib.lit. 3-Feb-3 Christie's, London #169/R est:180000
£160000 $267200 €240000 Le Palais de Rideaux II (73x54cm-29x21in) s. i.verso painted 1928 prov.exhib.lit. 23-Jun-3 Sotheby's, London #34/R est:180000-250000
£320000 $534400 €480000 Le colloque sentimental (54x65cm-21x26in) s.i.d.1945 verso prov.exhib.lit. 23-Jun-3 Sotheby's, London #30/R est:300000-400000
£320000 $534400 €464000 Le miroir vivant (41x33cm-16x13in) s. panel painted 1935 prov.exhib.lit. 24-Jun-3 Sotheby's, London #164/R est:100000-150000
£512821 $800000 €769232 La belle captive (53x66cm-21x26in) s. painted 1947 prov.exhib.lit. 5-Nov-2 Sotheby's, New York #38/R est:600000-800000
£520000 $847600 €780000 Victoire (72x53cm-28x21in) s. s.i.d.1939 verso prov.exhib.lit. 3-Feb-3 Christie's, London #166/R est:900000
£616438 $961644 €900000 Femme cachee (73x54cm-29x21in) s. i.on stretcher painted 1929 exhib.lit. 14-Apr-3 Laurence Calmels, Paris #4045/R est:800000
£720000 $1202400 €1044000 La magie noire (73x54cm-29x21in) s. painted 1942 prov.lit. 24-Jun-3 Christie's, London #38/R est:400000-600000
£750000 $1230000 €1125000 Belle de nuit (81x116cm-32x46in) s. painted 1932 prov.exhib.lit. 4-Feb-3 Sotheby's, London #47/R est:900000
£1700000 $2839000 €2550000 L'Acte de Foi (130x97cm-51x38in) s. i.d.1960 verso prov.exhib.lit. 23-Jun-3 Sotheby's, London #24/R est:900000-1200000
£1900000 $3097000 €2850000 Barricades mysterieuses (81x128cm-32x50in) s. s.i.d.1961 verso prov.exhib.lit. 3-Feb-3 Christie's, London #173/R est:2200000
£2361111 $3754167 €3400000 L'oiseau de ciel (68x48cm-27x19in) 1966. 5-May-3 Bernaerts, Antwerp #461/R

Prints
£1899 $3000 €3000 La belle captive (30x12cm-12x5in) s.num.69/100 etching. 26-Nov-2 Sotheby's, Amsterdam #367/R est:900-1200
£2083 $3312 €3000 Untitled. i.num.125/200 col lithograph. 5-May-3 Bernaerts, Antwerp #256
£2083 $3312 €3000 Untitled. i.num.126/200 col lithograph. 5-May-3 Bernaerts, Antwerp #257
£2083 $3312 €3000 Untitled. i.num.127/200 col lithograph. 5-May-3 Bernaerts, Antwerp #258
£2083 $3312 €3000 Untitled. i.num.129/200 col lithograph. 5-May-3 Bernaerts, Antwerp #423
£2083 $3312 €3000 Untitled. i.num.131/200 col lithograph. 5-May-3 Bernaerts, Antwerp #425
£2083 $3312 €3000 Untitled. i.num.132/200 col lithograph. 5-May-3 Bernaerts, Antwerp #426
£2083 $3312 €3000 Untitled. i.num.134/200 col lithograph. 5-May-3 Bernaerts, Antwerp #454
£2083 $3312 €3000 Untitled. i.num.135/200 col lithograph. 5-May-3 Bernaerts, Antwerp #455
£2083 $3312 €3000 Untitled. i.num.137/200 col lithograph. 5-May-3 Bernaerts, Antwerp #457
£2083 $3312 €3000 Untitled. i.num.138/200 col lithograph. 5-May-3 Bernaerts, Antwerp #458
£2083 $3312 €3000 Untitled. i.num.139/200 col lithograph. 5-May-3 Bernaerts, Antwerp #459
£2083 $3312 €3000 Untitled. i.num.140/200 col lithograph. 5-May-3 Bernaerts, Antwerp #460
£2222 $3533 €3200 Untitled. i.num.133/200 col lithograph. 5-May-3 Bernaerts, Antwerp #427
£7692 $12000 €11538 Paysage de Baucis (38x29cm-15x11in) s.i. etching edition of 100. 5-Nov-2 Christie's, Rockefeller NY #167/R est:6000-8000

Sculpture
£40000 $65200 €60000 Bouchon d'epouvante (13x25x31cm-5x10x12in) s.d.1966 bowler hat label prov.exhib.lit. 3-Feb-3 Christie's, London #178/R est:50000
£80000 $133600 €116000 Paysage au clair de lune (30cm-12in) oil glass bottle exec.c.1950 prov.exhib.lit. 24-Jun-3 Christie's, London #45/R est:80000-120000

Works on paper
£890 $1389 €1300 Composition (11x19cm-4x7in) s.i. ball point pen dr. 14-Apr-3 Horta, Bruxelles #127
£1151 $1842 €1600 Pipe smoking. s.i.d.1961 ball-point pen dr lit. 17-May-3 De Vuyst, Lokeren #248 est:750-1000
£1736 $2760 €2500 Caricature de son ami Colinet (32x16cm-13x6in) mono.i. ball point pen dr. 29-Apr-3 Artcurial Briest, Paris #132/R est:2500-3000
£1944 $3091 €2800 Etude pour les chants de maldoror (26x20cm-10x8in) s.i. pencil prov. 29-Apr-3 Artcurial Briest, Paris #131/R est:2600-3000
£2051 $3200 €3077 Etude d'un chien et un chat (14x12cm-6x5in) s. pencil exec.c.1948 exhib. 18-Sep-2 Swann Galleries, New York #52/R est:2500-3500
£2960 $4796 €4500 Locomotive et poisson (10x13cm-4x5in) s. ink pencil col crayon dr exhib. 22-Jan-3 Tajan, Paris #229/R est:5000-7000
£3000 $4620 €4500 L'etoile du matin (14x18cm-6x7in) s. pencil prov.lit. 23-Oct-2 Sotheby's, Olympia #785/R est:2000-3000
£4676 $7482 €6500 Roses. Gallows. March. Window (14x10cm-6x4in) three s. pencil col pen sketches four prov. 15-May-3 Neumeister, Munich #309/R est:4000-5000
£8000 $13120 €12000 Lion rugissant (34x22cm-13x9in) i. gouache double-sided exec.1964 prov. 6-Feb-3 Christie's, London #492/R est:15000
£10000 $16400 €15000 Etude pour 'Lieu commun' (21x28cm-8x11in) s. pencil double-sided prov.exhib. 6-Feb-3 Christie's, London #485/R est:15000
£12950 $21237 €18000 L'aiguillon - envy (27x21cm-11x8in) s. pencil executed c.1945 prov.exhib.lit. 3-Jun-3 Christie's, Amsterdam #297/R est:14000-22000
£14388 $23597 €20000 Projet de fanion du lions club de Bruxelles Cite (30x20cm-12x8in) i.verso gouache executed 1964. 3-Jun-3 Christie's, Amsterdam #286/R est:20000-25000
£35000 $58450 €50750 Les yeux bleus (18x13cm-7x5in) s. s.i.d.1947 verso gouache col crayon prov.exhib.lit. 24-Jun-3 Sotheby's, London #245/R est:40000-60000
£40000 $65600 €60000 Voix du sang (36x26cm-14x10in) s.i.d.1946 s.i.d.verso gouache col crayon over pencil prov.exhib. 5-Feb-3 Sotheby's, London #200/R est:60000
£45000 $73800 €67500 Soir d'orage (36x26cm-14x10in) s.i.d.1946 s.i.d.verso gouache col crayon over pencil prov.exhib. 5-Feb-3 Sotheby's, London #201/R est:65000
£65000 $105950 €97500 Retour au pays natal (15x20cm-6x8in) s. gouache exec.1959 prov.exhib.lit. 3-Feb-3 Christie's, London #183/R est:90000
£82192 $128219 €120000 Paris en 1930 (12x16cm-5x6in) i.verso collage exec.1929 exhib.lit. 14-Apr-3 Laurence Calmels, Paris #4046/R est:50000
£100000 $167000 €145000 Untitled (60x44cm-24x17in) s. W/C black chk pencil collage exec.1926 prov.exhib.lit. 24-Jun-3 Christie's, London #36/R est:70000-100000

£110000 $180400 €165000 Sheherazade (23x19cm-9x7in) s. gouache W/C paper on card exec.1947 prov.exhib.lit. 4-Feb-3 Sotheby's, London #45/R est:160000
£120000 $195600 €180000 Affinites electives (31x19cm-12x7in) s.d.1932 gouache W/C ink chl prov. 3-Feb-3 Christie's, London #156/R est:120000
£120000 $200400 €174000 Le domaine enchante VI (12x24cm-5x9in) s. gouache exec.1953 prov.exhib.lit. 24-Jun-3 Christie's, London #42/R est:80000-120000
£130000 $217100 €188500 Untitled (62x45cm-24x18in) s. W/C col crayon collage exec.1926 prov.exhib.lit. 24-Jun-3 Christie's, London #35/R est:90000-120000
£210000 $350700 €304500 La grande table (32x42cm-13x17in) s. gouache exec.c.1965 prov.exhib.lit. 24-Jun-3 Christie's, London #43/R est:160000-220000
£260000 $423800 €390000 Eclair (25x20cm-10x8in) s. gouache pencil exec.1959 prov.exhib.lit. 3-Feb-3 Christie's, London #152/R est:180000
£322981 $520000 €484472 Reveries du promeneur solitaire (59x44cm-23x17in) s. gouache brush ink chl collage exec.1926 prov.exhib.lit. 7-May-3 Christie's, Rockefeller NY #22/R est:250000-350000

MAGROTTI, Ercole (1890-1958) Italian
£205 $320 €308 Fishing boats at dusk (48x67cm-19x26in) s. canvas on board. 11-Nov-2 Stephan Welz, Johannesburg #33 (SA.R 3200)
£344 $554 €516 Winter village scene with a woman on a roadway (48x67cm-19x26in) s. canvas on board. 12-May-3 Stephan Welz, Johannesburg #28 est:4000-6000 (SA.R 4000)
£450 $684 €675 Herder and cattle by a mountainous farmstead (69x98cm-27x39in) s. canvas on board. 29-Aug-2 Christie's, Kensington #98/R
£568 $886 €852 Hauserkulisse with sailing boats (49x69cm-19x27in) s. canvas on masonite prov. 9-Nov-2 Galerie Gloggner, Luzern #96/R (S.FR 1300)
£641 $994 €1000 Village in the hills (69x49cm-27x19in) s. cardboard. 5-Dec-2 Stadion, Trieste #857/R
£952 $1514 €1400 Varese lake (29x40cm-11x16in) s. board. 18-Mar-3 Finarte, Milan #234/R
£1075 $1730 €1613 Italian village on a lake (67x97cm-26x38in) s. canvas on board. 12-May-3 Stephan Welz, Johannesburg #430/R est:8000-10000 (SA.R 12500)
£1384 $2131 €2200 Farm on the lake (60x120cm-24x47in) s. 23-Oct-2 Finarte, Milan #160/R
£1720 $2769 €2580 Extensive Italian winter landscape with figures near houses (58x116cm-23x46in) s. canavs on board. 12-May-3 Stephan Welz, Johannesburg #429/R est:10000-12000 (SA.R 20000)

MAGSAYSAY-HO, Anita Corpus (1914-) Philippino
£28998 $44656 €43497 Lavandera - laundry women (45x53cm-18x21in) s.d.1957 s.d.verso board exhib.lit. 27-Oct-2 Christie's, Hong Kong #66/R est:220000-320000 (HK.D 350000)
£42735 $70513 €61966 Banana vendors (50x40cm-20x16in) s.d.1954 board prov. 6-Jul-3 Christie's, Hong Kong #42/R est:220000-320000 (HK.D 550000)

MAGUET, Richard (1896-1940) French
£278 $458 €400 Still life with flowers in a vase on a red cloth (50x60cm-20x24in) s. 1-Jul-3 Christie's, Amsterdam #316

MAGUIRE, Brian (20th C) Irish
£701 $1093 €1100 Jewish family, Brooklyn, New York (59x37cm-23x15in) i.verso acrylic. 6-Nov-2 James Adam, Dublin #144/R
£1139 $1766 €1800 Dubliners lovelessness (127x102cm-50x40in) s. acrylic. 24-Sep-2 De Veres Art Auctions, Dublin #142 est:2000-3000

MAGUIRE, Cecil (1930-) British
£1200 $1908 €1800 Connemare landscape (30x61cm-12x24in) s.d.62 board. 5-Mar-3 John Ross, Belfast #13 est:700-800
£1667 $2583 €2600 Life on Aran (25x30cm-10x12in) s. board. 3-Dec-2 Bonhams & James Adam, Dublin #45/R est:2500-3500
£1700 $2635 €2550 Mending nets (46x36cm-18x14in) s. board. 2-Oct-2 John Ross, Belfast #237 est:800-1200
£2000 $3180 €3000 Connemara lake (35x91cm-14x36in) s.d.68 board. 5-Mar-3 John Ross, Belfast #201 est:1200-1400
£2100 $3255 €3150 Gathering ribbonweed, Aran (25x30cm-10x12in) s. board. 2-Oct-2 John Ross, Belfast #3 est:1500-2000
£2200 $3410 €3300 Lough Anya, July 94 (46x61cm-18x24in) s.d.95 board. 2-Oct-2 John Ross, Belfast #130 est:2200-2500
£2282 $3674 €3400 Pucan (25x30cm-10x12in) s. board. 18-Feb-3 Whyte's, Dublin #29/R est:3000-4000
£2500 $3875 €3750 Launching the curragh (25x30cm-10x12in) s.d.90 board. 2-Oct-2 John Ross, Belfast #111 est:1800-2000
£3000 $4380 €4500 Lifting prawn pots, Roundstone (36x46cm-14x18in) s. board. 12-Jun-2 John Ross, Belfast #77 est:3250-3500
£3100 $4526 €4650 Early one morning Roundstone (36x46cm-14x18in) s.d.88 board. 12-Jun-2 John Ross, Belfast #186 est:1600-1800
£3700 $5735 €5550 Pucan evening, Roundstone, Connemara (50x61cm-20x24in) s.d.91 board. 4-Dec-2 John Ross, Belfast #170 est:3000-3500
£4214 $6574 €6700 Evening light at the Benab (38x89cm-15x35in) s. i.verso. 17-Sep-2 Whyte's, Dublin #13/R est:5000-7000
£5000 $7950 €7500 Conversation at Kilronan II (50x61cm-20x24in) s.d.73 board. 5-Mar-3 John Ross, Belfast #142/R est:3500-4000
£6164 $9678 €9000 Home to Inishman (41x51cm-16x20in) s.d.82 i.verso. 15-Apr-3 De Veres Art Auctions, Dublin #103 est:5000-7000
£6376 $10265 €9500 Harbour afternoon (46x61cm-18x24in) s. i.verso board. 18-Feb-3 Whyte's, Dublin #116/R est:8000-10000
£6500 $10400 €9750 Portbradden (57x91cm-22x36in) s.d.82 s.i.verso board. 15-May-3 Christie's, London #99/R est:5000-8000
£8333 $13250 €12000 Humanity Dick's window, shop street, Galway (61x38cm-24x15in) s. i.verso board lit. 29-Apr-3 Whyte's, Dublin #120/R est:8000-10000

MAGUIRE, Helena (1860-1909) British
Works on paper
£283 $438 €425 Peasant girl in barn (24x20cm-9x8in) s. W/C. 9-Dec-2 Philippe Schuler, Zurich #4171/R (S.FR 650)
£750 $1170 €1088 The good book (15x12cm-6x5in) s. W/C. 27-Mar-3 Neales, Nottingham #962/R

MAGUIRE, Robert (1921-) American
£932 $1500 €1398 Ecstatic woman, standing couple and exploding boat (61x46cm-24x18in) board painted c.1970. 10-May-3 Illustration House, New York #124/R est:1500-2500
£1180 $1900 €1770 Young sheriff with gun drawn (76x51cm-30x20in) s. board. 20-Feb-3 Illustration House, New York #108/R est:1200-1800
£1242 $2000 €1863 Woman standing on moors (58x46cm-23x18in) s. board. 20-Feb-3 Illustration House, New York #106/R est:1200-1800
Works on paper
£248 $400 €372 Man holding seated nude, television in background (20x13cm-8x5in) s. gouache. 20-Feb-3 Illustration House, New York #107/R

MAGUIRE, Tim (1958-) Australian/British
£1607 $2523 €2411 Sturt's vision, the mirage a device for viewing the landscape (121x182cm-48x72in) composition board prov. 25-Nov-2 Christie's, Melbourne #236/R est:4500-6000 (A.D 4500)
£3654 $5809 €5481 Slit (91x91cm-36x36in) s.i.d.94 verso. 4-Mar-3 Deutscher-Menzies, Melbourne #175/R est:3800-4500 (A.D 9500)
£5000 $7950 €7500 Two tanks (91x91cm-36x36in) s.i.d.1990 verso prov. 4-Mar-3 Deutscher-Menzies, Melbourne #174/R est:5500-7500 (A.D 13000)
£5179 $8494 €7769 Slit 93.63 (100x50cm-39x20in) s.i.d.verso. 4-Jun-3 Deutscher-Menzies, Melbourne #273/R est:4000-6000 (A.D 13000)
£7200 $11592 €10800 Untitled 2000 U32 (150x110cm-59x43in) s.i.d.2000 verso prov. 6-May-3 Christie's, Melbourne #100a/R est:18000-25000 (A.D 18000)
£10714 $16714 €16071 Untitled, grapes (120x119cm-47x47in) s.i.d.2000 verso. 11-Nov-2 Deutscher-Menzies, Melbourne #51/R est:10000-15000 (A.D 30000)
£13846 $22015 €20769 Untitled, oranges (119x120cm-47x47in) s.i.d.98 verso prov. 4-Mar-3 Deutscher-Menzies, Melbourne #73/R est:28000-35000 (A.D 36000)
£15139 $24829 €22709 Untitled 95-72 white flowers (99x99cm-39x39in) s.i.d.95 verso prov. 4-Jun-3 Deutscher-Menzies, Melbourne #20/R est:30000-40000 (A.D 38000)
£16154 $25685 €24231 Untitled, 98U54 (200x399cm-79x157in) s.i.d.98 verso prov.exhib. 4-Mar-3 Deutscher-Menzies, Melbourne #74/R est:40000-60000 (A.D 42000)
£21429 $33214 €32144 Untitled, 2002 0201 (160x148cm-63x58in) 29-Oct-2 Lawson Menzies, Sydney #63/R est:60000-80000 (A.D 60000)
£22857 $35200 €34286 Untitled (107x214cm-42x84in) painted 1993 prov. 8-Sep-2 Sotheby's, Melbourne #1/R est:15000-25000 (A.D 64000)
£34000 $54740 €51000 Untitled - 99 59U (176x160cm-69x63in) s.i.d.99 prov.exhib. 6-May-3 Christie's, Melbourne #13/R est:60000-80000 (A.D 85000)
£38462 $61154 €57693 Untitled, apples (150x200cm-59x79in) s.i.d.98 verso prov. 4-Mar-3 Deutscher-Menzies, Melbourne #32/R est:65000-85000 (A.D 100000)
Prints
£1714 $2640 €2571 Night blooms II (40x50cm-16x20in) s.i.d.90 montype. 8-Sep-2 Sotheby's, Melbourne #6/R est:3000-5000 (A.D 4800)
£1786 $2750 €2679 Rose (37x49cm-15x19in) monotype executed c.1991. 8-Sep-2 Sotheby's, Melbourne #7/R est:3000-5000 (A.D 5000)
£2071 $3190 €3107 Night blooms III (50x40cm-20x16in) s.i.d.91 monotype. 8-Sep-2 Sotheby's, Melbourne #8/R est:3000-5000 (A.D 5800)
£3770 $6258 €6424 Untitled (100x70cm-39x28in) monotype prov. 10-Jun-3 Shapiro, Sydney #77/R est:6000-9000 (A.D 9500)

£22908 $37569 €34362 Untitled, still life with fruit, crayfish and vase (211x268cm-83x106in) monotype oil nine sheets prov. 4-Jun-3 Deutscher-Menzies, Melbourne #31/R est:35000-45000 (A.D 57500)

Works on paper

£438 $718 €657 Horizon (15x30cm-6x12in) s.i.d.92 verso pastel prov. 4-Jun-3 Deutscher-Menzies, Melbourne #275/R (A.D 1100)
£478 $784 €717 Canal study (22x22cm-9x9in) pastel prov. 4-Jun-3 Deutscher-Menzies, Melbourne #169/R (A.D 1200)
£518 $849 €777 Three column study (25x35cm-10x14in) s.d.87 pastel prov. 4-Jun-3 Deutscher-Menzies, Melbourne #274/R (A.D 1300)

MAGUIRE, William Henry (fl.1830-1840) British

Works on paper

£350 $543 €525 Bangor, Co. Down (30x56cm-12x22in) s.d.July 16 1840 W/C. 4-Dec-2 John Ross, Belfast #92

MAHAFFEY, Josephine (1903-1982) American

£1410 $2200 €2115 Mexican village (97x127cm-38x50in) 19-Oct-2 David Dike, Dallas #151/R est:1500-2500

MAHAINZ, Julius (1882-1966) Austrian

£897 $1391 €1400 Nude (102x70cm-40x28in) s.d.1940 i. verso lit. 6-Dec-2 Karlheinz Kaupp, Staufen #2101

MAHDAOUI, Nja (1937-) Tunisian

Works on paper

£2800 $4452 €4200 Calligraphy (99x68cm-39x27in) ink htd gold parchment. 30-Apr-3 Sotheby's, London #163/R est:2000-3000

MAHDY, Wadie (1921-) Canadian

£311 $510 €467 Arranging flowers (77x62cm-30x24in) s. 3-Jun-3 Joyner, Toronto #436/R (C.D 700)
£333 $546 €500 L'Eglise de village (62x80cm-24x31in) s. 3-Jun-3 Joyner, Toronto #451/R (C.D 750)

MAHER, Steve (20th C) Australian

Works on paper

£344 $543 €499 Miss Image 1977 (40x28cm-16x11in) s. gouache. 7-Apr-3 Australian Art Auctions, Sydney #178 (A.D 900)

MAHLANGU, Esther (1935-) South African

£338 $533 €507 Abstract design (54x72cm-21x28in) s.d.2001. 1-Apr-3 Stephan Welz, Johannesburg #506 est:4000-6000 (SA.R 4200)

MAHLANGU, Speelman (1958-) South African

£418 $660 €627 Mother Africa (51x79cm-20x31in) s. 1-Apr-3 Stephan Welz, Johannesburg #513 est:4000-6000 (SA.R 5200)

Works on paper

£269 $420 €404 Winnie thinking (59x75cm-23x30in) s.d.96 i.d.94 verso mixed media collage board. 11-Nov-2 Stephan Welz, Johannesburg #266 (SA.R 4200)

MAHLKNECHT, Edmund (1820-1903) Austrian

£1013 $1600 €1600 Goat (50x42cm-20x17in) s.d.892. 28-Nov-2 Dorotheum, Vienna #88/R est:2000-2600
£3200 $5088 €4800 Herdsman with cattle and sheep in a landscape (55x71cm-22x28in) s.d.1859. 20-Mar-3 Christie's, Kensington #159/R est:3000-5000
£3425 $5342 €5000 Alpine meadow (35x30cm-14x12in) s. paper on board. 10-Apr-3 Dorotheum, Vienna #17/R est:4500-5000
£4292 $6781 €6438 Mountain landscape with cows (26x52cm-10x20in) s. 29-Nov-2 Zofingen, Switzerland #2495 est:12000 (S.FR 10000)
£5036 $8058 €7000 Landscape with cattle and goats by water (36x45cm-14x18in) s. panel. 17-May-3 Lempertz, Koln #1430/R est:7500

MAHLKNECHT, Edmund (attrib) (1820-1903) Austrian

£3022 $5017 €4382 Farmer on horseback with livestock by lakeside shrine (38x38cm-15x15in) s. 16-Jun-3 Waddingtons, Toronto #15/R est:1000-1500 (C.D 6800)

MAHN, Richard (1866-1951) German

£417 $633 €650 Mountain hunter in winter camouflage suit and skis under a pine tree (58x44cm-23x17in) s. lit. 11-Jul-2 Allgauer, Kempten #2592/R
£1027 $1603 €1500 Allgauer landscape with village and high mountains in background (70x88cm-28x35in) s. s.i.verso. 10-Apr-3 Allgauer, Kempten #2881/R est:1500
£1301 $2030 €1900 Winter woods with chapel and view of Allgauer mountains (80x100cm-31x39in) s. s.i.verso. 10-Apr-3 Allgauer, Kempten #2882/R est:1500

MAHONEY, Charles (1903-1968) British

£375 $600 €563 Buccaneer (61x48cm-24x19in) s.d.1932. 15-Mar-3 Eldred, East Dennis #421/R
£750 $1193 €1125 English garden (26x61cm-10x24in) init.d.52. 26-Feb-3 Sotheby's, Olympia #135/R

MAHONEY, Ron (20th C) American

Works on paper

£3226 $5000 €4839 Dawn of the dead (74x46cm-29x18in) s. mixed media exec.c.1978 prov. 8-Dec-2 Toomey, Oak Park #763/R est:7500-10000

MAHONY, M (19th C) American

£1384 $2200 €2076 Steam engine E F Holden (27x46cm-11x18in) s. board. 4-Mar-3 Christie's, Rockefeller NY #7/R est:1500-2500

MAHOOD, Kenneth (20th C) ?

£3478 $5704 €4800 Three boats (92x45cm-36x18in) s. i.d.1955 verso board. 28-May-3 Bonhams & James Adam, Dublin #75/R est:5000-7000

MAHRENHOLZ, Harald (1904-1994) British?

£700 $1078 €1050 Red bonnet (76x63cm-30x25in) board exhib. 5-Sep-2 Christie's, Kensington #639

MAHRINGER, Anton (1902-1974) German

£5405 $8432 €8000 Two boys (78x58cm-31x23in) mono. s.d.1932 verso. 25-Mar-3 Wiener Kunst Auktionen, Vienna #119/R est:8000-12000
£11824 $18446 €17500 Gail valley (90x69cm-35x27in) s.mono.d.1938. 25-Mar-3 Wiener Kunst Auktionen, Vienna #120/R est:9000-15000
£22695 $36766 €32000 Dobratsch (77x70cm-30x28in) mono.d.1950 i. verso masonite prov. 20-May-3 Dorotheum, Vienna #189/R est:18000-26000
£24113 $39064 €34000 Winter in St Georgen, Gailtal (84x85cm-33x33in) s.d.52 masonite prov. 20-May-3 Dorotheum, Vienna #185/R est:18000-26000

Works on paper

£1111 $1767 €1600 River landscape (35x47cm-14x19in) s.d.33 W/C prov. 29-Apr-3 Wiener Kunst Auktionen, Vienna #595/R est:1200-1500
£1987 $3238 €3000 Gailtal landscape with piles of hay (35x48cm-14x19in) i. W/C. 28-Jan-3 Dorotheum, Vienna #108/R est:1400-1800

MAHU, Cornelis (attrib) (1613-1689) Flemish

£4000 $6680 €5800 Peasants carousing in a barn (40x53cm-16x21in) indis.s. i.d.1644 panel. 9-Jul-3 Bonhams, New Bond Street #109/R est:4000-6000

MAHU, Victor (?-1700) Flemish

£10135 $15811 €15000 Merry making peasants in village (27x37cm-11x15in) mono. panel. 27-Mar-3 Dorotheum, Vienna #168/R est:15000-20000
£20000 $31200 €30000 Interior with alchemist and assistant at work (58x84cm-23x33in) s. prov. 10-Apr-3 Sotheby's, London #39/R est:8000

MAHY-BOSSU, Maria (1880-?) Belgian

£417 $658 €650 Child sleeping on a chair (80x53cm-31x21in) s. 18-Nov-2 Bernaerts, Antwerp #390/R
£545 $861 €850 Landscape with haystack and farmer's wife (46x60cm-18x24in) s. 18-Nov-2 Bernaerts, Antwerp #395/R
£1154 $1823 €1800 Zonnige dag (131x106cm-52x42in) s. 18-Nov-2 Bernaerts, Antwerp #398/R est:1500-2000

MAI THU (1906-1980) Vietnamese

£12432 $20513 €18026 Conversation (47x60cm-19x24in) s.d.Mai 66 silk. 6-Jul-3 Christie's, Hong Kong #38/R est:120000-140000 (HK.D 160000)
£20570 $32089 €32500 Danseuse vietnamienne (100x70cm-39x28in) s. 20-Oct-2 Chayette & Cheval, Paris #61 est:12000-15000

Works on paper

£3314 $5104 €4971 Femme a l'enfant - mother and child (23x16cm-9x6in) s.d.54 gouache ink on silk. 27-Oct-2 Christie's, Hong Kong #43/R est:50000-70000 (HK.D 40000)
£5385 $8293 €8078 Femme a l'eventail et a l'oiseau - lady with a fan and bird (19x11cm-7x4in) s.d.56 gouache ink on silk. 27-Oct-2 Christie's, Hong Kong #42/R est:50000-70000 (HK.D 65000)

MAI-THU (1906-1980) ?

£11783 $18382 €18500 Belle endormie (66x55cm-26x22in) s.d.1938 silk. 10-Nov-2 Eric Pillon, Calais #163/R

MAIDMENT, Henry (19/20th C) British

£227 $351 €341 Livestock near duck pond (25x35cm-10x14in) s. 3-Dec-2 Ritchie, Toronto #3041b (C.D 550)

£453 $702 €680 Shepherd and flock in an extensive landscape (41x31cm-16x12in) s. 3-Dec-2 Ritchie, Toronto #3041a/R est:800-1000 (C.D 1100)
£950 $1482 €1425 At a ford (76x63cm-30x25in) mono.d.72. 26-Mar-3 Hamptons Fine Art, Godalming #122

MAIDMENT, Henry (attrib) (19/20th C) British
£329 $510 €494 Sheep grazing beyond the village (40x60cm-16x24in) bears init.d.1876. 3-Dec-2 Ritchie, Toronto #3041/R (C.D 800)

MAIDMENT, Thomas (1871-?) British
£350 $546 €525 Cornish street (36x46cm-14x18in) s. 17-Oct-2 David Lay, Penzance #1314

MAIER, Cloud (19/20th C) Austrian?
£513 $805 €800 Playing dice (95x80cm-37x31in) s. 10-Dec-2 Dorotheum, Vienna #62/R

MAIGNAN, Albert Pierre René (1845-1908) French
£897 $1409 €1400 Venise. Rome (15x24cm-6x9in) s.i.d. panel pair. 13-Dec-2 Piasa, Paris #167
Works on paper
£709 $1107 €1050 Saltimbanques en representation a Seville (14x20cm-6x8in) s.d.1868 W/C. 26-Mar-3 Piasa, Paris #115
£743 $1159 €1100 Untitled. i.d. crayon set of 12. 26-Mar-3 Piasa, Paris #114

MAIGRET, G (19th C) French
£417 $654 €650 Faggott gatherer on wintry riverbank with skaters (122x96cm-48x38in) s.d.1897. 23-Nov-2 Arnold, Frankfurt #797/R

MAIK, Henri (20th C) ?
£559 $900 €839 Dans la nuit (145x114cm-57x45in) s.d.70 i.verso prov. 20-Jan-3 Arthur James, Florida #368

MAILE, Alfred (fl.1882-1889) British
Works on paper
£400 $652 €580 Highland landscape with sheep (39x55cm-15x22in) s.d.1897 W/C. 17-Jul-3 Tennants, Leyburn #739

MAILE, Ben (20th C) British
£260 $406 €390 Blue boats and nets (49x81cm-19x32in) s. board. 26-Mar-3 Woolley & Wallis, Salisbury #50/R
£310 $481 €465 Beached boat in harbour (76x211cm-30x83in) s. board. 26-Sep-2 Lane, Penzance #119
£550 $913 €798 Micklegate Bar, York (76x51cm-30x20in) s. 10-Jun-3 David Lay, Penzance #504
£1600 $2656 €2320 Fishing boats, low tide (56x99cm-22x39in) 10-Jun-3 David Lay, Penzance #262 est:1500-2000

MAILEY, Arthur (20th C) British
Works on paper
£450 $707 €675 H L Collins leading out the Australians for the 5th Test (9x15cm-4x6in) s. pen ink exec.1926 reverse has signatures. 16-Apr-3 Anthemion, Cardiff #481

MAILLARD, Jean (1901-1993) Belgian
£705 $1093 €1100 Elegante a la voilette (60x47cm-24x19in) s. 9-Dec-2 Horta, Bruxelles #401

MAILLART, Diogene Ulysse Napoleon (1840-1926) French
£2800 $4424 €4200 La jolie petite (117x82cm-46x32in) s.d.1859. 14-Nov-2 Christie's, Kensington #303/R est:2500-3500
Works on paper
£380 $600 €600 Etudes de mains (29x23cm-11x9in) s. crayon. 28-Nov-2 Tajan, Paris #194
£759 $1200 €1200 Etude de nu feminin (28x41cm-11x16in) s. crayon double-sided. 28-Nov-2 Tajan, Paris #197

MAILLAUD, Fernand (1863-1948) French
£1006 $1560 €1600 Jeune femme a l'ombrelle dans un parc luxuriant (40x30cm-16x12in) s. 4-Oct-2 Tajan, Paris #161 est:2000-3000
£1161 $1800 €1742 Paysage de Vermarton, Yonne (33x26cm-13x10in) s. canvas on board. 26-Sep-2 Christie's, Rockefeller NY #609/R est:2000-3000
£1218 $1912 €1900 Enfants sur la place du village (32x41cm-13x16in) s. cardboard. 25-Nov-2 Rieunier, Bailly-Pommery, Mathias, Paris #9
£1486 $2319 €2200 Retour du chariot au printemps (27x35cm-11x14in) st.sig. cardboard. 26-Mar-3 Millon & Associes, Paris #73/R
£1931 $3225 €2800 Bergere et son troupeau (60x73cm-24x29in) s. 10-Jul-3 Artcurial Briest, Paris #140/R est:3000-4000
£1950 $3022 €3100 Le labourage (69x88cm-27x35in) s. panel. 4-Oct-2 Tajan, Paris #162 est:2400-3000
£2113 $3507 €3000 La chapelle du village sous la neige (33x41cm-13x16in) s. panel. 11-Jun-3 Beaussant & Lefèvre, Paris #93/R est:1000
£2115 $3321 €3300 Depart dans la brume (54x65cm-21x26in) s. panel. 22-Nov-2 Millon & Associes, Paris #61/R
£2244 $3522 €3500 Moissons dans la Creuse (46x5cm-18x2in) s. mono.i.verso. 22-Nov-2 Millon & Associes, Paris #60/R
£2848 $4500 €4500 Dindons (50x65cm-20x26in) s. i.verso. 2-Dec-2 Rieunier, Paris #6/R
Works on paper
£500 $790 €750 Study of shirehorse. Study of a bay hunter (13x20cm-5x8in) pencil W/C htd white two. 28-Nov-2 Christie's, Kensington #184/R
£1486 $2319 €2200 Relais (37x25cm-15x10in) s. gouache cardboard. 26-Mar-3 Millon & Associes, Paris #72/R

MAILLOL, Aristide (1861-1944) French
£5556 $8944 €8056 Nu couche (21x33cm-8x13in) mono. pastel chk. 7-May-3 Dobiaschofsky, Bern #803/R est:7500 (S.FR 12000)
£54487 $85000 €81731 Baigneuse au bord de la riviere (74x60cm-29x24in) painted c.1935 prov.exhib. 7-Nov-2 Christie's, Rockefeller NY #240/R est:80000-120000
£55000 $90200 €82500 Environs de Banyuls (60x73cm-24x29in) mono. painted c.1943-44 prov. 4-Feb-3 Christie's, London #246/R est:35000
Prints
£3800 $5928 €5700 La vague (24x26cm-9x10in) woodcut. 25-Mar-3 Sotheby's, London #90/R est:2000-3000
Sculpture
£3205 $5000 €4808 Femme debout se coiffant (39cm-15in) mono. brown pat bronze exec.c.1900-05. 18-Sep-2 Swann Galleries, New York #14/R est:7000-10000
£8216 $13474 €11913 Eva (59cm-23in) i. num.4/6 Cast.Alexis Rudier Paris. 4-Jun-3 Fischer, Luzern #1368/R est:1000-1200 (S.FR 17500)
£9000 $15030 €13050 Jeune boxeur (30cm-12in) mono. bronze i.f.Alexis Rudier prov.exhib. 24-Jun-3 Sotheby's, London #135/R est:10000-15000
£12422 $20000 €18633 Nabis (28cm-11in) mono.num.2/6 green black pat. bronze cast 1952. 8-May-3 Christie's, Rockefeller NY #150/R est:25000-35000
£16346 $25337 €25500 Nageurs dans la vague (29x33cm-11x13in) mono. num.1/6 brown green pat bronze Cast Rudier exec.1896 lit. 9-Dec-2 Piasa, Paris #5/R est:20000-30000
£18000 $30060 €26100 Etude pour l'action enchainee (32cm-13in) mono.num.6/6 bronze i.f.Alexis Rudier executed c.1905-06 prov.lit. 24-Jun-3 Sotheby's, London #136/R est:20000-30000
£19231 $30000 €28847 Nabis (29cm-11in) mono.num.5/6 brown green pat. bronze i.f.Alexis Rudier cast.1920. 7-Nov-2 Christie's, Rockefeller NY #236/R est:35000-45000
£19939 $32500 €29909 Nu debout (27cm-11in) mono.i. terracotta prov.exhib.lit. 12-Feb-3 Sotheby's, New York #9/R est:15000-20000
£22000 $36740 €31900 Jeune fille debout a la draperie (30cm-12in) mono.num.6/6 bronze i.f.Alexis Rudier executed 1930. 24-Jun-3 Sotheby's, London #140/R est:28000-35000
£23006 $37500 €34509 Torse de femme (20cm-8in) terracotta prov. 12-Feb-3 Sotheby's, New York #8/R est:20000-30000
£28500 $47595 €41325 Femme vetue assise (20cm-8in) mono.num.2/6 brown pat. bronze st.f. Alexis Rudier prov.exhib. 25-Jun-3 Christie's, London #118/R est:30000-40000
£29503 $47500 €44255 Mediterranee (15x16cm-6x6in) mono. dark green pat. bronze st.f.Alexis Rudier prov. 7-May-3 Sotheby's, New York #129/R est:40000-60000
£31056 $50000 €46584 Etude pour la Mediterranee (17x20cm-7x8in) mono.num.2/6 brown pat. bronze st.f.Alexis Rudier prov. 7-May-3 Sotheby's, New York #113/R est:40000-60000
£37267 $60000 €55901 Etude pour la Mediterranee (62cm-24in) mono. dark green pat. bronze st.f.Alexis Rudier prov.exhib.lit. 7-May-3 Sotheby's, New York #138/R est:60000-80000
£56000 $93520 €81200 Debout les bras ecartes (31cm-12in) mono.num.1/6 bronze i.f.Alexis Rudier executed 1924 lit. 24-Jun-3 Sotheby's, London #102/R est:35000-45000
£64103 $100000 €96155 Dina socle mobile (20cm-8in) mono.num.2 black pat. bronze st.f.A Rudier cast 1930-40 prov.lit. 7-Nov-2 Christie's, Rockefeller NY #206/R est:60000-80000
£64103 $100000 €96155 La petite Marie (69cm-27in) mono. black pat. bronze i.f.Alexis Rudier prov.exhib.lit. 7-Nov-2 Christie's, Rockefeller NY #264/R est:120000-160000

£67308 $104327 €105000 Agenouillee (20cm-8in) mono. green brown pat bronze Cast Rudier exec.1900 lit. 9-Dec-2 Piasa, Paris #4/R est:80000-120000
£70000 $114800 €105000 Baigneuse a l'echarpe (34cm-13in) mono.st.f.Rudier brown pat bronze lit. 4-Feb-3 Christie's, London #219/R est:40000
£80000 $131200 €120000 Baigneuse debout se coiffant (36cm-14in) mono.st.f.Rudier num.2/6 brown green pat bronze prov.exhib.lit. 4-Feb-3 Christie's, London #249/R est:80000
£95000 $155800 €142500 Torse (66cm-26in) mono.stf.Godard brown green pat bronze prov.exhib. 4-Feb-3 Christie's, London #247/R est:160000
£102837 $171738 €145000 Petite flore vetue (66cm-26in) s. num.2/6 pat bronze Cast A Rudier, Paris prov.lit. 20-Jun-3 Piasa, Paris #19/R est:120000-150000
£105000 $172200 €157500 Nuit (17cm-7in) mono. num.4/6 bronze prov.exhib.lit. 5-Feb-3 Sotheby's, London #131/R est:80000
£108974 $170000 €163461 Petite Flore nue (66cm-26in) init.green pat. bronze f.A.Bingen conceived 1907 prov.lit. 5-Nov-2 Sotheby's, New York #30/R est:200000-300000
£280000 $456400 €420000 Jeunesse (110cm-43in) st.mono.st.f.Bingen et Costenoble green pat bronze exhib.lit. 3-Feb-3 Christie's, London #63/R est:450000
£298137 $480000 €447206 Torse de la nymphe (132cm-52in) mono.st.sf.Rudier green pat bronze lit. 7-May-3 Christie's, Rockefeller NY #19/R est:500000-700000
£301282 $470000 €451923 Baigneuse aux bras leves (82cm-32in) mono.dark brown pat. bronze i.f.Alexis Rudier cast 1952 prov.exhib. 6-Nov-2 Christie's, Rockefeller NY #27/R est:400000-600000
£307692 $480000 €461538 Marie (158cm-62in) mono. green pat. bronze i.f.Alexis Rudier prov.lit. 6-Nov-2 Christie's, Rockefeller NY #22/R est:500000-700000
£576923 $900000 €865385 Venus - san collier (175cm-69in) mono. brown green pat. bronze i.f.Alexis Rudier prov.exhib.lit. 5-Nov-2 Sotheby's, New York #47/R est:650000-850000
£576923 $900000 €865385 La nymphe (156cm-61in) mono.num.3/4 dark green brown pat. bronze cast 1952 prov.exhib.li. 6-Nov-2 Christie's, Rockefeller NY #17/R est:1000000-1500000

Works on paper
£385 $562 €600 Que ton ame soit blanche ou noire - le desir (8x7cm-3x3in) mono. pen over pencil. 4-Jun-2 Karl & Faber, Munich #342
£570 $889 €900 Que ton ame soit blanche ou noire - le desir (11x14cm-4x6in) st.mono. Indian ink pencil paper on board. 18-Oct-2 Dr Fritz Nagel, Stuttgart #246/R
£608 $949 €900 Etude de nus (25x18cm-10x7in) mono. graphite dr double-sided. 26-Mar-3 Millon & Associes, Paris #25
£704 $1155 €1021 Femme debout (31x19cm-12x7in) mono. chk prov. 4-Jun-3 Fischer, Luzern #2534/R est:1600-1800 (S.FR 1500)
£1158 $1865 €1737 Couple de baigneurs (11x8cm-4x3in) red chk lit. 7-May-3 AB Stockholms Auktionsverk #1100/R est:12000-15000 (S.KR 15000)
£1408 $2338 €2000 Femme nue (21x14cm-8x6in) mono. col pen. 14-Jun-3 Hauswedell & Nolte, Hamburg #1367/R est:3000
£1583 $2500 €2375 Nu (27x22cm-11x9in) mono. pencil prov. 22-Apr-3 Butterfields, San Francisco #6013/R est:2500-3500
£1612 $2514 €2418 Model (34x21cm-13x8in) mono. red chk. 5-Nov-2 Bukowskis, Stockholm #290/R est:20000-25000 (S.KR 23000)
£2000 $3100 €3000 Dos debout (28x14cm-11x6in) mono. red chk. 5-Dec-2 Christie's, Kensington #44/R est:2000-3000
£2600 $4108 €3900 Jeune fille a la draperie (28x20cm-11x8in) mono. pencil. 3-Apr-3 Christie's, Kensington #34/R
£5000 $7700 €7500 Nu de dos (38x27cm-15x11in) mono. sanguine white chk prov. 22-Oct-2 Sotheby's, London #126/R est:6000-8000
£7051 $11071 €11000 Femme accroupie (28x23cm-11x9in) mono. chl exec.1942 prov.lit. 10-Dec-2 Piasa, Paris #265/R
£7419 $11723 €11500 Ida (43x26cm-17x10in) mono. chl. 19-Dec-2 Delvaux, Paris #18/R est:10000
£9816 $16000 €14724 Etude pour L'harmonie (45x27cm-18x11in) s.i. chl prov.exhib. 12-Feb-3 Sotheby's, New York #5/R est:12000-18000
£11538 $18115 €18000 Dina debout (39x25cm-15x10in) mono. chl chk dr exec.1942 prov.exhib.lit. 10-Dec-2 Piasa, Paris #263/R est:20000
£12000 $20040 €18000 Dina a la natte (25x25cm-10x10in) mono. chl. exec 1940 prov.exhib. 26-Jun-3 Christie's, London #356/R est:12000-15000
£12179 $19122 €19000 Dina a la natte, etude (25x25cm-10x10in) mono. chl exec.1940 prov.exhib.lit. 10-Dec-2 Piasa, Paris #264/R est:15000
£35256 $54647 €55000 Etude pour 'La tulipe' (30x23cm-12x9in) mono. chl dr exec.1942 lit. 9-Dec-2 Piasa, Paris #3/R est:15000-20000

MAILLOL, Aristide (attrib) (1861-1944) French
Works on paper
£1389 $2250 €2014 Standing female nude (48x30cm-19x12in) bears mono. sanguine white chk paper on board. 21-May-3 Doyle, New York #213/R est:3000-5000

MAIN, Herbert Degruff (20th C) American
£1497 $2500 €2171 Landscape, down to the sea (66x91cm-26x36in) s. i.verso. 17-Jun-3 John Moran, Pasadena #152 est:2000-3000

MAIN, Irene Lesley (20th C) British
Works on paper
£360 $558 €540 Eton Collage (18x26cm-7x10in) s.i.d.1984 W/C. 3-Dec-2 Bonhams, Knightsbridge #212/R

MAIN, William (1796-1876) American
£481 $750 €722 Portrait of a lady (36x30cm-14x12in) s. 22-Sep-2 Susanin's, Chicago #5077/R

MAINCENT, Gustave (1850-1887) French
£423 $701 €600 La chevriere (37x46cm-15x18in) s. panel. 11-Jun-3 Beaussant & Lefèvre, Paris #106/R
£4500 $7335 €6750 Riverside lunch (37x46cm-15x18in) s. 29-Jan-3 Sotheby's, Olympia #336/R est:1500-2000

MAINELLA, Raffaele (1858-1907) Italian
£745 $1200 €1118 Castle in summer landscape (64x43cm-25x17in) s. 20-Jan-3 Arthur James, Florida #810
Works on paper
£800 $1248 €1200 Lagoon view, Venice (23x43cm-9x17in) s.i. W/C. 9-Oct-2 Woolley & Wallis, Salisbury #182/R
£909 $1427 €1364 Venetian children in a lagoon (41x56cm-16x22in) s.i. W/C gouache. 24-Jul-2 Walker's, Ottawa #39/R est:2500-3000 (C.D 2200)
£2000 $3240 €3000 Gondola on the lagoon. Boats sailing on the lagoon (30x15cm-12x6in) s. pencil pen brown ink W/C pair. 23-Jan-3 Christie's, Kensington #326/R est:1000-1500

MAINOLFI, Luigi (1948-) Italian
Sculpture
£1149 $1792 €1700 Taso (21x39x23cm-8x15x9in) num.37006 terracotta exec.1992. 26-Mar-3 Finarte Semenzato, Milan #186/R
Works on paper
£612 $973 €900 Dust (30x60cm-12x24in) s.i.d.1995 mixed media board. 1-Mar-3 Meeting Art, Vercelli #332

MAINSSIEUX, Lucien (1885-1958) French
£310 $497 €450 A la fontaine (46x55cm-18x22in) s.d.1942 panel. 12-Mar-3 E & Eve, Paris #87
£896 $1497 €1300 Jeune femme sur un chemin en Provence (54x65cm-21x26in) s. 10-Jul-3 Artcurial Briest, Paris #138 est:1200-1500

MAIRE, Andre (1898-1985) French
£570 $889 €900 Bord de canal, Venise (50x38cm-20x15in) s.d.1927 cardboard. 20-Oct-2 Charbonneaux, Paris #141/R
£641 $1006 €1000 Egyptians riding camels before the pyramids of Gizeh (41x47cm-16x19in) s. panel. 21-Nov-2 Van Ham, Cologne #1771
£1122 $1785 €1650 Indochinoises au bord d'un fleuve (34x49cm-13x19in) s. cardboard painted c.1950. 26-Feb-3 Artcurial Briest, Paris #336 est:1000-1200
£1122 $1785 €1650 Femme a sa toilette (49x35cm-19x14in) s. cardboard painted c.1950. 26-Feb-3 Artcurial Briest, Paris #337 est:1000-1200
£1327 $2109 €1950 Odalisque Indochinoise (38x46cm-15x18in) s. panel painted c.1950. 26-Feb-3 Artcurial Briest, Paris #338 est:1000-1200
£1474 $2315 €2300 Nature morte (50x65cm-20x26in) s.d.1960 d.verso cardboard. 20-Nov-2 Claude Boisgirard, Paris #42/R
£1923 $3019 €3000 Sur la plage (65x92cm-26x36in) s.d.1974 panel. 20-Nov-2 Claude Boisgirard, Paris #41/R
£2885 $4529 €4500 Sieste (60x92cm-24x36in) s.d.1970 masonite. 20-Nov-2 Claude Boisgirard, Paris #40/R
£3148 $4848 €4722 L'autel dans l'arbre pres du fleuve - altar on the tree near the river (64x91cm-25x36in) s.d.1979 panel. 27-Oct-2 Christie's, Hong Kong #49/R est:45000-55000 (HK.D 38000)
£5036 $8057 €7000 Ronda (93x121cm-37x48in) s. panel lit. 19-May-3 Tajan, Paris #15/R est:4000-6000
£7194 $11511 €10000 Leda (109x169cm-43x67in) s. lit. 19-May-3 Tajan, Paris #5/R est:10000-12000
Works on paper
£272 $433 €400 Le caire (16x24cm-6x9in) s.i. W/C gouache. 28-Feb-3 Tajan, Paris #11/R
£316 $494 €500 Les Sampans, Indochine (31x49cm-12x19in) s.d.1951 black chk sanguine. 20-Oct-2 Charbonneaux, Paris #71/R est:500-600
£443 $691 €700 Porteurs de jarre, Indochine (49x64cm-19x25in) s.d.1955 black chk sanguine. 20-Oct-2 Charbonneaux, Paris #69 est:800-1000
£443 $691 €700 Ruines du site d'Angkor, Indochine (64x49cm-25x19in) s.d.1959 black chk sanguine. 20-Oct-2 Charbonneaux, Paris #70 est:800-1000
£696 $1079 €1100 Canal a Venise (36x28cm-14x11in) s.d.1925 sepia. 29-Sep-2 Eric Pillon, Calais #6/R

£746 $1148 €1119 Le retour de la chasse - return from the hunt (60x50cm-24x20in) s.d.1950 gouache prov. 27-Oct-2 Christie's, Hong Kong #48/R est:12000-16000 (HK.D 9000)
£881 $1365 €1400 Paris, les quais (29x37cm-11x15in) s.d.1929 wash. 6-Oct-2 Feletin, Province #122
£962 $1510 €1500 Escurial (48x54cm-19x21in) s.d.1930 ink dr panel. 11-Dec-2 Piasa, Paris #16/R
£971 $1593 €1350 Elephants s'abreuvant (50x65cm-20x26in) s.d.1955 conte crayon sanguine. 3-Jun-3 Piasa, Paris #11/R
£1020 $1622 €1500 Marchande devant pagode (50x65cm-20x26in) s.d.1952 crayon sanguine. 19-Mar-3 Claude Boisgirard, Paris #23/R
£1020 $1622 €1500 Femmes malagaches assises (50x65cm-20x26in) s.d.1959 crayon sanguine. 19-Mar-3 Claude Boisgirard, Paris #24/R
£1103 $1754 €1600 Vue d'Italie dans les environs de Naples (29x37cm-11x15in) s.d.1932 ink wash. 5-Mar-3 Oger, Dumont, Paris #20 est:500-600
£1151 $1888 €1600 La cour de la fontaine au lions (75x60cm-30x24in) s.d.1923 sepia. 3-Jun-3 Piasa, Paris #10/R est:2000-2500
£1241 $1974 €1800 La mosquee de Cordoue (73x57cm-29x22in) s.d.1928 pen sepia wash. 5-Mar-3 Oger, Dumont, Paris #19/R est:1000-1500
£1439 $2302 €2000 Chantier naval au bord du fleuve en orient (58x74cm-23x29in) s. W/C gouache. 18-May-3 Eric Pillon, Calais #121/R
£1538 $2415 €2400 Femme malgache (65x50cm-26x20in) crayon sanguine exec.1959. 20-Nov-2 Claude Boisgirard, Paris #20/R
£1538 $2415 €2400 Femme vietnamienne (50x33cm-20x13in) s.d.1954 sanguine chl. 20-Nov-2 Claude Boisgirard, Paris #21/R
£1701 $2704 €2500 Famille Moi sur les hauts plateaux (50x65cm-20x26in) s.d.1949. 19-Mar-3 Claude Boisgirard, Paris #21/R
£1731 $2717 €2700 Marche a Madagascar (50x65cm-20x26in) s.d.1959 crayon sanguine. 20-Nov-2 Claude Boisgirard, Paris #22/R
£1795 $2818 €2800 Long de fleuve (50x65cm-20x26in) s. gouache. 22-Nov-2 Millon & Associes, Paris #130
£1823 $2807 €2735 Le temple hindou - Hindu temple (75x58cm-30x23in) s. chl gouache prov. 27-Oct-2 Christie's, Hong Kong #47/R est:28000-35000 (HK.D 22000)
£1987 $3120 €3100 Venise (75x57cm-30x22in) s.d.1927 sepia ink. 20-Nov-2 Claude Boisgirard, Paris #19/R

MAIRE, Ferdinand Henri (1901-1963) Swiss
£324 $522 €486 Lakeshore on summer afternoon (73x79cm-29x31in) s.d.1943. 7-May-3 Dobiaschofsky, Bern #804/R (S.FR 700)

MAIROVICH, Zvi (1911-1973) Israeli
£1931 $3052 €2897 Two peasant woman (81x63cm-32x25in) s. 3-Apr-3 Heffel, Vancouver #59/R est:2500-3500 (C.D 4500)
Works on paper
£1139 $1800 €1709 Untitled (32x34cm-13x13in) s. pastel executed c.1970. 27-Apr-3 Sotheby's, Tel Aviv #70/R est:2000-3000

MAIS, Hilarie (1952-) Australian/British
£1964 $3064 €2946 Blind similie (59x59cm-23x23in) s.i.d.1997 verso one on timber pair prov. 11-Nov-2 Deutscher-Menzies, Melbourne #50/R est:4000-6000 (A.D 5500)
Sculpture
£1200 $1932 €1800 Nubes III, 2001 (73x53x6cm-29x21x2in) s.i.d.2001 painted wood prov. 6-May-3 Christie's, Melbourne #249/R est:4000-6000 (A.D 3000)
£1786 $2785 €2679 Chance 11 (95x94cm-37x37in) s.d.1991/92 verso painted wood. 11-Nov-2 Deutscher-Menzies, Melbourne #8/R est:3000-5000 (A.D 5000)

MAISIERE, Jean Luc (1956-) French
£370 $526 €600 Zebre (30x90cm-12x35in) 17-Mar-2 Galerie de Chartres, Chartres #149

MAISON, Mary Edith (1886-1954) American
£220 $350 €330 Crashing waves (51x61cm-20x24in) s. 7-Mar-3 Skinner, Boston #508/R
£346 $550 €519 Mountain landscapes (50x61cm-20x24in) s. pair. 7-Mar-3 Skinner, Boston #354/R

MAISON, Rudolf (1854-1904) German
Sculpture
£2630 $4129 €3945 Father time (63cm-25in) s.d.1900 bronze. 25-Nov-2 Stephan Welz, Johannesburg #211/R est:9000-12000 (SA.R 40000)

MAISONNEUVE, Pascal Desir (1863-1934) French
Sculpture
£15068 $23658 €22000 Tete (14cm-6in) carved shell. 15-Apr-3 Laurence Calmels, Paris #4341/R est:8000
£65068 $101507 €95000 La Reine Victoria (31x36x23cm-12x14x9in) shells wood plaster exec.1927-28 exhib.lit. 14-Apr-3 Laurence Calmels, Paris #4022/R est:50000

MAISTRE, Roy de (1894-1968) Australian
£420 $668 €630 Portrait of Lucy Dynevor (45x36cm-18x14in) 26-Feb-3 Sotheby's, Olympia #89/R
£1300 $2067 €1950 Portrait of Lucy Dynevor (45x35cm-18x14in) s. 26-Feb-3 Sotheby's, Olympia #90/R est:400-600
£2713 $4314 €4070 Lady Ashbourne in France (30x37cm-12x15in) s. board. 5-May 3 Sotheby's, Melbourne #260/R est:7000-10000 (A.D 7000)
£3600 $5724 €5400 Landscape with church spire (16x23cm-6x9in) s.d.1920 board. 26-Feb-3 Sotheby's, Olympia #86/R est:1200-1800
£4270 $6534 €6405 St. Jean Cap Ferrat (29x39cm-11x15in) s.i. board prov. 25-Aug-2 Sotheby's, Paddington #174/R est:12000-18000 (A.D 12000)
£6071 $9593 €9107 Angel of Peace (60x48cm-24x19in) s. board painted c.1930 prov.lit. 17-Nov-2 Sotheby's, Paddington #55/R est:10000-15000 (A.D 17000)
£8800 $14168 €13200 Studio at Compiegne (46x38cm-18x15in) s. board prov. 6-May-3 Christie's, Melbourne #33/R est:20000-30000 (A.D 22000)
£10000 $15500 €15000 Interior (60x45cm-24x18in) s. i.verso painted c.1928 prov. 29-Oct-2 Lawson Menzies, Sydney #50/R est:35000-45000 (A.D 28000)
£11388 $17423 €17082 Organist (51x61cm-20x24in) painted 1943 prov. 26-Aug-2 Sotheby's, Paddington #550/R est:40000-60000 (A.D 32000)
£13000 $20670 €19500 Searchers (91x142cm-36x56in) s. board exhib. 26-Feb-3 Sotheby's, Olympia #91/R est:4000-6000
£14000 $22260 €21000 Landscape (24x33cm-9x13in) s.d.1920 board. 26-Feb-3 Sotheby's, Olympia #87/R est:2000-3000
£18327 $30056 €27491 Berry's Bay, Sydney harbour (24x33cm-9x13in) s.d.1920 board prov. 4-Jun-3 Deutscher-Menzies, Melbourne #36/R est:45000-55000 (A.D 46000)
£20000 $31800 €30000 Wharfside (61x41cm-24x16in) s. board. 26-Feb-3 Sotheby's, Olympia #88/R est:3000-4000
Works on paper
£14643 $23136 €21965 Paris studio (78x52cm-31x20in) s.d.56 prov. 26-Nov-2 Sotheby's, Melbourne #22/R est:30000-50000 (A.D 41000)

MAITLAND, Captain Alexander Fuller (fl.1887-1904) British
£350 $532 €525 Line of windmills on the coast (24x30cm-9x12in) s.d.1906 i.verso board. 29-Aug-2 Christie's, Kensington #57/R

MAITLAND, Paul (1869-1909) British
£1500 $2505 €2175 Mills and barges, Chelsea (25x36cm-10x14in) indis.sig. 24-Jun-3 Bonhams, New Bond Street #25/R est:1500-2000
£2600 $4056 €3900 Low tide at Chelsea embankment (25x20cm-10x8in) s. prov. 25-Mar-3 Bonhams, New Bond Street #16/R est:2800-3200
£3800 $5928 €5700 Barge on the Thames (46x61cm-18x24in) s. 27-Mar-3 Christie's, Kensington #456/R est:4000-6000
£4500 $6975 €6750 Daffodils in Kensington Gardens (30x41cm-12x16in) s. exhib. 3-Dec-2 Bonhams, New Bond Street #15/R est:4000-6000
£7500 $12300 €11250 Chelsea Embankment, plane trees (21x18cm-8x7in) s.i.d.08 board prov. 6-Jun-3 Christie's, London #46/R est:6000-8000
£15000 $23400 €22500 Kensington Palace from the gardens (37x51cm-15x20in) s. prov.exhib. 25-Mar-3 Bonhams, New Bond Street #17/R est:4000-6000

MAJERSKY, Ladislav (1900-1965) Czechoslovakian
Sculpture
£1074 $1664 €1611 Misery (32cm-13in) bronze exec.1933. 3-Dec-2 SOGA, Bratislava #54/R est:39000 (SL.K 68000)

MAJEWICZ, George (1897-1965) German?
£272 $433 €400 Deer (80x120cm-31x47in) s. panel. 28-Mar-3 Bolland & Marotz, Bremen #566/R
£513 $795 €800 Savannah landscape with crouching leopard (60x80cm-24x31in) s. lit. 6-Dec-2 Karlheinz Kaupp, Staufen #2421

MAJOR, Ernest (1864-1935) American
£1623 $2500 €2435 Still life with flowers (33x41cm-13x16in) s.d.98 panel. 27-Oct-2 Grogan, Boston #26 est:1000-1500
£2885 $4500 €4328 Lake landscape with house (61x76cm-24x30in) s. 28-Mar-3 Eldred, East Dennis #684/R est:2000-3000

MAJOR, Theodore (1908-1999) British
£820 $1304 €1230 Canal and chimneys at sunset (25x35cm-10x14in) s.i.verso board. 27-Feb-3 Bonhams, Chester #362
£1050 $1670 €1575 Figure in the rain (26x31cm-10x12in) s.i. verso board. 27-Feb-3 Bonhams, Chester #361 est:900-1200
£3500 $5565 €5250 Chimney stack's and mills at dusk (31x47cm-12x19in) s.i.verso board. 27-Feb-3 Bonhams, Chester #360/R est:1200-1600
£5400 $8586 €8100 Still life with bottles (58x95cm-23x37in) s.i.verso board. 27-Feb-3 Bonhams, Chester #359/R est:4000-6000

MAJORELLE, Jacques (1886-1962) French
£1923 $3019 €3000 Porteuses d'eau sur les bords nu Nil (26x33cm-10x13in) panel. 16-Dec-2 Gros & Delettrez, Paris #66/R est:3000-4500

£3526 $5571 €5500 Dans l'atelier (155x117cm-61x46in) s.d.1908 exhib. 18-Nov-2 Sotheby's, Paris #98/R
£11076 $17500 €17500 Fougeres geantes (87x76cm-34x30in) i.d.1952. 28-Nov-2 Piasa, Paris #20/R est:15000-18000
£12179 $19122 €19000 Bananiers au negresses (63x49cm-25x19in) s.i. on sand paper exec.c.1934 lit. 20-Nov-2 Binoche, Paris #52 est:15000-20000
£17949 $28359 €28000 Divan gris (128x190cm-50x75in) s.d.08 exhib. 18-Nov-2 Sotheby's, Paris #95/R est:30000
£22436 $35224 €35000 Souk aux djellabahs (42x53cm-17x21in) mono. s.i.verso panel painted 1920 exhib. 20-Nov-2 Claude Boisgirard, Paris #43/R est:24000-25000
£44872 $70449 €70000 Marche aux chameaux, Souk el Had Des An Zamer (76x106cm-30x42in) s. cardboard. 16-Dec-2 Gros & Delettrez, Paris #399/R est:50000-60000

Works on paper
£2244 $3545 €3500 Deux femmes assises (49x63cm-19x25in) s.i. sanguine. 18-Nov-2 Sotheby's, Paris #97/R est:3000
£19231 $30192 €30000 Midi sur la Casbah (61x52cm-24x20in) s.i. i.verso mixed media gold powder. 16-Dec-2 Gros & Delettrez, Paris #68/R est:30000-45000
£19872 $31199 €31000 Marche au Soudan francais, Mali (64x49cm-25x19in) s.i.d.46 gouache. 16-Dec-2 Gros & Delettrez, Paris #459/R est:15000-18000
£22436 $35224 €35000 Nu (70x44cm-28x17in) s.i. gouache gold powder. 20-Nov-2 Binoche, Paris #50 est:20000-30000
£25641 $40256 €40000 Penetration pacifique (47x62cm-19x24in) s.i. gouache gold powder. 20-Nov-2 Binoche, Paris #49 est:20000-30000
£26923 $42269 €42000 Kasbah du Grand Atlas (70x85cm-28x33in) s.i.d.1943 gouache. 10-Dec-2 Tajan, Paris #194/R est:45000
£32051 $50321 €50000 Porteuses d'amphore et couffin a Marrakech (55x46cm-22x18in) s.i. stump mixed media paper on panel. 10-Dec-2 Tajan, Paris #195/R est:40000
£38462 $60769 €60000 Nus aux dattes rouges (74x53cm-29x21in) s.i.d.1931 stump gouache htd exhib. 18-Nov-2 Sotheby's, Paris #96/R est:25000
£45946 $71676 €68000 Beautes noires (74x86cm-29x34in) s.i. mixed media. 31-Mar-3 Ribeyre & Baron, Paris #40/R est:20000-25000

MAJUMDAR, B (20th C) Indian
£1800 $2808 €2700 River landscape (51x69cm-20x27in) s.d.1943. 17-Oct-2 Bonhams, Knightsbridge #563/R est:2000-3000
£3000 $4680 €4500 Rural landscape (60x84cm-24x33in) s. 17-Oct-2 Bonhams, Knightsbridge #567/R est:3000-4000

MAJZNER, Victor (1945-) Australian
Works on paper
£575 $856 €863 Road 2000 (70x90cm-28x35in) W/C prov. 27-Aug-2 Christie's, Melbourne #167 est:1800-2500 (A.D 1500)
£1143 $1783 €1715 Book of origin (122x122cm-48x48in) s.d.1999 synthetic polymer paint canvas. 11-Nov-2 Deutscher-Menzies, Melbourne #142/R est:3000-5000 (A.D 3200)
£1571 $2451 €2357 Earth conceals (167x182cm-66x72in) s.d.1991 s.i.d.1991 verso synthetic polymer paint canvas. 11-Nov-2 Deutscher-Menzies, Melbourne #141/R est:4000-6000 (A.D 4400)
£2326 $3698 €3489 Earth flight (183x167cm-72x66in) s.d.1991 s.i.d.1991 verso synthetic polymer prov. 5-May-3 Sotheby's, Melbourne #299 est:6000-9000 (A.D 6000)
£2491 $3811 €3737 Guardian to our unremembered home (183x167cm-72x66in) s.d.1998 synthetic polymer on canvas. 25-Aug-2 Sotheby's, Paddington #109/R est:8000-12000 (A.D 7000)

MAK, Paul (20th C) Russian
Works on paper
£890 $1389 €1300 La flute de pan, Cupidon et faunesse sous le charme (27x18cm-11x7in) s.d.1954 mixed media. 14-Apr-3 Horta, Bruxelles #203

MAK, Petr Petrovich (1885-c.1960) Russian
£10000 $15800 €15000 Tristan and Isolde (80x70cm-31x28in) s.i.d.1946. 26-Nov-2 Christie's, Kensington #48/R est:12000-16000

MAKART, Hans (1840-1884) Austrian
£6962 $11000 €11000 Reclining Baccante (32x42cm-13x17in) canvas on canvas. 28-Nov-2 Dorotheum, Vienna #205/R est:11000-13000
£9000 $14310 €13500 Portrait of a lady in a black hat and fur trimmed coat (74x59cm-29x23in) 20-Mar-3 Christie's, Kensington #166/R est:10000-15000

Works on paper
£1006 $1570 €1600 Moses destroying the tablets (35x38cm-14x15in) pencil. 23-Sep-2 Wiener Kunst Auktionen, Vienna #53/R
£1090 $1711 €1700 Study for "Die Gaben der Erde" (29x38cm-11x15in) pencil. 21-Nov-2 Dorotheum, Vienna #397/R est:1200-2000
£1189 $1700 €1784 Study of one of the fates (51x44cm-20x17in) black crayon. 23-Jan-3 Swann Galleries, New York #385/R est:1000-1500

MAKART, Johann Baptist Alois (1815-1849) Austrian
£1233 $1923 €1800 Alpine lake at night (14x22cm-6x9in) s.d.1846 board. 10-Apr-3 Dorotheum, Vienna #43 est:1800-2000

MAKELA, Jukka (1949-) Finnish
£494 $796 €741 Untitled (46x91cm-18x36in) s.d.89 verso acrylic canvas on panel. 7-May-3 AB Stockholms Auktionsverk #1026/R (S.KR 6400)

MAKELA, Marika (1947-) Finnish
£3294 $5138 €4941 Once upon a time (230x150cm-91x59in) s.d.83 verso oil acrylic prov.exhib. 6-Nov-2 AB Stockholms Auktionsverk #904/R est:50000-60000 (S.KR 47000)

Works on paper
£645 $1019 €1000 Composition (55x75cm-22x30in) s. mixed media. 19-Dec-2 Hagelstam, Helsinki #923

MAKILA, Otto (1904-1955) Finnish
£2585 $4110 €3800 Composition with head of woman (36x37cm-14x15in) s.d.1949. 27-Feb-3 Hagelstam, Helsinki #988/R est:4000

Works on paper
£377 $581 €600 Nude (18x13cm-7x5in) s. W/C. 27-Oct-2 Bukowskis, Helsinki #244/R

MAKIN, Jeffrey (1943-) Australian
£2143 $3343 €3215 Cape Schanck (152x122cm-60x48in) s. exhib. 11-Nov-2 Deutscher-Menzies, Melbourne #143/R est:4000-6000 (A.D 6000)

MAKKINK, Jan Henri (1868-1953) Dutch
£310 $499 €440 Landscape with birch trees (16x33cm-6x13in) s.d.31. 6-May-3 Vendu Notarishuis, Rotterdam #12

MAKOKIAN, Vartan (1869-1937) Armenian
£2025 $3159 €3200 Boat at sunset (61x95cm-24x37in) s. 16-Sep-2 Horta, Bruxelles #86

MAKOVSKY, Konstantin (1839-1915) Russian
£12658 $20000 €18987 Boyar and boyarina (55x46cm-22x18in) s. 24-Apr-3 Sotheby's, New York #117/R est:20000-30000
£48000 $77760 €72000 Cavalier (41x27cm-16x11in) s. board. 21-May-3 Sotheby's, London #33/R est:8000-12000
£55000 $89100 €82500 Treasures in the Granovitaya Palata (80x60cm-31x24in) s. 21-May-3 Sotheby's, London #34/R est:12000-18000
£60000 $97200 €90000 Russian beauty in summer garland (35x27cm-14x11in) s. board. 21-May-3 Sotheby's, London #37/R est:35000-50000
£74038 $115500 €111057 Three-quarter length portrait of a lady (142x122cm-56x48in) s. oval prov. 28-Mar-3 Aspire, Cleveland #6/R est:20000-30000
£115000 $180550 €172500 Charka of Honey (93x72cm-37x28in) s. 20-Nov-2 Sotheby's, London #20/R est:50000-60000
£125000 $196250 €187500 Young Russian beauty in a kokoshnik (56x45cm-22x18in) s. board. 20-Nov-2 Sotheby's, London #24/R est:50000-70000

Works on paper
£321 $497 €500 Children's heads (27x19cm-11x7in) s.i.d.1903 W/C. 5-Dec-2 Schopman, Hamburg #537
£6608 $9846 €9912 Woman in costume carrying fruit bowl (39x25cm-15x10in) s. w/C. 25-Jun-2 Koller, Zurich #6655 est:800-1200 (S.FR 15000)

MAKOVSKY, Vladimir (1846-1920) Russian
£6211 $10000 €9317 Market day (30x51cm-12x20in) s.d.1891 panel. 19-Feb-3 Doyle, New York #73/R est:5000-7000
£14000 $22680 €21000 Dancing crane (36x27cm-14x11in) s.d.97. 21-May-3 Sotheby's, London #36/R est:8000-12000
£18440 $28582 €27660 The guitar player (31x40cm-12x16in) s.d.1895 panel. 4-Dec-2 AB Stockholms Auktionsverk #1849/R est:20000-25000 (S.KR 260000)
£20886 $33000 €31329 Elegant outing (41x27cm-16x11in) s.d.1877-1918 panel. 24-Apr-3 Sotheby's, New York #118/R est:15000-20000
£28481 $45000 €42722 Children's games (32x46cm-13x18in) s.d.1890 panel. 24-Apr-3 Sotheby's, New York #115/R est:25000-35000
£120000 $188400 €180000 Rest on the way from Kiev (101x139cm-40x55in) s.d.1888 prov.exhib.lit. 20-Nov-2 Sotheby's, London #19/R est:150000-200000

MAKOVSKY, Vladimir (attrib) (1846-1920) Russian
£3125 $5000 €4688 Young boy clutching his jacket and hat (34x23cm-13x9in) s.d.1871 panel. 14-May-3 Butterfields, San Francisco #1102/R est:5000-7000

MAKOWSKI, Alexander W (1869-1924) Russian
£6962 $11000 €11000 By the river (26x42cm-10x17in) s.d.97. 1-Dec-2 Bukowskis, Helsinki #265/R est:4500-5500

MAKOWSKI, Alexander W (attrib) (1869-1924) Russian
£4000 $6280 €6000 View of a Russian provincial church (29x41cm-11x16in) bears sig. 20-Nov-2 Sotheby's, London #22/R est:600-800

MAKOWSKI, Tade (1882-1932) Polish
£40541 $63243 €60000 Trois enfants sous les petits drapraux (40x49cm-16x19in) s. 28-Mar-3 Claude Aguttes, Neuilly #133/R est:60000-80000

MAKS, Cornelis Johannes (1876-1967) Dutch
£12658 $20000 €20000 Souvenir de Paris (42x72cm-17x28in) s. i.on stretcher painted c.1908. 26-Nov-2 Sotheby's, Amsterdam #115/R est:20000-30000
£22436 $34776 €35000 New dress (82x71cm-32x28in) s. prov. 3-Dec-2 Christie's, Amsterdam #194/R est:20000-30000
Works on paper
£1727 $2832 €2400 Horses in the ring (50x64cm-20x25in) s. W/C. 3-Jun-3 Christie's, Amsterdam #35/R est:2000-3000

MAL-KELBERGHE, Josef van (19th/20th C) Dutch
£258 $407 €387 Still life of flowers (80x60cm-31x24in) s. 29-Nov-2 Zofingen, Switzerland #2496 (S.FR 600)

MALACREA, Francesco (1812-1886) Italian
£638 $1034 €900 Natura morta con melone et fichi. Natura morta con ostriche e limone (21x31cm-8x12in) s. pair. 22-May-3 Stadion, Trieste #253/R
£709 $1149 €1000 Natura morta con melone (39x53cm-15x21in) 22-May-3 Stadion, Trieste #326/R
£833 $1292 €1300 Still life with parrot (31x24cm-12x9in) canvas on cardboard. 5-Dec-2 Stadion, Trieste #888/R
£1064 $1723 €1500 Il picchio (51x44cm-20x17in) s.i. 22-May-3 Stadion, Trieste #245/R est:700-1000
£1312 $2126 €1850 Natura morta con viole (58x45cm-23x18in) s. 22-May-3 Stadion, Trieste #252/R est:2000-3000
£1773 $2872 €2500 Grande natura morta di pesci e animali (108x87cm-43x34in) s.d.1873. 22-May-3 Stadion, Trieste #244/R est:2500-3500
£2949 $4571 €4600 Still life with melon and grapes (76x52cm-30x20in) 5-Dec-2 Stadion, Trieste #887/R

MALACREA, Francesco (attrib) (1812-1886) Italian
£709 $1149 €1000 Natura morta con pesche e bicchiere (39x53cm-15x21in) 22-May-3 Stadion, Trieste #325/R

MALATESTA, C (19th C) Italian
Sculpture
£3145 $4843 €5000 Lady (68cm-27in) bears sig.d.1868 white marble. 23-Oct-2 Finarte, Rome #129/R

MALATESTA, Giuseppe (c.1650-1719) Italian
£3846 $5962 €6000 Saint Romualdo with angel (133x97cm-52x38in) 4-Dec-2 Christie's, Rome #446/R est:6000-9000

MALAVAL, Robert (1937-1980) French
£586 $979 €850 Anne, genoux pubis (51x36cm-20x14in) s.i.d. acrylic. 9-Jul-3 Cornette de St.Cyr, Paris #315
£1735 $2758 €2500 Petit glaire (27x46cm-11x18in) s. i.d.avril 1961 verso oil gourdon paper mache panel prov. 29-Apr-3 Artcurial Briest, Paris #547/R est:1500-1800
£1736 $2865 €2500 Un carton dans le parking (100x81cm-39x32in) s.i.d.1980 acrylic silver spray prov. 3-Jul-3 Christie's, Paris #8/R est:3000-5000
£2917 $4638 €4200 SSSS (56x74cm-22x29in) s. acrylic glitter paper on canvas prov.exhib. 29-Apr-3 Artcurial Briest, Paris #546/R est:3000-4000
£14437 $23965 €20500 Rouge, blanc, bleu (150x150cm-59x59in) acrylic paillettes prov. 18-Jun-3 Anaf, Lyon #55/R est:5000-6000
Sculpture
£11111 $18333 €16000 Nicole G vue de dos (125x70x24cm-49x28x9in) s.i.d.1968 verso polyester prov. 3-Jul-3 Christie's, Paris #11/R est:3000-5000
Works on paper
£423 $701 €600 San Diego 2 (23x32cm-9x13in) s.i.d.dec.1974 verso wax pastel. 18-Jun-3 Anaf, Lyon #54/R
£612 $973 €900 Corps noir (52x38cm-20x15in) s.d.1959 ink wash. 24-Mar-3 Claude Boisgirard, Paris #170
£972 $1604 €1400 Untitled (29x21cm-11x8in) Indian ink tracing paper lit. 3-Jul-3 Christie's, Paris #116/R est:600-800
£4088 $6377 €6500 Boyauderie (50x70cm-20x28in) s.i.d.1962 mixed media exhib.lit. 11-Oct-2 Binoche, Paris #135/R

MALCHUS, Carl Freiherr von (1835-1889) German
£510 $795 €800 Fishing boat in Venice (13x33cm-5x13in) s.d.1882 panel. 6-Nov-2 Hugo Ruef, Munich #1199

MALCOLM, Ellen (1923-2002) British
£360 $562 €540 Children in the street, dusk (63x76cm-25x30in) s. 17-Oct-2 Bonhams, Edinburgh #17/R

MALCZEWSKI, Jacek (1854-1929) Polish
Works on paper
£353 $546 €550 Farmer's wife (25x16cm-10x6in) s. pencil dr lit. 7-Dec-2 Bergmann, Erlangen #850/R

MALCZEWSKI, Rafal (1892-1965) Polish
Works on paper
£217 $339 €363 Mts Unwin and Warren, Maligne Lake (36x51cm-14x20in) s. W/C paper on board. 13-Apr-3 Levis, Calgary #501/R (C.D 500)
£309 $475 €464 Chalets en hiver (34x49cm-13x19in) s. W/C. 22-Oct-2 Iegor de Saint Hippolyte, Montreal #68 (C.D 750)

MALDARELLI, Giuseppe (1885-1958) Italian
£952 $1514 €1400 Female nude (70x50cm-28x20in) s. 18-Mar-3 Finarte, Milan #209/R
£1020 $1622 €1500 Girl at window (70x50cm-28x20in) s. board. 1-Mar-3 Meeting Art, Vercelli #113

MALEAS, Constantine (1879-1928) Greek
£9000 $13950 €13500 Attiki (23x23cm-9x9in) s. board. 2-Oct-2 Sotheby's, London #43/R
£10000 $15800 €15000 Landscape in Attica (18x29cm-7x11in) 1-Apr-3 Bonhams, New Bond Street #54 est:10000-15000
£20000 $31000 €30000 Lavrio (33x46cm-13x18in) s. board painted c.1918-20. 2-Oct-2 Sotheby's, London #28/R est:15000-20000
£40000 $63200 €60000 Monastery, Kessariani (46x55cm-18x22in) painted c.1917. 1-Apr-3 Bonhams, New Bond Street #52 est:40000-50000

MALEMPRE, Leo (fl.1887-1901) British
£1310 $2070 €1900 Portrait en pied de SAR le prince Albert de Belgique en habit de marin (68x37cm-27x15in) s.d.1881. 2-Apr-3 Vanderkindere, Brussels #188/R est:300-400

MALERBA, Frank (1950-) Australian?
£1200 $1932 €1800 18 (152x101cm-60x40in) s. acrylic. 6-May-3 Christie's, Melbourne #230/R est:3000-5000 (A.D 3000)

MALESCI, Giovanni (1884-1969) Italian
£516 $815 €800 Euganei hills (32x46cm-13x18in) s.d.1961 cardboard on canvas. 18-Dec-2 Finarte, Milan #3
£851 $1379 €1200 Lavandaie a Bocca d'Arno (29x44cm-11x17in) s. board. 22-May-3 Stadion, Trieste #256/R
£1216 $1897 €1800 Wicker basket makers (49x70cm-19x28in) s. board. 28-Mar-3 Farsetti, Prato #699/R

MALESPINA, Louis Ferdinand (1874-1940) French
£775 $1286 €1100 Steeple chase (33x46cm-13x18in) s. 11-Jun-3 Beaussant & Lefèvre, Paris #102/R
£1056 $1754 €1500 Auteuil, riviere du huit (38x61cm-15x24in) s. panel. 11-Jun-3 Beaussant & Lefèvre, Paris #99/R est:1500-2000
£2075 $3217 €3300 Jockeys (55x74cm-22x29in) s. 5-Oct-2 De Vuyst, Lokeren #550/R est:4000-5000

MALET, Albert (1905-1986) French
£348 $543 €550 Villers-sur-Mer (46x65cm-18x26in) s. i.verso. 20-Oct-2 Chayette & Cheval, Paris #90
£506 $790 €800 Giverny, le jardin (54x65cm-21x26in) s. 20-Oct-2 Chayette & Cheval, Paris #89
£1139 $1777 €1800 Bord de mer (24x33cm-9x13in) s. panel. 20-Oct-2 Claude Boisgirard, Paris #15 est:1800-2200
£1392 $2172 €2200 Le remorqueur sur la Seine (38x61cm-15x24in) s. i.verso. 20-Oct-2 Mercier & Cie, Lille #326/R est:2000-2500
£1901 $3061 €2700 Barques de pecheurs a quai (50x65cm-20x26in) s. 11-May-3 Lombrail & Teucquam, Paris #227/R
£3095 $4921 €4550 Meules (46x65cm-18x26in) s. 2-Mar-3 Lombrail & Teucquam, Paris #184

MALET, Guy (1900-1973) British
Works on paper
£280 $445 €420 Dixcart Bay, Sark (29x46cm-11x18in) s. W/C. 20-Mar-3 Martel Maides, Guernsey #57

MALEVAL, Henri (20th C) French
£377 $581 €600 Palmerai de gabes (32x45cm-13x18in) s.i. cardboard. 23-Oct-2 Rabourdin & Choppin de Janvry, Paris #88/R

MALEVICH, Kasimir (1878-1935) Russian
Works on paper
£7692 $11923 €12000 Suprematist composition (21x19cm-8x7in) pencil prov.exhib. 4-Dec-2 Lempertz, Koln #872/R est:15000-18000
£10256 $16000 €15384 Suprematist composition (18x11cm-7x4in) pencil exec.c.1920. 18-Sep-2 Swann Galleries, New York #33/R est:15000-20000

MALFAIT, Hubert (1898-1971) Belgian
£629 $969 €1000 Travail au champ (64x81cm-25x32in) s. 22-Oct-2 Campo, Vlaamse Kaai #554/R
£5479 $8548 €8000 La chevre (80x64cm-31x25in) s. i.verso. 14-Apr-3 Horta, Bruxelles #126/R est:10000-15000
£5556 $8833 €8000 Chenal (65x80cm-26x31in) s. 29-Apr-3 Campo, Vlaamse Kaai #203/R est:8000-9000
£6329 $9873 €10000 Mare and foal (49x67cm-19x26in) s. 21-Oct-2 Bernaerts, Antwerp #539/R est:10000-15000
£7092 $11844 €10000 Cavaliers dans le bois (61x75cm-24x30in) s. 17-Jun-3 Palais de Beaux Arts, Brussels #607/R est:7500-10000
£10828 $16892 €17000 Deux paysans sur une charrette attelee faisant la recolte (50x68cm-20x27in) mono. 11-Nov-2 Horta, Bruxelles #189/R est:20000-30000
Works on paper
£417 $646 €650 Potatoes (26x34cm-10x13in) s. felt-tip pen dr. 7-Dec-2 De Vuyst, Lokeren #209

MALFAIT, Hubert (attrib) (1898-1971) Belgian
£3448 $5517 €5000 Barques de peche sur la plage (49x65cm-19x26in) 17-Mar-3 Amberes, Antwerp #234/R

MALFRAY, Charles Alexandre (1887-1940) French
£2532 $4000 €4000 Martigues (38x55cm-15x22in) s.d.1908. 2-Dec-2 Rieunier, Paris #8/R
Sculpture
£1100 $1705 €1650 Etude d'une figure allegorique (22cm-9in) s.d.1927 num.6/8 green pat. bronze st.f.Valauani. 5-Dec-2 Christie's, Kensington #43/R est:1000-1500
£1200 $1860 €1800 Tete de jeune femme (12cm-5in) num.5/8 brown pat. bronze. 5-Dec-2 Christie's, Kensington #42/R est:1000-1500
£1309 $2107 €1950 Baigneuse (34cm-13in) num.4/8 brown pat bronze Cast Valsuani. 23-Feb-3 Lesieur & Le Bars, Le Havre #109/R
£1761 $2835 €2500 Femme drapee (61cm-24in) num 5/8 brown green pat bronze f.Godard cire perdue. 12-May-3 Lesieur & Le Bars, Le Havre #68/R
£3821 $5961 €6000 Printemps (60cm-24in) s.st.f.Rudier num.3/9 black pat bronze. 6-Nov-2 Tajan, Paris #10/R est:6000-8000
£4564 $7348 €6800 Sur les cimes de l'Olympe (83x33x56cm-33x13x22in) num.1/8 gold brown pat bronze Cast Alexis Rodier. 23-Feb-3 Lesieur & Le Bars, Le Havre #101/R

MALFROY, Charles (1862-1918) French
£926 $1315 €1500 Petite barque pres des Martigues (18x24cm-7x9in) s. panel. 16-Mar-3 Eric Pillon, Calais #100/R
£1037 $1700 €1556 Port scene (33x41cm-13x16in) s. panel. 5-Feb-3 Doyle, New York #43/R est:1500-2000
£3287 $5489 €4700 Martigues, le port (50x73cm-20x29in) s.indis.d.1894. 27-Jun-3 Claude Aguttes, Neuilly #41/R est:5000-6000
£3378 $5270 €5000 Petit port (46x65cm-18x26in) s. 28-Mar-3 Claude Aguttes, Neuilly #130b/R
£3648 $5618 €5800 Caiques sur le Bosphore (46x65cm-18x26in) s. 23-Oct-2 Rabourdin & Choppin de Janvry, Paris #76/R
£4194 $6626 €6500 Petit port (46x55cm-18x22in) s. 19-Dec-2 Claude Aguttes, Neuilly #221/R
£5944 $9927 €8500 Martigues (65x92cm-26x36in) s. 27-Jun-3 Claude Aguttes, Neuilly #42/R est:6000-8000

MALFROY, Henry (1895-1944) French
£961 $1519 €1500 Martigues en Provence (31x60cm-12x24in) s. panel. 18-Nov-2 Tajan, Paris #200/R est:1200-1500
£1203 $1900 €1900 Martigues (38x55cm-15x22in) 27-Nov-2 Blanchet, Paris #11/R
£1783 $2782 €2800 Village en Mediterranee (49x63cm-19x25in) s. canvas on panel. 11-Nov-2 Horta, Bruxelles #660 est:1000-1500
£2051 $3241 €3200 Martigues (11x16cm-4x6in) two mono. cardboard three in one frame. 18-Nov-2 Tajan, Paris #201 est:1200-1500
£2179 $3422 €3400 Paris, peniches a quai (36x46cm-14x18in) s.d.1919. 15-Dec-2 Eric Pillon, Calais #96/R
£2692 $4227 €4200 Port de martigues (46x65cm-18x26in) s. 22-Nov-2 Millon & Associes, Paris #74/R
£5743 $8959 €8500 View of Venice (60x92cm-24x36in) s. 28-Mar-3 Claude Aguttes, Neuilly #47/R
£7372 $11574 €11500 Caique sur le Bosphore (54x65cm-21x26in) s. 16-Dec-2 Gros & Delettrez, Paris #250/R est:5500-6500

MALHERBE, Louis (19th C) French
Works on paper
£321 $487 €500 Famille d'astro-physicien sur la terrase de sa maison (49x69cm-19x27in) s.indis.d.188 W/C gouache. 10-Jul-2 Rabourdin & Choppin de Janvry, Paris #102

MALHERBE, William (1884-1951) French
£878 $1370 €1300 Nature morte au vase de fleurs (54x45cm-21x18in) s.d.1913. 26-Mar-3 Millon & Associes, Paris #97
£1013 $1600 €1600 Bouquet (33x24cm-13x9in) s. panel. 27-Nov-2 Blanchet, Paris #26/R
£1013 $1600 €1600 Bouquet (32x24cm-13x9in) s. panel. 27-Nov-2 Blanchet, Paris #24/R
£1014 $1581 €1500 Jeune femme a la rose (59x45cm-23x18in) s. 26-Mar-3 Millon & Associes, Paris #95
£3716 $5797 €5500 Ete au jardin (66x81cm-26x32in) s.d.1927. 26-Mar-3 Millon & Associes, Paris #93/R

MALI, Christian (1832-1906) German
£482 $800 €699 Rural landscape with figures (30x61cm-12x24in) s. 11-Jun-3 Boos Gallery, Michigan #554/R
£541 $843 €800 Sheep in mountain landscape (28x24cm-11x9in) s. canvas on board prov. 27-Mar-3 Dr Fritz Nagel, Stuttgart #835/R
£574 $896 €850 Goat in extensive landscape (31x23cm-12x9in) i. verso canvas on board. 27-Mar-3 Dr Fritz Nagel, Stuttgart #836/R
£1013 $1570 €1600 Animals on path down from mountain pasture (43x31cm-17x12in) canvas on board. 25-Sep-2 Neumeister, Munich #645/R
£1351 $2108 €2000 Sheep (31x36cm-12x14in) canvas on board. 27-Mar-3 Dr Fritz Nagel, Stuttgart #838/R est:2000
£1351 $2108 €2000 Herdress with cows by village pond (14x36cm-6x14in) s. panel. 27-Mar-3 Dr Fritz Nagel, Stuttgart #839/R est:2800
£1646 $2551 €2600 Herdress with animals drinking at lakeshore (51x36cm-20x14in) s.i. bears d. 25-Sep-2 Neumeister, Munich #644/R est:2500
£2806 $4489 €3900 Alpine landscape with peasants harvesting (36x45cm-14x18in) s. panel. 17-May-3 Lempertz, Koln #1431/R est:4000
£8451 $13606 €12000 Upper Swabian village in summer (42x55cm-17x22in) s.d.1860 board. 7-May-3 Michael Zeller, Lindau #822/R est:12000

MALI, Hubertus (1818-1839) German
£968 $1423 €1500 Wooded, hilly landscape (62x83cm-24x33in) s. prov. 20-Jun-2 Dr Fritz Nagel, Stuttgart #793/R

MALIAR, Neznamy Madarsky (20th C) Czechoslovakian
£458 $710 €687 Still life with porcelain (67x53cm-26x21in) painted c.1910. 3-Dec-2 SOGA, Bratislava #93/R (SL.K 29000)

MALIAVINE, Philippe (1869-1940) Russian
£813 $1318 €1179 Portrait of merchant Johan Havemann (100x80cm-39x31in) s.d.1940. 24-May-3 Rasmussen, Havnen #4371/R (D.KR 8500)
£1923 $2981 €3000 Jeune russe au chale colore (36x50cm-14x20in) cardboard. 6-Dec-2 Rieunier, Bailly-Pommery, Mathias, Paris #85/R est:3500
£9000 $14130 €13500 Summer fun in the fields (38x61cm-15x24in) s. 20-Nov-2 Sotheby's, London #139/R est:6000-8000
£32278 $50354 €51000 Portrait de paysanne (92x73cm-36x29in) s.i. 18-Oct-2 Rabourdin & Choppin de Janvry, Paris #34/R est:4000
£45000 $70650 €67500 Dancing to the accordion (81x130cm-32x51in) s. i.verso. 20-Nov-2 Sotheby's, London #95/R est:25000-35000
£45000 $72900 €67500 Russian beauty with beads and scarf (100x79cm-39x31in) s. 21-May-3 Sotheby's, London #129/R est:40000-60000
£65000 $105300 €97500 Showing off the new arrival (81x100cm-32x39in) s. 21-May-3 Sotheby's, London #132/R est:50000-70000
£190000 $307800 €285000 Nude lady in floral hat (143x97cm-56x38in) s. prov. 21-May-3 Sotheby's, London #130/R est:50000-70000
Works on paper
£252 $387 €400 Michele Biancale and his family (42x31cm-17x12in) s.d.1932 mixed media. 28-Oct-2 Il Ponte, Milan #191
£432 $708 €600 Two girls (43x32cm-17x13in) s. dr. 4-Jun-3 Bukowskis, Helsinki #488/R
£541 $843 €800 Portrait d'une elegante (32x20cm-13x8in) conte crayon. 25-Mar-3 Chochon-Barre & Allardi, Paris #165/R
£543 $880 €787 Russian peasant woman (31x28cm-12x11in) s. pencil prov. 25-May-3 Uppsala Auktionskammare, Uppsala #132/R (S.KR 7000)
£582 $943 €844 Russian peasant (31x28cm-12x11in) s. pencil prov. 25-May-3 Uppsala Auktionskammare, Uppsala #133/R (S.KR 7500)
£755 $1239 €1050 Women (30x40cm-12x16in) s. dr. 4-Jun-3 Bukowskis, Helsinki #490/R
£791 $1298 €1100 Gustav V (44x30cm-17x12in) s. mixed media. 4-Jun-3 Bukowskis, Helsinki #489/R
£950 $1501 €1425 Two peasant women (45x33cm-18x13in) s. pastel. 26-Nov-2 Christie's, Kensington #46/R
£1396 $2262 €2024 Russian peasant woman (31x24cm-12x9in) s. chk prov. 25-May-3 Uppsala Auktionskammare, Uppsala #131/R est:10000-12000 (S.KR 18000)
£1800 $2916 €2700 Young women (21x30cm-8x12in) s. pencil set of five. 21-May-3 Sotheby's, London #100 est:1800-2500
£2000 $3140 €3000 Peasant couple (41x30cm-16x12in) s. pencil crayon. 20-Nov-2 Sotheby's, London #96/R est:3000-5000
£2200 $3454 €3300 Peasant girls (28x20cm-11x8in) s. pencil seven. 20-Nov-2 Sotheby's, London #93/R est:1500-2000

£2400 $3768 €3600 Peasant girls (28x20cm-11x8in) s. pencil one htd crayon seven. 20-Nov-2 Sotheby's, London #94/R est:1500-2000
£8400 $13944 €8400 Rejouissances paysannes (55x72cm-22x28in) s. mixed media two. 16-Jun-3 Horta, Bruxelles #303 est:600-800

MALIK (20th C) ?
£14000 $22680 €21000 Vision of paradise (131x138cm-52x54in) s.d.1918. 21-May-3 Sotheby's, London #119/R est:10000-15000

MALINCONICO, Nicola (1654-1721) Italian
Works on paper
£1111 $1800 €1667 Jonah and the whale (26x43cm-10x17in) pen ink wash over chk prov. 21-Jan-3 Sotheby's, New York #162/R

MALINOWSKI, Adam (1829-1892) Polish
£4359 $6756 €6800 Extensive landscape with farmsteads and figures (56x70cm-22x28in) s.d.1868 lit. 6-Dec-2 Karlheinz Kaupp, Staufen #2339/R est:6800

MALISSARD, Georges (1877-1942) French
Sculpture
£2089 $3258 €3300 Jeanette (34x36cm-13x14in) s.d.1909 pat bronze st.f.Siot. 20-Oct-2 Mercier & Cie, Lille #131/R est:3500-4000

MALKINE, Georges (1898-1970) French
£20548 $32055 €30000 Espoir (35x27cm-14x11in) s.d.1926 verso. 14-Apr-3 Laurence Calmels, Paris #4008/R est:9000
Works on paper
£3767 $5914 €5500 Untitled (32x25cm-13x10in) Chinese ink exhib. 15-Apr-3 Laurence Calmels, Paris #4343/R est:4000
£6164 $9678 €9000 Sirenes (32x25cm-13x10in) Chinese ink exhib. 15-Apr-3 Laurence Calmels, Paris #4342/R est:4000
£6849 $10753 €10000 Untitled (25x32cm-10x13in) Chinese ink exhib. 15-Apr-3 Laurence Calmels, Paris #4345/R est:4000
£7534 $11829 €11000 Untitled (25x32cm-10x13in) Chinese ink exhib. 15-Apr-3 Laurence Calmels, Paris #4344/R est:4000
£8219 $12904 €12000 Escalier chaud (63x48cm-25x19in) s.i.d.27 gouache ink wax crayon collage exhib. 15-Apr-3 Laurence Calmels, Paris #4348/R est:6000
£9589 $15055 €14000 Denrees (48x63cm-19x25in) s.i.d.1927 gouache ink wax crayon collage exhib. 15-Apr-3 Laurence Calmels, Paris #4349/R est:6000
£10959 $17205 €16000 Boudoir (48x63cm-19x25in) s.i.d.27 gouache ink wax crayon exhib. 15-Apr-3 Laurence Calmels, Paris #4350/R est:6000
£13699 $21507 €20000 Visit (48x63cm-19x25in) s.i.d.27 gouache ink crayon collage exhib. 15-Apr-3 Laurence Calmels, Paris #4347/R est:6000
£17808 $27959 €26000 Place Falguiere (63x48cm-25x19in) s.i.d.27 gouache ink graphite exhib. 15-Apr-3 Laurence Calmels, Paris #4346/R est:6000

MALLARME, Stephane (19th C) French
Prints
£2778 $4417 €4000 Pages. i. eau forte one of 50 exec.1891. 29-Apr-3 Piasa, Paris #269 est:1500-1800

MALLE, Charles (1935-) French
£669 $1077 €950 L'arrivee du poisson (33x41cm-13x16in) s. 12-May-3 Lesieur & Le Bars, Le Havre #69
£689 $1151 €1000 Paris, le Pont des Invalides (46x55cm-18x22in) s. 10-Jul-3 Artcurial Briest, Paris #286
£823 $1284 €1300 Le manege anime (46x55cm-18x22in) s. 20-Oct-2 Charbonneaux, Paris #142 est:1300-1500
£833 $1308 €1300 Nantes (46x55cm-18x22in) s. 15-Dec-2 Eric Pillon, Calais #212/R
£863 $1381 €1200 Neuilly-sur-Seine, rue de Chartres (33x46cm-13x18in) s. 18-May-3 Charbonneaux, Paris #178 est:1800-2000
£864 $1227 €1400 Plage animee a Lions-sur-Mer (50x65cm-20x26in) s. 16-Mar-3 Eric Pillon, Calais #224/R
£897 $1409 €1400 Neige sur le rivage Gayant (54x65cm-21x26in) s. s.i.verso. 16-Dec-2 Charbonneaux, Paris #276/R
£935 $1496 €1300 Le pont tournant du Treport (46x55cm-18x22in) s. 18-May-3 Eric Pillon, Calais #258/R
£1079 $1727 €1500 Paris, quai de l'Hotel de Ville, St Gervais (54x65cm-21x26in) s. 18-May-3 Charbonneaux, Paris #177/R est:1800-2000
£1389 $2209 €2000 Paris, quai de Seine (54x73cm-21x29in) s. 29-Apr-3 Artcurial Briest, Paris #195 est:2300-2500
£1656 $2699 €2500 Paris, Place Pigalle sous la neige (60x73cm-24x29in) s. 31-Jan-3 Charbonneaux, Paris #131/R est:2500-3000
£1772 $2747 €2800 Rue a Montmartre (73x92cm-29x36in) s. 29-Sep-2 Eric Pillon, Calais #261/R
Works on paper
£1007 $1621 €1500 Normandie, plage de Houlgate (50x61cm-20x24in) s. 23-Feb-3 Lesieur & Le Bars, Le Havre #111

MALLEBRANCHE, Louis-Claude (1790-1838) French
£1548 $2400 €2322 Skaters in a snowy landscape (65x93cm-26x37in) s. prov. 3-Dec-2 Christie's, Rockefeller NY #655/R est:3000-5000
£2878 $4604 €4000 La porte Saint-Andre de Versailles (32x40cm-13x16in) panel. 15-May-3 Christie's, Paris #457/R est:4000-6000
£3061 $4867 €4500 Convoi militaire sous la neige (27x40cm-11x16in) s. 26-Feb-3 Marc Kohn, Paris #26/R

MALLEBRANCHE, Louis-Claude (attrib) (1790-1838) French
£755 $1162 €1200 Paysage de neige (23x27cm-9x11in) panel. 25-Oct-2 Tajan, Paris #158

MALLET, Jean Baptiste (1759-1835) French
Works on paper
£5128 $7949 €8000 Deux femmes dans un interieur (20x14cm-8x6in) W/C gouache. 4-Dec-2 Piasa, Paris #106/R
£6901 $11456 €9800 Le bouillon de l'accouchee (31x39cm-12x15in) gouache prov. 13-Jun-3 Rossini, Paris #79/R est:10000-12000

MALLET, Jean Baptiste (attrib) (1759-1835) French
Works on paper
£577 $912 €900 Two women in studio (26x20cm-10x8in) W/C. 16-Nov-2 Lempertz, Koln #1258

MALLINA, Erich (1873-1954) Austrian
£448 $717 €650 In the grotto (55x37cm-22x15in) mixed media gold silver. 11-Mar-3 Dorotheum, Vienna #49/R
Works on paper
£360 $562 €540 Composition (30x41cm-12x16in) pencil ink gouache gold silver paint. 15-Oct-2 Bonhams, Knightsbridge #144/R
£1457 $2375 €2200 Woodland fairies (20x20cm-8x8in) gouache. 28-Jan-3 Dorotheum, Vienna #25/R est:1300-1800

MALLINSON, Ethel M (fl.1917-1940) British
Works on paper
£280 $440 €420 Washerwoman, Baveno (31x40cm-12x16in) s.d.28 W/C. 16-Dec-2 Bonhams, Bury St Edmunds #374

MALLO, Cristino (1905-1987) Spanish?
Works on paper
£270 $422 €400 Vase of flowers (18x12cm-7x5in) s. mixed media. 25-Mar-3 Durán, Madrid #641/R
£271 $428 €420 Woman cuddling baby (29x22cm-11x9in) s. wash col pencil. 17-Dec-2 Segre, Madrid #117/R
£323 $510 €500 Maternity (34x22cm-13x9in) s. ink wash. 17-Dec-2 Segre, Madrid #119/R
£403 $648 €600 Vase of flowers (22x19cm-9x7in) s. gouache. 18-Feb-3 Durán, Madrid #109/R

MALLO, Maruja (1908-1995) Spanish
£178082 $277808 €260000 Scarecrows (138x198cm-54x78in) s.d.1930 prov.exhib.lit. 14-Apr-3 Laurence Calmels, Paris #4048/R est:80000

MALLOCH, Stirling (19/20th C) British
£250 $398 €375 My mother bade me braid my hair (30x23cm-12x9in) board exhib. 6-Mar-3 Christie's, Kensington #116/R

MALLOL SUAZO, Josep M (1910-1986) Spanish
£4605 $7461 €7000 Young lady with shawl (59x38cm-23x15in) s. board. 21-Jan-3 Ansorena, Madrid #159/R est:5500
£11373 $18651 €17400 Woman (81x60cm-32x24in) 5-Feb-3 Arte, Seville #768/R

MALLY, Gustav (1879-1952) Czechoslovakian
£693 $984 €1040 Sitting nude (40x30cm-16x12in) painted c.1910-12. 26-Mar-2 SOGA, Bratislava #45/R (SL.K 44000)
£2048 $3174 €3072 Portrait of Andrej Hlinka (120x90cm-47x35in) painted c.1930. 1-Oct-2 SOGA, Bratislava #41/R est:130000 (SL.K 130000)
£4883 $7129 €7325 Women in a field (71x82cm-28x32in) painted c.1935-37. 4-Jun-2 SOGA, Bratislava #53a/R est:220000 (SL.K 310000)

MALM, Ulla (20th C) Finnish
£1020 $1622 €1500 Landscape (70x59cm-28x23in) s. 27-Feb-3 Hagelstam, Helsinki #1013 est:2000
£1727 $2763 €2400 Coastal landscape (66x78cm-26x31in) s. 17-May-3 Hagelstam, Helsinki #181/R est:2500

MALMBERG, Victor (1867-1936) Finnish
Sculpture
£1197 $1927 €1700 The summer girl (45cm-18in) s. bronze. 10-May-3 Bukowskis, Helsinki #8/R est:1000-1300

MALMSTROM, August (1829-1901) Swedish
£635 $997 €953 Girls on bridge (49x36cm-19x14in) 16-Dec-2 Lilla Bukowskis, Stockholm #876 (S.KR 9000)
£1021 $1675 €1480 Children on stone bridge (49x36cm-19x14in) 4-Jun-3 AB Stockholms Auktionsverk #2197/R (S.KR 13000)
£5674 $8794 €8511 Youth (70x58cm-28x23in) lit. 3-Dec-2 Bukowskis, Stockholm #281/R est:100000-125000 (S.KR 80000)
£11348 $17589 €17022 In confidence - boys in backyard (60x40cm-24x16in) s. lit. 3-Dec-2 Bukowskis, Stockholm #369/R est:200000-225000 (S.KR 160000)
Works on paper
£309 $481 €464 Fairy dance (73x51cm-29x20in) s. W/C. 13-Sep-2 Lilla Bukowskis, Stockholm #725 (S.KR 4500)
£1439 $2302 €2000 Scene from the Finnish war 1808-09 with soldiers marching (47x70cm-19x28in) s. gouache en grisaille. 17-May-3 Hagelstam, Helsinki #35/R est:2000

MALMSTROM, Henning (1890-1968) Swedish
£309 $488 €464 Flowers in jug (90x70cm-35x28in) s.d.19. 30-Nov-2 Goteborg Auktionsverk, Sweden #582/R (S.KR 4400)

MALONE, Electra (20th C) American
Works on paper
£417 $650 €626 Down San Antonio (53x28cm-21x11in) W/C. 19-Oct-2 David Dike, Dallas #321/R

MALONEY, Martin (1961-C) British
£830 $1294 €1245 Beauty with cruelty (167x198cm-66x78in) s.i.d.1999 verso prov. 6-Nov-2 Dobiaschofsky, Bern #801/R (S.FR 1900)
£1500 $2505 €2175 Untitled portrait, lilac sweater (76x56cm-30x22in) s.i.d.Nov. 1966 verso oil pastel paper prov. 24-Jun-3 Sotheby's, Olympia #12/R est:1500-2000
£6000 $10020 €8700 Baby, baby, baby (244x549cm-96x216in) s.i.d.1999 stretcher two panels after Poussin prov. 24-Jun-3 Sotheby's, Olympia #18/R est:6000-8000
£8500 $14195 €12325 Gemma III (61x45cm-24x18in) s.i.d.1999 stretcher prov. 26-Jun-3 Sotheby's, London #289/R est:3000-4000

MALPIERI, Roniolo (19th C) Italian
Sculpture
£5769 $8942 €9000 Madness (237cm-93in) s. bronze exec.1892. 4-Dec-2 Finarte, Rome #112/R est:4000

MALRIC, Charles Louis (1872-1942) French
Sculpture
£3846 $6038 €6000 Nu aux roses (87cm-34in) white marble. 22-Nov-2 Millon & Associes, Paris #152 est:1000-1500
£8000 $13360 €11600 Adolesence (87cm-34in) s. white marble. 8-Jul-3 Sotheby's, London #222/R est:8000-12000

MALSKAT, Lothar (1913-1988) German
£570 $900 €900 Corn field with poppies (70x60cm-28x24in) s. i.verso. 29-Nov-2 Bolland & Marotz, Bremen #891/R
Works on paper
£634 $1020 €900 Waterlilies (72x55cm-28x22in) s.mono. gouache lit. 9-May-3 Schloss Ahlden, Ahlden #1549/R
£634 $1020 €900 Sunflowers (46x96cm-18x38in) s.mono. W/C lit. 9-May-3 Schloss Ahlden, Ahlden #1550/R

MALSKAT, Lothar (attrib) (1913-1988) German
Works on paper
£276 $436 €400 Sunflowers in garden (68x52cm-27x20in) W/C gouache. 5-Apr-3 Hans Stahl, Hamburg #101/R

MALTBY, Peg (1899-1984) Australian
Works on paper
£681 $1035 €1022 Berry vendor (28x22cm-11x9in) s. W/C. 27-Aug-2 Goodman, Sydney #41 (A.D 1900)
£753 $1144 €1130 Singing together (28x22cm-11x9in) s. W/C. 27-Aug-2 Goodman, Sydney #40/R (A.D 2100)
£824 $1253 €1236 Fairy and bush babies (27x21cm-11x8in) s. W/C. 27-Aug-2 Goodman, Sydney #42/R (A.D 2300)

MALTERRE, Andre (1889-?) French
£448 $713 €650 SL. (90x146cm-35x57in) s.d.1916. 4-Mar-3 Ansorena, Madrid #7/R

MALTHOUSE, Eric (1914-1997) British
£400 $624 €600 Two pigeons, pigeons view (41x33cm-16x13in) s. canvas on panel. 11-Sep-2 Bonhams, Newport #384
£420 $668 €630 Family at work (45x24cm-18x9in) s. 5-Mar-3 Bonhams, Bury St Edmunds #399
£1200 $1872 €1800 Still life (76x55cm-30x22in) s. 12-Sep-2 Sotheby's, Olympia #142/R est:1000-1500
£1400 $2184 €2100 Drying surgical instruments. Cleaning operating theatre (46x60cm-18x24in) s.d.49 two. 27-Mar-3 Christie's, Kensington #576/R est:600-800

MALTINO, Francis (attrib) (?) Italian
£280 $454 €406 Waiting for the tide. board. 23-May-3 Dee Atkinson & Harrison, Driffield #635a/R

MALTON, James (attrib) (1761-1803) British
Works on paper
£380 $585 €570 Figures and horses (25x38cm-10x15in) pen ink wash. 25-Oct-2 Gorringes, Lewes #874

MALTON, Thomas (jnr) (1748-1804) British
Works on paper
£1850 $3034 €2775 St. Paul's Cathedral (31x23cm-12x9in) i.on mount pencil W/C htd white. 4-Feb-3 Bonhams, Leeds #313 est:1000-1500

MALVITO DE SUMALVITO, Giovanni Tommaso (16th C) Italian
Sculpture
£17361 $27604 €25000 Angels (84cm-33in) white marble pair. 4-May-3 Finarte, Venice #619/R est:25000-26000

MALY, Elga (1921-) German
£481 $745 €750 Untitled (80x100cm-31x39in) s. acrylic mixed media. 5-Dec-2 Dorotheum, Graz #41/R

MALY, Jan (?) ?
£759 $1200 €1200 Family dressed in Sunday best in meadow (61x70cm-24x28in) s. 29-Nov-2 Schloss Ahlden, Ahlden #1384/R

MALY, Michel (1936-) French
£420 $659 €630 Morning mist Venice (34x54cm-13x21in) s. 10-Dec-2 Lane, Penzance #46

MALY, Vaclav (1874-1935) Czechoslovakian
£351 $554 €527 Forest (68x47cm-27x19in) s.d.1902. 30-Nov-2 Dorotheum, Prague #63/R (C.KR 17000)

MAMBELLI, Adriana (20th C) Italian
£641 $1006 €1000 Nude on the sofa (50x70cm-20x28in) s. s.i.d.1999 verso. 21-Nov-2 Finarte, Rome #199/R

MAMBOUR, Auguste (1896-1968) Belgian
£1538 $2415 €2400 Le pianiste (54x65cm-21x26in) s.i.d.1918. 11-Dec-2 Hotel des Ventes Mosan, Brussels #298/R est:1800-2200
£3767 $5877 €5500 Jeune fille nue de face (35x26cm-14x10in) s. cardboard. 14-Apr-3 Horta, Bruxelles #124/R est:5000-7000
£7643 $11924 €12000 Maternite (61x41cm-24x16in) s. panel. 11-Nov-2 Horta, Bruxelles #166/R est:10000-15000
Works on paper
£1736 $2760 €2500 Femme nue assise (66x46cm-26x18in) s. dr. 29-Apr-3 Campo & Campo, Antwerp #208/R est:800-1200

MAMMEN, Jeanne (1890-1976) German
£1887 $2906 €3000 Still life with violin (71x49cm-28x19in) s.1933-36 board. 26-Oct-2 Dr Lehr, Berlin #294/R est:4000
Works on paper
£1408 $2338 €2000 Female nude sitting on chair (48x31cm-19x12in) mono. pencil. 14-Jun-3 Hauswedell & Nolte, Hamburg #1371/R est:1600

MAMMEN, Olga (19th C) ?
£431 $659 €647 Still life of flowers (95x64cm-37x25in) s.d.20/12 1890. 24-Aug-2 Rasmussen, Havnen #2197/R (D.KR 5000)

MAMMERI, Azouaou (1890-1954) Algerian
£481 $750 €722 Street in Morocco (46x56cm-18x22in) s. indis.i.stretcher. 9-Oct-2 Doyle, New York #69
£1034 $1655 €1500 Casbah de l'Atlas, Maroc (32x41cm-13x16in) s. panel. 12-Mar-3 E & Eve, Paris #93 est:1500-1800
Works on paper
£769 $1208 €1200 Le conteur (24x31cm-9x12in) s. gouache. 16-Dec-2 Gros & Delettrez, Paris #426

MAN, Cornelis de (1621-1706) Dutch

£38000 $59280 €57000 Interior of elegant town house with couple by fire (66x80cm-26x31in) s. prov. 10-Apr-3 Sotheby's, London #41/R est:40000

MAN-RAY (1890-1976) American

£1346 $1965 €2100 Le serieux (61x43cm-24x17in) s.i. assemblage lit.exhib. 4-Jun-2 Karl & Faber, Munich #345/R est:4000
£13699 $21507 €20000 Untitled (37x46cm-15x18in) s.d.1927. 15-Apr-3 Laurence Calmels, Paris #4351/R est:15000
£18000 $29520 €27000 Pain (38x46cm-15x18in) s.d.1926 s.i.d.on stretcher prov.exhib. 5-Feb-3 Sotheby's, London #192/R est:30000
£22000 $36080 €33000 Wave (27x35cm-11x14in) s.d.1923 panel. 4-Feb-3 Christie's, London #320/R est:30000
£25000 $41750 €36250 Voiliers (38x46cm-15x18in) s.d.1924. 25-Jun-3 Christie's, London #209/R est:25000-35000
£26000 $42640 €39000 Swedish landscape (46x65cm-18x26in) s. painted c.1924-25 prov.exhib.lit. 5-Feb-3 Sotheby's, London #191/R est:35000
£34932 $54842 €51000 Femme figure (35x26cm-14x10in) s.d.1923 panel exhib. 15-Apr-3 Laurence Calmels, Paris #4352/R est:25000
£60000 $97800 €90000 Narcissus (35x27cm-14x11in) s.d.1917 s.i.d.verso panel oval prov.exhib.lit. 3-Feb-3 Christie's, London #154/R est:90000
£958904 $1495890 €1400000 Impossibilite dancer-danger (61x35cm-24x14in) s.i.d.20 paint exhib.lit. 14-Apr-3 Laurence Calmels, Paris #4050/R est:1200000

Photographs

£1899 $3000 €3000 Adi et nush (7x5cm-3x2in) silver print prov.lit. 26-Nov-2 Sotheby's, Amsterdam #190/R est:2000-3000
£2000 $3240 €3000 Yeswant Rao Holkar Bahadur, Maharadja of Indore (23x17cm-9x7in) s.i. silver print card exec.c.1930. 22-May-3 Sotheby's, London #83/R est:1000-1500
£2532 $4000 €3798 Bettina (29x22cm-11x9in) s.i. gelatin silver print mounted on board prov. 24-Apr-3 Phillips, New York #96/R est:4000-6000
£2532 $4000 €3798 Nude study (8x6cm-3x2in) photograph prov.exhib. 23-Apr-3 Sotheby's, New York #168/R est:5000-8000
£2658 $4200 €3987 Ady and Nusch (7x5cm-3x2in) gelatin silver print lit. 22-Apr-3 Christie's, Rockefeller NY #168/R est:2000-3000
£2848 $4500 €4500 Man Ray's studio in Rue Denfert-Rochereau with painting Le Retour a la Raison III (29x23cm-11x9in) i.d.1939 silver print. 26-Nov-2 Sotheby's, Amsterdam #189/R est:4500-5500
£3006 $4750 €4509 Nude study (22x16cm-9x6in) with sig.num.7/50 gelatin silver print. 22-Apr-3 Butterfields, San Francisco #2490/R est:2000-4000
£3681 $6000 €5522 Mr and Mrs Woodman (23x29cm-9x11in) s.d.1976 gelatin silver print. 12-Feb-3 Christie's, Rockefeller NY #227/R est:4000-6000
£3896 $6000 €5844 Cyclamen (22x17cm-9x7in) i.verso photograph prov. 22-Oct-2 Sotheby's, New York #22/R est:10000-15000
£4114 $6500 €6171 Starfish (24x20cm-9x8in) gelatin silver print prov. 24-Apr-3 Phillips, New York #139/R est:4000-6000
£4795 $7479 €7000 Trompe l'oeil (23x19cm-9x7in) i. verso gelatine silver prov. 12-Apr-3 Lempertz, Koln #150/R est:6000-8000
£5063 $8000 €7595 Portrait (23x18cm-9x7in) gelatin silver print exhib.lit. 22-Apr-3 Christie's, Rockefeller NY #167/R est:8000-10000
£11688 $18000 €17532 Study of a woman (29x23cm-11x9in) photograph prov.lit. 22-Oct-2 Sotheby's, New York #23/R est:20000-30000
£11688 $18000 €17532 Pablo Picasso (30x23cm-12x9in) photograph prov.exhib.lit. 22-Oct-2 Sotheby's, New York #21/R est:20000-30000
£14286 $22000 €21429 Study of a woman face (23x17cm-9x7in) photograph prov.lit. 22-Oct-2 Sotheby's, New York #18/R est:25000-35000
£16000 $25920 €24000 Fireworks, le bouquet (29x31cm-11x12in) i.verso solarised silver print prov.lit. 22-May-3 Sotheby's, London #85/R est:10000-15000
£16000 $25920 €24000 Elsa Schiaparelli (29x22cm-11x9in) i.verso solarised silver print exec.c.1930 prov. 22-May-3 Sotheby's, London #87/R est:4000-6000
£16234 $25000 €24351 Meret Oppwnheim in bathing cap (18x12cm-7x5in) i.d.1930 verso photograph prov.exhib.lit. 22-Oct-2 Sotheby's, New York #24/R est:20000-30000
£25316 $40000 €37974 Magnolia blossom (40x49cm-16x19in) s.d.1926 gelatin silver print mounted on board prov.lit. 24-Apr-3 Phillips, New York #29/R est:40000-60000
£25325 $39000 €37988 Nude (29x22cm-11x9in) i. photograph prov.exhib.lit. 22-Oct-2 Sotheby's, New York #19/R est:50000-70000
£26000 $42120 €39000 Antoine (29x22cm-11x9in) i.verso silver print prov.lit. 22-May-3 Sotheby's, London #86/R est:4000-6000
£28000 $45360 €42000 Study of a woman's face through netting (29x23cm-11x9in) st.verso silver print exec.c.1930 prov. 22-May-3 Sotheby's, London #84/R est:4000-6000
£32000 $49600 €48000 Mr and Mrs Woodman (30x27cm-12x11in) s. gelatin silver prints 27. 5-Dec-2 Sotheby's, London #180/R est:27000-40000
£71429 $110000 €107144 Untitled - Rayograph with lock of hair (24x18cm-9x7in) s.d.1922 photograph prov.exhib.lit. 22-Oct-2 Sotheby's, New York #16/R est:100000-150000
£75000 $121500 €112500 Rayograph (24x18cm-9x7in) s.d. i.verso silver print photogram prov. 22-May-3 Sotheby's, London #79/R est:12000-18000
£194805 $300000 €292208 Noire et blanche (22x50cm-9x20in) s.i.d.26 gelatin sliver print prov.lit. 25-Oct-2 Phillips, New York #19/R est:375000-450000
£194805 $300000 €292208 Untitled - Rayograph with flowers and ferns (29x23cm-11x9in) s.i. photograph prov.lit. 22-Oct-2 Sotheby's, New York #17/R est:150000-250000

Prints

£1899 $3000 €3000 Danger - L'impossible (67x43cm-26x17in) silkscreen on altuglass. 26-Nov-2 Sotheby's, Amsterdam #188/R est:2000-3000
£3343 $5216 €5015 Untitled compostion (63x54cm-25x21in) init.num.42/120 screenprint. 17-Sep-2 Peter Webb, Auckland #186/R est:8000-12000 (NZ.D 11000)
£4452 $6990 €6500 Portrait d'Andre Breton (16x11cm-6x4in) lead plaque. 15-Apr-3 Laurence Calmels, Paris #4353/R
£12579 $20000 €18869 Keeps London going (92x62cm-36x24in) grey black lithograph. 2-May-3 Sotheby's, New York #200/R est:20000-30000

Sculpture

£949 $1500 €1500 Compass 1920 (51x35x5cm-20x14x2in) s.num.65/110. 26-Nov-2 Sotheby's, Amsterdam #147/R est:1200-1500
£949 $1500 €1500 Herma (27cm-11in) i.num.5/350 polished bronze. 26-Nov-2 Sotheby's, Amsterdam #175/R est:1500-1800
£994 $1560 €1550 Hermaphrodite (28cm-11in) s.num.129/350 bronze sold with socle. 16-Dec-2 Charbonneaux, Paris #318 est:1500-2000
£1076 $1700 €1700 Cadeau (17cm-7in) s.i.num.2004/5000 iron executed 1974 lit. 26-Nov-2 Sotheby's, Amsterdam #176/R est:1000-1500
£1135 $1838 €1600 Cadeau (16x10x8cm-6x4x3in) s.i. num.1519/5000 iron lit. 26-May-3 Christie's, Milan #114/R est:1500-2000
£1192 $1943 €1800 La femme ailee (38cm-15in) s. green pat bronze marble socle edition 76/350 Cast Venini. 1-Feb-3 Claude Aguttes, Neuilly #181/R est:1830-2135
£1295 $2072 €1800 Herma (36x11x7cm-14x4x3in) s.i. polished tin wood socle. 15-May-3 Neumeister, Munich #512/R est:1800-2000
£1449 $2377 €2000 Cadeau (16cm-6in) st.sig. iron nails lit. 29-May-3 Lempertz, Koln #767/R est:2000
£2013 $3200 €3020 Hermaphrodite (24cm-9in) i.num.162/350 bronze. 3-Mar-3 Swann Galleries, New York #76/R est:3000-5000
£2083 $3292 €3000 Priape (50x30x30cm-20x12x12in) s.num.191/500 Paros marble four parts lit. 27-Apr-3 Perrin, Versailles #126/R est:3500-4000
£2215 $3500 €3500 Le voyeur - peeping Tom (11x17x3cm-4x7x1in) mono.i.num. spy hole mounted in block of wood lit. 26-Nov-2 Sotheby's, Amsterdam #148/R est:1200-1500
£2886 $4646 €4300 Priape (50x30x30cm-20x12x12in) mono. num.179/500 marble lit. 23-Feb-3 Mercier & Cie, Lille #130/R
£3038 $4800 €4800 Presse papier a priape - priapus paperweight (50x29cm-20x11in) marble cast 1972 lit. 26-Nov-2 Sotheby's, Amsterdam #144/R est:2000-3000
£3800 $5852 €5700 Presse-papier a priape (53cm-21in) init.num.141/500 marble four parts lit. 23-Oct-2 Sotheby's, Olympia #790/R est:1000-1500
£8176 $13000 €12264 Chess set. st.init. anodized aluminium set of 32 prov.lit. 27-Feb-3 Christie's, Rockefeller NY #41/R est:15000
£9028 $14896 €13000 L'inconnue de la Seine (37x43cm-15x17in) plaster wood exec.c.1960 prov.lit. 2-Jul-3 Artcurial Briest, Paris #702/R est:10000-15000
£17081 $27500 €25622 Optical hopes and illusions (71cm-28in) wood banjo neck magnifying glass yellow ball. 7-May-3 Sotheby's, New York #325/R est:15000-20000
£24038 $37500 €36057 Chess set (46cm-18in) s.d.1947 aluminum panel chess board prov.lit. 6-Nov-2 Sotheby's, New York #273/R est:15000-20000

Works on paper

£759 $1200 €1200 Landscape with cow (50x70cm-20x28in) mono. ink prov.lit. 26-Nov-2 Sotheby's, Amsterdam #140/R est:1200-1500
£863 $1381 €1200 Personnages (33x26cm-13x10in) s. felt pen dr prov.lit. 18-May-3 Charbonneaux, Paris #180/R
£900 $1395 €1350 Stage show (28x39cm-11x15in) pencil pen ink executed c.1953 prov. 5-Dec-2 Christie's, Kensington #140/R est:1000-1500
£1899 $3000 €3000 Untitled (36x51cm-14x20in) s.d.71 ink black chk prov. 26-Nov-2 Sotheby's, Amsterdam #136/R est:3000-4000
£2013 $3200 €3020 Maquette pour 'Les grands transparents' (91x63cm-36x25in) s. col felt-tip pen ink pencil paper on board. 27-Feb-3 Christie's, Rockefeller NY #75/R
£2405 $3800 €3800 Jean Michel Franck, 1927 (22x17cm-9x7in) s.i. silver print prov. 26-Nov-2 Sotheby's, Amsterdam #178/R est:1500-2000
£2621 $4193 €3800 Hand with shell (39x29cm-15x11in) s. photograph exec.1931 lit. 11-Mar-3 Babuino, Rome #265/R
£3104 $5183 €4500 L'acrobate (53x38cm-21x15in) s.d.52 gouache Indian ink. 10-Jul-3 Artcurial Briest, Paris #83/R est:4500-5000
£3264 $5385 €4700 Guitare woman (27x17cm-11x7in) mono. col crayon Indian ink. 2-Jul-3 Artcurial Briest, Paris #701/R est:5000-7000

MAN-RAY and MIRO, Joan (20th C) American/French
Works on paper
£51370 $80137 €75000 Cadavre exquis (36x23cm-14x9in) i.verso ink col crayon exec.1927 with Max Morise and Yves Tanguy. 14-Apr-3 Laurence Calmels, Paris #4019/R est:30000

MANAGO, Vincent (1880-1936) French
£679 $964 €1100 Rivage mediterraneen (46x55cm-18x22in) s. panel. 16-Mar-3 Eric Pillon, Calais #99/R
£769 $1208 €1200 Cavaliers au crepuscule (21x26cm-8x10in) s. panel. 16-Dec-2 Gros & Delettrez, Paris #427
£816 $1298 €1200 Caravane au coucher du soleil (30x40cm-12x16in) s. cardboard prov. 24-Mar-3 Rabourdin & Choppin de Janvry, Paris #230/R
£1258 $2051 €1900 View of the Bosphorus (60x81cm-24x32in) s. 11-Feb-3 Segre, Madrid #117/R
£2244 $3545 €3500 Venise (50x65cm-20x26in) s. pair. 18-Nov-2 Tajan, Paris #151/R est:2400-3000
£4717 $7264 €7500 Lavandieres tunisiennes (65x92cm-26x36in) s. 23-Oct-2 Rabourdin & Choppin de Janvry, Paris #218/R

MANAIGO, Silvestro (1670-1734) Italian
Works on paper
£490 $700 €735 Crucifixion with St. John the Baptist, the Virgin and Mary Magdalene (28x19cm-11x7in) pen ink grey wash. 23-Jan-3 Swann Galleries, New York #115/R

MANARESI, Ugo (attrib) (1851-1917) Italian
£377 $581 €600 Port (27x37cm-11x15in) s. paper. 28-Oct-2 Il Ponte, Milan #213

MANAUT VIGLIETTI, Jose (1899-1971) Spanish
£302 $465 €480 Bouquet (85x70cm-33x28in) s. 28-Oct-2 Segre, Madrid #257/R
£479 $748 €700 Garden with statue (72x59cm-28x23in) 8-Apr-3 Ansorena, Madrid #42/R

MANCADAN, Jacobus Sibrandi (1602-1680) Dutch
£7006 $10930 €11000 Shepherds resting with their cattle, goats and dog in a hilly landscape (49x83cm-19x33in) mono. panel prov. 5-Nov-2 Sotheby's, Amsterdam #219/R est:12000-18000

MANCEAU, Lucien (1873-1937) French
£1316 $2132 €2000 Flowers in a stoneware vase with tropical bird (90x60cm-35x24in) s. oval top. 21-Jan-3 Christie's, Amsterdam #4/R est:1200-1600

MANCEAUX, Louis Antoine (1862-?) French
Works on paper
£417 $679 €600 Attente sur la greve (30x47cm-12x19in) mixed media. 19-Jul-3 Thierry & Lannon, Brest #279

MANCEBO, Julio (1933-) Uruguayan
£258 $408 €400 Untitled (58x48cm-23x19in) s. 18-Dec-2 Castellana, Madrid #52/R
£258 $408 €400 Untitled (58x39cm-23x15in) s. 18-Dec-2 Castellana, Madrid #50/R
£258 $408 €400 Untitled (60x49cm-24x19in) s.d.2001. 18-Dec-2 Castellana, Madrid #54/R

MANCHADO PASCUAL, Faustino (1951-) Spanish
£1090 $1722 €1700 Spanish horse (60x73cm-24x29in) s.d.99 s.i.d.verso acrylic. 13-Nov-2 Ansorena, Madrid #33/R
£2500 $3950 €3900 Spanish musician. s.d.2002. 13-Nov-2 Ansorena, Madrid #177/R

MANCINELLI, Gustavo (1842-1906) Italian
Works on paper
£2903 $4500 €4355 Portrait of a young man (17x14cm-7x6in) s.d.1882 i.verso pencil exhib. 29-Oct-2 Sotheby's, New York #116/R est:1500-2000

MANCINI, Antonio (1852-1930) Italian
£8861 $13823 €14000 Self-portrait (87x60cm-34x24in) s. 19-Oct-2 Semenzato, Venice #165/R
£11392 $18000 €18000 Young woman in profile (40x30cm-16x12in) s. 26-Nov-2 Christie's, Rome #269/R
£23270 $35836 €37000 Woman (101x60cm-40x24in) s. 23-Oct-2 Finarte, Milan #144/R est:35000-40000
Works on paper
£30645 $47500 €45968 Portrait of a young boy (57x73cm-22x29in) s. pasrel htd white prov. 29-Oct-2 Sotheby's, New York #77/R est:20000-30000

MANCINI, Antonio (attrib) (1852-1930) Italian
Works on paper
£218 $338 €340 Portrait (60x44cm-24x17in) chk. 5-Dec-2 Stadion, Trieste #839

MANCINI, Bartolommeo (fl.1630) Italian
£1887 $2943 €3000 La vierge de douleur - L'addolarata (27x20cm-11x8in) i. verso copper oval. 9-Oct-2 Lombrail & Teucquam, Paris #3/R

MANCINI, Carlo (1829-1910) Italian
£1517 $2412 €2200 Woman in the woods (33x23cm-13x9in) s. board. 5-Mar-3 Sotheby's, Milan #63

MANCINI, Francesco (18/19th C) Italian
Works on paper
£506 $800 €800 Warriors on horseback (36x26cm-14x10in) s. W/C card. 26-Nov-2 Christie's, Rome #99

MANCINI, V (19th C) Italian
£955 $1490 €1500 Coach ride in southern Italy (18x28cm-7x11in) s.d.83 panel. 6-Nov-2 Hugo Ruef, Munich #1200/R est:900

MANCOBA, Sonja Ferlov (1911-1984) Danish
Sculpture
£15799 $24963 €23699 Effort commun (106cm-42in) init.num.IV/VI green pat.bronze executed 1963-64 lit. 1-Apr-3 Rasmussen, Copenhagen #109/R est:150000-200000 (D.KR 170000)
Works on paper
£255 $398 €383 Composition (25x10cm-10x4in) init. paper collage. 5-Aug-2 Rasmussen, Vejle #363 (D.KR 3000)

MANDEL, Jura (1886-?) Czechoslovakian
£284 $440 €426 On the road (34x38cm-13x15in) painted c.1910. 3-Dec-2 SOGA, Bratislava #220/R (SL.K 18000)

MANDELLI, Pompilio (1912-) Italian
£1160 $1822 €1810 Landscape (45x65cm-18x26in) s. 23-Nov-2 Meeting Art, Vercelli #342/R
£1389 $2208 €2000 Autumn (60x50cm-24x20in) s.d.1990 s.i.d.verso. 1-May-3 Meeting Art, Vercelli #154

MANDER, Karel van I (attrib) (1548-1606) Dutch
Works on paper
£1216 $1897 €1800 Saint Augustin (17cm-7in circular) i. pen ink wash htd gouache prov. 26-Mar-3 Piasa, Paris #31

MANDER, Karel van III (1610-1672) Dutch
£4737 $7201 €7106 Portrait of Christian IV with white lace collar (50x37cm-20x15in) oval panel prov. 27-Aug-2 Rasmussen, Copenhagen #1401/R est:60000 (D.KR 55000)

MANDER, W H (fl.1880-1922) British
£1400 $2170 €2100 Old bridge near Capel Curig, mountainous landscape with house (90x60cm-35x24in) s. i.verso. 1-Oct-2 Fellows & Sons, Birmingham #51/R est:1500-2500

MANDER, William Henry (fl.1880-1922) British
£714 $1129 €1071 Llyn Gurrnon (35x46cm-14x18in) s. s.i.verso prov. 26-Nov-2 Sotheby's, Melbourne #218/R est:2000-3000 (A.D 2000)
£980 $1529 €1470 Near Aberglaslyn, looking towards Snowdon (32x48cm-13x19in) s. 19-Sep-2 John Bellman, Billingshurst #1482
£1000 $1630 €1500 Near Talylln, North Wales (76x101cm-30x40in) s. i.verso. 29-Jan-3 Sotheby's, Olympia #135/R est:1000-1500
£1500 $2460 €2250 Tributary of the Lledr (38x28cm-15x11in) s.d.95 s.i.d.95 verso. 4-Feb-3 Sworder & Son, Bishops Stortford #110/R est:1000-1500
£1900 $2755 €2850 Near Dolgelly. Conway Valley (38x23cm-15x9in) s.i.verso pair. 3-May-2 Biddle & Webb, Birmingham #323 est:1800-2600
£1935 $3058 €2903 At Dr-y-nant, near Dolgellay (30x46cm-12x18in) s. s.i.verso prov. 18-Nov-2 Waddingtons, Toronto #115/R est:1200-1800 (C.D 4800)
£2044 $3394 €2964 Glen on the Llugwy near Capel Curig (61x91cm-24x36in) s. prov. 16-Jun-3 Waddingtons, Toronto #167/R est:7000-9000 (C.D 4600)

£2500 $3875 €3750 On a Welsh river (51x76cm-20x30in) s.d.03. 25-Sep-2 Hamptons Fine Art, Godalming #400/R est:2500-4000
£2800 $4452 €4200 A Bit of the Llugy, Moel Siabod (46x36cm-18x14in) s. s.i.verso. 5-Mar-3 Bonhams, Bury St Edmunds #375/R est:1250-1750
£3000 $4620 €4500 Near Bala, North Wales (41x61cm-16x24in) s.d.11 s.i.d.11 verso. 5-Sep-2 Christie's, Kensington #175/R est:2500-3500
£3000 $4710 €4500 Festiniog Valley, North Wales (48x74cm-19x29in) s.d.09. 13-Dec-2 Keys, Aylsham #666 est:3000-4000
£3000 $4950 €4350 Man and woman fishing from a rocky riverbank (41x61cm-16x24in) s.d.1914. 3-Jul-3 Duke & Son, Dorchester #238/R est:500-1000
£3500 $5530 €5250 On the Wnion, near Dolgelly, North Wales (39x59cm-15x23in) s.d.12. 2-Dec-2 Bonhams, Bath #85/R est:1200-1800
£3500 $5565 €5250 Hedr Valley, North Wales (50x75cm-20x30in) s. 29-Apr-3 Henry Adams, Chichester #328/R est:1500-2500
£5000 $8350 €7250 Evening nr Upton On Severn. Ford nr Tewkesbury (51x76cm-20x30in) s. s.i.verso one d.12 one d.11 pair. 24-Jun-3 Bonhams, Knowle #84/R est:5000-8000
£6000 $9780 €9000 Elsie Mount, Bettws-Y-Coed, North Wales (56x96cm-22x38in) s.d.87. 29-Jan-3 Sotheby's, Olympia #138/R est:5000-7000

Works on paper
£5800 $9106 €8700 Waterfall (93x68cm-37x27in) s. W/C. 16-Dec-2 Bonhams, Bury St Edmunds #553/R est:3000-5000

MANDEVARE, Alphonse Nicolas Michel (attrib) (?-c.1829) French
Works on paper
£222 $350 €350 Vue de vallee fluviale (19x31cm-7x12in) crayon stump. 28-Nov-2 Tajan, Paris #142
£2500 $3925 €3750 Views of a Roman campagna (57x84cm-22x33in) black chk ink framing lines. 11-Dec-2 Sotheby's, Olympia #259/R est:3000-4000

MANDIN, Richard (1909-) French
£409 $638 €650 Nature morte (46x61cm-18x24in) s. 9-Oct-2 Marc Kohn, Paris #28
£409 $638 €650 Nature morte au verre de vin (54x65cm-21x26in) s.d.1949. 9-Oct-2 Marc Kohn, Paris #27

MANDLICK, Auguste (1860-?) Austrian
Works on paper
£338 $527 €500 St Stephan, Choir (47x37cm-19x15in) s. W/C. 28-Mar-3 Dorotheum, Vienna #352/R

MANDO, Helmut (20th C) ?
£266 $420 €420 Girls and pizza (50x40cm-20x16in) s.d.Feb 2002 verso acrylic collage. 30-Nov-2 Arnold, Frankfurt #359/R

MANDON, Edouard (20th C) French
£300 $495 €435 Marine (49x100cm-19x39in) s. prov. 1-Jul-3 Bearnes, Exeter #544/R

MANDYN, Jan (1500-1560) Dutch
£22642 $35094 €36000 Christ in limbo (72x101cm-28x40in) panel lit. 2-Oct-2 Dorotheum, Vienna #109/R est:35000-45000

MANDYN, Jan (circle) (1500-1560) Dutch
£9000 $13950 €13500 Guardian angel showing lost soul through the underworld (32x56cm-13x22in) panel prov. 31-Oct-2 Sotheby's, Olympia #23/R est:8000-12000
£13000 $20280 €19500 Descent into limbo (45x71cm-18x28in) panel prov.exhib. 9-Apr-3 Christie's, London #17/R est:12000-18000

MANE KATZ (1894-1962) French
£2500 $3975 €3750 Le reveur (18x14cm-7x6in) init. panel oval prov.exhib. 20-Mar-3 Sotheby's, Olympia #212/R est:2500-3500
£3289 $5329 €5000 Paysage d'Ukraine avec Chaumieres (75x90cm-30x35in) s. 21-Jan-3 Galerie Moderne, Brussels #227/R est:8000-10000
£5696 $9000 €8544 Student (60x50cm-24x20in) s.d.29. 27-Apr-3 Sotheby's, Tel Aviv #16a/R est:8000-12000
£6748 $11000 €10122 School (39x46cm-15x18in) s. 12-Feb-3 Sotheby's, New York #129/R est:12000-18000
£6884 $11290 €9500 Paysage (73x92cm-29x36in) s. prov. 29-May-3 Lempertz, Koln #770/R est:10000-14000
£6987 $10970 €10900 Jeune femme au chale (46x55cm-18x22in) s. painted c.1950. 24-Nov-2 Chayette & Cheval, Paris #270/R est:10000-12000
£10163 $15955 €15245 Hassidic musicians serenading their children (76x42cm-30x17in) s. 10-Dec-2 Pinneys, Montreal #65 est:14000-18000 (C.D 25000)
£11000 $16940 €16500 Deux femmes Arabes (159x119cm-63x47in) s. exhib.lit. 23-Oct-2 Sotheby's, Olympia #714/R est:12000-15000
£12821 $20128 €20000 Vase de fleurs (100x81cm-39x32in) s.d.1933. 12-Dec-2 Rabourdin & Choppin de Janvry, Paris #49/R est:30000
£17949 $28179 €28000 Course de chevaux (64x74cm-25x29in) s. prov.lit. 12-Dec-2 Rabourdin & Choppin de Janvry, Paris #89/R
£34000 $52360 €51000 Les deux musiciens (100x81cm-39x32in) s. prov.exhib. 22-Oct-2 Sotheby's, London #237/R est:25000-35000
£40000 $66800 €58000 Music (92x73cm-36x29in) s. lit. 25-Jun-3 Christie's, London #175/R est:20000-30000

Sculpture
£2051 $3221 €3200 Remouleur (29x18x22cm-11x7x9in) mono. num.9/10 bronze. 12-Dec-2 Rabourdin & Choppin de Janvry, Paris #103/R

Works on paper
£541 $845 €850 Rabin et son eleve (32x25cm-13x10in) s. Indian ink W/C. 6-Nov-2 Claude Boisgirard, Paris #34
£550 $858 €825 Revolt in the Ghetto (45x30cm-18x12in) s. ink lit. 15-Oct-2 Bonhams, Knightsbridge #227/R
£552 $883 €800 Rabbin a la priere (27x35cm-11x14in) s.i.d.1948 Chinese ink dr. 12-Mar-3 Rabourdin & Choppin de Janvry, Paris #57/R
£577 $906 €900 Auto-portrait (20x16cm-8x6in) mono. ink prov. 22-Nov-2 Millon & Associes, Paris #37/R
£609 $956 €950 Joueurs de cartes (30x23cm-12x9in) s. ink dr. 16-Dec-2 Eric Coutrier, Paris #88
£931 $1490 €1350 Rabbin et enfant (31x24cm-12x9in) s. W/C Chinese ink. 12-Mar-3 Rabourdin & Choppin de Janvry, Paris #38
£943 $1462 €1500 Le rabbin (48x34cm-19x13in) s.d.27 Indian ink wash prov. 30-Oct-2 Artcurial Briest, Paris #44 est:1000-1500
£1290 $2000 €1935 Deux rabins (61x51cm-24x20in) s. gouache board on canvas. 26-Sep-2 Christie's, Rockefeller NY #574/R est:3000-5000
£1290 $2000 €1935 Vase en fleurs (66x51cm-26x20in) s. gouache board on canvas. 26-Sep-2 Christie's, Rockefeller NY #594/R est:3000-5000
£1795 $2818 €2800 Desert de Judee (50x65cm-20x26in) s. gouache. 12-Dec-2 Rabourdin & Choppin de Janvry, Paris #61/R
£1800 $2772 €2700 Tete (59x44cm-23x17in) s. brush ink wash lit. 23-Oct-2 Sotheby's, Olympia #713/R est:2000-3000
£1887 $2924 €3000 Les heros de Varsovie (51x71cm-20x28in) s. ink. 4-Oct-2 Tajan, Paris #164 est:2400-2500
£2279 $3623 €3350 La lac de Tiberiade (44x53cm-17x21in) s. gouache. 26-Feb-3 Artcurial Briest, Paris #218/R est:3500-4000
£2436 $3824 €3800 Provincetown, NY (50x65cm-20x26in) s.d. gouache prov. 24-Nov-2 Chayette & Cheval, Paris #240/R est:3800-4500
£2600 $4004 €3900 Etude de chevaux (58x74cm-23x29in) s. pastel exhib.lit. 23-Oct-2 Sotheby's, Olympia #712/R est:2000-3000
£2759 $4607 €4000 Femme de Djerba (58x47cm-23x19in) s. gouache lit. 10-Jul-3 Artcurial Briest, Paris #89/R est:6000-7000
£3526 $5535 €5500 Bord de mer (65x50cm-26x20in) s.d. gouache prov.lit. 24-Nov-2 Chayette & Cheval, Paris #241/R est:3800-4500
£3548 $5500 €5322 Homme lisant (61x51cm-24x20in) s. gouache board on canvas. 26-Sep-2 Christie's, Rockefeller NY #573/R est:3000-5000
£5128 $8051 €8000 Jeune etudiant (77x60cm-30x24in) s. W/Cpastel. 12-Dec-2 Rabourdin & Choppin de Janvry, Paris #39/R

MANERA, Enrico (1947-) Italian
£359 $575 €550 Super family hero (100x35cm-39x14in) s.i.d.2001 verso acrylic plastic exhib.lit. 4-Jan-3 Meeting Art, Vercelli #376
£451 $718 €650 Portrait of Dorian Grey (111x111cm-44x44in) s.d.2000 verso oil acrylic lit. 1-May-3 Meeting Art, Vercelli #172
£475 $741 €750 Nick Fuy (100x50cm-39x20in) sidd.2001 verso acrylic plastic lit. 14-Sep-2 Meeting Art, Vercelli #30
£475 $741 €750 War (80x80cm-31x31in) s.i.d.2001 verso acrylic plastiv. 14-Sep-2 Meeting Art, Vercelli #500/R
£490 $784 €750 Kentucky (91x91cm-36x36in) s.i.d.2001 acrylic. 4-Jan-3 Meeting Art, Vercelli #84
£490 $784 €750 Power (80x100cm-31x39in) s.i.d.2000 verso acrylic. 4-Jan-3 Meeting Art, Vercelli #620
£490 $784 €750 Wisconsin BGA678 (91x101cm-36x40in) s.i.d.2000 verso acrylic collage. 4-Jan-3 Meeting Art, Vercelli #721
£510 $811 €750 Spiderman 2 (80x80cm-31x31in) s.i.d.2001 acrylic PVC. 1-Mar-3 Meeting Art, Vercelli #640
£521 $828 €750 Iron man (100x60cm-39x24in) s.i.d.2001 verso acrylic. 1-May-3 Meeting Art, Vercelli #217
£544 $865 €800 Cafe des Artistes (50x50cm-20x20in) s.i.d.2000 verso acrylic collage. 1-Mar-3 Meeting Art, Vercelli #636
£621 $993 €950 Spiderman (100x80cm-39x31in) s.i.d.2001 acrylic plastic. 4-Jan-3 Meeting Art, Vercelli #622
£633 $987 €1000 Universe (82x82cm-32x32in) s.i.d.1986 verso acrylic. 14-Sep-2 Meeting Art, Vercelli #369/R
£660 $1049 €950 Olimpias (131x111cm-52x44in) s.d.2000 verso oil acrylic lit. 1-May-3 Meeting Art, Vercelli #447
£696 $1086 €1100 Towards 2000 (71x52cm-28x20in) s.i.d.2000 verso acrylic plastic. 14-Sep-2 Meeting Art, Vercelli #80/R
£719 $1150 €1100 Arabian nights (100x100cm-39x39in) s.i.d.1999 acrylic lit. 4-Jan-3 Meeting Art, Vercelli #397
£962 $1510 €1500 Diabolik (165x210cm-65x83in) s.d.2000 verso acrylic. 23-Nov-2 Meeting Art, Vercelli #322/R
£972 $1546 €1400 Mirage (111x131cm-44x52in) s.i.d.2000 verso oil acrylic. 1-May-3 Meeting Art, Vercelli #38
£1156 $1839 €1700 Portrait of Dorian Gray (160x210cm-63x83in) s.d.1989 acrylic. 1-Mar-3 Meeting Art, Vercelli #367
£1181 $1877 €1700 Kangaroo woman (150x200cm-59x79in) s.d.2000 verso acrylic pvc. 1-May-3 Meeting Art, Vercelli #439
£1772 $2765 €2800 Jim dine with love (165x213cm-65x84in) s.d.1983 acrylic. 14-Sep-2 Meeting Art, Vercelli #818/R

Works on paper
£380 $592 €600 Marilyn Monroe (24x18cm-9x7in) s.d.2000 verso mixed media collage cardboard. 14-Sep-2 Meeting Art, Vercelli #117

£385 $608 €600 View of the Alps (80x80cm-31x31in) mixed media on canvas exec.1999. 12-Nov-2 Babuino, Rome #207/R

MANES, Antonin (attrib) (1784-1843) Czechoslovakian
Works on paper
£537 $838 €806 Study of deciduous trees (30x22cm-12x9in) s.d.832 wash dr. 12-Oct-2 Dorotheum, Prague #164/R (C.KR 26000)

MANES, Guido (attrib) (1828-1880) Bohemian
£620 $967 €930 Looking-up (17x13cm-7x5in) mono. oval. 12-Oct-2 Dorotheum, Prague #30/R (C.KR 30000)

MANESSIER, Alfred (1911-1993) French
£1348 $2183 €1900 La vigne (22x35cm-9x14in) s.d.65 prov. 26-May-3 Christie's, Milan #298 est:1500-2000
£3270 $5102 €5200 Composition (27x22cm-11x9in) s. i.d.1947 verso panel prov. 11-Oct-2 Pierre Berge, Paris #28/R est:3000
£8742 $13463 €13900 Composition (50x73cm-20x29in) s.d.1967. 26-Oct-2 Cornette de St.Cyr, Paris #21/R est:15000
£11728 $19000 €17006 St Adele (61x48cm-24x19in) s.d.49. 21-May-3 Doyle, New York #26/R est:6000-8000
£13043 $21391 €18000 Composition (33x55cm-13x22in) s.d.57 prov. 29-May-3 Lempertz, Koln #771/R est:18000-20000
£15603 $25277 €22000 Lumiere d'avril (100x80cm-39x31in) s.d. 23-May-3 Binoche, Paris #55/R est:20000-25000
£22436 $35224 €35000 Prix du sang (114x195cm-45x77in) s.d.65-67 i.d.verso. 11-Dec-2 Artcurial Briest, Paris #711/R est:40000
Sculpture
£2885 $4471 €4500 Composition (33x23x32cm-13x9x13in) plastic wallets paper CD case. 6-Dec-2 Hauswedell & Nolte, Hamburg #250/R est:5000
Works on paper
£486 $802 €700 Bleu et noir (24x18cm-9x7in) init.d.54 ink gouache collage. 1-Jul-3 Artcurial Briest, Paris #772
£725 $1188 €1000 Untitled (36x28cm-14x11in) s. bodycol board. 31-May-3 Villa Grisebach, Berlin #868/R
£949 $1472 €1500 La commune (35x26cm-14x10in) s.i. gouache W/C. 28-Sep-2 Cornette de St.Cyr, Paris #373/R est:1500-1800
£1277 $2068 €1800 Untitled (99x65cm-39x26in) s.d.59 Indian ink. 24-May-3 Van Ham, Cologne #374/R est:2200

MANET, Edouard (1832-1883) French
£190000 $311600 €285000 Lecon d'anatomie (25x39cm-10x15in) panel prov.exhib.lit. 4-Feb-3 Sotheby's, London #10/R est:120000
Prints
£1603 $2532 €2500 Les chats. etching. 14-Nov-2 Libert, Castor, Paris #120/R est:1500
£1923 $3000 €2885 Olympia (9x18cm-4x7in) etching aquatint. 7-Nov-2 Swann Galleries, New York #449/R est:2500-3500
£2308 $3646 €3600 Le torero mort. etching aquatint. 14-Nov-2 Libert, Castor, Paris #119 est:2250
£2639 $4196 €3800 Le guitarrero (30x24cm-12x9in) s.i. etching drypoint. 5-May-3 Ketterer, Munich #34/R est:3000-4000
£3077 $4862 €4800 Lola de Valence. etching. 14-Nov-2 Libert, Castor, Paris #116/R est:3000
£3797 $6000 €6000 Berthe Morisot en noir (20x14cm-8x6in) lithograph. 30-Nov-2 Villa Grisebach, Berlin #101/R est:6000-8000
£3916 $6500 €5678 Chanteur Espagnol (30x23cm-12x9in) etching. 13-Jun-3 Du Mouchelle, Detroit #2118/R est:1000-1500
£4444 $7067 €6400 Au Prado II (22x15cm-9x6in) aquatint. 5-May-3 Ketterer, Munich #35/R est:3500-4500
£7051 $11141 €11000 Le chanteur espagnol. etching. 14-Nov-2 Libert, Castor, Paris #113/R est:6000
£8974 $14000 €13461 La toilette (29x23cm-11x9in) etching. 7-Nov-2 Swann Galleries, New York #448/R est:7000-10000
£11538 $18000 €17307 Guerre civile (40x51cm-16x20in) col lithograph edition of 100. 7-Nov-2 Swann Galleries, New York #451/R est:18000-22000
Works on paper
£17949 $28000 €26924 Chanteuse de cafe-concert (14x9cm-6x4in) black conte crayon brush wash executed c.1876 prov.lit. 7-Nov-2 Christie's, Rockefeller NY #109/R est:30000-40000
£30000 $49200 €45000 Lettre a Albert Hecht (20x13cm-8x5in) s.i. W/C pen ink prov.lit. 6-Feb-3 Christie's, London #403/R est:50000

MANET, Edouard (attrib) (1832-1883) French
Works on paper
£3270 $5036 €5200 Mademoiselle Elise (30x22cm-12x9in) s. mixed media. 28-Oct-2 Il Ponte, Milan #272/R

MANETTI, Domenico (1609-1663) Italian
£1959 $3057 €2900 Religieuse faisant benir la maquette d'une eglise (27x33cm-11x13in) paper. 31-Mar-3 Piasa, Paris #20/R

MANFREDI, Alberto (1930-2001) Italian
£2027 $3162 €3000 Maria with black jacket (48x34cm-19x13in) s. painted 1959. 28-Mar-3 Farsetti, Prato #355/R

MANFREDI, Bartolomeo (attrib) (1580-1620) Italian
Works on paper
£300 $471 €450 Clasped hands, the fingers entwined (7x10cm-3x4in) i. black chk prov. 13-Dec-2 Christie's, Kensington #283

MANFREDI, Bartolomeo (circle) (1580-1620) Italian
£8000 $12480 €12000 Portrait of a gentleman wearing a feathered cap (43x34cm-17x13in) 10-Apr-3 Christie's, Kensington #231/R est:1200-1800
£31447 $48742 €50000 Christ's capture (119x172cm-47x68in) 2-Oct-2 Dorotheum, Vienna #267/R est:40000-50000

MANFREDI, Emilio (?-1801) Italian
Works on paper
£700 $1099 €1050 Two caricatures of heads (20x15cm-8x6in) red black chk prov. 11-Dec-2 Sotheby's, Olympia #26/R

MANFREDINI, Gaetano (1800-1870) Italian
Sculpture
£22642 $35094 €36000 Harvest (138cm-54in) s. marble. 29-Oct-2 Finarte, Milan #377/R est:12000-16000

MANGAN, Steven (1964-) British
£750 $1170 €1125 Beach (72x67cm-28x26in) s. 17-Oct-2 Bonhams, Edinburgh #58/R
£750 $1170 €1125 Gathering (70x75cm-28x30in) s. s.i.verso. 17-Oct-2 Bonhams, Edinburgh #59
£1200 $1872 €1800 Rendezvous (95x75cm-37x30in) s. 17-Oct-2 Bonhams, Edinburgh #57 est:1000-1500

MANGLARD, Adrien (1695-1760) French
£68966 $108966 €100000 Seascape (107x212cm-42x83in) prov. 3-Apr-3 Porro, Milan #29/R est:150000
Works on paper
£1701 $2704 €2500 Marine (22x34cm-9x13in) pen ink wash. 24-Mar-3 Tajan, Paris #23/R

MANGLARD, Adrien (attrib) (1695-1760) French
£6241 $9674 €9362 Naval battle with the Turkish fleet (74x97cm-29x38in) 3-Dec-2 Bukowskis, Stockholm #475/R est:30000-40000 (S.KR 88000)

MANGLARD, Adrien (style) (1695-1760) French
£6200 $10354 €8990 Mediterranean harbour scene with figures before a barque (74x136cm-29x54in) 8-Jul-3 Sotheby's, Olympia #479/R est:3000-5000

MANGO, Leonardo de (studio) (1843-?) Italian
£6061 $9394 €9092 Tripoli (55x76cm-22x30in) s.i. board. 24-Sep-2 Koller, Zurich #6761/R est:15000-25000 (S.FR 14000)

MANGOLD, Carl (20th C) Canadian
£242 $394 €363 Lake (38x44cm-15x17in) s.d.44 board. 12-Feb-3 Iegor de Saint Hippolyte, Montreal #132 (C.D 600)

MANGOLD, Josef (1884-1942) German
£897 $1426 €1300 Horse and cows by river bend (91x120cm-36x47in) s. 8-Mar-3 Arnold, Frankfurt #639/R

MANGOLD, Robert (1937-) American
£4430 $7000 €6645 Study for irregular area no.4 (75x56cm-30x22in) s.d.1985 acrylic pencil prov. 13-Nov-2 Sotheby's, New York #310/R est:8000-10000
£17089 $27000 €25634 Irregular red orange area with drawn ellipse (54x40cm-21x16in) s.d.1986 verso acrylic pencil on wood prov. 13-Nov-2 Sotheby's, New York #107/R est:10000-15000

MANGRAVITE, Peppino (1896-1978) American
£2258 $3500 €3387 Fishing (64x76cm-25x30in) s. painted c.1940. 8-Dec-2 Toomey, Oak Park #772/R est:3000-4000

MANGUIN, Henri (1874-1949) French
£1923 $3000 €2885 Bride with two women and a parrot (24x25cm-9x10in) s. paper. 19-Sep-2 Swann Galleries, New York #548/R est:4000-6000
£2532 $4000 €4000 Bassin (59x32cm-23x13in) s. 2-Dec-2 Tajan, Paris #168a/R
£5946 $9276 €8800 L'Ile de la Grande Jatte (28x28cm-11x11in) st.sig. lit. 31-Mar-3 Rossini, Paris #58/R
£6552 $10942 €9500 Nature morte aux fruits (38x47cm-15x19in) s. exec.c.1925 prov. 10-Jul-3 Artcurial Briest, Paris #176/R est:10000-12000

£7194 $11511 €10000 Jeanne Manguin et sa fille Lucile (25x33cm-10x13in) s. lit. 18-May-3 Eric Pillon, Calais #60/R
£9557 $14813 €15100 Nu assis (32x29cm-13x11in) s. canvas on panel. 29-Sep-2 Eric Pillon, Calais #224/R
£11043 $18000 €16565 Grenades et figues (39x47cm-15x19in) s. prov.lit. 12-Feb-3 Sotheby's, New York #52/R est:20000-25000
£11392 $17658 €18000 Peches dans un moustiers blanc (33x41cm-13x16in) s. painted c.1926 prov.exhib.lit. 28-Sep-2 Christie's, Paris #17/R est:8000-10000
£14085 $23380 €20000 Paysage (33x41cm-13x16in) s. canvas on cardboard. 16-Jun-3 Oger, Dumont, Paris #50/R est:20000-30000
£15000 $25050 €21750 Vase d'anemones (73x60cm-29x24in) s. painted 1921 prov.lit. 25-Jun-3 Christie's, London #151/R est:15000-20000
£15385 $24000 €23078 Torso de femme, la petite Marie (65x54cm-26x21in) s. painted 1912 prov.exhib.lit. 7-Nov-2 Christie's, Rockefeller NY #278/R est:30000-40000
£18634 $30000 €27951 Nu au peignoir la tcheque (73x60cm-29x24in) s. painted c.1942 prov.exhib.lit. 7-May-3 Sotheby's, New York #402/R est:35000-45000
£18777 $29293 €28166 Anemones et narcisses (55x46cm-22x18in) s. 6-Nov-2 Dobiaschofsky, Bern #803/R est:38000 (S.FR 43000)
£19580 $32699 €28000 Nu assis, Jeanne (66x54cm-26x21in) s. prov.exhib.lit. 30-Jun-3 Artcurial Briest, Paris #78/R est:20000-30000
£32000 $49280 €48000 Les barques (54x65cm-21x26in) s. prov.lit. 22-Oct-2 Sotheby's, London #202/R est:15000-20000
£34161 $55000 €51242 Les pavots (65x55cm-26x22in) s. painted 1937 prov.exhib.lit. 7-May-3 Sotheby's, New York #404/R est:35000-45000
£55000 $91850 €79750 Nu accoude (92x73cm-36x29in) s. painted 1919 prov.lit. 24-Jun-3 Sotheby's, London #139/R est:50000-70000
£158228 $245253 €250000 Les oliviers a Cavaliere (81x65cm-32x26in) s.d.1906 prov.exhib.lit. 28-Sep-2 Christie's, Paris #20/R est:90000-135000

Works on paper

£403 $648 €600 Femme assise (20x18cm-8x7in) ink dr. 23-Feb-3 Mercier & Cie, Lille #32
£532 $862 €750 Portrait de femme (30x32cm-12x13in) st.sig. graphite. 21-May-3 Cornette de St.Cyr, Paris #15/R
£550 $869 €825 Nu couche, Jeanne (15x19cm-6x7in) s. ink prov. 3-Apr-3 Christie's, Kensington #36/R
£1736 $2760 €2500 Paysage de Provence (17x24cm-7x9in) s. W/C pencil exec.c.1930. 29-Apr-3 Artcurial Briest, Paris #5/R est:3000-4000
£5484 $8500 €8226 Le port de Saint-Tropez (38x48cm-15x19in) s. W/C over pencil prov. 26-Sep-2 Christie's, Rockefeller NY #607/R est:7000-9000
£6500 $10335 €9750 Vase de fleurs (36x29cm-14x11in) s. W/C over pencil. 20-Mar-3 Sotheby's, Olympia #57/R est:4000-6000

MANHART, Eduard (1880-?) Austrian

Works on paper

£331 $517 €520 View from Innsbruck (40x34cm-16x13in) s.d.1940 W/C lit. 7-Nov-2 Allgauer, Kempten #2690
£504 $806 €700 Fort Hensel with Mittagskogel and Strelitza (24x15cm-9x6in) s.d.1925 s.i.d. verso W/C. 14-May-3 Dorotheum, Klagenfurt #42/R
£504 $806 €700 Place of help on the Strelitza (24x15cm-9x6in) s.d.18.4.16 s.i.d. verso W/C. 14-May-3 Dorotheum, Klagenfurt #43
£1295 $2072 €1800 Worthersee with Mittagskogel from Krumpendorf (30x42cm-12x17in) s.d.1925 s.i.d. verso W/C. 14-May-3 Dorotheum, Klagenfurt #41/R est:1300

MANIATTY, Stephen G (1910-) American

£435 $700 €653 East Gloucester (61x76cm-24x30in) 9-May-3 Douglas, South Deerfield #14

MANIATTY, Stephen G (attrib) (1910-) American

£1384 $2200 €2076 Conway brook (48x74cm-19x29in) 28-Feb-3 Douglas, South Deerfield #1

MANICARDI, Cirillo (1857-1925) Italian

£4221 $6500 €6332 Little weaver (36x25cm-14x10in) s. prov. 24-Oct-2 Shannon's, Milford #129/R est:2500-3500

MANKES, Jan (1889-1920) Dutch

£20253 $32000 €32000 Olieflesje (20x13cm-8x5in) s.d.09 prov.exhib.lit. 26-Nov-2 Sotheby's, Amsterdam #127/R est:18000-25000

Works on paper

£3481 $5500 €5500 Garden (14x20cm-6x8in) s. ink on vellum prov. 26-Nov-2 Sotheby's, Amsterdam #125/R est:5000-7000

MANLY, Charles MacDonald (1855-1924) Canadian

£444 $701 €666 Veiled sunset, bonaventure Island, P.Q (23x32cm-9x13in) s. board prov. 14-Nov-2 Heffel, Vancouver #270 est:400-600 (C.D 1100)

Works on paper

£444 $701 €666 Pool in the moor (30x46cm-12x18in) s. i.verso W/C. 14-Nov-2 Heffel, Vancouver #225/R est:700-900 (C.D 1100)
£644 $1057 €934 Cows at rest (17x24cm-7x9in) s. W/C. 9-Jun-3 Hodgins, Calgary #370/R est:700-900 (C.D 1450)

MANN, Alexander (1853-1908) British

£1400 $2156 €2100 Church, Isola Bella Maggiore (30x22cm-12x9in) board. 5-Sep-2 Christie's, Kensington #541/R
£1500 $2310 €2250 Tangiers over the marshes (30x46cm-12x18in) 5-Sep-2 Christie's, Kensington #547/R est:1200-1800
£3200 $4928 €4800 Tangier from the dunes (43x53cm-17x21in) s.d.1892 prov. 5-Sep-2 Christie's, Kensington #551/R est:2000-3000
£60000 $93000 €90000 Gleaners (76x91cm-30x36in) s.d.1889 prov.exhib. 31-Oct-2 Christie's, London #104/R est:60000-80000

MANN, Cathleen (1896-1959) British

£280 $437 €420 Soldiers with tanks training in a field by a river in Evreux (51x61cm-20x24in) s.i.d.1944. 17-Sep-2 Rosebery Fine Art, London #548/R
£300 $465 €450 Grand Canal, Venice (45x60cm-18x24in) s.d.1949. 29-Oct-2 Henry Adams, Chichester #519
£550 $858 €825 Flowerpiece. Portrait of a WAFF officer (77x64cm-30x25in) s.d.1943 double-side prov. 17-Sep-2 Rosebery Fine Art, London #623/R
£620 $980 €930 Grand Canal, Venice (45x60cm-18x24in) s.d.1949. 5-Apr-3 Windibank, Dorking #220/R
£800 $1240 €1200 Still life of anemones and tulips (61x46cm-24x18in) s. prov. 3-Dec-2 Bonhams, Knightsbridge #382/R

MANN, David (1948-) American

£4969 $8050 €7205 Sign of the smoke (61x91cm-24x36in) 23-May-3 Altermann Galleries, Santa Fe #47
£6849 $10000 €10274 The healer's art (61x91cm-24x36in) 18-May-2 Altermann Galleries, Santa Fe #16/R
£9416 $14500 €14124 Buffalo dreamer (122x91cm-48x36in) 25-Oct-2 Morris & Whiteside, Hilton Head Island #44 est:15000-20000
£12006 $19450 €17409 Cry of the nightwatch (152x102cm-60x40in) 23-May-3 Altermann Galleries, Santa Fe #46
£12179 $19000 €18269 Thunderbird shield (91x122cm-36x48in) 9-Nov-2 Altermann Galleries, Santa Fe #75
£15068 $22000 €22602 Cheyenne summer (122x91cm-48x36in) 18-May-2 Altermann Galleries, Santa Fe #17/R

MANN, Edward (19th C) ?

£466 $740 €699 Blind man and young girl (51x45cm-20x18in) s.d.61 panel. 5-Mar-3 Rasmussen, Copenhagen #1781/R (D.KR 5000)

MANN, Gother Victor Fyers (1863-1948) Australian

£1538 $2446 €2307 The Rocks, Sydney (30x40cm-12x16in) s. 4-Mar-3 Deutscher-Menzies, Melbourne #240/R est:5000-7000 (A.D 4000)

MANN, Harrington (1864-1937) British

£480 $802 €696 Montreaux - boats on the river (19x25cm-7x10in) s.d.1898 panel. 17-Jun-3 Anderson & Garland, Newcastle #366
£980 $1548 €1470 From the Palatine (16x25cm-6x10in) s. board. 7-Apr-3 Bonhams, Bath #59/R
£2400 $3864 €3600 Maid of Letuan, Tangiers (41x31cm-16x12in) i. prov.exhib. 20-Feb-3 Christie's, London #288/R

Works on paper

£650 $1007 €975 Young girl in a fur bonnet (32x21cm-13x8in) s. col chk pencil. 5-Dec-2 Bonhams, Edinburgh #101/R

MANN, James Scrimgeour (1883-1946) British

Works on paper

£340 $554 €510 Sunset over rocky island with three passing steam boats (38x17cm-15x7in) s. W/C htd white. 11-Feb-3 Fellows & Sons, Birmingham #110/R

MANN, Robert (19th C) British

£260 $426 €377 Country landscape, Harvest (28x43cm-11x17in) s. indis.i. 3-Jun-3 Capes Dunn, Manchester #127
£650 $1079 €975 Stratford on Avon church from the meadows (31x46cm-12x18in) s.i. 10-Jun-3 Bonhams, Knightsbridge #114/R

MANN, Sally (1951-) American

Photographs

£1899 $3000 €2849 Jessie at six (20x24cm-8x9in) s.i.d.1988 num.1/25 photograph. 23-Apr-3 Sotheby's, New York #249/R est:2500-3500
£2308 $3600 €3462 Hang nail (48x58cm-19x23in) s.i.d. verso silver. 21-Oct-2 Swann Galleries, New York #314/R est:4000-6000
£2331 $3800 €3497 Gorjus (19x24cm-7x9in) s.i.d.1989 num.8/25 gelatin silver print. 12-Feb-3 Christie's, Rockefeller NY #129/R est:4000-6000

£2454 $4000 €3681 Perfect tomato (19x25cm-7x10in) s.i.d.1990 num.17/25 gelatin silver print. 12-Feb-3 Christie's, Rockefeller NY #128/R est:5000-7000
£2922 $4500 €4383 At warm springs (59x48cm-23x19in) s.i.d.1991 num.3/25 photograph. 24-Oct-2 Sotheby's, New York #258/R est:6000-8000
£3797 $6000 €5696 Untitled, deep South no.29 (119x95cm-47x37in) s.i.d.1998 gelatin silver print toned with tea mounted on board. 24-Apr-3 Phillips, New York #61/R est:7000-10000
£5195 $8000 €7793 Holding Virginia (59x48cm-23x19in) s.i.d.1988 num.4/25 photograph. 24-Oct-2 Sotheby's, New York #257/R est:6000-8000
£5696 $9000 €8544 Naptime (48x61cm-19x24in) s.i.d.1989 num.20/25 gelatin silver print lit. 22-Apr-3 Christie's, Rockefeller NY #130/R est:8000-10000
£6013 $9500 €9020 Untitled - Virginia no.7 from mother land (76x98cm-30x39in) s.i.d.1996 num.2/10 verso gelatin silver print mounted on board. 24-Apr-3 Phillips, New York #207/R est:10000-15000

MANN, Sargy (1937-) British
£1000 $1550 €1500 Girl reading in a conservatory (97x76cm-38x30in) i.verso. 30-Sep-2 Bonhams, Ipswich #388/R est:1000-1500

MANNERS, W (fl.1885-c.1910) British
Works on paper
£1100 $1749 €1650 Ribble valley with figures, horse and cart (34x49cm-13x19in) s.d.1912. 19-Mar-3 James Thompson, Kirby Lonsdale #165/R

MANNERS, William (fl.1885-c.1910) British
£400 $624 €600 Rural landscape with farm buildings, figures and sheep (19x31cm-7x12in) s.d.1890 board. 6-Nov-2 Bonhams, Chester #330
£750 $1223 €1088 Country track in autumn (26x41cm-10x16in) s.d.1889. 16-Jul-3 Sotheby's, Olympia #14/R
£800 $1336 €1160 Rural landscape with travelers in lane, houses watering at a fountain (28x43cm-11x17in) s.d.1897. 20-Jun-3 Keys, Aylsham #659/R
Works on paper
£320 $502 €480 Shepherd and sheep on a country lane with a distant landscape beyond (17x24cm-7x9in) s. W/C gouache. 19-Nov-2 Bonhams, Leeds #61
£320 $499 €480 Wooded landscape with timber-wain (24x34cm-9x13in) s. W/C bodycol. 10-Apr-3 Tennants, Leyburn #857
£410 $644 €615 Landscape with cottages and two figures (24x34cm-9x13in) s. W/C. 19-Nov-2 James Thompson, Kirby Lonsdale #46
£420 $659 €630 Landscape with figures and cattle by a stream (19x29cm-7x11in) s.d.1911 W/C. 21-Nov-2 Tennants, Leyburn #630
£460 $750 €667 Moorland landscape with shepherd and flock (30x46cm-12x18in) s. W/C. 17-Jul-3 Richardson & Smith, Whitby #479
£470 $743 €705 Scene in Westmoreland (17x25cm-7x10in) s. W/C. 7-Apr-3 David Duggleby, Scarborough #352/R
£580 $957 €841 Returning home (24x35cm-9x14in) s. pencil W/C bodycol. 3-Jul-3 Christie's, Kensington #84/R
£600 $930 €900 Figures by a lake. Watching the horseman (16x24cm-6x9in) s. W/C bodycol pair. 24-Sep-2 Bonhams, Knightsbridge #24/R
£625 $969 €938 Off the hay field (18x25cm-7x10in) s. 4-Dec-2 Andrew Hartley, Ilkley #1122/R
£700 $1148 €1015 Figures gathering firewood in a wooded landscape (33x23cm-13x9in) s. W/C bodycol pair. 6-Jun-3 Halls, Shrewsbury #710
£825 $1279 €1238 Springtime, Levens (18x25cm-7x10in) s. 4-Dec-2 Andrew Hartley, Ilkley #1124/R
£825 $1279 €1238 Home sweet home (18x25cm-7x10in) s. 4-Dec-2 Andrew Hartley, Ilkley #1123/R
£900 $1449 €1350 Snowballing scene (17x25cm-7x10in) s. W/C. 15-Jan-3 James Thompson, Kirby Lonsdale #49
£900 $1467 €1305 Figure with a horse and cart on a country lane. Figures gathering wood beside a river (16x24cm-6x9in) s. W/C pair. 17-Jul-3 Tennants, Leyburn #727/R
£1300 $2067 €1950 Evening street scene in Kendall (19x29cm-7x11in) s. W/C sold with a companion. 5-Mar-3 Bonhams, Bury St Edmunds #272 est:1000-1500
£1500 $2340 €2250 Bustling street scenes by moonlight (20x30cm-8x12in) s. W/C pair. 6-Nov-2 Bonhams, Chester #331 est:700-1000
£1600 $2576 €2400 Horse fair, New Road, Kendal (24x24cm-9x9in) s. W/C. 15-Jan-3 James Thompson, Kirby Lonsdale #50

MANNFELD, Bernhard (1848-1925) German
Works on paper
£324 $538 €460 Beerfelder gallows (98x66cm-39x26in) s. pastel. 14-Jun-3 Arnold, Frankfurt #802/R

MANNHEIM, Jean (1863-1945) American/German
£1899 $3000 €2849 Nude combing her hair (41x38cm-16x15in) s. 5-Apr-3 Neal Auction Company, New Orleans #221/R est:2000-3000
£1946 $3250 €2822 Landscape near Pasadena (33x41cm-13x16in) s. board. 17-Jun-3 John Moran, Pasadena #27 est:2500-3500
£2229 $3500 €3344 Pond, Chapman Ranch (28x36cm-11x14in) s. i.verso board prov. 19-Nov-2 Butterfields, San Francisco #8294/R est:3000-5000
£2581 $4000 €3872 Cabin and figures in eucalyptus landscape (51x61cm-20x24in) s. masonite. 29-Oct-2 John Moran, Pasadena #642 est:4000-6000
£4459 $7000 €6689 View from the back patio (51x61cm-20x24in) s. masonite prov. 19-Nov-2 Butterfields, San Francisco #8272/R est:8000-12000
£6369 $10000 €9554 Dairy farm in the Arroyo Seco (71x91cm-28x36in) s. 20-Nov-2 Christie's, Los Angeles #80/R est:10000-15000
£6452 $10000 €9678 Boats and workers, San Pedro Harbour (51x61cm-20x24in) s. prov. 29-Oct-2 John Moran, Pasadena #730a est:10000-15000
£46584 $75000 €69876 Reminiscence (99x86cm-39x34in) indis.sig. prov. 18-Feb-3 John Moran, Pasadena #50 est:15000-20000

MANNIKKO, Esko (1959-) Finnish
Photographs
£2281 $3605 €3422 Organized freedom 2 (101x84cm-40x33in) s.num.3/20 C-print executed 1999-2000 prov. 28-Apr-3 Bukowskis, Stockholm #954/R est:25000-30000 (S.KR 30000)
£2281 $3605 €3422 Organized freedom 8 (101x84cm-40x33in) s.num.3/20 verso C-print prov. executed 1999-2000. 28-Apr-3 Bukowskis, Stockholm #955/R est:25000-30000 (S.KR 30000)
£2523 $3936 €3785 Kuivaniemi (33x37cm-13x15in) s.d.1994 verso num.4/20 C-print prov. 5-Nov-2 Bukowskis, Stockholm #479/R est:15000-20000 (S.KR 36000)
£4747 $7500 €7121 Frank and Christine. Untitled - Batesville. Alex, Batesville. s.verso set of three chromogenic col prints prov.lit. 24-Apr-3 Phillips, New York #212/R est:8000-12000
£6000 $9240 €9000 Frank and Christina, San Antonio. Cowboy. Kuivaniemi (74x98cm-29x39in) three col photographs prov. 22-Oct-2 Sotheby's, London #311/R est:3000-4000

MANNING, Constance Tempe (1896-1960) Australian
£269 $409 €404 Road to the homestead (15x37cm-6x15in) s. board. 27-Aug-2 Goodman, Sydney #53 (A.D 750)
£308 $489 €462 Market stall (23x28cm-9x11in) s. canvasboard. 4-Mar-3 Deutscher-Menzies, Melbourne #247/R (A.D 800)
£357 $564 €536 Seated man (30x22cm-12x9in) s. board. 27-Nov-2 Deutscher-Menzies, Melbourne #238/R est:2000-3000 (A.D 1000)
£357 $564 €536 Portrait of a boy (30x22cm-12x9in) s. board. 27-Nov-2 Deutscher-Menzies, Melbourne #239/R est:2000-3000 (A.D 1000)
£577 $917 €866 Bowral landscape (38x56cm-15x22in) s.d.38 i.verso canvas on board. 4-Mar-3 Deutscher-Menzies, Melbourne #255/R (A.D 1500)
£786 $1241 €1179 Peace - the clown (30x22cm-12x9in) i.d.Nov 8 18 board. 27-Nov-2 Deutscher-Menzies, Melbourne #240/R est:2000-3000 (A.D 2200)

MANNIX, Max (1939-) Australian
£282 $448 €423 How do you spell measles (35x45cm-14x18in) s.i. board. 3-Mar-3 Lawson Menzies, Sydney #364 (A.D 750)
£301 $478 €452 Can't go fast dad your not as young as you used to be (34x47cm-13x19in) s.i. board. 3-Mar-3 Lawson Menzies, Sydney #302 (A.D 800)
£358 $545 €537 Wash day (39x49cm-15x19in) s.i. board. 27-Aug-2 Goodman, Sydney #227 (A.D 1000)
£466 $708 €699 Old rogue (44x59cm-17x23in) s.i. board. 27-Aug-2 Goodman, Sydney #228 (A.D 1300)
£563 $879 €845 Another ruined card night (35x45cm-14x18in) s. board. 21-Oct-2 Australian Art Auctions, Sydney #133 (A.D 1600)

MANNUCCI, Cipriano (1882-1970) Italian
£314 $484 €500 Portraitof girl (46x35cm-18x14in) s. board. 28-Oct-2 Il Ponte, Milan #312
£833 $1317 €1300 Rialto Bridge (22x27cm-9x11in) i.verso canvas on cardboard. 15-Nov-2 Farsetti, Prato #522/R

MANNUCCI, Edgardo (1904-1986) Italian
Sculpture
£1538 $2246 €2400 Idea (65cm-26in) bronze. 5-Jun-2 Il Ponte, Milan #159/R
£2128 $3447 €3000 Studio per idea n. 1 (63cm-25in) bronze brass. 26-May-3 Christie's, Milan #144/R est:3000-4000

MANOIR, Irving (1891-1982) American
£1205 $2000 €1747 Summer in the garden (61x61cm-24x24in) s. 11-Jun-3 Butterfields, San Francisco #4277/R est:3000-5000

MANOL, John (20th C) Greek
£449 $700 €674 Harbour scene (91x91cm-36x36in) s. 5-Nov-2 Arthur James, Florida #168

MANOLO (1872-1945) Spanish
£3019 $4709 €4800 Catalan landscape (21x25cm-8x10in) cardboard. 17-Sep-2 Segre, Madrid #125/R est:4800
Sculpture
£1032 $1631 €1600 Youths (33x24x2cm-13x9x1in) s. terracotta relief. 17-Dec-2 Segre, Madrid #97/R
£5000 $7700 €7500 Deux Espagnoles (25cm-10in) terracotta edition of 10 prov. 23-Oct-2 Sotheby's, Olympia #769/R est:6000-8000
£6765 $11094 €10350 Singer with fan (27cm-11in) bronze lit. 5-Feb-3 Arte, Seville #315/R

MANPO, Francisco (20th C) French
Works on paper
£915 $1520 €1300 Nueva tipografia (151x156cm-59x61in) s.i.verso mixed media collage panel. 18-Jun-3 Anaf, Lyon #55a/R

MANRIQUE, Cesar (1920-1992) Spanish
£1377 $2258 €1900 Untitled (66x50cm-26x20in) s.d.74 s.d. verso acrylic mixed media board. 28-May-3 Lempertz, Koln #267/R est:2000
£3571 $5214 €5500 Growing up (100x70cm-39x28in) s.d.1984 s.i.d.verso board. 17-Jun-2 Ansorena, Madrid #346/R
Works on paper
£617 $901 €950 Composition in blue (16x24cm-6x9in) gouache. 17-Jun-2 Ansorena, Madrid #301/R
£779 $1138 €1200 Untitled (18x20cm-7x8in) mixed media. 17-Jun-2 Ansorena, Madrid #46/R

MANSER, Albert (1937-) Swiss
£858 $1356 €1287 Winter in Schneiele with figures and transport sledge (20x34cm-8x13in) s.d.71 pavatex. 26-Nov-2 Hans Widmer, St Gallen #1465/R est:1000-3000 (S.FR 2000)
£926 $1491 €1343 On the mountain pasture (11x20cm-4x8in) s.d.83 panel. 9-May-3 Dobiaschofsky, Bern #262/R (S.FR 2000)
£1747 $2725 €2621 Taking the cattle up to the mountains (25x62cm-10x24in) s. pavatex. 6-Nov-2 Hans Widmer, St Gallen #65/R est:4000-8500 (S.FR 4000)
£2402 $3747 €3603 Taking the cattle up the mountain (44x64cm-17x25in) s.d.70 pavatex. 6-Nov-2 Hans Widmer, St Gallen #63/R est:5500-10000 (S.FR 5500)

MANSFELD, Josef (1819-1894) Austrian
£556 $917 €800 Kaffeestilleben (32x27cm-13x11in) s.d.1887 panel. 1-Jul-3 Christie's, Amsterdam #38
£577 $906 €900 Breakfast still life (32x26cm-13x10in) s.d.1891 panel. 10-Dec-2 Dorotheum, Vienna #106/R
£833 $1308 €1300 Still life with china and fruit (32x27cm-13x11in) s.d. panel. 10-Dec-2 Dorotheum, Vienna #9

MANSFELD, Moritz (fl.1850-1890) Austrian
£1282 $1987 €2000 Still life with owl, wine glass, photo of ballerina and cookbook (30x18cm-12x7in) s. board. 6-Dec-2 Michael Zeller, Lindau #840/R

MANSFIELD, John W (1849-1933) American
£258 $400 €387 Equine portrait of Diana (30x36cm-12x14in) i.d.June 1906 verso board. 2-Nov-2 Thomaston Place, Thomaston #195

MANSFIELD, Louise (1876-?) American
£800 $1168 €1200 Summer days (51x76cm-20x30in) s. board. 12-Jun-2 John Ross, Belfast #154
£850 $1318 €1275 Little fishermen (61x51cm-24x20in) s. board. 2-Oct-2 John Ross, Belfast #169
£950 $1387 €1425 Summer days (51x76cm-20x30in) s. board. 12-Jun-2 John Ross, Belfast #147

MANSHIP, Paul Howard (1885-1966) American
Sculpture
£7742 $12000 €11613 Maenad (22cm-9in) i. gilded bronze marble base prov.exhib. 4-Dec-2 Sotheby's, New York #99/R est:6000-8000
£21127 $30000 €31691 Untitled (74x74cm-29x29in) cast bronze. 8-Aug-1 Barridorf, Portland #73/R est:30000-50000
£22581 $35000 €33872 Venus anadyomene (19cm-7in) i. yellow brown pat. black marble base prov.lit. 4-Dec-2 Sotheby's, New York #98/R est:20000-30000
£153846 $240000 €230769 Flight of night (94cm-37in) s. brown pat bronze marble base prov. 18-Sep-2 Boos Gallery, Michigan #167/R est:200000-300000
£253012 $420000 €366867 Dancer and gazelles (83cm-33in) s.i.d.1916 green pat bronze one of twelve. 11-Jun-3 Butterfields, San Francisco #4038/R est:75000-100000

MANSKIRCH, Bernhard Gottfried (attrib) (1736-1817) German
£4487 $7090 €7000 Wooded landscape with faggot gatherer (104x170cm-41x67in) 16-Nov-2 Lempertz, Koln #1050a/R est:5000

MANSON, Donald (1948-) British
£280 $456 €420 Fishing village (26x32cm-10x13in) 14-Feb-3 Lyon & Turnbull, Edinburgh #114

MANSON, George (1850-1876) British
£280 $440 €420 Celt, head study (13x12cm-5x5in) 17-Apr-3 Bonhams, Edinburgh #303

MANSON, James Bolivar (1879-1945) British
£450 $734 €675 Still life study of mixed flowers in a bowl on a table (46x56cm-18x22in) s. 14-Feb-3 Keys, Aylsham #720/R
£1000 $1640 €1500 Still life of flowers in front of a window (51x61cm-20x24in) s. 3-Jun-3 Sotheby's, Olympia #56/R
£2600 $4004 €3900 Spring comes to Chelsea (61x51cm-24x20in) s. prov. 5-Sep-2 Christie's, Kensington #560/R est:2000-4000
£3400 $5270 €5100 Still life of tulips (60x50cm-24x20in) s. 3-Dec-2 Bonhams, New Bond Street #24/R est:1500-2000

MANSOUROFF, Paul (1896-1983) French
£6944 $11042 €10000 Untitled (104x22cm-41x9in) s. board painted 1963. 1-May-3 Meeting Art, Vercelli #461 est:10000
£13462 $21135 €21000 Formule picturale, hommage a Cannes (68x156cm-27x61in) s.i.d.62 s.i.d.verso prov.exhib. 24-Nov-2 Laurence Calmels, Paris #187/R est:5000
£14103 $22141 €22000 Formule picturale (118x30cm-46x12in) s.d.71 s.i.d.verso panel prov.exhib. 24-Nov-2 Laurence Calmels, Paris #190/R
£15385 $24154 €24000 Formule picturale (125x30cm-49x12in) s. s.i.d.71 verso panel prov.exhib. 24-Nov-2 Laurence Calmels, Paris #189/R est:5000
£17308 $27173 €27000 Formule picturale (125x23cm-49x9in) s. panel prov.exhib. 24-Nov-2 Laurence Calmels, Paris #191/R est:5000
Works on paper
£312 $496 €450 Construction orthogonale (25x13cm-10x5in) s. pastel graphite. 29-Apr-3 Artcurial Briest, Paris #112
£317 $526 €450 Gamme chromatique 1225 (31x21cm-12x8in) s. wax pastel. 18-Jun-3 Anaf, Lyon #57/R
£347 $552 €500 Composition a la sphere (21x13cm-8x5in) s. graphite dr. 29-Apr-3 Artcurial Briest, Paris #113
£884 $1406 €1300 Composition (30x22cm-12x9in) s.d.1938 mixed media. 1-Mar-3 Meeting Art, Vercelli #316
£1923 $3019 €3000 Untitled (38x13cm-15x5in) s. pastel. 24-Nov-2 Laurence Calmels, Paris #188/R

MANSSON, Per (1896-1949) Swedish
£423 $665 €635 Landscape - view from my window (65x80cm-26x31in) s. 16-Dec-2 Lilla Bukowskis, Stockholm #448 (S.KR 6000)
£595 $946 €893 Oriental scene (100x63cm-39x25in) s.i.d.1921 exhib. 3-Mar-3 Lilla Bukowskis, Stockholm #10 (S.KR 8000)
£736 $1163 €1104 Model on spiral staircase (176x102cm-69x40in) i.verso panel. 27-Nov-2 Falkkloos, Malmo #77569/R (S.KR 10500)
£1901 $3004 €2852 Atlantis (90x70cm-35x28in) s.d.1924 exhib.lit. 28-Apr-3 Bukowskis, Stockholm #59/R est:25000-30000 (S.KR 25000)

MANSUROFF, Pavel (1896-1984) Russian
£15000 $24300 €22500 Tower, pictorial formula (125x23cm-49x9in) s. panel painted c.1970. 21-May-3 Sotheby's, London #187/R est:15000-20000
£15000 $24300 €22500 Pictorial formula (125x30cm-49x12in) s.i. panel. 21-May-3 Sotheby's, London #188/R est:15000-20000

MANTEGAZZA, Giacomo (1853-1920) Italian
£2075 $3217 €3300 Still life with vase of flowers (47x64cm-19x25in) s. 29-Oct-2 Finarte, Milan #448
£5507 $8040 €8261 The secret (84x56cm-33x22in) s.i. 17-Jun-2 Philippe Schuler, Zurich #4353/R est:4000-6000 (S.FR 12500)
£6000 $9420 €9000 Go-between (84x56cm-33x22in) s.i. 21-Nov-2 Christie's, Kensington #63/R est:6000-8000
£12319 $20203 €17000 Presentazione dell'erede (89x122cm-35x48in) s.d.1888. 27-May-3 Finarte, Milan #59/R est:17000-20000
£12335 $18009 €18503 Hunt for a mouse (120x70cm-47x28in) s.i. 17-Jun-2 Philippe Schuler, Zurich #4354/R est:6000-8000 (S.FR 28000)
£12500 $20375 €18750 Entertainer (41x60cm-16x24in) s.d.1875. 30-Jan-3 Lawrence, Crewkerne #737/R est:4000-6000
£14978 $21868 €22467 Group making music (120x70cm-47x28in) s.i. 17-Jun-2 Philippe Schuler, Zurich #4355/R est:6000-8000 (S.FR 34000)
£20701 $32500 €31052 Dancing lesson (82x122cm-32x48in) s.i. 21-Nov-2 Sotheby's, New York #178/R est:30000-40000
Works on paper
£323 $510 €500 Woman (27x17cm-11x7in) s. W/C. 18-Dec-2 Finarte, Milan #199/R

MANTEGNA, Andrea (1431-1506) Italian
£15740740 $25500000 €23611110 Descent into Limbo (39x42cm-15x17in) tempera gold panel. 23-Jan-3 Sotheby's, New York #62/R est:20000000-30000000
Prints
£26923 $42538 €42000 Combat de dieux marins. drypoint engraving. 14-Nov-2 Libert, Castor, Paris #18/R est:20000
£38462 $60769 €60000 La vierge. drypoint. 14-Nov-2 Libert, Castor, Paris #17/R est:18500

MANTOVANI, Luigi (1880-1957) Italian
£220 $341 €350 Lake landscape (13x27cm-5x11in) s. board. 29-Oct-2 Finarte, Milan #404
£481 $755 €750 Venice (19x29cm-7x11in) s.i.indis.d. board. 21-Nov-2 Dorotheum, Vienna #224/R
£581 $917 €900 Vase of flowers (44x28cm-17x11in) s. cardboard. 18-Dec-2 Finarte, Milan #160/R
£680 $1082 €1000 Milan, Naviglio Grande (17x23cm-7x9in) s. 18-Mar-3 Finarte, Milan #238/R
£2564 $4026 €4000 View of Milan (96x70cm-38x28in) s.d.1943. 16-Dec-2 Pandolfini, Florence #255/R

MANTYNEN, Jussi (1886-1978) Finnish
Sculpture
£1408 $2268 €2000 Elks on path (40x89cm-16x35in) s.d.1923 bronze lit. 10-May-3 Bukowskis, Helsinki #27/R est:1500-1700
£1439 $2302 €2000 Lynx sitting (18cm-7in) s.d.1933 pat.bronze. 17-May-3 Hagelstam, Helsinki #7/R est:2500
£1799 $2878 €2500 Elk walking proudly (35cm-14in) s.d.1940 bronze lit. 17-May-3 Hagelstam, Helsinki #8/R est:3000
£2113 $3401 €3000 Polar-bear (33cm-13in) s.d.1943 bronze lit. 10-May-3 Bukowskis, Helsinki #30/R est:4000-5000
£2278 $3736 €3303 Lynx on the sly (21cm-8in) s.d.1945 green pat.bronze. 4-Jun-3 AB Stockholms Auktionsverk #2370/R est:30000-35000 (S.KR 29000)
£2342 $3700 €3700 The elk cleaning his foot (20cm-8in) s.d.1948 bronze lit. 1-Dec-2 Bukowskis, Helsinki #10/R est:3500-4000
£2676 $4308 €3800 Ready for a fight (22cm-9in) s.d.1948 bronze lit. 10-May-3 Bukowskis, Helsinki #3/R est:3500-4000
£2734 $4374 €3800 Lynx hunting (27cm-11in) s.d.1936 bronze. 17-May-3 Hagelstam, Helsinki #4/R est:3500
£2950 $4719 €4100 Lynx (32cm-13in) s.d.1940 pat.bronze Cast Pettersson lit. 17-May-3 Hagelstam, Helsinki #9/R est:3000
£2975 $4700 €4700 Calves in spring meadow (19cm-7in) s. bronze lit. 1-Dec-2 Bukowskis, Helsinki #7/R est:4700-5000
£3103 $5027 €4499 Elk (51cm-20in) s.d.1947 brown pat.bronze Cast Pettersson. 26-May-3 Bukowskis, Stockholm #296/R est:40000-50000 (S.KR 40000)
£3191 $4947 €4787 Lynx (35cm-14in) s.d.1940 green pat.bronze incl.stone socle st.f.Pettersson. 4-Dec-2 AB Stockholms Auktionsverk #1808/R est:20000-25000 (S.KR 45000)
£3291 $5200 €5200 The ruler of the ice plateau (31cm-12in) s.d.1945 bronze lit. 1-Dec-2 Bukowskis, Helsinki #9/R est:4000-4500
£4051 $6400 €6400 Swans (28cm-11in) s.d.1955 bronze. 30-Nov-2 Hagelstam, Helsinki #3/R est:4000
£4173 $6676 €5800 Excelsior (56cm-22in) s.d.1946 pat.bronze. 17-May-3 Hagelstam, Helsinki #3/R est:5000
£4225 $6803 €6000 The lynx scenting danger (20cm-8in) s.d.1940 bronze lit. 10-May-3 Bukowskis, Helsinki #15/R est:4000-4500
£4241 $6700 €6700 Swans taking off (28cm-11in) s.d.1955 bronze. 1-Dec-2 Bukowskis, Helsinki #8/R est:4500-5000
£8201 $13122 €11400 Lynx (80cm-31in) s.d.1935 mahogany. 17-May-3 Hagelstam, Helsinki #2/R est:12000
£14789 $23810 €21000 Cranes by well - fountain sculpture (105cm-41in) s. bronze incl.socle. 10-May-3 Bukowskis, Helsinki #24/R est:12000-15000

MANTZ, Werner (1901-1983) German
Photographs
£3481 $5500 €5500 Dr Grobel house in Elberfeld (17x23cm-7x9in) s.d.1927 s. verso bromide silver gelatin on board lit.exhib. 28-Nov-2 Villa Grisebach, Berlin #1309/R est:6000-8000
£3797 $6000 €6000 Department store, Gelsenkirchen (23x17cm-9x7in) i. verso bromide silver gelatin. 28-Nov-2 Villa Grisebach, Berlin #1310/R est:6000-8000

MANUEL, Victor (1897-1969) Cuban
Works on paper
£6098 $10000 €9147 Retratos de mujeres (30x24cm-12x9in) s. one pastel crayon one gouache ink pencil exec.c.1960 prov. two. 28-May-3 Christie's, Rockefeller NY #125/R est:8000-10000

MANYAI, Jozsef (1875-?) Hungarian
£1132 $1811 €1698 Female nude (115x135cm-45x53in) s. 17-Mar-3 Philippe Schuler, Zurich #4630/R est:3500-4000 (S.FR 2400)

MANYOKI, Adam de (1673-1756) Hungarian
£5660 $8774 €9000 Portrait of young nobleman wearing wig (91x73cm-36x29in) prov. 2-Oct-2 Dorotheum, Vienna #196/R est:9000-12000

MANZ, Curt (1900-1989) Swiss
£386 $610 €579 Cherries (27x35cm-11x14in) s. 29-Nov-2 Zofingen, Switzerland #2975 (S.FR 900)

MANZ, Jean Luc (1952-) Swiss
£655 $956 €983 Untitled (56x56cm-22x22in) s.d.1987 verso. 4-Jun-2 Germann, Zurich #799 (S.FR 1500)

MANZANA-PISSARRO, Georges (1871-1961) French
£1603 $2516 €2500 La pie perchee (38x46cm-15x18in) s. lacquer panel. 16-Dec-2 Millon & Associes, Paris #172/R est:2500-3500
£1603 $2516 €2500 Le poisson Saint-Pierre (38x46cm-15x18in) bears sig. lacquer arrachee. 16-Dec-2 Millon & Associes, Paris #173/R est:2500-3500
£2405 $3800 €3800 Port de Dieppe (27x17cm-11x7in) s. panel. 2-Dec-2 Tajan, Paris #65
£3000 $4620 €4500 Bord de riviere (48x40cm-19x16in) s. board. 23-Oct-2 Sotheby's, Olympia #617/R est:4000-6000
£3500 $5390 €5250 L'eglise de Moisson sur Seine (38x47cm-15x19in) s.d.1952 i.verso board. 23-Oct-2 Sotheby's, Olympia #618/R est:4000-6000
£7362 $12000 €11043 Moret sur Loing (54x65cm-21x26in) s. 12-Feb-3 Sotheby's, New York #26/R est:15000-20000
£9607 $15179 €14411 Bord de Seine pres de Rouen (45x53cm-18x21in) s.d.1904. 17-Nov-2 Koller, Geneva #1227/R est:5000 (S.FR 22000)
Works on paper
£560 $935 €800 Coq et femme a la pomme (47x58cm-19x23in) s. wash gold. 26-Jun-3 Tajan, Paris #65
£577 $894 €900 Lapin a la pomme (22x30cm-9x12in) st.sig. gouache. 9-Dec-2 Beaussant & Lefèvre, Paris #74/R
£979 $1635 €1400 Les canards (28x45cm-11x18in) s. gouache ink gold silver pair. 26-Jun-3 Tajan, Paris #64 est:1500-2000
£2400 $3840 €3600 Indian girl dancing in an interior (61x48cm-24x19in) s. bodycol two. 13-Mar-3 Duke & Son, Dorchester #69

MANZELLI, Margherita (1968-) Italian
Works on paper
£1844 $2987 €2600 Untitled (19x57cm-7x22in) W/C. 20-May-3 Porro, Milan #40/R est:2800-3000

MANZINI, F (?) ?
Works on paper
£894 $1413 €1296 Oriental scene (51x41cm-20x16in) s. W/C. 22-Jul-3 Lawson Menzies, Sydney #285/R est:1500-2000 (A.D 2200)

MANZOCCHI, Francesco (attrib) (1502-1584) Italian
Works on paper
£1200 $2004 €1740 Madonna and Child with Saint Joseph and John the Baptist (29x50cm-11x20in) i.verso black chk squared. 8-Jul-3 Christie's, London #13/R est:1500-2000

MANZONE, Giuseppe (1887-1983) Italian
£850 $1352 €1250 Labour in the fields (30x35cm-12x14in) s. board. 1-Mar-3 Meeting Art, Vercelli #148

MANZONI, Francesco (19th C) Italian
£1772 $2747 €2800 Figures making music in wine cellar (27x43cm-11x17in) s.d.1896 panel. 25-Sep-2 Neumeister, Munich #646/R est:1500

MANZONI, P (?) ?
£1074 $1729 €1600 Ramasseuses de fagots (85x112cm-33x44in) 18-Feb-3 Vanderkindere, Brussels #80

MANZONI, Piero (1933-1963) Italian
£36000 $59040 €54000 Achrome (40x23cm-16x9in) s.d.59 verso sewn painted canvas prov.exhib.lit. 7-Feb-3 Sotheby's, London #203/R est:20000-30000
£80000 $123200 €120000 Achrome (18x24cm-7x9in) s.i.d.59 on stretcher prov.lit. 22-Oct-2 Christie's, London #25/R est:80000-100000
£350000 $574000 €525000 Achrome (100x70cm-39x28in) kaolin on canvas painted 1958 prov.exhib.lit. 5-Feb-3 Christie's, London #16/R est:300000-500000

£380000 $592800 €570000 Achrome (70x100cm-28x39in) s.d.58verso s.i.d.on stretcher kaolin on canvas prov.exhib.lit. 21-Oct-2 Sotheby's, London #22/R est:350000-450000

Prints

£16901 $28056 €24000 Eight Tavole di accertamento (49x35cm-19x14in) s.d.1958-1960 num.10/60 lithograph eight. 10-Jun-3 Finarte Semenzato, Milan #221/R est:22000-28000

Sculpture

£15000 $25050 €21750 Merda d'artista no.077 (5x6cm-2x2in) s.num.077 sealed tin paper label executed 1961 prov.exhib.lit. 27-Jun-3 Christie's, London #151/R est:15000-20000

£16000 $26240 €24000 Achrome (45x55cm-18x22in) s.i. paper string lead wax oil burlap. 6-Feb-3 Christie's, London #643/R est:15000-20000

£55000 $84700 €82500 Achrome (40x60cm-16x24in) i. s.v, newspaper string wax lead cardboard oil burlap. 22-Oct-2 Christie's, London #30/R est:60000-80000

£80000 $133600 €120000 Achrome (45x45cm-18x18in) bread rolls and kaolin on panel exc.1962 prov.exhib.lit. 26-Jun-3 Christie's, London #9/R est:80000-120000

Works on paper

£43750 $70000 €65625 Achrome (25x19cm-10x7in) 35 wool cotton balls on blue velvet executed 1961. 16-May-3 Phillips, New York #172/R est:40000-60000

£130000 $202800 €195000 Achrome (59x45cm-23x18in) s.d.1960 verso sewn canvas prov.exhib.lit. 21-Oct-2 Sotheby's, London #58/R est:120000-150000

£562500 $900000 €843750 Achrome (60x80cm-24x31in) s.verso kaolin burlap prov.exhib.lit. 14-May-3 Christie's, Rockefeller NY #38/R est:600000-800000

MANZONI, Ridolfo (1675-1743) Italian

£4430 $7000 €6645 Tree stump with birds and shepherds with their flocks beyond (279x206cm-110x81in) s.d.1715 vellum. 1-Apr-3 Christie's, Rockefeller NY #385/R est:10000-15000

MANZU, Giacomo (1908-1991) Italian

Sculpture

£27950 $45000 €41925 Cardinale seduto (38cm-15in) st.sig. brown pat. bronze cast c.1970-72 prov. 8-May-3 Christie's, Rockefeller NY #193/R est:50000-70000

£30000 $46800 €45000 Cardinali in preghiera (26cm-10in) st. bronze executed c.1979 prov. 21-Oct-2 Sotheby's, London #14/R est:35000-45000

£32051 $50000 €48077 Cardinale seduto (42cm-17in) brown pat. bronze st.f.Maf executed 1961 prov. 5-Nov-2 Phillips, New York #135/R est:90000-120000

£65000 $106600 €97500 Double dance step (72cm-28in) stsig.st.f.MAF bronze exec.1946 prov.exhib. 5-Feb-3 Sotheby's, London #246/R est:80000

Works on paper

£417 $663 €600 Etude pour Passo de Danza (20x12cm-8x5in) s. graphite dr. 29-Apr-3 Artcurial Briest, Paris #127b

MANZUOLI, Egisto (19th C) Italian?

£2000 $3260 €3000 Portrait of a lady, in a blue dress and red cloak (70x55cm-28x22in) s.i.verso feigned oval. 13-Feb-3 Christie's, Kensington #35/R est:2000-3000

MANZUOLI, Tommaso D'Antonio (1536-1571) Italian

£32000 $49920 €48000 Gabriel appearing to Zacharias. Birth of Sait John the Baptist (29x50cm-11x20in) panel pair prov.lit. 10-Apr-3 Sotheby's, London #25/R est:30000

£32051 $50641 €50000 Holy Family with Saint John the Baptist (64x46cm-25x18in) tempera board exhib.lit. 16-Nov-2 Farsetti, Prato #333/R est:40000-50000

MANZUR, David (1929-) Colombian

£577 $900 €866 Ave Mechanica (84x99cm-33x39in) s.d.67. 20-Sep-2 New Orleans Auction, New Orleans #1414/R est:1500-2500

MAPPLETHORPE, Robert (1946-1989) American

Photographs

£1840 $3000 €2760 Jack Walls (38x39cm-15x15in) s.i.d.1982 num.1/2 gelatin silver print. 12-Feb-3 Christie's, Rockefeller NY #266/R est:4000-6000

£2273 $3500 €3410 Michael (61x51cm-24x20in) s.d.87 num.1/10 gelatin silver print board prov.lit. 25-Oct-2 Phillips, New York #161/R est:4000-6000

£2400 $3888 €3600 Thomas (45x45cm-18x18in) s.i.d.num.2/10 verso gelatin silver print. 21-May-3 Christie's, London #202/R est:3000-5000

£2500 $4050 €3750 Lisa Lyon, San Francisco (50x40cm-20x16in) s.d.80 num.1/15 i.verso silver print card. 22-May-3 Sotheby's, London #139/R est:2500-3500

£2532 $4000 €3798 Lisa Lyon (50x40cm-20x16in) s.i.d.1981 num.2/10 verso gelatin silver print prov. 24-Apr-3 Phillips, New York #196/R est:7000-9000

£2639 $4354 €3800 Black nude (45x34cm-18x13in) s.d.81 num.7/15 gelatin silver print prov. 3-Jul-3 Christie's, Paris #2/R est:2500-3000

£2727 $4200 €4091 Ken Moody (69x58cm-27x23in) s.d.84 polaroid print aluminum prov.exhib. 25-Oct-2 Phillips, New York #162/R est:3000-4000

£2945 $4800 €4418 African daisy (38x38cm-15x15in) s.d.1982 num.6/10 gelatin silver print. 12-Feb-3 Christie's, Rockefeller NY #235/R est:5000-7000

£3067 $5000 €4601 Arnold Schwarzenegger (60x61cm-24x24in) gelatin silver print executed 1976. 12-Feb-3 Christie's, Rockefeller NY #42/R est:8000-10000

£3067 $5000 €4601 Melody (120x101cm-47x40in) gelatin silver print. 12-Feb-3 Christie's, Rockefeller NY #269/R est:7000-9000

£3822 $6000 €5733 Poppy (41x51cm-16x20in) s.verso num.6 of 10 gelatin silver print. 21-Apr-3 Phillips, New York #17 est:5000-7000

£5063 $8000 €7595 Orchid (38x38cm-15x15in) s.i.d.1982 num.8/10 gelatin silver print prov.lit. 24-Apr-3 Phillips, New York #51/R est:8000-12000

£5380 $8500 €8070 Ken Moody (48x49cm-19x19in) s.d.1983 num.2/3 platinum print lit. 22-Apr-3 Christie's, Rockefeller NY #183/R est:10000-15000

£6250 $10313 €9000 Robe drapeau (50x40cm-20x16in) s.d.82 num.1/10 gelatin silver print on board. 3-Jul-3 Christie's, Paris #3/R est:4000-6000

£6329 $10000 €9494 Anthurium (49x49cm-19x19in) s.i.d.1988 num.4/10 verso gelatin silver print prov.lit. 24-Apr-3 Phillips, New York #197/R est:5000-7000

£6329 $10000 €9494 Orchids (39x39cm-15x15in) i.d.1982 num.10/10 gelatin silver print prov.lit. 24-Apr-3 Phillips, New York #198/R est:7000-10000

£6494 $10000 €9741 Apples and urn (61x51cm-24x20in) s.d.87 num.4/7 dye transfer print prov.exhib.lit. 25-Oct-2 Phillips, New York #163/R est:10000-15000

£6748 $11000 €10122 Orchid (39x39cm-15x15in) s.d.1988 num.3/3 gelatin silver print. 12-Feb-3 Christie's, Rockefeller NY #76/R est:5000-7000

£9494 $15000 €14241 Hyacinth (83x83cm-33x33in) s.d.1987 num.9/27 photograph. 23-Apr-3 Sotheby's, New York #278/R est:10000-15000

£10127 $16000 €15191 Rose (48x47cm-19x19in) s.d.1987 num5/7 dye transfer print prov. 24-Apr-3 Phillips, New York #199/R est:18000-22000

£10625 $17000 €15938 Cindy Sherman (50x40cm-20x16in) s.i.d.1983 num.3/10 gelatin silver print prov. 14-May-3 Sotheby's, New York #403/R est:6000-8000

£12025 $19000 €18038 Tulips (47x47cm-19x19in) s.d.1988 num.5/7 dye transfer print prov.lit. 24-Apr-3 Phillips, New York #52/R est:20000-25000

£13636 $21000 €20454 Orchid (61x51cm-24x20in) s.i.d.verso dye transfer print 7 from edition of 7 prov.exhib.lit. 25-Oct-2 Phillips, New York #55/R est:20000-25000

£13924 $22000 €20886 Irises (83x83cm-33x33in) s.d.1986 num.13/27 photograph. 23-Apr-3 Sotheby's, New York #277/R est:10000-15000

£13924 $22000 €20886 Lydia Cheng (60x49cm-24x19in) s.i.d.1985 platinum print. 23-Apr-3 Sotheby's, New York #279/R est:25000-35000

£20253 $32000 €30380 Y Portfolio (19x19cm-7x7in) portfolio of 13 photograph. 23-Apr-3 Sotheby's, New York #275/R est:25000-35000

£25316 $40000 €37974 Lisa Marie (122x102cm-48x40in) oversized photograph prov. 23-Apr-3 Sotheby's, New York #280/R est:40000-60000

£31646 $50000 €47469 Flowers (48x49cm-19x19in) s.d.1988 num.20/25 suite of 10 lit. 23-Apr-3 Sotheby's, New York #276/R est:50000-70000

MAQHUBELA, Louis Khela (1939-) South African

Works on paper

£352 $550 €528 Workmen (33x21cm-13x8in) s. chl pastel. 11-Nov-2 Stephan Welz, Johannesburg #453 (SA.R 5500)

£430 $692 €645 Yellow sun (56x70cm-22x28in) s.d.71 mixed media. 12-May-3 Stephan Welz, Johannesburg #386 est:5000-7000 (SA.R 5000)

MAR, David de la (19/20th C) ?

£2158 $3453 €3000 La faneuse (160x90cm-63x35in) s.d.1887. 13-May-3 Palais de Beaux Arts, Brussels #58/R est:2800-4000

MARA, Pol (1920-1998) Belgian

£748 $1190 €1100 Sous-ile (146x114cm-57x45in) s.d.80 verso. 24-Mar-3 Bernaerts, Antwerp #859/R est:1500-2000

£1379 $2207 €2000 Nu tenant une fleur (110x130cm-43x51in) 17-Mar-3 Amberes, Antwerp #236

Works on paper

£347 $552 €500 Boulonner des ouvertures (70x100cm-28x39in) s.d.1990 W/C. 29-Apr-3 Campo, Vlaamse Kaai #204/R

£360 $576 €500 Meteore lesbienne (42x61cm-17x24in) s.d.72 mixed media. 13-May-3 Palais de Beaux Arts, Brussels #284
£417 $663 €600 Lila-Lila (110x72cm-43x28in) s.d.1973 mixed media. 29-Apr-3 Campo & Campo, Antwerp #210
£1258 $1937 €2000 Miroiter la realite (88x125cm-35x49in) s.1986 W/C. 22-Oct-2 Campo, Vlaamse Kaai #556/R
£1528 $2429 €2200 Venetiaanse (108x72cm-43x28in) s.d.1961 W/C. 29-Apr-3 Campo & Campo, Antwerp #211 est:2200-2500
£4717 $7264 €7500 Reve de glace (110x72cm-43x28in) s.1977 W/C. 22-Oct-2 Campo, Vlaamse Kaai #557

MARAINI, Adelaide (1843-?) Italian
Sculpture
£34810 $55000 €52215 Figure of Pomona with a Bacchic herm (213cm-84in) i. marble on granite plinth. 24-Apr-3 Christie's, Rockefeller NY #297/R est:40000-60000

MARAIS, Adolphe Charles (1856-1940) French
£520 $822 €780 Cattle in water meadow (41x58cm-16x23in) s.d.78. 17-Dec-2 Gorringes, Lewes #1477
£5513 $8655 €8600 Troupeau sous les arbres (243x300cm-96x118in) s.d.1881. 13-Dec-2 Rossini, Paris #176/R est:10000
Works on paper
£400 $636 €600 Cattle watering in pasture beneath stormy skies (40x53cm-16x21in) s.d.78. 18-Mar-3 Rosebery Fine Art, London #756

MARAIS, Wessel (20th C) South African
£205 $320 €308 Still life with gaillardias in a brass vase (60x90cm-24x35in) s. board. 11-Nov-2 Stephan Welz, Johannesburg #265 (SA.R 3200)
£256 $400 €384 Street scene with cottage, on an autumn day (50x75cm-20x30in) s. canvas on board. 11-Nov-2 Stephan Welz, Johannesburg #247 (SA.R 4000)

MARAIS-MILTON, Victor (1872-1968) French
£1538 $2385 €2400 Au regime (46x38cm-18x15in) s. 3-Dec-2 Campo & Campo, Antwerp #192/R est:3500-4500
£2700 $4266 €4050 Pet parrot (33x26cm-13x10in) s. 2-Dec-2 Bonhams, Bath #167/R est:1200-1800
£3000 $4800 €4500 Au regime (46x38cm-18x15in) s. 13-May-3 Bonhams, Knightsbridge #168/R est:3000-5000
£7911 $12342 €12500 Interior with two cardinals (65x54cm-26x21in) s. 21-Oct-2 Bernaerts, Antwerp #88/R est:2000-2500
£9000 $14130 €13500 Recital (53x71cm-21x28in) s. 19-Nov-2 Bonhams, New Bond Street #176/R est:3000-5000
£9000 $14760 €13500 Les connaisseurs (66x55cm-26x22in) s. 3-Jun-3 Sotheby's, London #173/R est:8000-10000
£9375 $15000 €14063 Checkmate (56x71cm-22x28in) s. paperboard. 14-May-3 Butterfields, San Francisco #1115/R est:8000-12000
£10000 $16400 €15000 Card game (50x61cm-20x24in) s. 3-Jun-3 Sotheby's, London #172/R est:7000-10000
£14000 $22820 €21000 Lavish interior with cardinal teaching his dog a new trick. Good vintage (36x45cm-14x18in) s.i. board pair. 11-Feb-3 Fellows & Sons, Birmingham #61/R est:5000-8000
£14184 $23688 €20000 Un mauvais cigare (72x90cm-28x35in) s. 23-Jun-3 Bernaerts, Antwerp #135/R est:20000-25000
Works on paper
£800 $1264 €1200 The cardinal (38x33cm-15x13in) s. W/C. 2-Dec-2 Gorringes, Lewes #2666

MARAK, Julius Eduard (1832-1899) Bohemian
£12658 $20000 €20000 Woodland interior with wild (67x44cm-26x17in) s. panel. 28-Nov-2 Dorotheum, Vienna #171/R est:3600-4500
Works on paper
£1342 $2094 €2013 Mountainous landscape (44x31cm-17x12in) s. Indian ink dr. 12-Oct-2 Dorotheum, Prague #172 est:50000-75000 (C.KR 65000)

MARANDAT, Louis (1850-1899) French
£633 $987 €1000 Lavandieres au bord de l'eau (44x71cm-17x28in) s.d.1884. 20-Oct-2 Chayette & Cheval, Paris #17

MARANIELLO, Giuseppe (1945-) Italian
Works on paper
£1026 $1610 €1600 Echos (22x54cm-9x21in) s.i.d.1999 mixed media on canvas on board. 23-Nov-2 Meeting Art, Vercelli #273/R
£1154 $1812 €1800 Everything in my mind (23x56cm-9x22in) s.i.d.1992 verso mixed media collage canvas on board. 23-Nov-2 Meeting Art, Vercelli #297/R
£1410 $2214 €2200 Everything in my mind (27x72cm-11x28in) s.i.d.1992 verso mixed media collage on canvas. 23-Nov-2 Meeting Art, Vercelli #59/R
£1905 $3029 €2800 Portrait (46x57cm-18x22in) s.i.d.1996 mixed media board. 1-Mar-3 Meeting Art, Vercelli #400

MARASCO, Antonio (1886-1975) Italian
£694 $1104 €1000 Anacapri (30x45cm-12x18in) s. cardboard on canvas. 1-May-3 Meeting Art, Vercelli #98
£917 $1448 €1430 Revelation (60x50cm-24x20in) painted 1970. 12-Nov-2 Babuino, Rome #248/R
£1295 $2046 €2020 Landscape (50x60cm-20x24in) 12-Nov-2 Babuino, Rome #353/R

MARATTA, C (1625-1713) Italian
£2100 $3276 €3150 Penitent Madonna (61x51cm-24x20in) 11-Apr-3 Keys, Aylsham #646/R est:700-900

MARATTA, Carlo (1625-1713) Italian
Works on paper
£1329 $1900 €1994 Virgin and child (25x18cm-10x7in) red chk. 23-Jan-3 Swann Galleries, New York #96/R est:3000-5000
£2797 $4000 €4196 Virgin and Child adored by Saints (25x17cm-10x7in) red chk. 23-Jan-3 Swann Galleries, New York #95/R est:5000-8000
£4545 $6500 €6818 Woman holding a bowl (42x24cm-17x9in) red chk htd white. 23-Jan-3 Swann Galleries, New York #98/R est:6000-9000
£4895 $7000 €7343 Head of a man looking up and to the left (38x27cm-15x11in) black chk htd white. 23-Jan-3 Swann Galleries, New York #97/R est:4000-6000

MARATTA, Carlo (attrib) (1625-1713) Italian
Works on paper
£262 $414 €393 Cupid (31x18cm-12x7in) s. ochre. 14-Nov-2 Stuker, Bern #9575 (S.FR 600)
£1013 $1600 €1600 Un homme nu regardant vers le bas (30x11cm-12x4in) col chk. 27-Nov-2 Christie's, Paris #75/R est:1500-2000

MARATTA, Carlo (style) (1625-1713) Italian
£5822 $9140 €8500 Madonna holding sleeping Infant Jesus and reading (74x63cm-29x25in) 16-Apr-3 Dorotheum, Salzburg #21/R est:4000-5000

MARATTA, Carlo and TAMM, Franz Werner (attrib) (17th C) Italian/German
£12057 $18688 €18086 Offering to the bust of Flora (94x135cm-37x53in) 4-Dec-2 AB Stockholms Auktionsverk #1948/R est:200000-250000 (S.KR 170000)

MARBLE, John Nelson (1855-1918) American
£617 $950 €926 Fifth Avenue, New York (13x20cm-5x8in) s. i.verso panel. 27-Oct-2 Grogan, Boston #94 est:300-500

MARC, Franz (1880-1916) German
£580645 $900000 €870968 Crouching deer (41x49cm-16x19in) tempera cardboard on wood prov.exhib.lit. 4-Nov-2 Phillips, New York #17/R est:700000-900000
Prints
£2089 $3258 €3300 Birth of a horse (22x14cm-9x6in) col woodcut. 18-Oct-2 Dr Fritz Nagel, Stuttgart #565/R est:3000
£3459 $5500 €5189 Tierlegende (20x24cm-8x9in) i.num.2 hand printed woodcut W/C. 2-May-3 Sotheby's, New York #202/R est:6000-8000
£4710 $7725 €6500 Horse and hedgehog (16x22cm-6x9in) bears sig. verso woodcut. 29-May-3 Lempertz, Koln #776/R est:4000
Works on paper
£5000 $7750 €7500 Katze (17x10cm-7x4in) pencil executed c.1908 prov. 5-Dec-2 Christie's, Kensington #111/R est:2500-3500
£9859 $16366 €14000 Snowy branches (21x16cm-8x6in) d.4.III.06 gouache. 14-Jun-3 Hauswedell & Nolte, Hamburg #1373/R est:15000
£35000 $57400 €52500 Red and yellow little horses (12x15cm-5x6in) gouache W/C exec.1913 prov.lit. 6-Feb-3 Christie's, London #456/R est:60000

MARC, Robert (1943-1993) French
£943 $1462 €1500 Composition (66x54cm-26x21in) s. 7-Oct-2 Claude Aguttes, Neuilly #185
£1069 $1657 €1700 Composition (60x42cm-24x17in) s. 7-Oct-2 Claude Aguttes, Neuilly #252
Works on paper
£377 $585 €600 Composition abstraite (33x22cm-13x9in) s. mixed media cardboard. 6-Oct-2 Livinec, Gaudcheau & Jezequel, Rennes #44

MARCA-RELLI, Conrad (1913-2000) American
£272 $425 €408 Still life (25x56cm-10x22in) s.d.39 masonite. 5-Nov-2 Arthur James, Florida #176
£288 $450 €432 Day and night (51x69cm-20x27in) s. masonite. 5-Nov-2 Arthur James, Florida #92
£321 $500 €482 City landscape (23x30cm-9x12in) s.d.39 board. 5-Nov-2 Arthur James, Florida #93

£355 $550 €533 Composition (76x61cm-30x24in) board. 16-Jul-2 Arthur James, Florida #90
£417 $650 €626 Fruit and plant still life (51x61cm-20x24in) s.d.1939 masonite. 5-Nov-2 Arthur James, Florida #94
£1026 $1600 €1539 Composition (48x66cm-19x26in) s. oil paper collage. 5-Nov-2 Arthur James, Florida #174
£3025 $4750 €4538 Untitled, M-10-69 (36x36cm-14x14in) s. s.d.verso painted canvas collage prov. 19-Nov-2 Wright, Chicago #204/R est:5000-7000

Works on paper
£256 $400 €384 Horse drawn carriage in the park (43x53cm-17x21in) s. W/C. 5-Nov-2 Arthur James, Florida #173
£11290 $17839 €17500 Untitled (52x46cm-20x18in) s.d.56 collage oil on canvas prov. 18-Dec-2 Christie's, Rome #91/R est:3000

MARCACCIO, Fabian (1963-) Argentinian
£1911 $3000 €2867 Untitled (68x66cm-27x26in) s.d.93 verso oil mixed media brush. 20-Nov-2 Christie's, Rockefeller NY #159/R
Sculpture
£5096 $8000 €7644 Untitled (143x148x18cm-56x58x7in) acrylic metal cords exec.1996 prov. 19-Nov-2 Sotheby's, New York #137/R est:15000

MARCARD-CUCUEL, Clara Lotte von (20th C) German?
£513 $810 €800 Still life of flowers (68x76cm-27x30in) s. board. 14-Nov-2 Neumeister, Munich #624/R

MARCEL, Didier (1961-) French
Works on paper
£621 $1037 €900 Sans titre (50x76cm-20x30in) s.verso ink prov. 9-Jul-3 Cornette de St.Cyr, Paris #317

MARCEL-BERONNEAU, Pierre Amedee (1869-1937) French
£280 $454 €420 Sunset landscape (46x61cm-18x24in) s. 20-May-3 Sotheby's, Olympia #308/R
£280 $454 €420 Rocheurs en corse (81x64cm-32x25in) s. 20-May-3 Sotheby's, Olympia #321/R
£350 $567 €525 Study for faunesse (17x14cm-7x6in) s. s.i.verso board. 20-May-3 Sotheby's, Olympia #302/R
£350 $567 €525 Monlight (26x34cm-10x13in) s. panel. 20-May-3 Sotheby's, Olympia #309/R
£350 $567 €525 Madonna (30x19cm-12x7in) board. 20-May-3 Sotheby's, Olympia #316/R
£350 $567 €525 Le pecheur (27x22cm-11x9in) board. 20-May-3 Sotheby's, Olympia #320/R
£380 $616 €570 Study of a seated nude (71x58cm-28x23in) st.atelier board oval. 20-May-3 Sotheby's, Olympia #289/R
£480 $778 €720 Male nude in the studio of Gustave Moreau (61x54cm-24x21in) s. s.verso. 20-May-3 Sotheby's, Olympia #333/R
£520 $842 €780 Ophelia (13x12cm-5x5in) board. 20-May-3 Sotheby's, Olympia #297/R
£550 $891 €825 Nude study foe Salome (35x18cm-14x7in) board. 20-May-3 Sotheby's, Olympia #291/R
£550 $891 €825 Salome with the head of John the Baptist (22x16cm-9x6in) 20-May-3 Sotheby's, Olympia #317/R
£550 $891 €825 Cote de Corse Mediternea (55x43cm-22x17in) board. 20-May-3 Sotheby's, Olympia #323/R
£550 $891 €825 In the kitchen (54x65cm-21x26in) 20-May-3 Sotheby's, Olympia #342/R
£600 $972 €900 Funeral in Paris (65x81cm-26x32in) s.verso. 20-May-3 Sotheby's, Olympia #341/R
£620 $1004 €930 Sphinx (16x22cm-6x9in) 20-May-3 Sotheby's, Olympia #339/R
£650 $1053 €975 Male nude in the studio of Gustave Moreau (81x65cm-32x26in) s. 20-May-3 Sotheby's, Olympia #334/R
£680 $1102 €1020 Temple at Versailles (34x27cm-13x11in) s. board. 20-May-3 Sotheby's, Olympia #318/R
£750 $1215 €1125 Sirene et poete (50x47cm-20x19in) board. 20-May-3 Sotheby's, Olympia #301/R
£750 $1215 €1125 Cloisters (73x54cm-29x21in) 20-May-3 Sotheby's, Olympia #331/R
£760 $1231 €1140 Le Mas (59x73cm-23x29in) board. 20-May-3 Sotheby's, Olympia #304/R
£800 $1296 €1200 At the dressing table (72x60cm-28x24in) board oval. 20-May-3 Sotheby's, Olympia #292/R
£900 $1458 €1350 Au soir (54x46cm-21x18in) i. board oval. 20-May-3 Sotheby's, Olympia #290/R
£900 $1458 €1350 Susanna and the Elders (60x50cm-24x20in) i. on stretcher. 20-May-3 Sotheby's, Olympia #327/R
£920 $1490 €1380 Salome (55x46cm-22x18in) 20-May-3 Sotheby's, Olympia #326/R
£950 $1539 €1425 Cherry blossom (65x91cm-26x36in) s. 20-May-3 Sotheby's, Olympia #305/R
£950 $1539 €1425 Study for the Salle de Mariages in the town hall, Bordeaux (64x54cm-25x21in) oil pencil on canvas. 20-May-3 Sotheby's, Olympia #330/R
£1100 $1782 €1650 Classical ruins (65x81cm-26x32in) s. 20-May-3 Sotheby's, Olympia #311/R est:1000-1500
£1100 $1782 €1650 Study for femme au parfume (60x73cm-24x29in) board. 20-May-3 Sotheby's, Olympia #335/R est:600-800
£1300 $2106 €1950 Le repose au laboureur (27x40cm-11x16in) s.i. 20-May-3 Sotheby's, Olympia #343/R est:600-800
£1300 $2106 €1950 Cherry blossom (81x65cm-32x26in) s. 20-May-3 Sotheby's, Olympia #345/R est:800-1200
£1400 $2268 €2100 Femme au parfume (54x54cm-21x21in) s. board circular. 20-May-3 Sotheby's, Olympia #300/R est:1000-1500
£1400 $2268 €2100 Red sunset (65x81cm-26x32in) s. 20-May-3 Sotheby's, Olympia #310/R est:1000-2000
£1450 $2349 €2175 Letter (73x60cm-29x24in) s. oval exhib. 20-May-3 Sotheby's, Olympia #298/R est:1000-1500
£1600 $2592 €2400 Village in Provence (81x56cm-32x22in) s. board. 20-May-3 Sotheby's, Olympia #319/R est:1000-2000
£1600 $2592 €2400 Sappho (60x81cm-24x32in) 20-May-3 Sotheby's, Olympia #338/R est:1000-1500
£1700 $2754 €2550 Studio interior (69x50cm-27x20in) s. s.i.d.1895 verso canvas on board. 20-May-3 Sotheby's, Olympia #344/R est:1000-1500
£1900 $3078 €2850 Les falaise de corse (73x60cm-29x24in) s. 20-May-3 Sotheby's, Olympia #322/R est:1000-1500
£2800 $4536 €4200 Orphee (45x81cm-18x32in) s.i.d.1901 i.verso. 20-May-3 Sotheby's, Olympia #294/R est:3000-5000
£3200 $5184 €4800 Sirene (72x60cm-28x24in) 20-May-3 Sotheby's, Olympia #313/R est:3000-5000
£9800 $15876 €14700 Salome avec la tete de Saint Jean Baptiste (60x73cm-24x29in) s. 20-May-3 Sotheby's, Olympia #296/R est:8000-12000
£15500 $25110 €23250 Interieur de l'atelier, 47 Boulevard Montparnasse (100x81cm-39x32in) s. exhib. 20-May-3 Sotheby's, Olympia #299/R est:8000-12000

MARCEL-CLEMENT, Amedee Julien (1873-?) French
£1338 $2087 €2100 Le cotre a la voile rouge (46x42cm-18x17in) s. panel. 7-Nov-2 Claude Aguttes, Neuilly #62/R est:1000-1200

MARCEL-LAURENT, Emmanuel (1892-1948) French
£1793 $2851 €2600 Pardon de Saint Anne la Palud (46x60cm-18x24in) s.d.1928. 4-Mar-3 Livinec, Gaudcheau & Jezequel, Rennes #73/R

MARCEL-LAURENT, Ernest (20th C) French
£1090 $1711 €1700 Retour de peche (38x46cm-15x18in) s.d.1928. 15-Dec-2 Thierry & Lannon, Brest #167

MARCETTE, Alexandre (1853-1929) Belgian
£392 $612 €620 Composition aux pommes et aux poires (38x60cm-15x24in) s.d.78. 16-Sep-2 Horta, Bruxelles #301
Works on paper
£272 $433 €400 Le moulin de Groenendyck (54x45cm-21x18in) s. s.i. verso gouache. 19-Mar-3 Hotel des Ventes Mosan, Brussels #177

MARCH, Giovanni (1894-1974) Tunisian
£385 $604 €600 Calambrone (51x70cm-20x28in) s. s.i.d.1972 verso. 16-Dec-2 Pandolfini, Florence #316/R
£481 $755 €750 Still life of fruit and bottle (50x70cm-20x28in) s. d.70 verso prov. 16-Dec-2 Pandolfini, Florence #309/R
£1026 $1621 €1600 Livorno harbour (35x50cm-14x20in) s.d.1936 board. 15-Nov-2 Farsetti, Prato #462/R
£1603 $2516 €2500 Ardenza resort (43x61cm-17x24in) prov. 16-Dec-2 Pandolfini, Florence #300/R
£2308 $3623 €3600 Under the parasol (32x43cm-13x17in) s. card. 16-Dec-2 Pandolfini, Florence #301/R

MARCH, Sidney (1875-1968) British
Sculpture
£8500 $13685 €12750 Orpheus descending into Hades (57cm-22in) bronze prov.exhib. 20-Feb-3 Christie's, London #153/R

MARCH, Vicente (1859-1914) Spanish
£5000 $7850 €7500 Orange sellers (34x18cm-13x7in) s.i. panel. 19-Nov-2 Bonhams, New Bond Street #97/R est:5000-8000
£10067 $16208 €15000 Orange sellers (34x19cm-13x7in) s. board. 18-Feb-3 Durán, Madrid #242/R est:9000
£30000 $47100 €45000 Plazza del Arco di Tito (25x42cm-10x17in) s.i. panel. 19-Nov-2 Bonhams, New Bond Street #96/R est:20000-30000

MARCHAIS (19/20th C) French
Works on paper
£3200 $4960 €4800 Hollande, Port Jackson - vue de l'Eglise de Paramatta 1818. Port Jackson vue de la maison du Gouvern (39x30cm-15x12in) i. pencil brown wash four after L C de Saulces de Freycinet. 26-Sep-2 Christie's, London #81/R est:3000
£3500 $5425 €5250 Port Jackson (30x39cm-12x15in) pencil wash sold with three proof engraving. 26-Sep-2 Christie's, London #93/R est:3000-4000
£14000 $21700 €21000 Aborigines fighting (28x39cm-11x15in) pencil W/C. 26-Sep-2 Christie's, London #95/R est:8000-12000

MARCHAIS, Pierre Antoine (1864-1889) French
£2581 $4078 €4000 Paysages de la campagne italienne anime (38x46cm-15x18in) s.d.1835 pair. 20-Dec-2 Tajan, Paris #174

MARCHAL, A (?) ?
£696 $1100 €1044 French townscape (48x58cm-19x23in) s.d.1925. 26-Apr-3 Thomaston Place, Thomaston #265

MARCHAND, Andre (1907-1998) French
£660 $1017 €1050 Piqueux et chiens (41x46cm-16x18in) s.d.1947. 27-Oct-2 Muizon & Le Coent, Paris #61/R
£1000 $1550 €1500 Fox hound running in a river landscape (56x64cm-22x25in) s.d.1936 panel. 26-Sep-2 Lane, Penzance #348 est:1000-1200
£1389 $2194 €2000 Le cloitre San Gimi Grano, Italie (35x27cm-14x11in) s. s.i.d.verso. 28-Apr-3 Cornette de St.Cyr, Paris #282/R est:800-1000
£1474 $2241 €2300 Deux oranges (32x40cm-13x16in) s. painted 1946-47. 16-Aug-2 Deauville, France #135/R
£2381 $3786 €3500 Barques (54x65cm-21x26in) s. 24-Mar-3 Claude Boisgirard, Paris #81
£2911 $4542 €4600 Fruits et objets (81x65cm-32x26in) s. i. verso prov.exhib. 20-Oct-2 Claude Boisgirard, Paris #85/R est:4000-4500
Works on paper
£278 $439 €400 Flamants dans la lumiere des roseaux (75x55cm-30x22in) s. W/C. 25-Apr-3 Piasa, Paris #131

MARCHAND, Andre (1877-1951) French
£314 $502 €480 Horses in the paddock by the stream (32x41cm-13x16in) s. panel lit. 10-Jan-3 Allgauer, Kempten #1683/R

MARCHAND, Jean Hippolyte (1883-1940) French
£500 $775 €750 Le jardin (33x41cm-13x16in) s. board. 5-Dec-2 Christie's, Kensington #40/R
£700 $1085 €1050 Lady with a black shawl (82x66cm-32x26in) s. 5-Dec-2 Christie's, Kensington #38/R
£950 $1473 €1425 Un vase chinois et un verte (33x30cm-13x12in) s. 5-Dec-2 Christie's, Kensington #41/R
£1200 $1860 €1800 Bateaux au port (55x65cm-22x26in) s. prov.exhib. 5-Dec-2 Christie's, Kensington #9/R est:1000-1200
£1700 $2703 €2550 Rue a Damas (40x33cm-16x13in) s. canvasboard painted c.1932. 20-Mar-3 Sotheby's, Olympia #153/R est:1200-1500
£3000 $4620 €4500 Paysans dans le foret (73x60cm-29x24in) s. prov. 23-Oct-2 Sotheby's, Olympia #705/R est:3000-4000
Works on paper
£280 $451 €420 Landscape, Chambery (32x24cm-13x9in) s.d.1915 W/C. 14-Jan-3 Bonhams, Knightsbridge #125/R

MARCHANT, Bob (1938-) Australian
£1526 $2411 €2645 Catching a wheat bag full of yabbies (100x150cm-39x59in) s. 1-Apr-3 Goodman, Sydney #39/R est:4000-8000 (A.D 4000)
£6607 $10175 €9911 Grand parade, Moore Park (160x275cm-63x108in) s. 3-Sep-2 Shapiro, Sydney #424/R est:18000-22000 (A.D 18500)

MARCHANT, Francis A le (20th C) French
£350 $546 €525 Environs des vegennes (30x50cm-12x20in) s.d.1968 board. 8-Oct-2 Sotheby's, Olympia #427/R

MARCHANT, Jean (1808-1864) Belgian
£5517 $8828 €8000 Saint Anthony's temptations (40x46cm-16x18in) s.d.1840 board. 17-Mar-3 Pandolfini, Florence #596/R est:10000

MARCHANT, Willy (?) ?
Works on paper
£510 $795 €800 Grieving children (66x47cm-26x19in) s. pastel. 5-Nov-2 Vendu Notarishuis, Rotterdam #270

MARCHE, Ernest Gaston (1864-1932) French
£1274 $2000 €1911 Pastoral river scene (51x66cm-20x26in) s. 23-Nov-2 Jackson's, Cedar Falls #24/R est:1200-1500

MARCHEGIANI, Elio (1929-) Italian
£348 $543 €550 Innocent dreams (100x70cm-39x28in) acrylic board painted 1958. 19-Oct-2 Semenzato, Venice #150/R

MARCHES SCHOOL (15th C) Italian
£12658 $20000 €20000 Madonna and Child (77x31cm-30x12in) tempera board. 2-Dec-2 Finarte, Milan #182/R est:30000

MARCHESSAULT, Robert (1953-) Canadian
£522 $814 €870 Last light, full moon, late March (88x125cm-35x49in) s. s.i.d.1991 verso. 13-Apr-3 Levis, Calgary #315 est:1500-2000 (C.D 1200)

MARCHETTI DA FAENZA, Marco (?-1588) Italian
Works on paper
£2778 $4500 €4167 Design for frieze (14x29cm-6x11in) i. pen ink wash over chk prov. 21-Jan-3 Sotheby's, New York #33/R

MARCHETTI, Giuseppe (18th C) Italian
£458 $760 €650 La Madonna (20x16cm-8x6in) s.d.1745 verso copper. 11-Jun-3 Dorotheum, Vienna #273/R

MARCHETTI, Ludovico (1853-1909) Italian
£2937 $4905 €4200 Jeune femme au bouquet de fleurs (80x65cm-31x26in) s.d.92. 25-Jun-3 Artcurial Briest, Paris #526/R est:4000-5000
Works on paper
£304 $474 €450 Couple sur les quais devant Notre-Dame (36x23cm-14x9in) s. black ink wash. 31-Mar-3 Rossini, Paris #28
£2098 $3504 €3000 Le souper (43x31cm-17x12in) s. W/C gouache two sheets. 26-Jun-3 Tajan, Paris #24/R est:2800-3000
£2308 $3854 €3300 Le concert (40x30cm-16x12in) s.d. W/C gouache. 26-Jun-3 Tajan, Paris #25/R est:2800-3000

MARCHI, Mario Vellani (1895-1979) Italian
£1923 $3019 €3000 Burano, seamstress at rest (52x40cm-20x16in) s.d.1944 cardboard. 23-Nov-2 Meeting Art, Vercelli #234/R
£2027 $3162 €3000 Summer in the lagoon (50x68cm-20x27in) init.d.1938. 26-Mar-3 Finarte Semenzato, Milan #259/R
£2027 $3162 €3000 Vineyard in autumn (50x68cm-20x27in) init.d.1938. 26-Mar-3 Finarte Semenzato, Milan #268/R
Works on paper
£408 $649 €600 Vegetable gardens in Burano (24x34cm-9x13in) init.d.32 Chinese ink. 24-Mar-3 Finarte Semenzato, Rome #293/R

MARCHI, Vincenzo (1818-1894) Italian
Works on paper
£2000 $3120 €3000 Chambres de maman a Rome dans le palais Freoli au Corso (37x50cm-15x20in) s.d.1857 W/C over pencil htd gum arabic. 5-Nov-2 Bonhams, New Bond Street #9a/R est:1000-1500

MARCHIG, Giannino (1897-1983) Italian
£9574 $15511 €13500 La vita allegra (160x214cm-63x84in) s.d.1928. 22-May-3 Stadion, Trieste #231/R est:14000-18000

MARCHIONI, Elisabetta (18th C) Italian
£9459 $14757 €14000 Bouquet of flowers in earthenware vase (105x78cm-41x31in) prov. 27-Mar-3 Dorotheum, Vienna #32/R est:14000-18000
£9459 $14757 €14000 Bouquet of flowers in earthenware vase (105x78cm-41x31in) prov. 27-Mar-3 Dorotheum, Vienna #33/R est:14000-18000

MARCHIONNI, Carlo (attrib) (1702-1786) Italian
Works on paper
£844 $1308 €1266 Fianco dalla Cappella di S Forma (46x34cm-18x13in) s. pen wash. 3-Oct-2 Koller, Zurich #3060/R est:2500-4000 (S.FR 1965)

MARCHIS, Alessio de (1684-1752) Italian
£4795 $7479 €7000 Fishing by the castle (55x80cm-22x31in) s.d.1748. 8-Apr-3 Ansorena, Madrid #86/R
£5263 $8526 €8000 Fishing by the castle (55x80cm-22x31in) s.i.d.1748. 21-Jan-3 Ansorena, Madrid #177/R
Works on paper
£699 $1090 €1049 Landscape near Frascati (28x42cm-11x17in) bister brush. 20-Nov-2 Fischer, Luzern #2402/R est:1200-1300 (S.FR 1600)
£845 $1361 €1200 Veduta del Tempio di Vesta e Snta Maria in Cosmedin, Roma (19x27cm-7x11in) bears i. point of brush grey W/C pen brown ink. 12-May-3 Sotheby's, Milan #52/R

MARCHISIO, Andrea (1850-1927) Italian
£1859 $2919 €2900 After the bath (21x27cm-8x11in) s.d.1989 cardboard lit. 10-Dec-2 Della Rocca, Turin #364a

MARCHOU, Georges (1898-1984) ?
£302 $486 €450 Paysage a l'arbre rouge (54x65cm-21x26in) s. 23-Feb-3 Lesieur & Le Bars, Le Havre #113
£417 $654 €650 Paysage (65x81cm-26x32in) s.d.66. 24-Nov-2 Lesieur & Le Bars, Le Havre #107

MARCIL, René (1917-) Canadian
Works on paper
£247 $383 €371 Head of a man (64x49cm-25x19in) s.d.83 W/C. 3-Dec-2 Joyner, Toronto #465 (C.D 600)
£1467 $2405 €2201 Still life with fruit and flowers (34x26cm-13x10in) s.i.d.54 pencil. 3-Jun-3 Joyner, Toronto #399/R est:3000-5000 (C.D 3300)

£1511	$2478	€2267	Reclining female nude (26x34cm-10x13in) s.d.50 wash prov. 3-Jun-3 Joyner, Toronto #415/R est:3000-5000 (C.D 3400)

MARCKE DE LUMMEN, E van (1827-1890) French

£257	$405	€400	Vaches dans un pre (23x34cm-9x13in) canvas on cardboard. 18-Nov-2 Tajan, Paris #125/R

MARCKE DE LUMMEN, Émile van (1827-1890) French

£1923	$3000	€2885	Cattle in the meadows (56x81cm-22x32in) s. 30-Mar-3 Susanin's, Chicago #6039/R est:3000-5000
£2877	$4488	€4200	Cows in meadow (57x84cm-22x33in) s. 10-Apr-3 Van Ham, Cologne #1583/R est:2500
£7742	$12000	€11613	Approaching storm (74x93cm-29x37in) s. prov.exhib.lit. 30-Oct-2 Christie's, Rockefeller NY #128/R est:12000-16000

MARCKE, Joseph van (attrib) (1806-1885) Belgian

£1026	$1610	€1600	Scene animee en bord de riviere (33x46cm-13x18in) 11-Dec-2 Hotel des Ventes Mosan, Brussels #212 est:800-900

MARCKS, Gerhard (1889-1981) German

Sculpture

£1923	$2981	€3000	Flautist (30cm-12in) st.sig. bronze exhib. 4-Dec-2 Lempertz, Koln #883/R est:4000
£1923	$2981	€3000	Mother with child in arms (39cm-15in) st.sig. bronze Cast.Barth exhib. 4-Dec-2 Lempertz, Koln #888/R est:3200
£1923	$2981	€3000	Little singer (26cm-10in) st.sig. bronze Cast.Barth Berlin exhib. 4-Dec-2 Lempertz, Koln #890/R est:4000
£1986	$3217	€2800	Female singer (25x13x11cm-10x5x4in) st.sig. num.5/10 dark pat.bronze Cast.Barth Rinteln. 24-May-3 Van Ham, Cologne #382/R est:3000
£2436	$3776	€3800	Mother and sun (15cm-6in) st.sig. pat.bronze exhib. 4-Dec-2 Lempertz, Koln #886/R est:3000
£2695	$4366	€3800	Small sitting Sapho (49x14x23cm-19x6x9in) terrakotta. 24-May-3 Van Ham, Cologne #384/R est:3500
£3043	$4991	€4200	Cassandra (54cm-21in) terracotta prov.exhib.lit. 29-May-3 Lempertz, Koln #781/R est:3000-4000
£3099	$5144	€4400	Meeting between old woman and pregnant woman (18x10x5cm-7x4x2in) bronze. 14-Jun-3 Hauswedell & Nolte, Hamburg #1377/R est:4500
£3797	$5886	€6000	Female nude (53cm-21in) num.3/12 gold brown pat.bronze Cast.Barth Rinteln. 28-Sep-2 Ketterer, Hamburg #182/R est:7000-9000
£3846	$5962	€6000	Two women (26x15x11cm-10x6x4in) mono. bronze. 7-Dec-2 Hauswedell & Nolte, Hamburg #878/R est:8000
£4808	$7452	€7500	Gross old nag (26cm-10in) s.i. bronze exhib.lit. 4-Dec-2 Lempertz, Koln #879/R est:7500
£5769	$8942	€9000	Crouching negro (26cm-10in) st.sig. i. gold brown pat.bronze exhib.lit. 4-Dec-2 Lempertz, Koln #882/R est:7000
£6289	$9811	€10000	Deklamierends Sybille - declaiming Sybill (19cm-7in) mono. bronze indis.f.st. executed 1943. 9-Oct-2 Sotheby's, London #208/R est:9000-12000
£7092	$11489	€10000	Diana (30x32x15cm-12x13x6in) st.sig. dark yellow bronze pat.bronze Cast.Batrth BLN exhib. 24-May-3 Van Ham, Cologne #383/R est:6000
£20290	$33275	€28000	Albertus Magnus - Model I (24cm-9in) s. bronze Cast. Barth Bln exhib.lit. 29-May-3 Lempertz, Koln #782/R est:10000
£26415	$41208	€42000	Ver sacrum (126cm-50in) mono. bronze executed 1943 prov.exhib.lit. 9-Oct-2 Sotheby's, London #164/R est:60000-90000
£44872	$69551	€70000	Albertus Magnus (85cm-33in) s.st.f.Guss bronze exec.1955-70. 4-Dec-2 Lempertz, Koln #15/R est:60000-70000
£53459	$83396	€85000	Maximilian (120cm-47in) bronze executed 1939 prov.exhib.lit. 9-Oct-2 Sotheby's, London #172/R est:60000-90000

Works on paper

£317	$526	€450	Nude boys (40x19cm-16x7in) s. pencil. 14-Jun-3 Hauswedell & Nolte, Hamburg #1378/R
£943	$1472	€1500	Two standing male nudes, shot-putters (42x26cm-17x10in) s. pencil set of three prov. 9-Oct-2 Sotheby's, London #166/R est:2200-3200
£1258	$1962	€2000	Standing male nude. Shot-putter (41x31cm-16x12in) s. one s.i. pencil set of three executed c.1945 prov. 9-Oct-2 Sotheby's, London #174/R est:3000-4000

MARCO, A de (?) Italian

£1020	$1622	€1500	Beach with fishermen (50x70cm-20x28in) s. oil tempera paper on canvas. 18-Mar-3 Finarte, Milan #74/R

MARCO, Angelo di (1927-) Italian?

Works on paper

£1528	$2521	€2200	Fait d'Hiver (64x66cm-25x26in) s.i. ink wash crayon. 3-Jul-3 Christie's, Paris #118/R

MARCOLA, Giovanni Battista (1711-1780) Italian

Works on paper

£1200	$2004	€1740	Roman soldiers around dying man. Woman by a well and pair of classical lovers (29x42cm-11x17in) pen blk ink over red chk double-sided. 9-Jul-3 Sotheby's, London #41/R est:1500-2000

MARCOLA, Marco (1740-1793) Italian

Works on paper

£1500	$2355	€2250	Aeneas receiving his armour from Venus (38x50cm-15x20in) bear i. pen ink wash over red chk framing lines. 11-Dec-2 Sotheby's, Olympia #134/R est:1800-2200

MARCON, Charles (1920-) French

£1418	$2298	€2000	Le cirque (100x65cm-39x26in) s. paper on cardboard. 23-May-3 Camard, Paris #169 est:2000-2300

MARCOTTE, Joseph (19th C) Belgian

£801	$1258	€1250	Nature morte aux framboises. Nature morte aux raisins (26x36cm-10x14in) s. pair. 19-Nov-2 Vanderkindere, Brussels #45

MARCOTTE, M A (1869-1929) French

£1384	$2158	€2200	Serre (43x53cm-17x21in) 14-Oct-2 Amberes, Antwerp #172

MARCOUSSIS, Louis (1883-1941) French

£62000	$101680	€93000	Personnage ecrivant et personnage (100x81cm-39x32in) s.d.1931 prov.lit. 5-Feb-3 Sotheby's, London #161/R est:60000

Prints

£4110	$6452	€6000	Portrait d'Andre Breton (44x30cm-17x12in) s.i. burin. 15-Apr-3 Laurence Calmels, Paris #4354/R
£4403	$7000	€6605	La table (24x18cm-9x7in) s.num.42/120 col etching engraving. 2-May-3 Sotheby's, New York #203/R est:3000-5000

Works on paper

£1513	$2452	€2300	Composition (20x21cm-8x8in) pencil estompe dr exec.c.1933. 22-Jan-3 Tajan, Paris #112/R est:3000-3500

MARCUCCI, Mario (1910-1992) Italian

£385	$608	€600	Vase of flowers (53x38cm-21x15in) s.d.1958 canvas on cardboard. 15-Nov-2 Farsetti, Prato #427/R
£676	$1054	€1000	Basket with fruit (30x40cm-12x16in) s. board. 28-Mar-3 Farsetti, Prato #502/R
£676	$1054	€1000	Beached boats (33x31cm-13x12in) cardboard on board. 28-Mar-3 Farsetti, Prato #755/R
£1284	$2003	€1900	Shell and potato (23x32cm-9x13in) s.d.1964 cardboard. 28-Mar-3 Farsetti, Prato #647/R

MARCUSE, Rudolf (1878-?) German

Sculpture

£2264	$3532	€3600	Figures riding water buffalo (53cm-21in) s. dark brown pat.bronze marble socle. 20-Sep-2 Schloss Ahlden, Ahlden #636/R est:2800

MARDEN, Brice (1938-) American

£72785	$115000	€109178	Sketch no.3 (51x67cm-20x26in) oil on linen painted 1983 prov.lit. 13-Nov-2 Sotheby's, New York #314/R est:80000-120000

Prints

£2051	$3200	€3077	Ten days (76x56cm-30x22in) s.d.71 num.27/30 etching aquatint. 5-Nov-2 Christie's, Rockefeller NY #459/R est:3000-4000
£3145	$5000	€4718	Five plates, one print (69x49cm-27x19in) s.d.num.27/50 etching aquatint. 2-May-3 Sotheby's, New York #524/R est:3000-4000
£20440	$32500	€30660	After Botticelli 1-5 (21x30cm-8x12in) s.d.num.33/45 etching aquatint set of five. 2-May-3 Sotheby's, New York #525/R est:20000-30000

Works on paper

£7000	$11690	€10150	Untitled (29x20cm-11x8in) init.d.72-3 ink prov. 26-Jun-3 Sotheby's, London #135/R est:5000-7000
£15190	$24000	€22785	Untitled - suicide notes (29x18cm-11x7in) one s.d.72 one s.d.73 three ink dr. prov. 14-Nov-2 Christie's, Rockefeller NY #374/R est:18000-22000
£17405	$27500	€26108	Untitled (104x75cm-41x30in) chl executed 1973 prov. 13-Nov-2 Sotheby's, New York #106/R est:22000-28000
£40625	$65000	€60938	Untitled (53x76cm-21x30in) s.d.70 graphite beeswax prov.exhib. 13-May-3 Sotheby's, New York #2/R est:60000-80000
£69620	$110000	€104430	Untitled (51x51cm-20x20in) s.d.1969 chl beeswax prov.exhib. 13-Nov-2 Sotheby's, New York #108/R est:100000-150000

MARDEROSOV, Leonid (?-1930) Russian
£1397 $2221 €2096 Picnic - man opening the wine while two ladies playing music (40x50cm-16x20in) s. oval prov. 5-Mar-3 Rasmussen, Copenhagen #1999/R est:6000-8000 (D.KR 15000)

MARE, Andre (1885-1932) French
£506 $790 €800 Cavalier (54x65cm-21x26in) mono. 18-Oct-2 Rabourdin & Choppin de Janvry, Paris #44

MARECHAL, Charles (attrib) (1801-1887) French
Works on paper
£1266 $1975 €2000 L'enface d'Apollon (37x28cm-15x11in) pastel. 15-Oct-2 Regis & Thiollet, Argentuil #164

MARECHAL, Claude (20th C) French
Works on paper
£397 $648 €600 La lande Bretonne (44x36cm-17x14in) s.d. torn paper panel prov. 31-Jan-3 Charbonneaux, Paris #135/R
£662 $1079 €1000 Pommes ramassees (81x400cm-32x157in) s.i.d.verso torn paper on canvas prov. 31-Jan-3 Charbonneaux, Paris #134/R

MARECHAL, Jean Baptiste (18th C) French
£2323 $3670 €3600 Portrait d'Henri IV (33x20cm-13x8in) s. 18-Dec-2 Beaussant & Lefèvre, Paris #28/R

MARECHAL, Jean Baptiste (attrib) (18th C) French
Works on paper
£612 $972 €900 Paysage anime (19x31cm-7x12in) wash. 24-Mar-3 Tajan, Paris #60

MARECHAL, le (1928-) French
Works on paper
£3767 $5914 €5500 Imperceptible abime (22x26cm-9x10in) i. ink exhib. 15-Apr-3 Laurence Calmels, Paris #4334/R est:2000-2500

MAREES, Hans von (1837-1887) German
Works on paper
£1887 $2943 €3000 Male nude with two horses (47x42cm-19x17in) sanguine on paper executed c.1880-85 prov. 9-Oct-2 Sotheby's, London #183/R est:2000-3000

MAREMBERT, Jean (c.1900-1968) French
£705 $1107 €1100 Fete foraine (81x100cm-32x39in) s. 22-Nov-2 Millon & Associes, Paris #115/R
£1899 $2962 €3000 Metamorphose au violon (73x60cm-29x24in) s. 20-Oct-2 Charbonneaux, Paris #143 est:1000-1200
Works on paper
£348 $543 €550 Visage aux barques (37x28cm-15x11in) s. graphite. 20-Oct-2 Charbonneaux, Paris #74 est:300-450

MARESCA, S (19th C) Italian
£600 $948 €900 Fishing boats in the Bay of Naples. Fishing boats in the Bay of Naples with Vesuvius beyond (25x39cm-10x15in) s. pair. 14-Nov-2 Christie's, Kensington #247/R

MARESCH, Ferdinand and Johann (19/20th C) French?
Sculpture
£1511 $2478 €2100 Combattant grec (61cm-24in) mono. polychrome terracotta lit. 4-Jun-3 Tajan, Paris #283/R est:2200-3000

MAREVNA, Marie (1892-1984) Russian
£12000 $19440 €18000 Cubist still life with flowers (100x60cm-39x24in) s.d.59 board. 21-May-3 Sotheby's, London #220/R est:12000-18000
Works on paper
£1104 $1843 €1600 Composition cubiste (41x29cm-16x11in) s.i.d.1917 gouache pastel. 10-Jul-3 Artcurial Briest, Paris #81 est:1000-1200

MAREZ-DARLEY, Nelly (20th C) French
£1321 $2047 €2100 Composition (100x81cm-39x32in) s. 7-Oct-2 Claude Aguttes, Neuilly #100

MARFAING, Andre (1925-1987) French
£1016 $1575 €1524 Calligraphy composition (61x50cm-24x20in) s.d.74. 1-Oct-2 Rasmussen, Copenhagen #40/R est:8000 (D.KR 12000)
£1258 $1950 €2000 1984 F, 1984 (35x27cm-14x11in) s.d.84 acrylic. 30-Oct-2 Artcurial Briest, Paris #438 est:2500-3000
£1693 $2625 €2540 Venus Angelique - black and white composition (80x60cm-31x24in) s. prov. 1-Oct-2 Rasmussen, Copenhagen #42/R est:15000-20000 (D.KR 20000)
£1738 $2902 €2450 Composition en noir (61x50cm-24x20in) s.d. 18-Jun-3 Pierre Berge, Paris #91/R est:2500-3000
£1899 $2962 €3000 Composition (27x16cm-11x6in) s. s.d.1959 verso. 20-Oct-2 Claude Boisgirard, Paris #59/R est:3000-3500
£1962 $3041 €3100 Sans titre (130x97cm-51x38in) s. d.22 mai 1986 verso. 28-Sep-2 Cornette de St.Cyr, Paris #374 est:3000-4000
£4898 $7788 €7200 Composition (116x89cm-46x35in) s.d.65. 26-Feb-3 Artcurial Briest, Paris #458/R est:5000-6000
Works on paper
£748 $1190 €1100 Composition (24x32cm-9x13in) s.d.1970 ink wash. 24-Mar-3 Claude Boisgirard, Paris #123/R

MARFFY, Odon (1878-1959) Hungarian
£1537 $2398 €2306 Morning on the River Danube (47x62cm-19x24in) s. board. 11-Apr-3 Kieselbach, Budapest #13/R est:450000-550000 (H.F 550000)
£4034 $6253 €6051 Self portrait with a red blue scarf (80x65cm-31x26in) cardboard. 6-Dec-2 Kieselbach, Budapest #149/R (H.F 1500000)
£4303 $6669 €6455 In circus (35x25cm-14x10in) s. cardboard. 6-Dec-2 Kieselbach, Budapest #191/R (H.F 1600000)
£4303 $6669 €6239 Chrysanthemums in a vase (60x50cm-24x20in) s. 9-Dec-2 Mu Terem Galeria, Budapest #122/R est:950000 (H.F 1600000)
£6992 $10838 €10138 Italian seaside (50x72cm-20x28in) s. 9-Dec-2 Mu Terem Galeria, Budapest #82/R est:2500000 (H.F 2600000)
£7021 $11234 €10532 Mountain landscape (34x49cm-13x19in) s. paper. 16-May-3 Kieselbach, Budapest #17/R (H.F 2400000)
£15000 $24600 €22500 Portrait of Czinska (65x51cm-26x20in) s. prov. 3-Jun-3 Sotheby's, London #116/R est:4000-6000
£18825 $29178 €28238 Lights by waterside (50x68cm-20x27in) s. 6-Dec-2 Kieselbach, Budapest #61/R (H.F 7000000)
£32271 $50020 €46793 Female nude standing (59x45cm-23x18in) s. prov.lit. 9-Dec-2 Mu Terem Galeria, Budapest #131/R est:6000000 (H.F 12000000)
Works on paper
£877 $1368 €1272 Saying farewell (39x28cm-15x11in) s. W/C. 13-Sep-2 Mu Terem Galeria, Budapest #25/R est:190000 (H.F 340000)
£1118 $1744 €1677 Loving couple on a bench (43x33cm-17x13in) mixed media. 11-Apr-3 Kieselbach, Budapest #22/R est:220000-400000 (H.F 400000)
£1174 $1831 €1761 Kertben (27x24cm-11x9in) W/C. 11-Apr-3 Kieselbach, Budapest #33/R est:60000-420000 (H.F 420000)
£1187 $1851 €1721 Standing male nude (36x22cm-14x9in) s. Indian ink W/C lit. 13-Sep-2 Mu Terem Galeria, Budapest #99/R est:280000 (H.F 460000)
£5309 $8283 €7698 Still life with fruits (40x59cm-16x23in) s. W/C. 12-Apr-3 Mu Terem Galeria, Budapest #20/R est:750000 (H.F 1900000)

MARGANTIN, Louis (1900-) French
£283 $441 €425 Still life with fish and lemons (47x54cm-19x21in) s.d.47 board. 16-Sep-2 Philippe Schuler, Zurich #6472 (S.FR 650)

MARGAT, Andre (1903-1999) French
£897 $1409 €1400 Leda et le cygne (100x50cm-39x20in) s. lacquer panel. 24-Nov-2 Lesieur & Le Bars, Le Havre #109
£1622 $2530 €2400 Leda et le cygne (100x50cm-39x20in) s. panel. 28-Mar-3 Camard, Paris #144/R
Works on paper
£538 $850 €850 Deux pantheres (17x23cm-7x9in) s. gouache. 27-Nov-2 Lemoine & Ferrando, Paris #156/R

MARGEOT, Theodore de (19th C) French
Works on paper
£1656 $2583 €2600 Touques (23x28cm-9x11in) W/C htd gouachepair. 10-Nov-2 Deauville, France #21/R est:2800

MARGETSON, William Henry (1861-1940) British
£14000 $22260 €21000 Lady ofvthe house (76x51cm-30x20in) bears sig exhib. 18-Mar-3 Bonhams, New Bond Street #110/R est:6000-8000

MARGITAY, Tihamer (1859-1922) Hungarian
£287 $447 €450 Young lady with flower garland (46x58cm-18x23in) s. canvas on canvas lit. 7-Nov-2 Allgauer, Kempten #2896/R
£615 $959 €923 Monarchy (49x60cm-19x24in) s. panel. 11-Apr-3 Kieselbach, Budapest #18/R est:220000 (H.F 220000)

MARGITSON, Marie (1857-1864) British
£440 $695 €660 Still life of peaches, pears and grapes in a basket (29x39cm-11x15in) s.d.1879. 26-Nov-2 Bonhams, Oxford #65

MARGO, Boris (1902-1995) American/Russian
£319 $500 €479 From the city (81x63cm-32x25in) s. 22-Nov-2 Skinner, Boston #393/R

MARGOLIES, Samuel L (1898-1974) American
Prints
£2564 $4000 €3846 Men of steel (38x30cm-15x12in) s. drypoint exec.c.1940. 7-Nov-2 Swann Galleries, New York #700/R est:5000-8000
£2724 $4250 €4086 Men of steel (36x28cm-14x11in) s.i. etching. 21-Sep-2 Rachel Davis, Shaker Heights #309/R est:4000-6000

MARGOSCY, Paul (1945-) Australian
Works on paper
£290 $442 €435 Birds Quetzel and south east Asian Shama (52x27cm-20x11in) s. W/C. 27-Aug-2 Goodman, Sydney #196 (A.D 810)
£362 $572 €543 Great horned owl (36x40cm-14x16in) s. W/C. 18-Nov-2 Goodman, Sydney #49 (A.D 1015)

MARGOT (?) ?
£625 $1019 €900 Femme aux iris devant la mer (85x59cm-33x23in) s. 19-Jul-3 Thierry & Lannon, Brest #150/R

MARGOTEAU, Rene Pierre (1902-) French
£1589 $2591 €2400 Model (61x50cm-24x20in) s.d.1941. 28-Jan-3 Dorotheum, Vienna #97/R est:500-700

MARGUERAY, Michel (1938-) French
£694 $1132 €1000 Ramassage du goemon devant Notre Dame de la joie (35x51cm-14x20in) s.d.71 cardboard. 19-Jul-3 Thierry & Lannon, Brest #216
£1218 $1912 €1900 Sevre a Coulon (73x92cm-29x36in) s. 24-Nov-2 Lesieur & Le Bars, Le Havre #110/R

MARGULIES, Joseph (1896-1984) American
£566 $900 €849 Breton fisherman of Concorneau (46x61cm-18x24in) s. i.verso canvasboard. 7-Mar-3 Skinner, Boston #482/R
Works on paper
£219 $350 €318 Gloucester Harbour (44x53cm-17x21in) s. W/C graphite paper on board. 16-May-3 Skinner, Boston #272/R

MARIA, Arturo di (1940-) Italian
£371 $583 €557 Variable continuo (50x50cm-20x20in) s.d.1996 verso acrylic. 23-Nov-2 Burkhard, Luzern #59/R (S.FR 850)
£568 $891 €852 Composition 13 (98x20cm-39x8in) s.d.1988 acrylic over panel. 23-Nov-2 Burkhard, Luzern #60/R (S.FR 1300)
£786 $1234 €1179 Composition 37 C (50x50cm-20x20in) s.d.2000 verso acrylic. 23-Nov-2 Burkhard, Luzern #78/R (S.FR 1800)
Sculpture
£1310 $2057 €1965 Sculpture (25x53cm-10x21in) chrome nickel steel. 23-Nov-2 Burkhard, Luzern #80/R est:3000-4000 (S.FR 3000)

MARIA, Mario de (1853-1924) Italian
£779 $1161 €1200 Evening on the coast (28x42cm-11x17in) s.d.98. 27-Jun-2 Neumeister, Munich #2799
£1519 $2400 €2400 Houses in Anticoli (41x77cm-16x30in) s.verso. 26-Nov-2 Christie's, Rome #100

MARIA, Nicola de (1954-) Italian
£4295 $6657 €6700 Regno dei fiori in memoriam Ivan Puni (30x40cm-12x16in) s.i. verso oil W/C Indian ink pencil. 3-Dec-2 Lempertz, Koln #293/R est:8000
£4397 $7123 €6200 Testa orfica (350x500cm-138x197in) s.i.d.1992 verso tempera pencil collage board. 26-May-3 Christie's, Milan #93/R est:3500-5000
£5674 $9191 €8000 Testa orfica (39x22cm-15x9in) s.i.d.1992 tempera collage board. 26-May-3 Christie's, Milan #91/R est:4000-6000
£7911 $12500 €12500 Faithful head of romantic queen (45x18cm-18x7in) i.d.1988. 29-Nov-2 Farsetti, Prato #470/R est:12500
£8000 $12320 €12000 Regno dei Fiori (40x30cm-16x12in) s. i.d.1984 on stretcher prov. 23-Oct-2 Christie's, London #137/R est:8000-12000
£8974 $14090 €14000 Enchanted head in sleep (50x40cm-20x16in) s.i.d.1991 verso prov. 20-Nov-2 Pandolfini, Florence #128/R est:14000
£10000 $15400 €15000 Nel Giorno di Santo Stefano (50x40cm-20x16in) i.on stretcher s.i.d.1986 verso prov. 23-Oct-2 Christie's, London #136/R est:10000-15000
£10000 $16700 €14500 Sera (56x40cm-22x16in) i.on stretcher prov. 27-Jun-3 Christie's, London #178/R est:10000-15000
£14744 $22853 €23000 Thoughts (50x40cm-20x16in) s.i.d.1988. 4-Dec-2 Finarte, Milan #546/R est:16000
£15385 $23846 €24000 White, blue, yellow, red and green musician angel (50x40cm-20x16in) s.i.d.1988 verso. 4-Dec-2 Finarte, Milan #483/R est:16000
£18000 $28080 €27000 Testa fatata (50x40cm-20x16in) s.i.verso painted 1990-91 prov. 21-Oct-2 Sotheby's, London #66/R est:14000-18000
£28000 $46760 €40600 Pax et bonum semper tecum, tecum, sempre regno dei fiori celeste con gli angeli (152x107cm-60x42in) i.d.1993 verso prov. 27-Jun-3 Christie's, London #181/R est:30000-40000
Works on paper
£719 $1180 €1000 Untitled (23x23cm-9x9in) s. pencil wax crayon executed 1989. 3-Jun-3 Christie's, Amsterdam #109/R est:1000-1500
£2600 $4108 €3900 Untitled (26x20cm-10x8in) i.d.1980 wax crayon gouache collage prov. 3-Apr-3 Christie's, Kensington #259/R
£2620 $4114 €3930 I suoni di tutte le anime (48x36cm-19x14in) s. verso mixed media collage prov. 25-Nov-2 Germann, Zurich #30/R est:9000-13000 (S.FR 6000)

MARIANI, Carlo Maria (1931-) Italian
£5128 $8051 €8000 Thoughts flowing smoothly in the artist's soul (56x45cm-22x18in) s.i.verso. 23-Nov-2 Meeting Art, Vercelli #416/R est:5000
£5556 $8889 €8500 Pictor arte insignis (73x60cm-29x24in) s.verso lit. 4-Jan-3 Meeting Art, Vercelli #724
£6597 $10490 €9500 Dionisus (66x50cm-26x20in) s.i.d.1985 verso lit. 1-May-3 Meeting Art, Vercelli #112
Works on paper
£2123 $3312 €3100 Portrait of Francesco Clemente (75x66cm-30x26in) s. pencil lead prov. 10-Apr-3 Finarte Semenzato, Rome #299/R

MARIANI, Cesare (1826-1901) Italian
Works on paper
£372 $584 €580 Moses (42x34cm-17x13in) s.i. pencil pastel. 16-Dec-2 Pandolfini, Florence #4a

MARIANI, Cesare (attrib) (1826-1901) Italian
£1677 $2466 €2600 Jospeh with fellow prisoners (100x138cm-39x54in) s. 20-Jun-2 Dr Fritz Nagel, Stuttgart #794/R est:2300

MARIANI, Pompeo (1857-1927) Italian
£442 $703 €650 Feeding hens (13x9cm-5x4in) init. W/C tempera. 18-Mar-3 Finarte, Milan #133/R
£1419 $2243 €2200 Flooding (19x26cm-7x10in) s.d.917. 18-Dec-2 Finarte, Milan #136/R
£2308 $3646 €3600 Reading in the woods (28x17cm-11x7in) s. board exhib.lit. 15-Nov-2 Farsetti, Prato #530/R
£2532 $4000 €4000 Zelada (53x33cm-21x13in) s. board. 26-Nov-2 Christie's, Rome #220/R est:6000
£4839 $7645 €7500 Lady strolling (20x13cm-8x5in) s. board prov. 18-Dec-2 Finarte, Milan #1/R est:4500
£4839 $7645 €7500 On stage (24x19cm-9x7in) s. cardboard. 18-Dec-2 Finarte, Milan #131/R est:2000
£7742 $12232 €12000 Seascape with fishermen (47x70cm-19x28in) s.d.1889 board. 18-Dec-2 Finarte, Milan #45/R est:15000
£8387 $13252 €13000 English women at the seaside (48x79cm-19x31in) s. i.verso board. 18-Dec-2 Finarte, Milan #89/R est:18000
Works on paper
£248 $402 €350 Pescatori (11x17cm-4x7in) s. W/C. 22-May-3 Stadion, Trieste #286
£374 $595 €550 Washerwomen (13x9cm-5x4in) init. W/C tempera. 18-Mar-3 Finarte, Milan #139/R
£748 $1190 €1100 Casino interior, Montecarlo (14x9cm-6x4in) init. W/C tempera. 18-Mar-3 Finarte, Milan #134/R
£748 $1190 €1100 Woman (24x16cm-9x6in) init. W/C tempera. 18-Mar-3 Finarte, Milan #135/R
£2721 $4327 €4000 Seascape with fishermen (24x32cm-9x13in) s. W/C tempera. 18-Mar-3 Finarte, Milan #130/R

MARIATTON, Eugen (19/20th C) French
Sculpture
£1034 $1655 €1500 Mere et son enfant (32cm-13in) s.d.1911 terracotta. 12-Mar-3 E & Eve, Paris #133/R est:1500-1600

MARIE, Adrien Emmanuel (1848-1891) French
Works on paper
£613 $950 €920 Study of a man in top hat and cane (20x12cm-8x5in) pencil. 29-Oct-2 Sotheby's, New York #58/R est:600-800

MARIE, Raoul-Edmond (1850-?) French
£432 $709 €626 Lake landscape in summer (38x55cm-15x22in) s.d.08. 4-Jun-3 AB Stockholms Auktionsverk #2444/R (S.KR 5500)
£9677 $15000 €14516 Boating on the Seine, Chatou (93x72cm-37x28in) s. 30-Oct-2 Christie's, Rockefeller NY #211/R est:12000-16000

MARIEN, Marcel (1920-1993) Belgian
£1614 $2518 €2550 Object (37x30cm-15x12in) s.d.75 on velum prov.exhib. 21-Oct-2 Bernaerts, Antwerp #652 est:2000-2500

Sculpture
£943 $1453 €1500 Les noces de Cana. s.d.1990 verso assemblage plexiglas box. 22-Oct-2 Campo, Vlaamse Kaai #561/R
£2158 $3453 €3000 Le voyant (36x36x36cm-14x14x14in) s.d18 mai 1973 assemblage exhib. 13-May-3 Palais de Beaux Arts, Brussels #97/R est:3000-4500

Works on paper
£897 $1434 €1300 Madone distraite (32x22cm-13x9in) s.i.d.1967 exhib. 15-Mar-3 De Vuyst, Lokeren #203/R
£1329 $2073 €2100 Lettre ouverte aux psychanalystes (102x175cm-40x69in) s.d.1955 collage. 21-Oct-2 Bernaerts, Antwerp #649/R est:1000-1500

MARIENHOF, Jan (1610-1650) Dutch
£3716 $5797 €5500 Christ and the Woman of Smaria (51x61cm-20x24in) s.panel prov. 27-Mar-3 Dorotheum, Vienna #171/R est:6000-9000

MARIESCHI, Michele (1696-1743) Italian
£75000 $117750 €112500 Capriccio landscape with palace and tower (33x53cm-13x21in) prov.lit. 11-Dec-2 Christie's, London #119/R est:60000-80000
£129630 $210000 €194445 Architectural capriccio of a city (51x75cm-20x30in) 24-Jan-3 Christie's, Rockefeller NY #168/R est:200000-300000

MARIESCHI, Michele (after) (1696-1743) Italian
£5500 $8580 €8250 Architectural capriccio with a gothic portico and an obelisk (36x54cm-14x21in) 9-Apr-3 Bonhams, New Bond Street #65/R est:3000-5000

MARIESCHI, Michele (circle) (1696-1743) Italian
£28000 $43960 €42000 Rialto Bridge (46x92cm-18x36in) prov. 11-Dec-2 Christie's, London #121/R est:20000-30000

MARIESCHI, Michele (style) (1696-1743) Italian
£6329 $10000 €10000 Vue de San Giorgio dei Greci, Venise (52x75cm-20x30in) 27-Nov-2 Christie's, Paris #68/R est:10000-15000
£7000 $10920 €10500 Capriccio scene with figures before classical ruins (121x154cm-48x61in) 8-Apr-3 Sotheby's, Olympia #257/R est:8000-12000
£14000 $21980 €21000 Venice, view of San Giorgio Maggiore (45x59cm-18x23in) 10-Dec-2 Sotheby's, Olympia #411/R est:6000-8000
£16000 $26720 €23200 Grand Canal, Venice, Fondaco dei Tedeschi and Palazzo dei Camerlenghi (48x70cm-19x28in) bears init. 9-Jul-3 Bonhams, New Bond Street #164/R est:8000-12000
£17000 $28390 €24650 Grand Canal, Venice, looking south towards Santa Maria della Salute and the Dogana (68x127cm-27x50in) 11-Jul-3 Christie's, Kensington #266/R est:15000-20000
£27673 $43170 €44000 Gondola before a Venetian church (53x77cm-21x30in) 20-Sep-2 Millon & Associes, Paris #612/R
£42000 $65940 €63000 Grand canal, Venice and the entrance to the Cannaregio (76x127cm-30x50in) prov. 13-Dec-2 Christie's, Kensington #275/R est:10000-15000

MARILHAT, Prosper (1811-1847) French
£1000 $1550 €1500 Landscape, an Arab woman carrying a pitcher (33x26cm-13x10in) s. panel. 25-Sep-2 John Nicholson, Haslemere #1026/R est:1500-2500
£2000 $3180 €3000 Watercarrier at the river's edge (35x26cm-14x10in) s. panel. 20-Mar-3 Christie's, Kensington #183/R est:2000-3000
£70000 $116900 €105000 Travellers at an oasis (40x58cm-16x23in) s. 19-Jun-3 Christie's, London #14/R est:15000-20000

Works on paper
£474 $720 €711 Mountain landscape with lake (17x22cm-7x9in) s. gouache. 27-Aug-2 Rasmussen, Copenhagen #1697/R (D.KR 5500)
£541 $843 €800 Oasis au soleil couchant (8x20cm-3x8in) s. W/C. 27-Mar-3 Maigret, Paris #202/R

MARILLIER, Clement (1740-1808) French

Works on paper
£1218 $1924 €1900 Revuedu dauphin (24x36cm-9x14in) pen ink wash. 18-Nov-2 Sotheby's, Paris #11/R

MARIN CARES, Isidoro (1863-1926) Spanish

Works on paper
£338 $527 €500 Landscape with houses (29x21cm-11x8in) s. pen dr. 25-Mar-3 Durán, Madrid #59/R

MARIN LOPEZ, Diego (1865-?) Spanish
£839 $1325 €1300 Soldiers (23x11cm-9x4in) s. board pair. 17-Dec-2 Segre, Madrid #60/R

MARIN MARIE (1901-1987) French

Works on paper
£621 $987 €900 Trois mats au mouillage (19x25cm-7x10in) s.i. blue ink. 4-Mar-3 Livinec, Gaudcheau & Jezequel, Rennes #412
£6218 $9762 €9700 Trois-mats tribord amures par mer formee (54x74cm-21x29in) s. W/C double-sided. 15-Dec-2 Thierry & Lannon, Brest #63
£10690 $17103 €15500 Bateaux a quai (40x50cm-16x20in) s. graphite W/C gouache. 12-Mar-3 Libert, Castor, Paris #145/R est:10000-12000

MARIN RAMOS, Eustaquio (1873-1959) Spanish
£897 $1434 €1300 L'espagnole (49x33cm-19x13in) cardboard. 12-Mar-3 Libert, Castor, Paris #147

MARIN Y MOLINAS, Adolfo (19th C) ?
£1442 $2279 €2250 Landscape (44x70cm-17x28in) s.d.1899. 14-Nov-2 Arte, Seville #338/R

MARIN, Enrique (1876-1940) Spanish
£1415 $2208 €2250 Granada street (32x17cm-13x7in) s. board. 23-Sep-2 Durán, Madrid #231/R
£1572 $2453 €2500 Street in Granada (32x17cm-13x7in) s. board. 23-Sep-2 Durán, Madrid #232/R

Works on paper
£1069 $1668 €1700 Patio in Granada (46x32cm-18x13in) s. W/C. 23-Sep-2 Durán, Madrid #233/R
£1415 $2208 €2250 Street in Granada (46x32cm-18x13in) s. W/C. 23-Sep-2 Durán, Madrid #234/R

MARIN, Javier (1962-) Mexican

Sculpture
£3023 $4715 €4535 Hombre sentado (66x29x24cm-26x11x9in) s. terracotta. 17-Oct-2 Louis Morton, Mexico #16/R est:22000-26000 (M.P 48000)

MARIN, John (1870-1953) American
£141975 $230000 €212963 Off cape split.Maine I (56x71cm-22x28in) s.d.34 prov.exhib.lit. 21-May-3 Sotheby's, New York #114/R est:250000-350000
£419355 $650000 €629033 Mid-Manhattan II (71x56cm-28x22in) s.d.32 prov.exhib.lit. 5-Dec-2 Christie's, Rockefeller NY #135/R est:700000-900000

Works on paper
£3171 $5200 €4598 Figure study (15x25cm-6x10in) s.d. pencil. 5-Jun-3 Swann Galleries, New York #175/R est:4000-6000
£3774 $6000 €5661 New York Stock Exchange (25x19cm-10x7in) s. pencil prov. 4-Mar-3 Christie's, Rockefeller NY #75/R est:6000-8000
£12963 $21000 €18796 Sea - Off Cape Split - Maine (25x36cm-10x14in) s.d.47 W/C prov. 21-May-3 Doyle, New York #150/R est:15000-20000
£16129 $25000 €24194 Castorland landscape cloud forms no.4 (36x45cm-14x18in) s.d.13 i.verso W/C prov.exhib. 4-Dec-2 Sotheby's, New York #62/R est:25000-35000
£17742 $27500 €26613 Deer Isle, Maine (37x44cm-15x17in) s.d.24 W/C chl prov. 4-Dec-2 Sotheby's, New York #86/R est:20000-30000
£20062 $32500 €30093 Maine Island (46x36cm-18x14in) s.d.14 W/C prov.lit. 21-May-3 Sotheby's, New York #108/R est:25000-35000
£20968 $32500 €31452 White mountain country no.34 Franconua Range, mountain and fir trees (41x56cm-16x22in) s.d.27 W/C prov.exhib.lit. 4-Dec-2 Sotheby's, New York #63/R est:30000-50000
£21605 $35000 €32408 Maine Rocks (42x49cm-17x19in) s.d.17 W/C chl prov.exhib.lit. 21-May-3 Sotheby's, New York #23/R est:40000-60000
£29321 $47500 €43982 Marin Island, Small Point, Maine (39x48cm-15x19in) s.d.16 W/C prov.exhib.lit. 21-May-3 Sotheby's, New York #95/R est:50000-75000
£29321 $47500 €43982 Maine coast (41x48cm-16x19in) s.d.14 W/C prov.lit. 21-May-3 Sotheby's, New York #107/R est:30000-50000
£92593 $150000 €138890 Street movement, New York City (46x56cm-18x22in) s.d.34 W/C prov.exhib.lit. 22-May-3 Christie's, Rockefeller NY #73/R est:150000-250000
£187097 $290000 €280646 New York (67x54cm-26x21in) s.d.27 W/C gouache chl prov.exhib.lit. 3-Dec-2 Phillips, New York #72/R est:150000-200000

MARIN, John (attrib) (1870-1953) American

Works on paper
£314 $500 €471 Along the coast. W/C exec.1940. 20-Mar-3 Skinner, Bolton #811/R

MARIN, Joseph Charles (1759-1834) French

Sculpture
£6410 $9936 €10000 Jeune femme a l'antique (20cm-8in) terracotta. 9-Dec-2 Rabourdin & Choppin de Janvry, Paris #116/R est:6000
£6993 $11678 €10000 Bacchus (23cm-9in) s.d.1823 terracotta lit. 25-Jun-3 Sotheby's, Paris #79/R est:10000-15000

£9615 $14904 €15000 Portrait de femme de l'epoque revolutionnaire (55x33x21cm-22x13x8in) s.verso terracotta. 9-Dec-2 Rabourdin & Choppin de Janvry, Paris #114/R est:22000
£17308 $26827 €27000 Portrait de jeune homme (34x17x12cm-13x7x5in) s.d.1794 terracotta exhib. 9-Dec-2 Rabourdin & Choppin de Janvry, Paris #113/R est:15000
£20513 $31795 €32000 Vestale portant une corbeille de fleurs (32x13x13cm-13x5x5in) terracotta exec.1790 exhib.lit. 9-Dec-2 Rabourdin & Choppin de Janvry, Paris #115/R est:30000

MARINALI, Orazio (attrib) (1643-1720) Italian
Sculpture
£12282 $19774 €18300 Triton (125cm-49in) stone. 19-Feb-3 Semenzato, Venice #97/R
£12349 $19882 €18400 Satyrs (73x123x77cm-29x48x30in) stone pair. 19-Feb-3 Semenzato, Venice #90/R
£12349 $19882 €18400 Triton (93cm-37in) stone pair. 19-Feb-3 Semenzato, Venice #91/R
£12349 $19882 €18400 Sea horses (60x150x50cm-24x59x20in) stone. 19-Feb-3 Semenzato, Venice #95/R

MARINARI, Onorio (1627-1715) Italian
£3526 $5465 €5500 Saint John the Evangelist (93x77cm-37x30in) octagonal. 6-Dec-2 Maigret, Paris #74/R est:8000

MARINE SCHOOL, 19th C
£12500 $20875 €18125 Shipping off Cape Town (54x74cm-21x29in) 18-Jun-3 Sotheby's, Olympia #26/R est:1200-1500

MARINI, Antonio (1788-1861) Italian
£6338 $10521 €9000 Cavalry battle (74x96cm-29x38in) prov. 11-Jun-3 Dorotheum, Vienna #40/R est:10000-15000
£24691 $40000 €37037 Landscape with rocky arch and figures (140x95cm-55x37in) 23-Jan-3 Sotheby's, New York #181/R est:60000

MARINI, Antonio (circle) (19th C) Italian
£7000 $11690 €10150 Shipping in a storm off the coast (58x102cm-23x40in) panel. 8-Jul-3 Sotheby's, Olympia #480/R est:2000-3000

MARINI, Antonio Maria (attrib) (1668-1725) Italian
£2621 $4193 €3800 Stormy seascape (68x30cm-27x12in) init. 17-Mar-3 Pandolfini, Florence #599/R est:4500
£3797 $6000 €6000 Combats de cavaliers autour d'un pont (65x99cm-26x39in) 27-Nov-2 Christie's, Paris #58/R est:6000-8000

MARINI, Marino (1901-1980) Italian
£3241 $5218 €4862 Standing female nude (27x19cm-11x7in) s. Indian ink w/C. 7-May-3 Dobiaschofsky, Bern #806/R est:9500 (S.FR 7000)
£14194 $22426 €22000 Man and horse (38x29cm-15x11in) tempera ink pen prov. 18-Dec-2 Christie's, Rome #314/R est:20000
£21250 $34000 €31875 Cavallo negro (44x63cm-17x25in) s.d.1953 tempera ink paper on canvas prov. 16-May-3 Phillips, New York #171/R est:40000-60000
£24823 $40213 €35000 Cavaliere in rosso (62x43cm-24x17in) s.d.1954 tempera oil paper prov.lit. 26-May-3 Christie's, Milan #275/R est:35000-45000
£45000 $75150 €65250 Cavallo e cavaliere (150x106cm-59x42in) s.d.1959 oil paper on canvas prov.lit. 24-Jun-3 Sotheby's, London #282/R est:45000-65000
£210000 $327600 €315000 Cavallo e giocoliere - acrobata con cavallo rosso (150x120cm-59x47in) init. s.verso painted 1958 prov.lit. 21-Oct-2 Sotheby's, London #13/R est:220000-260000
Prints
£2564 $3974 €4000 Marino from Shakespeare II (76x56cm-30x22in) s.num.5/75 col aquatint drypoint exec.1978. 6-Dec-2 Ketterer, Munich #119/R est:3500-4000
Sculpture
£4516 $7135 €7000 Reclining figure (20x9x1cm-8x4x0in) num.4/5 bronze lit. 18-Dec-2 Christie's, Rome #156/R
£12883 $21000 €19325 Piccola Venere seduta (22cm-9in) st.int.d.1929 brown pat. bronze prov.lit. 12-Feb-3 Sotheby's, New York #63/R est:10000-15000
£13462 $21000 €20193 Composition (18cm-7in) black pat. bronze executed 1965 prov.lit. 6-Nov-2 Sotheby's, New York #262/R est:20000-30000
£19872 $31199 €31000 Portrait of woman (31x19x24cm-12x7x9in) concrete exec.1925-26 lit. 19-Nov-2 Finarte, Milan #219/R est:26000-32000
£60000 $93600 €90000 Piccolo toro (32cm-13in) st.init. bronze executed 1951 prov.lit. 21-Oct-2 Sotheby's, London #2/R est:40000-60000
£80000 $123200 €120000 Piccola giuditta (65cm-26in) init.d.1944 chiselled bronze brown pat. prov.exhib.lit. 22-Oct-2 Christie's, London #16/R est:90000-120000
£200000 $308000 €300000 Composizione - cavaliere (56cm-22in) st.init. green grey white pat. bronze conceived 1955-56 prov.lit. 22-Oct-2 Christie's, London #23/R est:200000-300000
£520000 $800800 €780000 Piccolo cavaliere (59cm-23in) bronze conceived 1948 exhib.lit. 22-Oct-2 Christie's, London #18/R est:520000-600000
Works on paper
£1069 $1700 €1604 Horse and rider (17x12cm-7x5in) s.i. pen ink. 27-Feb-3 Christie's, Rockefeller NY #3/R
£1135 $1658 €1703 Paesaggio con bicicletta (14x20cm-6x8in) col pen paper on canvas prov. 4-Jun-2 Germann, Zurich #800 est:1000-1500 (S.FR 2600)
£1519 $2370 €2400 Horse (27x19cm-11x7in) s.d.1972 pastel. 14-Sep-2 Meeting Art, Vercelli #716/R
£1528 $2429 €2200 Horse (27x19cm-11x7in) s. ink lit. 1-May-3 Meeting Art, Vercelli #194
£1549 $2572 €2200 Il sogno della Venere (18x28cm-7x11in) s.i. Indian ink. 10-Jun-3 Finarte Semenzato, Milan #203/R est:2200-3000
£2207 $3487 €3200 Woman sitting on horse (36x26cm-14x10in) s.d. s.i.d. verso W/C Indian ink prov. 2-Apr-3 Dr Fritz Nagel, Stuttgart #9506/R est:4500
£3548 $5500 €5322 Horse and rider (29x21cm-11x8in) s. pen brush ink collage prov. 26-Sep-2 Christie's, Rockefeller NY #542/R est:5000-7000
£3659 $6000 €5306 Horse and rider (28x20cm-11x8in) pen ink gouache prov. 1-Jun-3 Wright, Chicago #114/R est:6000-8000
£3718 $5837 €5800 Nude (39x29cm-15x11in) s.d.1944 ink. 19-Nov-2 Finarte, Milan #12/R
£4114 $6377 €6500 Rider with horse (29x22cm-11x9in) s.d.1944 Indian ink prov. 28-Sep-2 Ketterer, Hamburg #22/R est:6000-6500
£9500 $14820 €14250 Cavallo e cavaliere (38x29cm-15x11in) s.i.d.1949 pen ink prov. 21-Oct-2 Sotheby's, London #1/R est:10000-15000
£10692 $17000 €16038 Four horses (48x34cm-19x13in) s.d.1950 col wax crayon brush ink tempera. 27-Feb-3 Christie's, Rockefeller NY #44/R est:9000
£12000 $18480 €18000 Cavaliere II (29x26cm-11x10in) s.d.1949 gouache enamel paper on canvas prov.lit. 22-Oct-2 Sotheby's, London #230/R est:15000-20000
£17628 $27676 €27500 Cavalier (62x43cm-24x17in) s.d.1952 gouache W/C ink prov. 10-Dec-2 Pierre Berge, Paris #49/R est:35000
£22000 $33880 €33000 Cavallo e cavaliere (62x43cm-24x17in) s.d.1952 gouache brush India ink pencil prov.exhib. 22-Oct-2 Christie's, London #19/R est:25000-35000
£23602 $38000 €35403 Cavallo e cavaliere (43x34cm-17x13in) s. gouache pen india ink executed 1950-51 prov. 8-May-3 Christie's, Rockefeller NY #135/R est:20000-30000
£25000 $39000 €37500 Cavallo e cavaliere (47x33cm-19x13in) s.d.1951 W/C pen ink prov.lit. 21-Oct-2 Sotheby's, London #16/R est:15000-20000
£75000 $117000 €112500 Cavallo e cavaliere (78x57cm-31x22in) s.d.1955 gouache pen ink prov. 21-Oct-2 Sotheby's, London #9/R est:40000-60000

MARINKO, George (1908-1989) American
£375 $600 €544 Clown (61x51cm-24x20in) s. 16-May-3 Skinner, Boston #385/R

MARINO, Francesco di (?) Italian
£393 $613 €590 Southern Italian street scene (35x25cm-14x10in) s. panel. 6-Nov-2 Dobiaschofsky, Bern #809/R (S.FR 900)
£759 $1200 €1200 Coastal views (22x26cm-9x10in) s. panel pair. 26-Nov-2 Christie's, Rome #266

MARINO, Giuseppe (1903-1980) Italian
£449 $655 €700 In my study (70x50cm-28x20in) s. 5-Jun-2 Il Ponte, Milan #209

MARINUS, Ferdinand Joseph Bernard (1808-1890) Belgian
£535 $851 €803 Pastoral landscape with figures by waterway (28x35cm-11x14in) s.indis.d.1836. 3-Mar-3 Lilla Bukowskis, Stockholm #219 (S.KR 7200)

MARIONI, Joseph (1943-) American
£24638 $40406 €34000 Painting No 9 - red (200x200cm-79x79in) s.i.d.1985 verso acrylic exhib. 28-May-3 Lempertz, Koln #273/R est:10000-15000

MARIOTON, Eugène (1854-1925) French
Sculpture
£1399 $2169 €2099 Viking family (76cm-30in) s. dark brown pat. bronze. 3-Dec-2 Ritchie, Toronto #3130/R est:4000-6000 (C.D 3400)
£2051 $3241 €3200 Napoleon en buste (68cm-27in) black pat bronze marble socle. 17-Nov-2 Osenat, Fontainebleau #258

MARIOTTI, Leopoldo (attrib) (1848-1916) Italian
Works on paper
£932 $1500 €1607 Farmers and cattle (64x97cm-25x38in) s. W/C. 9-May-3 Eldred, East Dennis #772/R est:300-500

MARIS, Ferdinand Johannes Jacobus (1873-1935) Dutch
£333 $550 €480 Poland rooster and hens by a forest (29x38cm-11x15in) s. 1-Jul-3 Christie's, Amsterdam #566

MARIS, Fritz (?) ?
£321 $497 €500 Nature morte de chasse (75x100cm-30x39in) s. 3-Dec-2 Campo & Campo, Antwerp #193

MARIS, Jacob (1837-1899) Dutch
£1500 $2505 €2175 Loading the hay barge (35x23cm-14x9in) s. 9-Jul-3 George Kidner, Lymington #172/R est:1500-2000
£4088 $6296 €6500 Moored sailing barges along a canal (40x60cm-16x24in) s. 23-Oct-2 Christie's, Amsterdam #214/R est:8000-12000
£6250 $9938 €9000 La chaumiere (69x85cm-27x33in) s. prov.exhib.lit. 29-Apr-3 Christie's, Amsterdam #128/R est:10000-15000
£9028 $14354 €13000 Bomschuit in the breakers (24x31cm-9x12in) s. prov. 29-Apr-3 Christie's, Amsterdam #143/R est:12000-16000
£23899 $36805 €38000 Molens aan de vaart (39x65cm-15x26in) s. prov.exhib. 23-Oct-2 Christie's, Amsterdam #209/R est:40000-60000
Works on paper
£9434 $14528 €15000 Girl playing with a cat (36x23cm-14x9in) s. W/C. 22-Oct-2 Sotheby's, Amsterdam #188/R est:15000-20000

MARIS, Jacob (attrib) (1837-1899) Dutch
£1494 $2181 €2300 Dutch mother warns her son (40x32cm-16x13in) s. prov. 15-Jun-2 Hans Stahl, Hamburg #90/R
£1529 $2385 €2400 Self portrait (32x25cm-13x10in) s. panel. 6-Nov-2 Vendue Huis, Gravenhage #587/R est:1500-2000

MARIS, Matthijs (1839-1917) Dutch
£1887 $2906 €3000 Study of a boy (56x46cm-22x18in) oil paper on triplex. 23-Oct-2 Christie's, Amsterdam #168/R est:3000-4000
£12329 $19356 €18000 Portrait of a girl (34x27cm-13x11in) init.d.72 canvas on panel. 15-Apr-3 Sotheby's, Amsterdam #219/R est:20000-30000
Works on paper
£987 $1599 €1500 Drying the nets, Norway (18x44cm-7x17in) s.i. W/C bodycol. 21-Jan-3 Christie's, Amsterdam #235/R est:1800-2200

MARIS, Simon (1873-1935) Dutch
£1645 $2664 €2500 Mother and child (69x49cm-27x19in) s. 21-Jan-3 Christie's, Amsterdam #261 est:2500-3500

MARIS, Willem (1844-1910) Dutch
£1164 $1816 €1700 Portrait of an Egyptian girl (35x26cm-14x10in) s. prov. 14-Apr-3 Glerum, Amsterdam #68 est:1500-2000
£1830 $2946 €2800 Vache et oies sur fond de traie (69x99cm-27x39in) s. 20-Jan-3 Horta, Bruxelles #72/R est:3500-4500
£2113 $3401 €3000 Cows at the feeding trough (31x22cm-12x9in) s. prov. 7-May-3 Vendue Huis, Gravenhage #433/R est:2000-3000
Works on paper
£428 $693 €650 Milking time (12x21cm-5x8in) init. black chk htd white. 21-Jan-3 Christie's, Amsterdam #208
£2516 $3874 €4000 View of a Dutch canal (33x48cm-13x19in) s. W/C prov. 22-Oct-2 Sotheby's, Amsterdam #120/R est:4000-6000
£2740 $4301 €4000 Milking time (57x39cm-22x15in) s. W/C. 15-Apr-3 Sotheby's, Amsterdam #102/R est:4000-6000
£3082 $4839 €4500 Watering cows in a polder landscape (27x40cm-11x16in) s. W/C. 15-Apr-3 Sotheby's, Amsterdam #222/R est:5000-7000

MARIS, Willem Matthijs (1872-1929) Dutch
£278 $458 €400 Cat's trick (26x17cm-10x7in) s.i.d.1889 verso panel. 1-Jul-3 Christie's, Amsterdam #197

MARISALDI, Elena Falco (1902-1986) Italian
£510 $811 €750 Hounds (35x50cm-14x20in) s.d.1960 board. 1-Mar-3 Meeting Art, Vercelli #91
£641 $1006 €1000 Hens (35x50cm-14x20in) s. cardboard. 10-Dec-2 Della Rocca, Turin #290/R
£1020 $1622 €1500 Still life of flowers (70x100cm-28x39in) s. canvas on board. 1-Mar-3 Meeting Art, Vercelli #89

MARISOL (1930-) American/Venezulean
Sculpture
£3049 $5000 €4421 Totem (269x15x20cm-106x6x8in) wood. 1-Jun-3 Wright, Chicago #310/R est:5000-7000

MARISSAL-CALBERG, Andree (1903-1986) Belgian
£288 $460 €400 Nature morte aux fleurs, fruits et legumes (64x65cm-25x26in) s. 13-May-3 Vanderkindere, Brussels #29

MARJORAM, Gerard (1936-) Irish
£295 $466 €460 Glenmalure (25x34cm-10x13in) board. 12-Nov-2 Mealy's, Castlecomer #1262
£308 $486 €480 Summer day (25x34cm-10x13in) s. board. 12-Nov-2 Mealy's, Castlecomer #1263
£338 $561 €480 Off Achill (25x34cm-10x13in) s. board. 10-Jun-3 James Adam, Dublin #244/R
£345 $548 €500 Sheep grazing on Roundstone Bogg (26x36cm-10x14in) s. board. 4-Mar-3 Mealy's, Castlecomer #1236
£345 $548 €500 Summers day, near Ballynahinch, Connemara (26x36cm-10x14in) s. board. 4-Mar-3 Mealy's, Castlecomer #1237
£352 $585 €500 Connemara coast (25x34cm-10x13in) s. board. 10-Jun-3 James Adam, Dublin #243/R
£355 $574 €500 Sheep grazing near Letterfrack, Connemara (26x36cm-10x14in) s. board. 20-May-3 Mealy's, Castlecomer #1300
£432 $614 €700 Bens near Toombeola, Co.Galway (43x58cm-17x23in) s. 29-Mar-2 Woodwards, Cork #177
£496 $804 €700 Sunlight on the bog, Connemara (26x36cm-10x14in) s. board. 20-May-3 Mealy's, Castlecomer #1301/R
£521 $859 €750 Woodland stream (35x52cm-14x20in) s. board. 7-Jul-3 Hamilton Osborne King, Dublin #227
£521 $859 €750 Connemara Coast (28x37cm-11x15in) s. 7-Jul-3 Hamilton Osborne King, Dublin #228
£647 $1036 €900 Connemara mountain landscape (61x91cm-24x36in) s. 13-May-3 Thomas Adams, Dublin #389
£660 $1030 €1050 Twelve pins near Clifden (61x71cm-24x28in) s. 8-Oct-2 Loughlin Bowe, Kilkenny #219
£833 $1317 €1300 Shades of Summer (41x51cm-16x20in) board. 12-Nov-2 Mealy's, Castlecomer #1227

MARK, Lajos (1867-1942) Hungarian
£1887 $3000 €2831 Red kimono (137x86cm-54x34in) s. 22-Mar-3 New Orleans Auction, New Orleans #415/R est:3500-5000
£2465 $3968 €3500 Woman's portrait (120x150cm-47x59in) s.d.95. 9-May-3 Schloss Ahlden, Ahlden #1510/R est:4500

MARKEL, Otto (attrib) (19/20th C) ?
£469 $751 €680 Girl with butterfly (46x35cm-18x14in) s.d.1907. 18-May-3 Anders Antik, Landskrona #87 (S.KR 6000)

MARKELBACH, Alexandre (attrib) (1824-1906) Belgian
£2785 $4344 €4400 Historical scene (253x234cm-100x92in) 21-Oct-2 Bernaerts, Antwerp #194/R est:3750-4000

MARKES, Albert Ernest (1865-1901) British
Works on paper
£390 $608 €585 Vessels in a calm (13x36cm-5x14in) s. sepia. 9-Oct-2 Woolley & Wallis, Salisbury #53/R
£400 $648 €580 Seascape with fishing vessels (15x27cm-6x11in) s. mono. W/C. 20-May-3 Dreweatt Neate, Newbury #211/R
£600 $972 €900 On the crest of a wave. Brig at anchor, offshore, drying her sails (16x23cm-6x9in) W/C one with scratching out pair. 21-May-3 Christie's, Kensington #421/R
£3800 $6156 €5700 Wrecked three master on the sands with inhabitants salvaging (61x95cm-24x37in) s. pencil W/C. 21-May-3 Christie's, Kensington #422/R est:4000-6000

MARKES, Richmond (19th C) British
Works on paper
£300 $489 €450 Three-masted ship in a storm (24x52cm-9x20in) init. W/C htd white rubbing out. 17-Feb-3 Bonhams, Bath #112
£300 $477 €450 Two men or war in rough seas (25x52cm-10x20in) s. W/C. 29-Apr-3 Sworder & Son, Bishops Stortford #339b/R

MARKHAM, Kyra (1891-1967) American
£1623 $2500 €2435 Woodland interior (48x69cm-19x27in) s.d.1944 board. 8-Sep-2 Treadway Gallery, Cincinnati #656/R est:800-1200
Prints
£2516 $4000 €3774 Flag raising in Leroy Street (33x24cm-13x9in) s.i.d.1942 lithograph. 4-Mar-3 Swann Galleries, New York #440/R est:2000-3000

MARKHAM, Philip (20th C) New Zealander
£561 $893 €842 Shearing shed, Wairarpa (58x89cm-23x35in) s.i.d.1987 verso acrylic. 25-Feb-3 Peter Webb, Auckland #212/R est:800-1200 (NZ.D 1600)

MARKINO, Yoshio (1874-1956) British/Japanese
£3500 $5810 €5250 Church of SS San Giovanni e Paolo from the Aventine, Rome (53x72cm-21x28in) s. 12-Jun-3 Bonhams, New Bond Street #815/R est:4000-6000

£4500 $7470 €6750 Looking down the river from Waterloo Bridge, London (50x70cm-20x28in) s. 12-Jun-3 Bonhams, New Bond Street #812/R est:5000-8000
£4800 $7968 €7200 Palace of Westminster, London (52x86cm-20x34in) s. 12-Jun-3 Bonhams, New Bond Street #803/R est:5000-8000
£5000 $8300 €7500 Turl, Oxford (72x49cm-28x19in) s. board. 12-Jun-3 Bonhams, New Bond Street #811/R est:5000-8000
£6500 $10790 €9750 Forum, Rome, Italy (49x72cm-19x28in) s. 12-Jun-3 Bonhams, New Bond Street #804/R est:7000-10000
£8000 $13280 €12000 Hyde Park from the Serpentine Bridge, London (51x76cm-20x30in) s. 12-Jun-3 Bonhams, New Bond Street #805/R est:6000-9000

Works on paper
£2700 $4482 €4050 First church of Christian Science, Boston (28x24cm-11x9in) s. W/C. 12-Jun-3 Bonhams, New Bond Street #808/R est:3000-5000
£3000 $4980 €4500 Miss John Bull (27x18cm-11x7in) s. W/C. 12-Jun-3 Bonhams, New Bond Street #809/R est:3000-5000
£3800 $6308 €5700 Busy London street, evening (16x25cm-6x10in) init. W/C. 12-Jun-3 Bonhams, New Bond Street #814/R est:3000-4000
£3800 $6308 €5700 Hotel entrance, Knightsbridge (23x34cm-9x13in) s. W/C. 12-Jun-3 Bonhams, New Bond Street #820/R est:2500-3500
£4000 $6640 €6000 Palace of Westminster (48x66cm-19x26in) s. W/C. 12-Jun-3 Bonhams, New Bond Street #819/R est:4000-6000
£4200 $6972 €6300 Aldwych site (25x32cm-10x13in) s. W/C. 12-Jun-3 Bonhams, New Bond Street #816/R est:4000-6000
£4500 $7470 €6750 Evening, Trafalgar Square (30x38cm-12x15in) s. W/C. 12-Jun-3 Bonhams, New Bond Street #823/R est:4000-6000
£5000 $8300 €7500 Victoria and Albert Museum (22x35cm-9x14in) s. W/C. 12-Jun-3 Bonhams, New Bond Street #818/R est:4000-6000
£5200 $8632 €7800 In the broad, Oxford (24x35cm-9x14in) s. W/C. 12-Jun-3 Bonhams, New Bond Street #825/R est:4000-6000
£6500 $10790 €9750 Evening outside the Adelphi Theatre, London (32x20cm-13x8in) init. W/C. 12-Jun-3 Bonhams, New Bond Street #810/R est:4000-6000
£7000 $11620 €10500 Embankment, London (14x17cm-6x7in) s. W/C. 12-Jun-3 Bonhams, New Bond Street #801/R est:7000-10000
£8500 $14110 €12750 New York Harbour (70x50cm-28x20in) s. W/C. 12-Jun-3 Bonhams, New Bond Street #807/R est:6000-9000
£9000 $14940 €13500 Evening exodus West End, entering Victoria railway station, London (23x30cm-9x12in) s. W/C. 12-Jun-3 Bonhams, New Bond Street #806/R est:5000-8000
£11000 $18260 €16500 Autumn (25x17cm-10x7in) s. W/C. 12-Jun-3 Bonhams, New Bond Street #802/R est:7000-10000

MARKITANTE, Sam (1885-1960) ?
£321 $497 €500 Allee ensoleillee et fleurie (80x64cm-31x25in) s. 9-Dec-2 Horta, Bruxelles #399

MARKKULA, Mauno (1905-1959) Finnish
£345 $545 €500 Landscape (26x32cm-10x13in) s. 3-Apr-3 Hagelstam, Helsinki #945
£475 $750 €750 Storm (21x16cm-8x6in) s. cardboard. 30-Nov-2 Hagelstam, Helsinki #157/R
£490 $775 €760 Moonlight (23x35cm-9x14in) s. 19-Dec-2 Hagelstam, Helsinki #881
£588 $965 €900 Nude (40x25cm-16x10in) s. 9-Feb-3 Bukowskis, Helsinki #303/R
£633 $1000 €1000 Train in the mountains by Sierra Madre (61x50cm-24x20in) s. board. 1-Dec-2 Bukowskis, Helsinki #335/R
£791 $1266 €1100 Evening (24x33cm-9x13in) s. board. 17-May-3 Hagelstam, Helsinki #195/R
£886 $1400 €1400 Dawn (36x45cm-14x18in) s. 1-Dec-2 Bukowskis, Helsinki #336/R
£1094 $1750 €1520 Landscape (25x34cm-10x13in) s. board. 17-May-3 Hagelstam, Helsinki #196/R est:700

MARKO, Andreas (1824-1895) Austrian
£2405 $3800 €3800 Cattle watering (55x65cm-22x26in) s.d.1879. 26-Nov-2 Christie's, Rome #127/R
£3125 $4969 €4500 Shepherdess in southern landscape (33x41cm-13x16in) s.d.1880. 29-Apr-3 Wiener Kunst Auktionen, Vienna #542/R est:1500-3000
£12102 $18758 €18153 Italian landscape with a shepherdess resting by the mountain spring (93x80cm-37x31in) s. 6-Dec-2 Kieselbach, Budapest #57/R (H.F 4500000)
£15479 $24147 €23219 Italian landscape with riding horses, 1871 (104x138cm-41x54in) s.d.1871. 11-Sep-2 Kieselbach, Budapest #101/R (H.F 6000000)

MARKO, Ferenc (1832-1874) Hungarian
£1548 $2415 €2322 Roving barbar, 1863 (32x40cm-13x16in) s.d.1863 cardboard. 11-Sep-2 Kieselbach, Budapest #158/R (H.F 600000)
£4644 $7244 €6966 Courting, 1866 (62x93cm-24x37in) s.d.1866. 11-Sep-2 Kieselbach, Budapest #159/R (H.F 1800000)

MARKO, Henry (1855-1921) Italian
£673 $1057 €1050 Landscape with trees (45x70cm-18x28in) s. 16-Dec-2 Pandolfini, Florence #99/R
£881 $1356 €1400 Landscape with figures (60x100cm-24x39in) s. 23-Oct-2 Finarte, Milan #22

MARKO, Karl (attrib) (19th C) Hungarian
£3169 $5261 €4500 Mountainous southern landscape with stone bridge and traveller (52x65cm-20x26in) prov. 11-Jun-3 Dorotheum, Vienna #157/R est:4000-6000

MARKO, Karl (elder and younger) (19th C) Hungarian
£8228 $13000 €13000 Landscape in Lazio with mythological scene (35x50cm-14x20in) s. 26-Nov-2 Christie's, Rome #122/R est:5000-6000
£12296 $19181 €17829 Mythological scene next to Tivoli (33x49cm-13x19in) s. 12-Apr-3 Mu Terem Galeria, Budapest #51/R est:2500000 (H.F 4400000)

MARKO, Karl (elder) (1791-1860) Hungarian
£1800 $2826 €2700 Travellers in an Italian landscape (13x16cm-5x6in) S. 21-Nov-2 Christie's, Kensington #151/R est:1800-2200
£2078 $3200 €3117 Landscape with rainbow and figures (20x28cm-8x11in) s.d.1831. 27-Oct-2 Grogan, Boston #55/R est:4000-5000
£7500 $11775 €11250 Miraculous draught of fishes (38x51cm-15x20in) s.i.d.1857 board. 21-Nov-2 Christie's, Kensington #150/R est:4000-6000
£19561 $30516 €29342 Italian landscape (19x28cm-7x11in) s.d.1851 paper on canvas. 11-Apr-3 Kieselbach, Budapest #188/R est:6500000-7000000 (H.F 7000000)
£33537 $52318 €48629 Founding of Moses (51x76cm-20x30in) lit. 13-Sep-2 Mu Terem Galeria, Budapest #122/R est:8000000 (H.F 13000000)
£43856 $68416 €65784 Italian landscape with viadust and rainbow, 1838 (75x100cm-30x39in) s.d.1838. 11-Sep-2 Kieselbach, Budapest #52/R (H.F 17000000)
£100000 $164000 €150000 Classical landscape (110x166cm-43x65in) s.i.d.1851 prov.exhib.lit. 3-Jun-3 Sotheby's, London #11/R est:30000-40000

Works on paper
£353 $515 €550 Peasants harvesting in Campagna (23x29cm-9x11in) s.d.1851 W/C Indian ink. 4-Jun-2 Karl & Faber, Munich #112
£3765 $5836 €5648 Italian landscape with harvesters (28x23cm-11x9in) s. W/C. 6-Dec-2 Kieselbach, Budapest #94/R (H.F 1400000)

MARKO, Karl (younger) (1822-1891) Hungarian
£900 $1404 €1350 Rocky landscape (20x23cm-8x9in) s.d.1857. 17-Sep-2 Bonhams, Oxford #49/R
£1090 $1722 €1700 Crossing the stream (33x40cm-13x16in) s.d.1874. 15-Nov-2 Farsetti, Prato #526/R
£4516 $7135 €7000 Tuscan landscape (45x60cm-18x24in) s.d.1885. 18-Dec-2 Finarte, Milan #30/R est:6500
£4841 $7503 €7019 Excursionists in Italian landscape (23x33cm-9x13in) s.d.845. 9-Dec-2 Mu Terem Galeria, Budapest #42/R est:1200000 (H.F 1800000)
£5160 $8049 €7482 Excursionists in Italian landscape (24x32cm-9x13in) s.d.1862. 13-Sep-2 Mu Terem Galeria, Budapest #53/R est:1200000 (H.F 2000000)
£7000 $11480 €10500 Classical landscape (28x38cm-11x15in) s.i. board prov. 3-Jun-3 Sotheby's, London #4/R est:10000-15000
£8974 $14090 €14000 Harbour in Corsica (90x120cm-35x47in) s.d.1877. 16-Dec-2 Pandolfini, Florence #61/R est:18000
£9681 $15006 €14522 Italian landscape (30x46cm-12x18in) s. 6-Dec-2 Kieselbach, Budapest #168/R (H.F 3600000)
£19348 $30183 €28055 Landscape with sunset and figures (60x87cm-24x34in) 13-Sep-2 Mu Terem Galeria, Budapest #200/R est:4000000 (H.F 7500000)
£23753 $37055 €34442 Harbour in Korika (90x122cm-35x48in) s.d.1877 s.i.verso. 12-Apr-3 Mu Terem Galeria, Budapest #131/R est:3800000 (H.F 8500000)

MARKO, Karl (19th C) Hungarian
£720 $1181 €1080 Rocky landscape (20x23cm-8x9in) s.d.1857. 3-Jun-3 Bonhams, Oxford #69

MARKO, Serge (1925-) ?
Works on paper
£385 $608 €600 Chalutiers au sec (50x32cm-20x13in) s. W/C. 12-Nov-2 Thierry & Lannon, Brest #76/R

MARKOFF, Natacha (1911-) Russian
£1020 $1622 €1500 Le port de Bizerte (54x65cm-21x26in) s. 24-Mar-3 Raboudin & Choppin de Janvry, Paris #118/R est:1100-1300

MARKOS, Lajos (1917-1993) American/Rumanian
£851 $1379 €1200 Il ritorno dell'ussaro (100x80cm-39x31in) s.d.1941. 22-May-3 Stadion, Trieste #387/R
£922 $1494 €1300 Ballerina gitana (80x60cm-31x24in) s. 22-May-3 Stadion, Trieste #386/R est:1500-2000
£1442 $2250 €2163 Standing nude female (41x51cm-16x20in) s. board. 30-Mar-3 Simpson's, Houston #333
£1534 $2500 €2301 Duck hunters (41x51cm-16x20in) s. 2-Feb-3 Simpson's, Houston #412
£1840 $3000 €2760 City bank (46x61cm-18x24in) s. 2-Feb-3 Simpson's, Houston #403
£2548 $4000 €3822 Boy and skittish horse in a barn (76x91cm-30x36in) s. prov. 19-Nov-2 Butterfields, San Francisco #8114/R est:5000-7000

MARKOV, Leonid (1926-) Russian
£280 $434 €420 Winter in a village (27x22cm-11x9in) s. board. 8-Dec-2 John Nicholson, Haslemere #15

MARKOWICZ, Arthur (1872-1934) Polish
Works on paper
£513 $805 €800 Portrait d'un rabin (56x39cm-22x15in) s.d.1910 pastel. 10-Dec-2 Vanderkindere, Brussels #23

MARKS, Albert (1870-1941) French
Works on paper
£350 $546 €525 Vessels in a harbour (18x13cm-7x5in) s. W/C. 26-Mar-3 Woolley & Wallis, Salisbury #68/R

MARKS, Barnett Samuel (1827-1916) British
£5743 $8959 €8500 Portrait de famille (153x196cm-60x77in) s.d. 26-Mar-3 Pierre Berge, Paris #31/R

MARKS, Claude (19th C) ?
£1266 $1962 €2000 Danseuses a Seville (69x92cm-27x36in) s.i. 27-Sep-2 Rabourdin & Choppin de Janvry, Paris #73/R est:2000-2500
Works on paper
£1000 $1560 €1500 Grande Canal, Venice. Doge's Palace (51x36cm-20x14in) s. W/C pair. 5-Nov-2 Bristol Auction Rooms #854/R est:1000-1400

MARKS, George (fl.1876-1922) British
Works on paper
£645 $1000 €968 Summertime (38x26cm-15x10in) s. W/C gouache. 29-Oct-2 Sotheby's, New York #143/R est:2000-3000
£645 $1000 €968 Surrey common (26x38cm-10x15in) s. W/C gouache. 29-Oct-2 Sotheby's, New York #144/R est:2000-3000
£645 $1000 €968 Three rabbits in a dry riverbed (28x39cm-11x15in) s. W/C gouache. 29-Oct-2 Sotheby's, New York #145/R est:2000-3000
£700 $1134 €1050 In the garden, Granada (25x18cm-10x7in) s. pencil W/C. 23-Jan-3 Christie's, Kensington #372/R
£967 $1500 €1451 Haystacks and an August Eve in a hayfield (17x27cm-7x11in) s. W/C gouache two prov. 29-Oct-2 Sotheby's, New York #139/R est:3000-4000
£967 $1500 €1451 Evening's final hour. Mill pond (27x18cm-11x7in) s. one s.d.1885 pencil W/C gouache. 29-Oct-2 Sotheby's, New York #141/R est:3000-4000
£1139 $1800 €1709 Summer evening (61x91cm-24x36in) s. W/C gouache prov. 24-Apr-3 Sotheby's, New York #178/R est:1500-2000
£1290 $2000 €1935 Flowers in the graveyard (36x47cm-14x19in) s.d.1886 W/C gouache prov. 29-Oct-2 Sotheby's, New York #140/R est:3000-4000
£1500 $2340 €2175 Albury Heath, Surrey (27x38cm-11x15in) s. W/C. 13-May-3 Holloways, Banbury #627/R est:1500-2000

MARKS, Hans (1946-) British
Sculpture
£2878 $4604 €4000 Comme le vent (86cm-34in) s.d.1986 num.1/8 col pat bronze Cast Zavattero. 18-May-3 Rabourdin & Choppin de Janvry, Paris #165/R est:8000-10000

MARKS, Henry Stacy (1829-1898) British
£1000 $1590 €1500 Quiet pipe (46x36cm-18x14in) s.d.1860 i.on stretcher. 6-Mar-3 Christie's, Kensington #543/R est:1500-2000
£1200 $1908 €1800 Sexton's sermon (66x50cm-26x20in) s.d.1860 s.i.stretcher. 5-Mar-3 Bonhams, Bury St Edmunds #417/R est:1000-1500
£6500 $10465 €9750 Father's study (30x41cm-12x16in) s.d.1861 prov.exhib.lit. 20-Feb-3 Christie's, London #41/R est:10000
Works on paper
£500 $780 €750 Study of a sparrowhawk (11x7cm-4x3in) init. W/C. 10-Sep-2 Sworder & Son, Bishops Stortford #762/R
£650 $1073 €943 The sleep of reason (21x25cm-8x10in) init.d.1855 pencil pen pen brown ink W/C htd white. 3-Jul-3 Christie's, Kensington #219/R
£1200 $1872 €1800 Study of an umbrella cockatoo, cacatua alba (19x11cm-7x4in) init. W/C bodycol. 5-Nov-2 Bonhams, New Bond Street #127/R est:1000-1500
£1200 $1872 €1800 Study of a sulphur crested cockatoo, Galerita galerita (24x11cm-9x4in) init. W/C. 5-Nov-2 Bonhams, New Bond Street #128/R est:1000-1500
£1419 $2200 €2129 Paroquette (15x10cm-6x4in) init. W/C exec.c.1911. 8-Dec-2 Toomey, Oak Park #658/R est:800-1200
£1500 $2340 €2250 Study of Leadbetter's cockatoo, plyctolophus leadbetter's cockatoo (18x11cm-7x4in) init. W/C bodycol. 5-Nov-2 Bonhams, New Bond Street #129/R est:1000-1500

MARKUS, Antoon (1870-1955) Dutch
£255 $392 €400 River landscape with a borough (33x47cm-13x19in) s. 3-Sep-2 Christie's, Amsterdam #354

MARLATT, H Irving (1860-1929) American
Works on paper
£774 $1200 €1161 River landscape (71x56cm-28x22in) s. mixed media oil gouache board. 29-Oct-2 John Moran, Pasadena #724

MARLE, Felix del (1889-1952) French
Works on paper
£759 $1200 €1200 Veuves (44x29cm-17x11in) mono. chl. 26-Nov-2 Camard, Paris #67
£2778 $4416 €4000 Composition neo-plastique (25x21cm-10x8in) gouache ink graphite exec.c.1925 prov.exhib. 29-Apr-3 Artcurial Briest, Paris #110/R est:1200-1500
£7000 $11480 €10500 Metro (51x31cm-20x12in) W/C chl exec.c.1912-13 prov. 6-Feb-3 Christie's, London #440/R
£13208 $20604 €21000 Catch as catch can (48x63cm-19x25in) s.d.1913 Chinese ink W/C exhib.lit. 11-Oct-2 Binoche, Paris #123/R est:15000-20000

MARLIAVE, François (1874-1953) French
Works on paper
£535 $823 €850 Ponts de Constantine (30x21cm-12x8in) s.d.42 W/C. 23-Oct-2 Rabourdin & Choppin de Janvry, Paris #251/R

MARLOW, William (1740-1813) British
£12195 $20000 €18293 View of Matlock, Derbyshire (38x53cm-15x21in) prov. 29-May-3 Sotheby's, New York #25/R est:10000-15000

MARLOW, William (circle) (1740-1813) British
£5800 $9512 €8700 Hornby Castle (70x89cm-28x35in) prov.exhib. 29-May-3 Christie's, Kensington #63/R est:3000-5000

MARMA, Rodolfo (1923-1997) Italian
£321 $503 €500 Clock tower in Pontassieve (60x50cm-24x20in) s. 16-Dec-2 Pandolfini, Florence #366
£405 $632 €600 Nuns with girls (40x8cm-16x3in) s.d.1972 board. 28-Mar-3 Farsetti, Prato #420
£449 $704 €700 Market (30x60cm-12x24in) s. 16-Dec-2 Pandolfini, Florence #364
Works on paper
£1026 $1621 €1600 Views of Florence (68x49cm-27x19in) gouache card set of 3. 15-Nov-2 Farsetti, Prato #443

MARMION, Simon (attrib) (1425-1489) French
£21622 $33730 €32000 Adoration of a Magus (55x37cm-22x15in) panel prov. 27-Mar-3 Dorotheum, Vienna #154/R est:30000-40000

MARMOL, Ignacio (1934-1994) Spanish
£760 $1223 €1140 Diona (34x41cm-13x16in) s.d.1970 oil enamel on board. 6-May-3 Christie's, Melbourne #265 est:800-1200 (A.D 1900)
£2400 $3864 €3600 Woman with ribbons (122x122cm-48x48in) s.d.1968 s.d.verso oil enamel on board. 6-May-3 Christie's, Melbourne #296 est:2000-5000 (A.D 6000)

MARNEFFE, Ernest (1866-1921) Belgian
£2621 $4141 €3800 Portrait d'une elegante (48x60cm-19x24in) s. 2-Apr-3 Vanderkindere, Brussels #513/R est:100
£6115 $9784 €8500 Jeune femme au corsage rouge (45x35cm-18x14in) s.d.1916 board. 13-May-3 Vanderkindere, Brussels #1 est:1000-1500

MARNY, Paul (1829-1914) British

£400 $640 €600 River scene with bridge, buildings and church in the background (36x58cm-14x23in) s. 11-Mar-3 David Duggleby, Scarborough #66/R
£460 $736 €690 River townscape with bridge (33x60cm-13x24in) s. 11-Mar-3 David Duggleby, Scarborough #64

Works on paper

£260 $424 €390 Figures beneath a town gateway and clock (46x32cm-18x13in) s. W/C over pencil htd white. 17-Feb-3 Bonhams, Bath #82
£260 $406 €390 European town scene with gothic clock building behind market place (28x38cm-11x15in) s. W/C. 12-Apr-3 Jim Railton, Durham #825
£310 $490 €465 Storm, South Bay Scarborough (46x66cm-18x26in) s. W/C. 24-Apr-3 Richardson & Smith, Whitby #196
£335 $533 €503 Continental street scene (37x65cm-15x26in) s. W/C. 25-Feb-3 John Taylors, Louth #441
£400 $632 €580 St Malo, Brittany (15x24cm-6x9in) s.i. W/C. 28-Jul-3 David Duggleby, Scarborough #232/R
£400 $632 €580 Continental market place (44x30cm-17x12in) s. W/C. 28-Jul-3 David Duggleby, Scarborough #255
£440 $686 €660 Morleix, continental street scene with figures washing clothes (44x32cm-17x13in) W/C. 10-Sep-2 David Duggleby, Scarborough #198
£450 $711 €653 Corner at Etienne (44x30cm-17x12in) s.i. W/C bodycol. 22-Jul-3 Bonhams, Knightsbridge #82/R
£450 $711 €653 Rouen, Basse-Tour (44x30cm-17x12in) s.i. W/C bodycol. 22-Jul-3 Bonhams, Knightsbridge #83/R
£520 $816 €780 Rouen (76x50cm-30x20in) s.i. pen ink W/C. 21-Nov-2 Tennants, Leyburn #647/R
£800 $1296 €1200 Caen, Normandy (37x64cm-15x25in) s.i. W/C. 21-May-3 Bonhams, Knightsbridge #44/R
£900 $1395 €1350 Bassigny, Haute Marne, France (59x108cm-23x43in) s. W/C. 25-Sep-2 Hamptons Fine Art, Godalming #147/R

MAROCHETTI, Baron Charles (1805-1867) French

Sculpture

£2500 $3900 €3750 Equestrian study of Wellington (43cm-17in) bronze with wooden plinth prov. 10-Sep-2 Riddetts, Bournemouth #226/R

MAROHN, Ferdinand (19th C) French

£1800 $2988 €2700 Figures on a haycart (38x45cm-15x18in) s.i. 10-Jun-3 Bonhams, Knightsbridge #99/R est:2000-3000

Works on paper

£340 $551 €510 Fishing on a pond (20x26cm-8x10in) s. W/C. 21-May-3 Bonhams, Knightsbridge #204/R
£1300 $2054 €1950 Swiss family cottage beside a lake (40x56cm-16x22in) s. W/C bodycol. 26-Nov-2 Bonhams, Knightsbridge #178/R est:1000-1500

MAROLA (1905-1986) Spanish

£1258 $1937 €2000 Peasant (70x115cm-28x45in) s. 22-Oct-2 Durán, Madrid #138/R
£1282 $2026 €2000 Reading (64x50cm-25x20in) s. cardboard. 19-Nov-2 Durán, Madrid #125/R

MAROLD, Ludwig (1865-1898) Czechoslovakian

Works on paper

£338 $527 €500 The latest fashion (30x17cm-12x7in) mono. W/C htd white over pencil. 28-Mar-3 Dorotheum, Vienna #143/R
£1091 $1734 €1637 Parisian (31x14cm-12x6in) mono. pencil W/C. 8-Mar-3 Dorotheum, Prague #237/R est:30000-45000 (C.KR 50000)

MARONEY, Ken (?) ?

£184 $287 €276 Fishing boats moored at Hout Bay (70x89cm-28x35in) s. 15-Oct-2 Stephan Welz, Johannesburg #413 est:4000-6000 (SA.R 3000)
£307 $479 €461 Still life in an interior (58x58cm-23x23in) s. board. 15-Oct-2 Stephan Welz, Johannesburg #414 est:4000-6000 (SA.R 5000)

MARONIEZ, Georges Philibert Charles (1865-1933) French

£269 $423 €420 Voiliers (11x15cm-4x6in) s. cardboard. 13-Dec-2 Piasa, Paris #187
£288 $453 €450 Voiliers au couchant (24x31cm-9x12in) s. cardboard. 13-Dec-2 Piasa, Paris #202
£288 $453 €450 Maison verte au bord de canal (16x10cm-6x4in) s. cardboard. 13-Dec-2 Piasa, Paris #196
£288 $453 €450 Coucher de soleil (12x16cm-5x6in) s. cardboard. 13-Dec-2 Piasa, Paris #188
£321 $503 €500 Port (12x16cm-5x6in) s. cardboard. 13-Dec-2 Piasa, Paris #198
£347 $549 €500 Ville mediterraneenne (15x24cm-6x9in) s. cardboard. 25-Apr-3 Piasa, Paris #139
£353 $554 €550 Paysanne (25x16cm-10x6in) s. panel. 13-Dec-2 Piasa, Paris #193
£382 $603 €550 Cote rocheuse (24x31cm-9x12in) s. panel. 25-Apr-3 Piasa, Paris #138
£449 $696 €700 Maison au bord de l'eau (22x30cm-9x12in) s. panel. 4-Dec-2 Pierre Berge, Paris #148/R
£451 $713 €650 Cote sauvage (16x24cm-6x9in) s. cardboard. 25-Apr-3 Piasa, Paris #143
£577 $906 €900 Paysage d'Afrique du Nord (16x24cm-6x9in) s. cardboard. 13-Dec-2 Piasa, Paris #190
£650 $1021 €975 Riviere en hiver (21x27cm-8x11in) s. panel. 12-Dec-2 Iegor de Saint Hippolyte, Montreal #63 (C.D 1600)
£673 $1057 €1050 Concarneau (16x24cm-6x9in) s. cardboard. 13-Dec-2 Piasa, Paris #201/R
£696 $1079 €1100 Rue de village pres de l'eglise (24x16cm-9x6in) s. panel. 29-Sep-2 Eric Pillon, Calais #133/R
£1026 $1610 €1600 POrt (15x24cm-6x9in) s. cardboard. 13-Dec-2 Piasa, Paris #199/R
£1186 $1862 €1850 Temple de Philae (9x13cm-4x5in) s. cardboard pair. 13-Dec-2 Piasa, Paris #192
£1218 $1912 €1900 Paysage d'Afrique du Nord (16x24cm-6x9in) s. cardboard pair. 13-Dec-2 Piasa, Paris #191
£1310 $2044 €1965 Retour de la peche (60x73cm-24x29in) s. 6-Nov-2 Dobiaschofsky, Bern #810/R est:6000 (S.FR 3000)
£2222 $3622 €3200 Retour de peche au soleil couchant (44x58cm-17x23in) s. 19-Jul-3 Thierry & Lannon, Brest #151/R est:2800-3000

Works on paper

£417 $654 €650 Voiliers (24x17cm-9x7in) s. W/C. 13-Dec-2 Piasa, Paris #197

MAROSAN, Gyula (1915-) Hungarian

£1118 $1744 €1621 Composition (54x67cm-21x26in) s. 12-Apr-3 Mu Terem Galeria, Budapest #113/R est:380000 (H.F 400000)

MARPLE, William (1827-1910) American

£683 $1100 €1025 River landscape with a couple on the shore (48x74cm-19x29in) s. 22-Feb-3 Pook & Pook, Downington #96/R
£4777 $7500 €7166 Mt Uncle Sam across the Narrows, Clear Lake, California (51x81cm-20x32in) init.d.69 i.verso prov. 19-Nov-2 Butterfields, San Francisco #8158/R est:5000-7000

MARQUANT, Peter (1956-) Austrian

£1266 $1962 €2000 Untitled (120x95cm-47x37in) s.d.87 dispersion. 24-Sep-2 Wiener Kunst Auktionen, Vienna #323/R est:2000-3000

MARQUARD, Otto (1881-1969) German

£347 $559 €521 Bodensee in morning light (27x39cm-11x15in) s. board. 7-May-3 Dobiaschofsky, Bern #808/R (S.FR 750)
£547 $776 €880 Bodensee landscape (65x47cm-26x19in) mono. 23-Mar-2 Geble, Radolfzell #561/R

MARQUET, Albert (1875-1947) French

£4403 $6824 €7000 Le pont (16x26cm-6x10in) s. panel lit. 30-Oct-2 Artcurial Briest, Paris #322/R est:7500-10000
£8633 $13813 €12000 Le pont soleil couchant (16x26cm-6x10in) s. canvas on cardboard. 18-May-3 Eric Pillon, Calais #74/R
£12037 $17093 €19500 Petit village des Vosges (26x34cm-10x13in) s. panel lit. 16-Mar-3 Eric Pillon, Calais #108/R
£12903 $20387 €20000 Port d'Alger (15x25cm-6x10in) s. cardboard prov.lit. 18-Dec-2 Tajan, Paris #63/R est:15000
£19580 $32699 €28000 Hauteurs de Chennevieres (50x61cm-20x24in) s. prov. 30-Jun-3 Pierre Berge, Paris #54/R est:25000-30000
£21154 $33212 €33000 Port d'Alger (33x41cm-13x16in) s. panel. 13-Dec-2 Piasa, Paris #182/R
£21795 $34000 €32693 Panorama de l'estaque (33x41cm-13x16in) s. canvasboard painted c.1918 prov. 7-Nov-2 Christie's, Rockefeller NY #243/R est:35000-45000
£22535 $37408 €32000 La goulette, une rue (22x27cm-9x11in) s. init.i.d.26 verso cardboard prov.lit. 11-Jun-3 Beaussant & Lefèvre, Paris #95/R est:30000-35000
£24887 $41561 €36086 Le port d'Alger (33x46cm-13x18in) s. prov. 24-Jun-3 Koller, Zurich #108/R est:55000-70000 (S.FR 55000)
£25000 $41750 €36250 Vue d'Alger (22x33cm-9x13in) s. painted 1924-32 prov.lit. 25-Jun-3 Christie's, London #150/R est:15000-20000
£26582 $42000 €42000 Place du marche, Ghardaia (33x41cm-13x16in) s. panel prov.lit. 1-Dec-2 Anaf, Lyon #121/R est:80000
£32051 $50321 €50000 Port de Bougie (33x41cm-13x16in) s. canvas on masonite exhib. 13-Dec-2 Piasa, Paris #10/R est:45000
£34694 $55163 €51000 La place du marche, Ghardaia (33x41cm-13x16in) s. painted c.1921 prov.lit. 24-Mar-3 Rabourdin & Choppin de Janvry, Paris #166/R est:55000-60000
£35000 $57400 €52500 Plongeoir a la Frette (33x41cm-13x16in) s. canvas on board painted 1945 prov. 4-Feb-3 Christie's, London #289/R est:60000
£35000 $58450 €50750 Alger, le Palais Consulaire et la Place du Gouvernement (50x61cm-20x24in) s. painted 1920 prov.lit. 25-Jun-3 Christie's, London #160/R est:50000-70000

£41667	$65000	€62501	Fenetre ouverte sur la baie d'alger (55x38cm-22x15in) s. painted c.1943 prov. 6-Nov-2 Sotheby's, New York #183/R est:70000-90000
£47297	$73784	€70000	Agay, les roches rouges (65x81cm-26x32in) s. painted c.1905. 30-Mar-3 Anaf, Lyon #187/R
£55172	$87172	€80000	Femme nue couchee (46x55cm-18x22in) s.prov. 2-Apr-3 Christie's, Paris #1/R est:90000
£60000	$92400	€90000	Le Seine a poissy (51x61cm-20x24in) s. s.i.d.1929 verso prov. 22-Oct-2 Sotheby's, London #115/R est:60000-80000
£80000	$133600	€116000	Le gros olivier (65x82cm-26x32in) s. painted c.1943 prov.exhib.lit. 25-Jun-3 Christie's, London #162/R est:80000-120000
£83974	$131840	€131000	Pont transbordeur (65x81cm-26x32in) s.d.1912 prov.exhib. 10-Dec-2 Pierre Berge, Paris #47/R est:220000
£86538	$135865	€135000	Vieux port, Marseille (65x81cm-26x32in) s. painted c.1916-18 prov.exhib. 10-Dec-2 Pierre Berge, Paris #45/R est:220000
£90000	$147600	€135000	Port, temps calme (65x81cm-26x32in) s. painted c.1932-34 prov.exhib.lit. 5-Feb-3 Sotheby's, London #134/R est:150000
£95000	$155800	€142500	La Marne a Chenneviere (65x81cm-26x32in) s. painted c.1914. 4-Feb-3 Christie's, London #295/R est:150000
£98592	$163662	€140000	Tanger, le Palais de Justice (66x81cm-26x32in) s.d. prov.exhib.lit. 12-Jun-3 Tajan, Paris #35/R est:100000-120000

Works on paper

£230	$373	€350	Silhouette e militaire (6x6cm-2x2in) mono. pen dr. 22-Jan-3 Tajan, Paris #85/R
£362	$586	€550	Homme tenant un bebe (12x7cm-5x3in) mono. chl dr. 22-Jan-3 Tajan, Paris #86
£395	$640	€600	Etude de voiliers. mono. ink chl dr pair in one frame. 22-Jan-3 Tajan, Paris #77
£395	$640	€600	Fille de joie (10x15cm-4x6in) mono. ink dr. 22-Jan-3 Tajan, Paris #88
£414	$691	€600	Paysage (10x15cm-4x6in) init. ink dr. 10-Jul-3 Artcurial Briest, Paris #20
£426	$689	€600	Femme (23x17cm-9x7in) mono. chl double-sided. 23-May-3 Camard, Paris #57
£428	$693	€650	Pont sur la Seine (8x11cm-3x4in) mono. Indian ink. 22-Jan-3 Tajan, Paris #87/R
£428	$693	€650	Etude de voiliers (12x7cm-5x3in) mono. ink dr. 22-Jan-3 Tajan, Paris #90
£472	$750	€708	Paysage a jardin (24x30cm-9x12in) init. brush ink prov.exhib. 27-Feb-3 Christie's, Rockefeller NY #56/R
£527	$853	€800	Silhouette pres d'une maison (16x21cm-6x8in) mono. chl dr. 22-Jan-3 Tajan, Paris #82/R
£592	$959	€900	Femme au parapluie (12x7cm-5x3in) mono. chl dr. 22-Jan-3 Tajan, Paris #89
£719	$1151	€1000	Homme tenant un enfant (11x6cm-4x2in) init. chl dr double-sided. 18-May-3 Eric Pillon, Calais #83/R
£723	$1172	€1100	Sur les hauteurs de la ville (11x16cm-4x6in) mono. Indian ink. 22-Jan-3 Tajan, Paris #78
£759	$1267	€1100	Rouen, pont Transbordeur (10x17cm-4x7in) ink dr paper on cardboard. 10-Jul-3 Artcurial Briest, Paris #19
£798	$1300	€1197	Portrait of a man walking (13x9cm-5x4in) init. pen ink wash prov. 12-Feb-3 Sotheby's, New York #3/R est:600-800
£833	$1317	€1200	Personnage au bord d'un oued (19x11cm-7x4in) s. pen dr. 25-Apr-3 Piasa, Paris #16/R
£868	$1372	€1250	Oasis anime (10x19cm-4x7in) s. pen dr. 25-Apr-3 Piasa, Paris #17/R
£987	$1599	€1500	Le modele nu (17x10cm-7x4in) mono. pencil dr. 22-Jan-3 Tajan, Paris #84 est:800-1000
£1053	$1705	€1600	L'homme (26x17cm-10x7in) mono. Indian ink. 22-Jan-3 Tajan, Paris #83/R est:800-1000
£1154	$1812	€1800	Figures (32x23cm-13x9in) st.sig. pen dr. 13-Dec-2 Piasa, Paris #168
£1266	$1962	€2000	Au bord de la Marne (13x19cm-5x7in) init. ink paper on cardboard prov. 28-Sep-2 Christie's, Paris #8/R est:300-450
£1474	$2241	€2300	Nu allonge au canape (31x22cm-12x9in) s. Chinese ink dr. 16-Aug-2 Deauville, France #42/R
£1550	$2465	€2325	Porquerolles (10x16cm-4x6in) s. i.d.39 verso pen ink. 20-Mar-3 Sotheby's, Olympia #2/R est:600-800
£1944	$3072	€2800	Femme et enfants, Lagouat (19x28cm-7x11in) W/C. 25-Apr-3 Piasa, Paris #21/R est:4000
£2222	$3511	€3200	Cheval tirant charrette (15x26cm-6x10in) s. dr. 25-Apr-3 Piasa, Paris #18/R
£2237	$3624	€3400	L'etreinte (30x18cm-12x7in) mono. Indian ink. 22-Jan-3 Tajan, Paris #79/R est:2000-3000
£2431	$3840	€3500	Matinee sur le Danube (11x13cm-4x5in) s. W/C. 25-Apr-3 Piasa, Paris #22/R
£2695	$4366	€3800	Saint Jean de Luz (11x16cm-4x6in) s.i.d. W/C pencil prov.exhib. 21-May-3 Cornette de St.Cyr, Paris #22/R est:2000-3000
£2766	$4481	€3900	Saint Jean de Luz (12x17cm-5x7in) s.i.d. W/C pencil prov. 21-May-3 Cornette de St.Cyr, Paris #23/R est:2000-3000
£2895	$4689	€4400	Deux meres Algeriennes et un enfant (20x29cm-8x11in) s. W/C. 22-Jan-3 Tajan, Paris #81/R est:5000-7000
£2911	$4513	€4600	Port de Collioure (13x18cm-5x7in) init. ink paper on cardboard prov. 28-Sep-2 Christie's, Paris #7/R est:450-600
£3312	$5167	€5200	Port (13x19cm-5x7in) s. Chinese ink wash dr. 10-Nov-2 Eric Pillon, Calais #21/R
£3718	$5874	€5800	Venice (23x29cm-9x11in) s.i.d.36 W/C pencil. 14-Nov-2 Neumeister, Munich #625/R est:3000-3500
£3819	$6035	€5500	Danube (11x13cm-4x5in) s.i. W/C. 25-Apr-3 Piasa, Paris #23/R
£6250	$9875	€9000	Rue a Lagouat (24x16cm-9x6in) s.i.d.1929 W/C. 25-Apr-3 Piasa, Paris #20/R est:5000
£6835	$10935	€9500	Les Orientales (19x28cm-7x11in) s. W/C. 18-May-3 Eric Pillon, Calais #67/R
£6908	$11191	€10500	Bateaux dans le port (17x25cm-7x10in) s.i.d.1932 W/C. 22-Jan-3 Tajan, Paris #76/R est:4000-5500
£8489	$13583	€11800	Petits bateaux sur le lac (17x25cm-7x10in) s. W/C. 18-May-3 Eric Pillon, Calais #69/R
£11000	$18370	€15950	Venise (23x29cm-9x11in) s.d.36 W/C pencil. 24-Jun-3 Sotheby's, London #213/R est:8000-10000

MARQUET, Aristide (1796-?) French

£346	$536	€550	Nu oriental (27x21cm-11x8in) s.d.1833 panel. 30-Oct-2 Coutau Begarie, Paris #68/R

MARQUET, René-Paul (1875-?) French

Sculpture

£1500	$2370	€2250	Female figure (48cm-19in) s. cold painted gilt bronze. 14-Nov-2 Christie's, Kensington #211/R est:1500-2000
£6000	$9540	€9000	Kernalan Indian dancer (39cm-15in) gilt bronze on onyx pedestal. 27-Feb-3 Sotheby's, Olympia #180/R est:6000-8000

MARQUIS, J Richard (?-1885) British

£9615	$14904	€15000	Summer breeze, fishing boats making for Boulogne (75x121cm-30x48in) exhib. 3-Dec-2 Bonhams & James Adam, Dublin #22/R est:15000-20000

MARR, Carl Ritter von (1858-1936) German/American

£515	$814	€773	Reclining female nude in the dunes (55x69cm-22x27in) s. 29-Nov-2 Zofingen, Switzerland #2499/R (S.FR 1200)
£2746	$4559	€3900	Small goose herder (37x27cm-15x11in) s.i. panel. 14-Jun-3 Arnold, Frankfurt #803/R est:2400

Works on paper

£308	$481	€450	Jester and king (38x41cm-15x16in) mono. W/C gouache. 10-Apr-3 Allgauer, Kempten #2632/R
£342	$534	€500	Oriental bazaar (33x24cm-13x9in) mono. W/C gouache lit. 10-Apr-3 Allgauer, Kempten #2631/R
£570	$889	€900	Mythological composition (59x39cm-23x15in) W/C pencil. 18-Oct-2 Dr Fritz Nagel, Stuttgart #249/R

MARRCESY, Flora (?) ?

£260	$406	€390	Still life of lilac (78x101cm-31x40in) s. 19-Sep-2 John Bellman, Billingshurst #1481

MARREL, Jacob (1614-1681) Dutch

£42000	$65940	€63000	Tulips in vase with caterpillar and grasshopper (48x36cm-19x14in) s. panel oval prov.exhib. 11-Dec-2 Christie's, London #53/R est:30000-50000

Works on paper

£2564	$3974	€4000	Tulipe Isabella Gabriela (21x15cm-8x6in) i. gouache vellum prov.exhib. 6-Dec-2 Rieunier, Bailly-Pommery, Mathias, Paris #3/R

MARREL, Jacob (attrib) (1614-1681) Dutch

Works on paper

£2436	$3849	€3800	Tulips (19x15cm-7x6in) gouache four. 16-Nov-2 Lempertz, Koln #1260/R est:4000

MARRIS, Robert (attrib) (1750-1827) British

Works on paper

£280	$434	€420	River landscape (23x30cm-9x12in) W/C dr. 1-Oct-2 Capes Dunn, Manchester #827

MARS, Peter Joseph Lawrence (1874-1949) American

£897	$1400	€1346	Louisiana landscape (61x91cm-24x36in) s.d.1945. 12-Oct-2 Neal Auction Company, New Orleans #1348/R est:1200-1800

MARSANS, Luis (1930-) Spanish

Works on paper

£816	$1298	€1200	Coffe grinder (18x21cm-7x8in) s. graphite gouache prov. 26-Feb-3 Artcurial Briest, Paris #538/R est:1000-1200

MARSH, Mary C (fl.1912-1930) British

£270	$427	€405	Grakle, winner of the 1931 Grand National (43x55cm-17x22in) s. board. 27-Nov-2 Bonhams, Knowle #231

MARSH, Reginald (1898-1954) American

£1032	$1600	€1548	Seated girl (13x10cm-5x4in) init. masonite. 3-Dec-2 Christie's, Rockefeller NY #616/R est:2500-3500
£1039	$1600	€1559	Exotic dancer (11x14cm-4x6in) init. masonite. 4-Sep-2 Christie's, Rockefeller NY #363/R est:1500-2500
£2160	$3500	€3132	Two women (18x13cm-7x5in) s.d.51 masonite. 21-May-3 Doyle, New York #146/R est:2500-3500
£6707	$11000	€9725	Motorcycle (20x30cm-8x12in) s. tempera ink on paper exhib. 1-Jun-3 Wright, Chicago #181/R est:9000-12000

£24691 $40000 €35802 Waiting for the subway (76x56cm-30x22in) s. tempera paper on board. 21-May-3 Doyle, New York #145/R est:6000-8000
£41935 $65000 €62903 Broadway and East 14th street (92x30cm-36x12in) s.d.1952 masonite prov.exhib.lit. 5-Dec-2 Christie's, Rockefeller NY #111/R est:60000-80000
£77419 $120000 €116129 Food store - Death of Dillinger (71x51cm-28x20in) s.d.38 tempera on paper prov.exhib.lit. 4-Dec-2 Sotheby's, New York #77/R est:80000-120000
£483871 $750000 €725807 Wooden horses (61x102cm-24x40in) s. tempera on board painted 1936 prov.lit. 4-Dec-2 Sotheby's, New York #67/R est:300000-500000

Prints
£2044 $3250 €3066 Striptease at New Gotham (30x23cm-12x9in) s.i. etching edition of 40. 2-May-3 Sotheby's, New York #39/R est:4000-6000
£2830 $4500 €4245 Chop Suey dancers no 2 (17x28cm-7x11in) s. hand col etching. 2-May-3 Sotheby's, New York #37/R est:4000-6000
£3205 $5000 €4808 Gaiety burlesk (35x28cm-14x11in) s.num.36 etching. 5-Nov-2 Christie's, Rockefeller NY #92/R est:4000-6000
£5484 $8500 €8226 Barker (28x22cm-11x9in) s.num.5 etching. 25-Sep-2 Christie's, Rockefeller NY #27/R est:6000-8000
£5660 $9000 €8490 Tatoo-shave haircut (25x25cm-10x10in) s. by another hand etching. 2-May-3 Sotheby's, New York #38/R est:9000-12000

Works on paper
£382 $600 €573 Sketch of a young woman (8x5cm-3x2in) init.d.48 pen ink. 22-Nov-2 Skinner, Boston #196/R
£513 $800 €770 Two figures in front of a country schoolhouse (13x15cm-5x6in) i. dr. 1-Aug-2 Eldred, East Dennis #931/R
£715 $1100 €1073 Figure studies (23x30cm-9x12in) s. pencil pen ink wash. 4-Sep-2 Christie's, Rockefeller NY #362/R est:2000-4000
£915 $1500 €1327 Illustration studies. s.i. pen ink three. 5-Jun-3 Swann Galleries, New York #180/R est:1000-1500
£1509 $2400 €2264 Backyard (36x51cm-14x20in) s. indis d. W/C gouache pencil prov. 5-Mar-3 Christie's, Rockefeller NY #110/R est:3000-5000
£1948 $3000 €2922 Woman walking (25x20cm-10x8in) s.d.45 W/C prov. 4-Sep-2 Christie's, Rockefeller NY #361/R est:1500-2500
£2229 $3500 €3344 Brooklyn museum (43x36cm-17x14in) s.i. ink prov. 19-Nov-2 Butterfields, San Francisco #8074/R est:5000-7000
£3049 $5000 €4421 Young woman walking in a summer dress (70x52cm-28x20in) s.d. brush ink wash. 5-Jun-3 Swann Galleries, New York #179/R est:3000-5000
£3171 $5200 €4598 Industrial landscape (38x55cm-15x22in) s.d. W/C. 5-Jun-3 Swann Galleries, New York #178/R est:3000-5000
£3704 $6000 €5371 Coney Island (33x51cm-13x20in) s.d.1944 pen ink W/C paper on card. 21-May-3 Doyle, New York #151/R est:5000-7000
£7143 $11000 €10715 Study for the death of Dillinger (43x28cm-17x11in) s.i. ink W/C pastel exec.c.1934 prov. 8-Sep-2 Treadway Gallery, Cincinnati #684/R est:8000-10000
£9259 $15000 €13889 City street corner (55x76cm-22x30in) s.d.47 W/C double-sided prov. 21-May-3 Sotheby's, New York #121/R est:15000-25000
£29032 $45000 €43548 Bowery scene (78x57cm-31x22in) s.d.1944 W/C wash prov. 5-Dec-2 Christie's, Rockefeller NY #112/R est:60000-80000

MARSHALL, Ben (1767-1835) British
£7000 $11060 €10500 Sancho, bay pony (45x54cm-18x21in) s.d.1810 prov. 27-Nov-2 Christie's, London #43/R
£30000 $48600 €45000 Gentleman with a bay hunter and terrier in a landscape (84x100cm-33x39in) prov.exhib. 22-May-3 Christie's, London #37/R est:25000-35000

MARSHALL, Charles (1806-1896) British
Works on paper
£280 $451 €406 By the river (20x37cm-8x15in) s. W/C. 12-May-3 Joel, Victoria #368 (A.D 700)

MARSHALL, Charles Edward (fl.1872-1903) British
£2500 $4000 €3750 Portrait of a woman in Oriental dress holding a cigarette (102x76cm-40x30in) s.d.1911. 14-May-3 Butterfields, San Francisco #1148/R est:4000-6000

MARSHALL, Clark Summers (1861-1944) American
£1911 $3000 €2867 Boat on an inlet with farmhouse and rolling hills beyond (63x76cm-25x30in) s. prov. 19-Nov-2 Butterfields, San Francisco #8025/R est:3000-5000

MARSHALL, Frank H (1866-1934) American
£1355 $2250 €1965 High country (45x60cm-18x24in) s.d.1928 canvasboard. 11-Jun-3 Butterfields, San Francisco #4321/R est:3000-5000

MARSHALL, Herbert Menzies (1841-1913) British
Works on paper
£300 $495 €435 Street in Rotterdam (30x20cm-12x8in) s.d.1898 pencil W/C htd white lit. 3-Jul-3 Christie's, Kensington #160/R
£1100 $1760 €1650 Westminster from the river (14x22cm-6x9in) W/C htd white. 11-Mar-3 Bonhams, New Bond Street #90/R est:1200-1800
£1500 $2490 €2250 Winter morning, Westminster (21x17cm-8x7in) s.d.1881 W/C. 12-Jun-3 Bonhams, New Bond Street #693/R est:1500-2000
£2000 $3040 €3000 Frosty sunrise, Lambeth Palace (25x51cm-10x20in) s.d.1887 W/C. 15-Aug-2 Bonhams, New Bond Street #437/R est:2000-3000
£2900 $4524 €4350 Dusk on Westminster bridge (36x26cm-14x10in) s. W/C. 5-Nov-2 Bonhams, New Bond Street #148/R est:1500-2000

MARSHALL, John Fitz (1859-1932) British
£2300 $3588 €3450 Guardian (53x36cm-21x14in) s. s.verso. 6-Nov-2 Sotheby's, Olympia #164/R est:1000-1500

MARSHALL, R A K (1849-1902) British
Works on paper
£316 $480 €474 Weary traveller (22x38cm-9x15in) s. W/C. 19-Aug-2 Joel, Victoria #188 (A.D 900)
£561 $853 €842 Gateway and moat Michelham Priory (24x34cm-9x13in) s. W/C. 19-Aug-2 Joel, Victoria #198/R est:1200-1500 (A.D 1600)

MARSHALL, Richard (1944-) British
£1020 $1612 €1479 Summer on the beach at Scarborough, with donkeys (19x24cm-7x9in) s. board. 28-Jul-3 David Duggleby, Scarborough #292/R est:600-800

MARSHALL, Roberto Angelo Kittermaster (1849-1902) British
Works on paper
£250 $405 €375 Girl on a country lane in a rural landscape (34x59cm-13x23in) s. pencil W/C. 23-Jan-3 Christie's, Kensington #314
£350 $553 €525 Gateway and moat, Michelham Priory (25x34cm-10x13in) s. W/C bodycol. 26-Nov-2 Bonhams, Knightsbridge #21/R
£450 $729 €675 Young girl on a country path (33x58cm-13x23in) s. W/C. 23-May-3 Honiton Galleries, Honiton #689

MARSHALL, Vicky (1952-) Canadian
£214 $340 €321 Untitled landscape (20x29cm-8x11in) init. oil pastel paper. 6-Mar-3 Heffel, Vancouver #24/R (C.D 500)

MARSHALL, William Calder (1813-1894) British
Sculpture
£900 $1405 €1350 Bust of a girl (54cm-21in) s.d.1849 white marble bust. 18-Sep-2 Sotheby's, Olympia #334/R est:600-900

MARSHAM, Grace Margaret (19th C) British
£300 $456 €450 Portrait of Rubens first wife, Isabella Brandt (76x56cm-30x22in) d.1898 verso after Rubens. 16-Aug-2 Keys, Aylsham #272

MARSHINGTON, Philip (?) British?
£360 $569 €540 Coastal scene (44x59cm-17x23in) s. 27-Nov-2 Peter Wilson, Nantwich #17

MARSILLACH, Joaquim (1905-) Spanish
£1452 $2294 €2250 Landscape (54x74cm-21x29in) s. 17-Dec-2 Durán, Madrid #94/R

MARSTON, Charles Gordon (1898-1980) American
£256 $400 €384 Town street scene (53x64cm-21x25in) s. 11-Aug-2 Thomaston Place, Thomaston #100

MARSTON, Freda (1895-1949) British
£330 $545 €479 Cerne Abbass, Dorset (46x61cm-18x24in) s. 3-Jul-3 Christie's, Kensington #439
Works on paper
£350 $546 €525 Lake Orta near Varses (37x53cm-15x21in) s. i.verso W/C. 23-Apr-3 Rupert Toovey, Partridge Green #156

MARSTON, Harry (?) British
£360 $562 €540 Figure before an old watermill in landscape (23x33cm-9x13in) s.d.96. 11-Apr-3 Keys, Aylsham #663

MARSTON, Reginald St Clair (1886-1943) British
£520 $858 €754 Summer in the Alps (51x61cm-20x24in) s. 3-Jul-3 Christie's, Kensington #460/R

MARSTRAND, Wilhelm (1810-1873) Danish
£390 $617 €585 Interior scene with two women (31x25cm-12x10in) panel. 5-Apr-3 Rasmussen, Havnen #2158/R (D.KR 4200)
£746 $1187 €1119 Italian woman resting (60x38cm-24x15in) i.stretcher. 5-May-3 Rasmussen, Vejle #518/R (D.KR 8000)

£931 $1480 €1397 Portrait of Frederik Thekla Lutken (19x16cm-7x6in) painted c.1835. 5-Mar-3 Rasmussen, Copenhagen #1672/R (D.KR 10000)
£1914 $3100 €2775 Landscape from Leksand with peasants on Sunday outing in horse and cart (46x58cm-18x23in) mono.d.1860. 26-May-3 Rasmussen, Copenhagen #1167/R est:25000 (D.KR 20000)
£2043 $3227 €3065 Roman prisoner (46x33cm-18x13in) painted c.1837 prov. 2-Dec-2 Rasmussen, Copenhagen #1317/R est:20000-25000 (D.KR 24000)
£2979 $4706 €4469 From the Roman Carnival (45x33cm-18x13in) prov. 2-Dec-2 Rasmussen, Copenhagen #1147/R est:40000-50000 (D.KR 35000)
£3165 $5191 €4400 Olevano (51x53cm-20x21in) i. stretcher. 4-Jun-3 Reiss & Sohn, Konigstein #156/R est:4500

Works on paper

£255 $403 €383 Rider, possibly Sancho Panza (13x13cm-5x5in) pen prov. 27-Nov-2 Museumsbygningen, Copenhagen #27 (D.KR 3000)
£270 $435 €405 Three Italian girls talking (13x12cm-5x5in) pen pencil study prov. 26-Feb-3 Museumsbygningen, Copenhagen #113 (D.KR 3000)
£288 $464 €432 Carneval scene (18x14cm-7x6in) pen wash Indian ink prov. 26-Feb-3 Museumsbygningen, Copenhagen #112 (D.KR 3200)
£298 $471 €447 Profile studies of men (27x20cm-11x8in) with sig.verso pencil pen. 27-Nov-2 Museumsbygningen, Copenhagen #21 (D.KR 3500)
£315 $508 €473 Half draped female figure (19x11cm-7x4in) pencil wash pen prov. 26-Feb-3 Museumsbygningen, Copenhagen #89 (D.KR 3500)
£360 $580 €540 Maria visiting Elisabeth (45x36cm-18x14in) s. pen Indian ink wash prov. 26-Feb-3 Museumsbygningen, Copenhagen #70 (D.KR 4000)
£378 $609 €567 Women by well, Italy (19x26cm-7x10in) pencil. 26-Feb-3 Museumsbygningen, Copenhagen #84 (D.KR 4200)
£423 $701 €600 Ospizio di Cosimato in Rome (26x40cm-10x16in) i. Indian ink. 12-Jun-3 Hauswedell & Nolte, Hamburg #373/R
£494 $780 €741 Study of nude men and women dancing. Study of men (25x34cm-10x13in) init. pencil pen W/C double-sided. 27-Nov-2 Museumsbygningen, Copenhagen #89/R (D.KR 5800)
£861 $1309 €1292 Travellers in front of Caffe Greco (22x21cm-9x8in) s. studies verso pencil pen. 27-Aug-2 Rasmussen, Copenhagen #1987/R (D.KR 10000)
£1050 $1660 €1575 Italian woman spinning by window (55x39cm-22x15in) s.i.d.1847 pastel. 16-Nov-2 Crafoord, Lund #55/R est:3000 (S.KR 15000)

MARSTRAND, Wilhelm (attrib) (1810-1873) Danish

£359 $552 €539 Entrance to an Italian villa (55x36cm-22x14in) paper on canvas. 4-Sep-2 Kunsthallen, Copenhagen #191/R (D.KR 4200)
£696 $1079 €1100 Returning home from the harvest (29x40cm-11x16in) mono. 28-Sep-2 Hans Stahl, Hamburg #120/R

MARSZALKIEWICZ, Stanislaw (1789-1872) Polish

Miniatures

£5000 $7800 €7500 Officer wearing dark green coat silver embroidered collar (13cm-5in) s. gilt mounted black wood frame oval prov.exhib.lit. 5-Nov-2 Bonhams, New Bond Street #112/R est:5000-7000

MART, Frank Griffiths (fl.1892-1904) British

£360 $601 €522 Portrait of a young lady wearing a flower trimmed black dress (56x48cm-22x19in) s. 20-Jun-3 Keys, Aylsham #310

MARTEL, Jan and Joel (1896-1966) French

Sculpture

£1603 $2484 €2500 Coq chantant (36cm-14in) zinc panel. 9-Dec-2 Artcurial Briest, Paris #103/R
£2587 $4321 €3700 Chat assis (40x13x17cm-16x5x7in) s. varnished wood lit. 25-Jun-3 Tajan, Paris #27/R est:3500-4000
£3013 $4670 €4700 Moineau (18x7x7cm-7x3x3in) s. pat bronze exec.c.1924 prov. 7-Dec-2 Martinot & Savignat, Pontoise #130/R
£16455 $26000 €26000 Joueur de polo (60x61x11cm-24x24x4in) s.st.f.Susse num.EAII/IV brown pat bronze lit. 26-Nov-2 Tajan, Paris #90/R est:30000
£17986 $28777 €25000 Nu (90cm-35in) s. terracotta lit. 19-May-3 Tajan, Paris #63/R est:30000-35000
£17986 $28777 €25000 Joueur de polo (60x40x11cm-24x16x4in) s. black pat.bronze lit. 19-May-3 Tajan, Paris #66/R est:30000-35000
£18987 $29620 €30000 Joueur de polo (61x40x11cm-24x16x4in) s. num.III/IV black brown pat.bronze lit. 31-Jul-2 Tajan, Paris #27/R est:30000-40000

MARTELAERE, Lodewyck de (1819-1904) Belgian

£1931 $3090 €2800 Herdswoman with cows in the forest (34x42cm-13x17in) s. panel. 15-Mar-3 De Vuyst, Lokeren #94/R est:2700-3000

MARTEN, Dimitrij E (1860-1918) Russian

Works on paper

£352 $567 €500 Russian village (31x60cm-12x24in) s.d.1916 gouache. 10-May-3 Bukowskis, Helsinki #389/R

MARTEN, Elliot H (fl.1886-1910) British

Works on paper

£250 $390 €375 Chanctonbury from Lancing Clump (20x32cm-8x13in) W/C. 9-Oct-2 Woolley & Wallis, Salisbury #173/R
£360 $562 €540 Farm buildings on the downs (26x49cm-10x19in) s. W/C. 25-Mar-3 Bonhams, Knightsbridge #50/R
£440 $713 €660 Old Shoreham church (25x35cm-10x14in) s. W/C. 20-May-3 Sotheby's, Olympia #33/R
£560 $907 €840 View above Shoreham (24x54cm-9x21in) s. W/C. 20-May-3 Sotheby's, Olympia #34/R
£600 $990 €870 Highland track. View across the lowlands (18x25cm-7x10in) s. pencil W/C two. 3-Jul-3 Christie's, Kensington #110/R

MARTEN, John I (fl.1782-1808) British

Works on paper

£1300 $2080 €1950 At Faversham. Cottages by a road (25x33cm-10x13in) s.d.1803 W/C three. 11-Mar-3 Bonhams, New Bond Street #17/R est:1200-1800

MARTENS, Albert (?) ?

£943 $1472 €1500 Still life (66x87cm-26x34in) s. board lit. 20-Sep-2 Schloss Ahlden, Ahlden #1263/R est:1800

MARTENS, Alfred (1888-1936) Danish?

£595 $928 €893 Near Norre Virum bridge and church, evening (121x139cm-48x55in) s. painted c.1928-29 exhib. 5-Aug-2 Rasmussen, Vejle #235 (D.KR 7000)

MARTENS, Conrad (1801-1878) Australian

£8000 $12880 €12000 Forest scene, Illawarra (41x31cm-16x12in) s. i.verso board. 6-May-3 Christie's, Melbourne #133/R est:15000-20000 (A.D 20000)

Works on paper

£643 $1015 €965 Tower near Coolangatta (36x26cm-14x10in) i. W/C prov.exhib.lit. 27-Nov-2 Deutscher-Menzies, Melbourne #98/R est:2000-3000 (A.D 1800)
£786 $1234 €1179 Cunningham's gap (27x18cm-11x7in) i.d.Sep 11th 1852 pencil. 25-Nov-2 Christie's, Melbourne #418/R (A.D 2200)
£929 $1430 €1394 Untitled - boats (11x16cm-4x6in) pencil prov.exhib. 3-Sep-2 Shapiro, Sydney #389/R est:1800-2500 (A.D 2600)
£1000 $1540 €1500 New inn on the Ashburton Road near Birkington, 7 July 1831 (13x22cm-5x9in) i. pencil. 3-Sep-2 Shapiro, Sydney #431 (A.D 2800)
£1107 $1705 €1661 Clovelly, July 1824. Pew Torr (13x22cm-5x9in) i. pencil W/C two prov.exhib. 3-Sep-2 Shapiro, Sydney #429 est:2000-3000 (A.D 3100)
£1220 $1927 €1769 Untitled (14x21cm-6x8in) i.verso W/C prov. 22-Jul-3 Lawson Menzies, Sydney #168/R est:3500-4500 (A.D 3000)
£1786 $2768 €2679 Sydney harbour (17x28cm-7x11in) W/C. 29-Oct-2 Lawson Menzies, Sydney #72/R est:8000-10000 (A.D 5000)
£10687 $16885 €16031 View from Flagstaff Hill, Sydney, New South Wales (29x44cm-11x17in) s.d.1865 W/C htd bodycol prov. 2-Apr-3 Christie's, Melbourne #52/R est:20000-30000 (A.D 28000)
£12100 $18512 €18150 Road across the Blue Mountains with Mount Tomah in the distance (45x65cm-18x26in) s. W/C gouache executed 1845 prov.exhib. 26-Aug-2 Sotheby's, Paddington #532/R est:40000-80000 (A.D 34000)

MARTENS, Hans Ditlev Christian (1795-1864) German

£3349 $5426 €4856 From the Roman Campagna with shepherds resting with their flock (59x71cm-23x28in) s. 26-May-3 Rasmussen, Copenhagen #1116/R est:20000-30000 (D.KR 35000)

MARTENS, Johann Heinrich (1815-1843) German

£1397 $2221 €2096 Coastal landscape south of Helsingor (21x31cm-8x12in) 10-Mar-3 Rasmussen, Vejle #177/R est:20000 (D.KR 15000)

MARTENS, Luise Henriette von (attrib) (1828-1897) German

£4930 $7937 €7000 Mother and child (97x73cm-38x29in) s. 10-May-3 Bukowskis, Helsinki #363/R est:3000-4000

MARTENS, Max (1887-?) German
Works on paper
£385 $585 €600 Chiemgau landscape (45x60cm-18x24in) s. W/C. 11-Jul-2 Hugo Ruef, Munich #912
£833 $1267 €1300 On the Fraueninsel (40x58cm-16x23in) s. W/C. 11-Jul-2 Hugo Ruef, Munich #913/R

MARTENS, Willem Johannes (1838-1895) Dutch
£1646 $2567 €2600 Young lady with mandoline (44x37cm-17x15in) s.d.58 panel. 21-Oct-2 Glerum, Amsterdam #93/R est:2800-3200
£6500 $10205 €9750 Happy family (51x63cm-20x25in) s. 21-Nov-2 Christie's, Kensington #25/R est:7000-10000

MARTENS, Willy (1856-1927) Dutch
£786 $1234 €1179 Girl (54x73cm-21x29in) s. 25-Nov-2 Germann, Zurich #140/R est:2000-3000 (S.FR 1800)

MARTENSEN, Peter (20th C) Danish
£851 $1345 €1277 Still life of fruit, wine and mirror (70x116cm-28x46in) s.d.1983. 27-Nov-2 Museumsbygningen, Copenhagen #669/R (D.KR 10000)

MARTI Y ALSINA, Ramon (1826-1894) Spanish
£1447 $2345 €2200 Landscape with lake (25x44cm-10x17in) s.d.1851 cardboard. 21-Jan-3 Ansorena, Madrid #72/R
£2673 $4170 €4250 Nudes (14x12cm-6x5in) s. board pair. 23-Sep-2 Durán, Madrid #169/R
£2830 $4415 €4500 Seascape (24x40cm-9x16in) s. 23-Sep-2 Durán, Madrid #217/R
£3548 $5606 €5500 Saint Francis holding crucified Christ (94x61cm-37x24in) s.i. 18-Dec-2 Ansorena, Madrid #105/R

MARTIKAINEN, Olavi (1920-1979) Finnish
£340 $526 €540 The sun's admirers (96x76cm-38x30in) s.d.74. 6-Oct-2 Bukowskis, Helsinki #224/R

MARTIN (?) ?
£950 $1463 €1425 Portrait of Mary Anne Spencer (70x56cm-28x22in) s.i. 24-Oct-2 Christie's, Kensington #41/R

MARTIN, Agnes (1912-) American/Canadian
£258 $402 €387 Above the falls (61x76cm-24x30in) s. 25-Mar-3 Ritchie, Toronto #90/R (C.D 600)
£601266 $950000 €901899 Untitled no.14 (183x183cm-72x72in) s.verso acrylic graphite painted 1980 prov.exhib. 13-Nov-2 Christie's, Rockefeller NY #52/R est:700000-900000

Works on paper
£11875 $19000 €17813 Untitled (30x30cm-12x12in) s.d.77 W/C pencil ink prov. 14-May-3 Sotheby's, New York #227/R est:20000-30000
£39241 $62000 €58862 Untitled (20x20cm-8x8in) s.d.60 ink prov. 14-Nov-2 Christie's, Rockefeller NY #370/R est:60000-80000

MARTIN, Alex Louis (1887-1954) Belgian
£425 $684 €650 Fillette au jupon rose (75x55cm-30x22in) s.d.25. 20-Jan-3 Horta, Bruxelles #490
£475 $741 €750 Portrait de fillette a la poupee (93x77cm-37x30in) s. 15-Oct-2 Vanderkindere, Brussels #74

MARTIN, Andreas (attrib) (18th C) Dutch
£2064 $3262 €3200 Scenes de cour de ferme (13x15cm-5x6in) panel pair. 20-Dec-2 Tajan, Paris #123

MARTIN, C Hargrave (fl.1912-1919) British
Works on paper
£650 $929 €975 Fairies bed time (20x28cm-8x11in) s. W/C. 28-Feb-2 Greenslade Hunt, Taunton #387a/R

MARTIN, Clement (?) British?
£250 $403 €375 Iffley Mill, Oxford (48x74cm-19x29in) s. i.verso. 19-Feb-3 Mallams, Oxford #421/R

MARTIN, Conny (20th C) American
£417 $650 €626 Hondo Valley fruit stand (51x41cm-20x16in) painted c.1959. 19-Oct-2 David Dike, Dallas #127/R

MARTIN, David (fl.1887-1935) British
Works on paper
£280 $437 €420 Pittenweem (34x52cm-13x20in) s.i. W/C. 13-Sep-2 Lyon & Turnbull, Edinburgh #43/R
£360 $558 €540 Crail Harbour, with boats returning (33x50cm-13x20in) s. W/C. 7-Dec-2 Shapes, Edinburgh #302
£1000 $1590 €1500 Largo Harbour. Anstruther. Stonehaven Harbour (27x37cm-11x15in) s.i. W/C set of three. 6-Mar-3 Christie's, Kensington #145/R est:800-1200

MARTIN, David McLeod (1922-) British
£1000 $1630 €1500 Portland mill (91x96cm-36x38in) 14-Feb-3 Lyon & Turnbull, Edinburgh #57

MARTIN, Elias (1739-1818) Swedish
£8511 $13191 €12767 Landscape with Aspa Bruk (129x240cm-51x94in) prov.exhib.lit. 3-Dec-2 Bukowskis, Stockholm #414/R est:140000-160000 (S.KR 120000)

Works on paper
£465 $754 €674 Johan Wedholm in Bybacka (13x10cm-5x4in) s. W/C Indian ink prov. 26-May-3 Bukowskis, Stockholm #491/R (S.KR 6000)
£737 $1194 €1069 Seated boy (16x11cm-6x4in) s. W/C. 26-May-3 Bukowskis, Stockholm #490/R (S.KR 9500)
£3200 $5344 €4640 View of Stockholm (44x70cm-17x28in) pen blk ink W/C. 9-Jul-3 Sotheby's, London #72/R est:3000-4000

MARTIN, Eugène-Louis (1880-1954) Swiss
£266 $420 €399 Small boat (24x33cm-9x13in) s.d.45 i.verso panel. 29-Nov-2 Zofingen, Switzerland #2976 (S.FR 620)

MARTIN, Fletcher (1904-1979) American
£4870 $7500 €7305 Challenger (86x76cm-34x30in) s.i.verso prov. 24-Oct-2 Shannon's, Milford #43/R est:5000-7000

MARTIN, Gerald Trice (1893-1961) British
£500 $815 €750 Eggs and roses (36x44cm-14x17in) s. board prov.exhib. 13-Feb-3 Christie's, Kensington #241

MARTIN, Gilbert (19th C) ?
£1154 $1812 €1800 Panier de dahlias (38x46cm-15x18in) s. 15-Dec-2 Eric Pillon, Calais #58/R

MARTIN, H (?) ?
£380 $578 €570 Playtime (31x41cm-12x16in) s. 29-Aug-2 Christie's, Kensington #200
£1000 $1600 €1500 Estate, Bedminster, NJ (51x61cm-20x24in) s. lit. 12-Jan-3 William Jenack, New York #216

MARTIN, Henri (19th C) French
£5594 $9343 €8000 Dans la serre (46x32cm-18x13in) s.d.1873 pair. 25-Jun-3 Sotheby's, Paris #82/R est:8000-12000

MARTIN, Henri (1860-1943) French
£7362 $12000 €11043 Portrait d'une jeune fille (38x25cm-15x10in) s. board prov. 12-Feb-3 Sotheby's, New York #111/R est:12000-18000
£7692 $12846 €11000 Bateau au port. Paysage du Lot (46x38cm-18x15in) s. panel double-sided. 30-Jun-3 Pierre Berge, Paris #57/R est:15000-20000
£11538 $18115 €18000 Arbre fleuri (38x46cm-15x18in) s. prov. 10-Dec-2 Pierre Berge, Paris #22/R est:20000
£12179 $19122 €19000 Port de Marseille (46x38cm-18x15in) s. panel prov. 10-Dec-2 Pierre Berge, Paris #21/R est:25000
£12821 $20000 €19232 Nature morte (60x37cm-24x15in) s. prov. 6-Nov-2 Sotheby's, New York #163/R est:25000-35000
£16770 $27000 €25155 Vase de fleurs (48x46cm-19x18in) s. panel prov. 7-May-3 Sotheby's, New York #152/R est:25000-35000
£17308 $27000 €25962 Deux paysans (55x38cm-22x15in) s. prov. 6-Nov-2 Sotheby's, New York #185/R est:25000-35000
£18000 $29520 €27000 Bassin de la Reine, Versailles (69x81cm-27x32in) s. canvas on cardboard painted c.1920. 4-Feb-3 Christie's, London #244/R est:24000
£18000 $29520 €27000 Vue de la bastide du vert (42x57cm-17x22in) s.i. painted c.1900 prov. 5-Feb-3 Sotheby's, London #123/R est:30000
£18710 $29561 €29000 Autoportrait. Paysage (53x38cm-21x15in) s. panel double-sided prov. 17-Dec-2 Rossini, Paris #109/R
£21203 $33500 €33500 Bassin de Marquayrol (67x100cm-26x39in) s. 2-Dec-2 Rieunier, Paris #16/R est:50000
£23776 $39706 €34000 Le pont dans la vallee du Vert (73x90cm-29x35in) s. 30-Jun-3 Pierre Berge, Paris #55/R est:60000-70000
£25641 $40256 €40000 Cote mediterraneenne (43x59cm-17x23in) s. prov. 10-Dec-2 Pierre Berge, Paris #23/R est:40000
£30000 $50100 €43500 Le pont de Labastide du vert, vue de l'Ouest (47x48cm-19x19in) s. painted c.1920 prov. 25-Jun-3 Christie's, London #134/R est:30000-40000
£30449 $47500 €45674 Portrait de femme (65x46cm-26x18in) s. prov. 6-Nov-2 Sotheby's, New York #158/R est:40000-60000
£32051 $50000 €48077 La prairie (54x73cm-21x29in) s. prov. 7-Nov-2 Christie's, Rockefeller NY #244/R est:35000-45000
£33108 $51649 €49000 Reverie (46x56cm-18x22in) s. 26-Mar-3 Millon & Associes, Paris #67/R est:55000

£38462 $60000 €57693 Groupe de maisons a Saint-Cirq-Lapopie (72x93cm-28x37in) s. painted 1920 prov. 7-Nov-2 Christie's, Rockefeller NY #231/R est:60000-80000
£41667 $65000 €62501 Jeune fille lisant (73x50cm-29x20in) s. i.verso prov. 6-Nov-2 Sotheby's, New York #171/R est:40000-60000
£45000 $75150 €65250 La pergola a marqueyrol (66x71cm-26x28in) s. panel painted 1930-40. 24-Jun-3 Sotheby's, London #132/R est:50000-70000
£59006 $95000 €88509 Garcon au bord du bassin, jardin du Luxembourg (65x54cm-26x21in) s. painted 1932-35 prov. 8-May-3 Christie's, Rockefeller NY #143/R est:60000-80000
£70513 $110000 €105770 Le bassin de Marquayrol (81x83cm-32x33in) s. prov. 7-Nov-2 Christie's, Rockefeller NY #260/R est:120000-160000
£76923 $120000 €115385 Le bassin sud-est de parc de Marquayrol (83x85cm-33x33in) s. i.on stretcher painted c.1930 prov. 7-Nov-2 Christie's, Rockefeller NY #252/R est:120000-160000
£86806 $137153 €125000 La riviere au bas de la Bastide (84x78cm-33x31in) s. 23-Apr-3 Rabourdin & Choppin de Janvry, Paris #23/R est:150000
£100000 $167000 €145000 Le pont a Labastide du vert au printemps (90x120cm-35x47in) s.d.1911 prov. 25-Jun-3 Christie's, London #138/R est:100000-150000
£108974 $170000 €163461 Le pont de la Bastide du vert (90x110cm-35x43in) s. painted c.1905 prov. 6-Nov-2 Sotheby's, New York #152/R est:120000-180000

MARTIN, Henry (1835-1908) British
£780 $1271 €1170 Newlyn (13x20cm-5x8in) s.i. pair. 13-Feb-3 David Lay, Penzance #20
£1500 $2324 €2250 Portrait of General Terry, XV hussars (40x32cm-16x13in) 3-Dec-2 Sotheby's, Olympia #52/R est:800-1400
£1700 $2839 €2465 Mounts Bay (13x22cm-5x9in) s. i.verso panel pair. 19-Jun-3 Lane, Penzance #430/R est:1700-2000

Works on paper
£420 $647 €630 View of St Michaels Mount, Cornwall (48x69cm-19x27in) s. W/C. 22-Oct-2 Sworder & Son, Bishops Stortford #656a/R

MARTIN, Henry Byam (1837-1902) Canadian
Works on paper
£244 $401 €366 Lynmouth, Devon (30x47cm-12x19in) s. W/C. 3-Jun-3 Joyner, Toronto #575 (C.D 550)

MARTIN, Hernandez (1940-) Spanish
£422 $616 €650 Beach scene (54x73cm-21x29in) s. board. 17-Jun-2 Ansorena, Madrid #135/R

MARTIN, Jacques (1844-1919) French
£1899 $2962 €3000 Pivoines (54x64cm-21x25in) s. 20-Oct-2 Anaf, Lyon #192/R est:3000-3500

MARTIN, James Kay (fl.1865-1885) British
£900 $1404 €1350 Duet - vocal and instrumental (46x37cm-18x15in) s. 10-Sep-2 Bonhams, Knightsbridge #46/R

MARTIN, Jason (1970-) British
£7000 $10780 €10500 Goldi Oldie no.6 (180x190cm-71x75in) oil cotton duck canvas painted 1995 prov. 23-Oct-2 Christie's, London #224/R est:8000-12000

Works on paper
£7000 $11690 €10150 Untitled - trevalley I-V (30x26cm-12x10in) s.d.Feb 95 blue pigment set of six. 27-Jun-3 Christie's, London #273/R est:7000-9000

MARTIN, Johan Fredrik (1755-1816) Swedish
Works on paper
£1939 $3142 €2812 Norrstrom and Gullo slopes and Ekeblad lock by Trollhatta (37x54cm-15x21in) s. W/C. 26-May-3 Bukowskis, Stockholm #506a/R est:20000-25000 (S.KR 25000)
£3404 $5277 €5106 The Royal Palace Drottningholm (35x51cm-14x20in) i. W/C over etching lit. 4-Dec-2 AB Stockholms Auktionsverk #1616/R est:35000-40000 (S.KR 48000)
£3546 $5496 €5319 Northern Malm's Square (35x51cm-14x20in) i. W/C over line etching lit. 4-Dec-2 AB Stockholms Auktionsverk #1615/R est:40000-50000 (S.KR 50000)
£4399 $7214 €6379 Vue de Stockholm vers la Mer Baltique (37x54cm-15x21in) W/C over etching lit. 4-Jun-3 AB Stockholms Auktionsverk #2134/R est:50000-60000 (S.KR 56000)

MARTIN, John (1789-1854) British
£1500000 $2415000 €2250000 Pandemonium (123x184cm-48x72in) s.d.1841. 19-Feb-3 Christie's, London #3/R est:800000-1200000

Works on paper
£300 $474 €450 Landscape with castle (13x19cm-5x7in) W/C. 27-Nov-2 Hamptons Fine Art, Godalming #160/R
£650 $1027 €975 Castle by a bridge (13x19cm-5x7in) W/C. 27-Nov-2 Hamptons Fine Art, Godalming #159/R
£780 $1208 €1170 Parkland with manor house in the distance (12x20cm-5x8in) W/C grey wash. 3-Dec-2 Sotheby's, Olympia #23/R
£1000 $1600 €1450 Along the Tiber, view of Castel Sant'Angelo and St Peter's Basilica (47x65cm-19x26in) s.i. W/C graphite gouache paper on board. 16-May-3 Skinner, Boston #115/R est:600-800
£24000 $39840 €36000 Nymph bathing by a lake in a woodland (61x89cm-24x35in) s. W/C over pencil htd bodycol gum arabic. 12-Jun-3 Sotheby's, London #134/R est:25000-35000

MARTIN, John Jack (1904-1965) Canadian
£258 $402 €387 Facade at Bamburg (28x36cm-11x14in) s.i.d.1954. 25-Mar-3 Ritchie, Toronto #165 (C.D 600)
£333 $546 €500 Morning (40x50cm-16x20in) s. board prov. 3-Jun-3 Joyner, Toronto #445/R (C.D 750)

MARTIN, Jolanda (1968-) Spanish
£353 $554 €550 Aerial transit XXX (80x60cm-31x24in) s.i.d.2002 verso acrylic board. 23-Nov-2 Meeting Art, Vercelli #13/R

MARTIN, Keith (20th C) American
Works on paper
£577 $900 €866 Elegant journey (36x46cm-14x18in) s.d.1957 s.i.d.verso gouache board. 10-Nov-2 Selkirks, St. Louis #876

MARTIN, Mandy (1952-) Australian
£1643 $2563 €2465 Abyss (135x244cm-53x96in) s.i.d.1991 verso linen prov. 11-Nov-2 Deutscher-Menzies, Melbourne #117/R est:5000-7000 (A.D 4600)
£3600 $5796 €5400 Brown coal to oil site (180x396cm-71x156in) s.i.d.1990 oil on linen prov. 6-May-3 Christie's, Melbourne #325/R est:8000-12000 (A.D 9000)

MARTIN, Martin (1792-1865) German
£775 $1208 €1163 Carved sawtooth (60x50cm-24x20in) s. 21-Oct-2 Australian Art Auctions, Sydney #150 (A.D 2200)

MARTIN, Noel (20th C) American
£579 $950 €840 Untitled (38x48cm-15x19in) s.d.1947 verso oil sand on board. 1-Jun-3 Wright, Chicago #131/R

MARTIN, Paul (1821-1901) German
£2651 $4215 €3977 Kitchen interior with dog and two children steeling apples (73x60cm-29x24in) s. 26-Feb-3 Kunsthallen, Copenhagen #548/R est:18000 (D.KR 29000)

MARTIN, R (19th C) French?
£1370 $2151 €2000 Untitled (50x65cm-20x26in) s.d.1962 exhib. 15-Apr-3 Laurence Calmels, Paris #4304/R est:200

MARTIN, Ronald Albert (1943-) Canadian
£4000 $6560 €6000 Unconscious (229x154cm-90x61in) s.i.d.Sept 18 1978 acrylic prov. 27-May-3 Sotheby's, Toronto #58/R est:8000-10000 (C.D 9000)
£6222 $10204 €9333 Fragments of occurrence (229x154cm-90x61in) s.i.d.Nov 18 1978 prov.lit. 27-May-3 Sotheby's, Toronto #57/R est:8000-10000 (C.D 14000)

MARTIN, S (19th C) British
£800 $1320 €1160 After a fast forty minutes, with the hounds and huntsmen (48x74cm-19x29in) s.i.d.1901 set of three. 3-Jul-3 Duke & Son, Dorchester #237

MARTIN, Sylvester (fl.1856-1906) British
£560 $930 €812 Gamekeeper with his dogs (20x15cm-8x6in) s. panel. 12-Jun-3 Christie's, Kensington #291/R
£800 $1328 €1160 Tally ho! (25x46cm-10x18in) s. 12-Jun-3 Christie's, Kensington #15/R

MARTIN, Thomas Mower (1838-1934) Canadian
£239 $373 €399 Untitled - Spaniel (36x26cm-14x10in) s. oil paper board prov. 13-Apr-3 Levis, Calgary #505 (C.D 550)
£300 $469 €450 Cattle by a creek (43x66cm-17x26in) s. 25-Mar-3 Ritchie, Toronto #54/R (C.D 700)
£533 $875 €800 West coast (26x61cm-10x24in) s. board. 3-Jun-3 Joyner, Toronto #255/R est:1000-1200 (C.D 1200)
£1156 $1895 €1734 On the portage, northern Ontario (27x42cm-11x17in) s. prov. 3-Jun-3 Joyner, Toronto #420/R est:800-1200 (C.D 2600)
£1778 $2916 €2667 Cattle watering at pasture stream (77x127cm-30x50in) s. prov. 27-May-3 Sotheby's, Toronto #71/R est:5000-7000 (C.D 4000)
£1867 $3061 €2801 In search of a dinner (40x50cm-16x20in) s. 3-Jun-3 Joyner, Toronto #368/R est:2000-3000 (C.D 4200)
£4000 $6560 €6000 Indian encampment (76x127cm-30x50in) s,. 27-May-3 Sotheby's, Toronto #211/R est:9000-12000 (C.D 9000)
Works on paper
£178 $292 €258 Homesteads overlooking the lake (26x44cm-10x17in) s. W/C. 9-Jun-3 Hodgins, Calgary #74/R (C.D 400)
£289 $473 €434 In the Rockies (49x31cm-19x12in) s.d.1898 W/C. 3-Jun-3 Joyner, Toronto #473 (C.D 650)
£359 $574 €539 Rocky mountains (21x50cm-8x20in) s.i.d.1898 W/C prov. 15-May-3 Heffel, Vancouver #50 (C.D 800)
£422 $692 €612 Country road (23x36cm-9x14in) s.d.1919 W/C. 9-Jun-3 Hodgins, Calgary #368/R est:700-900 (C.D 950)

MARTIN-FERRIERES, Jac (1893-1972) French
£1179 $1863 €1769 Bouquet (62x50cm-24x20in) s.d.31. 17-Nov-2 Koller, Geneva #1243/R (S.FR 2700)
£2000 $3260 €3000 Nature morte (59x45cm-23x18in) s. 3-Feb-3 Bonhams, New Bond Street #36/R est:2500-3500
£2797 $4671 €4000 Place animee sous la neige (55x65cm-22x26in) s. 26-Jun-3 Tajan, Paris #277/R est:4600-6000
£3000 $4770 €4500 Bouquet de roses (64x53cm-25x21in) s.d.46. 20-Mar-3 Sotheby's, Olympia #63/R est:3000-4000
£3019 $4800 €4529 Jardin anglais (60x81cm-24x32in) s. prov. 27-Feb-3 Christie's, Rockefeller NY #108/R est:8000
£6000 $9240 €9000 Fleurs en foule - mon jardin (81x100cm-32x39in) s. prov. 22-Oct-2 Sotheby's, London #200/R est:6000-8000
£6748 $11000 €10122 La bastide du vert, la route ombragee (65x85cm-26x33in) s.d.1923 prov. 12-Feb-3 Sotheby's, New York #39/R est:10000-15000

MARTIN-KAVEL, François (1861-1918) French
£4430 $7000 €6645 Lady with a parasol (93x73cm-37x29in) s. prov. 24-Apr-3 Sotheby's, New York #157/R est:7000-9000
£5000 $8100 €7500 Reclining nude (65x81cm-26x32in) s. 20-May-3 Sotheby's, Olympia #406/R est:3000-5000

MARTINE, Martine (1932-) French
£2128 $3447 €3000 Orage (116x89cm-46x35in) s. 23-May-3 Camard, Paris #183/R est:3000-3800

MARTINEAU, Edith (1842-1909) British
Works on paper
£1200 $1860 €1800 Horse drawn plough at work in the fields with extensive landscape in the distance (30x48cm-12x19in) s.d.1889 W/C. 3-Oct-2 Ewbank, Send #514/R est:600-1000
£1700 $2703 €2550 Outside the kitchen door (24x17cm-9x7in) s.d.1879 W/C. 4-Mar-3 Bearnes, Exeter #393/R est:400-600

MARTINELLI, Ezio (1913-1980) American
Works on paper
£637 $1000 €956 Untitled (24x38cm-9x15in) s. ink dr. 19-Nov-2 Wright, Chicago #173/R est:1000-1500

MARTINELLI, Giovanni (attrib) (1610-1659) Italian
£709 $1099 €1064 The art's Muse (64x51cm-25x20in) 4-Dec-2 AB Stockholms Auktionsverk #2044/R (S.KR 10000)

MARTINELLI, Nicholas (20th C) American
£281 $450 €422 Bathers in a classical landscape (86x74cm-34x29in) indis sig. 8-Jan-3 Doyle, New York #52/R

MARTINET, Pierre (1781-?) French
Works on paper
£3077 $4862 €4800 Battle scenes (31x44cm-12x17in) pen wash set of 4. 18-Nov-2 Sotheby's, Paris #20/R est:7000

MARTINETTI, Angelo (19th C) Italian
£1100 $1749 €1650 Courting couple (41x27cm-16x11in) s.d.1870. 27-Feb-3 Bonhams, Chester #256/R est:1200-1600

MARTINEZ (19th C) French
£1854 $3023 €2800 Chiens de chasse (65x54cm-26x21in) s. 2-Feb-3 Perrin, Versailles #1/R

MARTINEZ CELAYA, Enrique (1964-) Mexican
Sculpture
£7317 $12000 €10976 Quiet night, dirt (102cm-40in) dirt fibreglass resin exec.2000 prov.exhib. 28-May-3 Christie's, Rockefeller NY #53/R est:15000-20000

MARTINEZ CHECA, Fernando (?) Spanish
£608 $949 €900 Vase of flowers (74x40cm-29x16in) s. 25-Mar-3 Durán, Madrid #719/R
£608 $949 €900 Vase of flowers (74x40cm-29x16in) s. 25-Mar-3 Durán, Madrid #720/R
£805 $1297 €1200 Flowers (50x23cm-20x9in) s. pair. 18-Feb-3 Durán, Madrid #646/R

MARTINEZ DE LEON, Andres (1895-1978) Spanish
£245 $387 €368 Bulls in the field (50x64cm-20x25in) s. 14-Nov-2 Louis Morton, Mexico #22 (M.P 4000)
£245 $387 €368 Bulls in the field (50x64cm-20x25in) s. 14-Nov-2 Louis Morton, Mexico #65 (M.P 4000)
Works on paper
£377 $588 €550 Seville Fair (18x24cm-7x9in) s. W/C. 8-Apr-3 Ansorena, Madrid #407/R

MARTINEZ DE PEDROSA, Carlota Rosales (1872-1958) Spanish
£628 $993 €980 Landscape with trees (16x26cm-6x10in) s.i. board. 13-Nov-2 Ansorena, Madrid #276/R

MARTINEZ NOVILLO, Cirilo (1921-) Spanish
£4808 $7596 €7500 Houses (55x65cm-22x26in) s. 13-Nov-2 Ansorena, Madrid #36/R
Works on paper
£705 $1114 €1100 View of village (16x24cm-6x9in) s. W/C. 13-Nov-2 Ansorena, Madrid #205/R
£1447 $2228 €2300 Landscape with houses (24x33cm-9x13in) s. W/C wax crayon. 28-Oct-2 Segre, Madrid #123/R

MARTINEZ ORTIZ, Nicolas (1907-1990) Spanish
Works on paper
£321 $506 €500 Flags (22x16cm-9x6in) s. col dr. 19-Nov-2 Durán, Madrid #100/R
£355 $561 €550 Church (21x16cm-8x6in) s. dr. 17-Dec-2 Durán, Madrid #22/R

MARTINEZ PEDRO, Luis (1910-1990) Cuban
Works on paper
£889 $1476 €1289 Fishermen (71x58cm-28x23in) s.d.41 crayon prov. 16-Jun-3 Waddingtons, Toronto #209/R est:2000-3000 (C.D 2000)

MARTINEZ TARRASSO, Casimiro (1900-1980) Spanish
£1509 $2325 €2400 Majorca (16x22cm-6x9in) s. board painted 1948. 28-Oct-2 Segre, Madrid #99/R
£2516 $3925 €4000 Majorca (22x27cm-9x11in) s. s.i.1948 verso board. 17-Sep-2 Segre, Madrid #116/R

MARTINEZ VAZQUEZ, Eduardo (1886-1971) Spanish
£1921 $2805 €2882 Mas Andaluz (60x79cm-24x31in) s. 4-Jun-2 Germann, Zurich #108/R est:2500-3500 (S.FR 4400)
Works on paper
£2673 $4170 €4250 Landscape by Guisando, near Avila (75x110cm-30x43in) s. 23-Sep-2 Durán, Madrid #216/R

MARTINEZ, Alfredo Ramos (1872-1946) Mexican
£17516 $27500 €26274 Resting (33x41cm-13x16in) s. i.verso tempera pastel paper painted 1945 prov.lit. 19-Nov-2 Sotheby's, New York #83/R est:18000
£30255 $47500 €45383 Yalala (33x41cm-13x16in) s. tempera pastel paper painted c.1945 prov.lit. 19-Nov-2 Sotheby's, New York #84/R est:18000
£32012 $52500 €46417 El almuerzo (61x67cm-24x26in) s. board painted c.1942 prov. 27-May-3 Sotheby's, New York #8
£229299 $360000 €343949 Indian wedding (76x86cm-30x34in) s. painted c.1934 prov. 19-Nov-2 Sotheby's, New York #15/R est:175000
Works on paper
£7927 $13000 €11494 Virgen de San Juan (56x42cm-22x17in) s. gouache pastel newsprint prov. 27-May-3 Sotheby's, New York #96
£9446 $14736 €14169 Indio sentado (57x43cm-22x17in) s.d.Mayo 7 1933 mixed media newspaper. 17-Oct-2 Louis Morton, Mexico #82/R est:130000-150000 (M.P 150000)

£11585 $19000 €17378 Flores alucinogenas (173x38cm-68x15in) s. gouache pastel paper on masonite painted c.1935 two prov. 28-May-3 Christie's, Rockefeller NY #9/R est:25000-30000
£14013 $22000 €21020 Our Lady of Loneliness (51x47cm-20x19in) s. gouache chl pen ink exec.1942. 20-Nov-2 Christie's, Rockefeller NY #127/R est:18000-22000
£17516 $27500 €26274 Basket with flowers (57x73cm-22x29in) s. pastel board. 19-Nov-2 Sotheby's, New York #72/R est:18000

MARTINEZ, Domingo (attrib) (c.1688-1750) Spanish
£7000 $10990 €10500 Dream of Saint Joseph (90x113cm-35x44in) copper. 12-Dec-2 Sotheby's, London #190/R est:7000-10000

MARTINEZ, Gabrielle (?) ?
£1456 $2271 €2300 Moissons (71x91cm-28x36in) s. 20-Oct-2 Anaf, Lyon #194/R est:2500-3000

MARTINEZ, Julian (1879-1943) American
Works on paper
£875 $1400 €1313 Untitled (28x35cm-11x14in) s. W/C. 13-Jan-3 Christie's, Rockefeller NY #58/R

MARTINEZ, Ramon (19th C) Philippino
£3873 $6430 €5500 Portrait of a Spanish lady (30x26cm-12x10in) s. i.d.1934 verso panel. 14-Jun-3 Arnold, Frankfurt #804/R est:600

MARTINEZ, Raymundo (1938-) Mexican
£3092 $4947 €4483 Paisaje del Valle de Mexico (70x150cm-28x59in) s.d.24 V 58. 15-May-3 Louis Morton, Mexico #125/R est:55000-65000 (M.P 50000)

MARTINEZ, Ricardo (1918-) Mexican
£2215 $3500 €3323 Untitled - female head with fruit basket (56x41cm-22x16in) s.d.1959. 22-Apr-3 Butterfields, San Francisco #6032/R est:4000-6000
£3797 $6000 €5696 Untitled - man eating ice cream (66x51cm-26x20in) s.d.55. 22-Apr-3 Butterfields, San Francisco #6033/R est:6000-8000
£7051 $11000 €10577 La platica (50x150cm-20x59in) s.d.56 prov. 14-Oct-2 Butterfields, San Francisco #2142/R est:10000-15000
£10976 $18000 €15915 Figura en fondo verde (85x115cm-33x45in) s.d.63. 27-May-3 Sotheby's, New York #106
£14013 $22000 €21020 Couple (80x125cm-31x49in) s.d.1957 i.on stretcher prov.exhib. 20-Nov-2 Christie's, Rockefeller NY #135/R est:16000-18000
£21341 $35000 €30944 Figura y acente (109x200cm-43x79in) s.d.63 prov. 27-May-3 Sotheby's, New York #101

MARTINEZ, Xavier (1869-1943) American
£2640 $4250 €3960 Landscape, haymaking (20x13cm-8x5in) mono. board prov. 18-Feb-3 John Moran, Pasadena #128 est:1500-2500
£2866 $4500 €4299 Gate to the mission (41x51cm-16x20in) mono. prov. 19-Nov-2 Butterfields, San Francisco #8176/R est:3000-5000

MARTINI, Alberto (1876-1954) Italian
£4795 $7527 €7000 Venus' mirror (27x35cm-11x14in) s. panel. 15-Apr-3 Laurence Calmels, Paris #4355/R est:6000
£13699 $21370 €20000 Portrait of Andre Breton (36x29cm-14x11in) s. canvas on panel lit. 14-Apr-3 Laurence Calmels, Paris #4002/R est:8000
£13699 $21507 €20000 Cortege de Venus (35x50cm-14x20in) s. cardboard. 15-Apr-3 Laurence Calmels, Paris #4357/R est:8000
£14384 $22582 €21000 Look movement (27x35cm-11x14in) s. oil tempera cardboard. 15-Apr-3 Laurence Calmels, Paris #4356/R est:4000
Works on paper
£327 $523 €500 Plant (28x33cm-11x13in) init. mixed media exec.1894. 4-Jan-3 Meeting Art, Vercelli #472
£513 $795 €800 Ile de la Fee (27x18cm-11x7in) s. pencil. 4-Dec-2 Finarte, Milan #187
£1090 $1689 €1700 Female nude (28x18cm-11x7in) s. Chinese ink. 4-Dec-2 Finarte, Milan #213/R

MARTINI, Arturo (1889-1947) Italian
Sculpture
£1667 $2617 €2600 Bathers (26cm-10in) s. ceramic. 19-Nov-2 Finarte, Milan #284/R
£1923 $2808 €3000 Jesus naked (38x29cm-15x11in) terracotta. 5-Jun-2 Il Ponte, Milan #103/R
£2135 $3373 €3330 Untitled (27cm-11in) terracotta. 12-Nov-2 Babuino, Rome #315/R
£4054 $6324 €6000 Woman in the wind (35cm-14in) s. bronze lit. 26-Mar-3 Finarte Semenzato, Milan #340/R
£11348 $18383 €16000 Cavallino "Peroni" (21x30x10cm-8x12x4in) s.base terracotta lit. 26-May-3 Christie's, Milan #257/R est:10000-15000
£17308 $25269 €27000 Procession (54x40x9cm-21x16x4in) stone exec.1933 prov.exhib.lit. 5-Jun-2 Il Ponte, Milan #93/R est:30000-40000
£17949 $26205 €28000 King trilogy (90x35x40cm-35x14x16in) terracotta prov. 5-Jun-2 Il Ponte, Milan #98/R est:30000-40000
£141026 $205897 €220000 Woman from Pisa II (132x36x60cm-52x14x24in) s. bronze prov.lit. 5-Jun-2 Il Ponte, Milan #95/R est:200000-250000

MARTINI, Biagio (1761-1840) Italian
Works on paper
£280 $400 €420 Mary Magdalene (28x19cm-11x7in) red black white chk over pencil. 23-Jan-3 Swann Galleries, New York #164/R

MARTINI, Herbert E (1896-?) American
£566 $900 €849 Cattle watering. Wooded landscape (30x46cm-12x18in) s.d.1914-15 pair. 7-Mar-3 Jackson's, Cedar Falls #738/R est:750-1000

MARTINI, Max (1867-1920) German
£540 $885 €750 Valley in spring (51x76cm-20x30in) s.d.1911. 5-Jun-3 Dorotheum, Salzburg #527/R

MARTINI, Vivaldo (1908-1989) Italian
£278 $447 €417 Standing female nude (41x27cm-16x11in) s.d.49. 7-May-3 Dobiaschofsky, Bern #3435 (S.FR 600)

MARTINO, Antonio Pietro (1902-1989) American
£1317 $2200 €1910 Baileys Island (41x61cm-16x24in) s. s.i.on stretcher. 22-Jun-3 Freeman, Philadelphia #144/R est:2500-4000
£1497 $2500 €2171 Mixed bouquet (51x20cm-20x8in) s. s.i.on stretcher. 22-Jun-3 Freeman, Philadelphia #153/R est:2500-4000
£2581 $4000 €3872 Harbour scene (38x51cm-15x20in) s. board. 8-Dec-2 Freeman, Philadelphia #176/R est:2500-4000
£2903 $4500 €4355 Manayunk (69x91cm-27x36in) s.i. 8-Dec-2 Freeman, Philadelphia #146/R est:5000-8000
£3065 $4750 €4598 Corner house (76x102cm-30x40in) s. s.i.verso exhib. 8-Dec-2 Freeman, Philadelphia #147/R est:5000-8000
£6479 $9200 €9719 The street, Manayunk (84x114cm-33x45in) 8-Aug-1 Barridorf, Portland #62/R est:6000-9000
£12258 $19000 €18387 Canal, New Hope (63x76cm-25x30in) s. 8-Dec-2 Freeman, Philadelphia #175/R est:8000-12000
Works on paper
£705 $1100 €1058 Seascape with rocky coast (25x43cm-10x17in) s. pastel. 18-Sep-2 Alderfer's, Hatfield #332/R

MARTINO, Edoardo (1838-1912) Italian
£280 $456 €406 Coast of Portugal (20x25cm-8x10in) s. i.verso board. 21-Jul-3 Sotheby's, London #69/R
£340 $554 €493 Italian alpine lake scene with stone jetty and watch towers (11x14cm-4x6in) board. 21-Jul-3 Sotheby's, London #846
£520 $848 €754 Argentine frigate 'Uruguay' at the South Pole (10x15cm-4x6in) s. board. 21-Jul-3 Sotheby's, London #620
£550 $897 €798 Launch of the cruiser Esmeralda, Newcastle June 6th, 1888 (22x37cm-9x15in) s.i.d.1888. 21-Jul-3 Sotheby's, London #82
£600 $978 €870 Seascape by moonlight (23x15cm-9x6in) s. panel. 21-Jul-3 Sotheby's, London #68/R
£700 $1141 €1015 Duke of Edinburgh on board the S.S. Servia at Greenock (17x25cm-7x10in) s.i.d.23 Aug 81. 21-Jul-3 Sotheby's, London #80/R
£750 $1223 €1088 Tsukushi or one of her class (35x53cm-14x21in) s. 21-Jul-3 Sotheby's, London #79/R
£764 $1100 €1146 Whalers breaking through ice (28x38cm-11x15in) s. board. 15-Jan-3 Christie's, Rockefeller NY #140/R
£800 $1304 €1160 H.M.S. Temeraire known as the Great Brig (26x37cm-10x15in) s. 21-Jul-3 Sotheby's, London #342/R est:800-1200
£850 $1386 €1233 H.M.S. Nelson or her sister ship H.M.S. Northampton (30x45cm-12x18in) s. 21-Jul-3 Sotheby's, London #76/R
£950 $1473 €1425 Royal mail steamer Atrato anchored off Montevideo with her tender approaching (13x18cm-5x7in) s.d. oil on card. 31-Oct-2 Christie's, Kensington #563/R
£1000 $1630 €1450 Brazilian landscape with man and a woman with a red parasol in a boat (11x15cm-4x6in) s. board. 21-Jul-3 Sotheby's, London #610/R est:500-700
£1200 $1956 €1740 Paraguay, Il Ritorno che feinde (15x21cm-6x8in) s.d.1870 board. 21-Jul-3 Sotheby's, London #67/R est:800-1200
£1400 $2282 €2030 H.M.S. Inflexible firing a Salvo (45x74cm-18x29in) s.i. 21-Jul-3 Sotheby's, London #75/R est:1500-2000
£1400 $2282 €2030 Chilean warship Blanco Encalada and the Almirante Cochrane (18x28cm-7x11in) board. 21-Jul-3 Sotheby's, London #66/R est:800-1200
£1442 $2279 €2250 Cruiser Infanta Maria Teresa (26x35cm-10x14in) s. i.verso cardboard. 19-Nov-2 Durán, Madrid #180/R
£1800 $2934 €2610 Captain Blackwood leaving the frigate Euryalus (64x44cm-25x17in) s. 21-Jul-3 Sotheby's, London #73/R est:1000-1500
£1800 $2934 €2610 Stella Polare at the North Pole (26x37cm-10x15in) sketch. 21-Jul-3 Sotheby's, London #78/R est:1000-1500
£2000 $3040 €3000 Steamer of the Orient Line taking on passengers (12x18cm-5x7in) s.i. board. 15-Aug-2 Bonhams, New Bond Street #435/R est:1500-2000
£2800 $4564 €4060 Argentine cruiser with a frigate in the background (44x72cm-17x28in) s. 21-Jul-3 Sotheby's, London #77/R est:2000-3000

£4200 $6552 €6300 Promenade des Anglais, Nice (32x67cm-13x26in) s. 17-Sep-2 Sotheby's, Olympia #258/R est:3000-5000
£6000 $9780 €8700 Landing of the Duke and Duchess of York at Sydney, on S.S. Ophir (34x75cm-13x30in) s. 21-Jul-3 Sotheby's, London #72/R est:3000-5000

Works on paper
£500 $815 €725 Kaiser's Yacht Hohenzollern (20x15cm-8x6in) W/C. 21-Jul-3 Sotheby's, London #83
£1600 $2608 €2320 View of Sydney harbour with the Royal Barge in the foreground (19x49cm-7x19in) i.d.1911 W/C card. 21-Jul-3 Sotheby's, London #74/R est:1000-1500
£2400 $3912 €3480 Marine subjects. pen ink W/C eight. 21-Jul-3 Sotheby's, London #619 est:1000-2000

MARTINO, G de (20th C) Italian
Sculpture
£1887 $2906 €3000 Young angler (120cm-47in) s.i.d.1931 bronze. 28-Oct-2 Il Ponte, Milan #318

MARTINO, Giovanni (1908-1998) American
£1026 $1600 €1539 Manayunk landscape on a cloudy day (30x46cm-12x18in) s. 18-Sep-2 Alderfer's, Hatfield #329/R est:1500-2500
£1437 $2400 €2084 Spring (28x41cm-11x16in) a. board exhib. 22-Jun-3 Freeman, Philadelphia #156/R est:1500-2500
£2903 $4500 €4355 Reflections (64x76cm-25x30in) s.d.31 i.verso board. 8-Dec-2 Freeman, Philadelphia #134/R est:3000-5000
Works on paper
£897 $1400 €1346 Manayunk landscape in winter (43x58cm-17x23in) s. W/C. 18-Sep-2 Alderfer's, Hatfield #328/R

MARTINO, Giovanni di (1870-1935) Italian
Sculpture
£1000 $1540 €1500 Fisherboy (40cm-16in) s. bronze. 28-Oct-2 Sotheby's, Olympia #87/R est:1200-1800

MARTINS, Gomes (20th C) Portuguese
£280 $454 €420 Harbour at Lisbon (70x110cm-28x43in) s.i. 23-Jan-3 Christie's, Kensington #267/R
£750 $1170 €1125 Tejou, Lisbon (70x111cm-28x44in) s. 9-Oct-2 Woolley & Wallis, Salisbury #279/R

MARTINSEN, Kaare (1912-1986) Norwegian
£362 $586 €543 The model (29x26cm-11x10in) s. s.i.d.1962 stretcher. 26-May-3 Grev Wedels Plass, Oslo #14/R (N.KR 4000)

MARTINSSON, Harry (1904-1978) Swedish
£1164 $1885 €1688 Fairy story lamp (70x50cm-28x20in) s.i. panel. 25-May-3 Uppsala Auktionskammare, Uppsala #227/R est:10000-12000 (S.KR 15000)

MARTINZ, Fritz (1924-) ?
£504 $826 €700 Reclining cow (47x60cm-19x24in) s.d.71 oil crayon col pencil. 5-Jun-3 Dorotheum, Salzburg #840/R
£1111 $1756 €1600 Fishes (65x80cm-26x31in) s.d.77. 24-Apr-3 Dorotheum, Vienna #237/R est:1800-2600
Works on paper
£382 $603 €550 Catastrophe landscape (76x56cm-30x22in) s.i.d.28.VII.75 col pen col chk. 24-Apr-3 Dorotheum, Vienna #235/R

MARTORELL PUIGDOMENECH, Jose (19/20th C) Spanish
£679 $1060 €1080 Two vases of flowers (33x41cm-13x16in) s. 17-Sep-2 Segre, Madrid #53/R
£679 $1060 €1080 Vases of flowers with fruit in landscape (33x41cm-13x16in) s. 17-Sep-2 Segre, Madrid #52/R

MARTSEN, Jan (younger-attrib) (1609-c.1647) Flemish
£3878 $6165 €5700 Cavalry battle (61x90cm-24x35in) 19-Mar-3 Neumeister, Munich #453/R est:2500

MARTTINEN, Veikko (1917-) Finnish
£1044 $1629 €1650 House on shore (39x70cm-15x28in) s.d.1963. 12-Sep-2 Hagelstam, Helsinki #884 est:1500
£1392 $2200 €2200 Head (61x35cm-24x14in) s.d.1961. 30-Nov-2 Hagelstam, Helsinki #180/R est:2000
£2405 $3800 €3800 Woman with violin (100x70cm-39x28in) s.d.68 board. 1-Dec-2 Bukowskis, Helsinki #337/R est:3500-4000

MARTY, Andre Edouard (1882-1974) French
£5063 $8000 €8000 Persee et Andromede (166x167cm-65x66in) s.d.39 panel. 26-Nov-2 Tajan, Paris #147/R est:7500-8000

MARTYN, Thomas J (19th C) British
£400 $652 €600 French boat in a squall, with a frigate in the background (53x41cm-21x16in) panel arched top. 14-Feb-3 Bracketts, Tunbridge Wells #967

MARUGAN, Amal (1934-) Spanish
£283 $450 €410 Jerusalem, holy town (33x41cm-13x16in) s. s.i.verso board. 4-Mar-3 Ansorena, Madrid #26/R

MARULLO, Giuseppe (?-1685) Italian
£19310 $30510 €28000 Rachel meeting Jacob (177x231cm-70x91in) s. lit. 3-Apr-3 Porro, Milan #21/R est:40000
£140000 $233800 €203000 Flight into Egypt (232x178cm-91x70in) prov. 9-Jul-3 Christie's, London #99/R est:100000-150000

MARUSIC, Zjuho (1949-) Balkan
£1277 $2068 €1800 L'omino della pioggia (50x35cm-20x14in) s.d.1993. 22-May-3 Stadion, Trieste #213/R est:1000-1500

MARUSSIG, Guido (1885-1938) Italian
£1282 $1987 €2000 Poles in Venice (77x62cm-30x24in) s. tempera cardboard exhib. 5-Dec-2 Stadion, Trieste #673

MARUSSIG, Piero (1879-1937) Italian
£5229 $8366 €8000 Little bridge (48x68cm-19x27in) s. s.i.verso cardboard. 4-Jan-3 Meeting Art, Vercelli #226 est:8000
£5556 $8833 €8000 Landscape (50x60cm-20x24in) s. board painted 1933. 1-May-3 Meeting Art, Vercelli #321
£13462 $21135 €21000 Landscape (67x88cm-26x35in) s. s.i.verso painted 1910. 23-Nov-2 Meeting Art, Vercelli #496/R
£17730 $28723 €25000 Interno con fiori e quadro (66x45cm-26x18in) s. 22-May-3 Stadion, Trieste #395/R est:16000-20000

MARUSSO, Vittorio (?) Italian
Works on paper
£306 $477 €480 Venice (72x45cm-28x18in) s. W/C. 5-Nov-2 Hartung & Hartung, Munich #5257/R

MARVAL, Jacqueline (1866-1932) French
£1709 $2700 €2700 Chloe dansant (30x50cm-12x20in) s. 2-Dec-2 Tajan, Paris #151/R
£3205 $4968 €5000 Bouquet de roses au tournesol (92x70cm-36x28in) s. lit. 9-Dec-2 Beaussant & Lefèvre, Paris #76/R

MARVILLE, Charles (1816-c.1880) French
Photographs
£3718 $5874 €5800 Rue Saint-Julien-le-Pauvre (32x27cm-13x11in) albumin print lit. 16-Nov-2 Christie's, Paris #90/R est:5000-7000

MARWAN (1934-) Syrian
£1006 $1550 €1600 Still life with fruit (27x46cm-11x18in) s.d.1978 verso. 26-Oct-2 Dr Lehr, Berlin #309/R est:1500
£1069 $1647 €1700 Still life of pears (27x46cm-11x18in) s. s.d.1978 verso. 26-Oct-2 Dr Lehr, Berlin #310/R est:1500
£1384 $2131 €2200 Still life on central heating I (55x40cm-22x16in) s.d.1977 s.i.d. verso. 26-Oct-2 Dr Lehr, Berlin #308/R est:2000
Works on paper
£362 $594 €500 Poster sketch (92x69cm-36x27in) W/C pencil pastel chk. 31-May-3 Villa Grisebach, Berlin #873/R
£417 $658 €600 Head (85x60cm-33x24in) s.i. W/C over pencil board. 26-Apr-3 Dr Lehr, Berlin #343/R
£556 $878 €800 Head (88x64cm-35x25in) i. W/C over pencil board. 26-Apr-3 Dr Lehr, Berlin #344/R
£629 $969 €1000 Figures (42x60cm-17x24in) s.d.1970 W/C. 26-Oct-2 Dr Lehr, Berlin #311/R
£1258 $1937 €2000 Parisian head (78x84cm-31x33in) s.i.d.1973. 26-Oct-2 Dr Lehr, Berlin #312/R est:1500

MARX, Franz (1889-1960) German
£321 $468 €500 Zebras in Africa (60x80cm-24x31in) s. 4-Jun-2 Karl & Faber, Munich #347
£350 $546 €550 Departure on horseback in southern landscape (50x60cm-20x24in) s. lit. 7-Nov-2 Allgauer, Kempten #2897/R
£425 $697 €650 Bull fight (48x60cm-19x24in) s. 5-Feb-3 Neumeister, Munich #762
£759 $1185 €1200 Oriental scene (70x80cm-28x31in) s. 18-Oct-2 Dr Fritz Nagel, Stuttgart #253/R
£980 $1569 €1500 Football game between Nurnberg and Furth (60x69cm-24x27in) s.d.26 masonite lit. 10-Jan-3 Allgauer, Kempten #1684/R est:1500
£1103 $1754 €1600 Zebres dans la savane (60x80cm-24x31in) s. 7-Mar-3 Rabourdin & Choppin de Janvry, Paris #5/R est:1600-1800

MARX, Karl (1929-) German
£705 $1093 €1100 Untitled (189x200cm-74x79in) s.d.80 verso prov. 7-Dec-2 Van Ham, Cologne #335/R

MARXER, Alfred (1876-1945) Swiss
£611 $954 €917 Rowing boat group on a lake (38x50cm-15x20in) s.d.17. 8-Nov-2 Dobiaschofsky, Bern #214/R (S.FR 1400)
£944 $1492 €1416 Notre Dame in Paris (111x96cm-44x38in) s. 29-Nov-2 Zofingen, Switzerland #2977 est:2000 (S.FR 2200)
£1965 $3085 €2948 Winter landscape by the Zurichsee (60x70cm-24x28in) s.d.1929 prov. 25-Nov-2 Sotheby's, Zurich #124/R est:4000-5000 (S.FR 4500)

MARYAN (1927-1977) American
£1270 $1969 €1905 Personnage (81x64cm-32x25in) s.d.58 s.stretcher prov. 1-Oct-2 Rasmussen, Copenhagen #56/R est:20000-25000 (D.KR 15000)
£3836 $5947 €6100 Sans titre (114x98cm-45x39in) s.d.1973 acrylic exhib.lit. 30-Oct-2 Artcurial Briest, Paris #486/R est:4000-5000

MARYAN, Burstein Pinchas (1927-1977) American
£764 $1215 €1100 Sans titre (65x50cm-26x20in) s.d.60 gold paint paper on canvas. 29-Apr-3 Artcurial Briest, Paris #613
£1633 $2596 €2400 Tete a chapeau (55x46cm-22x18in) s.d.65 prov. 26-Feb-3 Artcurial Briest, Paris #539/R est:2000-3000
£2069 $3310 €3000 Composition (92x73cm-36x29in) s. 12-Mar-3 Rabourdin & Choppin de Janvry, Paris #193/R
£2414 $3814 €3500 Untitled (146x114cm-57x45in) s.d.59 prov. 2-Apr-3 Christie's, Paris #37/R

MARZELLE, Jean (1916-) French
£345 $548 €500 Le port de la Rochelle (14x22cm-6x9in) s. 9-Mar-3 Feletin, Province #142
£625 $1031 €900 Collines au village et viaduc (65x81cm-26x32in) s. 1-Jul-3 Rossini, Paris #108/R

MARZI, Ezio (20th C) Italian
£1203 $1876 €1900 Young girl in the kitchen (40x50cm-16x20in) s. 19-Oct-2 Semenzato, Venice #85/R

MARZIN, Alfred (20th C) French
£1600 $2560 €2400 Fishing boats in a harbour by moonlight (73x100cm-29x39in) s. 11-Mar-3 Bonhams, Knightsbridge #221/R est:1500-2000

MARZOCCHI DE BELLUCI, Numa (19/20th C) French
£2381 $3786 €3500 Jeune fille sur la terrase (36x27cm-14x11in) s.d.1882. 24-Mar-3 Rabourdin & Choppin de Janvry, Paris #256/R est:3500-4000

MAS Y FONDEVILA, Arcadio (1852-1934) Spanish
£4088 $6377 €6500 Venetian canal (14x25cm-6x10in) s. cardboard. 23-Sep-2 Durán, Madrid #251/R
Works on paper
£1645 $2664 €2500 Walkers (56x39cm-22x15in) s. W/C. 21-Jan-3 Ansorena, Madrid #50/R

MAS Y MASCARO, Juan (1892-?) Spanish
£855 $1386 €1300 Landscape with lonely man (36x71cm-14x28in) s.d.89. 21-Jan-3 Durán, Madrid #93/R

MASANOBU, Okumura (1686-1764) Japanese
Prints
£3077 $4800 €4616 Young dandy astride a lion in a parody of the bodhisattva Monju (31x15cm-12x6in) s. print prov. 25-Mar-3 Christie's, Rockefeller NY #3/R est:3000-4000
£12821 $20000 €19232 Entrance of the great gate to the Shin Yoshiwara (34x45cm-13x18in) s. col print prov.lit. 25-Mar-3 Christie's, Rockefeller NY #2/R est:20000-22000

MASAREEL, Frans (1889-?) German
Works on paper
£3700 $5698 €5550 Marseille harbour (52x73cm-20x29in) init.d.1926 W/C gouache brush ink. 23-Oct-2 Sotheby's, Olympia #704/R est:3000-5000

MASARYK, Herbert G (attrib) (1880-1915) Austrian
£305 $486 €458 Landscape with house (38x49cm-15x19in) mono. verso. 8-Mar-3 Dorotheum, Prague #145/R est:12000-18000 (C.KR 14000)

MASCART, Gustave (1834-1914) French
£696 $1100 €1100 Summer river landscape (50x66cm-20x26in) s. lit. 29-Nov-2 Schloss Ahlden, Ahlden #1319/R
£851 $1421 €1200 Deux incroyables (26x19cm-10x7in) s. panel. 18-Jun-3 Hotel des Ventes Mosan, Brussels #184
£1600 $2672 €2400 Le canal de gand (21x41cm-8x16in) s. 18-Jun-3 Christie's, Kensington #1/R est:2000-3000
£1862 $2961 €2700 Vue de Bruges ou de Gand (51x66cm-20x26in) s. 5-Mar-3 Oger, Dumont, Paris #42/R est:3000-4500
£3200 $5024 €4800 Place de la Republique. Place de Clichy (38x46cm-15x18in) s. pair. 21-Nov-2 Christie's, Kensington #1/R est:2000-3000

MASCAUX, Albert (1900-1963) Belgian
£405 $652 €575 Brittany harbour (48x58cm-19x23in) s. 7-May-3 Vendue Huis, Gravenhage #90

MASCELLANI, Norma (1909-) Italian
£603 $977 €850 Pesca sul fiume (24x33cm-9x13in) s. board. 22-May-3 Stadion, Trieste #272

MASCHERINI, Marcello (1906-1983) Italian
Sculpture
£2244 $3478 €3500 Pan (350x70cm-138x28in) s.d.50 pat. plaster. 5-Dec-2 Stadion, Trieste #760/R
Works on paper
£481 $745 €750 Horse fight (45x48cm-18x19in) s.d.43 W/C. 5-Dec-2 Stadion, Trieste #678

MASCI, Edolo (1938-) Italian
£494 $780 €770 Hill landscape (90x100cm-35x39in) 12-Nov-2 Babuino, Rome #255/R

MASEK, Vitezlav Karel (1865-1925) Bohemian
£5500 $9020 €8250 Batyhers by a riverbank (115x115cm-45x45in) init.d.1907. 3-Jun-3 Sotheby's, London #44/R est:5000-7000

MASELLI, Titina (1924-) Italian
£1026 $1610 €1600 Lights in the sky (60x60cm-24x24in) s.d.1969. 21-Nov-2 Finarte, Rome #263/R
£1410 $2214 €2200 Boxeur (89x115cm-35x45in) s.i.d.1991 verso. 19-Nov-2 Finarte, Milan #97/R
£2885 $4471 €4500 Untitled (195x130cm-77x51in) s.i.d.1986 verso acrylic. 4-Dec-2 Finarte, Milan #294/R est:7000
£6410 $10064 €10000 Stadium (81x180cm-32x71in) s.i.d.1975 acrylic. 21-Nov-2 Finarte, Rome #306/R est:10000

MASEREEL, Frans (1889-1972) Belgian
£517 $828 €750 Divers (46x62cm-18x24in) mono.d.1953 paper prov.lit. 15-Mar-3 De Vuyst, Lokeren #210/R
£897 $1391 €1400 Couple en maillot sur la plage (48x63cm-19x25in) mono. paper on panel painted 1959 lit. 7-Dec-2 De Vuyst, Lokeren #214
£1014 $1664 €1400 Gitane au corsage vert (60x37cm-24x15in) mono. board. 29-May-3 Lempertz, Koln #786/R
£1026 $1590 €1600 Diver (65x48cm-26x19in) mono. paper on board painted 1958 exhib.lit. 7-Dec-2 De Vuyst, Lokeren #212/R est:1400-2000
£1739 $2852 €2400 L'escaut a Tamise, remorqeurs et chalands (33x49cm-13x19in) mono.d.1948 s.i.d. verso board prov.exhib. 31-May-3 Villa Grisebach, Berlin #139/R est:3000-4000
£2532 $3949 €4000 Sidonie - dans la vitrine du coiffeur (50x65cm-20x26in) s.d.1966 i.d. verso paper on masonite. 18-Oct-2 Dr Fritz Nagel, Stuttgart #567/R est:6500
£2532 $3949 €4000 Father with child (46x33cm-18x13in) mono.d.1944 board. 18-Oct-2 Dr Fritz Nagel, Stuttgart #569/R est:5800
£2535 $4208 €3600 Maisons sur la falaise (38x55cm-15x22in) mono.d. s.d. verso. 14-Jun-3 Hauswedell & Nolte, Hamburg #1381/R est:3500
£2564 $4026 €4000 Un crime II (50x65cm-20x26in) mono.d.1964 paper. 21-Nov-2 Dorotheum, Vienna #249/R est:6800-9000
£2609 $4278 €3600 Dormeuse au torse nu (60x73cm-24x29in) mono.d.1951 s.d.1951 verso exhib. 29-May-3 Lempertz, Koln #787/R est:2500
£2817 $4676 €4000 Blonde sailor (92x73cm-36x29in) mono.d. s.d. verso. 14-Jun-3 Hauswedell & Nolte, Hamburg #1380/R est:5000
£3797 $5924 €6000 Mediterranean still life (50x65cm-20x26in) s.d.1963 s.d. verso. 18-Oct-2 Dr Fritz Nagel, Stuttgart #568/R est:8000
£4967 $8096 €7500 Mere assise avec sa fille dans les bras (66x92cm-26x36in) mono. s.i.d.1955 verso. 28-Jan-3 Dorotheum, Vienna #131/R est:8000-12000
£5380 $8500 €8500 Harbour scene (55x46cm-22x18in) mono.d.1929 i. verso. 30-Nov-2 Villa Grisebach, Berlin #303/R est:6000-8000
£6090 $9439 €9500 Lock (73x92cm-29x36in) mono. 7-Dec-2 Hauswedell & Nolte, Hamburg #880/R est:12500
Works on paper
£269 $417 €420 Man's head (21x15cm-8x6in) Indian ink brush. 7-Dec-2 Hauswedell & Nolte, Hamburg #882/R
£316 $500 €500 Chat noir (46x62cm-18x24in) mono.d.1954 Indian ink. 26-Nov-2 Palais de Beaux Arts, Brussels #123
£360 $576 €500 Batelier (48x63cm-19x25in) mono.d.1956 ink dr lit. 17-May-3 De Vuyst, Lokeren #252
£385 $596 €600 Nude (24x16cm-9x6in) d. Indian ink brush. 7-Dec-2 Hauswedell & Nolte, Hamburg #881/R

£393 $613 €590 Evening landscape (20x28cm-8x11in) mono. W/C. 6-Nov-2 Dobiaschofsky, Bern #3515 (S.FR 900)
£432 $691 €600 Famille (16x50cm-6x20in) mono.d.1941 Indian ink dr. 17-May-3 De Vuyst, Lokeren #253
£818 $1259 €1300 Atelier (46x62cm-18x24in) mono. wash. 22-Oct-2 Campo, Vlaamse Kaai #564
£861 $1403 €1300 Ville a la tombee de la nuit (48x63cm-19x25in) mono.d.1957 gouache. 28-Jan-3 Dorotheum, Vienna #129/R
£870 $1426 €1200 Church - set design for Goethe's Urfaust (49x63cm-19x25in) mono.d.1960 chl prov. 29-May-3 Lempertz, Koln #789/R
£897 $1391 €1400 Nude at window (49x39cm-19x15in) mono.d. Indian ink brush. 7-Dec-2 Hauswedell & Nolte, Hamburg #884/R
£949 $1481 €1500 Female nude (30x21cm-12x8in) mono. Indian ink. 18-Oct-2 Dr Fritz Nagel, Stuttgart #566/R est:2400
£962 $1490 €1500 Repos dans les foins (48x63cm-19x25in) mono.d.1959 Indian ink brush w/C. 4-Dec-2 Lempertz, Koln #901/R est:1500
£1127 $1870 €1600 Promenade (50x57cm-20x22in) mono.d. Indian ink brush. 14-Jun-3 Hauswedell & Nolte, Hamburg #1385/R est:1000
£1132 $1743 €1800 Femme pleurant (46x30cm-18x12in) mono. d.1957 wash. 22-Oct-2 Campo, Vlaamse Kaai #563
£1135 $1771 €1703 Canal landscape in evening (48x63cm-19x25in) mono.d.31 w/C. 6-Nov-2 Dobiaschofsky, Bern #814/R est:3700 (S.FR 2600)
£1218 $1888 €1900 Couple (64x49cm-25x19in) mono.d. W/C. 7-Dec-2 Hauswedell & Nolte, Hamburg #885/R est:1500
£1258 $1937 €2000 La marchande de fleurs (41x29cm-16x11in) mono.d.1945 wash. 22-Oct-2 Campo, Vlaamse Kaai #562
£1677 $2650 €2600 Femme dans la rue (105x73cm-41x29in) mono.d.1923 chl. 17-Dec-2 Palais de Beaux Arts, Brussels #572 est:1000-1500
£1799 $2950 €2500 At the tram stop (36x53cm-14x21in) init.d.1926 brush ink W/C. 3-Jun-3 Christie's, Amsterdam #292/R est:2500-3500
£2676 $4442 €3800 Maison de pecheurs (49x63cm-19x25in) mono.d. W/C. 14-Jun-3 Hauswedell & Nolte, Hamburg #1382/R est:3000
£2754 $4516 €3800 America (31x25cm-12x10in) mono. Indian ink brush exhib.lit. 29-May-3 Lempertz, Koln #788/R est:3500
£4085 $6780 €5800 Matelot dansant (64x49cm-25x19in) mono.d. W/C. 14-Jun-3 Hauswedell & Nolte, Hamburg #1384/R est:1500
£4348 $7130 €6000 Scene sous la lampe (107x72cm-42x28in) mono.d.1923 chl prov. 31-May-3 Villa Grisebach, Berlin #152/R est:6000-8000
£4487 $6955 €7000 Au restaurant (105x73cm-41x29in) mono.d.1923 Indian ink brush exhib. 4-Dec-2 Lempertz, Koln #899/R est:5200
£6410 $9936 €10000 Le trottoir (74x53cm-29x21in) mono.d.1927 s.d. verso Indian ink W/C prov. 4-Dec-2 Lempertz, Koln #900/R est:6000-7000
£6410 $9936 €10000 Small cafe (55x49cm-22x19in) mono.d. W/C. 7-Dec-2 Hauswedell & Nolte, Hamburg #883/R est:6000
£8803 $14613 €12500 Plage le dimanche (54x74cm-21x29in) mono.d. i. verso W/C. 14-Jun-3 Hauswedell & Nolte, Hamburg #1383/R est:2500
£13291 $21000 €21000 Sur le banc (50x65cm-20x26in) mono.d.1923 i. verso Indian ink brush W/C prov.exhib. 30-Nov-2 Villa Grisebach, Berlin #176/R est:4000-5000

MASHKOV, Ilya (1881-1944) Russian
£5517 $8828 €8000 Still life with lemons (61x43cm-24x17in) s. 12-Mar-3 Rabourdin & Choppin de Janvry, Paris #98/R

MASI, Roberto (1940-) Italian
£285 $444 €450 Angler seen from the back (20x20cm-8x8in) s. s.verso. 14-Sep-2 Meeting Art, Vercelli #842
£714 $1136 €1050 Fishermen (40x50cm-16x20in) s. 1-Mar-3 Meeting Art, Vercelli #440

MASIDE, Carlos (1897-1958) Spanish
£5975 $9201 €9500 Model (48x40cm-19x16in) s. 22-Oct-2 Durán, Madrid #198/R est:5750
Works on paper
£1452 $2294 €2250 Party (37x45cm-15x18in) s. ink dr. 17-Dec-2 Durán, Madrid #166/R

MASIP, Vicente Juan (circle) (c.1523-1579) Spanish
£10490 $17517 €15000 Tete de Saint Jean Baptiste (38x55cm-15x22in) panel. 25-Jun-3 Pierre Berge, Paris #17/R est:6000-8000

MASKELL, Christopher M (1846-1933) British
£480 $763 €720 Figure before a cottage in a wooded landscape (22x17cm-9x7in) init. board prov. 6-Mar-3 Christie's, Kensington #465/R
£720 $1130 €1080 Suffolk river landscape with figures by cottages (38x56cm-15x22in) init. pair. 13-Dec-2 Keys, Aylsham #643/R

MASOLLE, Helmer (1884-1969) Swedish
£1277 $1979 €1916 Mountain landscape from Dalarne (100x130cm-39x51in) s.d.08. 4-Dec-2 AB Stockholms Auktionsverk #1786/R est:8000-10000 (S.KR 18000)

MASON, Alice Frances Kolb (1895-1977) American
£452 $700 €678 Two turtle doves (91x76cm-36x30in) s. exhib. 21-Jul-2 Jeffery Burchard, Florida #30/R

MASON, Bateson (1910-1977) British
£1300 $2132 €1950 Boatyard, Finisterre (51x76cm-20x30in) s. prov.exhib. 6-Jun-3 Christie's, London #116/R est:1200-1800
£2200 $3608 €3300 Battersea church (25x35cm-10x14in) s. s.i.verso board sold with W/C by same hand prov.exhib. 6-Jun-3 Christie's, London #115/R est:1200-1800

MASON, E (?) British?
£253 $395 €380 Children fishing (49x74cm-19x29in) s. 23-Sep-2 Rasmussen, Vejle #2357 (D.KR 3000)
£253 $395 €380 Coastal landscape (50x75cm-20x30in) s. 23-Sep-2 Rasmussen, Vejle #2358 (D.KR 3000)

MASON, E C (19th C) British
£288 $450 €432 Two women in a field with a basket of flowers (46x36cm-18x14in) s. 14-Sep-2 Selkirks, St. Louis #200

MASON, Eric (?) British
£390 $651 €566 Blues on parade, Household Cavalry (60x90cm-24x35in) mono. 19-Jun-3 Lane, Penzance #351

MASON, Frank H (1876-1965) British
£270 $437 €392 Stormy weather (20x48cm-8x19in) s. board. 22-May-3 Richardson & Smith, Whitby #535
£300 $501 €435 MV Frederick T Everland passing Europa Point, Gibraltar (28x38cm-11x15in) s. board. 26-Jun-3 Richardson & Smith, Whitby #520
£320 $509 €480 M.V Centurity (61x81cm-24x32in) s.i. 29-Apr-3 Sworder & Son, Bishops Stortford #358/R
£360 $547 €540 Loading the fleet (30x38cm-12x15in) s.i. board. 15-Aug-2 Bonhams, New Bond Street #359
£400 $608 €600 Pordinoni boats landing pottery, Venice (25x40cm-10x16in) s. panel. 15-Aug-2 Bonhams, New Bond Street #361
£430 $671 €645 Cargo vessel passing a lighthouse (33x51cm-13x20in) s. 20-Sep-2 Richardson & Smith, Whitby #110
£1500 $2430 €2250 Whaler Hope at work in polar waters (49x76cm-19x30in) sd.1944. 21-May-3 Christie's, Kensington #580/R est:1500-2000
£1500 $2430 €2250 Off Flamboro Head, lights are burning bright and all's well (61x91cm-24x36in) s.d.1944 i.stretcher. 21-May-3 Christie's, Kensington #681/R est:1000-1500
£1900 $3078 €2850 Clearing Tower Bridge (51x76cm-20x30in) s. 21-May-3 Christie's, Kensington #677/R est:1000-1500
£4600 $7176 €6900 Loch Torridon, off Ushant, racing yacht in full sail (49x74cm-19x29in) s.d.1944. 10-Sep-2 David Duggleby, Scarborough #345/R est:3000-5000
Works on paper
£340 $544 €510 Three masted sailing boat at sea (25x17cm-10x7in) s. gouache. 11-Mar-3 David Duggleby, Scarborough #119
£380 $593 €570 Fishing boats at low tide (22x35cm-9x14in) s. W/C. 10-Apr-3 Tennants, Leyburn #826
£400 $656 €600 Wheatcroft Towers Filey Road, Scarborough (16x21cm-6x8in) mono.i.d.August 1911 W/C. 10-Feb-3 David Duggleby, Scarborough #559
£420 $655 €630 Mediterranean coastal scenes (23x33cm-9x13in) s. W/C pair. 9-Apr-3 Andrew Hartley, Ilkley #929
£550 $864 €825 Harbour scene (21x32cm-8x13in) s. W/C gum arabic. 21-Nov-2 Tennants, Leyburn #663
£574 $900 €861 Anchored, Holy Island (15x23cm-6x9in) s.i. W/C gouache. 22-Nov-2 Skinner, Boston #118/R est:300-500
£580 $916 €870 Water gate, Bruges (39x28cm-15x11in) s.i. W/C bodycol. 2-Dec-2 Bonhams, Bath #36/R
£580 $945 €870 Water Gate, Bruges (39x28cm-15x11in) s.i. W/C bodycol. 17-Feb-3 Bonhams, Bath #151
£600 $936 €900 Off Berwick (36x52cm-14x20in) s.d.47 W/C. 10-Oct-2 Bonhams, Edinburgh #301
£600 $936 €900 Beach scene with figures and boats (23x30cm-9x12in) init.d.1895 W/C. 20-Sep-2 Richardson & Smith, Whitby #103
£650 $929 €975 Low tide, figures and boats near a spit (16x23cm-6x9in) s. W/C htd white. 28-Feb-2 Greenslade Hunt, Taunton #388
£660 $1043 €990 Busy harbour scene with figures unloading a fishing vessel by a wall (46x33cm-18x13in) s. W/C htd white. 7-Apr-3 David Duggleby, Scarborough #343/R
£700 $1141 €1015 Bruges (38x28cm-15x11in) s. mixed media. 17-Jul-3 Richardson & Smith, Whitby #579
£800 $1336 €1160 Caldra, probably Portugal (23x33cm-9x13in) s.i. W/C. 26-Jun-3 Richardson & Smith, Whitby #552
£900 $1494 €1350 Wreck in the Channel (37x74cm-15x29in) s. W/C htd white. 10-Jun-3 Bonhams, Leeds #64/R
£920 $1500 €1334 Heavy weather in the North Sea (50x75cm-20x30in) s.d.1900 W/C bodycol. 21-Jul-3 Bonhams, Bath #14/R
£950 $1444 €1425 Cutty Sark and Thermopylae (33x51cm-13x20in) s. W/C htd white. 15-Aug-2 Bonhams, New Bond Street #237/R
£1000 $1620 €1450 Study of a fishing trawler caught in stormy waters (47x74cm-19x29in) s.d.99 W/C gouache. 21-May-3 Rupert Toovey, Partridge Green #21/R est:500-800
£1350 $2106 €2025 Penzance harbour (25x46cm-10x18in) s. W/C. 20-Sep-2 Richardson & Smith, Whitby #99/R est:1000-1500

£1400 $2184 €2100 Fishing fleet, Newlyn (25x46cm-10x18in) s. i.verso W/C. 20-Sep-2 Richardson & Smith, Whitby #101 est:1000-1500
£1900 $2964 €2850 In company, clipper ships in full sail (60x96cm-24x38in) s.d.28 W/C. 10-Sep-2 David Duggleby, Scarborough #128/R est:1200-1800
£2200 $3674 €3190 Entrance to the Tyne (24x76cm-9x30in) s. W/C. 17-Jun-3 Anderson & Garland, Newcastle #264/R est:450-750
£5000 $7900 €7500 Off Dover, shipping scene (43x109cm-17x43in) s.i. W/C. 18-Dec-2 John Nicholson, Haslemere #1139/R est:4000-5000

MASON, George Finch (1850-1915) British
£964 $1600 €1398 Quiet river (76x127cm-30x50in) s.d.1879. 14-Jun-3 Jackson's, Cedar Falls #217/R est:800-1200

MASON, George Hemming (1818-1872) British
£7000 $11270 €10500 Drinking fountain in the campagna (32x62cm-13x24in) s.i. prov.exhib. 20-Feb-3 Christie's, London #158/R

MASON, Gilbert (20th C) British
£850 $1326 €1275 Figures in a landscape. Study of a seated nude (71x92cm-28x36in) s.d.1963 double-sided. 10-Apr-3 Tennants, Leyburn #1140

MASON, J R (19th C) British?
£650 $1001 €975 St Paul's from the Thames (49x75cm-19x30in) s. 8-Sep-2 Lots Road, London #335/R

MASON, Robin (1958-) British
Works on paper
£280 $456 €420 Flowers with long stems (79x53cm-31x21in) compressed chl. 3-Feb-3 Sotheby's, Olympia #139/R

MASON, Roy M (1886-1972) American
Works on paper
£629 $1000 €944 Chopping wood (9x12cm-4x5in) s. W/C exec.c.1940. 4-May-3 Treadway Gallery, Cincinnati #560/R
£949 $1500 €1376 Gastenaux guide (41x30cm-16x12in) s. W/C. 26-Jul-3 Coeur d'Alene, Hayden #228/R est:2000-3000

MASON, William (1906-2002) British
£1007 $1621 €1500 Evening in the busy street at sunset, Belfast (25x33cm-10x13in) s. i.verso board prov. 18-Feb-3 Whyte's, Dublin #3/R est:1500-2000
£1042 $1656 €1500 Galway, 1970 (20x25cm-8x10in) s. i.verso board. 29-Apr-3 Whyte's, Dublin #22/R est:1500-2000
£1258 $1962 €2000 Fishing boats (61x79cm-24x31in) s. board. 17-Sep-2 Whyte's, Dublin #203/R est:2000-3000
£1477 $2377 €2200 Street scene (66x57cm-26x22in) s. panel. 18-Feb-3 Whyte's, Dublin #25/R est:2500-3500

MASON, William Sanford (1824-1864) American
Works on paper
£449 $700 €674 View from Lemon Hill, Fairmount Park canal road from Pratt's gate (6x8cm-2x3in) d. July 1827 W/C pencil prov. 12-Apr-3 Freeman, Philadelphia #14/R

MASQUERIER, John James (1778-1855) British
£982 $1600 €1473 Marie Anee Bellingham (76x64cm-30x25in) 2-Feb-3 Grogan, Boston #16 est:1500-2500
£1800 $2790 €2700 Half length portrait of Sarah, Lady Ogilvy (59x48cm-23x19in) oval. 6-Dec-2 Lyon & Turnbull, Edinburgh #24/R est:600-800

MASRELIEZ, Louis (1748-1810) Swedish
Works on paper
£892 $1445 €1293 King Carl Gustaf on a triumph wagon (33x48cm-13x19in) Indian ink squared. 26-May-3 Bukowskis, Stockholm #494/R (S.KR 11500)

MASRIERA Y MANOVENS, Francisco (1842-1902) Spanish
£256 $405 €400 Nude (46x38cm-18x15in) s. exhib. 19-Nov-2 Durán, Madrid #46/R
£12227 $19074 €18341 Penitente (88x191cm-35x75in) s.d.1893 prov.lit. 9-Nov-2 Galerie Gloggner, Luzern #97/R est:7500-8500 (S.FR 28000)
£41139 $65000 €61709 Penitent Magdalene (89x191cm-35x75in) s.d.1895 exhib. 24-Apr-3 Sotheby's, New York #52/R est:40000-60000

MASRIERA Y ROSES, Luis (1872-1958) Spanish
£20000 $31400 €30000 Sombrillas en la playa - parasols on the the beach (48x62cm-19x24in) s.d.28 prov. 19-Nov-2 Sotheby's, London #17/R est:20000-30000

MASSANI, P (1850-1920) Italian
£1650 $2607 €2393 Interior scene with seated monk and man in period costume (43x64cm-17x25in) s.d.1882. 22-Jul-3 Riddetts, Bournemouth #505/R

MASSANI, Pompeo (1850-1920) Italian
£1410 $2200 €2115 Interesting read (30x23cm-12x9in) s. 9-Oct-2 Doyle, New York #71/R est:3000-5000
£1418 $2369 €2000 Old man smoking a pipe (34x25cm-13x10in) s. 23-Jun-3 Bernaerts, Antwerp #103/R est:2000-3000
£9286 $14671 €13929 Betrothal (51x76cm-20x30in) s.i. 26-Nov-2 Sotheby's, Melbourne #188/R est:25000-35000 (A.D 26000)

MASSAU, Edmond (1860-?) German
£596 $941 €894 Am Fenster - woman waiting by window with her knitting (71x57cm-28x22in) s.i. 2-Dec-2 Rasmussen, Copenhagen #1738/R (D.KR 7000)

MASSE, Emmanuel Auguste (1818-1881) French
Works on paper
£513 $795 €800 Champigny battle (26x40cm-10x16in) s.i. W/C. 5-Dec-2 Stadion, Trieste #556

MASSE, Jean Baptiste (attrib) (1687-1767) French
Miniatures
£4800 $8016 €6960 Lady, seated with a cat in her lap (7cm-3in) gilt metal frame rec. exec.c.1750. 25-Jun-3 Sotheby's, Olympia #15/R est:4000-6000

MASSEN, Daniel (1896-c.1970) Swedish/American
£3185 $5000 €4778 Composition 57-8 (43x24cm-17x9in) s. init.verso board prov. 19-Nov-2 Wright, Chicago #142/R est:5000-7000
£3185 $5000 €4778 Form arrangement no 8 3-40 (25x22cm-10x9in) s.i.num.verso board prov. 19-Nov-2 Wright, Chicago #143/R est:5000-7000

MASSENOT, Charles Antoine Auguste (1821-1871) French
£2700 $4293 €4050 Southern mountain landscape with family resting by water-hole (102x162cm-40x64in) s.d.1849. 5-Mar-3 Rasmussen, Copenhagen #1703/R est:40000 (D.KR 29000)
£3176 $4954 €4700 Pommes et raisins au pied de colonne (116x90cm-46x35in) s. 26-Mar-3 Rossini, Paris #119/R

MASSHOLDER, Eric (1960-) French
£1103 $1754 €1600 Chamane (100x81cm-39x32in) s. d.98v. 10-Mar-3 Millon & Associes, Paris #117/R

MASSMANN, Hans (1887-1973) Rumanian
£483 $772 €700 Winter landscape (50x50cm-20x20in) s. 11-Mar-3 Dorotheum, Vienna #110/R
£570 $889 €900 Valley view (63x63cm-25x25in) s. panel. 15-Oct-2 Dorotheum, Vienna #124/R
£962 $1519 €1500 Landscape in early spring (57x61cm-22x24in) i. canvas on board. 12-Nov-2 Dorotheum, Vienna #127/R est:1200-1800
Works on paper
£439 $685 €650 Drosendorf (44x55cm-17x22in) s. gouache board exhib. 28-Mar-3 Dorotheum, Vienna #270/R

MASSMANN, Siegfried (1829-1853) German
£1500 $2505 €2175 Rhineland landscape with figures by a chalet (54x75cm-21x30in) s.d.50. 17-Jun-3 Bonhams, New Bond Street #22/R est:2000-3000

MASSON, Andre (1896-1987) French
£4730 $7378 €7000 Marche (48x32cm-19x13in) s. tempera paper on canvas. 26-Mar-3 Finarte Semenzato, Milan #83/R
£5479 $8603 €8000 Paysage aux nuages (63x49cm-25x19in) s. painted c.1950 prov. 21-Apr-3 Rabourdin & Choppin de Janvry, Paris #171/R est:10000-12000
£6463 $10276 €9500 Poissons et oeillets (73x40cm-29x16in) init.d.52 prov. 26-Feb-3 Fraysse & Associes, Paris #23/R est:10000-12000
£7000 $11060 €10500 Trois figures dans un tunnel (39x51cm-15x20in) painted 1947. 3-Apr-3 Christie's, Kensington #146/R
£9494 $15000 €15000 Paysanne au bord de ruisseau (82x96cm-32x38in) s. painted 1951 prov. 2-Dec-2 Tajan, Paris #11/R est:6000-8000
£10870 $17826 €15000 Visages dans la nuit des fleurs (40x80cm-16x31in) s. s.i.d.1959 verso tempera pastel sand prov. 29-May-3 Lempertz, Koln #791/R est:15000
£12579 $20000 €18869 Crane de tigre (20x23cm-8x9in) s.i.d.1945 tempera sand. 27-Feb-3 Christie's, Rockefeller NY #2/R est:23000

£16096 $25271 €23500 Au creux de l'arbre (55x46cm-22x18in) s. d.verso prov. 21-Apr-3 Rabourdin & Choppin de Janvry, Paris #186/R est:19000-21000
£19178 $29918 €28000 Paysage a Collioure (45x63cm-18x25in) s. painted 1919. 14-Apr-3 Laurence Calmels, Paris #4074/R est:12000
£30128 $47301 €47000 Figure a la rose poignardee (116x89cm-46x35in) s. i.d.1974 verso prov. 15-Dec-2 Perrin, Versailles #96/R est:50000
£76923 $120000 €115385 Les vieux souliers sous la pluie (60x73cm-24x29in) s. i.d.1947 on stretcher prov.exhib. 7-Nov-2 Christie's, Rockefeller NY #333/R est:30000-40000
£204969 $330000 €307454 La poursuite (92x60cm-36x24in) s.i.verso painted 1927 prov.exhib.lit. 7-May-3 Sotheby's, New York #309/R est:150000-200000
£242236 $390000 €363354 L'homme (100x66cm-39x26in) s.verso i.on stretcher painted 1924 prov.exhib.lit. 8-May-3 Christie's, Rockefeller NY #215/R est:120000-160000
£250000 $407500 €375000 Sybille aux presages (80x96cm-31x38in) s. s.i.d.1945 verso tempera sand prov.exhib. 3-Feb-3 Christie's, London #172/R est:150000
£496894 $800000 €745341 Pasiphae (102x127cm-40x50in) s. i.d.XLIII verso oil tempera sand prov.exhib.lit. 6-May-3 Sotheby's, New York #38/R est:400000-600000

Sculpture
£3800 $5852 €5700 Femmes (19x19cm-7x7in) s.d.21 painted glazed ceramic dish prov. 23-Oct-2 Sotheby's, Olympia #754/R est:4000-6000

Works on paper
£1026 $1590 €1600 Sonnet 7 (50x37cm-20x15in) s.i. ink. 7-Dec-2 Cornette de St.Cyr, Paris #37/R
£1042 $1656 €1500 Mulet (65x49cm-26x19in) s. Indian ink wash dr prov. 29-Apr-3 Artcurial Briest, Paris #134/R est:1000-1200
£1189 $1986 €1700 Homme attaque par des poissons (31x23cm-12x9in) s. Indian ink. 26-Jun-3 Tajan, Paris #171/R est:1200-1500
£1282 $2013 €2000 Etreinte (21x28cm-8x11in) mono. ink. 22-Nov-2 Millon & Associes, Paris #32/R
£1497 $2380 €2200 Composition (22x21cm-9x8in) s. mixed media paper on canvas prov. 24-Mar-3 Cornette de St.Cyr, Paris #26/R
£1740 $2750 €2610 Nun's dream (46x63cm-18x25in) s.i. ink. 22-Apr-3 Butterfields, San Francisco #6018/R est:3000-5000
£1761 $2730 €2800 Mathilde (36x28cm-14x11in) s. col ink Indian ink. 30-Oct-2 Artcurial Briest, Paris #263/R est:1800-2200
£2708 $4279 €3900 Couple (43x50cm-17x20in) s. col ink dr prov. 27-Apr-3 Perrin, Versailles #69/R est:4000-4500
£3165 $4937 €5000 Profils (31x24cm-12x9in) s.d.1965 gouache ink feltpen. 20-Oct-2 Claude Boisgirard, Paris #29/R est:5000-6000
£3425 $5377 €5000 Untitled (26x20cm-10x8in) ink. 15-Apr-3 Laurence Calmels, Paris #4363/R
£4167 $6583 €6000 Entre l'oiseau et la plante (26x19cm-10x7in) i. pastel ball point pen. 27-Apr-3 Perrin, Versailles #67/R est:5000-6000
£5000 $8350 €7250 Les fruits insolites. Goya (37x25cm-15x10in) s. indis i. brush ink double-sided executed 1947 exhib.lit. 24-Jun-3 Sotheby's, London #247/R est:5000-7000
£6500 $10595 €9750 Mandolines et cartes (48x63cm-19x25in) s. pastel exec.1923 prov.exhib. 3-Feb-3 Christie's, London #167/R
£7292 $11594 €10500 Paysage aux chasseurs (24x31cm-9x12in) pastel prov. 29-Apr-3 Artcurial Briest, Paris #125/R est:6000-8000
£8392 $14014 €12000 L'enfant au livre (49x41cm-19x16in) s. pastel prov. 26-Jun-3 Tajan, Paris #170/R est:12000-15000
£8654 $13587 €13500 Baladins (32x24cm-13x9in) i. s.d.1947 verso pastel. 15-Dec-2 Perrin, Versailles #83/R est:12000
£9000 $13860 €13500 Metamorphose (66x51cm-26x20in) s.d.1954 i.d.verso brush ink prov. 22-Oct-2 Sotheby's, London #140/R est:6000-8000
£10764 $17760 €15500 Promethee (37x46cm-15x18in) studio st. pastel ink. 2-Jul-3 Artcurial Briest, Paris #703/R est:9000-12000
£13699 $21507 €20000 Glory (37x29cm-15x11in) s.d.1928 ink. 15-Apr-3 Laurence Calmels, Paris #4362/R est:5000
£16000 $24640 €24000 Chevalier (62x47cm-24x19in) s. pastel black crayon executed 1926 prov. 22-Oct-2 Sotheby's, London #141/R est:18000-25000
£174658 $272466 €255000 Le jeu de Marseille (27x17cm-11x7in) gouache crayon ink exhib.lit. 14-Apr-3 Laurence Calmels, Paris #4054/R est:6000

MASSON, Clovis (1838-1913) French

Sculpture
£2302 $3683 €3200 Cerf, Biche et Faon, famille de chevreuils (60x60cm-24x24in) s. black pat. bronze. 17-May-3 De Vuyst, Lokeren #254/R est:3300-4000
£7194 $11511 €10000 Gorille terrassant un lion (51x61x41cm-20x24x16in) s. gilt brown pat bronze exhib. 18-May-3 Rabourdin & Choppin de Janvry, Paris #100 est:12500-15000

MASSON, E (?) French

Works on paper
£253 $395 €400 Nature morte a la chruche fleurie (70x50cm-28x20in) pastel. 16-Sep-2 Amberes, Antwerp #224

MASSON, Edouard (1881-1950) Belgian
£385 $596 €600 Industrial landscape (29x36cm-11x14in) canvas on plywood lit. 7-Dec-2 Bergmann, Erlangen #800/R
£544 $865 €800 Vue rue de Montmartre a Paris (56x46cm-22x18in) s. 19-Mar-3 Hotel des Ventes Mosan, Brussels #240

Works on paper
£340 $541 €500 Un bouquet de roses (58x50cm-23x20in) s. pastel. 19-Mar-3 Hotel des Ventes Mosan, Brussels #241
£532 $888 €750 Le bouquet champetre (73x100cm-29x39in) pastel canvas. 18-Jun-3 Hotel des Ventes Mosan, Brussels #202
£696 $1086 €1100 Salome (41x50cm-16x20in) s. pastel. 15-Oct-2 Horta, Bruxelles #91
£701 $1093 €1100 Jeune fille nue au collier (55x45cm-22x18in) s.i.d.1918 pastel. 11-Nov-2 Horta, Bruxelles #22

MASSON, Henri Jacques (1908-1995) French
£324 $516 €470 Les amandiers (37x55cm-15x22in) s. prov. 1-May-3 Heffel, Vancouver #67/R (C.D 750)

MASSON, Henri L (1907-1996) Canadian
£930 $1460 €1395 Pouch Cove (30x41cm-12x16in) i.d.69 s.verso board. 24-Jul-2 Walker's, Ottawa #235/R est:2500-3000 (C.D 2250)
£987 $1470 €1481 Quidi vidi NFLD (41x51cm-16x20in) s. i.verso masonite. 26-Jun-2 Iegor de Saint Hippolyte, Montreal #63/R (C.D 2250)
£1029 $1584 €1544 Automne a Buckingham (30x40cm-12x16in) s. 22-Oct-2 Iegor de Saint Hippolyte, Montreal #72 (C.D 2500)
£1073 $1674 €1556 Indian harbour, Nova Scotia (25x30cm-10x12in) s.i. board. 26-Mar-3 Walker's, Ottawa #412/R est:2000-2500 (C.D 2500)
£1152 $1786 €1728 Pond (25x30cm-10x12in) s. canvasboard painted c.1940 prov. 3-Dec-2 Joyner, Toronto #92/R est:2500-3000 (C.D 2800)
£1317 $2028 €1976 Riviere du Loup (41x51cm-16x20in) s. 22-Oct-2 Iegor de Saint Hippolyte, Montreal #70 (C.D 3200)
£1333 $2187 €2000 November, Wakefield (37x42cm-15x17in) s. board painted 1940. 3-Jun-3 Joyner, Toronto #170/R est:3500-4500 (C.D 3000)
£1378 $2260 €1998 Fishing village (45x60cm-18x24in) s. 9-Jun-3 Hodgins, Calgary #46/R est:4000-5000 (C.D 3100)
£1422 $2332 €2133 Autumn landscape (40x50cm-16x20in) s. board. 3-Jun-3 Joyner, Toronto #253/R est:3000-4000 (C.D 3200)
£1440 $2233 €2160 Notre Dame du portage (40x50cm-16x20in) s. 3-Dec-2 Joyner, Toronto #166/R est:3000-4000 (C.D 3500)
£1457 $2332 €2186 Rain mood, Hull (38x46cm-15x18in) s. i.verso prov. 15-May-3 Heffel, Vancouver #18/R est:2500-3500 (C.D 3250)
£1564 $2424 €2346 Fall's palette (45x60cm-18x24in) s. board. 3-Dec-2 Joyner, Toronto #4/R est:5000-6000 (C.D 3800)
£1689 $2770 €2534 March landscape near Old Chelsea (50x65cm-20x26in) s. 3-Jun-3 Joyner, Toronto #35/R est:4000-6000 (C.D 3800)
£1824 $2845 €2645 Recital (20x25cm-8x10in) s. board exhib. 26-Mar-3 Walker's, Ottawa #271/R est:2000-3000 (C.D 4250)
£1867 $3061 €2801 Melting snow, Buckingham, Que (40x50cm-16x20in) s. prov. 3-Jun-3 Joyner, Toronto #213/R est:3000-5000 (C.D 4200)
£2222 $3644 €3333 Village in the Gatineau Hills (45x52cm-18x20in) s.d.Sept 1938. 3-Jun-3 Joyner, Toronto #25/R est:5000-7000 (C.D 5000)
£2510 $3966 €3765 Still life in landscape (66x81cm-26x32in) d.1960. 1-Dec-2 Levis, Calgary #64/R est:3500-4500 (C.D 6250)
£3333 $5467 €5000 October, Farm Point, Que (76x102cm-30x40in) s. s.i.d.1985 on stretcher. 27-May-3 Sotheby's, Toronto #134/R est:4000-6000 (C.D 7500)
£4449 $7074 €6674 Near Perkins, Quebec (60x75cm-24x30in) s.i.d.1965 prov. 23-Mar-3 Hodgins, Calgary #79/R est:8000-10000 (C.D 10500)
£4638 $7606 €6957 Backyard hockey (60x75cm-24x30in) s. prov.exhib. 3-Jun-3 Joyner, Toronto #94/R est:12000-15000 (C.D 10435)

Works on paper
£215 $335 €312 Kingston (46x61cm-18x24in) s.i.d.1950 chl dr. 26-Mar-3 Walker's, Ottawa #421/R (C.D 500)
£215 $335 €312 Honda Valley, California (46x58cm-18x23in) s.i.d.1949 chl. 26-Mar-3 Walker's, Ottawa #464/R (C.D 500)
£343 $559 €515 Vivaldi (35x43cm-14x17in) s. pastel. 12-Feb-3 Iegor de Saint Hippolyte, Montreal #135 (C.D 850)
£386 $603 €560 Forest pool (36x51cm-14x20in) s. W/C. 26-Mar-3 Walker's, Ottawa #434/R est:1000-1500 (C.D 900)
£429 $670 €622 Plazza del Campo (35x41cm-14x16in) s.i. mixed media. 26-Mar-3 Walker's, Ottawa #458/R est:1000-1500 (C.D 1000)
£522 $814 €870 Claridorme, Quebec (35x43cm-14x17in) s.i. W/C mixed media paper on board prov. 13-Apr-3 Levis, Calgary #83/R est:1500-2000 (C.D 1200)

MASSON, Jules-Edmond (1871-1932) French

Sculpture
£1000 $1540 €1500 Stag and a doe (43x40cm-17x16in) s. bronze. 5-Sep-2 Sotheby's, Olympia #119/R est:1200-1500
£1086 $1760 €1575 Stag (53cm-21in) s. brown pat.bronze on stone socle. 26-May-3 Bukowskis, Stockholm #310/R (S.KR 14000)
£1258 $2051 €1900 Deux groenendaels (52cm-20in) s. pat bronze. 17-Feb-3 Horta, Bruxelles #41
£1795 $2782 €2800 Couple de cerfs (70cm-28in) s. bronze. 3-Dec-2 Campo & Campo, Antwerp #196/R est:3000-4000
£1987 $3238 €3000 Napoleon (46cm-18in) s. pat bronze. 17-Feb-3 Horta, Bruxelles #42

MASSON, M (1911-1988) French
£296 $476 €420 Chapelle de Kerdevot pres de Quimper (60x73cm-24x29in) s. 11-May-3 Thierry & Lannon, Brest #381

MASSON, Marcel (1911-1988) French
£278 $447 €417 Montmartre street (46x55cm-18x22in) s. 7-May-3 Dobiaschofsky, Bern #813/R (S.FR 600)

MASSONET, Armand (1892-1979) Belgian
£360 $576 €500 Couple se promenant sur les quais de Paris (27x22cm-11x9in) s. 13-May-3 Vanderkindere, Brussels #81
£532 $888 €750 Le Torero (64x54cm-25x21in) s. 18-Jun-3 Hotel des Ventes Mosan, Brussels #269
£532 $888 €750 Chateau Beauvoorde, Wulveringen (50x34cm-20x13in) s.d.1917 canvas laid down. 17-Jun-3 Palais de Beaux Arts, Brussels #596
£823 $1284 €1300 Portrait d'homme au journal (80x70cm-31x28in) s.d.decembre 1968. 10-Sep-2 Vanderkindere, Brussels #292
£1076 $1678 €1700 Elegante au bouquet de fleurs (27x22cm-11x9in) s. panel. 15-Oct-2 Horta, Bruxelles #27
£1203 $1876 €1900 Elegante se mirant (27x22cm-11x9in) s. panel. 15-Oct-2 Horta, Bruxelles #26
Works on paper
£315 $492 €460 Les musiciens (30x23cm-12x9in) s. W/C. 14-Apr-3 Horta, Bruxelles #29

MASSONI, Egisto (fl.1880-1885) Italian
£2600 $4316 €3900 Venetian canal view. Marano (29x50cm-11x20in) s.i. panel pair. 10-Jun-3 Bonhams, Knightsbridge #101/R est:1800-2500

MASSOULE, Andre Paul Arthur (1851-1901) French
Sculpture
£962 $1490 €1500 Fille assise sur un banc (71cm-28in) s. bronze. 3-Dec-2 Campo & Campo, Antwerp #197/R est:1800-2200

MASTENBROEK, Clary (1947-) Dutch
£828 $1316 €1200 Noodlot (35x40cm-14x16in) init.d.84 board prov. 10-Mar-3 Sotheby's, Amsterdam #306/R est:900-1200
£896 $1425 €1300 Uitzicht (27x43cm-11x17in) init.d.83 board prov. 10-Mar-3 Sotheby's, Amsterdam #305/R est:900-1200

MASTENBROEK, Johann Hendrik van (1875-1945) Dutch
£1146 $1789 €1800 Unsettled evening in Schiedam (21x32cm-8x13in) s.d.1905. 5-Nov-2 Vendu Notarishuis, Rotterdam #180/R est:1800-2200
£1549 $2494 €2200 Arensdorf building site (68x179cm-27x70in) s.i.d.1940. 7-May-3 Vendue Huis, Gravenhage #88 est:1000-1500
£1911 $2981 €3000 Storm (69x129cm-27x51in) s.d.38. 6-Nov-2 Vendue Huis, Gravenhage #568/R est:3000-4000
£6500 $10855 €9750 Rotterdam sunset (40x60cm-16x24in) s.d.1910 prov. 18-Jun-3 Christie's, Kensington #45/R est:7000-10000
£9434 $14528 €15000 Een haven vol schepen - harbour full of ships (71x131cm-28x52in) s.d.1928 prov. 22-Oct-2 Sotheby's, Amsterdam #213/R est:15000-20000
Works on paper
£287 $441 €450 Sailing barge - a study (18x20cm-7x8in) s.i.d.1895 pencil black chk W/C htd white. 3-Sep-2 Christie's, Amsterdam #293
£724 $1172 €1100 Three men hunting (24x32cm-9x13in) s. black crayon W/C htd white. 21-Jan-3 Christie's, Amsterdam #211/R est:1000-1500
£915 $1474 €1300 Town view with moored boats (26x19cm-10x7in) s.d.54 W/C. 7-May-3 Vendue Huis, Gravenhage #529
£2532 $3949 €4000 Activity in Rotterdam harbour (22x31cm-9x12in) s.d.21 W/C. 21-Oct-2 Glerum, Amsterdam #105/R est:4500-5500
£2917 $4638 €4200 Barges along a quay in a city (32x16cm-13x6in) s. W/C htd white. 29-Apr-3 Christie's, Amsterdam #149/R est:4000-6000
£3774 $5811 €6000 Canal scene (52x71cm-20x28in) s.d.1910 W/C. 22-Oct-2 Sotheby's, Amsterdam #108/R est:6000-8000
£3822 $5962 €6000 Rotterdam market scene (20x33cm-8x13in) s.d.1906 gouache W/C htd white. 6-Nov-2 Vendue Huis, Gravenhage #575 est:1000-1500
£5263 $8526 €8000 Drawbridge at Delftshaven (49x70cm-19x28in) s.d.1907 col crayon W/C bodycol htd white. 21-Jan-3 Christie's, Amsterdam #342/R est:2500-3500

MASTER G Z (circle) (15th C) German
£17986 $28777 €25000 Madonna with Child in rose bower (65x45cm-26x18in) tempera on panel prov. 17-May-3 Lempertz, Koln #1078/R est:25000

MASTER M Z (c.1477-c.1555) German
Prints
£2692 $4200 €4038 King's sons shooting their father's corpse (18x25cm-7x10in) engraving exec.c.1500. 6-Nov-2 Swann Galleries, New York #12/R est:4000-6000
£3718 $5800 €5577 Embrace (16x12cm-6x5in) engraving. 6-Nov-2 Swann Galleries, New York #16/R est:7000-10000
£4487 $7000 €6731 Aristotle and Phyllis (18x12cm-7x5in) engraving. 6-Nov-2 Swann Galleries, New York #13/R est:5000-8000

MASTER OF 1458 (15th C) Italian
£29000 $45240 €43500 Saint Jerome (90x46cm-35x18in) i. tempera panel gold ground arched top prov. 10-Apr-3 Sotheby's, London #19/R est:20000

MASTER OF 1518 (16th C) Flemish
£86331 $138130 €120000 Biblical scenes (106x30cm-42x12in) triptych panel prov.lit. 17-May-3 Lempertz, Koln #1079/R est:120000-130000

MASTER OF 1518 (circle) (16th C) Flemish
£10976 $18000 €16464 Adoration of the Magi (82x58cm-32x23in) panel. 29-May-3 Sotheby's, New York #127/R est:20000-30000

MASTER OF ALKMAAR (15th C) Flemish
£6757 $10541 €10000 David dansant devant Abigail (143x47cm-56x19in) panel diptych. 28-Mar-3 Piasa, Paris #10/R

MASTER OF ASTORGA (16th C) Italian?
£5183 $8500 €7775 Salome presenting the head of St John the Baptist (86x83cm-34x33in) panel on board prov.lit. 5-Feb-3 Christie's, Rockefeller NY #273 est:4000-6000

MASTER OF BORGO ALLA COLLINA (?) ?
£39000 $60840 €58500 Madonna and Child with saints (85x58cm-33x23in) tempera panel gold ground arched top prov.lit. 10-Apr-3 Sotheby's, London #20/R est:60000

MASTER OF CARMIGNANO (15th C) Italian
£42759 $68414 €62000 Madonna and Child enthroned (89x52cm-35x20in) tempera board. 17-Mar-3 Pandolfini, Florence #679/R est:65000-70000

MASTER OF CUBELLS (14th C) Spanish
£6757 $10541 €10000 Mise au tombeau entre Saint Jean et Sainte Catherine, la Vierge et Marie Madeleine (56x32cm-22x13in) panel prov.lit. 28-Mar-3 Piasa, Paris #13/R est:8000

MASTER OF FRANKFURT (c.1490-1515) Dutch
£18519 $30000 €27779 Saint Elizabeth. Saint James of Compostella (74x44cm-29x17in) panel pair exhib.lit. 23-Jan-3 Sotheby's, New York #147/R est:35000
£75342 $117534 €110000 Saint Isabelle of Hungary and Santiago de Compostela (74x44cm-29x17in) board pair part of triptych. 8-Apr-3 Ansorena, Madrid #76/R est:100000

MASTER OF LANAJA (attrib) (15th C) Spanish
£15385 $25693 €22000 Joachime et Anne expulses du temple (142x88cm-56x35in) gold panel five boards prov. 25-Jun-3 Tajan, Paris #2/R est:25000-35000

MASTER OF LANAJA (studio) (15th C) Spanish
£25176 $42043 €36000 Le deposition de croix. La fuite en Egypte (83x69cm-33x27in) panel pair. 25-Jun-3 Tajan, Paris #3/R est:40000-60000

MASTER OF MARTINEZ (15/16th C) Spanish
£25000 $39250 €37500 Adoration of the Magi (58x46cm-23x18in) panel. 12-Dec-2 Sotheby's, London #108/R est:15000-20000

MASTER OF OSMA (15th C) Spanish
£35000 $54600 €52500 Madonna and Child (21x28cm-8x11in) panel. 10-Apr-3 Sotheby's, London #18/R est:8000-12000

MASTER OF PANZANO (14th C) Italian
£208333 $331250 €300000 Madonna and Child with Saints (56x141cm-22x56in) tempera gold board triptych prov.lit. 4-May-3 Finarte, Venice #578/R est:350000-400000

MASTER OF PEREA (attrib) (fl.1490-1505) Spanish
£23148 $37500 €34722 Holy Family (42x31cm-17x12in) panel prov.lit. 23-Jan-3 Sotheby's, New York #148/R est:60000

MASTER OF SAINT BENTO (16th C) Portuguese
£80301 $126876 €125270 Scenes from Saint Michael's life (167x215cm-66x85in) board lit. 14-Nov-2 Arte, Seville #155/R

MASTER OF SAINT CATERINA GUALINO (14th C) Italian
Sculpture
£167785 $270134 €250000 Madonna and Child enthroned (137cm-54in) painted wood lit. 19-Feb-3 Semenzato, Venice #79/R est:280000

MASTER OF SAINT GILLES (attrib) (fl.1490-1510) French
£85000 $141950 €123250 Virgin and child (32x21cm-13x8in) i. oil gold ground panel prov. 9-Jul-3 Christie's, London #3/R est:15000-25000

MASTER OF SAN MARTINO ALFIERI (16th C) Italian
£25610 $42000 €38415 Assumption of the Virgin (211x134cm-83x53in) panel arched top prov.lit. 30-May-3 Christie's, Rockefeller NY #23/R est:20000-30000

MASTER OF THE ACQUAVELLA STILL LIFE (attrib) (17th C) Italian
£7000 $10850 €10500 Still life of fruit and almonds on stone ledge (48x63cm-19x25in) 31-Oct-2 Sotheby's, Olympia #144/R est:5000-7000

MASTER OF THE ANNUNCIATION TO THE SHEPHERDS (attrib) (17th C) Italian
£15385 $25692 €22000 Homme mourant entoure de deux personnages (100x125cm-39x49in) 27-Jun-3 Piasa, Paris #15/R est:22000-25000

MASTER OF THE APOLLO AND DAPHNE LEGEND (style) (c.1480-c.1510) Italian
£23022 $36835 €32000 Christ on the cross (149x108cm-59x43in) tempera oil panel crucifix. 13-May-3 Sotheby's, Amsterdam #76/R est:4000-6000

MASTER OF THE ARGONAUTS (15th C) Italian
£33951 $55000 €50927 Mystic marriage of Saint Catherine of Alexandria (69x44cm-27x17in) panel top corners made up prov.lit. 24-Jan-3 Christie's, Rockefeller NY #27/R est:10000-15000

MASTER OF THE ASHMOLEAN PREDELLA (15th C) Italian
£82278 $130000 €130000 Madonna and Child with Saint Francis and Saint Margaret (74x50cm-29x20in) tempera gold board prov.lit. 29-Nov-2 Semenzato, Venice #614/R est:60000-75000

MASTER OF THE BADIA A ISOLA (attrib) (fl.1290-1320) Italian
£11585 $19000 €17378 Madonna and Child (67x44cm-26x17in) gold ground panel arched top prov.exhib. 29-May-3 Sotheby's, New York #80/R est:10000-15000

MASTER OF THE BERGWOLKEN (studio) (fl.1470-1480) German
Prints
£30000 $46500 €45000 Madonna nursing the child (18x12cm-7x5in) dotted metal cut executed c.1470-80 prov. 3-Dec-2 Christie's, London #87/R est:35000-45000

MASTER OF THE CORRADINO BIBLE (13th C) Italian
Miniatures
£53691 $86443 €80000 Saint Benedict delivering the code (34x27cm-13x11in) paper. 19-Feb-3 Semenzato, Venice #212/R est:100000

MASTER OF THE CORTONA TONDO (15/16th C) Italian
£50000 $78500 €75000 Holy Family with St John the Baptist and female saint (76cm-30in circular) panel prov. 12-Dec-2 Sotheby's, London #103/R est:12000-18000

MASTER OF THE FEMALE HALF LENGTHS (16th C) Flemish
£25601 $41474 €37121 Christ being stared at (25x19cm-10x7in) panel prov.lit. 26-May-3 Bukowskis, Stockholm #373/R est:100000-125000 (S.KR 330000)

MASTER OF THE FEMALE HALF LENGTHS (attrib) (16th C) Flemish
£5256 $8147 €8200 Vanitas allegory - Young lute player and old man holding a skull (77x62cm-30x24in) panel. 4-Dec-2 Neumeister, Munich #613/R est:6500
£12000 $20040 €17400 Penitent Saint Jerome (48x38cm-19x15in) panel. 9-Jul-3 Christie's, London #22/R est:15000-20000

MASTER OF THE GAMES (17th C) French
£195804 $326993 €280000 La danse d'enfants au joueur de pochette (95x120cm-37x47in) prov.exhib.lit. 25-Jun-3 Sotheby's, Paris #9/R est:300000-400000

MASTER OF THE GIOVANELLI MADONNA (14/15th C) Italian
£27848 $44000 €44000 Madonna and Child (46x29cm-18x11in) board. 27-Nov-2 Finarte, Milan #125/R est:35000-45000
£164528 $256664 €261600 Christ with other figures (28x20cm-11x8in) tempera gold. 21-Sep-2 Semenzato, Venice #140/R

MASTER OF THE HOLY BLOOD (attrib) (16th C) Flemish
£32000 $53440 €46400 Virgin and Child (30x23cm-12x9in) oil gold ground panel arched top prov.exhib. 9-Jul-3 Christie's, London #4/R est:15000-20000

MASTER OF THE HOLY BLOOD (style) (16th C) Flemish
£16000 $25120 €24000 Adoration of the Magi (102x139cm-40x55in) panel triptych. 10-Dec-2 Sotheby's, Olympia #326/R est:8000-12000

MASTER OF THE JOHNSON ASSUMPTION OF THE MAGDALEN (fl.1500) Italian
£49383 $80000 €74075 Madonna and Child (88cm-35in circular) tempera on panel prov.lit. 23-Jan-3 Sotheby's, New York #33/R est:100000-150000

MASTER OF THE LANGMATT FOUNDATION VIEW (fl.1740-1770) Italian
£28000 $46760 €40600 Elegant figures in the Piazzetta, Venice with view of San Giorgio Maggiore (56x80cm-22x31in) 9-Jul-3 Bonhams, New Bond Street #32/R est:12000-18000
£35127 $54446 €55500 Vue de Grand Canal avec le pont Rialto (81x124cm-32x49in) 27-Sep-2 Rabourdin & Choppin de Janvry, Paris #168/R est:30000-45000

MASTER OF THE LANGMATT FOUNDATION VIEW (circle) (fl.1740-1770) Italian
£6962 $11000 €11000 View of the Arsenal in Venice (45x72cm-18x28in) 27-Nov-2 Finarte, Milan #68/R
£18000 $28080 €27000 Rome, view of the Arch of Constantine (52x88cm-20x35in) 10-Apr-3 Sotheby's, London #97/R est:20000

MASTER OF THE LANGMATT FOUNDATION VIEW (style) (fl.1740-1770) Italian
£11000 $18370 €15950 Piazzetta, Venice looking south towards S. Giorgio Maggiore (74x113cm-29x44in) 9-Jul-3 Bonhams, New Bond Street #163/R est:6000-8000

MASTER OF THE MADONNA CAGNOLA (?-1476) Italian
£106250 $168938 €153000 Saint Christopher (72x44cm-28x17in) tempera gold board prov.lit. 4-May-3 Finarte, Venice #572/R est:165000-185000
£106250 $168938 €153000 Saint Lawrence (72x44cm-28x17in) tempera gold board prov.lit. 4-May-3 Finarte, Venice #573/R est:165000-185000
£106944 $170042 €154000 Saint Jerome (72x44cm-28x17in) tempera gold board prov.lit. 4-May-3 Finarte, Venice #574/R est:165000-185000

MASTER OF THE MADONNA D'ORTE (fl.1525) Italian
£4630 $7500 €6945 Madonna and Child with cherubs (49x35cm-19x14in) panel. 24-Jan-3 Christie's, Rockefeller NY #77/R est:8000-12000

MASTER OF THE MADONNA LAZZARONE (15th C) Italian
£27000 $42390 €40500 Madonna and Child enthroned with Saints and angels (65x44cm-26x17in) tempera gold ground panel. 12-Dec-2 Sotheby's, London #101/R est:15000-20000

MASTER OF THE METROPOLITAN (17th C) Italian
£35000 $58450 €50750 Melon, peaches, figs and other fruits, carnations on a step on a rocky ledge (50x38cm-20x15in) prov. 9-Jul-3 Christie's, London #85/R est:18000-25000

MASTER OF THE METROPOLITAN MUSEUM (attrib) (17th C) ?
£16352 $25346 €26000 Still life of fruit in palace gardens (97x122cm-38x48in) 2-Oct-2 Dorotheum, Vienna #48/R est:25000-35000

MASTER OF THE PARROT (circle) (16th C) Flemish
£17000 $28390 €24650 Mary Magdalene reading, seated before an open window (45x29cm-18x11in) panel. 10-Jul-3 Sotheby's, London #108/R est:15000-20000

MASTER OF THE PRODIGAL SON (attrib) (16th C) Flemish
£24460 $39137 €34000 Susanna and the elders (101x127cm-40x50in) panel. 13-May-3 Sotheby's, Amsterdam #36/R est:18000-20000

MASTER OF THE STERZINGER ALTARPIECE (circle) (15th C) German
£15000 $23400 €22500 Saint Odile (56x30cm-22x12in) panel from wing of a triptych prov.lit. 9-Apr-3 Christie's, London #63/R est:10000-15000

MASTER OF THE TIBURTINE SIBYL (fl.1480-1495) Flemish
£231707 $380000 €347561 Virgin seated on a low wall picking a flower for Christ (35x23cm-14x9in) d.1468 prov.exhib.lit. 29-May-3 Sotheby's, New York #128/R est:200000-300000

MASTER OF THE UNRULY CHILDREN (16th C) Italian
Sculpture
£14839 $23445 €23000 Charity (54x38x22cm-21x15x9in) painted terracotta. 19-Dec-2 Semenzato, Venice #46/R est:30000

MASTER OF THE UNRULY CHILDREN (attrib) (16th C) Italian
Sculpture
£15432 $25000 €23148 Virgin (55cm-22in) painted terracotta prov.lit. 23-Jan-3 Sotheby's, New York #193a/R est:20000

MASTER OF TRESSA (13th C) Italian
£296774 $468903 €460000 Nativity (33x43cm-13x17in) i. tempera board lit. 19-Dec-2 Semenzato, Venice #29/R est:300000
£296774 $468903 €460000 Eraclius bringing the Cross back to Jerusalem (29x43cm-11x17in) i. tempera board lit. 19-Dec-2 Semenzato, Venice #30/R est:300000

MASTER OF VOLTERRA (16th C) Italian
£8974 $13910 €14000 Madonna and Child (100x72cm-39x28in) board. 4-Dec-2 Christie's, Rome #481/R est:20000

MASTER WITH THE PINK (c.1480-c.1510) Swiss
£7595 $11772 €12000 St Barbara and St Elisabeth of Thuringen (68x46cm-27x18in) i. verso panel prov. 25-Sep-2 Neumeister, Munich #507/R est:14000

MASTERS, Edward (19th C) British
£1100 $1804 €1650 Start of the day (25x46cm-10x18in) 29-May-3 Christie's, Kensington #252/R est:1000-1500
£1700 $2788 €2550 End of the day (25x46cm-10x18in) bears sig. 29-May-3 Christie's, Kensington #254/R est:1500-2000

MASTERS, Edward (attrib) (19th C) British
£260 $406 €390 Stagecoach before an inn (31x46cm-12x18in) 23-Sep-2 Bonhams, Chester #952

MASTERS, Edwin (19th C) British
£2500 $3900 €3750 Outside, The Horse's Head, Village Green, Hampstead (51x75cm-20x30in) 17-Sep-2 Sotheby's, Olympia #175a/R est:1500-2000
£6200 $10106 €9300 Extemsive imaginary rural landscapes with numerous figures and animals (48x74cm-19x29in) s. pair prov. 14-Feb-3 Keys, Aylsham #678/R est:3000-4000

MASTERS, Edwin (attrib) (19th C) British
£2000 $3160 €3000 Wayfarers meeting outside a village inn. Farmyard scene with figures on horseback (44x34cm-17x13in) pair. 26-Nov-2 Bonhams, Oxford #67/R est:2000-3000

MASTROIANNI, Umberto (1910-1998) Italian
£769 $1208 €1200 Composition (16x16cm-6x6in) s. varnish on lead plate. 21-Nov-2 Finarte, Rome #14/R
£972 $1546 €1400 Europe (22x30cm-9x12in) s. enamel copper. 1-May-3 Meeting Art, Vercelli #159
£994 $1570 €1550 Untitled (50x70cm-20x28in) 12-Nov-2 Babuino, Rome #305/R
Sculpture
£962 $1510 €1500 Assiria (21x38cm-8x15in) s. Carrara marble. 23-Nov-2 Meeting Art, Vercelli #40/R
£962 $1510 €1500 Towards the centre (21x40cm-8x16in) s. marble. 23-Nov-2 Meeting Art, Vercelli #264/R
£1154 $1812 €1800 Centre of gravity (21x40x7cm-8x16x3in) s. Carrara marble. 19-Nov-2 Finarte, Milan #266/R
£1781 $2778 €2600 Composition (100x70cm-39x28in) s. copper enamel board exec.1967. 10-Apr-3 Finarte Semenzato, Rome #218/R
£1835 $2863 €2900 Woman (32x17x8cm-13x7x3in) s. bronze. 14-Sep-2 Meeting Art, Vercelli #796/R
£2138 $3421 €3100 Untitled (28cm-11in) s. num.4/9 gilt pat bronze. 11-Mar-3 Babuino, Rome #267/R
£3165 $4937 €5000 Mask (17x12cm-7x5in) s. bronze marble base exec.1937. 14-Sep-2 Meeting Art, Vercelli #798/R
Works on paper
£694 $1104 €1000 Summer (35x25cm-14x10in) s. mixed media card. 1-May-3 Meeting Art, Vercelli #473
£962 $1510 €1500 Limina (25x40cm-10x16in) s. painted lead. 20-Nov-2 Pandolfini, Florence #144/R
£980 $1569 €1500 Mythological bird (50x35cm-20x14in) s. mixed media card. 4-Jan-3 Meeting Art, Vercelli #556
£1307 $2092 €2000 Space car (40x50cm-16x20in) s. mixed media card lit. 4-Jan-3 Meeting Art, Vercelli #355/R
£1701 $2704 €2500 Natural cells (56x41cm-22x16in) s. mixed media card exhib.lit. 1-Mar-3 Meeting Art, Vercelli #626

MASTURZIO, Marzio (fl.1670) Italian
£7233 $11138 €11500 Battle scene (73x108cm-29x43in) 23-Oct-2 Finarte, Rome #516/R

MASTURZIO, Marzio (attrib) (fl.1670) Italian
£4000 $6200 €6000 Landscape with an army on the march (45x66cm-18x26in) 31-Oct-2 Sotheby's, Olympia #132/R est:4000-8000
£18354 $29000 €29000 Battle scenes (90x134cm-35x53in) pair. 27-Nov-2 Finarte, Milan #84/R est:30000-40000

MASUCCI, Agostino (attrib) (1691-1758) Italian
Works on paper
£2500 $4175 €3625 Annunciation (36x26cm-14x10in) i. i.verso black white red chk prov. 8-Jul-3 Christie's, London #12/R est:3000-5000

MASUDA, Makoto (20th C) Japanese?
Works on paper
£517 $822 €750 Vue de port (54x81cm-21x32in) s. 4-Mar-3 Livinec, Gaudcheau & Jezequel, Rennes #120

MASUI, Paul Auguste (1888-1981) Luxembourger
£377 $591 €550 La digue (34x40cm-13x16in) s. cardboard. 15-Apr-3 Galerie Moderne, Brussels #397
£596 $972 €900 Martigues (34x40cm-13x16in) s. panel. 17-Feb-3 Horta, Bruxelles #462
£637 $994 €1000 Le passeur (88x78cm-35x31in) s.i.d.1976 verso. 11-Nov-2 Horta, Bruxelles #639
£4114 $6418 €6500 Quai de Paris anime (50x65cm-20x26in) s. panel. 15-Oct-2 Horta, Bruxelles #90/R

MASULLI, Pietro (19th C) Italian
Sculpture
£3600 $6012 €5220 Giordano Bruno (58cm-23in) s.d.1861 brown pat bronze. 8-Jul-3 Sotheby's, London #225/R est:3000-5000

MASURE, Jules (1819-1910) French
£633 $981 €1000 Jardin potager pres d'un rivage mediteraneen (24x32cm-9x13in) s. panel. 29-Sep-2 Eric Pillon, Calais #21/R

MASUREL, Johannes Engel (1826-1915) Dutch
£526 $853 €800 Farmer at work in a stable (36x46cm-14x18in) s.d.1842 panel. 21-Jan-3 Christie's, Amsterdam #23/R

MASUTTI (?) ?
£1075 $1634 €1613 Preparing potatoes (56x73cm-22x29in) s.d.1948. 28-Aug-2 Deutscher-Menzies, Melbourne #444/R est:800-1200 (A.D 3000)

MASZYNSKI, Julian (1848-1901) Polish
£3205 $5000 €4808 Refusal (51x38cm-20x15in) s. 30-Mar-3 Susanin's, Chicago #6024/R est:1000-1500

MATAL, Bohumir (1922-1988) Czechoslovakian
£590 $956 €885 Composition with birds (20x15cm-8x6in) s.d.58 tempera. 24-May-3 Dorotheum, Prague #192/R est:10000-15000 (C.KR 26000)
Works on paper
£454 $736 €681 Figure (21x16cm-8x6in) s.d.64 ink. 24-May-3 Dorotheum, Prague #190/R est:10000-15000 (C.KR 20000)
£590 $956 €885 Dancer (21x16cm-8x6in) s.d.64 gouache. 24-May-3 Dorotheum, Prague #191/R est:10000-15000 (C.KR 26000)

MATANIA, Fortunino (1881-1963) Italian
£600 $936 €900 Pink and cream roses in a bowl (59x49cm-23x19in) s. 16-Oct-2 Mervyn Carey, Tenterden #159
£1700 $2652 €2550 Seeking father approval (24x29cm-9x11in) s. panel. 16-Oct-2 Mervyn Carey, Tenterden #160/R
£2400 $3912 €3600 Still life of roses (60x50cm-24x20in) s. 29-Jan-3 Sotheby's, Olympia #305/R est:2000-3000
£9000 $14040 €13500 Musical soiree with Beethoven playing the pianoforte (52x44cm-20x17in) s. 16-Oct-2 Mervyn Carey, Tenterden #163/R

Works on paper
£280 $445 €420 Lord Byron, take away as much blood as you will but have done with it (18x27cm-7x11in) s.i. pencil wash dr with drs by the same hand and 1 by another. 5-Mar-3 Bonhams, Bury St Edmunds #295
£380 $600 €570 Challenge of the champion (31x51cm-12x20in) s. i.verso W/C bodycol. 26-Nov-2 Bonhams, Oxford #18
£520 $822 €780 Check-mate, naked maiden seated on a rock in a bay (25x41cm-10x16in) s. W/C. 26-Nov-2 Bonhams, Oxford #17
£18250 $28470 €27375 Elegant Edwardian scene with males and female figures at a polo match (46x67cm-18x26in) W/C. 16-Oct-2 Mervyn Carey, Tenterden #164/R

MATARE, Ewald (1887-1965) German
Prints
£2138 $3336 €3400 Drei kuhe (32x24cm-13x9in) s.i. black brown woodcut. 9-Oct-2 Sotheby's, London #496/R est:3000-5000
£2345 $3705 €3400 Four horses in field (31x54cm-12x21in) s.i. col woodcut. 4-Apr-3 Venator & Hansten, Koln #1926/R est:1200
£2390 $3728 €3800 Gruss an meine kuh III (25x36cm-10x14in) s.i. col woodcut executed c.1950. 9-Oct-2 Sotheby's, London #495/R est:4500-6500
£2482 $4021 €3500 Autumn landscape (40x49cm-16x19in) s. woodcut W/C. 24-May-3 Van Ham, Cologne #397/R est:5000
£2893 $4513 €4600 Zeichen einer weide I (42x42cm-17x17in) s.i. black turquoise woodcut. 9-Oct-2 Sotheby's, London #497/R est:3000-5000
Sculpture
£1408 $2338 €2000 Plaque with hen (25x24cm-10x9in) bronze. 14-Jun-3 Hauswedell & Nolte, Hamburg #1391/R est:1800
£3205 $4968 €5000 Four cows (26x34cm-10x13in) s. verso marquetry wood. 7-Dec-2 Hauswedell & Nolte, Hamburg #888/R est:5000
£9615 $14904 €15000 Mathematical cow I (4x12x150cm-2x5x59in) s. bronze exhib.lit. 4-Dec-2 Lempertz, Koln #906/R est:10000-13000
£11859 $18381 €18500 Horse (9x10cm-4x4in) bronze prov.exhib. 4-Dec-2 Lempertz, Koln #905/R est:14000-15000
£13000 $21320 €19500 Dancing horse (21cm-8in) s. pat bronze lit. 5-Feb-3 Sotheby's, London #240/R est:20000
£14493 $23768 €20000 Mathematical cow I (4cm-2in) bronze prov.exhib.lit. 29-May-3 Lempertz, Koln #796/R est:15000
£15217 $24957 €21000 Reclining calf (5cm-2in) bronze exhib.lit. 29-May-3 Lempertz, Koln #795/R est:10000-12000
£16197 $26887 €23000 Mathematical cow I (4x12x7cm-2x5x3in) bronze. 14-Jun-3 Hauswedell & Nolte, Hamburg #1390/R est:8000
Works on paper
£2222 $3511 €3200 Woodland path (25x35cm-10x14in) s. W/C over pencil board. 26-Apr-3 Dr Lehr, Berlin #349/R est:3000

MATCHITT, Paratene (1933-) New Zealander
Works on paper
£1302 $2031 €1953 Figure with guitar (76x30cm-30x12in) s. crayon paper on board exec.c.1965 prov. 8-Apr-3 Peter Webb, Auckland #69/R est:4000-6000 (NZ.D 3750)

MATEO CHARRIS, Angel (1962-) Spanish
£993 $1619 €1500 Picturesque (27x41cm-11x16in) s. s.i.d.1996 verso prov.exhib. 11-Feb-3 Segre, Madrid #253/R

MATEOS, Francisco (1894-1976) Spanish
£2258 $3568 €3500 Toy (60x97cm-24x38in) s. s.i.d.1961 verso. 18-Dec-2 Ansorena, Madrid #176/R
Works on paper
£483 $763 €700 Friends (15x12cm-6x5in) s. W/C. 1-Apr-3 Segre, Madrid #315/R

MATHEO, Terezo (attrib) (?) ?
£600 $960 €900 Marc Rey (109x84cm-43x33in) 11-Mar-3 Bonhams, Knightsbridge #297/R

MATHER, John (1848-1916) British
£775 $1233 €1163 Trail (75x50cm-30x20in) s.d.1914. 5-May-3 Sotheby's, Melbourne #340 (A.D 2000)
£992 $1568 €1488 Colonial homestead (21x35cm-8x14in) s.d.1881 board. 2-Apr-3 Christie's, Melbourne #43 est:1000-1500 (A.D 2600)

MATHER, Sydney (1944-) Australian
£500 $790 €750 Morning cuppa on the Wallangarauh River (59x90cm-23x35in) s. canvasboard. 18-Nov-2 Joel, Victoria #246 est:1800-2200 (A.D 1400)

MATHEU, Cornelis (17th C) Flemish
£4114 $6500 €6500 Moonlit landscape with fishermen (43x35cm-17x14in) s. panel. 29-Nov-2 Bassenge, Berlin #5374/R est:7500

MATHEWS, John Chester (fl.1884-1912) British
£1900 $3097 €2850 Major Eustace Crawley, mounted on Field Marshall, a bay before a race course (70x91cm-28x36in) s.d.1896. 11-Feb-3 Bonhams, Knowle #77 est:2000-3000

MATHEWS, Michael (20th C) British
Works on paper
£250 $390 €375 Battle of Trafalgar (47x67cm-19x26in) s. W/C. 23-Sep-2 Bonhams, Chester #858

MATHEWSON, Frank Convers (1862-1941) American
£3797 $6000 €5696 Laurel and white birch (64x76cm-25x30in) s.d.1932 s.i.verso. 24-Apr-3 Shannon's, Milford #184/R est:4000-6000

MATHIESEN, Axel (1882-1973) Danish
Works on paper
£478 $775 €693 Children in front of a Christmas display at Stroget (30x24cm-12x9in) s. pencil gouache. 26-May-3 Rasmussen, Copenhagen #1599/R (D.KR 5000)

MATHIESEN, Egon (1907-1976) Danish
£254 $394 €381 Evening II (65x54cm-26x21in) init.d.60 s.d.1960 verso. 1-Oct-2 Rasmussen, Copenhagen #203 (D.KR 3000)
£304 $474 €456 Composition (52x65cm-20x26in) init. masonite. 18-Sep-2 Kunsthallen, Copenhagen #120 (D.KR 3600)
£354 $564 €531 Cyclist in wet snow (100x78cm-39x31in) init.d.marts 70. 29-Apr-3 Kunsthallen, Copenhagen #101 (D.KR 3800)
£517 $801 €776 Cyclist in a snow flurry (100x130cm-39x51in) init.d.52 verso. 4-Dec-2 Kunsthallen, Copenhagen #29/R (D.KR 6000)
£1525 $2547 €2211 Nature morte (131x100cm-52x39in) mono.d.1944-53 verso masonite exhib. 17-Jun-3 Rasmussen, Copenhagen #35/R est:15000-20000 (D.KR 16000)

MATHIESON, J Muir (?) British
£360 $587 €540 Fruit stall by the ferry (56x48cm-22x19in) s. 14-Feb-3 Keys, Aylsham #709/R

MATHIEU, Cornelius (17th C) Dutch
£6051 $9439 €9500 Wooded river landscape with a shepherd and his flock resting (37x50cm-15x20in) indis sig. panel prov.exhib.lit. 5-Nov-2 Sotheby's, Amsterdam #21/R est:10000-15000
£8917 $13911 €14000 Italianate hilly landscape with horsemen resting (66x91cm-26x36in) indis sig.d.43 panel prov.exhib.lit. 5-Nov-2 Sotheby's, Amsterdam #90/R est:15000-20000

MATHIEU, Georges (1921-) French
£2878 $4719 €4000 Composition (48x38cm-19x15in) s.i.d.58 oil brush canvas on cardboard. 3-Jun-3 Christie's, Amsterdam #96/R est:5000-7000
£4200 $6888 €6300 Chissay (92x60cm-36x24in) s.d.69 i.stretcher prov. 7-Feb-3 Sotheby's, London #219/R est:4000-6000
£4430 $7000 €7000 Temps infidele (91x73cm-36x29in) s. i.verso painted 1989 prov. 27-Nov-2 Tajan, Paris #32/R est:9000-10000
£4686 $7216 €7450 Composition (49x64cm-19x25in) s paper prov.exhib. 26-Oct-2 Cornette de St.Cyr, Paris #8/R
£5000 $8200 €7500 Ghythion (60x73cm-24x29in) s.d.76 i.stretcher prov. 7-Feb-3 Sotheby's, London #220/R est:4000-6000
£5161 $8155 €8000 Vieillesse de roses (73x92cm-29x36in) s. alkyde. 17-Dec-2 Gioffredo, Nice #12/R
£5200 $8008 €7800 Chora (73x92cm-29x36in) s.d.76 i.on stretcher prov. 22-Oct-2 Sotheby's, London #359/R est:5000-7000
£6500 $10010 €9750 Seringa (59x72cm-23x28in) s.d.79 i.on stretcher prov. 22-Oct-2 Sotheby's, London #358/R est:4000-6000
£6500 $10855 €9425 Arbousier (60x73cm-24x29in) s.d.79 i.stretcher prov. 26-Jun-3 Sotheby's, London #195/R est:4000-6000
£8176 $12673 €13000 Dassia (60x80cm-24x31in) s.d.76 i.verso prov. 30-Oct-2 Artcurial Briest, Paris #437/R est:10000-12000
£8805 $13648 €14000 Composition rouge et noire (97x62cm-38x24in) s.d.50 paper. 30-Oct-2 Artcurial Briest, Paris #721/R est:12000-15000
£9000 $15030 €13050 Soothsayer (73x60cm-29x24in) s.d.72 i.stretcher prov. 26-Jun-3 Sotheby's, London #194/R est:5000-7000
£9220 $14936 €13000 Avadel (50x81cm-20x32in) s.d. i.stretcher prov. 26-May-3 Christie's, Milan #367/R est:10000-12000
£9615 $14904 €15000 Plaintes d'epines (145x114cm-57x45in) s. i.verso. 7-Dec-2 Cornette de St.Cyr, Paris #88/R est:15000-20000
£9810 $15500 €15500 Regards las (73x91cm-29x36in) s.d.1969 s.i.verso prov. 27-Nov-2 Tajan, Paris #25/R est:12000-15000
£10417 $17188 €15000 Chimaires (74x92cm-29x36in) s. exhib.lit. 1-Jul-3 Artcurial Briest, Paris #510/R est:15000-20000
£10759 $16785 €17000 Mensonges tendres (100x81cm-39x32in) s. i.verso. 14-Sep-2 Meeting Art, Vercelli #833/R est:15000
£10884 $17306 €16000 Temps infideles (92x72cm-36x28in) s. 1-Mar-3 Meeting Art, Vercelli #366

£11076 $17500 €17500 Daon (92x60cm-36x24in) s. s.i.verso prov. 27-Nov-2 Tajan, Paris #24/R est:9000-12000
£11321 $17547 €18000 Agnetz (92x54cm-36x21in) s.d.65 i.verso. 30-Oct-2 Artcurial Briest, Paris #436/R est:8000-12000
£11950 $18522 €19000 L'ombrage frivole (73x92cm-29x36in) s. 30-Oct-2 Artcurial Briest, Paris #435/R est:15000-18000
£12179 $19122 €19000 Paranadomo (65x130cm-26x51in) s.d.70 prov. 11-Dec-2 Artcurial Briest, Paris #717/R est:22000
£13542 $21396 €19500 Composition (97x162cm-38x64in) painted c.1960 prov. 27-Apr-3 Perrin, Versailles #46/R est:20000-25000
£13924 $22000 €22000 Obscuration verte (130x192cm-51x76in) s.d.1952 s.i.d.verso prov. 27-Nov-2 Tajan, Paris #12/R est:24000-26000
£15000 $25050 €21750 Hommage a Vivaldi (97x162cm-38x64in) s.d.70 i.d.24 Novembre 1970 stretcher prov. 26-Jun-3 Sotheby's, London #200/R est:7000-10000
£26088 $42784 €36000 Untitled (130x84cm-51x33in) s.d.1957. 27-May-3 Tajan, Paris #9/R est:20000-25000
£27000 $45090 €39150 Victoire di Philippe d'Alsatie sur les sarrasins en syrie (98x162cm-39x64in) s.d.58 s.i.d.58 stretcher prov.exhib. 26-Jun-3 Sotheby's, London #198/R est:20000-30000
£30272 $48133 €44500 La bataille d'hiver a Osaka (110x160cm-43x63in) 26-Feb-3 Artcurial Briest, Paris #459/R est:30000-40000

Works on paper

£345 $552 €500 Composition (31x29cm-12x11in) s.d.80 red felt catalogue sheet. 12-Mar-3 Libert, Castor, Paris #149
£828 $1382 €1200 Composition (9x20cm-4x8in) s.i. gold paint collage. 10-Jul-3 Artcurial Briest, Paris #318
£1057 $1575 €1586 Untitled (73x53cm-29x21in) s.d.60 Indian ink W/C. 25-Jun-2 Koller, Zurich #6076 est:1500-2500 (S.FR 2400)
£1300 $2119 €1950 Bois Robert (49x65cm-19x26in) s.d.71 i.verso pastel on card prov. 3-Feb-3 Sotheby's, Olympia #76/R est:1000-1500
£1430 $2231 €2260 Composition (22x27cm-9x11in) mixed media. 15-Oct-2 Babuino, Rome #341/R
£1500 $2505 €2175 Corydon (49x65cm-19x26in) s.d.71 i.verso mixed media collage card prov. 24-Jun-3 Sotheby's, Olympia #80/R est:1000-1500
£1600 $2672 €2320 Untitled (64x49cm-25x19in) s.d.63 mixed media collage card prov. 24-Jun-3 Sotheby's, Olympia #81/R est:1000-1500
£1700 $2771 €2550 Nissaki (50x65cm-20x26in) s.d.71 mixed media collage prov. 3-Feb-3 Sotheby's, Olympia #74/R est:1000-1500
£1710 $2771 €2600 Composition (40x60cm-16x24in) s.d. Indian ink red ink dr. 22-Jan-3 Tajan, Paris #271/R est:2000-3000
£1806 $2871 €2600 Composition (54x75cm-21x30in) s.d.65 mixed media. 29-Apr-3 Artcurial Briest, Paris #583/R est:3500-4000
£1942 $3108 €2700 Composition (69x48cm-27x19in) s.d. gouache mixed media cardboard. 18-May-3 Charbonneaux, Paris #182/R est:3000-4000
£2009 $2933 €3014 Composition sur fond rouge (59x39cm-23x15in) s.d.1958 Indian ink gouache. 4-Jun-2 Germann, Zurich #13/R est:3500-4500 (S.FR 4600)
£2083 $3437 €3000 Composition (55x77cm-22x30in) s.d.68 W/C ink collage. 1-Jul-3 Artcurial Briest, Paris #791/R est:3000-4000
£2152 $3400 €3400 Composition (23x35cm-9x14in) s.d.1961 gouache cardboard prov. 27-Nov-2 Tajan, Paris #21/R
£2201 $3412 €3500 Composition (75x44cm-30x17in) s.d.68 W/C ink. 30-Oct-2 Artcurial Briest, Paris #719/R est:2500-3500
£2449 $3894 €3600 Composition (44x58cm-17x23in) s.d.1948 ink wash. 24-Mar-3 Claude Boisgirard, Paris #121
£2516 $3899 €4000 Composition (75x44cm-30x17in) s.d.68 s.i.d.68 verso W/C ink. 30-Oct-2 Artcurial Briest, Paris #720/R est:2500-3500
£2721 $4327 €4000 Composition (57x77cm-22x30in) s.d.1957 W/C Chinese ink card. 1-Mar-3 Meeting Art, Vercelli #643
£4340 $6726 €6900 Nuits bannies (56x76cm-22x30in) s. gouache. 7-Oct-2 Claude Aguttes, Neuilly #264
£5031 $7849 €8000 Composition (59x64cm-23x25in) s.i.d.64 gouache prov. 10-Oct-2 Ribeyre & Baron, Paris #58/R est:6000-8000

MATHIEU, Jean Adam (1698-1753) French

Miniatures

£2000 $3240 €3000 Lady in the guise of a shepherdess (8cm-3in) enamel rectangular black wood frame. 22-May-3 Bonhams, New Bond Street #15/R est:2000-3000

MATHIEU, Paul (1872-1932) Belgian

£833 $1292 €1300 Poplar lined track in Flanders (99x71cm-39x28in) s. prov. 7-Dec-2 Ketterer, Hamburg #187/R
£1806 $2979 €2600 Tree lined country road with village in the distance (100x72cm-39x28in) s. 1-Jul-3 Christie's, Amsterdam #106/R est:3000-4000
£2025 $3159 €3200 Bord de Meuse (39x55cm-15x22in) s. panel. 16-Sep-2 Horta, Bruxelles #192/R

MATHIEU, Pol Francois (1895-1979) Belgian

£346 $533 €550 Maree basse en Bretagne (31x40cm-12x16in) s.d.1939 panel. 22-Oct-2 Campo & Campo, Antwerp #180

MATHIOPOULOS, Pavlos (1876-1956) Greek

£1100 $1738 €1650 En vogue (31x22cm-12x9in) 1-Apr-3 Bonhams, New Bond Street #48 est:1000-2000

MATHIOT, Alain (1938-) French

£420 $701 €600 Pointe dojon jaune (50x50cm-20x20in) s.verso. 25-Jun-3 Claude Aguttes, Neuilly #130

MATHIS, Adolphe (1873-1940) French

£480 $754 €720 La maison du pecheur, Provence (38x46cm-15x18in) s. panel. 16-Apr-3 Christie's, Kensington #923/R
£800 $1240 €1200 Le miroir aux oiseaux Martigues (38x46cm-15x18in) s. panel. 5-Dec-2 Christie's, Kensington #73/R
£1200 $1860 €1800 Une maison aux jardins exotiques. Une maison a l'eau (27x41cm-11x16in) s. panel pair. 5-Dec-2 Christie's, Kensington #76/R est:1200-1500

Works on paper

£900 $1395 €1350 Un port a Martiques (32x46cm-13x18in) s. W/C. 5-Dec-2 Christie's, Kensington #78/R
£900 $1395 €1350 Un port au sud de la France (50x65cm-20x26in) s. W/C. 5-Dec-2 Christie's, Kensington #79/R
£1000 $1550 €1500 Passage du cloitre de la collegiate, Villeneuve-les-Avignon (32x46cm-13x18in) s. W/C. 5-Dec-2 Christie's, Kensington #78a/R est:1000-1500
£1200 $1860 €1800 Un canal a Martigues. Un rue a Martigues. Un coin de port (33x46cm-13x18in) s. W/C set of three. 5-Dec-2 Christie's, Kensington #75/R est:1500-2000
£1200 $1860 €1800 Le jardin au bord de la Meditteranee (65x45cm-26x18in) s. W/C. 5-Dec-2 Christie's, Kensington #80/R est:1500-2000

MATHIS, Jean Jacques (1906-) Swiss

£952 $1514 €1400 Lamentation devant l'eglise (100x120cm-39x47in) s. 18-Mar-3 Galerie Moderne, Brussels #518/R

MATHISON, W (?) British

Works on paper

£820 $1279 €1230 Evening St Ives harbour (33x51cm-13x20in) s. W/C. 26-Mar-3 Woolley & Wallis, Salisbury #86/R

MATHISON, William (?) British

£260 $416 €390 Country walker rambling down rural wooded track (53x43cm-21x17in) s. 10-Jan-3 Biddle & Webb, Birmingham #205

MATHON, Émile (19th C) French

£321 $503 €500 Ebre a Tortosa (34x60cm-13x24in) s. d.1882 verso panel. 24-Nov-2 Lesieur & Le Bars, Le Havre #115

MATHORNE, Carl (1878-1942) Danish

£372 $603 €558 Women dancing (125x165cm-49x65in) mono. 25-Jan-3 Rasmussen, Havnen #2033 (D.KR 4200)

MATHY, Henri (1897-1956) Belgian

£340 $547 €510 Le Chantier (58x71cm-23x28in) s. 15-Jan-3 Cheffins Grain & Comins, Cambridge #435/R

MATHYS, Albert François (1885-1956) Belgian

£949 $1481 €1500 Nature morte aux legumes (50x60cm-20x24in) s. panel. 15-Oct-2 Horta, Bruxelles #47
£1096 $1710 €1600 Herder with his sheep flock on a country road (97x119cm-38x47in) s. 14-Apr-3 Glerum, Amsterdam #100/R est:600-800

MATHYS, Hendrik (20th C) Belgian

£300 $456 €450 Sunlit wooded track (116x77cm-46x30in) s. 29-Aug-2 Christie's, Kensington #137

MATIGNON, Albert (1869-?) French

£800 $1248 €1200 Looking out to sea (43x73cm-17x29in) s. 26-Mar-3 Sotheby's, Olympia #244/R

MATILLA Y MARINA, Segundo (1862-1937) Spanish

£2318 $3778 €3500 Self-portrait (37x41cm-15x16in) s.d.1912. 11-Feb-3 Segre, Madrid #138/R
£3289 $5329 €5000 Fishermen (26x29cm-10x11in) s. board. 21-Jan-3 Ansorena, Madrid #194/R est:4600
£8609 $14033 €13000 Beach with fishermen (73x50cm-29x20in) s.d.1909 cardboard. 11-Feb-3 Segre, Madrid #129/R
£8805 $13736 €14000 Marsh (75x150cm-30x59in) s.d.1891. 17-Sep-2 Segre, Madrid #105/R est:10500
£10897 $17326 €15800 Boats on the coast (36x42cm-14x17in) s. 4-Mar-3 Ansorena, Madrid #167/R

MATISSE, Camille (20th C) French

£320 $525 €480 Roses, daisies and other summer flowers in a vase (49x40cm-19x16in) s. oval. 5-Jun-3 Christie's, Kensington #796
£480 $744 €720 Chrysanthemums in a stone vase (48x62cm-19x24in) s.i. panel. 1-Nov-2 Moore Allen & Innocent, Cirencester #478

£654 $1072 €1000 Flowers in vase (52x41cm-20x16in) s. 9-Feb-3 Bukowskis, Helsinki #421/R

MATISSE, Henri (1869-1954) French

£75000 $123000 €112500 Nouages blancs, vieux port de Marseille (27x35cm-11x14in) s. panel painted 1918 prov.lit. 4-Feb-3 Christie's, London #294/R est:120000

£2820513 $4400000 €4230770 Nature morte, serviette a carreaux (52x55cm-20x22in) s. painted c.1903 prov.exhib.lit. 5-Nov-2 Sotheby's, New York #19/R est:4000000-6000000

Prints

£1698 $2700 €2547 Vierge a l'Enfant debout (29x13cm-11x5in) s.num.168/200 lithograph. 7-Mar-3 Skinner, Boston #89a/R est:1500-2000
£1740 $2750 €2610 From cinquante dessin mlle M M (15x11cm-6x4in) s. drypoint. 22-Apr-3 Butterfields, San Francisco #2163/R est:2000-3000
£1923 $3000 €2885 Jeune femme au foulard (38x28cm-15x11in) st.mono.num.23/25 col lithograph. 5-Nov-2 Christie's, Rockefeller NY #190/R est:2500-3500
£1923 $3019 €3000 Odalisque couchee (199x299cm-78x118in) etching. 12-Dec-2 Piasa, Paris #77
£1944 $3092 €2800 Odalisque couchee (20x30cm-8x12in) s. etching. 5-May-3 Ketterer, Munich #40/R est:1500-2500
£2044 $3250 €3066 Jazz, M Loyal (42x65cm-17x26in) col pochoir. 2-May-3 Sotheby's, New York #217
£2065 $3200 €3098 Etudes pour Saint Dominique (49x37cm-19x15in) s.num.63/100 lithograph. 25-Sep-2 Christie's, Rockefeller NY #139/R est:2500-3500
£2113 $3507 €3000 Loulou, visage de face (16x6cm-6x2in) s.i. etching. 14-Jun-3 Hauswedell & Nolte, Hamburg #1397/R est:4000
£2215 $3500 €3500 Nu couche, sol en damier (14x20cm-6x8in) etching. 30-Nov-2 Villa Grisebach, Berlin #382/R est:3500-4000
£2215 $3500 €3323 D Galanis, paysan (14x10cm-6x4in) s. drypoint. 22-Apr-3 Butterfields, San Francisco #2162/R est:3500-4500
£2215 $3500 €3323 Etude de jambes (25x50cm-10x20in) s.num.33/50 lithograph. 22-Apr-3 Butterfields, San Francisco #2164/R est:4000-6000
£2308 $3623 €3600 Emma L, Riviere (179x129cm-70x51in) s.i. etching. 12-Dec-2 Piasa, Paris #75/R
£2331 $3800 €3497 Orientale assise (15x11cm-6x4in) s.i. drypoint exec.1929. 13-Feb-3 Christie's, Rockefeller NY #100/R
£2516 $4000 €3774 Nu accroupi, profil a la chevelure noire (107x56cm-42x22in) d.1906 num.14/25 lithograph. 30-Apr-3 Doyle, New York #236/R est:3000-4000
£2532 $4000 €3798 Nu a demi allonge (15x10cm-6x4in) s.num12 drypoint. 22-Apr-3 Butterfields, San Francisco #2160/R est:4000-6000
£2564 $4051 €4000 Fanny - Mme D G. etching. 14-Nov-2 Libert, Castor, Paris #123/R est:3000
£2564 $3974 €4000 La persane (13x10cm-5x4in) s.i. drypoint etching. 7-Dec-2 Hauswedell & Nolte, Hamburg #895/R est:3000
£2600 $4056 €3900 Odalisque couchee (20x30cm-8x12in) etching. 25-Mar-3 Sotheby's, London #100/R est:2000-3000
£2767 $4400 €4151 Vierge a l enfant debout (32x24cm-13x9in) s.num.168/200 lithograph. 1-May-3 Swann Galleries, New York #516/R est:5000-8000
£2817 $4676 €4000 Marie Jose en robe jaune (54x41cm-21x16in) aquatint etching. 14-Jun-3 Hauswedell & Nolte, Hamburg #1398/R est:5000
£2838 $4427 €4200 Visage (20x14cm-8x6in) s.i. num.235/300 lithograph. 28-Mar-3 Ketterer, Hamburg #495/R est:3000-4000
£2885 $4471 €4500 Jeune fille en robe fleurie au col d'organdi (22x15cm-9x6in) s. lithograph. 4-Dec-2 Lempertz, Koln #908/R est:5000-6000
£2903 $4500 €4355 Vierge et enfant sans indication des visages (48x37cm-19x15in) s.num.38/100 lithograph. 25-Sep-2 Christie's, Rockefeller NY #138/R est:4000-6000
£3077 $4800 €4616 Jeune fille au col d'organdi (38x29cm-15x11in) s.num.13/50 lithograph prov. 5-Nov-2 Christie's, Rockefeller NY #174/R est:4000-6000
£3077 $4800 €4616 Martiniquaise (38x28cm-15x11in) s.num.16/25 etching prov. 5-Nov-2 Christie's, Rockefeller NY #183/R est:6000-8000
£3097 $4800 €4646 Patitcha souriante (33x25cm-13x10in) aquatint. 25-Sep-2 Christie's, Rockefeller NY #137/R est:4000-6000
£3165 $5000 €4748 Nu pour Cleveland (37x29cm-15x11in) s. num.70/250 etching gray chine colle executed c.1932. 12-Nov-2 Doyle, New York #299/R est:4000-6000
£3243 $5222 €4865 Le destin - Jazz pl.XVI (42x65cm-17x26in) pochoir printed in col. after collage. 7-May-3 AB Stockholms Auktionsverk #1234/R est:40000-50000 (S.KR 42000)
£3333 $5233 €5200 Personnage de droite de la pl (435x242cm-171x95in) s.i. lithograph. 12-Dec-2 Piasa, Paris #88
£3333 $5300 €4800 Visage (20x15cm-8x6in) s. num.138/300 lithograph. 5-May-3 Ketterer, Munich #37/R est:1400-1800
£3459 $5500 €5189 Nu pour Cleveland (36x28cm-14x11in) s.num.59/250 etching chine colle exec.1932. 22-Mar-3 Rachel Davis, Shaker Heights #616 est:6000-8000
£3459 $5500 €5189 Le grand collier (25x18cm-10x7in) s.num.12/25 etching prov. 29-Apr-3 Christie's, Rockefeller NY #483/R est:4000-6000
£3459 $5500 €5189 Nu, etude d'un mouvement de jambes (43x56cm-17x22in) s.num.4/10 lithograph edition of 46 prov. 29-Apr-3 Christie's, Rockefeller NY #485/R est:5000-8000
£3459 $5500 €5189 Jazz, clown (42x65cm-17x26in) col pochoir. 2-May-3 Sotheby's, New York #216/R est:3500-4500
£3472 $5521 €5000 Le repos du modele (22x30cm-9x12in) s. lithograph. 5-May-3 Ketterer, Munich #39/R est:4000-6000
£3526 $5500 €5289 Le repos du modele (28x37cm-11x15in) s. lithograph edition of 100. 5-Nov-2 Christie's, Rockefeller NY #173/R est:5000-7000
£3526 $5500 €5289 Paul Leautaud (25x17cm-10x7in) s.num.5/5 lithograph prov. 5-Nov-2 Christie's, Rockefeller NY #184/R est:6000-8000
£3662 $6079 €5200 Nu, jambe repliee, etude de jambes (29x54cm-11x21in) s.num. lithograph. 12-Jun-3 Piasa, Paris #145/R
£3726 $5887 €5589 Odalisque sur fond a Carreaux (15x12cm-6x5in) s.num.13/25 drypoint lit. 28-Apr-3 Bukowskis, Stockholm #457/R est:50000-70000 (S.KR 49000)
£3774 $6000 €5661 Tete de jeune femme, la chevelure dans le vent (18x20cm-7x8in) s.num.17/25 etching. 1-May-3 Swann Galleries, New York #515/R est:6000-9000
£3797 $6000 €5696 Figure assise (15x10cm-6x4in) s.num.7/12 drypoint. 22-Apr-3 Butterfields, San Francisco #2161/R est:5000-7000
£3800 $5928 €5700 Vierge a l'enfant debout (45x32cm-18x13in) s.num.11/200 lithograph. 10-Oct-2 Sotheby's, London #59/R est:2500-3000
£3803 $6313 €5400 Marguerite (18x13cm-7x5in) s.num. drypoint edition of 20. 12-Jun-3 Piasa, Paris #141/R
£3846 $6000 €5769 Nu pour Cleveland (36x28cm-14x11in) s.num.66/250 etching chine colle executed c.1932. 21-Sep-2 Rachel Davis, Shaker Heights #525/R est:6000-9000
£3846 $6038 €6000 Danseuse endormie (220x456cm-87x180in) s.i. lithograph. 12-Dec-2 Piasa, Paris #85
£3846 $5962 €6000 Odalisque couchee (20x30cm-8x12in) s. etching. 7-Dec-2 Hauswedell & Nolte, Hamburg #894/R est:8000
£3974 $6477 €6000 Danseuse allongee (28x46cm-11x18in) s. num.93/100 lithograph prov. 3-Feb-3 Cornette de St.Cyr, Paris #185/R
£4000 $6360 €5800 Vierge et enfant (51x73cm-20x29in) s.num.13/200 lithograph vellum. 5-Mar-3 Doutrebente, Paris #12/R est:4500-5000
£4088 $6500 €6132 Nu assis de trois-quarts, le visage de face (12x9cm-5x4in) s.i. etching. 2-May-3 Sotheby's, New York #206/R est:5000-7000
£4167 $6542 €6500 La main (154x205cm-61x81in) i. etching. 12-Dec-2 Piasa, Paris #80/R
£4200 $6552 €6300 Nadia visage aux yeux obliques (43x35cm-17x14in) s.num.10/25 aquatint. 25-Mar-3 Sotheby's, London #106/R est:3000-4000
£4318 $7211 €6261 Sleeping (33x42cm-13x17in) s.indis.num.49/50 lithograph. 18-Jun-3 Grev Wedels Plass, Oslo #57/R est:30000-50000 (N.KR 50000)
£4403 $7000 €6605 Masque blanc sur fond noir (32x25cm-13x10in) init.num.13/25 aquatint prov. 29-Apr-3 Christie's, Rockefeller NY #492/R est:5000-7000
£4403 $7000 €6605 Nu drape sur fond compose de cercles (12x9cm-5x4in) s.num.25/25 etching. 2-May-3 Sotheby's, New York #208/R est:6000-8000
£4430 $7000 €6645 Dix danseuses (28x46cm-11x18in) num.92 lithograph executed c.1927. 15-Nov-2 Du Mouchelle, Detroit #2006/R est:5000-8000
£4487 $7000 €6731 Visage de jeune femme (56x38cm-22x15in) s.num.25/25 aquatint prov. 5-Nov-2 Christie's, Rockefeller NY #186/R est:6000-8000
£4577 $7599 €6500 Catherinette (28x16cm-11x6in) s.i. lithograph. 14-Jun-3 Hauswedell & Nolte, Hamburg #1401/R est:7500
£4633 $7459 €6950 From Dix danseuses (27x45cm-11x18in) s.num.5/5 lithograph executed 1925-26 lit. 7-May-3 AB Stockholms Auktionsverk #1233/R est:60000-70000 (S.KR 60000)
£4645 $7339 €7200 La pompadour (36x30cm-14x12in) s.num.8/200 lithograph vellum lit. 17-Dec-2 Rossini, Paris #5
£4717 $7500 €7076 Trois tetes (34x28cm-13x11in) init.num.17/25 aquatint prov. 29-Apr-3 Christie's, Rockefeller NY #494/R est:5000-7000
£4808 $7500 €7212 Danseuse allongee, tete accoudee (16x42cm-6x17in) s.num.7/120 lithograph. 7-Nov-2 Swann Galleries, New York #705/R est:6000-9000
£4808 $7500 €7212 Icarus (43x65cm-17x26in) col pochoir. 7-Nov-2 Swann Galleries, New York #706/R est:10000-15000
£5000 $7750 €7500 Danseuse couchee (32x50cm-13x20in) s.num.4/130 lithograph. 3-Dec-2 Christie's, London #143/R est:5000-7000
£5031 $8000 €7547 Danseuse du fauteuil de bois (46x26cm-18x10in) s.num.110/150 lithograph. 1-May-3 Swann Galleries, New York #514/R est:8000-12000
£5200 $8164 €7800 Jules Romain (25x19cm-10x7in) s. lithograph. 17-Apr-3 Christie's, Kensington #288/R est:2500-3000
£5323 $8411 €7985 Danseuse debout, Accoudee - Dix danseuses (46x28cm-18x11in) s.num.14/130 lithograph executed 1925-26. 28-Apr-3 Bukowskis, Stockholm #456/R est:80000-100000 (S.KR 70000)

£5323	$8411	€7985	Jeune fille arrangeant ses cheveux (15x11cm-6x4in) s.num.8/25 etching executed 1934-35. 28-Apr-3 Bukowskis, Stockholm #458/R est:50000-60000 (S.KR 70000)
£5346	$8500	€8019	Nu assis dans un fauteuil, une jambe repliee (42x28cm-17x11in) s.num.33/50 lithograph. 2-May-3 Sotheby's, New York #210/R est:6000-8000
£5380	$8500	€8070	Dix danseuses (28x46cm-11x18in) num.91 or 99 lithograph executed c.1927. 15-Nov-2 Du Mouchelle, Detroit #2007/R est:5000-8000
£5449	$8554	€8500	Figure endormie (237x385cm-93x152in) s.i. lithograph. 12-Dec-2 Piasa, Paris #86/R
£5663	$9175	€8211	Dancer seated on sofa (46x32cm-18x13in) s.num.82/130 lithograph exhib. 25-May-3 Uppsala Auktionskammare, Uppsala #345/R est:60000-80000 (S.KR 73000)
£5769	$9000	€8654	Danseuse debout (50x33cm-20x13in) s.i. lithograph. 14-Oct-2 Butterfields, San Francisco #1139/R est:10000-15000
£5769	$9000	€8654	Figure voilee aux deux bracelets (43x36cm-17x14in) s.num.3/25 lithograph. 7-Nov-2 Swann Galleries, New York #707/R est:10000-15000
£5800	$9048	€8700	Nu allonge, jambers repliees (38x28cm-15x11in) s.num.16/25 etching. 25-Mar-3 Sotheby's, London #101/R est:3000-4000
£5903	$9385	€8500	Danseuse allogee (28x46cm-11x18in) s. num.13/130 lithograph. 5-May-3 Ketterer, Munich #43/R est:6500-7500
£6090	$9500	€9135	Grand masque (35x25cm-14x10in) s.num.21/50 lithograph. 18-Sep-2 Swann Galleries, New York #71/R est:6000-9000
£6289	$10000	€9434	Nu couche, drape dans un etoffe fleurie (10x25cm-4x10in) s.num.24/25 etching prov. 29-Apr-3 Christie's, Rockefeller NY #482/R est:7000-10000
£6289	$10000	€9434	Nu renversee au brasero (57x46cm-22x18in) s.i. lithograph edition of 50. 29-Apr-3 Christie's, Rockefeller NY #484/R est:9000-11000
£6289	$10000	€9434	Danseuse etendue au divan (28x45cm-11x18in) s.num.127/130 lithograph. 2-May-3 Sotheby's, New York #214/R est:6000-8000
£6289	$10000	€9434	Nu assis, chevelure claire (39x24cm-15x9in) s.num.23/50 lithograph. 1-May-3 Swann Galleries, New York #512/R est:10000-15000
£6301	$9830	€9200	Une religieuse a l'expression candide (15x12cm-6x5in) s. etching. 11-Apr-3 Winterberg, Heidelberg #1354/R est:9800
£6738	$10915	€9500	Odalisque couchee (44x55cm-17x22in) s. etching. 20-May-3 Dorotheum, Vienna #21/R est:9000-9500
£6768	$10694	€10152	Danseuse au tabouret - Dix danseuses (45x27cm-18x11in) s.num.43/130 lithograph executed 1925-26 lit. 28-Apr-3 Bukowskis, Stockholm #455/R est:70000-90000 (S.KR 89000)
£7000	$10920	€10500	Les trois modeles (55x85cm-22x33in) s.num.34/50 lithograph. 25-Mar-3 Sotheby's, London #105/R est:5000-7000
£7547	$12000	€11321	Danseuse au tabouret (45x28cm-18x11in) s.num.42/130 lithograph. 2-May-3 Sotheby's, New York #213/R est:8000-10000
£7692	$12000	€11538	Petit bois noir (46x29cm-18x11in) s.num.50/50 woodcut prov. 5-Nov-2 Christie's, Rockefeller NY #169/R est:14000-18000
£7692	$12000	€11538	Odalisque au magnolia (37x49cm-15x19in) s.num.44/50 lithograph. 5-Nov-2 Christie's, Rockefeller NY #175/R est:15000-20000
£7692	$12000	€11538	La robe d'organdi (43x28cm-17x11in) s.num.11/50 lithograph. 7-Nov-2 Swann Galleries, New York #704/R est:8000-12000
£7692	$12077	€12000	Nu de trois-quarts, une partie de la tete coupee (501x303cm-197x119in) init.i. lithograph. 12-Dec-2 Piasa, Paris #82/R
£7862	$12186	€12500	Danseuse au tabouret (50x33cm-20x13in) s.num.90/130 black lithograph. 30-Oct-2 Artcurial Briest, Paris #538/R est:11000-12000
£8013	$12580	€12500	Figure endormie aux babouches (272x378cm-107x149in) s.i. lithograph. 12-Dec-2 Piasa, Paris #87/R
£8176	$13000	€12264	Jeune etudiant de profil (44x35cm-17x14in) s.num.4/15 aquatint prov. 29-Apr-3 Christie's, Rockefeller NY #493/R est:3500-4500
£8176	$13000	€12264	Danseuse endormie (44x60cm-17x24in) s.i. lithograph. 2-May-3 Sotheby's, New York #212/R est:10000-15000
£8333	$13000	€12500	Figure endormie, chale sur les jambes (44x56cm-17x22in) s.i. lithograph prov. 5-Nov-2 Christie's, Rockefeller NY #180/R est:10000-15000
£8333	$13250	€12000	Danseuse au tabouret (46x26cm-18x10in) s. num.53/130 lithograph. 5-May-3 Ketterer, Munich #42/R est:8000-12000
£8805	$14000	€13208	La robe jaune au ruban noir (53x36cm-21x14in) s.num.14/50 lithograph. 2-May-3 Sotheby's, New York #211/R est:10000-12000
£8805	$14000	€13208	Odalisque, brasero et coupe de fruits (28x37cm-11x15in) s.i. lithograph. 2-May-3 Sotheby's, New York #215/R est:10000-15000
£8974	$14000	€13461	Nu de trois quarts, une partie de la tete coupee (50x33cm-20x13in) s.num.39/50 i.verso lithograph. 5-Nov-2 Christie's, Rockefeller NY #171/R est:12000-15000
£9028	$14354	€13000	Jeune fille accoudee au paravent fleuri (18x26cm-7x10in) s. num.7/60 lithograph. 5-May-3 Ketterer, Munich #41/R est:8000-12000
£9155	$15197	€13000	Danseuse (46x27cm-18x11in) s. lithograph. 14-Jun-3 Hauswedell & Nolte, Hamburg #1400/R est:15000
£9494	$15000	€15000	Odalisque a la culotte rayee reflectee dans la glace (40x30cm-16x12in) s. lithograph. 27-Nov-2 Dorotheum, Vienna #24/R est:18000-19000
£9615	$15000	€14423	La pause (28x38cm-11x15in) s.num.3/4 etching prov. 5-Nov-2 Christie's, Rockefeller NY #179/R est:10000-12000
£9859	$16366	€14000	Figure devant un tapa Africain (53x44cm-21x17in) s.num. lithograph edition of 70. 12-Jun-3 Piasa, Paris #148
£10063	$16000	€15095	Danseuse au tabouret (46x28cm-18x11in) s.num.58/130 lithograph. 3-Mar-3 Swann Galleries, New York #50/R est:8000-12000
£10563	$17535	€15000	Nu assis, les bras etendus (49x41cm-19x16in) s.num. lithograph edition of 65. 12-Jun-3 Piasa, Paris #146/R
£10897	$17000	€16346	Danseuse au tabouret (50x33cm-20x13in) s.num.31/130 lithograph. 5-Nov-2 Christie's, Rockefeller NY #178/R est:10000-15000
£11321	$18000	€16982	Le grand nu (28x25cm-11x10in) s.num.36/50 lithograph. 2-May-3 Sotheby's, New York #209/R est:20000-30000
£11500	$17825	€17250	Interieur le lecture (38x28cm-15x11in) s.num.4/50 lithograph. 5-Dec-2 Sotheby's, London #150/R est:12000-15000
£11538	$18000	€17307	Le grand nu (45x34cm-18x13in) s.num.29/50 lithograph prov. 5-Nov-2 Christie's, Rockefeller NY #170/R est:20000-30000
£11972	$19873	€17000	Nu couche de dos (46x56cm-18x22in) s.num. lithograph edition of 63. 12-Jun-3 Piasa, Paris #147/R
£12179	$19000	€18269	Nu assis a chemis de tulle (55x37cm-22x15in) s.num.3/10 lithograph edition of 50 prov. 5-Nov-2 Christie's, Rockefeller NY #176/R est:18000-22000
£12658	$20000	€20000	Nadia - vissage aux yeux obliques (43x35cm-17x14in) s. aquatint. 30-Nov-2 Villa Grisebach, Berlin #373/R est:16000-18000
£13836	$22000	€20754	Florilege des amours de Ronsard (40x30cm-16x12in) eight init. sanguine lithograph set of 126 album prov. 29-Apr-3 Christie's, Rockefeller NY #490/R est:15000-20000
£14744	$23147	€23000	Femme au collier (515x395cm-203x156in) s.i. lithograph. 12-Dec-2 Piasa, Paris #84/R
£16352	$26000	€24528	La sieste (28x33cm-11x13in) s.i. linocut edition of 25. 29-Apr-3 Christie's, Rockefeller NY #487/R est:12000-15000
£17610	$28000	€26415	Repos sur la banquette (44x54cm-17x21in) s.num.23/50 lithograph. 29-Apr-3 Christie's, Rockefeller NY #486/R est:20000-30000
£20000	$31000	€30000	Nu assis a la chemise de tulle (53x36cm-21x14in) s.num.15/50 lithograph. 5-Dec-2 Sotheby's, London #147/R est:22000-24000
£22436	$35000	€33654	Le renard blanc (67x50cm-26x20in) s.i.d.17/11 29 lithograph edition of 75 prov. 5-Nov-2 Christie's, Rockefeller NY #181/R est:40000-60000
£26923	$42000	€40385	Odalisque a la coupe de fruits (44x33cm-17x13in) s.num.27/50 lithograph. 5-Nov-2 Christie's, Rockefeller NY #177/R est:35000-40000
£54487	$85000	€81731	Marie-Jose en robe jaune (76x56cm-30x22in) s.num.34/100 col aquatint. 5-Nov-2 Christie's, Rockefeller NY #187/R est:70000-90000

Sculpture

£20833	$32292	€32500	Petite tete au peigne (9cm-4in) mono. num.8/10 brown pat bronze lit. 5-Dec-2 Gros & Delettrez, Paris #122/R est:35000
£41925	$67500	€62888	Tete de Marguerite (12x12cm-5x5in) s.i. glazed ceramic executed c.1906 prov. 7-May-3 Sotheby's, New York #372/R est:30000-40000

Works on paper

£2628	$4074	€4100	Nude girl standing (33x21cm-13x8in) s. pencil paper on paper. 7-Dec-2 Van Ham, Cologne #333/R est:5000
£4259	$6729	€6389	Untitled (26x20cm-10x8in) s. Indian ink sketch. 28-Apr-3 Bukowskis, Stockholm #300/R est:40000-50000 (S.KR 56000)
£4601	$7500	€6902	Deux barques, Collioure (32x20cm-13x8in) s. green pencil executed 1905 prov.lit. 12-Feb-3 Sotheby's, New York #62/R est:8000-12000
£8500	$13260	€12750	Nadia masque (31x25cm-12x10in) s.num.20/25 aquatint. 25-Mar-3 Sotheby's, London #107/R est:8000-10000
£9028	$14354	€13000	Les acrobates (27x21cm-11x8in) mono. graphite dr. prov. 29-Apr-3 Artcurial Briest, Paris #99/R est:13000-18000
£9500	$14630	€14250	Nu (21x26cm-8x10in) s. brush ink executed 1906 prov. 22-Oct-2 Sotheby's, London #133/R est:10000-15000
£12000	$18600	€18000	Les bateaux a Collioure (21x30cm-8x12in) s. pen ink cardboard. 5-Dec-2 Christie's, Kensington #125/R est:8000-12000
£20000	$32800	€30000	Danseuse (31x24cm-12x9in) st.init. pencil prov. 6-Feb-3 Christie's, London #476/R
£20833	$34375	€30000	Orphee, les musiciens celebres (32x24cm-13x9in) s.d.45 ink dr. 2-Jul-3 Artcurial Briest, Paris #686/R est:18000-25000
£22000	$33880	€33000	Baigneuse debout contre un arbre (27x21cm-11x8in) s. pen ink executed 1909 prov. 22-Oct-2 Sotheby's, London #174/R est:18000-25000
£26000	$42640	€39000	Visages de Jean (30x24cm-12x9in) s.i. pen ink prov. 5-Feb-3 Sotheby's, London #211/R est:25000

£26000 $43420 €37700 Angele Lamotte (31x24cm-12x9in) s.i. chl prov.exhib.lit. 24-Jun-3 Christie's, London #6/R est:20000-30000
£28571 $46000 €42857 La Japonaise au bord de l'eau - Portrait de Madame Matisse (26x20cm-10x8in) init. W/C executed 1905 exhib. 8-May-3 Christie's, Rockefeller NY #109/R est:40000-60000
£30000 $50100 €43500 Remember (36x26cm-14x10in) s. black ink prov.lit. 24-Jun-3 Christie's, London #30/R est:10000-15000
£30769 $48000 €46154 Nue assise sur la divan (24x31cm-9x12in) st.sig. pen ink executed 1929 prov. 7-Nov-2 Christie's, Rockefeller NY #138/R est:50000-70000
£32000 $53440 €46400 Fruits (36x27cm-14x11in) s. pen ink prov.lit. 24-Jun-3 Christie's, London #12/R est:10000-15000
£34161 $55000 €51242 Figure au corselet (25x32cm-10x13in) s. pencil executed 1935 prov.exhib.lit. 7-May-3 Sotheby's, New York #351a/R est:60000-80000
£38000 $63460 €57000 Portrait de femme (33x24cm-13x9in) s.i.d.1943 pen ink prov.lit. 26-Jun-3 Christie's, London #433/R est:20000-30000
£46474 $72500 €69711 Nu allonge (25x33cm-10x13in) s.d.30 pencil prov. 6-Nov-2 Sotheby's, New York #287/R est:70000-90000
£51282 $80000 €76923 Le modele - Henriette (46x31cm-18x12in) s. chl prov.lit. 6-Nov-2 Sotheby's, New York #302/R est:80000-120000
£53409 $88660 €75840 Portrait de femme (53x41cm-21x16in) s.d. chl dr. prov. 12-Jun-3 Tajan, Paris #28/R est:40000-60000
£86538 $135000 €129807 Femme aux mains agrafees (42x32cm-17x13in) st.sig. pen ink executed 1944 prov.lit. 6-Nov-2 Sotheby's, New York #254/R est:80000-120000
£102564 $160000 €153846 Nu debout (61x41cm-24x16in) s.d.1950 chl prov. 6-Nov-2 Sotheby's, New York #308/R est:180000-250000
£130000 $213200 €195000 Baudelaire (40x30cm-16x12in) s.i.d.44 chl prov.lit. 6-Feb-3 Christie's, London #498/R est:120000
£192547 $310000 €288821 Auto-portrait de face, chemise ouverte (40x26cm-16x10in) s.d.44 India ink prov.exhib.lit. 6-May-3 Sotheby's, New York #28/R est:250000-300000
£192712 $300631 €289068 Lilian - the artist's daughter (52x40cm-20x16in) s.d.45 chl prov. 5-Nov-2 Bukowskis, Stockholm #287a/R est:1000000-1200000 (S.KR 2750000)
£205128 $322051 €320000 Danseuse (51x37cm-20x15in) s.d.49 chl dr prov.exhib.lit. 10-Dec-2 Artcurial Briest, Paris #475/R est:200000-250000

MATISSE, Henri (after) (1869-1954) French

Prints

£2564 $4000 €3846 Vierge a l'enfant debout (22x40cm-9x16in) col lithograph. 7-Nov-2 Swann Galleries, New York #711/R est:2500-3500
£6918 $11000 €10377 Odalisque sur la terrace (48x60cm-19x24in) s.num.95/200 col aquatint. 3-Mar-3 Swann Galleries, New York #51/R est:10000-15000

MATON, G (20th C) ?

£550 $875 €825 Singing robin (41x30cm-16x12in) i.verso panel. 6-Mar-3 Christie's, Kensington #586/R

MATORIN, N (19/20th C) Russian

£1300 $2042 €1950 Russian symbolist painting (59x30cm-23x12in) s.d.1899. 20-Nov-2 Sotheby's, London #63 est:1200-1800

MATOS, Ana de (1969-) Spanish

£377 $581 €600 Untitled (100x81cm-39x32in) s.d.1999 verso oil pencil collage fabric on canvas. 28-Oct-2 Segre, Madrid #173/R

MATOUT, Louis (1811-1888) French

£4800 $8016 €7200 Elegant figures by the Pont-des-Arts, with the Palais du Louvre beyond (38x50cm-15x20in) s.verso. 18-Jun-3 Christie's, Kensington #19/R est:5000-7000

MATSCH, Franz von (1861-1942) Austrian

£5072 $8319 €7000 Still life with mimosa (51x46cm-20x18in) s. canvas on board. 27-May-3 Wiener Kunst Auktionen, Vienna #93/R est:7000-14000

MATSCHINSKY-DENNINGHOFF, Brigitte and Martin (20th C) German

Sculpture

£9494 $15000 €15000 Embrace (99x49x54cm-39x19x21in) mono.d.90 brass zinc. 30-Nov-2 Villa Grisebach, Berlin #420/R est:15000-17000

MATSON, Victor (1898-1972) American

£581 $900 €872 Chartreuse (64x76cm-25x30in) s. 29-Oct-2 John Moran, Pasadena #630

MATT, Dennis (20th C) American

£292 $450 €438 Nude in an interior (91x84cm-36x33in) s. painted c.1945. 8-Sep-2 Treadway Gallery, Cincinnati #724/R

MATTA (1911-2002) Chilean

£4103 $6441 €6400 Elle and Sei (40x52cm-16x20in) s. i.verso prov. 20-Nov-2 Pandolfini, Florence #166/R
£8654 $12635 €13500 Untitled (58x49cm-23x19in) s. painted 1966 prov. 5-Jun-2 Il Ponte, Milan #133/R est:13000 15000
£11000 $18370 €15950 Les dangers interieurs (103x95cm-41x37in) s. i.d.1974 verso prov.lit. 27-Jun-3 Christie's, London #180/R est:10000-15000
£11538 $16846 €18000 Composition (65x78cm-26x31in) s. 5-Jun-2 Il Ponte, Milan #141/R est:16000-18000
£12167 $19224 €18251 La Seine des Seins (118x110cm-46x43in) mono. i.verso prov. 28-Apr-3 Bukowskis, Stockholm #327/R est:100000-125000 (S.KR 160000)
£12258 $19368 €19000 Bomb fruit (100x100cm-39x39in) painted 1960 prov.exhib. 18-Dec-2 Christie's, Rome #305/R est:25000
£15000 $24600 €22500 Untitled (105x88cm-41x35in) s. prov. 6-Feb-3 Christie's, London #621/R est:14000-18000
£15924 $25000 €23886 Untitled (57x59cm-22x23in) s.i.verso painted c.1978 prov. 19-Nov-2 Sotheby's, New York #133/R est:40000
£17568 $27405 €26000 Composition (84x64cm-33x25in) s. 25-Mar-3 Chochon-Barre & Allardi, Paris #167/R est:19000-22000
£19817 $32500 €28735 Passo interno di mercurio (70x65cm-28x26in) s. i.verso prov. 27-May-3 Sotheby's, New York #112
£22000 $36740 €31900 Composition (81x100cm-32x39in) mono. prov. 26-Jun-3 Sotheby's, London #209/R est:10000-15000
£28000 $46760 €40600 Untitled (59x71cm-23x28in) s. painted 1962 prov. 27-Jun-3 Christie's, London #111/R est:15000-20000
£28082 $43808 €41000 Untitled (84x94cm-33x37in) s. painted 1961. 10-Apr-3 Finarte Semenzato, Rome #314/R est:48000
£28662 $45000 €42993 Scie le desir (60x73cm-24x29in) s.verso acrylic painted 1957 prov. 20-Nov-2 Christie's, Rockefeller NY #83/R est:55000-75000
£30488 $50000 €44208 Composition (73x60cm-29x24in) s. painted c.1955-57 exhib. 27-May-3 Sotheby's, New York #74
£35000 $57400 €52500 Forces de la nature (81x100cm-32x39in) s. s.i.d.56 verso prov. 6-Feb-3 Christie's, London #622/R est:30000-40000
£37975 $60000 €60000 Untitled (60x73cm-24x29in) s.d.53 verso. 29-Nov-2 Farsetti, Prato #541/R est:70000
£38956 $61550 €58434 Untitled (83x102cm-33x40in) s. 15-Nov-2 Naón & Cia, Buenos Aires #4/R
£41401 $65000 €62102 Cosmic creator (117x172cm-46x68in) s.d.52 prov. 20-Nov-2 Christie's, Rockefeller NY #38/R est:60000-80000
£50955 $80000 €76433 Untitled. s. canvas on board double-sided triptych painted 1961 prov. 19-Nov-2 Sotheby's, New York #101/R est:80000
£62821 $98628 €98000 Jouer sa vue (117x150cm-46x59in) s. s.d.58-59 verso. 24-Nov-2 Laurence Calmels, Paris #193/R est:60000
£79618 $125000 €119427 Untitled (114x146cm-45x57in) s.d.58 prov. 20-Nov-2 Christie's, Rockefeller NY #26/R est:100000-150000
£85000 $141950 €127500 Les roses sont belles (205x170cm-81x67in) exc.1952 prov. 25-Jun-3 Sotheby's, London #26/R est:70000-90000
£112805 $185000 €169208 Composicion (144x124cm-57x49in) painted 1948 prov. 28-May-3 Christie's, Rockefeller NY #38/R est:100000-150000
£158537 $260000 €229879 Psychological morphology (30x41cm-12x16in) prov. 27-May-3 Sotheby's, New York #12
£396341 $650000 €594512 Morphology of desire (73x92cm-29x36in) painted 1938 prov.exhib.lit. 28-May-3 Christie's, Rockefeller NY #28/R est:700000-900000
£914634 $1500000 €1371951 Endless nudes (72x91cm-28x36in) painted 1941-1942 prov.exhib.lit. 28-May-3 Christie's, Rockefeller NY #21/R est:1000000-1500000

Sculpture

£1367 $2242 €1900 Untitled. various. 6-Jun-3 Rabourdin & Choppin de Janvry, Paris #43/R est:1500-2000
£5449 $7955 €8500 Untitled (114x45x55cm-45x18x22in) s. wood. 5-Jun-2 Il Ponte, Milan #142/R est:6000-8000
£15244 $25000 €22104 Design of intention (39x72x22cm-15x28x9in) black pat steel edition of 30 prov.exhib. 27-May-3 Sotheby's, New York #111

Works on paper

£694 $1104 €1000 Tatoucha cherie (18x12cm-7x5in) s.i. pastel pencil two in one frame. 29-Apr-3 Artcurial Briest, Paris #616/R
£949 $1481 €1500 Untitled (20x32cm-8x13in) s. mixed media card. 14-Sep-2 Meeting Art, Vercelli #772/R
£1456 $2300 €2300 Musiciens. s. s.i.verso pastel graphite frottage. 27-Nov-2 Tajan, Paris #58/R
£1622 $2530 €2400 Untitled (64x48cm-25x19in) s. pastel. 28-Mar-3 Farsetti, Prato #72/R
£1622 $2530 €2400 Return to Livorno with Rodolfo (42x59cm-17x23in) s.i. pastel. 28-Mar-3 Farsetti, Prato #286/R
£1736 $2865 €2500 L'impensable (48x64cm-19x25in) s.i.d.1955 black crayon. 1-Jul-3 Artcurial Briest, Paris #795a/R est:3000-4000
£1973 $3137 €2900 Journee des intellectuels pour le Viet-Nam (41x60cm-16x24in) wax crayon tracing paper. 26-Feb-3 Artcurial Briest, Paris #424/R est:2500-3000
£2200 $3410 €3300 Untitled (49x49cm-19x19in) s.indis i. pencil col crayon. 5-Dec-2 Christie's, Kensington #223/R est:2500-3500

£2600 $4238 €3900 Le centre du milieu (128x134cm-50x53in) mono. pastel marker on printed paper executed 1967 prov. 3-Feb-3 Sotheby's, Olympia #69/R est:2500-3500
£2642 $4094 €4200 Vers une structure de l'individu alerte (48x68cm-19x27in) i. pencil pastel dr. 30-Oct-2 Artcurial Briest, Paris #490/R est:4500-6000
£2676 $4442 €3800 Untitled (63x48cm-25x19in) bears sig. wax pastel prov. 11-Jun-3 Beaussant & Lefèvre, Paris #112/R est:4000-5000
£3077 $4769 €4800 Composition (35x50cm-14x20in) s. mixed media. 4-Dec-2 Finarte, Milan #271/R
£3095 $4921 €4550 Aux etudiants (50x64cm-20x25in) s.i.d.68 col crayon graphite prov. 26-Feb-3 Artcurial Briest, Paris #425/R est:3500-4000
£3265 $5192 €4800 Nous sommes les problemes a l'interieur du couple (50x65cm-20x26in) s.i. mixed media. 26-Feb-3 Artcurial Briest, Paris #426/R est:3000-4000
£3473 $5521 €5000 Composition (44x39cm-17x15in) s. wax pastel prov. 29-Apr-3 Artcurial Briest, Paris #615/R est:5000-7000
£4345 $6778 €6518 Untitled (48x64cm-19x25in) s. mixed media painted 1950s-1960s. 5-Nov-2 Bukowskis, Stockholm #311/R est:50000-60000 (S.KR 62000)
£5096 $8000 €7644 Explication picturale (50x65cm-20x26in) s.i.d.65 crayon graphite lit. 19-Nov-2 Sotheby's, New York #131/R
£7927 $13000 €11891 Sin titulo (49x64cm-19x25in) mono.indis.i. col crayon exec.c.1960 prov. 28-May-3 Christie's, Rockefeller NY #136/R est:10000-15000
£13415 $22000 €20123 Lettre sur la bombe atomique (36x48cm-14x19in) i.d.1945 verso col chk paper collage prov. 28-May-3 Christie's, Rockefeller NY #111/R est:22000-28000
£24390 $40000 €36585 Sin titulo (33x41cm-13x16in) pencil crayon exec.c.1938 prov.lit. 28-May-3 Christie's, Rockefeller NY #19/R est:50000-70000
£54140 $85000 €81210 Untitled (50x65cm-20x26in) col crayon pencil exec.1937 lit. 20-Nov-2 Christie's, Rockefeller NY #151/R est:70000-90000
£54878 $90000 €79573 Untitled (49x65cm-19x26in) s. wax crayon graphite prov.exhib.lit. 27-May-3 Sotheby's, New York #45
£101911 $160000 €152867 Scenery 1 (50x64cm-20x25in) s.i.d.37 crayon graphite prov.lit. 19-Nov-2 Sotheby's, New York #24/R est:200000
£123288 $192329 €180000 Untitled (31x49cm-12x19in) s. col crayon stump exec.c.1939 exhib. 14-Apr-3 Laurence Calmels, Paris #4047/R est:80000
£191781 $301096 €280000 Untitled (49x65cm-19x26in) col crayon graphite. 15-Apr-3 Laurence Calmels, Paris #4366/R est:60000-80000

MATTAS, Ake (1920-1962) Finnish
£460 $755 €640 Pine trees (28x33cm-11x13in) s.d.1961. 5-Jun-3 Hagelstam, Helsinki #995
£1799 $2878 €2500 Coastal landscape (42x34cm-17x13in) s.d.1945 canvas on board. 17-May-3 Hagelstam, Helsinki #173/R est:2000
£1899 $3000 €3000 Self portrait (39x31cm-15x12in) s.d.1940 cardboard. 30-Nov-2 Hagelstam, Helsinki #151/R est:2500
£2158 $3453 €3000 Irma (80x66cm-31x26in) s. board prov. 17-May-3 Hagelstam, Helsinki #174/R est:3500
£2532 $4000 €4000 Seated woman (64x53cm-25x21in) s.d.1946 exhib.lit. 30-Nov-2 Hagelstam, Helsinki #150/R est:5000
£5493 $8844 €7800 Portrait of Olavi Martikainen (56x43cm-22x17in) s.d.1961 board exhib. 10-May-3 Bukowskis, Helsinki #144/R est:4000-5000
£5696 $9000 €9000 Self portrait (70x55cm-28x22in) s.d.61 board exhib.lit. 1-Dec-2 Bukowskis, Helsinki #118/R est:6000-7000
Works on paper
£345 $566 €480 Coastal cliff (20x30cm-8x12in) s.d.1955 mixed media. 5-Jun-3 Hagelstam, Helsinki #803
£372 $588 €540 Breasts (33x40cm-13x16in) s. pastel. 3-Apr-3 Hagelstam, Helsinki #1001/R
£1338 $2154 €1900 Green back (32x24cm-13x9in) s.d.1960 gouache exhib. 10-May-3 Bukowskis, Helsinki #138/R est:800-900

MATTEI, Pasquale (1813-1879) Italian
£12414 $19614 €18000 The Bacino di Raddobbo inauguration (29x44cm-11x17in) tempera paper. 3-Apr-3 Porro, Milan #65/R est:25000
£25862 $40862 €37500 Pius IX blessing people from Naples Royal Palace (39x61cm-15x24in) s. exhib.lit. 3-Apr-3 Porro, Milan #64/R est:50000

MATTEINI, Theodoro (attrib) (1754-1831) Italian
£1489 $2413 €2100 Portrait of an officer (62x48cm-24x19in) lit. 20-May-3 Babuino, Rome #48/R est:2000-3000

MATTEIS, Francesco de (1852-?) Italian
Sculpture
£5696 $8886 €9000 Le concert des enfants (35x85x18cm-14x33x7in) s. brown pat.bronze. 31-Jul-2 Tajan, Paris #15/R est:9000-12000

MATTEIS, Paolo de (1662-1728) Italian
£5000 $7850 €7500 Finding of Moses (54x54cm-21x21in) 13-Dec-2 Christie's, Kensington #258/R est:5000-7000
£6500 $10205 €9750 Adam and Eve crying over the dead body of Abel. Cain slaying Abel (75x62cm-30x24in) pair. 10-Dec-2 Bonhams, New Bond Street #275/R est:7000-10000
£7927 $13000 €11891 Holy Family (29x37cm-11x15in) 29-May-3 Sotheby's, New York #83/R est:8000-12000
£19481 $29026 €30000 Caritas (128x101cm-50x40in) s.d.1717 prov. 26-Jun-2 Neumeister, Munich #642/R est:12000
£20000 $31400 €30000 Triumph of Galatea (125x97cm-49x38in) oval prov. 10-Dec-2 Bonhams, New Bond Street #305/R est:18000-25000
£20270 $31622 €30000 Venus presenting Helena to Paris (171x207cm-67x81in) 27-Mar-3 Dorotheum, Vienna #16/R est:30000-40000
£22069 $34869 €32000 Assumption of the Virgin (121x101cm-48x40in) prov. oval. 3-Apr-3 Porro, Milan #28/R est:30000
Works on paper
£950 $1587 €1378 Study of angles and putti on clouds. Saint attended by putti adoring the name of Jesus (20x24cm-8x9in) pen ink over black chk squared for transfer double-sided. 9-Jul-3 Bonhams, Knightsbridge #20/R

MATTEIS, Paolo de (attrib) (1662-1728) Italian
£11724 $18524 €17000 Apollus against Marsia (256x305cm-101x120in) 5-Apr-3 Finarte Semenzato, Milan #34/R est:20000
Works on paper
£1600 $2672 €2320 Orpheus and Eurydice (17x19cm-7x7in) pen brown ink brown pink wash traces blk chk prov.lit. 9-Jul-3 Sotheby's, London #48/R est:1000-1500

MATTENHEIMER, Theodor (younger) (1787-1856) German
£7407 $12000 €11111 Flowers in vase (46x38cm-18x15in) s.d.1831. 23-Jan-3 Sotheby's, New York #220/R est:8000

MATTERN, Walter (20th C) American
£769 $1200 €1154 Winter landscape with covered bridge and farmhouse (64x76cm-25x30in) s. masonite. 18-Sep-2 Alderfer's, Hatfield #374/R
£1154 $1800 €1731 Autumn landscape with bridge and town (51x61cm-20x24in) s. masonite. 18-Sep-2 Alderfer's, Hatfield #373/R est:1200-1500
£1282 $2000 €1923 South Allentown, autumn landscape (64x76cm-25x30in) s. masonite. 18-Sep-2 Alderfer's, Hatfield #371/R est:2000-3000
£2244 $3500 €3366 Winter afternoon (64x76cm-25x30in) s. masonite. 18-Sep-2 Alderfer's, Hatfield #368/R est:3000-5000
£2404 $3750 €3606 Autumn landscape with view of valley and farm (64x76cm-25x30in) s. masonite. 18-Sep-2 Alderfer's, Hatfield #370/R est:3000-5000

MATTESON, Tompkins Harrison (1813-1884) American
£3012 $5000 €4367 Still life with an ewer, melons, apples and other fruit (51x75cm-20x30in) s.indis.d. prov. 11-Jun-3 Butterfields, San Francisco #4021/R est:6000-8000
£14151 $22500 €21227 Meeting of Hetty and Hist (61x48cm-24x19in) s.d.1857 prov.exhib. 5-Mar-3 Sotheby's, New York #9/R est:8000-12000

MATTEUCCI, Renzo (1930-) Italian
£387 $600 €581 Ancestor portrait (89x69cm-35x27in) s.d.1963. 28-Sep-2 Charlton Hall, Columbia #364/R

MATTHEWS, James (19th C) British
Works on paper
£250 $395 €375 At Watersfield, Sussex (33x49cm-13x19in) s.i. W/C htd white scratching out. 13-Nov-2 Bonhams, Knowle #208

MATTHEWS, Marmaduke (1837-1913) Canadian
Works on paper
£201 $315 €302 Rider beside a mountain river (14x35cm-6x14in) s. W/C. 25-Nov-2 Hodgins, Calgary #354/R (C.D 500)
£222 $364 €333 At the edge of the forest (46x32cm-18x13in) s. W/C prov. 3-Jun-3 Joyner, Toronto #556 (C.D 500)
£258 $402 €374 Sailing at sunset (53x41cm-21x16in) s. W/C. 26-Mar-3 Walker's, Ottawa #253/R (C.D 600)
£261 $410 €392 National Park from Stoney Squaw Mountain (14x26cm-6x10in) s.i. W/C. 25-Nov-2 Hodgins, Calgary #379/R (C.D 650)
£300 $469 €435 Sunlight through the trees (53x39cm-21x15in) s. W/C. 26-Mar-3 Walker's, Ottawa #252/R (C.D 700)
£369 $572 €554 Mountain landscape (34x27cm-13x11in) s. W/C prov. 24-Sep-2 Ritchie, Toronto #3093/R (C.D 900)
£383 $605 €575 Public school house, Nanaimo, BC (15x30cm-6x12in) s.i.d.1896 W/C. 14-Nov-2 Heffel, Vancouver #26 est:900-1200 (C.D 950)
£400 $656 €580 Grey day in the Rockies (34x56cm-13x22in) s. W/C. 9-Jun-3 Hodgins, Calgary #73/R (C.D 900)
£533 $875 €773 Above Spuzzum (37x54cm-15x21in) s.i.d.1894 W/C. 9-Jun-3 Hodgins, Calgary #151/R est:1500-2000 (C.D 1200)
£756 $1239 €1096 Mt. Stephen and Kicking Horse Pass (49x37cm-19x15in) s. W/C. 9-Jun-3 Hodgins, Calgary #367/R est:1500-2000 (C.D 1700)
£1606 $2522 €2409 Mt Washington (49x74cm-19x29in) s. W/C. 25-Nov-2 Hodgins, Calgary #369/R est:4500-5000 (C.D 4000)

MATTHEWS, Michael (20th C) British
Works on paper
£260 $424 €390 Brig and other sailing ships off Jersey (40x28cm-16x11in) s. i.verso gouache. 11-Feb-3 Fellows & Sons, Birmingham #86/R

MATTHEY, Gill Julien (1889-1956) French?
£3205 $5032 €5000 Jeune femme aux tatouages (81x60cm-32x24in) s. 10-Dec-2 Tajan, Paris #198/R est:8000

MATTHIESEN, Oscar Adam Otto (1861-1957) German
£300 $489 €450 When the boats come in (51x90cm-20x35in) s.d.1923. 13-Feb-3 Christie's, Kensington #112/R

MATTHIESEN, Oscar Adam Otto (attrib) (1861-1957) German
£333 $537 €500 Boy riding calves across river (24x35cm-9x14in) 22-Feb-3 Rasmussen, Havnen #2097 (D.KR 3700)

MATTHIEU, Georg David (attrib) (1737-1776) German
£2958 $4762 €4200 Princess Sophie Friederike von Mecklenbug-Schwerin (64x50cm-25x20in) i. verso oval. 10-May-3 Hans Stahl, Toestorf #97/R est:3500
£5732 $8943 €9000 Southern wooded landscape with a travellers near a stream, mountains beyond (35x32cm-14x13in) panel prov.exhib.lit. 5-Nov-2 Sotheby's, Amsterdam #17/R est:10000-15000

MATTHISON, William (fl.1883-1923) British
Works on paper
£1600 $2496 €2400 Views of Whitby harbour (25x53cm-10x21in) s. W/C pair. 17-Sep-2 Rosebery Fine Art, London #614/R est:1000-1500

MATTIACCI, Eliseo (1940-) Italian
Sculpture
£2581 $4077 €4000 Untitled (95cm-37in) init.d. iron stone prov. 18-Dec-2 Christie's, Rome #46/R

MATTINEN, Seppo (1930-) Finnish
£637 $994 €956 Reclining female nude (74x100cm-29x39in) s.d.66.67.68. 5-Aug-2 Rasmussen, Vejle #340/R (D.KR 7500)

MATTIO, Laurent-Marius-Auguste (1892-1965) French
£980 $1608 €1500 Falaise de Sainte-Marguerite (81x65cm-32x26in) s.i.d.1916. 9-Feb-3 Anaf, Lyon #183/R

MATTIOLI, Carlo (1911-1994) Italian
£1154 $1812 €1800 Landscape (20x27cm-8x11in) s.d.1991 tempera card. 23-Nov-2 Meeting Art, Vercelli #54/R
Works on paper
£609 $957 €950 Tree (44x63cm-17x25in) s.d.76 Chinese ink W/C. 20-Nov-2 Pandolfini, Florence #2/R
£1538 $2246 €2400 Tree and table (22x14cm-9x6in) s. mixed media card. 5-Jun-2 Il Ponte, Milan #106
£1923 $3019 €3000 Landscape with tree (23cm-9in circular) s. mixed media card lit. 19-Nov-2 Finarte, Milan #140/R
£1923 $3019 €3000 Manzu' (44x65cm-17x26in) s.d.1970 W/C. 19-Nov-2 Finarte, Milan #137/R

MATTIOLI, Silvio (1929-) Swiss
Sculpture
£5240 $7651 €7860 Comet I (81x121x77cm-32x48x30in) mno.d.1972 verso prov.el. 4-Jun-2 Germann, Zurich #78/R est:12000-15000 (S.FR 12000)

MATTIS-TEUTSCH, Janos (1884-1960) Bohemian
£7739 $12073 €11609 Blue composition with figures (50x29cm-20x11in) 11-Sep-2 Kieselbach, Budapest #107/R (H.F 3000000)
£15479 $24147 €23219 Landscape with trees (15x19cm-6x7in) s. cardboard. 11-Sep-2 Kieselbach, Budapest #81/R (H.F 6000000)
Sculpture
£6191 $9659 €8977 Dancer (36cm-14in) s. aluminium marble base. 13-Sep-2 Mu Terem Galeria, Budapest #5/R est:1600000 (H.F 2400000)
£9143 $14172 €13257 Kneeling nude (33cm-13in) s. lacquered panel. 9-Dec-2 Mu Terem Galeria, Budapest #119/R est:2400000 (H.F 3400000)
Works on paper
£8606 $13339 €12909 Landscape (25x29cm-10x11in) s. mixed media. 6-Dec-2 Kieselbach, Budapest #188/R (H.F 3200000)
£9803 $15293 €14705 Hilly landscape (27x37cm-11x15in) s. mixed media. 11-Sep-2 Kieselbach, Budapest #112/R (H.F 3800000)

MATTON, Arsene (1873-1933) Belgian
Sculpture
£8219 $12822 €12000 Porteurs de pierre (210x170x137cm-83x67x54in) s. green pat bronze. 14-Apr-3 Horta, Bruxelles #94/R est:20000-30000

MATTONI DE LA FUENTE, Virgilio (1842-1923) Spanish
£141935 $220000 €212903 Baths of Caracalla (118x235cm-46x93in) s. 30-Oct-2 Christie's, Rockefeller NY #39/R est:220000-280000

MATULKA, Jan (1890-1972) American
£6289 $10000 €9434 Summer day in the park (62x77cm-24x30in) s. executed c.1917-18. 4-Mar-3 Christie's, Rockefeller NY #55/R est:10000-15000
Prints
£14103 $22000 €21155 Arrangement, New York (34x42cm-13x17in) s.i.d.1927 lithograph. 7-Nov-2 Swann Galleries, New York #713/R est:20000-30000
Works on paper
£335 $550 €486 Untitled - woman's head (18x15cm-7x6in) s. pencil prov. 1-Jun-3 Wright, Chicago #189/R
£610 $1000 €885 Female nude (46x20cm-18x8in) s. pencil. 5-Jun-3 Swann Galleries, New York #182/R
£671 $1100 €973 Still life with an owl, phonograph and shell (38x28cm-15x11in) s. brush ink pencil exec.c.1930. 5-Jun-3 Swann Galleries, New York #183/R
£1786 $2750 €2679 Houses over a bridge. Head of a man (36x30cm-14x12in) s. W/C crayon double-sided. 27-Oct-2 Grogan, Boston #99 est:3000-5000
£2435 $3750 €3653 Docks, Rockport (36x56cm-14x22in) s. W/C prov. 24-Oct-2 Shannon's, Milford #111/R est:4000-6000

MATULLA, Oskar (1900-1983) Austrian
£641 $1013 €1000 Windmill in Deutsch Altenburg (70x97cm-28x38in) mono.d.1937 panel double-sided. 12-Nov-2 Dorotheum, Vienna #120/R

MAUBERT, James (1666-1746) British
£2308 $3623 €3600 Portrait of girl with flowers and dog (126x100cm-50x39in) s.d.1729. 21-Nov-2 Van Ham, Cologne #1391/R est:1600

MAUBOULES, Jean (1943-) Swiss
Sculpture
£1223 $1920 €1835 Sculpture (43cm-17in) s.d.1991 iron glass. 23-Nov-2 Burkhard, Luzern #55/R est:2000-2800 (S.FR 2800)
Works on paper
£284 $446 €426 Untitled (18x28cm-7x11in) s.d.1990 Indian ink pencil glass collage on paper. 23-Nov-2 Burkhard, Luzern #51/R (S.FR 650)

MAUDSLEY, Helen (1927-) Australian
Works on paper
£500 $795 €750 From white to coral (39x31cm-15x12in) s.d.84 W/C exhib. 4-Mar-3 Deutscher-Menzies, Melbourne #209/R (A.D 1300)

MAUFRA, Maxime (1861-1918) French
£1899 $3000 €3000 Petit port, quai Rostin (18x24cm-7x9in) s. panel. 2-Dec-2 Tajan, Paris #49/R
£2158 $3453 €3000 Portrait du fils de l'artiste (92x73cm-36x29in) s. 18-May-3 Eric Pillon, Calais #52/R
£3544 $5600 €5600 Inondations (70x135cm-28x53in) s.d.1882. 2-Dec-2 Tajan, Paris #48/R
£4114 $6500 €6500 Effets de ciel sur le rivage breton (54x73cm-21x29in) s. prov. 2-Dec-2 Tajan, Paris #46
£4430 $7000 €6645 Martin brumeux, chateaulin (61x73cm-24x29in) s.d.1901 i.on stretcher prov. 22-Apr-3 Butterfields, San Francisco #6001/R est:8000-12000
£5380 $8500 €8070 L'appel du large (38x46cm-15x18in) s. 16-Nov-2 New Orleans Auction, New Orleans #319/R est:8000-12000
£6410 $10064 €10000 Ruches (60x73cm-24x29in) s.d.1902. 22-Nov-2 Millon & Associes, Paris #62/R est:7500-9000
£9317 $15000 €13976 Paysage aux environs de Douarnenez Brittany (54x65cm-21x26in) s. painted 1897 prov.lit. 7-May-3 Sotheby's, New York #396/R est:15000-20000
£10897 $17109 €17000 Mare Cadol, Rosporden, Finistere (65x81cm-26x32in) s.d.1903 lit. 10-Dec-2 Artcurial Briest, Paris #481/R est:15000-23000
£11972 $19275 €17000 Village du Morbihan (65x81cm-26x32in) s.d.1908. 11-May-3 Thierry & Lannon, Brest #202/R est:22000-25000
£13548 $21406 €21000 Orage (74x60cm-29x24in) s. prov.lit. 18-Dec-2 Tajan, Paris #21/R est:20000
£14557 $22709 €23000 Voiliers au large de la cote (46x55cm-18x22in) s. prov.lit. 31-Jul-2 Tajan, Paris #36/R est:15000-18000
£15000 $24600 €22500 Semaphore (55x82cm-22x32in) s.d.1904 prov. 5-Feb-3 Sotheby's, London #228/R est:12000

£15000 $23850 €22500 Les ruches, la vacheries pres d'Andelys (61x73cm-24x29in) s.d.1902 prov. 20-Mar-3 Sotheby's, Olympia #48/R est:9000-12000
£17391 $28000 €26087 La mare cadol, Rosporden, Finistere (65x81cm-26x32in) s.d.1903 prov. 8-May-3 Christie's, Rockefeller NY #165/R est:25000-35000
£21739 $35000 €32609 Voiliers au large de la cote (46x56cm-18x22in) s. prov. 7-May-3 Sotheby's, New York #165/R est:25000-30000

Works on paper

£355 $550 €533 Le bateau (25x32cm-10x13in) s. graphite exhib. 3-Dec-2 Christie's, Rockefeller NY #39/R
£833 $1358 €1200 Etude d'oies (21x25cm-8x10in) W/C. 19-Jul-3 Thierry & Lannon, Brest #70
£1300 $2002 €1950 Lac Killean (12x14cm-5x6in) s. W/C over pencil prov. 23-Oct-2 Sotheby's, Olympia #623/R est:700-900
£1795 $2818 €2800 Chaloupe sardiniere (24x35cm-9x14in) s. W/C chl. 15-Dec-2 Thierry & Lannon, Brest #36
£1806 $2943 €2600 Sortie du bateau de Belle Ile a Quiberon (24x35cm-9x14in) s. chl W/C. 19-Jul-3 Thierry & Lannon, Brest #67 est:2800-3000
£2083 $3396 €3000 Le port du Havre (30x47cm-12x19in) studio st. chl W/C. 19-Jul-3 Thierry & Lannon, Brest #68/R est:3000-3500
£2083 $3396 €3000 Animation au port du Havre (24x31cm-9x12in) s. W/C chl. 19-Jul-3 Thierry & Lannon, Brest #69/R est:3000-3500
£2179 $3422 €3400 Solitude Ecosse (23x31cm-9x12in) init. W/C chl. 15-Dec-2 Thierry & Lannon, Brest #39
£2436 $3824 €3800 Paysage d'automne (21x27cm-8x11in) init. gouache chl. 15-Dec-2 Thierry & Lannon, Brest #37
£2778 $4416 €4000 Les phares du Havre (32x48cm-13x19in) s.i.d.20 mars 1905 W/C lit. 29-Apr-3 Artcurial Briest, Paris #27/R est:4000-6000
£3169 $5102 €4500 Le cheval blanc (34x32cm-13x13in) pastel. 11-May-3 Thierry & Lannon, Brest #71/R est:3600-4000
£4028 $6404 €5800 Belle-ile (27x44cm-11x17in) s.d.1905 W/C gouache lit. 29-Apr-3 Artcurial Briest, Paris #26/R est:4000-6000

MAUGHAN, Karl (1964-) New Zealander

£478 $750 €717 View through key hole (77x51cm-30x20in) oil construction by Banard Mcintyre. 10-Dec-2 Peter Webb, Auckland #55/R (NZ.D 1500)
£1123 $1785 €1685 Garden painting (37x35cm-15x14in) s.d.March 1993 verso. 25-Feb-3 Peter Webb, Auckland #49/R est:1500-2500 (NZ.D 3200)
£1625 $2599 €2356 Love lies bleeding suite no 1 (31x46cm-12x18in) s.d.1996 verso. 13-May-3 Watson's, Christchurch #42/R est:3500-5000 (NZ.D 4500)

MAUKE, Rudolf (1924-) German

£385 $596 €600 Untitled (72x65cm-28x26in) s.d.55 board prov. 7-Dec-2 Van Ham, Cologne #338/R

MAULBERTSCH, Franz Anton (attrib) (1724-1796) Austrian

£6757 $10541 €10000 Visigothic King Wamba finding St Aegidius (97x53cm-38x21in) i. verso prov. 27-Mar-3 Dorotheum, Vienna #251/R est:10000-15000

MAUND, George C (fl.1853-1871) British

Works on paper

£280 $454 €406 Forester's family (72x105cm-28x41in) s. W/C after Edwin Henry Landseer. 20-May-3 Dreweatt Neate, Newbury #158

MAURA, Bartolome (19th C) Spanish

£503 $810 €750 Adam and Eve in Paradise (33x25cm-13x10in) s. s.i.d.1869 verso. 18-Feb-3 Durán, Madrid #102/R

MAURER, Albert (1889-1935) Swiss

£449 $704 €700 Farmhouse (34x41cm-13x16in) s. canvas on board. 21-Nov-2 Dorotheum, Vienna #259/R

MAURER, Alfred H (1868-1932) American

£40123 $65000 €60185 Still life with pears and Indian bowl (34x77cm-13x30in) painted c.1928-30 prov. 21-May-3 Sotheby's, New York #93/R est:20000-30000
£49383 $80000 €74075 Bridge landscape no.2 (55x46cm-22x18in) s. s.verso board double-sided prov.exhib.lit. 21-May-3 Sotheby's, New York #3/R est:80000-120000
£80247 $130000 €120371 Two heads - two women (55x46cm-22x18in) s. painted c.1929-30 prov.exhib.lit. 21-May-3 Sotheby's, New York #35/R est:50000-75000

Works on paper

£10494 $17000 €15741 Portrait of a girl (55x46cm-22x18in) s. W/C gouache pencil executed c.1923 prov.exhib. 21-May-3 Sotheby's, New York #86/R est:15000-25000
£16975 $27500 €25463 Abstract head (55x46cm-22x18in) s. W/C gouache chl executed c.1930 prov. 21-May-3 Sotheby's, New York #94/R est:15000-25000

MAURER, Friedrich (19th C) German

£1266 $1962 €2000 Farmstead in mountain valley (60x73cm-24x29in) s. 25-Sep-2 Neumeister, Munich #648/R est:1800

MAURER, Jacob (18/19th C) Dutch/German

£641 $1006 €1000 Mountain landscape (63x96cm-25x38in) s.d.1850 panel. 21-Nov-2 Van Ham, Cologne #1778
£7382 $11885 €11000 Travellers in a summer landscape (65x95cm-26x37in) s.d.1850 i.verso. 18-Feb-3 Sotheby's, Amsterdam #424/R est:3000-5000

MAURICE, Charles (19/20th C) British

£250 $388 €375 Pass near Glencoe, Argyllshire, figure on a path by a pool (38x58cm-15x23in) s. s.i.verso. 18-Jul-2 Neales, Nottingham #687

MAURIE, Gaston (?-1912) French

Works on paper

£641 $994 €1000 Elegante au bouquet (24x12cm-9x5in) s.d.1903 W/C. 4-Dec-2 Pierre Berge, Paris #86/R

MAURIER, Georges du (1834-1896) French

Works on paper

£340 $541 €510 Warning of the honeymoon (11x17cm-4x7in) s.i. sepia. 25-Feb-3 Bonhams, Knightsbridge #17/R

MAURITZ-LARSEN, Bjarne (1897-1967) Norwegian

£349 $548 €524 From the skerries (80x100cm-31x39in) s. 25-Nov-2 Blomqvist, Lysaker #1183/R (N.KR 4000)
£708 $1154 €1062 Horses at the mountain farm (70x124cm-28x49in) s. 17-Feb-3 Blomqvist, Lysaker #1124 (N.KR 8000)

MAURUS, Hans (1901-1942) German

£325 $494 €500 Tegernsee (78x97cm-31x38in) s. 5-Jul-2 Weidler, Nurnberg #8692/R
£486 $768 €700 Wetterstein peaks near Mittenwald (78x63cm-31x25in) s. i. verso. 25-Apr-3 Weidler, Nurnberg #9152/R
£500 $790 €720 Waxensteine in autumn near Grainau (64x78cm-25x31in) s. i. verso. 25-Apr-3 Weidler, Nurnberg #9151/R
£510 $811 €750 St Leonhard in Pitztal (66x81cm-26x32in) s.i. i. verso. 20-Mar-3 Neumeister, Munich #2690/R
£577 $894 €900 Konigssee (80x100cm-31x39in) s.i. 5-Dec-2 Neumeister, Munich #2840/R
£633 $1000 €1000 Gschwandtne farmhouse in Zugspitze Alp (65x80cm-26x31in) s. i.verso. 29-Nov-2 Bolland & Marotz, Bremen #802/R
£641 $1006 €1000 Wisurina lake with view of Drei Zinnen (100x80cm-39x31in) s. i.verso. 21-Nov-2 Dorotheum, Vienna #300/R
£755 $1177 €1200 Old courtyard in Meran with vines (80x60cm-31x24in) s.i. prov. 19-Sep-2 Dr Fritz Nagel, Stuttgart #967/R
£759 $1200 €1200 Village street in Garmisch with view of Zugspitze (70x100cm-28x39in) s.d.1924. 29-Nov-2 Sigalas, Stuttgart #1113/R
£828 $1292 €1300 High mountain pasture (65x80cm-26x31in) s. 6-Nov-2 Hugo Ruef, Munich #1201/R
£1064 $1489 €1596 Matterhorn from Winkelmatten (59x78cm-23x31in) s. 29-Nov-1 Falk & Falk, Zurich #684/R (S.FR 2500)
£1370 $2137 €2000 View over the Tegersee with abbey (81x101cm-32x40in) s. i.verso. 10-Apr-3 Allgauer, Kempten #2890/R est:1800

MAURY, François (1861-1933) French

£545 $855 €850 Barque au crepuscule (27x35cm-11x14in) s.d.1895 panel. 24-Nov-2 Lesieur & Le Bars, Le Havre #118
£1013 $1580 €1600 La cueillette (65x49cm-26x19in) s. panel. 20-Oct-2 Mercier & Cie, Lille #305 est:1000-1500
£1203 $1876 €1900 Eloge du desir (60x73cm-24x29in) s. 20-Oct-2 Mercier & Cie, Lille #308/R est:1500-2500
£1266 $1975 €2000 Femmes dans un sous-bois (60x73cm-24x29in) s. 20-Oct-2 Mercier & Cie, Lille #325 est:1500-2500
£2656 $4250 €3984 Landscape with elegant ladies in the wood (61x81cm-24x32in) s. 14-May-3 Butterfields, San Francisco #1135/R est:3000-5000

MAUTHAUSER, J (19th C) ?

£1154 $1788 €1800 After a successful hunt in snow (56x68cm-22x27in) s. canvas on panel. 5-Dec-2 Schopman, Hamburg #528 est:1200

MAUVE, Anton (1838-1888) Dutch

£556 $917 €800 Interior of a barn (35x49cm-14x19in) s. paper on panel. 1-Jul-3 Christie's, Amsterdam #193
£986 $1587 €1400 Country path (40x30cm-16x12in) s. 7-May-3 Vendue Huis, Gravenhage #453/R
£1250 $2000 €1875 Cows by a stream (28x51cm-11x20in) s. canvas on board. 15-Mar-3 Jeffery Burchard, Florida #82/R
£1301 $2030 €1900 Still life (22x23cm-9x9in) s. panel prov. 14-Apr-3 Glerum, Amsterdam #59/R est:2000-3000
£1806 $2979 €2600 Sunny farmyard (55x34cm-22x13in) s. panel prov.exhib. 1-Jul-3 Christie's, Amsterdam #188/R est:2000-3000

£2397 $3764 €3500 Summer landscape (22x39cm-9x15in) s. canvas on panel. 15-Apr-3 Sotheby's, Amsterdam #223/R est:4000-6000
£7895 $12000 €11843 Herdsman with sheep and dog (61x86cm-24x34in) s. 30-Aug-2 Thomaston Place, Thomaston #85
£11644 $18281 €17000 Cows in a meadow (54x83cm-21x33in) s. 15-Apr-3 Sotheby's, Amsterdam #150/R est:8000-12000
£13699 $21370 €20000 Portrait of Mrs Mauve sitting in the dunes (19x33cm-7x13in) s. canvas on panel prov. 14-Apr-3 Glerum, Amsterdam #60/R est:8000-10000
£51370 $80651 €75000 Fishing boats on Scheveningen beach (83x122cm-33x48in) s. 15-Apr-3 Sotheby's, Amsterdam #243/R est:80000-120000
Works on paper
£329 $533 €500 Sheep (26x33cm-10x13in) pencil prov. 21-Jan-3 Christie's, Amsterdam #207
£556 $917 €800 Bring in the sheep (23x16cm-9x6in) s. pencil W/C. 1-Jul-3 Christie's, Amsterdam #189/R
£2877 $4516 €4200 Young wood gatherer (24x34cm-9x13in) s. W/C htd white. 15-Apr-3 Sotheby's, Amsterdam #103/R est:3000-5000
£6051 $9500 €9077 Digging in the fields (7x16cm-3x6in) s. W/C. 10-Dec-2 Doyle, New York #191/R est:5000-7000
£22318 $34815 €32361 Sunlight and shade (57x90cm-22x35in) s. W/C htd gouache exhib. 26-Mar-3 Walker's, Ottawa #3/R est:25000-30000 (C.D 52000)

MAUVE, Anton (attrib) (1838-1888) Dutch
£650 $1021 €975 Unharnessing the cart at dusk (52x67cm-20x26in) s. 16-Apr-3 Christie's, Kensington #742/R

MAUVE, Anton Rudolf (1876-1962) Dutch
£461 $746 €700 Tending to the fields (45x60cm-18x24in) 21-Jan-3 Christie's, Amsterdam #247/R

MAUZAISSE, Jean Baptiste (1784-1844) French
£2027 $3162 €3000 Portrait d'homme au manteau borde de fourrure (64x53cm-25x21in) s. 28-Mar-3 Delvaux, Paris #128/R

MAUZAN, Achille (1883-1952) Italian/French
£256 $403 €400 Italian recorder (53x38cm-21x15in) s.d.925 tempera paper. 19-Nov-2 Finarte, Milan #26

MAVRO, Mania (1889-?) Russian
£451 $736 €650 La biae de Douarnenez (37x46cm-15x18in) s. cardboard. 19-Jul-3 Thierry & Lannon, Brest #364

MAVROGORDATO, Alexander James (fl.1892-1933) British
Works on paper
£350 $557 €525 Entrance to the Forum at Rome (33x48cm-13x19in) s.d.1901 W/C. 29-Apr-3 Bonhams, Knightsbridge #21/R
£1150 $1817 €1725 Sphinx with the Pyramids behind (30x47cm-12x19in) s.d.97 W/C. 26-Nov-2 Bonhams, Knightsbridge #206b/R est:800-1200

MAVROIDIS, Giorgios (1913-) Greek
£2300 $3634 €3450 Artist's materials (62x52cm-24x20in) 1-Apr-3 Bonhams, New Bond Street #66 est:2000-3000

MAW, W D (?) American?
£2467 $3750 €3701 Clipper ships at sea (41x41cm-16x16in) s. 17-Aug-2 North East Auctions, Portsmouth #412/R

MAWDSLEY, Henry (1878-1937) British
Works on paper
£280 $437 €420 Continental market place (30x38cm-12x15in) s. W/C. 9-Apr-3 Andrew Hartley, Ilkley #921

MAWLEY, George (1838-1873) British
Works on paper
£280 $437 €420 River landscape with cattle, probably in Yorkshire (22x28cm-9x11in) s.d.1871 W/C. 10-Apr-3 Tennants, Leyburn #842

MAX, Gabriel von (1840-1915) Czechoslovakian
£662 $1079 €1000 Praying (49x40cm-19x16in) 28-Jan-3 Dorotheum, Vienna #15/R
£677 $1050 €1016 Bust portrait of a bearded gentleman wearing a red cap (38x28cm-15x11in) s. prov. 6-Dec-2 Eldred, East Dennis #1019/R
£844 $1258 €1300 Woman's portrait (59x43cm-23x17in) s. 26-Jun-2 Neumeister, Munich #798/R
£945 $1550 €1370 Portrait of a beauty in Greek clothing (46x36cm-18x14in) s. 30-May-3 Aspire, Cleveland #33/R est:1500-3000
£950 $1577 €1425 Reclining beauty (34x27cm-13x11in) s. 10-Jun-3 Bonhams, Knightsbridge #268/R
£1000 $1560 €1500 Nature scene (29x23cm-11x9in) s.i. panel. 10-Oct-2 Rupert Toovey, Partridge Green #1574
£1088 $1731 €1600 Isolde (58x42cm-23x17in) s.i. canvas on panel. 20-Mar-3 Neumeister, Munich #2691/R est:800
£1923 $3019 €3000 Portrait of girl (18x14cm-7x6in) s. panel. 21-Nov-2 Van Ham, Cologne #1779 est:3200
£1948 $2961 €3000 Monkeys (59x79cm-23x31in) 6-Jul-2 Berlinghof, Heidelberg #226/R est:6000
£2800 $4396 €4200 Palm reader (126x98cm-50x39in) s.d.87. 21-Nov-2 Christie's, Kensington #35/R est:3000-5000
£3774 $5887 €6000 Monkey with bandaged arm (35x26cm-14x10in) s.i. 19-Sep-2 Dr Fritz Nagel, Stuttgart #968/R est:2000
£4762 $7571 €7000 Mother with child (63x50cm-25x20in) s. 19-Mar-3 Neumeister, Munich #644/R est:2500
£9000 $14760 €13500 Odalisque (127x170cm-50x67in) s. 3-Jun-3 Sotheby's, London #45/R est:8000-12000
£16000 $26240 €24000 Abelard and Heloise (41x36cm-16x14in) s. prov. 3-Jun-3 Sotheby's, London #38/R est:5000-7000
Works on paper
£380 $589 €600 Portrait of Eleonora Duse (30x24cm-12x9in) s. pen Indian ink brush gouache chk board. 27-Sep-2 Venator & Hansten, Koln #1188/R

MAX, Heinrich (1847-1900) Czechoslovakian
£450 $743 €653 Liberty (79x64cm-31x25in) s. 3-Jul-3 Duke & Son, Dorchester #309/R

MAXENCE, Edgard (1871-1954) French
£705 $1107 €1100 Je ferai tomber une pluie de roses (60x44cm-24x17in) s. panel. 13-Dec-2 Piasa, Paris #175
£1111 $1811 €1600 Vase de fleurs (63x44cm-25x17in) s. 19-Jul-3 Thierry & Lannon, Brest #152 est:1000-1200
Works on paper
£506 $800 €800 Cour de ferme (12x19cm-5x7in) s.i. W/C. 1-Dec-2 Peron, Melun #6

MAXFIELD, James Emery (1848-?) American
£650 $1008 €975 Picking flowers (36x28cm-14x11in) s. 3-Dec-2 Sotheby's, Olympia #227/R

MAXWELL, Carolyn (20th C) Irish?
£282 $468 €400 Abstract (40x56cm-16x22in) mono.d. acrylic. 10-Jun-3 James Adam, Dublin #186/R
£282 $468 €400 Abstract (76x60cm-30x24in) mono.d.2003 acrylic. 10-Jun-3 James Adam, Dublin #205/R
£296 $491 €420 Abstract (76x50cm-30x20in) mono.d.2003 verso acrylic. 10-Jun-3 James Adam, Dublin #206/R

MAXWELL, Christian (1909-1980) British
Works on paper
£480 $802 €696 Gavin convalescing (31x19cm-12x7in) W/C over pencil. 25-Jun-3 Bonhams, Bury St Edmunds #518/R

MAXWELL, John (1905-1962) British
Works on paper
£2400 $3720 €3600 Window (48x35cm-19x14in) s.d.44 W/C pastel col crayon prov.exhib. 31-Oct-2 Christie's, London #161/R est:2500-3500

MAY, Elisabeth M Messiter (1913-) American
£387 $600 €581 Native American family gathering sticks. Surreal explosion of colours (51x61cm-20x24in) double-sided. 21-Jul-2 Jeffery Burchard, Florida #54/R

MAY, Ferdinand (?) British?
£800 $1272 €1200 Farmers' hunt (46x56cm-18x22in) s. 30-Apr-3 Halls, Shrewsbury #264/R

MAY, Henrietta Mabel (1884-1971) Canadian
£2889 $4738 €4334 Daffodils in a vase (40x33cm-16x13in) s. canvas on masonite prov. 27-May-3 Sotheby's, Toronto #42/R est:3000-4000 (C.D 6500)
£2915 $4664 €4373 Still life with geraniums (33x25cm-13x10in) s. panel double-sided prov. 15-May-3 Heffel, Vancouver #204/R est:4000-5000 (C.D 6500)
£4435 $7008 €6653 Village in the hills (25x36cm-10x14in) s. panel double-sided. 14-Nov-2 Heffel, Vancouver #154/R est:5000-6000 (C.D 11000)
£6855 $10831 €10283 Farm, Comeau (57x69cm-22x27in) s. painted 1943 prov. 14-Nov-2 Heffel, Vancouver #153/R est:18000-22000 (C.D 17000)

MAY, Olivier le (1734-1797) French
£1400 $2184 €2100 Dutch river scene (13x26cm-5x10in) panel. 8-Oct-2 Bonhams, Knightsbridge #128/R est:800-1200

MAY, Phil (1864-1903) British
Works on paper
£300 $462 €450 Lagonda V12 no 5 at Le Mans 1939, Dobson, Brackenbury (43x33cm-17x13in) s. W/C. 6-Sep-2 Bonhams, Knightsbridge #42a
£720 $1195 €1080 The coming race. pencil ink. 10-Jun-3 Lawrences, Bletchingley #1370

MAY, Walter William (1831-1896) British
£589 $931 €884 Waiting for the time (28x41cm-11x16in) s. 27-Nov-2 Falkkloos, Malmo #77585/R (S.KR 8400)
Works on paper
£320 $499 €480 Sailing barge on a beach, with horses tendered nearby (14x26cm-6x10in) s. W/C. 9-Apr-3 Cheffins Grain & Comins, Cambridge #565/R
£320 $525 €480 An offshore breeze, sailing vessels off a coastline (21x34cm-8x13in) s.d.62 W/C. 3-Jun-3 Bonhams, Oxford #26
£420 $689 €630 Amsterdam from the west dock (18x26cm-7x10in) W/C. 7-Feb-3 Honiton Galleries, Honiton #360/R
£450 $725 €675 Before the squall, yacht off a rocky headland (17x24cm-7x9in) i. pencil W/C htd white. 18-Feb-3 Rowley Fine Art, Newmarket #339/R
£550 $897 €825 Barges in a Dutch landscape (49x77cm-19x30in) s.d.86 W/C. 29-Jan-3 Sotheby's, Olympia #119/R est:600-800
£1200 $1860 €1800 On the Scheldt, near Antwerp (49x70cm-19x28in) s.d.74 i. verso W/C over pencil htd bodycol scratching out. 2-Oct-2 Bonhams, Knowle #48 est:250-350

MAYAN, Earl (20th C) American
£481 $750 €722 Southern belle firing pistols (41x58cm-16x23in) s. board. 9-Nov-2 Illustration House, New York #149/R

MAYBURGER, Josef (1813-1908) Austrian
£1026 $1610 €1600 Dachstein with the Gosau lake (27x36cm-11x14in) s.i. paper on board. 21-Nov-2 Dorotheum, Vienna #121/R est:1400-2000
£1154 $1812 €1800 Alpine way near Gosau-Zwang (95x140cm-37x55in) s.d.1889. 21-Nov-2 Dorotheum, Vienna #123/R est:3600-5000
£1410 $2214 €2200 Alpine way near Gosau-Zwang (83x116cm-33x46in) s. 21-Nov-2 Dorotheum, Vienna #120/R est:3000-4000
£1667 $2617 €2600 Evening time on the Salzburg alpine pasture (26x37cm-10x15in) s. 21-Nov-2 Dorotheum, Vienna #122/R est:2000-3000
£2152 $3400 €3400 South Italian abbey buildings (70x92cm-28x36in) s.indis.d. 28-Nov-2 Dorotheum, Vienna #103/R est:3200-3600
£2431 $3865 €3500 Seekirchen (16x43cm-6x17in) i. verso board. 29-Apr-3 Wiener Kunst Auktionen, Vienna #551/R est:3000-5000
£2655 $4141 €3983 Idyllic landscape (88x136cm-35x54in) s. 11-Apr-3 Kieselbach, Budapest #118/R est:500000-950000 (H.F 950000)

MAYER, Erich (1876-1960) South African
£344 $554 €516 Goats in a wooded landscape (35x50cm-14x20in) s.d.1942 board. 12-May-3 Stephan Welz, Johannesburg #235 est:4000-6000 (SA.R 4000)
£381 $606 €560 South African landscape (95x51cm-37x20in) s. 28-Mar-3 Bolland & Marotz, Bremen #567/R
£384 $600 €576 Women with two children in a Veld landscape (19x27cm-7x11in) s.d.1914 board. 11-Nov-2 Stephan Welz, Johannesburg #554 (SA.R 6000)
£473 $761 €710 Hartebeespoort dam near Pretoria (22x30cm-9x12in) s.d.1923 s.i.d.verso board. 12-May-3 Stephan Welz, Johannesburg #122 est:5000-8000 (SA.R 5500)
£545 $849 €818 Bushveld Koppie in the winter (26x36cm-10x14in) s.d.1941 board. 11-Nov-2 Stephan Welz, Johannesburg #547 (SA.R 8500)
£817 $1315 €1226 Pilansberg (19x29cm-7x11in) s.d.1927 i.d.verso board. 12-May-3 Stephan Welz, Johannesburg #129/R est:5000-7000 (SA.R 9500)
£1290 $2077 €1935 Sunday in the Pretoria Zoo (24x35cm-9x14in) s. indis d.1946 canvasboard. 12-May-3 Stephan Welz, Johannesburg #518/R est:15000-20000 (SA.R 15000)
Works on paper
£192 $300 €288 Street, Port Elizabeth (18x29cm-7x11in) s. W/C over pencil. 11-Nov-2 Stephan Welz, Johannesburg #469 (SA.R 3000)
£275 $443 €413 Tussen Letaba en Thabina, N TVL (18x24cm-7x9in) s.d.1931 i.verso W/C. 12-May-3 Stephan Welz, Johannesburg #124 est:1200-1800 (SA.R 3200)

MAYER, Frank Blackwell (1827-1899) American
£10063 $16000 €15095 Man of the house (37x28cm-15x11in) s.d.1867 s.i.on stretcher. 5-Mar-3 Sotheby's, New York #54b/R est:7000-10000

MAYER, Georg (1765-c.1830) Swiss
Works on paper
£545 $855 €850 Portrait of painter Karl Spitzweg (34x26cm-13x10in) s. chl. 21-Nov-2 Dorotheum, Vienna #396/R

MAYER, Leopold Ernest and PIERSON, Pierre Louis (19th C) French
Photographs
£3205 $5064 €5000 Gioacchino Rossini (10x16cm-4x6in) s.i.num.12510 salt print exec.c.1855. 16-Nov-2 Christie's, Paris #219/R est:6000-8000

MAYER, Louis (1869-?) American
Sculpture
£943 $1500 €1415 Head of negro (46cm-18in) s.i. plaster exec.c.1925. 2-Mar-3 Toomey, Oak Park #580/R est:1000-2000

MAYER, Luigi (18th C) Italian
Works on paper
£1064 $1777 €1500 L'ancien theatre de Myra, Turquie (23x32cm-9x13in) W/C gouache. 23-Jun-3 Beaussant & Lefèvre, Paris #101 est:200-250

MAYER, Michael (fl.1550-1570) German
Works on paper
£1224 $1750 €1836 Adoration of the Shepherds (33x45cm-13x18in) mono.d.1565 pen ink. 23-Jan-3 Swann Galleries, New York #317/R est:2500-3500

MAYER, Nicolas (1852-1929) French
Sculpture
£2200 $3432 €3300 Duel (25x41cm-10x16in) s.d.1887 brown pat bronze. 5-Nov-2 Sotheby's, London #140/R est:2500-3500

MAYER, Peter Bela (1888-?) American
£484 $750 €726 House by birch trees (23x30cm-9x12in) canvasboard. 7-Dec-2 South Bay, Long Island #178/R
£1796 $3000 €2604 Afternoon (30x41cm-12x16in) s. s.i.verso canvasboard. 18-Jun-3 Christie's, Los Angeles #43/R est:3000-5000

MAYER, Ralph (1898-1979) American
£1398 $2250 €2097 Avalon, Catalina Island (41x51cm-16x20in) s. canvasboard. 18-Feb-3 John Moran, Pasadena #126 est:1000-1500
£6098 $10000 €8842 Firehouse (66x84cm-26x33in) 1-Jun-3 Wright, Chicago #213/R est:10000-15000

MAYER, W (19th C) German
£811 $1265 €1200 Man and woman before landscape (68x53cm-27x21in) s. d.1855 verso two. 26-Mar-3 Hugo Ruef, Munich #173

MAYER-MARTON, Georg (1897-?) Hungarian
£2899 $4754 €4000 Boats in the harbour (51x70cm-20x28in) masonite prov.lit. 27-May-3 Hassfurther, Vienna #48/R est:4000-5000

MAYER-SEEON (?) ?
£541 $845 €850 Isar landscape (78x10cm-31x4in) s.d.20. 6-Nov-2 Hugo Ruef, Munich #1203/R

MAYES, William Edward (1861-1952) British
Works on paper
£300 $468 €450 At Brandall (27x45cm-11x18in) s.i.d.1926 W/C. 27-Mar-3 Christie's, Kensington #340
£320 $522 €480 Norfolk keel at Runham Vauxhall (25x41cm-10x16in) s. W/C. 14-Feb-3 Keys, Aylsham #635
£350 $546 €525 Farm buildings by the river (29x42cm-11x17in) s.d.1922 W/C. 27-Mar-3 Christie's, Kensington #310
£480 $802 €696 Wherry and yacht on the Norfolk Broads approaching a cottage (25x33cm-10x13in) s. W/C. 20-Jun-3 Keys, Aylsham #596
£500 $780 €750 Hensted Mill, Norfolk (29x27cm-11x11in) s.d.1926 indis i.verso pencil W/C. 27-Mar-3 Christie's, Kensington #313/R
£620 $1035 €899 Wherry passing a windmill on the Norfolk Broads (20x30cm-8x12in) s.d.1927 W/C. 20-Jun-3 Keys, Aylsham #594/R
£620 $1035 €899 Wherry and a white hulled yacht on the Norfolk Broads (20x30cm-8x12in) s. W/C. 20-Jun-3 Keys, Aylsham #595

MAYET, Léon (1858-?) French
£2607 $4145 €3911 Young nude girl sewing (123x92cm-48x36in) s.d.1914. 5-Mar-3 Rasmussen, Copenhagen #1771/R est:25000 (D.KR 28000)

MAYEUR, Adrien le (1844-1923) Belgian
£440 $682 €700 Port de peche (35x50cm-14x20in) s. 1-Oct-2 Palais de Beaux Arts, Brussels #502

£3226 $5097 €4839 Entrance of a farm near Brussels (35x48cm-14x19in) s. panel. 30-Nov-2 Goteborg Auktionsverk, Sweden #188/R est:6000 (S.KR 46000)

MAYEUR, Jean le (1880-1958) Belgian
£949 $1481 €1500 Coucher de soleil sur Mer du Nord (15x22cm-6x9in) s. panel. 16-Sep-2 Horta, Bruxelles #124
£1126 $1835 €1700 Vapeur dans l'entree du chenal (36x54cm-14x21in) panel. 17-Feb-3 Horta, Bruxelles #141
£1192 $1943 €1800 Peniche amarree au bord de canal (35x53cm-14x21in) s. 17-Feb-3 Horta, Bruxelles #142
£1781 $2778 €2600 Venise (22x27cm-9x11in) s. i.verso panel. 14-Apr-3 Horta, Bruxelles #125/R est:3000-4000
£1795 $2782 €2800 Peniche amarree au bord du canal (35x53cm-14x21in) s. panel. 9-Dec-2 Horta, Bruxelles #160/R est:4000-6000
£1854 $3023 €2800 Voilier (30x42cm-12x17in) s. canvas on panel. 17-Feb-3 Horta, Bruxelles #140/R
£2961 $4796 €4500 Lake at sunset (28x39cm-11x15in) s. canvas on board. 21-Jan-3 Christie's, Amsterdam #438/R est:1500-2000
£3597 $5899 €5000 Landscape with a boat in a canal (36x55cm-14x22in) s. panel. 3-Jun-3 Christie's, Amsterdam #282/R est:6000-8000
£3974 $6240 €6200 Port de peche (22x26cm-9x10in) s. panel. 19-Nov-2 Vanderkindere, Brussels #82 est:1000-1500
£6410 $10064 €10000 La kermesse au village (36x55cm-14x22in) s. panel. 19-Nov-2 Vanderkindere, Brussels #32/R est:2000-3000
£10771 $16587 €16157 Coffee pickers in Djibouti, Africa (22x27cm-9x11in) s. cardboard. 27-Oct-2 Christie's, Hong Kong #5/R est:35000-45000 (HK.D 130000)
£11511 $18417 €16000 Sunbathers in St Tropez. Algerian woman seated (46x52cm-18x20in) s. board painted c.1928 double-sided. 17-May-3 De Vuyst, Lokeren #559/R est:6500-7500
£18227 $28070 €27341 Port (72x97cm-28x38in) s. canvas on board. 27-Oct-2 Christie's, Hong Kong #4/R est:200000-400000 (HK.D 220000)
£18987 $29620 €30000 Jour de marche (90x120cm-35x47in) s. 16-Sep-2 Horta, Bruxelles #123/R est:10000-15000
£21541 $33173 €32312 Dancing Balinese women (25x31cm-10x12in) s. ap. 27-Oct-2 Christie's, Hong Kong #6/R est:90000-120000 (HK.D 260000)
£93617 $147915 €140426 Joie de vivre - de soleil (76x90cm-30x35in) s. lit. 2-Dec-2 Rasmussen, Copenhagen #1199/R est:800000-1200000 (D.KR 1100000)
£147630 $243590 €214064 Four Balinese girls resting in the jungle (75x90cm-30x35in) s. prov. 6-Jul-3 Christie's, Hong Kong #28/R est:1200000-1500000 (HK.D 1900000)

Works on paper
£377 $581 €600 A bord de l'Anthinous (19x26cm-7x10in) s. dr. 22-Oct-2 Campo, Vlaamse Kaai #183
£3145 $4843 €5000 Jeune garcon dans une rue de Kairouan (42x52cm-17x20in) s.i.d.1919 pastel. 23-Oct-2 Rabourdin & Choppin de Janvry, Paris #163/R
£3145 $4843 €5000 Marche aux chameaux (42x57cm-17x22in) s.i.d.1919 pastel. 23-Oct-2 Rabourdin & Choppin de Janvry, Paris #161/R
£7042 $10845 €10563 Ballinese girl in the garden (22x27cm-9x11in) s. pastel chl. 27-Oct-2 Christie's, Hong Kong #1/R est:40000-80000 (HK.D 85000)
£31080 $51282 €45066 Women around the table (53x68cm-21x27in) s. chl pastel prov. 6-Jul-3 Christie's, Hong Kong #7/R est:100000-150000 (HK.D 400000)

MAYNADIE, Charles Emmanuel (20th C) French?
£897 $1409 €1400 Souk de Taza (33x55cm-13x22in) s.i. cardboard. 20-Nov-2 Claude Boisgirard, Paris #44/R
£1973 $3137 €2900 Scene de marche a Taza (33x55cm-13x22in) s.i. panel. 24-Mar-3 Rabourdin & Choppin de Janvry, Paris #242/R est:3000-3500

MAYNARD, Arthur F (?) American?
£285 $450 €428 Before the rain (61x76cm-24x30in) s. 5-Apr-3 Harvey Clar, Oakland #1339

MAYNARD, Thomas (attrib) (fl.1777-1812) British
£4200 $6720 €6300 Young girl standing on a terrace holding basket of fruit (107x76cm-42x30in) 13-Mar-3 Duke & Son, Dorchester #261/R

MAYNE, Jean (19th C) Belgian
£3082 $4808 €4500 In a garden in Veere (53x65cm-21x26in) s.i. 14-Apr-3 Glerum, Amsterdam #89/R est:4500-5500

MAYO, Antoine Malliarakis (1905-1990) French/Egyptian
£255 $397 €400 Fillette aux nattes (35x27cm-14x11in) st.sig. 6-Nov-2 Le Mouel, Paris #92
£255 $397 €400 La foret (73x60cm-29x24in) st.sig. painted c.1963. 6-Nov-2 Le Mouel, Paris #94
£255 $397 €400 Bord de mer (38x61cm-15x24in) st.sig. painted c.1958. 6-Nov-2 Le Mouel, Paris #101
£255 $397 €400 Paysage vallonne (60x73cm-24x29in) st.sig. 6-Nov-2 Le Mouel, Paris #113
£255 $397 €400 Composition (114x72cm-45x28in) st.sig. painted c.1960. 6-Nov-2 Le Mouel, Paris #121
£255 $397 €400 Bord de mer (60x73cm-24x29in) st.sig. 6-Nov-2 Le Mouel, Paris #126
£255 $397 €400 Fleurs (65x54cm-26x21in) st.sig. 6-Nov-2 Le Mouel, Paris #132
£255 $397 €400 Le lit de depart (60x73cm-24x29in) s. 6-Nov-2 Le Mouel, Paris #192
£255 $397 €400 Lianes, vagues (65x93cm-26x37in) s. 6-Nov-2 Le Mouel, Paris #183
£255 $397 €400 Poires (81x65cm-32x26in) st.sig. 6-Nov-2 Le Mouel, Paris #200
£255 $397 €400 Montagne (50x61cm-20x24in) st.sig. 6-Nov-2 Le Mouel, Paris #215
£255 $397 €400 Bord de mer (60x73cm-24x29in) st.sig. 6-Nov-2 Le Mouel, Paris #228
£255 $397 €400 Crepuscule (64x55cm-25x22in) st.sig. 6-Nov-2 Le Mouel, Paris #230
£287 $447 €450 Eurydice (73x60cm-29x24in) st.sig. 6-Nov-2 Le Mouel, Paris #63
£287 $447 €450 Reflet (92x73cm-36x29in) st.sig. 6-Nov-2 Le Mouel, Paris #100
£287 $447 €450 Tete (41x33cm-16x13in) st.sig. 6-Nov-2 Le Mouel, Paris #116
£287 $447 €450 Mer eternelle (60x73cm-24x29in) s. 6-Nov-2 Le Mouel, Paris #174
£287 $447 €450 Le figuier (65x54cm-26x21in) st.sig. 6-Nov-2 Le Mouel, Paris #214
£287 $447 €450 La revelation (54x65cm-21x26in) s. 6-Nov-2 Le Mouel, Paris #222
£287 $447 €450 Deux mondes (65x54cm-26x21in) st.sig. 6-Nov-2 Le Mouel, Paris #234
£287 $447 €450 Reve blanc (65x81cm-26x32in) st.sig. s.i.d.verso. 6-Nov-2 Le Mouel, Paris #240
£287 $447 €450 Coupe de fruits (50x61cm-20x24in) st.sig. 6-Nov-2 Le Mouel, Paris #242
£318 $497 €500 Perspective (73x92cm-29x36in) s. 6-Nov-2 Le Mouel, Paris #103
£318 $497 €500 Les grands arbres (54x65cm-21x26in) st.sig. 6-Nov-2 Le Mouel, Paris #108
£318 $497 €500 Le lac (60x73cm-24x29in) st.sig. 6-Nov-2 Le Mouel, Paris #110
£318 $497 €500 Chien (33x41cm-13x16in) st.sig. 6-Nov-2 Le Mouel, Paris #114
£318 $497 €500 Corso (46x38cm-18x15in) st.sig. 6-Nov-2 Le Mouel, Paris #117
£318 $497 €500 Lianes (91x73cm-36x29in) st.sig. 6-Nov-2 Le Mouel, Paris #137
£318 $497 €500 Nu couche (19x27cm-7x11in) st.sig. 6-Nov-2 Le Mouel, Paris #210
£318 $497 €500 Coquetterie (46x38cm-18x15in) s. 6-Nov-2 Le Mouel, Paris #213
£318 $497 €500 Echafaudage (60x73cm-24x29in) st.sig. 6-Nov-2 Le Mouel, Paris #219
£318 $497 €500 Aphrodite (54x81cm-21x32in) s. 6-Nov-2 Le Mouel, Paris #226
£318 $497 €500 Le chien (60x73cm-24x29in) st.sig. 6-Nov-2 Le Mouel, Paris #227
£350 $546 €550 Spectacle (54x65cm-21x26in) st.sig. 6-Nov-2 Le Mouel, Paris #233
£382 $596 €600 Tete (35x27cm-14x11in) st.sig. s.i.d.01.1937 verso panel. 6-Nov-2 Le Mouel, Paris #27
£382 $596 €600 Fleurs (61x46cm-24x18in) st.sig. 6-Nov-2 Le Mouel, Paris #76
£382 $596 €600 Le parc, grands arbres (47x61cm-19x24in) s. 6-Nov-2 Le Mouel, Paris #96
£382 $596 €600 La danse de marbre (65x92cm-26x36in) s. 6-Nov-2 Le Mouel, Paris #99
£382 $596 €600 L'homme (81x55cm-32x22in) st.sig. 6-Nov-2 Le Mouel, Paris #111
£382 $596 €600 Fruits de sang (81x65cm-32x26in) st.sig. 6-Nov-2 Le Mouel, Paris #145
£382 $596 €600 Renis, mon ame (46x55cm-18x22in) s. 6-Nov-2 Le Mouel, Paris #150
£382 $596 €600 Jeux de jambes (65x81cm-26x32in) st.sig. 6-Nov-2 Le Mouel, Paris #191
£382 $596 €600 Le pain quotidien (73x60cm-29x24in) s. i.d.verso. 6-Nov-2 Le Mouel, Paris #223
£382 $596 €600 L'atelier (73x60cm-29x24in) st.sig. 6-Nov-2 Le Mouel, Paris #237
£414 $646 €650 Jeune garcon (55x46cm-22x18in) st.sig. wood painted c.1945. 6-Nov-2 Le Mouel, Paris #22
£414 $646 €650 Jardin de Ravenne (100x81cm-39x32in) s. 6-Nov-2 Le Mouel, Paris #124
£414 $646 €650 Les oeufs (100x100cm-39x39in) st.sig. 6-Nov-2 Le Mouel, Paris #216
£414 $646 €650 Danseuses (60x73cm-24x29in) st.sig. 6-Nov-2 Le Mouel, Paris #244
£446 $696 €700 Paysanne (100x65cm-39x26in) st.sig. i.d.verso. 6-Nov-2 Le Mouel, Paris #18
£446 $696 €700 Femme pensive (41x33cm-16x13in) st.sig. i.d.verso. 6-Nov-2 Le Mouel, Paris #29
£446 $696 €700 Oignons (54x73cm-21x29in) s. 6-Nov-2 Le Mouel, Paris #79

£446 $696 €700 A travers les arbres (65x92cm-26x36in) st.sig. 6-Nov-2 Le Mouel, Paris #81
£446 $696 €700 Fillette aux nattes (46x33cm-18x13in) st.sig. 6-Nov-2 Le Mouel, Paris #91
£446 $696 €700 Le depart (60x73cm-24x29in) st.sig. 6-Nov-2 Le Mouel, Paris #102
£446 $696 €700 Rome (54x73cm-21x29in) st.sig. 6-Nov-2 Le Mouel, Paris #107
£446 $696 €700 Bord de mer (38x55cm-15x22in) s. painted c.1958. 6-Nov-2 Le Mouel, Paris #115
£446 $696 €700 Pigeons volent (60x73cm-24x29in) s. 6-Nov-2 Le Mouel, Paris #139
£446 $696 €700 Les figures (38x55cm-15x22in) s. 6-Nov-2 Le Mouel, Paris #141
£446 $696 €700 Dunes (46x55cm-18x22in) s. 6-Nov-2 Le Mouel, Paris #161
£446 $696 €700 Paysage (54x65cm-21x26in) st.sig. 6-Nov-2 Le Mouel, Paris #172
£446 $696 €700 La grande vague (73x92cm-29x36in) s. 6-Nov-2 Le Mouel, Paris #181
£446 $696 €700 La providence (54x65cm-21x26in) s. 6-Nov-2 Le Mouel, Paris #184
£446 $696 €700 L'envol (46x55cm-18x22in) s. 6-Nov-2 Le Mouel, Paris #196
£446 $696 €700 Les oeufs (100x100cm-39x39in) st.sig. 6-Nov-2 Le Mouel, Paris #221
£446 $696 €700 Montagne (50x65cm-20x26in) st.sig. 6-Nov-2 Le Mouel, Paris #231
£478 $745 €750 Le bretonne. st.sig. i.d.verso. 6-Nov-2 Le Mouel, Paris #30
£478 $745 €750 Femme nue (54x73cm-21x29in) st.sig. 6-Nov-2 Le Mouel, Paris #225
£510 $795 €800 Fleurs (16x27cm-6x11in) st.sig. panel painted c.1943. 6-Nov-2 Le Mouel, Paris #49
£510 $795 €800 Portrait d'homme (27x22cm-11x9in) st.sig. 6-Nov-2 Le Mouel, Paris #71
£510 $795 €800 Femme peintre (27x22cm-11x9in) st.sig. painted c.1953. 6-Nov-2 Le Mouel, Paris #90
£510 $795 €800 Bataille (38x65cm-15x26in) st.sig. 6-Nov-2 Le Mouel, Paris #97/R
£510 $795 €800 Composition (147x116cm-58x46in) st.sig. 6-Nov-2 Le Mouel, Paris #129
£510 $795 €800 Composition (164x131cm-65x52in) s. 6-Nov-2 Le Mouel, Paris #130
£510 $795 €800 Composition (150x104cm-59x41in) st.sig. 6-Nov-2 Le Mouel, Paris #131
£510 $795 €800 Feminite (46x38cm-18x15in) s. 6-Nov-2 Le Mouel, Paris #178
£510 $795 €800 Vacances (60x73cm-24x29in) st.sig. 6-Nov-2 Le Mouel, Paris #186
£510 $795 €800 Figuier petrifiee (83x100cm-33x39in) st.sig. 6-Nov-2 Le Mouel, Paris #232/R
£541 $845 €850 Fleurs (24x19cm-9x7in) st.sig. canvas on panel. 6-Nov-2 Le Mouel, Paris #44
£541 $845 €850 La jeune fille (27x19cm-11x7in) st.sig. 6-Nov-2 Le Mouel, Paris #51
£541 $845 €850 Deux poires, une pomme (19x24cm-7x9in) st.sig. 6-Nov-2 Le Mouel, Paris #88
£541 $845 €850 Composition (146x126cm-57x50in) s. 6-Nov-2 Le Mouel, Paris #122/R
£541 $845 €850 Volutes (27x35cm-11x14in) st.sig. wood. 6-Nov-2 Le Mouel, Paris #203
£541 $845 €850 Les athletes (60x49cm-24x19in) st.sig. 6-Nov-2 Le Mouel, Paris #204
£573 $894 €900 La truite (24x41cm-9x16in) st.sig. painted c.1963. 6-Nov-2 Le Mouel, Paris #87
£573 $894 €900 Rue a Rome (50x73cm-20x29in) s. 6-Nov-2 Le Mouel, Paris #104
£573 $894 €900 La lutte (50x61cm-20x24in) st.sig. 6-Nov-2 Le Mouel, Paris #106
£573 $894 €900 Soleil (65x81cm-26x32in) s. 6-Nov-2 Le Mouel, Paris #127
£573 $894 €900 Pomme (27x35cm-11x14in) st.sig. 6-Nov-2 Le Mouel, Paris #160
£573 $894 €900 Femme aux masques blancs (73x60cm-29x24in) st.sig. 6-Nov-2 Le Mouel, Paris #163
£573 $894 €900 Le bouquet (73x60cm-29x24in) s. 6-Nov-2 Le Mouel, Paris #171
£573 $894 €900 Le professeur (60x73cm-24x29in) st.sig. 6-Nov-2 Le Mouel, Paris #177
£573 $894 €900 Trois personnages (100x81cm-39x32in) st.sig. 6-Nov-2 Le Mouel, Paris #189
£573 $894 €900 Mykonos (16x27cm-6x11in) st.sig. painted c.1960. 6-Nov-2 Le Mouel, Paris #207
£573 $894 €900 Nu (28x22cm-11x9in) st.sig. 6-Nov-2 Le Mouel, Paris #209
£605 $944 €950 Cinq personnages (60x50cm-24x20in) st.sig. 6-Nov-2 Le Mouel, Paris #243
£637 $994 €1000 Portrait (54x42cm-21x17in) s.d. s.i.d.verso. 6-Nov-2 Le Mouel, Paris #25
£637 $994 €1000 Femme a la coiffe (27x22cm-11x9in) st.sig. 6-Nov-2 Le Mouel, Paris #52
£637 $994 €1000 Deux femmes sur un fond bleu (56x39cm-22x15in) st.sig. paper. 6-Nov-2 Le Mouel, Paris #61
£637 $994 €1000 Roses de Noel (43x33cm-17x13in) st.sig. 6-Nov-2 Le Mouel, Paris #66
£637 $994 €1000 Femme de trois-quart (40x33cm-16x13in) st.sig. 6-Nov-2 Le Mouel, Paris #70
£637 $994 €1000 Une belle poire (54x65cm-21x26in) s. 6-Nov-2 Le Mouel, Paris #144
£637 $994 €1000 L'equipe (60x73cm-24x29in) s. 6-Nov-2 Le Mouel, Paris #167/R
£637 $994 €1000 Double nu (46x55cm-18x22in) s. 6-Nov-2 Le Mouel, Paris #170
£637 $994 €1000 Oiseaux (55x46cm-22x18in) s. wood. 6-Nov-2 Le Mouel, Paris #218
£637 $994 €1000 Le petit matin (64x64cm-25x25in) s. 6-Nov-2 Le Mouel, Paris #241/R
£669 $1043 €1050 Le pas (72x50cm-28x20in) s. 6-Nov-2 Le Mouel, Paris #173/R
£701 $1093 €1100 La Tunisienne (55x46cm-22x18in) s. 6-Nov-2 Le Mouel, Paris #20
£701 $1093 €1100 L'echelle (65x54cm-26x21in) st.sig. wood. 6-Nov-2 Le Mouel, Paris #21
£701 $1093 €1100 Les mains (46x33cm-18x13in) st.sig. wood painted c.1935. 6-Nov-2 Le Mouel, Paris #24
£701 $1093 €1100 Femme et enfant (81x65cm-32x26in) st.sig. wood. painted c.1936. 6-Nov-2 Le Mouel, Paris #56
£701 $1093 €1100 Les cerises (38x46cm-15x18in) s.d.1946. 6-Nov-2 Le Mouel, Paris #58
£701 $1093 €1100 La flute imaginaire (116x89cm-46x35in) st.sig. 6-Nov-2 Le Mouel, Paris #89
£701 $1093 €1100 Monsieur Madame (55x46cm-22x18in) s. s.i.d.verso. 6-Nov-2 Le Mouel, Paris #149
£701 $1093 €1100 Le torrent (55x46cm-22x18in) st.sig. 6-Nov-2 Le Mouel, Paris #155
£701 $1093 €1100 L'emerveille (46x38cm-18x15in) s. s.i.d.verso. 6-Nov-2 Le Mouel, Paris #166
£701 $1093 €1100 Propheties (55x46cm-22x18in) s. painted c.1972-77. 6-Nov-2 Le Mouel, Paris #169
£701 $1093 €1100 L'arbre-personnage (60x73cm-24x29in) st.sig. 6-Nov-2 Le Mouel, Paris #175/R
£701 $1093 €1100 Sur le sable (38x46cm-15x18in) s. 6-Nov-2 Le Mouel, Paris #194
£764 $1192 €1200 Portrait de femme (46x38cm-18x15in) st.sig. panel painted c.1936. 6-Nov-2 Le Mouel, Paris #10
£764 $1192 €1200 Femme pensive (35x24cm-14x9in) st.sig. painted c.1935. 6-Nov-2 Le Mouel, Paris #16
£764 $1192 €1200 Le vagabond (80x98cm-31x39in) st.sig. painted c.1935. 6-Nov-2 Le Mouel, Paris #17
£764 $1192 €1200 Danseurs (25x14cm-10x6in) s. wood. 6-Nov-2 Le Mouel, Paris #48
£764 $1192 €1200 Nu assis (92x73cm-36x29in) st.sig. wood painted c.1935. 6-Nov-2 Le Mouel, Paris #75
£764 $1192 €1200 Fruits (46x38cm-18x15in) s. 6-Nov-2 Le Mouel, Paris #77
£764 $1192 €1200 Paysage (73x100cm-29x39in) st.sig. painted c.1950. 6-Nov-2 Le Mouel, Paris #93
£764 $1192 €1200 Tete (24x19cm-9x7in) s. wood painted c.1965. 6-Nov-2 Le Mouel, Paris #159
£764 $1192 €1200 Les comediens (65x50cm-26x20in) s. 6-Nov-2 Le Mouel, Paris #176
£764 $1192 €1200 La blanchisseuse (116x89cm-46x35in) st.sig. 6-Nov-2 Le Mouel, Paris #187
£764 $1192 €1200 Personnages dans les arbres (81x65cm-32x26in) st.sig. 6-Nov-2 Le Mouel, Paris #198
£828 $1292 €1300 Deux Soudanaise (73x60cm-29x24in) st.sig. 6-Nov-2 Le Mouel, Paris #7
£828 $1292 €1300 Fatma (65x54cm-26x21in) s. 6-Nov-2 Le Mouel, Paris #8
£828 $1292 €1300 Arabe (35x27cm-14x11in) s. 6-Nov-2 Le Mouel, Paris #9
£828 $1292 €1300 Helene (72x53cm-28x21in) st.sig. s.i.d.verso. 6-Nov-2 Le Mouel, Paris #19
£828 $1292 €1300 Palette et tomate (21x12cm-8x5in) s. wood. 6-Nov-2 Le Mouel, Paris #37
£828 $1292 €1300 Palette et ombre (24x19cm-9x7in) s.d. panel. 6-Nov-2 Le Mouel, Paris #43
£828 $1292 €1300 Les forgerons (100x80cm-39x31in) st.sig. painted c.1935-40. 6-Nov-2 Le Mouel, Paris #59
£828 $1292 €1300 Ismailia, la bouteille de Chaindy (38x46cm-15x18in) st.sig. wood. 6-Nov-2 Le Mouel, Paris #69
£828 $1292 €1300 La fuite (26x34cm-10x13in) st.sig. painted c.1946. 6-Nov-2 Le Mouel, Paris #72
£828 $1292 €1300 Fleurs (81x65cm-32x26in) st.sig. 6-Nov-2 Le Mouel, Paris #74/R
£828 $1292 €1300 Souvenir d'Andalousie (45x65cm-18x26in) s. 6-Nov-2 Le Mouel, Paris #140
£828 $1292 €1300 Dans les nuages (40x31cm-16x12in) st.sig. panel. 6-Nov-2 Le Mouel, Paris #156
£828 $1292 €1300 Femme (46x55cm-18x22in) s. 6-Nov-2 Le Mouel, Paris #165/R
£828 $1292 €1300 Le palais desert (60x73cm-24x29in) st.sig. s.i.d.verso. 6-Nov-2 Le Mouel, Paris #193
£828 $1292 €1300 Le bain turc (50x102cm-20x40in) s. 6-Nov-2 Le Mouel, Paris #229
£892 $1391 €1400 Femme pensive (55x46cm-22x18in) s. s.i.d.verso. 6-Nov-2 Le Mouel, Paris #60
£892 $1391 €1400 La guitare (48x59cm-19x23in) st.sig. painted c.1946. 6-Nov-2 Le Mouel, Paris #62
£892 $1391 €1400 Femme, seins nus (61x50cm-24x20in) s. painted c.1937. 6-Nov-2 Le Mouel, Paris #65/R

£892 $1391 €1400 Le gui (54x65cm-21x26in) s. 6-Nov-2 Le Mouel, Paris #80
£955 $1490 €1500 Le dormeur (46x55cm-18x22in) st.sig. panel painted c.1928. 6-Nov-2 Le Mouel, Paris #2
£955 $1490 €1500 Pichet et oignons (54x73cm-21x29in) s. 6-Nov-2 Le Mouel, Paris #78
£955 $1490 €1500 Charpentiers (55x81cm-22x32in) s. 6-Nov-2 Le Mouel, Paris #105/R
£955 $1490 €1500 Figuiers (72x92cm-28x36in) st.sig. 6-Nov-2 Le Mouel, Paris #138
£955 $1490 €1500 La chute d'eau (73x60cm-29x24in) st.sig. 6-Nov-2 Le Mouel, Paris #190
£1019 $1590 €1600 Tendresse (45x38cm-18x15in) s. 6-Nov-2 Le Mouel, Paris #1/R
£1019 $1590 €1600 Tete de femme (55x46cm-22x18in) st.sig. panel exec.c.1936. 6-Nov-2 Le Mouel, Paris #6
£1019 $1590 €1600 Palette et ambre (73x116cm-29x46in) st.sig. 6-Nov-2 Le Mouel, Paris #36/R
£1019 $1590 €1600 Rue de la gaiete (35x27cm-14x11in) st.sig. 6-Nov-2 Le Mouel, Paris #179
£1019 $1590 €1600 Petit matin (48x36cm-19x14in) s. 6-Nov-2 Le Mouel, Paris #197
£1019 $1590 €1600 Personnage (18x14cm-7x6in) st.sig. painted c.1956. 6-Nov-2 Le Mouel, Paris #206
£1083 $1689 €1700 Femme sur fond bleu (63x51cm-25x20in) st.sig. painted c.1943. 6-Nov-2 Le Mouel, Paris #67
£1083 $1689 €1700 Elsa (65x54cm-26x21in) s. 6-Nov-2 Le Mouel, Paris #143
£1083 $1689 €1700 Naissance (92x70cm-36x28in) s. s.i.d.verso lit. 6-Nov-2 Le Mouel, Paris #224/R
£1146 $1789 €1800 Deux femmes (81x65cm-32x26in) st.sig. 6-Nov-2 Le Mouel, Paris #5
£1146 $1789 €1800 Volutes (16x22cm-6x9in) st.sig. painted c.1940. 6-Nov-2 Le Mouel, Paris #38
£1146 $1789 €1800 Composition (16x22cm-6x9in) s. panel. 6-Nov-2 Le Mouel, Paris #40
£1210 $1888 €1900 Tete de femme (45x37cm-18x15in) st.sig. painted c.1937. 6-Nov-2 Le Mouel, Paris #28
£1210 $1888 €1900 Femme a la pomme (77x56cm-30x22in) s. paper. 6-Nov-2 Le Mouel, Paris #64
£1210 $1888 €1900 Le port de Piree (46x61cm-18x24in) s. 6-Nov-2 Le Mouel, Paris #112
£1274 $1987 €2000 Forcat nubien (65x54cm-26x21in) st.sig. wood. painted c.1934. 6-Nov-2 Le Mouel, Paris #53/R
£1274 $1987 €2000 La vie des ombres (61x50cm-24x20in) s. 6-Nov-2 Le Mouel, Paris #146/R
£1338 $2087 €2100 La petite bergere (28x23cm-11x9in) st.sig. 6-Nov-2 Le Mouel, Paris #3
£1338 $2087 €2100 Personnages (35x27cm-14x11in) st.sig. wood. painted c.1930. 6-Nov-2 Le Mouel, Paris #39
£1338 $2087 €2100 Le dandi (144x73cm-57x29in) st.sig. painted c.1940. 6-Nov-2 Le Mouel, Paris #68
£1338 $2087 €2100 Vacances (61x50cm-24x20in) s. s.i.d.verso. 6-Nov-2 Le Mouel, Paris #142
£1338 $2087 €2100 Visages (55x46cm-22x18in) st.sig. 6-Nov-2 Le Mouel, Paris #154
£1338 $2087 €2100 La Bocca della Verita (55x46cm-22x18in) s. 6-Nov-2 Le Mouel, Paris #180/R
£1401 $2186 €2200 Les passants egyptiens (19x24cm-7x9in) st.sig. i.d.verso panel. 6-Nov-2 Le Mouel, Paris #42
£1401 $2186 €2200 La table de jardin (83x73cm-33x29in) s. 6-Nov-2 Le Mouel, Paris #73
£1465 $2285 €2300 La table grise (54x65cm-21x26in) s. 6-Nov-2 Le Mouel, Paris #57
£1465 $2285 €2300 Dina Verny (46x38cm-18x15in) st.sig. 6-Nov-2 Le Mouel, Paris #217
£1592 $2484 €2500 Rideaux bleus (100x100cm-39x39in) s. s.i.d.verso lit. 6-Nov-2 Le Mouel, Paris #239/R
£1656 $2583 €2600 Foret secrete (65x54cm-26x21in) s. lit. 6-Nov-2 Le Mouel, Paris #152
£1656 $2583 €2600 Le passage (61x50cm-24x20in) s. 6-Nov-2 Le Mouel, Paris #153
£1656 $2583 €2600 Soleil couchant (60x73cm-24x29in) s. 6-Nov-2 Le Mouel, Paris #205/R
£1656 $2583 €2600 La clairiere (100x81cm-39x32in) s. 6-Nov-2 Le Mouel, Paris #212/R
£1689 $2635 €2500 Baiser a la reine (61x50cm-24x20in) s. s.i.d.64-70 verso. 28-Mar-3 Delvaux, Paris #51/R
£1720 $2683 €2700 L'endormie du crepuscule (65x54cm-26x21in) s. s.i.d.verso. 6-Nov-2 Le Mouel, Paris #148
£1783 $2782 €2800 Ma dame (23x33cm-9x13in) s. lit. 6-Nov-2 Le Mouel, Paris #4/R
£1783 $2782 €2800 Le beau Gilles (116x90cm-46x35in) s. 6-Nov-2 Le Mouel, Paris #54/R
£1847 $2882 €2900 Reflet (60x73cm-24x29in) s. 6-Nov-2 Le Mouel, Paris #157
£1847 $2882 €2900 Groissance (100x100cm-39x39in) s. lit. 6-Nov-2 Le Mouel, Paris #208/R
£1911 $2981 €3000 Le chinois (95x64cm-37x25in) st.sig. painted c.1936. 6-Nov-2 Le Mouel, Paris #12
£1911 $2981 €3000 Composition surrealiste (55x66cm-22x26in) st.sig. painted c.1936. 6-Nov-2 Le Mouel, Paris #33
£1911 $2981 €3000 Personnages (130x146cm-51x57in) st.sig. 6-Nov-2 Le Mouel, Paris #46/R
£1911 $2981 €3000 L'ami nocturne (73x60cm-29x24in) s. 6-Nov-2 Le Mouel, Paris #182/R
£1975 $3080 €3100 Portrait (55x46cm-22x18in) st.sig. 6-Nov-2 Le Mouel, Paris #147
£1975 $3080 €3100 L'annonce (65x54cm-26x21in) s. 6-Nov-2 Le Mouel, Paris #192/R
£1975 $3080 €3100 Les freres de la nuit (50x61cm-20x24in) s. 6-Nov-2 Le Mouel, Paris #220/R
£1975 $3080 €3100 Une nuit (81x65cm-32x26in) s. lit. 6-Nov-2 Le Mouel, Paris #236/R
£2038 $3180 €3200 Premier amour (54x65cm-21x26in) s. 6-Nov-2 Le Mouel, Paris #164/R
£2038 $3180 €3200 Le visiteur (65x54cm-26x21in) s. 6-Nov-2 Le Mouel, Paris #168/R
£2102 $3279 €3300 Deux femmes (65x54cm-26x21in) st.sig. painted c.1936. 6-Nov-2 Le Mouel, Paris #13
£2102 $3279 €3300 La concierge (33x47cm-13x19in) st.sig. i.d.12.11.35 verso. 6-Nov-2 Le Mouel, Paris #15
£2102 $3279 €3300 La vie augemente toujours (81x65cm-32x26in) s. 6-Nov-2 Le Mouel, Paris #195/R
£2166 $3378 €3400 Le froid physiologique (38x46cm-15x18in) st.sig. wood lit. 6-Nov-2 Le Mouel, Paris #41/R
£2229 $3478 €3500 Palette et ombre (60x71cm-24x28in) s.d. s.i.verso. 6-Nov-2 Le Mouel, Paris #35
£2229 $3478 €3500 L'infini (92x65cm-36x26in) s. lit. 6-Nov-2 Le Mouel, Paris #199/R
£2548 $3975 €4000 Autoportrait (54x65cm-21x26in) s. 6-Nov-2 Le Mouel, Paris #26/R
£2548 $3975 €4000 Abondance (54x65cm-21x26in) s. lit. 6-Nov-2 Le Mouel, Paris #185/R
£2611 $4074 €4100 Les ivorgnes (27x35cm-11x14in) st.sig. s.i.d.verso panel. 6-Nov-2 Le Mouel, Paris #47
£2866 $4471 €4500 Elle est bissilhide (49x81cm-19x32in) st.sig. wood. 6-Nov-2 Le Mouel, Paris #32/R
£2930 $4571 €4600 Deux femmes (80x63cm-31x25in) st.sig. wood painted c.1940. 6-Nov-2 Le Mouel, Paris #31/R
£3057 $4769 €4800 Le reveuse (18x24cm-7x9in) st.sig. i.d.6.8.34 verso panel. 6-Nov-2 Le Mouel, Paris #14/R
£3185 $4968 €5000 Composition surrealiste (33x42cm-13x17in) st.sig. 6-Nov-2 Le Mouel, Paris #34
£3503 $5465 €5500 Le joueur de pipeau (113x92cm-44x36in) st.sig. painted c.1950. 6-Nov-2 Le Mouel, Paris #86
£4140 $6459 €6500 Visage de femme (46x38cm-18x15in) st.sig. painted c.1936. 6-Nov-2 Le Mouel, Paris #11/R
£4586 $7154 €7200 Ma poire (54x65cm-21x26in) st.sig. 6-Nov-2 Le Mouel, Paris #135/R
£10255 $15997 €16100 Souvenir de Sonia (55x46cm-22x18in) s. wood. lit. 6-Nov-2 Le Mouel, Paris #45/R
£11465 $17885 €18000 Armours (55x46cm-22x18in) s. lit. 6-Nov-2 Le Mouel, Paris #85/R

Works on paper

£613 $968 €950 Deux visages (28x75cm-11x30in) s.d. i.verso mixed media. 17-Dec-2 Rossini, Paris #111
£1401 $2186 €2200 Les chercheurs (37x47cm-15x19in) s.i.d. gouache lit. 6-Nov-2 Le Mouel, Paris #151/R

MAYO, Luis (1964-) Spanish

Works on paper

£962 $1519 €1500 Ruins. s. mixed media board. 14-Nov-2 Arte, Seville #442b/R

MAYODON, Jean (1893-1967) French

Works on paper

£633 $987 €1000 Triton et sirene (39x32cm-15x13in) s.i.d.1938 W/C. 20-Oct-2 Charbonneaux, Paris #77 est:450-500

MAYOL, Manuel (1865-1929) Spanish

£1523 $2483 €2300 Street in Cadiz (54x41cm-21x16in) s. cardboard. 11-Feb-3 Segre, Madrid #102/R

MAYOR, Fred (1868-1916) British

£900 $1413 €1350 Garden (54x43cm-21x17in) 15-Apr-3 Bonhams, Knightsbridge #6/R
£3400 $5508 €5100 Fisherman on the beach (51x69cm-20x27in) s. 20-May-3 Sotheby's, Olympia #287/R est:800-1200

Works on paper

£580 $928 €870 Cottage landscape with figure returning home (21x35cm-8x14in) s. W/C. 11-Mar-3 David Duggleby, Scarborough #139/R

MAYR, Johann Ulrich (1630-1704) German

£20382 $31796 €32000 Self portrait of the artist, wearing a blue velvet jacket with a cuirass (92x79cm-36x31in) s. prov.lit. 5-Nov-2 Sotheby's, Amsterdam #238/R est:20000-30000

MAYR, Johann Ulrich (attrib) (1630-1704) German

£818 $1267 €1300 Portrait of a novice, order of St Clare (89x71cm-35x28in) 2-Oct-2 Dorotheum, Vienna #254/R est:1600-2200

MAYR, Karl Viktor (1881-1975) Austrian
£602 $969 €903 Coffee time (94x77cm-37x30in) s.d.1921. 7-May-3 Dobiaschofsky, Bern #816/R (S.FR 1300)
£3165 $5000 €5000 Exotic model (105x69cm-41x27in) s.d.1903. 28-Nov-2 Dorotheum, Vienna #115/R est:6000-8000

MAYR, Peter (1758-1836) German
Miniatures
£5769 $9115 €9000 Marie Louise of Austria (8x7cm-3x3in) s.d.1810 oval. 17-Nov-2 Osenat, Fontainebleau #246

MAYR-GRAZ, Karl (1850-1929) German
Works on paper
£264 $420 €380 Studies of children (20x22cm-8x9in) s. pencil double-sided. 5-May-3 Ketterer, Munich #309/R

MAYRHOFER, Johann Nepomuk (1764-1832) Austrian
£6143 $9521 €9215 Still life with fruit, flowers and butterfly (29x23cm-11x9in) wood painted c.1820. 1-Oct-2 SOGA, Bratislava #169/R est:390000 (SL.K 390000)

MAYRSHOFER, Max (1875-1950) German
£272 $433 €400 Still life of flowers (35x33cm-14x13in) s. board. 20-Mar-3 Neumeister, Munich #2692/R
£510 $795 €800 Flowers in vase (49x36cm-19x14in) s. board. 6-Nov-2 Hugo Ruef, Munich #1205/R
£647 $1036 €900 Still life of flowers (40x31cm-16x12in) i. verso paper on panel. 15-May-3 Neumeister, Munich #315/R

MAYS, Maxwell (20th C) American
£890 $1300 €1335 Peaceable Kingdom (58x74cm-23x29in) s.d.63 masonite. 3-Nov-1 North East Auctions, Portsmouth #816

MAZAL, Ricardo (1950-) Mexican
£5488 $9000 €8232 Marzo 27 (147x137cm-58x54in) s.d.2002 i.verso prov.exhib. 28-May-3 Christie's, Rockefeller NY #157/R est:10000-15000
£5793 $9500 €8400 Febrero-2 (203x157cm-80x62in) s.i.d.2002 verso prov.lit. 27-May-3 Sotheby's, New York #64

MAZARD, Alphonse-Henri (1865-?) French
£700 $1099 €1050 Rowing on still waters (50x73cm-20x29in) s.d.1893. 16-Apr-3 Christie's, Kensington #722/R
£1935 $3058 €3000 Wood (90x131cm-35x52in) s.d.1893. 18-Dec-2 Castellana, Madrid #3/R

MAZE, Paul (1887-1979) French
£250 $400 €375 Tall trees (44x59cm-17x23in) s. board. 11-Mar-3 David Duggleby, Scarborough #263/R
£285 $444 €450 Lake (46x58cm-18x23in) s. W/C. 15-Oct-2 Dorotheum, Vienna #131/R
£450 $702 €675 Sailing off the coast (22x27cm-9x11in) s. board prov. 27-Mar-3 Christie's, Kensington #463/R
£580 $905 €870 Still life with anemones in a bowl (23x32cm-9x13in) s. board. 26-Mar-3 Woolley & Wallis, Salisbury #153/R
£1800 $3006 €2610 Susquehanna yacht club, Pennsylvania (74x53cm-29x21in) s. paper. 24-Jun-3 Bonhams, New Bond Street #97/R est:2000-3000
£2000 $3160 €3000 Cheyne Walk, Chelsea (46x30cm-18x12in) s. i.d.1923 verso. 27-Nov-2 Sotheby's, Olympia #102/R est:2000-3000
£2200 $3432 €3300 Jessie on the beach. Jessie and her dog's (46x61cm-18x24in) s. board two. 27-Mar-3 Christie's, Kensington #283/R est:1000-1500
£2400 $3744 €3600 Gondolas, Venice (65x80cm-26x31in) s. prov. 25-Mar-3 Bonhams, New Bond Street #70/R est:2000-3000
£3800 $6156 €5700 Tug and regatta (33x41cm-13x16in) s. board. 23-May-3 Lyon & Turnbull, Edinburgh #44/R est:2500-3500
£5500 $9020 €8250 Port of Le Havre (33x41cm-13x16in) s.d.1930 prov.exhib. 6-Jun-3 Christie's, London #134/R est:6000-8000
Works on paper
£250 $398 €375 Portrait of a girl (34x28cm-13x11in) s. red chk. 4-May-3 Lots Road, London #338/R
£310 $490 €450 Continental coastal landscape (20x32cm-8x13in) s. W/C. 28-Jul-3 David Duggleby, Scarborough #244
£320 $512 €480 Building beside an estuary (28x38cm-11x15in) s. col chk. 13-Mar-3 Duke & Son, Dorchester #78
£320 $534 €464 Black boat on beach (18x24cm-7x9in) s. pastel. 24-Jun-3 Holloways, Banbury #476/R
£380 $585 €570 Jessie at her dressing table (20x33cm-8x13in) s. pastel dr. 22-Oct-2 Bonhams, Bath #46
£380 $589 €570 Village in Normandy (33x60cm-13x24in) s. pastel. 3-Dec-2 Bonhams, Knightsbridge #100/R
£400 $632 €600 Monaco (12x16cm-5x6in) s.i. pastel. 2-Dec-2 Bonhams, Bath #45/R
£420 $664 €630 Guardsman (31x16cm-12x6in) s. pencil chl col crayon. 27-Nov-2 Sotheby's, Olympia #27/R
£420 $655 €630 Yachts entering harbour. Escorial, Spain (21x33cm-8x13in) s. pencil black felt tip pen W/C two. 27-Mar-3 Christie's, Kensington #345/R
£443 $691 €700 Paysage au moulin (26x32cm-10x13in) s. pastel gouache. 20-Oct-2 Mercier & Cie, Lille #337
£450 $715 €675 Woman dressing (28x22cm-11x9in) s. pastel. 26-Feb-3 Sotheby's, Olympia #205/R
£450 $707 €675 View from the artist window (35x52cm-14x20in) s. pastel. 15-Apr-3 Bonhams, Knightsbridge #203/R
£450 $752 €653 Sussex landscape (33x23cm-13x9in) s. pastel. 20-Jun-3 Keys, Aylsham #511
£500 $795 €750 Boats on the Solent (29x40cm-11x16in) s. ink wash. 26-Feb-3 Sotheby's, Olympia #163/R
£500 $780 €750 Naval regatta (23x54cm-9x21in) s. pastel. 27-Mar-3 Christie's, Kensington #343/R
£550 $853 €825 Scene at Henley with numerous figures boating (23x43cm-9x17in) s. pastel. 29-Oct-2 Gorringes, Lewes #1284/R
£600 $936 €900 Sunset on the heath, Sussex. Heath, Sussex (18x37cm-7x15in) s. pastel two prov.exhib. 27-Mar-3 Christie's, Kensington #284
£700 $1092 €1050 Girl seated on a rock (37x35cm-15x14in) s. col chk. 18-Sep-2 Dreweatt Neate, Newbury #86/R
£700 $1092 €1050 Garden, Mill Cottage (76x56cm-30x22in) s. pastel prov. 27-Mar-3 Christie's, Kensington #311/R
£750 $1193 €1125 Boats in the estuary (20x33cm-8x13in) s. pencil W/C. 26-Feb-3 Sotheby's, Olympia #162/R
£800 $1216 €1200 Harbour scene (25x35cm-10x14in) s. pastel. 17-Sep-2 Henry Adams, Chichester #116/R
£800 $1216 €1200 Harbour scene (37x53cm-15x21in) s. pastel. 17-Sep-2 Henry Adams, Chichester #117
£823 $1284 €1300 Vue de Londres (37x55cm-15x22in) s. pastel gouache. 20-Oct-2 Mercier & Cie, Lille #336
£850 $1351 €1275 Poole harbour ferry (19x25cm-7x10in) s.i.d.1956 pastel. 26-Feb-3 Sotheby's, Olympia #164/R est:700-900
£900 $1404 €1350 Jessie on the beach (53x73cm-21x29in) s. pen ink W/C prov. 27-Mar-3 Christie's, Kensington #280/R
£900 $1404 €1350 Black boat at anchor. Jessie gardening (38x56cm-15x22in) s. pastel two prov. 27-Mar-3 Christie's, Kensington #341/R
£950 $1568 €1378 Quayside, Venice, Italy (37x54cm-15x21in) s. pastel prov. 3-Jul-3 Christie's, Kensington #290/R
£1000 $1590 €1500 At the dressing table (20x33cm-8x13in) s. pencil W/C sold with dr. of Jessie by same hand. 26-Feb-3 Sotheby's, Olympia #157/R est:800-1200
£1013 $1600 €1520 Place de la concorde (30x41cm-12x16in) s. pastel. 22-Apr-3 Butterfields, San Francisco #6004/R est:2000-3000
£1200 $1860 €1800 HM Yacht Britannia at Cowes (20x23cm-8x9in) s. pencil W/C bodycol. 4-Dec-2 Christie's, Kensington #261/R est:1000-1500
£1200 $1872 €1800 Making for the course. By the rails (41x53cm-16x21in) black felt tip pen W/C bodycol two prov. 27-Mar-3 Christie's, Kensington #339/R est:1200-1800
£1266 $2000 €1899 View of the Tuileries (38x52cm-15x20in) s.d.1955 pastel. 22-Apr-3 Butterfields, San Francisco #6005/R est:3000-5000
£1300 $2015 €1950 Quayside, Venice, Italy (37x54cm-15x21in) s. pastel prov. 4-Dec-2 Christie's, Kensington #259/R est:1000-1500
£1400 $2128 €2100 Sailing boats off Medeira (36x53cm-14x21in) s. pastel. 17-Sep-2 Henry Adams, Chichester #118/R est:1200-1800
£1400 $2156 €2100 Hillside (56x76cm-22x30in) s. W/C. 5-Sep-2 Christie's, Kensington #572/R est:1500-2500
£1600 $2544 €2400 Henley on Thames (20x33cm-8x13in) s. pencil W/C. 26-Feb-3 Sotheby's, Olympia #155/R est:1500-2000
£1600 $2624 €2400 At the dressing table (27x38cm-11x15in) s. col chk. 3-Jun-3 Sotheby's, Olympia #49/R est:1000-1500
£1800 $2916 €2700 St. Pauls from the river (37x53cm-15x21in) s. pastel. 22-Jan-3 Bonhams, New Bond Street #256/R est:2000-3000
£1800 $2808 €2700 Jessie at her dressing table. Jessie in her boudoir. Jessie getting dressed (37x56cm-15x22in) pastel set of three. 27-Mar-3 Christie's, Kensington #285/R est:1000-1500
£1800 $2826 €2700 Yachting off Cowes (47x61cm-19x24in) s. W/C. 15-Apr-3 Bonhams, Knightsbridge #31/R est:1800-2500
£1900 $2888 €2850 Tethered yachts (61x45cm-24x18in) s. W/C. 15-Aug-2 Bonhams, New Bond Street #285/R est:700-1000
£1900 $2964 €2850 Jessie shielding from the wind. Jessie in the garden (27x37cm-11x15in) s. pastel two prov. 27-Mar-3 Christie's, Kensington #281/R est:800-1200
£2000 $3040 €3000 Naval review (37x54cm-15x21in) s. pastels W/C. 15-Aug-2 Bonhams, New Bond Street #286/R est:2000-3000
£2000 $3280 €3000 Jessie (38x32cm-15x13in) s.i.d.Dec 16th 1965 i.verso pastel. 3-Jun-3 Sotheby's, Olympia #48/R est:2000-3000
£2000 $3300 €2900 Boating on the Cam (28x37cm-11x15in) s.d.1960 pastel. 1-Jul-3 Bonhams, Norwich #195/R est:2000-3000
£2500 $3900 €3750 View of the Eiffel Tower (56x76cm-22x30in) s. pastel prov. 27-Mar-3 Christie's, Kensington #335/R est:800-1200
£3800 $5776 €5700 Yacht race off Cowes (20x33cm-8x13in) s. pencil W/C. 15-Aug-2 Bonhams, New Bond Street #452/R est:2000-3000
£3800 $6042 €5700 Itchenor Harbour (54x74cm-21x29in) s.i. pastel. 26-Feb-3 Sotheby's, Olympia #156/R est:2000-3000
£3800 $5928 €5700 Yachting, Cowes week (53x74cm-21x29in) studio st. pastel prov. 27-Mar-3 Christie's, Kensington #336/R est:1000-1500
£3800 $5928 €5700 Paddock at Goodwood. In the saddling ring (56x76cm-22x30in) s. pastel two. 27-Mar-3 Christie's, Kensington #338/R est:1800-2500

MAZELLA, J (19th C) French
£1923 $3038 €3000 Pecheurs sur un rivage en Normandie (42x82cm-17x32in) s.d.1877. 18-Nov-2 Tajan, Paris #58 est:1200-1500

MAZER, Karl Peter (attrib) (1807-1884) Swedish
£1064 $1649 €1596 Portrait of Molly and Axel Rohtlieb (55x57cm-22x22in) lit. 4-Dec-2 AB Stockholms Auktionsverk #1682/R est:18000-20000 (S.KR 15000)
£2676 $4308 €3800 Brother and sister - possibly Axel and Molly Rothlieb (55x57cm-22x22in) prov. 10-May-3 Bukowskis, Helsinki #189/R est:3000-4000

MAZEROLLE, Alexis Joseph (1826-1889) French
Works on paper
£621 $993 €900 Figure feminine nue et ailee (33x33cm-13x13in) black pencil htd white chk. 12-Mar-3 E & Eve, Paris #54

MAZOT, Louis (1919-) French
£241 $403 €350 Nature morte (130x89cm-51x35in) s. 10-Jul-3 Artcurial Briest, Paris #139

MAZUMDAR, Hemen (1894-1943) Indian
£17094 $28205 €24786 Woman with pitcher (119x70cm-47x28in) indis.sig. 6-Jul-3 Christie's, Hong Kong #72/R est:160000-200000 (HK.D 220000)

MAZZA, Salvatore (1819-1886) Italian
£506 $800 €800 Fisherman's family. Simple meal (23x19cm-9x7in) paper on board pair. 26-Nov-2 Christie's, Rome #54
£1076 $1700 €1700 Praying. Pipe player (35x28cm-14x11in) pair. 26-Nov-2 Christie's, Rome #113/R
£2405 $3800 €3800 Resting in the woods. Back from the fields (60x43cm-24x17in) one s.d.1845 two. 26-Nov-2 Christie's, Rome #55
£2532 $4000 €4000 Fishermen waiting (80x110cm-31x43in) s. 26-Nov-2 Christie's, Rome #114/R

MAZZACURATI, Marino (1907-1969) Italian
£1282 $2013 €2000 Machines (70x49cm-28x19in) s.d.941 tempera cardboard. 21-Nov-2 Finarte, Rome #148/R
Sculpture
£1203 $1876 €1900 Nude (48cm-19in) bronze exec.1954. 15-Oct-2 Babuino, Rome #355/R

MAZZANOVICH, Lawrence (1872-1946) American
£1037 $1700 €1556 Late autumn afternoon (30x41cm-12x16in) s. panel. 5-Feb-3 Doyle, New York #45/R est:1500-2000
£2532 $4000 €3798 River landscape (53x74cm-21x29in) s. 24-Apr-3 Shannon's, Milford #226/R est:4000-6000

MAZZOCHI, Guido (19/20th C) Italian
£324 $518 €450 Lac au Crepuscule (26x37cm-10x15in) s.d.1907 wood. 13-May-3 Galerie Moderne, Brussels #20

MAZZOLA, Francesco (1503-1540) Italian
Prints
£3797 $6000 €6000 Study sheet of St John the Baptist (15x18cm-6x7in) mono. etching chiaroscuro woodcut wash. 29-Nov-2 Bassenge, Berlin #5226/R est:6000
Works on paper
£95000 $158650 €137750 Two lovers seated on a couch (13x15cm-5x6in) i.verso pen ink prov.lit. 8-Jul-3 Christie's, London #20/R est:60000-90000

MAZZOLA, Francesco (circle) (1503-1540) Italian
Works on paper
£26389 $41958 €38000 Torment of St Laurentius (21x20cm-8x8in) pen sepia chk wash htd white squared paper. 5-May-3 Ketterer, Munich #361/R est:3000-4000

MAZZOLA, Giuseppe (attrib) (1748-1838) Italian
£5128 $8000 €7692 Madonna (76x56cm-30x22in) panel. 11-Apr-3 Du Mouchelle, Detroit #2006/R est:8000-10000

MAZZOLENI, Martino (1935-1995) Italian
£272 $433 €400 Untitled (100x80cm-39x31in) s.d.1989 verso acrylic. 1-Mar-3 Meeting Art, Vercelli #577
£272 $433 €400 Black mistery (70x70cm-28x28in) s.d.1989 verso acrylic. 1-Mar-3 Meeting Art, Vercelli #566

MAZZOLINI, Giuseppe (1806-1876) Italian
£3600 $5976 €5400 On the way to market (75x62cm-30x24in) s.i. 10-Jun-3 Bonhams, Knightsbridge #93/R est:2000-2500

MAZZOLINI, Giuseppe (attrib) (1806-1876) Italian
£1300 $1976 €1950 Girl with basket of fruit, a storm approaching (63x49cm-25x19in) 29-Aug-2 Christie's, Kensington #262/R est:700-900

MAZZON, Galliano (1896-1978) Italian
£563 $935 €800 Composition (70x50cm-28x20in) s. acrylic paper on panel. 10-Jun-3 Finarte Semenzato, Milan #250/R
Works on paper
£256 $403 €400 Composition (32x24cm-13x9in) s.d.948 gouache prov. 20-Nov-2 Pandolfini, Florence #99/R
£321 $503 €500 Composition (42x32cm-17x13in) s.d.948 gouache prov. 20-Nov-2 Pandolfini, Florence #102

MAZZONI, Cesare Giuseppe (1678-1763) Italian
Works on paper
£629 $900 €944 Saint Marcel receiving a scarf from the Holy Spirit (27x20cm-11x8in) pen brown ink wash. 23-Jan-3 Swann Galleries, New York #119/R

MAZZONI, Franco (20th C) Italian
£349 $545 €524 City with wide river (45x67cm-18x26in) s. panel. 6-Nov-2 Dobiaschofsky, Bern #817/R (S.FR 800)

MAZZUCHELLI, Pietro Francesco (1571-1626) Italian
£3378 $5270 €5000 Madonna and Child with bishop and two saints (41x30cm-16x12in) paper on canvas prov. 27-Mar-3 Dorotheum, Vienna #356/R est:5000-8000
Works on paper
£2800 $4396 €4200 Adoration of the Magi (27x41cm-11x16in) black chk wash he. chk. 11-Dec-2 Sotheby's, Olympia #20/R est:2000-3000

MEAD, David (19/20th C) British
£260 $406 €390 River running through a wooded landscape (51x76cm-20x30in) s. 10-Sep-2 Bonhams, Knightsbridge #237
£350 $571 €508 Woodland ride (61x91cm-24x36in) s. s.i.verso. 16-Jul-3 Sotheby's, Olympia #132/R
£440 $686 €660 View of woodland glade (60x49cm-24x19in) s. i.verso board. 10-Oct-2 Rupert Toovey, Partridge Green #1507/R
£480 $758 €720 Winter sunshine, near Canterbury (51x61cm-20x24in) s.i.verso. 2-Dec-2 Gorringes, Lewes #2732

MEAD, Larkin Goldsmith (1835-1910) American
Sculpture
£3085 $4750 €4628 Venezia (56cm-22in) s.i. white marble. 27-Oct-2 Grogan, Boston #117 est:3000-5000
£19753 $32000 €29630 Venezia (60cm-24in) i. marble. 22-May-3 Christie's, Rockefeller NY #51/R est:25000-35000

MEAD, Philip (1948-) British
£300 $477 €450 Overgrown garden II (45x67cm-18x26in) s.d.89 oil on paper. 18-Mar-3 Bonhams, Knightsbridge #153

MEAD, Ray John (1921-1998) Canadian
£2444 $4009 €3666 Cloud cover (102x132cm-40x52in) s.d.94 i.verso acrylic prov. 27-May-3 Sotheby's, Toronto #55/R est:4000-6000 (C.D 5500)

MEADE, Arthur (1863-1948) British
£350 $546 €525 Ploughing (41x32cm-16x13in) s. panel. 7-Nov-2 Christie's, Kensington #162/R

MEADE-KING, Eric (1911-) British
Works on paper
£600 $936 €900 Worcestershire hounds, Grafton Flyford (36x56cm-14x22in) s. W/C bodycol. 17-Oct-2 Lawrence, Crewkerne #1578/R

MEADMORE, Clement (1929-) American/Australian
Sculpture
£5658 $8827 €9803 Trio III (55x77x48cm-22x30x19in) corten prov. 31-Mar-3 Goodman, Sydney #170/R (A.D 15000)
£7732 $12063 €13397 Stormy weather (18cm-7in) s.d.1997 num.1/8 bronze prov. 31-Mar-3 Goodman, Sydney #156/R (A.D 20500)

MEADOR, Joshua (1911-1965) American
£778 $1300 €1128 Cabins in foothill landscape (51x69cm-20x27in) s. prov. 17-Jun-3 John Moran, Pasadena #154 est:800-1200

MEADOWS, Arthur Joseph (1843-1907) British

£450 $707 €675 On the Maas near Dordrecht (35x61cm-14x24in) s.d.1878. 16-Dec-2 Sotheby's, Olympia #31/R
£800 $1248 €1200 On the canal at Ostend, morning (25x35cm-10x14in) s.d.1888 s.i.d.verso. 10-Apr-3 Tennants, Leyburn #949/R
£980 $1558 €1470 Dutch boats preparing for sea, near Scheveningen (35x61cm-14x24in) s.d.1886. 5-Mar-3 Bonhams, Bury St Edmunds #345
£2200 $3432 €3300 Menton on the Riviera (20x30cm-8x12in) s.d.1904 panel. 9-Oct-2 Woolley & Wallis, Salisbury #287/R est:2000-3000
£2200 $3476 €3300 French riverscape, possibly Samur (23x46cm-9x18in) s. 12-Nov-2 Bonhams, Knightsbridge #301/R est:2000-3000
£2400 $3912 €3600 Hay barge (35x46cm-14x18in) s. 29-Jan-3 Sotheby's, Olympia #134/R est:600-800
£2800 $4536 €4200 Schooner aground off Dungeness Beach (46x81cm-18x32in) bears sig. 22-Jan-3 Bonhams, New Bond Street #377/R est:1500-2000
£2900 $4524 €4350 Fishing boats on shoreline with woman washing nets (33x58cm-13x23in) s. 18-Sep-2 Wingetts, Wrexham #220 est:3000-4000
£4000 $6360 €6000 Venice from the public gardens (56x43cm-22x17in) s.i.d.1903 verso. 19-Mar-3 Rupert Toovey, Partridge Green #20/R est:2000-3000
£4500 $7290 €6750 Preparing the fishing fleet (36x61cm-14x24in) s.d.1877. 22-Jan-3 Bonhams, New Bond Street #381/R est:4000-6000
£4600 $7498 €6900 Sussex coast (40x61cm-16x24in) s.d.63. 29-Jan-3 Sotheby's, Olympia #157/R est:2500-3500
£7000 $10990 €10500 Venice, flood tide, Dogana and Santa Maria della salute (61x107cm-24x42in) s.d.1907 s.i.d.verso. 19-Nov-2 Bonhams, New Bond Street #114/R est:6000-8000
£7000 $11690 €10150 Choppy seas off Pierhead, Yarmouth (40x66cm-16x26in) s.d.1873. 18-Jun-3 Sotheby's, Olympia #66/R est:4000-6000
£7200 $11304 €10800 Beaugency on the Loire. On the Italian Lakes (20x30cm-8x12in) s.d.95 panel two. 19-Nov-2 Bonhams, New Bond Street #115/R est:4000-6000
£7500 $12150 €11250 Corfu, in the Adriatic (46x36cm-18x14in) s.d.1901 s.i.d.1901 verso. 21-May-3 Christie's, Kensington #591/R est:6000-8000
£7800 $13026 €11310 Harbour entrance (76x127cm-30x50in) s. indis d. 18-Jun-3 Sotheby's, Olympia #67/R est:6000-9000

MEADOWS, Bernard (1915-) British

Sculpture

£903 $1400 €1355 Seated armed figure (43x41x28cm-17x16x11in) init.num.2/6 bronze. 29-Sep-2 Butterfields, Los Angeles #4430/R est:1000-1200
£1032 $1600 €1548 Bust version 1 2/6 (48x38x20cm-19x15x8in) bronze. 29-Sep-2 Butterfields, Los Angeles #4429/R est:1200-1500
£1800 $2970 €2610 Pointing figure with child (20cm-8in) mono.num.2/6 gilt pat. bronze conceived 1971. 3-Jul-3 Christie's, Kensington #598/R est:1500-2000
£4800 $7872 €7200 Running bird (38cm-15in) init. black pat. bronze. 6-Jun-3 Christie's, London #57/R est:3000-5000

Works on paper

£300 $473 €450 Sculptural sketch (32x28cm-13x11in) s. gouache. 27-Nov-2 Sotheby's, Olympia #162/R
£350 $574 €525 Sculpture drawing (10x16cm-4x6in) mono. pencil ink gouache. 3-Jun-3 Sotheby's, Olympia #283/R
£380 $616 €570 Still life with apples and pears (15x15cm-6x6in) mono.d.79 i.verso pencil W/C. 20-May-3 Bonhams, Knightsbridge #147
£400 $624 €600 Study of a female nude (39x21cm-15x8in) s.d.40 chl grey wash exhib. 27-Mar-3 Christie's, Kensington #407
£550 $869 €825 Pointing and frightened figure (26x21cm-10x8in) mono.d.64 pencil W/C. 27-Nov-2 Sotheby's, Olympia #160/R
£900 $1404 €1350 Studies for sculpture (26x21cm-10x8in) s.d.59 pencil W/C htd white four on one mount. 17-Sep-2 Rosebery Fine Art, London #607/R

MEADOWS, Christopher (fl.1883-1901) British

£280 $442 €420 Cattle by a loch (51x76cm-20x30in) s.d.1882. 27-Nov-2 Bonhams, Knowle #226
£350 $571 €525 Cottage interior (40x50cm-16x20in) 14-Feb-3 Lyon & Turnbull, Edinburgh #95

MEADOWS, Edwin L (fl.1854-1872) British

£316 $494 €500 Resting (61x50cm-24x20in) s.d.1892. 12-Sep-2 Hagelstam, Helsinki #933
£510 $796 €765 Haycart in a river landscape (61x107cm-24x42in) s.d.1868. 7-Nov-2 Christie's, Kensington #123/R
£3354 $5500 €5031 Travelers resting at the great temple at Paestum (91x71cm-36x28in) s.i.d.1863 i.d.verso. 5-Feb-3 Christie's, Rockefeller NY #204/R est:7000-9000
£3600 $5868 €5220 Extensive landscape with Canterbury in the distance (75x122cm-30x48in) s.d.1877. 16-Jul-3 Sotheby's, Olympia #65/R est:4000-6000

MEADOWS, Gordon Arthur (1868-?) British

£1100 $1716 €1650 St Pauls from Southwark (51x76cm-20x30in) s.d.1887 s.i.d.verso. 10-Sep-2 Bonhams, Knightsbridge #50/R est:1200-1800

MEADOWS, James Edwin (1828-1888) British

£260 $429 €377 Happy fisherman (25x20cm-10x8in) s. board. 1-Jul-3 Bearnes, Exeter #509/R
£380 $593 €570 Washerwoman by thatched cottage in mountains landscape (15x23cm-6x9in) 11-Apr-3 Keys, Aylsham #634
£800 $1264 €1200 Figures with a horse and dog crossing a ford. Figures beside a river (24x29cm-9x11in) s. pair. 2-Dec-2 Bonhams, Bath #128/R
£1200 $1824 €1800 Fishing smack off the coast (30x56cm-12x22in) s.d.1866. 15-Aug-2 Bonhams, New Bond Street #328/R est:1200-1800
£1300 $2015 €1950 Fishing boats in coastal waters. Fishing vessel running. Beached vessel at moonrise (14x13cm-6x5in) one s. three in one frame. 31-Oct-2 Christie's, Kensington #524/R est:1500-2500
£4000 $6080 €6000 Return from the fishing grounds (61x106cm-24x42in) s.d.1880. 15-Aug-2 Bonhams, New Bond Street #327/R est:4000-6000
£5000 $8300 €7500 Gypsy shelter (76x127cm-30x50in) s.d.1877. 12-Jun-3 Sotheby's, London #267/R est:5000-7000

MEADOWS, John (19th C) British

£20000 $33200 €30000 Bay of Scarborough with the castle beyond (90x183cm-35x72in) s.d.1856. 12-Jun-3 Sotheby's, London #235a/R est:20000-30000

MEADOWS, Joseph (attrib) (1790-1874) British

£481 $750 €722 Nineteenth century battle scene (30x38cm-12x15in) mono.d.1841 canvas on board. 22-Sep-2 Jeffery Burchard, Florida #10

MEADOWS, W (19th C) British

£639 $990 €959 Venetian scene with figures (52x41cm-20x16in) s.d.1914. 28-Sep-2 Rasmussen, Havnen #2133/R (D.KR 7500)

MEADOWS, William (fl.1870-1895) British

£280 $445 €420 Figures loading a boat with a view of a continental town beyond (23x18cm-9x7in) s. 30-Apr-3 Halls, Shrewsbury #302
£400 $640 €600 Continental street scene (56x41cm-22x16in) s. 7-Jan-3 Bonhams, Knightsbridge #60/R
£520 $806 €780 Grand Canal, Venice (35x66cm-14x26in) s. 3-Dec-2 Sotheby's, Olympia #133/R
£1700 $2652 €2550 Venetian canal scenes (20x40cm-8x16in) s. pair. 10-Sep-2 Bonhams, Knightsbridge #225/R est:1200-1800
£2000 $3280 €3000 Grand Canal, Venice. The Guidecca, Venice (41x61cm-16x24in) one s. pair. 29-May-3 Christie's, Kensington #212/R est:2000-3000
£2600 $4160 €3900 Venetian canal with figures in the foreground (38x81cm-15x32in) s. 13-Mar-3 Duke & Son, Dorchester #200/R est:600-1200

MEADOWS, William (attrib) (19th C) British

£750 $1162 €1125 Cattle approaching a ford (56x91cm-22x36in) i. 3-Dec-2 Sotheby's, Olympia #144/R
£1000 $1570 €1500 Trading vessels on the Grand Canal, Venice (46x81cm-18x32in) init. 16-Apr-3 Christie's, Kensington #573/R est:1200-1800

MEADOWS, William G (19th C) British

£1006 $1600 €1509 Stable interior (51x76cm-20x30in) s.d.1898. 5-Mar-3 Doyle, New York #45/R est:1000-1500

MEARNS, Fanny (fl.1870-1888) British

Works on paper

£211 $350 €306 Children gathering flowers (29x49cm-11x19in) s. W/C. 16-Jun-3 Waddingtons, Toronto #43/R (C.D 475)

MEARNS, Louisa (19th C) British

Works on paper

£760 $1201 €1102 Figures beside country lanes (36x61cm-14x24in) s.d.1875 W/C pair. 22-Jul-3 Gorringes, Lewes #1566

MEARS, George (1865-1910) British

£2700 $4266 €4050 Study of clipper (48x89cm-19x35in) s.d.02. 17-Dec-2 Gorringes, Lewes #1401

MEARS, George (attrib) (1865-1910) British

£450 $752 €653 S.S Maharaja (22x56cm-9x22in) board. 18-Jun-3 Sotheby's, Olympia #56/R
£800 $1264 €1200 S S Orizaba (48x74cm-19x29in) 24-Apr-3 Scarborough Perry Fine Arts, Hove #678

MEATYARD, Ralph Eugene (1925-1972) American
Photographs
£2373 $3750 €3560 Boy holding dolls (17x17cm-7x7in) photograph. 23-Apr-3 Sotheby's, New York #247/R est:3000-5000
£2532 $4000 €3798 Boy below white mask (18x17cm-7x7in) s. photograph. 23-Apr-3 Sotheby's, New York #251/R est:3000-5000
£2625 $4200 €3938 Boy with glass shard (17x17cm-7x7in) silver print. 15-May-3 Swann Galleries, New York #426/R est:5000-7500
£3571 $5500 €5357 Boy in old man's mask with doll (19x20cm-7x8in) bears another sig.verso gelatin silver print exec.c.1960 prov.lit. 25-Oct-2 Phillips, New York #116/R est:3000-5000

MECHAU, Frank (1904-1946) American
Works on paper
£350 $550 €525 Study for Battle of Alamo (41x104cm-16x41in) pencil on tracing paper prov.exhib. 10-Dec-2 Doyle, New York #60

MECHAU, Jakob Wilhelm (1745-1808) German
Works on paper
£1538 $2200 €2307 River landscape with a ruined tower and bridge (25x29cm-10x11in) black chk col wash. 23-Jan-3 Swann Galleries, New York #351/R est:3000-5000

MECHAU, Jakob Wilhelm (attrib) (1745-1808) German
Works on paper
£949 $1472 €1500 Nemi in the Campagna (24x33cm-9x13in) i. pen wash. 27-Sep-2 Venator & Hansten, Koln #1033/R

MECHELAERE, Leo (1880-1964) Belgian
£346 $536 €550 Begiunage of Bruges (87x110cm-34x43in) s. 5-Oct-2 De Vuyst, Lokeren #239

MECHLEN, Paul (1888-1961) German
£292 $427 €450 Market scene in North Africa (49x39cm-19x15in) s. oil pastel tempera panel. 15-Jun-2 Hans Stahl, Hamburg #203/R

MECKENEM, Israhel van (15/16th C) German
Prints
£2911 $4600 €4600 St Catherine of Siena (16x11cm-6x4in) copperplate. 29-Nov-2 Bassenge, Berlin #5375 est:4500
£3205 $5000 €4808 Foolish virgin (8x13cm-3x5in) copper engraving prov. 28-Mar-3 Aspire, Cleveland #18/R est:7000-10000

MECKSEPER, Friedrich (1936-) German?
Works on paper
£1603 $2484 €2500 One of three X fades out (12x13cm-5x5in) s.d.1962 gouache gold. 6-Dec-2 Hauswedell & Nolte, Hamburg #258/R est:2500
£1795 $2782 €2800 Letters (12x15cm-5x6in) s.d.1963 gouache gold. 6-Dec-2 Hauswedell & Nolte, Hamburg #259/R est:2800

MECRAY, John (1939-) American
Works on paper
£2600 $4212 €3900 Enterprise (29x57cm-11x22in) s.d.82 pencil. 22-Jan-3 Bonhams, New Bond Street #307/R est:1000-1500

MEDARD, Eugène (1847-1897) French
£1923 $3000 €2885 Battle scene at St Cloud (74x91cm-29x36in) s.d.1881. 14-Sep-2 Selkirks, St. Louis #716/R est:4000-6000

MEDARD, Jules Ferdinand (c.1853-1927) French
£2278 $3600 €3600 Roses (27x21cm-11x8in) s. panel. 1-Dec-2 Anaf, Lyon #127/R
£2405 $3800 €3800 Roses blanches (27x21cm-11x8in) s.d.1917 panel. 1-Dec-2 Anaf, Lyon #126

MEDICI DEL VASCELLO, Osvaldo (1902-) Italian
£1700 $2686 €2550 River crossing (54x65cm-21x26in) s. 3-Apr-3 Christie's, Kensington #44/R

MEDINA VERA, Inocenzio (1876-1917) Spanish
£1635 $2551 €2600 Young woman from Murcia (41x34cm-16x13in) s.d.1914. 8-Oct-2 Ansorena, Madrid #273/R
Works on paper
£548 $855 €800 Seller (24x17cm-9x7in) s. en grisaille. 8-Apr-3 Ansorena, Madrid #406/R
£1300 $2028 €1950 Going to the fete (24x35cm-9x14in) s. gouache. 26-Mar-3 Sotheby's, Olympia #269/R est:600-800

MEDINA, Angel (1924-) Spanish
£577 $877 €900 Untitled (49x69cm-19x27in) cardboard. 28-Aug-2 Castellana, Madrid #224/R

MEDINA, Antonio (19th C) Spanish
£1216 $1897 €1800 Carnival (26x39cm-10x15in) s. board. 25-Mar-3 Durán, Madrid #158/R
£1284 $2003 €1900 Market (26x39cm-10x15in) s. board. 25-Mar-3 Durán, Madrid #157/R

MEDINA, Enrique (?) ?
Works on paper
£353 $550 €530 Puerta (80x80cm-31x31in) s. aerografo fabric. 30-Jul-2 Galleria Y Remates, Montevideo #94

MEDINA, Sir John (attrib) (1659-1710) British
£20000 $31600 €30000 Portrait of Thomas Boothby (123x100cm-48x39in) prov. 28-Nov-2 Sotheby's, London #154/R est:20000-30000

MEDIZ, Karl (1868-1944) Austrian
£625 $994 €900 Adriatic near Luino, study of breaking waves (49x61cm-19x24in) 29-Apr-3 Wiener Kunst Auktionen, Vienna #626/R
Works on paper
£795 $1295 €1200 Tyrolean landscape (46x76cm-18x30in) s.d.1901 pencil black chk chl col pencil triptych. 28-Jan-3 Dorotheum, Vienna #3/R

MEDIZ-PELIKAN, Emilie (1861-1908) Austrian
£27848 $44000 €44000 Evening on Corfu (96x106cm-38x42in) s. i. stretcher. 26-Nov-2 Wiener Kunst Auktionen, Vienna #78/R est:15000-25000
Works on paper
£304 $474 €450 Fairytale illustration (19x16cm-7x6in) s. Indian ink board. 28-Mar-3 Dorotheum, Vienna #164/R

MEDLEY, Robert (1905-) British
£400 $648 €600 Thebes (103x126cm-41x50in) s.i.d.October 71 verso acrylic prov.exhib. 20-May-3 Bonhams, Knightsbridge #189/R
£400 $648 €600 Mogul (107x122cm-42x48in) s.i.d.Sept 71 verso acrylic. 20-May-3 Bonhams, Knightsbridge #192/R

MEDLYCOTT, Sir Hubert (1841-1920) British
Works on paper
£250 $413 €363 Tower of London from the Thames (29x62cm-11x24in) s.d.1884 W/C. 1-Jul-3 Bearnes, Exeter #461/R
£400 $624 €600 Verdun, riverside scene (24x43cm-9x17in) s.i.d.1916. 5-Nov-2 Bristol Auction Rooms #952/R
£520 $801 €780 London pool (23x36cm-9x14in) s.d.1893. 3-Sep-2 Gorringes, Lewes #2158
£1800 $2988 €2700 Thames at Blackfriars (35x51cm-14x20in) s.d.1894 W/C. 12-Jun-3 Bonhams, New Bond Street #655/R est:2000-3000

MEDNYANSZKY, Laszlo von (1852-1919) Hungarian
£1074 $1664 €1611 Trees (21x29cm-8x11in) painted c.1890. 3-Dec-2 SOGA, Bratislava #28/R est:85000 (SL.K 68000)
£1135 $1771 €1703 Old carrier (60x42cm-24x17in) s. 11-Sep-2 Kieselbach, Budapest #152/R (H.F 440000)
£1187 $1851 €1781 Sentry (35x24cm-14x9in) estate st. cardboard. 11-Sep-2 Kieselbach, Budapest #118/R (H.F 460000)
£1213 $1880 €1820 Landscape with shepherd (20x25cm-8x10in) board painted c.1885. 1-Oct-2 SOGA, Bratislava #26/R est:90000 (SL.K 77000)
£1237 $1917 €1856 Sunset (27x42cm-11x17in) s. 6-Dec-2 Kieselbach, Budapest #56/R (H.F 460000)
£1548 $2415 €2322 Ruins of Castle Becko (27x36cm-11x14in) s. cardboard. 11-Sep-2 Kieselbach, Budapest #50/R (H.F 600000)
£2064 $3220 €3096 Cottage in winter landscape (32x27cm-13x11in) s. 11-Sep-2 Kieselbach, Budapest #2/R (H.F 800000)
£2205 $3418 €3308 Man in cap (52x32cm-20x13in) painted c.1890-95. 1-Oct-2 SOGA, Bratislava #25/R est:120000 (SL.K 140000)
£2236 $3487 €3354 Boy in hat (45x30cm-18x12in) s. 11-Apr-3 Kieselbach, Budapest #196/R est:650000-800000 (H.F 800000)
£2286 $3543 €3429 Boy in a hat (40x27cm-16x11in) s. board painted c.1900. 6-Dec-2 Kieselbach, Budapest #71/R (H.F 850000)
£2958 $4585 €4437 Soldiers in winter forest (35x42cm-14x17in) s. 6-Dec-2 Kieselbach, Budapest #14/R (H.F 1100000)
£3087 $4507 €4631 Before the storm (47x59cm-19x23in) plywood painted c.1890. 4-Jun-2 SOGA, Bratislava #28/R est:245000 (SL.K 196000)
£3612 $5634 €5418 Nightfall at full moon (80x101cm-31x40in) s. 11-Sep-2 Kieselbach, Budapest #15/R (H.F 1400000)
£4303 $6669 €6455 Soldiers in the forest (35x52cm-14x20in) s. 6-Dec-2 Kieselbach, Budapest #67/R (H.F 1600000)
£4386 $6842 €6579 Gunners in snowy landscape (50x34cm-20x13in) s. 11-Sep-2 Kieselbach, Budapest #194/R (H.F 1700000)
£4644 $7244 €6966 On the shore (75x100cm-30x39in) s. 11-Sep-2 Kieselbach, Budapest #119/R (H.F 1800000)
£4681 $7489 €7022 Fishing boy (42x28cm-17x11in) panel. 16-May-3 Kieselbach, Budapest #62/R (H.F 1600000)

£5160 $8049 €7740 Snowy peaks (109x180cm-43x71in) s. 11-Sep-2 Kieselbach, Budapest #105/R (H.F 2000000)
£5589 $8719 €8384 Riverside lit by afternoon sunlight (26x36cm-10x14in) s. 11-Apr-3 Kieselbach, Budapest #17/R est:50000-2000000 (H.F 2000000)
£6000 $9840 €9000 Landscape at dusk (75x100cm-30x39in) s. 3-Jun-3 Sotheby's, London #55/R est:4000-6000
£6191 $9659 €9287 Spring hillside (24x32cm-9x13in) s. 11-Sep-2 Kieselbach, Budapest #213/R (H.F 2400000)
£6436 $10298 €9654 Early spring (27x33cm-11x13in) s. canvas on cardboard. 16-May-3 Kieselbach, Budapest #65/R (H.F 2200000)
£6458 $9428 €9687 Orchard in spring (51x66cm-20x26in) cardboard. 4-Jun-2 SOGA, Bratislava #29/R est:320000 (SL.K 410000)
£6707 $10464 €10061 Lakelet with snowy peaks (55x68cm-22x27in) s. 11-Sep-2 Kieselbach, Budapest #51/R (H.F 2600000)
£7000 $11480 €10500 Spring landscape (26x36cm-10x14in) s. canvas on board. 3-Jun-3 Sotheby's, London #66/R est:4000-6000
£7606 $12170 €11409 View in the Tatra Mountains (27x38cm-11x15in) s. panel. 16-May-3 Kieselbach, Budapest #35/R (H.F 2600000)
£8068 $12505 €12102 Riverside with light (70x100cm-28x39in) s. 6-Dec-2 Kieselbach, Budapest #43/R (H.F 3000000)
£9143 $14172 €13257 Mountain lake (42x52cm-17x20in) s. 9-Dec-2 Mu Terem Galeria, Budapest #46/R est:1500000 (H.F 3400000)
£9501 $14822 €13776 Landscape at spring (31x56cm-12x22in) s. canvas on board. 12-Apr-3 Mu Terem Galeria, Budapest #130/R est:1200000 (H.F 3400000)
£10619 $16566 €15398 Part of a courtyard with well (23x31cm-9x12in) s. canvas on board prov.exhib.lit. 12-Apr-3 Mu Terem Galeria, Budapest #54/R est:1500000 (H.F 3800000)
£10894 $16885 €16341 View over High Tatras (73x100cm-29x39in) painted c.1905. 3-Dec-2 SOGA, Bratislava #29a/R est:590000 (SL.K 690000)
£12236 $18965 €18354 Road in forest (76x50cm-30x20in) painted c.1890. 3-Dec-2 SOGA, Bratislava #29b/R est:470000 (SL.K 775000)
£12899 $20122 €18704 Landscape in the Tatra (72x100cm-28x39in) s. 13-Sep-2 Mu Terem Galeria, Budapest #57/R est:2600000 (H.F 5000000)
£12908 $20008 €18717 Mountain stream with bridge (67x54cm-26x21in) s. 9-Dec-2 Mu Terem Galeria, Budapest #154/R est:1800000 (H.F 4800000)
£15370 $23977 €22287 Lake in the Tatra (70x100cm-28x39in) s. 12-Apr-3 Mu Terem Galeria, Budapest #139/R est:3000000 (H.F 5500000)
£19015 $30424 €28523 Sunrise by the snowy riverside (72x121cm-28x48in) s. 16-May-3 Kieselbach, Budapest #13/R (H.F 6500000)
£45717 $70862 €66290 At the iron gate (110x176cm-43x69in) s.i. 9-Dec-2 Mu Terem Galeria, Budapest #44/R est:8000000 (H.F 17000000)

Works on paper

£253 $392 €380 Head of a soldier (25x21cm-10x8in) pencil dr cardboard exec.c.1914. 3-Dec-2 SOGA, Bratislava #29/R (SL.K 16000)
£440 $682 €700 Street (29x39cm-11x15in) s.i. pencil. 1-Oct-2 Dorotheum, Vienna #159/R
£504 $736 €756 Beggar (20x28cm-8x11in) ink W/C. 4-Jun-2 SOGA, Bratislava #30/R est:28000 (SL.K 32000)
£583 $903 €875 Head of young man (28x17cm-11x7in) ink W/C painted c.1890-95. 1-Oct-2 SOGA, Bratislava #27/R est:35000 (SL.K 37000)
£861 $1334 €1292 Landscape, hillside at Felsokubin (38x54cm-15x21in) s. W/C. 6-Dec-2 Kieselbach, Budapest #66/R (H.F 320000)
£1129 $1751 €1637 In a highland village (31x47cm-12x19in) s. mixed media. 9-Dec-2 Mu Terem Galeria, Budapest #36/R est:220000 (H.F 420000)
£1290 $2012 €1871 Rainy woods (31x43cm-12x17in) s. W/C pencil chk. 13-Sep-2 Mu Terem Galeria, Budapest #51/R est:350000 (H.F 500000)

MEDOW, Augustin (?-1660) German

Works on paper

£1944 $3092 €2800 Susanna bathing (18x14cm-7x6in) s.i.d.1616 pen lit. 5-May-3 Ketterer, Munich #236/R est:600-800

MEDREZ, Miriam (1958-) Latin American?

Sculpture

£7006 $11000 €10509 I do not want to see (161x31x24cm-63x12x9in) ceramic graphite wax exec.2002 prov. 19-Nov-2 Sotheby's, New York #139/R est:15000

MEDVECKA, Maria (1914-1987) Czechoslovakian

£316 $489 €474 Rest on field (18x48cm-7x19in) painted c.1975. 3-Dec-2 SOGA, Bratislava #251/R (SL.K 20000)
£347 $538 €521 End of winter (18x49cm-7x19in) painted 1976. 3-Dec-2 SOGA, Bratislava #252/R (SL.K 22000)
£394 $559 €591 Haymakers (19x49cm-7x19in) board painted 1981. 26-Mar-2 SOGA, Bratislava #247/R (SL.K 25000)
£410 $636 €615 Winter in the Orava region (18x49cm-7x19in) veneer painted c.1975. 3-Dec-2 SOGA, Bratislava #253/R (SL.K 26000)
£457 $708 €686 Orava region (24x35cm-9x14in) board. 1-Oct-2 SOGA, Bratislava #238/R est:25000 (SL.K 29000)
£504 $781 €756 Holy Family (37x28cm-15x11in) tempera gouache board painted c.1947. 1-Oct-2 SOGA, Bratislava #236/R est:25000 (SL.K 32000)
£583 $851 €875 Pastures (48x60cm-19x24in) 4-Jun-2 SOGA, Bratislava #245/R est:29000 (SL.K 37000)
£1181 $1831 €1772 Orava region (38x52cm-15x20in) wood. 1-Oct-2 SOGA, Bratislava #235/R est:35000 (SL.K 75000)

Works on paper

£709 $1099 €1064 Woman with child (36x30cm-14x12in) pastel exec.c.1947. 1-Oct-2 SOGA, Bratislava #237/R est:25000 (SL.K 45000)

MEDVECZKY, Jeno (1902-1969) Hungarian

£516 $805 €748 Spring flower bouquet (49x39cm-19x15in) s. tempera cardboard. 13-Sep-2 Mu Terem Galeria, Budapest #83/R est:160000 (H.F 200000)
£2838 $4427 €4115 Thinking woman with a dog (80x60cm-31x24in) s. cardboard. 13-Sep-2 Mu Terem Galeria, Budapest #68/R est:800000 (H.F 1100000)
£7825 $12206 €11738 Art Deco landscape (64x98cm-25x39in) s. canvas on board. 11-Apr-3 Kieselbach, Budapest #127/R est:1000000-2800000 (H.F 2800000)

MEE, Anne (c.1770-1851) British

Miniatures

£1300 $2106 €1950 Princess, probably princess Charlotte Augusta (12cm-5in) shaped velvet frame. 22-May-3 Bonhams, New Bond Street #129/R est:1500-2000
£1600 $2544 €2400 Barbara, Countess of Shaftesbury (8cm-3in) painted c.1800. 6-Mar-3 Sotheby's, Olympia #9/R est:800-1200
£3800 $6232 €5510 Two young ladies in white dress with ruffled collar (6cm-2in) gilt metal frame pair. 3-Jun-3 Christie's, London #226/R est:1000-1500

MEEGAN, H (19/20th C) British

£2500 $4150 €3750 Moonlit Thames with St. Paul's beyond. Moonlit Thames with Tower Bridge beyond (25x34cm-10x13in) s. board pair. 10-Jun-3 Bonhams, Leeds #158/R est:1000-1500

MEEGAN, Walter (1859-1944) British

£350 $571 €508 Lakeland landscape with figures fishing from a boat (41x61cm-16x24in) s. 17-Jul-3 Tennants, Leyburn #841
£500 $780 €750 Boats in a harbour (21x31cm-8x12in) s. 10-Apr-3 Tennants, Leyburn #954
£600 $954 €900 Moonlit street scene (29x44cm-11x17in) s. 29-Apr-3 Henry Adams, Chichester #298/R
£950 $1558 €1425 View across the bay (36x51cm-14x20in) s. canvas on board. 5-Jun-3 Christie's, Kensington #731/R
£1100 $1738 €1650 Moonlight view of the embankment (76x127cm-30x50in) s. 12-Nov-2 Bonhams, Knightsbridge #82/R est:1000-2000
£2200 $3586 €3300 Fishing boats at the quay by moonlight. (25x36cm-10x14in) s. sold with another similar. 13-Feb-3 Christie's, Kensington #99/R est:800-1200

MEEGAN, Walter (attrib) (1859-1944) British

£820 $1287 €1230 Moonlit street scene (35x50cm-14x20in) 19-Nov-2 Bonhams, Leeds #235

MEEGEREN, Han van (1889-1947) Dutch

£224 $350 €336 Young boy making bubbles (32x27cm-13x11in) s. board. 11-Nov-2 Stephan Welz, Johannesburg #20 (SA.R 3500)
£1064 $1723 €1500 Interior with piano playing gentleman and two ladies standing, by lamplight (39x58cm-15x23in) s. 26-May-3 Glerum, Amsterdam #53 est:1200-1600
£1447 $2345 €2200 Inquistive goat (71x50cm-28x20in) s.d.16 exhib. 21-Jan-3 Christie's, Amsterdam #157/R est:1500-2000

Works on paper

£1379 $2193 €2000 Sunny day at the beach (22x30cm-9x12in) s. W/C. 10-Mar-3 Sotheby's, Amsterdam #240/R est:2000-3000

MEEKER, Joseph R (1827-1889) American

£7143 $11000 €10715 Bayou plaguemines (51x23cm-20x9in) s.i.d.80 prov. 24-Oct-2 Shannon's, Milford #97/R est:4000-6000
£8974 $14000 €13461 Near lake Pontchartain (30x25cm-12x10in) mono.i.d.1874. 20-Sep-2 New Orleans Auction, New Orleans #1227/R est:15000-25000
£30255 $47500 €45383 Bayou at sunrise (61x51cm-24x20in) s. prov. 19-Nov-2 Butterfields, San Francisco #8000/R est:10000-15000

MEELES, Derk Willem (1872-1958) Dutch

£915 $1474 €1300 Still life with anemones (38x48cm-15x19in) s. 6-May-3 Vendu Notarishuis, Rotterdam #132/R

MEENAN, Anton (20th C) Irish?
£380 $589 €570 Changing storm turned against HMS Wasp 1884 (59x122cm-23x48in) s. board. 4-Dec-2 John Ross, Belfast #161
£650 $1040 €975 HMS Wasp sinking off Tory Island (58x119cm-23x47in) s.i.d.1884 board. 15-May-3 Christie's, Kensington #171/R

MEERBERGEN, Rudolf (1908-1987) Belgian
£503 $775 €800 Composition orange (92x62cm-36x24in) s. 22-Oct-2 Campo & Campo, Antwerp #181

MEERE, Charles M (1890-1961) Australian
£65385 $103962 €98078 Australian beach pattern (65x88cm-26x35in) init.i. painted c.1938 prov. 4-Mar-3 Deutscher-Menzies, Melbourne #29/R est:160000-200000 (A.D 170000)

MEERHOUD, Jan (?-1677) Dutch
£2200 $3410 €3300 River landscape with villa, travellers and fishermen (65x84cm-26x33in) panel. 30-Oct-2 Bonhams, New Bond Street #147/R est:2000-3000

MEERSCHE, Gustaaf van den (1891-1970) Belgian
Sculpture
£1793 $2833 €2600 Femme en priere (79cm-31in) s.d.1926 green pat bronze. 2-Apr-3 Vanderkindere, Brussels #560/R est:600-800

MEERSMAN, Arthur (1908-1984) Belgian
£340 $541 €500 Composition (120x120cm-47x47in) s. 24-Mar-3 Bernaerts, Antwerp #857/R
£362 $594 €500 Fermes (90x110cm-35x43in) s.d.43. 27-May-3 Campo, Vlaamse Kaai #246

MEERTENS, Victor (1955-) Australian
Sculpture
£1357 $2117 €2036 Untitled (102x66x34cm-40x26x13in) corrugated iron timber. 11-Nov-2 Deutscher-Menzies, Melbourne #133/R est:2000-3000 (A.D 3800)

MEERTS, Frans (1836-1896) Belgian
£417 $654 €650 Drinking monks (53x43cm-21x17in) s. 16-Dec-2 Bernaerts, Antwerp #827
£481 $755 €750 Jeune femme a la couture (58x46cm-23x18in) s. 10-Dec-2 Vanderkindere, Brussels #101
£2055 $3226 €3000 Jeune femme et chaton (65x49cm-26x19in) s. 15-Apr-3 Galerie Moderne, Brussels #372/R est:3000-4000
£2564 $4026 €4000 Presentation de la fiancee (69x92cm-27x36in) s. 19-Nov-2 Servarts Themis, Bruxelles #117/R
£10526 $17053 €16000 La marchande de legumes (85x130cm-33x51in) 21-Jan-3 Galerie Moderne, Brussels #195/R est:7500-10000

MEESER, Lillian B (1864-1942) American
£692 $1100 €1038 Gloucester Harbor (23x20cm-9x8in) s. 7-Mar-3 Jackson's, Cedar Falls #649/R est:500-700

MEESON, Dora (1869-1955) Australian
£250 $395 €375 Water garden, Buckingham Palace (33x41cm-13x16in) board. 14-Nov-2 Christie's, Kensington #44

MEESTER DE BETZENBROECK, Raymond de (1904-1995) Belgian
Sculpture
£1176 $1894 €1800 Mouflon sur un rocher (60cm-24in) s. green pat bronze Cast Charles Storms. 20-Jan-3 Horta, Bruxelles #129 est:2000-3000
£1307 $2105 €2000 Chevreuil a trois semaines (53cm-21in) s. brown pat bronze. 20-Jan-3 Horta, Bruxelles #128 est:2200-2800
£1410 $2214 €2200 Belier se tenant debout sur un rocher. brown pat bronze. 16-Dec-2 Amberes, Antwerp #439
£1772 $2765 €2800 Chevreuil de trois semaines (53cm-21in) s. pat bronze. 16-Sep-2 Horta, Bruxelles #120/R
£2911 $4600 €4600 Jeune faon (36x28x17cm-14x11x7in) i. green pat bronze Cast Batardy. 26-Nov-2 Palais de Beaux Arts, Brussels #68/R est:4000-5000
£2917 $4638 €4200 Jeune dromadaire (40x38x17cm-16x15x7in) s.i. bronze lit. 29-Apr-3 Campo & Campo, Antwerp #77/R est:4250-5250
£3019 $4679 €4800 Chevreuil de trois semaines (53x46cm-21x18in) s. brown black pat bronze lit. 5-Oct-2 De Vuyst, Lokeren #456/R est:5000-6000
£3038 $4739 €4800 Elephanteau (45x40cm-18x16in) s. pat bronze exec.1944. 15-Oct-2 Horta, Bruxelles #123/R
£3793 $6069 €5500 Le bison d'Amerique (38x63x18cm-15x25x7in) s.d.1930. 17-Mar-3 Horta, Bruxelles #158 est:3500-4500
£6962 $10861 €11000 Aigle royal (60cm-24in) s. pat bronze. 15-Oct-2 Horta, Bruxelles #122/R est:10000-15000

MEESTERS, Dirk (1899-1950) British
£360 $562 €540 Marshland with cows watering in the foreground (57x78cm-22x31in) s.d.45. 8-Apr-3 Bonhams, Knightsbridge #240/R

MEGANCK, Joseph (1807-1891) German
£728 $1135 €1150 La cantiniere (24x20cm-9x8in) s. panel. 15-Oct-2 Vanderkindere, Brussels #57
£2878 $4604 €4000 La lecture de la lettre (57x45cm-22x18in) s.d.1836 panel. 13-May-3 Vanderkindere, Brussels #258 est:2500-4000

MEGGESON, J T (fl.1869-1871) British
£3600 $5904 €5220 Gentleman hunting with hounds (102x140cm-40x55in) s.d.1861. 9-Jun-3 Bonhams, Bath #104/R est:4000-6000

MEHEUT, François (?) French
Sculpture
£962 $1510 €1500 Trois marins aux paniers (50cm-20in) s. terracotta. 15-Dec-2 Thierry & Lannon, Brest #19

MEHEUT, Mathurin (1882-1958) French
£1282 $2013 €2000 Fonds marins (73x57cm-29x22in) tempera paper on canvas. 15-Dec-2 Thierry & Lannon, Brest #40
£1757 $2741 €2600 Debacle au soir couchant (41x150cm-16x59in) s. paper on canvas. 28-Mar-3 Claude Aguttes, Neuilly #50b
£1859 $2919 €2900 Campement de nomades (30x20cm-12x8in) mono. cardboard. 15-Dec-2 Thierry & Lannon, Brest #171
£3205 $5032 €5000 Chalutiers dans la tempete (50x65cm-20x26in) s.i. 15-Dec-2 Thierry & Lannon, Brest #169
£4839 $7645 €7500 Biche et son faon en foret de Fontainebleau (126x159cm-50x63in) mono. panel. 19-Dec-2 Claude Aguttes, Neuilly #186/R
£10577 $16606 €16500 Grande Tromenie (104x144cm-41x57in) mono.d.1954 oil casein. 15-Dec-2 Thierry & Lannon, Brest #170
Works on paper
£269 $423 €420 Etude de squelette de faisan (39x30cm-15x12in) W/C wash. 15-Dec-2 Thierry & Lannon, Brest #343
£288 $453 €450 Etude de serpent et salamandre (37x26cm-15x10in) mono. W/C gouache. 15-Dec-2 Thierry & Lannon, Brest #344
£308 $483 €480 Etude de scorpion (34x24cm-13x9in) mono. W/C gouache. 15-Dec-2 Thierry & Lannon, Brest #345
£308 $483 €480 Barque sous voiles (16x23cm-6x9in) mono. W/C. 15-Dec-2 Thierry & Lannon, Brest #341
£321 $503 €500 Etude de salamandre (38x38cm-15x15in) studio st. crayon. 15-Dec-2 Thierry & Lannon, Brest #306
£333 $543 €480 Les casiers sur la jetee a Roscoff (14x19cm-6x7in) mono. crayon. 19-Jul-3 Thierry & Lannon, Brest #44
£345 $548 €500 La harde (19x26cm-7x10in) mono. Indian ink. 4-Mar-3 Livinec, Gaudcheau & Jezequel, Rennes #62
£353 $554 €550 Etude d'animaux (36x26cm-14x10in) mono. W/C htd gouache. 15-Dec-2 Thierry & Lannon, Brest #346
£353 $554 €550 Etude de poissons (16x30cm-6x12in) mono. gouache. 15-Dec-2 Thierry & Lannon, Brest #342
£361 $589 €520 Scene Orientaliste, deux jeunes filles assises (17x22cm-7x9in) studio st. chl col crayon. 19-Jul-3 Thierry & Lannon, Brest #45
£372 $584 €580 Deux bretonnes assises (19x29cm-7x11in) chl. 15-Dec-2 Thierry & Lannon, Brest #302
£397 $624 €620 Bretons en conversations (12x17cm-5x7in) mono. chl. 15-Dec-2 Thierry & Lannon, Brest #311
£417 $654 €650 Etude de lucane (40x30cm-16x12in) mono. W/C gouache. 15-Dec-2 Thierry & Lannon, Brest #347
£423 $680 €600 Service pour l'appartement breton (41x55cm-16x22in) i. chl W/C gouache. 11-May-3 Thierry & Lannon, Brest #298
£436 $684 €680 Animation pres de l'abreuvoir (20x30cm-8x12in) mono. chl. 15-Dec-2 Thierry & Lannon, Brest #304
£462 $725 €720 Etude de tetes (38x48cm-15x19in) s. crayon htd chk. 15-Dec-2 Thierry & Lannon, Brest #308
£481 $755 €750 Etude desauterelles (30x40cm-12x16in) studio st. wash. 15-Dec-2 Thierry & Lannon, Brest #305
£517 $822 €750 Les geomoniers (18x36cm-7x14in) mono. col crayon dr. 4-Mar-3 Livinec, Gaudcheau & Jezequel, Rennes #64
£625 $1019 €900 Etude de dindons (40x55cm-16x22in) gouache double-sided. 19-Jul-3 Thierry & Lannon, Brest #1hc
£660 $1075 €950 Marchande de ficelle Auray (20x26cm-8x10in) chl. 19-Jul-3 Thierry & Lannon, Brest #43
£704 $1134 €1000 Maternite (25x15cm-10x6in) mono. chl. 11-May-3 Thierry & Lannon, Brest #299
£769 $1208 €1200 Barque sur la grande Briere (21x24cm-8x9in) s. gouache. 15-Dec-2 Thierry & Lannon, Brest #90
£986 $1587 €1400 Scene de repas en Bretagne (22x33cm-9x13in) mono. chl. 11-May-3 Thierry & Lannon, Brest #72
£1056 $1701 €1500 Cote rocheuse et tourelle (22x36cm-9x14in) mono. W/C. 11-May-3 Thierry & Lannon, Brest #97 est:1500-1800
£1090 $1711 €1700 Locronan (31x39cm-12x15in) mono.d.1929 gouache. 15-Dec-2 Thierry & Lannon, Brest #87
£1090 $1711 €1700 Bord de la Penze (29x43cm-11x17in) mono. gouache. 15-Dec-2 Thierry & Lannon, Brest #93
£1218 $1912 €1900 Scene de moisson (19x31cm-7x12in) s. gouache. 15-Dec-2 Thierry & Lannon, Brest #88
£1456 $2300 €2300 Chevres dans la clairiere (45x30cm-18x12in) mono. gouache. 1-Dec-2 Livinec, Gaudcheau & Jezequel, Rennes #38c

£2115 $3321 €3300 Gerbes de ble (19x31cm-7x12in) s. gouache. 15-Dec-2 Thierry & Lannon, Brest #89
£2244 $3522 €3500 Pardon de Saint-Yves a Treguier (16x21cm-6x8in) i. gouache. 15-Dec-2 Thierry & Lannon, Brest #92
£2308 $3623 €3600 Fontaine sacree (22x33cm-9x13in) init.i. w htd gouache. 15-Dec-2 Thierry & Lannon, Brest #64
£3077 $4831 €4800 Jeune bretonne et son enfant (29x40cm-11x16in) s.i. chl gouache. 15-Dec-2 Thierry & Lannon, Brest #41

MEHRLE, Josef (20th C) German
£449 $682 €700 Kappadokien - central Turkey (92x63cm-36x25in) s. 11-Jul-2 Hugo Ruef, Munich #745

MEHTA, Tyeb (1925-) Indian
£62160 $102564 €90132 Untitled (150x125cm-59x49in) s.d.74. 6-Jul-3 Christie's, Hong Kong #84/R est:600000-700000 (HK.D 800000)

MEHUS, Livio (1630-1691) Flemish
£3514 $5481 €5200 Jesus baptise par St Jean Baptiste dans le Jourdain. 25-Mar-3 Chochon-Barre & Allardi, Paris #13/R est:5000-6000
£5000 $8350 €7250 The Creation of Adam (78x56cm-31x22in) 8-Jul-3 Sotheby's, Olympia #386/R est:6000-8000
£5517 $8717 €8000 Isaac's sacrifice (88x65cm-35x26in) 5-Apr-3 Finarte Semenzato, Milan #141/R est:12000
£12579 $19497 €20000 Bridge over river. Riverside fortress (59x88cm-23x35in) pair. 2-Oct-2 Dorotheum, Vienna #71/R est:20000-30000

MEI, Bernardino (1615-1676) Italian
£16000 $25120 €24000 Roman charity (98x131cm-39x52in) 10-Dec-2 Bonhams, New Bond Street #262/R est:15000-20000

MEI, Paolo (19th C) Italian
£2500 $3925 €3750 Sleeping seamstress (63x52cm-25x20in) s.d.1863 prov. 21-Nov-2 Christie's, Kensington #33/R est:2500-3500

MEID, Hans (1883-1957) German
£506 $800 €800 Tiergarten (30x39cm-12x15in) s. Indian ink pencil chk. 29-Nov-2 Villa Grisebach, Berlin #800/R

Works on paper
£633 $1000 €1000 Woman sleeping - Wagner singer Berta Morena (38x48cm-15x19in) chk ochre wash htd white. 29-Nov-2 Villa Grisebach, Berlin #802/R

MEIDE, Jacobus Leonardus van der (20th C) Belgian
£283 $442 €450 Capri and Gulf of Naples in evening light (70x120cm-28x47in) s.s. 21-Sep-2 Bolland & Marotz, Bremen #624

MEIDNER, Ludwig (1884-1966) German
£2532 $3773 €3900 Landscape with resting travellers (24x33cm-9x13in) mono.d.54 board. 28-Jun-2 Sigalas, Stuttgart #647/R
£7692 $11923 €12000 Self portrait (74x57cm-29x22in) mono. bears d.193 board double-sided prov. 4-Dec-2 Lempertz, Koln #910/R est:8000-10000

Sculpture
£12057 $19532 €17000 Untitled (57x33x30cm-22x13x12in) s.d.1959 steel pewter wood socle prov. 24-May-3 Van Ham, Cologne #406/R est:6000

Works on paper
£1702 $2757 €2400 Portrait of a man (47x31cm-19x12in) mono.d.1917 Indian ink pencil. 24-May-3 Van Ham, Cologne #405/R est:2400
£2278 $3600 €3417 Self portait (29x21cm-11x8in) init.d.1924 chl. 27-Apr-3 Sotheby's, Tel Aviv #17/R est:5000-7000
£2899 $4754 €4000 Prophet (75x56cm-30x22in) mono.d.1920 wax chk board. 31-May-3 Villa Grisebach, Berlin #215/R est:4000-5000
£15000 $24600 €22500 Apocalyptic landscape (52x37cm-20x15in) s.d.1914 pen ink pencil prov. 6-Feb-3 Christie's, London #455/R est:12000

MEIER, Paul Louis (1950-) Swiss

Works on paper
£343 $542 €515 Female nude (76x52cm-30x20in) mono. collage. 29-Nov-2 Zofingen, Switzerland #2981 (S.FR 800)
£408 $644 €612 Two figures meeting (150x41cm-59x16in) mono. mixed media. 29-Nov-2 Zofingen, Switzerland #2982 (S.FR 950)
£687 $1085 €1031 Figures (156x54cm-61x21in) mono. mixed media. 29-Nov-2 Zofingen, Switzerland #2985 est:850 (S.FR 1600)

MEIER, Theo (1908-1982) Swiss
£1572 $2452 €2358 Portrait of asiatic woman (54x44cm-21x17in) s.d.36. 6-Nov-2 Dobiaschofsky, Bern #820/R est:6000 (S.FR 3600)
£2620 $4087 €3930 Portrait of asiatic woman against red backdrop (51x41cm-20x16in) s. 6-Nov-2 Dobiaschofsky, Bern #821/R est:5000 (S.FR 6000)
£3930 $6131 €5895 Buddhist temple (100x76cm-39x30in) s.d.61. 6-Nov-2 Dobiaschofsky, Bern #818/R est:14000 (S.FR 9000)
£5385 $8293 €8078 Portrait of a Chinese girl (55x45cm-22x18in) s.d.36. 27-Oct-2 Christie's, Hong Kong #31/R est:35000-45000 (HK.D 65000)
£6207 $9807 €9000 Girl from South Sea Island (60x70cm-24x28in) s.d. s.i. verso. 2-Apr-3 Dr Fritz Nagel, Stuttgart #9507/R est:9500
£10878 $17949 €15773 Sunset in Sanur (133x65cm-52x26in) s.d.1971-73 prov. 6-Jul-3 Christie's, Hong Kong #11/R est:110000-160000 (HK.D 140000)
£49710 $76553 €74565 Balinese beauty combing her hair (67x37cm-26x15in) s.d.1948 prov.exhib. 27-Oct-2 Christie's, Hong Kong #29/R est:340000-440000 (HK.D 600000)

MEIER-DENNINGHOFF, Brigitte (1923-) German

Sculpture
£2374 $3799 €3300 Form in pewter Nr 26 (37cm-15in) i.d. brass pewter lit. 15-May-3 Neumeister, Munich #728/R est:3000-3500

Works on paper
£641 $994 €1000 Untitled - head (70x50cm-28x20in) s.d.1952 chl board. 3-Dec-2 Lempertz, Koln #294/R

MEIFREN Y ROIG, Eliseo (1859-1940) Spanish
£774 $1223 €1200 Landscape with river (56x35cm-22x14in) s. chl dr. 17-Dec-2 Durán, Madrid #79/R
£5379 $8553 €7800 Garden (23x22cm-9x9in) s. 4-Mar-3 Ansorena, Madrid #154/R
£8553 $13855 €13000 Seascape at nightfall (28x23cm-11x9in) s. 21-Jan-3 Ansorena, Madrid #176/R est:10000
£9211 $14921 €14000 Fishing harbour (38x46cm-15x18in) s.i. s.i.verso cardboard. 21-Jan-3 Ansorena, Madrid #169/R
£18000 $28260 €27000 Atardecer - evening light (86x52cm-34x20in) s.i. prov. 19-Nov-2 Sotheby's, London #1/R est:20000-30000

MEIJER, Fritz (1900-) Swiss?
£283 $441 €425 Ascona (30x40cm-12x16in) s. masonite. 16-Sep-2 Philippe Schuler, Zurich #6632 (S.FR 650)

MEIJER, Jan (1927-) Dutch
£1026 $1590 €1600 Landschap in geel - landscape in yellow (100x80cm-39x31in) s.d.8/60 s.i.d.verso. 3-Dec-2 Christie's, Amsterdam #176/R est:1000-1300

MEILERTS, Ludmilla (1908-1997) Australian
£351 $533 €527 Still life (48x58cm-19x23in) s.d.80 board. 19-Aug-2 Joel, Victoria #158 est:1200-1500 (A.D 1000)
£526 $800 €789 Flowers (75x59cm-30x23in) s.d.70 board. 19-Aug-2 Joel, Victoria #334 est:1500-2000 (A.D 1500)
£643 $1016 €965 Melbourne general post office (74x59cm-29x23in) s. 18-Nov-2 Joel, Victoria #190/R est:2000-3000 (A.D 1800)
£1075 $1634 €1613 Still life with apples (74x59cm-29x23in) s.d.76 board. 27-Aug-2 Goodman, Sydney #173 est:3000-4000 (A.D 3000)
£1076 $1764 €1560 Still life, flowers in vase (75x58cm-30x23in) s.d.54. 3-Jun-3 Lawson Menzies, Sydney #885 (A.D 2700)

MEILI, Conrad (1895-1969) Swiss
£347 $559 €521 Still life with apples and small wooden bowl (15x21cm-6x8in) s.d.58 s.d.60 verso board. 7-May-3 Dobiaschofsky, Bern #817/R (S.FR 750)
£755 $1208 €1133 Still life with garden chair (65x54cm-26x21in) s.d. 17-Mar-3 Philippe Schuler, Zurich #4538 (S.FR 1600)
£1132 $1811 €1698 Seated female nude (66x46cm-26x18in) s.d. 17-Mar-3 Philippe Schuler, Zurich #4537 est:1500-2000 (S.FR 2400)
£2707 $4224 €4061 Woman seated in front of drape (121x80cm-48x31in) s.d.27. 20-Nov-2 Fischer, Luzern #1289/R est:4000-5000 (S.FR 6200)

MEINDL, Albert (1891-1967) Austrian
£224 $351 €336 In the Alps (30x41cm-12x16in) s. prov. 10-Dec-2 Pinneys, Montreal #30 (C.D 550)
£962 $1510 €1500 Inner courtyard with park landscape beyond (41x40cm-16x16in) s.d.26. 20-Nov-2 Dorotheum, Klagenfurt #14/R est:1500

MEINES, H W V (20th C) ?
£402 $631 €603 Reading in a summer meadow (46x34cm-18x13in) s.d.1931. 25-Nov-2 Hodgins, Calgary #73/R (C.D 1000)

MEINTJES, Johannes (1923-1980) South African
£243 $380 €365 Portrait of Herbert McWilliam (44x34cm-17x13in) s.d.51 canvasboard. 11-Nov-2 Stephan Welz, Johannesburg #474 (SA.R 3800)
£965 $1524 €1448 Adolescent longing (75x39cm-30x15in) s.d.1971 prov. 1-Apr-3 Stephan Welz, Johannesburg #491/R est:10000-15000 (SA.R 12000)

MEIREN, Jan Baptist van der (1664-1708) Flemish
£1064 $1649 €1596 Naval battle (18x24cm-7x9in) 4-Dec-2 AB Stockholms Auktionsverk #1978/R est:25000-30000 (S.KR 15000)

MEIRHANS, Joseph (1890-1981) American
£321 $500 €482 Abstract composition (81x71cm-32x28in) s. masonite. 18-Sep-2 Alderfer's, Hatfield #386/R
£353 $550 €530 Abstract composition (81x51cm-32x20in) s. masonite. 18-Sep-2 Alderfer's, Hatfield #385
£1442 $2250 €2163 Landscape of cloudy day (61x76cm-24x30in) s. masonite. 18-Sep-2 Alderfer's, Hatfield #384/R est:700-900

MEIRVENNE, Alfons van (1932-) Belgian
£252 $387 €400 Hibou (95x70cm-37x28in) s.d.1972. 22-Oct-2 Campo & Campo, Antwerp #308/R
£340 $541 €500 Landscape with farmhouse (80x100cm-31x39in) s.d.1963. 24-Mar-3 Bernaerts, Antwerp #819
£346 $533 €550 Chevre au repos (120x180cm-47x71in) s.d.1961. 22-Oct-2 Campo, Vlaamse Kaai #323

MEISENBACH, Karl (1898-1976) German
£955 $1490 €1500 Hut in lower alpine landscape (77x94cm-30x37in) s.d.38. 6-Nov-2 Hugo Ruef, Munich #1206/R est:900

MEISSER, Leonhard (1902-1977) Swiss
£448 $717 €672 Wood in late autumn (45x34cm-18x13in) s. i.d. verso. 17-Mar-3 Philippe Schuler, Zurich #4540 (S.FR 950)
£556 $894 €834 Sunday - Lenzburg (27x35cm-11x14in) s. i.d.1954 verso. 7-May-3 Dobiaschofsky, Bern #818/R (S.FR 1200)
£613 $981 €920 Evening (35x27cm-14x11in) s.d. i. verso. 17-Mar-3 Philippe Schuler, Zurich #4539 (S.FR 1300)
£1157 $1863 €1678 Fading sun (81x65cm-32x26in) s.d.59. 9-May-3 Dobiaschofsky, Bern #153/R est:5000 (S.FR 2500)
£1204 $1938 €1746 La neige s'en va (55x33cm-22x13in) s.d.72. 9-May-3 Dobiaschofsky, Bern #151/R est:4000 (S.FR 2600)
£1747 $2725 €2621 First snow (73x54cm-29x21in) s.d.67. 8-Nov-2 Dobiaschofsky, Bern #157/R est:4800 (S.FR 4000)

MEISSNER, Adolf Ernst (1837-1902) German
£274 $427 €400 Standing white cow (46x55cm-18x22in) mono. canvas on board. 10-Apr-3 Allgauer, Kempten #2893/R
£443 $687 €700 Peasant woman with cows drinking from trough (20x31cm-8x12in) paper on board. 25-Sep-2 Neumeister, Munich #649/R
£720 $1159 €1044 Shepherd (34x59cm-13x23in) s.i. 12-May-3 Joel, Victoria #335 est:1500-2000 (A.D 1800)

MEISSNER, Gustav (1830-?) German
£1086 $1760 €1575 Landscape with figures and cattle (60x90cm-24x35in) s. prov. 25-May-3 Uppsala Auktionskammare, Uppsala #64/R (S.KR 14000)
£2260 $3526 €3300 Swiss alpine landscape with gathering storm (52x88cm-20x35in) s.d.80. 10-Apr-3 Van Ham, Cologne #1587/R est:4000

MEISSONIER, Jean Charles (1848-1917) French
£2532 $4000 €3798 Art amateurs (23x18cm-9x7in) s. panel prov. 24-Apr-3 Sotheby's, New York #138/R est:2000-3000

MEISSONIER, Jean Louis Ernest (1815-1891) French
£1299 $2013 €1949 White horse (19x18cm-7x7in) mono. panel. 24-Sep-2 Koller, Zurich #6494 est:2500-4500 (S.FR 3000)
£2893 $4600 €4340 Cheval alezan (23x25cm-9x10in) s. panel. 22-Mar-3 New Orleans Auction, New Orleans #411/R est:5000-8000
£6452 $10000 €9678 Self portrait along the route de la salice, Antibes (14x26cm-6x10in) s.d.1868 board prov.exhib.lit. 29-Oct-2 Sotheby's, New York #10/R est:12000-15000
£316129 $490000 €474194 Guide (112x88cm-44x35in) s.d.1883 prov.exhib.lit. 29-Oct-2 Sotheby's, New York #11/R est:150000-250000

Works on paper
£385 $550 €578 Seascape with fishing boats (11x19cm-4x7in) mono.i. pencil prov. 22-Jan-3 Doyle, New York #46
£1235 $2000 €1853 Portrait of Doctor Lefebvre (21x14cm-8x6in) lead prov. 21-Jan-3 Sotheby's, New York #179/R
£2258 $3500 €3387 Seated boy with a book (35x26cm-14x10in) mono. pencil black chk prov.exhib. 29-Oct-2 Sotheby's, New York #60/R est:1500-2000
£10968 $17000 €16452 Bacchus (57x37cm-22x15in) init. W/C gouache ink exhib. 29-Oct-2 Sotheby's, New York #62/R est:15000-20000

MEISSONIER, Jean Louis Ernest (attrib) (1815-1891) French
£1006 $1550 €1600 Portrait of French soldier (46x38cm-18x15in) init. 28-Oct-2 Il Ponte, Milan #239/R

MEISTER, Pierre (1814-?) French
£1964 $3221 €2848 Hunting still life (88x69cm-35x27in) s. 4-Jun-3 AB Stockholms Auktionsverk #2457/R est:20000-25000 (S.KR 25000)

MEISTERMANN, Georg (1911-1990) German

Works on paper
£2642 $4121 €4200 Blooming zone (37x45cm-15x18in) mono.i.d.1929 pen ink W/C prov. 9-Oct-2 Sotheby's, London #230/R est:6000-9000

MEIT, Conrad (attrib) (1485-1544) German

Sculpture
£1948 $3000 €2922 Eve - pensive figure with braided hair, outstretched hand holding an apple (34cm-13in) pat bronze prov. 28-Oct-2 Butterfields, San Francisco #3176/R est:4000-6000

MEIXNER, Ludwig (1828-1885) German
£855 $1386 €1300 Pleasure boating (36x61cm-14x24in) s.d.1869. 21-Jan-3 Christie's, Amsterdam #56 est:800-1200

MELBYE, Anton (1818-1875) Danish
£317 $511 €476 Sailing boat off the coast, autumn (24x33cm-9x13in) s. panel. 19-Jan-3 Hindemae, Ullerslev #7471/R (D.KR 3600)
£601 $949 €902 Sunset over the sea, sailing vessel by coast (42x55cm-17x22in) s.d.1855. 17-Nov-2 Hindemae, Ullerslev #7222/R (D.KR 7000)
£617 $963 €926 Sailing vessel off rocky reef (13x21cm-5x8in) s.i.d.1844 panel. 11-Nov-2 Rasmussen, Vejle #623/R (D.KR 7200)
£681 $1076 €1022 Sunset over fjord landscape with castle ruins (11x17cm-4x7in) s.d.1851. 2-Dec-2 Rasmussen, Copenhagen #1399/R (D.KR 8000)
£1064 $1681 €1596 Seascape with high seas (33x48cm-13x19in) s.i.d.25 Januar 1847. 30-Nov-2 Rasmussen, Havnen #2252/R est:15000-20000 (D.KR 12500)
£1319 $2084 €1979 Seascape in high seas (52x78cm-20x31in) s.d.1846. 30-Nov-2 Rasmussen, Havnen #2270/R est:20000-25000 (D.KR 15500)
£1531 $2480 €2220 Alexander Nevskis shipwreck off the west coast of Jylland (106x150cm-42x59in) s.d.1871. 26-May-3 Rasmussen, Copenhagen #1190/R est:25000-35000 (D.KR 16000)
£2153 $3273 €3230 Fishermen by their boats on beach, in background The White Lighthouse, Skagen (48x66cm-19x26in) s. 27-Aug-2 Rasmussen, Copenhagen #1474/R est:30000-40000 (D.KR 25000)
£2273 $3773 €3296 Seascape with sailing ship in high seas at sunset (37x50cm-15x20in) s.i. 12-Jun-3 Kunsthallen, Copenhagen #342/R est:25000 (D.KR 24000)
£3830 $6051 €5745 Vessels by The Gold Horn, entrance to Constantinople (42x76cm-17x30in) s.d.1860. 27-Nov-2 Museumsbygningen, Copenhagen #70/R est:30000-40000 (D.KR 45000)
£8511 $13447 €12767 Seascape with sailing vessels and fishing boats off an island (100x150cm-39x59in) s.d.1862. 2-Dec-2 Rasmussen, Copenhagen #1154/R est:125000-150000 (D.KR 100000)

Works on paper
£335 $543 €486 Evening by the sea (20x28cm-8x11in) s.d.1866 pen W/C. 26-May-3 Rasmussen, Copenhagen #1582 (D.KR 3500)

MELBYE, Fritz (1826-1896) Danish
£775 $1178 €1163 Paddlesteamer off Kullen (37x56cm-15x22in) s.d.1849. 27-Aug-2 Rasmussen, Copenhagen #1766/R (D.KR 9000)

MELBYE, Fritz (attrib) (1826-1896) Danish
£270 $417 €405 Coastal landscape with figures, boat and house (36x46cm-14x18in) s. 26-Oct-2 Rasmussen, Havnen #2071 (D.KR 3200)

MELBYE, Wilhelm (1824-1882) Danish
£258 $393 €387 Large stones at water's edge near Aalsgaarde (27x36cm-11x14in) s.d.9 July 49. 27-Aug-2 Rasmussen, Copenhagen #1758/R (D.KR 3000)
£478 $775 €693 Coastal landscape, Cornwall (31x54cm-12x21in) init.d.1865. 26-May-3 Rasmussen, Copenhagen #1419/R (D.KR 5000)
£840 $1335 €1260 Seascape with sailing vessels (37x56cm-15x22in) s.i.d.21 Juni 49. 5-May-3 Rasmussen, Vejle #269/R (D.KR 9000)
£947 $1440 €1421 Seascape with sailing vessels off coast at sunset (33x47cm-13x19in) s.d.1878. 27-Aug-2 Rasmussen, Copenhagen #1465/R (D.KR 11000)
£1170 $1814 €1755 Sailing vessel at dusk (46x83cm-18x33in) s.d.1859. 3-Dec-2 Bukowskis, Stockholm #237/R est:20000-25000 (S.KR 16500)
£1500 $2325 €2250 Running up the beach in a heavy swell (51x76cm-20x30in) s.d.1867. 31-Oct-2 Christie's, Kensington #508/R est:2000-3000
£1500 $2355 €2250 The Rock of Gibraltar (45x65cm-18x26in) s.d.1851. 16-Dec-2 Sotheby's, Olympia #97/R est:1500-2000
£1667 $2617 €2600 Fishing boats returning home in stormy seas (28x42cm-11x17in) s.d.79. 21-Nov-2 Van Ham, Cologne #1782 est:1200
£2392 $3876 €3468 Clipper off the Scottish coast (68x78cm-27x31in) s.d.1856. 26-May-3 Rasmussen, Copenhagen #1196/R est:30000 (D.KR 25000)

£2756 $4189 €4134 Life boat in action in the North Sea (43x68cm-17x27in) s. 27-Aug-2 Rasmussen, Copenhagen #1726/R est:25000 (D.KR 32000)
£3519 $5561 €5279 Seascape with vessels off southern coastal fort (61x36cm-24x14in) s.d.60. 13-Nov-2 Kunsthallen, Copenhagen #1/R est:25000 (D.KR 41000)
£3526 $5535 €5500 Two master stranded off Scandinavian coast (67x107cm-26x42in) s.d.1863. 21-Nov-2 Van Ham, Cologne #1781/R est:3500
£4000 $6480 €6000 Reefing down in heavy weather (71x109cm-28x43in) s.d.1852. 21-May-3 Christie's, Kensington #669/R est:3000-5000
£4255 $6723 €6383 Calm evening - Loch Limnke in Scotland (49x76cm-19x30in) s.d.1866. 2-Dec-2 Rasmussen, Copenhagen #1359/R est:60000 (D.KR 50000)
£4321 $7000 €6265 Man-o-war firing a salute off a headland with other shipping in the distance (80x159cm-31x63in) s.d.1860. 29-Jul-3 Christie's, Rockefeller NY #132/R est:8000-12000
£4414 $6797 €6621 Seascape with sailing boats and vessel in rough seas (94x138cm-37x54in) s.d.1850. 27-Oct-2 Anders Antik, Landskrona #317/R est:30000-40000 (S.KR 64000)
£4777 $7500 €7166 Shipping along the coast (26x38cm-10x15in) s.d.1972. 10-Dec-2 Doyle, New York #181/R est:8000-12000
£5431 $8798 €7875 Shipwreck (86x145cm-34x57in) s.d.1867. 26-May-3 Bukowskis, Stockholm #277/R est:70000-80000 (S.KR 70000)
£10638 $16809 €15957 Coastal landscape near Malaga, Spain (58x86cm-23x34in) s.d.1863. 2-Dec-2 Rasmussen, Copenhagen #1155/R est:125000-150000 (D.KR 125000)

Works on paper
£287 $465 €431 Sailing vessels off town (19x35cm-7x14in) s.indis.i. pencil W/C. 21-May-3 Museumsbygningen, Copenhagen #80 (D.KR 3000)

MELCHERS, Franz (1868-1944) Dutch
£506 $790 €800 Vues de la Tamise a Londres (23x32cm-9x13in) s. panel pair. 16-Sep-2 Horta, Bruxelles #463

MELCHERS, Gari (1860-1932) American
£13836 $22000 €20754 Debutante, portrait of Mrs Gari Melchers (58x46cm-23x18in) s. board prov.exhib. 4-Mar-3 Christie's, Rockefeller NY #48/R est:12000-18000

Works on paper
£1698 $2750 €2462 Look of concern (38x25cm-15x10in) s. W/C gouache over pencil. 21-May-3 Doyle, New York #110/R est:5000-7000
£2037 $3300 €2954 Standing woman (48x33cm-19x13in) s. W/C gouache htd white over pencil. 21-May-3 Doyle, New York #107/R est:6000-8000
£2037 $3300 €2954 Woman holding a bundle of sticks (48x28cm-19x11in) s. W/C gouache htd white over chl. 21-May-3 Doyle, New York #108/R est:6000-8000
£2716 $4400 €3938 Mother and child (48x28cm-19x11in) s. gouache over pencil. 21-May-3 Doyle, New York #109/R est:8000-10000

MELCHERT, Samuel (1916-) Swiss
£279 $441 €419 Paris - my friend (60x80cm-24x31in) mono. masonite. 29-Nov-2 Zofingen, Switzerland #2988 (S.FR 650)

MELCHIOR, Joseph Wilhelm (1810-1883) German
£649 $968 €1000 Man on horseback driving cattle (25x30cm-10x12in) s. 26-Jun-2 Neumeister, Munich #800/R

MELCHIOR, Ludovica Augusta (1808-1882) Danish
£861 $1395 €1248 Camellias in basket on ledge (40x52cm-16x20in) mono. 26-May-3 Rasmussen, Copenhagen #1222/R (D.KR 9000)

MELCHIOR, Wilhelm (1817-1860) German
£2308 $3623 €3600 Grazing animals and drowsy sheep with view of a lake in background (53x64cm-21x25in) s. 21-Nov-2 Dorotheum, Vienna #110/R est:3600-5000
£4545 $6773 €7000 Peasant family with cows, sheep and goats (46x40cm-18x16in) s.d.1844. 26-Jun-2 Neumeister, Munich #799/R est:8000

MELCHIOR, Wilhelm (attrib) (1817-1860) German
£2179 $3422 €3400 Sheep and goat in meadow (53x64cm-21x25in) indis.i. 21-Nov-2 Dorotheum, Vienna #102/R est:2200-3000

MELDRUM, Duncan Max (1875-1955) Australian
£645 $981 €968 Still life (42x45cm-17x18in) s.d.25 s.d.1925 verso canvasboard. 28-Aug-2 Deutscher-Menzies, Melbourne #375/R (A.D 1800)
£804 $1246 €1206 Ranuncluses (43x36cm-17x14in) s. board. 29-Oct-2 Lawson Menzies, Sydney #310 (A.D 2250)

MELENDEZ, Luis (style) (1716-1780) Italian
£7000 $11690 €10150 Earthenware jug, a basket with a white table cloth, pewter lid, wooden spoon and pears (50x66cm-20x26in) prov. 11-Jul-3 Christie's, Kensington #155/R est:8000-12000

MELENDEZ, Miguel Jacinto (1679-1734) Spanish
£6289 $9748 €10000 Immaculate Conception (165x110cm-65x43in) 7-Oct-2 Ansorena, Madrid #44/R est:9000

MELGAARD, Bjarne (1967-) Norwegian
£5204 $8118 €7806 Untitled composition (180x170cm-71x67in) s.d.1997 verso exhib. 21-Oct-2 Blomqvist, Oslo #449/R est:80000-100000 (N.KR 60000)

Sculpture
£9183 $15060 €13315 Mr Black Pearl (31x18x20cm-12x7x8in) bronze. 2-Jun-3 Blomqvist, Oslo #209/R est:110000-130000 (N.KR 100000)

Works on paper
£290 $453 €435 Tortoise (27x21cm-11x8in) s. mixed media executed 1997 exhib. 23-Sep-2 Blomqvist, Lysaker #1154 (N.KR 3400)
£341 $532 €512 Home alone 5 - age 30 - Obsessed about Bob Hund Consert (40x32cm-16x13in) s. mixed media executed 1997. 23-Sep-2 Blomqvist, Lysaker #1155/R (N.KR 4000)
£384 $599 €576 Green head (35x50cm-14x20in) s. W/C Indian ink executed 1997. 23-Sep-2 Blomqvist, Lysaker #1153/R (N.KR 4500)
£427 $666 €641 Recycled misery, 91-97 Lost drawing at last - Oslo Maastricht (31x43cm-12x17in) s. mixed media. 23-Sep-2 Blomqvist, Lysaker #1156/R (N.KR 5000)
£491 $765 €737 Untitled (67x49cm-26x19in) s.d.1997 collage pastel chk. 6-Nov-2 AB Stockholms Auktionsverk #892/R (S.KR 7000)

MELGERS, Hendrik Johan (1899-1973) Dutch

Works on paper
£1582 $2500 €2500 Paard en clown (55x45cm-22x18in) s. gouache. 26-Nov-2 Sotheby's, Amsterdam #12/R est:2500-3500

MELIDA Y ALINARI, Don Enrique (1834-1892) Spanish
£8588 $13569 €12882 Untitled, procession of Spanish penitents in the 18th Century (116x207cm-46x81in) s. prov. 7-Apr-3 Shapiro, Sydney #505/R est:20000-30000 (A.D 22500)

MELINGUE, Gaston (1840-1914) French
£3205 $5032 €5000 Juif errant (65x87cm-26x34in) s.d.1874 lit. 12-Dec-2 Rabourdin & Choppin de Janvry, Paris #9/R

MELISSENT, Maurice (?) French

Works on paper
£283 $436 €450 Voiliers a quai dans le bassin de la Barre au Harve (66x93cm-26x37in) s. chl. 27-Oct-2 Lesieur & Le Bars, Le Havre #59
£423 $680 €600 L'entree du port du Havre (45x60cm-18x24in) s. W/C. 12-May-3 Lesieur & Le Bars, Le Havre #71/R
£458 $737 €700 Vue du Havre (97x60cm-38x24in) s. gouache. 18-Jan-3 Neret-Minet, Paris #170/R

MELKOV, A (20th C) Russian

Works on paper
£1900 $3078 €2850 Stage design of a Georgian interior (42x60cm-17x24in) init. gouache on card. 21-May-3 Sotheby's, London #151/R est:3000-5000

MELKUS, H (20th C) ?
£1156 $1839 €1700 Peasant with pipe (30x24cm-12x9in) s.i. board two. 20-Mar-3 Neumeister, Munich #2695/R est:1500
£1923 $2981 €3000 Upper Bavarian farmer with pipe and beer tankard (30x24cm-12x9in) board. 4-Dec-2 Neumeister, Munich #817/R est:1500

MELLAN, Claude (1598-1688) French

Prints
£8176 $12754 €12100 Souriciere (22x31cm-9x12in) drypoint. 31-Mar-3 Piasa, Paris #164/R

Works on paper
£2128 $3553 €3000 Portrait d'un eveque (22x17cm-9x7in) black crayon. 19-Jun-3 Piasa, Paris #79/R est:3000

MELLE (1908-1976) Dutch
£2025 $3200 €3200 Abraham's bosom (27x32cm-11x13in) s. panel painted 1963. 26-Nov-2 Sotheby's, Amsterdam #80/R est:2500-3500

£3597 $5899 €5000 Landscape with cows (29x32cm-11x13in) s. canvas on board prov. 3-Jun-3 Christie's, Amsterdam #221/R est:5000-7000
£6475 $10619 €9000 Bird on stilts (40x40cm-16x16in) s. 3-Jun-3 Christie's, Amsterdam #222/R est:6000-8000

MELLE, Henri van (1859-1930) Belgian
£1111 $1800 €1667 Four sisters (61x97cm-24x38in) s. 24-Jan-3 New Orleans Auction, New Orleans #461/R est:2000-4000

MELLE, Léon Auguste (1816-1889) French
£931 $1480 €1397 Castelli Romani (38x28cm-15x11in) 5-Mar-3 Rasmussen, Copenhagen #1769/R (D.KR 10000)

MELLEN, Mary (1817-?) American
£4375 $7000 €6344 Three master in rough seas (33x51cm-13x20in) lit. 16-May-3 Skinner, Boston #114/R est:8000-12000

MELLER, Reijo (1944-) Finnish
£354 $562 €520 Testament of the Sea (25x28cm-10x11in) s.d.76. 24-Mar-3 Bukowskis, Helsinki #184/R
£494 $770 €780 Blue flowers (40x30cm-16x12in) s.d.89. 15-Sep-2 Bukowskis, Helsinki #236/R

MELLERUP, Tage (1910-1988) Danish
£763 $1274 €1106 Flower picture with red background (100x66cm-39x26in) s.i.d.1958 verso. 17-Jun-3 Rasmussen, Copenhagen #38/R (D.KR 8000)

MELLERY, Xavier (1845-1921) Belgian
£284 $474 €400 Village au clair de lune (30x20cm-12x8in) s. 18-Jun-3 Hotel des Ventes Mosan, Brussels #273
Works on paper
£4000 $6400 €5800 Interior of Marken (24x32cm-9x13in) mono. black chk dr prov. 15-Mar-3 De Vuyst, Lokeren #214/R est:1000-1250

MELLET, Janetta (20th C) Irish?
£423 $701 €600 Hazel wood flowers (39x39cm-15x15in) s.verso board. 10-Jun-3 James Adam, Dublin #184/R

MELLIN, Charles (c.1597-1647) French
Works on paper
£559 $800 €839 Jacob commanding the sun and moon to stand still (17x21cm-7x8in) brush brown ink wash. 23-Jan-3 Swann Galleries, New York #232/R

MELLING, Antoine Ignace (1763-1831) French
Works on paper
£473 $738 €700 Town in the mountains (28x43cm-11x17in) i. graphite pen ink wash. 27-Mar-3 Christie's, Paris #156/R

MELLING, Joseph (1724-1796) French
£8805 $13648 €14000 Putti by fire in landscape at dusk (77x138cm-30x54in) prov. 2-Oct-2 Dorotheum, Vienna #242/R est:8000-12000

MELLIS, Margaret (20th C) ?
Works on paper
£800 $1240 €1200 Construction (50x30cm-20x12in) gouache wood copper construction. 4-Dec-2 Christie's, Kensington #619/R

MELLISH, Thomas (attrib) (18th C) British
£3200 $4960 €4800 Men-o-war laid up off Chatham, with a view of Rochester beyond (81x133cm-32x52in) indis sig. 31-Oct-2 Christie's, Kensington #418a/R est:1000-1500

MELLON, Campbell (1876-1955) British
£222 $369 €322 Hopton Nov 1 and 2, 1924 (24x30cm-9x12in) s.i.verso panel prov. 16-Jun-3 Waddingtons, Toronto #111/R (C.D 500)
£400 $664 €580 Cattle on a river bank (61x51cm-24x20in) s. 10-Jun-3 David Lay, Penzance #46
£555 $922 €805 Stround Valley late October (30x41cm-12x16in) s. i.verso panel. 16-Jun-3 Waddingtons, Toronto #149/R est:2000-3000 (C.D 1250)
£950 $1530 €1425 Cattle grazing in the Wye Valley (23x28cm-9x11in) board exhib. 9-May-3 Mallams, Oxford #144/R
£1500 $2385 €2250 Figures walking at dusk by the river Trent (31x41cm-12x16in) s. i.verso. 5-Mar-3 Bonhams, Bury St Edmunds #405/R est:1500-2500
£2000 $3100 €3000 Children flying a kite on a Mousehold Heath, Norwich (23x29cm-9x11in) s. board. 30-Sep-2 Bonhams, Ipswich #415 est:1200-1800
£2800 $4340 €4200 View of Norwich (22x30cm-9x12in) board. 30-Sep-2 Bonhams, Ipswich #435/R est:1000-1500
£2800 $4340 €4200 Hopton cliff (23x30cm-9x12in) board. 30-Sep-2 Bonhams, Ipswich #441/R est:1200-1800
£2844 $4722 €4124 Hopton Beach, Norfolk (51x61cm-20x24in) s. prov. 16-Jun-3 Waddingtons, Toronto #172/R est:5000-7000 (C.D 6400)
£4200 $6510 €6300 Corton beach, near Charnoc, August Bank Holiday (23x30cm-9x12in) board. 30-Sep-2 Bonhams, Ipswich #439/R est:2000-3000
£4200 $6510 €6300 North wind, Hopton, last September (23x30cm-9x12in) board. 30-Sep-2 Bonhams, Ipswich #440/R est:2000-3000
£4400 $7172 €6600 Gorleston beach scene with figures (23x25cm-9x10in) s. 14-Feb-3 Keys, Aylsham #657/R est:2000-3000
£5000 $7850 €7500 Hopton cliffs (30x41cm-12x16in) s. i.d.Sept 1929 verso panel. 22-Nov-2 Christie's, London #36/R est:5000-7000
£8000 $12160 €12000 Gorleston Beach low tide (43x53cm-17x21in) s. d.1925 verso prov. 16-Aug-2 Keys, Aylsham #647/R
£15000 $23400 €22500 August Bank Holiday (48x58cm-19x23in) s. prov. 18-Oct-2 Keys, Aylsham #683/R est:15000-20000

MELLOR, Everett W (1878-1965) British
Works on paper
£300 $468 €450 Barden Moor, Nr. Bolton Abbey, Yorkshire (19x29cm-7x11in) s. W/C. 25-Mar-3 Bonhams, Leeds #516

MELLOR, Joseph (fl.1850-1885) British
£300 $468 €450 Woodland stream (23x19cm-9x7in) s. 25-Mar-3 Bonhams, Leeds #621
£680 $1068 €1020 River landscape with an angler and a lady nearby (61x91cm-24x36in) s. 19-Nov-2 Bonhams, Leeds #241
£3000 $4680 €4500 River Wharfe, with cattle among trees on the banks (61x91cm-24x36in) s. 10-Apr-3 Tennants, Leyburn #990/R est:1500-2000

MELLOR, W (1851-1931) British
£1200 $1944 €1740 Mountainous landscape with cattle watering and foreground fisherman (49x74cm-19x29in) s. 22-May-3 Wintertons, Lichfield #579/R est:1200-1800

MELLOR, William (1851-1931) British
£458 $750 €687 On the wharf (46x30cm-18x12in) s. i.verso. 8-Feb-3 Neal Auction Company, New Orleans #550
£700 $1092 €1050 Figure on a bridge in a rocky river landscape (61x91cm-24x36in) s. 7-Nov-2 Christie's, Kensington #109/R
£800 $1264 €1200 On the hills, near Ambleside, Westmoreland. Grasmere Lake, Westmoreland (30x51cm-12x20in) s. i.verso pair. 27-Nov-2 Hamptons Fine Art, Godalming #369
£1000 $1570 €1500 On the Conwaym, North Wales (48x74cm-19x29in) s. 19-Nov-2 Riddetts, Bournemouth #878/R
£1000 $1660 €1500 On the Burbage, Derbyshire (30x46cm-12x18in) s. 10-Jun-3 Bonhams, Leeds #195/R est:1500-2000
£1400 $2212 €2100 Bolton Woods, Yorkshire (15x23cm-6x9in) s. board. 2-Dec-2 Gorringes, Lewes #2691 est:500-800
£1500 $2445 €2250 Wooded river view in Yorkshire, probably on the wharf near Bolton (58x83cm-23x33in) s. canvas on board. 30-Jan-3 Lawrence, Crewkerne #719/R est:2000-3000
£1500 $2445 €2175 Skelwith force Ambleside. 16-Jul-3 James Thompson, Kirby Lonsdale #202
£1600 $2480 €2400 Black Foss, near Ilkley (43x28cm-17x11in) s. i.verso. 4-Dec-2 Andrew Hartley, Ilkley #1240/R est:2000-3000
£1700 $2771 €2465 Falls on the Llugny, North Wales (20x30cm-8x12in) s. s.i.verso board. 16-Jul-3 Sotheby's, Olympia #74/R est:1000-1500
£1850 $2886 €2775 On the Lledr, Bettys Y Coed (58x89cm-23x35in) s. 9-Apr-3 Andrew Hartley, Ilkley #985/R est:1500-2200
£2200 $3432 €3300 On Barden Moor, near Bolton (30x51cm-12x20in) s. i.verso. 7-Nov-2 Christie's, Kensington #158/R est:1000-1500
£2200 $3432 €3300 Near Birk Crag, Harrogate (46x28cm-18x11in) s. i.verso. 9-Apr-3 Andrew Hartley, Ilkley #982/R est:1800-2500
£2600 $4030 €3900 Bow Beck, near Ilkley (43x33cm-17x13in) s. i.verso. 4-Dec-2 Andrew Hartley, Ilkley #1241/R est:2500-3500
£2700 $4482 €4050 Farmstead with a figure and cattle (20x30cm-8x12in) s. 10-Jun-3 Bonhams, Leeds #194/R est:1400-1600
£2756 $4300 €4134 Welsh river landscape (92x72cm-36x28in) s. 9-Nov-2 Sloan, North Bethesda #563/R est:2000-4000
£2800 $4452 €4200 Rydal Beck (46x76cm-18x30in) s. i.verso. 6-Mar-3 Christie's, Kensington #461/R est:3000-5000
£2800 $4452 €4200 Landscape with cattle watering and sheep grazing in the distance (89x69cm-35x27in) s. 19-Mar-3 Rupert Toovey, Partridge Green #26/R est:2000-4000
£2900 $4495 €4350 Fishing on the River Wharfe. Tranquil lake with heron (23x41cm-9x16in) s. board pair. 4-Oct-2 Mallams, Oxford #567/R est:3000-5000

£3000 $4680 €4500 On the Lledr nr Bettys Y Coed. On the hills near Keswick, Cumberland (28x43cm-11x17in) s. i.verso pair. 9-Oct-2 Andrew Hartley, Ilkley #784/R est:3000-4000
£3000 $4890 €4500 Oak Beck near Harrogate (8x11cm-3x4in) s. board. 12-Feb-3 Andrew Hartley, Ilkley #954/R est:3000-4000
£3000 $4680 €4500 View of Goathland near Whitby, South Yorkshire (76x127cm-30x50in) s. i.verso. 26-Mar-3 Sotheby's, Olympia #47/R est:3000-5000
£3000 $4680 €4500 Easdale Tarn, Westmorland. Near Capel Curig, North Wales (30x23cm-12x9in) s. i.verso board pair. 25-Mar-3 Bonhams, Leeds #619/R est:2400-2600
£3200 $5216 €4800 Brook near Froggatt Edge, Derbyshire (17x13cm-7x5in) s. i.verso. 12-Feb-3 Andrew Hartley, Ilkley #956/R est:2000-3000
£3500 $5565 €5250 On the Conway, North wales (46x35cm-18x14in) s. i.verso pair prov. 6-Mar-3 Christie's, Kensington #460/R est:1500-2000
£3556 $5902 €5156 On the Rothay near Grasmere (41x77cm-16x30in) s. s.i.verso. 16-Jun-3 Waddingtons, Toronto #161/R est:5000-7000 (C.D 8000)
£3600 $5868 €5400 Nidd, near Knaresborough (8x11cm-3x4in) s. board. 12-Feb-3 Andrew Hartley, Ilkley #950/R est:3000-4000
£3600 $5616 €5400 Untitled. pair. 25-Mar-3 Tayler & Fletcher, Cheltenham #2/R
£3600 $5976 €5400 View near Grasmere, Westmorland. Posforth Gill, Bolton Woods, Yorkshire (44x33cm-17x13in) s.i.verso pair. 10-Jun-3 Bonhams, Leeds #197/R est:3000-5000
£3800 $5966 €5700 On the Lledr, North Wales (22x30cm-9x12in) s. board. 21-Nov-2 Tennants, Leyburn #808/R est:1500-2000
£3800 $5890 €5700 View near Capel Curig, North Wales (30x46cm-12x18in) s. 4-Dec-2 Andrew Hartley, Ilkley #1260/R est:3000-5000
£3800 $5928 €5700 View near Rydal lake, Westmoreland (30x46cm-12x18in) s.i i.verso. 26-Mar-3 Sotheby's, Olympia #50/R est:1200-1800
£4200 $6510 €6300 On the Wharfe, Bolton Woods (28x46cm-11x18in) s. 4-Dec-2 Andrew Hartley, Ilkley #1247/R est:3000-5000
£4300 $6708 €6450 View near Loughrigg, Ambleside, Westmorland (51x76cm-20x30in) s. i.verso. 15-Oct-2 Bearnes, Exeter #415/R est:2000-3000
£4321 $7000 €6265 Woodland interior with waterfall (76x51cm-30x20in) s. canvas on board. 21-May-3 Doyle, New York #180/R est:8000-12000
£4800 $7536 €7200 On the Llugwy, North Wales (51x77cm-20x30in) s. i.verso. 21-Nov-2 Tennants, Leyburn #809/R est:3500-4500
£5000 $7750 €7500 Peep of the Wharfe, Bolton Woods (28x43cm-11x17in) s. 4-Dec-2 Andrew Hartley, Ilkley #1246/R est:3000-5000
£5000 $7800 €7500 Cattle watering with a figure on a woodland track, possibly a stretch on the river Wharfe (72x117cm-28x46in) s. 25-Mar-3 Bonhams, Leeds #618/R est:4000-6000
£5200 $8528 €7540 Washburn Valley, Yorkshire (40x61cm-16x24in) s. 5-Jun-3 Morphets, Harrogate #371/R est:2500-3000
£5414 $8500 €8121 On the wharfe near Bolton, Yorkshire. Valley of the Lledr, north Wales (23x58cm-9x23in) s. board two. 10-Dec-2 Doyle, New York #163/R est:2000-3000
£6250 $10438 €9063 View near Goathland, Whitby, Yorkshire (74x124cm-29x49in) s. s.i.verso. 18-Jun-3 Andrew Hartley, Ilkley #1185/R est:6000-9000
£6600 $10362 €9900 On the Derwent, Derbyshire (51x76cm-20x30in) s. i.verso. 19-Nov-2 Bonhams, Leeds #239/R est:6000-8000
£8200 $12710 €12300 Wharfe, Bolton Woods, Yorkshire (48x74cm-19x29in) s. i.verso. 4-Dec-2 Andrew Hartley, Ilkley #1239 est:4000-5000
£8200 $13366 €11890 On the Lleder, North Wales. On the Hebden, near Hardcastle Crage, Yorkshire (30x46cm-12x18in) s. pair. 16-Jul-3 Sotheby's, Olympia #75/R est:2000-3000
£9400 $15322 €13630 Langdale Pikes from Elterwater, Westmoreland. Grasmere, from Loughrigg, Westmooreland (31x46cm-12x18in) s.i. pair. 17-Jul-3 Tennants, Leyburn #838/R est:5000-6000
£9500 $15390 €13775 Nidd, near Knaresboro. Wharfe, Yorkshire (20x25cm-8x10in) s. pair. 1-Aug-3 Dee Atkinson & Harrison, Driffield #645/R est:3500-5000
£14000 $21840 €21000 On the Nidd, near Knaresborough. Lledr Valley North Wales. On Conway (22x29cm-9x11in) s.i. board set of six. 25-Mar-3 Bonhams, Leeds #620/R est:12000-18000

MELLOR, William (attrib) (1851-1931) British
£600 $942 €900 On the Lledr, North Wales (46x61cm-18x24in) i.on stretcher. 21-Nov-2 Tennants, Leyburn #806/R

MELLSTROM, Rolf (1896-1953) Swedish
£834 $1384 €1209 Sunshine and eiderducks (90x126cm-35x50in) s.d.1945 panel. 16-Jun-3 Lilla Bukowskis, Stockholm #111 (S.KR 10800)

MELNICK, Camillo (19th C) Austrian
£2632 $4263 €4000 The flirt (43x34cm-17x13in) s.i.d.1891 panel. 21-Jan-3 Christie's, Amsterdam #126/R est:3000-5000

MELOCHE, Suzanne (1926-) Canadian
£309 $475 €464 Abstraction en orange et bleu (42x52cm-17x20in) s.d. 22-Oct-2 Iegor de Saint Hippolyte, Montreal #73 (C.D 750)
£350 $539 €525 La vue oblongue (55x51cm-22x20in) s.d. prov. 22-Oct-2 Iegor de Saint Hippolyte, Montreal #74 (C.D 850)

MELONI, Gino (1905-1989) Italian
£962 $1510 €1500 Landscape (65x80cm-26x31in) s. painted 1961. 23-Nov-2 Meeting Art, Vercelli #101/R
Works on paper
£257 $401 €380 Village (31x44cm-12x17in) s. gouache card. 26-Mar-3 Finarte Semenzato, Milan #60
£449 $696 €700 Seated figure. Square head (28x21cm-11x8in) s. Chinese ink dr. pair. 4-Dec-2 Finarte, Milan #183

MELOTTI, Fausto (1901-1986) Italian
Sculpture
£2297 $3584 €3400 Changing subject (48x45x18cm-19x18x7in) s. num.9/50 copper lit. 26-Mar-3 Finarte Semenzato, Milan #20/R
£3333 $5167 €5200 Triangle (37x27x12cm-15x11x5in) s. num.9/10 brass exec.1975. 4-Dec-2 Finarte, Milan #498/R
£4730 $7378 €7000 Paris' judgement (21x20x20cm-8x8x8in) s. num.19/40 brass lit. 26-Mar-3 Finarte Semenzato, Milan #21/R
£10256 $16103 €16000 Hug (35x11x12cm-14x4x5in) d.1961 brass exhib.lit. 20-Nov-2 Pandolfini, Florence #148/R est:20000
£16129 $25484 €25000 H (70x58x7cm-28x23x3in) s. stainless steel prov.exhib.lit. 18-Dec-2 Christie's, Rome #243/R est:30000
£70000 $109200 €105000 La barca (267x90x70cm-105x35x28in) brass executed 1966 prov.exhib.lit. 21-Oct-2 Sotheby's, London #59/R est:40000-60000
Works on paper
£1538 $2415 €2400 Untitled (24x18cm-9x7in) s.verso mixed media lit. 20-Nov-2 Pandolfini, Florence #125/R

MELROSE, Andrew (1836-1901) American
£1795 $2800 €2693 Rural setting with mill, stream, and fishermen in a rowboat (28x43cm-11x17in) s. 8-Nov-2 York Town, York #591

MELSEN, Marten (1870-1947) Belgian
£535 $823 €850 Carrefour (30x46cm-12x18in) s.d.1917 cardboard prov. 22-Oct-2 Campo & Campo, Antwerp #185/R
£566 $872 €900 Amour contadin (47x39cm-19x15in) s.d.1897 prov. 22-Oct-2 Campo & Campo, Antwerp #184
£1887 $2906 €3000 Tracee (51x70cm-20x28in) s.d.1906 prov.exhib. 22-Oct-2 Campo & Campo, Antwerp #187/R
£2013 $3099 €3200 Winter evening (40x55cm-16x22in) s. exhib. 22-Oct-2 Campo & Campo, Antwerp #188/R est:3000
£2222 $3533 €3200 L'abatteur de porc (41x56cm-16x22in) s. exhib. 29-Apr-3 Campo & Campo, Antwerp #214/R est:3250-4250
£2778 $4417 €4000 La vente publique (41x56cm-16x22in) s.d.1920. 29-Apr-3 Campo & Campo, Antwerp #213/R est:4500-5500
£3401 $5408 €5000 Arrivee de la course cycliste (40x50cm-16x20in) s. 18-Mar-3 Campo, Vlaamse Kaai #155/R est:5000-6000
£7500 $12450 €7500 Fete villageoise (70x59cm-28x23in) s. 16-Jun-3 Horta, Bruxelles #138/R est:2500-3000
£7547 $11623 €12000 Generosite et convoitise (94x124cm-37x49in) s.d.1901 prov.exhib. 22-Oct-2 Campo & Campo, Antwerp #183/R est:8500
£8176 $12673 €13000 Procession (41x130cm-16x51in) s. lit. 5-Oct-2 De Vuyst, Lokeren #536/R est:5500-6500
Works on paper
£1635 $2518 €2600 Lampe (42x56cm-17x22in) s. mixed media exhib. 22-Oct-2 Campo & Campo, Antwerp #186/R

MELTSNER, Paul R (1905-1966) American
£5519 $8500 €8279 Builders (91x71cm-36x28in) s. i.verso prov. 24-Oct-2 Shannon's, Milford #15/R est:8000-12000
£6169 $9500 €9254 Man and machinery (76x61cm-30x24in) s. i.verso prov. 24-Oct-2 Shannon's, Milford #16/R est:8000-12000

MELTZER, Anna Elkan (20th C) American
£281 $450 €422 Two young girls, one black, one white (20x20cm-8x8in) i.stretcher. 15-Mar-3 Jeffery Burchard, Florida #12/R

MELTZER, Arthur (1893-?) American
£958 $1600 €1389 Rocky shore (30x36cm-12x14in) s. 22-Jun-3 Freeman, Philadelphia #160/R est:1000-1500
£1161 $1800 €1742 Yellow lemon (41x51cm-16x20in) s. board. 8-Dec-2 Freeman, Philadelphia #129/R est:1500-2500
£1161 $1800 €1742 Gladiolas (51x41cm-20x16in) s. board. 8-Dec-2 Freeman, Philadelphia #169/R est:1500-2500
£1484 $2300 €2226 Swans (41x51cm-16x20in) s. 8-Dec-2 Freeman, Philadelphia #191/R est:2000-3000
£2581 $4000 €3872 Silver Springs Nevada (41x51cm-16x20in) s. 8-Dec-2 Freeman, Philadelphia #140/R est:4000-6000
£10256 $16000 €15384 Dolton's Oak in Feasterville, Bucks County, PA (51x61cm-20x24in) s. board painted c.1944. 18-Sep-2 Alderfer's, Hatfield #333/R est:4000-6000

£10897 $17000 €16346 By the mill stream, winter scene (41x51cm-16x20in) s. 21-Sep-2 Pook & Pook, Downington #23/R est:14000-18000
£27097 $42000 €40646 Golden quarry (30x36cm-12x14in) s. i.verso board. 8-Dec-2 Freeman, Philadelphia #137/R est:15000-25000

MELTZOFF, Stanley (1917-) American
£807 $1300 €1211 Thomas Jefferson and laborers on the grounds of Monticello (41x30cm-16x12in) init. 20-Feb-3 Illustration House, New York #117/R est:800-1200

MELVILLE, Arthur (1858-1904) British
£950 $1558 €1425 Grand Canal, Venice (33x41cm-13x16in) s.d.91 board. 29-May-3 Christie's, Kensington #210/R
£3000 $4680 €4500 Miss Doris Spence (140x90cm-55x35in) 10-Apr-3 Bonhams, Edinburgh #79 est:4000-6000
£14000 $21280 €21000 French peasant (32x21cm-13x8in) s.i.d.79 panel. 28-Aug-2 Sotheby's, London #1061/R est:8000-12000
Works on paper
£44000 $68200 €66000 Outside the bull ring (60x85cm-24x33in) s. W/C exhib.lit. 6-Dec-2 Lyon & Turnbull, Edinburgh #111/R est:20000-30000

MELVILLE, Eliza Anne (fl.1854-1868) British
£1500 $2340 €2250 Portrait of Queen Victoria (29x21cm-11x8in) 26-Mar-3 Woolley & Wallis, Salisbury #244/R est:1500-2000

MELVILLE, H S (fl.1837-1881) British
£300 $462 €450 Ploughing scene (18x28cm-7x11in) s. 6-Sep-2 Biddle & Webb, Birmingham #38

MELVILLE, John (1902-1986) British
£250 $388 €375 Tauromachie (71x81cm-28x32in) s.d.55. 1-Oct-2 Bonhams, Leeds #299
£270 $443 €405 Abstract symbol (84x99cm-33x39in) s. 7-Feb-3 Biddle & Webb, Birmingham #20
£300 $462 €450 Abstract mountainous landscape with vivid colours (97x127cm-38x50in) s.d.1974. 6-Sep-2 Biddle & Webb, Birmingham #401
£300 $477 €450 Artist in a woodland (102x76cm-40x30in) s.d.1968. 7-Mar-3 Biddle & Webb, Birmingham #32
£420 $701 €609 Forest (76x101cm-30x40in) s.d.57. 17-Jun-3 Bonhams, Knightsbridge #9/R
£490 $755 €735 Post modern desert landscape with Don Quixote on horse back (107x122cm-42x48in) s. 6-Sep-2 Biddle & Webb, Birmingham #384
£500 $770 €750 Post modern landscape composition of trees and fields (132x132cm-52x52in) s. 6-Sep-2 Biddle & Webb, Birmingham #383
£600 $930 €900 Sleeping nude (61x91cm-24x36in) s.d.48. 1-Oct-2 Bonhams, Leeds #293/R
£700 $1169 €1015 Forest (76x89cm-30x35in) s.d.68 board. 17-Jun-3 Bonhams, Knightsbridge #74/R
£850 $1403 €1233 Girl with fruit (57x35cm-22x14in) s.d.36 board. 3-Jul-3 Christie's, Kensington #545/R
£900 $1503 €1305 Standing Christ figure (101x79cm-40x31in) s.d.1950. 17-Jun-3 Bonhams, Knightsbridge #169/R
£1000 $1570 €1500 On the shores of Oblivion (53x101cm-21x40in) s. i.verso. 15-Apr-3 Bonhams, Knightsbridge #33/R est:1000-1500
£1000 $1570 €1500 Nude (120x90cm-47x35in) board. 15-Apr-3 Bonhams, Knightsbridge #91/R est:1000-1500
Works on paper
£250 $388 €375 Head of a woman (25x39cm-10x15in) s. indis d.1945 gouache. 1-Oct-2 Bonhams, Leeds #296
£280 $440 €420 Standing figure (41x34cm-16x13in) s.d.1943 gouache. 10-Dec-2 Rosebery Fine Art, London #580/R
£280 $440 €420 Reclining figure by a window (29x54cm-11x21in) s.d.1946 gouache. 10-Dec-2 Rosebery Fine Art, London #581

MELYN, Mattheus (1589-1653) ?
Works on paper
£1519 $2400 €2400 Le siege de Juliers par Ambrogio Spinola (23x43cm-9x17in) indis.i. graphite pen brown ink brown wash three sheets. 27-Nov-2 Christie's, Paris #4/R est:4000-6000

MELZER, Moritz (1877-1966) German
£316 $500 €500 Ascension of Christ (153x113cm-60x44in) s.i.d.1953 panel. 30-Nov-2 Bassenge, Berlin #6507/R
£1899 $3000 €3000 Ach - smoke (126x84cm-50x33in) s. s.i. verso oil silverbronze paper on masonite. 30-Nov-2 Villa Grisebach, Berlin #268/R est:5000-7000

MEMKOBI, A (?) ?
£884 $1406 €1300 Back from fishing (78x54cm-31x21in) s. 18-Mar-3 Finarte, Milan #39/R

MEMLING, Hans (style) (?-1494) Flemish
£24000 $37440 €36000 Portrait of a young man (17x14cm-7x6in) panel. 19-Sep-2 Christie's, Kensington #143/R est:1000-2000

MENA, Daniel (1945-) French?
£298 $486 €450 Factory (41x33cm-16x13in) s. 11-Feb-3 Segre, Madrid #349/R
£428 $693 €650 Still life (50x40cm-20x16in) s. lit. 21-Jan-3 Durán, Madrid #708/R
£690 $1097 €1000 Nature morte au grenade (60x73cm-24x29in) s. i.verso. 10-Mar-3 Millon & Associes, Paris #111/R
£690 $1152 €1000 Arlequin (73x60cm-29x24in) s. 9-Jul-3 Millon & Associes, Paris #203/R
£789 $1279 €1200 Still life with newspaper (63x52cm-25x20in) s. 21-Jan-3 Ansorena, Madrid #309/R

MENARD, Emile René (1862-1930) French
£551 $866 €860 Troupeau dans la montagne (40x55cm-16x22in) st.sig. 11-Dec-2 Maigret, Paris #99/R
£1042 $1646 €1500 Jugement de Paris (69x145cm-27x57in) s. 25-Apr-3 Piasa, Paris #159 est:1500
£1081 $1686 €1600 Paysage italien avec aqueduc en ruine (48x72cm-19x28in) s. panel. 28-Mar-3 Delvaux, Paris #15
£1216 $1897 €1800 Baigneuses (50x73cm-20x29in) 25-Mar-3 Chochon-Barre & Allardi, Paris #169/R est:1800-2000
£3057 $4769 €4800 Reve de la nymphe au crepuscule (51x73cm-20x29in) s. 7-Nov-2 Chochon-Barre & Allardi, Paris #196/R
£3226 $5000 €4839 Beauty guided by wisdom (49x76cm-19x30in) s.d.1909. 2-Oct-2 Christie's, Rockefeller NY #771/R est:7000-9000

MENARDEAU, Maurice (1897-1977) French
£556 $906 €800 L'appartement de l'artiste (54x65cm-21x26in) s.i.d.1944. 19-Jul-3 Thierry & Lannon, Brest #366
£625 $1019 €900 Le Tombereau (46x55cm-18x22in) studio st. 19-Jul-3 Thierry & Lannon, Brest #153
£845 $1361 €1200 Vue de port breton (38x46cm-15x18in) s. cardboard. 11-May-3 Lombrail & Teucquam, Paris #220/R
£1285 $2120 €1850 La baie d'Along, Indochine (38x46cm-15x18in) s. 1-Jul-3 Rossini, Paris #110
£1319 $2177 €1900 Temple du vieux port a Soochang, Chine (46x55cm-18x22in) s. 1-Jul-3 Rossini, Paris #109
£1901 $3061 €2700 Guenole, la Tour Carree, trois Bigoudenes sur le chemin (38x46cm-15x18in) s. 11-May-3 Thierry & Lannon, Brest #383/R est:1200-1500
£2324 $3742 €3300 Thoniers sous voiles (64x80cm-25x31in) s. 11-May-3 Thierry & Lannon, Brest #204/R est:2600-3000

MENASSIER, Andre (fl.c.1600) French
£1500 $2355 €2250 Raising of Lazurus (81x64cm-32x25in) s.d.1603. 13-Dec-2 Christie's, Kensington #169/R est:2500-3500

MENASSIER, Isaac (fl.c.1596) French
Works on paper
£256 $397 €400 Scene de bataille (11x23cm-4x9in) pen ink after Jacques Callot. 4-Dec-2 Piasa, Paris #56

MENCHI, Bruno (?) Italian?
£298 $474 €447 Still life of fruit and candleholder on table (40x31cm-16x12in) s.i.verso panel. 10-Mar-3 Rasmussen, Vejle #602 (D.KR 3200)

MENDELSON, Dinora (1924-) British
£380 $608 €570 Study of two semi nude male figures (69x51cm-27x20in) s.d.56. 14-Mar-3 Gardiner & Houlgate, Bath #41/R

MENDELSON, Marc (1915-) Belgian
£3165 $5000 €5000 Nature morte au reveil (81x100cm-32x39in) mono.d.1948 verso. 26-Nov-2 Palais de Beaux Arts, Brussels #251/R est:5000-7000
£8333 $13250 €12000 Le dejeuner de coreil (130x130cm-51x51in) s.verso. 29-Apr-3 Campo & Campo, Antwerp #216/R est:13000-16000
Works on paper
£468 $748 €650 Black and white (25x32cm-10x13in) mono.i.d.54 s.i.verso Indian ink. 17-May-3 De Vuyst, Lokeren #257

MENDES DA COSTA, Joseph (1863-1939) Dutch
Sculpture
£5755 $9439 €8000 Spinoza (33cm-13in) mono.d.1909 bronze prov.exhib.lit. 3-Jun-3 Christie's, Amsterdam #150/R est:8000-12000
£5755 $9439 €8000 St. Francis of Assisi (32cm-13in) mono.d. bronze i.f.Natle prov.lit. 3-Jun-3 Christie's, Amsterdam #152/R est:8000-12000
£7194 $11799 €10000 Abraham - t offer (26cm-10in) mono.i.d.1907 gres ceramics prov.lit. 3-Jun-3 Christie's, Amsterdam #155/R est:10000-15000
£7194 $11799 €10000 Ziek aapje, met gesloten ogen - sick monkey with eyes closed (20cm-8in) mono. gres ceramics conceived c.1900 prov.exhib.lit. 3-Jun-3 Christie's, Amsterdam #154/R est:10000-15000

£10791 $17698 €15000 Vincent van Gogh - mijn god mag het (40cm-16in) mono.i. bronze i.f.Natle des conceived c.1098 prov.exhib.lit. 3-Jun-3 Christie's, Amsterdam #149/R est:10000-15000
£10791 $17698 €15000 Jan Steen (35cm-14in) mono.d.1911 bronze i.f.Natie prov.lit. 3-Jun-3 Christie's, Amsterdam #151/R est:8000-12000

MENDEZ BRINGA, Narciso (1868-1933) Spanish
Works on paper
£256 $405 €400 Office (28x28cm-11x11in) s. W/C. 19-Nov-2 Durán, Madrid #656/R

MENDEZ RUIZ, Jose (1936-) Spanish
£414 $654 €600 New being (73x92cm-29x36in) s.d.1973 lit. 1-Apr-3 Segre, Madrid #343/R

MENDIETA, Ana (1948-1985) Cuban
Photographs
£14013 $22000 €21020 Untitled (136x91cm-54x36in) gelatin silver print exec.c.1982 prov. 20-Nov-2 Christie's, Rockefeller NY #47/R est:25000-35000

MENDJISKY, Serge (1929-) French
£711 $1180 €1031 Defile a longchamps (63x51cm-25x20in) s. sold with a letter. 10-Jun-3 Ritchie, Toronto #122/R est:1200-1800 (C.D 1600)
£1795 $2782 €2800 Pin maritime au bord de mer (41x27cm-16x11in) s. 9-Dec-2 Beaussant & Lefèvre, Paris #77/R
Sculpture
£962 $1510 €1500 Composition constructiviste (60x90cm-24x35in) s. ceramic relief panel exec.c.1966. 16-Dec-2 Charbonneaux, Paris #271 est:1200-1500
Works on paper
£4710 $7725 €6500 Le Pont Neuf (100x100cm-39x39in) s.d.2003 collage black white photographs. 27-May-3 Tajan, Paris #77/R est:7000-8000

MENDOLA, Rosolino (1949-) Italian
£316 $494 €500 Alphabet (100x100cm-39x39in) s. s.i.d.2001 verso. 14-Sep-2 Meeting Art, Vercelli #707
£340 $541 €500 Alphabet (100x100cm-39x39in) s. painted 2001. 1-Mar-3 Meeting Art, Vercelli #358
£340 $541 €500 Alphabet (90x116cm-35x46in) s. painted 2001. 1-Mar-3 Meeting Art, Vercelli #574
£380 $592 €600 Patterns (90x116cm-35x46in) s. 14-Sep-2 Meeting Art, Vercelli #300
£392 $627 €600 Alphabet (90x116cm-35x46in) s. painted 2001. 4-Jan-3 Meeting Art, Vercelli #167
£417 $654 €650 Alphabet (120x120cm-47x47in) s.d.2000. 23-Nov-2 Meeting Art, Vercelli #275/R
£458 $732 €700 Composition (100x100cm-39x39in) s. oil pigment enamel. 4-Jan-3 Meeting Art, Vercelli #351
Works on paper
£316 $494 €500 Composition (100x100cm-39x39in) s. mixed media on canvas. 14-Sep-2 Meeting Art, Vercelli #314

MENDOLY, Grzegorz S (20th C) American?
£253 $400 €367 Man cutting wheat (58x79cm-23x31in) s.d.1933. 5-Apr-3 DeFina, Austinburg #1340

MENDOZA, Jane (20th C) American
£377 $600 €566 Portrait of Irene Worth (51x61cm-20x24in) s. 5-Mar-3 Doyle, New York #101/R

MENDOZA, Ryan (1971-) American
£4808 $7452 €7500 Untitled (80x80cm-31x31in) s.verso painted 1998. 4-Dec-2 Finarte, Milan #547/R est:3500
Works on paper
£1859 $2881 €2900 Untitled (40x50cm-16x20in) s.verso pastel plastic. 4-Dec-2 Finarte, Milan #460/R est:3300

MENE, P J (1810-1879) French
Sculpture
£1200 $1908 €1800 Gigi and Gisele (15cm-6in) s. brown pat bronze. 29-Apr-3 Sotheby's, Olympia #147/R est:800-1200
£2100 $3255 €3150 Model of a setter (33cm-13in) s. bronze with rustic oval base. 4-Nov-2 Brightwells, Leominster #968/R est:800-1200
£3000 $4770 €4500 Ibrahim etalon Arabe (30cm-12in) s.i. bronze. 29-Apr-3 Sotheby's, Olympia #142/R est:3000-5000

MENE, Pierre Jules (1810-1879) French
Sculpture
£909 $1518 €1300 Deux levrettes jouant avec une boule (15x22cm-6x9in) s. bob. 30-Jun-3 Pierre Berge, Paris #25 est:1000-1200
£909 $1518 €1300 Chien de meute attache a un arbre (23x32cm-9x13in) s. medaille pat bronze. 30-Jun-3 Pierre Berge, Paris #34/R est:800-1000
£962 $1471 €1500 Vainqueur (32cm-13in) s.d.1866 brown green pat bronze. 23-Aug-2 Deauville, France #269
£979 $1635 €1400 Levrette et King Charles a l'eventail (16x25cm-6x10in) s. brown pat bronze. 30-Jun-3 Pierre Berge, Paris #23/R est:800-1000
£1020 $1622 €1500 Setter irlandais (14x33x12cm-6x13x5in) s. brown pat bronze. 24-Mar-3 Claude Boisgirard, Paris #33/R
£1111 $1800 €1667 Retriever with a swan (13x18cm-5x7in) s. 24-Jan-3 New Orleans Auction, New Orleans #1424/R est:1800-2500
£1122 $1716 €1750 Pouliniere (26cm-10in) brown pat bronze. 23-Aug-2 Deauville, France #270
£1154 $1812 €1800 Chien se lechant la patte (11x12cm-4x5in) s. brown pat bronze. 10-Dec-2 Renaud, Paris #105/R
£1208 $1945 €1800 Trois chiens au terrier ou chasse au lapin (37x19cm-15x7in) s. pat.bronze. 18-Feb-3 Galerie Moderne, Brussels #1006/R est:1500-2000
£1218 $1900 €1827 Greyhounds playing with a ball (15cm-6in) s. brown pat bronze oval base pair. 14-Sep-2 Selkirks, St. Louis #931/R est:600-700
£1300 $2003 €1950 Basset hound (11x27cm-4x11in) s. bronze. 5-Sep-2 Sotheby's, Olympia #140/R est:1000-1500
£1367 $2187 €1900 Trois chiens sur un terrier (20x37cm-8x15in) s. brown pat bronze. 19-May-3 Horta, Bruxelles #40/R est:2200-2800
£1534 $2500 €2301 Terriers ratting (38cm-15in) s. brown pat. bronze. 11-Feb-3 Bonhams & Doyles, New York #14 est:1500-2500
£1565 $2488 €2300 Cerf a la branche (38x39cm-15x15in) s. pat bronze. 23-Mar-3 Herbette, Doullens #164/R
£1576 $2522 €2364 Jument a l'ecurie jouant avec un chen (25x47cm-10x19in) s. pat.bronze lit. 13-Jan-3 Rasmussen, Vejle #360/R est:10000 (D.KR 18000)
£1646 $2567 €2600 Fauconnier arabe a pied (67cm-26in) s.d.1873 pat bronze. 15-Oct-2 Horta, Bruxelles #230/R
£1837 $2920 €2700 Taureau (24x40cm-9x16in) s.d.1844 plaster. 23-Mar-3 Herbette, Doullens #163/R
£1900 $2888 €2850 Nanny goat and kid (23x23cm-9x9in) s. brown pat. bronze. 28-Aug-2 Sotheby's, London #845 est:1500-2000
£2000 $3120 €3000 Fabio, a French spaniel (16x30cm-6x12in) s. brown pat bronze. 9-Apr-3 Sotheby's, London #107/R est:1800-2500
£2053 $3346 €3100 Chasse a la perdrix, setter et pointer (22x43cm-9x17in) s.i. brown pat bronze Cast F. Barbedienne. 2-Feb-3 Muizon & Le Coent, Paris #75
£2083 $3313 €3000 Taureau normand (22x37x15cm-9x15x6in) brown pat bronze. 30-Apr-3 Tajan, Paris #41/R
£2342 $3653 €3700 La chasse a la perdrix (22x40cm-9x16in) s. brown pat bronze. 20-Oct-2 Mercier & Cie, Lille #125/R est:2300-3000
£2400 $3792 €3480 Gisella and Jiji - pair of whippets with ball (23x15cm-9x6in) s. bronze exec.c.1850-1875. 24-Jul-3 John Nicholson, Haslemere #262/R est:2200-2500
£2500 $4000 €3750 Mare with frolicking colt (28x48x23cm-11x19x9in) s. golden brown pat bronze. 4-Jan-3 Brunk, Ashville #173/R est:4000-8000
£2500 $3900 €3750 Rabbit hunt (20x38cm-8x15in) s. brown pat bronze lit. 9-Apr-3 Sotheby's, London #171/R est:3000-5000
£2600 $4316 €2600 Djinn, etalon barde (30x37cm-12x15in) s.d.1846 dark pat bronze. 16-Jun-3 Horta, Bruxelles #130 est:2000-3000
£2624 $4250 €3936 Arab mare and stallion (20x33cm-8x13in) s.num.27 bronze with naturalistic base. 25-Jan-3 Skinner, Boston #809/R est:600-800
£2901 $4120 €4700 Cheval Ibrahim (31x40cm-12x16in) s. brown black pat bronze. 16-Mar-3 Eric Pillon, Calais #40/R
£3165 $5000 €4748 Saddled horse with dog (25cm-10in) i. bronze. 3-Apr-3 Christie's, Rockefeller NY #312/R est:3000-5000
£3500 $5460 €5250 Partridge hunt (22x41cm-9x16in) s.d.1847 brown pat bronze. 9-Apr-3 Sotheby's, London #168/R est:4000-6000
£3718 $5837 €5800 Chien de race (24x45x21cm-9x18x8in) brown pat bronze. 24-Nov-2 Lesieur & Le Bars, Le Havre #120/R
£3797 $6000 €5696 Fauconnier Arabe (77cm-30in) i. bronze. 24-Apr-3 Christie's, Rockefeller NY #229/R est:6000-8000
£3930 $6210 €5895 Cerf attaque (40x63cm-16x25in) s. bronze. 17-Nov-2 Koller, Geneva #1231/R est:12000 (S.FR 9000)
£4000 $6240 €6000 Chasseur Africain - Arabian huntsman (51x36cm-20x14in) s. brown pat. bronze. 15-Oct-2 Sotheby's, London #155/R est:4000-6000
£4277 $6629 €6800 Chasseur ecossais montrant un renard (56cm-22in) s. pat bronze. 6-Oct-2 Livinec, Gaudcheau & Jezequel, Rennes #84/R
£4304 $6714 €6800 Le vainqueur du Derby (42x43cm-17x17in) s. medaille pat bronze. 20-Oct-2 Mercier & Cie, Lille #129/R est:6800-7200
£5500 $8580 €8250 Accolade (34x54cm-13x21in) s. brown pat bronze. 9-Apr-3 Sotheby's, London #173/R est:6000-8000
£5755 $9209 €8000 Amazone no 2 (26x24cm-10x9in) s.d.1865 brown pat bronze. 18-May-3 Rabourdin & Choppin de Janvry, Paris #66/R est:8000-9000
£5800 $9048 €8700 Djinn, a Barbary stallion (29x38cm-11x15in) s.i.d.1846 brown pat bronze lit. 5-Nov-2 Sotheby's, London #123/R est:6000-8000
£7200 $11232 €10800 Vainquer du derby (42x43cm-17x17in) s. copper brown pat. bronze. 6-Nov-2 Sotheby's, Olympia #177/R est:5000-7000
£7500 $11400 €11250 La chasse en ecosse (53x54cm-21x21in) s.d.1861 dark brown pat. bronze lit. 28-Aug-2 Sotheby's, London #847/R est:8000-12000

£7914 $12662 €11000 L'accolade, groupe d'un couple de chevaux (44x70x24cm-17x28x9in) s.d.1865 pat bronze. 13-May-3 Palais de Beaux Arts, Brussels #466/R est:7500-12500
£9028 $14354 €13000 Accolade des chevaux arabes (35cm-14in) s. brown pat bronze lit. 30-Apr-3 Tajan, Paris #50/R est:3800
£17308 $27173 €27000 Valet de chasse Louis XV avec cinq chiens (68x76x40cm-27x30x16in) s.st.f.Barbedienne gilt pat bronze. 13-Dec-2 Lombrail & Teucquam, Paris #1/R

MENE, Pierre Jules (attrib) (1810-1879) French
Sculpture
£2075 $3238 €3300 Horses (33x52x21cm-13x20x8in) i. pat.bronze lit. 20-Sep-2 Karlheinz Kaupp, Staufen #989/R est:900

MENEGAZZI, Carlo (19/20th C) Italian
Works on paper
£541 $845 €850 Venice (20x30cm-8x12in) s. gouache. 6-Nov-2 Vendue Huis, Gravenhage #512/R

MENENDEZ ROJAS, Jose Manuel (1956-) Spanish
£1589 $2591 €2400 Composition with cock and chess game (92x73cm-36x29in) s.d.1989 s.d.verso. 11-Feb-3 Segre, Madrid #300/R

MENESCARDI, Giustino (18th C) Italian
Works on paper
£1972 $3175 €2800 Il ratto di Elena (32x20cm-13x8in) pen brown ink W/C blk pencil. 12-May-3 Sotheby's, Milan #51/R est:2000-3000

MENGE, Charles (1920-) ?
£833 $1342 €1208 Still life with cherries (16x20cm-6x8in) s.d.1992 masonite. 9-May-3 Dobiaschofsky, Bern #157/R est:2600 (S.FR 1800)
£1204 $1938 €1746 View of village at night (29x37cm-11x15in) s. panel. 9-May-3 Dobiaschofsky, Bern #156/R est:2600 (S.FR 2600)
Works on paper
£1092 $1703 €1638 Landscape with vineyard (37x48cm-15x19in) s. W/C bodycol. 8-Nov-2 Dobiaschofsky, Bern #93/R est:3000 (S.FR 2500)

MENGIN, Charles Auguste (1853-1933) French
£2244 $3522 €3500 Portrait de Jacques Baudry (151x103cm-59x41in) s.d.1891. 13-Dec-2 Piasa, Paris #173/R

MENGOLINI, Aldo (1939-) Italian
£548 $855 €800 Untitled (80x80cm-31x31in) s.d.76 verso acrylic. 10-Apr-3 Finarte Semenzato, Rome #300

MENGS, Anton Raphael (1728-1779) German
£18790 $30252 €28000 Adoration of the shepherds (253x163cm-100x64in) prov.exhib.lit. 18-Feb-3 Sotheby's, Amsterdam #279/R est:30000-50000

MENGS, Anton Raphael (attrib) (1728-1779) German
£380 $593 €570 Madonna and Child (22x18cm-9x7in) copper prov. 23-Sep-2 Rasmussen, Vejle #235/R (D.KR 4500)
£6028 $10067 €8500 Portrait du pere John Gahagan (62x48cm-24x19in) 18-Jun-3 Hotel des Ventes Mosan, Brussels #152/R est:8000-12000
£19753 $32000 €29630 Portrait of a man, said to be the artist's father, Ismael Mengs (35x27cm-14x11in) 23-Jan-3 Sotheby's, New York #102/R est:8000-12000

MENGUY, Frederic (1927-) French
£284 $474 €400 Paysage vallonne (61x46cm-24x18in) s.d.64. 18-Jun-3 Charbonneaux, Paris #105
£556 $878 €800 Chevaux (46x54cm-18x21in) s. 28-Apr-3 Cornette de St.Cyr, Paris #284/R
£689 $1089 €1000 Deux femmes (80x80cm-31x31in) s. i.verso. 4-Apr-3 Tajan, Paris #240/R
£1439 $2302 €2000 La chaise rouge (73x93cm-29x37in) s. i.verso. 18-May-3 Eric Pillon, Calais #289/R

MENINSKY, Bernard (1891-1950) British
£800 $1296 €1200 Portrait of the artist's sister (52x42cm-20x17in) s. prov. 20-May-3 Bonhams, Knightsbridge #61/R
£900 $1423 €1350 Vase of flowers (75x51cm-30x20in) s.d.27. 27-Nov-2 Sotheby's, Olympia #106/R est:600-800
£1300 $2132 €1950 Portrait of Lady Passfield (61x46cm-24x18in) s. i.stretcher. 3-Jun-3 Sotheby's, Olympia #61/R est:1000-1500
£2000 $3280 €3000 Landscape in Provence (51x61cm-20x24in) s.d.1923 s.d.verso prov. 3-Jun-3 Sotheby's, Olympia #60/R est:2000-3000
£2000 $3340 €2900 Wooded landscape (41x56cm-16x22in) s.d.25. 24-Jun-3 Bonhams, New Bond Street #21/R est:2000-3000
£2200 $3410 €3300 Still life with bread and pear (51x61cm-20x24in) s. 4-Dec-2 Christie's, Kensington #590/R est:2000-3000
Works on paper
£260 $419 €390 Sleeping baby (32x18cm-13x7in) s. pen ink. 14-Jan-3 Bonhams, Knightsbridge #96
£600 $954 €900 Rural landscape South of France (45x61cm-18x24in) s. gouache. 29-Apr-3 Sworder & Son, Bishops Stortford #334/R
£800 $1248 €1200 Dance (30x21cm-12x8in) black brown ink prov. 12-Sep-2 Sotheby's, Olympia #43/R
£800 $1312 €1200 Illustration for Il Penseroso (33x20cm-13x8in) pen ink W/C. 3-Jun-3 Sotheby's, Olympia #18/R
£7000 $11060 €10500 Picking flowers (33x30cm-13x12in) pen ink gouache prov.exhib. 27-Nov-2 Sotheby's, Olympia #252/R est:4000-6000

MENJAUD, Alexandre (attrib) (1773-1832) French
£1698 $2615 €2700 Raphael jeune arrivant a l'atelier du Perugin (54x43cm-21x17in) 25-Oct-2 Tajan, Paris #127/R est:3000-4000

MENKEL, Ludwig (19th C) German
£588 $965 €900 River landscape with figures on path (37x53cm-15x21in) s.d.1875. 7-Feb-3 Auktionhaus Georg Rehm, Augsburg #8056/R

MENKEN, Johann Heinrich (1766-1834) German
£1195 $1864 €1900 Herdsmen resting beneath trees (80x100cm-31x39in) s. 21-Sep-2 Bolland & Marotz, Bremen #434/R est:1500
£3500 $5425 €5250 Landscape with drovers beside stream (81x106cm-32x42in) i.verso. 31-Oct-2 Sotheby's, Olympia #174/R est:3000-5000

MENKES, Zygmunt (1896-1986) Polish
£2778 $4500 €4028 Releasing the doves (61x46cm-24x18in) s. 21-May-3 Doyle, New York #223/R est:3000-5000
£5782 $9194 €8500 Nature morte au masque (82x100cm-32x39in) s.d. 3-Mar-3 Claude Boisgirard, Paris #69/R est:7000-8000

MENN, Barthelemy (1815-1893) Swiss
£961 $1499 €1442 Village street (26x36cm-10x14in) 20-Nov-2 Fischer, Luzern #1251/R est:2500-3500 (S.FR 2200)
Works on paper
£328 $514 €492 Landscape with fruit trees (9x14cm-4x6in) pencil prov. 25-Nov-2 Sotheby's, Zurich #24/R (S.FR 750)
£699 $1097 €1049 Riverside (9x18cm-4x7in) pencil prov. 25-Nov-2 Sotheby's, Zurich #23/R (S.FR 1600)

MENN, Barthelemy (attrib) (1815-1893) Swiss
£348 $543 €522 Wooded river landscape (19x27cm-7x11in) oil study panel. 16-Sep-2 Philippe Schuler, Zurich #3388 (S.FR 800)

MENNESSIER, Auguste Dominique (1803-1890) French
Works on paper
£256 $392 €400 Sortie de l'ecurie (10x12cm-4x5in) s. wash. 23-Aug-2 Deauville, France #145

MENNESSONS, Jacques (1923-1983) French
£1014 $1581 €1500 Beatitudes (90x71cm-35x28in) s. 26-Mar-3 Finarte Semenzato, Milan #99/R

MENNET, Louis (1829-1875) Swiss
£301 $484 €452 Seascape (34x29cm-13x11in) s. 7-May-3 Dobiaschofsky, Bern #820/R (S.FR 650)
£1204 $1938 €1746 Lakeside in summer (22x35cm-9x14in) s. masonite. 9-May-3 Dobiaschofsky, Bern #48/R est:2600 (S.FR 2600)
£1934 $3133 €2901 Swiss mountain town (114x162cm-45x64in) s. canvas on panel. 3-Feb-3 Lilla Bukowskis, Stockholm #423 est:12000-15000 (S.KR 27000)

MENOCAL, Juan Adriaenses (1936-) Cuban
£538 $851 €840 Gardens of Villa Adriana (55x46cm-22x18in) s.d.1985 verso cardboard. 14-Nov-2 Arte, Seville #454/R

MENPES, Mortimer L (1860-1938) British
£520 $848 €780 Portrait of whistler (16x15cm-6x6in) 14-Feb-3 Lyon & Turnbull, Edinburgh #118
£1200 $1992 €1800 Shinto priest on horseback (15x10cm-6x4in) s. board. 12-Jun-3 Bonhams, New Bond Street #835/R est:1000-1500
£1339 $2116 €2009 Breton woman (38x24cm-15x9in) s. s.i. board. 18-Nov-2 Joel, Victoria #166/R est:2000-2500 (A.D 3750)
£1500 $2490 €2250 Japanese children in a shop (15x11cm-6x4in) s. board. 12-Jun-3 Bonhams, New Bond Street #833/R est:1500-2000
£1800 $2988 €2700 Busy Japanese street (15x10cm-6x4in) s. board. 12-Jun-3 Bonhams, New Bond Street #836/R est:1500-2000
£2200 $3652 €3300 Japanese children in the street (15x11cm-6x4in) s. board. 12-Jun-3 Bonhams, New Bond Street #832/R est:2000-3000
£2800 $4340 €4200 Potato peeler. Japanese lady with Koto (16x12cm-6x5in) s. board pair prov. 3-Dec-2 Bonhams, New Bond Street #7/R est:2000-3000

£5200 $8632 €7800 Showers (19x21cm-7x8in) s. board. 12-Jun-3 Bonhams, New Bond Street #834/R est:2000-3000

Works on paper

£300 $477 €450 Young girl holding a book (58x49cm-23x19in) init. i.verso W/C bodycol. 27-Feb-3 Greenslade Hunt, Taunton #1252
£600 $936 €900 Bridge of Sighs and Straw Bridge, Venice (32x42cm-13x17in) s. W/C lit. 26-Mar-3 Hamptons Fine Art, Godalming #84/R
£1600 $2592 €2400 Portrait of a girl (40x32cm-16x13in) s. W/C col chk gouache. 20-May-3 Sotheby's, Olympia #277/R est:500-700
£3000 $4980 €4500 Sunny garden (32x41cm-13x16in) s. mixed media on board. 12-Jun-3 Bonhams, New Bond Street #830/R est:3000-5000

MENS, Isidorus Maria Cornelis van (1890-1985) Belgian

£497 $810 €750 Jeune berbere (30x25cm-12x10in) s. panel. 17-Feb-3 Horta, Bruxelles #373
£1079 $1727 €1500 Vue animee de Ghardaia (40x50cm-16x20in) s.d.1933. 13-May-3 Vanderkindere, Brussels #110 est:500-750
£1583 $2532 €2200 Porte de ville animee au Maroc (60x75cm-24x30in) s.d.1931. 13-May-3 Vanderkindere, Brussels #125 est:750-1000
£2194 $3466 €3400 Souk a Fez (51x40cm-20x16in) s.i.d.1910. 18-Dec-2 Rieunier, Bailly-Pommery, Mathias, Paris #55/R

Works on paper

£355 $574 €500 Marchand des legumes a Tunis (47x59cm-19x23in) s.d.1928 pastel. 26-May-3 Glerum, Amsterdam #167
£709 $1184 €1000 Rabat (28x38cm-11x15in) s. W/C. 23-Jun-3 Bernaerts, Antwerp #431/R est:1000-1250
£1224 $1947 €1800 Devant le marabout (37x30cm-15x12in) s.i.d.1937 W/C. 24-Mar-3 Rabourdin & Choppin de Janvry, Paris #137/R est:1800-2000

MENSE, Carlo (1886-1965) German

£2436 $3776 €3800 Moselle landscape (39x57cm-15x22in) s. panel prov. 4-Dec-2 Lempertz, Koln #914/R est:3500

MENSION, Cornelis Jan (1882-1950) Dutch

£517 $823 €750 Dinner time (16x19cm-6x7in) s. panel. 10-Mar-3 Sotheby's, Amsterdam #136/R
£2535 $4082 €3600 Nude sitting with cat (82x56cm-32x22in) s. 7-May-3 Vendue Huis, Gravenhage #544/R est:3500-4500

MENTA, Edouard (1858-1915) Swiss/French

£1456 $2300 €2300 Musical time in the studio (37x28cm-15x11in) s. 30-Nov-2 Hagelstam, Helsinki #49/R est:2500
£2043 $3167 €3065 La Vaoudoise, chargee de bois (38x54cm-15x21in) s.d.1883 prov. 7-Dec-2 Galerie du Rhone, Sion #457/R est:3000-4000 (S.FR 4700)

MENTOR, Blasco (1918-) Spanish

£897 $1497 €1300 Nu (65x54cm-26x21in) s.d.91. 9-Jul-3 Millon & Associes, Paris #184
£1119 $1868 €1600 Bouquet de fleurs (65x50cm-26x20in) s. 26-Jun-3 Tajan, Paris #306 est:1800-2500
£1127 $1870 €1600 Bouquet de roses rouges (61x50cm-24x20in) s. 11-Jun-3 Beaussant & Lefèvre, Paris #97 est:1000-1200
£1250 $1988 €1800 Le torero (41x27cm-16x11in) s. 29-Apr-3 Artcurial Briest, Paris #309 est:1500-1800
£2695 $4501 €3800 La creation du monde (162x114cm-64x45in) s.d. i.verso. 23-Jun-3 Claude Boisgirard, Paris #193/R est:3500-4000
£2885 $4529 €4500 Concert for reclining woman (81x116cm-32x46in) s.d.1995. 15-Dec-2 Eric Pillon, Calais #258/R
£4808 $7548 €7500 Musician (100x85cm-39x33in) s. 13-Dec-2 Piasa, Paris #176
£5172 $8638 €7500 L'oiseau se frotte les mains (11x414cm-4x163in) s. 9-Jul-3 Millon & Associes, Paris #177 est:6500-8000
£5448 $9099 €7900 Le petit cirque (162x130cm-64x51in) s. 9-Jul-3 Millon & Associes, Paris #176/R est:7000-8000

Works on paper

£280 $467 €400 Nature morte (24x32cm-9x13in) s. W/C. 25-Jun-3 Claude Aguttes, Neuilly #68
£931 $1555 €1350 Chloe au jardin (65x50cm-26x20in) s. pastel. 9-Jul-3 Millon & Associes, Paris #173/R

MENU, Julien (20th C) ?

£2299 $3425 €3449 Garden of Eden (47x61cm-19x24in) s. 27-Aug-2 Christie's, Melbourne #246/R est:3000-5000 (A.D 6000)

MENZEL, Adolph (1815-1905) German

£171674 $266094 €257511 Frederick the Great and the dancer Barbarina with other figures (34x26cm-13x10in) s.d.1852 prov.exhib.lit. 3-Oct-2 Koller, Zurich #3097/R est:380000-500000 (S.FR 400000)

Works on paper

£1575 $2458 €2300 Head of crying newborn (9x10cm-4x4in) pencil. 11-Apr-3 Winterberg, Heidelberg #480/R est:2200
£4114 $6500 €6500 Woman with umbrella and hat (8x4cm-3x2in) mono. pencil board. 30-Nov-2 Villa Grisebach, Berlin #102/R est:3500-4500
£4223 $6588 €6335 Portrait of Miss Daler (13x7cm-5x3in) mono.d.1 feb.90 pencil. 23-Sep-2 Rasmussen, Vejle #128/R est:5000 (D.KR 50000)
£4500 $7515 €6525 Seated man in a hat (18x11cm-7x4in) s.d.92 black lead prov.lit. 8-Jul-3 Christie's, London #116/R est:5000-8000
£6173 $10000 €9260 Piano recital (6x10cm-2x4in) s. chk. 22-Jan-3 Christie's, Rockefeller NY #128/R est:15000
£6173 $10000 €9260 Head of woman looking down (20x13cm-8x5in) s.d.90 chk. 22-Jan-3 Christie's, Rockefeller NY #127/R est:15000
£6452 $10000 €9678 Study of hands (18x11cm-7x4in) init.d.84 pencil stumping. 29-Oct-2 Sotheby's, New York #91/R est:18000-25000
£6962 $11000 €11000 Landscape of Mark Brandenburg (13x20cm-5x8in) exec.c.1850/60. 29-Nov-2 Villa Grisebach, Berlin #1/R est:12000-15000
£7407 $12000 €11111 Seated old man with beard (12x17cm-5x7in) init.d.99. 21-Jan-3 Sotheby's, New York #178/R est:18000
£10870 $17826 €15000 Man at grindstone (21x13cm-8x5in) mono.i. pencil. 30-May-3 Villa Grisebach, Berlin #2/R est:20000-25000
£10968 $17000 €16452 Mountainous landscape (13x21cm-5x8in) init. pencil stumping. 29-Oct-2 Sotheby's, New York #93/R est:12000-18000
£14194 $22000 €21291 Study of a woman holding a stein (23x15cm-9x6in) init.i.d.84 pencil stumping. 29-Oct-2 Sotheby's, New York #92/R est:30000-40000
£14839 $23000 €22259 Study of a wooden bridge (12x21cm-5x8in) init. indis i. pencil stumping prov.exhib. 29-Oct-2 Sotheby's, New York #95/R est:15000-20000
£30556 $48583 €44000 Portrait of young Italian man (12x20cm-5x8in) mono.d.1888 pencil. 5-May-3 Ketterer, Munich #311/R est:1600-1800
£33871 $52500 €50807 Study of a woman holding a fan (13x21cm-5x8in) init. pencil stumping prov.exhib.lit. 29-Oct-2 Sotheby's, New York #90/R est:50000-70000
£34000 $55760 €51000 Das Nurnberger rathaus - Nuremberg town hall (27x21cm-11x8in) init.i.d.52 pencil prov.exhib.lit. 3-Jun-3 Sotheby's, London #42/R est:6000-8000
£100000 $155000 €150000 Head of a workman, for iron rolling mill (20x13cm-8x5in) s. pencil stumping prov.exhib.lit. 29-Oct-2 Sotheby's, New York #88/R est:80000-120000

MENZEL, Adolph (attrib) (1815-1905) German

Works on paper

£886 $1400 €1400 Portrait d'homme portant des lunettes (21x13cm-8x5in) indis.sig.indis.d.91 black chk estompe prov. 27-Nov-2 Christie's, Paris #313/R

MENZIO, Francesco (1899-1979) Italian

£1899 $3000 €3000 Figures (100x66cm-39x26in) s. tempera paper on canvas. 30-Nov-2 Farsetti, Prato #751/R est:3500
£2323 $3670 €3600 Still life with vase of flowers and fruit (41x27cm-16x11in) s. board prov. 18-Dec-2 Christie's, Rome #134
£2695 $4366 €3800 Ritratto (79x49cm-31x19in) paper on canvas prov.exhib. 26-May-3 Christie's, Milan #131/R est:3000-5000
£3205 $5032 €5000 Portrait of lady in sitting room (100x70cm-39x28in) s.i. tempera card. 10-Dec-2 Della Rocca, Turin #331/R
£4430 $6911 €7000 Figure with still life (100x70cm-39x28in) s. painted 1959. 14-Sep-2 Meeting Art, Vercelli #957/R
£5063 $7899 €8000 Nude (80x120cm-31x47in) s masonite painted 1958. 14-Sep-2 Meeting Art, Vercelli #979/R
£5319 $8617 €7500 Donna con cappellino (100x77cm-39x30in) s.d.33 prov.exhib. 26-May-3 Christie's, Milan #130/R est:8000-12000
£5806 $9174 €9000 Nude (100x58cm-39x23in) s. 18-Dec-2 Christie's, Rome #131/R

Works on paper

£510 $811 €750 From a window in Oneglia (35x52cm-14x20in) s. pencil. 1-Mar-3 Meeting Art, Vercelli #729

MENZLER, Wilhelm (1846-1926) German

£517 $822 €750 Girl's portrait (43x36cm-17x14in) s.d.1915 oval. 8-Mar-3 Arnold, Frankfurt #643
£909 $1327 €1400 Female nude with rose (16x24cm-6x9in) s. panel exhib. 15-Jun-2 Hans Stahl, Hamburg #41/R

Works on paper

£2549 $4078 €3900 Elegant female company in park with blossoming fruit trees (46x61cm-18x24in) s. gouache lit. 10-Jan-3 Allgauer, Kempten #1440/R est:3500

MENZLER, Wilhelm (attrib) (1846-1926) German

£287 $448 €431 Moulin pres d'un canal (25x31cm-10x12in) panel. 10-Sep-2 Iegor de Saint Hippolyte, Montreal #82 (C.D 700)

MERANO, Giovanni Battista (attrib) (1632-c.1698) Italian

£53793 $84993 €78000 Saint Peter and the angel (200x133cm-79x52in) 5-Apr-3 Finarte Semenzato, Milan #133/R est:45000

MERCADE, Jaime (1889-1967) Spanish
£2450 $3994 €3700 Landscape (50x60cm-20x24in) s.d.1918. 11-Feb-3 Segre, Madrid #141/R
£3145 $4843 €5000 Vase of flowers (53x44cm-21x17in) s. lit. 28-Oct-2 Segre, Madrid #118/R est:5000

MERCADE, Jordi (1923-) Spanish
£395 $639 €600 Still life of fruit (56x73cm-22x29in) s. 21-Jan-3 Durán, Madrid #73/R
£1090 $1722 €1700 Still life with grapes (65x92cm-26x36in) s. s.i.d.1973 verso lit. 19-Nov-2 Durán, Madrid #198/R

MERCANTI, Gaetano (19th C) Italian
Sculpture
£3103 $4966 €4500 Young bather with urn (83cm-33in) white marble. 13-Mar-3 Artcurial Briest, Paris #184/R

MERCER, Frederick (fl.1881-1937) British
Works on paper
£250 $405 €375 Horle de Ville, Brussels (13x9cm-5x4in) W/C. 21-Jan-3 Bonhams, Knightsbridge #79/R
£300 $477 €450 Hagia Sofia, Istanbul (9x14cm-4x6in) W/C. 29-Apr-3 Bonhams, New Bond Street #78b
£550 $853 €825 View of the Doge's Palace, Venice. View of the Forum, Rome (9x14cm-4x6in) W/C pair. 24-Sep-2 Bonhams, Knightsbridge #182/R

MERCER, Mary Cockburn (1882-1963) British
£2713 $4314 €4070 Birth of Venus, study in diagonals (69x72cm-27x28in) s. board painted 1941 exhib. 5-May-3 Sotheby's, Melbourne #258/R est:7000-9000 (A.D 7000)
£7257 $11465 €10523 Prosepina returns to Earth (54x48cm-21x19in) s. canvasboard. 22-Jul-3 Lawson Menzies, Sydney #20/R est:9000-12000 (A.D 17850)

MERCER, Stanley (1889-1932) British
£1000 $1650 €1450 Portrait of a lady (90x69cm-35x27in) s. 6-Jul-3 Lots Road, London #332

MERCHANT, Albert Wyndon (1881-1936) American
£321 $500 €482 Off Sprucehead, seascape (23x25cm-9x10in) canvas on board. 11-Aug-2 Thomaston Place, Thomaston #136
£368 $600 €552 Summer reflections (30x25cm-12x10in) board. 1-Feb-3 Thomaston Place, Thomaston #217
£385 $600 €578 Sunset, New York harbour (38x43cm-15x17in) canvas on board. 11-Aug-2 Thomaston Place, Thomaston #175
£429 $700 €644 The garden gate (30x23cm-12x9in) with sig. canvas on board. 1-Feb-3 Thomaston Place, Thomaston #184
£491 $800 €737 Out back, Rockland, me subject (41x36cm-16x14in) s.verso. 1-Feb-3 Thomaston Place, Thomaston #183
Works on paper
£428 $650 €642 Moored sailboats (36x33cm-14x13in) W/C. 30-Aug-2 Thomaston Place, Thomaston #177
£592 $900 €888 Sailboats dockside under orange sky (36x41cm-14x16in) W/C. 30-Aug-2 Thomaston Place, Thomaston #178
£855 $1300 €1283 Sailboats dockside at low tide (41x46cm-16x18in) W/C. 30-Aug-2 Thomaston Place, Thomaston #179

MERCIE, M J A (1845-1916) French
Sculpture
£2837 $4738 €4000 La decapitation. dark brown pat bronze green marble rectangular base. 23-Jun-3 Amberes, Antwerp #259/R

MERCIE, Marius Jean Antonin (1845-1916) French
Sculpture
£1282 $2000 €1923 Standing figure sheathing his sword (61cm-24in) s. bronze. 9-Oct-2 Doyle, New York #434 est:1500-2500
£1418 $2199 €2127 Quand meme - woman with wounded soldier (52cm-20in) s. pat.bronze st.f.Barbedienne. 8-Dec-2 Uppsala Auktionskammare, Uppsala #343/R est:20000-25000 (S.KR 20000)
£1698 $2750 €2462 David slays Goliath (112x56cm-44x22in) s.i. brown pat bronze Cast Barbedienne. 21-May-3 Doyle, New York #192/R est:5000-7000
£2000 $3100 €3000 David and Goliath, the boy with his foot on the head of the giant (74cm-29in) s. golden brown pat bronze circular base. 29-Oct-2 Bonhams, New Bond Street #153/R est:2500-3000
£3800 $5852 €5700 Goria Victis (59cm-23in) s.st.f.F Barbedienne bronze ebonised plinth lit. 28-Oct-2 Sotheby's, Olympia #74/R est:3000-4000
£5200 $8060 €7800 David and Goliath, the boy with his foot on the head of the giant (110cm-43in) s. green brown pat bronze circular base. 29-Oct-2 Bonhams, New Bond Street #152/R est:4000-5000
£6129 $9500 €9194 David (90cm-35in) s. brown pat. bronze i.f.Barbedienne lit. 29-Oct-2 Sotheby's, New York #234/R est:5000-7000
£6259 $9951 €9200 Gloria Victis (100cm-39in) s. yellow brown pat.bronze marble socle lit. 24-Mar-3 Bernaerts, Antwerp #48/R est:3750-5000
£6369 $10000 €9554 Gloria Victus (91cm-36in) s.st.f.F.Barbedienne bronze. 21-Nov-2 Sotheby's, New York #119/R est:10000-15000
£7800 $12090 €11700 Gloria Victus holding aloft a defeated naked male warrior (93cm-37in) s.i. gilt brown pat bronze circular base st.f.F.Barbedienne. 29-Oct-2 Bonhams, New Bond Street #156/R est:7000-10000
£9500 $15105 €14250 David with the head of Goliath (95cm-37in) s. gilt bronze exhib. 29-Apr-3 Sotheby's, Olympia #154/R est:7000-10000
£12500 $19500 €18750 Dave apres le combat (124cm-49in) s.st.f.F Barbedienne gilt brown pat bronze marble plinth exhib. 9-Apr-3 Sotheby's, London #205/R est:10000-15000

MERCIER, Major Charles (1834-?) British
£3300 $5115 €4950 Portrait of a young lady with a horse and dog (143x112cm-56x44in) s.d.1873. 25-Sep-2 John Nicholson, Haslemere #1066/R est:500-1000

MERCIER, Mathieu (20th C) French?
Works on paper
£476 $757 €700 Projet Koln (21x30cm-8x12in) s.i.d.1997 W/C gouache graphite prov. 24-Mar-3 Cornette de St.Cyr, Paris #195/R

MERCIER, Philippe (1689-1760) French
£6500 $10790 €9750 Young drummer boy (76x63cm-30x25in) prov. 10-Jun-3 Christie's, London #29/R est:6000-8000
£10000 $15800 €15000 Blowing bubbles (75x61cm-30x24in) mono. prov. 26-Nov-2 Christie's, London #22/R est:8000-12000
£155000 $257300 €232500 Portrait of a young woman, possibly Hannah, the artist maid, holding a tea tray (92x71cm-36x28in) s. prov.exhib.lit. 10-Jun-3 Christie's, London #33/R est:25000-35000
Works on paper
£750 $1163 €1125 Woman gesturing to the left (32x26cm-13x10in) red white chk. 9-Dec-2 Bonhams, New Bond Street #98/R
£1048 $1635 €1572 Girl asleep (70x80cm-28x31in) chl htd white. 20-Nov-2 Fischer, Luzern #2438/R est:1500-1800 (S.FR 2400)

MERCIER, Philippe (attrib) (1689-1760) French
Works on paper
£355 $592 €500 Femme assise vue de dos (27x25cm-11x10in) black pen white chk. 23-Jun-3 Beaussant & Lefèvre, Paris #255/R

MERCK, Jacob Franz van der (attrib) (1610-1664) Dutch
£1200 $2004 €1740 Officers playing cards with courtesans in an interior (46x62cm-18x24in) panel. 8-Jul-3 Bonhams, Knightsbridge #72/R est:1200-1800

MERCKAERT, Jules (1872-1924) Belgian
£256 $403 €400 Bord de riviere (30x41cm-12x16in) panel. 19-Nov-2 Vanderkindere, Brussels #57
£532 $888 €750 Canal en Flandres (50x75cm-20x30in) s.d.1909. 17-Jun-3 Palais de Beaux Arts, Brussels #597
£545 $855 €850 La Semois (50x60cm-20x24in) s.d.1923. 19-Nov-2 Vanderkindere, Brussels #78
£550 $913 €550 Barque de plaisance (30x41cm-12x16in) panel. 16-Jun-3 Horta, Bruxelles #417
£915 $1473 €1400 Vue de la vallee de la Marne (50x60cm-20x24in) s.d.1921. 20-Jan-3 Horta, Bruxelles #137 est:1800-2200
£1392 $2172 €2200 L'inondation a Testelt (70x80cm-28x31in) s.d.1916 i.verso. 21-Oct-2 Bernaerts, Antwerp #519/R est:750-1000
£1900 $3154 €1900 Le geranium sur l'appui de fenetre (65x54cm-26x21in) s.d.21. 16-Jun-3 Horta, Bruxelles #416 est:1500-2000

MERCKER, Erich (1891-1973) German
£261 $418 €400 Waves at sandy beach (50x65cm-20x26in) s.i. masonite. 10-Jan-3 Allgauer, Kempten #1690/R
£276 $427 €430 View over Alster to Hamburg (39x49cm-15x19in) s.i. masonite prov. 7-Dec-2 Ketterer, Hamburg #190/R
£327 $523 €500 Fontag in Allgau (60x80cm-24x31in) s.i. 10-Jan-3 Allgauer, Kempten #1692/R
£392 $643 €600 Capri: view of Sorrento - III (50x40cm-20x16in) s. i. verso board. 8-Feb-3 Hans Stahl, Hamburg #34/R
£439 $685 €650 Stoking the oven in the Thyssen Hutte, Duisburg (40x50cm-16x20in) s. i. verso canvas on board on panel. 26-Mar-3 Hugo Ruef, Munich #174
£458 $732 €700 Rough seas with sailing ships at sunset (42x70cm-17x28in) s.i. masonite lit. 10-Jan-3 Allgauer, Kempten #1689/R

£481 $755 €750 Empty fields (61x81cm-24x32in) s. 21-Nov-2 Van Ham, Cologne #1783
£513 $805 €800 Venice (60x80cm-24x31in) s. 21-Nov-2 Van Ham, Cologne #1785/R
£513 $795 €800 Hamburg harbour (40x52cm-16x20in) s. panel. 5-Dec-2 Schopman, Hamburg #665
£588 $941 €900 Fishing boats in front of Venice (80x60cm-31x24in) s.i. 10-Jan-3 Allgauer, Kempten #1693/R
£612 $973 €900 Nurnberg in winter (86x65cm-34x26in) s. i. stretcher. 28-Mar-3 Bolland & Marotz, Bremen #569/R
£654 $1046 €1000 Sands at Sylt (60x80cm-24x31in) s.i. 10-Jan-3 Allgauer, Kempten #1691/R
£692 $1079 €1100 Coast near Monaco (90x130cm-35x51in) s. 19-Sep-2 Dr Fritz Nagel, Stuttgart #969/R
£764 $1177 €1200 Fishing boats in harbour (82x100cm-32x39in) s.i. 5-Sep-2 Arnold, Frankfurt #814/R
£1156 $1839 €1700 Landscape near Elbing (100x110cm-39x43in) s. i. stretcher. 28-Mar-3 Bolland & Marotz, Bremen #568/R est:1900
£1410 $2228 €2200 August Thyssen Hutte Hamborn - factory (80x100cm-31x39in) s.i. panel. 14-Nov-2 Neumeister, Munich #630/R est:1300-1400

MEREDITH, John (1933-2000) Canadian
£1889 $3098 €2834 Untitled abstract (127x62cm-50x24in) s.d.60 s.d.verso prov. 27-May-3 Sotheby's, Toronto #89/R est:4000-6000 (C.D 4250)

MEREDITH, William (1851-1916) British
Works on paper
£700 $1092 €1050 Two fishermen in a cottage (53x66cm-21x26in) s. gouache. 9-Oct-2 Woolley & Wallis, Salisbury #71/R

MERET, Émile Louis (19/20th C) French
£491 $746 €737 Part of the Seine with river boat (38x61cm-15x24in) s.d.1902. 28-Aug-2 Museumsbygningen, Copenhagen #35/R (D.KR 5700)

MERIAN, Maria Sibylla (1647-1717) German
Works on paper
£29000 $48430 €42050 Spurge hawk-moth in various stages of life-cycle with insects and spurge (38x31cm-15x12in) W/C gouache over blk chk vellum. 9-Jul-3 Sotheby's, London #109/R est:22000-28000
£29000 $48430 €42050 Convolvulus hawk moth as pupa, caterpillar and moth on sprig of betony (38x30cm-15x12in) bears i.d.1661 W/C touches gouache blk chk vellum. 9-Jul-3 Sotheby's, London #111/R est:22000-28000

MERIDA, Carlos (1891-1984) Guatemalan
£3822 $6000 €5733 Mother and blind son (49x60cm-19x24in) s. s.i.d.MCMXIV verso prov. 19-Nov-2 Sotheby's, New York #75/R
£5414 $8500 €8121 Heart (31x25cm-12x10in) s.d.1979 s.i.d.verso masonite prov. 20-Nov-2 Christie's, Rockefeller NY #88/R est:10000-15000
£11465 $18000 €17198 Exorcist (77x56cm-30x22in) s.d.1968 s.i.d.verso acrylic paper prov. 20-Nov-2 Christie's, Rockefeller NY #87/R est:25000-35000
£16561 $26000 €24842 Planetarium (80x64cm-31x25in) s.d.1965 i.on stretcher prov. 20-Nov-2 Christie's, Rockefeller NY #123/R est:15000-20000
£20701 $32500 €31052 Drawing on the wall (90x66cm-35x26in) s.d.1960 s.i.d.verso petroplastic panel prov.lit. 19-Nov-2 Sotheby's, New York #88/R est:60000
£24390 $40000 €35366 Pajaro muerto (100x81cm-39x32in) s.d.1944 prov.exhib. 27-May-3 Sotheby's, New York #100
£35032 $55000 €52548 Young king (66x49cm-26x19in) s.d.1956 prov.lit. 19-Nov-2 Sotheby's, New York #10/R est:60000
Prints
£5312 $8074 €7702 En tono mayor (80x240cm-31x94in) s.d.1981 serigraph 23/100. 24-Jul-2 Louis Morton, Mexico #57/R est:85000-90000 (M.P 80000)
Works on paper
£1258 $2000 €1887 Abstract composition (15x23cm-6x9in) s. W/C exec.c.1973. 2-Mar-3 Toomey, Oak Park #813/R est:2500-4500
£1290 $2000 €1935 Guatemalan scene (23x28cm-9x11in) s. gouache board exec.c.1925. 8-Dec-2 Toomey, Oak Park #821/R est:8000-10000
£1385 $2161 €2078 Boceto (7x27cm-3x11in) s. lapiz. 17-Oct-2 Louis Morton, Mexico #145/R est:22000-26000 (M.P 22000)
£2015 $3144 €3023 Luz radiante (23x18cm-9x7in) s.d.1974 col crayon. 17-Oct-2 Louis Morton, Mexico #53/R est:40000-50000 (M.P 32000)
£7317 $12000 €10976 Prestidigitador (76x56cm-30x22in) s. pastel chl exec.1981 prov. 28-May-3 Christie's, Rockefeller NY #109/R est:15000-20000

MERIEL-BUSSY, Andre (1902-1985) French
£288 $453 €450 Sur les dunes en Bretagne (65x96cm-26x38in) s.d.1923. 15-Dec-2 Thierry & Lannon, Brest #401
Works on paper
£775 $1247 €1100 Maternite (44x36cm-17x14in) s. gouache. 11-May-3 Thierry & Lannon, Brest #128

MERITE, Edouard Paul (1867-1941) French
£915 $1520 €1300 Fauconnerie (23x34cm-9x13in) s. cardboard. 11-Jun-3 Beaussant & Lefèvre, Paris #98/R
£1410 $2214 €2200 Col vert survolant la lande (52x70cm-20x28in) s. 16-Dec-2 Rabourdin & Choppin de Janvry, Paris #84/R
Works on paper
£828 $1316 €1200 Etude de chevreuils (19x18cm-7x7in) s. chl. 10-Mar-3 Coutau Begarie, Paris #129/R
£3448 $5483 €5000 Etude de chats sauvages (24x15cm-9x6in) chl htd col. 10-Mar-3 Coutau Begarie, Paris #132/R

MERIVALE, Louisa Ann (1819-?) British
Works on paper
£600 $984 €870 Barton Place, Exeter (26x37cm-10x15in) i. pencil pen ink wash. 5-Jun-3 Christie's, London #52/R

MERK, Eduard (1816-1888) German
£2188 $3500 €3282 Moment of harmony (67x56cm-26x22in) s.i. 14-May-3 Butterfields, San Francisco #1085/R est:3000-5000

MERKEL, Georg (1881-1976) Austrian
£7801 $12638 €11000 Lovers, shepherd and flock in landscape with windmill (57x71cm-22x28in) s. prov. 20-May-3 Dorotheum, Vienna #145/R est:12000-16000
£8511 $13787 €12000 Mother and child (60x34cm-24x13in) s. board prov. 20-May-3 Dorotheum, Vienna #138/R est:12000-17000
£10127 $16000 €16000 Meeting (57x42cm-22x17in) s. prov. 27-Nov-2 Dorotheum, Vienna #146/R est:12000-18000
£11392 $18000 €18000 Summer fairy tale (47x61cm-19x24in) s. i. stretcher prov. 27-Nov-2 Dorotheum, Vienna #156/R est:12000-16000
£12025 $19000 €19000 Lovers in landscape (50x68cm-20x27in) s. 27-Nov-2 Dorotheum, Vienna #147/R est:13000-19000
Works on paper
£709 $1149 €1000 The source (43x38cm-17x15in) chl chk prov. 20-May-3 Dorotheum, Vienna #131/R

MERKEL, Georg (attrib) (1881-1976) Austrian
£779 $1138 €1200 Wachau village (52x63cm-20x25in) s. 15-Jun-2 Hans Stahl, Hamburg #42/R

MERKER, Max (1861-1928) German
£1410 $2214 €2200 Concordia Temple in Agrigent, Scicily (92x142cm-36x56in) s. 21-Nov-2 Van Ham, Cologne #1786 est:1600

MERLE, Georges Hugues (19th C) French
£15385 $25692 €22000 L'envouteuse (145x114cm-57x45in) s. exhib. 25-Jun-3 Sotheby's, Paris #99/R est:25000-35000

MERLE, Hughes (1823-1881) French
£3344 $5250 €5016 Eagle's flight (127x89cm-50x35in) s.d.1857 canvas on board. 23-Nov-2 Jackson's, Cedar Falls #1/R est:6000-8000
£3659 $6000 €5489 Portrait of d'une Bohemienne (56x46cm-22x18in) s.d.1878. 5-Feb-3 Christie's, Rockefeller NY #177/R est:7000-9000
£17610 $27472 €28000 Vintaging (110x196cm-43x77in) s.d.1850. 20-Sep-2 Millon & Associes, Paris #717/R est:35000-60000
£19355 $30000 €29033 Maternal affection (56x46cm-22x18in) s.d.1867 prov. 29-Oct-2 Sotheby's, New York #12/R est:40000-60000
£20979 $35035 €30000 Portrait de jeune fille en robe bleue (116x71cm-46x28in) s. 25-Jun-3 Sotheby's, Paris #78/R est:15000-20000

MERLIN, Daniel (1861-1933) French
£2051 $3221 €3200 Jeunes chatons jouant avec des fleurs (38x55cm-15x22in) s. 19-Nov-2 Vanderkindere, Brussels #115/R est:2500-5000
£2838 $4428 €4257 Cat with kittens (46x55cm-18x22in) s. 6-Nov-2 Dobiaschofsky, Bern #825/R est:8500 (S.FR 6500)
£2975 $4700 €4700 Cinq chatons devant la grenouille (38x55cm-15x22in) s. 1-Dec-2 Peron, Melun #100

MERLINO, Silvio (1952-) American
£1206 $1953 €1700 Affiora (121x186cm-48x73in) i.d.1986 oil mixed media prov. 26-May-3 Christie's, Milan #180/R est:1500-2000

MERLO, Camillo (1856-1931) Italian
£578 $919 €850 Countryside near Turin (23x30cm-9x12in) s.d.1920 cardboard. 1-Mar-3 Meeting Art, Vercelli #151

MERLO, Metello (1886-1964) Italian
£340 $541 €500 Amongst chestnut trees (37x29cm-15x11in) s. board. 1-Mar-3 Meeting Art, Vercelli #108
£340 $541 €500 The Po at San Mauro (28x34cm-11x13in) i.verso card on masonite. 1-Mar-3 Meeting Art, Vercelli #195
£510 $811 €750 Oggebbio (35x30cm-14x12in) s.d.1931 board. 1-Mar-3 Meeting Art, Vercelli #47
£884 $1406 €1300 Street in Grugliasco (35x30cm-14x12in) s. board. 1-Mar-3 Meeting Art, Vercelli #50

Works on paper
£340 $541 €500 Women in the garden (27x33cm-11x13in) s.d.1943 mixed media cardboard. 1-Mar-3 Meeting Art, Vercelli #190

MERODE, Carl von (1853-1909) Austrian
£1582 $2453 €2500 Vegetable seller standing in doorway of shop (31x21cm-12x8in) s. panel. 25-Sep-2 Neumeister, Munich #654/R est:3000

MERODIO, Carlos (1944-) Spanish
£526 $853 €800 Structures in balance (55x70cm-22x28in) s.d.1973. 21-Jan-3 Ansorena, Madrid #320/R

MEROTE, B (19th C) Belgian
£962 $1510 €1500 Arrestation de la famille royale (79x119cm-31x47in) s. 15-Dec-2 Mercier & Cie, Lille #374

MERRIAM, James Arthur (1880-1951) American
£510 $800 €765 Desert landscape (76x99cm-30x39in) s. 14-Dec-2 CRN Auctions, Cambridge #205/R
£1234 $1900 €1851 California coast (91x122cm-36x48in) s. painted c.1930. 8-Sep-2 Treadway Gallery, Cincinnati #604/R est:2500-3500

MERRIAM, James Arthur (attrib) (1880-1951) American
£281 $450 €422 Untitled. 1-Jan-3 Fallon, Copake #585

MERRICK, Emily M (c.1842-1921) British
£8000 $12320 €12000 In Wonderland, portrait of Margery Merrick reading a book (150x99cm-59x39in) 5-Sep-2 Christie's, Kensington #84/R est:5000-8000

MERRIFIELD, Tom (1932-) Australian
Sculpture
£1300 $2015 €1950 Pas de deux (42cm-17in) s.num.7/9 golden brown pat. 3-Dec-2 Bonhams, New Bond Street #66/R est:1500-2000
£2200 $3432 €3300 Dancing nude (63cm-25in) s.num.1/9 dark brown pat. bronze marble base. 27-Mar-3 Christie's, Kensington #454/R est:1500-2000
£8500 $13175 €12750 Juliet (252cm-99in) s. green black pat. bronze. 3-Dec-2 Bonhams, New Bond Street #63/R est:8000-12000
Works on paper
£300 $486 €450 Seated ballerina (90x84cm-35x33in) s. pencil chl. 20-May-3 Bonhams, Knightsbridge #22/R

MERRILL, E W (?) American?
Works on paper
£1301 $1900 €1952 Love in Blackville, wooing of the twins. i. W/C ink China white birchbark dr. 3-Nov-1 North East Auctions, Portsmouth #237/R

MERRIOTT, Jack (1901-1968) British
Works on paper
£300 $474 €450 Farmyard (55x76cm-22x30in) s. W/C. 27-Nov-2 Hamptons Fine Art, Godalming #212
£620 $992 €930 Afternoon in Venice (46x53cm-18x21in) s. pastel. 11-Mar-3 Gorringes, Lewes #2542

MERRITT, Anna Lea (1844-1930) British
£1605 $2600 €2408 Young girl with flowers (51x61cm-20x24in) s. 24-Jan-3 Freeman, Philadelphia #198/R est:400-600

MERRITT, Warren Chase (1897-1968) American
£1442 $2250 €2163 Sausalito and Belvedere. 21-Sep-2 Harvey Clar, Oakland #1520

MERRY, Godfrey (fl.1883-1903) British
Works on paper
£3400 $5270 €5100 Stand aside for Scotland's Pride (152x229cm-60x90in) s. W/C. 26-Sep-2 Lane, Penzance #285/R est:3500-4500

MERSCH, Cecile (1905-) Belgian
£538 $839 €850 Les moissons (97x127cm-38x50in) s. 15-Oct-2 Vanderkindere, Brussels #43

MERSFELDER, Jules (1865-1937) American
£437 $700 €656 Landscape with oaks (41x61cm-16x24in) s. 16-Mar-3 Butterfields, San Francisco #1033
£964 $1600 €1398 Evening glow, Marin (56x72cm-22x28in) s. i.verso. 11-Jun-3 Butterfields, San Francisco #4194/R est:3000-5000

MERSON, Luc-Olivier (1846-1920) French
£1736 $2743 €2500 Illustrations (42x31cm-17x12in) s. set of 4. 25-Apr-3 Piasa, Paris #166/R
Works on paper
£284 $474 €400 Vignette (13x23cm-5x9in) i. pen W/C. 23-Jun-3 Beaussant & Lefèvre, Paris #155
£633 $981 €1000 Femme drapee (64x23cm-25x9in) init. chl chk. 29-Sep-2 Eric Pillon, Calais #102/R
£823 $1275 €1300 Scene allegorique avec femme et angelot musicien (34x15cm-13x6in) init. gouache. 29-Sep-2 Eric Pillon, Calais #100/R

MERTEN, T (19th C) ?
£478 $736 €750 River landscape in afternoon (69x96cm-27x38in) s. 5-Sep-2 Arnold, Frankfurt #816/R

MERTENS, Fernande de (19/20th C) Belgian?
Works on paper
£1064 $1777 €1500 Portrait de femme (78x65cm-31x26in) s. pastel oval. 20-Jun-3 Rieunier, Paris #35 est:800-1200

MERTIKAS, Katerina (20th C) ?
£222 $364 €322 Cross country skiers (30x40cm-12x16in) s.i.d.2003 board. 9-Jun-3 Hodgins, Calgary #68/R (C.D 500)
£467 $765 €677 Stormy morning (60x75cm-24x30in) s.i.d.2003 acrylic board. 9-Jun-3 Hodgins, Calgary #15 est:800-1200 (C.D 1050)

MERTON, Erling (1898-1967) Norwegian
£431 $656 €647 Evening sunshine (51x60cm-20x24in) s.d.34 s.i.verso. 31-Aug-2 Grev Wedels Plass, Oslo #64/R (N.KR 5000)

MERTON, Owen Heathcote Grierson (1887-1931) New Zealander
Works on paper
£351 $547 €527 Artist's residence, France (44x29cm-17x11in) s.d.1942 W/C. 27-Mar-3 International Art Centre, Auckland #127/R (NZ.D 1000)
£408 $636 €612 Spanish border town (29x22cm-11x9in) s.d.1911 W/C. 7-Nov-2 International Art Centre, Auckland #190/R est:1000-2000 (NZ.D 1300)
£644 $915 €966 St. Ives (24x31cm-9x12in) s. W/C. 20-Mar-2 Watson's, Christchurch #49/R est:1500-2400 (NZ.D 2100)

MERTZ, Albert (1920-1990) Danish
£347 $552 €521 The yellow food bowl (31x36cm-12x14in) s.d.57 verso. 26-Feb-3 Kunsthallen, Copenhagen #84/R (D.KR 3800)
£420 $669 €630 Sick flowers (40x57cm-16x22in) s.d.24/7-57 verso cardboard exhib. 26-Feb-3 Kunsthallen, Copenhagen #87/R (D.KR 4600)
£558 $881 €837 L'heure bleue (47x27cm-19x11in) s.d.August 58 verso panel exhib. 1-Apr-3 Rasmussen, Copenhagen #354/R (D.KR 6000)
£686 $1090 €1029 Atom age (60x73cm-24x29in) s.d.60 verso exhib. 26-Feb-3 Kunsthallen, Copenhagen #91/R (D.KR 7500)
£994 $1651 €1441 Barber's sign (165x110cm-65x43in) s.d.56 masonite exhib. 12-Jun-3 Kunsthallen, Copenhagen #4/R (D.KR 10500)
Works on paper
£283 $451 €425 Bonne Annee (30x21cm-12x8in) gouache postcard exhib. 26-Feb-3 Kunsthallen, Copenhagen #89/R (D.KR 3100)
£384 $610 €576 Green man (24x25cm-9x10in) init.d.25/1-67 gouache. 26-Feb-3 Kunsthallen, Copenhagen #88/R (D.KR 4200)
£392 $623 €588 Compositions. init.d.64 two in one frame. 29-Apr-3 Kunsthallen, Copenhagen #103 (D.KR 4200)
£560 $868 €840 Cut and tear (34x45cm-13x18in) init.d.28-6-58 collage. 4-Dec-2 Kunsthallen, Copenhagen #39 (D.KR 6500)
£931 $1444 €1397 Theatre (36x49cm-14x19in) init.d.11-7-65 i.verso gouache htd gold. 1-Oct-2 Rasmussen, Copenhagen #16a (D.KR 11000)

MERTZ, Johann Cornelius (1819-1891) Dutch
£599 $964 €850 Endorsement of jewel (49x38cm-19x15in) s.d.1858 panel. 6-May-3 Vendu Notarishuis, Rotterdam #110/R

MERWART, Paul (1855-1902) Polish
£382 $600 €573 Portrait of a gentleman (36x25cm-14x10in) s. i.d.Avril 1888 verso panel. 14-Dec-2 Weschler, Washington #632/R

MERY, Alfred Émile (1824-1896) French
Works on paper
£690 $1090 €1000 Heron cendre (47x66cm-19x26in) s. gouache. 6-Apr-3 Herbette, Doullens #592/R

MERYON, Charles (1821-1868) French
Prints
£1887 $3000 €2831 Le Stryge (17x13cm-7x5in) etching. 1-May-3 Swann Galleries, New York #331/R est:4000-6000
£2756 $4355 €4300 Le petit pont. etching. 14-Nov-2 Libert, Castor, Paris #125/R est:3000
£5449 $8609 €8500 La morgue. etching. 14-Nov-2 Libert, Castor, Paris #126/R est:7500
£6200 $9610 €9300 Le stryge (23x27cm-9x11in) etching. 5-Dec-2 Sotheby's, London #163/R est:2000-3000

MERZ, Albert (1942-) Swiss
Works on paper
£306 $480 €459 Composition (38x28cm-15x11in) s.d.1992 mixed media. 25-Nov-2 Germann, Zurich #769 (S.FR 700)

MERZ, Gerhard (1947-) German
£8000 $13120 €12000 Rappel a l'ordre (210x210cm-83x83in) i.d.MCMLXXXIX prov.exhib. 7-Feb-3 Sotheby's, London #162/R est:8000-12000

MERZ, Karl (1890-1970) German
£411 $650 €650 Furstenberg in early spring (32x49cm-13x19in) s. i.verso panel. 30-Nov-2 Geble, Radolfzell #679

MERZ, Mario (1925-) Italian
Sculpture
£13768 $22580 €19000 Untitled - outrigger (96x146cm-38x57in) s.d.Merz 82 collage clay corn leaves plastic board. 28-May-3 Lempertz, Koln #282/R est:18000-20000
Works on paper
£1585 $2600 €2298 Luce e sette appogiagi (48x69cm-19x27in) s.i. pencil W/C chl. 1-Jun-3 Wright, Chicago #331/R est:2000-3000
£5319 $8617 €7500 Progetto per spirale (33x45cm-13x18in) s. pastel ink polish exec.1978-79 prov. 26-May-3 Christie's, Milan #104/R est:7500-9000

MESCHERSKY, Arsenii Ivanovich (1834-1902) Russian
£25000 $40500 €37500 Tranquil woodland lake (43x60cm-17x24in) s.d.1896. 21-May-3 Sotheby's, London #59/R est:6000-8000

MESCHIS, Renzo (1945-) Italian
£340 $541 €500 Sicilian landscape (60x70cm-24x28in) s. 1-Mar-3 Meeting Art, Vercelli #694

MESDAG VAN HOUTEN, Sientje (1834-1909) Dutch
£745 $1184 €1118 View across the meadows towards Delft (50x80cm-20x31in) s.d.1879. 5-Mar-3 Rasmussen, Copenhagen #2072/R (D.KR 8000)
£962 $1490 €1500 Still life with flowers and jug (36x52cm-14x20in) mono. 7-Dec-2 Hans Stahl, Hamburg #47/R est:1500
£5732 $8943 €9000 Flock of sheep near fold (99x125cm-39x49in) s. 6-Nov-2 Vendue Huis, Gravenhage #549/R est:4000-5000

MESDAG, H W (1831-1915) Dutch
£304 $474 €456 Coastal landscape with figures and fishing boats (77x106cm-30x42in) s. 23-Sep-2 Rasmussen, Vejle #2108 (D.KR 3600)

MESDAG, Hendrik-Willem (1831-1915) Dutch
£1736 $2760 €2500 Flowering oostindische kers (38x28cm-15x11in) init.d.67 canvas on board prov.lit. 29-Apr-3 Christie's, Amsterdam #119/R est:1500-2000
£2740 $4274 €4000 Seascape with a boat in the distance (43x102cm-17x40in) prov. 14-Apr-3 Glerum, Amsterdam #61/R est:8000-12000
£4861 $7729 €7000 View on the church of Vries, Drenthe (52x41cm-20x16in) s. prov.exhib.lit. 29-Apr-3 Christie's, Amsterdam #118/R est:7000-9000
£12821 $19872 €20000 Stormy seascape with fishing boat on choppy sea (44x69cm-17x27in) s. 4-Dec-2 Neumeister, Munich #818/R est:2500
£18493 $29034 €27000 Rowing boat on a choppy sea (44x103cm-17x41in) s.d.1869. 15-Apr-3 Sotheby's, Amsterdam #253/R est:10000-15000
£37736 $58113 €60000 Soleil couchant (39x50cm-15x20in) s. prov.lit. 23-Oct-2 Christie's, Amsterdam #224/R est:60000-80000
£69182 $106541 €110000 Bomschuiten at sea (89x69cm-35x27in) s.d.1897 prov.lit. 22-Oct-2 Sotheby's, Amsterdam #209/R est:100000-150000
£75472 $116226 €120000 Return of the fishing fleet (77x49cm-30x19in) s. prov. 22-Oct-2 Sotheby's, Amsterdam #185/R est:90000-120000
£76389 $121458 €110000 Bomschuit in the breakers on a calm day (51x39cm-20x15in) s. panel. 29-Apr-3 Christie's, Amsterdam #140/R est:60000-80000
Works on paper
£584 $853 €900 Seascape (18x33cm-7x13in) s. chl dr. 17-Jun-2 Ansorena, Madrid #19/R
£7547 $11623 €12000 Bomschuiten near the coast of Scheveningen (43x46cm-17x18in) s. gouache black chk. 23-Oct-2 Christie's, Amsterdam #196/R est:15000-20000

MESENS, E L T (1903-1971) British
Works on paper
£696 $1100 €1100 Figure (24x19cm-9x7in) s. mixed media. 26-Nov-2 Palais de Beaux Arts, Brussels #249/R
£728 $1150 €1150 Main (24x19cm-9x7in) s. mixed media. 26-Nov-2 Palais de Beaux Arts, Brussels #250/R

MESENS, Edouard Léon Theodore (1903-1971) British
Works on paper
£506 $790 €800 Surreal composition with hand and balls (27x23cm-11x9in) s. collage W/C. 21-Oct-2 Bernaerts, Antwerp #648/R
£633 $987 €1000 Surreal composition with pears (23x30cm-9x12in) s. collage. 21-Oct-2 Bernaerts, Antwerp #645/R
£1712 $2688 €2500 Quartiers inegaux et reserves (34x23cm-13x9in) s.i.d.1954 gouache collage cardboard exhib.lit. 15-Apr-3 Laurence Calmels, Paris #4364/R

MESGRINY, Claude François Auguste de (1836-1884) French
£2000 $3160 €3000 Tranquil lake (51x80cm-20x31in) s. 14-Nov-2 Christie's, Kensington #128/R est:1000-1500
£3226 $5000 €4839 Bord de la riviere (36x56cm-14x22in) s. 2-Oct-2 Christie's, Rockefeller NY #768/R est:8000-12000

MESHILDOT, Albert du (?) ?
Works on paper
£380 $593 €570 Troupe (31x24cm-12x9in) s. pen ink W/C. 10-Apr-3 Tennants, Leyburn #920

MESKER, Theodorus Ludovicus (1853-1894) Dutch
£11111 $17667 €16000 Buying flowers on the market on a sunny day (131x91cm-52x36in) s.d.1881. 29-Apr-3 Christie's, Amsterdam #171/R est:15000-20000
£20000 $31400 €30000 At the book stall (43x75cm-17x30in) s.d.1877. 19-Nov-2 Bonhams, New Bond Street #6/R est:6000-8000

MESLY, David (1918-) ?
Sculpture
£1506 $2335 €2350 Ours debout (35cm-14in) s. num.EA4/4 black pat bronze. 4-Dec-2 Libert, Castor, Paris #168/R
£1731 $2717 €2700 Surprise (26cm-10in) s. num.IV/IV brown pat bronze Cast Serralheiro. 24-Nov-2 Lesieur & Le Bars, Le Havre #121/R
£1799 $2878 €2500 Igor, ours assis (18x22cm-7x9in) s.num.4/8 black pat bronze Cast Serralheiro. 18-May-3 Charbonneaux, Paris #231/R est:2500-3000
£2887 $4649 €4100 Manchot (38cm-15in) num 4/4 black pat bronze f.Serrhalheiro cire perdue. 12-May-3 Lesieur & Le Bars, Le Havre #72/R
£2911 $4542 €4600 Ingenue (40x15x11cm-16x6x4in) s.num.II/IV black pat bronze Cast Serralheiro. 20-Oct-2 Charbonneaux, Paris #199/R est:3500-3800
£5036 $8058 €7000 Seduisante (56cm-22in) num.III/IV black pat bronze Cast Serralheiro. 18-May-3 Charbonneaux, Paris #232/R est:6000-7000
£5960 $9715 €9000 Sensuelle (56x30cm-22x12in) s.num.4/8 blue pat bronze. 31-Jan-3 Charbonneaux, Paris #183 est:6000-7000

MESNAGER, Jerome (1961-) French
£408 $649 €600 Femme assise (65x54cm-26x21in) s.d.1993 acrylic. 24-Mar-3 Claude Boisgirard, Paris #169/R
£517 $822 €750 Silhouettes sur fond rouge (130x80cm-51x31in) s.d.90 oil acrylic. 8-Mar-3 Peron, Melun #63
£633 $1000 €1000 Silhouette (116x89cm-46x35in) s.d.1989 acrylic. 2-Dec-2 Tajan, Paris #249/R
£764 $1207 €1100 Ho hisse (78x38cm-31x15in) s. painted wood. 27-Apr-3 Perrin, Versailles #138/R
£833 $1317 €1200 Bacchus et a Bercy (193x97cm-76x38in) s.d. s.i.verso acrylic metal wood prov. 27-Apr-3 Perrin, Versailles #146/R
£894 $1457 €1350 La danse (116x89cm-46x35in) s. acrylic. 1-Feb-3 Claude Aguttes, Neuilly #292/R
£1226 $1901 €1950 Vive le roi (95x65cm-37x26in) s. acrylic panel. 7-Oct-2 Claude Aguttes, Neuilly #136
£1879 $3026 €2800 Danse bleue (162x130cm-64x51in) s.d.1999 acrylic. 23-Feb-3 Mercier & Cie, Lille #138/R
£1944 $3091 €2800 Alors (73x129cm-29x51in) s. acrylic panel exhib. 29-Apr-3 Artcurial Briest, Paris #421 est:3000-3500

MESPLES, Paul Eugène (1849-?) French
£1300 $2028 €1950 Ballerinas (59x72cm-23x28in) s. 8-Oct-2 Bonhams, Knightsbridge #54/R est:1500-2000

MESS, George J (1898-1962) American

£584 $900 €876 Hillside farm (30x41cm-12x16in) s. board painted c.1940. 8-Sep-2 Treadway Gallery, Cincinnati #661/R
£755 $1200 €1133 Winter landscape, Indiana (16x22cm-6x9in) s. painted c.1940. 4-May-3 Treadway Gallery, Cincinnati #601/R

MESSAC, Ivan (1948-) French

£4723 $7509 €6800 Passion Hindoue/Ravi Sahnkar (100x100cm-39x39in) s.d.70 verso acrylic exhib. 29-Apr-3 Artcurial Briest, Paris #419/R est:4500-6000

MESSAGER, Annette (1943-) French

Sculpture

£10127 $16000 €15191 Mes voeux (300x15cm-118x6in) i.verso photograph tape string assemblage exec.1989 prov.exhib. 13-Nov-2 Sotheby's, New York #469/R est:10000-15000

MESSAGIER, Jean (1920-1999) French

£772 $1204 €1158 Moteur a orages (32x90cm-13x35in) s. d.Juin 1967 verso prov.exhib. 11-Nov-2 Rasmussen, Vejle #108/R (D.KR 9000)
£845 $1403 €1200 La lecon de juin (26x60cm-10x24in) s.i. paint paillettes. 18-Jun-3 Anaf, Lyon #60/R
£1064 $1777 €1500 Deux paysages timides (195x298cm-77x117in) s.i. s.verso acrylic. 23-Jun-3 Claude Boisgirard, Paris #153/R est:1500-2000
£1101 $1706 €1652 Composition in red and brown (35x75cm-14x30in) s. s.i.d.Aout 1963 and 1966 verso prov. 1-Oct-2 Rasmussen, Copenhagen #153/R est:8000 (D.KR 13000)
£1127 $1870 €1600 Reposoir pour les Iles, Cannes (27x46cm-11x18in) s. s.i.d.verso paint. 18-Jun-3 Anaf, Lyon #61/R est:1200-1500
£1156 $1839 €1700 Composition (19x33cm-7x13in) s. s.d.avril 1960 verso prov. 26-Feb-3 Artcurial Briest, Paris #461/R est:1000-1500
£1397 $2221 €2096 Theatre Bleu (60x92cm-24x36in) s.verso d.1962 stretcher exhib.prov. 10-Mar-3 Rasmussen, Vejle #675/R est:20000-25000 (D.KR 15000)
£1410 $2214 €2200 Wounded knee (107x197cm-42x78in) s. s.i.verso acrylic. 15-Dec-2 Perrin, Versailles #27/R
£1456 $2300 €2300 Untitled (160x240cm-63x94in) s. panel in 4 parts. 2-Dec-2 Tajan, Paris #210/R
£2465 $4092 €3500 Vallee franchie (56x100cm-22x39in) s.i.d.Aout 1955 verso paint. 18-Jun-3 Anaf, Lyon #62/R est:1500-1800
£2482 $4145 €3500 Les paupieres fermees (195x298cm-77x117in) s.i.d. acrylic. 23-Jun-3 Claude Boisgirard, Paris #154/R est:1500-2000
£2535 $4208 €3600 Excroissance apres frottements (76x105cm-30x41in) s.i. paint. 18-Jun-3 Anaf, Lyon #63/R est:4000-4500
£2639 $4196 €3800 Noeuds d'iles (60x92cm-24x36in) s. s.i.d.1961 verso acrylic prov. 29-Apr-3 Artcurial Briest, Paris #584 est:1500-2000
£2958 $4910 €4200 Passage d'une vallee a l'autre (64x116cm-25x46in) s.i.d.verso paint. 18-Jun-3 Anaf, Lyon #64/R est:2000-2200
£2958 $4910 €4200 Couronne le jour (194x223cm-76x88in) s.i. paint. 18-Jun-3 Anaf, Lyon #67/R est:6000-7000
£3265 $5192 €4800 Composition (71x119cm-28x47in) s. 26-Feb-3 Artcurial Briest, Paris #460/R est:2500-3000
£3269 $5133 €5100 Oiseaux atteles (131x191cm-52x75in) s. s.i.d.1965 verso prov.lit. 11-Dec-2 Artcurial Briest, Paris #718/R
£3803 $6313 €5400 Les chevreuils fous (132x191cm-52x75in) s. s.i.d.verso paint. 18-Jun-3 Anaf, Lyon #65/R est:4000-5000
£3944 $6546 €5600 Faut-il vraiment regarder un paysage (130x195cm-51x77in) s.i. paint. 18-Jun-3 Anaf, Lyon #68/R est:3000-4000
£4167 $6875 €6000 Hommage a Chambord (105x170cm-41x67in) s.i.d.Septembre 1964 s.verso exhib. 1-Jul-3 Artcurial Briest, Paris #796/R est:4000-6000
£4225 $7014 €6000 Capture d'une apres-midi (128x191cm-50x75in) s.d.verso paint. 18-Jun-3 Anaf, Lyon #66/R est:3000-4000
£5080 $7875 €7620 Machine a aimer, Kuala Lumpur - orange red composition (130x195cm-51x77in) s. prov. 1-Oct-2 Rasmussen, Copenhagen #49/R est:60000-80000 (D.KR 60000)
£8397 $13184 €13100 Septembre en equilibre (192x221cm-76x87in) s. s.i.d.1960 verso prov. 15-Dec-2 Perrin, Versailles #57/R

Works on paper

£252 $390 €400 Un printemps pour Isabelle (50x65cm-20x26in) s. aerosol col wax crayon. 30-Oct-2 Artcurial Briest, Paris #722
£563 $935 €800 Sans titre, brun/bleu (73x106cm-29x42in) s.d.juin W/C. 18-Jun-3 Anaf, Lyon #58/R
£897 $1497 €1300 Signature d'une matinee vers midi (76x107cm-30x42in) s. pastel. 9-Jul-3 Cornette de St.Cyr, Paris #323/R

MESSEL, Oliver (1904-1978) British

£700 $1084 €1050 Jug off azaleas (61x49cm-24x19in) s. 30-Sep-2 Sotheby's, Olympia #174/R
£750 $1162 €1125 Head study of Mrs Maud Messel (40x31cm-16x12in) canvasboard. 30-Sep-2 Sotheby's, Olympia #37/R
£900 $1396 €1350 Portrait of Maud Messel, the artist's mother (43x34cm-17x13in) 30-Sep-2 Sotheby's, Olympia #172/R est:1000-1500
£900 $1396 €1350 Portrait of a lady wearing Edwardian costume (33x47cm-13x19in) board. 30-Sep-2 Sotheby's, Olympia #177/R est:500-700
£1300 $2041 €1950 Portrait of David Robertson (39x30cm-15x12in) s. board. 16-Dec-2 Sotheby's, London #96/R est:600-800
£1800 $2790 €2700 Lilies (99x74cm-39x29in) board painted c.1930. 30-Sep-2 Sotheby's, Olympia #173/R est:1500-2000
£1800 $2790 €2700 Portrait of Mrs Maud Messel, artist's mother (58x48cm-23x19in) canvasboard. 30-Sep-2 Sotheby's, Olympia #175/R est:2000-3000
£2400 $3720 €3600 Basket of roses (58x51cm-23x20in) board prov. 30-Sep-2 Sotheby's, Olympia #194/R est:1000-1500

Works on paper

£300 $464 €450 Delia (36x49cm-14x19in) s. W/C over pencil. 30-Sep-2 Sotheby's, Olympia #178/R
£350 $542 €525 Mother and child (74x56cm-29x22in) s. black chk htd white. 30-Sep-2 Sotheby's, Olympia #190
£400 $624 €600 Theatrical costume study (51x36cm-20x14in) s.i. pencil W/C htd white. 26-Mar-3 Hamptons Fine Art, Godalming #52
£400 $632 €580 Pages in Cinderella (23x28cm-9x11in) s. chl gouache. 22-Jul-3 Gorringes, Lewes #1655
£450 $711 €675 Flower girl (54x40cm-21x16in) s. pencil ink W/C gouache. 27-Nov-2 Sotheby's, Olympia #6/R
£560 $918 €840 Study of a young man's head (47x37cm-19x15in) charcoal wash pastel. 2-Jun-3 David Duggleby, Scarborough #283
£580 $900 €870 Masked Greek dancer (44x36cm-17x14in) s.d.1926 W/C over pencil. 30-Sep-2 Sotheby's, Olympia #192/R
£600 $930 €900 Study of young black boy (71x53cm-28x21in) s. W/C. 30-Sep-2 Sotheby's, Olympia #189/R
£700 $1084 €1050 Design for the Osterley Ball (48x35cm-19x14in) s.i. W/C over pencil. 30-Sep-2 Sotheby's, Olympia #180/R
£800 $1240 €1200 Costume designs - princess Auroura (38x29cm-15x11in) s. W/C over pencil pair. 30-Sep-2 Sotheby's, Olympia #176/R
£800 $1240 €1200 Costume design - Sally Grey (51x35cm-20x14in) s. gouache W/C over pencil. 30-Sep-2 Sotheby's, Olympia #183/R
£800 $1240 €1200 Costume designs (48x30cm-19x12in) s. one d.1936 verso W/C over pencil three. 30-Sep-2 Sotheby's, Olympia #184/R
£1200 $1860 €1800 Portrait of a lady in a feather bonnet (36x25cm-14x10in) s.d.1934 i.verso pencil pen ink. 30-Sep-2 Sotheby's, Olympia #193/R est:600-800
£1300 $2016 €1950 Juliet's bedroom (31x43cm-12x17in) W/C over pencil exhib. 30-Sep-2 Sotheby's, Olympia #186/R est:500-700
£1600 $2480 €2400 Tyrolean girls (43x33cm-17x13in) s. W/C over pencil pair. 30-Sep-2 Sotheby's, Olympia #187/R est:800-1200
£1700 $2636 €2550 Costume design of warriors (48x32cm-19x13in) W/C over pencil pair. 30-Sep-2 Sotheby's, Olympia #188/R est:1500-2000
£2200 $3410 €3300 Lady in 18th century costume with her poodle (48x35cm-19x14in) s. W/C over pencil. 30-Sep-2 Sotheby's, Olympia #191/R est:500-900
£4200 $6510 €6300 Costume designs (48x33cm-19x13in) s. W/C over pencil pair. 30-Sep-2 Sotheby's, Olympia #185/R est:1500-2000
£5500 $8524 €8250 Dr Rosings libary in Brussels (31x50cm-12x20in) s. W/C gouache over pen ink. 30-Sep-2 Sotheby's, Olympia #169/R est:800-1200

MESSENSEE, Jurgen (1937-) Austrian

£4430 $6867 €7000 Woman smoking. s.i.d.89 verso acrylic. 24-Sep-2 Wiener Kunst Auktionen, Vienna #274/R est:7000-12000
£10759 $17000 €17000 Taking a walk (218x170cm-86x67in) s.d.83 acrylic. 27-Nov-2 Dorotheum, Vienna #311/R est:15000-20000

MESSER, Mable B (fl.1910-1940) British

£340 $530 €510 Still life of pedestal glass vase filled with flowers (74x61cm-29x24in) s. 17-Sep-2 Bonhams, Knightsbridge #120/R

MESSERSCHMIDT, Franz Xavier (1736-1783) German

Sculpture

£1266 $2000 €2000 Second head (31cm-12in) pat.plaster lit. 27-Nov-2 Wiener Kunst Auktionen, Vienna #549/R est:2000-4000

MESSERSCHMITT, Pius Ferdinand (1858-1915) German

£283 $436 €450 Coach trip (46x66cm-18x26in) s. 23-Oct-2 Neumeister, Munich #704

MESSIER, Gregory F (20th C) American

Works on paper

£949 $1500 €1424 Canada geese in flight (51x70cm-20x28in) s. W/C gouache on board prov. 3-Apr-3 Christie's, Rockefeller NY #196/R est:1000-1500

MESSINA, Francesco (1900-1995) Italian

Sculpture

£2532 $3949 €4000 Dancer (14x42cm-6x17in) brown pat bronze exec.1969. 14-Sep-2 Meeting Art, Vercelli #718/R
£2837 $4596 €4000 Fanciullo con arpione (54cm-21in) s.base bronze. 26-May-3 Christie's, Milan #172 est:3500-5000

£3846 $6038 €6000 Head of boy (24cm-9in) s. bronze. 20-Nov-2 Pandolfini, Florence #59

MESSMANN, Carl Ludvig Ferd (1826-1893) Danish
£287 $465 €416 Coastal landscape, North Sjaelland, from Klampenborg towards Copenhagen (39x63cm-15x25in) s.d.1891. 26-May-3 Rasmussen, Copenhagen #1522/R (D.KR 3000)
£386 $610 €579 Landscape with fields, sheep and houses (50x73cm-20x29in) s. 17-Nov-2 Hindemae, Ullerslev #7570/R (D.KR 4500)

MESTELLE, J H (?) German?
£548 $806 €850 Beach near Ebbe (40x80cm-16x31in) s. 24-Jun-2 Dr Fritz Nagel, Stuttgart #6083

MESZOLY, Geza (1844-1887) Hungarian
£3633 $5667 €5268 Dusk at Lake Balaton (34x42cm-13x17in) s.d.1886. 12-Apr-3 Mu Terem Galeria, Budapest #46/R est:1000000 (H.F 1300000)
£3633 $5667 €5268 Poultry (10x13cm-4x5in) s. panel. 12-Apr-3 Mu Terem Galeria, Budapest #135/R est:950000 (H.F 1300000)
£5030 $7847 €7545 Waterside landscape with clouds (15x33cm-6x13in) s. board. 11-Apr-3 Kieselbach, Budapest #6/R est:1800000 (H.F 1800000)
£6707 $10462 €9725 Landscape in summer (17x33cm-7x13in) s.d.873 panel. 12-Apr-3 Mu Terem Galeria, Budapest #55/R est:1700000 (H.F 2400000)
£16136 $25010 €23397 Fisherman's cottage at Szantod (40x74cm-16x29in) s.d.873 exhib.lit. 9-Dec-2 Mu Terem Galeria, Budapest #156/R est:3500000 (H.F 6000000)

METCALF, Conger (1914-1998) American
£414 $650 €621 Divertimento, II Segreto (10x18cm-4x7in) s. oil graphite clay coated panel exhib. 23-Nov-2 Jackson's, Cedar Falls #323/R
£755 $1200 €1133 Studies of Sicilian vase bearers (59x89cm-23x35in) s. i.verso oil graphite. 7-Mar-3 Skinner, Boston #607/R
£764 $1200 €1146 La famiglia (25x20cm-10x8in) s. panel exhib. 23-Nov-2 Jackson's, Cedar Falls #307/R est:800-1200
£1847 $2900 €2771 Portrait of a young girl in a blue hat (30x25cm-12x10in) s. oil graphite clay coated paper exhib. 23-Nov-2 Jackson's, Cedar Falls #304/R est:1000-2000

Works on paper
£452 $700 €678 Portrait with figures (25x25cm-10x10in) s.d.Dec 74 ink W/C. 2-Nov-2 North East Auctions, Portsmouth #74/R
£482 $800 €699 Contemplative thought. Young girl (28x20cm-11x8in) one s. graphite oil pair. 14-Jun-3 Jackson's, Cedar Falls #25/R

METCALF, Eliab (1785-1834) American
£818 $1300 €1227 Portrait of Julia Metcalf and James, John T and William H Metcalf (51x38cm-20x15in) panel double-sided prov. 29-Apr-3 Doyle, New York #25

METCALF, Paul (20th C) British
Works on paper
£300 $495 €435 Wymondham Abbey in the snow (32x47cm-13x19in) s. W/C. 1-Jul-3 Bonhams, Norwich #180

METCALF, Willard Leroy (1858-1925) American
£2215 $3500 €3323 Palm trees (51x36cm-20x14in) est.st dr paper pair. 26-Apr-3 Jeffery Burchard, Florida #40
£7595 $12000 €11393 Smith homestead (30x51cm-12x20in) s.d.74. 24-Apr-3 Shannon's, Milford #54/R est:12000-18000
£14286 $22000 €21429 Late afternoon, Manchester, Massachusetts (33x23cm-13x9in) s. s.i.d.1877 verso prov. 24-Oct-2 Shannon's, Milford #26/R est:12000-18000
£14744 $23000 €22116 Summer landscape with creek (40x38cm-16x15in) s.d.1911 canvasboard. 14-Sep-2 Weschler, Washington #619/R est:10000-15000

METCALFE, Colin J (20th C) British
£280 $445 €420 Sheep on the moors (28x76cm-11x30in) s.d.1998 board. 27-Feb-3 Richardson & Smith, Whitby #451
£460 $731 €690 Proud mother (48x58cm-19x23in) s.d.1995 board. 27-Feb-3 Richardson & Smith, Whitby #423

METCALFE, Gerald Fenwick (fl.1894-1929) British
Works on paper
£20967 $32500 €31451 Vindemia (35x72cm-14x28in) s.i. pencil W/C gouache board. 29-Oct-2 Sotheby's, New York #119/R est:7000-10000

METEIN-GILLIARD, Valentine (1891-) Swiss
£282 $462 €409 Fruit trees in bloom (65x50cm-26x20in) s. 4-Jun-3 Fischer, Luzern #2246/R (S.FR 600)

METEYARD, Thomas B (1865-1928) American
£1975 $3100 €2963 Misty day, New England Coast (38x56cm-15x22in) 14-Dec-2 CRN Auctions, Cambridge #22/R
Works on paper
£250 $400 €363 Breakwater, Cavalaire (26x37cm-10x15in) s. W/C. 16-May-3 Skinner, Boston #349/R

METHER-BORGSTROM, Ernst (1917-1996) Finnish
£1268 $2041 €1800 Composition (39x55cm-15x22in) s.d.1975. 10-May-3 Bukowskis, Helsinki #252/R est:1200-1500
Works on paper
£286 $454 €420 Surfaces - composition (42x60cm-17x24in) s.d.72 gouache. 24-Mar-3 Bukowskis, Helsinki #185/R

METHFESSEL, Adolf (1836-1909) Argentinian
£480 $749 €720 Small chapel in wood (35x28cm-14x11in) mono.d.XI/86 canvas on board. 6-Nov-2 Dobiaschofsky, Bern #3529/R (S.FR 1100)

METHUEN, Lord (1886-1974) British
£300 $465 €450 View of Claverton Manor (77x102cm-30x40in) s. 3-Dec-2 Bonhams, Knightsbridge #354
£800 $1312 €1200 Pantheon at Stourhead (36x45cm-14x18in) s. board exhib. 3-Jun-3 Sotheby's, Olympia #37/R
£1200 $1860 €1800 View over the House of Parliament from my studio window at 12 Medway Street (54x77cm-21x30in) s. exhib. 4-Dec-2 Sotheby's, London #59/R est:1200-1800
Works on paper
£280 $456 €420 Avoncliff Mill (30x42cm-12x17in) s.i.d.1965 pen ink wash. 17-Feb-3 Bonhams, Bath #71

METSYS, Jan (circle) (c.1509-1575) Flemish
£24000 $37440 €36000 Madonna and Child (61x49cm-24x19in) panel prov. 9-Apr-3 Christie's, London #13/R est:20000-30000

METSYS, Jan (studio) (c.1509-1575) Flemish
£5479 $8548 €8219 Caritas (62x57cm-24x22in) 28-Mar-3 Koller, Zurich #3068/R est:8000-12000 (S.FR 12000)

METSYS, Quentin (attrib) (1466-1530) Flemish
£12676 $21042 €18000 Portrait of old woman (29x24cm-11x9in) i. verso panel prov. 11-Jun-3 Dorotheum, Vienna #94/R est:6000-10000

METSYS, Quentin (circle) (1466-1530) Flemish
£11511 $18417 €16000 Christ as Salvator Mundi (46x36cm-18x14in) panel. 13-May-3 Sotheby's, Amsterdam #91a/R est:4000-6000

METTENHOVEN, Marcel (20th C) French
£276 $439 €400 Paysage fluvial (46x65cm-18x26in) s.d.1933. 10-Mar-3 Thierry & Lannon, Brest #121
Works on paper
£292 $475 €420 Devant la chapelle (24x37cm-9x15in) s.d.1913 W/C. 19-Jul-3 Thierry & Lannon, Brest #284

METTENLEITER, Peter (19th C) German
Works on paper
£255 $397 €400 Hohenaschau (12x17cm-5x7in) wash pencil. 5-Nov-2 Hartung & Hartung, Munich #5184/R

METTLING, Louis (1847-1904) French
£696 $1100 €1100 Jeune fille allongee sur l'herbe (24x42cm-9x17in) s. panel. 1-Dec-2 Peron, Melun #59
£850 $1343 €1275 Peaches, white grapes, black grapes a glass and a decanter (55x66cm-22x26in) s. 14-Nov-2 Christie's, Kensington #81/R
£1200 $1896 €1800 Copper cleaner (49x27cm-19x11in) s. panel exhib. 12-Nov-2 Bonhams, Knightsbridge #165/R est:600-800

METZ, Alois (1869-?) German
£1500 $2325 €2250 Orchards in blossom (100x115cm-39x45in) mono. 5-Dec-2 Christie's, Kensington #127/R est:1000-1500

METZ, Caesar (1823-1895) German
£1844 $2987 €2600 Moon rising over Ammersee (70x120cm-28x47in) s. 22-May-3 Dorotheum, Vienna #103/R est:2800-3200
£2721 $4327 €4000 Mountain valley with river (130x170cm-51x67in) s.d.1848. 19-Mar-3 Neumeister, Munich #646/R est:4000

METZ, Conrad Martin (1749-1827) British
Works on paper
£1006 $1560 €1600 Merkur and Argus (32x23cm-13x9in) mono.d.1823 wash pen htd white. 1-Oct-2 Dorotheum, Vienna #63/R est:1900-2000

METZ, Friedrich (1820-1901) German
Works on paper
£288 $449 €420 Concordia Temple in Agrigent (41x55cm-16x22in) s.i. pencil. 11-Apr-3 Winterberg, Heidelberg #485

METZ, Johann Martin (1717-1790) German
£7143 $11357 €10500 Bouquet by tree in landscape (86x67cm-34x26in) s.d.1770. 21-Mar-3 Millon & Associes, Paris #23/R est:20000

METZGER, Henry (1876-1934) Canadian
£225 $349 €338 Autumn lake scene (41x55cm-16x22in) s. 24-Sep-2 Ritchie, Toronto #3135 (C.D 550)
£225 $349 €338 Our camping place on Whitewood Lake (41x50cm-16x20in) s. i.verso. 24-Sep-2 Ritchie, Toronto #3136 (C.D 550)
£266 $413 €399 Mountain view (41x56cm-16x22in) s. 24-Sep-2 Ritchie, Toronto #3134/R (C.D 650)
£656 $1016 €984 Distinguished drummer (52x41cm-20x16in) s. 24-Sep-2 Ritchie, Toronto #3132/R (C.D 1600)
£943 $1461 €1415 Chief O-Hoo (42x34cm-17x13in) s.i. 24-Sep-2 Ritchie, Toronto #3131/R est:1500-2000 (C.D 2300)
£1200 $1884 €1800 Portrait of Sonia Peasis (25x20cm-10x8in) s. 13-Dec-2 Keys, Aylsham #734/R est:1200-1500

METZINGER, Jean (1883-1956) French
£4140 $6500 €6210 Coucher du Soleil (60x74cm-24x29in) mono.i. prov. 14-Dec-2 Weschler, Washington #607/R est:8000-10000
£5000 $7700 €7500 Deux jeunes filles a la fenetre (27x22cm-11x9in) init. board painted c.1904. 23-Oct-2 Sotheby's, Olympia #648/R est:6000-8000
£7742 $12232 €12000 Paysage avec maison (35x27cm-14x11in) s. painted c.1930. 18-Dec-2 Tajan, Paris #48/R est:15000
£11224 $17847 €16500 Paysage du Midi (46x55cm-18x22in) s. painted c.1940. 24-Mar-3 Claude Boisgirard, Paris #56/R
£17195 $28715 €24933 Tete de femme (34x23cm-13x9in) s. panel prov.exhib. 24-Jun-3 Koller, Zurich #135/R est:30000-40000 (S.FR 38000)
£27950 $45000 €41925 Femme assise au bouquet de feuilage (65x54cm-26x21in) s. painted c.1905 prov. 8-May-3 Christie's, Rockefeller NY #142/R est:30000-40000
£32374 $53094 €45000 Paris, le Parc Monceau (53x72cm-21x28in) s. painted c.1906. 4-Jun-3 Marc Kohn, Paris #46/R est:50000-60000
£38462 $60000 €57693 Nu au perrouquet (91x73cm-36x29in) s. canvas on panel painted c.1953 prov. 6-Nov-2 Sotheby's, New York #326/R est:60000-80000
£55000 $90200 €82500 Ecuyere au cirque (81x65cm-32x26in) s.d.27 prov. 5-Feb-3 Sotheby's, London #165/R est:70000
£67308 $105000 €100962 Les arlequins (89x130cm-35x51in) s.d.1925 prov. 7-Nov-2 Christie's, Rockefeller NY #285/R est:90000-120000
£93168 $150000 €139752 Paysage imaginaire (116x89cm-46x35in) s. painted 1928 prov.lit. 7-May-3 Sotheby's, New York #348/R est:150000-200000
£397436 $620000 €596154 L'invitation au voyage (130x195cm-51x77in) s. i.on stretcher painted c.1927 prov. 6-Nov-2 Sotheby's, New York #265/R est:300000-400000
Works on paper
£1122 $1785 €1650 Figure dans un paysage (15x24cm-6x9in) st.sig. pencil dr. 26-Feb-3 Artcurial Briest, Paris #92/R est:1200-1500
£2885 $4529 €4500 Paysage cubiste (13x10cm-5x4in) st.sig. gouache. 12-Dec-2 Rabourdin & Choppin de Janvry, Paris #72/R est:5000
£5500 $8745 €8250 Portrait de femme (29x22cm-11x9in) s.d.1920 gouache paper on canvas. 20-Mar-3 Sotheby's, Olympia #204/R est:6000-8000

METZKER, Ray K (1931-) American
Photographs
£4114 $6500 €6171 Philadelphia, from series city whispers (20x30cm-8x12in) s.verso gelatin silver print prov.exhib. 25-Apr-3 Phillips, New York #185/R est:3000-5000

METZKES, Harald (1929-) German
£1384 $2131 €2200 Self portrait before window (60x50cm-24x20in) s.d.1977. 26-Oct-2 Dr Lehr, Berlin #335/R est:2500
£1698 $2615 €2700 Seated nude (50x60cm-20x24in) s.d.1979. 26-Oct-2 Dr Lehr, Berlin #336/R est:3000
£2264 $3487 €3600 Still life with beer glass and herring (50x60cm-20x24in) s.d.1976. 26-Oct-2 Dr Lehr, Berlin #334/R est:3000

METZL, Ervine (1899-?) American
Works on paper
£745 $1200 €1118 Night train in landscape (38x28cm-15x11in) s.d.1923 gouache linen. 18-Feb-3 John Moran, Pasadena #118

METZLER, Johann Jakob (attrib) (1804-1839) German
£1090 $1711 €1700 Holy Family with Infant St John the Baptist (76x62cm-30x24in) 21-Nov-2 Van Ham, Cologne #1787/R est:800

METZLER, Kurt Laurenz (1941-) Swiss
Sculpture
£1674 $2444 €2511 Untitled figure (79x19x28cm-31x7x11in) iron. 17-Jun-2 Philippe Schuler, Zurich #4244/R est:4000-6000 (S.FR 3800)

METZOLDT, Max (1859-?) German?
£2431 $3865 €3500 First daffodils, girl from Laren, Holland (81x61cm-32x24in) s. i.on stretcher. 29-Apr-3 Christie's, Amsterdam #66/R est:4000-6000

MEUCCI, Angiola (1880-1966) Italian
£288 $453 €450 Mountainous landscape (41x63cm-16x25in) s. cardboard. 10-Dec-2 Della Rocca, Turin #304
£340 $541 €500 On the bench (43x29cm-17x11in) s. cardboard. 1-Mar-3 Meeting Art, Vercelli #103
£340 $541 €500 Mountainous landscape (44x35cm-17x14in) s.d.1923 cardboard. 1-Mar-3 Meeting Art, Vercelli #198
£481 $755 €750 Mountainous landscape (82x100cm-32x39in) 10-Dec-2 Della Rocca, Turin #275

MEUCCI, Michelangelo (19th C) Italian
£300 $456 €450 Hanging songbirds (21x17cm-8x7in) s.i.d.1875 board oval. 29-Aug-2 Christie's, Kensington #125
£385 $604 €600 Robins (45x21cm-18x8in) s.i. card. 16-Dec-2 Pandolfini, Florence #126
£446 $700 €669 Game bird (48x38cm-19x15in) s.i.d.1877 board. 22-Nov-2 Skinner, Boston #36a/R est:400-600
£542 $850 €813 Still lifes with game birds (49x38cm-19x15in) s.i.d.1877 board two. 22-Nov-2 Skinner, Boston #39/R
£550 $897 €825 Hanging birds (22x18cm-9x7in) s.d.1875 pair. 12-Feb-3 Bonhams, Knightsbridge #22
£720 $1138 €1080 Hanging songbirds (21x16cm-8x6in) s.d.1875 panel oval pair. 6-Apr-3 Lots Road, London #345/R
£890 $1398 €1300 Still lfie of pomegranates, peaches, grapes and plums (90x70cm-35x28in) s.d.1902. 16-Apr-3 Dorotheum, Salzburg #121/R
£1006 $1560 €1600 Still lives of birds (21x17cm-8x7in) s.i.d.1871 board oval two. 29-Oct-2 Dorotheum, Vienna #256/R est:1600-1800
£1250 $2000 €1875 Still life with songbirds and a letter (23x18cm-9x7in) s.i.d.1873 board trompe l'oeil sold with a companion. 14-May-3 Butterfields, San Francisco #1057/R est:3000-5000
£2400 $3888 €3600 Tulips, roses, magnolias, lilies and other summer flowers in a basket (75x62cm-30x24in) s.i.d.1875 oval. 23-Jan-3 Christie's, Kensington #177/R est:800-1200
£2500 $3975 €3750 Cornucopia of fruit (90x60cm-35x24in) s.d.1885. 20-Mar-3 Christie's, Kensington #36/R est:3000-5000
£3145 $5000 €4718 Hanging fowl with cherries (54x46cm-21x18in) s.d.1875 pair. 5-Mar-3 Christie's, Rockefeller NY #78/R est:6000-8000

MEULEN, Adam Frans van der (1632-1690) Flemish
£7000 $10920 €10500 Cavalry skirmish with a windmill on a hill beyond (42x58cm-17x23in) 9-Apr-3 Christie's, London #9/R est:7000-10000
£9434 $14717 €15000 Horsemen in wood (72x97cm-28x38in) s. 23-Sep-2 Wiener Kunst Auktionen, Vienna #63/R est:25000-50000
£15000 $25050 €21750 Extensive river landscape with a cavalry troops on a path (54x64cm-21x25in) s. 11-Jul-3 Christie's, Kensington #100/R est:5000-8000
Works on paper
£2800 $4676 €4060 Battle scene (43x61cm-17x24in) i.d.1686 pen brown ink blk red chk. 9-Jul-3 Sotheby's, London #102/R est:3000-5000

MEULEN, Adam Frans van der (attrib) (1632-1690) Flemish
£1370 $2137 €2000 Soldiers in military camp by river (23x33cm-9x13in) panel. 10-Apr-3 Van Ham, Cologne #1240/R est:3000
£5390 $8355 €8085 Battle scene (48x72cm-19x28in) 3-Dec-2 Bukowskis, Stockholm #474/R est:35000-40000 (S.KR 76000)

MEULEN, Adam Frans van der (circle) (1632-1690) Flemish
£6918 $10723 €11000 Elegant hunting party outside chateau (114x160cm-45x63in) prov. 2-Oct-2 Dorotheum, Vienna #78/R est:12000-16000
£15000 $23550 €22500 Landscape with noblemen in carriages and other figures by a moated town (119x176cm-47x69in) prov. 12-Dec-2 Sotheby's, London #201/R est:12000-18000

MEULEN, Adam Frans van der (style) (1632-1690) Flemish
£11783 $19324 €17085 Landscape with riders and figures (48x71cm-19x28in) 4-Jun-3 AB Stockholms Auktionsverk #2523/R est:50000-70000 (S.KR 150000)

MEULEN, Edmond van der (1841-1905) Belgian
£577 $906 €900 Chiens de chasse. s.i. 19-Nov-2 Servarts Themis, Bruxelles #130

MEULEN, Sieuwert van der (?-1730) Dutch
Works on paper
£1400 $2338 €2030 Four birds and a mouse (25x36cm-10x14in) W/C prov. 9-Jul-3 Sotheby's, London #123/R est:2000-3000

MEULEN, Steven van der (studio) (16th C) Flemish
£11000 $17270 €16500 Portrait of a gentleman, aged 26 in a white tunic, gold chain (43x33cm-17x13in) i.d.1568 panel. 10-Dec-2 Bonhams, New Bond Street #274/R est:4000-6000

MEULEN, van der (17th C) Dutch
£5833 $9217 €9100 Battle by Mont-Cassel (50x61cm-20x24in) 13-Nov-2 Marc Kohn, Paris #43/R

MEULENER, Pieter (1602-1654) Dutch
£13636 $20318 €21000 Entry of Spanish nobleman into Antwerp (73x100cm-29x39in) panel. 26-Jun-2 Neumeister, Munich #643/R est:18000
£14013 $21860 €22000 Cavalry battle scene on an open field near a farm (44x64cm-17x25in) s.d.1650 panel. 5-Nov-2 Sotheby's, Amsterdam #331/R est:8000-12000

MEUNIER, C (19th C) Belgian
Sculpture
£1325 $2159 €2000 Forgeron au repos. green brown pat bronze. 17-Feb-3 Amberes, Antwerp #446

MEUNIER, Constantin (1831-1905) Belgian
£577 $906 €900 Apparition de la Vierge (45x32cm-18x13in) s. panel. 19-Nov-2 Servarts Themis, Bruxelles #120/R
£609 $950 €914 Self portrait (53x43cm-21x17in) s. 29-Mar-3 Charlton Hall, Columbia #229/R
£851 $1421 €1200 Le Borinage en hiver (17x25cm-7x10in) s. 17-Jun-3 Palais de Beaux Arts, Brussels #608/R
£2069 $3310 €3000 Digne a Ostende (25x38cm-10x15in) s.i. panel. 15-Mar-3 De Vuyst, Lokeren #519/R est:2500-3500
£2734 $4374 €3800 L'ouvriere (70x44cm-28x17in) s.d. panel prov. 13-May-3 Palais de Beaux Arts, Brussels #104/R est:3750-5000
Sculpture
£1083 $1689 €1700 Buste masculin (46cm-18in) s. brown pat bronze Cast Verbeyst. 11-Nov-2 Horta, Bruxelles #99 est:2000-3000
£1126 $1835 €1700 Hiercheur debout (47cm-19in) s. pat bronze. 17-Feb-3 Horta, Bruxelles #178/R
£1987 $3238 €3000 Hiercheur assis (38cm-15in) s. black pat bronze. 17-Feb-3 Horta, Bruxelles #180/R
£1987 $3238 €3000 Hiercheur debout (51cm-20in) s. black pat bronze. 17-Feb-3 Horta, Bruxelles #179/R
£2778 $4417 €4000 Maternite (45cm-18in) s. bronze. 29-Apr-3 Campo, Vlaamse Kaai #218/R est:3000-3500
£5396 $8633 €7500 Coup de grisou (26x39x20cm-10x15x8in) s. pat bronze Cast B Verbeyst. 13-May-3 Palais de Beaux Arts, Brussels #101/R est:5000-7500
£6835 $10935 €9500 Blacksmith (47x26cm-19x10in) s. st.f.Peterman dark brown pat bronze exec.1890 exhib. 17-May-3 De Vuyst, Lokeren #452/R est:9000-11000
£9434 $14623 €15000 Pecheur ostendais (81x28cm-32x11in) s. st.f.Petermann dark brown pat bronze exec.1890 prov.lit. 5-Oct-2 De Vuyst, Lokeren #442/R est:15000-16000
Works on paper
£597 $926 €950 Pecheur d'Ostende (36x26cm-14x10in) s. chl sepia dr lit. 5-Oct-2 De Vuyst, Lokeren #243/R
£2759 $4414 €4000 Old mine horse (45x60cm-18x24in) s.d.93 gouache W/C exhib.lit. 15-Mar-3 De Vuyst, Lokeren #522/R est:3500-4500
£3453 $5525 €4800 Moisson (38x48cm-15x19in) mono.i. chl dr exec.c.1894 lit. 17-May-3 De Vuyst, Lokeren #451/R est:3000-4000

MEUNIER, Georgette (1859-1951) Belgian
£1787 $2824 €2681 Still life of white chrysanthemums, porcelain elephant and mirror (140x100cm-55x39in) s. 2-Dec-2 Rasmussen, Copenhagen #1472/R est:15000 (D.KR 21000)

MEURER, Charles A (1865-1955) American
£1154 $1800 €1731 Trompe l'oeil still life (13x22cm-5x9in) s. panel prov. 12-Apr-3 Weschler, Washington #559/R est:1000-1500
£3526 $5500 €5289 Trompe l'oeil still life of pipe and currency (11x23cm-4x9in) s. panel prov. 12-Apr-3 Weschler, Washington #560/R est:3000-5000
£32258 $50000 €48387 Royal flush (36x56cm-14x22in) panel painted c.1899 prov.exhib.lit. 3-Dec-2 Phillips, New York #34/R est:50000-70000

MEURET, François (1800-1887) French
Miniatures
£1100 $1716 €1650 Bespectacled gentleman wearing dark grey suit white waistcoat and shirt (9cm-4in) s.d.1859 gilt mount. 5-Nov-2 Bonhams, New Bond Street #134/R est:1000-1500

MEURIS, Emmanuel (1894-1969) Italian
£253 $395 €400 Les maisons sur la crete a La Haze sur Ourthe (54x65cm-21x26in) s.d.47 panel. 16-Oct-2 Hotel des Ventes Mosan, Brussels #170
Works on paper
£506 $790 €800 La baie de Naples animee (37x30cm-15x12in) s. gouache oval. 15-Oct-2 Vanderkindere, Brussels #35

MEURON, Albert de (1823-1897) Swiss
£437 $681 €656 Interior (37x51cm-15x20in) mono.i.d.Sept 64-6 canvas on board. 20-Nov-2 Fischer, Luzern #2181/R (S.FR 1000)

MEURS, Harmen (1891-1964) Dutch
£993 $1609 €1400 Farmer's wife in front of farm and garden (70x45cm-28x18in) s.d.1925. 26-May-3 Glerum, Amsterdam #87/R

MEXICAN COLONIAL SCHOOL, 17th C
£17683 $29000 €25640 La inmaculada (29x22cm-11x9in) oil feather collage paper on sheet metal prov. 27-May-3 Sotheby's, New York #128

MEXICAN COLONIAL SCHOOL, 18th C
£11585 $19000 €16798 Virgen de Guadalupe (28x22cm-11x9in) i.d.Abril 15 de 1771 copper. 27-May-3 Sotheby's, New York #38

MEY, Carl (1747-1822) German
£327 $510 €520 Portrait of Abraham Lange (37x20cm-15x8in) s.d.1782 verso panel. 9-Oct-2 Michael Zeller, Lindau #587/R

MEY, Gaston de (1933-) Belgian?
£306 $487 €450 Structuur Nuxes. Structuur Mukar (60x50cm-24x20in) s. verso pair. 24-Mar-3 Bernaerts, Antwerp #918

MEY, Jos de (1928-) Belgian
£288 $460 €400 Winter near the farms (36x24cm-14x9in) s. panel. 17-May-3 De Vuyst, Lokeren #143
£604 $972 €900 Farm by the water (84x128cm-33x50in) s. 24-Feb-3 Bernaerts, Antwerp #6/R

MEY, Phil de (19th C) Belgian?
£331 $540 €500 Nature morte aux fleurs et aux fruits (89x102cm-35x40in) 17-Feb-3 Amberes, Antwerp #187

MEYBODEN, Hans (1901-1965) German
£2089 $3258 €3300 Two men with cigarette (63x49cm-25x19in) mono.d.1963 board. 18-Oct-2 Dr Fritz Nagel, Stuttgart #570/R est:3800

MEYER VON BREMEN, Johann Georg (1813-1886) German
£1404 $2050 €2106 The letter, woman reflecting after having read a letter (15x10cm-6x4in) s.i. panel. 17-Jun-2 Schrager Galleries, Milwaukee #1193/R
£2113 $3401 €3000 Baby brother (22x17cm-9x7in) copper lit. 9-May-3 Schloss Ahlden, Ahlden #1390/R est:2500
£2432 $3795 €3600 Boy reading at wooden table (20x16cm-8x6in) s.d.1852 lit. 27-Mar-3 Dr Fritz Nagel, Stuttgart #843/R est:2000
£4423 $6856 €6900 Girl returning home (19x13cm-7x5in) s.d.1884 panel. 7-Dec-2 Hauswedell & Nolte, Hamburg #902/R est:8000
Works on paper
£333 $517 €520 Girl standing with basket (40x22cm-16x9in) s. pencil dr lit. 7-Dec-2 Bergmann, Erlangen #849/R

MEYER, Auguste (19th C) French
£2740 $4274 €4000 Battle of Waterloo (66x99cm-26x39in) s. i. verso. 10-Apr-3 Van Ham, Cologne #1588/R est:3000

MEYER, Baron Adolph de (1868-1946) American?
Photographs
£2597 $4000 €3896 Claude Monet (21x16cm-8x6in) s. photograph prov.lit. 24-Oct-2 Sotheby's, New York #84/R est:3000-5000
£2922 $4500 €4383 John Barrymore (24x18cm-9x7in) i. photograph prov.lit. 24-Oct-2 Sotheby's, New York #85/R est:5000-8000
£7595 $12000 €11393 Olga de Meyer (42x27cm-17x11in) oversized warm toned platinum print prov. 23-Apr-3 Sotheby's, New York #57/R est:6000-9000

MEYER, Carl Diethelm (1840-1884) German
£1217 $1899 €1826 Two children in garden (70x56cm-28x22in) s.d.1880. 16-Sep-2 Philippe Schuler, Zurich #3389/R est:3500-4500 (S.FR 2800)

MEYER, Claus (1856-1919) German
£1310 $2044 €1965 Old man walking down steps lit by lamp (52x71cm-20x28in) s. 20-Nov-2 Fischer, Luzern #1176/R est:3000-4000 (S.FR 3000)

MEYER, Conrad (1618-1689) Swiss
£870 $1348 €1305 Portrait of a 46 year old Zurich official (10x8cm-4x3in) mono.i. copper. 9-Dec-2 Philippe Schuler, Zurich #3828 (S.FR 2000)
£6481 $10435 €9397 Portrait of Salomon Hirtzel (88x69cm-35x27in) s.i.d.1637. 9-May-3 Dobiaschofsky, Bern #11/R est:5500 (S.FR 14000)

MEYER, Elias (1763-1809) Danish
£1550 $2357 €2325 Horse and carriage in the area near Dyrehaven (42x52cm-17x20in) with sig.stretcher prov. 27-Aug-2 Rasmussen, Copenhagen #1489/R est:20000-25000 (D.KR 18000)

MEYER, Elias (attrib) (1763-1809) Danish
£603 $916 €905 Landscape from Naestved with lake (30x44cm-12x17in) panel. 28-Aug-2 Museumsbygningen, Copenhagen #70/R (D.KR 7000)

MEYER, Émile (19th C) French
£510 $795 €800 Compositions aux prunes et peches sur un entablement (38x50cm-15x20in) s.d.1893. 11-Nov-2 Horta, Bruxelles #681
£1528 $2429 €2200 Allegorie de l'Industrie (138x80cm-54x31in) s.d.1891. 30-Apr-3 Tajan, Paris #142/R

MEYER, Emma Eleonore (1859-1921) Danish
£861 $1309 €1292 Summer's day by the old vicarage in Fjellerup near Mejlgaard (78x98cm-31x39in) mono.d.1913. 27-Aug-2 Rasmussen, Copenhagen #1868/R (D.KR 10000)

MEYER, Emmanuel (1836-?) French
£4717 $7311 €7500 Rose bush (116x83cm-46x33in) s. 29-Oct-2 Finarte, Milan #395/R est:5000-6000

MEYER, Ernst (1796-1861) Danish
£405 $653 €608 Well near a monastery in Italy (26x34cm-10x13in) i.verso mahogany study. 26-Feb-3 Museumsbygningen, Copenhagen #18 (D.KR 4500)
£1117 $1777 €1676 Two Italian women, Rome (27x32cm-11x13in) s.stretcher. 5-Mar-3 Rasmussen, Copenhagen #1569/R est:10000-15000 (D.KR 12000)
Works on paper
£443 $718 €665 Woman on steps about to spin wool, cat and chickens watching (17x14cm-7x6in) s.d.1859 W/C. 25-Jan-3 Rasmussen, Havnen #2260 (D.KR 5000)

MEYER, Ernst (attrib) (1796-1861) Danish
£297 $470 €446 Italian monks in front of monastery, evening (33x44cm-13x17in) 5-Apr-3 Rasmussen, Havnen #2036 (D.KR 3200)

MEYER, Frederick William (?-1922) British
£380 $600 €570 White Wings on a summer sea (34x57cm-13x22in) mono. i.on stretcher. 7-Apr-3 Bonhams, Bath #105

MEYER, Hubert (19th C) Swiss
Works on paper
£2105 $3411 €3200 Fabrique de tonneaux sur fond de ville d'anvers (45x70cm-18x28in) s.d.1885 pen ink W/C htd white. 21-Jan-3 Christie's, Amsterdam #91/R est:3000-4000

MEYER, Jeremiah (1735-1789) German
Miniatures
£1000 $1640 €1450 Young gentleman in gold bordered maroon coat (3cm-1in) silver gilt frame oval. 3-Jun-3 Christie's, London #119/R est:1000-1500
£1600 $2624 €2320 Young lady in lace white dress (3cm-1in) gilt metal bracelet clasp oval prov. 3-Jun-3 Christie's, London #76/R est:1500-2500
£3000 $4710 €4500 Young lady in a lilac dress (8cm-3in) gold frame oval. 10-Dec-2 Christie's, London #127/R est:2500-3500
£3000 $4920 €4350 Gentleman in raspberry pink coat (4cm-2in) silver gilt oval. 3-Jun-3 Christie's, London #115/R est:3000-4000
£4200 $6888 €6090 Young lady in a palc blue dress (7cm-3in) painted on a snuff box oval. 3-Jun-3 Christie's, London #96/R est:4000-6000
£5500 $8635 €8250 Young officer in a red coat (4cm-2in) gold fausse montre frame oval. 10-Dec-2 Christie's, London #168/R est:3000-5000

MEYER, Johan (1885-?) Dutch
£789 $1279 €1200 Herfstmorgen aan de beek - autumn morning (45x85cm-18x33in) s.i. s.i.on stretcher. 21-Jan-3 Christie's, Amsterdam #382 est:1200-1600

MEYER, Johan Hendrik Louis (1809-1866) Dutch
£962 $1462 €1500 Wooded river landscape with figures (23x32cm-9x13in) s.d.1833 panel. 17-Aug-2 Hans Stahl, Toestorf #45/R
£2778 $4583 €4000 Mountain landscape with countrymen taking a break (38x47cm-15x19in) s.d.1833 panel. 1-Jul-3 Christie's, Amsterdam #55/R est:4000-6000
£3425 $5377 €5000 River landscape with figures on a path (23x32cm-9x13in) s.d.1833 panel. 15-Apr-3 Sotheby's, Amsterdam #82/R est:5000-7000
£10274 $16130 €15000 Sailing vessels on the shore with Katwijk in the background (39x49cm-15x19in) s. 15-Apr-3 Sotheby's, Amsterdam #189/R est:15000-20000

MEYER, Johann Heinrich (1755-1829) Swiss
Works on paper
£503 $785 €800 Italian landscape with mountain stream (38x54cm-15x21in) s.d.1787 wash brush pen pencil. 11-Oct-2 Winterberg, Heidelberg #436

MEYER, Johann Jakob (1787-1858) Swiss
£1674 $2444 €2511 Landscape near Ragaz (46x60cm-18x24in) s.d.1846 prov. 17-Jun-2 Philippe Schuler, Zurich #4283/R est:3000-4000 (S.FR 3800)
Works on paper
£2000 $3140 €3000 View of Kameny Ostrov Palace, St Petersburg (24x34cm-9x13in) s.d.1844 W/C. 20-Nov-2 Sotheby's, London #5/R est:2500-3500

MEYER, John (1942-) South African
£1433 $2250 €2150 Early storms, High Sierras (62x92cm-24x36in) s. i.stretcher prov. 19-Nov-2 Butterfields, San Francisco #8360/R est:3000-5000
£2580 $4153 €3870 Green house (24x43cm-9x17in) init. i.d.1977 verso acrylic on board. 12-May-3 Stephan Welz, Johannesburg #503/R est:15000-20000 (SA.R 30000)
£8228 $13000 €11931 Wild lilies (91x122cm-36x48in) s. 26-Jul-3 Coeur d'Alene, Hayden #91/R est:8000-12000

MEYER, Maurice de (1911-) Belgian
£445 $695 €650 Charrois dans une allee (50x65cm-20x26in) s. 14-Apr-3 Horta, Bruxelles #347
£540 $863 €750 Bouquinistes a Paris (33x46cm-13x18in) s. s.i.verso panel. 17-May-3 De Vuyst, Lokeren #144
£570 $889 €900 Plaisirs dominicaux a la plage (45x60cm-18x24in) s. 16-Sep-2 Horta, Bruxelles #354
£705 $1135 €1050 Rue de Paris animee (46x38cm-18x15in) s. panel. 18-Feb-3 Vanderkindere, Brussels #432

MEYER, Melissa (1947-) American
£549 $900 €796 Untitled (76x114cm-30x45in) oil stick on paper diptych exhib. 1-Jun-3 Wright, Chicago #335/R

MEYER, Rudolf (20th C) German?
£267 $379 €430 Insel Reichenau (36x42cm-14x17in) s. board. 23-Mar-2 Geble, Radolfzell #562

MEYER, Sal (1877-1965) Dutch
£1103 $1754 €1600 Still life with a blue bowl (23x31cm-9x12in) s. board. 10-Mar-3 Sotheby's, Amsterdam #352/R est:600-800

MEYER, Sophie (?-1921) German
£601 $932 €950 Fisherwoman in costume (40x28cm-16x11in) s.d.1878 panel. 27-Sep-2 Weidler, Nurnberg #8704/R

MEYER-AMDEN, Otto (1885-1933) Swiss
Works on paper
£2146 $3391 €3219 Harvest (27x21cm-11x8in) pencil col pen. 28-Nov-2 Christie's, Zurich #71/R est:5000-7000 (S.FR 5000)
£4717 $7358 €7500 Ascent to the cross (31x27cm-12x11in) s.d.04 W/C paper on card prov.exhib. 9-Oct-2 Sotheby's, London #371/R est:7000-10000
£5975 $9321 €9500 Young male nude (29x20cm-11x8in) pencil executed c.1925-28 prov.exhib. 9-Oct-2 Sotheby's, London #370/R est:3000-5000
£7547 $11774 €12000 Preparatory study (21x27cm-8x11in) col pencil pencil on tracing paper prov.exhib. 9-Oct-2 Sotheby's, London #380/R est:4000-6000
£9434 $14717 €15000 Studie XII for a stained glass window (64x31cm-25x12in) d.1924 pencil col pencil on two sheets prov.exhib. 9-Oct-2 Sotheby's, London #375/R est:1200-1800
£13100 $20568 €19650 Guest room of Hermann Huber in Gut Schooren near Kilchberg (62x43cm-24x17in) W/C prov.exhib. 25-Nov-2 Sotheby's, Zurich #121/R est:30000-40000 (S.FR 30000)
£22642 $35321 €36000 Two nude youths on an Amden country road (30x23cm-12x9in) pencil paper on board executed c.1925-28 prov.exhib. 9-Oct-2 Sotheby's, London #381/R est:12000-15000

MEYER-BASEL, Carl Theodor (1860-1932) Swiss
£798 $1309 €1157 Millstream (37x49cm-15x19in) s.d.1916 board. 4-Jun-3 Fischer, Luzern #2249/R est:1200-1500 (S.FR 1700)

MEYER-EBERHARDT, Curt (1895-1977) German
£446 $687 €700 Garden on the Cote d'Azur (75x111cm-30x44in) s. 5-Sep-2 Arnold, Frankfurt #817/R
£573 $894 €900 Dalmatian landscape (91x115cm-36x45in) lit. 7-Nov-2 Allgauer, Kempten #2903/R
£786 $1288 €1140 Landscape with horse and cart (75x111cm-30x44in) init. 4-Jun-3 AB Stockholms Auktionsverk #2481/R (S.KR 10000)
£1493 $2448 €2165 Donkey and cart in garden (99x110cm-39x43in) s.d.35. 4-Jun-3 AB Stockholms Auktionsverk #2480/R est:12000-15000 (S.KR 19000)

MEYER-WALDECK, Kunz (1859-1953) German
£1644 $2564 €2400 Two boys by boat (27x30cm-11x12in) s.i. board. 10-Apr-3 Dorotheum, Vienna #197/R est:2200-2500

MEYERHEIM, Franz Eduard (1838-1880) German
£4452 $6945 €6500 Audience with Cardinal (59x47cm-23x19in) s.d.1864. 10-Apr-3 Van Ham, Cologne #1589/R est:8000

MEYERHEIM, Friedrich Edouard (1808-1879) German
£2628 $3995 €4100 Grandmother with granddaughter reading book (36x30cm-14x12in) bears sig. 17-Aug-2 Hans Stahl, Toestorf #73/R est:3000
£7000 $11480 €10500 Fang die maus - catch the mouse (43x50cm-17x20in) s.d.1850 prov. 3-Jun-3 Sotheby's, London #18/R est:4000-6000

MEYERHEIM, Hermann (1840-1880) German
£3585 $5557 €5700 Passau with figures (40x56cm-16x22in) s. 2-Nov-2 Hans Stahl, Toestorf #21/R est:4800
£9375 $15000 €14063 Dutch river scene with figures on the bank (68x97cm-27x38in) indis.sig. 14-May-3 Butterfields, San Francisco #1079/R est:8000-12000

MEYERHEIM, Paul Friedrich (1842-1915) German
£897 $1426 €1300 Wooded landscape (35x41cm-14x16in) s.d.1864 i. verso. 8-Mar-3 Arnold, Frankfurt #645/R
£5128 $8051 €8000 Lion et lionne (50x60cm-20x24in) s. 16-Dec-2 Gros & Delettrez, Paris #192/R est:4000-5000

MEYERHEIM, Wilhelm Alexander (1815-1882) German
£2273 $3386 €3500 Ahrweiler - Walporzheimer Tor (34x50cm-13x20in) s. 26-Jun-2 Neumeister, Munich #802/R est:6000
£2740 $4274 €4000 In the winter (59x82cm-23x32in) s. 10-Apr-3 Schopman, Hamburg #583a est:4800
£8387 $13000 €12581 Arrival of the ferry (70x96cm-28x38in) s. 30-Oct-2 Christie's, Rockefeller NY #116/R est:15000-20000

MEYERHOFF, Pedro Moreno (1951-) Spanish
£7547 $11698 €12000 Night harbour scene (51x42cm-20x17in) s. board. 7-Oct-2 Ansorena, Madrid #82/R est:12000

MEYERN, Ellen von (19/20th C) New Zealander
Works on paper
£547 $853 €821 Portrait of Ena Te Papatahi. Portrait of a Maori man smoking a pipe (21x13cm-8x5in) s.d.1903 W/C pair. 17-Sep-2 Peter Webb, Auckland #88/R est:1800-2500 (NZ.D 1800)

MEYEROWITZ, Joel (1938-) American
Photographs
£1911 $3000 €2867 Winter morning, Tuscany (28x36cm-11x14in) s.i.d.verso chromogenic col print. 21-Apr-3 Phillips, New York #30/R est:1500-2000

MEYEROWITZ, William (1887-1981) American
£566 $900 €849 Floral still life (71x61cm-28x24in) s. 7-Mar-3 Skinner, Boston #578/R
£881 $1400 €1322 Tree study (62x47cm-24x19in) s. canvasboard. 7-Mar-3 Skinner, Boston #407/R est:2000-2500
£2070 $3250 €3105 Theresa in the garden (41x50cm-16x20in) s.d.20 board double-sided. 22-Nov-2 Skinner, Boston #375/R est:3000-5000
Photographs
£5696 $9000 €8544 Broadway at 46th Street, New York City (39x60cm-15x24in) s.i.d.1976 verso dye transfer print prov.exhib.lit. 25-Apr-3 Phillips, New York #61/R est:3000-5000

MEYERS, Isidore (1836-1917) Belgian
£346 $533 €550 Jeune fille au parapluie (40x27cm-16x11in) s. 22-Oct-2 Campo, Vlaamse Kaai #570
£377 $581 €600 Chasseur dans un paysage (98x63cm-39x25in) s. 22-Oct-2 Campo & Campo, Antwerp #191
£449 $704 €700 Paysanne (27x40cm-11x16in) 16-Dec-2 Amberes, Antwerp #271
£481 $755 €750 Voiliers (80x50cm-31x20in) s. 10-Dec-2 Campo, Vlaamse Kaai #327
£633 $987 €1000 Voilier devant la cote (61x94cm-24x37in) 16-Sep-2 Amberes, Antwerp #226
£791 $1266 €1100 Summer landscape with mill (15x28cm-6x11in) s. panel. 17-May-3 De Vuyst, Lokeren #260
£1384 $2145 €2200 On the River Scheldt (85x64cm-33x25in) s. lit. 5-Oct-2 De Vuyst, Lokeren #244/R est:2400-2800
£2041 $3245 €3000 Lonely wanderer near farms by water. s. 24-Mar-3 Bernaerts, Antwerp #76/R est:800-1000
£3061 $4867 €4500 Figures dans un paysage (100x152cm-39x60in) s. 18-Mar-3 Campo, Vlaamse Kaai #156/R est:5000-7000

MEYERS, O (19th C) American
£2013 $3200 €3020 Five dollars (20x25cm-8x10in) s.d.1899 panel. 4-Mar-3 Christie's, Rockefeller NY #16/R est:4000-6000

MEYIER, Anthony Andreas de (1806-1867) Dutch
£1974 $3197 €3000 Frozen waterway with figures skating (16x21cm-6x8in) s. panel. 21-Jan-3 Christie's, Amsterdam #79/R est:1500-2000

MEYNIER, Jules Joseph (1826-c.1903) French
£550 $836 €825 Sleeping beauties (24x31cm-9x12in) s. 29-Aug-2 Christie's, Kensington #78

MEYS, Louis (1902-1995) Dutch
£1210 $1888 €1900 Town garden in winter (78x58cm-31x23in) s. board. 6-Nov-2 Vendue Huis, Gravenhage #240/R est:2000-3000

MEZA, Guillermo (1917-) Mexican
£629 $1000 €944 Night (50x28cm-20x11in) s.d.1970 s.i.d.verso panel. 7-Mar-3 Skinner, Boston #632/R
£5353 $8350 €8030 Tierra quemada, el cerro del Tecajete, Hgo (50x100cm-20x39in) s.d.1958. 17-Oct-2 Louis Morton, Mexico #69/R est:100000-120000 (M.P 85000)
£17516 $27500 €26274 Exodus (90x70cm-35x28in) s.d.1951 prov.lit. 19-Nov-2 Sotheby's, New York #86/R est:22000

MEZIAT, Renato (1952-) Latin American
£5096 $8000 €7644 Fruits in harmony (90x130cm-35x51in) s. s.i.d.2002 verso. 19-Nov-2 Sotheby's, New York #154/R est:15000

MGUDLANDLU, Gladys (1925-1979) South African
£1206 $1905 €1809 Portrait of a warrior (64x44cm-25x17in) s.d.1962 board. 1-Apr-3 Stephan Welz, Johannesburg #497/R est:15000-20000 (SA.R 15000)
Works on paper
£1527 $2413 €2291 House beyond the trees (36x49cm-14x19in) s.d.1961 gouache. 1-Apr-3 Stephan Welz, Johannesburg #496/R est:10000-15000 (SA.R 19000)

MICAELLES, Ruggero (1898-1976) Italian
£1149 $1792 €1700 Reclining female nude (50x73cm-20x29in) s.d.49 on stretcher. 28-Mar-3 Farsetti, Prato #640/R

MICAS, Jeanne Sarah Natalie (19th C) French
£720 $1195 €1044 Chickens with their chicks (18x23cm-7x9in) s.d.1896. 10-Jun-3 Louis Taylor, Stoke on Trent #920
£1100 $1793 €1650 Hen and chicks. Ducks and ducklings at water's edge (15x20cm-6x8in) s. panel pair. 11-Feb-3 Bonhams, Knowle #120 est:600-800

MICEU, Giuseppe (1873-1908) Italian
£1090 $1689 €1700 Fishermen (17x25cm-7x10in) s.i. cardboard. 5-Dec-2 Stadion, Trieste #823

MICHA, Maurice Jean (1890-1969) Belgian
£342 $534 €500 Dahlias (70x60cm-28x24in) s. 14-Apr-3 Horta, Bruxelles #350
£1600 $2656 €1600 Le violoniste (90x59cm-35x23in) s. 16-Jun-3 Horta, Bruxelles #21 est:1000-1500

MICHAEL (19th C) British?
£1122 $1750 €1683 Listening to records (71x76cm-28x30in) 20-Sep-2 Du Mouchelle, Detroit #2087/R est:600-900

MICHAEL, Anne (20th C) British?
£300 $438 €450 Van plays the blues (41x30cm-16x12in) s. board. 12-Jun-2 John Ross, Belfast #187

MICHAEL, Loui (1933-) Danish
£429 $669 €644 Composition with birds (122x122cm-48x48in) mono. s.d.1979-80 verso cut panel exhib. 11-Nov-2 Rasmussen, Vejle #140/R (D.KR 5000)
£466 $742 €699 Sunset (100x81cm-39x32in) mono. s.d.1977 verso. 5-May-3 Rasmussen, Vejle #95/R (D.KR 5000)
£466 $742 €699 Composition with female torso and birds (100x81cm-39x32in) mono. 5-May-3 Rasmussen, Vejle #96/R (D.KR 5000)

MICHAEL, Max (1823-1891) German
£696 $1100 €1100 Young woman knitting by a cradle (29x26cm-11x10in) s.d.1869 board. 29-Nov-2 Bolland & Marotz, Bremen #738/R

MICHAELIS, Alexander (attrib) (?-1869) German
£1392 $2158 €2200 Wooded landscape with two figures and dog (35x39cm-14x15in) bears sig. panel. 25-Sep-2 Neumeister, Munich #656/R est:1000

MICHAELIS, Heinrich (1837-?) German
£296 $476 €420 Portrait of old woman (120x80cm-47x31in) s.d.1898. 10-May-3 Berlinghof, Heidelberg #275

MICHAELIS, Oskar (1872-?) German
£296 $465 €444 Woman (45x36cm-18x14in) s. 16-Dec-2 Lilla Bukowskis, Stockholm #384 (S.KR 4200)

MICHAELS, Eric (1948-) American
£1039 $1600 €1559 Southbound (30x41cm-12x16in) 25-Oct-2 Morris & Whiteside, Hilton Head Island #141 est:1800-2000

MICHAELSON, Hans (1872-?) German
£380 $597 €570 Figures on a country path (45x61cm-18x24in) s. 15-Apr-3 Bonhams, Knightsbridge #116

MICHAILOW, Nikola (1876-1960) Bulgarian
£886 $1373 €1400 Villa park near Dubrovnik (44x53cm-17x21in) s. board. 28-Sep-2 Hans Stahl, Hamburg #95/R
£1139 $1766 €1800 Dubrovnik (44x53cm-17x21in) s. board. 28-Sep-2 Hans Stahl, Hamburg #94 est:1400

MICHALS, Duane (1932-) American
Photographs
£2222 $3667 €3200 Andy Warhol (18x24cm-7x9in) s.i. num.14/25 gelatin silver print. 3-Jul-3 Christie's, Paris #73/R est:1000-1500
£2340 $3791 €3300 Portrait of Andy Warhol (9x13cm-4x5in) silver gelatin three on one sheet. 23-May-3 Van Ham, Cologne #166/R est:3000

MICHAU, Raoul (1897-) French
£417 $658 €600 L'instant (100x77cm-39x30in) s.d. s.verso. 28-Apr-3 Cornette de St.Cyr, Paris #462

MICHAU, Theobald (1676-1765) Flemish
£305 $500 €458 Peasants and cattle in a village (28x25cm-11x10in) panel prov. 5-Feb-3 Christie's, Rockefeller NY #260/R
£14000 $21980 €21000 Boors resting before a tavern, with cattle by a stream beyond (28x40cm-11x16in) s. panel prov. 12-Dec-2 Sotheby's, London #131/R est:10000-15000
£16667 $26333 €26000 Paysage fluvial anime de nombreux personnages (37x59cm-15x23in) bears sig. 12-Nov-2 Palais de Beaux Arts, Brussels #461/R est:25000-35000
£23288 $36329 €34932 Farmstead with figures (31x37cm-12x15in) panel. 28-Mar-3 Koller, Zurich #3022/R est:70000-90000 (S.FR 51000)

MICHAU, Theobald (style) (1676-1765) Flemish
£18000 $28260 €27000 Fishing boats before a house. Fishermen selling their catch (30x35cm-12x14in) bears sig. copper pair. 12-Dec-2 Sotheby's, London #136/R est:8000-12000

MICHAUD, Hippolyte (1831-1886) French
£475 $750 €750 Landscape in summer with cows at a pond (39x50cm-15x20in) s. canvas on board. 29-Nov-2 Sigalas, Stuttgart #1116/R
£1899 $3000 €3000 Loge (95x115cm-37x45in) mono. 1-Dec-2 Livinec, Gaudcheau & Jezequel, Rennes #95/R

MICHAUT, Angel Alexio (1879-?) French
Works on paper
£1931 $3070 €2800 Le cortege. La traversee. Athena. Elephant Indien (27x19cm-11x7in) s.d.1915-1916 W/C gour. 4-Mar-3 Palais de Beaux Arts, Brussels #353 est:2800-4000

MICHAUX, Henri (1899-1984) Belgian
£1923 $2981 €3000 Untitled (32x49cm-13x19in) mono. acrylic. 7-Dec-2 Van Ham, Cologne #345/R est:6000
£4494 $7100 €7100 Untitled (54x73cm-21x29in) mono. prov. 27-Nov-2 Tajan, Paris #22/R est:8000-10000
Works on paper
£345 $552 €500 Composition (64x49cm-25x19in) init. W/C gouache ink paper on masonite. 11-Mar-3 Christie's, Paris #428/R
£496 $829 €700 Composition (13x16cm-5x6in) Indian ink. 18-Jun-3 Pierre Berge, Paris #63/R
£641 $994 €1000 Untitled (8x11cm-3x4in) mono. pen ink. 3-Dec-2 Christie's, Amsterdam #137/R est:1000-1500
£641 $1006 €1000 Untitled (15x28cm-6x11in) W/C. 11-Dec-2 Artcurial Briest, Paris #703a/R
£755 $1170 €1200 Sans titre (37x27cm-15x11in) mono. gouache W/C exec.c.1946. 30-Oct-2 Artcurial Briest, Paris #416/R
£962 $1510 €1500 Untitled (24x31cm-9x12in) W/C. 11-Dec-2 Artcurial Briest, Paris #703b/R
£1277 $2132 €1800 Composition (31x24cm-12x9in) Indian ink. 18-Jun-3 Pierre Berge, Paris #61/R est:3000-3500
£1776 $2859 €2664 Tete (32x24cm-13x9in) init. mixed media prov. 7-May-3 AB Stockholms Auktionsverk #1104/R est:20000-30000 (S.KR 23000)
£2172 $3389 €3258 Untitled (28x48cm-11x19in) init. W/C. 6-Nov-2 AB Stockholms Auktionsverk #933/R est:25000-30000 (S.KR 31000)
£2449 $3894 €3600 Composition (39x57cm-15x22in) mono. ink acrylic. 24-Mar-3 Claude Boisgirard, Paris #118/R
£2516 $3899 €4000 Flammes (37x54cm-15x21in) mono. W/C. 30-Oct-2 Artcurial Briest, Paris #418/R est:4500-5000
£2708 $4279 €3900 Personnage (36x27cm-14x11in) mono. W/C gouache. 28-Apr-3 Cornette de St.Cyr, Paris #463/R est:4000-4500
£2721 $4327 €4000 Composition (50x65cm-20x26in) mono. ink acrylic. 24-Mar-3 Claude Boisgirard, Paris #117/R
£3404 $5515 €4800 Untitled (39x54cm-15x21in) mono. W/C gouache exhib. 24-May-3 Van Ham, Cologne #410/R est:5500
£3478 $5704 €4800 Untitled (58x77cm-23x30in) mono. Indian ink brush. 28-May-3 Lempertz, Koln #284/R est:6000-8000
£3861 $6216 €5792 Dessin mescalien (41x32cm-16x13in) init. crayon prov. 7-May-3 AB Stockholms Auktionsverk #1153/R est:60000-80000 (S.KR 50000)
£4200 $7014 €6090 Untitled (58x78cm-23x31in) init. ink. 24-Jun-3 Sotheby's, Olympia #77/R est:3000-4000
£4479 $7211 €6719 Visage (32x25cm-13x10in) init. gouache prov. 7-May-3 AB Stockholms Auktionsverk #1114/R est:30000-40000 (S.KR 58000)
£4633 $7459 €6950 Sans titre (56x76cm-22x30in) mono. Indian ink prov. 7-May-3 AB Stockholms Auktionsverk #1105/R est:60000-80000 (S.KR 60000)
£4684 $7400 €7400 Composition (51x73cm-20x29in) mono. gouache. 26-Nov-2 Palais de Beaux Arts, Brussels #274/R est:5000-7000
£6250 $9938 €9000 Sans titre (66x97cm-26x38in) mono. Indian ink dr prov. 29-Apr-3 Artcurial Briest, Paris #614/R est:10000-12000
£6289 $9748 €10000 Sans titre (74x107cm-29x42in) mono. ink dr. 30-Oct-2 Artcurial Briest, Paris #419/R est:12000-15000
£6500 $10010 €9750 Composition (70x100cm-28x39in) init. ink W/C executed 1958 prov. 23-Oct-2 Christie's, London #110/R est:8000-12000
£6962 $11000 €11000 Untitled (75x106cm-30x42in) mono. Indian ink col chk. 27-Nov-2 Dorotheum, Vienna #93/R est:11000-15000

£9653 $15541 €14480 Dessin mescalien (31x24cm-12x9in) init. Indian ink exhib.prov. 7-May-3 AB Stockholms Auktionsverk #1151/R est:60000-80000 (S.KR 125000)
£11054 $17577 €16250 Sans titre (72x105cm-28x41in) mono. Indian ink dr. prov. 26-Feb-3 Artcurial Briest, Paris #438/R est:10000-12000
£11218 $17612 €17500 Composition (77x110cm-30x43in) mono. ink. 16-Dec-2 Millon & Associes, Paris #70a/R est:10000-12000
£11218 $17612 €17500 Composition (77x110cm-30x43in) mono. ink. 16-Dec-2 Millon & Associes, Paris #70b/R est:10000-12000
£12000 $18960 €18000 Composition (74x104cm-29x41in) init. brush ink. 3-Apr-3 Christie's, Kensington #225/R
£13103 $20966 €19000 Composition (78x140cm-31x55in) init. ink. 11-Mar-3 Christie's, Paris #426/R

MICHEL, Alfonso (1897-1957) Mexican
£10366 $17000 €15031 Cabeza de mujer (46x41cm-18x16in) s. painted c.1952. 27-May-3 Sotheby's, New York #91

MICHEL, Charles (19th C) French/Belgian
£654 $1052 €1000 Elegante au bouquet (33x24cm-13x9in) s. panel. 20-Jan-3 Horta, Bruxelles #469

MICHEL, Ernest (1833-1902) French
£2500 $3900 €3750 La robe verte (61x43cm-24x17in) s. 7-Nov-2 Christie's, Kensington #230/R est:1500-2000

MICHEL, Georges (1763-1843) French
£3846 $5962 €6000 Landscape with vehicle, traveller and cow (42x53cm-17x21in) s. panel. 4-Dec-2 Neumeister, Munich #821/R est:4000
£3957 $6331 €5500 Montmartre in the evening with peasants returning home (32x42cm-13x17in) i. verso panel prov. 17-May-3 Lempertz, Koln #1439/R est:6000
£4577 $6500 €6866 Paysage au moulin d'un garcon avec son chien (51x66cm-20x26in) s. 8-Aug-1 Barridorf, Portland #76/R est:6000-8000
£4721 $7318 €7082 Landscape with windmill (26x35cm-10x14in) 3-Oct-2 Koller, Zurich #3073/R est:5000-8000 (S.FR 11000)
£7000 $11130 €10500 View over a village in a rainstorm (56x79cm-22x31in) exhib. 20-Mar-3 Christie's, Kensington #6/R est:6000-8000
£7097 $11000 €10646 Shepherd and his herd crossing the river before the storm (52x71cm-20x28in) prov.exhib. 30-Oct-2 Christie's, Rockefeller NY #139/R est:10000-15000
£8176 $12673 €13000 Orage au dessus de la colline au moulin (51x74cm-20x29in) 29-Oct-2 Artcurial Briest, Paris #55/R est:6000

MICHEL, Georges (attrib) (1763-1843) French
£1667 $2683 €2501 Summer countryside (51x60cm-20x24in) 7-May-3 Dobiaschofsky, Bern #826/R est:4000 (S.FR 3600)

MICHEL, Robert (1897-1983) German
Works on paper
£1950 $3042 €3100 Mijnheer van Haken-acht (59x61cm-23x24in) mono.d.1924 mono.i.d.verso Chinese ink gouache collage. 11-Oct-2 Binoche, Paris #148
£2075 $3238 €3300 Do-de-bild (64x66cm-25x26in) s.d.1922 collage gouache paper on cardboard. 11-Oct-2 Binoche, Paris #149
£2516 $3925 €4000 Noch eine Olympiade (64x68cm-25x27in) s.i. s.i.d.1922 verso gouache collage cardboard. 11-Oct-2 Binoche, Paris #147/R
£5634 $9352 €8000 Another olympiade (64x68cm-25x27in) s.i.d. gouache collage. 14-Jun-3 Hauswedell & Nolte, Hamburg #1408/R est:8000
£5755 $9439 €8000 Do-De-Bild (64x66cm-25x26in) s.i.d. W/C ink airbrush silverpoint pen collage papers on board. 6-Jun-3 Ketterer, Munich #57/R est:6000-8000
£26923 $41731 €42000 Clocks (58x62cm-23x24in) s.i.d. paper on board. 7-Dec-2 Hauswedell & Nolte, Hamburg #903/R est:40000

MICHEL-LEVY, Henri (1845-1914) French
£2115 $3321 €3300 La marchande de fleurs (61x47cm-24x19in) s. 19-Nov-2 Vanderkindere, Brussels #162/R est:3000-5000

MICHELACCI, Luigi (1879-1959) Italian
£387 $612 €600 Study of village (12x18cm-5x7in) s. board. 18-Dec-2 Finarte, Milan #238
£439 $685 €650 Venice (21x11cm-8x4in) s. cardboard. 28-Mar-3 Farsetti, Prato #664
£507 $791 €750 Children (13x12cm-5x5in) s. board. 28-Mar-3 Farsetti, Prato #678
£2215 $3500 €3500 Gipsy cart (20x30cm-8x12in) s. cardboard. 26-Nov-2 Christie's, Rome #183/R

MICHELANGELO (1475-1564) Italian
Works on paper
£260000 $434200 €377000 Study of a left thigh and knee, separate study of right knee and right foot (19x16cm-7x6in) blk chk prov.exhib. 9-Jul-3 Sotheby's, London #9/R est:200000-300000

MICHELETTI, Mario (1892-1975) Italian
£340 $541 €500 Bordighera (50x60cm-20x24in) s. painted 1970. 1-Mar-3 Meeting Art, Vercelli #105
£538 $839 €850 Rocks and houses (50x70cm-20x28in) s.d.1970 lit. 14-Sep-2 Meeting Art, Vercelli #469/R

MICHELOT, J (19th C) ?
£533 $831 €800 Nature morte a la colombe et cerises (52x77cm-20x30in) s.d.1874. 10-Sep-2 Iegor de Saint Hippolyte, Montreal #83/R (C.D 1300)

MICHELOZZI, Corrado (1883-1965) Italian
£321 $503 €500 Ship in background (11x18cm-4x7in) init. canvas on board. 16-Dec-2 Pandolfini, Florence #305
£372 $580 €550 Potted plant (50x35cm-20x14in) s. board. 28-Mar-3 Farsetti, Prato #454

MICHETTI, Francesco Paolo (1851-1929) Italian
£1603 $2532 €2500 Figure (31x40cm-12x16in) s. tempera. 15-Nov-2 Farsetti, Prato #529/R
£4747 $7500 €7500 Shepherdess with oxen (40x50cm-16x20in) s. cardboard. 26-Nov-2 Christie's, Rome #166/R est:12000
Works on paper
£577 $842 €900 Portrait of Caludia (25x15cm-10x6in) s. W/C. 5-Jun-2 Il Ponte, Milan #248
£1772 $2800 €2800 Head of young woman (34x25cm-13x10in) s. mixed media on canvas. 26-Nov-2 Christie's, Rome #168/R

MICHETTI, Francesco Paolo (attrib) (1851-1929) Italian
£748 $1190 €1100 Portrait of man (38x31cm-15x12in) i.d.1869. 18-Mar-3 Finarte, Milan #218

MICHIE, Alastair (1921-) British
£1000 $1560 €1500 Continental terrace (50x61cm-20x24in) s. board. 17-Oct-2 Bonhams, Edinburgh #50 est:300-500

MICHIE, David (1928-) British
£400 $648 €600 Spring day, Newburgh (50x60cm-20x24in) s.i.verso board. 23-May-3 Lyon & Turnbull, Edinburgh #35
£460 $718 €690 Ringed plovers, Aires, Isle of Man (19x19cm-7x7in) s. 17-Oct-2 Bonhams, Edinburgh #90
£600 $924 €900 Duck and fish (56x56cm-22x22in) s. exhib. 5-Sep-2 Christie's, Kensington #732/R
£1100 $1694 €1650 House in Lisbon (61x51cm-24x20in) s. board. 5-Sep-2 Christie's, Kensington #684/R est:600-800
£2400 $3816 €3600 Cats in an ornamental garden (66x101cm-26x40in) s. prov.exhib. 6-Mar-3 Christie's, Kensington #258/R est:1800-2500

MICHIE, James Coutts (1861-1919) British
£195 $303 €293 Seville (23x14cm-9x6in) s. board. 3-Dec-2 Ritchie, Toronto #3054/R (C.D 475)
£3000 $4770 €4500 Study of a seated nude female (76x51cm-30x20in) s.d.1879. 18-Mar-3 Lawrences, Bletchingley #1230
£3000 $4860 €4500 Normandy orchard (80x63cm-31x25in) s.d.1885. 23-May-3 Lyon & Turnbull, Edinburgh #41/R est:2000-3000
£3600 $5472 €5400 An autumn landscape (91x133cm-36x52in) s. 28-Aug-2 Sotheby's, London #925/R est:2000-3000

MICHIELI, Andrea dei (attrib) (1542-1617) Italian
Works on paper
£700 $1099 €1050 Mythological scene with a river God and two female figures (13x18cm-5x7in) pen ink wash over red chk prov. 11-Dec-2 Sotheby's, Olympia #33/R

MICHIELS, Dirk (1943-) Belgian
£633 $987 €1000 Portrait of a woman and tulips (110x90cm-43x35in) s. 21-Oct-2 Bernaerts, Antwerp #783/R

MICHONZE, Gregoire (1902-1982) French
£545 $855 €850 Chevaux et chevres (16x22cm-6x9in) s.d.63. 12-Dec-2 Rabourdin & Choppin de Janvry, Paris #160
£609 $956 €950 La ferme (27x35cm-11x14in) s. paint. 24-Nov-2 Chayette & Cheval, Paris #279
£641 $1006 €1000 Animaux dans un paysage (33x46cm-13x18in) s.d.67 paper on canvas. 12-Dec-2 Rabourdin & Choppin de Janvry, Paris #158
£701 $1093 €1100 Vue des environs de Paris (19x24cm-7x9in) s.d.1953 panel. 10-Nov-2 Eric Pillon, Calais #27/R
£701 $1093 €1100 Vue des environs de Paris (19x24cm-7x9in) s.d.1953 panel. 10-Nov-2 Eric Pillon, Calais #26/R
£943 $1462 €1500 La zone, scene de rue (24x35cm-9x14in) s. s.d.58 verso panel. 30-Oct-2 Artcurial Briest, Paris #46 est:1500-2000

£1035 $1635 €1500 Marchand de fleurs au village (24x35cm-9x14in) s.d.1955 masonite. 4-Apr-3 Tajan, Paris #164
£1250 $1963 €1950 Dance (33x46cm-13x18in) s.d. 12-Dec-2 Rabourdin & Choppin de Janvry, Paris #157
£1282 $2013 €2000 Scene surrealiste (48x70cm-19x28in) s. 12-Dec-2 Rabourdin & Choppin de Janvry, Paris #156/R
£1300 $2015 €1950 Devant le lac. Composition (33x33cm-13x13in) s. board two prov. 5-Dec-2 Christie's, Kensington #138/R est:800-1200
£1346 $2113 €2100 Enfant au drapeau (54x45cm-21x18in) s. 12-Dec-2 Rabourdin & Choppin de Janvry, Paris #159
£1631 $2724 €2300 Scene paysanne (27x22cm-11x9in) s.d. canvas on cardboard. 17-Jun-3 Claude Boisgirard, Paris #88/R est:1800-2200
£1655 $2615 €2400 Porteur de sac (30x52cm-12x20in) s. masonite painted 1957. 4-Apr-3 Tajan, Paris #163/R
£1793 $2869 €2600 Scene de village (15x29cm-6x11in) s.d.57 panel. 12-Mar-3 Rabourdin & Choppin de Janvry, Paris #143/R
£2207 $3531 €3200 Devant le lac (33x33cm-13x13in) s.d.58 panel. 12-Mar-3 Rabourdin & Choppin de Janvry, Paris #141/R

Works on paper

£306 $487 €450 Scene allegorique (11x18cm-4x7in) s.d.40 ink dr. 26-Feb-3 Artcurial Briest, Paris #219
£769 $1208 €1200 Groupe de personnages (37x52cm-15x20in) s.d. W/C. 24-Nov-2 Chayette & Cheval, Paris #245

MICKELBORG, Finn (1932-) Danish

£258 $401 €387 Composition (56x45cm-22x18in) s.d.94 verso. 4-Dec-2 Kunsthallen, Copenhagen #225 (D.KR 3000)
£384 $610 €576 Maximum (66x90cm-26x35in) mono. prov. 26-Feb-3 Kunsthallen, Copenhagen #27/R (D.KR 4200)
£423 $656 €635 Surrealistic composition (80x121cm-31x48in) mono. prov. 1-Oct-2 Rasmussen, Copenhagen #237/R (D.KR 5000)
£530 $843 €795 Conception mutation (64x55cm-25x22in) mono. exhib. 26-Feb-3 Kunsthallen, Copenhagen #28/R (D.KR 5800)
£1206 $1869 €1809 Modulation (180x140cm-71x55in) s. acrylic. 4-Dec-2 Kunsthallen, Copenhagen #271/R est:18000 (D.KR 14000)

MICKER, Jan Christiansz (1600-1664) Dutch

£10274 $16027 €15000 Landscape with figures (39x52cm-15x20in) board oval. 8-Apr-3 Ansorena, Madrid #109/R est:15000

MIDDEL, Maurits van (1886-?) Belgian

£268 $432 €400 Vue du Palais de Justice a Bruges (82x75cm-32x30in) s. 24-Feb-3 Bernaerts, Antwerp #771/R

MIDDENDORF, Helmut (1953-) German

£2532 $4000 €4000 Gefuhl und harte (220x170cm-87x67in) s.i.d.1984 acrylic prov. 27-Nov-2 Tajan, Paris #115/R
£2658 $4200 €4200 Blue dance (190x230cm-75x91in) s.i.d.1983 verso. 30-Nov-2 Arnold, Frankfurt #383/R est:6000
£4348 $7130 €6000 Painter (230x180cm-91x71in) s.i.d.1984 verso acrylic. 31-May-3 Villa Grisebach, Berlin #395/R est:6000-8000
£4937 $7652 €7800 About to dive II (190x230cm-75x91in) s.i.d.1981 verso dispersion prov. 28-Sep-2 Ketterer, Hamburg #814/R est:10000-12000
£5031 $7799 €8000 Kopf and mond (100x70cm-39x28in) s.d. acrylic panel. 30-Oct-2 Artcurial Briest, Paris #481/R est:6000-8000
£5797 $9507 €8000 Self (150x120cm-59x47in) i. s.d.1986/87 verso prov. 28-May-3 Lempertz, Koln #286/R est:8000-10000
£7547 $11623 €12000 Under the umbrella (250x190cm-98x75in) s.i.d.1985 verso acrylic exhib. 26-Oct-2 Cornette de St.Cyr, Paris #106/R est:12000
£7609 $12478 €10500 Two (230x100cm-91x39in) s.i.d.1982 cotton prov.exhib. 28-May-3 Lempertz, Koln #285/R est:8000

Works on paper

£385 $596 €600 Study for 'Loneliness of the heads' (34x28cm-13x11in) s.i.d.1982 W/C chk pencil. 6-Dec-2 Hauswedell & Nolte, Hamburg #264/R
£497 $810 €750 Portrait (23x17cm-9x7in) s.d.2001 gouache acrylic prov. 3-Feb-3 Cornette de St.Cyr, Paris #485/R
£513 $795 €800 Untitled (40x30cm-16x12in) s.i.d.82 gouache pencil. 3-Dec-2 Lempertz, Koln #307/R
£513 $795 €800 Big dream (29x42cm-11x17in) s.i.d.1979 W/C chk pencil. 6-Dec-2 Hauswedell & Nolte, Hamburg #263/R
£625 $1031 €900 Untitled (28x66cm-11x26in) s.d.83 W/C crayon lit. 3-Jul-3 Christie's, Paris #83/R
£764 $1215 €1100 New York dream (29x41cm-11x16in) s.i.d.80 i.verso W/C pencil prov. 29-Apr-3 Artcurial Briest, Paris #461/R
£769 $1192 €1200 City landscape with couple (56x76cm-22x30in) s.d.1986 ink. 7-Dec-2 Van Ham, Cologne #346/R
£903 $1490 €1300 Untitled (28x69cm-11x27in) s.d.83 W/C crayon lit. 3-Jul-3 Christie's, Paris #82/R
£1111 $1833 €1600 Untitled (28x67cm-11x26in) s.d.83 gouache W/C crayon lit. 3-Jul-3 Christie's, Paris #84/R est:1500-2000
£1266 $2000 €2000 S. and sunset (138x107cm-54x42in) s.i.d.84 gouache. 30-Nov-2 Villa Grisebach, Berlin #472/R est:3000-5000
£2245 $3569 €3300 Self-portrait (42x30cm-17x12in) s.i.d.1982 W/C gouache prov. 24-Mar-3 Cornette de St.Cyr, Paris #32/R
£2837 $4596 €4000 Untitled (138x108cm-54x43in) s.d.89 mixed media. 24-May-3 Van Ham, Cologne #411/R est:6000
£4966 $8292 €7200 Falling figure (61x88cm-24x35in) s.d. W/C charbon. 9-Jul-3 Cornette de St.Cyr, Paris #324/R est:6000-8000

MIDDLE RHINE SCHOOL (15th C) German

£7692 $12154 €12000 Altar pieces (102x44cm-40x17in) panel prov. 16-Nov-2 Lempertz, Koln #1057/R est:12000

MIDDLEDITCH, Edward (1923-1987) British

£500 $825 €725 Two roses (108x139cm-43x55in) 3-Jul-3 Christie's, Kensington #661/R
£6500 $10660 €9425 Winter (260x208cm-102x82in) painted 1960 prov.exhib.lit. 4-Jun-3 Sotheby's, London #40/R est:8000-12000

Works on paper

£350 $578 €508 Two roses (46x62cm-18x24in) chl brush ink executed 1965. 3-Jul-3 Christie's, Kensington #578
£420 $693 €609 Olive tree, Ronda, Spain (87x75cm-34x30in) chl. 3-Jul-3 Christie's, Kensington #662/R
£500 $820 €750 Thistles, Guadaljara (49x69cm-19x27in) chl pastel sold with a linocut by same hand. 6-Jun-3 Christie's, London #121/R
£600 $984 €900 Oak tree and hedgerow (63x53cm-25x21in) crayon prov.exhib. 3-Jun-3 Sotheby's, Olympia #217/R

MIDDLETON, Colin (1910-1983) British

£2819 $4538 €4200 Lettermore (15x15cm-6x6in) mono. board prov.exhib. 18-Feb-3 Whyte's, Dublin #33/R est:1500-2000
£3087 $4970 €4600 Moss, Drumrush (30x30cm-12x12in) mono. board prov. 18-Feb-3 Whyte's, Dublin #56/R est:3000-4000
£3500 $5425 €5250 Dungloe Bay, Lechengh (20x20cm-8x8in) s.d.71 board. 4-Dec-2 John Ross, Belfast #176 est:800-1000
£3500 $5600 €5250 Seven creatures (122x122cm-48x48in) s. s.i.d.1970 verso board. 15-May-3 Christie's, London #88/R est:6000
£4027 $6483 €6000 Mourne landscape, Rostrevor II (30x30cm-12x12in) s. board prov. 18-Feb-3 Whyte's, Dublin #31/R est:3000-4000
£4790 $8000 €6946 Figures (76x64cm-30x25in) mono. oil mixed media collage on masonite. 22-Jun-3 Freeman, Philadelphia #50/R est:10000-15000
£5000 $7750 €7500 Mussenden Temple (61x122cm-24x48in) s. board. 4-Dec-2 John Ross, Belfast #154 est:5000-6000
£5346 $8340 €8500 Prisoners and guards (76x76cm-30x30in) s.i.d.2 October 1966 s.verso prov.exhib. 17-Sep-2 Whyte's, Dublin #73/R est:10000-12000
£6500 $10400 €9750 Vines Tossa (30x30cm-12x12in) s.i.verso board prov. 16-May-3 Sotheby's, London #114/R est:2500-3500
£8333 $13250 €12000 Table with teapot (61x122cm-24x48in) s. s.i.verso board prov.exhib. 29-Apr-3 Whyte's, Dublin #66/R est:10000-12000
£9434 $14717 €15000 Buildings with distant spinney (41x51cm-16x20in) s.d.1939. 17-Sep-2 Whyte's, Dublin #44/R est:10000-12000
£9459 $14757 €14000 Glenwherry (50x75cm-20x30in) s. s.i.d.16 July 1948 verso. 26-Mar-3 James Adam, Dublin #83/R est:14000-18000
£11409 $18369 €17000 Untitled, 1983 (58x58cm-23x23in) panel prov. 18-Feb-3 Whyte's, Dublin #36/R est:15000-20000
£12575 $21000 €18234 Dutch seaman (61x51cm-24x20in) s. s.i.d.1952 verso. 22-Jun-3 Freeman, Philadelphia #49/R est:10000-15000
£13514 $21081 €20000 Dark April landscape (45x60cm-18x24in) s. s.i.d.1954 verso. 26-Mar-3 James Adam, Dublin #49/R est:18000-22000
£14000 $22400 €21000 Dick's farm, Carnalridge (46x61cm-18x24in) mono. painted 1961 lit. 15-May-3 Christie's, London #87/R est:5000-8000
£15385 $24154 €24000 Dear sir (61x61cm-24x24in) s.i. mono.d.1972/1974 verso board prov.exhib. 19-Nov-2 Whyte's, Dublin #37/R est:25000-35000
£16987 $26330 €26500 John and Jane, Ballyholme Strand, winter 1953 (46x61cm-18x24in) s. 3-Dec-2 Bonhams & James Adam, Dublin #116/R est:12000-15000
£26389 $41958 €38000 Music (51x66cm-20x26in) s.i.d.1953 exhib. 29-Apr-3 Whyte's, Dublin #62/R est:30000-40000
£26923 $42269 €42000 Queen of Spain's daughter (43x43cm-17x17in) s.i. mono.d.1972/1974 verso board prov.exhib. 19-Nov-2 Whyte's, Dublin #33/R est:25000-35000

Works on paper

£300 $462 €450 Two dancers (27x16cm-11x6in) studio st.verso chl. 5-Sep-2 Christie's, Kensington #719
£450 $698 €675 Male study (20x17cm-8x7in) mono.d.72 pen ink dr. 4-Dec-2 John Ross, Belfast #261
£650 $1034 €975 Head (15x10cm-6x4in) s.d.Dec 1950 pen ink dr. 5-Mar-3 John Ross, Belfast #21
£700 $1085 €1050 Females studies (25x20cm-10x8in) s.d.41 pen ink dr. set of three. 2-Oct-2 John Ross, Belfast #73
£897 $1391 €1400 Yellow tent, Castle Archdale (15x15cm-6x6in) init. W/C. 17-Jul-2 Woodwards, Cork #236
£1000 $1550 €1500 White Island, autumn 1969 (38x61cm-15x24in) mono.d.1969 verso mixed media. 2-Oct-2 John Ross, Belfast #131a est:1000-1500
£1100 $1606 €1650 Dhu Varren (20x20cm-8x8in) s. W/C. 12-Jun-2 John Ross, Belfast #93 est:1000-1200
£1350 $2147 €2025 Feeding sardines (22x17cm-9x7in) mono. pencil. 5-Mar-3 John Ross, Belfast #209 est:1500-1800
£1800 $2628 €2700 Clouds (10x10cm-4x4in) mono. W/C. 12-Jun-2 John Ross, Belfast #65/R est:1400-1600
£3205 $5032 €5000 Dancing forms (50x62cm-20x24in) mono. gouache paper on board prov. 19-Nov-2 Whyte's, Dublin #35/R est:3000-5000
£6000 $9540 €9000 Untitled (61x61cm-24x24in) mono.d.June 1968 verso mixed media. 5-Mar-3 John Ross, Belfast #149 est:7000-8000

£10738 $17289 €16000 Standing figure (56x36cm-22x14in) mono. mixed media board prov. 18-Feb-3 Whyte's, Dublin #57/R est:12000-15000

MIDDLETON, James Godsell (attrib) (fl.1826-1872) British
£300 $489 €450 Portrait of a young girl standing half length in a formal garden (72x58cm-28x23in) board. 17-Feb-3 Bonhams, Bath #140

MIDDLETON, John (1828-1856) British
Works on paper
£5000 $8200 €7250 Pile of logs by a barn in a clearing (43x66cm-17x26in) pencil W/C prov. 5-Jun-3 Christie's, London #91/R est:5000-8000

MIDDLETON, Max (1922-) Australian
£357 $564 €536 Still life, flowers (34x29cm-13x11in) s. board. 18-Nov-2 Joel, Victoria #299 est:1000-2000 (A.D 1000)
£502 $763 €753 Golden water (15x20cm-6x8in) s. canvasboard. 27-Aug-2 Goodman, Sydney #32 (A.D 1400)

MIDDLETON, Sam (1927-) American
Works on paper
£451 $745 €650 Harlem speaks (47x77cm-19x30in) s.d.63 collage mixed media. 1-Jul-3 Christie's, Amsterdam #519/R
£674 $1091 €950 Composition (50x77cm-20x30in) s.d.85 mixed media. 26-May-3 Glerum, Amsterdam #269/R

MIDELFART, Willi (1904-1975) Norwegian
£345 $577 €500 Marianne (61x50cm-24x20in) init.d.48 i.verso panel. 18-Jun-3 Grev Wedels Plass, Oslo #201 (N.KR 4000)
£694 $1082 €1041 Roof t ops, Paris (37x46cm-15x18in) s. panel painted 1936. 21-Oct-2 Blomqvist, Oslo #398/R (N.KR 8000)
£1404 $2218 €2106 Boys on bare rock-face (67x52cm-26x20in) init.d.65. 17-Dec-2 Grev Wedels Plass, Oslo #255/R est:8000-10000 (N.KR 16000)

MIDOLLINI, Sirio (1925-) Italian
Works on paper
£284 $443 €420 Boy in the courtyard (120x80cm-47x31in) s.d.60 mixed media collage on canvas. 28-Mar-3 Farsetti, Prato #38

MIDWOOD, William Henry (fl.1867-1871) British
£1850 $3034 €2775 Cottage courtship (66x56cm-26x22in) indis.sig. 29-May-3 Christie's, Kensington #271/R est:2000-3000
£11500 $18170 €17250 Courting the seamstress (91x71cm-36x28in) indis.sig.d.82 prov. 26-Nov-2 Christie's, London #127/R est:7000-10000
£12000 $19680 €18000 At the stile. Conversation (91x68cm-36x27in) s. pair. 10-Feb-3 Robin Fenner, Tavistock #702/R est:14000-18000
£17000 $26690 €25500 Calm sea (86x112cm-34x44in) s.d.1878. 19-Nov-2 Bonhams, New Bond Street #129/R est:8000-12000

MIDY, Adolphe (1797-1874) French
Works on paper
£685 $1068 €1000 Lovesick (32x26cm-13x10in) s. W/C. 10-Apr-3 Van Ham, Cologne #1590/R
£1923 $3019 €3000 Lovesick woman (32x26cm-13x10in) s. W/C. 21-Nov-2 Van Ham, Cologne #1792/R est:1400

MIDY, Arthur (1887-1944) French
£552 $883 €800 Rue a Bou-Saada (55x46cm-22x18in) s.i. panel. 12-Mar-3 E & Eve, Paris #98
£986 $1587 €1400 Bretonnes sur le chemin (38x46cm-15x18in) s. 11-May-3 Thierry & Lannon, Brest #205/R
£986 $1587 €1400 Les lavandieres (41x33cm-16x13in) s. panel. 11-May-3 Thierry & Lannon, Brest #384
£2113 $3401 €3000 Washerwomen of Faouet, Brittany (81x100cm-32x39in) s. 7-May-3 Michael Zeller, Lindau #830/R est:3000

MIEDEMA, Rein (1835-1912) Dutch
£1100 $1782 €1650 In still waters at dusk (40x60cm-16x24in) s. 23-Jan-3 Christie's, Kensington #78/R est:500-700

MIEDUCH, Dan (1947-) American
£3425 $5000 €5138 Last stage to Prescott (61x91cm-24x36in) 18-May-2 Altermann Galleries, Santa Fe #178/R
£8519 $13800 €12353 More N a penny fight (61x91cm-24x36in) board. 23-May-3 Altermann Galleries, Santa Fe #134
£20570 $32500 €29827 Cradle on wheels (61x91cm-24x36in) s. board. 26-Jul-3 Coeur d'Alene, Hayden #204/R est:12000-18000

MIEG, Peter (1906-1990) Swiss
£370 $596 €555 Flowers in white vase (52x68cm-20x27in) mono.d.19.V.64 W/C. 7-May-3 Dobiaschofsky, Bern #827/R (S.FR 800)
Works on paper
£300 $475 €450 White roses before blue (28x19cm-11x7in) d.1967 mono.verso W/C. 29-Nov-2 Zofingen, Switzerland #2989 (S.FR 700)

MIEGHEM, E van (?) Belgian
£993 $1619 €1500 Havenboefje voor de Schelde (22x19cm-9x7in) 17-Feb-3 Amberes, Antwerp #249

MIEGHEM, Eugène van (1875-1930) Belgian
£472 $726 €750 Mere et enfant au port (37x29cm-15x11in) mono. paper. 22-Oct-2 Campo, Vlaamse Kaai #659/R
£903 $1435 €1300 Scene de carnaval au cafe (12x20cm-5x8in) chl. 29-Apr-3 Campo, Vlaamse Kaai #334/R
£3774 $5811 €6000 Couple au fumoir (21x44cm-8x17in) s. 22-Oct-2 Campo, Vlaamse Kaai #657
£10127 $16000 €16000 L'accordeoniste du port (75x130cm-30x51in) s. 26-Nov-2 Palais de Beaux Arts, Brussels #398/R est:15000-20000
£54167 $86125 €78000 Au bord de l'Escaut (72x82cm-28x32in) s.d.1926 cardboard. 29-Apr-3 Campo, Vlaamse Kaai #332/R est:68000-72000
Prints
£10063 $15497 €16000 Femme pres de l'armoire (17x13cm-7x5in) s. monotype. 22-Oct-2 Campo, Vlaamse Kaai #662
Works on paper
£313 $497 €450 Tasse et pommes (12x14cm-5x6in) mono. dr. 29-Apr-3 Campo & Campo, Antwerp #917
£313 $497 €450 Agent de police ecrivant (19x11cm-7x4in) studio st. chl. 29-Apr-3 Campo, Vlaamse Kaai #336/R
£347 $552 €500 Homme a la casquette (10x12cm-4x5in) studio st. chl. 29-Apr-3 Campo, Vlaamse Kaai #338
£347 $552 €500 Elegante au manteau (11x12cm-4x5in) studio st. chl. 29-Apr-3 Campo, Vlaamse Kaai #340
£347 $552 €500 Nu (11x12cm-4x5in) studio st. sanguine. 29-Apr-3 Campo, Vlaamse Kaai #341
£347 $552 €500 Couple au bord de l'Escaut (11x12cm-4x5in) studio st. chl. 29-Apr-3 Campo, Vlaamse Kaai #342
£347 $552 €500 Femme assise (10x12cm-4x5in) studio st. chl. 29-Apr-3 Campo, Vlaamse Kaai #343
£347 $552 €500 Homme debout (12x10cm-5x4in) studio st. chl. 29-Apr-3 Campo, Vlaamse Kaai #344
£347 $552 €500 Vieil homme a la canne (11x12cm-4x5in) studio st. chl. 29-Apr-3 Campo, Vlaamse Kaai #347
£347 $552 €500 Homme allonge (11x12cm-4x5in) studio st. chl. 29-Apr-3 Campo, Vlaamse Kaai #349
£347 $552 €500 Avocat (10x12cm-4x5in) studio st. chl. 29-Apr-3 Campo, Vlaamse Kaai #350
£347 $552 €500 Avocat (10x12cm-4x5in) studio st. chl. 29-Apr-3 Campo, Vlaamse Kaai #351
£347 $552 €500 Fumeur de pipe assis (10x12cm-4x5in) studio st. chl. 29-Apr-3 Campo, Vlaamse Kaai #352
£347 $552 €500 Fillette devant les hangars (20x19cm-8x7in) mono. chl. 29-Apr-3 Campo, Vlaamse Kaai #353
£382 $607 €550 Elegante (11x12cm-4x5in) studio st. chl. 29-Apr-3 Campo, Vlaamse Kaai #339
£382 $607 €550 Avocat assis (10x12cm-4x5in) studio st. chl. 29-Apr-3 Campo, Vlaamse Kaai #345/R
£382 $607 €550 Femme debout (10x12cm-4x5in) studio st. sanguine. 29-Apr-3 Campo, Vlaamse Kaai #346
£382 $607 €550 Femme au livre (10x12cm-4x5in) studio st. sanguine. 29-Apr-3 Campo, Vlaamse Kaai #348
£417 $663 €600 Femme assise (24x15cm-9x6in) mono. chl. 29-Apr-3 Campo & Campo, Antwerp #324/R
£461 $770 €650 Gypsies (45x70cm-18x28in) s. pastel. 23-Jun-3 Bernaerts, Antwerp #171/R
£486 $773 €700 Het vliegend wiel (13x22cm-5x9in) studio st. sanguine. 29-Apr-3 Campo, Vlaamse Kaai #337
£764 $1215 €1100 Couple (15x24cm-6x9in) mono.d.1899 chl. 29-Apr-3 Campo & Campo, Antwerp #323/R
£1042 $1656 €1500 Moquerie du Christ (24x33cm-9x13in) sanguine. 29-Apr-3 Campo & Campo, Antwerp #322/R est:1100-1300
£1277 $2132 €1800 Harbour view (27x35cm-11x14in) s. Indian ink dr. 23-Jun-3 Bernaerts, Antwerp #169/R est:1000-1250
£2083 $3312 €3000 Deux vieilles dames (18x27cm-7x11in) mono. chl. 29-Apr-3 Campo, Vlaamse Kaai #354/R est:2000-2500
£2778 $4417 €4000 Deux elegantes (13x22cm-5x9in) studio st. sanguine. 29-Apr-3 Campo, Vlaamse Kaai #358 est:600-800
£3774 $5811 €6000 Nu assis (34x24cm-13x9in) mono. dr. 22-Oct-2 Campo, Vlaamse Kaai #660
£6289 $9686 €10000 Quartier populaire (24x35cm-9x14in) s. dr. 22-Oct-2 Campo, Vlaamse Kaai #663/R

MIEL, Jan (1599-1663) Flemish
£16216 $25297 €24000 After the hunt (59x74cm-23x29in) lit.prov. 27-Mar-3 Dorotheum, Vienna #96/R est:20000-30000
Works on paper
£8861 $14000 €14000 Jeune garcon allonge (15x10cm-6x4in) i. red chk prov. 27-Nov-2 Christie's, Paris #6/R est:5000-8000

MIEL, Jan (attrib) (1599-1663) Flemish
£8865 $13741 €13298 Commedia del'arte (57x78cm-22x31in) prov. 4-Dec-2 AB Stockholms Auktionsverk #1969/R est:125000-150000 (S.KR 125000)

MIELDS, Rune (1935-) German
£2029 $3328 €2800 B 28/70 (150x96cm-59x38in) s.i.d.28/70 verso prov. 28-May-3 Lempertz, Koln #287/R est:2600
£2821 $4372 €4400 B 47 (180x120cm-71x47in) s.i.d.1971 verso. 3-Dec-2 Lempertz, Koln #308/R est:4000

MIELICH, Alfons Leopold (1863-1929) Austrian
£4317 $7079 €6000 Detente dans un cafe au Caire (74x100cm-29x39in) s. 4-Jun-3 Tajan, Paris #277/R est:5000-6000

MIEREVELT, Michiel Jans van (attrib) (1567-1641) Dutch
£506 $790 €800 Portrait d'homme a la collerette (30x22cm-12x9in) panel. 18-Oct-2 Rabourdin & Choppin de Janvry, Paris #134
£4577 $7599 €6500 Portrait of gentleman with lace collar (40x33cm-16x13in) panel prov. 11-Jun-3 Dorotheum, Vienna #87/R est:6000-9000
£6757 $10541 €10000 Portrait of bearded man in white ruff and Bordeaux doublet (58x44cm-23x17in) i. panel prov. 27-Mar-3 Dorotheum, Vienna #199/R est:8000-12000

MIEREVELT, Michiel Jans van (circle) (1567-1641) Dutch
£19108 $29809 €30000 Portrait of a young woman, small bust length (25x19cm-10x7in) panel. 6-Nov-2 Christie's, Amsterdam #21/R est:2200-2600

MIERIS, Frans van (attrib) (17/18th C) Dutch
£2958 $4762 €4200 Eating oysters (27x21cm-11x8in) lit. 9-May-3 Schloss Ahlden, Ahlden #1329/R est:4800

MIERIS, Frans van (elder) (1635-1681) Dutch
£8861 $14000 €14000 Portrait presume de Francois de le Boe (19x15cm-7x6in) s.i.d.1665 panel prov.lit. 2-Dec-2 Rieunier, Paris #58/R est:8000
Works on paper
£110000 $183700 €159500 Young woman seated at a table, reading a letter by candlelight (20x17cm-8x7in) s. blk chk vellum prov. 9-Jul-3 Sotheby's, London #95/R est:60000-80000

MIERIS, Frans van (younger) (1689-1763) Dutch
£18000 $30060 €26100 Self-portrait of the artist in his studio (27x24cm-11x9in) s.d.1747 oak panel prov.exhib.lit. 10-Jul-3 Sotheby's, London #138/R est:20000-30000

MIERIS, Willem van (1662-1747) Dutch
£2229 $3478 €3500 Portrait of a gentleman wearing a orange coat (3x2cm-1x1in) s. oil prov. 5-Nov-2 Sotheby's, Amsterdam #151/R est:4000-6000
£4676 $7482 €6500 Portrait of a lady in a white gown and fuchsia shawl (9x7cm-4x3in) s.d.1707 copper oval. 14-May-3 Christie's, Amsterdam #201/R est:7000-9000
£19000 $29830 €28500 Rest on the Flight into Egypt (49x43cm-19x17in) indis.sig.d.1734 panel. 11-Dec-2 Christie's, London #64/R est:20000-30000
£19000 $31730 €27550 Rest on the flight into Egypt (49x43cm-19x17in) indis sig.d.1734 panel. 9-Jul-3 Christie's, London #49/R est:20000-30000
£19231 $30192 €30000 Portrait of lady (27x23cm-11x9in) panel. 13-Dec-2 Pierre Berge, Paris #62/R est:15000
Works on paper
£955 $1471 €1500 Two figures, half length, standing at a bench (70x17cm-28x7in) black chk prov. 3-Sep-2 Christie's, Amsterdam #80/R est:1500-2500
£1900 $3173 €2755 Bearded man holding bags of gold seducing a lady at her dressing table (24x20cm-9x8in) black white chk prov. 8-Jul-3 Christie's, London #106/R est:2000-3000

MIERIS, Willem van (after) (1662-1747) Dutch
£7500 $11700 €11250 Young girl at window, holding parrot (31x25cm-12x10in) bears sig. panel prov. 10-Apr-3 Sotheby's, London #45/R

MIERZEJEWSKI, Andrzej (1915-1982) Polish
£3481 $5500 €5500 Composition (65x80cm-26x31in) s.d.1960 on stretcher. 2-Dec-2 Tajan, Paris #170/R est:6000-7500

MIESENBERGER, Maria (1965-) Swedish
Photographs
£2890 $4566 €4335 Hands (120x100cm-47x39in) s. d.95 verso num.7/10 C-print lit. 28-Apr-3 Bukowskis, Stockholm #949/R est:30000-35000 (S.KR 38000)
£2966 $4686 €4449 Untitled - the ball, or Sverige/Sweden (109x92cm-43x36in) num.1/3 gelatin silver print prov.exhib. 28-Apr-3 Bukowskis, Stockholm #890/R est:40000-45000 (S.KR 39000)
£5606 $8746 €8409 Untitled - gentlemen in the garden (99x157cm-39x62in) s.d.93-98 C-print one of three prov.lit. 6-Nov-2 AB Stockholms Auktionsverk #829/R est:60000-80000 (S.KR 80000)

MIETTINEN, Olli (1899-1969) Finnish
£316 $494 €500 Landscape (34x42cm-13x17in) s.d.1943. 12-Sep-2 Hagelstam, Helsinki #845/R
£642 $994 €1020 Group of houses (28x35cm-11x14in) s.d.45 exhib. 6-Oct-2 Bukowskis, Helsinki #229/R

MIFELEW, Chananel (1920-1999) Polish
£250 $388 €375 Desert house (56x75cm-22x30in) s.d.68 board. 6-Oct-2 Lots Road, London #344

MIGLIARA, Giovanni (1785-1837) Italian
£31090 $49122 €48500 Grand Canal.abstrait Piazzetta with figures (26x34cm-10x13in) pair. 13-Nov-2 Marc Kohn, Paris #63/R est:60000-70000
£36709 $58000 €58000 Landscape with church and figures. Landscape with ruins and figures (47x62cm-19x24in) one s. tempera paper on canvas pair. 2-Dec-2 Finarte, Milan #78/R est:50000

MIGLIARA, Giovanni (attrib) (1785-1837) Italian
£490 $804 €750 Cloister with monks (31x25cm-12x10in) cardboard. 5-Feb-3 Il Ponte, Milan #200
£3049 $5000 €4574 Capriccios of the Venetian lagoons (14x24cm-6x9in) 5-Feb-3 Christie's, Rockefeller NY #299/R est:5000-7000
£19444 $30722 €28000 Views of Venice (61x98cm-24x39in) pair. 23-Apr-3 Rabourdin & Choppin de Janvry, Paris #60/R est:32000

MIGLIARO, Vincenzo (1858-1938) Italian
£9494 $15000 €15000 Adalgisa (66x86cm-26x34in) s. prov.lit. 26-Nov-2 Christie's, Rome #261/R est:20000
£17722 $28000 €28000 Two women praying (48x32cm-19x13in) s.d.1882 lit. 26-Nov-2 Christie's, Rome #262/R est:23000-28000

MIGNARD (17/18th C) French
£5449 $8500 €8174 Trompe l'oeil still life (54x43cm-21x17in) s. 20-Sep-2 Sloan, North Bethesda #405/R est:2000-4000

MIGNARD, Nicolas (1606-1668) French
Works on paper
£769 $1192 €1200 Hercule entre le Vice et la Vertu (24x34cm-9x13in) sanguine. 4-Dec-2 Piasa, Paris #63
£6790 $11000 €10185 Studies of legs and arms (41x28cm-16x11in) chk double-sided prov. 22-Jan-3 Christie's, Rockefeller NY #62/R est:10000

MIGNARD, Nicolas (attrib) (1606-1668) French
£7095 $11068 €10500 Christ a la couronne d'epines (39x32cm-15x13in) oval. 26-Mar-3 Tajan, Paris #55/R

MIGNARD, Pierre (17/18th C) French
£3427 $5415 €5141 Portrait of Marguerite Louise D'Orleans, Grand Duchess of Tuscany (116x90cm-46x35in) prov. 18-Nov-2 Waddingtons, Toronto #250/R est:10000-15000 (C.D 8500)
£18293 $30000 €27440 Young girl playing a guitar (72x50cm-28x20in) oval prov. 30-May-3 Christie's, Rockefeller NY #40/R est:30000-50000

MIGNARD, Pierre (attrib) (17/18th C) French
£6993 $11678 €10000 L'Archange Saint Michel terrassant le dragon (179x116cm-70x46in) 25-Jun-3 Tajan, Paris #46/R est:12000-15000

MIGNARD, Pierre (circle) (17/18th C) French
£5800 $9512 €8700 Portrait of Louise Renee de Penancoet de Kerouaille (96x84cm-38x33in) 29-May-3 Christie's, Kensington #11/R est:6000-8000

MIGNARD, Pierre (style) (17/18th C) French
£5696 $8886 €9000 Portrait de femme (74x59cm-29x23in) oval. 16-Oct-2 Fraysse & Associes, Paris #24/R est:2500-3000
£6000 $9420 €9000 Allegory of music (82x80cm-32x31in) indis d.1627. 10-Dec-2 Sotheby's, Olympia #342/R est:2000-3000
£7436 $11526 €11600 Portrait de Louis XIV a cheval (103cm-41in circular) 6-Dec-2 Rieunier, Bailly-Pommery, Mathias, Paris #336/R est:18000

MIGNARD, Pierre I (1612-1695) French
£8333 $13083 €13000 Portrait of girl with dog (86x79cm-34x31in) 10-Dec-2 Della Rocca, Turin #166/R est:15000
£96154 $150962 €150000 Louis XIV devant une ville de Flandres (168x137cm-66x54in) painted c.1680 exhib. 20-Nov-2 Binoche, Paris #55/R est:150000-200000

MIGNARD, Pierre I (attrib) (1612-1695) French
£1959 $3057 €2900 Portrait de madame de maintenon et du Duc du Maine (43x52cm-17x20in) panel oval. 28-Mar-3 Piasa, Paris #40/R

£4112 $6661 €5962 Diana - Goddess of hunting (58x72cm-23x28in) 26-May-3 Bukowskis, Stockholm #447/R est:40000-50000 (S.KR 53000)

MIGNECO, Giuseppe (1908-1997) Italian

£1757 $2741 €2600 Workmen at bar (51x35cm-20x14in) s.d.52 tempera paper on cardboard. 28-Mar-3 Farsetti, Prato #358/R
£1923 $3019 €3000 Lady and gentleman (40x30cm-16x12in) s. tempera paper on canvas. 23-Nov-2 Meeting Art, Vercelli #187/R
£3014 $4701 €4400 Fisherman leaving (24x18cm-9x7in) s. lit. 10-Apr-3 Finarte Semenzato, Rome #210/R
£4861 $7729 €7000 Peasant woman (30x24cm-12x9in) s. painted 1987 lit. 1-May-3 Meeting Art, Vercelli #340
£6329 $10000 €10000 Woman with basket of fish (45x35cm-18x14in) s. painted 1987. 30-Nov-2 Farsetti, Prato #659/R est:13000
£6329 $10000 €10000 Reclining fisherman (35x45cm-14x18in) s. s.i.verso painted 1981. 30-Nov-2 Farsetti, Prato #669/R est:12000
£7801 $12638 €11000 Contadino (55x44cm-22x17in) s. prov. 26-May-3 Christie's, Milan #307/R est:10000-12000
£9615 $15096 €15000 Fishermen (81x65cm-32x26in) s. painted 1965 exhib.lit. 23-Nov-2 Meeting Art, Vercelli #491/R est:15000

Works on paper

£541 $843 €800 Woman (29x21cm-11x8in) s. gouache paper on canvas. 26-Mar-3 Finarte Semenzato, Milan #61
£608 $949 €900 Woman (28x23cm-11x9in) s.d.1969 Chinese ink W/C. 26-Mar-3 Finarte Semenzato, Milan #37/R
£676 $1054 €1000 Couple (28x21cm-11x8in) s. gouache paper on canvas. 26-Mar-3 Finarte Semenzato, Milan #35/R
£816 $1298 €1200 Fisherman (28x22cm-11x9in) s. Chinese ink W/C paper on canvas. 1-Mar-3 Meeting Art, Vercelli #546
£833 $1325 €1200 Woman (28x22cm-11x9in) s.d.1960 W/C. 1-May-3 Meeting Art, Vercelli #588
£1176 $1882 €1800 Figure (32x24cm-13x9in) s. Chinese ink paper on canvas exec.1984. 4-Jan-3 Meeting Art, Vercelli #477

MIGNERY, Herb (1937-) American

Sculpture

£2397 $3500 €3596 The hungry loop (56cm-22in) one of 20 bronze. 18-May-2 Altermann Galleries, Santa Fe #182/R
£2397 $3500 €3596 Bronc rider (36cm-14in) one of 10 bronze. 18-May-2 Altermann Galleries, Santa Fe #183/R

MIGNON, Léon (1847-1898) Belgian

Sculpture

£1589 $2591 €2400 Uhlan a cheval (73cm-29in) s. bronze. 17-Feb-3 Horta, Bruxelles #177/R
£1611 $2593 €2400 La vedette ou la sentinelle (73cm-29in) s. brown pat.bronze. 18-Feb-3 Galerie Moderne, Brussels #1023/R est:3000-4000
£2848 $4443 €4500 Fermier et son taureau (52x60x23cm-20x24x9in) s. brown pat bronze. 15-Oct-2 Horta, Bruxelles #121

MIGNON, Lucien (1865-1944) French

£826 $1280 €1239 Les deux amies (27x34cm-11x13in) s.d.1917 board prov. 9-Dec-2 Philippe Schuler, Zurich #3949/R (S.FR 1900)

MIGNOT, Louis Remy (1831-1870) American

£10200 $16116 €14790 Morning, Guayaquil River (25x36cm-10x14in) i.verso. 23-Jul-3 Mallams, Oxford #264/R est:3000-5000

MIGONNEY, Jules (1876-1929) French

£650 $1053 €975 Reclining female nude (22x35cm-9x14in) s.d.1926 canvas on board. 23-Jan-3 Christie's, Kensington #52/R
£676 $1054 €1000 Auto-portrait (35x27cm-14x11in) s.i. cardboard. 30-Mar-3 Anaf, Lyon #410

MIHAILOV, Ivan (19th C) Russian

£314 $487 €500 The guest (19x24cm-7x9in) s.d.1892. 6-Oct-2 Bukowskis, Helsinki #341/R

MIHAILOVITCH, Milorad Batta (1923-) Yugoslavian

£339 $525 €509 Composition (146x114cm-57x45in) s.d.60 s.d.1960 verso paper on canvas prov. 1-Oct-2 Rasmussen, Copenhagen #152 (D.KR 4000)

MIHALOVITS, Miklos (1888-1960) Hungarian

£1145 $1809 €1718 Untitled, slave girl (80x60cm-31x24in) s. 7-Apr-3 Shapiro, Sydney #552/R est:3000-5000 (A.D 3000)
£1298 $2050 €1947 Untitled, slave girl (80x60cm-31x24in) s. 7-Apr-3 Shapiro, Sydney #553/R est:3000-5000 (A.D 3400)

MIHICH, Vasa (20th C) ?

Sculpture

£1602 $2500 €2403 Untitled (216cm-85in) plexiglass. 30-Mar-3 Butterfields, Los Angeles #1423/R est:800-1200

MIKHAILOV, Oleg (1934-) Russian

£250 $388 €375 Spring garden (73x54cm-29x21in) s. 8-Dec-2 John Nicholson, Haslemere #179

MIKL, Josef (1929-) Austrian

£1241 $1986 €1800 Untitled (29x21cm-11x8in) mono.d.61 paper. 11-Mar-3 Dorotheum, Vienna #174/R est:1800-2200
£2152 $3400 €3400 Rollers in Theresienthal (87x61cm-34x24in) s.d.1982 board. 27-Nov-2 Dorotheum, Vienna #283/R est:2200-3000
£6329 $10000 €10000 Glass with flowers (50x50cm-20x20in) 27-Nov-2 Dorotheum, Vienna #277/R est:7000-9000
£14493 $23768 €20000 Composition with blue figure (198x198cm-78x78in) s.indis.i.d.92 lit. 27-May-3 Wiener Kunst Auktionen, Vienna #205/R est:20000-35000

MIKLOS, Gustave (1888-1967) French

Works on paper

£1079 $1727 €1500 Bleu marine (31x8cm-12x3in) init. gouache prov. 15-May-3 Sotheby's, Paris #174/R

MIKOLA, Andreas Armas (1884-1970) Finnish

£671 $1046 €1007 Landscape in Nagybanya with shadowy field (33x51cm-13x20in) s. 11-Apr-3 Kieselbach, Budapest #125/R est:120000-240000 (H.F 240000)

MIKOLA, Armas (1901-1983) Finnish

£432 $708 €600 Reval (42x51cm-17x20in) s. 5-Jun-3 Hagelstam, Helsinki #974
£576 $944 €800 Summer evening (39x46cm-15x18in) s.d.42. 4-Jun-3 Bukowskis, Helsinki #363/R
£612 $1003 €850 Boathouse (39x50cm-15x20in) s.d.50. 4-Jun-3 Bukowskis, Helsinki #364/R
£673 $1036 €1070 Aabo - boat by harbour (35x45cm-14x18in) s.d.1943. 24-Oct-2 Hagelstam, Helsinki #844/R
£691 $1133 €960 Fishermen (60x43cm-24x17in) s.d.1942. 5-Jun-3 Hagelstam, Helsinki #892/R
£728 $1135 €1150 Paris (50x40cm-20x16in) s.d.60. 12-Sep-2 Hagelstam, Helsinki #1032
£728 $1135 €1150 Beach huts (43x55cm-17x22in) s.i. 15-Sep-2 Bukowskis, Helsinki #240/R
£850 $1393 €1300 Bridge in Paris (18x27cm-7x11in) s.i.d.55. 9-Feb-3 Bukowskis, Helsinki #309/R
£1031 $1599 €1640 From Aura river (42x53cm-17x21in) s.d.45. 6-Oct-2 Bukowskis, Helsinki #230/R est:1500
£1079 $1770 €1500 Aabo (45x55cm-18x22in) s. 5-Jun-3 Hagelstam, Helsinki #970/R est:600
£1156 $1839 €1700 Venice (50x81cm-20x32in) s.d.1964. 27-Feb-3 Hagelstam, Helsinki #868 est:1000
£1172 $1852 €1700 Akaslompolo - mountain landscape (50x84cm-20x33in) s.d.1977. 3-Apr-3 Hagelstam, Helsinki #1013/R est:1200
£1582 $2468 €2500 Rymattyla (50x80cm-20x31in) s. 12-Sep-2 Hagelstam, Helsinki #935 est:1200

MIKOLA, Nandor (1911-) Finnish

Works on paper

£396 $610 €630 Landscape (66x96cm-26x38in) s. W/C. 24-Oct-2 Hagelstam, Helsinki #1040
£423 $680 €600 View from Madeira (34x50cm-13x20in) s.i.d.87 W/C. 10-May-3 Bukowskis, Helsinki #90/R

MIKULICZ-BREYER, Isabella von (1887-1973) Czechoslovakian

£1111 $1767 €1600 Standing female nude (75x46cm-30x18in) i. verso. 29-Apr-3 Wiener Kunst Auktionen, Vienna #593/R est:800-1500

MILA, Joel (1895-1990) Swedish

£266 $421 €399 Beautiful flowers (75x57cm-30x22in) s.d.1945 panel. 30-Nov-2 Goteborg Auktionsverk, Sweden #585/R (S.KR 3800)
£442 $698 €663 View from Katarinahissen, Stockholm (62x52cm-24x20in) s.d.1946 panel. 30-Nov-2 Goteborg Auktionsverk, Sweden #584/R (S.KR 6300)

MILANESE SCHOOL (16th C) Italian

£5743 $8959 €8500 Lucrece (69x48cm-27x19in) panel painted c.1580. 26-Mar-3 Tajan, Paris #2

MILANI, Aureliano (1675-1749) Italian

Works on paper

£1757 $2741 €2600 Three male nudes (21x30cm-8x12in) i. pen ink wash. 27-Mar-3 Christie's, Paris #80/R

MILANI, Umberto (1912-1969) Italian

£641 $994 €1000 Reclining female nude (28x37cm-11x15in) s. tempera paper on canvas prov. 4-Dec-2 Finarte, Milan #318

MILATZ, Frans Andreas (1763-1808) Dutch
Works on paper
£605 $944 €950 Landscape with peasants near a farm, cornfield and woods behind (29x38cm-11x15in) s. pen brown ink W/C over black chk. 5-Nov-2 Sotheby's, Amsterdam #177/R

MILDE, J (20th C) German
Sculpture
£1145 $1672 €1718 Seated female nude (56cm-22in) s.i.d. bronze. 17-Jun-2 Philippe Schuler, Zurich #4081 est:1400-2100 (S.FR 2600)

MILEHAM, Harry Robert (1873-1957) British
£3000 $4740 €4500 Joseph sold to the Ishmaeilites (131x115cm-52x45in) s.d.98 exhib.lit. 2-Dec-2 Sotheby's, London #66/R est:4000-6000

MILEN, J R (?) ?
£414 $654 €600 Landscape view by the fjord Lorn (60x91cm-24x36in) s. 3-Apr-3 Hagelstam, Helsinki #937

MILES, Annie Stewart (fl.1888-1907) British
£440 $712 €620 Still life with cornflowers (55x39cm-22x15in) s. 21-May-3 James Adam, Dublin #66
£450 $716 €675 Little girl praying with an old woman in an interior (92x61cm-36x24in) s. 18-Mar-3 Rosebery Fine Art, London #751

MILES, J (19th C) ?
£449 $750 €651 Farm in the hills (41x51cm-16x20in) s.d.1941 prov. 21-Jun-3 Selkirks, St. Louis #161/R

MILES, Thomas Rose (fl.1869-1906) British
£800 $1336 €1160 Before the storm, Mounts Bay, Cornwall (36x51cm-14x20in) s. s.i.verso. 18-Jun-3 Sotheby's, Olympia #76/R
£900 $1458 €1350 After a stormy night, Ramsgate (112x86cm-44x34in) s. s.i.verso. 21-May-3 Christie's, Kensington #630/R
£900 $1503 €1305 Morning off Whitby (61x107cm-24x42in) s. s.i.verso. 18-Jun-3 Sotheby's, Olympia #75/R
£1400 $2310 €2030 Fishing boats returning to shore in choppy seas (35x61cm-14x24in) s.d.1870. 1-Jul-3 Bearnes, Exeter #492/R est:800-1200
£1410 $2214 €2200 Morning, Kilkeiran Bay (29x58cm-11x23in) s. exhib. 19-Nov-2 Hamilton Osborne King, Dublin #442 est:2000-3000
£1500 $2280 €2250 Connemara coast (46x82cm-18x32in) s. 15-Aug-2 Bonhams, New Bond Street #339/R est:1500-2500
£2200 $3410 €3300 Waiting for the catch (61x108cm-24x43in) s. 31-Oct-2 Christie's, Kensington #530/R est:1500-2000
£2282 $3674 €3400 Morning, Kilkieran Bay, Co Galway (29x60cm-11x24in) s. canvas on panel prov. 18-Feb-3 Whyte's, Dublin #88/R est:2500-3500
£2500 $3925 €3750 Wind and rain off Sheerness (53x102cm-21x40in) s. 13-Dec-2 Keys, Aylsham #673 est:2500-3500
£2516 $3925 €4000 Killary Bay, Connemara (41x66cm-16x26in) s. s.i.verso. 17-Sep-2 Whyte's, Dublin #125/R est:3000-4000
£3200 $4960 €4800 Running into Peel Harbour, Isle of Man (102x76cm-40x30in) s. 31-Oct-2 Christie's, Kensington #537/R est:3000-5000
£3500 $5495 €5250 Return of the Douglas lifeboat (91x145cm-36x57in) s. 16-Dec-2 Sotheby's, Olympia #133/R est:1500-2500
£6400 $9536 €9600 Breezy morning, Peel Harbour, Isle of Man (61x107cm-24x42in) s.i. verso. 28-Jun-2 Chrystals Auctions, Isle of Man #175a est:3000-5000

MILES, Thomas Rose (attrib) (fl.1869-1906) British
£1400 $2212 €2100 Fisherman rowing out to their catch (61x107cm-24x42in) s. 14-Nov-2 Christie's, Kensington #232/R est:800-1200

MILESI, Alessandro (1856-1945) Italian
£850 $1343 €1275 Portrait, bust length, of a gentleman (70x52cm-28x20in) s. i.verso. 12-Nov-2 Bonhams, Knightsbridge #63/R
£2564 $4026 €4000 Small child in front of a soup bowl (31x21cm-12x8in) s. board. 10-Dec-2 Dorotheum, Vienna #251/R est:4500-5800
£3797 $6000 €6000 Boats in the Lagoon (38x55cm-15x22in) s.d.1900. 26-Nov-2 Christie's, Rome #202/R est:9000
£3871 $6116 €6000 Laggon (23x30cm-9x12in) s. cardboard. 18-Dec-2 Finarte, Milan #38/R est:7000
£3871 $6116 €6000 Marghera (34x48cm-13x19in) s. cardboard. 18-Dec-2 Finarte, Milan #67/R
Works on paper
£284 $460 €400 Busto d'uomo (16x11cm-6x4in) s.i. pencil. 22-May-3 Stadion, Trieste #261
£503 $775 €800 Woman in profile (45x32cm-18x13in) s. pencil chl dr. 28-Oct-2 Il Ponte, Milan #298

MILHOUS, Katherine (1894-1977) American
£353 $550 €530 Sun and shadow (25x20cm-10x8in) s. board exhib. 18-Sep-2 Alderfer's, Hatfield #276

MILIADIS, Stelios (1881-1965) Greek
£4500 $7110 €6750 Fishermen in a boat (45x70cm-18x28in) 1-Apr-3 Bonhams, New Bond Street #30 est:3500-5000

MILICH, Adolphe (1884-1964) Polish
£750 $1163 €1125 Portrait of a woman (115x88cm-45x35in) s. canvas on board. 3-Dec-2 Bonhams, Knightsbridge #291/R

MILIOTI, Nikolai Dimitrievich (1874-1962) Russian
£180000 $282600 €270000 Fete galante (53x55cm-21x22in) mono.d.1905. 20-Nov-2 Sotheby's, London #74/R est:40000-60000

MILJAN, Niko (1861-?) Yugoslavian
£611 $971 €917 Trabancula (68x74cm-27x29in) s.d.37. 8-Mar-3 Dorotheum, Prague #157/R est:15000-23000 (C.KR 28000)

MILL, J (fl.1855) British
£7000 $11060 €10500 River in a jungle, South America (240x141cm-94x56in) s. 15-Nov-2 Sotheby's, London #91/R est:8000-12000

MILLAIS, John Guille (1865-1931) British
Works on paper
£570 $900 €855 Birds of Patagonia and waterbirds (38x60cm-15x24in) s.d.1901 W/C gouache on board prov. 3-Apr-3 Christie's, Rockefeller NY #223/R
£1139 $1800 €1709 White tailed gnus (30x45cm-12x18in) s.d.1895 gouache on board prov.lit. 3-Apr-3 Christie's, Rockefeller NY #177/R est:1500-2500
£2405 $3800 €3608 Six Orvis poli against snow capped mountains (45x55cm-18x22in) s.d.1912 W/C chl gouache on board prov. 3-Apr-3 Christie's, Rockefeller NY #178/R est:2000-3000
£3165 $5000 €4748 Red grouse over the moors (43x56cm-17x22in) s.d.1908 W/C gouache on board prov. 3-Apr-3 Christie's, Rockefeller NY #190/R est:3000-5000
£41139 $65000 €61709 Skull inset with English stag antlers (114x132cm-45x52in) s.d.1917 pen ink on antlers prov. 3-Apr-3 Christie's, Rockefeller NY #172/R est:8000-12000
£48101 $76000 €72152 Skull inset with Alaskan moose antlers (155x122cm-61x48in) s.d.1915 pen ink on antlers prov.lit. 3-Apr-3 Christie's, Rockefeller NY #173/R est:10000-15000

MILLAIS, Raoul (1901-) British
£1900 $3097 €2850 Stable (18x23cm-7x9in) s. board prov. 29-Jan-3 Sotheby's, Olympia #242/R est:800-1200
£2400 $3792 €3600 Grey Arab horse and two dogs in paddocks (51x61cm-20x24in) s. 28-Nov-2 Bonhams, Knightsbridge #62/R est:2000-3000
£4000 $6560 €6000 Mares and foals grazing in a paddock (51x61cm-20x24in) s. 3-Jun-3 Bonhams, Knightsbridge #33/R est:2500-3500

MILLAIS, Sir John Everett (1829-1896) British
£32000 $50560 €48000 The Romans leaving Britain (46x70cm-18x28in) mono. i.verso panel prov.exhib.lit. 26-Nov-2 Christie's, London #112/R est:30000-50000
£70000 $110600 €105000 Portrait of the artist daughter, Mary (60x46cm-24x18in) prov.exhib.lit. 27-Nov-2 Christie's, London #20/R est:70000-100000
£180000 $298800 €270000 Early days (114x95cm-45x37in) mono.d.1873 prov.exhib.lit. 11-Jun-3 Christie's, London #8/R est:200000-300000
£1100000 $1826000 €1650000 Sleeping (89x68cm-35x27in) mono. prov.exhib.lit. 11-Jun-3 Christie's, London #9/R est:1200000-1800000
Works on paper
£320 $534 €464 Group of people (18x18cm-7x7in) pencil prov. 20-Jun-3 Keys, Aylsham #470
£1600 $2592 €2400 Sketch of a coat of arms (15x12cm-6x5in) s.i.d.1862 with sketch and engraving three. 21-Jan-3 Bonhams, Knightsbridge #47/R est:300-500
£11000 $17710 €16500 Roundhead conventicle (88x177cm-35x70in) s.d.1841 i.verso pencil W/C oil htd white prov.exhib.lit. 20-Feb-3 Christie's, London #77/R est:10000

MILLAIS, Sir John Everett (attrib) (1829-1896) British
£3000 $4650 €4500 Sketch, portrait of Lady Millais and his infant daughter (43x34cm-17x13in) board. 25-Sep-2 John Nicholson, Haslemere #1031/R est:2500-5000

MILLAIS, William Henry (1814-1899) British
Works on paper
£360 $569 €540 Continental lake scene with town in distance and figures on bank (15x24cm-6x9in) s. W/C. 4-Apr-3 Moore Allen & Innocent, Cirencester #436/R
£440 $686 €660 Woodland stream (33x48cm-13x19in) W/C exhib. 26-Mar-3 Woolley & Wallis, Salisbury #30/R
£1300 $2132 €1950 Lynmouth, North Devon (23x51cm-9x20in) s. W/C. 5-Feb-3 John Nicholson, Haslemere #1006 est:1250-1500

MILLAN, Joaquin (1964-) Spanish
£1859 $2937 €2900 Gran Via, Madrid (114x146cm-45x57in) s. s.i.d.1996 verso. 14-Nov-2 Arte, Seville #458/R

MILLAN, Manuel (1948-) Spanish
£641 $1013 €1000 Still life (55x39cm-22x15in) s. board. 19-Nov-2 Durán, Madrid #132/R

MILLAR, Addison T (1860-1913) American
£416 $650 €603 Arab street scene (31x23cm-12x9in) 13-Apr-3 Butterfields, Los Angeles #7030
£769 $1200 €1154 Arab street (30x25cm-12x10in) bears sig. 9-Oct-2 Doyle, New York #74
£778 $1300 €1128 Rue des Abencerages Alger (30x25cm-12x10in) s. 22-Jun-3 Freeman, Philadelphia #110/R est:1500-2500
£1205 $2000 €1747 Mountainous river landscape (36x25cm-14x10in) s.d.1887 prov. 11-Jun-3 Butterfields, San Francisco #4014/R est:3000-5000
£2111 $3250 €3167 Middle Eastern Bazaar (18x23cm-7x9in) s. board. 24-Oct-2 Shannon's, Milford #178/R est:4000-6000

MILLAR, Jack (1921-) British
£633 $981 €1000 Winter sun (64x76cm-25x30in) s. 24-Sep-2 De Veres Art Auctions, Dublin #161a est:1000-2000
£4000 $6200 €6000 Studio at night (89x105cm-35x41in) s. board. 4-Dec-2 Christie's, Kensington #584/R est:600-800

MILLAR, James H C (fl.1884-1903) British
£350 $550 €525 HMS Montague ashore on Lundy Island (24x37cm-9x15in) s. oil on linen. 16-Dec-2 Sotheby's, Olympia #123/R
£500 $780 €750 Steep cliffs (76x10cm-30x4in) s. 17-Oct-2 David Lay, Penzance #1332
£580 $905 €870 Coastal scene (41x61cm-16x24in) s. exhib. 8-Oct-2 Bonhams, Oxford #167
£1600 $2464 €2400 Loch Lyne, Scotland (41x61cm-16x24in) s. 5-Sep-2 Christie's, Kensington #151/R est:1000-1500

MILLAR, Judy (1957-) New Zealander
£880 $1452 €1276 Abstract (95x86cm-37x34in) s.d.1981 verso acrylic collage. 1-Jul-3 Peter Webb, Auckland #87/R est:2500-3500 (NZ.D 2500)

MILLARD, Daryl (20th C) American
£1146 $1800 €1719 Lake Hodges (30x36cm-12x14in) s. i.verso canvas on board. 19-Nov-2 Butterfields, San Francisco #8361/R est:2000-3000

MILLARD, Frederick (1857-1937) British
£5063 $8000 €7595 Latest news (71x91cm-28x36in) s. 23-Apr-3 Christie's, Rockefeller NY #85/R est:10000-15000

MILLARES, Manolo (1926-1972) Spanish
£10256 $16103 €16000 Untitled (50x65cm-20x26in) s. i.verso paper on canvas. 24-Nov-2 Laurence Calmels, Paris #194/R
£10897 $17109 €17000 Untitled (49x64cm-19x25in) s. paper on canvas. 24-Nov-2 Laurence Calmels, Paris #196/R est:15000
£11538 $18115 €18000 Peace victims (50x65cm-20x26in) s. paper on canvas. 24-Nov-2 Laurence Calmels, Paris #195/R est:15000
£26000 $43420 €37700 Insula (32x41cm-13x16in) s. s.i.d.1967 verso oil string on burlap prov. 27-Jun-3 Christie's, London #149/R est:18000-22000
£39744 $62397 €62000 Painting (54x65cm-21x26in) s. s.i.d.69 verso oil mixed media. 24-Nov-2 Laurence Calmels, Paris #197/R est:50000
£51799 $82878 €72000 El Grito - the cry (73x60cm-29x24in) s. s.i.d. verso oil collage exhib.prov.lit. 15-May-3 Neumeister, Munich #729/R est:30000-40000
£65000 $100100 €97500 Personaje (81x100cm-32x39in) s. s.i.d.1969 verso oil on burlap prov. 23-Oct-2 Christie's, London #118/R est:40000-60000
£80000 $131200 €120000 Cuadro 44 (130x97cm-51x38in) s..i.on stretcher oil on burlap painted 1958 prov.exhib.lit. 5-Feb-3 Christie's, London #30/R est:80000-120000
£140000 $233800 €210000 Cuadro 140 (128x160cm-50x63in) s. s.i.d.1961 stretcher oil burlap on burlap bags prov.lit. 26-Jun-3 Christie's, London #37/R est:100000-150000
Works on paper
£748 $1100 €1122 Abstract collage (18x25cm-7x10in) s. mixed media. 23-Jun-2 Susanin's, Chicago #5062/R
£2086 $3338 €2900 Harbour workers (25x21cm-10x8in) s. W/C exec.c.1948. 17-May-3 Hagelstam, Helsinki #37/R est:3500
£7097 $11000 €10646 Pintura sobre papel (49x71cm-19x28in) s. s.i.d.1968 verso gouache ink prov. 26-Sep-2 Christie's, Rockefeller NY #708/R est:7000-9000

MILLASSON, Anne (20th C) French?
Works on paper
£400 $636 €580 Promeneurs au bois de pins (48x64cm-19x25in) s. pastel. 10-Mar-3 Thierry & Lannon, Brest #182

MILLER, Alfred Jacob (1810-1874) American
£12258 $19000 €18387 Critic (30x26cm-12x10in) mono. board prov. 4-Dec-2 Sotheby's, New York #133/R est:12000-18000
£23885 $37500 €35828 American Indians on horseback in a river landscape (23x30cm-9x12in) s. paper panel prov. 19-Nov-2 Butterfields, San Francisco #8080/R est:40000-60000
£53797 $85000 €78006 Scene on the Big Sandy River (23x30cm-9x12in) s. oil paper on board. 26-Jul-3 Coeur d'Alene, Hayden #161/R est:60000-90000
£601266 $950000 €871836 Indian village (79x122cm-31x48in) painted c.1850 prov.exhib.lit. 26-Jul-3 Coeur d'Alene, Hayden #148/R est:600000-900000
£967742 $1500000 €1451613 Buffalo hunt (55x86cm-22x34in) s.d.58 prov.lit. 4-Dec-2 Sotheby's, New York #143/R est:800000-1200000
Works on paper
£14013 $22000 €21020 Louison Crevier (22x17cm-9x7in) W/C ink prov.exhib. 20-Nov-2 Christie's, Los Angeles #58/R est:5000-7000
£14423 $22500 €21635 Portrait of an Indian Chief, Kansas (15x13cm-6x5in) init.i. graphite wash prov.lit. 9-Nov-2 Santa Fe Art, Santa Fe #157/R est:25000-35000
£24516 $38000 €36774 Running a bank of Elk, near the cut rocks of the platte (17x27cm-7x11in) pencil pen ink executed c.1837 prov.exhib.lit. 5-Dec-2 Christie's, Rockefeller NY #155/R est:30000-50000
£24516 $38000 €36774 Young woman of the flat head tribe (19cm-7in circular) W/C gouache prov. 5-Dec-2 Christie's, Rockefeller NY #175/R est:15000-25000
£45161 $70000 €67742 Crow Indian on the lookout (32x24cm-13x9in) mono.i. W/C gouache pencil prov. 5-Dec-2 Christie's, Rockefeller NY #165/R est:30000-50000
£51613 $80000 €77420 Shoshone Indian and his pet horse (23x30cm-9x12in) mono, W/C gouache pencil prov. 5-Dec-2 Christie's, Rockefeller NY #156/R est:40000-60000
£51613 $80000 €77420 Scalp lock (30x24cm-12x9in) mono. W/C gouache pencil prov. 5-Dec-2 Christie's, Rockefeller NY #176/R est:40000-60000
£61290 $95000 €91935 Indians on the war path (22x31cm-9x12in) mono. W/C gouache pencil prov. 5-Dec-2 Christie's, Rockefeller NY #166/R est:50000-70000

MILLER, Barse (1904-1973) American
£4516 $7000 €6774 South wind (64x76cm-25x30in) s. i.verso prov. 29-Oct-2 John Moran, Pasadena #740 est:3000-5000

MILLER, Charles Frederic (20th C) American
£262 $425 €393 Boat in Tahitian Harbor (61x51cm-24x20in) s. i.verso. 24-Jan-3 Freeman, Philadelphia #214/R

MILLER, Charles Henry (1842-1922) American
£710 $1100 €1065 Old mill (46x61cm-18x24in) s. board painted c.1880. 8-Dec-2 Toomey, Oak Park #645/R

MILLER, Curtis (20th C) British?
£347 $500 €521 Omaha (76x63cm-30x25in) s.d.1941 s.i.d.verso. 15-Jan-3 Christie's, Rockefeller NY #161/R

MILLER, Edgar (1899-?) American
Works on paper
£319 $500 €479 Dowager (53x30cm-21x12in) s. gouache. 22-Nov-2 Skinner, Boston #192/R

MILLER, Evylena Nunn (1888-1966) American
£559 $900 €839 Snow capped mountain landscape (76x91cm-30x36in) s. prov. 18-Feb-3 John Moran, Pasadena #178
£1144 $1900 €1659 Coast Royal (63x76cm-25x30in) s. prov. 11-Jun-3 Butterfields, San Francisco #4276/R est:3000-5000

MILLER, Frederick (19th C) British
Works on paper
£400 $632 €600 Three deckers and hulks in harbour (28x53cm-11x21in) s. W/C. 2-Dec-2 Gorringes, Lewes #2670

MILLER, Godfrey Clive (1893-1964) Australian
£2692 $4281 €4038 Figure design (42x26cm-17x10in) init. 4-Mar-3 Deutscher-Menzies, Melbourne #99/R est:8000-12000 (A.D 7000)
£7117 $10890 €10676 Compote series (47x59cm-19x23in) oil pencil canvas on board prov.exhib. 25-Aug-2 Sotheby's, Paddington #41/R est:22000-28000 (A.D 20000)
Works on paper
£4800 $7728 €7200 Still life (38x28cm-15x11in) init. pastel pencil chl paper on board prov. 6-May-3 Christie's, Melbourne #32/R est:8000-12000 (A.D 12000)

MILLER, Harrison (fl.1891-1892) British
Works on paper
£378 $627 €548 Woman in country garden (37x28cm-15x11in) s. W/C. 16-Jun-3 Waddingtons, Toronto #62/R (C.D 850)

MILLER, Henry (1891-1980) American
Works on paper
£854 $1324 €1350 Paris (31x24cm-12x9in) s.i.d.12/61 W/C board. 28-Sep-2 Ketterer, Hamburg #313/R
£943 $1472 €1500 City panorama (34x27cm-13x11in) s.i.d.12/59 W/C. 21-Sep-2 Bolland & Marotz, Bremen #751/R

MILLER, James Robertson (fl.1880-1912) British
Works on paper
£440 $682 €660 Canal in Holland (37x28cm-15x11in) s. W/C. 24-Sep-2 Anderson & Garland, Newcastle #387/R
£540 $837 €810 Rowing boat on a Dutch canal (37x28cm-15x11in) s. W/C. 24-Sep-2 Anderson & Garland, Newcastle #388/R

MILLER, John (1911-1975) British
£350 $571 €525 Turkish village, Cyprus (51x76cm-20x30in) s.d.1974 i.verso. 13-Feb-3 David Lay, Penzance #373
£550 $875 €825 Bluebells in a vase (54x38cm-21x15in) s. panel. 6-Mar-3 Christie's, Kensington #215/R
£850 $1326 €1275 Garden (71x76cm-28x30in) s. s.verso. 27-Mar-3 Christie's, Kensington #435

MILLER, John (fl.1876-1890) British
£600 $942 €900 Rabbits in a pen (33x77cm-13x30in) s. 21-Nov-2 Tennants, Leyburn #777/R

MILLER, John (1931-2002) British
£250 $415 €363 Beacon, evening (30x71cm-12x28in) s.d.1974. 10-Jun-3 David Lay, Penzance #151
£280 $468 €406 Bell tower (61x61cm-24x24in) s. 17-Jun-3 Bonhams, Knightsbridge #87
£800 $1280 €1200 Two men seated in interior with Staffordshire cat and dog, bold geometric rug (91x61cm-36x24in) 13-Mar-3 Duke & Son, Dorchester #199/R
£900 $1440 €1350 St. Just evening (56x61cm-22x24in) s.i.d.1973 board. 13-Mar-3 Duke & Son, Dorchester #264/R
£2750 $4593 €3988 St. Mawes, panoramic view of the armour with castles in the distance (70x100cm-28x39in) s. 19-Jun-3 Lane, Penzance #130/R est:3000-4000
£4000 $6680 €5800 West country fishing boats (70x100cm-28x39in) s.d.1977. 19-Jun-3 Lane, Penzance #95/R est:3000-4000
Works on paper
£300 $471 €450 Waves (13x10cm-5x4in) s.i. gouache. 10-Dec-2 Lane, Penzance #24
£380 $631 €551 Penwith landscape (25x25cm-10x10in) s. gouache. 10-Jun-3 David Lay, Penzance #306
£380 $631 €551 Cornish beach (15x10cm-6x4in) s. gouache. 10-Jun-3 David Lay, Penzance #307
£600 $936 €900 Beach at Tresco (15x15cm-6x6in) s.i.verso gouache. 16-Oct-2 David Lay, Penzance #264/R
£600 $942 €900 Sunrise (37x16cm-15x6in) s. i. gouache collage. 10-Dec-2 Lane, Penzance #139
£1450 $2277 €2175 Sunset (41x36cm-16x14in) s.i. gouache. 10-Dec-2 Lane, Penzance #193/R est:1200-1400
£1900 $3173 €2755 Beach. s.i. gouache. 19-Jun-3 Lane, Penzance #353 est:850-1250
£2050 $3219 €3075 Island beach (30x25cm-12x10in) s.i. gouache. 10-Dec-2 Lane, Penzance #5/R est:900-1200

MILLER, John (1893-1975) British
£580 $905 €870 Clyde at Rhu (40x60cm-16x24in) s. board. 17-Oct-2 Bonhams, Edinburgh #25/R

MILLER, Lewis (1795-1882) American
Works on paper
£897 $1400 €1346 Strawberries, with kneeling Amish man (15x8cm-6x3in) s.i. W/C ink prov. 21 Sep-2 Pook & Pook, Downington #466/R est:800-1000

MILLER, Lewis (1959-) Australian
£358 $559 €621 Schnapper (25x30cm-10x12in) s.i.d.95 prov. 31-Mar-3 Goodman, Sydney #30 (A.D 950)
£717 $1176 €1076 Bust of a girl (50x40cm-20x16in) s.i.d.03 verso prov. 4-Jun-3 Deutscher-Menzies, Melbourne #112/R est:2000-3000 (A.D 1800)
£1120 $1803 €1680 Reclining nude (50x60cm-20x24in) init.d.97 s.i.d.verso prov. 6-May-3 Christie's, Melbourne #349/R est:2500-3500 (A.D 2800)

MILLER, Melissa (1951-) American
£299 $500 €434 Ocean dance, 1982 (79x64cm-31x25in) s. oil on paper. 29-Jun-3 Butterfields, Los Angeles #7076/R
£539 $900 €782 Bear dance in clearing (58x79cm-23x31in) s. acrylic on paper. 29-Jun-3 Butterfields, Los Angeles #7070/R est:400-600
£599 $1000 €869 Studies for the ark, buffaloes (64x79cm-25x31in) s. acrylic. 29-Jun-3 Butterfields, Los Angeles #7071/R est:400-600

MILLER, Mildred Bunting (1892-?) American
£1198 $2000 €1737 Summer afternoon (46x61cm-18x24in) s. canvasboard. 22-Jun-3 Freeman, Philadelphia #123/R est:2000-3000

MILLER, Norman James Miller (1914-2001) British
£270 $419 €405 Group of horses (71x91cm-28x36in) 5-Oct-2 Shapes, Edinburgh #363/R
£280 $434 €420 Portrait of a young girl with a shell to her ear (43x56cm-17x22in) 5-Oct-2 Shapes, Edinburgh #351
£280 $434 €420 Bay and foal (66x74cm-26x29in) 5-Oct-2 Shapes, Edinburgh #364
£290 $450 €435 HRH Princess Anne on horseback (71x91cm-28x36in) 5-Oct-2 Shapes, Edinburgh #362/R
£520 $806 €780 Young lady with her horse (68x84cm-27x33in) 5-Oct-2 Shapes, Edinburgh #361/R
£980 $1519 €1470 Jackie's ready for the off (51x61cm-20x24in) board. 5-Oct-2 Shapes, Edinburgh #360

MILLER, Oscar (1867-?) American
£1069 $1700 €1604 Haystacks (46x61cm-18x24in) s.i.d.95. 7-Mar-3 Skinner, Boston #381/R est:1000-1500

MILLER, Ralph Davison (1858-1946) American
£1026 $1600 €1539 Mt Tallac, Lake Tahoe. board. 21-Sep-2 Harvey Clar, Oakland #1522

MILLER, Richard E (1875-1943) American
£26235 $42500 €39353 Portrait of Frederick Hammett. Nude in an interior (74x78cm-29x31in) s. masonite double-sided painted 1935 prov.lit. 21-May-3 Sotheby's, New York #153/R est:30000-50000
£42254 $68028 €60000 Reverie (92x73cm-36x29in) 11-May-3 Thierry & Lannon, Brest #207/R est:60000-80000

MILLER, Stuart McAlpine (1964-) British
£700 $1155 €1015 In need of an immediate change of face (137x122cm-54x48in) s. s.i.verso. 3-Jul-3 Christie's, Kensington #526

MILLER, Vance (20th C) American
£968 $1500 €1452 Autumn woods (79x61cm-31x24in) s. 28-Sep-2 Charlton Hall, Columbia #549/R est:700-1000

MILLER, William Rickarby (1818-1893) American
£1730 $2750 €2595 Still life with exotic fruits (43x54cm-17x21in) 5-Mar-3 Sotheby's, New York #36/R est:4000-6000
£3247 $5000 €4871 Summer walk (20x30cm-8x12in) s.d.1869 prov. 24-Oct-2 Shannon's, Milford #181/R est:5000-7000

MILLER, Winfried von (1854-1925) German
£943 $1472 €1500 Smiling girl with slice of bread (53x44cm-21x17in) s. 9-Oct-2 Michael Zeller, Lindau #821/R

MILLER-DIFLO, Otto (1878-1949) German
£548 $855 €800 Extensive landscape near Fussen with view of Alps (56x72cm-22x28in) s. i.verso. 10-Apr-3 Allgauer, Kempten #2897/R
£719 $1122 €1050 Allgauer winter landscape (41x50cm-16x20in) s. lit. 10-Apr-3 Allgauer, Kempten #2896/R

MILLES, Carl (1875-1955) Swedish/American

Sculpture

£1135 $1759 €1703 Angel playing the flute (22x20cm-9x8in) s. green pat.bronze cire perdue. 3-Dec-2 Bukowskis, Stockholm #226/R est:20000-25000 (S.KR 16000)

£1348 $2089 €2022 Head of Europa (14cm-6in) s. green pat.bronze sold with stone base st.f.Rasmussen. 3-Dec-2 Bukowskis, Stockholm #225/R est:12000-15000 (S.KR 19000)

£1348 $2089 €2022 The philosopher (57cm-22in) s. pat.bronze cire perdue incl. granite socle. 3-Dec-2 Bukowskis, Stockholm #228/R est:25000-30000 (S.KR 19000)

£1474 $2388 €2137 Girl standing in the wind (25cm-10in) s. green pat.bronze. 26-May-3 Bukowskis, Stockholm #304/R est:20000-25000 (S.KR 19000)

£1487 $2349 €2231 Bust of young woman (24cm-9in) s. green pat.bronze st.f.Rasmussen incl socle. 1-Apr-3 Rasmussen, Copenhagen #74/R est:20000-25000 (D.KR 16000)

£2128 $3298 €3192 Laughter - fencing-master Janken Wiel-Hansen (42cm-17in) s. dark pat.bronze st.f.H Bergman lit. 8-Dec-2 Uppsala Auktionskammare, Uppsala #344/R est:30000-35000 (S.KR 30000)

£2749 $4509 €3986 The battle for survival (20x40cm-8x16in) s. pat.bronze Cast. Andro exec.1899-1900 lit. 4-Jun-3 AB Stockholms Auktionsverk #2361/R est:35000-40000 (S.KR 35000)

£2948 $4776 €4275 Water-carrier (22cm-9in) s. gold pat.bronze Cast Bergman. 26-May-3 Bukowskis, Stockholm #303/R est:20000-25000 (S.KR 38000)

£3050 $4727 €4575 Small girl (21cm-8in) s. green pat.bronze cire perdue prov. 4-Dec-2 AB Stockholms Auktionsverk #1810/R est:30000-35000 (S.KR 43000)

£3103 $5027 €4499 Boy with dolphin (60cm-24in) s.d.1956 green pat.bronze fountain sculpture. 26-May-3 Bukowskis, Stockholm #306/R est:50000-60000 (S.KR 40000)

£3404 $5277 €5106 Girl standing (27cm-11in) s.d.97 marble. 3-Dec-2 Bukowskis, Stockholm #224/R est:45000-50000 (S.KR 48000)

£5000 $8350 €7250 Struggle for existence (19cm-7in) s.i. dk brown pat bronze Cast Andro. 8-Jul-3 Sotheby's, London #230/R est:6000-8000

£7092 $10993 €10638 Diana - from Dianabrunnen, Stockholm (70cm-28in) s. green pat.bronze incl.stone socle st.f.Rasmussen lit. 4-Dec-2 AB Stockholms Auktionsverk #1803/R est:60000-80000 (S.KR 100000)

£7447 $11543 €11171 Plesiosaurs (100cm-39in) s. green pat.bronze st.f.Bergman executed 1903-1904 lit. 4-Dec-2 AB Stockholms Auktionsverk #1816/R est:60000-80000 (S.KR 105000)

£17021 $26383 €25532 The elephants blowing their trumpets (118x110cm-46x43in) s. green pat.bronze st.f.Bergman. 3-Dec-2 Bukowskis, Stockholm #62/R est:300000-350000 (S.KR 240000)

£18440 $28582 €27660 Torso of Europa (66cm-26in) s. green pat.bronze st.f.Pettersson. 3-Dec-2 Bukowskis, Stockholm #227/R est:300000-350000 (S.KR 260000)

£19007 $30791 €27560 The flying horse (86x54cm-34x21in) s.num.11/12 green pat.bronze Cast Gunnar Pettersson. 26-May-3 Bukowskis, Stockholm #307/R est:180000-200000 (S.KR 245000)

£28369 $43972 €42554 Europa and the bull (78cm-31in) s.d.1950 num.2 green pat.bronze st.f.Bergman. 3-Dec-2 Bukowskis, Stockholm #223/R est:500000-700000 (S.KR 400000)

£111111 $180000 €166667 Europa and the bull (78cm-31in) i. greenish brown pat. bronze prov.exhib.lit. 21-May-3 Sotheby's, New York #184/R est:200000-300000

MILLES, Ruth (1873-1955) Swedish

Sculpture

£1135 $1759 €1703 Girl on a windy day (25cm-10in) s. green pat.bronze on wood base st.f.Pettersson. 3-Dec-2 Bukowskis, Stockholm #72/R est:8000-10000 (S.KR 16000)

£1474 $2241 €2300 La petite Hollandaise assise (28x20x17cm-11x8x7in) red brown pat bronze exec.c.1920. 10-Jul-2 Rabourdin & Choppin de Janvry, Paris #53/R est:2300-2500

£1844 $2858 €2766 Water carrier (35cm-14in) s.d.1906 dark pat.bronze st.f.Bergman. 3-Dec-2 Bukowskis, Stockholm #71/R est:15000-20000 (S.KR 26000)

MILLESON, Royal Hill (1849-1926) American

Works on paper

£419 $650 €629 Sunset river landscape (33x48cm-13x19in) s. W/C prov. 29-Oct-2 John Moran, Pasadena #627

MILLET, Clarence (1897-1959) American

£1220 $2000 €1830 Market (15x20cm-6x8in) s. s.i.verso masonite prov. 8-Feb-3 Neal Auction Company, New Orleans #366/R est:2000-3000

£4268 $7000 €6189 Sculptor's holiday (69x53cm-27x21in) s. 7-Jun-3 Neal Auction Company, New Orleans #395/R est:10000-15000

£6707 $11000 €9725 Antique shop Rue Royale (25x33cm-10x13in) s.i.verso board. 7-Jun-3 Neal Auction Company, New Orleans #363/R est:7000-10000

£10897 $17000 €16346 Oak Alley plantation home (76x91cm-30x36in) s. s.i.verso. 12-Oct-2 Neal Auction Company, New Orleans #631/R est:20000-30000

£11613 $18000 €17420 Cathedral Jackson Square (61x66cm-24x26in) s. s.i.verso. 7-Dec-2 Neal Auction Company, New Orleans #480/R est:2000-3000

MILLET, Francisque (attrib) (17/18th C) French

£638 $1066 €900 Marie-Madeleine dans un paysage (38x44cm-15x17in) 20-Jun-3 Rieunier, Paris #21/R

MILLET, Francisque I (attrib) (1642-1679) French

£4810 $7792 €6975 Landscape with the Penitent Magdalena (115x160cm-45x63in) prov. 26-May-3 Bukowskis, Stockholm #420/R est:40000-50000 (S.KR 62000)

MILLET, Jean Baptiste (1831-1906) French

Works on paper

£350 $574 €525 Hay making (15x18cm-6x7in) s. pencil W/C. 5-Jun-3 Christie's, Kensington #929

£949 $1500 €1500 Paturage pres de Barbizon (23x32cm-9x13in) s. W/C. 1-Dec-2 Peron, Melun #89

£2482 $4145 €3500 La ferme (25x21cm-10x8in) s. crayon drawing. 20-Jun-3 Piasa, Paris #4/R est:3000-4000

£3800 $6346 €5510 Landscape with a field of mangold wurzels, figures beyond (18x25cm-7x10in) s. pen ink W/C bodycol. 8-Jul-3 Christie's, London #90/R est:2000-3000

MILLET, Jean François (1814-1875) French

£96774 $150000 €145161 Norman milkmaid - Laitiere Normande (33x26cm-13x10in) s. painted 1853-54 prov.exhib.lit. 30-Oct-2 Christie's, Rockefeller NY #22/R est:100000-150000

Prints

£1887 $3000 €2831 La grande bergere (32x24cm-13x9in) etching. 1-May-3 Swann Galleries, New York #44/R est:4000-6000

£2564 $4026 €4000 Le semeur (191x156cm-75x61in) lithograph. 12-Dec-2 Piasa, Paris #90

£2642 $4094 €4200 Depart pour le travail (55x38cm-22x15in) brown engraving vellum. 30-Oct-2 Artcurial Briest, Paris #539 est:2300-2500

£3226 $5000 €4839 Les glaneuses (26x36cm-10x14in) etching executed c.1855. 25-Sep-2 Christie's, Rockefeller NY #142/R est:3500-4500

£4000 $6600 €5800 Les glaneuses (19x25cm-7x10in) brown etching. 1-Jul-3 Sotheby's, London #95/R est:4000-6000

£4000 $6600 €5800 Les glaneuses (19x25cm-7x10in) col etching exec.c.1855. 2-Jul-3 Christie's, London #107/R est:4000-6000

£4200 $6930 €6090 Le semeur (19x16cm-7x6in) lithograph. 2-Jul-3 Christie's, London #108/R est:3000-5000

£4487 $7000 €6731 Les glaneuses (29x34cm-11x13in) brown ink etching prov. 14-Oct-2 Butterfields, San Francisco #1145/R est:6000-8000

£4487 $7000 €6731 Les glaneuses (30x38cm-12x15in) brown ink etching prov. 14-Oct-2 Butterfields, San Francisco #1146/R est:6000-8000

Works on paper

£559 $934 €800 Vierge a l'Enfant sur un croissant de lune (13x6cm-5x2in) studio st. black crayon. 27-Jun-3 Claude Aguttes, Neuilly #3a/R

£903 $1427 €1400 Village breton (9x12cm-4x5in) st.mono. pen brown ink htd blue. 17-Dec-2 Rossini, Paris #41

£993 $1658 €1400 Mere et ses enfants (25x19cm-10x7in) bears st.init. black pencil dr. 23-Jun-3 Beaussant & Lefèvre, Paris #329/R

£1139 $1800 €1800 Grands arbres (6x12cm-2x5in) st.init. pen Chinese ink wash. 27-Nov-2 Blanchet, Paris #10/R

£1181 $1877 €1700 Jeune femme a la cape. Etude de jeune femme a la cape (22x15cm-9x6in) studio st. graphite dr double-sided. 29-Apr-3 Artcurial Briest, Paris #19 est:1200-1500

£1552 $2514 €2250 Studies (26x18cm-10x7in) s. pair prov. 25-May-3 Uppsala Auktionskammare, Uppsala #117 est:5000-6000 (S.KR 20000)

£1689 $2635 €2500 Etude de baigneuses (22x31cm-9x12in) studio st. chl. 27-Mar-3 Maigret, Paris #122/R

£1800 $2808 €2700 Sleeping lovers (16x23cm-6x9in) black chk two prov. 26-Mar-3 Sotheby's, Olympia #184/R est:2000-3000

£2138 $3314 €3400 Paysan ramenant son troupeau (13x19cm-5x7in) st.init. chl. 30-Oct-2 Coutau Begarie, Paris #36/R est:4500-5000

£4000 $6280 €6000 Carrefour de l'epine, foret de Fontainbleau (9x14cm-4x6in) pen ink over pencil stumping blue crayon prov. 19-Nov-2 Sotheby's, London #158/R est:1500-2000
£4000 $6560 €6000 Wooded hillside above Vichy (11x19cm-4x7in) studio st. W/C pen ink prov. 6-Feb-3 Christie's, London #401/R
£5556 $9000 €8334 Woman spinning and other figures (18x13cm-7x5in) chl prov. 21-Jan-3 Sotheby's, New York #177/R est:8000
£5674 $9475 €8000 La baratteuse (29x17cm-11x7in) st. black crayon prov. 19-Jun-3 Piasa, Paris #176/R est:7000-9000
£5769 $9058 €9000 Reve (18x25cm-7x10in) sanguine dr prov. 14-Dec-2 Artcurial Briest, Paris #6/R
£7387 $11894 €11081 Landscape with houses (10x15cm-4x6in) st.init.i. brown ink pencil executed 1866-69 lit. 26-Feb-3 Museumsbygningen, Copenhagen #42/R est:25000-30000 (D.KR 82000)
£12838 $20027 €19000 Portrait de Leopold Debrosses en buste (54x42cm-21x17in) chk prov.exhib.lit. 27-Mar-3 Christie's, Paris #175/R
£23649 $36892 €35000 Portrait de narcisse Virgile Diaz de la Pena (56x43cm-22x17in) s. chk prov.exhib.lit. 27-Mar-3 Christie's, Paris #173/R est:12000
£35484 $55000 €53226 Pastures in Normandy (29x23cm-11x9in) st.sig. pen ink W/C prov.exhib. 30-Oct-2 Christie's, Rockefeller NY #17/R est:70000-90000
£41935 $65000 €62903 Milkmaid leaning against a tree (30x19cm-12x7in) s. chl stumping prov.exhib. 30-Oct-2 Christie's, Rockefeller NY #16/R est:80000-120000
£43919 $68514 €65000 Portrait de Victor Dupre (60x46cm-24x18in) s. chk prov.exhib.lit. 27-Mar-3 Christie's, Paris #174/R est:12000

MILLET, Jean François (attrib) (1814-1875) French
£2264 $3487 €3600 Retour de foret (64x52cm-25x20in) init. lit. 28-Oct-2 Il Ponte, Milan #219/R
Works on paper
£503 $775 €800 Rural house (11x8cm-4x3in) pencil dr. 28-Oct-2 Il Ponte, Milan #215

MILLIERE, Maurice (1871-1946) French
£403 $648 €600 La petite Christiane (21x18cm-8x7in) s.d.1914 W/C. 23-Feb-3 Lesieur & Le Bars, Le Havre #119
£915 $1474 €1300 La meule (64x80cm-25x31in) s.d.1915. 11-May-3 Thierry & Lannon, Brest #386
£1479 $2381 €2100 Belle Ile, la crique (65x65cm-26x26in) s. 11-May-3 Thierry & Lannon, Brest #385 est:1000-1200
£3500 $5495 €5250 Au restaurant (49x26cm-19x10in) s. panel. 21-Nov-2 Christie's, Kensington #60/R est:4000-6000

MILLIKEN, J W (fl.1887-1930) British
Works on paper
£650 $1066 €975 Venetian scenes (20x28cm-8x11in) s. W/C pair. 5-Feb-3 John Nicholson, Haslemere #999
£700 $1092 €1050 Vegetable market, Bruges (25x35cm-10x14in) s. W/C. 6-Nov-2 Bonhams, Chester #318
£1800 $2826 €2700 Views of Venice (16x23cm-6x9in) s. W/C over pencil htd gouache pair. 11-Dec-2 Rupert Toovey, Partridge Green #150/R

MILLIKEN, James W (fl.1887-1930) British
Works on paper
£250 $388 €375 Village cross, Long Wittenham, Berkshire (18x25cm-7x10in) s. i.verso W/C on board. 5-Oct-2 Finan Watkins & Co, Mere #202/R
£300 $465 €450 Continental street market (17x24cm-7x9in) s. W/C. 25-Sep-2 Hamptons Fine Art, Godalming #158
£420 $659 €630 Raby village, Cheshire (24x34cm-9x13in) s. W/C. 16-Apr-3 George Kidner, Lymington #88/R
£650 $1053 €975 Market day, Lanion. Evening, Hesden (24x34cm-9x13in) s. W/C pair. 21-May-3 Bonhams, Knightsbridge #20/R
£800 $1304 €1160 Figures at a Continental fruit market. Figures at a flower market (18x50cm-7x20in) s. W/C pair. 17-Jul-3 Tennants, Leyburn #765

MILLIKEN, R W (1920-) British
Works on paper
£350 $546 €525 Mallards ascending the Quoile River, Downpatrick (20x28cm-8x11in) s. 20-Sep-2 Dee Atkinson & Harrison, Driffield #656

MILLIKEN, Robert W (1920-) British
Works on paper
£320 $496 €480 Pheasant (35x48cm-14x19in) s. W/C. 4-Dec-2 John Ross, Belfast #224
£500 $815 €725 Goldies across the fairway (48x61cm-19x24in) s. W/C gouache. 17-Jul-3 Thomson, Roddick & Medcalf, Carlisle #65/R

MILLINGTON, John (1891-1948) British
Works on paper
£320 $534 €464 Fully rigged sip (25x37cm-10x15in) s. W/C. 25-Jun-3 Bonhams, Bury St Edmunds #506

MILLNER, Karl (1825-1894) German
£321 $497 €500 Upper Bavarian farmstead (28x38cm-11x15in) s. 5-Dec-2 Neumeister, Munich #2843/R
£352 $515 €528 Mountain landscape (28x40cm-11x16in) s. paper on canvas. 17-Jun-2 Philippe Schuler, Zurich #7350 (S.FR 800)
£701 $1093 €1100 Tal Vedro (34x52cm-13x20in) 6-Nov-2 Hugo Ruef, Munich #1212/R
£1042 $1656 €1500 Mountain landscape (38x46cm-15x18in) s.d.1869 panel. 29-Apr-3 Wiener Kunst Auktionen, Vienna #526/R est:1500-3000
£3576 $5543 €5650 Shepherd and flock on track (51x67cm-20x26in) s.d.1852. 25-Sep-2 Neumeister, Munich #657/R est:5800
£10000 $16000 €15000 Springtime Alpine landscape with figures and cattle in the village square (110x142cm-43x56in) s.i.d.1867. 14-May-3 Butterfields, San Francisco #1081/R est:10000-150000

MILLNER, Karl (attrib) (1825-1894) German
£338 $527 €500 High mountains (40x28cm-16x11in) board. 26-Mar-3 Hugo Ruef, Munich #175
£2857 $4543 €4200 Farmstead in mountain valley (111x143cm-44x56in) 19-Mar-3 Neumeister, Munich #648/R est:2000

MILLNER, William Edward (1849-1885) British
£3000 $4710 €4500 Springtime (101x76cm-40x30in) s.d.85 s.i.on stretcher. 19-Nov-2 Bonhams, New Bond Street #144/R est:3000-5000

MILLS, Arthur W (19/20th C) British
£260 $403 €390 HMS Antrim (24x44cm-9x17in) s.d.1904. 31-Oct-2 Locke & England, Leamington Spa #157

MILLS, Reginald (20th C) British
£300 $465 €450 Silhouette, nude in an interior (28x23cm-11x9in) s. panel double-sided. 1-Nov-2 Moore Allen & Innocent, Cirencester #417

MILLWARD, Clem (1929-) Australian
£320 $508 €480 Near Frome Downs (91x106cm-36x42in) s. 3-Mar-3 Lawson Menzies, Sydney #386 (A.D 850)

MILLY, Dezider (1906-1971) Czechoslovakian
£284 $439 €426 Landscape (40x100cm-16x39in) painted c.1970. 1-Oct-2 SOGA, Bratislava #232/R est:22000 (SL.K 18000)
£882 $1252 €1323 Krivy Jarok landscape (43x60cm-17x24in) tempera painted 1942. 26-Mar-2 SOGA, Bratislava #93/R est:32000 (SL.K 56000)

MILNE, Barbara (1956-) Canadian
£221 $347 €332 Field (40x60cm-16x24in) s.i.d.1992 panel prov. 25-Nov-2 Hodgins, Calgary #153/R (C.D 550)

MILNE, David Brown (1882-1953) Canadian
£9274 $14653 €13911 Landscape (51x41cm-20x16in) prov.lit. 18-Nov-2 Sotheby's, Toronto #123/R est:15000-20000 (C.D 23000)
£13333 $21867 €20000 Rapids (30x41cm-12x16in) prov.exhib.lit. 27-May-3 Sotheby's, Toronto #216/R est:20000-25000 (C.D 30000)
£22222 $36444 €33333 Blossoming tree (46x51cm-18x20in) i.d.May 11 11 prov.exhib. 27-May-3 Sotheby's, Toronto #30/R est:60000-80000 (C.D 50000)
£29234 $46190 €43851 Winter sky (30x41cm-12x16in) s.d.1935 prov.exhib.lit. 18-Nov-2 Sotheby's, Toronto #30/R est:50000-60000 (C.D 72500)
£32258 $50968 €48387 Slashing (42x56cm-17x22in) s. prov.lit. 18-Nov-2 Sotheby's, Toronto #124/R est:70000-90000 (C.D 80000)
£33632 $53812 €50448 Cabin in the snow, Mount Riga, NY (30x41cm-12x16in) s. d.January 12.1922 verso prov.lit. 15-May-3 Heffel, Vancouver #41/R est:35000-45000 (C.D 75000)
£44444 $72889 €66666 Black spruce (41x56cm-16x22in) s.d.1927 i.verso prov.lit. 27-May-3 Sotheby's, Toronto #135/R est:60000-80000 (C.D 100000)
£44843 $71749 €67265 Landscape with barn, Palgrave, Ontario (51x67cm-20x26in) s. painted c.1930 prov.exhib.lit. 15-May-3 Heffel, Vancouver #56/R est:80000-100000 (C.D 100000)
£48387 $76452 €72581 Old Horan Place, Palgrave, Ontario (46x62cm-18x24in) s.d.1930 verso prov.lit. 14-Nov-2 Heffel, Vancouver #78/R est:80000-100000 (C.D 120000)
£53333 $87467 €80000 Tin cans in the bush, morning (42x51cm-17x20in) s.d.1929 i.verso. 27-May-3 Sotheby's, Toronto #136/R est:50000-70000 (C.D 120000)
£75556 $123911 €113334 Temagami from above the railroad (40x50cm-16x20in) s. painted 1929 prov.lit. 3-Jun-3 Joyner, Toronto #46/R est:125000-150000 (C.D 170000)

£82661 $130605 €123992 White rocker (51x41cm-20x16in) i. prov.lit. 18-Nov-2 Sotheby's, Toronto #73/R est:120000-150000 (C.D 205000)

Works on paper

£3086 $4784 €4629 Sun dogs II (30x40cm-12x16in) s.i.verso painted c.June 1950 prov.exhib.lit. 3-Dec-2 Joyner, Toronto #64/R est:8000-10000 (C.D 7500)

£4115 $6379 €6173 Ripe wheat and green oats III (36x54cm-14x21in) W/C executed September 1947 prov.lit. 3-Dec-2 Joyner, Toronto #87/R est:12000-15000 (C.D 10000)

£7258 $11468 €10887 Balsam tree no.1 (37x54cm-15x21in) i.verso W/C prov.exhib. 18-Nov-2 Sotheby's, Toronto #164/R est:20000-25000 (C.D 18000)

£7258 $11468 €10887 First snow on the cabin roof (36x53cm-14x21in) i.d. W/C prov.exhib.lit. 18-Nov-2 Sotheby's, Toronto #188/R est:20000-25000 (C.D 18000)

£8072 $12915 €12108 Spring showers - budding poplars III (37x55cm-15x22in) W/C prov.exhib.lit. 15-May-3 Heffel, Vancouver #181/R est:20000-25000 (C.D 18000)

£8230 $12757 €12345 Hyacinths in a window (37x50cm-15x20in) W/C executed 1939 prov.lit. 3-Dec-2 Joyner, Toronto #53/R est:15000-20000 (C.D 20000)

£17937 $28700 €26906 Brown Hill, Boston corners (22x56cm-9x22in) s.d.April 24 1920 W/C prov.exhib.lit. 15-May-3 Heffel, Vancouver #42/R est:60000-80000 (C.D 40000)

£33333 $54667 €50000 Glass jar II (36x55cm-14x22in) i. W/C prov.exhib.lit. 27-May-3 Sotheby's, Toronto #147/R est:20000-30000 (C.D 75000)

MILNE, James (?-1918) British

£1200 $1860 €1800 Cattle grazing by stream with farmbuildings in the background (31x46cm-12x18in) s. 5-Oct-2 Shapes, Edinburgh #256 est:500-700

MILNE, Joe (fl.1905-1908) British

£850 $1377 €1275 Tending the calf (25x38cm-10x15in) s. board. 23-May-3 Lyon & Turnbull, Edinburgh #75

£1000 $1620 €1500 Gathering wrack (30x45cm-12x18in) s. panel. 23-May-3 Lyon & Turnbull, Edinburgh #1/R est:1000-1500

£1250 $1950 €1875 Fisherfolk in the East Neuk (30x45cm-12x18in) s. 17-Oct-2 Bonhams, Edinburgh #258/R est:600-800

£1400 $2282 €2100 Gathering sea-wrack (30x45cm-12x18in) 14-Feb-3 Lyon & Turnbull, Edinburgh #65

£2200 $3366 €3300 Harbour scene, probably Leith (51x31cm-20x12in) s.d.93. 22-Aug-2 Bonhams, Edinburgh #1079 est:800-1200

£3100 $4743 €4650 Tug towing a sailing ship into harbour (51x31cm-20x12in) s.d.93. 22-Aug-2 Bonhams, Edinburgh #952/R est:800-1200

MILNE, John E (1931-1978) British

Sculpture

£1000 $1670 €1450 Sakkara, Egyptian city (21cm-8in) init.d.1978 num.1/9 polished bronze prov.lit. 24-Jun-3 Bonhams, New Bond Street #121/R est:1000-1500

£1200 $1860 €1800 Propylaea II (142cm-56in) cold cast bronze prov.lit. 3-Dec-2 Bonhams, New Bond Street #99/R est:1200-1800

£2000 $3260 €3000 Persepolis (206x170x254cm-81x67x100in) fibreglass pat bronze. 13-Feb-3 David Lay, Penzance #482 est:2000-3000

£2500 $3900 €3750 Totemic II (180cm-71in) Cold cast aluminium. 17-Oct-2 David Lay, Penzance #1544/R est:3000-4000

Works on paper

£240 $379 €360 Untitled (38x28cm-15x11in) s.d.1962 verso chl W/C crayon. 27-Nov-2 Sotheby's, Olympia #161/R

MILNE, John Maclaughlan (1885-1957) British

£3000 $4680 €4500 Corrie, Isle of Arran (38x44cm-15x17in) s. panel prov. 14-Apr-3 Sotheby's, London #115/R est:4000-6000

£4000 $6120 €6000 Mountains of Midi (32x40cm-13x16in) bears sig board prov. 22-Aug-2 Bonhams, Edinburgh #1178/R est:4000-6000

£7000 $10850 €10500 Village of Corrie, Arran (36x44cm-14x17in) s. panel prov. 5-Dec-2 Bonhams, Edinburgh #42/R est:7000-10000

£8000 $12480 €12000 Flowers in a blue vase (61x50cm-24x20in) s. prov.exhib. 14-Apr-3 Sotheby's, London #114/R est:8000-12000

£8500 $13175 €12750 Reflections at corrie (51x61cm-20x24in) s. board. 6-Dec-2 Lyon & Turnbull, Edinburgh #109/R est:6000-8000

£22000 $33440 €33000 View in the South of France (99x125cm-39x49in) s. 28-Aug-2 Sotheby's, London #1094/R est:10000-15000

Works on paper

£600 $936 €900 Ferryden, Montrose (14x22cm-6x9in) s. W/C prov. 10-Apr-3 Bonhams, Edinburgh #164

£800 $1248 €1200 St Paul's from the Thames (25x31cm-10x12in) s. W/C. 13-Sep-2 Lyon & Turnbull, Edinburgh #137/R

£1000 $1560 €1500 Ferryden, Montrose (17x22cm-7x9in) s. W/C prov. 10-Apr-3 Bonhams, Edinburgh #108/R est:600-800

MILNE, Joseph (1861-1911) British

£320 $502 €480 Untitled (33x53cm-13x21in) 15-Apr-3 Bonhams, Chester #855

£480 $749 €720 Drying the nets (15x23cm-6x9in) s. board. 17-Sep-2 Sotheby's, Olympia #33/R

£797 $1300 €1196 Peaceful evening (30x46cm-12x18in) s. 16-Feb-3 Butterfields, San Francisco #2055 est:1200-1800

£850 $1343 €1233 Sheep in an open landscape (23x30cm-9x12in) s. board. 22-Jul-3 Gorringes, Lewes #1741/R

£1500 $2325 €2250 Evening on a Thames backwater with barges moored by the bank (41x61cm-16x24in) s. 31-Oct-2 Christie's, Kensington #548/R est:1000-1500

£4200 $6510 €6300 Stormy day on the Fife coast (51x77cm-20x30in) s. i.verso prov. 31-Oct-2 Christie's, London #91/R est:4000-6000

MILNE, William (19/20th C) British

£800 $1248 €1200 Shepherdess (41x51cm-16x20in) s.d.1904. 14-Apr-3 Sotheby's, London #143/R

MILNE, William Watt (fl.1900-1915) British

£536 $846 €804 Changing pastures (22x30cm-9x12in) s.d.1910 canvasboard. 26-Nov-2 Sotheby's, Melbourne #245/R est:1500-2000 (A.D 1500)

£800 $1328 €1160 Fisherfolk on the beach (25x36cm-10x14in) s. masonite. 16-Jun-3 Waddingtons, Toronto #205/R est:2000-3000 (C.D 1800)

£900 $1440 €1350 View of a thatched cottage, with a well in the foreground (61x51cm-24x20in) s. 13-May-3 Bonhams, Knightsbridge #292/R

£950 $1482 €1425 Shepherdess with her flock (25x32cm-10x13in) s. panel. 14-Apr-3 Sotheby's, London #121/R

£1050 $1733 €1523 Feeding the sheep (20x24cm-8x9in) s. board. 1-Jul-3 Bonhams, Norwich #344 est:1000-1500

£1600 $2496 €2400 Bringing in the nets (29x40cm-11x16in) s. panel. 14-Apr-3 Sotheby's, London #131/R est:1000-1500

£2600 $4056 €3900 Calves watering (54x88cm-21x35in) s. 17-Oct-2 Bonhams, Edinburgh #153a est:1000-1500

£2600 $4056 €3900 Poplars. Cottage (31x25cm-12x10in) s. board two. 14-Apr-3 Sotheby's, London #134/R est:1500-2000

£3000 $4650 €4500 Angler with women washing at a stream (36x50cm-14x20in) s. board. 30-Sep-2 Bonhams, Ipswich #481/R est:3000-4000

MILNE, William Watt (attrib) (fl.1900-1915) British

£390 $608 €585 River landscape at dawn (38x61cm-15x24in) 13-Sep-2 Lyon & Turnbull, Edinburgh #120/R

MILNER, Frederick (1863-1939) British

£900 $1404 €1350 St Ives Harbour (33x41cm-13x16in) s. 17-Oct-2 David Lay, Penzance #1056

£1900 $3116 €2850 Bickton Mill, Hampshire Avon (71x91cm-28x36in) s. 3-Jun-3 Sotheby's, Olympia #26/R est:1000-1500

MILO, Jean (1906-1993) Belgian

£475 $741 €750 Composition (38x55cm-15x22in) s.d.1959 exhib. 20-Oct-2 Charbonneaux, Paris #145 est:500-600

£662 $1079 €1000 Composition aux objets de verre (50x35cm-20x14in) s.d.1947. 17-Feb-3 Horta, Bruxelles #23

£949 $1500 €1500 Composition (61x92cm-24x36in) s.d.61 paper on canvas. 26-Nov-2 Palais de Beaux Arts, Brussels #242 est:1500-2000

£1090 $1689 €1700 Composition au objets de verre devant la fenetre (50x35cm-20x14in) s.d.1947 panel. 9-Dec-2 Horta, Bruxelles #168 est:2000-3000

MILOCH, D (20th C) ?

£333 $523 €520 Sainte-Marine (45x78cm-18x31in) s. 15-Dec-2 Thierry & Lannon, Brest #402

MILOCH, Henri (20th C) French

£769 $1208 €1200 Pardon en Bretagne (50x73cm-20x29in) s. 15-Dec-2 Eric Pillon, Calais #122/R

MILONE, Antonio (?-1920) Italian

£1139 $1800 €1800 Calves in the stable (21x25cm-8x10in) s.d.1897 board. 26-Nov-2 Christie's, Rome #58/R

MILOVITCH, Tanasko (1900-) American/Yugoslavian

£256 $400 €384 Mary (58x46cm-23x18in) s. paper prov. 10-Nov-2 Selkirks, St. Louis #885/R

MILROY, Lisa (1959-) Canadian

£4375 $7000 €6563 Personal items (143x180cm-56x71in) painted 1984 exhib. 14-May-3 Sotheby's, New York #339/R est:8000-12000

£8861 $14000 €13292 Plates (193x284cm-76x112in) init.d.93 overlap prov. 13-Nov-2 Sotheby's, New York #588/R est:15000-20000

MILSTEIN, Zvi (1934-) Israeli

£833 $1308 €1300 Retour de Grece (66x100cm-26x39in) s.d. paint panel exhib. 24-Nov-2 Chayette & Cheval, Paris #314

MILTON-JENSEN, C (1855-1928) Danish

£287 $465 €416 Sunlit tree trunks, Selistria (50x39cm-20x15in) s.d.1904. 26-May-3 Rasmussen, Copenhagen #1310/R (D.KR 3000)

£372 $592 €558 Fjord landscape with geese (40x61cm-16x24in) s.d.1897. 10-Mar-3 Rasmussen, Vejle #119/R (D.KR 4000)

£431 $655 €647 Warm summer's day around Midsummer, Bjerringbro (53x53cm-27x21in) s.d.1893 exhib. 27-Aug-2 Rasmussen, Copenhagen #1927/R (D.KR 5000)

£437 $690 €656 Wooded landscape (95x68cm-37x27in) s.d.1907. 5-Apr-3 Rasmussen, Havnen #2056 (D.KR 4700)

MILTON-JENSEN, Carl (1855-1928) Danish

£1132 $1755 €1800 Goose maid (39x62cm-15x24in) mono.d.82. 29-Oct-2 Dorotheum, Vienna #159/R est:1800-2200

MIN, Jaap (1914-1987) Dutch

Works on paper

£1772 $2800 €2800 Beach scene (48x62cm-19x24in) W/C gouache black chk. 26-Nov-2 Sotheby's, Amsterdam #11/R est:1200-1500

MINARTZ, Tony (1873-1944) French

£775 $1286 €1100 Voiliers dans un port mediterraneen (50x64cm-20x25in) s. 13-Jun-3 Rabourdin & Choppin de Janvry, Paris #105

£15484 $24000 €23226 Fete foraine (40x80cm-16x31in) s. board prov. 30-Oct-2 Christie's, Rockefeller NY #219/R est:18000-25000

MINAUX, Andre (1923-1988) French

£260 $408 €390 Woman standing holding a bouquet of flowers (71x30cm-28x12in) s. prov. 10-Dec-2 Rosebery Fine Art, London #639

£800 $1264 €1200 Two women with a bowl of fruit (82x112cm-32x44in) s. 14-Nov-2 Christie's, Kensington #125/R

£1088 $1731 €1600 Portrait de femme (65x54cm-26x21in) s. 24-Mar-3 Claude Boisgirard, Paris #80

£3000 $4770 €4500 Jeune femme portant une corbeille de fruits (178x93cm-70x37in) s. prov. 20-Mar-3 Sotheby's, Olympia #161/R est:1800-2500

MIND, Gottfried (1768-1814) Swiss

Works on paper

£437 $690 €656 Cat family (11x17cm-4x7in) W/C. 14-Nov-2 Stuker, Bern #9269 (S.FR 1000)

£524 $828 €786 Cat (11x9cm-4x4in) W/C. 14-Nov-2 Stuker, Bern #9270 (S.FR 1200)

MINDEN, Olga Potthast von (1869-1942) German

£1517 $2428 €2200 Heath in bloom (51x117cm-20x46in) s. 11-Mar-3 Dorotheum, Vienna #72/R est:2500-3000

MINDERHOUT, Hendrik van (1632-1696) Dutch

£34532 $55252 €48000 Mediterranean harbour scene with merchants (170x246cm-67x97in) mono. 13-May-3 Sotheby's, Amsterdam #74/R est:30000-50000

MINDERHOUT, Hendrik van (attrib) (1632-1696) Dutch

£7463 $12239 €10821 Harbour scene with figures by temple ruins (73x125cm-29x49in) 4-Jun-3 AB Stockholms Auktionsverk #2550/R est:80000-100000 (S.KR 95000)

MINE, Casper (1905-) French

£976 $1600 €1415 Rabbi. Man with pipe, man in profile (33x23cm-13x9in) s. masonite two. 4-Jun-3 Doyle, New York #71 est:600-800

MINET, Louis Émile (1855-1920) French

£1677 $2800 €2432 River near Stratford on Avon (67x107cm-26x42in) s. 22-Jun-3 Freeman, Philadelphia #38/R est:2000-3000

£2069 $3290 €3000 Jeune fille au bouquet. Jeune fille a genoux. Jeune femmes. two ovals set of four. 5-Mar-3 Oger, Dumont, Paris #44/R est:12000-15000

£11724 $18641 €17000 Grands vases de pivoines, branches de pommier et panier de pensees (148x207cm-58x81in) 5-Mar-3 Oger, Dumont, Paris #46/R est:7000-8000

Works on paper

£1034 $1645 €1500 Les bords de Seine a Rouen (33x50cm-13x20in) s.i.d.1908 pencil pastel. 5-Mar-3 Oger, Dumont, Paris #21/R est:800-900

MING DYNASTY, Chinese

Works on paper

£6962 $11000 €11000 Guanyin assise sur une terrasse, sous un arbre en fleurs (271x126cm-107x50in) ink polychrome silk. 29-Nov-2 Tajan, Paris #295/R est:6000-6500

MINGRET, Jose (20th C) Spanish

£449 $696 €700 Mount Rosa (21x32cm-8x13in) s.i.d.1922. 6-Dec-2 Maigret, Paris #122

MINGUZZI, Luciano (1911-) Italian

Sculpture

£1521 $2403 €2282 Untitled (59cm-23in) s. dark pat.bronze wood socle. 28-Apr-3 Bukowskis, Stockholm #311/R est:25000-30000 (S.KR 20000)

£1795 $2818 €2800 Study for 'Wind amongst canes' (27x39x14cm-11x15x6in) init. bronze exec.1961. 19-Nov-2 Finarte, Milan #239/R

£5128 $7487 €8000 Horse (67x64x20cm-26x25x8in) s. bronze. 5-Jun-2 Il Ponte, Milan #102/R

Works on paper

£372 $580 €550 Face (47x35cm-19x14in) s.d.1967 gouache. 28-Mar-3 Farsetti, Prato #42

MINIAN, John van (fl.1805-1842) American

Works on paper

£11180 $18000 €16770 Birth certificate for Suzanna Beidelman, with elaborate border (38x33cm-15x13in) d.1801 W/C ink. 22-Feb-3 Pook & Pook, Downington #111/R est:7000-9000

MINNAERT, Frans (1929-) Belgian

£338 $527 €500 Fermier dans un paysage (65x85cm-26x33in) s. panel exhib. 25-Mar-3 Campo & Campo, Antwerp #120

£473 $738 €700 Fermiers sure le champs (120x150cm-47x59in) s. 25-Mar-3 Campo & Campo, Antwerp #119

MINNE, George (1866-1941) Belgian

Sculpture

£1727 $2763 €2400 Mother and child (54x18cm-21x7in) s. gypsum. 17-May-3 De Vuyst, Lokeren #262/R est:2200-2400

£2414 $3862 €3500 Small kneeler (47x20cm-19x8in) s.d.96 brown pat plaster prov.lit. 15-Mar-3 De Vuyst, Lokeren #520/R est:4000-5000

£2414 $3862 €3500 Small wound (25x10cm-10x4in) s.d.98 dark brown pat bronze prov.lit. 15-Mar-3 De Vuyst, Lokeren #521/R est:2800-3600

£2658 $4200 €4200 Le petit blesse (25cm-10in) s. green pat bronze marble base. 26-Nov-2 Palais de Beaux Arts, Brussels #126/R est:1250-1750

£3077 $4769 €4800 David (41cm-16in) s. bronze conceived 1928 exhib.lit. 3-Dec-2 Christie's, Amsterdam #50/R est:4000-6000

£3205 $4968 €5000 Maternite (38cm-15in) s. bronze conceived c.1928 exhib. 3-Dec-2 Christie's, Amsterdam #49/R est:5000-7000

£3846 $5962 €6000 Adolescent II (47cm-19in) s. bronze conceived 1923 prov.exhib. 3-Dec-2 Christie's, Amsterdam #56/R est:6000-8000

£4317 $7079 €6000 Christ en croix (65x52cm-26x20in) s. bronze wood prov.exhib. 3-Jun-3 Christie's, Amsterdam #164/R est:6000-8000

£4828 $7724 €7000 Kneeling (71x44cm-28x17in) s. plaster exec.1925 prov.lit. 15-Mar-3 De Vuyst, Lokeren #455/R est:7000-8000

£5500 $8470 €8250 Le grand blesse (40cm-16in) init. bronze lit. 23-Oct-2 Sotheby's, Olympia #762/R est:3000-4000

£6410 $9936 €10000 Bearer of a relic (103cm-41in) s. green pat. bronze lit. 3-Dec-2 Christie's, Amsterdam #55/R est:10000-15000

£8176 $12591 €13000 Baigneuse (58cm-23in) s.d.1931 bronze lit. 22-Oct-2 Campo & Campo, Antwerp #192/R est:15000

£13462 $20865 €21000 Man with water sack (63cm-25in) s.i. bronze prov.lit. 4-Dec-2 Lempertz, Koln #915/R est:20000-30000

£14388 $23597 €20000 L'Agenouille (80cm-31in) plaster conceived c.1898 lit. 3-Jun-3 Christie's, Amsterdam #162/R est:3000-5000

£17241 $27586 €25000 Kneeling man and woman (43x29cm-17x11in) s. brown pat bronze exec.1889 prov.exhib.lit. 15-Mar-3 De Vuyst, Lokeren #423/R est:20000-24000

£19718 $32732 €28000 L'homme a l'outre (64x41x25cm-25x16x10in) bronze. 14-Jun-3 Hauswedell & Nolte, Hamburg #1409/R est:15000

Works on paper

£346 $536 €550 Motherhood (25x17cm-10x7in) s. pencil dr. 5-Oct-2 De Vuyst, Lokeren #249

£1172 $1876 €1700 Eucharist Christ (15x12cm-6x5in) s. chl dr prov. 15-Mar-3 De Vuyst, Lokeren #222 est:1400-1800

£1447 $2345 €2200 Maternite. s. dr. 21-Jan-3 Galerie Moderne, Brussels #279/R est:2000-3000

MINNEBO, Hubert (1940-) Belgian

Sculpture

£1006 $1560 €1600 Bird (60x36cm-24x14in) s.num.1/1 brown pat bronze. 5-Oct-2 De Vuyst, Lokeren #250/R est:1600-1800

MINNS, Benjamin Edward (1864-1937) Australian

£2509 $3814 €3764 Still life (45x56cm-18x22in) s.d.1929. 28-Aug-2 Deutscher-Menzies, Melbourne #247/R est:6500-7500 (A.D 7000)

Works on paper

£575 $856 €863 Little Bo Peep (30x20cm-12x8in) s. W/C. 27-Aug-2 Christie's, Melbourne #327 est:1500-2000 (A.D 1500)
£651 $1023 €977 Untitled - an afternoon stroll (31x23cm-12x9in) s.d.05 W/C. 15-Apr-3 Lawson Menzies, Sydney #218/R est:1500-2000 (A.D 1700)
£690 $1083 €1035 Sydney Harbour (23x31cm-9x12in) s. W/C executed c.1910. 15-Apr-3 Lawson Menzies, Sydney #65/R est:2200-3200 (A.D 1800)
£714 $1129 €1071 Harbour from Middle Head (25x34cm-10x13in) s. W/C. 18-Nov-2 Goodman, Sydney #80/R (A.D 2000)
£763 $1206 €1145 Untitled, ducks in farmyard (25x30cm-10x12in) s. W/C. 7-Apr-3 Shapiro, Sydney #422/R (A.D 2000)
£766 $1142 €1149 Surf (27x36cm-11x14in) s. W/C. 27-Aug-2 Christie's, Melbourne #346 est:2000-3000 (A.D 2000)
£893 $1411 €1340 Drover's camp (25x36cm-10x14in) s.d.1935 W/C. 18-Nov-2 Goodman, Sydney #91 (A.D 2500)
£1527 $2412 €2291 Nude seated by a stream (36x26cm-14x10in) s.d.1918 W/C. 2-Apr-3 Christie's, Melbourne #20 est:1000-2000 (A.D 4000)
£2672 $4221 €4008 Negotiating the pond (25x35cm-10x14in) s.d.1902 W/C. 2-Apr-3 Christie's, Melbourne #13 est:2000-4000 (A.D 7000)
£4122 $6265 €6183 The Spit, Sydney (25x36cm-10x14in) s.d.1926 W/C. 28-Aug-2 Deutscher-Menzies, Melbourne #220/R est:5000-8000 (A.D 11500)

MINOLI, Paolo (1942-) Italian

£1834 $2678 €2751 Permutations (80x80cm-31x31in) acrylic panel prov. 4-Jun-2 Germann, Zurich #68/R est:4000-6000 (S.FR 4200)

MINOR, Anne Rogers (1864-?) American

£353 $550 €530 Sail boats in harbour (33x41cm-13x16in) s. i.stretcher. 15-Oct-2 Winter Associates, Plainville #226

MINOR, Robert Crannell (1839-1904) American

£802 $1300 €1163 Giant of the valley (56x76cm-22x30in) s. 21-May-3 Doyle, New York #59/R
£3438 $5500 €5157 Near Waterford, Conn (36x48cm-14x19in) s. 11-Jan-3 James Julia, Fairfield #301 est:3500-5000

MINORU, Niizuma (1930-) Japanese

Sculpture

£1852 $3000 €2685 Untitled (36cm-14in) s.d.69 blk marble incl blk marble base. 21-May-3 Doyle, New York #43/R est:1500-2500
£3086 $5000 €4475 Untitled (160cm-63in) s.d.1930 white marble wood pedestal. 21-May-3 Doyle, New York #39/R est:3000-5000

MINOZZI, Bernardino (1699-1769) Italian

£10345 $16448 €15000 Landscape with shepherd. Landscape with river (274x109cm-108x43in) tempera pair. 9-Mar-3 Semenzato, Venice #28/R

MINOZZI, Filiberto (1887-1936) Italian

£324 $522 €486 Evening park landscape (21x24cm-8x9in) s. board. 7-May-3 Dobiaschofsky, Bern #831/R (S.FR 700)

MINOZZI, Flaminio (1735-1817) Italian

Works on paper

£5068 $7905 €7500 David's triumph (39x53cm-15x21in) pen ink wash W/C prov. 27-Mar-3 Christie's, Paris #42/R

MINOZZI, Flaminio (attrib) (1735-1817) Italian

Works on paper

£1119 $1600 €1679 Study for the decoration of a rectangular ceiling (20x34cm-8x13in) pen ink W/C. 23-Jan-3 Swann Galleries, New York #148/R est:800-1200

MINTCHINE, Abraham (1898-1931) Russian

£1935 $3058 €3000 Auction (50x65cm-20x26in) s. prov. 18-Dec-2 Christie's, Rome #83/R
£4487 $7045 €7000 Street scene (38x55cm-15x22in) s. 12-Dec-2 Rabourdin & Choppin de Janvry, Paris #17/R
£4615 $7246 €7200 Nature morte au violon (38x46cm-15x18in) s. 12-Dec-2 Rabourdin & Choppin de Janvry, Paris #16/R

MINTON, John (1917-1957) British

£12000 $19680 €18000 Circus baker (63x76cm-25x30in) init. painted 1956 prov.lit. 6-Jun-3 Christie's, London #185/R est:10000-15000

Works on paper

£300 $465 €450 Study for Corialanus (22x29cm-9x11in) pen black ink. 4-Dec-2 Christie's, Kensington #295
£320 $528 €464 Printing (46x31cm-18x12in) i. pen ink. 3-Jul-3 Christie's, Kensington #539
£380 $585 €570 Seated male (37x27cm-15x11in) pen ink. 5-Sep-2 Christie's, Kensington #601
£500 $825 €725 Seated male nude (56x27cm-22x11in) pen brush ink. 3-Jul-3 Christie's, Kensington #530/R
£550 $908 €798 Portrait of a young man (38x27cm-15x11in) pen ink. 3-Jul-3 Christie's, Kensington #534
£600 $930 €900 Standing male nude (38x26cm-15x10in) pen brush blue ink. 4-Dec-2 Christie's, Kensington #297/R
£600 $990 €870 Seated male nude. Seated male nude (32x26cm-13x10in) pencil two. 3-Jul-3 Christie's, Kensington #535
£700 $1085 €1050 Norwegian landscape (26x37cm-10x15in) s.d.1953 pen brush black brown ink prov. 4-Dec-2 Christie's, Kensington #342/R
£750 $1238 €1088 Clown (27x21cm-11x8in) s. pen ink brown wash prov.exhib. 3-Jul-3 Christie's, Kensington #536
£850 $1403 €1233 Portrait of Owen Wood (39x28cm-15x11in) pencil W/C. 3-Jul-3 Christie's, Kensington #531/R
£850 $1403 €1233 Corsican landscape (35x28cm-14x11in) pen brush ink. 3-Jul-3 Christie's, Kensington #649/R
£1500 $2475 €2175 Self portrait (20x18cm-8x7in) pencil executed c.1949 prov. 3-Jul-3 Christie's, Kensington #529/R est:800-1200
£1600 $2496 €2400 Bullfighter (36x27cm-14x11in) s.d.1949 prov. 6-Nov-2 Dreweatt Neate, Newbury #11/R est:1000-1500
£2800 $4340 €4200 Corsican cemetery (28x38cm-11x15in) s.d.1947 pen ink wash wax crayon. 3-Dec-2 Bonhams, New Bond Street #75/R est:2000-3000

MINTREP, Theodor (1814-1870) German

Works on paper

£449 $709 €700 Ludwig van Beethoven composing outside (18x14cm-7x6in) s. Indian ink brush over pencil. 16-Nov-2 Lempertz, Koln #1362
£449 $709 €700 Wolfgang Amadeus Mozart composing Don Giovanni (18x14cm-7x6in) s. Indian ink brush over pencil. 16-Nov-2 Lempertz, Koln #1363
£449 $709 €700 Raffael painting surrounded by onlookers (18x14cm-7x6in) s. Indian ink brush over pencil. 16-Nov-2 Lempertz, Koln #1364

MION, Luigi (19th C) Italian

£2500 $4000 €3750 Loving look (84x53cm-33x21in) 11-Mar-3 Bonhams, Knightsbridge #245/R est:3000-4000

MIORI, Luciano (20th C) Italian?

Works on paper

£3226 $5000 €4839 Standing male nude with fish (76x51cm-30x20in) s. pencil black ink gouache. 29-Oct-2 Sotheby's, New York #299 est:2000-3000

MIOTTE, Jean (1926-) French

£297 $495 €430 Elan (32x24cm-13x9in) s. acrylic. 9-Jul-3 Cornette de St.Cyr, Paris #325
£641 $1006 €1000 Composition et nu cubisant (151x49cm-59x19in) studio st. panel double-sided. 16-Dec-2 Eric Coutrier, Paris #96
£1076 $1678 €1700 En passant par la (14x18cm-6x7in) s. s.i. verso prov. 20-Oct-2 Claude Boisgirard, Paris #63/R est:1600-1800
£1367 $2132 €2051 Untitled (131x96cm-52x38in) s.d.73. 5-Nov-2 Bukowskis, Stockholm #298/R est:15000-20000 (S.KR 19500)
£3019 $4679 €4800 Composition (130x97cm-51x38in) s. 7-Oct-2 Claude Aguttes, Neuilly #268/R
£4430 $7000 €6645 Distances (50x65cm-20x26in) s. s.d.1964 verso oil on paper prov.lit. 12-Nov-2 Phillips, New York #254/R est:5000-7000
£13125 $21000 €19688 Untitled (100x81cm-39x32in) s. painted 1958 prov.lit. 16-May-3 Phillips, New York #178/R est:6000-8000

Works on paper

£475 $741 €750 Composition (63x48cm-25x19in) s.d.86 W/C. 20-Oct-2 Mercier & Cie, Lille #358

MIR Y TRINXET, Joaquin (1873-1940) Spanish

£11950 $18403 €19000 Wood (32x23cm-13x9in) s. painted c.1903 prov.exhib.lit. 22-Oct-2 Durán, Madrid #274/R est:19000
£15484 $24465 €24000 Village (32x40cm-13x16in) 18-Dec-2 Ansorena, Madrid #82/R est:24000
£19310 $30703 €28000 House and garden (41x33cm-16x13in) s. 4-Mar-3 Ansorena, Madrid #160/R
£68966 $109655 €100000 White house in the sun (81x94cm-32x37in) s. 4-Mar-3 Ansorena, Madrid #161/R

MIRA, Victor (1949-) Spanish

£736 $1148 €1104 Mesa desmontable con marmol rojo (46x38cm-18x15in) s.d.1987 verso. 5-Nov-2 Bukowskis, Stockholm #304/R (S.KR 10500)
£1069 $1647 €1700 Lonely bird (90x122cm-35x48in) s.d.1987 cardboard. 22-Oct-2 Durán, Madrid #215/R

£1370 $2137 €2000 Abyss and fork (100x80cm-39x31in) s.d.1995 cardboard. 8-Apr-3 Ansorena, Madrid #271/R
£1742 $2752 €2700 Beggar burning Crucifix (99x79cm-39x31in) s.d.1995 cardboard. 18-Dec-2 Ansorena, Madrid #192/R
£1742 $2752 €2700 Anti-hero (99x79cm-39x31in) s.d.1995 cardboard. 18-Dec-2 Ansorena, Madrid #191/R
£1793 $2851 €2600 Still life with table upside down (80x100cm-31x39in) s.d.1995 cardboard. 4-Mar-3 Ansorena, Madrid #222/R
£2468 $3603 €3800 Anti-hero (120x140cm-47x55in) s.i.d.1993 mixed media on canvas. 17-Jun-2 Ansorena, Madrid #59/R

Works on paper

£383 $559 €590 Chain (50x40cm-20x16in) s.i.d.1998 verso mixed media. 17-Jun-2 Ansorena, Madrid #50/R
£419 $663 €650 Bull scene (43x60cm-17x24in) s. mixed media. 18-Dec-2 Ansorena, Madrid #216/R
£422 $616 €650 Chair (40x27cm-16x11in) s. mixed media. 17-Jun-2 Ansorena, Madrid #45/R
£519 $758 €800 Closed house (50x40cm-20x16in) s.d.1998 mixed media collage on canvas. 17-Jun-2 Ansorena, Madrid #49/R
£584 $853 €900 Antiffetoe (65x45cm-26x18in) s.i.d.1996 mixed media. 17-Jun-2 Ansorena, Madrid #52/R
£613 $968 €950 Bull scene (60x42cm-24x17in) s. mixed media. 18-Dec-2 Ansorena, Madrid #212/R
£645 $1019 €1000 Esterlita (40x28cm-16x11in) s. mixed media. 18-Dec-2 Ansorena, Madrid #215/R
£1793 $2851 €2600 Europe (74x143cm-29x56in) s.i.d.1983 mixed media over engraving. 4-Mar-3 Ansorena, Madrid #221/R
£1793 $2851 €2600 Still life in the light (100x79cm-39x31in) s.d.1999 mixed media cardboard. 4-Mar-3 Ansorena, Madrid #220/R
£2468 $3603 €3800 Anti-hero (120x100cm-47x39in) s.i.d.1993 verso mixed media on canvas. 17-Jun-2 Ansorena, Madrid #75/R est:2400

MIRABELLA, Mario (1870-1931) Italian

£4082 $6490 €6000 Punta Zafferano, Palermo (26x48cm-10x19in) s. board. 18-Mar-3 Finarte, Milan #29/R

MIRABELLA, Saro (1914-) Italian

£570 $889 €900 Landscape with olive trees (54x65cm-21x26in) s.d.1950 s.d.verso. 19-Oct-2 Semenzato, Venice #105/R
£633 $987 €1000 Marine landscape (50x70cm-20x28in) s. s.i.verso. 19-Oct-2 Semenzato, Venice #120/R

MIRADORI, Luigi (attrib) (17th C) Italian

£5128 $7949 €8000 Abraham and the three angels (86x72cm-34x28in) 4-Dec-2 Christie's, Rome #443/R est:8000-12000
£19231 $29808 €30000 Landscape with Putto stung by bees (55x74cm-22x29in) 4-Dec-2 Christie's, Rome #413/R est:5000-8000

MIRAGLIA, Ermogene (1907-1964) Italian

£759 $1200 €1200 Little market (30x40cm-12x16in) s. 26-Nov-2 Christie's, Rome #83/R
£818 $1259 €1300 Market in Naples (30x40cm-12x16in) s. 23-Oct-2 Finarte, Milan #20/R
£1519 $2400 €2400 Still life with fish (75x100cm-30x39in) s. 26-Nov-2 Christie's, Rome #234
£1613 $2371 €2500 Guitar player (110x79cm-43x31in) 24-Jun-2 Babuino, Rome #346

MIRALLES DARMANIN, Jose (1851-1900) Spanish

£890 $1389 €1300 Garden (13x21cm-5x8in) s. board. 8-Apr-3 Ansorena, Madrid #15/R
£1528 $2429 €2200 Elegant entertainment (38x46cm-15x18in) s. 29-Apr-3 Christie's, Amsterdam #100/R est:1500-2000
£2349 $3782 €3500 Gallant scene (72x60cm-28x24in) s. 18-Feb-3 Durán, Madrid #176/R
£2349 $3782 €3500 Gallant scene (72x60cm-28x24in) s. 18-Feb-3 Durán, Madrid #177/R
£5371 $8379 €8057 Tavern interior (51x59cm-20x23in) s. 6-Nov-2 Dobiaschofsky, Bern #829/R est:8000 (S.FR 12300)

MIRALLES, Francisco (1848-1901) Spanish

£3712 $5790 €5568 Palace interior (33x40cm-13x16in) s. 6-Nov-2 Dobiaschofsky, Bern #830/R est:8500 (S.FR 8500)
£7000 $10990 €10500 Retrato de la Reina Maria Cristina (45x34cm-18x13in) s.d.1883 prov. 19-Nov-2 Sotheby's, London #29/R est:5000-7000
£9655 $15352 €14000 Stroll (26x42cm-10x17in) s. 4-Mar-3 Ansorena, Madrid #166/R
£18868 $29434 €30000 Spanish beauty (55x39cm-22x15in) s. 23-Sep-2 Durán, Madrid #223/R est:27500
£26316 $42632 €40000 Ladies on the beach (48x60cm-19x24in) s. board. 21-Jan-3 Ansorena, Madrid #164/R est:36000

MIRAMOND, Alexis (19th C) French

£884 $1406 €1300 Couple a cheval (60x73cm-24x29in) s. 18-Mar-3 Vanderkindere, Brussels #102

MIRANDA, Celso (1954-) Spanish

£345 $545 €500 Seascape (23x33cm-9x13in) s. 1-Apr-3 Segre, Madrid #113/R

MIRANI, Everardus Pagano (1810-1881) Dutch

£1592 $2452 €2500 Woodcutter with a mallejan in a winter forest (22x29cm-9x11in) s. panel. 3-Sep-2 Christie's, Amsterdam #104/R est:3000-5000

MIRBACH (?) French

Works on paper

£528 $750 €850 Elegante sur un quai de Seine (39x43cm-15x17in) pen Indian ink blue crayon. 20-Mar-2 Chayette & Cheval, Paris #68

MIRECOURT, Adolphe (19th C) French

£298 $486 €450 Les bords de Seine a Paris. s.i.d.verso panel. 16-Feb-3 Mercier & Cie, Lille #251

MIRER, Rudolf (1937-) Swiss

£2957 $4612 €4436 Chalanda Marz (69x40cm-27x16in) s. 16-Sep-2 Philippe Schuler, Zurich #3390 est:3500-4000 (S.FR 6800)

MIRET ALEU, Jose (1912-) Spanish

£472 $736 €750 Landscape with tree (60x50cm-24x20in) s.d.1975 board. 23-Sep-2 Durán, Madrid #606/R
£1053 $1705 €1600 Landscape with mill (54x65cm-21x26in) s.d.1951. 21-Jan-3 Ansorena, Madrid #272/R

MIRET ALEU, Jose (attrib) (1912-) Spanish

£1053 $1705 €1600 Flowers (73x60cm-29x24in) s. 21-Jan-3 Durán, Madrid #642
£2632 $4263 €4000 Mountainous landscape (73x92cm-29x36in) s. 21-Jan-3 Durán, Madrid #641/R

MIRKO (1910-1969) Italian

£603 $977 €850 Figure (24x19cm-9x7in) s. tempera crayon cardboard on masonite prov. 26-May-3 Christie's, Milan #78
£1844 $2987 €2600 Chimera (40x62cm-16x24in) s.d.54 canvas on panel prov. 26-May-3 Christie's, Milan #364/R est:2000-2500
£2837 $4596 €4000 Composizione per il monumento delle Fosse Ardeatine (101x70cm-40x28in) s.d.1949 tempera paer on canvas prov. 26-May-3 Christie's, Milan #303/R est:3000-4000
£4839 $7645 €7500 Untitled (159x380cm-63x150in) tempera wax crayon. 18-Dec-2 Christie's, Rome #105/R est:12000

MIRO DE COMPTE, Esteban (19/20th C) Spanish

£268 $432 €400 Sale in Andalucia (35x55cm-14x22in) s. 18-Feb-3 Durán, Madrid #123/R
£270 $422 €400 Catalan farm (35x55cm-14x22in) s. 25-Mar-3 Durán, Madrid #637/R

MIRO LLEO, Gaspar (1859-1930) Spanish

£4800 $7776 €7200 Promeneurs sur l'avenue du bois a Paris (33x23cm-13x9in) s. panel. 20-May-3 Sotheby's, Olympia #413/R est:3000-4000

MIRO, Joachim (1875-1941) Spanish

£2564 $4026 €4000 Scene du rue, Maroc (27x17cm-11x7in) s.d.78 panel. 16-Dec-2 Gros & Delettrez, Paris #329/R est:3800-4500

MIRO, Joan (1893-1983) Spanish

£24000 $36960 €36000 Femmes (56x45cm-22x18in) s. gouache over woodcut print prov. 22-Oct-2 Sotheby's, London #178/R est:15000-20000
£29412 $49118 €42647 Les voyants (66x51cm-26x20in) s.d. prov.lit. 24-Jun-3 Koller, Zurich #162b/R est:65000-100000 (S.FR 65000)
£45000 $73800 €67500 Femme I (51x34cm-20x13in) s. s.i.d.75 verso oil pastel wax crayon grattage prov. 6-Feb-3 Christie's, London #509/R est:60000
£52795 $85000 €79193 Personnage (48x57cm-19x22in) s. oil gouache over monotype on paper painted 1978 prov. 7-May-3 Sotheby's, New York #332/R est:70000-90000
£96154 $150000 €144231 Paysage (27x22cm-11x9in) s. i.d.27/XI/77 verso prov. 5-Nov-2 Phillips, New York #134/R est:180000-250000
£105590 $170000 €158385 Personnage (35x24cm-14x9in) s. i.d.15/XI/77 verso. 8-May-3 Christie's, Rockefeller NY #216/R est:120000-160000
£105769 $165000 €158654 Femme oiseaux (35x22cm-14x9in) s.i.d.XI/77 verso prov.exhib. 6-Nov-2 Sotheby's, New York #293/R est:80000-120000
£125000 $205000 €187500 Oiseau nocturne (70x99cm-28x39in) s. s.i.d.62 verso oil brush ink wash pastel col wax crayon prov. 6-Feb-3 Christie's, London #502/R est:180000
£130000 $211900 €195000 Reveil des oiseaux II (195x50cm-77x20in) s. s.i.d.1965 verso prov.exhib.lit. 3-Feb-3 Christie's, London #190/R est:150000
£130380 $206000 €206000 Naissance du crepuscule (104x73cm-41x29in) s. s.d.62 verso cardboard. 27-Nov-2 Marc Kohn, Paris #39/R est:300000-450000
£169014 $280563 €240000 Femme, oiseaux, etoile II (81x54cm-32x21in) s. prov.lit. 12-Jun-3 Tajan, Paris #38/R est:250000-300000
£254658 $410000 €381987 Paroles du poete (130x195cm-51x77in) s.i.d.68 prov.exhib.lit. 8-May-3 Christie's, Rockefeller NY #230/R est:300000-400000

£307692 $480000 €461538 Oiseaux dans l'espace (116x89cm-46x35in) init. s.i.d.18.2.60 verso prov.exhib.lit. 6-Nov-2 Christie's, Rockefeller NY #54/R est:450000-650000
£314103 $490000 €471155 Femme, etoile, echelle de l'evasion (22x16cm-9x6in) s.i.d.1944 verso prov.lit. 6-Nov-2 Sotheby's, New York #269/R est:300000-400000
£465839 $750000 €698759 Peinture (74x187cm-29x74in) s. s.d.1952 verso prov.exhib.lit. 7-May-3 Christie's, Rockefeller NY #31/R est:400000-600000
£1250000 $1950000 €1875000 L'oiseau boum-boum fait sa priere a la tete pelure d'oignon (81x100cm-32x39in) s. s.i.d.1952 verso prov.exhib.lit. 5-Nov-2 Sotheby's, New York #34/R est:2500000-3500000
£1712329 $2671233 €2500000 Piege (93x73cm-37x29in) s.d.1924 s.i.d.verso exhib.lit. 14-Apr-3 Laurence Calmels, Paris #4040/R est:5000000

Prints

£1456 $2300 €2300 Untitled (23x30cm-9x12in) s.d. col aquatint etching. 30-Nov-2 Villa Grisebach, Berlin #391/R est:3000-4000
£1740 $2750 €2610 Ritual combat (60x90cm-24x35in) s.num.46/75 col lithograph. 22-Apr-3 Butterfields, San Francisco #2171/R est:3000-5000
£1763 $2750 €2645 Japanese woman (36x50cm-14x20in) s.num.19/30 lithograph. 14-Oct-2 Butterfields, San Francisco #1156 est:1500-2500
£1763 $2750 €2645 Altamira (51x66cm-20x26in) s.num.11/25 col lithograph. 14-Oct-2 Butterfields, San Francisco #1153/R est:3000-4000
£1887 $3000 €2831 Comet bird (55x38cm-22x15in) s.d.num.20/75 col lithograph. 29-Apr-3 Christie's, Rockefeller NY #497/R est:1000-1500
£1887 $3000 €2831 Paroles peinter III (38x29cm-15x11in) s.num.41/50 col aquatint. 1-May-3 Swann Galleries, New York #523/R est:1800-2200
£1887 $3000 €2831 Le miroir de l'homme par les betes (46x35cm-18x14in) s.num.18/40 col aquatint. 1-May-3 Swann Galleries, New York #528/R est:1500-2500
£1887 $3000 €2831 Young artists (226x155cm-89x61in) s.d.1973 num.56/75 col lithograph. 30-Apr-3 Doyle, New York #246/R est:2000-3000
£1899 $2962 €3000 Lezard aux plumes d'or (33x98cm-13x39in) s. col lithograph. 15-Oct-2 Dorotheum, Vienna #146/R est:4400-5100
£1899 $3000 €3000 Composition - Maravillas con variaciones acrosticas (47x36cm-19x14in) s. col lithograph. 30-Nov-2 Bassenge, Berlin #6521/R est:2200
£1923 $2808 €3000 Personnage dans le jardin IV (36x59cm-14x23in) s.d.1951 col lithograph. 4-Jun-2 Karl & Faber, Munich #357/R est:5000
£1923 $2981 €3000 For: Louis Aragon, je n'ai jamais appris a ecrire ou les incipit (22x28cm-9x11in) s. num.167/175 col etching. 4-Dec-2 Lempertz, Koln #920/R est:2500
£1935 $3000 €2903 Family of bird catchers (76x56cm-30x22in) s.d.1955 num.20/50 col lithograph. 25-Sep-2 Christie's, Rockefeller NY #145/R est:2800-3500
£2000 $3100 €3000 Le marteau sans morteau Maitre (44x66cm-17x26in) s.num.XLV/L col etching aquatint. 3-Dec-2 Christie's, London #158/R est:1000-1500
£2000 $3300 €2900 Signes and meteors (43x46cm-17x18in) s.num.48/100 col lithograph. 2-Jul-3 Christie's, London #282/R est:1500-2500
£2006 $3250 €3009 Series XVII (30x41cm-12x16in) s.num.VII/XV col lithograph prov. 23-Jan-3 Aspire, Cleveland #38
£2051 $3200 €3077 Giboulees (35x47cm-14x19in) s.num.43/90 col soft ground etching aquatint. 7-Nov-2 Swann Galleries, New York #723/R est:3500-5000
£2051 $3179 €3200 Le prophete (15x11cm-6x4in) s.i. col etching aquatint. 7-Dec-2 Ketterer, Hamburg #562/R est:3000-3500
£2057 $3250 €3086 Petite Barriere (26x10cm-10x4in) s. num.55/75 drypoint col aquatint executed c.1967. 12-Nov-2 Doyle, New York #313/R est:5000-7000
£2083 $3250 €3125 Fissures (49x59cm-19x23in) s.num.56/75 col aquatint. 14-Oct-2 Butterfields, San Francisco #1149/R est:3000-3500
£2083 $3250 €3125 Exhibition XXIIe Salon de Mai (67x52cm-26x20in) s.i. col lithograph. 14-Oct-2 Butterfields, San Francisco #1154/R est:2000-3000
£2100 $3255 €3150 Composition (61x71cm-24x28in) s.num.127/300 col print. 4-Dec-2 Bonhams, New Bond Street #201/R est:1200-1800
£2100 $3297 €3150 One plate from Fissures (49x58cm-19x23in) s.num.68/75 col etching aquatint. 17-Apr-3 Christie's, Kensington #294/R est:1500-2000
£2115 $3279 €3300 Hommage to Picasso (56x76cm-22x30in) s.num.XXVIII/XXX col etching aquatinta exec.1972. 7-Dec-2 Van Ham, Cologne #352/R est:3400
£2138 $3400 €3207 Le lezard aux plumes d'or (34x48cm-13x19in) s.num.40/50 col lithograph. 1-May-3 Swann Galleries, New York #526/R est:2500-3500
£2152 $3335 €3400 Hommage a Joan Prats (65x86cm-26x34in) s.num.8/75 col lithograph lit. 28-Sep-2 Cornette de St.Cyr, Paris #84/R est:2800-3000
£2158 $3540 €3000 Mavena (30x10cm-12x4in) s.num.2/20 lithograph. 3-Jun-3 Christie's, Amsterdam #441/R est:2500-3500
£2160 $3500 €3240 Sun and starfish (33x43cm-13x17in) s.mu,46/60 col lithograph. 23-Jan-3 Aspire, Cleveland #39 est:1000-2000
£2179 $3400 €3269 Le marteau sans maitre (45x67cm-18x26in) s. col aquatint sold with a col lithograph. 7-Nov-2 Swann Galleries, New York #740a/R est:3500-5000
£2183 $3515 €3100 From the series - Oda a Joan Miro (88x61cm-35x24in) s.num.73/75 col.lithograph. 10-May-3 Bukowskis, Helsinki #276/R est:3000-4000
£2200 $3630 €3190 Els castellers (72x54cm-28x21in) s.num.7/50 col etching aquatint. 1-Jul-3 Sotheby's, London #98/R est:1500-2200
£2200 $3630 €3190 Suite La Bague d'Aurore (14x12cm-6x5in) s.num.40/60 col etching aquatint. 2-Jul-3 Christie's, London #274 est:1500-2000
£2200 $3630 €3190 Escalade (66x51cm-26x20in) s.num.57/75 col etching aquatint carborundum. 2-Jul-3 Christie's, London #279/R est:2500-3500
£2201 $3434 €3500 Lithograph I (24x32cm-9x13in) s. num.46/75 lithograph. 11-Oct-2 Winterberg, Heidelberg #1484/R est:4500
£2201 $3500 €3302 Young girl in the moonlight (37x52cm-15x20in) s.d.num.16/75 col lithograph. 29-Apr-3 Christie's, Rockefeller NY #498/R est:2000-3000
£2201 $3500 €3302 Joan Miro (21x40cm-8x16in) s.num.95/100 col lithograph. 29-Apr-3 Christie's, Rockefeller NY #512/R est:3500-4500
£2218 $3615 €3327 Prise a l'hamencon (99x60cm-39x24in) s. col etching aquatint. 12-Feb-3 Iegor de Saint Hippolyte, Montreal #137 (C.D 5500)
£2222 $3511 €3200 Strip-tease (32x49cm-13x19in) s.num.16/75 col etching W/C prov.lit. 26-Apr-3 Cornette de St.Cyr, Paris #71/R est:2500-3000
£2244 $3478 €3500 Vitrier lunaire (66x50cm-26x20in) s.i. col aquatint exec.1973. 6-Dec-2 Ketterer, Munich #191/R est:3500-4000
£2292 $3781 €3300 Ancre et fumee (75x56cm-30x22in) s.num.75/75 aquatint etching carborundum. 2-Jul-3 Artcurial Briest, Paris #52/R est:3000-4000
£2300 $3795 €3335 Suite la bague d'aurore (11x13cm-4x5in) s.num.16/60 col etching aquatint. 1-Jul-3 Sotheby's, London #97/R est:1500-2500
£2323 $3670 €3600 Freedom (47x36cm-19x14in) s. eau forte exec.1971 lit. 17-Dec-2 Segre, Madrid #194/R
£2358 $3750 €3537 Hommage aux prix nobel (76x56cm-30x22in) s.num.93/100 col lithograph. 2-May-3 Sotheby's, New York #232/R est:2500-3500
£2372 $3700 €3558 Le chien blue (61x47cm-24x19in) s.num.266/300 col etching aquatint. 20-Sep-2 Sloan, North Bethesda #302/R est:3000-4000
£2373 $3750 €3560 Sculptures en montagne (77x55cm-30x22in) s.num.8/150 col lithograph. 22-Apr-3 Butterfields, San Francisco #2173/R est:3500-4500
£2376 $3850 €3564 Series XVI (30x41cm-12x16in) s.num.7/15 col lithograph. 23-Jan-3 Aspire, Cleveland #40 est:1000-2000
£2400 $3720 €3600 L'homme au balancier (68x50cm-27x20in) s.i. col etching aquatint. 3-Dec-2 Christie's, London #161/R est:2500-3500
£2400 $3720 €3600 L'antitete (15x11cm-6x4in) s.i. col etching pochoir. 5-Dec-2 Sotheby's, London #157/R est:2000-2500
£2405 $3800 €3800 Libre de sis sentits II (77x64cm-30x25in) s. col etching. 27-Nov-2 Dorotheum, Vienna #75/R est:3400-3600
£2405 $3800 €3800 Altamira (51x66cm-20x26in) s. col lithograph. 30-Nov-2 Bassenge, Berlin #6517/R est:3500
£2436 $3800 €3654 Le lezard aux plumes d'or (36x50cm-14x20in) s.num.40/50 col lithograph. 7-Nov-2 Swann Galleries, New York #730/R est:5000-8000
£2452 $3800 €3678 Archipel sauvage II (75x105cm-30x41in) s.num.32/35 col etching aquatint. 25-Sep-2 Christie's, Rockefeller NY #156/R est:3000-5000
£2452 $3800 €3678 Lithographs for the International plastic Arts Association, Unesco (58x56cm-23x22in) s.num.63/75 col lithograph. 25-Sep-2 Christie's, Rockefeller NY #159/R est:2800-3500
£2500 $3875 €3750 Le marteau sans maitre (44x66cm-17x26in) s.num.XXVII/L col etching aquatint two. 5-Dec-2 Sotheby's, London #154/R est:2800-3600
£2500 $4125 €3625 Les forestiers (50x32cm-20x13in) s.i. col aquatint. 2-Jul-3 Christie's, London #275/R est:3000-5000
£2516 $3925 €4000 Femmes, lune, etoile I (50x63cm-20x25in) s. col lithograph. 11-Oct-2 Winterberg, Heidelberg #1501/R est:2000
£2516 $4000 €3774 Nocturnal germination (67x51cm-26x20in) s.d.num.35/50 col lithograph. 29-Apr-3 Christie's, Rockefeller NY #502/R est:3000-4000
£2518 $4129 €3500 Battement (60x57cm-24x22in) s.i. col lithograph prov. 3-Jun-3 Christie's, Amsterdam #442/R est:4000-6000
£2564 $3744 €4000 Derriere le miroir (40x58cm-16x23in) s.num.74/100 lithograph. 5-Jun-2 Il Ponte, Milan #168/R
£2564 $4026 €4000 Hommage a Joan Prats, pl 15 de la suite (54x74cm-21x29in) s.i. col lithograph. 22-Nov-2 Tajan, Paris #360/R est:3000
£2569 $4060 €3700 Pygmees sous la lune (70x94cm-28x37in) s. col etching wash W/C edition of 50 lit. 26-Apr-3 Cornette de St.Cyr, Paris #67/R est:2500-3000
£2581 $4000 €3872 Pierrot le fou (90x61cm-35x24in) s.num.30/75 col lithograph. 25-Sep-2 Christie's, Rockefeller NY #150/R est:4000-5000

£2586 $4085 €3879 From - Serie noire et rouge (17x25cm-7x10in) s.num.2/2 etching. 28-Apr-3 Bukowskis, Stockholm #463/R est:35000-40000 (S.KR 34000)
£2639 $4169 €3800 Feuilles eparses (38x28cm-15x11in) s.num.III/XII col etching lit. 26-Apr-3 Cornette de St.Cyr, Paris #30/R est:3500-4000
£2642 $4200 €3963 Person in a garden (37x60cm-15x24in) s.d.num.43/75 col lithograph. 29-Apr-3 Christie's, Rockefeller NY #499/R est:3000-4000
£2658 $4200 €4200 Le bleu de la cible (65x50cm-26x20in) s.i. col aquatint relief. 30-Nov-2 Villa Grisebach, Berlin #390/R est:3500-4000
£2724 $4250 €4086 From Parler Seul (38x28cm-15x11in) s.d. col lithograph. 14-Oct-2 Butterfields, San Francisco #1151/R est:2000-4000
£2738 $4325 €4107 Les armes du sommeil (51x62cm-20x24in) s.num.66/75 col etching aquatint carborundum lit. 28-Apr-3 Bukowskis, Stockholm #470/R est:40000-60000 (S.KR 36000)
£2767 $4400 €4151 Ubu roi (41x62cm-16x24in) s.num.42/75 col lithograph. 1-May-3 Swann Galleries, New York #522/R est:5000-8000
£2778 $4417 €4000 Composition with green background (34x46cm-13x18in) s.d.1950 chromolithograph prov. 29-Apr-3 Whyte's, Dublin #48/R est:2000-3000
£2778 $4583 €4000 Prise a l'hamecon (134x96cm-53x38in) s.num.11/50 col etching aquatint. 2-Jul-3 Artcurial Briest, Paris #54/R est:4000-5000
£2778 $4583 €4000 Fugitive (134x96cm-53x38in) s.num.11/50 col etching aquatint. 2-Jul-3 Artcurial Briest, Paris #57/R est:4500-6000
£2800 $4340 €4200 Miro, oiseau solaire (31x24cm-12x9in) s.num.37/75 col etching aquatint. 3-Dec-2 Christie's, London #160/R est:3000-5000
£2800 $4620 €4060 Salvat papasseit (90x64cm-35x25in) s.num.HC XIV col etching aquatint. 1-Jul-3 Sotheby's, London #107/R est:2000-3000
£2800 $4620 €4060 Le lezard au plumes d'or (34x48cm-13x19in) s.num.V/X col lithograph from the set of 18. 2-Jul-3 Christie's, London #131/R est:2000-3000
£2821 $4400 €4232 Le lezard aux plumes d'or (33x98cm-13x39in) s.num.66/100 col lithograph. 18-Sep-2 Swann Galleries, New York #96/R est:5000-8000
£2830 $4500 €4245 Barcelona (70x105cm-28x41in) s.num.22/50 col etching aquatint carborundum. 2-May-3 Sotheby's, New York #231/R est:3000-5000
£2837 $4596 €4000 Enrajolats (39x52cm-15x20in) s.i. col etching. 20-May-3 Dorotheum, Vienna #196/R est:4000-4500
£2897 $4577 €4200 Lettre rouge (87x63cm-34x25in) s. lithograph on canvas lit. 1-Apr-3 Segre, Madrid #261/R
£2900 $4495 €4350 Miro, cartones (54x71cm-21x28in) s.num.64/75 col lithograph. 3-Dec-2 Christie's, London #175/R est:1500-2500
£2903 $4500 €4355 Young artists (90x61cm-35x24in) s.num.75/75 col lithograph. 25-Sep-2 Christie's, Rockefeller NY #163/R est:3000-4000
£3000 $4650 €4500 Polypheme (103x75cm-41x30in) s.num.16/75 engraving aquatint. 3-Dec-2 Christie's, London #159/R est:1500-2500
£3000 $4650 €4500 Le styx (18x23cm-7x9in) s.num.51/75 etching aquatint. 5-Dec-2 Sotheby's, London #153/R est:3000-4000
£3000 $4950 €4350 Salvat papasseit (90x64cm-35x25in) s.num.HC XIV col etching aquatint. 1-Jul-3 Sotheby's, London #105/R est:2000-3000
£3000 $4950 €4350 Le lezard au plumes d'or (36x99cm-14x39in) s.num.97/100 col lithograph from the set of 18. 2-Jul-3 Christie's, London #130/R est:3000-5000
£3000 $4950 €4350 Le lezard aux plumes d'or (36x100cm-14x39in) s.num.97/100 col lithograph from the set of 18. 2-Jul-3 Christie's, London #132/R est:2000-5000
£3019 $4800 €4529 La baigneuse (18x30cm-7x12in) s.num.18/30 drypoint. 29-Apr-3 Christie's, Rockefeller NY #495/R est:4000-6000
£3019 $4800 €4529 The indifferent (56x76cm-22x30in) s.d.num.25/50 col lithograph. 29-Apr-3 Christie's, Rockefeller NY #501/R est:2500-3500
£3077 $4800 €4616 Le guerrier mongol (85x59cm-33x23in) s.num.18/50 col lithograph. 5-Nov-2 Christie's, Rockefeller NY #202/R est:3500-4500
£3097 $4800 €4646 Oda a Joan Miro (88x61cm-35x24in) s.num.40/75 col lithograph. 25-Sep-2 Christie's, Rockefeller NY #162/R est:6000-10000
£3165 $5000 €4748 Pierrot le fou (90x61cm-35x24in) s. num.60/75 col lithograph executed c.1964. 12-Nov-2 Doyle, New York #311/R est:3500-4500
£3165 $5000 €4748 Partie de campagne IV (59x93cm-23x37in) s. num.34/75 col aquatint etching executed c.1967. 12-Nov-2 Doyle, New York #312/R est:5000-7000
£3165 $5000 €4748 Vladimir (90x63cm-35x25in) s.num.7/50 col lithograh. 22-Apr-3 Butterfields, San Francisco #2174/R est:6000-8000
£3179 $5181 €4800 Strindberg mappen (75x56cm-30x22in) s. num.83/100 lithograph lit. 11-Feb-3 Segre, Madrid #303/R
£3200 $5280 €4640 Salvat papasseit (90x64cm-35x25in) s.num.HC XIV col etching aquatint. 1-Jul-3 Sotheby's, London #104/R est:2000-3000
£3200 $5280 €4640 Salvat papasseit (90x64cm-35x25in) s.num.HC XIV col etching aquatint. 1-Jul-3 Sotheby's, London #106/R est:2000-3000
£3205 $5000 €4808 Plate V, from Oda a Joan Miro (104x77cm-41x30in) s.num.I/XXV col lithograph. 5-Nov-2 Christie's, Rockefeller NY #196/R est:4000-6000
£3208 $5132 €4812 Montroig 4 (74x56cm-29x22in) s.i. col lithograph num.22/30 lit.prov. 17-Mar-3 Philippe Schuler, Zurich #4069/R est:5000-7000 (S.FR 6800)
£3226 $5000 €4839 Les Essencies de la Terra (50x36cm-20x14in) s. col lithograph. 25-Sep-2 Christie's, Rockefeller NY #153/R est:3000-4000
£3398 $5470 €5097 Quatre colors aparien el mon (90x63cm-35x25in) s.num.35/50 col etching aquatint. 7-May-3 AB Stockholms Auktionsverk #1247/R est:50000-60000 (S.KR 44000)
£3459 $5500 €5189 Parler seul (38x28cm-15x11in) s. hand col lithograph deluxe edition of 50. 29-Apr-3 Christie's, Rockefeller NY #496/R est:6000-8000
£3500 $5425 €5250 Vers la gauche (72x104cm-28x41in) s.num.60/75 col etching aquatint. 3-Dec-2 Christie's, London #163/R est:4000-6000
£3500 $5425 €5250 L'Astre du Marecage (104x72cm-41x28in) s.num.57/75 col aquatint. 3-Dec-2 Christie's, London #171/R est:4000-6000
£3522 $5600 €5283 Figure and bird (57x41cm-22x16in) s.d.1948 num.18/75 col lithograph. 1-May-3 Swann Galleries, New York #519/R est:7000-10000
£3526 $5465 €5500 From: The lizard with the golden feathers (33x97cm-13x38in) s.i. col lithograph. 7-Dec-2 Ketterer, Hamburg #571/R est:5500-7500
£3546 $5745 €5000 From 'Essencies de la terre' (50x36cm-20x14in) s. Indian ink brush on lithograph. 20-May-3 Dorotheum, Vienna #85/R est:5000-5500
£3623 $5942 €5000 From: Ode to Joan Miro (83x58cm-33x23in) s. col lithograph. 31-May-3 Villa Grisebach, Berlin #315/R est:3000-4000
£3774 $6000 €5661 Le lezard aux d'or (34x99cm-13x39in) s.num.XV/XX col lithograph. 1-May-3 Swann Galleries, New York #527/R est:5000-8000
£3813 $6368 €5529 Le grand ordonnateur (104x67cm-41x26in) s.num.47/75 aquatint. 17-Jun-3 Rasmussen, Copenhagen #247/R est:40000-50000 (D.KR 40000)
£3846 $6000 €5769 From La Bague d'aurore (38x28cm-15x11in) s.d.1958 handcol etching. 14-Oct-2 Butterfields, San Francisco #1147/R est:3500-4500
£3846 $6000 €5769 Le lezard aux plumes d'or (33x98cm-13x39in) s.num.82/100 col lithograph. 18-Sep-2 Swann Galleries, New York #95/R est:5000-8000
£3846 $5962 €6000 Personnage dans un jardin IV (36x59cm-14x23in) s.d.1951 col lithograph. 7-Dec-2 Hauswedell & Nolte, Hamburg #907/R est:6000
£4025 $6400 €6038 Barcelona XXXI (178x132cm-70x52in) s.d.1944 num.4/5 lithograph. 30-Apr-3 Doyle, New York #243/R est:3000-4000
£4064 $6341 €6096 Trace sir la paroi I (58x93cm-23x37in) s.num.50/75 col etching aquatint carborundum lit. 5-Nov-2 Bukowskis, Stockholm #595/R est:60000-80000 (S.KR 58000)
£4064 $6341 €6096 L'exile verts (102x59cm-40x23in) s.num.38/75 col etching aquatint carborundum lit. 5-Nov-2 Bukowskis, Stockholm #597/R est:60000-80000 (S.KR 58000)
£4088 $6500 €6132 Palotin giron (72x48cm-28x19in) s.d.num.29/50 col lithograph. 29-Apr-3 Christie's, Rockefeller NY #504/R est:3500-4500
£4161 $6699 €6200 Captive (93x71cm-37x28in) s.i. eau forte exhib.lit. 23-Feb-3 Mercier & Cie, Lille #18/R
£4167 $6500 €6251 Joan Miro lithographe II (44x61cm-17x24in) s.num.XLIX/LXXX col lithograph pair. 5-Nov-2 Christie's, Rockefeller NY #199/R est:4500-5500
£4167 $6542 €6500 Tres Joan : en hommage a Joan Prats (52x107cm-20x42in) s.i. etching aquatint. 22-Nov-2 Tajan, Paris #361/R est:6000
£4200 $6930 €6090 Salvat Papasseit (90x64cm-35x25in) s.num.HC XIV col etching aquatint. 1-Jul-3 Sotheby's, London #103/R est:2000-3000
£4205 $6559 €6308 Partie de campagne I (58x92cm-23x36in) s.num.62/75 col etching aquatint lit. 5-Nov-2 Bukowskis, Stockholm #594/R est:60000-80000 (S.KR 60000)
£4403 $7000 €6605 Family of bird catchers (76x56cm-30x22in) s.d.num.45/50 col lithograph vellum. 29-Apr-3 Christie's, Rockefeller NY #505/R est:3500-4500
£4485 $6996 €6728 La caissier (90x69cm-35x27in) s.num.26/75 col etching aquatint carborundum lit. 5-Nov-2 Bukowskis, Stockholm #596/R est:50000-70000 (S.KR 64000)
£4487 $6551 €7000 Gaudi 46 (96x78cm-38x31in) s. col aquatint etching. 4-Jun-2 Karl & Faber, Munich #360/R est:8000-10000
£4487 $7000 €6731 Penseur puissant (102x66cm-40x26in) s.num.22/75 col etching aquatint. 20-Sep-2 Sloan, North Bethesda #304/R est:7000-9000
£4500 $6975 €6750 L'Aigle et la femme (33x45cm-13x18in) s.num.11/30 etching drypoint. 3-Dec-2 Christie's, London #147/R est:5000-7000
£4525 $7557 €6561 L'etrangle (117x74cm-46x29in) s.i. etching aquatint. 24-Jun-3 Koller, Zurich #463/R est:24000-34000 (S.FR 10000)
£4717 $7500 €7076 Suite la bague d'aurore (14x12cm-6x5in) s.d.1958 hand col engraving vellum. 29-Apr-3 Christie's, Rockefeller NY #506/R est:4000-6000

£4717	$7500	€7076	Nymphomaniac president (120x77cm-47x30in) s.num.49/50 col lithograph. 2-May-3 Sotheby's, New York #229/R est:3000-5000
£4789	$7136	€7184	L'adorateur du soleil (103x65cm-41x26in) s.mum.H C col etching aquatint with carborundrum prov. 27-Aug-2 Christie's, Melbourne #107/R est:12000-16000 (A.D 12500)
£4800	$7392	€7200	One plate, Barcelona (105x69cm-41x27in) s.num.29/50 etching aquatint. 24-Oct-2 Christie's, Kensington #293/R est:3000-5000
£4800	$7488	€7200	L'ogre enjoue (73x106cm-29x42in) s.num.11/75 col etching aquatint. 10-Oct-2 Sotheby's, London #64/R est:4000-6000
£5000	$7750	€7500	L'halterophile (23x107cm-9x42in) s.num.18/30 col lithograph. 5-Dec-2 Sotheby's, London #156/R est:5000-7000
£5000	$8250	€7250	Le chef d'orchestre (114x74cm-45x29in) s.num.50/50 col etching aquatint. 2-Jul-3 Christie's, London #280/R est:3500-4500
£5031	$8000	€7547	Vers la gauche (104x73cm-41x29in) s.num.34/75 col etching aquatint carborundum. 29-Apr-3 Christie's, Rockefeller NY #511/R est:7000-9000
£5288	$8250	€7932	Le Samourai (74x53cm-29x21in) s.num.57/75 col aquatint carborundum. 20-Sep-2 Sloan, North Bethesda #303/R est:7000-9000
£5346	$8500	€8019	Le tambour-major (107x75cm-42x30in) s.num.33/50 col etching aquatint. 29-Apr-3 Christie's, Rockefeller NY #514/R est:4000-6000
£5500	$9075	€7975	Le rebelle (94x64cm-37x25in) s.num.40/75 col etching aquatint carborundum. 2-Jul-3 Christie's, London #116/R est:5000-7000
£5660	$9000	€8490	Tete au soleil (28x38cm-11x15in) s.num.49/75 col aquatint carborundum. 1-May-3 Swann Galleries, New York #525/R est:6000-9000
£5677	$8856	€8516	Trace sur la paroi (58x92cm-23x36in) s.i. col etching. 6-Nov-2 Dobiaschofsky, Bern #1742/R est:12000 (S.FR 13000)
£5677	$8913	€8516	Cantic del Sol (39x52cm-15x20in) s. num.11/12 col aquatint etching. 23-Nov-2 Burkhard, Luzern #112/R est:12000-16000 (S.FR 13000)
£5696	$9000	€8544	Trace sur la paroi (58x93cm-23x37in) s.num.19/75 col lithograh. 22-Apr-3 Butterfields, San Francisco #2172 est:7000-9000
£5779	$9132	€8669	La rebelle (93x64cm-37x25in) s.num.12/75 col etching aquatint carborundum lit. 28-Apr-3 Bukowskis, Stockholm #468/R est:80000-100000 (S.KR 76000)
£5975	$9500	€8963	Derriere le miroir. Miro. Oiseau solaire - oiseau lunaire - etincelles (38x28cm-15x11in) init.num.96/150 col lithograph text 4 portfolio. 2-May-3 Sotheby's, New York #226/R est:8000-10000
£6000	$9300	€9000	L'oiseau mongol (103x70cm-41x28in) s.num.64/75 col etching aquatint. 3-Dec-2 Christie's, London #170/R est:4000-6000
£6000	$9900	€8700	Trace sur la Paroi IV (59x93cm-23x37in) s.num.10/75 col etching aquatint carborundum. 2-Jul-3 Christie's, London #278/R est:7000-10000
£6071	$9593	€9107	Femme et volcan (39x28cm-15x11in) s.num.2/4 etching pastel. 26-Nov-2 Sotheby's, Melbourne #249/R est:8000-12000 (A.D 17000)
£6090	$9500	€9135	Gaudi series (130x85cm-51x33in) s.num.41/50 col etching aquatint. 20-Sep-2 Sloan, North Bethesda #300/R est:8000-12000
£6090	$9500	€9135	Serie gaudi (115x72cm-45x28in) s.num.45/50 col etching aquatint collage white chk. 20-Sep-2 Sloan, North Bethesda #305/R est:10000-15000
£6410	$10000	€9615	Barcelona III (70x52cm-28x20in) s.d.num.4/5 lithograph. 5-Nov-2 Christie's, Rockefeller NY #193/R est:5000-7000
£6868	$10713	€10302	From Barcelona (105x69cm-41x27in) s.num.30/50 col etching aquatint carborundum lit. 5-Nov-2 Bukowskis, Stockholm #601/R est:100000-120000 (S.KR 98000)
£6918	$11000	€10377	Partie de campagne V (31x93cm-12x37in) s.num.1/75 col etching aquatint. 29-Apr-3 Christie's, Rockefeller NY #508/R est:7000-10000
£6944	$10972	€10000	L'invite du dimanche I (80x116cm-31x46in) s.num.62/75 col etching W/C lit. 26-Apr-3 Cornette de St.Cyr, Paris #70/R est:10000-15000
£7000	$10920	€10500	L'libre dels sis sentis I and VI (72x54cm-28x21in) s.num.33/50 one num.17/50 etching aquatint two. 10-Oct-2 Sotheby's, London #67/R est:3500-4500
£7500	$12375	€10875	Charivari (121x160cm-48x63in) s.i. col aquatint. 2-Jul-3 Christie's, London #281 est:3000-5000
£7692	$12000	€11538	Hibou blasphemateur (118x146cm-46x57in) s.num.30/50 col etching aquatint carbourundum. 20-Sep-2 Sloan, North Bethesda #301/R est:12000-15000
£8805	$14000	€13208	Le rebelle (94x64cm-37x25in) s.num.59/75 col etching aquatint carborundum. 29-Apr-3 Christie's, Rockefeller NY #509/R est:10000-15000
£8805	$14000	€13208	L'aigrette rouge (115x74cm-45x29in) s.num.13/50 col etching aquatint carborundum. 29-Apr-3 Christie's, Rockefeller NY #513/R est:9000-12000
£9434	$15000	€14151	Le sarrasin a l'etoile bleue (138x60cm-54x24in) s.num.31/50 col etching aquatint carborundum. 2-May-3 Sotheby's, New York #230/R est:8000-10000
£10256	$16000	€15384	La femme toupie (137x96cm-54x38in) s.num.48/50 col etching aquatint. 5-Nov-2 Christie's, Rockefeller NY #197/R est:18000-22000
£10692	$17000	€16038	Le grand sorcier (89x68cm-35x27in) s.i. col etching aquatint drypoint carborundum edition of 75. 29-Apr-3 Christie's, Rockefeller NY #510/R est:18000-22000
£12000	$19800	€17400	Le cracheur de flammes (113x74cm-44x29in) s.i. col etching aquatint carborundum. 2-Jul-3 Christie's, London #120/R est:7000-10000
£12000	$19800	€17400	Oda a Joan Miro (88x61cm-35x24in) s.num.27/75 and 35/75 col lithograph four from the set of nine. 2-Jul-3 Christie's, London #128/R est:10000-14000
£12500	$20125	€18750	L'enfance d'Ubu. folio of 20 col lithographs. 7-May-3 Dobiaschofsky, Bern #2192/R est:17000 (S.FR 27000)
£14000	$21700	€21000	Femme et chien devant la lune (65x50cm-26x20in) s.d.1935 num.28/60 col pochoir print. 3-Dec-2 Christie's, London #149/R est:15000-20000
£14000	$23100	€20300	La femme aux bijoux (47x34cm-19x13in) s.num.16/75 col aquatint carborundum. 2-Jul-3 Christie's, London #117/R est:8000-12000
£14744	$23000	€22116	Equinoxe (104x74cm-41x29in) s.num.30/75 col etching aquatint carborundum. 20-Sep-2 Sloan, North Bethesda #299/R est:25000-35000
£16000	$24960	€24000	Raymond Queneau (71x56cm-28x22in) init,num.67/75 col lithograph album. 10-Oct-2 Sotheby's, London #66/R est:12000-15000
£16667	$26000	€25001	Le somnambule (138x97cm-54x38in) s.num.15/50 col etching aquatint. 5-Nov-2 Christie's, Rockefeller NY #198/R est:25000-35000
£17610	$28000	€26415	Carlos Franqui (66x51cm-26x20in) s.num. col lithograph set of 21 portfolio wooden case. 29-Apr-3 Christie's, Rockefeller NY #515/R est:25000-30000
£20000	$31000	€30000	Ubu aux baleares (53x68cm-21x27in) col lithograph album. 3-Dec-2 Christie's, London #154/R est:20000-30000
£20440	$32500	€30660	Equinoxe (104x74cm-41x29in) s.num.30/75 col etching aquatint carborundum. 2-May-3 Sotheby's, New York #225/R est:30000-40000
£21101	$35239	€30596	Equinoxe (104x74cm-41x29in) s.i. col etching. 20-Jun-3 Kornfeld, Bern #113/R est:50000 (S.FR 46000)
£22013	$35000	€33020	A toute epreuve (33x26cm-13x10in) s. black and col woodcut 79 edition of 130 book. 2-May-3 Sotheby's, New York #221/R est:15000-25000
£24359	$38000	€36539	Equinoxe (104x74cm-41x29in) s.num.42/75 col etching aquatint carborundum. 5-Nov-2 Christie's, Rockefeller NY #194/R est:35000-45000
£25688	$42899	€37248	Tristan Tzara. Parler Seul (39x30cm-15x12in) s.d.12/VI/1950 lithographs 70. 20-Jun-3 Kornfeld, Bern #112/R est:60000 (S.FR 56000)
£38000	$58900	€57000	L'enfance d'ubu, teriade, Paris (35x53cm-14x21in) s. col lithograph album. 3-Dec-2 Christie's, London #156/R est:25000-35000
£38462	$60000	€57693	L'enfance d'ubu, Paris, Teriade Editeur (36x53cm-14x21in) 20 s.col lithographs portfolio. 5-Nov-2 Christie's, Rockefeller NY #201/R est:35000-45000
£44015	$70865	€66023	Suite - La Bague d'Aurore (14x11cm-6x4in) s.d.1958 portfolio 23 etchings aquatint prov.lit. 7-May-3 AB Stockholms Auktionsverk #1238/R est:300000-400000 (S.KR 570000)
£50000	$77500	€75000	Suites pour ubu roi, teriade, Paris (78x57cm-31x22in) s.i.num.39/75 col lithograph album. 3-Dec-2 Christie's, London #155/R est:40000-60000
£64000	$99200	€96000	Suite la bague a'aurore (42x31cm-17x12in) s.d.1958 etching album. 3-Dec-2 Christie's, London #151/R est:45000-65000
£80000	$124000	€120000	Le lezard aux plumes d'or (39x53cm-15x21in) s. lithograph album. 3-Dec-2 Christie's, London #153/R est:50000-70000
£2500000	$4175000	€3750000	Personnages et l'etoile (65x51cm-26x20in) s.d.1949 verso prov.exhib.lit. 23-Jun-3 Sotheby's, London #25/R est:1500000-2000000

Sculpture

£44872	$70000	€67308	Personnage (50x66cm-20x26in) s.num.2 green brown pat. bronze st.f.Clementi cast 1972 prov.exhib. 7-Nov-2 Christie's, Rockefeller NY #338/R est:70000-90000

£80745 $130000 €121118 Personnage et oiseau (153cm-60in) i. brown red green pat. bronze executed 1970 prov.lit. 7-May-3 Sotheby's, New York #333/R est:180000-250000

£161491 $260000 €242237 Projet pour un monument pour la ville de Barcelone (130cm-51in) i.num.8/8 broen red green pat. bronze st.f.Susse executed 1967. 7-May-3 Sotheby's, New York #328/R est:200000-300000

Works on paper

£694 $1104 €1000 Personnage surrealiste (24x19cm-9x7in) s.d.1969 ball point pen. 29-Apr-3 Campo & Campo, Antwerp #225

£4500 $6975 €6750 En souvenir d'Elsa (23x18cm-9x7in) s.i.d.1870 pen brush ink sold with a photo. 5-Dec-2 Christie's, Kensington #151/R est:3000-4000

£5031 $8000 €7547 Joyeux Noel, bonne nouvelle annee (27x21cm-11x8in) s.i.d.1961 col wax crayon ink prov.lit. 27-Feb-3 Christie's, Rockefeller NY #72/R

£6250 $10125 €9500 Composition (30x42cm-12x17in) s.i. col wax crayon dr lit. 22-Jan-3 Tajan, Paris #224/R est:9000-12000

£6579 $10658 €10000 Silhouette (37x26cm-15x10in) s.i. pastel dr. 22-Jan-3 Tajan, Paris #225/R est:8000-10000

£14068 $22228 €21102 Characters on white background (11x32cm-4x13in) s. i.d.57 verso gouache prov.exhib.lit. 28-Apr-3 Bukowskis, Stockholm #307/R est:100000-150000 (S.KR 185000)

£14348 $22239 €21522 L'oiseau migrateur (66x51cm-26x20in) s.d.13/VI/64 gouache prov. 4-Dec-2 Koller, Zurich #164/R est:35000-55000 (S.FR 33000)

£15000 $24600 €22500 Composition a l'etoile (25x18cm-10x7in) s.i.d.1944 W/C pen ink prov. 6-Feb-3 Christie's, London #478/R est:15000

£15837 $26448 €22964 L'oiseau migrateur (66x51cm-26x20in) s.d. gouache prov.lit. 24-Jun-3 Koller, Zurich #160/R est:35000-50000 (S.FR 35000)

£15837 $26448 €22964 L'oiseau migrateur (66x51cm-26x20in) s.d.31/12/62 and 15/2/64 gouache prov.lit. 24-Jun-3 Koller, Zurich #160a/R est:35000-50000 (S.FR 35000)

£18000 $28440 €27000 Arc-en-ciel (55x40cm-22x16in) s. chl W/C gouache. 3-Apr-3 Christie's, Kensington #145/R est:30000

£19205 $31305 €29000 Untitled (44x61cm-17x24in) s. ink exec.1967 prov. 3-Feb-3 Cornette de St.Cyr, Paris #487/R est:35000

£20000 $31000 €30000 L'oiseau migrateur (66x51cm-26x20in) s.d.13/VI/64 gouache prov. 4-Dec-2 Koller, Zurich #165/R est:50000-70000 (S.FR 46000)

£32394 $53775 €46000 Two characters (21x32cm-8x13in) s. Indian ink W/C lit. 12-Jun-3 Laurence Calmels, Paris #77/R est:30000-40000

£32609 $50543 €48914 Voyants (66x51cm-26x20in) s.d.69 gouache on lithographed paper prov.lit. 4-Dec-2 Koller, Zurich #49/R est:80000-120000 (S.FR 75000)

£35000 $58450 €52500 Personnage (41x41cm-16x16in) s. i.d.75 verso crayon india ink prov. 26-Jun-3 Christie's, London #439/R est:30000-40000

£44872 $70000 €67308 Figures et animaux dans un paysage (27x47cm-11x19in) s. s.i.d.1942 verso pencil prov. 6-Nov-2 Sotheby's, New York #299/R est:90000-120000

£45000 $73800 €67500 Personnage, oiseau II (44x57cm-17x22in) s. s.i.d.69 verso W/C ink brush wash prov. 6-Feb-3 Christie's, London #495/R est:70000

£48000 $78720 €72000 Oiseau volant vers le soleil (28x78cm-11x31in) s. i.d.70 verso gouache wash prov. 6-Feb-3 Christie's, London #494/R est:60000

£51282 $80000 €76923 Untitled (63x46cm-25x18in) s.d.21/2/34 verso pastel pen India ink prov. 6-Nov-2 Sotheby's, New York #282/R est:90000-120000

£57692 $90000 €86538 Composition (32x25cm-13x10in) s. W/C pastel brush ink. 7-Nov-2 Christie's, Rockefeller NY #148/R est:40000-60000

£80000 $131200 €120000 Souvenir de Montroig (50x65cm-20x26in) s. s.i.d.37 verso gouache brush ink pencil prov. 6-Feb-3 Christie's, London #505/R est:80000

£110000 $180400 €165000 Femme, oiseau III (84x70cm-33x28in) s. s.i.d.76 verso gouache ink wash prov. 6-Feb-3 Christie's, London #504/R est:70000

£179487 $280000 €269231 Personnage (37x30cm-15x12in) s. s.i.d.22.8.1935 gouache pen ink prov. 5-Nov-2 Sotheby's, New York #49/R est:350000-450000

£245000 $409150 €367500 Personnage (65x52cm-26x20in) s. i.d.1.Vl.80 verso gouache W/C pencil exhib. 26-Jun-3 Christie's, London #440/R est:130000-160000

£1600000 $2672000 €2320000 Le coq (63x49cm-25x19in) s. s.i.d.1940 verso gouache W/C pencil prov.lit. 24-Jun-3 Christie's, London #29/R est:250000-350000

MIRON SIMA (1902-) Palestinian

£417 $658 €650 Still life of flowers with roses in vase (65x45cm-26x18in) s.d.1958. 15-Nov-2 Reiss & Sohn, Konigstein #689/R

MIROU, Antoine (1583-1669) Flemish

£14388 $23022 €20000 Extensive wooded river landscape with huntsman and dogs (49x59cm-19x23in) panel. 13-May-3 Sotheby's, Amsterdam #7/R est:20000-30000

MIROU, Antoine (attrib) (1583-1669) Flemish

Works on paper

£6369 $9936 €10000 Panoramic view of Frankenthal (20x33cm-8x13in) i. pen brown ink brown blue wash prov.exhib. 5-Nov-2 Sotheby's, Amsterdam #196/R est:900-1200

MIROU, Antoine (circle) (1583-1669) Flemish

£6000 $9360 €9000 Extensive landscape with elegant company and villagers, a village beyond (30x42cm-12x17in) copper. 10-Apr-3 Christie's, Kensington #5/R est:4000-6000

MIRVAL, C (20th C) French

Sculpture

£4966 $7896 €7300 Untitled (60cm-24in) s. silver pat bronze onyx marble. 24-Mar-3 Digard, Paris #74/R

£11000 $17600 €16500 Female dancer (64cm-25in) s. bronze ivory. 15-May-3 Christie's, Kensington #453/R est:7000-9000

MISCHENKOV, Alexei (1947-) Russian

£250 $388 €375 In the park (40x50cm-16x20in) s. 8-Dec-2 John Nicholson, Haslemere #56

MISONNE, Leonard (1870-1943) Belgian

Photographs

£1829 $3000 €2744 Amsterdam le matin (39x29cm-15x11in) s.d. s.i.verso mediabrome print. 10-Feb-3 Swann Galleries, New York #28/R est:4000-5000

£1887 $2925 €3000 Le pommier (30x40cm-12x16in) s.d.1918 bromine oil print lit. 2-Nov-2 Lempertz, Koln #71/R est:2800

MISRACH, Richard (1949-) American

Photographs

£3247 $5000 €4871 Flooded house foundation, Salton Sea (76x102cm-30x40in) s.i.verso col chromogenic print 5 of 10 prov.lit. 25-Oct-2 Phillips, New York #171/R est:3000-5000

£3766 $5800 €5649 Cloud no 5 (96x122cm-38x48in) i.verso chromogenic col print 9 of 10 prov.lit. 25-Oct-2 Phillips, New York #172/R est:3000-5000

£4375 $7000 €6563 Salton sea (46x58cm-18x23in) s.i.d.1984 verso chromogenic print. 15-May-3 Swann Galleries, New York #442/R est:2000-3000

£4878 $8000 €7317 Desert fire no 249 (67x85cm-26x33in) s.i.d. num.1/10 col chromogenic print. 10-Feb-3 Swann Galleries, New York #99/R est:8000-12000

MISSAKIAN, Berge (20th C) American?

£481 $750 €722 Afternoon blues (51x41cm-20x16in) s. s.i.d.2001 verso. 20-Sep-2 Sloan, North Bethesda #480/R

MISSELHORN, Roscoe (1902-1997) American

£346 $550 €502 Ozark cabin (16x20cm-6x8in) s. board painted c.1940. 4-May-3 Treadway Gallery, Cincinnati #597/R

MITCHELL OF MARYPORT, William (c.1806-1900) British

£900 $1503 €1305 Herring fishing boats leaving port (51x76cm-20x30in) s. July 7 1889. 17-Jun-3 Anderson & Garland, Newcastle #460/R

£950 $1549 €1378 Crummock water. St. Johns. Beck Patterdale. Ullswater and Rydal Water (23x33cm-9x13in) s.i.verso panel set of four. 16-Jul-3 James Thompson, Kirby Lonsdale #40

£2100 $3297 €3150 View of Ullswater from Birk Grag (120x75cm-47x30in) s.i.d.1878 verso. 25-Nov-2 Cumbria Auction Rooms, UK #338 est:2000-3000

MITCHELL, Alfred (19/20th C) British

£9639 $16000 €13977 Peaceful morning (40x51cm-16x20in) s. board exhib. 11-Jun-3 Butterfields, San Francisco #4240/R est:15000-20000

MITCHELL, Alfred R (1888-1972) American

£2259 $3750 €3276 Monterey headland (20x25cm-8x10in) s. i.verso board prov. 11-Jun-3 Butterfields, San Francisco #4288/R est:4000-6000

£4969 $8000 €7454 White barn (41x51cm-16x20in) s. board prov. 18-Feb-3 John Moran, Pasadena #95 est:8000-12000
£7186 $12000 €10420 Old mill at Carversville PA (41x51cm-16x20in) s. i.verso board prov. 17-Jun-3 John Moran, Pasadena #46 est:12000-18000
£7453 $12000 €11180 Brisk day (41x51cm-16x20in) s. i.verso board. 18-Feb-3 John Moran, Pasadena #30 est:10000-15000
£7784 $13000 €11287 Smoke trees (61x76cm-24x30in) s.i. s.i.stretcher prov. 18-Jun-3 Christie's, Los Angeles #49/R est:15000-25000
£9677 $15000 €14516 Outskirts of San Diego (41x51cm-16x20in) s.i.verso board prov. 29-Oct-2 John Moran, Pasadena #624 est:15000-20000
£9677 $15000 €14516 On Palomar (41x51cm-16x20in) s. i.verso board prov. 29-Oct-2 John Moran, Pasadena #755 est:10000-15000
£25478 $40000 €38217 Late afternoon, El Capitan near El Cajon (61x76cm-24x30in) s. i.verso prov.exhib. 19-Nov-2 Butterfields, San Francisco #8265/R est:20000-30000
£30645 $47500 €45968 Emerald Cove, La Jolla (61x76cm-24x30in) s. i.stretcher prov. 29-Oct-2 John Moran, Pasadena #654b est:35000-50000

MITCHELL, Arthur Croft (1872-?) British
£5800 $9164 €8700 Morning (63x64cm-25x25in) 26-Nov-2 Christie's, London #164/R est:4000-6000

MITCHELL, Arthur Roy (1886-1977) American
£3313 $5500 €4804 Cowboy on horseback shooting his guns (91x63cm-36x25in) s.d.1933 prov. 11-Jun-3 Butterfields, San Francisco #4329/R est:3000-5000

MITCHELL, Denis (1912-1993) British
£950 $1511 €1425 Standing stones (66x96cm-26x38in) s.d.47 board. 18-Mar-3 Bonhams, Knightsbridge #156

Sculpture
£1200 $1956 €1800 Trew (13cm-5in) s.i.d.1974 bronze stepped slate base. 13-Feb-3 David Lay, Penzance #272/R est:450-650
£1500 $2490 €2175 Paphos II (30cm-12in) s.d.1974 num.1 polished bronze. 10-Jun-3 David Lay, Penzance #471/R est:1000-1500
£1800 $2790 €2700 Circle within triangular form (40cm-16in) stone. 3-Dec-2 Bonhams, New Bond Street #98/R est:2000-3000
£5500 $9020 €8250 Zennor (80cm-31in) init.i.d.1969 num.0/5 bronze marble base. 3-Jun-3 Sotheby's, Olympia #299/R est:2000-3000

MITCHELL, E (19th C) British
£1200 $1896 €1800 Heavy horse in a field. Heavy horse in a stable (63x76cm-25x30in) s.d.1885 pair. 28-Nov-2 Christie's, Kensington #114/R est:1500-2000

MITCHELL, Flora H (1890-1973) Irish

Works on paper
£506 $785 €800 Royal College of Surgeons, Dublin (22x29cm-9x11in) s. monochrome pen ink. 25-Sep-2 James Adam, Dublin #13/R
£1216 $1897 €1800 Crampton Court, Dublin (30x26cm-12x10in) s.i. pen ink W/C. 26-Mar-3 James Adam, Dublin #120/R est:1200-1500
£1266 $1962 €2000 O'Connell Street Bridge from Burgh Quay, Dublin (22x34cm-9x13in) s. W/C. 25-Sep-2 James Adam, Dublin #12 est:1500-2500
£1319 $2177 €1900 Entrance to Lower castle Yard, Dublin (20x19cm-8x7in) s.i.d.57 W/C over pen. 7-Jul-3 Hamilton Osborne King, Dublin #205/R est:1000-1500
£1342 $2161 €2000 Crampton Court, Dublin (27x22cm-11x9in) s.i. pen ink W/C. 18-Feb-3 Whyte's, Dublin #26/R est:2000-2500
£1509 $2355 €2400 York Street, Dublin (21x29cm-8x11in) s.i. pen ink W/C prov. 17-Sep-2 Whyte's, Dublin #53 est:1800-2200
£1635 $2551 €2600 Moore street market, Dublin (27x25cm-11x10in) s.i.d.1971 pen ink W/C. 17-Sep-2 Whyte's, Dublin #147/R est:2000-2500
£1667 $2750 €2400 Weaver's Hall, Dublin (20x25cm-8x10in) s.i. W/C over pen. 7-Jul-3 Hamilton Osborne King, Dublin #204/R est:1000-1500
£1745 $2809 €2600 O'Connell Bridge from Burgh Quay, Dublin (23x36cm-9x14in) s.i. pen ink W/C prov. 18-Feb-3 Whyte's, Dublin #193/R est:2000-3000
£2222 $3667 €3200 O'Connell Street, Dublin, with Nelson's Column (21x29cm-8x11in) s.i. W/C over pen. 7-Jul-3 Hamilton Osborne King, Dublin #203/R est:2000-3000

MITCHELL, George Bertrand (1874-1966) American
£500 $800 €725 Glacier from Larch Valley, Canadian Rockies (11x30cm-4x12in) s. canvasboard. 16-May-3 Skinner, Boston #249/R

MITCHELL, Gladys Vinson (1894-1968) American
£281 $450 €422 Moonlight on Baldwin Lake (25x20cm-10x8in) s. board. 15-Mar-3 Selkirks, St. Louis #329

MITCHELL, Glen (1894-1972) American
£375 $600 €544 Modern figural composition (61x50cm-24x20in) bears sig.verso. 16-May-3 Skinner, Boston #374/R

MITCHELL, Helen Lillias (1915-2000) Irish
£321 $503 €500 Lilian Davidson's Toby Jug (43x33cm-17x13in) s. canvas on board painted c.1936. 19-Nov-2 Whyte's, Dublin #134/R

MITCHELL, Janet (1912-1998) Canadian
£402 $635 €603 Autumn (43x71cm-17x28in) hardboard. 1-Dec-2 Levis, Calgary #68/R (C.D 1000)
£652 $1017 €1088 Lake shore (51x61cm-20x24in) s. i.verso acrylic board prov. 13-Apr-3 Levis, Calgary #86/R est:1800-2000 (C.D 1500)
£723 $1142 €1085 Spring garden (51x102cm-20x40in) d.1960 hardboard. 1-Dec-2 Levis, Calgary #67/R est:1500-2000 (C.D 1800)
£924 $1459 €1386 Whimsical figures (61x76cm-24x30in) d.1974 acrylic hardboard. 1-Dec-2 Levis, Calgary #66/R est:2500-3000 (C.D 2300)
£978 $1604 €1418 Sunflowers and shack (55x60cm-22x24in) s.i.d.1947 board. 9-Jun-3 Hodgins, Calgary #129/R est:2500-3000 (C.D 2200)

Works on paper
£261 $410 €392 Autumn colours (11x16cm-4x6in) s. W/C. 25-Nov-2 Hodgins, Calgary #251/R (C.D 650)
£361 $567 €542 West of Bragg Creek (35x53cm-14x21in) s. W/C prov. 25-Nov-2 Hodgins, Calgary #14/R (C.D 900)
£361 $567 €542 Rain in the mountains (33x43cm-13x17in) s.d. W/C. 25-Nov-2 Hodgins, Calgary #66/R (C.D 900)
£890 $1415 €1335 Dreamers (50x73cm-20x29in) s.d.1980 W/C. 23-Mar-3 Hodgins, Calgary #2/R est:1500-2000 (C.D 2100)
£1525 $2425 €2288 Stampede time (35x53cm-14x21in) s.d.1979 W/C. 23-Mar-3 Hodgins, Calgary #5/R est:1500-2000 (C.D 3600)
£1610 $2560 €2415 Stampede merry-go-round (34x51cm-13x20in) s.d.1979 W/C prov. 23-Mar-3 Hodgins, Calgary #25/R est:1500-2000 (C.D 3800)

MITCHELL, Joan (1926-1992) American
£41139 $65000 €61709 Untitled (31x24cm-12x9in) s.d.58/59 i.verso oil graphite on paper prov. 13-Nov-2 Sotheby's, New York #217a/R est:40000-60000
£80272 $127633 €118000 Untitled (77x102cm-30x40in) s. prov. 24-Mar-3 Cornette de St.Cyr, Paris #12/R est:180000
£137500 $220000 €206250 Ecole buissonniere (100x81cm-39x32in) s.i. painted c.1959 prov. 15-May-3 Christie's, Rockefeller NY #111/R est:100000-150000
£190000 $317300 €275500 Untitled (89x116cm-35x46in) prov. 26-Jun-3 Sotheby's, London #175/R est:70000-90000
£227848 $360000 €341772 Vetheuil (195x129cm-77x51in) painted 1967-68 prov.exhib. 13-Nov-2 Sotheby's, New York #217/R est:250000-350000
£250000 $400000 €375000 River III (260x201cm-102x79in) s. i.verso painted 1967-68 prov.exhib. 14-May-3 Christie's, Rockefeller NY #11/R est:400000-600000
£253165 $400000 €379748 Maple leave forever (251x147cm-99x58in) s. i.d.1968 on stretcher prov.exhib. 14-Nov-2 Christie's, Rockefeller NY #151/R est:300000-400000
£343750 $550000 €515625 Temps des lilas (195x129cm-77x51in) s. painted 1966 prov. 13-May-3 Sotheby's, New York #24/R est:400000-600000
£430380 $680000 €645570 Landscape ting (170x198cm-67x78in) i.verso painted c.1958-59 prov. 13-Nov-2 Christie's, Rockefeller NY #16/R est:400000-600000

Prints
£1887 $3000 €2831 Trees II (145x208cm-57x82in) s.i.d. col lithograph two sheets. 2-May-3 Sotheby's, New York #530/R est:2000-3000
£1887 $3000 €2831 Trees III (145x208cm-57x82in) s.i.d. col lithograph. 2-May-3 Sotheby's, New York #531/R est:2000-3000
£2201 $3500 €3302 Brush. Tree (108x82cm-43x32in) s.one num.AP 9/16 one num.68/94 col lithograph two. 2-May-3 Sotheby's, New York #529/R est:2200-2800
£2673 $4250 €4010 Sunflowers III (145x209cm-57x82in) s.i.d. col lithograph two sheets. 2-May-3 Sotheby's, New York #532/R est:3000-4000

MITCHELL, John (1838-1926) British

Works on paper
£1400 $2226 €2100 Highland river scene with sheep grazing and cattle in the distance (38x53cm-15x21in) s.d.1899 W/C. 18-Mar-3 Lawrences, Bletchingley #1435 est:500-700

MITCHELL, John Campbell (1862-1922) British
£420 $697 €609 Open sea (45x75cm-18x30in) s.d.1910. 13-Jun-3 Lyon & Turnbull, Edinburgh #48
£900 $1467 €1350 Argyllshire (40x46cm-16x18in) 14-Feb-3 Lyon & Turnbull, Edinburgh #152
£2200 $3366 €3300 Near North Berwick (37x45cm-15x18in) s. 22-Aug-2 Bonhams, Edinburgh #1042/R est:1000-1500

Works on paper
£600 $918 €900 Scrats Rock, Machrihanish, Paps of Jura in the distance (20x35cm-8x14in) s.d.1918 W/C. 22-Aug-2 Bonhams, Edinburgh #1166

MITCHELL, Mike (20th C) Irish?
£288 $449 €420 Geo 1 (36x36cm-14x14in) s. acrylic collage paper. 8-Apr-3 James Adam, Dublin #104/R

MITCHELL, Neil Reid (1858-1934) American
Works on paper
£710 $1100 €1065 Sail ship on moonlight seas (30x61cm-12x24in) s. pastel prov. 29-Oct-2 John Moran, Pasadena #688b

MITCHELL, Philip (1814-1896) British
Works on paper
£300 $471 €450 Burg Rheinstein on the river Rhine (47x72cm-19x28in) s.i.d.1857 pencil W/C bodycol. 16-Apr-3 Christie's, Kensington #1063

MITCHELL, Reine (19/20th C) American
£321 $500 €465 Fishing boats off the coast (56x84cm-22x33in) s. 30-Mar-3 Simpson's, Houston #266

MITCHELL, W (?) ?
£450 $702 €675 Dunderave Castle, head of Loch Fyne (61x92cm-24x36in) s.i.d.March 1888 verso. 17-Sep-2 Sotheby's, Olympia #23/R

MITCHELL, William Frederick (1845-1914) British
Works on paper
£250 $385 €375 HMS Black Prince (15x28cm-6x11in) s.i.d.1902 W/C. 5-Sep-2 Clevedon Sale Rooms #135
£320 $506 €480 Black Prince in full sail at sea (15x28cm-6x11in) s.d.1902 pen ink W/C. 18-Dec-2 Mallams, Oxford #587
£340 $517 €510 HMS Calliope (24x33cm-9x13in) s.i.d.1890 W/C over pencil htd white. 15-Aug-2 Bonhams, New Bond Street #235/R
£1000 $1520 €1500 HMS Britannia under full sail in a light breeze (15x22cm-6x9in) s.d.1874 i.verso W/C htd white. 15-Aug-2 Bonhams, New Bond Street #405/R est:1000-1500
£2300 $3634 €3450 Royal yacht Victoria and Albert III with escort (36x51cm-14x20in) s.d.June 1904 W/C. 13-Nov-2 Halls, Shrewsbury #364/R est:1000-1500

MITELLI, Giuseppe Maria (attrib) (1634-1718) Italian
Works on paper
£507 $791 €750 Paysans discutant (17x28cm-7x11in) crayon. 31-Mar-3 Piasa, Paris #53

MITELMAN, Allan (1946-) Australian
Works on paper
£232 $358 €348 Untitled - orange (34x22cm-13x9in) s.d.90 W/C. 8-Sep-2 Sotheby's, Melbourne #82 (A.D 650)
£304 $467 €456 Untitled - black (22x18cm-9x7in) s.d.90 W/C. 8-Sep-2 Sotheby's, Melbourne #63 est:500-800 (A.D 850)

MITI-ZANETTI, Giuseppe (1859-1929) Italian
£362 $594 €500 Paesaggio con lago (20x33cm-8x13in) s. panel. 27-May-3 Finarte, Milan #68/R

MITORAJ, Igor (1944-) German
Sculpture
£962 $1510 €1500 Grepol (30x21x12cm-12x8x5in) num.247/250 pat bronze sold with base exec.1978. 16-Dec-2 Eric Coutrier, Paris #130/R

MITTERFELLNER, Andreas (1912-1972) German
£272 $433 €400 Simssee (60x80cm-24x31in) s. board. 20-Mar-3 Neumeister, Munich #2696
£1351 $2108 €2000 Hay harvest (20x40cm-8x16in) s. panel. 26-Mar-3 Hugo Ruef, Munich #176 est:1500
£1497 $2380 €2200 Chiemsee with Kampenwand (46x79cm-18x31in) s. i. verso panel. 19-Mar-3 Neumeister, Munich #649/R est:1500
£1892 $2951 €2800 Returning home after the harvest (20x40cm-8x16in) s. panel. 26-Mar-3 Hugo Ruef, Munich #177/R est:1500

MIYAJIMA, Tatsuo (1957) Japanese
Sculpture
£13750 $22000 €20625 Line of time (10x99x4cm-4x39x2in) 38 light emitting diodes electric wire executed 1988 prov. 14-May-3 Sotheby's, New York #381/R est:12000-18000

Works on paper
£1000 $1640 €1500 Drawing for region no 103550-103598 (45x62cm-18x24in) s.i.d.91 pencil ink cardboard collage prov.exhib. 7-Feb-3 Sotheby's, London #129/R est:2000-3000

MIYAO (?) Japanese
Sculpture
£9204 $14451 €13806 Shou Lao (38cm-15in) s. bronze. 25-Nov-2 Stephan Welz, Johannesburg #174/R est:30000-40000 (SA.R 140000)

MIZERA, Otto (attrib) (1919-1951) Czechoslovakian
£524 $817 €786 Still life with apples on dish (20x31cm-8x12in) i. panel. 6-Nov-2 Dobiaschofsky, Bern #3537/R (S.FR 1200)

MNGUNI, Simoni (1885-1956) South African
Works on paper
£243 $380 €365 Portrait of a man in a suit (37x28cm-15x11in) s.i. W/C. 11-Nov-2 Stephan Welz, Johannesburg #218 (SA.R 3800)
£333 $520 €500 Medicine man (37x27cm-15x11in) s.i. W/C. 11-Nov-2 Stephan Welz, Johannesburg #217 (SA.R 5200)
£372 $580 €558 Ndongeni, portrait of a man (35x28cm-14x11in) s.i. W/C. 11-Nov-2 Stephan Welz, Johannesburg #219 (SA.R 5800)

MOBBS, Rick (20th C) American
£342 $550 €513 Old factory (122x244cm-48x96in) s.i.verso masonite. 22-Feb-3 Brunk, Ashville #551/R

MOCARELLI, Emanuele (1968-) Italian
£981 $1530 €1550 Ninive I (80x60cm-31x24in) s.i.d.1994. 14-Sep-2 Meeting Art, Vercelli #779/R
£1026 $1610 €1600 With a flute (80x60cm-31x24in) s.i.d.1998 verso. 23-Nov-2 Meeting Art, Vercelli #16/R
£1156 $1839 €1700 Beginner (60x80cm-24x31in) s. s.i.verso. 1-Mar-3 Meeting Art, Vercelli #502

MODEL, Lisette (1902-) American
Photographs
£3896 $6000 €5844 East side, New York (34x27cm-13x11in) d.1944 photograph prov.exhib.lit. 22-Oct-2 Sotheby's, New York #74/R est:3000-5000
£3896 $6000 €5844 Block party, East side, New York (34x27cm-13x11in) i.d.circa 1942 photograph prov.lit. 22-Oct-2 Sotheby's, New York #75/R est:3000-5000

MODERSOHN, Otto (1865-1943) German
£5128 $7949 €8000 Evening at River Wumme (56x74cm-22x29in) s.d.39. 7-Dec-2 Van Ham, Cologne #356/R est:14000
£5282 $8768 €7500 Moor landscape (24x36cm-9x14in) mono.d. panel. 14-Jun-3 Hauswedell & Nolte, Hamburg #1419/R est:10000
£5286 $7718 €7929 Village street in Dobben (17x24cm-7x9in) mono. panel prov. 17-Jun-2 Philippe Schuler, Zurich #4387/R est:8000-12000 (S.FR 12000)
£6463 $10276 €9500 Enjoying the ice on the meadows by the Wumme (46x64cm-18x25in) s.d.1932. 28-Mar-3 Bolland & Marotz, Bremen #357a est:12000
£7547 $11623 €12000 Hindelang with dark pine trees (57x73cm-22x29in) s.d.1933. 26-Oct-2 Dr Lehr, Berlin #339/R est:15000
£7595 $12000 €12000 Windblown bushes (32x41cm-13x16in) mono. board. 30-Nov-2 Villa Grisebach, Berlin #133/R est:12000-15000
£8228 $13000 €13000 Starry sky over the Wumme (60x38cm-24x15in) painted c.1912. 29-Nov-2 Bolland & Marotz, Bremen #546/R est:14000
£8511 $13787 €12000 Wumme with melting snows (46x61cm-18x24in) s.d.37. 24-May-3 Van Ham, Cologne #419/R est:9000
£8861 $14000 €14000 Spring morning (50x70cm-20x28in) s.d.37. 29-Nov-2 Bolland & Marotz, Bremen #545/R est:8700
£9420 $15449 €13000 Gailenberg - Allgau (56x73cm-22x29in) s.d.31 prov. 31-May-3 Villa Grisebach, Berlin #140/R est:12000-15000
£9494 $15000 €15000 Stormy day in Teufels fen (56x73cm-22x29in) s. 29-Nov-2 Bolland & Marotz, Bremen #541/R est:15000
£9494 $15000 €15000 Winter in the fens (50x61cm-20x24in) s.d.39. 29-Nov-2 Bolland & Marotz, Bremen #542/R est:16000
£9615 $14904 €15000 Bridge over the Wumme (40x58cm-16x23in) s. board. 7-Dec-2 Kastern, Hannover #50/R est:14000
£10127 $16000 €16000 Boats on the Wumme at dusk (47x67cm-19x26in) s. 29-Nov-2 Bolland & Marotz, Bremen #540/R est:17000
£10563 $17535 €15000 Calm river (74x67cm-29x26in) s.d. 14-Jun-3 Hauswedell & Nolte, Hamburg #1418/R est:20000
£10870 $16848 €16305 Village by water near Worpswede (40x50cm-16x20in) s.d.27 panel prov. 4-Dec-2 Koller, Zurich #160/R est:25000-35000 (S.FR 25000)

£11392 $18000 €18000 Autumn (40x56cm-16x22in) s. double-sided. 27-Nov-2 Dorotheum, Vienna #32/R est:18000-25000
£12455 $20800 €18060 Summer Wumme landscape (50x35cm-20x14in) d.VII/II board prov. 24-Jun-3 Koller, Zurich #126/R est:25000-40000 (S.FR 27525)
£12658 $20000 €20000 Approaching storm over Fisherhude fields in early summer (41x58cm-16x23in) d.11 i.verso board. 29-Nov-2 Bolland & Marotz, Bremen #543/R est:15000
£15190 $23696 €24000 Moorland near Worpswede in summer (71x78cm-28x31in) s. board prov. 18-Oct-2 Dr Fritz Nagel, Stuttgart #572/R est:12000
£15942 $26145 €22000 Spring on the Wumme (50x70cm-20x28in) s.d.35 i. stretcher prov. 31-May-3 Villa Grisebach, Berlin #141/R est:14000-18000

Works on paper

£775 $1286 €1100 Houses and trees (16x25cm-6x10in) chk chl ochre. 14-Jun-3 Hauswedell & Nolte, Hamburg #1422/R
£845 $1403 €1200 Moorland canal with bridge (18x22cm-7x9in) chk ochre. 14-Jun-3 Hauswedell & Nolte, Hamburg #1421/R
£897 $1391 €1400 Moorland canal with bridges and houses (16x26cm-6x10in) chl chk. 7-Dec-2 Hauswedell & Nolte, Hamburg #910/R

MODERSOHN-BECKER, Paula (1876-1907) German

£55128 $85449 €86000 Fairground (36x49cm-14x19in) panel double-sided. 7-Dec-2 Hauswedell & Nolte, Hamburg #911/R est:60000
£132912 $210000 €210000 Two girls before the stem of a birch tree (71x52cm-28x20in) d.04 cardboard prov.lit. 29-Nov-2 Villa Grisebach, Berlin #20/R est:160000-180000
£200000 $326000 €300000 Liegender weiblicher akt (70x112cm-28x44in) init. painted 1905-06 prov.exhib.lit. 3-Feb-3 Christie's, London #4/R est:200000-300000

Prints

£2215 $3500 €3323 Die frau mit der gans (13x18cm-5x7in) s.i. etching aquatint executed c.1902. 12-Nov-2 Doyle, New York #316/R est:4000-6000
£4710 $7725 €6500 Goose maid (25x20cm-10x8in) etching aquatint. 31-May-3 Villa Grisebach, Berlin #129/R est:4500-5500

Works on paper

£1899 $3000 €3000 Woman walking (31x24cm-12x9in) i. chl. 30-Nov-2 Villa Grisebach, Berlin #138/R est:4000-5000
£3129 $4976 €4600 Houses behind trees (16x32cm-6x13in) mono. col chk. 28-Mar-3 Bolland & Marotz, Bremen #358/R est:2800
£5282 $8768 €7500 Houses behind trees (17x33cm-7x13in) mono.i. col chk. 14-Jun-3 Hauswedell & Nolte, Hamburg #1423/R est:7500

MODESITT, John (1955-) American

£1242 $2000 €1863 Autumn morning (61x61cm-24x24in) s. i.verso. 18-Feb-3 John Moran, Pasadena #123 est:2000-3000
£1497 $2500 €2171 Coast near Point Loma (51x41cm-20x16in) s. i.verso. 17-Jun-3 John Moran, Pasadena #131a est:2000-3000
£2096 $3500 €3039 Landscape, High Sierras Bishop (64x76cm-25x30in) s. i.verso. 17-Jun-3 John Moran, Pasadena #131 est:3000-4000
£2861 $4750 €4148 Imperial coast, near Rosarito Beach (91x91cm-36x36in) s. prov. 11-Jun-3 Butterfields, San Francisco #4343/R est:4000-6000
£5689 $9500 €8249 Alpine splendor (152x147cm-60x58in) s. s.i.on stretcher. 18-Jun-3 Christie's, Los Angeles #51/R est:10000-15000

MODIGLIANI, Amedeo (1884-1920) Italian

£269231 $420000 €403847 Le typographe - Pedro (55x46cm-22x18in) bears sig painted c.1909 prov.exhib.lit. 6-Nov-2 Christie's, Rockefeller NY #13/R est:500000-700000
£2435898 $3800000 €3653847 Beatrice hastings devant une porte (81x46cm-32x18in) s.d.1915 prov.exhib.lit. 6-Nov-2 Christie's, Rockefeller NY #35/R est:3000000-4000000
£4935898 $7700000 €7403847 Giovanotto dai capelli rossi (101x63cm-40x25in) s. painted 1919 prov.exhib.lit. 5-Nov-2 Sotheby's, New York #59/R est:6000000-8000000

Sculpture

£9028 $14896 €13000 Tete de femme (25x21cm-10x8in) s.st.f.Valsuani black pat bronze sold with marble socle. 1-Jul-3 Rossini, Paris #54/R
£26087 $40435 €39131 Tete de jeune fille a la frange (50cm-20in) i. num.III/IV dark brown pat bronze prov.exhib.lit. 4-Dec-2 Koller, Zurich #40/R est:50000-60000 (S.FR 60000)

Works on paper

£5674 $9475 €8000 Jeune femme assise (42x26cm-17x10in) s. lead pencil. 20-Jun-3 Piasa, Paris #92/R est:10000-12000
£11000 $18040 €16500 Nu assis sur une chaise (43x28cm-17x11in) crayon exec.1908 prov.exhib.lit. 5-Feb-3 Sotheby's, London #149/R est:7000
£11043 $18000 €16565 Portrait de femme nue (55x41cm-22x16in) s.d.1914 col pencil prov. 12-Feb-3 Sotheby's, New York #89/R est:6000-8000
£11972 $19873 €17000 Profil (40x24cm-16x9in) s. ink pencil dr lit. 11-Jun-3 Beaussant & Lefèvre, Paris #113/R est:12000-15000
£15000 $24600 €22500 Nu assis, bras le long du corps (43x26cm-17x10in) bruh ink exec.1909 prov.exhib.lit. 5-Feb-3 Sotheby's, London #147/R est:25000
£16218 $25462 €25300 Portrait d'homme (22x17cm-9x7in) s. graphite dr prov.lit. 11-Dec-2 Artcurial Briest, Paris #515/R
£16667 $26000 €25001 Tete de femme (49x31cm-19x12in) s. pencil card exec.c.1910. 18-Sep-2 Swann Galleries, New York #22/R est:10000-15000
£17000 $26180 €25500 Femme assise (42x25cm-17x10in) s. pencil prov.exhib. 22-Oct-2 Sotheby's, London #137/R est:18000-25000
£17467 $25502 €26201 Henri Laurens (38x27cm-15x11in) s. pencil lit. 4-Jun-2 Germann, Zurich #17/R est:50000-70000 (S.FR 40000)
£18000 $29520 €27000 Nu allonge de dos (26x43cm-10x17in) crayon exec.1908 prov.exhib.lit. 5-Feb-3 Sotheby's, London #150/R est:25000
£24000 $39360 €36000 Tete de face (31x24cm-12x9in) crayon exec.c.1910-11 prov.exhib.lit. 5-Feb-3 Sotheby's, London #148/R est:15000
£26207 $41931 €38000 Henri Laurens (38x27cm-15x11in) s. crayon dr exec.c.1915 lit. 12-Mar-3 Rabourdin & Choppin de Janvry, Paris #146/R est:45000
£37267 $60000 €55901 Jeune femme assise (43x28cm-17x11in) s. W/C executed c.1918 prov. 8-May-3 Christie's, Rockefeller NY #113/R est:25000-35000
£41259 $68902 €59000 Tete de Cariatide (42x25cm-17x10in) s. blk crayon c.1911-1912 prov.lit. 30-Jun-3 Artcurial Briest, Paris #52/R est:40000-60000
£48000 $80160 €69600 Tete et epaules de face avec frange (43x26cm-17x10in) s. black crayon executed 1911-12 prov.exhib.lit. 24-Jun-3 Sotheby's, London #230/R est:50000-70000
£57692 $89423 €90000 Cariatide (43x29cm-17x11in) s. pencil col chk. 7-Dec-2 Hauswedell & Nolte, Hamburg #912/R est:100000
£80000 $131200 €120000 Caraiatide agenouillee assise sur ses talons (43x26cm-17x10in) crayon exec.c.1911-13 prov.exhib.lit. 5-Feb-3 Sotheby's, London #146/R est:80000

MODIGLIANI, Corinna (19/20th C) Italian

£444 $738 €644 Young boy holding a bird (31x16cm-12x6in) s. canvasboard. 16-Jun-3 Waddingtons, Toronto #332/R est:800-1200 (C.D 1000)

MODIGLIANI, Jeanne (1918-1984) French

£331 $540 €500 Sans titre (82x130cm-32x51in) s. 1-Feb-3 Claude Aguttes, Neuilly #294

MODOTTI, Tina (1896-1962) Italian

Photographs

£3049 $5000 €4574 Orozco mural from the entrance to the Great Patio (25x20cm-10x8in) i.verso silver print. 10-Feb-3 Swann Galleries, New York #42/R est:6000-9000

MOE, Carl (1889-1942) Norwegian

£364 $556 €546 Winter by the coast (50x80cm-20x31in) s. 26-Aug-2 Blomqvist, Lysaker #1257 (N.KR 4200)
£425 $692 €638 Winter landscape (19x45cm-7x18in) s. 17-Feb-3 Blomqvist, Lysaker #1127 (N.KR 4800)
£442 $676 €663 Winter landscape in moonlight (50x80cm-20x31in) s. 26-Aug-2 Blomqvist, Lysaker #1256/R (N.KR 5100)

MOE, Louis (1859-1945) Norwegian

£266 $431 €399 Mountain brook in Telemarken (45x37cm-18x15in) init.i.d.1 Aug 89 prov. 25-Jan-3 Rasmussen, Havnen #2225/R (D.KR 3000)
£355 $574 €533 Log cabin (36x44cm-14x17in) s.i.d.90 prov. 25-Jan-3 Rasmussen, Havnen #2261/R (D.KR 4000)

MOE, Odd (1944-) Norwegian

£419 $666 €629 Landscape, La Verna (165x120cm-65x47in) s.d.1990 verso. 10-Mar-3 Rasmussen, Vejle #684 (D.KR 4500)
£512 $814 €768 Composition (144x116cm-57x46in) s.d.90 verso. 10-Mar-3 Rasmussen, Vejle #685 (D.KR 5500)

MOEBUS, Peter (1954-) German

£897 $1391 €1400 Morning light (55x70cm-22x28in) s.d.1997 verso i. stretcher prov. 3-Dec-2 Lempertz, Koln #309/R
£1538 $2385 €2400 Mist on Skaro (75x100cm-30x39in) s.d.2000 i. stretcher prov. 3-Dec-2 Lempertz, Koln #310/R est:2500

MOELLER, Arnold (1886-1963) German

£314 $491 €500 Shepherd in mountains (60x50cm-24x20in) 23-Sep-2 Dr Fritz Nagel, Stuttgart #6960
£969 $1415 €1454 Homeward (51x60cm-20x24in) s.d.1930. 17-Jun-2 Philippe Schuler, Zurich #4388/R (S.FR 2200)
£1266 $1962 €2000 Woman driving ox cart home between mountain pastures (50x61cm-20x24in) s.d.1930. 25-Sep-2 Neumeister, Munich #658/R est:2000

MOELLER, Louis C (1855-1930) American

£4545 $7000 €6818 News from the Front (30x41cm-12x16in) s. prov. 24-Oct-2 Shannon's, Milford #103/R est:8000-12000

£9091 $14000 €13637 Man's best friend (41x30cm-16x12in) s.i. 24-Oct-2 Shannon's, Milford #145/R est:6000-8000
£10494 $17000 €15741 Tea party (46x62cm-18x24in) s. indis d.1905 prov. 21-May-3 Sotheby's, New York #214/R est:10000-15000
£12346 $20000 €18519 Reading the will (46x61cm-18x24in) s.d.1888 prov. 21-May-3 Sotheby's, New York #213/R est:20000-30000

MOENS, Robert (1908-1977) Belgian
£288 $460 €400 Landscape (80x100cm-31x39in) s. 17-May-3 De Vuyst, Lokeren #264

MOER, Jean Baptiste van (1819-1884) Belgian
£2244 $3478 €3500 Vue d'une eglise (48x56cm-19x22in) s. panel. 3-Dec-2 Campo & Campo, Antwerp #323/R est:3750-4250
£2313 $3678 €3400 Scene de port Mediterranean (26x35cm-10x14in) s.d.1864. 19-Mar-3 Hotel des Ventes Mosan, Brussels #174/R est:2000-2500
£3930 $6131 €5895 Drawing room in Portman Square (36x52cm-14x20in) s.d.1859 panel. 20-Nov-2 Fischer, Luzern #1086/R est:9000-12000 (S.FR 9000)
£6897 $11034 €10000 Artist in his attic (93x112cm-37x44in) s.d.1855. 15-Mar-3 De Vuyst, Lokeren #406/R est:13000-16000

Works on paper
£2911 $4542 €4600 Venise (67x48cm-26x19in) s. W/C graphite. 16-Oct-2 Hotel des Ventes Mosan, Brussels #160/R est:2000-3000

MOER, Jean Baptiste van (attrib) (1819-1884) Belgian
£2680 $4314 €4100 La piazzetta a Venise (37x54cm-15x21in) i.verso. 14-Jan-3 Vanderkindere, Brussels #4/R est:1500-2500

MOERENHOUT, Edouard Joris (1801-?) Belgian
£350 $581 €525 Country landscape with boy resting and horse in the foreground (25x31cm-10x12in) s.d.1857 panel. 10-Jun-3 Bonhams, Knightsbridge #27

MOERENHOUT, Edward (19th C) Belgian
£319 $533 €450 Chien dans un paysage hivernal (33x45cm-13x18in) 23-Jun-3 Amberes, Antwerp #112
£822 $1282 €1200 Port de peche au clair de lune (73x55cm-29x22in) s. 14-Apr-3 Horta, Bruxelles #238
£915 $1473 €1400 Port de peche au clair de lune (73x55cm-29x22in) s. 20-Jan-3 Horta, Bruxelles #74
£1266 $1975 €2000 Au secours des naufrages, effect de lune (42x84cm-17x33in) s. s.i.d.1877 verso. 21-Oct-2 Bernaerts, Antwerp #177/R est:1500-2000
£1266 $1975 €2000 Vue sur l'Escaut (42x84cm-17x33in) s. s.i.d.1887 verso. 21-Oct-2 Bernaerts, Antwerp #178/R est:1500-2000
£2949 $4629 €4600 Vue de village anime au clair de lune (131x102cm-52x40in) s.d.1883. 19-Nov-2 Vanderkindere, Brussels #117/R est:4500-6250

MOERENHOUT, Joseph Jodocus (1801-1874) Belgian
£1761 $2835 €2500 Woman on horse with falcon (62x80cm-24x31in) s. 10-May-3 Berlinghof, Heidelberg #276/R est:5000

MOERKERK, Herman (1879-1949) Dutch
£775 $1247 €1100 City harbour (48x58cm-19x23in) s. 7-May-3 Vendue Huis, Gravenhage #91/R

MOERMAN, Albert Edouard (1808-1856) Belgian
£5172 $8276 €7500 Winter landscape with skaters (55x78cm-22x31in) s. 15-Mar-3 De Vuyst, Lokeren #503/R est:7500-8500

MOERMAN, Johannes Lodewyk (1850-1896) Belgian
£346 $540 €550 Untitled (27x32cm-11x13in) 14-Oct-2 Amberes, Antwerp #177
£689 $1047 €1034 Interior from an inn with men playing cards and smoking pipe (34x18cm-13x7in) s.d.94 panel. 27-Aug-2 Rasmussen, Copenhagen #1860/R (D.KR 8000)
£1795 $2836 €2800 Interior of tavern with three seated men smoking and reading the newspaper (15x21cm-6x8in) s.d.1893 panel. 18-Nov-2 Bernaerts, Antwerp #52/R est:2500-3000
£2830 $4415 €4500 Scene d'auberge (26x35cm-10x14in) panel. 14-Oct-2 Amberes, Antwerp #179
£3046 $4966 €4600 Lecture du journal (16x21cm-6x8in) s.d.93 panel. 17-Feb-3 Horta, Bruxelles #162/R
£3145 $4906 €5000 Scene de cafe (18x24cm-7x9in) panel. 14-Oct-2 Amberes, Antwerp #178/R
£4140 $6459 €6500 La lecture du journal (35x46cm-14x18in) s. panel. 11-Nov-2 Horta, Bruxelles #130/R est:5000-7000

MOES, Wally (1856-1918) Dutch
£1310 $2044 €1965 Peasant woman at spinning wheel, man smoking pipe (40x60cm-16x24in) s.d.98. 6-Nov-2 Dobiaschofsky, Bern #831/R est:3800 (S.FR 3000)

MOESELAGEN, Jean A (1827-?) German
£705 $1107 €1100 The seesaw (50x73cm-20x29in) s. 21-Nov-2 Van Ham, Cologne #1793/R

MOESMAN, Johannes Hendrikus (1909-1988) Dutch
£20144 $33036 €28000 Behoeftigen (29x44cm-11x17in) s.d.1931 prov.exhib.lit. 3-Jun-3 Christie's, Amsterdam #206/R est:18000-25000

Works on paper
£791 $1298 €1100 Standing nude seen from behind (49x30cm-19x12in) s.d.1933 pencil black chk lit. 3-Jun-3 Christie's, Amsterdam #218/R est:1000-1500
£791 $1298 €1100 Two nudes (54x35cm-21x14in) s.d.1929 black chk. 3-Jun-3 Christie's, Amsterdam #220/R est:1000-1500

MOEST, Hermann (1868-1945) German
£417 $654 €650 Park landscape in winter (32x39cm-13x15in) i.verso board. 21-Nov-2 Dorotheum, Vienna #201/R

MOEVIUS, Johann Jacob (1767-1836) German
£2564 $4026 €4000 Johanniskirche in Frankfurt-Bornheim (108x93cm-43x37in) s.d.1822 panel. 23-Nov-2 Arnold, Frankfurt #805/R est:6000

MOEYAERT, Nicolaes Cornelisz (attrib) (1592-1655) Dutch
£1408 $2338 €2000 Granida et Daifilo (78x95cm-31x37in) bears sig. panel prov. 16-Jun-3 Claude Aguttes, Neuilly #6 est:2000-2500

MOFFAT, A E (fl.1880-1898) British

Works on paper
£238 $379 €357 Midlands valley with river and cattle (54x76cm-21x30in) s.d. W/C. 4-Mar-3 Dales, Durban #18 (SA.R 3000)

MOFFATT, Tracey (1960-) Australian

Photographs
£7857 $12100 €11786 Untitled (122x152cm-48x60in) cibachrome exhib. 8-Sep-2 Sotheby's, Melbourne #2/R est:10000-15000 (A.D 22000)
£12143 $18700 €18215 Untitled (122x152cm-48x60in) cibachrome exhib. 8-Sep-2 Sotheby's, Melbourne #11/R est:20000-30000 (A.D 34000)
£15447 $24407 €22398 Something's more no.8 (98x127cm-39x50in) s.verso c-type photograph. 22-Jul-3 Lawson Menzies, Sydney #26/R est:30000-35000 (A.D 38000)
£15771 $23971 €23657 Scarred for life (80x60cm-31x24in) i. s.d.num.verso offset photo lithograph edition 21/50 nine exhib. 28-Aug-2 Deutscher-Menzies, Melbourne #38/R est:28000-35000 (A.D 44000)
£25714 $39600 €38571 Untitled (122x152cm-48x60in) cibachrome exhib. 8-Sep-2 Sotheby's, Melbourne #28/R est:80000-120000 (A.D 72000)

Prints
£1647 $2619 €2471 Up in the sky 16 (43x54cm-17x21in) s.d.97 num.65/99 offset print prov. 5-May-3 Sotheby's, Melbourne #215/R est:3000-5000 (A.D 4250)

MOFFITT, Trevor (1936-) New Zealander
£767 $1089 €1151 Series, Canterbury paddocks (50x60cm-20x24in) s.d.91 board. 20-Mar-2 Watson's, Christchurch #36/R est:2500-5000 (NZ.D 2500)
£1515 $2333 €2273 Southland series - Road to Dunedin (77x44cm-30x17in) s.i.verso board. 4-Sep-2 Dunbar Sloane, Wellington #21/R est:5000-7000 (NZ.D 5000)
£1818 $2800 €2727 Rakaia River series no.16 (48x58cm-19x23in) s.d.1982 board. 4-Sep-2 Dunbar Sloane, Wellington #40/R est:5000-7000 (NZ.D 6000)
£2014 $3142 €3021 Learning to kill for the king (56x64cm-22x25in) s.d.1979 i.verso board. 8-Apr-3 Peter Webb, Auckland #176/R est:5000-7000 (NZ.D 5800)
£2105 $3284 €3158 Self portrait (55x38cm-22x15in) s.d.1990 board. 27-Mar-3 International Art Centre, Auckland #20/R est:8000-12000 (NZ.D 6000)
£2572 $3987 €3858 Rakaia River series no 27 (58x88cm-23x35in) s.d.1984. 4-Dec-2 Dunbar Sloane, Auckland #55/R est:5000-8000 (NZ.D 8000)

MOGANO, Phoshoko David (1932-2000) South African

Works on paper
£764 $1207 €1146 Bustling township (47x69cm-19x27in) s.d.1985 W/C. 1-Apr-3 Stephan Welz, Johannesburg #503 est:4000-6000 (SA.R 9500)

£	$	€	
£1032	$1661	€1548	Ancestral figures with a drum (67x49cm-26x19in) s. W/C. 12-May-3 Stephan Welz, Johannesburg #396/R est:5000-8000 (SA.R 12000)

MOGELGAARD, Ludvig (1873-1928) Danish
£478 $775 €693 Trees in evening light (58x102cm-23x40in) s.i.d.1916. 26-May-3 Rasmussen, Copenhagen #1433/R (D.KR 5000)

MOGELGAARD, Ludvig (attrib) (1873-1928) Danish
£405 $653 €608 Wooded landscape (66x83cm-26x33in) 22-Feb-3 Rasmussen, Havnen #2007 (D.KR 4500)

MOGFORD, John (1821-1885) British
£1500 $2340 €2250 Seine, net fishermen at sunset (44x75cm-17x30in) s.i.verso. 17-Sep-2 Bonhams, Sevenoaks #199/R est:1500-2500

Works on paper
£300 $495 €435 Evening at Walberswick (12x23cm-5x9in) s. W/C. 1-Jul-3 Bonhams, Norwich #97
£480 $758 €720 Marroch Bay - fisherman's cottage (33x49cm-13x19in) s.d.1871 W/C. 2-Dec-2 Bonhams, Bath #8/R
£540 $886 €810 Cottages and a boathouse on an estuary (24x34cm-9x13in) s.d.1870 W/C. 3-Jun-3 Bearnes, Exeter #418
£880 $1338 €1320 Scarborough Pier in moonlight (17x31cm-7x12in) s. W/C. 15-Aug-2 Bonhams, New Bond Street #218
£1000 $1550 €1500 Looking out to sea (33x53cm-13x21in) s.d.1862 pencil W/C. 4-Dec-2 Christie's, Kensington #68 est:300-500
£1200 $1872 €1800 Runswick Bay (23x51cm-9x20in) s. W/C. 20-Sep-2 Richardson & Smith, Whitby #193 est:1200-1500
£1250 $2025 €1875 Salvaging the wreck (30x49cm-12x19in) s.d.1861 W/C htd white. 22-Jan-3 Bonhams, New Bond Street #334/R est:1000-1500
£1800 $2808 €2700 Sunset at Kynance Cove, Cornwall (42x75cm-17x30in) s.d.1867 pencil W/C htd white. 19-Sep-2 Christie's, Kensington #82/R est:2000-3000

MOHL, John Koenakeefe (1903-1985) South African
£559 $900 €839 Evening on the Vaal River near Vereeniging (25x35cm-10x14in) s. i.d.1908 verso canvas on board. 12-May-3 Stephan Welz, Johannesburg #474/R est:6000-8000 (SA.R 6500)

MOHL-HANSEN, Kristian (1876-1962) Danish
Works on paper
£491 $761 €737 Flowers and birds. s. W/C Indian ink pencil six in one frame. 1-Oct-2 Rasmussen, Copenhagen #438 (D.KR 5800)

MOHN, Victor Paul (1842-1911) German
Works on paper
£1438 $2244 €2100 Farmstead by stream (20x34cm-8x13in) s.d. W/C pencil. 11-Apr-3 Winterberg, Heidelberg #489/R est:1980

MOHOLY-NAGY, Laszlo (1895-1946) American/Hungarian
£17949 $28359 €28000 Composition with blue circle (22x21cm-9x8in) i. tempera Indian ink over pencil exhib.lit.prov. 14-Nov-2 Neumeister, Munich #635/R est:18000-20000

Photographs
£3896 $6000 €5844 In the swim (29x21cm-11x8in) photograph prov.exhib. 22-Oct-2 Sotheby's, New York #15/R est:10000-15000
£13924 $22000 €20886 Pont transbordeur, in the rain, Marseille (22x16cm-9x6in) i.verso gelatin silver print executed c.1929 prov. 24-Apr-3 Phillips, New York #15/R est:8000-12000
£16234 $25000 €24351 Sand architects, no.2 (29x21cm-11x8in) num.6 photograph prov.exhib.lit. 22-Oct-2 Sotheby's, New York #14/R est:10000-15000

Prints
£2516 $4000 €3774 Composition (12x16cm-5x6in) init.i. etching. 2-May-3 Sotheby's, New York #235/R est:4000-6000
£3145 $5000 €4718 Konstruktion I (59x36cm-23x14in) s.i. col lithograph. 3-Mar-3 Swann Galleries, New York #55/R est:5000-8000
£5660 $9000 €8490 Untitled, construction (12x8cm-5x3in) s. cut linoleum exec.c.1921. 2-May-3 Sotheby's, New York #234/R est:8000-12000

Works on paper
£3333 $5200 €5000 Komposition mit gelbem pfeil (22x28cm-9x11in) init.d.Apr.26 1941 W/C brush black ink. 18-Sep-2 Swann Galleries, New York #64/R est:5000-8000
£6832 $11000 €10248 Composition with three circles (43x35cm-17x14in) s.d.July 46 pen brush ink pencil col crayon prov. 7-May-3 Sotheby's, New York #199a/R est:5000-7000
£12899 $20122 €19349 Floating forms (21x27cm-8x11in) s. mixed media. 11-Sep-2 Kieselbach, Budapest #127/R (H.F 5000000)

MOHR, Alexandre Carl Adrian (1892-1974) German
Works on paper
£385 $604 €600 Composition with Greek and Roman figures (44x58cm-17x23in) s. gouache. 25-Nov-2 Glerum, Amsterdam #98/R

MOHR, Johann Georg (1864-1943) German
£483 $768 €700 Taunus landscape with town (17cm-7in circular) s. board. 8-Mar-3 Arnold, Frankfurt #646/R
£1410 $2214 €2200 Morning mist on autumn pond (51x20cm-20x8in) s. board. 23-Nov-2 Arnold, Frankfurt #806/R est:800

MOHRMANN, John Henry (1857-1916) American
£1563 $2500 €2345 Portrait of the Leopoldville in a harbour (50x70cm-20x28in) s.d.1905. 14-May-3 Butterfields, San Francisco #1152/R est:3000-5000
£1600 $2592 €2400 British steamer Aldgate in the Channel (60x99cm-24x39in) s. canvas on board. 21-May-3 Christie's, Kensington #643/R est:1500-2500
£3200 $5312 €4640 Spanish auxiliary steamer Gravina bound for a Belgian port (60x100cm-24x39in) s.d.1894. 12-Jun-3 Christie's, London #530/R est:1500-2500

MOHY, Yves (20th C) French?
Sculpture
£1223 $2006 €1700 Untitled (40x43cm-16x17in) sandstone enamel. 6-Jun-3 Rabourdin & Choppin de Janvry, Paris #36/R est:1700-2000

MOIGNIEZ, J (1835-1894) French
Sculpture
£1500 $2325 €2250 Horse and jockey (16cm-6in) s.d. bronze marble socle. 30-Oct-2 Mallams, Oxford #583/R est:800-1200
£1600 $2560 €2400 Panther (65cm-26in) s. green pat. bronze. 15-May-3 Christie's, Kensington #389/R est:800-1000

MOIGNIEZ, Jules (1835-1894) French
Sculpture
£993 $1619 €1500 Faucon, une belette et un oiseau (45x36cm-18x14in) s. medaille pat bronze. 16-Feb-3 Mercier & Cie, Lille #197 est:1200-1800
£1190 $1893 €1750 Faisan attaquant une belette (44cm-17in) s. brown pat bronze marble socle. 18-Mar-3 Vanderkindere, Brussels #181/R est:1750-2000
£1300 $2067 €1950 Pointer (20x31cm-8x12in) s. brown pat bronze. 29-Apr-3 Sotheby's, Olympia #139/R est:1000-1500
£1361 $2163 €2000 Lievre (30x23cm-12x9in) s. pat bronze. 23-Mar-3 Herbette, Doullens #165/R
£1400 $2282 €2030 French animalier group of two hares (10cm-4in) s. bronze oval base. 21-Jul-3 Sotheby's, London #18/R est:600-800
£1452 $2250 €2178 Figure of a quail amongst grasses (30cm-12in) i. bronze. 2-Nov-2 North East Auctions, Portsmouth #406/R
£1800 $2736 €2700 Pheasant with a stoat (34x30cm-13x12in) s. brown pat. bronze. 28-Aug-2 Sotheby's, London #861/R est:2000-3000
£2119 $3454 €3200 Faisan sur un rocher (50x52x25cm-20x20x10in) s. brown pat bronze. 17-Feb-3 Horta, Bruxelles #87
£2194 $3466 €3400 Accolade (35x46cm-14x18in) s. brown pat bronze lit. 19-Dec-2 Delvaux, Paris #58/R
£2200 $3388 €3300 Setter (28x43cm-11x17in) s. bronze. 5-Sep-2 Sotheby's, Olympia #142/R est:1800-2200
£2200 $3432 €3300 Retriever spotting a hare (19x32cm-7x13in) s. brown pat bronze. 9-Apr-3 Sotheby's, London #124/R est:2000-3000
£3200 $4992 €4800 Persian stallion (30x39cm-12x15in) s. brown pat bronze. 5-Nov-2 Sotheby's, London #121/R est:3000-5000
£11000 $16720 €16500 Prince Albert on horseback (64x60cm-25x24in) s. dark brown pat. bronze. 28-Aug-2 Sotheby's, London #835/R est:10000-15000

MOILLIET, Louis (1880-1962) Swiss
£2174 $3370 €3261 Tunisia (18x25cm-7x10in) s.d.1921. 4-Dec-2 Koller, Zurich #104/R est:2500-3500 (S.FR 5000)

Works on paper
£3524 $5145 €5286 Puerto de la Selva de Mar (36x47cm-14x19in) s.d.1948 W/C. 17-Jun-2 Philippe Schuler, Zurich #4205/R est:6000-8000 (S.FR 8000)
£6114 $9598 €9171 Harbour (33x40cm-13x16in) s.i.d.1928 W/C. 25-Nov-2 Sotheby's, Zurich #74/R est:14000-18000 (S.FR 14000)

MOIRA, Eduardo de Lobo (1817-1887) Portuguese
Miniatures
£1000 $1560 €1500 Rev William Rayner seated in oak tapestry chair wearing black suit (19cm-7in) s.i.d.1857 wood frame rec. arched top. 5-Nov-2 Bonhams, New Bond Street #157/R est:600-800

MOIRIGNOT, Edmond (1913-) French
Sculpture
£880 $1365 €1400 La toilette (30cm-12in) s.num.3/12 black pat bronze st.f.E Godard. 4-Oct-2 Tajan, Paris #170 est:1500-1800

MOISE, Gustave (1879-?) French
£436 $702 €650 Le peintre Boudin a son chevalet (72x51cm-28x20in) s. isorel. 23-Feb-3 Lesieur & Le Bars, Le Havre #121

MOISES, Julio (1888-1968) Spanish
£1452 $2294 €2250 Two women (70x60cm-28x24in) s.d.MCMLXI. 17-Dec-2 Durán, Madrid #194/R
Works on paper
£377 $589 €600 Study of male nude (52x45cm-20x18in) s.d.1908 chl dr. 8-Oct-2 Ansorena, Madrid #481/R

MOISO, Giorgio (1942-) Italian
£523 $837 €800 Beauty shop (100x80cm-39x31in) s.d.2001. 4-Jan-3 Meeting Art, Vercelli #584

MOISSET, Maurice (1860-1946) French
£570 $889 €900 Scene de plage en Normandie (15x23cm-6x9in) s. 15-Oct-2 Vanderkindere, Brussels #114

MOITTE, Alexandre (1750-1828) French
Works on paper
£699 $1168 €1000 Femme au chapeau attablee (19x15cm-7x6in) bears mono.d.1786 pierre noire. 27-Jun-3 Claude Aguttes, Neuilly #6/R

MOIX SOLE, Josep (1907-) Spanish
Works on paper
£288 $449 €420 The Elena (48x68cm-19x27in) s. mixed media. 8-Apr-3 Ansorena, Madrid #669/R

MOJA, Frederico (1802-1885) Italian
£6438 $10172 €9657 Canal landscape in Venice with Bogen bridge and figures in foreground (31x42cm-12x17in) s.d.72 canvas on canvas. 29-Nov-2 Zofingen, Switzerland #2348/R est:7500 (S.FR 15000)
£6962 $11000 €11000 Italian courtyard (59x48cm-23x19in) s.d.1835. 28-Nov-2 Dorotheum, Vienna #113/R est:8000-9500

MOKADY, Moshe (1902-1975) Israeli
£8500 $13175 €12750 Boy with guitar (93x72cm-37x28in) s. 5-Dec-2 Christie's, Kensington #191/R est:8000-12000
£31514 $49790 €47271 Study for on the balcony (42x52cm-17x20in) painted 1926-27 exhib. 27-Apr-3 Sotheby's, Tel Aviv #39/R est:60000-80000

MOL, Leo (1915-) Canadian
Sculpture
£884 $1387 €1326 Bust, young boy (34cm-13in) s.d.1982 bronze. 25-Nov-2 Hodgins, Calgary #33/R est:1000-1250 (C.D 2200)

MOLA, Pier Francesco (1612-1666) Italian
£3262 $5285 €4600 Saint Joseph Dream (43x28cm-17x11in) lit. 20-May-3 Babuino, Rome #42/R est:4000-6000
£43972 $71234 €62000 The death of Archimedes (135x122cm-53x48in) lit. 20-May-3 Babuino, Rome #22/R
Works on paper
£2800 $4396 €4200 Landscape with fishermen (13x20cm-5x8in) i. pen ink wash over black chk. 11-Dec-2 Sotheby's, Olympia #94/R est:2000-3000
£8966 $14345 €13000 Etude d'homme drape (22x16cm-9x6in) pen wash. 14-Mar-3 Libert, Castor, Paris #10/R

MOLA, Pier Francesco (attrib) (1612-1666) Italian
£1728 $2834 €2506 Figures on road (97x135cm-38x53in) 4-Jun-3 AB Stockholms Auktionsverk #2507/R est:40000-50000 (S.KR 22000)
£2979 $4617 €4469 Saint Hieronymus (45x73cm-18x29in) 4-Dec-2 AB Stockholms Auktionsverk #2021/R est:40000-50000 (S.KR 42000)
Works on paper
£459 $717 €680 Putti on donkey in landscape (18x25cm-7x10in) i. pen ink. 27-Mar-3 Christie's, Paris #187/R
£1300 $2041 €1950 Dwarf riding a mule, reading a letter to five others (20x29cm-8x11in) i. chk pen brown wash sold with landscape by attrib P. Wouverman. 13-Dec-2 Christie's, Kensington #288

MOLA, Pier Francesco (circle) (1612-1666) Italian
£9500 $14820 €14250 Saint Mark (99x74cm-39x29in) 10-Apr-3 Sotheby's, London #78/R est:12000

MOLANUS, Mattheus (?-1645) Dutch
£4938 $8000 €7407 Wooded landscape with a cavalry skirmish, city beyond (14x19cm-6x7in) copper prov.exhib. 24-Jan-3 Christie's, Rockefeller NY #3/R est:10000-15000

MOLARSKY, Maurice (1885-1950) American
£4088 $6500 €6132 Pipes and pan (164x54cm-65x21in) s. on four panel prov. 5-Mar-3 Sotheby's, New York #73/R est:8000-12000

MOLAS SABARTE, Juan (1887-?) Spanish
£346 $540 €550 Apples (14x9cm-6x4in) s. vellum. 23-Sep-2 Durán, Madrid #1260/R

MOLDOVAN, Kurt (1918-1977) Austrian
Works on paper
£360 $590 €500 Car racing (24x18cm-9x7in) s.i.d.68 pen brush Indian ink. 4-Jun-3 Dorotheum, Vienna #185
£625 $987 €900 A man between two women (21x30cm-8x12in) brush pen Indian ink. 24-Apr-3 Dorotheum, Vienna #175/R
£641 $994 €1000 Border (21x22cm-8x9in) i.d.57 verso W/C. 5-Dec-2 Dorotheum, Graz #123/R
£795 $1295 €1200 Wild dogs on the lead (31x47cm-12x19in) s.d.65 pen ink. 28-Jan-3 Dorotheum, Vienna #192/R
£861 $1403 €1300 Griffin and the mock turtle soup (47x64cm-19x25in) s.i.d.70 pen ink wash. 28-Jan-3 Dorotheum, Vienna #236/R
£1139 $1800 €1800 Venetian carneval (48x32cm-19x13in) s.i.d. pen brush Indian ink. 27-Nov-2 Dorotheum, Vienna #270/R est:1800-2400
£1139 $1800 €1800 Composition with figures (47x32cm-19x13in) s.d.68 pen Indian ink wash. 27-Nov-2 Dorotheum, Vienna #272/R est:1800-2400
£1923 $3038 €3000 London (32x48cm-13x19in) s.i.d.71 W/C. 12-Nov-2 Dorotheum, Vienna #233/R est:3400-5000
£2025 $3200 €3200 Harbour (32x48cm-13x19in) s.d.70 s.i.d. verso W/C. 27-Nov-2 Dorotheum, Vienna #275/R est:3200-5000
£2244 $3522 €3500 Harbour (32x48cm-13x19in) s.d.61 W/C. 25-Nov-2 Hassfurther, Vienna #56 est:2500-3000
£2278 $3600 €3600 St Margarethen quarry, Burgenland (32x48cm-13x19in) s.d.70 s.i.d. verso W/C. 27-Nov-2 Dorotheum, Vienna #276/R est:3200-5000

MOLE, Frank (20th C) British
Works on paper
£260 $406 €390 Polperro (33x46cm-13x18in) s.d.1948 W/C. 17-Oct-2 David Lay, Penzance #1348

MOLE, John Henry (1814-1886) British
£460 $754 €690 In Borrowdale, Cumberland (34x53cm-13x21in) s.d.1886. 4-Jun-3 Bonhams, Chester #341
Works on paper
£268 $415 €402 Leisurely figures by the cottage gates (15x24cm-6x9in) s.d.1863 W/C gouache. 29-Oct-2 Lawson Menzies, Sydney #86 (A.D 750)
£270 $440 €405 Up river, Salcombe (29x44cm-11x17in) s. W/C pencil. 30-Jan-3 Lawrence, Crewkerne #630/R
£300 $462 €450 Coniston Falls (33x51cm-13x20in) s.i.d.1871 W/C. 24-Oct-2 Richardson & Smith, Whitby #458/R
£520 $806 €780 Country girl (27x37cm-11x15in) s.d.1863 W/C. 25-Sep-2 Hamptons Fine Art, Godalming #209/R
£525 $835 €788 Man and two children fishing in a pond (25x37cm-10x15in) s. W/C. 29-Apr-3 Rowley Fine Art, Newmarket #418/R
£550 $858 €825 Fair water carrier (39x29cm-15x11in) s.d.1857 W/C bodycol. 17-Sep-2 Bonhams, Sevenoaks #250/R
£700 $1084 €1050 Drawing water in the Highlands (33x50cm-13x20in) s. W/C exhib. 3-Dec-2 Sotheby's, Olympia #131/R
£700 $1113 €1050 Man and young girl walking across heath land (24x28cm-9x11in) s.d.1877 W/C. 29-Apr-3 Rowley Fine Art, Newmarket #417/R
£820 $1304 €1230 Riding through the harvest field with lake and mountains beyond (29x44cm-11x17in) s.d.1870 W/C. 5-Mar-3 Bonhams, Bury St Edmunds #284/R
£920 $1426 €1380 Bust portraits of a lady and two gentlemen (23x18cm-9x7in) s.d.1843 and 1847 W/C three in one frame. 24-Sep-2 Anderson & Garland, Newcastle #218/R

£954 $1508 €1431 Untitled, winkle picker (38x28cm-15x11in) s.d.1853 W/C boducol pencil prov. 7-Apr-3 Shapiro, Sydney #492/R (A.D 2500)
£1100 $1804 €1650 Gypsies' camp (20x31cm-8x12in) s.d.1877 W/C. 4-Jun-3 Bonhams, Chester #373/R est:1200-1600
£1750 $2818 €2625 Landing the day's catch (28x46cm-11x18in) s.d.1860 W/C. 9-May-3 Mallams, Oxford #10/R est:500-700
£1910 $2979 €2865 Collecting cockles (32x58cm-13x23in) s.d.1864 W/C. 8-Apr-3 Peter Webb, Auckland #118/R est:4500-6500 (NZ.D 5500)
£2200 $3586 €3300 Fisherfolk above the Bay at Freshwater, Isle of Wight (33x59cm-13x23in) s.d.1862 W/C. 29-Jan-3 Dreweatt Neate, Newbury #31/R est:2500-3000
£2800 $4592 €4200 Landscape with mother and child resting before watermill (41x67cm-16x26in) s.d.1873 W/C. 4-Jun-3 Bonhams, Chester #372/R est:3000-5000
£3800 $6308 €5700 Shepherd boy and his dog (47x68cm-19x27in) s.d.1866 W/C htd white. 12-Jun-3 Bonhams, New Bond Street #652/R est:4000-6000

MOLE, John Henry (attrib) (1814-1886) British
Works on paper
£300 $501 €435 Overshot watermill (24x36cm-9x14in) W/C over pencil. 25-Jun-3 Bonhams, Bury St Edmunds #478/R

MOLENAAR, Hein (1909-) Dutch?
£340 $541 €500 Rue de Tunis (31x23cm-12x9in) s. panel. 24-Mar-3 Coutau Begarie, Paris #218

MOLENAAR, Johannes Petrus (1914-1989) Dutch
£634 $1020 €900 View of harbour (49x69cm-19x27in) s. 6-May-3 Vendu Notarishuis, Rotterdam #223
£986 $1587 €1400 Activity in Rotterdam harbour (59x99cm-23x39in) s. 6-May-3 Vendu Notarishuis, Rotterdam #196/R
£6338 $10204 €9000 Four-mast ship in storm (39x29cm-15x11in) s. 6-May-3 Vendu Notarishuis, Rotterdam #19/R est:200-250

MOLENAER, Bartholomeus (1612-1650) Dutch
£3145 $4874 €5000 Peasants at the inn (32x46cm-13x18in) panel. 2-Oct-2 Dorotheum, Vienna #352/R est:5000-7000
£3200 $5344 €4640 Peasants making merry in a tavern (33x44cm-13x17in) panel. 11-Jul-3 Christie's, Kensington #111/R est:3000-5000
£10811 $16865 €16000 Peasants dancing in village (39x53cm-15x21in) mono. panel oval. 27-Mar-3 Dorotheum, Vienna #182/R est:15000-20000

MOLENAER, Jan Jacobz (1654-?) Dutch
£4777 $7452 €7500 Grace before the meal (28x27cm-11x11in) s. panel. 5-Nov-2 Sotheby's, Amsterdam #205/R est:8000-12000

MOLENAER, Jan Miense (1610-1668) Dutch
£1351 $2108 €2000 Couples in interior (16x12cm-6x5in) mono. panel pair. 28-Mar-3 Delvaux, Paris #124
£2215 $3500 €3500 Tavern scene (40x55cm-16x22in) s. panel. 30-Nov-2 Berlinghof, Heidelberg #345/R est:3900
£3145 $4906 €5000 Kitchen interior (47x38cm-19x15in) s. panel prov. 19-Sep-2 Dr Fritz Nagel, Stuttgart #885/R est:1500
£12676 $21042 €18000 Merry company outside tavern (70x66cm-28x26in) bears sig. panel prov. 11-Jun-3 Dorotheum, Vienna #95/R est:8000-12000
£26000 $40820 €39000 Village landscape with crowds gathering around quack doctors (61x92cm-24x36in) panel prov.exhib. 11-Dec-2 Christie's, London #66/R est:15000-20000

MOLENAER, Jan Miense (attrib) (1610-1668) Dutch
£6475 $10360 €9000 Interior scene with children making music (54x65cm-21x26in) panel. 13-May-3 Sotheby's, Amsterdam #31/R est:10000-15000
£11728 $19000 €17592 Children playing cards around a barrel (36x56cm-14x22in) panel prov.exhib.lit. 23-Jan-3 Sotheby's, New York #5/R est:10000-15000

MOLENAER, Klaes (1630-1676) Dutch
£3700 $5809 €5550 Winter landscape with skaters on a foren river (23x31cm-9x12in) s. panel. 10-Dec-2 Bonhams, New Bond Street #35/R est:3000-5000
£3822 $5962 €6000 Villagers on the beach near Scheveningen (77x67cm-30x26in) s.d.1670 prov. 6-Nov-2 Christie's, Amsterdam #6/R est:4000-6000
£8176 $12755 €13000 Scheveningen street scene (63x82cm-25x32in) s. 23-Sep-2 Wiener Kunst Auktionen, Vienna #20/R est:11000-22000
£8273 $13237 €11500 Village scene with peasants and children by ruined tower (65x80cm-26x31in) s. prov. 13-May-3 Sotheby's, Amsterdam #25/R est:4000-6000
£8280 $12917 €13000 River landscape with figures fishing near a windmill, church beyond (33x31cm-13x12in) s.d.1653 panel. 5-Nov-2 Sotheby's, Amsterdam #292/R est:4000-6000
£10191 $15898 €16000 Winter landscape with skaters, two horsedrawn sledges (26x32cm-10x13in) panel prov.exhib.lit. 5-Nov-2 Sotheby's, Amsterdam #105/R est:15000-20000
£16216 $25297 €24000 Wintry village with traveller and ice skaters (25x34cm-10x13in) panel exhib. 27-Mar-3 Dorotheum, Vienna #125/R est:20000-25000
£21605 $35000 €32408 Figures in a landscape with a bleaching field (47x63cm-19x25in) s. panel prov.exhib. 23-Jan-3 Sotheby's, New York #9/R est:40000-60000

MOLENAZ, A (18th C) Spanish
Works on paper
£1477 $2377 €2200 Venus in a landscape with three other miniatures (10x9cm-4x4in) s.d.1770 oval four. 18-Feb-3 Whyte's, Dublin #97/R est:1500-2000

MOLES, Francisco (19/20th C) Spanish
£6452 $10194 €10000 Antique shop (48x68cm-19x27in) 17-Dec-2 Durán, Madrid #221/R est:4500

MOLETTE, Jean (19th C) ?
Sculpture
£2134 $3500 €3201 Napoleon Le Grand (91cm-36in) i. fruitwood plinth. 8-Feb-3 Neal Auction Company, New Orleans #185/R est:4000-6000

MOLEVELD, Pieter (1919-) Dutch
£385 $604 €600 Still life with a tin can and grapes and a bowl (38x48cm-15x19in) s.d.1950. 25-Nov-2 Glerum, Amsterdam #19

MOLEZUN SUAREZ, Manuel (1920-) Spanish
Works on paper
£345 $548 €500 Flowers in blue (50x70cm-20x28in) s. gouache. 4-Mar-3 Ansorena, Madrid #278/R
£385 $608 €600 Composition (48x53cm-19x21in) s.d.75 mixed media. 19-Nov-2 Durán, Madrid #105/R

MOLFENTER, Hans (1884-?) German
£881 $1374 €1400 Travellers (34x45cm-13x18in) i. verso. 19-Sep-2 Dr Fritz Nagel, Stuttgart #970/R
£1032 $1517 €1600 Evening landscape (33x40cm-13x16in) s. canvas on panel. 20-Jun-2 Dr Fritz Nagel, Stuttgart #797/R est:800
£1290 $1897 €2000 Circus study (33x34cm-13x13in) s. canvas on panel. 20-Jun-2 Dr Fritz Nagel, Stuttgart #796/R est:800

MOLFENTER, Hans (attrib) (1884-?) German
£516 $759 €800 Pelican (27x17cm-11x7in) s. 24-Jun-2 Dr Fritz Nagel, Stuttgart #5979/R

MOLIER, Jacobus Henri (1904-1998) Dutch?
Works on paper
£1690 $2721 €2400 Ontwerp with dancers, art deco style (43x54cm-17x21in) ink dr gouache. 7-May-3 Vendue Huis, Gravenhage #125/R est:150-200

MOLIN, Oreste da (1856-1921) Italian
Works on paper
£314 $491 €500 Head of elderly man (18x14cm-7x6in) s. pen. 20-Sep-2 Semenzato, Venice #214/R

MOLINA CAMPOS, Florencio (1891-1959) Argentinian
Works on paper
£15924 $25000 €23886 Celebrations (32x50cm-13x20in) s. gouache paper on board exec.c.1940 lit. 19-Nov-2 Sotheby's, New York #43/R est:45000

MOLINA SANCHEZ, Jose Antonio (1918-) Spanish
£1447 $2257 €2300 Galician fishermen (110x125cm-43x49in) s. 23-Sep-2 Durán, Madrid #124/R

MOLINARI, Guido (19th C) Italian
£4839 $7645 €7259 Structure (114x91cm-45x36in) s. i.d.6/70 verso col geometries. 18-Nov-2 Sotheby's, Toronto #62/R est:15000-20000 (C.D 12000)

MOLINIER, Pierre (1900-1976) French

Photographs

£1899 $3000 €2849 L'enfant - self portrait (16x13cm-6x5in) photocollage hand cut out photograph. 23-Apr-3 Sotheby's, New York #272/R est:3000-5000

Prints

£3425 $5377 €5000 Figure feminine (12x17cm-5x7in) s.i.d.1956 eau forte prov. 15-Apr-3 Laurence Calmels, Paris #4368/R

Works on paper

£1712 $2688 €2500 Portrait d'Andre Breton (32x23cm-13x9in) s.verso chl crayon. 15-Apr-3 Laurence Calmels, Paris #4369/R

£3767 $5914 €5500 Untitled (46x55cm-18x22in) s. mixed media paper on canvas. 15-Apr-3 Laurence Calmels, Paris #4370/R

£9932 $15592 €14500 Untitled (40x32cm-16x13in) mono. i.verso mixed media paper on canvas prov. 15-Apr-3 Laurence Calmels, Paris #4371/R

£21918 $34192 €32000 Comtesse Midralgar (80x66cm-31x26in) mixed media paper on canvas exhib.lit. 14-Apr-3 Laurence Calmels, Paris #4035/R est:40000

£21918 $34411 €32000 Succube (94x85cm-37x33in) s.d.1952 mixed media paper on cardboard on canvas exhib.lit. 15-Apr-3 Laurence Calmels, Paris #4372/R

MOLINO, Walter (1915-1997) Italian

£253 $395 €400 Dancers (35x25cm-14x10in) s. tempera W/C card on masonite. 14-Sep-2 Meeting Art, Vercelli #389

MOLITOR, Martin von (1759-1812) Austrian

Works on paper

£881 $1313 €1322 Family by pond in wooded landscape. Old man and boy on bridge (16cm-6in circular) s.d.1797 W/C pair. 25-Jun-2 Koller, Zurich #6448/R (S.FR 2000)

MOLITOR, Mathieu (1873-1929) German

£417 $646 €650 Woman by sea (44x52cm-17x20in) s. board. 5-Dec-2 Schopman, Hamburg #529

MOLL, Carl (1861-1945) Austrian

£6369 $9936 €10000 Italian landscape - possibly Ischia (17x23cm-7x9in) s.d.1888 panel. 6-Nov-2 Hugo Ruef, Munich #1213/R est:1200

£21519 $34000 €34000 Asters and canister (35x35cm-14x14in) s. panel prov. 27-Nov-2 Dorotheum, Vienna #157/R est:26000-32000

£21622 $33730 €32000 Schloss Neudorf near Wildon (35x35cm-14x14in) s. i. verso panel. 25-Mar-3 Wiener Kunst Auktionen, Vienna #133/R est:18000-28000

£24051 $38000 €38000 Country road (60x60cm-24x24in) mono.d.43. 27-Nov-2 Dorotheum, Vienna #180/R est:30000-50000

£25362 $41594 €35000 Alley of birch trees (45x43cm-18x17in) mono. panel. 27-May-3 Hassfurther, Vienna #49/R est:20000-25000

£30405 $47432 €45000 Schloss Neudorf near Wildon (35x35cm-14x14in) mono. i. verso panel. 25-Mar-3 Wiener Kunst Auktionen, Vienna #132/R est:18000-35000

£64189 $100135 €95000 Poppy field (35x35cm-14x14in) mono. panel. 25-Mar-3 Wiener Kunst Auktionen, Vienna #131/R est:18000-50000

£94937 $150000 €150000 Heiligenstadter Church in winter (100x100cm-39x39in) s. i. stretcher prov.lit. 26-Nov-2 Wiener Kunst Auktionen, Vienna #81/R est:18000-250000

Prints

£2754 $4516 €3800 Hohe Warte in winter (56x45cm-22x18in) s. col woodcut exec.1903 lit. 27-May-3 Hassfurther, Vienna #50/R est:1200-1700

MOLL, Evert (1878-1955) Dutch

£296 $476 €420 View of harbour (29x39cm-11x15in) s. 6-May-3 Vendu Notarishuis, Rotterdam #224

£316 $494 €500 Dahlia's in a vase (49x58cm-19x23in) s. 21-Oct-2 Glerum, Amsterdam #83/R

£340 $530 €510 Still life of flowers in a green vase (48x69cm-19x27in) s. 15-Oct-2 Bonhams, Knightsbridge #187

£366 $590 €520 View of south coast of France (20x26cm-8x10in) s. 6-May-3 Vendu Notarishuis, Rotterdam #68

£385 $600 €578 Street scene of Italian town Capri. 19-Oct-2 Harvey Clar, Oakland #1527

£417 $688 €600 Choppy surf (40x60cm-16x24in) s. 1-Jul-3 Christie's, Amsterdam #214

£437 $681 €656 Sunny garden (32x23cm-13x9in) s. panel. 6-Nov-2 Dobiaschofsky, Bern #833/R (S.FR 1000)

£493 $794 €700 Sea port (19x25cm-7x10in) s. 7-May-3 Vendue Huis, Gravenhage #106/R

£528 $850 €750 View of harbour with three-mast ship (29x39cm-11x15in) s. 6-May-3 Vendu Notarishuis, Rotterdam #69/R

£637 $981 €1000 Harbour activities at dusk (21x27cm-8x11in) s. panel. 3-Sep-2 Christie's, Amsterdam #329

£669 $1077 €950 Harbour view (37x56cm-15x22in) s. 7-May-3 Vendue Huis, Gravenhage #108/R

£690 $1097 €1000 Harbour scene (24x36cm-9x14in) s. panel. 10-Mar-3 Sotheby's, Amsterdam #237/R est:1000-1500

£696 $1086 €1100 Activity in Rotterdam harbour (18x24cm-7x9in) s. 21-Oct-2 Glerum, Amsterdam #152

£704 $1134 €1000 Still life (74x59cm-29x23in) s. 6-May-3 Vendu Notarishuis, Rotterdam #95/R

£789 $1279 €1200 Busy harbour scene, Rotterdam (39x38cm-15x15in) s. 21-Jan-3 Christie's, Amsterdam #338/R est:1500-2000

£833 $1375 €1200 Activities in Rotterdam harbour (37x64cm-15x25in) s. 1-Jul-3 Christie's, Amsterdam #184/R

£886 $1382 €1400 Houses and a mill by a shipyard (19x28cm-7x11in) s. panel. 21-Oct-2 Glerum, Amsterdam #72/R

£921 $1492 €1400 Tall ship in Rotterdam harbour (30x40cm-12x16in) s. 21-Jan-3 Christie's, Amsterdam #349 est:1500-2000

£955 $1490 €1500 Sea port (10x8cm-4x3in) s. board. 6-Nov-2 Vendue Huis, Gravenhage #499/R est:800-1200

£955 $1490 €1500 Activity in Rotterdam harbour (30x44cm-12x17in) s. 6-Nov-2 Vendue Huis, Gravenhage #646/R est:1500-2000

£1019 $1569 €1600 Activities around an ocean steamer (50x61cm-20x24in) s. 3-Sep-2 Christie's, Amsterdam #342/R est:1500-2000

£1083 $1689 €1700 City harbour in Old-Rotterdam (18x27cm-7x11in) s. panel. 6-Nov-2 Vendue Huis, Gravenhage #648/R est:3000-4000

£1127 $1814 €1600 Harbour activity (39x59cm-15x23in) s. 6-May-3 Vendu Notarishuis, Rotterdam #67/R est:1600-2000

£1268 $2041 €1800 Breakwater (35x60cm-14x24in) s. 6-May-3 Vendu Notarishuis, Rotterdam #187 est:1000-1500

£1301 $2030 €1900 Rotterdam harbour (40x60cm-16x24in) s. 10-Apr-3 Van Ham, Cologne #1592/R est:2200

£1379 $2193 €2000 Vue portuaire (61x101cm-24x40in) s. 4-Mar-3 Palais de Beaux Arts, Brussels #356 est:1700-2500

£1389 $2292 €2000 Activities in Rotterdam harbour (60x105cm-24x41in) s. 1-Jul-3 Christie's, Amsterdam #122/R est:1200-1600

£1538 $2385 €2400 Le port de Rotterdam (60x100cm-24x39in) s. 9-Dec-2 Horta, Bruxelles #95 est:2000-3000

£1549 $2494 €2200 Fishing port (19x37cm-7x15in) s. panel. 7-May-3 Vendue Huis, Gravenhage #107 est:2500-3000

£1644 $2564 €2400 Harbour activity (59x69cm-23x27in) s. canvas on panel. 14-Apr-3 Glerum, Amsterdam #127/R est:2500-3000

£1645 $2664 €2500 Harbour of Rotterdam with the Holland-America building in the distance (60x80cm-24x31in) s. 21-Jan-3 Christie's, Amsterdam #348/R est:3000-5000

£1656 $2583 €2600 Dutch city with fishing port (25x34cm-10x13in) s. panel. 6-Nov-2 Vendue Huis, Gravenhage #644/R est:3000-5000

£1690 $2721 €2400 Harbour view (39x59cm-15x23in) s. 7-May-3 Vendue Huis, Gravenhage #109/R est:2500-3000

£1711 $2771 €2600 View of Dordrecht (41x81cm-16x32in) s. 21-Jan-3 Christie's, Amsterdam #337/R est:3000-5000

£1842 $2984 €2800 Busy day in the Rotterdam harbour (60x100cm-24x39in) s. 21-Jan-3 Christie's, Amsterdam #352 est:2000-3000

£1911 $2943 €3000 Busy harbour (22x30cm-9x12in) s. panel. 3-Sep-2 Christie's, Amsterdam #328/R est:2800-3200

£2105 $3411 €3200 View on the Grote Kerk, Dordrecht (57x54cm-22x21in) s. 21-Jan-3 Christie's, Amsterdam #334/R est:1200-1600

£2113 $3401 €3000 Sea port (34x49cm-13x19in) s. 7-May-3 Vendue Huis, Gravenhage #95/R est:2000-2500

£2303 $3730 €3500 White threemaster in the harbour of Rotterdam (60x100cm-24x39in) s. 21-Jan-3 Christie's, Amsterdam #341/R est:3000-5000

£2420 $3776 €3800 River scene with many ships (49x79cm-19x31in) s. 5-Nov-2 Vendu Notarishuis, Rotterdam #268/R est:3000-5000

Works on paper

£450 $698 €675 Shipping in the harbour at Rotterdam (25x28cm-10x11in) s. pencil W/C. 31-Oct-2 Christie's, Kensington #334/R

MOLL, Oskar (1875-1947) German

£1765 $2894 €2700 River, meadow and wood in sunlight (39x58cm-15x23in) s. board. 8-Feb-3 Hans Stahl, Hamburg #99/R est:6000

£10870 $17826 €15000 Dahlias and cress in crystal blue vase (64x58cm-25x23in) s. bears d.38 i. verso prov. 31-May-3 Villa Grisebach, Berlin #257/R est:20000-30000

£15799 $24963 €23699 Vorgarten im Winter - garden covered in snow (120x105cm-47x41in) s.d.17 lit. 1-Apr-3 Rasmussen, Copenhagen #47/R est:150000-200000 (D.KR 170000)

Works on paper

£2986 $4748 €4300 Female nude in the outdoors (34x25cm-13x10in) s.d. W/C col crayon. 5-May-3 Ketterer, Munich #913/R est:3000-5000

£4348 $7130 €6000 Moyenne Corniche (50x70cm-20x28in) s.d.35 i. verso W/C exhib. 31-May-3 Villa Grisebach, Berlin #253/R est:8000-10000

MOLLEKOT, Eugen van (19/20th C) German?

Works on paper

£288 $438 €450 Art Nouveau style lady (71x45cm-28x18in) s.i.d.1915 W/C. 11-Jul-2 Allgauer, Kempten #2357/R

MOLLER, Aenderly (1863-?) German
£274 $427 €400 Evening (23x33cm-9x13in) s. board. 10-Apr-3 Schopman, Hamburg #681

MOLLER, Carl Henrik Koch (1845-1920) Danish
£287 $448 €431 Coastal landscape (38x56cm-15x22in) s.d.1901. 23-Sep-2 Rasmussen, Vejle #2280 (D.KR 3400)
£838 $1332 €1257 Young girl on road through woodland (38x56cm-15x22in) s.i.d.8 August 1900. 5-Mar-3 Rasmussen, Copenhagen #2059/R (D.KR 9000)

MOLLER, Caroline (1827-1883) Danish
£876 $1401 €1314 Roses and butterfly on tree trunk in woodland (27x37cm-11x15in) s.d.1854. 13-Jan-3 Rasmussen, Vejle #56/R (D.KR 10000)

MOLLER, Gunnar (1946-1991) Danish
£325 $514 €488 Jeweller fantasy (69x75cm-27x30in) mono.d.80-79 verso. 1-Apr-3 Rasmussen, Copenhagen #322/R (D.KR 3500)
£455 $755 €660 Composition (70x100cm-28x39in) 12-Jun-3 Kunsthallen, Copenhagen #74 (D.KR 4800)
£1689 $2635 €2534 View towards land (170x190cm-67x75in) exhib. 18-Sep-2 Kunsthallen, Copenhagen #228/R est:20000 (D.KR 20000)

MOLLER, J F (1797-1871) Danish
£909 $1473 €1364 View from Norrebro towards the nursing home (36x51cm-14x20in) s.indis.d. prov. 21-May-3 Museumsbygningen, Copenhagen #11/R (D.KR 9500)

MOLLER, J P (1783-1854) Danish
£659 $1028 €989 Landscape (21x28cm-8x11in) i.verso. 23-Sep-2 Rasmussen, Vejle #70/R (D.KR 7800)
£1532 $2420 €2298 View towards Frislev Mill and Church (100x135cm-39x53in) d.1819 exhib. 2-Dec-2 Rasmussen, Copenhagen #1266/R est:30000 (D.KR 18000)

MOLLER, Jeanette (1825-1872) Norwegian
£864 $1417 €1253 The love letter (32x24cm-13x9in) s.i.d.1853 panel prov. 4-Jun-3 AB Stockholms Auktionsverk #2229/R (S.KR 11000)

MOLLER, Jens Peter (1783-1854) Danish
£1715 $2676 €2573 Hilly landscape with figures and horses, Torring near Lemvig (48x68cm-19x27in) init. exhib. 11-Nov-2 Rasmussen, Vejle #471/R est:25000 (D.KR 20000)

MOLLER, Jens Peter (attrib) (1783-1854) Danish
£931 $1480 €1397 Park landscape with figures (62x91cm-24x36in) 10-Mar-3 Rasmussen, Vejle #265/R (D.KR 10000)
£1586 $2521 €2379 Danish landscape with church and lock (100x135cm-39x53in) d.1819. 5-May-3 Rasmussen, Vejle #364/R est:20000 (D.KR 17000)

MOLLER, Johan Frederik (1797-1871) Danish
£436 $723 €632 Portrait of gentleman wearing red uniform (40x34cm-16x13in) s.d.1825. 12-Jun-3 Kunsthallen, Copenhagen #353 (D.KR 4600)
£638 $1009 €957 Young woman wearing pink dress (32x25cm-13x10in) s.d.1848. 2-Dec-2 Rasmussen, Copenhagen #1698/R (D.KR 7500)

MOLLER, Mogens (1934-) Danish
£283 $451 €425 Men offering a dream (75x58cm-30x23in) s.d.1981 verso acrylic underwear material exhib. 26-Feb-3 Kunsthallen, Copenhagen #205/R (D.KR 3100)
£283 $451 €425 Longing - station to station by David Bowie (75x58cm-30x23in) mono. exhib. 26-Feb-3 Kunsthallen, Copenhagen #206/R (D.KR 3100)

MOLLER, Niels Bjornsson (1827-1887) Norwegian
£867 $1353 €1301 Wooded landscape with two small girls (40x55cm-16x22in) s.d.79. 21-Oct-2 Blomqvist, Oslo #335/R (N.KR 10000)
£3186 $5034 €4779 Reindeer in the high mountains (42x60cm-17x24in) s.d.1853. 28-Apr-3 Blomqvist, Oslo #305/R est:35000-40000 (N.KR 36000)

MOLLER, Olaf (1903-) American
£1677 $2600 €2516 Impressionist landscape (91x76cm-36x30in) s. 8-Dec-2 Freeman, Philadelphia #109/R est:2000-3000

MOLLER, Olivia Holm (1875-1970) Danish
£266 $431 €399 Indian buffalo lying down (50x65cm-20x26in) init. 25-Jan-3 Rasmussen, Havnen #2064/R (D.KR 3000)
£296 $456 €444 Bedouin woman (46x36cm-18x14in) init. 26-Oct-2 Rasmussen, Havnen #2219 (D.KR 3500)
£422 $659 €633 The colours rhythm (64x105cm-25x41in) init. 18-Sep-2 Kunsthallen, Copenhagen #34 (D.KR 5000)
£511 $808 €767 Ocean (92x73cm-36x29in) init. exhib. 1-Apr-3 Rasmussen, Copenhagen #99/R (D.KR 5500)
£719 $1107 €1079 Mountain landscape (100x78cm-39x31in) 23-Oct-2 Kunsthallen, Copenhagen #159/R (D.KR 8500)
£836 $1322 €1254 Young girl going through life (135x160cm-53x63in) init.d.46. 1-Apr-3 Rasmussen, Copenhagen #89/R (D.KR 9000)

MOLLER, Otto (1883-1964) German
£7692 $11923 €12000 Steglitz in the snow (80x60cm-31x24in) s. i.d.1928 verso lit. 6-Dec-2 Karlheinz Kaupp, Staufen #2403/R est:350

MOLLER, Rudolf (1881-1964) German
Works on paper
£261 $407 €392 Country track with farmstead (21x28cm-8x11in) s. w/C over chl. 16-Sep-2 Philippe Schuler, Zurich #3050 (S.FR 600)

MOLLER, Sigurd (1895-1984) Swedish
£448 $713 €650 Female bathers on the beach (38x46cm-15x18in) s.d.45 board. 10-Mar-3 Sotheby's, Amsterdam #369

MOLLER, Thorvald Christian Benjamin (1842-1925) Danish
£560 $857 €840 Seascape with many vessels off Kronborg (81x107cm-32x42in) s.d.78. 24-Aug-2 Rasmussen, Havnen #2298/R (D.KR 6500)

MOLLGAARD, Christian (1919-) Danish
£338 $527 €507 Coastal landscape with shipwreck, fishermen and lifeboat on shore (70x101cm-28x40in) s. 23-Sep-2 Rasmussen, Vejle #114/R (D.KR 4000)
£420 $638 €630 Sailing boat off the coast (29x39cm-11x15in) s. 15-Aug-2 Bonhams, New Bond Street #370
£425 $663 €638 Seascape with naval battle (67x97cm-26x38in) s. 5-Aug-2 Rasmussen, Vejle #59/R (D.KR 5000)
£560 $890 €840 Summer landscape with shepherd boy and sheep near Himmelbjerget, Denmark (90x125cm-35x49in) s. 5-May-3 Rasmussen, Vejle #702/R (D.KR 6000)
£628 $1031 €911 Seascape with vessel in full sail (68x100cm-27x39in) s. 4-Jun-3 AB Stockholms Auktionsverk #2425/R (S.KR 8000)

MOLLIET, Clemence (19th C) French
£633 $1000 €1000 Bretonne et son enfant au clair de lune (9x19cm-4x7in) s. panel. 1-Dec-2 Anaf, Lyon #129
£949 $1500 €1500 Allee fleurie (28x21cm-11x8in) s. 1-Dec-2 Anaf, Lyon #128

MOLLOY, Sylvia Clark (1914-) British
£650 $1027 €975 Seahouses (48x74cm-19x29in) s. exhib. 18-Dec-2 Mallams, Oxford #628/R

MOLLWEIDE, Werner (1889-1978) German
£443 $700 €700 View of Ludwigs harbour at Bodensee at dusk (50x70cm-20x28in) s. pavatex. 30-Nov-2 Geble, Radolfzell #681

MOLNAR, C Pal (1894-1981) Hungarian
£838 $1308 €1215 Nude in front of the mirror (43x57cm-17x22in) s. s.i.d.1979 verso panel. 12-Apr-3 Mu Terem Galeria, Budapest #141/R est:200000 (H.F 300000)
£1006 $1569 €1509 Landscape with lights (54x34cm-21x13in) s. board. 11-Apr-3 Kieselbach, Budapest #70/R est:280000-360000 (H.F 360000)
£1118 $1744 €1621 Reflection at the waterfront (60x71cm-24x28in) s. s.d.1979 verso panel. 12-Apr-3 Mu Terem Galeria, Budapest #70/R est:280000 (H.F 400000)
£1537 $2398 €2229 Italian landscape (31x41cm-12x16in) s. panel. 12-Apr-3 Mu Terem Galeria, Budapest #69/R est:320000 (H.F 550000)
£1935 $3018 €2806 Pilgrims in the Cypher Grove (40x50cm-16x20in) s. cardboard. 13-Sep-2 Mu Terem Galeria, Budapest #22/R est:340000 (H.F 750000)
£2555 $3960 €3833 Dome in Milan (52x58cm-20x23in) s. wood fibre board. 6-Dec-2 Kieselbach, Budapest #76/R (H.F 950000)
£3496 $5419 €5069 Flight to Egypt (51x65cm-20x26in) s. 9-Dec-2 Mu Terem Galeria, Budapest #32/R est:450000 (H.F 1300000)
£4034 $6253 €5849 Italian landscape (46x65cm-18x26in) s. tempera panel. 9-Dec-2 Mu Terem Galeria, Budapest #182/R est:650000 (H.F 1500000)
Works on paper
£1006 $1569 €1459 Bathers (29x22cm-11x9in) s.d.1922 pencil. 12-Apr-3 Mu Terem Galeria, Budapest #14/R est:220000 (H.F 360000)
£2689 $4168 €4034 On the bank of the River Tevere (23x25cm-9x10in) s. Indian ink. 6-Dec-2 Kieselbach, Budapest #190/R (H.F 1000000)

MOLNAR, Janos Z (1880-1960) Czechoslovakian

£320 $512 €480 Still life of spring flowers in a vase (68x55cm-27x22in) s. 7-Jan-3 Bonhams, Knightsbridge #248
£1024 $1587 €1536 Bunch of cornpoppies (68x55cm-27x22in) painted c.1920. 1-Oct-2 SOGA, Bratislava #130/R est:32000 (SL.K 65000)

MOLNAR, Josef (1821-1899) Hungarian

£3912 $6103 €5672 Creek side (28x42cm-11x17in) s. panel. 12-Apr-3 Mu Terem Galeria, Budapest #52/R est:950000 (H.F 1400000)
£4303 $6669 €6455 Capri (33x60cm-13x24in) s. canvas on cardboard. 6-Dec-2 Kieselbach, Budapest #63/R (H.F 1600000)
£5110 $7920 €7410 River bank with figures (37x53cm-15x21in) s. 9-Dec-2 Mu Terem Galeria, Budapest #45/R est:1300000 (H.F 1900000)
£7223 $11268 €10473 Town by a lake (33x57cm-13x22in) s. cardboard. 13-Sep-2 Mu Terem Galeria, Budapest #50/R est:1100000 (H.F 2800000)
£7530 $11671 €10919 Villa in Tivoli (62x26cm-24x10in) s. papercard. 9-Dec-2 Mu Terem Galeria, Budapest #41/R est:550000 (H.F 2800000)

MOLNAR, Roza (1900-1977) Hungarian

£727 $1133 €1054 Still life with tulips (52x36cm-20x14in) s.i.d.930. 12-Apr-3 Mu Terem Galeria, Budapest #24/R est:180000 (H.F 260000)

MOLS, Florent (19th C) Belgian

£3000 $4650 €4500 Lake at sunset (62x97cm-24x38in) s. panel. 3-Dec-2 Sotheby's, Olympia #222/R est:1500-2000

MOLS, N P (1859-1921) Danish

£337 $546 €506 Hazy landscape with cows and thatched houses (34x53cm-13x21in) init.d.09. 25-Jan-3 Rasmussen, Havnen #2112 (D.KR 3800)
£388 $589 €582 Driving the cattle home in evening sunshine (33x46cm-13x18in) init.d.08. 27-Aug-2 Rasmussen, Copenhagen #1898/R (D.KR 4500)
£405 $632 €608 Geese and cattle in meadow (35x27cm-14x11in) s. 23-Sep-2 Rasmussen, Vejle #179/R (D.KR 4800)
£470 $761 €705 Stable interior with cows (75x98cm-30x39in) s. 25-Jan-3 Rasmussen, Havnen #2114/R (D.KR 5300)
£532 $862 €798 Landscape with cows (48x66cm-19x26in) s.d.09. 25-Jan-3 Rasmussen, Havnen #2113 (D.KR 6000)
£746 $1187 €1119 Sailing ship unloading corn at the coast near Fanoe (34x23cm-13x9in) init. 5-May-3 Rasmussen, Vejle #706/R (D.KR 8000)
£1152 $1867 €1728 Stable interior with woman and calves (77x69cm-30x27in) s.d.83. 25-Jan-3 Rasmussen, Havnen #2115/R est:10000-12000 (D.KR 13000)

MOLS, Niels Pedersen (1859-1921) Danish

£904 $1375 €1356 In the stable - man wearing bowler hat with horse and foal (59x57cm-23x22in) s.d.87 exhib. 28-Aug-2 Museumsbygningen, Copenhagen #73/R (D.KR 10500)
£2365 $3689 €3548 Home from milking - cattle on road by Ribe (106x142cm-42x56in) s.d.18. 23-Sep-2 Rasmussen, Vejle #101/R est:25000 (D.KR 28000)
£2549 $3976 €3824 Cattle returning home, Fano (102x145cm-40x57in) s.i.d.17. 5-Aug-2 Rasmussen, Vejle #201/R est:25000 (D.KR 30000)

MOLS, Robert (1848-1903) Belgian

£1007 $1621 €1500 Pecheur solitaire (107x168cm-42x66in) s.d.1867. 24-Feb-3 Bernaerts, Antwerp #10/R

Prints

£285 $444 €450 La Rade van Antwerpen. col etching. 16-Sep-2 Amberes, Antwerp #10

MOLSTED, Chr (1862-1930) Danish

£254 $391 €381 Old farm with cows and chickens (51x63cm-20x25in) s. 26-Oct-2 Rasmussen, Havnen #2123 (D.KR 3000)
£306 $496 €444 Seascape with many ship, lighthouse in background (21x35cm-8x14in) s.d.19/6 80. 24-May-3 Rasmussen, Havnen #2185 (D.KR 3200)
£372 $592 €558 Sailing vessels off Dragor (33x35cm-13x14in) s. 5-Mar-3 Rasmussen, Copenhagen #1959 (D.KR 4000)
£372 $587 €558 Seascape with sailing vessels (27x40cm-11x16in) s. 5-Apr-3 Rasmussen, Havnen #2121 (D.KR 4000)
£2700 $4293 €4050 Girls dressed in national costumes dancing ring dance, evening (35x45cm-14x18in) s.d.85. 5-Mar-3 Rasmussen, Copenhagen #1504/R est:40000-50000 (D.KR 29000)
£3404 $5379 €5106 In the harbour inlet to Dragor, stormy weather (127x172cm-50x68in) s.d.1919. 2-Dec-2 Rasmussen, Copenhagen #1403/R est:40000-50000 (D.KR 40000)
£3574 $5648 €5361 Storm in Drogden (128x171cm-50x67in) s.d.1916-17 prov. 27-Nov-2 Museumsbygningen, Copenhagen #61/R est:40000-50000 (D.KR 42000)

Works on paper

£851 $1345 €1277 Naval battle between Swedes and Danes (92x127cm-36x50in) s.d.1930 pastel. 2-Dec-2 Rasmussen, Copenhagen #1623/R (D.KR 10000)

MOLTENI, Giuseppe (1800-1867) Italian

£13423 $21611 €20000 Portrait of lady (64x50cm-25x20in) lit. 19-Feb-3 Semenzato, Venice #39/R est:26000
£13423 $21611 €20000 Portrait of lady (73x65cm-29x26in) lit. 19-Feb-3 Semenzato, Venice #42/R est:26000

MOLTINO, Francis (1818-1874) British

£360 $576 €540 In the pool on the Thames (29x60cm-11x24in) 15-May-3 Lawrence, Crewkerne #974
£1200 $1920 €1800 St Marks, Venice (35x30cm-14x12in) mono. board with companion two. 11-Mar-3 Bonhams, Knightsbridge #120/R est:300-500
£1400 $2128 €2100 Berthed ships at river dock (29x24cm-11x9in) board pair. 15-Aug-2 Bonhams, New Bond Street #316/R est:600-800
£2400 $3816 €3600 Venetian canal scenes (25x30cm-10x12in) init. board oval pair. 18-Mar-3 Bonhams, New Bond Street #56/R est:2000-3000
£2800 $4312 €4200 Westminster Bridge, Houses of Parliament and Westminster Abbey (61x91cm-24x36in) 5-Sep-2 Christie's, Kensington #225/R est:2000-3000
£3200 $4928 €4800 Royal Naval College, Greenwich, from the Thames (61x91cm-24x36in) s. 5-Sep-2 Christie's, Kensington #224/R est:2000-3000

MOLTINO, Francis (attrib) (1818-1874) British

£1400 $2184 €2100 Thames looking towards the Houses of Parliament (61x92cm-24x36in) 10-Apr-3 Tennants, Leyburn #959/R est:1500-2500
£2200 $3476 €3300 View of Greenwich (49x74cm-19x29in) 12-Nov-2 Bonhams, Knightsbridge #241/R est:700-1000

MOLTKE, Harald (1871-1960) Danish

£769 $1184 €1154 Young woman from Greenland dancing (120x100cm-47x39in) init.d.1933. 4-Sep-2 Kunsthallen, Copenhagen #143/R (D.KR 9000)

MOLVIG, John (1923-1970) Australian

£968 $1598 €1404 Eden industrial - hand and bird (73x47cm-29x19in) s.d.1962 acrylic on paper prov. 1-Jul-3 Peter Webb, Auckland #117/R est:3000-4000 (NZ.D 2750)
£1149 $1805 €1724 Still life (30x37cm-12x15in) s. board painted c.1952. 15-Apr-3 Lawson Menzies, Sydney #154/R est:3000-4000 (A.D 3000)
£1912 $3136 €2868 Three jesters (52x69cm-20x27in) s.d.51 i.d.51 verso composition board prov.exhib.lit. 4-Jun-3 Deutscher-Menzies, Melbourne #191/R est:4000-6000 (A.D 4800)
£1971 $2996 €2957 Old warrior (51x70cm-20x28in) s.d.58 i.verso composition board prov. 28-Aug-2 Deutscher-Menzies, Melbourne #244/R est:6000-8000 (A.D 5500)
£1992 $3267 €2988 Juggler (52x70cm-20x28in) s.d.51 i.verso composition board prov.exhib.lit. 4-Jun-3 Deutscher-Menzies, Melbourne #190/R est:4000-6000 (A.D 5000)

Works on paper

£575 $902 €863 Nude (75x49cm-30x19in) s. ink. 15-Apr-3 Lawson Menzies, Sydney #155/R est:1500-2000 (A.D 1500)

MOLYN, Petrus Marius (1819-1849) Belgian

£1795 $2836 €2800 La partie de Des (25x31cm-10x12in) s.d.1844 panel. 18-Nov-2 Tajan, Paris #12 est:3000-3500

MOLYN, Pieter (1595-1661) Dutch

£19108 $29809 €30000 Wooded landscape with travellers in wagons on a road (67x112cm-26x44in) panel. 6-Nov-2 Christie's, Amsterdam #80/R est:16000-22000
£25610 $42000 €38415 Dune landscape with travellers on a path (25x37cm-10x15in) s. panel prov.lit. 30-May-3 Christie's, Rockefeller NY #18/R est:15000-20000

Works on paper

£688 $1100 €1032 Herders at rest in a landscape (20x28cm-8x11in) mono. black chk stumping out. 14-May-3 Doyle, New York #15/R est:2000-3000
£3200 $5344 €4640 Wooded path with mounted travelers and herdsman with cattle (14x19cm-6x7in) s. black chk prov.lit. 8-Jul-3 Christie's, London #102/R est:4000-6000

£15287 $23847 €24000 Travellers on a village street (15x20cm-6x8in) s.d.1654 black chk grey wash prov.lit. 5-Nov-2 Sotheby's, Amsterdam #41/R est:20000-30000

MOLYN, Pieter (attrib) (1595-1661) Dutch
£9615 $15192 €15000 Paysage boise anime de pecheurs et de voyageurs (50x78cm-20x31in) bears sig. panel. 12-Nov-2 Palais de Beaux Arts, Brussels #460/R est:4000-6000

MOLYNEUX, Edward (1896-?) American
£500 $820 €725 Peniche sur la Seine (32x40cm-13x16in) s. 1-Jun-3 Lots Road, London #339

MOLYNEUX, Edward (fl.1899-1904) British
£250 $403 €375 Kashmir Glen (89x127cm-35x50in) i. 14-Jan-3 Bonhams, Knowle #348

MOMAL, Jacques François (1754-1832) French
£3481 $5430 €5500 La lecon de dessin (6x54cm-2x21in) s. 20-Oct-2 Mercier & Cie, Lille #272/R est:4500-6000

MOMBELLI, Eugenio (1950-) Italian
Works on paper
£316 $494 €500 Meditation on art (80x100cm-31x39in) s.i.verso mixed media collage on canvas exec.1999. 14-Sep-2 Meeting Art, Vercelli #876/R

MOMBELLO, Luca (1520-?) Italian
£4300 $6708 €6450 Allegorical marriage portrait (90x88cm-35x35in) 8-Apr-3 Sotheby's, Olympia #128/R est:4000-6000

MOMMERS, Hendrik (1623-1693) Dutch
£1039 $1600 €1559 Vegetable sellers in a landscape, a village beyond (48x65cm-19x26in) s. panel on panel. 4-Sep-2 Christie's, Rockefeller NY #235/R est:3000-5000
£3378 $5270 €5000 Shepherdess and flock in southern landscape (70x57cm-28x22in) s. panel prov. 27-Mar-3 Dorotheum, Vienna #105/R est:6000-9000
£6711 $10804 €10000 Southern landscape with figures selling vegetables in the foreground (60x84cm-24x33in) s. panel. 18-Feb-3 Sotheby's, Amsterdam #224/R est:7000-9000
£7000 $11690 €10150 Italianate river landscape with shepherd and shepherdess with their flock (66x86cm-26x34in) 11-Jul-3 Christie's, Kensington #91/R est:5000-7000

MOMMERS, Hendrik (style) (1623-1693) Dutch
£17610 $27472 €28000 View of Paris from the Pont-Neuf (76x181cm-30x71in) 8-Oct-2 Christie's, Paris #24/R est:50000

MOMPER, Frans de (1603-1660) Flemish
£3333 $5067 €5200 Villageois sur un chemin de montagne (41x59cm-16x23in) 10-Jul-2 Rabourdin & Choppin de Janvry, Paris #81/R est:3800-4000
£8805 $13648 €14000 Riverside village with fishermen (46x62cm-18x24in) panel lit. 2-Oct-2 Dorotheum, Vienna #123/R est:12000-16000
£9434 $14623 €15000 View of Antwerp (60x83cm-24x33in) bears sig. panel. 2-Oct-2 Dorotheum, Vienna #181/R est:15000-20000
£11184 $18118 €17000 Landscape with peasants (44x62cm-17x24in) board. 21-Jan-3 Ansorena, Madrid #95/R est:15000
£17568 $27405 €26000 View of Flemish village (19cm-7in circular) panel. 27-Mar-3 Dorotheum, Vienna #122/R est:25000-30000

MOMPER, Jan de (attrib) (16/17th C) Flemish
£2000 $3120 €3000 Forest floor still life with a chaffinch, swallow and other birds, in a landscape with farmhouse (103x86cm-41x34in) 10-Apr-3 Christie's, Kensington #117/R est:3000-5000
£2041 $3245 €3000 Fouille des tombes (50x98cm-20x39in) canvas on cardboard. 21-Mar-3 Rieunier, Bailly-Pommery, Mathias, Paris #55/R

MOMPER, Joos de (1564-1635) Flemish
£6738 $10443 €10107 River landscape (56x67cm-22x26in) 4-Dec-2 AB Stockholms Auktionsverk #1955/R est:50000-60000 (S.KR 95000)
£10063 $15597 €16000 Landscape with horsemen (49x39cm-19x15in) panel lit. 2-Oct-2 Dorotheum, Vienna #183/R est:12000-15000
£17266 $27626 €24000 Extensive river landscape with Elijah fed by ravens (49x91cm-19x36in) painted with studio. 13-May-3 Sotheby's, Amsterdam #2/R est:20000-30000
£18705 $29928 €26000 Mountain landscape with fallen tree on a path (46x70cm-18x28in) panel prov.exhib.lit. 14-May-3 Christie's, Amsterdam #164/R est:20000-30000
Works on paper
£2692 $4254 €4200 Extensive mountain landscape with riders (26x41cm-10x16in) ochre prov. 16-Nov-2 Lempertz, Koln #1265/R est:3500

MOMPER, Joos de (attrib) (1564-1635) Flemish
£700 $1127 €1050 Landscape with a drover and hid cattle (24x30cm-9x12in) panel. 20-Feb-3 Christie's, Kensington #212/R
£16000 $25120 €24000 Wooded landscape with overturned wagon before a village (81x69cm-32x27in) bears sig.d.1620 panel. 12-Dec-2 Sotheby's, London #129/R est:10000-15000
£19481 $30195 €29222 Landscape with riders (30x42cm-12x17in) panel. 24-Sep-2 Koller, Zurich #6433/R est:3500-5500 (S.FR 45000)
Works on paper
£892 $1391 €1400 Landscape with windmill in the distance (20x38cm-8x15in) pen brown ink wash prov.exhib. 5-Nov-2 Sotheby's, Amsterdam #197/R

MOMPER, Joos de (circle) (1564-1635) Flemish
£5000 $7750 €7500 Landscape with waggoners beside river, village beyond (54x48cm-21x19in) i.verso panel fragment. 31-Oct-2 Sotheby's, Olympia #45/R est:4000-6000

MOMPER, Joos de (style) (1564-1635) Flemish
£5755 $9209 €8000 Mountain landscape with travellers (49x66cm-19x26in) panel. 17-May-3 Lempertz, Koln #1088/R est:5000
£7800 $13026 €11310 River landscape with huntsmen and hounds (50x81cm-20x32in) panel. 8-Jul-3 Sotheby's, Olympia #361/R est:8000-12000

MOMPER, Philips de (elder) (1598-1634) Flemish
£37975 $59241 €60000 Bord de canal anime de personnages (60x120cm-24x47in) panel. 20-Oct-2 Mercier & Cie, Lille #253/R est:60000-75000

MOMPER, Philips de (elder-attrib) (1598-1634) Flemish
£5256 $8305 €8200 Vues de Rome (13x36cm-5x14in) panel pair. 12-Nov-2 Palais de Beaux Arts, Brussels #56/R est:5000-7000

MONACHESI, Sante (1910-1991) Italian
£541 $843 €800 Landscape (70x50cm-28x20in) s. acrylic. 26-Mar-3 Finarte Semenzato, Milan #255
£833 $1308 €1300 Idroglass. Imponderabilita' (70x50cm-28x20in) s. pair. 20-Nov-2 Pandolfini, Florence #73
£1560 $2528 €2200 Urban landscape (60x50cm-24x20in) s. 26-May-3 Christie's, Milan #319/R est:2500-3000
£1622 $2530 €2400 Landscape (50x60cm-20x24in) s. 26-Mar-3 Finarte Semenzato, Milan #394/R
£1644 $2564 €2400 Landscape in Casaamicciola (50x60cm-20x24in) s.verso painted 1949. 10-Apr-3 Finarte Semenzato, Rome #268/R
£1667 $2617 €2600 Blind walls (50x70cm-20x28in) s. oil mixed media. 23-Nov-2 Meeting Art, Vercelli #460/R
£1677 $2650 €2600 Venice (49x70cm-19x28in) s. painted c.1946. 18-Dec-2 Christie's, Rome #179
£2083 $3312 €3000 Still life (60x80cm-24x31in) s. oil silver powder. 1-May-3 Meeting Art, Vercelli #170
£2192 $3419 €3200 Still life with teapot and plant (50x60cm-20x24in) s. 10-Apr-3 Finarte Semenzato, Rome #159/R
£3283 $5252 €4760 Old painting (48x68cm-19x27in) s. s.i.verso. 11-Mar-3 Babuino, Rome #314/R

MONAHAN, Hugh (1914-1970) Irish
£600 $996 €870 Geese at sunset (50x64cm-20x25in) s. canvas on board prov. 12-Jun-3 Christie's, Kensington #153
£1200 $1896 €1800 Morning flight (46x61cm-18x24in) s. 28-Nov-2 Christie's, Kensington #16/R est:1200-1800

MONALDI, Paolo (18th C) Italian
£2244 $3478 €3500 Simple meal (17x22cm-7x9in) copper prov. 4-Dec-2 Christie's, Rome #310/R
£6207 $9931 €9000 Grape harvest (50x65cm-20x26in) 17-Mar-3 Pandolfini, Florence #713/R
£7547 $11623 €12000 Peasants celebrating (56x63cm-22x25in) 23-Oct-2 Finarte, Rome #480/R est:7500-8500
£10345 $16448 €15000 Genre scenes (41x32cm-16x13in) pair. 5-Mar-3 Sotheby's, Milan #424/R est:20000

MONAMY, Peter (1689-1749) British
£1400 $2338 €2030 Man-o-war on the rocks (38x73cm-15x29in) s. 18-Jun-3 Sotheby's, Olympia #4/R est:1500-2500
£9000 $14580 €13500 Flagship joining the fleet at its anchorage at sunset, probably Medway (76x113cm-30x44in) s.i. 21-May-3 Christie's, Kensington #523/R est:10000-15000

£24691 $40000 €35802 Flagship at anchor and firing an Admiral's salute (79x117cm-31x46in) prov. 29-Jul-3 Christie's, Rockefeller NY #124/R est:30000-50000
£50000 $83000 €75000 Flagship arriving at her anchorage to join the squadron of the Red (122x132cm-48x52in) 10-Jun-3 Christie's, London #50/R est:20000-30000

MONCHABLON, Alphonse (1835-1907) French
£2069 $3269 €3000 Jeunes femmes au chaton (46x61cm-18x24in) s.d.1885. 4-Apr-3 Tajan, Paris #142/R

MONCHABLON, Jean Ferdinand (1855-1904) French
£1509 $2400 €2264 Cows resting near a stream in a summer landscape (55x40cm-22x16in) s. 5-Mar-3 Christie's, Rockefeller NY #72/R est:3000-5000
£2342 $3700 €3700 Buissons fleuris, pres Chatillon, Vosges (32x46cm-13x18in) s. i.verso. 1-Dec-2 Peron, Melun #1
£2800 $4368 €4200 Forest at Fontainbleau (55x73cm-22x29in) s.d.1885. 26-Mar-3 Sotheby's, Olympia #259/R est:2000-3000
£3125 $5000 €4688 Haute Saone (25x30cm-10x12in) s. 11-Jan-3 James Julia, Fairfield #117a est:4000-6000

MONCRIEFF, Colonel Alexander (fl.1883) British
£580 $905 €870 Portrait of a young blackamoor page, Alfred Augustus Jordan (45x38cm-18x15in) s.i.d.1853 verso board painted oval. 17-Oct-2 Lawrence, Crewkerne #467

MONCUR, Jane (1891-1983) British
£260 $429 €377 Bury field, Clavering, Essex (61x56cm-24x22in) s. 1-Jul-3 Bonhams, Norwich #318/R
£260 $429 €377 Lane in Clavering, Essex (61x51cm-24x20in) s. 1-Jul-3 Bonhams, Norwich #327
£300 $495 €435 Old house, Clavering, Essex (35x46cm-14x18in) s. 1-Jul-3 Bonhams, Norwich #317/R

MONDINO, Aldo (1938-) Italian
£506 $790 €800 Bacino (25x35cm-10x14in) i. painted 1983. 14-Sep-2 Meeting Art, Vercelli #717/R
£641 $1006 €1000 Saint mark's (25x35cm-10x14in) i. s.d.1983 verso. 23-Nov-2 Meeting Art, Vercelli #391/R
£696 $1086 €1100 Danse des Jardes (60x25cm-24x10in) s.d.1998 linoleum. 14-Sep-2 Meeting Art, Vercelli #749/R
£903 $1435 €1300 Clapping (50x35cm-20x14in) i. s.d.1983 verso. 1-May-3 Meeting Art, Vercelli #161
£1014 $1581 €1500 Arlequin (90x60cm-35x24in) painted 1975. 26-Mar-3 Finarte Semenzato, Milan #134/R
£1565 $2488 €2300 Konia (80x60cm-31x24in) s.i.d.1996 linoleum. 1-Mar-3 Meeting Art, Vercelli #374
£2692 $4227 €4200 Green Turkish dance (90x120cm-35x47in) s.i.d.1997 verso linoleum. 23-Nov-2 Meeting Art, Vercelli #357/R

Works on paper
£897 $1310 €1400 Bon ton (70x70cm-28x28in) s. mixed media on canvas prov. 5-Jun-2 Il Ponte, Milan #55
£1154 $1685 €1800 Composition (80x80cm-31x31in) s. s.verso mixed media on canvas. 5-Jun-2 Il Ponte, Milan #39/R

MONDO, Domenico (1717-1806) Italian
Works on paper
£443 $700 €700 L'ascension de la Vierge. Une eveque a sa table (27x20cm-11x8in) i.verso red chk pen black ink double-sided prov. 27-Nov-2 Christie's, Paris #104/R
£1049 $1700 €1574 Classical scene of judgement (20x35cm-8x14in) pen ink wash htd white. 21-Jan-3 Sotheby's, New York #161/R
£1631 $2724 €2300 Apelle peignant Campaspe sous le regard d'Alexandre (18x28cm-7x11in) pen black ink sanguine wash. 19-Jun-3 Piasa, Paris #38 est:1500

MONDOR, Henri (20th C) French
Works on paper
£806 $1274 €1250 Coquillages (17x13cm-7x5in) s.i.d.1937 dr. 18-Dec-2 Ferri, Paris #97

MONDRIAAN, Frits (1853-1932) Dutch
£348 $543 €550 Willow along a ditch (27x43cm-11x17in) 21-Oct-2 Glerum, Amsterdam #215

MONDRIAN, Piet (1872-1944) Dutch
£46584 $75000 €69876 Landscape in Montmorency (47x55cm-19x22in) s. s.i.d.8 Aug 30 verso prov.lit. 7-May-3 Sotheby's, New York #131/R est:40000-60000
£179487 $278205 €280000 Ditch near landzicht farm (45x64cm-18x25in) s. W/C prov.lit. 3-Dec-2 Christie's, Amsterdam #209/R est:300000-500000
£302158 $495540 €420000 Avond - evening (38x49cm-15x19in) init. painted c.1907-08 prov. 3-Jun-3 Christie's, Amsterdam #235/R est:60000-80000
£4472050 $7200000 €6708075 Composition in white, blue and yellow: C (72x69cm-28x27in) init.d.36 prov.lit. 7-May-3 Christie's, Rockefeller NY #23/R est:6000000-9000000

Works on paper
£51282 $80000 €76923 Dahlia (23x17cm-9x7in) s. W/C pencil gouache paper on card executed c.1920-25 prov.exhib. 6-Nov-2 Sotheby's, New York #207/R est:80000-120000

MONDZAIN, Simon François Stanislas (1890-1979) French
£886 $1373 €1400 Portrait de femme (46x38cm-18x15in) s.d. 28-Sep-2 Cornette de St.Cyr, Paris #177
£1139 $1800 €1800 Maison de Garde (50x61cm-20x24in) s. 29-Nov-2 Drouot Estimations, Paris #93
£1401 $2186 €2200 Nu allonge (46x55cm-18x22in) s. 7-Nov-2 Chochon-Barre & Allardi, Paris #200/R
£1447 $2242 €2300 La Place du Gouvernement a Alger (80x65cm-31x26in) s. 30-Oct-2 Artcurial Briest, Paris #319 est:1500-2000
£2548 $3975 €4000 Vue de village (73x60cm-29x24in) s.d.1926. 7-Nov-2 Claude Aguttes, Neuilly #67/R est:1000-1200
£2739 $4273 €4300 Maison en bord de mer (60x73cm-24x29in) s.d.1923. 7-Nov-2 Claude Aguttes, Neuilly #64 est:1200-1500

MONEDERO, Manuel (1925-) Spanish
£1509 $2325 €2400 Figures chatting (60x81cm-24x32in) s. 28-Oct-2 Segre, Madrid #79/R

MONES, A de (19th C) ?
£16000 $24960 €24000 Scholars debate (51x69cm-20x27in) s.d.1850. 15-Oct-2 Sotheby's, London #71/R est:5000-7000

MONET, Claude (1840-1926) French
£200000 $328000 €300000 La Seine a Argenteuil (29x59cm-11x23in) st.sig. painted c.1872 prov.exhib.lit. 4-Feb-3 Christie's, London #211/R est:350000
£352564 $550000 €528846 Soleil couchant, temps brumeux, pourville (62x75cm-24x30in) s.d.82 prov.exhib.lit. 5-Nov-2 Sotheby's, New York #17/R est:600000-800000
£372671 $600000 €559007 Vagues a Manneporte (74x93cm-29x37in) s. painted c.1885 prov.exhib.lit. 7-May-3 Christie's, Rockefeller NY #5/R est:600000-800000
£400000 $668000 €580000 Bord de Seine a Port-Villez (61x80cm-24x31in) s. prov.exhib. 24-Jun-3 Christie's, London #51/R est:600000-800000
£580000 $945400 €870000 Chemin creux a Giverny (60x81cm-24x32in) s. prov.exhib.lit. 3-Feb-3 Christie's, London #69/R est:800000
£650000 $1059500 €975000 Glacons a Lavacourt (50x81cm-20x32in) s. painted 1879 prov.exhib.lit. 3-Feb-3 Christie's, London #64/R est:900000
£705128 $1100000 €1057692 Au bord du fjord de Christiania (65x91cm-26x36in) s.d.95 prov.exhib.lit. 5-Nov-2 Sotheby's, New York #7/R est:1200000-1600000
£993789 $1600000 €1490684 Poste de douaniers a Dieppe (59x70cm-23x28in) s.d.82 prov.exhib.lit. 7-May-3 Christie's, Rockefeller NY #8/R est:2000000-3000000
£1500000 $2505000 €2175000 Le Dam a Zaandam, le soir (44x72cm-17x28in) s. painted 1871 prov.exhib.lit. 24-Jun-3 Christie's, London #59/R est:1700000-2200000
£1794872 $2800000 €2692308 Fleurs dans un pot - roses et brouillard (83x62cm-33x24in) s.d.1878 prov.exhib.lit. 5-Nov-2 Sotheby's, New York #10/R est:3000000-4000000
£1925466 $3100000 €2888199 Bateaux de peche (65x93cm-26x37in) s.d.83 prov.exhib.lit. 6-May-3 Sotheby's, New York #19/R est:2500000-3500000
£10897437 $17000000 €16346156 Nympheas (89x92cm-35x36in) s.d.1906 prov.exhib.lit. 5-Nov-2 Sotheby's, New York #12/R est:16000000-20000000

Works on paper
£42000 $68880 €63000 Waterloo bridge (31x47cm-12x19in) pastel exec.1901 prov.lit. 6-Feb-3 Christie's, London #414/R est:70000

MONET, Claude and THORNLEY, Georges W (19th C) French
Prints
£2738 $4325 €4107 Tempete a Belle-ile (20x24cm-8x9in) s. one of 25 greenish blue lithograph executed c.1908. 28-Apr-3 Bukowskis, Stockholm #483/R est:25000-30000 (S.KR 36000)
£4403 $7000 €6605 Falaises (20x24cm-8x9in) s. col lithograph executed c.1892. 3-Mar-3 Swann Galleries, New York #14/R est:7000-10000
£4403 $7000 €6605 Une anse dans un aber (23x29cm-9x11in) s. col lithograph executed c.1892. 3-Mar-3 Swann Galleries, New York #15/R est:7000-10000

£5769 $9000 €8654 Trois barques sur la Greve (21x27cm-8x11in) s. col lithograph exec.c.1892 edition of 25. 18-Sep-2 Swann Galleries, New York #2/R est:12000-18000

MONFALLET, Adolphe François (1816-1900) French

£890 $1397 €1335 Elegant lady in her boudoir (22x16cm-9x6in) s. panel. 16-Apr-3 Christie's, Kensington #844/R
£4839 $7645 €7500 Scene de ripaille (42x62cm-17x24in) s. 19-Dec-2 Claude Aguttes, Neuilly #59/R

MONFARDINI, Alfonso (1887-1965) Italian

£725 $1188 €1000 Piano de Resinelli e Grignetta (59x50cm-23x20in) s.d.1922 board. 27-May-3 Finarte, Milan #10/R

MONFORT, Nicolas (fl.1840) French

£3000 $4770 €4500 Farewell to Napoleon at the chateau de Fontainebleau, 30th April 1814 (72x100cm-28x39in) after Antoine Charles Horace Vernet. 20-Mar-3 Christie's, Kensington #136/R est:3000-5000

MONFORT, Octavianus (attrib) (17th C) Italian

Works on paper

£15484 $24465 €24000 Natures mortes aux carpes, brochets et ecrevisses (26x40cm-10x16in) W/C paper on panel pair. 18-Dec-2 Piasa, Paris #48/R est:15000

MONGIN, Antoine Pierre (1761-1827) French

£1200 $1884 €1800 Courtyard of a ruined villa (37x52cm-15x20in) black chk bodycol. 13-Dec-2 Christie's, Kensington #319/R est:1200-1800

MONGIN, Antoine Pierre (attrib) (1761-1827) French

Works on paper

£769 $1192 €1200 Promenade au parc (21x33cm-8x13in) W/C gouache. 4-Dec-2 Piasa, Paris #93
£1361 $2164 €2000 Promenade dans un parc (58x42cm-23x17in) W/C gouache. 24-Mar-3 Tajan, Paris #94/R

MONGINOT, Charles (1825-1900) French

£900 $1458 €1350 Dangerous game (43x63cm-17x25in) s. 20-May-3 Sotheby's, Olympia #414/R
£2051 $3241 €3200 Le chaton effronte (50x61cm-20x24in) s. 18-Nov-2 Tajan, Paris #158/R est:1800-2400
£2800 $4256 €4200 Jeune fille aux perroquets (134x89cm-53x35in) s. 29-Aug-2 Christie's, Kensington #173/R est:3000-5000

MONGRELL Y TORRENT, Jose (1870-1934) Spanish

£1442 $2279 €2250 Sailorman (50x33cm-20x13in) s. board. 19-Nov-2 Durán, Madrid #182/R
£1603 $2532 €2500 Fisherman (49x33cm-19x13in) s. board. 19-Nov-2 Durán, Madrid #183/R
£62893 $98113 €100000 Fisherman's family (71x115cm-28x45in) s. 23-Sep-2 Durán, Madrid #257/R est:100000

MONI, Louis de (1698-1771) Dutch

£1026 $1621 €1600 Feeding the chickens (33x24cm-13x9in) s. panel. 18-Nov-2 Bernaerts, Antwerp #48/R est:1500-2000
£3462 $5469 €5400 La cuisiniere (38x31cm-15x12in) s. panel. 14-Nov-2 Credit Municipal, Paris #21 est:7000-9000

MONICO, dal (19th C) Italian?

Works on paper

£484 $765 €750 Nice vue de la route de Genes (14x23cm-6x9in) s. W/C. 17-Dec-2 Claude Boisgirard, Paris #15
£503 $795 €780 Entree du port de Nice (12x22cm-5x9in) s. W/C. 17-Dec-2 Claude Boisgirard, Paris #16

MONIES, David (1812-1894) Danish

£355 $553 €533 Figures by fisherman's house (21x29cm-8x11in) 23-Sep-2 Rasmussen, Vejle #2071/R (D.KR 4200)
£431 $698 €625 Faggot gatherers in beech wood (23x32cm-9x13in) s. 26-May-3 Rasmussen, Copenhagen #1523/R (D.KR 4500)
£559 $888 €839 Portrait of Professor Edvard August Dahlerup (65x56cm-26x22in) s.d.1854 oval lit. 5-Mar-3 Rasmussen, Copenhagen #1712/R (D.KR 6000)
£1036 $1668 €1554 From a loggia with figures (47x38cm-19x15in) s.i. 22-Feb-3 Rasmussen, Havnen #2019/R (D.KR 11500)
£1401 $2242 €2102 Landscape with two children crying on road (70x60cm-28x24in) s.d.1855. 13-Jan-3 Rasmussen, Vejle #236/R est:20000 (D.KR 16000)

MONINOT, Bernard (20th C) French

Works on paper

£900 $1503 €1305 Peinture (41x44cm-16x17in) s.d.78 assemblage prov. 24-Jun-3 Sotheby's, Olympia #84/R

MONJO, Hernandez (1862-1939) Spanish

£3800 $6308 €5510 Spanish steamers off the coast at dusk (97x112cm-38x44in) s. 12-Jun-3 Christie's, London #534/R est:1200-1800

MONK, William (1863-1937) British

Works on paper

£260 $434 €377 Turfers working in steep valley (25x36cm-10x14in) s. W/C. 25-Jun-3 Brightwells, Leominster #1028
£260 $434 €377 Windsor Castle, with fair in the foreground (19x25cm-7x10in) s. pastel prov. 25-Jun-3 Cheffins, Cambridge #734
£360 $601 €522 Fair day at Mann, Connemara (23x36cm-9x14in) s. W/C. 25-Jun-3 Brightwells, Leominster #1030/R

MONKS, John Austin Sands (1850-1917) American

£1146 $1800 €1719 Sheep grazing in a landscape (41x51cm-16x20in) s. 14-Dec-2 Charlton Hall, Columbia #206/R est:1000-1500

MONNET, Charles (1732-c.1808) French

Works on paper

£22152 $35000 €35000 Famille royale (36x40cm-14x16in) pen ink wash crayon prov.exhib. 28-Nov-2 Tajan, Paris #82/R est:12000-15000

MONNICKENDAM, Jules (19/20th C) Dutch

£246 $383 €369 Sailing boats in a harbour (29x39cm-11x15in) s. 15-Oct-2 Stephan Welz, Johannesburg #409 est:2000-3000 (SA.R 4000)

MONNICKENDAM, Martin (1874-1943) Dutch

Works on paper

£284 $460 €400 Street in Rome (37x25cm-15x10in) s.d.1934 W/C. 26-May-3 Glerum, Amsterdam #41/R

MONNICKENDAM, Maurits (1863-?) Dutch

£592 $959 €900 Doelenhotel, Amsterdam (36x27cm-14x11in) s.d.1890 panel. 21-Jan-3 Christie's, Amsterdam #300/R est:1000-1500

MONNIER, Charles (1925-) Swiss

£524 $817 €786 Sortie de la foret (33x24cm-13x9in) s. s.i.d.1976 verso prov. 9-Nov-2 Galerie Gloggner, Luzern #99/R (S.FR 1200)
£1223 $1907 €1835 Hameau in winter (33x55cm-13x22in) s. i.d.1967 verso. 8-Nov-2 Dobiaschofsky, Bern #91/R est:3000 (S.FR 2800)

MONNIER, Claire Lise (20th C) Swiss

£408 $644 €612 Still life composition in red (46x27cm-18x11in) s. s.i.d.63 verso. 29-Nov-2 Zofingen, Switzerland #2992 (S.FR 950)

MONNOYER, Jean Baptiste (1636-1699) French

£3526 $5535 €5500 Corbeille de fleurs sur entablement (99x130cm-39x51in) 14-Dec-2 Artcurial Briest, Paris #45/R
£5406 $8433 €8000 Nature morte au vase de fleurs sur entablement (42x32cm-17x13in) s. 26-Mar-3 Tajan, Paris #64/R
£51282 $81026 €80000 Flowers, fruit, animals and works of art (190x158cm-75x62in) prov. 13-Nov-2 Ansorena, Madrid #131/R est:80000

MONNOYER, Jean Baptiste (circle) (1636-1699) French

£6475 $10360 €9000 Still life of flowers and fruit (66x77cm-26x30in) 17-May-3 Lempertz, Koln #1089/R est:9000
£6604 $10698 €9576 Still life of flowers (41x32cm-16x13in) prov. 24-May-3 Galerie Gloggner, Luzern #84/R est:3800-4500 (S.FR 14000)
£7000 $10850 €10500 Crysanthemums, morning glory and other flowers in a glass vase (68x63cm-27x25in) 30-Oct-2 Christie's, Kensington #104/R est:7000-10000

MONNOYER, Jean Baptiste (style) (1636-1699) French

£5096 $7949 €8000 Flowers in a sculpted vase on a draped ledge (86x98cm-34x39in) 6-Nov-2 Christie's, Amsterdam #84/R est:10000-15000
£6250 $10000 €9375 Still life with swag of flowers around an urn (98x74cm-39x29in) bears sig. 14-May-3 Butterfields, San Francisco #1038/R est:10000-15000
£6500 $10205 €9750 Roses, carnations and other flowers in a basket on a stone ledge (63x90cm-25x35in) 13-Dec-2 Christie's, Kensington #176/R est:5000-7000
£6875 $11000 €10313 Still life with tulips, roses and other flowers in a vase (71x52cm-28x20in) 14-May-3 Butterfields, San Francisco #1039/R est:3000-5000

£9500 $14915 €14250 Roses, carnations and other flowers in a basket by a tree in a hilly landscape (78x107cm-31x42in) 13-Dec-2 Christie's, Kensington #183/R est:8000-12000

MONOGRAMMIST A (?) ?
£2532 $4000 €4000 Foret et dreve (140x170cm-55x67in) pair. 2-Dec-2 Amberes, Antwerp #1327

MONOGRAMMIST A D (?) ?
£764 $1177 €1200 Resting point (43x54cm-17x21in) i. 5-Sep-2 Arnold, Frankfurt #818/R
£2087 $3235 €3131 Three girls in traditional costume teasing miller and companions (81x65cm-32x26in) mono.i.d.1886. 9-Dec-2 Philippe Schuler, Zurich #3922 est:3000-5000 (S.FR 4800)

Works on paper
£823 $1300 €1300 Sketch for fountain allegory (27x19cm-11x7in) mono.d.1629 pen wash. 29-Nov-2 Bassenge, Berlin #5388/R

MONOGRAMMIST A E (?) ?
£772 $1096 €1158 Three ladies in a park (85x58cm-33x23in) painted c.1830. 26-Mar-2 SOGA, Bratislava #161/R (SL.K 49000)

MONOGRAMMIST A G (?) ?
£1410 $2186 €2200 Old small city on the bend of a river (12x18cm-5x7in) mono. indis.i.verso iron plate. 4-Dec-2 Neumeister, Munich #823/R est:2200
£1816 $2834 €2724 Revelling (59x74cm-23x29in) init. 11-Apr-3 Kieselbach, Budapest #78/R est:650000 (H.F 650000)

MONOGRAMMIST A K (?) ?
£1164 $1816 €1700 Head of child (37x37cm-15x15in) mono. canvas on board. 10-Apr-3 Van Ham, Cologne #1594 est:1500

Works on paper
£957 $1492 €1436 Houses (39x47cm-15x19in) mono.d.1926 gouache. 16-Sep-2 Philippe Schuler, Zurich #6822 (S.FR 2200)

MONOGRAMMIST A M (?) ?
£2146 $3391 €3219 Soldiers with child in front of the burning town of Moscow (33x44cm-13x17in) mono.d.1867. 29-Nov-2 Zofingen, Switzerland #2350/R est:6000 (S.FR 5000)

Works on paper
£435 $713 €600 Figures de femmes (50x30cm-20x12in) pastel. 27-May-3 Campo & Campo, Antwerp #137

MONOGRAMMIST A P (?) ?
£419 $611 €629 Landscape with lake and figures (22x30cm-9x12in) mono. 17-Jun-2 Philippe Schuler, Zurich #7351 (S.FR 950)
£892 $1400 €1338 Arab on horseback (20x28cm-8x11in) panel. 13-Dec-2 Du Mouchelle, Detroit #2347/R est:800-1200

MONOGRAMMIST A W (?) ?
£609 $944 €950 Mountain landscape in summer with peasant and child on path (33x41cm-13x16in) mono.d.1878. 7-Dec-2 Dannenberg, Berlin #705/R

MONOGRAMMIST B A C (?) ?
£816 $1298 €1200 Hot soup being served in Spanish market (44x33cm-17x13in) mono. canvas on board. 19-Mar-3 Neumeister, Munich #652/R est:1000

MONOGRAMMIST B L S (?) ?
£409 $634 €650 Schloss Marzoll (31x42cm-12x17in) mono.d.74. 29-Oct-2 Dorotheum, Vienna #155/R

MONOGRAMMIST B V K (?) ?
£3851 $6008 €5700 Southern scene (99x135cm-39x53in) mono.d.1844. 27-Mar-3 Dr Fritz Nagel, Stuttgart #847/R est:1800

MONOGRAMMIST C R (?) ?
£276 $441 €400 Early morning (15x19cm-6x7in) mono. i. verso canvas on panel. 11-Mar-3 Dorotheum, Vienna #67
£321 $503 €500 Hydrangeas (45x48cm-18x19in) mono. 22-Nov-2 Karrenbauer, Konstanz #1854
£1034 $1634 €1500 Jewish portrait (34x26cm-13x10in) mono.d.1910 board. 5-Apr-3 Hans Stahl, Hamburg #66/R est:500

MONOGRAMMIST C V B (?) ?
£692 $1079 €1100 Hilly landscape with figures, ruins, animals and bust on pillar (46x59cm-18x23in) panel. 9-Oct-2 Michael Zeller, Lindau #588/R

MONOGRAMMIST C V L (?) ?
£11000 $18370 €15950 Idolatory of Solomon (60x85cm-24x33in) mono.d.1658 panel. 10-Jul-3 Sotheby's, London #132/R est:12000-18000

MONOGRAMMIST D L (?) ?
£513 $805 €800 Portrait d'une dame de qualite en robe blanche (81x65cm 32x26in) mono. painted c.1830. 10-Dec-2 Vanderkindere, Brussels #59

MONOGRAMMIST D V (17th C) Flemish?
£432 $709 €626 Shipwreck (24x38cm-9x15in) mono. panel. 4-Jun-3 AB Stockholms Auktionsverk #2421/R (S.KR 5500)

MONOGRAMMIST E C W (?) ?
£962 $1490 €1500 Children by a stream in front of farmhouse (30x40cm-12x16in) mono. i.verso. 4-Dec-2 Neumeister, Munich #824/R est:1500

MONOGRAMMIST E D (?) ?

Works on paper
£2400 $3960 €3480 Crescent at Buxton, Derbyshire (30x48cm-12x19in) mono.d.1839 W/C bodycol. 3-Jul-3 Duke & Son, Dorchester #161/R est:2000-3000

MONOGRAMMIST E F (?) ?
£962 $1462 €1500 Cale de la Fenetre (50x32cm-20x13in) mono. panel. 17-Aug-2 Livinec, Gaudcheau & Jezequel, Rennes #42

MONOGRAMMIST E L (?) ?
£2979 $4617 €4469 Bedouins and camels in the desert (100x133cm-39x52in) mono.d.1855. 4-Dec-2 AB Stockholms Auktionsverk #1882/R est:20000-25000 (S.KR 42000)

MONOGRAMMIST E R T (?) ?
£1633 $2596 €2400 Italian coast (82x119cm-32x47in) mono.d.1840. 19-Mar-3 Neumeister, Munich #654/R est:2200

MONOGRAMMIST E W (?) ?
£1972 $3175 €2800 Hunting dogs chasing cat (33x23cm-13x9in) two. 7-May-3 Michael Zeller, Lindau #837/R est:2800

MONOGRAMMIST F B (?) ?
£892 $1463 €1293 Flowers on stone (21x29cm-8x11in) s.i.d.15.Mrtz 1827 tempera. 4-Jun-3 Fischer, Luzern #2456/R est:1200-1500 (S.FR 1900)

MONOGRAMMIST F D K (?) ?
£1361 $2163 €2000 Girl eating cherries (32x22cm-13x9in) mono. 25-Feb-3 Dorotheum, Vienna #63/R est:2000-2200

MONOGRAMMIST F G S (?) ?
£601 $938 €950 Seated nude (89x74cm-35x29in) mono. board. 15-Oct-2 Dorotheum, Vienna #100/R

MONOGRAMMIST F M B (?) ?
£2394 $3975 €3400 Portrait of a youth. mono. 11-Jun-3 Dorotheum, Vienna #4/R est:2000-3000

MONOGRAMMIST F V B (?) ?
£252 $392 €400 Portrait of a noble man (27x23cm-11x9in) mono.d.1832 panel. 23-Sep-2 Bernaerts, Antwerp #221/R

MONOGRAMMIST G S (?) ?
£1090 $1722 €1700 Sunrise (55x110cm-22x43in) mono.d.02. 12-Nov-2 Dorotheum, Vienna #7/R est:1600-2200

MONOGRAMMIST G T (?) ?
£1258 $1962 €2000 River landscape with anglers and thatched cottages (27x37cm-11x15in) bears i.mono. verso. 21-Sep-2 Bolland & Marotz, Bremen #435/R est:1300

MONOGRAMMIST H B (?) ?
£620 $961 €930 Sheep in a landscape (16x20cm-6x8in) mono. panel. 1-Nov-2 Moore Allen & Innocent, Cirencester #498/R

MONOGRAMMIST H C (?) ?
£1879 $3026 €2800 Interior with a peasant family beside a fire (42x60cm-17x24in) mono. panel prov.lit. 18-Feb-3 Sotheby's, Amsterdam #212/R est:1800-2200

MONOGRAMMIST H H (?) ?
£325 $484 €500 Cat couple on Sunday stroll (17x15cm-7x6in) mono. panel. 27-Jun-2 Neumeister, Munich #2859/R

MONOGRAMMIST H M (?) ?
£563 $907 €800 Bacchantal procession (28x123cm-11x48in) supraporte. 7-May-3 Michael Zeller, Lindau #839
£685 $1068 €1000 Italian mountain landscape with waterfall and figures (51x67cm-20x26in) mono.d.1861. 10-Apr-3 Schopman, Hamburg #584
£775 $1247 €1100 Kiel Regatta 1907 (25x40cm-10x16in) mono.d.07. 10-May-3 Hans Stahl, Toestorf #63/R

MONOGRAMMIST I F A (?) ?
£2121 $3478 €3075 Seascape with sailing vessel flying the American flag (48x63cm-19x25in) mono. 4-Jun-3 AB Stockholms Auktionsverk #2422/R est:20000-25000 (S.KR 27000)

MONOGRAMMIST I H (?) ?
£776 $1257 €1125 View on the Old London Road, Sneinton in distance (31x46cm-12x18in) mono.d.1850. 25-May-3 Uppsala Auktionskammare, Uppsala #74/R (S.KR 10000)

MONOGRAMMIST I K (?) ?
£610 $1001 €885 Southern river landscape with figures (71x92cm-28x36in) mono. 4-Jun-3 Fischer, Luzern #2253/R (S.FR 1300)

MONOGRAMMIST J A H (?) ?
£1250 $2063 €1813 Young boy holding a pond yacht (76x56cm-30x22in) mono.d.1867. 3-Jul-3 Duke & Son, Dorchester #248/R est:500-1000

MONOGRAMMIST J E (?) ?
£779 $1239 €1169 Whaling crew capsizing in arctic waters. Whaling with a Three masted ship in arctic waters (30x43cm-12x17in) mono. pair. 1-May-3 Waddingtons, Toronto #94/R est:1500-2000 (C.D 1800)

MONOGRAMMIST J H (?) ?
£769 $1192 €1200 Winter landscape with hunters (50x102cm-20x40in) mono.i. after G Wimmer. 6-Dec-2 Auktionhaus Georg Rehm, Augsburg #8086/R

MONOGRAMMIST J H V B (?) ?
£2830 $4415 €4500 Ambush on country track (50x65cm-20x26in) bears mono. panel. 20-Sep-2 Schloss Ahlden, Ahlden #1063/R est:4500

MONOGRAMMIST J J (?) ?
£519 $774 €800 Mountain valley with stream (79x71cm-31x28in) mono. 27-Jun-2 Neumeister, Munich #2861/R

MONOGRAMMIST J L (?) ?
£5449 $8446 €8500 Winter amusement on the ice-rink (72x114cm-28x45in) mono. canvas on canvas lit. 4-Dec-2 Neumeister, Munich #614/R est:4000

MONOGRAMMIST J P (?) ?
£2548 $3975 €4000 Wooded river landscape with a nymph bathing (41x39cm-16x15in) mono. 5-Nov-2 Sotheby's, Amsterdam #59/R est:5000-7000
Works on paper
£281 $436 €422 Harbour with Chinese people (9x14cm-4x6in) mono.d.1771 gouache oval. 24-Sep-2 Koller, Zurich #6472/R (S.FR 650)

MONOGRAMMIST J W (?) ?
£680 $1082 €1000 Gypsy woman with child. Kettle peddler (21x13cm-8x5in) mono.d.83 two. 19-Mar-3 Neumeister, Munich #656/R est:1200

MONOGRAMMIST L F (?) ?
£422 $629 €650 Farmstead in pre-Alpine landscape (15x22cm-6x9in) mono.d.1869 panel. 27-Jun-2 Neumeister, Munich #2862/R

MONOGRAMMIST L M (?) ?
£1069 $1668 €1700 Portrait of Kaiser Wilhelm I (88x71cm-35x28in) mono.i. 20-Sep-2 Schloss Ahlden, Ahlden #1113/R est:900

MONOGRAMMIST M B (?) ?
£2564 $4026 €4000 Paysage anime de figures (17x23cm-7x9in) copper. 15-Dec-2 Mercier & Cie, Lille #310/R
£2885 $4471 €4500 River landscapes (18x27cm-7x11in) panel pair. 6-Dec-2 Maigret, Paris #91/R est:7000
£9091 $15182 €13000 Paysages de riviere animes de personnages (23x27cm-9x11in) one mono. panel pair. 25-Jun-3 Tajan, Paris #31/R est:12000-15000

MONOGRAMMIST M G (?) ?
£1277 $2068 €1800 Study of a Pomeranian (42x33cm-17x13in) mono.d.1876. 20-May-3 Mealy's, Castlecomer #965/R est:300-500

MONOGRAMMIST M H (?) ?
£513 $810 €800 Landscape (54x62cm-21x24in) mono. board. 12-Nov-2 Dorotheum, Vienna #132/R

MONOGRAMMIST M I S (?) ?
Works on paper
£380 $608 €551 Bleaching the linen (27x37cm-11x15in) W/C. 17-May-3 Thomson Roddick & Medcalf, Edinburgh #667/R

MONOGRAMMIST M S (?) ?
£510 $795 €800 Agony in the garden (49x37cm-19x15in) mono. 5-Nov-2 Sotheby's, Amsterdam #127
£8276 $13241 €12000 Garden (142x140cm-56x55in) mono. three part screen prov. 11-Mar-3 Dorotheum, Vienna #40/R est:2200-3000

MONOGRAMMIST N H (?) ?
Works on paper
£2300 $3749 €3450 Royal favourites at Windsor (30x44cm-12x17in) init.d.1900 pencil W/C pair. 29-Jan-3 Dreweatt Neate, Newbury #33 est:200-250

MONOGRAMMIST O P (?) ?
£2516 $3925 €4000 Scene from 18th C battle (66x98cm-26x39in) mono. 23-Sep-2 Wiener Kunst Auktionen, Vienna #60/R est:1000-2200

MONOGRAMMIST P B B (?) ?
Works on paper
£400 $664 €600 London, Portland Place and Broadcasting House (33x38cm-13x15in) mono. W/C. 12-Jun-3 Scarborough Perry Fine Arts, Hove #447

MONOGRAMMIST P L (?) ?
£353 $536 €550 Peasant with pipe resting (27x35cm-11x14in) panel. 11-Jul-2 Hugo Ruef, Munich #574

MONOGRAMMIST P S (?) ?
£1747 $2760 €2621 Icy pleasures (57x74cm-22x29in) mono.d.1817. 14-Nov-2 Stuker, Bern #411/R est:2500-3000 (S.FR 4000)

MONOGRAMMIST P V B (?) ?
£1429 $2129 €2200 River landscape with oriental figures (29x21cm-11x8in) mono. bears d.1711 copper. 26-Jun-2 Neumeister, Munich #644/R

MONOGRAMMIST P W L (?) ?
£4292 $6652 €6438 Orpheus with animals (75x160cm-30x63in) mono. d.1581/17 panel. 3-Oct-2 Koller, Zurich #3003/R est:15000-25000 (S.FR 10000)

MONOGRAMMIST R A H (?) ?
£3355 $5402 €5000 Fishboats near the coast at sunset (45x57cm-18x22in) mono.d.1836. 18-Feb-3 Sotheby's, Amsterdam #644/R est:2500-3500

MONOGRAMMIST S A (?) ?
Miniatures
£2300 $3726 €3450 Gentleman wearing crimson cloak (7cm-3in) mono. oval gilt frame. 22-May-3 Bonhams, New Bond Street #18/R est:2500-3500

MONOGRAMMIST T H (?) ?
Works on paper
£1007 $1612 €1400 Walk in the woods (22x17cm-9x7in) mono. W/C. 17-May-3 Lempertz, Koln #1321/R

MONOGRAMMIST V B (?) ?
Miniatures
£1000 $1550 €1500 Nina Boucault, as a young girl (6cm-2in) mono. gilt metal frame oval. 1-Oct-2 Bonhams, New Bond Street #310/R est:400-600

MONOGRAMMIST V E (?) ?
£2767 $4317 €4400 Flower arrangement (55x43cm-22x17in) mono. 19-Sep-2 Dr Fritz Nagel, Stuttgart #887/R est:1500

MONOGRAMMIST V H (?) ?
£710 $1043 €1100 Still life of flowers in glass vase (51x43cm-20x17in) mono. 20-Jun-2 Dr Fritz Nagel, Stuttgart #718/R

MONOGRAMMIST W B (?) ?
£1700 $2635 €2550 Portrait of a young boy in a brimmed hat (107x91cm-42x36in) mono. canvas on panel. 26-Sep-2 Lane, Penzance #328 est:1500-1700

MONOGRAMMIST W C (?) ?
Works on paper
£566 $871 €849 King Arthur's Castle (36x56cm-14x22in) s.indis.d.187. 27-Oct-2 Anders Antik, Landskrona #46/R (S.KR 8200)

MONOGRAMMIST W M (?) ?
£652 $1011 €978 Still life with fruit and wine glass (33x41cm-13x16in) mono. 9-Dec-2 Philippe Schuler, Zurich #3923/R (S.FR 1500)
£1918 $2992 €2800 Returning home after the harvest (29x40cm-11x16in) mono. 10-Apr-3 Dorotheum, Vienna #3/R est:2800-3200

MONOGRAMMIST W Q (?) ?
£692 $1079 €1100 Man watching three young women looking in mirror (60x95cm-24x37in) mono.d.88. 19-Sep-2 Dr Fritz Nagel, Stuttgart #971/R

MONORY, Jacques (1924-) French
£972 $1546 €1400 Etude pour la premiere version de la terrasse no 9 (120x126cm-47x50in) i. acrylic plexiglas photos cardboard. 29-Apr-3 Artcurial Briest, Paris #427 est:1200-1500
£1111 $1766 €1600 Etude pour la premiere version de la terrasse no 10 (121x126cm-48x50in) i. acrylic plexiglas photos cardboard lit. 29-Apr-3 Artcurial Briest, Paris #426/R est:1200-1500
£3946 $6273 €5800 Death Valley 7 (146x114cm-57x45in) s.i.d.1975 lit. 24-Mar-3 Cornette de St.Cyr, Paris #71/R
£4487 $7045 €7000 Mademoiselle (92x73cm-36x29in) s.d.1966 s.i.d.verso. 20-Nov-2 Binoche, Paris #37/R
£5128 $8051 €8000 J'ai vecu une autre vie (89x130cm-35x51in) s.i.d.1969. 20-Nov-2 Binoche, Paris #38/R
£6944 $10972 €10000 Exercice de style (83x73cm-33x29in) s.d. s.i.d.verso prov.lit. 27-Apr-3 Perrin, Versailles #75/R est:10000-12000
£7823 $12439 €11500 Images incurables (114x162cm-45x64in) s.i.d.1974 verso exhib.lit. 24-Mar-3 Cornette de St.Cyr, Paris #55/R est:15000
£8334 $13250 €12000 Les voyeuses (150x500cm-59x197in) s.i.d.verso prov.exhib.lit. 29-Apr-3 Artcurial Briest, Paris #376/R est:12000-15000
£13648 $21018 €21700 REvolution impossible (140x162cm-55x64in) s.d.1966 panel exhib.lit. 26-Oct-2 Cornette de St.Cyr, Paris #71/R
£14584 $23188 €21000 La terrasse no 7 (150x160cm-59x63in) s.d.1989 verso acrylic lit. 29-Apr-3 Artcurial Briest, Paris #394/R est:16000-18000
£19445 $30917 €28000 La voleuse no 6 (170x340cm-67x134in) s.d.1986 i.verso exhib.lit. 29-Apr-3 Artcurial Briest, Paris #384/R est:30000-35000

MONOSTORI-MOLLER, Pal (1894-?) Hungarian
£2420 $3752 €3509 Coffee house terrace in Paris (61x71cm-24x28in) s. panel. 9-Dec-2 Mu Terem Galeria, Budapest #9/R est:380000 (H.F 900000)

MONOT, Pierre Étienne (1657-1733) French
Works on paper
£333 $517 €520 Bacchus couronne (18x22cm-7x9in) s. pen ink over crayon. 4-Dec-2 Piasa, Paris #94

MONRO, Alasdair (1946-) Canadian
£271 $425 €407 My studio (34x27cm-13x11in) s. paper. 25-Nov-2 Hodgins, Calgary #90/R (C.D 675)

MONSTED, P (1859-1941) Danish
£769 $1184 €1154 Nature morte (24x21cm-9x8in) init.d.77. 4-Sep-2 Kunsthallen, Copenhagen #55/R (D.KR 9000)

MONSTED, Peder (1859-1941) Danish
£298 $471 €447 Portrait of Captain Olsen (44x30cm-17x12in) s.i.d.12.7.1907. 2-Dec-2 Rasmussen, Copenhagen #1795/R (D.KR 3500)
£391 $622 €587 Horses grazing in front of wagon (9x12cm-4x5in) init.d.1881. 10-Mar-3 Rasmussen, Vejle #145/R (D.KR 4200)
£400 $632 €600 Brewing storm (19x25cm-7x10in) s.i.d.1892 panel. 14-Nov-2 Christie's, Kensington #13
£680 $1060 €1020 Portrait of lady wearing black dress (47x39cm-19x15in) s.d.1907. 5-Aug-2 Rasmussen, Vejle #255/R (D.KR 8000)
£1288 $2034 €1932 Wooded glade (27x40cm-11x16in) s.d.1898. 3-Apr-3 Heffel, Vancouver #67/R est:3500-4500 (C.D 3000)
£1288 $2034 €1932 Portrait of an African (27x22cm-11x9in) s.d.1886. 13-Nov-2 Kunsthallen, Copenhagen #83/R est:18000 (D.KR 15000)
£1306 $2103 €1959 Portrait of Edvard Munch's psychiatrist dr.med. Daniel Eduard Jacobson (48x34cm-19x13in) i. 26-Feb-3 Museumsbygningen, Copenhagen #49/R est:6000-8000 (D.KR 14500)
£1397 $2221 €2096 Still life of branch of cherries, wild flowers in vase and fly on wall (25x22cm-10x9in) init.d.77. 5-Mar-3 Rasmussen, Copenhagen #1845/R est:20000 (D.KR 15000)
£1397 $2221 €2096 From Aalsgaarde towards the coast of Sweden (30x36cm-12x14in) s.d.1919. 5-Mar-3 Rasmussen, Copenhagen #2013/R est:15000 (D.KR 15000)
£1605 $2503 €2408 View from woodland across Sundet (23x32cm-9x13in) s.d.1901. 23-Sep-2 Rasmussen, Vejle #39/R est:12000 (D.KR 19000)
£1715 $2676 €2573 Landscape from Julso seen from Himmelbjerget (67x48cm-26x19in) s.i.d.1937. 11-Nov-2 Rasmussen, Vejle #659/R est:25000 (D.KR 20000)
£1872 $2958 €2808 Lake landscape with washerwomen (24x41cm-9x16in) s.d.1889. 2-Dec-2 Rasmussen, Copenhagen #1204/R est:25000 (D.KR 22000)
£1879 $2893 €2819 Spring landscape with sheep grazing near farm (47x62cm-19x24in) s.i.d.1923. 4-Sep-2 Kunsthallen, Copenhagen #131/R est:30000 (D.KR 22000)
£2048 $3257 €3072 Farmyard with chickens (35x52cm-14x20in) s.i.d.1923. 10-Mar-3 Rasmussen, Vejle #231/R est:25000 (D.KR 22000)
£2105 $3411 €3052 Landscape with the river in Sorgenfri (23x38cm-9x15in) init.d.1886. 26-May-3 Rasmussen, Copenhagen #1495/R est:15000 (D.KR 22000)
£2216 $3590 €3324 Figures praying on riverbank, North Africa (33x24cm-13x9in) s.d.1894 cardboard. 25-Jan-3 Rasmussen, Havnen #2247/R est:20000 (D.KR 25000)
£2357 $3865 €3418 Woman on terrace (32x22cm-13x9in) s.d.1892. 4-Jun-3 AB Stockholms Auktionsverk #2477/R est:40000-50000 (S.KR 30000)
£2390 $3681 €3800 Caravane (22x16cm-9x6in) s.d.1893 cardboard. 23-Oct-2 Rabourdin & Choppin de Janvry, Paris #150/R
£2421 $3849 €3632 Wooded landscape with river (40x60cm-16x24in) s.d.1905. 10-Mar-3 Rasmussen, Vejle #248/R est:20000 (D.KR 26000)
£2452 $3923 €3678 Interior scene with woman seated by window (45x42cm-18x17in) s.i.d.85. 13-Jan-3 Rasmussen, Vejle #5/R est:30000 (D.KR 28000)
£2584 $3928 €3876 Children with sleigh in Dyrehaven (31x41cm-12x16in) s.i.d.1924. 27-Aug-2 Rasmussen, Copenhagen #1421/R est:30000 (D.KR 30000)
£2679 $4341 €3885 Camels and figures by a pyramid (27x20cm-11x8in) s.d.1894. 26-May-3 Rasmussen, Copenhagen #1322/R est:35000 (D.KR 28000)
£2799 $4450 €4199 Harvest scene at the outskirts of Asminderod (40x45cm-16x18in) s.i.d.1922. 5-May-3 Rasmussen, Vejle #446/R est:20000-25000 (D.KR 30000)
£2804 $4374 €4206 Figures with horse and sleigh near Herstedoster (35x50cm-14x20in) s.i.d.1929. 5-Aug-2 Rasmussen, Vejle #229/R est:30000 (D.KR 33000)
£2871 $4651 €4163 Ducks in front of farmhouse, summer (41x61cm-16x24in) s.i.d.1919. 26-May-3 Rasmussen, Copenhagen #1304/R est:50000 (D.KR 30000)
£2871 $4651 €4163 Boat bridge at Faeno (50x38cm-20x15in) s.i.d.1915. 26-May-3 Rasmussen, Copenhagen #1436/R est:20000 (D.KR 30000)
£3015 $4582 €4523 Spring landscape, Marselisborg Woods (36x58cm-14x23in) init.d.81. 27-Aug-2 Rasmussen, Copenhagen #1422/R est:35000-40000 (D.KR 35000)
£3349 $5426 €4856 Autumn forest with lake (16x22cm-6x9in) s.d.1891. 26-May-3 Rasmussen, Copenhagen #1172/R est:15000 (D.KR 35000)
£3404 $5379 €5106 Landscape from Aarhus bay with children playing at water's edge (43x65cm-17x26in) s. 2-Dec-2 Rasmussen, Copenhagen #1260/R est:40000-50000 (D.KR 40000)
£3797 $6000 €6000 At the farmyard - two children by house (35x49cm-14x19in) s.i.d.1908. 30-Nov-2 Hagelstam, Helsinki #43/R est:6000
£3885 $6061 €5828 Sunset over water (26x36cm-10x14in) s.d.1900. 23-Sep-2 Rasmussen, Vejle #38/R est:15000-20000 (D.KR 46000)
£4000 $6200 €6000 Winter landscape (46x62cm-18x24in) s.i.d.1924. 3-Dec-2 Sotheby's, Olympia #302/R est:4000-6000
£4139 $6456 €6209 Ducks at watercourse near mill (58x40cm-23x16in) s.d.1909. 23-Sep-2 Rasmussen, Vejle #44/R est:50000 (D.KR 49000)
£4500 $7380 €6750 View of Cairo (33x23cm-13x9in) s.d.1894 panel. 3-Jun-3 Sotheby's, London #161/R est:5000-7000

£4500 $7380 €6750 Strandparti - view of the seashore (53x86cm-21x34in) s.i.d.1919 prov. 3-Jun-3 Sotheby's, London #256/R est:4000-6000
£4615 $7015 €7200 Idyllic village street with peasant girls, oxen and hens (52x78cm-20x31in) s.d.1906. 17-Aug-2 Hans Stahl, Toestorf #93/R est:3500
£4645 $7247 €6968 The bay at Hjortnaes, Soro, with man fishing from rowing boat (53x79cm-21x31in) s.d.1903. 23-Sep-2 Rasmussen, Vejle #42/R est:75000-80000 (D.KR 55000)
£4655 $7402 €6983 Birds in river landscape (43x66cm-17x26in) s.d.1898. 5-Mar-3 Rasmussen, Copenhagen #1531/R est:50000 (D.KR 50000)
£4816 $7706 €7224 Children playing under flowering chestnut tree (43x57cm-17x22in) s.i.d.1921. 13-Jan-3 Rasmussen, Vejle #22/R est:50000-75000 (D.KR 55000)
£5000 $8200 €7500 Blomster plukkes - picking flowers (16x23cm-6x9in) s.d.87. 3-Jun-3 Sotheby's, London #249/R est:5000-7000
£5200 $8112 €7800 Bather (56x39cm-22x15in) s.i.d.1917. 17-Sep-2 Sotheby's, Olympia #279/R est:4000-6000
£5742 $9301 €8326 Spring forest with waterway (40x60cm-16x24in) s.d.1905. 26-May-3 Rasmussen, Copenhagen #1185/R est:50000 (D.KR 60000)
£5777 $9013 €8666 Woodland lake with swallow and wood anemones (28x48cm-11x19in) s.d.1900. 5-Aug-2 Rasmussen, Vejle #186/R est:30000-40000 (D.KR 68000)
£6099 $9454 €9149 Trollhattefallen - landscape with waterfall (83x120cm-33x47in) s.d.1897. 3-Dec-2 Bukowskis, Stockholm #303a/R est:80000-100000 (S.KR 86000)
£6220 $10077 €9019 A pergola from Anacapri (31x26cm-12x10in) s.d.1895. 26-May-3 Rasmussen, Copenhagen #1323/R est:15000 (D.KR 65000)
£6284 $10306 €9112 River landscape with ducks (70x100cm-28x39in) s.i.d.1935. 4-Jun-3 AB Stockholms Auktionsverk #2433/R est:100000-135000 (S.KR 80000)
£6460 $9819 €9690 Landscape from Villa d'Este, Tivoli (122x95cm-48x37in) s.d.1884. 27-Aug-2 Rasmussen, Copenhagen #1440/R est:75000-125000 (D.KR 75000)
£6460 $9819 €9690 Talking by a farmhouse with flowers in garden (44x65cm-17x26in) s. 27-Aug-2 Rasmussen, Copenhagen #1463/R est:75000-100000 (D.KR 75000)
£6699 $10852 €9714 Autumn day in Frederiksberg Garden (61x90cm-24x35in) s.i.d.1923. 26-May-3 Rasmussen, Copenhagen #1186/R est:50000-75000 (D.KR 70000)
£6800 $11152 €10200 Pa terrassen, Ravello - terrace, Ravello (62x40cm-24x16in) s.i. 3-Jun-3 Sotheby's, London #269/R est:5000-7000
£6982 $11311 €10124 Lac Leman (33x25cm-13x10in) init.d.1887. 26-May-3 Bukowskis, Stockholm #279/R est:70000-80000 (S.KR 90000)
£7234 $11430 €10851 View of a North Italian lake (70x100cm-28x39in) s.d.1913. 2-Dec-2 Rasmussen, Copenhagen #1140/R est:50000-75000 (D.KR 85000)
£7321 $11128 €10982 Children playing by farmhouse (46x62cm-18x24in) s.i.d.1924. 27-Aug-2 Rasmussen, Copenhagen #1462/R est:60000-75000 (D.KR 85000)
£7660 $12102 €11490 Mending the fishing nets (47x62cm-19x24in) s.i.d.1933. 2-Dec-2 Rasmussen, Copenhagen #1188/R est:75000-100000 (D.KR 90000)
£7843 $12863 €12000 Woodland path in spring (52x79cm-20x31in) s.d.1903. 29-Mar-3 Dannenberg, Berlin #625/R est:8500
£8183 $12438 €12275 Landscape with pond and white ducks (98x71cm-39x28in) s.i.d.1918. 27-Aug-2 Rasmussen, Copenhagen #1491/R est:50000-75000 (D.KR 95000)
£8500 $13346 €12750 Outskirts of Cario (37x55cm-15x22in) s.d.1893 prov. 19-Nov-2 Sotheby's, London #181/R est:6000-8000
£8511 $13447 €12767 Heather hills, Silkeborg Islands (123x200cm-48x79in) s.d.1908. 2-Dec-2 Rasmussen, Copenhagen #1165/R est:100000-150000 (D.KR 100000)
£8612 $13952 €12918 Bedouin camp at Gerzereh after sunset (55x80cm-22x31in) s.d.1892. 21-May-3 Museumsbygningen, Copenhagen #70/R est:75000-100000 (D.KR 90000)
£10000 $16700 €15000 Haystacks in an alpine pasture (50x70cm-20x28in) s.d.1924. 18-Jun-3 Christie's, Kensington #67/R est:10000-15000
£10764 $17007 €15500 Landscape covered in snow with figures (50x36cm-20x14in) s.i.d.1914. 25-Apr-3 Piasa, Paris #24/R
£12259 $19615 €18389 Spring landscape with river along path (81x124cm-32x49in) s.d.1909. 13-Jan-3 Rasmussen, Vejle #21/R est:150000 (D.KR 140000)
£12903 $20000 €19355 Fishing boats on the water, Cap Martin (70x100cm-28x39in) s.d.1907. 30-Oct-2 Christie's, Rockefeller NY #209/R est:20000-30000
£13397 $21703 €19426 Spring in garden - small girl watering flowers (72x48cm-28x19in) s.i.d.1920. 26-May-3 Rasmussen, Copenhagen #1184/R est:150000 (D.KR 140000)
£14935 $22253 €23000 Spreewald idyll near Lehde (81x121cm-32x48in) s.d.1914. 26-Jun-2 Neumeister, Munich #803/R est:14000
£17000 $27880 €25500 Skovstraekning - woodland landscape (100x70cm-39x28in) s.d.1907. 3-Jun-3 Sotheby's, London #244/R est:15000-20000
£17266 $27626 €24000 Farmsteads by river (70x100cm-28x39in) s.d.1910. 17-May-3 Lempertz, Koln #1442/R est:16000
£19718 $32732 €28000 Summer day in a wooded river stream with path and figure (81x123cm-32x48in) s.d.1908. 14-Jun-3 Arnold, Frankfurt #817/R est:12000
£22000 $36080 €33000 Vandlob i skoven - stream in the woods (90x149cm-35x59in) s.d.1905. 3-Jun-3 Sotheby's, London #232/R est:18000-25000
£26899 $42500 €40349 Charlottendun Forest (70x99cm-28x39in) s.d.1908. 24-Apr-3 Sotheby's, New York #85/R est:30000-50000
£27000 $44280 €40500 Flodbred - on the river (81x120cm-32x47in) s.i.d.1914. 3-Jun-3 Sotheby's, London #231/R est:18000-25000
£32258 $50000 €48387 An afternoon stroll (65x123cm-26x48in) s.d.1888 prov. 29-Oct-2 Sotheby's, New York #123/R est:40000-60000
£40000 $65600 €60000 Den rode paraply - red umbrella (68x122cm-27x48in) s.i.d.1888. 3-Jun-3 Sotheby's, London #241/R est:40000-60000

MONT, Hans (attrib) (16th C) Flemish
Works on paper
£12057 $20135 €17000 Defile militaire (18x26cm-7x10in) brown wash gouache. 19-Jun-3 Piasa, Paris #48/R est:2000-3000

MONTAG, Carl (1880-1956) Swiss
£793 $1181 €1190 Flowers in green vase (61x50cm-24x20in) s.d.1908 verso double-sided. 25-Jun-2 Koller, Zurich #6645/R (S.FR 1800)

MONTAGNE, Émile Pierre de la (1873-1956) Belgian
£260 $411 €390 Portrait, half length, of a gentleman seated at a desk (85x108cm-33x43in) s.d.1921. 12-Nov-2 Bonhams, Knightsbridge #173/R
£3514 $5481 €5200 Femme nue (84x111cm-33x44in) s. 25-Mar-3 Campo & Campo, Antwerp #52/R est:3500-4500
£3546 $5745 €5000 Picture of Paris (50x65cm-20x26in) s. 22-May-3 Dorotheum, Vienna #188/R est:5000-6000

MONTAGNE, Louis (1879-1960) French
£660 $1042 €950 Crepuscule a Venise (26x34cm-10x13in) s. i.verso panel. 28-Apr-3 Cornette de St.Cyr, Paris #285
Works on paper
£1172 $1864 €1700 Le port de Cannes (44x62cm-17x24in) s.i. W/C. 5-Mar-3 Oger, Dumont, Paris #24/R est:700-800

MONTAGUE, Alfred (fl.1832-1883) British
£700 $1169 €1015 Old grass market, Edinburgh. Old Folkstone, Kent (29x44cm-11x17in) s. pair. 8-Jul-3 Bonhams, Knightsbridge #33/R
£800 $1296 €1200 Hay barge and other vessels at a riverside town (15x35cm-6x14in) s.d.1878. 23-Jan-3 Christie's, Kensington #81/R
£827 $1324 €1150 Marina con pescatori (14x32cm-6x13in) s. cardboard. 17-May-3 Meeting Art, Vercelli #372/R
£1150 $1806 €1725 Fishing boats on the Medway (36x62cm-14x24in) s.d.1878. 16-Dec-2 Sotheby's, Olympia #44/R est:1000-1500
£1300 $2067 €1950 Rotterdam (41x61cm-16x24in) s. prov. 6-Mar-3 Christie's, Kensington #509/R est:1000-1500
£1806 $2655 €2800 Old English town street (30x24cm-12x9in) s. bears d. board. 20-Jun-2 Dr Fritz Nagel, Stuttgart #798/R est:1500
£2000 $3260 €3000 Guy Cliff, Nr Warwick (38x58cm-15x23in) s. prov. 14-Feb-3 Keys, Aylsham #679/R est:2000-3000
£2300 $3841 €3335 Shipping in a harbour (52x71cm-20x28in) s. indis d. 18-Jun-3 Sotheby's, Olympia #65/R est:1500-2500
£2400 $3912 €3480 Bringing in the catch (25x35cm-10x14in) s.d.1874 board. 16-Jul-3 Sotheby's, Olympia #90/R est:800-1200
£2800 $4536 €4200 View of Rotterdam (40x61cm-16x24in) s.d.1871 i.on overlap. 20-May-3 Sotheby's, Olympia #266/R est:1000-2000

MONTAGUE, Alfred (attrib) (fl.1832-1883) British
£400 $644 €600 Canal scene in a Continental town. Painted shipwreck (20x16cm-8x6in) mono. double-sided board. 18-Feb-3 Rowley Fine Art, Newmarket #345
£430 $671 €645 Sailing barges near the quayside (23x34cm-9x13in) 10-Sep-2 David Duggleby, Scarborough #341

MONTAGUE, Clifford (fl.1883-1900) British
£570 $889 €855 In the Aberglasyn district. Old Mill near Dolgelly (40x66cm-16x26in) one s.i. pair. 11-Sep-2 Bonhams, Newport #231
£600 $954 €900 Continental street (51x41cm-20x16in) s. indis d. 6-Mar-3 Christie's, Kensington #505/R
£780 $1271 €1170 Windsor Castle, Eton College. d.1916 i.verso. 12-Feb-3 Bonhams, Knightsbridge #53/R
£850 $1309 €1275 Angler on a bridge (30x46cm-12x18in) s.d.1891. 24-Oct-2 Christie's, Kensington #151/R
£1150 $1806 €1725 Dutch boats drying the sails. On the French river (34x59cm-13x23in) s. i.verso pair. 10-Dec-2 Bristol Auction Rooms #920/R est:1200-1500

MONTALBA, Clara (1842-1929) British
£1433 $2250 €2150 Harbor scene (39x32cm-15x13in) indis sig.i. on stretcher. 10-Dec-2 Doyle, New York #194/R est:4000-6000
Works on paper
£380 $616 €570 An early start (30x22cm-12x9in) s.d.77 W/C. 21-May-3 Bonhams, Knightsbridge #225/R
£400 $620 €600 Fishing boats moored at a quayside (27x37cm-11x15in) s.i.d.83 W/C. 25-Sep-2 Hamptons Fine Art, Godalming #274

MONTALBA, Clara (attrib) (1842-1929) British
£800 $1232 €1200 St Marco, Venice (46x61cm-18x24in) 3-Sep-2 Gorringes, Lewes #2289

MONTALBA, Hilda (?-1919) British
£423 $665 €635 Sunset over the lagoon (52x97cm-20x38in) s. 16-Dec-2 Lilla Bukowskis, Stockholm #780 (S.KR 6000)

MONTALD, Constant (1862-1944) Belgian
£385 $604 €600 Vase de roses (39x29cm-15x11in) mono. cardboard. 19-Nov-2 Servarts Themis, Bruxelles #129
£949 $1481 €1500 Maternite (140x85cm-55x33in) s. oil mixed media. 10-Sep-2 Vanderkindere, Brussels #395 est:1000-1500
£1007 $1612 €1400 Ferme a la levee de la brume (38x46cm-15x18in) s.d.09 panel. 19-May-3 Horta, Bruxelles #374
£4808 $7452 €7500 Orchard (67x110cm-26x43in) s.d.03. 3-Dec-2 Christie's, Amsterdam #238/R est:5000-7000
£5096 $7949 €8000 Deux jeunes femmes dans un jardin fleuri (80x30cm-31x12in) s.d.1898. 11-Nov-2 Horta, Bruxelles #170/R est:3500-4000
£5696 $9000 €9000 Paysage de neige (70x90cm-28x35in) s.d.16 cardboard. 26-Nov-2 Palais de Beaux Arts, Brussels #348/R est:7500-10000
£8176 $12673 €13000 Winter landscape (76x101cm-30x40in) s.d.28 exhib. 5-Oct-2 De Vuyst, Lokeren #540/R est:14000-16000
Works on paper
£7051 $10929 €11000 Libation (137x73cm-54x29in) s.d.02 W/C pastel prov. 7-Dec-2 De Vuyst, Lokeren #435b/R est:11000-13000

MONTALLIER, Alexandre (17th C) French
£20253 $32000 €32000 Paiement de la dime (57x70cm-22x28in) prov.lit. 27-Nov-2 Christie's, Paris #33/R est:20000-30000

MONTALVO, Bartolome (attrib) (1769-1846) Spanish
£1761 $2923 €2500 Pecheurs pres d'un rivage mediterraneen (21x27cm-8x11in) pair. 13-Jun-3 Rossini, Paris #93/R est:2000-3000

MONTAN, Anders (1846-1917) Swedish
£1164 $1885 €1688 Interior scene with woman and man playing concertina (47x60cm-19x24in) s.i.d.82. 25-May-3 Uppsala Auktionskammare, Uppsala #92/R est:15000-18000 (S.KR 15000)
£1571 $2577 €2278 Cottage interior with woman (48x38cm-19x15in) s.d.82. 4-Jun-3 AB Stockholms Auktionsverk #2193/R est:35000-40000 (S.KR 20000)
£2189 $3503 €3174 View towards the farm (67x79cm-26x31in) s. 18-May-3 Anders Antik, Landskrona #112 est:30000 (S.KR 28000)

MONTANA, Pietro (1890-1978) American
£446 $700 €669 Three men training horses with hilly background (64x86cm-25x34in) s. 19-Apr-3 James Julia, Fairfield #287/R

MONTANARI, Daniela (1969-) Italian
£1489 $2413 €2100 Untitled (150x200cm-59x79in) s.i.d.2002 verso. 20-May-3 Porro, Milan #42/R est:2200-2400

MONTANARINI, Luigi (1906-1998) Italian
£442 $703 €650 Impressions (48x68cm-19x27in) s. card. 1-Mar-3 Meeting Art, Vercelli #596
£833 $1317 €1300 Untitled (60x50cm-24x20in) painted 1973. 12-Nov-2 Babuino, Rome #298/R
£1282 $2013 €2000 Storm (55x64cm-22x25in) init.d.1943. 23-Nov-2 Meeting Art, Vercelli #425/R
£1526 $2411 €2380 Via Margutta (60x50cm-24x20in) painted 1950. 12-Nov-2 Babuino, Rome #310/R
£1986 $3099 €2900 Variations (80x100cm-31x39in) s. 10-Apr-3 Finarte Semenzato, Rome #239/R
Works on paper
£256 $403 €400 Maternity (27x18cm-11x7in) s. Chinese ink. 21-Nov-2 Finarte, Rome #70
£886 $1382 €1400 Composition (63x48cm-25x19in) s.d.1958 mixed media on canvas. 19-Oct-2 Semenzato, Venice #29/R
£949 $1481 €1500 Composition (63x48cm-25x19in) s.d.1958 mixed media on canvas. 19-Oct-2 Semenzato, Venice #30/R

MONTANE, Roger (1916-) French
£223 $350 €335 La Garde Barriere (65x81cm-26x32in) s.i. prov. 24-Nov-2 Butterfields, San Francisco #2624/R
£255 $400 €383 Les baigneuses (33x46cm-13x18in) s. canvasboard. 24-Nov-2 Butterfields, San Francisco #2674/R
£350 $550 €525 Port d'Elburg, Hollande (61x81cm-24x32in) s. prov. 24-Nov-2 Butterfields, San Francisco #2623/R
£420 $664 €630 La Barriere Blanche (91x74cm-36x29in) s. painted 1959-60. 14-Nov-2 Christie's, Kensington #122

MONTANEZ, Juan Martinez (1568-1649) Spanish
Sculpture
£14198 $23000 €21297 Christ Child (87cm-34in) painted lead lit. 23-Jan-3 Sotheby's, New York #201/R est:35000

MONTANEZ, Juan Martinez (attrib) (1568-1649) Spanish
Sculpture
£75000 $117750 €112500 Figure of st. Dominic (125cm-49in) polychrome giltwood prov.lit. 10-Dec-2 Sotheby's, London #116/R est:50000-80000

MONTANIER, Francis (1895-1974) French
£769 $1285 €1100 Aloes noir (46x33cm-18x13in) s. panel. 25-Jun-3 Claude Aguttes, Neuilly #118/R

MONTE, Alberto del (1933-) Argentinian
£258 $408 €400 Untitled (49x26cm-19x10in) s.d.95 board. 18-Dec-2 Castellana, Madrid #47/R

MONTEL, Alfred (20th C) ?
£750 $1230 €1125 Mixed summer flowers in a vase (50x61cm-20x24in) s. 5-Jun-3 Christie's, Kensington #790/R

MONTELATICI, Mario (1884-1974) Italian
Works on paper
£32911 $52000 €49367 Return from market (104x82cm-41x32in) s. pietre dure panel. 24-Apr-3 Christie's, Rockefeller NY #299/R est:50000-70000

MONTELUPO, Baccio da (1469-1535) Italian
Sculpture
£3548 $5606 €5500 Crucifixion (32x33cm-13x13in) painted wood. 19-Dec-2 Semenzato, Venice #74/R

MONTEMEZZO, Antonio (1841-1898) German
£11000 $17600 €16500 Playing on a swing with geese in the foreground (20x33cm-8x13in) s. panel. 13-Mar-3 Duke & Son, Dorchester #300/R est:5000-8000

MONTENARD, Frederic (1849-1926) French
£1319 $2085 €1900 Paysage provencal (37x46cm-15x18in) s. panel. 25-Apr-3 Piasa, Paris #170/R
£3694 $5763 €5800 Marseille, le vieux port (38x58cm-15x23in) s. 7-Nov-2 Claude Aguttes, Neuilly #68/R est:1500-1800
£3822 $5962 €6000 Trois mats sortant du vieux port de Marseille (38x46cm-15x18in) s. 7-Nov-2 Claude Aguttes, Neuilly #69 est:1000-1500

MONTENEGRO CAPELL, Jose (1855-1924) Spanish
£452 $714 €700 Patio in Jerez (49x22cm-19x9in) s.i.d.1901 board. 18-Dec-2 Ansorena, Madrid #33
£548 $866 €850 Cloister (49x19cm-19x7in) s.d.1901 board. 18-Dec-2 Ansorena, Madrid #393/R
£1301 $2030 €1900 Alcaceres patio, Seville (31x17cm-12x7in) s.d.1984 board. 8-Apr-3 Ansorena, Madrid #209/R

MONTENEGRO, Roberto (1881-1968) Mexican
£3401 $5442 €4931 Retrato do Roberto Segovia (80x80cm-31x31in) s.d.MCXXI. 15-May-3 Louis Morton, Mexico #121/R est:65000-70000 (M.P 55000)
£5668 $8841 €8502 Tres indigenas (70x71cm-28x28in) s. 17-Oct-2 Louis Morton, Mexico #111/R est:62000-66000 (M.P 90000)

MONTERO BUSTAMANTE, Jose Pedro (1875-1927) South American
£346 $540 €519 En la rada (25x31cm-10x12in) s. cardboard. 30-Jul-2 Galleria Y Remates, Montevideo #25

MONTERO MADRAZO, Nazario (1883-?) Spanish
£309 $501 €470 Village (50x75cm-20x30in) s.d.49. 21-Jan-3 Ansorena, Madrid #224/R

MONTERO, Manuel (?) Spanish?
£658 $1066 €1000 Virgin of Guadaloupe (84x64cm-33x25in) s. 21-Jan-3 Durán, Madrid #146/R

MONTES ITURRIOZ, Gaspar (1901-?) Spanish
£1161 $1835 €1800 Yauci farm (25x34cm-10x13in) s. s.i.d.1983 canvas on cardboard. 18-Dec-2 Ansorena, Madrid #15/R

MONTES LENGUAS, Jose (1929-2001) Uruguayan?
£256 $400 €384 From Zabala Square (40x51cm-16x20in) s.d.96. 10-Oct-2 Galleria Y Remates, Montevideo #44/R

MONTES, Pepe (1929-) Uruguayan
£385 $604 €600 Untitled (39x49cm-15x19in) s. cardboard. 16-Dec-2 Castellana, Madrid #975/R
£801 $1258 €1250 Untitled (52x42cm-20x17in) s. cardboard. 16-Dec-2 Castellana, Madrid #921/R

MONTESANO, Gian Marco (1949-) Italian
£886 $1400 €1400 Ange des pauvres (90x60cm-35x24in) s.i.verso. 29-Nov-2 Farsetti, Prato #252/R
£1013 $1600 €1600 Ange des riches (90x60cm-35x24in) s.i.verso. 29-Nov-2 Farsetti, Prato #438/R
£1282 $2026 €2000 You must know how to fight (120x100cm-47x39in) s.i.d.1992 verso acrylic. 15-Nov-2 Farsetti, Prato #14/R
£1282 $1987 €2000 Fresh waters at Cinecitta' (100x120cm-39x47in) s.i.d.1993 verso. 4-Dec-2 Finarte, Milan #540/R
£1351 $2108 €2000 Masks (59x69cm-23x27in) s.d.1975 verso acrylic. 26-Mar-3 Finarte Semenzato, Milan #168
£1835 $2900 €2900 Queen of Peace (55x45cm-22x18in) s.i.d.1991 verso. 29-Nov-2 Farsetti, Prato #65/R est:3300
£2703 $4216 €4000 Jeux de mains (104x115cm-41x45in) s.i.d.1975 verso. 26-Mar-3 Finarte Semenzato, Milan #164/R
Works on paper
£385 $596 €600 Saint George and the dragon (70x50cm-28x20in) s. pastel exec.1991. 4-Dec-2 Finarte, Milan #479/R

MONTESINOS, Ricardo (1942-) Spanish
£252 $387 €400 Washerwomen (38x46cm-15x18in) s.d.84. 22-Oct-2 Durán, Madrid #109/R
£566 $883 €900 Battle (66x81cm-26x32in) s. 8-Oct-2 Ansorena, Madrid #433/R

MONTEYNE, Roland (1932-) Belgian
Sculpture
£2222 $3533 €3200 De tuin van Loplop (107cm-42in) s.d.1970 num.3/3 bronze. 29-Apr-3 Campo, Vlaamse Kaai #226/R est:2000-2500
£2778 $4417 €4000 De echo van de stilte (75cm-30in) bronze. 29-Apr-3 Campo & Campo, Antwerp #228/R est:5000-6000

MONTEYS, Esperanza (20th C) Spanish
£315 $492 €460 Flowers (100x82cm-39x32in) s.d.91. 8-Apr-3 Ansorena, Madrid #299/R

MONTEZIN, Pierre Eugène (1874-1946) French
£3300 $5247 €4950 Nature morte aux oeillets (65x81cm-26x32in) s. oval prov. 20-Mar-3 Sotheby's, Olympia #34/R est:2000-3000
£3427 $5722 €4900 Vaches en sous bois (51x61cm-20x24in) s. 30-Jun-3 Pierre Berge, Paris #56/R est:5000-7000
£4276 $6799 €6200 Les abords du village (65x53cm-26x21in) s. 7-Mar-3 Rabourdin & Choppin de Janvry, Paris #19/R est:7500-9500
£5128 $8051 €8000 Verger (33x46cm-13x18in) s. prov. 10-Dec-2 Pierre Berge, Paris #12/R
£5449 $8554 €8500 Vaches au paturage (60x72cm-24x28in) s. 13-Dec-2 Piasa, Paris #174/R
£6013 $9320 €9500 La drague (60x73cm-24x29in) s. i.verso painted c.1942-43 prov.exhib. 28-Sep-2 Christie's, Paris #44/R est:12000-18000
£6918 $10792 €11000 Bord d'etang et roupeau (54x73cm-21x29in) s. prov. 10-Oct-2 Ribeyre & Baron, Paris #62/R est:10000-12000
£7975 $13000 €11963 Promeneurs au bord de la maison fleurie (54x65cm-21x26in) s. 12-Feb-3 Sotheby's, New York #37/R est:8000-12000
£8544 $13244 €13500 Venise, Canal de Saint Marc (50x65cm-20x26in) s. i.verso oil gouache paper on canvas painted c.1937-38 prov. 28-Sep-2 Christie's, Paris #28/R est:15000-22000
£8974 $14090 €14000 Moulin sur la riviere (60x73cm-24x29in) s. prov. 10-Dec-2 Pierre Berge, Paris #14/R est:20000
£9202 $15000 €13803 Au bord de la riviere (60x73cm-24x29in) s. board. 12-Feb-3 Sotheby's, New York #28/R est:18000-20000
£10000 $15400 €15000 Bord de riviere (43x61cm-17x24in) st.sig. 22-Oct-2 Sotheby's, London #110/R est:8000-12000
£10256 $16000 €15384 Personnage au bord de la route (73x73cm-29x29in) s. 7-Nov-2 Christie's, Rockefeller NY #259/R est:18000-22000
£10577 $16712 €16500 Neige a Saint-Mammes (60x73cm-24x29in) s. i.verso. 15-Nov-2 Laurence Calmels, Paris #15a/R est:30000
£10645 $16819 €16500 Automne (73x73cm-29x29in) s. 18-Dec-2 Beaussant & Lefèvre, Paris #45/R est:10000
£11000 $17490 €16500 La Place des Tilleuls a Moret-sur-Loing (73x73cm-29x29in) s. i.verso. 20-Mar-3 Sotheby's, Olympia #148/R est:7000-9000
£11392 $17658 €18000 Brume matinale (60x73cm-24x29in) studio st. i.d.1942 verso prov. 28-Sep-2 Christie's, Paris #25/R est:20000-24000
£14103 $22000 €21155 Terrasse a Cannes (60x73cm-24x29in) s. 6-Nov-2 Sotheby's, New York #177/R est:25000-30000
£14103 $22282 €22000 Nature morte a la fenetre (74x60cm-29x24in) s. exhib. 15-Nov-2 Laurence Calmels, Paris #13a/R est:15000
£14907 $24000 €22361 Nature morte a la fenetre (74x60cm-29x24in) s. burlap exhib. 7-May-3 Sotheby's, New York #167/R est:25000-35000
£16026 $25160 €25000 Jardinier dans le verger fleuri (55x73cm-22x29in) s. prov. 10-Dec-2 Pierre Berge, Paris #13/R est:20000
£16149 $26000 €24224 Le quai D'Orsay (54x65cm-21x26in) s. prov.exhib. 7-May-3 Sotheby's, New York #162/R est:20000-30000
£21118 $34000 €31677 Le jardin dans le potager a Veneux les Sablons (53x72cm-21x28in) s. oil on burlap. 7-May-3 Sotheby's, New York #391/R est:25000-35000
£44872 $70000 €67308 Les nympheas (76x71cm-30x28in) s. 6-Nov-2 Sotheby's, New York #169/R est:30000-40000
Works on paper
£577 $906 €900 Cueillette (15x25cm-6x10in) s. gouache. 21-Nov-2 Neret-Minet, Paris #22
£645 $1019 €1000 Paysage aux bottes de foin (15x36cm-6x14in) s. gouache. 17-Dec-2 Rossini, Paris #42
£759 $1185 €1200 Paysage champetre (9x9cm-4x4in) mono. gouache pair. 20-Oct-2 Mercier & Cie, Lille #342
£1019 $1590 €1600 Scene animee, bord de riviere (14x20cm-6x8in) gouache. 6-Nov-2 Gioffredo, Nice #53/R
£1032 $1631 €1600 Travail au champs (9x17cm-4x7in) s. W/C gouache. 18-Dec-2 Digard, Paris #103/R
£1586 $2522 €2300 Rue de village (22x30cm-9x12in) s. gouache. 7-Mar-3 Rabourdin & Choppin de Janvry, Paris #20/R
£6135 $10000 €9203 Pont de Paris anime (34x63cm-13x25in) s. gouache chl paper on panel. 12-Feb-3 Sotheby's, New York #33/R est:12000-18000

MONTFALCON, C (19th C) French
£264 $386 €396 Still life with roses (27x35cm-11x14in) s. 17-Jun-2 Philippe Schuler, Zurich #7353 (S.FR 600)

MONTFORT, Franz van (1889-1980) Belgian
£633 $987 €1000 Pichet fleuri avec citrons (39x47cm-15x19in) s.d.1923. 16-Sep-2 Horta, Bruxelles #27

MONTGOMERY, Eugene Alexander (attrib) (1905-) American
£325 $500 €488 Carnation milk baby (51x56cm-20x22in) painted c.1940 prov. 8-Sep-2 Treadway Gallery, Cincinnati #650/R
£357 $550 €536 Carnation milk baby (56x51cm-22x20in) painted c.1940 prov. 8-Sep-2 Treadway Gallery, Cincinnati #652/R

MONTGOMERY, George (1916-2000) American
Sculpture
£2342 $3700 €3396 Self sculpture, George Montgomery (61cm-24in) s.d. bronze prov. 26-Jul-3 Coeur d'Alene, Hayden #53/R est:4000-8000
£2532 $4000 €3671 John Wayne, the legend (71cm-28in) s.d. bronze prov.lit. 26-Jul-3 Coeur d'Alene, Hayden #54/R est:4000-8000
£20570 $32500 €29827 Custer's final moments (51x145cm-20x57in) bronze prov.lit. 26-Jul-3 Coeur d'Alene, Hayden #223/R est:50000-75000

MONTGOMERY, Robert (1839-1893) Belgian
£769 $1192 €1200 Cote Rocheuse en Irlande (72x55cm-28x22in) s. 7-Dec-2 De Vuyst, Lokeren #227/R

MONTHOLON, François de (1856-1940) French
£578 $919 €850 Morning (22x35cm-9x14in) st.sig. board. 25-Feb-3 Dorotheum, Vienna #71/R

MONTI, Cesare (1891-1952) Italian
£1613 $2548 €2500 Balcony in bloom (80x48cm-31x19in) s.d.1949. 18-Dec-2 Finarte, Milan #164/R

MONTI, Francesco (attrib) (17/18th C) Italian
£36000 $60120 €52200 Still life with a relief of the death of Cleopatra. Still life with Haratius Cocles (121x175cm-48x69in) pair prov. 10-Jul-3 Sotheby's, London #196/R est:30000-40000

MONTI, Francesco (circle) (1646-1712) Italian
£4487 $6955 €7000 Battle by bridge (50x92cm-20x36in) 4-Dec-2 Christie's, Rome #364 est:7000-10000

MONTI, Francesco (1685-1768) Italian
£9655 $15255 €14000 Portrait of woman as Minerva (122x90cm-48x35in) 5-Apr-3 Finarte Semenzato, Milan #46/R est:20000

MONTI, Piero (1910-1994) Italian
£641 $1006 €1000 Tree in landscape covered in snow (49x60cm-19x24in) s. 10-Dec-2 Della Rocca, Turin #332/R

MONTI, R (19/20th C) Italian
Sculpture
£7600 $12084 €11400 Bust of nineteenth century veiled bride with floral garland around her head (41cm-16in) i.d.1848 white marble. 7-Mar-3 Moore Allen & Innocent, Cirencester #158/R est:1000-1500

MONTICELLI (?) Italian
£680 $1082 €1000 Women with children in park landscape (30x45cm-12x18in) i. panel. 19-Mar-3 Neumeister, Munich #658/R est:3000

MONTICELLI, Adolphe (1824-1886) French
£1258 $2000 €1887 Feeding the chickens (36x26cm-14x10in) s. panel. 7-Mar-3 Skinner, Boston #243/R est:3000-5000
£1538 $2415 €2400 Moonlit figures in park (33x28cm-13x11in) s. panel. 23-Nov-2 Arnold, Frankfurt #807/R est:4000
£3648 $5618 €5800 Wood (65x43cm-26x17in) s. board. 28-Oct-2 Il Ponte, Milan #244/R
£4140 $6459 €6500 Enfants au parc (30x23cm-12x9in) s. panel. 7-Nov-2 Chochon-Barre & Allardi, Paris #201/R
£4808 $7548 €7500 Figures conversant dans une foret (53x36cm-21x14in) s. 16-Dec-2 Rabourdin & Choppin de Janvry, Paris #13/R
£6731 $10635 €10500 Scene de parc (51x102cm-20x40in) s. 18-Nov-2 Sotheby's, Paris #42/R est:9500
£8333 $13083 €13000 La ceremonie (40x53cm-16x21in) s. 16-Dec-2 Millon & Associes, Paris #123/R est:15000-20000
£9103 $14291 €14200 Assemblee dans une foret (43x73cm-17x29in) panel. 16-Dec-2 Rabourdin & Choppin de Janvry, Paris #11/R est:4000
£12821 $20256 €20000 Women chatting (29x46cm-11x18in) s. panel prov. 16-Nov-2 Lempertz, Koln #1537/R est:30000-35000
£15000 $24450 €21750 Bouquet of flowers (33x50cm-13x20in) s. panel prov. 16-Jul-3 Sotheby's, Olympia #235/R est:6000-8000

MONTICELLI, Adolphe (attrib) (1824-1886) French
£755 $1162 €1200 Figures in park (15x40cm-6x16in) s. board prov. 28-Oct-2 Il Ponte, Milan #248/R
£2500 $3925 €3750 La terrasse du chateau de St. Germain (136x108cm-54x43in) indis sig. exhib. 21-Nov-2 Christie's, Kensington #18/R est:3000-5000
Works on paper
£1100 $1705 €1650 Spandrel design, San Giovanni (11x20cm-4x8in) pen ink wash sold with three similar. 9-Dec-2 Bonhams, New Bond Street #90/R est:1200-1500

MONTIEL, Jonio (1924-1986) South American
£314 $500 €471 Harbour (31x42cm-12x17in) s.verso panel. 2-Mar-3 Galleria Y Remates, Montevideo #40/R
£321 $500 €482 Fishing in the Tajo (60x70cm-24x28in) 17-Oct-2 Galleria Y Remates, Montevideo #39
£408 $640 €612 Harbour (48x62cm-19x24in) s. 20-Nov-2 Galleria Y Remates, Montevideo #23/R
£510 $800 €765 Buenos Aires harbour (51x62cm-20x24in) s. 20-Nov-2 Galleria Y Remates, Montevideo #22/R
£535 $850 €803 Still life (49x67cm-19x26in) s.d.51 cardboard. 2-Mar-3 Galleria Y Remates, Montevideo #39/R
£1154 $1800 €1731 Harbour (34x99cm-13x39in) s. cardboard. 10-Oct-2 Galleria Y Remates, Montevideo #42/R

MONTIGNY, Jenny (1875-1937) Belgian
£1042 $1656 €1500 Le chemin de campagne (30x40cm-12x16in) s. 29-Apr-3 Campo, Vlaamse Kaai #229 est:2000-2500
£2152 $3400 €3400 Vue de la Lys sous un ciel pluvieux (60x95cm-24x37in) prov. 26-Nov-2 Palais de Beaux Arts, Brussels #134/R est:3750-5000
£2532 $4000 €4000 Vase de narcisses et bouquet de bleuets devant la fenetre (66x88cm-26x35in) prov. 26-Nov-2 Palais de Beaux Arts, Brussels #136/R est:4500-6500
£4430 $7000 €7000 Effet de neige (44x59cm-17x23in) s. prov. 26-Nov-2 Palais de Beaux Arts, Brussels #130/R est:7500-12500
£4483 $7172 €6500 Returning from the field (33x45cm-13x18in) s. 15-Mar-3 De Vuyst, Lokeren #441/R est:6000-8000
£6013 $9500 €9500 Mere et enfant (58x59cm-23x23in) s. prov. 26-Nov-2 Palais de Beaux Arts, Brussels #131/R est:10000-12500

MONTIGNY, Jules Léon (1847-1899) Belgian
£479 $753 €700 Charrette et chevaux (10x15cm-4x6in) panel. 15-Apr-3 Galerie Moderne, Brussels #369
£962 $1510 €1500 Paysage (60x85cm-24x33in) s. 19-Nov-2 Galerie Moderne, Brussels #261 est:1500-2000
£1200 $1908 €1800 Cattle in a meadow on a summer's day (60x85cm-24x33in) s. 20-Mar-3 Christie's, Kensington #2/R est:1500-2000
£1410 $2214 €2200 Le retour de la fermiere (60x50cm-24x20in) s. 19-Nov-2 Galerie Moderne, Brussels #225/R est:2000-2400
£3145 $4874 €5000 Landscape with horse and cart (65x100cm-26x39in) s.d.90. 5-Oct-2 De Vuyst, Lokeren #530/R est:2800-3300

MONTINI, Umberto (1897-1978) Italian
£340 $541 €500 Milan suburbs (9x13cm-4x5in) s. board. 18-Mar-3 Finarte, Milan #196/R

MONTLEVAULT, Charles (c.1835-1897) French
£1419 $2214 €2100 Pont fortifie (24x35cm-9x14in) s. i.verso cardboard prov.lit. 30-Mar-3 Anaf, Lyon #411
£3797 $6000 €6000 Paysage aux bouleau (54x81cm-21x32in) s. 1-Dec-2 Anaf, Lyon #145/R

MONTMORENCY, Miles Fletcher de (1893-?) British
£1300 $2067 €1950 Portrait of Freda Walker seated half-length with painting amongst foliage (76x64cm-30x25in) i. i.verso. 18-Mar-3 Rosebery Fine Art, London #752/R est:700-900

MONTOBIO, Guillaume (1883-1962) Belgian
£2055 $3205 €3000 L'etang aux canards (38x48cm-15x19in) s. canvas on panel. 14-Apr-3 Horta, Bruxelles #106/R est:4000-6000
£2621 $4193 €3800 View of park in the summer (50x65cm-20x26in) s. 15-Mar-3 De Vuyst, Lokeren #224/R est:2800-3300
£3165 $5065 €4400 Apple trees in blossom (80x100cm-31x39in) s. 17-May-3 De Vuyst, Lokeren #266/R est:4400-5000

MONTONI, Prof E (19/20th C) Italian?
Sculpture
£1410 $2059 €2200 Bather (94cm-37in) alabaster. 5-Jun-2 Il Ponte, Milan #228/R

MONTOYA, Gustavo (1905-) Mexican
£1104 $1800 €1656 Nino (56x46cm-22x18in) painted c.1960. 14-Feb-3 Du Mouchelle, Detroit #1031/R est:2500-3000
£1104 $1800 €1656 Nina (56x46cm-22x18in) painted c.1960. 14-Feb-3 Du Mouchelle, Detroit #1032/R est:2500-3000
£1242 $2000 €1863 Nina's con bicicletas (61x51cm-24x20in) s. s.i.d.1967 verso prov. 20-Jan-3 Arthur James, Florida #365
£1242 $2000 €1863 Nina's corriendo (61x51cm-24x20in) s. s.i.d.1967 verso. 20-Jan-3 Arthur James, Florida #367
£1366 $2200 €2049 Group of items on a tiled table (61x102cm-24x40in) s. 20-Jan-3 Arthur James, Florida #366
£2108 $3500 €3057 Eva (104x76cm-41x30in) s. prov. 11-Jun-3 Butterfields, San Francisco #4309/R est:5000-7000

MONTOYA, Robert (1947-) American
Works on paper
£250 $400 €375 Untitled - woman with olla (20x18cm-8x7in) s.d.8.88 mixed media. 11-Jan-3 Skinner, Boston #339/R
£313 $500 €470 Rain God (23x18cm-9x7in) s.d.4 89 casein. 11-Jan-3 Skinner, Boston #338

MONTPEZAT, Henri d'Ainecy Comte de (1817-1859) French
£1921 $2997 €2882 Landscape with horse and foal (73x59cm-29x23in) s. 6-Nov-2 Dobiaschofsky, Bern #307/R est:4600 (S.FR 4400)
£7639 $12146 €11000 Amazone et deux levriers (60x74cm-24x29in) s.d.1847 oval. 30-Apr-3 Tajan, Paris #46/R est:12000

MONTROSE, C M (19th C) British
Works on paper
£440 $700 €660 Classical scene with figures in foreground (61x76cm-24x30in) s.d.1812 sepia ink pencil. 27-Feb-3 Brightwells, Leominster #792

MONTROSE, Herbert (19/20th C) ?
£360 $558 €540 Wooded landscape with a figure collecting wood (51x75cm-20x30in) s.d.1900. 25-Sep-2 Hamptons Fine Art, Godalming #426

MONTVALLON, Valerie de (20th C) French
Works on paper
£324 $518 €450 La momiflee (51x39cm-20x15in) s. mixed media canvas. 18-May-3 Neret-Minet, Paris #46
£1151 $1842 €1600 L'Egyptienne (197x82cm-78x32in) s. mixed media canvas. 18-May-3 Neret-Minet, Paris #105 est:1840-2080

MONVOISIN, Simon (20th C) French
£544 $865 €800 Fantasia (50x100cm-20x39in) s. 24-Mar-3 Coutau Begarie, Paris #214

MONZO, Rafael (1952-) French?
£250 $390 €375 Macier (30x23cm-12x9in) s.d.77 canvasboard. 10-Apr-3 Tennants, Leyburn #1142
£320 $493 €480 Port villa Nova Y Geltru (24x32cm-9x13in) s. i.verso board. 24-Oct-2 Christie's, Kensington #4
£320 $493 €480 Paysage rouge (16x22cm-6x9in) s. i.d.1976 verso board. 24-Oct-2 Christie's, Kensington #6/R

£400 $624 €600 San Pedro de Ribes (28x40cm-11x16in) s. i.verso. 10-Apr-3 Tennants, Leyburn #1143
£420 $647 €630 Bodeco (66x81cm-26x32in) s. i.d.1988 verso. 24-Oct-2 Christie's, Kensington #23
£420 $647 €630 Barcas (51x64cm-20x25in) s. s.i.verso. 24-Oct-2 Christie's, Kensington #5/R
£420 $647 €630 Eglise Vinyet, 78 (18x25cm-7x10in) s. i.verso board. 24-Oct-2 Christie's, Kensington #13/R
£420 $647 €630 Puigmalto (60x92cm-24x36in) s. s.i.d.1980 verso. 24-Oct-2 Christie's, Kensington #16/R
£650 $1001 €975 El bany (131x54cm-52x21in) s. i.d.1978-79 verso. 24-Oct-2 Christie's, Kensington #28
£800 $1232 €1200 Pina (66x65cm-26x26in) s. i.verso. 24-Oct-2 Christie's, Kensington #8/R
£850 $1309 €1275 Sitges el paseo de la ribera (74x93cm-29x37in) s. s.i.d.1988 verso. 24-Oct-2 Christie's, Kensington #3/R

MOODIE, Donald (1892-1963) British
£260 $424 €390 Carradale from the surrounding hills (34x48cm-13x19in) 14-Feb-3 Lyon & Turnbull, Edinburgh #147
£300 $489 €450 Boats and bathing huts, Beer, Devon (33x47cm-13x19in) 14-Feb-3 Lyon & Turnbull, Edinburgh #129
£360 $587 €540 Camaret sur mer (27x56cm-11x22in) 14-Feb-3 Lyon & Turnbull, Edinburgh #148
£1800 $2916 €2700 Midlothian landscape, Kirkliston (70x90cm-28x35in) s. 23-May-3 Lyon & Turnbull, Edinburgh #64 est:800-1200
Works on paper
£300 $498 €435 By the lochside, Arisaig (35x57cm-14x22in) s.d.48 pen ink W/C. 13-Jun-3 Lyon & Turnbull, Edinburgh #105
£400 $664 €580 Camaret sur mer (30x43cm-12x17in) s.d.1951 pencil W/C. 13-Jun-3 Lyon & Turnbull, Edinburgh #51

MOODY, Fannie (fl.1885-1897) British
£2969 $4750 €4305 Scotland, England and Ireland (41x62cm-16x24in) s. board. 16-May-3 Skinner, Boston #124/R est:5000-7000
Works on paper
£500 $810 €750 Three Jack Russells (34x49cm-13x19in) s. col chk. 20-May-3 Sotheby's, Olympia #210/R
£736 $1200 €1104 Wire fox terriers (48x36cm-19x14in) s. pastel. 11-Feb-3 Bonhams & Doyles, New York #222/R est:1200-1500
£920 $1500 €1380 Wire fox terrier (39x29cm-15x11in) s. col chk. 11-Feb-3 Bonhams & Doyles, New York #221/R est:1500-2000
£1166 $1900 €1749 Scotties (51x61cm-20x24in) s. col chk. 11-Feb-3 Bonhams & Doyles, New York #217/R est:1500-2000
£1687 $2750 €2531 Left behind (45x61cm-18x24in) s. col chk. 11-Feb-3 Bonhams & Doyles, New York #219/R est:1200-1800

MOODY, John Charles (1884-1962) British
Works on paper
£460 $712 €690 Amberley chalk pits from Houghton, Sussex (37x52cm-15x20in) s. W/C. 3-Dec-2 Sotheby's, Olympia #184/R

MOODY, Rufus (20th C) Canadian
Sculpture
£16129 $25484 €24194 Longhouse (32x28x39cm-13x11x15in) s. argillite prov. 14-Nov-2 Heffel, Vancouver #178/R est:10000-15000 (C.D 40000)

MOOK, Friedrich (1888-1944) German
£255 $392 €400 Taunus in winter (60x80cm-24x31in) i.d.1934. 5-Sep-2 Arnold, Frankfurt #826/R
£255 $392 €400 Nidda meadows (51x68cm-20x27in) i.d.1930. 5-Sep-2 Arnold, Frankfurt #827/R
£256 $403 €400 Winter landscape (81x60cm-32x24in) s.d.1934. 23-Nov-2 Arnold, Frankfurt #811/R
£308 $483 €480 Neckar in summer (51x68cm-20x27in) s.d.1932 i. verso. 23-Nov-2 Arnold, Frankfurt #815/R
£417 $654 €650 Autumn wood (89x66cm-35x26in) s.d.1930. 23-Nov-2 Arnold, Frankfurt #810/R

MOOLHUIZEN, Jan Jurrien (1900-) Dutch
£356 $590 €516 Village street (49x63cm-19x25in) s. exhib. 16-Jun-3 Waddingtons, Toronto #233/R (C.D 800)

MOON, Carl (1878-1948) American
£683 $1100 €1025 Southwest landscape (15x20cm-6x8in) s. canvas on board. 18-Feb-3 John Moran, Pasadena #174
£1118 $1800 €1677 Cotton woods in fall, Taos Valley, New Mexico (41x51cm-16x20in) s. i.verso canvasboard prov. 18-Feb-3 John Moran, Pasadena #173 est:2500-3500
£4839 $7500 €7259 Indian riders in south west landscape (51x71cm-20x28in) s. prov. 29-Oct-2 John Moran, Pasadena #788 est:2000-3000
Photographs
£3038 $4800 €4557 Navaho boy (28x20cm-11x8in) gelatin silver print prov.lit. 24-Apr-3 Phillips, New York #81/R est:5000-7000
£4878 $8000 €7317 Cho-bah-begay, the wolf, Navajo boy (43x33cm-17x13in) i.verso sepia silver print. 10-Feb-3 Swann Galleries, New York #20/R est:7000-10000
£5215 $8500 €7823 Navajo boy (34x26cm-13x10in) s. orotone executed c.1904. 12-Feb-3 Christie's, Rockefeller NY #28/R est:9000-12000

MOON, Jeremy (1934-1974) British
£300 $495 €435 Plaque no.2 (145x145cm-57x57in) init.i.d.12.62. 3-Jul-3 Christie's, Kensington #620
£900 $1476 €1350 Untitled (106x132cm-42x52in) i.d.1970 stretcher acrylic prov. 3-Jun-3 Sotheby's, Olympia #303/R

MOON, Mick (1937-) British?
£1000 $1630 €1500 Commodities (237x177cm-93x70in) s.d.96 verso acrylic collage on calico prov. 3-Feb-3 Sotheby's, Olympia #19/R est:1000-1500

MOON, Sarah (1938-) British
Photographs
£2215 $3500 €3500 Eva (49x39cm-19x15in) s.i.d.1997 verso silver gelatin from polaroid negative. 28-Nov-2 Villa Grisebach, Berlin #1330/R est:3599-4500

MOONEY, E Hartley (fl.1926-1932) British
£260 $426 €377 Floral still life (53x58cm-21x23in) s. 3-Jun-3 Capes Dunn, Manchester #1
£378 $627 €548 Still life chrysanthemums in a vase (76x63cm-30x25in) s. 16-Jun-3 Waddingtons, Toronto #102/R (C.D 850)
£3000 $4740 €4500 Rural view of North Wales (62x74cm-24x29in) s.d.1929. 27-Nov-2 Peter Wilson, Nantwich #63 est:250-300

MOONEY, Martin (20th C) Irish?
£3043 $4991 €4200 Bridge in France (20x40cm-8x16in) init. s.i.d.1998 verso prov. 28-May-3 Bonhams & James Adam, Dublin #59/R est:3000-4000
£3188 $5229 €4400 Udaipur rooftop (25x50cm-10x20in) init. s.i.d.1999 verso panel prov. 28-May-3 Bonhams & James Adam, Dublin #92/R est:3000-4000
£6159 $10101 €8500 Bacino Di San Marco, Venice (30x60cm-12x24in) init. s.i.d.2000 verso board prov. 28-May-3 Bonhams & James Adam, Dublin #102/R est:4500-5500
£8333 $13250 €12000 Facade Giron cathedral. Facade I (117x89cm-46x35in) init.d.1988 i.verso pair prov. 29-Apr-3 Whyte's, Dublin #128/R est:10000-12000
£10870 $17826 €15000 Sta Maria della Salute from the Redentore, Venice (61x122cm-24x48in) init. prov. 28-May-3 Bonhams & James Adam, Dublin #62/R est:7000-8000

MOONY, Robert James Enraght (1879-1946) British
£2051 $3221 €3200 Night and the poet (56x66cm-22x26in) s.d.1912 i.verso tempera board on canvas exhib. 19-Nov-2 Whyte's, Dublin #90/R est:3000-4000
Works on paper
£750 $1170 €1125 Nymphs in a woodland setting (48x58cm-19x23in) s. W/C. 11-Apr-3 Keys, Aylsham #450/R

MOOR, Karel de (1695-?) Dutch
£9500 $14915 €14250 Shepherd kneeling over a lady sleeping under a canopy in a wooded landscape (28x35cm-11x14in) panel exhib. 13-Dec-2 Christie's, Kensington #134/R est:4000-6000

MOOR, Karl (1904-1991) Swiss
£429 $678 €644 Poppy field in bloom in Leomental (35x60cm-14x24in) s.i.verso. 29-Nov-2 Zofingen, Switzerland #2993 (S.FR 1000)
£611 $954 €917 Oberbeinwil (50x100cm-20x39in) s. 8-Nov-2 Dobiaschofsky, Bern #140/R (S.FR 1400)

MOORE OF IPSWICH, John (1820-1902) British
£650 $1053 €975 Harvest time (15x20cm-6x8in) s. panel. 23-Jan-3 Christie's, Kensington #211
£850 $1420 €1233 Fishing boats in rough water (23x38cm-9x15in) s. 20-Jun-3 Keys, Aylsham #638/R
£1050 $1733 €1523 Looking across the Orwell (23x28cm-9x11in) s.d.1886 board. 1-Jul-3 Bonhams, Norwich #253/R est:600-900
£1100 $1716 €1650 Cottage scenes (14x20cm-6x8in) one indis sig. panel pair. 26-Mar-3 Sotheby's, Olympia #12/R est:600-800
£1250 $1963 €1875 Fishing boats on a moonlit sea (24x38cm-9x15in) s. panel. 16-Dec-2 Bonhams, Bury St Edmunds #516/R est:1000-1500
£1500 $2475 €2175 Gypsy camp (21x31cm-8x12in) i.on stretcher. 1-Jul-3 Bonhams, Norwich #243/R est:1000-1500

£1750 $2888 €2538 Figures walking towards a moored boat at dusk (19x26cm-7x10in) s. panel. 1-Jul-3 Bonhams, Norwich #244/R est:1200-1800
£2000 $3100 €3000 Moonlit river scene with post mill (20x28cm-8x11in) s. 30-Sep-2 Bonhams, Ipswich #465 est:1000-1500
£2000 $3300 €2900 Deben from Woodbridge with a train in the foreground (86x112cm-34x44in) 1-Jul-3 Bonhams, Norwich #240/R est:1000-1500
£2200 $3410 €3300 Fishing vessels off the shore (23x50cm-9x20in) 30-Sep-2 Bonhams, Ipswich #453/R est:1500-2000
£2200 $3630 €3190 Shipping close to shore in choppy sea (15x35cm-6x14in) s. canvas on panel. 1-Jul-3 Bonhams, Norwich #248/R est:1500-2000
£2600 $4212 €3900 Barges on an East Anglian river at dusk (41x61cm-16x24in) s. 21-May-3 Christie's, Kensington #611/R est:3000-5000
£2700 $4293 €4050 Fishing boats and other vessels in a choppy sea (34x44cm-13x17in) s. 5-Mar-3 Bonhams, Bury St Edmunds #371/R est:3000-5000
£3200 $4960 €4800 Fishing boats offshore, early morning (40x61cm-16x24in) 30-Sep-2 Bonhams, Ipswich #491/R est:1500-2000

MOORE OF IPSWICH, John (attrib) (1820-1902) British
£2500 $3975 €3750 Fishing vessels in a rough sea (48x66cm-19x26in) 5-Mar-3 Bonhams, Bury St Edmunds #413/R est:2500-4000

MOORE, Abel Buel (19th C) American
£427 $700 €641 Portrait of a woman (58x51cm-23x20in) s.d.1849 verso oval. 8-Feb-3 Neal Auction Company, New Orleans #329

MOORE, Albert Joseph (1841-1893) British
£420000 $676200 €630000 Lighting and light (88x146cm-35x57in) s. exhib.lit. 19-Feb-3 Christie's, London #27/R est:500000-700000

Works on paper
£40000 $63200 €60000 Girl gathering Wooded landscape (25x42cm-10x17in) bears i. W/C bodycol prov.exhib.lit. 28-Nov-2 Sotheby's, London #22/R est:8000-12000

MOORE, Benson Bond (1882-1974) American
£705 $1100 €1058 North Carolina mountain home (50x38cm-20x15in) s.d.1954 i.verso. 14-Sep-2 Weschler, Washington #605/R est:1000-1500

MOORE, Claude T S (1853-1901) British
£6500 $10335 €9750 Thames at Greenwich (76x112cm-30x44in) s.d.85. 19-Mar-3 Sotheby's, London #244/R est:7000-10000

MOORE, E W (1857-1938) American
£253 $400 €380 Two hanging dead ducks and a woodcock (61x41cm-24x16in) s. 26-Apr-3 Thomaston Place, Thomaston #190

MOORE, Ernest (1865-1940) British
£779 $1200 €1169 Girl in a blue dress (61x51cm-24x20in) s. painted c.1890. 8-Sep-2 Treadway Gallery, Cincinnati #546/R

MOORE, Fay (20th C) American
£265 $425 €384 Sliding into home (68x99cm-27x39in) s. 16-May-3 Skinner, Boston #378/R

MOORE, Frank Montague (1877-1967) American/British
£609 $950 €914 Kern River, morning mists, California (64x76cm-25x30in) s. s.i.verso board. 20-Sep-2 Freeman, Philadelphia #60/R
£898 $1500 €1302 Sands dunes in spring (48x66cm-19x26in) s. canvasboard. 17-Jun-3 John Moran, Pasadena #97 est:2000-3000
£1266 $2000 €1899 Wooded California coastal scene (51x66cm-20x26in) s. 3-Apr-3 Boos Gallery, Michigan #276/R est:4000-6000
£1274 $2000 €1911 Mojave desert, California. Desert smoke trees and spring carpets (36x51cm-14x20in) s. canvasboard. 10-Dec-2 Doyle, New York #116/R est:2000-3000
£1582 $2500 €2373 Wooded mountain landscape (51x76cm-20x30in) s. 3-Apr-3 Boos Gallery, Michigan #277/R est:4000-6000
£2560 $4250 €3712 Pines and surf (76x102cm-30x40in) s. masonite prov. 11-Jun-3 Butterfields, San Francisco #4285/R est:3000-5000
£3915 $6500 €5677 California wildflowers (51x70cm-20x28in) s. board. 11-Jun-3 Butterfields, San Francisco #4248/R est:4000-6000

MOORE, Harry Humphrey (1844-1926) American
£241 $375 €362 Guitar player. s. panel. 9-Aug-2 Skinner, Bolton #840

MOORE, Henry O M (1898-1986) British

Photographs
£1829 $3000 €2744 Sculpture (25x30cm-10x12in) s.i.d. st.d.verso silver print. 10-Feb-3 Swann Galleries, New York #57/R est:4000-5000

Prints
£2200 $3432 €3300 Head (170x118cm-67x46in) printed sig. num.37/65 silkscreen on linen. 27-Mar-3 Christie's, Kensington #553/R est:2500-3500
£2270 $3677 €3200 Seated figures (53x36cm-21x14in) s. col lithograph. 24-May-3 Van Ham, Cologne #422/R est:4800
£2564 $4000 €3846 Standing figures (27x22cm-11x9in) s.d. num.48/50 col lithograph. 7-Nov-2 Swann Galleries, New York #743/R est:5000-8000
£3988 $6500 €5982 Woman holding cat (29x48cm-11x19in) s.d.1949 num.44/75 col colograph. 13-Feb-3 Christie's, Rockefeller NY #108/R

Sculpture
£3800 $6270 €5510 Single female figure (52cm-20in) s.num.3/7 green pat. bronze prov.lit. 3-Jul-3 Christie's, Kensington #600/R est:2000-3000
£4200 $6468 €6300 Reclining nude (7cm-3in) s.num.3/6 bronze exec.c.1945 prov.exhib.lit. 23-Oct-2 Sotheby's, Olympia #781/R est:4000-6000
£6000 $9540 €9000 Maquette for wall relief no 7 (47cm-19in) bronze edition of 5 Cast Art Bronze prov.lit. 20-Mar-3 Sotheby's, Olympia #94/R est:4000-6000
£6289 $10000 €9434 Maquette for sheep piece (11cm-4in) s.num.1/7 green brown pat bronze lit. 27-Feb-3 Christie's, Rockefeller NY #5/R est:16000
£7500 $12300 €11250 Mother and child (13cm-5in) s.num.8/9 dark brown pat. bronze lit. 6-Jun-3 Christie's, London #173/R est:7000-10000
£8230 $12675 €12345 Standing woman, shell skirt (17x7x7cm-7x3x3in) brown pat bronze. 26-Oct-2 Heffel, Vancouver #29 est:25000-30000 (C.D 20000)
£9000 $14040 €13500 Standing figure no.4 (25cm-10in) brown pat. bronze conceived 1952. 25-Mar-3 Bonhams, New Bond Street #108/R est:10000-15000
£9677 $15000 €14516 Draped torso (8cm-3in) num.1 bronze prov. 8-Dec-2 Wright, Chicago #190/R est:10000-15000
£11321 $18000 €16982 Reclining female nude (13cm-5in) brown gold pat bronze lit. 27-Feb-3 Christie's, Rockefeller NY #37/R est:28000
£11538 $17885 €18000 Architectural prize (26x32cm-10x13in) s.i. num.9/9 dark brown pat.bronze Cast.Noack Berlin. 4-Dec-2 Lempertz, Koln #931/R est:20000-25000
£12258 $19000 €18387 Helmet head and shoulders (16cm-6in) brown pat. bronze lit. 26-Sep-2 Christie's, Rockefeller NY #555/R est:18000-22000
£14000 $21980 €21000 Standing figure relief no.1 (25cm-10in) s.num.6/12 dark brown pat. bronze conceived 1960 lit. 22-Nov-2 Christie's, London #64/R est:15000-25000
£14000 $21980 €21000 Standing figure relief no.2 (25cm-10in) s.num.5/12 dark brown pat. bronze conceived 1960 lit. 22-Nov-2 Christie's, London #65/R est:15000-25000
£17391 $28000 €26087 Architecture prize (32cm-13in) i.num.9/9 brown pat. bronze st.f.Noack conceived 1979 prov.lit. 7-May-3 Sotheby's, New York #347/R est:25000-35000
£17391 $28000 €26087 Mother and child (17cm-7in) i.num.3/6 brown pat. bronze cast 1965 prov.lit. 7-May-3 Sotheby's, New York #347a/R est:35000-45000
£18341 $26777 €27512 Standing figure No 3 (21x4x4cm-8x2x2in) bronze prov.lit. 4-Jun-2 Germann, Zurich #27/R est:50000-60000 (S.FR 42000)
£19231 $30000 €28847 Small mother and child (13cm-5in) s.num.5/9 brown pat. bronze cast 1982 lit. 7-Nov-2 Christie's, Rockefeller NY #354/R est:22000-28000
£22000 $34540 €33000 Upright motive, maquette 1 (30cm-12in) green pat. bronze cast 1955 prov.lit. 22-Nov-2 Christie's, London #67/R est:10000-15000
£24000 $36960 €36000 Maquette for two piece reclining figure no.9 (23cm-9in) i.num.4/9 bronze executed 1967 prov.lit. 22-Oct-2 Sotheby's, London #227/R est:20000-30000
£26398 $42500 €39597 Reclining figure (13cm-5in) i.num.2/7 golden brown pat. bronze st.f.Noack lit. 7-May-3 Sotheby's, New York #339/R est:40000-60000
£29814 $48000 €44721 Upright connected forms (20cm-8in) s.num.2/7 brown pat. bronze prov.lit. 8-May-3 Christie's, Rockefeller NY #228/R est:30000-40000
£35256 $55000 €52884 Maquette for reclining figure (17cm-7in) brown pat. bronze cast 1955 lit. 7-Nov-2 Christie's, Rockefeller NY #346/R est:70000-90000
£40000 $66800 €58000 Reclining mother and child IV (20cm-8in) s.num.4/9 green brown pat. bronze conceived 1979 prov.lit. 25-Jun-3 Christie's, London #232/R est:45000-65000
£40064 $62500 €60096 Pointed reclining figure (12x23cm-5x9in) i.num.5/9 light brown pat. bronze conceived 1948 prov.lit. 6-Nov-2 Sotheby's, New York #321/R est:50000-70000
£41667 $65000 €62501 Maquette for reclining figure no.7 (20cm-8in) s.num.2/9 brown pat. bronze cast 1978 lit. 7-Nov-2 Christie's, Rockefeller NY #343/R est:40000-60000

£41925 $67500 €62888 Reclining figure (18cm-7in) i. brown pat. bronze conceived 1945 prov.lit. 7-May-3 Sotheby's, New York #343/R est:70000-90000
£45031 $72500 €67547 Reclining figure, goujon (24cm-9in) i.num.2/9 brown pat. bronze cast 1971 prov.lit. 7-May-3 Sotheby's, New York #348a/R est:80000-120000
£57692 $90000 €86538 Rocking chair no.4 miniature (15cm-6in) brown pat. bronze conceived 1950 prov.exhib.lit. 6-Nov-2 Sotheby's, New York #249/R est:100000-150000
£64103 $100000 €96155 Composition (42cm-17in) i.num.1/9 brown pat. bronze conceived 1934 prov.lit. 6-Nov-2 Sotheby's, New York #300a/R est:90000-120000
£75000 $125250 €108750 Pointed torso (66cm-26in) i.num.4/12 bronze prov.lit. 24-Jun-3 Sotheby's, London #178/R est:70000-90000
£89744 $140000 €134616 No.10 interlocking (54x91x53cm-21x36x21in) s.num.4/7 gold brown pat. bronze two piece cast 1968 lit. 7-Nov-2 Christie's, Rockefeller NY #341/R est:180000-220000
£102564 $160000 €153846 Working model for upright internal external form (63cm-25in) green pat. bronze conceived 1951. 6-Nov-2 Sotheby's, New York #247/R est:200000-300000
£105590 $170000 €158385 Working model for mother and child, block seat (62cm-24in) s.num.9/9 brown pat. bronze cast 1983 prov.lit. 8-May-3 Christie's, Rockefeller NY #238/R est:250000-350000
£108974 $170000 €163461 Family group (15cm-6in) dark brown pat. bronze executed 1944 prov.lit. 6-Nov-2 Sotheby's, New York #244/R est:200000-300000
£124224 $200000 €186336 Reclining figure (35cm-14in) i. dark brown pat. bronze cast 1945 prov.exhib.lit. 7-May-3 Sotheby's, New York #315/R est:200000-300000
£124224 $200000 €186336 Three quarter figure, lines (82cm-32in) s.num.8/9 green brown pat. bronze cast 1982 prov.exhib.lit. 8-May-3 Christie's, Rockefeller NY #231/R est:200000-300000
£125000 $195000 €187500 Helmet head no.5 (34cm-13in) num.1/6 brown pat. bronze cast 1966 prov.exhib.lit. 6-Nov-2 Sotheby's, New York #246/R est:120000-180000
£145000 $237800 €217500 Family group (13cm-5in) s. green pat. bronze conceived 1945 prov.lit. 6-Jun-3 Christie's, London #107/R est:120000-180000
£150000 $250500 €225000 Two piece reclining figure - armless (61cm-24in) i.num.2/9 base bronze Cast Fiorini exc.1975 prov.lit. 23-Jun-3 Sotheby's, London #31/R est:150000-200000
£217391 $350000 €326087 Family group (24cm-9in) s. black pat bronze prov.lit. 7-May-3 Christie's, Rockefeller NY #24/R est:250000-350000
£232919 $375000 €349379 Upright internal external form, flower (76cm-30in) s.num.3/6 brown pat. bronze lit. 8-May-3 Christie's, Rockefeller NY #229/R est:150000-200000
£310559 $500000 €465839 Seated figure against a curved wall (91cm-36in) brown pat bronze prov.lit. 6-May-3 Sotheby's, New York #4/R est:700000-900000
£400000 $668000 €600000 Working model for sheep piece (151cm-59in) i.num. 9/9 top base bronze Cast Fiorini exc.1971 prov.lit. 23-Jun-3 Sotheby's, London #28/R est:200000-300000
£822785 $1300000 €1234178 Reclining mother and child (84x120cm-33x47in) green pat. bronze cast 1961 prov.exhib.lit. 13-Nov-2 Christie's, Rockefeller NY #20/R est:1000000-1500000
£931677 $1500000 €1397516 Mother and child with apple (76cm-30in) brown green pat bronze prov.lit. 7-May-3 Christie's, Rockefeller NY #27/R est:1000000-1500000

Works on paper

£2200 $3388 €3300 Seated woman (18x14cm-7x6in) s. pencil ballpoint pen prov. 5-Sep-2 Christie's, Kensington #606/R est:1200-1800
£4000 $6160 €6000 Artist's daughter, Mary (28x23cm-11x9in) s.d. pencil W/C dr. 5-Sep-2 Christie's, Kensington #610/R est:4000-6000
£5128 $8000 €7692 Three trees (21x29cm-8x11in) s. W/C gouache chl ballpoint pen executed 1982 prov.exhib.lit. 6-Nov-2 Sotheby's, New York #263/R est:6000-8000
£9450 $14648 €14175 Ideas of sculptures (48x37cm-19x15in) Indian ink W/C. 1-Oct-2 SOGA, Bratislava #198/R est:400000 (SL.K 600000)
£9500 $14724 €14250 Artist's sister Mary (37x27cm-15x11in) s.d.27 pen black ink wash prov.exhib.lit. 4-Dec-2 Sotheby's, London #37/R est:6000-8000
£11000 $17050 €16500 Seated nude (55x36cm-22x14in) s.d.34 pen ink wash prov.lit. 4-Dec-2 Sotheby's, London #35/R est:10000-15000
£13400 $22110 €19430 Sleeping figure (28x23cm-11x9in) s.d.41 pencil col crayon W/C wash. 3-Jul-3 Christie's, Kensington #533/R est:6000-8000
£18000 $30060 €27000 Miner drilling in drift (30x22cm-12x9in) s.d.42 W/C wash pen ink crayon pencil prov.lit. 26-Jun-3 Christie's, London #413/R est:20000-30000
£24845 $40000 €37268 Drawing for sculpture, reclining figures (27x37cm-11x15in) s.d.38 pencil crayon prov.exhib.lit. 7-May-3 Sotheby's, New York #342/R est:25000-35000
£25641 $40000 €38462 Figures in a shelter (18x25cm-7x10in) s.d.41 pencil wax crayon col crayon W/C wash pen ink. 6-Nov-2 Sotheby's, New York #245/R est:50000-70000
£33333 $51667 €52000 Standing figures (28x38cm-11x15in) s.d.40 mixed media prov.exhib. 4-Dec-2 Lempertz, Koln #28/R est:55000-65000

MOORE, Henry R A (1831-1895) British

£400 $668 €580 Coastal view at sunset (23x28cm-9x11in) s. 20-Jun-3 Keys, Aylsham #777
£440 $678 €660 Fishing boats at sea (30x53cm-12x21in) s.d.1881. 3-Sep-2 Gorringes, Lewes #2273
£1268 $2104 €1800 Barque sur le lac (50x91cm-20x36in) s.d. 11-Jun-3 Beaussant & Lefèvre, Paris #104/R est:1500-2000
£1300 $2015 €1950 Coastal landscape with a sailing vessel aground and a lifeboat approaching (41x81cm-16x32in) s.d.1875. 31-Oct-2 Duke & Son, Dorchester #250/R est:600-900
£2100 $3297 €3150 Seascape with vessels on the horizon (66x117cm-26x46in) s. canvas on board. 16-Dec-2 Sotheby's, Olympia #43/R est:2000-3000
£3900 $6162 €5850 Breezy day (30x60cm-12x24in) s.d.1879 exhib. 2-Dec-2 Bonhams, Bath #168/R est:2000-3000
£5200 $8372 €7800 Breezy day in the channel (59x99cm-23x39in) s. exhib. 15-Jan-3 Cheffins Grain & Comins, Cambridge #427/R
£5500 $8745 €8250 Breezy day (30x61cm-12x24in) s.d.1879 exhib. 6-Mar-3 Christie's, Kensington #499/R est:5000-7000
£9500 $14440 €14250 Sunset over the sea (52x77cm-20x30in) s.d.1888. 15-Aug-2 Bonhams, New Bond Street #433/R est:4000-6000
£22000 $35420 €33000 Half a gale (66x102cm-26x40in) s.d.1892 prov.exhib.lit. 20-Feb-3 Christie's, London #211/R est:20000

Works on paper

£300 $480 €450 Yacht on an open sea (22x29cm-9x11in) s. W/C. 15-May-3 Lawrence, Crewkerne #825
£337 $525 €506 Fog study (20x28cm-8x11in) s.d.July 18th 1881 i.verso W/C paperboard. 14-Sep-2 Weschler, Washington #593/R

MOORE, John (19th C) British

£3200 $4960 €4800 Lowestoft Beach (33x46cm-13x18in) s. 4-Dec-2 Neal & Fletcher, Woodbridge #251/R est:3500-4500
£3800 $5890 €5700 River landscape (20x41cm-8x16in) s.d.1881 panel. 4-Dec-2 Neal & Fletcher, Woodbridge #252 est:2000-3000

MOORE, L G (19th C) British

£1000 $1550 €1500 Fishing boats and merchant brig beached at low tide with white cliffs (30x46cm-12x18in) s.d.1855. 31-Oct-2 Christie's, Kensington #483/R est:700-900

MOORE, Leslie L H (1907-1997) British

Works on paper

£300 $489 €450 Fishing boats off the East Anglian coast (36x51cm-14x20in) s. W/C. 14-Feb-3 Keys, Aylsham #582
£300 $495 €435 Oby Mill (26x37cm-10x15in) s. W/C. 1-Jul-3 Bonhams, Norwich #150
£300 $495 €435 Walberswick (26x37cm-10x15in) s. W/C. 1-Jul-3 Bonhams, Norwich #152/R
£310 $487 €465 River Alde (36x51cm-14x20in) s. W/C. 13-Dec-2 Keys, Aylsham #513
£320 $528 €464 Morston Creek (26x37cm-10x15in) s. W/C. 1-Jul-3 Bonhams, Norwich #151
£400 $652 €600 Norwich Castle (38x51cm-15x20in) s. W/C. 14-Feb-3 Keys, Aylsham #583/R

MOORE, Nelson Augustus (1823-1902) American

£1019 $1600 €1529 Summer landscape with stream (33x38cm-13x15in) s. 23-Nov-2 Jackson's, Cedar Falls #63/R est:1000-1500
£18750 $30000 €28125 New England winter landscape (61x97cm-24x38in) s. 1-Jan-3 Nadeau, Windsor #150/R est:10000-15000

MOORE, Robert (?) ?

£850 $1326 €1275 Fishing vessels in harbour. Dingy rowing from shore to ship (28x40cm-11x16in) s. board pair prov. 18-Sep-2 Dreweatt Neate, Newbury #169
£2800 $4256 €4200 Ranger and Endeavour II rounding the mark, America's Cup 1937 (41x61cm-16x24in) s. board. 15-Aug-2 Bonhams, New Bond Street #371/R est:3000-4000

Works on paper

£943 $1471 €1634 Surfboard (275cm-108in) s.d.89 mixed media fibreglass prov. 31-Mar-3 Goodman, Sydney #151/R (A.D 2500)

MOORE, Rubens Arthur (fl.1881-1920) British
£520 $811 €780 Fordham, Norfolk (18x23cm-7x9in) s.d.09. 26-Mar-3 Sotheby's, Olympia #15/R

MOORE, Thomas Cooper (1827-1901) British
£580 $928 €870 Shipping off the French coast (39x51cm-15x20in) s. 13-May-3 Bonhams, Knightsbridge #186/R

MOORE, William (snr) (1790-1851) British
Works on paper
£650 $1060 €975 Portrait of a family group (49x40cm-19x16in) s.d.1839 W/C pencil. 30-Jan-3 Lawrence, Crewkerne #625/R

MOORE, Yvonne (20th C) Irish
£329 $513 €480 Flower bowl (20x20cm-8x8in) init. board. 8-Apr-3 James Adam, Dublin #25/R
£342 $538 €500 Bogland, West of Ireland (20x19cm-8x7in) init. s.i.verso canvasboard. 15-Apr-3 De Veres Art Auctions, Dublin #84
£353 $554 €550 Blaskets from Slea Head (24x29cm-9x11in) s.d.2002 canvasboard. 19-Nov-2 Whyte's, Dublin #186/R
£459 $720 €670 Cellar door (31x24cm-12x9in) init. s.i.verso canvasboard. 15-Apr-3 De Veres Art Auctions, Dublin #85/R
£537 $864 €800 Carafes (25x20cm-10x8in) init. canvasboard. 18-Feb-3 Whyte's, Dublin #179
£616 $968 €900 Table top still life (41x41cm-16x16in) init. 15-Apr-3 De Veres Art Auctions, Dublin #83/R

MOOREN, Josef (1885-?) German
£705 $1107 €1100 Harvest near Kleve (50x60cm-20x24in) s. 21-Nov-2 Van Ham, Cologne #1797/R
£897 $1409 €1400 Schwanenburg in Kleve (50x60cm-20x24in) s. 21-Nov-2 Van Ham, Cologne #1798/R

MOORHOUSE, George Mortram (1882-?) British
Works on paper
£600 $996 €900 Village street at twilight with a girl beside a cottage door feeding ducks (42x32cm-17x13in) s. i.verso pastel. 10-Jun-3 Bonhams, Leeds #86

MOORMANS, Franz (1832-1893) Dutch
£458 $737 €650 Interior with elegant couple near a bird cage (39x31cm-15x12in) s. 7-May-3 Vendue Huis, Gravenhage #365/R
£1589 $2591 €2400 Scene d'interieur hollandais (38x46cm-15x18in) s. panel. 16-Feb-3 Mercier & Cie, Lille #219/R est:2700-3200
£2621 $4193 €3800 Cerises (32x23cm-13x9in) s.d.74 s.i.d.1874 verso panel. 15-Mar-3 De Vuyst, Lokeren #226/R est:4000-4500

MOR, Antonis (studio) (1519-1575) Dutch
£18868 $29245 €30000 Portrait of Fernando Alvarez de Toledo, Duke of Alba (96x71cm-38x28in) 2-Oct-2 Dorotheum, Vienna #132/R est:22000-30000

MOR, Antonis (style) (1519-1575) Dutch
£7200 $11232 €10800 Portrait of Emperor Charles V (63x49cm-25x19in) i. panel. 8-Apr-3 Sotheby's, Olympia #134/R est:2000-3000

MORA, Francis Luis (1874-1940) American
£425 $680 €638 Sunset in winter harbor, Maine (51x76cm-20x30in) s. i.on stretcher. 11-Jan-3 James Julia, Fairfield #461
£1083 $1700 €1625 Daily news (40x30cm-16x12in) s.i. canvasboard. 22-Nov-2 Skinner, Boston #157/R est:1000-1500
£1592 $2500 €2388 Dancing nymphs (102x89cm-40x35in) 10-Dec-2 Doyle, New York #64/R est:5000-7000
£1667 $2600 €2501 Portrait of a young woman (41x30cm-16x12in) s. 14-Sep-2 Weschler, Washington #628/R est:2500-3500
£1911 $3000 €2867 Spanish beauty (102x91cm-40x36in) s. 10-Dec-2 Doyle, New York #65/R est:4000-6000
Works on paper
£1266 $1962 €2000 Le combat de coqs (48x35cm-19x14in) s. Indian ink wash W/C. 29-Sep-2 Eric Pillon, Calais #226/R

MORA, Joseph Jacinto (1876-1947) American
Prints
£2885 $4500 €4328 Salinas rodeo (76x58cm-30x23in) col lithograph on cardboard prov. 9-Nov-2 Santa Fe Art, Santa Fe #75/R est:3500-4500

MORA, Mirka Madeleine (1928-) Australian
Works on paper
£597 $980 €896 Innocent love (55x71cm-22x28in) s.i.d.May 1969 pen col ink prov. 4-Jun-3 Deutscher-Menzies, Melbourne #369/R (A.D 1500)
£1075 $1634 €1613 Two figures (63x49cm-25x19in) s.d.69 gouache pastel. 28-Aug-2 Deutscher-Menzies, Melbourne #365/R est:2000-3000 (A.D 3000)

MORACH, Otto (1887-1973) Swiss
£10730 $16953 €16095 Viaduct and boat (59x45cm-23x18in) prov.exhib.lit. 28-Nov-2 Christie's, Zurich #43/R est:15000-20000 (S.FR 25000)

MORADO, Jose Chavez (1909-) Mexican
£4093 $6385 €6140 La danza de las doncellas y el brujo (80x100cm-31x39in) s.d.1964 acrylic. 17-Oct-2 Louis Morton, Mexico #106/R est:60000-70000 (M.P 65000)
£12594 $19647 €18891 Figura barroca (92x76cm-36x30in) s.d.1949. 17-Oct-2 Louis Morton, Mexico #88/R est:250000-300000 (M.P 200000)

MORAGAS, Jose (?) Spanish
Works on paper
£280 $437 €420 Italian shepherd boy resting (46x34cm-18x13in) s.i.d.91 W/C. 26-Mar-3 Hamptons Fine Art, Godalming #32

MORAGO, Carlos (1957-) Spanish
£629 $981 €1000 Terrace (20x50cm-8x20in) s. board. 8-Oct-2 Ansorena, Madrid #438/R

MORALES, Armando (1927-) Nicaraguan
£1667 $2633 €2600 Venise, Saint-Simon Piccolo (24x19cm-9x7in) s.d. prov. 14-Nov-2 Credit Municipal, Paris #65/R est:1500-1800
£24390 $40000 €35366 Deux baingeuses et canal (54x73cm-21x29in) s.d.94 prov.exhib.lit. 27-May-3 Sotheby's, New York #30
£38217 $60000 €57326 Afternoon dream (73x91cm-29x36in) s.d.83 prov. 19-Nov-2 Sotheby's, New York #41/R est:120000
£101911 $160000 €152867 Three nudes and bike (114x93cm-45x37in) s.d.96 i.d.verso oil beeswax prov. 20-Nov-2 Christie's, Rockefeller NY #42/R est:140000-160000
£103659 $170000 €150306 Trapiche, moulin a sucre (130x162cm-51x64in) s.d.91 i.d.verso prov.exhib.lit. 27-May-3 Sotheby's, New York #42

MORALES, Dario (1944-1988) Colombian
Sculpture
£4484 $6996 €6726 Standing female nude undressing (98cm-39in) s.st.d.82 num.1/6 bronze rec. base. 11-Nov-2 Stephan Welz, Johannesburg #440/R est:80000-120000 (SA.R 70000)

MORALES, Francisco (19th C) Mexican?
Works on paper
£1900 $3154 €2755 Brigantine Armistad in Spanish waters (43x59cm-17x23in) s.i.d.1869 pen ink W/C. 12-Jun-3 Christie's, London #551/R est:1500-2000

MORALES, Juan Antonio (19/20th C) Spanish
£755 $1162 €1200 Landscape (47x113cm-19x44in) s. board. 22-Oct-2 Durán, Madrid #84/R

MORALES, Luis de (c.1509-1586) Spanish
£520000 $868400 €754000 The birth of the Virgin (69x93cm-27x37in) panel prov. 10-Jul-3 Sotheby's, London #41/R est:200000-300000

MORALES, Luis de (circle) (c.1509-1586) Spanish
£24000 $40080 €34800 Saint John the Baptist (56x35cm-22x14in) i.verso panel. 11-Jul-3 Christie's, Kensington #157/R est:5000-7000

MORALES, Rodolfo (1925-2001) Mexican
£7006 $11000 €10509 Sonrosada (70x100cm-28x39in) s. prov.lit. 19-Nov-2 Sotheby's, New York #149/R est:18000
£23500 $37600 €34075 Untitled (150x120cm-59x47in) s. 15-May-3 Louis Morton, Mexico #81/R est:400000-450000 (M.P 380000)
£30573 $48000 €45860 Untitled (127x175cm-50x69in) s. painted 1989-90 prov. 20-Nov-2 Christie's, Rockefeller NY #131/R est:50000-70000
Sculpture
£22293 $35000 €33440 Column. Box (198x41x41cm-78x16x16in) s. oil canvas on cardboard tube exec.c.1983 two prov. 20-Nov-2 Christie's, Rockefeller NY #93/R est:60000-80000

MORALT, Ludwig (1815-1888) German
£2949 $4571 €4600 Poet Dante on the way to worldly paradise (109x135cm-43x53in) s.d.1842. 4-Dec-2 Neumeister, Munich #827/R est:3500

MORALT, Willy (1884-1947) German

£395 $639 €600 Landscape with mountains in the distance (51x66cm-20x26in) s. indis i. 21-Jan-3 Christie's, Amsterdam #38
£2405 $3728 €3800 Peasant girl crossing stream on the way to hermit (38x24cm-15x9in) s.i. panel. 25-Sep-2 Neumeister, Munich #669/R est:4500
£3038 $4709 €4800 Cactus lover standing outside house examining plant (38x27cm-15x11in) s.i. paper on panel. 25-Sep-2 Neumeister, Munich #668/R est:4800
£3401 $5408 €5000 Tending the flowers (30x21cm-12x8in) s.i. i. verso panel. 19-Mar-3 Neumeister, Munich #663/R est:4500
£3537 $5624 €5200 Biedermeier family taking Sunday walk (28x38cm-11x15in) s.i. panel. 19-Mar-3 Neumeister, Munich #662/R est:6000
£3571 $5321 €5500 Elderly flautist playing on terrace (52x35cm-20x14in) s.i. panel. 26-Jun-2 Neumeister, Munich #813/R est:4500
£4054 $6324 €6000 Mountain landscape with figures (57x40cm-22x16in) s.i. panel. 27-Mar-3 Dr Fritz Nagel, Stuttgart #848/R est:3000
£4221 $6289 €6500 Bavarian border station (34x49cm-13x19in) s.i. panel. 26-Jun-2 Neumeister, Munich #812/R est:7000

Works on paper

£353 $546 €550 Farmhouse in spring, with grandmother knitting (43x57cm-17x22in) s.d.98 W/C htd white lit. 7-Dec-2 Bergmann, Erlangen #836/R
£641 $974 €1000 Nine ducks on the water (40x55cm-16x22in) s.i. W/C gouache lit. 11-Jul-2 Allgauer, Kempten #2362/R
£833 $1317 €1300 Tegernsee in spring (44x60cm-17x24in) s. i. verso mixed media. 16-Nov-2 Lempertz, Koln #1368/R
£974 $1451 €1500 Near Bichl (44x61cm-17x24in) s.i. i. verso gouache. 26-Jun-2 Neumeister, Munich #592/R

MORALT, Willy (attrib) (1884-1947) German

£1935 $2845 €3000 Girls leaving school (25x36cm-10x14in) bears sig. panel. 20-Jun-2 Dr Fritz Nagel, Stuttgart #800 est:4800
£3205 $4968 €5000 Cactus friend standing on the steps in front of his house (29x22cm-11x9in) i. panel. 4-Dec-2 Neumeister, Munich #826/R est:6000

MORAN, Cythnia (20th C) Irish?

Sculpture

£1301 $2043 €1900 Seated nude (33x36cm-13x14in) bronze. 15-Apr-3 De Veres Art Auctions, Dublin #260/R est:900-1200

MORAN, E Percy (1862-1935) American

£385 $600 €578 Untitled (23x15cm-9x6in) s. board. 20-Oct-2 Susanin's, Chicago #5079/R
£545 $850 €818 Good read (18x15cm-7x6in) s. canvas on board. 9-Oct-2 Doyle, New York #79
£943 $1500 €1415 Pastoral landscape (25x30cm-10x12in) s. painted c.1900. 2-Mar-3 Toomey, Oak Park #602/R est:2000-3000
£1429 $2200 €2144 Feeding the parrot (48x38cm-19x15in) s. prov. 24-Oct-2 Shannon's, Milford #174/R est:2500-3500
£5031 $8000 €7547 Washington at valley forge (56x46cm-22x18in) s. prov. 5-Mar-3 Sotheby's, New York #6/R est:8000-12000

MORAN, Earl (1893-1984) American

£719 $1200 €1043 Reclining nude (61x122cm-24x48in) s. prov. 17-Jun-3 John Moran, Pasadena #218 est:1500-2000

MORAN, Edward (1829-1901) American

£641 $1000 €962 Seascape. s. 19-Oct-2 Harvey Clar, Oakland #1413
£6918 $11000 €10377 Noon day rest (91x168cm-36x66in) s.d.1879 prov.exhib. 4-Mar-3 Christie's, Rockefeller NY #25/R est:10000-15000
£8654 $13500 €12981 New York harbour with tugboat assisting sailing ship (41x71cm-16x28in) s. 21-Sep-2 Nadeau, Windsor #275/R est:7000-10000
£9434 $15000 €14151 On the beach at Digby (79x118cm-31x46in) s.d.1886 verso prov. 5-Mar-3 Sotheby's, New York #52/R est:12000-18000
£11111 $18000 €16667 Shipping off Calais (86x162cm-34x64in) s.d.1878 prov. 21-Jan-3 Christie's, Rockefeller NY #380/R est:18000

MORAN, Patricia (?) Australian

£893 $1410 €1340 Camellias in a glass bowl (44x59cm-17x23in) s. 18-Nov-2 Joel, Victoria #301 est:2500-3500 (A.D 2500)

MORAN, Percy (1862-?) American

£1438 $2300 €2085 Courting favour with the grandparents (46x61cm-18x24in) s. 17-May-3 CRN Auctions, Cambridge #25

MORAN, Peter (1841-1914) American

Works on paper

£244 $400 €366 Mountain lake landscape (10x25cm-4x10in) s. W/C. 8-Feb-3 Neal Auction Company, New Orleans #926

MORAN, Thomas (1837-1926) American

£13924 $22000 €20886 Grand Canal, Venice (28x41cm-11x16in) s.d.1892 prov. 5-Apr-3 Neal Auction Company, New Orleans #220/R est:25000-35000
£23226 $36000 €34839 In the Rockies (25x32cm-10x13in) mono. oil paper on canvas prov. 5-Dec-2 Christie's, Rockefeller NY #160/R est:40000-60000
£27097 $42000 €40646 Hunter in a landscape (23x35cm-9x14in) mono.d.1886 prov.exhib. 5-Dec-2 Christie's, Rockefeller NY #68/R est:50000-70000
£41935 $65000 €62903 Autumn (23x33cm-9x13in) s. painted c.1880 prov. 8-Dec-2 Toomey, Oak Park #706/R est:145000-175000
£58065 $90000 €87098 View of the Doge's Palace (36x51cm-14x20in) mono.d.1916 exhib. 5-Dec-2 Christie's, Rockefeller NY #63/R est:80000-120000
£58642 $95000 €87963 Mexican sunset (51x76cm-20x30in) mono.d.1884 prov. 21-May-3 Sotheby's, New York #192/R est:80000-120000
£64516 $100000 €96774 Venice (36x51cm-14x20in) mono. indis d. 5-Dec-2 Christie's, Rockefeller NY #58/R est:80000-120000
£90323 $140000 €135485 Venice (51x77cm-20x30in) mono. prov. 4-Dec-2 Sotheby's, New York #128/R est:75000-100000
£117284 $190000 €175926 Passing shower, East Hampton (51x76cm-20x30in) mono.d.1918. 22-May-3 Christie's, Rockefeller NY #28/R est:120000-180000
£193548 $300000 €290322 Looking over Niagara Falls (36x76cm-14x30in) mono.d.1885 prov.lit. 4-Dec-2 Sotheby's, New York #127/R est:200000-300000
£234568 $380000 €351852 Castle Rock, Green River, Wyoming (51x76cm-20x30in) mono.d.1907 s.i.d.verso prov.lit. 22-May-3 Christie's, Rockefeller NY #20/R est:250000-350000
£580645 $900000 €870968 Badlands of the Dakota (51x76cm-20x30in) mono.d.1901 prov.lit. 3-Dec-2 Phillips, New York #44/R est:700000-900000
£1709678 $2650000 €2564517 Green river, Wyoming (29x91cm-11x36in) mono.d.1878 panel prov. 5-Dec-2 Christie's, Rockefeller NY #167/R est:1500000-2500000

Works on paper

£11180 $18000 €16770 Two boats steaming through steep passageway, looming mountains (18x13cm-7x5in) s. i.verso carbon pencil ink. 10-May-3 Illustration House, New York #50/R est:5000-7500
£32258 $50000 €48387 Icebergs (27x37cm-11x15in) mono.d.1891 W/C prov.exhib. 5-Dec-2 Christie's, Rockefeller NY #60/R est:60000-80000
£56090 $87500 €84135 Deer in a mountain landscape (25x36cm-10x14in) s. W/C graphite prov.lit. 9-Nov-2 Santa Fe Art, Santa Fe #154/R est:100000-150000

MORAN, Thomas Sydney (19/20th C) American

£313 $500 €470 Trees (21x15cm-8x6in) s. board. 18-May-3 Butterfields, Los Angeles #7032

MORANDI, Giorgio (1890-1964) Italian

£65000 $105950 €97500 Fiori (20x19cm-8x7in) s. oil over chl prov.lit. 3-Feb-3 Bonhams, New Bond Street #75/R est:35000-45000
£88608 $140000 €140000 Flowers (25x20cm-10x8in) s. painted 1963 lit. 30-Nov-2 Farsetti, Prato #727/R est:120000
£125000 $205000 €187500 Still life (26x30cm-10x12in) s. painted 1958 prov.exhib.lit. 4-Feb-3 Sotheby's, London #41/R est:200000
£144231 $226442 €225000 Still life (25x30cm-10x12in) s. painted 1956 prov.lit. 20-Nov-2 Pandolfini, Florence #50/R est:300000
£185897 $291859 €290000 Still life (30x45cm-12x18in) painted 1954 prov.lit. 20-Nov-2 Pandolfini, Florence #49/R est:350000
£200000 $308000 €300000 Paesaggio (33x53cm-13x21in) s. painted 1941 prov.exhib.lit. 22-Oct-2 Christie's, London #13/R est:200000-300000
£210000 $327600 €315000 Cortile di via fondazza (47x50cm-19x20in) s. painted 1954 prov.exhib.lit. 21-Oct-2 Sotheby's, London #11/R est:250000-350000
£250000 $390000 €375000 Natura morta (40x45cm-16x18in) s. painted 1952 prov.lit. 21-Oct-2 Sotheby's, London #6/R est:250000-350000
£300000 $489000 €450000 Still life (36x40cm-14x16in) s. painted 1952 prov.exhib.lit. 3-Feb-3 Christie's, London #87/R est:400000
£319149 $517021 €450000 Fiori (64x50cm-25x20in) exhib.lit. 26-May-3 Christie's, Milan #269/R est:300000-350000
£350000 $539000 €525000 Natura morta (31x42cm-12x17in) s. painted 1944 prov.exhib.lit. 22-Oct-2 Christie's, London #10/R est:300000-400000
£400000 $624000 €600000 Nature morta (38x45cm-15x18in) s. painted 1951 prov.exhib.lit. 21-Oct-2 Sotheby's, London #15/R est:300000-400000

Prints

£2958 $4910 €4200 Natura morta con si oggetti (20x24cm-8x9in) s.d. etching. 14-Jun-3 Hauswedell & Nolte, Hamburg #1431/R est:3000
£3774 $6000 €5661 Natura morta con zuccheriera, limone e pane (8x10cm-3x4in) s.d. etching. 2-May-3 Sotheby's, New York #239/R est:8000-10000
£4717 $7500 €7076 Vaso a strisce con fiori (24x20cm-9x8in) s.d.num.38/60 etching. 2-May-3 Sotheby's, New York #240/R est:10000
£4717 $7500 €7076 Gruppo di zinnie (23x19cm-9x7in) s.num.16/30 etching. 2-May-3 Sotheby's, New York #243/R est:10000-15000
£4965 $8043 €7000 Landscape, Chiesanuova (15x16cm-6x6in) s.d.1924 eau forte lit. 26-May-3 Christie's, Milan #202/R est:6000-8000
£6383 $10340 €9000 Natura morta di vasi su un tavolo (34x25cm-13x10in) s.d.1931 eau forte. 26-May-3 Christie's, Milan #201/R est:8000-12000
£9434 $15000 €14151 Natura morta con oggetti bianchi su fondo scuro (24x29cm-9x11in) s.i.num.16/30 etching. 2-May-3 Sotheby's, New York #242/R est:20000

£11538 $18115 €18000 Still life of vases, bottles and glasses ontable (20x14cm-8x6in) s. num.18/62 eau forte exhib.lit. 20-Nov-2 Pandolfini, Florence #37/R est:18000
£14151 $22500 €21227 Natura morta (24x24cm-9x9in) s.num.4/21 etching. 2-May-3 Sotheby's, New York #245/R est:25000-35000
£14151 $22500 €21227 Natura morta (26x30cm-10x12in) s.num.15/30 etching. 2-May-3 Sotheby's, New York #246/R est:20000-30000
£15878 $24770 €23500 Still life of vases on table (25x33cm-10x13in) s.d.1931 eau forte on copper lit. 28-Mar-3 Farsetti, Prato #298/R est:26000
£16000 $24800 €24000 Grande natura morta con undici oggetti (37x48cm-15x19in) s.num.21/50 etching. 5-Dec-2 Sotheby's, London #160/R est:12000-18000
£16667 $26167 €26000 Flowers in white vase (16x25cm-6x10in) d.1917 eau forte exhib.lit. 20-Nov-2 Pandolfini, Florence #38/R est:30000
£17021 $27574 €24000 Still life with jugs (23x28cm-9x11in) s.i.d.1930 etching. 20-May-3 Dorotheum, Vienna #22/R est:24000-26000
£19266 $32174 €27936 Natura morta a tratti sottilisimi (26x23cm-10x9in) s.i. etching. 20-Jun-3 Kornfeld, Bern #114/R est:25000 (S.FR 42000)
£28205 $44282 €44000 Big still life with oil lamp (36x30cm-14x12in) s.d.1930 num.4/40 eau forte on copper lit. 20-Nov-2 Pandolfini, Florence #45/R est:50000
£42000 $64680 €63000 Grande natura morta con la lampada a petrolio (30x36cm-12x14in) s.num.26/40 etching prov.exhib.lit. 22-Oct-2 Christie's, London #8/R est:30000-40000

Works on paper
£29000 $44660 €43500 Paesaggio (16x21cm-6x8in) s.d.1957 prov.exhib.lit. 22-Oct-2 Christie's, London #11/R est:18000-25000

MORANDI, Martha (1936-) Uruguayan
£256 $403 €400 Untitled (25x26cm-10x10in) s. cardboard. 16-Dec-2 Castellana, Madrid #917/R
£385 $604 €600 Untitled (34x43cm-13x17in) s. cardboard. 16-Dec-2 Castellana, Madrid #850/R

MORANDINI, Francesco (attrib) (1544-1597) Italian
Works on paper
£1795 $2818 €2800 Holy Family and Saint Catherine (31x42cm-12x17in) pierre noire sanguine htd white. 13-Dec-2 Pierre Berge, Paris #27/R

MORANDIS, Gino (1915-) Italian
£1519 $2370 €2400 Untitled (70x51cm-28x20in) s. 19-Oct-2 Semenzato, Venice #40/R

MORANDO, Pietro (1892-1980) Italian
£1582 $2468 €2500 Toubadors (65x55cm-26x22in) s. 14-Sep-2 Meeting Art, Vercelli #975/R
£1603 $2516 €2500 Story teller (65x55cm-26x22in) s. painted 1965. 23-Nov-2 Meeting Art, Vercelli #415/R
£1634 $2614 €2500 Life (65x55cm-26x22in) s. 4-Jan-3 Meeting Art, Vercelli #209
£1973 $3137 €2900 Priest with flower (65x55cm-26x22in) s. exhib.lit. 1-Mar-3 Meeting Art, Vercelli #765
£2500 $3975 €3600 Candle maker (60x50cm-24x20in) s. painted 1952 lit. 1-May-3 Meeting Art, Vercelli #554 est:3000
£2564 $4026 €4000 Traveller (100x60cm-39x24in) s. 10-Dec-2 Della Rocca, Turin #333/R
£2564 $4026 €4000 Shirt in the sun (90x70cm-35x28in) s. s.i.verso. 23-Nov-2 Meeting Art, Vercelli #445/R
£2885 $4529 €4500 Cart (50x59cm-20x23in) s. 10-Dec-2 Della Rocca, Turin #362/R
£3846 $6038 €6000 Fields' apostle (70x60cm-28x24in) s. painted 1926 lit. 23-Nov-2 Meeting Art, Vercelli #474/R
Works on paper
£521 $828 €750 Peasant (73x60cm-29x24in) s.verso pencil paper on canvas. 1-May-3 Meeting Art, Vercelli #53

MORANG, Alfred (1901-1958) American
£4167 $6500 €6251 Acequia Madre (38x48cm-15x19in) s.d.52 panel prov.lit. 9-Nov-2 Santa Fe Art, Santa Fe #123/R est:10000-15000
£5769 $9000 €8654 Summer shadows (36x48cm-14x19in) s. board prov.lit. 9-Nov-2 Santa Fe Art, Santa Fe #124/R est:10000-15000

MORANT, Elise (?) ?
£353 $569 €530 Irish village, Galway (28x36cm-11x14in) s. board. 7-May-3 Dunbar Sloane, Auckland #18/R (NZ.D 1000)

MORAS, Walter (1856-1925) German
£344 $550 €499 Farm by bridge (25x40cm-10x16in) s. 18-May-3 Anders Antik, Landskrona #9 (S.KR 4400)
£479 $748 €700 Running steam in winter forest (27x44cm-11x17in) s. canvas on board. 10-Apr-3 Allgauer, Kempten #2905/R
£1233 $1923 €1800 Factory in the Ruhr (31x43cm-12x17in) s. canvas on board. 10-Apr-3 Van Ham, Cologne #1599/R est:1400
£1519 $2354 €2400 Lubeck (36x55cm-14x22in) s. 28-Sep-2 Hans Stahl, Hamburg #124/R est:2800
£2405 $3728 €3800 Snowy pine wood (81x120cm-32x47in) s. 25-Sep-2 Neumeister, Munich #670/R est:2500
£2436 $3824 €3800 Winter wood in evening light (81x120cm-32x47in) s. 21-Nov-2 Van Ham, Cologne #1799/R est:2000
£3234 $5110 €4851 Snow covered pine forest (80x120cm-31x47in) S. 2-Dec-2 Rasmussen, Copenhagen #1563/R est:40000 (D.KR 38000)

MORAT, Francois (20th C) French
£1165 $1900 €1748 Stream in a pastoral landscape with flock of sheep (39x49cm-15x19in) s. canvas on board. 16-Feb-3 Butterfields, San Francisco #2073 est:700-900

MORAT, Johann Martin (1805-1867) German
Works on paper
£1384 $2158 €2200 View over the Wutach to Morat's birthplace, Stuhlingen (25x34cm-10x13in) i. gouache prov.lit. 20-Sep-2 Karlheinz Kaupp, Staufen #2157/R est:2200

MORBELLI, Angelo (1853-1919) Italian
£5442 $8653 €8000 Portrait of lady (59x50cm-23x20in) lit. 18-Mar-3 Finarte, Milan #79/R

MORBIDUCCI, Publio (1888-1963) Italian
Sculpture
£1026 $1610 €1600 Hunting scene (22x32cm-9x13in) s. brown pat bronze relief. 21-Nov-2 Finarte, Rome #225

MORBY, Walter J (fl.1880-90) British
Works on paper
£600 $960 €900 Sheep at a field side (53x36cm-21x14in) s.d.87 W/C. 11-Mar-3 Gorringes, Lewes #2550

MORCHAIN, Paul-Bernard (1876-1938) French
£276 $439 €400 Thoniers sous voiles pres de la cale (16x22cm-6x9in) panel. 10-Mar-3 Thierry & Lannon, Brest #124/R
£338 $544 €480 Eglise du Finistere (17x14cm-7x6in) board. 11-May-3 Thierry & Lannon, Brest #387
£345 $548 €500 Bateau a quai (38x55cm-15x22in) 10-Mar-3 Thierry & Lannon, Brest #126
£400 $636 €580 Voiliers au mouillage et barque a la Godille (22x16cm-9x6in) panel. 10-Mar-3 Thierry & Lannon, Brest #125/R
£769 $1208 €1200 Sur le chemin (16x22cm-6x9in) panel prov. 15-Dec-2 Thierry & Lannon, Brest #175
£903 $1472 €1300 Barques au mouillage et sous voiles (50x65cm-20x26in) s. cardboard. 19-Jul-3 Thierry & Lannon, Brest #156
£972 $1585 €1400 La baie de Douarnenez (38x45cm-15x18in) s. panel. 19-Jul-3 Thierry & Lannon, Brest #367
£1154 $1812 €1800 Thonier (35x27cm-14x11in) cardboard prov. 15-Dec-2 Thierry & Lannon, Brest #176
£1171 $1815 €1850 Bateau a quai (50x65cm-20x26in) s. 29-Sep-2 Eric Pillon, Calais #181/R
£1603 $2516 €2500 Retour de peche (27x35cm-11x14in) s. prov. 15-Dec-2 Thierry & Lannon, Brest #174
Works on paper
£472 $770 €680 Ste Marie du Menez Hom (30x44cm-12x17in) s. chl crayon. 19-Jul-3 Thierry & Lannon, Brest #410

MORCILLO, Gabriel (19th C) Spanish
£769 $1215 €1200 Portrait of gentleman (65x47cm-26x19in) s.i. 19-Nov-2 Durán, Madrid #138/R

MORDECAI, Frances (20th C) American
£283 $450 €425 Rockport (51x61cm-20x24in) s.d.51. 7-Mar-3 Skinner, Boston #474/R

MORDINA, J (19th C) Spanish?
£2200 $3652 €3190 Spanish brig Brillante off the North African coast (62x81cm-24x32in) s.i.d.1852. 12-Jun-3 Christie's, London #524/R est:1500-2000

MORDSTEIN, Karl Ludwig (1937-) German
£641 $994 €1000 Still life (50x65cm-20x26in) mono.d.1979 acrylic panel. 7-Dec-2 Ketterer, Hamburg #529/R

MORDT, Gustav (1826-1856) Norwegian
£594 $915 €891 Duck hunt in moonlight (31x44cm-12x17in) s. painted 1851. 28-Oct-2 Blomqvist, Lysaker #1191 (N.KR 7000)
£640 $998 €960 Duck hunting in moonlight (31x44cm-12x17in) s. painted 1851. 23-Sep-2 Blomqvist, Lysaker #1158/R (N.KR 7500)

MORE, J H C (19th C) British?
£1019 $1600 €1529 Ships in harbour at twilight (30x51cm-12x20in) s. 22-Nov-2 Eldred, East Dennis #666/R est:600-900

MORE, Jacob (circle) (1740-1793) British
£8000 $13280 €12000 View of the Falls at Tivoli and Villa of Maecenas, an artist sketching and sportsmen beyond (99x141cm-39x56in) prov. 10-Jun-3 Christie's, London #48/R est:10000-15000

MORE, Paul le (1863-1914) French
£256 $392 €400 Chevaux et cavaliers (40x32cm-16x13in) s. 23-Aug-2 Deauville, France #139
£449 $687 €700 Chevaux a l'oree du bois (100x80cm-39x31in) s. 23-Aug-2 Deauville, France #140
£641 $981 €1000 Perce-neige (36x43cm-14x17in) s.i. 23-Aug-2 Deauville, France #131
£865 $1324 €1350 Sporting scenes (130x83cm-51x33in) s. set of 3. 23-Aug-2 Deauville, France #130
£962 $1471 €1500 Ferme normande (29x39cm-11x15in) s. 23-Aug-2 Deauville, France #128/R
£1282 $1962 €2000 Paysans au retour des champs (87x130cm-34x51in) s. 23-Aug-2 Deauville, France #136
£1795 $2746 €2800 En route vers Falaise (87x130cm-34x51in) s. 23-Aug-2 Deauville, France #132/R
£3526 $5394 €5500 Course d'obstacles (130x83cm-51x33in) s. 23-Aug-2 Deauville, France #133/R

MOREA, Jose (1951-) Spanish
£645 $1019 €1000 Figures. s. s.i.d.1980-81 verso acrylic prov.exhib.lit. 17-Dec-2 Segre, Madrid #189/R

MOREAU (?) French
Sculpture
£4114 $6500 €6171 Nymph and putti (57cm-22in) i. bronze marble plinth. 24-Apr-3 Christie's, Rockefeller NY #187/R est:6000-8000

MOREAU DE TOURS, Georges (1848-1901) French
£1923 $2981 €3000 Palefrenier et son cheval. 6-Dec-2 Millon & Associes, Paris #78/R
£4167 $6625 €6000 Printemps. Automne (81x54cm-32x21in) s. pair. 30-Apr-3 Tajan, Paris #134/R est:3000

MOREAU, Adrien (1843-1906) French
£319 $533 €450 Scene antique, esquisse (40x32cm-16x13in) 23-Jun-3 Beaussant & Lefèvre, Paris #156
£980 $1528 €1450 Rue des Chats a Troyes (33x27cm-13x11in) s.i. 28-Mar-3 Charbonneaux, Paris #120/R
£2100 $3360 €3150 Flirtation (22x27cm-9x11in) s. panel prov. 13-May-3 Bonhams, Knightsbridge #175/R est:2000-3000
Works on paper
£400 $636 €600 Gift (23x31cm-9x12in) s. W/C. 27-Feb-3 Bonhams, Chester #459

MOREAU, Auguste (19th C) French
Sculpture
£962 $1519 €1500 Dancing nymph (106cm-42in) i. zinc brass electrified marble socle. 14-Nov-2 Neumeister, Munich #467/R est:1200-1500
£1100 $1749 €1650 Children kissing (37cm-15in) s. bronze marble base. 4-Mar-3 Bearnes, Exeter #534/R est:800-1200
£1156 $1839 €1700 Angel (60cm-24in) s. brown pat.bronze. 24-Mar-3 Bernaerts, Antwerp #41/R est:2000-3000
£1172 $1852 €1700 Young girl sitting on cushion (36x30x170cm-14x12x67in) s. brown pat.bronze. 5-Apr-3 Hans Stahl, Hamburg #494/R est:1800
£1266 $1975 €2000 Amours a la guirlande (34cm-13in) s. green pat bronze red marble socle. 15-Oct-2 Horta, Bruxelles #243
£1282 $2013 €2000 Flora (63cm-25in) i. brown pat.bronze. 21-Nov-2 Van Ham, Cologne #1231/R est:1600
£1392 $2172 €2200 Aiurore (65cm-26in) s. brown pat bronze. 16-Sep-2 Horta, Bruxelles #35
£1429 $2300 €2465 Cupid holding an arrow with a quiver at his feet (76cm-30in) s. bronze. 9-May-3 Eldred, East Dennis #613/R est:500-1000
£1667 $2617 €2600 Porteur de fagots (47cm-19in) s. pat bronze. 13-Dec-2 Piasa, Paris #114/R
£2252 $3670 €3400 Eglantine (71cm-28in) s. brown pat bronze. 17-Feb-3 Horta, Bruxelles #86
£2278 $3554 €3600 Les deux enfants (54cm-21in) medaille pat bronze marble socle. 20-Oct-2 Mercier & Cie, Lille #117 est:1800-2000
£3500 $5460 €5250 Mignon (59cm-23in) s. white marble lit. 5-Nov-2 Sotheby's, London #168/R est:4000-6000

MOREAU, Auguste Louis Mathurin (1834-1917) French
Sculpture
£1154 $1754 €1800 Allegorie du Printemps (53cm-21in) bronze marble base. 17-Aug-2 Livinec, Gaudcheau & Jezequel, Rennes #102
£2300 $3541 €3450 Infant cupids holding garlands (41cm-16in) s. bronze on marble bases pair. 5-Sep-2 Sotheby's, Olympia #127/R est:2000-2500
£20946 $32676 €31000 Cupid (152cm-60in) s. Carrara marble. 31-Mar-3 Finarte Semenzato, Milan #294/R

MOREAU, Charles (1830-?) French
£641 $1006 €1000 Femme assise (35x24cm-14x9in) s. 15-Dec-2 Mercier & Cie, Lille #391

MOREAU, François Hippolyte (19th C) French
Sculpture
£2400 $3816 €3600 Raphael (76cm-30in) s. brown pat bronze. 29-Apr-3 Sotheby's, Olympia #157/R est:600-900

MOREAU, Gustave (1826-1898) French
£92000 $153640 €138000 Christ and Mary Magdalene (81x64cm-32x25in) s. panel painted c.1889 prov.exhib.lit. 19-Jun-3 Christie's, London #64/R est:40000-60000

MOREAU, Henri (1869-1943) Belgian
£321 $503 €500 Nu de dos (40x20cm-16x8in) s.d.1917. 19-Nov-2 Vanderkindere, Brussels #53
£350 $539 €525 Curious glance (50x27cm-20x11in) s.d.1917. 24-Oct-2 Christie's, Kensington #179
£548 $855 €800 Vase fleuri (60x50cm-24x20in) s. 14-Apr-3 Horta, Bruxelles #325
£641 $994 €1000 Roses d'hiver. Vase fleuri (40x30cm-16x12in) s. pair. 9-Dec-2 Horta, Bruxelles #425
£1931 $3090 €2800 Lady in evening dress (80x60cm-31x24in) s.d.1921. 15-Mar-3 De Vuyst, Lokeren #228/R est:3000-3600

MOREAU, Hippolite (19th C) French
Sculpture
£7095 $11068 €10500 Le printemps (69cm-27in) s. marble. 31-Mar-3 Rossini, Paris #37/R

MOREAU, Hippolyte François (1832-1927) French
Sculpture
£955 $1500 €1433 Jeanne d'Arc (48cm-19in) s. brown pat bronze. 23-Nov-2 Jackson's, Cedar Falls #257/R est:1500-2500
£1448 $2317 €2100 Mignon (49x18cm-19x7in) s. brown pat lit. 15-Mar-3 De Vuyst, Lokeren #229/R est:2000-2400
£2949 $4571 €4600 Jeune fille assise (78cm-31in) s. bronze. 3-Dec-2 Campo & Campo, Antwerp #209/R est:1000-1500
£3077 $4769 €4800 Jeune femme a la lampe a huile (60cm-24in) s.st.f.Compagnie des Bronzes pat bronze red marble socle. 9-Dec-2 Horta, Bruxelles #156/R est:6000-8000
£4500 $7020 €6750 Two young maidens (83cm-33in) s. brown pat bronze green marble base. 9-Apr-3 Sotheby's, London #150/R est:4000-6000
£4676 $7482 €6500 Mignon (81x30cm-32x12in) s. brown pat bronze lit. 17-May-3 De Vuyst, Lokeren #432/R est:6000-6500
£8500 $13260 €12750 Girl with dove (82cm-32in) s. white marble. 5-Nov-2 Sotheby's, London #163/R est:7000-10000

MOREAU, Jean Baptiste (1797-1855) French
Sculpture
£3800 $6308 €3800 Vase avec fleurs de lys et chardons (63cm-25in) s. pat bronze. 16-Jun-3 Horta, Bruxelles #81 est:2200-3000

MOREAU, Jean Michel (younger) (1741-1814) French
Works on paper
£1772 $2800 €2800 Une petite fille endormie sur un tabouret (19x23cm-7x9in) col chk. 27-Nov-2 Christie's, Paris #163/R est:3000-5000
£1795 $2818 €2800 Bacchante et jeune satyre (22x17cm-9x7in) s.d.1772 pen wash. 16-Dec-2 Eric Coutrier, Paris #31/R
£2378 $3400 €3567 Untitled (8x9cm-3x4in) pen ink wash bound volume with five drawings. 23-Jan-3 Swann Galleries, New York #272/R est:2000-3000
£2585 $4110 €3800 Scene galante dans un parc (17x12cm-7x5in) i.verso W/C htd gouache pen ink. 24-Mar-3 Tajan, Paris #91/R
£3108 $4849 €4600 Chene et roseau (29x37cm-11x15in) i. pen ink wash over crayon. 26-Mar-3 Piasa, Paris #75

MOREAU, Louis Gabriel (1740-1806) French
£283871 $448516 €440000 Vue des coteaux de Bellevue prise du Parc de Saint-Cloud (56x82cm-22x32in) paper on canvas exhib. 18-Dec-2 Piasa, Paris #63/R est:300000-350000
Works on paper
£385 $550 €578 Landscape with a cottage (17x24cm-7x9in) brush ink wash black chk. 23-Jan-3 Swann Galleries, New York #269/R

£3094 $4950 €4300 Landscape with elegant figures and ruins (40x30cm-16x12in) mono.d.1784. 17-May-3 Lempertz, Koln #1244/R est:3800
£4422 $7031 €6500 Paysage au bord de la mer (21x43cm-8x17in) gouache over crayon. 24-Mar-3 Tajan, Paris #82/R
£28481 $45000 €45000 Paysage montagneux avec une cascade, figures au premier plan (22x33cm-9x13in) gouache prov.exhib.lit. 27-Nov-2 Christie's, Paris #199/R est:25000-35000

MOREAU, Louis Gabriel (attrib) (1740-1806) French
Works on paper
£1329 $1900 €1994 Landscape with a house by a pond and church ruins (14x18cm-6x7in) gouache. 23-Jan-3 Swann Galleries, New York #270/R est:2000-3000

MOREAU, Louis-Auguste (1855-1919) French
Sculpture
£1000 $1630 €1450 Young girl dancing (50cm-20in) s. dark brown pat. bronze. 15-Jul-3 Sotheby's, Olympia #128/R est:1200-1800

MOREAU, Mathurin (1822-1912) French
Sculpture
£1053 $1705 €1600 Diane au bain (53cm-21in) s. brown pat bronze. 21-Jan-3 Galerie Moderne, Brussels #1526/R est:1200-1600
£1164 $1816 €1700 Jeune bergere (52cm-20in) s. brown pat bronze Cast G. Godeau. 14-Apr-3 Horta, Bruxelles #117 est:1800-2200
£1172 $1876 €1700 Fillette au pigeon assis sur une gerbe. brown pat bronze Cast Cie de Bronzes. 17-Mar-3 Amberes, Antwerp #439
£1258 $2051 €1900 Cueillette (50cm-20in) s. pat bronze. 17-Feb-3 Horta, Bruxelles #43
£1268 $2041 €1800 La liseuse (60cm-24in) s. yellow pat bronze. 12-May-3 Bernaerts, Antwerp #57/R est:2000-3000
£1497 $2380 €2200 Printemps (87cm-34in) s. terracotta. 26-Feb-3 Fraysse & Associes, Paris #39/R est:1000-1200
£1879 $3026 €2800 La chanson de la mer (74cm-29in) s. gold pat.bronze. 18-Feb-3 Galerie Moderne, Brussels #1021 est:2500-3000
£2095 $3268 €3100 Baigneuse aux fleurs (76cm-30in) s. marble. 31-Mar-3 Rossini, Paris #36/R
£2098 $3504 €3000 Venus aux fleurs (85cm-33in) green pat bronze onyx socle. 25-Jun-3 Artcurial Briest, Paris #714/R est:3000-4000
£2448 $4087 €3500 Femme a la lyre (107cm-42in) s. brown pat bronze. 25-Jun-3 Artcurial Briest, Paris #42/R est:2500-3000
£2564 $4000 €3846 Classical figures with putti (48cm-19in) s. bronze pair. 22-Sep-2 Susanin's, Chicago #5051/R est:5000-7000
£2642 $4094 €4200 Source (72cm-28in) i. pat bronze. 6-Oct-2 Livinec, Gaudcheau & Jezequel, Rennes #86/R
£2953 $4754 €4400 Homme accompagne d'une victoire (97cm-38in) s. black pat bronze. 18-Feb-3 Vanderkindere, Brussels #128/R
£3608 $5592 €5700 La source (61cm-24in) s. brown pat bronze Cast Colin a Paris. 29-Sep-2 Eric Pillon, Calais #98/R
£3797 $6000 €5696 Figure of Bacchante, emblematic of autumn (86cm-34in) i. brown pat. bronze on marble pedestal. 24-Apr-3 Christie's, Rockefeller NY #185/R est:6000-8000
£4317 $6906 €6000 Retour de moisson (84x40cm-33x16in) s. brown pat bronze lit. 17-May-3 De Vuyst, Lokeren #420/R est:6000-7000
£6500 $10140 €9750 Winged maidens allegorical of summer and autumn (76cm-30in) s. brown pat bronze pair. 9-Apr-3 Sotheby's, London #130/R est:5000-7000
£10759 $16785 €17000 Allegory of Victory (175cm-69in) brown pat bronze. 19-Oct-2 Semenzato, Venice #235/R est:16000-22000

MOREAU, Mathurin (after) (1822-1912) French
Sculpture
£8228 $13000 €13000 Jeunes enfants endormis (154x90x50cm-61x35x20in) bears sig. white marble wooden base. 2-Dec-2 Cornette de St.Cyr, Paris #143/R est:9000

MOREAU, Mathurin (attrib) (1822-1912) French
Sculpture
£3444 $5613 €5200 Femme avec deux enfants (86cm-34in) brown pat bronze marble base. 29-Jan-3 Tajan, Paris #59

MOREAU, Max (1902-1992) Belgian
£903 $1490 €1300 Roasting chestnuts (92x74cm-36x29in) s. 1-Jul-3 Christie's, Amsterdam #304/R
£927 $1511 €1400 Ruelle animee (38x31cm-15x12in) s.d.30 panel. 17-Feb-3 Horta, Bruxelles #355
£5036 $8259 €7000 La lecture sur la terrasse d'un palais a Tunis (80x60cm-31x24in) s. 4-Jun-3 Tajan, Paris #293/R est:4000-6000
£5756 $9439 €8000 Portrait d'un jeune Africain (100x80cm-39x31in) s.d.1938. 4-Jun-3 Tajan, Paris #285/R est:4000-6000

MOREAU, Nicolas (19th C) French
£3418 $5400 €5400 Le relais de chiens (27x35cm-11x14in) s. panel. 1-Dec-2 Peron, Melun #41b

MOREAU, Nikolaus (1805-1834) Austrian
£300 $474 €450 Bassett hounds leashed to a bush on a forest track (27x35cm-11x14in) s. panel. 14-Nov-2 Christie's, Kensington #124

MOREAU-DESCHANVRES, Auguste (19th C) French
£705 $1072 €1100 Fermiere et veaux (54x66cm-21x26in) 17-Aug-2 Livinec, Gaudcheau & Jezequel, Rennes #46

MOREAU-NELATON, Étienne (1859-1927) French
£700 $1141 €1050 Arched cliff at Etretat (60x74cm-24x29in) s. prov. 13-Feb-3 Christie's, Kensington #121/R

MOREELSE, Paulus (attrib) (1571-1638) Dutch
£4800 $7488 €7200 Portrait of a lady, wearing a black dress (41x35cm-16x14in) panel fragment prov.lit. 8-Apr-3 Sotheby's, Olympia #144/R est:3000-5000

MOREELSE, Paulus (circle) (1571-1638) Dutch
£8500 $13345 €12750 Portrait of a lady in black and white lace costume holding a black dog (91x72cm-36x28in) with sig.d.1629. 13-Dec-2 Christie's, Kensington #37/R est:5000-7000

MOREL FATIO, Antoine Léon (1810-1871) French
£5031 $8000 €7547 On the high seas (66x58cm-26x23in) init. 7-Mar-3 Skinner, Boston #318/R est:5000-7000
Works on paper
£310 $493 €450 Trois mats vent arriere (22x27cm-9x11in) mono. graphite dr tracing paper. 4-Mar-3 Livinec, Gaudcheau & Jezequel, Rennes #408
£345 $548 €500 Cotre grand largue (22x27cm-9x11in) mono. graphite dr tracing paper. 4-Mar-3 Livinec, Gaudcheau & Jezequel, Rennes #407

MOREL, Charles (1861-1908) French
Works on paper
£360 $587 €540 Officer and guards review (31x26cm-12x10in) s.i.d.1891 W/C. 29-Jan-3 Sotheby's, Olympia #260/R

MOREL, E (19th C) French
£1835 $2863 €2900 Le Moulin des Cinq Ormes (68x98cm-27x39in) s.d.1886. 20-Oct-2 Galerie de Chartres, Chartres #112 est:1500-2500

MOREL, Henriette (20th C) French
£633 $987 €1000 Femme rousse (51x39cm-20x15in) s/. cardboard. 20-Oct-2 Anaf, Lyon #197

MOREL, Jan Baptist (1662-1732) Flemish
£5594 $9343 €8000 Guirlandes de fleurs retenues par des rubans bleus (55x77cm-22x30in) pair. 27-Jun-3 Piasa, Paris #35/R est:8000-10000

MOREL, Jan Evert II (1835-1905) Dutch
£1027 $1613 €1500 Travelers in a wooded summer landscape (30x38cm-12x15in) s. panel. 15-Apr-3 Sotheby's, Amsterdam #11/R est:1500-2000
£1159 $1900 €1739 Landscape with figures by stream (33x25cm-13x10in) s. panel. 9-Feb-3 William Jenack, New York #193 est:600-1000
£2025 $3200 €3200 Landscape (26x36cm-10x14in) s. panel. 26-Nov-2 Wiener Kunst Auktionen, Vienna #20/R est:1500-2500
£2431 $3865 €3500 Haycart by a farm in a panoramic river landscape (22x36cm-9x14in) s. panel. 29-Apr-3 Christie's, Amsterdam #84/R est:4000-6000
£2740 $4301 €4000 Travelers in a summer landscape (44x68cm-17x27in) s. 15-Apr-3 Sotheby's, Amsterdam #54/R est:4000-6000
£3014 $4701 €4400 Extensive Dutch river landscape with windmill and peasants (51x38cm-20x15in) s. panel. 10-Apr-3 Van Ham, Cologne #1601/R est:3800
£5479 $8603 €8000 Conversing figures on a frozen ditch (40x55cm-16x22in) s. 15-Apr-3 Sotheby's, Amsterdam #28/R est:9000-12000
£9028 $14354 €13000 Panoramic river landscape with a town in the distance (35x51cm-14x20in) s. panel. 29-Apr-3 Christie's, Amsterdam #1/R est:3000-5000

MOREL, Jan Evert II and SEVERDONCK, Franz van (19th C) Dutch/Belgian
£1887 $2906 €3000 Shepherd and his flock in a wooded landscape (28x36cm-11x14in) s.i. 22-Oct-2 Sotheby's, Amsterdam #14/R est:2000-3000
£3767 $5914 €5500 Shepherd with his flock in a wooded landscape (36x51cm-14x20in) s. 15-Apr-3 Sotheby's, Amsterdam #21/R est:4000-6000

MOREL, Willem F A I Vaarzon (1868-1955) Dutch

£506 $790 €800 Still life of poppies (54x70cm-21x28in) s. prov. 21-Oct-2 Glerum, Amsterdam #86/R
£696 $1086 €1100 Roses in a glass vase (34x26cm-13x10in) s. prov. 21-Oct-2 Glerum, Amsterdam #87/R
£1899 $2962 €3000 View of church and houses in Veere from a garden (100x100cm-39x39in) s. prov. 21-Oct-2 Glerum, Amsterdam #43/R est:2000-3000
£2038 $3180 €3200 View of the buildings on Veere quay (68x85cm-27x33in) s. 5-Nov-2 Vendu Notarishuis, Rotterdam #98/R est:800-1000
£16667 $26167 €26000 Figures in the market in Middelburg (53x83cm-21x33in) s. 25-Nov-2 Glerum, Amsterdam #103/R est:3500-5000

MORELL, Abelardo (1948-) ?

Photographs

£2675 $4200 €4013 Book with wavy pages (61x51cm-24x20in) s.i.d.verso num.21 of 30 gelatin silver print. 21-Apr-3 Phillips, New York #22/R est:3000-4000
£3165 $5000 €4748 Camera obscura image of houses across the street in our living room (45x57cm-18x22in) s.i.d.1991 large format photograph. 23-Apr-3 Sotheby's, New York #269/R est:5000-7000
£3571 $5500 €5357 Camera obscura image of Manhattan (51x61cm-20x24in) s.i.d.1996 num.27/30 verso gelatin silver print prov.lit. 25-Oct-2 Phillips, New York #62/R est:4000-6000
£5519 $8500 €8279 Camera obscura image of Times Square in hotel room (46x57cm-18x22in) s.i.d.1997 photograph. 24-Oct-2 Sotheby's, New York #255/R est:5000-7000
£5828 $9500 €8742 Dictionary (75x99cm-30x39in) s.i.d.1994 gelatin silver print. 12-Feb-3 Christie's, Rockefeller NY #132/R est:7000-9000

MORELLE, John P (fl.1884-1886) British

£1586 $2443 €2379 Fishergirls on beach near Tynemouth (11x86cm-4x34in) s. 27-Oct-2 Anders Antik, Landskrona #251/R est:5000-7000 (S.KR 23000)

MORELLET, François (1926-) French

£1000 $1580 €1580 10 lignes au hasard No 75091 No 2 (60x60cm-24x24in) s.i.d.1975 stretcher. 29-Nov-2 Villa Grisebach, Berlin #815/R est:1200-1500
£3546 $5922 €5000 La vague (125x92cm-49x36in) s.i.d.verso oil acrylic. 18-Jun-3 Pierre Berge, Paris #103 est:5000-6000

Sculpture

£6550 $10284 €9825 7 lignes au hasard (80x80x3cm-31x31x1in) s.i.d.1986 verso acrylic panel. 23-Nov-2 Burkhard, Luzern #65/R est:10000-12000 (S.FR 15000)
£12903 $20387 €20000 Untitled (60x60x60cm-24x24x24in) metal prov. 19-Dec-2 Ruellan, Paris #148/R est:30000

MORELLI, Domenico (1826-1901) Italian

£1282 $1987 €2000 PO. of man (52x64cm-20x25in) s. 4-Dec-2 Finarte, Rome #786/R

Works on paper

£833 $1292 €1300 Woman in interior (24x17cm-9x7in) s. ink. 4-Dec-2 Finarte, Rome #730
£968 $1529 €1500 Odalisk (44x29cm-17x11in) s. Chinese ink. 18-Dec-2 Finarte, Milan #201/R

MORELLON LAPUENTE, Jose (1944-) Spanish

£383 $559 €590 Bull scene (100x81cm-39x32in) s.i.d.verso. 17-Jun-2 Ansorena, Madrid #48/R
£481 $760 €750 Speak to her (100x81cm-39x32in) s. s.i.d.2002 verso. 13-Nov-2 Ansorena, Madrid #74/R

MORENA, Manuel de la (?) Spanish

£487 $711 €750 River by Hares (20x25cm-8x10in) s. s.i.verso board. 17-Jun-2 Ansorena, Madrid #122/R

MORENI, Mattia (1920-1999) Italian

£7092 $11489 €10000 Anguria sulla neve (47x90cm-19x35in) s.d.1965 s.i.d.verso prov.exhib. 26-May-3 Christie's, Milan #178/R est:10000-12000
£16774 $26503 €26000 Wind (130x130cm-51x51in) s.d.1953 s.i.d.verso exhib. 18-Dec-2 Christie's, Rome #300/R
£20513 $32205 €32000 Fire (81x100cm-32x39in) s. s.i.d.1957 verso prov. 20-Nov-2 Pandolfini, Florence #114/R

Works on paper

£2083 $3312 €3000 Life revolution (71x47cm-28x19in) s.d.1997 mixed media. 1-May-3 Meeting Art, Vercelli #221
£2244 $3545 €3500 Electronic shoe (66x48cm-26x19in) s.d.1995 mixed media. 15-Nov-2 Farsetti, Prato #309/R

MORENO RODRIGUEZ, Manuel (19th C) Spanish

£1572 $2421 €2500 Princess hall (98x78cm-39x31in) s.d.1887. 22-Oct-2 Durán, Madrid #129/R

MORENO VILLA, Jose (1887-1960) Spanish

Works on paper

£1226 $1937 €1900 Stone figures (13x14cm-5x6in) s. gouache. 17-Dec-2 Durán, Madrid #153/R
£1290 $2039 €2000 Surrealist landscape (15x15cm-6x6in) s. gouache. 17-Dec-2 Durán, Madrid #184/R

MORENO YRIBERRY, J (20th C) Spanish

£671 $1081 €1000 Bucholic scene (140x230cm-55x91in) s.i.d.1912. 18-Feb-3 Durán, Madrid #639/R

MORENO, Luis (?) Spanish

£586 $932 €850 Young woman with basket of fruit (41x33cm-16x13in) s. board. 4-Mar-3 Ansorena, Madrid #321/R
£642 $1001 €950 Portrait of girl (61x50cm-24x20in) s. canvas on board. 25-Mar-3 Durán, Madrid #113/R
£1069 $1668 €1700 Girl with flowers (41x27cm-16x11in) s. 8-Oct-2 Ansorena, Madrid #275/R
£1316 $2132 €2000 Embroidering (35x44cm-14x17in) s. board. 21-Jan-3 Durán, Madrid #117/R
£1572 $2453 €2500 Flower seller (46x27cm-18x11in) s. board. 23-Sep-2 Durán, Madrid #148/R

MORENO, Michel (1945-) French

£769 $1285 €1100 Le joueur de mandoline (80x65cm-31x26in) s. 25-Jun-3 Claude Aguttes, Neuilly #147

MORENO, Rafael (1911-1951) Spanish

£340 $530 €540 Landscape with dog (73x105cm-29x41in) s. painted c.1940. 17-Sep-2 Segre, Madrid #222/R

MORERA Y GALICIA, Jaime (1854-1927) Spanish

£541 $845 €850 Allee ensoleillee (55x55cm-22x22in) s.d.05. 11-Nov-2 Horta, Bruxelles #540
£15723 $24528 €25000 Lagoon (65x117cm-26x46in) s. 23-Sep-2 Durán, Madrid #218/R est:15000

Works on paper

£1083 $1689 €1700 Gitane (68x48cm-27x19in) s. pastel. 11-Nov-2 Horta, Bruxelles #539 est:1800-2500

MOREROD, Edouard (1879-1919) Swiss

Works on paper

£239 $371 €359 Jeunes filles au foulard (61x46cm-24x18in) s. pierre noire pastel. 7-Dec-2 Galerie du Rhone, Sion #408/R (S.FR 550)
£371 $579 €557 Portrait of Spanish woman (62x44cm-24x17in) s. chl col chk. 6-Nov-2 Dobiaschofsky, Bern #843/R (S.FR 850)

MORESCAUX, Kathleen (20th C) Irish

£496 $804 €700 Still life of bowl of flowers (32x49cm-13x19in) s. 20-May-3 Mealy's, Castlecomer #1325/R

MORET, Henry (1856-1913) French

£15385 $24000 €23078 La Manche a Dieppe (54x73cm-21x29in) s.d.1912 prov. 7-Nov-2 Christie's, Rockefeller NY #249/R est:25000-35000
£15823 $24684 €25000 La peche au homard (54x64cm-21x25in) s.d.1892. 20-Oct-2 Galerie de Chartres, Chartres #150 est:18000-25000
£17000 $27710 €25500 Doelan basse mer (65x80cm-26x31in) s.d.1903. 3-Feb-3 Bonhams, New Bond Street #25/R est:15000-20000
£24434 $40805 €35429 Quimper, la riviere (46x55cm-18x22in) s. prov. 24-Jun-3 Koller, Zurich #110/R est:40000-70000 (S.FR 54000)
£24653 $40184 €35500 Cote rocheuse ensoleillee en Bretagne (60x73cm-24x29in) s. 19-Jul-3 Thierry & Lannon, Brest #158/R est:35000-40000
£24891 $39328 €37337 Breton peasants in the fields (54x64cm-21x25in) s. 14-Nov-2 Stuker, Bern #416/R est:15000-20000 (S.FR 57000)
£26351 $41108 €39000 Le pilote, Cote de Bretagne (60x81cm-24x32in) s.d. prov. 31-Mar-3 Rossini, Paris #62/R
£28846 $45288 €45000 Semaphore (65x92cm-26x36in) s. i.verso. 15-Dec-2 Thierry & Lannon, Brest #179/R est:50000
£30769 $51385 €44615 Le loch, pres Audierne (48x61cm-19x24in) s.d.1911 prov. 24-Jun-3 Koller, Zurich #115/R est:50000-80000 (S.FR 68000)
£32639 $53201 €47000 Le Pouldu (117x105cm-46x41in) s. 19-Jul-3 Thierry & Lannon, Brest #157 est:50000-60000
£35256 $55000 €52884 Rochers de porspoder, finistere (51x65cm-20x26in) s.d.1910 prov. 6-Nov-2 Sotheby's, New York #164/R est:45000-60000
£45000 $75150 €65250 Jour de calme (61x74cm-24x29in) s.d.97 prov. 25-Jun-3 Christie's, London #101/R est:30000-40000

Works on paper

£285 $450 €450 Personnages au bord de la mer (28x38cm-11x15in) s.d.92 pastel. 27-Nov-2 Christie's, Paris #280/R

£382 $607 €550 Le verger (26x38cm-10x15in) studio st. graphite chl dr. 29-Apr-3 Artcurial Briest, Paris #6

MORETTI, G (?) Italian
Sculpture
£3065 $4750 €4598 Figure of Dante seated with the doomed lovers (109cm-43in) s.d.1911 white marble. 7-Dec-2 Selkirks, St. Louis #401/R est:6000-7000

MORETTI, Lucien Philippe (1922-) French
£403 $648 €600 Jeune femme a la chevelure rousse (27x22cm-11x9in) s. 23-Feb-3 Lesieur & Le Bars, Le Havre #122
£701 $1093 €1052 Cafe interior (73x92cm-29x36in) s. 6-Nov-2 AB Stockholms Auktionsverk #935/R (S.KR 10000)
£1849 $2885 €2700 Animation a Paris, la Seine (27x41cm-11x16in) s.d.55. 13-Apr-3 Feletin, Province #94

MORETTI, Luigi (1884-?) Italian
£400 $632 €620 Baie de Dieppe (37x46cm-15x18in) s. panel. 18-Dec-2 Ferri, Paris #98
£2025 $3200 €3200 La Salute, Venice (60x73cm-24x29in) s.d.1930. 26-Nov-2 Christie's, Rome #102/R
£2500 $4175 €3750 Venetian Canal (111x80cm-44x31in) s. 18-Jun-3 Christie's, Kensington #138/R est:2000-3000

MORETTI, R (19/20th C) ?
Works on paper
£1000 $1620 €1500 Promotion (36x54cm-14x21in) s.i. W/C. 21-May-3 Bonhams, Knightsbridge #43/R est:800-1200

MORETTI, Raymond (1931-) French
£364 $594 €550 Composition (167x116cm-66x46in) s.verso. 1-Feb-3 Claude Aguttes, Neuilly #154/R
£397 $648 €600 Espgane 4/5000 F (116x89cm-46x35in) s.d.1986 verso. 1-Feb-3 Claude Aguttes, Neuilly #156/R
Works on paper
£2518 $4029 €3500 Hommage a Philippe Solers (73x103cm-29x41in) s. mixed media. 18-May-3 Eric Pillon, Calais #298/R

MOREUX, Jean Charles (1889-1956) French
Sculpture
£6329 $10000 €10000 Untitled (147cm-58in) pat cast iron lit. 26-Nov-2 Tajan, Paris #148/R est:15000-18000

MORGAN, Alfred (fl.1862-1904) British
£1900 $3097 €2755 Angel Gabriel appearing to the shepherds (74x136cm-29x54in) mono.d.1876. 16-Jul-3 Sotheby's, Olympia #125/R est:1000-1500
£420000 $697200 €630000 Omnibus ride to Piccadilly Circus, Mr Gladstone travelling with ordinary passengers (82x109cm-32x43in) s.d.1885 prov.exhib.lit. 12-Jun-3 Sotheby's, London #38/R est:200000-300000

MORGAN, Alfred George (fl.1896-1919) British
£450 $711 €675 Boots corner, Whitby (58x48cm-23x19in) s. 24-Apr-3 Richardson & Smith, Whitby #50/R

MORGAN, Barbara (1902-1992) American
Photographs
£1899 $3000 €2849 Fossil in formation (25x34cm-10x13in) s.d.1965 gelatin silver print prov.exhib.lit. 25-Apr-3 Phillips, New York #268/R est:1500-2500
£2805 $4600 €4208 Martha Graham, letter to the world, kick (38x48cm-15x19in) s.i.d. s.i.verso silver print. 10-Feb-3 Swann Galleries, New York #66/R est:4500-5500

MORGAN, Baxter (fl.1905-1932) British
£480 $744 €720 Sheep barn (36x53cm-14x21in) s. 3-Dec-2 Sotheby's, Olympia #84/R
Works on paper
£250 $405 €375 Sheep watering (25x35cm-10x14in) s. W/C. 20-May-3 Sotheby's, Olympia #281/R

MORGAN, Charlotte E (1867-1947) American
£542 $900 €786 Untitled (69x84cm-27x33in) 13-Jun-3 Du Mouchelle, Detroit #2492/R

MORGAN, Cole (1950-) Dutch
£1266 $2000 €2000 Untitled (24x34cm-9x13in) s.d.86 acrylic pencil col crayon collage on paper. 26-Nov-2 Sotheby's, Amsterdam #60/R est:1000-1200
£2564 $3974 €4000 Glass mountain (58x77cm-23x30in) s. cardboard painted 2001. 3-Dec-2 Christie's, Amsterdam #292/R est:4000-6000
£5036 $8259 €7000 Can we talk (80x160cm-31x63in) s.d.90 s.i.d.verso acrylic pencil collage on two canvases diptych. 3-Jun-3 Christie's, Amsterdam #358/R est:7000-9000
Works on paper
£2532 $4000 €4000 Stripes Xi (160x190cm-63x75in) s.d.90 s.i.d. verso mixed media. 27-Nov-2 Dorotheum, Vienna #337/R est:4000-5000
£6090 $9561 €9500 Five eyes (140x120cm-55x47in) s.d.1998 mixed media. 25-Nov-2 Glerum, Amsterdam #353/R est:10000-15000

MORGAN, Evelyn de (1855-1919) British
Works on paper
£620 $1004 €930 Study of an arm from queen Eleanor and fair Rosamund (31x20cm-12x8in) col chk exhib. 20-May-3 Sotheby's, Olympia #239/R
£1300 $2080 €1950 Draped figure study with accompanying nude (48x59cm-19x23in) col chk prov. 15-May-3 Lawrence, Crewkerne #826/R est:1000-1500
£2400 $3864 €3600 Study of two female nudes (42x58cm-17x23in) chk prov.exhib. 20-Feb-3 Christie's, London #283/R
£2581 $4000 €3872 Female nude (37x23cm-15x9in) pencil pastel htd white prov. 29-Oct-2 Sotheby's, New York #120/R est:600-800

MORGAN, Fred (19/20th C) British
£500 $790 €725 Ploughing team with hunt passing in distance (43x58cm-17x23in) s.d.1906. 28-Jul-3 David Duggleby, Scarborough #296/R

MORGAN, Frederick (1856-1927) British
£3500 $5529 €5250 Flower gatherer (25x20cm-10x8in) s. board oval. 2-Dec-2 Sotheby's, London #27/R est:4000-6000
£4800 $7776 €6960 Looking Glass (60x45cm-24x18in) s.d.1873. 29-Jul-3 Henry Adams, Chichester #551/R est:4000-6000
£24825 $40217 €35996 The rowing trip - small girl and old man (98x110cm-39x43in) s. 26-May-3 Bukowskis, Stockholm #233/R est:400000-500000 (S.KR 320000)
£70968 $110000 €106452 Motherly love (67x49cm-26x19in) s. prov. 30-Oct-2 Christie's, Rockefeller NY #44/R est:70000-90000
£129032 $200000 €193548 First tooth (88x119cm-35x47in) s. prov. 30-Oct-2 Christie's, Rockefeller NY #47/R est:220000-280000

MORGAN, Frederick (attrib) (1856-1927) British
£2033 $3211 €2948 Maid of the Netherlands (105x65cm-41x26in) bears sig. 22-Jul-3 Lawson Menzies, Sydney #289/R est:4000-6000 (A.D 5000)

MORGAN, Gareth (1978-) British
£976 $1600 €1415 Telephone (90x62cm-35x24in) s.d.2001 acrylic on board. 28-May-3 Sotheby's, Amsterdam #166/R est:1200-1800
£1000 $1600 €1450 Scratched car (90x62cm-35x24in) s.d.2001 verso acrylic on board. 13-May-3 Sotheby's, Tel Aviv #81/R est:1200-1800
£1000 $1600 €1450 Flood (73x100cm-29x39in) s.d.2002 verso acrylic on perspex. 13-May-3 Sotheby's, Tel Aviv #82/R est:1800-2200
£1677 $2800 €2432 Caryatid (134x94cm-53x37in) s.d.2001 verso acrylic on perspex. 25-Jun-3 Sotheby's, Moscow #230/R est:2200-2800
£1951 $3200 €2829 Arm (130x103cm-51x41in) s.d.2002 acrylic on perspex. 28-May-3 Sotheby's, Amsterdam #167/R est:2200-2800
£2096 $3500 €3039 I dreamt I was human and I had to eat and drink and shit and piss and wash and shave it was horrible (152x104cm-60x41in) s.d.2002 verso acrylic on perspex. 25-Jun-3 Sotheby's, Moscow #229/R est:2500-3000

MORGAN, Glenn William (1955-) Australian
£377 $589 €654 The City (50x172cm-20x68in) s.d.96 wood. 31-Mar-3 Goodman, Sydney #34 (A.D 1000)

MORGAN, Gwyn (20th C) British
£820 $1304 €1230 Still life of roses and carnation (66x52cm-26x20in) s. board. 6-Mar-3 Bonhams, Cornwall #727

MORGAN, Jane (1832-1899) American
£641 $1000 €962 Midy Morgan in Greek costume (47x38cm-19x15in) s. 20-Sep-2 Sloan, North Bethesda #490/R est:500-700

MORGAN, Jenny (20th C) British
£1400 $2338 €2030 On station - the Elbe pilot schooner Cuxhaven (61x76cm-24x30in) s. 18-Jun-3 Sotheby's, Olympia #141/R est:1000-1500

MORGAN, John (1823-1886) British
£600 $936 €900 Burial in a country churchyard (90x134cm-35x53in) s. 8-Oct-2 Bonhams, Oxford #219
£230000 $370300 €345000 Fight (68x104cm-27x41in) prov.exhib.lit. 19-Feb-3 Christie's, London #16/R est:250000-350000

MORGAN, Mary de Neale (1868-1948) American
£1708 $2750 €2562 Carmel shore (18x23cm-7x9in) estate st. prov. 18-Feb-3 John Moran, Pasadena #13a est:1000-2000
£5901 $9500 €8852 Cypress trees in Carmel coastal (41x51cm-16x20in) s. board prov. 18-Feb-3 John Moran, Pasadena #24 est:7000-9000
£8280 $13000 €12420 Oaks and lupin, Carmel Valley (61x61cm-24x24in) s. i.stretcher prov. 20-Nov-2 Christie's, Los Angeles #1/R est:7000-9000
Works on paper
£1078 $1800 €1563 House in landscape (15x15cm-6x6in) s. gouache. 17-Jun-3 John Moran, Pasadena #18a est:2000-3000
£2484 $4000 €3726 Early moonrise, Carmel lagoon (30x20cm-12x8in) s. i.verso W/C pastel prov. 18-Feb-3 John Moran, Pasadena #13 est:3000-5000
£2903 $4500 €4355 Carmel dunes and cypress (15x15cm-6x6in) s. i.verso gouache. 29-Oct-2 John Moran, Pasadena #610b est:2500-3500

MORGAN, Patrick (1904-) American
£289 $480 €419 Novembre a la malbaie (61x81cm-24x32in) s. i.verso prov. 10-Jun-3 Ritchie, Toronto #96/R (C.D 650)

MORGAN, Phyllis (?) British?
£320 $496 €480 Harbour scene with shrimp boats unloading. board. 3-Oct-2 Bonhams, Cornwall #181

MORGAN, R F (1929-) American
£6646 $10500 €9637 Captain Clark and party at the Big Hole (76x102cm-30x40in) s. 26-Jul-3 Coeur d'Alene, Hayden #222/R est:4000-6000

MORGAN, Randall (1920-) American
£1699 $2735 €2549 Natura morta (150x190cm-59x75in) s. painted c.1985 prov. 7-May-3 AB Stockholms Auktionsverk #1094/R est:18000-20000 (S.KR 22000)

MORGAN, Sister Gertrude (1900-1980) American
Works on paper
£3640 $5750 €5460 Heavenly wedding with angels attending (28x28cm-11x11in) s. mixed media cardboard. 16-Nov-2 New Orleans Auction, New Orleans #1569/R est:3500-5000

MORGAN, Walter Jenks (1847-1924) British
Works on paper
£270 $432 €405 Arabian street scene with figures of a musician and a young boy (33x23cm-13x9in) s. W/C. 10-Jan-3 Biddle & Webb, Birmingham #268
£330 $538 €495 Aberdovey, North Wales (19x29cm-7x11in) s. i.verso W/C over pencil htd bodycol. 11-Feb-3 Bonhams, Knowle #61

MORGAN, William (1826-1900) American
£12500 $19751 €18750 Young soldiers (51x76cm-20x30in) s.d.1883 prov. 18-Nov-2 Waddingtons, Toronto #21/R est:10000-15000 (C.D 31000)

MORGAN, William F de (1839-1917) British
Works on paper
£4000 $6440 €6000 Perseus and Andromeda (29x29cm-11x11in) pencil chk prov. 20-Feb-3 Christie's, London #232/R

MORGARI INGARANO, Emilia (1881-1950) Italian
£324 $522 €470 Roses in glass vase (41x32cm-16x13in) s. panel. 7-May-3 Dobiaschofsky, Bern #845/R (S.FR 700)
£884 $1406 €1300 Vase with roses (50x50cm-20x20in) s.d.1931 board. 1-Mar-3 Meeting Art, Vercelli #16

MORGARI, Luigi (1857-1935) Italian
£2700 $4239 €4050 In the baths of the harem (90x42cm-35x17in) s. 19-Nov-2 Bonhams, New Bond Street #90 est:3000-5000
£12838 $20027 €19000 Young women bathing (91x43cm-36x17in) s. 28-Mar-3 Claude Aguttes, Neuilly #195/R est:8000-12000

MORGARI, Rodolfo (1827-1909) Italian
£833 $1308 €1300 Assumption (55x36cm-22x14in) 10-Dec-2 Della Rocca, Turin #315/R
£1020 $1622 €1500 Portrait of girl (50x40cm-20x16in) s.d.1867. 18-Mar-3 Finarte, Milan #127/R

MORGENROTH, Johann Martin (1800-1859) German
Miniatures
£1200 $1848 €1800 Princess Auguste of Wurttemberg (17cm-7in) s. i.verso porcelain giltwood frame rec. 24-Oct-2 Sotheby's, Olympia #84/R est:700-900

MORGENSTERN, Christian (1805-1867) German
£6220 $10077 €9019 Wasserfall bei Hoog Foss - Norwegian landscape with huts by waterfall (53x64cm-21x25in) mono.d.1828. 26-May-3 Rasmussen, Copenhagen #1178/R est:20000-30000 (D.KR 65000)
Works on paper
£519 $774 €800 Entry to the Tyrol near Lofer (25x33cm-10x13in) mnoo.i.d.1830 pencil. 26-Jun-2 Neumeister, Munich #593/R

MORGENSTERN, Friedrich Ernst (1853-1919) German
£318 $490 €500 High mountain river landscape (28x40cm-11x16in) s. 5-Sep-2 Arnold, Frankfurt #828/R
£833 $1292 €1300 Romantic coastal landscape at Ostend with various boats (44x66cm-17x26in) s.i.d.1881 lit. 7-Dec-2 Bergmann, Erlangen #768/R

MORGENSTERN, Karl (1811-1893) German
£2009 $3134 €3014 Beach with anchored ships (19x26cm-7x10in) s.d.1852. 20-Nov-2 Fischer, Luzern #1165/R est:5000-7000 (S.FR 4600)
£9155 $15197 €13000 View of Tivoli (56x74cm-22x29in) s.i.d.1836. 14-Jun-3 Arnold, Frankfurt #818/R est:9000
£15823 $24525 €25000 Mainz (31x47cm-12x19in) s.d.184. 25-Sep-2 Neumeister, Munich #671/R est:15000

MORGENSTERN, Karl Ernst (1847-1928) German
£1793 $2851 €2600 Konigssee (21x31cm-8x12in) i. verso. 8-Mar-3 Arnold, Frankfurt #654/R est:3000

MORGENSTERNE MUNTHE, Gerhard (1875-1927) Dutch
£1871 $2993 €2600 Fishing cutter in harbour (41x31cm-16x12in) s. 17-May-3 Lempertz, Koln #1443/R est:3000
£2105 $3411 €3200 Sorting the catch (20x15cm-8x6in) s.d.24 cardboard. 21-Jan-3 Christie's, Amsterdam #223/R est:1500-2000
£2113 $3401 €3000 Fisherman (29x17cm-11x7in) init.d.22. 7-May-3 Vendue Huis, Gravenhage #479/R est:3000-5000
£3158 $5116 €4800 Sorting the catch (13x16cm-5x6in) s. panel. 21-Jan-3 Christie's, Amsterdam #225/R est:1500-2000
£3205 $4968 €5000 Fisherwoman on beach (40x30cm-16x12in) s.d.14. 5-Dec-2 Schopman, Hamburg #668 est:2000
£7746 $12472 €11000 Shell cart (79x89cm-31x35in) s. panel. 7-May-3 Vendue Huis, Gravenhage #480/R est:12000-15000
Works on paper
£925 $1442 €1350 Fishing boat on a choppy sea (8x12cm-3x5in) s.d.20 W/C. 14-Apr-3 Glerum, Amsterdam #64/R
£1645 $2664 €2500 Bomschuit in the surf (7x12cm-3x5in) s. black ink gouache. 21-Jan-3 Christie's, Amsterdam #209 est:800-1200
£2877 $4516 €4200 Sorting the catch (17x24cm-7x9in) s.d.22 gouache. 15-Apr-3 Sotheby's, Amsterdam #107/R est:3000-5000

MORGENTHALER, Ernst (1887-1962) Swiss
£300 $475 €450 Extensive field landscape with riders on horseback (22x93cm-9x37in) mono.d.1958 masonite. 29-Nov-2 Zofingen, Switzerland #2995 (S.FR 700)
£429 $678 €644 Lady on a garden bench (46x38cm-18x15in) mono.d.1962 i.verso. 29-Nov-2 Zofingen, Switzerland #2994 (S.FR 1000)
£773 $1221 €1160 Houses (23x28cm-9x11in) mono.d.51 oil chk. 28-Nov-2 Christie's, Zurich #88/R (S.FR 1800)
£1217 $1899 €1826 Le cheval, Mourazki (50x73cm-20x29in) s.d.1940 i. verso prov. 16-Sep-2 Philippe Schuler, Zurich #3391/R est:3000-3500 (S.FR 2800)
£1357 $2267 €1968 Still life with jug (37x45cm-15x18in) mono. panel. 24-Jun-3 Koller, Zurich #78/R est:2200-3000 (S.FR 3000)
£1429 $2214 €2144 Early spring (80x69cm-31x27in) mono.d.39. 24-Sep-2 Koller, Zurich #6682/R est:1800-2500 (S.FR 3300)
£1454 $2166 €2181 On the Sihl (129x89cm-51x35in) s.d.52. 25-Jun-2 Koller, Zurich #6619/R est:4000-5500 (S.FR 3300)
£2620 $4087 €3930 Mountain landscape near Fuorn at Ofenpass (72x78cm-28x31in) mono.d.56 i.verso. 8-Nov-2 Dobiaschofsky, Bern #212/R est:6000 (S.FR 6000)
Works on paper
£303 $470 €455 Servant boy, Hellsau (19x26cm-7x10in) mono.d.18. 24-Sep-2 Koller, Zurich #6685/R (S.FR 700)

£1288 $2034 €1932 Albistrasse. Wollishofen (28x32cm-11x13in) mono. W/C over pencil two. 28-Nov-2 Christie's, Zurich #89/R est:2500-3500 (S.FR 3000)

MORGNER, Wilhelm (1891-1917) German
Works on paper
£870 $1426 €1200 Male bust (24x31cm-9x12in) mono.d.12 Indian ink. 29-May-3 Lempertz, Koln #814/R
£1594 $2614 €2200 Girl in field (27x37cm-11x15in) mono.d.11 chk. 29-May-3 Lempertz, Koln #812/R est:1000

MORI SANDRINI, Corrado (20th C) Italian
Works on paper
£316 $494 €500 Composition (69x100cm-27x39in) pastel. 19-Oct-2 Semenzato, Venice #102/R

MORI, Mariko (1967-) American
Photographs
£12500 $20000 €18750 Head in the clouds (61x51cm-24x20in) photogram in aluminum lightbox executed 1996 prov. 14-May-3 Sotheby's, New York #404/R est:20000-30000
£15385 $24154 €24000 Initiation (300x600cm-118x236in) photograph on polystyrene in 10 parts exec.1993 prov.exhib. 11-Dec-2 Artcurial Briest, Paris #769/R est:25000
£18750 $30000 €28125 Beginning of the end, Egypt (274x368cm-108x145in) c-print aluminum wood in three parts executed 1996 prov.exhib. 14-May-3 Sotheby's, New York #397/R est:40000-60000
£56962 $90000 €85443 Red light (305x381cm-120x150in) fuji super gloss photo set of three prov.exhib.lit. 14-Nov-2 Christie's, Rockefeller NY #471/R est:100000-150000
Sculpture
£2215 $3500 €3323 Miko no inori (83x29x16cm-33x11x6in) s.i.d.1996 num.100 VHS cassette glass sphere capsule. 12-Nov-2 Phillips, New York #236/R est:4000-6000

MORI, Neno (1898-1970) Italian
£823 $1284 €1300 Boats in Venice (24x35cm-9x14in) s.d.1958 cardboard. 19-Oct-2 Semenzato, Venice #99/R

MORIER, David (1705-1770) Swiss
£36000 $56880 €54000 Equestrian portrait of field marshal Sir Jean Louis Ligonier (122x101cm-48x40in) 28-Nov-2 Sotheby's, London #166/R est:15000-20000

MORIGGIA, Giovanni (1796-1878) Italian
£262 $409 €393 Portrait of Emmanuel Vonder Muhll-Bischoff von Basel (55x47cm-22x19in) 20-Nov-2 Fischer, Luzern #2192/R (S.FR 600)

MORIGUCHI, Kunihiko (1941-) ?
Works on paper
£270 $422 €400 Vert 19 (86x78cm-34x31in) s. yuzen prov. 26-Mar-3 Peschetau-Badin Godeau & Leroy, Paris #24

MORIMURA, Yasumasa (1951-) Japanese
Photographs
£1935 $3000 €2903 Self portrait - bathtub (29x44cm-11x17in) s.d.1996 num.4/10 black white gelatin silver print prov. 26-Sep-2 Christie's, Rockefeller NY #844/R est:4000-6000
£2500 $4000 €3750 Self portrait, actress, after Marlene Dietrich 1 (119x93cm-47x37in) s.num.3/10 llfochrome print acrylic sheet prov. 14-May-3 Sotheby's, New York #405/R est:5000-7000
£3481 $5500 €5222 Self portrait - actress after Greta Garbo 1 (120x95cm-47x37in) lifochrome on acrylic sheet executed 1996. 12-Nov-2 Phillips, New York #213/R est:5000-7000
£4747 $7500 €7121 Self portrait - actress, after Brigitte Bardot (122x96cm-48x38in) s.num.5/10 oversized ilfochrome print. 23-Apr-3 Sotheby's, New York #288/R est:7000-10000
£4800 $7392 €7200 Portrait of the family - wife (139x119cm-55x47in) s. cibachrome print executed 1994. 23-Oct-2 Christie's, London #178/R est:6000-8000
£7406 $11700 €11700 Auto-portrait (118x94cm-46x37in) s. num.9/10 Ilfochrome panel prov. 27-Nov-2 Tajan, Paris #118/R est:12000-18000
£7595 $12000 €11393 Self portrait - actress white Marilyn (160x195cm-63x77in) col coupler print executed 1996 prov. 14-Nov-2 Christie's, Rockefeller NY #458/R est:15000-20000
£12658 $20000 €18987 Self-portrait (43x36cm-17x14in) s.d.1996 num.8/10 verso gelatin silver print set of 8 prov. 13-Nov-2 Sotheby's, New York #446/R est:25000-35000

MORIN, Arturo (1953-) Mexican
Works on paper
£1385 $2161 €2078 Jinete (120x120cm-47x47in) s.d.2002 mixed media canvas. 17-Oct-2 Louis Morton, Mexico #147/R est:22000-26000 (M.P 22000)

MORIN, Gustave François (1809-1886) French
Works on paper
£516 $800 €774 Seated young man in renaissance costume (35x23cm-14x9in) s.i. chl black white chk prov. 29-Oct-2 Sotheby's, New York #73/R

MORIN, Louis (1855-?) French
Works on paper
£356 $590 €516 Cardinals playing chess (49x39cm-19x15in) s. W/C. 16-Jun-3 Waddingtons, Toronto #263/R (C.D 800)

MORIS, Louis Marie (1818-1883) French
Sculpture
£2469 $3802 €3704 Napoleon on horseback (63x3x25cm-25x1x10in) bronze. 26-Oct-2 Heffel, Vancouver #32 est:6000-7000 (C.D 6000)
£2724 $4250 €4086 Napoleon Bonaparte (64x66cm-25x26in) bronze. 11-Apr-3 Du Mouchelle, Detroit #2108/R est:4500-7000

MORISON, J H (19th C) Irish?
£300 $468 €450 Country house in an extensive summer landscape (50x76cm-20x30in) s.d.1857. 12-Sep-2 Bonhams, Edinburgh #313

MORISOT, Berthe (1841-1895) French
£25316 $39241 €40000 Devant la toilette (55x46cm-22x18in) studio st. prov.lit. 28-Sep-2 Christie's, Paris #6/R est:45000-60000
£31056 $50000 €46584 Paysage (38x46cm-15x18in) st.sig. painted 1883 prov.lit. 8-May-3 Christie's, Rockefeller NY #154/R est:35000-45000
£83333 $130000 €125000 Tete de Jeannie (33x37cm-13x15in) prov.lit. 6-Nov-2 Sotheby's, New York #110/R est:120000-180000
Works on paper
£3000 $4890 €4500 Jeannie tendant un panier - etude pour le cerisier (21x17cm-8x7in) st.sig red crayon pencil on tracing paper prov. 3-Feb-3 Bonhams, New Bond Street #2/R est:3000-5000
£3226 $5097 €5000 Jeune femme a l'ouvrage (18x25cm-7x10in) graphite col crayon dr. 18-Dec-2 Ferri, Paris #99/R
£6200 $9548 €9300 Samois (24x24cm-9x9in) init. W/C executed 1893 prov.exhib.lit. 22-Oct-2 Sotheby's, London #103/R est:6000-8000
£14286 $23000 €21429 Le cerf-volant (27x19cm-11x7in) init.i. W/C over pencil prov.exhib.lit. 8-May-3 Christie's, Rockefeller NY #108/R est:20000-30000
£16000 $26720 €24000 Portrait de Mlle Labillois (49x41cm-19x16in) st.sig. pastel exec 1885 exhib.lit. 26-Jun-3 Christie's, London #354/R est:15000-20000
£22973 $35838 €34000 Dans le bois de Maurecourt (52x41cm-20x16in) mono. pastel chl prov.exhib.lit. 26-Mar-3 Piasa, Paris #121/R

MORISOT, Edma (19th C) French
£1678 $2803 €2400 Paysage lacustre (49x65cm-19x26in) s. 26-Jun-3 Tajan, Paris #206 est:2400-3000

MORISSET, Andre (1876-1954) French
£5380 $8500 €8500 Bord de mer au soleil couchant (108x134cm-43x53in) s. 26-Nov-2 Palais de Beaux Arts, Brussels #409/R est:8700-17500

MORISSET, François Henri (1870-?) French
£818 $1300 €1227 His favourite toy (32x41cm-13x16in) s.d.1908 panel. 7-Mar-3 Skinner, Boston #568/R est:1000-1500

MORITZ, Fritz (1922-) German
£353 $536 €550 Winter hunt (30x40cm-12x16in) s. 11-Jul-2 Hugo Ruef, Munich #752

MORITZ, Karl (1896-1963) German
Works on paper
£248 $353 €400 Bodensee landscape near Constance (30x45cm-12x18in) s.d.54 W/C. 23-Mar-2 Geble, Radolfzell #596
£497 $706 €800 Hilzingen (25x35cm-10x14in) s.d.46 W/C. 23-Mar-2 Geble, Radolfzell #595/R

MORITZ, Louis (1773-1850) Dutch
£903 $1328 €1400 Interior of stable (33x44cm-13x17in) s. 24-Jun-2 Dr Fritz Nagel, Stuttgart #6075/R

MORITZ, Marie Elisabeth (1860-?) German
£385 $585 €600 House on Sylt (22x36cm-9x14in) s.i.d.1911 i. verso. 17-Aug-2 Hans Stahl, Toestorf #94/R

MORIZET, Paul (19/20th C) French
£314 $487 €500 Personnage dans un sous-bois (38x55cm-15x22in) s.i. 30-Oct-2 Artcurial Briest, Paris #193
£552 $877 €800 Wooded landscape (99x64cm-39x25in) s. 4-Mar-3 Ansorena, Madrid #120/R

MORLAN, Dorothy (20th C) American
£1161 $1800 €1742 Southern Indiana landscape (61x48cm-24x19in) s. painted c.1920. 8-Dec-2 Toomey, Oak Park #725/R est:500-700

MORLAND, George (1763-1804) British
£340 $530 €510 Study of a sow in a stable (14x17cm-6x7in) i.verso panel. 13-Sep-2 Lyon & Turnbull, Edinburgh #142/R
£650 $988 €975 Swineherd with pigs in yard (43x51cm-17x20in) s. 16-Aug-2 Keys, Aylsham #623
£1000 $1560 €1500 Pig sty (18x23cm-7x9in) board prov. 8-Oct-2 Bonhams, Knightsbridge #175/R est:1000-1500
£1750 $2870 €2625 Figures by a frozen stream (36x44cm-14x17in) mono. 29-May-3 Christie's, Kensington #222/R est:2000-3000
£3900 $6045 €5850 In full cry (71x91cm-28x36in) init. 2-Oct-2 Bonhams, Knowle #101/R est:4000-6000
£5000 $8300 €7500 Portrait of a lady said to be Ann, the artist's wife with her child, cottage beyond (30x24cm-12x9in) painted oval prov. 12-Jun-3 Sotheby's, London #68/R est:4000-6000
£16000 $26560 €24000 Scene in Westmoreland with a farmer and his family driving a white horse towards a lake (99x141cm-39x56in) s. prov. 12-Jun-3 Sotheby's, London #111/R est:15000-25000
£45000 $74700 €67500 Fox Inn (126x162cm-50x64in) s.d.1792 prov.lit. 10-Jun-3 Christie's, London #55/R est:40000-60000
Works on paper
£710 $1101 €1065 Man seated on chair reading (21x17cm-8x7in) s.d.1795 pencil htd red chk. 2-Oct-2 Bonhams, Knowle #29
£1600 $2624 €2320 Pigs in a sty (48x36cm-19x14in) s.d.1972 pencil white chk. 5-Jun-3 Christie's, London #4/R est:1200-1800

MORLAND, George (attrib) (1763-1804) British
£400 $656 €600 Turnpike gate (17x21cm-7x8in) prov. 29-May-3 Christie's, Kensington #220/R
£480 $758 €720 Horses sheltering from the snow (30x45cm-12x18in) 2-Dec-2 Bonhams, Bath #142/R
£1400 $2310 €2030 Peasants talking outside a ruined cottage in a coastal landscape (49x64cm-19x25in) prov. 2-Jul-3 Sotheby's, Olympia #89/R est:1500-2000

MORLAND, Henry Robert (c.1719-1797) British
£4800 $7584 €7200 Portrait of Queen Charlotte (74x61cm-29x24in) prov.exhib. 28-Nov-2 Sotheby's, London #179/R est:4000-6000
£9000 $14130 €13500 General post (74x64cm-29x25in) prov.exhib. 16-Dec-2 Sotheby's, London #56/R est:10000-15000

MORLAND, Henry Robert (attrib) (c.1719-1797) British
£1796 $3000 €2604 Boy with guinea pig (76x64cm-30x25in) 22-Jun-3 Freeman, Philadelphia #46/R est:2000-3000

MORLE, Stuart (1960-) British
£1132 $1766 €1800 Still life with oysters and pewter tankard (23x29cm-9x11in) s. panel. 17-Sep-2 Whyte's, Dublin #162/R est:2000-2500
£1538 $2415 €2400 Still life with artist's palette (36x51cm-14x20in) s. canvas on board. 19-Nov-2 Whyte's, Dublin #131/R est:2500-3500
£1745 $2809 €2600 Ballet shoes IV (65x32cm-26x13in) s. canvasboard. 18-Feb-3 Whyte's, Dublin #142/R est:2000-3000

MORLEY, D (19th C) British
£520 $811 €780 Highland scenes (24x44cm-9x17in) s. board pair. 17-Sep-2 Sotheby's, Olympia #22/R

MORLEY, Harry (1881-1943) British
Works on paper
£260 $421 €390 Village scene in the hills of Italy (24x37cm-9x15in) s. W/C. 21-Jan-3 Bonhams, Knightsbridge #49/R

MORLEY, Malcolm (1931-) British
£20000 $32000 €30000 Picture from the Azores (74x89cm-29x35in) s.d.94 oil painted airplane on canvas prov.lit. 15-May-3 Christie's, Rockefeller NY #375/R est:30000-40000
Sculpture
£10127 $16000 €15191 Navy (143x20x10cm-56x8x4in) grey pat bronze exec.1990 prov.exhib. 13-Nov-2 Sotheby's, New York #539/R est:10000-15000
Works on paper
£605 $950 €908 Man reading newspaper (30x20cm-12x8in) s.d.1972 pencil. 21-Nov-2 Swann Galleries, New York #118/R
£1154 $1788 €1800 Windy breeze (77x56cm-30x22in) s.i. ink W/C. 7-Dec-2 Van Ham, Cologne #358/R est:2000
£1600 $2528 €2400 Untitled (48x62cm-19x24in) s. pencil exec.1983. 3-Apr-3 Christie's, Kensington #260/R
£4000 $6680 €5800 Hollywood film stars and their homes, Doris Day fragment (64x102cm-25x40in) W/C pencil prov.exhib. 26-Jun-3 Sotheby's, London #221/R est:4000-6000

MORLEY, T W (1859-1925) British
Works on paper
£260 $416 €390 Coastal view of Whitby (33x20cm-13x8in) W/C. 10-Jan-3 Biddle & Webb, Birmingham #195
£380 $600 €570 Leading sheep (36x53cm-14x21in) s.d.14 W/C. 24-Apr-3 Richardson & Smith, Whitby #158

MORLON, Alexandre (1878-?) French
Sculpture
£1702 $2638 €2553 Nude woman playing with goat (58cm-23in) s. bronze incl.socle cire perdue st.f.Valsuani. 8-Dec-2 Uppsala Auktionskammare, Uppsala #346/R est:12000-15000 (S.KR 24000)

MORLOTTI, Ennio (1910-1992) Italian
£926 $1491 €1389 Nude (33x39cm-13x15in) s. mixed media. 7-May-3 Dobiaschofsky, Bern #847/R (S.FR 2000)
£7051 $11071 €11000 Rocks (44x45cm-17x18in) s. painted 1979. 23-Nov-2 Meeting Art, Vercelli #100/R est:9000
£7595 $12000 €12000 Two heads (70x55cm-28x22in) s.i.d.1944 verso. 30-Nov-2 Farsetti, Prato #655/R est:13000
£8333 $12917 €13000 Bathers at Oggiono Lake (60x60cm-24x24in) s. painted 1990 prov.exhib.lit. 4-Dec-2 Finarte, Milan #321/R est:14000
£9615 $15096 €15000 Vegetals (35x51cm-14x20in) s. s.d.1960 verso. 23-Nov-2 Meeting Art, Vercelli #332/R est:10000
£21769 $34612 €32000 Rocks (150x150cm-59x59in) s. painted 1984 exhib.lit. 1-Mar-3 Meeting Art, Vercelli #647
Works on paper
£897 $1409 €1400 Flowers (50x35cm-20x14in) s.d.62 chl pencil. 20-Nov-2 Pandolfini, Florence #100/R
£980 $1569 €1500 Landscape (23x28cm-9x11in) s. pastel. 4-Jan-3 Meeting Art, Vercelli #674
£1923 $3019 €3000 Nude (50x35cm-20x14in) s. wax crayon paper on canvas. 23-Nov-2 Meeting Art, Vercelli #308/R
£2083 $3312 €3000 Study of nude (35x47cm-14x19in) s. pastel oil. 1-May-3 Meeting Art, Vercelli #463
£2244 $3478 €3500 Roses (28x35cm-11x14in) s. oil pastel exec.1989. 4-Dec-2 Finarte, Milan #231/R
£2436 $3824 €3800 Landscape (24x35cm-9x14in) s. wax pastel. 21-Nov-2 Finarte, Rome #153/R est:3200

MORNARD, Henri (?) ?
£876 $1401 €1314 Battle scene with soldiers on horseback (82x129cm-32x51in) s. 13-Jan-3 Rasmussen, Vejle #207/R (D.KR 10000)

MORNER, Hjalmar (1794-1837) Swedish
£1474 $2388 €2137 Visiting the shoe-maker (53x42cm-21x17in) s.indis.d.1823 verso panel. 26-May-3 Bukowskis, Stockholm #368/R est:25000-28000 (S.KR 19000)

MORNER, Stellan (1896-1979) Swedish
£275 $417 €413 The last day at the summer house (19x24cm-7x9in) s. 16-Aug-2 Lilla Bukowskis, Stockholm #30 (S.KR 4000)
£596 $929 €894 Interior scene with silver candle holder (24x33cm-9x13in) s. panel. 6-Nov-2 AB Stockholms Auktionsverk #523/R (S.KR 8500)
£618 $995 €927 Le vent se leve (23x32cm-9x13in) s.d.56 i.verso panel. 7-May-3 AB Stockholms Auktionsverk #741/R (S.KR 8000)
£927 $1492 €1391 Composition (37x31cm-15x12in) s. i.d.1947 verso panel. 7-May-3 AB Stockholms Auktionsverk #727/R (S.KR 12000)
£1074 $1741 €1611 Church with domes (36x28cm-14x11in) s. 3-Feb-3 Lilla Bukowskis, Stockholm #828 est:7000-8000 (S.KR 15000)

£	$	€	Details
£1544	$2486	€2316	Near Christmas the snow came down (33x41cm-13x16in) s. 7-May-3 AB Stockholms Auktionsverk #660/R est:25000-30000 (S.KR 20000)
£1901	$3004	€2852	Message at night (60x73cm-24x29in) init. d.34 verso panel. 28-Apr-3 Bukowskis, Stockholm #192/R est:30000-35000 (S.KR 25000)
£2357	$3725	€3536	The church (46x55cm-18x22in) s. exhib. 28-Apr-3 Bukowskis, Stockholm #191/R est:30000-35000 (S.KR 31000)
£2780	$4476	€4170	Landscape with house (36x44cm-14x17in) s.d.78. 7-May-3 AB Stockholms Auktionsverk #739/R est:30000-35000 (S.KR 36000)
£3042	$4806	€4563	In memory of Greta (64x92cm-25x36in) s. painted 1940 exhib. 28-Apr-3 Bukowskis, Stockholm #140/R est:40000-60000 (S.KR 40000)
£4106	$6488	€6159	August Malmstrom showing the country to visitors (46x56cm-18x22in) s. panel. 28-Apr-3 Bukowskis, Stockholm #142/R est:25000-30000 (S.KR 54000)

Works on paper

£	$	€	Details
£494	$776	€741	In the park (23x32cm-9x13in) s. gouache. 16-Dec-2 Lilla Bukowskis, Stockholm #191 (S.KR 7000)
£6950	$11189	€10425	Rings (41x26cm-16x10in) s.d.30 gouache exhib.lit. 7-May-3 AB Stockholms Auktionsverk #698/R est:80000-100000 (S.KR 90000)

MORNEWICK, Charles Augustus (19th C) British

£	$	€	Details
£300	$480	€450	Still life of a robin and plate of fruit and vegetables (34x45cm-13x18in) 13-May-3 Bonhams, Knightsbridge #40/R
£780	$1186	€1170	Dutch trading barges running towards a three master riding out the squall (18x25cm-7x10in) s.d.1869. 15-Aug-2 Bonhams, New Bond Street #304/R

MORO, Ferruccio (1859-?) Italian

£	$	€	Details
£2949	$4600	€4424	Legal advisor (58x48cm-23x19in) s. 22-Sep-2 Susanin's, Chicago #5038/R est:2400-3400

Works on paper

£	$	€	Details
£449	$700	€674	Love Gate Castle Court-Florence (51x30cm-20x12in) s.i.d.1890 W/C. 5-Nov-2 Arthur James, Florida #379

MORO, Franz (1900-1940) Austrian

Works on paper

£	$	€	Details
£377	$585	€600	Melting snow - riverbed (29x34cm-11x13in) s. Indian ink W/C board. 1-Oct-2 Dorotheum, Vienna #236

MOROHN, Ferdinand (fl.1846-1859) British

£	$	€	Details
£2400	$3816	€3600	Winter scene with wood cutters family preparing for work. Woodman's lunch (25x35cm-10x14in) s. panel pair. 27-Feb-3 Bonhams, Chester #445/R est:2500-3500

MORONEY, Ken (1949-) British

£	$	€	Details
£280	$440	€420	Cherries in a bowl (30x38cm-12x15in) s. board. 15-Apr-3 Bonhams, Knightsbridge #142/R
£280	$440	€420	Seated lady with lamp (21x27cm-8x11in) s. board. 15-Apr-3 Bonhams, Knightsbridge #160
£280	$454	€420	Harbour scene at dusk (35x38cm-14x15in) s. board. 20-May-3 Bonhams, Knightsbridge #154
£300	$471	€450	Mother and child on a beach (16x21cm-6x8in) s. oil on paper. 15-Apr-3 Bonhams, Knightsbridge #202/R
£380	$616	€570	Horse and cart in the snow (49x59cm-19x23in) s. board. 20-May-3 Bonhams, Knightsbridge #135/R
£380	$627	€551	Stroll along the cliff tops (30x41cm-12x16in) 3-Jul-3 Christie's, Kensington #411
£400	$624	€600	Figures on a quayside (35x46cm-14x18in) s. board. 27-Mar-3 Christie's, Kensington #441/R
£400	$624	€600	Steam train entering the station (46x61cm-18x24in) s. 27-Mar-3 Christie's, Kensington #442
£400	$640	€600	Still life of a vase of flowers and a tea tray (59x44cm-23x17in) s. 15-May-3 Lawrence, Crewkerne #1022
£420	$659	€630	Moored boats (36x42cm-14x17in) s. board. 15-Apr-3 Bonhams, Knightsbridge #138/R
£450	$698	€675	Family outing (33x38cm-13x15in) s. board. 3-Dec-2 Bonhams, Knightsbridge #4/R
£480	$758	€720	Street scene (29x39cm-11x15in) s. board. 27-Nov-2 Sotheby's, Olympia #115/R
£480	$773	€720	Figures on a beach (31x41cm-12x16in) s. board. 14-Jan-3 Bonhams, Knightsbridge #189/R
£500	$800	€750	Fishing scene, probably on the Shannon (74x49cm-29x19in) s. canvasboard. 15-May-3 Lawrence, Crewkerne #959
£500	$825	€725	Artist's table (46x61cm-18x24in) s. 3-Jul-3 Christie's, Kensington #632/R
£550	$858	€825	Tea party on the beach. s. 15-Oct-2 Bonhams, Knightsbridge #235/R
£550	$858	€825	Figures on a promenade (29x38cm-11x15in) s. board. 15-Oct-2 Bonhams, Knightsbridge #237/R
£550	$858	€825	Boats in the harbour (33x38cm-13x15in) s. board. 15-Oct-2 Bonhams, Knightsbridge #238/R
£550	$886	€825	Fight outside the Crown, Kilburn (46x61cm-18x24in) s. 18-Feb-3 Bonhams, Knightsbridge #81/R
£580	$934	€870	On the beach (45x60cm-18x24in) s. board. 18-Feb-3 Bonhams, Knightsbridge #84/R
£600	$948	€900	Picking flowers (29x22cm-11x9in) s. board. 27-Nov-2 Sotheby's, Olympia #153/R
£650	$1027	€975	Figures on street (21x29cm-8x11in) s. board. 27-Nov-2 Sotheby's, Olympia #114/R
£650	$1047	€975	Lady and the lamp (61x51cm-24x20in) s. board. 14-Jan-3 Bonhams, Knightsbridge #144/R
£700	$1085	€1050	Mother and daughter picking flowers (40x30cm-16x12in) s. board. 3-Dec-2 Bonhams, Knightsbridge #95/R
£700	$1127	€1050	Artist at work (44x64cm-17x25in) s. board. 18-Feb-3 Bonhams, Knightsbridge #193/R
£720	$1152	€1080	On the beach (28x39cm-11x15in) s.i.d.91 verso. 15-May-3 Lawrence, Crewkerne #1021/R
£750	$1230	€1125	Horse and trap (17x22cm-7x9in) s. card. 3-Jun-3 Sotheby's, Olympia #189/R
£800	$1248	€1200	Family on the beach (50x61cm-20x24in) s. board. 15-Oct-2 Bonhams, Knightsbridge #234/R
£850	$1369	€1275	Looking out to sea (51x61cm-20x24in) s. board. 18-Feb-3 Bonhams, Knightsbridge #68/R
£850	$1326	€1275	At the market (76x61cm-30x24in) s. 27-Mar-3 Christie's, Kensington #443/R
£950	$1482	€1425	Cherries in a bowl (30x40cm-12x16in) s. board. 15-Oct-2 Bonhams, Knightsbridge #82
£1300	$2028	€1950	Punch and Judy at the beach (56x76cm-22x30in) s. board. 27-Mar-3 Christie's, Kensington #444/R est:800-1200
£1300	$2106	€1950	Clown with green jacket (76x55cm-30x22in) s. board double-sided. 20-May-3 Bonhams, Knightsbridge #78 est:1200-1800
£1342	$2161	€2000	Boats moored along the quay at Cobh, Co Cork (46x61cm-18x24in) s. 18-Feb-3 Whyte's, Dublin #216/R est:1500-2000
£1900	$2926	€2850	Punch and Judy (37x48cm-15x19in) s. board. 5-Sep-2 Christie's, Kensington #685/R est:2000-3000

MORONI, Giovan Battista (circle) (1525-1578) Italian

£	$	€	Details
£5000	$7800	€7500	Portrait of a young girl, with a beaded necklace (66x55cm-26x22in) 19-Sep-2 Christie's, Kensington #215/R est:4000-6000
£6323	$9990	€9800	Portrait of gentleman in black (66x51cm-26x20in) panel. 18-Dec-2 Piasa, Paris #7/R est:9000
£7643	$11924	€12000	Portrait of a scholar, bust length (48x39cm-19x15in) 6-Nov-2 Christie's, Amsterdam #61/R est:12000-18000

MORONI, Giovan Battista (style) (1525-1578) Italian

£	$	€	Details
£34043	$52766	€51065	Florianus Morattus (114x100cm-45x39in) 3-Dec-2 Bukowskis, Stockholm #425/R est:60000-80000 (S.KR 480000)

MOROT, Aime (1850-1913) French

£	$	€	Details
£1370	$2151	€2000	Portrait of man (40x43cm-16x17in) s.i.d.1880 panel. 16-Apr-3 Dorotheum, Salzburg #135/R est:1800-2400

MOROZOV, Aleksandr Ivanovich (1835-1904) Russian

Works on paper

£	$	€	Details
£3200	$5024	€4800	Stacking the hay (31x45cm-12x18in) s.d.1891 W/C. 20-Nov-2 Sotheby's, London #57/R est:1800-2200

MORRELL, Wayne (1923-) American

£	$	€	Details
£256	$400	€384	Spring pond (20x25cm-8x10in) i. board. 18-Sep-2 Alderfer's, Hatfield #369
£288	$450	€432	Oriental garden pool, Palm Beach, Florida (41x28cm-16x11in) s. masonite. 18-Sep-2 Alderfer's, Hatfield #381
£385	$600	€578	Canal bridge (30x41cm-12x16in) s. s.i.verso board. 18-Sep-2 Alderfer's, Hatfield #366/R
£385	$600	€578	Rockport landscape with woman in flower field and ocean (203x25cm-80x10in) s. masonite. 18-Sep-2 Alderfer's, Hatfield #378
£542	$850	€813	Storys boat yard, Essex Mass (31x40cm-12x16in) s.i.d.1972 masonite. 22-Nov-2 Skinner, Boston #377/R
£833	$1300	€1250	Spring meadows (61x76cm-24x30in) s. i.verso board. 18-Sep-2 Alderfer's, Hatfield #382
£1250	$2000	€1875	Seaside (61x91cm-24x36in) s. masonite. 11-Jan-3 James Julia, Fairfield #230 est:3000-5000
£1442	$2250	€2163	Monet's pond, Giverny, France (76x99cm-30x39in) s. i.d.Sept 28 1987 verso board. 18-Sep-2 Alderfer's, Hatfield #380/R est:1500-2500
£2083	$3250	€3125	New Hope barn (61x76cm-24x30in) s.d.Oct 1976 board. 18-Sep-2 Alderfer's, Hatfield #367/R est:800-1200

MORREN, Georges (1868-1941) Belgian

£	$	€	Details
£380	$600	€600	Fillette aux mains jointes (20x19cm-8x7in) mono. chl exec.c.1892. 26-Nov-2 Palais de Beaux Arts, Brussels #350
£414	$658	€600	Portrait d'Hermann Paul (28x32cm-11x13in) s.d.1935 lit. 4-Mar-3 Palais de Beaux Arts, Brussels #368
£3038	$4800	€4800	Mon portrait (100x80cm-39x31in) s.d.1936 exhib. 26-Nov-2 Palais de Beaux Arts, Brussels #360/R est:4500-6000
£3310	$5297	€4800	Bassin de Neptune a Versailles (60x49cm-24x19in) s. s.i.d.1922 verso board exhib.lit. 15-Mar-3 De Vuyst, Lokeren #438/R est:5000-6200

£12025 $19000 €19000 Le baton de rouge (90x91cm-35x36in) s.d.1941. 26-Nov-2 Palais de Beaux Arts, Brussels #361/R est:18500-25000
£12414 $19738 €18000 Le sommeil de Gilberte (80x80cm-31x31in) s.d.1941 exhib.lit. 4-Mar-3 Palais de Beaux Arts, Brussels #383/R est:14000-19000

Works on paper

£253 $400 €400 Alex Charpentier (22x14cm-9x6in) d.1892 chl pastel lit. 26-Nov-2 Palais de Beaux Arts, Brussels #354
£266 $420 €420 Femme endormie (13x29cm-5x11in) pastel exec.c.1893 lit. 26-Nov-2 Palais de Beaux Arts, Brussels #355
£655 $1042 €950 Concarneau (22x240cm-9x94in) s.d.26 juillet 29 pastel exhib.lit. 4-Mar-3 Palais de Beaux Arts, Brussels #358/R
£759 $1200 €1200 Chrysanthemes (59x39cm-23x15in) s.i.verso col crayon exec.c.1893 exhib.lit. 26-Nov-2 Palais de Beaux Arts, Brussels #357
£1793 $2851 €2600 Cabaret - Saint Tropez (45x56cm-18x22in) s.d.29.3.29 pastel lit. 4-Mar-3 Palais de Beaux Arts, Brussels #365/R est:2000-2400
£2278 $3600 €3600 Beaulieu (23x31cm-9x12in) s.d.avril 1900 pastel lit. 26-Nov-2 Palais de Beaux Arts, Brussels #349/R est:3000-4000
£2278 $3600 €3600 Point du jour (14x23cm-6x9in) mono.d.23 mars 93 pastel exhib.lit. 26-Nov-2 Palais de Beaux Arts, Brussels #353/R est:1000-1500
£2278 $3600 €3600 Le gouter (23x31cm-9x12in) mono.d.95 col crayon. 26-Nov-2 Palais de Beaux Arts, Brussels #359/R est:3000-4500
£7595 $12000 €12000 Trois jeunes filles en peignoir (11x59cm-4x23in) s.d.1901 sanguine lit. 26-Nov-2 Palais de Beaux Arts, Brussels #352/R est:10000-15000

MORREN, René (19/20th C) Belgian

£320 $522 €464 Vase of flowers with statue (86x101cm-34x40in) s. 15-Jul-3 Bonhams, Knightsbridge #4/R

MORRICE, James Wilson (1865-1924) Canadian

£4016 $6305 €6024 Landscape (13x18cm-5x7in) panel prov. 25-Nov-2 Hodgins, Calgary #357b/R est:15000-18000 (C.D 10000)
£4444 $7289 €6666 Paysage en France (20x23cm-8x9in) board prov. 27-May-3 Sotheby's, Toronto #217/R est:10000-15000 (C.D 10000)
£6173 $9568 €9260 After the rainstorm (19x21cm-7x8in) studio st. verso panel prov. 3-Dec-2 Joyner, Toronto #137/R est:20000-30000 (C.D 15000)
£15556 $25511 €23334 Cafe scene (10x15cm-4x6in) panel prov. 27-May-3 Sotheby's, Toronto #109/R est:40000-50000 (C.D 35000)
£17284 $26790 €25926 Tangiers, the rainbow (12x15cm-5x6in) studio st.verso panel painted c.1912-14 prov.lit. 3-Dec-2 Joyner, Toronto #22/R est:30000-40000 (C.D 42000)
£22222 $36444 €33333 Return of the fishing fleet, Britanny (15x12cm-6x5in) i.verso panel painted c.1905 prov.lit. 3-Jun-3 Joyner, Toronto #52/R est:50000-60000 (C.D 50000)
£24194 $38226 €36291 Flemish peasants on the beach (18x25cm-7x10in) panel prov.lit. 14-Nov-2 Heffel, Vancouver #104/R est:40000-45000 (C.D 60000)
£34783 $57043 €52175 Jeune fille Hollandaise (55x32cm-22x13in) s. prov.lit. 3-Jun-3 Joyner, Toronto #67/R est:100000-150000 (C.D 78260)
£77778 $127556 €116667 Breton pardon (38x46cm-15x18in) s. prov.exhib.lit. 27-May-3 Sotheby's, Toronto #110/R est:180000-200000 (C.D 175000)

Works on paper

£1156 $1895 €1734 Venetian girl. Sawing logs. Forest (15x10cm-6x4in) pencil sold with painting by Coburn and Gagnon. 3-Jun-3 Joyner, Toronto #449/R est:3000-4000 (C.D 2600)
£7296 $11382 €10944 Lively street (23x31cm-9x12in) s. W/C. 25-Mar-3 Iegor de Saint Hippolyte, Montreal #95/R (C.D 17000)

MORRIS, Alfred (19th C) British

£350 $546 €525 Sheep resting in a highland landscape (76x127cm-30x50in) s.d.75. 7-Nov-2 Christie's, Kensington #119
£620 $980 €930 Scottish blackface sheep in a highland landscape (61x91cm-24x36in) s. 2-Dec-2 Bonhams, Bath #95/R
£709 $1149 €1000 Black faced sheep on a cliff (61x107cm-24x42in) s.d.1883. 20-May-3 Mealy's, Castlecomer #970 est:800-1500
£1550 $2542 €2325 Sheep and lambs on upland fells (76x127cm-30x50in) s.d.1881. 2-Jun-3 David Duggleby, Scarborough #324/R est:1200-1800
£2500 $4175 €3625 Shepherd boy and his flock in the hills (76x127cm-30x50in) s.d.1867. 25-Jun-3 Bonhams, Bury St Edmunds #561/R est:2500-4000

MORRIS, C (19/20th C) British/American

£801 $1266 €1250 Landscape with figures (30x34cm-12x13in) 12-Nov-2 Mealy's, Castlecomer #1030

MORRIS, Cedric (1889-1982) British

£1400 $2296 €2100 Pool at Benton End (47x55cm-19x22in) s.d.47. 3-Jun-3 Sotheby's, Olympia #58/R
£1500 $2340 €2175 Portrait of Bettina Shaw-Lawrence. exhib. 27-Mar-3 Neales, Nottingham #1038/R est:800-1200
£1800 $2952 €2700 Wooded hills, west Suffolk (51x76cm-20x30in) s. i.verso. 3-Jun-3 Sotheby's, Olympia #57/R est:2000-3000
£2300 $3795 €3335 Flight from Medina (51x61cm-20x24in) s.d.26. 3-Jul-3 Christie's, Kensington #424/R est:2500-3500
£4300 $6708 €6235 Zennor, North Cornwall (24x19cm-9x7in) s.i. exhib. 27-Mar-3 Neales, Nottingham #1039/R est:2000-3000
£5500 $8524 €8250 Artist cottage, Dorset (40x51cm-16x20in) board prov. 4-Dec-2 Sotheby's, London #12/R est:4000-6000
£6500 $10660 €9750 Still life, the iron birds (56x66cm-22x26in) s.d.42 exhib. 3-Jun-3 Sotheby's, Olympia #59/R est:4000-6000
£8000 $12720 €12000 Kiln Farm Higham (62x75cm-24x30in) s. s.i.d.29 verso. 26-Feb-3 Sotheby's, Olympia #243/R est:8000-12000
£9500 $14724 €14250 Back garden at Benton End (103x76cm-41x30in) s.d.70 prov. 4-Dec-2 Sotheby's, London #13/R est:8000-12000

Works on paper

£500 $780 €750 Springbok (23x21cm-9x8in) s.d.25 silverpoint. 15-Oct-2 Bonhams, Knightsbridge #130/R

MORRIS, Charles (19th C) British

£280 $456 €420 Weir (29x24cm-11x9in) s.d.1871. 2-Feb-3 Lots Road, London #335/R
£350 $539 €525 Old farm (25x36cm-10x14in) s. 5-Sep-2 Christie's, Kensington #134/R
£400 $620 €600 Horse and cart on a woodland track (30x25cm-12x10in) s. 30-Sep-2 Bonhams, Ipswich #520

MORRIS, Charles (attrib) (19th C) British

£350 $546 €525 Cottage by a stream (20x16cm-8x6in) 7-Nov-2 Christie's, Kensington #159/R

MORRIS, Charles (snr-attrib) (19th C) British

£500 $815 €750 Watermill (38x48cm-15x19in) bears sig. 29-Jan-3 Sotheby's, Olympia #136/R

MORRIS, Charles Alfred (1898-?) British

Works on paper

£280 $454 €420 New Shoreham Church (23x30cm-9x12in) s. W/C. 21-Jan-3 Bonhams, Knightsbridge #36/R

MORRIS, Franklin E (1938-) American

£346 $540 €519 Beach scene (13x18cm-5x7in) s. canvasboard. 28-Mar-3 Aspire, Cleveland #30/R

MORRIS, Garman (fl.c.1900-1930) British

Works on paper

£410 $668 €615 Fishing fleet (20x53cm-8x21in) s.i. mixed media pair. 13-Feb-3 David Lay, Penzance #166
£500 $790 €750 Night coast off Kent. Night on the river (18x53cm-7x21in) s.i. W/C pair. 26-Nov-2 Bonhams, Knightsbridge #154/R
£1040 $1664 €1560 Misty evening Whitby (18x53cm-7x21in) s.i. W/C. 11-Mar-3 David Duggleby, Scarborough #116/R est:400-600

MORRIS, George L K (1905-1975) American

£5975 $9500 €8963 Abstract composition (46x36cm-18x14in) mono.d.1937 panel prov. 1-Mar-3 North East Auctions, Portsmouth #736/R est:4000-6000

MORRIS, George Spencer (20th C) American

£645 $1000 €968 Harbour scene (41x51cm-16x20in) s. board painted c.1925 prov. 8-Dec-2 Toomey, Oak Park #696/R

MORRIS, J (19th C) British

£297 $473 €446 Landscape with sheep resting (30x50cm-12x20in) s. 3-Mar-3 Lilla Bukowskis, Stockholm #595 (S.KR 4000)

MORRIS, J C (19th C) British

£1800 $2808 €2700 Sheep and cattle resting in a river landscape (76x127cm-30x50in) s. 7-Nov-2 Christie's, Kensington #184/R est:2000-3000

MORRIS, J W (19th C) British

£489 $767 €734 Fishermen by lake (30x61cm-12x24in) s. 25-Nov-2 Blomqvist, Lysaker #1188 (N.KR 5600)
£506 $800 €759 Guarding the sheep (61x51cm-24x20in) s.d.1881. 17-Nov-2 CRN Auctions, Cambridge #30/R

MORRIS, James Charles (19th C) British

£280 $462 €406 Shepherd and sheep in a highland landscape (61x91cm-24x36in) s. indis d. 3-Jul-3 Duke & Son, Dorchester #269

MORRIS, John (19th C) British

£400 $624 €600 Brigand at a window (61x51cm-24x20in) s.i.d.1838 verso trompe l'oeil. 23-Sep-2 Bonhams, Chester #930
£400 $624 €600 Farmyard friends (24x34cm-9x13in) s.d.80. 6-Nov-2 Sotheby's, Olympia #69/R

£1214 $1918 €1821 Farmyard scene with horses, pigs and ducks (76x127cm-30x50in) s. 27-Nov-2 Deutscher-Menzies, Melbourne #265a/R est:6000-8000 (A.D 3400)
£5556 $8000 €8334 Waiting for master (90x69cm-35x27in) s. 15-Jan-3 Christie's, Rockefeller NY #168/R

MORRIS, John W (19th C) British
£600 $1002 €870 Sheep resting by a highland burn. Highland cattle grazing (29x49cm-11x19in) s. pair. 25-Jun-3 Cheffins, Cambridge #791/R

MORRIS, Kathleen (1893-1986) Canadian
£484 $750 €726 Winter cabin (33x41cm-13x16in) board. 7-Dec-2 Harvey Clar, Oakland #1151
£861 $1334 €1292 Sheep in a pasture. Study of cows (31x36cm-12x14in) s. panel double-sided. 24-Sep-2 Ritchie, Toronto #3151/R est:2000-3000 (C.D 2100)
£5333 $8747 €8000 Sheep and barn (30x35cm-12x14in) panel. 3-Jun-3 Joyner, Toronto #36/R est:15000-20000 (C.D 12000)
£9073 $14335 €13610 Barn, St. Genevieve (26x36cm-10x14in) s. panel prov. 14-Nov-2 Heffel, Vancouver #156/R est:10000-12000 (C.D 22500)
£9877 $15309 €14816 St. Cecile Street, Montreal (35x26cm-14x10in) s. panel. 3-Dec-2 Joyner, Toronto #97/R est:20000-25000 (C.D 24000)
£10288 $15947 €15432 Street market with fowl and goats (26x35cm-10x14in) s. panel prov. 3-Dec-2 Joyner, Toronto #196/R est:12000-15000 (C.D 25000)
£10700 $16584 €16050 St. Stanislas St. Quebec City (35x25cm-14x10in) s. panel. 3-Dec-2 Joyner, Toronto #147/R est:15000-20000 (C.D 26000)
£11382 $17870 €17073 Fruit stall (26x34cm-10x13in) s. board exhib. 10-Dec-2 Pinneys, Montreal #148 est:25000-35000 (C.D 28000)
£11523 $17860 €17285 Leaving Mass (22x31cm-9x12in) s. panel prov. 3-Dec-2 Joyner, Toronto #161/R est:15000-20000 (C.D 28000)
£11934 $18498 €17901 Old shop, Mountain Hill, Quebec (25x35cm-10x14in) s. panel. 3-Dec-2 Joyner, Toronto #171/R est:20000-25000 (C.D 29000)
£13169 $20412 €19754 Figures in a flower market (26x35cm-10x14in) panel prov. 3-Dec-2 Joyner, Toronto #83/R est:20000-25000 (C.D 32000)
£22177 $35040 €33266 Dominion Square, Montreal (25x36cm-10x14in) s. board painted c.1923 prov.lit. 14-Nov-2 Heffel, Vancouver #113/R est:40000-45000 (C.D 55000)

MORRIS, Lincoln Godfrey (1887-1967) Canadian
£267 $412 €401 Afternoon late winter (51x61cm-20x24in) s. 22-Oct-2 Iegor de Saint Hippolyte, Montreal #76 (C.D 650)

MORRIS, Margaret (1891-1980) British
£1500 $2280 €2250 Behind Pourville (34x26cm-13x10in) s.i.d.1922 verso board. 28-Aug-2 Sotheby's, London #1096/R est:1000-1500
£2500 $3800 €3750 White clouds (27x35cm-11x14in) s.i.verso board. 28-Aug-2 Sotheby's, London #1097/R est:2000-3000
£3200 $4864 €4800 In Harlech (35x26cm-14x10in) i. s.d.1921 verso board. 28-Aug-2 Sotheby's, London #1095/R est:2000-3000
£7600 $11552 €11400 Picnic at Harlech (27x36cm-11x14in) s.d.1921 verso board. 28-Aug-2 Sotheby's, London #1090/R est:5000-7000
Works on paper
£1100 $1672 €1650 Harlech (17x20cm-7x8in) W/C chl. 28-Aug-2 Sotheby's, London #1098/R est:700-900

MORRIS, Mary (fl.1919-1950) British
£780 $1217 €1170 Quiet cove (44x60cm-17x24in) s.d.1913. 28-Mar-3 Bonhams, Edinburgh #147

MORRIS, Oliver (19th C) British
£550 $897 €825 Edinburgh from Calton Hill (18x27cm-7x11in) sold with a companion. 14-Feb-3 Lyon & Turnbull, Edinburgh #141
Works on paper
£620 $980 €930 Edinburgh. View from an Edinburgh park (19x27cm-7x11in) mono.d.1895 W/C pair. 27-Nov-2 Hamptons Fine Art, Godalming #138/R

MORRIS, Pascale (1955-) Spanish
£288 $472 €400 Star bush (32x20cm-13x8in) s. panel. 5-Jun-3 Dorotheum, Salzburg #662/R

MORRIS, Philip Richard (1838-1902) British
£706 $1108 €1059 The keeper's daughter (82x61cm-32x24in) s. 16-Dec-2 Lilla Bukowskis, Stockholm #22 (S.KR 10000)
£886 $1400 €1329 Waiting for Morris (76x51cm-30x20in) s. 16-Nov-2 New Orleans Auction, New Orleans #545/R est:1800-2500
£1632 $2596 €2448 Mother and child in cornfield (76x51cm-30x20in) s. 5-May-3 Rasmussen, Vejle #678/R est:15000 (D.KR 17500)
Works on paper
£4200 $6762 €6300 Farewell. Return (36x29cm-14x11in) one s. pencil W/C htd bodycol gum arabic pair prov.exhib. 20-Feb-3 Christie's, London #118/R

MORRIS, Roger (1935-) British
£351 $547 €527 Archibald Russell (75x58cm-30x23in) s. board. 27-Mar-3 International Art Centre, Auckland #171/R (NZ.D 1000)

MORRIS, S (?) ?
£451 $703 €677 Table en Provence (51x61cm-20x24in) s. 10-Sep-2 Iegor de Saint Hippolyte, Montreal #86 (C.D 1100)

MORRIS, Sarah (1967-) American
£10127 $16000 €15191 NMCBLL (256x199cm-101x78in) s. i.d.98 verso gloss household paint on canvas prov. 14-Nov-2 Christie's, Rockefeller NY #347/R est:15000-20000
£17500 $28000 €26250 First bank - Miami (213x213cm-84x84in) s.i.d.98 on overlap gloss household paint prov.exhib. 16-May-3 Phillips, New York #110/R est:18000-25000

MORRIS, William (1834-1896) British
£900 $1494 €1305 Terriers ratting (19x23cm-7x9in) s.d.56. 12-Jun-3 Christie's, Kensington #235/R

MORRIS, William E (1935-) Canadian
£202 $323 €303 Vieux Montreal (51x41cm-20x16in) s.i.verso. 15-May-3 Heffel, Vancouver #71 (C.D 450)
£206 $327 €299 Chinese bowl, fruit and flowers (41x51cm-16x20in) s. i.verso board. 1-May-3 Heffel, Vancouver #68/R (C.D 475)
£262 $414 €393 Cote de la Montagnes Quebec (41x51cm-16x20in) s. i.verso board prov. 14-Nov-2 Heffel, Vancouver #260 (C.D 650)
£281 $447 €407 Hazelton Lanes (41x51cm-16x20in) s. i.verso. 1-May-3 Heffel, Vancouver #69/R (C.D 650)
£343 $542 €515 Houses North of Queen Street - Toronto (30x41cm-12x16in) s. i.verso board prov. 14-Nov-2 Heffel, Vancouver #261 (C.D 850)

MORRIS, William Walker (fl.1850-1867) British
£320 $499 €480 Toy spaniels chasing a pheasant in the undergrowth (19x29cm-7x11in) s.d.1857. 23-Sep-2 Bonhams, Chester #955

MORRISH, W S (1844-1917) British
Works on paper
£480 $778 €720 Moorland landscape (28x44cm-11x17in) s.d.1895 W/C. 21-Jan-3 Bonhams, Knightsbridge #5/R

MORRISH, William S (1844-1917) British
£340 $527 €510 Crossing the bridge in a rocky river valley (99x152cm-39x60in) s. 26-Sep-2 Lane, Penzance #302
Works on paper
£400 $636 €600 Near Kedar Rock, Bittaford Tor, Dartmoor (19x47cm-7x19in) s.d.1894 W/C. 29-Apr-3 Bearnes, Exeter #498
£460 $736 €667 Dartmoor stream (28x78cm-11x31in) s. W/C. 19-May-3 Bearnes, Exeter #113
£750 $1170 €1125 Cornish moorland scene. Stream running across a Cornish landscape (27x36cm-11x14in) s. pencil W/C pair. 27-Mar-3 Christie's, Kensington #41
£880 $1426 €1320 Cattle resting in an extensive landscape with Bath in distance (33x56cm-13x22in) s.d.1883 W/C. 23-May-3 Honiton Galleries, Honiton #657/R

MORRISON, George William (20th C) Irish
Works on paper
£250 $365 €375 Tyrella (18x25cm-7x10in) s. W/C. 12-Jun-2 John Ross, Belfast #19
£250 $365 €375 Cushendun, Co. Antrim (25x36cm-10x14in) s. W/C. 12-Jun-2 John Ross, Belfast #315
£250 $365 €375 Colleen Bawn Rock, Killarney (25x36cm-10x14in) s.d.36 W/C. 12-Jun-2 John Ross, Belfast #319
£250 $398 €375 Errigal, County Donegal (25x35cm-10x14in) s.d.37 W/C. 5-Mar-3 John Ross, Belfast #195
£260 $380 €390 Mount Errigal, Donegal (25x36cm-10x14in) s.d.37 W/C. 12-Jun-2 John Ross, Belfast #160
£260 $403 €390 Bryansford, Co. Down (25x35cm-10x14in) s. W/C. 4-Dec-2 John Ross, Belfast #149
£270 $422 €400 Rathlin from Ballintoy (14x28cm-6x11in) s. W/C. 26-Mar-3 James Adam, Dublin #144/R
£280 $445 €420 Barnsmore, Donegal (15x30cm-6x12in) s. W/C. 5-Mar-3 John Ross, Belfast #18
£280 $445 €420 St. Patricks, Lough Derg, Donegal (15x28cm-6x11in) s.d.1935 W/C. 5-Mar-3 John Ross, Belfast #214
£280 $434 €420 Narrowwater, Co. Down (25x35cm-10x14in) s. W/C. 4-Dec-2 John Ross, Belfast #17

£300 $465 €450 Cushendun (25x36cm-10x14in) s. W/C. 2-Oct-2 John Ross, Belfast #8
£300 $477 €450 Murlough Bay, County Antrim (15x30cm-6x12in) s. W/C. 5-Mar-3 John Ross, Belfast #9
£300 $477 €450 Muckish, Donegal (17x25cm-7x10in) s.d.1935 W/C. 5-Mar-3 John Ross, Belfast #28
£300 $465 €450 Mount Errigal (25x35cm-10x14in) s. W/C. 4-Dec-2 John Ross, Belfast #8
£320 $467 €480 Dhu Lough, Mayo (25x36cm-10x14in) s. W/C. 12-Jun-2 John Ross, Belfast #2
£320 $509 €480 Roshine, Errigal (17x25cm-7x10in) s.d.1933 W/C. 5-Mar-3 John Ross, Belfast #36
£320 $509 €480 Sheephaven, Donegal (15x28cm-6x11in) s.d.37 W/C. 5-Mar-3 John Ross, Belfast #50
£324 $506 €480 Sugar loaf mountain, Glengariff (14x28cm-6x11in) s. W/C. 26-Mar-3 James Adam, Dublin #145/R
£350 $511 €525 Murlough Bay, Co. Antrim (25x38cm-10x15in) s. W/C. 12-Jun-2 John Ross, Belfast #48
£350 $543 €525 Cushendun Bay, Co. Antrim (25x36cm-10x14in) s. W/C. 2-Oct-2 John Ross, Belfast #17
£419 $654 €620 Mourne mountains, Co. Down (25x37cm-10x15in) s. W/C. 26-Mar-3 James Adam, Dublin #80/R
£500 $775 €750 Portsalon, Co. Donegal (23x58cm-9x23in) s. W/C. 4-Dec-2 John Ross, Belfast #155

MORRISON, James (1932-) British
£360 $587 €540 Small landscape (15x16cm-6x6in) 14-Feb-3 Lyon & Turnbull, Edinburgh #42
£600 $972 €900 Thorn (24x26cm-9x10in) s.d.1980 board. 23-May-3 Lyon & Turnbull, Edinburgh #76
£750 $1215 €1125 Tundra 1 (32x49cm-13x19in) s.d.29.VII.1990 board exhib. 23-May-3 Lyon & Turnbull, Edinburgh #82
£780 $1217 €1170 Tree at Craig House (44x28cm-17x11in) s.d.1976 gesso board. 17-Oct-2 Bonhams, Edinburgh #24
£980 $1529 €1470 Mains of Catterline (24x87cm-9x34in) s.d.1959 board exhib. 17-Oct-2 Bonhams, Edinburgh #53
£1000 $1560 €1500 Towards old Montrose (27x88cm-11x35in) s. board. 17-Oct-2 Bonhams, Edinburgh #111/R est:1000-1500
£1600 $2592 €2400 Bush and field (30x110cm-12x43in) s.d.19.11.1992 board exhi. 23-May-3 Lyon & Turnbull, Edinburgh #91 est:1200-1500
£1900 $3078 €2850 February landscape (80x113cm-31x44in) s.d.1978 board exhib. 23-May-3 Lyon & Turnbull, Edinburgh #37/R est:2000-3000
£4200 $6804 €6300 Near Maryton (83x151cm-33x59in) s.d.26.1.1983 board. 23-May-3 Lyon & Turnbull, Edinburgh #63/R est:2500-3500
£5200 $8268 €7800 Montreathmont Beach (119x179cm-47x70in) s.d.1976 board exhib. 6-Mar-3 Christie's, Kensington #229/R est:3000-5000
£6200 $10044 €9300 Snow with farmhouses (98x148cm-39x58in) s.d.11.2.1991 board. 23-May-3 Lyon & Turnbull, Edinburgh #29/R est:3000-5000
Works on paper
£1500 $2340 €2250 Angus (72x88cm-28x35in) s.d.1979 gouache wash board. 17-Sep-2 Sotheby's, Olympia #74/R est:800-1200

MORRISON, L (20th C) ?
£643 $990 €965 Untitled - cattle in a mountain field (92x71cm-36x28in) s. 3-Sep-2 Shapiro, Sydney #425 est:2000-4000 (A.D 1800)

MORRISON, Robert Edward (1852-1925) British
£1150 $1794 €1725 Low tide at shore (29x39cm-11x15in) s. panel. 26-Mar-3 Hamptons Fine Art, Godalming #209/R est:500-700

MORRISSEAU, Norval (1932-) Canadian
£241 $378 €362 Bird Spirit (75x55cm-30x22in) s. acrylic. 25-Nov-2 Hodgins, Calgary #349/R (C.D 600)
£287 $445 €431 Young girl (38x56cm-15x22in) s. acrylic. 24-Sep-2 Maynards, Vancouver #392 (C.D 700)
£1111 $1822 €1611 Two figures and serpent (75x58cm-30x23in) init.d.1974 acrylic prov. 9-Jun-3 Hodgins, Calgary #94/R est:2000-2500 (C.D 2500)
£1406 $2221 €2109 Medicine bear (71x130cm-28x51in) d.1979 acrylic. 1-Dec-2 Levis, Calgary #70/R est:4000-4500 (C.D 3500)

MORRO-HENZE, Ingfried Paul (1925-1972) German
£720 $1181 €1080 Still life with flowers with Venice in the background (38x49cm-15x19in) s. 2-Jun-3 David Duggleby, Scarborough #323/R

MORROCCO, Alberto (1917-1998) British
£820 $1279 €1230 Sunflower (41x42cm-16x17in) s. conte. 17-Oct-2 Bonhams, Edinburgh #26
£1800 $2862 €2700 Study for the sculpture two centaurs (53x74cm-21x29in) s.i.d.75 chl bodycol. 6-Mar-3 Christie's, Kensington #260/R est:2000-3000
£4600 $7038 €6900 Tunisian girl, blue cushion (36x41cm-14x16in) s. board. 22-Aug-2 Bonhams, Edinburgh #972/R est:5000-7000
£5200 $7904 €7800 Low tide, Benholm (38x91cm-15x36in) s. exhib. 28-Aug-2 Sotheby's, London #1100/R est:5000-7000
£5800 $9048 €8700 Ellen and Gordon Cameron, at Murcar beach (41x49cm-16x19in) s.d.48 panel. 17-Oct-2 Bonhams, Edinburgh #3/R est:4000-6000
£7000 $10850 €10500 Red beach (46x40cm-18x16in) s. 6-Dec-2 Lyon & Turnbull, Edinburgh #73/R est:3000-5000
£7200 $10944 €10800 Child and water melon (41x46cm-16x18in) s.d.82 i.verso board prov. 28-Aug-2 Sotheby's, London #1020/R est:5000-7000
£7200 $11664 €10800 Still life with pear and banana (42x48cm-17x19in) s.d.70 exhib. 23-May-3 Lyon & Turnbull, Edinburgh #34/R est:4000-6000
£7500 $11400 €11250 Low tide, Johnshaven (45x70cm-18x28in) s.d.61 board. 28-Aug-2 Sotheby's, London #1099/R est:6000-8000
£8000 $12400 €12000 Two clowns with birds (61x56cm-24x22in) s.d.97 panel. 31-Oct-2 Christie's, London #173/R est:8000-12000
£8000 $12400 €12000 Small shrine, Pellestrina (61x75cm-24x30in) s. i.verso board. 6-Dec-2 Lyon & Turnbull, Edinburgh #91/R est:6000-8000
£8000 $12720 €12000 Still life and striped cloth (46x49cm-18x19in) s. panel exhib. 6-Mar-3 Christie's, Kensington #262/R est:4000-6000
£8800 $13464 €13200 Ponte de san Pantalone, Venice (50x47cm-20x19in) s.d.80 cardboard prov. 22-Aug-2 Bonhams, Edinburgh #1056/R est:8000-12000
£10000 $15800 €15000 Still life with apples (59x84cm-23x33in) s. i.verso board. 27-Nov-2 Sotheby's, Olympia #259/R est:8000-12000
£11000 $16830 €16500 Clown with bird (61x31cm-24x12in) s.d.96 s.i.verso board. 22-Aug-2 Bonhams, Edinburgh #963/R est:5000-8000
£14500 $22475 €21750 Clown thinking (56x46cm-22x18in) s. 6-Dec-2 Lyon & Turnbull, Edinburgh #62/R est:15000-20000
£18000 $29880 €26100 Homage a Kees van Dongen (81x86cm-32x34in) s.d.1989 i.verso. 10-Jun-3 David Lay, Penzance #95/R est:1800-2000

MORROCCO, Léon (1942-) Australian
£260 $424 €390 Olive grove (40x58cm-16x23in) 14-Feb-3 Lyon & Turnbull, Edinburgh #106
£880 $1373 €1320 Sunrise from the studio (12x18cm-5x7in) s.i.d.1994 board. 17-Oct-2 Bonhams, Edinburgh #2/R
£1200 $1872 €1800 Self portrait in bedroom (126x152cm-50x60in) s.d.70 prov. 17-Sep-2 Sotheby's, Olympia #82/R est:1500-2500
£7500 $11700 €11250 Romolo's balcony, Tuscany (46x46cm-18x18in) s.d.96 board prov. 14-Apr-3 Sotheby's, London #182/R est:4000-6000
Works on paper
£500 $795 €750 Figure on a patio (65x47cm-26x19in) s.i.d.69 pencil squared for transfer. 6-Mar-3 Christie's, Kensington #261/R

MORSE, Jonathan Bradley (1834-1898) American
£625 $1000 €938 Forest interior (91x53cm-36x21in) s. prov. 18-May-3 Butterfields, Los Angeles #7023

MORSING, Ivar (1919-) Swedish
£384 $584 €576 A different life (63x70cm-25x28in) s.d.67 s.i.d.1967 verso canvas on panel. 16-Aug-2 Lilla Bukowskis, Stockholm #393 (S.KR 5600)
£847 $1330 €1271 Figure composition (62x56cm-24x22in) s. 16-Dec-2 Lilla Bukowskis, Stockholm #417 (S.KR 12000)
£917 $1440 €1376 Figure composition (88x99cm-35x39in) s.d.70. 16-Dec-2 Lilla Bukowskis, Stockholm #544 (S.KR 13000)

MORSS, Edward (1906-) British
£280 $434 €420 Ready money cove (50x60cm-20x24in) s. board. 3-Dec-2 Bonhams, Knightsbridge #286/R

MORSTAD, Torbjorn (20th C) Norwegian
£289 $469 €434 Figures (27x53cm-11x21in) s. panel. 27-Jan-3 Blomqvist, Lysaker #1150/R (N.KR 3200)

MORTEL, Jan (1650-1719) Dutch
£30000 $47100 €45000 Fruit on ledge with squirrel and dragonfly (68x84cm-27x33in) bears sig. 11-Dec-2 Christie's, London #54/R est:30000-50000

MORTELL, Bernard (?) ?
£340 $482 €550 American dream (38x58cm-15x23in) s.d. 29-Mar-2 Woodwards, Cork #162

MORTELMANS, F (19/20th C) Belgian
£2201 $3434 €3500 Nature morte: vase de violettes (18x26cm-7x10in) panel. 14-Oct-2 Amberes, Antwerp #180/R
Works on paper
£316 $494 €500 Vase fleuri (51x24cm-20x9in) W/C. 16-Sep-2 Amberes, Antwerp #227

MORTELMANS, Frank (1898-1986) Belgian
£2885 $4529 €4500 Bouquet de fleurs (130x104cm-51x41in) s. 21-Nov-2 Neret-Minet, Paris #32

MORTELMANS, Frans (1865-c.1936) Belgian
£503 $780 €800 Landscape with mill (18x25cm-7x10in) s. panel. 5-Oct-2 De Vuyst, Lokeren #256
£1087 $1783 €1500 Roses (32x42cm-13x17in) s. 27-May-3 Campo & Campo, Antwerp #141 est:900-1200
£1594 $2614 €2200 Roses dans un vase (45x25cm-18x10in) s. panel. 27-May-3 Campo & Campo, Antwerp #142/R est:1500-2000

£3038 $4739 €4800 Still life with roses (45x22cm-18x9in) 21-Oct-2 Bernaerts, Antwerp #723/R est:3000-4000
£4110 $6411 €6000 Still life with apples and cut melon (60x80cm-24x31in) s. 10-Apr-3 Dorotheum, Vienna #254/R est:6000-6500
£4114 $6418 €6500 Still life with pears and beakers (54x50cm-21x20in) s. panel. 21-Oct-2 Bernaerts, Antwerp #112/R est:7000-8000
£8000 $13360 €11600 Still life of roses (100x61cm-39x24in) s.i. 17-Jun-3 Bonhams, New Bond Street #13/R est:8000-12000

Works on paper
£252 $387 €400 Zaanstraat, Kiel (30x40cm-12x16in) s. pastel. 22-Oct-2 Campo, Vlaamse Kaai #211
£1151 $1842 €1600 Flowers in blue vase (54x25cm-21x10in) s. W/C. 17-May-3 De Vuyst, Lokeren #270/R est:2000-2500
£4167 $6458 €6500 Still life with roses (50x80cm-20x31in) s. W/C. 7-Dec-2 De Vuyst, Lokeren #533/R est:6500-7500

MORTENSEN, Richard (1910-1994) Danish
£1907 $3184 €2765 Composition (48x68cm-19x27in) s.i.d.1949 verso paper prov. 17-Jun-3 Rasmussen, Copenhagen #1/R est:20000-25000 (D.KR 20000)
£2144 $3345 €3216 Abstract composition (67x56cm-26x22in) mono.d.1958 verso. 11-Nov-2 Rasmussen, Vejle #133/R est:40000-60000 (D.KR 25000)
£3002 $4683 €4503 Composition (87x68cm-34x27in) painted c.1946. 11-Nov-2 Rasmussen, Vejle #116/R est:75000-100000 (D.KR 35000)
£4833 $7636 €7250 Composition (31x42cm-12x17in) s.d.1958 verso. 1-Apr-3 Rasmussen, Copenhagen #188/R est:20000-25000 (D.KR 52000)
£7435 $11747 €11153 Bastille Day (54x65cm-21x26in) init.d.14 VII 54 verso lit. 1-Apr-3 Rasmussen, Copenhagen #191/R est:90000-100000 (D.KR 80000)
£7495 $11918 €11243 Composition - Birkerod (54x65cm-21x26in) init.d.II.I3.53 verso exhib.lit. 26-Feb-3 Kunsthallen, Copenhagen #9/R est:75000 (D.KR 82000)
£7770 $12354 €11655 Ventoux (50x61cm-20x24in) prov.exhib.lit. 26-Feb-3 Kunsthallen, Copenhagen #25/R est:75000 (D.KR 85000)
£8044 $12468 €12066 Composition (87x68cm-34x27in) painted 1942 prov. 1-Oct-2 Rasmussen, Copenhagen #34/R est:90000-100000 (D.KR 95000)
£8467 $13124 €12701 Abstract composition (90x68cm-35x27in) init.d.42 verso s.stretcher lit. 1-Oct-2 Rasmussen, Copenhagen #36/R est:100000 (D.KR 100000)
£10584 $16406 €15876 Paris - Birkerod (65x90cm-26x35in) init.i.d.1958 verso lit.prov. 1-Oct-2 Rasmussen, Copenhagen #23/R est:150000-200000 (D.KR 125000)
£13091 $20422 €19637 Composition - Ajaccio, spring (65x90cm-26x35in) s. s.d.1959 verso lit. 18-Sep-2 Kunsthallen, Copenhagen #60/R est:175000 (D.KR 155000)
£13711 $21801 €20567 Opus 7, Havdrup (100x81cm-39x32in) s.d.21/VIII/78 lit. 26-Feb-3 Kunsthallen, Copenhagen #107/R est:160000 (D.KR 150000)
£14358 $22399 €21537 Opus 7 - Tune (100x81cm-39x32in) s.i.d.12/VII.78 verso exhib.lit. 18-Sep-2 Kunsthallen, Copenhagen #110/R est:175000 (D.KR 170000)
£22382 $34916 €33573 Sirmione No.2 - Hameau Boileau summer (130x97cm-51x38in) init.i.d.1953 verso exhib. 18-Sep-2 Kunsthallen, Copenhagen #9/R est:175000 (D.KR 265000)
£27872 $43480 €41808 Shape of the world in a cold room (100x120cm-39x47in) i.d.24.8-6.9.1938 verso exhib.lit. 18-Sep-2 Kunsthallen, Copenhagen #47/R est:300000 (D.KR 330000)

Sculpture
£2288 $3821 €3318 Relief number IV (100x70cm-39x28in) s.d.1962 verso cut black painted wood white background. 17-Jun-3 Rasmussen, Copenhagen #24/R est:18000-20000 (D.KR 24000)
£3432 $5731 €4976 Floating relief (81x100cm-32x39in) s.d.1962 black white wood white background. 17-Jun-3 Rasmussen, Copenhagen #23/R est:18000-20000 (D.KR 36000)

Works on paper
£388 $601 €582 Composition (75x56cm-30x22in) s.d.30-VI-89 Indian ink. 4-Dec-2 Kunsthallen, Copenhagen #198 (D.KR 4500)
£423 $656 €635 Composition (48x63cm-19x25in) s.d.18 IX 48 Indian ink prov.lit. 1-Oct-2 Rasmussen, Copenhagen #8/R (D.KR 5000)
£490 $764 €735 Composition (55x70cm-22x28in) mono.d.52 Indian ink collage prov. 18-Sep-2 Kunsthallen, Copenhagen #75 (D.KR 5800)
£524 $876 €760 Composition with calligraphy (46x60cm-18x24in) Indian ink exhib.prov. 17-Jun-3 Rasmussen, Copenhagen #110/R (D.KR 5500)
£732 $1135 €1098 Composition (51x65cm-20x26in) s. gouache. 4-Dec-2 Kunsthallen, Copenhagen #136/R (D.KR 8500)
£763 $1274 €1106 Composition (48x63cm-19x25in) s.d.1960 collage prov. 17-Jun-3 Rasmussen, Copenhagen #197/R (D.KR 8000)
£836 $1322 €1254 Composition (48x63cm-19x25in) s.i.d.61 gouache pencil. 1-Apr-3 Rasmussen, Copenhagen #262/R (D.KR 9000)
£858 $1433 €1244 Composition (46x60cm-18x24in) s.d.28-V-59 gouache pencil. 17-Jun-3 Rasmussen, Copenhagen #21/R (D.KR 9000)
£913 $1442 €1370 Collage (64x60cm-25x24in) s.d.24-VIII-89 collage. 28-Apr-3 Bukowskis, Stockholm #340/R (S.KR 12000)
£1098 $1713 €1647 Composition (41x30cm-16x12in) s.d.65 gouache W/C. 18-Sep-2 Kunsthallen, Copenhagen #13/R est:8000 (D.KR 13000)
£1121 $1749 €1682 Souvenirs de bal negre (56x76cm-22x30in) s.d.4-III-91 collage. 5-Nov-2 Bukowskis, Stockholm #313/R est:18000-20000 (S.KR 16000)

MORTEO, Ettore (1874-1939) Italian
£2536 $4159 €3500 La marinaretta. S. Giacomo in Carignano. Porta aurea o di Piccapietra. La guardia Val Polcervera (36x28cm-14x11in) all s. i.verso panel four. 27-May-3 Finarte, Milan #114/R est:1000-1200

MORTIER, Antoine (1908-1998) Belgian
£3038 $4800 €4800 Phantasma (116x81cm-46x32in) s.d.71 verso. 26-Nov-2 Palais de Beaux Arts, Brussels #252/R est:5000-7000

Works on paper
£1736 $2760 €2500 Nu (150x100cm-59x39in) s. chl. 29-Apr-3 Campo, Vlaamse Kaai #231 est:2600-3500
£2083 $3312 €3000 Composition (110x72cm-43x28in) s.d.1967. 29-Apr-3 Campo, Vlaamse Kaai #233 est:3000-3500

MORTIER, Emile (20th C) ?
£385 $596 €600 Vue de port d'Ostende (40x50cm-16x20in) s. 9-Dec-2 Horta, Bruxelles #510

MORTIMER, Alexander (fl.1885-1895) British
£720 $1116 €1080 By the cliffs, Stonehaven (51x76cm-20x30in) s.d.1897 two. 7-Dec-2 Shapes, Edinburgh #349

MORTIMER, Anne (1958-) British

Works on paper
£320 $496 €480 Swatting yellow yarn balls round the playroom floor (14x32cm-6x13in) s. W/C. 31-Oct-2 Greenslade Hunt, Taunton #612

MORTIMER, John Hamilton (1740-1779) British

Works on paper
£1800 $2808 €2700 Falstaff (33x26cm-13x10in) pen black ink oval prov.exhib. 17-Sep-2 Rosebery Fine Art, London #510 est:300-400

MORTIMER, John Hamilton (attrib) (1740-1779) British
£10000 $16700 €14500 Edward the Black Prince at the Battle of Poitiers. Black Prince receiving John, King of France (30x44cm-12x17in) pair. 9-Jul-3 Bonhams, New Bond Street #12/R est:10000-15000

MORTIMER, Lewis (20th C) British

Works on paper
£250 $410 €375 A quiet moment in a Cornish harbour (34x24cm-13x9in) s. W/C. 3-Jun-3 Bearnes, Exeter #423
£280 $465 €406 Rose cottage (36x25cm-14x10in) s. W/C. 10-Jun-3 David Lay, Penzance #18
£350 $581 €508 Thatched cottages (25x38cm-10x15in) s. W/C. 10-Jun-3 David Lay, Penzance #19

MORTON, Alastair (1910-1963) British

Works on paper
£300 $468 €450 Abstract composition (33x25cm-13x10in) init.d.46 gouache. 17-Sep-2 Bonhams, Knightsbridge #223/R
£650 $1014 €975 Untitled (25x35cm-10x14in) s.d.1939verso pen ink gouache. 15-Oct-2 Bonhams, Knightsbridge #211/R

MORTON, Cavendish (1911-) British
£300 $465 €450 Barge going up river to Snape Bridge (54x70cm-21x28in) s.d.1969 board. 4-Dec-2 Christie's, Kensington #532

Works on paper
£260 $413 €390 Thaxted church (62x49cm-24x19in) s.d.1974 ink W/C. 24-Mar-3 Trembath Welch, Great Dunmow #476
£380 $597 €570 Boats on the shore (18x50cm-7x20in) s.d.1966 W/C. 16-Dec-2 Bonhams, Bury St Edmunds #370/R

MORTON, Gary (1951-) American
£3205 $5000 €4808 Noon change (46x61cm-18x24in) s. acrylic prov. 9-Nov-2 Santa Fe Art, Santa Fe #26/R est:7500-8500

Works on paper
£801 $1250 €1202 Leather throne (33x43cm-13x17in) s. W/C prov. 9-Nov-2 Santa Fe Art, Santa Fe #25/R est:1800-2250

MORTON, Thomas Corsan (1859-1928) British
£300 $498 €435 June afternoon (62x67cm-24x26in) s. board. 13-Jun-3 Lyon & Turnbull, Edinburgh #37
£400 $620 €600 Harvest from the sea (30x43cm-12x17in) mono. canvasboard prov. 31-Oct-2 Duke & Son, Dorchester #297/R
£606 $933 €909 Mother and child on country lane (23x51cm-9x20in) s. 4-Sep-2 Dunbar Sloane, Wellington #92/R est:2000-3000 (NZ.D 2000)

MORTON, William (20th C) American
Works on paper
£250 $380 €375 Matlock Dale with Abrahams Heights (33x48cm-13x19in) s. W/C. 14-Aug-2 Andrew Hartley, Ilkley #564

MORTON-JOHNSON, Francis (1878-1931) French
£1418 $2369 €2000 Jeune femme dans la mansarde (50x61cm-20x24in) s. board. 20-Jun-3 Piasa, Paris #105 est:1400-1500

MORVAN, Jean Jacques (1928-) French
£355 $574 €500 Corse (81x65cm-32x26in) s. s.i.verso isorel. 23-May-3 Camard, Paris #175

MORZENTI, Natale (19th C) Italian
£3623 $5942 €5000 Giocatori di carte (90x115cm-35x45in) 27-May-3 Finarte, Milan #52/R est:5000-6000

MOSBACHER, Alois (1954-) Austrian
£3623 $5942 €5000 Hiding (115x80cm-45x31in) mono.d.83. 27-May-3 Wiener Kunst Auktionen, Vienna #220/R est:5000-8000
Works on paper
£2703 $4216 €4000 Stones (240x140cm-94x55in) W/C exhib.lit. 25-Mar-3 Wiener Kunst Auktionen, Vienna #38/R est:4000-7500

MOSBLECH, Wilhelm (elder) (19/20th C) German
£350 $574 €525 Fishing vessels on calm waters offshore (70x81cm-28x32in) s. board. 5-Jun-3 Christie's, Kensington #737/R

MOSCA, August (1909-) American/Russian
£2830 $4500 €4245 Seated nude (64x74cm-25x29in) s. board painted c.1948 prov. 2-Mar-3 Toomey, Oak Park #646/R est:5000-7000

MOSCARDO, Jose (1953-) Spanish
£1169 $1706 €1800 Night view of the harbour (65x130cm-26x51in) s. 17-Jun-2 Ansorena, Madrid #79/R

MOSCARDO, Ramon (1953-) Spanish
£839 $1325 €1300 Study of study (24x35cm-9x14in) s. s.i.verso cardboard. 17-Dec-2 Durán, Madrid #148/R
Works on paper
£552 $872 €800 Full (47x67cm-19x26in) s. gouache. 1-Apr-3 Segre, Madrid #344/R

MOSCHELES, Felix (1833-1917) British
£1392 $2200 €2200 Family (65x80cm-26x31in) s.d.1902. 26-Nov-2 Christie's, Rome #31/R
£3500 $5425 €5250 Henry Morton Stanley, in tropical dress (56x42cm-22x17in) s.i. 24-Sep-2 Christie's, London #56/R est:3000-5000

MOSEBEKK, Olav (1910-2001) Norwegian
Works on paper
£340 $523 €510 Small girl (63x52cm-25x20in) s. chl. 28-Oct-2 Blomqvist, Lysaker #1193 (N.KR 4000)

MOSELEY, Austin (20th C) British
£700 $1092 €1050 Wind and rain (76x56cm-30x22in) s. board exhib. 27-Mar-3 Christie's, Kensington #563/R

MOSER, Anna Maria (1756-1838) Austrian
£629 $981 €1000 Portrait of the mother of God holding Infant Christ (72x57cm-28x22in) s.d.1833 verso lit. 20-Sep-2 Karlheinz Kaupp, Staufen #1840/R

MOSER, Frank H (1886-1964) American
£375 $600 €563 Road home, landscape with snow covered land and trees (30x41cm-12x16in) s. canvasboard. 17-Mar-3 Winter Associates, Plainville #51

MOSER, Hermann (1835-?) Austrian
£390 $597 €585 Cottage in a landscape at dusk (37x58cm-15x23in) s. 21-Aug-2 Bonhams, Knowle #248

MOSER, Karl (younger) (1873-1939) Austrian
Prints
£2403 $3797 €3605 Paradise (32x35cm-13x14in) s.i.d.1908 col woodcut. 29-Nov-2 Zofingen, Switzerland #2605/R est:3000 (S.FR 5600)
£3165 $5000 €5000 Croatian woman with hen (45x33cm-18x13in) s.i.d.08 col woodcut. 27-Nov-2 Dorotheum, Vienna #128/R est:3600-3800
£3546 $5745 €5000 Breton wedding (43x53cm-17x21in) s.mono.i.d.06 woodcut. 20-May-3 Dorotheum, Vienna #113/R est:3600-4500

MOSER, Kolo (1868-1918) Austrian
£8861 $14000 €14000 Hyacinths (50x50cm-20x20in) prov. 27-Nov-2 Dorotheum, Vienna #139/R est:6000-9000
£60000 $100200 €87000 Fruhling (100x99cm-39x39in) mono. painted c.1900 prov. 25-Jun-3 Christie's, London #176/R est:60000-80000
Works on paper
£1944 $3092 €2800 Kneeling figure (40x28cm-16x11in) pencil. 29-Apr-3 Wiener Kunst Auktionen, Vienna #568/R est:1800-2500
£4255 $6894 €6000 Female nude with arms raised (47x30cm-19x12in) i. pen Indian ink htd white. 20-May-3 Dorotheum, Vienna #126/R est:2000-2800

MOSER, Kurt (20th C) German
£272 $425 €408 Tripolis (61x91cm-24x36in) 22-Sep-2 Susanin's, Chicago #5154/R

MOSER, M (?) ?
£550 $869 €825 Interior with man drinking wine (41x50cm-16x20in) s.d.1936. 18-Dec-2 John Nicholson, Haslemere #1236

MOSER, Oswald (1874-1953) British
Works on paper
£264 $412 €420 Market (52x37cm-20x15in) s.d.1929 pastel. 17-Sep-2 Segre, Madrid #127/R

MOSER, Richard (1874-?) Austrian
Works on paper
£2639 $4196 €3800 Griechengasse (33x22cm-13x9in) s.i.d.1917 W/C. 29-Apr-3 Wiener Kunst Auktionen, Vienna #560/R est:1500-2500

MOSER, Wilfried (1914-1997) Swiss
£783 $1213 €1175 Otea (42x22cm-17x9in) s. oil chk. 4-Dec-2 Koller, Zurich #185/R est:1200-1800 (S.FR 1800)
£1010 $1657 €1465 Voyage au bout de la nuit (74x92cm-29x36in) s. i.stretcher. 2-Jun-3 Blomqvist, Oslo #215/R (N.KR 11000)
£1397 $2040 €2096 Untitled (49x68cm-19x27in) s. i. verso oil collage paper on canvas. 4-Jun-2 Germann, Zurich #28/R est:3500-4000 (S.FR 3200)
£2402 $3507 €3603 St Remy (65x81cm-26x32in) s. s.i.d.1958 verso prov. 4-Jun-2 Germann, Zurich #30/R est:5000-7000 (S.FR 5500)
£2620 $4114 €3930 Apres la tempete (92x65cm-36x26in) s. s.i.d.1958 verso prov. 25-Nov-2 Sotheby's, Zurich #149/R est:6000-9000 (S.FR 6000)
£5093 $8199 €7385 La concierge (113x145cm-44x57in) s.d.63 i.verso. 9-May-3 Dobiaschofsky, Bern #243/R est:11000 (S.FR 11000)
Sculpture
£3930 $6170 €5895 Eudymion (117x54cm-46x21in) s.i.d.1960 verso painted wood prov. 25-Nov-2 Sotheby's, Zurich #168/R est:9000-12000 (S.FR 9000)

MOSES, Anna Mary Robertson (Grandma) (1860-1961) American
£12903 $20000 €19355 In camp (36x26cm-14x10in) s.d.June 17 1942 masonite prov.lit. 4-Dec-2 Sotheby's, New York #163/R est:15000-25000
£17949 $28000 €26924 Farm in autumn (33x69cm-13x27in) s. masonite prov. 12-Oct-2 Neal Auction Company, New Orleans #471/R est:30000-50000
£23899 $38000 €35849 Winter (25x41cm-10x16in) s. board prov.lit. 4-Mar-3 Christie's, Rockefeller NY #99/R est:30000-50000
£28302 $45000 €42453 Cambridge valley (44x60cm-17x24in) s. board painted 1943 prov.lit. 5-Mar-3 Sotheby's, New York #103/R est:25000-35000
£29032 $45000 €43548 Last road (46x61cm-18x24in) s.d.Sept 18 1953 board prov.lit. 4-Dec-2 Sotheby's, New York #162/R est:30000-50000
£29032 $45000 €43548 Birthday cake (41x51cm-16x20in) d.Feb 1953 tempera on board prov.lit. 5-Dec-2 Christie's, Rockefeller NY #215/R est:30000-50000
£33548 $52000 €50322 We are coming to church (39x42cm-15x17in) s. board prov.lit. 5-Dec-2 Christie's, Rockefeller NY #217/R est:30000-50000

MOSES, Ed (1926-) American
£961 $1500 €1442 Untitled (25x36cm-10x14in) s. 14-Oct-2 Butterfields, San Francisco #2058/R est:2500-3500
Works on paper
£4114 $6500 €6171 Untitled (151x102cm-59x40in) s.d.85 W/C prov. 13-Nov-2 Sotheby's, New York #122/R est:5000-7000

MOSES, Forrest K (1893-1974) American
£1415 $2250 €2123 Yellow straw, winter snow scene (41x61cm-16x24in) s. board. 1-Mar-3 North East Auctions, Portsmouth #767/R

MOSES, Walter Farrington (1874-?) ?
£256 $400 €384 Landscape (20x25cm-8x10in) s. board. 21-Sep-2 Harvey Clar, Oakland #1642

MOSLER, Henry (1841-1920) American
£318 $500 €477 Portrait of a fisherman (33x23cm-13x9in) s. board. 23-Nov-2 Pook & Pook, Downington #473/R
£1224 $1947 €1800 Young peasant girl with ducks in courtyard (55x38cm-22x15in) s. 19-Mar-3 Neumeister, Munich #665/R est:2000

MOSMAN, William (c.1700-1771) British
£4000 $6200 €6000 Portrait of a lady with a white shawl (60x62cm-24x24in) s.d.1742 feigned oval. 31-Oct-2 Christie's, London #1/R est:3000-5000

MOSNIER, Jean (attrib) (1600-1656) French
£26235 $42500 €39353 Saint Sebastian (116x90cm-46x35in) 23-Jan-3 Sotheby's, New York #246/R est:40000

MOSS, Charles Eugène (1860-1901) Canadian
£333 $546 €500 Roadside farmhouse near Orangeville (18x33cm-7x13in) s. canvas on board. 3-Jun-3 Joyner, Toronto #516 (C.D 750)
£987 $1540 €1431 Collecting the harvest (46x76cm-18x30in) s. 26-Mar-3 Walker's, Ottawa #202/R est:2000-2500 (C.D 2300)

MOSS, Colin (1914-) British
£600 $942 €900 Still life of gladioli in a vase (76x61cm-30x24in) s.d.53 board. 16-Dec-2 Bonhams, Bury St Edmunds #459/R

MOSS, Gary (20th C) American
£1899 $3000 €2754 Distant drummer (51x71cm-20x28in) s. prov. 26-Jul-3 Coeur d'Alene, Hayden #22/R est:3000-5000

MOSS, Henry William (fl.1885-1938) Irish
£641 $994 €1000 Captain and cattle going home (51x66cm-20x26in) s. 3-Dec-2 Thomas Adams, Dublin #386
£1377 $2258 €1900 Woman washing in alpine setting (50x61cm-20x24in) init. s.d.1911 verso. 28-May-3 Bonhams & James Adam, Dublin #121/R est:1000-1500

MOSS, Michael (?) British?
Works on paper
£250 $398 €375 Armada Street (18x33cm-7x13in) s.i.verso W/C. 19-Mar-3 Anthemion, Cardiff #406

MOSSA, Gustave Adolf (1883-1971) French
Works on paper
£566 $872 €900 Femme et ange (55x44cm-22x17in) s. W/C. 22-Oct-2 Campo, Vlaamse Kaai #573

MOSSER, Christine (20th C) American
£478 $750 €717 Still life with T'ang figure, ginger jar (48x63cm-19x25in) s. 22-Nov-2 Skinner, Boston #165/R

MOSSET, Olivier (1944-) Swiss
£2183 $3428 €3275 Untitled (100x100cm-39x39in) s.d.1990 verso acrylic prov. 25-Nov-2 Germann, Zurich #49/R est:9000-13000 (S.FR 5000)
£6597 $10424 €9500 Sans titre (100x100cm-39x39in) s.verso prov. 27-Apr-3 Perrin, Versailles #114/R est:6000-7000
£7292 $11594 €10500 Peinture (200x210cm-79x83in) s.d.74 verso prov. 29-Apr-3 Artcurial Briest, Paris #511/R est:8000-12000
£8844 $14061 €13000 Monochrome vert (200x200cm-79x79in) s.d.1981 verso acrylic. 24-Mar-3 Cornette de St.Cyr, Paris #115/R
£12013 $18499 €19100 Rond (100x100cm-39x39in) s.d.1970 verso. 26-Oct-2 Cornette de St.Cyr, Paris #140/R est:5000

MOSSMER, Raimund (1813-1874) Austrian
£1905 $3029 €2800 Alpine lake scene with paddle-steamer (11x18cm-4x7in) s. board. 25-Feb-3 Dorotheum, Vienna #137/R est:1400-1800

MOSSON, Georges (1851-1933) German
Works on paper
£1135 $1838 €1600 Boy playing (114x82cm-45x32in) s. pastel. 24-May-3 Van Ham, Cologne #425/R est:1600

MOSTAERT, Gillis (elder) (1534-1598) Flemish
£160000 $267200 €232000 Village kermesse (68x98cm-27x39in) mono. panel prov.exhib.lit. 9-Jul-3 Christie's, London #21/R est:80000-120000

MOSTAERT, Gillis (elder-circle) (1534-1598) Flemish
£20000 $31200 €30000 Village kermesse (69x101cm-27x40in) panel. 10-Apr-3 Christie's, Kensington #3/R est:6000-8000

MOSTYN, Marjorie (1893-?) British
£280 $462 €406 Still life with roses (35x46cm-14x18in) s. 3-Jul-3 Christie's, Kensington #416

MOSTYN, Tom (1864-1930) British
£260 $413 €390 Marshland river landscape (51x68cm-20x27in) s. 18-Mar-3 Rosebery Fine Art, London #787
£320 $499 €480 Picnic in the forest (51x68cm-20x27in) s. 17-Sep-2 Sotheby's, Olympia #189/R
£320 $522 €480 Girls on the edge of a pond (41x53cm-16x21in) s. 13-Feb-3 David Lay, Penzance #264
£360 $569 €540 River landscape (48x66cm-19x26in) s. 17-Dec-2 Gorringes, Lewes #1479
£620 $998 €930 Spring garden with Bougainvillaea (50x67cm-20x26in) s. 18-Feb-3 Bonhams, Knightsbridge #96
£800 $1280 €1200 Lovers (31x36cm-12x14in) s. 7-Jan-3 Bonhams, Knightsbridge #28
£800 $1264 €1160 River landscape across the valley, two figures at waters edge (53x76cm-21x30in) s.d.Sep6/2. 24-Jul-3 John Nicholson, Haslemere #1194
£850 $1326 €1275 Parisian garden (44x59cm-17x23in) s. 10-Sep-2 Bonhams, Knightsbridge #185/R
£880 $1373 €1320 Garden scene (46x61cm-18x24in) s. 26-Mar-3 Sotheby's, Olympia #179/R
£1100 $1793 €1650 Figures in a Mediterranean garden (49x67cm-19x26in) s. 13-Feb-3 Mellors & Kirk, Nottingham #820/R est:800-1200
£2600 $4238 €3770 Figure standing on steps in midnight wooded garden (51x70cm-20x28in) s. 17-Jul-3 Tennants, Leyburn #927/R est:600-900
£3000 $4680 €4500 Enchanted garden (71x91cm-28x36in) s. 27-Mar-3 Christie's, Kensington #526/R est:2000-3000
Works on paper
£600 $942 €900 Edge of the village (50x37cm-20x15in) s. W/C. 21-Nov-2 Clevedon Sale Rooms #237

MOSTYN, Tom (attrib) (1864-1930) British
£450 $716 €653 Cottage garden (64x77cm-25x30in) bears sig. 26-Feb-3 John Bellman, Billingshurst #1811/R
£620 $967 €930 Garden in fall (49x64cm-19x25in) bears sig. 19-Sep-2 John Bellman, Billingshurst #1456

MOTA Y MORALES, Vicente (19/20th C) Spanish
£288 $456 €450 Trees (15x24cm-6x9in) s. board. 14-Nov-2 Arte, Seville #339/R

MOTAU, Julian (1948-1968) South African
Works on paper
£192 $300 €288 Portrait of a man kneeling (53x36cm-21x14in) s.d.69 ink W/C. 11-Nov-2 Stephan Welz, Johannesburg #264 (SA.R 3000)

MOTE, George William (1832-1909) British
£500 $790 €750 On a Surrey heath (51x76cm-20x30in) s. 27-Nov-2 Hamptons Fine Art, Godalming #380
Works on paper
£400 $624 €600 View across a calm bay (20x33cm-8x13in) s.d.1886 W/C. 15-Oct-2 Bearnes, Exeter #375

MOTELEY, Jules Georges (1865-1923) French
£823 $1284 €1300 Lac de Clairaux sous la neige (40x65cm-16x26in) s. cardboard. 15-Sep-2 Etude Bailleul, Bayeux #96/R
£854 $1333 €1350 Effet de brouillard (27x35cm-11x14in) s.d.1915 s.i.verso cardboard. 15-Sep-2 Etude Bailleul, Bayeux #97/R

MOTHERWELL, Robert (1915-1991) American
£7097 $11000 €10646 Drunk with turpentine (51x41cm-20x16in) s.d.1979 board prov. 26-Sep-2 Christie's, Rockefeller NY #706/R est:9000-12000
£10625 $17000 €15938 Untitled - number a sketch (76x58cm-30x23in) s.d.1988 acrylic prov. 14-May-3 Sotheby's, New York #234/R est:15000-20000
£18750 $30000 €28125 Gauloises on scarlet over yellow no.3 (75x37cm-30x15in) init.d.72 acrylic printed paper collage canvas on board prov. 14-May-3 Sotheby's, New York #154/R est:20000-30000

£20000 $32000 €30000 Open 148 (35x46cm-14x18in) s. painted 1970 prov. 15-May-3 Christie's, Rockefeller NY #181/R est:20000-30000
£40000 $65600 €60000 Untitled, anchor (74x59cm-29x23in) init.d.63 paper on board prov. 7-Feb-3 Sotheby's, London #257/R est:25000-35000
£62500 $100000 €93750 Beside the sea (74x58cm-29x23in) s.d.1962 s.i.d.verso oil on paper prov.exhib. 14-May-3 Sotheby's, New York #153/R est:30000-40000

Prints
£1923 $3000 €2885 Untitled (76x56cm-30x22in) s.num.66/96 col aquatint etching. 14-Oct-2 Butterfields, San Francisco #1319/R est:1500-2500
£2044 $3250 €3066 St Michael (160x644cm-63x254in) s.num.14/14 col lithograph screenprint monoprint. 2-May-3 Sotheby's, New York #537/R est:3000-4000
£2293 $3600 €3440 Hermitage (103x73cm-41x29in) s.i. col lithograph. 21-Nov-2 Swann Galleries, New York #128/R est:4000-6000
£2516 $4000 €3774 Lament for Lorca (103x143cm-41x56in) init.d.num.AP II/XVII col lithograph edition of 25. 29-Apr-3 Christie's, Rockefeller NY #688/R est:5000-7000
£2516 $4000 €3774 Green studio (33x76cm-13x30in) s.d.1985 num.36/50 etching aquatint green black. 30-Apr-3 Doyle, New York #251/R est:2000-3000
£2564 $4000 €3846 Australian stone (61x76cm-24x30in) s.num.18/52 col etching aquatint. 14-Oct-2 Butterfields, San Francisco #1321/R est:5000-7000
£2692 $4200 €4038 Red sea (87x73cm-34x29in) s.num.23/100 red black aquatint etching. 5-Nov-2 Christie's, Rockefeller NY #462/R est:4000-6000
£2830 $4500 €4245 Calligraphy (137x102cm-54x40in) s.indis.num.36/50 col lithograph. 2-May-3 Sotheby's, New York #556/R est:3000-3500
£2903 $4500 €4355 In white with green stripe (86x61cm-34x24in) s.num.10/16 col etching embossing collage. 25-Sep-2 Christie's, Rockefeller NY #359/R est:2000-3000
£2903 $4500 €4355 Black cathedral (170x119cm-67x47in) s.num.8/14 col lithograph. 25-Sep-2 Christie's, Rockefeller NY #361/R est:4000-6000
£3067 $5000 €4601 Dance III (70x77cm-28x30in) s. num.8/50 etching aquatint. 13-Feb-3 Christie's, Rockefeller NY #306/R
£3145 $5000 €4718 Lament for Lorca (101x143cm-40x56in) init.i. col lithograph. 2-May-3 Sotheby's, New York #543/R est:6000-8000
£3226 $5000 €4839 Games of chance (88x69cm-35x27in) s.num.2/1000 col aquatint lithograph collage. 25-Sep-2 Christie's, Rockefeller NY #358/R est:4000-6000
£3459 $5500 €5189 Black cathedral (170x119cm-67x47in) init.num.3/40 col lithograph. 2-May-3 Sotheby's, New York #558/R est:4500-5500
£4088 $6500 €6132 Untitled (60x90cm-24x35in) s.num.4/50 col aquatint etching. 2-May-3 Sotheby's, New York #533/R est:3000-4000
£4088 $6500 €6132 Game of chance (61x42cm-24x17in) s.num.49/100 col lithograph aquatint. 2-May-3 Sotheby's, New York #552/R est:4000-5000
£4403 $7000 €6605 Signs on copper (45x60cm-18x24in) init.num.4/53 col aquatint. 29-Apr-3 Christie's, Rockefeller NY #687/R est:4000-5000
£4403 $7000 €6605 Australian stone (45x60cm-18x24in) s.num.42/52 col aquatint collage. 29-Apr-3 Christie's, Rockefeller NY #690/R est:5000-7000
£4403 $7000 €6605 Game of chance (58x43cm-23x17in) s.num.95/100 col aquatint lithograph collage. 29-Apr-3 Christie's, Rockefeller NY #691/R est:4000-6000
£4403 $7000 €6605 Elegy study I (81x139cm-32x55in) s.i. col lithograph. 2-May-3 Sotheby's, New York #554/R est:8000-10000
£4487 $7000 €6731 Flags (92x76cm-36x30in) init.num.52/68 lithograph. 5-Nov-2 Christie's, Rockefeller NY #466/R est:7000-9000
£4717 $7500 €7076 Red sea II (88x74cm-35x29in) s.i. col etching aquatint. 2-May-3 Sotheby's, New York #538/R est:2500-3500
£5346 $8500 €8019 Gesture IV (49x40cm-19x16in) s.num.73/100 col aquatint etching. 2-May-3 Sotheby's, New York #536/R est:6000-8000
£7051 $11000 €10577 Mexican night (64x61cm-25x24in) s.num.28/70 red black aquatint. 5-Nov-2 Christie's, Rockefeller NY #464/R est:12000-16000
£7547 $12000 €11321 Mexican night (45x45cm-18x18in) s.num.14/70 col aquatint. 2-May-3 Sotheby's, New York #550/R est:12000-15000
£7692 $12000 €11538 Elegy black black (38x96cm-15x38in) s.num.46/98 black white lithograph. 5-Nov-2 Christie's, Rockefeller NY #463/R est:8000-12000
£8176 $13000 €12264 Elegy black black (38x96cm-15x38in) s.num.92/98 col lithograph. 29-Apr-3 Christie's, Rockefeller NY #689/R est:10000-15000
£8805 $14000 €13208 Three figures (104x102cm-41x40in) s.num.71/80 col lithograph. 2-May-3 Sotheby's, New York #555/R est:8000-10000
£10063 $16000 €15095 Redness of red (61x41cm-24x16in) init.i. col lithograph screenprint collage. 2-May-3 Sotheby's, New York #551/R est:10000-15000
£10500 $17325 €15225 Mediterranean light (56x169cm-22x67in) init.num.28/40 col lithograph. 2-Jul-3 Christie's, London #296/R est:8000-12000
£15094 $24000 €22641 Mediterranean light (57x167cm-22x66in) init.num.1/40 col lithograph. 2-May-3 Sotheby's, New York #557/R est:15000-20000

MOTLEY, David (fl.1898) British
£1235 $2000 €1853 Urquhart Castle, Loch Ness (30x61cm-12x24in) s.i. 24-Jan-3 New Orleans Auction, New Orleans #179/R est:1200-1800

MOTLEY, Wilton (19/20th C) British
£400 $608 €600 Highland cattle resting by a loch (61x91cm-24x36in) s. 29-Aug-2 Christie's, Kensington #250/R

MOTTA, Raffaellino (1550-1578) Italian
Works on paper
£2532 $4000 €4000 La circoncision (33x24cm-13x9in) black chk pen brown ink brown wash. 27-Nov-2 Christie's, Paris #38/R est:4000-6000

MOTTA, Raffaellino (attrib) (1550-1578) Italian
Works on paper
£1000 $1550 €1500 Study of a standing warrior (37x15cm-15x6in) i. pen ink wash prov. 9-Dec-2 Bonhams, New Bond Street #26/R est:700-1000
£3716 $5797 €5500 Tarquine and Lucrece (16x18cm-6x7in) pen ink wash prov. 27-Mar-3 Christie's, Paris #59/R

MOTTARD VAN MARCKE, Leonie (1862-1936) Belgian
£545 $855 €850 Nature morte au lapin (90x73cm-35x29in) s. 11-Dec-2 Hotel des Ventes Mosan, Brussels #227

MOTTET, Yvonne (1906-1968) French
£880 $1373 €1320 Still life with pot of flowers (56x45cm-22x18in) s. prov. 6-Nov-2 Dreweatt Neate, Newbury #227/R

MOTTEZ, Henri Paul (1855-?) French
£3200 $5216 €4640 Portrait of Mrs Frederick Hill (58x43cm-23x17in) s.d.1902. 21-Jul-3 Sotheby's, London #835/R est:400-600

MOTTEZ, Victor (1809-1897) French
£11806 $18653 €17000 Portrait de Francois Guizot (100x81cm-39x32in) s.i.d.1849 prov.lit. 25-Apr-3 Beaussant & Lefèvre, Paris #27/R est:15000

MOTTI, Giuseppe (1908-1988) Italian
£316 $494 €500 Pink reflections (50x60cm-20x24in) s. 14-Sep-2 Meeting Art, Vercelli #843
£510 $811 €750 Anguri (50x60cm-20x24in) s. painted 1979. 1-Mar-3 Meeting Art, Vercelli #740

MOTTRAM, Charles Sim (fl.1880-1919) British
Works on paper
£185 $287 €278 Fishing boats at dawn (25x45cm-10x18in) s. W/C gouache prov. 3-Dec-2 Ritchie, Toronto #3010 (C.D 450)
£300 $501 €435 Off Brighton (40x60cm-16x24in) s.d.93 W/C. 23-Jun-3 Bonhams, Bath #208
£380 $593 €570 Herring boats at St Ives (17x13cm-7x5in) s.d.06 W/C htd white. 18-Sep-2 Dreweatt Neate, Newbury #69
£600 $972 €900 View of fishing boats surrounded by gulls on Cornish coastal waters (29x24cm-11x9in) s.d.09 W/C htd gouache. 21-Jan-3 Rupert Toovey, Partridge Green #1/R
£700 $1134 €1050 High tide, Clodgy Point, St. Ives (42x36cm-17x14in) s.d.1903 W/C htd white. 21-May-3 Bonhams, Knightsbridge #38/R
£2300 $3749 €3335 Boats on the Thames - upstream from Blackfriars (35x86cm-14x34in) s.d.1911 W/C scratching out. 21-Jul-3 Bonhams, Bath #23/R est:800-1000

MOUALLA, Fikret (1903-1967) Turkish
£1258 $1950 €2000 Feuillage et fleurs (50x35cm-20x14in) s.d.11.6.48. 30-Oct-2 Artcurial Briest, Paris #278 est:2000-2500
£1400 $2184 €2100 Study of a seated man (27x19cm-11x7in) s. 15-Oct-2 Sotheby's, London #102/R est:1500-2000
£1410 $2214 €2200 Femme debout (37x14cm-15x6in) s.d.1949. 13-Dec-2 Piasa, Paris #34/R
£3521 $5845 €5000 Les toits (17x27cm-7x11in) s.d.941 panel prov. 11-Jun-3 Beaussant & Lefèvre, Paris #116/R est:5000
£5556 $8778 €8000 Reprise des filets (29x45cm-11x18in) s.d.52. 25-Apr-3 Piasa, Paris #197
£18065 $28542 €28000 Banquet, fond vert (55x38cm-22x15in) st.sig. 19-Dec-2 Claude Aguttes, Neuilly #145/R est:50000
£19355 $30581 €30000 Dejeuner, fond jaune (48x55cm-19x22in) st.sig. 19-Dec-2 Claude Aguttes, Neuilly #144/R est:50000
£19355 $30581 €30000 Enfants au ballon (33x51cm-13x20in) s.d.1959 panel. 19-Dec-2 Claude Aguttes, Neuilly #147/R est:50000
£27097 $42813 €42000 Elegante a l'ombrelle (55x33cm-22x13in) s. 19-Dec-2 Claude Aguttes, Neuilly #149/R est:50000
£29032 $45871 €45000 Dejeuner bleu (46x55cm-18x22in) s.d.1956. 19-Dec-2 Claude Aguttes, Neuilly #148/R est:50000
£33548 $53006 €52000 Promenade au parc (46x55cm-18x22in) s. 19-Dec-2 Claude Aguttes, Neuilly #146/R
£41935 $66258 €65000 Peniches au quai a Paris (63x52cm-25x20in) s. 19-Dec-2 Claude Aguttes, Neuilly #143/R est:60000

Works on paper
£352 $585 €500 Soleil rouge sur le village (22x30cm-9x12in) s. felt crayon. 11-Jun-3 Beaussant & Lefèvre, Paris #115
£426 $711 €600 Port (23x17cm-9x7in) s.d.53 W/C gouache. 20-Jun-3 Piasa, Paris #177
£426 $711 €600 Nature morte aux fruits (17x22cm-7x9in) s.d.53 W/C gouache. 20-Jun-3 Piasa, Paris #178
£426 $711 €600 Nature morte aux raisins (22x18cm-9x7in) s.d.53 wash W/C. 20-Jun-3 Piasa, Paris #179
£496 $829 €700 Nature morte a la carafe et aux fruits (17x22cm-7x9in) s.d.53 W/C. 20-Jun-3 Piasa, Paris #182/R
£496 $829 €700 Elegantes (24x17cm-9x7in) s.d.53 col.ink. 20-Jun-3 Piasa, Paris #183
£496 $829 €700 La belle et le musicien (17x23cm-7x9in) s.d.53 W/C. 20-Jun-3 Piasa, Paris #184
£638 $1066 €900 Port (22x17cm-9x7in) s.d.53 W/C. 20-Jun-3 Piasa, Paris #180/R
£709 $1184 €1000 Voilier au port (18x22cm-7x9in) s.d.53 W/C gouache. 20-Jun-3 Piasa, Paris #181/R
£755 $1170 €1200 Scene de cafe (24x19cm-9x7in) s. gouache ink. 30-Oct-2 Artcurial Briest, Paris #277
£759 $1267 €1100 Le coiffeur (24x32cm-9x13in) s.d.55 gouache. 10-Jul-3 Artcurial Briest, Paris #90
£896 $1497 €1300 Scene de cafe (20x26cm-8x10in) s.d.53 gouache. 10-Jul-3 Artcurial Briest, Paris #91 est:1500-1800
£1000 $1560 €1500 Woman with a bottle of chianti (19x25cm-7x10in) s.d.54 W/C. 15-Oct-2 Sotheby's, London #104/R est:1200-1800
£1135 $1838 €1600 Deux portraits (18x28cm-7x11in) s.d.51 ink W/C two. 26-May-3 Joron-Derem, Paris #44 est:600-750
£1484 $2345 €2300 Notre-Dame (18x29cm-7x11in) s.d.1947 gouache. 19-Dec-2 Delvaux, Paris #25/R est:1800
£1701 $2704 €2500 Paris, terrasse du Cafe George V (46x33cm-18x13in) s.i.d.1.8.50 W/C ink paper on canvas. 26-Feb-3 Artcurial Briest, Paris #100 est:1600-1800
£2258 $3568 €3500 Ravaudeurs de filet (27x46cm-11x18in) s.d.1947 s.i.d.verso W/C oil. 19-Dec-2 Delvaux, Paris #24/R est:4500
£2632 $4264 €4000 La partie de cartes (18x24cm-7x9in) s.d.54 gouache. 22-Jan-3 Tajan, Paris #151/R est:4000-6000
£2632 $4264 €4000 Scene de bar (25x38cm-10x15in) s.d. gouache. 22-Jan-3 Tajan, Paris #153/R est:4000-6000
£2778 $4583 €4000 Tete de femme (49x34cm-19x13in) s. gouache. 2-Jul-3 Artcurial Briest, Paris #715/R est:4000-6000
£3291 $5134 €5200 Nature morte aux poires (31x53cm-12x21in) s. gouache. 20-Oct-2 Chayette & Cheval, Paris #5/R
£4722 $7461 €6800 Vase de fleurs (39x26cm-15x10in) s.d.1951 W/C gouache. 25-Apr-3 Piasa, Paris #196
£5000 $7800 €7500 Study of figures in a bar (31x53cm-12x21in) s. W/C gouache bodycol paper on canvas. 15-Oct-2 Sotheby's, London #101/R est:2000-3000
£5128 $7795 €8000 Personnages dans la rue, fond jaune (30x47cm-12x19in) s.d.59 gouache. 10-Jul-2 Rabourdin & Choppin de Janvry, Paris #23/R est:10000-12000
£5500 $8580 €8250 Conversation at the bar (35x52cm-14x20in) s.d.54 W/C bodycol. 15-Oct-2 Sotheby's, London #100/R est:2500-3500
£5806 $9174 €9000 Cinq femmes (37x49cm-15x19in) s.d.1954 gouache. 19-Dec-2 Delvaux, Paris #23/R est:10000
£6289 $9748 €10000 Quatre personnages en promenade (33x54cm-13x21in) s. gouache. 30-Oct-2 Artcurial Briest, Paris #274/R est:10000-12000
£7500 $11700 €11250 Woman with flowers (32x54cm-13x21in) s. W/C bodycol. 15-Oct-2 Sotheby's, London #103/R est:3000-5000
£8058 $12892 €11200 Femme assis pres du vase de fleurs (32x54cm-13x21in) s. gouache. 18-May-3 Eric Pillon, Calais #234/R
£8803 $14613 €12500 Interieur de bar (37x51cm-15x20in) s.d.55 prov. 11-Jun-3 Beaussant & Lefèvre, Paris #114/R est:8000
£15278 $25208 €22000 Paris, scene de rue devant le Moulin Rouge (44x64cm-17x25in) s. gouache. 2-Jul-3 Artcurial Briest, Paris #716/R est:8000-12000
£16783 $28028 €24000 Personnages sur fond bleu (64x54cm-25x21in) s.d.1960 gouache. 27-Jun-3 Claude Aguttes, Neuilly #101/R est:25000-30000
£20833 $34375 €30000 Scene de cafe dans un village Provencal (52x65cm-20x26in) s. gouache. 2-Jul-3 Artcurial Briest, Paris #714/R est:15000-20000

MOUBAIN, Paul (?) ?
£280 $456 €420 Harbour scene (48x53cm-19x21in) s. panel. 28-Jan-3 Henry Adams, Chichester #459

MOUCHERON, Frederic de (1633-1686) Dutch
£1280 $2074 €1856 Italianate landscape with figures (25x31cm-10x12in) panel prov. 26-May-3 Bukowskis, Stockholm #422/R est:18000-20000 (S.KR 16500)
£3503 $5465 €5500 Southern wooded landscape with fishermen in a stream and shepherds with their herd in the background (71x80cm-28x31in) bears sig. 5-Nov-2 Sotheby's, Amsterdam #212/R est:6000-8000
£5484 $8665 €8500 Paysage boise (110x132cm-43x52in) 18-Dec-2 Tajan, Paris #19/R est:12000
£10494 $17000 €15741 Italianate wooded landscape with figures on path (75x67cm-30x26in) prov. 23-Jan-3 Sotheby's, New York #188/R est:30000
Works on paper
£955 $1490 €1500 Italianate landscape with revellers in a clearing (21x26cm-8x10in) pen brown ink grey wash black chk prov. 5-Nov-2 Sotheby's, Amsterdam #85/R est:1500-2000

MOUCHERON, Frederic de (attrib) (1633-1686) Dutch
Works on paper
£1140 $1779 €1710 Classical landscapes. pen W/C four in one frame prov. 23-Sep-2 Rasmussen, Vejle #223/R est:8000-10000 (D.KR 13500)

MOUCHERON, Frederic de (circle) (1633-1686) Dutch
£8280 $12917 €13000 Italianate river landscape with nietherd, his family and flock before cascade (121x99cm-48x39in) s. 6-Nov-2 Christie's, Amsterdam #73/R est:10000-20000

MOUCHOT, Louis (19th C) French
£7051 $11071 €11000 La priere devant le minbar (66x52cm-26x20in) s.i.d.69 panel. 16-Dec-2 Gros & Delettrez, Paris #356/R est:10000-15000

MOUCHOT, Louis Claude (1830-1891) French
£3500 $5460 €5250 Ruins at Karnak (60x45cm-24x18in) s.d.1859. 15-Oct-2 Sotheby's, London #235/R est:4000-6000

MOUCLIER, Marc (1866-1948) French
£272 $433 €400 Maison jaune dans la foret (18x25cm-7x10in) s. cardboard. 27-Feb-3 Chochon-Barre & Allardi, Paris #49
£544 $865 €800 Porte au rideau rouge (33x25cm-13x10in) s. paper. 27-Feb-3 Chochon-Barre & Allardi, Paris #92

MOUGIN, Eugene Marcel (1895-1981) French
£315 $488 €500 Vue sur la Marne a la Varenne Saint-Hilaire (44x53cm-17x21in) s. 4-Oct-2 Tajan, Paris #176

MOUILLARD, Lucien (1842-1912) French
£284 $474 €400 Bateaux a maree basse (32x41cm-13x16in) s. panel. 23-Jun-3 Beaussant & Lefèvre, Paris #160
£780 $1303 €1100 Paysage en Algerie (17x31cm-7x12in) 23-Jun-3 Beaussant & Lefèvre, Paris #159/R
£851 $1421 €1200 Scene de village Arabe (16x21cm-6x8in) s. 23-Jun-3 Beaussant & Lefèvre, Paris #157
£1560 $2606 €2200 Scene de la vie Arabe a Garshia (33x41cm-13x16in) s.i. 23-Jun-3 Beaussant & Lefèvre, Paris #161/R est:200-250

MOUILLE, Serge (1922-1988) French
Sculpture
£5578 $8869 €8200 Untitled (172x100cm-68x39in) metal exec.c.1953 prov.lit. 24-Mar-3 Digard, Paris #91/R

MOULD, John (20th C) British
£850 $1411 €1233 Family portrait (46x58cm-18x23in) s. acrylic. 12-Jun-3 Christie's, Kensington #304/R

MOULIN, Felix Jacques Antoine (19th C) French?
Photographs
£3205 $5064 €5000 Nu feminin allonge, Amelie (16x22cm-6x9in) albumin print exec.c.1852-53 prov.lit. 16-Nov-2 Christie's, Paris #172/R est:3000-5000

MOULIN, Hippolyte (1832-1884) French
Sculpture
£2096 $3250 €3144 Excavation worker of Pompeii (84cm-33in) s. brown pat. bronze prov.exhib. 29-Oct-2 Sotheby's, New York #235/R est:6000-8000

MOULTRAY, James Douglas (fl.1860-1880s) British
£3200 $4864 €4800 Sanctuary on the Cairngorms (51x76cm-20x30in) s. 28-Aug-2 Sotheby's, London #889/R est:1500-2000

MOULTRAY, John Elder (1865-1922) New Zealander
£251 $391 €377 Fisherman in a riverbed (30x45cm-12x18in) s. board. 5-Nov-2 Peter Webb, Auckland #124/R (NZ.D 800)

MOULY, Marcel (1920-) French
£1141 $1802 €1712 Lumiere du soir (53x72cm-21x28in) s. 28-Apr-3 Bukowskis, Stockholm #334/R est:20000-25000 (S.KR 15000)

£4132 $6777 €5991 La femme en bleu fenetre grecque (146x114cm-57x45in) s.d.85 s.i.d.1985 verso lit. 2-Jun-3 Blomqvist, Oslo #191/R est:18000-20000 (N.KR 45000)

MOUNCEY, William (1852-1901) British
£2000 $3040 €3000 Sheep grazing (61x51cm-24x20in) s.i.on stretcher prov. 28-Aug-2 Sotheby's, London #884/R est:2000-3000

MOUNIER, Andre (20th C) French?
Sculpture
£1056 $1754 €1500 Relief (34x34cm-13x13in) i.num.1/1 duralumin on metal sheet exec.c.1960. 12-Jun-3 Laurence Calmels, Paris #81/R est:2000-3000

MOUNT, Rita (1888-1967) Canadian
£372 $584 €558 Port activity (23x28cm-9x11in) s. s.verso canvasboard. 24-Jul-2 Walker's, Ottawa #203/R (C.D 900)
£387 $604 €581 Study of a senora (69x61cm-27x24in) s. 30-Jul-2 Iegor de Saint Hippolyte, Montreal #105 (C.D 960)
£444 $729 €666 Gaspe (12x17cm-5x7in) init. board. 3-Jun-3 Joyner, Toronto #580 est:600-800 (C.D 1000)
£620 $973 €930 Lake Louise, Banff, Alberta (36x41cm-14x16in) i. s.d.1918 verso. 24-Jul-2 Walker's, Ottawa #250/R est:1500-2000 (C.D 1500)
£649 $1000 €974 Sunset Barachois-Gaspe (23x28cm-9x11in) s.i. board painted c.1930. 8-Sep-2 Treadway Gallery, Cincinnati #562/R
£649 $1000 €974 Autumn riviere aux Benards (23x28cm-9x11in) s.i. board painted c.1930. 8-Sep-2 Treadway Gallery, Cincinnati #563/R
£700 $1084 €1050 Gaspesie (22x27cm-9x11in) s. canvas on board. 3-Dec-2 Joyner, Toronto #156/R est:1500-1800 (C.D 1700)
£738 $1143 €1107 Bonsecours Market, Old Montreal (13x22cm-5x9in) i.d.1963 verso panel. 24-Sep-2 Ritchie, Toronto #3122/R est:600-800 (C.D 1800)

MOUNT, William Sidney (1807-1868) American
Works on paper
£566 $900 €849 Writer (10x18cm-4x7in) init. pencil prov. 29-Apr-3 Doyle, New York #28

MOURANT, Elise (?) ?
£325 $520 €471 Landscape near Katikati (45x49cm-18x19in) s. board. 13-May-3 Watson's, Christchurch #115/R (NZ.D 900)

MOURIER-PETERSEN, Christian (1858-1945) Danish
£595 $928 €893 Heath landscape with cabin (44x65cm-17x26in) mono.d.87. 5-Aug-2 Rasmussen, Vejle #195/R (D.KR 7000)

MOURIK, Hendrikus Cornelis van (1877-1944) Dutch
£1056 $1701 €1500 Still life with onions and copper pot (30x33cm-12x13in) s. 7-May-3 Vendue Huis, Gravenhage #152/R est:700-900

MOUS, Jos (1896-1968) Belgian
£252 $392 €400 Vue portuaire (40x49cm-16x19in) 14-Oct-2 Amberes, Antwerp #181

MOUSSEAU, Jean Paul (1927-1991) Canadian
Works on paper
£244 $383 €366 Bandes de couleurs (30x23cm-12x9in) s. pastel. 12-Dec-2 Iegor de Saint Hippolyte, Montreal #72 (C.D 600)

MOUSSON, Jozef Teodor (1887-1946) Czechoslovakian
£553 $856 €830 Artist's studio (26x32cm-10x13in) cardboard painted c.1924. 3-Dec-2 SOGA, Bratislava #32/R (SL.K 35000)
£599 $850 €899 Reading woman (22x18cm-9x7in) board painted c.1910. 26-Mar-2 SOGA, Bratislava #37/R (SL.K 38000)
£740 $1051 €1110 Winter landscape (36x39cm-14x15in) painted c.1910. 26-Mar-2 SOGA, Bratislava #35/R est:38000 (SL.K 47000)
£821 $1272 €1232 On balcony (75x81cm-30x32in) painted c.1910. 3-Dec-2 SOGA, Bratislava #31/R (SL.K 52000)
£914 $1297 €1371 Sitting woman (48x33cm-19x13in) painted c.1910. 26-Mar-2 SOGA, Bratislava #34/R est:58000 (SL.K 58000)
£1181 $1831 €1772 Judita and Edita, on walk (61x76cm-24x30in) painted c.1920. 1-Oct-2 SOGA, Bratislava #32/R est:75000 (SL.K 75000)
£1374 $2129 €2061 Market in Lucenec (35x47cm-14x19in) cardboard painted 1923. 3-Dec-2 SOGA, Bratislava #30/R est:78000 (SL.K 87000)
£1890 $2930 €2835 On the beach (60x72cm-24x28in) painted c.1910. 1-Oct-2 SOGA, Bratislava #31/R est:95000 (SL.K 120000)

MOUSSON, Viliam Euzeb (1914-) Czechoslovakian
£284 $440 €426 Bouquet of cherry flowers (82x90cm-32x35in) veneer painted c.1940. 3-Dec-2 SOGA, Bratislava #34/R (SL.K 18000)

MOUVAU, Cesar (?) ?
£308 $484 €450 Paysage de campagne (90x120cm-35x47in) s. 15-Apr-3 Galerie Moderne, Brussels #357

MOVALLI, Charles (20th C) American
£548 $850 €822 Winter landscape, with boat at shore edge and distant hills (102x102cm-40x40in) 3-Nov-2 Van Blarcom, South Natick #166
£796 $1250 €1194 Boatyard with boat tied to edge of dock with buildings (51x61cm-20x24in) s. 19-Apr-3 James Julia, Fairfield #264/R

MOY, Joseph (1905-1992) French
£12950 $20719 €18000 Spring, young man and shepherdess in a landscape (86x96cm-34x38in) indis.sig.d.1760 prov. 13-May-3 Christie's, Amsterdam #66/R est:10000-15000

MOYA Y CALVO, Victor (1884-1972) Spanish
£1678 $2701 €2500 Flower seller from Valencia (91x75cm-36x30in) s.d.1929. 18-Feb-3 Durán, Madrid #173/R
£2013 $3242 €3000 Flowers (90x75cm-35x30in) s.d.1929. 18-Feb-3 Durán, Madrid #172/R

MOYA, Victor (20th C) Spanish
£1702 $2757 €2400 Coqueteria (75x60cm-30x24in) s.d.1930 s.i.d.verso. 20-May-3 Segre, Madrid #263/R est:2100

MOYAUX, Constant (1835-1911) French
Works on paper
£1773 $2961 €2500 Athenes, vue du nord ouest (12x26cm-5x10in) s.i. W/C prov. 23-Jun-3 Beaussant & Lefèvre, Paris #66 est:500-600

MOYERS, John (1958-) American
£1299 $2000 €1949 Evening shadows (25x30cm-10x12in) 25-Oct-2 Morris & Whiteside, Hilton Head Island #30 est:2000-2500
£3333 $5200 €5000 Roberta (58x33cm-23x13in) 9-Nov-2 Altermann Galleries, Santa Fe #56
£7534 $11000 €11301 Tomasita's parrot pot (112x76cm-44x30in) 18-May-2 Altermann Galleries, Santa Fe #99/R
£8904 $13000 €13356 Dramatic sky (91x76cm-36x30in) 18-May-2 Altermann Galleries, Santa Fe #79/R
£9259 $15000 €13426 Songs of his ancestors (102x76cm-40x30in) 23-May-3 Altermann Galleries, Santa Fe #48
£10897 $17000 €16346 Winter above Taos (122x86cm-48x34in) 9-Nov-2 Altermann Galleries, Santa Fe #73

MOYERS, Terri Kelly (1953-) American
£3082 $4500 €4623 The road not taken (51x61cm-20x24in) 18-May-2 Altermann Galleries, Santa Fe #158/R
£4795 $7000 €7193 Yellow rocker (76x61cm-30x24in) 18-May-2 Altermann Galleries, Santa Fe #147/R
£13462 $21000 €20193 Santa Fe style (102x97cm-40x38in) 9-Nov-2 Altermann Galleries, Santa Fe #72

MOYERS, William (1916-1976) American
£1026 $1600 €1539 Seat warmer (58x74cm-23x29in) s. prov.lit. 9-Nov-2 Santa Fe Art, Santa Fe #180/R
£5556 $9000 €8056 Eye to eye (61x91cm-24x36in) 23-May-3 Altermann Galleries, Santa Fe #6
Sculpture
£1122 $1750 €1683 Bronc (28x28x38cm-11x11x15in) i. bronze prov.lit. 9-Nov-2 Santa Fe Art, Santa Fe #210/R est:1500-2500
£1562 $2530 €2265 Loser buys the drinks (36x23x48cm-14x9x19in) bronze. 23-May-3 Altermann Galleries, Santa Fe #124
£1775 $2875 €2574 Bronco (33cm-13in) bronze. 23-May-3 Altermann Galleries, Santa Fe #5

MOYES, Isabelle (20th C) American
Works on paper
£256 $400 €384 Circus (28x36cm-11x14in) W/C. 19-Oct-2 David Dike, Dallas #110/R

MOZERT, Zoe (1904-1993) American
Works on paper
£563 $900 €816 Seated scantily clad woman reading a newspaper (38x28cm-15x11in) s. pastel. 17-May-3 Selkirks, St. Louis #385/R
£938 $1500 €1360 How'd you like to hold my hand (38x28cm-15x11in) s. pastel. 17-May-3 Selkirks, St. Louis #386/R est:2000-3000

MOZIER, Joseph (1812-1870) American
Sculpture
£25806 $40000 €38709 Pocahontas (122cm-48in) i. white marble lit. 4-Dec-2 Sotheby's, New York #138/R est:25000-35000

MOZIN, Charles Louis (1806-1862) French
£2138 $3336 €3400 Fishing boats in choppy seas (107x149cm-42x59in) s.i. prov. 19-Sep-2 Dr Fritz Nagel, Stuttgart #972/R est:2500
£3459 $5362 €5500 Bateau de peche dans la tempete (83x113cm-33x44in) s.d.1859. 4-Oct-2 Tajan, Paris #177 est:1500-1800
Works on paper
£317 $500 €500 Vue de Nantes et d'Amiens (9x18cm-4x7in) i. crayon. 28-Nov-2 Tajan, Paris #199
£577 $894 €900 On the Mole (13x21cm-5x8in) s. prov. 7-Dec-2 Ketterer, Hamburg #13/R

MOZLEY, Charles (1914-1991) British
£250 $398 €363 Hespin, Normandy, town scene with figures (74x99cm-29x39in) s.d.78. 1-May-3 Amersham Auction Rooms, UK #233

MOZOS, Pedro (1915-1983) Spanish
Works on paper
£258 $408 €400 Dancer (45x29cm-18x11in) s. chl dr. 18-Dec-2 Ansorena, Madrid #427/R
£268 $432 €400 Couple at balcony (27x22cm-11x9in) s. W/C. 18-Feb-3 Durán, Madrid #51/R
£342 $534 €500 Orchestra (26x19cm-10x7in) s. pencil dr. 8-Apr-3 Ansorena, Madrid #683

MPETYANE, Arthur Turner (20th C) Australian
Works on paper
£600 $966 €900 Snake dreaming (129x130cm-51x51in) with sig.i. synthetic polymer paint on linen prov. 6-May-3 Christie's, Melbourne #324/R est:1200-1800 (A.D 1500)

MPUANGA, Liyolo Limbe (1943-) African
Sculpture
£993 $1619 €1500 Tete masque (45cm-18in) s. green pat bronze. 17-Feb-3 Horta, Bruxelles #112

MRKUSICH, Milan (1925-) New Zealander
£3521 $5810 €5105 Collage red (59x30cm-23x12in) s.i.d.1977 acrylic on card. 1-Jul-3 Peter Webb, Auckland #57/R est:7000-9000 (NZ.D 10000)
£5414 $8500 €8121 Painting purple (46x46cm-18x18in) s.d.1968 i.verso acrylic prov. 10-Dec-2 Peter Webb, Auckland #41/R est:15000-25000 (NZ.D 17000)
£16549 $27306 €23996 Four elements above (64x46cm-25x18in) s.d.1965 board. 1-Jul-3 Peter Webb, Auckland #34/R est:45000-65000 (NZ.D 47000)

MRKVICKA, Otakar (1898-?) Czechoslovakian
£1132 $1743 €1800 Untitled abstract still life (55x39cm-22x15in) mono.d.1927. 26-Oct-2 Dr Lehr, Berlin #370/R est:1200

MUBIN, Othon (1924-1981) Turkish
£411 $654 €617 Composition (100x100cm-39x39in) s.i.d.1960-61 verso. 26-Feb-3 Kunsthallen, Copenhagen #99 (D.KR 4500)
£709 $1184 €1000 Composition sur fond bleu (20x27cm-8x11in) s. 23-Jun-3 Claude Boisgirard, Paris #146/R
£1600 $2576 €2400 Abstract (162x130cm-64x51in) i.d.October 1963 sold with two others by the same hand. 14-Jan-3 Bonhams, Knightsbridge #49 est:400-600

MUCCI, Rosalba de (1942-) Italian
£253 $395 €400 Basket seller (50x40cm-20x16in) s. cardboard painted 1997. 14-Sep-2 Meeting Art, Vercelli #422
£316 $494 €500 Umbrella repair (30x40cm-12x16in) s. s.i.d.1977 verso. 14-Sep-2 Meeting Art, Vercelli #394
£443 $691 €700 Life swirl (70x80cm-28x31in) s. s.i.d.1985 verso. 14-Sep-2 Meeting Art, Vercelli #456

MUCHA, A (1860-1939) Czechoslovakian
Prints
£4783 $7843 €6600 Panonceau, flirt (64x30cm-25x12in) chromolithographie paper on cardboard exec.c.1901. 27-May-3 Artcurial Briest, Paris #135/R est:4500-5500
£7391 $12122 €10200 Panonceau, biscuit champagne (53x36cm-21x14in) chromolithographie paper on cardboard. 27-May-3 Artcurial Briest, Paris #109/R est:8000-9000
£7609 $12478 €10500 Panonceau, Sarah Bernhardt (72x53cm-28x21in) chromolithographie paper on cardboard. 27-May-3 Artcurial Briest, Paris #111/R est:5000-6000
£7754 $12716 €10700 Panonceau, Gaufrettes vanille (62x45cm-24x18in) chromolithographie paper on cardboard exec.c.1900. 27-May-3 Artcurial Briest, Paris #130/R est:7000-9000

MUCHA, Alphonse (1860-1939) Czechoslovakian
£2200 $3608 €3300 Contemplation (28x20cm-11x8in) s. panel prov. 3-Jun-3 Sotheby's, London #72/R est:2000-3000
£24359 $37756 €38000 Flowers (106x46cm-42x18in) s. lithograph on silk 4 parts. 3-Dec-2 Sotheby's, Paris #4/R est:15000-20000
£54348 $89130 €75000 Sarah Bernhardt (68x53cm-27x21in) s.d.1903 panel. 27-May-3 Artcurial Briest, Paris #110/R est:90000-110000
Prints
£1899 $3000 €3000 The Lily (104x43cm-41x17in) s.d.97 col lithograph lit. 26-Nov-2 Wiener Kunst Auktionen, Vienna #75/R est:3000-7000
£2025 $3200 €3200 Eclat du jour (101x36cm-40x14in) s.d.99 col lithograph board. 27-Nov-2 Dorotheum, Vienna #120/R est:2800-3800
£2532 $4000 €3798 Zdenka czerny (185x111cm-73x44in) col lithograph on two sheets. 22-Apr-3 Butterfields, San Francisco #2176/R est:4000-6000
£2564 $4000 €3846 Flirt biscuits lefevre utile (63x30cm-25x12in) print. 30-Mar-3 Butterfields, Los Angeles #1060/R est:2000-2500
£2692 $4200 €4038 Reading (64x46cm-25x18in) s. lithograph. 22-Sep-2 Susanin's, Chicago #5003/R est:1200-1500
£3521 $5669 €5000 Salon des Cent (64x43cm-25x17in) i. col lithograph. 10-May-3 Quittenbaum, Munich #153/R est:6000
£4032 $6250 €6048 Job, 1898 (148x100cm-58x39in) s. lithograph colour linen. 6-Dec-2 Sotheby's, New York #149/R est:6000-9000
£5806 $9000 €8709 Reverie, 1898 (64x50cm-25x20in) s. lithograph colour prov. 6-Dec-2 Sotheby's, New York #148/R est:600-9000
£5944 $9927 €8500 Tete Byzantine brune. Tete Byzantine blonde (54x37cm-21x15in) s. col lithograph pair. 25-Jun-3 Tajan, Paris #3/R est:8000-10000
Sculpture
£467742 $725000 €701613 La nature (69cm-27in) st.sig. patinated bronze lapis lazuli executed c.1900. 6-Dec-2 Sotheby's, New York #150/R est:400000-600000
Works on paper
£273 $425 €410 Woman's profile (10x8cm-4x3in) s.d.1897 graphite. 21-Sep-2 Rachel Davis, Shaker Heights #536
£273 $425 €410 Seated man (13x10cm-5x4in) s.d.1897 graphite. 21-Sep-2 Rachel Davis, Shaker Heights #535
£1266 $2000 €2000 Woman standing (11x8cm-4x3in) s. pencil. 29-Nov-2 Villa Grisebach, Berlin #817/R est:1500-1700
£1572 $2437 €2500 L'art, projection (50x69cm-20x27in) s. i.verso W/C col crayon graphite prov.lit. 30-Oct-2 Artcurial Briest, Paris #197/R est:2000-3000
£1613 $2500 €2420 Young woman, separate study of her hands embracing a man's head (48x34cm-19x13in) s. pencil black crayon on board prov.exhib. 29-Oct-2 Sotheby's, New York #106/R est:2000-3000
£1875 $3094 €2700 Patere (23x28cm-9x11in) s. W/C Indian ink gouache. 1-Jul-3 Claude Aguttes, Neuilly #114/R est:3000-3200
£2244 $3522 €3500 Portrait de femme (31x23cm-12x9in) s. crayon dr. 16-Dec-2 Rabourdin & Choppin de Janvry, Paris #14/R
£10000 $16400 €15000 Portrait of a girl (58x43cm-23x17in) s.i.d.1913 chl pastel prov. 3-Jun-3 Sotheby's, London #74/R est:10000-15000
£26000 $42640 €39000 Poppies (41x30cm-16x12in) s.i.d.1935 pastel prov. 3-Jun-3 Sotheby's, London #70/R est:20000-30000
£39130 $64174 €54000 Biscuits champagne (52x35cm-20x14in) s. W/C paper laid down. 27-May-3 Artcurial Briest, Paris #108/R est:65000-75000

MUCHA, Alphonse (attrib) (1860-1939) Czechoslovakian
Works on paper
£288 $450 €432 Figure of a woman (13x10cm-5x4in) s.d.1897 graphite. 21-Sep-2 Rachel Davis, Shaker Heights #533/R
£288 $450 €432 Seated man (15x15cm-6x6in) s.d.1897 graphite. 21-Sep-2 Rachel Davis, Shaker Heights #534/R

MUCHA, Willy (c.1920-) French
£530 $864 €800 Port vendres-collioure (40x90cm-16x35in) s. i.d.verso. 31-Jan-3 Charbonneaux, Paris #143

MUCHE, J F (19th C) German
£1282 $2000 €1923 Portrait of a young girl seated (79x64cm-31x25in) s.d.1870 prov. 14-Sep-2 Selkirks, St. Louis #729/R est:1000-1500

MUCKE, Carl Emil (1847-1923) German
£1731 $2683 €2700 The dance (42x35cm-17x14in) s.d.75. 5-Dec-2 Schopman, Hamburg #530 est:2300
£1918 $3011 €2800 In Gedanken (33x22cm-13x9in) s. panel. 15-Apr-3 Sotheby's, Amsterdam #91/R est:3000-5000
£5000 $7950 €7500 Grandfather's joy, a little girl dancing (46x58cm-18x23in) s.d.73. 20-Mar-3 Ewbank, Send #400/R est:3000-5000

MUCKLEY, William Jabez (1837-1905) British

Works on paper

£260 $400 €390 Still life with red and white grapes (32x25cm-13x10in) s.d.1873 W/C bodycol. 22-Oct-2 Bonhams, Knightsbridge #92/R

MUDIE, Charles F (fl.1900-1935) Australian

£597 $980 €896 Summer day, Sorrento (40x60cm-16x24in) s. i.verso canvas on board. 4-Jun-3 Deutscher-Menzies, Melbourne #318/R (A.D 1500)

MUDROCH, Jan (1909-1968) Czechoslovakian

£868 $1346 €1302 Nude sitting (33x45cm-13x18in) painted c.1938. 3-Dec-2 SOGA, Bratislava #75/R (SL.K 55000)
£2363 $3662 €3545 Unfinished chronicle (51x62cm-20x24in) glass. 1-Oct-2 SOGA, Bratislava #81/R est:150000 (SL.K 150000)
£2993 $4639 €4490 Still life with bunch of flowers. lemons and apples (31x39cm-12x15in) cardboard. 1-Oct-2 SOGA, Bratislava #79/R est:190000 (SL.K 190000)
£3386 $4944 €5079 Still life with apples (46x52cm-18x20in) 4-Jun-2 SOGA, Bratislava #84a/R est:145000 (SL.K 215000)
£4725 $7324 €7088 Bunch of flowers (65x50cm-26x20in) 1-Oct-2 SOGA, Bratislava #80/R est:160000 (SL.K 300000)

Works on paper

£394 $559 €591 Victim (20x34cm-8x13in) chl exec.c.1948. 26-Mar-2 SOGA, Bratislava #88/R (SL.K 25000)
£457 $649 €686 Reclining nude (45x59cm-18x23in) gouache exec.c.1938. 26-Mar-2 SOGA, Bratislava #87/R (SL.K 29000)

MUE, Maurice August del (1875-1955) American/French

£552 $900 €828 Cathedral Rocks, Yosemite (25x34cm-10x13in) s. paperboard. 16-Feb-3 Butterfields, San Francisco #2091

MUELLER, Henry (19/20th C) ?

£581 $900 €872 In the Luxembourg Gardens (46x36cm-18x14in) s. board painted c.1920. 8-Dec-2 Toomey, Oak Park #660/R

MUENIER, Jules Alexis (1863-1942) French

£1487 $2350 €2350 Marin assis sur le port (46x38cm-18x15in) s.d.1891. 1-Dec-2 Livinec, Gaudcheau & Jezequel, Rennes #84/R

MUGHAL SCHOOL, Asian

£5128 $8000 €7692 Portrait of a prince visiting Holy men (17x10cm-7x4in) i. s.Muhammad Ali verso. 27-Mar-3 Christie's, Rockefeller NY #204/R est:8000-12000

MUGHAL SCHOOL (16th C) Asian

£6410 $10000 €9615 Portrait of a royal youth and his tutor (14x9cm-6x4in) attributed to Jaganath. 27-Mar-3 Christie's, Rockefeller NY #206/R est:12000-15000

MUGUERZA, Jose Maria (1907-1985) Spanish

Works on paper

£345 $548 €500 Card players (33x48cm-13x19in) s. W/C. 4-Mar-3 Ansorena, Madrid #689/R

MUHEIM, Jost (1837-1919) Swiss

£611 $960 €917 In the mountains (84x116cm-33x46in) s.d.1872. 25-Nov-2 Germann, Zurich #141/R (S.FR 1400)
£987 $1560 €1481 Farmer's wife with cows in the meadow and inner Swiss landscape in background (67x103cm-26x41in) s.verso. 29-Nov-2 Zofingen, Switzerland #2997/R est:3000 (S.FR 2300)

MUHL, Otto (1924-) Russian

£396 $633 €550 Female nude (45x31cm-18x12in) s.d.20.8.82 oil chk. 15-May-3 Neumeister, Munich #492/R
£414 $654 €600 Abstract composition (31x24cm-12x9in) s. acrylic. 4-Apr-3 Venator & Hansten, Koln #1932
£612 $978 €850 Head (44x30cm-17x12in) d.17.8.82 oil chk. 14-May-3 Dorotheum, Klagenfurt #67
£2837 $4596 €4000 Super Gau (100x80cm-39x31in) s.i.d.8.4.96 acrylic. 20-May-3 Dorotheum, Vienna #297/R est:5000-8000
£3481 $5500 €5500 Christophorus (130x71cm-51x28in) acrylic prov. 27-Nov-2 Dorotheum, Vienna #349/R est:8000-10000
£3716 $5797 €5500 Vincent (89x69cm-35x27in) s.i.d.3.4.87 verso acrylic board on panel. 25-Mar-3 Wiener Kunst Auktionen, Vienna #26/R est:5500-9000

Works on paper

£360 $576 €500 Head (42x28cm-17x11in) s.d.26.8.85 W/C. 14-May-3 Dorotheum, Klagenfurt #48
£396 $633 €550 Woman (32x44cm-13x17in) s.d.21.8.85 gouache pencil. 15-May-3 Neumeister, Munich #494/R
£468 $767 €650 Head (44x30cm-17x12in) s.d.85 ink W/C. 5-Jun-3 Dorotheum, Salzburg #897/R
£576 $921 €800 Claudia (42x28cm-17x11in) s.i.d.14.8.85 W/C. 14-May-3 Dorotheum, Klagenfurt #47
£577 $894 €900 Couple with umbrella (27x37cm-11x15in) s.d.10.12.85 chl W/C. 5-Dec-2 Dorotheum, Graz #125
£769 $1192 €1200 Pianist (27x37cm-11x15in) s.d.5.12.85 chl W/C. 5-Dec-2 Dorotheum, Graz #124/R
£897 $1434 €1300 Untitled (59x85cm-23x33in) d.21.11.83 mixed media. 11-Mar-3 Dorotheum, Vienna #241/R
£1899 $2943 €3000 Untitled (86x60cm-34x24in) s.d.2.3.96 mixed media. 24-Sep-2 Wiener Kunst Auktionen, Vienna #320/R est:4000-7000

MUHL, Roger (1929-) French

£451 $713 €650 Paysage (19x34cm-7x13in) s. 28-Apr-3 Cornette de St.Cyr, Paris #287/R
£676 $1054 €1000 Nature morte a la bouteille (50x53cm-20x21in) s. 28-Mar-3 Claude Aguttes, Neuilly #138
£764 $1192 €1200 Vase de fleurs (41x33cm-16x13in) s. 10-Nov-2 Eric Pillon, Calais #271/R
£845 $1403 €1200 La plaine au printemps (119x130cm-47x51in) s. i.verso. 11-Jun-3 Beaussant & Lefèvre, Paris #105
£979 $1635 €1400 Printemps (50x53cm-20x21in) s. 25-Jun-3 Claude Aguttes, Neuilly #50
£1007 $1612 €1400 Nu assis (80x85cm-31x33in) s. 18-May-3 Eric Pillon, Calais #155/R
£1800 $2844 €2700 Eggalieres (39x46cm-15x18in) s. painted 1962 exhib. 3-Apr-3 Christie's, Kensington #193/R
£2452 $3800 €3678 Nature morte aux fruits (63x79cm-25x31in) s. s.i.d.1961 verso prov. 26-Sep-2 Christie's, Rockefeller NY #552/R est:3000-5000

MUHLBECK, Joseph (1878-1948) German

£286 $426 €440 Dachau landscape (18x24cm-7x9in) s.i. board. 27-Jun-2 Neumeister, Munich #2792

MUHLENHAUPT, Kurt (1921-) German

£295 $466 €460 Blucherstrasse (43x25cm-17x10in) mono.d.1969. 14-Nov-2 Neumeister, Munich #637/R

Works on paper

£314 $484 €500 Robel an der Muritz (50x64cm-20x25in) s.i.d.1981 W/C over biro board. 26-Oct-2 Dr Lehr, Berlin #373/R

MUHLFIELD, Charles O (20th C) American

£621 $1000 €932 Showgirls in feathered outfits with long black gloves (102x76cm-40x30in) s. 20-Feb-3 Illustration House, New York #121/R est:2000-4000

MUHLHAN, Adolf (1886-?) German

£255 $400 €383 Ewer und hapag Lloyd Dampfer vor Blankenese, coastal view (35x50cm-14x20in) s.i. panel. 22-Nov-2 Skinner, Boston #140/R
£414 $650 €621 See ewer auf der unterelbe - off the coast (35x50cm-14x20in) s.i. panel. 22-Nov-2 Skinner, Boston #142/R

MUHLIG, Albert Ernst (1862-?) German

£1027 $1603 €1500 Peasant woman in kitchen (28x28cm-11x11in) s.d. 5/5 86 board on canvas. 10-Apr-3 Dorotheum, Vienna #164/R est:1800-2200

MUHLIG, Bernard (1829-1910) German

£283 $442 €450 Countryside near Dresden with figures (9x15cm-4x6in) board. 9-Oct-2 Michael Zeller, Lindau #831/R
£897 $1391 €1400 Romantic Swiss mountain landscape with cattle (16x26cm-6x10in) s. lit. 7-Dec-2 Bergmann, Erlangen #774/R
£962 $1490 €1500 Elbe landscape (17x27cm-7x11in) s. lit. 7-Dec-2 Bergmann, Erlangen #776/R est:1500
£1361 $2163 €2000 View from mountain pasture of extensive river valley (18x31cm-7x12in) mono. i. stretcher. 19-Mar-3 Neumeister, Munich #666/R est:2100

MUHLIG, Hugo (1854-1929) German

£1282 $1949 €2000 Extensive landscape with peasants ploughing (17x33cm-7x13in) s. canvas on panel. 17-Aug-2 Hans Stahl, Toestorf #47/R
£2014 $3223 €2800 Lower Rhine landscape (17x25cm-7x10in) s. board. 17-May-3 Lempertz, Koln #1447/R est:3000
£2089 $3300 €3300 Homebound hunter (18x17cm-7x7in) s. panel. 29-Nov-2 Bolland & Marotz, Bremen #744/R est:1600
£5036 $8058 €7000 Summer landscape with windmill (20x27cm-8x11in) s. i. verso board prov. 17-May-3 Lempertz, Koln #1444/R est:8000
£33813 $54101 €47000 After the autumn hunt (61x80cm-24x31in) 17-May-3 Lempertz, Koln #1445/R est:20000

Works on paper

£1056 $1754 €1500 Beach with donkeys and walkers (19x27cm-7x11in) s. gouache W/C. 14-Jun-3 Arnold, Frankfurt #819/R est:1400

£1370 $2137 €2000 Old peasant woman in courtyard entrance (29x22cm-11x9in) s.d.24 W/C. 10-Apr-3 Van Ham, Cologne #1603 est:1000

MUHLIG, Meno (1823-1873) German
£481 $755 €750 Abduction of the Princess (43x33cm-17x13in) s. 21-Nov-2 Van Ham, Cologne #1803/R
£621 $1018 €950 Hilltop bivouac (25x36cm-10x14in) s. 29-Mar-3 Dannenberg, Berlin #626/R

MUHLMANN, Joseph (1805-1865) German
Works on paper
£284 $443 €426 Two Italien girls (21x18cm-8x7in) s.i.d.1842 gouache W/C mixed media prov. 9-Nov-2 Galerie Gloggner, Luzern #101/R (S.FR 650)

MUHLSTOCK, Louis (1904-2001) Canadian
£193 $302 €290 Laurentians (16x20cm-6x8in) s. isorel. 25-Mar-3 Iegor de Saint Hippolyte, Montreal #99 (C.D 450)
£1317 $2041 €1976 Lane in Montreal (75x65cm-30x26in) s. exhib. 3-Dec-2 Joyner, Toronto #221/R est:1000-1500 (C.D 3200)
Works on paper
£309 $478 €464 Reclining female nude (62x48cm-24x19in) s. ink pastel exhib. 3-Dec-2 Joyner, Toronto #370 (C.D 750)
£323 $526 €485 Portrait of a man (44x34cm-17x13in) s. chl. 12-Feb-3 Iegor de Saint Hippolyte, Montreal #140 (C.D 800)
£413 $649 €620 Sleeping nude (66x53cm-26x21in) s. dr. executed c.1960. 24-Jul-2 Walker's, Ottawa #415/R est:1200-1600 (C.D 1000)

MUHRMAN, Henry (1854-1916) American
Works on paper
£350 $550 €525 Male dancers (38x28cm-15x11in) ink wash. 13-Dec-2 Du Mouchelle, Detroit #2185/R

MUIJSENBERG, Toon van den (1901-1967) Dutch
£704 $1134 €1000 Still life with bottle, book and pipe (49x39cm-19x15in) s.d.42 exhib. 7-May-3 Vendue Huis, Gravenhage #525/R
£1316 $2132 €2000 View on a church (100x75cm-39x30in) s. 21-Jan-3 Christie's, Amsterdam #484/R est:1500-2000

MUIR, Anne Davidson (?-1951) British
£600 $936 €900 Flowers of summer (45x35cm-18x14in) s. canvasboard exhib. 10-Oct-2 Bonhams, Edinburgh #334

MUIR, James Nathan (1945-) American
Sculpture
£781 $1265 €1132 Through shot and shell (46x56x36cm-18x22x14in) bronze. 23-May-3 Altermann Galleries, Santa Fe #129
£1065 $1725 €1544 Black horse (25x33cm-10x13in) bronze. 23-May-3 Altermann Galleries, Santa Fe #99
£1207 $1955 €1750 Whitworth sharpshooter (18cm-7in) bronze. 23-May-3 Altermann Galleries, Santa Fe #131
£1233 $1800 €1850 Southern steel II (33cm-13in) one of 25 bronze. 18-May-2 Altermann Galleries, Santa Fe #172/R
£1370 $2000 €2055 In Tierce Point (25x41cm-10x16in) one of 30 bronze. 18-May-2 Altermann Galleries, Santa Fe #171/R
£1370 $2000 €2055 The Texan (30x30cm-12x12in) one of 30 bronze. 18-May-2 Altermann Galleries, Santa Fe #173/R
£1775 $2875 €2574 Letter from home (43cm-17in) bronze. 23-May-3 Altermann Galleries, Santa Fe #130
£3205 $5000 €4808 Rescue under fire (58x64cm-23x25in) bronze. 9-Nov-2 Altermann Galleries, Santa Fe #170
£6389 $10350 €9264 Rescue under fire (58x64cm-23x25in) bronze. 23-May-3 Altermann Galleries, Santa Fe #127
£9877 $16000 €14322 June 25, 1876 (66cm-26in) bronze. 23-May-3 Altermann Galleries, Santa Fe #128

MUIRHEAD, David (1867-1930) British
£385 $600 €578 Mill (15x20cm-6x8in) s. board. 20-Oct-2 Susanin's, Chicago #5084/R
£565 $892 €848 Figure in pasture with church in distance (43x72cm-17x28in) s.d.1919. 18-Nov-2 Waddingtons, Toronto #178/R (C.D 1400)
£740 $1162 €1110 Portrait of a girl in a red dress (67x49cm-26x19in) 17-Apr-3 Bonhams, Edinburgh #387
£1200 $1956 €1800 Stonehaven (63x75cm-25x30in) 14-Feb-3 Lyon & Turnbull, Edinburgh #10

MUIRHEAD, John (1863-1927) British
£634 $1020 €900 Polder landscape (46x56cm-18x22in) s. 7-May-3 Vendue Huis, Gravenhage #176/R

MULAS, Franco (1938-) Italian
£1090 $1711 €1700 Roman landscape (84x98cm-33x39in) s. s.i.d.1988 verso board. 21-Nov-2 Finarte, Rome #67/R

MULCAHY, Michael (1952-) Irish
£324 $538 €460 Traitors dance (76x51cm-30x20in) s. 10-Jun-3 James Adam, Dublin #104/R
£633 $981 €1000 Coastal landscape (71x68cm-28x27in) s. 24-Sep-2 De Veres Art Auctions, Dublin #151 est:1000-2000
£881 $1374 €1400 Ch'uksoam XII (91x76cm-36x30in) s.d.1994 s.verso prov. 17-Sep-2 Whyte's, Dublin #94/R
£1026 $1610 €1600 Female reclining on a bed (64x91cm-25x36in) s.d.1981 verso. 19-Nov-2 Whyte's, Dublin #178/R est:1200-1500
£1218 $1912 €1900 Untitled (122x152cm-48x60in) s. 19-Nov-2 Whyte's, Dublin #172/R est:2500-3000
£1268 $2104 €1800 Vaira (130x162cm-51x64in) s. 10-Jun-3 James Adam, Dublin #92/R est:2000-3000
£1389 $2208 €2000 Chuk'soam. Headland (76x91cm-30x36in) s.i.d.1994 verso. 29-Apr-3 Whyte's, Dublin #147/R est:2000-3000
£1667 $2650 €2400 Flower (51x61cm-20x24in) s. s.i.verso. 29-Apr-3 Whyte's, Dublin #148/R est:1200-1500
£2308 $3623 €3600 Keyhole (51x76cm-20x30in) paper six. 19-Nov-2 Whyte's, Dublin #168 est:3500-4500
£2949 $4629 €4600 Islands 9 (132x165cm-52x65in) s. s.d.1998 verso exhib. 19-Nov-2 Whyte's, Dublin #167/R est:4000-5000
Works on paper
£510 $795 €800 Abstract (70x99cm-28x39in) s.d.1996 gouache. 6-Nov-2 James Adam, Dublin #159/R
£685 $1075 €1000 Island series (45x65cm-18x26in) s. mixed media prov. 15-Apr-3 De Veres Art Auctions, Dublin #59/R est:1000-1500
£685 $1075 €1000 Warriors song (56x75cm-22x30in) s. mixed media prov. 15-Apr-3 De Veres Art Auctions, Dublin #98 est:1000-1500
£981 $1521 €1550 Camping out at the weekend (56x76cm-22x30in) s.d.1984 mixed media. 24-Sep-2 De Veres Art Auctions, Dublin #140/R est:1000-2000

MULDER, A R (1903-1971) American
£541 $850 €812 Setter on point (61x91cm-24x36in) s. 14-Dec-2 Weschler, Washington #653/R

MULDERS, Camille van (1868-1949) Belgian
Works on paper
£449 $696 €700 Vase de cuivre fleuri de roses (75x40cm-30x16in) s. pastel. 9-Dec-2 Horta, Bruxelles #329

MULDERS, Jean (1913-) Belgian
£949 $1481 €1500 Marchand et son ane (100x74cm-39x29in) s. 16-Sep-2 Horta, Bruxelles #122 est:2000-3000

MULDERS, Marc (1958-) Dutch
£3165 $5000 €5000 Stilleven VI (150x100cm-59x39in) s.i.d.1988 verso. 26-Nov-2 Sotheby's, Amsterdam #301/R est:5000-7000

MULHAUPT, Frederick J (1871-1938) American
£1899 $3000 €2849 Landscape (28x41cm-11x16in) s. i.verso. 24-Apr-3 Shannon's, Milford #200/R est:2000-3000
£5975 $9500 €8963 Winter landscape (66x91cm-26x36in) s.d.1912. 7-Mar-3 Skinner, Boston #458/R est:3000-5000
£48387 $75000 €72581 Gloucester Harbour (63x76cm-25x30in) s. prov. 4-Dec-2 Sotheby's, New York #47/R est:60000-80000

MULHOLLAND, Craig (1969-) British
£600 $936 €900 Portrait of Peter McCaughey (46x35cm-18x14in) init. 17-Oct-2 Bonhams, Edinburgh #37/R

MULHOLLAND, Henry (1962-) Australian
£245 $382 €425 Untitled (137x168cm-54x66in) s. 31-Mar-3 Goodman, Sydney #161 (A.D 650)
£491 $765 €849 Untitled (175x175cm-69x69in) s.d.April 1992 verso prov. 31-Mar-3 Goodman, Sydney #69 (A.D 1300)
£535 $846 €803 Morning mist III (152x182cm-60x72in) s.i.d.1996. 27-Nov-2 Deutscher-Menzies, Melbourne #162/R est:2000-3000 (A.D 1500)
£566 $883 €981 Rhythms of a burnt bush (183x152cm-72x60in) s.verso prov. 31-Mar-3 Goodman, Sydney #114 (A.D 1500)
£660 $1030 €1143 Jack Klompe (238x118cm-94x46in) board prov. 31-Mar-3 Goodman, Sydney #157/R (A.D 1750)
£1018 $1589 €1764 Pool crossing (155x270cm-61x106in) i.d.1990 verso prov. 31-Mar-3 Goodman, Sydney #112 (A.D 2700)

MULHOLLAND, S A (19th C) British
Works on paper
£385 $600 €578 Venetian scene with sailboats and buildings on the canal (41x56cm-16x22in) s.d.1905 W/C. 18-Sep-2 Alderfer's, Hatfield #250/R

MULHOLLAND, Sydney A (19th C) British
Works on paper
£446 $700 €669 Coastal landscape with boats and figures (25x56cm-10x22in) s. W/C. 20-Nov-2 Boos Gallery, Michigan #418/R

MULHOLLAND, Sydney A (attrib) (19th C) British
£4400 $7084 €6600 Towards the Bascilica of Santa Maria della Salute, Venice (73x124cm-29x49in) indis sig. 6-May-3 Christie's, Melbourne #130/R est:12000-15000 (A.D 11000)

MULIER, Pieter (circle) (17th C) Dutch
£8966 $14345 €13000 Tobias aand the angel (86x126cm-34x50in) 17-Mar-3 Pandolfini, Florence #656/R est:6000
£8966 $14345 €13000 Moses saved from the river (86x126cm-34x50in) 17-Mar-3 Pandolfini, Florence #655/R est:6000

MULIER, Pieter (younger) (1637-1701) Dutch
£2600 $4030 €3900 Deluge with animals on a rocky promontory (28x34cm-11x13in) 6-Dec-2 Lyon & Turnbull, Edinburgh #12/R est:3000-4000
£7693 $12847 €11000 La rencontre du Christ et de St Jean Baptiste sur le Jourdain (140x112cm-55x44in) prov. 25-Jun-3 Tajan, Paris #37/R est:10000-12000
£14388 $23022 €20000 Pastoral landscape with shepherds and sheep (99x73cm-39x29in) 13-May-3 Sotheby's, Amsterdam #73/R est:20000-30000

MULIER, Pieter (younger-attrib) (1637-1701) Dutch
£25641 $39744 €40000 Landscape with figures nd ruins (124x168cm-49x66in) 4-Dec-2 Christie's, Rome #415/R est:20000-30000

MULIERE, Claude (20th C) French
£276 $439 €400 In the orchard (40x30cm-16x12in) s. panel. 10-Mar-3 Sotheby's, Amsterdam #363

MULINARI, Stefano (attrib) (c.1741-1790) Italian
Works on paper
£577 $912 €900 Jesus and the Apostles (30x41cm-12x16in) sepia ink dr. 14-Nov-2 Arte, Seville #197/R

MULKENS, Jose (?) ?
£621 $993 €900 Nature morte au vase fleuri et a une coupe de fraises (80x82cm-31x32in) 17-Mar-3 Amberes, Antwerp #237

MULLER, Albert (1897-1926) Swiss
£944 $1492 €1416 Female nude (39x27cm-15x11in) chl pencil. 26-Nov-2 Hans Widmer, St Gallen #1290/R est:2000-3500 (S.FR 2200)
£1019 $1640 €1478 Obino (16x18cm-6x7in) oilstick dr prov. 9-May-3 Dobiaschofsky, Bern #225/R (S.FR 2200)
£3704 $5963 €5371 Landscape with village (36x50cm-14x20in) mono. prov.lit. 9-May-3 Dobiaschofsky, Bern #155/R est:7500 (S.FR 8000)
£7971 $13072 €11000 Sunrise (71x63cm-28x25in) s.d.17 oil sketch verso prov.exhib.lit. 31-May-3 Villa Grisebach, Berlin #218/R est:7000-9000
£184549 $291588 €276824 Veglione a Mendrisio (150x115cm-59x45in) s.d.26 prov.exhib.lit. 28-Nov-2 Christie's, Zurich #82/R est:180000-250000 (S.FR 430000)

Works on paper
£601 $949 €902 Anna, portrait of the artist's wife (21x17cm-8x7in) pencil chk. 29-Nov-2 Zofingen, Switzerland #3001 (S.FR 1400)
£644 $1017 €966 Tessin village with church (17x22cm-7x9in) Indian ink chk. 28-Nov-2 Christie's, Zurich #81/R (S.FR 1500)
£648 $1044 €972 The twins Judith and Kaspar (33x50cm-13x20in) Indian ink. 7-May-3 Dobiaschofsky, Bern #1803/R (S.FR 1400)
£1073 $1695 €1610 Self-portrait (24x19cm-9x7in) chl pencil. 26-Nov-2 Hans Widmer, St Gallen #1289 est:2000-3800 (S.FR 2500)
£1322 $1969 €1983 Family on balcony (33x38cm-13x15in) W/C over pencil. 25-Jun-2 Koller, Zurich #6610/R est:1000-1500 (S.FR 3000)

MULLER, Andreas (1831-1901) German
Works on paper
£563 $935 €800 Portrait of Carl Muller (17x15cm-7x6in) s.i. pencil. 12-Jun-3 Hauswedell & Nolte, Hamburg #376/R

MULLER, Anton (1853-1897) Austrian
Works on paper
£507 $791 €750 Tiefe Graben, Vienna (40x30cm-16x12in) s. W/C. 28-Mar-3 Dorotheum, Vienna #329/R

MULLER, August (1836-1885) German
£377 $588 €550 St Cecilia (64cm-25in circular) s.d.1867 board. 10-Apr-3 Van Ham, Cologne #1606

MULLER, Carl Wilhelm (1839-1904) German
Works on paper
£1200 $2004 €1740 Church of Santa Maria Assunta at Castello Gragnano, near Naples (38x31cm-15x12in) s. graphite W/C scratching out set of three. 8-Jul-3 Christie's, London #19/R est:700-1000

MULLER, Charles Louis (1815-1892) French
£5280 $8500 €7920 Girl in landscape (94x66cm-37x26in) s. prov. 15-Jan-3 Boos Gallery, Michigan #582/R est:12000-15000

MULLER, Charles Louis (attrib) (1815-1892) French
£7143 $11000 €10715 La Ronde du Mai (121x77cm-48x30in) 4-Sep-2 Christie's, Rockefeller NY #309/R est:7000-9000

MULLER, Dan (1888-1976) American
£2293 $3600 €3440 Cowboy sport (74x58cm-29x23in) s. i.verso. 23-Nov-2 Jackson's, Cedar Falls #66/R est:2500-3500
£2420 $3800 €3630 Two ponies for little fawn (61x76cm-24x30in) s. i.verso. 23-Nov-2 Jackson's, Cedar Falls #67/R est:2500-3000

MULLER, E (20th C) German
£1204 $1938 €1806 Matterhorn in summer (150x102cm-59x40in) s.d.1894. 7-May-3 Dobiaschofsky, Bern #3466/R est:1200 (S.FR 2600)

MULLER, Edmund Gustavus (fl.1836-1871) British
£5500 $8745 €8250 Ferry. At the eel trap (30x23cm-12x9in) s.d.1852 panel on board pair prov. 6-Mar-3 Christie's, Kensington #427/R est:6000-8000

MULLER, Eduard Josef (1851-1922) German
£692 $1079 €1100 Moor landscape with deer (43x73cm-17x29in) s.d.1919 board. 11-Oct-2 Winterberg, Heidelberg #656/R

MULLER, Emma von (1859-1925) Austrian
£952 $1514 €1400 Tyrolean girl (25x20cm-10x8in) s. board. 19-Mar-3 Neumeister, Munich #668 est:800
£1069 $1668 €1700 Portrait of young girl in traditional costume (55x45cm-22x18in) s.d.1902 prov. 19-Sep-2 Dr Fritz Nagel, Stuttgart #974/R
£1266 $1962 €2000 Young peasant man in traditional costume and hat (24x18cm-9x7in) s. panel. 25-Sep-2 Neumeister, Munich #672/R est:1000

MULLER, Erich Martin (1888-1972) German
£535 $834 €850 Figures in old town street (64x82cm-25x32in) s.i.d.1912. 21-Sep-2 Dannenberg, Berlin #583/R
£868 $1346 €1302 Flowers in a vase (80x58cm-31x23in) painted c.1950. 3-Dec-2 SOGA, Bratislava #155/R (SL.K 55000)
£1071 $1521 €1607 Flowers in a vase (80x58cm-31x23in) painted c.1950. 26-Mar-2 SOGA, Bratislava #167/R est:33000 (SL.K 68000)

MULLER, Ernst Emmanuel (1844-1915) German
£1197 $1927 €1700 Two musicians playing flute and oboe (37x32cm-15x13in) s. 7-May-3 Michael Zeller, Lindau #847/R est:1700

MULLER, Eva (?) German
£377 $589 €600 Girl (20x15cm-8x6in) i. 23-Sep-2 Dr Fritz Nagel, Stuttgart #7039/R

MULLER, F (19th C) German?
£652 $1017 €978 Deer grazing by wood (28x55cm-11x22in) s.d.1884. 16-Sep-2 Philippe Schuler, Zurich #6477 (S.FR 1500)
Works on paper
£340 $541 €500 Castle on the Flakenstein near Pfronten (13x17cm-5x7in) s.d.1870 W/C sketch verso sold with another W/C. 20-Mar-3 Neumeister, Munich #2504/R

MULLER, Franz Wilhelm (18/19th C) German
Works on paper
£704 $1169 €1000 Le palais de la Seigneurie a Florence (22x33cm-9x13in) s.d.1810 black crayon W/C. 13-Jun-3 Rossini, Paris #78/R

MULLER, Friedrich Wilhelm (18/19th C) German
£961 $1499 €1442 Thun lake with Hunegg castle (36x48cm-14x19in) s.d.1866 board. 8-Nov-2 Dobiaschofsky, Bern #22/R (S.FR 2200)

MULLER, Fritz (19th C) German
£350 $550 €525 Good vintage (29x23cm-11x9in) s.i. board sold with two oils by same hand. 16-Apr-3 Christie's, Kensington #801
£460 $731 €690 Cellarman (28x22cm-11x9in) board. 18-Mar-3 Bonhams, Sevenoaks #191

£800 $1256 €1200 Good joke. Tyroleans reading the news (50x60cm-20x24in) s.i two. 16-Apr-3 Christie's, Kensington #799/R
£1322 $1930 €1983 Winter mountain landscape (60x80cm-24x31in) s.d.1926. 17-Jun-2 Philippe Schuler, Zurich #7432 est:1000-1500 (S.FR 3000)
£5921 $9000 €8882 US Naval frigate (51x76cm-20x30in) s. 17-Aug-2 North East Auctions, Portsmouth #860/R

MULLER, Georg Friedrich (1708-1792) German
£1509 $2355 €2400 Still life (25x34cm-10x13in) i.d.1841 lit. 20-Sep-2 Schloss Ahlden, Ahlden #1206/R est:1900

MULLER, Gerrit (1779-1826) Dutch
£1096 $1710 €1600 Dutch landscape with farmstead by water (36x49cm-14x19in) s. 10-Apr-3 Van Ham, Cologne #1618/R est:2000

MULLER, Hans (?) German
Sculpture
£962 $1510 €1500 Medieval hunter on horseback (47cm-19in) i. brown pat.bronze. 11-Dec-2 Dorotheum, Vienna #164/R est:1500-2000

MULLER, Heinrich (1885-1960) Swiss
£330 $528 €495 Still life with camellias (35x28cm-14x11in) s.d. 17-Mar-3 Philippe Schuler, Zurich #8466 (S.FR 700)
£1415 $2292 €2052 Orchids (79x64cm-31x25in) s.d.1929. 26-May-3 Sotheby's, Zurich #114/R est:3000-5000 (S.FR 3000)

MULLER, Heinrich (1903-1978) Swiss
£326 $509 €489 Interior with still life (46x26cm-18x10in) mono.d.1965 masonite. 16-Sep-2 Philippe Schuler, Zurich #3394 (S.FR 750)
£652 $1017 €978 Girl with wine carafe (80x79cm-31x31in) s.d.1932 i. verso. 16-Sep-2 Philippe Schuler, Zurich #3393 est:2000-2500 (S.FR 1500)
£687 $1085 €1031 An outraged woman and a calm figure standing behind her (120x90cm-47x35in) s.d.30. 26-Nov-2 Hans Widmer, St Gallen #1292 est:1400-3400 (S.FR 1600)
£2402 $3507 €3603 Girl with guitar (120x100cm-47x39in) s.d.1932 s.i.d. verso. 4-Jun-2 Germann, Zurich #98/R est:2000-3000 (S.FR 5500)

MULLER, Jacques (1930-) Belgian
£926 $1315 €1500 Paris, Grands Boulevards (24x33cm-9x13in) s. 16-Mar-3 Eric Pillon, Calais #212/R

MULLER, Jakob (attrib) (19th C) Swiss
£377 $604 €566 Children playing in front of house (46x37cm-18x15in) s.d. 17-Mar-3 Philippe Schuler, Zurich #8467 (S.FR 800)

MULLER, Jan (1922-1958) American
£28481 $45000 €42722 Virgins (122x192cm-48x76in) painted 1957 prov.exhib. 14-Nov-2 Christie's, Rockefeller NY #118/R est:15000-20000

MULLER, Jan Harmensz (c.1571-1628) Dutch
Prints
£2013 $3200 €3020 Apollo killing the serpent python (45x34cm-18x13in) engraving. 1-May-3 Swann Galleries, New York #196/R est:4000-6000
£3500 $5425 €5250 Raising of Lazarus (37x49cm-15x19in) engraving executed c.1600 after A. Bloemaert. 5-Dec-2 Sotheby's, London #22/R est:4000-6000

Works on paper
£18919 $29514 €28000 Prophet Elija fed by crows (17x21cm-7x8in) i. pen ink wash htd white prov.lit. 27-Mar-3 Christie's, Paris #48/R est:30000

MULLER, Jan Jakub (1780-1828) Czechoslovakian
Works on paper
£646 $943 €969 View of the High Tatras (35x47cm-14x19in) gouache W/C pencil. 4-Jun-2 SOGA, Bratislava #24/R est:35000 (SL.K 41000)

MULLER, Johann Georg (1913-1986) German
£9615 $15192 €15000 Flowers (64x78cm-25x31in) s. 14-Nov-2 Neumeister, Munich #841/R est:15000-16000
£14493 $23768 €20000 Mother and child (100x84cm-39x33in) s.d.80 bears i.d. verso panel. 31-May-3 Villa Grisebach, Berlin #359/R est:20000-30000
£24051 $38000 €38000 Interieur rouge (95x115cm-37x45in) s.d.1967 mono.i. verso exhib. 30-Nov-2 Villa Grisebach, Berlin #363/R est:35000-45000

Works on paper
£5755 $9209 €8000 Couple (63x75cm-25x30in) s.d. Indian ink col pen paper on board. 15-May-3 Neumeister, Munich #495/R est:8000-10000
£5755 $9209 €8000 Figural composition (63x76cm-25x30in) mono.d. Indian ink col pen. 15-May-3 Neumeister, Munich #496/R est:8000-10000

MULLER, Johann Gotthard von (1747-1830) German
Works on paper
£755 $1170 €1200 Male nude (53x35cm-21x14in) s. chl. 1-Oct-2 Dorotheum, Vienna #127/R

MULLER, Johann Marius Hartmann (1863-1945) Norwegian
£433 $662 €650 From a cheese farm (51x64cm-20x25in) s. painted 1931 exhib. 26-Aug-2 Blomqvist, Lysaker #1275/R (N.KR 5000)

MULLER, Johannes (19/20th C) German?
£3974 $6199 €5961 Peasants with cows (16x22cm-6x9in) paper. 6-Nov-2 Hans Widmer, St Gallen #81/R est:7000-12000 (S.FR 9100)
£6987 $10969 €10481 Trip to the mountain pastures (19x28cm-7x11in) tempera gold bronze board. 25-Nov-2 Sotheby's, Zurich #33/R est:7000-9000 (S.FR 16000)

MULLER, Josef Felix (1955-) Swiss
Works on paper
£568 $829 €852 Untitled (99x64cm-39x25in) s.d.1986 verso W/C. 4-Jun-2 Germann, Zurich #810/R (S.FR 1300)
£568 $829 €852 Untitled (99x64cm-39x25in) s.d.1986 verso W/C. 4-Jun-2 Germann, Zurich #811 (S.FR 1300)
£568 $829 €852 Untitled (99x64cm-39x25in) s.d.1986 verso W/C. 4-Jun-2 Germann, Zurich #812 (S.FR 1300)

MULLER, Karl (1818-1893) German
£775 $1286 €1100 Tower with shrine (22x20cm-9x8in) s.i. 12-Jun-3 Hauswedell & Nolte, Hamburg #377/R

MULLER, Karl Erich (1917-) German
£556 $878 €800 Farmstead in Dierhagen (53x62cm-21x24in) s.d.1953 i.d. verso panel. 26-Apr-3 Dr Lehr, Berlin #383/R
£629 $969 €1000 Seated figures (40x50cm-16x20in) s. 26-Oct-2 Dr Lehr, Berlin #378/R

MULLER, Leopold Carl (1834-1892) German
£2692 $4227 €4200 Portrait of young Egyptian woman (63x51cm-25x20in) s.d. lit. 25-Nov-2 Hassfurther, Vienna #57/R est:4000-6000
£3191 $5170 €4500 Indecisive traveller (66x52cm-26x20in) s. 22-May-3 Dorotheum, Vienna #154/R est:5000-6500

MULLER, M (19th C) ?
£419 $624 €629 Still life of flowers with bottle on cloth (35x41cm-14x16in) s.d.1925 board. 25-Jun-2 Koller, Zurich #6594 (S.FR 950)
£2201 $3390 €3500 Chasse au tigre (56x74cm-22x29in) s.i.d.1894. 23-Oct-2 Rabourdin & Choppin de Janvry, Paris #190/R

MULLER, Maria (1847-?) Austrian
£4082 $6490 €6000 Portrait of an African (39x26cm-15x10in) s.i.d.1897 panel. 25-Feb-3 Dorotheum, Vienna #100/R est:2500-3000

MULLER, Max (1911-1991) Danish
£372 $592 €558 Woman selling fish (40x49cm-16x19in) s.d.58. 10-Mar-3 Rasmussen, Vejle #590/R (D.KR 4000)

MULLER, Moritz (jnr) (20th C) German
£949 $1472 €1500 Deer running across woodland meadow (53x73cm-21x29in) s.i. 25-Sep-2 Neumeister, Munich #675/R est:1800
£1497 $2380 €2200 Hunting dog chasing deer (70x90cm-28x35in) s.d.1906. 19-Mar-3 Neumeister, Munich #670/R est:900

MULLER, Moritz (snr) (1841-1899) German
£390 $604 €585 Cows and rabbits inside barn (13x18cm-5x7in) s. panel. 24-Sep-2 Koller, Zurich #6566 (S.FR 900)
£601 $949 €902 Surprise about the rest of the hunt (39x51cm-15x20in) s.d.1892. 29-Nov-2 Zofingen, Switzerland #2352 (S.FR 1400)

MULLER, Moritz Karl Friedrich (1807-1865) German
£609 $944 €950 Study of a girl by candlelight (37x31cm-15x12in) lit. 7-Dec-2 Bergmann, Erlangen #793/R
£2564 $3974 €4000 Small girl fruit seller in Upper Bavarian costume (24x22cm-9x9in) s. canvas on canvas. 4-Dec-2 Neumeister, Munich #830/R est:2800
£3291 $5101 €5200 Man with girl at window (31x24cm-12x9in) s.d.1854 painted oval panel. 25-Sep-2 Neumeister, Munich #674/R est:2500

MULLER, Morten (1828-1911) Norwegian
£777 $1180 €1166 Southern landscape with house (25x38cm-10x15in) s. paper on panel. 31-Aug-2 Grev Wedels Plass, Oslo #67 (N.KR 9000)
£785 $1233 €1178 Waterfall (29x47cm-11x19in) s. 25-Nov-2 Blomqvist, Lysaker #1196/R (N.KR 9000)
£1038 $1640 €1557 Man in rowing boat on lake (28x46cm-11x18in) s.d.90. 2-Dec-2 Blomqvist, Oslo #303/R (N.KR 12000)
£1175 $1904 €1763 Waterfall (29x47cm-11x19in) s. 27-Jan-3 Blomqvist, Lysaker #1161 est:15000-18000 (N.KR 13000)

£1305 $2089 €1958 Steam boat on fjord, west coast of Norway (18x47cm-7x19in) s.d.90. 17-Mar-3 Blomqvist, Oslo #304/R est:20000-25000 (N.KR 15000)
£1309 $2055 €1964 Cattle by woodland tarn (90x128cm-35x50in) s. 25-Nov-2 Blomqvist, Lysaker #1195/R est:25000-30000 (N.KR 15000)
£1561 $2560 €2263 Landscape in moonlight (50x78cm-20x31in) s/. 2-Jun-3 Blomqvist, Oslo #169/R est:20000-25000 (N.KR 17000)
£1741 $2785 €2612 Fjord landscape (43x65cm-17x26in) s. 17-Mar-3 Blomqvist, Oslo #365/R est:30000-40000 (N.KR 20000)
£2327 $3770 €3374 Landscape with rapids (55x74cm-22x29in) s.d.1861. 26-May-3 Bukowskis, Stockholm #265/R est:20000-25000 (S.KR 30000)
£4700 $7520 €7050 Figures and buildings by water's edge (100x70cm-39x28in) s. 17-Mar-3 Blomqvist, Oslo #345/R est:30000-40000 (N.KR 54000)
£7965 $12584 €11948 View across Stockholm (86x123cm-34x48in) s. let. 28-Apr-3 Blomqvist, Oslo #309/R est:100000-120000 (N.KR 90000)

MULLER, Otto (1874-1930) German
£10791 $17698 €15000 Standing female nude (68x45cm-27x18in) s. oil crayon prov. 6-Jun-3 Ketterer, Munich #72/R est:15000-20000

Prints
£2083 $3312 €3000 Circus couple - variety (26x19cm-10x7in) mono. lithograph. 5-May-3 Ketterer, Munich #915/R est:1500-2500
£2089 $3258 €3300 Russian house with sunflowers (41x56cm-16x22in) s.i. lithograph. 18-Oct-2 Dr Fritz Nagel, Stuttgart #578/R est:2800
£2174 $3565 €3000 Three figures behind crossed tree trunks (26x21cm-10x8in) s.i. lithograph. 29-May-3 Lempertz, Koln #818/R est:4000
£3099 $5144 €4400 Seated girl surrounded by leaves (30x21cm-12x8in) s. lithograph. 14-Jun-3 Hauswedell & Nolte, Hamburg #1444/R est:6000
£3145 $5000 €4718 Waldlandschaft mit kleinen figuren (38x29cm-15x11in) s. i.d.1912 num.54/60 verso lithograph. 29-Apr-3 Christie's, Rockefeller NY #518/R est:7000-9000
£3404 $5515 €4800 Wooded landscape with small figures (40x29cm-16x11in) s. lithograph. 24-May-3 Van Ham, Cologne #431/R est:6000
£3478 $5426 €5217 Wooded landscape with small figures - 2 (51x38cm-20x15in) s.i. num.16/60 lithograph lit. 16-Sep-2 Philippe Schuler, Zurich #3052/R est:10000-15000 (S.FR 8000)
£3481 $5500 €5500 Half naked girl (22x17cm-9x7in) s. lithograph. 30-Nov-2 Villa Grisebach, Berlin #186/R est:4000-5000
£3521 $5845 €5000 Seated lovers (37x28cm-15x11in) s.i. lithograph. 14-Jun-3 Hauswedell & Nolte, Hamburg #1435/R est:7500
£3526 $5465 €5500 Standing, sitting and bathing girls at a tree (35x26cm-14x10in) s. lithograph one of 30. 6-Dec-2 Ketterer, Munich #61/R est:6500-8000
£3546 $5745 €5000 Reclining girl (29x39cm-11x15in) s. lithograph. 24-May-3 Van Ham, Cologne #430/R est:7400
£3623 $5942 €5000 Forest lake with bathers and seated girls (33x27cm-13x11in) s. lithograph. 31-May-3 Villa Grisebach, Berlin #188/R est:5000-7000
£3623 $5942 €5000 Girl on sofa (29x39cm-11x15in) s. lithograph. 31-May-3 Villa Grisebach, Berlin #189/R est:5000-6000
£3623 $5942 €5000 Half naked girl in profile (22x17cm-9x7in) s. lithograph. 29-May-3 Lempertz, Koln #821/R est:5000
£3662 $6079 €5200 Girl between leaves (28x37cm-11x15in) s. woodcut. 14-Jun-3 Hauswedell & Nolte, Hamburg #1453/R est:3000
£3797 $6000 €6000 Circus couple - variety (26x19cm-10x7in) s. W/C col chk lithograph board. 30-Nov-2 Villa Grisebach, Berlin #192/R est:7000-9000
£3803 $6313 €5400 Potsdam Summer of Art (95x70cm-37x28in) woodcut. 14-Jun-3 Hauswedell & Nolte, Hamburg #1456/R est:8000
£4167 $6458 €6500 Girl sitting (42x30cm-17x12in) s. lithograph exec.1923. 7-Dec-2 Van Ham, Cologne #364/R est:5000
£4808 $7452 €7500 Mother and child II (26x18cm-10x7in) s. lithograph. 7-Dec-2 Hauswedell & Nolte, Hamburg #925/R est:4000
£5070 $8417 €7200 Girl standing in water and girl wearing hat sitting on bank (39x29cm-15x11in) s. lithograph. 14-Jun-3 Hauswedell & Nolte, Hamburg #1447/R est:8000
£5208 $8281 €7500 Seated figure (30x21cm-12x8in) s. lithograph. 5-May-3 Ketterer, Munich #921/R est:2500-3500
£5208 $8281 €7500 Three girls in front of mirror (35x26cm-14x10in) s. num.48/50 lithograph. 5-May-3 Ketterer, Munich #922/R est:3000-5000
£5608 $8749 €8300 Reclining girl (29x39cm-11x15in) s.i. num.IV/XXX lithograph. 28-Mar-3 Ketterer, Hamburg #514/R est:6000-7000
£6250 $9938 €9000 Mother and child 2 (26x18cm-10x7in) s. lithograph. 5-May-3 Ketterer, Munich #918/R est:4000-6000
£7042 $11690 €10000 Girl reclining on couch (33x32cm-13x13in) s. lithograph W/C. 14-Jun-3 Hauswedell & Nolte, Hamburg #1449/R est:9000
£7639 $12146 €11000 Two seated girls 2 (29x40cm-11x16in) s.i. lithograph. 5-May-3 Ketterer, Munich #917/R est:5000-7000
£7692 $11923 €12000 Two bathers in stream (25x17cm-10x7in) s. col lithograph. 7-Dec-2 Hauswedell & Nolte, Hamburg #926/R est:10000
£8333 $13250 €12000 Self portrait with model and mask (39x29cm-15x11in) s. lithograph. 5-May-3 Ketterer, Munich #919/R est:7000-9000
£8451 $14028 €12000 Seated nude (37x31cm-15x12in) mono. woodcut. 14-Jun-3 Hauswedell & Nolte, Hamburg #1455/R est:4000
£9615 $14904 €15000 Couple at table (39x29cm-15x11in) s. col lithograph. 4-Dec-2 Lempertz, Koln #943/R est:16000
£10417 $16563 €15000 Finding of Moses (29x39cm-11x15in) s. num.7/30 col lithograph. 5-May-3 Ketterer, Munich #916/R est:5000-7000
£11268 $18704 €16000 Two girls - Russian girls (44x34cm-17x13in) mono. lithograph. 14-Jun-3 Hauswedell & Nolte, Hamburg #1445/R est:15000
£12179 $18878 €19000 Gypsy family resting with goat (68x48cm-27x19in) col lithograph. 7-Dec-2 Hauswedell & Nolte, Hamburg #928/R est:12000
£12676 $21042 €18000 Three bathers - nudes in water (43x54cm-17x21in) s.i. s.i. verso lithograph. 14-Jun-3 Hauswedell & Nolte, Hamburg #1437/R est:10000
£13194 $20979 €19000 Five yellow nudes by water (33x44cm-13x17in) s. col lithograph. 5-May-3 Ketterer, Munich #920/R est:9000-12000
£14103 $21859 €22000 Two girls in dunes (30x39cm-12x15in) s. lithograph. 7-Dec-2 Hauswedell & Nolte, Hamburg #927/R est:13000
£15000 $23400 €22500 Zigeuner zwei zigeunermadchen im wohnraum - Two gipsy girls in a room (70x50cm-28x20in) black orange lithograph. 9-Oct-2 Sotheby's, London #2/R est:18000-25000
£15000 $23400 €22500 Zwei madchen und stehender jungling - Two girls and a standing boy (43x33cm-17x13in) s. hand col lithograph prov.lit. 9-Oct-2 Sotheby's, London #11/R est:18000-25000
£15823 $25000 €25000 Gypsy family at a covered wagon (70x50cm-28x20in) col lithograph exec.1926/27 one of 60 prov. 29-Nov-2 Villa Grisebach, Berlin #30/R est:25000-30000
£17606 $29225 €25000 Five yellow nudes by water (33x44cm-13x17in) s. col lithograph. 14-Jun-3 Hauswedell & Nolte, Hamburg #2450/R est:24000
£20253 $32000 €32000 Gypsy Madonna (70x50cm-28x20in) col lithograph exec.1926-1927 one of 60 prov. 29-Nov-2 Villa Grisebach, Berlin #31/R est:35000-40000
£21528 $34229 €31000 Couple at table (38x29cm-15x11in) s. col lithograph. 5-May-3 Ketterer, Munich #923/R est:10000-15000

Works on paper
£1901 $3156 €2700 Gisi (46x34cm-18x13in) col chk. 14-Jun-3 Hauswedell & Nolte, Hamburg #1434/R est:4000
£5556 $8833 €8000 Dance study (32x36cm-13x14in) s. chlk. 5-May-3 Ketterer, Munich #914/R est:6000-8000
£5696 $9000 €9000 Seated naked girl (67x50cm-26x20in) chk. 30-Nov-2 Villa Grisebach, Berlin #191/R est:10000-12000
£12676 $21042 €18000 Two nudes (28x39cm-11x15in) s. pen chl pencil. 14-Jun-3 Hauswedell & Nolte, Hamburg #1433/R est:12000
£23913 $39217 €33000 Girl at the beach (35x50cm-14x20in) s. col crayons W/C prov. 30-May-3 Villa Grisebach, Berlin #26/R est:20000-30000
£33945 $56688 €49220 Two nudes standing in wood (68x52cm-27x20in) s. verso col chk. 20-Jun-3 Kornfeld, Bern #116/R est:80000 (S.FR 74000)
£49645 $80426 €70000 Girl sitting by woodland stream (68x50cm-27x20in) i. verso chl chk W/C prov.lit. 24-May-3 Van Ham, Cologne #429/R est:70000
£65217 $106957 €90000 Two girls in grass (52x69cm-20x27in) s. i. verso W/C col chk prov. 29-May-3 Lempertz, Koln #816/R est:70000-80000
£201835 $337064 €292661 Couple with green fan - youth and girl (100x85cm-39x33in) mono. s.i. verso distemper linen prov.lit.exhib. 20-Jun-3 Kornfeld, Bern #115/R est:450000 (S.FR 440000)

MULLER, Paul Jakob (1894-1982) Swiss
£347 $559 €503 Clochard (63x53cm-25x21in) i. panel. 7-May-3 Dobiaschofsky, Bern #869/R (S.FR 750)

MULLER, Paul Lothar (1869-?) German
£480 $749 €720 Landscape with ox cart (45x50cm-18x20in) s.d.1919 i. verso board. 6-Nov-2 Dobiaschofsky, Bern #851/R (S.FR 1100)

MULLER, R (?) ?
£1807 $2963 €2620 In the oasis (32x23cm-13x9in) s.i.d.1882 panel. 4-Jun-3 AB Stockholms Auktionsverk #2404/R est:25000-30000 (S.KR 23000)

MULLER, Riccardo (20th C) Italian
£320 $493 €480 Interior scene with cavalier figures and fortune teller (46x69cm-18x27in) 5-Sep-2 Clevedon Sale Rooms #139

MULLER, Richard (1874-1954) Austrian
£2958 $4762 €4200 Old windmill in Poitzsch near Wurzen (43x32cm-17x13in) s.d.1940 s.i.d. stretcher lit. 9-May-3 Schloss Ahlden, Ahlden #1539/R est:3800

MULLER, Robert (1859-1895) German
£1783 $2746 €2800 Having fun outside the blacksmiths (68x83cm-27x33in) s. 5-Sep-2 Arnold, Frankfurt #830/R est:1000

MULLER, Robert Antoine (19th C) British
£2000 $3180 €3000 Letter. Lovers (25x20cm-10x8in) s.d.1870 panel pair. 20-Mar-3 Christie's, Kensington #108/R est:2000-3000
£2200 $3630 €3190 Butterfly (40x30cm-16x12in) s. panel. 2-Jul-3 Sotheby's, Olympia #311/R est:1000-1500

MULLER, Rudolf (1892-1972) Swiss

£524 $817 €786 Tauffelen beach with St Peter island (46x100cm-18x39in) mono. 6-Nov-2 Dobiaschofsky, Bern #852/R (S.FR 1200)

MULLER, Rudolph (1802-1885) Swiss

Works on paper

£2146 $3391 €3219 Italian landscape near Olevano (48x68cm-19x27in) s.d.1838 W/C over pencil sketch. 29-Nov-2 Falk & Falk, Zurich #441/R est:3500 (S.FR 5000)

£2146 $3391 €3219 Roman Campagna with San Giovanni in Laterano with aqueducts (46x66cm-18x26in) s.d.49 W/C over pencil sketch. 29-Nov-2 Falk & Falk, Zurich #442 est:3500 (S.FR 5000)

£3261 $5054 €4892 Ruins near Rome. Tivoli (37x54cm-15x21in) s. one bears d.188 W/C pair. 9-Dec-2 Philippe Schuler, Zurich #4173/R est:3000-4000 (S.FR 7500)

MULLER, Wilhelm Andreas (1733-1816) German

Miniatures

£4000 $6480 €6000 Juliane Marie, Queen of Denmark (13cm-5in) indis i. ivory panel gilded wood frame. 22-May-3 Bonhams, New Bond Street #46/R est:3000-5000

MULLER, William James (1812-1845) British

£330 $538 €495 Figures by an old water mill (28x23cm-11x9in) s. 14-Feb-3 Keys, Aylsham #711

£450 $729 €675 Attentive audience (20x27cm-8x11in) s. 23-Jan-3 Christie's, Kensington #144

£600 $948 €900 Selling a slave (28x38cm-11x15in) s. board. 12-Nov-2 Bonhams, Knightsbridge #250/R

£600 $936 €900 Zurich fishing boat (28x42cm-11x17in) s.d.1840 panel exhib. 8-Apr-3 Bonhams, Knightsbridge #229/R

£1076 $1700 €1614 Winter landscape (76x137cm-30x54in) s.d.1881. 16-Nov-2 New Orleans Auction, New Orleans #311/R est:2000-4000

£1800 $2988 €2700 Hampstead Heath, bird trap (42x58cm-17x23in) s. prov. 10-Jun-3 Christie's, London #64/R est:2000-3000

£2000 $3180 €3000 Loading barges on the Thames (30x51cm-12x20in) 19-Mar-3 Sotheby's, London #235/R est:2000-3000

£2800 $4648 €4200 Wooded landscape with sheep (23x39cm-9x15in) s.d.1843 panel. 10-Jun-3 Christie's, London #62/R est:3000-5000

£11000 $17710 €16500 Good Samaritan (56x81cm-22x32in) s.d.1843 prov.exhib.lit. 20-Feb-3 Christie's, London #157/R est:8000

Works on paper

£300 $474 €435 Fontainebleau, the age of Francis I (38x28cm-15x11in) W/C bodycol. 22-Jul-3 Bonhams, Knightsbridge #226/R

£480 $739 €720 Children fishing by a stream before a village (22x16cm-9x6in) s.d.1840 W/C. 7-Sep-2 Shapes, Edinburgh #522

£650 $1014 €975 Arab smoking a hookah (25x37cm-10x15in) W/C. 25-Mar-3 Bonhams, Knightsbridge #190/R

£1200 $1908 €1800 Figures unloading fishing boats on the shore (16x24cm-6x9in) s. W/C over pencil htd bodycol prov. 19-Mar-3 Sotheby's, London #160/R est:1200-1800

£1800 $2952 €2610 Villeneuve-les-Avignon, Provence (15x35cm-6x14in) pencil W/C prov. 5-Jun-3 Christie's, London #109/R est:2000-3000

£1800 $2952 €2610 River at Angers (28x43cm-11x17in) s.i.d.1840 pencil W/C prov. 5-Jun-3 Christie's, London #110/R est:2000-3000

£2400 $3936 €3480 Figure before a mosque, Egypt (16x31cm-6x12in) i. pencil W/C. 5-Jun-3 Christie's, London #149/R est:2000-3000

£3500 $5005 €5250 The Avon near Bath (23x31cm-9x12in) pencil W/C htd white prov.exhib.lit. 22-Jan-3 Christie's, London #46/R est:3500

£4000 $6560 €5800 Vines o the bank of a river near Masry, Asia minor (50x33cm-20x13in) s.i.d.1844 pencil W/C arched prov.exhib. 5-Jun-3 Christie's, London #111/R est:3000-5000

£8000 $11440 €12000 Great Bazaar, Constantinople (27x20cm-11x8in) indis.sig. pencil W/C htd bodycol scratching out prov.exhib.lit. 22-Jan-3 Christie's, London #64/R est:10000

£12500 $17875 €18750 Turk smoking pipe beneath awning (17x13cm-7x5in) pencil W/C gum htd white prov. 22-Jan-3 Christie's, London #65/R est:15000

MULLER, Willy (1889-1953) Swiss

£279 $441 €419 Beach near Arbon, Bodensee (33x46cm-13x18in) s.d.1943. 26-Nov-2 Hans Widmer, St Gallen #1299 (S.FR 650)

MULLER, Wout (1946-2000) Dutch

£3481 $5500 €5500 Schimmenspel (43x38cm-17x15in) mono.d.90 s.i.d.1990 verso panel. 26-Nov-2 Sotheby's, Amsterdam #84/R est:2000-3000

MULLER-BAUMGARTEN, Carl (1879-1946) German

£2064 $3220 €3096 Over the map (73x105cm-29x41in) s. 11-Sep-2 Kieselbach, Budapest #192/R (H.F 800000)

MULLER-BRITTNAU, Willy (1938-) Swiss

£328 $511 €492 Refief 1965-72 (63x63cm-25x25in) acrylic panel prov. 6-Nov-2 Dobiaschofsky, Bern #1760/R (S.FR 750)

MULLER-CORNELIUS, Ludwig (1864-1946) German

£316 $491 €500 Post coach halted outside farmstead (10x16cm-4x6in) s. panel. 25-Sep-2 Neumeister, Munich #678/R

£411 $641 €600 Haymaking in extensive lower foothills (12x17cm-5x7in) s.verso panel. 10-Apr-3 Allgauer, Kempten #2913/R

£417 $646 €650 Farming couple and cow-maid in front of Upper Bavarian farmhouse (7x16cm-3x6in) s. panel. 4-Dec-2 Neumeister, Munich #833

£633 $981 €1000 Post coach halted outside farmstead (65x84cm-26x33in) s. 26-Sep-2 Neumeister, Munich #2795/R

£705 $1107 €1100 Hay wagon outside farmhouse (16x23cm-6x9in) s. board. 21-Nov-2 Dorotheum, Vienna #190/R

£769 $1192 €1200 Potato harvest with maids with baskets and farmer with vehicle (8x13cm-3x5in) s. panel. 4-Dec-2 Neumeister, Munich #832/R

£878 $1370 €1300 Peasants harvesting (13x20cm-5x8in) s. panel. 26-Mar-3 Hugo Ruef, Munich #180/R

£962 $1490 €1500 Dachau landscape with figures and carriage in front of a house (10x19cm-4x7in) s. i.verso panel. 4-Dec-2 Neumeister, Munich #831/R est:1400

£2157 $3451 €3300 Three horses and wagon and figures resting on the path (30x50cm-12x20in) s. lit. 10-Jan-3 Allgauer, Kempten #1704/R est:1800

MULLER-GOSSEN, Franz (1871-1946) German

£769 $1192 €1200 Steamer at sea (61x79cm-24x31in) s.d. 7-Dec-2 Ketterer, Hamburg #28/R

£974 $1451 €1500 Hamburg harbour with steamers and barges (100x150cm-39x59in) s. 26-Jun-2 Neumeister, Munich #816/R

MULLER-HUFSCHMID, Willi (1890-1966) German

Works on paper

£629 $981 €1000 Veils of the night descend (34x43cm-13x17in) i. s.verso brush ink wash executed c.1950 prov. 9-Oct-2 Sotheby's, London #228/R est:1500-2000

MULLER-KAEMPFF, Paul (1861-1941) German

£269 $417 €420 Sun drenched woodland clearing (51x41cm-20x16in) s. 7-Dec-2 Dannenberg, Berlin #711/R

£748 $1190 €1100 Path through field (71x100cm-28x39in) s. 28-Mar-3 Bolland & Marotz, Bremen #500/R

£1197 $1927 €1700 Farm (78x118cm-31x46in) s. 7-May-3 Vendue Huis, Gravenhage #72/R est:1000-1200

£2264 $3532 €3600 Ostsee coast (51x70cm-20x28in) s. lit. 20-Sep-2 Schloss Ahlden, Ahlden #1168/R est:2400

£2767 $4289 €4400 Landscape near Ahrenshoop (80x120cm-31x47in) s. 2-Nov-2 Hans Stahl, Toestorf #51/R est:4600

£5380 $8500 €8500 Village in stormy weather (96x105cm-38x41in) s. painted c.1900/02. 29-Nov-2 Bolland & Marotz, Bremen #745/R est:8500

Works on paper

£714 $1043 €1100 Ahrenshoop with wide sandy path, houses and gardens (23x35cm-9x14in) s. W/C gouache. 15-Jun-2 Hans Stahl, Hamburg #132/R

£714 $1043 €1100 Early spring view of blue house over meadows and shrub (23x41cm-9x16in) s.i.d.1908 W/C gouache. 15-Jun-2 Hans Stahl, Hamburg #133/R

MULLER-KURZWELLY, Konrad Alexander (attrib) (1855-1914) German

£314 $515 €480 Boat, jetty and house near Ahrenshoop (45x64cm-18x25in) mono. 8-Feb-3 Hans Stahl, Hamburg #100/R

MULLER-LANDAU, Rolf (1903-1956) Austrian

£440 $687 €700 Amaryllis (43x31cm-17x12in) s. lit. 20-Sep-2 Karlheinz Kaupp, Staufen #1987/R

MULLER-MASSDORF, Julius (1863-?) German

£4088 $6377 €6500 Kitchen interior (72x61cm-28x24in) s.i. prov. 19-Sep-2 Dr Fritz Nagel, Stuttgart #975/R est:1000

MULLER-MOHR, Hugo (1863-1912) German

£483 $763 €700 Alpine landscape with Bozen (63x88cm-25x35in) s. 4-Apr-3 Venator & Hansten, Koln #1817

MULLER-MUNSTER, Franz (1867-?) German

£380 $592 €600 Female nude in landscape (52x43cm-20x17in) mono. i. verso board lit. 14-Sep-2 Bergmann, Erlangen #764/R

£2553 $4034 €3830 Die Kinder von Naumburg. Pictures of crowds (85x295cm-33x116in) s. triptych exhib. 2-Dec-2 Rasmussen, Copenhagen #1751/R est:30000 (D.KR 30000)

MULLER-SAMERBERG, Karl Hermann (1869-?) German
Works on paper
£408 $644 €612 Village street (61x46cm-24x18in) s.d.1907 exhib. 29-Nov-2 Zofingen, Switzerland #2511 (S.FR 950)

MULLER-SCHEESEL, Ernst (1863-1936) German
£696 $1100 €1100 White lilies and other flowers in glass vase (76x54cm-30x21in) s.d.1931. 29-Nov-2 Bolland & Marotz, Bremen #549/R
£1266 $2000 €2000 Fen landscape with cotton-grass and young birch trees (51x70cm-20x28in) s.d.1936. 29-Nov-2 Bolland & Marotz, Bremen #548/R est:2200
Works on paper
£316 $500 €500 Dune landscape with moor and juniper at dusk (35x45cm-14x18in) s.d.1917 gouache. 29-Nov-2 Bolland & Marotz, Bremen #550/R

MULLER-SCHWABEN, Fritz (1879-1957) German
£261 $429 €400 Street in Garmisch in the spring (70x95cm-28x37in) s. 5-Feb-3 Neumeister, Munich #775
£288 $472 €440 Fishing boat on the Fraueninsel (45x65cm-18x26in) s. 5-Feb-3 Neumeister, Munich #774
£380 $589 €600 Still life of flowers (48x58cm-19x23in) s. 26-Sep-2 Neumeister, Munich #2797
£411 $638 €650 Still life of flowers (65x84cm-26x33in) s. 26-Sep-2 Neumeister, Munich #2798
£490 $784 €750 Shepherd with flock in front of farm buildings in Swabian landscape (70x100cm-28x39in) s. 10-Jan-3 Allgauer, Kempten #1706/R
£769 $1169 €1200 Ducks in front of a watermill (70x100cm-28x39in) s. lit. 11-Jul-2 Allgauer, Kempten #2624/R
£850 $1393 €1300 Farm buildings in the mountains (70x100cm-28x39in) s. 5-Feb-3 Neumeister, Munich #772/R

MULLER-WERLAU, Peter Paul (attrib) (1864-1945) German
£1006 $1550 €1600 Cochem fortress on the Mosel (61x77cm-24x30in) s. i. verso. 23-Oct-2 Neumeister, Munich #710 est:1200

MULLER-WIEHL, Helmut (20th C) German
£256 $397 €400 Sunny cornfield with village. mono.d.89 board. 6-Dec-2 Karlheinz Kaupp, Staufen #2397/R
£353 $546 €550 Ohningen, Hori (40x80cm-16x31in) mono.d.80 i. verso. 6-Dec-2 Karlheinz Kaupp, Staufen #2148
£417 $646 €650 The Donau at Donaueschingen (80x100cm-31x39in) mono.d.97. 6-Dec-2 Karlheinz Kaupp, Staufen #2382
Works on paper
£256 $397 €400 Snowy village (40x50cm-16x20in) mono.d.88 gouache. 6-Dec-2 Karlheinz Kaupp, Staufen #2099

MULLER-WISCHIN, Anton (1865-1949) German
£2707 $4224 €4061 Still life with roses and jewellery (105x90cm-41x35in) s. oval. 20-Nov-2 Fischer, Luzern #2195/R est:1800-2500 (S.FR 6200)
£3038 $4709 €4800 Roses (56x46cm-22x18in) s. board. 25-Sep-2 Neumeister, Munich #679/R est:4000

MULLER-WUNSCHE, Heinrich Hermann (1893-?) German
£288 $449 €420 Rococo group in salon (70x50cm-28x20in) s.d.29 board on panel. 10-Apr-3 Van Ham, Cologne #1608/R

MULLERS, Albert (1921-) Belgian
£255 $397 €400 Ice skaters in front of an abbey (40x50cm-16x20in) s.i. panel. 7-Nov-2 Allgauer, Kempten #2910/R
£541 $845 €850 Children at the forest edge in winter (50x40cm-20x16in) s. panel. 7-Nov-2 Allgauer, Kempten #2911/R

MULLEY (20th C) Austrian
£8228 $12753 €13000 Mountain farm with flowers and washing (83x160cm-33x63in) i. 27-Sep-2 Dr Fritz Nagel, Leipzig #3901/R est:7400
£8544 $13244 €13500 Village in the high mountains with mountain range beyond (86x160cm-34x63in) i. 27-Sep-2 Dr Fritz Nagel, Leipzig #3900/R est:8000

MULLEY, Oskar (1891-1949) Austrian
£1613 $2371 €2500 Mountain village (60x50cm-24x20in) i. verso. 20-Jun-2 Dr Fritz Nagel, Stuttgart #802/R est:2500
£1944 $3092 €2800 House in landscape (59x80cm-23x31in) s. i. verso. 29-Apr-3 Wiener Kunst Auktionen, Vienna #552/R est:3000-5500
£2113 $3401 €3000 Alpine landscape in the autumn (74x89cm-29x35in) s. panel lit. 9-May-3 Schloss Ahlden, Ahlden #1495/R est:3900
£3226 $4742 €5000 Mountain farm (80x120cm-31x47in) s. 20-Jun-2 Dr Fritz Nagel, Stuttgart #801/R est:5000
£3481 $5430 €5500 Landscape (33x31cm-13x12in) s. oil chk. 15-Oct-2 Dorotheum, Vienna #44/R est:3000-4000
£3597 $5899 €5000 Farmhouse in the evening light (22x35cm-9x14in) s. board. 5-Jun-3 Dorotheum, Salzburg #532/R est:4400-6000
£7692 $11923 €12000 Two farmhouses on high mountain-chain (104x180cm-41x71in) s. s.i.verso. 4-Dec-2 Neumeister, Munich #834/R est:10000
£7971 $13072 €11000 House in the mountains (96x79cm-38x31in) s. 27-May-3 Wiener Kunst Auktionen, Vienna #105/R est:10000-15000
Works on paper
£1139 $1777 €1800 Rocky shore (22x22cm-9x9in) s. mixed media. 15-Oct-2 Dorotheum, Vienna #43/R est:1500-2200

MULLEY, Oskar (attrib) (1891-1949) Austrian
£1154 $1754 €1800 High mountain-chain with Tirol farmhouse (65x90cm-26x35in) lit. 11-Jul-2 Allgauer, Kempten #2620/R
£2372 $3676 €3700 Chapel on forest path (61x80cm-24x31in) i. 4-Dec-2 Neumeister, Munich #835/R est:3800

MULLIKIN, Mary Augusta (1874-?) American
£1592 $2500 €2388 View of Shanghai (21x27cm-8x11in) i.verso canvasboard. 19-Nov-2 Butterfields, San Francisco #8251/R est:2000-3000

MULNIER (18/19th C) French
£9500 $14725 €14250 Le coucher de la mariee (81x65cm-32x26in) s. 30-Oct-2 Bonhams, New Bond Street #160/R est:6000-8000

MULOCK, Frederick C (1888-1932) British
£300 $471 €450 Garden (92x51cm-36x20in) exhib. 21-Nov-2 Tennants, Leyburn #823
£800 $1256 €1200 Huntress (81x54cm-32x21in) s. exhib. 21-Nov-2 Tennants, Leyburn #849
£2800 $4396 €4200 Protected from harm on the river (244x205cm-96x81in) s. 21-Nov-2 Tennants, Leyburn #754/R est:1000-2000

MULPHIN, Albert (?) French
£316 $500 €500 Nature morte aux grappes de raisins (48x63cm-19x25in) 2-Dec-2 Amberes, Antwerp #1349

MULREADY, A E (fl.1863-1905) British
£1300 $2171 €1885 Sister's two street urchins (53x32cm-21x13in) s.d.1883. 9-Jul-3 Edgar Horn, Eastbourne #295/R est:400-600

MULREADY, Augustus E (fl.1863-1905) British
£350 $571 €508 London flower seller (68x50cm-27x20in) i.verso. 16-Jul-3 Sotheby's, Olympia #106/R
£535 $829 €850 Rainy day (38x31cm-15x12in) s.d.1874. 29-Oct-2 Finarte, Milan #443
£600 $978 €900 Fallen bird (29x22cm-11x9in) s.d.1901 board. 29-Jan-3 Sotheby's, Olympia #67/R
£12258 $19000 €18387 Little spies (40x31cm-16x12in) s.d.86 prov. 30-Oct-2 Christie's, Rockefeller NY #159/R est:10000-15000

MULREADY, W (1786-1863) British
£460 $699 €690 Woodland clearing with figures and dog (43x33cm-17x13in) s. 14-Aug-2 Andrew Hartley, Ilkley #664

MULREADY, William (1786-1863) British
£833 $1267 €1300 Country house (28x36cm-11x14in) s. board. 31-Aug-2 Geble, Radolfzell #652/R
£2016 $3185 €3024 Dispute outside cobbler's shop (20x18cm-8x7in) prov. 18-Nov-2 Waddingtons, Toronto #158/R est:6000-8000 (C.D 5000)
Works on paper
£2300 $3680 €3450 Vessels in squall off the coast (32x49cm-13x19in) chk. 15-May-3 Christie's, London #31/R est:1500-2000

MULREADY, William (attrib) (1786-1863) British
£7200 $11448 €10800 Farmer's daughters (91x71cm-36x28in) 6-Mar-3 Christie's, Kensington #604/R est:4000-6000

MULTRUS, Josef (19/20th C) Austrian?
£372 $580 €558 Singing lesson (32x41cm-13x16in) s. cardboard. 12-Oct-2 Dorotheum, Prague #74 (C.KR 18000)
£873 $1387 €1310 Bouquet in blue vase (69x49cm-27x19in) s. 8-Mar-3 Dorotheum, Prague #69/R est:26000-40000 (C.KR 40000)

MULTSCHER, Hans (circle) (1400-1467) German
Sculpture
£9259 $15000 €13889 Madonna and Child (82cm-32in) carved wood exhib.lit. 23-Jan-3 Sotheby's, New York #145b/R est:30000

MULVAD, Emma (1838-1903) Danish
£1277 $2017 €1916 Still life of Christmas roses in glass vase on table (43x34cm-17x13in) s.d.1890. 2-Dec-2 Rasmussen, Copenhagen #1473/R est:20000 (D.KR 15000)
£1507 $2351 €2200 Still life of roses in a basket (41x32cm-16x13in) s.d.1888 lit. 10-Apr-3 Allgauer, Kempten #2915/R est:2200

MULVANY, Thomas James (1779-1845) British
£2500 $3975 €3750 Coast scene, noon (30x45cm-12x18in) 5-Mar-3 John Ross, Belfast #101 est:3500-4000

MUMPRECHT, Walter Rudolf (1918-) Swiss
£1659 $2589 €2489 Abstract composition (97x130cm-38x51in) s.d.62. 8-Nov-2 Dobiaschofsky, Bern #267/R est:6000 (S.FR 3800)
Works on paper
£309 $500 €448 Springtaufel (25x30cm-10x12in) s. gouache ink prov. 21-May-3 Doyle, New York #4/R

MUNAKATA, Shiko (1903-1975) Japanese
Prints
£1887 $3000 €2831 Landscape with a bird in a tree (30x30cm-12x12in) s.d.1960 woodcut. 1-May-3 Swann Galleries, New York #537/R est:4000-6000
£1923 $3000 €2885 Pair of goddesses, Sohi no saku (60x46cm-24x18in) s.i.num.71/100 woodcut. 14-Oct-2 Butterfields, San Francisco #1158/R est:2500-3500
£2516 $4000 €3774 Landscape with distant mountains (39x31cm-15x12in) s.d.1962 woodcut hand col W/C. 1-May-3 Swann Galleries, New York #538/R est:5000-8000
£2821 $4400 €4232 Sho kei sho (49x36cm-19x14in) s.i.d. col woodcut. 19-Sep-2 Swann Galleries, New York #624/R est:4000-6000
£3205 $5000 €4808 Jizo on Sado Island (54x31cm-21x12in) s.i.d.1960 hand col woodcut. 25-Mar-3 Christie's, Rockefeller NY #429/R est:5000-7000
£4487 $7000 €6731 Seated deity (45x31cm-18x12in) s.i. hand col W/C woodcut. 7-Nov-2 Swann Galleries, New York #747/R est:10000-15000
£4808 $7500 €7212 Avalokitesvara of Salvation (43x31cm-17x12in) s.i. hand col woodcut. 25-Mar-3 Christie's, Rockefeller NY #430/R est:5000-7000
£5346 $8500 €8019 Seated female nude (31x20cm-12x8in) s.d.1962 woodcut hand col W/C. 1-May-3 Swann Galleries, New York #541/R est:8000-12000
£6090 $9500 €9135 Sariputra (93x31cm-37x12in) s.i. woodcut. 7-Nov-2 Swann Galleries, New York #746/R est:15000-20000
£6410 $10000 €9615 Fugen (66x40cm-26x16in) s.d.1958 hand col W/C woodcut. 7-Nov-2 Swann Galleries, New York #748/R est:10000-15000
£7547 $12000 €11321 Two goddesses (43x23cm-17x9in) s.d.1962 woodcut. 1-May-3 Swann Galleries, New York #542/R est:12000-18000
£10063 $16000 €15095 Seated goddess and fish (41x30cm-16x12in) s.d.1962 woodcut hand col W/C. 1-May-3 Swann Galleries, New York #540/R est:7000-10000
£10692 $17000 €16038 Samantabhadra (93x30cm-37x12in) s.d.1958 woodcut. 1-May-3 Swann Galleries, New York #535/R est:10000-15000

MUNARI, Bruno (1907-1998) Italian
Works on paper
£634 $1052 €900 Composition (25x25cm-10x10in) s.d.1996 verso collage cardboard. 10-Jun-3 Finarte Semenzato, Milan #235/R
£811 $1265 €1200 Papyrus. Composition (20x14cm-8x6in) s.d.1995 one W/C one pastel pencil two. 26-Mar-3 Finarte Semenzato, Milan #158/R
£1408 $2338 €2000 Untitled (70x120cm-28x47in) s.d.1954-1984 cut wood. 10-Jun-3 Finarte Semenzato, Milan #126/R est:1000-1400

MUNCASTER, Claude (1903-1974) British
Works on paper
£280 $442 €420 River landscape (35x50cm-14x20in) s. pen ink W/C. 27-Nov-2 Sotheby's, Olympia #37/R
£300 $486 €450 Windy afternoon, Hornay rock, Orkney (34x50cm-13x20in) s. W/C. 23-May-3 Honiton Galleries, Honiton #681
£340 $541 €510 Near Petworth (18x25cm-7x10in) s.d.1944 W/C. 4-Mar-3 Bearnes, Exeter #398/R
£400 $636 €600 Low tide at Nonscholi (19x28cm-7x11in) s. W/C. 4-Mar-3 Bearnes, Exeter #397/R

MUNCH, Anna E (1876-1960) Danish
£321 $517 €482 Young woman having a rest in summer (46x57cm-18x22in) init.d.34. 11-May-3 Hindemae, Ullerslev #355/R (D.KR 3400)
£949 $1472 €1500 Femme lisant dans le jardin (47x57cm-19x22in) init.d.1917. 29-Sep-2 Eric Pillon, Calais #164/R

MUNCH, Axel (20th C) Danish?
£1119 $1780 €1679 Figures in gate opening, Bornholm (52x86cm-20x34in) init. 29-Apr-3 Kunsthallen, Copenhagen #217/R est:5000 (D.KR 12000)
£1144 $1910 €1659 Figures by open gate, Bornholm (52x86cm-20x34in) init. 17-Jun-3 Rasmussen, Copenhagen #139/R est:5000 (D.KR 12000)

MUNCH, Edvard (1863-1944) Norwegian
£10897 $16891 €17000 Early morning river landscape (14x18cm-6x7in) board. 3-Dec-2 Christie's, Amsterdam #208/R est:15000-20000
£12766 $20170 €19149 Norwegian summer landscape with man fishing by fjord (18x25cm-7x10in) i.verso. 2-Dec-2 Rasmussen, Copenhagen #1102/R est:150000-200000 (D.KR 150000)
£19231 $30000 €28847 Bildnis senator Brunings (106x76cm-42x30in) s.d.1919 prov.exhib.lit. 7-Nov-2 Christie's, Rockefeller NY #274/R est:60000-80000
£22436 $35000 €33654 Bildnis Andreas Munch. Mannerstudie (40x28cm-16x11in) double-sided painted c.1883-85. 7-Nov-2 Christie's, Rockefeller NY #209/R est:25000-35000
£29591 $47346 €44387 Portrait of Charlotte Dornberger (48x35cm-19x14in) prov.exhib.lit. 17-Mar-3 Blomqvist, Oslo #385y/R est:400000-600000 (N.KR 340000)
£63149 $99775 €94724 Edvard Munch's house and studio in Aasgaardstrand (31x41cm-12x16in) s. canvas on panel painted c.1899 prov.lit. 2-Dec-2 Blomqvist, Oslo #375/R est:800000-900000 (N.KR 730000)
£64103 $100000 €96155 Das rote Haus (45x55cm-18x22in) s. panel painted 1926 lit. 7-Nov-2 Christie's, Rockefeller NY #247/R est:140000-180000
£950000 $1548500 €1425000 Mermaid (100x320cm-39x126in) s.d.1896 burlap prov. 3-Feb-3 Christie's, London #84/R est:800000
£1050000 $1753500 €1575000 From Asgardstrand (68x90cm-27x35in) s. painted summer 1904 prov.exhib. 23-Jun-3 Sotheby's, London #19/R est:1200000-1800000
Prints
£2422 $3827 €3633 Landscape with beach (12x19cm-5x7in) s. etching printed in black executed 1902. 2-Dec-2 Blomqvist, Oslo #407/R est:20000-25000 (N.KR 28000)
£2516 $4000 €3774 Bohemian's wedding (34x49cm-13x19in) s.i. lithograph. 2-May-3 Sotheby's, New York #247/R est:6000-8000
£2560 $3993 €3840 Old man praying (46x33cm-18x13in) s. black white woodcut. 23-Sep-2 Blomqvist, Lysaker #1160/R est:40000-45000 (N.KR 30000)
£2595 $4100 €3893 Lubeck (48x63cm-19x25in) s. etching printed in black executed 1903. 2-Dec-2 Blomqvist, Oslo #412/R est:50000-60000 (N.KR 30000)
£2602 $4059 €3903 Holger Drachmann (59x45cm-23x18in) s. lithograph printed in green executed 1902. 21-Oct-2 Blomqvist, Oslo #467/R est:40000-50000 (N.KR 30000)
£2743 $4335 €4115 Holger Drachmann (59x45cm-23x18in) s. lithograph printed in green. 28-Apr-3 Blomqvist, Oslo #346/R est:35000-45000 (N.KR 31000)
£2785 $4456 €4178 Head of woman (30x23cm-12x9in) s. etching printed in black. 17-Mar-3 Blomqvist, Oslo #408/R est:15000-18000 (N.KR 32000)
£3054 $4795 €4581 Pretenders to the throne - Skule and Jatgeir I (29x52cm-11x20in) executed 1929 lithograph printed in black. 21-Nov-2 Grev Wedels Plass, Oslo #16/R est:40000-60000 (N.KR 35000)
£3363 $5313 €5045 Half nude resting (57x46cm-22x18in) lithograph printed in black executed 1919-20. 28-Apr-3 Blomqvist, Oslo #339/R est:25000-35000 (N.KR 38000)
£3490 $5480 €5235 Clothes drying in Travemund (21x26cm-8x10in) s.d.1904 etching printed in black. 21-Nov-2 Grev Wedels Plass, Oslo #2/R est:30000 (N.KR 40000)
£3578 $5617 €5367 Self portrait with beard (43x61cm-17x24in) s.d.1919 lithograph printed in black. 21-Nov-2 Grev Wedels Plass, Oslo #7/R est:40000-60000 (N.KR 41000)
£3633 $5740 €5450 Ghosts - family scene (42x62cm-17x24in) s. lithograph printed in black executed 1920. 2-Dec-2 Blomqvist, Oslo #406/R est:30000-35000 (N.KR 42000)
£3633 $5740 €5450 The lion tamer (50x69cm-20x27in) s. lithograph printed in black executed 1916. 2-Dec-2 Blomqvist, Oslo #414/R est:50000-60000 (N.KR 42000)
£3643 $5683 €5465 Idyll (44x37cm-17x15in) s. lithograph printed in black executed 1912. 21-Oct-2 Blomqvist, Oslo #463/R est:35000-45000 (N.KR 42000)

£3839 $6028 €5759 Houses in Kragero (23x35cm-9x14in) s.d.1916 lithograph printed in black. 21-Nov-2 Grev Wedels Plass, Oslo #5/R est:30000-40000 (N.KR 44000)
£3839 $6028 €5759 Genthinerstrasse in Berlin after the war (28x40cm-11x16in) s.d.1920 lithograph printed in black. 21-Nov-2 Grev Wedels Plass, Oslo #18/R est:30000-40000 (N.KR 44000)
£3982 $6292 €5973 The seducer (44x63cm-17x25in) s. lithograph printed in black. 28-Apr-3 Blomqvist, Oslo #343/R est:55000-65000 (N.KR 45000)
£4000 $6600 €5800 Tete a tete (22x33cm-9x13in) s.i. etching drypoint prov. 2-Jul-3 Christie's, London #145/R est:4000-6000
£4683 $7306 €7025 Lion resting II (35x45cm-14x18in) s. lithograph executed 1920 exhib. 21-Oct-2 Blomqvist, Oslo #464/R est:20000-25000 (N.KR 54000)
£5204 $8118 €7806 The seducer (44x63cm-17x25in) s. lithograph printed in black executed 1913. 21-Oct-2 Blomqvist, Oslo #470/R est:55000-65000 (N.KR 60000)
£5363 $8474 €8045 Young woman (33x34cm-13x13in) s.d.1914 hand col lithograph printed in black. 2-Dec-2 Blomqvist, Oslo #409/R est:40000-50000 (N.KR 62000)
£5769 $9000 €8654 Das weib an der urne (43x29cm-17x11in) s. lithograph edition of 20. 18-Sep-2 Swann Galleries, New York #21/R est:10000-15000
£6000 $9900 €8700 Modellstudie (28x21cm-11x8in) s.i. drypoint prov. 2-Jul-3 Christie's, London #143/R est:6000-8000
£6918 $11000 €10377 Das madchen am fenster (22x16cm-9x6in) s. drypoint roulette burnishing. 29-Apr-3 Christie's, Rockefeller NY #520/R est:8000-12000
£6938 $10824 €10407 Kristiania-Boheme I - 1895 (21x30cm-8x12in) s.i. etching printed in black. 21-Oct-2 Blomqvist, Oslo #465/R est:90000-120000 (N.KR 80000)
£7155 $11234 €10733 Two people (63x55cm-25x22in) i. lithograph printed in black. 21-Nov-2 Grev Wedels Plass, Oslo #9/R est:80000-100000 (N.KR 82000)
£7504 $11782 €11256 Neutralia - girls picking apples (53x50cm-21x20in) s.d.1915 col lithograph in five col. 21-Nov-2 Grev Wedels Plass, Oslo #1/R est:70000-90000 (N.KR 86000)
£7806 $12177 €11709 Women bathing (22x32cm-9x13in) aquatint dry-point papir colle executed 1895. 21-Oct-2 Blomqvist, Oslo #472/R est:60000-80000 (N.KR 90000)
£9811 $15305 €14717 Death and the women (30x22cm-12x9in) s. drypoint printed in black grey lit. 5-Nov-2 Bukowskis, Stockholm #604a/R est:150000-175000 (S.KR 140000)
£10161 $15851 €15242 Moonlight, night in St Cloud (31x25cm-12x10in) s. drypoint aquatint lit. 5-Nov-2 Bukowskis, Stockholm #605/R est:60000-80000 (S.KR 145000)
£12111 $19135 €18167 The violin concert (48x56cm-19x22in) s.i. lithograph printed in black executed 1903. 2-Dec-2 Blomqvist, Oslo #408/R est:180000-220000 (N.KR 140000)
£12821 $19872 €20000 The day after (21x29cm-8x11in) s. drypoint etching. 7-Dec-2 Hauswedell & Nolte, Hamburg #930/R est:15000
£13089 $20550 €19634 Mystical shore (37x57cm-15x22in) s. woodcut printed in black green from two wood blocks. 21-Nov-2 Grev Wedels Plass, Oslo #17/R est:150000-200000 (N.KR 150000)
£13761 $22982 €19953 Henrik Ibsen in Cafe des Grand Hotel, Christiania (43x59cm-17x23in) s. lithograph. 20-Jun-3 Kornfeld, Bern #118/R est:30000 (S.FR 30000)
£13962 $21920 €20943 The girl at the window (20x14cm-8x6in) s.d.1894 etching printed in black. 21-Nov-2 Grev Wedels Plass, Oslo #6/R est:170000-200000 (N.KR 160000)
£14103 $22000 €21155 On the waves of love (32x42cm-13x17in) brown ink burnished aquatint. 5-Nov-2 Christie's, Rockefeller NY #208/R est:15000-25000
£15000 $24750 €21750 Zwei menschen, die einsamen (17x23cm-7x9in) s. i.verso drypoint prov. 2-Jul-3 Christie's, London #140/R est:12000-18000
£16514 $27578 €23945 Comfort (22x32cm-9x13in) s.i. drypoint brush etching. 20-Jun-3 Kornfeld, Bern #117/R est:25000 (S.FR 36000)
£17452 $27400 €26178 Madonna (60x44cm-24x17in) with sig.d.1895/1902 lithograph printed in black. 21-Nov-2 Grev Wedels Plass, Oslo #11/R est:200000-300000 (N.KR 200000)
£17949 $28000 €26924 Puberty (37x30cm-15x12in) s. brownish black etching. 5-Nov-2 Christie's, Rockefeller NY #210/R est:20000-30000
£18599 $29386 €27899 Self portrait (46x32cm-18x13in) s. lithograph printed in black executed 1895. 2-Dec-2 Blomqvist, Oslo #411/R est:150000-200000 (N.KR 215000)
£19000 $31350 €27550 Separation II (41x63cm-16x25in) lithograph prov. 1-Jul-3 Sotheby's, London #111/R est:20000-30000
£21758 $34813 €32637 Old fisherman (44x35cm-17x14in) s.i. handcol woodcut lit. 17-Mar-3 Blomqvist, Oslo #409/R est:150000-200000 (N.KR 250000)
£24359 $38000 €36539 Sick child (51x64cm-20x25in) col lithograph. 5-Nov-2 Christie's, Rockefeller NY #209/R est:18000-22000
£27305 $42323 €40958 The sick child (38x29cm-15x11in) s.d.95 drypoint polished steel on copper panel prov.lit. 8-Dec-2 Uppsala Auktionskammare, Uppsala #303/R est:300000-400000 (S.KR 385000)
£28000 $46200 €40600 Junge frau aum strand (30x22cm-12x9in) col woodcut. 2-Jul-3 Christie's, London #136/R est:30000-50000
£28621 $44649 €42932 Woman with red hair and green eyes (70x40cm-28x16in) s. col lithograph in three colours executed 1902 lit. 21-Oct-2 Blomqvist, Oslo #469/R est:450000-550000 (N.KR 330000)
£29225 $48514 €41500 Madonna - the brooch - Eva Mudocci (68x47cm-27x19in) s.i. lithograph. 14-Jun-3 Hauswedell & Nolte, Hamburg #1461/R est:70000
£34615 $53654 €54000 The heart (25x19cm-10x7in) s. col woodcut. 7-Dec-2 Hauswedell & Nolte, Hamburg #934/R est:26000
£38000 $62700 €55100 Das kranke kink I (36x27cm-14x11in) s.i.d. drypoint prov. 2-Jul-3 Christie's, London #138/R est:20000-30000
£40000 $66000 €58000 Das kranke kind I (42x60cm-17x24in) s. col lithograph prov. 2-Jul-3 Christie's, London #139/R est:25000-35000
£47993 $75349 €71990 The brooch, Eva Mudocci (69x46cm-27x18in) s.i.d.1916 lithograph printed in black. 21-Nov-2 Grev Wedels Plass, Oslo #20/R est:600000-800000 (N.KR 550000)
£59748 $95000 €89622 Madonna (60x44cm-24x17in) s.d.1896 lithograph. 1-May-3 Swann Galleries, New York #544/R est:150000-200000
£95403 $148829 €143105 Moonlight - 1896 (41x47cm-16x19in) s. woodcut in five colours from three plates lit. 21-Oct-2 Blomqvist, Oslo #466/R est:1100000-1300000 (N.KR 1100000)
£120000 $198000 €174000 Das kranke kind (42x57cm-17x22in) s. col lithograph. 2-Jul-3 Christie's, London #137/R est:60000-80000
£135000 $222750 €195750 On the waves of love (50x62cm-20x24in) s. hand col Indian ink graphite lithograph prov. 1-Jul-3 Sotheby's, London #112/R est:70000-80000
£310000 $480500 €465000 Ashes - after the fall (42x53cm-17x21in) hand col lithograph W/C prov. 5-Dec-2 Sotheby's, London #164/R est:250000-300000

Works on paper
£3307 $5292 €4961 Old man with beard (35x25cm-14x10in) s. pencil chl spray technique paper on panel executed c.1883-84. 17-Mar-3 Blomqvist, Oslo #412/R est:70000-80000 (N.KR 38000)
£7500 $12525 €11250 Nude (45x29cm-18x11in) crayons pencil exec c.1920 prov. 26-Jun-3 Christie's, London #373/R est:8000-12000
£11000 $18370 €16500 Portrait of a woman (45x27cm-18x11in) s. W/C exec c.1930 prov. 26-Jun-3 Christie's, London #372/R est:12000-18000
£17000 $27880 €25500 Nude couple (27x41cm-11x16in) i.verso chl prov. 5-Feb-3 Sotheby's, London #132/R est:15000

MUNCH, Gustav Heinrich (1882-?) German
£1083 $1689 €1700 Landscape with river and houses (35x41cm-14x16in) s.i. board lit. 8-Nov-2 Auktionhaus Georg Rehm, Augsburg #8112/R est:2000

MUNCK, Johannes Jacobus Willem de (1866-1943) Dutch
Works on paper
£1250 $2025 €1900 Cigar vendor (49x64cm-19x25in) s.d.1897 pencil W/C htd white. 21-Jan-3 Christie's, Amsterdam #155 est:600-800

MUND, Hugo (1892-1962) Hungarian
£782 $1221 €1134 Nude in front of the drapery (35x48cm-14x19in) s. board. 12-Apr-3 Mu Terem Galeria, Budapest #147/R est:220000 (H.F 280000)

MUNDELL, John (1818-1875) British
£500 $820 €750 Figures on the river bank beside a mill (26x46cm-10x18in) s. 7-Feb-3 Honiton Galleries, Honiton #248/R
£1111 $1800 €1611 Rough seas. Shipping off the coast (25x30cm-10x12in) s. panel pair. 29-Jul-3 Christie's, Rockefeller NY #138/R est:2000-3000
£1440 $2318 €2088 Seascapes (23x44cm-9x17in) s. pair. 12-May-3 Joel, Victoria #400 est:2000-3000 (A.D 3600)
£2450 $3822 €3675 Shipping off the coast in choppy seas (24x44cm-9x17in) s. pair. 10-Sep-2 David Duggleby, Scarborough #281/R est:2500-3500

MUNDO, Ignasi (1918-) Spanish
£709 $1149 €1000 Jardin interior (36x19cm-14x7in) s. panel. 20-May-3 Segre, Madrid #110/R

£1316 $2132 €2000 View of village (60x92cm-24x36in) s.d.74. 21-Jan-3 Ansorena, Madrid #307/R
£1321 $2060 €2100 Landscape (89x116cm-35x46in) s.verso. 8-Oct-2 Ansorena, Madrid #467/R

Works on paper
£258 $408 €400 Street in Barcelona (28x39cm-11x15in) s. wax crayon. 17-Dec-2 Durán, Madrid #586/R

MUNDT, Caroline Emilie (1849-1922) Danish
£299 $475 €449 Landscape with lake (32x22cm-13x9in) s.d.1914. 5-May-3 Rasmussen, Vejle #531 (D.KR 3200)
£553 $874 €830 Interior scene with girl (35x45cm-14x18in) s. 30-Nov-2 Rasmussen, Havnen #2018/R (D.KR 6500)
£555 $899 €805 Garden scene with small girl (37x29cm-15x11in) s.d.84. 24-May-3 Rasmussen, Havnen #2133 (D.KR 5800)
£653 $1038 €980 Children playing (30x25cm-12x10in) mono. 5-May-3 Rasmussen, Vejle #662/R (D.KR 7000)
£1362 $2151 €2043 Girl standing by jetty (118x70cm-46x28in) s.i.d.1886. 2-Dec-2 Rasmussen, Copenhagen #1520/R est:20000 (D.KR 16000)

MUNDUWALAWALA, Ginger Riley (c.1937-) Australian
£2800 $4508 €4200 Untitled (50x63cm-20x25in) acrylic painted c.1990. 6-May-3 Christie's, Melbourne #317/R est:2000-3000 (A.D 7000)

MUNDY, Henry (1919-) British
£1000 $1560 €1500 Indicator (160x152cm-63x60in) s.d.61 s.i.d.verso board. 27-Mar-3 Christie's, Kensington #657/R est:1000-1500

Works on paper
£250 $388 €375 Rooftops (39x32cm-15x13in) d.1961 black chk gouache collage. 4-Dec-2 Christie's, Kensington #362

MUNGER, Anne Wells (1862-1945) American
£3481 $5500 €5222 French Quarter patio (51x56cm-20x22in) s. 5-Apr-3 Neal Auction Company, New Orleans #315/R est:6000-8000

MUNICH SCHOOL (19th C) German
£7051 $10929 €11000 Munich Max-Vorstadt scene with figures (29x40cm-11x16in) 4-Dec-2 Neumeister, Munich #836/R est:2500

MUNIER, Émile (1810-1895) French
£53797 $85000 €80696 Portrait de marie Louise (46x53cm-18x21in) s.d.1880. 24-Apr-3 Sotheby's, New York #60/R est:40000-60000
£69620 $110000 €104430 La jeune fille et la poupee (83x62cm-33x24in) s.d.1882. 24-Apr-3 Sotheby's, New York #9/R est:60000-80000

MUNIER, Hubert (20th C) ?
£1014 $1581 €1500 Milarepa (190x140cm-75x55in) s.i.d.1985 prov. 28-Mar-3 Charbonneaux, Paris #122

MUNIZ, Vik (1961-) Brazilian

Photographs
£2420 $3800 €3630 Orchids (51x41cm-20x16in) s.i.d. gelatin silver print 3 of 3 after Hokusai. 21-Apr-3 Phillips, New York #23/R est:3000-5000
£2744 $4500 €4116 Nietzche, Prodocto de Parma; from the series of philosophers (56x73cm-22x29in) s.i.d.1998 polaroid print one of one prov. 28-May-3 Christie's, Rockefeller NY #154/R est:4000-6000
£3896 $6000 €5844 Lake 18,000 yards (47x58cm-19x23in) s.i.d.1996 num.2/5 gelatin silver print. 25-Oct-2 Phillips, New York #192/R est:6000-8000
£5063 $8000 €7595 Socrates (183x122cm-72x48in) cibachrome print executed 1998 prov.exhib. 14-Nov-2 Christie's, Rockefeller NY #459/R est:10000-15000
£6013 $9500 €9020 Disaster (129x105cm-51x41in) s.i.d.verso cibachrome print prov. 24-Apr-3 Phillips, New York #63/R est:10000-15000
£6329 $10000 €9494 Monster (156x126cm-61x50in) s.i.d.2000 cibachrome print prov. 24-Apr-3 Phillips, New York #228/R est:10000-15000
£7500 $12000 €11250 Wrestlers (160x129cm-63x51in) s.i.d.1998 num.2/3 cibachrome print mounted on foamcore. 15-May-3 Christie's, Rockefeller NY #368/R est:12000-18000
£7595 $12000 €11393 Lincoln (102x96cm-40x38in) s.d.2000 c-print one of 5 prov. 13-Nov-2 Sotheby's, New York #492/R
£10000 $16000 €15000 Fossil (105x146cm-41x57in) s.i.d.1998 num.4/5 verso gelatin silver print prov.lit. 14-May-3 Sotheby's, New York #409/R est:15000-20000
£10759 $17000 €16139 Nadia comaneci (122x152cm-48x60in) s.i.d.2000 cibachrome print prov. 14-Nov-2 Christie's, Rockefeller NY #460/R est:15000-20000
£12658 $20000 €18987 Andy Warhol (152x122cm-60x48in) cibachrome mounted to foamcore executed 1999 prov. 14-Nov-2 Christie's, Rockefeller NY #456/R est:18000-25000
£16456 $26000 €24684 Untitled - after Rodin's kiss picture of chocolate series (213x126cm-84x50in) col coupler print executed 1999 prov. 12-Nov-2 Phillips, New York #172/R est:20000-30000
£18750 $30000 €28125 Chocolate disaster (46x61cm-18x24in) seven cibachrome prints executed 1999 prov. 15-May-3 Christie's, Rockefeller NY #367/R est:25000-35000
£20570 $32500 €30855 Brando (95x82cm-37x32in) c-print exec.1999 prov. 13-Nov-2 Sotheby's, New York #449/R est:18000-22000
£24051 $38000 €36077 Action painter - from picture of chocolate (137x107cm-54x42in) cibachrome print on foamcore executed 1998 prov. 14-Nov-2 Christie's, Rockefeller NY #455/R est:25000-35000
£25316 $40000 €37974 Bloody Marilyn (99x85cm-39x33in) c-print exec.2001 prov. 13-Nov-2 Sotheby's, New York #447/R est:18000-25000
£29688 $47500 €44532 Self portrait - Andy Warhol (157x123cm-62x48in) s.i.d.1999 num.2/3 c-print prov. 14-May-3 Sotheby's, New York #401/R est:20000-30000
£32500 $52000 €48750 Bela Lugosi (122x149cm-48x59in) s.i.d.1999 num.3/3 c-print prov. 14-May-3 Sotheby's, New York #402/R est:20000-30000

MUNKACSI, Martin (20th C) ?

Photographs
£5380 $8500 €8070 Fred Astaire (30x23cm-12x9in) photograph prov.lit. 23-Apr-3 Sotheby's, New York #152/R est:5000-8000

MUNKACSY, Mihaly Lieb (1844-1900) Hungarian
£78245 $122062 €113455 Composition sketch for the painting, Christ before Pilats (107x67cm-42x26in) s.d.1882 prov.exhib. 12-Apr-3 Mu Terem Galeria, Budapest #138/R est:20000000 (H.F 28000000)
£83871 $130000 €125807 Lady seated in an elegant interior (115x90cm-45x35in) s. panel. 30-Oct-2 Christie's, Rockefeller NY #62/R est:40000-60000
£90000 $147600 €135000 Tin drum (92x69cm-36x27in) s.d.1872 panel prov.lit. 3-Jun-3 Sotheby's, London #50/R est:60000-80000
£447115 $697499 €648317 Baby's visitors (110x149cm-43x59in) s.d.1879 panel. 12-Apr-3 Mu Terem Galeria, Budapest #56/R est:60000000 (H.F 160000000)

Works on paper
£474 $734 €711 Sketch for the picture "Ecce homo" (24x21cm-9x8in) pencil dr exec.1895-96. 3-Dec-2 SOGA, Bratislava #92/R (SL.K 30000)
£646 $917 €969 Study for picture "Ecce homo" (21x17cm-8x7in) pencil paper on board. 26-Mar-2 SOGA, Bratislava #122/R (SL.K 41000)
£755 $1170 €1200 Studies of men's heads (21x17cm-8x7in) s.i. pencil. 1-Oct-2 Dorotheum, Vienna #75/R
£17949 $28359 €28000 Collection (22x17cm-9x7in) s.i. pencil 96. 15-Nov-2 Reiss & Sohn, Konigstein #336/R est:10000

MUNN, Paul Sandby (1773-1845) British

Works on paper
£300 $468 €450 Pont-oben-glas, Monmothshire (27x38cm-11x15in) s.indis.d. W/C. 17-Sep-2 Sotheby's, Olympia #100/R
£500 $825 €725 View of Cader Idris (13x22cm-5x9in) s.d.1832 pencil W/C. 3-Jul-3 Christie's, Kensington #119/R
£700 $1092 €1050 Fishing off a beach (21x32cm-8x13in) W/C. 25-Mar-3 Bonhams, Knightsbridge #46/R
£1050 $1565 €1575 View of the Pantheon, Stourhead Gardens, Wilts (20x29cm-8x11in) s.d.1871 W/C. 27-Jun-2 Greenslade Hunt, Taunton #683/R est:700-900

MUNN, Paul Sandby (attrib) (1773-1845) British

Works on paper
£300 $477 €450 Caernarvon Castle (16x23cm-6x9in) i. pen ink W/C. 4-Mar-3 Bearnes, Exeter #349/R

MUNN, Thomas H (fl.1880-1908) British

Works on paper
£260 $411 €377 Flowers and lake in a garden (23x36cm-9x14in) s. W/C. 22-Jul-3 Gorringes, Lewes #1714/R

MUNNICH, Heinz (19/20th C) German
£417 $633 €650 View of Berchtesgaden with Watzmann (80x100cm-31x39in) s. lit. 11-Jul-2 Allgauer, Kempten #2626/R
£881 $1374 €1400 Snowy winter landscape (104x165cm-41x65in) s. 9-Oct-2 Michael Zeller, Lindau #840/R

MUNNIK, Henk (1912-1997) Dutch
£288 $450 €432 Bridge over river. 21-Sep-2 Harvey Clar, Oakland #1414
£704 $1134 €1000 Untitled (79x59cm-31x23in) s. board. 7-May-3 Vendue Huis, Gravenhage #193

MUNNINGHOFF, Xeno (1873-1944) Dutch
£293 $457 €460 Heather landscape with brook and birch trees (59x99cm-23x39in) s. 5-Nov-2 Vendu Notarishuis, Rotterdam #104

MUNNINGS, Sir A (1878-1959) British
£450 $711 €653 Huntsman on horseback with hounds on pathway (20x28cm-8x11in) 24-Jul-3 John Nicholson, Haslemere #1209

MUNNINGS, Sir Alfred (1878-1959) British
£3800 $6080 €5700 Woodland landscape with pond in foreground (56x41cm-22x16in) s.indis.d. 11-Mar-3 Gorringes, Lewes #2353/R est:2000-3000
£7500 $11850 €11250 Willows near Dedham (25x30cm-10x12in) s. panel painted c.1930-35 prov. 27-Nov-2 Christie's, London #16/R
£8000 $12960 €12000 Lamorna cove (30x44cm-12x17in) s. canvas on panel painted c.1913-14. 22-May-3 Christie's, London #69/R est:8000-12000
£9000 $14220 €13500 Portrait of Charles Baxter Nurse (51x41cm-20x16in) s.d.04 prov. 27-Nov-2 Christie's, London #12/R
£10000 $15500 €15000 Cows drinking in a brook (17x25cm-7x10in) panel prov. 4-Dec-2 Sotheby's, London #1/R est:10000-15000
£16500 $26730 €24750 Country lane with distant figures (30x25cm-12x10in) s.indis.d. prov. 22-May-3 Christie's, London #67/R est:15000-25000
£19000 $30780 €28500 Cornish coast between Penzance and Lamorna (51x61cm-20x24in) s.d.1914 prov. 22-May-3 Christie's, London #68/R est:20000-30000
£20000 $31600 €30000 Cow in landscape (63x74cm-25x29in) s. painted c.1910 prov. 27-Nov-2 Christie's, London #15/R est:20000-30000
£25000 $39500 €37500 Study for 'Autumn Tapestry' (30x40cm-12x16in) s. on canvasboard. 27-Nov-2 Christie's, London #58/R est:25000-35000
£30000 $47400 €45000 Polperro (38x46cm-15x18in) s. prov. 27-Nov-2 Christie's, London #11/R est:15000-20000
£32000 $51840 €48000 Study for going to the post (30x39cm-12x15in) s. panel prov. 22-May-3 Christie's, London #70/R est:30000-50000
£68000 $107440 €102000 Langham Mill Pool (51x61cm-20x24in) s.i.d.1923 exhib. 27-Nov-2 Christie's, London #14/R est:30000-50000
£76000 $118560 €114000 Her caravan (63x76cm-25x30in) s. i.stretcher prov. 9-Oct-2 Woolley & Wallis, Salisbury #302/R est:60000-80000
£80000 $124000 €120000 Western hunt, from Zennor Hill (51x61cm-20x24in) s.d.1912 prov. 3-Dec-2 Bonhams, New Bond Street #48/R est:80000-120000
£280000 $442400 €420000 Tightening the girth (41x51cm-16x20in) s.d.1912 prov. 27-Nov-2 Christie's, London #60/R est:300000-500000
£540000 $874800 €810000 Sidney Webster Fish on a dark bay (76x81cm-30x32in) s. prov.lit. 22-May-3 Christie's, London #71/R est:500000-800000
£1350000 $2133000 €2025000 Beryl Riley-Smith on Snowflake (102x126cm-40x50in) s. painted 1925 prov.exhib. 27-Nov-2 Christie's, London #61/R est:600000-800000

Works on paper
£640 $1011 €960 Jockey saddling up (14x20cm-6x8in) s. pencil. 27-Nov-2 Bonhams, Knowle #174
£800 $1336 €1160 Bull (36x28cm-14x11in) init.d.April 9 1902 pencil W/C. 20-Jun-3 Keys, Aylsham #542/R
£820 $1271 €1230 Artist's room (31x50cm-12x20in) s.i.d.Dec.21 98 pen ink wash prov.lit. 30-Sep-2 Bonhams, Ipswich #329/R
£1050 $1649 €1575 Saddling up (18x18cm-7x7in) s. pencil dr. 13-Dec-2 Keys, Aylsham #640 est:500-800
£1100 $1727 €1650 First World War Canadian Cavalry (18x25cm-7x10in) init. pencil dr. 13-Dec-2 Keys, Aylsham #641/R est:1000-1500
£1300 $2054 €1950 Jockey saddling up (16x20cm-6x8in) init. pencil prov. 27-Nov-2 Bonhams, Knowle #173 est:400-600
£1450 $2364 €2175 Huntsman with dogs going out (15x23cm-6x9in) s. pencil dr. 14-Feb-3 Keys, Aylsham #562/R est:500-700
£1725 $2726 €2588 Study of Steve Donohue on horseback (22x17cm-9x7in) s. pencil. 15-Nov-2 Rowley Fine Art, Newmarket #382
£2200 $3432 €3300 Three studies of a race horse (25x18cm-10x7in) s. pencil dr. 11-Apr-3 Keys, Aylsham #562/R est:600-800
£3000 $5010 €4350 Return from the fields (29x15cm-11x6in) s.d.1906 W/C over pencil. 24-Jun-3 Bonhams, New Bond Street #15/R est:2500-4000
£3200 $5056 €4800 Woods near Noyon, 1918 attack our retreat (22x26cm-9x10in) s.i. W/C prov. 27-Nov-2 Sotheby's, Olympia #34/R est:3000-4000
£3500 $5705 €5250 Poster designs for Bullards (36x28cm-14x11in) init. W/C. 14-Feb-3 Keys, Aylsham #563/R est:3500-4500
£3800 $5966 €5700 Sweet fragrance (41x25cm-16x10in) s.d.99 monotone W/C htd white. 13-Dec-2 Keys, Aylsham #642 est:5000-7000
£10000 $16500 €14500 White cow and others in a landscape (20x27cm-8x11in) s.d.01 W/C prov. 1-Jul-3 Bonhams, Norwich #197/R est:10000-15000
£17000 $26860 €25500 Cavalry brigade headquarters, France (25x35cm-10x14in) s.i.d.1918 W/C bodycol prov.exhib. 27-Nov-2 Christie's, London #59/R est:12000-18000
£20000 $32000 €30000 Study for the ford (25x30cm-10x12in) s. W/C. 11-Mar-3 Gorringes, Lewes #2403/R est:20000-25000
£58000 $89900 €87000 Gypsy camp with horses and hens (31x47cm-12x19in) s.d.1908 W/C exhib. 4-Dec-2 Sotheby's, London #5/R est:60000-80000
£78000 $127920 €113100 The Halfway House (34x49cm-13x19in) s.d.1907 W/C gouache pencil prov. 4-Jun-3 Sotheby's, London #8/R est:25000-35000

MUNNS, Henry Turner (1832-1898) British
£1026 $1559 €1600 English beauty wearing hat in windy weather (61x51cm-24x20in) s.d.1889 lit. 17-Aug-2 Hans Stahl, Toestorf #59 est:1700
£12500 $20375 €18750 Gambler (87x107cm-34x42in) s.d.1894. 29-Jan-3 Sotheby's, Olympia #212/R est:3000-5000

MUNOZ BARBERAN, Manuel (1921-) Spanish
£1509 $2355 €2400 Aguilas beach (50x61cm-20x24in) s.d.85 s.i.d.verso board. 8-Oct-2 Ansorena, Madrid #469/R

MUNOZ LORENTE, Jose (1932-1988) Spanish
£252 $392 €400 Bull (61x50cm-24x20in) s. s.i.d.1956 verso board. 23-Sep-2 Durán, Madrid #636/R

MUNOZ RUBIO (19th C) Spanish
£3600 $5616 €5400 Greeting. Courtship (74x40cm-29x16in) s. pair. 26-Mar-3 Sotheby's, Olympia #203/R est:2000-3000

MUNOZ RUBIO, Ramon (19th C) Spanish
£1149 $1792 €1700 Procession (30x41cm-12x16in) s. 25-Mar-3 Durán, Madrid #165/R

Works on paper
£1517 $2412 €2200 Snack in the fields (23x34cm-9x13in) s. gouache. 4-Mar-3 Ansorena, Madrid #308/R

MUNOZ Y CUESTA, Domingo (1850-1912) Spanish
£2044 $3189 €3250 Military mail (50x60cm-20x24in) s.d.1905. 23-Sep-2 Durán, Madrid #249/R
£5031 $7849 €8000 Fight in the inn (38x46cm-15x18in) s. 23-Sep-2 Durán, Madrid #250/R

MUNOZ Y LUCENA, Tomas (1860-1943) Spanish
£2120 $3350 €3180 Spanish party (15x29cm-6x11in) s. board. 15-Nov-2 Naón & Cia, Buenos Aires #116/R
£16250 $24700 €24375 Deleitandose con el canario (75x121cm-30x48in) 3-Jul-2 Naón & Cia, Buenos Aires #2/R est:12000-15000

MUNOZ Y LUCENA, Tomas (attrib) (1860-1943) Spanish
£3019 $4679 €4800 At the well (74x48cm-29x19in) 7-Oct-2 Ansorena, Madrid #60/R est:3600

MUNOZ, Ana Maria (1947-) Spanish
£755 $1162 €1200 Landscape (36x27cm-14x11in) s. board. 22-Oct-2 Durán, Madrid #155/R
£755 $1177 €1200 Girl combing her hair (35x40cm-14x16in) s. board. 23-Sep-2 Durán, Madrid #89/R

MUNOZ, Blas (1620-?) Spanish
£1293 $2055 €1900 Saint Francis imploring Christ (102x77cm-40x30in) s.d.1687. 21-Mar-3 Millon & Associes, Paris #4

MUNOZ, Godofredo Ortega (1905-1982) Spanish
£11724 $18759 €17000 Landscape (42x35cm-17x14in) s. board. 11-Mar-3 Castellana, Madrid #68/R est:15000
£14286 $20857 €22000 Landscape (65x81cm-26x32in) s. 12-Jun-2 Castellana, Madrid #102/R est:25000
£38961 $56883 €60000 Landscape with donkey (68x60cm-27x24in) s. s.verso painted 1948. 17-Jun-2 Ansorena, Madrid #63/R est:36000

MUNOZ, Juan (1953-2001) Spanish
£5500 $8690 €8250 Raincoat drawing (115x95cm-45x37in) paint oilstick prov. 3-Apr-3 Christie's, Kensington #191/R

Sculpture
£10500 $17220 €15750 Pullover (97x118x54cm-38x46x21in) wooden chest of drawers pullovers loudspeakers CD player disc. 6-Feb-3 Christie's, London #760/R est:6000-8000
£11000 $16940 €16500 Untitled (27x12x10cm-11x5x4in) chk terracotta executed c.1992 prov. 22-Oct-2 Sotheby's, London #373/R est:10000-15000
£24000 $39360 €36000 Untitled, handrail (9x189x12cm-4x74x5in) wood bronze iron exec.c.1988 prov.exhib. 7-Feb-3 Sotheby's, London #152/R est:4000-6000
£60000 $98400 €90000 Untitled (98x54x55cm-39x21x22in) painted papier-mache exec.c.1996 prov. 7-Feb-3 Sotheby's, London #130/R est:35000-45000
£70000 $114800 €105000 London conversation piece I (155x88x67cm-61x35x26in) resin fibreglass sand executed 1993 prov.exhib. 5-Feb-3 Christie's, London #24/R est:60000-80000
£80000 $131200 €120000 Untitled (87x135x87cm-34x53x34in) table resin mirrors exec.2001 prov. 6-Feb-3 Sotheby's, London #48/R est:120000

MUNOZ, Lucio (1929-1998) Spanish
£9655 $15255 €14000 True blue (73x60cm-29x24in) s.i.d.1980 verso panel prov.lit. 1-Apr-3 Segre, Madrid #208/R est:14000

MUNOZ-DEGRAIN, Antoine (1843-1924) French
£1818 $2655 €2800 Rocky landscape (21x34cm-8x13in) s. canvas on board. 17-Jun-2 Ansorena, Madrid #149
£2404 $3798 €3750 Deposition (46x30cm-18x12in) s. board. 19-Nov-2 Durán, Madrid #191/R
£4138 $6538 €6000 Coastal landscape (51x76cm-20x30in) s. 1-Apr-3 Segre, Madrid #115/R

MUNOZ-VERA, Guillermo (1949-) Chilean
£14189 $22135 €21000 Oriente Palace (134x113cm-53x44in) s.d.87. 25-Mar-3 Durán, Madrid #204/R est:21000
£19817 $32500 €28735 Alacena azul IV (100x152cm-39x60in) s.d.02 oil acrylic canvas on wood prov. 27-May-3 Sotheby's, New York #69
£26829 $44000 €40244 Libros antiguos y palmatoria (100x150cm-39x59in) mono.d.2002 canvas on panel prov.exhib. 28-May-3 Christie's, Rockefeller NY #31/R est:50000-70000
£44586 $70000 €66879 Three capes (122x200cm-48x79in) s.i. canvas on panel painted 1999-2000 prov. 20-Nov-2 Christie's, Rockefeller NY #35/R est:80000-100000
Works on paper
£4110 $6411 €6000 Still life (39x90cm-15x35in) s.d.92 pastel. 8-Apr-3 Ansorena, Madrid #265/R

MUNRO, Alexander (1825-1871) British
Sculpture
£4000 $6240 €6000 Portrait relief of Lady Constance Grosvenor (57cm-22in) mono. white painted plaster giltwood oval lit. 9-Apr-3 Sotheby's, London #105/R est:1000-1500

MUNRO, Alexander Graham (fl.1923-1940) British
£6000 $9360 €9000 Martigues (10x127cm-4x50in) s. 14-Apr-3 Sotheby's, London #119/R est:6000-8000

MUNRO, Hugh (1873-1928) British
£1500 $2340 €2250 Travelers on the moor (40x40cm-16x16in) panel. 14-Apr-3 Sotheby's, London #163/R est:1000-1500
£2800 $4284 €4200 Home from the fields (46x35cm-18x14in) s. 22-Aug-2 Bonhams, Edinburgh #1067/R est:3000-5000

MUNRO, Peter (1954-) British
£900 $1494 €1305 Two springer spaniels on a moor (46x61cm-18x24in) s.d.2000. 12-Jun-3 Christie's, Kensington #306/R

MUNRO, Robert Henry (1886-?) British
£620 $1035 €899 Fall of Icarus (60x91cm-24x36in) s. 17-Jun-3 Anderson & Garland, Newcastle #418/R

MUNSCH, Josef (1832-1896) Austrian
£1027 $1603 €1500 Mountain landscape on moonlit night (74x101cm-29x40in) bears sig. 10-Apr-3 Dorotheum, Vienna #231 est:1600-1800
£9000 $13950 €13500 Gamblers (31x42cm-12x17in) s.i. panel prov. 4-Dec-2 Christie's, London #83/R est:10000-15000

MUNSCH, Leopold (1826-1888) Austrian
£890 $1389 €1300 Working on the farmstead (29x22cm-11x9in) s. board. 10-Apr-3 Dorotheum, Vienna #15/R

MUNSON, J S (19th C) American
£2884 $4500 €4326 Portrait of a girl holding a basket of flowers (124x99cm-49x39in) i.d.1847 verso sold with an oil and family bible prov. 21-Sep-2 Pook & Pook, Downington #249/R est:15000-20000

MUNSON, K O (20th C) American
Works on paper
£1656 $2600 €2484 Young woman (81x61cm-32x24in) s. pastel. 20-Nov-2 Boos Gallery, Michigan #451/R est:2500-3500

MUNSTERFELD, F (?) ?
Works on paper
£576 $921 €800 Rural district (35x49cm-14x19in) s.d.6.9.1895 pencil. 17-May-3 Hagelstam, Helsinki #57/R

MUNSTERHJELM, Ali (1873-1944) Finnish
£252 $390 €400 Church in evening light (62x46cm-24x18in) s. 6-Oct-2 Bukowskis, Helsinki #231/R
£432 $708 €600 Stansvik (58x108cm-23x43in) s.d.1927. 5-Jun-3 Hagelstam, Helsinki #883
£612 $973 €900 Church (65x46cm-26x18in) s. 24-Mar-3 Bukowskis, Helsinki #186/R
£791 $1298 €1100 Landscape with Skatudden (51x66cm-20x26in) s. 5-Jun-3 Hagelstam, Helsinki #975/R
£918 $1460 €1350 Ship-yard (60x47cm-24x19in) s. 27-Feb-3 Hagelstam, Helsinki #974
£1069 $1647 €1700 In the harbour (56x76cm-22x30in) s.i.d.1914. 27-Oct-2 Bukowskis, Helsinki #242/R est:1500
£1088 $1731 €1600 The shore by Aura river (606x989cm-239x389in) s. 24-Mar-3 Bukowskis, Helsinki #187/R est:1700
£1307 $2144 €2000 Snow covered pine (64x48cm-25x19in) s. 9-Feb-3 Bukowskis, Helsinki #310/R est:1700
£1307 $2144 €2000 Autumn in Aabo (67x48cm-26x19in) s.d.32. 9-Feb-3 Bukowskis, Helsinki #311/R est:1000
£1392 $2200 €2200 Aura river (50x67cm-20x26in) s. 30-Nov-2 Hagelstam, Helsinki #138/R est:2500
£1392 $2200 €2200 View from Aabo (52x67cm-20x26in) s. 1-Dec-2 Bukowskis, Helsinki #120/R est:2500-3000
£1519 $2370 €2400 Aura river (50x67cm-20x26in) s. 12-Sep-2 Hagelstam, Helsinki #946/R est:3000
£1582 $2500 €2500 Winter view from Sandviken (50x66cm-20x26in) s. 1-Dec-2 Bukowskis, Helsinki #121/R est:2500-3000
£1613 $2548 €2500 Landscape (150x130cm-59x51in) s. 19-Dec-2 Hagelstam, Helsinki #947 est:3000
£1698 $2615 €2700 Harbour (53x68cm-21x27in) s. 24-Oct-2 Hagelstam, Helsinki #869/R est:2500
£2041 $3245 €3000 View from Aura river (51x67cm-20x26in) s. 24-Mar-3 Bukowskis, Helsinki #189/R est:2000
£2177 $3461 €3200 Aura river (46x67cm-18x26in) s. 27-Feb-3 Hagelstam, Helsinki #951/R est:2500
£2278 $3600 €3600 Beach huts (80x120cm-31x47in) s. 30-Nov-2 Hagelstam, Helsinki #137/R est:3200
£3165 $5000 €5000 Aura river in winter (46x66cm-18x26in) s. 30-Nov-2 Hagelstam, Helsinki #80/R est:3000
£12658 $20000 €20000 Winter night (23x37cm-9x15in) s. panel. 1-Dec-2 Bukowskis, Helsinki #124/R est:20000-22000

MUNSTERHJELM, Hjalmar (1840-1905) Finnish
£619 $1015 €860 Landscape (28x42cm-11x17in) sketch lit. 5-Jun-3 Hagelstam, Helsinki #913
£2314 $3656 €3471 Stone wall covered in moss (27x35cm-11x14in) s.d.1863 paper prov. 27-Nov-2 Falkkloos, Malmo #77529/R est:40000 (S.KR 33000)
£2484 $4073 €3800 The old wall (28x35cm-11x14in) s.d.1863. 9-Feb-3 Bukowskis, Helsinki #312/R est:4000
£6329 $10000 €10000 The road to the Alpine mountains (19x31cm-7x12in) s. board. 1-Dec-2 Bukowskis, Helsinki #128/R est:10000-12000
£6479 $10431 €9200 Moonlit landscape (23x31cm-9x12in) s. panel. 10-May-3 Bukowskis, Helsinki #152/R est:8000-10000
£10127 $16000 €16000 Landscape from Ekenas skerries (22x29cm-9x11in) s. board. 1-Dec-2 Bukowskis, Helsinki #127/R est:12000-15000
£11268 $18141 €16000 Coastal landscape with beached boat (47x34cm-19x13in) s. 10-May-3 Bukowskis, Helsinki #170/R est:15000-18000
£12658 $20000 €20000 Cattle in by coast, Tulois (57x63cm-22x25in) s. 30-Nov-2 Hagelstam, Helsinki #96/R est:20000
£12676 $20408 €18000 Sailing in Ekenas skerries (17x36cm-7x14in) s. panel. 10-May-3 Bukowskis, Helsinki #185/R est:10000-12000
£13380 $21542 €19000 Hazy morning (36x65cm-14x26in) s.d.79. 10-May-3 Bukowskis, Helsinki #143/R est:20000-25000
£16456 $26000 €26000 Summer haze (25x42cm-10x17in) s. board. 1-Dec-2 Bukowskis, Helsinki #125/R est:20000-22000
£35211 $56690 €50000 Winter landscape with horses and sleighs (53x89cm-21x35in) s.d.1869. 10-May-3 Bukowskis, Helsinki #50/R est:50000-60000
Works on paper
£1266 $2000 €2000 Reflections (8x13cm-3x5in) s. W/C. 1-Dec-2 Bukowskis, Helsinki #129/R est:1200-1500

MUNTEAN, Markus and ROSENBLUM, Adi (1962-) Austrian/Israeli
£962 $1490 €1500 Untitled (40x30cm-16x12in) i. 4-Dec-2 Finarte, Milan #453/R

MUNTER, David Heinrich (1816-1879) German
£510 $811 €750 Windmill and shepherd with flock near windmill (44x63cm-17x25in) 28-Mar-3 Bolland & Marotz, Bremen #502/R
£2381 $3786 €3500 Farmstead in trees near Bremen (66x86cm-26x34in) s. 28-Mar-3 Bolland & Marotz, Bremen #501/R est:3500

MUNTER, Gabriele (1877-1962) German
£10256 $15897 €16000 White irises in vase (48x34cm-19x13in) s.i.d.1916 board. 4-Dec-2 Lempertz, Koln #945/R est:12000-15000
£11538 $16846 €18000 Poppies and other flowers (43x30cm-17x12in) mono.i.d.55 paper. 4-Jun-2 Karl & Faber, Munich #366/R est:15000-17000
£13462 $20865 €21000 Flowers M 4 (45x33cm-18x13in) s.i. board on panel prov. 4-Dec-2 Lempertz, Koln #946/R est:25000-30000
£16026 $25000 €24039 Dorfkirche in Froschhausen (39x26cm-15x10in) init. d.1908 verso paperboard prov. 14-Oct-2 Butterfields, San Francisco #2010/R est:30000-50000
£17986 $29496 €25000 Pink tree trunk and landscape (37x48cm-15x19in) mono.i.d.5/60 oil pen Indian ink over pencil prov. 6-Jun-3 Ketterer, Munich #87/R est:25000-35000

£18116 $29710 €25000 Still life with oranges (48x39cm-19x15in) mono. board. 31-May-3 Villa Grisebach, Berlin #233/R est:25000-30000
£22436 $34776 €35000 Tunis landscape (25x48cm-10x19in) painted 1905 prov.exhib. 6-Dec-2 Ketterer, Munich #23/R est:40000-60000
£23718 $34628 €37000 Peonies and other flowers in blue vases (33x41cm-13x16in) s. paper on board. 4-Jun-2 Karl & Faber, Munich #365/R est:30000-32000
£25316 $40000 €40000 Melting snows in village - Murnau (33x45cm-13x18in) s.d.1948 s.i.d. verso board exhib.prov. 30-Nov-2 Villa Grisebach, Berlin #257/R est:40000-50000
£26923 $41731 €42000 In Stockholm (60x45cm-24x18in) init.d.1916 s.i.d. verso prov. 6-Dec-2 Ketterer, Munich #38/R est:40000-60000
£27536 $45159 €38000 Mountain mill near Marone (33x41cm-13x16in) i. stretcher prov. 31-May-3 Villa Grisebach, Berlin #167/R est:35000-45000
£37324 $61958 €53000 St Cloud park in autumn (21x32cm-8x13in) s.d. 14-Jun-3 Hauswedell & Nolte, Hamburg #1459/R est:60000
£43590 $67564 €68000 Avenue of birch trees (33x41cm-13x16in) s.d.1923 i.verso cardboard prov. 6-Dec-2 Ketterer, Munich #84/R est:50000-70000
£50000 $81500 €75000 Rosa stilleben (42x73cm-17x29in) s. s.i.d.1908-9 verso board. 3-Feb-3 Bonhams, New Bond Street #23/R est:8000-12000
£50641 $78494 €79000 Study of landscape with autumnal tree (41x33cm-16x13in) st.sig.verso card painted 1937. 4-Dec-2 Lempertz, Koln #22/R est:60000-80000
£64103 $99359 €100000 Lake Staffel (33x44cm-13x17in) s.d.1932 cardboard prov. 6-Dec-2 Ketterer, Munich #91/R est:80000-100000
£85443 $135000 €135000 Lake on Easter day (50x65cm-20x26in) s.d.1935 s.i.d.1935 verso prov. 29-Nov-2 Villa Grisebach, Berlin #22/R est:100000-150000
£86957 $142609 €120000 Vase with two miniature Madonna's (30x40cm-12x16in) s. s. verso i. stretcher prov. 29-May-3 Lempertz, Koln #822/R est:130000-150000
£105129 $153488 €164000 Portrait of young woman wearing large hat - Polin (70x50cm-28x20in) d.1909 verso board. 4-Jun-2 Karl & Faber, Munich #364/R est:130000-135000
£124224 $200000 €186336 Entwurf heuwagen - study of a haywagon (33x41cm-13x16in) s.d.1908 i.verso board prov.exhib. 7-May-3 Sotheby's, New York #222/R est:150000-200000
£130435 $213913 €180000 Clouds over castle, Murnau (73x54cm-29x21in) s.d.1939 i.stretcher prov. 30-May-3 Villa Grisebach, Berlin #13/R est:130000-160000

Prints

£2297 $3584 €3400 Gabriele Munter's house in Murnau (9x12cm-4x5in) linocut board. 28-Mar-3 Ketterer, Hamburg #517 est:1200-1400

Works on paper

£10759 $17000 €17000 Wilting poppies (61x45cm-24x18in) mono.d.1960 s.i.verso W/C gouache brush ink over pencil prov. 29-Nov-2 Villa Grisebach, Berlin #46/R est:14000-16000
£13768 $22580 €19000 Birthday table (32x45cm-13x18in) mono.i.d.54.26.11 gouache over pencil prov. 29-May-3 Lempertz, Koln #824/R est:16000-18000

MUNTHE, Gerhard Peter Franz Vilhelm (1849-1929) Norwegian

£954 $1488 €1431 Farmer's wife from Elverum (22x23cm-9x9in) s. canvas on panel. 21-Oct-2 Blomqvist, Oslo #336/R (N.KR 11000)
£1416 $2237 €2124 Figures by edge of river (26x35cm-10x14in) s.d.85 panel. 28-Apr-3 Blomqvist, Oslo #300/R est:20000-30000 (N.KR 16000)
£1500 $2355 €2250 Boats moored on the beach (21x32cm-8x13in) s. 16-Dec-2 Sotheby's, Olympia #36/R est:300-500
£6071 $9471 €9107 An apple seller in a mountain village (24x38cm-9x15in) s.d.77 prov.lit. 21-Oct-2 Blomqvist, Oslo #302/R est:25000-35000 (N.KR 70000)
£15707 $24660 €23561 Sitting room with open fire place in the artist's home, Leveld, Lysaker (60x90cm-24x35in) s.d.1917 i.verso exhib. 21-Nov-2 Grev Wedels Plass, Oslo #11/R est:180000-200000 (N.KR 180000)
£19147 $30635 €28721 Interior of the room with open fire at Leveld (65x80cm-26x31in) s.i.indis.d. lit. 17-Mar-3 Blomqvist, Oslo #364/R est:150000-180000 (N.KR 220000)

Works on paper

£346 $530 €519 From Etzenhausen (22x33cm-9x13in) s. W/C executed 1907. 26-Aug-2 Blomqvist, Lysaker #1272/R (N.KR 4000)
£645 $1000 €968 Bringing the catch (18x23cm-7x9in) s.d.22 W/C. 7-Dec-2 Neal Auction Company, New Orleans #634 est:1000-1500
£1730 $2734 €2595 Christmas Day from the artist's home Leveld at Lysaker (21x22cm-8x9in) s.d.27 i.d.verso W/C. 2-Dec-2 Blomqvist, Oslo #395/R est:15000-18000 (N.KR 20000)
£6028 $9344 €9042 The suitors (36x45cm-14x18in) s. W/C exhib. 3-Dec-2 Bukowskis, Stockholm #55/R est:60000-80000 (S.KR 85000)

MUNTHE, Ludvig (1841-1896) Norwegian

£1286 $2108 €1865 Boy and fox by bridge in winter landscape (33x49cm-13x19in) s.d.63 exhib. 2-Jun-3 Blomqvist, Oslo #167/R est:20000-25000 (N.KR 14000)
£2483 $4022 €3600 Coastal landscape with boats and fishermen, evening (68x101cm-27x40in) s. prov. 25-May-3 Uppsala Auktionskammare, Uppsala #70/R est:40000-60000 (S.KR 32000)
£4799 $7535 €7199 German landscape with figures (76x110cm-30x43in) s.i.d.1869. 21-Nov-2 Grev Wedels Plass, Oslo #28/R est:80000-100000 (N.KR 55000)

MUNTHE-NORSTEDT, Anna (1854-1936) Swedish

£746 $1224 €1082 Tulips and narcissus - and A frog (19x24cm-7x9in) s.i.d.1907 panel two in one frame. 4-Jun-3 AB Stockholms Auktionsverk #2120/R (S.KR 9500)
£851 $1319 €1277 Still life of green grapes, apple and hock-glass (22x31cm-9x12in) s.d.1884 panel. 3-Dec-2 Bukowskis, Stockholm #21/R (S.KR 12000)
£860 $1376 €1247 Still life (24x13cm-9x5in) s.d.1916 panel. 18-May-3 Anders Antik, Landskrona #25 (S.KR 11000)
£931 $1508 €1350 Still life of green grapes and wine (38x46cm-15x18in) s.d.1902. 26-May-3 Bukowskis, Stockholm #135/R (S.KR 12000)
£970 $1571 €1407 Still life of fruit and flowers (23x32cm-9x13in) s.d.1903 canvas on panel. 26-May-3 Bukowskis, Stockholm #136/R (S.KR 12500)

MUNTZ-ADAMS, Josephine (1861-1950) Australian

£561 $853 €842 Corotesque (14x22cm-6x9in) s. exhib. 19-Aug-2 Joel, Victoria #146 est:1500-2500 (A.D 1600)
£1280 $2061 €1920 Studio nude in mirror. Study two nudes (43x33cm-17x13in) board double-sided. 6-May-3 Christie's, Melbourne #275/R est:3000-4000 (A.D 3200)
£4070 $6471 €6105 Portrait of Stella White (99x73cm-39x29in) s. 5-May-3 Sotheby's, Melbourne #290/R est:5000-7000 (A.D 10500)

MURA, Angelo della (1867-1922) Italian

£1307 $2105 €2000 Vue d'Amalfi (38x19cm-15x7in) s.i. panel. 20-Jan-3 Horta, Bruxelles #245 est:2000-3000

MURA, Francesco de (1696-1782) Italian

£8500 $13345 €12750 Madonna and Child (45x36cm-18x14in) copper oval. 10-Dec-2 Bonhams, New Bond Street #288/R est:3000-5000
£14465 $22277 €23000 Agar and the angel (73x98cm-29x39in) 23-Oct-2 Finarte, Rome #531/R est:25000-30000

MURA, Francesco de (circle) (1696-1782) Italian

£6000 $9420 €9000 Daughter of Jethro (115x184cm-45x72in) 10-Dec-2 Bonhams, New Bond Street #187/R est:6000-8000

MURA, Frank (1861-?) American

£400 $624 €600 Abbeville (18x29cm-7x11in) indis.sig. paper laid down. 10-Apr-3 Bonhams, Edinburgh #103

MURAKAMI, Takashi (1962-) Japanese

£3000 $4920 €4500 Untitled (89x59cm-35x23in) s.d.1992 verso acrylic plastic toy soldiers board. 7-Feb-3 Sotheby's, London #128/R est:4000-6000
£10127 $16000 €15191 Untitled (40x40cm-16x16in) s.d.00 verso acrylic canvas on panel prov. 14-Nov-2 Christie's, Rockefeller NY #303/R est:15000-20000
£15000 $24000 €22500 Tara (53x65cm-21x26in) s.d.97 acrylic prov.exhib. 15-May-3 Christie's, Rockefeller NY #325/R est:15000-20000
£16456 $26000 €24684 Mushroom painting no.2 (40x40cm-16x16in) s.d.00 verso acrylic canvas on panel prov. 14-Nov-2 Christie's, Rockefeller NY #301/R est:15000-20000
£21528 $35521 €31000 Mushrooms (40x40cm-16x16in) s.d.00 acrylic canvas on panel prov. 1-Jul-3 Artcurial Briest, Paris #545/R est:20000-25000
£27083 $44688 €39000 Jellyfish eyes cream (40x40cm-16x16in) s.d.2000 verso acrylic canvas on wood prov. 1-Jul-3 Artcurial Briest, Paris #544/R est:20000-25000
£93750 $150000 €140625 Fujisan (100x100cm-39x39in) acrylic canvas on board painted 2000 prov. 14-May-3 Sotheby's, New York #316/R est:40000-60000
£162500 $260000 €243750 Magic ball II - negative (240x630cm-94x248in) acrylic canvas mounted on board in seven parts painted 1999. 15-May-3 Phillips, New York #6/R est:250000-350000
£175000 $280000 €262500 Dream of opposite world (180x180cm-71x71in) s.d.99 verso acrylic canvas on panel prov.exhib.lit. 15-May-3 Christie's, Rockefeller NY #324/R est:100000-150000

£210000 $350700 €315000 And then, and then and then and then and then (100x100cm-39x39in) acrylic canvas on board i exc.1994 ii exc.1996 two prov.exhib. 25-Jun-3 Sotheby's, London #8/R est:70000-90000

£240506 $380000 €360759 When the double helix is aroused l hear a familiar voice (250x399cm-98x157in) s. acrylic canvas on three panel painted 1999 prov.exhib. 13-Nov-2 Christie's, Rockefeller NY #6/R est:150000-200000

Sculpture

£312500 $500000 €468750 Miss Ko (188x61x89cm-74x24x35in) painted fiberglass one of 3 exec.1966 prov.lit. 14-May-3 Christie's, Rockefeller NY #4/R est:300000-400000

MURANT, Emanuel (1622-1700) Dutch

£8917 $13911 €14000 Two women, some sheep and a rooster near a pond in the courtyard of a farmhouse (33x44cm-13x17in) s. panel prov. 5-Nov-2 Sotheby's, Amsterdam #218/R est:10000-15000

MURATA, San (20th C) Canadian/Japanese

Works on paper

£191 $299 €287 France (31x39cm-12x15in) s.d.2000 W/C pastel. 25-Nov-2 Hodgins, Calgary #362/R (C.D 475)

MURATON, Alfonso (19th C) French

£435 $635 €670 Franciscan monk (76x57cm-30x22in) s.indis.d. 17-Jun-2 Ansorena, Madrid #198/R

MURATON, Euphemie (1840-?) French

£1572 $2452 €2358 Still life with peaches, apples and pears (35x50cm-14x20in) s. 6-Nov-2 Dobiaschofsky, Bern #855/R est:3500 (S.FR 3600)

MURATON, Frederic Alphonse (1824-1911) French

Works on paper

£3793 $6031 €5500 Lady with jewels. Lady with flowers (81x65cm-32x26in) s.d.1861 pastel pair oval. 9-Mar-3 Semenzato, Venice #3/R

MURATTA, Kishio (20th C) Japanese

£265 $425 €398 Cinta Roja (52x45cm-20x18in) s.d.1966 i.verso. 16-Mar-3 Butterfields, San Francisco #31207

MURAVIEV, Graf (19/20th C) Russian

£15823 $25000 €25000 Birds in winter forest (98x143cm-39x56in) s.d.1912. 1-Dec-2 Bukowskis, Helsinki #268/R est:15000-20000

Works on paper

£2658 $4200 €4200 Winter landscape with fox (50x34cm-20x13in) s.d.1901 gouache. 1-Dec-2 Bukowskis, Helsinki #267/R est:2000-3000

MURAVYOV, Count Vladimir Leonidovich (1861-1915) Russian

£818 $1267 €1300 Animals in winter wood (20x30cm-8x12in) s.cyrillic panel. 29-Oct-2 Dorotheum, Vienna #193

£14789 $23810 €21000 Blackcocks in forest (66x102cm-26x40in) s.d.1909 oil tempera board. 10-May-3 Bukowskis, Helsinki #404/R est:16000-18000

Works on paper

£11000 $17820 €16500 Hunting scenes (30x48cm-12x19in) s.d.1905-07 gouache on card set of three. 21-May-3 Sotheby's, London #49/R est:9000-12000

£13000 $21060 €19500 Hunting scenes with capercaille (48x65cm-19x26in) one s. s.d.1900 gouache on card two. 21-May-3 Sotheby's, London #50/R est:8000-12000

£17000 $27540 €25500 Hunting scenes with fox and elk (30x48cm-12x19in) s.d.1907 gouache on card set of three. 21-May-3 Sotheby's, London #48/R est:9000-12000

MURCH, Arthur (1902-1990) Australian

£498 $762 €747 Memory of Albury (51x61cm-20x24in) board painted c.1958 prov. 26-Aug-2 Sotheby's, Paddington #588 est:1500-2500 (A.D 1400)

£536 $841 €804 Still life camellias (39x29cm-15x11in) s. board. 25-Nov-2 Christie's, Melbourne #264/R (A.D 1500)

£573 $872 €860 Road to the mountains (45x56cm-18x22in) s. board. 28-Aug-2 Deutscher-Menzies, Melbourne #374/R (A.D 1600)

£690 $1083 €1035 Mother and child (37x30cm-15x12in) s. board. 15-Apr-3 Lawson Menzies, Sydney #165/R est:2000-4000 (A.D 1800)

£786 $1218 €1179 Flowers (58x44cm-23x17in) s. board. 29-Oct-2 Lawson Menzies, Sydney #18/R (A.D 2200)

£1071 $1682 €1607 Mother and child (29x37cm-11x15in) s. board. 25-Nov-2 Christie's, Melbourne #465 est:1500-2000 (A.D 3000)

£1163 $1849 €1745 Resting (39x49cm-15x19in) s. board. 5-May-3 Sotheby's, Melbourne #278/R est:3000-5000 (A.D 3000)

£1423 $2178 €2135 Boy and goat (39x55cm-15x22in) s. canvas on panel. 25-Aug-2 Sotheby's, Paddington #170/R est:2000-4000 (A.D 4000)

Works on paper

£287 $436 €431 Seated nude (47x42cm-19x17in) s.d.1960 pastel. 27-Aug-2 Goodman, Sydney #73 (A.D 800)

MURCH, Walter (1907-1967) American/Canadian

£3822 $6000 €5733 Radio telescope (18x18cm 7x7in) s. prov.exhib. 19-Nov-2 Wright, Chicago #213/R est:2000-3000

£14151 $22500 €21227 Gear (58x41cm-23x16in) s. painted 1950 prov.exhib.lit. 5-Mar-3 Sotheby's, New York #79/R est:10000-15000

Works on paper

£1210 $1900 €1815 I-beam, kettle, ball bearing. Telex, head maps (9x14cm-4x6in) mixed media drs pair prov. 19-Nov-2 Wright, Chicago #214/R est:600-800

MURDFIELD, Carl (1868-?) German

£335 $520 €530 Portrait of Wilhelm II (72x52cm-28x20in) s. 27-Sep-2 Venator & Hansten, Koln #1186

MURDOCH, C R (19th C) British

£982 $1600 €1473 Setter seated in a landscape (33x41cm-13x16in) s.i.d.1864. 11-Feb-3 Bonhams & Doyles, New York #112 est:2000-3000

MURDOCH, William Duff (fl.1899-1923) British

£457 $750 €663 Cows watering at a stream (61x46cm-24x18in) s.d.76. 4-Jun-3 Doyle, New York #72

MURER, Augusto (1922-1985) Italian

Sculpture

£1026 $1497 €1600 Female bust (22x28x15cm-9x11x6in) s. bronze. 5-Jun-2 Il Ponte, Milan #65

£1026 $1497 €1600 Faunes (35x40x30cm-14x16x12in) s.d.1977 num.1/9 bronze. 5-Jun-2 Il Ponte, Milan #66

£2065 $3262 €3200 Horse (32x31x14cm-13x12x6in) s.d.83 prov. 18-Dec-2 Christie's, Rome #41/R

£2065 $3262 €3200 Bull (22x33x16cm-9x13x6in) s.d.84 bronze prov. 18-Dec-2 Christie's, Rome #42/R

Works on paper

£1096 $1710 €1600 Rice picker (70x50cm-28x20in) s. mixed media paper on board. 10-Apr-3 Finarte Semenzato, Rome #107/R

MURER, Eugène (1845-1906) French

£2000 $3180 €3000 Fleurs (65x54cm-26x21in) s. 20-Mar-3 Sotheby's, Olympia #150/R est:2500-3000

MURFIN, Michael (1954-) British

£280 $434 €420 Portrait of Manfred Freitag (54x61cm-21x24in) s.d.85 prov. 3-Dec-2 Bonhams, Knightsbridge #42

£520 $837 €780 Crowd assembly (137x137cm-54x54in) s.d.1983 verso. 18-Feb-3 Bonhams, Knightsbridge #72/R

MURILLO (after) (17th C) Spanish

£8600 $13932 €12470 Portrait of a lady, head and shoulders holding playing cards with a monkey (65x54cm-26x21in) 29-Jul-3 Henry Adams, Chichester #552/R est:400-600

MURILLO BRACHO, Jose Maria (1827-1882) Spanish

£1242 $2000 €1863 Floral still life in a chinese decorated vase (46x36cm-18x14in) s. panel. 19-Feb-3 Doyle, New York #2 est:2000-3000

MURILLO, Bartolome Esteban (1618-1682) Spanish

£300000 $501000 €435000 The Immaculate Conception (27x18cm-11x7in) i.verso copper prov.exhib.lit. 10-Jul-3 Sotheby's, London #43/R est:50000-70000

MURILLO, Bartolome Esteban (attrib) (1618-1682) Spanish

Works on paper

£577 $894 €900 Saints in adoration (25x14cm-10x6in) pen ink wash over crayon prov. 4-Dec-2 Piasa, Paris #25

MURPHY, Caroline Boles (19/20th C) American

Works on paper

£446 $700 €669 Under the sea (41x23cm-16x9in) mono. W/C. 22-Nov-2 Skinner, Boston #174/R

MURPHY, Diana (1906-1976) British
Works on paper
£550 $875 €825 Rain storm (20x26cm-8x10in) init.d.1929 ink W/C. 26-Feb-3 Sotheby's, Olympia #80/R

MURPHY, Fiona (1958-) Australian
Sculpture
£760 $1223 €1140 Night landscape - Mungo 2002 (45x95x7cm-18x37x3in) wood resin wax prov. 6-May-3 Christie's, Melbourne #329/R est:2000-3000 (A.D 1900)

MURPHY, Herman Dudley (1867-1945) American
£283 $450 €425 Woman in profile (74x38cm-29x15in) mono. 7-Mar-3 Skinner, Boston #545/R
£531 $850 €770 Sketch for "The Opal Sunset" (25x35cm-10x14in) studio st. verso canvasboard. 16-May-3 Skinner, Boston #226/R
£531 $850 €770 Coastal view, Italian sketch (25x36cm-10x14in) studio st. verso canvasboard. 16-May-3 Skinner, Boston #348/R
£818 $1300 €1227 New England landscape with distant church steeple (30x40cm-12x16in) estate st.verso board. 7-Mar-3 Skinner, Boston #452/R est:1500-2500
£956 $1500 €1434 Gulf stream (30x41cm-12x16in) mono. s.i.verso panel. 22-Nov-2 Skinner, Boston #369/R est:3000-3500
£1258 $2000 €1887 In a tropic garden (41x30cm-16x12in) s. s.i.verso panel. 7-Mar-3 Skinner, Boston #437/R est:3000-5000
£3247 $5000 €4871 Helen Martha Woods (46x36cm-18x14in) s.d.1902 i.verso canvas on board oval prov. 24-Oct-2 Shannon's, Milford #13/R est:3000-5000
£3846 $6000 €5769 Guayama Road (74x91cm-29x36in) s. exhib. 28-Mar-3 Eldred, East Dennis #683/R est:10000-15000
£31447 $50000 €47171 Peonies and tapestry (77x63cm-30x25in) s. s.i.d.1937 verso prov. 5-Mar-3 Sotheby's, New York #4/R est:20000-30000

MURPHY, J Francis (1853-1921) American
£549 $850 €824 The hill (8x18cm-3x7in) s. panel. 7-Dec-2 South Bay, Long Island #190/R
£1290 $2000 €1935 Autumn landscape (20x30cm-8x12in) s.d.97. 3-Dec-2 Christie's, Rockefeller NY #582/R est:3000-5000
£1751 $2750 €2627 New England farm, in summer, nestled atop hillside with dirt roads (41x61cm-16x24in) s. 19-Apr-3 James Julia, Fairfield #237/R est:1500-2500
£1958 $3250 €2839 Wooded landscape with fisherman (36x53cm-14x21in) s. 11-Jun-3 Boos Gallery, Michigan #428/R est:2500-3500
£3019 $4800 €4529 Little farm (36x48cm-14x19in) s.d.1904 canvas over panel prov. 4-Mar-3 Christie's, Rockefeller NY #1/R est:6000-8000
£3797 $6000 €5696 An old farm (30x23cm-12x9in) s.d.07 mono.i.d.1907 verso canvas on panel. 24-Apr-3 Shannon's, Milford #7/R est:5000-7000
£4459 $7000 €6689 Sunset landscape (23x28cm-9x11in) s. 10-Dec-2 Doyle, New York #77/R est:3000-5000
£5031 $8000 €7547 Sunset landscape (21x26cm-8x10in) s. prov. 5-Mar-3 Sotheby's, New York #14/R est:7000-10000
£6452 $10000 €9678 Summer afternoon (61x91cm-24x36in) mono. i.verso prov. 2-Nov-2 North East Auctions, Portsmouth #69/R est:8000-12000

MURPHY, J Francis (attrib) (1853-1921) American
£422 $700 €612 Early spring (18x28cm-7x11in) indis.i.verso wood panel. 14-Jun-3 Jackson's, Cedar Falls #10/R

MURPHY, Martin (1949-) British
£255 $397 €400 Wave XXI (92x92cm-36x36in) acrylic. 6-Nov-2 James Adam, Dublin #56
£255 $397 €400 Blue slab (61x61cm-24x24in) acrylic. 6-Nov-2 James Adam, Dublin #61/R
£274 $427 €400 Abstract (60x60cm-24x24in) s.d.2003 acrylic diptych. 8-Apr-3 James Adam, Dublin #199/R
£285 $441 €450 Wave L.I (76x76cm-30x30in) s.i.verso acrylic exhib. 24-Sep-2 De Veres Art Auctions, Dublin #131
£382 $596 €600 Blue slab (75x46cm-30x18in) acrylic. 6-Nov-2 James Adam, Dublin #63/R
£401 $666 €570 Wave splash (60x122cm-24x48in) acrylic diptych. 10-Jun-3 James Adam, Dublin #119/R
£423 $701 €600 Wave splash (60x60cm-24x24in) acrylic four panel. 10-Jun-3 James Adam, Dublin #118/R

MURPHY, Noel (?) Irish?
£800 $1240 €1200 Sideward glance (20x17cm-8x7in) s. board. 4-Dec-2 John Ross, Belfast #61

MURPHY, Rowley Walter (20th C) Canadian
£289 $473 €434 Sail boats at rest (30x40cm-12x16in) s.d.1947 board. 3-Jun-3 Joyner, Toronto #561 (C.D 650)
£844 $1385 €1266 Home on the lagoon (81x85cm-32x33in) exhib. 3-Jun-3 Joyner, Toronto #390/R est:800-1200 (C.D 1900)
Works on paper
£242 $382 €363 Merchanr Dock, WW II (23x30cm-9x12in) s. pastel prov. 14-Nov-2 Heffel, Vancouver #269 (C.D 600)

MURPHY, Sandy (1956-) British
£350 $578 €508 Striped tablecloth (29x29cm-11x11in) s. board prov. 3-Jul-3 Christie's, Kensington #492
£700 $1155 €1015 Wild flowers (38x41cm-15x16in) s. board. 3-Jul-3 Christie's, Kensington #634/R
£1000 $1650 €1450 Yellow jug (30x30cm-12x12in) s. board. 3-Jul-3 Christie's, Kensington #630/R est:400-600

MURPHY, William (20th C) Irish
£288 $449 €420 Ireland's Eye, Howth (62x73cm-24x29in) s. paper. 8-Apr-3 James Adam, Dublin #65/R
£310 $514 €440 On the Wicklow Way (81x81cm-32x32in) s. board. 10-Jun-3 James Adam, Dublin #93/R
£329 $513 €480 Dalkey Island (62x73cm-24x29in) s. paper. 8-Apr-3 James Adam, Dublin #66/R

MURRAY, Bob (20th C) ?
Works on paper
£280 $437 €420 Fighter aircraft, MG sports car and figures on a runway (57x41cm-22x16in) s. W/C. 14-Sep-2 Cumbria Auction Rooms, UK #90a/R

MURRAY, Charles (1894-1954) British
£1215 $1896 €1823 Deer in a landscape (184x108cm-72x43in) s. 8-Apr-3 Peter Webb, Auckland #121/R est:3500-4000 (NZ.D 3500)

MURRAY, Eben H (fl.1880-1886) British
£1000 $1630 €1500 Portrait study of a young boy in a ruff (51x41cm-20x16in) 14-Feb-3 Lyon & Turnbull, Edinburgh #122

MURRAY, Eileen (1885-1962) British
£510 $795 €800 Kashmir fisherman (24x32cm-9x13in) mono. board. 6-Nov-2 James Adam, Dublin #90/R
£1700 $2635 €2550 Tending sheep (30x25cm-12x10in) s.d.26. 4-Dec-2 John Ross, Belfast #181 est:750-800
£1761 $2747 €2800 Evening in the west (36x25cm-14x10in) mono. i.verso paper. 17-Sep-2 Whyte's, Dublin #197/R est:1800-2000

MURRAY, Elizabeth (1940-) American
Works on paper
£1290 $2000 €1935 Hand drawing (53x75cm-21x30in) s. i.d.1989 verso col chk paper collage prov. 26-Sep-2 Christie's, Rockefeller NY #831/R est:4000-6000

MURRAY, Frank (1848-1915) British
Works on paper
£396 $650 €594 Extensive landscape (13x20cm-5x8in) s.d.1900 W/C paper on board. 5-Feb-3 Doyle, New York #2/R

MURRAY, George (1875-1933) British
£300 $501 €435 Scottish city parkland scene (25x34cm-10x13in) s.d.1902. 17-Jun-3 Gildings, Market Harborough #444

MURRAY, H (fl.1850-1860) British
Works on paper
£475 $751 €689 Scottish loch scene with cattle and man fishing (38x58cm-15x23in) s. W/C. 24-Jul-3 John Nicholson, Haslemere #1061
£500 $780 €750 Coaching scenes - stage coach pausing by a cottage (29x44cm-11x17in) s. W/C pair. 6-Nov-2 Bonhams, Chester #495

MURRAY, John (1908-1988) American
Works on paper
£1111 $1800 €1667 Untitled (60x45cm-24x18in) W/C ink prov. 27-Jan-3 Christie's, Rockefeller NY #80/R est:2000-3000

MURRAY, Olive (?) Irish?
£1090 $1711 €1700 Extensive beach landscape (122x184cm-48x72in) board. 19-Nov-2 Hamilton Osborne King, Dublin #463/R est:500-1000

MURRAY, Richard Deibel (1921-) American
£266 $415 €399 Summer street scene with houses, trees and white picket fence (41x51cm-16x20in) s. 19-Apr-3 James Julia, Fairfield #394/R

MURRAY, Robert D (1884-1953) American
£253 $400 €380 Coastal landscape with a figure and boat (25x48cm-10x19in) s.d. board. 1-Dec-2 Susanin's, Chicago #5042/R

Works on paper
£450 $716 €675 Fisherman dream buoys (91x122cm-36x48in) mixed media exhib. 6-Mar-3 Christie's, Kensington #250

MURRAY, Sir David (1849-1933) British
£400 $624 €600 Fishing on Loch Awe (38x45cm-15x18in) s. cardboard. 17-Sep-2 Sotheby's, Olympia #29/R
£400 $652 €580 River landscape with two young girls fishing in the foreground (25x46cm-10x18in) s.d.1875. 17-Jul-3 Tennants, Leyburn #844
£520 $811 €780 Castle in a Highland landscape (36x44cm-14x17in) s. paper. 17-Oct-2 Bonhams, Edinburgh #156
£550 $858 €825 River landscape (37x46cm-15x18in) s. board. 27-Mar-3 Christie's, Kensington #481/R
£600 $936 €900 Clearing a wood (35x46cm-14x18in) s.d.1906. 15-Oct-2 Bearnes, Exeter #426/R
£660 $1096 €990 Harbour mouth, evening effect (39x47cm-15x19in) board. 10-Jun-3 Sworder & Son, Bishops Stortford #542/R
£763 $1213 €1145 Near Royan, Poitou (23x33cm-9x13in) s. 18-Mar-3 Maynards, Vancouver #21/R (C.D 1800)
£900 $1413 €1350 Clovelly. Seascape (37x45cm-15x18in) s. board two. 16-Dec-2 Sotheby's, Olympia #135/R
£2415 $3840 €3623 Village street scene (61x91cm-24x36in) s. 18-Mar-3 Maynards, Vancouver #20/R est:4000-6000 (C.D 5700)
£2500 $3850 €3750 Haunt of the red deer (47x63cm-19x25in) s.d.1928. 23-Oct-2 Hamptons Fine Art, Godalming #149 est:2500-3500
£14000 $21700 €21000 Day in October, Venice (122x183cm-48x72in) s.d.1915 s.i.d.verso prov.exhib. 31-Oct-2 Christie's, London #93/R est:8000-12000

MURRAY, Sir James (19th C) British
Works on paper
£2800 $4424 €4200 View of the Palace Hotel, Buckingham Gate, London (71x125cm-28x49in) wash pencil. 28-Nov-2 Sotheby's, London #280/R est:3000-5000

MURRAY, Thomas (1663-1734) British
£7200 $11952 €10800 Portrait of a lady (74x61cm-29x24in) oval. 12-Jun-3 Sotheby's, London #55/R est:6000-8000

MURRAY, Thomas (circle) (1663-1734) British
£5500 $8690 €8250 Portrait of lady, thought to be wife of Captain H Baker (127x102cm-50x40in) prov. 26-Nov-2 Christie's, London #12/R est:2000-3000

MURRAY, William Grant (1877-1950) British
£350 $560 €525 View of Swansea (30x51cm-12x20in) 11-Mar-3 Gorringes, Lewes #2522
Works on paper
£550 $858 €825 Devils elbow, Gower (36x39cm-14x15in) s.d.1926 W/C. 11-Sep-2 Bonhams, Newport #293

MURRIE, Desmond (?) ?
£250 $365 €375 Polo match (36x30cm-14x12in) s. board. 12-Jun-2 John Ross, Belfast #110
£260 $413 €390 Head to head (30x25cm-12x10in) s. board. 5-Mar-3 John Ross, Belfast #14
£280 $434 €420 Close cluster (30x36cm-12x14in) s. board. 2-Oct-2 John Ross, Belfast #84
£280 $434 €420 Final furlong (30x36cm-12x14in) s. board. 2-Oct-2 John Ross, Belfast #214
£280 $434 €420 Break for the finish (30x35cm-12x14in) s. board. 4-Dec-2 John Ross, Belfast #246
£480 $763 €720 On the last turn (46x66cm-18x26in) s. board. 5-Mar-3 John Ross, Belfast #200
£520 $827 €780 Cluster on the last furlong (61x66cm-24x26in) s. board. 5-Mar-3 John Ross, Belfast #169
£550 $853 €825 Full gallop (61x61cm-24x24in) s. board. 4-Dec-2 John Ross, Belfast #124

MURRY, Richard (1902-1984) British
Works on paper
£260 $403 €390 Thripskin farm (36x53cm-14x21in) s.i. gouache. 24-Sep-2 Bonhams, New Bond Street #63

MURTIC, Edo (1921-) Yugoslavian
Works on paper
£484 $765 €750 Composition (94x60cm-37x24in) s.d.72 enamel metal prov. 18-Dec-2 Christie's, Rome #104/R

MUS, Italo (1892-1967) Italian
£8013 $12580 €12500 Mountain people's meal (70x100cm-28x39in) s. 10-Dec-2 Della Rocca, Turin #398/R est:14000
£8163 $12980 €12000 Workman (60x50cm-24x20in) s. board painted 1940. 1-Mar-3 Meeting Art, Vercelli #238

MUSANTE, Francesco (1950-) Italian
£408 $649 €600 Mariella's dream (30x30cm-12x12in) s. board. 1-Mar-3 Meeting Art, Vercelli #572
£442 $703 €650 Moon tamer (31x23cm-12x9in) s. board. 1-Mar-3 Meeting Art, Vercelli #301
£510 $811 €750 Plant wizard (30x25cm-12x10in) s. board. 1-Mar-3 Meeting Art, Vercelli #534
£748 $1190 €1100 One and true love story between Mirabilia King's jolly joker and the Queen (70x50cm-28x20in) s. oval. 1-Mar-3 Meeting Art, Vercelli #738
£764 $1215 €1100 Flying at night amongst music and olive trees (60x60cm-24x24in) s. board lit. 1-May-3 Meeting Art, Vercelli #289
£884 $1406 €1300 Turning my back to the world to see my last dream running away in a frosty wind (60x60cm-24x24in) s. board. 1-Mar-3 Meeting Art, Vercelli #482
Works on paper
£321 $506 €500 My dream houses (20x20cm-8x8in) s. mixed media panel. 15-Nov-2 Farsetti, Prato #234

MUSATOV, Grigorij (1899-1941) Czechoslovakian
£513 $805 €800 Paysage (50x65cm-20x26in) s. 16-Dec-2 Millon & Associes, Paris #179/R
£10326 $16109 €15489 Procession (182x95cm-72x37in) s.d.1922 exhib. 12-Oct-2 Dorotheum, Prague #79/R est:500000-750000 (C.KR 500000)

MUSCHAMP, F Sydney (1851-1929) British
£983 $1533 €1475 Recital (52x42cm-20x17in) init. 15-Oct-2 Stephan Welz, Johannesburg #385 (SA.R 16000)
£1200 $1908 €1800 Recital (53x43cm-21x17in) init. 6-Mar-3 Christie's, Kensington #542/R est:1500-2000
£1500 $2430 €2250 Unloading the catch (40x61cm-16x24in) s.d.1887. 20-May-3 Sotheby's, Olympia #232/R est:500-700
£1500 $2460 €2250 Love letter, a jester and young lady waiting outside a hall (65x90cm-26x35in) s.d.1880. 3-Jun-3 Bonhams, Oxford #77/R est:2000-3000
£2214 $3498 €3321 Surprise (32x17cm-13x7in) s. prov. 7-Apr-3 Shapiro, Sydney #548 est:6000-8000 (A.D 5800)
Works on paper
£443 $700 €665 Broken string (25x38cm-10x15in) W/C. 15-Nov-2 Du Mouchelle, Detroit #2001/R

MUSHKYETOV, V I (20th C) Russian
£549 $900 €796 Duel of Pushkin. Russian festival (81x99cm-32x39in) s.d.1953 two. 4-Jun-3 Doyle, New York #73

MUSIC, Zoran (1909-) Italian
£432 $691 €600 Italian landscape (11x17cm-4x7in) s. pencil. 14-May-3 Dorotheum, Klagenfurt #68
£7278 $11500 €11500 Landscape in the Appennini (38x61cm-15x24in) s.d.68 s.i.d.verso. 30-Nov-2 Farsetti, Prato #668/R est:10000
£7595 $12000 €12000 Women at the market (43x61cm-17x24in) s.d.1939 tempera cardboard lit. 30-Nov-2 Farsetti, Prato #665/R est:15000
£7692 $11923 €12000 Paysage rocheux (46x65cm-18x26in) s.d.1978 s.i.d.1978 prov. 6-Dec-2 Ketterer, Munich #156/R est:7000-9000
£8500 $14195 €12325 La giudecca (38x60cm-15x24in) s.i.d.1983 verso prov. 27-Jun-3 Christie's, London #139/R est:8000-12000
£9494 $15000 €15000 Custom (50x65cm-20x26in) s.d.82 s.i.d.verso. 30-Nov-2 Farsetti, Prato #670/R est:22000
£9615 $15096 €15000 Giudecca Canal (33x41cm-13x16in) s.d.1980 s.i.d.verso. 19-Nov-2 Finarte, Milan #215/R est:11000-14000
£11149 $17392 €16500 Paris (50x61cm-20x24in) s.d.1988. 26-Mar-3 Finarte Semenzato, Milan #313/R
£11538 $18115 €18000 Dalmatian hill (40x50cm-16x20in) s.d.1966. 19-Nov-2 Finarte, Milan #168/R est:15000-18000
£16340 $26144 €25000 Self-portrait (55x38cm-22x15in) s.d.1992. 4-Jan-3 Meeting Art, Vercelli #630 est:25000
Works on paper
£1151 $1842 €1600 Self portrait (49x43cm-19x17in) s.d. chk wash. 15-May-3 Neumeister, Munich #498/R est:1500-1800
£1282 $2013 €2000 Flowers in Cortina (25x35cm-10x14in) s.d.64 pastel. 19-Nov-2 Finarte, Milan #167/R
£1351 $2108 €2000 Paysage (38x56cm-15x22in) s.d pastel. 31-Mar-3 Rossini, Paris #104/R
£1438 $2301 €2200 Dalmatian lands (20x30cm-8x12in) s.d.1980 W/C. 4-Jan-3 Meeting Art, Vercelli #345
£2025 $3200 €3200 Untitled (20x29cm-8x11in) s.d.80 W/C prov. 27-Nov-2 Dorotheum, Vienna #103/R est:2000-3000
£2179 $3378 €3400 Untitled (26x35cm-10x14in) s.d.1986 W/C gouache. 6-Dec-2 Hauswedell & Nolte, Hamburg #265/R est:3000
£2302 $3683 €3200 Dalmatian landscapes (13x22cm-5x9in) one s.d. two W/C two Indian ink paper one on board four. 15-May-3 Neumeister, Munich #497/R est:1500-1800

£2532 $4000 €4000 Dalmatian earth (50x57cm-20x22in) s.d.1959 gouache col chk. 30-Nov-2 Villa Grisebach, Berlin #413/R est:5000-6000
£2564 $4026 €4000 Dalmatian lands (50x66cm-20x26in) s.d.1960 mixed media. 21-Nov-2 Finarte, Rome #126/R
£2800 $4424 €4200 Dalmatian lands (18x28cm-7x11in) s.d.1959 gouache. 3-Apr-3 Christie's, Kensington #186/R
£3000 $4740 €4500 Colline (37x56cm-15x22in) s.d.64 pastel. 3-Apr-3 Christie's, Kensington #187/R
£3094 $5073 €4300 Paysage vide (50x65cm-20x26in) s.d. s.i.d. verso gouache tempera. 6-Jun-3 Ketterer, Munich #157/R est:5000-6000
£3401 $5408 €5000 Self-portrait (36x30cm-14x12in) s.d.90 chl pastel prov. 24-Mar-3 Cornette de St.Cyr, Paris #27/R
£3901 $6319 €5500 Terre dalmate (50x70cm-20x28in) s.d.1958 mixed media prov. 26-May-3 Christie's, Milan #224/R est:5000-7000
£4353 $6877 €6790 Landscape in Dalmatia (46x64cm-18x25in) mixed media paper on board exec.1958. 12-Nov-2 Babuino, Rome #340/R
£5800 $9164 €8700 Dalmatian pattern (33x49cm-13x19in) s. W/C gouache exec.c.1952-53 prov.exhib. 3-Apr-3 Christie's, Kensington #184/R
£5897 $9318 €9200 Landscape in Umbria (42x60cm-17x24in) s.d.1952 W/C tempera paper on cardboard. 15-Nov-2 Farsetti, Prato #352/R est:8500
£7692 $12077 €12000 Auto-portrait (40x26cm-16x10in) s.d.82 mixed media prov.exhib. 11-Dec-2 Artcurial Briest, Paris #721a/R est:16000
£10256 $16103 €16000 Ida (40x26cm-16x10in) s.i.d.1986 mixed media paper on board prov.exhib.lit. 11-Dec-2 Artcurial Briest, Paris #721b/R est:18000

MUSIN, Auguste (1852-1920) Belgian
£1088 $1731 €1600 Chaloupes de peche echouees (19x33cm-7x13in) s. panel. 18-Mar-3 Campo, Vlaamse Kaai #160 est:450-550
£2041 $3245 €3000 Moulins a vent au bord de l'eau (43x37cm-17x15in) s.d.1874 panel. 18-Mar-3 Vanderkindere, Brussels #55/R est:3000-5000
£10000 $16600 €10000 Scene hivernale animee (41x74cm-16x29in) s. panel. 16-Jun-3 Horta, Bruxelles #184/R est:6000-8000
Works on paper
£253 $395 €400 Route d'Adinkerke a la Panne (22x26cm-9x10in) s. W/C chl. 15-Oct-2 Vanderkindere, Brussels #49

MUSIN, François Etienne (1820-1888) Belgian
£641 $994 €1000 Le haleur au coucher du soleil (13x22cm-5x9in) s. panel. 9-Dec-2 Horta, Bruxelles #299
£1224 $1947 €1800 Le naufrage (54x73cm-21x29in) s. 19-Mar-3 Hotel des Ventes Mosan, Brussels #164/R est:1900-2200
£3741 $5986 €5200 Pecheurs par gros temps (51x76cm-20x30in) s. 19-May-3 Horta, Bruxelles #130 est:4000-6000
£4430 $6911 €7000 Le retour de pecheurs (41x74cm-16x29in) s. panel. 15-Oct-2 Vanderkindere, Brussels #40/R est:5000-7000
£4460 $7137 €6200 Sailing ships in front of the coast of Dover (38x57cm-15x22in) s.d.1846 verso panel. 17-May-3 De Vuyst, Lokeren #271/R est:6000-7500
£5036 $8058 €7000 Canot des pilotes, gros temps devant Nieuport (46x81cm-18x32in) s. 17-May-3 De Vuyst, Lokeren #434/R est:8000-12000
£5705 $9185 €8500 Combat naval (30x38cm-12x15in) s.d.46. 24-Feb-3 Bernaerts, Antwerp #156/R
£6051 $9439 €9500 L'abordage (29x40cm-11x16in) s. 11-Nov-2 Horta, Bruxelles #83/R est:5000-7000
£9353 $14964 €13000 Depart pour la peche (65x124cm-26x49in) s. 14-May-3 Rabourdin & Choppin de Janvry, Paris #33/R est:10000-12000
£9400 $15604 €9400 Retour des pecheurs (21x37cm-8x15in) s. panel. 16-Jun-3 Horta, Bruxelles #139/R est:5000-7000
£12821 $19872 €20000 Shipwreck (52x84cm-20x33in) s. panel. 7-Dec-2 De Vuyst, Lokeren #421/R est:22000-25000
£17857 $28214 €26786 Fleet in distress (117x181cm-46x71in) s. 26-Nov-2 Sotheby's, Melbourne #187/R est:50000-70000 (A.D 50000)
£23022 $36835 €32000 Combat naval (60x90cm-24x35in) s. 19-May-3 Horta, Bruxelles #129/R est:12000-15000

MUSIN, François Etienne (attrib) (1820-1888) Belgian
£2323 $3670 €3600 Paysage cotier avec voiliers (38x58cm-15x23in) s. 17-Dec-2 Palais de Beaux Arts, Brussels #576/R est:3200-4800

MUSIN, Maurice (1939-) Belgian
£306 $487 €450 Maternite (25x45cm-10x18in) s. 19-Mar-3 Hotel des Ventes Mosan, Brussels #338
£748 $1190 €1100 Le cavalier (70x60cm-28x24in) s.d.66 s.i.d. verso. 19-Mar-3 Hotel des Ventes Mosan, Brussels #343

MUSS-ARNOLT, Gustav (1858-1927) American
£2215 $3500 €3212 Redhead duck (23x30cm-9x12in) s. prov. 26-Jul-3 Coeur d'Alene, Hayden #14/R est:1500-2500

MUSSAIJASSUL, Halil-Bey (1896-1931) Russian
£1400 $2198 €2100 Turkish beauty in a garden (70x49cm-28x19in) s. board. 16-Apr-3 Christie's, Kensington #789/R est:800-1200

MUSSARD, Jean V (1681-1754) Swiss
Miniatures
£6000 $9360 €9000 Peter I, The Great Romanov, column and trees in background (5cm-2in) s.d.1714 verso enamel oval. 5-Nov-2 Bonhams, New Bond Street #25/R est:1200-1500

MUSSCHER, Michiel van (1645-1705) Dutch
£8917 $13911 €14000 Portrait of Gerard Pietersz, Hulft, seated with maps a sword and globe (49x40cm-19x16in) s.d.1677 prov.exhib.lit. 5-Nov-2 Sotheby's, Amsterdam #70/R est:15000-20000

MUSSILL, William (19th C) Austrian?
£4012 $6500 €6018 Study of roses (43x36cm-17x14in) s.d. board. 23-Jan-3 Sotheby's, New York #213/R est:7000

MUT, Antonio (1921-1990) Spanish
£314 $491 €500 Clown (60x46cm-24x18in) s. 23-Sep-2 Durán, Madrid #625/R

MUTCH, Tom (20th C) New Zealander
£702 $1095 €1053 Tracking down the strongman, lizard (90x62cm-35x24in) s. paper. 27-Mar-3 International Art Centre, Auckland #24/R (NZ.D 2000)
£2456 $3832 €3684 Coromandel Kiwi (120x93cm-47x37in) s.d.2001 board. 27-Mar-3 International Art Centre, Auckland #61/R est:10000-14000 (NZ.D 7000)

MUTER, Mela (1886-1967) French
£1795 $2818 €2800 Jeune femme pensive (55x38cm-22x15in) s.verso. 16-Dec-2 Millon & Associes, Paris #174/R est:2500-3500
£2500 $3875 €3750 Promeneur au bord du Rhone (53x44cm-21x17in) panel. 5-Dec-2 Christie's, Kensington #83/R est:1500-2500
£2778 $4583 €4000 Mere et enfant (153x117cm-60x46in) contreplaque prov. 2-Jul-3 Artcurial Briest, Paris #653/R est:5000-7000
£3048 $4785 €4450 Nature morte a la pasteque (46x38cm-18x15in) panel prov. 21-Apr-3 Rabourdin & Choppin de Janvry, Paris #106/R est:1600-1800
£3901 $6319 €5500 Scene de rue animee (64x50cm-25x20in) s. 21-May-3 Cornette de St.Cyr, Paris #50/R est:5000-7000
£4430 $7000 €7000 Southern harbour (71x90cm-28x35in) s. 30-Nov-2 Villa Grisebach, Berlin #204/R est:7000-9000
£6122 $9735 €9000 La marne a Charenton (54x65cm-21x26in) s. 3-Mar-3 Claude Boisgirard, Paris #71/R est:7000-8000
£8334 $13250 €12000 Repos au bord de l'eau, grand-mere et petite fille (100x90cm-39x35in) s. painted c.1917 prov.exhib. 29-Apr-3 Artcurial Briest, Paris #245/R est:5000-7000

MUTI, Rutilio (1904-1995) Italian
£481 $760 €750 Farm (35x49cm-14x19in) s.d.1939 board. 15-Nov-2 Farsetti, Prato #418/R
£676 $1054 €1000 Calambrone (35x58cm-14x23in) s. board. 28-Mar-3 Farsetti, Prato #608

MUTRIE, Annie Feray (1826-1893) British
Works on paper
£340 $554 €510 Black and green grapes in a pearlware basket (18x23cm-7x9in) s.d.1875 W/C. 11-Feb-3 Bonhams, Knowle #48

MUTRIE, Martha Darley (1824-1885) British
£6000 $10020 €8700 Still life of flowers and grapes on a ledge (61x91cm-24x36in) mono. 17-Jun-3 Bonhams, New Bond Street #52/R est:2000-3000
Works on paper
£950 $1511 €1425 Still life of roses (19x13cm-7x5in) init.d.1877 W/C htd white. 25-Feb-3 Bonhams, Knightsbridge #46/R

MUTZNER, Sammys (1869-1958) Rumanian
£1429 $2199 €2144 Le cerisiers de maruyama (69x50cm-27x20in) canvas on board. 3-Sep-2 Shapiro, Sydney #398/R est:5000-7000 (A.D 4000)

MUUKKA, Elias (1853-1938) Finnish
£345 $545 €500 Beach (16x24cm-6x9in) s. 3-Apr-3 Hagelstam, Helsinki #942
£540 $885 €750 Landscape, Aabo (16x24cm-6x9in) s. 5-Jun-3 Hagelstam, Helsinki #848/R
£597 $920 €950 Coastal landscape (15x31cm-6x12in) 27-Oct-2 Bukowskis, Helsinki #243/R
£633 $987 €1000 Road (60x91cm-24x36in) s.d.1914. 12-Sep-2 Hagelstam, Helsinki #980
£719 $1179 €1100 The red gate (28x41cm-11x16in) s.d.13. 9-Feb-3 Bukowskis, Helsinki #315/R
£968 $1529 €1500 Winter landscape (31x27cm-12x11in) s.d.1989. 19-Dec-2 Hagelstam, Helsinki #859/R est:2000

£980 $1608 €1500 Hay stooks (30x42cm-12x17in) s.d.31. 9-Feb-3 Bukowskis, Helsinki #313/R est:1800
£1076 $1700 €1700 Reeds by water (29x49cm-11x19in) s.d.19. 1-Dec-2 Bukowskis, Helsinki #136/R est:1500-1700
£1266 $2000 €2000 Tervaniemi, Viborg - coastal view (16x23cm-6x9in) s. canvas on board. 1-Dec-2 Bukowskis, Helsinki #135/R est:2500-3000
£1295 $2124 €1800 Birch grove (41x61cm-16x24in) s.d.1912. 4-Jun-3 Bukowskis, Helsinki #368/R est:2000
£1392 $2200 €2200 Coastal landscape with no wind (41x67cm-16x26in) s.d.23. 1-Dec-2 Bukowskis, Helsinki #134/R est:2500-2800
£1565 $2488 €2300 Coastal landscape (30x40cm-12x16in) s.d.1901. 27-Feb-3 Hagelstam, Helsinki #803 est:2000
£1655 $2714 €2300 Coastal landscape (32x60cm-13x24in) s.d.1918. 4-Jun-3 Bukowskis, Helsinki #369/R est:4300
£1831 $2948 €2600 Lake landscape (21x35cm-8x14in) s.d.89. 10-May-3 Bukowskis, Helsinki #48/R est:1700-1900
£1835 $2900 €2900 Beach in winter (57x79cm-22x31in) s.d.1890. 30-Nov-2 Hagelstam, Helsinki #111/R est:3300
£1871 $2993 €2600 Road through woods (32x44cm-13x17in) s.d.1893. 17-May-3 Hagelstam, Helsinki #114/R est:3000
£2278 $3600 €3600 Large stone in forest (50x68cm-20x27in) s.d.1911. 1-Dec-2 Bukowskis, Helsinki #132/R est:2500-2800
£2278 $3600 €3600 Coastal road (32x60cm-13x24in) s.d.1914. 1-Dec-2 Bukowskis, Helsinki #133/R est:2500-2700
£2595 $4100 €4100 The beach at home (25x41cm-10x16in) s.d.1882. 1-Dec-2 Bukowskis, Helsinki #131/R est:3300-3500
£2876 $4716 €4400 Children fishing (27x46cm-11x18in) s. 9-Feb-3 Bukowskis, Helsinki #314/R est:1300
£3797 $6000 €6000 Coastal landscape with cattle by bay (46x72cm-18x28in) s.d.1886. 30-Nov-2 Hagelstam, Helsinki #112/R est:6000
£3885 $6216 €5400 Horse and carriage with figures on country road (34x56cm-13x22in) s.d.1877. 17-May-3 Hagelstam, Helsinki #112/R est:5000

MUXART, Jaime (1922-) Spanish
£685 $1068 €1000 Heads (58x45cm-23x18in) s. 8-Apr-3 Ansorena, Madrid #286/R
£1558 $2275 €2400 Face (30x50cm-12x20in) s. paper. 17-Jun-2 Ansorena, Madrid #43/R

MUYDEN, Alfred van (1818-1898) Swiss
£633 $1000 €1000 Portrait of man (46x36cm-18x14in) mono.d.51. 1-Dec-2 Anaf, Lyon #146
£1409 $2269 €2100 Praying monk (44x31cm-17x12in) s.d.1863. 18-Feb-3 Sotheby's, Amsterdam #569/R est:800-1000
£2130 $3429 €3089 Gypsy woman with child in her arms (63x45cm-25x18in) s.d.1853. 9-May-3 Dobiaschofsky, Bern #38/R est:3000 (S.FR 4600)
Works on paper
£286 $427 €429 Mother and child (18x13cm-7x5in) mono. W/C. 25-Jun-2 Koller, Zurich #6551 (S.FR 650)

MUYDEN, Charles Henri van (1860-1936) Swiss
£4721 $7459 €7082 In wine cellar (49x62cm-19x24in) s.d.1912. 29-Nov-2 Zofingen, Switzerland #3000 est:1500 (S.FR 11000)

MUZIANO, Girolamo (attrib) (1528-1592) Italian
Works on paper
£1852 $3000 €2778 Saint paul (25x11cm-10x4in) i. red chk prov. 21-Jan-3 Sotheby's, New York #41/R est:2500

MUZIKA, Frantisek (1900-1974) Czechoslovakian
£2957 $4612 €4436 Citadelle III (69x55cm-27x22in) s.d.1964 tempera oil prov. 16-Sep-2 Philippe Schuler, Zurich #6478 est:1500-2000 (S.FR 6800)

MUZZIOLI, Giovanni (1854-1894) Italian
£6803 $10816 €10000 Scene in ancient Rome (40x30cm-16x12in) s. 18-Mar-3 Finarte, Milan #68/R
£10884 $17306 €16000 Scene in ancient Rome (40x30cm-16x12in) s.d.1889. 18-Mar-3 Finarte, Milan #62/R

MYERS, Frank Harmon (1899-1956) American
£812 $1300 €1218 Fog at sea (61x81cm-24x32in) s. i.verso. 16-Mar-3 Butterfields, San Francisco #1050 est:2000-3000
£3614 $6000 €5240 Pacific surf (63x76cm-25x30in) s. prov. 11-Jun-3 Butterfields, San Francisco #4289/R est:3000-5000

MYERS, Harry (1886-1961) American
£563 $900 €845 Coastal scene with lighthouse (38x99cm-15x39in) 10-Jan-3 Du Mouchelle, Detroit #2072/R

MYERS, J (20th C) ?
£982 $1600 €1473 Best friends, hound and terrier (41x30cm-16x12in) s.d.1901. 11-Feb-3 Bonhams & Doyles, New York #230/R est:1200-1800

MYERS, Jerome (1867-1940) American
£1786 $2750 €2679 Swimming class (30x41cm-12x16in) s.d.1938 canvasboard. 24-Oct-2 Shannon's, Milford #176/R est:3000-5000
£4516 $7000 €6774 Recitation (25x20cm-10x8in) s.d.1922 board prov. 4-Dec-2 Sotheby's, New York #79/R est:8000-12000
£5096 $8000 €7644 Houston street (61x43cm-24x17in) s.d.08 prov. 20-Nov-2 Christie's, Los Angeles #38/R est:8000-12000
Works on paper
£481 $750 €722 At the movies (20x28cm-8x11in) ink dr. 20-Sep-2 Du Mouchelle, Detroit #2190/R
£865 $1350 €1298 Street group (25x36cm-10x14in) s. 21-Sep-2 Nadeau, Windsor #176/R
£964 $1600 €1398 Burlesque comrades (28x36cm-11x14in) gouache. 13-Jun-3 Du Mouchelle, Detroit #2221/R est:700-1200
£1392 $2200 €2088 Street group (25x36cm-10x14in) s.d.1925 W/C exhib. 24-Apr-3 Shannon's, Milford #203/R est:2500-3500

MYGATT, Robertson K (1861-1919) American
£600 $942 €900 Wood and marsh (22x27cm-9x11in) s. board. 16-Dec-2 Bonhams, Bury St Edmunds #521/R

MYLIUS, Stanley (19th C) British
Works on paper
£1439 $2360 €2000 Promeneurs a Eyup (30x42cm-12x17in) s. one d.1892 W/C pair. 4-Jun-3 Tajan, Paris #183/R est:2000-2500

MYN, Herman van der (1684-1741) Dutch
£7000 $11690 €10150 Two parrots, and fruit in a wooded landscape (91x71cm-36x28in) s. prov. 11-Jul-3 Christie's, Kensington #131/R est:4000-6000

MYN, Herman van der (attrib) (1684-1741) Dutch
£3000 $4710 €4500 Gentleman showing the day's bag to a lady in an interior, with servants and pug dog (84x67cm-33x26in) panel prov. 13-Dec-2 Christie's, Kensington #116/R est:3000-5000

MYN, Herman van der (circle) (1684-1741) Dutch
£13000 $20540 €19500 Portrait of young girl beside an orange tree, page offering her flowers (110x163cm-43x64in) 26-Nov-2 Christie's, London #10/R est:5000-8000

MYNTTI, Eemu (1890-1943) Finnish
£1103 $1743 €1600 Landscape (60x71cm-24x28in) s. 3-Apr-3 Hagelstam, Helsinki #977/R est:1800

MYNTTI, Eemu (attrib) (1890-1943) Finnish
£377 $581 €600 Composition (55x60cm-22x24in) 24-Oct-2 Hagelstam, Helsinki #1039

MYRAH, Newman (1921-) Canadian
£5696 $9000 €8259 Off the hunt (61x91cm-24x36in) s. 26-Jul-3 Coeur d'Alene, Hayden #221/R est:6000-9000

MYTENS, Daniel (circle) (17th C) Dutch
£4573 $7500 €6631 Portrait of a girl in a red dress with a dog (116x82cm-46x32in) 4-Jun-3 Christie's, Rockefeller NY #157/R est:5000-7000

MYTENS, Daniel (style) (17th C) Dutch
£5000 $7950 €7500 Portrait of Sir Thomas Bowes (181x106cm-71x42in) prov.lit. 19-Mar-3 Sotheby's, London #14/R est:6000-8000

MYTENS, Jan (attrib) (1614-1670) Dutch
£11465 $17885 €18000 Portrait of family a la antique in a wooded landscape (152x121cm-60x48in) prov.lit. 6-Nov-2 Christie's, Amsterdam #64/R est:10000-15000

MYTENS, Martin (attrib) (17/18th C) Dutch/Swedish
£3333 $5167 €5000 Portrait of Queen Maria Theresa of Austria (236x122cm-93x48in) 4-Dec-2 AB Stockholms Auktionsverk #1690/R est:35000-40000 (S.KR 47000)

MYTENS, Martin II (1695-1770) Swedish
£5660 $8774 €9000 Empress Maria Theresia with Royal Hungarian Crown (92x62cm-36x24in) 2-Oct-2 Dorotheum, Vienna #193/R est:9000-15000

MYTENS, Martin II (attrib) (1695-1770) Swedish
£1197 $1987 €1700 Empress Maria Theresa (93x73cm-37x29in) prov. 11-Jun-3 Dorotheum, Vienna #396/R est:1400-1800
£4054 $6324 €6000 Portrait of Empress Maria Theresa (80x61cm-31x24in) oval prov. 27-Mar-3 Dorotheum, Vienna #428/R est:5000-8000

NABAA, Nazir (1938-) Syrian
£1500 $2385 €2250 Nude in purple (54x39cm-21x15in) s.d.1991. 30-Apr-3 Sotheby's, London #149/R est:1500-2000

NABERT, Wilhelm (1830-1904) German
£1139 $1800 €1800 Deer in landscape (73x111cm-29x44in) s. lit. 29-Nov-2 Schloss Ahlden, Ahlden #1194a/R est:2400
£2397 $3740 €3500 Sunday walk (46x65cm-18x26in) s. 10-Apr-3 Van Ham, Cologne #1619/R est:4200
Works on paper
£315 $500 €473 Mountain traveler (27x41cm-11x16in) s.d.1860 W/C. 7-Mar-3 Skinner, Boston #228/R

NABINGER, Dollie (1905-1988) American
£449 $700 €674 Colorado landscape (61x91cm-24x36in) 19-Oct-2 David Dike, Dallas #360/R

NACCIARONE, Gustavo (1833-1929) Italian
£5380 $8500 €8500 On the beach (29x45cm-11x18in) s. 26-Nov-2 Christie's, Rome #235/R

NACERADSKY, Jiri (1939-) Czechoslovakian
£454 $736 €658 Figure (32x36cm-13x14in) s.d.66 panel. 24-May-3 Dorotheum, Prague #133/R est:20000-30000 (C.KR 20000)

NACHENIUS, Jan Coenraad (1890-?) Dutch
£955 $1471 €1500 Glass vase with primroses and daffodils. Still life of wild roses (18x24cm-7x9in) one mono. two. 3-Sep-2 Christie's, Amsterdam #270 est:800-1200

NADAL, Carlos (1917-1998) Spanish
£1338 $2087 €2100 Port (41x33cm-16x13in) s. paper on canvas. 10-Nov-2 Eric Pillon, Calais #172/R
£1800 $2844 €2700 Beach (19x26cm-7x10in) s.indis.d. paper. 3-Apr-3 Christie's, Kensington #205/R
£1935 $3058 €3000 Souvenir of Florence (55x46cm-22x18in) s.prov. 17-Dec-2 Segre, Madrid #249/R
£2192 $3419 €3200 Barques de peche sur la plage. s. cardboard. 14-Apr-3 Horta, Bruxelles #215 est:3000-4000
£3500 $5460 €5250 Sainte Marie (23x28cm-9x11in) s. s.i.d.74 verso. 10-Apr-3 Tennants, Leyburn #1141 est:4000-5000
£4088 $6296 €6500 French town (50x61cm-20x24in) s.d.1953 s.verso. 28-Oct-2 Segre, Madrid #117/R est:6500
£4500 $7110 €6750 Beach (27x35cm-11x14in) s. paper on canvas. 3-Apr-3 Christie's, Kensington #201/R
£5310 $8390 €7700 Landscape with villa (46x55cm-18x22in) s.d.1982. 1-Apr-3 Segre, Madrid #312/R
£5379 $8553 €7800 Champ de ble (44x55cm-17x22in) s. s.i.verso. 4-Mar-3 Ansorena, Madrid #224/R
£5500 $8690 €8250 Red houses (50x61cm-20x24in) s. i.d.72 verso paper on canvas. 3-Apr-3 Christie's, Kensington #203/R
£6897 $10897 €10000 Landscape and sea (65x54cm-26x21in) s. prov. 1-Apr-3 Segre, Madrid #147/R est:10000
£7285 $11874 €11000 Beach (48x66cm-19x26in) s.d.1954 cardboard. 11-Feb-3 Segre, Madrid #154/R est:8500
£8387 $13252 €13000 Horses (65x81cm-26x32in) s. 17-Dec-2 Segre, Madrid #107/R est:5900
£12000 $18480 €18000 Plage aux estivants (73x92cm-29x36in) s. s.i.d.1994 verso prov.exhib. 22-Oct-2 Sotheby's, London #248/R est:12000-15000
Works on paper
£345 $548 €500 L (29x20cm-11x8in) s. gouache. 4-Mar-3 Ansorena, Madrid #273/R
£1300 $2015 €1950 Damme (32x31cm-13x12in) s.i.d.5-84 s.i.d.verso black felt tipped pen brush ink bodycol. 5-Dec-2 Christie's, Kensington #214/R est:1000-1500
£1400 $2170 €2100 Eglise (30x34cm-12x13in) s.d.78 s.i.d.verso black felt tipped pen W/C. 5-Dec-2 Christie's, Kensington #215/R est:1000-1500

NADAL, R (?) Spanish?
£4934 $7993 €7500 Still life (50x61cm-20x24in) s. 21-Jan-3 Durán, Madrid #640/R

NADELMAN, Elie (1882-1946) American/Polish
Prints
£3462 $5400 €5193 Head of a woman (18x13cm-7x5in) engraving exec.c.1904-7. 7-Nov-2 Swann Galleries, New York #749/R est:2000-3000
Sculpture
£4839 $7500 €7259 Dancer and figure (23cm-9in) plaster one exec.c.1944 pair prov. 2-Oct-2 Christie's, Rockefeller NY #81/R est:2500-3500
£5183 $8500 €7515 Standing woman (20x5x8cm-8x2x3in) terracotta prov. 1-Jun-3 Wright, Chicago #257/R est:5000-7000
£16129 $25000 €24194 Wounded bull (28cm-11in) dark brown pat. bronze green marble base prov.lit. 4-Dec-2 Sotheby's, New York #101/R est:25000-35000
£23457 $38000 €35186 Classical head (39cm-15in) i. reddish brown pat. bronze executed c.1910-11. 22-May-3 Christie's, Rockefeller NY #67/R est:25000-35000
£70988 $115000 €106482 Classical head (32cm-13in) i. white marble executed c.1909 prov.exhib.lit. 21-May-3 Sotheby's, New York #37/R est:50000-75000
Works on paper
£510 $800 €765 Standing nude (7x3cm-3x1in) init. pen ink exec.c.1907 prov. 19-Nov-2 Wright, Chicago #125/R
£2469 $4000 €3580 Standing female nude (18x10cm-7x4in) sepia ink wash prov. 21-May-3 Doyle, New York #1/R est:1200-1600

NADERA, Ida Bagus Made (1910-1998) Indonesian
Works on paper
£7042 $10845 €10563 Funeral procession (53x76cm-21x30in) wash pen ink W/C executed c.1938 prov.exhib. 27-Oct-2 Christie's, Hong Kong #20/R est:90000-120000 (HK.D 85000)

NADJA (1902-1941) French
Works on paper
£8904 $13890 €13000 Untitled (50x64cm-20x25in) ink on napkin exec.1926 lit. 14-Apr-3 Laurence Calmels, Paris #4020/R est:8000

NADLER, Istvan (1938-) Hungarian
£699 $1084 €1049 Florence (100x70cm-39x28in) s. acrylic on paper. 6-Dec-2 Kieselbach, Budapest #127/R (H.F 260000)
Works on paper
£826 $1288 €1198 Florence (98x68cm-39x27in) s.d.83 mixed media. 13-Sep-2 Mu Terem Galeria, Budapest #129/R est:250000 (H.F 320000)

NADLER, Robert (1858-?) Hungarian
£2375 $3705 €3444 At the workplace (46x55cm-18x22in) s.d.1888 prov. 12-Apr-3 Mu Terem Galeria, Budapest #49/R est:380000 (H.F 850000)
Works on paper
£439 $684 €637 Venetian barques (24x33cm-9x13in) s. W/C. 13-Sep-2 Mu Terem Galeria, Budapest #12/R est:150000 (H.F 170000)

NADORP, Franz (1794-1876) Italian
£1961 $3216 €3000 Hagar and Ismael in the desert (73x99cm-29x39in) mono.i. 8-Feb-3 Hans Stahl, Hamburg #58/R est:4000
Works on paper
£342 $534 €500 Taking Christ down from the cross (41x29cm-16x11in) s.i.d. pencil. 11-Apr-3 Winterberg, Heidelberg #498/R
£513 $810 €800 Portrait of old man (33x28cm-13x11in) s.d.43 pencil W/C prov. 16-Nov-2 Lempertz, Koln #1370/R

NADUE, Hugo (?) ?
£650 $1073 €943 Coastal scene (23x28cm-9x11in) s.i.verso board. 3-Jul-3 Duke & Son, Dorchester #293

NAEGELY, H (?) ?
£968 $1529 €1500 Fisherman (23x19cm-9x7in) s. board. 18-Dec-2 Finarte, Milan #240

NAEKE, Gustav Heinrich (1786-1835) German
Works on paper
£324 $518 €450 Italian buildings (10x11cm-4x4in) pencil studies prov. two. 17-May-3 Lempertz, Koln #1323
£411 $650 €650 Mother with daughters (12x8cm-5x3in) pencil. 29-Nov-2 Bassenge, Berlin #5999

NAFTEL, Isabel (fl.1862-1891) British
Works on paper
£950 $1482 €1425 Tumble of stones (36x25cm-14x10in) s.d.1891 W/C white. 26-Mar-3 Hamptons Fine Art, Godalming #88
£1719 $2750 €2579 Grandfather with children outside a cottage (37x27cm-15x11in) s.d.1881 pencil W/C. 14-May-3 Butterfields, San Francisco #1168/R est:3000-5000

NAFTEL, Paul Jacob (1817-1891) British
£300 $477 €450 Rural path with silver birches (25x25cm-10x10in) s.d.1886. 18-Mar-3 Sworder & Son, Bishops Stortford #402e/R
Works on paper
£316 $500 €474 Landscape (25x18cm-10x7in) mono.d.1869. 26-Apr-3 Thomaston Place, Thomaston #339
£320 $509 €480 Silver birches and stream with woodland beyond (35x25cm-14x10in) s.d.1889 W/C. 18-Mar-3 Sworder & Son, Bishops Stortford #402f/R

£600 $972 €900 View of a lakeside town (29x22cm-11x9in) s. W/C. 21-May-3 Bonhams, Knightsbridge #10/R
£2600 $4134 €3900 Boy gathering firewood beside a thatched cottage (60x47cm-24x19in) indis.s. W/C. 20-Mar-3 Martel Maides, Guernsey #54/R est:2000-2500

NAFTEL, Paul Jacob (attrib) (1817-1891) British
Works on paper
£2000 $3180 €3000 Landing of Queen Victoria at Guernsey (36x26cm-14x10in) W/C htd white exec.1846. 20-Mar-3 Martel Maides, Guernsey #53/R est:2000-2500

NAGEL, Andres (1947-) Spanish
Sculpture
£3205 $5032 €5000 Prisoner (84x120x40cm-33x47x16in) s. glass fiber string. 16-Dec-2 Castellana, Madrid #801/R

NAGEL, Jan (?-1616) Dutch
£10000 $15600 €15000 Miracle at the grave of Elisha (69x60cm-27x24in) s.d.1596 panel. 9-Apr-3 Christie's, London #64/R est:12000-18000

NAGEL, Johann Friedrich (1765-1825) German
Works on paper
£2518 $4129 €3500 Sornitz near Meissen (29x39cm-11x15in) s.i. gouache. 4-Jun-3 Reiss & Sohn, Konigstein #272/R est:4000

NAGEL, Otto (1894-1967) German
£1931 $3108 €2897 Portrait of the Russian poet Majakowskij (71x59cm-28x23in) s.d.1929. 7-May-3 AB Stockholms Auktionsverk #1123/R est:25000-30000 (S.KR 25000)
Works on paper
£1314 $2037 €2050 Street in Wedding (21x15cm-8x6in) s. pastel exec.1933 lit. 7-Dec-2 Dannenberg, Berlin #712/R est:1500
£2532 $4000 €4000 Jungfern bridge (37x28cm-15x11in) s. pastel. 30-Nov-2 Bassenge, Berlin #6534/R est:2200
£4430 $7000 €7000 Fischerstrasse II (44x58cm-17x23in) s. pastel. 30-Nov-2 Bassenge, Berlin #6535/R est:3000

NAGEL, Wilhelm (1866-1945) German
£292 $444 €450 Peasant on country road in summer landscape (38x53cm-15x21in) s. board. 6-Jul-2 Berlinghof, Heidelberg #233/R
£503 $785 €800 Tree lined country road to village in summer heat (7x86cm-3x34in) 21-Sep-2 Berlinghof, Heidelberg #134/R
£685 $1068 €1000 Snowy lower Rhine landscape (85x110cm-33x43in) s. 10-Apr-3 Van Ham, Cologne #1620
Works on paper
£385 $596 €600 March snows (56x78cm-22x31in) s. s.i. verso gouache lit. 6-Dec-2 Karlheinz Kaupp, Staufen #2228/R
£566 $883 €900 Mountains in morning light (68x100cm-27x39in) s. W/C bodycol. 11-Oct-2 Winterberg, Heidelberg #1547/R

NAGELE, Reinhold (1884-1972) German
£629 $981 €1000 Snowy valley (34x44cm-13x17in) s.d.1935 tempera paper. 19-Sep-2 Dr Fritz Nagel, Stuttgart #978/R
£881 $1374 €1400 Mountain village in winter (34x44cm-13x17in) s.d.1935 tempera paper one of pair. 19-Sep-2 Dr Fritz Nagel, Stuttgart #979/R
£1282 $1987 €2000 Coffee house (18x12cm-7x5in) s.i.d.1917 tempera. 5-Dec-2 Dr Fritz Nagel, Stuttgart #681/R est:4500
£1923 $2981 €3000 Self portrait (15x18cm-6x7in) mono. tempera. 5-Dec-2 Dr Fritz Nagel, Stuttgart #680/R est:6000
£2323 $3414 €3600 Rocket launchpad (23x17cm-9x7in) mono.d.1966 behind glass. 20-Jun-2 Dr Fritz Nagel, Stuttgart #803/R est:4000
£3145 $4906 €5000 Athlete's graveyard (30x24cm-12x9in) mono.d.48 tempera paper. 20-Sep-2 Sigalas, Stuttgart #1121/R est:4800
£3226 $4742 €5000 Still life (26x24cm-10x9in) mono.d.1966 behind glass. 20-Jun-2 Dr Fritz Nagel, Stuttgart #804/R est:4000
£3459 $5396 €5500 Galerie Thannhauser, New York (19x20cm-7x8in) init.d.1960 oil on glass prov. 9-Oct-2 Sotheby's, London #255/R est:8000-12000
£3846 $5962 €6000 Officer's mess in Boblingen (20x26cm-8x10in) mono. tempera. 5-Dec-2 Dr Fritz Nagel, Stuttgart #684/R est:10000
£4167 $6458 €6500 The artist and actress (29x23cm-11x9in) mono.d.1963 glass. 5-Dec-2 Dr Fritz Nagel, Stuttgart #682/R est:6000
£6918 $10792 €11000 Boblingen (34x50cm-13x20in) s.i.d.1916 tempera board. 19-Sep-2 Dr Fritz Nagel, Stuttgart #977/R est:3000
£11321 $17660 €18000 Guggenheim Museum, New York (29x34cm-11x13in) oil on glass painted c.1962 prov.exhib. 9-Oct-2 Sotheby's, London #257/R est:12000-18000
£12179 $18878 €19000 Figures at night looking into brightly lit windows of jewellery shop (27x30cm-11x12in) s.d.1910 tempera. 5-Dec-2 Dr Fritz Nagel, Stuttgart #685/R est:12000
Prints
£2903 $4268 €4500 Station Square, Stuttgart (31x48cm-12x19in) s.i.d.1926 etching. 20-Jun-2 Dr Fritz Nagel, Stuttgart #674/R est:1200

NAGL, Hazel (?) ?
£440 $717 €660 Bamboo border, Lot et Garonne (52x73cm-20x29in) 14-Feb-3 Lyon & Turnbull, Edinburgh #14

NAGORNOV, Vladislav (1974-) Russian
£350 $543 €525 Girl near the fountain (46x27cm-18x11in) s. 29-Sep-2 John Nicholson, Haslemere #140
£450 $698 €675 On the terrace (27x46cm-11x18in) s. 29-Sep-2 John Nicholson, Haslemere #136/R
£500 $775 €750 Near the mirror (61x46cm-24x18in) s. 8-Dec-2 John Nicholson, Haslemere #164/R
£550 $853 €825 Rest on the deck (38x55cm-15x22in) s. 29-Sep-2 John Nicholson, Haslemere #137
£550 $853 €825 Near a blooming rose (77x43cm-30x17in) s. 29-Sep-2 John Nicholson, Haslemere #141
£592 $959 €900 Nude (33x46cm-13x18in) s. 21-Jan-3 Durán, Madrid #733/R
£692 $1065 €1100 Young painter (58x40cm-23x16in) s. 22-Oct-2 Durán, Madrid #697/R
£700 $1085 €1050 Two friends (46x61cm-18x24in) s. 29-Sep-2 John Nicholson, Haslemere #139/R
£750 $1163 €1125 While reading (55x33cm-22x13in) s. 29-Sep-2 John Nicholson, Haslemere #138/R

NAGSH, Jamil (20th C) Indian
Works on paper
£600 $936 €900 Figure of a man (53x38cm-21x15in) s.d.83 W/C. 17-Oct-2 Bonhams, Knightsbridge #664/R

NAGY, Bela Fekete (1904-1983) Hungarian
Works on paper
£531 $828 €770 Remembering (60x47cm-24x19in) s.d.39 chl exhib.lit. 12-Apr-3 Mu Terem Galeria, Budapest #105/R est:120000 (H.F 190000)

NAGY, Ernoi (1881-1951) Hungarian?
£379 $603 €550 Goose market (68x55cm-27x22in) s. 8-Mar-3 Arnold, Frankfurt #659

NAGY, Gabor (1945-) Canadian
£281 $441 €422 Lilies (75x60cm-30x24in) s.i.d.1994. 25-Nov-2 Hodgins, Calgary #324/R (C.D 700)
£894 $1395 €1341 Memory (40x51cm-16x20in) s.d.1983 panel. 11-Apr-3 Kieselbach, Budapest #156/R est:180000-320000 (H.F 320000)

NAGY, Imre (1893-?) Hungarian
£2193 $3421 €3290 Shepherds (100x87cm-39x34in) s. 11-Sep-2 Kieselbach, Budapest #197/R (H.F 850000)

NAGY, Istvan (1873-1937) Hungarian
£903 $1409 €1355 Farm (38x48cm-15x19in) s. 11-Sep-2 Kieselbach, Budapest #69/R (H.F 350000)
£2041 $3245 €3000 Cattle market (100x121cm-39x48in) s.d.923. 24-Mar-3 Bernaerts, Antwerp #131/R est:2000-3000
£3633 $5667 €5450 The Horgas Street in Mindszent (44x60cm-17x24in) s. 11-Apr-3 Kieselbach, Budapest #169/R est:480000-1300000 (H.F 1300000)
Works on paper
£753 $1167 €1130 House before blue sky (25x34cm-10x13in) s. pastel. 6-Dec-2 Kieselbach, Budapest #7/R (H.F 280000)
£1022 $1584 €1533 Cottage (25x33cm-10x13in) s. pastel. 6-Dec-2 Kieselbach, Budapest #121/R (H.F 380000)
£1290 $2012 €1935 Woman in blue shawl, 1917 (43x30cm-17x12in) s.d.1917 pastel. 11-Sep-2 Kieselbach, Budapest #3/R (H.F 500000)
£1290 $2012 €1871 Hills in Transylvania (49x66cm-19x26in) s. pastel. 13-Sep-2 Mu Terem Galeria, Budapest #77/R est:450000 (H.F 500000)
£1341 $2092 €2012 Self portrait with hat (48x35cm-19x14in) s. pastel. 11-Apr-3 Kieselbach, Budapest #137/R est:380000-480000 (H.F 480000)
£3227 $5002 €4841 Stacks (50x70cm-20x28in) s. pastel. 6-Dec-2 Kieselbach, Budapest #8/R (H.F 1200000)

NAGY, Oszkar (20th C) Hungarian
£2451 $3823 €3554 Nagybanya (55x90cm-22x35in) s. 13-Sep-2 Mu Terem Galeria, Budapest #39/R est:750000 (H.F 950000)
£2655 $4141 €3850 Bridge over the river Zazar (70x76cm-28x30in) s. 12-Apr-3 Mu Terem Galeria, Budapest #98/R est:850000 (H.F 950000)
£3227 $5002 €4841 Sunlit houses in Nagybanya (43x58cm-17x23in) s. 6-Dec-2 Kieselbach, Budapest #29/R (H.F 1200000)
£3765 $5836 €5459 Twilight at Nagybanya (52x45cm-20x18in) s.d.932. 9-Dec-2 Mu Terem Galeria, Budapest #71/R est:600000 (H.F 1400000)

£4192 $6539 €6078 Street in Nagabanya (44x70cm-17x28in) s.d.955. 12-Apr-3 Mu Terem Galeria, Budapest #39/R est:850000 (H.F 1500000)
£4303 $6669 €6455 Forest in Nagybanya (90x105cm-35x41in) s. 6-Dec-2 Kieselbach, Budapest #110/R (H.F 1600000)
£4303 $6669 €6239 Sunny street (66x97cm-26x38in) s.d.957. 9-Dec-2 Mu Terem Galeria, Budapest #170/R est:900000 (H.F 1600000)
£5030 $7847 €7294 House in Nagybanyai at dusk (30x31cm-12x12in) s.d.39 panel. 12-Apr-3 Mu Terem Galeria, Budapest #94/R est:600000 (H.F 1800000)
£5916 $9170 €8578 Sunlit house at Nagybanya (64x71cm-25x28in) s.d.958. 9-Dec-2 Mu Terem Galeria, Budapest #174/R est:850000 (H.F 2200000)
£9681 $15006 €14037 Snowy street in Nagybanya (80x70cm-31x28in) s.d.924. 9-Dec-2 Mu Terem Galeria, Budapest #69/R est:1400000 (H.F 3600000)
£11833 $18341 €17158 In the park (72x89cm-28x35in) s.d.1937 exhib. 9-Dec-2 Mu Terem Galeria, Budapest #63/R est:1800000 (H.F 4400000)

NAGY, Sandor (1869-1950) Hungarian
£1076 $1667 €1560 Colour study for the glasses of the Culture Palace in Marosvasarhely (39x17cm-15x7in) papercard three. 9-Dec-2 Mu Terem Galeria, Budapest #49/R est:300000 (H.F 400000)
£5558 $8893 €8337 Spring garden, blossoming (65x81cm-26x32in) init. painted c.1908. 16-May-3 Kieselbach, Budapest #29/R (H.F 1900000)
Works on paper
£335 $523 €503 Mother with child (24x36cm-9x14in) s. W/C. 11-Sep-2 Kieselbach, Budapest #212/R (H.F 130000)

NAGY, Vilmos (1874-1953) Hungarian
£360 $590 €500 Lovers serenade (100x75cm-39x30in) s. 5-Jun-3 Dorotheum, Salzburg #518/R
£411 $638 €650 Woman with dog in landscape (60x80cm-24x31in) s. i. verso. 26-Sep-2 Neumeister, Munich #2800/R
£850 $1343 €1275 Love letter (79x60cm-31x24in) s. 14-Nov-2 Christie's, Kensington #61/R
£5676 $8854 €8514 Ladies in interior, 1904 (166x125cm-65x49in) s.d.1904. 11-Sep-2 Kieselbach, Budapest #89/R (H.F 2200000)

NAHCEPE, E (19th C) Austrian
Sculpture
£6452 $10000 €9355 Three thoroughbreds taking a water jump (36x48x25cm-14x19x10in) s. bronze. 7-Dec-2 South Bay, Long Island #76/R

NAHL, Carl (19th C) ?
£1076 $1700 €1700 Saxon prince robbery (38x31cm-15x12in) s.d.1843 copper. 30-Nov-2 Berlinghof, Heidelberg #350/R est:1500

NAHL, Charles C (1818-1878) American
£1144 $1900 €1659 Quit thoughts (17x13cm-7x5in) s. paper on board. 11-Jun-3 Butterfields, San Francisco #4153/R est:3000-5000
Works on paper
£285 $450 €428 Life in Sacramento Valley. s. pencil dr. 16-Nov-2 Harvey Clar, Oakland #1235

NAHL, Johann August (18/19th C) German
Works on paper
£267 $425 €401 Roman scene (46x61cm-18x24in) s.d.1800 dr. 8-Mar-3 Harvey Clar, Oakland #1148

NAIDA, Dmitri (1969-) Russian
£622 $945 €970 Still life of flowers (100x70cm-39x28in) s.d.01. 11-Jul-2 Hugo Ruef, Munich #759/R

NAIDITCH, Vladimir (1903-1980) Russian
£385 $604 €600 Les amoureuses (48x38cm-19x15in) mono. cardboard prov. 24-Nov-2 Chayette & Cheval, Paris #281
£442 $703 €650 Jeune femme a la cheminee (40x30cm-16x12in) s. cardboard. 26-Feb-3 Artcurial Briest, Paris #222
£1135 $1895 €1600 Peintre devant son modele (73x60cm-29x24in) s. 17-Jun-3 Claude Boisgirard, Paris #95/R est:1500-1800
£1361 $2163 €2000 Paysage (65x101cm-26x40in) s. 3-Mar-3 Claude Boisgirard, Paris #72/R est:2000-2500

NAIRN, Cecilia (1791-1857) British
£2051 $3179 €3200 Landscape with figures (43x60cm-17x24in) prov. 3-Dec-2 Bonhams & James Adam, Dublin #20/R est:2000-3000

NAIRN, James (20th C) New Zealander
£2736 $4267 €4104 Moonrise at Ohau, Tararua Mountain (33x48cm-13x19in) s.d.92 board. 17-Sep-2 Peter Webb, Auckland #102/R est:15000-25000 (NZ.D 9000)

NAIRN, James McLachlan (1859-1904) British
Works on paper
£1300 $2171 €1885 Fisherman by a highland river. Returning home from the fields (24x34cm-9x13in) s.d.1883 W/C pair. 17-Jun-3 Rosebery Fine Art, London #617/R est:600-800
£2456 $3832 €3684 Silverstream (27x45cm-11x18in) s.d.1905 W/C. 27-Mar-3 International Art Centre, Auckland #96/R est:5000-8000 (NZ.D 7000)

NAISH, John George (1824-1905) British
£900 $1386 €1350 Gurnard's head, north Cornwall (71x442cm-28x174in) s. 23-Oct-2 Hamptons Fine Art, Godalming #137/R

NAIVE SCHOOL, 19th C
£18000 $27900 €27000 Benthall Hall and church, with children and dog in foreground (69x79cm-27x31in) 25-Sep-2 Brightwells, Leominster #969/R est:2000-3000

NAIVEU, Matthys (1647-1721) Dutch
£15000 $23400 €22500 Candle-lit interior with Arlequin (54x64cm-21x25in) prov.exhib. 10-Apr-3 Sotheby's, London #43/R est:20000

NAKAMURA, Kazuo (1926-2002) Canadian/Japanese
£2222 $3644 €3333 Solitude (48x61cm-19x24in) s.d.86 masonite prov. 27-May-3 Sotheby's, Toronto #185/R est:2500-3000 (C.D 5000)
£4222 $6924 €6333 Core suspension (102x99cm-40x39in) s. prov. 3-Jun-3 Joyner, Toronto #107/R est:5000-7000 (C.D 9500)
Works on paper
£820 $1270 €1230 Bridge under construction. Untitled (35x52cm-14x20in) s. i.verso ink double-sided. 24-Sep-2 Ritchie, Toronto #3204/R est:1800-2200 (C.D 2000)

NAKAMURA, Nandu (20th C) Japanese?
Works on paper
£2279 $3623 €3350 Jeune fille a l'eventail (69x53cm-27x21in) s.d.1955 gouache ink. 26-Feb-3 Artcurial Briest, Paris #309/R est:3000-4000

NAKAMURA, Naondo (20th C) Japanese
£1236 $1989 €1854 Woman with cockerel (94x49cm-37x19in) s.i.d.1959 tempera. 7-May-3 AB Stockholms Auktionsverk #1130/R est:15000-20000 (S.KR 16000)

NAKIAN, Reuben (1897-1986) American
Sculpture
£1401 $2200 €2102 Seal (30cm-12in) s.d.1930 alabaster prov. 14-Dec-2 Weschler, Washington #700/R est:800-1200
£2690 $4250 €4035 Europa and the bull (28x14x34cm-11x6x13in) s. fired terracota executed c.1962 prov. 13-Nov-2 Sotheby's, New York #221/R est:2000-3000

NAKKEN, Willem Carel (1835-1926) Dutch
£446 $696 €700 Hay wagon (33x43cm-13x17in) s. 6-Nov-2 Vendue Huis, Gravenhage #550/R
£955 $1490 €1500 Farmer with goat (21x26cm-8x10in) s. panel. 5-Nov-2 Vendu Notarishuis, Rotterdam #216 est:1500-2000
£2345 $3728 €3400 Cows near the waterside (33x52cm-13x20in) s. panel. 10-Mar-3 Sotheby's, Amsterdam #150/R est:2000-3000
£4110 $6452 €6000 Landweg achter marlot bij wassenaar (35x49cm-14x19in) s. i.verso board on panel. 15-Apr-3 Sotheby's, Amsterdam #122/R est:5000-7000
£7547 $11623 €12000 In ryes, horse in a sunny farmyard (40x56cm-16x22in) s.d.99. 23-Oct-2 Christie's, Amsterdam #12/R est:6000-8000
£8000 $12560 €12000 At the quarry (75x114cm-30x45in) s. 21-Nov-2 Christie's, Kensington #106/R est:8000-12000
£10692 $16465 €17000 Bringing in the hay (40x60cm-16x24in) s. 22-Oct-2 Sotheby's, Amsterdam #12/R est:8000-12000
Works on paper
£450 $711 €675 Village beam pump (24x32cm-9x13in) s. W/C. 2-Dec-2 Bonhams, Bath #25/R
£949 $1481 €1500 Figures and horse-drawn sledges on the ice (13x24cm-5x9in) s. W/C. 21-Oct-2 Glerum, Amsterdam #187 est:1000-1500
£1069 $1647 €1700 Horse drawn wagons halting by a barn (33x54cm-13x21in) s.d.76 pencil W/C htd white. 23-Oct-2 Christie's, Amsterdam #79/R est:2000-3000

£2830 $4358 €4500 Farmer with his horses entering a courtyard (38x56cm-15x22in) s.d.1906 W/C. 22-Oct-2 Sotheby's, Amsterdam #2/R est:4000-6000

NALDINI, Giovan Battista (1537-1591) Italian
Works on paper
£625 $994 €900 Mary with child worshipped by saints (20x17cm-8x7in) i. i. verso pen wash prov. 5-May-3 Ketterer, Munich #368/R
£6500 $10855 €9425 Diana and Endymion in a landscape with putti and a dog. Horse drawing a chariot (10x14cm-4x6in) i. black chk ink double-sided. 8-Jul-3 Christie's, London #24/R est:4000-6000

NALDINI, Giovan Battista (attrib) (1537-1591) Italian
Works on paper
£3000 $4710 €4500 Standing female nude (40x18cm-16x7in) black chk prov. 11-Dec-2 Sotheby's, Olympia #13/R est:3000-5000

NALDINI, Paolo (attrib) (c.1615-1691) Italian
Sculpture
£12000 $18840 €18000 Head of an angel (38cm-15in) white marble on octagonal base prov. 10-Dec-2 Sotheby's, London #128/R est:15000-20000

NALLARD, Louis (1918-) French
£1351 $2108 €2000 Atelier (72x81cm-28x32in) s. painted 1975 prov. 26-Mar-3 Peschetau-Badin Godeau & Leroy, Paris #26/R

NAM KWAN (1911-1990) Korean
£7547 $12000 €11321 Untitled (73x93cm-29x37in) s.d.65. 24-Mar-3 Christie's, Rockefeller NY #323/R est:8000-12000

NAM, Jacques (1881-1974) French
Works on paper
£256 $397 €400 Chat tigre allonge (25x35cm-10x14in) s. felt-tip pen dr. 7-Dec-2 Martinot & Savignat, Pontoise #10
£288 $447 €450 Etudes de chats et chiot (22x30cm-9x12in) s. pen W/C dr prov. 7-Dec-2 Martinot & Savignat, Pontoise #18
£288 $447 €450 Chat tigre surpris (29x44cm-11x17in) studio st. chl crayon dr prov. 7-Dec-2 Martinot & Savignat, Pontoise #19
£288 $447 €450 Chat tigre au repos (15x24cm-6x9in) s. ink dr. 7-Dec-2 Martinot & Savignat, Pontoise #13/R
£353 $546 €550 Chats accroupis (23x40cm-9x16in) s. Chinese ink dr prov. 7-Dec-2 Martinot & Savignat, Pontoise #30
£365 $566 €570 Chats couches (17x26cm-7x10in) s. pen ink wash htd gouache dr prov. 7-Dec-2 Martinot & Savignat, Pontoise #22
£385 $596 €600 Chat accroupi (21x28cm-8x11in) s. ink dr prov. 7-Dec-2 Martinot & Savignat, Pontoise #12
£564 $874 €880 Etude de chatons blancs (38x28cm-15x11in) s. ink W/C gouache dr prov. 7-Dec-2 Martinot & Savignat, Pontoise #29/R
£577 $894 €900 Fastagette assise (44x32cm-17x13in) s. ink dr. 7-Dec-2 Martinot & Savignat, Pontoise #23/R

NAMATJIRA, Albert (1902-1959) Australian
£438 $719 €635 Painted woomerah (14x56cm-6x22in) 3-Jun-3 Lawson Menzies, Sydney #787 (A.D 1100)
Works on paper
£1057 $1670 €1533 Gum tree in Central Australia (9x14cm-4x6in) s. i.verso W/C prov. 22-Jul-3 Lawson Menzies, Sydney #132/R est:1000-2000 (A.D 2600)
£1805 $2869 €2708 Blue hills (21x38cm-8x15in) s. W/C. 3-Mar-3 Lawson Menzies, Sydney #422 est:5000-7000 (A.D 4800)
£2143 $3364 €3215 Kariltynja, Western Australia (27x38cm-11x15in) s. i.verso W/C. 25-Nov-2 Christie's, Melbourne #265/R est:6000-8000 (A.D 6000)
£2400 $3816 €3600 Central Australian mountain range (26x37cm-10x15in) s. W/C. 29-Apr-3 Bonhams, New Bond Street #16/R est:1500-2000
£3036 $4705 €4554 Blue ranges (30x45cm-12x18in) s. W/C. 29-Oct-2 Lawson Menzies, Sydney #44/R est:8000-12000 (A.D 8500)
£3101 $4930 €4652 Gorge, Central Australia (36x25cm-14x10in) s. W/C. 5-May-3 Sotheby's, Melbourne #289/R est:7000-9000 (A.D 8000)
£3257 $4852 €4886 Gorge (22x27cm-9x11in) s. W/C. 27-Aug-2 Christie's, Melbourne #278/R est:2000-3000 (A.D 8500)
£3400 $5474 €5100 McDonnell Ranges (25x36cm-10x14in) s. W/C. 6-May-3 Christie's, Melbourne #272 est:8000-12000 (A.D 8500)
£3448 $5414 €5172 Gap at Glen Gorge (21x25cm-8x10in) s.i. W/C. 15-Apr-3 Lawson Menzies, Sydney #137/R est:14500-16500 (A.D 9000)
£3559 $5445 €5339 Receding hills, Mcdonnell Ranges (25x34cm-10x13in) s. i.verso W/C executed c.1950 prov. 26-Aug-2 Sotheby's, Paddington #568/R est:9000-12000 (A.D 10000)
£3584 $5448 €5376 Landscape (38x53cm-15x21in) s. W/C prov. 27-Aug-2 Goodman, Sydney #127/R est:10000-15000 (A.D 10000)
£3640 $5715 €5460 Palm Valley, James Range, Central Australia (28x27cm-11x11in) s.i. W/C prov. 15-Apr-3 Lawson Menzies, Sydney #33/R est:8000-12000 (A.D 9500)
£3929 $6207 €5894 Mount Sonder (25x37cm-10x15in) s. W/C. 26-Nov-2 Sotheby's, Melbourne #121/R est:8000-10000 (A.D 11000)
£4286 $6643 €6429 Landscape (25x36cm-10x14in) s. W/C. 29-Oct-2 Lawson Menzies, Sydney #43/R est:8000-12000 (A.D 12000)
£5364 $8421 €8046 Towards Mt. Gillen, west of Alice (26x36cm-10x14in) s. W/C executed c.1955. 15-Apr-3 Lawson Menzies, Sydney #32/R est:15500-18500 (A.D 14000)
£5776 $8953 €8664 Untitled, central desert landscape with gum tree (25x35cm-10x14in) s. W/C. 3-Dec-2 Shapiro, Sydney #141/R est:12000-18000 (A.D 16000)
£6429 $9964 €9644 Mount Sonder MacDonnell Ranges (38x55cm-15x22in) s.d.1945 W/C. 29-Oct-2 Lawson Menzies, Sydney #23/R est:20000-25000 (A.D 18000)
£6504 $10276 €9431 Kwaratnama Quaraitnama (38x28cm-15x11in) s. W/C. 22-Jul-3 Lawson Menzies, Sydney #131/R est:12000-15000 (A.D 16000)
£7321 $11568 €10982 Central Australian landscape (35x25cm-14x10in) s. W/C. 26-Nov-2 Sotheby's, Melbourne #76/R est:8000-12000 (A.D 20500)
£8527 $13558 €12791 Glen Helen landscape, Macdonnell ranges (27x38cm-11x15in) s. W/C prov. 5-May-3 Sotheby's, Melbourne #119/R est:18000-22000 (A.D 22000)
£8571 $13543 €12857 Ghost gums and Ranges (26x35cm-10x14in) s. W/C prov. 26-Nov-2 Sotheby's, Melbourne #71/R est:12000-14000 (A.D 24000)
£10000 $16100 €15000 Mount Sonder (25x36cm-10x14in) s. W/C. 6-May-3 Christie's, Melbourne #124/R est:10000-15000 (A.D 25000)
£11155 $18295 €16733 Ghost gums and ranges, central Australia (28x36cm-11x14in) s. W/C exec.c.1958 prov. 4-Jun-3 Deutscher-Menzies, Melbourne #61/R est:14000-18000 (A.D 28000)

NAMATJIRA, Ewald (1930-1984) Australian
Works on paper
£359 $588 €521 Ghost gums, Macdonell Ranges (35x26cm-14x10in) s. W/C. 3-Jun-3 Lawson Menzies, Sydney #790 (A.D 900)
£440 $708 €638 Tree (36x26cm-14x10in) s. W/C prov. 12-May-3 Joel, Victoria #237 est:800-1200 (A.D 1100)
£500 $775 €750 After rain McDonnell Range Valley (38x52cm-15x20in) s. W/C exec.c.1960. 29-Oct-2 Lawson Menzies, Sydney #129 (A.D 1400)

NAMATJIRA, Gabriel (1941-1969) Australian
Works on paper
£325 $514 €471 Mount Sonder (34x50cm-13x20in) s. W/C. 22-Jul-3 Lawson Menzies, Sydney #133/R (A.D 800)

NAMATJIRA, Keith (1938-1977) Australian
Works on paper
£279 $457 €405 Central Australian landscape (41x55cm-16x22in) s. W/C. 3-Jun-3 Lawson Menzies, Sydney #794 (A.D 700)

NAMATJIRA, Oscar (1922-) Australian
Works on paper
£722 $1119 €1083 Aranda tribal country at Mt Sonder (53x73cm-21x29in) s. W/C exhib. 3-Dec-2 Shapiro, Sydney #143 (A.D 2000)

NANGALA, Ningie (1934-) Australian
£383 $602 €575 Untitled (80x80cm-31x31in) s.verso acrylic. 15-Apr-3 Lawson Menzies, Sydney #115/R est:900-1200 (A.D 1000)

NANGALA, Tatali (c.1928-2000) Australian
Works on paper
£939 $1455 €1409 Women gathering mungilypa seeds at Kaakurantinja (91x61cm-36x24in) synthetic polymer paint linen prov. 3-Dec-2 Shapiro, Sydney #162/R est:2500-4000 (A.D 2600)

NANNI DI BARTOLO (15th C) Italian
Sculpture
£91321 $142460 €145200 Madonna with Child (65x43cm-26x17in) painted plaster. 21-Sep-2 Semenzato, Venice #125/R est:160000-200000

NANNI, Mario (1922-) Italian
Works on paper
£696 $1086 €1100 Composition (48x69cm-19x27in) s. burning on canvas. 19-Oct-2 Semenzato, Venice #32/R

NANNINGA, Dirk Berend (1868-1954) Dutch
£2803 $4372 €4400 Still life of wild flowers (49x60cm-19x24in) s. 6-Nov-2 Vendue Huis, Gravenhage #119/R est:600-800

NANNINGA, Jaap (1904-1962) Dutch
£4777 $7452 €7500 Abstract composition (40x50cm-16x20in) s.d.50. 6-Nov-2 Vendue Huis, Gravenhage #259/R est:2500-3000
Works on paper
£4167 $6458 €6500 Venetie (60x72cm-24x28in) s.d.59 gouache exhib. 3-Dec-2 Christie's, Amsterdam #241/R est:4000-6000

NANTEMBO, Nakahara (1839-1925) Japanese
Works on paper
£950 $1587 €1378 Staff and Tassels (143x50cm-56x20in) i. ink hanging scroll. 18-Jun-3 Christie's, London #307/R
£1300 $2171 €1885 Procession of Monks (145x34cm-57x13in) s. ink hanging scrolls pair. 18-Jun-3 Christie's, London #308/R est:1500-2000

NANTEUIL, Celestin Francois (1837-1873) French
Works on paper
£476 $757 €700 Portrait d'homme en pied (31x22cm-12x9in) W/C gouache over crayon. 24-Mar-3 Tajan, Paris #171

NANTEUIL, Robert (1623-1678) French
Prints
£2949 $4659 €4600 Le Cardinal de Furstenberg. drypoint engraving. 14-Nov-2 Libert, Castor, Paris #22/R est:225

NAONOBU, Kano (1607-1650) Japanese
Works on paper
£1635 $2600 €2453 Kikyorai, Gui-Qu-Lai (30x78cm-12x31in) s. ink col silk hanging scroll. 24-Mar-3 Christie's, Rockefeller NY #8/R est:2000-3000

NAPALTJARRI, Tjunkiya (20th C) Australian
£843 $1323 €1265 Lingakurra rockhole, South of Kintore (137x137cm-54x54in) s.verso acrylic. 15-Apr-3 Lawson Menzies, Sydney #109/R est:2500-3500 (A.D 2200)

NAPANANGKA, Warlangkara (c.1946-) Australian
Works on paper
£866 $1343 €1299 Designs associated with the travels of Kutungka Napanangka (91x91cm-36x36in) synthetic polymer paint linen prov. 3-Dec-2 Shapiro, Sydney #148/R (A.D 2400)

NAPARRULA, Mitjilli (c.1930-) Australian
£1073 $1684 €1610 Untitled (153x62cm-60x24in) acrylic. 15-Apr-3 Lawson Menzies, Sydney #101/R est:2200-2800 (A.D 2800)
£1626 $2569 €2358 Untitled (122x92cm-48x36in) acrylic. 22-Jul-3 Lawson Menzies, Sydney #65/R est:2500-3000 (A.D 4000)

NAPPER, John (1916-) British
£2800 $4368 €4200 Autobus (42x61cm-17x24in) s. exhib. 12-Sep-2 Sotheby's, Olympia #101/R est:3000-5000
Works on paper
£480 $763 €720 Still lifes of pots and spoons (26x20cm-10x8in) s.d.1980 gouache pair. 26-Feb-3 Sotheby's, Olympia #381/R

NAPPI, Sigismondo (1804-1832) Italian
£1935 $3058 €3000 Portrait of Carlo Prayer (64x49cm-25x19in) board. 18-Dec-2 Finarte, Milan #98/R est:4000

NAPURRULA, Mitjili (c.1930-) Australian
£976 $1541 €1415 Untitled (55x152cm-22x60in) s.verso acrylic. 22-Jul-3 Lawson Menzies, Sydney #71/R est:2800-3500 (A.D 2400)

NARA, Yoshimoto (1959-) American
£12658 $20000 €18987 So far apart (60x50cm-24x20in) i.d.97 verso prov. 14-Nov-2 Christie's, Rockefeller NY #304/R est:20000-30000
£12658 $20000 €18987 Little black bunny (70x50cm-28x20in) s.i.d.96 on overlap acrylic prov. 14-Nov-2 Christie's, Rockefeller NY #305/R est:20000-30000
£22152 $35000 €33228 Q at A (68x55cm-27x22in) s.i.d.95 on overlap prov. 13-Nov-2 Sotheby's, New York #416/R est:25000-35000
£29688 $47500 €44532 Planet doll (170x110cm-67x43in) s.on stretcher i.d.93 verso prov. 14-May-3 Sotheby's, New York #319/R est:30000-40000
Sculpture
£13291 $21000 €19937 Little pilgrims (72x46x43cm-28x18x17in) s. fabric acrylic exec.1999 one of 10 prov. 13-Nov-2 Sotheby's, New York #421/R est:18000-22000
£37500 $60000 €56250 Bunny heads (13x11x9cm-5x4x4in) init.d.98 num.W1 acrylic cast composite gauze seven parts. 14-May-3 Sotheby's, New York #337/R est:15000-20000
Works on paper
£2187 $3500 €3281 Miss Mountain (30x23cm-12x9in) s.i.d.2000 verso col pencil on board prov. 16-May-3 Phillips, New York #217/R est:4000-6000
£2848 $4500 €4272 Untitled (27x21cm-11x8in) s.d.99 W/C wax crayon graphite prov. 12-Nov-2 Phillips, New York #220/R est:5000-7000
£3000 $4800 €4500 Three heads for you (30x23cm-12x9in) s.i.d.00 verso col pencil on board prov. 16-May-3 Phillips, New York #218/R est:4000-6000

NARAHA, Takashi (1930-) Japanese
Sculpture
£53125 $85000 €79688 Dog form your childhood (106x59x248cm-42x23x98in) d.Jan 2000 fiberglass reinforced plastics plywwod cotton acrylic. 15-May-3 Christie's, Rockefeller NY #327/R est:50000-70000

NARAIN, Laxmi (?) Indian
Works on paper
£3885 $5634 €6100 Mado Singh of Jaipur (29x24cm-11x9in) s. gouache htd gold. 31-May-2 Blanchet, Paris #25/R est:4000-5000

NARANJO, Eduardo (1944-) Spanish
£62500 $101250 €95000 Dream with white jacket (130x116cm-51x46in) s.d.76 exhib.lit. 21-Jan-3 Durán, Madrid #167/R est:95000
Works on paper
£980 $1578 €1500 Alchemist (18x12cm-7x5in) s. W/C prov. 14-Jan-3 Castellana, Madrid #68/R

NARAY, Aurel (1883-1948) Hungarian
£520 $759 €780 Sisters (33x26cm-13x10in) board painted c.1930. 4-Jun-2 SOGA, Bratislava #120/R est:25000 (SL.K 33000)

NARBONA BELTRAN, Francisco (1860-1926) Spanish
£517 $822 €750 Landscape (14x21cm-6x8in) s. board. 4-Mar-3 Ansorena, Madrid #127/R
£855 $1386 €1300 Flowers (100x50cm-39x20in) s. 21-Jan-3 Durán, Madrid #107/R

NARDI, Antonio M (?) Italian
£570 $889 €900 Still life with hat (45x55cm-18x22in) s. 19-Oct-2 Semenzato, Venice #6/R

NARDI, Enrico (1864-?) Italian
Works on paper
£750 $1230 €1125 In the Roman campagna (27x44cm-11x17in) s. pencil W/C. 5-Jun-3 Christie's, Kensington #937/R

NARDI, François (1861-1936) French
£2917 $4696 €4376 Sailing ships in the Lagoon, Venice (54x73cm-21x29in) s. 7-May-3 Dobiaschofsky, Bern #854/R est:7000 (S.FR 6300)
£3521 $5845 €5000 Vue de Nice (33x55cm-13x22in) s. 16-Jun-3 Oger, Dumont, Paris #47/R est:1800-2000

NARDI, Piero (20th C) ?
£1803 $2866 €2650 Souvenirs d'une ile Grecque (65x54cm-26x21in) s. 26-Feb-3 Artcurial Briest, Paris #341/R est:2400-2800

NARDI, Ugo (20th C) Italian
£500 $790 €750 Architect (59x69cm-23x27in) s. acrylic painted c.1990. 18-Nov-2 Joel, Victoria #321 est:1100-1600 (A.D 1400)

NARDINI, P (?) ?
£320 $493 €480 Italian marina (25x25cm-10x10in) s.d.99 acrylic. 7-Sep-2 Shapes, Edinburgh #448

NARES, James (1953-) American
£3165 $5000 €4748 Untitled (91x61cm-36x24in) s.d.1995 verso oil on paper prov. 12-Nov-2 Phillips, New York #224/R est:2000-3000

NARJOT, Ernest (1826-1898) American
£17964 $30000 €26048 Pike's Peak, Platt River (51x76cm-20x30in) s.i. exhib. 18-Jun-3 Christie's, Los Angeles #63/R est:30000-50000

NARODITSKY, Mikhail (1946-) Russian
£503 $775 €800 Study of dogs (22x27cm-9x11in) s. canvas on cardboard. 22-Oct-2 Durán, Madrid #699/R
£550 $836 €825 Two Russian wolfhounds (60x21cm-24x8in) s. 14-Jul-2 John Nicholson, Haslemere #77/R

NASH, David (1945-) British
Sculpture
£1800 $2808 €2700 Mosaic egg (50x62cm-20x24in) carved wood. 15-Oct-2 Bonhams, Knightsbridge #134/R est:2000-3000

NASH, Frederick (1782-1856) British
Works on paper
£400 $648 €580 Kensington Gardens (14x19cm-6x7in) W/C. 23-May-3 Bracketts, Tunbridge Wells #963/R
£1200 $1920 €1800 Pont Neuf, Paris - sunrise (38x53cm-15x21in) W/C exhib. 11-Mar-3 Bonhams, New Bond Street #12/R est:1200-1800

NASH, John (1893-1977) British
£1800 $2808 €2700 Reclining nude (67x56cm-26x22in) s. board. 17-Sep-2 Bonhams, Knightsbridge #111/R est:2000-3000
£2100 $3318 €3150 Weir (38x43cm-15x17in) board exhib. 18-Dec-2 Mallams, Oxford #659/R est:1500-2000
£21000 $32550 €31500 Wooded landscape (61x51cm-24x20in) s.d.1914. 4-Dec-2 Sotheby's, London #9/R est:7000-10000
Works on paper
£650 $1066 €975 From a Cornish notebook (21x29cm-8x11in) i. pen ink wash squared for transfer. 6-Jun-3 Christie's, London #103/R
£800 $1248 €1200 Tree study, Buckinghamshire (55x38cm-22x15in) s.d.1929 wash pencil prov. 25-Mar-3 Bonhams, New Bond Street #99/R
£1700 $2635 €2550 Botallack Hill (39x52cm-15x20in) s. W/C executed c.1971 prov. 3-Dec-2 Bonhams, New Bond Street #72/R est:800-1200
£1800 $2790 €2700 Weir (44x53cm-17x21in) s. W/C pencil prov. 3-Dec-2 Bonhams, New Bond Street #74/R est:2000-3000
£2200 $3542 €3300 Pond by trees (39x55cm-15x22in) s. W/C over pencil prov. 14-Jan-3 Bonhams, Knightsbridge #151/R est:1500-2000
£2400 $3912 €3600 Ash Grove, Firle Park, Sussex (33x43cm-13x17in) s.d.1957 W/C prov.exhib. 28-Jan-3 Henry Adams, Chichester #412/R est:1400-1600
£2600 $4082 €3900 Autumn landscape (39x49cm-15x19in) s. W/C pencil. 21-Nov-2 Christie's, London #133/R est:2000-3000
£3000 $4680 €4500 French landscape (43x53cm-17x21in) s. pencil W/C prov. 27-Mar-3 Christie's, Kensington #330/R est:1500-2000
£4000 $6320 €6000 Sand dunes and rocky coast (37x54cm-15x21in) s. pencil W/C prov. 27-Nov-2 Sotheby's, Olympia #3/R est:2000-3000
£4400 $6952 €6380 Bathers (36x25cm-14x10in) s.i.verso gouache. 23-Jul-3 Brightwells, Leominster #999/R est:800-1200

NASH, Jorgen (1920-) Danish
£508 $813 €762 A Kvanki-Vanki (50x65cm-20x26in) s.d.69. 13-Jan-3 Rasmussen, Vejle #299 (D.KR 5800)
£1524 $2362 €2286 A bird of the twenties (150x114cm-59x45in) s.d.1989 prov. 1-Oct-2 Rasmussen, Copenhagen #206/R est:18000 (D.KR 18000)

NASH, Joseph (1808-1878) British
Works on paper
£343 $542 €515 Playing soldier (33x48cm-13x19in) s.d.1873 W/C. 18-Nov-2 Waddingtons, Toronto #73/R (C.D 850)
£350 $546 €525 Knole House, Kent Armoury (28x40cm-11x16in) s. pencil W/C scratching out. 27-Mar-3 Christie's, Kensington #71/R
£380 $593 €570 Long galley, Haddon Hall (33x48cm-13x19in) s.d.1872 W/C. 6-Nov-2 Bonhams, Chester #418
£550 $869 €798 Entrance to a cathedral (34x25cm-13x10in) s.d.Jan 5 W/C htd bodycol. 22-Jul-3 Bonhams, Knightsbridge #80/R
£550 $869 €798 Watching the cloisters (52x40cm-20x16in) s.d.1865 W/C bodycol. 22-Jul-3 Bonhams, Knightsbridge #81/R
£800 $1240 €1200 Levens, Westmoreland (33x48cm-13x19in) s.d.1855 W/C. 3-Dec-2 Sotheby's, Olympia #43/R

NASH, Paul (1889-1946) British
£20000 $31400 €30000 Portrait of Alice Daglish (61x46cm-24x18in) s.d.1921. 22-Nov-2 Christie's, London #26/R est:20000-30000
£45000 $73800 €65250 The French farm (54x73cm-21x29in) s. s.i. on stretcher painted 1926 prov.exhib.lit. 4-Jun-3 Sotheby's, London #24/R est:20000-30000
Works on paper
£800 $1248 €1200 Hilly landscape, possibly Maiden Castle, Dorset (18x25cm-7x10in) s.i. pencil crayon. 17-Sep-2 Bonhams, Knightsbridge #266/R
£2600 $4264 €3900 Black farm on the marsh (35x49cm-14x19in) s.i.d.1922 pencil W/C prov.exhib.lit. 6-Jun-3 Christie's, London #32/R est:2500-3500
£4000 $6560 €6000 Russell Square (38x57cm-15x22in) s.i.d.1942 black crayon W/C prov.exhib.lit. 6-Jun-3 Christie's, London #143/R est:4000-6000
£5500 $9020 €8250 Badbury Rings, Dorset (28x39cm-11x15in) s. i.verso pencil W/C prov.exhib. 6-Jun-3 Christie's, London #33/R est:2500-3500
£10000 $15500 €15000 Backwater (28x38cm-11x15in) s.d.1919 W/C pencil prov.exhib.lit. 4-Dec-2 Sotheby's, London #27/R est:5000-7000
£11000 $17490 €16500 In the trenches (25x35cm-10x14in) chl white chk sold with letters. 26-Feb-3 Sotheby's, Olympia #75/R est:1000-1500
£11000 $18040 €15950 Wittenham Clumps (28x38cm-11x15in) s. W/C pencil prov. 4-Jun-3 Sotheby's, London #19/R est:3000-4000
£18000 $27900 €27000 Swanage, low tide (38x56cm-15x22in) s. W/C panel executed 1935 prov.exhib.lit. 4-Dec-2 Sotheby's, London #34/R est:10000-15000

NASINI, Giuseppe Niccolo (1657-1736) Italian
Works on paper
£1300 $2171 €1885 Bishop and other figures adoring a vision of Christ in glory (34x21cm-13x8in) blk chk pen brown ink wash htd white prov. 9-Jul-3 Sotheby's, London #38/R est:1500-2000

NASKE, Edith (1901-1963) Russian
Works on paper
£256 $403 €400 Still life of flowers (78x54cm-31x21in) s.d.62 W/C. 20-Nov-2 Dorotheum, Klagenfurt #53/R

NASKE, Franitisek Xaver (1884-?) Czechoslovakian
£327 $520 €491 Gardener (50x35cm-20x14in) s. canvas on board. 8-Mar-3 Dorotheum, Prague #137/R est:15000-23000 (C.KR 15000)
£347 $538 €521 Woman with basket (33x48cm-13x19in) painted 1942. 3-Dec-2 SOGA, Bratislava #218/R (SL.K 22000)
£654 $1041 €981 Lady with camellia - Anna Sedlackova (140x107cm-55x42in) s.d.1911 oval. 8-Mar-3 Dorotheum, Prague #93/R est:30000-45000 (C.KR 30000)

NASMYTH, Alexander (1758-1840) British
£800 $1248 €1200 Scottish castle (71x91cm-28x36in) s. 10-Sep-2 Bonhams, Knightsbridge #143/R
£1135 $1759 €1703 View of a chateau on the Lake of Lucerne, Switzerland (22x30cm-9x12in) s.i.d.1817 verso panel. 4-Dec-2 AB Stockholms Auktionsverk #1943/R est:20000-25000 (S.KR 16000)
£4200 $7014 €6090 Kambuskenneth Tower, with Stirling Castle in the distance (45x61cm-18x24in) panel. 25-Jun-3 Bonhams, Bury St Edmunds #564/R est:2500-3500
£5500 $8525 €8250 Highland landscape with figures by a river (47x61cm-19x24in) init. 31-Oct-2 Christie's, London #22/R est:4000-6000
£6000 $9300 €9000 View of Dunnottar Castle, with figures on a beach, and ship on the rocks (46x61cm-18x24in) panel prov.exhib.lit. 31-Oct-2 Christie's, London #12/R est:7000-10000
£10000 $15900 €15000 Dumbarton Castle and town with Ben Lomond (32x49cm-13x19in) s.i.verso prov. 20-Mar-3 Sotheby's, London #272/R est:10000-15000
£12000 $19080 €18000 Ardencaple from Roseneath, Dumbartonshire (44x60cm-17x24in) s. i.verso prov. 20-Mar-3 Sotheby's, London #271/R est:12000-18000
£50000 $79000 €75000 View of Durham from North-East with Cathedral, Castle and river Wear (69x89cm-27x35in) s.d.1809 prov.exhib. 26-Nov-2 Christie's, London #57/R est:25000-35000
£400000 $668000 €580000 Prospect of London, seen from the Earl of Cassillis's privy garden (139x208cm-55x82in) bears i.verso prov.exhib.lit. 17-Jun-3 Bonhams, New Bond Street #58/R est:400000-600000

NASMYTH, Alexander (attrib) (1758-1840) British
£900 $1404 €1350 Figure seated in Scottish West Coast scene (60x80cm-24x31in) indis sig. 28-Mar-3 Bonhams, Edinburgh #140
£4400 $6864 €6600 View of St Albans Abbey (46x60cm-18x24in) 26-Mar-3 Woolley & Wallis, Salisbury #227/R est:1000-1500

NASMYTH, Anne (1793-?) British
£4000 $6360 €6000 Where two rivers meet, Severn and Avon, near Newham (33x46cm-13x18in) i.d.1854 verso prov. 6-Mar-3 Christie's, Kensington #31/R est:2000-3000

NASMYTH, Barbara (1790-1870) British
£1400 $2226 €2100 Figures before a cottage in a loch landscape (23x30cm-9x12in) panel. 6-Mar-3 Christie's, Kensington #29/R est:1200-1800

NASMYTH, Charlotte (1804-1884) British
£4000 $6200 €6000 Wooded landscape with travellers on a path (71x91cm-28x36in) s.d.1813. 31-Oct-2 Christie's, London #23/R est:4000-6000

NASMYTH, Elizabeth Wemyss (attrib) (1793-?) British
£3304 $4824 €4956 The ferry (47x61cm-19x24in) mono. 17-Jun-2 Philippe Schuler, Zurich #4356/R est:2500-3000 (S.FR 7500)

NASMYTH, James (1808-1890) British
£700 $1155 €1015 Figure and a dog on a wooded track, with castle and extensive landscape beyond (18x28cm-7x11in) mono.d.1886 panel. 3-Jul-3 Duke & Son, Dorchester #314
£9000 $14310 €13500 Alchemist (30x41cm-12x16in) panel prov. 6-Mar-3 Christie's, Kensington #32/R est:4000-6000

NASMYTH, Jane (1788-1867) British
£1200 $1908 €1800 Mill at woodhall (22x30cm-9x12in) i. panel. 6-Mar-3 Christie's, Kensington #27/R est:800-1200

NASMYTH, Jane (attrib) (1788-1867) British
£1400 $2170 €2100 Hawthornden Castle from the river (46x61cm-18x24in) panel. 6-Dec-2 Lyon & Turnbull, Edinburgh #80/R est:1500-2000

NASMYTH, Margaret (1791-1869) British
£6500 $10335 €9750 Monastery of St Scholastica, Subiaco (44x60cm-17x24in) s.i. prov. 20-Mar-3 Sotheby's, London #273/R est:4000-6000

NASMYTH, Patrick (1787-1831) British
£650 $1027 €975 House in the woods with a figure on the garden path (36x28cm-14x11in) s. 2-Dec-2 Bonhams, Bath #111/R
£650 $1014 €975 Avenue of trees (30x23cm-12x9in) d.1825 i.verso panel. 11-Apr-3 Keys, Aylsham #734
£1600 $2448 €2400 By an English mill (44x57cm-17x22in) s. panel. 22-Aug-2 Bonhams, Edinburgh #1158/R est:1200-1800
£2000 $3340 €2900 Suffolk river landscape with figures conversing by a cottage (43x69cm-17x27in) s.d.1828. 20-Jun-3 Keys, Aylsham #739 est:2000-3000
£4200 $6594 €6300 Overshot flint mill (37x52cm-15x20in) s.d.1831 panel prov. 19-Nov-2 Bonhams, New Bond Street #49/R est:3000-4000
£6000 $9960 €9000 Wooded landscape in Surrey with figures, the villages of Godstone beyond (69x91cm-27x36in) s.d.1828 panel. 10-Jun-3 Christie's, London #59/R est:7000-10000

NASMYTH, Patrick (attrib) (1787-1831) British
£700 $1113 €1050 Bather in a wooded landscape, castle beyond (27x20cm-11x8in) panel. 6-Mar-3 Christie's, Kensington #30/R
£800 $1248 €1200 River landscape with small craft near houses in a copes (40x53cm-16x21in) bears sig indis d. 10-Sep-2 Bonhams, Knightsbridge #242/R
£1000 $1630 €1500 Boy beside a loch (26x35cm-10x14in) bears sigd.1823. 29-Jan-3 Sotheby's, Olympia #23/R est:1000-1500
£1600 $2544 €2400 Figures on a path in an extensive landscape (23x32cm-9x13in) with sig.d.1821 panel. 6-Mar-3 Christie's, Kensington #24/R est:1000-1500

NASON, Pieter (1612-1688) Dutch
£18000 $28260 €27000 Portrait of a gentleman, in an embroidered jacket with satin sash (74x59cm-29x23in) s.d.1646 panel painted oval prov. 12-Dec-2 Sotheby's, London #145/R est:8000-12000

NASSIVET, Paul (20th C) French
£282 $468 €400 Bord de Loire (60x73cm-24x29in) s. 11-Jun-3 Beaussant & Lefèvre, Paris #107

NAST, Thomas (1840-1902) American
Works on paper
£1667 $2600 €2501 Dozing city official's dream of the future (41x36cm-16x14in) s. pen ink. 9-Nov-2 Illustration House, New York #74/R est:3000-4500

NAT, W H van der (1864-1929) Dutch
£875 $1278 €1400 Canal lock in snow (27x36cm-11x14in) s.d.1904 panel. 14-May-2 Thomas Adams, Dublin #385
£938 $1369 €1500 Thatched house and yard (39x52cm-15x20in) s. 14-May-2 Thomas Adams, Dublin #384/R

NAT, Willem Hendrik van der (1864-1929) Dutch
Works on paper
£333 $553 €483 Kerkstraatje te Noordroyk (32x46cm-13x18in) s. s.i.verso W/C. 16-Jun-3 Waddingtons, Toronto #218/R (C.D 750)
£526 $853 €800 Polder landscape with a farm under trees. Flock of sheep near a farm (34x49cm-13x19in) s. pencil W/C htd white two. 21-Jan-3 Christie's, Amsterdam #206
£900 $1404 €1350 Sheepfold (30x47cm-12x19in) s. W/C. 5-Nov-2 Bonhams, New Bond Street #3/R est:1000-1500
£1139 $1777 €1800 View of a village (32x47cm-13x19in) s. W/C. 21-Oct-2 Glerum, Amsterdam #48/R est:1500-2000

NATALI, Renato (1883-1979) Italian
£535 $835 €803 On the pier (48x34cm-19x13in) s. panel. 13-Sep-2 Lilla Bukowskis, Stockholm #105 (S.KR 7800)
£1603 $2516 €2500 Sassaia bridge (42x67cm-17x26in) s. s.i.d.1938 verso masonite. 16-Dec-2 Pandolfini, Florence #307/R
£1635 $2518 €2600 Man with umbrella (30x20cm-12x8in) s board. 23-Oct-2 Finarte, Milan #197/R
£2179 $3378 €3400 Carnival party (54x70cm-21x28in) s. board. 5-Dec-2 Stadion, Trieste #738/R
£2436 $3824 €3800 Road at sunset (31x49cm-12x19in) s. 16-Dec-2 Pandolfini, Florence #321/R est:5000
£3871 $6116 €6000 Carnival (50x69cm-20x27in) s. board prov. 18-Dec-2 Finarte, Milan #158/R
£4808 $7596 €7500 Popular meeting (49x70cm-19x28in) s. board. 15-Nov-2 Farsetti, Prato #580/R est:7500
£10145 $16638 €14000 Il veglione (52x88cm-20x35in) s. panel. 27-May-3 Finarte, Milan #94/R est:8000-9000

NATANSON, Joseph (attrib) (1921-) French
£306 $475 €459 Still life with lemon (43x53cm-17x21in) masonite. 28-Sep-2 Charlton Hall, Columbia #175/R

NATH, Friedrich (1859-?) German
£685 $1068 €1000 Fjord in the autumn (26x45cm-10x18in) s.d.96. 10-Apr-3 Van Ham, Cologne #1621

NATIVI, Gualtiero (1921-1997) Italian
£385 $604 €600 Solarity (70x50cm-28x20in) s. tempera paper prov. 20-Nov-2 Pandolfini, Florence #87/R
£917 $1448 €1430 Composition (70x70cm-28x28in) painted 1968. 12-Nov-2 Babuino, Rome #330/R
£1389 $2208 €2000 Grandonio souvenir (80x60cm-31x24in) s. acrylic painted 1998. 1-May-3 Meeting Art, Vercelli #419
£1528 $2429 €2200 Untitled (60x80cm-24x31in) s. acrylic tempera. 1-May-3 Meeting Art, Vercelli #169
£1709 $2700 €2700 Elements, space (37x15cm-15x6in) s.d.48 tempera paper on board. 29-Nov-2 Farsetti, Prato #421/R
£4839 $7645 €7500 Space energy (100x80cm-39x31in) s. s.d.1951. 18-Dec-2 Christie's, Rome #93/R
Works on paper
£1772 $2800 €2800 Composition (73x53cm-29x21in) s. i.d.1988 verso waterpaint on canvas. 29-Nov-2 Farsetti, Prato #258/R
£1772 $2800 €2800 Untitled (112x91cm-44x36in) s.d.1980 waterpaint on canvas. 29-Nov-2 Farsetti, Prato #475/R

NATKIN, Robert (1930-) American
£1442 $2250 €2163 Untitled (91x149cm-36x59in) s. acrylic prov. 14-Oct-2 Butterfields, San Francisco #2112/R est:2000-3000

NATOIRE, Charles-Joseph (1700-1777) French
£25137 $41225 €36449 La muse de la Musique, Erato (106x141cm-42x56in) s.i.d.1751. 4-Jun-3 AB Stockholms Auktionsverk #2518/R est:250000-300000 (S.KR 320000)
Works on paper
£2658 $4200 €4200 Clovis, couronne par la Victoire, fait fleurir la religion (25x23cm-10x9in) black chk. 27-Nov-2 Christie's, Paris #182/R est:4000-6000
£3041 $4743 €4500 Etude pour allegorie du Temps (52x35cm-20x14in) i. crayon chk stump prov. 26-Mar-3 Piasa, Paris #69/R
£6962 $11000 €11000 Tete d'homme (33x23cm-13x9in) i. sanguine chk. 28-Nov-2 Tajan, Paris #78/R
£8228 $13000 €13000 La Vierge a l'Enfant (24x18cm-9x7in) s. red chk prov. 27-Nov-2 Christie's, Paris #187/R est:8000-12000
£20946 $32676 €31000 Oriental coiffe d'un turban (38x28cm-15x11in) i. sanguine chk. 26-Mar-3 Piasa, Paris #60/R est:10000
£21986 $36716 €31000 Moines dans le jardin des Camaldules a Frascati (34x24cm-13x9in) gouache W/C pen brown ink black crayon. 19-Jun-3 Piasa, Paris #128/R est:20000-25000
£29054 $45324 €43000 Triton soufflant dans une conque (24x29cm-9x11in) i. sanguine chk. 26-Mar-3 Piasa, Paris #59/R est:10000

NATOIRE, Charles-Joseph (attrib) (1700-1777) French
Works on paper
£900 $1413 €1350 Psyche, with two further studies of her left hand (36x25cm-14x10in) black chk htd white. 11-Dec-2 Sotheby's, Olympia #252/R

NATOIRE, Charles-Joseph (studio) (1700-1777) French
Works on paper
£577 $912 €900 Diane abandonnant la chasse pour eclairer le monde (59x44cm-23x17in) sanguine. 15-Nov-2 Drouot Estimations, Paris #58/R

NATTES, John Claude (1765-1822) British
Works on paper
£5190 $8044 €8200 Waterfall in the Dargle. Mill at Bray. View of Essex Bridge from the Old Custom House (23x30cm-9x12in) s.i.d.1801-07 monochrome wash set of three. 25-Sep-2 James Adam, Dublin #22/R est:3000-4000

NATTIER, Jean Marc (1685-1766) French
£420000 $701400 €609000 Portrait of Madame Pompadour in the guise of Diana (102x82cm-40x32in) prov.exhib.lit. 10-Jul-3 Sotheby's, London #52/R est:200000-300000

Works on paper
£3500 $5845 €5075 Portrait of Jean Baptist Le Gobien, seigneur de Saint Jouan holding a gun (41x26cm-16x10in) i. black white chk. 8-Jul-3 Christie's, London #66/R est:4000-6000

NATTIER, Jean Marc (attrib) (1685-1766) French
Works on paper
£1216 $1897 €1800 Graveur assis (30x25cm-12x10in) chk prov.exhib.lit. 27-Mar-3 Christie's, Paris #90/R

NATTIER, Jean Marc (studio) (1685-1766) French
£6173 $10000 €9260 Portrait of a lady, said to be la Duchesse de Chevreuse (109x84cm-43x33in) prov. 24-Jan-3 Christie's, Rockefeller NY #102/R est:10000-15000

NATTINI, Amos (1892-?) Italian
£1384 $2131 €2200 Mountain problem (55x65cm-22x26in) s. board exhib. 23-Oct-2 Finarte, Milan #5/R

NATTINO, Vittorio (1890-1971) Italian
£680 $1054 €1020 Venice at dusk (35x46cm-14x18in) s. board. 22-Jul-2 Bonhams, Bury St Edmunds #441

NATUS, Johannes (17th C) Dutch
£7500 $11775 €11250 Interior with men drinking and one playing a recorder (37x28cm-15x11in) bears mono. panel. 12-Dec-2 Sotheby's, London #150/R est:8000-12000

NAU (fl.1733-1735) French
Sculpture
£10490 $17517 €15000 Satyre poursuivant une nymphe (44x65x6cm-17x26x2in) s. gilt pat bronze green marble socle. 25-Jun-3 Tajan, Paris #30/R est:8500-9000

NAUDE, Hugo (1869-1941) South African
£1206 $1905 €1809 Extensive landscape, Western Cape (19x27cm-7x11in) s. panel. 1-Apr-3 Stephan Welz, Johannesburg #433/R est:16000-20000 (SA.R 15000)
£1537 $2398 €2306 Seascape (27x37cm-11x15in) s. board. 11-Nov-2 Stephan Welz, Johannesburg #489/R est:12000-15000 (SA.R 24000)
£1548 $2492 €2322 Mountains near Worcester (19x28cm-7x11in) board exhib. 12-May-3 Stephan Welz, Johannesburg #590/R est:9000-12000 (SA.R 18000)
£1548 $2492 €2322 Drakensberg under snow (22x26cm-9x10in) s. board. 12-May-3 Stephan Welz, Johannesburg #592/R est:9000-12000 (SA.R 18000)
£2434 $3798 €3651 Seascape, Hermanus (29x39cm-11x15in) s. board. 11-Nov-2 Stephan Welz, Johannesburg #490 est:20000-30000 (SA.R 38000)
£2691 $4197 €4037 Walker Bay (24x34cm-9x13in) s. board. 11-Nov-2 Stephan Welz, Johannesburg #491/R est:20000-30000 (SA.R 42000)
£2826 $4408 €4239 Hermanus seascape (24x29cm-9x11in) s. panel. 15-Oct-2 Stephan Welz, Johannesburg #420/R est:20000-30000 (SA.R 46000)
£3376 $5334 €5064 Extensive winter landscape (24x34cm-9x13in) s. canvasboard. 1-Apr-3 Stephan Welz, Johannesburg #434/R est:20000-30000 (SA.R 42000)
£4612 $7195 €6918 Dar-es-Salaam, harbour (35x55cm-14x22in) s. i.verso. 11-Nov-2 Stephan Welz, Johannesburg #493/R est:40000-60000 (SA.R 72000)
£7687 $11992 €11531 Namaqualand daisies (25x35cm-10x14in) s. board. 11-Nov-2 Stephan Welz, Johannesburg #533/R est:70000-90000 (SA.R 120000)
£8648 $13491 €12972 Spring, Namaqualand (29x39cm-11x15in) s. board. 11-Nov-2 Stephan Welz, Johannesburg #534/R est:90000-120000 (SA.R 135000)
£12038 $19381 €18057 Klipfontein, Namaqualand (29x39cm-11x15in) s. i.verso panel. 12-May-3 Stephan Welz, Johannesburg #485/R est:90000-120000 (SA.R 140000)

Works on paper
£817 $1315 €1226 View of a marshland (16x23cm-6x9in) s. W/C. 12-May-3 Stephan Welz, Johannesburg #153 est:4000-6000 (SA.R 9500)

NAUEN, Heinrich (1880-1941) German
£7971 $13072 €11000 Still life of flowers (50x42cm-20x17in) s. oil tempera prov. 29-May-3 Lempertz, Koln #825/R est:12000
£14388 $23597 €20000 Flower vase on round table (67x71cm-26x28in) s. prov.exhib. 6-Jun-3 Ketterer, Munich #46/R est:25000-35000
Works on paper
£362 $594 €500 Seated woman (21x16cm-8x6in) s.d.0.12. Indian ink bodycol col chk. 31-May-3 Villa Grisebach, Berlin #642/R

NAUMAN, Bruce (1941-) American
Photographs
£6875 $11000 €10313 Coffee spilled because the cup was too hot (51x60cm-20x24in) s.i.d.1966 num.5/8 verso c-print on foamcore prov.lit. 14-May-3 Sotheby's, New York #220/R est:10000-15000

Prints
£8861 $14000 €13292 Studies for holograms (66x66cm-26x26in) s.d.70 num. five screenprint black yellow green prov. 14-Nov-2 Christie's, Rockefeller NY #361/R est:15000-20000
£14103 $22000 €21155 Studies for holograms (66x66cm-26x26in) s.num.87/100 col screenprints set of five. 5-Nov-2 Christie's, Rockefeller NY #467/R est:20000-25000

Sculpture
£6250 $10000 €9375 Untitled - cross beams (25x217x217cm-10x85x85in) incised sig.d.85 num.BN83 2123 B/B 21/25 iron 2 elements. 15-May-3 Christie's, Rockefeller NY #302/R est:15000-20000
£11392 $18000 €17088 Untitled - crossbeams (13x217x11cm-5x85x4in) init.d.88 num.25 iron element two parts prov.exhib.lit. 12-Nov-2 Phillips, New York #114/R est:18000-25000
£12658 $20000 €18987 Untitled - cross beams (25x217x217cm-10x85x85in) incised sig.num.9/25 two cast iron elements prov.exhib.lit. 14-Nov-2 Christie's, Rockefeller NY #362/R est:18000-22000
£26250 $42000 €39375 Double poke in the eye II (61x91x16cm-24x36x6in) s.num.13 neon tubing mounted on aluminum monolith prov.exhib.lit. 15-May-3 Christie's, Rockefeller NY #301/R est:50000-70000
£240506 $380000 €360759 Run from fear fun from rear. yellow pink neon tubing glass tubing executed 1972 prov.exhib.lit. 13-Nov-2 Christie's, Rockefeller NY #35/R est:400000-600000
£265823 $420000 €398735 Untitled - hand circle (13x74x70cm-5x29x28in) st.BN 1996 copper bronze silver solder wire steel prov.exhib. 13-Nov-2 Christie's, Rockefeller NY #34/R est:250000-350000

Works on paper
£10500 $17220 €15750 Untitled (76x102cm-30x40in) s.d.75 pencil prov. 7-Feb-3 Sotheby's, London #139/R est:10000-15000
£18354 $29000 €27531 Untitled (58x77cm-23x30in) s.d.93 graphite executed 1993 prov. 14-Nov-2 Christie's, Rockefeller NY #360/R est:30000-40000
£21875 $35000 €32813 Templates for right half of my body (47x61cm-19x24in) W/C ink prov.exhib. 13-May-3 Sotheby's, New York #7/R est:50000-70000
£37975 $60000 €56963 Double size head on hand (145x110cm-57x43in) s.d.89 col chks graphite tape on three sheets prov.exhib. 13-Nov-2 Christie's, Rockefeller NY #38/R est:100000-150000

£50000 $80000 €75000 Shoulder with three arms (40x62cm-16x24in) init.d.1967 W/C ink prov.exhib. 13-May-3 Sotheby's, New York #1/R est:60000-80000
£75000 $123000 €112500 Drawing for Stadium Day (97x127cm-38x50in) s.d.83 W/C pencil prov.exhib. 6-Feb-3 Christie's, London #702/R est:80000-120000
£75949 $120000 €113924 Masturbating man (134x107cm-53x42in) s. graphite gouache col crayon W/C executed 1985 prov.exhib.lit. 13-Nov-2 Christie's, Rockefeller NY #36/R est:150000-200000
£101266 $160000 €151899 Bst tu (51x292cm-20x115in) graphite col chk gouache acrylic tape collage paper executed 1967. 13-Nov-2 Christie's, Rockefeller NY #37/R est:200000-300000

NAUMANN, Hermann (1930-) German
£451 $713 €650 Anna II dancing on table (68x50cm-27x20in) s.d. varnish board. 26-Apr-3 Dr Lehr, Berlin #394/R
Works on paper
£347 $549 €500 Untitled (60x42cm-24x17in) s.d.1959 mixed media monotype board. 26-Apr-3 Dr Lehr, Berlin #393/R

NAUMANN, Karl Georg (1827-1902) German
£2391 $3730 €3587 Lesson (62x72cm-24x28in) s.d.559. 16-Sep-2 Philippe Schuler, Zurich #3488/R est:5000-7000 (S.FR 5500)

NAUMOVA, Tamara Sergeevna (1923-) Russian
£4000 $6280 €6000 Celebrating the harvest (130x179cm-51x70in) s. 20-Nov-2 Sotheby's, London #198/R est:4000-6000

NAUMOW, E (?) Russian?
£449 $714 €660 The beach (79x116cm-31x46in) s. 24-Mar-3 Bukowskis, Helsinki #387/R

NAUR, Albert (1889-1973) Danish
£270 $417 €405 Summer landscape (67x87cm-26x34in) s. 23-Oct-2 Kunsthallen, Copenhagen #40 (D.KR 3200)
£280 $445 €420 Summer day by the fjord (67x85cm-26x33in) s. 29-Apr-3 Kunsthallen, Copenhagen #221 (D.KR 3000)
£293 $448 €440 Flowers (74x93cm-29x37in) s.d.1920. 24-Aug-2 Rasmussen, Havnen #2168 (D.KR 3400)
£305 $509 €442 Landscape with high sky (67x89cm-26x35in) s. 17-Jun-3 Rasmussen, Copenhagen #162 (D.KR 3200)
£333 $532 €500 White star of Bethlehem - potted plant on chair (50x65cm-20x26in) s.d.58. 13-Jan-3 Rasmussen, Vejle #285/R (D.KR 3800)
£343 $535 €515 Garden with trees in blossom (74x93cm-29x37in) s,. 11-Nov-2 Rasmussen, Vejle #46/R (D.KR 4000)
£366 $581 €549 Summer landscape (82x100cm-32x39in) s. 26-Feb-3 Kunsthallen, Copenhagen #327 (D.KR 4000)
£400 $669 €580 Bouquet of flowers (75x93cm-30x37in) mono.d.1918. 17-Jun-3 Rasmussen, Copenhagen #160/R (D.KR 4200)
£408 $661 €612 Flowers in pot (67x86cm-26x34in) s. 25-Jan-3 Rasmussen, Havnen #2012/R (D.KR 4600)
£423 $651 €635 Summer landscape (65x86cm-26x34in) s. 23-Oct-2 Kunsthallen, Copenhagen #97 (D.KR 5000)
£510 $795 €765 Landscape near Tibirke (67x98cm-26x39in) s. 5-Aug-2 Rasmussen, Vejle #2013 (D.KR 6000)
£560 $890 €840 Landscape (67x90cm-26x35in) s. 5-May-3 Rasmussen, Vejle #53/R (D.KR 6000)
£1144 $1910 €1659 Still life of fruit and books (50x66cm-20x26in) s.d.28. 17-Jun-3 Rasmussen, Copenhagen #146/R est:12000 (D.KR 12000)

NAUTSCHUTZ, Rudolf Franke (1860-?) German
Sculpture
£2000 $3080 €3000 Snake charmer (33cm-13in) s. alabaster bronze. 28-Oct-2 Sotheby's, Olympia #22/R est:2000-3000

NAUWENS, Jozef (1830-?) Belgian
£519 $810 €820 Nature morte au gibier (50x68cm-20x27in) s.d.1887 i.verso. 15-Oct-2 Horta, Bruxelles #373

NAVA, Ambrogio de (19th C) Italian
£5405 $8432 €8000 Wooded landscape with shepherds (97x73cm-38x29in) s.d.1822. 28-Mar-3 Piasa, Paris #7/R est:6000-8000

NAVA, Hector (1875-1940) ?
£357 $521 €550 Playing ball (85x59cm-33x23in) s. 17-Jun-2 Ansorena, Madrid #308/R

NAVARRA, Gerolamo (1852-1920) Italian
£252 $392 €400 Portrait of old man with beard (69x50cm-27x20in) s.d.1898 paper on board. 20-Sep-2 Semenzato, Venice #578

NAVARRETE OPPELT, Jose (1872-?) Spanish
£769 $1215 €1200 Kids (40x53cm-16x21in) canvas on cardboard. 14-Nov-2 Arte, Seville #330/R

NAVARRO LLORENS, Jose (1867-1923) Spanish
£6000 $9420 €9000 Peasant family (21x31cm-8x12in) s. panel. 21-Nov-2 Christie's, Kensington #183/R est:5000-7000
£6000 $9420 €9000 Lover's tiff (42x63cm-17x25in) s. 21-Nov-2 Christie's, Kensington #184/R est:6000-8000
£6289 $9686 €10000 Marine (29x44cm-11x17in) s. 28-Oct-2 Segre, Madrid #93/R est:10000
£7742 $12232 €12000 Couple of gypsies (42x35cm-17x14in) s. 18-Dec-2 Ansorena, Madrid #160/R est:12000
£9000 $13950 €13500 Arab street market (35x39cm-14x15in) s. 4-Dec-2 Christie's, London #4/R est:10000-15000
Works on paper
£1509 $2355 €2400 Women from Valencia (12x17cm-5x7in) s. W/C. 17-Sep-2 Segre, Madrid #28/R
£3526 $5571 €5500 To the market (40x36cm-16x14in) s. W/C. 13-Nov-2 Ansorena, Madrid #186/R
£6383 $10340 €9000 Jietes bereberes (28x45cm-11x18in) s.d.1900 W/C. 20-May-3 Segre, Madrid #93/R est:9000
£6383 $10340 €9000 Jinetes (27x45cm-11x18in) s.d.1900 W/C. 20-May-3 Segre, Madrid #92/R est:9000

NAVARRO, Jose (19th C) Spanish
£3548 $5606 €5500 Jockey (24x50cm-9x20in) s. 17-Dec-2 Durán, Madrid #158/R

NAVARRO, Miquel (1945-) Spanish
Works on paper
£597 $920 €950 Sculpture (28x21cm-11x8in) s.d.1980 ink dr prov. 28-Oct-2 Segre, Madrid #180/R
£1007 $1621 €1500 Pearl III (66x49cm-26x19in) s. W/C card. 18-Feb-3 Durán, Madrid #154/R

NAVE, Henri Auguste la (19th C) French
£260 $434 €377 Figures around a table in a stone interior (35x27cm-14x11in) i.verso board. 8-Jul-3 Bonhams, Knightsbridge #20

NAVELLIER, Edouard (1865-1944) French
Sculpture
£4490 $7139 €6600 Rhinoceros de l'Inde (20x38cm-8x15in) s. pat bronze. 23-Mar-3 Herbette, Doullens #166/R

NAVEZ, Arthur (1881-1931) Belgian
£496 $829 €700 Nature morte au vase rose (46x39cm-18x15in) s. panel. 18-Jun-3 Hotel des Ventes Mosan, Brussels #243
£1135 $1895 €1600 Interieur (58x40cm-23x16in) s.indis.d.1916 cardboard. 17-Jun-3 Palais de Beaux Arts, Brussels #610 est:150-200
£2014 $3223 €2800 La fillette a la poupee (45x30cm-18x12in) s. canvas on panel. 19-May-3 Horta, Bruxelles #86 est:1500-2000
£3597 $5755 €5000 Le bassin houiller (52x63cm-20x25in) s.d.1906. 13-May-3 Vanderkindere, Brussels #175/R est:4000-6000

NAVEZ, François Joseph (1787-1869) Belgian
£1603 $2532 €2500 Visage d'Orientale pensive (42x35cm-17x14in) s.d.1826. 18-Nov-2 Tajan, Paris #13 est:1200-1500
£3000 $4770 €4500 Portrait of Alexandre Henne (77x72cm-30x28in) s.d.1851 prov.lit. 20-Mar-3 Christie's, Kensington #135/R est:3000-5000
£54487 $84455 €85000 Elegant Roman woman giving alms to young mother with children (113x137cm-44x54in) s.i.d.1821. 5-Dec-2 Dr Fritz Nagel, Stuttgart #686/R
£81761 $126730 €130000 Scene de brigands avec la diseuse de bonne aventure (104x148cm-41x58in) s.i.d.1821 prov.exhib.lit. 30-Oct-2 Coutau Begarie, Paris #57/R est:120000-150000

NAVEZ, François Joseph (attrib) (1787-1869) Belgian
£3597 $5755 €5000 Mere et enfant dans un paysage Italianisant (73x60cm-29x24in) oval. 13-May-3 Palais de Beaux Arts, Brussels #108/R est:5000-7000

NAVEZ, Geo (20th C) Belgian
£342 $534 €500 Rue de village ensoleillee (76x66cm-30x26in) s. 14-Apr-3 Horta, Bruxelles #60

NAVEZ, Léon (1900-1967) Belgian
£695 $1133 €1050 Femme a la robe bleue (60x50cm-24x20in) s. 17-Feb-3 Horta, Bruxelles #22

NAVIASKY, Philip (1894-1983) British
£250 $393 €375 Study of a young lady seated wearing a blue evening dress (76x50cm-30x20in) s. i.verso board. 19-Nov-2 Bonhams, Leeds #151

£250 $398 €375 Portrait of a woman (39x30cm-15x12in) s. board. 4-Mar-3 Bristol Auction Rooms #321
£260 $400 €390 Still life study of flowers in a vase (58x48cm-23x19in) s. board. 24-Oct-2 Richardson & Smith, Whitby #495
£300 $468 €450 Portrait of the artist's mother wearing a headscarf (43x33cm-17x13in) s. 9-Oct-2 Andrew Hartley, Ilkley #763
£300 $471 €450 Still life of flowers in a pottery jug (51x61cm-20x24in) s. 21-Nov-2 Tennants, Leyburn #844
£300 $501 €435 Portrait of a lady wearing a purple scarf (64x53cm-25x21in) s.d.1928. 17-Jun-3 Anderson & Garland, Newcastle #412/R
£350 $553 €525 Two seated figures (48x38cm-19x15in) s. board. 29-Nov-2 Dee Atkinson & Harrison, Driffield #814
£400 $628 €600 Portrait of a young girl (61x51cm-24x20in) s. 19-Nov-2 Bonhams, Leeds #150
£420 $655 €630 Portrait of a young girl in a turquoise skirt (38x28cm-15x11in) s. board. 9-Oct-2 Andrew Hartley, Ilkley #764
£460 $699 €690 Portrait of Millie Naviasky seated by a table (38x33cm-15x13in) s. board. 14-Aug-2 Andrew Hartley, Ilkley #699
£620 $1004 €930 Vase of red and orange flowers (60x50cm-24x20in) s. 20-May-3 Bonhams, Knightsbridge #24/R

NAVLET, Joseph (1821-1889) French
£755 $1170 €1200 Scene biblique (50x65cm-20x26in) s.d.1876. 4-Oct-2 Tajan, Paris #178

NAVLET, Victor (1819-1886) French
£2800 $4396 €4200 Sistine chapel (195x131cm-77x52in) s.d.1870. 21-Nov-2 Christie's, Kensington #161/R est:2000-3000

NAVOZOV, Vassily Ivanovich (1862-1919) Russian
£45000 $70650 €67500 Baptism of Russia (96x179cm-38x70in) s.d.1887 exhib. 20-Nov-2 Sotheby's, London #42/R est:50000-70000

NAVRATIL, Joseph (1798-1865) Czechoslovakian
Works on paper
£928 $1467 €1392 Organ grinder (21x30cm-8x12in) s. pencil dr exhib.lit. 30-Nov-2 Dorotheum, Prague #141 (C.KR 45000)

NAVRATIL, Walter (1950-) Austrian
£993 $1609 €1400 Black cat looking at a (69x100cm-27x39in) tempera prov. 20-May-3 Dorotheum, Vienna #209/R
£993 $1609 €1400 Landscape with singular animals (60x90cm-24x35in) pen Indian ink tempera canvas prov. 20-May-3 Dorotheum, Vienna #210/R
£1379 $2179 €2000 Hearing voices 6 (90x76cm-35x30in) s. i.d. stretcher. 2-Apr-3 Dr Fritz Nagel, Stuttgart #9511/R est:1500
£6757 $10541 €10000 Dream of Mr Marquant (180x240cm-71x94in) s. 25-Mar-3 Wiener Kunst Auktionen, Vienna #25/R est:12000-18000

NAVTSCHVETZ, Franke (?) ?
Sculpture
£1772 $2765 €2800 Charmeur de serpent assis (15cm-6in) s. pat bronze marble. 16-Sep-2 Horta, Bruxelles #158/R

NAY, Ernst Wilhelm (1902-1968) German
£7595 $12000 €12000 Playing with a ball on the beach (40x66cm-16x26in) s.d.34 d. verso. 30-Nov-2 Bassenge, Berlin #6537/R est:18000
£22436 $34776 €35000 Couple (60x78cm-24x31in) s.d.1938 i.d.1938 verso prov.exhib. 6-Dec-2 Ketterer, Munich #102/R est:30000-40000
£38462 $59615 €60000 Femme rose (55x70cm-22x28in) s.d.47 prov.exhib.lit. 4-Dec-2 Lempertz, Koln #30/R est:80000-100000
£44025 $68679 €70000 Persiches gedicht - Persian poem (65x110cm-26x43in) s.d.49 s.i.d.1949 on stretcher prov.lit. 8-Oct-2 Sotheby's, London #31/R est:100000-150000
£70000 $114800 €105000 Arkadische melodie (120x100cm-47x39in) s.d.57 s.i.d.on stretcher prov.exhib.lit. 5-Feb-3 Christie's, London #5/R est:80000-120000
£75472 $117736 €120000 Bukolisches bild - Bucolic painting (74x95cm-29x37in) s.d.47 s.i.d.on stretcher prov.exhib.lit. 8-Oct-2 Sotheby's, London #29/R est:130000-200000
£79114 $125000 €125000 With festive blue (100x120cm-39x47in) s.d.53 s.i.d.1953 verso prov.exhib. 29-Nov-2 Villa Grisebach, Berlin #82/R est:150000-200000
£90000 $147600 €135000 Alpha (116x89cm-46x35in) s.d.57 s.verso i.d.on stretcher prov.exhib.lit. 6-Feb-3 Sotheby's, London #18/R est:150000
£101449 $166377 €140000 Of volcanic grey (100x120cm-39x47in) s.d.53 s.i.d. stretcher prov.exhib. 30-May-3 Villa Grisebach, Berlin #68/R est:120000-150000
£125000 $208750 €187500 Reihung in Gelb und Grun (125x201cm-49x79in) s.d.56 s.i.d.1956 stretcher prov.exhib.lit. 26-Jun-3 Christie's, London #47/R est:130000-160000

Prints
£2174 $3565 €3000 Coloured lithograph 1966 - 1 - NOR (65x59cm-26x23in) s.d. col lithograph. 31-May-3 Villa Grisebach, Berlin #339/R est:2500-3500
£2174 $3565 €3000 Seated woman (41x44cm-16x17in) s.d. num.19/30 col lithograph. 28-May-3 Lempertz, Koln #299/R est:3500
£2270 $3677 €3200 Plants (40x30cm-16x12in) s. col aquatint. 24-May-3 Van Ham, Cologne #435/R est:2800
£33544 $53000 €53000 Lofoton landscapes (49x64cm-19x25in) s.d.1938 col woodcut one of 8-10 prov.exhib. four. 29-Nov-2 Villa Grisebach, Berlin #78/R est:30000-35000

Works on paper
£2113 $3507 €3000 Composition (49x62cm-19x24in) s.d. 14-Jun-3 Hauswedell & Nolte, Hamburg #1464/R est:4000
£4493 $7368 €6200 Untitled (41x32cm-16x13in) s.d.65 W/C pencil. 28-May-3 Lempertz, Koln #298/R est:3800
£5755 $9439 €8000 Untitled (48x62cm-19x24in) s.d. brush Indian ink. 6-Jun-3 Ketterer, Munich #96/R est:8000-12000
£5769 $8942 €9000 Untitled (26x42cm-10x17in) s.d.55 W/C. 3-Dec-2 Lempertz, Koln #323/R est:12000
£6115 $10029 €8500 Untitled (48x62cm-19x24in) s.d. brush Indian ink. 6-Jun-3 Ketterer, Munich #98/R est:9000-12000
£6129 $9500 €9194 Untitled - head (41x31cm-16x12in) s.d.46 gouache paper on linen prov. 26-Sep-2 Christie's, Rockefeller NY #730/R est:12000-16000
£7042 $11690 €10000 Composition (42x60cm-17x24in) s.d. W/C. 14-Jun-3 Hauswedell & Nolte, Hamburg #1465/R est:15000
£7862 $12264 €12500 Composition (50x70cm-20x28in) s.d.55 brush ink pencil prov. 9-Oct-2 Sotheby's, London #219/R est:18000-25000
£8491 $13245 €13500 Fisherman (48x62cm-19x24in) s.d.35 pen ink pencil prov. 9-Oct-2 Sotheby's, London #224/R est:9000-12000
£9353 $15338 €13000 Untitled (41x59cm-16x23in) s.d.60 W/C. 3-Jun-3 Christie's, Amsterdam #326/R est:10000-12000
£10063 $15698 €16000 Empress Theodora (21x18cm-8x7in) s.d.47 gouache prov. 9-Oct-2 Sotheby's, London #221/R est:20000-30000
£13208 $20604 €21000 Nocturnal tragedy (26x34cm-10x13in) s.d.45 i.verso W/C gouache pencil ink prov. 9-Oct-2 Sotheby's, London #222/R est:30000-40000
£21739 $35652 €30000 Adam and Eve (20x30cm-8x12in) gouache board prov. 30-May-3 Villa Grisebach, Berlin #62/R est:30000-40000
£24528 $38264 €39000 Komposition mit gelben scheiben - Composition with yellow disks (42x60cm-17x24in) s.d.55 W/C prov. 9-Oct-2 Sotheby's, London #220/R est:30000-40000

NAZARENE SCHOOL (19th C) German
£19000 $29830 €28500 Saint Apollonia (134x63cm-53x25in) panel prov. 10-Dec-2 Bonhams, New Bond Street #145/R est:7000-10000

NAZZARI, Bartolommeo (1699-1758) Italian
£10000 $15700 €15000 Portraits of a young man and young lady in masquerade costume (56x43cm-22x17in) pair prov. 12-Dec-2 Sotheby's, London #195/R est:12000-18000

NDIMANDE, Francina (1940-) South African
£281 $445 €422 Mural design (39x50cm-15x20in) s. acrylic canvas on board. 1-Apr-3 Stephan Welz, Johannesburg #507 est:4000-6000 (SA.R 3500)
£513 $795 €800 Untitled (140x133cm-55x52in) s.d.April 1990 acrylic prov. 3-Dec-2 Christie's, Amsterdam #183
£769 $1192 €1200 Untitled (98x134cm-39x53in) s.d.July 1990 acrylic prov. 3-Dec-2 Christie's, Amsterdam #182/R est:600-800

NEAGLE, John (1796-1865) American
£621 $1000 €932 Bust length portrait of a gentleman (76x61cm-30x24in) s. 22-Feb-3 Pook & Pook, Downington #179/R
Works on paper
£5414 $8500 €8121 Red Jacket, a celebrated Indian chief (9x8cm-4x3in) s.i.d.March 22 1823 graphite. 20-Nov-2 Christie's, Los Angeles #110/R est:4000-6000
£7006 $11000 €10509 Iskatupee, Pawnee Chief (16x15cm-6x6in) s.i.d.1827 graphite brown pencil. 20-Nov-2 Christie's, Los Angeles #109/R est:6000-8000

NEAGLE, John (attrib) (1796-1865) American
£19231 $30000 €28847 Portrait of Henry Clay (70x52cm-28x20in) s.d.1843 prov. 12-Apr-3 Freeman, Philadelphia #194/R est:8000-12000

NEAL, James (1918-) British
£300 $489 €450 Farm near Paull (28x46cm-11x18in) s. board. 7-Feb-3 Dee Atkinson & Harrison, Driffield #680

£480 $782 €720 Leven (30x30cm-12x12in) s. board. 7-Feb-3 Dee Atkinson & Harrison, Driffield #681
£550 $897 €825 Princes Dock, Hull (20x23cm-8x9in) s. board painted 1926. 7-Feb-3 Dee Atkinson & Harrison, Driffield #679
£650 $1007 €975 The Audrey, boat in dock (38x51cm-15x20in) s. 30-Sep-2 Bonhams, Ipswich #395

NEAL, Walter O (20th C) American
£513 $800 €770 Untitled (183x64cm-72x25in) s.d.79 s.d.verso. 20-Sep-2 Sloan, North Bethesda #459/R

NEALE, George Hall (fl.1883-1935) British
£714 $1129 €1071 Acre (29x22cm-11x9in) s.i.d.94 panel. 26-Nov-2 Sotheby's, Melbourne #241/R est:2000-3000 (A.D 2000)

NEAPOLITAN SCHOOL (15th C) Italian
£20886 $33000 €33000 Madonna and Child (88x92cm-35x36in) tempera board. 2-Dec-2 Finarte, Milan #125/R est:45000

NEAPOLITAN SCHOOL (17/18th C) Italian
£8219 $12822 €12000 Vase of flowers in landscape (65x51cm-26x20in) 8-Apr-3 Ansorena, Madrid #83/R est:12000

NEAPOLITAN SCHOOL (17th C) Italian
£4828 $7628 €7000 Presentation of the Virgin at Temple (145x206cm-57x81in) 5-Apr-3 Finarte Semenzato, Milan #21/R est:9000
£7370 $11939 €10687 Still life of food on table with small dog watching (46x61cm-18x24in) 26-May-3 Bukowskis, Stockholm #403/R est:50000-60000 (S.KR 95000)
£8438 $13079 €12657 St Augustinus and his mother St Monica (107x58cm-42x23in) 3-Oct-2 Koller, Zurich #3053/R est:20000-30000 (S.FR 19660)
£13141 $20631 €20500 Autoportrait d'un artiste a la palette (68x52cm-27x20in) painted c.1660. 16-Dec-2 Chochon-Barre & Allardi, Paris #7/R est:5500-6500
£15000 $23550 €22500 Supper at Emmaus (146x182cm-57x72in) after Michelangelo. 10-Dec-2 Bonhams, New Bond Street #302/R est:15000-20000
£148148 $240000 €222222 David with the head of Goliath (126x173cm-50x68in) 23-Jan-3 Sotheby's, New York #26/R est:40000-60000

NEAPOLITAN SCHOOL (18th C) Italian
£5570 $8689 €8800 Madonna and Child and angels (98x72cm-39x28in) 15-Oct-2 Babuino, Rome #42/R
£7152 $11157 €11300 Vessels in trouble (97x130cm-38x51in) 15-Oct-2 Babuino, Rome #188/R
£7372 $11574 €11500 Landscape with figures (87x110cm-34x43in) 10-Dec-2 Della Rocca, Turin #125/R est:14000
£10000 $15800 €14500 Storm on the coast (130x165cm-51x65in) 1-Apr-3 Babuino, Rome #72/R
£45732 $75000 €68598 Cauliflower, fennel, eggplant, celery, lettuce, grapes, pomegranate on a ledge (76x106cm-30x42in) 30-May-3 Christie's, Rockefeller NY #1/R est:10000-15000

Miniatures
£6552 $10352 €9500 Portrait of Mary Caroline of Asburg (8x7cm-3x3in) s. 3-Apr-3 Porro, Milan #168/R
£10000 $15800 €14500 Portrait of Ferdinand IV of Borbone (8cm-3in circular) 3-Apr-3 Porro, Milan #166/R est:12000

NEAPOLITAN SCHOOL (19th C) Italian
£7241 $11441 €10500 View of Naples from Posillipo (42x33cm-17x13in) 3-Apr-3 Porro, Milan #42/R est:15000
£8387 $13252 €13000 View of Naples Bay (54x132cm-21x52in) 20-Dec-2 Ribeyre & Baron, Paris #42/R est:18000
£31507 $49151 €46000 Vues Napolitaines animees de personnages (76x102cm-30x40in) pair. 8-Apr-3 Gioffredo, Nice #57/R

Miniatures
£3448 $5448 €5000 Portrait of princess (17x15cm-7x6in) sd.1839. 3-Apr-3 Porro, Milan #169/R
£4828 $7628 €7000 Portrait of Murat (10x8cm-4x3in) s. painted c.1810. 3-Apr-3 Porro, Milan #170/R

NEATBY, William James (1860-1910) British
Works on paper
£450 $734 €653 Redcap (18x12cm-7x5in) s.d.1906 W/C. 16-Jul-3 Sotheby's, Olympia #111/R

NEAVE, David (fl.1903-1936) British
£480 $749 €720 Topsham Quay (34x44cm-13x17in) s. 15-Oct-2 Bearnes, Exeter #435/R
£620 $967 €930 Topsham Quay (46x61cm-18x24in) pair. 15-Oct-2 Bearnes, Exeter #436

NEBBIA, Cesare (1536-1614) Italian
Works on paper
£2517 $3600 €3776 Ecce Homo (31x28cm-12x11in) pen ink black red chk. 23-Jan-3 Swann Galleries, New York #44/R est:3000-5000
£2838 $4427 €4200 Christ au jardin des oliviers (31x27cm-12x11in) pen ink wash prov. 31-Mar-3 Piasa, Paris #15/R

NEBEKER, Bill (1942-) American
Sculpture
£2397 $3500 €3596 Medicine shield (23cm-9in) one of 25 bronze. 18-May-2 Altermann Galleries, Santa Fe #42/R
£6962 $11000 €10095 Good hand with a horse. Ain't no fence mender. Nose bag (43cm-17in) bronze set of three different sizes. 26-Jul-3 Coeur d'Alene, Hayden #70/R est:8000-12000

NEBEL, Otto (1892-1975) German
Works on paper
£602 $969 €903 Marina di Ravenna (24x31cm-9x12in) s.i.d.1955 Indian ink. 7-May-3 Dobiaschofsky, Bern #1832/R (S.FR 1300)
£851 $1379 €1200 Ein blatt mit zutter laune (42x45cm-17x18in) s.i.d. W/C. 23-May-3 Binoche, Paris #24/R

NECHUTUNY, Franz (19th C) German
£1000 $1560 €1500 Storming of Algiers (75x63cm-30x25in) s. 15-Oct-2 Sotheby's, London #220/R est:1000-2000

NEDER, Johann Michael (1807-1882) Austrian
£584 $871 €900 Portrait of Viennese woman (39x32cm-15x13in) mono. board prov.lit. 26-Jun-2 Neumeister, Munich #819/R

NEDJAR, Michel (1947-) French
£679 $1100 €1019 Untitled - two figures (22x16cm-9x6in) s. i.d.86 verso oil on paper prov. 27-Jan-3 Christie's, Rockefeller NY #29/R est:700-900
£4012 $6500 €6018 Untitled (99x75cm-39x30in) paint prov.exhib. 27-Jan-3 Christie's, Rockefeller NY #53/R est:7000-9000

Sculpture
£6173 $10000 €9260 Poupee (76x21cm-30x8in) fabric string soil prov. 27-Jan-3 Christie's, Rockefeller NY #52/R est:12000-18000

Works on paper
£446 $714 €620 Figural composition (57x36cm-22x14in) s.i.d. distemper on French newspaper. 15-May-3 Neumeister, Munich #736/R

NEEDHAM, Alfred Carter (1872-?) American
£692 $1100 €1038 Iceberg (41x51cm-16x20in) s.d.21. 7-Mar-3 Skinner, Boston #318a/R

NEEFFS, Pieter (elder) (1578-1658) Flemish
£9353 $14964 €13000 Interior of a gothic cathedral by night (42x58cm-17x23in) s.d.1659 prov. 14-May-3 Christie's, Amsterdam #143/R est:8000-12000

NEEFFS, Pieter (elder-attrib) (1578-1658) Flemish
£3121 $5055 €4400 Interieur d'eglise (24x31cm-9x12in) copper. 26-May-3 Joron-Derem, Paris #73/R est:6000-9000

NEEFFS, Pieter (style) (16/17th C) Flemish
£6494 $10000 €9741 St Jerome in his study (27x38cm-11x15in) 23-Oct-2 Doyle, New York #15 est:1000-1500

NEEFFS, Pieter (younger) (1620-1675) Flemish
£5000 $7850 €7500 Elegant figures in gothic church interiors (6x9cm-2x4in) one init.d.1650 copper oval pair. 10-Dec-2 Bonhams, New Bond Street #9/R est:5000-7000
£8000 $12560 €12000 Interior of a Gothic Cathedral by night (25x34cm-10x13in) panel. 13-Dec-2 Christie's, Kensington #61/R est:6000-8000
£9146 $15000 €13719 Church interior (42x60cm-17x24in) indis.s.d.1659. 30-May-3 Christie's, Rockefeller NY #27/R est:12000-18000
£13415 $22000 €20123 Cathedral interior with a mass. Cathedral interior with candlelit procession (7x9cm-3x4in) init. copper pair. 30-May-3 Christie's, Rockefeller NY #26/R est:10000-15000
£33103 $52303 €48000 Interieur d'eglise (26x38cm-10x15in) s. panel. 2-Apr-3 Marc Kohn, Paris #18/R

NEEFFS, Pieter (younger-attrib) (1620-1675) Flemish
£9434 $14623 €15000 Gothic church interior (47x63cm-19x25in) panel. 2-Oct-2 Dorotheum, Vienna #256/R est:15000-20000

NEEL, Alice (1900-1984) American
£48387 $75000 €72581 Peter B. Kaplan (71x51cm-28x20in) s. painted 1950 prov. 26-Sep-2 Christie's, Rockefeller NY #738/R est:60000-80000

£53125 $85000 €79688 Portrait of Dr John J Lucca (102x81cm-40x32in) s.d.74 prov. 15-May-3 Christie's, Rockefeller NY #168/R est:80000-120000

NEER, Aert van der (attrib) (1603-1677) Dutch
£1135 $1759 €1703 Moonlit landscape (15x20cm-6x8in) panel. 3-Dec-2 Bukowskis, Stockholm #482/R est:18000-20000 (S.KR 16000)
£4167 $6583 €6500 Bord de riviere anime, au clair de lune (51x64cm-20x25in) panel. 12-Nov-2 Palais de Beaux Arts, Brussels #73/R est:5000-7000
£7500 $11625 €11250 Moonlit landscape with two peasant conversing near a lake in the foreground (41x56cm-16x22in) mono. prov.lit. 30-Oct-2 Christie's, Kensington #24/R est:5000-7000

NEERVOORT, Jan (1863-1940) Belgian
£496 $829 €700 Berger avec son troupeau (13x23cm-5x9in) panel. 23-Jun-3 Amberes, Antwerp #113
£1172 $1864 €1700 Farmers in the field (100x80cm-39x31in) s. 10-Mar-3 Sotheby's, Amsterdam #186a est:1000-1500

NEFF, Sibylle (1929-) Swiss
Works on paper
£1223 $1907 €1835 Cattle market in Appenzell (25x35cm-10x14in) s. pencil. 6-Nov-2 Hans Widmer, St Gallen #54/R est:2000-3800 (S.FR 2800)

NEFF, Timoleon Karl (1805-1876) Russian
£4762 $7571 €7000 Young Italian woman (35x28cm-14x11in) s.d.1855. 19-Mar-3 Neumeister, Munich #672/R est:4000

NEFKENS, Martinus Jacobus (1866-1941) Dutch
£414 $658 €600 Peasant with a flock of sheep (60x100cm-24x39in) s. 10-Mar-3 Sotheby's, Amsterdam #249
£451 $745 €650 Seascape with sailing vessels in the distance (50x70cm-20x28in) s. 1-Jul-3 Christie's, Amsterdam #141
£481 $750 €722 Herder with flock of sheep (32x52cm-13x20in) s. 9-Nov-2 Sloan, North Bethesda #565/R
£658 $1066 €1000 Ploughteam (50x71cm-20x28in) s. 21-Jan-3 Christie's, Amsterdam #150/R est:1000-1500
£822 $1282 €1200 Interior with a mother near her two children (80x61cm-31x24in) s. 14-Apr-3 Glerum, Amsterdam #76/R
£1056 $1701 €1500 Landscape with cattle on edge of forest (72x122cm-28x48in) s. 6-May-3 Vendu Notarishuis, Rotterdam #7/R est:1000-1500

NEFORS, Petrus (1790-1876) Belgian
£5000 $8100 €7500 H.M.S Castor running down the Cameleon cutter of Dover (48x61cm-19x24in) init. i.d.Aug 27 1834 verso painting on glass. 22-Jan-3 Bonhams, New Bond Street #322/R est:5000-8000

NEGELY, Rudolph (1883-?) Hungarian
£400 $636 €600 View of a continental harbour with figures and moored sailing vessels (59x79cm-23x31in) s. 19-Mar-3 Rupert Toovey, Partridge Green #30/R

NEGRE, Charles (1820-1880) French
Photographs
£2436 $3849 €3800 Autoportrait (15x10cm-6x4in) salt print exec.c.1853 prov. 16-Nov-2 Christie's, Paris #236/R est:4000-6000
£7692 $12154 €12000 Pericles, Jardin des Tuileries (33x25cm-13x10in) salt print prov. 16-Nov-2 Christie's, Paris #127/R est:15000-20000

NEGRET, Edgar (1920-) Colombian
Sculpture
£1529 $2400 €2294 Moon clock (35cm-14in) s.d.1988 num.7/30 painted aluminium prov. 20-Nov-2 Christie's, Rockefeller NY #104/R
£4878 $8000 €7317 Celestial navigator (145x66cm-57x26in) s.d.1958 verso paint bolted aluminium on wood prov. 28-May-3 Christie's, Rockefeller NY #138/R est:12000-16000

NEGULESCU, Jean (1900-1993) Rumanian/American
Works on paper
£300 $471 €450 Seated figure with dancer behind (75x55cm-30x22in) s.i.d.62 pen ink. 15-Apr-3 Bonhams, Knightsbridge #60
£800 $1240 €1200 Seated female nude (75x49cm-30x19in) s.d. W/C three. 3-Dec-2 Bonhams, Knightsbridge #359/R
£1100 $1705 €1650 Dancer (76x50cm-30x20in) s.d.53 W/C four. 3-Dec-2 Bonhams, Knightsbridge #362/R est:800-1000

NEHMER, Rudolf (1912-1983) German
£1013 $1600 €1600 Portrait of semi nude Lisl Wachsmann (65x54cm-26x21in) s.d.1940 panel. 30-Nov-2 Arnold, Frankfurt #404/R
£1572 $2421 €2500 Marrows (39x81cm-15x32in) s.d.1949. 26-Oct-2 Dr Lehr, Berlin #387/R est:3500
£6013 $9500 €9500 Self portrait (90x85cm-35x33in) mono.d.38 panel exhib. 30-Nov-2 Villa Grisebach, Berlin #291/R est:8000-10000

NEIF, Arifien (1955-) Javanese
£2154 $3317 €3231 Singer and the pianist (68x58cm-27x23in) s.d.94. 27-Oct-2 Christie's, Hong Kong #95/R est:22000-30000 (HK.D 26000)
£3885 $6410 €5633 On the red bridge in Surabaya (58x68cm-23x27in) s.d.2003. 6-Jul-3 Christie's, Hong Kong #60/R est:24000-30000 (HK.D 50000)
£5385 $8293 €8078 Tequila (80x90cm-31x35in) s.d.99. 27-Oct-2 Christie's, Hong Kong #94/R est:45000-55000 (HK.D 65000)

NEILAND, Brendan (1941-) British
£600 $990 €870 Reflection of concrete and glass (48x70cm-19x28in) acrylic. 3-Jul-3 Christie's, Kensington #617/R

NEILL, Henry Echlin (1888-?) British
£400 $624 €600 Port Salon from Buncrana, Co Donegal (28x33cm-11x13in) s.i. panel. 17-Sep-2 Goldings, Lincolnshire #617

NEILLOT, Louis (1898-1973) French
£442 $703 €650 Eglise du village (60x73cm-24x29in) s.d.27. 24-Mar-3 Coutau Begarie, Paris #245
£680 $1082 €1000 Les sauges (33x41cm-13x16in) s.d.1968. 2-Mar-3 Lombrail & Teucquam, Paris #177/R
£793 $1261 €1150 Environs de Maillard (38x46cm-15x18in) s.d.66. 7-Mar-3 Claude Aguttes, Neuilly #7
£811 $1265 €1200 Paysage (38x46cm-15x18in) s.d.46. 26-Mar-3 Rieunier, Paris #13/R
£987 $1540 €1550 Clairiere aux acacias (50x61cm-20x24in) s. painted 1947 lit. 10-Nov-2 Eric Pillon, Calais #93/R
£1079 $1727 €1500 Le pont de Bellevue a Meudon (60x73cm-24x29in) s.d.29. 15-May-3 Christie's, Paris #123/R est:1500-2000
£1210 $1888 €1900 Ananas (60x73cm-24x29in) s. painted 1960 lit. 10-Nov-2 Eric Pillon, Calais #89
Works on paper
£282 $468 €400 Let toits rouges (27x36cm-11x14in) s.i.d.52 W/C. 11-Jun-3 Beaussant & Lefèvre, Paris #109

NEIMAN, Leroy (1926-) American
£2563 $4100 €3716 Jockey (30x20cm-12x8in) s. artist board painted c.1967 prov. 17-May-3 Selkirks, St. Louis #389/R est:4500-6000
£2969 $4750 €4305 French jockeys (43x64cm-17x25in) s.d. board prov. 17-May-3 Selkirks, St. Louis #388/R est:5000-7000
Works on paper
£353 $550 €530 America's Cup (66x79cm-26x31in) s.d.1964 seriograph. 30-Mar-3 Simpson's, Houston #361
£696 $1100 €1044 Fine art expert (46x48cm-18x19in) s. W/C. 1-Dec-2 Susanin's, Chicago #5007/R

NEITSCHE, Paul (20th C) Irish?
£2100 $3255 €3150 Tree reflection (61x51cm-24x20in) s. board. 2-Oct-2 John Ross, Belfast #149 est:1500-2000
£2100 $3255 €3150 Country Down farmhouse (61x51cm-24x20in) s.d.38 board. 2-Oct-2 John Ross, Belfast #219 est:1500-2000
Works on paper
£320 $496 €480 Male portrait (51x41cm-20x16in) s.d.1929 pastel. 2-Oct-2 John Ross, Belfast #193

NEIZVESTNY, Ernst (1926-) Russian
Works on paper
£1800 $2916 €2700 Torso (74x62cm-29x24in) s.d.65 chl brush. 21-May-3 Sotheby's, London #224/R est:2000-3000

NEJEDLY, Otakar (1883-1957) Czechoslovakian
£1135 $1793 €1703 Forest landscape (52x81cm-20x32in) s. 30-Nov-2 Dorotheum, Prague #65/R est:40000-60000 (C.KR 55000)
£1341 $2119 €2012 Landscape with rocks (81x116cm-32x46in) s.d.29. 30-Nov-2 Dorotheum, Prague #71/R est:50000-75000 (C.KR 65000)
£1549 $2416 €2324 Summer landscape with Rip (49x68cm-19x27in) s. 12-Oct-2 Dorotheum, Prague #130/R est:50000-75000 (C.KR 75000)

NELIMARKKA, Eero (1891-1977) Finnish
£538 $839 €850 Interior (68x46cm-27x18in) s.d.1936. 12-Sep-2 Hagelstam, Helsinki #836
£629 $975 €1000 Still life (83x53cm-33x21in) s.d.1934. 6-Oct-2 Bukowskis, Helsinki #236/R
£719 $1179 €1100 Landscape from Tel Aviv (34x46cm-13x18in) s.i.d.1954. 9-Feb-3 Bukowskis, Helsinki #321/R
£748 $1190 €1100 Road (55x47cm-22x19in) s. 27-Feb-3 Hagelstam, Helsinki #905
£755 $1170 €1200 Landscape (46x38cm-18x15in) s.d.1935. 6-Oct-2 Bukowskis, Helsinki #238/R
£759 $1185 €1200 Landscape (40x50cm-16x20in) s. 12-Sep-2 Hagelstam, Helsinki #1020

£759 $1199 €1100 Winter (40x32cm-16x13in) s. 3-Apr-3 Hagelstam, Helsinki #807/R
£774 $1223 €1200 Notre Dame, Paris (46x55cm-18x22in) s.d.36. 19-Dec-2 Hagelstam, Helsinki #939
£784 $1286 €1200 River landscape (47x55cm-19x22in) s.d.1952. 9-Feb-3 Bukowskis, Helsinki #319/R
£786 $1211 €1250 Winter landscape (39x79cm-15x31in) s. 24-Oct-2 Hagelstam, Helsinki #826
£816 $1298 €1200 Cloudy day (38x87cm-15x34in) s.d.1950. 24-Mar-3 Bukowskis, Helsinki #206/R
£816 $1298 €1200 Autumn colours (46x79cm-18x31in) s.d.1973. 24-Mar-3 Bukowskis, Helsinki #207/R
£828 $1308 €1200 Mountain landscape (52x77cm-20x30in) s.d.1974. 3-Apr-3 Hagelstam, Helsinki #1014/R
£828 $1308 €1200 Landscape (46x92cm-18x36in) s.d.1976. 3-Apr-3 Hagelstam, Helsinki #1019
£849 $1308 €1350 Mountain (40x95cm-16x37in) s.d.1974. 24-Oct-2 Hagelstam, Helsinki #825
£849 $1308 €1350 Landscape (50x65cm-20x26in) s. 24-Oct-2 Hagelstam, Helsinki #873
£850 $1393 €1300 The plain (60x80cm-24x31in) s.d.55. 9-Feb-3 Bukowskis, Helsinki #320/R
£850 $1393 €1300 The last snow (47x64cm-19x25in) s.d.1937. 9-Feb-3 Bukowskis, Helsinki #323/R
£862 $1362 €1250 Landscape (40x50cm-16x20in) s.d.1935. 3-Apr-3 Hagelstam, Helsinki #830/R
£863 $1416 €1200 Landscape (46x88cm-18x35in) s.d.1945. 5-Jun-3 Hagelstam, Helsinki #1010
£881 $1356 €1400 Reindeer in autumn landscape (46x70cm-18x28in) s.d.1938 prov. 27-Oct-2 Bukowskis, Helsinki #246/R
£918 $1432 €1450 View from Koli (65x45cm-26x18in) s.i.d.1957. 15-Sep-2 Bukowskis, Helsinki #246/R
£943 $1453 €1500 Winter landscape (65x81cm-26x32in) s.d.1967. 24-Oct-2 Hagelstam, Helsinki #1004 est:2000
£986 $1587 €1400 Autumn (65x82cm-26x32in) s.d.1949. 10-May-3 Bukowskis, Helsinki #43/R
£1013 $1600 €1600 Cattle grazing (47x56cm-19x22in) s.d.1950. 1-Dec-2 Bukowskis, Helsinki #140/R est:1400-1700
£1020 $1622 €1500 Landscape (31x55cm-12x22in) s.d.1945. 27-Feb-3 Hagelstam, Helsinki #1035 est:1000
£1034 $1634 €1500 Landscape (46x55cm-18x22in) s.d.1915. 3-Apr-3 Hagelstam, Helsinki #980/R est:1800
£1088 $1731 €1600 Winter felds (81x46cm-32x18in) s.d.1960. 27-Feb-3 Hagelstam, Helsinki #917 est:1500
£1127 $1814 €1600 Mountain landscape in autumn (65x80cm-26x31in) s.d.1948. 10-May-3 Bukowskis, Helsinki #72/R est:1500-2000
£1132 $1755 €1800 Summer clouds (47x100cm-19x39in) s.d.1938. 6-Oct-2 Bukowskis, Helsinki #239/R est:1700
£1172 $1852 €1700 Winter landscape (46x87cm-18x34in) s.d.1964. 3-Apr-3 Hagelstam, Helsinki #823 est:1500
£1197 $1927 €1700 Pelargonium (63x46cm-25x18in) s.d.1937. 10-May-3 Bukowskis, Helsinki #55/R est:1200-1500
£1241 $1961 €1800 Horses grazing (50x72cm-20x28in) s.d.1921. 3-Apr-3 Hagelstam, Helsinki #974/R est:2000
£1266 $2000 €2000 Evening light (66x83cm-26x33in) s.d.1944. 1-Dec-2 Bukowskis, Helsinki #138/R est:2500-2800
£1321 $2034 €2100 Landscape (65x162cm-26x64in) s. 24-Oct-2 Hagelstam, Helsinki #830 est:1800
£1367 $2242 €1900 Winter (70x121cm-28x48in) s.d.1962. 5-Jun-3 Hagelstam, Helsinki #951/R est:2000
£1415 $2179 €2250 Autumn colours (66x146cm-26x57in) s. 24-Oct-2 Hagelstam, Helsinki #822 est:2500
£1429 $2271 €2100 Farm view (55x52cm-22x20in) s.d.1916. 27-Feb-3 Hagelstam, Helsinki #821 est:1500
£1634 $2680 €2500 Still life (55x46cm-22x18in) s.d.1929. 9-Feb-3 Bukowskis, Helsinki #318/R est:1000
£1724 $2724 €2500 Interior (125x125cm-49x49in) s.d.1927-33. 3-Apr-3 Hagelstam, Helsinki #1017/R est:2500
£1772 $2800 €2800 The last snow (45x46cm-18x18in) s.d.1921. 1-Dec-2 Bukowskis, Helsinki #139/R est:1500-1800
£1831 $2948 €2600 The water carrier (54x65cm-21x26in) s.d.1921. 10-May-3 Bukowskis, Helsinki #61/R est:2000-2500

NELIMARKKA, Tuomas (1925-1997) Finnish
£316 $494 €500 Landscape (40x83cm-16x33in) s.d.1971. 12-Sep-2 Hagelstam, Helsinki #811
£327 $536 €500 Winter's day in Osterbotten (38x68cm-15x27in) s.d.75. 9-Feb-3 Bukowskis, Helsinki #324/R
£345 $545 €500 Winter landscape (40x85cm-16x33in) s.d.1976. 3-Apr-3 Hagelstam, Helsinki #841
£380 $592 €600 Landscape (40x84cm-16x33in) s. 12-Sep-2 Hagelstam, Helsinki #942/R

NELLE, Anthony (19/20th C) Russian/American
Works on paper
£705 $1100 €1058 Dancers amidst charred remains of Luna Park amusement park (33x48cm-13x19in) s. gouache W/C prov.lit. 9-Nov-2 Illustration House, New York #105/R

NELLENS, Roger (1937-) Belgian
£253 $400 €400 Signal 10 (65x61cm-26x24in) s.d.69. 26-Nov-2 Palais de Beaux Arts, Brussels #363/R
£316 $500 €500 Composition (91x73cm-36x29in) s. 26-Nov-2 Palais de Beaux Arts, Brussels #362
£915 $1473 €1400 Composition mecanique (90x136cm-35x54in) i.d.72 verso. 20-Jan-3 Horta, Bruxelles #178

NELLIUS, Martinus (fl.1670-1706) Dutch
£7914 $12662 €11000 Partly peeled lemon in a giant roemer and other fruits on a partly draped stone table (61x51cm-24x20in) s. 14-May-3 Christie's, Amsterdam #148/R est:7000-9000
£12230 $19568 €17000 Still life with peeled lemon, oyster, pipe and apples (43x38cm-17x15in) s. panel prov.exhib. 17-May-3 De Vuyst, Lokeren #519/R est:17000-20000
£12739 $19873 €20000 Still life of an orange, grapes and red berries, together with a white butterfly (26x24cm-10x9in) panel prov. 5-Nov-2 Sotheby's, Amsterdam #12/R est:12000-18000

NELLY (1899-1998) Turkish
Photographs
£12000 $19440 €18000 Nikolska dancing in the parthenon (21x28cm-8x11in) i. silver bromide print card lit. 22-May-3 Sotheby's, London #68/R est:2000-3000

NELSON, Alphonse Henri (1854-?) French
Sculpture
£1154 $1812 €1800 L'aurore (55cm-22in) s.st.f.H. Luppens brown pat bronze. 19-Nov-2 Vanderkindere, Brussels #125/R est:1500-2000

NELSON, Ernest Bruce (1888-1952) American
£2987 $4750 €4481 April in the park (58x74cm-23x29in) 28-Feb-3 Douglas, South Deerfield #7

NELSON, Frank Bronson Jagamara (20th C) Australian
£268 $415 €402 Fly ants dreaming (126x78cm-50x31in) acrylic. 29-Oct-2 Lawson Menzies, Sydney #278 (A.D 750)

NELSON, George Laurence (1887-1978) American
£5380 $8500 €8070 Portrait of Bessie Hutty (76x64cm-30x25in) s.d.1910. 24-Apr-3 Shannon's, Milford #150/R est:6000-8000

NELSON, George Laurence (attrib) (1887-1978) American
£446 $700 €669 Mary Lyons founder of Mt Holyoke College on centennial of founding (91x91cm-36x36in) 19-Apr-3 James Julia, Fairfield #410/R

NELSON, Joan (1958-) American
£6329 $10000 €9494 Untitled, number 244 (38x38cm-15x15in) s.i.d.1989 verso oil wax wood prov. 13-Nov-2 Sotheby's, New York #601/R est:10000-15000

NELSON, Michael Tjakamarra (1949-) Australian
£414 $658 €621 Sweet potato dreaming (90x119cm-35x47in) painted 1986 prov. 23-Mar-3 Goodman, Sydney #19 (A.D 1100)

NELSON, Robert A (20th C) American
£1419 $2200 €2129 Birds (137x173cm-54x68in) prov. 25-Sep-2 Doyle, New York #54/R est:800-1200

NEMES, Endre (1909-1985) Hungarian
£268 $421 €402 Figures in snow (50x65cm-20x26in) s. enamel. 16-Dec-2 Lilla Bukowskis, Stockholm #555 (S.KR 3800)
£463 $746 €695 Controversial figure (19x23cm-7x9in) s.d.81 tempera pencil collage. 7-May-3 AB Stockholms Auktionsverk #771/R (S.KR 6000)
£1081 $1741 €1622 Crowding (22x25cm-9x10in) s.d.41 tempera pencil exhib.lit. 7-May-3 AB Stockholms Auktionsverk #715/R est:6000-8000 (S.KR 14000)
£1121 $1749 €1682 Portrait of man (74x55cm-29x22in) s. i.verso painted 1930-31. 5-Nov-2 Bukowskis, Stockholm #224/R est:25000-30000 (S.KR 16000)
£2857 $4600 €4286 Downfall shapes (92x73cm-36x29in) s. painted 1957-58. 7-May-3 AB Stockholms Auktionsverk #690/R est:20000-25000 (S.KR 37000)
£3475 $5595 €5213 Formations against plaited work (200x160cm-79x63in) s. exhib.lit. 7-May-3 AB Stockholms Auktionsverk #885/R est:40000-50000 (S.KR 45000)

£3644 $5685 €5466 The large metamorphosis (160x200cm-63x79in) s. d.1958 verso exhib. 6-Nov-2 AB Stockholms Auktionsverk #568/R est:40000-50000 (S.KR 52000)
£3994 $6231 €5991 Journey in the past (90x115cm-35x45in) s.d.1967 acrylic tempera collage exhib.lit. 6-Nov-2 AB Stockholms Auktionsverk #589/R est:40000-50000 (S.KR 57000)
£4015 $6465 €6023 Visit in the studio (138x224cm-54x88in) s. exhib.lit. 7-May-3 AB Stockholms Auktionsverk #691/R est:50000-60000 (S.KR 52000)
£7708 $12025 €11562 The toy doll (120x100cm-47x39in) s.d.43 exhib. 6-Nov-2 AB Stockholms Auktionsverk #521/R est:40000-50000 (S.KR 110000)
£8494 $13676 €12741 A teaspoon Bleriot (215x155cm-85x61in) s.d.1970 tempera oil acrylic exhib.lit. 7-May-3 AB Stockholms Auktionsverk #719/R est:60000-80000 (S.KR 110000)
£15417 $24050 €23126 The sleep-walker saying Good-bye (152x122cm-60x48in) s.d.46 tempera panel exhib.lit. 6-Nov-2 AB Stockholms Auktionsverk #539/R est:100000-125000 (S.KR 220000)
£20077 $32324 €30116 The large interior (134x185cm-53x73in) s. tempera exhib.lit. 7-May-3 AB Stockholms Auktionsverk #695/R est:100000-125000 (S.KR 260000)

Works on paper
£372 $587 €558 The skater (60x50cm-24x20in) s.d.1968 W/C over aquatint. 30-Nov-2 Goteborg Auktionsverk, Sweden #588/R (S.KR 5300)
£386 $622 €579 Different battle-fields (20x28cm-8x11in) s.d.1966 collage mixed media exhib.lit. 7-May-3 AB Stockholms Auktionsverk #718/R (S.KR 5000)
£541 $870 €812 Screws, weapon and a little greenery (31x40cm-12x16in) s.d.1965 collage acrylic exhib.lit. 7-May-3 AB Stockholms Auktionsverk #716/R (S.KR 7000)
£567 $879 €851 Itchy fingers (41x38cm-16x15in) s.d.1967 collage tempera exhib. 8-Dec-2 Uppsala Auktionskammare, Uppsala #250/R (S.KR 8000)
£656 $1057 €984 Wrecked engine (33x21cm-13x8in) s.d.1981 collage pencil exhib.lit. 7-May-3 AB Stockholms Auktionsverk #711/R (S.KR 8500)
£736 $1148 €1104 Prelude (32x23cm-13x9in) s.d.1967 collage tempera exhib. 6-Nov-2 AB Stockholms Auktionsverk #703/R (S.KR 10500)
£772 $1243 €1158 Mussel concert (31x19cm-12x7in) s.d.1966 collage exhib.lit. 7-May-3 AB Stockholms Auktionsverk #712/R (S.KR 10000)
£927 $1492 €1391 Seated woman with stereometric projections (58x50cm-23x20in) s.d.1983 pencil gouache exhib.lit. 7-May-3 AB Stockholms Auktionsverk #770/R (S.KR 12000)
£1081 $1741 €1622 Renaissance inheritance (29x27cm-11x11in) s.d.1976-77 collage tempera Indian ink exhib.lit. 7-May-3 AB Stockholms Auktionsverk #714/R est:8000-12000 (S.KR 14000)
£1313 $2114 €1970 Meeting with the baroque (31x24cm-12x9in) s.d.1967 collage tempera exhib.lit. 7-May-3 AB Stockholms Auktionsverk #713/R est:8000-12000 (S.KR 17000)

NEMES, Endre (attrib) (1909-1985) Hungarian
£351 $554 €527 Composition (64x80cm-25x31in) tempera. 30-Nov-2 Goteborg Auktionsverk, Sweden #589/R (S.KR 5000)

NEMES, Jozsef Haranglabi (1889-1976) Hungarian
£699 $1084 €1014 Sailing boats (22x29cm-9x11in) s. card. 9-Dec-2 Mu Terem Galeria, Budapest #23/R est:150000 (H.F 260000)

NEMES-LAMPERTH, Jozsef (1891-1924) Hungarian
£38000 $58900 €57000 Still life with flowers (55x68cm-22x27in) s.d.1916 exhib. 1-Oct-2 Bonhams, Leeds #289/R est:2000-3000
£134134 $209250 €194494 Still life with plants and plate (58x69cm-23x27in) s.d.1916 exhib.lit. 12-Apr-3 Mu Terem Galeria, Budapest #221/R est:15000000 (H.F 48000000)

Works on paper
£3227 $5002 €4841 Interior (49x36cm-19x14in) Indian ink. 6-Dec-2 Kieselbach, Budapest #97/R (H.F 1200000)
£4386 $6842 €6360 Nude woman. Parisian landscape (53x43cm-21x17in) s.i.d.1913 Indian ink double-sided lit. 13-Sep-2 Mu Terem Galeria, Budapest #61/R est:800000 (H.F 1700000)
£78245 $122062 €117368 Kolosvar, 1920 (72x100cm-28x39in) s.d.7.IV.1920 Indian ink. 11-Apr-3 Kieselbach, Budapest #37/R est:15000-28000000 (H.F 28000000)

NEMETH, Lajos (1861-?) Hungarian
£4572 $7086 €6858 Park of the castle with count (90x141cm-35x56in) s. 6-Dec-2 Kieselbach, Budapest #103/R (H.F 1700000)

NEMETH, Miklos (1934-) Hungarian
£531 $828 €797 Fairytale landscape (100x70cm-39x28in) s. board. 11-Apr-3 Kieselbach, Budapest #159/R est:190000 (H.F 190000)
£968 $1501 €1404 Clown (63x52cm-25x20in) s.d.79 card exhib.lit. 9-Dec-2 Mu Terem Galeria, Budapest #104/R est:240000 (H.F 360000)
£1006 $1569 €1459 Autumn on Kapy street (70x100cm-28x39in) s.d.1964 board prov.lit. 12-Apr-3 Mu Terem Galeria, Budapest #109/R est:240000 (H.F 360000)

NEMETHY, Albert (1920-) American
£506 $800 €759 Couple fishing near covered bridge in Catskill mountains (79x102cm-31x40in) s.i. 22-Apr-3 Arthur James, Florida #176
£920 $1500 €1380 Middletown (58x74cm-23x29in) 31-Jan-3 Douglas, South Deerfield #6

NEMON, Oscar (1906-1985) British

Sculpture
£1300 $2067 €1950 Queen Mother (36cm-14in) init.num.1/2 brown pat. bronze. 26-Feb-3 Sotheby's, Olympia #268/R est:600-800

NEMOURS, Aurelie (1910-) French
£1048 $1530 €1572 Untitled (15x15cm-6x6in) s.d.1977 panel. 4-Jun-2 Germann, Zurich #1/R est:1400-1800 (S.FR 2400)
£1135 $1658 €1703 Untitled (15x15cm-6x6in) s.d.1976 panel. 4-Jun-2 Germann, Zurich #2/R est:1400-1800 (S.FR 2600)
£13100 $20568 €19650 Couronne pour un carre (120x120cm-47x47in) s.d.1983 verso exhib.lit.prov. 23-Nov-2 Burkhard, Luzern #173/R est:28000-32000 (S.FR 30000)

NEOCLASSICAL SCHOOL (18th C)

Sculpture
£4747 $7405 €7500 Ganimedes' kidnapping (106x92cm-42x36in) painted carved wood. 19-Oct-2 Meeting Art, Vercelli #288/R est:7000

NEOGRADY, Antal (1861-1942) Hungarian
£510 $795 €800 Young woman at woodland spring (44x33cm-17x13in) s. board. 6-Nov-2 Hugo Ruef, Munich #1223
£614 $952 €921 Hunters in winter (58x78cm-23x31in) painted c.1920. 1-Oct-2 SOGA, Bratislava #118/R est:39000 (SL.K 39000)
£641 $1013 €1000 By the water (36x48cm-14x19in) s. 12-Nov-2 Dorotheum, Vienna #83/R
£662 $1025 €993 Brook (25x39cm-10x15in) painted c.1935. 1-Oct-2 SOGA, Bratislava #120/R est:24000 (SL.K 42000)
£759 $1185 €1200 Girl sitting on jetty (29x39cm-11x15in) s. paper. 16-Oct-2 Dorotheum, Vienna #10/R
£1174 $1831 €1761 Girls picking flowers by brook (49x69cm-19x27in) s. oil tempera. 11-Apr-3 Kieselbach, Budapest #42/R est:360000-420000 (H.F 420000)
£1392 $2200 €2200 Apple tree (56x60cm-22x24in) s. 28-Nov-2 Dorotheum, Vienna #174/R est:2800-3400
£2500 $4100 €3750 Springtime (33x56cm-13x22in) s. 3-Jun-3 Sotheby's, London #82/R est:3000-5000

Works on paper
£503 $780 €800 Children chatting in Hungarian courtyard (28x38cm-11x15in) s. W/C. 1-Oct-2 Dorotheum, Vienna #343/R
£536 $830 €804 In front of the house (28x41cm-11x16in) W/C exec.c.1910. 1-Oct-2 SOGA, Bratislava #119/R est:18000 (SL.K 34000)
£614 $897 €921 Near brook (50x60cm-20x24in) W/C board exec.c.1935. 4-Jun-2 SOGA, Bratislava #114/R est:29000 (SL.K 39000)
£1345 $2084 €1950 Little gardener (85x45cm-33x18in) s. W/C. 9-Dec-2 Mu Terem Galeria, Budapest #200/R est:250000 (H.F 500000)

NEOGRADY, L (1896-1962) Hungarian
£769 $1200 €1154 Snowy landscape (58x76cm-23x30in) 11-Apr-3 Douglas, South Deerfield #3

NEOGRADY, Laszlo (1896-1962) Hungarian
£247 $400 €371 Winter scene (61x91cm-24x36in) s. 25-Jan-3 Susanin's, Chicago #5007
£314 $491 €500 Girl going home in blooming autumn landscape (24x35cm-9x14in) s.d.12 board on panel. 21-Sep-2 Bolland & Marotz, Bremen #531
£316 $500 €474 Country scene with woman and duck (23x33cm-9x13in) s. board. 5-Apr-3 DeFina, Austinburg #1318
£321 $503 €500 Girl with geese by village pond in summer (25x39cm-10x15in) s. 23-Nov-2 Arnold, Frankfurt #825/R
£347 $538 €521 Way home (20x33cm-8x13in) cardboard painted c.1930. 3-Dec-2 SOGA, Bratislava #102/R (SL.K 22000)
£404 $650 €606 Mountain landscape in winter (41x51cm-16x20in) s. 18-Feb-3 Arthur James, Florida #317
£484 $750 €726 Winter landscape (61x81cm-24x32in) s. 1-Oct-2 Arthur James, Florida #62
£536 $782 €804 In front of the house (25x37cm-10x15in) 4-Jun-2 SOGA, Bratislava #115/R est:22000 (SL.K 34000)

£590 $950 €885 Winter landscape in the mountains (61x91cm-24x36in) s. 20-Jan-3 Arthur James, Florida #698
£590 $974 €850 Abundant flower garden (60x80cm-24x31in) s. 1-Jul-3 Christie's, Amsterdam #76
£680 $1082 €1000 Summer landscape (61x91cm-24x36in) s. 1-Mar-3 Meeting Art, Vercelli #88
£695 $1077 €1043 By the brook (23x33cm-9x13in) panel painted c.1935. 3-Dec-2 SOGA, Bratislava #104/R (SL.K 44000)
£889 $1476 €1289 In the heart of the mountains, winter (61x91cm-24x36in) s. 16-Jun-3 Waddingtons, Toronto #311/R est:2000-3000 (C.D 2000)
£900 $1440 €1350 Snowy wooded landscape (61x76cm-24x30in) s. 13-May-3 Bonhams, Knightsbridge #63/R
£931 $1444 €1397 In front of a house (24x34cm-9x13in) cardboard painted c.1930. 3-Dec-2 SOGA, Bratislava #103/R est:24000 (SL.K 59000)
£931 $1444 €1397 Goose herd (23x33cm-9x13in) panel painted c.1935. 3-Dec-2 SOGA, Bratislava #105/R est:20000 (SL.K 59000)
£968 $1500 €1452 Young ladies and geese by the river (61x91cm-24x36in) s. 1-Oct-2 Arthur James, Florida #63
£1000 $1540 €1500 Cattle grazing before a bay (61x76cm-24x30in) s. 24-Oct-2 Christie's, Kensington #122/R est:600-800
£1100 $1738 €1650 River running through a sunlit alpine landscape (60x80cm-24x31in) s. 14-Nov-2 Christie's, Kensington #113/R est:1000-1500
£1677 $2600 €2516 Wooded winter landscape (61x76cm-24x30in) s. 16-Jul-2 Arthur James, Florida #374
£1781 $2778 €2600 Plattensee on summer's day (60x80cm-24x31in) s. 10-Apr-3 Dorotheum, Vienna #141/R est:3000-3600
£1928 $3200 €2796 Fresh snow on a wooded winter landscape (58x69cm-23x27in) s. 14-Jun-3 Jackson's, Cedar Falls #202/R est:3000-3500

NEPO, Ernst (1895-1971) Austrian
£6329 $10000 €10000 Flowers (32x31cm-13x12in) s.d.1945 i. verso masonite. 27-Nov-2 Dorotheum, Vienna #183/R est:10000-13000

NEPOTE, Alexander (1913-1986) American
Works on paper
£244 $400 €366 Snow forest (112x74cm-44x29in) s. mixed media. 31-May-3 Harvey Clar, Oakland #1169

NERDRUM, Odd (1944-) Norwegian
£17406 $27850 €26109 The arrest (76x63cm-30x25in) s. painted c.1975-76 lit. 17-Mar-3 Blomqvist, Oslo #454/R est:40000-60000 (N.KR 200000)
£83643 $132156 €125465 Male twins - twins with knives (101x108cm-40x43in) s.verso prov.exhib.lit. 1-Apr-3 Rasmussen, Copenhagen #161/R est:1000000-1200000 (D.KR 900000)

NERI, Manuel (1930-) American
£3165 $5000 €4748 Gesture study no.87 (21x23cm-8x9in) s.d.1980 acrylic oil stick pencil magazine sheet. 22-Apr-3 Butterfields, San Francisco #6043/R est:6000-8000
Sculpture
£25316 $40000 €37974 Prietas series 1 (165cm-65in) s.d.1993 bronze enamel paint. 22-Apr-3 Butterfields, San Francisco #6050/R est:25000-35000

NERI, Paul (1910-1966) Italian?
£2158 $3540 €3000 Ksar de l'Anti-Atlas (59x72cm-23x28in) s.i. 4-Jun-3 Tajan, Paris #291/R est:3000-4000

NERLI, G P B (?) ?
£915 $1399 €1373 Native woman outside trading house (20x33cm-8x13in) s. board. 21-Aug-2 Dunbar Sloane, Auckland #34/R est:3000-5000 (NZ.D 3000)

NERLI, Marchese Girolamo Ballatti (1860-1926) Italian
£3659 $5780 €5306 Goose girl (44x33cm-17x13in) s. prov. 22-Jul-3 Lawson Menzies, Sydney #77/R est:10000-12000 (A.D 9000)
£5344 $8443 €8016 Regent Park (22x30cm-9x12in) s.i. board. 2-Apr-3 Christie's, Melbourne #3/R est:6000-8000 (A.D 14000)
£10000 $15900 €15000 Sydney (38x55cm-15x22in) s.i.d.1886 prov. 4-Mar-3 Deutscher-Menzies, Melbourne #46/R est:20000-30000 (A.D 26000)
Works on paper
£382 $603 €662 Elaborately dressed figure (31x21cm-12x8in) s. W/C. 1-Apr-3 Goodman, Sydney #26 (A.D 1000)
£637 $1045 €924 Imperial concubine (30x20cm-12x8in) s. W/C. 4-Jun-3 Deutscher-Menzies, Melbourne #313/R (A.D 1600)

NERLY, Friedrich (19th C) Italian/Austrian
£5660 $8830 €9000 Sunset on Venice (52x85cm-20x33in) s.d.1855 painted oval. 11-Oct-2 Winterberg, Heidelberg #658/R est:11500
£6849 $10685 €10274 Doges Palace in morning light (47x61cm-19x24in) 28-Mar-3 Koller, Zurich #3128/R est:15000-20000 (S.FR 15000)
Works on paper
£382 $608 €550 Kneeling girl (17x21cm-7x8in) mono. pen Indian ink over pencil double-sided. 5-May-3 Ketterer, Munich #310/R
£945 $1475 €1380 Palazzo Grassi in Venice (23x34cm-9x13in) s.i.d. pencil. 11-Apr-3 Winterberg, Heidelberg #503/R est:680
£1859 $2937 €2900 For Thorwaldsen (27x37cm-11x15in) s.d.1833 pen wash. 16-Nov-2 Lempertz, Koln #1372/R est:1000

NERLY, Friedrich (elder) (1807-1878) Italian/Austrian
£42000 $68880 €63000 Der Canale Grande, Venedig - Grand Canal Venice (63x98cm-25x39in) s. prov. 3-Jun-3 Sotheby's, London #182/R est:18000-25000
£53425 $83877 €78000 At the cafe Florian, Venice (96x78cm-38x31in) s. s.i.verso exhib. 15-Apr-3 Sotheby's, Amsterdam #89/R est:70000-90000

NERLY, Friedrich (elder-attrib) (1807-1878) Italian/Austrian
£2041 $3245 €3000 Venice by moonlight (64x88cm-25x35in) 19-Mar-3 Neumeister, Munich #673/R est:3000

NERLY, Friedrich (younger) (1824-1919) Italian
£1700 $2652 €2550 Capri (23x46cm-9x18in) s. 11-Apr-3 Keys, Aylsham #632/R est:1500-2000
£2600 $4342 €3900 Capri - veduta de Maifa (24x48cm-9x19in) s. i.verso. 18-Jun-3 Christie's, Kensington #170/R est:3000-5000
£6500 $10205 €9750 Fishing boats off the Naples coast, Capri beyond (51x91cm-20x36in) s. 21-Nov-2 Christie's, Kensington #136/R est:6000-8000

NERONI, Bartolomeo (1500-c.1573) Italian
Works on paper
£9877 $16000 €14816 Alexander the Great kneeling in front of Jaddus, The High Priest of Jerusalem (19x26cm-7x10in) pen brown ink over balck chk cut edge prov.lit. 21-Jan-3 Sotheby's, New York #5/R est:15000-20000

NERONI, Bartolomeo (attrib) (1500-c.1573) Italian
Works on paper
£1200 $1884 €1800 Two male figures and a female figures (15x20cm-6x8in) pen ink prov. 11-Dec-2 Sotheby's, Olympia #1/R est:1000-1500

NERUD, Josef Karl (1900-1982) German
£955 $1490 €1500 Mountain farmstead (83x100cm-33x39in) s.d.37. 6-Nov-2 Hugo Ruef, Munich #1220/R est:900
Works on paper
£256 $405 €400 Winter landscape with snow (42x45cm-17x18in) s. W/C. 14-Nov-2 Neumeister, Munich #641
£385 $608 €600 Seated peasant girl (58x44cm-23x17in) s. bears i. col chk Indian ink. 14-Nov-2 Neumeister, Munich #640/R
£1079 $1727 €1500 Ibiza (56x44cm-22x17in) s.i. col wax chk board. 15-May-3 Neumeister, Munich #322/R est:1200-1500

NESBITT, Frances E (1864-1934) British
Works on paper
£325 $517 €488 Fishing boats (36x53cm-14x21in) s. W/C. 20-Mar-3 Ewbank, Send #387
£380 $597 €570 Bowl of roses (18x24cm-7x9in) s. W/C. 10-Dec-2 Rosebery Fine Art, London #681/R

NESBITT, John (1831-1904) British
Works on paper
£280 $437 €420 Newark castle (34x50cm-13x20in) s.i.d.1876 W/C. 17-Oct-2 Bonhams, Edinburgh #170

NESBITT, Lowell (1933-1993) American
£221 $350 €332 Ivory rose (61x76cm-24x30in) s.i.d.1982 verso. 5-Apr-3 Neal Auction Company, New Orleans #369
£323 $500 €485 Pink lily (30x30cm-12x12in) s.i.d.1982 verso. 7-Dec-2 Neal Auction Company, New Orleans #643
£563 $924 €816 Blue iris (41x41cm-16x16in) s.d.82 verso. 4-Jun-3 Fischer, Luzern #2264/R (S.FR 1200)
£613 $1000 €920 Dutch iris (62x61cm-24x24in) s.i.d.65 verso. 16-Feb-3 Butterfields, San Francisco #2131
£1154 $1800 €1731 Cherries (152x152cm-60x60in) s.i.d.1965 prov. 20-Sep-2 New Orleans Auction, New Orleans #1404/R est:2000-4000
£4715 $7449 €7073 Amntethyst iris (112x96cm-44x38in) s.d.1981 prov. 28-Apr-3 Bukowskis, Stockholm #907/R est:8000-10000 (S.KR 62000)
£5449 $8500 €8174 Giant tulips (178x127cm-70x50in) s.i.d.1964 exhib. 20-Sep-2 New Orleans Auction, New Orleans #1405/R est:2500-4000
Works on paper
£558 $881 €837 Composition with white flower (101x75cm-40x30in) s.d.80 W/C gouache. 1-Apr-3 Rasmussen, Copenhagen #355/R (D.KR 6000)

NESBITT, Tom (?) Irish
Works on paper
£382 $630 €550 Canal bridge (30x37cm-12x15in) s. W/C. 7-Jul-3 Hamilton Osborne King, Dublin #224
£694 $1146 €1000 Baily Howth (30x37cm-12x15in) s. W/C. 7-Jul-3 Hamilton Osborne King, Dublin #222/R est:600-800

NESCH, Rolf (1893-1975) Norwegian
Prints
£2536 $4159 €3500 Pine trees (57x43cm-22x17in) s.i. metal print monotype prov. 29-May-3 Lempertz, Koln #827/R est:3000
£3982 $6292 €5973 Snake glutton (57x41cm-22x16in) s. col metal print trial print executed c.1965-66. 28-Apr-3 Blomqvist, Oslo #353/R est:40000-50000 (N.KR 45000)
£5724 $8930 €8586 Vardohus Fort (33x50cm-13x20in) s. num.6/10 col metal print executed 1947-48. 21-Oct-2 Blomqvist, Oslo #483/R est:30000-40000 (N.KR 66000)
£5759 $9042 €8639 Angel (59x49cm-23x19in) s.i.num.3/5 col metal print. 21-Nov-2 Grev Wedels Plass, Oslo #50/R est:80000-100000 (N.KR 66000)
£6981 $10960 €10472 Fish (48x63cm-19x25in) s.i.d.5 november 1970 col metal print. 21-Nov-2 Grev Wedels Plass, Oslo #49/R est:60000-80000 (N.KR 80000)
£7042 $11690 €10000 Bridge over lake (45x60cm-18x24in) s.i. metal print col chk. 14-Jun-3 Hauswedell & Nolte, Hamburg #1471/R est:12000
£7257 $11465 €10886 To swim (44x57cm-17x22in) s.d.22 juli 1971 col metal print. 28-Apr-3 Blomqvist, Oslo #352/R est:60000-80000 (N.KR 82000)
£9083 $14351 €13625 Oh to fly (61x46cm-24x18in) s.d.20 Februar 1971 col metal print lit. 2-Dec-2 Blomqvist, Oslo #419/R est:120000-140000 (N.KR 105000)
£10841 $16912 €16262 Nesoen - from the Snow serie (58x43cm-23x17in) s. metal print executed 1933-34. 21-Oct-2 Blomqvist, Oslo #478/R est:50000-70000 (N.KR 125000)

Works on paper
£485 $742 €728 Landscape with trees (37x49cm-15x19in) s. mixed media. 26-Aug-2 Blomqvist, Lysaker #1279 (N.KR 5600)
£513 $795 €800 Portrait of soldier (38x33cm-15x13in) s.d. 7-Dec-2 Hauswedell & Nolte, Hamburg #940/R
£737 $1150 €1106 Head of an animal (27x40cm-11x16in) s.d.34 pastel. 21-Oct-2 Blomqvist, Oslo #477/R (N.KR 8500)
£1301 $2029 €1952 Two men on horsebacks (48x63cm-19x25in) s.d.44 Indian ink pastel. 21-Oct-2 Blomqvist, Oslo #491/R est:25000-35000 (N.KR 15000)
£1735 $2706 €2603 Memory of Lofoten (50x66cm-20x26in) s.d.1936 pastel. 21-Oct-2 Blomqvist, Oslo #481/R est:15000-18000 (N.KR 20000)

NESHAT, Shirin (1957-) American
Photographs
£3797 $6000 €5696 Rapture series (56x75cm-22x30in) s.i.d.1999 verso c-print one of 35 prov. 13-Nov-2 Sotheby's, New York #462/R est:8000-12000
£5000 $8000 €7500 Untitled - rapture series (122x182cm-48x72in) s.i.d.1999 num.3/5 gelatin silver print fiber panel prov.exhib.lit. 15-May-3 Christie's, Rockefeller NY #401/R est:10000-15000
£7500 $12000 €11250 Untitled - rapture series (51x61cm-20x24in) s.i.num.5/10 gelatin silver print executed 1999 prov.exhib. 14-May-3 Sotheby's, New York #386/R est:6000-8000
£7595 $12000 €11393 Untitled - rapture series (116x177cm-46x70in) s.i.d.1999 num. gelatin silver print prov.exhib. 12-Nov-2 Phillips, New York #158/R est:15000-20000
£8000 $13360 €11600 Moon song (28x36cm-11x14in) s.i.d.1995 verso gelatin silver print ink prov.lit. 27-Jun-3 Christie's, London #251/R est:6000-8000
£8800 $14696 €12760 Rapture series (36x58cm-14x23in) s.i.d.1999 num.1/10 verso gelatin silver print prov.lit. 26-Jun-3 Sotheby's, London #278/R est:4000-6000
£9000 $13860 €13500 Untitled (152x112cm-60x44in) s.i.d.1999 num.4/5 silver dye bleach print. 23-Oct-2 Christie's, London #206/R est:10000-15000
£10127 $16000 €15191 Untitled - rapture series (112x178cm-44x70in) s.i.d.1999 num. gelatin silver print prov.exhib. 12-Nov-2 Phillips, New York #155/R est:20000-30000
£10127 $16000 €15191 Untitled - rapture series (108x169cm-43x67in) s.i.d.1999 num. gelatin silver print on board prov.exhib.lit. 12-Nov-2 Phillips, New York #157/R est:20000-30000
£11000 $18040 €16500 Rapture (107x175cm-42x69in) s. verso num.three of five gelatin silver print. 6-Feb-3 Christie's, London #762/R est:7000-9000
£12000 $20040 €17400 Untitled - rapture series (117x177cm-46x70in) s.i.d.1999 num.4/5 verso gelatin silver print prov.lit. 27-Jun-3 Christie's, London #267/R est:8000-12000
£18750 $30000 €28125 Modern building - solilouy series (122x152cm-48x60in) s.i.num.1999 verso c-print on aluminum prov.exhib. 16-May-3 Phillips, New York #205/R est:15000-20000
£18750 $30000 €28125 Identified - woman of Allah series (141x100cm 56x39in) gelatin silver print pen ink on board prov.exhib. 16-May-3 Phillips, New York #207/R est:30000-40000
£21250 $34000 €31875 Untitled - bonding (70x103cm-28x41in) s.i.d.1995 num.10 verso gelatin silver printacrylic pen ink. 16-May-3 Phillips, New York #206/R est:20000-30000

Works on paper
£12658 $20000 €18987 Rebellious silence (36x25cm-14x10in) s.d.1994 ink over photograph prov. 13-Nov-2 Sotheby's, New York #463/R est:15000-20000
£15625 $25000 €23438 Whispers (125x198cm-49x78in) s.i.d.1997 num.2 verso gelatin silver print prov. 14-May-3 Sotheby's, New York #383/R est:30000-40000
£19000 $29260 €28500 Birthmark (102x75cm-40x30in) s.i.d.1994 num.2/3 verso ink gelatin silver print prov.lit. 22-Oct-2 Sotheby's, London #492/R est:15000-20000

NESPOLO, Ugo (1941-) Italian
£475 $741 €750 Composition (36x25cm-14x10in) s. tempera card on canvas. 14-Sep-2 Meeting Art, Vercelli #704/R
£510 $811 €750 Bursting apple (36x24cm-14x9in) s. tempera paper. 1-Mar-3 Meeting Art, Vercelli #690
£654 $1046 €1000 Sunflower (100x70cm-39x28in) s. tempera card. 4-Jan-3 Meeting Art, Vercelli #518
£660 $1049 €950 Lightening (36x24cm-14x9in) s. tempera paper. 1-May-3 Meeting Art, Vercelli #187
£833 $1308 €1300 Untitled (100x70cm-39x28in) s. acrylic paper prov. 20-Nov-2 Pandolfini, Florence #164/R
£1203 $1876 €1900 Faces (40x30cm-16x12in) s. acrylic panel. 14-Sep-2 Meeting Art, Vercelli #971/R
£1528 $2429 €2200 Red belt (40x30cm-16x12in) s. acrylic panel. 1-May-3 Meeting Art, Vercelli #547
£1634 $2614 €2500 Window (50x70cm-20x28in) s. acrylic panel. 4-Jan-3 Meeting Art, Vercelli #705
£1731 $2717 €2700 Doll house (71x51cm-28x20in) s. acrylic panel. 23-Nov-2 Meeting Art, Vercelli #110/R
£3526 $5535 €5500 Perfect museum (70x100cm-28x39in) s. acrylic panel. 23-Nov-2 Meeting Art, Vercelli #321/R

Works on paper
£1370 $2137 €2000 Little writer (50x67cm-20x26in) s.verso alabaster collage oval. 10-Apr-3 Finarte Semenzato, Rome #204/R
£3521 $5845 €5000 L'uomo dal faro febbrile (100x70cm-39x28in) s. s.i.verso wood acrylic panel. 10-Jun-3 Finarte Semenzato, Milan #275/R est:5000-5400

NESSENTHALER, Johann David (c.1717-1766) German
Works on paper
£714 $1064 €1100 The brave amazon (47x37cm-19x15in) s.i. pen wash htd white. 26-Jun-2 Neumeister, Munich #553/R

NESSI, Marie Lucie (1900-1992) French
£528 $850 €792 Buissons au pritemps (46x56cm-18x22in) s. i.verso prov. 20-Jan-3 Arthur James, Florida #502

NESTE, Alfred van (1874-1969) Belgian
£414 $662 €600 Chateau dans un paysage fluvial (63x73cm-25x29in) 17-Mar-3 Amberes, Antwerp #279
£417 $646 €650 Old quay in Bruges (33x46cm-13x18in) s. panel. 7-Dec-2 De Vuyst, Lokeren #364
£514 $801 €750 Deux pecheurs au carrelet (60x90cm-24x35in) s.d.1944 s.i.d.verso. 14-Apr-3 Horta, Bruxelles #368
£710 $1100 €1065 Dutch harbour scene (36x46cm-14x18in) s. board. 7-Dec-2 Harvey Clar, Oakland #1132
£1006 $1550 €1600 Market in Brugges (40x42cm-16x17in) s. cardboard. 22-Oct-2 Campo & Campo, Antwerp #309/R
£1013 $1580 €1600 Deux pecheurs au carrelet (60x90cm-24x35in) s.d.1944 s.i.d.verso. 16-Sep-2 Horta, Bruxelles #407

Works on paper
£327 $526 €500 Quai de Bruges anime (28x35cm-11x14in) s. gouache cardboard. 14-Jan-3 Vanderkindere, Brussels #63

NESTEROV, Mikhail Vasilievich (1862-1942) Russian
£450000 $729000 €675000 Vision of the boy Bartholomew (94x110cm-37x43in) s.d.1917 s.d.verso. 21-May-3 Sotheby's, London #134/R est:180000-220000

NESTEROVA, Natalia (1944-) Russian
£2500 $3926 €3750 The sea (70x90cm-28x35in) s.i.d.2001 verso. 20-Nov-2 Sotheby's, London #195/R est:3000-5000

NESTOR (19/20th C) Spanish
Works on paper
£2452 $3874 €3800 Fish (20x27cm-8x11in) s.d.1931 col pencil dr. 17-Dec-2 Segre, Madrid #111/R est:1500

NESVIK, Ole (1941-) Norwegian
£262 $411 €393 North Cape (50x70cm-20x28in) s. 25-Nov-2 Blomqvist, Lysaker #1207 (N.KR 3000)

NETER, Laurentius de (1600-?) German
£2866 $4471 €4500 Interior with elegant figures playing music, singing and dancing (37x50cm-15x20in) mono.d.1638 panel oval. 5-Nov-2 Sotheby's, Amsterdam #326/R est:5000-7000

NETHERLANDISH SCHOOL, 15th C
Prints
£5500 $9075 €7975 Apocalypsis Sancti Johannis (26x19cm-10x7in) brown woodcut exec.c.1451-52. 1-Jul-3 Sotheby's, London #29/R est:6000-8000

NETHERLANDISH SCHOOL, 15th/16th C
Works on paper
£6051 $9439 €9500 Interior scene with four figures (12cm-5in circular) pen brown ink exec.c.1500 prov.exhib. 5-Nov-2 Sotheby's, Amsterdam #2/R est:7000-9000

NETHERLANDISH SCHOOL, 16th C
£7500 $12525 €10875 The Agony in the Garden (32x23cm-13x9in) panel prov. 8-Jul-3 Sotheby's, Olympia #338/R est:5000-7000
£8000 $12560 €12000 Portrait of a lady, in a dark dress with red sleeves (72x57cm-28x22in) d.1551 panel prov. 16-Dec-2 Sotheby's, London #31/R est:6000-8000
£9000 $13950 €13500 Portrait of elderly gentleman wearing cloak and hat (31x25cm-12x10in) i.d.1591 panel. 31-Oct-2 Sotheby's, Olympia #22/R est:2000-3000
£54487 $86090 €85000 Virgin and Child (28cm-11in circular) panel prov.exhib. 18-Nov-2 Bernaerts, Antwerp #189/R est:37000-54000

NETHERLANDISH SCHOOL, 17th C
£12903 $18968 €20000 Mocking of Christ (190x137cm-75x54in) bears sig. 20-Jun-2 Dr Fritz Nagel, Stuttgart #719/R est:20000

NETHERLANDISH SCHOOL, 19th C
£5063 $7899 €8000 Marine with fishermen at the beach and fishing boat on stormy sea (64x86cm-25x34in) indis.s. 21-Oct-2 Bernaerts, Antwerp #139/R est:3000-4000

NETHERWOOD, Arthur (1864-1930) British
£400 $652 €600 Country lane with figure and ducks before a cottage (11x18cm-4x7in) s. 12-Feb-3 Andrew Hartley, Ilkley #901
£420 $685 €630 Dalgelly (56x86cm-22x34in) s. 14-Feb-3 Keys, Aylsham #730
£975 $1511 €1463 Mousehole, Cornwall (51x76cm-20x30in) s. 4-Dec-2 Andrew Hartley, Ilkley #1234
Works on paper
£700 $1106 €1050 Conway quay scene with old salts chatting and a coal cart (48x89cm-19x35in) s.d.1893/4 W/C. 26-Nov-2 Rogers Jones, Clwyd #136/R
£1500 $2445 €2175 On the River Severn. Telford church on the Severn (58x92cm-23x36in) s.i.verso W/C pair. 17-Jul-3 Tennants, Leyburn #731 est:1000-1500

NETHERWOOD, Arthur (attrib) (1864-1930) British
£290 $447 €435 Cornish coastal scene (51x74cm-20x29in) 6-Sep-2 Biddle & Webb, Birmingham #139

NETSCHER, Caspar (1639-1684) Dutch
£1397 $2180 €2096 Woman at spinning wheel (20cm-8in circular) bears sig.d.1675 i. verso. 6-Nov-2 Dobiaschofsky, Bern #860/R est:4500 (S.FR 3200)

NETSCHER, Caspar (attrib) (1639-1684) Dutch
£2110 $3270 €3165 Young woman with landscape beyond (41x34cm-16x13in) 3-Oct-2 Koller, Zurich #3057/R est:5000-8000 (S.FR 4915)
£4839 $7645 €7259 Portrait of Madame Grigon, daughter of Marquis de Sevigny (70x56cm-28x22in) i. prov. 18-Nov-2 Waddingtons, Toronto #201/R est:4000-6000 (C.D 12000)

NETSCHER, Constantyn (1668-1723) Dutch
£4839 $7500 €7259 Portrait of a lady, holding a posy of roses (54x45cm-21x18in) s.d.Fec.1681 prov. 2-Oct-2 Christie's, Rockefeller NY #170/R est:8000-12000

NETSCHER, Constantyn (attrib) (1668-1723) Dutch
£961 $1499 €1442 Portrait of Henrietta Elisabeth (42x34cm-17x13in) i. verso prov. 6-Nov-2 Dobiaschofsky, Bern #861/R est:4000 (S.FR 2200)
£2448 $4087 €3500 Portrait d'une jeune mere avec son fils et leur chien (124x94cm-49x37in) oval. 27-Jun-3 Piasa, Paris #86/R est:3000-4000
£2516 $3899 €4000 Portrait of armoured Prince (131x98cm-52x39in) prov.lit. 2-Oct-2 Dorotheum, Vienna #432/R est:3500-5500

NETSCHER, Theodoor (attrib) (1661-1728) French
£1778 $2951 €2578 Portrait of a lady in blue with vase of carnations (114x87cm-45x34in) canvas on masonite. 10-Jun-3 Ritchie, Toronto #165/R est:7000-9000 (C.D 4000)

NETTI, Francesco (1834-1894) Italian
£26000 $43420 €39000 River nymph (65x58cm-26x23in) indis sig. oval prov. 18-Jun-3 Christie's, Kensington #124/R est:3000-5000

NETZER, Remigius (1960-) German
£396 $633 €550 Southern city (40x60cm-16x24in) s. 15-May-3 Neumeister, Munich #323/R

NEUBAUER, Max (19/20th C) Austrian
Works on paper
£881 $1365 €1400 Schwedenplatz bridge with Cafe Siller (30x40cm-12x16in) i. verso Indian ink W/C. 1-Oct-2 Dorotheum, Vienna #244/R

NEUBURGER, Elie (1891-?) Dutch
£625 $1013 €950 View of the Qudeschans, Amsterdam (48x62cm-19x24in) s. 21-Jan-3 Christie's, Amsterdam #295

NEUENSCHWANDER, Albert (1902-1984) Swiss
£655 $1022 €983 Rhein harbour in Basel in summer (65x81cm-26x32in) s.d.51. 8-Nov-2 Dobiaschofsky, Bern #133/R (S.FR 1500)

NEUFF, G (19th C) Austrian
£1268 $2104 €1800 Annunciation (78x67cm-31x26in) s.d.838. 11-Jun-3 Dorotheum, Vienna #454/R est:1000-1500

NEUGEBAUER, Josef (1810-1895) Austrian
£514 $801 €750 Little dog (12x10cm-5x4in) board. 10-Apr-3 Dorotheum, Vienna #9

NEUHAUS, Eugen (1879-1963) American
£1347 $2250 €1953 Study of tress (46x61cm-18x24in) s.i. prov. 17-Jun-3 John Moran, Pasadena #79 est:2000-3000
Works on paper
£1274 $2000 €1911 Idle hour (25x37cm-10x15in) s. gouache prov. 19-Nov-2 Butterfields, San Francisco #8170/R est:2500-3500

NEUHAUS, J F (19th C) ?
£272 $424 €408 The Last Supper (47x72cm-19x28in) i.d.1838 verso. 5-Aug-2 Rasmussen, Vejle #146/R (D.KR 3200)

NEUHAUS, Sigfred (1879-1955) Danish
£344 $558 €499 Interior scene with the artist's wife and children (99x92cm-39x36in) s.d.1914. 24-May-3 Rasmussen, Havnen #2272 (D.KR 3600)

NEUHAUS, Werner (1897-1934) Swiss
£23853 $39835 €34587 St Jakob an der Birs (110x100cm-43x39in) i. verso exhib. 20-Jun-3 Kornfeld, Bern #120/R est:30000 (S.FR 52000)

NEUHOF, Walthere Joseph (1904-1984) Dutch
£1899 $3000 €2849 Landscape near Maastricht (51x71cm-20x28in) s. 3-Apr-3 Boos Gallery, Michigan #237/R est:500-700

NEUHUYS, Albert (1844-1914) Dutch
£1629 $2639 €2362 Interior scene with mother and child at kitchen table (42x60cm-17x24in) s. 25-May-3 Uppsala Auktionskammare, Uppsala #137 est:8000-10000 (S.KR 21000)
Works on paper
£1056 $1701 €1500 Asleep in mother's lap (17x13cm-7x5in) st.sig. W/C prov.exhib. 7-May-3 Vendue Huis, Gravenhage #439/R est:1500-2000

NEUMAN, Robert S (1926-) American
Works on paper
£497 $800 €746 Voyage (33x38cm-13x15in) init.d.1966 mixed media pen ink W/C. 10-May-3 Skinner, Boston #578/R

NEUMANN, Anne (fl.1950s) German
£356 $590 €516 Refugees in the forest (65x85cm-26x33in) s.d.1950 prov. 16-Jun-3 Waddingtons, Toronto #288/R (C.D 800)

NEUMANN, Carl (1833-1891) Danish
£1218 $1912 €1900 Calm seas off coast near Bornholm (40x57cm-16x22in) s.d.1856. 21-Nov-2 Van Ham, Cologne #1816 est:1600
£1277 $2017 €1916 Waves breaking at northern point of Jylland (35x51cm-14x20in) s.i.d.69. 2-Dec-2 Rasmussen, Copenhagen #1410/R est:6000 (D.KR 15000)
£1795 $2818 €2800 Fishermen with boats on shore (37x59cm-15x23in) s.d.1878. 21-Nov-2 Van Ham, Cologne #1817/R est:1600
£3731 $5933 €5597 Skaters on the ice at Kastrup Harbour (50x76cm-20x30in) init.d.1876. 29-Apr-3 Kunsthallen, Copenhagen #515/R est:40000 (D.KR 40000)
£11500 $17940 €17250 View of the Acropolis from the Elissos River (47x66cm-19x26in) indis sig. 15-Oct-2 Sotheby's, London #23/R est:5000-7000

NEUMANN, Ernst (1907-1955) Canadian
£279 $435 €419 Portrait of the artist's father (16x12cm-6x5in) s. cardboard on canvas. 25-Mar-3 Iegor de Saint Hippolyte, Montreal #106 (C.D 650)
Works on paper
£605 $986 €908 Portrait of Alexander Bridt playing the cello (25x19cm-10x7in) mono. ink chl. 12-Feb-3 Iegor de Saint Hippolyte, Montreal #146 (C.D 1500)

NEUMANN, Fritz (1881-?) German
£955 $1490 €1500 Bavarian infantry in battle with French (60x80cm-24x31in) s. 6-Nov-2 Hugo Ruef, Munich #1221/R est:1400

NEUMANN, Johan (1860-1940) Danish
£279 $444 €419 Herring boats in a calm (85x64cm-33x25in) s. 5-Mar-3 Rasmussen, Copenhagen #1991/R (D.KR 3000)
£335 $536 €503 Boats on land (32x53cm-13x21in) s. 16-Mar-3 Hindemae, Ullerslev #387/R (D.KR 3600)
£337 $546 €506 Seascape off Skagen (31x47cm-12x19in) s. 25-Jan-3 Rasmussen, Havnen #2084 (D.KR 3800)
£345 $528 €518 Seascape off Helsingor (44x68cm-17x27in) s. 24-Aug-2 Rasmussen, Havnen #2137 (D.KR 4000)
£526 $853 €763 Sundet off Snekkersten (63x95cm-25x37in) s. 26-May-3 Rasmussen, Copenhagen #1360/R (D.KR 5500)
£559 $888 €839 Sailing vessels off Copenhagen (45x62cm-18x24in) s. 5-Mar-3 Rasmussen, Copenhagen #1987/R (D.KR 6000)
£652 $1036 €978 Gunboats in battle (53x86cm-21x34in) s. 10-Mar-3 Rasmussen, Vejle #431/R (D.KR 7000)
£700 $1112 €1050 Summer day in Sundet, morning (62x95cm-24x37in) s.d.1899. 5-May-3 Rasmussen, Vejle #291/R (D.KR 7500)
£745 $1184 €1118 The shore south of Helsingor (68x100cm-27x39in) s.d.1918. 5-Mar-3 Rasmussen, Copenhagen #1980/R (D.KR 8000)
£775 $1178 €1163 Sundet off Snekkersten (63x95cm-25x37in) s. 27-Aug-2 Rasmussen, Copenhagen #1755/R (D.KR 9000)
£1030 $1627 €1545 Harbour scene (57x82cm-22x32in) s,. 17-Nov-2 Hindemae, Ullerslev #7208/R est:12000-15000 (D.KR 12000)
£1357 $2172 €2036 Seascape with sailing ship off Kronborg (87x116cm-34x46in) s. 13-Jan-3 Rasmussen, Vejle #65/R est:8000-12000 (D.KR 15500)
£3774 $5849 €6000 Sea battle off Helgoland (75x115cm-30x45in) s. 29-Oct-2 Dorotheum, Vienna #143/R est:4500-4800

NEUMANN, Max (1949-) German
£2174 $3565 €3000 Untitled (60x50cm-24x20in) s.d.6.11.86 acrylic. 31-May-3 Villa Grisebach, Berlin #388/R est:3500-4500
Works on paper
£284 $460 €400 Brock, Purcell, Joyce (21x28cm-8x11in) s.i.d.1.4.1982 mixed media. 24-May-3 Van Ham, Cologne #438/R
£316 $500 €500 Untitled (32x23cm-13x9in) s.d.6.3.81 Indian ink brush bodycol pencil chk. 29-Nov-2 Villa Grisebach, Berlin #825/R
£543 $891 €750 Untitled (49x40cm-19x16in) s.d.19. Marz 1991 i. verso W/C graphite. 28-May-3 Lempertz, Koln #304/R

NEUMANN, Robert von (1888-1976) American
Works on paper
£311 $500 €467 Bringing in the catch (43x58cm-17x23in) s. W/C. 20-Jan-3 Schrager Galleries, Milwaukee #1040

NEUMANS, Alphonse (19th C) British
£2600 $4264 €3900 The South Bay, Scarborough by moonlight. By daylight (14x30cm-6x12in) s.d.1875 paper pair. 2-Jun-3 David Duggleby, Scarborough #350/R est:2000-3000

NEUQUELMAN, Lucien (1909-1988) French
£897 $1418 €1400 Bord de la Sioule an Auvergne (33x46cm-13x18in) s.i. panel. 14-Nov-2 Credit Municipal, Paris #59
£943 $1462 €1500 Inside the harbour (37x55cm-15x22in) s. 5-Oct-2 De Vuyst, Lokeren #257/R est:1500-1800
£1307 $2144 €2000 Port de Saint-Tropez (27x41cm-11x16in) s. 7-Feb-3 Oger, Dumont, Paris #119
Works on paper
£377 $600 €566 Villa (27x40cm-11x16in) s.d.1932 W/C. 7-Mar-3 Skinner, Boston #537/R
£612 $973 €900 View of Saint-Tropez (38x50cm-15x20in) s. W/C graphite. 24-Mar-3 Claude Boisgirard, Paris #186

NEUREUTHER, Eugen Napoleon (1806-1882) German
£1026 $1610 €1600 Romantic wooded landscape with fortress (56x47cm-22x19in) s.d.1873. 21-Nov-2 Van Ham, Cologne #1818/R est:2000

NEUREUTHER, Ludwig (fl.1830-1854) German
Works on paper
£2597 $3870 €4000 Kloster Benediktbeuren (28x39cm-11x15in) W/C. 26-Jun-2 Neumeister, Munich #594/R est:3000

NEUSTAEDTER, Chissandra (20th C) Canadian
£221 $347 €332 Before dinner (60x75cm-24x30in) s.i. acrylic board. 25-Nov-2 Hodgins, Calgary #384/R (C.D 550)

NEUSTATTER, Ludwig (1829-1899) German
£4348 $7000 €6522 Children playing (53x41cm-21x16in) s.d.1872 prov. 15-Jan-3 Boos Gallery, Michigan #583/R est:6000-8000
£5280 $8500 €7920 Children playing (53x41cm-21x16in) s.d.1872 prov. 15-Jan-3 Boos Gallery, Michigan #584/R est:6000-8000

NEUTRA, Richard Joseph (1892-1970) American
Works on paper
£710 $1100 €1065 Floor plan (14x25cm-6x10in) ink pencil dr. 8-Dec-2 Wright, Chicago #234/R est:1000-1500
£1161 $1800 €1742 California military academy (18x22cm-7x9in) s. ink dr. 8-Dec-2 Wright, Chicago #233/R est:2000-3000

NEUVILLE, Alphonse Marie de (1835-1885) French
£280 $437 €420 Figures in an Alpine landscape (17x25cm-7x10in) s. panel. 8-Apr-3 Bonhams, Knightsbridge #200/R

NEUVILLE, Bernard (19/20th C) French
£2000 $3200 €3000 Kitchen still life with prawns (48x63cm-19x25in) s. 7-Jan-3 Bonhams, Knightsbridge #182/R est:2000-3000

NEUVONEN, Antti (1937-) Finnish
Sculpture
£1307 $2144 €2000 The twins (59cm-23in) s.d.71 bronze incl.base. 9-Feb-3 Bukowskis, Helsinki #187/R est:2000

NEUWIRTH, Arnulf (20th C) Austrian?
Works on paper
£621 $993 €900 Manhattan (29x40cm-11x16in) s. i. verso pen Indian ink col pen w/C. 11-Mar-3 Dorotheum, Vienna #134/R
£764 $1207 €1100 Acrobats in Eggenburg (31x25cm-12x10in) s.i.d.1972 verso Indian ink collage W/C parchment on masonite. 24-Apr-3 Dorotheum, Vienna #216/R

NEVAN, Eugen (1914-1967) ?
£1134 $1656 €1701 Self portrait (53x51cm-21x20in) painted c.1944. 4-Jun-2 SOGA, Bratislava #84/R est:90000 (SL.K 72000)

NEVELSON, Louise (1899-1988) American
Sculpture
£1852 $3000 €2685 Pendant (10x28x23cm-4x11x9in) blk painted wood metal strips mounted prov. 21-May-3 Doyle, New York #18/R est:2000-3000
£3111 $5164 €4511 Untitled composition (56x17x10cm-22x7x4in) brushed aluminum box painted wood assemblage prov. 10-Jun-3 Ritchie, Toronto #99/R est:2500-4000 (C.D 7000)
£3750 $6000 €5625 Diminishing reflection xix (37x25x11cm-15x10x4in) wood formica mirror in plexiglas box executed 1965 prov. 16-May-3 Phillips, New York #202/R est:7000-10000
£4062 $6500 €5890 Primitive figure (17cm-7in) s.verso wood acrylic base sold with letter. 16-May-3 Skinner, Boston #368/R est:5000-7000
£4194 $6500 €6291 Black cryptic XIII (27x23x10cm-11x9x4in) wood painted black prov. 26-Sep-2 Christie's, Rockefeller NY #709/R est:6000-8000
£4516 $7000 €6774 End of day cryptic XIV (12x23x21cm-5x9x8in) wood panited black executed 1972 prov.exhib. 26-Sep-2 Christie's, Rockefeller NY #705/R est:7000-9000
£5556 $9167 €8000 Untitled (90x59x6cm-35x23x2in) s.d.76 wood paper collage prov.exhib. 1-Jul-3 Artcurial Briest, Paris #493/R est:8000-12000
£9554 $15000 €14331 Untitled (184cm-72in) painted wooden construction exhib. 22-Nov-2 Skinner, Boston #399/R est:30000-50000
£12346 $20000 €17902 Skygate II (102x66x20cm-40x26x8in) blk painted wood prov. 21-May-3 Doyle, New York #17/R est:40000-60000
£24204 $38000 €36306 Night zag VI (32x59cm-13x23in) painted wood prov.exhib. 19-Nov-2 Wright, Chicago #255/R est:4000-50000
£34375 $55000 €51563 Open zag XII (172x157x22cm-68x62x9in) wood painted black executed 1974 prov. 14-May-3 Sotheby's, New York #229/R est:70000-90000
£41139 $65000 €61709 Sky zag V (134x170x21cm-53x67x8in) wall relief wood painted black executed 1974 prov. 14-Nov-2 Christie's, Rockefeller NY #218/R est:70000-90000
£60127 $95000 €90191 Luminous Voyage/mirror image (419x335x25cm-165x132x10in) wall relief wood painted black executed 1969-1977 prov. 14-Nov-2 Christie's, Rockefeller NY #181/R est:90000-120000
Works on paper
£1098 $1800 €1592 Female nude (45x19cm-18x7in) s. pencil exec.c.1930. 5-Jun-3 Swann Galleries, New York #188/R est:1000-1500
£1829 $3000 €2652 Untitled - nude (28x23cm-11x9in) s. pencil prov. 1-Jun-3 Wright, Chicago #107/R est:3000-4000
£2187 $3500 €3281 Untitled (45x31cm-18x12in) s.d.1933 pastel ink prov. 16-May-3 Phillips, New York #203/R est:2000-2500
£5660 $8717 €9000 Collage (88x88cm-35x35in) s.d.1974 spray collage cardboard on panel. 26-Oct-2 Cornette de St.Cyr, Paris #90/R est:12000

NEVIL, E (19th C) British
Works on paper
£680 $1061 €1020 Staithes and Argument Yard, Whitby (39x28cm-15x11in) s.i. W/C pair. 10-Sep-2 David Duggleby, Scarborough #100

NEVILLE, Bernard (?) ?
£904 $1500 €1311 Interior with kittens (30x46cm-12x18in) s. 11-Jun-3 Boos Gallery, Michigan #541/R est:3000-5000

NEVINSON, C R W (1889-1946) British
Prints
£2200 $3432 €3300 Broadway girls (14x17cm-6x7in) s. drypoint printed in brown. 10-Oct-2 Sotheby's, London #73/R est:1000-1500
£2600 $4160 €3900 Industrial scene. etching. 8-Jan-3 Brightwells, Leominster #1091
£3400 $5338 €5100 Assembling parts (47x38cm-19x15in) s. num.78 lithograph. 17-Apr-3 Christie's, Kensington #95/R est:1500-2000
£3600 $5544 €5400 Cursed wood (25x34cm-10x13in) s.d.1918 drypoint. 24-Oct-2 Christie's, Kensington #23/R est:1000-1500

NEVINSON, Christopher Richard Wynne (1889-1946) British
£520 $816 €780 Untitled (35x25cm-14x10in) 15-Apr-3 Bonhams, Chester #820
£2600 $4342 €3770 Summer meadow (40x30cm-16x12in) s. canvasboard. 24-Jun-3 Bonhams, New Bond Street #61/R est:2500-3500
£7500 $12300 €11250 On the fringe of a wood (56x76cm-22x30in) s. painted c.1926 prov.exhib. 6-Jun-3 Christie's, London #17/R est:8000-12000
Prints
£3000 $4650 €4500 Le port (50x39cm-20x15in) s.d.1919 lithograph. 24-Sep-2 Bonhams, New Bond Street #27/R est:3000-5000
£3200 $4960 €4800 Sur la Terrasse (38x49cm-15x19in) s. lithograph executed c.1920. 4-Dec-2 Bonhams, New Bond Street #338/R est:3000-5000
£4400 $6820 €6600 Communist meeting at Tower Bridge (51x35cm-20x14in) s.d.1919 lithograph. 24-Sep-2 Bonhams, New Bond Street #26 est:800-1200
Works on paper
£600 $954 €900 Portrait of Sisley Huddleston (51x35cm-20x14in) s. pencil. 26-Feb-3 Sotheby's, Olympia #170/R
£4200 $6510 €6300 Mediterranean Beach scene (24x35cm-9x14in) s. W/C gouache pencil prov. 4-Dec-2 Sotheby's, London #31/R est:3000-4000

NEWBOLT, John (fl.1868) British
£850 $1394 €1275 In the campagna (32x47cm-13x19in) s.i.d.1840. 29-May-3 Christie's, Kensington #213/R

NEWCOMB, Marie Guise (1865-?) American
£1104 $1800 €1656 Bloodhound head study (51x35cm-20x14in) s. 11-Feb-3 Bonhams & Doyles, New York #207/R est:2000-3000

NEWCOMB, Mary (1922-) British
£5500 $8635 €8250 Stinking mayweed and the fried egg sun (53x54cm-21x21in) s. i.d.October 73 verso oil pencil on board prov. 22-Nov-2 Christie's, London #112/R est:6000-8000
Works on paper
£1200 $1872 €1800 Three dandelions (20x28cm-8x11in) s.i. pencil W/C exhib. 27-Mar-3 Christie's, Kensington #641/R est:600-800

NEWCOMBE, Frederick Clive (1847-1894) British
£250 $380 €375 Cattle grazing in a meadow (23x34cm-9x13in) s. board. 29-Aug-2 Christie's, Kensington #259
£600 $930 €900 Derwent Water from Waterlily Bay (107x178cm-42x70in) s. 26-Sep-2 Lane, Penzance #179

NEWCOMBE, Peter (20th C) British
£550 $919 €798 Evening near Brixworth (29x39cm-11x15in) s.d.1973 i.verso. 17-Jun-3 Gildings, Market Harborough #419
£1225 $1936 €1838 Stormy landscape with river, bridges and church spire (43x53cm-17x21in) s.d.1985. 26-Nov-2 Rogers Jones, Clwyd #175

NEWCOMBE, William John Bertram (1907-1969) Canadian
£550 $875 €825 Usurper. s.i.d.1967 verso. 18-Mar-3 Bonhams, Knightsbridge #163
Works on paper
£1411 $2230 €2117 Market, San Miguel de Allende, Mexico (49x61cm-19x24in) s.d.46 s.i.d.verso W/C prov. 18-Nov-2 Sotheby's, Toronto #47/R est:3000-4000 (C.D 3500)

NEWELL, Hugh (1830-?) British
£701 $1100 €1052 Boys fishing (43x33cm-17x13in) s.d.1893 canvas on board. 10-Dec-2 Doyle, New York #21/R est:2000-3000
Works on paper
£472 $750 €708 Figures in a landscape (38x53cm-15x21in) s. pastel exec.c.1900. 4-May-3 Treadway Gallery, Cincinnati #499/R

NEWEY, Harry Foster (1858-1933) British
£500 $795 €750 On the Alcester Road in winter (61x91cm-24x36in) i.verso. 29-Apr-3 Peter Francis, Wales #1/R

NEWHALL, Kate W (19/20th C) American
£449 $700 €674 Afterglow at Lake Tahoe (13x25cm-5x10in) s.d.1906 panel. 1-Aug-2 Eldred, East Dennis #1075/R

NEWMAN, Anna Mary (?-1930) American
£1761 $2800 €2553 Brookville Indiana (41x51cm-16x20in) 4-May-3 Treadway Gallery, Cincinnati #521/R est:4000-6000
£3459 $5500 €5016 An old heirloom (51x33cm-20x13in) s. painted c.1905. 4-May-3 Treadway Gallery, Cincinnati #457/R est:6000-8000
£10692 $17000 €15503 Love letter (20x16cm-8x6in) s. painted c.1910. 4-May-3 Treadway Gallery, Cincinnati #530/R est:15000-25000

NEWMAN, Arnold (1918-) American
Photographs
£9494 $15000 €14241 Portrait of Arp (34x25cm-13x10in) s. gelatin silver print two. 22-Apr-3 Christie's, Rockefeller NY #174/R est:4000-6000

NEWMAN, Barnett (1905-1970) American
£2215190 $3500000 €3322785 White fire 1 (122x152cm-48x60in) s.d.1954 prov.exhib.lit. 13-Nov-2 Christie's, Rockefeller NY #14/R est:4000000-6000000

Prints
£8805 $14000 €13208 Note VII (15x8cm-6x3in) num.HC 2/2 bears another sig.d.1978 verso etching. 29-Apr-3 Christie's, Rockefeller NY #699/R est:12000-15000
£44025 $70000 €66038 Untitled (76x56cm-30x22in) s.d.num.19/30 lithograph. 2-May-3 Sotheby's, New York #560/R est:40000-50000

NEWMAN, Henry (1843-1921) American
£1709 $2700 €2700 Portrait of young man (54x43cm-21x17in) s. bears i. lit. 29-Nov-2 Schloss Ahlden, Ahlden #1158/R est:2300

NEWMAN, Henry Roderick (c.1833-1918) American
Works on paper
£7325 $11500 €10988 Pagoda in the woods, Nikko, Japan (40x30cm-16x12in) s.i.d.1897 W/C gouache prov. 20-Nov-2 Christie's, Los Angeles #105/R est:15000-25000
£33951 $55000 €50927 Peony garden, Kyoto, Japan (36x51cm-14x20in) s. i.verso W/C on board prov. 21-May-3 Sotheby's, New York #190/R est:40000-60000

NEWMAN, Howard (1943-) American
Sculpture
£1524 $2500 €2210 Winter (36x20x15cm-14x8x6in) bronze prov. 1-Jun-3 Wright, Chicago #263/R est:2000-3000

NEWMAN, John (1952-) American
Sculpture
£1402 $2300 €2033 Shell shock (122x81x46cm-48x32x18in) bronze exhib. 1-Jun-3 Wright, Chicago #344/R est:4000-6000
Works on paper
£3481 $5500 €5222 Untitled (175x175cm-69x69in) chk pastel Chinese ink marker graphite prov. 13-Nov-2 Sotheby's, New York #605/R

NEWMAN, Joseph (1890-1979) American
£822 $1200 €1233 Summer, Cold Spring Harbour (36x46cm-14x18in) s. panel. 10-May-2 Skinner, Boston #233/R est:1000-1500

NEWMAN, Robert Loftin (1827-1912) American
Works on paper
£366 $600 €531 Woman of Samaria (35x28cm-14x11in) chl exec.c.1860. 5-Jun-3 Swann Galleries, New York #189/R

NEWMARCH, G B (19th C) British
£1800 $2988 €2610 Chestnut hunter and spaniel before a stable (66x76cm-26x30in) s. 12-Jun-3 Christie's, Kensington #40/R est:2000-3000

NEWNHAM, Mary (1848-1937) American
£390 $600 €585 Nashotah mission (10x30cm-4x12in) s. painted c.1895. 9-Sep-2 Schrager Galleries, Milwaukee #1017/R

NEWSON, Marc (1963-) Australian
Sculpture
£44586 $70000 €66879 Skoda boutique, Berlin. comprising long rail clothes hooks spheroid desk. 19-Nov-2 Phillips, New York #7/R est:80000-120000

NEWTON, Algernon (1880-1968) British
£900 $1423 €1350 Snow scene (26x36cm-10x14in) s.d.1939 verso board prov. 27-Nov-2 Sotheby's, Olympia #92/R est:1000-1500
£2200 $3630 €3190 Yorkshire landscape (61x91cm-24x36in) 3-Jul-3 Christie's, Kensington #438/R est:1500-2000
£4200 $6930 €6090 Gap in the hedge (61x61cm-24x24in) mono. 3-Jul-3 Christie's, Kensington #441/R est:1200-1800
£5000 $7800 €7500 Outskirts of London (41x30cm-16x12in) mono.d.32 panel exhib. 27-Mar-3 Christie's, Kensington #487/R est:800-1200
£13000 $20670 €19500 Evening sky over church street (92x76cm-36x30in) init. prov. 26-Feb-3 Sotheby's, Olympia #241/R est:3000-5000

NEWTON, G S (1794-1835) British
£290 $464 €421 Reversal (40x30cm-16x12in) 17-May-3 Thomson Roddick & Medcalf, Edinburgh #678/R

NEWTON, Gilbert Stuart (1794-1835) British
Works on paper
£5000 $8000 €7500 Portrait of Thomas Moore (22x17cm-9x7in) i. black white chk. 16-May-3 Sotheby's, London #20/R est:5000-7000

NEWTON, Helmut (1920-) German
Photographs
£2222 $3534 €3200 Viviane F, Hotel Volney (37x25cm-15x10in) s.i.d.1972 verso black white photo. 29-Apr-3 Artcurial Briest, Paris #512/R est:1000-1500
£2273 $3500 €3410 In my studio, Paris (30x44cm-12x17in) s.i.d.1978 photograph. 24-Oct-2 Sotheby's, New York #227/R est:3500-5000
£3165 $5000 €4748 Domestic nude 10, Hollywood (31x46cm-12x18in) s.i.d.1992 num.14/15 gelatin silver print prov. 24-Apr-3 Phillips, New York #205/R est:5000-7000
£3247 $5000 €4871 Woman into man, Paris (58x38cm-23x15in) s.i.d.1979 num.1/10 photograph. 24-Oct-2 Sotheby's, New York #228/R est:5000-7000
£3625 $5800 €5438 Tied up toros, ramatuelie (47x47cm-19x19in) with sig.i.d.1980 silver print. 15-May-3 Swann Galleries, New York #453/R est:6000-9000
£7911 $12500 €12500 Brescia, Italy 11 o'clock, dressed. Brescia, Italy, midday, nude (61x50cm-24x20in) s.i.d.1981 verso silver gelatin lit.exhib. two. 28-Nov-2 Villa Grisebach, Berlin #1340/R est:5000-7000
£12025 $19000 €18038 Panoramic nude, the school teacher, Grand Hotel Villa Serbellon (158x58cm-62x23in) s.i.d.1989 verso gelatin silver print prov.exhib.lit. 24-Apr-3 Phillips, New York #60/R est:20000-30000
£20408 $32449 €30000 Domestic nude II (129x114cm-51x45in) s. num.2/5 verso silver print exhib. 24-Mar-3 Cornette de St.Cyr, Paris #82/R est:40000
£71429 $110000 €107144 Big nude III, Paris (200x120cm-79x47in) gelatin silver print board 3 from edition of 3 prov.lit. 25-Oct-2 Phillips, New York #53/R est:120000-160000

NEWTON, John Edward (19th C) British
Works on paper
£450 $702 €675 Hare coursing (42x68cm-17x27in) s.d.70 pencil W/C bodycol. 27-Mar-3 Christie's, Kensington #90/R

NEWTON, Kenneth (20th C) British
£560 $874 €840 Harlesden Station (61x91cm-24x36in) i.verso board on panel. 15-Oct-2 Canterbury Auctions, UK #125/R

NEWTON, Lilias Torrance (1896-1980) Canadian
£3778 $6196 €5667 Portrait of Wilma (29x23cm-11x9in) s.i.d.1931-32 panel prov. 27-May-3 Sotheby's, Toronto #2/R est:6000-8000 (C.D 8500)

NEWTON, P (20th C) British?
£650 $1021 €975 Chickens and ducks in a farmyard (61x91cm-24x36in) s. 21-Nov-2 Tennants, Leyburn #776

NEWTON, Richard (jnr) (20th C) British?
£1104 $1800 €1656 Muffin (64x74cm-25x29in) s. i.verso. 2-Feb-3 Grogan, Boston #68 est:400-600

NEWTON, Sir William John (1785-1869) British
Miniatures
£1100 $1815 €1595 Edward J Cooper (11cm-4in) s.i.d.1833 rec. prov.exhib. 1-Jul-3 Bonhams, New Bond Street #160/R est:700-900

NEWTON, Sir William John (attrib) (1785-1869) British
Miniatures
£1400 $2184 €2100 Officer of Cavalry or Yeomanry wearing black braided dark blue frock coat (8cm-3in) gilt mount laurel leaf border oval. 5-Nov-2 Bonhams, New Bond Street #128/R est:500-700

NEY, Lancelot (1900-1965) Hungarian
£280 $437 €420 Ile de la Cite (73x60cm-29x24in) s. 10-Apr-3 Tennants, Leyburn #1135
£552 $922 €800 Composition (73x92cm-29x36in) studio st.verso. 10-Jul-3 Artcurial Briest, Paris #317
£1046 $1715 €1600 Composition (97x131cm-38x52in) s. s.d.52 verso. 7-Feb-3 Oger, Dumont, Paris #118
£2096 $3270 €3144 Cote d'azur (129x96cm-51x38in) s.d.52. 11-Apr-3 Kieselbach, Budapest #155/R est:650000-750000 (H.F 750000)

NEY, Lloyd Raymond (1893-1964) American
Works on paper
£305 $500 €442 Mexico (34x49cm-13x19in) W/C pencil crayon. 5-Jun-3 Swann Galleries, New York #190/R

£897 $1400 €1346 Landscape with figures and cat (46x38cm-18x15in) s.d.25 W/C. 18-Sep-2 Alderfer's, Hatfield #388/R

NEYLAND, Harry A (1877-1958) American
£563 $900 €816 Blooming forsythia (30x23cm-12x9in) s. 17-May-3 CRN Auctions, Cambridge #40

NEYN, Pieter de (circle) (1597-1639) Dutch
£5449 $8554 €8500 Horse and cart with figures in village landscape (63x109cm-25x43in) mono.d.1632. 21-Nov-2 Van Ham, Cologne #1397/R est:7000
£12000 $20040 €17400 Travelers halting by a village inn (59x72cm-23x28in) with sig panel. 11-Jul-3 Christie's, Kensington #29/R est:10000-15000

NEYTS, Gillis (1623-1687) Flemish
£10135 $15811 €15000 Mountainous landscape with view of ruined Castle of Huy (43x60cm-17x24in) s. lit. 27-Mar-3 Dorotheum, Vienna #378/R est:15000-20000
Works on paper
£1149 $1792 €1700 Church in landscape (20x31cm-8x12in) s. chk pen ink wash. 27-Mar-3 Christie's, Paris #144/R
£1772 $2800 €2800 Deux chasseurs et un chien pres d 'un arbre (28x20cm-11x8in) pen brown ink prov. 27-Nov-2 Christie's, Paris #17/R est:1500-2400

NGALE, Angelina Pwerle (c.1952-) Australian
£1423 $2248 €2063 Untitled (184x122cm-72x48in) acrylic. 22-Jul-3 Lawson Menzies, Sydney #60/R est:4000-6000 (A.D 3500)

NGAMANDARRA, Terry (c.1952-) Australian
Works on paper
£1571 $2420 €2357 Waterlily dreaming (197x105cm-78x41in) ochre pigments on bark. 8-Sep-2 Sotheby's, Melbourne #49/R est:5000-8000 (A.D 4400)

NGATANE, Ephraim (1938-1971) South African
£448 $700 €672 Figure by a ruin (39x49cm-15x19in) s.indis.d. canvas on board. 11-Nov-2 Stephan Welz, Johannesburg #262 (SA.R 7000)
Works on paper
£833 $1299 €1250 Street scene in a township (52x72cm-20x28in) mixed media. 11-Nov-2 Stephan Welz, Johannesburg #581 (SA.R 13000)
£1290 $2077 €1935 Two penny whistlers (57x70cm-22x28in) s.d.70 mixed media on board. 12-May-3 Stephan Welz, Johannesburg #550/R est:10000-15000 (SA.R 15000)
£2408 $3876 €3612 Pensive seated man (74x60cm-29x24in) s. mixed media on board. 12-May-3 Stephan Welz, Johannesburg #523/R est:12000-18000 (SA.R 28000)

NGUYEN DIN HAM (20th C) Vietnamese
£2866 $4471 €4500 Young dancer and musician (56x41cm-22x16in) s.d.1972 silk. 10-Nov-2 Eric Pillon, Calais #164/R

N'GUYEN PHAN CHANH (1892-1984) Vietnamese
Works on paper
£5891 $9307 €8837 Girl bathing (57x37cm-22x15in) s.d.1936 Indian ink. 27-Nov-2 Falkkloos, Malmo #78003/R est:50000 (S.KR 84000)
£10771 $16587 €16157 Bather (69x49cm-27x19in) s.i.d.1970 ink on silk prov. 27-Oct-2 Christie's, Hong Kong #61/R est:130000-160000 (HK.D 130000)

NGUYEN TU NGHIEM (1922-) Vietnamese
Works on paper
£994 $1531 €1491 Ancient dance (31x43cm-12x17in) init.d.69 gouache prov. 27-Oct-2 Christie's, Hong Kong #54/R est:12000-16000 (HK.D 12000)
£1988 $3062 €2982 Year of the dragon (54x76cm-21x30in) init.d.88 gouache prov. 27-Oct-2 Christie's, Hong Kong #53/R est:24000-34000 (HK.D 24000)

NHLENGETHWA, Sam (1955-) South African
£817 $1315 €1226 Zulu wedding (160x261cm-63x103in) s.d.90. 12-May-3 Stephan Welz, Johannesburg #552 est:6000-9000 (SA.R 9500)

NI TIAN (1855-1919) Chinese
Works on paper
£435 $713 €600 Rider and horse (132x61cm-52x24in) s.d.1894 seals Indian ink col hanging scroll. 30-May-3 Dr Fritz Nagel, Stuttgart #1278/R

NIBBRIG, Ferdinand Hart (1866-1915) Dutch
£2930 $4571 €4600 Farmers doing carpentry (60x42cm-24x17in) s. 6-Nov-2 Vendue Huis, Gravenhage #572/R est:4000-5000
£61644 $96781 €90000 Panoramic view on the Eng, Blaricum (60x90cm-24x35in) s.d.1902. 15-Apr-3 Sotheby's, Amsterdam #211/R est:50000-70000

NIBBS, Richard Henry (1816-1893) British
£600 $960 €900 Hay barges off coast (44x57cm-17x22in) s.d.1856. 13-May-3 Bonhams, Knightsbridge #78/R
£650 $1040 €975 Figures in a market place (91x70cm-36x28in) s. 11-Mar-3 Bonhams, Knightsbridge #78/R
£1500 $2325 €2250 Shoreham harbour (27x45cm-11x18in) i. 6-Dec-2 ELR Auctions, Sheffield #252 est:1500-1800
Works on paper
£400 $608 €600 Bonchurch, Isle of Wight (51x76cm-20x30in) W/C. 15-Aug-2 Bonhams, New Bond Street #230
£440 $722 €660 Towing out of port (48x75cm-19x30in) s.i. W/C. 4-Jun-3 Bonhams, Chester #337
£700 $1106 €1050 Ships sailing into their moorings (43x73cm-17x29in) s.d.86 W/C htd bodycol. 26-Nov-2 Bonhams, Knightsbridge #161/R
£2800 $4536 €4200 Shoreham Harbour (37x70cm-15x28in) s. W/C gouache. 20-May-3 Sotheby's, Olympia #23/R est:1000-2000

NIBBS, Richard Henry (attrib) (1816-1893) British
Works on paper
£250 $408 €375 Village street scene, with church tower beyond (25x36cm-10x14in) W/C htd white. 29-Jan-3 Hampton & Littlewood, Exeter #355

NIBLETT, Gary (1943-) American
£2808 $4100 €4212 Coming home (36x51cm-14x20in) 18-May-2 Altermann Galleries, Santa Fe #179/R
£8333 $13000 €12500 Unloading at the Pueblo (61x91cm-24x36in) 9-Nov-2 Altermann Galleries, Santa Fe #165

NICCOLO DEI CORI, Domenico (14/15th C) Italian
Sculpture
£49677 $78490 €77000 SDaint Francis (60x21x16cm-24x8x6in) polychrome wood lit. 19-Dec-2 Semenzato, Venice #14/R

NICCOLO DI LIBERATORE (c.1430-1502) Italian
£20690 $32897 €30000 Madonna adoring the Child (15x14cm-6x6in) board prov.lit. 9-Mar-3 Semenzato, Venice #48/R

NICCOLO DI TOMMASO (14/15th C) Italian
£46296 $75000 €69444 Madonna and Child (47x37cm-19x15in) tempera gold ground panel. 24-Jan-3 Christie's, Rockefeller NY #21/R est:60000-80000
£110000 $172700 €165000 Madonna and Child with Saints and angels (48x45cm-19x18in) tempera gold ground panel prov.exhib.lit. 16-Dec-2 Sotheby's, London #18/R est:60000-80000

NICHOL, Alfred (19/20th C) British
£3000 $4620 €4500 Cattle watering in a continental landscape (63x100cm-25x39in) s. 5-Sep-2 Christie's, Kensington #119/R est:3000-4000

NICHOLAES, K S (?) ?
£460 $718 €690 Still life with fruit, carpet and glass vase on a ledge (50x40cm-20x16in) indis sig. board. 6-Nov-2 Bonhams, Chester #504

NICHOLAS, Thomas Andrew (1934-) American
Works on paper
£239 $375 €359 Lobster man's shacks (41x56cm-16x22in) s. i.verso W/C. 23-Nov-2 Jackson's, Cedar Falls #77/R
£271 $450 €393 New England marsh (48x71cm-19x28in) s. W/C exhib. 14-Jun-3 Jackson's, Cedar Falls #28/R
£302 $475 €453 Picnic (25x33cm-10x13in) s. i.verso W/C. 23-Nov-2 Jackson's, Cedar Falls #76/R

NICHOLL, Agnes Rose (1842-c.1892) British
Works on paper
£2000 $3260 €3000 Industrious mood (40x21cm-16x8in) s. W/C. 29-Jan-3 Sotheby's, Olympia #140/R est:1000-1500

NICHOLL, Andrew (1804-1886) British
£300 $438 €450 Bridge in Tullymore Forest, Co. Down (25x36cm-10x14in) s. 12-Jun-2 John Ross, Belfast #225

Works on paper

£500 $830 €750 Valetta Harbour, Malta (22x36cm-9x14in) s.i. pencil htd white. 12-Jun-3 Sotheby's, London #185/R

£580 $963 €870 Fishing boats on the coast of Antrim (15x19cm-6x7in) s. W/C. 10-Jun-3 Bonhams, Leeds #90

£600 $954 €900 Foreshore, West of Ireland (35x50cm-14x20in) s. W/C. 5-Mar-3 John Ross, Belfast #151

£633 $981 €1000 Reeded riverbank at sunset with flying ducks (34x48cm-13x19in) s. W/C. 25-Sep-2 James Adam, Dublin #132/R est:1000-2000

£900 $1494 €1350 Sunset on the Indian Ocean (24x33cm-9x13in) i.verso W/C htd stopping out scratching out. 12-Jun-3 Sotheby's, London #192/R

£900 $1494 €1350 Sunrise near the Cape (25x36cm-10x14in) i.verso W/C htd stopping out. 12-Jun-3 Sotheby's, London #193/R

£950 $1387 €1425 Giants causeway, Co. Antrim (25x36cm-10x14in) s. W/C. 12-Jun-2 John Ross, Belfast #70

£950 $1577 €1425 Shipping off Aden in the Red Sea (26x38cm-10x15in) s. i.verso W/C over pencil. 12-Jun-3 Sotheby's, London #183/R

£1000 $1660 €1500 View of Newtownbreda church, Co. Down (18x27cm-7x11in) i. W/C over pencil two. 12-Jun-3 Sotheby's, London #175/R est:800-1200

£1000 $1660 €1500 View of cape Town (27x67cm-11x26in) i. W/C over pencil htd stopping out. 12-Jun-3 Sotheby's, London #184/R est:800-1200

£1000 $1660 €1500 Sunrise, Indian Ocean (25x35cm-10x14in) i.verso W/C htd stopping out. 12-Jun-3 Sotheby's, London #191/R est:1200-1800

£1100 $1826 €1650 Distant view of Glengariff Castle. Glengariff harbour, mountains beyond (18x29cm-7x11in) one i. W/C over pencil two. 12-Jun-3 Sotheby's, London #174/R est:1000-1500

£1200 $1920 €1800 Giant's causeway Co. Antrim (25x31cm-10x12in) bears sig W/C over pencil htd bodycol. 16-May-3 Sotheby's, London #25/R est:1500-2000

£1300 $2015 €1950 Portmullan castle, Co Donegal (28x46cm-11x18in) s. W/C. 2-Oct-2 John Ross, Belfast #129 est:1250-1500

£1400 $2324 €2100 Sunrise on the Indian Ocean (24x35cm-9x14in) i.verso W/C htd stopping out scratching out. 12-Jun-3 Sotheby's, London #190/R est:1200-1800

£2000 $3320 €3000 Dunstaffnage Castle, Argyllshire (34x49cm-13x19in) s. W/C over pencil gum arabic. 12-Jun-3 Sotheby's, London #181/R est:1000-1500

£2000 $3320 €3000 Squall, Indian Ocean (26x36cm-10x14in) one i. W/C four. 12-Jun-3 Sotheby's, London #194/R est:1500-2000

£2025 $3139 €3200 Reeded river bank (23x34cm-9x13in) s. W/C. 25-Sep-2 James Adam, Dublin #131/R est:1200-1600

£2100 $3486 €3150 Studies of fir trees in Kensington Gardens, London (30x39cm-12x15in) i. W/C over pencil two. 12-Jun-3 Sotheby's, London #176/R est:1200-1800

£2200 $3652 €3300 Studies of tress (24x35cm-9x14in) one i. W/C over pencil five. 12-Jun-3 Sotheby's, London #179/R est:800-1200

£2600 $4316 €3900 Yachts on Belfast Lough (26x36cm-10x14in) i.verso W/C over pencil htd stopping out. 12-Jun-3 Sotheby's, London #182/R est:800-1200

£3145 $4906 €5000 View of the river Foyle (32x46cm-13x18in) s. W/C pen ink scratching out. 17-Sep-2 Whyte's, Dublin #117/R est:5000-6000

£3500 $5460 €5250 Scene in the Island of Ceylon (49x71cm-19x28in) s. W/C. 26-Mar-3 Sotheby's, Olympia #33/R est:3000-5000

£4200 $6972 €6300 Irish views. i. W/C over pencil set of 14 various sizes. 12-Jun-3 Sotheby's, London #172/R est:1500-2000

£4400 $7304 €6600 Irish views (20x29cm-8x11in) i.d.1834-61 W/C over pencil set of seven. 12-Jun-3 Sotheby's, London #171/R est:1500-2000

£5000 $8300 €7500 Bank of wild flowers with a shore and sea beyond (28x48cm-11x19in) W/C over pencil htd bodycol. 12-Jun-3 Sotheby's, London #170/R est:2000-3000

£5800 $9164 €8700 Bank of wild flowers (35x51cm-14x20in) s. W/C over pencil htd bodycol stopping out. 28-Nov-2 Sotheby's, London #294/R est:4000-6000

£6000 $9420 €9000 View of loch (35x51cm-14x20in) s. W/C htd gouache. 11-Dec-2 Rupert Toovey, Partridge Green #22/R

£6600 $10956 €9900 Irish coastal scenes. i. W/C over pencil set of 14 various sizes. 12-Jun-3 Sotheby's, London #173/R est:1500-2000

£6800 $11288 €10200 Bank of wild flowers, sea beyond (31x49cm-12x19in) W/C over pencil htd bodycol. 12-Jun-3 Sotheby's, London #169/R est:2500-3500

£7000 $11200 €10500 Poppies, daisies and dandelions at the edge of a field (32x51cm-13x20in) s. pencil W/C gum arabic scratching out. 15-May-3 Christie's, London #25/R est:7000-10000

£7000 $11200 €10500 Dunluce Castle, County Antrim (34x50cm-13x20in) s.i. W/C over pencil htd bodycol stopping out prov. 16-May-3 Sotheby's, London #27/R est:6000-8000

£8176 $12755 €13000 Bank of wild flowers, morning (50x74cm-20x29in) s. W/C htd white scratching out prov. 17-Sep-2 Whyte's, Dublin #114/R est:12000-15000

£10000 $16000 €15000 Poppies, daisises, dandelions and foxgloves (35x52cm-14x20in) s. pencil W/C gum arabic scratching out. 15-May-3 Christie's, London #24/R est:10000-15000

NICHOLLS, Charles Wynne (1831-1903) British

£7500 $12450 €11250 What are the wild waves saying?, Florence and Paul Dombey (56x79cm-22x31in) s.i.verso. 10-Jun-3 Christie's, London #88/R est:7000-10000

Works on paper

£1208 $1945 €1800 Young woman in distress, attended by her maid (25x36cm-10x14in) one s. one init. gouache board pair. 18-Feb-3 Whyte's, Dublin #203/R est:2000-3000

NICHOLLS, John E (fl.1922-1955) British

£1312 $2100 €1902 Iris and gladiola (24x20cm-9x8in) s. board. 16-May-3 Skinner, Boston #165/R est:2000-3000

NICHOLS, Dale (1904-1995) American

£1847 $2900 €2771 Birch in winter (53x94cm-21x37in) s. board. 14-Dec-2 Charlton Hall, Columbia #463 est:1000-2000

£3481 $5500 €5222 Fort Gaines, Dauphin Island, Alabama (36x48cm-14x19in) s.d.55 canvasboard. 5-Apr-3 Neal Auction Company, New Orleans #332/R est:6000-9000

£9434 $15000 €14151 Last log (76x102cm-30x40in) s. 4-Mar-3 Christie's, Rockefeller NY #98/R est:7000-10000

£16456 $26000 €24684 Platte valley farm, Nebraska (76x102cm-30x40in) s.d.1965 prov. 24-Apr-3 Shannon's, Milford #86/R est:6000-8000

£17516 $27500 €26274 Through the clouds (46x61cm-18x24in) s.d.1939 s.verso prov. 19-Nov-2 Butterfields, San Francisco #8070/R est:15000-20000

NICHOLS, H (20th C) American

£1154 $1800 €1731 Fishermen by the cliffs at low tide (56x91cm-22x36in) s. 12-Apr-3 Weschler, Washington #514/R est:500-700

NICHOLS, Henry Hobart (1869-1962) American

£481 $750 €722 After the storm '95 (38x64cm-15x25in) s. 18-Sep-2 Alderfer's, Hatfield #273

£962 $1500 €1443 Sunset over a forest clearing (51x41cm-20x16in) s. 12-Apr-3 Weschler, Washington #566/R est:2000-3000

NICHOLS, Perry (1911-1992) American

£321 $500 €482 Still life with eggplant (51x61cm-20x24in) masonite. 19-Oct-2 David Dike, Dallas #227/R

£1987 $3100 €2981 West Texas farm (30x41cm-12x16in) masonite. 19-Oct-2 David Dike, Dallas #228/R est:2000-3000

£4808 $7500 €7212 Furrows (41x61cm-16x24in) masonite. 19-Oct-2 David Dike, Dallas #243/R est:8000-12000

NICHOLSON, Ben (1894-1982) British

£17000 $28390 €25500 Oct 55 (62x44cm-24x17in) oil gouache wash pencil paper exec 1955 prov. 26-Jun-3 Christie's, London #411/R est:18000-24000

£31739 $49196 €47609 San Gimignano (24x32cm-9x13in) s.verso canvas on board painted 1950 prov. 4-Dec-2 Koller, Zurich #46/R est:50000-75000 (S.FR 73000)

£32000 $50240 €48000 1934 relief (11x11cm-4x4in) s.d.34 verso oil pencil carved board prov. 22-Nov-2 Christie's, London #91/R est:15000-25000

£38000 $62320 €57000 Feb28-53 (22x17cm-9x7in) oil pencil canvas on board painted 1953 prov.exhib.lit. 5-Feb-3 Sotheby's, London #244/R est:35000

£55000 $86350 €82500 Sept - dark relief (61x52cm-24x20in) s. i.d.62 verso carved hardboard prov.exhib. 22-Nov-2 Christie's, London #93/R est:60000-80000

£86538 $135000 €129807 Painting 1943 version 3 - Midget (21x21cm-8x8in) s.i.d.1942 verso board prov.exhib.lit. 6-Nov-2 Sotheby's, New York #243/R est:50000-70000

£124224 $200000 €186336 July 1959 - Londos (155x81cm-61x32in) s. i.d.July 1959 verso board masonite on canavs prov.exhib.lit. 7-May-3 Sotheby's, New York #344/R est:180000-250000

£420000 $701400 €609000 White relief (178x73cm-70x29in) s.d.1936 verso walnut prov.exhib.lit. 24-Jun-3 Christie's, London #72/R est:200000-300000

Sculpture

£9800 $15190 €14700 Offertory box (98cm-39in) wooden stand prov.exhib. 4-Dec-2 Sotheby's, London #40/R est:10000-15000

Works on paper

£4200 $6930 €6090 Greek columns, 1965 (25x13cm-10x5in) init.i.d.1965 gouache. 3-Jul-3 Christie's, Kensington #653/R est:2000-3000

£7000 $11480 €10150 Hubberholme (36x44cm-14x17in) s.i.d.1975 verso pencil wash exhib. 4-Jun-3 Sotheby's, London #76/R est:8000-12000

£18000 $30060 €27000 Bright blue and black (23x18cm-9x7in) s.i.d.April 78 verso pen blk.ink W/C paper on mount prov.exhib. 26-Jun-3 Christie's, London #406/R est:10000-15000

£28000 $46760 €42000 Mountain landscape (37x42cm-15x17in) s.d.68 s.i.d.69 verso W/C pastel wash pencil on mount prov.exhib. 26-Jun-3 Christie's, London #410/R est:10000-15000

£30000 $49200 €45000 Still life 1965 (51x36cm-20x14in) pen ink brush oil gouache paper on board prov.exhib.lit. 5-Feb-3 Sotheby's, London #174/R est:40000

£48000 $80160 €72000 Painting (22x19cm-9x7in) s.d.1937 verso gouache pencil cardboard prov.exhib. 26-Jun-3 Christie's, London #405/R est:12000-18000

£61338 $96914 €92007 Piet Mondrian painting, version 5/12 (38x50cm-15x20in) s.d.1936 verso prov.lit. 1-Apr-3 Rasmussen, Copenhagen #64/R est:300000-500000 (D.KR 660000)

NICHOLSON, Charles H (1900-?) British

Works on paper

£540 $880 €810 Berwick, possibly, with fishing boats moored by the harbour wall (49x74cm-19x29in) s. W/C. 30-Jan-3 Lawrence, Crewkerne #656

NICHOLSON, F (1753-1844) British

£750 $1193 €1125 Portrait group of two children within an interior (59x49cm-23x19in) 19-Mar-3 Rupert Toovey, Partridge Green #107/R

NICHOLSON, Francis (1753-1844) British

Works on paper

£300 $468 €450 Scarborough (25x36cm-10x14in) i. monochrome wash. 20-Sep-2 Richardson & Smith, Whitby #87
£330 $548 €495 Ben Arthur from Arrochar (35x51cm-14x20in) W/C. 10-Jun-3 Bonhams, Leeds #80
£400 $620 €600 Figures by a mill (38x54cm-15x21in) W/C. 3-Dec-2 Sotheby's, Olympia #36/R
£750 $1155 €1125 Tintern Abbey, river landscape with figures (25x39cm-10x15in) W/C. 5-Sep-2 Morphets, Harrogate #368/R
£750 $1230 €1125 Derwentwater, looking towards Lodore (34x50cm-13x20in) i.d.1808 pencil W/C. 4-Feb-3 Bonhams, Leeds #307
£1400 $2240 €2100 Views on the river Nidd opposite the dripping rock of Knaresborough (18x26cm-7x10in) W/C exhib. 11-Mar-3 Bonhams, New Bond Street #19/R est:1000-1500
£2300 $3588 €3450 Windermere, near Low Wood Inn, Cumbria (39x57cm-15x22in) s.d.11 i.verso W/C. 5-Nov-2 Bonhams, New Bond Street #29/R est:2000-3000

NICHOLSON, Francis (attrib) (1753-1844) British

Works on paper

£800 $1248 €1200 Mossdale, Yorkshire. Borrowdale, Cumberland (30x40cm-12x16in) i.verso W/C pair. 10-Sep-2 David Duggleby, Scarborough #88

NICHOLSON, George W (1832-1912) American

£300 $475 €450 Walk in the hills of the Southwest (30x41cm-12x16in) s. 16-Nov-2 New Orleans Auction, New Orleans #1118/R
£414 $650 €621 Arab market scene (30x41cm-12x16in) s. canvas on panel. 23-Nov-2 Pook & Pook, Downington #288
£597 $950 €896 Village street (51x41cm-20x16in) s. painted c.1880. 4-May-3 Treadway Gallery, Cincinnati #461/R
£710 $1100 €1065 Family around a campfire (36x48cm-14x19in) s. board. 2-Nov-2 North East Auctions, Portsmouth #52/R
£6494 $10000 €9741 European harbour (61x107cm-24x42in) s. canvas on board painted c.1880. 8-Sep-2 Treadway Gallery, Cincinnati #526/R est:7000-9000

NICHOLSON, John H (1911-1988) British

Works on paper

£280 $434 €420 Castletown from Hango Hill (28x48cm-11x19in) s. i.verso W/C. 6-Dec-2 Chrystals Auctions, Isle of Man #164
£320 $496 €480 Grenaby Bridge (33x46cm-13x18in) s. i.verso W/C. 6-Dec-2 Chrystals Auctions, Isle of Man #163
£420 $651 €630 Castletown Harbour (25x36cm-10x14in) s. i.verso W/C ink. 6-Dec-2 Chrystals Auctions, Isle of Man #165
£420 $651 €630 S.S Peverill, Douglas Harbour (43x64cm-17x25in) s. col chk. 6-Dec-2 Chrystals Auctions, Isle of Man #272p
£440 $682 €660 Peel Harbour (36x53cm-14x21in) s. W/C. 6-Dec-2 Chrystals Auctions, Isle of Man #152
£450 $698 €675 Regitz thalstrap in Douglas Harbour (36x53cm-14x21in) s. i.verso W/C. 6-Dec-2 Chrystals Auctions, Isle of Man #162
£900 $1395 €1350 Port St. Mary Harbour. Castletown Harbour (28x48cm-11x19in) s. W/C pair. 6-Dec-2 Chrystals Auctions, Isle of Man #161

NICHOLSON, John Millar (fl.1877-1888) British

Works on paper

£650 $1007 €975 Dub, Sulby (8x13cm-3x5in) init.d.1904 W/C. 6-Dec-2 Chrystals Auctions, Isle of Man #257
£1400 $2170 €2100 Douglas Harbour (8x13cm-3x5in) init.d.1904 W/C. 6-Dec-2 Chrystals Auctions, Isle of Man #256 est:200-400

NICHOLSON, Kate (20th C) ?

£300 $468 €450 Shell magic (51x40cm-20x16in) canvasboard prov. 27-Mar-3 Christie's, Kensington #486

Works on paper

£650 $1014 €975 Viking ship III (30x41cm-12x16in) s.i.verso gouache. 16-Oct-2 David Lay, Penzance #258/R
£1200 $1872 €1800 Rock plants (41x43cm-16x17in) s.i.verso mixed media. 16-Oct-2 David Lay, Penzance #279/R est:1000-1500

NICHOLSON, Lillie May (1884-1964) American

£745 $1200 €1118 Fisherman repairing a net or basket (25x18cm-10x7in) init. canvasboard prov. 18-Feb-3 John Moran, Pasadena #161

NICHOLSON, Mabel Pryde (?-c.1920) British

£2400 $3816 €3480 Portrait of Sybil Hart Davis (52x42cm-20x17in) 26-Feb-3 John Bellman, Billingshurst #1824/R est:500-700

NICHOLSON, Peter Walker (1856-1885) British

Works on paper

£5778 $9591 €8378 Burning weeds (63x107cm-25x42in) s.d.84 W/C. 10-Jun-3 Ritchie, Toronto #13/R est:3000-5000 (C.D 13000)

NICHOLSON, Rachel (1934-) British

£600 $936 €900 Striped jug on blue (29x25cm-11x10in) init. d.1980 verso board. 12-Sep-2 Sotheby's, Olympia #78/R

NICHOLSON, Sir William (1872-1949) British

£12500 $20500 €18750 Bonfire in the valley (32x40cm-13x16in) s.d.1922 canvas on board prov. 3-Jun-3 Sotheby's, Olympia #23/R est:5000-7000
£16000 $24800 €24000 Black sanders - the beachcomber (33x40cm-13x16in) init. board prov.exhib.lit. 4-Dec-2 Sotheby's, London #28/R est:6000-8000
£36000 $59040 €52200 La fin de saison, Sirocco (37x46cm-15x18in) init. panel prov.exhib.lit. 4-Jun-3 Sotheby's, London #3/R est:25000-35000
£52000 $81640 €78000 Pink cyclamen in a vase (32x41cm-13x16in) init. s.i.verso canvasboard prov.exhib.lit. 22-Nov-2 Christie's, London #14/R est:40000-60000
£95000 $155800 €137750 White Stone Pond, Hampstead (35x43cm-14x17in) init.d.1909 prov.exhib.lit. 4-Jun-3 Sotheby's, London #11/R est:30000-40000

Works on paper

£850 $1326 €1275 Girl reading at a table (20x25cm-8x10in) i.d.1932 chl col chk. 27-Mar-3 Christie's, Kensington #251/R
£1700 $2788 €2550 Swans and a punt, Chartwell (19x24cm-7x9in) i. chl prov. 3-Jun-3 Sotheby's, Olympia #7/R est:800-1200

NICHOLSON, W (19th C) British

£327 $536 €500 The fish shop (46x84cm-18x33in) s. prov. 9-Feb-3 Bukowskis, Helsinki #438/R

NICHOLSON, Winifred (1893-1981) British

£900 $1440 €1350 Rivulet, brook scene with trees (56x41cm-22x16in) i.verso board. 8-Jan-3 Brightwells, Leominster #1083/R
£9000 $14130 €13500 Melon flowers (48x39cm-19x15in) 25-Nov-2 Cumbria Auction Rooms, UK #344 est:3000-5000
£11800 $18290 €17700 Narcissi in firelight (60x50cm-24x20in) 24-Sep-2 Anderson & Garland, Newcastle #415/R est:7000-9000
£19500 $31980 €29250 Flowers in a green jug (51x61cm-20x24in) canvasboard. 6-Jun-3 Christie's, London #130/R est:5000-7000
£36000 $56160 €54000 Hellibore and hyacinth (63x77cm-25x30in) board prov. 25-Mar-3 Bonhams, New Bond Street #94/R est:25000-30000
£55000 $90200 €79750 Lilies and moonlight (63x76cm-25x30in) s.d.1930 on stretcher prov.exhib.lit. 4-Jun-3 Sotheby's, London #26/R est:25000-35000

Works on paper

£2800 $4368 €4200 Seeds of Trefoil (34x50cm-13x20in) pastel exhib. 17-Oct-2 Lawrence, Crewkerne #437/R est:1200-1800

NICKEL, Hans (1916-1986) German

£345 $548 €500 Peasant with horse drawn plough (60x80cm-24x31in) s. 8-Mar-3 Arnold, Frankfurt #660/R
£769 $1169 €1200 Horse-drawn log wagon (80x120cm-31x47in) s. lit. 11-Jul-2 Allgauer, Kempten #2627/R

NICKEL, Heinz (1919-) German

£449 $696 €700 Ploughing in the Rhon (73x81cm-29x32in) s. 5-Dec-2 Schopman, Hamburg #588

NICKELE, Isaak van (?-1703) Dutch
£1800 $2808 €2700 Interior of Saint Bavo's, Haarlem (30x35cm-12x14in) prov. 10-Apr-3 Christie's, Kensington #105/R est:2000-3000
£3200 $5344 €4640 Interior of Saint Bavo's Haarlem (50x42cm-20x17in) s. indis d. 11-Jul-3 Christie's, Kensington #94/R est:2000-3000
£46763 $74820 €65000 Haarlem: interior of the St Bavo (106x124cm-42x49in) s.d.1693. 13-May-3 Sotheby's, Amsterdam #93/R est:20000-30000

NICKELE, Jacoba Maria van (attrib) (c.1690-?) Dutch
£9790 $14000 €14685 Floral still life with red squirrel and salamander (153x92cm-60x36in) s.d.1743. 22-Jan-3 Doyle, New York #122/R est:18000

NICKERSON, Reginald E (1915-) American
£1975 $3100 €2963 Three masted ship Alfred Gibb (56x91cm-22x36in) s. 26-Jul-2 Eldred, East Dennis #363c/R est:3000-4000

NICKISCH, Alfred (1872-?) German
£516 $805 €820 Stream in early spring (68x81cm-27x32in) s. i. stretcher. 11-Oct-2 Winterberg, Heidelberg #1553

NICKOL, Adolf (1824-1905) German
£1623 $2419 €2500 Toblinosee, southern Tyrol in the morning (63x100cm-25x39in) s. 26-Jun-2 Neumeister, Munich #820/R est:4000
£2177 $3461 €3200 Sheep returning home before the storm (112x94cm-44x37in) s.d.1885. 28-Mar-3 Bolland & Marotz, Bremen #506/R est:3800
£2517 $4002 €3700 Alpine lake landscape with cattle grazing in morning sunshine (59x80cm-23x31in) s. 28-Mar-3 Bolland & Marotz, Bremen #505/R est:4400

NICKOLLS, Joseph (attrib) (18th C) British
£55000 $86900 €82500 View of Ranelagh House and Garden with Chelsea Hospital (91x140cm-36x55in) i. prov. 26-Nov-2 Christie's, London #23/R est:40000-60000

NICKOLLS, Trevor (1949-) Australian
Works on paper
£2107 $3308 €3161 Birds in forest (91x75cm-36x30in) synthetic polymer on linen. 15-Apr-3 Lawson Menzies, Sydney #112/R est:6000-10000 (A.D 5500)
£17073 $26976 €24756 Roving in Thomas Town (152x212cm-60x83in) s. polyvinylacetate on canvas exhib. 22-Jul-3 Lawson Menzies, Sydney #51/R est:35000-45000 (A.D 42000)

NICOL, Erskine (1825-1904) British
£250 $395 €375 Huntsman and hounds (23x28cm-9x11in) panel. 1-Apr-3 Patersons, Paisley #521
£782 $1244 €1150 Reading time (66x51cm-26x20in) s.d.38. 24-Mar-3 Bukowskis, Helsinki #388/R
£3229 $5037 €4844 Summer landscape with figures in flower meadow (69x109cm-27x43in) s.d.89. 5-Aug-2 Rasmussen, Vejle #138/R est:40000-60000 (D.KR 38000)
£3716 $5797 €5500 Pastoral landscape with figures on a bridge (30x32cm-12x13in) s.d.1861 board. 26-Mar-3 James Adam, Dublin #19/R est:5000-7000
£8108 $12649 €12000 Card players (70x121cm-28x48in) s.d.1859. 26-Mar-3 James Adam, Dublin #31/R est:10000-15000
£11000 $17710 €16500 Thunder and turf. Off to Philadelphia (29x20cm-11x8in) s. pair prov. 20-Feb-3 Christie's, London #50/R est:12000
£21000 $32550 €31500 Looking out for a safe investment (109x82cm-43x32in) s.d.1876 prov.exhib. 31-Oct-2 Christie's, London #63/R est:8000-12000
Works on paper
£500 $790 €750 Portrait of a gentleman (24x20cm-9x8in) s.d.85 W/C bodycol. 26-Nov-2 Bonhams, Knightsbridge #168/R
£600 $930 €900 Boy with dog (23x20cm-9x8in) s.d.1851 W/C. 2-Oct-2 John Ross, Belfast #63
£660 $1082 €990 Study of an Irish donkey with wicker panniers (30x41cm-12x16in) s.d.1855 W/C. 4-Feb-3 Lawrences, Bletchingley #1573
£720 $1102 €1080 Salmon spearing (51x32cm-20x13in) s.d.93 W/C scratching out. 22-Aug-2 Bonhams, Edinburgh #948
£1300 $2067 €1950 Wanderer (35x25cm-14x10in) mono.d.1851 pastel. 5-Mar-3 John Ross, Belfast #62 est:1500-2000
£2200 $3520 €3300 Emigrant. Man on a stool (32x25cm-13x10in) one s.d.49 one s.i.d.1849 pencil W/C htd white pair. 15-May-3 Christie's, Kensington #128/R est:1200-1800
£18000 $28800 €27000 Salmon fishing (52x33cm-20x13in) s.d.93 pencil W/C scratching out prov. 15-May-3 Christie's, Kensington #127/R est:2000-3000

NICOL, Erskine (attrib) (1825-1904) British
£260 $400 €390 Portrait of an old man and girl (43x33cm-17x13in) 6-Sep-2 Richardson & Smith, Whitby #461
£1629 $2639 €2362 Children playing (53x43cm-21x17in) bears sig.d.1861. 25-May-3 Uppsala Auktionskammare, Uppsala #93/R est:10000-12000 (S.KR 21000)
Works on paper
£769 $1208 €1200 Sir Walter Scott seated, holding a book (38x31cm-15x12in) W/C htd bodycol. 19-Nov-2 Hamilton Osborne King, Dublin #430/R

NICOL, John Watson (?-1926) British
£3400 $5542 €5100 Court jester (41x57cm-16x22in) s.d.1895. 29-Jan-3 Sotheby's, Olympia #129/R est:1000-1500
£6048 $9556 €9072 Pouting school girl (62x46cm-24x18in) s.d.1875. 18-Nov-2 Waddingtons, Toronto #133/R est:3000-5000 (C.D 15000)
£15000 $24150 €22500 Cause. Effect (25x20cm-10x8in) s.d.1887 pair prov.exhib. 20-Feb-3 Christie's, London #246/R est:8000

NICOLA, Francesco de (1882-?) Italian
£2146 $3391 €3219 Female nude (73x84cm-29x33in) s. 29-Nov-2 Zofingen, Switzerland #2512/R est:2500 (S.FR 5000)

NICOLAIDES, Kimon (1892-1938) American
£466 $750 €699 Portrait, red beads (36x28cm-14x11in) s. i.verso. 18-Feb-3 John Moran, Pasadena #153a

NICOLAISEN, Peter (1894-1989) Danish
£354 $564 €531 Landscape with country road (76x79cm-30x31in) init. 5-May-3 Rasmussen, Vejle #628 (D.KR 3800)
£372 $580 €558 Still life of apples and flowers in vase (76x80cm-30x31in) init. 23-Sep-2 Rasmussen, Vejle #295/R (D.KR 4400)

NICOLAUS, Martin (1870-1945) German
£769 $1169 €1200 Grape gatherers in Kraeherwald with view of Stuttgart (81x101cm-32x40in) s.d.28 lit. 11-Jul-2 Allgauer, Kempten #2629/R

NICOLET, Gabriel Emile Edouard (1856-1921) Swiss
£1500 $2325 €2250 Portrait of Blanche, daughter of Lord Eustace Cecil 1898 (64x51cm-25x20in) s. i.verso. 31-Oct-2 Duke & Son, Dorchester #283/R est:300-600

NICOLINI, Aldo (1934-) Italian
£353 $554 €550 Oasis (70x100cm-28x39in) s.d.1992 verso oil enamel. 23-Nov-2 Meeting Art, Vercelli #315

NICOLL, Archibald Frank (1886-1953) New Zealander
£351 $547 €527 Canterbury road (30x40cm-12x16in) s. canvasboard. 27-Mar-3 International Art Centre, Auckland #158/R (NZ.D 1000)
£456 $712 €684 Canterbury landscape (30x40cm-12x16in) s. board. 27-Mar-3 International Art Centre, Auckland #117/R (NZ.D 1300)
£704 $1126 €1021 Styx Mill Road (21x29cm-8x11in) s. board. 13-May-3 Watson's, Christchurch #3/R (NZ.D 1950)
Works on paper
£379 $606 €550 Akaroa Harbour (24x35cm-9x14in) s. W/C. 13-May-3 Watson's, Christchurch #44/R (NZ.D 1050)

NICOLL, James Craig (1846-1918) American
£2357 $3700 €3536 Shore scene (46x76cm-18x30in) s. 22-Nov-2 Eldred, East Dennis #1104/R est:2000-3000
£3006 $4750 €4509 Near the sea (61x102cm-24x40in) s. s.i.d.1915 verso. 24-Apr-3 Shannon's, Milford #205/R est:4000-6000

NICOLL, James McLaren (1892-1986) Canadian
Works on paper
£267 $437 €387 Imperial oil refineries (24x38cm-9x15in) i.d.1938 pencil. 9-Jun-3 Hodgins, Calgary #49/R (C.D 600)

NICOLL, Marion Florence (1909-1985) Canadian
Works on paper
£267 $437 €387 Corral (31x40cm-12x16in) s. W/C. 9-Jun-3 Hodgins, Calgary #358/R (C.D 600)
£593 $943 €890 Big Horn (25x34cm-10x13in) s.d.1936 W/C. 23-Mar-3 Hodgins, Calgary #49/R est:600-900 (C.D 1400)
£805 $1280 €1208 Canmore (34x39cm-13x15in) s.d.1955 W/C. 23-Mar-3 Hodgins, Calgary #38/R est:800-1200 (C.D 1900)

NICOLLE, Victor Jean (1754-1826) French
Works on paper
£340 $541 €500 Classical temple (12x19cm-5x7in) s. W/C pen. 19-Mar-3 Neumeister, Munich #334

£545 $866 €800 Figures pres d'une eglise (7cm-3in circular) pen ink W/C. 24-Mar-3 Tajan, Paris #95
£545 $866 €800 Paysages (11x15cm-4x6in) pen ink pair. 24-Mar-3 Tajan, Paris #99
£601 $950 €950 Figures devant le Colisee (7cm-3in circular) W/C. 28-Nov-2 Tajan, Paris #85/R
£1013 $1600 €1600 Vue de Castel Gandolfo (16x24cm-6x9in) W/C over pen ink. 28-Nov-2 Tajan, Paris #101/R
£4000 $6280 €6000 View of Rome (20x31cm-8x12in) s. brown ink pen wash W/C. 11-Dec-2 Sotheby's, Olympia #249/R est:2500-3500
£4054 $6324 €6000 Vue du Forum a Rome (21x31cm-8x12in) s. pen ink W/C. 26-Mar-3 Piasa, Paris #61/R
£10577 $16394 €16500 Colonnade du Bernin a Rome (23x40cm-9x16in) W/C pen ink. 4-Dec-2 Piasa, Paris #107/R est:15000

NICOLS, Audley Dean (1875-1941) American
£6051 $9500 €9077 Desert landscape (46x36cm-18x14in) s.d.1914 canvas on board. 10-Dec-2 Doyle, New York #128/R est:4000-6000

NICOLSON, John T (?) British
Works on paper
£500 $775 €750 Harbour, Douglas, Isle of Man (29x67cm-11x26in) W/C. 26-Sep-2 Locke & England, Leamington Spa #283

NICZKY, Edouard (1850-1919) German
£1164 $1816 €1700 Couple in park (27x19cm-11x7in) s.d.1876 panel. 10-Apr-3 Van Ham, Cologne #1449 est:800

NIDZGORSKI, Adam (20th C) ?
Works on paper
£360 $576 €500 Sans titre (29x41cm-11x16in) s. Indian ink wax pastel. 18-May-3 Neret-Minet, Paris #39

NIEDERMAYR, Walter (1952-) German?
Photographs
£3526 $5535 €5500 Mittel Allain III (106x266cm-42x105in) s.i.d.1997 col photograph prov. 11-Dec-2 Artcurial Briest, Paris #780/R

NIEDMANN, August Heinrich (1826-1910) German
£1688 $2516 €2600 Blindman's bluff (75x86cm-30x34in) s. bears i. 26-Jun-2 Neumeister, Munich #824/R est:1200

NIEHAUS, Kaspar (1889-1974) Dutch
£1800 $2790 €2700 Boats on a river in summer (110x140cm-43x55in) mono.d.09. 3-Dec-2 Sotheby's, Olympia #317/R est:2000-3000

NIEKERK, Maurits (1871-1940) Dutch
£397 $648 €600 Brise-lames a la mer du Nord (71x100cm-28x39in) s. 17-Feb-3 Horta, Bruxelles #378

NIELSEN, Amaldus Clarin (1838-1932) Norwegian
£5570 $8912 €8355 Evening in Staveneas (38x64cm-15x25in) s.d.1876. 17-Mar-3 Blomqvist, Oslo #359/R est:80000-100000 (N.KR 64000)
£13055 $20888 €19583 Old farm on the west coast (39x71cm-15x28in) s. canvas on panel. 17-Mar-3 Blomqvist, Oslo #342/R est:100000-120000 (N.KR 150000)
£19284 $31625 €27962 Landscape from Ny Hellesund (34x58cm-13x23in) s. 2-Jun-3 Blomqvist, Oslo #4/R est:250000-300000 (N.KR 210000)

NIELSEN, Carl (1848-1908) Norwegian
£297 $458 €446 Wooded landscape with water (29x39cm-11x15in) s. painted 1872. 28-Oct-2 Blomqvist, Lysaker #1206/R (N.KR 3500)
£354 $577 €531 Norwegian mountain landscape with river (34x53cm-13x21in) s.d.1877. 17-Feb-3 Blomqvist, Lysaker #1142 (N.KR 4000)

NIELSEN, Carl Leopold (1888-1960) Danish
£1537 $2367 €2306 View of Stockholm with Slusebroen (58x83cm-23x33in) s. 4-Sep-2 Kunsthallen, Copenhagen #141/R est:20000 (D.KR 18000)

NIELSEN, Christian Vilhelm (1833-1910) Danish
£426 $672 €639 Woodland lake with rowing boat (39x46cm-15x18in) init.d.1888. 2-Dec-2 Rasmussen, Copenhagen #1810/R (D.KR 5000)
Works on paper
£258 $407 €387 Part of Maria Church, Lubeck (28x22cm-11x9in) init.d.1887 W/C. 17-Nov-2 Hindemae, Ullerslev #7198 (D.KR 3000)

NIELSEN, Eivind (1864-1939) Norwegian
£1131 $1810 €1697 Morning in the kitchen (26x21cm-10x8in) s. canvas on panel. 17-Mar-3 Blomqvist, Oslo #376/R est:10000-12000 (N.KR 13000)
£2855 $4510 €4283 Milkmaids at the outfarm (48x60cm-19x24in) s. 2-Dec-2 Blomqvist, Oslo #377/R est:20000-25000 (N.KR 33000)

NIELSEN, Ejnar (1872-1956) Danish
£293 $454 €440 Landscape from Svolvaer, Lofoten (40x33cm-16x13in) mono.d.1947 exhib. 4-Dec-2 Kunsthallen, Copenhagen #309 (D.KR 3400)
£338 $521 €507 Still life (45x39cm-18x15in) mono.d.1937. 23-Oct-2 Kunsthallen, Copenhagen #9 (D.KR 4000)
£431 $668 €647 The sky above the hills (32x41cm-13x16in) mono. cardboard. 4-Dec-2 Kunsthallen, Copenhagen #310 (D.KR 5000)
£677 $1050 €1016 Insane recluse from the town Scanno in Italy (48x39cm-19x15in) mono.d.1925 prov. 1-Oct-2 Rasmussen, Copenhagen #276/R (D.KR 8000)
£746 $1209 €1119 Interior scene with woman seated at table (24x23cm-9x9in) s.d.1904. 21-May-3 Museumsbygningen, Copenhagen #60 (D.KR 7800)
£1073 $1706 €1610 Mountain landscape, Vjottastjoka, Lapland (44x38cm-17x15in) mono.i.d.09. 5-May-3 Rasmussen, Vejle #635/R (D.KR 11500)

NIELSEN, Jais (1885-1961) Danish
£321 $495 €482 Summer landscape, Bornholm (65x74cm-26x29in) s.d.26. 23-Oct-2 Kunsthallen, Copenhagen #71 (D.KR 3800)
£456 $703 €684 Figure picture (58x65cm-23x26in) s.d.42. 23-Oct-2 Kunsthallen, Copenhagen #106 (D.KR 5400)
£651 $1028 €977 The Judas Kiss (99x80cm-39x31in) s.d.45. 1-Apr-3 Rasmussen, Copenhagen #90/R (D.KR 7000)
£746 $1209 €1082 From the artist's studio, female model in background (135x100cm-53x39in) prov. 24-May-3 Rasmussen, Havnen #4259/R (D.KR 7800)
£1096 $1831 €1589 Orange pickers (102x87cm-40x34in) s.d.23 painted on cloth prov. 17-Jun-3 Rasmussen, Copenhagen #184/R (D.KR 11500)
£1239 $2070 €1797 Bathing girls (128x100cm-50x39in) s.d.48 prov. 17-Jun-3 Rasmussen, Copenhagen #193/R est:8000-10000 (D.KR 13000)
£1693 $2625 €2540 Hilly landscape with figures (80x86cm-31x34in) s. painted c.1917. 1-Oct-2 Rasmussen, Copenhagen #132/R est:12000-15000 (D.KR 20000)
£1920 $3052 €2880 Figure among cliffs by the sea, Bornholm (95x116cm-37x46in) s.d.47. 26-Feb-3 Kunsthallen, Copenhagen #310/R est:20000 (D.KR 21000)
£2967 $4806 €4302 Landscape with horses (49x58cm-19x23in) s.d.17. 24-May-3 Rasmussen, Havnen #4224/R est:5000-7000 (D.KR 31000)
£10161 $15749 €15242 Cafe scene - woman with mask and couple dancing. Figure composition (43x35cm-17x14in) s.d.18 cardboard double-sided. 1-Oct-2 Rasmussen, Copenhagen #131/R est:80000-100000 (D.KR 120000)
£11426 $18167 €17139 Circus picture, Paris (84x72cm-33x28in) s.d.16 compoboard lit. 26-Feb-3 Kunsthallen, Copenhagen #278/R est:150000 (D.KR 125000)
Works on paper
£334 $557 €484 Standing female model seen from behind (31x22cm-12x9in) s.i.d.13 Indian ink. 17-Jun-3 Rasmussen, Copenhagen #186/R (D.KR 3500)

NIELSEN, Jens (1891-1978) Danish
£297 $481 €431 Composition with figures, sunset (85x88cm-33x35in) s. 24-May-3 Rasmussen, Havnen #4139 (D.KR 3100)

NIELSEN, Johan (1835-1912) Norwegian
£2071 $3148 €3107 Harbour for sailing vessels (61x97cm-24x38in) s.d.1880. 31-Aug-2 Grev Wedels Plass, Oslo #68/R est:15000-20000 (N.KR 24000)

NIELSEN, Kai (1882-1924) Danish
Sculpture
£1208 $1909 €1812 Lady at her toilet (25cm-10in) s. pat.bronze lit. 1-Apr-3 Rasmussen, Copenhagen #567/R est:8000 (D.KR 13000)
£1270 $1969 €1905 Old woman (38cm-15in) s.i. brown pat.bronze executed 1917-1919 lit. 1-Oct-2 Rasmussen, Copenhagen #273/R est:15000-20000 (D.KR 15000)
£1766 $2790 €2649 Young girl seated picking her feet (20cm-8in) s. pat.bronze lit. 1-Apr-3 Rasmussen, Copenhagen #566/R est:10000 (D.KR 19000)

NIELSEN, Kay (1886-1957) Danish
£360 $562 €540 Self portrait (39x31cm-15x12in) init.d.04. 11-Nov-2 Rasmussen, Vejle #43/R (D.KR 4200)

NIELSEN, Kehnet (1947-) Danish
£1394 $2203 €2091 Villa Falconieri (100x81cm-39x32in) s.d.1996/97 verso. 1-Apr-3 Rasmussen, Copenhagen #281/R est:15000 (D.KR 15000)
£2196 $3426 €3294 La solitude No.1 (205x70cm-81x28in) s.d.1995 verso exhib.lit. 18-Sep-2 Kunsthallen, Copenhagen #156/R est:30000 (D.KR 26000)
£2670 $4139 €4005 Untitled composition (120x100cm-47x39in) s.d.1999 verso prov. 4-Dec-2 Kunsthallen, Copenhagen #125/R est:25000 (D.KR 31000)
Works on paper
£953 $1592 €1382 Composition (200x149cm-79x59in) s.d.94 gouache. 17-Jun-3 Rasmussen, Copenhagen #49/R (D.KR 10000)
£953 $1592 €1382 Composition (200x149cm-79x59in) s.d.94 gouache. 17-Jun-3 Rasmussen, Copenhagen #52/R (D.KR 10000)
£1430 $2388 €2074 Composition (200x194cm-79x76in) s.d.94 gouache. 17-Jun-3 Rasmussen, Copenhagen #46/R est:20000 (D.KR 15000)

NIELSEN, Knud (1916-) Danish
£255 $398 €383 Hystade - composition (32x26cm-13x10in) s.d.85. 5-Aug-2 Rasmussen, Vejle #326/R (D.KR 3000)
£284 $472 €412 Composition (61x48cm-24x19in) s.d.1961. 12-Jun-3 Kunsthallen, Copenhagen #68 (D.KR 3000)
£306 $477 €459 May - number five (34x38cm-13x15in) s. s.d.71 verso. 5-Aug-2 Rasmussen, Vejle #325/R (D.KR 3600)
£357 $557 €536 Composition (69x48cm-27x19in) s. paper on masonite. 5-Aug-2 Rasmussen, Vejle #321/R (D.KR 4200)
£391 $610 €587 Composition (69x48cm-27x19in) s. paper on masonite. 5-Aug-2 Rasmussen, Vejle #316/R (D.KR 4600)
£418 $661 €627 Stripes (55x46cm-22x18in) s.d.55 verso. 1-Apr-3 Rasmussen, Copenhagen #268/R (D.KR 4500)
£442 $689 €663 Composition (69x48cm-27x19in) s. paper on masonite. 5-Aug-2 Rasmussen, Vejle #331/R (D.KR 5200)
£482 $771 €723 Composition (73x60cm-29x24in) s.d.64. 13-Jan-3 Rasmussen, Vejle #290/R (D.KR 5500)
£606 $964 €909 Folding composition (56x65cm-22x26in) s.d.56 verso prov. 29-Apr-3 Kunsthallen, Copenhagen #32/R (D.KR 6500)
£640 $1017 €960 Composition (87x50cm-34x20in) s.d.52 verso exhib.prov. 26-Feb-3 Kunsthallen, Copenhagen #29/R (D.KR 7000)
£914 $1453 €1371 Okker - composition (47x56cm-19x22in) init.d.54 verso. 26-Feb-3 Kunsthallen, Copenhagen #21/R (D.KR 10000)
£929 $1449 €1394 Composition (90x68cm-35x27in) init.d.48 double-sided. 18-Sep-2 Kunsthallen, Copenhagen #2/R (D.KR 11000)
£931 $1444 €1397 Umage par (65x40cm-26x16in) painted 1991. 1-Oct-2 Rasmussen, Copenhagen #75/R (D.KR 11000)
£952 $1484 €1428 Pessimist in spring mood (65x50cm-26x20in) s. s.d.85 verso. 5-Aug-2 Rasmussen, Vejle #324/R (D.KR 11200)
£979 $1557 €1469 Slippery (55x46cm-22x18in) s.d.73. 29-Apr-3 Kunsthallen, Copenhagen #187/R (D.KR 10500)
£1005 $1599 €1508 Composition (73x60cm-29x24in) s.d.64 exhib.prov. 26-Feb-3 Kunsthallen, Copenhagen #30/R (D.KR 11000)
£1143 $1817 €1715 Black sign (55x46cm-22x18in) s.d.86 verso. 26-Feb-3 Kunsthallen, Copenhagen #219/R est:12000 (D.KR 12500)
£1213 $1928 €1820 Composition (100x81cm-39x32in) s.d.61. 29-Apr-3 Kunsthallen, Copenhagen #100/R est:12000 (D.KR 13000)
£1430 $2388 €2074 Bride and groom (55x46cm-22x18in) s/d/1988 prov. 17-Jun-3 Rasmussen, Copenhagen #36/R est:10000 (D.KR 15000)
£1444 $2253 €2166 Abstract composition (160x115cm-63x45in) s.d.57 verso. 5-Aug-2 Rasmussen, Vejle #322/R est:20000-25000 (D.KR 17000)
£1716 $2866 €2488 Concrete composition (89x122cm-35x48in) s.d.53 verso. 17-Jun-3 Rasmussen, Copenhagen #30/R est:30000 (D.KR 18000)
£1778 $2756 €2667 Aggressive bird (81x65cm-32x26in) s. s.d.91 verso. 1-Oct-2 Rasmussen, Copenhagen #76/R est:8000-12000 (D.KR 21000)
£2383 $3980 €3455 Bolero (97x30cm-38x12in) s. prov. 17-Jun-3 Rasmussen, Copenhagen #5/R est:30000-40000 (D.KR 25000)
£2449 $3821 €3674 Composition (127x127cm-50x50in) plywood double-sided exhib.lit. painted 1946. 18-Sep-2 Kunsthallen, Copenhagen #62/R est:30000 (D.KR 29000)
£3125 $4875 €4688 Blue composition (130x162cm-51x64in) s.d.86. 18-Sep-2 Kunsthallen, Copenhagen #204/R est:40000 (D.KR 37000)
£5303 $8803 €7689 Ekely V (220x160cm-87x63in) s.d.1996 verso. 12-Jun-3 Kunsthallen, Copenhagen #70/R est:40000 (D.KR 56000)

NIELSEN, Marius (1882-1971) Danish?
£270 $435 €405 Interior scene with woman sewing (40x41cm-16x16in) mono. 22-Feb-3 Rasmussen, Havnen #2042 (D.KR 3000)

NIELSEN, Palle (20th C) Danish
Works on paper
£1140 $1779 €1710 Necropolis (33x42cm-13x17in) d.8.7.67 gouache Indian ink exhib. 18-Sep-2 Kunsthallen, Copenhagen #221/R est:8000 (D.KR 13500)

NIELSEN, Peter (1873-1965) American/Danish
£385 $600 €578 Ducks on a river (41x51cm-16x20in) s. 20-Sep-2 Freeman, Philadelphia #122/R
£621 $1000 €932 River landscape with ducks (41x51cm-16x20in) s. canvas on board. 18-Feb-3 John Moran, Pasadena #49

NIELSEN, Poul (1920-1998) Danish
£254 $391 €381 Girl at window (50x60cm-20x24in) mono. 26-Oct-2 Rasmussen, Havnen #2019 (D.KR 3000)
£326 $518 €489 Mother and child in the bathroom (68x91cm-27x36in) mono. 10-Mar-3 Rasmussen, Vejle #630/R (D.KR 3500)
£346 $560 €519 Skaters in the park (90x96cm 35x38in) mono.d.54. 25-Jan-3 Rasmussen, Havnen #2195 (D.KR 3900)
£356 $551 €534 Seated girl seen from behind (60x50cm-24x20in) mono.d.59. 1-Oct-2 Rasmussen, Copenhagen #378 (D.KR 4200)
£405 $653 €608 Interior scene with young girl (60x50cm-24x20in) mono. 22-Feb-3 Rasmussen, Havnen #2232/R (D.KR 4500)
£508 $787 €762 Girl looking out of window (60x70cm-24x28in) mono.d.62. 1-Oct-2 Rasmussen, Copenhagen #334a (D.KR 6000)
£1045 $1661 €1568 Interior scene with girl (70x100cm-28x39in) init. 5-May-3 Rasmussen, Vejle #6/R (D.KR 11200)

NIELSEN, Ville Jais (1886-1949) Danish
£728 $1128 €1150 Vence (80x66cm-31x26in) s. s.i.d.verso. 28-Sep-2 Cornette de St.Cyr, Paris #178/R
£1859 $2937 €2789 Still life of peace lily, bowls and oranges (85x94cm-33x37in) s. painted c.1937. 1-Apr-3 Rasmussen, Copenhagen #76/R est:20000-25000 (D.KR 20000)

NIELSSEN, Clemence (19/20th C) German
£1090 $1656 €1700 Young dogs feuding with lobsters (39x49cm-15x19in) s.d.1889 lit. 11-Jul-2 Allgauer, Kempten #2634/R

NIEMANN, E H (fl.1863-1867) British
£800 $1272 €1200 Tintern Abbey (51x76cm-20x30in) s. 19-Mar-3 John Nicholson, Haslemere #1156

NIEMANN, E J (1813-1876) British
£5200 $8424 €7540 Wooden walls walks of Old England (62x113cm-24x44in) i. 21-May-3 Edgar Horn, Eastbourne #248/R est:1000-1500

NIEMANN, Edmund John (1813-1876) British
£299 $466 €449 Barden Tower (33x51cm-13x20in) s. painted 1875. 23-Sep-2 Blomqvist, Lysaker #1170 (N.KR 3500)
£360 $576 €540 On the moors, Yorks (17x31cm-7x12in) s. board. 13-May-3 Bonhams, Knightsbridge #131/R
£470 $743 €682 Guildford, Surrey (18x36cm-7x14in) s.d.62. 23-Jul-3 Mallams, Oxford #307/R
£1500 $2355 €2250 Extensive wooded lake landscape (71x111cm-28x44in) 15-Apr-3 Bonhams, Knowle #110 est:1500-2500
£1500 $2340 €2250 On the coast at low tide (11x16cm-4x6in) s. 26-Mar-3 Hamptons Fine Art, Godalming #113 est:300-500
£2400 $3936 €3600 Windsor (51x76cm-20x30in) s. 29-May-3 Christie's, Kensington #149/R est:2000-3000
£2500 $4100 €3750 Filey, north Yorkshire (63x112cm-25x44in) s.i.d.71. 29-May-3 Christie's, Kensington #152/R est:3000-5000
£3000 $4710 €4500 View of Richmond across the Swale (54x46cm-21x18in) s.i.d.67. 21-Nov-2 Tennants, Leyburn #796/R est:2500-3500

NIEMANN, Edmund John (attrib) (1813-1876) British
£445 $650 €668 River near Windsor (50x76cm-20x30in) 10-May-2 Skinner, Boston #9/R

NIEMANN, Edward H (fl.1863-1887) British
£300 $462 €450 On the moors, Yorkshire (17x30cm-7x12in) s. board prov. 5-Sep-2 Christie's, Kensington #172/R
£350 $546 €525 Extensive landscape with ruined castle, figures and sheep (35x61cm-14x24in) s. 18-Sep-2 Dreweatt Neate, Newbury #102
£400 $664 €580 On the River Severn (51x76cm-20x30in) s. 16-Jun-3 Waddingtons, Toronto #117/R est:1000-1500 (C.D 900)
£550 $897 €798 River Wharfe (51x77cm-20x30in) s. 16-Jul-3 Sotheby's, Olympia #62/R
£600 $930 €900 Saw mill (36x58cm-14x23in) s. 26-Sep-2 Mellors & Kirk, Nottingham #740/R
£800 $1280 €1200 Near Birk Crags, Yorkshire (54x95cm-21x37in) s. s.i.on overlap. 15-May-3 Lawrence, Crewkerne #983/R
£1000 $1630 €1450 Woking common, Surrey (51x76cm-20x30in) s. 16-Jul-3 Sotheby's, Olympia #88/R est:1000-1500
£2200 $3432 €3300 View over a valley (51x76cm-20x30in) s. 26-Mar-3 Sotheby's, Olympia #60/R est:1200-1800

NIEMEYER, John Henry (1839-1932) American
£556 $890 €834 Summer landscape (36x41cm-14x16in) s.d. 11-Jan-3 James Julia, Fairfield #592 est:900-1200

NIEMEYER-HOLSTEIN, Otto (1896-?) German
£641 $994 €1000 Study of a nude lying down (45x70cm-18x28in) i.verso masonite. 7-Dec-2 Dannenberg, Berlin #714/R
£1509 $2325 €2400 Woodland lake (27x41cm-11x16in) mono. canvas on masonite. 26-Oct-2 Dr Lehr, Berlin #395/R est:2800

Works on paper

£755 $1162 €1200 Fishing boat on beach (36x47cm-14x19in) s. W/C over pencil board. 26-Oct-2 Dr Lehr, Berlin #396/R

NIERMAN, Leonardo (1932-) Mexican

£288 $450 €432 Pajaro de Fuego (13x25cm-5x10in) s.d.63 masonite. 12-Oct-2 Neal Auction Company, New Orleans #1378
£398 $650 €597 Untitled, abstract (60x40cm-24x16in) s. masonite. 16-Feb-3 Butterfields, San Francisco #2128
£449 $700 €674 Ciudad dorado (58x79cm-23x31in) masonite. 22-Sep-2 Susanin's, Chicago #5036/R
£503 $800 €755 Abstract (81x60cm-32x24in) s. masonite. 7-Mar-3 Skinner, Boston #634/R
£566 $900 €849 Magic flame (60x80cm-24x31in) s.d.67 i.verso masonite. 7-Mar-3 Skinner, Boston #636/R
£759 $1200 €1139 Cityscape (81x61cm-32x24in) s. board. 1-Dec-2 Susanin's, Chicago #5183/R
£822 $1250 €1233 Abstract composition (41x58cm-16x23in) s.d.68 board. 18-Aug-2 Jeffery Burchard, Florida #139a/R
£921 $1400 €1382 Abstract composition (58x41cm-23x16in) s.d.68 board. 18-Aug-2 Jeffery Burchard, Florida #139/R
£1282 $2000 €1923 Bird in flight (175x105cm-69x41in) s.d.59 masonite. 14-Sep-2 Weschler, Washington #660/R est:3000-5000
£1538 $2400 €2307 Magic flight (122x89cm-48x35in) s.i.verso masonite. 22-Sep-2 Susanin's, Chicago #5008/R est:3000-5000
£2564 $4000 €3846 Enchanted landscape. s. board. 22-Sep-2 Susanin's, Chicago #5067/R est:4000-6000

Works on paper

£269 $425 €404 Abstract (30x33cm-12x13in) s. W/C. 1-Dec-2 Susanin's, Chicago #5182/R

NIESSMANN, Adolf (1899-?) German

Works on paper

£472 $736 €750 Lovers in evening market (55x77cm-22x30in) s.d.31 W/C tempera. 21-Sep-2 Bolland & Marotz, Bremen #388/R

NIESTLE, Jean Bloe (1884-1942) German

Works on paper

£5072 $8319 €7000 Crows in treetops (18x37cm-7x15in) s.d.1915 gouache prov.exhib. 29-May-3 Lempertz, Koln #828/R est:7000-8000

NIETO URIBARRI, Enrique (1890-1963) Spanish

£1548 $2446 €2400 Algorta beach (12x19cm-5x7in) s. board. 18-Dec-2 Ansorena, Madrid #62/R est:2000

NIETO, Anselmo Miguel (1881-1964) Spanish

£1558 $2275 €2400 Portrait of woman (45x38cm-18x15in) s. 17-Jun-2 Ansorena, Madrid #330/R
£3205 $5064 €5000 Woman sowing (54x65cm-21x26in) s.d.1937. 14-Nov-2 Arte, Seville #398/R

NIETO, John W (1936-) American

£2564 $4000 €3846 Shrouded Indian (152x122cm-60x48in) s. i.verso acrylic prov. 9-Nov-2 Santa Fe Art, Santa Fe #249/R est:5000-7000

NIETO, Rodolfo (1936-1988) Mexican

Works on paper

£989 $1583 €1434 Panda (46x36cm-18x14in) s.d.2-67 chl. 15-May-3 Louis Morton, Mexico #18/R est:18000-30000 (M.P 16000)

NIETSCHE, Paul (fl.1930s) British

£750 $1200 €1125 Impressionist landscape (51x61cm-20x24in) s. board. 18-May-3 Jeffery Burchard, Florida #35/R
£2500 $3875 €3750 Still life, rose (61x51cm-24x20in) s.d.26. 2-Oct-2 John Ross, Belfast #91 est:1500-2000
£2899 $4754 €4000 Tree reflection (61x50cm-24x20in) s. board. 28-May-3 Bonhams & James Adam, Dublin #118/R est:4000-5000

NIEULANDT, Adriaen van I (1587-1658) Flemish

£6369 $9936 €10000 Amaryllis crowing Mirtillo (52x67cm-20x26in) s.d.1648 panel prov. 5-Nov-2 Sotheby's, Amsterdam #57/R est:12000-18000
£8562 $13356 €12500 Suzanne and the elderly (66x85cm-26x33in) board. 8-Apr-3 Ansorena, Madrid #78/R

NIEULANDT, Adriaen van I (attrib) (1587-1658) Flemish

£6500 $10205 €9750 Meeting of Abraham and Melchizedek (25x35cm-10x14in) panel. 10-Dec-2 Bonhams, New Bond Street #273/R est:3000-5000

NIEULANDT, Willem van (16/17th C) Flemish

£22973 $35838 €34000 Triumph of war. Triumph of peace (54x74cm-21x29in) s.d.1627 panel two. 27-Mar-3 Dorotheum, Vienna #301/R est:30000-40000

NIEULANDT, Willem van II (1584-1635) Flemish

£3226 $5097 €5000 Enee et Anchise fuyant Troie (28x34cm-11x13in) copper. 18-Dec-2 Tajan, Paris #10/R
£33951 $55000 €50927 Roman forum with drovers and watercarriers on a path in the foreground (93x123cm-37x48in) s. indis d. panel prov. 24-Jan-3 Christie's, Rockefeller NY #18/R est:40000-60000

NIEUWAEL, Jan van (fl.1620-1661) Dutch

£1829 $3000 €2652 Portrait of a lady, holding a bouquet of narcissi (75x60cm-30x24in) prov.exhib. 4-Jun-3 Christie's, Rockefeller NY #162/R est:5000-7000

NIEUWENHOVEN, Willem van (1879-1979) Dutch

£1210 $1888 €1900 Shoemaker in his workshop (39x29cm-15x11in) s. 5-Nov-2 Vendu Notarishuis, Rotterdam #110/R est:1000-1500
£4605 $7461 €7000 Old sailor, Volendam (71x51cm-28x20in) s. 21-Jan-3 Christie's, Amsterdam #313/R est:3000-5000

NIEUWERKERKE, Comte de Alfred-Emilien (1811-1892) French

Sculpture

£2885 $4529 €4500 Portrait de la Duchesse de Cadore (60x29x27cm-24x11x11in) s.d.1860 white marble. 10-Dec-2 Renaud, Paris #111/R
£3500 $5460 €5250 Combat of the Duke of Clarence and Garin de Fontaine (26x30cm-10x12in) s.st.f.Susse brown pat bronze and 2 bronzes by C E de Beaumont. 5-Nov-2 Sotheby's, London #139/R est:4000-6000

NIEZKY, Eduard (?) ?

£2300 $3565 €3450 Young lady on a balcony (36x25cm-14x10in) s. panel. 3-Dec-2 Sworder & Son, Bishops Stortford #931/R est:2000-3000

NIFTERIK, Gustaaf van (1886-1954) Dutch

£318 $497 €500 Cows in the meadow (32x45cm-13x18in) s. 6-Nov-2 Vendue Huis, Gravenhage #29/R

NIGG, Joseph (1782-1863) Austrian

£3500 $5495 €5250 Assorted summer flowers in a vase on a stone ledge (65x53cm-26x21in) s. 21-Nov-2 Christie's, Kensington #78/R est:4000-6000
£10127 $16000 €16000 Large arrangement of flowers including crown imperials, tulips and roses (81x65cm-32x26in) s. 28-Nov-2 Dorotheum, Vienna #68/R est:16000-18000
£10127 $16000 €16000 Large flower arrangement including roses, tulips, peaches and grapes (81x65cm-32x26in) s. 28-Nov-2 Dorotheum, Vienna #69/R est:12000-14000

NIGHTINGALE, Basil (1864-1940) British

Works on paper

£310 $477 €465 Hunting scene (36x48cm-14x19in) s.d.1906 W/C. 6-Sep-2 Biddle & Webb, Birmingham #79
£400 $624 €600 Limbs with no check to their freedom of stride (46x67cm-18x26in) s.i.d.1917 pastel. 10-Oct-2 Greenslade Hunt, Taunton #549
£720 $1116 €1080 Musical honours (50x44cm-20x17in) s.i.d.1918 W/C htd white. 1-Oct-2 Gildings, Market Harborough #289/R
£920 $1435 €1380 Grief (43x58cm-17x23in) s.i.d.1908 W/C bodycol. 10-Oct-2 Greenslade Hunt, Taunton #548/R
£962 $1510 €1500 Horse (33x44cm-13x17in) s.i.d.1902 chl dr. 19-Nov-2 Castellana, Madrid #483/R
£1500 $2385 €2250 With the quorn (43x61cm-17x24in) s.d.1896 pastel bodycol. 30-Apr-3 Goldings, Lincolnshire #127/R
£3000 $4680 €4500 Frank Gillard of the Belvoir on grey Bob with the celebrated hounds Gamble, Norminal (54x75cm-21x30in) s.i.d.1891 W/C. 5-Nov-2 Bonhams, New Bond Street #144/R est:2000-3000
£4200 $6678 €6300 Young girl holding bouquet to a foal by a country stile (54x74cm-21x29in) s.i. chl W/C. 1-May-3 Locke & England, Leamington Spa #181/R est:1000-1500

NIGHTINGALE, Leonard Charles (19/20th C) British

£645 $1000 €968 Uniformed officer standing in a field (51x25cm-20x10in) s.d.1879. 7-Dec-2 Selkirks, St. Louis #119 est:3000-4000
£28000 $44240 €42000 Under the blossom (88x142cm-35x56in) init. exhib. 26-Nov-2 Christie's, London #156/R est:20000-30000

NIGHTINGALE, R (1815-1895) British

Works on paper

£250 $403 €375 Barn and farmyard probably Essex (32x46cm-13x18in) s.d.1885 pencil W/C. 18-Feb-3 Rowley Fine Art, Newmarket #329/R

NIGHTINGALE, Robert (1815-1895) British
£320 $499 €480 In a field (33x44cm-13x17in) s.d.1894 panel. 26-Mar-3 Hamptons Fine Art, Godalming #120
£1600 $2464 €2400 Beeleigh Abbey, Maldon (38x55cm-15x22in) 5-Sep-2 Christie's, Kensington #218/R est:2000-3000

NIGRO, Jan (1920-) ?
Works on paper
£1111 $1733 €1667 Two woman and a cat in an interior (84x62cm-33x24in) s.d.1989 mixed media. 8-Apr-3 Peter Webb, Auckland #174/R est:3000-5000 (NZ.D 3200)

NIGRO, Mario (1917-1992) Italian
£897 $1418 €1400 Composition (35x46cm-14x18in) s.d.1953 tempera paper. 15-Nov-2 Farsetti, Prato #275/R
£1923 $2981 €3000 Untitled (91x64cm-36x25in) s.d.1956. 4-Dec-2 Finarte, Milan #345
£1935 $3058 €3000 Seven reds (100x62cm-39x24in) s.i.d.1971 prov. 18-Dec-2 Christie's, Rome #198/R
£2500 $3975 €3600 Net (32x9cm-13x4in) s.d.1967 verso board. 1-May-3 Meeting Art, Vercelli #229
£2532 $3949 €4000 Composition (75x52cm-30x20in) s.d.1956 acrylic paper. 19-Oct-2 Semenzato, Venice #143/R
£2721 $4327 €4000 Untitled (70x100cm-28x39in) s. 1-Mar-3 Meeting Art, Vercelli #354
£6456 $10071 €10200 Composition (60x80cm-24x31in) s.d.1958 acrylic. 19-Oct-2 Semenzato, Venice #155/R
£12903 $20387 €20000 Total space (120x120cm-47x47in) s.i.d.1954 lit. 18-Dec-2 Christie's, Rome #303/R
Works on paper
£405 $632 €600 Untitled (17x24cm-7x9in) mixed media paper on canvas. 26-Mar-3 Finarte Semenzato, Milan #124/R
£1135 $1838 €1600 Composition (34x46cm-13x18in) s. crayon prov.exhib. 26-May-3 Christie's, Milan #105/R est:1500-2000
£2083 $3312 €3000 Vibrations (70x50cm-28x20in) s.d.1961 pastel paper on canvas. 1-May-3 Meeting Art, Vercelli #476

NIJLAND, Dirk (1881-1955) Dutch
£1844 $2987 €2600 Pastoral garden in Rhone (45x60cm-18x24in) mono.d.12 prov. 26-May-3 Glerum, Amsterdam #23/R est:2500-3000
£2303 $3730 €3500 Wilgenlaantje - Willow Lane (30x32cm-12x13in) init.d.41 prov. 21-Jan-3 Christie's, Amsterdam #378/R est:2500-3500
Works on paper
£395 $639 €600 Boerenbegrafenis - peasant's funeral (26x34cm-10x13in) init. black chk prov. 21-Jan-3 Christie's, Amsterdam #379

NIJMEGEN, Dionys van (1705-1789) Dutch
Works on paper
£406 $650 €609 Courting couple at a window (34x23cm-13x9in) gray brown wash over black chk. 14-May-3 Doyle, New York #11

NIKEL, Lea (1918-) Israeli
£1646 $2600 €2469 Untitled (76x56cm-30x22in) s. oil mixed media on paper painted c.1990. 27-Apr-3 Sotheby's, Tel Aviv #89/R est:2200-2800
£1772 $2800 €2658 Untitled (64x49cm-25x19in) s.d.1993 oil mixed media on paper. 27-Apr-3 Sotheby's, Tel Aviv #88/R est:2200-2800
£6962 $11000 €10443 Composition (65x54cm-26x21in) s.d.1962. 27-Apr-3 Sotheby's, Tel Aviv #68/R est:10000-15000

NIKIFOR (c.1893-1968) Polish
Works on paper
£961 $1499 €1442 City with onion dome church (35x47cm-14x19in) i. gouache exhib. 6-Nov-2 Dobiaschofsky, Bern #3572/R (S.FR 2200)

NIKITIN, A (19th C) Russian
Works on paper
£327 $536 €500 Italian woman (29x24cm-11x9in) s.i.d.1858 W/C gouache. 9-Feb-3 Bukowskis, Helsinki #423/R

NIKODEM, Artur (1870-1940) Austrian
£5652 $8817 €8478 Landscape with trees (75x66cm-30x26in) s.d.1912 exhib.prov. 16-Sep-2 Philippe Schuler, Zurich #3517/R est:4000-6000 (S.FR 13000)
Works on paper
£2222 $3533 €3200 Witches (26x28cm-10x11in) i. verso mixed media. 29-Apr-3 Wiener Kunst Auktionen, Vienna #636/R est:2000-4000

NIKRITIN, Solomon (1898-1965) Russian
£8000 $12960 €12000 Classical figures (32x38cm-13x15in) canvas on board. 21-May-3 Sotheby's, London #175/R est:8000-12000

NIKUTOWSKI, Erich (1872-1921) German
£586 $926 €850 Rudesheim am Rhein in the evening (59x83cm-23x33in) s. 5-Apr-3 Hans Stahl, Hamburg #37/R

NILOUSS, Piotr (1869-1943) Russian
£816 $1298 €1200 Les toits de l'hotel de ville (18x23cm-7x9in) panel. 3-Mar-3 Claude Boisgirard, Paris #74
£1923 $3000 €2885 Untitled, Paris street scene (65x91cm-26x36in) s.indis.d. prov. 14-Oct-2 Butterfields, San Francisco #2001/R est:3000-5000

NILSON, Friedrich Christoph (1811-1879) German
Works on paper
£580 $900 €870 Male nude (45x39cm-18x15in) s.d.28.6.33 pencil. 29-Oct-2 Sotheby's, New York #102/R est:800-1200

NILSON, Johann Jacob (attrib) (1756-1826) German
£485 $707 €728 Rococo woman beneath garland held by angels (15x12cm-6x5in) grisaille prov. 17-Jun-2 Philippe Schuler, Zurich #4811/R (S.FR 1100)

NILSON, Karl Gustaf (1942-) Swedish
£532 $824 €798 Composition in green and yellow with white background (110x116cm-43x46in) s.d.1963 verso. 8-Dec-2 Uppsala Auktionskammare, Uppsala #279/R (S.KR 7500)
£596 $929 €894 Twilight (225x26cm-89x10in) s.d.1974 exhib. 6-Nov-2 AB Stockholms Auktionsverk #699/R (S.KR 8500)
£1749 $2763 €2624 Untitled (63x189cm-25x74in) s.d.1997 panel. 28-Apr-3 Bukowskis, Stockholm #276/R est:12000-15000 (S.KR 23000)
£2873 $4482 €4310 Se-Sam I (99x76cm-39x30in) s.d.1965 prov.exhib.lit. 6-Nov-2 AB Stockholms Auktionsverk #611/R est:35000-40000 (S.KR 41000)

NILSON, Severin (1846-1918) Swedish
£317 $489 €476 Farm in landscape (33x59cm-13x23in) s. 27-Oct-2 Anders Antik, Landskrona #300/R (S.KR 4600)
£412 $626 €618 Girl on road (40x70cm-16x28in) s. 16-Aug-2 Lilla Bukowskis, Stockholm #408 (S.KR 6000)
£461 $715 €692 Lake landscape with cottage (40x70cm-16x28in) s.d.1915. 8-Dec-2 Uppsala Auktionskammare, Uppsala #136/R (S.KR 6500)
£463 $769 €671 Boy fishing (24x16cm-9x6in) s. panel. 16-Jun-3 Lilla Bukowskis, Stockholm #66 (S.KR 6000)
£480 $753 €720 Country idyll (42x65cm-17x26in) s. 16-Dec-2 Lilla Bukowskis, Stockholm #867 (S.KR 6800)
£496 $770 €744 Interior scene with woman and flowers, Halland (18x24cm-7x9in) s. d.1914 verso panel. 4-Dec-2 AB Stockholms Auktionsverk #1771/R (S.KR 7000)
£617 $963 €926 Landscape from Gripsholm (22x34cm-9x13in) s. 13-Sep-2 Lilla Bukowskis, Stockholm #887 (S.KR 9000)
£618 $1025 €896 Cottage by shore (68x85cm-27x33in) s. 16-Jun-3 Lilla Bukowskis, Stockholm #609 (S.KR 8000)
£674 $1044 €1011 Landscape (17x46cm-7x18in) s. panel. 4-Dec-2 AB Stockholms Auktionsverk #1666/R (S.KR 9500)
£780 $1209 €1170 View towards the church in Mariefred (20x34cm-8x13in) s. panel. 4-Dec-2 AB Stockholms Auktionsverk #1551/R (S.KR 11000)
£818 $1300 €1227 Spring farming (42x66cm-17x26in) s. 3-Mar-3 Lilla Bukowskis, Stockholm #147 (S.KR 11000)
£849 $1410 €1231 Rosebush by fence (37x32cm-15x13in) s/ canvas on panel. 16-Jun-3 Lilla Bukowskis, Stockholm #739 (S.KR 11000)
£931 $1508 €1350 Old farmhouse, south Gotland (54x65cm-21x26in) s. 25-May-3 Uppsala Auktionskammare, Uppsala #144/R (S.KR 12000)
£943 $1546 €1367 Swedish spring landscape with lake (28x47cm-11x19in) s. panel. 4-Jun-3 AB Stockholms Auktionsverk #2206/R (S.KR 12000)
£960 $1498 €1440 Lake landscape with cottage (60x108cm-24x43in) s. 13-Sep-2 Lilla Bukowskis, Stockholm #570 (S.KR 14000)
£1844 $2858 €2766 By the stile - young couple from Runmaro (90x55cm-35x22in) s. 8-Dec-2 Uppsala Auktionskammare, Uppsala #105/R est:30000-40000 (S.KR 26000)
£2595 $4100 €3893 Autumn evening, lake landscape from Malaren (67x100cm-26x39in) s. 27-Nov-2 Falkkloos, Malmo #77583/R est:35000 (S.KR 37000)
£6383 $9894 €9575 Mother and child by well in farmyard (68x48cm-27x19in) s. panel. 4-Dec-2 AB Stockholms Auktionsverk #1587/R est:125000-150000 (S.KR 90000)

NILSON, Severin (attrib) (1846-1918) Swedish
£776 $1219 €1125 Untitled. 15-Dec-2 Anders Antik, Landskrona #265 (S.KR 11000)

NILSSON, Axel (1889-1981) Swedish

£561 $875 €842 Autumn in the garden (45x55cm-18x22in) s. panel painted 1967. 6-Nov-2 AB Stockholms Auktionsverk #639/R (S.KR 8000)
£561 $875 €842 Fruit orchard in Skaane (46x55cm-18x22in) s. painted 1965. 6-Nov-2 AB Stockholms Auktionsverk #656/R (S.KR 8000)
£561 $875 €842 Autumn (48x61cm-19x24in) s. panel painted 1968. 6-Nov-2 AB Stockholms Auktionsverk #657/R (S.KR 8000)
£565 $886 €848 Interior (47x40cm-19x16in) s. canvas on panel. 16-Dec-2 Lilla Bukowskis, Stockholm #43 (S.KR 8000)
£580 $922 €870 View from a window (53x45cm-21x18in) s. 3-Mar-3 Lilla Bukowskis, Stockholm #358 (S.KR 7800)
£701 $1093 €1052 Still life of yellow chrysanthemums (73x54cm-29x21in) s. painted 1957 exhib. 6-Nov-2 AB Stockholms Auktionsverk #655/R (S.KR 10000)
£772 $1243 €1158 Tree turning yellow (65x54cm-26x21in) s/ panel. 7-May-3 AB Stockholms Auktionsverk #707/R (S.KR 10000)
£876 $1367 €1314 Autumn landscape (50x65cm-20x26in) s. 5-Nov-2 Bukowskis, Stockholm #175/R (S.KR 12500)
£1016 $1585 €1524 Field with trees in blossom, view from Vaison la Romaine (52x72cm-20x28in) s.d.50 exhib. 6-Nov-2 AB Stockholms Auktionsverk #668/R est:10000-12000 (S.KR 14500)
£1121 $1749 €1682 Fishing village in snow (46x55cm-18x22in) s. panel lit. 5-Nov-2 Bukowskis, Stockholm #174/R est:20000-22000 (S.KR 16000)
£1402 $2186 €2103 Still life (57x55cm-22x22in) s. panel. 6-Nov-2 AB Stockholms Auktionsverk #638/R est:20000-25000 (S.KR 20000)
£1542 $2405 €2313 Still life of flowers and fruit (60x81cm-24x32in) s. 5-Nov-2 Bukowskis, Stockholm #168/R est:30000-35000 (S.KR 22000)
£1699 $2735 €2549 By the window (46x40cm-18x16in) s. i.d.1951 verso panel. 7-May-3 AB Stockholms Auktionsverk #706/R est:12000-15000 (S.KR 22000)
£1962 $3061 €2943 The Roman Wall - landscape in France (33x46cm-13x18in) s. 5-Nov-2 Bukowskis, Stockholm #169/R est:20000-25000 (S.KR 28000)
£1977 $3124 €2966 View of town hall quay Stockholm (65x50cm-26x20in) s. 28-Apr-3 Bukowskis, Stockholm #89/R est:20000-25000 (S.KR 26000)
£3861 $6216 €5792 Rhododendron (92x73cm-36x29in) s.d.1933 prov.exhib.lit. 7-May-3 AB Stockholms Auktionsverk #819/R est:25000-30000 (S.KR 50000)
£3954 $6248 €5931 Still life of objects on table (30x30cm-12x12in) s.d.1921 panel lit. 28-Apr-3 Bukowskis, Stockholm #10/R est:60000-80000 (S.KR 52000)
£4788 $7708 €7182 Still life of flowers and fruit (46x38cm-18x15in) s. panel. 7-May-3 AB Stockholms Auktionsverk #648/R est:30000-40000 (S.KR 62000)
£6167 $9620 €9251 View from Smedsuuden, Stockholm (46x46cm-18x18in) s. 5-Nov-2 Bukowskis, Stockholm #1/R est:60000-70000 (S.KR 88000)

NILSSON, Bert Johnny (1934-) Swedish

£427 $691 €619 Surrealistic female portrait (47x30cm-19x12in) s.d.1973 panel. 25-May-3 Uppsala Auktionskammare, Uppsala #337/R (S.KR 5500)

NILSSON, Ernst (1892-1937) Swedish

£372 $591 €558 Academy mill from Jarnbron (75x98cm-30x39in) s. 2-Mar-3 Uppsala Auktionskammare, Uppsala #227 (S.KR 5000)

NILSSON, Nils (1901-1949) Swedish

£337 $532 €506 Portrait of lady wearing green dress (60x48cm-24x19in) s. 30-Nov-2 Goteborg Auktionsverk, Sweden #591/R (S.KR 4800)
£849 $1368 €1274 Portrait of woman (81x65cm-32x26in) init. exhib. 7-May-3 AB Stockholms Auktionsverk #845/R (S.KR 11000)
£1407 $2223 €2111 Landscape with road (65x81cm-26x32in) init. 28-Apr-3 Bukowskis, Stockholm #101/R est:12000-15000 (S.KR 18500)

NILSSON, Olof (1868-1956) Swedish

£275 $417 €413 Evening in the mountains, possibly Norrland (54x70cm-21x28in) s.d.1932. 16-Aug-2 Lilla Bukowskis, Stockholm #325 (S.KR 4000)

NILSSON, Vera (1888-1979) Swedish

£989 $1562 €1484 By the window (34x27cm-13x11in) init. canvas on panel. 28-Apr-3 Bukowskis, Stockholm #75/R (S.KR 13000)
£1065 $1682 €1598 Sailor (41x33cm-16x13in) init. 28-Apr-3 Bukowskis, Stockholm #70/R est:18000-20000 (S.KR 14000)
£1236 $1989 €1854 Still life of flowers (70x64cm-28x25in) init. 7-May-3 AB Stockholms Auktionsverk #844/R est:12000-15000 (S.KR 16000)
£1293 $2043 €1940 Girl at table (74x60cm-29x24in) s. panel painted 1939 exhib. 28-Apr-3 Bukowskis, Stockholm #68/R est:12000-15000 (S.KR 17000)
£1445 $2283 €2168 Portrait of a friend (46x33cm-18x13in) init. exhib. 28-Apr-3 Bukowskis, Stockholm #76/R est:25000-30000 (S.KR 19000)
£2471 $3978 €3707 Town scene from Stockholm (56x61cm-22x24in) init. prov. 7-May-3 AB Stockholms Auktionsverk #663/R est:40000-50000 (S.KR 32000)
£2738 $4325 €4107 In the shade (60x73cm-24x29in) init. painted 1946 exhib.lit. 28-Apr-3 Bukowskis, Stockholm #71/R est:40000-50000 (S.KR 36000)
£6178 $9946 €9267 Gubbhuset in snow - tall wooden house in Glasbruksgatan (65x66cm-26x26in) init. prov.exhib.lit. 7-May-3 AB Stockholms Auktionsverk #665/R est:100000-120000 (S.KR 80000)
£19972 $31156 €29958 Landscape with horses (110x106cm-43x42in) painted 1916 exhib.lit. 6-Nov-2 AB Stockholms Auktionsverk #726/R est:300000-400000 (S.KR 285000)
£23166 $37297 €34749 Barbro (92x65cm-36x26in) init. d.1934 verso prov.exhib.lit. 7-May-3 AB Stockholms Auktionsverk #843/R est:300000-350000 (S.KR 300000)
£44149 $68872 €66224 The lamplight - Ginga asleep at table (78x88cm-31x35in) init. painted c.1930 exhib.lit. 6-Nov-2 AB Stockholms Auktionsverk #691/R est:400000-500000 (S.KR 630000)

Works on paper

£849 $1368 €1274 Barbro (41x48cm-16x19in) s.i. W/C prov. 7-May-3 AB Stockholms Auktionsverk #842/R (S.KR 11000)

NILSSON, Wiven (1897-1974) Swedish

Sculpture

£1655 $2549 €2483 Woman (36cm-14in) plaster prov. 27-Oct-2 Anders Antik, Landskrona #639/R est:15000-18000 (S.KR 24000)

NILUS, Pjotr Alexandrowitsch (1869-1943) Russian

£1013 $1600 €1600 Lady on sofa (24x41cm-9x16in) s. 1-Dec-2 Bukowskis, Helsinki #269/R est:2000-3000
£2055 $3205 €3000 Girls swimming (28x42cm-11x17in) s.cyrillisch board. 10-Apr-3 Dorotheum, Vienna #60/R est:3400-3600
£4422 $7031 €6500 Ladies bathing (26x36cm-10x14in) indis.s. board. 25-Feb-3 Dorotheum, Vienna #125/R est:4000-4500
£12000 $19440 €18000 Still life with artist's paintings in background. Ladies promenading in the park (50x61cm-20x24in) s.i. double-sided. 21-May-3 Sotheby's, London #196/R est:6000-8000
£18000 $29160 €27000 Parisian square with kiosks (65x92cm-26x36in) s.i. 21-May-3 Sotheby's, London #82/R est:6000-8000

NINGURRAY, Nancy Ross (20th C) Australian

£366 $578 €531 Untitled (130x52cm-51x20in) acrylic. 22-Jul-3 Lawson Menzies, Sydney #63/R est:1500-2000 (A.D 900)

NINHAM, Henry (1793-1874) British

Works on paper

£250 $380 €375 On Trowse Common (15x25cm-6x10in) W/C sketch. 16-Aug-2 Keys, Aylsham #585

NINNES, Bernard (1899-1971) British

£250 $388 €375 Still life of glass bowl of summer flowers (79x99cm-31x39in) s. board. 26-Sep-2 Lane, Penzance #2
£1100 $1837 €1595 Harbour and Smeatons Pier St. Ives (63x76cm-25x30in) s. 19-Jun-3 Lane, Penzance #357 est:1000-1500
£2600 $4238 €3900 St Ives harbour (51x79cm-20x31in) s. 13-Feb-3 David Lay, Penzance #362 est:1000-2000

NIQUILLE, Armand (1912-) Swiss

£1033 $1694 €1498 Les verres (61x105cm-24x41in) s. i.d.1966 verso panel. 4-Jun-3 Fischer, Luzern #1257/R est:2500-3500 (S.FR 2200)
£1596 $2618 €2314 Le Bourg, vu de l'ouest au printemps (48x65cm-19x26in) s.d.67. 4-Jun-3 Fischer, Luzern #2268/R est:1500-1800 (S.FR 3400)

NISBET, Marc (20th C) American

£375 $600 €563 Evening ships. s.i. masonite. 12-Jan-3 William Jenack, New York #432

NISBET, Noel Laura (1887-1956) British

£9220 $14936 €13000 Procession of a bacchanalian revellers (75x100cm-30x39in) s. 21-May-3 James Adam, Dublin #69/R est:3000-5000

NISBET, Pollock (1848-1922) British

£1511 $2508 €2191 Shepherd and long horned sheep on a highland path (107x81cm-42x32in) s.d.1879. 16-Jun-3 Waddingtons, Toronto #206/R est:2000-2500 (C.D 3400)

NISBET, R B (1857-1942) British
£420 $668 €630 View of a harbour with trawlers and figures on the quay at sunset (19x29cm-7x11in) s.d.1882. 19-Mar-3 Rupert Toovey, Partridge Green #51/R

NISBET, Robert Buchan (1857-1942) British
£440 $691 €660 October day near Crieff, cattle grazing (25x34cm-10x13in) s. panel. 10-Dec-2 Lane, Penzance #292
Works on paper
£250 $408 €375 Early autumn (18x25cm-7x10in) s.d.1886. 14-Feb-3 Keys, Aylsham #317
£267 $443 €387 Farmer and workhorses in an open field (55x66cm-22x26in) s. W/C. 16-Jun-3 Waddingtons, Toronto #198/R (C.D 600)
£400 $624 €600 Sheep on a headland (32x47cm-13x19in) s.d.1886 W/C. 26-Mar-3 Sotheby's, Olympia #130/R

NISBET, Robert H (1879-1961) American
£2597 $4000 €3896 Summer clouds (66x81cm-26x32in) s. prov. 24-Oct-2 Shannon's, Milford #218/R est:4000-6000
£5195 $8000 €7793 Snowy hillside (64x76cm-25x30in) s. prov. 24-Oct-2 Shannon's, Milford #167/R est:4000-6000

NISBET, Tom (1909-?) Irish
Works on paper
£274 $430 €400 Along the canal (28x37cm-11x15in) s. W/C. 15-Apr-3 De Veres Art Auctions, Dublin #100u
£293 $457 €460 Stroll along the towpath (26x36cm-10x14in) s. W/C. 6-Nov-2 James Adam, Dublin #37/R
£310 $514 €440 Grand canal, autumn (26x36cm-10x14in) s. W/C. 10-Jun-3 James Adam, Dublin #150/R
£361 $559 €570 Morning chat, St. Stephen's Green (30x36cm-12x14in) s. i.verso W/C. 24-Sep-2 De Veres Art Auctions, Dublin #6
£500 $775 €750 Old bridge, Milltown, Dublin (28x38cm-11x15in) s. W/C. 2-Oct-2 John Ross, Belfast #67
£940 $1513 €1400 St Stephen's Green with a view of the Russell Hotel (28x38cm-11x15in) s. W/C. 18-Feb-3 Whyte's, Dublin #215/R

NISBET-SMITH, Alistair (20th C) New Zealander
£313 $489 €470 Acrobat (168x120cm-66x47in) s.i. s.verso. 5-Nov-2 Peter Webb, Auckland #123 est:500-1000 (NZ.D 1000)

NISEN, Jean Baptiste (1819-1885) Belgian
Works on paper
£1203 $1876 €1900 Tete de jeune homme effraye (42x37cm-17x15in) s. chl htd white chk dr. 10-Sep-2 Vanderkindere, Brussels #411 est:300-500

NISHIZAWA, Luis (1926-) Mexican
£2103 $3364 €3049 Paisaje de Tlahuac (20x37cm-8x15in) s. wood. 15-May-3 Louis Morton, Mexico #136/R est:38000-40000 (M.P 34000)
Works on paper
£3092 $4947 €4483 El nevado desde Zacualpan (60x90cm-24x35in) s. Indian ink. 15-May-3 Louis Morton, Mexico #54/R est:60000-70000 (M.P 50000)

NISS, Thorvald (1842-1905) Danish
£270 $435 €405 Snow-covered woodland (63x41cm-25x16in) mono. 22-Feb-3 Rasmussen, Havnen #2260 (D.KR 3000)
£301 $458 €452 Landscape from Funkedammen, Hillerod (37x46cm-15x18in) mono. 27-Aug-2 Rasmussen, Copenhagen #1677 (D.KR 3500)
£324 $502 €486 Winter landscape with river through wood (52x55cm-20x22in) s.d.1901. 28-Sep-2 Rasmussen, Havnen #2155 (D.KR 3800)
£343 $535 €515 Heather hills in Vendsyssel (24x42cm-9x17in) s.indis.d. 11-Nov-2 Rasmussen, Vejle #683/R (D.KR 4000)
£455 $729 €683 Landscape with lake, farm in background (48x85cm-19x33in) mono.d.1897. 13-Jan-3 Rasmussen, Vejle #157/R (D.KR 5200)
£574 $930 €832 Garden walk behind farmhouse (46x58cm-18x23in) mono.d.1886. 26-May-3 Rasmussen, Copenhagen #1409/R (D.KR 6000)
£766 $1210 €1149 Autumn landscape, Jaegersborg Dyrehave (79x125cm-31x49in) s.d.1897 exhib. 2-Dec-2 Rasmussen, Copenhagen #1494/R (D.KR 9000)
£773 $1221 €1160 Landscape with shepherd boy (30x50cm-12x20in) 13-Nov-2 Kunsthallen, Copenhagen #47/R (D.KR 9000)
£1447 $2286 €2171 Man walking on road in autumn (77x59cm-30x23in) mono.d.Novr.1883 prov. 27-Nov-2 Museumsbygningen, Copenhagen #24/R est:15000-20000 (D.KR 17000)
£1447 $2286 €2171 Oxen and cart on heath, Jylland (56x86cm-22x34in) mono.d.1878. 2-Dec-2 Rasmussen, Copenhagen #1307/R est:20000-25000 (D.KR 17000)
£4655 $7402 €6983 Landscape with road along fjord (107x158cm-42x62in) s.d.1884. 5-Mar-3 Rasmussen, Copenhagen #1529/R est:50000-60000 (D.KR 50000)
Works on paper
£256 $395 €384 Winter landscape (50x65cm-20x26in) s.d.1886 pastel. 4-Sep-2 Kunsthallen, Copenhagen #26 (D.KR 3000)
£438 $701 €657 Winter landscape (50x65cm-20x26in) s.d.1886 pastel. 13-Jan-3 Rasmussen, Vejle #119/R (D.KR 5000)

NISSL, Rudolf (1870-1955) Austrian
£1020 $1622 €1500 Still life of ornaments (66x50cm-26x20in) i.d.1916 verso. 19-Mar-3 Neumeister, Munich #678/R est:1600
£1923 $3038 €3000 Woman resting (58x73cm-23x29in) s. 12-Nov-2 Dorotheum, Vienna #81/R est:3000-4000

NITSCH, Hermann (1938-) Austrian
£1583 $2532 €2200 Untitled (59x77cm-23x30in) s.i.d. board on canvas prov. 15-May-3 Neumeister, Munich #740/R est:2000-2500
£2532 $3924 €4000 Relic in Schomerhaus, Klosterneuberg (98x137cm-39x54in) s.d.1996 verso paper. 24-Sep-2 Wiener Kunst Auktionen, Vienna #316/R est:4000-6000
£2695 $4366 €3800 Frammento della pittura dell'Origin Misterien Theatre (175x28cm-69x11in) s.1984 verso painted mural juta on plywood prov. 26-May-3 Christie's, Milan #169/R est:2800-3200
£2703 $4216 €4000 Shaken picture (100x80cm-39x31in) s.d.2000 verso. 25-Mar-3 Wiener Kunst Auktionen, Vienna #31/R est:4000-6500
£2703 $4216 €4000 Shaken picture (100x80cm-39x31in) s.d.2000 verso. 25-Mar-3 Wiener Kunst Auktionen, Vienna #32/R est:4000-7000
£3623 $5942 €5000 Picture of debris (104x80cm-41x31in) s.d.1986 verso. 27-May-3 Wiener Kunst Auktionen, Vienna #213/R est:4000-6500
£4317 $6906 €6000 Spray painting (105x79cm-41x31in) s.d. stretcher hessian. 15-May-3 Neumeister, Munich #739/R est:6000-8000
£5435 $8913 €7500 Untitled (105x80cm-41x31in) s.d.1978 verso s.i.d. stretcher dispersion blood hessian two. 28-May-3 Lempertz, Koln #307/R est:8000-10000
Works on paper
£396 $633 €550 Untitled (53x37cm-21x15in) s. d. verso W/C col aquatint. 15-May-3 Neumeister, Munich #499/R
£414 $662 €600 Relic (28x20cm-11x8in) s.d.98 blood. 11-Mar-3 Dorotheum, Vienna #282
£1154 $1823 €1800 Action picture (24x38cm-9x15in) s.d.1988 i. stretcher mixed media canvas. 18-Nov-2 Dorotheum, Linz #445/R est:2000-2400
£1855 $2931 €2783 Untitled (99x75cm-39x30in) s.i.d.1987 mixed media. 18-Nov-2 Waddingtons, Toronto #29/R est:4000-5000 (C.D 4600)
£3623 $5942 €5000 Om theatre (128x100cm-50x39in) s.d.1965 verso overpainted photo canvas exhib.lit. 28-May-3 Lempertz, Koln #306/R est:5000

NITSCH, Richard (1866-?) German
£437 $681 €656 Portrait of a musketeer (125x72cm-49x28in) s.d.1904. 6-Nov-2 Dobiaschofsky, Bern #3573/R (S.FR 1000)

NITSCHKE, Detlev (?) German
£955 $1490 €1500 Park in Bad Worishofen (12x9cm-5x4in) s. panel. 8-Nov-2 Auktionhaus Georg Rehm, Augsburg #8114/R est:1700
£1154 $1788 €1800 Augsburg flower market (20x15cm-8x6in) s. panel. 6-Dec-2 Auktionhaus Georg Rehm, Augsburg #8093/R est:2400

NITTIS, Giuseppe de (1846-1884) Italian
£6410 $10064 €10000 Courtyard (16x21cm-6x8in) s.d.68 panel. 13-Dec-2 Piasa, Paris #11/R est:12000
£20834 $33126 €30000 Place des Pyramides, Paris (40x32cm-16x13in) s. prov.lit. 30-Apr-3 Tajan, Paris #113/R est:25000
£21935 $34658 €34000 Small lake (18x31cm-7x12in) s. board lit. 18-Dec-2 Finarte, Milan #96/R est:50000
£38710 $61161 €60000 Figures in the park (39x25cm-15x10in) s.d.1874 prov. 18-Dec-2 Finarte, Milan #87/R est:80000
Works on paper
£2839 $4485 €4400 Sleeping figures (26x22cm-10x9in) s. i.verso W/C. 18-Dec-2 Finarte, Milan #88/R

NIVELT, Roger (1899-1962) French
Works on paper
£897 $1409 €1400 Tete d'africaine (53x40cm-21x16in) s.i.d.avril 1926 pencil gold silver powder. 16-Dec-2 Gros & Delettrez, Paris #307

NIVISON, Angus (1953-) Australian
£282 $448 €423 Study for compassion 1987 (75x74cm-30x29in) s. acrylic on paper. 3-Mar-3 Lawson Menzies, Sydney #367 (A.D 750)

NIXON, James (c.1741-1812) British
Miniatures
£1300 $2106 €1950 Officer, possibly a cavalry officer wearing a scralet coat (3cm-1in) gold bracelet clasp frame with pearl border. 22-May-3 Bonhams, New Bond Street #50/R est:500-700

NIXON, John (1949-) Australian
£1075 $1634 €1613 Untitled (76x57cm-30x22in) painted c.1985 prov. 28-Aug-2 Deutscher-Menzies, Melbourne #140/R est:3500-4500 (A.D 3000)
£1084 $1712 €1626 Architecture of life 1980 (76x61cm-30x24in) oil synthetic polymer on plywood prov. 27-Nov-2 Deutscher-Menzies, Melbourne #115/R est:2000-4000 (A.D 3035)
£2411 $3761 €3617 Untitled (61x45cm-24x18in) 11-Nov-2 Deutscher-Menzies, Melbourne #57/R est:3000-5000 (A.D 6750)
Works on paper
£709 $1127 €1064 Untitled, red cross (67x51cm-26x20in) enamel composition board. 4-Mar-3 Deutscher-Menzies, Melbourne #148/R (A.D 1840)

NIXON, John (1760-1818) British
Works on paper
£250 $388 €375 My cook (18x13cm-7x5in) i. pencil pen brown ink W/C. 4-Dec-2 Christie's, Kensington #157
£320 $506 €480 On board the Wellington packet from Brighton to Dieppe (12x10cm-5x4in) init.i.d.1814 pen ink wash. 7-Apr-3 Bonhams, Bath #1
£320 $506 €480 W Northager on board the packet going to Boulogne (12x10cm-5x4in) i. pen ink. 7-Apr-3 Bonhams, Bath #2
£2600 $4264 €3900 Margate Hoy unloading her cargo (42x63cm-17x25in) s. indis i.d. pen ink W/C. 4-Feb-3 Bonhams, Leeds #271 est:1000-1500

NIXON, Kay (1895-1988) British
Works on paper
£300 $465 €450 Barn owls (27x33cm-11x13in) s. W/C htd white. 24-Sep-2 Bonhams, Knightsbridge #239/R

NIXON, Nicholas (1947-) American
Photographs
£6494 $10000 €9741 Brown Sisters, 1976/1981/1984/1987/1989 (124x42cm-49x17in) s.i.d.num.verso gelatin silver print 5 in one frame prov.lit. 25-Oct-2 Phillips, New York #45/R est:7000-10000

NIZZOLI, Marcello (20th C) Italian
£462 $729 €720 Landscape (30x43cm-12x17in) tempera board. 12-Nov-2 Babuino, Rome #40/R
Works on paper
£994 $1570 €1550 Landscape (37x48cm-15x19in) W/C. 12-Nov-2 Babuino, Rome #243/R

NOAILLES, Marie-Laure de (1902-1970) French
£2051 $3221 €3200 Enlevement (73x92cm-29x36in) s.i.d.57. 24-Nov-2 Laurence Calmels, Paris #192/R

NOAKES, Michael (1933-) British
£300 $477 €450 Spanish landscape (63x76cm-25x30in) s.i. i.d.1979 verso. 26-Feb-3 Sotheby's, Olympia #350/R

NOBBE, Jacob (1850-1919) Danish
£429 $669 €644 Thoughtful (46x37cm-18x15in) s.d.1908. 11-Nov-2 Rasmussen, Vejle #537/R (D.KR 5000)
£564 $857 €880 Flensburg Fjord (28x17cm-11x7in) s.d.08 canvas board. 17-Aug-2 Hans Stahl, Toestorf #99
£745 $1184 €1118 Kitchen interior with woman by fireplace (48x40cm-19x16in) s.d.1894 cardboard. 10-Mar-3 Rasmussen, Vejle #83/R (D.KR 8000)
£1603 $2436 €2500 Stone bridge near Alnor (46x68cm-18x27in) s.d.1896 board. 17-Aug-2 Hans Stahl, Toestorf #98 est:2450

NOBBE, Ortwin (1926-) Danish
£557 $870 €836 Family portrait - Jacob Nobbe and his sisters, artist's summerhouse (125x96cm-49x38in) 11-Nov-2 Rasmussen, Vejle #536/R (D.KR 6500)

NOBBIT, M (19th C) ?
£897 $1381 €1346 Girl with apple (43x33cm-17x13in) after Jean Baptiste Greuze. 27-Oct-2 Anders Antik, Landskrona #250 (S.KR 13000)

NOBELE, Henri de (c.1820-1870) Belgian
£1441 $2277 €2162 Bernese Oberland woman by mountain stream (54x44cm-21x17in) s. 14-Nov-2 Stuker, Bern #435/R est:2700-3200 (S.FR 3300)

NOBLE, Edwin (1876-?) British
Works on paper
£700 $1099 €1050 On the scent (37x34cm-15x13in) s. W/C over pencil. 15-Apr-3 Bonhams, Knowle #84

NOBLE, James (1919-1989) British
£410 $640 €615 Still life of yellow roses in a vase (24x19cm-9x7in) s. prov. 11-Sep-2 Bonhams, Knowle #194
£550 $891 €825 Mixed roses (51x41cm-20x16in) s.d.51. 23-Jan-3 Christie's, Kensington #201/R
£600 $912 €900 Golden times, study of a yellow rose (18x13cm-7x5in) s. i.verso panel sold with a companion. 4-Jul-2 Duke & Son, Dorchester #245
£650 $1014 €975 White roses in a silver vase (25x20cm-10x8in) s. 15-Oct-2 Bonhams, Knightsbridge #76
£650 $1027 €975 Roses in a glass (25x20cm-10x8in) s. prov. 27-Nov-2 Sotheby's, Olympia #75/R
£650 $1053 €975 Flowerpiece (51x41cm-20x16in) s.d.51. 23-Jan-3 Christie's, Kensington #198/R
£700 $1092 €1050 Still life of yellow and white roses (41x30cm-16x12in) s. prov. 12-Sep-2 Sotheby's, Olympia #114/R
£700 $1092 €1050 Still life of pink, yellow and white roses (41x30cm-16x12in) s. prov. 12-Sep-2 Sotheby's, Olympia #115/R
£800 $1312 €1200 Peppers, plums, punnet of cherries and a pot plant on draped table (40x76cm-16x30in) s. 5-Jun-3 Christie's, Kensington #803/R
£1100 $1782 €1650 From the hedgerow (20x25cm-8x10in) s.d.July 1981 i.verso board sold with dandelions by Claire Dalby. 20-May-3 Sotheby's, Olympia #154/R est:500-700
£1500 $2355 €2250 Still life with eggs and mushrooms (30x40cm-12x16in) s. exhib. 15-Apr-3 Bonhams, Knightsbridge #139/R est:1500-2000
£2000 $3280 €3000 Spring flowers in a glass vase (51x56cm-20x22in) s. 29-May-3 Christie's, Kensington #322/R est:500-700

NOBLE, James Campbell (1846-1913) British
£700 $1113 €1050 Sun after rain (30x51cm-12x20in) s. 6-Mar-3 Christie's, Kensington #169/R
£1650 $2690 €2393 Dordrecht harbour (50x60cm-20x24in) s. 21-Jul-3 Bonhams, Bath #72/R est:1000-1500
£2800 $4284 €4200 Dutch waterway (71x92cm-28x36in) s. 22-Aug-2 Bonhams, Edinburgh #1045/R est:3000-5000
£4000 $6120 €6000 Bringing the boats ashore (52x38cm-20x15in) s. indis d. 22-Aug-2 Bonhams, Edinburgh #1041/R est:6000-8000

NOBLE, James Campbell (attrib) (1846-1913) British
£256 $400 €384 Afternoon following the blessing of the boats. 19-Oct-2 Harvey Clar, Oakland #1380

NOBLE, Jill (1962-) Australian
£1240 $1972 €1860 Female nude (123x112cm-48x44in) s.d.1994. 5-May-3 Sotheby's, Melbourne #266/R est:2000-3000 (A.D 3200)
£2321 $3668 €3482 East Gippsland (110x151cm-43x59in) s.d.89 s.i.verso. 27-Nov-2 Deutscher-Menzies, Melbourne #36/R est:4500-6000 (A.D 6500)
£2422 $3852 €3633 Landscape (87x111cm-34x44in) s.i.d.1985 verso. 5-May-3 Sotheby's, Melbourne #216/R est:2000-4000 (A.D 6250)
Works on paper
£1085 $1726 €1628 Cityscape (50x104cm-20x41in) mixed media. 5-May-3 Sotheby's, Melbourne #224 est:800-1500 (A.D 2800)

NOBLE, John (1874-1935) American
£420 $672 €630 Gun dogs resting by the basket with pheasants by a fence (51x76cm-20x30in) s. 13-May-3 Rosebery Fine Art, London #723

NOBLE, John Sargeant (1848-1896) British
£440 $695 €660 Winter, figures on a lane under snow (23x18cm-9x7in) s.verso panel. 2-Dec-2 Gorringes, Lewes #2779
£1000 $1580 €1500 Rustic gossip (38x44cm-15x17in) s.i.verso panel. 2-Dec-2 Bonhams, Bath #157/R est:1200-1800

NOBLE, Mamie (1871-1958) American
£897 $1400 €1346 Bluebonnets (51x46cm-20x18in) painted c.1930 exhib. 19-Oct-2 David Dike, Dallas #358/R

NOBLE, Richard Pratchett (fl.1830-1861) British
Works on paper
£400 $660 €580 Ploughman (30x47cm-12x19in) W/C. 1-Jul-3 Bonhams, Norwich #120/R

£480 $802 €696 Contemplation by a riverside (45x65cm-18x26in) s. W/C. 24-Jun-3 Bonhams, Knightsbridge #154/R

NOBLE, Robert (1857-1917) British
£900 $1494 €1305 Riverside trees, a church beyond (51x61cm-20x24in) s.d.96. 12-Jun-3 Gorringes, Lewes #1757
£2300 $3519 €3450 Children playing on the River Tyne, East Lothian (61x74cm-24x29in) s. 22-Aug-2 Bonhams, Edinburgh #1145 est:2500-3500
Works on paper
£440 $726 €638 Near Brancaster (31x46cm-12x18in) i.verso W/C scratching out. 1-Jul-3 Bonhams, Norwich #82/R

NOBLE, Tim and WEBSTER, Sue (20th C) American
Sculpture
£31646 $50000 €47469 Yes (148x295x25cm-58x116x10in) lacquered brass 335 ice white turbo reflector caps executed 2001. 14-Nov-2 Christie's, Rockefeller NY #349/R est:50000-70000
£34375 $55000 €51563 Vicious (79x243x10cm-31x96x4in) init.d.1999 num.4/5 verso reflector caps bulbs fittings 2 parts. 13-May-3 Sotheby's, New York #44/R est:60000-80000
£34375 $55000 €51563 Dollar (182x130x25cm-72x51x10in) UFO cups lighbulbs brass electronic fittings sequencer prov. 15-May-3 Christie's, Rockefeller NY #344/R est:35000-45000
£60000 $98400 €90000 Excessive, sensual indulgence (190x90x25cm-75x35x10in) multicoloured light fittings UFO caps foamex vinyl executed 1996. 5-Feb-3 Christie's, London #11/R est:50000-70000
£65000 $106600 €97500 One of us (54x38x52cm-21x15x20in) s.i.d.1999 rubbish light projector wood prov.exhib. 6-Feb-3 Sotheby's, London #43/R est:35000

NOCK, L F (20th C) American
Sculpture
£2215 $3500 €3323 Standing moose (25cm-10in) i. reddish brown pat. prov. 3-Apr-3 Christie's, Rockefeller NY #134/R est:2000-3000

NOCK, Leo F (20th C) American
Sculpture
£1911 $3000 €2867 Standing moose (23x33cm-9x13in) s. bronze cast Gorham Co. 20-Nov-2 Boos Gallery, Michigan #435 est:2000-3000

NOCKEN, Wilhelm Theodor (1830-1905) German
£446 $696 €700 Mountain landscape (75x100cm-30x39in) s. 6-Nov-2 Hugo Ruef, Munich #1224/R
£1384 $2145 €2200 Konigssee with St Bartholoma (48x85cm-19x33in) s. 29-Oct-2 Dorotheum, Vienna #77/R est:2600-3200

NOCKOLDS, Roy (1911-1979) British
£260 $403 €390 Coculey works of the Fuller Earth Union, Nutfield Surrey (61x76cm-24x30in) s. 3-Oct-2 Amersham Auction Rooms, UK #297
Works on paper
£650 $1014 €975 Hurrying south (60x50cm-24x20in) s.d.1951 W/C black chk. 12-Sep-2 Sotheby's, Olympia #74/R

NOCRET, Jean (attrib) (1617-1672) French
£1065 $1778 €1500 Saint Jean Baptiste (29x24cm-11x9in) panel. 18-Jun-3 Tajan, Paris #115 est:600-800
£1383 $2144 €2075 Saint Katarina of Alexandria (37x45cm-15x18in) oval. 3-Dec-2 Bukowskis, Stockholm #523/R est:20000-25000 (S.KR 19500)

NOEH, Anna T (1926-) Canadian
£222 $350 €333 Family at the airport (51x41cm-20x16in) s.d.1978 s.i.verso board prov. 14-Nov-2 Heffel, Vancouver #108 (C.D 550)

NOEL, Alexandre Jean (1752-1834) French
£900 $1413 €1350 Harbour seen in winter, under a stormy sky (55x74cm-22x29in) chk bodycol sold with drawing by different hand. 13-Dec-2 Christie's, Kensington #320/R
Works on paper
£2721 $4327 €4000 View of Portugal (31x39cm-12x15in) s. gouache. 24-Mar-3 Tajan, Paris #112/R
£5743 $8959 €8500 Ships on a stormy sea off southern coastline (62x94cm-24x37in) s. gouache board prov. 27-Mar-3 Dorotheum, Vienna #92/R est:9000-12000

NOEL, Alexandre Jean (attrib) (1752-1834) French
Works on paper
£2797 $4671 €4000 Scene d'incendie dans un port mediterraneen (55x64cm-22x25in) gouache. 25-Jun-3 Tajan, Paris #81/R est:4000-6000
£4196 $7007 €6000 Scene de cavalerie avec l'incendie d'une ville assiegee (54x68cm-21x27in) gouache. 25-Jun-3 Tajan, Paris #80/R est:6000-9000

NOEL, Alphonse Leon (1807-1884) French
Works on paper
£645 $1000 €968 Portrait of the artist sister-in-law Louise Stephanie Rouget (33x24cm-13x9in) s.d.1837 pencil gouache col chk htd white prov. 29-Oct-2 Sotheby's, New York #13/R est:2000-3000

NOEL, Edme Antony Paul (1845-1909) French
Sculpture
£1700 $2635 €2550 Orpheus and Cerberus (74cm-29in) s. brown pat bronze circular base. 29-Oct-2 Bonhams, New Bond Street #178/R est:1800-2200
£2229 $3500 €3344 Gladiators (48x51cm-19x20in) s.i. brown pat bronze. 23-Nov-2 Jackson's, Cedar Falls #256/R est:3000-4000

NOEL, Emile Laurent (20th C) French?
£2390 $3704 €3800 Composition (97x130cm-38x51in) s. 7-Oct-2 Claude Aguttes, Neuilly #193

NOEL, Georges (1924-) French
£3264 $5157 €4700 Palimpseste (73x116cm-29x46in) s.d.1960 oil scratching out. 27-Apr-3 Perrin, Versailles #26/R est:4500-5500
Works on paper
£468 $748 €650 Assemblage (58x55cm-23x22in) s.d.verso mixed media wood. 14-May-3 Blanchet, Paris #185/R
£986 $1568 €1450 Palimpseste (73x54cm-29x21in) mono.d. s.d.1967 verso pigments sand canvas. 26-Feb-3 Artcurial Briest, Paris #462
£1390 $2238 €2085 Palimpseste bleu du NIL (100x73cm-39x29in) s.d.1965 verso mixed media canvas. 7-May-3 AB Stockholms Auktionsverk #1148/R est:8000-10000 (S.KR 18000)
£1552 $2514 €2250 Vieux teste archaique (130x97cm-51x38in) s.d.64 mixed media. 25-May-3 Uppsala Auktionskammare, Uppsala #311/R est:8000-10000 (S.KR 20000)
£1772 $2800 €2800 Hommage a un peintre d'Orient (180x162cm-71x64in) s. s.i.d.1962 verso mixed media collage cardboard prov. 2-Dec-2 Tajan, Paris #204
£2017 $3268 €2925 Bleu egyptien (130x97cm-51x38in) s.d.64 mixed media collage. 25-May-3 Uppsala Auktionskammare, Uppsala #310/R est:8000-10000 (S.KR 26000)
£3957 $6331 €5500 Hommage a un peintre d'Orient (162x130cm-64x51in) s. i.d.verso mixed media. 14-May-3 Blanchet, Paris #184/R est:4000-6000

NOEL, Hippolyte (1828-1902) French
£506 $800 €800 Seamstress (18x24cm-7x9in) s. panel. 29-Nov-2 Bassenge, Berlin #6002

NOEL, John Bates (fl.1893-1909) British
£550 $858 €825 Ham Hill, Somerset (34x46cm-13x18in) s.d.1910. 26-Mar-3 Hamptons Fine Art, Godalming #226
£1600 $2528 €2400 Duck pool, near Malvern (41x61cm-16x24in) s. 28-Nov-2 Christie's, Kensington #92/R est:1500-2000
Works on paper
£320 $534 €464 Girl and dog by a mountain stream (35x51cm-14x20in) s. W/C. 24-Jun-3 Bonhams, Knowle #15

NOEL, Jules (1815-1881) French
£1029 $1595 €1544 Rouen (47x77cm-19x30in) s.i. 3-Dec-2 Ritchie, Toronto #3075/R est:1000-1500 (C.D 2500)
£1951 $3200 €2829 Dutch fishing boats moored on the shore (38x46cm-15x18in) s. 4-Jun-3 Christie's, Rockefeller NY #233/R est:4000-6000
£2908 $4856 €4100 Retour de peche (38x54cm-15x21in) s. 20-Jun-3 Piasa, Paris #37/R est:3000-4000
£3662 $5896 €5200 Riviere pres d'Hennebont dans le Morbihan (54x38cm-21x15in) s.d.1878. 11-May-3 Thierry & Lannon, Brest #209/R est:4500-5000
£3987 $6220 €6300 Les remparts pres du port (51x40cm-20x16in) s.d.1842. 20-Oct-2 Galerie de Chartres, Chartres #113 est:6000-8000
£4255 $7106 €6000 Bateaux sur la Greve (38x54cm-15x21in) s. 20-Jun-3 Piasa, Paris #36/R est:4000-5000
£5696 $8886 €9000 Vue d'un port de peche (38x66cm-15x26in) s.i.d. 20-Oct-2 Mercier & Cie, Lille #295/R est:10000-12000
£17925 $27962 €28500 Tempete sur la cote normande (38x56cm-15x22in) s.d.1875. 9-Oct-2 Lombrail & Teucquam, Paris #8/R

Works on paper
£290 $459 €450 Une place de village breton (22x37cm-9x15in) graphite dr. 17-Dec-2 Rossini, Paris #43
£380 $600 €600 Port anime (17x25cm-7x10in) s. chl dr htd col. 29-Nov-2 Drouot Estimations, Paris #36
£1210 $1888 €1900 Paysage de neige (12x16cm-5x6in) W/C. 6-Nov-2 Gioffredo, Nice #54/R

NOEL, Jules (attrib) (1815-1881) French
£826 $1289 €1239 Canal landscape with sailing ships (27x38cm-11x15in) s. 16-Sep-2 Philippe Schuler, Zurich #6479 est:1500-2000 (S.FR 1900)

NOEL, Martin (1956-) German
£1538 $2385 €2400 Bierhoff (84x60cm-33x24in) s.i.d.1996 verso panel. 3-Dec-2 Lempertz, Koln #328/R est:2000

NOEL, Matthias Joseph de (1782-1849) German
Works on paper
£4430 $6867 €7000 Schloss Blankenheim (17x29cm-7x11in) s.i. W/C. 27-Sep-2 Venator & Hansten, Koln #1330/R est:2500

NOEL, Peter Paul Joseph (1789-1822) Belgian
£10828 $16892 €17000 Wooded landscape with shepherds watering their herd near a well (71x103cm-28x41in) s.d.1815 panel. 5-Nov-2 Sotheby's, Amsterdam #246/R est:8000-12000

NOELSMITH (fl.1889-1900) British
Works on paper
£260 $406 €390 River landscape with figures punting (16x26cm-6x10in) s. W/C. 9-Oct-2 Woolley & Wallis, Salisbury #93/R
£800 $1304 €1200 Windsor from the Runnymead (38x61cm-15x24in) s. W/C. 13-Feb-3 David Lay, Penzance #260/R

NOELSMITH, Thomas (fl.1889-1900) British
Works on paper
£406 $650 €589 Within the garden walls (27x44cm-11x17in) s. W/C gouache paperboard. 16-May-3 Skinner, Boston #36/R

NOERR, Julius (1827-1897) German
£2027 $3162 €3000 Peasant with horses in meadow (25x48cm-10x19in) s.d.1870. 26-Mar-3 Hugo Ruef, Munich #182/R est:3000
£4487 $6955 €7000 Resting after the harvest by Starnberger See (25x32cm-10x13in) s.d.1862. 5-Dec-2 Dr Fritz Nagel, Stuttgart #690/R est:8000
£7234 $11430 €10851 River landscape with children playing (23x34cm-9x13in) s.d.1878 panel exhib. 2-Dec-2 Rasmussen, Copenhagen #1529/R est:50000 (D.KR 85000)

NOGARI, Giuseppe (attrib) (1699-1763) Italian
£1554 $2424 €2300 Man reading (54x46cm-21x18in) 25-Mar-3 Finarte Semenzato, Rome #102/R

NOGUCHI, Isamu (1904-1988) American
Sculpture
£5313 $8500 €7970 Plus equals minus (8x32x25cm-3x13x10in) s.num.1/8 gold plated bronze prov.lit. 14-May-3 Sotheby's, New York #173/R est:6000-8000
£8387 $13000 €12581 Pebble for fish (34x18cm-13x7in) incised init. executed 1978 prov. 26-Sep-2 Christie's, Rockefeller NY #783/R est:7000-9000
£13548 $21000 €20322 Kaki persimmons (13x19x10cm-5x7x4in) galvanized steel. 8-Dec-2 Wright, Chicago #186/R est:15000-20000
£18750 $30000 €28125 Cloud mountain (176x128x65cm-69x50x26in) init.d.82 num.15/18 galvanized steel prov.lit. 14-May-3 Sotheby's, New York #230/R est:20000-30000
£87500 $140000 €131250 Target (79x69x60cm-31x27x24in) init.d.84 black granite prov.exhib. 14-May-3 Sotheby's, New York #233/R est:120000-180000

NOGUCHI, Yokoku (1827-1898) Japanese
Works on paper
£563 $900 €845 Carp with water weeds (208x312cm-82x123in) s. W/C silk. 15-Mar-3 Selkirks, St. Louis #413/R

NOIRE, Maxime (1861-1927) French
£769 $1207 €1200 Caravane dans le Sud algerien (33x118cm-13x46in) s. 10-Dec-2 Tajan, Paris #208/R
£769 $1208 €1200 Village au bord de l'oued, sud algerien (33x55cm-13x22in) s. 16-Dec-2 Gros & Delettrez, Paris #69/R
£968 $1529 €1500 Ville Orientale dans le desert (36x95cm-14x37in) s. 17-Dec-2 Rossini, Paris #114
£1871 $3068 €2600 Vue de Constantine (33x55cm-13x22in) s. 4-Jun-3 Tajan, Paris #289/R est:1800-2000
£2390 $3681 €3800 Vue de la baie d'Alger (30x55cm-12x22in) s. 23-Oct-2 Rabourdin & Choppin de Janvry, Paris #145/R
£2800 $4340 €4200 Sultry beauty (43x34cm-17x13in) s. 3-Dec-2 Sotheby's, Olympia #276/R est:3000-5000

NOIROT, Émile (1853-1924) French
£1266 $1962 €2000 Route de Saint Clair, Var (32x55cm-13x22in) s. s.i.d.1907 verso. 27-Sep-2 Rabourdin & Choppin de Janvry, Paris #28/R est:2400-2600
£1887 $2924 €3000 Rivage de Mediterranee (150x250cm-59x98in) s.d.1893. 4-Oct-2 Tajan, Paris #179 est:3000-4000

NOLAN, Sidney (1917-1992) Australian
£692 $1101 €1038 Desert flowers II (29x24cm-11x9in) s. paper prov. 4-Mar-3 Deutscher-Menzies, Melbourne #217/R (A.D 1800)
£766 $1142 €1149 Swimmer, New York (16x30cm-6x12in) init. s.i.d.1958 verso ripolin. 27-Aug-2 Christie's, Melbourne #243 est:2000-3000 (A.D 2000)
£846 $1345 €1269 Desert flowers III (29x24cm-11x9in) s. paper prov. 4-Mar-3 Deutscher-Menzies, Melbourne #218/R (A.D 2200)
£880 $1417 €1320 Figure and tree (30x25cm-12x10in) init. ripolin on paper. 6-May-3 Christie's, Melbourne #226 est:1000-2000 (A.D 2200)
£880 $1417 €1320 Head study (30x25cm-12x10in) s.d.6 July 69 verso ripolin on paper. 6-May-3 Christie's, Melbourne #299 est:2000-3000 (A.D 2200)
£880 $1417 €1320 Skull with helicopter (30x25cm-12x10in) s.i.d.67 ripolin on card. 6-May-3 Christie's, Melbourne #354/R est:2000-3000 (A.D 2200)
£928 $1467 €1392 Landscape (24x30cm-9x12in) s. card. 27-Nov-2 Deutscher-Menzies, Melbourne #141/R est:3000-4000 (A.D 2600)
£958 $1427 €1437 Convict (30x25cm-12x10in) s.d.68 verso ripolin on paper. 27-Aug-2 Christie's, Melbourne #187 est:2500-3500 (A.D 2500)
£981 $1530 €1700 Head (56x37cm-22x15in) s.d.83 oil pastel prov. 31-Mar-3 Goodman, Sydney #159/R (A.D 2600)
£1000 $1570 €1500 Asia. Leda and Swan (25x30cm-10x12in) one s.d.67 s.i.d.1 June 1969 verso ripolin paper pair. 25-Nov-2 Christie's, Melbourne #445 est:3000-5000 (A.D 2800)
£1000 $1610 €1500 Two figures (29x24cm-11x9in) init.d.3rd Oct ripolin ink on paper. 6-May-3 Christie's, Melbourne #256 est:2500-3500 (A.D 2500)
£1036 $1699 €1554 Greek fragments (30x25cm-12x10in) s.d.54 card on board. 4-Jun-3 Deutscher-Menzies, Melbourne #341/R est:2000-3000 (A.D 2600)
£1040 $1674 €1560 Native flowers (30x25cm-12x10in) s. s.d.10 Feb 70 verso ripolin on paper. 6-May-3 Christie's, Melbourne #236 est:2000-3000 (A.D 2600)
£1040 $1674 €1560 Head study (30x25cm-12x10in) s.d.July 6 69 ripolin on paper. 6-May-3 Christie's, Melbourne #366 est:2000-3000 (A.D 2600)
£1071 $1682 €1607 Face. Obstructed face. Head in profile (30x25cm-12x10in) s.d.1968 verso ripolin paper three. 25-Nov-2 Christie's, Melbourne #213 est:3000-5000 (A.D 3000)
£1071 $1682 €1607 Sonnet (63x51cm-25x20in) one s.i.d.17th Oct 63 verso one s.i. ripolin paper pair. 25-Nov-2 Christie's, Melbourne #270 est:3000-5000 (A.D 3000)
£1071 $1682 €1607 Central Australia (25x30cm-10x12in) s.d.67 s.d.April/May 1967 verso ripolin paper. 25-Nov-2 Christie's, Melbourne #426/R est:2000-3000 (A.D 3000)
£1073 $1598 €1610 Lowell No.90 (30x25cm-12x10in) s. s.i.verso ripolin on paper. 27-Aug-2 Christie's, Melbourne #335 est:3000-4000 (A.D 2800)
£1149 $1713 €1724 Convict and figure (25x30cm-10x12in) s.d.10 Feb 68 ripolin on paper. 27-Aug-2 Christie's, Melbourne #306 est:3000-4000 (A.D 3000)
£1153 $1799 €1730 Desert flowers II. Desert flowers III (28x23cm-11x9in) ripolin enamel board pair. 11-Nov-2 Stephan Welz, Johannesburg #434/R est:9000-12000 (SA.R 18000)
£1200 $1932 €1800 Head study (30x25cm-12x10in) s.d.6 July 69 ripolin. 6-May-3 Christie's, Melbourne #290 est:2000-3000 (A.D 3000)
£1226 $1827 €1839 Convict dancing (26x30cm-10x12in) init. s.verso ripolin on paper. 27-Aug-2 Christie's, Melbourne #308 est:2500-3500 (A.D 3200)
£1429 $2243 €2144 Flowers (36x25cm-14x10in) s.d.23 June 69 verso ripolin paper sold with another similar. 25-Nov-2 Christie's, Melbourne #201 est:3000-5000 (A.D 4000)
£1520 $2447 €2280 Shakespeare's sonnets (63x50cm-25x20in) s. s.i.d.1967 verso ripolin on paper. 6-May-3 Christie's, Melbourne #233 est:2000-3000 (A.D 3800)

£1545 $2441 €2240 Gallipoli landscape (25x30cm-10x12in) s. ripolin paper on board prov. 22-Jul-3 Lawson Menzies, Sydney #120/R est:3000-4000 (A.D 3800)
£1786 $2804 €2679 New Guina dance (52x76cm-20x30in) s. i.verso ripolin paper on board. 25-Nov-2 Christie's, Melbourne #400 est:5000-7000 (A.D 5000)
£1800 $2898 €2700 Leda and the swan series (30x25cm-12x10in) s.d.1959 verso ripolin. 6-May-3 Christie's, Melbourne #350 est:2500-3500 (A.D 4500)
£2000 $3220 €3000 Bird (76x61cm-30x24in) s. s.d.3 Aug 84 ripolin on paper. 6-May-3 Christie's, Melbourne #208 est:4000-6000 (A.D 5000)
£2061 $3133 €3092 Landscape (51x75cm-20x30in) s. board. 27-Aug-2 Goodman, Sydney #120 est:7000-10000 (A.D 5750)
£2107 $3140 €3161 Central Australian landscape (74x51cm-29x20in) s. ripolin on paper. 27-Aug-2 Christie's, Melbourne #271 est:5000-7000 (A.D 5500)
£2200 $3542 €3300 Shark (30x25cm-12x10in) s.i. verso ripolin on paper two. 6-May-3 Christie's, Melbourne #202 est:3000-5000 (A.D 5500)
£2200 $3542 €3190 Hydra (25x30cm-10x12in) s. board. 12-May-3 Joel, Victoria #345a est:5500-7500 (A.D 5500)
£2357 $3724 €3536 Landscape (50x75cm-20x30in) s. paper on board prov. 26-Nov-2 Sotheby's, Melbourne #158 est:6000-10000 (A.D 6600)
£2400 $3864 €3600 Reclining figure (25x30cm-10x12in) s. ripolin on paper. 6-May-3 Christie's, Melbourne #210 est:3000-5000 (A.D 6000)
£2400 $3864 €3600 Central Australian landscape (50x75cm-20x30in) s. ripolin pastel on board. 6-May-3 Christie's, Melbourne #345/R est:5000-7000 (A.D 6000)
£2884 $4586 €4326 Jungle pool (29x24cm-11x9in) s. ripolin paper. 4-Mar-3 Deutscher-Menzies, Melbourne #197/R est:3500-5500 (A.D 7500)
£2888 $4477 €4332 Crocodile attack no 10 (120x208cm-47x82in) s. spray enamel masonite. 3-Dec-2 Shapiro, Sydney #12/R est:8000-12000 (A.D 8000)
£2888 $4477 €4332 Crocodile attack no 4 (120x208cm-47x82in) s. spray enamel masonite. 3-Dec-2 Shapiro, Sydney #13/R est:8000-12000 (A.D 8000)
£3036 $4796 €4554 Bather (122x91cm-48x36in) s. ripolin enamel on board prov.exhib. 26-Nov-2 Sotheby's, Melbourne #113/R est:10000-15000 (A.D 8500)
£3101 $4930 €4652 Two heads (26x21cm-10x8in) s.i. paper prov. 5-May-3 Sotheby's, Melbourne #17/R est:8000 (A.D 8000)
£3175 $5270 €5409 Waterlily series (178x120cm-70x47in) s.verso enamel. 10-Jun-3 Shapiro, Sydney #24/R est:8000-12000 (A.D 8000)
£3175 $5270 €5409 Waterlily series (178x120cm-70x47in) enamel on masonite board. 10-Jun-3 Shapiro, Sydney #25/R est:8000-12000 (A.D 8000)
£3175 $5270 €5409 Waterlily series no.4 (178x120cm-70x47in) enamel masonite on board. 10-Jun-3 Shapiro, Sydney #26/R est:8000-12000 (A.D 8000)
£3175 $5270 €5409 Waterlily series no.8 (178x120cm-70x47in) i.verso enamel on masonite board. 10-Jun-3 Shapiro, Sydney #26a est:8000-12000 (A.D 8000)
£3200 $5152 €4800 Leda and the swan (25x30cm-10x12in) s. ripolin on paper. 6-May-3 Christie's, Melbourne #224 est:4000-6000 (A.D 8000)
£3295 $5238 €4943 Man on horseback (20x25cm-8x10in) i. paper prov. 5-May-3 Sotheby's, Melbourne #29/R est:5000 (A.D 8500)
£3461 $5504 €5192 Native and bird, New Guinea (52x76cm-20x30in) s. paper on board painted c.1972. 4-Mar-3 Deutscher-Menzies, Melbourne #157/R est:10000-15000 (A.D 9000)
£3770 $6258 €6424 Dreamtime no.57 (242x120cm-95x47in) s.verso spray enamel on masonite board. 10-Jun-3 Shapiro, Sydney #27 est:7000-9000 (A.D 9500)
£3791 $5876 €5687 Crocodile attack no 5 (208x120cm-82x47in) s. spray enamel masonite. 3-Dec-2 Shapiro, Sydney #14/R est:8000-12000 (A.D 10500)
£3984 $6534 €5976 Dusk at Dimboola (49x62cm-19x24in) canvas on board prov. 4-Jun-3 Deutscher-Menzies, Melbourne #131/R est:12000-18000 (A.D 10000)
£4056 $6286 €6084 Dreamtime no 47 (242x120cm-95x47in) s. i.verso spray enamel masonite. 3-Dec-2 Shapiro, Sydney #7/R est:12000-18000 (A.D 11200)
£4286 $6771 €6429 Bather (122x91cm-48x36in) s. ripolin enamel painted 1975 prov.exhib. 26-Nov-2 Sotheby's, Melbourne #114/R est:10000-15000 (A.D 12000)
£4332 $6715 €6498 Dreamtime no 55 (242x120cm-95x47in) s. i.d.March 1989 verso spray enamel masonite. 3-Dec-2 Shapiro, Sydney #6/R est:12000-18000 (A.D 12000)
£4338 $6593 €6507 The dance (51x75cm-20x30in) s. board. 28-Aug-2 Deutscher-Menzies, Melbourne #111/R est:8000-10000 (A.D 12100)
£4513 $6995 €6770 Dreamtime no 59 (242x120cm-95x47in) s. i.d.March 1989 verso spray enamel masonite. 3-Dec-2 Shapiro, Sydney #4/R est:12000-18000 (A.D 12500)
£4660 $7082 €6990 Landscape (91x122cm-36x48in) s. s.i.1981 verso composition board. 28-Aug-2 Deutscher-Menzies, Melbourne #87/R est:15000-20000 (A.D 13000)
£4660 $7082 €6990 Central Australian landscape (91x122cm-36x48in) s. composition board. 28-Aug 2 Deutscher-Menzies, Melbourne #88/R est:15000-20000 (A.D 13000)
£4800 $7728 €7200 Leda and the swan (30x25cm-12x10in) s. ripolin paper on board. 6-May-3 Christie's, Melbourne #213/R est:9000-12000 (A.D 12000)
£4874 $7554 €7311 Dreamtime no 52 (242x120cm-95x47in) s. i.d.Jan 89 verso spray enamel masonite. 3-Dec-2 Shapiro, Sydney #2/R est:12000-18000 (A.D 13500)
£4981 $7421 €7472 Kelly (75x52cm-30x20in) s. ripolin pastel paper on board. 27-Aug-2 Christie's, Melbourne #150/R est:9000-12000 (A.D 13000)
£5376 $8172 €8064 Central Australian landscape IV (91x122cm-36x48in) s. i.verso composition board. 28-Aug-2 Deutscher-Menzies, Melbourne #89/R est:15000-20000 (A.D 15000)
£5376 $8172 €8064 Inland landscape II (91x122cm-36x48in) s. s.i.d.1981 verso composition board. 28-Aug-2 Deutscher-Menzies, Melbourne #91/R est:15000-20000 (A.D 15000)
£5596 $8674 €8394 Dreamtime no 50 (242x120cm-95x47in) s. i.verso spray enamel masonite. 3-Dec-2 Shapiro, Sydney #1 est:12000-18000 (A.D 15500)
£5600 $9016 €8400 Figure and landscape (90x121cm-35x48in) s. s.i.verso ripolin on board. 6-May-3 Christie's, Melbourne #143/R est:15000-20000 (A.D 14000)
£5725 $9046 €8588 Burke and Wills (90x70cm-35x28in) s.d.8 Dec 1967 verso paper composition board. 7-Apr-3 Shapiro, Sydney #440 est:12000-18000 (A.D 15000)
£5735 $8717 €8603 Central Australian landscape I (91x122cm-36x48in) s. i.1981 verso composition board. 28-Aug-2 Deutscher-Menzies, Melbourne #93/R est:15000-20000 (A.D 16000)
£5769 $9173 €8654 Bald native head (122x91cm-48x36in) init. d.27/12/62 verso composition board prov. 4-Mar-3 Deutscher-Menzies, Melbourne #86/R est:18000-25000 (A.D 15000)
£6000 $9660 €9000 Kelly (64x52cm-25x20in) s.d.1961 verso ripolin on paper. 6-May-3 Christie's, Melbourne #309/R est:7000-10000 (A.D 15000)
£6318 $9793 €9477 Dreamtime no 64 (120x120cm-47x47in) s. i.d.1989 verso spray enamel masonite. 3-Dec-2 Shapiro, Sydney #8/R est:10000-15000 (A.D 17500)
£7143 $11286 €10715 Bather (122x91cm-48x36in) s. s.verso ripolin enamel on board prov.exhib. 26-Nov-2 Sotheby's, Melbourne #46/R est:15000-20000 (A.D 20000)
£7581 $11751 €11372 Dreamtime no 31 (242x120cm-95x47in) s. i.d.Jan 89 verso spray enamel masonite. 3-Dec-2 Shapiro, Sydney #5/R est:12000-18000 (A.D 21000)
£7724 $12203 €11200 Figures in a landscape (90x120cm-35x47in) s. ripolin on board prov. 22-Jul-3 Lawson Menzies, Sydney #121/R est:16000-20000 (A.D 19000)
£7857 $12414 €11786 Woman. init.d.1962 board prov. 26-Nov-2 Sotheby's, Melbourne #44/R est:15000-25000 (A.D 22000)
£7885 $11986 €11828 Dam near Glenrowan (122x152cm-48x60in) init.d.70 i.verso composition board. 28-Aug-2 Deutscher-Menzies, Melbourne #85/R est:15000-20000 (A.D 22000)
£9195 $13701 €13793 Kelly in landscape (46x63cm-18x25in) init. ripolin. 27-Aug-2 Christie's, Melbourne #159/R est:8000-10000 (A.D 24000)
£9286 $14579 €13929 Man and parrot (76x63cm-30x25in) s.i.d.1946 verso ripolin board. 25-Nov-2 Christie's, Melbourne #119/R est:25000-35000 (A.D 26000)
£9319 $14165 €13979 Bush (152x122cm-60x48in) s. i.d.1970 verso composition board. 28-Aug-2 Deutscher-Menzies, Melbourne #94/R est:12000-15000 (A.D 26000)
£9677 $14710 €14516 Rimbaud at Harar (152x122cm-60x48in) s. i.d.1963 verso ripolin enamel composition board. 28-Aug-2 Deutscher-Menzies, Melbourne #86/R est:12000-15000 (A.D 27000)
£9677 $14710 €14516 Central Australian landscape III (91x122cm-36x48in) s. i.verso composition board. 28-Aug-2 Deutscher-Menzies, Melbourne #92/R est:15000-20000 (A.D 27000)
£11388 $17423 €17082 Explorer in landscape (50x74cm-20x29in) s. oil crayon paper on board prov. 25-Aug-2 Sotheby's, Paddington #78/R est:15000-20000 (A.D 32000)

£12000 $19320 €18000 Leda and the swan (122x91cm-48x36in) init. s.d.28 April 1960 verso board prov.exhib. 6-May-3 Christie's, Melbourne #136/R est:30000-40000 (A.D 30000)
£12903 $19613 €19355 Soldier bathing, Galipoli (149x119cm-59x47in) init. s.d.12th Jan 1959 verso polyvinyl acetate board exhib. 28-Aug-2 Deutscher-Menzies, Melbourne #83/R est:40000-60000 (A.D 36000)
£13178 $20953 €19767 Kweilin river I (121x150cm-48x59in) init. prov. 5-May-3 Sotheby's, Melbourne #55/R est:20000 (A.D 34000)
£15771 $23971 €23657 Central Australian landscape (91x122cm-36x48in) s. composition board. 28-Aug-2 Deutscher-Menzies, Melbourne #90/R est:15000-20000 (A.D 44000)
£16667 $26500 €25001 Miner (121x121cm-48x48in) s. board prov. 5-May-3 Sotheby's, Melbourne #24/R est:30000-50000 (A.D 43000)
£16800 $27048 €25200 Swimmer (72x35cm-28x14in) s. ripolin on board painted c.1945 prov.exhib. 6-May-3 Christie's, Melbourne #90/R est:45000-60000 (A.D 42000)
£17241 $25690 €25862 New Guinea (121x121cm-48x48in) i. s.i.verso ripolin on board prov.exhib. 27-Aug-2 Christie's, Melbourne #75/R est:45000-55000 (A.D 45000)
£17857 $28214 €26786 Elephant (120x150cm-47x59in) init. board painted c.1953 prov. 26-Nov-2 Sotheby's, Melbourne #53/R est:25000-35000 (A.D 50000)
£22857 $36114 €34286 Fitzroy river (122x92cm-48x36in) s.d.17.2.50 oil ripolin enamel on board. 17-Nov-2 Sotheby's, Paddington #13/R est:80000-100000 (A.D 64000)
£28470 $43559 €42705 Central Australia (92x122cm-36x48in) s.d.1956 s.i.d.verso ripolan enamel board prov. 25-Aug-2 Sotheby's, Paddington #50/R est:80000-120000 (A.D 80000)
£29457 $46837 €44186 Kelly and reflection (91x122cm-36x48in) s. s.i.d.1980 verso ripolin enamel board prov.exhib. 5-May-3 Sotheby's, Melbourne #6/R est:50000-80000 (A.D 76000)
£44574 $70872 €66861 Girl and township (121x91cm-48x36in) s.d.62 s.i.d.1962 verso ripolin enamel board prov.exhib. 5-May-3 Sotheby's, Melbourne #161/R est:80000-120000 (A.D 115000)
£46000 $74060 €69000 Explorer (122x122cm-48x48in) s.i. verso ripolin on board prov.lit. 6-May-3 Christie's, Melbourne #52/R est:90000-120000 (A.D 115000)
£46429 $73357 €69644 Kelly in bush (61x51cm-24x20in) s.i.d.55 ripolin enamel board prov.exhib. 17-Nov-2 Sotheby's, Paddington #6/R est:120000-160000 (A.D 130000)
£46512 $73953 €69768 Kelly gang: bushranger portrait (76x63cm-30x25in) s. s.i.d.1945 verso ripolin enamel prov.exhib. 5-May-3 Sotheby's, Melbourne #43/R est:120000-180000 (A.D 120000)
£47809 $78406 €71714 Dimboola (34x76cm-13x30in) s.i.d.1943 verso enamel board prov.exhib. 4-Jun-3 Deutscher-Menzies, Melbourne #38/R est:140000-180000 (A.D 120000)
£50000 $79500 €75000 Luna Park (67x84cm-26x33in) i.d.41 prov.exhib.lit. 4-Mar-3 Deutscher-Menzies, Melbourne #41/R est:70000-90000 (A.D 130000)
£56940 $87117 €85410 Crossing river - Burke and Wills expedition (122x122cm-48x48in) init.d.23 i.verso board prov.exhib. 25-Aug-2 Sotheby's, Paddington #58/R est:160000-210000 (A.D 160000)
£96899 $154070 €145349 Robbed (90x121cm-35x48in) i.d.1947 verso ripolin enamel board exhib.lit. 5-May-3 Sotheby's, Melbourne #48/R est:350000-550000 (A.D 250000)
£100775 $160233 €151163 Ned Kelly and policeman (122x152cm-48x60in) init. board painted 1964 prov.exhib. 5-May-3 Sotheby's, Melbourne #16/R est:200000-300000 (A.D 260000)
£160142 $245018 €240213 Glenrowan - Ned Kelly series (90x70cm-35x28in) init.d.15.2.55 i.verso ripolin enamel on board. 25-Aug-2 Sotheby's, Paddington #31/R est:400000-500000 (A.D 450000)

Prints

£3682 $5855 €5523 Ned Kelly kneeling in landscape (24x20cm-9x8in) s.verso monotype prov. 5-May-3 Sotheby's, Melbourne #25/R est:7000 (A.D 9500)
£15000 $23700 €22500 Ned Kelly (54x70cm-21x28in) s.num. silkscreen prints set of 15. 26-Nov-2 Sotheby's, Melbourne #52/R est:25000-35000 (A.D 42000)

Works on paper

£250 $395 €375 Carcass (30x25cm-12x10in) ink felt tip pen. 27-Nov-2 Deutscher-Menzies, Melbourne #232/R (A.D 700)
£393 $621 €590 Untitled - horse (29x22cm-11x9in) init. pencil. 27-Nov-2 Deutscher-Menzies, Melbourne #230/R est:800-1200 (A.D 1100)
£571 $903 €857 Untitled - Christ (30x25cm-12x10in) s. s.i.d.1955 verso mixed media. 27-Nov-2 Deutscher-Menzies, Melbourne #231/R est:900-1200 (A.D 1600)
£577 $917 €866 Central Australian landscape (24x29cm-9x11in) mixed media. 4-Mar-3 Deutscher-Menzies, Melbourne #268/R (A.D 1500)
£643 $1009 €965 Australian outback (29x22cm-11x9in) s. crayon. 25-Nov-2 Christie's, Melbourne #448 (A.D 1800)
£645 $981 €968 Crucifix and baboon (61x49cm-24x19in) s. mixed media prov. 28-Aug-2 Deutscher-Menzies, Melbourne #131/R (A.D 1800)
£717 $1090 €1076 Crucifix and fish (61x49cm-24x19in) s. mixed media prov. 28-Aug-2 Deutscher-Menzies, Melbourne #130/R (A.D 2000)
£775 $1233 €1163 Shooting (34x25cm-13x10in) s. crayon. 5-May-3 Sotheby's, Melbourne #256/R (A.D 2000)
£786 $1241 €1179 Untitled - figures (76x56cm-30x22in) s. wax crayon. 27-Nov-2 Deutscher-Menzies, Melbourne #233/R est:900-1200 (A.D 2200)
£1008 $1602 €1512 Landscape with flower (25x30cm-10x12in) init.i.d.56 verso mixed media prov. 5-May-3 Sotheby's, Melbourne #12/R est:3000 (A.D 2600)
£1040 $1674 €1560 Crowned Kelly (39x29cm-15x11in) s. ink prov. 6-May-3 Christie's, Melbourne #262/R est:1200-1500 (A.D 2600)
£1047 $1623 €1571 Untitled, wild flowers (30x25cm-12x10in) s. ripolin paper on board painted c.1968. 3-Dec-2 Shapiro, Sydney #16/R est:3000-5000 (A.D 2900)
£1071 $1682 €1607 Near the ocean, Cleopatra (61x48cm-24x19in) s. pastel exhib. 25-Nov-2 Christie's, Melbourne #283/R est:2500-3500 (A.D 3000)
£1071 $1693 €1607 Central Australian landscape (23x30cm-9x12in) s. W/C executed c.1950. 26-Nov-2 Sotheby's, Melbourne #134 est:3000-5000 (A.D 3000)
£1149 $1713 €1724 Cal (30x25cm-12x10in) s. s.i.d.69 verso ripolin on paper. 27-Aug-2 Christie's, Melbourne #328 est:2000-3000 (A.D 3000)
£1260 $2003 €1890 Cross (25x30cm-10x12in) init.d.1960 mixed media prov. 5-May-3 Sotheby's, Melbourne #30/R est:3500 (A.D 3250)
£1357 $2144 €2036 Figures in landscape (25x30cm-10x12in) s.d.69 mixed media. 27-Nov-2 Deutscher-Menzies, Melbourne #175/R est:3000-4000 (A.D 3800)
£1473 $2342 €2210 Orange floating figure (25x30cm-10x12in) s.i.d.1982 verso mixed media prov. 5-May-3 Sotheby's, Melbourne #11/R est:3500 (A.D 3800)
£1495 $2287 €2243 Shakespeare sonnet no.136 (63x50cm-25x20in) mixed media executed 1967 prov. 26-Aug-2 Sotheby's, Paddington #662/R est:5000-7000 (A.D 4200)
£1550 $2465 €2325 Leda and swan (30x25cm-12x10in) i.d.55 verso mixed media prov. 5-May-3 Sotheby's, Melbourne #37/R (A.D 4000)
£1628 $2588 €2442 Crouching figure, oeil (30x25cm-12x10in) init.d.57 mixed media prov. 5-May-3 Sotheby's, Melbourne #26/R est:6000 (A.D 4200)
£1628 $2588 €2442 Dancer (30x25cm-12x10in) s.d.67 verso dr mixed media prov. 5-May-3 Sotheby's, Melbourne #39/R (A.D 4200)
£1649 $2506 €2474 Frazer and trees (29x24cm-11x9in) init. mixed media exec.c.1962. 28-Aug-2 Deutscher-Menzies, Melbourne #305/R est:5000-7000 (A.D 4600)
£1793 $2940 €2690 Plant (24x29cm-9x11in) init.d.9.4.49 ink enamel glass prov. 4-Jun-3 Deutscher-Menzies, Melbourne #373/R est:3000-4000 (A.D 4500)
£1860 $2958 €2790 Blue sea, red cliffs, Gallipoli (25x30cm-10x12in) s. s.d.1958 verso mixed media prov.lit. 5-May-3 Sotheby's, Melbourne #40/R est:5000 (A.D 4800)
£1938 $3081 €2907 Butterfly and flower (30x25cm-12x10in) init. wax crayon dyes prov. 5-May-3 Sotheby's, Melbourne #4/R est:5000 (A.D 5000)
£1938 $3081 €2907 Bird and flower (30x25cm-12x10in) init. wax crayon dyes prov. 5-May-3 Sotheby's, Melbourne #54/R est:5000 (A.D 5000)
£1957 $2995 €2936 Shakespeare sonnet No.110 (63x51cm-25x20in) s. mixed media executed 1967 prov.exhib. 26-Aug-2 Sotheby's, Paddington #661/R est:7000-10000 (A.D 5500)
£2132 $3390 €3198 Figure II (30x25cm-12x10in) init.i.d.57 wax crayon dyes prov. 5-May-3 Sotheby's, Melbourne #45/R est:3500 (A.D 5500)
£2143 $3321 €3215 Mrs Fraser and convict (23x29cm-9x11in) s.i.d.1958 mixed media. 29-Oct-2 Lawson Menzies, Sydney #102/R est:6000-8000 (A.D 6000)
£2229 $3544 €3344 Floating figure, Gallipoli (25x30cm-10x12in) init.d.57 mixed media prov. 5-May-3 Sotheby's, Melbourne #57/R (A.D 5750)
£2500 $3975 €3750 Africa (37x27cm-15x11in) s.i.d.June 1977 col crayon set of nine. 29-Apr-3 Bonhams, New Bond Street #12/R est:2500-3000
£2519 $4006 €3779 Swimmer, Gallipoli (29x24cm-11x9in) init. s.i.d.1958 verso mixed media prov. 5-May-3 Sotheby's, Melbourne #51/R est:6000 (A.D 6500)
£2688 $4085 €4032 Leda and the swan (24x29cm-9x11in) init. mixed media exec.c.1962. 28-Aug-2 Deutscher-Menzies, Melbourne #304/R est:5000-7000 (A.D 7500)

£2847 $4356 €4271 Head hunters pursued by bird of paradise (50x74cm-20x29in) s. mixed media paper on board. 25-Aug-2 Sotheby's, Paddington #201/R est:6000-8000 (A.D 8000)
£3025 $4628 €4538 Central Australia (52x76cm-20x30in) s.d.1967 mixed media prov. 26-Aug-2 Sotheby's, Paddington #643/R est:6000-8000 (A.D 8500)
£3101 $4930 €4652 Red and blue Kelly head (30x25cm-12x10in) init.i.d.56 mixed media prov. 5-May-3 Sotheby's, Melbourne #18/R est:10000 (A.D 8000)
£3200 $5216 €4800 Burke and Wills (56x65cm-22x26in) synthetic polymer hardboard. 28-Jan-3 Henry Adams, Chichester #473/R est:2000-3000
£3295 $5238 €4943 Verve (30x25cm-12x10in) init.i. wax dyes prov. 5-May-3 Sotheby's, Melbourne #3/R est:6000 (A.D 8500)
£3488 $5547 €5232 Gallipoli soldier (28x24cm-11x9in) init. s.i.d.1958 verso mixed media prov. 5-May-3 Sotheby's, Melbourne #50/R est:7000 (A.D 9000)
£3800 $6118 €5700 Ned Kelly (65x48cm-26x19in) init. col chk etching. 6-May-3 Christie's, Melbourne #294/R est:8000-12000 (A.D 9500)
£3831 $6015 €5747 Figure and rainbow serpent (52x75cm-20x30in) s. mixed media. 15-Apr-3 Lawson Menzies, Sydney #130/R est:8000-14000 (A.D 10000)
£3915 $5989 €5873 Burke and camel (50x75cm-20x30in) s.d.15.7.66 mixed media on board prov. 25-Aug-2 Sotheby's, Paddington #155/R est:10000-15000 (A.D 11000)
£4400 $7084 €6600 Ned Kelly and Drought (65x48cm-26x19in) init. col chks etching. 6-May-3 Christie's, Melbourne #356/R est:8000-12000 (A.D 11000)
£4464 $7054 €6696 Outback landscape (52x76cm-20x30in) s. mixed media. 26-Nov-2 Sotheby's, Melbourne #103/R est:8000-12000 (A.D 12500)
£4981 $7820 €7472 New Guinea series (52x75cm-20x30in) s. mixed media. 15-Apr-3 Lawson Menzies, Sydney #26/R est:12000-18000 (A.D 13000)
£5814 $9244 €8721 Kelly (30x25cm-12x10in) init.d.57 mixed media prov. 5-May-3 Sotheby's, Melbourne #36/R est:7000-10000 (A.D 15000)
£6429 $10157 €9644 Leda and Swan (150x120cm-59x47in) polyvinyl acetate on board painted c.1960 board. 26-Nov-2 Sotheby's, Melbourne #59/R est:20000-30000 (A.D 18000)
£9562 $15681 €14343 Kelly on horseback (30x25cm-12x10in) init.i.d.10-7-56 verso mixed media. 4-Jun-3 Deutscher-Menzies, Melbourne #6/R est:12000-18000 (A.D 24000)
£11155 $18295 €16733 Kelly and running horse (51x74cm-20x29in) s.d.21 July 1966 verso mixed media exhib. 4-Jun-3 Deutscher-Menzies, Melbourne #85/R est:25000-30000 (A.D 28000)
£15504 $24651 €23256 Heron (151x120cm-59x47in) s. polymer spray prov. 5-May-3 Sotheby's, Melbourne #31/R est:14000-18000 (A.D 40000)

NOLAN, Sidney and WARHOL, Andy (20th C) Australian/American

Works on paper

£1900 $3097 €2850 Campbells soup (17x22cm-7x9in) s.i. one d.6 Sept 76 pen ink two. 3-Feb-3 Sotheby's, Olympia #152/R est:800-1200

NOLAND, Cady (1956-) American

Sculpture

£6027 $9402 €9041 Five-Lane-Maniac (28x33x40cm-11x13x16in) metal ready-mades executed 1988 prov. 6-Nov-2 AB Stockholms Auktionsverk #846/R est:10000-12000 (S.KR 86000)

NOLAND, Kenneth (1924-) American

£9375 $15000 €14063 Right pitch (210x132cm-83x52in) s. i.d.1977 verso acrylic prov. 14-May-3 Sotheby's, New York #148/R est:10000-15000
£12658 $20000 €18987 Southline (114x114cm-45x45in) s. i.d.1966 verso acrylic prov.lit. 13-Nov-2 Sotheby's, New York #222/R est:30000-40000
£26250 $42000 €39375 Elide (110x260cm-43x102in) s.i.d.1969 verso acrylic prov. 15-May-3 Christie's, Rockefeller NY #134/R est:30000-40000
£28261 $43804 €42392 Open trough (250x60cm-98x24in) s.d.1967 acrylic prov. 4-Dec-2 Koller, Zurich #48/R est:60000-80000 (S.FR 65000)

Prints

£2044 $3250 €3066 Shadow line (43x121cm-17x48in) s.d.verso col screenprint canvas laminated board edition of 150. 2-May-3 Sotheby's, New York #561/R est:2500-3500

Works on paper

£3681 $6000 €5522 Untitled 1 (84x85cm-33x33in) s.d.1977 verso cast paper pulp. 13-Feb-3 Christie's, Rockefeller NY #320/R

NOLDE, Emil (1867-1956) German

£6597 $10490 €9500 In the morning (30x24cm-12x9in) s.i.d. drypoint aquatint. 5-May-3 Ketterer, Munich #924/R est:3000-4000
£185897 $288141 €290000 Hay field (47x70cm-19x28in) s.i. painted 1907 prov.exhib.lit. 6-Dec-2 Ketterer, Munich #24/R est:250000-350000
£850000 $1385500 €1275000 Sonnenblumenbild I (73x89cm-29x35in) s. s.i.verso panel painted 1928 prov.exhib.lit. 3-Feb-3 Christie's, London #11/R est:900000-1200000

Prints

£1772 $2800 €2800 Woodland children (25x30cm-10x12in) s.i. drypoint brush etching. 30-Nov-2 Villa Grisebach, Berlin #193/R est:3500-4500
£1923 $3000 €2885 Zwei frauen (19x15cm-7x6in) s.i.d.06 num.15 col etching. 7-Nov-2 Swann Galleries, New York #755/R est:3500-5000
£1923 $2981 €3000 Figures round table (15x19cm-6x7in) s.d. etching. 7-Dec-2 Hauswedell & Nolte, Hamburg #953/R est:3000
£2113 $3507 €3000 Sailing boat (19x15cm-7x6in) s.d. drypoint etching. 14-Jun-3 Hauswedell & Nolte, Hamburg #1480/R est:3500
£2264 $3600 €3396 Abschied (17x12cm-7x5in) drypoint etching aquatint. 1-May-3 Swann Galleries, New York #109/R est:4000-6000
£2516 $3925 €4000 Tug (20x28cm-8x11in) s.i. 21-Sep-2 Bolland & Marotz, Bremen #764/R est:5500
£2564 $3974 €4000 Woman N (23x19cm-9x7in) etching prov. 4-Dec-2 Lempertz, Koln #954/R est:2800
£2586 $4085 €3879 Frau N - Ada Nolde (23x18cm-9x7in) s.i. drypoint lit. 28-Apr-3 Bukowskis, Stockholm #485/R est:40000-50000 (S.KR 34000)
£2673 $4250 €4010 Waldkinder, wood sprites (25x30cm-10x12in) s. drypoint etching. 2-May-3 Sotheby's, New York #248/R est:4000-6000
£2821 $4456 €4400 Head with pipe, E N - self portrait (40x28cm-16x11in) s. lithograph paper on board. 14-Nov-2 Neumeister, Munich #643/R est:2500-3000
£3472 $5521 €5000 Young mother (21x15cm-8x6in) s.i. woodcut. 5-May-3 Ketterer, Munich #932/R est:2500-3500
£3521 $5845 €5000 Woodland children (25x30cm-10x12in) s. drypoint etching aquatint. 14-Jun-3 Hauswedell & Nolte, Hamburg #1486/R est:5000
£3526 $5465 €5500 Peasant (23x31cm-9x12in) s.i. etching. 7-Dec-2 Hauswedell & Nolte, Hamburg #958 est:6000
£4225 $7014 €6000 Solomon and his women (30x25cm-12x10in) s.i. etching. 14-Jun-3 Hauswedell & Nolte, Hamburg #1485/R est:8000
£4514 $7177 €6500 Double portrait (31x23cm-12x9in) s.i. woodcut. 5-May-3 Ketterer, Munich #931/R est:4000-6000
£4514 $7177 €6500 Woman's face in profile (21x15cm-8x6in) s.i. woodcut. 5-May-3 Ketterer, Munich #934/R est:5000-7000
£4514 $7177 €6500 Death as a dancer (21x26cm-8x10in) s. etching. 5-May-3 Ketterer, Munich #937/R est:3000-5000
£4600 $7682 €6670 Expressionist, woman with bird on her arm in a field horses (31x22cm-12x9in) s. etching. 11-Jul-3 Bracketts, Tunbridge Wells #781/R est:300-500
£4800 $7440 €7200 Hamburg, schiff im dock (46x58cm-18x23in) s.i. etching. 3-Dec-2 Christie's, London #178/R est:5000-7000
£5068 $7905 €7500 Young girl I (21x32cm-8x13in) s. woodcut. 28-Mar-3 Ketterer, Hamburg #525/R est:8000-10000
£5072 $8319 €7000 Admiration (32x25cm-13x10in) s. etching drypoint. 31-May-3 Villa Grisebach, Berlin #225/R est:5000-7000
£5072 $8319 €7000 Woman's head III (29x23cm-11x9in) s. woodcut board. 31-May-3 Villa Grisebach, Berlin #181/R est:7000-9000
£5211 $8651 €7400 Sailing ship and smoke (41x31cm-16x12in) s.i. etching. 14-Jun-3 Hauswedell & Nolte, Hamburg #1484/R est:8000
£5449 $8446 €8500 Double portrait (32x23cm-13x9in) s. woodcut. 7-Dec-2 Hauswedell & Nolte, Hamburg #960/R est:7500
£5634 $9352 €8000 Sailing ship and three steamers (31x41cm-12x16in) s.i. etching. 14-Jun-3 Hauswedell & Nolte, Hamburg #1483/R est:9000
£5769 $8942 €9000 Alice (33x21cm-13x8in) s.i. col lithograph. 7-Dec-2 Hauswedell & Nolte, Hamburg #959/R est:6000
£6250 $9938 €9000 Young girl I (22x32cm-9x13in) s.i. woodcut. 5-May-3 Ketterer, Munich #926/R est:6000-8000
£6410 $10000 €9615 Segler und drei kleine dampfer (31x41cm-12x16in) s. etching. 7-Nov-2 Swann Galleries, New York #756/R est:12000-18000
£6690 $11106 €9500 Nude (47x31cm-19x12in) s.i.d. etching. 14-Jun-3 Hauswedell & Nolte, Hamburg #1481/R est:10000
£8333 $12917 €13000 Hamburg (31x41cm-12x16in) s. etching. 7-Dec-2 Hauswedell & Nolte, Hamburg #957/R est:10000
£8491 $13245 €13500 Junges paar (40x34cm-16x13in) s.i. woodcut. 9-Oct-2 Sotheby's, London #502/R est:12500-16000
£8681 $13802 €12500 Mother and child (48x44cm-19x17in) s.i. col lithograph. 5-May-3 Ketterer, Munich #925/R est:3000-4000
£9028 $14354 €13000 Frau N - Frau Ada Nolde (23x18cm-9x7in) s.i. drypoint. 5-May-3 Ketterer, Munich #936/R est:5000-7000
£9615 $15000 €14423 Junger furst und tanzerinnen (26x22cm-10x9in) s.i. etching. 7-Nov-2 Swann Galleries, New York #761/R est:15000-20000
£11806 $18771 €17000 Conversation (24x31cm-9x12in) s.i. woodcut. 5-May-3 Ketterer, Munich #935/R est:4500-6500
£12500 $19875 €18000 Candle dancer (26x22cm-10x9in) s.i. aquatint. 5-May-3 Ketterer, Munich #938/R est:5000-7000
£12821 $19872 €20000 Kneeling girl (30x22cm-12x9in) s. drypoint etching. 7-Dec-2 Hauswedell & Nolte, Hamburg #955/R est:20000
£12844 $21450 €18624 Hamburg, inner harbour (31x41cm-12x16in) s.i. etching. 20-Jun-3 Kornfeld, Bern #123/R est:20000 (S.FR 28000)
£13194 $20979 €19000 Young girl (32x23cm-13x9in) s.i. woodcut. 5-May-3 Ketterer, Munich #933/R est:3000-5000
£14493 $23768 €20000 Steam trawler (30x38cm-12x15in) s. woodcut. 30-May-3 Villa Grisebach, Berlin #33/R est:20000-30000
£15094 $24000 €22641 Kopf mit pfeife (40x28cm-16x11in) s. lithograph. 1-May-3 Swann Galleries, New York #6/R est:30000-40000
£16352 $25509 €26000 Mann und weibchen (24x30cm-9x12in) s.i. woodcut. 9-Oct-2 Sotheby's, London #503/R est:19000-24000
£18349 $30642 €26606 Prophet (32x22cm-13x9in) s.i. woodcut. 20-Jun-3 Kornfeld, Bern #124/R est:50000 (S.FR 40000)

£18987 $30000 €30000 Kneeling Girl (57x45cm-22x18in) s.i. dry point etching one of 37 exec.1907 prov. 29-Nov-2 Villa Grisebach, Berlin #32/R est:35000-40000
£19231 $30000 €28847 Prophet (32x23cm-13x9in) s.i. woodcut edition of 20-30. 7-Nov-2 Swann Galleries, New York #760/R est:30000-50000
£21622 $33730 €32000 Windmill (56x71cm-22x28in) s.i. col lithograph. 28-Mar-3 Ketterer, Hamburg #526/R est:25000-30000
£26408 $43838 €37500 Actress (55x47cm-22x19in) s.i. col lithograph. 14-Jun-3 Hauswedell & Nolte, Hamburg #1488/R est:60000

Sculpture

£2899 $4754 €4000 Crouching woman (12cm-5in) s. verso bronze Cast.Noack Berlin dark pat.bronze prov. 29-May-3 Lempertz, Koln #829/R est:5000

Works on paper

£2860 $4776 €4147 Figure composition (29x44cm-11x17in) s. Indian ink prov.lit. 17-Jun-3 Rasmussen, Copenhagen #73/R est:40000 (D.KR 30000)
£6289 $9811 €10000 Tischgesellschaft - Cafe society (21x26cm-8x10in) s.d.08 brush ink wash prov. 9-Oct-2 Sotheby's, London #109/R est:12000-18000
£7595 $12000 €12000 Two ships on the Baltic (18x22cm-7x9in) s. pen Indian ink W/C paper on board. 29-Nov-2 Schloss Ahlden, Ahlden #1411/R est:9500
£7639 $12146 €11000 At the piano (16x31cm-6x12in) s. Indian ink. 5-May-3 Ketterer, Munich #929/R est:5000-7000
£13889 $22083 €20000 In the cafe (21x31cm-8x12in) s. Indian ink wash. 5-May-3 Ketterer, Munich #927/R est:5000-7000
£18000 $30060 €27000 Madonnenfigur und Hyazinthen (32x47cm-13x19in) s. W/C exec c.1954-55 prov. 26-Jun-3 Christie's, London #415/R est:18000-24000
£18987 $30000 €30000 Turk's head (23x17cm-9x7in) s. W/C brush prov. 30-Nov-2 Villa Grisebach, Berlin #249/R est:30000-40000
£20000 $31200 €30000 Eidechsen - Lizards (35x47cm-14x19in) s.d.25 W/C prov. 9-Oct-2 Sotheby's, London #36/R est:15000-20000
£20833 $33125 €30000 In the ballroom (21x31cm-8x12in) s. Indian ink wash. 5-May-3 Ketterer, Munich #928/R est:7000-9000
£22152 $35000 €35000 Red and yellow cacti (35x47cm-14x19in) s. W/C prov.lit. 30-Nov-2 Villa Grisebach, Berlin #248/R est:40000-50000
£23077 $35769 €36000 White house in hilly landscape (30x49cm-12x19in) s. W/C Indian ink brush. 7-Dec-2 Hauswedell & Nolte, Hamburg #949/R est:30000
£25641 $40000 €38462 Zwei dschunken (28x23cm-11x9in) s. W/C prov. 5-Nov-2 Phillips, New York #129/R est:40000-60000
£26582 $42000 €42000 Boy's portrait (35x28cm-14x11in) s. Indian ink W/C. 30-Nov-2 Villa Grisebach, Berlin #194/R est:30000-40000
£29496 $48374 €41000 Woman's portrait (21x16cm-8x6in) s. W/C prov. 6-Jun-3 Ketterer, Munich #63/R est:30000-40000
£32911 $52000 €52000 Steamboat and sailing boats (34x47cm-13x19in) s. W/C Indian ink exec.c.1920/25 prov. 29-Nov-2 Villa Grisebach, Berlin #36/R est:35000-45000
£34000 $55760 €51000 Portrait of lady (45x36cm-18x14in) s. W/C brush ink exec.c.1920-25 prov. 6-Feb-3 Christie's, London #468/R est:60000
£35971 $58993 €50000 Sea - high sky, dark green water, steamer (17x23cm-7x9in) s. W/C. 6-Jun-3 Ketterer, Munich #80/R est:50000-70000
£37975 $60000 €60000 South sea landscape (35x48cm-14x19in) s. W/C prov. 29-Nov-2 Villa Grisebach, Berlin #29/R est:60000-70000
£38000 $59280 €57000 Roter mohn und fingerhut - Red poppy and foxglove (35x48cm-14x19in) s. W/C executed c.1925 prov. 9-Oct-2 Sotheby's, London #14/R est:40000-60000
£43165 $70791 €60000 Woman's portrait with lily (46x33cm-18x13in) s. W/C pen prov. 6-Jun-3 Ketterer, Munich #73/R est:70000-80000
£43478 $70000 €65217 Zwei kopfe - two heads (34x46cm-13x18in) s. W/C executed c.1920-25 prov. 7-May-3 Sotheby's, New York #208/R est:80000-120000
£50000 $77500 €78000 South Seas native (53x39cm-21x15in) s. W/C exec.1913-14. 4-Dec-2 Lempertz, Koln #24/R est:68000-72000
£51799 $84950 €72000 Three Chinese junks (28x40cm-11x16in) s. W/C prov.lit. 6-Jun-3 Ketterer, Munich #31/R est:45000-55000
£55000 $85800 €82500 Sonnenuntergang - Sunset (33x48cm-13x19in) s. W/C executed c.1925 prov. 9-Oct-2 Sotheby's, London #37/R est:40000-60000
£55000 $90200 €82500 Calla, anemonen und gerbera (45x34cm-18x13in) s. W/C exec.1925-30 prov.lit. 6-Feb-3 Christie's, London #467/R est:70000
£56962 $90000 €90000 Marshy landscape with windmill (35x49cm-14x19in) s. W/C black brush paper on paper prov. 29-Nov-2 Villa Grisebach, Berlin #38/R est:90000-120000
£59748 $93208 €95000 Marschlandschaft mit wolken - Marsh landscape with clouds (34x48cm-13x19in) s. W/C prov. 9-Oct-2 Sotheby's, London #104/R est:80000-100000
£60897 $96218 €95000 Sunflowers (49x36cm-19x14in) s. W/C prov. 14-Nov-2 Neumeister, Munich #642/R est:120000-140000
£64748 $106187 €90000 Flowers (32x47cm-13x19in) s. W/C prov. 6-Jun-3 Ketterer, Munich #82/R est:80000-120000
£65217 $106957 €90000 Red tulips (35x47cm-14x19in) s. W/C prov. 30-May-3 Villa Grisebach, Berlin #35/R est:90000-100000
£65972 $104896 €95000 Diseuse in red dress (34x24cm-13x9in) s. W/C. 5-May-3 Ketterer, Munich #930/R est:30000-40000
£85000 $132600 €127500 Zwei vasen mit blumen und keramischer figur - Two vases with flowers and ceramic (33x47cm-13x19in) s.i. W/C executed c.1930-1935 prov. 9-Oct-2 Sotheby's, London #19/R est:60000-80000
£86331 $141583 €120000 Low red sun - above green marsh landscape (34x46cm-13x18in) s. W/C prov. 6-Jun-3 Ketterer, Munich #64/R est:120000-150000
£104431 $165000 €165000 Head of a woman with blue eyes and reddish golden hair (47x34cm-19x13in) s. W/C gouache prov. 29-Nov-2 Villa Grisebach, Berlin #34/R est:100000-150000
£105000 $163800 €157500 Abendlandschaft - Evening landscape (36x47cm-14x19in) s. W/C executed c.1925 prov. 9-Oct-2 Sotheby's, London #13/R est:30000-40000
£180000 $295200 €270000 Young couple (50x35cm-20x14in) s. W/C pen ink exec.c.1931-35. 4-Feb-3 Sotheby's, London #23/R est:250000

NOLKEN, Franz (1884-1918) German

£6410 $9936 €10000 Seated female nude wearing stockings. s.d. 7-Dec-2 Hauswedell & Nolte, Hamburg #948/R est:2500
£12987 $18961 €20000 Artist's mother sewing by the window (60x60cm-24x24in) mono. 15-Jun-2 Hans Stahl, Hamburg #205/R est:20000

NOLL, Alexandre (1890-1970) French

Sculpture

£2381 $3786 €3500 Hippopotame (30x13x6cm-12x5x2in) s. wood prov. 24-Mar-3 Digard, Paris #90/R
£3741 $5949 €5500 Forme libre (25x14cm-10x6in) s. ebony prov. 24-Mar-3 Digard, Paris #86/R
£4218 $6706 €6200 Untitled (21x10x8cm-8x4x3in) s. ebony prov. 24-Mar-3 Digard, Paris #5/R
£4898 $7788 €7200 Poisson (26x18x12cm-10x7x5in) s. ebony prov. 24-Mar-3 Digard, Paris #29/R
£22449 $35694 €33000 Untitled (124x25cm-49x10in) ebony prov. 24-Mar-3 Digard, Paris #43/R est:30000

NOLLEKENS (?) ?

Sculpture

£9677 $15000 €14516 Bust of Spencer Percival (65cm-26in) s.d.1813 white marble turned socle. 3-Dec-2 Christie's, Rockefeller NY #515/R est:5000-8000

NOLLEKENS, J F (1702-1748) Flemish

£3100 $4805 €4650 Departure for the hunt, figures and horses gathering in a formal garden (30x36cm-12x14in) copper panel. 4-Oct-2 Mallams, Oxford #561/R est:3500-4500

NOLLEKENS, Joseph (1737-1823) British

Sculpture

£8000 $12560 €12000 Bust of a man (75cm-30in) s.d.1777 white marble. 10-Dec-2 Sotheby's, London #142/R est:3000-5000

NOLLET, Paul (1911-1996) Belgian

£256 $403 €400 Nature morte sur une table (140x94cm-55x37in) s. 11-Dec-2 Hotel des Ventes Mosan, Brussels #274

NOLTEE, Cornelis (1903-1967) Dutch

£350 $546 €550 Park view (58x48cm-23x19in) s. 5-Nov-2 Vendu Notarishuis, Rotterdam #17
£414 $646 €650 Demolished street (34x39cm-13x15in) s. 5-Nov-2 Vendu Notarishuis, Rotterdam #146
£512 $794 €768 Farm landscape (41x51cm-16x20in) s. 24-Sep-2 Maynards, Vancouver #365 (C.D 1250)
£625 $1031 €900 Artist with a red beret (40x30cm-16x12in) s. 1-Jul-3 Christie's, Amsterdam #107
£637 $981 €1000 Low tide (50x60cm-20x24in) s. prov. 3-Sep-2 Christie's, Amsterdam #237/R
£704 $1134 €1000 Farm with farmer's wife and nanny goat (39x59cm-15x23in) s. 7-May-3 Vendue Huis, Gravenhage #47
£1146 $1789 €1800 Dordrecht street with figures (17x26cm-7x10in) s. panel. 5-Nov-2 Vendu Notarishuis, Rotterdam #204/R est:1250-1500
£2345 $3728 €3400 Children plying on the beach with sailing vessels in the background (18x24cm-7x9in) s. cardboard. 10-Mar-3 Sotheby's, Amsterdam #228/R est:1500-2000
£2483 $3948 €3600 Children playing on the beach at low tide (18x24cm-7x9in) s. cardboard. 10-Mar-3 Sotheby's, Amsterdam #229/R est:1500-2000

NOLTHENIUS, Robert Claude Jacques Tutein (1851-1915) Dutch
£633 $1000 €918 Impressionist pastoral landscape (53x74cm-21x29in) s. board. 26-Apr-3 Jeffery Burchard, Florida #53a
£892 $1391 €1400 Farm in the woods (52x72cm-20x28in) s.d.92. 6-Nov-2 Vendue Huis, Gravenhage #647

NOMEIER, Alfred (1939-) German
£316 $494 €500 Octoberfest, Munich (72x87cm-28x34in) s. 18-Oct-2 Dr Fritz Nagel, Stuttgart #273/R

NOMELLINI, Plinio (1866-1943) Italian
£9864 $15684 €14500 Hunter (26x30cm-10x12in) s.d.902 board. 18-Mar-3 Finarte, Milan #99/R
£19928 $32681 €27500 Elba selvaggia (63x77cm-25x30in) s. exhib. 27-May-3 Finarte, Milan #80/R est:30000-35000
£54054 $84324 €80000 Spring celebration (215x155cm-85x61in) s. 28-Mar-3 Farsetti, Prato #740/R est:65000
Works on paper
£8844 $14061 €13000 Landscape (48x68cm-19x27in) s. W/C. 18-Mar-3 Finarte, Milan #22/R

NONELL Y MONTURIOL, Isidro (1873-1911) Spanish
£59355 $93781 €92000 Winter landscape (43x68cm-17x27in) s.d.1896. 19-Dec-2 Claude Aguttes, Neuilly #178/R est:40000
£100671 $162081 €150000 Landscape by Sant Marti (43x68cm-17x27in) s.d.96. 18-Feb-3 Durán, Madrid #224/R est:130000
Works on paper
£3378 $5270 €5000 Gypsy woman with baby (26x19cm-10x7in) s. W/C over chl. 28-Mar-3 Claude Aguttes, Neuilly #62/R
£3514 $5481 €5200 Man wearing scarf (26x19cm-10x7in) s. W/C over chl. 28-Mar-3 Claude Aguttes, Neuilly #61/R
£3716 $5797 €5500 Washerwoman (26x19cm-10x7in) s. W/C over chl. 28-Mar-3 Claude Aguttes, Neuilly #60/R
£4000 $6280 €6000 Mujer sentada - seated woman (29x20cm-11x8in) c. chl. 19-Nov-2 Sotheby's, London #37/R est:1500-2000
£7000 $10990 €10500 Mujer rezando - woman praying (39x31cm-15x12in) s. black crayon chk col chk. 19-Nov-2 Sotheby's, London #38/R est:4000-6000

NONN, Carl (1876-1949) German
£641 $1006 €1000 Beilstein an der Mosel (100x150cm-39x59in) s. 21-Nov-2 Van Ham, Cologne #1839/R
£935 $1496 €1300 Houses in Bacharach am Rhein (52x69cm-20x27in) s. i. verso. 17-May-3 Lempertz, Koln #1451
£1295 $2072 €1800 Winter evening in the Eifel (50x60cm-20x24in) s. i. verso. 17-May-3 Lempertz, Koln #1450 est:1500

NONNOTTE, Donat (1708-1785) French
£4196 $7007 €6000 Portraits de Monsieur et de Madame Moreau de Besigny (102x81cm-40x32in) s.d.1740 pair. 25-Jun-3 Tajan, Paris #60/R est:8000-10000

NONO, Luigi (1850-1918) Italian
£55000 $86350 €82500 La cucitrice - seamstress (58x76cm-23x30in) s.d.1886 prov. 19-Nov-2 Sotheby's, London #126/R est:60000-80000

NOOMS, Reinier (1623-1667) Dutch
£15000 $23400 €22500 Ferry and shipping in calm off a coastline (71x94cm-28x37in) 9-Apr-3 Christie's, London #35/R est:15000-20000
£16438 $25644 €24000 Boats being loaded and unloaded in bay (41x67cm-16x26in) s.d.16. 10-Apr-3 Van Ham, Cologne #1289/R est:17000

NOOMS, Reinier (attrib) (1623-1667) Dutch
£8800 $13728 €13200 Naval engagement with sailors in a rowing boat (32x37cm-13x15in) 9-Apr-3 Bonhams, New Bond Street #7/R est:3000-4000

NOONAN, Kay (20th C) British
£320 $496 €480 Female nude at a mirror (76x50cm-30x20in) 3-Dec-2 Bonhams, Knightsbridge #82

NOORDE, Cornelis van (1731-1795) Dutch
Works on paper
£510 $785 €800 Peasants with cattle among ruins, road to the right (15x21cm-6x8in) mono. black chk W/C. 3-Sep-2 Christie's, Amsterdam #86/R
£637 $994 €1000 Boats on a choppy river estuary (14x18cm-6x7in) s.indis.d.1768 brush black ink grey wash black chk. 5-Nov-2 Sotheby's, Amsterdam #110/R

NOORDHOF, Els (20th C) New Zealander
£294 $432 €441 Portrait (34x29cm-13x11in) s.d.1975 board prov. 19-Jun-2 Watson's, Christchurch #70/R est:300-600 (NZ.D 900)

NOORDIJK, Willem Frederik (1887-1970) Dutch
£789 $1279 €1200 Procession (45x71cm-18x28in) s. 21-Jan-3 Christie's, Amsterdam #198 est:600-800

NOORT, Adrianus Cornelis van (1914-) Dutch
£755 $1170 €1200 Animated beach view (50x70cm-20x28in) s. 5-Oct-2 De Vuyst, Lokeren #386
£818 $1267 €1300 Pleasure beach (40x60cm-16x24in) s. 5-Oct-2 De Vuyst, Lokeren #385
£1197 $1927 €1700 Amusement on the beach (50x70cm-20x28in) s. 6-May-3 Vendu Notarishuis, Rotterdam #114/R est:1000-1500

NOORT, B H van (19th C) Dutch
£573 $836 €860 Seasape (30x39cm-12x15in) panel. 17-Jun-2 Philippe Schuler, Zurich #7354 (S.FR 1300)

NOORT, Jan van (16/18th C) Dutch
£9500 $14915 €14250 Adoration of the Shepherds (66x58cm-26x23in) bears i.verso. 12-Dec-2 Sotheby's, London #178/R est:8000-12000

NOORT, Jan van (circle) (16/18th C) Dutch
£9494 $15000 €15000 Adoration of the Magi (93x128cm-37x50in) board. 2-Dec-2 Finarte, Milan #167/R est:9000

NOOTEBOOM, Jacobus Hendricus Johannes (1811-1878) Dutch
£2113 $3465 €3064 Coastal landscape with fishing boats (35x34cm-14x13in) s. panel. 4-Jun-3 Fischer, Luzern #1052/R est:4500-6000 (S.FR 4500)

NORAMIES, Kaj (1918-1976) Finnish
Sculpture
£1690 $2721 €2400 The first step (22cm-9in) s. bronze. 10-May-3 Bukowskis, Helsinki #22/R est:800-1000

NORBERTO (1927-) Italian
£1408 $2338 €2000 Spello (14x9cm-6x4in) s. s.i.d.1975 verso tempera cardboard on panel. 10-Jun-3 Finarte Semenzato, Milan #289/R est:1600-2200

NORBLIN DE LA GOURDAINE, Jean Pierre (attrib) (1745-1830) French
£676 $1054 €1000 Paysage pastoral (32x40cm-13x16in) 26-Mar-3 Tajan, Paris #76

NORBURY, Richard (1815-1886) British
£280 $440 €420 Sampans (30x51cm-12x20in) s. board. 16-Dec-2 Bonhams, Bury St Edmunds #488

NORCIA, Paolo da (1953-) Italian
£256 $403 €400 Tunis (90x100cm-35x39in) s. painted 2000. 23-Nov-2 Meeting Art, Vercelli #455

NORDAN, Henriette (1826-1903) Danish
£745 $1184 €1118 Norwegian cottage interior with women and children (46x60cm-18x24in) s.d.18de September 1870. 10-Mar-3 Rasmussen, Vejle #158/R (D.KR 8000)

NORDBERG, Olle (1905-1986) Swedish
£358 $580 €537 Family meal (16x38cm-6x15in) s.d.50 panel. 3-Feb-3 Lilla Bukowskis, Stockholm #215 (S.KR 5000)
£450 $729 €653 In the garden - scene with elderly man resting (46x56cm-18x22in) s. panel. 25-May-3 Uppsala Auktionskammare, Uppsala #286/R (S.KR 5800)
£465 $754 €674 Winter landscape with farmer and horse (54x64cm-21x25in) s.d.57. 25-May-3 Uppsala Auktionskammare, Uppsala #301 (S.KR 6000)
£824 $1335 €1236 Walking with children (75x61cm-30x24in) s. panel. 3-Feb-3 Lilla Bukowskis, Stockholm #859 (S.KR 11500)

NORDELL, Carl J (1885-1934) American
£769 $1200 €1154 October still life (81x102cm-32x40in) s. i.verso. 14-Sep-2 Weschler, Washington #624/R
£1125 $1800 €1631 Lady with prints (82x64cm-32x25in) s. exhib. 16-May-3 Skinner, Boston #137/R est:3000-5000

NORDELL, Carl J (attrib) (1885-1934) American
£286 $450 €429 Landscape with Cape Cod style home and boathouse (25x36cm-10x14in) s. 23-Nov-2 Pook & Pook, Downington #259

NORDELL, Emma Parker (1876-1956) American
£297 $475 €431 From the hill tops (20x25cm-8x10in) s. i.verso board. 16-May-3 Skinner, Boston #203/R

NORDENBERG, Bengt (1822-1902) Swedish
£1517 $2337 €2276 Officer offering young lady money (64x53cm-25x21in) s.d.1857 after Gerard ter Borch. 27-Oct-2 Anders Antik, Landskrona #130/R est:20000-30000 (S.KR 22000)
£3015 $4764 €4523 Cottage interior with couple seated (56x81cm-22x32in) s.d.89. 27-Nov-2 Falkkloos, Malmo #77682/R est:50000 (S.KR 43000)
£4468 $6926 €6702 Girl and boy with rabbits (63x51cm-25x20in) s.d.91. 3-Dec-2 Bukowskis, Stockholm #173/R est:70000-80000 (S.KR 63000)
£4500 $7289 €6525 The small goat kid (48x60cm-19x24in) s.d.1856. 26-May-3 Bukowskis, Stockholm #153/R est:40000-50000 (S.KR 58000)
£19395 $31420 €28123 After the bear hunt (73x110cm-29x43in) s.d.1882. 26-May-3 Bukowskis, Stockholm #156/R est:80000-100000 (S.KR 250000)

NORDENBERG, Hendrick (1857-1928) Swedish
£786 $1288 €1140 Interior scene with woman sewing (60x51cm-24x20in) s. panel. 4-Jun-3 AB Stockholms Auktionsverk #2132/R (S.KR 10000)

NORDENCREUTZ, Brita (1899-1982) Swedish
Works on paper
£304 $481 €456 Facial expressions (20x14cm-8x6in) init. pencil. 28-Apr-3 Bukowskis, Stockholm #145/R (S.KR 4000)
£304 $481 €456 Triangle drama (46x31cm-18x12in) s.d.22 pencil. 28-Apr-3 Bukowskis, Stockholm #146/R (S.KR 4000)
£426 $673 €639 Backyard artists (34x24cm-13x9in) init. pencil. 28-Apr-3 Bukowskis, Stockholm #144/R (S.KR 5600)

NORDFELDT, Bror Julius Olsson (1878-1955) American
£1899 $3000 €2849 Mary Louise (69x61cm-27x24in) s. s.i.d.1916 verso. 24-Apr-3 Shannon's, Milford #212/R est:2000-3000
£6369 $10000 €9554 Snow flurry (81x102cm-32x40in) s.i.d.1939 prov. 10-Dec-2 Doyle, New York #101/R est:10000-15000

NORDGREN, Anna (1847-1916) Swedish
£570 $900 €900 Baby Moses among the reeds (95x70cm-37x28in) s.d.1879. 1-Dec-2 Bukowskis, Helsinki #270/R
£745 $1154 €1118 Grandfather reading a story (40x25cm-16x10in) s.d.1882 panel. 4-Dec-2 AB Stockholms Auktionsverk #1630/R (S.KR 10500)

NORDGREN, Axel (1828-1888) Swedish
£709 $1099 €1064 Lake landscape with high mountains (44x61cm-17x24in) s. 8-Dec-2 Uppsala Auktionskammare, Uppsala #49/R (S.KR 10000)
£709 $1099 €1064 Fishermen by Husqvarna waterfall (43x68cm-17x27in) s. 8-Dec-2 Uppsala Auktionskammare, Uppsala #52/R (S.KR 10000)
£1403 $2216 €2105 Das Siebengebirge am Rhein (39x63cm-15x25in) s. 27-Nov-2 Falkkloos, Malmo #77601/R est:15000 (S.KR 20000)
£1667 $2617 €2600 Small fishing harbour on snowy Scandinavian coast (71x117cm-28x46in) s.d.1876. 21-Nov-2 Van Ham, Cologne #1841/R est:3000
£2817 $4535 €4000 Huskvarna waterfall (42x67cm-17x26in) s. 10-May-3 Bukowskis, Helsinki #360/R est:4000-5000
£5674 $9191 €8000 Small fishing port at snowy Scandinavian coast (71x117cm-28x46in) s.d.1876. 22-May-3 Dorotheum, Vienna #196/R est:5500-6000

NORDGREN, Wilhelm (1804-1857) Swedish
£530 $859 €795 Portrait of Jonas Liebert Gagge (65x54cm-26x21in) s.d.1837. 3-Feb-3 Lilla Bukowskis, Stockholm #50 (S.KR 7400)
£811 $1346 €1176 Self-portrait (52x47cm-20x19in) i. verso. 16-Jun-3 Lilla Bukowskis, Stockholm #559 (S.KR 10500)
£3121 $4837 €4682 Portrait of Karl XIV Johan wearing uniform (14x13cm-6x5in) s. panel oval. 4-Dec-2 AB Stockholms Auktionsverk #1621/R est:8000-10000 (S.KR 44000)

NORDHAGEN, Johan (1856-1956) Norwegian
Works on paper
£1995 $3112 €2993 From Saltstenen, Bardset in Ringaker - horse by farm (63x84cm-25x33in) s.i.d.Juli 1934 W/C exhib. 21-Oct-2 Blomqvist, Oslo #504/R est:15000-18000 (N.KR 23000)

NORDLIEN, Olaf (1864-1919) Norwegian
£256 $399 €384 Mountain landscape (51x66cm-20x26in) s. 23-Sep-2 Blomqvist, Lysaker #1172/R (N.KR 3000)
£297 $470 €446 Norwegian fjord landscape with vessel and houses (47x85cm-19x33in) s. 5-Apr-3 Rasmussen, Havnen #2023 (D.KR 3200)
£433 $662 €650 Milkmaid with cattle by the outfarm (34x55cm-13x22in) s. 26-Aug-2 Blomqvist, Lysaker #1287/R (N.KR 5000)
£619 $1010 €929 Wooded landscape with rapids (77x125cm-30x49in) s. 17-Feb-3 Blomqvist, Lysaker #1145 (N.KR 7000)
£814 $1318 €1221 From Nordmarka (73x99cm-29x39in) s. 27-Jan-3 Blomqvist, Lysaker #1169 (N.KR 9000)

NORDQVIST, Per (1770-1805) Swedish
£12000 $19080 €18000 St. James's Palace, Pall Mall beyond (66x97cm-26x38in) s.d.1796 on stretcher prov. 6-Mar-3 Christie's, Kensington #527/R est:4000-6000

NORDSTRAND, Ragna (1878-1976) Danish
£721 $1160 €1082 The violin player Gerda Hoeberg wearing red dress (100x82cm-39x32in) s.d.1904 prov. 26-Feb-3 Museumsbygningen, Copenhagen #10/R (D.KR 8000)

NORDSTROM, Jockum (1963-) Swedish
£2433 $3845 €3650 Poet (54x36cm-21x14in) s.d.94 panel. 28-Apr-3 Bukowskis, Stockholm #936/R est:20000-25000 (S.KR 32000)
£6084 $9612 €9126 Musician in New York (160x125cm-63x49in) s.d.89 exhib. 28-Apr-3 Bukowskis, Stockholm #935/R est:50000-60000 (S.KR 80000)

NORDSTROM, Karl (1855-1923) Swedish
£938 $1501 €1360 French street scene (24x18cm-9x7in) s. panel. 18-May-3 Anders Antik, Landskrona #24 (S.KR 12000)
£2908 $4507 €4362 Beach by Trekanten, Stockholm (70x90cm-28x35in) init.d.1919 lit. 4-Dec-2 AB Stockholms Auktionsverk #1552/R est:50000-60000 (S.KR 41000)
£3262 $5057 €4893 Seascape, Vesterhavet (100x138cm-39x54in) init.d.1906 prov.exhib.lit. 3-Dec-2 Bukowskis, Stockholm #94/R est:25000-30000 (S.KR 46000)
£4043 $6266 €6065 Lake landscape (29x59cm-11x23in) s.d.89 prov. 3-Dec-2 Bukowskis, Stockholm #144/R est:50000-60000 (S.KR 57000)
£25532 $39574 €38298 Sunflowers, garden scene from Grez (41x15cm-16x6in) s.d.84 panel exhib. 4-Dec-2 AB Stockholms Auktionsverk #1607/R est:225000-250000 (S.KR 360000)

NORDSTROM, Lars Gunnar (1924-) Finnish
£3165 $5000 €5000 Composition in red (70x122cm-28x48in) s.verso board. 1-Dec-2 Bukowskis, Helsinki #340/R est:5000-6000
£3418 $5400 €5400 Composition (52x62cm-20x24in) s.verso board. 1-Dec-2 Bukowskis, Helsinki #341/R est:3000-3500
Works on paper
£823 $1300 €1300 Composition in green and yellow (30x30cm-12x12in) s.verso gouache. 1-Dec-2 Bukowskis, Helsinki #342/R

NORDT, M (?) ?
£1021 $1614 €1532 Birds in fight (50x38cm-20x15in) s. 2-Dec-2 Rasmussen, Copenhagen #1322/R est:10000 (D.KR 12000)

NOREAU, Francine (20th C) American
£533 $875 €773 Spring bouquet (75x60cm-30x24in) s.i. 9-Jun-3 Hodgins, Calgary #21/R est:1000-1500 (C.D 1200)

NORGA, Silvain (20th C) Belgian
Sculpture
£949 $1481 €1500 Panthere (30x70x20cm-12x28x8in) s. green pat brown black marble base. 16-Oct-2 Hotel des Ventes Mosan, Brussels #261 est:1200-1400

NORGARD, Lars (1956-) Danish
£466 $742 €699 Composition (73x60cm-29x24in) s.d.91 verso. 29-Apr-3 Kunsthallen, Copenhagen #193/R (D.KR 5000)
£524 $817 €786 Composition (59x42cm-23x17in) s.d.85 paper on canvas. 18-Sep-2 Kunsthallen, Copenhagen #136 (D.KR 6200)
£548 $872 €822 Composition (59x42cm-23x17in) init.d.86 paper. 26-Feb-3 Kunsthallen, Copenhagen #155/R (D.KR 6000)
£560 $890 €840 Composition (73x60cm-29x24in) s.d.91 verso. 29-Apr-3 Kunsthallen, Copenhagen #137 (D.KR 6000)
£616 $1022 €893 Clean nails (100x81cm-39x32in) s.d.90 verso. 12-Jun-3 Kunsthallen, Copenhagen #100/R (D.KR 6500)

NORIE, Orlando (1832-1901) British
Works on paper
£300 $465 €450 Troops on the march (31x47cm-12x19in) s. W/C. 29-Oct-2 Henry Adams, Chichester #417
£320 $509 €480 Mounted detachment of Victorian Lancers with military encampment beyond (30x43cm-12x17in) s. W/C. 29-Apr-3 Peter Francis, Wales #69/R

£320 $525 €464 Officer of the Royal Foot Artillery (30x18cm-12x7in) s. W/C. 6-Jun-3 Halls, Shrewsbury #835
£520 $832 €780 The Eighth, Hussars Chobham 1853 (13x23cm-5x9in) W/C prov. 13-Mar-3 Duke & Son, Dorchester #174/R
£540 $837 €810 Troop 4th Dragoon Guards charging into battle (49x32cm-19x13in) s. W/C htd white. 1-Oct-2 Fellows & Sons, Birmingham #112/R
£550 $908 €798 Officer of the third Dragoon Guards. Officer of the Royal Horse Artillery (18x13cm-7x5in) s. W/C over pencil htd bodycol pair. 2-Jul-3 Sotheby's, Olympia #174/R
£600 $972 €900 The 93rd Sutherland Highlanders engaging the enemy (30x43cm-12x17in) s. W/C. 21-May-3 Bonhams, Knightsbridge #14/R
£1400 $2240 €2100 6th Dragoon Guards on manoeuvres (32x48cm-13x19in) s. W/C. 11-Mar-3 Bonhams, New Bond Street #109/R est:1500-2000
£1400 $2240 €2100 4th Irish Dragoon Guards charging (32x49cm-13x19in) s. W/C. 11-Mar-3 Bonhams, New Bond Street #113/R est:1500-2000
£1600 $2560 €2400 93rd Sutherland Highlanders storming the walls of Begum Kothi (30x47cm-12x19in) s. W/C. 11-Mar-3 Bonhams, New Bond Street #111/R est:1000-1500
£1600 $2656 €2400 The 1st Battalion of the Gordon highlanders on parade near Aldershot (36x21cm-14x8in) s. W/C exhib. 12-Jun-3 Bonhams, New Bond Street #690/R est:1500-2000
£3900 $6084 €5850 Battle scene (55x99cm-22x39in) W/C. 6-Aug-2 Outhwaite & Litherland, Liverpool #264

NORIE, Orlando (attrib) (1832-1901) British
Works on paper
£1389 $2264 €2000 Cavalier arabe (46x32cm-18x13in) s. W/C gouache. 19-Jul-3 Thierry & Lannon, Brest #287 est:1800-2000

NORIE, Robert (19th C) British
£2700 $4212 €4050 Fisherfolk on the coast (86x125cm-34x49in) indis.sig.d.1869. 17-Oct-2 Bonhams, Edinburgh #247/R est:2000-3000

NORLIND, Ernst (1877-1952) Swedish
£351 $554 €527 Stork (70x60cm-28x24in) s.d.47 panel. 30-Nov-2 Goteborg Auktionsverk, Sweden #593/R (S.KR 5000)

NORMAN, Dorothy (1905-) American
Photographs
£3165 $5000 €5000 Hunter College (9x3cm-4x1in) s.i. verso silver gelatin. 28-Nov-2 Villa Grisebach, Berlin #1341/R est:5000-6000

NORMAN, Gunner (20th C) American
Works on paper
£318 $500 €477 Two tulips (21x16cm-8x6in) s.d.1978 crayon. 21-Nov-2 Swann Galleries, New York #136/R

NORMAN, W T (19th C) British
£288 $450 €432 Italianate landscape with figures on a path (30x25cm-12x10in) s. panel. 14-Sep-2 Selkirks, St. Louis #201

NORMAND, Ernest (1857-1923) British
£420 $647 €630 Portrait of Sir John Henry Corner, bust length (53x43cm-21x17in) mono.i.d.1881. 9-Sep-2 Bonhams, Ipswich #118
£450 $711 €675 Study, three quarter length, of a female nude from behind (35x28cm-14x11in) s. board. 12-Nov-2 Bonhams, Knightsbridge #204/R

NORMANN, Adelsteen (1848-1918) Norwegian
£411 $641 €600 Summer fjord landscape (20x24cm-8x9in) s. 10-Apr-3 Schopman, Hamburg #715
£752 $1226 €1128 Cheese farm in the mountains (35x52cm-14x20in) s.verso panel. 17-Feb-3 Blomqvist, Lysaker #1146/R (N.KR 8500)
£1730 $2734 €2595 Fjord landscape with boat, Vestlandet (50x72cm-20x28in) s. 2-Dec-2 Blomqvist, Oslo #307/R est:35000-40000 (N.KR 20000)
£3121 $4837 €4682 Coastal landscape from Lofoten (33x48cm-13x19in) s. 3-Dec-2 Bukowskis, Stockholm #169/R est:20000-25000 (S.KR 44000)
£4034 $6535 €5849 Fishing village at dusk (24x36cm-9x14in) s. panel. 26-May-3 Bukowskis, Stockholm #266/R est:12000-15000 (S.KR 52000)
£4255 $6596 €6383 Fjord landscape with steamboat and figures in rowing boat (74x123cm-29x48in) s.d.1877. 3-Dec-2 Bukowskis, Stockholm #164/R est:60000-80000 (S.KR 60000)
£4808 $7548 €7500 Norwegian fjord landscape with fishing village (43x72cm-17x28in) s. 21-Nov-2 Dorotheum, Vienna #166/R est:1600-2000
£4844 $7654 €7266 Fishermen pulling in nets (90x140cm-35x55in) s. 2-Dec-2 Blomqvist, Oslo #353/R est:70000-90000 (N.KR 56000)
£5000 $8200 €7500 Fjordutsikt - view of a Norwegian fjord (72x100cm-28x39in) s. 3-Jun-3 Sotheby's, London #261/R est:5000-7000
£5061 $7946 €7592 Figures and boats on the coast of Northern Norway (24x36cm-9x14in) s. panel. 21-Nov-2 Grev Wedels Plass, Oslo #62/R est:30000-40000 (N.KR 58000)
£5204 $8118 €7806 Sunrise on the coast (93x124cm-37x49in) s. 21-Oct-2 Blomqvist, Oslo #328/R est:70000-90000 (N.KR 60000)
£5396 $8634 €8094 Fishing village in Midnight sun (72x100cm-28x39in) s. 17-Mar-3 Blomqvist, Oslo #336/R est:50000-70000 (N.KR 62000)
£6500 $10206 €9750 Norwegian fjord (49x73cm-19x29in) s. 19-Nov-2 Sotheby's, London #198/R est:5000-7000
£6500 $10660 €9750 Sommerdag ved fjorden - summer's day in a Norwegian fjord (72x97cm-28x38in) s. 3-Jun-3 Sotheby's, London #262/R est:6000-8000
£6527 $10444 €9791 Fjord landscape with figure rowing the hay (60x80cm-24x31in) s. 17-Mar-3 Blomqvist, Oslo #367/R est:80000-100000 (N.KR 75000)
£6690 $11106 €9500 Fjord in summer (64x104cm-25x41in) s. 14-Jun-3 Arnold, Frankfurt #822/R est:1600
£6842 $10811 €10263 Fjord landscape with figures (121x160cm-48x63in) s,. 17-Dec-2 Grev Wedels Plass, Oslo #176/R est:80000-100000 (N.KR 78000)
£7111 $11804 €10311 Fjord (113x150cm-44x59in) s. 10-Jun-3 Ritchie, Toronto #136/R est:7000-9000 (C.D 16000)
£8000 $13120 €12000 Fjorden - fjord (104x156cm-41x61in) s. 3-Jun-3 Sotheby's, London #259/R est:8000-12000
£8000 $13120 €12000 Norsk fjord - Norwegian fjord (36x54cm-14x21in) s. 3-Jun-3 Sotheby's, London #264/R est:4000-6000
£8333 $12917 €13000 Norwegian fjord landscape (104x156cm-41x61in) s. lit. 7-Dec-2 Bergmann, Erlangen #769/R est:9000
£8500 $13940 €12750 Fiske pa fjorden - fishing on the fjord (72x100cm-28x39in) s. 3-Jun-3 Sotheby's, London #260/R est:6000-8000
£9000 $14760 €13500 Fjord ved solnegang - fjord at sunset (113x150cm-44x59in) s. 3-Jun-3 Sotheby's, London #258/R est:10000-15000
£20253 $32000 €30380 Boats on a Norwegian fjord (104x155cm-41x61in) s. prov. 23-Apr-3 Christie's, Rockefeller NY #80/R est:20000-30000

NORMANN, Emma (1871-1954) Norwegian
£1062 $1731 €1593 Fjord landscape (60x80cm-24x31in) s. 17-Feb-3 Blomqvist, Lysaker #1147/R (N.KR 12000)

NORREGAARD, Asta (1853-1933) Norwegian
£3633 $5740 €5450 Interior scene with woman at piano (40x50cm-16x20in) s.d.1890. 2-Dec-2 Blomqvist, Oslo #337/R est:50000-70000 (N.KR 42000)

NORRIE, Susan (1953-) Australian
£357 $561 €536 Whistling Joe (37x31cm-15x12in) paper prov. 25-Nov-2 Christie's, Melbourne #237 (A.D 1000)
£400 $644 €600 Milk chocolates (23x23cm-9x9in) s.i.d.92 oil varnish screenprint on canvas prov. 6-May-3 Christie's, Melbourne #313/R est:1000-1500 (A.D 1000)
£714 $1129 €1071 Equivalence - multiple series I (31x30cm-12x12in) s. i.d.92. 27-Nov-2 Deutscher-Menzies, Melbourne #117/R est:2500-3500 (A.D 2000)
£731 $1162 €1097 Untitled (38x26cm-15x10in) 4-Mar-3 Deutscher-Menzies, Melbourne #213/R (A.D 1900)
£4286 $6600 €6429 Installment 5 (244x122cm-96x48in) s. i.d.92 verso. 8-Sep-2 Sotheby's, Melbourne #37/R est:20000-30000 (A.D 12000)
£4286 $6771 €6429 Untitled (240x189cm-94x74in) prov. 26-Nov-2 Sotheby's, Melbourne #42/R est:12000-18000 (A.D 12000)
£5536 $8525 €8304 Untitled (152x122cm-60x48in) s.i.d.93 in two parts. 8-Sep-2 Sotheby's, Melbourne #15/R est:20000-30000 (A.D 15500)
£7143 $11000 €10715 Untitled (161x113cm-63x44in) prov. 8-Sep-2 Sotheby's, Melbourne #9/R est:25000-35000 (A.D 20000)
£9609 $14701 €14414 Untitled (240x189cm-94x74in) prov. 25-Aug-2 Sotheby's, Paddington #11/R est:28000-35000 (A.D 27000)
Works on paper
£529 $835 €767 In the trees (14x16cm-6x6in) i.d.2002 verso gouache on card prov. 22-Jul-3 Lawson Menzies, Sydney #192/R est:1500-2000 (A.D 1300)
£600 $966 €900 Untitled (28x40cm-11x16in) s. i.d.92 verso chocolate oil varnish on canvas prov. 6-May-3 Christie's, Melbourne #248/R est:1500-2000 (A.D 1500)
£929 $1467 €1394 Souvenir of Sydney (101x151cm-40x59in) mixed media on board. 17-Nov-2 Sotheby's, Paddington #86/R est:3000-5000 (A.D 2600)

NORRIS, Hugh L (fl.1882-1904) British
Works on paper
£250 $400 €375 Willow trees beside a river (25x36cm-10x14in) s. W/C. 11-Mar-3 Gorringes, Lewes #2558

NORRIS, Joe (1924-) Canadian
£1210 $1911 €1815 Shipwreck (26x34cm-10x13in) s. board. 14-Nov-2 Heffel, Vancouver #15/R est:3000-4000 (C.D 3000)
£1333 $2187 €2000 Wildlife gathering (40x60cm-16x24in) s.d.19.83 panel. 27-May-3 Sotheby's, Toronto #46/R est:3000-5000 (C.D 3000)
£2444 $4009 €3666 Making friends (51x91cm-20x36in) s.d.1977 prov. 27-May-3 Sotheby's, Toronto #48/R est:4000-6000 (C.D 5500)

NORRLIN, S (20th C) ?
£1266 $2000 €2000 Belle creole (51x40cm-20x16in) indis.sig. 28-Nov-2 Piasa, Paris #2/R est:2000-2500

NORRMAN, Herman (1864-1906) Swedish
£543 $880 €787 Fishing village in Bohuslan (38x58cm-15x23in) s.d.86 panel. 25-May-3 Uppsala Auktionskammare, Uppsala #165/R (S.KR 7000)

NORRMAN, Lars (1915-1979) Swedish
Works on paper
£295 $460 €443 Les modistes suedoise (53x73cm-21x29in) s. gouache. 13-Sep-2 Lilla Bukowskis, Stockholm #652 (S.KR 4300)

NORTH EUROPEAN SCHOOL (16th C)
Works on paper
£9929 $16582 €14000 Fete en l'honneur d'un souverain. Paysage fluvial (24x39cm-9x15in) i.verso pen brown ink wash gouache double-sided. 19-Jun-3 Piasa, Paris #50/R est:15000-18000

NORTH ITALIAN SCHOOL (14th C)
£9259 $15000 €13889 Saints Catherine and Bartholomew (70x44cm-28x17in) fresco on canvas pair. 23-Jan-3 Sotheby's, New York #160/R est:30000

NORTH ITALIAN SCHOOL (15th C)
£5500 $9185 €7975 Recurrection of Christ (11x11cm-4x4in) tempera on gold ground panel on panel round. 9-Jul-3 Bonhams, New Bond Street #58/R est:6000-8000

NORTH ITALIAN SCHOOL (16th C)
£17000 $26350 €25500 Madonna and Child with infant St John the Baptist (43x34cm-17x13in) i.d.1510 oil gold panel. 31-Oct-2 Sotheby's, Olympia #2/R est:4000-6000
£20548 $32055 €30822 The four senses: taste, hearing, sensation, sight (76x55cm-30x22in) four. 28-Mar-3 Koller, Zurich #3047/R est:20000-30000 (S.FR 45000)
Works on paper
£6500 $10855 €9425 Study after Michelangelo's Aurora (28x25cm-11x10in) black chk htd white. 8-Jul-3 Christie's, London #9/R est:7000-10000

NORTH ITALIAN SCHOOL (17th C)
£4808 $7596 €7500 Still life with peaches (40x56cm-16x22in) 13-Nov-2 Marc Kohn, Paris #56/R est:7500-8500
£5674 $9475 €8000 Nature morte a la corbeille de fleurs et coupe de fruits (96x130cm-38x51in) 18-Jun-3 Tajan, Paris #22/R est:4000-6000
£6800 $10608 €10200 Portrait of a lady, possibly a member of the Frigmelica family (203x113cm-80x44in) i. 8-Apr-3 Sotheby's, Olympia #131/R est:3000-5000
£14000 $21980 €21000 Moses receiving the commandments and Israelites adoring the golden calf (98x133cm-39x52in) 12-Dec-2 Sotheby's, London #119/R est:15000-20000
£16000 $25120 €24000 Madonna and Child with infant St John the Baptist by architectural ruins (81x64cm-32x25in) painted c.1600. 12-Dec-2 Sotheby's, London #110/R est:8000-12000
£22051 $32194 €33077 Triumph of crucifix (148x124cm-58x49in) painted c.1600. 4-Jun-2 SOGA, Bratislava #139/R est:1300000 (SL.K 1400000)
Sculpture
£10490 $17517 €15000 Figurant Gian Giacomo Trivulzio avec cheval (26x27cm-10x11in) pat bronze wood socle after drs by Leonard de Vinci. 25-Jun-3 Piasa, Paris #15/R est:15000-18000

NORTH ITALIAN SCHOOL (18th C)
£3548 $5500 €5322 Miracle of the Scaffold (71x43cm-28x17in) possibly attributed to Biagio Bellotti. 2-Oct-2 Christie's, Rockefeller NY #127/R est:7000-10000
£6000 $10020 €8700 Interior with a young lady playing a spinnet (112x139cm-44x55in) 8-Jul-3 Sotheby's, Olympia #457/R est:6000-8000
£9000 $14130 €13500 Man wearing a green coat and holding baskets of fruit (96x73cm-38x29in) 10-Dec-2 Sotheby's, Olympia #394/R est:3000-5000
£14000 $21980 €21000 Architectural capricci with figures disputing amongst ruins (49x64cm-19x25in) pair. 10-Dec-2 Sotheby's, Olympia #410/R est:10000-15000
£23000 $36110 €34500 Cavalry engagements in hilly and mountainous landscapes (89x122cm-35x48in) pair prov. 12-Dec-2 Sotheby's, London #203/R est:12000-18000
£55000 $91850 €79750 Still life of musical instuments. Interior with still life of instruments (113x165cm-44x65in) pair prov. pair. 10-Jul-3 Sotheby's, London #48/R est:60000-80000
Sculpture
£10500 $16485 €15750 Head of the young Hermes (27cm-11in) white marble. 10-Dec-2 Sotheby's, London #140/R est:3000-4000

NORTH, Charles (18th C) British
Works on paper
£280 $440 €420 Lovers in a wood (46x56cm-18x22in) s. pen ink W/C. 10-Dec-2 Cheffins Grain & Comins, Cambridge #342/R

NORTH, John William (1842-1924) British
Works on paper
£420 $676 €630 Off Golden Cap, Dorset (27x33cm-11x13in) W/C. 15-Jan-3 Cheffins Grain & Comins, Cambridge #383/R

NORTH, Sidney V (20th C) British
£550 $864 €825 Citadel at dusk, thought to be Durham (35x46cm-14x18in) s. 16-Apr-3 Christie's, Kensington #860/R

NORTHCOAT, J (1822-1904) American
£321 $500 €482 Deer in a forest stream (36x46cm-14x18in) s. 1-Aug-2 Eldred, East Dennis #141/R

NORTHCOTE, James (1746-1831) British
£1037 $1700 €1556 Portrait of a lady holding a book (76x63cm-30x25in) s.i.d.1816. 5-Feb-3 Christie's, Rockefeller NY #245/R est:3000-5000
£3000 $4680 €4500 Death of the Earl of Argyll (41x26cm-16x10in) s. panel. 14-Apr-3 Sotheby's, London #3/R est:3000-5000

NORTHCOTE, James (attrib) (1746-1831) British
£3000 $4980 €4500 Lioness with her cubs (50x63cm-20x25in) panel. 12-Jun-3 Sotheby's, London #93/R est:4000-6000

NORTHCOTE, James (circle) (1746-1831) British
£8200 $13612 €12300 Portrait of General the Hon Sir Henry Murray, K.C.B (126x110cm-50x43in) 12-Jun-3 Sotheby's, London #69/R est:4000-6000

NORTHEN, Adolf (1828-1876) German
£915 $1474 €1300 Cavalry battle (26x34cm-10x13in) s.i.d.1868 lit. 9-May-3 Schloss Ahlden, Ahlden #1367/R

NORTHERN SCHOOL, 17th C
Works on paper
£5743 $8959 €8500 Cabaret scene (21x18cm-8x7in) pen ink wash. 26-Mar-3 Piasa, Paris #30/R

NORTON, Benjamin Cam (1835-1900) British
£300 $474 €450 Two prize pedigree Ayrshire cows at Knockdon (71x91cm-28x36in) s.d.1890. 7-Apr-3 Bonhams, Bath #103
£820 $1337 €1189 Pinky II and Polly II, two prize pedigree cows in a spring landscape (71x94cm-28x37in) s.d.1890. 16-Jul-3 Sotheby's, Olympia #18/R
£1534 $2500 €2301 White terrier in a landscape (33x43cm-13x17in) s.d.1879. 11-Feb-3 Bonhams & Doyles, New York #198/R est:3000-5000
£3500 $5810 €5075 Chestnut racehorse in a stable (71x91cm-28x36in) s.d.1882 prov. 12-Jun-3 Christie's, Kensington #43/R est:2000-3000
£5500 $8525 €8250 Guernsey cattle in coastal landscape with Martello Fort (71x92cm-28x36in) s.d.1887 sold with a companion. 30-Sep-2 Bonhams, Ipswich #485/R est:6000-9000

NORTON, Jim C (1953-) American
£1059 $1684 €1589 Ahead of the storm (60x45cm-24x18in) s.i.d.1982. 23-Mar-3 Hodgins, Calgary #13/R est:1500-2000 (C.D 2500)
£2179 $3400 €3269 Hunter in the Aspen (41x30cm-16x12in) 9-Nov-2 Altermann Galleries, Santa Fe #164
£2338 $3600 €3507 Along ridge top (46x61cm-18x24in) 25-Oct-2 Morris & Whiteside, Hilton Head Island #37 est:4000-6000
£3846 $6000 €5769 Chance meeting (61x81cm-24x32in) 9-Nov-2 Altermann Galleries, Santa Fe #61

£9228 $14950 €13381 The old trapper (61x91cm-24x36in) 23-May-3 Altermann Galleries, Santa Fe #100
£11327 $18350 €16424 At the falls (61x91cm-24x36in) 23-May-3 Altermann Galleries, Santa Fe #101

NORTON, L D (1867-?) American
Works on paper
£500 $800 €750 Shore scene with sailboats, marshes and trees (33x48cm-13x19in) s.d.1922 pastel. 17-Mar-3 Winter Associates, Plainville #140

NORTON, Larry (1963-) Zimbabwean
£641 $1000 €962 Water bucks (76x102cm-30x40in) s. 30-Mar-3 Simpson's, Houston #101

NORTON, Rosaleen (1917-) Australian
£1073 $1684 €1610 Devil's tree (74x59cm-29x23in) s. board. 15-Apr-3 Lawson Menzies, Sydney #262/R est:3000-4000 (A.D 2800)
Works on paper
£1073 $1684 €1610 Self portrait with accomplices of Evil (74x57cm-29x22in) s. pastel. 15-Apr-3 Lawson Menzies, Sydney #261/R est:2700-3500 (A.D 2800)

NORTON, William Edward (1843-1916) American
£304 $475 €456 Haystack (20x28cm-8x11in) s. panel. 9-Nov-2 Sloan, North Bethesda #622/R
£1050 $1680 €1575 Off Dieppe (49x39cm-19x15in) s.d.89. 11-Mar-3 David Duggleby, Scarborough #237/R est:1000-1500
£1100 $1837 €1595 Sailing barge (40x30cm-16x12in) s. 18-Jun-3 Sotheby's, Olympia #90/R est:600-800
£1461 $2250 €2192 Honfleur (41x30cm-16x12in) s.i. prov. 24-Oct-2 Shannon's, Milford #205/R est:2500-3500
£1700 $2839 €2465 Harbour scene (40x30cm-16x12in) 18-Jun-3 Sotheby's, Olympia #88/R est:800-1200
Works on paper
£617 $1000 €895 View of the coast of Belgium (39x49cm-15x19in) s. s.i.verso W/C on board. 29-Jul-3 Christie's, Rockefeller NY #118/R est:1500-2000

NORTON, William Edward (attrib) (1843-1916) American
£822 $1250 €1233 Ships passing a lighthouse (64x127cm-25x50in) 17-Aug-2 North East Auctions, Portsmouth #947/R

NORWELL, Graham Noble (1901-1967) Canadian
£198 $325 €297 Cabin in winter (20x25cm-8x10in) s. canvasboard. 6-Feb-3 Heffel, Vancouver #038/R (C.D 500)
£198 $325 €297 Winter cabins (46x61cm-18x24in) s. board. 6-Feb-3 Heffel, Vancouver #039/R (C.D 500)
£203 $319 €305 Paysage d'automne (30x41cm-12x16in) s. board. 10-Dec-2 Pinneys, Montreal #190 (C.D 500)
£238 $378 €345 Laurentian cabin (10x23cm-4x9in) s. board. 1-May-3 Heffel, Vancouver #73/R (C.D 550)
£260 $413 €377 Sunset in the Laurentians (10x23cm-4x9in) s. board. 1-May-3 Heffel, Vancouver #74/R (C.D 600)
£905 $1403 €1358 Farm on Tremaine Road (50x60cm-20x24in) s. canvasboard prov. 3-Dec-2 Joyner, Toronto #247/R est:2000-2500 (C.D 2200)
Works on paper
£195 $309 €283 Cabins in the Laurentians (3x48cm-1x19in) s. W/C. 1-May-3 Heffel, Vancouver #72/R (C.D 450)
£215 $335 €312 Orange chalet (32x46cm-13x18in) s. W/C. 26-Mar-3 Walker's, Ottawa #266a (C.D 500)
£236 $368 €342 Skiier (48x66cm-19x26in) s. W/C. 26-Mar-3 Walker's, Ottawa #226a (C.D 550)

NORWOOD, Arthur Harding (fl.1889-1893) British
£520 $811 €780 Loading the hay (51x76cm-20x30in) s. 9-Oct-2 Woolley & Wallis, Salisbury #359/R

NOSKE, Hugo (1886-1960) Austrian
£2069 $3310 €3000 Evening in Venice (98x147cm-39x58in) i. 11-Mar-3 Dorotheum, Vienna #64/R est:1200-1800

NOTEN, Jean van (1903-1982) ?
£349 $548 €524 Three women and a sailor (115x69cm-45x27in) s. panel. 25-Nov-2 Blomqvist, Lysaker #1209 (N.KR 4000)
£354 $577 €531 Three women and a sailor (115x69cm-45x27in) s.d.1938 panel. 17-Feb-3 Blomqvist, Lysaker #1153 (N.KR 4000)

NOTER, David de (1825-1875) Belgian
£1439 $2302 €2000 Fraises, legumes et gibier sur une table (27x25cm-11x10in) s. panel. 13-May-3 Palais de Beaux Arts, Brussels #57/R est:2000-3000
£1500 $2324 €2250 Still life of flowers and fruit (50x61cm-20x24in) s. 3-Dec-2 Sotheby's, Olympia #296/R est:800-1200
£2885 $4529 €4500 Bouquet de fleurs avec des oranges sur un entablement (51x64cm-20x25in) s. 16-Dec-2 Millon & Associes, Paris #71/R est:5000-6000
£12000 $18840 €18000 Moment of rest (54x44cm-21x17in) s.d.50 panel prov. 19-Nov-2 Sotheby's, London #133/R est:12000-18000
Works on paper
£292 $481 €420 Kitchen still life (41x34cm-16x13in) s. W/C. 1-Jul-3 Christie's, Amsterdam #11
£5365 $8315 €8048 Still life of fruit and dead birds (51x43cm-20x17in) s. pastel paper on canvas oval. 3-Oct-2 Koller, Zurich #3100/R est:9000-12000 (S.FR 12500)

NOTER, Jean Baptiste Andre de (1787-1855) Belgian
Works on paper
£2446 $3914 €3400 Views of buildings (15x19cm-6x7in) s. pen W/C dr six. 13-May-3 Palais de Beaux Arts, Brussels #244/R est:1200-1800

NOTER, Josephine de (1805-?) Belgian
£4114 $6377 €6500 Vase garni de roses (72x57cm-28x22in) s.d.1830 panel. 24-Sep-2 Galerie Moderne, Brussels #921 est:750-1000

NOTERMAN, Zacharias (1820-1890) German
£955 $1490 €1500 La fin du duel, singerie (28x36cm-11x14in) s. panel. 11-Nov-2 Horta, Bruxelles #35 est:1000-1500
£2676 $4308 €3800 Dogs playing (54x65cm-21x26in) s. lit. 9-May-3 Schloss Ahlden, Ahlden #1389/R est:4500
£2721 $4327 €4000 Reunion de chiens et singe (36x47cm-14x19in) s. panel. 2-Mar-3 Lombrail & Teucquam, Paris #157/R
£3597 $5755 €5000 Singes lisant, le rappel, dans une auberge (45x37cm-18x15in) s. panel. 19-May-3 Horta, Bruxelles #197/R est:5000-7000
£4967 $8096 €7500 Singe tirant l'oreille d'un chien (64x81cm-25x32in) s. 17-Feb-3 Horta, Bruxelles #160/R

NOTT, P (19th C) British?
£2400 $3792 €3600 In full cry (46x107cm-18x42in) s. indis d. 28-Nov-2 Christie's, Kensington #78/R est:2000-3000

NOTT, Raymond (1888-1948) American
£807 $1300 €1211 Flower field landscape (48x61cm-19x24in) s. board prov. 18-Feb-3 John Moran, Pasadena #32

NOTTE, Emilio (1891-1982) Italian
£705 $1107 €1100 Composition (35x44cm-14x17in) s.d.1972. 16-Dec-2 Pandolfini, Florence #338
£1370 $2137 €2000 Flowers (42x27cm-17x11in) s. board. 10-Apr-3 Finarte Semenzato, Rome #183/R

NOTTINGHAM, Robert A (jnr) (fl.1853-1875) British
Works on paper
£290 $452 €435 River landscape, probably a Lake District scene (27x50cm-11x20in) W/C. 31-Jul-2 Bonhams, Knowle #233

NOUAKISCH, K (?) ?
£1722 $2807 €2600 Amateur de poteries (52x80cm-20x31in) s. 17-Feb-3 Horta, Bruxelles #124

NOURSE, Elizabeth (1859-1938) American
£1506 $2500 €2184 Springtime: head of a girl (33x23cm-13x9in) s. i.verso oil pencil panel prov. 11-Jun-3 Butterfields, San Francisco #4029/R est:3000-5000
£2108 $3500 €3057 Paysage Penmarch (43x61cm-17x24in) s. prov. 11-Jun-3 Butterfields, San Francisco #4028/R est:3000-5000
£3025 $4750 €4538 Roses in a glass vase (41x33cm-16x13in) s. 19-Nov-2 Butterfields, San Francisco #8054/R est:4000-6000
£8784 $13703 €13000 Jeunes bretonnes (130x161cm-51x63in) 28-Mar-3 Claude Aguttes, Neuilly #87/R est:15000

NOURY, Gaston (1866-?) French
Works on paper
£385 $604 €600 Bateau sur mer formee (25x42cm-10x17in) s. pastel. 24-Nov-2 Lesieur & Le Bars, Le Havre #127/R
£417 $654 €650 Cour de ferme (27x43cm-11x17in) s.d.1902 pastel. 24-Nov-2 Lesieur & Le Bars, Le Havre #128
£641 $1006 €1000 Pecheurs a pied a Etretat (50x27cm-20x11in) s.i.d.1901 pastel. 24-Nov-2 Lesieur & Le Bars, Le Havre #126

NOURY, Jacques (1747-1832) French
£2027 $3162 €3000 Pere de famille et ses quatre enfants (71x91cm-28x36in) s.d.1778. 26-Mar-3 Rossini, Paris #114/R

NOUVEAU, Henri (1901-1959) Rumanian
£759 $1267 €1100 Sans titre (44x315cm-17x124in) init.d.1952. 10-Jul-3 Artcurial Briest, Paris #306
£839 $1401 €1200 Sans titre (48x34cm-19x13in) mono. d. paper. 26-Jun-3 Tajan, Paris #184/R
£839 $1401 €1200 Sans titre (30x47cm-12x19in) s.d. i.verso paper. 26-Jun-3 Tajan, Paris #182/R
£2013 $3119 €3200 So goetze icht (55x39cm-22x15in) mono.d.1948 mono.i.d.27.10.48 verso paper. 30-Oct-2 Artcurial Briest, Paris #287 est:3000-4000
£3265 $5192 €4800 Sans titre (35x27cm-14x11in) mono.d.27 mono.d.29.IV.27 prov. 26-Feb-3 Artcurial Briest, Paris #75/R est:1000-1500
£4167 $6542 €6500 Gris (47x33cm-19x13in) init.d.1947 paper on canvas prov.exhib. 24-Nov-2 Laurence Calmels, Paris #203/R
£10256 $16103 €16000 Improvisation (51x36cm-20x14in) init.d.1958 paper on canvas prov.exhib. 24-Nov-2 Laurence Calmels, Paris #205/R est:6000
Works on paper
£705 $1107 €1100 Graffiti d'enfant (30x48cm-12x19in) s.i.d.46 Chinese ink wash. 24-Nov-2 Laurence Calmels, Paris #200/R
£987 $1599 €1500 Sans titre (44x32cm-17x13in) ink W/C dr. 22-Jan-3 Tajan, Paris #249/R est:2000-3000
£1667 $2583 €2600 Sans titre (33x18cm-13x7in) mono.d.1943 s.i. verso gouache bodycol. 7-Dec-2 Ketterer, Hamburg #299/R est:2800-3200
£1944 $3091 €2800 Sans titre (20x14cm-8x6in) mono.d.21.IV.27 verso gouache collage. 29-Apr-3 Artcurial Briest, Paris #119/R est:1500-2000
£3205 $5032 €5000 Kinderbild (27x21cm-11x8in) init.d.30 collage prov.exhib. 24-Nov-2 Laurence Calmels, Paris #201/R
£3205 $5032 €5000 Composition (27x21cm-11x8in) init.d.1930 collage prov.exhib. 24-Nov-2 Laurence Calmels, Paris #199/R
£3205 $5032 €5000 Interior (27x38cm-11x15in) init.d.1940 gouache prov.exhib. 24-Nov-2 Laurence Calmels, Paris #204/R
£3718 $5837 €5800 Composition (27x21cm-11x8in) init.d.1930 collage prov.exhib. 24-Nov-2 Laurence Calmels, Paris #198/R
£5449 $8554 €8500 Copie (27x21cm-11x8in) init.d.1929 collage prov.exhib. 24-Nov-2 Laurence Calmels, Paris #202/R

NOUVEL, Jean (1945-) French
Works on paper
£581 $917 €900 Ile de Awaji (60x84cm-24x33in) collage pair. 19-Dec-2 Ruellan, Paris #146/R

NOVAK, Ada (1912-1990) Czechoslovakian
£318 $515 €461 Landscape viewed from Duby (120x85cm-47x33in) s. 24-May-3 Dorotheum, Prague #140/R est:8000-12000 (C.KR 14000)

NOVAK, Andor (1887-?) Hungarian
£4751 $7411 €7127 Femme fatale (131x100cm-52x39in) s. 11-Apr-3 Kieselbach, Budapest #19/R est:650000-1700000 (H.F 1700000)

NOVATI, Marco (1895-1975) Italian
£513 $795 €800 Still life (34x48cm-13x19in) s. paper. 5-Dec-2 Stadion, Trieste #877/R
£823 $1284 €1300 La Salute (35x50cm-14x20in) s. board. 19-Oct-2 Semenzato, Venice #20/R

NOVELLI, Gastone (1925-1968) Italian
£10284 $16660 €14500 Cuba creatore (40x50cm-16x20in) s.d.67 s.i.d.verso prov.exhib. 26-May-3 Christie's, Milan #342/R est:9000-12000
£19355 $30581 €30000 Full flood (50x60cm-20x24in) s.d.62 s.i.d.1962 verso oil pencil prov.lit. 18-Dec-2 Christie's, Rome #304/R
Sculpture
£1712 $2671 €2500 Average mountain (17x23cm-7x9in) s. num.1/12 brown pat bronze. 10-Apr-3 Finarte Semenzato, Rome #217/R
Works on paper
£548 $855 €800 Untitled (20x22cm-8x9in) s. ink pencil paper on card. 10-Apr-3 Finarte Semenzato, Rome #195
£1935 $3058 €3000 Fifty suns plus one (35x51cm-14x20in) s.i.d.66 pencil felt-tip pen pastel prov.exhib. 18-Dec-2 Christie's, Rome #189/R
£2740 $4274 €4000 Forms (49x71cm-19x28in) s. ink exec.1967 exhib.lit. 10-Apr-3 Finarte Semenzato, Rome #97/R

NOVELLI, Pietro (1603-1647) Italian
£23448 $37048 €34000 Moses (116x81cm-46x32in) 3-Apr-3 Porro, Milan #23/R est:40000
£150943 $235472 €240000 Apollo and Coronide (146x180cm-57x71in) 22-Sep-2 Semenzato, Venice #304/R
Works on paper
£324 $518 €450 Riders and other figures by spring (7x18cm-3x7in) i.d.MDCC.LXXXVI pen wash prov. 17-May-3 Lempertz, Koln #1248
£1818 $2600 €2727 Coronation of the Virgin (34x21cm-13x8in) pen ink brown wash over black chk. 23-Jan-3 Swann Galleries, New York #55/R est:3000-5000

NOVELLI, Pietro Antonio (1729-1804) Italian
Works on paper
£664 $950 €996 Standing female figure with an anchor in a niche (43x19cm-17x7in) brush ink grey wash pen. 23-Jan-3 Swann Galleries, New York #161/R
£1013 $1600 €1520 Nude male with an outstretched arm (231x157cm-91x62in) i. red chk prov. 1-Apr-3 Christie's, Rockefeller NY #380/R est:2000-3000
£5000 $8350 €7250 Three studies of a dog frolicking (33x23cm-13x9in) black chk pen ink wash prov. 8-Jul-3 Christie's, London #55/R est:4000-6000

NOVELLI, Pietro Antonio (attrib) (1729-1804) Italian
Works on paper
£385 $596 €600 Mythological scene (11x19cm-4x7in) pen W/C. 4-Dec-2 Piasa, Paris #15

NOVICE, William (fl.1809-1833) British
£1043 $1628 €1565 Self portrait with picture (48x37cm-19x15in) s. panel prov. 16-Sep-2 Philippe Schuler, Zurich #3489/R est:3000-3500 (S.FR 2400)

NOVICE, William (attrib) (fl.1809-1833) British
£2600 $4290 €3770 Kitchen interior (100x145cm-39x57in) 2-Jul-3 Sotheby's, Olympia #130/R est:800-1200

NOVIS, Barry (1944-) British
£11250 $17888 €16875 John Lennon (150x120cm-59x47in) linen. 10-Mar-3 Christie's, London #4

NOVO, Stefano (1862-1902) Italian
£1361 $2163 €2000 Young Venetian woman (20x16cm-8x6in) s. 18-Mar-3 Finarte, Milan #36/R
£5200 $8268 €7800 Woman before a vegetable stall. Three women at a canal side (76x51cm-30x20in) one s.i.d.1907 pair. 18-Mar-3 Capes Dunn, Manchester #525/R
£13000 $21710 €19500 Awaiting the gondola. Fruit stall (81x56cm-32x22in) s. pair. 18-Jun-3 Christie's, Kensington #113a/R est:8000-12000

NOVOA, Leopoldo (1929-) Uruguayan
Works on paper
£676 $1054 €1000 Next time the fire (60x73cm-24x29in) s.d.92 mixed media on canvas. 26-Mar-3 Finarte Semenzato, Milan #95/R

NOVOPACKY, Johann (1821-1908) Austrian
Works on paper
£386 $625 €579 Landscape with stream (16x13cm-6x5in) s.d.857 col pencil. 24-May-3 Dorotheum, Prague #210/R est:4000-6000 (C.KR 17000)

NOWAK, Ernst (1853-1919) Austrian
£641 $1006 €1000 A good drop (21x16cm-8x6in) s. wood. 21-Nov-2 Dorotheum, Vienna #182/R

NOWAK, Otto (1874-1945) Austrian
Works on paper
£566 $877 €900 Schanigarten (34x37cm-13x15in) s. W/C. 1-Oct-2 Dorotheum, Vienna #328/R

NOWAK, Suzanne and WALKER, Elizabeth A Kelly (20th C) American
£10828 $17000 €16242 Panoramic view of Wychmere Harbour, Harwichport, MA. (104x1280cm-41x504in) s.d.1977 board 45 panel folding wall mural. 22-Nov-2 Eldred, East Dennis #1061/R est:500-1000

NOWAK, Wilhelm (1886-1977) Austrian
£222 $369 €322 Still life with porcelain and wine carafe (32x36cm-13x14in) s. panel. 16-Jun-3 Waddingtons, Toronto #14/R (C.D 500)
£2113 $3401 €3000 Summer's day by river (67x83cm-26x33in) s. lit. 9-May-3 Schloss Ahlden, Ahlden #1514/R est:2800
Works on paper
£351 $554 €527 Autumn (42x27cm-17x11in) s. W/C gouache. 30-Nov-2 Dorotheum, Prague #150 (C.KR 17000)

NOWEY, A (1835-?) British?
£516 $759 €800 Stable with sheep and goats (28x35cm-11x14in) s. 24-Jun-2 Dr Fritz Nagel, Stuttgart #5946/R

NOWEY, Adolf (1835-?) British?
£550 $869 €825 Chickens and ducks in a farmyard (26x39cm-10x15in) s. panel. 14-Nov-2 Christie's, Kensington #156
£634 $1052 €900 Fox family with slain duck (42x58cm-17x23in) s. 14-Jun-3 Arnold, Frankfurt #823/R
£755 $1170 €1200 Girl holding lamb in barn with sheep (36x58cm-14x23in) s. panel. 29-Oct-2 Dorotheum, Vienna #44/R
£1000 $1520 €1500 Unwanted visitor. Mischief makers (43x34cm-17x13in) s. panel pair. 29-Aug-2 Christie's, Kensington #268/R est:1500-2000
£1162 $1871 €1650 Goat, sheep and poultry in barn (29x47cm-11x19in) s.d.76. 7-May-3 Michael Zeller, Lindau #862/R est:1450

NOWLAN, Frank (1835-1919) British
Works on paper
£310 $484 €465 Young lady with black ribbons in her hair (25x18cm-10x7in) s. W/C. 15-Oct-2 Canterbury Auctions, UK #185/R

NOYER, Philippe (1917-1985) French
Works on paper
£224 $375 €325 Jeune fille assise a la terrasse d'un cafe (64x48cm-25x19in) s.d.69 mixed media. 29-Jun-3 Butterfields, Los Angeles #7052/R
£479 $800 €695 Having a drink (74x58cm-29x23in) s. mixed media on canvas. 29-Jun-3 Butterfields, Los Angeles #7051/R

NOYES, George L (1864-1954) Canadian
£2229 $3500 €3344 City interior (64x46cm-25x18in) s. 10-Dec-2 Doyle, New York #83/R est:4000-6000
£4114 $6500 €6171 Gloucester fishing craft (20x23cm-8x9in) s. i.verso panel prov. 24-Apr-3 Shannon's, Milford #65/R est:3000-5000
£4221 $6500 €6332 Hillside in summer (41x36cm-16x14in) s. 24-Oct-2 Shannon's, Milford #193/R est:3000-5000
£6013 $9500 €9020 Harbor view, Gloucester (30x41cm-12x16in) s. prov. 24-Apr-3 Shannon's, Milford #52/R est:6000-8000
£6329 $10000 €9494 From the shore, Rockport (30x41cm-12x16in) s. canvasboard prov. 24-Apr-3 Shannon's, Milford #53/R est:5000-7000
£15584 $24000 €23376 Gloucester Harbour (36x38cm-14x15in) s. prov. 24-Oct-2 Shannon's, Milford #143/R est:15000-20000
£15753 $23000 €23630 Haystacks (61x63cm-24x25in) s. 10-May-2 Skinner, Boston #167/R est:18000-22000

NOYES, Walter Fiske (20th C) American
£764 $1100 €1146 Morning ride (122x91cm-48x36in) s. 15-Jan-3 Christie's, Rockefeller NY #158/R

NOZAL, Alexandre (1852-1929) French
£483 $768 €700 La faneuse (31x16cm-12x6in) s.d.1892 panel. 5-Mar-3 Oger, Dumont, Paris #49
£483 $768 €700 La faneuse (32x28cm-13x11in) panel. 5-Mar-3 Oger, Dumont, Paris #47/R
£714 $1136 €1050 Crepuscule en bord de lac (38x55cm-15x22in) s.i.d.1922. 24-Mar-3 Coutau Begarie, Paris #229/R
£1655 $2632 €2400 Le pont sur la Durance (83x147cm-33x58in) s. 5-Mar-3 Oger, Dumont, Paris #48/R est:1500

NUCCI, Avanzino (1551-1629) Italian
Works on paper
£1338 $2154 €1900 Santa che si comunica (24x17cm-9x7in) pen brown ink htd white blk pencil blue paper. 12-May-3 Sotheby's, Milan #18/R est:1500-2000

NUCCI, Benedetto (1515-1587) Italian
£26000 $40820 €39000 Pilgrim with supplicants. Madonna of Mercy with female donors (81x47cm-32x19in) one s. i. pair. 12-Dec-2 Sotheby's, London #104/R est:12000-18000

NUCKEL, Otto (1888-1956) German
£377 $581 €600 Starnberger See (32x24cm-13x9in) s. W/C over pencil board. 26-Oct-2 Dr Lehr, Berlin #401/R
£3077 $4862 €4800 Street scene - possibly Berlin (78x78cm-31x31in) s. i. stretcher. 14-Nov-2 Neumeister, Munich #644/R est:6000-8000
£8333 $12167 €13000 Couple in restaurant (91x76cm-36x30in) s.d.21. 4-Jun-2 Karl & Faber, Munich #373/R est:16000-17000
£9615 $14038 €15000 Acrobats (136x92cm-54x36in) s. 4-Jun-2 Karl & Faber, Munich #374/R est:16000-17000

NUDERSCHER, Frank (1880-1959) American
Works on paper
£337 $525 €506 Landscape with haystacks and view of Missouri State Capitol Building (20x20cm-8x8in) s. W/C prov. 10-Nov-2 Selkirks, St. Louis #895

NUNEN, David van (1952-) Australian
£1071 $1693 €1607 Sydney Harbour Bridge (168x137cm-66x54in) s.d.1982 i.verso prov. 17-Nov-2 Sotheby's, Paddington #83/R est:4000-6000 (A.D 3000)
Works on paper
£786 $1225 €1179 Middle harbour, Sugarloaf (122x121cm-48x48in) s.d.86 synthetic polymer paint linen. 11-Nov-2 Deutscher-Menzies, Melbourne #168/R (A.D 2200)

NUNEZ DE CELIS, Francisco (1919-1996) Spanish
£321 $506 €500 Landscape with lake (46x55cm-18x22in) s. board. 13-Nov-2 Ansorena, Madrid #296/R
£395 $639 €600 Landscape (46x55cm-18x22in) board. 21-Jan-3 Ansorena, Madrid #247/R
£523 $842 €800 Landscape (40x57cm-16x22in) s. d.65 verso board. 14-Jan-3 Castellana, Madrid #15/R
£523 $842 €800 Beach (40x57cm-16x22in) s. board. 14-Jan-3 Castellana, Madrid #358/R
£728 $1187 €1100 Istambul (50x75cm-20x30in) s. board. 11-Feb-3 Castellana, Madrid #28/R
£828 $1349 €1250 Mogrovejo Tower (50x70cm-20x28in) s. board. 11-Feb-3 Castellana, Madrid #333/R
£974 $1422 €1500 Spain is this (73x93cm-29x37in) s. s.i.d.verso. 17-Jun-2 Ansorena, Madrid #325/R

NUNEZ LOSADA, Francisco (1889-1973) Spanish
£2586 $4086 €3750 Mountains (80x90cm-31x35in) s. 7-Apr-3 Castellana, Madrid #435/R

NUNEZ LOSADA, Francisco (attrib) (1889-1973) Spanish
£705 $1100 €1058 Dutch figures on shore (41x61cm-16x24in) s. 29-Mar-3 Charlton Hall, Columbia #223/R est:1000-1500

NUNEZ, Armando Garcia (20th C) Mexican
£1763 $2751 €2645 Frente a la tienda (15x20cm-6x8in) s. wood. 17-Oct-2 Louis Morton, Mexico #26/R est:20000-25000 (M.P 28000)
Works on paper
£561 $887 €842 Man (58x42cm-23x17in) s. chl. 26-Nov-2 Louis Morton, Mexico #94/R est:12000 (M.P 9000)
£630 $982 €945 Paisaje (15x27cm-6x11in) s. chl. 17-Oct-2 Louis Morton, Mexico #12 est:12000-14000 (M.P 10000)

NUNZIANTE, Antonio (1956-) Italian
£3537 $5624 €5200 Travelling to the Isle of Eros (70x100cm-28x39in) s. 1-Mar-3 Meeting Art, Vercelli #733

NUNZIO (1954-) American
Sculpture
£3846 $6038 €6000 Untitled (113cm-44in) burnt wood exec.1996. 21-Nov-2 Finarte, Rome #281/R est:7000
Works on paper
£347 $552 €500 Composition (33x46cm-13x18in) s.d.1984 mixed media. 1-May-3 Meeting Art, Vercelli #155
£1282 $2013 €2000 Untitled (71x50cm-28x20in) s.d.90 mixed media cardboard. 21-Nov-2 Finarte, Rome #162/R
£1765 $2824 €2700 Untitled (72x51cm-28x20in) s.d.2001 lead chl panel. 4-Jan-3 Meeting Art, Vercelli #365
£3378 $5270 €5000 Scare (80x78cm-31x31in) s.i.d.1992 verso mixed media wood lead diptych. 26-Mar-3 Finarte Semenzato, Milan #169/R

NUPEN, Kjell (1955-) Norwegian
£887 $1383 €1331 Composition (65x54cm-26x21in) s.d.1991 verso. 18-Sep-2 Kunsthallen, Copenhagen #133 (D.KR 10500)
£5044 $7970 €7566 Restored landscape (195x130cm-77x51in) s. d.1991 verso exhib.prov. 28-Apr-3 Blomqvist, Oslo #394/R est:35000-45000 (N.KR 57000)

NUREMBERG SCHOOL (15th C) German
£576923 $905769 €900000 Adoration of the Magi with Saint Anthony (88x171cm-35x67in) panel painted c.1410 prov.lit. 14-Dec-2 Artcurial Briest, Paris #27/R est:350000-420000

NUSCHELER, Hans Jakob II (1614-1658) Swiss
Works on paper
£455 $700 €683 Battle scene with men praying in the background (229x171cm-90x67in) s.indis.i.d.1638 black chk pen ink brown wash prov. 4-Sep-2 Christie's, Rockefeller NY #276/R

NUSE, Roy Cleveland (1885-?) American
£16168 $27000 €23444 McComas Farm, Rushland, Pennsylvania (51x56cm-20x22in) s. 22-Jun-3 Freeman, Philadelphia #158/R est:15000-25000

NUSSBAUM, Jacob (1873-1936) German
£493 $818 €700 Bank of River Main in winter with walkers (57x40cm-22x16in) indis.s.d.1923. 14-Jun-3 Arnold, Frankfurt #824/R
£552 $877 €800 Autumn pond (43x54cm-17x21in) s. 8-Mar-3 Arnold, Frankfurt #662/R

NUSSBAUMER, Paul (1934-) Swiss
£524 $817 €786 Vierwaldstattersee (64x110cm-25x43in) s.d.63. 20-Nov-2 Fischer, Luzern #2205/R (S.FR 1200)

NUSSI, Arnaldo (1906-) Italian
£507 $832 €700 Paesaggio montano (31x40cm-12x16in) s. panel. 27-May-3 Finarte, Milan #117/R

NUSSIO, Oscar (1899-1976) Swiss
£266 $420 €399 Piz Bernina, Scherschen and Piz Rosegg in front of the Fuorcla Surlej (45x66cm-18x26in) s.i.d.1949 verso. 29-Nov-2 Zofingen, Switzerland #3011 (S.FR 620)
£283 $441 €425 Melting snow in the Alps (56x70cm-22x28in) s.d.1964. 16-Sep-2 Philippe Schuler, Zurich #6639 (S.FR 650)
£340 $543 €510 Silvretta (38x52cm-15x20in) s.d. 17-Mar-3 Philippe Schuler, Zurich #8472 (S.FR 720)
£648 $1044 €972 Matterhorn from Findeln (59x69cm-23x27in) s.d.1930 i. verso. 7-May-3 Dobiaschofsky, Bern #862/R (S.FR 1400)

NUTTER, J (?) British
£620 $986 €930 Views in the Lakeland fells (51x40cm-20x16in) s. pair. 27-Feb-3 Bonhams, Chester #325

NUVOLONE, Carlo Francesco (1608-1665) Italian
£3846 $5962 €6000 Putto with martyrdom symbols (66x73cm-26x29in) 4-Dec-2 Christie's, Rome #414/R est:4000-6000
£9877 $16000 €14816 Penitent Magdalene (67x52cm-26x20in) prov. 23-Jan-3 Sotheby's, New York #66/R est:12000-18000
£10000 $16700 €14500 Sleeping Christ child, God the Father and putti with instruments of passion (157x121cm-62x48in) 10-Jul-3 Sotheby's, London #166/R est:12000-18000

NUVOLONE, Carlo Francesco (attrib) (1608-1665) Italian
£1032 $1631 €1600 Madonna and Child (100x77cm-39x30in) 19-Dec-2 Delvaux, Paris #85
£4930 $7937 €7000 Madonna with sleeping child (116x92cm-46x36in) 10-May-3 Hans Stahl, Toestorf #98/R est:9000
£14685 $21000 €22028 Still life of fruit and flowers (80x110cm-31x43in) 22-Jan-3 Doyle, New York #103/R
Works on paper
£507 $800 €800 Young boy (10x7cm-4x3in) crayon sanguine. 28-Nov-2 Tajan, Paris #22

NUVOLONE, Carlo Francesco (style) (1608-1665) Italian
£2254 $3741 €3200 Santa Caterina d'Alessandria (74x61cm-29x24in) 11-Jun-3 Dorotheum, Vienna #5/R est:3000-5000

NUVOLONE, Giuseppe (attrib) (1619-1703) Italian
£11034 $17655 €16000 Samaritan at the well (123x153cm-48x60in) 17-Mar-3 Pandolfini, Florence #693/R est:34000
£11034 $17655 €16000 Christ and the magdalene (123x153cm-48x60in) 17-Mar-3 Pandolfini, Florence #694/R est:34000
£11034 $17655 €16000 Charity (67x57cm-26x22in) 17-Mar-3 Pandolfini, Florence #701/R est:15000

NUVOLONE, Panfilo (circle) (c.1581-1651) Italian
£5172 $8224 €7500 Still life with peaches (19x26cm-7x10in) board octagonal. 5-Mar-3 Sotheby's, Milan #209/R

NUYEN, Wijbrand Johannes Josephus (1813-1839) Dutch
£1911 $2981 €3000 Landscape with Batavieren (40x60cm-16x24in) 6-Nov-2 Vendue Huis, Gravenhage #442/R est:3000-4000
£6944 $11042 €10000 Activities on a sunlit beach (27x32cm-11x13in) s.d.1831 panel prov. 29-Apr-3 Christie's, Amsterdam #19/R est:10000-15000
£53459 $82327 €85000 Hiver, winter landscape with figure near a fishermans house (60x46cm-24x18in) s.d.37 panel prov. 23-Oct-2 Christie's, Amsterdam #111/R est:40000-60000
Works on paper
£2420 $3776 €3800 Church interior (9x5cm-4x2in) s.verso pen brown ink W/C over black chk prov.exhib.lit. 5-Nov-2 Sotheby's, Amsterdam #174/R est:4000-6000
£3694 $5763 €5800 Beach scene on the Normandy coast with figures (9x13cm-4x5in) s. W/C gouache over pencil prov.exhib. 5-Nov-2 Sotheby's, Amsterdam #173/R est:6000-8000

NUYEN, Wijbrand Johannes Josephus (attrib) (1813-1839) Dutch
Works on paper
£526 $853 €800 Fisherfolk overlooking the sea (25x33cm-10x13in) s.d.36 pencil pen ink W/C. 21-Jan-3 Christie's, Amsterdam #73

NUZI, Allegretto (1346-1385) Italian
£75000 $125250 €108750 Arrest and miracles of Saint Blaise (25x34cm-10x13in) gold ground panel prov.lit. 9-Jul-3 Christie's, London #80/R est:80000-100000

NUZZI, Mario (1603-1673) Italian
£15190 $24000 €24000 Vase of flowers (95x72cm-37x28in) lit. 27-Nov-2 Finarte, Milan #86/R
£28000 $43960 €42000 Still life of various flowers in an ormolu vase with putti (98x75cm-39x30in) 12-Dec-2 Sotheby's, London #52/R est:25000-35000
£62069 $98069 €90000 Still life of flowers in metal vase (65x49cm-26x19in) 5-Apr-3 Finarte Semenzato, Milan #125/R est:80000-120000
£128205 $198718 €200000 Vases of flowers on table (98x73cm-39x29in) pair prov.exhib.lit. 6-Dec-2 Millon & Associes, Paris #11/R

NUZZI, Mario (attrib) (1603-1673) Italian
£12950 $20719 €18000 Still life of flowers in blue stone vase (74x61cm-29x24in) 13-May-3 Sotheby's, Amsterdam #83/R est:20000-30000

NUZZI, Mario (style) (1603-1673) Italian
£5704 $9184 €8500 Flower still life in a stone vase (45x34cm-18x13in) prov. 18-Feb-3 Sotheby's, Amsterdam #244/R est:3000-5000

NYBERG, Ivar (1855-1925) Swedish
£1795 $2818 €2800 Peintre dans son atelier (34x25cm-13x10in) s. 16-Dec-2 Rabourdin & Choppin de Janvry, Paris #22/R
Works on paper
£1681 $2655 €2522 Interior scene with two woman at the piano (90x72cm-35x28in) s.d.92 pastel. 16-Nov-2 Crafoord, Lund #90/R est:5000 (S.KR 24000)

NYBOE, Friis (1869-1929) Danish
£253 $395 €380 Interior scene with man seated (45x61cm-18x24in) s. 22-Sep-2 Hindemae, Ullerslev #7210/R (D.KR 3000)
£262 $408 €393 Interior scene with mother and child by fireplace (47x50cm-19x20in) s. 23-Sep-2 Rasmussen, Vejle #2172 (D.KR 3100)
£306 $490 €459 Interior scene with woman seen from behind looking in mirror (50x42cm-20x17in) s. 13-Jan-3 Rasmussen, Vejle #167/R (D.KR 3500)
£466 $740 €699 Evening party at the home of the artist Viggo Johansen (100x70cm-39x28in) s. 10-Mar-3 Rasmussen, Vejle #543 (D.KR 5000)
£517 $786 €776 Girl wearing red dress at piano in evening light (45x48cm-18x19in) s. 27-Aug-2 Rasmussen, Copenhagen #1943/R (D.KR 6000)

NYBORG, Asle (1966-) Norwegian
£778 $1260 €1167 Talking to you about our furniture (200x115cm-79x45in) s. 27-Jan-3 Blomqvist, Lysaker #1181 (N.KR 8600)
£814 $1318 €1221 Small girl's world (200x120cm-79x47in) s. 27-Jan-3 Blomqvist, Lysaker #1182/R (N.KR 9000)
£1175 $1904 €1763 Show a traveller a winter night (227x146cm-89x57in) s. 27-Jan-3 Blomqvist, Lysaker #1180 est:17000 (N.KR 13000)

NYBORG, Peter (1937-) Danish
£271 $420 €407 The possessed (81x100cm-32x39in) s.i.d.1966 verso. 1-Oct-2 Rasmussen, Copenhagen #190/R (D.KR 3200)
£362 $561 €543 Night bird (100x131cm-39x52in) s.d.62 verso. 4-Dec-2 Kunsthallen, Copenhagen #172 (D.KR 4200)
£378 $609 €567 Castles of the Kings (96x80cm-38x31in) s.d.91. 22-Feb-3 Rasmussen, Havnen #2185 (D.KR 4200)
£450 $725 €675 Oceans of Dreams (96x111cm-38x44in) s.d.1991 verso. 22-Feb-3 Rasmussen, Havnen #2182 (D.KR 5000)
£508 $787 €762 Gnomes' party (128x190cm-50x75in) s.d.64 s.i.d.1964. 1-Oct-2 Rasmussen, Copenhagen #189 (D.KR 6000)
£861 $1335 €1292 Le depart d'amour (92x73cm-36x29in) s. 4-Dec-2 Kunsthallen, Copenhagen #252/R (D.KR 10000)
£913 $1415 €1370 Composition (140x95cm-55x37in) s.d.92 acrylic. 4-Dec-2 Kunsthallen, Copenhagen #270/R (D.KR 10600)
£1723 $2670 €2585 L'hiver de Mahler (17x126cm-7x50in) s. 4-Dec-2 Kunsthallen, Copenhagen #258/R est:18000 (D.KR 20000)

NYE, Edgar (1879-1943) American
£446 $700 €669 Farmstead. River landscape (69x81cm-27x32in) s. board double-sided. 23-Nov-2 Jackson's, Cedar Falls #109/R

£705 $1100 €1058 Boats along the canal (71x84cm-28x33in) s.d.22. 20-Sep-2 Sloan, North Bethesda #464/R est:2000-3000
£705 $1100 €1058 Rocky shoreline on a misty day (94x104cm-37x41in) s.d.23. 12-Apr-3 Weschler, Washington #578/R est:1200-1800
£897 $1400 €1346 Pasture beside rolling hills (94x107cm-37x42in) s. 12-Apr-3 Weschler, Washington #576/R est:1000-1500
£1346 $2100 €2019 Vegetable sellers (36x46cm-14x18in) s.d.21. 20-Sep-2 Sloan, North Bethesda #465/R est:800-1200

NYFELLER, Albert (1883-1969) German
£304 $472 €456 Alp Buhl on Hohenweg (50x61cm-20x24in) s.d.1943 i. verso. 9-Dec-2 Philippe Schuler, Zurich #8745 (S.FR 700)
£515 $814 €773 Sunny winter day in Kippel (60x49cm-24x19in) d.1966 s.i.verso board. 29-Nov-2 Zofingen, Switzerland #2013 (S.FR 1200)

NYGN, Ba (20th C) Asian
£414 $658 €600 Flowers in a garden (96x44cm-38x17in) s. 10-Mar-3 Sotheby's, Amsterdam #260
£620 $986 €900 People at the entrance of a temple (41x51cm-16x20in) s.d.1933. 10-Mar-3 Sotheby's, Amsterdam #262 est:600-900

NYHOLM, Arvid Frederick (1866-1927) American/Swedish
£417 $650 €626 Landscape and mountains (25x76cm-10x30in) 10-Nov-2 Selkirks, St. Louis #897

NYILASY, Sandor (1873-?) Hungarian
£488 $800 €708 Windmill (64x53cm-25x21in) s. 4-Jun-3 Doyle, New York #74
£782 $1221 €1173 Spring (80x65cm-31x26in) s. 11-Apr-3 Kieselbach, Budapest #2/R (H.F 280000)

NYKYRI, Susanna (20th C) Finnish
£387 $612 €600 Home-coming (65x80cm-26x31in) s.d.1941. 19-Dec-2 Hagelstam, Helsinki #910

NYL-FROSCH, Marie (1857-1914) German
£573 $883 €900 Basket of flowers hanging on wall (48x32cm-19x13in) s. 5-Sep-2 Arnold, Frankfurt #834/R

NYLUND, Felix (1878-1940) Finnish?
Sculpture
£2405 $3800 €3800 Nude female bending forward (26cm-10in) s.i.d.1908 bronze st.f.Rasmussen lit. 30-Nov-2 Hagelstam, Helsinki #5/R est:2000

NYMAN, Bjorn (1934-) Swedish
£458 $737 €650 Still life of glass and medal (32x27cm-13x11in) s.d.1976. 10-May-3 Bukowskis, Helsinki #33/R
£588 $965 €900 Still life towards heaven (72x57cm-28x22in) s.d.1993 acrylic. 9-Feb-3 Bukowskis, Helsinki #327/R

NYMAN, Olle (1909-1999) Swedish
£327 $520 €491 Portrait of lady (56x46cm-22x18in) s.d.1987 panel. 3-Mar-3 Lilla Bukowskis, Stockholm #23 (S.KR 4400)
£473 $766 €710 Flowers in green jug (66x44cm-26x17in) s. canvas on panel. 3-Feb-3 Lilla Bukowskis, Stockholm #946 (S.KR 6600)
£479 $795 €695 Still life of shoe-tree and wood anemones (41x49cm-16x19in) s. canvas on panel exhib. 16-Jun-3 Lilla Bukowskis, Stockholm #359 (S.KR 6200)
Sculpture
£1892 $2952 €2838 Woman (52cm-20in) s. scrap sculpture. 5-Nov-2 Bukowskis, Stockholm #235/R est:18000-20000 (S.KR 27000)
Works on paper
£561 $886 €842 Architecture (50x85cm-20x33in) s. gouache. 30-Nov-2 Goteborg Auktionsverk, Sweden #594/R (S.KR 8000)
£3042 $4806 €4563 Composition Y (40x32cm-16x13in) s. collage exhib. 28-Apr-3 Bukowskis, Stockholm #260/R est:12000-15000 (S.KR 40000)

NYMEYER, Joop (20th C) Dutch
£1915 $3102 €2700 Still life with red thread (80x70cm-31x28in) s.d.84 verso. 26-May-3 Glerum, Amsterdam #255/R est:1200-1600

NYROP, Borge (1881-1948) Danish
£337 $525 €506 Sheaths of hay (76x109cm-30x43in) 28-Mar-3 Douglas, South Deerfield #3

NYS, Alexis (20th C) Belgian
£1053 $1705 €1600 Quai aux briques (40x50cm-16x20in) s. 21-Jan-3 Galerie Moderne, Brussels #208/R est:1000-1500

NYS, Carl (1858-?) Belgian
£1772 $2765 €2800 Alice (125x65cm-49x26in) s. 21-Oct-2 Bernaerts, Antwerp #144/R est:1500-2000
£2014 $3223 €2800 Jeune fille dans les dunes (100x125cm-39x49in) s. 13-May-3 Palais de Beaux Arts, Brussels #109/R est:2800-3500

NYS, Francis (1863-1900) Belgian
£633 $987 €1000 Mediterranean village view in the mountains (38x46cm-15x18in) s. 21-Oct-2 Bernaerts, Antwerp #521/R

NYST, Jacques Louis (1942-1996) Belgian
£503 $775 €800 Boule de corde (109x72cm-43x28in) s. dr. 22-Oct-2 Campo, Vlaamse Kaai #216

NYSTROM, Jenny (1854-1946) Swedish
£897 $1381 €1346 River landscape (92x146cm-36x57in) s.d.1901 after Gottfrid Kallstenius. 27-Oct-2 Anders Antik, Landskrona #320/R (S.KR 13000)
£1125 $1822 €1631 Harvesting time (24x32cm-9x13in) s.d.1941. 25-May-3 Uppsala Auktionskammare, Uppsala #199/R est:18000-20000 (S.KR 14500)
£1482 $2327 €2223 Wood anemones (27x23cm-11x9in) s.d.1944. 16-Dec-2 Lilla Bukowskis, Stockholm #446 est:10000-12000 (S.KR 21000)
£2677 $4069 €4016 Loves me, loves me not (67x53cm-26x21in) s.d.1873 after Joseph W Wallander. 16-Aug-2 Lilla Bukowskis, Stockholm #862 est:30000-35000 (S.KR 39000)
Works on paper
£340 $564 €493 Lady wearing hat (34x16cm-13x6in) s.i.d.1885 Indian ink. 16-Jun-3 Lilla Bukowskis, Stockholm #547 (S.KR 4400)
£347 $577 €503 The sickbed (14x19cm-6x7in) s. Indian ink wash htd white. 16-Jun-3 Lilla Bukowskis, Stockholm #249 (S.KR 4500)
£352 $563 €510 Horse taxi (13x22cm-5x9in) s. Indian ink wash. 18-May-3 Anders Antik, Landskrona #66 (S.KR 4500)
£360 $575 €522 The kiss (17x10cm-7x4in) s. Indian ink wash htd white. 18-May-3 Anders Antik, Landskrona #68 (S.KR 4600)
£360 $575 €522 Hesitation (16x10cm-6x4in) s. Indian ink wash htd white. 18-May-3 Anders Antik, Landskrona #69 (S.KR 4600)
£360 $575 €522 The proposal (17x10cm-7x4in) s. Indian ink wash htd white. 18-May-3 Anders Antik, Landskrona #70 (S.KR 4600)
£367 $576 €551 Children picking flowers (25x16cm-10x6in) s. W/C Indian ink. 16-Dec-2 Lilla Bukowskis, Stockholm #160 (S.KR 5200)
£395 $620 €593 The doctor is visiting (18x13cm-7x5in) s. Indian ink book illustration. 16-Dec-2 Lilla Bukowskis, Stockholm #116 (S.KR 5600)
£412 $642 €618 Evening on the terrace (25x17cm-10x7in) s. W/C htd white paper on cardboard. 13-Sep-2 Lilla Bukowskis, Stockholm #220 (S.KR 6000)
£423 $665 €635 The angel (22x14cm-9x6in) s. W/C. 16-Dec-2 Lilla Bukowskis, Stockholm #422 (S.KR 6000)
£607 $953 €911 Easter chick (10x15cm-4x6in) s. W/C. 16-Dec-2 Lilla Bukowskis, Stockholm #420 (S.KR 8600)
£638 $989 €957 The Princess (22x18cm-9x7in) s. Indian ink W/C. 3-Dec-2 Bukowskis, Stockholm #272/R (S.KR 9000)
£638 $989 €957 Children picking apples (20x12cm-8x5in) mono. Indian ink htd white. 8-Dec-2 Uppsala Auktionskammare, Uppsala #147/R (S.KR 9000)
£780 $1209 €1170 Lintott among tulips (22x17cm-9x7in) s. W/C. 3-Dec-2 Bukowskis, Stockholm #279/R (S.KR 11000)
£860 $1393 €1290 Boy on jetty (19x14cm-7x6in) s. W/C. 3-Feb-3 Lilla Bukowskis, Stockholm #104 (S.KR 12000)
£993 $1539 €1490 Happy New Year (17x28cm-7x11in) s. W/C. 3-Dec-2 Bukowskis, Stockholm #271/R est:18000-20000 (S.KR 14000)
£1099 $1704 €1649 Congratulations on your birthday (11x15cm-4x6in) s. W/C oval. 3-Dec-2 Bukowskis, Stockholm #272a/R est:12000-15000 (S.KR 15500)
£1257 $2061 €1823 Winter landscape with red cottage (16x24cm-6x9in) s. W/C. 4-Jun-3 AB Stockholms Auktionsverk #2270/R est:12000-15000 (S.KR 16000)
£1277 $1979 €1916 Meeting of the Christmas gnomes (15x23cm-6x9in) s. gouache W/C. 3-Dec-2 Bukowskis, Stockholm #46/R est:20000-25000 (S.KR 18000)
£1348 $2089 €2022 Christmas Day early service (28x25cm-11x10in) s. W/C. 3-Dec-2 Bukowskis, Stockholm #47/R est:25000-30000 (S.KR 19000)
£1348 $2089 €2022 By the lighthouse (30x19cm-12x7in) s. W/C. 3-Dec-2 Bukowskis, Stockholm #270/R est:25000-30000 (S.KR 19000)
£1383 $2144 €2075 Christmas Eve (21x15cm-8x6in) s. W/C htd white oval. 3-Dec-2 Bukowskis, Stockholm #48/R est:18000-20000 (S.KR 19500)
£1396 $2262 €2024 Happy Easter (20x17cm-8x7in) s. W/C. 26-May-3 Bukowskis, Stockholm #26/R est:20000-25000 (S.KR 18000)
£1418 $2199 €2127 Christmas Eve's morning (18x11cm-7x4in) s. W/C. 3-Dec-2 Bukowskis, Stockholm #50/R est:15000-18000 (S.KR 20000)
£1474 $2388 €2137 Snoklockan - young girl dressed in white playing the piano (36x26cm-14x10in) s. W/C. 26-May-3 Bukowskis, Stockholm #28/R est:25000-30000 (S.KR 19000)
£1560 $2418 €2340 Feeding the Christmas pig (14x22cm-6x9in) s. gouache W/C. 3-Dec-2 Bukowskis, Stockholm #45/R est:20000-25000 (S.KR 22000)

£1560 $2418 €2340 Factory owner Kukeliku - patronising Swedish industry (24x18cm-9x7in) s. W/C. 4-Dec-2 AB Stockholms Auktionsverk #1795/R est:20000-25000 (S.KR 22000)
£1629 $2639 €2362 The squirrel (14x13cm-6x5in) s. W/C. 26-May-3 Bukowskis, Stockholm #24/R est:15000-18000 (S.KR 21000)
£1724 $2655 €2586 Girl with daffodils (29x20cm-11x8in) s.i.d.Nov.1941 Indian ink W/C. 27-Oct-2 Anders Antik, Landskrona #165/R est:25000-30000 (S.KR 25000)
£1862 $3016 €2700 Small boy by Christmas tree (33x25cm-13x10in) s. W/C. 25-May-3 Uppsala Auktionskammare, Uppsala #197/R est:18000-20000 (S.KR 24000)
£1862 $3016 €2700 Father Christmas's helper and the pig (15x18cm-6x7in) s. W/C. 26-May-3 Bukowskis, Stockholm #34/R est:15000-18000 (S.KR 24000)
£1905 $2992 €2858 Girl with basket of flowers, cockerel and hen (20x14cm-8x6in) s. W/C. 16-Dec-2 Lilla Bukowskis, Stockholm #1038/R est:12000-15000 (S.KR 27000)
£1986 $3078 €2979 Small boy and girl embracing (16x12cm-6x5in) s. gouache oval. 4-Dec-2 AB Stockholms Auktionsverk #1753/R est:30000-35000 (S.KR 28000)
£2172 $3519 €3149 Young knights with swans (20x16cm-8x6in) s. Indian ink W/C. 26-May-3 Bukowskis, Stockholm #27/R est:20000-25000 (S.KR 28000)
£2340 $3628 €3510 Delivering Christmas cards (21x14cm-8x6in) s. W/C. 3-Dec-2 Bukowskis, Stockholm #51/R est:20000-22000 (S.KR 33000)
£2405 $3896 €3487 Summer's day on the fjord, sailing boat with children (38x26cm-15x10in) s. W/C. 25-May-3 Uppsala Auktionskammare, Uppsala #196/R est:25000-30000 (S.KR 31000)
£2482 $3848 €3723 King Heimer and Aslog (39x27cm-15x11in) s. W/C htd white. 3-Dec-2 Bukowskis, Stockholm #278/R est:40000-50000 (S.KR 35000)
£2483 $4022 €3600 Dachshund with basket of eggs and daffodils (11x17cm-4x7in) s. W/C oval. 26-May-3 Bukowskis, Stockholm #25/R est:10000-15000 (S.KR 32000)
£3142 $5153 €4556 Girl playing small piano - Christmas time (27x17cm-11x7in) s.i. W/C. 4-Jun-3 AB Stockholms Auktionsverk #2110/R est:40000-50000 (S.KR 40000)
£5106 $8374 €7404 Lost in the forest (34x21cm-13x8in) s. W/C. 4-Jun-3 AB Stockholms Auktionsverk #2347/R est:80000-100000 (S.KR 65000)
£5586 $9049 €8100 Small girl feeding the farm's chickens (34x69cm-13x27in) s. W/C. 26-May-3 Bukowskis, Stockholm #32/R est:50000-60000 (S.KR 72000)
£6950 $10773 €10425 Father Christmas and the Christmas pig arriving (36x80cm-14x31in) s. W/C. 3-Dec-2 Bukowskis, Stockholm #49/R est:120000-140000 (S.KR 98000)
£8865 $13741 €13298 Father Christmas' helpers having porridge for breakfast (36x80cm-14x31in) s. W/C. 3-Dec-2 Bukowskis, Stockholm #273/R est:140000-150000 (S.KR 125000)

NYSTROM, Valdemar (1864-1924) Swedish
£628 $1031 €911 Coastal landscape, Sandhamn (38x59cm-15x23in) s.i.d.98. 4-Jun-3 AB Stockholms Auktionsverk #2225/R (S.KR 8000)
£14140 $23189 €20503 Scirocco - view from Capri (150x245cm-59x96in) s.i.d.1892. 4-Jun-3 AB Stockholms Auktionsverk #2080/R est:60000-80000 (S.KR 180000)

NYUMI, Elizabeth (c.1946-) Australian
Works on paper
£650 $1007 €975 Parwalla (80x30cm-31x12in) i.verso synthetic polymer paint linen prov. 3-Dec-2 Shapiro, Sydney #230/R (A.D 1800)

OAKES, John Wright (1820-1887) British
£469 $751 €680 Old mill at Naulittle, Carnavonshire 1856 (29x46cm-11x18in) i. verso prov. 18-May-3 Anders Antik, Landskrona #150e (S.KR 6000)
£1600 $2496 €2400 Creek on the Severn (30x46cm-12x18in) s. board prov. 26-Mar-3 Sotheby's, Olympia #52/R est:1000-1500

OAKLEY, Lawson (20th C) British
£275 $459 €399 Still life basket of apples (29x39cm-11x15in) s. board exhib. 19-Jun-3 Lane, Penzance #194

OAKLEY, Maria L (fl.1854-1865) British
Works on paper
£500 $830 €725 Portrait of a young lady (52x38cm-20x15in) s.d.1859 W/C. 12-Jun-3 Martel Maides, Guernsey #141

OAKLEY, Octavius (1800-1867) British
Works on paper
£700 $1134 €1050 At Limehouse (25x36cm-10x14in) s. pencil W/C bodycol. 21-May-3 Christie's, Kensington #454/R
£1613 $2500 €2420 Student of beauty (76x55cm-30x22in) s.d.1861 pencil gouache W/C. 29-Oct-2 Sotheby's, New York #127/R est:4000-6000
£2800 $4620 €4060 Boy playing cricket (31x24cm-12x9in) W/C over pencil htd scratching out. 2-Jul-3 Sotheby's, Olympia #177/R est:1000-1500

OAKLEY, Violet (1874-1961) American
Works on paper
£3526 $5500 €5289 Woman guarding Italian artistic treasures (74x53cm-29x21in) s. gouache pastel chl ink exhib. 9-Nov-2 Illustration House, New York #62/R est:6000-9000

OATES, Bennett (1928-) British
£1200 $1860 €1800 Summer flowers (22x51cm-9x20in) s.d.82 board. 4-Dec-2 Christie's, Kensington #464/R est:1000-1500
£1200 $1860 €1800 Yellow lilies and white peonies (22x51cm-9x20in) s.d.82 board. 4-Dec-2 Christie's, Kensington #468/R est:1000-1500
£5400 $8910 €7830 Hollyhocks (61x51cm-24x20in) s.d.84 panel. 1-Jul-3 Bonhams, Norwich #352/R est:5000-6000

OATES, Daniel (1964-) American
Sculpture
£1266 $2000 €1899 Lunch box and thermos. s.i.1992 num. in two parts prov. 12-Nov-2 Phillips, New York #226/R est:3000-4000

OBENICHE, Dominique (20th C) ?
£319 $500 €479 Still life with cherries (23x28cm-9x11in) s. 22-Nov-2 Skinner, Boston #53/R
£319 $500 €479 Still life with peaches, grapes and currants (23x28cm-9x11in) s. 22-Nov-2 Skinner, Boston #55/R

OBER, Artemi (1843-1917) Russian
Sculpture
£2014 $3303 €2800 Cavalier Kirguize (38x35x13cm-15x14x5in) s.d.1872 num.3/1881 brown pat bronze. 4-Jun-3 Tajan, Paris #294/R est:2000-2500

OBER, Hermann (?) ?
£863 $1416 €1200 Tree (115x100cm-45x39in) mono.d.67. 5-Jun-3 Dorotheum, Salzburg #656/R

OBERHAUSER, Emanuel (19/20th C) Austrian
£1200 $1872 €1800 Night in Pompeii (68x107cm-27x42in) bears sig. 9-Oct-2 Woolley & Wallis, Salisbury #259/R est:1200-1800
£5696 $9000 €8544 Roman dance with swords (76x150cm-30x59in) s. 16-Nov-2 Harvey Clar, Oakland #1299

OBERHUBER, Oswald (1931-) Austrian
Works on paper
£310 $497 €450 Untitled (42x56cm-17x22in) s.d.89 pencil col pen oil chk. 11-Mar-3 Dorotheum, Vienna #262/R
£310 $497 €450 Untitled (42x56cm-17x22in) s.d.85 col pen pencil. 11-Mar-3 Dorotheum, Vienna #263/R
£1351 $2108 €2000 Untitled (50x35cm-20x14in) s.d.1949 W/C. 25-Mar-3 Wiener Kunst Auktionen, Vienna #4/R est:2800-4000
£1519 $2370 €2400 Untitled (34x50cm-13x20in) mixed media. 15-Oct-2 Dorotheum, Vienna #144/R est:1300-1900

OBERLE, Jean (1900-1961) French
£1571 $2577 €2278 Ingrid Dardel en tutu (91x60cm-36x24in) s. exhib. 4-Jun-3 AB Stockholms Auktionsverk #2498/R est:20000-25000 (S.KR 20000)

OBERMAN, Anthony (1781-1845) Dutch
£12000 $18720 €18000 Parrot tulips, roses, morning glory and other flowers in a terracotta pot on a marble ledge (53x41cm-21x16in) oil on paper card. 9-Apr-3 Christie's, London #59/R est:12000-18000

OBERTEUFFER, George (1878-1940) American
£1761 $2730 €2800 Eglise de Macon, Sarthe (46x55cm-18x22in) s. i.verso prov. 30-Oct-2 Artcurial Briest, Paris #149 est:2800-3200
Works on paper
£2273 $3500 €3410 Washington Square Park (36x51cm-14x20in) s. W/C prov. 24-Oct-2 Shannon's, Milford #2/R est:200-3000

OBIOLS DELGADO, Mariano (19th C) Spanish
£828 $1316 €1200 Toledo Gate, Madrid (35x17cm-14x7in) s. cardboard. 4-Mar-3 Ansorena, Madrid #147/R
£828 $1316 €1200 Street in Cordoba (23x38cm-9x15in) s. cardboard. 4-Mar-3 Ansorena, Madrid #327/R

OBIOLS, Gustave (19th C) Spanish
Sculpture
£803 $1300 €1205 Love struck - art deco figure of cupid and lady (38x58cm-15x23in) s. green pat. bronze with marble base. 25-Jan-3 Skinner, Boston #975/R est:800-1200
£1000 $1580 €1500 Le Nid (78cm-31in) i. pottery. 14-Nov-2 Christie's, Kensington #126/R est:500-700

O'BRADY, Gertrude (1901-) American
£1716 $2402 €2745 Autoportrait au chat (33x22cm-13x9in) mono. s.i.d.1939 verso. 29-Nov-1 Piasa, Paris #480 est:900-1200
£9554 $14904 €15000 Theatre Hebertot (64x91cm-25x36in) s.d.1946 prov. 5-Nov-2 Tajan, Paris #102/R est:10000-12000
Works on paper
£828 $1308 €1200 Promenade dans l'allee (11x18cm-4x7in) mono. gouache. 4-Apr-3 Tajan, Paris #54/R
£896 $1416 €1300 Portrait d'Alexandra Stepanoff (31x23cm-12x9in) s.i. crayon dr. 4-Apr-3 Tajan, Paris #2/R

OBREEN, Hendrik van der Speck (1888-1950) Dutch
£298 $483 €420 Extensive landscape (35x54cm-14x21in) st.sig. verso. 26-May-3 Glerum, Amsterdam #77

OBREGON, Alejandro (1920-1992) Colombian
£9554 $15000 €14331 Homage to Saint-Exupery (72x72cm-28x28in) s. i.verso masonite prov.exhib. 20-Nov-2 Christie's, Rockefeller NY #105/R est:18000-22000
£17516 $27500 €26274 Souvenir of Venice (131x97cm-52x38in) s. painted 1954 prov.lit. 19-Nov-2 Sotheby's, New York #100/R est:50000

O'BRIEN, Daniel (19/20th C) American
£1090 $1700 €1635 Winter landscape with horse drawn sled (56x61cm-22x24in) s. board. 20-Sep-2 Freeman, Philadelphia #132/R est:1000-1500

O'BRIEN, Dermod (1865-1945) British
£1304 $2139 €1800 Portrait of a seated lady in a black dress (32x24cm-13x9in) board. 28-May-3 Bonhams & James Adam, Dublin #167/R est:2000-3000

O'BRIEN, Geraldine (1922-) Irish
£377 $591 €550 Still life (39x41cm-15x16in) s. 15-Apr-3 De Veres Art Auctions, Dublin #100b
£1346 $2113 €2100 Fleeting splendour (74x61cm-29x24in) s.d.1954. 19-Nov-2 Whyte's, Dublin #132/R est:2000-2500

O'BRIEN, Greta (20th C) Irish
£329 $510 €520 Summer bouquet (41x51cm-16x20in) s. canvasboard. 24-Sep-2 De Veres Art Auctions, Dublin #8
£331 $526 €480 Middle Lake Killarney (49x65cm-19x26in) s.d.79. 4-Mar-3 Mealy's, Castlecomer #1221/R

O'BRIEN, John (1834-1904) British
£8228 $13000 €12342 Passenger packets Boston and Alice Rogers off Halifax Nova Scotia (53cm-21in) s.d.1858. 26-Apr-3 Thomaston Place, Thomaston #55

O'BRIEN, Justin Maurice (1917-1996) Australian
£5694 $8712 €8541 Madonna and child (51x26cm-20x10in) s. paper on board. 25-Aug-2 Sotheby's, Paddington #64/R est:15000-20000 (A.D 16000)
£10714 $16821 €16071 Death of the Virgin (69x79cm-27x31in) s. prov. 25-Nov-2 Christie's, Melbourne #70/R est:40000-50000 (A.D 30000)
£14286 $22429 €21429 Clowns picnic (75x48cm-30x19in) s. i.verso. 25-Nov-2 Christie's, Melbourne #8a/R est:40000-60000 (A.D 40000)
£21429 $35571 €36452 Untitled - interior with two figures (78x58cm-31x23in) masonite prov. 10-Jun-3 Shapiro, Sydney #30/R est:50000-70000 (A.D 54000)
£24911 $38114 €37367 Three jugglers (57x70cm-22x28in) s. painted 1955 prov.exhib. 26-Aug-2 Sotheby's, Paddington #504/R est:50000-70000 (A.D 70000)
£27907 $44372 €41861 Still life against window (73x53cm-29x21in) s. painted 1984 exhib. 5-May-3 Sotheby's, Melbourne #121/R est:60000-80000 (A.D 72000)

O'BRIEN, Kitty Wilmer (1910-1982) British
£1000 $1600 €1500 Evening, Croagh Patrick, Co Mayo (43x54cm-17x21in) s. board prov. 15-May-3 Christie's, Kensington #178/R est:1000-1500
£1795 $2782 €2800 Low tide Clew Bay (40x50cm-16x20in) s. board prov. 3-Dec-2 Bonhams & James Adam, Dublin #80/R est:3000-5000
£1923 $3019 €3000 Leeson Park, in snow (53x41cm-21x16in) s. i.verso board prov. 19-Nov 2 Whyte's, Dublin #144/R est:2000-3000
£2390 $3728 €3800 Peter Murphy's yard, Ringsend (41x51cm-16x20in) s. i.verso canvasboard prov.exhib. 17-Sep-2 Whyte's, Dublin #109/R est:4000-6000
£3418 $5297 €5400 Westport, Co. Mayo (50x62cm-20x24in) s. board. 25-Sep-2 James Adam, Dublin #76/R est:3000-5000
Works on paper
£548 $860 €800 Black mountains, Dingle (33x74cm-13x29in) s. gouache. 15-Apr-3 De Veres Art Auctions, Dublin #73/R
£3019 $4709 €4800 Mall, Westport (30x46cm-12x18in) s. gouache board. 17-Sep-2 Whyte's, Dublin #144/R est:3500-4500
£4027 $6483 €6000 Figures in the street, Westport, County Mayo (38x48cm-15x19in) gouache board. 18-Feb-3 Whyte's, Dublin #11/R est:4500-5500

O'BRIEN, Lucius Richard (1832-1899) Canadian
£1111 $1822 €1667 Rocky shoreline with distant figures (42x61cm-17x24in) s.d.1881. 27-May-3 Sotheby's, Toronto #37/R est:2000-3000 (C.D 2500)
£1556 $2551 €2334 Acadian harvest (33x55cm-13x22in) s.d.1894 canvas on board prov. 27-May-3 Sotheby's, Toronto #101/R est:5000-7000 (C.D 3500)
£1778 $2916 €2667 Break in the clouds (34x46cm-13x18in) s.d.1895 board. 3-Jun-3 Joyner, Toronto #318/R est:3000-4000 (C.D 4000)
Works on paper
£635 $1041 €953 Chateay Roche (36x27cm-14x11in) s.d.1879 W/C. 6-Feb-3 Heffel, Vancouver #040/R (C.D 1600)
£656 $1016 €984 Hunters in a snowstorm (11x14cm-4x6in) s.d.75 W/C prov. 24-Sep-2 Ritchie, Toronto #3065/R (C.D 1600)
£905 $1403 €1358 Ramparts, Quebec (25x17cm-10x7in) s.d.1884 W/C. 3-Dec-2 Joyner, Toronto #374 est:800-1000 (C.D 2200)
£984 $1554 €1476 Landscape with rapids (20x36cm-8x14in) d.1889 W/C. 1-Dec-2 Levis, Calgary #72/R est:2800-3000 (C.D 2450)
£1008 $1593 €1512 Landscape with covered bridge (27x38cm-11x15in) s.d.1892 W/C prov. 14-Nov-2 Heffel, Vancouver #28/R est:3000-4000 (C.D 2500)
£1030 $1607 €1545 Lake Rousseau (25x34cm-10x13in) s.d.1895 W/C. 25-Mar-3 Ritchie, Toronto #56/R est:2000-3000 (C.D 2400)
£2479 $3893 €3719 Guided canoe excursion (41x66cm-16x26in) s.d.1893 W/C. 24-Jul-2 Walker's, Ottawa #246/R est:8000-10000 (C.D 6000)
£2881 $4465 €4322 Collingwood Harbour (12x26cm-5x10in) s. ink w, htd white prov. 3-Dec-2 Joyner, Toronto #13/R est:5000-7000 (C.D 7000)
£2889 $4738 €4334 Haying in Albeta (41x68cm-16x27in) s.d.1894 W/C prov. 27-May-3 Sotheby's, Toronto #13/R est:6000-8000 (C.D 6500)
£3400 $5678 €4930 Barges in front on the Houses of Parliament (52x75cm-20x30in) s.d.1889 W/C. 18-Jun-3 Sotheby's, Olympia #86/R est:600-800

OCAMPO, Manuel (1965-) ?
£4114 $6500 €6171 Prognosticatio (183x274cm-72x108in) s. i.d.1.6.91 verso prov.exhib.lit. 13-Nov-2 Sotheby's, New York #148/R est:8000-12000

OCANA, Mariano (?) Spanish?
£503 $775 €800 Inn interior (45x36cm-18x14in) s. board. 22-Oct-2 Durán, Madrid #672/R

O'CASEY, Breon (1928-) British
£300 $480 €450 St. Ives - abstract (91x61cm-36x24in) painted 1967. 14-Mar-3 Gardiner & Houlgate, Bath #29/R
£641 $1006 €1000 Paul song (28x38cm-11x15in) s. i.d.1987 verso acrylic board. 19-Nov-2 Whyte's, Dublin #44/R

O'CEALLACHAIN, Diarmuid (1915-1993) Irish
£676 $1054 €1000 Blind (28x38cm-11x15in) s. board. 26-Mar-3 James Adam, Dublin #78/R est:1000-1500
£1477 $2377 €2200 Boat on the river Lee, Cork. Portrait of a man (29x41cm-11x16in) s. i.verso board double-sided. 18-Feb-3 Whyte's, Dublin #191/R est:1500-2000

OCHOA, Enrique (1890-1978) Spanish
£2419 $3823 €3750 Woman from Majorca (100x90cm-39x35in) s. s.verso. 17-Dec-2 Durán, Madrid #111/R

Works on paper

£503	$785	€800	Spanish women in a garden (39x36cm-15x14in) s. gouache. 17-Sep-2 Segre, Madrid #117/R

OCHTMAN, Leonard (1854-1934) American

£316	$500	€474	Farm in spring (30x41cm-12x16in) painted c.1912 panel. 26-Apr-3 Thomaston Place, Thomaston #324
£1613	$2500	€2420	Hill in February (30x41cm-12x16in) s.d.1913 panel. 2-Nov-2 North East Auctions, Portsmouth #67/R est:1500-2500
£2373	$3750	€3560	Hills in February (30x41cm-12x16in) s.d.1913 panel. 24-Apr-3 Shannon's, Milford #120/R est:2500-3500

OCKEL, Eduard (1834-1910) German

£641	$974	€1000	Autumn evening at the border of Gamen-See (96x160cm-38x63in) s. s.i.verso lit. 11-Jul-2 Allgauer, Kempten #2637/R
£1735	$2758	€2550	Lake in the Mark on autumn evening (95x160cm-37x63in) s. i. stretcher. 19-Mar-3 Neumeister, Munich #681a/R est:1800

OCKERT, Carl Friedrich (1825-1899) German

£417	$633	€650	Fox catching duck (21x27cm-8x11in) s. panel. 11-Jul-2 Hugo Ruef, Munich #762/R
£481	$731	€750	Deer in forest clearing (21x27cm-8x11in) s. panel. 11-Jul-2 Hugo Ruef, Munich #761/R
£793	$1261	€1150	Deer by wood in winter (18x26cm-7x10in) s. panel. 8-Mar-3 Arnold, Frankfurt #663/R
£890	$1389	€1300	Fox and hare (17x33cm-7x13in) s. panel. 10-Apr-3 Van Ham, Cologne #1633

O'COLMAIN, Seamus (1925-1990) Irish

£458	$760	€650	Ancient Irish landscape (44x54cm-17x21in) s. board. 10-Jun-3 James Adam, Dublin #106/R
£548	$860	€800	Roundstone (38x52cm-15x20in) s.i.d.1965 oil paper. 15-Apr-3 De Veres Art Auctions, Dublin #99e
£685	$1075	€1000	Looking towards Christ Church (41x51cm-16x20in) s. board prov. 15-Apr-3 De Veres Art Auctions, Dublin #99d est:1200-1600
£949	$1472	€1500	Dublin street scene (40x50cm-16x20in) s. board. 24-Sep-2 De Veres Art Auctions, Dublin #119/R est:900-1200
£1090	$1711	€1700	Pint drinker (41x30cm-16x12in) s. board. 19-Nov-2 Whyte's, Dublin #88/R est:1200-1500
£1392	$2158	€2200	Coal man (40x50cm-16x20in) s. board. 24-Sep-2 De Veres Art Auctions, Dublin #112a est:900-1200
£2899	$4754	€4000	Spanish slums (68x254cm-27x100in) s. board. 28-May-3 Bonhams & James Adam, Dublin #123/R est:4000-6000

OCON Y RIVAS, Emilio (1848-1904) Spanish

£1700	$2822	€2465	Spanish trader and a xebec drying their sails off a beach (19x32cm-7x13in) indis sig.d.1874 panel. 12-Jun-3 Christie's, London #572/R est:400-600
£2051	$3179	€3200	Malaga (56x89cm-22x35in) s.i.d.1897. 9-Dec-2 Beaussant & Lefèvre, Paris #83/R
£18456	$29715	€27500	Getting ready (56x89cm-22x35in) s.i.d.1897. 18-Feb-3 Durán, Madrid #223/R est:4500

O'CONNELL, John (20th C) Irish?

£1338	$2221	€1900	Breakers, Antrim coast (59x73cm-23x29in) s. acrylic panel. 10-Jun-3 James Adam, Dublin #116/R est:1800-2200

Works on paper

£280	$437	€440	Practise on strings (29x29cm-11x11in) s. pastel. 6-Nov-2 James Adam, Dublin #40/R

O'CONNOR, Declan (1957-) Irish

£545	$855	€850	Horse fair (43x60cm-17x24in) s. canvasboard. 19-Nov-2 Whyte's, Dublin #179

O'CONNOR, J (1830-1889) British

£1150	$1886	€1725	Still pool (68x51cm-27x20in) s. 29-May-3 Christie's, Kensington #124/R est:500-700

O'CONNOR, James Arthur (1792-1841) British

£4167	$6458	€6500	Moonlight (25x35cm-10x14in) init. panel prov. 3-Dec-2 Bonhams & James Adam, Dublin #24/R est:6000-10000
£4800	$7680	€7200	Lower Lake Killarney (18x23cm-7x9in) s. panel. 11-Mar-3 Gorringes, Lewes #2309/R est:3000-5000
£5350	$8292	€8025	Extensive landscape with traveller on road (64x76cm-25x30in) 3-Dec-2 Ritchie, Toronto #3033/R est:5000-7000 (C.D 13000)
£6500	$10010	€9750	Wooded river landscape with bridge (20x25cm-8x10in) s.d.1827. 25-Oct-2 Gorringes, Lewes #871
£9000	$14400	€13500	View of Bullock Castle and Bawn, Dalkey (30x35cm-12x14in) s.d.1830. 15-May-3 Christie's, London #7/R
£9459	$14757	€14000	Fisherman on a riverbank with figures on a bridge outside a town (19x24cm-7x9in) s.d.1827. 26-Mar-3 James Adam, Dublin #15/R est:14000-18000
£13768	$22580	€19000	An oncoming storm (28x33cm-11x13in) s.d.1832 panel. 28-May-3 Bonhams & James Adam, Dublin #10/R est:15000-20000
£14493	$23768	€20000	Travelers in extensive wooded landscape mountain landscape (62x75cm-24x30in) 28-May-3 Bonhams & James Adam, Dublin #9/R est:20000-30000
£26000	$41600	€39000	Wooded river landscape (62x75cm-24x30in) s.d.1826 prov.exhib. 15-May-3 Christie's, London #6/R est:15000-25000

Works on paper

£833	$1308	€1300	Flirtation (15x22cm-6x9in) s.d.1815 ink brown wash over pencil. 19-Nov-2 Hamilton Osborne King, Dublin #401/R est:600-1000

O'CONNOR, James Arthur (attrib) (1792-1841) British

£1069	$1668	€1700	Jerpoint Abbey, Waterford (11x13cm-4x5in) i.verso. 17-Sep-2 Whyte's, Dublin #198/R est:2000-4000
£4487	$6955	€7000	Figures walking in a wooded country lane (20x25cm-8x10in) 3-Dec-2 Bonhams & James Adam, Dublin #17/R est:5000-7000
£9494	$15000	€14241	Landscape near Dublin (46x61cm-18x24in) s.d.1826 prov. 24-Apr-3 Shannon's, Milford #132/R est:15000-25000

O'CONNOR, John (1830-1889) British

£2400	$3984	€3600	View of Waterloo Bridge, with St. Paul's in the distance (26x44cm-10x17in) mono.d.75 prov. 10-Jun-3 Christie's, London #79/R est:2000-3000

O'CONNOR, Roderic (1908-2001) Irish

£352	$585	€500	Still life in grey (63x76cm-25x30in) s.d.94 board. 10-Jun-3 James Adam, Dublin #170/R
£1944	$3092	€2800	Study of a boy (53x43cm-21x17in) i.verso panel exhib. 29-Apr-3 Whyte's, Dublin #34/R est:1500-2000

O'CONNOR, Sean (20th C) Irish

£320	$509	€480	Golf course view, Ireland (39x49cm-15x19in) s. board. 27-Feb-3 Greenslade Hunt, Taunton #1318/R

O'CONNOR, Victor G (1918-) Australian

£1354	$2221	€1963	Street scene (53x83cm-21x33in) s. canvas on board. 4-Jun-3 Deutscher-Menzies, Melbourne #342/R est:3800-5000 (A.D 3400)

O'CONOR, Roderic (1860-1940) Irish

£7500	$11775	€11250	Bay (37x46cm-15x18in) studio st. canvasboard painted c.1913 exhib.lit. 22-Nov-2 Christie's, London #49/R est:10000-15000
£23077	$36231	€36000	Head of an old man (46x37cm-18x15in) st.sig.verso wood painted c.1891 prov.exhib.lit. 19-Nov-2 Whyte's, Dublin #68/R est:30000-40000
£27000	$43200	€40500	Etude, femme a contre-jour (62x51cm-24x20in) s.d.07 s.i.verso board prov.exhib.lit. 15-May-3 Christie's, London #67/R est:20000-30000
£60000	$96000	€90000	Montigny landscape (91x73cm-36x29in) 16-May-3 Sotheby's, London #62/R est:60000-80000
£70000	$112000	€105000	Jeune fille (91x72cm-36x28in) s.i. prov.exhib.lit. 15-May-3 Christie's, London #63/R est:50000-80000
£92000	$147200	€138000	Red rocks and foam (50x61cm-20x24in) prov. 16-May-3 Sotheby's, London #52/R est:60000-80000
£320000	$512000	€480000	Nature morte aux pommes et aux pots Bretons (49x55cm-19x22in) painted c.1896-97 prov.exhib.lit. 16-May-3 Sotheby's, London #53/R est:200000-300000

Prints

£3767	$5914	€5500	Landscape (29x41cm-11x16in) drypoint. 15-Apr-3 Laurence Calmels, Paris #4373/R
£4452	$6990	€6500	Field with trees (42x34cm-17x13in) s.d.1893 eau forte lit. 15-Apr-3 Laurence Calmels, Paris #4375/R
£4795	$7527	€7000	Extensive landscape (30x42cm-12x17in) eau forte lit. 15-Apr-3 Laurence Calmels, Paris #4378/R
£5479	$8603	€8000	Landscape (33x43cm-13x17in) s.d.1893 drypoint. 15-Apr-3 Laurence Calmels, Paris #4374/R
£6849	$10753	€10000	Landscape with trees (35x41cm-14x16in) eau forte lit. 15-Apr-3 Laurence Calmels, Paris #4376/R
£6849	$10753	€10000	Falaise (24x39cm-9x15in) s.d.1893 drypoint eau forte lit. 15-Apr-3 Laurence Calmels, Paris #4380/R est:1800
£6849	$10753	€10000	Femme assise sur un banc (34x26cm-13x10in) s.d.1897 monotype. 15-Apr-3 Laurence Calmels, Paris #4382/R est:800
£9589	$15055	€14000	Landscape (29x43cm-11x17in) eau forte drypoint. 15-Apr-3 Laurence Calmels, Paris #4377/R est:1500
£10274	$16130	€15000	Verger (51x60cm-20x24in) eau forte lit. 15-Apr-3 Laurence Calmels, Paris #4379/R est:2000
£12329	$19356	€18000	Glaneuses (49x56cm-19x22in) eau forte lit. 15-Apr-3 Laurence Calmels, Paris #4381/R est:1800

Works on paper

£2200	$3520	€3300	Reclining nude (24x34cm-9x13in) init.d.1916 chl pastel. 15-May-3 Christie's, Kensington #155/R est:2000-3000
£12000	$19200	€18000	White houses in a landscape (24x32cm-9x13in) W/C prov.exhib.lit. 16-May-3 Sotheby's, London #99/R est:4000-6000

ODAZZI, Giovanni (1663-1731) Italian
£6000 $10020 €8700 Vision of Saint Bruno (101x60cm-40x24in) within painted arch prov. 10-Jul-3 Sotheby's, London #182/R est:6000-8000

ODEKERKEN, Willem van (?-1677) Dutch
£1282 $1987 €2000 Woman drinking and smoking (63x46cm-25x18in) panel. 6-Dec-2 Maigret, Paris #58/R
£5096 $7949 €8000 Shepherd playing the flute (75x62cm-30x24in) panel prov.exhib.lit. 5-Nov-2 Sotheby's, Amsterdam #348/R est:8000-12000
£40123 $65000 €60185 Still life with a lute (79x62cm-31x24in) s. panel prov.exhib.lit. 23-Jan-3 Sotheby's, New York #46/R est:60000-80000

ODELMARK, F W (1849-1937) Swedish
£2196 $3426 €3250 Venice (91x68cm-36x27in) s. 25-Mar-3 Durán, Madrid #166/R

ODELMARK, Frans Wilhelm (1849-1937) Swedish
£311 $488 €467 Man with donkey (56x37cm-22x15in) s.d.1889 panel. 16-Dec-2 Lilla Bukowskis, Stockholm #880 (S.KR 4400)
£329 $501 €494 Man reading (40x33cm-16x13in) s.d.1892 panel. 16-Aug-2 Lilla Bukowskis, Stockholm #203 (S.KR 4800)
£631 $997 €947 Farm with chickens, Skaane (90x70cm-35x28in) s.i. 30-Nov-2 Goteborg Auktionsverk, Sweden #161/R (S.KR 9000)
£877 $1385 €1316 Canal scene, Venice (66x56cm-26x22in) s. 30-Nov-2 Goteborg Auktionsverk, Sweden #163/R (S.KR 12500)
£922 $1429 €1383 On the farm - boy surrounded by pigs, geese and chickens (71x53cm-28x21in) s.i.d.1915. 8-Dec-2 Uppsala Auktionskammare, Uppsala #88/R (S.KR 13000)
£967 $1537 €1451 From the well, Seville (90x55cm-35x22in) s.i. 3-Mar-3 Lilla Bukowskis, Stockholm #87 (S.KR 13000)
£1122 $1773 €1683 Woman and chickens in farmyard, Skaane (50x75cm-20x30in) s. 30-Nov-2 Goteborg Auktionsverk, Sweden #164/R est:15000 (S.KR 16000)
£1152 $1832 €1728 Collecting water in Venice (110x66cm-43x26in) s. 3-Mar-3 Lilla Bukowskis, Stockholm #494 est:15000-20000 (S.KR 15500)
£1164 $1885 €1688 Venice (113x75cm-44x30in) s. 26-May-3 Bukowskis, Stockholm #69/R est:20000-25000 (S.KR 15000)
£1348 $2089 €2022 Farm yard with woman feeding chickens, Falsterbo, Skane (51x65cm-20x26in) s.i. 4-Dec-2 AB Stockholms Auktionsverk #1777/R est:15000-18000 (S.KR 19000)
£1500 $2340 €2250 Santa Maria della Salute, Venice (89x66cm-35x26in) s.i. 17-Oct-2 Lawrence, Crewkerne #480/R est:1500-2000
£1629 $2639 €2362 Portal in Cairo (94x67cm-37x26in) s. 26-May-3 Bukowskis, Stockholm #197/R est:35000-40000 (S.KR 21000)
£2482 $3848 €3723 Venetian canal scene (65x92cm-26x36in) s. 4-Dec-2 AB Stockholms Auktionsverk #1599/R est:20000-25000 (S.KR 35000)
£2483 $4022 €3600 Bazaar street, Cairo (100x60cm-39x24in) s. 26-May-3 Bukowskis, Stockholm #189/R est:25000-30000 (S.KR 32000)
£3226 $4903 €4839 Bazaar street, Cairo (100x71cm-39x28in) s. 16-Aug-2 Lilla Bukowskis, Stockholm #1024 est:30000-35000 (S.KR 47000)

Works on paper
£915 $1500 €1327 Snake charmers in a courtyard, Cairo (74x48cm-29x19in) s.i. W/C htd white. 4-Jun-3 Doyle, New York #75 est:1000-1500
£1583 $2595 €2200 Le bain de la princesse (57x44cm-22x17in) s. W/C. 4-Jun-3 Tajan, Paris #185/R est:2800-3000
£1707 $2765 €2475 Street scene in Cairo (69x38cm-27x15in) s.i.d.1900 W/C. 25-May-3 Uppsala Auktionskammare, Uppsala #102/R est:16000-18000 (S.KR 22000)

ODEVAERE, Joseph Denis (1778-1830) Belgian
£1277 $2132 €1800 Portrait d'un jeune garcon dans un fauteuil (64x78cm-25x31in) s.d.1806. 18-Jun-3 Tajan, Paris #101 est:2500-3000

ODIER, Jacques (1853-1930) Swiss
£742 $1158 €1113 Cypres a Pardigon (35x55cm-14x22in) s. i. stretcher. 6-Nov-2 Dobiaschofsky, Bern #863/R (S.FR 1700)

ODIERNO, Guido (1913-) Italian
£301 $500 €436 Rocky coastline (69x99cm-27x39in) s. 11-Jun-3 Boos Gallery, Michigan #579/R
£356 $590 €516 Capri (69x99cm-27x39in) s.i.d.62. 16-Jun-3 Waddingtons, Toronto #329/R (C.D 800)
£400 $644 €600 Terrace in summer (40x50cm-16x20in) s. 18-Feb-3 Bonhams, Knightsbridge #24/R
£800 $1296 €1200 Sunlit terrace, Anacapri (68x99cm-27x39in) s.i. board. 23-Jan-3 Christie's, Kensington #158/R

ODIN, Blanche (1865-?) French

Works on paper
£1170 $1954 €1650 Bouquet de fleurs (28x35cm-11x14in) s. W/C. 19-Jun-3 Piasa, Paris #183 est:1000
£1300 $2028 €1950 Roses in a glass bowl (45x54cm-18x21in) s. W/C oval. 17-Sep-2 Sotheby's, Olympia #262/R est:600-800
£1400 $2184 €2100 Still life of mimosa and other flowers in a bowl (37x54cm-15x21in) s. W/C. 17-Sep-2 Sotheby's, Olympia #265/R est:700-900
£1474 $2315 €2300 Raisin et bouteille de vin (56x37cm-22x15in) s. W/C. 10-Dec-2 Renaud, Paris #35
£1600 $2496 €2400 Still life study of roses, book and vase (54x75cm-21x30in) s. W/C. 17-Sep-2 Sotheby's, Olympia #264/R est:800-1200
£1800 $2808 €2700 Bowl of apple blossom, lilac and peonies (55x76cm-22x30in) s. W/C. 17-Sep-2 Sotheby's, Olympia #263/R est:1000-1500
£2372 $3724 €3700 Cloche a fromage (55x38cm-22x15in) s. W/C. 10-Dec-2 Renaud, Paris #34

ODJIG, Daphne (1928-) Canadian
£622 $983 €933 Two mythological figures (48x69cm-19x27in) d.1968 acrylic. 1-Dec-2 Levis, Calgary #73/R (C.D 1550)

O'DONNELL, Hugh (20th C) American
£1100 $1705 €1650 Untitled 7 (87x92cm-34x36in) s.d.1990 verso prov. 3-Dec-2 Bonhams, New Bond Street #126/R est:1000-1500

O'DONOGHUE, John (20th C) Irish?
£377 $588 €550 Female torso, study for bronze (14x11cm-6x4in) s.d.1983 canvasboard. 8-Apr-3 James Adam, Dublin #108/R

O'DOWD, Gwen (?) ?

Works on paper
£1918 $3011 €2800 Crevass on the ice fields Canada (123x107cm-48x42in) s. verso mixed media. 15-Apr-3 De Veres Art Auctions, Dublin #196/R est:3000-4000

OECONOMO, Aristide (1821-1887) Austrian
£2000 $3100 €3000 Portrait of girl (40x32cm-16x13in) s.d.1882. 2-Oct-2 Sotheby's, London #22/R est:4000-6000

OEHLEN, Albert (1954-) German
£9615 $14904 €15000 Untitled (180x135cm-71x53in) s.d.87 oil varnish oats collaged on canvas. 3-Dec-2 Lempertz, Koln #329/R est:10000
£9615 $14904 €15000 Untitled (135x180cm-53x71in) s.d.87 oil varnish collage oats. 3-Dec-2 Lempertz, Koln #330/R est:15000

OEHLEN, Markus (1956-) German
£1410 $2186 €2200 Untitled (200x100cm-79x39in) s.d.1987 cotton. 3-Dec-2 Lempertz, Koln #333/R est:2600
£1449 $2377 €2000 Untitled (120x100cm-47x39in) s.d.1986 cotton. 28-May-3 Lempertz, Koln #310/R est:2200
£1449 $2377 €2000 Untitled (120x100cm-47x39in) s.d.1986 cotton lit. 28-May-3 Lempertz, Koln #311/R est:1800
£1667 $2583 €2600 Untitled (150x120cm-59x47in) s.d.1987 varnish oil gouache cotton. 3-Dec-2 Lempertz, Koln #332/R est:2500
£1884 $3090 €2600 Untitled (120x100cm-47x39in) s.d.1986 cotton. 28-May-3 Lempertz, Koln #309/R est:2200
£2051 $3179 €3200 Untitled (150x200cm-59x79in) s.d.83 dispersion two part. 3-Dec-2 Lempertz, Koln #331/R est:4000-5000

OEHLER, Christoph Friedrich (1881-1964) German
£880 $1416 €1276 Stockhorn from Merligen (78x97cm-31x38in) s. i.d.1919 verso. 9-May-3 Dobiaschofsky, Bern #121/R (S.FR 1900)

OEHLER, Helen Gapen (1893-1979) American
£301 $500 €436 Clouds over an island lake (51x76cm-20x30in) s. board. 14-Jun-3 Jackson's, Cedar Falls #15/R

OEHME, Erwin (1831-1907) German

Works on paper
£323 $507 €485 Winter sunshine (99x80cm-39x31in) s. gouache. 25-Nov-2 Blomqvist, Lysaker #1214/R (N.KR 3700)
£352 $585 €500 In the wood (60x51cm-24x20in) s.d. W/c. 12-Jun-3 Hauswedell & Nolte, Hamburg #380/R

OEHME, Georg Egmont (1890-1955) German
£1165 $1900 €1748 Scholar in a library (59x67cm-23x26in) s.d.1924. 16-Feb-3 Butterfields, San Francisco #2040 est:1200-1800

OEHMICHEN, Hugo (1843-1933) German
£3333 $5267 €5200 Young girl knitting (58x36cm-23x14in) s. 16-Nov-2 Lempertz, Koln #1546/R est:6000

OEHRING, Hedwig (1855-?) German
£200 $332 €290 Kittens playing with a butterfly (16x24cm-6x9in) s. panel. 16-Jun-3 Waddingtons, Toronto #291/R (C.D 450)
£287 $447 €450 Three kittens with red umbrella (12x24cm-5x9in) s. panel. 6-Nov-2 Hugo Ruef, Munich #1225/R
£816 $1298 €1200 Three cats under a red umbrella (16x24cm-6x9in) s.i. panel. 25-Feb-3 Dorotheum, Vienna #92/R
£2568 $4005 €3800 Locals round tavern table (31x41cm-12x16in) s. panel. 25-Mar-3 Wiener Kunst Auktionen, Vienna #103/R est:3500-7000

£2838 $4427 €4200 Locals at tavern table (32x44cm-13x17in) s. panel. 25-Mar-3 Wiener Kunst Auktionen, Vienna #104/R est:3500-7000

OELENHAINZ, Friedrich (1745-1804) German

£4362 $7023 €6500 Portrait of a gentleman. Portrait of a lady wearing a white dress (70x53cm-28x21in) pair prov.exhib.lit. 18-Feb-3 Sotheby's, Amsterdam #278/R est:4000-6000

OELENHAINZ, Friedrich (attrib) (1745-1804) German

£1203 $1876 €1900 Portrait of lady (59x48cm-23x19in) lit. one of pair. 14-Sep-2 Bergmann, Erlangen #702/R est:1900
£1203 $1876 €1900 Portrait of lady (59x48cm-23x19in) lit. one of pair. 14-Sep-2 Bergmann, Erlangen #703/R est:1900

OEPTS, Willem Anthonie (1904-1988) Dutch

£3846 $5962 €6000 Village in Southern France (33x41cm-13x16in) s.d.66 prov. 3-Dec-2 Christie's, Amsterdam #166/R est:6000-8000

OER, Theobald Reinhold von (1807-1885) German

£1200 $1956 €1740 Offering (110x89cm-43x35in) s.i.d.1850. 16-Jul-3 Sotheby's, Olympia #240/R est:1000-1500

OERDER, Frans (1866-1944) Dutch

£269 $423 €420 Landscape in South Africa (28x52cm-11x20in) s. 25-Nov-2 Glerum, Amsterdam #25
£399 $623 €599 Pretoria Zoo garden (42x67cm-17x26in) s. 15-Oct-2 Stephan Welz, Johannesburg #418/R est:7000-10000 (SA.R 6500)
£526 $853 €800 Farming community (46x55cm-18x22in) s. 21-Jan-3 Christie's, Amsterdam #189
£1085 $1715 €1628 View of Rome (59x104cm-23x41in) s. 1-Apr-3 Stephan Welz, Johannesburg #432/R est:15000-20000 (SA.R 13500)
£1233 $1923 €1800 School place in Marabastad, Pretoria (24x31cm-9x12in) s.d.1901. 14-Apr-3 Glerum, Amsterdam #166/R est:1800-2200
£1720 $2769 €2580 Chrysanthemums (50x75cm-20x30in) s. 12-May-3 Stephan Welz, Johannesburg #567/R est:20000-30000 (SA.R 20000)
£1842 $2984 €2800 Magnolia (70x100cm-28x39in) s. 21-Jan-3 Christie's, Amsterdam #181/R est:2200-2800
£2236 $3599 €3354 Man resting in a forest clearing (46x57cm-18x22in) s. 12-May-3 Stephan Welz, Johannesburg #576/R est:12000-18000 (SA.R 26000)
£2562 $3997 €3843 By Wonderboom. s.d.1902. 11-Nov-2 Stephan Welz, Johannesburg #544/R est:40000-60000 (SA.R 40000)
£3523 $5496 €5285 Still life of azaleas (68x88cm-27x35in) s. 11-Nov-2 Stephan Welz, Johannesburg #524/R est:40000-60000 (SA.R 55000)

Works on paper

£258 $415 €387 Field near houses (43x62cm-17x24in) s. chl htd. 12-May-3 Stephan Welz, Johannesburg #187 est:2000-4000 (SA.R 3000)

OERTEL, Johannes Adam Simon (1823-1909) German

£1410 $2200 €2115 Head of St Peter (20x15cm-8x6in) s.d.1855 verso. 18-Sep-2 Jackson's, Cedar Falls #955/R

OESCH, Albert Sebastian (1893-1920) Swiss

Works on paper

£522 $809 €783 Peasant from Appenzell (33x25cm-13x10in) s.i.d.1918 pastel chk chl. 9-Dec-2 Philippe Schuler, Zurich #3587 (S.FR 1200)
£730 $1153 €1095 Farmer smoking a tobacco pipe (41x32cm-16x13in) pastel chk. 26-Nov-2 Hans Widmer, St Gallen #1307/R est:700-2000 (S.FR 1700)
£957 $1483 €1436 Hand organ player sitting by oven (65x40cm-26x16in) s.i.d.1918 pastel chl. 9-Dec-2 Philippe Schuler, Zurich #3586/R est:3000-4000 (S.FR 2200)

OESER, Auguste (1821-?) German

£4194 $6165 €6500 Riva on Lake Garda (83x116cm-33x46in) s.i. 20-Jun-2 Dr Fritz Nagel, Stuttgart #805/R est:3000

OESTERHELD, Oliver (19th/20th C) ?

£255 $397 €400 Chalk cliff on the Dieppe coast (33x59cm-13x23in) i.verso after Ernst Rieck. 7-Nov-2 Allgauer, Kempten #2917/R

OESTERLEY, Marie (1842-1916) German

£318 $497 €500 Rapid stream in forest clearing (50x40cm-20x16in) s. board lit. 7-Nov-2 Allgauer, Kempten #2918

OESTERREICH, H (fl.1856-1887) German

£709 $1099 €1064 Port (73x99cm-29x39in) painted c.1880. 1-Oct-2 SOGA, Bratislava #183/R est:45000 (SL.K 45000)

OFFEL, Edmond van (1871-1959) Belgian

£1060 $1727 €1600 Nu assis (66x53cm-26x21in) 17-Feb-3 Amberes, Antwerp #250

OFFERMANS, Anthony Jacob (1796-1872) Dutch

£1282 $1987 €2000 Wooded landscape with pair of herdsmen and cows, sheep and goats drinking (82x129cm-32x51in) s.d.1862-1863 canvas on canvas. 4-Dec-2 Neumeister, Munich #840a/R est:2500

OFFERMANS, Tony Lodewyk George (1854-1911) Dutch

£955 $1490 €1500 Clog maker (47x67cm-19x26in) s. 6-Nov-2 Vendue Huis, Gravenhage #494/R est:1000-1500
£1274 $1987 €2000 Farmer in stable (33x23cm-13x9in) s. panel. 6-Nov-2 Vendue Huis, Gravenhage #493/R est:2000-3000

Works on paper

£517 $823 €750 Stable interior (43x59cm-17x23in) s. W/C. 10-Mar-3 Sotheby's, Amsterdam #113/R

OFFINGER, Adam (attrib) (fl.1575-1598) German

£2013 $3119 €3200 Portrait of a lady with ruff and pearls (74x58cm-29x23in) 2-Oct-2 Dorotheum, Vienna #255/R est:3500-5000

OFILI, Chris (1968-) British

£54487 $85000 €81731 Mono Rojo (183x123cm-72x48in) s.i.d.2000 acrylic collage glitter polyester resin prov. 11-Nov-2 Phillips, New York #43/R est:80000-120000

Works on paper

£1899 $3000 €2849 Untitled (24x16cm-9x6in) s.d.99 verso W/C pencil prov. 13-Nov-2 Sotheby's, New York #409/R est:4000
£1899 $3000 €2849 Untitled (24x16cm-9x6in) s.d.99 verso W/C pencil prov. 13-Nov-2 Sotheby's, New York #408/R
£2581 $4000 €3872 Untitled (24x16cm-9x6in) s.d.99 verso W/C graphite. 26-Sep-2 Christie's, Rockefeller NY #876/R est:3000-5000
£4747 $7500 €7121 Untitled. Salzau (24x16cm-9x6in) s.d.1999 verso W/C graphite two. 12-Nov-2 Phillips, New York #235/R est:5000-7000
£5000 $7750 €7500 Untitled (24x16cm-9x6in) s.d.98 verso pencil W/C set of three. 5-Dec-2 Christie's, Kensington #286/R est:6000-8000
£6000 $10020 €8700 Untitled (24x16cm-9x6in) s.d.98 verso W/C pencil prov. 26-Jun-3 Sotheby's, London #299/R est:3000-4000
£6329 $10000 €9494 Untitled (24x16cm-9x6in) W/C pencil paper exec.2000 prov. 13-Nov-2 Sotheby's, New York #402/R est:8000-12000
£7500 $12000 €11250 Untitled (24x16cm-9x6in) pencil W/C in two parts executed 2000 prov. 14-May-3 Sotheby's, New York #317/R est:8000-12000
£7500 $12000 €11250 Untitled (24x16cm-9x6in) pencil W/C in two parts executed 2000 prov. 14-May-3 Sotheby's, New York #318/R est:8000-12000
£8000 $12320 €12000 Untitled (24x15cm-9x6in) s.d.99 pencil W/C four prov. 23-Oct-2 Christie's, London #235/R est:8000-12000
£11709 $18500 €17564 Untitled. Salzau (24x16cm-9x6in) s.d.1999 verso two prov. 12-Nov-2 Phillips, New York #232/R est:5000-7000
£25000 $40000 €37500 Afro lips to check (76x57cm-30x22in) s.i.d.2001-02 graphite prov. 15-May-3 Christie's, Rockefeller NY #346/R est:25000-35000

OFVERSTROM, Hugo (1900-1973) Swedish

£295 $465 €443 Coastal landscape with sailing boat (47x58cm-19x23in) s. 30-Nov-2 Goteborg Auktionsverk, Sweden #668/R (S.KR 4200)
£324 $499 €486 Harbour scene with boats and boathouses (50x67cm-20x26in) s. 27-Oct-2 Anders Antik, Landskrona #28/R (S.KR 4700)

OGIER, Marie Louise (1912-) French

£270 $422 €400 Vase au bouquet de fleurs (55x38cm-22x15in) s. 26-Mar-3 Millon & Associes, Paris #110

OGILVIE, Edward (c.1911-) British

Works on paper

£400 $636 €600 Dundee (34x56cm-13x22in) s.d.1911 W/C. 6-Mar-3 Christie's, Kensington #204

OGILVIE, Frederick Dove (1850-1921) British

Works on paper

£280 $437 €420 Scottish loch with castle in winter (36x54cm-14x21in) s.d.96 W/C. 26-Mar-3 Sotheby's, Olympia #82/R
£380 $597 €570 Coastal scene. s.d.1911 W/C. 25-Nov-2 Bonhams, Chester #807

OGILVIE, John Clinton (1838-1900) American

£786 $1288 €1140 Wooded landscape (92x66cm-36x26in) s. 4-Jun-3 AB Stockholms Auktionsverk #2447/R (S.KR 10000)

OGILVIE, William Abernethy (1901-1989) Canadian

Works on paper

£267 $437 €387 Untitled - glacial river (36x53cm-14x21in) W/C. 1-Jun-3 Levis, Calgary #91/R (C.D 600)
£516 $846 €774 Fall reflections, Algonquin (51x71cm-20x28in) s.d.1979 W/C. 6-Feb-3 Heffel, Vancouver #041/R (C.D 1300)

O'GORMAN, Lance (fl.1970s) New Zealander
£282 $440 €423 Fruits of the sea, Puketu Island, Tokerau Beach (44x60cm-17x24in) s. acrylic canvasboard. 7-Nov-2 International Art Centre, Auckland #184/R (NZ.D 900)
£561 $876 €842 Seclusion (50x60cm-20x24in) s. board. 27-Mar-3 International Art Centre, Auckland #187 (NZ.D 1600)
£1083 $1733 €1570 Sand hoppers, Coromandel (50x50cm-20x20in) s. board. 13-May-3 Watson's, Christchurch #22/R est:3000-4000 (NZ.D 3000)

OGUISS, Takanari (1901-1986) Japanese
£11000 $17490 €16500 Paysage de Marne (24x33cm-9x13in) s. s.i.verso panel painted c.1952 prov.exhib. 20-Mar-3 Sotheby's, Olympia #154/R est:5000-7000
£27149 $45339 €39366 Vieille maison a Vanves (65x81cm-26x32in) s. prov. 24-Jun-3 Koller, Zurich #139/R est:40000-60000 (S.FR 60000)
£29677 $46890 €46000 Rue (46x56cm-18x22in) s. prov. 18-Dec-2 Tajan, Paris #36a/R est:30000-40000

O'HALLORAN, James (1955-) Irish
£1346 $2127 €2100 Morning light (34x45cm-13x18in) s. i.verso board. 12-Nov-2 Mealy's, Castlecomer #1258a/R
£1859 $2937 €2900 Drawing room (44x34cm-17x13in) s. i.verso board. 12-Nov-2 Mealy's, Castlecomer #1260a

O'HALRAHAN, James (?) Irish
£1180 $1711 €1900 Launching the currach carraroes (51x58cm-20x23in) s. 3-May-2 Woodwards, Cork #228

O'HARA, Helen (fl.1881-1908) British
Works on paper
£1603 $2484 €2500 Rocks near Portrush (36x53cm-14x21in) mono. i.verso w/v prov. 3-Dec-2 Bonhams & James Adam, Dublin #8/R est:2000-2500
£1879 $3026 €2800 Pathway near Lismore, Co Waterford (23x32cm-9x13in) mono.d.1897 i.verso W/C htd bodycol. 18-Feb-3 Whyte's, Dublin #195/R est:1800-2200

O'HIGGINS, Pablo (1904-1983) Mexican
£3778 $5894 €5667 Mujer pensativa (74x53cm-29x21in) s. 17-Oct-2 Louis Morton, Mexico #42/R est:45000-50000 (M.P 60000)
£9895 $15832 €14348 Roaslio tejiendo (80x57cm-31x22in) s. 15-May-3 Louis Morton, Mexico #104/R est:166000-170000 (M.P 160000)

OHL, Fritz (1904-1976) Dutch
£704 $1134 €1000 Fishing boat (19x15cm-7x6in) s. board. 7-May-3 Vendue Huis, Gravenhage #239/R
£828 $1292 €1300 Balinese (45x33cm-18x13in) s. board. 6-Nov-2 Vendue Huis, Gravenhage #283
£1146 $1789 €1800 Balanese by temple door (49x39cm-19x15in) s. board. 6-Nov-2 Vendue Huis, Gravenhage #284/R est:450-550
£2331 $3846 €3380 By the temple gate (50x40cm-20x16in) s. panel. 6-Jul-3 Christie's, Hong Kong #1/R est:24000-30000 (HK.D 30000)
£3263 $5385 €4731 Junk under full sail (90x70cm-35x28in) s. 6-Jul-3 Christie's, Hong Kong #2/R est:35000-55000 (HK.D 42000)

OHLSEN, Jeppe Madsen (1891-1948) Danish
£373 $593 €560 Scene from the story - About a mother (44x38cm-17x15in) 5-May-3 Rasmussen, Vejle #10/R (D.KR 4000)
£507 $791 €761 Still life of book and metal cup on table (37x28cm-15x11in) s. exhib. 23-Sep-2 Rasmussen, Vejle #47/R (D.KR 6000)
£560 $890 €840 Still life of red glass (45x41cm-18x16in) s. 5-May-3 Rasmussen, Vejle #9/R (D.KR 6000)
£591 $922 €887 Farmyard with figures (42x36cm-17x14in) s. 23-Sep-2 Rasmussen, Vejle #45/R (D.KR 7000)
£676 $1054 €1014 Avenue with canal and dam, houses in background (51x60cm-20x24in) s. exhib. 23-Sep-2 Rasmussen, Vejle #48/R (D.KR 8000)
£845 $1318 €1268 The old farm (57x65cm-22x26in) s. 23-Sep-2 Rasmussen, Vejle #46/R (D.KR 10000)
£1351 $2108 €2027 Knife grinder outside old house (65x55cm-26x22in) s. exhib. 23-Sep-2 Rasmussen, Vejle #50/R est:15000 (D.KR 16000)
£1866 $2966 €2799 Evening by the sea (50x60cm-20x24in) s. exhib. 29-Apr-3 Kunsthallen, Copenhagen #296/R est:20000 (D.KR 20000)
£2014 $3222 €3021 By the old weight house (68x82cm-27x32in) s. exhib. 13-Jan-3 Rasmussen, Vejle #218/R est:20000-30000 (D.KR 23000)
£2111 $3294 €3167 Enkehuset seen from the North (55x66cm-22x26in) s. exhib. 23-Sep-2 Rasmussen, Vejle #49/R est:15000 (D.KR 25000)

OHLSEN, Theodor (1855-?) German
£612 $973 €900 Young woman in the sugar cane (69x41cm-27x16in) s. board. 19-Mar-3 Neumeister, Munich #683/R
£816 $1298 €1200 Desert landscape with camels by salt lake (37x67cm-15x26in) s. board. 19-Mar-3 Neumeister, Munich #682/R est:1500

OHM, Wilhelm (1905-1965) German
£1410 $2186 €2200 Track in path (53x43cm-21x17in) tempera. 7-Dec-2 Hans Stahl, Hamburg #131/R est:2000
£2014 $3304 €2800 Summer landscape (55x66cm-22x26in) board painted c.1960. 3-Jun-3 Christie's, Amsterdam #47/R est:3000-5000
£2536 $4159 €3500 Sunflowers (66x49cm-26x19in) panel prov. 29-May-3 Lempertz, Koln #834/R est:3000

OINONEN, Mikko (1883-1956) Finnish
£422 $671 €620 Stones in the forest (19x27cm-7x11in) s. 24-Mar-3 Bukowskis, Helsinki #221/R
£430 $671 €680 Waterfall (55x65cm-22x26in) s.d.1938. 12-Sep-2 Hagelstam, Helsinki #919
£581 $917 €900 Landscape (46x47cm-18x19in) s. 19-Dec-2 Hagelstam, Helsinki #927/R
£586 $926 €850 Flowers (54x65cm-21x26in) s. 3-Apr-3 Hagelstam, Helsinki #979/R
£621 $1018 €950 Green landscape (38x54cm-15x21in) s.d.1937. 9-Feb-3 Bukowskis, Helsinki #330/R
£782 $1244 €1150 Still life of flowers (70x66cm-28x26in) s. 27-Feb-3 Hagelstam, Helsinki #807/R
£980 $1608 €1500 Foaming river (66x81cm-26x32in) s.d.1930 exhib. 9-Feb-3 Bukowskis, Helsinki #328/R est:1300
£1032 $1631 €1600 Colourful clouds (40x55cm-16x22in) s.d.1925. 19-Dec-2 Hagelstam, Helsinki #925 est:1800
£1127 $1814 €1600 The old shed (34x43cm-13x17in) s. 10-May-3 Bukowskis, Helsinki #65/R est:700-1000

OITICICA, Helio (1937-1980) Brazilian
£8917 $14000 €13376 Untitled (37x29cm-15x11in) i.verso tempera cardboard painted 1956 prov. 20-Nov-2 Christie's, Rockefeller NY #44/R est:10000-15000

OJA, Arvi (?) Finnish
£390 $601 €620 Landscape (30x40cm-12x16in) s. 24-Oct-2 Hagelstam, Helsinki #978

OJA, Onni (1909-) Finnish
£912 $1404 €1450 Woman wearing hat (55x46cm-22x18in) s. 27-Oct-2 Bukowskis, Helsinki #252/R
£1025 $1589 €1630 Sun behind town (38x61cm-15x24in) s. painted 1979. 6-Oct-2 Bukowskis, Helsinki #247/R est:1500
£1038 $1608 €1650 Landscape from Mantsala (30x60cm-12x24in) s. 6-Oct-2 Bukowskis, Helsinki #246/R est:1300
£1088 $1731 €1600 Landscape from Lappo (32x45cm-13x18in) s.d.45. 24-Mar-3 Bukowskis, Helsinki #222/R est:1200
£1203 $1900 €1900 Brook in Orimattila (27x41cm-11x16in) s. 1-Dec-2 Bukowskis, Helsinki #142/R est:1500-1700
£1519 $2370 €2400 Landscape, Borgnas (54x81cm-21x32in) s. 12-Sep-2 Hagelstam, Helsinki #934/R est:1750
£1582 $2500 €2500 Houses in village, Tavastland (50x81cm-20x32in) s. 1-Dec-2 Bukowskis, Helsinki #141/R est:2500-3000
£1701 $2704 €2500 Winter landscape from Sjundeaa (54x80cm-21x31in) s. 24-Mar-3 Bukowskis, Helsinki #224/R est:2500
£2109 $3353 €3100 Road in Fiskars (40x80cm-16x31in) s. 24-Mar-3 Bukowskis, Helsinki #223/R est:2500
£2606 $4195 €3700 Mantsala in March with farm (60x81cm-24x32in) s. painted 1958. 10-May-3 Bukowskis, Helsinki #44/R est:3000-3500

OKADA, Kenzo (1902-1982) American/Japanese
£10000 $16000 €15000 Tanabata (109x93cm-43x37in) s. painted 1955 prov.lit. 14-May-3 Sotheby's, New York #104/R est:15000-20000

OKAMOTO KAKYO (19th C) Oriental
Works on paper
£573 $894 €900 Monkey with tree in blossom (100x35cm-39x14in) s. Indian ink col silk hanging scroll. 9-Nov-2 Dr Fritz Nagel, Stuttgart #1852/R

O'KEEFFE, Georgia (1887-1986) American
£222222 $360000 €333333 Antelope head with pedernal (51x61cm-20x24in) painted 1953 prov.exhib.lit. 22-May-3 Christie's, Rockefeller NY #77/R est:300000-500000
£225806 $350000 €338709 Alligator pears (23x30cm-9x12in) board prov.exhib.lit. 5-Dec-2 Christie's, Rockefeller NY #143/R est:300000-500000
£462963 $750000 €694445 Little barn (27x34cm-11x13in) panel painted 1932 prov.exhib.lit. 21-May-3 Sotheby's, New York #123/R est:300000-500000
£740741 $1200000 €1111112 Red hills perernal, white clouds (51x76cm-20x30in) painted 1936 prov.exhib.lit. 21-May-3 Sotheby's, New York #119/R est:1000000-1500000
£838710 $1300000 €1258065 Antelope (36x81cm-14x32in) painted 1954 prov.exhib.lit. 4-Dec-2 Sotheby's, New York #70/R est:750000-1000000

Works on paper
£25806 $40000 €38709 Woman with blue hat (51x39cm-20x15in) gouache on board prov.lit. 5-Dec-2 Christie's, Rockefeller NY #126/R est:25000-35000
£38710 $60000 €58065 Like an early blue abstraction (76x57cm-30x22in) s.d.77 W/C prov.lit. 4-Dec-2 Sotheby's, New York #75/R est:60000-80000
£200000 $310000 €300000 Indian beads (63x48cm-25x19in) chl prov.exhib.lit. 3-Dec-2 Phillips, New York #67/R est:100000-150000

O'KELLY, Aloysius (1853-1929) Irish
£1852 $3000 €2685 Village church (33x51cm-13x20in) bears sig. canvas on masonite. 21-May-3 Doyle, New York #181/R est:4000-6000
£2200 $3520 €3300 Evening on the coast of Brittany (25x33cm-10x13in) s. panel. 16-May-3 Sotheby's, London #44/R est:1000-1500
£2208 $3400 €3312 Coastal scene at Concarneau, Brittany, France (23x33cm-9x13in) s. i.verso panel. 26-Oct-2 Brunk, Ashville #665/R est:1500-2500
£5192 $8048 €8100 Breton church interior, with two figures and stained glass window (91x64cm-36x25in) s. 3-Dec-2 Thomas Adams, Dublin #396
£5500 $8800 €8250 Le passage (24x33cm-9x13in) s. panel. 16-May-3 Sotheby's, London #42/R est:6000-8000
£11218 $17388 €17500 Ville de Concarneau (23x31cm-9x12in) s. i.verso panel. 3-Dec-2 Bonhams & James Adam, Dublin #36/R est:8000-12000
£11500 $17824 €17250 Two Breton women (56x47cm-22x19in) s. 3-Dec-2 Sotheby's, Olympia #190/R est:8000-12000

OKIMOTO, Jerry T (20th C) American
£288 $450 €432 Black conception no 1 (152x130cm-60x51in) 10-Nov-2 Selkirks, St. Louis #899/R

OKNINSKI, Ryszard (1848-1925) Polish
£1900 $2964 €2850 Polish cavalry during the uprising of 1863 (29x41cm-11x16in) prov. 17-Sep-2 Sotheby's, Olympia #237/R est:1500-2000

OLAFSSON, Sigurjon (1908-1982) Icelandic
Sculpture
£4833 $7636 €7250 Two contrasts - symbolising man and woman (175cm-69in) wood pair prov.lit. 1-Apr-3 Rasmussen, Copenhagen #166/R est:40000 (D.KR 52000)

OLAI, Johan Petter (1842-1885) Swedish
£1079 $1770 €1500 Cattle in landscape (94x134cm-37x53in) s.d.79. 4-Jun-3 Bukowskis, Helsinki #492/R est:1500

OLARIA, Frederico (1849-1898) French
£1184 $1918 €1800 Spring with flowers and bird (55x38cm-22x15in) s. 21-Jan-3 Durán, Madrid #127/R

OLAUSSON, Lennart (1944-) Swedish
Works on paper
£575 $896 €863 Studio visit (67x46cm-26x18in) s. W/C. 5-Nov-2 Bukowskis, Stockholm #396/R (S.KR 8200)

OLBRICH, P (?) ?
£323 $474 €500 Stormy waves in front of Usedom (46x96cm-18x38in) s. 24-Jun-2 Dr Fritz Nagel, Stuttgart #5999/R

OLBRICH, Viktor (1887-1960) Austrian
£345 $552 €500 Winter village (67x94cm-26x37in) s.d.1948 tempera board. 11-Mar-3 Dorotheum, Vienna #109/R

OLDE, Hans (1855-1917) German
£513 $805 €800 Venice (42x41cm-17x16in) s. board. 21-Nov-2 Dorotheum, Vienna #172/R

OLDENBURG, Claes (1929-) American
Prints
£1840 $3000 €2760 Soft saxophone (89x112cm-35x44in) init. num.20/30 col lithograph. 13-Feb-3 Christie's, Rockefeller NY #321/R
£5031 $8000 €7547 Floating three-way plug (107x82cm-42x32in) s.d.num.AP VII/XV col soft ground etching spitbite aquatint. 29-Apr-3 Christie's, Rockefeller NY #702/R est:4000-5000
£13836 $22000 €20754 Screwarch bridge (59x128cm-23x50in) s.i.d. col etching aquatint monoprint. 2-May-3 Sotheby's, New York #567/R est:18000-22000
Sculpture
£3500 $5775 €5075 London knees (38x12cm-15x5in) init.d. polyurethane latex travelling case sold with notes. 1-Jul-3 Sotheby's, London #206/R est:4000-5000
£17500 $28000 €26250 Sof inverted Q (46x46x33cm-18x18x13in) init.d.76 num.1/2 cast resin prov.lit. 15-May-3 Christie's, Rockefeller NY #197/R est:8000-10000
£101266 $160000 €151899 Soft juicit - ghost version (48x46x41cm-19x18x16in) s.d.1965 canvas filled with kapok liquitex on wood base. 14-Nov-2 Christie's, Rockefeller NY #141/R est:150000-200000
£113924 $180000 €170886 Soft tires for airflow - scale 5 (76x76cm-30x30in) enamel on canvas kapok executed 1965 prov.exhib. 13-Nov-2 Christie's, Rockefeller NY #27/R est:400000-600000
£116981 $186000 €175472 Profile airflow (85x166cm-33x65in) s.i.d.num.39/75 col lithograph cast-polyurethane relief. 2-May-3 Sotheby's, New York #565/R est:30000-40000
£225000 $360000 €337500 Soft light switches (104x104x28cm-41x41x11in) vinyl executed 1963-69 prov.exhib. 15-May-3 Phillips, New York #18/R est:500000-700000
£272152 $430000 €408228 Soft typewriter (23x66x69cm-9x26x27in) vinyl filled with kapok plexiglass nylon card executed 1963. 14-Nov-2 Christie's, Rockefeller NY #140/R est:200000-300000
£397436 $620000 €596154 Light switches - hard version (121x121x30cm-48x48x12in) painted wood formica metal executed 1964 prov.exhib. 11-Nov-2 Phillips, New York #13/R est:500000-700000
Works on paper
£5128 $8000 €7692 Pat in black underwear, seated (35x28cm-14x11in) init.d.59 black crayon lit. 5-Nov-2 Doyle, New York #56/R est:8000-12000
£8000 $13360 €11600 Floating watch (22x28cm-9x11in) init.i.d.68 chl paper on paper prov. 26-Jun-3 Sotheby's, London #149/R est:6000-8000
£10000 $16700 €14500 Proposal for a sculpture in the form of a steaming baked potato (20x24cm-8x9in) init.d.70 ink W/C pastel col pencil prov. 26-Jun-3 Sotheby's, London #150/R est:10000-15000
£12658 $20000 €18987 Prosposal for a building in form of a colossal flashlight in place of the Hoover dam Nevada (102x76cm-40x30in) s.i.d.1982 pencil col pencil W/C prov.exhib. 13-Nov-2 Sotheby's, New York #261/R est:15000-20000
£20312 $32500 €30468 Study for bottle of notes (102x76cm-40x30in) s.d.88 chl pastel prov. 14-May-3 Sotheby's, New York #201b/R est:12000-18000
£20312 $32500 €30468 7-up pie, pink characters, green background (58x74cm-23x29in) init.d.72 crayon chl prov. 14-May-3 Sotheby's, New York #201c/R est:20000-30000

OLDEROCK, Max (1895-1972) German
£641 $994 €1000 Red glow (81x60cm-32x24in) s.d.62 board. 7-Dec-2 Van Ham, Cologne #378/R

OLDERT, Johan (1912-1984) South African?
£205 $320 €308 Bluegums near a lake (44x59cm-17x23in) s. board. 11-Nov-2 Stephan Welz, Johannesburg #260 (SA.R 3200)
£205 $320 €308 Bluegums alongside a river (44x60cm-17x24in) s. board. 11-Nov-2 Stephan Welz, Johannesburg #261 (SA.R 3200)

OLDFIELD, Alan (1943-) Australian
£244 $388 €366 Colourfully constructed painting (153x245cm-60x96in) s.i.d.70 verso. 23-Mar-3 Goodman, Sydney #37 (A.D 650)
Works on paper
£846 $1345 €1269 Expulsion from the temple (63x76cm-25x30in) s.i.d.17/6/73 verso synthetic polymer paint canvas. 4-Mar-3 Deutscher-Menzies, Melbourne #262/R (A.D 2200)

OLDFIELD, David Jupurrula (c.1942-) Australian
£260 $419 €377 Warna jukurrpa - snake dreaming (116x120cm-46x47in) acrylic on linen. 12-May-3 Joel, Victoria #379 (A.D 650)

OLDFIELD, Otis (1890-1969) American
£2229 $3500 €3344 Rooftops, Telegraph Hill, San Francisco (41x33cm-16x13in) s.d.1932 i.d.April 29 1932 stretcher prov. 19-Nov-2 Butterfields, San Francisco #8181/R est:3000-5000
£2711 $4500 €3931 Rooftops, Telegraph Hill, San Francisco (41x33cm-16x13in) s.d.1932 i. on stretcher prov. 11-Jun-3 Butterfields, San Francisco #4304/R est:3000-5000

OLDS, Paul (1922-) New Zealander
£702 $1095 €1053 Boats on the Hard (42x54cm-17x21in) s.d.1950 board. 27-Mar-3 International Art Centre, Auckland #149/R (NZ.D 2000)

OLEFFE, Auguste (1867-1931) Belgian
£633 $987 €1000 La mer a Nieuport (37x57cm-15x22in) s.d.1909. 10-Sep-2 Vanderkindere, Brussels #307

£833 $1292 €1300 View of a street (75x55cm-30x22in) s.d.1924. 7-Dec-2 De Vuyst, Lokeren #236/R
£972 $1546 €1400 Mer du Nord agitee (44x65cm-17x26in) mono.d.1909. 29-Apr-3 Campo & Campo, Antwerp #236/R
£1111 $1767 €1600 Paysage mediterraneen (33x49cm-13x19in) s.d.1920. 29-Apr-3 Campo & Campo, Antwerp #235/R est:2000-2500
£1655 $2648 €2400 Elegante dans un interieur (71x50cm-28x20in) s. 17-Mar-3 Horta, Bruxelles #190 est:3200-3800

Works on paper
£641 $994 €1000 Sight of Zeebrugge harbour (55x70cm-22x28in) s.i.d.1927 W/C chl paper on panel. 7-Dec-2 De Vuyst, Lokeren #237
£647 $1036 €900 Nature morte aux fleurs et aux fruits (54x45cm-21x18in) s.i.d.1912 mixed media. 19-May-3 Horta, Bruxelles #439

OLEJNIK, Janka (1887-1954) Hungarian
£645 $1000 €935 Detail of a street (15x19cm-6x7in) s. canvas on card. 9-Dec-2 Mu Terem Galeria, Budapest #169/R est:120000 (H.F 240000)
£968 $1501 €1404 Sweet smelling garden (80x64cm-31x25in) s.d.1927. 9-Dec-2 Mu Terem Galeria, Budapest #57/R est:300000 (H.F 360000)

OLESEN, Eyvind (1907-1995) Danish
£279 $447 €419 Self portrait (41x35cm-16x14in) s.d.36. 16-Mar-3 Hindemae, Ullerslev #352/R (D.KR 3000)

OLESEN, G (18/19th C) Danish
Works on paper
£306 $496 €459 Prospect view of Aalborg Harbour (30x40cm-12x16in) i.d.1807 pen W/C oval. 21-May-3 Museumsbygningen, Copenhagen #41/R (D.KR 3200)

OLESEN, Olaf (1873-?) American?
Works on paper
£3614 $6000 €5240 Winter sunlight (81x122cm-32x48in) s.d.1929 mixed media board exhib. 11-Jun-3 Butterfields, San Francisco #4094/R est:3000-5000

OLINSKY, Ivan G (1878-1962) American
£897 $1400 €1346 Student (46x36cm-18x14in) s. 14-Sep-2 Weschler, Washington #627/R est:2000-3000
Works on paper
£1258 $2000 €1887 Mirror (62x42cm-24x17in) s. pastel exhib. 5-Mar-3 Christie's, Rockefeller NY #101/R est:3000-5000

OLIS, Jan (1610-1676) Dutch
£3200 $4960 €4800 Interior scene with three soldiers beside fireplace (29x21cm-11x8in) panel prov. 31-Oct-2 Sotheby's, Olympia #55/R est:3000-4000

OLIS, Jan (attrib) (1610-1676) Dutch
£1629 $2639 €2362 Kitchen interior with woman and child (27x26cm-11x10in) panel prov. 25-May-3 Uppsala Auktionskammare, Uppsala #37/R est:20000-25000 (S.KR 21000)

OLIS, Jan (style) (1610-1678) Dutch
£5517 $8828 €8000 La lecon de musique (39x37cm-15x15in) 17-Mar-3 Horta, Bruxelles #182/R est:12000-15000

OLITSKI, Jules (1922-) American/Russian
£2083 $3250 €3125 Samaria Sin-Kr-12 (145x91cm-57x36in) s.i.d.78 verso acrylic prov. 14-Oct-2 Butterfields, San Francisco #2087/R est:4000-6000
£4487 $7000 €6731 Yarmuk wal-6 (216x140cm-85x55in) s.d.75 verso acrylic prov. 14-Oct-2 Butterfields, San Francisco #2086/R est:10000-12000
£7097 $11000 €10646 Other flesh-9 (165x134cm-65x53in) s.i.d.1972 verso acrylic prov. 26-Sep-2 Christie's, Rockefeller NY #779/R est:4000-6000
£22152 $35000 €33228 Ishtar bra box (203x305cm-80x120in) acrylic painted 1962 prov.exhib. 12-Nov-2 Phillips, New York #125/R est:40000-60000

OLIVA Y RODRIGO, Eugenio (1854-1925) Spanish
£286 $417 €440 Dog head (31x46cm-12x18in) s. 17-Jun-2 Ansorena, Madrid #228
£320 $509 €464 Portrait of an elderly lady (61x46cm-24x18in) s. 29-Apr-3 Gorringes, Lewes #2348
£2583 $4210 €3900 Street in Granada (27x17cm-11x7in) s. board. 11-Feb-3 Segre, Madrid #101/R
£8710 $13761 €13500 Lady in the garden (116x83cm-46x33in) s. 18-Dec-2 Ansorena, Madrid #163/R est:13500
Works on paper
£514 $801 €750 Village square (31x22cm-12x9in) s. W/C. 8-Apr-3 Ansorena, Madrid #597/R

OLIVA, Eugenio (19/20th C) Spanish
Works on paper
£284 $460 €400 Vista desde San Sebastian (40x55cm-16x22in) s.i. chl sketch. 20-May-3 Segre, Madrid #79/R

OLIVA, Pedro Pablo (1949-) Cuban
£12102 $19000 €18153 Great artist and his models (117x105cm-46x41in) s.d.98 s.i.verso prov. 20-Nov-2 Christie's, Rockefeller NY #109/R est:15000-20000

OLIVA, Victor (elder) (1861-1928) Czechoslovakian
£785 $1249 €1178 Future telling (49x71cm-19x28in) s. board. 8-Mar-3 Dorotheum, Prague #20/R est:36000-50000 (C.KR 36000)

OLIVA, Victor (younger) (1898-?) Czechoslovakian
£454 $736 €658 On the Charles Bridge (50x60cm-20x24in) mono. panel. 24-May-3 Dorotheum, Prague #56/R est:12000-18000 (C.KR 20000)

OLIVE, Ceferi (1907-1995) Spanish
Works on paper
£321 $500 €510 Landscape (48x63cm-19x25in) s.d.MCMLXVI W/C exec.1966. 17-Sep-2 Segre, Madrid #206/R
£390 $569 €600 Landscape (26x47cm-10x19in) s.d.MCMLXXXIII W/C. 17-Jun-2 Ansorena, Madrid #2/R
£395 $639 €600 View of castle (29x38cm-11x15in) s.d.MCMLV W/C. 21-Jan-3 Ansorena, Madrid #3/R
£609 $962 €950 Harbour (21x27cm-8x11in) s. W/C. 19-Nov-2 Durán, Madrid #623/R
£1103 $1754 €1600 River (68x98cm-27x39in) s.d.1975 W/C. 4-Mar-3 Ansorena, Madrid #687/R
£1161 $1835 €1800 Seascape (49x64cm-19x25in) s.d.MCMLXXXIV W/C. 18-Dec-2 Ansorena, Madrid #250/R

OLIVE, Jean Baptiste (1848-1936) French
£2590 $4144 €3600 Petit port mediterraneen (13x22cm-5x9in) s.i. cardboard. 14-May-3 Blanchet, Paris #58/R est:3000-4000
£5532 $9238 €7800 Cassis (24x33cm-9x13in) s. 20-Jun-3 Piasa, Paris #80/R est:5000-7000
£5577 $8756 €8700 Rochers en bord de mer (31x41cm-12x16in) s.i.d.1893 panel. 13-Dec-2 Piasa, Paris #178/R
£7432 $11595 €11000 Trois-mats a quai (46x61cm-18x24in) s. 28-Mar-3 Claude Aguttes, Neuilly #42/R est:15000
£8861 $13734 €14000 L'epave de la Navarre pres de Marseille (51x73cm-20x29in) s. 29-Sep-2 Eric Pillon, Calais #149/R

OLIVEIRA, Nathan (1928-) American
£177215 $280000 €265823 Seated figure with pink background (208x157cm-82x62in) s.d.60 prov.exhib.lit. 12-Nov-2 Sotheby's, New York #8/R est:150000-200000

OLIVEIRO, Hugh (20th C) Australian
£400 $644 €580 Mother and child with flowers (50x60cm-20x24in) mono. enamel on board. 12-May-3 Joel, Victoria #407 est:1000-1500 (A.D 1000)

OLIVER, Bronwyn (1959-) Australian
Sculpture
£1358 $2118 €2352 Feather (200cm-79in) silk bone prov. 31-Mar-3 Goodman, Sydney #164/R (A.D 3600)

OLIVER, C (20th C) ?
£377 $581 €600 Landscape (100x150cm-39x59in) s.d.1902. 22-Oct-2 Durán, Madrid #654/R

OLIVER, Emma Sophie (1819-1885) British
Works on paper
£320 $525 €480 Troutbeck, Westmorland (34x47cm-13x19in) s. W/C htd white. 4-Feb-3 Bonhams, Leeds #301

OLIVER, Herbert (attrib) (19th C) British
£250 $400 €363 Lake view (30x46cm-12x18in) s.i. 16-May-3 Skinner, Boston #38/R

OLIVER, Isaac (c.1550-1617) British
Miniatures
£15000 $23400 €22500 Mrs Holland wearing black dress with gold and silver braid and silver rosette (5cm-2in) mono. gilt frame gold border W/C vellum stuck to playing card oval. 5-Nov-2 Bonhams, New Bond Street #14/R est:25000-35000

OLIVER, Kate (?) British?
£400 $616 €600 Portrait of a lady holding a book (61x51cm-24x20in) s. 3-Sep-2 Gorringes, Lewes #2293

OLIVER, Peter (1594-1648) British
£480 $763 €720 Two figures (62x52cm-24x20in) board. 18-Mar-3 Bonhams, Knightsbridge #166
£600 $930 €900 Man with baskets (66x91cm-26x36in) s. board prov. 4-Dec-2 Christie's, Kensington #567/R

OLIVER, Richard Aldworth (1811-1889) New Zealander
Works on paper
£3659 $5598 €5489 Maorie girls, Auckland (37x26cm-15x10in) W/C. 21-Aug-2 Dunbar Sloane, Auckland #16/R est:12000-20000 (NZ.D 12000)
£3859 $5981 €5789 Interior of a Maori hut at Waiheke Island, Hauraki Gulf (24x35cm-9x14in) i.verso W/C double-sided. 4-Dec-2 Dunbar Sloane, Auckland #7/R est:12000-25000 (NZ.D 12000)

OLIVER, T Clark (?-1893) American
£1039 $1600 €1559 Sunrise over the harbor (76x61cm-30x24in) s.d.1887. 27-Oct-2 Grogan, Boston #67 est:1500-2000

OLIVER, Thomas (1979-) British
£900 $1458 €1350 America's Cup trials, Long Island Sound, Yankee v Rainbow (61x91cm-24x36in) s.d.02 i.stretcher. 21-May-3 Christie's, Kensington #496/R
£1200 $1944 €1800 America's Cup Jubilee Round the Island Race, Mariette and Cambria (61x91cm-24x36in) s.d.02 i.stretcher. 21-May-3 Christie's, Kensington #497/R est:1500-2500
£2600 $4030 €3900 Velsheda and Shamrock off Seaview on their way to the Nab Tower, America's cup jubilee, 2001 (61x91cm-24x36in) s.d.2002. 31-Oct-2 Christie's, Kensington #412/R est:800-1200

OLIVER, William (attrib) (fl.1867-1882) British
£4000 $6360 €6000 Expectation (103x36cm-41x14in) s. 19-Mar-3 Sotheby's, London #284/R est:4000-6000

OLIVER, William (1805-1853) British
£568 $886 €852 Dinant (24x37cm-9x15in) s.d.1852 W/C over pencil. 6-Nov-2 Dobiaschofsky, Bern #864/R (S.FR 1300)
£600 $978 €900 Portrait of a young lady (61x46cm-24x18in) s. 29-Jan-3 Sotheby's, Olympia #68/R
£3459 $5327 €5500 News from afar (61x46cm-24x18in) s. 22-Oct-2 Sotheby's, Amsterdam #84/R est:3000-5000
Works on paper
£769 $1100 €1154 View from the Villa Matteri, Rome (21x29cm-8x11in) s.d.1840 verso W/C. 23-Jan-3 Swann Galleries, New York #400/R est:600-900

OLIVER, William (fl.1865-1897) British
£1500 $2490 €2250 Farewell (92x70cm-36x28in) s. 10-Jun-3 Bonhams, Knightsbridge #226/R est:2000-3000
£3404 $5277 €5106 Young lady with rose (103x35cm-41x14in) s. 4-Dec-2 AB Stockholms Auktionsverk #1841/R est:25000-30000 (S.KR 48000)
£3404 $5277 €5106 Young lady by wall (103x35cm-41x14in) s. 4-Dec-2 AB Stockholms Auktionsverk #1842/R est:25000-30000 (S.KR 48000)
£3800 $6232 €5700 Snake in the grass (76x43cm-30x17in) s.d.1883 i.verso. 29-May-3 Christie's, Kensington #240/R est:3000-5000
Works on paper
£600 $942 €900 Portrait of a young woman in a bonnet (20x15cm-8x6in) s.d.1883 W/C. 21-Nov-2 Tennants, Leyburn #688

OLIVERO, Pietro Domenico (circle) (?-1754) Italian
£6000 $9360 €9000 Market scene with peasants gathered before the walls of a town (76x93cm-30x37in) i.on stretcher. 10-Apr-3 Sotheby's, London #72/R

OLIVETTI, Ercole (1874-1941) Italian
£577 $906 €900 Portrait of girl with flower in her hair (57cm-22in circular) on terracotta. 10-Dec-2 Della Rocca, Turin #301

OLIVETTI, Luigi (16th C) Italian
Works on paper
£2620 $4087 €3930 Two figures in Italian landscape. Flower girl (52x35cm-20x14in) s.i. one d.MCMIII W/C over pencil two. 6-Nov-2 Dobiaschofsky, Bern #865/R est:6400 (S.FR 6000)

OLIVETTI, S (?) Italian
£325 $510 €471 Landscape. 15-Dec-2 Anders Antik, Landskrona #47 (S.KR 4600)

OLIVIER, Emile (20th C) American
£1596 $2650 €2314 Landscape with sheep (86x122cm-34x48in) s. 11-Jun-3 Boos Gallery, Michigan #342/R est:2000-3000

OLIVIER, Ferdinand (1873-?) French
Prints
£79739 $130771 €122000 Salzburg landscapes (20x27cm-8x11in) lithographs nine. 6-Feb-3 Weidler, Nurnberg #307/R est:21000

OLIVIER, Friedrich (1791-1859) German
Works on paper
£1667 $2633 €2600 Daniel's prayer (16x26cm-6x10in) sepia htd white prov. 16-Nov-2 Lempertz, Koln #1374/R est:2000

OLIVIER, Herbert Arnould (1861-1952) British
£396 $614 €630 La peche a la sardine (39x29cm-15x11in) s. board. 6-Oct-2 Feletin, Province #128/R

OLIVIER, Olivier O (20th C) French
Works on paper
£312 $496 €450 Untitled (64x49cm-25x19in) s. chl graphite dr. 29-Apr-3 Artcurial Briest, Paris #653

OLIVIER, René (19th C) French
£897 $1391 €1400 Equilibriste (97x131cm-38x52in) s. panel. 9-Dec-2 Beaussant & Lefèvre, Paris #80/R

OLIVIERA, Jao Marques de (1853-1927) Portuguese
£2568 $4005 €3800 House and tropical garden (70x80cm-28x31in) s. 28-Mar-3 Claude Aguttes, Neuilly #68/R

OLIVIERI, Claudio (1934-) Italian
£897 $1391 €1400 Blue-yellow (100x70cm-39x28in) s.d.1971. 4-Dec-2 Finarte, Milan #268/R
£1218 $1912 €1900 Untitled (100x150cm-39x59in) s.d.1971 verso. 23-Nov-2 Meeting Art, Vercelli #294

OLLERS, Edvin (1888-1959) Swedish
£423 $665 €635 Landscape, Tuscany (60x73cm-24x29in) s.d.1938. 16-Dec-2 Lilla Bukowskis, Stockholm #140 (S.KR 6000)

OLLEY, Margaret Hannah (1923-) Australian
£1429 $2200 €2144 Untitled - Portrait of a man (30x19cm-12x7in) s.d.68 prov. 3-Sep-2 Shapiro, Sydney #385/R est:3000-5000 (A.D 4000)
£6786 $10450 €10179 Wallflowers (61x51cm-24x20in) s.d.72 board prov. 3-Sep-2 Shapiro, Sydney #387/R est:20000-30000 (A.D 19000)
£7168 $10896 €10752 Still life with brioche (49x65cm-19x26in) s. composition board. 28-Aug-2 Deutscher-Menzies, Melbourne #62/R est:25000-30000 (A.D 20000)
£7200 $11592 €10800 Still life with pears (45x60cm-18x24in) s. board. 6-May-3 Christie's, Melbourne #29/R est:25000-40000 (A.D 18000)
£7857 $12257 €11786 Boy at a table (61x76cm-24x30in) s. composition board prov. 11-Nov-2 Deutscher-Menzies, Melbourne #68/R est:25000-35000 (A.D 22000)
£11508 $19103 €19607 Untitled - evening interior (45x53cm-18x21in) s. masonite board prov. 10-Jun-3 Shapiro, Sydney #38/R est:30000-50000 (A.D 29000)
£12261 $19249 €18392 Boy at table (61x76cm-24x30in) s. composition board prov. 15-Apr-3 Lawson Menzies, Sydney #30/R est:34000-45000 (A.D 32000)
£14729 $23419 €22094 Still life with red pot and pomegranates (52x44cm-20x17in) s. board prov. 5-May-3 Sotheby's, Melbourne #105/R est:25000-35000 (A.D 38000)
£15200 $24472 €22800 Evening interior (45x53cm-18x21in) s. board painted c.1980 prov.exhib.lit. 6-May-3 Christie's, Melbourne #31/R est:25000-40000 (A.D 38000)
£16786 $26185 €25179 Evening kitchen still life with apples (68x92cm-27x36in) s. composition board prov. 11-Nov-2 Deutscher-Menzies, Melbourne #20/R est:35000-45000 (A.D 47000)
£17143 $26914 €25715 Cornflowers and Indian rug (74x60cm-29x24in) s. board prov.exhib. 25-Nov-2 Christie's, Melbourne #1/R est:25000-35000 (A.D 48000)

£20609 $31326 €30914 Daisies with pears and jug (75x121cm-30x48in) s. painted c.1976 composition board prov. 28-Aug-2 Deutscher-Menzies, Melbourne #82/R est:38000-45000 (A.D 57500)
£21352 $32669 €32028 Nippy in the red room (73x74cm-29x29in) s. board painted 2000 prov. 25-Aug-2 Sotheby's, Paddington #18/R est:50000-70000 (A.D 60000)
£22000 $35420 €33000 Still life with flowers (60x75cm-24x30in) s.d.66 board prov. 6-May-3 Christie's, Melbourne #48/R est:40000-60000 (A.D 55000)
£23256 $36977 €34884 Still life with banksia (90x120cm-35x47in) s. board prov. 5-May-3 Sotheby's, Melbourne #113/R est:40000-60000 (A.D 60000)
£25000 $39250 €37500 Yellow room, afternoon (75x75cm-30x30in) s. board painted c.1990 prov. 25-Nov-2 Christie's, Melbourne #36/R est:30000-40000 (A.D 70000)
£25000 $39750 €37500 Still life with lemons (76x101cm-30x40in) s. composition board prov. 4-Mar-3 Deutscher-Menzies, Melbourne #27/R est:40000-50000 (A.D 65000)
£26000 $41860 €39000 Flowers and persimmons (75x100cm-30x39in) s.d.65 board prov. 6-May-3 Christie's, Melbourne #6/R est:50000-70000 (A.D 65000)
£34000 $54740 €51000 Ranunculus and fruits I (74x120cm-29x47in) s. board painted 1973. 6-May-3 Christie's, Melbourne #21/R est:65000-80000 (A.D 85000)

Works on paper
£1301 $2055 €1886 Chinese New Year (30x50cm-12x20in) s. W/C. 22-Jul-3 Lawson Menzies, Sydney #177/R est:3000-5000 (A.D 3200)
£1607 $2491 €2411 Jardin des Tuileries (31x40cm-12x16in) s.d.1950 pen ink wash. 29-Oct-2 Lawson Menzies, Sydney #94 est:5500-7000 (A.D 4500)
£2107 $3308 €3161 Pont Louis Philippe Paris (35x45cm-14x18in) s.i.d.1971 ink W/C. 15-Apr-3 Lawson Menzies, Sydney #164/R est:5000-10000 (A.D 5500)
£4000 $6440 €6000 Place Dauphine, Paris (50x40cm-20x16in) s.i.d.1951 ink W/C. 6-May-3 Christie's, Melbourne #218/R est:7000-10000 (A.D 10000)

OLLGAARD, Hans (1911-1969) Danish
£254 $394 €381 Two women by Hellingdomsklipperne, Bornholm (88x76cm-35x30in) s,. 1-Oct-2 Rasmussen, Copenhagen #383/R (D.KR 3000)
£296 $456 €444 Girls in autumn, Bornholm (58x70cm-23x28in) mono. 23-Oct-2 Kunsthallen, Copenhagen #341 (D.KR 3500)
£339 $525 €509 Hostmark at night with view across the sea (116x97cm-46x38in) init.d.52. 1-Oct-2 Rasmussen, Copenhagen #272/R (D.KR 4000)
£343 $535 €515 Coastal landscape with women at edge of water (100x118cm-39x46in) mono. s.d.59 verso. 11-Nov-2 Rasmussen, Vejle #73/R (D.KR 4000)
£390 $617 €585 Outing in the woods (87x67cm-34x26in) mono. 1-Apr-3 Rasmussen, Copenhagen #599 (D.KR 4200)

OLLILA, Yrjo (1887-1932) Finnish
£421 $665 €610 Avenue (54x36cm-21x14in) s. 3-Apr-3 Hagelstam, Helsinki #993
£1176 $1929 €1800 Reflections (48x58cm-19x23in) s.d.1915. 9-Feb-3 Bukowskis, Helsinki #331/R est:1300
£2215 $3500 €3500 Evening light (47x47cm-19x19in) s.d.1911. 1-Dec-2 Bukowskis, Helsinki #145/R est:1500-1700

Works on paper
£374 $591 €580 The angel (46x62cm-18x24in) s.d.1932 pastel. 19-Dec-2 Hagelstam, Helsinki #941

OLLIVARY, Anette (20th C) French
£2600 $4082 €3900 Plantation (65x92cm-26x36in) s.d.1959 prov. 16-Dec-2 Sotheby's, London #91/R est:400-800

OLMO, Gregorio del (1921-1977) Spanish
£1410 $2228 €2200 Landscape (65x81cm-26x32in) s. 13-Nov-2 Ansorena, Madrid #280/R

OLOFSSON, Pierre (1921-1996) Swedish

Sculpture
£1141 $1802 €1712 Duo (42cm-17in) s.num.3/8 painted metal. 28-Apr-3 Bukowskis, Stockholm #245/R est:15000-18000 (S.KR 15000)

Works on paper
£420 $656 €630 October (38x44cm-15x17in) s. Indian ink wax gouache. 5-Nov-2 Bukowskis, Stockholm #270/R (S.KR 6000)
£491 $765 €737 The ghost sonata (54x38cm-21x15in) s. Indian ink wax gouache. 5-Nov-2 Bukowskis, Stockholm #269/R (S.KR 7000)
£526 $820 €789 Composition (39x27cm-15x11in) s. gouache. 6-Nov-2 AB Stockholms Auktionsverk #553/R (S.KR 7500)
£526 $820 €789 Composition (43x30cm-17x12in) s. mixed media. 6-Nov-2 AB Stockholms Auktionsverk #610/R (S.KR 7500)
£608 $961 €912 Untitled (48x78cm-19x31in) s. mixed media. 28-Apr-3 Bukowskis, Stockholm #247/R (S.KR 8000)
£1004 $1616 €1506 Composition (23x17cm-9x7in) s. Indian ink. 7-May-3 AB Stockholms Auktionsverk #921/R (S.KR 13000)
£1351 $2243 €1959 Circle in ring (30x38cm-12x15in) s.d.48 pastel. 16 Jun-3 Lilla Bukowskis, Stockholm #446 est:6000-8000 (S.KR 17500)

OLRICK, Henrik Benedikt (1830-1890) Danish
£331 $533 €497 Portrait of a Roman woman (45x37cm-18x15in) s.i.d.1863 verso. 11-May-3 Hindemae, Ullerslev #381/R (D.KR 3500)
£341 $528 €512 Portrait of girl (58x47cm-23x19in) s.d.1874 i.verso. 28-Sep-2 Rasmussen, Havnen #2045 (D.KR 4000)
£448 $686 €672 Portrait of woman (68x57cm-27x22in) s.d.1872 oval. 24-Aug-2 Rasmussen, Havnen #2303/R (D.KR 5200)

OLRIK, Balder (1966-) Danish
£465 $721 €698 Composition (81x81cm-32x32in) s.verso. 4-Dec-2 Kunsthallen, Copenhagen #189/R (D.KR 5400)
£1144 $1910 €1659 The gate to Hell (140x120cm-55x47in) with sig.verso prov. 17-Jun-3 Rasmussen, Copenhagen #62/R est:15000-18000 (D.KR 12000)

OLSEN, Alfred (1854-1932) Danish
£284 $457 €426 Ships at the harbour quay (42x60cm-17x24in) s. 11-May-3 Hindemae, Ullerslev #676/R (D.KR 3000)
£317 $504 €476 Sailing vessels in a calm (49x83cm-19x33in) s.d.1918. 5-May-3 Rasmussen, Vejle #295/R (D.KR 3400)
£388 $589 €582 Skagen, fishing boats at sea (49x68cm-19x27in) s.d.1915. 27-Aug-2 Rasmussen, Copenhagen #1754/R (D.KR 4500)
£474 $720 €711 Early morning, Oresund (40x67cm-16x26in) s.d.1910. 27-Aug-2 Rasmussen, Copenhagen #1728/R (D.KR 5500)
£517 $786 €776 Calm day at Sundet (50x66cm-20x26in) s.d.1917. 27-Aug-2 Rasmussen, Copenhagen #1747/R (D.KR 6000)
£525 $841 €788 Seascape with sailing ship (44x61cm-17x24in) s. 13-Jan-3 Rasmussen, Vejle #98/R (D.KR 6000)
£603 $916 €905 Calm summer evening, Svendborgsund (40x79cm-16x31in) s. 27-Aug-2 Rasmussen, Copenhagen #1761/R (D.KR 7000)
£680 $1060 €1020 Seascape with steamer and sailing ship (30x76cm-12x30in) s.d.1883. 5-Aug-2 Rasmussen, Vejle #54/R (D.KR 8000)
£1702 $2689 €2553 Danish and Swedish sailing vessels in Sundet (58x84cm-23x33in) s. 2-Dec-2 Rasmussen, Copenhagen #1376/R est:20000 (D.KR 20000)

OLSEN, Carl (1818-1878) Danish
£383 $620 €555 Seascape with sailing vessels at sunset (37x52cm-15x20in) s. 26-May-3 Rasmussen, Copenhagen #1379/R (D.KR 4000)
£583 $910 €875 Seascape with sailing vessels (53x80cm-21x31in) s. 11-Nov-2 Rasmussen, Vejle #611/R (D.KR 6800)
£652 $1036 €978 Rowing boat at sea before storm (25x33cm-10x13in) s.d.1861. 5-Mar-3 Rasmussen, Copenhagen #2016/R (D.KR 7000)
£732 $1113 €1098 Ships portrait of a Danish sailing ship (55x84cm-22x33in) s.d.8/9 65. 28-Aug-2 Museumsbygningen, Copenhagen #47/R (D.KR 8500)

OLSEN, Chr Benjamin (1873-1935) Danish
£302 $462 €453 Floating dock at Refshale Island (21x30cm-8x12in) s. 24-Aug-2 Rasmussen, Havnen #2036/R (D.KR 3500)
£306 $496 €444 Seascape with man-o-war (27x41cm-11x16in) s. 24-May-3 Rasmussen, Havnen #2027/R (D.KR 3200)
£317 $526 €450 Fishing boats setting sail in front of the coast in moonlight (42x62cm-17x24in) s. 14-Jun-3 Arnold, Frankfurt #826/R
£374 $583 €561 Seascape with vessels (27x42cm-11x17in) s.d.1923. 5-Aug-2 Rasmussen, Vejle #2182 (D.KR 4400)
£389 $599 €584 The frigate Jylland in the North Sea, evening light (41x61cm-16x24in) s. 26-Oct-2 Rasmussen, Havnen #3108 (D.KR 4600)
£399 $623 €599 Seascape with sailing ship (73x101cm-29x40in) s. 5-Aug-2 Rasmussen, Vejle #55/R (D.KR 4700)
£423 $651 €635 Seascape with sailing vessels on open seas (36x58cm-14x23in) s.d.1903. 26-Oct-2 Rasmussen, Havnen #3009 (D.KR 5000)
£511 $808 €767 Sailing vessels in Bay of Naples (24x37cm-9x15in) s.d.1929. 5-Apr-3 Rasmussen, Havnen #2119/R (D.KR 5500)
£541 $843 €812 Vessels by entrance to Assen's Harbour (32x44cm-13x17in) s.i.d.1908. 23-Sep-2 Rasmussen, Vejle #111/R (D.KR 6400)
£670 $1066 €1005 Seascape with ships, Copenhagen Harbour in background (68x101cm-27x40in) s. 10-Mar-3 Rasmussen, Vejle #495/R (D.KR 7200)
£1051 $1681 €1577 The motor ship Holger Danske on the way out of Copenhagen Harbour (41x57cm-16x22in) s.d.1914. 13-Jan-3 Rasmussen, Vejle #68/R est:6000-8000 (D.KR 12000)

£1182 $1891 €1773 The corvette Dagmar's last hours, 25 June 1901 (45x61cm-18x24in) s.d.1901. 13-Jan-3 Rasmussen, Vejle #69/R est:6000-8000 (D.KR 13500)
£1241 $2011 €1862 Training ship Ingolf and other vessels, Copenhagen Harbour (70x100cm-28x39in) s.d.1915. 25-Jan-3 Rasmussen, Havnen #2235/R est:10000-15000 (D.KR 14000)
£2553 $4034 €3830 Full sail ahead (65x100cm-26x39in) s. 2-Dec-2 Rasmussen, Copenhagen #1394/R est:30000 (D.KR 30000)

OLSEN, Christian (19th C) Norwegian
£366 $575 €549 Self portrait. s. 25-Nov-2 Blomqvist, Lysaker #1216 (N.KR 4200)

OLSEN, Gudmund (1913-1985) Danish
£257 $401 €386 Rudi (116x89cm-46x35in) s.d.57. 11-Nov-2 Rasmussen, Vejle #35 (D.KR 3000)
£280 $448 €420 Still life of objects on window ledge (75x60cm-30x24in) s.d.48 panel. 13-Jan-3 Rasmussen, Vejle #282 (D.KR 3200)

OLSEN, John (1928-) Australian
£4660 $7082 €6990 Portrait of Bill Rose (74x39cm-29x15in) init.d.93 i.verso card on board prov. 28-Aug-2 Deutscher-Menzies, Melbourne #106/R est:14000-18000 (A.D 13000)
£6773 $11107 €10160 Road to Hill End (30x38cm-12x15in) s. composition board prov. 4-Jun-3 Deutscher-Menzies, Melbourne #88/R est:18000-24000 (A.D 17000)
£7752 $12326 €11628 Australian landscape (35x45cm-14x18in) s.d.90. 5-May-3 Sotheby's, Melbourne #165/R est:14000-18000 (A.D 20000)
£13889 $21667 €20834 Wimmera river (71x81cm-28x32in) init.d.1969 prov. 8-Apr-3 Peter Webb, Auckland #105/R est:45000-65000 (NZ.D 40000)
£20000 $31600 €30000 Pilbara (135x150cm-53x59in) s.d.85 i.verso oil on linen. 27-Nov-2 Deutscher-Menzies, Melbourne #88/R est:65000-85000 (A.D 56000)
£30357 $47357 €45536 Ebb tide (137x152cm-54x60in) s.i.d.91 i.verso. 11-Nov-2 Deutscher-Menzies, Melbourne #23/R est:60000-80000 (A.D 85000)
£34615 $55038 €51923 Still life influenced by the desert (130x149cm-51x59in) s.d.82 prov.exhib. 4-Mar-3 Deutscher-Menzies, Melbourne #48/R est:100000-140000 (A.D 90000)
£37848 $62071 €56772 Rydal landscape (136x152cm-54x60in) s.d.92 prov.exhib. 4-Jun-3 Deutscher-Menzies, Melbourne #27/R est:120000-150000 (A.D 95000)
£40650 $64228 €58943 Self portrait - afternoon walk, Dunmoochin (183x122cm-72x48in) s.d.69 i.verso board prov.exhib. 22-Jul-3 Lawson Menzies, Sydney #36/R est:110000-140000 (A.D 100000)
£56911 $89919 €82521 Debussy's pool 1984-5 (120x180cm-47x71in) s.i. board prov. 22-Jul-3 Lawson Menzies, Sydney #25/R est:80000-100000 (A.D 140000)
£162791 $258837 €244187 Love in the kitchen (199x213cm-78x84in) init.d.69 prov.exhib. 5-May-3 Sotheby's, Melbourne #126/R est:300000-400000 (A.D 420000)

Prints
£2491 $3811 €3737 Giraffes and Mount Kenya (90x62cm-35x24in) s.d.80 num.16/30 col lithograph prov. 26-Aug-2 Sotheby's, Paddington #593 est:2500-3500 (A.D 7000)
£3187 $5227 €4781 Frog at Kakadu (76x56cm-30x22in) s.i.d.num.22/40 col lithograph. 4-Jun-3 Deutscher-Menzies, Melbourne #192/R est:3000-4000 (A.D 8000)

Works on paper
£491 $747 €737 Pelican (34x21cm-13x8in) s. ink. 19-Aug-2 Joel, Victoria #222 est:1200-1500 (A.D 1400)
£800 $1288 €1200 Mousetrap (19x25cm-7x10in) s. pastel. 6-May-3 Christie's, Melbourne #243 est:2000-3000 (A.D 2000)
£2000 $3220 €3000 Honey possum (28x21cm-11x8in) s. pastel. 6-May-3 Christie's, Melbourne #358 est:3000-4000 (A.D 5000)
£2390 $3920 €3585 Still life with crab (35x52cm-14x20in) s. pencil pastel. 4-Jun-3 Deutscher-Menzies, Melbourne #136/R est:7500-10000 (A.D 6000)
£2905 $4503 €4358 Frog spawn (39x27cm-15x11in) s.i.d.99 W/C prov. 3-Dec-2 Shapiro, Sydney #25/R est:10000-15000 (A.D 8000)
£3200 $5152 €4800 Interior with animals (38x52cm-15x20in) init. W/C prov. 6-May-3 Christie's, Melbourne #300/R est:7000-10000 (A.D 8000)
£3200 $5152 €4640 Nightjar studies (50x39cm-20x15in) s.i. pencil wash gouache. 12-May-3 Joel, Victoria #230 est:8000-12000 (A.D 8000)
£3257 $5113 €4886 Indian contemplation (75x55cm-30x22in) s.i.d.1984 W/C ink prov. 15-Apr-3 Lawson Menzies, Sydney #13/R est:8000-10000 (A.D 8500)
£3448 $5138 €5172 Vervet monkey and Mt. Kenya (77x56cm-30x22in) s.i.verso pastel chl. 27-Aug-2 Christie's, Melbourne #11/R est:10000-15000 (A.D 9000)
£3461 $5504 €5192 Life study (36x54cm-14x21in) i.verso pen ink W/C exec.c.1959. 4-Mar-3 Deutscher-Menzies, Melbourne #167/R est:10000-15000 (A.D 9000)
£4382 $7187 €6573 Black faced monkey, Kenya (71x51cm-28x20in) s.i.d.78 W/C prov. 4-Jun-3 Deutscher-Menzies, Melbourne #116/R est:12000-15000 (A.D 11000)
£4800 $7728 €7200 Sunburst (35x50cm-14x20in) init. W/C. 6-May-3 Christie's, Melbourne #225/R est:7000-10000 (A.D 12000)
£5426 $8628 €8139 Paddocks, wattle and moon (63x46cm-25x18in) s.d.70 i.d.1968 verso gouache. 5-May-3 Sotheby's, Melbourne #142/R est:14000-18000 (A.D 14000)
£5426 $8628 €8139 Escaping mouse (79x104cm-31x41in) s.i.d.89 W/C. 5-May-3 Sotheby's, Melbourne #211/R est:7000-9000 (A.D 14000)
£6050 $9256 €9075 Old dog (63x97cm-25x38in) s.d.86 W/C pastel prov. 25-Aug-2 Sotheby's, Paddington #76/R est:18000-22000 (A.D 17000)
£6071 $9471 €9107 Inland lake (79x88cm-31x35in) s. W/C pastel. 11-Nov-2 Deutscher-Menzies, Melbourne #19/R est:20000-30000 (A.D 17000)
£6452 $9806 €9678 Shadow over landscape (77x55cm-30x22in) s. gouache prov. 28-Aug-2 Deutscher-Menzies, Melbourne #109/R est:22000-26000 (A.D 18000)
£9286 $14579 €13929 Kimberley tree frog (74x57cm-29x22in) s.i.d.94 W/C pastel. 25-Nov-2 Christie's, Melbourne #20/R est:24000-34000 (A.D 26000)
£10078 $16023 €15117 Artist's camp and echidna (79x89cm-31x35in) s.i. W/C chl exhib. painted c.2000. 5-May-3 Sotheby's, Melbourne #150/R est:25000-35000 (A.D 26000)
£10359 $16988 €15539 Tree monkeys, Kenya (153x98cm-60x39in) s.i. W/C pastel gouache. 4-Jun-3 Deutscher-Menzies, Melbourne #77/R est:25000-35000 (A.D 26000)
£13167 $20146 €19751 Frutta misto del mare (99x94cm-39x37in) s.d.91 W/C mixed media prov. 26-Aug-2 Sotheby's, Paddington #501/R est:22000-28000 (A.D 37000)
£13214 $20879 €19821 Ostrich (151x135cm-59x53in) s.d.91 pastel W/C. 26-Nov-2 Sotheby's, Melbourne #35/R est:30000-50000 (A.D 37000)
£13600 $21896 €19720 Waterbird (79x104cm-31x41in) s. W/C gouache pastel. 12-May-3 Joel, Victoria #300/R est:35000-50000 (A.D 34000)
£13620 $20703 €20430 Bathurst butter II (93x99cm-37x39in) s.i.d.99 W/C pastel synthetic polymer paint prov.exhib. 28-Aug-2 Deutscher-Menzies, Melbourne #46/R est:32000-40000 (A.D 38000)
£14235 $21779 €21353 Desert and orange chats (95x99cm-37x39in) s.i.d.93 W/C mixed media. 25-Aug-2 Sotheby's, Paddington #57/R est:30000-40000 (A.D 40000)
£17073 $26976 €24756 Chats at Coopers Creek (94x99cm-37x39in) s.i. W/C pastel prov. 22-Jul-3 Lawson Menzies, Sydney #18a/R est:8000-12000 (A.D 42000)
£19713 $29964 €29570 Wet day at the lily pond (96x99cm-38x39in) s.i.d.94 W/C ink pastel prov. 28-Aug-2 Deutscher-Menzies, Melbourne #5/R est:34000-40000 (A.D 55000)
£22358 $35325 €32419 Pelican Rocky Lake, Alexandrina (134x121cm-53x48in) s.i.d.2002 mixed media paper on canvas. 22-Jul-3 Lawson Menzies, Sydney #22/R est:70000-90000 (A.D 55000)
£23200 $37352 €34800 Sausage makers (99x94cm-39x37in) s.i.d.92 W/C pastel gouache prov. 6-May-3 Christie's, Melbourne #2/R est:20000-30000 (A.D 58000)
£23904 $39203 €35856 Harbour tidal pool (100x190cm-39x75in) s.i.d.93 W/C prov. 4-Jun-3 Deutscher-Menzies, Melbourne #51/R est:65000-80000 (A.D 60000)
£29181 $44648 €43772 Spring by the little river (100x380cm-39x150in) s.i.d.93 gouache pastel on four panel. 25-Aug-2 Sotheby's, Paddington #1/R est:40000-60000 (A.D 82000)

OLSEN, Kjell Erik Killi (1952-) Norwegian
£4337 $6765 €6506 Taagen - composition (150x150cm-59x59in) exhib. 21-Oct-2 Blomqvist, Oslo #447/R est:60000-80000 (N.KR 50000)

OLSEN, Maria (1945-) New Zealander
£860 $1350 €1290 House of strain 4 (167x137cm-66x54in) s.d.1999. 10-Dec-2 Peter Webb, Auckland #113/R est:3000-4000 (NZ.D 2700)

Works on paper
£694 $1083 €1041 Reflection (123x153cm-48x60in) s. mixed media canvas. 8-Apr-3 Peter Webb, Auckland #145/R (NZ.D 2000)

OLSEN, Otto (1905-1966) Danish
£723 $1143 €1085 Winter's day at Kongen's Nytorv (41x52cm-16x20in) s. 2-Dec-2 Rasmussen, Copenhagen #1225/R (D.KR 8500)

OLSEN, William Skotte (1945-) Danish

£270 $422 €405 Figures in town (31x60cm-12x24in) init. panel. 18-Sep-2 Kunsthallen, Copenhagen #132 (D.KR 3200)
£270 $422 €405 Landscape with figure and houses (73x92cm-29x36in) init. 18-Sep-2 Kunsthallen, Copenhagen #247 (D.KR 3200)
£297 $481 €431 Sunny morning in town (50x60cm-20x24in) init. 24-May-3 Rasmussen, Havnen #4055 (D.KR 3100)
£329 $523 €494 Mester Jakel (60x50cm-24x20in) init. canvas on board. 26-Feb-3 Kunsthallen, Copenhagen #157 (D.KR 3600)
£340 $538 €510 Figures, house and bird (87x102cm-34x40in) init. 30-Nov-2 Rasmussen, Havnen #2114 (D.KR 4000)
£473 $738 €710 Figure composition (110x130cm-43x51in) init.d.79. 18-Sep-2 Kunsthallen, Copenhagen #106 (D.KR 5600)
£500 $774 €750 Composition with many figures and houses (60x80cm-24x31in) init. painted 1984-87-1988. 4-Dec-2 Kunsthallen, Copenhagen #34 (D.KR 5800)
£541 $870 €812 Born again (82x66cm-32x26in) 22-Feb-3 Rasmussen, Havnen #2287 (D.KR 6000)
£1309 $2042 €1964 Little green grass saga (73x60cm-29x24in) s.verso painted c.1967 exhib. 18-Sep-2 Kunsthallen, Copenhagen #163 est:6000 (D.KR 15500)

OLSOMMER, Charles Clos (1883-1966) Swiss

£535 $834 €850 Landscape with trees (40x40cm-16x16in) s. i. stretcher. 11-Oct-2 Winterberg, Heidelberg #1564/R
£742 $1173 €1113 Woman's portrait (28x30cm-11x12in) s. 14-Nov-2 Stuker, Bern #446/R est:2500-3000 (S.FR 1700)

Works on paper

£349 $545 €524 Songeuse (27x20cm-11x8in) s. mixed media on chl. 20-Nov-2 Fischer, Luzern #2668/R (S.FR 800)
£370 $596 €555 Jeune femme lisant un livre (15x15cm-6x6in) s.d.1915 Indian ink pencil. 7-May-3 Dobiaschofsky, Bern #1843/R (S.FR 800)
£1528 $2384 €2292 Apres-midi a la campagne (29x49cm-11x19in) s. i.d.1944 gouache. 8-Nov-2 Dobiaschofsky, Bern #76/R est:4500 (S.FR 3500)
£3275 $5109 €4913 Francoise (34x30cm-13x12in) s. pastel prov. 8-Nov-2 Dobiaschofsky, Bern #75/R est:12000 (S.FR 7500)
£6522 $10109 €9783 Enfant en priere (48x34cm-19x13in) s. mixed media. 7-Dec-2 Galerie du Rhone, Sion #483/R est:15000-20000 (S.FR 15000)

OLSON, Axel (1899-1986) Swedish

£521 $813 €782 Landscape with cliffs (24x33cm-9x13in) s. 13-Sep-2 Lilla Bukowskis, Stockholm #612 (S.KR 7600)
£567 $879 €851 On the beach in Tylosand (22x44cm-9x17in) s. panel. 8-Dec-2 Uppsala Auktionskammare, Uppsala #247/R (S.KR 8000)
£631 $997 €947 Stones from Crete (12x52cm-5x20in) s. panel. 30-Nov-2 Goteborg Auktionsverk, Sweden #600/R (S.KR 9000)
£771 $1203 €1157 Landscape with figures and community (32x21cm-13x8in) s. 6-Nov-2 AB Stockholms Auktionsverk #724/R (S.KR 11000)
£771 $1203 €1157 The white horse (33x41cm-13x16in) s.d.42 panel. 5-Nov-2 Bukowskis, Stockholm #46/R (S.KR 11000)
£876 $1367 €1314 Narrow street (27x22cm-11x9in) s. 6-Nov-2 AB Stockholms Auktionsverk #632/R (S.KR 12500)
£1003 $1625 €1505 Grotvik's Harbour, Sondrum (22x27cm-9x11in) s. 3-Feb-3 Lilla Bukowskis, Stockholm #30 est:8000-10000 (S.KR 14000)
£1331 $2077 €1997 Found on the beach (28x46cm-11x18in) s. 6-Nov-2 AB Stockholms Auktionsverk #719/R est:15000-18000 (S.KR 19000)
£1402 $2186 €2103 The bouquet (20x27cm-8x11in) s. 5-Nov-2 Bukowskis, Stockholm #44/R est:12000-15000 (S.KR 20000)
£1407 $2252 €2040 The fishing harbour (33x41cm-13x16in) s.d.40. 18-May-3 Anders Antik, Landskrona #42 est:20000 (S.KR 18000)
£1445 $2283 €2168 Flowers and house (41x27cm-16x11in) s. 28-Apr-3 Bukowskis, Stockholm #137/R est:15000-20000 (S.KR 19000)
£1613 $2548 €2420 Calla and iris (47x33cm-19x13in) s.d.45. 30-Nov-2 Goteborg Auktionsverk, Sweden #597/R est:20000 (S.KR 23000)
£1682 $2624 €2523 Finished walk (23x28cm-9x11in) s.d.45. 6-Nov-2 AB Stockholms Auktionsverk #720/R est:30000-35000 (S.KR 24000)
£1892 $2952 €2838 Harvesters resting (37x49cm-15x19in) s.d.42. 6-Nov-2 AB Stockholms Auktionsverk #584/R est:15000-18000 (S.KR 27000)
£1892 $2952 €2838 The jetty (35x43cm-14x17in) s.d.41. 5-Nov-2 Bukowskis, Stockholm #43/R est:20000-25000 (S.KR 27000)
£1962 $3061 €2943 The shell woman (48x75cm-19x30in) s. 6-Nov-2 AB Stockholms Auktionsverk #717/R est:30000-40000 (S.KR 28000)
£2129 $3364 €3194 The Royal mill at Nissan (35x45cm-14x18in) s. painted c.1924-27. 28-Apr-3 Bukowskis, Stockholm #37/R est:35000-40000 (S.KR 28000)
£2453 $3826 €3680 Window towards the garden (33x46cm-13x18in) s.d.48. 6-Nov-2 AB Stockholms Auktionsverk #713/R est:20000-25000 (S.KR 35000)
£7605 $12015 €11408 The monument (41x56cm-16x22in) s.d.37 prov.exhib.lit. 28-Apr-3 Bukowskis, Stockholm #45/R est:100000-125000 (S.KR 100000)

Works on paper

£297 $473 €446 Figures in southern town scene (16x13cm-6x5in) s.d.71 Indian ink chk mixed media. 3-Mar-3 Lilla Bukowskis, Stockholm #760 (S.KR 4000)
£631 $984 €947 Model I (30x20cm-12x8in) s.i.d.923 Indian ink. 5-Nov-2 Bukowskis, Stockholm #126/R (S.KR 9000)

OLSON, Bengt (1930-) Swedish

£412 $642 €618 Untitled (65x100cm-26x39in) s.d.1971. 13-Sep-2 Lilla Bukowskis, Stockholm #650 (S.KR 6000)
£543 $880 €787 Composition (60x83cm-24x33in) s.d.76 i. verso. 25-May-3 Uppsala Auktionskammare, Uppsala #315 (S.KR 7000)
£621 $1005 €900 Composition in purple and pink (80x100cm-31x39in) s. d.1967 verso. 25-May-3 Uppsala Auktionskammare, Uppsala #328/R (S.KR 8000)
£630 $996 €945 Untitled (100x80cm-39x31in) s. 16-Nov-2 Crafoord, Lund #20/R (S.KR 9000)
£698 $1131 €1012 Full of life (88x115cm-35x45in) s.d.64. 25-May-3 Uppsala Auktionskammare, Uppsala #327/R (S.KR 9000)
£967 $1567 €1451 Untitled (88x69cm-35x27in) s.i.d.1987. 3-Feb-3 Lilla Bukowskis, Stockholm #64 (S.KR 13500)

OLSON, Eric H (1909-1996) Swedish

Sculpture

£1472 $2296 €2208 Optochromi - S4 (48cm-19in) s.d.74 glass black plexi. 6-Nov-2 AB Stockholms Auktionsverk #757/R est:25000-30000 (S.KR 21000)
£2471 $3978 €3707 Optochromi - DR (28cm-11in) s.d.80 glass filter black plexiglass. 7-May-3 AB Stockholms Auktionsverk #939/R est:15000-18000 (S.KR 32000)

OLSON, Erik (1901-1986) Swedish

£352 $563 €510 The tool shed (31x39cm-12x15in) s.d.45. 18-May-3 Anders Antik, Landskrona #41 (S.KR 4500)
£701 $1093 €1052 Park landscape (24x28cm-9x11in) init.d.17 cardboard. 5-Nov-2 Bukowskis, Stockholm #34/R (S.KR 10000)
£837 $1322 €1256 Shelter for the night (29x38cm-11x15in) s.d.48. 28-Apr-3 Bukowskis, Stockholm #138/R (S.KR 11000)
£981 $1530 €1472 I am the way, the truth and life (30x63cm-12x25in) s.d.41. 5-Nov-2 Bukowskis, Stockholm #124/R est:20000-25000 (S.KR 14000)
£1892 $2952 €2838 Summer light (33x41cm-13x16in) s.d.1946 cardboard. 5-Nov-2 Bukowskis, Stockholm #125/R est:30000-35000 (S.KR 27000)
£2205 $3484 €3308 View from Lilla Torg, Halmstad (24x35cm-9x14in) s.d.1950. 28-Apr-3 Bukowskis, Stockholm #32/R est:20000-25000 (S.KR 29000)
£2242 $3498 €3363 The banana seller (24x22cm-9x9in) init.i.d.27 paper lit. 5-Nov-2 Bukowskis, Stockholm #42/R est:30000-35000 (S.KR 32000)
£2357 $3725 €3536 Landscape from Brittany (19x33cm-7x13in) s.d.19.8-29 canvas on board. 28-Apr-3 Bukowskis, Stockholm #130/R est:20000-25000 (S.KR 31000)
£2394 $3974 €3471 Summer visitors (20x50cm-8x20in) s.d.59 panel. 16-Jun-3 Lilla Bukowskis, Stockholm #451/R est:12000-15000 (S.KR 31000)
£3346 $5286 €5019 Landscape with figure in field (50x61cm-20x24in) s.d.1943 masonite. 1-Apr-3 Rasmussen, Copenhagen #80/R est:20000 (D.KR 36000)
£9811 $15305 €14717 Interior - Xenius (40x50cm-16x20in) s.d.1933 panel. 5-Nov-2 Bukowskis, Stockholm #41/R est:120000-130000 (S.KR 140000)
£14449 $22829 €21674 Summer's day on the beach, Halland (26x49cm-10x19in) s.d.26 canvas on panel. 28-Apr-3 Bukowskis, Stockholm #36/R est:130000-140000 (S.KR 190000)
£19392 $30639 €29088 The searcher I (48x38cm-19x15in) s.d.1934 exhib. 28-Apr-3 Bukowskis, Stockholm #194/R est:150000-175000 (S.KR 255000)
£20077 $32324 €30116 29 rue Boulard, Paris (56x46cm-22x18in) s.i.d.1927 prov.exhib.lit. 7-May-3 AB Stockholms Auktionsverk #880/R est:100000-125000 (S.KR 260000)

Works on paper

£532 $841 €798 Still life of jug (24x19cm-9x7in) init.d.24 pencil crayon. 28-Apr-3 Bukowskis, Stockholm #33/R (S.KR 7000)
£1141 $1802 €1712 Still life of table and vase (25x20cm-10x8in) s.d.1924 pencil. 28-Apr-3 Bukowskis, Stockholm #38/R est:12000-15000 (S.KR 15000)

OLSON, George Wallace (1876-1938) American

£569 $950 €825 Landscape (61x76cm-24x30in) s. 17-Jun-3 John Moran, Pasadena #97a est:1200-2000
£710 $1100 €1065 Sycamores in landscape (61x46cm-24x18in) s. 29-Oct-2 John Moran, Pasadena #697
£1032 $1600 €1548 Cottage in foothill flower fields (61x76cm-24x30in) s. 29-Oct-2 John Moran, Pasadena #696 est:1500-2000
£1398 $2250 €2097 California landscape (61x76cm-24x30in) s. prov. 18-Feb-3 John Moran, Pasadena #167 est:1500-2250

OLSON, Nils (1891-1953) Swedish

£420 $651 €630 Winter landscape (38x28cm-15x11in) d.1945. 2-Nov-2 Hogben, Folkstone #240

OLSON, Ragnar (?-1949) American?
£355 $550 €533 Spring in Washington (51x61cm-20x24in) s.d.38. 8-Dec-2 Uppsala Auktionskammare, Uppsala #229 (S.KR 5000)

OLSON, Victor (20th C) American
Works on paper
£264 $425 €396 Woman emerges from tent, aims rifle at big game hunter (48x74cm-19x29in) s. gouache en grisaille. 20-Feb-3 Illustration House, New York #127/R

OLSSON, Gottfrid (1890-1979) Scandinavian
£276 $425 €414 Village scene with men talking by fisherman's cottage, Skaane (46x55cm-18x22in) s,. 27-Oct-2 Anders Antik, Landskrona #29/R (S.KR 4000)

OLSSON, Julius (1864-1942) British
£380 $597 €570 Seascape (61x75cm-24x30in) s. 16-Dec-2 Bonhams, Bury St Edmunds #468
£700 $1092 €1050 Off the Isle of Wight (25x33cm-10x13in) s. i.verso board. 12-Sep-2 Sotheby's, Olympia #105/R
£750 $1223 €1125 Riverside cottage in a winter landscape at night (61x76cm-24x30in) s. 13-Feb-3 Christie's, Kensington #156
£893 $1410 €1340 Seascape (34x46cm-13x18in) s. board. 18-Nov-2 Joel, Victoria #303 est:1500-2500 (A.D 2500)
£950 $1549 €1425 Sunlit sea, Seaford (33x43cm-13x17in) s. 28-Jan-3 Gorringes, Lewes #1783
£3600 $5652 €5400 Moonlight on breakers (71x81cm-28x32in) s. 10-Dec-2 Lane, Penzance #245/R est:3500-5000
£3600 $5616 €5220 Cross swell (44x60cm-17x24in) s. 27-Mar-3 Lane, Penzance #155/R est:3000-4000
£5000 $7750 €7500 Sunlight on breaking waves (160x193cm-63x76in) s. 26-Sep-2 Lane, Penzance #215/R est:5000-6000
£6206 $10054 €8999 The golden shore - coast near St Ives with mermaids (124x182cm-49x72in) s. 25-May-3 Uppsala Auktionskammare, Uppsala #120/R est:30000-40000 (S.KR 80000)

OLSSON, Julius (attrib) (1864-1942) British
£976 $1385 €1600 Sunset (33x46cm-13x18in) s. board. 5-Mar-2 Thomas Adams, Dublin #333

OLSSON, Mats Anders (19th C) Swedish
£1699 $2820 €2464 When I'm in the desert with Jesus (94x108cm-37x43in) 16-Jun-3 Lilla Bukowskis, Stockholm #891 est:6000 (S.KR 22000)

OLSSON-HAGALUND, Olle (1904-1972) Swedish
£5186 $8090 €7779 The grocer's shop (33x41cm-13x16in) s. 6-Nov-2 AB Stockholms Auktionsverk #631/R est:80000-100000 (S.KR 74000)
£6097 $9511 €9146 From Haga (48x52cm-19x20in) s. 6-Nov-2 AB Stockholms Auktionsverk #583/R est:80000-100000 (S.KR 87000)
£6552 $10090 €9828 The launching of Dagmar Salen at Oresund ship-yard, Landskrona (50x64cm-20x25in) s. 27-Oct-2 Anders Antik, Landskrona #125/R est:100000-125000 (S.KR 95000)
£15444 $24865 €23166 The yellow twist biscuit (76x91cm-30x36in) s. exhib. 7-May-3 AB Stockholms Auktionsverk #702/R est:400000-500000 (S.KR 200000)
£21724 $33889 €32586 The red fence (38x46cm-15x18in) s. painted 1960s exhib. 5-Nov-2 Bukowskis, Stockholm #178c/R est:130000-150000 (S.KR 310000)
£22814 $36046 €34221 Karlbergs Palace (54x65cm-21x26in) s. 28-Apr-3 Bukowskis, Stockholm #92/R est:300000-350000 (S.KR 300000)
£23574 $37247 €35361 The white house in Hagalund (50x61cm-20x24in) s. 28-Apr-3 Bukowskis, Stockholm #178/R est:300000-350000 (S.KR 310000)
£27799 $44757 €41699 Crayfish-feast in Hagalund (54x80cm-21x31in) s. exhib. 7-May-3 AB Stockholms Auktionsverk #758/R est:450000-500000 (S.KR 360000)
£29344 $47243 €44016 The artist's studio - scene from Hagalund (50x61cm-20x24in) s. painted 1960s exhib.lit. 7-May-3 AB Stockholms Auktionsverk #677/R est:350000-400000 (S.KR 380000)
£31939 $50464 €47909 Vartan - Stockholm's harbour area (57x66cm-22x26in) s. lit. 28-Apr-3 Bukowskis, Stockholm #147a/R est:300000-350000 (S.KR 420000)

Works on paper
£1542 $2405 €2313 Hagalund at sunset (23x33cm-9x13in) s.d.37 gouache pencil dr verso. 6-Nov-2 AB Stockholms Auktionsverk #579/R est:20000-25000 (S.KR 22000)
£3364 $5247 €5046 Street in town (30x34cm-12x13in) s. W/C. 6-Nov-2 AB Stockholms Auktionsverk #528/R est:30000-40000 (S.KR 48000)
£3802 $6008 €5703 Street scene in autumn, Hagalund (50x63cm-20x25in) s. gouache. 28-Apr-3 Bukowskis, Stockholm #2/R est:50000-60000 (S.KR 50000)
£3854 $6013 €5781 Gustav III's pavillion, Haga Park (31x41cm-12x16in) s. gouache. 5-Nov-2 Bukowskis, Stockholm #167/R est:80000-100000 (S.KR 55000)
£4867 $7690 €7301 Still life of flowers (53x41cm-21x16in) s.i.d.6/7 1968 mixed media. 28-Apr-3 Bukowskis, Stockholm #1/R est:50000-70000 (S.KR 64000)
£4867 $7690 €7301 The fish and fruit shop, Hagalund (23x31cm-9x12in) s.i. gouache. 28-Apr-3 Bukowskis, Stockholm #3/R est:40000-50000 (S.KR 64000)
£6738 $10443 €10107 Girl with red jo-jo, the artist's daughter (64x45cm-25x18in) s. mixed media paper on canvas exhib. 8-Dec-2 Uppsala Auktionskammare, Uppsala #249/R est:100000-150000 (S.KR 95000)
£9886 $15620 €14829 Oresund boat builders, Landskrona, launching of the ship Dagmar Salen (50x61cm-20x24in) s. gouache exhib. 28-Apr-3 Bukowskis, Stockholm #88/R est:100000-125000 (S.KR 130000)

OLSTED, P (1824-1887) Danish
£422 $659 €633 View of Lyngby Lake (20x26cm-8x10in) s.d.1861. 23-Sep-2 Rasmussen, Vejle #72/R (D.KR 5000)

OLSTED, Peter (1824-1887) Danish
£574 $930 €861 Biert Church between Haderslep and Kolding (24x30cm-9x12in) s.d.1856. 21-May-3 Museumsbygningen, Copenhagen #1/R (D.KR 6000)
£1723 $2618 €2585 Large stone monument by fjord (64x85cm-25x33in) s.d.1853. 27-Aug-2 Rasmussen, Copenhagen #1414/R est:20000 (D.KR 20000)
£2756 $4189 €4134 View from Ermelunden towards Gentofte Church (54x80cm-21x31in) s.d.1855. 27-Aug-2 Rasmussen, Copenhagen #1409/R est:35000 (D.KR 32000)

OLVER, Kate Elizabeth (1881-1960) British
£12000 $18960 €18000 In the nursery (160x104cm-63x41in) s. prov.exhib. 26-Nov-2 Christie's, London #161/R est:15000-20000

O'LYNCH OF TOWN, Karl (1869-1942) German
£578 $919 €850 Schirocco on Capri (54x70cm-21x28in) s. i. verso. 20-Mar-3 Neumeister, Munich #2709
£582 $908 €850 In the cliffs (77x100cm-30x39in) s. i. verso. 9-Apr-3 Neumeister, Munich #723
£884 $1406 €1300 Melting snow near Berwang (50x65cm-20x26in) s. i. verso. 20-Mar-3 Neumeister, Munich #2710/R
£897 $1364 €1400 Sailing boat in Dortrecht harbour (70x86cm-28x34in) s. lit. 11-Jul-2 Allgauer, Kempten #2636/R
£962 $1490 €1500 Hilly landscape (42x55cm-17x22in) s. 5-Dec-2 Dorotheum, Graz #35/R est:1500
£1795 $2818 €2800 Mountain village by evening light (82x106cm-32x42in) s. 23-Nov-2 Arnold, Frankfurt #827/R est:1600
£1844 $2987 €2600 Cirocco of Capri (55x70cm-22x28in) s. i.verso. 22-May-3 Dorotheum, Vienna #189/R est:3000-3500
£1899 $3000 €3000 View of Dortrecht harbour (65x50cm-26x20in) s. 28-Nov-2 Dorotheum, Vienna #209/R est:3300-3500
£2564 $3974 €4000 Dutch harbour (70x86cm-28x34in) s. 5-Dec-2 Dorotheum, Graz #34/R est:4000
£3038 $4709 €4800 Fishing boats in Italian harbour (111x120cm-44x47in) s. 25-Sep-2 Neumeister, Munich #689/R est:2600

O'MALLEY, Jane (1944-) Irish
£300 $468 €450 Anemones in a jug (30x20cm-12x8in) s.d.1983 board. 16-Oct-2 David Lay, Penzance #295
£616 $968 €900 Untitled (41x30cm-16x12in) s.d.1981 board. 15-Apr-3 De Veres Art Auctions, Dublin #135/R
£962 $1510 €1500 Evening window by the sea. Morning window by the sea (24x28cm-9x11in) one s.i.d.1985 card pastel pair prov. 19-Nov-2 Whyte's, Dublin #11/R est:2000-2500

Works on paper
£582 $903 €920 Still life, white and ochre (30x42cm-12x17in) s.d.1989 gouache. 24-Sep-2 De Veres Art Auctions, Dublin #141/R

O'MALLEY, Tony (1913-2003) British/Irish
£2911 $4513 €4600 Burren greys (18x26cm-7x10in) init.d.1993 oil on paper prov.exhib. 24-Sep-2 De Veres Art Auctions, Dublin #68a/R est:2500-3500
£3000 $4680 €4500 Black trawler (23x18cm-9x7in) s.i.d.1977 i.verso paper on board. 16-Oct-2 David Lay, Penzance #344/R est:3000-5000
£5696 $8829 €9000 Inscape, Ireland (43x55cm-17x22in) s.i.d.19/3/55 oil on paper. 24-Sep-2 De Veres Art Auctions, Dublin #68/R est:6500-8000
£6507 $10216 €9500 Autumn field (64x52cm-25x20in) s.i.d.10/8/85 oil on paper. 15-Apr-3 De Veres Art Auctions, Dublin #244/R est:9000-12000

£7000 $10920 €10500 Ballykeefe Hill, Callan (51x76cm-20x30in) s.d.1962 s.i.d.verso board. 16-Oct-2 David Lay, Penzance #218/R est:4000-6000
£7000 $10920 €10500 Ship in winter (41x38cm-16x15in) board. 16-Oct-2 David Lay, Penzance #282/R est:4000-6000
£7000 $11620 €10150 Table, winter studio (64x28cm-25x11in) init. s.i.d.1984 verso board. 10-Jun-3 David Lay, Penzance #284/R est:8000-10000
£7671 $12044 €11200 Small spring Inscape (12x46cm-5x18in) init.d.5/86 s.i.d.verso. 15-Apr-3 De Veres Art Auctions, Dublin #200/R est:6000-8000
£8500 $13600 €12750 Garden, morning Bahamas 1982 (33x53cm-13x21in) oil.acrylic collage on board. 16-May-3 Sotheby's, London #144/R est:4000-6000
£10000 $16300 €15000 Work table and silence (38x64cm-15x25in) init. board lit. 13-Feb-3 David Lay, Penzance #442/R est:6000-7000
£10063 $15698 €16000 Spring sky with busy rooks (91x56cm-36x22in) init. i.d.1985 verso oil sand board prov. 17-Sep-2 Whyte's, Dublin #26/R est:15000-20000
£10500 $16380 €15750 Winter Orpheus (61x122cm-24x48in) s. s.i.verso board. 16-Oct-2 David Lay, Penzance #215/R est:5000-8000
£10500 $16380 €15750 Wind lover's morning (61x122cm-24x48in) init. s.i.d.1965 verso board. 16-Oct-2 David Lay, Penzance #216/R est:5000-8000
£10500 $16380 €15750 Winter landscape (122x61cm-48x24in) init. s.i.d.1966 verso board. 16-Oct-2 David Lay, Penzance #217/R est:5000-8000
£11644 $18281 €17000 Bahamas (36x56cm-14x22in) init.d.1/84 oil paper. 15-Apr-3 De Veres Art Auctions, Dublin #113/R est:10000-15000
£15000 $24000 €22500 Eleuthera, Bahamas (76x102cm-30x40in) s.i.d.1977 verso board exhib. 15-May-3 Christie's, London #107/R est:15000-25000
£20548 $32260 €30000 Window with birdsong (92x122cm-36x48in) init.d.5/88 board prov. 15-Apr-3 De Veres Art Auctions, Dublin #152/R est:30000-40000
£22500 $36675 €33750 Lava fields of Lanzarote (122x91cm-48x36in) init. s.i.verso board. 13-Feb-3 David Lay, Penzance #441/R est:14000-16000

Works on paper
£450 $702 €675 Still life with feathers (36x25cm-14x10in) s.d.1980 gouache. 16-Oct-2 David Lay, Penzance #260/R
£800 $1248 €1200 Untitled (25x33cm-10x13in) s.d.1965 bodycol. 16-Oct-2 David Lay, Penzance #341
£1200 $1872 €1800 Bird (23x28cm-9x11in) s.i.d.1967 mixed media. 16-Oct-2 David Lay, Penzance #343 est:1200-1800
£1500 $2340 €2250 Irish rain (18x25cm-7x10in) s.d.1970 i.verso mixed media. 17-Oct-2 David Lay, Penzance #1251 est:400-600
£1772 $2747 €2800 St. Martins (30x41cm-12x16in) init.d.5/75 gouache. 24-Sep-2 De Veres Art Auctions, Dublin #162/R est:3000-4000
£1944 $3092 €2800 Artists table (24x17cm-9x7in) s.d.1978 pastel W/C on board. 29-Apr-3 Whyte's, Dublin #15/R est:3000-4000
£1962 $3041 €3100 Untitled (7x9cm-3x4in) s. ink W/C on card set of five sketches. 25-Sep-2 James Adam, Dublin #64/R est:2000-3000
£2055 $3226 €3000 Still life (18x20cm-7x8in) init.d.9/83 mixed media. 15-Apr-3 De Veres Art Auctions, Dublin #219 est:3000-4000
£2342 $3630 €3700 Untitled (18x20cm-7x8in) init.d.12/75 gouache. 24-Sep-2 De Veres Art Auctions, Dublin #95/R est:2500-3500
£2466 $3871 €3600 Untitled (28x23cm-11x9in) init.d.1968 ink wash. 15-Apr-3 De Veres Art Auctions, Dublin #218 est:3500-4500
£2800 $4368 €4200 Winter sea (48x74cm-19x29in) s.i.verso mixed media. 16-Oct-2 David Lay, Penzance #219/R est:1500-2500
£2800 $4368 €4200 Morning bird and summer morning, Trevaylor (76x46cm-30x18in) init.i.d.1962 i.d.verso mixed media. 16-Oct-2 David Lay, Penzance #284 est:2500-3500
£2848 $4415 €4500 Nassau, Bahamas (22x26cm-9x10in) init.d.12/75 gouache. 24-Sep-2 De Veres Art Auctions, Dublin #163/R est:2500-3500
£3000 $4680 €4500 Birds in springtime (20x30cm-8x12in) s.d.1963 i.d.verso mixed media. 16-Oct-2 David Lay, Penzance #283/R est:800-1400
£3100 $4836 €4650 Untitled (43x53cm-17x21in) s.d.1963 mixed media. 16-Oct-2 David Lay, Penzance #342 est:800-1400
£3151 $4947 €4600 Bird (23x28cm-9x11in) init.i.d.1967 mixed media. 15-Apr-3 De Veres Art Auctions, Dublin #215/R est:4000-6000
£3826 $6159 €5700 Symphony of the ocean (23x30cm-9x12in) init. gouache. 18-Feb-3 Whyte's, Dublin #53/R est:6000-8000
£4247 $6667 €6200 River bed (41x28cm-16x11in) init.d.1981 mixed media prov. 15-Apr-3 De Veres Art Auctions, Dublin #198/R est:4000-6000
£4493 $7368 €6200 Glenmallure (23x31cm-9x12in) s. gouache on card. 28-May-3 Bonhams & James Adam, Dublin #147/R est:4000-6000
£4589 $7205 €6700 Country still life with crow and magpie feathers (28x38cm-11x15in) init.i. s.i.d.1990 verso gouache. 15-Apr-3 De Veres Art Auctions, Dublin #195/R est:4000-6000
£4800 $7488 €7200 Winter table (38x48cm-15x19in) s.i. gouache. 16-Oct-2 David Lay, Penzance #340/R est:2500-3500
£5000 $8000 €7500 Cornish landscape (30x49cm-12x19in) init.d.1963 gouache acrylic wash paper collage prov. 16-May-3 Sotheby's, London #119/R est:6000-8000
£5034 $8104 €7500 Composition for African screen (66x53cm-26x21in) s.d.1966 gouache. 18-Feb-3 Whyte's, Dublin #51/R est:10000-15000
£5769 $9058 €9000 Walking by moonlight (52x16cm-20x6in) init.d.1977 pastel gouache ink board. 19-Nov-2 Whyte's, Dublin #42/R est:12000-15000
£6000 $9360 €9000 Irish landscape (58x41cm-23x16in) s.i.d.1962 gouache newspaper. 16-Oct-2 David Lay, Penzance #231/R est:3000-4000
£9000 $14040 €13500 Spring (64x51cm-25x20in) init.i.d.1985 gouache. 16-Oct-2 David Lay, Penzance #345/R est:4000-6000
£10959 $17205 €16000 Morning bird and summer morning, Trevaylor (32x46cm-13x18in) init.i.d. mixed media prov. 15-Apr-3 De Veres Art Auctions, Dublin #178/R est:8000-12000

OMAN, Valentin (1935-) Austrian
Works on paper
£288 $453 €450 Reclining female nude (34x52cm-13x20in) s.i.d.72 chl. 20-Nov-2 Dorotheum, Klagenfurt #99

OMEGNA, Filippo (1881-1948) Italian
£1923 $3019 €3000 Portrait of girl (170x85cm-67x33in) s. 10-Dec-2 Della Rocca, Turin #391/R

OMENCINI, Eugenio (1939-) Italian
£321 $503 €500 On the quay (25x35cm-10x14in) s.d.1986 acrylic. 23-Nov-2 Meeting Art, Vercelli #453

OMERTH (fl.1895-1925) French
Sculpture
£2200 $3476 €3300 Female figures (28cm-11in) s.num.4951 bronze pair. 14-Nov-2 Christie's, Kensington #281/R est:1000-1500

OMERTH, Georges (fl.1895-1925) French
Sculpture
£2359 $3798 €3350 Danseuse orientale (29x20cm-11x8in) green pat bronze gold ivory marble base. 12-May-3 Lesieur & Le Bars, Le Havre #74
£2449 $3894 €3600 Art Deco figure of geisha with fan (28cm-11in) s. yellow pat bronze ivory. 24-Mar-3 Bernaerts, Antwerp #160/R est:3500-4000

OMICCIOLI, Giovanni (1901-1975) Italian
£321 $503 €500 Fish on the beach (25x32cm-10x13in) s. tempera card on canvas painted 1970. 21-Nov-2 Finarte, Rome #64
£556 $883 €800 Flowers (24x20cm-9x8in) s. cardboard on canvas. 1-May-3 Meeting Art, Vercelli #300
£581 $917 €900 Vase of flowers (51x36cm-20x14in) s. card. 18-Dec-2 Christie's, Rome #219
£822 $1282 €1200 Landscape with hut and canes (30x40cm-12x16in) s. cardboard on canvas. 10-Apr-3 Finarte Semenzato, Rome #163
£946 $1476 €1400 Street in Ischia (25x25cm-10x10in) s. canvas on cardboard. 28-Mar-3 Farsetti, Prato #245
£1026 $1610 €1600 Landscape (40x52cm-16x20in) s. masonite. 19-Nov-2 Finarte, Milan #52
£1027 $1603 €1500 Seascape (25x35cm-10x14in) s.verso. 10-Apr-3 Finarte Semenzato, Rome #142/R
£1149 $1792 €1700 Hut by the sea (50x60cm-20x24in) i.verso card on canvas. 26-Mar-3 Finarte Semenzato, Milan #119/R
£1859 $2919 €2900 Landscape (45x55cm-18x22in) s.d.1940. 19-Nov-2 Finarte, Milan #271/R
£1935 $3058 €3000 Houses and snow (50x70cm-20x28in) s. s.i.verso. 18-Dec-2 Christie's, Rome #73/R
£2436 $3824 €3800 Summer in the field (55x38cm-22x15in) s. painted 1948. 21-Nov-2 Finarte, Rome #193/R
£3425 $5342 €5000 Street in Chianalea (60x45cm-24x18in) s.i.verso. 10-Apr-3 Finarte Semenzato, Rome #130/R

OMMEGANCK, Balthasar Paul (1755-1826) Flemish
£382 $607 €550 Moutons a l'abreuvoir (23x28cm-9x11in) s. panel. 29-Apr-3 Campo, Vlaamse Kaai #237
£1677 $2616 €2516 Evening mood with flock coming home (99x58cm-39x23in) s.d.1807 panel. 11-Apr-3 Kieselbach, Budapest #117/R est:600000 (H.F 600000)
£1702 $2638 €2553 Landscape with sheep (28x35cm-11x14in) s. panel. 4-Dec-2 AB Stockholms Auktionsverk #1916/R est:18000-20000 (S.KR 24000)
£3400 $5304 €5100 Landscape with cattle on a riverbank (37x56cm-15x22in) s.d.1785 panel. 10-Apr-3 Christie's, Kensington #126/R est:3000-5000
£3548 $5500 €5322 Landscape with cows watering and shepherds mending a fence (30x43cm-12x17in) s. panel. 2-Oct-2 Christie's, Rockefeller NY #169/R est:6000-8000
£4717 $7264 €7500 Herdsmen with sheep in a landscape (42x53cm-17x21in) s.d.1811 panel. 22-Oct-2 Sotheby's, Amsterdam #65/R est:7000-9000

OMMEGANCK, Balthasar Paul (attrib) (1755-1826) Flemish
£833 $1267 €1300 Sheep and goats with young herder asleep (38x46cm-15x18in) panel. 11-Jul-2 Hugo Ruef, Munich #764

ONDERDONK, Julian (1882-1922) American
£2885 $4500 €4328 Twilight, Staten Island (10x18cm-4x7in) panel. 19-Oct-2 David Dike, Dallas #124/R est:5000-7000
£3205 $5000 €4808 Woods scene (15x23cm-6x9in) panel painted c.1908. 19-Oct-2 David Dike, Dallas #263/R est:5000-7000
£3548 $5500 €5322 Through the woods. s. s.i.verso board painted c.1915 prov. 8-Dec-2 Toomey, Oak Park #704/R est:8000-10000

£3799 $5850 €5699 Rising moon (10x18cm-4x7in) s. s.i.d.1909 verso panel prov. 24-Oct-2 Shannon's, Milford #24/R est:6000-8000
£3846 $6000 €5769 Woodland pool (15x23cm-6x9in) panel. 19-Oct-2 David Dike, Dallas #263a est:6000-8000
£4487 $7000 €6731 Evening landscape (15x23cm-6x9in) panel. 19-Oct-2 David Dike, Dallas #163/R est:5000-7000
£7051 $11000 €10577 Landscape (23x30cm-9x12in) board. 19-Oct-2 David Dike, Dallas #264/R est:12000-14000
£7186 $12000 €10420 Landscape with lady on a pathway and cattle (36x51cm-14x20in) s. 22-Jun-3 Freeman, Philadelphia #109/R est:5000-8000
£44872 $70000 €67308 Cactus in bloom, San Antonio, Texas 1918 (64x76cm-25x30in) 19-Oct-2 David Dike, Dallas #125a est:60000-80000

Works on paper

£6410 $10000 €9615 Mexican woman washing at old aqueduct near Mission San Juan (25x30cm-10x12in) gouache W/C. 19-Oct-2 David Dike, Dallas #126/R est:12000-15000

ONDERDONK, Robert Jenkins (1853-1917) American

Works on paper

£5449 $8500 €8174 Alamo in 1870 (15x18cm-6x7in) W/C painted 1885. 19-Oct-2 David Dike, Dallas #174/R est:6000-8000
£6164 $9000 €9246 Cattle in pasture with wagon in background (28x18cm-11x7in) pastel. 18-May-2 Altermann Galleries, Santa Fe #210/R

ONDREICKA, Karol (1904-1971) Czechoslovakian

£473 $671 €710 At bonfire (44x48cm-17x19in) painted 1931. 26-Mar-2 SOGA, Bratislava #12/R (SL.K 30000)

ONDREICKA, Peter (1947-) Czechoslovakian

£441 $644 €662 Salamander (51x40cm-20x16in) 4-Jun-2 SOGA, Bratislava #271/R est:12000 (SL.K 28000)
£473 $732 €710 Salamander (51x40cm-20x16in) 1-Oct-2 SOGA, Bratislava #252/R est:22000 (SL.K 30000)
£536 $782 €804 Mozartiana (70x70cm-28x28in) 4-Jun-2 SOGA, Bratislava #270/R est:28000 (SL.K 34000)
£1500 $2325 €2250 Hommage a Rembrant (160x130cm-63x51in) painted 1989-90. 3-Dec-2 SOGA, Bratislava #268/R est:95000 (SL.K 95000)

ONDRUSEK, Franz (1861-1932) Hungarian

£341 $552 €494 Portrait of an old lady (33x25cm-13x10in) s.d.1905 panel. 24-May-3 Dorotheum, Prague #49/R est:15000-23000 (C.KR 15000)

O'NEILL, Daniel (1920-1974) British

£4500 $7200 €6750 Bathers, homage to Rouault (23x35cm-9x14in) s.i.verso board prov. 15-May-3 Christie's, London #89/R
£6164 $9678 €9000 Moonlight (51x61cm-20x24in) s. board prov.exhib. 15-Apr-3 De Veres Art Auctions, Dublin #226/R est:9000-12000
£6800 $11152 €10200 Portrait of a young girl (46x36cm-18x14in) board. 3-Jun-3 Sotheby's, Olympia #249/R est:4000-6000
£9500 $15200 €14250 Western family (51x66cm-20x26in) s. canvas on board. 16-May-3 Sotheby's, London #83/R est:10000-15000
£10000 $16000 €15000 Girl sitting in her flat overlooking Belfast (51x61cm-20x24in) s. i.verso board prov. 15-May-3 Christie's, London #90/R est:10000-15000
£10274 $16130 €15000 Evening (36x44cm-14x17in) s. i.verso board prov. 15-Apr-3 De Veres Art Auctions, Dublin #165 est:15000-20000
£10870 $17826 €15000 Cornfield (50x68cm-20x27in) s. board. 28-May-3 Bonhams & James Adam, Dublin #127/R est:15000-20000
£11392 $17658 €18000 Harbour at dusk (43x68cm-17x27in) s. board. 24-Sep-2 De Veres Art Auctions, Dublin #90/R est:18000-22000
£13423 $21611 €20000 Fortress (61x91cm-24x36in) s. i.verso board prov. 18-Feb-3 Whyte's, Dublin #118/R est:20000-30000
£15068 $23658 €22000 White house (61x44cm-24x17in) s. i.verso board. 15-Apr-3 De Veres Art Auctions, Dublin #149/R est:18000-22000
£17123 $26884 €25000 Reclining figure (36x54cm-14x21in) s. i.verso board prov. 15-Apr-3 De Veres Art Auctions, Dublin #140/R est:25000-35000
£17500 $27825 €26250 Bath (50x40cm-20x16in) s. board. 5-Mar-3 John Ross, Belfast #146 est:22000-25000
£17722 $27468 €28000 One man band (61x41cm-24x16in) s. board prov. 25-Sep-2 James Adam, Dublin #77/R est:15000-20000
£18493 $29034 €27000 On the way home (49x66cm-19x26in) s. s.i.verso board prov. 15-Apr-3 De Veres Art Auctions, Dublin #157/R est:25000-35000
£25000 $40000 €37500 Couple (48x61cm-19x24in) s. board. 16-May-3 Sotheby's, London #89/R est:25000-35000
£28481 $44146 €45000 After dinner (55x63cm-22x25in) s. i.verso board. 24-Sep-2 De Veres Art Auctions, Dublin #81/R est:45000-60000

Works on paper

£1090 $1711 €1700 Madonna window - Christmas card (13x8cm-5x3in) s.i. pen ink W/C painted c.1954 prov. 19-Nov-2 Whyte's, Dublin #39 est:1000-1200
£1268 $2104 €1800 Coastal landscape (23x16cm-9x6in) s. W/C. 10-Jun-3 James Adam, Dublin #262/R est:1000-1500

O'NEILL, George Bernard (1828-1917) Irish

£8500 $13770 €12325 Tolling the bell (24x29cm-9x11in) s. panel. 29-Jul-3 Henry Adams, Chichester #561/R est:4000-6000
£12000 $19080 €18000 Little gardener (35x45cm-14x18in) s. 18-Mar-3 Bonhams, New Bond Street #65/R est:12000-18000
£12602 $19785 €18903 Gardner and his friends (41x51cm-16x20in) s. 10-Dec-2 Pinneys, Montreal #62 est:20000-25000 (C.D 31000)
£20000 $32200 €30000 Jury (63x100cm-25x39in) s.d.1854 panelprov.exhib.lit. 20-Feb-3 Christie's, London #315/R est:35000
£24000 $37920 €36000 Sympathy (46x35cm-18x14in) s. panel prov. 26-Nov-2 Christie's, London #130/R est:15000-25000
£24000 $37920 €36000 Hanging the mistletoe (30x25cm-12x10in) s.d.1892 panel. 26-Nov-2 Christie's, London #131/R est:18000-25000

Works on paper

£2500 $4025 €3750 Study (43x30cm-17x12in) pencil chk prov. 20-Feb-3 Christie's, London #316/R

O'NEILL, Henry (1798-1880) British

Works on paper

£460 $731 €690 Study of a fallen tree (20x36cm-8x14in) s.d.71 W/C. 25-Feb-3 Bonhams, Knightsbridge #168/R

O'NEILL, Henry Nelson (1817-1880) British

£6000 $9480 €9000 Letter writer (71x52cm-28x20in) mono.d.1860 panel prov.exhib.lit. 2-Dec-2 Sotheby's, London #22/R est:6000-8000
£20000 $33200 €30000 Consulting the astrologer (61x91cm-24x36in) s.d.1849 exhib.lit. 10-Jun-3 Christie's, London #126/R est:20000-30000

O'NEILL, Henry Nelson (attrib) (1817-1880) British

£1667 $2633 €2600 Home coming (61x49cm-24x19in) canvas on board. 12-Nov-2 Mealy's, Castlecomer #1031

O'NEILL, Liam (20th C) Irish

£616 $968 €900 Musicians. 15-Apr-3 De Veres Art Auctions, Dublin #70

O'NEILL, Mark (1963-) Irish?

£2192 $3441 €3200 Georgian blue (41x28cm-16x11in) s.d.1998 board prov. 15-Apr-3 De Veres Art Auctions, Dublin #100v est:2000-3000
£2264 $3532 €3600 Venice, Tuesday's colours (55x64cm-22x25in) s.d.1999 board prov. 17-Sep-2 Whyte's, Dublin #218/R est:3000-4000
£2464 $4041 €3400 Still life study of a robe on a chair (57x50cm-22x20in) s.d.1997 board. 28-May-3 Bonhams & James Adam, Dublin #101/R est:2200-2800
£2899 $4754 €4000 Young woman at a window (47x37cm-19x15in) s.d.1995. 28-May-3 Bonhams & James Adam, Dublin #60/R est:3000-4000
£3333 $5467 €4600 Venice side canal calm (47x37cm-19x15in) s.d.1999 board prov. 28-May-3 Bonhams & James Adam, Dublin #100/R est:2500-3500

O'NEILL, Rose (1875-1944) American

Works on paper

£1090 $1700 €1635 Little boy and parents, father holding carriage reins (48x56cm-19x22in) s. pencil. 9-Nov-2 Illustration House, New York #66/R est:2000-3000
£1090 $1700 €1635 Boy drills hole in fence of ballfield for enthusiastic girl to watch baseball (36x41cm-14x16in) s. pencil. 9-Nov-2 Illustration House, New York #91/R est:2000-3000

O'NEILL, Tom (1950-) British

Works on paper

£250 $395 €375 Eyes I dare not meet in dreams (59x39cm-23x15in) s.i. W/C. 27-Nov-2 Sotheby's, Olympia #157/R

ONG, Jimmy (1964-) Singaporean

Works on paper

£2720 $4487 €3944 Shear hero (127x226cm-50x89in) s.d.99 chl exhib. 6-Jul-3 Christie's, Hong Kong #48/R est:30000-40000 (HK.D 35000)

ONGANIA, Umberto (19th C) Italian

Works on paper

£650 $1053 €975 Santa Maria della Salute, Venice (29x18cm-11x7in) s. pencil W/C. 23-Jan-3 Christie's, Kensington #330

ONGENAE, Joseph (1921-1993) Belgian

£4937 $7800 €7800 Shivaki II (97x51cm-38x20in) s. i.d.1958/59 verso board. 26-Nov-2 Sotheby's, Amsterdam #280/R est:2500-3000

ONKEN, Karl (1846-1934) German

£3165 $5000 €5000 View of Waidhofen/Ybbs (61x83cm-24x33in) 28-Nov-2 Dorotheum, Vienna #129/R est:5000-6000

ONLEY, Toni (1928-) Canadian
£386 $603 €560 Ethereal landscape (51x65cm-20x26in) s.i.d.1967 panel prov. 26-Mar-3 Walker's, Ottawa #465/R est:900-1200 (C.D 900)
£556 $883 €834 Active pass (48x61cm-19x24in) s. i.verso acrylic collage board. 6-Mar-3 Heffel, Vancouver #26/R (C.D 1300)
Works on paper
£522 $820 €783 Kluane Lake at Condon Creek, Alaska Highway (26x38cm-10x15in) s.i.d.1990 W/C. 25-Nov-2 Hodgins, Calgary #319/R (C.D 1300)

ONNES, Harm Henrick Kamerlingh (1893-1985) Dutch
£340 $551 €480 Mother and her child holding hands and walking in the town (29x23cm-11x9in) init.d.50 board. 26-May-3 Glerum, Amsterdam #264/R
£719 $1180 €1000 Pension herta after the fire (60x40cm-24x16in) init.d.34. 3-Jun-3 Christie's, Amsterdam #44/R est:1000-1500
£955 $1490 €1500 Conversation (31x37cm-12x15in) s. panel. 5-Nov-2 Vendu Notarishuis, Rotterdam #120/R est:1500-2000
£1042 $1719 €1500 Dahlias in a ginger jar (32x27cm-13x11in) mono.d.sept.44. 1-Jul-3 Christie's, Amsterdam #355 est:1500-2000
£1250 $2063 €1800 Autumn leaves (28x32cm-11x13in) mono. 1-Jul-3 Christie's, Amsterdam #353 est:1200-1600
£2885 $4471 €4500 Stad bij avond (39x53cm-15x21in) s. painted c.1916 lit. 3-Dec-2 Christie's, Amsterdam #1/R est:5000-7000
£3901 $6319 €5500 Dune landscape with balloon (50x59cm-20x23in) s.d.59 board prov.exhib. 26-May-3 Glerum, Amsterdam #263/R est:1800-2200
£5036 $8259 €7000 Harwich (32x66cm-13x26in) mono.d.65 i.d.verso board prov. 3-Jun-3 Christie's, Amsterdam #1/R est:3000-5000
Works on paper
£526 $853 €800 On the trampoline (19x29cm-7x11in) init.d.71 W/C gouache sold with another by same hand. 21-Jan-3 Christie's, Amsterdam #477
£590 $974 €850 At the barber's (24x24cm-9x9in) mono.d.75 pastel ballpoint. 1-Jul-3 Christie's, Amsterdam #358

ONOSATO, Toshinobu (1912-1986) Japanese
Works on paper
£692 $1100 €1038 Abstract (15x20cm-6x8in) s.d.63 W/C pencil. 18-Mar-3 Doyle, New York #61/R

ONSAGER, Soren (1878-1946) Norwegian
£1184 $1871 €1776 Archipelago (50x60cm-20x24in) s. 17-Dec-2 Grev Wedels Plass, Oslo #260/R est:8000-10000 (N.KR 13500)
£1558 $2384 €2337 Brook in winter (87x77cm-34x30in) s. painted 1936. 26-Aug-2 Blomqvist, Lysaker #1295/R est:20000-25000 (N.KR 18000)
£1915 $3064 €2873 Autumn by the fjord, possibly Soon (57x84cm-22x33in) s.d.20 i.stretcher. 17-Mar-3 Blomqvist, Oslo #386/R est:25000-30000 (N.KR 22000)
£2655 $4195 €3983 Interior scene with two women (85x99cm-33x39in) 28-Apr-3 Blomqvist, Oslo #361/R est:40000-60000 (N.KR 30000)
£3540 $5593 €5310 Three generations (88x118cm-35x46in) s.d.35. 28-Apr-3 Blomqvist, Oslo #360/R est:70000-90000 (N.KR 40000)
£5585 $8768 €8378 Young girl (75x52cm-30x20in) s.indis.d.1938 exhib. 21-Nov-2 Grev Wedels Plass, Oslo #87/R est:60000-80000 (N.KR 64000)

ONSLOW-FORD, Edward (1852-1901) British
Sculpture
£6040 $9724 €9000 Ivy, bust of a young girl (39cm-15in) s.d. bronze. 18-Feb-3 Sotheby's, Amsterdam #312/R est:4500-7500
Works on paper
£319 $533 €450 Composition (30x22cm-12x9in) s.d. ink. 23-Jun-3 Claude Boisgirard, Paris #119

ONSLOW-FORD, Gordon (1912-) British
£19178 $30110 €28000 Untitled (73x92cm-29x36in) s.d.XXXVIII prov.exhib.lit. 15-Apr-3 Laurence Calmels, Paris #4383/R est:3000
Works on paper
£6849 $10753 €10000 Propaganda for love (61x48cm-24x19in) s.d.1940 gouache ink. 15-Apr-3 Laurence Calmels, Paris #4384/R est:1200

ONTANI, Luigi (1943-) Italian
Sculpture
£10256 $15897 €16000 Ecce Homo (32x23cm-13x9in) s.i.d.1982 verso num.9/85 painted wood exhib.lit. 4-Dec-2 Finarte, Milan #485/R est:20000

ONUS, Lin (1948-1996) Australian
£1434 $2179 €2151 Frosty morning (56x71cm-22x28in) s. canvas on composition board. 28-Aug-2 Deutscher-Menzies, Melbourne #185/R est:4500-6500 (A.D 4000)
Works on paper
£2867 $4358 €4301 Evening reflections (49x37cm-19x15in) s. synthetic polymer paint paper on board. 28-Aug-2 Deutscher-Menzies, Melbourne #164/R est:9500-12000 (A.D 8000)
£3200 $5152 €4640 Bulla djerriwa - two lizards (27x63cm-11x25in) s. gouache executed c.1995 prov. 12-May-3 Joel, Victoria #271 est:8000-10000 (A.D 8000)
£3386 $5554 €5079 Butterflies and wattle (49x37cm-19x15in) s. synthetic polymer paint paper on board. 4-Jun-3 Deutscher-Menzies, Melbourne #185/R est:6000-9000 (A.D 8500)
£4107 $6489 €6161 Yorta yorta language group frogs and lilies (49x37cm-19x15in) s. gouache on board. 27-Nov-2 Deutscher-Menzies, Melbourne #83/R est:9000-12000 (A.D 11500)
£4286 $6771 €6429 Yorta yorta language group butterflies (49x37cm-19x15in) s. gouache on board. 27-Nov-2 Deutscher-Menzies, Melbourne #82/R est:9000-12000 (A.D 12000)
£12500 $19500 €18750 Frog at Bullita crossing (91x121cm-36x48in) s. synthetic polymer paint canvas. 11-Nov-2 Deutscher-Menzies, Melbourne #48/R est:20000-30000 (A.D 35000)
£14286 $22429 €21429 Untitled (91x152cm-36x60in) s. synthetic polymer paint prov. 25-Nov-2 Christie's, Melbourne #42/R est:35000-50000 (A.D 40000)
£15000 $23700 €22500 Fish and waterlillies with evening reflections (60x121cm-24x48in) s. synthetic polymer on canvas. 27-Nov-2 Deutscher-Menzies, Melbourne #28/R est:28000-30000 (A.D 42000)

OOLEN, Adriaen van (?-1694) Dutch
£3800 $6194 €5510 Cockerels and ornamental fowl in a landscape (91x73cm-36x29in) 21-Jul-3 Sotheby's, London #91/R est:2000-3000

OOMS, Karel (1845-1900) Belgian
£570 $889 €900 Homer playing the harp with girl near a porch (38x28cm-15x11in) s.d.1866 panel. 21-Oct-2 Bernaerts, Antwerp #91/R

OORSCHOT, Dorus van (1910-1989) Dutch
£255 $397 €400 Moored barge (59x79cm-23x31in) s. 5-Nov-2 Vendu Notarishuis, Rotterdam #171
£478 $745 €750 Washing the dishes (48x59cm-19x23in) s. 5-Nov-2 Vendu Notarishuis, Rotterdam #53/R
£634 $1020 €900 Poppies (52x53cm-20x21in) s. 6-May-3 Vendu Notarishuis, Rotterdam #147
£915 $1474 €1300 Kitchen garden (49x59cm-19x23in) s. 6-May-3 Vendu Notarishuis, Rotterdam #153/R

OOST, Jacques van (elder) (1601-1671) Belgian
£19231 $29808 €30000 Portrait de Pieter Pruyssenaere (117x91cm-46x36in) s. 4-Dec-2 Libert, Castor, Paris #46/R est:30000
£73718 $114263 €115000 Young man studying (120x143cm-47x56in) 6-Dec-2 Maigret, Paris #89/R est:30000-40000

OOST, Jacques van (elder-circle) (1601-1671) Belgian
£9000 $15030 €13050 Holy Family with infant Saint John the Baptist (63x47cm-25x19in) panel. 11-Jul-3 Christie's, Kensington #95/R est:8000-12000
£26000 $40820 €39000 Five Senses (88x126cm-35x50in) 11-Dec-2 Christie's, London #34/R est:14000-18000

OOSTEN, Izaack van (1613-1661) Flemish
£15000 $23400 €22500 River landscape with stag hunt. River landscape with fox hunt (39x52cm-15x20in) init. panel oval pair. 10-Apr-3 Sotheby's, London #6/R est:15000
£19231 $30385 €30000 Landscapes with figures (30x19cm-12x7in) mono. panel pair. 13-Nov-2 Marc Kohn, Paris #26/R est:27000-30000
£40000 $62800 €60000 Landscape with wagon and figures passing through a village (40x71cm-16x28in) s. panel. 12-Dec-2 Sotheby's, London #9/R est:40000-60000

OOSTERDIJCK, Wybrant van (attrib) (fl.1665-1668) Dutch
£1800 $2790 €2700 Portrait of a gentleman, in black velvet robe with lace collar (28x22cm-11x9in) s.d.1677. 30-Oct-2 Bonhams, New Bond Street #112/R est:2000-3000

OOSTERHOUDT, Dirk van (1756-1830) Flemish
£2548 $3924 €4000 Portrait of Mr van Wessem. Portrait of Mrs van Wessem (63x52cm-25x20in) one s. pair. 3-Sep-2 Christie's, Amsterdam #132 est:800-1200

OOSTERLYNCK, Jean (1915-) Belgian
£382 $607 €550 Vue sur la Provence (30x40cm-12x16in) s. 29-Apr-3 Campo & Campo, Antwerp #237
£823 $1284 €1300 Fenaison (158x200cm-62x79in) s.d.69. 15-Oct-2 Horta, Bruxelles #309

OPALKA, Roman (1931-) Polish
£36000 $60120 €52200 1965/ 1-oo detail 2232834-2250960 (196x135cm-77x53in) s.i.verso acrylic prov. 26-Jun-3 Sotheby's, London #138/R est:30000-40000
£38000 $58520 €57000 1965/ 1 - detail 2010496-2032877 (195x135cm-77x53in) s.i. acrylic painted 1976 prov.exhib. 22-Oct-2 Sotheby's, London #323/R est:25000-35000
£48000 $78720 €72000 1965/1-00 detail 2032878-2053278 (196x135cm-77x53in) init.verso acrylic prov.exhib. 7-Feb-3 Sotheby's, London #143/R est:25000-35000

OPDAHL, Ornulf (1944-) Norwegian
£541 $843 €800 Slipsmenn (63x63cm-25x25in) s. oil mixed media painted 1981. 26-Mar-3 Peschetau-Badin Godeau & Leroy, Paris #27
Works on paper
£570 $901 €855 Landscape from Godoya (44x61cm-17x24in) s.d.1981 pencil W/C. 17-Dec-2 Grev Wedels Plass, Oslo #261/R (N.KR 6500)

OPDENHOFF, George Willem (1807-1873) Dutch
£577 $911 €900 Voiliers au port (32x39cm-13x15in) s. panel. 18-Nov-2 Tajan, Paris #55
£3871 $6000 €5807 Coastal scene with fishermen (30x38cm-12x15in) panel. 7-Dec-2 South Bay, Long Island #132/R
£4452 $6990 €6500 Unload the catch (31x42cm-12x17in) s. panel. 15-Apr-3 Sotheby's, Amsterdam #12/R est:7000-10000
£7547 $11623 €12000 Bringing the catch on board (47x67cm-19x26in) s. prov. 23-Oct-2 Christie's, Amsterdam #134/R est:12000-16000

OPHEY, Walter (1882-1930) German
£759 $1200 €1200 Couple by castle moat by moonlight (37x46cm-15x18in) panel. 29-Nov-2 Villa Grisebach, Berlin #828/R
£3205 $4968 €5000 Near Drevenack (60x81cm-24x32in) s. i. stretcher. 4-Dec-2 Lempertz, Koln #956/R est:6000
£5797 $9507 €8000 Blossom on trees in Zons (61x56cm-24x22in) s. mono. verso exhib.lit. 29-May-3 Lempertz, Koln #835/R est:7000-8000
£10145 $16638 €14000 House in park (66x65cm-26x26in) 29-May-3 Lempertz, Koln #836/R est:15000
Works on paper
£652 $1070 €900 Boats in harbour (39x47cm-15x19in) s. chk. 29-May-3 Lempertz, Koln #838/R
£1449 $2377 €2000 Rhine near Neuss (36x46cm-14x18in) s. pastel chk. 29-May-3 Lempertz, Koln #837/R est:2000

OPIE, Edward (1810-1894) British
£550 $897 €798 Portrait of the artist's niece Joanna, in profile (42x33cm-17x13in) i.d.November 15th 1831. 21-Jul-3 Sotheby's, London #566 est:400-600
£2000 $3340 €2900 Content (65x56cm-26x22in) s.d.1885. 17-Jun-3 Bonhams, New Bond Street #96/R est:2000-3000

OPIE, John (1761-1807) British
£1178 $1932 €1708 Portrait of man (52x42cm-20x17in) 4-Jun-3 AB Stockholms Auktionsverk #2505/R est:8000-10000 (S.KR 15000)
£1600 $2496 €2400 Portrait of Dr Sayer of Norwich (75x61cm-30x24in) prov. 18-Sep-2 Cheffins Grain & Comins, Cambridge #536/R est:1000-1500
£2800 $4312 €4200 Portrait of Samuel Favell, long bust length (76x63cm-30x25in) 9-Sep-2 Bonhams, Ipswich #115/R est:3000-5000

OPIE, John (attrib) (1761-1807) British
£4200 $6930 €6090 Portrait of a boy (61x51cm-24x20in) 2-Jul-3 Sotheby's, Olympia #57/R est:2000-3000

OPISSO, Alfredo (1907-1980) Spanish
£3288 $5129 €4800 Vase of flowers (92x72cm-36x28in) s. 8-Apr-3 Ansorena, Madrid #222/R est:4800
Works on paper
£597 $932 €950 Kiosk (24x31cm-9x12in) s. pastel. 8-Oct-2 Ansorena, Madrid #440/R
£1447 $2257 €2300 Circus figures (33x45cm-13x18in) s. pencil W/C dr. 8-Oct-2 Ansorena, Madrid #476/R

OPISSO, Ricardo (1880-1966) Spanish
Works on paper
£331 $540 €500 Man (21x14cm-8x6in) s.i.d.1905 pastel dr. 11-Feb-3 Segre, Madrid #365/R
£331 $523 €480 Cry (14x19cm-6x7in) s. W/C. 1-Apr-3 Segre, Madrid #381/R
£577 $906 €900 Granny and girl (23x18cm-9x7in) s. pencil dr lit. 19-Nov-2 Castellana, Madrid #507/R
£1097 $1733 €1700 Drunkards (42x54cm-17x21in) s. pastel. 18-Dec-2 Ansorena, Madrid #357/R

OPITZ, Franz Karl (1916-) Swiss
Works on paper
£472 $746 €708 Patmos stone (28x37cm-11x15in) s.i.verso pastel. 29-Nov-2 Zofingen, Switzerland #3017 (S.FR 1100)

OPITZ, Georg Emanuel (1775-1841) German
Works on paper
£500 $780 €750 Russian family wearing traditional dress (46x35cm-18x14in) s.i. W/C. 14-Apr-3 Hamilton Osborne King, Dublin #1417/R
£608 $949 €900 Marchand de coco (31x26cm-12x10in) s. graphite pen ink W/C prov. 27-Mar-3 Christie's, Paris #164/R
£1096 $1710 €1600 Progresser des idess liberales (36x26cm-14x10in) s.i. gouache W/C. 11-Apr-3 Winterberg, Heidelberg #507/R
£3000 $4710 €4500 Tobogganing down the ice mountain (48x37cm-19x15in) s. W/C over pencil. 20-Nov-2 Sotheby's, London #1/R est:2000-3000

OPPEL, Lisel (1897-1960) German
£4422 $7031 €6500 Garden on the Weyerberg (60x50cm-24x20in) s.d.47 i. verso panel. 28-Mar-3 Bolland & Marotz, Bremen #360/R est:8500

OPPENHEIM, Dennis (1938-) American
Works on paper
£500 $800 €750 An armature for projection from the fire works series -2 (96x127cm-38x50in) s.d.1981 gouache ink pencil. 18-May-3 Butterfields, Los Angeles #7059
£833 $1325 €1200 Study for virus (130x95cm-51x37in) s.d.1988 mixed media. 29-Apr-3 Artcurial Briest, Paris #513/R
£1220 $2000 €1769 Study for impersonation station, proposal for police precinct (246x211cm-97x83in) s.d.1988 pencil col pencil oil prov. 1-Jun-3 Wright, Chicago #353/R est:3000-5000
£2500 $4075 €3750 Between drinks (500x700cm-197x276in) fibreglass confetti executed 1991 prov.exhib. 3-Feb-3 Sotheby's, Olympia #102/R est:2500-3500
£2532 $4000 €4000 Study for wine glasses dancing back to back, industrial buffing disks (193x128cm-76x50in) s.d.1988 W/C pastel crayon. 26-Nov-2 Sotheby's, Amsterdam #311/R est:4000-5000

OPPENHEIM, Meret (1913-1986) Swiss
£15753 $24575 €23000 Lune, soleil et oeuf (22x29cm-9x11in) mono.d.53. 14-Apr-3 Laurence Calmels, Paris #4051/R est:6000
£47210 $74592 €70815 Tout toujours (90x104cm-35x41in) mono.i.d.1950 s. verso prov.lit. 28-Nov-2 Christie's, Zurich #96/R est:80000-120000 (S.FR 110000)
Works on paper
£1218 $1888 €1900 Parrot tulips (29x42cm-11x17in) mono.d. i.d. verso W/C over pencil. 7-Dec-2 Ketterer, Hamburg #626/R est:2100-2300

OPPENHEIM, Moritz Daniel (1800-1882) German
£4460 $7137 €6200 Young woman holding candle (72x56cm-28x22in) s. 17-May-3 Lempertz, Koln #1453/R est:5000

OPPENHEIM, Yves (1948-) French
£3061 $4867 €4500 Landscape 20 (200x150cm-79x59in) painted 1986 exhib. 24-Mar-3 Cornette de St.Cyr, Paris #159/R

OPPENHEIMER, Charles (1875-1961) British
£720 $1130 €1080 Whitby old town and abbey (55x45cm-22x18in) board. 19-Nov-2 Bonhams, Leeds #167
£9500 $14725 €14250 Kirkcudbright (46x61cm-18x24in) s. 31-Oct-2 Christie's, London #164/R est:4000-6000
Works on paper
£420 $655 €630 Winter sea and peaks (22x28cm-9x11in) s. W/C. 17-Oct-2 Bonhams, Edinburgh #186
£750 $1170 €1125 Italian hill town (56x40cm-22x16in) s. W/C. 17-Oct-2 Bonhams, Edinburgh #189
£750 $1245 €1088 Dee, Galloway (38x55cm-15x22in) s. W/C. 13-Jun-3 Lyon & Turnbull, Edinburgh #38

OPPENHEIMER, Josef (1876-1966) German
£380 $635 €551 Marble Arch, Kensington (18x23cm-7x9in) s.i.d.28 two in one frame. 17-Jun-3 Bonhams, Knightsbridge #61/R

£870 $1400 €1305 Portrait of Henry Pfungst examining an Oriental idol (86x81cm-34x32in) s.i.d.1907. 19-Jan-3 Jeffery Burchard, Florida #60/R
£1300 $2119 €1885 Portrait of two young children (112x93cm-44x37in) s. 15-Jul-3 Bonhams, Knightsbridge #181/R est:1500-2000
£1400 $2170 €2100 Pier on the beach, Heringsdorf (25x33cm-10x13in) panel prov. 4-Dec-2 Christie's, Kensington #418 est:200-300
Works on paper
£310 $484 €465 Half-length portrait of Miss Epstein (55x41cm-22x16in) s.i.d.1903 col chk. 17-Sep-2 Bearnes, Exeter #504

OPPENHEIMER, Max (1885-1954) Austrian
£2402 $3747 €3603 Etude pour piano par J B Cramer (22x27cm-9x11in) i. i. stretcher prov. 6-Nov-2 Dobiaschofsky, Bern #867/R est:7500 (S.FR 5500)
Works on paper
£529 $788 €794 Portrait of Pestalozzi (18x13cm-7x5in) mono. chl W/C. 25-Jun-2 Koller, Zurich #6698/R (S.FR 1200)
£2830 $4415 €4500 Violin quintet (26x33cm-10x13in) s.d.1949 mixed media board lit. 20-Sep-2 Schloss Ahlden, Ahlden #1324/R est:4500

OPPENOORTH, Willem (1847-1905) Dutch
£347 $552 €500 Fin de jour (28x17cm-11x7in) s. panel. 30-Apr-3 Tajan, Paris #64
£1083 $1689 €1700 Farmer on the polder lake (94x63cm-37x25in) s. prov. 6-Nov-2 Vendue Huis, Gravenhage #497/R est:1500-2000
£1316 $2132 €2000 Man and his dog on a day's outing (47x61cm-19x24in) s. 21-Jan-3 Christie's, Amsterdam #140/R est:2000-3000

OPPO, Cipriano Efisio (1891-1962) Italian
£3425 $5342 €5000 Still life (30x47cm-12x19in) s. board. 10-Apr-3 Finarte Semenzato, Rome #255/R

OPSOMER, Isidore (1878-1967) Belgian
£1019 $1590 €1600 Shady spot under trees by entrance gate (63x131cm-25x52in) s. 6-Nov-2 Vendue Huis, Gravenhage #41/R est:700-900
£1384 $2131 €2200 Petit pont sur canal a Lierre (55x55cm-22x22in) s. panel. 22-Oct-2 Campo & Campo, Antwerp #207/R
£1589 $2591 €2400 Entree du chateau (65x133cm-26x52in) s. 17-Feb-3 Horta, Bruxelles #161/R
£2222 $3533 €3200 Maison pre de l'eau (45x55cm-18x22in) s.d.1944 panel. 29-Apr-3 Campo & Campo, Antwerp #238/R est:1600-2000
£2276 $3641 €3300 King Albert in military uniform (130x102cm-51x40in) s. prov.lit. 15-Mar-3 De Vuyst, Lokeren #233/R est:3000-3500

ORAM, Ann (1956-) British
£420 $655 €630 Compotier of fruit (29x26cm-11x10in) s.d.94. 10-Apr-3 Bonhams, Edinburgh #4
Works on paper
£580 $899 €870 Spanish compote of fruit (53x66cm-21x26in) s.d.98. 24-Sep-2 Anderson & Garland, Newcastle #398/R
£1800 $2790 €2700 Seville (102x109cm-40x43in) s.d.94 W/C. 24-Sep-2 Anderson & Garland, Newcastle #399/R est:1200-2000
£1850 $2868 €2775 Flowers from my father's garden (103x104cm-41x41in) s.d.98 W/C. 24-Sep-2 Anderson & Garland, Newcastle #397/R est:1500-2500

ORAN, Ahmet (1957-) ?
£3472 $5521 €5000 Yagliboya/Tahta (180x100cm-71x39in) s.d.1999 verso panel lit. 29-Apr-3 Wiener Kunst Auktionen, Vienna #499/R est:4000-7000

ORANGE, Maurice Henri (1868-1916) French
Works on paper
£710 $1121 €1100 Kremlin under siege (19x20cm-7x8in) s. W/C. 17-Dec-2 Segre, Madrid #4/R

ORANT, Marthe (1874-1953) French
£645 $1019 €1000 Pivoines au vase vert (54x45cm-21x18in) s. cardboard. 19-Dec-2 Ruellan, Paris #38/R
£755 $1208 €1133 Chez l'artiste (41x35cm-16x14in) s. panel lit. 17-Mar-3 Philippe Schuler, Zurich #4645/R (S.FR 1600)
Works on paper
£417 $679 €600 La chapelle en bord de riviere (36x52cm-14x20in) s. pastel. 19-Jul-3 Thierry & Lannon, Brest #288

ORAZI, Manuel (1860-1934) French
Prints
£3000 $4770 €4500 Theatre de Loie exposition universelle (200x64cm-79x25in) col lithograph lit. 27-Feb-3 Sotheby's, Olympia #78/R est:1500-2500

ORBAN, Desiderius (1884-1986) Hungarian
£571 $886 €857 Still life, flowers (63x47cm-25x19in) s. 29-Oct-2 Lawson Menzies, Sydney #158 (A.D 1600)
£581 $918 €872 Olvasok II (68x85cm-27x33in) s. i.verso. 27-Nov-2 Deutscher-Menzies, Melbourne #144/R est:3000-5000 (A.D 1625)
£1076 $1667 €1614 Hills by the river (24x30cm-9x12in) s. board. 6-Dec-2 Kieselbach, Budapest #13/R (H.F 400000)
£1956 $3052 €2934 Mediterranean courtyard (50x40cm-20x16in) s. 11-Apr-3 Kieselbach, Budapest #56/R est:200000-700000 (H.F 700000)
£2064 $3220 €3096 Grove (52x70cm-20x28in) s. 11-Sep-2 Kieselbach, Budapest #145/R (H.F 800000)
£2515 $3923 €3773 Bunch of flowers in blue vase (66x50cm-26x20in) s. 11-Apr-3 Kieselbach, Budapest #172/R est:800000-900000 (H.F 900000)
£2689 $4168 €4034 Paris (38x47cm-15x19in) s. 6-Dec-2 Kieselbach, Budapest #33/R (H.F 1000000)
£4751 $7411 €6889 Venice (66x51cm-26x20in) s.d.1923. 12-Apr-3 Mu Terem Galeria, Budapest #80/R est:1600000 (H.F 1700000)
£11178 $17437 €16208 Lonely tree (72x97cm-28x38in) s. 12-Apr-3 Mu Terem Galeria, Budapest #99/R est:3800000 (H.F 4000000)
£20000 $32800 €30000 Blue lagoon (55x69cm-22x27in) s.d.1913. 3-Jun-3 Sotheby's, London #78/R est:25000-35000
£21514 $33347 €32271 Still life of fruit (60x80cm-24x31in) s. 6-Dec-2 Kieselbach, Budapest #151/R (H.F 8000000)
£26893 $41683 €38995 Still life of fruit (47x60cm-19x24in) s. panel. 9-Dec-2 Mu Terem Galeria, Budapest #215/R est:3500000 (H.F 10000000)
Works on paper
£500 $790 €750 Bronte Beach (48x62cm-19x24in) s. pastel. 26-Nov-2 Sotheby's, Melbourne #109/R est:1200-1800 (A.D 1400)
£500 $795 €750 Lines of thought (48x64cm-19x25in) s.d.1964 pastel exhib. 4-Mar-3 Deutscher-Menzies, Melbourne #264/R (A.D 1300)

ORBAN, Gabor (1798-1855) Hungarian
£394 $610 €591 Self portrait (22x16cm-9x6in) wood painted c.1845. 1-Oct-2 SOGA, Bratislava #112/R est:25000 (SL.K 25000)
Works on paper
£284 $439 €426 Abraham and Sara (35x26cm-14x10in) Indian ink W/C. 1-Oct-2 SOGA, Bratislava #113/R est:18000 (SL.K 18000)

ORCHARD, Ken (1959-) Australian
Works on paper
£992 $1647 €1438 Entrance to the Onkaparing Gorge (27x129cm-11x51in) s.d.2002 ink pastel. 10-Jun-3 Shapiro, Sydney #61 est:1500-2500 (A.D 2500)

ORCHARDSON, Sir William Quiller (1832-1910) British
£70000 $112700 €105000 Queen of the swords (84x135cm-33x53in) s.d.77 prov. 19-Feb-3 Christie's, London #9/R est:100000-150000
Works on paper
£400 $636 €600 Cattle watering in upland landscape (30x36cm-12x14in) mono.d.1864 W/C. 29-Apr-3 Peter Francis, Wales #43

ORCHART, Stanley (?) ?
£380 $623 €570 Late autumn mist near Woburn (51x61cm-20x24in) s.d.1960 i.verso. 5-Jun-3 Christie's, Kensington #810/R
£600 $936 €900 Arncliffe church (69x89cm-27x35in) s. 18-Oct-2 Keys, Aylsham #568
Works on paper
£330 $535 €495 Cambridge (48x58cm-19x23in) s. W/C gouache. 21-May-3 James Thompson, Kirby Lonsdale #81

ORCZY, Emina Baronne de (1865-?) Hungarian/British
£440 $717 €660 Elegant party watching a play (50x75cm-20x30in) s. 17-Feb-3 Bonhams, Bath #114

ORD, Joseph Biays (1805-1865) American
£5696 $9000 €8544 Still life with fruit (38x46cm-15x18in) s.d.1854 panel. 26-Apr-3 Thomaston Place, Thomaston #45

ORDWAY, Alfred (1819-1897) American
£297 $475 €431 Pond Road, Wayland (34x25cm-13x10in) s. i.verso board. 16-May-3 Skinner, Boston #63/R
£1226 $1900 €1839 Autumnal landscape with pumpkins (53x61cm-21x24in) s. 2-Nov-2 Thomaston Place, Thomaston #20

O'REILLY, Patrick (20th C) Irish
£833 $1308 €1300 Landscape with green fields (51x76cm-20x30in) s.i.d.1995 verso. 19-Nov-2 Whyte's, Dublin #21 est:1500-2000
Sculpture
£1519 $2354 €2400 Crow (42cm-17in) bronze. 24-Sep-2 De Veres Art Auctions, Dublin #136/R est:1500-2500
£2215 $3434 €3500 Married couple in their garden (46x23cm-18x9in) bronze. 24-Sep-2 De Veres Art Auctions, Dublin #135/R est:2500-3500

£3562 $5592 €5200 Striding horse II (112x56cm-44x22in) bronze. 15-Apr-3 De Veres Art Auctions, Dublin #248/R est:3500-4500
£3904 $6129 €5700 Why God why (143cm-56in) bronze. 15-Apr-3 De Veres Art Auctions, Dublin #249/R est:4500-5500

O'REILLY, Rosemary (20th C) Irish
£411 $641 €600 Coliemore Harbour (40x50cm-16x20in) s. canvasboard. 8-Apr-3 James Adam, Dublin #132/R

ORELL, Argio (1884-1942) Italian
£1026 $1590 €1600 Trieste from the terrace (38x45cm-15x18in) s.d.1908 cardboard. 5-Dec-2 Stadion, Trieste #775/R
Works on paper
£705 $1093 €1100 My mouth is as fresh as a cherry (34x42cm-13x17in) s. s.i.d.1932 verso col pastel. 5-Dec-2 Stadion, Trieste #855

ORELLANA, Gaston (1933-) Chilean
£1763 $2785 €2750 Figures (160x160cm-63x63in) exhib. 19-Nov-2 Durán, Madrid #171/R

OREN, John Clarkson (?) British?
Works on paper
£420 $638 €630 Rocky Cornish castal scene with distant shipping (43x33cm-17x13in) s. W/C. 16-Aug-2 Keys, Aylsham #310

ORFEI, Orfeo (19th C) Italian
£1594 $2614 €2200 Suonatore ambulante (28x15cm-11x6in) s.d.1872 panel. 27-May-3 Finarte, Milan #121/R est:1500-1700
£14194 $22000 €21291 Afternoon tipple (55x45cm-22x18in) s. 30-Oct-2 Christie's, Rockefeller NY #120/R est:10000-15000

ORGAN, Robert (1933-) British
£380 $604 €570 On the Croisette (45x60cm-18x24in) 18-Mar-3 Bonhams, Knightsbridge #165

ORI, Luciano (1928-) Italian
£385 $604 €600 Composition with cards and shadows (50x70cm-20x28in) cardboard. 20-Nov-2 Pandolfini, Florence #91/R
£481 $755 €750 Formal composition (80x70cm-31x28in) s.i.d.61 verso masonite prov. 20-Nov-2 Pandolfini, Florence #85/R

ORIANI, Pippo (1909-1972) Italian
£897 $1409 €1400 Villa at the seaside (50x60cm-20x24in) s. 10-Dec-2 Della Rocca, Turin #336/R
£2482 $4021 €3500 Bottiglia e chitarra (50x70cm-20x28in) s. s.i.verso oil collage prov. 26-May-3 Christie's, Milan #359/R est:4000-6000

ORIENTAL SCHOOL
£6552 $10417 €9500 Odalisque devant le Nil (81x126cm-32x50in) bears sig. 7-Mar-3 Rabourdin & Choppin de Janvry, Paris #35/R

ORIENTAL SCHOOL, 19th C
£26415 $40679 €42000 Pacha fumant le hookah (82x104cm-32x41in) 23-Oct-2 Rabourdin & Choppin de Janvry, Paris #83/R est:12000-15000
Works on paper
£5597 $8620 €8900 Port de Tripoli (30x43cm-12x17in) i. W/C. 23-Oct-2 Rabourdin & Choppin de Janvry, Paris #70/R

ORIOLA, Nora (1925-) Italian
£516 $800 €774 Venetian mariner, Zanni (41x30cm-16x12in) s. panel. 28-Sep-2 Charlton Hall, Columbia #374/R

ORIX, Bill (1900-1983) Belgian
£278 $442 €400 Composition (92x73cm-36x29in) s.d.1952. 29-Apr-3 Campo, Vlaamse Kaai #243

ORKIN, Ruth (1921-1985) American
Photographs
£1829 $3000 €2744 White trees (77x51cm-30x20in) s.i.d. col chromogenic print. 10-Feb-3 Swann Galleries, New York #82/R est:4000-5000
£2308 $3600 €3462 The last big peace march - Central Park West (23x34cm-9x13in) s.i. silver. 21-Oct-2 Swann Galleries, New York #221/R est:2500-3500
£3374 $5500 €5061 American girl in Florence, Italy (22x34cm-9x13in) s.i.d.1951/1970 gelatin silver print. 12-Feb-3 Christie's, Rockefeller NY #261/R est:6000-8000

ORLEY, Barend van (studio) (c.1492-1542) Flemish
£17000 $26520 €25500 Portrait of the Emperor Charles V (33x25cm-13x10in) i. pa. 10-Apr-3 Sotheby's, London #13/R est:15000
Works on paper
£5449 $8446 €8500 Visiting the farm (39x29cm-15x11in) pen ink wash over crayon. 4-Dec-2 Piasa, Paris #29/R
£10897 $16891 €17000 Hunting (34x31cm-13x12in) pen ink wash over crayon. 4-Dec-2 Piasa, Paris #30/R est:23000

ORLIK, Emil (1870-1932) Czechoslovakian
£1812 $2971 €2500 Villa with garden (38x42cm-15x17in) s. canvas on board. 31-May-3 Villa Grisebach, Berlin #125/R est:3000-4000
£2564 $3974 €4000 Still life of apples (33x44cm-13x17in) s.d.19. 4-Dec-2 Lempertz, Koln #957/R est:3000
£3103 $4903 €4500 Two Japanese women (52x36cm-20x14in) s. panel. 2-Apr-3 Dr Fritz Nagel, Stuttgart #9512/R est:2800
£3597 $5755 €5000 Portrait of Franz Marc (50x40cm-20x16in) s. i. stretcher. 15-May-3 Neumeister, Munich #324/R est:5000-7000
£4430 $6867 €7000 Two female nudes (50x75cm-20x30in) s.d.1913 prov. 28-Sep-2 Ketterer, Hamburg #75/R est:5000-7000
£8696 $14261 €12000 Still life of flowers (99x80cm-39x31in) s.d.18 prov. 31-May-3 Villa Grisebach, Berlin #266/R est:12000-16000
Works on paper
£411 $650 €650 Accordion player (20x26cm-8x10in) s. chk sold with anther. 29-Nov-2 Villa Grisebach, Berlin #829/R
£769 $1192 €1200 Still life of flowers in Chinese vase (45x30cm-18x12in) s.i.d.1.VII.17 W/C pen over pencil. 4-Dec-2 Lempertz, Koln #959/R
£797 $1307 €1100 Portrait of woman wearing hat (37x28cm-15x11in) s. gouache col chks pencil. 31-May-3 Villa Grisebach, Berlin #647/R
£1517 $2397 €2200 Two women on steamer (33x34cm-13x13in) s.d. gouache chl board. 2-Apr-3 Dr Fritz Nagel, Stuttgart #9513/R est:2000

ORLOFF, Alexander (1899-1979) Polish
£686 $1125 €1050 Spring (24x33cm-9x13in) s. 9-Feb-3 Bukowskis, Helsinki #424/R
£2000 $3240 €3000 Landscape spring and summer (21x35cm-8x14in) s. oil on card two. 21-May-3 Sotheby's, London #80/R est:3000-5000

ORLOFF, Chana (1878-1968) French
£263 $413 €410 Snow (73x50cm-29x20in) s. 22-Nov-2 Millon & Associes, Paris #139
£449 $704 €700 Bouquet de fleurs (60x49cm-24x19in) s. s.d.1958 verso. 22-Nov-2 Millon & Associes, Paris #137
Sculpture
£1667 $2733 €2300 Macha Skibin (45cm-18in) s.d.45 dark pat.bronze Cast.Alexis Rudier Fondeur Paris exhib. 29-May-3 Lempertz, Koln #841/R est:2300
£6115 $10029 €8500 Danseuse (58cm-23in) s.d.1939 terracotta lit. 3-Jun-3 Piasa, Paris #41/R est:8000-10000
£11392 $18000 €17088 Baigneuse nu couche (21x47cm-8x19in) s.d.1930 bronze st.f.Suisse prov.lit. 27-Apr-3 Sotheby's, Tel Aviv #61/R est:18000-25000
£50360 $80576 €70000 Torse (10x24x17cm-4x9x7in) s.d.1918 cement stone prov.exhib.lit. 15-May-3 Sotheby's, Paris #185/R

ORLOV, K (19th C) Russian
£1500 $2430 €2250 Pilgrims outside the cathedral of Saint Sofia, Kiev (66x47cm-26x19in) s. canvas on board. 21-May-3 Sotheby's, London #98 est:1500-2000

ORLOWSKI, Alexander (1777-1832) Polish
£7000 $10990 €10500 The Hay Market, St Petersburg (42x54cm-17x21in) board lit. 20-Nov-2 Sotheby's, London #4/R est:8000-10000
Works on paper
£3200 $5344 €4640 Oriental horseman holding a standard (35x27cm-14x11in) red chk ink wash. 8-Jul-3 Christie's, London #112/R est:2000-3000

ORLOWSKI, Vladimir (1842-1914) Russian
£28205 $44282 €44000 Carpet makers in the Caucasus (81x125cm-32x49in) s.cyrillic d.1866. 21-Nov-2 Van Ham, Cologne #1853/R est:2000

ORME, William (fl.1790-1820) British
Works on paper
£950 $1511 €1425 Shipping on the River Ghaghara, Faizabad, India (42x58cm-17x23in) W/C after Thomas and Wiliam Daniell prov. 29-Apr-3 Bonhams, New Bond Street #59/R

ORMSBY, J W (19th C) British
Works on paper
£400 $636 €600 Corfu from Govina, Greece (25x36cm-10x14in) s.i.d.1889 W/C. 29-Apr-3 Bonhams, New Bond Street #124a

OROSZ, Gellert (1919-2002) Hungarian
£619 $966 €898 Geometric shapes (50x60cm-20x24in) s.d.76. 13-Sep-2 Mu Terem Galeria, Budapest #124/R est:180000 (H.F 240000)
Works on paper
£1187 $1851 €1721 Glass mountain (30x42cm-12x17in) s.d.59 i.verso mixed media lit. 13-Sep-2 Mu Terem Galeria, Budapest #127/R est:240000 (H.F 460000)

OROZCO, Gabriel (1962-) Mexican
Photographs
£1899 $3000 €2849 Pathway (41x51cm-16x20in) s.i.d.1996 c-print prov. 13-Nov-2 Sotheby's, New York #484/R
£2452 $3800 €3678 Tinaco (41x51cm-16x20in) s.d.1999 num.4/5 verso cibachrome print prov. 26-Sep-2 Christie's, Rockefeller NY #847/R est:2000-3000
£2581 $4000 €3872 Relos humedo (51x41cm-20x16in) s.d.1993 num.2/5 cibachrome print prov. 26-Sep-2 Christie's, Rockefeller NY #862/R est:3000-5000
£2710 $4200 €4065 Ladrillo en Varillas - wire holding bricks (41x51cm-16x20in) s.d.1993 num.5/5 verso color coupler print prov. 26-Sep-2 Christie's, Rockefeller NY #841/R est:3000-5000
£2710 $4200 €4065 Autumn umbrella (41x51cm-16x20in) s.d.1993 verso cibachrome print prov. 26-Sep-2 Christie's, Rockefeller NY #845/R est:3000-5000
£5484 $8500 €8226 Turista Malvo (57x71cm-22x28in) s.i.d.1991 num.2/5 verso cibachrome print prov.exhib.lit. 26-Sep-2 Christie's, Rockefeller NY #840/R est:5000-7000
Works on paper
£3956 $6250 €5934 Time bubbles (10x15cm-4x6in) ink on c-print exec.1995 exhib. 13-Nov-2 Sotheby's, New York #485/R

OROZCO, Jose Clemente (1883-1949) Mexican
£195122 $320000 €282927 Acordadas y zapatistas (61x74cm-24x29in) s.d.Dec 9 1941 masonite prov. 27-May-3 Sotheby's, New York #9
Works on paper
£675 $1100 €1013 Prostitute (25x18cm-10x7in) pencil. 31-Jan-3 Douglas, South Deerfield #15
£1282 $2000 €1923 Untitled (36x29cm-14x11in) s. chl. 14-Oct-2 Butterfields, San Francisco #2133/R est:2500-3500
£2404 $3750 €3606 Untitled (29x41cm-11x16in) s. brush india ink. 5-Nov-2 Doyle, New York #22/R est:3000-4000
£3205 $5000 €4808 Velada (34x50cm-13x20in) s. i.verso W/C prov. 14-Sep-2 Weschler, Washington #655/R est:8000-12000
£7643 $12000 €11465 Nude (63x48cm-25x19in) s. i.verso chl double-sided. 19-Nov-2 Sotheby's, New York #81/R est:15000

ORPEN, Bea (1913-1980) British
Works on paper
£641 $1006 €1000 Spinner's house, Dunleavy, co Donegal. Marble hill (27x36cm-11x14in) s. W/C pair. 19-Nov-2 Hamilton Osborne King, Dublin #469
£1342 $2161 €2000 Gulls flying by rocky cliffs on a fine day (37x52cm-15x20in) s.d.1937 W/C. 18-Feb-3 Whyte's, Dublin #198/R est:1000-1500

ORPEN, Richard Caulfield (1863-1938) British
Works on paper
£451 $718 €650 Study of men in a public house (28x38cm-11x15in) mono. W/C over pencil. 29-Apr-3 Whyte's, Dublin #81/R

ORPEN, Sir William (1878-1931) Irish
£3500 $5600 €5250 Portrait of Mr Francis Henry Edward Livesay (112x86cm-44x34in) s. prov. 16-May-3 Sotheby's, London #66/R est:3000-5000
£120000 $192000 €180000 Edge of the cliff, Howth (50x61cm-20x24in) s. panel prov.exhib.lit. 16-May-3 Sotheby's, London #58/R est:80000-120000
£150000 $249000 €225000 Painter, self portrait with glasses (92x70cm-36x28in) painted 1907 prov.exhib.lit. 11-Jun-3 Christie's, London #19/R est:150000-250000
£200000 $320000 €300000 Portrait of Mrs Ella Fry (51x40cm-20x16in) s.d.1904. 16-May-3 Sotheby's, London #61/R est:50000-80000
£650000 $1040000 €975000 Gardenia Saint George on donkey (96x91cm-38x36in) s. painted 1910 prov.exhib.lit. 15-May-3 Christie's, London #56/R est:800000-1200000
£820000 $1312000 €1230000 Mrs St. George (216x119cm-85x47in) s. on overlap. 16-May-3 Sotheby's, London #57/R est:500000-700000
Works on paper
£903 $1435 €1300 Study for Swinton family portrait (28x22cm-11x9in) pen ink prov.exhib. 29-Apr-3 Whyte's, Dublin #83/R est:1500-1800
£950 $1520 €1425 Study of a lady (23x18cm-9x7in) chl prov.exhib. 15-May-3 Christie's, Kensington #148/R
£1042 $1656 €1500 Female nude with study of a man's head (23x18cm-9x7in) pencil dr. prov.exhib. 29-Apr-3 Whyte's, Dublin #100/R est:2000-3000
£1233 $1936 €1800 Zink my dear etc (25x21cm-10x8in) i. ink wash dr. 15-Apr-3 De Veres Art Auctions, Dublin #162/R est:1500-2000
£1522 $2496 €2100 Illustrated letter to his wife (32x51cm-13x20in) s. pen ink. 28-May-3 Bonhams & James Adam, Dublin #135/R est:1500-2000
£1538 $2415 €2400 Noll posing as an Eygptian (28x23cm-11x9in) mono.i. pencil dr prov. 19-Nov-2 Whyte's, Dublin #56/R est:2000-3000
£1575 $2473 €2300 Female nude study (23x18cm-9x7in) pencil exhib. 15-Apr-3 De Veres Art Auctions, Dublin #191/R est:1500-2000
£1800 $2880 €2700 Your damned whisky is finished (18x23cm-7x9in) i. pen ink prov. 15-May-3 Christie's, London #59/R
£2200 $3520 €3300 Getting more intimate with the rabbit (33x23cm-13x9in) i. pen ink W/C prov. 15-May-3 Christie's, London #58/R est:3500
£2264 $3532 €3600 Kildare street club (20x33cm-8x13in) i. pen black ink prov. 17-Sep-2 Whyte's, Dublin #50/R est:3000-4000
£5000 $8000 €7500 Self-portrait (28x22cm-11x9in) s.d.95 red chk exhib. 15-May-3 Christie's, Kensington #150/R est:5000-7000
£10968 $17000 €16452 Portrait of a kneeling boy (46x32cm-18x13in) s. pencil ink. 29-Oct-2 Sotheby's, New York #153/R est:6000-8000
£47000 $74730 €70500 Furniture painter (40x35cm-16x14in) s. pencil col wash. 29-Apr-3 Sworder & Son, Bishops Stortford #364/R est:5000-8000
£85000 $136000 €127500 Grace and Mary (33x49cm-13x19in) s.d.1910 pencil W/C prov. 15-May-3 Christie's, London #57/R est:40000-60000

ORR, Joseph (1949-) American
£449 $700 €674 Late snowfall (30x41cm-12x16in) s. i.verso prov. 9-Nov-2 Santa Fe Art, Santa Fe #237/R
£3194 $5175 €4631 Pecos palette (61x76cm-24x30in) acrylic. 23-May-3 Altermann Galleries, Santa Fe #174
£3205 $5000 €4808 Road to Lamy (61x76cm-24x30in) 9-Nov-2 Altermann Galleries, Santa Fe #201

ORR, Stewart (1872-1944) British
Works on paper
£1600 $2496 €2400 Traigh Nan Siolag, Iona (32x39cm-13x15in) s. W/C prov. 14-Apr-3 Sotheby's, London #117/R est:800-1200

ORRENTE, Pedro (1570-1644) Spanish
£25641 $40513 €40000 Adoration of the shepherds (157x117cm-62x46in) 13-Nov-2 Ansorena, Madrid #136/R est:40000

ORRENTE, Pedro (attrib) (1570-1644) Spanish
£4403 $6780 €7000 L'adoration des bergers. L'adoration des mages (58x56cm-23x22in) pair. 25-Oct-2 Tajan, Paris #12/R est:7500-10000

ORROCK, James (1829-1913) British
£800 $1312 €1200 Cattle resting in a wooded valley (61x91cm-24x36in) 29-May-3 Christie's, Kensington #98/R
Works on paper
£360 $587 €522 On the Downs near Brighton (39x66cm-15x26in) pencil W/C. 16-Jul-3 Sotheby's, Olympia #37/R
£380 $616 €570 Brighton (18x25cm-7x10in) init.i.d.1861 pencil W/C. 21-May-3 Christie's, Kensington #451/R
£400 $636 €600 Near Ludlow, Salop (34x48cm-13x19in) s.i. W/C. 27-Feb-3 Bonhams, Chester #407
£500 $780 €750 Barnbogle Castle, from the Forth (49x74cm-19x29in) s.i. W/C. 17-Oct-2 Bonhams, Edinburgh #213
£550 $919 €798 Near Milford, Surrey (21x49cm-8x19in) s.d.1897 pencil W/C. 26-Jun-3 Mellors & Kirk, Nottingham #785/R
£600 $1002 €870 Off Hindhead not Minehead from the Hog's back (90x130cm-35x51in) s.i.d.1910 blk chk W/C htd scratching out. 17-Jun-3 Rosebery Fine Art, London #471
£900 $1494 €1350 Caernarvon Castle, Wales (39x58cm-15x23in) s. W/C. 12-Jun-3 Bonhams, New Bond Street #650/R
£950 $1558 €1425 Landscape with border tower (23x33cm-9x13in) s. W/C. 7-Feb-3 Biddle & Webb, Birmingham #273
£1050 $1733 €1523 Barfield Mill. Bury, Sussex (18x47cm-7x19in) s.i. one d.1895 W/C pair. 2-Jul-3 Sotheby's, Olympia #346/R est:1200-1800
£2800 $4592 €4200 Bradgate Park, Leicestershire (59x97cm-23x38in) s.d.1893 s.i.d.verso pen ink W/C prov. 6-Jun-3 Christie's, London #95/R est:1500-2000

ORSELLI, Arturo (19th C) Italian
£1384 $2200 €2076 Suitor (61x51cm-24x20in) s. painted c.1880. 4-May-3 Treadway Gallery, Cincinnati #486/R est:3000-5000

ORSI, Lelio (1511-1587) Italian
Works on paper
£11000 $18370 €15950 Caryatid. Telamon (19x5cm-7x2in) pen brown ink two. 9-Jul-3 Sotheby's, London #5/R est:7000-9000

ORSI, Michel Angelo (19th C) Italian
£2800 $4340 €4200 Madonna della Sedia (84x73cm-33x29in) i. panel tondo after Raffaello Santi. 30-Oct-2 Bonhams, New Bond Street #145/R est:2000-3000

ORTEGA IBARRA, Hector (1950-) Spanish
£1169 $1706 €1800 Man by window (100x81cm-39x32in) s. s.i.d.1988 verso. 17-Jun-2 Ansorena, Madrid #77/R

ORTEGA, Epifanio (20th C) Mexican
£535 $850 €776 Still life (51x61cm-20x24in) s.d. 4-May-3 Treadway Gallery, Cincinnati #622/R

ORTEGA, Juan (?) Spanish
£755 $1177 €1200 Dance (50x61cm-20x24in) s. canvas on board. 23-Sep-2 Durán, Madrid #153/R

ORTH, Benjamin (1803-1875) German
£552 $877 €800 Portraits of Dr Wilhelm Zais and his wife Adolphine (77x65cm-30x26in) s.d.1865 two. 8-Mar-3 Arnold, Frankfurt #666/R

ORTH, Willy (1889-1976) American/German
£1859 $2900 €2789 Yellow roses (61x91cm-24x36in) 19-Oct-2 David Dike, Dallas #312/R est:3000-6000
£1923 $3000 €2885 White roses and stock with butterfly (61x76cm-24x30in) 19-Oct-2 David Dike, Dallas #241/R est:2500-5000

ORTHNER, Martin (18th C) German
Works on paper
£974 $1500 €1461 Untitled, trompe l'oeils. one s.d.1772 one s.d.1784 W/C gouache one s. W/C vellum three. 23-Oct-2 Doyle, New York #5 est:1000-1500

ORTIZ DE ZARATE, Manuel (1886-1946) French
£333 $550 €480 L'assiette aux legumes (26x32cm-10x13in) s. canvas on panel. 1-Jul-3 Rossini, Paris #112
£506 $800 €800 Elegante a la mantille (81x54cm-32x21in) s. 27-Nov-2 Blanchet, Paris #35/R
£884 $1406 €1300 Nu allonge (50x61cm-20x24in) s. 26-Feb-3 Artcurial Briest, Paris #263
£1844 $3079 €2600 Nature morte au bouquet de roses (46x55cm-18x22in) s. 20-Jun-3 Piasa, Paris #168/R est:2000-3000

ORTIZ, Angeles (1895-1984) Spanish
£1712 $2671 €2500 View of Lake Nahuel Huapi (34x35cm-13x14in) s. cardboard. 8-Apr-3 Ansorena, Madrid #67/R
£2129 $3364 €3300 Head of woman (27x22cm-11x9in) s. painted c.1954. 17-Dec-2 Segre, Madrid #131/R
£6507 $10151 €9500 Lake Mascardi (21x32cm-8x13in) s. cardboard. 8-Apr-3 Ansorena, Madrid #66/R est:950
Works on paper
£353 $557 €550 Mascardi Lake (27x35cm-11x14in) s. pencil ink dr. 19-Nov-2 Durán, Madrid #735/R
£483 $768 €700 House amongst trees (36x40cm-14x16in) s. ink dr. 4-Mar-3 Ansorena, Madrid #423/R

ORTIZ, Emilio (1936-) Mexican
£1763 $2751 €2645 Desdoblamiento (80x100cm-31x39in) s.d.1980. 17-Oct-2 Louis Morton, Mexico #32/R est:30000-34000 (M.P 28000)

ORTIZ, Manuel Angeles (1895-1984) Spanish
Works on paper
£705 $1107 €1100 Personnage cubique (30x21cm-12x8in) s.d.1925 collage chl dr. 16-Dec-2 Eric Coutrier, Paris #86
£1208 $1945 €1800 Shapes (24x35cm-9x14in) s. mixed media collage. 18-Feb-3 Durán, Madrid #158/R

ORTLIEB, Friedrich (1839-1909) German
£1389 $2292 €2000 Harmonious family (61x50cm-24x20in) s.i. 1-Jul-3 Christie's, Amsterdam #14/R est:2500-3500
£1942 $3108 €2700 Young hunter in conversation with girl (65x53cm-26x21in) s. 17-May-3 Lempertz, Koln #1454/R est:3000

ORTMANS, François-Auguste (1827-1884) French
£1277 $1800 €1916 Punting on a lake in autumn (30x38cm-12x15in) s. 12-Feb-2 Lincoln, Orange #468
£2405 $3800 €3800 Vaches a la mare (23x34cm-9x13in) s. panel. 1-Dec-2 Peron, Melun #19

ORTVAD, Erik (1917-) Danish
£593 $919 €890 Concrete composition (44x65cm-17x26in) s.d.1971 verso exhib. 1-Oct-2 Rasmussen, Copenhagen #36a (D.KR 7000)
£1715 $2676 €2573 Figures in landscape (73x91cm-29x36in) init. s.d.1963 verso. 11-Nov-2 Rasmussen, Vejle #131/R est:20000-25000 (D.KR 20000)
£2540 $3937 €3810 Kvanjarp - composition (76x106cm-30x42in) s.d.1963 verso. 1-Oct-2 Rasmussen, Copenhagen #87/R est:30000 (D.KR 30000)
£4234 $6562 €6351 Figures in sunny landscape (56x68cm-22x27in) init. s.d.1942 verso. 1-Oct-2 Rasmussen, Copenhagen #82/R est:50000-70000 (D.KR 50000)
£5027 $7994 €7541 Stiff breeze (76x89cm-30x35in) i.d.1945 verso. 26-Feb-3 Kunsthallen, Copenhagen #39/R est:50000 (D.KR 55000)
£7770 $12122 €11655 Composition (106x92cm-42x36in) init. painted 1948-1949. 18-Sep-2 Kunsthallen, Copenhagen #50/R est:75000 (D.KR 92000)

O'RYAN, Fergus (1911-1989) Irish
£500 $800 €750 Glendalough, Co Wicklow (35x46cm-14x18in) s. board. 15-May-3 Christie's, Kensington #199/R
£616 $968 €900 Dun Laoghaire and Howth from the mountains (24x56cm-9x22in) s.i.verso canvasboard. 15-Apr-3 De Veres Art Auctions, Dublin #32/R
£897 $1409 €1400 Connemara coastal scene (27x34cm-11x13in) s. canvasboard. 19-Nov-2 Hamilton Osborne King, Dublin #435/R
£903 $1435 €1300 Pine forest road (41x47cm-16x19in) s. board. 29-Apr-3 Whyte's, Dublin #199/R est:1800-2200
£940 $1513 €1400 Hazel wood, Kippure, Co Wicklow (30x41cm-12x16in) s. i.verso canvasboard. 18-Feb-3 Whyte's, Dublin #213/R
£1233 $1936 €1800 May day (39x50cm-15x20in) s. canvas on board. 15-Apr-3 De Veres Art Auctions, Dublin #18/R est:2000-3000
£1233 $1936 €1800 Near Renvyle, Connemara (37x50cm-15x20in) s. board. 15-Apr-3 De Veres Art Auctions, Dublin #112/R est:2000-3000
£1370 $2151 €2000 Glendalough, Connemara (38x48cm-15x19in) s.i. board. 15-Apr-3 De Veres Art Auctions, Dublin #221/R est:2000-3000
£1528 $2429 €2200 Orange door, Mykonos, Greece (30x41cm-12x16in) s. board. 29-Apr-3 Whyte's, Dublin #73/R est:1500-2000
£1635 $2551 €2600 Greek fisherman and family (51x61cm-20x24in) s. i.verso canvas on board. 17-Sep-2 Whyte's, Dublin #33/R est:2500-3500
£1946 $3134 €2900 View across the bay on a fine day (25x51cm-10x20in) s. canvasboard. 18-Feb-3 Whyte's, Dublin #211/R est:1500-2000
£2029 $3328 €2800 St. Patrick's Park, Bride Street, Dublin (52x62cm-20x24in) s. board. 28-May-3 Bonhams & James Adam, Dublin #99/R est:3000-4000

OS, Georgius Jacobus Johannes van (1782-1861) Dutch
£4500 $7019 €6750 Dead game, flowers, fruit and nuts on a ledge (59x48cm-23x19in) s.d.1835 panel. 19-Sep-2 Christie's, Kensington #133/R est:3000-5000
£4828 $7676 €7000 Still life with dead game and fruit (81x65cm-32x26in) 4-Mar-3 Ansorena, Madrid #62/R
£5500 $9185 €7975 Roses, jasmine and other flowers in a glass vase on a ledge (25x20cm-10x8in) s. oil paper on panel oval. 11-Jul-3 Christie's, Kensington #133/R est:5000-8000
Works on paper
£468 $748 €650 Vache (18x26cm-7x10in) s. ink wash. 13-May-3 Vanderkindere, Brussels #4
£12963 $21000 €19445 Five shells (24x31cm-9x12in) s. W/C. 21-Jan-3 Sotheby's, New York #153/R est:6000

OS, Georgius Jacobus Johannes van (attrib) (1782-1861) Dutch
£1795 $2818 €2800 Still life with dead bird, fruit and flowers (53x43cm-21x17in) i. 21-Nov-2 Van Ham, Cologne #1855/R est:3500
£5594 $9343 €8000 Nature morte de raisins, peches et prunes d'un tambourin (64x51cm-25x20in) 27-Jun-3 Piasa, Paris #36/R est:8000-10000

OS, J van (1744-1808) Dutch
Works on paper
£11465 $17885 €18000 Still life of fruit and flowers with a sparrow (48x35cm-19x14in) bears sig. W/C. 5-Nov-2 Sotheby's, Amsterdam #142/R est:10000-15000

OS, Jan van (1744-1808) Dutch
Works on paper
£15287 $23847 €24000 Flower still life (47x35cm-19x14in) bears sig. W/C. 5-Nov-2 Sotheby's, Amsterdam #143/R est:10000-15000

OS, Jan van (circle) (1744-1808) Dutch
£16000 $25120 €24000 Still life of flowers in a terracotta vase, with fruit on a marble table (99x69cm-39x27in) bears sig. 12-Dec-2 Sotheby's, London #213/R est:10000-15000

OS, Maria Margrita van (1780-1862) Dutch
£1757 $2741 €2600 Still life with peaches and grapes on stone (40x32cm-16x13in) s. panel. 27-Mar-3 Dr Fritz Nagel, Stuttgart #860/R est:2200

OS, Pieter Frederik van (1808-1860) Dutch
£4110 $6452 €6000 Groom tending the horses (15x23cm-6x9in) s. panel. 15-Apr-3 Sotheby's, Amsterdam #27/R est:7000-10000
Works on paper
£385 $608 €600 Winter scene with figures (21x28cm-8x11in) s. pen ink W/C. 18-Nov-2 Sotheby's, Paris #93/R

OS, Pieter Gerardus van (1776-1839) Dutch
£1132 $1743 €1800 Cow resting in a meadow (22x28cm-9x11in) s.d.1836 panel prov. 23-Oct-2 Christie's, Amsterdam #58/R est:2000-3000
£3459 $5327 €5500 Cows in a wooded landscape (46x62cm-18x24in) s.d.1823. 22-Oct-2 Sotheby's, Amsterdam #37/R est:6000-8000
£4577 $7370 €6500 Landscape with resting cows (35x45cm-14x18in) s.d.1826. 7-May-3 Vendue Huis, Gravenhage #344/R est:6500-7000

OS, Tony van (1886-1945) Belgian
£340 $541 €500 Ferme (60x50cm-24x20in) s. 18-Mar-3 Campo, Vlaamse Kaai #267
£377 $581 €600 Portrait de U Peeters (60x44cm-24x17in) s.d.1920. 22-Oct-2 Campo, Vlaamse Kaai #664
£405 $632 €600 Vue su l'Escaut (51x60cm-20x24in) s. panel. 25-Mar-3 Campo & Campo, Antwerp #235/R
£503 $775 €800 Untitled (50x70cm-20x28in) s. panel. 22-Oct-2 Campo & Campo, Antwerp #310/R
£521 $828 €750 Moulin pres de l'eau (73x91cm-29x36in) s. 29-Apr-3 Campo & Campo, Antwerp #325/R
£609 $956 €950 Mere et enfant au bord du canal (36x56cm-14x22in) s. 19-Nov-2 Vanderkindere, Brussels #43
£692 $1079 €1100 View of Temse (90x130cm-35x51in) s. 23-Sep-2 Bernaerts, Antwerp #46/R

OS-DELHEZ, Hendrik van (1880-1976) Dutch
£263 $426 €400 Dubbele tulp (25x19cm-10x7in) s. plywood. 21-Jan-3 Christie's, Amsterdam #152

OSA, Lars (1860-1958) Norwegian
£2176 $3481 €3264 From Setesdal - girl seated on steps (40x46cm-16x18in) s. 17-Mar-3 Blomqvist, Oslo #381/R est:20000-25000 (N.KR 25000)
£3481 $5570 €5222 Small girl selling flowers at the door (61x83cm-24x33in) s,. 17-Mar-3 Blomqvist, Oslo #375/R est:40000-50000 (N.KR 40000)

OSBERT, Alphonse (1857-1939) French
£5208 $8281 €7500 Quietude du soir (54x68cm-21x27in) s. panel. 30-Apr-3 Tajan, Paris #143/R

OSBORN, E M (1834-?) British
£2436 $3776 €3800 View of Algiers (80x160cm-31x63in) s.i.d.1881. 7-Dec-2 De Vuyst, Lokeren #238/R est:1300-1500

OSBORN, Emily Mary (1834-?) British
£850 $1326 €1275 Young girl dreaming (46x61cm-18x24in) s. 15-Oct-2 Canterbury Auctions, UK #132/R
£3200 $5152 €4800 Going home (28x38cm-11x15in) board prov.exhib. 20-Feb-3 Christie's, London #103/R

OSBORNE, Daisy (?) New Zealander
£1210 $1779 €1815 Mauve chrysanthemums (50x65cm-20x26in) s. prov. 19-Jun-2 Watson's, Christchurch #11/R est:2000-4000 (NZ.D 3700)

OSBORNE, Dennis Henry (1919-) British
£456 $706 €720 Busker outside the bank (34x45cm-13x18in) s. prov. 24-Sep-2 De Veres Art Auctions, Dublin #12

OSBORNE, E (19/20th C) ?
£700 $1113 €1050 Patriot (51x41cm-20x16in) s. 6-Mar-3 Christie's, Kensington #580/R

OSBORNE, Walter (1859-1903) Irish
£10965 $16338 €16448 Garcon assis au bord de l'eau (16x22cm-6x9in) s.d.92 panel. 26-Jun-2 Iegor de Saint Hippolyte, Montreal #68/R (C.D 25000)
£60000 $96000 €90000 La rue Jerzual, Dinan (27x29cm-11x11in) s.d.83 i.verso board prov. 16-May-3 Sotheby's, London #46/R est:60000-80000
£70513 $109295 €110000 Shepherd and his flock 1887 (39x22cm-15x9in) s.d.1887 board prov.exhib.lit. 3-Dec-2 Bonhams & James Adam, Dublin #78/R est:120000-180000
£100000 $160000 €150000 Small girl with a cat (30x23cm-12x9in) s. prov.lit. 16-May-3 Sotheby's, London #41/R est:120000-180000
£170000 $272000 €255000 Return of the flock (33x40cm-13x16in) s. board prov.exhib.lit. 15-May-3 Christie's, London #37/R est:120000-180000
£333333 $516667 €520000 By the sea, Portmarnock (58x71cm-23x28in) s. prov.lit. 3-Dec-2 Bonhams & James Adam, Dublin #50/R est:300000-400000

OSBORNE, William (1823-1901) Irish
£558 $876 €870 Portrait of a seated Jack Russell in a white cravat (35x45cm-14x18in) 19-Nov-2 Hamilton Osborne King, Dublin #478
£4000 $6360 €6000 Good day's work (35x46cm-14x18in) mono. 19-Mar-3 Sotheby's, London #249/R est:4000-6000
£30000 $48000 €45000 Dogs parliament (82x72cm-32x28in) mono. prov. 16-May-3 Sotheby's, London #30/R est:30000-40000

OSCARSSON, Bernhard (1894-1971) Swedish
£342 $544 €513 Portrait of the artist Robert Hogfeldt (27x22cm-11x9in) s.d.25 panel. 3-Mar-3 Lilla Bukowskis, Stockholm #2 (S.KR 4600)

OSEN, Erwin Dominik (1891-1970) Austrian
Works on paper
£54487 $85000 €81731 Die grungekleidete frau - woman in a green dress (44x40cm-17x16in) s.d.1912 W/C pencil prov. 6-Nov-2 Sotheby's, New York #206/R est:15000-20000

OSGOOD, Charles (1809-1890) American
£2097 $3250 €3146 Portraits of Mr and Mrs Edward (91x74cm-36x29in) i.verso pair. 2-Nov-2 North East Auctions, Portsmouth #751/R

OSHIVER, Harry J (1888-1974) American/Russian
£1226 $1900 €1839 Steamships in harbour (61x77cm-24x30in) s. 8-Dec-2 Freeman, Philadelphia #182/R est:1200-1800

OSIPOW, Paul (1937-) Finnish
£294 $482 €450 Composition (50x70cm-20x28in) s.d.77 paper. 9-Feb-3 Bukowskis, Helsinki #332/R
£443 $691 €700 February (178x61cm-70x24in) s.d.74 verso. 15-Sep-2 Bukowskis, Helsinki #250/R
£541 $870 €812 Untitled (153x76cm-60x30in) s.d.81. 7-May-3 AB Stockholms Auktionsverk #988/R (S.KR 7000)
£618 $995 €927 Untitled (153x122cm-60x48in) diptych prov. 7-May-3 AB Stockholms Auktionsverk #956/R (S.KR 8000)

OSKAR, J (19th C) ?
£500 $810 €750 Figures on a jetty hauling in a vessel in a storm (57x68cm-22x27in) s. 21-May-3 Christie's, Kensington #667/R

OSMERKIN, Alexander Alexandrovitch (1892-1953) Russian
£3261 $5348 €4500 Sankt Petersburg (68x83cm-27x33in) s.d.33 cyrillic prov. 29-May-3 Lempertz, Koln #842/R est:4000

OSNAGHI, Josefine (fl.1890-1920) Austrian
£419 $700 €608 Still life with cherries on a lace draped table top (21x26cm-8x10in) s. panel prov. 22-Jun-3 Freeman, Philadelphia #28/R

OSORIO, Trinidad (1929-) Mexican
£1546 $2474 €2242 Nina en caballo (76x50cm-30x20in) s. 15-May-3 Louis Morton, Mexico #36/R est:30000-32000 (M.P 25000)
£2267 $3537 €3401 Caballo sumergido (90x73cm-35x29in) s.d.1962. 17-Oct-2 Louis Morton, Mexico #136/R est:32000-36000 (M.P 36000)

OSSANI, Alessandro (fl.1857-1888) British
£3800 $6232 €5700 Street children (25x34cm-10x13in) s.d.1877 board. 4-Feb-3 Sworder & Son, Bishops Stortford #92/R est:3500-4000

OSSIF, Vladimir (1954-) Czechoslovakian
Works on paper
£315 $460 €473 Untitled (45x60cm-18x24in) mixed media. 4-Jun-2 SOGA, Bratislava #295/R est:18000 (SL.K 20000)
£441 $684 €662 Untitled II (60x80cm-24x31in) mixed media. 1-Oct-2 SOGA, Bratislava #306/R est:35000 (SL.K 28000)

OSSLUND, Helmer (1866-1938) Swedish
£274 $428 €411 Northern river landscape (14x14cm-6x6in) s. greaseproof paper on panel. 13-Sep-2 Lilla Bukowskis, Stockholm #252 (S.KR 4000)
£297 $473 €446 A storm (24x32cm-9x13in) s. i.verso greaseproof paper pan. 2-Mar-3 Uppsala Auktionskammare, Uppsala #299/R (S.KR 4000)
£297 $473 €446 Cloudy (31x45cm-12x18in) s. cardboard on panel. 3-Mar-3 Lilla Bukowskis, Stockholm #159 (S.KR 4000)
£535 $814 €803 River landscape (34x40cm-13x16in) s. greaseproof paper on cardboard. 16-Aug-2 Lilla Bukowskis, Stockholm #864 (S.KR 7800)
£550 $902 €798 Northern landscape (31x44cm-12x17in) s. greaseproof paper on panel. 4-Jun-3 AB Stockholms Auktionsverk #2298/R (S.KR 7000)

£558 $887 €837 Evening, Lapland (24x33cm-9x13in) s. cardboard. 3-Mar-3 Lilla Bukowskis, Stockholm #27 (S.KR 7500)
£579 $909 €869 House near hillside of wood anemones (15x18cm-6x7in) s. panel. 16-Dec-2 Lilla Bukowskis, Stockholm #900 (S.KR 8200)
£617 $963 €926 View towards Sollefteaa (34x45cm-13x18in) s. greaseproof paper on cardboard. 13-Sep-2 Lilla Bukowskis, Stockholm #42 (S.KR 9000)
£698 $1131 €1012 Spring flood (24x37cm-9x15in) s. greaseproof paper on panel. 25-May-3 Uppsala Auktionskammare, Uppsala #164/R (S.KR 9000)
£755 $1148 €1133 Interior scene with Laplander (54x44cm-21x17in) s. panel prov. 16-Aug-2 Lilla Bukowskis, Stockholm #189 (S.KR 11000)
£888 $1474 €1288 Twilight (35x46cm-14x18in) s. greaseproof paper on panel. 16-Jun-3 Lilla Bukowskis, Stockholm #63 (S.KR 11500)
£927 $1538 €1344 River landscape (32x41cm-13x16in) s. cardboard. 16-Jun-3 Lilla Bukowskis, Stockholm #322 (S.KR 12000)
£965 $1602 €1399 Northern landscape (33x43cm-13x17in) s. greaseproof paper on panel. 16-Jun-3 Lilla Bukowskis, Stockholm #957 (S.KR 12500)
£1028 $1594 €1542 Evening light over Ringkallen (23x35cm-9x14in) greaseproof paper on cardboard painted c.1920. 3-Dec-2 Bukowskis, Stockholm #97/R est:12000-15000 (S.KR 14500)
£1375 $2187 €2063 Coastal landscape (32x46cm-13x18in) s.d.1912 greaseproof paper on cardboard. 3-Mar-3 Lilla Bukowskis, Stockholm #86 est:8000-10000 (S.KR 18500)
£1418 $2199 €2127 Houses in evening glow (22x32cm-9x13in) s. panel. 4-Dec-2 AB Stockholms Auktionsverk #1580/R est:20000-25000 (S.KR 20000)
£1560 $2418 €2340 Evening clouds over Myrlandet (30x45cm-12x18in) s. panel. 4-Dec-2 AB Stockholms Auktionsverk #1578/R est:20000-25000 (S.KR 22000)
£1560 $2418 €2340 Lake landscape (37x53cm-15x21in) s. panel. 4-Dec-2 AB Stockholms Auktionsverk #1740/R est:30000-35000 (S.KR 22000)
£1571 $2577 €2278 View of a lake landscape (27x42cm-11x17in) s. panel. 4-Jun-3 AB Stockholms Auktionsverk #2216/R est:15000-20000 (S.KR 20000)
£1702 $2638 €2553 Tree in autumn (22x32cm-9x13in) s. panel. 4-Dec-2 AB Stockholms Auktionsverk #1648/R est:25000-30000 (S.KR 24000)
£1738 $2693 €2607 Reflections in mountain lake (24x34cm-9x13in) s. exhib. 4-Dec-2 AB Stockholms Auktionsverk #1787/R est:30000-35000 (S.KR 24500)
£1915 $2968 €2873 Autumn evening from Angerman river (29x34cm-11x13in) s. greaseproof paper on cardboard. 3-Dec-2 Bukowskis, Stockholm #350/R est:20000-25000 (S.KR 27000)
£1964 $3221 €2848 Town scene (24x38cm-9x15in) panel. 4-Jun-3 AB Stockholms Auktionsverk #2106/R est:20000-25000 (S.KR 25000)
£1964 $3221 €2848 Coastal landscape (36x63cm-14x25in) s. d.1912 greaseproof paper on canvas. 4-Jun-3 AB Stockholms Auktionsverk #2176/R est:40000-50000 (S.KR 25000)
£2128 $3298 €3192 Summer evening, Taxelven - river landscape with rapids and pine trees (43x78cm-17x31in) s.d.1918 verso greaseproof paper on panel exhib. 8-Dec-2 Uppsala Auktionskammare, Uppsala #152/R est:30000-40000 (S.KR 30000)
£2200 $3607 €3190 On the way to Stora Sjofallet (36x51cm-14x20in) s. greaseproof paper on canvas. 4-Jun-3 AB Stockholms Auktionsverk #2177/R est:25000-30000 (S.KR 28000)
£2340 $3628 €3510 Landscape, Osteras (32x42cm-13x17in) s. panel. 4-Dec-2 AB Stockholms Auktionsverk #1721/R est:30000-35000 (S.KR 33000)
£2411 $3738 €3617 Summer's day by Medelpad near Viforsen (35x99cm-14x39in) s. cardboard. 3-Dec-2 Bukowskis, Stockholm #252/R est:40000-50000 (S.KR 34000)
£2553 $3957 €3830 Summer time at Oregrund (34x75cm-13x30in) s. greaseproof paper on cardboard. 3-Dec-2 Bukowskis, Stockholm #260/R est:40000-50000 (S.KR 36000)
£2979 $4617 €4469 Coastal landscape (31x31cm-12x12in) s. greaseproof paper on cardboard. 3-Dec-2 Bukowskis, Stockholm #96/R est:30000-35000 (S.KR 42000)
£3456 $5669 €5011 Landscape (32x81cm-13x32in) s. greaseproof paper on panel. 4-Jun-3 AB Stockholms Auktionsverk #2108/R est:30000-35000 (S.KR 44000)
£3546 $5496 €5319 Landscape view across Angermanland, autumn colours (38x75cm-15x30in) s. greaseproof paper. 4-Dec-2 AB Stockholms Auktionsverk #1568/R est:60000-80000 (S.KR 50000)
£3546 $5496 €5319 Mountain landscape with birch in autumn colours (36x45cm-14x18in) s. greaseproof paper on panel. 8-Dec-2 Uppsala Auktionskammare, Uppsala #153/R est:20000-25000 (S.KR 50000)
£3724 $6033 €5400 Autumn in Alvdalen (34x73cm-13x29in) s. panel. 26-May-3 Bukowskis, Stockholm #143a/R est:35000-40000 (S.KR 48000)
£4397 $6816 €6596 Landscape with waterfall, Handolsforsen (42x61cm-17x24in) s. panel. 4-Dec-2 AB Stockholms Auktionsverk #1596/R est:40000-50000 (S.KR 62000)
£5586 $9049 €8100 Spring landscape at night, Abisko (43x51cm-17x20in) s. canvas on cardboard. 26-May-3 Bukowskis, Stockholm #142/R est:50000-60000 (S.KR 72000)
£5674 $8794 €8511 Landscape, Suorva (36x45cm-14x18in) s. greaseproof paper on cardboard. 3-Dec-2 Bukowskis, Stockholm #349/R est:80000-100000 (S.KR 80000)
£5887 $9124 €8831 Landscape, Kvikkjokk (32x45cm-13x18in) s. greaseproof paper on cardboard. 3-Dec-2 Bukowskis, Stockholm #259/R est:80000-100000 (S.KR 83000)
£6028 $9344 €9042 Autumn landscape (50x81cm-20x32in) s. 3-Dec-2 Bukowskis, Stockholm #250/R est:80000-100000 (S.KR 85000)
£6284 $10306 €9112 Landscape with Angerman river (33x82cm-13x32in) s. greaseproof paper on panel. 4-Jun-3 AB Stockholms Auktionsverk #2329/R est:30000-40000 (S.KR 80000)
£6517 $10557 €9450 Torne marshes (47x71cm-19x28in) s. canvas on panel. 26-May-3 Bukowskis, Stockholm #144/R est:60000-80000 (S.KR 84000)
£11702 $18138 €17553 Spring wind, Torne Trask (41x72cm-16x28in) s. greaseproof paper on cardboard painted 1915-20 prov.lit. 3-Dec-2 Bukowskis, Stockholm #98/R est:100000-150000 (S.KR 165000)
£14000 $22960 €21000 Kall Lake, Jamtland, Sweden (32x16cm-13x6in) s. oil paper on card prov. 3-Jun-3 Sotheby's, London #202/R est:3000-5000
£28000 $45920 €42000 Suorva (44x109cm-17x43in) s. canvas on board prov.exhib.lit. 3-Jun-3 Sotheby's, London #203/R est:30000-50000
£44220 $71637 €64119 Evening by Angerman river (113x136cm-44x54in) s. canvas on panel painted 1901-02 lit. 26-May-3 Bukowskis, Stockholm #141/R est:350000-400000 (S.KR 570000)

Works on paper

£520 $828 €780 Mountain village (37x76cm-15x30in) s. gouache greaseproof paper on panel. 3-Mar-3 Lilla Bukowskis, Stockholm #888 (S.KR 7000)
£1474 $2388 €2137 Northern landscape (43x62cm-17x24in) s. mixed media. 26-May-3 Bukowskis, Stockholm #145/R est:25000-30000 (S.KR 19000)
£1773 $2748 €2660 Landscape (49x70cm-19x28in) s. mixed media paper on panel. 3-Dec-2 Bukowskis, Stockholm #258/R est:25000-30000 (S.KR 25000)
£1885 $3092 €2733 Northern landscape with blue mountain tops (47x80cm-19x31in) s. gouache greaseproof paper on canvas. 4-Jun-3 AB Stockholms Auktionsverk #2286/R est:30000-40000 (S.KR 24000)
£2793 $4524 €4050 Spring day at Torne marsh (44x57cm-17x22in) s. gouache panel. 25-May-3 Uppsala Auktionskammare, Uppsala #213/R est:15000-18000 (S.KR 36000)

OSSWALD, Fritz (1878-1966) Swiss

£417 $654 €650 Field flowers (77x70cm-30x28in) s. panel. 23-Nov-2 Arnold, Frankfurt #829/R
£476 $757 €700 Still life of flowers (58x48cm-23x19in) s. board. 20-Mar-3 Neumeister, Munich #2711/R
£509 $820 €764 Gitschen and Uri-Rotstock (57x77cm-22x30in) s. i. verso panel. 7-May-3 Dobiaschofsky, Bern #866/R (S.FR 1100)

OSSWALD, Karl (1925-1972) German

Works on paper

£759 $1177 €1200 Hohenhewen (58x80cm-23x31in) mixed media pastel board. 27-Sep-2 Karrenbauer, Konstanz #1665

OSSWALD-LUTTIN, Ingeborg (1921-) German

Works on paper

£398 $564 €640 Still life of flowers (78x70cm-31x28in) s.d.88 W/C. 23-Mar-2 Geble, Radolfzell #597

OSSWALD-TOPPI, Margherita (1897-1971) Italian

£391 $607 €587 Girl's portrait (57x41cm-22x16in) s. board. 9-Dec-2 Philippe Schuler, Zurich #3831 (S.FR 900)
£708 $1132 €1062 Still life (52x71cm-20x28in) s.d. board. 17-Mar-3 Philippe Schuler, Zurich #4545 (S.FR 1500)
£858 $1356 €1287 Garden flowers in two clay pots (44x57cm-17x22in) s. board. 29-Nov-2 Zofingen, Switzerland #3018/R est:2500 (S.FR 2000)
£1019 $1640 €1478 Two girls in a garden (51x42cm-20x17in) s. board. 9-May-3 Dobiaschofsky, Bern #165/R est:3600 (S.FR 2200)
£1759 $2832 €2551 Girl from Tessin in a garden with sunflowers (75x39cm-30x15in) s. board. 9-May-3 Dobiaschofsky, Bern #163/R est:6000 (S.FR 3800)

OST, Alfred (1884-1945) Belgian
£316 $494 €500 Scene de famille (36x54cm-14x21in) Indian ink. 16-Sep-2 Amberes, Antwerp #229
Works on paper
£252 $387 €400 Chaloupes sur l'Escaut (28x43cm-11x17in) s. ink dr. 22-Oct-2 Campo, Vlaamse Kaai #578
£252 $390 €400 Village view (28x36cm-11x14in) mono.d.1926 W/C. 5-Oct-2 De Vuyst, Lokeren #261
£277 $429 €440 Mediaeval scene (33x26cm-13x10in) mono. pen Indian ink dr. 5-Oct-2 De Vuyst, Lokeren #263
£277 $429 €440 Consecration (27x35cm-11x14in) brush Indian ink dr exec.c.1923. 5-Oct-2 De Vuyst, Lokeren #265
£283 $436 €450 Mendiants (27x29cm-11x11in) dr exec.c.1909. 22-Oct-2 Campo, Vlaamse Kaai #577
£288 $460 €400 Snowy landscape (14x18cm-6x7in) i. W/C pen Indian ink dr. 17-May-3 De Vuyst, Lokeren #281
£302 $468 €480 Two horses (17x17cm-7x7in) s.d.X W/C pencil. 5-Oct-2 De Vuyst, Lokeren #272
£321 $497 €500 Old horses (27x36cm-11x14in) mono.d.19 pen dr. 7-Dec-2 De Vuyst, Lokeren #239
£346 $536 €550 View of the Antwerp stone (27x35cm-11x14in) d.39 W/C Indian ink. 5-Oct-2 De Vuyst, Lokeren #271
£377 $585 €600 Horse market (17x22cm-7x9in) d.X W/C black chk. 5-Oct-2 De Vuyst, Lokeren #273
£385 $596 €600 Delft fantasy (26x35cm-10x14in) mono.d.41 pen dr wash. 7-Dec-2 De Vuyst, Lokeren #240
£417 $668 €580 Brabancon en hiver (23x25cm-9x10in) mono.d.1912 W/C. 19-May-3 Horta, Bruxelles #309
£440 $678 €700 La petite charrete a charbon (20x33cm-8x13in) mono. dr. 22-Oct-2 Campo, Vlaamse Kaai #575
£472 $731 €750 Refugees (26x35cm-10x14in) mono.d.XIIII wash Indian ink. 5-Oct-2 De Vuyst, Lokeren #266/R
£472 $731 €750 Kijkend near the sea (27x36cm-11x14in) i.d.XXXII wash Indian ink. 5-Oct-2 De Vuyst, Lokeren #270
£483 $772 €700 Baiser (30x38cm-12x15in) mono.d.14 W/C. 15-Mar-3 De Vuyst, Lokeren #236
£503 $780 €800 Refugees (30x42cm-12x17in) mono.i.d.XIIII pen Indian ink dr. 5-Oct-2 De Vuyst, Lokeren #264/R
£504 $806 €700 Desire (31x16cm-12x6in) mono.d.6 W/C. 17-May-3 De Vuyst, Lokeren #279
£535 $829 €850 Refugees (26x35cm-10x14in) mono.i.d.XIIII pen Indian ink dr. 5-Oct-2 De Vuyst, Lokeren #262
£719 $1151 €1000 Near the theatre (27x18cm-11x7in) mono.d.29 W/C Indian ink. 17-May-3 De Vuyst, Lokeren #277
£818 $1267 €1300 Horse (51x66cm-20x26in) mono.d.24 W/C Indian ink. 5-Oct-2 De Vuyst, Lokeren #260
£818 $1267 €1300 Organ grinder (36x28cm-14x11in) mono.d.27 col pencil dr. 5-Oct-2 De Vuyst, Lokeren #267/R
£2319 $3803 €3200 En route en chariot et cheval vers la maison (32x48cm-13x19in) s.d.1925 W/C. 27-May-3 Campo & Campo, Antwerp #176/R est:3000-4000

OSTADE, Adriaen van (1610-1684) Dutch
£12838 $20027 €19000 Peasants in barn (19x20cm-7x8in) s.d.1637 panel. 27-Mar-3 Dorotheum, Vienna #216/R est:15000-20000
£22013 $34119 €35000 Peasants playing dice (40cm-16in circular) panel prov.lit. 2-Oct-2 Dorotheum, Vienna #166/R est:40000-60000
£40252 $62390 €64000 Men playing cards in a tavern (46x59cm-18x23in) s.d.1643 panel prov. exhib. 4-Nov-2 Glerum, Amsterdam #24/R est:65000-80000
£950000 $1491500 €1425000 Three boors drinking and smoking in spirit house (29x23cm-11x9in) s. panel prov.exhib.lit. 11-Dec-2 Christie's, London #70/R est:300000-500000
Prints
£4225 $7014 €6000 Painter (24x17cm-9x7in) etching. 12-Jun-3 Hauswedell & Nolte, Hamburg #139/R est:6000
£4808 $7500 €7212 Painter (24x17cm-9x7in) etching drypoint exec.c.1667. 6-Nov-2 Swann Galleries, New York #93/R est:3000-5000
£5449 $8500 €8174 Breakfast (22x26cm-9x10in) etching exec.c.1664. 6-Nov-2 Swann Galleries, New York #92/R est:5000-8000
£5500 $8525 €8250 Organ grinder (11x9cm-4x4in) etching. 5-Dec-2 Sotheby's, London #25/R est:4000-6000

OSTADE, Adriaen van (style) (1610-1684) Dutch
£604 $972 €900 Inn scene (33x42cm-13x17in) panel. 24-Feb-3 Bernaerts, Antwerp #141
£943 $1462 €1500 Scene d'auberge (25x32cm-10x13in) panel. 1-Oct-2 Palais de Beaux Arts, Brussels #417

OSTADE, Isaac van (1621-1649) Dutch
£10191 $15898 €16000 Barn interior with a pig's carcass and two children playing with its bladder in the background (61x46cm-24x18in) s.d.1642 panel prov.lit. 5-Nov-2 Sotheby's, Amsterdam #297/R est:18000-25000
£14388 $23022 €20000 Barn interior with three children playing with pig's bladder (35x47cm-14x19in) s. panel. 13-May-3 Sotheby's, Amsterdam #43/R est:10000-15000
£16000 $25120 €24000 Travellers halted at an inn (81x144cm-32x57in) prov.exhib. 12-Dec-2 Sotheby's, London #176/R est:15000-20000
Works on paper
£1282 $1987 €2000 Etudes de figures. pen ink wash 2 in one frame. 6-Dec-2 Rieunier, Bailly-Pommery, Mathias, Paris #1/R

OSTERLIN, Anders (1926-) Swedish
£541 $870 €812 Sign of green surface (73x60cm-29x24in) s.d.1959 prov. 7-May-3 AB Stockholms Auktionsverk #794/R (S.KR 7000)

OSTERLIND, Allan (1855-1938) Swedish
Works on paper
£287 $464 €431 Spanish ladies (44x56cm-17x22in) s. W/C. 3-Feb-3 Lilla Bukowskis, Stockholm #32 (S.KR 4000)
£561 $886 €842 Girl at table (46x61cm-18x24in) s. mixed media. 30-Nov-2 Goteborg Auktionsverk, Sweden #226/R (S.KR 8000)
£741 $1156 €1112 Fruit sellers (83x52cm-33x20in) s. W/C. 13-Sep-2 Lilla Bukowskis, Stockholm #316 (S.KR 10800)
£774 $1223 €1200 Gallant scene (95x44cm-37x17in) s. W/C. 18-Dec-2 Rieunier, Bailly-Pommery, Mathias, Paris #37
£1277 $1979 €1916 Portrait of Karl Nordstrom (33x24cm-13x9in) s.i.d.1881 W/C exhib. 4-Dec-2 AB Stockholms Auktionsverk #1715/R est:20000-25000 (S.KR 18000)

OSTERLIND, Anders (1887-1960) French
£256 $405 €400 Sous bois (54x73cm-21x29in) s.d. 14-Nov-2 Credit Municipal, Paris #51
£321 $503 €500 Paysage (60x73cm-24x29in) s. 11-Dec-2 Maigret, Paris #152
£346 $536 €550 Barque de pecheurs au levant (35x46cm-14x18in) s. 4-Oct-2 Tajan, Paris #181
£476 $757 €700 Barque echouee (65x80cm-26x31in) s. 18-Mar-3 Galerie Moderne, Brussels #288
£641 $1006 €1000 Paysage au pont (60x73cm-24x29in) s. 10-Dec-2 Renaud, Paris #41
£705 $1093 €1100 Ciel d'orage sur la ferme (60x73cm-24x29in) s. 9-Dec-2 Beaussant & Lefèvre, Paris #84/R
£949 $1481 €1500 Paysage de campagne (65x81cm-26x32in) s. s. verso. 20-Oct-2 Claude Boisgirard, Paris #19/R est:1500-1800
£1026 $1610 €1600 Paysage au ciel orageux (60x73cm-24x29in) s. panel. 10-Dec-2 Renaud, Paris #42
£1724 $2759 €2500 La Gargelesse, Indre (73x92cm-29x36in) s. 12-Mar-3 E & Eve, Paris #107/R est:2000-2500

OSTERLUND, Herman (1873-1964) Swedish
£423 $665 €635 Morning glow (31x44cm-12x17in) s.indis.d. 16-Dec-2 Lilla Bukowskis, Stockholm #178 (S.KR 6000)

OSTERSETZER, Carl (1865-1914) Austrian
£828 $1308 €1200 Tavern scene (20x26cm-8x10in) s.d.906 i. verso panel. 5-Apr-3 Hans Stahl, Hamburg #17/R
£1189 $1737 €1784 Sewing. Music lesson (48x32cm-19x13in) s.d.1905 panel pair. 17-Jun-2 Philippe Schuler, Zurich #4357/R est:4500-5000 (S.FR 2700)

OSTERWALD, George (1803-1884) German
£9797 $15284 €14500 View from Palazzo Orsini in Nemi over Lake Nemi towards the sea (92x149cm-36x59in) s.d.1868. 26-Mar-3 Hugo Ruef, Munich #187/R est:1200

OSTHAUS, Edmund H (1858-1928) American
£3526 $5500 €5289 Two hunters (61x112cm-24x44in) canvas on board. 18-Oct-2 Du Mouchelle, Detroit #2289/R est:7000-9000
£7051 $11000 €10577 On the point (51x71cm-20x28in) 20-Sep-2 Du Mouchelle, Detroit #2033/R est:12000-16000
£12329 $18000 €18494 Setter in a forest (41x61cm-16x24in) s. 3-Nov-1 North East Auctions, Portsmouth #747/R est:18000-24000
£15663 $26000 €22711 Landscape with two setters (46x56cm-18x22in) s. 11-Jun-3 Boos Gallery, Michigan #495/R est:22000-26000
£19355 $30000 €29033 Setters on point (61x102cm-24x40in) s. prov. 4-Dec-2 Sotheby's, New York #161/R est:30000-50000
£19620 $31000 €29430 Two setters in a landscape (61x86cm-24x34in) s. painted c.1900. 5-Apr-3 DeFina, Austinburg #1291 est:20000-30000
Works on paper
£355 $550 €533 On the point (13x20cm-5x8in) s. W/C exec.c.1892. 8-Dec-2 Toomey, Oak Park #636/R
£956 $1500 €1434 On the scent, hunting dog (15x22cm-6x9in) s. W/C. 22-Nov-2 Skinner, Boston #151/R est:2000-4000
£2110 $3250 €3060 Two hunting dogs (20x38cm-8x15in) s. W/C. 8-Sep-2 DeFina, Austinburg #518 est:800-1200
£3085 $4750 €4628 Hal pointer (38x53cm-15x21in) s.i. W/C. 27-Oct-2 Grogan, Boston #25 est:4000-6000

OSTHOFF, Hermann (1879-1918) German
£503 $785 €800 Early morning in the Black Forest (70x98cm-28x39in) s.d.1904. 11-Oct-2 Winterberg, Heidelberg #663/R

OSTLUND, Manne (1904-1957) Scandinavian
Works on paper
£471 $745 €707 The factory (47x37cm-19x15in) s.d.1933 W/C. 28-Apr-3 Bukowskis, Stockholm #34/R (S.KR 6200)

OSTMAR, Tommy (1934-) Swedish
£1121 $1749 €1682 Hokusai watching (115x68cm-45x27in) s. 5-Nov-2 Bukowskis, Stockholm #383/R est:8000-10000 (S.KR 16000)
Works on paper
£342 $541 €513 Capacity for growth (122x80cm-48x31in) s. chl executed 1985-90. 28-Apr-3 Bukowskis, Stockholm #994/R (S.KR 4500)

OSTROGOVICH, Carlo (1884-?) ?
£544 $865 €800 Boats at dusk (40x70cm-16x28in) s. board. 1-Mar-3 Stadion, Trieste #115

OSTROWSKY, Sam (1885-?) American
£267 $425 €401 Seated nude (20x18cm-8x7in) s. painted c.1935. 4-May-3 Treadway Gallery, Cincinnati #536/R
£346 $550 €519 Young model (22x18cm-9x7in) s. painted c.1935. 4-May-3 Treadway Gallery, Cincinnati #533/R

O'SULLIVAN, Sean (1906-1964) British
£2264 $3532 €3600 Haymaking (41x51cm-16x20in) s.d.1927. 17-Sep-2 Whyte's, Dublin #59/R est:3500-4000
Works on paper
£356 $559 €520 Portrait of a young traveller girl (35x30cm-14x12in) s. pastel. 15-Apr-3 De Veres Art Auctions, Dublin #43
£582 $908 €850 Portrait of a girl (33x26cm-13x10in) s. pastel. 8-Apr-3 James Adam, Dublin #105/R

O'SULLIVAN, Timothy (c.1840-1882) American
Photographs
£6962 $11000 €10443 Shoshone Falls. Glacial lake from the King Survey (20x27cm-8x11in) d.1868 verso albumen prints two prov.lit. 23-Apr-3 Sotheby's, New York #119/R est:1000-1500

OSUNA, Manuel (19th C) Spanish
£574 $896 €850 Boat with flowers in Cadiz (28x37cm-11x15in) s. 25-Mar-3 Durán, Madrid #703/R

OSWALD, C W (fl.1892) British
£1800 $2682 €2700 Castle Rushen (76x127cm-30x50in) s.i.d.1888. 28-Jun-2 Chrystals Auctions, Isle of Man #173 est:1500-2500

OSWALD, Charles W (19th C) British
£280 $440 €420 Cottage and figure by a river (24x34cm-9x13in) s. 15-Dec-2 Lots Road, London #334
£1000 $1550 €1500 Horses and cart on a country lane (46x81cm-18x32in) s. 6-Dec-2 Chrystals Auctions, Isle of Man #197 est:1000-1800

OSWALD, John H (1843-1895) British
£270 $427 €405 Sketch off the Bass (25x31cm-10x12in) s.i.d.1865 verso panel. 14-Nov-2 Bonhams, Edinburgh #307

OSZ, Denisch (1915-1980) Hungarian
£619 $966 €929 Panorama of Budapest (63x101cm-25x40in) s. 11-Sep-2 Kieselbach, Budapest #35/R (H.F 240000)

OTEIZA, Jorge de (1908-) Spanish
Sculpture
£1806 $2854 €2800 Carlos III and illustration (13x13cm-5x5in) s. green pat bronze exhib.lit. 17-Dec-2 Segre, Madrid #153/R
£55000 $90200 €82500 Homenaje a Mallarme (54x60x40cm-21x24x16in) s.i. painted iron prov.exhib. 6-Feb-3 Christie's, London #632/R est:50000-70000

OTERO ABELEDO LAXEIRO, Jose (1908-1996) Spanish
£7862 $12186 €12500 Forms (70x70cm-28x28in) s. 7-Oct-2 Ansorena, Madrid #78/R
Works on paper
£269 $417 €425 Untitled (16x22cm-6x9in) s. ink dr. 26-Sep-2 Castellana, Madrid #361/R
£269 $425 €420 Untitled (24x16cm-9x6in) s. W/C. 13-Nov-2 Ansorena, Madrid #212/R
£277 $432 €440 Menstrel and muse (14x10cm-6x4in) s.d.58 ink double-sided. 17-Sep-2 Segre, Madrid #201/R
£290 $458 €420 Two peasant women (14x11cm-6x4in) s. ink. 1-Apr-3 Segre, Madrid #380/R
£323 $510 €500 Figures (22x30cm-9x12in) s. ink dr. 17-Dec-2 Durán, Madrid #6/R
£325 $529 €490 Peasants (19x11cm-7x4in) s. chl. 11-Feb-3 Segre, Madrid #379/R
£348 $540 €550 Untitled (33x25cm-13x10in) s. ink dr. 26-Sep-2 Castellana, Madrid #360/R
£390 $632 €550 Retrato de hombre con gafas (19x14cm-7x6in) s. felt-tip pen. 20-May-3 Segre, Madrid #243/R
£443 $687 €700 Figures (34x23cm-13x9in) s.d.76 ink dr. 26-Sep-2 Castellana, Madrid #358/R
£448 $713 €650 Figure on horseback (19x16cm-7x6in) s.d.70 ink dr. 4-Mar-3 Ansorena, Madrid #425/R
£448 $713 €650 Crucifixion (19x16cm-7x6in) s. ink dr. 4-Mar-3 Ansorena, Madrid #426/R
£514 $801 €750 Figures (32x50cm-13x20in) s. ink dr cardboard. 8-Apr-3 Ansorena, Madrid #642/R
£974 $1481 €1500 Untitled (23x17cm-9x7in) s.d.77 mixed media. 3-Jul-2 Castellana, Madrid #157/R
£1887 $2943 €3000 Figure (68x48cm-27x19in) s.d.19554 gouache. 8-Oct-2 Ansorena, Madrid #580/R
£2027 $3162 €3000 Figure (24x17cm-9x7in) s. gouache. 25-Mar-3 Durán, Madrid #94/R
£2027 $3162 €3000 Figure (24x17cm-9x7in) s. gouache. 25-Mar-3 Durán, Madrid #93/R
£4277 $6629 €6800 Via Crucis (97x68cm-38x27in) s.d.63 ink dr. 7-Oct-2 Ansorena, Madrid #77/R

OTERO, Alejandro (1921-1990) Venezuelan
£22293 $35000 €33440 B (64x54cm-25x21in) i.d.50 verso prov.lit. 19-Nov-2 Sotheby's, New York #108/R est:60000

OTERO, Jaime (1880-?) Spanish
Sculpture
£3357 $5606 €4800 Jeune fille a la colombe (100x20x15cm-39x8x6in) s.num.1 black pat bronze oval base st.f.A.A. Hebrard. 25-Jun-3 Tajan, Paris #31/R est:5000-6000
£3357 $5606 €4800 Bacchus (110x38x18cm-43x15x7in) s.num.1 black pat bronze rec. base st.f.A.A. Hebrard. 25-Jun-3 Tajan, Paris #32/R est:5000-6000

OTHONEOS, Nicholaos (1877-1950) Greek
£6000 $9480 €9000 Sunset at Poros (43x64cm-17x25in) 1-Apr-3 Bonhams, New Bond Street #53 est:6000-8000

OTIS, Bass (1784-1861) American
£1104 $1700 €1656 Portrait of Marie Louise Vernier Besson (77x65cm-30x26in) s.i.d.1824. 28-Oct-2 Butterfields, San Francisco #3004a/R est:2000-3000
£1401 $2200 €2102 Portrait of a gentleman (127x102cm-50x40in) s.i.d.1853. 22-Nov-2 Skinner, Boston #120/R est:2000-3000

OTIS, George Demont (1877-1962) American
£613 $950 €920 Horse Shoe Bend-Car River (15x20cm-6x8in) s. i.verso board. 29-Oct-2 John Moran, Pasadena #698a
£1138 $1900 €1650 Sketch for afterglow (25x20cm-10x8in) i.verso board. 17-Jun-3 John Moran, Pasadena #11 est:1000-1500
£1290 $2000 €1935 Along the Trespe (15x20cm-6x8in) s. i.verso board. 29-Oct-2 John Moran, Pasadena #698b est:1000-2000
£2097 $3250 €3146 Shack in autumn river landscape (56x69cm-22x27in) s. prov. 29-Oct-2 John Moran, Pasadena #698 est:4000-5500
£5090 $8500 €7381 Country road (61x76cm-24x30in) s. i.verso. 17-Jun-3 John Moran, Pasadena #60 est:6000-8000
£5414 $8500 €8121 Old depot, Tomales Bay (71x91cm-28x36in) s. i.stretcher prov. 19-Nov-2 Butterfields, San Francisco #8154/R est:9000-12000
£6129 $9500 €9194 Valley Farm, San Geronimo Valley (61x76cm-24x30in) s. i.verso prov. 29-Oct-2 John Moran, Pasadena #750a est:7500-9500

OTREY, Alexander (1877-1939) Austrian
£694 $1104 €1000 Reclining female nude (52x65cm-20x26in) bears i. board. 29-Apr-3 Wiener Kunst Auktionen, Vienna #584/R

OTTA, D (19th C) ?
£297 $473 €446 Portrait of young girl (52x42cm-20x17in) s.d.86 oval. 2-Mar-3 Uppsala Auktionskammare, Uppsala #311 (S.KR 4000)

OTTANI, Gaetano (?-1790) Italian
£6993 $11678 €10000 Paysage de ruines architecturales anime de personnages (200x105cm-79x41in) s.d.1748 prov. 25-Jun-3 Tajan, Paris #12/R est:10000-12000

OTTAVIANI, Silvio (20th C) Italian
£769 $1200 €1154 Trompe l'oeil still life with umbrella, pistol and hat (79x58cm-31x23in) s. s.i.verso. 20-Sep-2 Sloan, North Bethesda #395/R est:1500-2500

OTTE, Christian (?) ?
Works on paper
£408 $649 €600 Hommage a l'Askoy (71x49cm-28x19in) s.i.d.79 Indian ink. 19-Mar-3 Hotel des Ventes Mosan, Brussels #345

OTTE, William Louis (1871-1957) American
£994 $1600 €1491 Monterey coastal (25x36cm-10x14in) s. canvasboard. 18-Feb-3 John Moran, Pasadena #14 est:1500-2500
£2903 $4500 €4355 Autumn dunes, Carmel, Cal, 1935 (41x51cm-16x20in) s. masonite. 29-Oct-2 John Moran, Pasadena #695a est:4000-6000
£4194 $6500 €6291 Lupin and poppies, San Gorgonio Pass (36x48cm-14x19in) s.i.d.1919 verso board prov. 29-Oct-2 John Moran, Pasadena #640c est:2500-4000
Works on paper
£4491 $7500 €6512 Flower field in foothill landscape (53x69cm-21x27in) s. pastel prov. 17-Jun-3 John Moran, Pasadena #109 est:8000-11000

OTTERNESS, Tom (1952-) American
Sculpture
£4430 $7000 €6645 Father and son. Mother and daughter (46x46x8cm-18x18x3in) s.d.1984 num.3/3 bronze pair. 13-Nov-2 Sotheby's, New York #569/R

OTTESEN, Otto Didrik (1816-1892) Danish
£1048 $1635 €1572 Meadow flowers (19x15cm-7x6in) mono. panel. 20-Nov-2 Fischer, Luzern #1143/R est:2400-3000 (S.FR 2400)
£1549 $2494 €2200 Still life with flowers (50x70cm-20x28in) s. 12-May-3 Bernaerts, Antwerp #610/R est:1500-2000
£8380 $13324 €12570 Strawberry plant among clemantis, yellow and red roses in greenhouse (55x42cm-22x17in) s.d.1880 mahogany exhib. 5-Mar-3 Rasmussen, Copenhagen #1555/R est:50000-60000 (D.KR 90000)
£23830 $37651 €35745 Flowers in vase in niche and bird's nest with eggs (81x61cm-32x24in) s.i.d.1886 mahogany. 2-Dec-2 Rasmussen, Copenhagen #1137/R est:300000-350000 (D.KR 280000)

OTTESEN, Otto Didrik (attrib) (1816-1892) Danish
£1090 $1689 €1700 Peach and hazelnuts (13x18cm-5x7in) panel. 7-Dec-2 Hans Stahl, Hamburg #99/R est:1500

OTTEVAERE, Henri (1870-1940) Belgian
£481 $745 €750 Summer landscape (38x60cm-15x24in) s.d.1912 canvas on panel. 7-Dec-2 De Vuyst, Lokeren #243

OTTEWELL, Benjamin John (fl.1885-1930) British
Works on paper
£380 $593 €570 After rain the Ballochbuie from old Brig O'Dee (35x54cm-14x21in) s.d.1899 W/C. 13-Sep-2 Lyon & Turnbull, Edinburgh #44/R
£550 $869 €825 Cattle by a river. Tranquil river landscape with angler by a bridge (44x64cm-17x25in) s.d.1882 W/C pair. 27-Nov-2 Hamptons Fine Art, Godalming #187

OTTINI, Pasquale (1580-1630) Italian
£80000 $133600 €116000 Deposition (46x39cm-18x15in) oil on slate prov.exhib.lit. 9-Jul-3 Christie's, London #101/R est:30000-50000

OTTMANN, Henri (1877-1927) French
£811 $1265 €1200 Sur le port de Marseille (34x46cm-13x18in) s. 26-Mar-3 Millon & Associes, Paris #71/R
£1139 $1800 €1800 Jeune fille au marche (64x46cm-25x18in) s. cardboard. 2-Dec-2 Tajan, Paris #89
£1146 $1789 €1800 Promenade a Fontainebleau (70x90cm-28x35in) s. 7-Nov-2 Chochon-Barre & Allardi, Paris #206/R
£1486 $2319 €2200 Jardin (52x63cm-20x25in) s. painted c.1920 prov. 28-Mar-3 Delvaux, Paris #30/R
£1899 $3000 €3000 Nu allonge au miroir (98x130cm-39x51in) 2-Dec-2 Tajan, Paris #88/R
£2390 $3704 €3800 La promenade (73x60cm-29x24in) s. 30-Oct-2 Artcurial Briest, Paris #323/R est:4000-6000
£2400 $3816 €3600 Les bicyclistes a Fontainbleau (70x90cm-28x35in) s. 20-Mar-3 Sotheby's, Olympia #137/R est:3000-4000
£4500 $6930 €6750 La poissonniere a Marseille (73x91cm-29x36in) s. i.verso prov.exhib. 22-Oct-2 Sotheby's, London #252/R est:5000-7000
Works on paper
£270 $422 €400 Paysage de campagne (21x29cm-8x11in) s. gouache. 25-Mar-3 Chochon-Barre & Allardi, Paris #174

OTTO, Ernst (1807-1847) German
£506 $800 €800 Elks on lake shore (54x102cm-21x40in) s. lit. 29-Nov-2 Schloss Ahlden, Ahlden #1323/R

OTTO, Johann Heinrich (attrib) (fl.1762-1797) American
Works on paper
£994 $1600 €1491 Cumberland County fraktur with elaborate surround (30x38cm-12x15in) d.1793 W/C ink. 22-Feb-3 Pook & Pook, Downington #163/R est:800-1200

OTTO, Walt (1895-1963) American
£1491 $2400 €2237 Beautiful woman cheering at football game (36x51cm-14x20in) s. 20-Feb-3 Illustration House, New York #129/R est:2500-3500

OTWAGIN, M (20th C) Russian
£256 $390 €400 October, first snow (50x70cm-20x28in) s. 11-Jul-2 Hugo Ruef, Munich #768/R

OUATTARA (20th C) American?
£4255 $7106 €6000 Sans titre (194x296cm-76x117in) s.d. acrylic. 23-Jun-3 Claude Boisgirard, Paris #170/R est:5000-6000

OUBORG, Piet (1893-1956) Dutch
£15190 $24000 €24000 Beweeglijke lichtheid (50x64cm-20x25in) s. painted c.1949 prov. 26-Nov-2 Sotheby's, Amsterdam #216/R est:18000-25000
Works on paper
£576 $944 €800 Untitled (31x13cm-12x5in) pencil brush ink executed c.1946-47. 3-Jun-3 Christie's, Amsterdam #72/R
£6835 $11209 €9500 Composition (55x65cm-22x26in) s.d.49 gouache W/C pastel. 3-Jun-3 Christie's, Amsterdam #311/R est:10000-15000

OUDART, P L (1796-1850) French
Works on paper
£2400 $3720 €3600 Marine life (36x28cm-14x11in) s. pencil wash three and two by Bevalet and Chazel. 26-Sep-2 Christie's, London #100/R est:2000-3000

OUDENDAG, Egbert (1914-) Canadian
£311 $510 €451 Beach (45x60cm-18x24in) s.i. board. 9-Jun-3 Hodgins, Calgary #175/R (C.D 700)

OUDENDYCK, Evert (17th C) Dutch
£4225 $7014 €6000 Gentilhomme a son bureau (48x39cm-19x15in) s.indis.d.1688. 16-Jun-3 Claude Aguttes, Neuilly #19/R est:4000-5000

OUDENDYK, Sonja (1958-) Dutch
Works on paper
£443 $700 €700 Untitled (300x45cm-118x18in) lead prov. 26-Nov-2 Sotheby's, Amsterdam #309

OUDERRA, Pierre van der (1841-1915) Belgian
£641 $994 €1000 Execution (50x70cm-20x28in) s. panel. 3-Dec-2 Campo & Campo, Antwerp #303
£2400 $3648 €3600 St Thomas of Villanueva (112x84cm-44x33in) s. after Bartolome Esteban Murillo. 29-Aug-2 Christie's, Kensington #86/R est:1500-2000
£3765 $6250 €5459 Classical scene (89x109cm-35x43in) s.d.1902 canvas laid down. 14-Jun-3 Jackson's, Cedar Falls #197/R est:6000-9000
£10256 $16103 €16000 Hoe de heillige Franciscus van Assisi zigne roeping begon (155x230cm-61x91in) 16-Dec-2 Amberes, Antwerp #307/R

OUDINOT, Achille (1820-1891) Flemish
£900 $1413 €1350 Cattle in a sunlit meadow (33x46cm-13x18in) s. 16-Apr-3 Christie's, Kensington #748/R
£4167 $6458 €6500 Boy under a tree by a pond with meadow and a village in the background (32x46cm-13x18in) s. 4-Dec-2 Neumeister, Munich #841/R est:5500
£4688 $7500 €7032 Extensive seaside view with children playing (100x132cm-39x52in) s. 14-May-3 Butterfields, San Francisco #1136/R est:4000-6000

OUDINOT, Achille (attrib) (1820-1891) French
£1346 $2087 €2100 Italian landscape (46x80cm-18x31in) 6-Dec-2 Rieunier, Bailly-Pommery, Mathias, Paris #55

OUDOT, Roland (1897-1981) French
£245 $383 €368 Les faneurs (27x22cm-11x9in) s. d.1962 verso prov. 6-Nov-2 AB Stockholms Auktionsverk #937/R (S.KR 3500)
£256 $405 €400 Beach cafe (16x22cm-6x9in) s. 14-Nov-2 Neumeister, Munich #651/R
£377 $585 €600 Le port (29x47cm-11x19in) s.d.1957 panel. 6-Oct-2 Feletin, Province #130
£380 $600 €600 Nu (41x28cm-16x11in) s. 2-Dec-2 Tajan, Paris #102
£609 $950 €914 Still life with crab, mussels, lemon and wine (38x46cm-15x18in) s. 9-Oct-2 Doyle, New York #81
£612 $978 €850 Nu dans un paysage (41x27cm-16x11in) s. 14-May-3 Blanchet, Paris #127/R
£705 $1114 €1100 Landscape (21x27cm-8x11in) s. board. 14-Nov-2 Neumeister, Munich #653/R
£1389 $2209 €2000 Paysage (65x81cm-26x32in) s.d.1927. 29-Apr-3 Artcurial Briest, Paris #261 est:2200-3100
£1410 $2186 €2200 Female nude (73x60cm-29x24in) s.d.30. 3-Dec-2 Christie's, Amsterdam #35/R est:1000-1500
£1418 $2369 €2000 Paysage (32x40cm-13x16in) s. canvas on board. 20-Jun-3 Piasa, Paris #216 est:2000-2500
£1644 $2581 €2400 Mikonos (54x81cm-21x32in) s. 21-Apr-3 Rabourdin & Choppin de Janvry, Paris #64/R est:2500-3000
£1795 $2818 €2800 Scene de corrida (65x81cm-26x32in) s. 13-Dec-2 Piasa, Paris #259/R
£3248 $5068 €5100 Table sur la terrasse en Provence (60x81cm-24x32in) s. 10-Nov-2 Eric Pillon, Calais #178/R
£4726 $7420 €6900 Jeune aventuriere (81x51cm-32x20in) s. prov. 21-Apr-3 Rabourdin & Choppin de Janvry, Paris #97/R est:8000-9000
£6250 $9938 €9000 Venise, Rio San-Barnabe (66x100cm-26x39in) s. prov. 29-Apr-3 Artcurial Briest, Paris #270/R est:8000-9000
£6429 $10157 €9644 Pastorale (250x320cm-98x126in) sig. woven wool tapestry exhib. 17-Nov-2 Sotheby's, Paddington #26/R est:10000-15000 (A.D 18000)

OUDRY, J B (1686-1755) French
£1392 $2158 €2200 Still life with violin and recorder (28x37cm-11x15in) i. 27-Sep-2 Dr Fritz Nagel, Leipzig #3906/R

OUDRY, Jacques-Charles (1720-1778) French
£8966 $14345 €13000 Heron effraye par un chien (100x81cm-39x32in) 11-Mar-3 Christie's, Paris #250/R
£12000 $20040 €17400 Still life with ham, procelain bowl, pot, oranges, rabbit and partridge (49x73cm-19x29in) s. indis.d.17.. 10-Jul-3 Sotheby's, London #198/R est:7000-10000
£21622 $33730 €32000 Trompe-l'oeil sur mur blanc (64x47cm-25x19in) s.d.1769. 26-Mar-3 Tajan, Paris #72/R est:15000

OUDRY, Jean Baptiste (1686-1755) French
£20271 $31622 €30000 Nature morte au lievre et perdreau gris attaches a un tronc d'arbre (79x86cm-31x34in) s.d.1728. 26-Mar-3 Tajan, Paris #71/R est:50000
£121622 $189730 €180000 Nature morte aux pieces de gibier (79x97cm-31x38in) indis.sig. 26-Mar-3 Tajan, Paris #70/R est:65000-70000

Works on paper
£1500 $2355 €2250 Portrait of a scholar (13x9cm-5x4in) pen ink wash htd white framing lines prov. 11-Dec-2 Sotheby's, Olympia #153/R est:1500-2000
£2000 $3340 €2900 Female archer in a landscape, snake to the right (20x20cm-8x8in) i. black chk pen ink htd white prov. 8-Jul-3 Christie's, London #64/R est:1500-2000
£6013 $9500 €9500 La tentation de St Pacome (43x38cm-17x15in) i. brush black ink grey wash. 27-Nov-2 Christie's, Paris #157/R est:10000-15000
£6081 $9486 €9000 Vue des Jardins d'Arcueil (29x49cm-11x19in) crayon chk. 31-Mar-3 Piasa, Paris #61/R est:20000
£17008 $27043 €25000 Forhu (28x22cm-11x9in) s.d.1746 pen ink wash htd gouache exhib. 24-Mar-3 Tajan, Paris #37/R
£28571 $45429 €42000 Vieille meute (28x22cm-11x9in) i. pen ink wash htd gouache exhib.lit. 24-Mar-3 Tajan, Paris #36/R est:20000

OUDRY, Jean Baptiste (attrib) (1686-1755) French
£4808 $7596 €7500 Portrait d'homme a la veste rouge (82x65cm-32x26in) i.verso. 15-Nov-2 Beaussant & Lefèvre, Paris #53/R est:4000-5000

OUDRY, Jean Baptiste (studio) (1686-1755) French

Works on paper
£641 $1013 €1000 Terrasse avec chiens et gibier (52x32cm-20x13in) pierre noire sanguine prov. 15-Nov-2 Drouot Estimations, Paris #60/R

OUDRY, Jean Baptiste (style) (1686-1755) French
£7500 $11775 €11250 Two parrots, a silver goblet, apple and an almond on a table (28x22cm-11x9in) 13-Dec-2 Christie's, Kensington #178/R est:1200-1800

OULESS, Philip J (1817-1885) British
£274 $427 €400 British sailing ship on choppy seas (31x41cm-12x16in) s.d.51 lit. 10-Apr-3 Allgauer, Kempten #2924
£500 $780 €750 Paddle steamer in rough seas (20x30cm-8x12in) board. 26-Mar-3 Bonhams & Langlois, Jersey #166
£4000 $6480 €6000 Markwell of Jersey under reduced sail in heavy weather (53x83cm-21x33in) mono.d.1865. 21-May-3 Christie's, Kensington #603/R est:6000-8000
£5000 $7800 €7500 Schooner Boadicea off Gronez (45x64cm-18x25in) mono.d.1866. 26-Mar-3 Bonhams & Langlois, Jersey #167/R est:5000-8000

OULTON, Therese (1953-) British
£800 $1248 €1200 Displaced (68x63cm-27x25in) s.i.d.1984 verso exhib. 27-Mar-3 Christie's, Kensington #659/R
£3000 $4650 €4500 Celestine (233x178cm-92x70in) s. i.d.Feb 1988 verso prov. 3-Dec-2 Bonhams, New Bond Street #121/R est:3000-4000

OUSEY, Buckley (1851-1889) British
£620 $980 €930 Buying fish from the boats, possibly Conway, North Wales (41x84cm-16x33in) s.d.1888. 27-Nov-2 Bonhams, Knowle #224

OUSLEY, William (1866-1953) American
£1026 $1600 €1539 Blue bonnets (61x91cm-24x36in) s. 12-Oct-2 Neal Auction Company, New Orleans #645/R est:2500-4000
£1524 $2500 €2210 Calcasieu River, near the Hortman's ferry (36x86cm-14x34in) s.i.d.Dec 1927 verso. 7-Jun-3 Neal Auction Company, New Orleans #358/R est:3000-5000
£2439 $4000 €3537 Scene at Chouoique near the Ellender House (38x84cm-15x33in) s.i.d.1930 verso. 7-Jun-3 Neal Auction Company, New Orleans #357/R est:3000-5000

OUTAKKA, Alvar (?) Finnish?

Works on paper
£253 $395 €400 Laplanders (32x48cm-13x19in) s. W/C. 12-Sep-2 Hagelstam, Helsinki #815

OUTER, Nestor (1865-1923) Belgian

Works on paper
£342 $534 €500 Virton a midi (53x36cm-21x14in) s.d.1902 W/C. 14-Apr-3 Horta, Bruxelles #370
£481 $745 €750 Soir a Chenois (53x35cm-21x14in) s.d.1897 W/C. 9-Dec-2 Horta, Bruxelles #298
£897 $1434 €1300 Les reveurs (36x53cm-14x21in) s.d.1905 w/C. 17-Mar-3 Horta, Bruxelles #233

OUTERBRIDGE, Paul (jnr) (1896-1958) American

Photographs
£2690 $4250 €4035 Still life with silk flowers (11x9cm-4x4in) warm toned. 23-Apr-3 Sotheby's, New York #155/R est:3000-5000
£3165 $5000 €4748 Chrysanthemums (42x32cm-17x13in) carbro col print executed c.1930 prov. 24-Apr-3 Phillips, New York #100 est:6000-8000
£3774 $5849 €6000 Still life with chrysanthemums (42x42cm-17x17in) carbro col print lit. 2-Nov-2 Lempertz, Koln #76/R est:6000-7000
£7143 $11000 €10715 Wall paper (38x28cm-15x11in) s.d.1936 col carbro print prov.exhib.lit. 22-Oct-2 Sotheby's, New York #77/R est:3000-5000
£15190 $24000 €24000 Egg in spotlight (26x34cm-10x13in) i. verso silver gelatin prov.lit.exhib. 28-Nov-2 Villa Grisebach, Berlin #1342/R est:15000-18000
£22785 $36000 €34178 Riding boot with feather (38x29cm-15x11in) s. col carbro print prov.lit. 23-Apr-3 Sotheby's, New York #156/R est:20000-30000
£39241 $62000 €58862 42nd Street elevated (11x8cm-4x3in) platinum print prov.lit. 25-Apr-3 Phillips, New York #4/R est:20000-30000

OUTHWAITE, Ida Rentoul (1888-1960) Australian

Works on paper
£929 $1467 €1394 She's really rather nice! (28x22cm-11x9in) s.i. ink pen brush. 18-Nov-2 Joel, Victoria #158/R est:2000-3000 (A.D 2600)

OUVRIE, Justin (1806-1879) French

Works on paper
£288 $447 €450 Ruines d'une tour (20x26cm-8x10in) s.d.1849 wash over pierre noire. 6-Dec-2 Maigret, Paris #35
£459 $717 €680 Vue de Heidelberg (12x17cm-5x7in) s.i. W/C over crayon htd gouache. 31-Mar-3 Piasa, Paris #100

£801 $1242 €1250 Heidelberg (12x17cm-5x7in) s.i. W/C over crayon htd gouache. 4-Dec-2 Piasa, Paris #152
£1605 $2279 €2600 Eglise au bord du lac (8x12cm-3x5in) s.d.1875 W/C gouache. 16-Mar-3 Eric Pillon, Calais #9/R
£3444 $5613 €5200 Artere animee a Munich (20x25cm-8x10in) s.d.i.1865 W/C. 16-Feb-3 Mercier & Cie, Lille #232/R est:2500-3000

OUWATER, Isaak (1750-1793) Dutch
£21656 $33783 €34000 View of the Spui of The Hague (37x44cm-15x17in) s.d.1788 prov. 6-Nov-2 Vendue Huis, Gravenhage #429/R est:40000-45000
£28000 $46760 €40600 View of Amsterdam from the T Spaarne canal in Slooterdijk with travelers on a towpath (32x42cm-13x17in) s.d.1782. 9-Jul-3 Christie's, London #54/R est:12000-18000
£100719 $161151 €140000 Amsterdam, the t'spaarne canal in Slooterdijk wityh the ferry office (40x53cm-16x21in) s.d.1778 prov. 14-May-3 Christie's, Amsterdam #203/R est:50000-70000

OUWATER, Isaak (circle) (1750-1793) Dutch
£13669 $21871 €19000 St. Bavo's cathedral and the Groote market, Haarlem (57x70cm-22x28in) panel. 14-May-3 Christie's, Amsterdam #206/R est:8000-12000

OVENS, Jurgen (attrib) (1623-1678) German
£1500 $2340 €2250 Portrait of a gentleman in a brown coat with white collar (64x52cm-25x20in) 10-Apr-3 Christie's, Kensington #146/R est:1500-2000
£4200 $7014 €6090 Portrait of a lady in black costume with a white lace collar (68x60cm-27x24in) 11-Jul-3 Christie's, Kensington #85/R est:2000-3000

OVERBECK, A V (20th C) ?
£253 $392 €400 Still life with porcelain figure and roses (38x35cm-15x14in) s.d.1929 panel. 27-Sep-2 Weidler, Nurnberg #8828

OVERBECK, Fritz (1869-1909) German
£2152 $3400 €3400 Landscape in May (39x58cm-15x23in) d. 29-Nov-2 Bolland & Marotz, Bremen #557/R est:1600
£2431 $3840 €3500 First snow in Klosters (38x46cm-15x18in) s.d.12.11.08 board. 26-Apr-3 Dr Lehr, Berlin #409/R est:4000
£5380 $8500 €8500 Spring in the fens (45x36cm-18x14in) s. board on panel painted c.1895/1900. 29-Nov-2 Bolland & Marotz, Bremen #556/R est:7000
£6329 $10000 €10000 Trees on the water-meadow in summer breeze (93x116cm-37x46in) painted c.1906/08. 29-Nov-2 Bolland & Marotz, Bremen #558/R est:11000

OVERBECK, Hannah Borger (?-1931) American
Works on paper
£1258 $2000 €1824 Untitled (20x13cm-8x5in) s. W/C. 4-May-3 Treadway Gallery, Cincinnati #231/R est:1000-2000

OVERBECK, Johann Friedrich (1789-1869) German
£9677 $15290 €15000 Annonciation (68x40cm-27x16in) mono. triptych. 17-Dec-2 Galerie Moderne, Brussels #821/R est:7000
Works on paper
£280 $400 €420 Study of a lower right arm and hand (10x19cm-4x7in) pencil. 23-Jan-3 Swann Galleries, New York #374/R
£8000 $13360 €11600 Madonna and child in a landscape (19x15cm-7x6in) pen grey ink brown wash blk chk. 9-Jul-3 Sotheby's, London #61/R est:4000-6000

OVERBEEK, G J van (1882-1947) Dutch
£295 $475 €440 Harbour view (59x99cm-23x39in) 18-Feb-3 Vendu Notarishuis, Rotterdam #29

OVERBEEK, Gijsbertus Johannes van (1882-1947) Dutch
£892 $1391 €1400 Caravans on the Rotterdam quay (59x99cm-23x39in) s. 5-Nov-2 Vendu Notarishuis, Rotterdam #275/R
£915 $1474 €1300 Caravans at the little tree (59x99cm-23x39in) s. 6-May-3 Vendu Notarishuis, Rotterdam #46
£1127 $1814 €1600 Haulage wagon on the quay (78x64cm-31x25in) s. 6-May-3 Vendu Notarishuis, Rotterdam #87/R est:1000-1500
£3289 $5329 €5000 View of the Nieuwe Haven with a horse-drawn cart on the quay, Rotterdam (60x80cm-24x31in) s. 21-Jan-3 Christie's, Amsterdam #339/R est:800-1200

OVERBERGHE, Cel (1937-) Belgian
£347 $552 €500 Soft relief (110x110cm-43x43in) panel d.1972 exhib. 29-Apr-3 Campo & Campo, Antwerp #240/R

OVERMAN, Gerard (1855-1906) Dutch
£261 $407 €410 Romantic landscape with cows by river (18x23cm-7x9in) panel lit. 8-Nov-2 Auktionhaus Georg Rehm, Augsburg #8115

OVERSTRAETEN, War van (1891-1981) Belgian
£340 $541 €500 La maison blanche (50x60cm-20x24in) s. 18-Mar-3 Galerie Moderne, Brussels #289
£440 $678 €700 Lady in interior (54x65cm-21x26in) s. 22-Oct-2 Campo & Campo, Antwerp #312
£966 $1545 €1400 Saint-Remy de Provence (60x80cm-24x31in) s. mono.i.d.1952 verso. 15-Mar-3 De Vuyst, Lokeren #351/R

OWEN, Bill (1942-) American
£16080 $26050 €23316 Nighthawk's evening song (71x51cm-28x20in) oil on linen. 23-May-3 Altermann Galleries, Santa Fe #19

OWEN, G O (19/20th C) British
Works on paper
£2800 $4340 €4200 Portrait of a religious cleric (49x70cm-19x28in) s.d.98 W/C. 1-Oct-2 Fellows & Sons, Birmingham #167/R est:150-250

OWEN, Joel (20th C) British
£420 $651 €630 Harbour scene with shipping (38x58cm-15x23in) s.d.1927. 4-Dec-2 Andrew Hartley, Ilkley #1179
£500 $780 €750 Sunrise, Queens view, Killicruik. Sunset, Queens view, Killicruik (48x74cm-19x29in) s.d.1916 pair. 11-Apr-3 Keys, Aylsham #688

OWEN, June L (1930-) American
£281 $450 €422 Standing male and seated female looking over a landscape (102x102cm-40x40in) s. i.verso acrylic. 17-Mar-3 Winter Associates, Plainville #69

OWEN, Robert Emmett (1878-1957) American
£1468 $2350 €2202 Study of the profile, Franconia Notch, New Hampshire (30x41cm-12x16in) s. board. 11-Jan-3 James Julia, Fairfield #196 est:2500-3500
£1687 $2750 €2531 Autumnal landscape with stream (41x56cm-16x22in) s. 16-Feb-3 Jeffery Burchard, Florida #26
£1887 $3000 €2831 New England church (46x51cm-18x20in) s. 5-Mar-3 Christie's, Rockefeller NY #81/R est:2500-3500
£2276 $3300 €3414 Autumn pool Stamford Ct (41x51cm-16x20in) 1-Jun-2 Russ Antiques, Waterford #170
£3481 $5500 €5222 Brook in winter near Ridgefield (38x48cm-15x19in) s. 26-Apr-3 Thomaston Place, Thomaston #105

OWEN, Samuel (1768-1857) British
Works on paper
£361 $600 €523 Stormy ocean with ships (15x20cm-6x8in) s. W/C. 11-Jun-3 Boos Gallery, Michigan #559/R
£1197 $1927 €1700 Ship on beach with figures and village beyond (14x21cm-6x8in) s. W/C. 7-May-3 Michael Zeller, Lindau #865/R est:200
£1300 $2106 €1950 Unloading the catch (14x11cm-6x4in) W/C. 22-Jan-3 Bonhams, New Bond Street #336/R est:1200-1800
£1300 $2093 €1950 Dutch boat in rough water (16x22cm-6x9in) W/C. 15-Jan-3 Cheffins Grain & Comins, Cambridge #354/R
£2600 $4134 €3900 Shipping in a rough sea (23x33cm-9x13in) s.d.1800 pen sepia W/C prov. 5-Mar-3 Bonhams, Bury St Edmunds #253/R est:1500-2500
£4800 $7776 €7200 Busy shipping lanes offshore under clearing skies. Running into danger (14x23cm-6x9in) s.d.1822 W/C htd white pair. 22-Jan-3 Bonhams, New Bond Street #328/R est:4000-6000

OWEN, William (1769-1825) British
£500 $770 €750 Portrait of Dr Cyril Jackson in clerics robes (76x63cm-30x25in) prov. 5-Sep-2 Christie's, Kensington #86
£2800 $4368 €4200 Hard is the fate of the infirm and poor (104x79cm-41x31in) s. 14-Apr-3 Hamilton Osborne King, Dublin #1511/R est:3000-5000
£3800 $6004 €5700 Portrait of Dorothy Westmacott (75x62cm-30x24in) 28-Nov-2 Sotheby's, London #168/R est:3000-5000
Works on paper
£304 $475 €456 Wyoming noon. pencil. 21-Sep-2 Harvey Clar, Oakland #1491

OWENS, Laura (1970-) American
£25316 $40000 €37974 Untitled (183x152cm-72x60in) s.on overlap oil acrylic painted 1995 prov.exhib. 13-Nov-2 Christie's, Rockefeller NY #1/R est:40000-60000

OWLES, Alfred (1894-1978) American
Works on paper
£306 $475 €459 Deck of WW1 aircraft carrier. s. W/C. 7-Dec-2 Harvey Clar, Oakland #1162
£419 $650 €629 WW1 fighter pilot. s. W/C. 7-Dec-2 Harvey Clar, Oakland #1161

OX, Jack (1948-) American
Works on paper
£298 $486 €450 Anton Bruckner symphony nr 8 (58x53cm-23x21in) s.d.1986 ink. 28-Jan-3 Dorotheum, Vienna #281

OYAGUEZ, Guillermo (1970-) Spanish
£462 $729 €720 Houses (40x102cm-16x40in) s. board. 13-Nov-2 Ansorena, Madrid #72/R

OYENS, D (1842-1902) Flemish
£3262 $5285 €4600 Au travail (37x29cm-15x11in) panel. 26-May-3 Amberes, Antwerp #58

OYENS, David (1842-1902) Flemish
£935 $1496 €1300 Jeune femme au piano (24x18cm-9x7in) s. panel. 13-May-3 Palais de Beaux Arts, Brussels #292
£1711 $2771 €2600 Sunny corner (19x15cm-7x6in) s. panel. 21-Jan-3 Christie's, Amsterdam #245/R est:1500-2000
£4114 $6418 €6500 At the dressing-table (28x38cm-11x15in) s.indis.d. panel. 21-Oct-2 Glerum, Amsterdam #133/R est:6500-8000

OYENS, David (attrib) (1842-1902) Flemish
£1410 $2228 €2200 Dans l'atelier (65x54cm-26x21in) 18-Nov-2 Tajan, Paris #170/R est:2400-3000

OYENS, Pierre (1842-1894) Flemish
£3521 $5669 €5000 Conversation (36x29cm-14x11in) s. panel. 6-May-3 Vendu Notarishuis, Rotterdam #9/R est:700-900
£5660 $8717 €9000 Italian beauty looking at an album in the artist studio (101x77cm-40x30in) s.d.1886. 23-Oct-2 Christie's, Amsterdam #167/R est:4000-6000
£5660 $8717 €9000 Vlijtig aan het werk (40x31cm-16x12in) s.d.93 panel exhib. 22-Oct-2 Sotheby's, Amsterdam #128/R est:3000-5000

OYSTON, George (c.1860-?) British
Works on paper
£300 $468 €450 Sheep grazing in a meadow (29x20cm-11x8in) s.d.96 W/C. 6-Nov-2 Bonhams, Chester #444
£400 $624 €600 Old Newlyn (36x23cm-14x9in) s.d.1901 W/C. 17-Oct-2 David Lay, Penzance #1216
£400 $620 €600 At Rusper, Sussex. Near Ockley, Dorking, Surrey (34x52cm-13x20in) s. W/C pair. 29-Oct-2 Henry Adams, Chichester #443
£400 $624 €600 Evensong, near Corfe Castle, Dorset (27x47cm-11x19in) s. pencil W/C htd white. 27-Mar-3 Christie's, Kensington #141/R
£400 $648 €600 Figure in a rural landscape (35x52cm-14x20in) s.d.1909 W/C. 21-May-3 Bonhams, Knightsbridge #50/R
£420 $655 €630 Sheep grazing (28x45cm-11x18in) s.d.1914 W/C gouache pastel. 10-Oct-2 Rupert Toovey, Partridge Green #1444/R
£580 $905 €870 River landscape with sheep and fishermen (22x51cm-9x20in) s.d.99 W/C. 15-Oct-2 Bearnes, Exeter #380/R

OZANNE, Pierre (1737-1813) French
Works on paper
£1149 $1792 €1700 Marine (9x15cm-4x6in) wash over crayon. 26-Mar-3 Piasa, Paris #112
£18519 $30000 €27779 Cherbourg (44x75cm-17x30in) i. pen ink wash htd white set of 3 prov.exhib.lit. 21-Jan-3 Sotheby's, New York #108/R est:40000

OZENFANT, Amedee (1886-1966) French
£8000 $12720 €12000 Maternite (148x114cm-58x45in) s. painted c.1941 prov.exhib.lit. 20-Mar-3 Sotheby's, Olympia #206/R est:8000-12000
£10638 $17234 €15000 Baigneuses au reflets (98x56cm-39x22in) s.d. oil stucco prov.lit. 23-May-3 Binoche, Paris #60/R est:13000-15000
£205000 $336200 €307500 Composition II (46x55cm-18x22in) s. painted 1929 prov.exhib.lit. 5-Feb-3 Sotheby's, London #162/R est:80000

OZERNY, Andriy (20th C) Irish?
£282 $468 €400 To be continued (77x104cm-30x41in) s.d.03. 10-Jun-3 James Adam, Dublin #180/R
£352 $585 €500 Fishing boats by a jetty (88x73cm-35x29in) s.d.03. 10-Jun-3 James Adam, Dublin #177/R

OZERNY, Michail (20th C) ?
£425 $662 €620 Wooded landscape in autumn (47x69cm-19x27in) s. 8-Apr-3 James Adam, Dublin #53/R

P B R (19th C) British?
£260 $403 €390 Small fishing boat and other shipping boat at sea (69x119cm-27x47in) init.d.1890 board. 26-Sep-2 Lane, Penzance #213
£380 $589 €570 Newcastle fishing boats at sea (104x142cm-41x56in) init.d.1891 board. 26-Sep-2 Lane, Penzance #212

PAAL, Ladislas de (1846-1879) Hungarian
£13500 $22140 €20250 Farmyard with haystacks (61x80cm-24x31in) s. prov. 3-Jun-3 Sotheby's, London #57/R est:15000-20000
£50000 $82000 €75000 Birch forest with faggot gatherer (74x92cm-29x36in) s. prov.lit. 3-Jun-3 Sotheby's, London #48/R est:25000-35000
£106190 $165656 €159285 Village end (50x85cm-20x33in) 11-Apr-3 Kieselbach, Budapest #58/R est:25000000-38000000 (H.F 38000000)
£140000 $219800 €210000 Soleil couchant (111x164cm-44x65in) s. 19-Nov-2 Sotheby's, London #155/R est:30000-50000

PAAL, Ladislas de (attrib) (1846-1879) Hungarian
£1899 $2962 €3000 La peinture en plein air (59x49cm-23x19in) s. panel. 15-Oct-2 Regis & Thiollet, Argentuil #85

PAALEN, Wolfgang (1905-1959) Austrian
£3125 $5156 €4500 La rosee de mai (46x65cm-18x26in) mono.i.d.1953 verso. 2-Jul-3 Artcurial Briest, Paris #705/R est:3000-4000
£3767 $5914 €5500 Untitled (27x35cm-11x14in) oil fumage lit. 15-Apr-3 Laurence Calmels, Paris #4391/R
£4795 $7527 €7000 Untitled (58x31cm-23x12in) paper on panel oval. 15-Apr-3 Laurence Calmels, Paris #4387/R
£4898 $7788 €7200 Composition (55x38cm-22x15in) mono. 26-Feb-3 Artcurial Briest, Paris #320 est:250-3000
£8219 $12904 €12000 Entre chien et loup (38x61cm-15x24in) mono.d.54 i.verso. 15-Apr-3 Laurence Calmels, Paris #4390/R est:12000
£17808 $27959 €26000 From the painter's logbook (49x44cm-19x17in) mono. mono.i.d.1948 verso paper on panel oval. 15-Apr-3 Laurence Calmels, Paris #4388/R est:10000
£17808 $27959 €26000 Passage du renard (50x65cm-20x26in) mono. oil fumage prov.lit. 15-Apr-3 Laurence Calmels, Paris #4392/R est:15000
£19178 $30110 €28000 Nuclear wheel (64x62cm-25x24in) i.verso pentagonal prov.lit. 15-Apr-3 Laurence Calmels, Paris #4389/R est:22000
£27397 $43014 €40000 Soeurs obsidiennes (91x73cm-36x29in) s.i.d.1952 verso prov.exhib.lit. 15-Apr-3 Laurence Calmels, Paris #4385/R est:30000
£35616 $55562 €52000 Orages magnetiques (73x100cm-29x39in) mono.i.d.1938 oil fumage. 14-Apr-3 Laurence Calmels, Paris #4031/R est:80000
£51370 $80651 €75000 Rencontre sur plage (195x141cm-77x56in) s.i.d.1936 prov.exhib.lit. 15-Apr-3 Laurence Calmels, Paris #4386/R est:60000

PAAP, Hans (1894-1966) American
£475 $750 €713 Wise elder. s.d.1952. 16-Nov-2 Harvey Clar, Oakland #1275
£629 $1000 €944 Indian portrait (64x53cm-25x21in) s. painted c.1950. 2-Mar-3 Toomey, Oak Park #704/R

PAATELA, Oskari (1888-1952) Finnish
£432 $708 €600 Winter (42x53cm-17x21in) s.d.1919. 5-Jun-3 Hagelstam, Helsinki #945/R
Works on paper
£405 $665 €620 Landscape from Hogland (27x35cm-11x14in) s.i.d.1938 W/C. 9-Feb-3 Bukowskis, Helsinki #334/R
£519 $810 €820 Village at Hogland (40x33cm-16x13in) s.i.d.1926 W/C. 15-Sep-2 Bukowskis, Helsinki #255/R

PACANOWSKA, Felicia (1915-2002) Polish
£692 $1072 €1100 Vue de Sorrento. Village (65x92cm-26x36in) one s.d.1957 one painted c.1959 pair. 30-Oct-2 Artcurial Briest, Paris #59/R
£818 $1267 €1300 Nature morte. Village (92x65cm-36x26in) s. one d.1954 pair. 30-Oct-2 Artcurial Briest, Paris #57/R
£1132 $1755 €1800 Le couple. Personnages de theatre (92x65cm-36x26in) s. one d.1953 pair. 30-Oct-2 Artcurial Briest, Paris #58/R est:400-500
£1132 $1755 €1800 Vue de village. Viaduc d'Arcueil. Bouquet de fleurs. L'orchestre a l'entracte (45x64cm-18x25in) s. four painted c.1940-1950. 30-Oct-2 Artcurial Briest, Paris #61 est:450-600
Works on paper
£535 $829 €850 Avallon. Banlieue Parisienne (26x37cm-10x15in) s.d.1952 pair. 30-Oct-2 Artcurial Briest, Paris #63
£786 $1219 €1250 Village. Homme assis. Funiculaire a Naples (37x27cm-15x11in) two s. pastel exec.c.1950 three. 30-Oct-2 Artcurial Briest, Paris #62

PACCHIA, Girolamo del (1477-1533) Italian
£22581 $35677 €35000 Tiresia transformed into a woman (61x40cm-24x16in) board prov.lit. 19-Dec-2 Semenzato, Venice #21/R est:40000

PACE, Achille (1923-) Italian
£1064 $1723 €1500 Itinerari vaganti (40x50cm-16x20in) s.i.d.1990 verso oil pigment prov. 26-May-3 Christie's, Milan #152/R est:2000-3000

PACETTI, Giovanni Battista (1693-1743) Italian
Works on paper
£1139 $1800 €1800 La montee au Calvaire (21x13cm-8x5in) red chk pen brown ink brown wash prov. 27-Nov-2 Christie's, Paris #83/R est:1500-2000

PACETTI, Michelangelo (1793-1855) Italian
£2390 $3704 €3800 Boar hunt (54x74cm-21x29in) s. 29-Oct-2 Dorotheum, Vienna #121/R est:4000-5000
£9864 $15684 €14500 Naples (66x87cm-26x34in) s.d.1830. 19-Mar-3 Neumeister, Munich #688/R est:11000

PACHECO, Fernando Castro (1918-) South American
£3711 $5937 €5381 Dos mujeres (60x45cm-24x18in) s.d.1954. 15-May-3 Louis Morton, Mexico #120/R est:65000-75000 (M.P 60000)
£8280 $13000 €12420 Lovers (52x62cm-20x24in) s.d.53. 19-Nov-2 Sotheby's, New York #123/R est:15000

PACHT, Wilhelm (1843-1912) Danish
£1435 $2325 €2081 Fisherman in rowing boat (74x54cm-29x21in) s.d.89. 26-May-3 Rasmussen, Copenhagen #1327/R est:7000-10000 (D.KR 15000)

PACHTA, Josef (1902-) Austrian
£313 $494 €450 St Johann Nepomukkirche in Gersthof (23x35cm-9x14in) s. s.d.76 verso canvas on masonite. 24-Apr-3 Dorotheum, Vienna #241/R
£417 $658 €600 River in city (36x50cm-14x20in) s. s.d.82 verso canvas on masonite. 24-Apr-3 Dorotheum, Vienna #240/R

PACHTER, Charles (1942-) Canadian
Works on paper
£289 $473 €434 Still life in blues (36x52cm-14x20in) s.d.61 W/C ink. 3-Jun-3 Joyner, Toronto #331/R (C.D 650)

PACKER, Monica (1960-) Uruguayan
£256 $400 €384 Azul infinito (43x82cm-17x32in) s. papel. 30-Jul-2 Galleria Y Remates, Montevideo #102/R

PACKER, Richard G (?-1998) American
£472 $750 €708 Stark NH (61x91cm-24x36in) s. i.verso board prov. 7-Mar-3 Skinner, Boston #296/R

PACX, Hendrick Ambrosius (1602-?) Dutch
£4430 $6911 €7000 Portrait equestre d'un commandant hollandais (96x121cm-38x48in) s.d.1644. 20-Oct-2 Mercier & Cie, Lille #263/R est:2500-3000

PACZKA FERENCZ, Franz (1856-1925) Hungarian
£1064 $1649 €1596 Visiting the tailor (73x52cm-29x20in) s.d.76 panel. 3-Dec-2 Bukowskis, Stockholm #183/R est:20000-25000 (S.KR 15000)
£1935 $3018 €2806 Spinning bride (91x62cm-36x24in) s. 13-Sep-2 Mu Terem Galeria, Budapest #136/R est:400000 (H.F 750000)

PADAMSEE, Akbar (1928-) Indian
£13209 $21795 €19153 Untitled (61x4cm-24x2in) s.d.62. 6-Jul-3 Christie's, Hong Kong #79/R est:95000-110000 (HK.D 170000)
£13986 $23077 €20280 Nude (137x92cm-54x36in) s.d.93. 6-Jul-3 Christie's, Hong Kong #80/R est:120000-150000 (HK.D 180000)
£20000 $31800 €30000 Landscape (92x60cm-36x24in) s.d.62. 2-May-3 Christie's, Kensington #568/R est:6000-8000

PADDAY, Charles Murray (1868-1954) British
Works on paper
£311 $516 €451 Landing, Dardanelles (18x30cm-7x12in) s. i.verso W/C en grisaille. 16-Jun-3 Waddingtons, Toronto #55/R (C.D 700)
£600 $954 €900 Arrival (25x35cm-10x14in) s.d.93 W/C. 4-Mar-3 Bonhams, Knightsbridge #226/R
£1300 $2027 €1950 Auction on the beach (41x90cm-16x35in) s.d.97 pencil W/C. 19-Sep-2 Christie's, Kensington #168 est:300-500

PADERLIK, Arnost (1919-) Czechoslovakian?
£413 $652 €620 Still life with bouquet and cherries (36x50cm-14x20in) s.d.62 canvas on cardboard. 30-Nov-2 Dorotheum, Prague #98/R (C.KR 20000)

PADILLA, Juan (attrib) (1906-1980) Spanish
£245 $400 €368 Still life of peaches in a torn paper sack (38x46cm-15x18in) s. 16-Feb-3 Jeffery Burchard, Florida #172a

PADILLA, Miguel (19th C) Italian
£473 $738 €700 Street in Rome (36x25cm-14x10in) s.i.d.1889. 25-Mar-3 Durán, Madrid #595/R

PADNIA, J (19th C) Spanish?
£1154 $1788 €1800 Turkey with chicks (37x68cm-15x27in) s. 5-Dec-2 Dr Fritz Nagel, Stuttgart #691/R est:1500

PADRONI, Luca (1973-) Italian
£1206 $1953 €1700 Studio, il giardino (65x90cm-26x35in) s.i.d.2002 verso. 20-May-3 Porro, Milan #43/R est:1400-1600

PADUA SCHOOL (16th C) Italian
Sculpture
£9494 $15000 €15000 Hercules fighting Cacus (28cm-11in) bronze. 2-Dec-2 Finarte, Milan #56/R est:14000

PADUA, Paul Matthias (1903-1981) Austrian
£1218 $1924 €1900 Landscape (61x51cm-24x20in) s.d.1970. 14-Nov-2 Neumeister, Munich #660/R est:1000-1200
£1923 $2981 €3000 Bust portrait of a farmer boy with felt hat (30x24cm-12x9in) s.d.1944 board. 4-Dec-2 Neumeister, Munich #843/R est:2500
£2345 $3705 €3400 Female nude (60x75cm-24x30in) s.d.1962. 5-Apr-3 Quittenbaum, Hamburg #158/R est:2200
Works on paper
£385 $608 €600 Female nude (63x40cm-25x16in) s.d.1972 chl htd pastel chk. 14-Nov-2 Neumeister, Munich #661/R

PADULA, Maria (20th C) Italian?
£833 $1317 €1300 Portrait oF Leonardo Sinisgalli (66x48cm-26x19in) painted 1944. 12-Nov-2 Babuino, Rome #47/R

PAEDE, Paul (1868-1929) German
£493 $794 €700 Woman's portrait (117x95cm-46x37in) s.d.1916. 10-May-3 Berlinghof, Heidelberg #186/R
£548 $855 €800 Portrait of a lady in white dress with fur stole (100x75cm-39x30in) s.i.d.09 lit. 10-Apr-3 Allgauer, Kempten #2925/R
£692 $1100 €1038 Nudes in the woods (43x53cm-17x21in) s.d. painted c.1919. 4-May-3 Treadway Gallery, Cincinnati #498/R
£1156 $1839 €1700 Female nude (94x59cm-37x23in) s. 19-Mar-3 Neumeister, Munich #690/R
£1346 $2127 €2100 Two girls by stream (44x35cm-17x14in) s. 14-Nov-2 Neumeister, Munich #662/R est:2000-2500

PAEDE, Paul (attrib) (1868-1929) German
£256 $390 €400 Female nude in bedroom (66x48cm-26x19in) indis.s. i.verso painted 1904 lit. 11-Jul-2 Allgauer, Kempten #2640/R

PAEFFGEN, C O (20th C) German
Sculpture
£1282 $1987 €2000 Rapsfeld on sea (51x58x17cm-20x23x7in) mono.d.94 num.85 wood mixed media. 7-Dec-2 Van Ham, Cologne #384/R est:3200
£4130 $6774 €5700 House altar (63x32x12cm-25x13x5in) mono.i.d.92 verso diverse objects wired together. 28-May-3 Lempertz, Koln #313/R est:5800
Works on paper
£641 $994 €1000 Untitled - Saddam (29x21cm-11x8in) mono.d.90 pen. 3-Dec-2 Lempertz, Koln #334/R

PAEFFGEN, Claes Otto (20th C) German
£1019 $1600 €1529 Harman, Mona Lisa (48x65cm-19x26in) init.d.1988 acrylic screenprint paper on wood. 21-Nov-2 Swann Galleries, New York #138/R est:3000-5000
Works on paper
£379 $599 €550 Question mark (73x23cm-29x9in) s.d. verso panel stone wire. 2-Apr-3 Dr Fritz Nagel, Stuttgart #9514/R

PAELLA, Chimicos (20th C) ?
£475 $736 €750 Sans titre (150x200cm-59x79in) s.d.verso acrylic. 28-Sep-2 Cornette de St.Cyr, Paris #385

PAERELS, Willem (1878-1962) Belgian/Dutch
£719 $1180 €1000 View of Cadaques, Spain (50x40cm-20x16in) oil paper on canvas prov. 3-Jun-3 Christie's, Amsterdam #272/R est:1500-2000
£1076 $1700 €1700 Paysage vallonne avec maisons (40x50cm-16x20in) s. 26-Nov-2 Palais de Beaux Arts, Brussels #140/R est:2000-3000
£1241 $1974 €1800 Portrait en pied de Madam Paerels (200x100cm-79x39in) s. exhib. 4-Mar-3 Palais de Beaux Arts, Brussels #388 est:1600-1800
£1250 $1987 €1800 Fleurs (52x41cm-20x16in) s. paper. 29-Apr-3 Campo, Vlaamse Kaai #245/R est:1800-2200
£1806 $2871 €2600 Terasse a la plage (39x49cm-15x19in) s. paper. 29-Apr-3 Campo & Campo, Antwerp #241/R est:2000-2500
£3448 $5517 €5000 Reclining nude (50x60cm-20x24in) s. 15-Mar-3 De Vuyst, Lokeren #447/R est:5500-6500
Works on paper
£274 $427 €400 Nu de dos (24x20cm-9x8in) sanguine dr. 14-Apr-3 Horta, Bruxelles #500
£377 $588 €550 Vue de Menton (40x52cm-16x20in) s. chl dr. 14-Apr-3 Horta, Bruxelles #499
£382 $596 €600 Fishing boats (68x89cm-27x35in) s. W/C. 6-Nov-2 Vendue Huis, Gravenhage #57/R
£570 $889 €900 Vapeur a quai a Ostende (23x30cm-9x12in) studio st. chl. 16-Sep-2 Horta, Bruxelles #458
£1295 $2072 €1800 Nu couche (43x53cm-17x21in) studio st. pastel. 13-May-3 Palais de Beaux Arts, Brussels #111 est:1750-2500

PAESCHKE, Paul (1875-1943) German
Works on paper
£443 $700 €700 Market day in an east German coastal town (32x24cm-13x9in) s. pastel board lit. 29-Nov-2 Schloss Ahlden, Ahlden #1397/R
£472 $746 €708 Concert in a pleasure garden (25x36cm-10x14in) s.i.d.1911 chl dr. 29-Nov-2 Zofingen, Switzerland #2517/R (S.FR 1100)
£2405 $3800 €3800 Berlin at dusk (32x41cm-13x16in) s.d.1926 pastel. 30-Nov-2 Villa Grisebach, Berlin #278/R est:3000-4000

PAEZ VILARO, Jorge (1922-) Uruguayan
£535 $850 €803 Couple (59x50cm-23x20in) s. 2-Mar-3 Galleria Y Remates, Montevideo #94/R

PAGAN DE PAGANIS, Tiziano (1858-1932) Italian
Works on paper
£479 $748 €700 Drinking wine (15x11cm-6x4in) s. W/C. 8-Apr-3 Ansorena, Madrid #409/R

PAGANI, Gregorio (1558-1605) Italian
£36879 $59745 €52000 Moses making water spring from a rock (217x288cm-85x113in) lit. 20-May-3 Babuino, Rome #36/R

PAGANI, Paolo (1661-1716) Italian
£41139 $65000 €65000 Hercules and his son preparing the fire (162x140cm-64x55in) oval prov.exhib.lit. 27-Nov-2 Finarte, Milan #131/R est:60000-70000

PAGANO, Michele (attrib) (1697-1732) Italian
£1090 $1689 €1700 Landscape with figures and village (39x46cm-15x18in) 4-Dec-2 Christie's, Rome #318

PAGANS MONSALVATJE, Jordi (1932-) Spanish
£346 $540 €550 View of the river (46x61cm-18x24in) s. 23-Sep-2 Durán, Madrid #42/R

PAGAVA, Vera (1907-) ?
£271 $425 €407 Sans titre (33x55cm-13x22in) s.d.1958. 25-Nov-2 Germann, Zurich #778 (S.FR 620)

PAGE, Edward A (1850-1928) American
£687 $1100 €996 Fishing shacks (15x22cm-6x9in) s. board prov. 16-May-3 Skinner, Boston #302/R
£750 $1200 €1088 Two-masted schooner ashore (25x30cm-10x12in) s. canvasboard prov. 16-May-3 Skinner, Boston #296/R est:800-1200
£1250 $2000 €1813 Two-masted schooner (13x17cm-5x7in) s. canvasboard prov. 16-May-3 Skinner, Boston #294/R est:800-1200
£1312 $2100 €1902 Schooner in the water with a beached dinghy (16x22cm-6x9in) s. board prov. 16-May-3 Skinner, Boston #306/R est:800-1200

PAGE, Evelyn (1899-?) New Zealander
£3537 $5482 €5306 Portrait of Frances (43x35cm-17x14in) s. board. 4-Dec-2 Dunbar Sloane, Auckland #22/R est:25000-35000 (NZ.D 11000)
£4823 $7476 €7235 Older Wellington , evening (29x49cm-11x19in) s.i.verso canvas on board painted 1969. 4-Dec-2 Dunbar Sloane, Auckland #16/R est:20000-30000 (NZ.D 15000)
£4930 $8134 €7149 Old Queenstown (30x43cm-12x17in) s.i. board. 1-Jul-3 Peter Webb, Auckland #80/R est:15000-25000 (NZ.D 14000)
£8333 $13000 €12500 City harbour, Wellington (40x67cm-16x26in) s. s.i.verso canvas on board prov. 8-Apr-3 Peter Webb, Auckland #37/R est:25000-35000 (NZ.D 24000)

PAGE, Fred (1908-1984) South African
Works on paper
£241 $381 €362 Dirge (50x34cm-20x13in) s.d.75 i.verso pen ink. 1-Apr-3 Stephan Welz, Johannesburg #205 est:3000-5000 (SA.R 3000)
£801 $1249 €1202 Extensive landscape with houses (26x41cm-10x16in) s.d.60 gouache. 11-Nov-2 Stephan Welz, Johannesburg #552/R (SA.R 12500)

PAGE, Henry Maurice (fl.1878-1890) British
£350 $532 €525 Loggers loading a cart in a winter landscape (61x51cm-24x20in) s.d.84. 29-Aug-2 Christie's, Kensington #49

PAGE, William (1811-1885) American
Works on paper
£800 $1272 €1200 Temple of Poseidon, Cape Sunium. Entrance to the Aora, Greece (23x20cm-9x8in) W/C two. 29-Apr-3 Bonhams, New Bond Street #124b

PAGE, William (attrib) (1811-1885) American
Works on paper
£7500 $11700 €11250 Athens and the Acropolis seen from the Pnyx (53x74cm-21x29in) W/C over pencil bodycol. 15-Oct-2 Sotheby's, London #25/R est:3000-5000

PAGENKOPF, Ursula (20th C) Canadian/German
£289 $474 €419 It's pumpkin time (45x60cm-18x24in) s.i.d.2003 acrylic. 9-Jun-3 Hodgins, Calgary #66/R (C.D 650)
£333 $547 €483 Referee (45x60cm-18x24in) s.i.d.2003 acrylic. 9-Jun-3 Hodgins, Calgary #260/R (C.D 750)

PAGES, Jules Eugene (1867-1946) American
£1911 $3000 €2867 View of Semur-en-Auxios (46x55cm-18x22in) prov. 19-Nov-2 Butterfields, San Francisco #8028/R est:4000-6000
£2410 $4000 €3495 Ranunculus. Zinnias (22x16cm-9x6in) s. one i.verso canvasboard pair. 11-Jun-3 Butterfields, San Francisco #4151/R est:4000-6000
£4777 $7500 €7166 Roses in a yellow vase. Roses in a blue vase (16x22cm-6x9in) s. canvasboard pair prov.exhib. 19-Nov-2 Butterfields, San Francisco #8260/R est:4000-6000
£5660 $9000 €8490 In the flower garden (54x65cm-21x26in) s. 5-Mar-3 Sotheby's, New York #70/R est:10000-15000

PAGES, Jules François (1833-1910) American
£4194 $6500 €6291 River and bridge in cityscape, Spain (46x61cm-18x24in) s.i. 29-Oct-2 John Moran, Pasadena #746 est:3000-5000

PAGET, Sidney (1861-1908) British
Works on paper
£280 $468 €406 Figures by a stream in a wooded mountain landscape (32x49cm-13x19in) s. W/C. 17-Jun-3 Rosebery Fine Art, London #640/R

PAGET, Walter Stanley (1863-1935) British
Works on paper
£600 $984 €900 Angel Gabriel appearing to the three shepherds (25x48cm-10x19in) s. pencil W/C bodycol htd gold. 5-Jun-3 Christie's, Kensington #872/R

PAGGI, Giovanni Battista (1554-1627) Italian
£8000 $12480 €12000 Holy Family with the infant Saint John the Baptist (91x85cm-36x33in) 9-Apr-3 Christie's, London #107/R est:8000-12000

PAGGI, Giovanni Battista (attrib) (1554-1627) Italian
Works on paper
£1216 $1897 €1800 Burial scene (27x41cm-11x16in) pen ink wash. 27-Mar-3 Maigret, Paris #51/R

PAGLIACCI, Mirko (1959-) Italian?
Works on paper
£1111 $1767 €1600 Night in the past (70x100cm-28x39in) s.i.verso polymer on canvas. 1-May-3 Meeting Art, Vercelli #206

PAGLIANO, Eleuterio (1826-1903) Italian
Works on paper
£1548 $2446 €2400 Page (38x24cm-15x9in) s. W/C. 18-Dec-2 Finarte, Milan #197/R est:1200
£1901 $3061 €2700 Portrait de femme assise (27x22cm-11x9in) s. gouache W/C. 12-May-3 Lesieur & Le Bars, Le Havre #74b/R

PAGNUELO, Francoise (20th C) Canadian?
£222 $364 €322 Untitled - small cottage amid trees (23x30cm-9x12in) hard board. 1-Jun-3 Levis, Calgary #277/R (C.D 500)
£225 $349 €338 Ste Faustin, Cape Cod (28x35cm-11x14in) s. i.d.1939 verso board. 24-Sep-2 Ritchie, Toronto #3162/R (C.D 550)

PAGUENAUD, Jean-Louis (1876-1952) French
£2767 $4262 €4400 Chameliers et marchands (46x61cm-18x24in) s. panel. 23-Oct-2 Rabourdin & Choppin de Janvry, Paris #196/R
Works on paper
£258 $397 €410 Batiment de guerre en vue des cotes bresiliennes (28x43cm-11x17in) s. gouache. 27-Oct-2 Lesieur & Le Bars, Le Havre #180

PAHL, Manfred (1900-1994) German
£621 $981 €900 Gas kettle (36x44cm-14x17in) s.i.d. verso board. 2-Apr-3 Dr Fritz Nagel, Stuttgart #9518/R
£690 $1090 €1000 Bodensee landscape (50x60cm-20x24in) mono.d. i. stretcher. 2-Apr-3 Dr Fritz Nagel, Stuttgart #9520/R

PAHR-IVERSEN, Kjell (1937-) Norwegian
£1474 $2300 €2211 A l'interieur de rouge (120x75cm-47x30in) s. s.i.verso. 21-Oct-2 Blomqvist, Oslo #418/R est:20000-30000 (N.KR 17000)

PAI, Laxman (1926-) Indian
£300 $468 €450 Sun and moon (91x91cm-36x36in) s.d.1997 acrylic lit. 17-Oct-2 Bonhams, Knightsbridge #660/R

PAICE, George (1854-1925) British
£241 $400 €349 Surf beauty (23x30cm-9x12in) s.d.02 artists board. 14-Jun-3 Jackson's, Cedar Falls #221/R
£350 $543 €525 Boxer , a terrier in a landscape (24x30cm-9x12in) s.i. board. 31-Oct-2 Greenslade Hunt, Taunton #638/R
£360 $598 €540 Ginger (29x21cm-11x8in) s.i. board. 10-Jun-3 Bonhams, Leeds #156
£420 $647 €630 Portrait of a hunter in a stable, Flexable (20x30cm-8x12in) s. board. 3-Sep-2 Gorringes, Lewes #2086
£420 $655 €630 Maybey (19x25cm-7x10in) s.i. board. 6-Nov-2 Sotheby's, Olympia #76/R
£420 $701 €609 Battle Dawn, a favourite hunter (21x29cm-8x11in) s. board. 25-Jun-3 Cheffins, Cambridge #795
£450 $734 €653 Mac, study of a terrier (23x30cm-9x12in) s.i. 17-Jul-3 Tennants, Leyburn #885
£465 $734 €725 Old grey (21x29cm-8x11in) s.i. 12-Nov-2 Mealy's, Castlecomer #1052/R
£480 $749 €720 Hunter in stable (23x30cm-9x12in) s.d.1908. 10-Apr-3 Brightwells, Leominster #928/R
£550 $869 €825 Flexible, a brown hunter in a stable (23x30cm-9x12in) s.i.d.91 board. 28-Nov-2 Christie's, Kensington #156/R
£550 $853 €825 Biddy horse in a landscape (35x43cm-14x17in) s.i. 25-Sep-2 John Nicholson, Haslemere #1036/R
£600 $930 €900 Satan, a bulldog (30x23cm-12x9in) s.i.d.07. 30-Sep-2 Bonhams, Ipswich #383/R
£600 $984 €900 Uncle Dick (36x46cm-14x18in) s.i. 3-Jun-3 Bonhams, Knightsbridge #57/R
£650 $1086 €943 Live Wire, a bay hunter in a stable (34x49cm-13x19in) s. 25-Jun-3 Cheffins, Cambridge #801/R
£650 $1086 €943 Beny, a dark bay hunter with a white blaze in a stable (34x49cm-13x19in) s. 25-Jun-3 Cheffins, Cambridge #802/R
£650 $1086 €943 Indian Ink, a dark bay hunter in a stable (34x49cm-13x19in) s. 25-Jun-3 Cheffins, Cambridge #803/R
£675 $1100 €1013 Greyhound in a landscape (41x56cm-16x22in) s.d.02. 11-Feb-3 Bonhams & Doyles, New York #168 est:800-1200
£750 $1253 €1088 Skylark, a dark bay hunter, with Jane, a lurcher in a landscape (34x49cm-13x19in) s. 25-Jun-3 Cheffins, Cambridge #800
£1000 $1640 €1500 Dignity and Impudence (23x30cm-9x12in) s.i. 3-Jun-3 Bonhams, Knightsbridge #58/R est:500-800
£1200 $1896 €1800 Ypsilanti, bay hunter in a stable (35x46cm-14x18in) s.i.d.04. 28-Nov-2 Christie's, Kensington #167/R est:700-900

PAIER, Theodor (19th C) German
£548 $855 €800 Herd of cows returning home (79x34cm-31x13in) s. one of pair. 10-Apr-3 Dorotheum, Vienna #125/R
£548 $855 €800 Village track (79x34cm-31x13in) s. verso one of pair. 10-Apr-3 Dorotheum, Vienna #126/R

PAIK, Nam June (1932-) American/Korean
£762 $1241 €1150 Untitled (25x20cm-10x8in) s.d.1991 verso prov. 3-Feb-3 Cornette de St.Cyr, Paris #494/R
Photographs
£1887 $2925 €3000 Sans titre (24x29cm-9x11in) bears num.NJP-0602 verso cibachrome prov. 30-Oct-2 Artcurial Briest, Paris #586/R est:1800-2300
Sculpture
£1923 $2981 €3000 Work for radio (49cm-19in) s. num.14/20 bronze cassette exec.1988. 7-Dec-2 Cornette de St.Cyr, Paris #117/R
£3397 $5266 €5300 Untitled (60x75cm-24x30in) s.i.d.91 African wooden mask TV oil pastel chk prov. 7-Dec-2 Ketterer, Hamburg #740/R est:5000-6000
£8500 $13090 €12750 Untitled - robot on wheels (118x63x48cm-46x25x19in) s.d.92 rubber bicycle wheels wireless sets mini TV. 23-Oct-2 Christie's, London #160/R est:7000-9000
£9500 $15580 €14250 Triangle (208x188x23cm-82x74x9in) s.d.88 silkscreen print, acrylic wood metal silk canvas prov. 6-Feb-3 Christie's, London #703/R est:8000-12000
£13000 $20020 €19500 Zen for T.V (49x57x52cm-19x22x20in) television set conceived 1963 prov. 22-Oct-2 Sotheby's, London #343/R est:5000-7000
£77925 $120004 €123900 Vol de nuit (220x445x35cm-87x175x14in) s.d.1990 monitor CD-player aluminium propellers. 26-Oct-2 Cornette de St.Cyr, Paris #101/R est:150000
Works on paper
£503 $775 €800 Lawrence welk show (46x64cm-18x25in) s.i. collage chk W/C. 26-Oct-2 Dr Lehr, Berlin #413/R

PAIL, Edouard (1851-1916) French
£845 $1403 €1200 Troupeau au paysage (37x46cm-15x18in) s. 15-Jun-3 Anaf, Lyon #178
£2609 $4043 €3914 Bruyeres en fleurs (78x110cm-31x43in) s. prov. 7-Dec-2 Galerie du Rhone, Sion #505/R est:3000-5000 (S.FR 6000)

PAILES, Isaac (1895-1978) French
£748 $1190 €1100 Nature morte (22x27cm-9x11in) s. 3-Mar-3 Claude Boisgirard, Paris #77

PAILHES, Fred (1902-1991) French
£321 $503 €500 Roulotte (60x73cm-24x29in) s.d.37. 24-Nov-2 Lesieur & Le Bars, Le Havre #138
Works on paper
£285 $450 €450 Marin au port (47x32cm-19x13in) s. W/C. 29-Nov-2 Drouot Estimations, Paris #40
£288 $453 €450 Parvis de Notre-Dame au Havre (45x62cm-18x24in) s. W/C gouache. 24-Nov-2 Lesieur & Le Bars, Le Havre #136
£353 $554 €550 Bohemiens (45x60cm-18x24in) s. W/C gouache. 24-Nov-2 Lesieur & Le Bars, Le Havre #130/R
£385 $604 €600 Scene de bar (42x58cm-17x23in) s.d.1940 gouache. 24-Nov-2 Lesieur & Le Bars, Le Havre #134
£449 $704 €700 Vive notre rosiere (37x45cm-15x18in) s.d.1949 W/C gouache. 24-Nov-2 Lesieur & Le Bars, Le Havre #135
£449 $704 €700 Couple de clochard (34x22cm-13x9in) s.d.1947 chl crayon. 24-Nov-2 Lesieur & Le Bars, Le Havre #132
£458 $737 €650 Les nudistes (50x61cm-20x24in) s. gouache. 12-May-3 Lesieur & Le Bars, Le Havre #75/R
£513 $805 €800 Marins en goguette (46x50cm-18x20in) s. gouache. 24-Nov-2 Lesieur & Le Bars, Le Havre #137

PAILLER, Henri (1876-1954) French
£280 $451 €420 Canal scene in winter (38x56cm-15x22in) s. 18-Feb-3 Bonhams, Knightsbridge #117
£440 $722 €660 L'Eglise de Triel et la Seine au couchant (46x61cm-18x24in) s. exhib. 4-Jun-3 Bonhams, Chester #362

PAILLET, Charles (attrib) (1871-1937) French
Sculpture
£1000 $1560 €1500 Pelican (18x7cm-7x3in) i. brown black pat bronze st.f.A.A.Hebrard. 5-Nov-2 Sotheby's, London #119/R est:1000-1500

PAILLOU, Peter (snr) (fl.1744-1784) British
Works on paper
£6500 $10855 €9425 Tawny owl on a branch (34x51cm-13x20in) bears i. W/C pen blk ink blk chk. 9-Jul-3 Sotheby's, London #121/R est:3000-5000

PAILOS, Manuel (1917-) Uruguayan
£755 $1200 €1133 Boat at harbour (30x36cm-12x14in) s.d.63 cardboard. 2-Mar-3 Galleria Y Remates, Montevideo #31/R
£1094 $1750 €1641 Moving (25x30cm-10x12in) s. cardboard. 5-Jan-3 Galleria Y Remates, Montevideo #26/R
Works on paper
£478 $750 €717 Adventures (43x29cm-17x11in) s. mixed media. 20-Nov-2 Galleria Y Remates, Montevideo #26/R
£705 $1100 €1058 Constructivo (25x25cm-10x10in) s.d.96 encaustica. 30-Jul-2 Galleria Y Remates, Montevideo #56/R

£875 $1400 €1313 Adventures (40x38cm-16x15in) s. mixed media. 5-Jan-3 Galleria Y Remates, Montevideo #25/R

PAIN, G (?) British?
£1200 $1896 €1800 Granite, docked grey hunter wearing saddle and bridle in a stable (51x69cm-20x27in) s.d.99. 20-Dec-2 Bigwood, Stratford on Avon #217/R est:200-300

PAINE, May (1873-?) American
£1037 $1700 €1504 South Carolina shoreline (48x61cm-19x24in) s. 1-Jun-3 Wright, Chicago #215/R est:2000-3000

PAIX, Josef de la (1854-1895) German
£699 $1090 €1049 Tyrolean tavern Eppan (37x29cm-15x11in) s.i.d.1896 mono.i. verso. 20-Nov-2 Fischer, Luzern #2210/R est:1600-2000 (S.FR 1600)

PAJETTA, Guido (1898-1987) Italian
£949 $1481 €1500 Figure (70x37cm-28x15in) s.d.1963. 14-Sep-2 Meeting Art, Vercelli #897/R
£980 $1569 €1500 Martyrdom (40x35cm-16x14in) s.d.1950 cardboard on canvas. 4-Jan-3 Meeting Art, Vercelli #74
£1282 $2013 €2000 Littl evillage (39x55cm-15x22in) s.d.1948. 23-Nov-2 Meeting Art, Vercelli #109
£1835 $2863 €2900 Private house (38x55cm-15x22in) s.d.1942. 14-Sep-2 Meeting Art, Vercelli #916/R
£1923 $3019 €3000 Woman (55x38cm-22x15in) s.d.1963. 23-Nov-2 Meeting Art, Vercelli #182/R
£2308 $3623 €3600 Beach in Liguria (54x73cm-21x29in) s.d.1939. 23-Nov-2 Meeting Art, Vercelli #211/R
£2778 $4417 €4000 Concert (101x82cm-40x32in) s.d.1952. 1-May-3 Meeting Art, Vercelli #574
£3205 $5032 €5000 Figures (80x60cm-31x24in) s.d.1976. 19-Nov-2 Finarte, Milan #40
£8108 $12649 €12000 Travelling through myth (115x69cm-45x27in) s. painted 1930. 26-Mar-3 Finarte Semenzato, Milan #275/R

PAJETTA, Pietro (1845-1911) Italian
£6038 $9419 €9600 Returning from the fields (15x38cm-6x15in) s.d.1883. 22-Sep-2 Semenzato, Venice #109/R est:4000-5000

PAJOT, Émile Paul (1870-1930) French
Works on paper
£2431 $3962 €3500 Le port de Douarnenez (42x60cm-17x24in) s.i. W/C. 19-Jul-3 Thierry & Lannon, Brest #73 est:3000-4000

PAJOT, Gilbert (?) French
Works on paper
£1549 $2572 €2200 Les Sables d'Olonne (40x33cm-16x13in) s. W/C. 11-Jun-3 Beaussant & Lefèvre, Paris #108/R est:800-1200

PAJOU, Augustin (1730-1809) French
Sculpture
£24679 $38253 €38500 Portrait de Jean Baptiste II Lemoyne (14x14cm-6x6in) s. terracotta relief. 9-Dec-2 Rabourdin & Choppin de Janvry, Paris #8/R est:9000
£70513 $109295 €110000 Portrait presumede Flore Pajou (67x42x30cm-26x17x12in) s.d.1786 terracotta exhib.lit. 9-Dec-2 Rabourdin & Choppin de Janvry, Paris #28/R est:120000
£89744 $139103 €140000 Portrait de Claude-Edme Labille (47x24x16cm-19x9x6in) terracotta exec.1784 exhib.lit. 9-Dec-2 Rabourdin & Choppin de Janvry, Paris #25/R
£90323 $142710 €140000 Madame de Bonnard (69cm-27in) s.d.1780 terracotta stone socle prov.lit. 17-Dec-2 Sotheby's, Paris #90/R est:80000
£500000 $775000 €780000 Tete d'expression (54x30x22cm-21x12x9in) s.d.1768 terracotta. 9-Dec-2 Rabourdin & Choppin de Janvry, Paris #30/R est:180000
Works on paper
£284 $474 €400 Etudes de vases d'apres l'antique (19x25cm-7x10in) black pencil prov. sold with two others by the same hand. 19-Jun-3 Piasa, Paris #120
£284 $474 €400 Etudes de pietement et de griffons (18x12cm-7x5in) black crayon grey wash prov. sold with a dr by the same hand. 19-Jun-3 Piasa, Paris #121
£426 $711 €600 Etude de femme d'apres l'Antique (18x12cm-7x5in) pen brown ink crayon prov. sold with 2 others by the same hand. 19-Jun-3 Piasa, Paris #122
£426 $711 €600 Etude de terme a l'effigie d'Hercule (18x12cm-7x5in) i. pen brown ink black crayon sold with 2 drs by the same hand. 19-Jun-3 Piasa, Paris #123
£496 $829 €700 Etudes de vaches, chevres et chien (12x17cm-5x7in) i. black crayon sold with two drs by the same hand. 19-Jun-3 Piasa, Paris #124
£1013 $1580 €1600 Couronnement de l'Amour (26x38cm-10x15in) s.d.1780 pierre noire htd white. 18-Oct-2 Rabourdin & Choppin de Janvry, Paris #86/R
£1899 $2962 €3000 Pyrrhus et Glaucias (55x78cm-22x31in) s. pen Chinese ink wash prov. 18-Oct-2 Rabourdin & Choppin de Janvry, Paris #88/R
£2215 $3456 €3500 Projet de medaille (29x23cm-11x9in) s.d.1784 crayon prov.lit. 18-Oct-2 Rabourdin & Choppin de Janvry, Paris #82/R
£2315 $3750 €3473 Design for medal (22cm-9in circular) i. chk prov.exhib. 21-Jan-3 Sotheby's, New York #110/R
£2848 $4443 €4500 Projet de medaille (25cm-10in circular) pierre noire double-sided prov.lit. 18-Oct-2 Rabourdin & Choppin de Janvry, Paris #83
£4012 $6500 €6018 Design for medal (29x23cm-11x9in) chk prov.lit. 21-Jan-3 Sotheby's, New York #111/R est:6000
£6962 $10861 €11000 Scene de sacrifice a Dionysos (60x90cm-24x35in) i. pen ink wash sanguine htd white. 18-Oct-2 Rabourdin & Choppin de Janvry, Paris #85/R est:4000

PAJOU, Augustin (after) (1730-1809) French
Sculpture
£11538 $17885 €18000 Buffon assis (43x23x23cm-17x9x9in) pat bronze exec.1788 lit. 9-Dec-2 Rabourdin & Choppin de Janvry, Paris #54/R
£21678 $36203 €31000 L'allegorie de la naissance du Dauphin (42cm-17in) terracotta sold with gilt wood socle prov.lit. 25-Jun-3 Sotheby's, Paris #72/R est:15000-20000

PAJOU, Augustin (attrib) (1730-1809) French
Sculpture
£7692 $11923 €12000 Portrait presume du Conventionnel Gerard (41x21cm-16x8in) terracotta. 9-Dec-2 Rabourdin & Choppin de Janvry, Paris #27/R

PAJOU, Jacques Augustin Catherine and Augustin (19th C) French
£16774 $26503 €26000 Etudes de figures d'hommes (100x82cm-39x32in) s.d.1785 pair exhib. 20-Dec-2 Tajan, Paris #149/R est:12000-15000

PAKOSTA, Florentine (1933-) Austrian
Works on paper
£1899 $2943 €3000 Smoker (140x97cm-55x38in) s.d.1986 pencil Indian ink sprayed. 24-Sep-2 Wiener Kunst Auktionen, Vienna #302/R est:3000-4500
£2848 $4415 €4500 Heads (97x148cm-38x58in) pencil Indian ink spray technique. 24-Sep-2 Wiener Kunst Auktionen, Vienna #276/R est:2500-5000

PAL, Fried (1914-) Hungarian
£491 $800 €737 Ballerina (79x51cm-31x20in) s. 2-Feb-3 Grogan, Boston #17
£611 $965 €917 Greta (81x59cm-32x23in) s. 7-Apr-3 Australian Art Auctions, Sydney #125 (A.D 1600)
£763 $1206 €1145 Ballerina (79x59cm-31x23in) s. 7-Apr-3 Australian Art Auctions, Sydney #126 (A.D 2000)
£1731 $2717 €2700 Female nude (61x76cm-24x30in) s. 21-Nov-2 Van Ham, Cologne #1857/R est:2800
£2885 $4500 €4328 Road west (61x76cm-24x30in) s. i.verso prov. 9-Nov-2 Santa Fe Art, Santa Fe #128/R est:3000-5000
£6250 $9750 €9375 Bucking bronco (79x61cm-31x24in) s. prov. 9-Nov-2 Santa Fe Art, Santa Fe #74/R est:4000-6000
Works on paper
£791 $1250 €1187 At the ball (33x30cm-13x12in) s. pastel gouache. 17-Nov-2 Jeffery Burchard, Florida #22/R

PALACIOS, Joaquin Vaquero (1900-1998) Spanish
£5660 $8717 €9000 Somiedo landscape (45x35cm-18x14in) s. board. 22-Oct-2 Durán, Madrid #213/R est:9000
Works on paper
£316 $499 €490 Farewell (15x17cm-6x7in) s. pencil dr. 18-Dec-2 Ansorena, Madrid #968/R
£338 $527 €500 Landscape (19x14cm-7x6in) s. dr lit. 25-Mar-3 Durán, Madrid #38

PALADINI, Vinicio (1902-1971) Italian
Photographs
£11392 $18000 €17088 Movement and space (34x24cm-13x9in) photomontage gelatin silver print lit. 22-Apr-3 Christie's, Rockefeller NY #144/R est:10000-15000

PALADINO, Mimmo (1948-) Italian
£3000 $4890 €4500 Gesso (35x25cm-14x10in) s.d.79 on overlap i.verso. 3-Feb-3 Sotheby's, Olympia #93/R est:2000-3000
£4000 $6160 €6000 Untitled (59x76cm-23x30in) oil gold silver paint collage on paper executed 1982 prov. 23-Oct-2 Christie's, London #141/R est:3000-4000
£7051 $10929 €11000 Untitled (103x72cm-41x28in) s.d.1988 cardboard. 4-Dec-2 Finarte, Milan #492/R est:10000
£13514 $21757 €20271 Senza titulo (140x150cm-55x59in) s.d.1977 verso oil collage. 7-May-3 AB Stockholms Auktionsverk #957/R est:30000-40000 (S.KR 175000)
£14000 $21560 €21000 Untitled (88x80cm-35x31in) s.d.1984 verso oil wood collage on hessian prov. 22-Oct-2 Sotheby's, London #381/R est:10000-15000
£15000 $23100 €22500 Camera Mozart (75x90cm-30x35in) init.d.1985 s.i.d.verso panel prov. 23-Oct-2 Christie's, London #139/R est:15000-20000
£25000 $41000 €37500 Untitled no.3 (145x205cm-57x81in) oil pastel sand fabric cardboard prov.exhib. 6-Feb-3 Christie's, London #652/R est:25000-35000
£30000 $46800 €45000 Untitled (121x90cm-48x35in) s.d.1983 verso acrylic on canvas collage painted wood prov.exhib. 21-Oct-2 Sotheby's, London #62/R est:25000-35000
£37975 $60000 €56963 Lucomone (142x112cm-56x44in) s.d.1983 oil wood canvas collage prov. 13-Nov-2 Sotheby's, New York #521/R est:30000-40000
£50000 $83500 €72500 Vespero (200x300cm-79x118in) s.i.d.1981 prov. 27-Jun-3 Christie's, London #183/R est:40000-60000
£55000 $90200 €82500 Poem at the gates of Bethlehem (300x300cm-118x118in) s.i.d.1982 verso oil mixed media prov.exhib. 6-Feb-3 Sotheby's, London #36/R est:70000
£58000 $89320 €87000 Untitled (210x150cm-83x59in) s.d.82 oil mixed media painted wood on cardboard prov. 22-Oct-2 Christie's, London #56/R est:65000-85000

Sculpture
£2536 $4159 €3500 Untitled, carafe with stopper (31cm-12in) s.d.1994 num.2/3 st.f.Venturi Arte pat bronze. 27-May-3 Wiener Kunst Auktionen, Vienna #218/R est:3500-7000
£13750 $22000 €20625 Disco (63x58x27cm-25x23x11in) s.d.1986 num.6/6 painted bronze prov. 14-May-3 Sotheby's, New York #416/R est:10000-15000
£16250 $26000 €24375 Untitled (62x62x57cm-24x24x22in) s.d.1986 num.5/5 brown pat. bronze prov. 14-May-3 Sotheby's, New York #417/R est:15000-20000
£21875 $35000 €32813 L'isola - island (218x53x76cm-86x21x30in) painted wood stone executed 1983 prov. 14-May-3 Sotheby's, New York #426/R est:30000-40000
£90000 $140400 €135000 Giardino chiuso (200x185x175cm-79x73x69in) sig.d.1982 painted bronze prov.lit. 21-Oct-2 Sotheby's, London #64/R est:90000-120000

Works on paper
£752 $1203 €1150 Smoky (20x24cm-8x9in) s. Chinese ink. 4-Jan-3 Meeting Art, Vercelli #545
£1013 $1600 €1600 Untitled (30x39cm-12x15in) mono. s.d.1987 verso pencil Indian ink. 27-Nov-2 Dorotheum, Vienna #98/R
£1048 $1530 €1572 Untitled (35x50cm-14x20in) s.d.1980 verso mixed media. 4-Jun-2 Germann, Zurich #21/R est:2500-3000 (S.FR 2400)
£1667 $2617 €2600 Untitled (45x35cm-18x14in) s.d.65 collage mixed media card. 20-Nov-2 Pandolfini, Florence #136/R
£1689 $2635 €2500 Untitled (30x40cm-12x16in) pastel htd bodycol wax over pencil. 28-Mar-3 Ketterer, Hamburg #535/R est:2500-3000
£1923 $3019 €3000 Untitled (31x43cm-12x17in) s. mixed media collage. 20-Nov-2 Pandolfini, Florence #156/R
£2313 $3608 €3470 Untitled (51x69cm-20x27in) s.d.1983 verso mixed media. 5-Nov-2 Bukowskis, Stockholm #435/R est:35000-40000 (S.KR 33000)
£2564 $3744 €4000 Composition (40x27cm-16x11in) s. mixed media collage prov. 5-Jun-2 Il Ponte, Milan #158/R
£2721 $4327 €4000 Mythological lands (12x8cm-5x3in) s.i.d.1992 verso gouache. 24-Mar-3 Cornette de St.Cyr, Paris #29/R
£4000 $6520 €6000 Untitled (47x35cm-19x14in) s.d.1990 pencil W/C gouache set of three prov. 3-Feb-3 Sotheby's, Olympia #213/R est:3000-4000
£4200 $6846 €6300 Untitled (39x30cm-15x12in) pencil crayon prov. 3-Feb-3 Sotheby's, Olympia #214/R est:2000-3000
£4600 $7498 €6900 Untitled (47x35cm-19x14in) s.d.1990 gouache pencil collage three. 3-Feb-3 Sotheby's, Olympia #212/R est:3000-4000
£5500 $8690 €8250 Untitled (56x78cm-22x31in) s. collage brush ink wax crayon acrylic Polyfilla exec.1981 prov. 3-Apr-3 Christie's, Kensington #243/R
£8760 $13665 €13140 Woman (103x73cm-41x29in) s.d.1984 verso mixed media paper on cardboard. 5-Nov-2 Bukowskis, Stockholm #431/R est:100000-120000 (S.KR 125000)
£30968 $48929 €48000 First lights at dawn (82x100cm-32x39in) s.i.d.1986 verso mixed media canvas on panel prov. 18-Dec-2 Christie's, Rome #301/R est:40000

PALAMEDES, Anthonie (1601-1673) Dutch
£2400 $3720 €3600 Guardroom interior with courtesans entertaining a gentleman (44x61cm-17x24in) indis.sig.d.1635 panel. 30-Oct-2 Bonhams, New Bond Street #90/R est:2000-3000
£3500 $5845 €5075 Guardroom interior with a cavalier conversing with a drummer. Guardroom interior, cavalier mother (34x39cm-13x15in) s. panel pair. 11-Jul-3 Christie's, Kensington #26/R est:3000-5000
£4088 $6296 €6500 Scene de banquet (24x31cm-9x12in) panel. 25-Oct-2 Tajan, Paris #65/R est:6000-9000
£4500 $7020 €6750 Guardroom interior with a cavalier conversing with a drummer. Guardroom interior (34x39cm-13x15in) one s. panel pair. 10-Apr-3 Christie's, Kensington #73/R est:3500-4500
£5732 $8943 €9000 Kortegaarje, soldiers smoking and making music (28x37cm-11x15in) bears sig panel prov. 5-Nov-2 Sotheby's, Amsterdam #209/R est:10000-15000
£20000 $31200 €30000 Elegant company in an interior with a gentleman playing the cello (60x79cm-24x31in) panel prov. 9-Apr-3 Christie's, London #40/R est:12000-18000

PALAMEDES, Anthonie (attrib) (1601-1673) Dutch
£3400 $5338 €5100 Portrait of a young woman in a black and gold dress (42x26cm-17x10in) panel prov. 21-Nov-2 Tennants, Leyburn #720/R est:3000-4000

PALAMEDES, Anthonie (circle) (1601-1673) Dutch
£7500 $11700 €11250 Portrait of a gentleman in a black jacket and white collar (33x26cm-13x10in) panel. 9-Apr-3 Christie's, London #45/R est:7000-10000

PALAMEDES, Palamedesz (17th C) Dutch
£2564 $3974 €4000 Extensive landscape with combat on horseback (37cm-15in circular) s.d.1626 i.verso panel lit. 4-Dec-2 Neumeister, Munich #630/R est:7000
£5405 $8432 €8000 Officer commanding cavalry engagement. bears sig.d.1620 panel. 27-Mar-3 Dorotheum, Vienna #321/R est:8000-12000

PALAMEDES, Palamedesz I (circle) (1607-1638) Dutch
£5000 $7800 €7500 Cavalry engagement (50x85cm-20x33in) panel. 10-Apr-3 Christie's, Kensington #69/R est:5000-7000

PALANTI, Giuseppe (1881-1946) Italian
Works on paper
£774 $1223 €1200 Exhibition Pavillion (22x33cm-9x13in) s. W/C pair. 18-Dec-2 Finarte, Milan #207/R

PALAU BUIXO, Juan de (1919-) Spanish
£1613 $2548 €2500 Landscape by Banolas (70x130cm-28x51in) s. s.verso. 17-Dec-2 Durán, Madrid #49/R

PALAU OLLER, Jose (1888-?) Spanish
£28767 $44877 €42000 Vase of flowers (61x50cm-24x20in) s. 8-Apr-3 Ansorena, Madrid #8/R est:420

PALAZZI, Bernardino (1907-1987) Italian
£392 $627 €600 Reclining female nude (18x27cm-7x11in) s.d.1949. 4-Jan-3 Meeting Art, Vercelli #165
£475 $741 €750 Woman from Sardinia (26x19cm-10x7in) i.d.1953 s.d.verso. 14-Sep-2 Meeting Art, Vercelli #854/R

PALDI, Israel (1892-1979) Israeli
Works on paper
£993 $1619 €1500 Tableau mystique (54x73cm-21x29in) s. mixed media on canvas. 3-Feb-3 Cornette de St.Cyr, Paris #495

PALENCIA, Benjamin (1894-1980) Spanish
£1419 $2243 €2200 Vase of flowers (50x34cm-20x13in) s. paper. 18-Dec-2 Ansorena, Madrid #946/R
£4091 $5973 €6300 Church (26x35cm-10x14in) s. cardboard. 17-Jun-2 Ansorena, Madrid #166/R
£11613 $18348 €18000 Spring landscape (33x41cm-13x16in) s.d.1973 exhib.lit. 17-Dec-2 Segre, Madrid #103/R est:17000
£11688 $17065 €18000 Untitled (45x64cm-18x25in) s.d. 12-Jun-2 Castellana, Madrid #281/R est:18000
£20645 $32000 €30968 El valle (76x66cm-30x26in) s.d.49. 26-Sep-2 Christie's, Rockefeller NY #572/R est:18000-22000
Works on paper
£288 $421 €450 Untitled (22x14cm-9x6in) s.d.1974 pencil dr double-sided. 6-Jun-2 Castellana, Madrid #542/R
£323 $510 €500 Peasant man (16x21cm-6x8in) s.d.1969 ink dr. 18-Dec-2 Ansorena, Madrid #967/R
£348 $550 €540 Basket with fruit (23x16cm-9x6in) s.i. ink dr. 17-Dec-2 Segre, Madrid #137/R
£449 $655 €700 Untitled (22x16cm-9x6in) s. ink dr. 6-Jun-2 Castellana, Madrid #543/R
£481 $702 €750 Wide street in Villafranca (31x21cm-12x8in) s.i. ink dr. 6-Jun-2 Castellana, Madrid #550/R
£493 $799 €750 Figures (38x28cm-15x11in) s.d.31 W/C. 21-Jan-3 Durán, Madrid #69/R
£503 $785 €800 Peasant and horse (22x33cm-9x13in) s.d.1969 ink. 17-Sep-2 Segre, Madrid #240/R
£507 $791 €750 Shepherdess (21x14cm-8x6in) s. mixed media exhib. 25-Mar-3 Durán, Madrid #34
£545 $861 €850 Margarita (40x32cm-16x13in) s.d.59 dr. 19-Nov-2 Durán, Madrid #117/R
£613 $968 €950 Landscape with peasants (33x49cm-13x19in) s.d.1968 ink dr. 18-Dec-2 Ansorena, Madrid #955/R
£641 $1006 €1000 Untitled (28x21cm-11x8in) s.d.63 pen dr. 19-Nov-2 Castellana, Madrid #56/R
£641 $936 €1000 Uncle Quico (26x18cm-10x7in) s.d. ink wax crayon lit. 6-Jun-2 Castellana, Madrid #2/R
£641 $1013 €1000 Goats (27x38cm-11x15in) s. ink dr. 13-Nov-2 Ansorena, Madrid #437/R
£685 $1068 €1000 Portrait of woman (24x14cm-9x6in) s.d.1920 col dr. 8-Apr-3 Ansorena, Madrid #674/R
£710 $1121 €1100 Boy. Horses (35x47cm-14x19in) s.d.44 ink dr double-sided. 17-Dec-2 Durán, Madrid #100/R
£710 $1121 €1100 Boys (47x38cm-19x15in) s.d.44 ink dr. 17-Dec-2 Durán, Madrid #155/R
£724 $1172 €1100 Fishermen (26x48cm-10x19in) s. ink dr. 21-Jan-3 Ansorena, Madrid #837/R
£755 $1177 €1200 Untitled (48x33cm-19x13in) s. felt-tip pen dr. 23-Sep-2 Durán, Madrid #676/R
£759 $1206 €1100 Boy. Horses (36x47cm-14x19in) s.d.44 ink dr double-sided. 4-Mar-3 Ansorena, Madrid #372/R
£774 $1223 €1200 Castilla (48x56cm-19x22in) s. felt-tip pen dr. 18-Dec-2 Ansorena, Madrid #960/R
£801 $1258 €1250 Kids (28x19cm-11x7in) s.d.53 pen dr. 19-Nov-2 Castellana, Madrid #506/R
£822 $1282 €1200 Landscape in the Mancha (50x34cm-20x13in) s. felt-tip pen dr. 8-Apr-3 Ansorena, Madrid #645/R
£828 $1316 €1200 Castilla (31x45cm-12x18in) s. felt-tip pen. 4-Mar-3 Ansorena, Madrid #375/R
£846 $1337 €1320 Figure (20x29cm-8x11in) s.d.1934 ink dr. 14-Nov-2 Arte, Seville #425/R
£881 $1356 €1400 Reclining female nude (27x44cm-11x17in) s.d.1926 prov. 28-Oct-2 Segre, Madrid #102/R
£890 $1389 €1300 Landscape (46x32cm-18x13in) s. felt-tip pen dr. 8-Apr-3 Ansorena, Madrid #646/R
£943 $1453 €1500 Two female nudes (43x28cm-17x11in) s. pencil dr prov. 28-Oct-2 Segre, Madrid #103/R
£968 $1529 €1500 Shepherds and horses (32x47cm-13x19in) s.d.1967 ink dr. 18-Dec-2 Ansorena, Madrid #962/R
£1032 $1631 €1600 Boy (42x30cm-17x12in) s.d.1942 ink. 17-Dec-2 Segre, Madrid #118/R
£1074 $1729 €1600 Boys and dogs (51x34cm-20x13in) s. ink dr. 18-Feb-3 Durán, Madrid #141/R
£1161 $1835 €1800 Grazing (20x30cm-8x12in) s.d.1961 Chinese ink dr. 17-Dec-2 Durán, Madrid #51/R
£1384 $2131 €2200 Figure in landscape (21x16cm-8x6in) s. ink prov. 28-Oct-2 Segre, Madrid #106/R
£1645 $2664 €2500 Landscape (33x48cm-13x19in) s. gouache. 21-Jan-3 Durán, Madrid #687/R
£2053 $3346 €3100 Two figures (29x23cm-11x9in) s.d.1931 ink dr. 11-Feb-3 Segre, Madrid #150/R
£2097 $3313 €3250 Surrealist figures (28x19cm-11x7in) s. W/C. 17-Dec-2 Durán, Madrid #181/R
£2201 $3390 €3500 Metamorphosis (46x32cm-18x13in) s.d.1934 ink prov. 28-Oct-2 Segre, Madrid #105/R
£2244 $3545 €3500 Altea, January 1927 (23x21cm-9x8in) s. gouache exhib. 19-Nov-2 Durán, Madrid #207/R
£2897 $4577 €4200 Surrealist figure moving (42x27cm-17x11in) s.d.1932 W/C col wax. 1-Apr-3 Segre, Madrid #152/R

PALERMO, Blinky (1943-1977) German
£210000 $350700 €315000 Untitled - braun / olive / olive (200x200cm-79x79in) s.d.69 stretcher cotton over wooden stretcher prov.exhib.lit. 26-Jun-3 Christie's, London #6/R est:80000-120000
Works on paper
£384615 $600000 €576923 Stoffbild (200x200cm-79x79in) s.d.69 verso dyed cotton over wooden stretcher prov.exhib.lit. 11-Nov-2 Phillips, New York #23/R est:500000-700000

PALEZIEUX, Edmond de (1850-1924) Swiss
£411 $600 €617 Stormy sea (68x102cm-27x40in) s.d.1879. 10-May-2 Skinner, Boston #120/R

PALEZIEUX, Gerard (1919-) Swiss
£957 $1483 €1436 Nature morte aux chardons (16x20cm-6x8in) s.d.43 prov. 7-Dec-2 Galerie du Rhone, Sion #489/R est:1500-2000 (S.FR 2200)
£1565 $2426 €2348 Nature morte aux pivoines blanches (23x31cm-9x12in) s.d.85 canvas on panel prov. 7-Dec-2 Galerie du Rhone, Sion #488/R est:2000-3000 (S.FR 3600)
£2087 $3235 €3131 Nature morte (12x21cm-5x8in) mono. canvas on panel prov. 7-Dec-2 Galerie du Rhone, Sion #487/R est:2000-3000 (S.FR 4800)
Works on paper
£652 $1011 €978 Pont sur le canal (19x21cm-7x8in) mono. W/C prov. 7-Dec-2 Galerie du Rhone, Sion #423/R (S.FR 1500)
£1826 $2830 €2739 Nature morte (17x18cm-7x7in) mono. wash. 7-Dec-2 Galerie du Rhone, Sion #421/R est:400-600 (S.FR 4200)
£2174 $3370 €3261 Nature morte (22x18cm-9x7in) mono. wash. 7-Dec-2 Galerie du Rhone, Sion #422/R est:400-600 (S.FR 5000)

PALFFY, Peter (1899-1988) Austrian
£16667 $27333 €23000 Madonna with Child (180x110cm-71x43in) painted 1950 lit. 27-May-3 Hassfurther, Vienna #57/R est:20000-26000

PALIZZI, Filippo (1818-1899) Italian
£2546 $4100 €3819 Young Roman woman in costume (46x34cm-18x13in) 7-May-3 Dobiaschofsky, Bern #867/R est:3000 (S.FR 5500)
£16327 $25959 €24000 Harvest (31x52cm-12x20in) s. 18-Mar-3 Finarte, Milan #141/R
£70886 $112000 €112000 Back from the fields (49x75cm-19x30in) s.d.71 lit. 26-Nov-2 Christie's, Rome #284/R est:80000-100000
Works on paper
£952 $1514 €1400 Sheep (17x20cm-7x8in) s. W/C cardboard. 18-Mar-3 Finarte, Milan #222/R

PALIZZI, Filippo (attrib) (1818-1899) Italian
£2245 $3569 €3300 Peasant woman at rest (52x39cm-20x15in) 18-Mar-3 Finarte, Milan #40/R

PALIZZI, Giuseppe (1812-1888) Italian
£2264 $3623 €3396 Landscape with goatherd and goats (22x16cm-9x6in) s. 17-Mar-3 Philippe Schuler, Zurich #4636/R est:3500-4500 (S.FR 4800)
£18710 $29561 €29000 Shepherd with herd at source (48x38cm-19x15in) s. 18-Dec-2 Finarte, Milan #72/R est:35000

PALLA, F (?) Italian?
Sculpture
£15190 $24000 €22785 Dancing figures (155x63x45cm-61x25x18in) s. white marble pedestal pair after Canova prov. 26-Nov-2 Christie's, Rockefeller NY #66/R est:30000-50000

PALLA, Garciosa (?) Italian?
£541 $850 €812 Still life of peaches (61x41cm-24x16in) board. 13-Dec-2 Du Mouchelle, Detroit #2297/R

PALLANDT, Charlotte van (1898-1997) Dutch
Sculpture
£1266 $2000 €2000 Liggende figuur leunend op linkerarm (17cm-7in) i. terracotta executed 1941 lit. 26-Nov-2 Sotheby's, Amsterdam #31/R est:2000-3000
£2014 $3304 €2800 Twee zittende figuren - two seated figures (13cm-5in) bronze conceived 1955 prov.lit. 3-Jun-3 Christie's, Amsterdam #175/R est:1800-2500
£4487 $6955 €7000 Jeanne bieruma Oosting (47cm-19in) s.d.79 bronze conceived 1976. 3-Dec-2 Christie's, Amsterdam #51/R est:7000-9000

PALLARES Y ALLUSTANTE, Joaquin (1853-1935) Spanish

£680 $1081 €1020 Rainy Parisian scene (43x53cm-17x21in) s. 18-Mar-3 Rosebery Fine Art, London #790/R
£12057 $18688 €18086 Paris, Place de l'Opera (55x67cm-22x26in) s. 3-Dec-2 Bukowskis, Stockholm #192/R est:50000-60000 (S.KR 170000)

Works on paper

£1132 $1766 €1800 Chess game (56x39cm-22x15in) s. W/C. 23-Sep-2 Durán, Madrid #144/R

PALLMANN, Gotz (1908-1966) German

£1026 $1610 €1600 Busy city street (35x40cm-14x16in) s. board. 21-Nov-2 Van Ham, Cologne #1858/R est:1200
£1667 $2617 €2600 Old bridge in Frankfurt am main with Cathedral. s. panel. 23-Nov-2 Arnold, Frankfurt #831/R est:2500
£1923 $3038 €3000 Evening city (44x67cm-17x26in) s. panel. 14-Nov-2 Neumeister, Munich #664/R est:1800-2000

Works on paper

£484 $765 €765 City ruins in Charlottenburg, Berlin (23x34cm-9x13in) s. W/C over pencil. 29-Nov-2 Bolland & Marotz, Bremen #809/R

PALLYA, Carolus (1875-1930) Hungarian

£267 $412 €401 Les oies (11x16cm-4x6in) s. panel. 22-Oct-2 Iegor de Saint Hippolyte, Montreal #79 (C.D 650)
£353 $550 €530 Untitled, figures with horses and wagon (10x18cm-4x7in) board. 18-Oct-2 Du Mouchelle, Detroit #260/R

PALM, Anna (1859-1924) Swedish

Works on paper

£238 $378 €357 Young soldier (26x18cm-10x7in) s. W/C. 3-Mar-3 Lilla Bukowskis, Stockholm #161 (S.KR 3200)
£238 $378 €357 Small game hunt (26x18cm-10x7in) s. W/C. 3-Mar-3 Lilla Bukowskis, Stockholm #167 (S.KR 3200)
£238 $378 €357 Attention! (26x18cm-10x7in) s. W/C. 3-Mar-3 Lilla Bukowskis, Stockholm #168 (S.KR 3200)
£238 $378 €357 Shot coming! (26x18cm-10x7in) s. W/C. 3-Mar-3 Lilla Bukowskis, Stockholm #169 (S.KR 3200)
£297 $473 €446 Ship at sunset (19x12cm-7x5in) s. W/C. 3-Mar-3 Lilla Bukowskis, Stockholm #379 (S.KR 4000)
£312 $497 €468 Sailing vessel (18x13cm-7x5in) s. W/C. 3-Mar-3 Lilla Bukowskis, Stockholm #381 (S.KR 4200)
£423 $665 €635 Hay harvest (24x34cm-9x13in) s.i.d.1908 W/C. 16-Dec-2 Lilla Bukowskis, Stockholm #563 (S.KR 6000)
£567 $879 €851 View towards Stockholm Palace (5x10cm-2x4in) s.i. W/C. 3-Dec-2 Bukowskis, Stockholm #7/R (S.KR 8000)
£567 $879 €851 Steam ship at anchor, view of the ocean (13x28cm-5x11in) s.i.d.93 W/C. 4-Dec-2 AB Stockholms Auktionsverk #1671/R (S.KR 8000)
£780 $1209 €1170 Stockholm Palace and river (8x26cm-3x10in) s.i. W/C. 4-Dec-2 AB Stockholms Auktionsverk #1670/R (S.KR 11000)
£800 $1312 €1200 Champs Elysee, Paris (39x29cm-15x11in) s.i. pencil W/C. 5-Jun-3 Christie's, Kensington #860/R
£864 $1417 €1253 Stockholm (10x13cm-4x5in) s.i. W/C. 4-Jun-3 AB Stockholms Auktionsverk #2271/R (S.KR 11000)
£931 $1508 €1350 Coastal landscape from Sandhamn (22x33cm-9x13in) s. gouache. 25-May-3 Uppsala Auktionskammare, Uppsala #212/R (S.KR 12000)
£1129 $1773 €1694 With white sails, Sandhamn (22x33cm-9x13in) s.i. W/C. 16-Dec-2 Lilla Bukowskis, Stockholm #802 est:12000-15000 (S.KR 16000)
£1202 $1948 €1743 Riddardholmen, Stockholm (13x24cm-5x9in) s. W/C. 26-May-3 Bukowskis, Stockholm #11/R est:12000-15000 (S.KR 15500)
£1206 $1869 €1809 Stockholm's Palace and Helgelandsholmen (9x26cm-4x10in) s.i. W/C. 3-Dec-2 Bukowskis, Stockholm #8/R est:10000-12000 (S.KR 17000)
£1206 $1869 €1809 Stockholm from Saltsjoen (23x31cm-9x12in) s. W/C. 3-Dec-2 Bukowskis, Stockholm #372/R est:10000-12000 (S.KR 17000)
£1312 $2034 €1968 Stockholm Palace and Helgeandsholmen (8x26cm-3x10in) s. W/C. 3-Dec-2 Bukowskis, Stockholm #373/R est:15000-18000 (S.KR 18500)
£1348 $2089 €2022 Stockholm (10x26cm-4x10in) s. W/C. 3-Dec-2 Bukowskis, Stockholm #337/R est:10000-12000 (S.KR 19000)
£1560 $2418 €2340 Stockholm (13x30cm-5x12in) s. W/C. 3-Dec-2 Bukowskis, Stockholm #311/R est:20000-25000 (S.KR 22000)
£1600 $2592 €2400 Shipping in the Strommen at Stockholm (31x46cm-12x18in) s.i.d.1887 pencil W/C htd white. 23-Jan-3 Christie's, Kensington #368/R est:300-500
£1844 $2858 €2766 Stockholm with Skeppsbron, the Palace and Helgelandsholmen (12x37cm-5x15in) s.i. W/C. 3-Dec-2 Bukowskis, Stockholm #310/R est:18000-20000 (S.KR 26000)
£1915 $2968 €2873 View of Stockholm with Riddarholm Church and the Palace (17x31cm-7x12in) s. W/C. 4-Dec-2 AB Stockholms Auktionsverk #1672/R est:18000-20000 (S.KR 27000)
£1964 $3221 €2848 Stockholm's Palace from Kungstradgarden (20x47cm-8x19in) s.i. W/C prov. 4-Jun-3 AB Stockholms Auktionsverk #2164/R est:25000-30000 (S.KR 25000)
£1964 $3221 €2848 Stockholm's entrance towards Saltsjon, roses in foreground (66x53cm-26x21in) s. W/C htd white. 4-Jun-3 AB Stockholms Auktionsverk #2167/R est:30000-35000 (S.KR 25000)
£2128 $3298 €3192 View towards the Royal Opera and the Grand Hotel, Stockholm (13x31cm-5x12in) s. W/C. 4-Dec-2 AB Stockholms Auktionsverk #1658/R est:20000-25000 (S.KR 30000)
£2357 $3865 €3418 Boats at Blasieholms quay, Stockholm (23x31cm-9x12in) s.i. W/C. 4-Jun-3 AB Stockholms Auktionsverk #2165/R est:18000-20000 (S.KR 30000)
£2514 $4123 €3645 View of Stockholm's Palace (17x42cm-7x17in) s.d.1890 W/C. 4-Jun-3 AB Stockholms Auktionsverk #2168/R est:20000-25000 (S.KR 32000)
£2793 $4524 €4050 Stockholm from Saltsjoen (26x47cm-10x19in) s. W/C. 26-May-3 Bukowskis, Stockholm #12/R est:25000-30000 (S.KR 36000)

PALM, Brian (20th C) Irish?

Works on paper

£634 $1052 €900 Snowcaps (39x73cm-15x29in) s. mixed media. 10-Jun-3 James Adam, Dublin #40/R

PALM, Ester (19/20th C) Finnish

£367 $584 €540 Portrait of lady (46x29cm-18x11in) s.d.1903. 24-Mar-3 Bukowskis, Helsinki #232/R

PALM, Gustaf Wilhelm (1810-1890) Swedish

£674 $1044 €1011 The croft Kulan by Drottningholm (47x39cm-19x15in) s.d.1873. 8-Dec-2 Uppsala Auktionskammare, Uppsala #64/R (S.KR 9500)
£2793 $4524 €4050 Italian landscape (55x75cm-22x30in) s.i.d.7 augusti 1847. 26-May-3 Bukowskis, Stockholm #183/R est:40000-45000 (S.KR 36000)

PALM, Torsten (1875-1934) Swedish

£386 $622 €579 Still life of mug with buildings in background (40x33cm-16x13in) s.d.27 panel. 7-May-3 AB Stockholms Auktionsverk #876/R (S.KR 5000)
£491 $765 €737 Still life of violin and jug (35x27cm-14x11in) init. panel. 6-Nov-2 AB Stockholms Auktionsverk #666/R (S.KR 7000)
£562 $877 €843 Landscape from Oland (32x42cm-13x17in) s. panel prov.lit. 13-Sep-2 Lilla Bukowskis, Stockholm #453 (S.KR 8200)
£646 $1021 €969 Avenue de la Gare (21x28cm-8x11in) s. panel prov.exhib.lit. 28-Apr-3 Bukowskis, Stockholm #52/R (S.KR 8500)
£855 $1334 €1283 Landscape with earth cellar. s.d.27 panel exhib. 6-Nov-2 AB Stockholms Auktionsverk #689/R (S.KR 12200)
£4556 $7335 €6834 Riddarfjarden - Stockholm from Smedsudden (37x49cm-15x19in) s.d.19 panel prov.exhib.lit. 7-May-3 AB Stockholms Auktionsverk #672/R est:18000-20000 (S.KR 59000)

PALMA, G di (19/20th C) ?

£1020 $1622 €1500 Rue animee en Orient (24x33cm-9x13in) s. 24-Mar-3 Rabourdin & Choppin de Janvry, Paris #167/R est:1000-1200

PALMA, Jacopo (il Giovane) (1544-1628) Italian

£10063 $15597 €16000 St Helena with the cross (96x73cm-38x29in) 2-Oct-2 Dorotheum, Vienna #253/R est:13000-16000

Works on paper

£845 $1361 €1200 Saint 'Antonio abate tormentato da un demone (20x25cm-8x10in) bears i. pen ink brown W/C blk pencil prov. 12-May-3 Sotheby's, Milan #29/R est:1200-1500
£1000 $1570 €1500 Mocking Christ (7x11cm-3x4in) pen ink wash htd white framing lines. 11-Dec-2 Sotheby's, Olympia #10/R est:800-1200
£2160 $3500 €3240 Christ disputing with the doctors (28x20cm-11x8in) d.1627 pen ink wash htd white prov. 21-Jan-3 Sotheby's, New York #53/R
£3704 $6000 €5556 Studies (17x21cm-7x8in) i. pen ink. 22-Jan-3 Christie's, Rockefeller NY #12/R
£4000 $6680 €5800 Praying woman, seen from behind (29x15cm-11x6in) black white chk. 8-Jul-3 Christie's, London #8/R est:1500-2000
£4500 $7515 €6525 Feeding of the five thousand. Seated figure, seen from behind (25x41cm-10x16in) d.1621 black chk ink wash double-sided prov. 8-Jul-3 Christie's, London #7/R est:5000-7000
£5449 $8446 €8500 Study of seated man (18x12cm-7x5in) i. pen ink over crayon prov. 4-Dec-2 Piasa, Paris #6/R

PALMA, Jacopo (il Giovane-attrib) (1544-1628) Italian

£3000 $4680 €4500 Madonna and Child (101x84cm-40x33in) prov. 10-Apr-3 Christie's, Kensington #224/R est:3000-5000

£9032 $14271 €14000 Deposition (99x130cm-39x51in) 20-Dec-2 Tajan, Paris #28/R est:10000

PALMAROLI Y GONZALEZ, Vicente (1834-1896) Spanish

£1316 $2132 €2000 Head of Ceasar (32x25cm-13x10in) s.i.verso board. 21-Jan-3 Durán, Madrid #112/R

£3145 $4906 €5000 Blessing (40x31cm-16x12in) s. board. 23-Sep-2 Durán, Madrid #237/R

£3188 $5133 €4750 Blessing (40x31cm-16x12in) s. board. 18-Feb-3 Durán, Madrid #238/R

£16774 $26000 €25161 Afternoon Sieta in the park (51x61cm-20x24in) s. panel prov. 30-Oct-2 Christie's, Rockefeller NY #176/R est:25000-35000

£27419 $43323 €42500 On the terrace (51x61cm-20x24in) s. board. 17-Dec-2 Durán, Madrid #230/R est:30000

Works on paper

£1007 $1621 €1500 Woma with fan (29x22cm-11x9in) s. W/C. 18-Feb-3 Durán, Madrid #151/R

PALME, Augustin (1808-1897) German

£478 $745 €750 St Norbert and saints with Pope Honorius II. 6-Nov-2 Hugo Ruef, Munich #1233/R

PALMEIRO, Jose (1903-1984) Spanish

£377 $585 €600 La fermette, vallee de chevreuse (55x66cm-22x26in) s. s.i.verso. 30-Oct-2 Artcurial Briest, Paris #341

£405 $632 €600 Bouquet de fleurs (55x46cm-22x18in) s. 31-Mar-3 Rossini, Paris #68

£475 $741 €750 Modele assis (73x60cm-29x24in) s. 20-Oct-2 Chayette & Cheval, Paris #85

£481 $760 €750 Vase of flowers (45x38cm-18x15in) s. paper. 13-Nov-2 Ansorena, Madrid #13/R

£705 $1114 €1100 Still life of fruit (65x50cm-26x20in) s. 13-Nov-2 Ansorena, Madrid #8/R

£818 $1275 €1300 Landscape with houses and lake (40x30cm-16x12in) s. 17-Sep-2 Segre, Madrid #133/R

£896 $1416 €1300 Bouquet (73x60cm-29x24in) s.d.1932 cardboard on canvas. 4-Apr-3 Tajan, Paris #219

£1034 $1645 €1500 Cubist still life (50x60cm-20x24in) s. board. 4-Mar-3 Ansorena, Madrid #18/R

£1034 $1645 €1500 Bouquet de fleurs (92x73cm-36x29in) s. 5-Mar-3 Doutrebente, Paris #70/R est:1800-2000

£1042 $1646 €1500 Eglise (52x64cm-20x25in) s.d.28 cardboard. 25-Apr-3 Piasa, Paris #192 est:500

£1195 $1864 €1900 Flowers in blue background (73x54cm-29x21in) s.d.60 s.i.d.verso. 23-Sep-2 Durán, Madrid #203/R

£1268 $2041 €1800 Morgat (45x54cm-18x21in) s. 11-May-3 Thierry & Lannon, Brest #268 est:1200-1500

£1275 $2053 €1900 Marne (51x82cm-20x32in) s. 18-Feb-3 Durán, Madrid #211/R

£1319 $2085 €1900 Nature morte (38x55cm-15x22in) s. 25-Apr-3 Piasa, Paris #191/R

£1415 $2208 €2250 Marne woods (51x82cm-20x32in) s. 23-Sep-2 Durán, Madrid #191/R

£1509 $2355 €2400 Venetian canal (60x71cm-24x28in) s.d.70 i.verso. 23-Sep-2 Durán, Madrid #195/R

£1510 $2431 €2250 Landscape in Lot (73x92cm-29x36in) s.d.79. 18-Feb-3 Durán, Madrid #210/R

£1678 $2701 €2500 Woman with lamp (81x65cm-32x26in) s.d.1950. 18-Feb-3 Durán, Madrid #236/R

£2000 $3100 €3000 St. Jea, Cap Ferrat, France (74x55cm-29x22in) s. prov. 5-Dec-2 Christie's, Kensington #90/R est:2000-3000

£2013 $3242 €3000 Normandy port (60x81cm-24x32in) s.d.57. 18-Feb-3 Durán, Madrid #209/R

£2041 $3245 €3000 Marchande de fleurs (74x92cm-29x36in) s. 21-Mar-3 Rieunier, Bailly-Pommery, Mathias, Paris #116

£13836 $21585 €22000 Still life (51x62cm-20x24in) s. board. 8-Oct-2 Ansorena, Madrid #315/R

PALMER HAWKINS, May (1879-?) American

£343 $500 €515 Still life with Zinnias (32x41cm-13x16in) s. 10-May-2 Skinner, Boston #320/R

PALMER, Alfred (1877-1951) British

£256 $400 €384 Venetian scene (36x44cm-14x17in) s. board. 11-Nov-2 Stephan Welz, Johannesburg #89 (SA.R 4000)

£420 $664 €630 Notre Dame, Paris (25x20cm-10x8in) s. card painted c.1908. 1-Dec-2 Lots Road, London #333

PALMER, Franklin (1912-1990) Canadian

£215 $335 €323 Harbour (30x41cm-12x16in) s. s.i.on stretcher. 25-Mar-3 Ritchie, Toronto #164/R (C.D 500)

£400 $656 €580 S.E corner, Heritage Drive and McLeod Trail (60x90cm-24x35in) s. 9-Jun-3 Hodgins, Calgary #141/R (C.D 900)

£402 $635 €603 Rock formation (81x91cm-32x36in) 1-Dec-2 Levis, Calgary #320/R (C.D 1000)

£975 $1550 €1463 Majorcan village (65x90cm-26x35in) s.i. prov. 23-Mar-3 Hodgins, Calgary #59/R est:1500-2000 (C.D 2300)

Works on paper

£551 $876 €827 Waterfront evening (43x47cm-17x19in) i. W/C. 23-Mar-3 Hodgins, Calgary #76/R est:700-900 (C.D 1300)

PALMER, Hannah (19th C) British

Works on paper

£4000 $6360 €6000 Street of Tombs, Pompeii (18x27cm-7x11in) s. W/C over pencil htd bodycol prov.exhib.lit. 19-Mar-3 Sotheby's, London #216/R est:2000-3000

PALMER, Harry Sutton (1854-1933) British

Works on paper

£340 $568 €493 Ballater, Deeside, Scotland (24x34cm-9x13in) s. i.verso W/C. 25-Jun-3 Bonhams, Bury St Edmunds #514

£520 $868 €754 River scene (36x25cm-14x10in) i.verso W/C. 25-Jun-3 Bonhams, Bury St Edmunds #515

£980 $1529 €1470 On the Thames (23x35cm-9x14in) s. W/C. 15-Oct-2 Bearnes, Exeter #364/R

£1100 $1826 €1650 Sheep resting by a moorland tor (33x69cm-13x27in) s.d.1872 W/C. 12-Jun-3 Bonhams, New Bond Street #685/R est:800-1200

£1700 $2822 €2550 Surrey hills looking towards Blackdown (35x51cm-14x20in) s. W/C. 12-Jun-3 Bonhams, New Bond Street #684/R est:1200-1800

£1700 $2839 €2465 Loch Achray, the Trossachs (56x76cm-22x30in) s. W/C bodycol prov. 25-Jun-3 Bonhams, Bury St Edmunds #504/R est:1800-2500

£2200 $3564 €3300 Arundel Castle (36x64cm-14x25in) s.d.84 W/C. 20-May-3 Sotheby's, Olympia #9/R est:2000-3000

£2400 $4008 €3480 Springtime, Surrey (63x43cm-25x17in) s. W/C bodycol. 25-Jun-3 Bonhams, Bury St Edmunds #508/R est:1400-1800

£2800 $4564 €4200 Avon near Stratford (35x52cm-14x20in) s. W/C. 29-Jan-3 Dreweatt Neate, Newbury #25/R est:1800-2200

£2900 $4843 €4205 Wye at Symonds Yat (76x54cm-30x21in) s. W/C bodycol prov. 25-Jun-3 Bonhams, Bury St Edmunds #507/R est:1200-1800

£3800 $6004 €5700 Chattering beck at Ullswater (53x35cm-21x14in) s. W/C. 2-Dec-2 Sotheby's, London #81/R est:2000-3000

PALMER, Herbert Sidney (1881-1970) Canadian

£489 $802 €734 Evening glow (26x21cm-10x8in) s. board. 3-Jun-3 Joyner, Toronto #278/R est:1000-1500 (C.D 1100)

£533 $874 €800 Autumn trees and ferns (26x33cm-10x13in) s. canvas on board. 3-Jun-3 Joyner, Toronto #531 est:1500-2000 (C.D 1200)

£576 $893 €864 Sunny hillside (11x17cm-4x7in) s. canvas on board. 3-Dec-2 Joyner, Toronto #300/R est:1500-1800 (C.D 1400)

£605 $956 €908 Old birch tree, Rice Lake (21x27cm-8x11in) s. i.verso panel prov. 14-Nov-2 Heffel, Vancouver #217/R est:2000-3000 (C.D 1500)

£620 $973 €930 Early snow in October (25x33cm-10x13in) s.i. s.verso board. 24-Jul-2 Walker's, Ottawa #403/R (C.D 1500)

£700 $1084 €1050 Rain Long Lake, near Whitney, ONT (21x26cm-8x10in) s. canvas on board prov. 3-Dec-2 Joyner, Toronto #288/R est:1000-1500 (C.D 1700)

£773 $1205 €1121 Changing skies near Weston (41x51cm-16x20in) s.i. 26-Mar-3 Walker's, Ottawa #205/R est:2000-3000 (C.D 1800)

£782 $1212 €1173 Muskoka Rocks near Bracebridge (21x26cm-8x10in) s. canvas on board prov. 3-Dec-2 Joyner, Toronto #291/R est:1000-1500 (C.D 1900)

£782 $1212 €1173 Across the lake, Haliburton (21x26cm-8x10in) s. panel. 3-Dec-2 Joyner, Toronto #415 est:1000-1500 (C.D 1900)

£800 $1312 €1200 Drifting clouds near Woodbridge (26x34cm-10x13in) s. canvas on board. 3-Jun-3 Joyner, Toronto #477 est:1000-1500 (C.D 1800)

£889 $1458 €1334 Summer sunset, Saskatchewan (40x50cm-16x20in) s. canvas on board. 3-Jun-3 Joyner, Toronto #233/R est:2000-3000 (C.D 2000)

£889 $1458 €1334 Highway to Madawaska (40x50cm-16x20in) s. 3-Jun-3 Joyner, Toronto #242/R est:2000-3000 (C.D 2000)

£1070 $1658 €1605 Caledon hills (21x26cm-8x10in) s. canvas on board. 3-Dec-2 Joyner, Toronto #434 est:1000-1500 (C.D 2600)

£1749 $2711 €2624 Road to the lake (40x50cm-16x20in) s. 3-Dec-2 Joyner, Toronto #183/R est:2000-3000 (C.D 4250)

£1778 $2916 €2667 Horseshore lake, Haliburton, Ontario (35x43cm-14x17in) s. s.i.verso canvasboard prov. 27-May-3 Sotheby's, Toronto #66/R est:2000-3000 (C.D 4000)

PALMER, James Lynwood (1868-1941) British

£1724 $2759 €2500 Georgina (25x30cm-10x12in) s.d.1895. 12-Mar-3 James Adam, Dublin #155/R est:2500-3500

£3500 $5810 €5075 Bay racehorse held by a groom (76x88cm-30x35in) s.d.1916. 12-Jun-3 Christie's, Kensington #75/R est:4000-6000

Works on paper

£1600 $2496 €2400 Cyllene (47x60cm-19x24in) s. chl. 6-Nov-2 Sotheby's, Olympia #88/R est:1200-1800

PALMER, Janet (1940-) Australian?
£1714 $2709 €2571 Sydney harbour (122x122cm-48x48in) i.verso board prov.exhib. 17-Nov-2 Sotheby's, Paddington #82/R est:2000-4000 (A.D 4800)

PALMER, Samuel (1805-1881) British
Prints
£2500 $3900 €3750 Skylark (12x11cm-5x4in) etching. 25-Mar-3 Sotheby's, London #60/R est:1200-1500
£3200 $4992 €4800 Lonely tower (19x25cm-7x10in) s. etching. 25-Mar-3 Sotheby's, London #58/R est:1200-1500
£5031 $8000 €7547 Christmas, or folding the last sheep. Sleeping shepherd, early morning (11x10cm-4x4in) one exec.1850 one exec.1857 etching pair. 2-May-3 Sotheby's, New York #249/R est:5000-7000
Works on paper
£5500 $8635 €8250 Windmill near Pulborough, West Sussex (12x16cm-5x6in) pencil W/C scratching out prov.exhib. 21-Nov-2 Christie's, London #31/R est:3000-5000
£20000 $33200 €30000 Evening, cottager returning home greeted by his children (19x41cm-7x16in) W/C over pencil htd bodycol gum arabic prov.lit. 12-Jun-3 Sotheby's, London #147/R est:20000-30000
£520000 $863200 €780000 Golden valley (13x16cm-5x6in) i. W/C bodycol gum arabic gold pencil ink scratching out. 11-Jun-3 Christie's, London #5/R est:500000-800000

PALMER, Samuel (attrib) (1805-1881) British
£734 $1218 €1064 The road home (48x64cm-19x25in) bears sig. 16-Jun-3 Lilla Bukowskis, Stockholm #228 (S.KR 9500)
Works on paper
£1200 $1896 €1800 Bridge over a stream (15x17cm-6x7in) W/C over pencil prov. 28-Nov-2 Sotheby's, London #336/R est:600-800

PALMER, Sutton (1854-1935) British
Works on paper
£630 $1021 €914 River landscape with hills in background, in Lake District (32x48cm-13x19in) s. W/C. 24-May-3 Windibank, Dorking #370

PALMER, W L (19th C) German
£1188 $1900 €1782 Genre scene of interior with seated gentleman and caged canary. s. 1-Jan-3 Nadeau, Windsor #139/R est:1000-2000

PALMER, Walter L (1854-1932) American
£5484 $8500 €8226 Medieval fort in Brittany. painted c.1876. 8-Dec-2 Toomey, Oak Park #665/R est:10000-15000
£10968 $17000 €16452 Magic hour (53x41cm-21x16in) s. painted c.1910 prov. 8-Dec-2 Toomey, Oak Park #647/R est:20000-22000
Works on paper
£466 $750 €699 Winter landscape (23x15cm-9x6in) s.i.d.April 23 1887 W/C. 15-Jan-3 Boos Gallery, Michigan #577/R
£8176 $13000 €12264 Normansvale (56x76cm-22x30in) s.i. W/C gouache prov.exhib.lit. 5-Mar-3 Sotheby's, New York #24/R est:15000-25000

PALMERO DE GREGORIO, Alfredo (1901-1991) Spanish
£425 $684 €650 Chevaux pres d'une barriere (60x120cm-24x47in) s. 20-Jan-3 Horta, Bruxelles #135
£1438 $2315 €2200 Vue des Champs Elysees anime (70x100cm-28x39in) s. 20-Jan-3 Horta, Bruxelles #134 est:1200-1800
£1474 $2285 €2300 Elegante au cafe (90x116cm-35x46in) s. 9-Dec-2 Horta, Bruxelles #352 est:1500-2000
£1569 $2525 €2400 St Germain des Pres a Paris (70x100cm-28x39in) s. 20-Jan-3 Horta, Bruxelles #133 est:1500-2000

PALMERO, Alfredo (19/20th C) Spanish
£516 $815 €800 Gypsy campment (54x65cm-21x26in) s. 17-Dec-2 Durán, Madrid #4/R
£516 $815 €800 Carnival in Madrid (55x46cm-22x18in) s.i. 17-Dec-2 Durán, Madrid #2/R
£516 $815 €800 Plaza Vieja, Madrid (65x81cm-26x32in) s.i. 17-Dec-2 Durán, Madrid #1/R
£1290 $2039 €2000 Cafe in Calle de Alcala' (89x116cm-35x46in) s.i. 17-Dec-2 Durán, Madrid #156/R
£1774 $2803 €2750 Opera, Paris (89x116cm-35x46in) s. 17-Dec-2 Durán, Madrid #157/R
£2097 $3313 €3250 Cafe de Paris (65x81cm-26x32in) s. 17-Dec-2 Durán, Madrid #188/R

PALMIE, Gisbert (1897-1986) German
£466 $750 €699 Woman in black (58x46cm-23x18in) s.i. board. 19-Feb-3 Doyle, New York #50

PALMIERI, Pietro Giacomo (?-c.1819) Italian
Works on paper
£506 $800 €800 Trois chevaux pres d'une ferme, un homme assis nourissant l'un d'eux (32x40cm-13x16in) s. pen brown ink brown wash. 27-Nov-2 Christie's, Paris #106/R

PALMORE, Tom (1944-) American
£723 $1150 €1085 Parrot (28x36cm-11x14in) i. on stretcher acrylic board prov. 5-Mar-3 Doyle, New York #99/R
£5732 $9000 €8598 In outer space (76x102cm-30x40in) s. 22-Nov-2 Skinner, Boston #402/R est:3000-5000

PALMU, Jan (1945-1995) Finnish
£288 $472 €400 Still life of oranges and grapes (25x25cm-10x10in) s.d.80. 4-Jun-3 Bukowskis, Helsinki #385/R
£338 $555 €470 Still life (25x25cm-10x10in) s. 5-Jun-3 Hagelstam, Helsinki #996
£576 $944 €800 Still life (50x62cm-20x24in) s. 5-Jun-3 Hagelstam, Helsinki #827
£662 $1085 €920 Still life (47cm-19in) s.d.89. 4-Jun-3 Bukowskis, Helsinki #386/R

PALMU, Juhani (1944-) Finnish
£345 $545 €500 Farm (28x43cm-11x17in) s. 3-Apr-3 Hagelstam, Helsinki #1012
£377 $581 €600 Door (34x30cm-13x12in) s. 24-Oct-2 Hagelstam, Helsinki #972
£409 $630 €650 Women (48x39cm-19x15in) s. 24-Oct-2 Hagelstam, Helsinki #1031
£612 $973 €900 Cabins (50x70cm-20x28in) s.d.76. 24-Mar-3 Bukowskis, Helsinki #233/R
£714 $1136 €1050 Landscape with town (50x90cm-20x35in) s.d.77. 24-Mar-3 Bukowskis, Helsinki #234/R
£918 $1460 €1350 Road to town (50x90cm-20x35in) s.d.77. 24-Mar-3 Bukowskis, Helsinki #235/R

PALSA, Kalervo (1947-1987) Finnish
Works on paper
£261 $429 €400 Self portrait (40x32cm-16x13in) s.d.23.3.87 Indian ink. 9-Feb-3 Bukowskis, Helsinki #336/R
£442 $703 €650 Memory from Auschwitz (44x56cm-17x22in) s.d.1980 W/C. 27-Feb-3 Hagelstam, Helsinki #979/R

PALTA, Josef (1886-?) German
£369 $575 €554 Portraits of a man and woman (23x17cm-9x7in) s. pair. 15-Oct-2 Stephan Welz, Johannesburg #395 est:6000-9000 (SA.R 6000)

PALTRINIERI, Oreste (1873-?) Italian
£544 $865 €800 Viareggio market (11x27cm-4x11in) s. cardboard. 18-Mar-3 Finarte, Milan #202/R

PALTRONIERI, Pietro (circle) (1673-1741) Italian
£5500 $8579 €8250 Raising of Lazarus (93x119cm-37x47in) 19-Sep-2 Christie's, Kensington #296/R est:3000-4000

PALUGYAY, Zoltan (1898-1935) Czechoslovakian
£1026 $1591 €1539 Piles of hay (31x35cm-12x14in) painted c.1930. 3-Dec-2 SOGA, Bratislava #59/R est:45000 (SL.K 65000)
Works on paper
£315 $460 €473 Krivan Peak (42x28cm-17x11in) W/C exec.c.1930. 4-Jun-2 SOGA, Bratislava #56/R est:18000 (SL.K 20000)
£662 $939 €993 Symbolic motive (28x20cm-11x8in) pastel exec.c.1930. 26-Mar-2 SOGA, Bratislava #68/R (SL.K 42000)

PALUMBO, Alphonse (?) ?
£414 $650 €621 Autumn leaves (35x43cm-14x17in) s. canvasboard. 22-Nov-2 Skinner, Boston #277/R
£915 $1500 €1327 After a long day (71x86cm-28x34in) 5-Jun-3 Swann Galleries, New York #191/R est:1500-2500
£1863 $3000 €2795 Couple dancing at a masquerade ball (79x76cm-31x30in) s. painted c.1930. 10-May-3 Illustration House, New York #96/R est:3000-5000

PALUMBO, Eduardo (1932-) Italian
£340 $541 €500 Light appearing (24x30cm-9x12in) s.i.d.2001 verso vinyl. 1-Mar-3 Meeting Art, Vercelli #328
£347 $552 €500 Fire wing (30x24cm-12x9in) s.i.d.2001 verso vinyl. 1-May-3 Meeting Art, Vercelli #16
£347 $552 €500 Green in the moonlight (24x30cm-9x12in) s.i.d.2001 vinyl. 1-May-3 Meeting Art, Vercelli #157
£1282 $2013 €2000 Untitled (50x70cm-20x28in) s.d.1986 vinyl. 23-Nov-2 Meeting Art, Vercelli #97/R

£1282 $2013 €2000 Remembering (70x100cm-28x39in) s.i.d.1988 verso acrylic vinyl. 23-Nov-2 Meeting Art, Vercelli #340/R
£1285 $2043 €1850 Endless (50x70cm-20x28in) s.i.d.1989 verso vinyl acrylic lit. 1-May-3 Meeting Art, Vercelli #398
£1307 $2092 €2000 Harvest (70x100cm-28x39in) s.i.d.1987 acrylic vinyl. 4-Jan-3 Meeting Art, Vercelli #610

Works on paper

£316 $494 €500 Veiled songs (50x35cm-20x14in) s.i. verso W/C exec.2000. 14-Sep-2 Meeting Art, Vercelli #367
£327 $523 €500 Island in the sky (35x50cm-14x20in) s.d.2000 W/C. 4-Jan-3 Meeting Art, Vercelli #549
£425 $680 €650 Whispered music (35x50cm-14x20in) s.i.verso W/C. 4-Jan-3 Meeting Art, Vercelli #361
£523 $837 €800 Beam in the sea (35x50cm-14x20in) s.d.2000 W/C. 4-Jan-3 Meeting Art, Vercelli #342
£570 $889 €900 Only dreams (50x35cm-20x14in) s.i.d.2000 W/C. 14-Sep-2 Meeting Art, Vercelli #78
£633 $987 €1000 Green afternoon (35x50cm-14x20in) s.i.verso W/C exec.2000. 14-Sep-2 Meeting Art, Vercelli #781/R

PALUMBO, Onofrio (17th C) Italian

£12346 $20000 €18519 Magdalen (121x153cm-48x60in) 23-Jan-3 Sotheby's, New York #228/R est:30000

PAMBOUJIAN, Gerard (1941-) French

£671 $1081 €1000 Cafe Florian a Venise (60x73cm-24x29in) s. 23-Feb-3 Mercier & Cie, Lille #245

PAN TIANSHOU (1897-1971) Chinese

Works on paper

£4065 $6423 €6098 Bird resting on the branch (69x38cm-27x15in) s. ink col hanging scroll. 28-Apr-3 Sotheby's, Hong Kong #631/R est:25000-35000 (HK.D 50000)
£13008 $20553 €19512 Cat lying on the rock (96x44cm-38x17in) s. ink col hanging scroll. 28-Apr-3 Sotheby's, Hong Kong #609/R est:50000-70000 (HK.D 160000)

PAN, Antonio (1937-2001) Spanish

£252 $392 €400 Carnival (18x33cm-7x13in) s. cardboard. 23-Sep-2 Durán, Madrid #653/R
£283 $442 €450 Procession (50x70cm-20x28in) s. s.i.d.1995 verso panel. 23-Sep-2 Durán, Madrid #41/R
£299 $466 €475 Beach (14x22cm-6x9in) board. 23-Sep-2 Durán, Madrid #656/R

PANABAKER, Frank S (1904-1992) Canadian

£511 $838 €767 Autumn landscape (40x50cm-16x20in) s. board. 3-Jun-3 Joyner, Toronto #496 est:1500-2000 (C.D 1150)
£978 $1604 €1467 Peaceful river in winter (50x60cm-20x24in) s. 3-Jun-3 Joyner, Toronto #306/R est:2000-3000 (C.D 2200)
£1022 $1676 €1482 Sugar bush, Ontario (63x75cm-25x30in) s.i. 9-Jun-3 Hodgins, Calgary #361/R est:2500-3500 (C.D 2300)
£1689 $2770 €2534 Red door (55x70cm-22x28in) s. board. 3-Jun-3 Joyner, Toronto #240/R est:2500-3000 (C.D 3800)
£1955 $3030 €2933 Early spring, Georgian Bay (40x50cm-16x20in) s. board. 3-Dec-2 Joyner, Toronto #205/R est:2000-3000 (C.D 4750)
£2058 $3189 €3087 After the snowfall (50x60cm-20x24in) s. 3-Dec-2 Joyner, Toronto #168/R est:3000-4000 (C.D 5000)

PANCHOUNETTE, Presence (20th C) French

£694 $1097 €1000 Monochrome jaune (23x33cm-9x13in) mono. s.i.d.verso prov. 27-Apr-3 Perrin, Versailles #116/R

PANCKOUCKE, Ernestine (1784-1860) French

Works on paper

£3200 $5344 €4640 Flowers in a Grecian urn (29x21cm-11x8in) s.d.1829 W/C vellum. 9-Jul-3 Sotheby's, London #122/R est:1500-2000

PANCOAST, Morris Hall (1877-?) American

£2675 $4200 €4013 Snowy landscape (56x66cm-22x26in) s. 22-Nov-2 Skinner, Boston #289/R est:1000-1500
£6962 $11000 €10443 Street in winter.By the river (20x25cm-8x10in) s. one i. board pair. 24-Apr-3 Shannon's, Milford #227/R est:5000-7000

PANDOLFINI, Joseph Paul (?) Italian

Works on paper

£620 $887 €930 Venice (69x116cm-27x46in) s. pencil W/C. 11-Apr-2 Mellors & Kirk, Nottingham #542a/R

PANEL, Louis (?) French?

£278 $453 €400 Beg-Meil petite plage Bretonne (24x33cm-9x13in) s. cardboard. 19-Jul-3 Thierry & Lannon, Brest #370
£361 $589 €520 Paysage Breton et barques sous voiles (24x33cm-9x13in) s. cardboard. 19-Jul-3 Thierry & Lannon, Brest #371

PANERAI, Ruggero (1862-1923) Italian

£2200 $3586 €3300 Shepherdess amongst her flock at dusk (41x56cm-16x22in) s. 13-Feb-3 Christie's, Kensington #230/R est:1000-1500
£3165 $5000 €5000 Cart (37x53cm-15x21in) s. 26-Nov-2 Christie's, Rome #174/R
£5102 $8112 €7500 Horse (81x60cm-32x24in) s. 18-Mar-3 Finarte, Milan #51/R

PANG JIUN (1936-) Chinese

£4662 $7692 €6760 Still life (60x72cm-24x28in) s.d. 2002. 6-Jul-3 Christie's, Hong Kong #116/R est:60000-90000 (HK.D 60000)
£4662 $7692 €6760 Corner of the community (60x50cm-24x20in) s.d.2002. 6-Jul-3 Christie's, Hong Kong #168/R est:40000-60000 (HK.D 60000)

PANG TSENG-YING (1916-1997) Chinese

£6216 $10256 €9013 Countryside at dusk (52x38cm-20x15in) s.d.1954 paperboard. 6-Jul-3 Christie's, Hong Kong #120/R est:100000-150000 (HK.D 80000)

Works on paper

£3108 $5128 €4507 Village in the green forest (39x31cm-15x12in) s. W/C. 6-Jul-3 Christie's, Hong Kong #123/R est:50000-80000 (HK.D 40000)

PANG XUNQIN (1906-1985) Chinese

Works on paper

£6216 $10256 €9013 Tang lady (38x40cm-15x16in) s. ink col. 6-Jul-3 Christie's, Hong Kong #164/R est:100000-140000 (HK.D 80000)

PANG, P T (20th C) Chinese

£1382 $2100 €2073 USS Mindanao, in Hong Kong (43x56cm-17x22in) s. board. 17-Aug-2 North East Auctions, Portsmouth #575/R

PANHUYSEN, E van den (1874-1929) Belgian

£725 $1188 €1000 La lecon (80x60cm-31x24in) s. 27-May-3 Campo & Campo, Antwerp #237/R

PANICHI (19th C) ?

£1159 $1900 €1681 Woman in landscape (28x10cm-11x4in) s. panel two. 4-Jun-3 Doyle, New York #76 est:500-700

PANINI, Giovanni Paolo (1691-1765) Italian

£41379 $66207 €60000 Roman ruins (72x98cm-28x39in) 17-Mar-3 Pandolfini, Florence #705/R est:65000
£52469 $85000 €78704 Architectural capriccio with Alexander visiting the tomb of Achilles (74x99cm-29x39in) with sig. prov.lit. 24-Jan-3 Christie's, Rockefeller NY #55/R est:30000-50000
£200000 $314000 €300000 Architectural capriccio with figures among Roman ruins (99x136cm-39x54in) s. prov. 12-Dec-2 Sotheby's, London #58/R est:120000-180000
£234568 $380000 €351852 Capriccio of classical ruins (77x103cm-30x41in) s.d.1736 prov.lit. 24-Jan-3 Christie's, Rockefeller NY #64/R est:300000-500000

Works on paper

£33784 $52703 €50000 Galerie de vues de la Rome antique (39x51cm-15x20in) pen ink wash. 27-Mar-3 Maigret, Paris #84/R est:40000

PANINI, Giovanni Paolo (circle) (1691-1765) Italian

£5816 $9014 €8724 Church architecture with figure scene (76x99cm-30x39in) 3-Dec-2 Bukowskis, Stockholm #490/R est:80000-100000 (S.KR 82000)
£6329 $10000 €10000 Old harbour with ruins in evening (36x47cm-14x19in) lit. 29-Nov-2 Schloss Ahlden, Ahlden #1116/R est:12000
£7134 $11129 €11200 Riders before castle (16x163cm-6x64in) 6-Nov-2 Hugo Ruef, Munich #938/R est:3000
£7278 $11500 €11500 Bay in southern Italy (36x47cm-14x19in) lit. 29-Nov-2 Schloss Ahlden, Ahlden #1117/R est:12000

PANITZSCH, Robert (1879-1949) German/Danish

£288 $464 €432 Interior bathed in sunshine (60x50cm-24x20in) s.d.35. 22-Feb-3 Rasmussen, Havnen #2018/R (D.KR 3200)
£320 $518 €480 Horse drawn stall before Copenhagen canal (80x65cm-31x26in) s.d.36. 23-Jan-3 Christie's, Kensington #166
£378 $609 €567 Interior scene with woman (45x48cm-18x19in) s. 11-May-3 Hindemae, Ullerslev #321/R (D.KR 4000)
£400 $632 €600 Elegant woman reading in a drawing room (71x65cm-28x26in) s.d.38. 14-Nov-2 Christie's, Kensington #210/R
£466 $742 €699 Interior scene with woman on sofa (66x53cm-26x21in) s.d.39. 5-May-3 Rasmussen, Vejle #652/R (D.KR 5000)
£488 $790 €732 Interior scene with rococo furniture (66x82cm-26x32in) s. 25-Jan-3 Rasmussen, Havnen #2038/R (D.KR 5500)
£515 $803 €773 Woman at piano (58x50cm-23x20in) s.d.33. 11-Nov-2 Rasmussen, Vejle #506/R (D.KR 6000)

£550 $864 €825 Danish interior leading to a sunlit hall (64x79cm-25x31in) s.d.27. 16-Apr-3 Christie's, Kensington #706/R
£600 $912 €900 Sunflowers in a vase (85x65cm-33x26in) s. 29-Aug-2 Christie's, Kensington #138/R
£676 $1041 €1014 Interior (64x79cm-25x31in) s.d.1924. 26-Oct-2 Rasmussen, Havnen #2032 (D.KR 8000)
£708 $1125 €1062 Nude female standing in garden with flowers (66x46cm-26x18in) s.d.1922. 10-Mar-3 Rasmussen, Vejle #566/R (D.KR 7600)
£745 $1184 €1118 Interior scene with girl reading by sunlit window (44x36cm-17x14in) s.d.1923. 5-Mar-3 Rasmussen, Copenhagen #1945/R (D.KR 8000)
£750 $1140 €1125 Fishing vessels at the quay, Copenhagen (66x81cm-26x32in) s.d.46. 29-Aug-2 Christie's, Kensington #133/R
£800 $1312 €1200 Rococo interior before a sunlit garden (66x82cm-26x32in) s. 5-Jun-3 Christie's, Kensington #791/R
£931 $1480 €1397 Else Norgaard at the piano (49x57cm-19x22in) s.i.d.X 27 i.verso. 5-Mar-3 Rasmussen, Copenhagen #1947/R (D.KR 10000)
£957 $1550 €1388 Interior scene with the artist's wife sewing by window (66x82cm-26x32in) s.d.1922. 26-May-3 Rasmussen, Copenhagen #1463/R (D.KR 10000)
£1000 $1630 €1500 Summer garden party (65x55cm-26x22in) s.d.37. 13-Feb-3 Christie's, Kensington #232/R est:1200-1800
£4000 $6080 €6000 Fishing boats at the quay, Copenhagen (120x100cm-47x39in) s.d.39. 29-Aug-2 Christie's, Kensington #158/R est:1000-1500

PANITZSCH, Robert (attrib) (1879-1949) German/Danish
£1497 $2380 €2200 Fountain in summer garden (62x86cm-24x34in) s. 19-Mar-3 Neumeister, Munich #691/R est:1500

PANKIEWICZ, Jozef (attrib) (1866-1940) Polish
£1392 $2172 €2200 Woodland stream (65x53cm-26x21in) i. 15-Oct-2 Dorotheum, Vienna #26/R est:1500-2200

PANKOK, Otto (1893-1966) German
Sculpture
£3261 $5087 €4892 Walking Jew (43cm-17in) mono. bronze lit.prov. 16-Sep-2 Philippe Schuler, Zurich #3095/R est:7000-9000 (S.FR 7500)

PANN, Abel (1883-1963) Israeli/Latvian
Works on paper
£11709 $18500 €17564 And Sara heard it in the tent door, therefore Sara laughed within (40x42cm-16x17in) s. pastel prov. 27-Apr-3 Sotheby's, Tel Aviv #32/R est:8000-10000

PANNAGGI, Ivo (1901-) Italian
£26027 $40603 €38000 Portrait of Vinicio Paladini (49x40cm-19x16in) s.d.22 tempera collage cardboard exhib.lit. 10-Apr-3 Finarte Semenzato, Rome #291/R est:52000
Works on paper
£2128 $3447 €3000 Funzione geometrica K5 (74x36cm-29x14in) s.i.verso pencil chl prov. 26-May-3 Christie's, Milan #214/R est:2500-3500

PANNO, Laura (20th C) Italian
£2465 $4092 €3500 Nudo (40x40cm-16x16in) s.i.d.1990 verso oil canvas metal meshing round. 10-Jun-3 Finarte Semenzato, Milan #362/R est:1300-1600

PANOW, Peter A (1902-1975) Australian
£325 $513 €488 Untitled, flowers (58x68cm-23x27in) s. canvas on board prov. 7-Apr-3 Shapiro, Sydney #498 (A.D 850)

PANSING, Fred (19th C) American
£9259 $15000 €13889 Steamship entering New York harbour (33x41cm-13x16in) s. board. 21-Jan-3 Christie's, Rockefeller NY #387/R est:12000
£27439 $45000 €39787 Portrait of the American steamer Puritan (56x89cm-22x35in) s. 8-Jun-3 Skinner, Boston #125/R est:8000-12000
Works on paper
£597 $950 €896 American line, Philadelphia-Liverpool service (16x28cm-6x11in) s. W/C pencil. 5-Mar-3 Christie's, Rockefeller NY #93/R

PANTALEON, Theodoros (1945-) Greek
£8500 $13430 €12750 Untitled (50x47cm-20x19in) 1-Apr-3 Bonhams, New Bond Street #107 est:6000-9000

PANTAZIS, Pericles (1849-1884) Greek
£15000 $23250 €22500 Portrait of girl (49x43cm-19x17in) s. prov. 2-Oct-2 Sotheby's, London #23/R
£16000 $24800 €24000 Portrait of boy (75x60cm-30x24in) prov. 2-Oct-2 Sotheby's, London #24/R est:18000-25000
£17000 $26860 €25500 Portrait du fils de l'artiste (21x18cm-8x7in) painted c.1878. 1-Apr-3 Bonhams, New Bond Street #19 est:15000-20000
£30000 $46500 €45000 Ride on the beach (50x70cm-20x28in) s. prov. 2-Oct-2 Sotheby's, London #17/R est:15000-20000
£30000 $46500 €45000 Portrait of woman knitting (103x74cm-41x29in) s.d.1870 canvas on board prov.exhib.lit. 2-Oct-2 Sotheby's, London #33/R est:30000-50000
Works on paper
£493 $799 €750 Portrait de femme. s. dr. 21-Jan-3 Galerie Moderne, Brussels #266/R

PANTOJA DE LA CRUZ (1551-1608) Spanish
£1351 $2108 €2000 Cebada Square (70x93cm-28x37in) s. 25-Mar-3 Durán, Madrid #73/R
£2740 $4274 €4110 Portrait of preacher (86x64cm-34x25in) i. 28-Mar-3 Koller, Zurich #3064/R est:6000-9000 (S.FR 6000)

PANTON, Alexander (fl.1861-1888) British
£2100 $3045 €3150 Mountainous scene with stream and deer grazing (76x119cm-30x47in) s.d. 3-May-2 Biddle & Webb, Birmingham #351/R

PANTON, Lawrence Arthur Colley (1894-1954) Canadian
£287 $445 €431 Wood interior no 1 (27x35cm-11x14in) s.d.36 board exhib. 24-Sep-2 Ritchie, Toronto #3149/R (C.D 700)
£844 $1385 €1266 Laketalon (22x28cm-9x11in) s.i.verso panel. 3-Jun-3 Joyner, Toronto #515 est:1500-2000 (C.D 1900)

PANUSKA, Jaroslav (1872-1958) Czechoslovakian
£341 $552 €512 Lime works at Beroun (42x35cm-17x14in) s. i. verso tempera paper. 24-May-3 Dorotheum, Prague #150/R est:10000-15000 (C.KR 15000)
£681 $1103 €1022 Landscape with river (50x65cm-20x26in) s. board. 24-May-3 Dorotheum, Prague #67/R est:3000-45000 (C.KR 30000)

PANZA, Giovanni (1894-1989) Italian
£1258 $1937 €2000 Boy with mandolin (40x30cm-16x12in) s. board. 23-Oct-2 Finarte, Milan #162/R
£1258 $1937 €2000 Print loer (47x38cm-19x15in) s. board. 23-Oct-2 Finarte, Milan #195/R
£1384 $2131 €2200 Fruit harvest (50x39cm-20x15in) s. 23-Oct-2 Finarte, Milan #163/R
£1519 $2400 €2400 Maternity (23x29cm-9x11in) s. panel. 26-Nov-2 Christie's, Rome #264/R
£2041 $3245 €3000 Mandolin player (40x30cm-16x12in) s. 1-Mar-3 Meeting Art, Vercelli #250
£2201 $3390 €3500 Pulcinella with laid table (30x40cm-12x16in) s. board. 23-Oct-2 Finarte, Milan #187/R est:2500-3000
£3269 $5133 €5100 Vomero market (50x69cm-20x27in) s. 10-Dec-2 Della Rocca, Turin #383/R est:8000
£3481 $5500 €5500 Deputy mum (25x35cm-10x14in) s. i.verso board. 26-Nov-2 Christie's, Rome #160/R est:4800

PANZENBERGER, Kurt (20th C) Austrian?
Works on paper
£279 $441 €419 Venice (48x61cm-19x24in) mono.d.1982 W/C. 29-Nov-2 Zofingen, Switzerland #2519 (S.FR 650)

PAOLETTI, Antonio (1834-1912) Italian
£2000 $3340 €2900 Venetian fruit seller (26x35cm-10x14in) s. panel. 17-Jun-3 Bonhams, New Bond Street #102/R est:4000-6000
£5500 $9185 €8250 Watermelon eaters (25x38cm-10x15in) s. prov. 18-Jun-3 Christie's, Kensington #136/R est:3000-5000
£6000 $9540 €9000 Venditore di legna da ardere (35x24cm-14x9in) s. panel. 20-Mar-3 Christie's, Kensington #46/R est:5000-7000
£7258 $11468 €10887 Courting gondolier (91x60cm-36x24in) s. prov. 18-Nov-2 Waddingtons, Toronto #285/R est:10000-15000 (C.D 18000)

PAOLETTI, Rodolfo (1866-1940) Italian
£409 $630 €650 View of Venice with masked figures (60x45cm-24x18in) s. board. 28-Oct-2 Il Ponte, Milan #295
£449 $655 €700 View of Venice with bridge and masks (53x36cm-21x14in) s. i.d.1936 verso board. 5-Jun-2 Il Ponte, Milan #207
£510 $811 €750 Gondola (40x29cm-16x11in) s. board. 1-Mar-3 Meeting Art, Vercelli #203
£962 $1404 €1500 View of Venice with balcony in bloom (70x50cm-28x20in) s. board. 5-Jun-2 Il Ponte, Milan #262

PAOLIERI, Ferdinando (1878-1928) Italian
£321 $503 €500 Copper mines (23x51cm-9x20in) i.d.on stretcher. 16-Dec-2 Pandolfini, Florence #134/R
£321 $503 €500 Summer sunset (25x43cm-10x17in) s. s.i.d.1925 verso board. 16-Dec-2 Pandolfini, Florence #136
£481 $755 €750 Novices strolling (25x44cm-10x17in) s.d.1925 board. 16-Dec-2 Pandolfini, Florence #137/R

PAOLINI, Giulio (1940-) Italian

£16774 $26503 €26000 Doublune (80x120cm-31x47in) prov. 18-Dec-2 Christie's, Rome #291/R est:30000
£20000 $31200 €30000 Ebla (100x90cm-39x35in) s.i.d.1976-77 verso oil postcard collage varnish on wood panel. 21-Oct-2 Sotheby's, London #39/R est:25000-35000

Photographs

£6383 $10340 €9000 174 (24x18cm-9x7in) s.i.d.1965 verso photograph wood. 26-May-3 Christie's, Milan #221/R est:8000-10000

Sculpture

£30000 $49200 €45000 Astrolabe (36x36x26cm-14x14x10in) plastic in 5 parts exec.1967 prov.lit. 6-Feb-3 Sotheby's, London #34/R est:70000
£32000 $53440 €48000 Averroe (197cm-78in) chromium-plated steel fifteen flags 1 of 7 exc.1967 prov.lit. 25-Jun-3 Sotheby's, London #38/R est:40000-60000
£65000 $101400 €97500 Averroe (197cm-78in) chromium plated steel and 15 flags prov.exhib.lit. 21-Oct-2 Sotheby's, London #34/R est:40000-60000
£170000 $261800 €255000 Mimesi (223cm-88in) plaster two incl wooden plinths executed 1975-76 prov.exhib.lit. 22-Oct-2 Christie's, London #48/R est:100000-160000

Works on paper

£1395 $2217 €2050 Ni le soleil, ni la mort (65x49cm-26x19in) s.i.d.15 avril 1989 collage drawing pin lithograph exhib. 26-Feb-3 Artcurial Briest, Paris #380 est:2000-2500
£1497 $2380 €2200 Ni le soleil ni la mort (65x49cm-26x19in) s.i.d.15 avril 1989 collage drawing pin lithograph exhib. 26-Feb-3 Artcurial Briest, Paris #379/R est:2000-2500
£2400 $3912 €3600 Le soleil ni la mort (64x48cm-25x19in) s.i.d.Marzo 1993 collage prov. 3-Feb-3 Sotheby's, Olympia #95/R est:2000-3000
£4167 $6542 €6500 Study (49x60cm-19x24in) collage pencil card. 20-Nov-2 Pandolfini, Florence #152/R
£4194 $6626 €6500 Globe (34x47cm-13x19in) s.d.1974 verso collage card prov. 18-Dec-2 Christie's, Rome #124/R
£19000 $31730 €27550 Untitled (89x80cm-35x31in) plywood brass steel fasteners photo verso prov. 26-Jun-3 Sotheby's, London #132/R est:15000-20000
£20000 $31200 €30000 Untitled (110x150cm-43x59in) s.d.1979/80 stretcher pencil canvas bz, on canvas. 21-Oct-2 Sotheby's, London #31/R est:15000-20000
£40000 $65600 €60000 Ronde (45x67cm-18x26in) s.i.d.1977 verso photographic emulsion canvas on panel prov. 6-Feb-3 Sotheby's, London #32/R est:40000

PAOLINI, Pietro (1603-1681) Italian

£40426 $65489 €57000 Young lute player (97x160cm-38x63in) 20-May-3 Babuino, Rome #41/R est:25000-30000
£60284 $97660 €85000 Young woman playing the lute with a child and a sleeping old man (105x161cm-41x63in) 20-May-3 Babuino, Rome #18/R est:30000-40000
£88652 $143617 €125000 Concert of an old man playing the violone and two young singers (105x160cm-41x63in) lit. 20-May-3 Babuino, Rome #17/R est:30000-40000

PAOLINI, Pietro (circle) (1603-1681) Italian

£8000 $12880 €12000 An old man stringing a lute (67x55cm-26x22in) lit. 20-Feb-3 Christie's, Kensington #355/R est:2000-3000

PAOLOZZI, Eduardo (1924-) British

Sculpture

£2800 $4368 €4200 Head (18cm-7in) s.d.1992 verso brown pat. bronze. 27-Mar-3 Christie's, Kensington #577/R est:2000-3000
£4500 $6930 €6750 Head (20cm-8in) s.d.1990 num.2/3 black pat bronze. 5-Sep-2 Christie's, Kensington #612/R est:2000-3000
£4500 $7380 €6750 Bandaged head (20cm-8in) dark brown pat. bronze conceived c.1953-54 prov. 6-Jun-3 Christie's, London #205/R est:2500-3500
£4800 $7872 €7200 Portrait of Matta (35cm-14in) s. black pat. bronze conceived c.1980 prov. 6-Jun-3 Christie's, London #206/R est:4000-6000
£9800 $16072 €14700 Bull (41cm-16in) s. dark brown pat. bronze conceived c.1946 prov. 6-Jun-3 Christie's, London #204/R est:3000-5000
£12000 $19680 €18000 Relief (109cm-43in) s.d.1975 light brown pat. bronze. 6-Jun-3 Christie's, London #41/R est:7000-10000
£14110 $23000 €21165 Krokodeel (93cm-37in) golden brown pat. bronze prov.lit. 12-Feb-3 Sotheby's, New York #112/R est:12000-18000
£22000 $36080 €33000 After Blake's Newton (60cm-24in) s.d.1993 black pat. bronze prov. 6-Jun-3 Christie's, London #203/R est:15000-25000
£55000 $90200 €82500 Portrait of the artist (150cm-59in) s.d.1988 num.2/3 black pat. bronze prov. 6-Jun-3 Christie's, London #202/R est:25000-35000

Works on paper

£339 $525 €509 Composition (34x26cm-13x10in) s.d.1973 pencil. 1-Oct-2 Rasmussen, Copenhagen #209 (D.KR 4000)
£2848 $4500 €4500 Untitled - head (52x38cm-20x15in) s.d.1954 collage gouache Indian ink. 27-Nov-2 Dorotheum, Vienna #43/R est:3000-4000
£3165 $5000 €5000 Untitled (35x28cm-14x11in) s. collage. 27-Nov-2 Dorotheum, Vienna #72/R est:2500-3500

PAOLUCCI, Flavio (1934-) Swiss

Works on paper

£611 $960 €917 Untitled (50x59cm-20x23in) mono.d.1986 s.d. verso mixed media collage paper on pavatex. 23-Nov-2 Burkhard, Luzern #245/R (S.FR 1400)

PAP, Domonkos (1894-1972) Hungarian

£782 $1221 €1134 Nagybanya (65x50cm-26x20in) s.d.1922. 12-Apr-3 Mu Terem Galeria, Budapest #87/R est:180000 (H.F 280000)

PAP, Emil (1884-?) Hungarian

£800 $1248 €1200 Young girl at a window with roses (100x75cm-39x30in) s. 8-Oct-2 Bonhams, Knightsbridge #215c/R
£833 $1375 €1200 Girl with apples and her cat (80x50cm-31x20in) s. 1-Jul-3 Christie's, Amsterdam #302/R
£1500 $2340 €2250 Lady playing a mandolin (80x60cm-31x24in) s. 8-Oct-2 Bonhams, Knightsbridge #215b/R est:1500-2500

PAP, Geza (1893-?) Hungarian

£2375 $3705 €3563 Town detail with red roofs - Taban (70x50cm-28x20in) s. board. 11-Apr-3 Kieselbach, Budapest #36/R est:650000-850000 (H.F 850000)

PAPADOPOULOS, Leonidas (1914-1988) Greek

£1200 $1896 €1800 Seasacape (32x45cm-13x18in) 1-Apr-3 Bonhams, New Bond Street #59 est:500-700

PAPAGEORGIOU, Michail (1896-1987) Greek

£1600 $2528 €2400 At the horse races (100x69cm-39x27in) 1-Apr-3 Bonhams, New Bond Street #49 est:1500-2000

PAPALOUCAS, Spyros (1892-1957) Greek

£14000 $21700 €21000 Church tower in Mitylene (32x26cm-13x10in) s. board painted 1925 exhib. 2-Oct-2 Sotheby's, London #46/R est:15000-20000
£19000 $29450 €28500 Houses on hillside, Mount Athos (33x27cm-13x11in) s.d.1924 cardboard. 2-Oct-2 Sotheby's, London #44/R est:10000-15000
£65000 $100750 €97500 View of Plagia village, Lesbos (56x51cm-22x20in) s. board exhib. 2-Oct-2 Sotheby's, London #50/R est:35000-55000

PAPALUCA, Louis (1890-1934) Italian

£360 $576 €540 Sunday boating in the bay (30x41cm-12x16in) 14-Mar-3 Gardiner & Houlgate, Bath #196/R
£422 $650 €633 Full sail (76x56cm-30x22in) s. 27-Oct-2 Grogan, Boston #59

Works on paper

£362 $572 €543 Fantome II R.Y.S (25x35cm-10x14in) s.i. gouache. 1-Apr-3 Stephan Welz, Johannesburg #425 est:5000-8000 (SA.R 4500)

PAPART, Max (1911-1994) French

£390 $632 €550 Madame Butterfly (54x65cm-21x26in) s. s.i.d.75 verso. 26-May-3 Joron-Derem, Paris #54
£503 $780 €800 Composition (27x41cm-11x16in) s.d.LX. 30-Oct-2 Artcurial Briest, Paris #398
£704 $1126 €1021 Still life (27x35cm-11x14in) s. panel. 18-May-3 Anders Antik, Landskrona #79 (S.KR 9000)
£786 $1219 €1250 Nature morte, rouge et noir (54x65cm-21x26in) s.d.55 s.i.d.55 verso. 30-Oct-2 Artcurial Briest, Paris #397
£841 $1312 €1262 Femme d'Alger (65x54cm-26x21in) s. 5-Nov-2 Bukowskis, Stockholm #332/R (S.KR 12000)
£841 $1312 €1262 Figure with red background (80x66cm-31x26in) s. 5-Nov-2 Bukowskis, Stockholm #335/R (S.KR 12000)
£927 $1492 €1391 Candide (47x64cm-19x25in) s. oil collage panel. 7-May-3 AB Stockholms Auktionsverk #1158/R (S.KR 12000)
£1656 $2699 €2500 Nature morte (50x65cm-20x26in) s. oil collage isorel. 31-Jan-3 Charbonneaux, Paris #144/R est:2000-2500
£2469 $4000 €3580 Nature morte (48x61cm-19x24in) s.i.d.50 d.46 verso. 21-May-3 Doyle, New York #29/R est:4000-6000
£4861 $7729 €7000 Dames II (130x130cm-51x51in) s. s.i.d.verso. 29-Apr-3 Artcurial Briest, Paris #290/R est:4500-5000
£5500 $8525 €8250 Le modele (100x100cm-39x39in) s.d.57 s.i.d.verso. 5-Dec-2 Christie's, Kensington #189/R est:6000-8000
£8861 $14000 €14000 Composition Romanesque (130x130cm-51x51in) s. 1-Dec-2 Bukowskis, Helsinki #389/R est:12000-15000

Sculpture

£1772 $2800 €2800 Humanite (38cm-15in) s.num.5/6 bronze. 1-Dec-2 Bukowskis, Helsinki #390/R est:2500-3000

£2172 $3389 €3258 Figure standing (129cm-51in) s.num.3/8 dark pat.bronze st.f.Guyot. 5-Nov-2 Bukowskis, Stockholm #242a/R est:18000-20000 (S.KR 31000)

Works on paper

£336 $540 €500 Le chateau fort (48x64cm-19x25in) s. collage dr. 23-Feb-3 Lesieur & Le Bars, Le Havre #128
£377 $585 €600 Composition (45x65cm-18x26in) s.d.LX mixed media collage panel. 30-Oct-2 Artcurial Briest, Paris #724
£556 $878 €800 Tete aux yeux bleus (33x23cm-13x9in) s. collage cardboard. 28-Apr-3 Cornette de St.Cyr, Paris #474
£631 $984 €947 Untitled (63x49cm-25x19in) s. mixed media collage. 5-Nov-2 Bukowskis, Stockholm #334/R (S.KR 9000)
£886 $1400 €1400 Couple (53x68cm-21x27in) s.d.1967 mixed media paper on canvas. 27-Nov-2 Blanchet, Paris #152/R
£927 $1492 €1391 Oiseau vert (50x65cm-20x26in) s. gouache collage panel. 7-May-3 AB Stockholms Auktionsverk #1120/R (S.KR 12000)
£1004 $1616 €1506 Sans titre (68x49cm-27x19in) s. mixed media. 7-May-3 AB Stockholms Auktionsverk #1119/R (S.KR 13000)
£1402 $2186 €2103 The Santos-Dumont (78x99cm-31x39in) s. s.d.1982 verso mixed media collage. 5-Nov-2 Bukowskis, Stockholm #331/R est:25000-30000 (S.KR 20000)

PAPAS, John (1942-) New Zealander

£281 $446 €422 Tell me of other cities (70x70cm-28x28in) s. i.verso oil collage on paper. 25-Feb-3 Peter Webb, Auckland #13 (NZ.D 800)

Works on paper

£482 $748 €723 Timn Eton Mata Anexandpo (59x49cm-23x19in) s. W/C. 4-Dec-2 Dunbar Sloane, Auckland #82 (NZ.D 1500)

PAPAZOFF, Georges (1894-1972) Bulgarian

£841 $1312 €1262 Figures on beach (19x27cm-7x11in) s. prov.exhib. 5-Nov-2 Bukowskis, Stockholm #287/R (S.KR 12000)
£2898 $4753 €4000 Feuilles eclairees par la chute d'un meteore (54x73cm-21x29in) s. 27-May-3 Tajan, Paris #1/R est:4000-4500

Works on paper

£327 $519 €480 Joueur de mandoline (28x20cm-11x8in) Indian ink paper on cardboard dr prov. 26-Feb-3 Artcurial Briest, Paris #63

PAPE, Abraham de (attrib) (1620-1666) Dutch

£2138 $3314 €3400 Farmstead (37x30cm-15x12in) panel. 2-Oct-2 Dorotheum, Vienna #339/R est:3000-4000

PAPE, Eric (1870-1938) American

£1096 $1600 €1644 Still life with autumn flowers in cream and marigold (51x41cm-20x16in) s.d.25. 3-Nov-1 North East Auctions, Portsmouth #250/R

PAPENDRECHT, Jan Hoynck van (1858-1933) Dutch

Works on paper

£382 $589 €600 Soldiers in uniform - a sketch (41x27cm-16x11in) pencil pen black ink W/C. 3-Sep-2 Christie's, Amsterdam #127
£423 $680 €600 Highlanders (14x22cm-6x9in) init.d.97 W/C. 7-May-3 Vendue Huis, Gravenhage #561/R
£1316 $2132 €2000 Gallery of Honour at the Rijksmuseum, Amsterdam (50x36cm-20x14in) s.d.1885 W/C htd white. 21-Jan-3 Christie's, Amsterdam #238/R est:2000-3000

PAPF, Karl Ernest (1833-1910) German

£20701 $32500 €31052 Exotic flowers (110x90cm-43x35in) s.d.1895. 19-Nov-2 Sotheby's, New York #70/R est:40000

PAPP, Aurelius (1879-1960) Hungarian

£929 $1449 €1347 Shady courtyard (34x47cm-13x19in) s.d.926 cardboard. 13-Sep-2 Mu Terem Galeria, Budapest #40/R est:280000 (H.F 360000)

PAPP, Oszkar (1925-) Hungarian

£774 $1207 €1122 Trio (51x80cm-20x31in) s.i.d.79. 13-Sep-2 Mu Terem Galeria, Budapest #150/R est:280000 (H.F 300000)

PAPPE, Carl Lewis (1900-1998) American

Works on paper

£252 $400 €378 Mexican villa, Taxco (41x51cm-16x20in) s.d.1938 W/C. 7-Mar-3 Jackson's, Cedar Falls #1026/R

PAPPERITZ, Fritz Georg (1846-1918) German

£1722 $2790 €2497 Lady wearing wide brimmed hat smoking a cigarette (63x72cm-25x28in) s. 26-May-3 Rasmussen, Copenhagen #1297/R est:20000 (D.KR 18000)

PAPPERITZ, Gustav Friedrich (attrib) (1813-1861) German

£424 $654 €636 By the coast (77x113cm-30x44in) indis.sig. 28-Oct-2 Blomqvist, Lysaker #1335 (N.KR 5000)
£575 $938 €863 By the coast (77x113cm-30x44in) indis.sig. 17-Feb-3 Blomqvist, Lysaker #1247/R (N.KR 6500)

PAPSDORF, Frederick (1887-?) American

£375 $600 €563 Virgin Island flowers (10x8cm-4x3in) 14 Mar-3 Du Mouchelle, Detroit #2342/R est:105
£391 $625 €587 Erythronium Americanum (10x8cm-4x3in) 14-Mar-3 Du Mouchelle, Detroit #2340/R
£438 $700 €657 Composition (10x8cm-4x3in) 14-Mar-3 Du Mouchelle, Detroit #2339/R
£563 $900 €845 Zinnias (13x12cm-5x5in) 14-Mar-3 Du Mouchelle, Detroit #2332/R
£625 $1000 €938 Flowers (10x16cm-4x6in) 14-Mar-3 Du Mouchelle, Detroit #2117/R
£625 $1000 €938 Still life of flowers in vase with clock (10x8cm-4x3in) 14-Mar-3 Du Mouchelle, Detroit #2333/R est:100-200
£688 $1100 €1032 Blue violets and dandelions (11x7cm-4x3in) 14-Mar-3 Du Mouchelle, Detroit #2337/R
£813 $1300 €1220 Still lifes of flowers (10x8cm-4x3in) three. 14-Mar-3 Du Mouchelle, Detroit #2338/R
£938 $1500 €1407 Flowers in vase (14x12cm-6x5in) 14-Mar-3 Du Mouchelle, Detroit #2335/R est:150-200
£938 $1500 €1407 Dish with tomatoes (12x16cm-5x6in) 14-Mar-3 Du Mouchelle, Detroit #2331/R est:200-400
£1000 $1600 €1500 Wild flower seed pots (15x13cm-6x5in) 14-Mar-3 Du Mouchelle, Detroit #2341/R est:100
£1250 $2000 €1875 The morning after (15x23cm-6x9in) 14-Mar-3 Du Mouchelle, Detroit #2118/R est:500-800
£1250 $2000 €1875 Wood in Michigan (19x15cm-7x6in) 14-Mar-3 Du Mouchelle, Detroit #2336/R est:250-350

PAPWORTH, Edgar George (jnr) (1832-1884) British

Sculpture

£55000 $91850 €79750 Vestal Virgin and Maidenhood (162cm-64in) s.d.1861 s.d.1860 white marble two. 8-Jul-3 Sotheby's, London #219/R est:55000-75000

PAQUETTE, Armand (1930-) Canadian

Works on paper

£478 $746 €798 Untitled - Horse team in rain storm (34x53cm-13x21in) s. W/C prov. 13-Apr-3 Levis, Calgary #88/R est:1500-2000 (C.D 1100)

PAQUIN, Pauline (1952-) Canadian

£348 $543 €580 On Relaxe (25x30cm-10x12in) s. s.i.d.2000 acrylic. 13-Apr-3 Levis, Calgary #89/R (C.D 800)
£1422 $2332 €2133 Un double jeu (60x75cm-24x30in) s. acrylic. 3-Jun-3 Joyner, Toronto #409/R est:2000-2500 (C.D 3200)

PARADIES, Herman Cornelis Adolf (1883-1966) Dutch

£1418 $2298 €2000 Beurs Square in Amsterdam (50x70cm-20x28in) s. 26-May-3 Glerum, Amsterdam #36/R est:1000-1200

Works on paper

£1056 $1701 €1500 Activity at Delft canal (38x48cm-15x19in) s. mixed media. 6-May-3 Vendu Notarishuis, Rotterdam #58/R est:1500-2000
£2113 $3401 €3000 Rotterdam canal with fishermen (48x38cm-19x15in) s. mixed media. 6-May-3 Vendu Notarishuis, Rotterdam #106/R est:1500-2000

PARADISE, John Wesley (attrib) (1809-1862) American

£1366 $2200 €2049 Portrait of a young lady in a white lace bodice (27x21cm-11x8in) board prov. 16-Jan-3 Christie's, Rockefeller NY #446/R est:3000-5000

PARAVANO, Dino (1935-) South African

£258 $424 €387 Seascape with dunes (45x60cm-18x24in) s. board. 4-Feb-3 Dales, Durban #9 (SA.R 3500)
£258 $424 €387 Fishermen pulling in nets on beach (45x60cm-18x24in) s. board. 4-Feb-3 Dales, Durban #10 (SA.R 3500)
£559 $900 €839 Cleaning fish (29x39cm-11x15in) s.d.1975 i.verso canvas on board. 12-May-3 Stephan Welz, Johannesburg #85 est:2000-4000 (SA.R 6500)
£705 $1099 €1058 Still life with pomegranates on a table (34x50cm-13x20in) s.d.76 canvas on board. 11-Nov-2 Stephan Welz, Johannesburg #242 (SA.R 11000)

Works on paper

£352 $550 €528 Seascape (74x109cm-29x43in) s.d.1978 pastel. 11-Nov-2 Stephan Welz, Johannesburg #606 (SA.R 5500)

PARC, Julio le (1928-) Argentinian
£2051 $3241 €3200 Serie 3, Nr 3 (105x105cm-41x41in) s.i. verso acrylic. 14-Nov-2 Neumeister, Munich #849/R est:3000-3500
£2051 $3241 €3200 Serie 15, Nr 8 (100x100cm-39x39in) s. verso i. stretcher acrylic. 14-Nov-2 Neumeister, Munich #850/R est:3000-3500
Sculpture
£7643 $12000 €11465 Untitled (122x42cm-48x17in) wood metal motor exec.1967 prov.exhib. 20-Nov-2 Christie's, Rockefeller NY #152/R est:15000-20000
£10500 $17535 €15225 Untitled (100x100x17cm-39x39x7in) metal discs thread light box exec.c.1970 prov. 26-Jun-3 Sotheby's, London #154/R est:3000-4000
Works on paper
£629 $975 €1000 Collage serie 48 no 1 (74x74cm-29x29in) s. collage. 4-Oct-2 Tajan, Paris #145

PARDI, Gian Franco (1933-) Italian
£256 $403 €400 Bathers (60x50cm-24x20in) s. 23-Nov-2 Meeting Art, Vercelli #217
£1282 $2013 €2000 Architecture (75x100cm-30x39in) s.i.d.73 verso acrylic wire. 21-Nov-2 Finarte, Rome #304/R
£1418 $2298 €2000 Architettura (51x32cm-20x13in) s.i.d.73 acrylic aluminium steel pencil canvas lit. 26-May-3 Christie's, Milan #173/R est:2000-3000

PARDO FORTEZA, J (?) Spanish
£452 $714 €700 Harbour (61x73cm-24x29in) s. 17-Dec-2 Durán, Madrid #574/R

PARDO, Jorge (1963-) German
Sculpture
£4375 $7000 €6563 Untitled - yellow no.343 (142x61x61cm-56x24x24in) single painted steel chandelier wax candle executed 1998. 15-May-3 Christie's, Rockefeller NY #339/R est:10000-15000

PAREDES, Vicenta de (1857-1903) Spanish
£1915 $2968 €2873 At the library (35x27cm-14x11in) s. 3-Dec-2 Bukowskis, Stockholm #190/R est:15000-18000 (S.KR 27000)

PAREDES, Vicente Garcia de (1845-1903) Spanish
£1800 $2808 €2700 Walk in the grounds (44x53cm-17x21in) s. 26-Mar-3 Sotheby's, Olympia #245/R est:2000-3000
£2201 $3434 €3500 Andalucian dance (64x81cm-25x32in) s. 23-Sep-2 Durán, Madrid #245/R
Works on paper
£897 $1400 €1346 In the study (33x25cm-13x10in) s. W/C gouache. 9-Oct-2 Doyle, New York #38

PAREKOWHAI, Michael (20th C) Australian
£2604 $4062 €3906 Bosom of Abraham; let there be light (127x22cm-50x9in) 8-Apr-3 Peter Webb, Auckland #21/R est:3000-4000 (NZ.D 7500)

PARELLO, A (19th C) Italian
Sculpture
£1700 $2636 €2550 Bust of Laura in Renaissance style (51cm-20in) s.i. gilt alabaster. 4-Dec-2 Sotheby's, Olympia #101/R est:1000-1500

PARENT, Jean (attrib) (19th C) French
Miniatures
£1800 $2808 €2700 Napoleon I wearing uniform of the chasseurs-a-cheval dark green red collar (5cm-2in) indis.sig. ormolu frame coronet surmount oval. 5-Nov-2 Bonhams, New Bond Street #114/R est:1200-1800

PARENT, Mimi (1925-) Canadian
Sculpture
£10274 $16130 €15000 Untitled (42x21x20cm-17x8x8in) doll wood straw sand pearls oil prov.exhib.lit. 15-Apr-3 Laurence Calmels, Paris #4394/R est:15000

PARENT, Roger (1881-?) French
£346 $533 €550 Nu (70x90cm-28x35in) s. 22-Oct-2 Campo, Vlaamse Kaai #583
£2055 $3226 €3000 Nus (80x100cm-31x39in) s.d.1927. 15-Apr-3 Galerie Moderne, Brussels #404/R est:5000-7000

PAREROULTJA, Edwin (1918-1986) Australian
Works on paper
£407 $642 €590 Ellery Creek, Big Hole, Near Alice Spring (34x52cm-13x20in) s. W/C. 22-Jul-3 Lawson Menzies, Sydney #129/R est:800-1200 (A.D 1000)

PAREROULTJA, Otto (1914-1973) Australian
Works on paper
£286 $443 €429 Gum tree and blue ridge (35x52cm-14x20in) s. W/C. 29-Oct-2 Lawson Menzies, Sydney #207 (A.D 800)
£469 $728 €704 Untitled, central desert landscape with gum tree (26x36cm-10x14in) s. W/C. 3-Dec-2 Shapiro, Sydney #142/R (A.D 1300)
£677 $1111 €982 Landscape with gum (27x36cm-11x14in) s. W/C. 3-Jun-3 Lawson Menzies, Sydney #791 (A.D 1700)
£712 $1089 €1068 Symbolic Mountain, Northern Territory (57x76cm-22x30in) s. W/C executed c.1950. 26-Aug-2 Sotheby's, Paddington #595 est:1000-2000 (A.D 2000)
£786 $1218 €1179 Symbolic rhythm, James Range (32x49cm-13x19in) s. W/C. 29-Oct-2 Lawson Menzies, Sydney #67/R (A.D 2200)
£1138 $1798 €1650 Mt. Hermannsberg and Finke River (36x51cm-14x20in) s. W/C. 22-Jul-3 Lawson Menzies, Sydney #130/R est:2500-3500 (A.D 2800)
£1250 $1938 €1875 Aranda country (27x38cm-11x15in) s. W/C exhib. 29-Oct-2 Lawson Menzies, Sydney #33/R est:4000-6000 (A.D 3500)

PARESCE, Renato (1886-1937) Italian
£10915 $18120 €15500 Paysage du Midi (60x73cm-24x29in) s.d.23. 11-Jun-3 Beaussant & Lefèvre, Paris #110/R est:5000-6000
£15190 $24000 €24000 Still life (50x40cm-20x16in) s. cardboard oval painted 1920. 30-Nov-2 Farsetti, Prato #688/R est:22000
Works on paper
£1438 $2244 €2100 Architecture and figures (34x25cm-13x10in) s. Chinese ink exec.1933. 10-Apr-3 Finarte Semenzato, Rome #275/R

PARESSANT, Jules (?) French
£1972 $3175 €2800 La route de Brest (48x71cm-19x28in) s.d.84 panel. 11-May-3 Thierry & Lannon, Brest #211/R est:1500-2000
£2676 $4308 €3800 Bruno a l'edredon rouge (38x62cm-15x24in) mono.d.88 panel. 11-May-3 Thierry & Lannon, Brest #212/R est:2000-2500

PAREY, Alonzo (19th/20th C) French
£344 $550 €516 Sleigh ride (51x30cm-20x12in) s. 12-Jan-3 William Jenack, New York #441

PARIGINI, Novella (1921-1993) Italian
£321 $503 €500 Nude (120x80cm-47x31in) s. 23-Nov-2 Meeting Art, Vercelli #205
£523 $837 €800 Flower (70x50cm-28x20in) s. 4-Jan-3 Meeting Art, Vercelli #662

PARIN, Gino (1876-1944) Italian
£506 $800 €800 Young lady (66x46cm-26x18in) s. cardboard. 26-Nov-2 Christie's, Rome #88
£633 $1000 €1000 Lady sowing (58x43cm-23x17in) s. wood. 26-Nov-2 Christie's, Rome #87
£1163 $1767 €1745 Lady wearing mint green dress and fur cape (70x40cm-28x16in) s. 27-Aug-2 Rasmussen, Copenhagen #1633/R est:8000 (D.KR 13500)
£1410 $2186 €2200 Evening (49x59cm-19x23in) s.d.26 exhib. 4-Dec-2 Finarte, Rome #791/R est:3500
£1667 $2583 €2600 Model (49x38cm-19x15in) s. canvas on cardboard. 5-Dec-2 Stadion, Trieste #698/R
£2721 $4327 €4000 Model with pearl necklace (84x60cm-33x24in) s.d.1917 cardboard. 1-Mar-3 Stadion, Trieste #300
£3688 $5974 €5200 In poltrona (64x64cm-25x25in) 22-May-3 Stadion, Trieste #162/R est:3500-4500
Works on paper
£1154 $1788 €1800 Loneliness (55x32cm-22x13in) s.d.1909 chl pencil. 5-Dec-2 Stadion, Trieste #777

PARIS, George de (1829-1911) British
Works on paper
£600 $936 €900 Salisbury Cathedral (76x109cm-30x43in) s.d.1868 W/C. 26-Mar-3 Woolley & Wallis, Salisbury #127/R

PARIS, Maurice (1903-1969) French
£290 $461 €420 La Coqueliere, Baie du Mont St Michel (38x55cm-15x22in) s. i.verso. 4-Mar-3 Livinec, Gaudcheau & Jezequel, Rennes #46

PARIS, Roland (1894-?) French
Sculpture
£1800 $2844 €2700 Clown figure (34cm-13in) i. cold painted bronze. 14-Nov-2 Christie's, Kensington #302/R est:2000-3000

PARISI, Francisco Paolo (1857-1948) Italian
£4608 $7280 €6912 View of the Tiber, Rome (55x100cm-22x39in) s. 15-Nov-2 Naón & Cia, Buenos Aires #101/R

PARISOT, Pierre Alexandre (1750-1820) French
Works on paper
£10638 $17766 €15000 Danse traditionnelle dans un paysage des environs de Moscou (57x87cm-22x34in) W/C gouache pen black ink. 19-Jun-3 Piasa, Paris #127a/R est:4000-6000

PARISY, Eugène (19th C) French
£283 $441 €425 Cows, sheep and figures by lake (45x60cm-18x24in) s.d.1901. 16-Sep-2 Philippe Schuler, Zurich #6480 (S.FR 650)

PARIZEAU, Edme Gratien (1783-?) French
Works on paper
£506 $800 €800 Soldat Romain avec une lance et un bouclier (27x43cm-11x17in) s. graphite white chk. 27-Nov-2 Christie's, Paris #192

PARIZEAU, Philippe-Louis (1740-1801) French
Works on paper
£270 $422 €400 Offrande du Temps a l'Amour (28x20cm-11x8in) s.d.1776 pen ink wash. 27-Mar-3 Maigret, Paris #91
£1288 $1996 €1932 Sacrifice (16x23cm-6x9in) s.d.1775 pen wash. 3-Oct-2 Koller, Zurich #3059/R est:2500-3500 (S.FR 3000)
£7770 $12122 €11500 Triomphe d'Amphitrite (51x69cm-20x27in) i. sanguine. 27-Mar-3 Maigret, Paris #90/R est:4000

PARIZEAU, Philippe-Louis (attrib) (1740-1801) French
Works on paper
£372 $580 €550 Sacriphice d'Iphigenie (36x49cm-14x19in) pen ink wash. 27-Mar-3 Maigret, Paris #61
£380 $600 €600 Offrande aux dieux (42x32cm-17x13in) pen ink wash crayon prov. 28-Nov-2 Tajan, Paris #87

PARK SOO KEUN (1914-1965) Korean
£628931 $1000000 €943397 Leisure time (33x53cm-13x21in) s. 24-Mar-3 Christie's, Rockefeller NY #326/R est:250000-300000

PARK, David (1911-1960) American
£443038 $700000 €664557 Boy with flute (127x102cm-50x40in) s.d.59 prov.exhib. 12-Nov-2 Sotheby's, New York #9/R est:500000-700000
Works on paper
£14423 $22500 €21635 Seated man (28x22cm-11x9in) i.verso ink wash prov. 14-Oct-2 Butterfields, San Francisco #2065/R est:30000-50000

PARK, J A (20th C) British
£500 $770 €750 Cornish fishing village (38x48cm-15x19in) s. board. 6-Sep-2 Biddle & Webb, Birmingham #13
£1550 $2542 €2248 North African street scenes. s. board sold with two paintings by other artists. 28-May-3 Riddetts, Bournemouth #844
£1950 $3081 €2925 Cornish harbour with fishing and pleasure boats (30x38cm-12x15in) s. board. 24-Apr-3 Scarborough Perry Fine Arts, Hove #587/R

PARK, John Anthony (1880-1962) British
£450 $752 €653 Rocky coast (16x23cm-6x9in) s.d.15 panel. 26-Jun-3 Mellors & Kirk, Nottingham #853
£500 $810 €725 Cornish coastal landscape (21x29cm-8x11in) s. panel. 29-Jul-3 Henry Adams, Chichester #485/R
£850 $1420 €1233 Cottage door (16x24cm-6x9in) s.d.15 canvasboard. 26-Jun-3 Mellors & Kirk, Nottingham #852/R
£1150 $1921 €1668 West country harbour scene with boats (18x33cm-7x13in) s. 20-Jun-3 Keys, Aylsham #702/R est:400-600
£1500 $2325 €2250 St. Ives (33x40cm-13x16in) s. s.i.verso board. 3-Dec-2 Bonhams, New Bond Street #2/R est:2000-3000
£1700 $2839 €2465 Back Road West, St Ives (28x39cm-11x15in) s. 24-Jun-3 Bonhams, New Bond Street #4/R est:1500-2000
£2800 $4340 €4200 Morning light, St. Ives (34x41cm-13x16in) s. board. 4-Dec-2 Christie's, Kensington #445/R est:3000-5000
£2800 $4368 €4060 High tide St. Ives (15x23cm-6x9in) s. board. 27-Mar-3 Lane, Penzance #20 est:3000-4000
£3300 $5115 €4950 Brixham harbour (76x99cm-30x39in) s. board. 26-Sep-2 Lane, Penzance #75/R est:3000-3500
£3400 $5372 €5100 Beach, St. Ives (32x39cm-13x15in) s. i.verso board. 7-Apr-3 Bonhams, Bath #55/R est:1200-1800
£4200 $6552 €6300 Harbour scene, St Ives (30x40cm-12x16in) s. 17-Sep-2 Bonhams, Knightsbridge #110/R est:3000-5000
£4200 $6552 €6300 Polperro (14x20cm-6x8in) s. board. 27-Mar-3 Christie's, Kensington #464/R est:1200-1800
£4800 $8016 €6960 At the quayside (32x41cm-13x16in) s. board. 24-Jun-3 Bonhams, New Bond Street #3/R est:3000-5000
£5500 $8580 €8250 Sailing boats (33x41cm-13x16in) s. board. 27-Mar-3 Christie's, Kensington #461/R est:2000-3000

PARK, Maria (1972-) German
£625 $1000 €906 Nomadic pilgrimage (145x145cm-57x57in) s.d.2001 verso acrylic ink transfer on canvas. 13-May-3 Sotheby's, Tel Aviv #83/R est:1200-1800

PARK, Stuart (1862-1933) British
£700 $1113 €1050 Roses in a vase (32x37cm-13x15in) s. verso. 6-Mar-3 Christie's, Kensington #182/R
£720 $1123 €1080 Pink roses (30x45cm-12x18in) s. 17-Oct-2 Bonhams, Edinburgh #257
£950 $1482 €1425 Iris (36x28cm-14x11in) s. 17-Oct-2 Bonhams, Edinburgh #200
£1000 $1530 €1500 Still life of red and white roses (51x41cm-20x16in) s. 22-Aug-2 Bonhams, Edinburgh #1109/R est:1000-1500
£1000 $1540 €1500 Still life with flowers (30x40cm-12x16in) s. 5-Sep-2 Christie's, Kensington #564/R est:1000-1500
£1100 $1705 €1650 Still life of pink and white roses (50x60cm-20x24in) s. 6-Dec-2 Lyon & Turnbull, Edinburgh #47 est:800-1200
£1200 $1908 €1800 Wild roses (30x38cm-12x15in) s. 6-Mar-3 Christie's, Kensington #179/R est:800-1200
£1300 $1989 €1950 Pink roses (39x49cm-15x19in) s. 22-Aug-2 Bonhams, Edinburgh #1179/R est:1500-2000
£1400 $2226 €2100 Pink and white camellias (35x35cm-14x14in) s. 6-Mar-3 Christie's, Kensington #180/R est:800-1200
£1500 $2295 €2250 Still life of cream and red roses (39cm-15in circular) s. 22-Aug-2 Bonhams, Edinburgh #1110/R est:1500-2000
£1500 $2340 €2250 Dove (41x51cm-16x20in) s. 27-Mar-3 Christie's, Kensington #534/R est:1500-2000
£1500 $2430 €2250 Still life of lilies (62x38cm-24x15in) s. 23-May-3 Lyon & Turnbull, Edinburgh #65/R est:1200-1800
£1650 $2574 €2393 Pedestal vase of geraniums (39x39cm-15x15in) s. 27-Mar-3 Lane, Penzance #225/R est:2000-2500
£1700 $2703 €2550 White and red roses (41x51cm-16x20in) indis sig. 6-Mar-3 Christie's, Kensington #181/R est:1200-1800
£1700 $2652 €2550 Yellow and pink roses (50x40cm-20x16in) s. oval. 10-Apr-3 Bonhams, Edinburgh #127/R est:1500-2000
£1800 $2754 €2700 Yellow and red roses in a glass vase (75x60cm-30x24in) s. 22-Aug-2 Bonhams, Edinburgh #1180/R est:2000-3000
£1800 $2790 €2700 White and red camelias (41x51cm-16x20in) 31-Oct-2 Christie's, London #125/R est:2000-3000
£2000 $3100 €3000 Yellow and red roses (62x91cm-24x36in) s. prov. 31-Oct-2 Christie's, London #124/R est:3000-5000
£2400 $3744 €3600 Still life of codling (23x43cm-9x17in) s.d.May 1886 canvas on board. 17-Oct-2 Bonhams, Edinburgh #153 est:400-600
£2400 $3648 €3600 Still life of geraniums (30x38cm-12x15in) s. 28-Aug-2 Sotheby's, London #1017/R est:1500-2000
£2500 $3900 €3750 White roses (46x30cm-18x12in) s. 14-Apr-3 Sotheby's, London #97/R est:1500-2000
£2500 $3900 €3750 Still life with camellias (51x41cm-20x16in) 14-Apr-3 Sotheby's, London #99/R est:2500-3000
£2500 $3900 €3750 Geraniums (29x36cm-11x14in) s. prov. 10-Apr-3 Bonhams, Edinburgh #86/R est:1000-1500
£2600 $4056 €3770 Still life with white roses (23x20cm-9x8in) s. 27-Mar-3 Neales, Nottingham #982/R est:2000-3000
£3000 $4590 €4500 Still life of pink roses (27x37cm-11x15in) s. canvas on board. 22-Aug-2 Bonhams, Edinburgh #1066/R est:2000-3000
£3400 $5304 €5100 Still life of pink roses (40x50cm-16x20in) s. 13-Sep-2 Lyon & Turnbull, Edinburgh #92/R est:1500-2500
£3800 $5776 €5700 Still life of roses (51x41cm-20x16in) s. 28-Aug-2 Sotheby's, London #1010/R est:3000-4000
£3800 $5776 €5700 Pink roses. White begonias (50cm-20in circular) s. pair. 28-Aug-2 Sotheby's, London #1012/R est:3000-5000
£6000 $9360 €9000 Pink roses (46x30cm-18x12in) s. prov. 14-Apr-3 Sotheby's, London #96/R est:4000-6000
£22000 $34320 €33000 Still life of roses in a blue vase (45x76cm-18x30in) mono. 14-Apr-3 Sotheby's, London #98/R est:7000-10000

PARKE, Walter (1909-) American
£316 $500 €474 Tee shade, cloud shade (38x51cm-15x20in) s. board. 26-Apr-3 Jeffery Burchard, Florida #48
£581 $900 €872 Slipping away (53x66cm-21x26in) s. painted c.1950. 8-Dec-2 Toomey, Oak Park #679/R

PARKEHARRISON, Robert (20th C) American
Photographs
£2454 $4000 €3681 Exchange (102x115cm-40x45in) s.i.d.1999 num.1/4 waxed gelatin silver print. 12-Feb-3 Christie's, Rockefeller NY #125/R est:8000-10000

PARKER, Anne Eaton (1919-) American
£286 $470 €415 Untitled - Portrait of in a landscape (43x58cm-17x23in) d.March 1940 board. 30-May-3 Aspire, Cleveland #48/R

PARKER, Colin Ross (1941-) Australian
£704 $1099 €1056 No respect for the bullnose cowley (60x90cm-24x35in) s. board. 21-Oct-2 Australian Art Auctions, Sydney #49 (A.D 2000)

PARKER, Ellen Grace (fl.1875-1903) British
£5200 $8112 €7800 Art students holiday (40x56cm-16x22in) s. 17-Sep-2 Sotheby's, Olympia #180/R est:5000-7000

PARKER, Frederick (?) British
£1100 $1694 €1650 Gardener's visit (71x93cm-28x37in) indis.sig. 5-Sep-2 Christie's, Kensington #288/R est:1500-2000

PARKER, George Waller (1888-1957) American
£291 $475 €437 Far East street (46x36cm-18x14in) board. 31-Jan-3 Douglas, South Deerfield #5

PARKER, Gill (1957-) British
Sculpture
£1400 $2268 €2100 Horse and groom (32cm-13in) s.d.1983 num.1/9 brown pat. bronze. 20-May-3 Sotheby's, Olympia #120/R est:500-700

PARKER, Henry (19/20th C) British
£380 $589 €570 Cumberland sands (29x44cm-11x17in) board. 25-Sep-2 Peter Wilson, Nantwich #71

PARKER, Henry H (1858-1930) British
£340 $568 €493 Harvesting scene, figures in the foreground (20x15cm-8x6in) s. board. 18-Jun-3 Andrew Hartley, Ilkley #1151
£823 $1276 €1235 Summer morning (25x20cm-10x8in) s..i.verso. 3-Dec-2 Ritchie, Toronto #3040/R est:2500-4000 (C.D 2000)
£847 $1330 €1271 Upland landscape with cattle grazing (47x77cm-19x30in) s. 16-Dec-2 Lilla Bukowskis, Stockholm #436 (S.KR 12000)
£2147 $3500 €3221 English landscape (36x61cm-14x24in) s. 2-Feb-3 Simpson's, Houston #429
£2600 $4238 €3770 River landscape with cattle grazing (28x36cm-11x14in) s. s.verso. 17-Jul-3 Tennants, Leyburn #842/R est:1000-1500
£2800 $4592 €4200 Harvesting (30x46cm-12x18in) s. 29-May-3 Christie's, Kensington #159 est:1000-1500
£3000 $4620 €4500 River Lea, Broxbourne (51x76cm-20x30in) s. s.i.verso. 5-Sep-2 Christie's, Kensington #186/R est:4000-6000
£3000 $4740 €4500 Sonning, Berkshire (30x51cm-12x20in) s.d.95 s.i.d.1895 verso. 26-Nov-2 Christie's, London #87/R est:3000-5000
£3000 $4920 €4500 Evening on the banks of the Ouse (51x76cm-20x30in) s. 29-May-3 Christie's, Kensington #113/R est:5000-8000
£3000 $5010 €4350 Extensive landscape with cattle by river in foreground. Cornfield Godalming (30x45cm-12x18in) s.i. s.i.verso pair. 8-Jul-3 Bonhams, Knightsbridge #239/R est:1000-1500
£3185 $5000 €4778 Homewards (61x91cm-24x36in) s. i.verso. 23-Nov-2 Jackson's, Cedar Falls #10/R est:5000-7500
£4000 $6280 €6000 Thames at Pangbourne (31x46cm-12x18in) s. i.verso. 19-Nov-2 Bonhams, New Bond Street #116/R est:3000-4000
£4200 $6636 €6300 Near Great Marlow on the Thames (30x51cm-12x20in) s. s.i.d.1895 verso. 26-Nov-2 Christie's, London #86/R est:3000-5000
£5000 $7800 €7500 The end of the day (61x91cm-24x36in) s. 17-Sep-2 Sotheby's, Olympia #176/R est:5000-7000
£5000 $7950 €7500 Thames near Henley (61x91cm-24x36in) s. s.i.verso. 6-Mar-3 Christie's, Kensington #454/R est:6000-8000
£5400 $8748 €8100 Haymaking by the Thames (27x43cm-11x17in) s. board. 20-May-3 Sotheby's, Olympia #217/R est:1500-2500
£7000 $11060 €10500 On the banks of the Thames at Streatley (61x91cm-24x36in) s. s.i.verso. 26-Nov-2 Christie's, London #85/R est:8000-12000
£7595 $12000 €11393 Surrey cornfield near Reigate (61x92cm-24x36in) s. prov. 23-Apr-3 Christie's, Rockefeller NY #79/R est:15000-20000
£8500 $13940 €12750 Surrey cornfield, Betchworth (61x91cm-24x36in) s. s.i.verso. 29-May-3 Christie's, Kensington #157/R est:5000-7000
Works on paper
£282 $446 €423 Children in a river landscape (36x25cm-14x10in) s. W/C. 18-Nov-2 Waddingtons, Toronto #57/R (C.D 700)
£500 $820 €750 Rural landscape with harvest scene and stream (64x81cm-25x32in) s. W/C. 7-Feb-3 Biddle & Webb, Birmingham #346
£500 $810 €750 Haymakers in a field (25x36cm-10x14in) s. W/C. 21-May-3 Bonhams, Knightsbridge #214/R
£600 $978 €900 Mill on the Thames (37x27cm-15x11in) s. W/C. 29-Jan-3 Dreweatt Neate, Newbury #89/R
£1000 $1580 €1500 Harvest time at Haslemere, Surrey (37x54cm-15x21in) s. W/C. 27-Nov-2 Peter Wilson, Nantwich #132/R

PARKER, Henry Perlee (1795-1873) British
£560 $918 €840 Shelling oysters (54x43cm-21x17in) s.d.1857. 2-Jun-3 David Duggleby, Scarborough #325/R
£800 $1264 €1200 Oyster eaters (56x45cm-22x18in) s.d.1857. 12-Nov-2 Bonhams, Knightsbridge #295/R
£10000 $15600 €15000 Home and happiness (76x63cm-30x25in) s.d.1853. 25-Mar-3 Bonhams, Leeds #657 est:10000-12000

PARKER, John (?) New Zealander?
Works on paper
£420 $655 €630 Haymaking near Dartford (29x41cm-11x16in) s.d.83 i.verso W/C. 25-Mar-3 Bonhams, Knightsbridge #214/R
£823 $1300 €1235 Annie Lott's garden (33x49cm-13x19in) s.d.70 W/C gouache htd white prov. 24-Apr-3 Sotheby's, New York #179/R est:1500-2000
£900 $1395 €1350 Boys angling beside a river with trees beyond (25x38cm-10x15in) s.d.71 W/C bodycol prov. 31-Oct-2 Duke & Son, Dorchester #115/R

PARKER, Lawton S (1868-1954) American
£389 $650 €564 Summer day, cottage in a landscape (25x15cm-10x6in) s. monotype panel. 17-Jun-3 John Moran, Pasadena #13b

PARKER, M (?) British
Works on paper
£280 $437 €420 Steam and sailing vessels in a city dock scene with gulls (25x42cm-10x17in) s. W/C. 10-Sep-2 David Duggleby, Scarborough #59/R

PARKER, Marge (20th C) American
£1948 $3000 €2922 Arnold Palmer at the first heritage (76x102cm-30x40in) 25-Oct-2 Morris & Whiteside, Hilton Head Island #174 est:2000-3000

PARKER, Robert Andrew (1927-) American
Works on paper
£285 $450 €428 Thelonius monk (58x46cm-23x18in) s.d.1961 W/C. 3-Apr-3 Boos Gallery, Michigan #226/R

PARKER, William (1946-) Canadian
£348 $543 €580 Canola fields (41x50cm-16x20in) s.d.1990 s.i.d.verso canvasboard prov. 13-Apr-3 Levis, Calgary #90 (C.D 800)
£978 $1604 €1467 Photographer's model (60x60cm-24x24in) s.i.d.Sept 1976 verso acrylic canvas on panel. 3-Jun-3 Joyner, Toronto #338/R est:1200-1500 (C.D 2200)

PARKINSON, Florence (fl.1890-1918) British
£950 $1492 €1425 William Haver as a young man (48x39cm-19x15in) s.d.1894 verso. 10-Dec-2 Lane, Penzance #351

PARKINSON, Norman (1913-1990) British
Photographs
£1948 $3000 €2922 Burn up the sun, Carmen Dell'Orifice (35x29cm-14x11in) st. gelatin silver print prov.exhib.lit. 25-Oct-2 Phillips, New York #122/R est:3000-5000
£2152 $3400 €3228 Celia's mouth (25x36cm-10x14in) gelatin silver print prov.lit. 24-Apr-3 Phillips, New York #142/R est:3000-5000
£3571 $5500 €5357 You can be walking, talkin, swimmin doll, Nena von Schlebrugge (56x45cm-22x18in) st.i.verso gelatin silver print prov.lit. 25-Oct-2 Phillips, New York #121/R est:3000-5000

PARKINSON, William H (fl.1892-1898) British
£1400 $2184 €2100 Gardener tending bonfire (36x25cm-14x10in) s.d.1892. 15-Oct-2 Gorringes, Lewes #2205/R est:800-1200

PARKMAN, Alfred Edward (1852-?) British
Works on paper
£270 $421 €405 Malpas Brough, angler on river bank (33x43cm-13x17in) s. W/C. 18-Oct-2 Keys, Aylsham #502
£680 $1061 €1020 Old lay up Mumbles (24x37cm-9x15in) s.i.d.1912 W/C. 11-Sep-2 Bonhams, Newport #211

PARKS, Frederick (fl.1900-1927) British
Works on paper
£1392 $2200 €2088 Moment of rest in the woods (28x35cm-11x14in) s. W/C. 1-Apr-3 Christie's, Rockefeller NY #203/R est:800-1200

PARMA SCHOOL (16th C) Italian
£60000 $94200 €90000 Madonna and Child with a male saint, landscape beyond (48x36cm-19x14in) panel prov.lit. 12-Dec-2 Sotheby's, London #48/R est:30000-50000

PARMENTIER, Paul Eugene (1854-1902) Belgian
Works on paper
£689 $1089 €1000 Chat qui dort (60x48cm-24x19in) mono. W/C. 4-Apr-3 Tajan, Paris #146

PARMIGGIANI, Claudio (1943-) Italian
Sculpture
£4514 $7448 €6500 De Sphaera (48x48x5cm-19x19x2in) s.i.d.1976 verso astronomy charts glass. 3-Jul-3 Christie's, Paris #9/R est:4000-6000
£16312 $26426 €23000 Invito al viaggio (77x46x31cm-30x18x12in) plaster oil painting canvas. 26-May-3 Christie's, Milan #238/R est:20000-30000
£26389 $43542 €38000 Phisiognomoniae Coelestis (124x185x4cm-49x73x2in) s.i.d.1975 plexiglass cibachrome W/C panel diptych prov.exhib. 3-Jul-3 Christie's, Paris #10/R est:3000-4000
Works on paper
£903 $1435 €1300 Sans titre (24x33cm-9x13in) s. col crayon pencil prov. 29-Apr-3 Artcurial Briest, Paris #462/R est:1500-2000

PARR, Mike (1945-) Australian
Sculpture
£1571 $2451 €2357 Head (19x19x30cm-7x7x12in) bronze. 11-Nov-2 Deutscher-Menzies, Melbourne #64/R est:5000-7000 (A.D 4400)
Works on paper
£1056 $1648 €1830 Anamorphii of God (103x71cm-41x28in) s.d.86 graphite dr prov. 31-Mar-3 Goodman, Sydney #152/R (A.D 2800)
£1286 $2031 €1929 Self portrait (127x97cm-50x38in) s.d.89 ink wash. 27-Nov-2 Deutscher-Menzies, Melbourne #118/R est:4000-5000 (A.D 3600)
£1792 $2724 €2688 Anamorphil of God, I self portraits, towards the other side (103x71cm-41x28in) s.d.85 chl pencil prov. 28-Aug-2 Deutscher-Menzies, Melbourne #150/R est:4000-6000 (A.D 5000)

PARR, Nuna (1949-) North American
Sculpture
£3629 $5734 €5444 Dancing bear (43x30x30cm-17x12x12in) s. serpentine stone. 14-Nov-2 Heffel, Vancouver #174/R est:6000-7000 (C.D 9000)
£5381 $8610 €8072 Dancing bear (51x41x23cm-20x16x9in) s. stone. 15-May-3 Heffel, Vancouver #138/R est:8000-12000 (C.D 12000)

PARRA, Gines (1895-1960) Spanish
£428 $693 €650 Head of woman (14x11cm-6x4in) s. cardboard. 21-Jan-3 Ansorena, Madrid #318/R
£1321 $2060 €2100 Portrait (35x27cm-14x11in) s. 17-Sep-2 Segre, Madrid #153/R
£1415 $2208 €2250 Lonely street (24x35cm-9x14in) s. 23-Sep-2 Durán, Madrid #192/R
£1438 $2244 €2100 Face (29x24cm-11x9in) s. 8-Apr-3 Ansorena, Madrid #260/R
£2308 $3646 €3600 Urban landscape (37x29cm-15x11in) s. cardboard. 13-Nov-2 Ansorena, Madrid #38/R
£2500 $4050 €3800 Landscape with Nahuel Huapi lake, Argentina (35x50cm-14x20in) s. 21-Jan-3 Ansorena, Madrid #190/R est:3600
£2911 $4541 €4250 The Seine, Paris (34x48cm-13x19in) s. board. 8-Apr-3 Ansorena, Madrid #261/R
£3205 $5064 €5000 View of the Seine (47x70cm-19x28in) s. 19-Nov-2 Durán, Madrid #233/R
£3459 $5362 €5500 The Seine, Paris (40x56cm-16x22in) s. paper on canvas on cardboard. 7-Oct-2 Ansorena, Madrid #69/R
£3793 $6031 €5500 Still life with figs (34x45cm-13x18in) s. cardboard. 4-Mar-3 Ansorena, Madrid #19/R
Works on paper
£968 $1529 €1500 Female nude (50x35cm-20x14in) s. wax crayon. 17-Dec-2 Durán, Madrid #129/R

PARRA, Jose Felipe (1824-?) Spanish
£1548 $2446 €2400 Still life with pineapples (82x56cm-32x22in) s. 18-Dec-2 Ansorena, Madrid #947/R

PARRAS, Alfonso (1934-) Spanish
£1447 $2345 €2200 Mountainous landscape (97x146cm-38x57in) s. 21-Jan-3 Ansorena, Madrid #280/R

PARRES, Alberto (1953-) Italian
£316 $494 €500 Animal on the left (40x50cm-16x20in) s.i.d.2001 acrylic. 14-Sep-2 Meeting Art, Vercelli #755/R

PARRINO, Steven (1958-) American
£3043 $4991 €4200 Untitled (182x152cm-72x60in) s.i.d.91 stretcher enamel exhib. 28-May-3 Lempertz, Koln #321/R est:2500

PARRIS, Edmond Thomas (1793-1873) British
Works on paper
£292 $450 €438 Mother with children at sea (33x23cm-13x9in) s.d.1836 W/C gouache. 27-Oct-2 Grogan, Boston #61

PARRIS, Edmond Thomas (attrib) (1793-1873) British
£6000 $9240 €9000 Portrait of Queen Victoria (41x33cm-16x13in) lit. 5-Sep-2 Christie's, Kensington #74/R est:3000-5000

PARRISH, Maxfield (1870-1966) American
£3313 $5500 €4804 The pickle man (22x18cm-9x7in) init. canvas on board. 11-Jun-3 Butterfields, San Francisco #4101/R est:5000-7000
£48387 $75000 €72581 Villa d'Este (71x46cm-28x18in) init.i.d.1903 paper on board prov.exhib.lit. 3-Dec-2 Phillips, New York #58/R est:50000-75000
£53459 $85000 €80189 Grape gatherer (51x61cm-20x24in) s. oil paper cutouts board on panel painted c.1904 prov. 5-Mar-3 Sotheby's, New York #104/R est:25000-35000
£95541 $150000 €143312 Sing a song of sixpence (23x56cm-9x22in) s.i. board prov.exhib.lit. 19-Nov-2 Butterfields, San Francisco #8066/R est:150000-200000
£108281 $170000 €162422 Heading for the knave of hearts (23x51cm-9x20in) init. i.d.1924 verso panel prov.exhib.lit. 19-Nov-2 Butterfields, San Francisco #8067/R est:100000-150000
£161290 $250000 €241935 King and Chancellor (51x42cm-20x17in) init. paper on board prov.exhib.lit. 3-Dec-2 Phillips, New York #59/R est:150000-250000
Works on paper
£15723 $25000 €23585 Solitude (41x43cm-16x17in) init. ink gouache chl prov. 5-Mar-3 Sotheby's, New York #105/R est:25000-35000

PARROCEL, Charles (1688-1752) French
Works on paper
£608 $949 €900 Homme attache a une potence (17x14cm-7x6in) s.d.35 chk. 27-Mar-3 Christie's, Paris #185/R

PARROCEL, Étienne (attrib) (1696-1776) French
Works on paper
£577 $894 €900 Etude de femme en buste (24x19cm-9x7in) crayon. 4-Dec-2 Piasa, Paris #81

PARROCEL, Joseph (1646-1704) French
£79861 $126181 €115000 Scenes de bataille (78x136cm-31x54in) pair prov. 25-Apr-3 Beaussant & Lefèvre, Paris #12/R est:40000-50000
Works on paper
£316 $500 €500 Deux etudes de sculpture, un guerrier et une femme drapee (26x19cm-10x7in) i. col chk. 27-Nov-2 Christie's, Paris #167

PARROCEL, Joseph (attrib) (1646-1704) French
£2439 $4000 €3537 Cavalry skirmish (50x64cm-20x25in) prov. 4-Jun-3 Christie's, Rockefeller NY #187/R est:6000-8000
£3500 $5845 €5075 Cavalry skirmish (28x32cm-11x13in) 9-Jul-3 Bonhams, New Bond Street #137/R est:4000-6000

PARROCEL, Joseph François (attrib) (1704-1781) French
Works on paper
£641 $1013 €1000 Scene de chasse (19x31cm-7x12in) pen ink wash. 18-Nov-2 Sotheby's, Paris #12/R

PARROCEL, Pierre (1670-1739) French
Works on paper
£922 $1540 €1300 Tete d'homme barbu (19x13cm-7x5in) black crayon white chk. 19-Jun-3 Piasa, Paris #108
£1076 $1700 €1700 Deux tetes d'enfants avec des etudes de bras (31x40cm-12x16in) col chk. 27-Nov-2 Christie's, Paris #152/R est:1500-2000

PARROCEL, Pierre (attrib) (1670-1739) French
Works on paper
£541 $843 €800 Christ et la Samaritaine (39x26cm-15x10in) sanguine. 27-Mar-3 Maigret, Paris #70/R

PARROW, Karin (1900-1986) Swedish
£452 $709 €678 Summer landscape with farm (60x80cm-24x31in) s. 16-Dec-2 Lilla Bukowskis, Stockholm #415 (S.KR 6400)
£1081 $1741 €1622 Apples (46x42cm-18x17in) 7-May-3 AB Stockholms Auktionsverk #823/R est:18000-20000 (S.KR 14000)
£1683 $2659 €2525 Flowers (66x57cm-26x22in) s. 30-Nov-2 Goteborg Auktionsverk, Sweden #603/R est:20000 (S.KR 24000)

£1964 $3102 €2946 Newspaper boys (72x72cm-28x28in) init. 30-Nov-2 Goteborg Auktionsverk, Sweden #602/R est:20000 (S.KR 28000)

PARRY, David (1942-) British
Works on paper
£250 $390 €375 Badger in undergrowth (14x19cm-6x7in) s. W/C. 9-Oct-2 Woolley & Wallis, Salisbury #174/R

PARRY, Joseph (1744-1826) British
Works on paper
£1000 $1600 €1500 Phoenix and Soho Foundaries of Peel and Williams, Manchester (14x23cm-6x9in) monochrome W/C executed c.1812 pair. 11-Mar-3 Bonhams, New Bond Street #44/R est:1000-1500

PARRY, Thomas Gambier (1816-1888) British
Works on paper
£300 $468 €450 Travellers by a waterfall (62x47cm-24x19in) s.d.1840 W. 18-Sep-2 Cheffins Grain & Comins, Cambridge #492/R

PARSHALL, Dewitt (1864-1956) American
£2070 $3250 €3105 View from Central Park, New York City (61x81cm-24x32in) s. 10-Dec-2 Doyle, New York #137/R est:2000-3000

PARSHALL, Douglas (1899-1990) American
£1356 $2250 €1966 Two horses grazing (61x91cm-24x36in) s. i.verso board. 11-Jun-3 Butterfields, San Francisco #4314/R est:3000-5000

PARSONS, A W (19/20th C) British
Works on paper
£1165 $1900 €1748 Study for the Frontenac Cellar, Spring Mountain, St Helena, California (71x93cm-28x37in) s. pencil W/C. 16-Feb-3 Butterfields, San Francisco #2110 est:1000-1500

PARSONS, Alfred William (1847-1920) British
£2200 $3520 €3300 Orange lilies (41x25cm-16x10in) s.i. 14-Mar-3 Gardiner & Houlgate, Bath #219/R est:2200-2800
£3200 $5216 €4640 Orange lilies (41x25cm-16x10in) s. exhib. 16-Jul-3 Sotheby's, Olympia #126/R est:2500-3500
Works on paper
£2400 $3744 €3600 Lily pond with dove cote (52x37cm-20x15in) s. W/C. 10-Sep-2 David Duggleby, Scarborough #267/R est:1200-1800
£4000 $6640 €6000 Mi Komori jinja near Yoshino (49x33cm-19x13in) s.i. W/C bodycol exhib. 12-Jun-3 Bonhams, New Bond Street #837/R est:4000-6000

PARSONS, Arthur Wilde (1854-1931) British
£400 $624 €600 Stormy coast (71x91cm-28x36in) s.d.1889. 17-Oct-2 David Lay, Penzance #1349
£600 $858 €900 Breezy day, shipping off a headland (41x61cm-16x24in) s.d.1876. 28-Feb-2 Greenslade Hunt, Taunton #431/R
£1850 $2923 €2775 Summertime - rocky seascape looking towards a headland (80x127cm-31x50in) s.d.1909 i.on stretcher. 2-Dec-2 Bonhams, Bath #132/R est:1200-1800
£3400 $5304 €5100 Fishing fleet of the coast (39x59cm-15x23in) s. 15-Oct-2 Bearnes, Exeter #434/R est:1500-2500
Works on paper
£330 $551 €479 Dogana, Venice with sailing boats and sailors (30x45cm-12x18in) s.d.1908 W/C. 17-Jun-3 Bristol Auction Rooms #462/R
£1300 $2028 €1950 Dirty weather, Falmouth (41x71cm-16x28in) s.d.1915 W/C htd gouache. 17-Oct-2 David Lay, Penzance #1203 est:1200-1600
£4200 $6510 €6300 Jealousy, fisherfolk in a cove (124x191cm-49x75in) s.d.1902 W/C. 26-Sep-2 Lane, Penzance #355/R est:3500-4500

PARSONS, Beatrice (1870-1955) British
Works on paper
£320 $496 €480 Mountains near Turin (17x25cm-7x10in) s. W/C prov. 3-Dec-2 Sotheby's, Olympia #72/R
£480 $749 €720 Blue fairy (12x8cm-5x3in) s. W/C. 15-Oct-2 Bearnes, Exeter #370
£550 $869 €825 Herbaceous border with delphiniums and roses (22x16cm-9x6in) s. W/C. 2-Dec-2 Bonhams, Bath #37/R
£1000 $1560 €1500 Flowering gorse on coastal path (25x36cm-10x14in) s. W/C. 15-Oct-2 Gorringes, Lewes #2148/R est:1000-1500
£1000 $1580 €1450 Pergola with an Alfred carrier roses climbing up it (34x24cm-13x9in) s. W/C. 22-Jul-3 Bonhams, Knightsbridge #209/R est:1000-1500
£1500 $2430 €2250 Pathway to the coast, bordered with pansies (17x25cm-7x10in) s. W/C. 21-May-3 Bonhams, Knightsbridge #117/R est:1500-2000
£2600 $4056 €3900 Herbaceous border (23x16cm-9x6in) s. W/C gum arabic. 27-Mar-3 Christie's, Kensington #63/R est:500-700
£3000 $4680 €4500 Bluebells (18x27cm-7x11in) s. pencil W/C. 19-Sep-2 Christie's, Kensington #67/R est:1000-1500
£3000 $4860 €4500 Path bordered with lupus, convolvulus and other flowers (25x35cm-10x14in) s. W/C. 21-May-3 Bonhams, Knightsbridge #149/R est:3000-4000
£5200 $8372 €7800 Japanese Gardens, The Pleasance, Over Strand (25x36cm-10x14in) W/C. 9-May-3 Mallams, Oxford #57/R est:1000-1500

PARSONS, Charles (1821-1910) American
Works on paper
£373 $600 €560 Coastal village inlet at low tide, probably a New England town (33x43cm-13x17in) s.d.04 W/C. 19-Jan-3 Jeffery Burchard, Florida #18/R
£497 $800 €746 Coastal shanty village with figures (28x53cm-11x21in) s.d.89 W/C. 19-Jan-3 Jeffery Burchard, Florida #18a/R

PARSONS, Edith Baretto (1878-1956) American
Sculpture
£24516 $38000 €36774 Duck baby (107cm-42in) i. verdigris pat. bronze st.f.Gorham executed c.1912. 5-Dec-2 Christie's, Rockefeller NY #106/R est:15000-25000
£24691 $40000 €37037 Frog baby - fountain (100cm-39in) i. verdigris pat. bronze prov. 22-May-3 Christie's, Rockefeller NY #44/R est:20000-30000

PARSONS, Elizabeth (1831-1897) Australian
£285 $450 €428 Italian riverside landscape (74x84cm-29x33in) s. 30-Nov-2 Thomaston Place, Thomaston #199

PARSONS, J V (19/20th C) British
£900 $1431 €1350 Boys rabbiting (51x61cm-20x24in) indis sig.d.1886. 6-Mar-3 Christie's, Kensington #587/R

PARSONS, Lloyd Halman (1893-1968) American
£299 $475 €449 At home (72x61cm-28x24in) s.d.51. 7-Mar-3 Skinner, Boston #565/R

PARSONS, Marion Randall (1878-1953) American
£545 $850 €818 Hispanic mission. 21-Sep-2 Harvey Clar, Oakland #1487

PARSONS, Max (19/20th C) British?
£634 $1020 €900 Le SS Chartered (45x60cm-18x24in) s. panel. 12-May-3 Lesieur & Le Bars, Le Havre #76/R

PARSONS, Sheldon (?) American?
£12821 $20000 €19232 Headwaters of the Rio Grande (61x91cm-24x36in) board. 9-Nov-2 Altermann Galleries, Santa Fe #180

PARTENHEIMER, Jurgen (1947-) German
£4167 $6458 €6500 Untitled (50x39cm-20x15in) mono.i.d.90.39 oil pencil paper strips collage. 3-Dec-2 Lempertz, Koln #343/R est:6000
£5797 $9507 €8000 Fools ship (115x103cm-45x41in) mono.i.d.87.12 s.i.d. stretcher oil graphite collaged paper prov. 28-May-3 Lempertz, Koln #322/R est:8000
£10256 $15897 €16000 Canto (200x140cm-79x55in) mono.d.89 s.i.d. stretcher oil paper stripes collage. 3-Dec-2 Lempertz, Koln #342/R est:15000-20000
Works on paper
£2244 $3478 €3500 Untitled (75x57cm-30x22in) mono.i.d.87.54 Indian ink graphite paper stripes collage board. 3-Dec-2 Lempertz, Koln #344/R est:4200
£2244 $3478 €3500 Untitled (76x57cm-30x22in) mono.i.d.88.50 Indian ink paper stripes collage board. 3-Dec-2 Lempertz, Koln #345/R est:4200
£2754 $4516 €3800 Brought me out of myself (75x57cm-30x22in) mono.i.d.87.58 pencil chl Indian ink paper collage board. 28-May-3 Lempertz, Koln #325/R est:4600
£3261 $5348 €4500 Thanathos (105x78cm-41x31in) mono.i.d.89 Indian ink graphite collaged paper strips. 28-May-3 Lempertz, Koln #326/R est:4800

PARTHENIS, Constantine (1878-1967) Greek
£6000 $9300 €9000 Hydra (24x31cm-9x12in) prov. 2-Oct-2 Sotheby's, London #41/R est:3000-5000

£7200 $11376 €10800 View of Corfu (23x30cm-9x12in) 1-Apr-3 Bonhams, New Bond Street #63 est:7000-10000
£9500 $14725 €14250 Wooded landscape (23x33cm-9x13in) canvas on board prov. 2-Oct-2 Sotheby's, London #42/R est:6000-8000
£10500 $16275 €15750 Poros (22x28cm-9x11in) s.i. board prov. 2-Oct-2 Sotheby's, London #40/R est:5000-7000
£45000 $69750 €67500 Man with flute (57x53cm-22x21in) s. board exhib. 2-Oct-2 Sotheby's, London #45/R est:30000-50000

Works on paper

£1000 $1550 €1500 Corfu (28x42cm-11x17in) s.i. pencil prov. 2-Oct-2 Sotheby's, London #92/R
£7000 $10850 €10500 Angel (48x33cm-19x13in) init.indis.d. pencil ink prov. 2-Oct-2 Sotheby's, London #93/R est:5000-7000
£11000 $17050 €16500 Reclining woman (32x50cm-13x20in) s. pencil ink prov. 2-Oct-2 Sotheby's, London #94/R est:6000-8000

PARTIKEL, Alfred (1888-1946) German

£1266 $2000 €2000 Flat landscape (49x61cm-19x24in) s. bears d.2927 panel. 29-Nov-2 Villa Grisebach, Berlin #839/R est:2000-3000
£1667 $2600 €2650 Landscape near Ahrenshoop (57x79cm-22x31in) s. 21-Sep-2 Dannenberg, Berlin #589/R est:1000

PARTON, Arthur (1842-1914) American

£1039 $1600 €1559 Hillside pasture, Pennsylvania (56x38cm-22x15in) s.d.1881. 4-Sep-2 Christie's, Rockefeller NY #338/R est:2000-4000
£1415 $2250 €2123 Cows watering at sunset (25x51cm-10x20in) s. canvas on masonite. 18-Mar-3 Doyle, New York #13/R est:800-1200
£2718 $4350 €4077 Spring orchard with cows (41x61cm-16x24in) s. prov. 11-Jan-3 James Julia, Fairfield #133 est:5000-7000
£3355 $5200 €5033 Quiet stream (41x36cm-16x14in) s.i. prov. 2-Nov-2 North East Auctions, Portsmouth #34/R est:2000-4000
£5696 $9000 €8544 Rowboat on the lake (61x102cm-24x40in) s.d.1876 prov. 24-Apr-3 Shannon's, Milford #114/R est:8000-12000

Works on paper

£285 $450 €428 American landscape of cows in field (23x33cm-9x13in) s.i. W/C. 26-Apr-3 Thomaston Place, Thomaston #288a

PARTON, Ernest (1845-1933) British

£667 $1107 €967 Burnham Beeches (36x25cm-14x10in) s. i.verso canvasboard prov. 16-Jun-3 Waddingtons, Toronto #7/R est:1000-1500 (C.D 1500)
£926 $1500 €1343 Landscape with punt (74x58cm-29x23in) s. 21-May-3 Doyle, New York #87/R est:2000-3000
£1500 $2340 €2250 Angler in a wooded lake landscape (91x74cm-36x29in) s. 7-Nov-2 Christie's, Kensington #195/R est:1500-2000
£1500 $2445 €2250 River landscape with silver birch on the bank, man rowing beyond (40x56cm-16x22in) s. 29-Jan-3 Dreweatt Neate, Newbury #116/R est:2000-2500
£1500 $2460 €2250 Cattle watering in a sunlit lake (43x69cm-17x27in) s. 29-May-3 Christie's, Kensington #114/R est:1800-2200

PARTON, Ernest (attrib) (1845-1933) British

£444 $719 €666 Landscape with brook and bridge (45x30cm-18x12in) bears sig.d.83. 3-Feb-3 Lilla Bukowskis, Stockholm #976 (S.KR 6200)

PARTON, Henry Woodbridge (1858-1933) American

£416 $650 €624 Country landscape with blue sky (25x35cm-10x14in) s. canvasboard. 14-Sep-2 Weschler, Washington #599/R

PARTON, Hulda (19/20th C) American

Works on paper

£510 $800 €765 Portrait of young girl seated in her best dress holding a bouquet (53x38cm-21x15in) s.d.1904 W/C. 19-Apr-3 James Julia, Fairfield #301/R

PARTOS, Paul (1943-) Australian

£6452 $9806 €9678 Untitled (137x111cm-54x44in) s.d.1979-80 verso exhib. 28-Aug-2 Deutscher-Menzies, Melbourne #56/R est:10000-15000 (A.D 18000)
£11538 $18346 €17307 Untitled (178x152cm-70x60in) s.i.d.1987 verso prov.exhib. 4-Mar-3 Deutscher-Menzies, Melbourne #22/R est:20000-30000 (A.D 30000)
£12000 $19320 €18000 Untitled 12 - X,O, painting series (177x145cm-70x57in) s.i.d.1996 prov. 6-May-3 Christie's, Melbourne #27/R est:30000-40000 (A.D 30000)
£12500 $19625 €18750 Untitled, blue border (178x145cm-70x57in) s.i.d.1996 verso prov. 25-Nov-2 Christie's, Melbourne #61/R est:20000-30000 (A.D 35000)

Works on paper

£786 $1225 €1179 Untitled (76x57cm-30x22in) s.d.88 pastel gouache. 11-Nov-2 Deutscher-Menzies, Melbourne #11/R (A.D 2200)

PARTRIDGE, Beatrice (1867-1963) New Zealander

£862 $1345 €1293 Otira Gorge (65x86cm-26x34in) s. 7-Nov-2 International Art Centre, Auckland #145/R est:2000-3000 (NZ.D 2750)

PARTRIDGE, Bernard (1861-1945) British

Works on paper

£400 $632 €600 Elegant girl in garden (75x55cm-30x22in) s.d. pastel oval. 19-Dec-2 Bonhams, Edinburgh #321

PARTRIDGE, E (?) British

£940 $1457 €1410 Winter landscape with congregation leaving the village church (44x32cm-17x13in) s.d.1875. 1-Oct-2 Fellows & Sons, Birmingham #11/R

PARTRIDGE, Frank H (20th C) British

Works on paper

£800 $1304 €1200 Gore Point, Holme-next-to-the-sea - sea lavender and ragwort (23x71cm-9x28in) s. W/C. 14-Feb-3 Keys, Aylsham #637/R
£2500 $3925 €3750 The 5th Great Yarmouth. Approaching to the 4th Great Yarmouth (25x56cm-10x22in) s.d.1910 W/C pair. 13-Dec-2 Keys, Aylsham #607/R est:2000-3000

PARTRIDGE, Frederick Henry (?) British

Works on paper

£2000 $3040 €3000 Blakeney Point (36x127cm-14x50in) s.d.1922/3 one i. W/C pair. 16-Aug-2 Keys, Aylsham #590/R

PARTRIDGE, Henry T (19/20th C) British

£3100 $4836 €4650 Billy. Empress. Harlequin. Daly (44x59cm-17x23in) s.d.1889 one s.verso set of four prov. 17-Oct-2 Lawrence, Crewkerne #1584/R est:1500-2500

PARTRIDGE, Henry T (attrib) (19/20th C) British

£270 $432 €405 Bay in a stable (44x53cm-17x21in) indis.s. 15-May-3 Lawrence, Crewkerne #945
£3400 $5304 €5100 Portraits of hunters in stables (44x60cm-17x24in) three prov. 17-Oct-2 Lawrence, Crewkerne #1583/R est:1000-1500

PARTRIDGE, J C (19th C) British

£828 $1300 €1242 Dark bat hunter in a stable (36x46cm-14x18in) s.d. prov. 14-Dec-2 Charlton Hall, Columbia #208a/R est:800-1200

PARTRIDGE, John (attrib) (1790-1872) British

£4200 $6636 €6300 Grenadier guards officer (51x40cm-20x16in) 7-Apr-3 Bonhams, Bath #76/R est:1000-1500

PARTURIER, Marcel (1901-1976) French

£255 $397 €400 La riviere (22x27cm-9x11in) s. panel. 7-Nov-2 Claude Aguttes, Neuilly #71
£256 $403 €400 Vue de Tunisie (24x33cm-9x13in) s. d.1921 verso cardboard. 11-Dec-2 Maigret, Paris #131/R
£283 $436 €450 La vente publique (65x52cm-26x20in) s. 22-Oct-2 Campo, Vlaamse Kaai #584
£321 $503 €500 Carolles, Pont du Ludes dans la Manche (27x35cm-11x14in) s.d.1933 panel. 11-Dec-2 Maigret, Paris #134
£545 $855 €850 Groupe de maisons dans les arbres (33x41cm-13x16in) s. panel. 11-Dec-2 Maigret, Paris #132/R
£647 $1036 €900 Bord de riviere Ombrage (22x27cm-9x11in) s. panel. 18-May-3 Eric Pillon, Calais #135/R
£833 $1308 €1300 Maisons a Douarnenez (18x24cm-7x9in) s. panel. 11-Dec-2 Maigret, Paris #133/R
£845 $1403 €1200 Le chemin creux, environs de Compiegne (50x61cm-20x24in) s. s.i.verso. 11-Jun-3 Beaussant & Lefèvre, Paris #120
£943 $1453 €1500 Port de peche (32x41cm-13x16in) s. panel. 27-Oct-2 Muizon & Le Coent, Paris #30/R
£1088 $1731 €1600 Marabout a Kairouan (24x33cm-9x13in) s.i. cardboard. 24-Mar-3 Rabourdin & Choppin de Janvry, Paris #263/R est:1800-2200
£1127 $1870 €1600 Le Rhu a Douarnenez (46x55cm-18x22in) s. i.d.verso. 11-Jun-3 Beaussant & Lefèvre, Paris #119/R est:1500-1800
£1154 $1812 €1800 Les Alpilles (60x81cm-24x32in) s.d.1938. 11-Dec-2 Maigret, Paris #135/R est:1500-2500
£1274 $1987 €2000 Marche a Douarnenez, Finistere (18x24cm-7x9in) s. s.i. verso panel. 7-Nov-2 Claude Aguttes, Neuilly #70/R est:800-1000
£1329 $2073 €2100 Port de Douarnenez (54x65cm-21x26in) s. 20-Oct-2 Mercier & Cie, Lille #341 est:900-1000

Works on paper

£321 $503 €500 Rue de Kerea, Quimper (38x26cm-15x10in) s. gouache. 11-Dec-2 Maigret, Paris #130/R

PASCAL, Leopold (1900-) French
£641 $1006 €1000 Le jardin fleuri (71x90cm-28x35in) s. 16-Dec-2 Chochon-Barre & Allardi, Paris #85

PASCAL, Paul (1832-1903) French
Works on paper
£399 $650 €599 Arabian encampment at sunset (28x43cm-11x17in) s.d.1902 gouache. 2-Feb-3 Grogan, Boston #30
£417 $654 €650 Paysage Orientaliste (18x24cm-7x9in) s.d.1870 gouache. 11-Dec-2 Maigret, Paris #114
£531 $850 €797 Shepherds and sheep in a mid-eastern landscape (43x61cm-17x24in) s. 15-Mar-3 Eldred, East Dennis #476/R
£617 $1000 €926 North African scene (23x46cm-9x18in) s.d.1899 gouache. 24-Jan-3 Freeman, Philadelphia #127/R est:500-800
£865 $1359 €1350 Sur la route d'Alger a El-Biar (44x31cm-17x12in) s.d.1890 W/C gouache. 16-Dec-2 Gros & Delettrez, Paris #287
£943 $1453 €1500 Rue en orient au claire de lune (20x30cm-8x12in) s.d.1883 W/C. 23-Oct-2 Rabourdin & Choppin de Janvry, Paris #188
£1500 $2340 €2250 Oriental scenes (30x43cm-12x17in) s. W/C pair. 26-Mar-3 Sotheby's, Olympia #233/R est:1500-2000

PASCALI, Pino (1935-1968) Italian
£903 $1427 €1400 Woman (24x29cm-9x11in) Chinese ink tempera. 18-Dec-2 Christie's, Rome #16/R
£160000 $262400 €240000 Rug (62x120cm-24x47in) steel wool exec.1968 prov. 6-Feb-3 Sotheby's, London #33/R est:60000
Sculpture
£70000 $109200 €105000 Sul ponte sventola bandiera bianca (83x113x7cm-33x44x3in) oil fabric on wooden structure executed 1964 prov.lit. 21-Oct-2 Sotheby's, London #37/R est:70000-90000
Works on paper
£1677 $2650 €2600 Aboriginal (25x35cm-10x14in) mixed media exec.1965 exhib. 18-Dec-2 Christie's, Rome #26
£1702 $2757 €2400 Lion (31x41cm-12x16in) mixed media sheet on board exec.1965. 26-May-3 Christie's, Milan #33/R est:2500-3000
£1795 $2818 €2800 Untitled (22x34cm-9x13in) mixed media collage. 20-Nov-2 Pandolfini, Florence #108/R
£1806 $2854 €2800 Letters (29x17cm-11x7in) mixed media card. 18-Dec-2 Christie's, Rome #61
£2065 $3262 €3200 Wizard (35x25cm-14x10in) mixed media card exhib. 18-Dec-2 Christie's, Rome #13/R
£2323 $3670 €3600 Africa (28x34cm-11x13in) mixed media exec.1964 exhib. 18-Dec-2 Christie's, Rome #14/R
£2658 $4200 €4200 Steady: fire!! (23x32cm-9x13in) mixed media exec.1963. 29-Nov-2 Farsetti, Prato #468/R

PASCH, Johan (elder-attrib) (1706-1769) Swedish
£6284 $10306 €9112 Africa and Europe - Still life of symbols against grey background (93x137cm-37x54in) overdoors pair. 4-Jun-3 AB Stockholms Auktionsverk #2254/R est:80000-120000 (S.KR 80000)

PASCH, Lorens (elder) (1702-1776) Swedish
£851 $1319 €1277 Portrait of young lady (53x44cm-21x17in) i.verso. 3-Dec-2 Bukowskis, Stockholm #401/R (S.KR 12000)

PASCH, Lorens (elder-attrib) (1702-1776) Swedish
£15318 $25122 €22211 Three brothers and sisters (76cm-30in) trompe l'oeil vertical lamellas three. 4-Jun-3 AB Stockholms Auktionsverk #2251/R est:225000-250000 (S.KR 195000)

PASCH, Lorens (younger) (1733-1805) Swedish
£2199 $3408 €3299 Portrait of Gustaf Miles Fleetwood (74x58cm-29x23in) i.d.1787 verso oval. 4-Dec-2 AB Stockholms Auktionsverk #1612/R est:25000-30000 (S.KR 31000)

PASCH, Ulrika (1735-1796) Swedish
£2532 $4000 €4000 Portraits of Ulrika Eleonora and Gustaf II Adolf (21x16cm-8x6in) s.verso panel pair. 30-Nov-2 Hagelstam, Helsinki #26/R est:2000

PASCH, Ulrika (attrib) (1735-1796) Swedish
£709 $1099 €1064 Portrait of young lady (58x45cm-23x18in) 4-Dec-2 AB Stockholms Auktionsverk #1613/R (S.KR 10000)
£771 $1219 €1157 Queen Kristina (10x9cm-4x4in) copper panel. 27-Nov-2 Falkkloos, Malmo #78124/R (S.KR 11000)
£20946 $33933 €30372 King Adolf Fredrik and Queen Lovisa Ulrika (75x62cm-30x24in) pair. 26-May-3 Bukowskis, Stockholm #361/R est:300000-350000 (S.KR 270000)

PASCHEN, Peter (19th C) German
£1200 $1992 €1740 Intruder (65x81cm-26x32in) s. 12-Jun-3 Christie's, Kensington #123/R est:1500-2000

PASCHETTA, Mario (1949-) Italian
£278 $442 €400 Tuscany (40x50cm-16x20in) s.i.verso oil pigment. 1-May-3 Meeting Art, Vercelli #262
£316 $494 €500 Sahara (80x40cm-31x16in) s.i.d.2000 oil pigment. 14-Sep-2 Meeting Art, Vercelli #328
£316 $494 €500 Lagoon and everglades (80x40cm-31x16in) s.i.d.2001 verso oil pigment. 14-Sep-2 Meeting Art, Vercelli #364/R
£347 $552 €500 Night scene (80x60cm-31x24in) s.i.d.1999 verso oil pigment. 1-May-3 Meeting Art, Vercelli #537
£417 $663 €600 Night scene in Tuscany (70x60cm-28x24in) s.i.d.2000 oil pigment. 1-May-3 Meeting Art, Vercelli #51
£481 $755 €750 Arctic (90x80cm-35x31in) s.i.d.2000 verso oil pigment. 23-Nov-2 Meeting Art, Vercelli #422/R
£490 $784 €750 Red land (100x80cm-39x31in) s.i.d.2001 verso oil pigment. 4-Jan-3 Meeting Art, Vercelli #69
£510 $811 €750 San Giminiano (120x60cm-47x24in) s.i.d.2000 oil pigment. 1-Mar-3 Meeting Art, Vercelli #736
£523 $837 €800 Trequanda at night (80x70cm-31x28in) s.i.d.1999 verso oil pigment. 4-Jan-3 Meeting Art, Vercelli #686
£545 $855 €850 Landscape by Volterra (100x90cm-39x35in) s.i.d.2000 verso oil pigment. 23-Nov-2 Meeting Art, Vercelli #394/R
£654 $1046 €1000 Blue (120x80cm-47x31in) s.i.d.2000 verso oil pigment. 4-Jan-3 Meeting Art, Vercelli #200
£764 $1215 €1100 Volterra hills (120x60cm-47x24in) s.i.d.2000 verso oil pigment. 1-May-3 Meeting Art, Vercelli #343
£1042 $1656 €1500 Sea in Forte, at night (120x100cm-47x39in) s.i.d.2000 verso oil pigment lit. 1-May-3 Meeting Art, Vercelli #575

PASCHINGER, Franz Stefan (attrib) (1862-?) Austrian
£420 $617 €630 Moonlit riverscene with cottage by a wood (17x30cm-7x12in) s. board. 24-Jun-2 Tiffin King & Nicholson, Carlisle #335/R

PASCHKE, Ed (1939-) American
Works on paper
£438 $700 €657 Bayou shoe (36x41cm-14x16in) s.d.71 col pencil dr. 11-Jan-3 Susanin's, Chicago #5014/R
£1098 $1800 €1592 Untitled (58x43cm-23x17in) s.d.1978 pastel. 1-Jun-3 Wright, Chicago #355/R est:2000-3000
£1280 $2100 €1856 Boyou shoe (36x41cm-14x16in) s.d.71 col pencil. 1-Jun-3 Wright, Chicago #354/R est:2000-3000

PASCIN (1885-1930) American/Bulgarian
Works on paper
£629 $1051 €900 Couple (17x14cm-7x6in) s. W/C ink. 26-Jun-3 Tajan, Paris #101

PASCIN, Jules (1885-1930) American/Bulgarian
£833 $1292 €1300 Femme nue etendue (48x35cm-19x14in) studio st. graphite. 5-Dec-2 Gros & Delettrez, Paris #101
£3500 $5565 €5250 Clair de lune (48x61cm-19x24in) s. oil Indian ink paper on canvas prov.exhib.lit. 20-Mar-3 Sotheby's, Olympia #162/R est:5000-7000
£9028 $14896 €13000 Hermine a l'ombrelle rouge (46x38cm-18x15in) st.sig. cardboard painted c.1908. 1-Jul-3 Rossini, Paris #113/R
£10000 $15400 €15000 Suzanne (48x33cm-19x13in) st.sig. prov.lit. 22-Oct-2 Sotheby's, London #240/R est:10000-15000
£34783 $56000 €52175 Cendrillon (93x74cm-37x29in) s. i.verso painted c.1925-26 prov.exhib.lit. 7-May-3 Sotheby's, New York #368/R est:70000-90000
£40000 $66800 €58000 Jeunes noirs a Cuba (74x86cm-29x34in) s. painted c.1917-18 prov.exhib.lit. 24-Jun-3 Sotheby's, London #148/R est:28000-35000
£64103 $100000 €96155 Zimette et mireille (101x81cm-40x32in) painted 1930 prov.exhib.lit. 6-Nov-2 Sotheby's, New York #217/R est:100000-150000
Works on paper
£250 $388 €375 Figure study (22x13cm-9x5in) s.i.d.1915 pen ink wash. 24-Sep-2 Bonhams, Knightsbridge #221/R
£263 $427 €400 Personnages et cavaliers (15x28cm-6x11in) s. ink dr. 22-Jan-3 Tajan, Paris #197
£306 $487 €450 Beau moustachu (32x23cm-13x9in) studio st. ink. 24-Mar-3 Claude Boisgirard, Paris #44
£345 $576 €500 Irene (19x27cm-7x11in) s. graphite. 9-Jul-3 Cornette de St.Cyr, Paris #186
£345 $576 €500 Nu feminin (19x26cm-7x10in) s.i.d.1909 ink. 9-Jul-3 Cornette de St.Cyr, Paris #187/R
£379 $633 €550 Nu feminin (19x27cm-7x11in) st.sig. ink. 9-Jul-3 Cornette de St.Cyr, Paris #188
£390 $651 €550 La sieste sur l'herbe (21x35cm-8x14in) studio st. graphite. 23-Jun-3 Claude Boisgirard, Paris #66
£390 $651 €550 Deux femmes enlacees (34x24cm-13x9in) studio st. graphite. 23-Jun-3 Claude Boisgirard, Paris #67

£417 $650 €626 Seated nude. Brothel scene (20x20cm-8x8in) studio st. one W/C brush ink exec.c.1925 one d.1927 pencil. 19-Sep-2 Swann Galleries, New York #639/R
£417 $658 €600 Femmes en promenade en Algerie (20x31cm-8x12in) pen ink. 25-Apr-3 Piasa, Paris #37
£507 $832 €700 Portrait de Germaine Eisenmann (23x32cm-9x13in) s. sepia Indian ink prov. 29-May-3 Lempertz, Koln #848/R
£518 $850 €751 Two seated woman (20x28cm-8x11in) s.d.1910 ink. 1-Jun-3 Wright, Chicago #192/R
£567 $948 €800 Marguerite, modele assis (20x16cm-8x6in) st.sig.i.d.1907 pencil dr. 18-Jun-3 Charbonneaux, Paris #58
£608 $949 €900 Reunion de femmes (26x21cm-10x8in) st.sig.i. crayon dr prov. 28-Mar-3 Charbonneaux, Paris #126
£613 $968 €950 Portrait de Madame Henri Laurens (42x28cm-17x11in) s. ink. 18-Dec-2 Digard, Paris #253
£619 $990 €860 Nu feminin de profil (29x19cm-11x7in) s. pencil dr prov. 18-May-3 Charbonneaux, Paris #195/R
£680 $1082 €1000 Reveil au Pensinnat Venus (64x49cm-25x19in) sttudo st. graphite. 24-Mar-3 Claude Boisgirard, Paris #43
£699 $1168 €1000 La presentation (22x28cm-9x11in) s. W/C Indian ink. 26-Jun-3 Tajan, Paris #102
£700 $1113 €1050 Sur la plage (27x21cm-11x8in) st.sig. pen ink over pencil lit. 20-Mar-3 Sotheby's, Olympia #74/R
£755 $1209 €1050 Nu feminin, une jambe levee (30x18cm-12x7in) bears studio st. pencil dr prov. 18-May-3 Charbonneaux, Paris #196
£789 $1279 €1200 Hermine David et Lucie Krohg (26x43cm-10x17in) s. dr lit. 22-Jan-3 Tajan, Paris #196
£814 $1360 €1180 Two nudes and poodle (13x18cm-5x7in) s. Indian ink W/C prov. 24-Jun-3 Koller, Zurich #138/R (S.FR 1800)
£816 $1298 €1200 Femmes de couleur (16x18cm-6x7in) st.sig. graphite W/C prov. 26-Feb-3 Artcurial Briest, Paris #229
£851 $1421 €1200 Personnages en Tunisie (24x19cm-9x7in) studio st. graphite prov. 23-Jun-3 Claude Boisgirard, Paris #68/R
£873 $1371 €1310 Trois jeunes filles (25x25cm-10x10in) s. W/C Indian ink prov.lit. 23-Nov-2 Burkhard, Luzern #143/R (S.FR 2000)
£884 $1406 €1300 Scene de rue a Cuba (20x16cm-8x6in) st.sig. chl W/C dr. 26-Feb-3 Artcurial Briest, Paris #225
£904 $1500 €1311 Continental village landscape with figures (18x28cm-7x11in) s. pen ink W/C. 11-Jun-3 Boos Gallery, Michigan #595/R est:3000-5000
£922 $1540 €1300 Maison close, l'attente (25x24cm-10x9in) studio st. brown ink. 23-Jun-3 Claude Boisgirard, Paris #64/R
£962 $1500 €1443 A la Nouvelle Orleans (20x26cm-8x10in) s. W/C pen black ink exhib. 18-Sep-2 Swann Galleries, New York #40/R est:2000-3000
£1006 $1600 €1509 Deux femmes. Homme et femme aux marches (24x16cm-9x6in) s. ink two. 4-Mar-3 Swann Galleries, New York #494/R est:2000-3000
£1006 $1600 €1509 Trois femmes. L'ete (16x26cm-6x10in) s. ink two. 4-Mar-3 Swann Galleries, New York #495/R est:2000-3000
£1020 $1622 €1500 Toilette au Chaussons (31x37cm-12x15in) studio st. ink. 24-Mar-3 Claude Boisgirard, Paris #45/R
£1026 $1610 €1600 Deux nus (21x32cm-8x13in) studio st.d. pencil prov. 16-Dec-2 Charbonneaux, Paris #174/R est:1800-2000
£1032 $1600 €1548 Femme assise. Etude de femme (63x48cm-25x19in) st.verso pen black ink double-sided prov. 26-Sep-2 Christie's, Rockefeller NY #565/R est:2000-3000
£1184 $1918 €1800 Nu allonge (24x31cm-9x12in) studio st. ink W/C. 22-Jan-3 Tajan, Paris #198 est:150-200
£1282 $2026 €2000 Scene de maison close (19x24cm-7x9in) st.sig. ink wash W/C. 15-Nov-2 Laurence Calmels, Paris #24/R
£1282 $2013 €2000 La conversation, Marseille (17x20cm-7x8in) st.sig. graphite double-sided prov. 24-Nov-2 Chayette & Cheval, Paris #242 est:1200-1500
£1410 $2200 €2115 Pauline, nue couchee (33x46cm-13x18in) studio st. pencil exec.c.1920. 18-Sep-2 Swann Galleries, New York #41/R est:3000-5000
£1463 $2326 €2150 Terrasse de cafe (27x28cm-11x11in) s.i.d.1924 pen ink wash. 3-Mar-3 Claude Boisgirard, Paris #81 est:2200-2500
£1528 $2384 €2292 Modele dans un fauteuil (43x30cm-17x12in) s. sepia pen wash lit. 6-Nov-2 Dobiaschofsky, Bern #1790/R est:5500 (S.FR 3500)
£1702 $2757 €2400 Monsieur Pascin, cher Maitre (49x49cm-19x19in) st.sig. ink W/C prov. 21-May-3 Cornette de St.Cyr, Paris #60/R est:2000-3000
£1731 $2717 €2700 Figures (17x24cm-7x9in) studio st. Chinese ink W/C double-sided. 19-Nov-2 Finarte, Milan #8/R
£1923 $3000 €2885 Jeune femme nue, sur une chaise (36x23cm-14x9in) studio st. pen ink pencil. 19-Sep-2 Swann Galleries, New York #638/R est:2000-3000
£2051 $3200 €3077 Jeune femme (32x24cm-13x9in) s. W/C pen ink. 18-Sep-2 Swann Galleries, New York #42/R est:2500-3500
£2516 $4000 €3774 Histoire antique: Socrate et ses disciples (31x45cm-12x18in) s.i. W/C pen ink chl prov. 27-Feb-3 Christie's, Rockefeller NY #24/R
£2619 $4164 €3850 Les deux amies (35x50cm-14x20in) s. graphite dr. 26-Feb-3 Artcurial Briest, Paris #231/R est:3000-4000
£2778 $4472 €4167 Trois jeunes filles (25x25cm-10x10in) s. prov.lit. 7-May-3 Dobiaschofsky, Bern #871/R est:4000 (S.FR 6000)
£3019 $4800 €4529 Chinoise (56x43cm-22x17in) s.i. pastel pencil prov. 27-Feb-3 Christie's, Rockefeller NY #52/R est:7000

PASCIUTI, Antonio (1937-) Italian
£340 $541 €500 Flowers in landscape (30x40cm-12x16in) s. 1-Mar-3 Meeting Art, Vercelli #457
£374 $595 €550 Summer (30x40cm-12x16in) s. 1-Mar-3 Meeting Art, Vercelli #751
£590 $939 €850 Labour (50x50cm-20x20in) s. 1-May-3 Meeting Art, Vercelli #36
£759 $1185 €1200 In the garden (40x50cm-16x20in) s. s.i.verso. 14-Sep-2 Meeting Art, Vercelli #498/R
£759 $1185 €1200 Souvenirs (40x50cm-16x20in) s. 14-Sep-2 Meeting Art, Vercelli #873/R

PASEVI, F (?) Italian
£1772 $2765 €2800 Harvesting (67x79cm-26x31in) s. 19-Oct-2 Semenzato, Venice #345/R

PASINELLI, Lorenzo (1629-1700) Italian
£3378 $5270 €5000 Madonna (92x73cm-36x29in) 25-Mar-3 Finarte Semenzato, Rome #103/R

PASINETTI, Antonio (1863-1940) Italian
£4295 $6271 €6700 Flags in Venice (78x98cm-31x39in) s. 5-Jun-2 Il Ponte, Milan #246/R est:2000-2200

PASINI, Alberto (1826-1899) Italian
£1410 $2228 €2200 ORiental daner (27x17cm-11x7in) s.d.1861 oil pen cardboard. 18-Nov-2 Sotheby's, Paris #92/R
£5405 $8432 €8000 Odalisk (27x36cm-11x14in) s.d.1878. 28-Mar-3 Claude Aguttes, Neuilly #198/R
£13462 $21135 €21000 Fantasia (23x39cm-9x15in) s.d. panel. 11-Dec-2 Maigret, Paris #102/R est:14000-16000
£15278 $24292 €22000 Quiet afternoon at the bazar (40x24cm-16x9in) s.i.d.1872 prov. 29-Apr-3 Christie's, Amsterdam #102/R est:15000-20000
£36000 $56520 €54000 Ottoman portico (28x35cm-11x14in) s.d.1886 canvas on b prov. 19-Nov-2 Sotheby's, London #183/R est:30000-50000
£36539 $57366 €57000 Cavaliers turcs dans la cour du palais (32x41cm-13x16in) s. lit. 10-Dec-2 Tajan, Paris #212/R est:40000
£42000 $70140 €63000 Market outside the city gate (35x27cm-14x11in) s.d.1881 prov. 19-Jun-3 Christie's, London #1/R est:25000-35000
£195000 $325650 €292500 Mercato Turco (48x73cm-19x29in) s.d.1884 prov.exhib.lit. 19-Jun-3 Christie's, London #23/R est:120000-160000

Works on paper
£2365 $3689 €3500 Market in Turkey (39x29cm-15x11in) s. dr. 28-Mar-3 Claude Aguttes, Neuilly #179/R
£14685 $24524 €21000 Scene animee en Turquie (32x40cm-13x16in) s.d.1870 W/C. 27-Jun-3 Claude Aguttes, Neuilly #115/R est:15000-20000
£17483 $29196 €25000 Scene animee de marche en Turquie (32x40cm-13x16in) s.d.1870 W/C. 27-Jun-3 Claude Aguttes, Neuilly #114/R est:15000-20000

PASINI, Bonifazio (1489-1540) Italian
£8176 $12673 €13000 Madonna with child (39x33cm-15x13in) 2-Oct-2 Dorotheum, Vienna #57/R est:13000-15000

PASINI, Ludwig (1832-1903) Austrian
Works on paper
£1538 $2385 €2400 Young Italian girl reading a letter leaning on a confessional box (50x34cm-20x13in) s.i.d.1884 W/C. 4-Dec-2 Neumeister, Munich #544/R est:900
£7500 $11625 €11250 Roman house with an edicola in a baroque surrounds (68x50cm-27x20in) s.d.1863 W/C. 4-Dec-2 Christie's, London #105/R est:8000-12000

PASINI, Ludwig (attrib) (1832-1903) Austrian
£482 $800 €699 Curiosity (56x41cm-22x16in) s.i.verso. 14-Jun-3 Jackson's, Cedar Falls #211

PASKELL, William (1866-1951) American
£321 $500 €482 Autumn landscape (30x41cm-12x16in) s. 1-Aug-2 Eldred, East Dennis #411
£433 $675 €650 Fall day Nantucket Harbour (41x61cm-16x24in) s. i.verso. 9-Nov-2 Sloan, North Bethesda #623

PASMORE, F G (jnr) (fl.1875-1884) British
£1026 $1600 €1539 Boys ratting (46x58cm-18x23in) s. 30-Mar-3 Susanin's, Chicago #6025/R est:3000-5000

PASMORE, Frederick George (jnr-attrib) (fl.1875-1884) British
£1400 $2184 €2100 Boys rabbiting (51x61cm-20x24in) bears sig.d. 10-Oct-2 Greenslade Hunt, Taunton #587/R est:1200-1600

PASMORE, John F (1820-1871) British
£1800 $2970 €2610 Egg collectors (61x50cm-24x20in) s.d.1853. 2-Jul-3 Sotheby's, Olympia #313/R est:2000-3000

PASMORE, Victor (1908-1998) British
£1500 $2340 €2250 Portrait of a frame master (35x25cm-14x10in) init. s.d.1939 verso panel prov. 27-Mar-3 Christie's, Kensington #575/R est:2000-3000
£5000 $7750 €7500 Untitled (23x149cm-9x59in) mono. acrylic chl painted c.1980. 3-Dec-2 Bonhams, New Bond Street #108/R est:4000-6000
£6200 $9610 €9300 Untitled (39x39cm-15x15in) mono.d.88 board with scoring. 3-Dec-2 Bonhams, New Bond Street #106/R est:5000-7000
£6500 $10140 €9750 Untitled (41x41cm-16x16in) mono.d.90 board. 25-Mar-3 Bonhams, New Bond Street #113/R est:4000-6000
£6800 $10608 €10200 Untitled (41x41cm-16x16in) mono. board. 25-Mar-3 Bonhams, New Bond Street #114/R est:4000-6000
£9800 $15190 €14700 Untitled (39x39cm-15x15in) mono. board with scoring. 3-Dec-2 Bonhams, New Bond Street #107/R est:5000-7000
£90000 $147600 €130500 View on the Cam from Magdalene Bridge, Cambridge, No 1 (56x81cm-22x32in) painted 1947 lit. 4-Jun-3 Sotheby's, London #52/R est:40000-60000

Works on paper
£280 $434 €420 Lady at her toilette (24x16cm-9x6in) init. pencil. 24-Sep-2 Bonhams, Knightsbridge #223/R
£620 $967 €930 Untitled (48x36cm-19x14in) init. chl. 17-Oct-2 David Lay, Penzance #1391
£1700 $2652 €2550 World and its shadow (79x76cm-31x30in) chl ink canvas on board. 25-Mar-3 Bonhams, New Bond Street #115/R est:1000-1500
£2600 $4056 €3900 Rooftops (20x33cm-8x13in) mono. pen ink collage airbrush. 25-Mar-3 Bonhams, New Bond Street #112/R est:1200-1800
£4205 $6559 €6308 Composition (40x46cm-16x18in) init.d.85 mixed media building board. 6-Nov-2 AB Stockholms Auktionsverk #967/R est:75000-100000 (S.KR 60000)
£10000 $15700 €15000 Linear image in 2 movements - relief (40x40cm-16x16in) init.d.75 paint gravure board prov.lit. 22-Nov-2 Christie's, London #101/R est:6000-8000

PASOTTO, Paolo (1930-) Italian
£1233 $1936 €1800 Untitled (81x65cm-32x26in) s.d.63 s.i.verso prov. 15-Apr-3 Laurence Calmels, Paris #4114/R

PASQUAROSA (1896-1973) Italian
£1154 $1812 €1800 Flowers in black vase (60x50cm-24x20in) s. board. 21-Nov-2 Finarte, Rome #358/R
£1646 $2600 €2600 Still life with carnations in vase (56x45cm-22x18in) s. 26-Nov-2 Christie's, Rome #133/R

PASQUE, Aubin (1903-1981) Belgian
£305 $497 €460 Paysage a Uccle (28x38cm-11x15in) s. panel. 17-Feb-3 Horta, Bruxelles #328
£850 $1368 €1300 L'epreuve du feu (70x60cm-28x24in) s. d.1950 verso panel. 20-Jan-3 Horta, Bruxelles #401

PASQUIER, Jacques (1930-) French
Works on paper
£253 $395 €400 Jardin I (70x50cm-28x20in) s.i.d.1977 mixed media. 15-Sep-2 Etude Bailleul, Bayeux #138/R

PASQUIER, Noel (20th C) French
Works on paper
£1013 $1652 €1530 La barcarolle (20x20cm-8x8in) s. mixed media. 1-Feb-3 Claude Aguttes, Neuilly #188 est:1680-1830

PASQUIER, Pierre (1731-1808) French
Miniatures
£3800 $6156 €5700 Marie Therese de Savoie, comtesse d'Artois (5cm-2in) s.d.1778 enamel. 22-May-3 Bonhams, New Bond Street #29/R est:1500-2000

PASSAGE, Comte Arthur Marie Gabriel du (1838-1909) French
Sculpture
£1475 $2330 €2300 Chien ratier (8x25x13cm-3x10x5in) s. brown pat bronze. 18-Nov-2 Tajan, Paris #69/R est:1800-2400
£3885 $6216 €5400 Le contrebandier (56x65cm-22x26in) s. brown pat bronze. 18-May-3 Rabourdin & Choppin de Janvry, Paris #54/R est:6000-8000
£10791 $17266 €15000 Cheval a l'entrainement avec son lad (83x113cm-33x44in) s. black brown pat bronze. 18-May-3 Eric Pillon, Calais #25/R
Works on paper
£353 $546 €550 Promenade sur la plage normande (12x17cm-5x7in) s.d.1890 W/C gouache. 6-Dec-2 Rieunier, Bailly-Pommery, Mathias, Paris #68/R

PASSAGE, Vicomte Charles Marie du (1848-1926) French
Works on paper
£1076 $1700 €1700 Course d'attelage (43x63cm-17x25in) s.d.1905 pen ink W/C. 28-Nov-2 Tajan, Paris #182/R est:1000-1500

PASSAROTTI, Bartolomeo (1529-1592) Italian
£23000 $38410 €33350 Study of Saint John the Baptist, bust length (43x28cm-17x11in) paper on panel. 10-Jul-3 Sotheby's, London #162/R est:6000-8000

PASSAROTTI, Bartolomeo (attrib) (1529-1592) Italian
£11585 $19000 €17378 Adoration of the Magi (28x22cm-11x9in) copper. 29-May-3 Sotheby's, New York #3/R est:10000-15000

PASSAURO, Edmondo (1893-1969) Italian
£532 $862 €750 Interno (39x25cm-15x10in) s.d.1932. 22-May-3 Stadion, Trieste #318/R
£1064 $1723 €1500 Ritratto di signora (69x59cm-27x23in) s.verso board. 22-May-3 Stadion, Trieste #314/R est:1500-2000
£1418 $2298 €2000 La spagnola (90x69cm-35x27in) board. 22-May-3 Stadion, Trieste #309/R est:2500-3500
£2270 $3677 €3200 Autoritratto (69x60cm-27x24in) s.d.1928 verso board. 22-May-3 Stadion, Trieste #310/R est:2500-3500
£2482 $4021 €3500 Idillio nei campi (104x128cm-41x50in) s. panel. 22-May-3 Stadion, Trieste #308/R est:2000-3000
Works on paper
£270 $437 €380 Gattino (30x21cm-12x8in) s. col pastel. 22-May-3 Stadion, Trieste #320
£390 $632 €550 Fiori (35x30cm-14x12in) mixed media panel. 22-May-3 Stadion, Trieste #316/R
£709 $1149 €1000 Signora con cagnolino (70x65cm-28x26in) s.d.1946 W/C. 22-May-3 Stadion, Trieste #290
£1064 $1723 €1500 Bambina con giocattolo di pezza (67x54cm-26x21in) s.d.44 col pastel. 22-May-3 Stadion, Trieste #312/R est:1400-1800

PASSE, Chrispijn van de (elder-attrib) (c.1564-1637) Dutch
Works on paper
£472 $736 €750 Christ (24x16cm-9x6in) pen wash htd bodycol. 11-Oct-2 Winterberg, Heidelberg #300/R
£1800 $2790 €2700 Annunciation (18x11cm-7x4in) pen ink wash htd white. 9-Dec-2 Bonhams, New Bond Street #78/R est:1200-1800

PASSERI, Giuseppe (1654-1714) Italian
Works on paper
£1000 $1570 €1500 Kneeling figure of a pope praying in front of a crucifix (23x16cm-9x6in) red chk pen ink wash htd white. 11-Dec-2 Sotheby's, Olympia #61/R est:1200-1500
£4500 $7515 €6525 Madonna and Child with Saints (22x21cm-9x8in) red chk ink pen wash htd white corner cut prov. 8-Jul-3 Christie's, London #39/R est:3000-4000

PASSERI, Giuseppe (attrib) (1654-1714) Italian
Works on paper
£704 $1134 €1000 Figure femminili che si affacciano da una tenda (20x14cm-8x6in) pen ink brown W/C htd white blk pencil oval. 12-May-3 Sotheby's, Milan #39/R

PASSET, Gerard (20th C) French
£449 $700 €674 Basket of fruit on a table (48x64cm-19x25in) s.d.1960. 10-Nov-2 Selkirks, St. Louis #589

PASSEY, Charles H (fl.1870-1885) British
£350 $567 €508 Harvesting scene (71x91cm-28x36in) s.d.1894. 22-May-3 Wintertons, Lichfield #589
£420 $685 €609 Landscape with figure gathering corn near stukes (90x70cm-35x28in) s. 16-Jul-3 Rupert Toovey, Partridge Green #9/R
£800 $1256 €1200 Reapers harvesting corn. Peaceful stretch of the river (51x76cm-20x30in) s. pair. 16-Apr-3 Christie's, Kensington #629/R
£3205 $5000 €4808 Forest lane (91x66cm-36x26in) s. 12-Oct-2 Neal Auction Company, New Orleans #154/R est:2500-3500

PASSIGLI, Carlo (1881-1953) Italian
£532 $862 €750 Nevicata, Arno alle Cascine (26x37cm-10x15in) s. panel. 22-May-3 Stadion, Trieste #255/R

PASSINI, Johann Nepomuk (1798-1874) Austrian
Works on paper
£1509 $2340 €2400 Puchberg (23x32cm-9x13in) i. W/C. 1-Oct-2 Dorotheum, Vienna #189/R est:1800-2000
£2264 $3509 €3600 View over Altausseer See to Trisselwand (29x44cm-11x17in) i. W/C. 1-Oct-2 Dorotheum, Vienna #186/R est:3600-3800

PASSMORE, John Richard (1904-1984) Australian
£976 $1541 €1415 Still life (20x25cm-8x10in) init. board. 22-Jul-3 Lawson Menzies, Sydney #222/R est:2500-4500 (A.D 2400)
£996 $1564 €1494 Figure in interior (25x26cm-10x10in) s. board prov. 15-Apr-3 Lawson Menzies, Sydney #14/R est:2500-4500 (A.D 2600)
£1423 $2178 €2135 Interior with figures (32x25cm-13x10in) init. board painted c.1950 prov. 25-Aug-2 Sotheby's, Paddington #126 est:4000-6000 (A.D 4000)
£1938 $3081 €2907 Ritual dance (23x29cm-9x11in) init. i.verso prov. 5-May-3 Sotheby's, Melbourne #198/R est:5000-6000 (A.D 5000)
£19231 $30577 €28847 Newcastle beach (33x83cm-13x33in) s.d.55 s.i.d.1955 verso composition board. 4-Mar-3 Deutscher-Menzies, Melbourne #43/R est:45000-50000 (A.D 50000)
Works on paper
£1071 $1693 €1607 Basket boys II (37x48cm-15x19in) W/C ink wash exhib. 27-Nov-2 Deutscher-Menzies, Melbourne #107/R est:4000-6000 (A.D 3000)

PASTEGA, Luigi (1858-1927) Italian
£1646 $2600 €2600 Carnival in Saint Mark's Square (22x33cm-9x13in) s. cardboard. 26-Nov-2 Christie's, Rome #131

PASTEKA, Milan (1931-1998) Czechoslovakian
Works on paper
£473 $732 €710 Figures (32x43cm-13x17in) pencil W/C. 1-Oct-2 SOGA, Bratislava #286/R est:38000 (SL.K 30000)
£553 $856 €830 Blue chair (45x55cm-18x22in) mixed media exec.1976. 3-Dec-2 SOGA, Bratislava #282/R (SL.K 35000)
£646 $917 €969 Sitting woman II (62x44cm-24x17in) pencil exec.1982. 26-Mar-2 SOGA, Bratislava #276/R (SL.K 41000)

PASTOR CALPENA, Vicente (1918-1993) Spanish
Works on paper
£822 $1282 €1200 Village street (42x57cm-17x22in) s.i.d.52 W/C. 8-Apr-3 Ansorena, Madrid #416/R
£833 $1317 €1300 Village (50x70cm-20x28in) s.d.1961 W/C. 19-Nov-2 Durán, Madrid #652/R

PASTOR, Andres (1922-) Spanish
Works on paper
£621 $987 €900 Mimosas (95x65cm-37x26in) s. W/C oval. 4-Mar-3 Ansorena, Madrid #693/R

PASTOUKHOFF, Boris (1894-1974) Russian
£567 $948 €800 Anemones et tulipes (65x54cm-26x21in) s.d. 17-Jun-3 Claude Boisgirard, Paris #107/R

PASTOUR, Louis (1876-1948) French
£300 $498 €435 Jetty and fishing boats (25x41cm-10x16in) s. panel. 12-Jun-3 Gorringes, Lewes #1633
£350 $550 €525 Street scene, Paris (42x32cm-17x13in) s. panel. 14-Dec-2 Weschler, Washington #619/R
£390 $651 €550 Le pont des Oliviers (27x41cm-11x16in) s. board. 20-Jun-3 Piasa, Paris #100
£500 $835 €725 Still life. Wilting flowers (13x22cm-5x9in) s.d.1916 board double-sided. 19-Jun-3 Clevedon Sale Rooms #137/R
£777 $1212 €1150 Marche aux poissons a Aix en Provence (24x33cm-9x13in) d.1923 panel. 25-Mar-3 Chochon-Barre & Allardi, Paris #177/R
£912 $1423 €1350 Barques et voileirs devant les Martigues (23x32cm-9x13in) s.d. panel. 31-Mar-3 Rossini, Paris #73/R
£1064 $1777 €1500 Apres la peche (27x46cm-11x18in) s. board. 20-Jun-3 Piasa, Paris #101 est:450-600
£1081 $1686 €1600 Port Mediterraneen (24x32cm-9x13in) s. panel. 25-Mar-3 Chochon-Barre & Allardi, Paris #176 est:1200-1400

PASZK, Jeno (1895-1948) Hungarian
£2580 $4024 €3870 Square in Nagybanya (68x94cm-27x37in) s. 11-Sep-2 Kieselbach, Budapest #78/R (H.F 1000000)

PATA, Cherubino (1827-1899) French
£1042 $1646 €1500 Chateau de Chillon (65x81cm-26x32in) bears sig. 23-Apr-3 Rabourdin & Choppin de Janvry, Paris #4/R

PATAKY VON SOSPATAK, Laszlo (1857-1912) Hungarian
£7000 $11200 €10500 Making posies (122x81cm-48x32in) s.i. 14-Mar-3 Gardiner & Houlgate, Bath #228/R est:8000-12000

PATAKY, Ferenc (1850-1910) Hungarian
£490 $784 €750 Reclining female nude on river bank (40x50cm-16x20in) s. lit. 10-Jan-3 Allgauer, Kempten #1714/R

PATCH, Thomas (1720-1782) British
£24691 $40000 €37037 Mediterranean coastal scene with a frigate flying the red ensign (90x127cm-35x50in) s. prov.lit. 23-Jan-3 Sotheby's, New York #48/R est:50000-70000

PATCH, Thomas (school) (1720-1782) British
£1800 $2772 €2700 Portrait od Dr Kilburn (33x28cm-13x11in) 25-Oct-2 Gorringes, Lewes #887

PATCHEN, M (20th C) American
£938 $1500 €1360 Fuji series 1 (183x152cm-72x60in) init.d. 17-May-3 Selkirks, St. Louis #397/R est:900-1100

PATEL, Antoine Pierre (younger) (1648-1707) French
Works on paper
£3147 $5255 €4500 Personnages dans un paysage de ruines (39x63cm-15x25in) gouache vellum on panel prov.lit. 25-Jun-3 Sotheby's, Paris #10/R est:5000-7000
£6962 $10861 €11000 Paysage au architectures antiques. Paysage au troupeau (21x28cm-8x11in) one s.d.1699 one s.d.1700 gouache pair. 16-Oct-2 Fraysse & Associes, Paris #31/R est:6000-9000

PATEL, Pierre (elder) (1605-1676) French
£220000 $367400 €319000 Classical landscape with drovers and animals resting on the banks of a river (61x81cm-24x32in) prov.lit. 10-Jul-3 Sotheby's, London #53/R est:30000-50000
Works on paper
£4054 $6324 €6000 Couple in classic landscape (19x25cm-7x10in) gouache. 26-Mar-3 Piasa, Paris #39/R

PATEL, Pierre (elder-attrib) (1605-1676) French
£2885 $4471 €4500 Satyr and nymphs in ruins (96x72cm-38x28in) 5-Dec-2 Dr Fritz Nagel, Stuttgart #625/R est:7000
Works on paper
£851 $1379 €1200 Paysage avec bateaux (16x22cm-6x9in) bears s. gouache. 23-May-3 Beaussant & Lefèvre, Paris #45/R

PATELLIERE, Amedee de la (1890-1932) French
£524 $875 €750 Personnages (30x40cm-12x16in) s. 26-Jun-3 Tajan, Paris #276
£5732 $8943 €9000 Buveur (50x60cm-20x24in) s. painted 1926 exhib. 7-Nov-2 Chochon-Barre & Allardi, Paris #174/R
Works on paper
£310 $497 €450 Interieur d'eglise (49x34cm-19x13in) s.d.1926 chl. 12-Mar-3 Libert, Castor, Paris #150
£774 $1223 €1200 Mas en Provence (44x59cm-17x23in) s. W/C exec.c.1930. 19-Dec-2 Ruellan, Paris #45/R

PATENIER, Joachim (circle) (1485-1524) Flemish
£7547 $11698 €12000 St Hieronymus in landscape (49x57cm-19x22in) panel prov. 2-Oct-2 Dorotheum, Vienna #108/R est:12000-15000
£14465 $22421 €23000 Sylvan landscape with Samaritan (80x109cm-31x43in) panel prov. 2-Oct-2 Dorotheum, Vienna #179/R est:24000-30000

PATER, Jean Baptiste (1695-1736) French
£15244 $25000 €22866 Fete champetre (29x37cm-11x15in) 29-May-3 Sotheby's, New York #61/R est:30000-40000
£19512 $32000 €29268 Fete champetre (29x37cm-11x15in) 29-May-3 Sotheby's, New York #62/R est:40000-60000
£32258 $50968 €50000 Scene galante dans un parc (47x37cm-19x15in) 18-Dec-2 Tajan, Paris #41/R est:15000
£87413 $145979 €125000 L'amour et le Badinage (42x56cm-17x22in) 27-Jun-3 Piasa, Paris #72/R est:125000-145000
£370370 $600000 €555555 Bathers. The swing (57x65cm-22x26in) pair prov.lit. 24-Jan-3 Christie's, Rockefeller NY #99/R est:400000-600000
Works on paper
£680 $1054 €1020 Reclining man (15x12cm-6x5in) black white red chk. 9-Dec-2 Bonhams, New Bond Street #97/R

£10205 $16226 €15000 Etudes de femmes dansant (22x27cm-9x11in) sanguine prov.exhib. 24-Mar-3 Tajan, Paris #29/R

PATER, Jean Baptiste (attrib) (1695-1736) French
£8263 $13138 €12395 Fetes chapters (58x46cm-23x18in) pair. 18-Mar-3 Maynards, Vancouver #24/R est:20000-30000 (C.D 19500)
£14000 $23380 €20300 Ladies bathing at a pool before a rococo pavilion, in a wooded clearing (51x63cm-20x25in) prov. 9-Jul-3 Christie's, London #64/R est:20000-30000

PATERSON, Emily Murray (1855-1934) British
£500 $825 €725 Still life with flowers in a vase (50x60cm-20x24in) s. canvas on board. 3-Jul-3 Christie's, Kensington #477/R
Works on paper
£380 $593 €570 Dutch canal scene (54x77cm-21x30in) s. W/C. 10-Apr-3 Tennants, Leyburn #832

PATERSON, George M (fl.1880-1904) British
£420 $685 €630 Feeding time (30x45cm-12x18in) 14-Feb-3 Lyon & Turnbull, Edinburgh #16

PATERSON, James (1854-1932) British
£4500 $7020 €6750 Ajaccio, Corsica from the quay (37x48cm-15x19in) s.d.1921. 14-Apr-3 Sotheby's, London #120/R est:3000-5000
£30000 $46500 €45000 Green jug. Portrait bust of a girl (46x58cm-18x23in) s.d.1923 double-sided exhib. 31-Oct-2 Christie's, London #122/R est:30000-40000
Works on paper
£950 $1568 €1378 Street, Burford, Oxfordshire (36x24cm-14x9in) s.i.d.1926 pencil. 3-Jul-3 Christie's, Kensington #496
£2300 $3841 €3335 Chatham Heath. s. W/C. 17-Jun-3 Rosebery Fine Art, London #415/R est:200-400
£3700 $5735 €5550 Earling morning, Place St Sauveur, Dinan. Old house on the Rance (25x18cm-10x7in) s.i. one s.i.verso one i.verso pencil W/C pair. 31-Oct-2 Christie's, London #120/R est:1500-2000

PATERSON, John Ford (1851-1912) Australian
£310 $493 €465 River bank at sunset (34x24cm-13x9in) board prov. 5-May-3 Sotheby's, Melbourne #311 (A.D 800)

PATERSON, Mary Viola (1899-1982) British
£460 $713 €690 Figures resting (46x58cm-18x23in) mono. board. 26-Sep-2 Lane, Penzance #44

PATERSON, Viola (1899-1981) British
£800 $1240 €1200 Reclining figures (19x23cm-7x9in) board. 6-Dec-2 Lyon & Turnbull, Edinburgh #69

PATIGIAN, Haig (1876-1950) American
Sculpture
£6024 $10000 €8735 Friendship (43cm-17in) i. brown pat bronze exhib. 11-Jun-3 Butterfields, San Francisco #4296/R est:8000-12000

PATINI, Teofilo (attrib) (1840-1906) Italian
£244 $383 €380 Under Marcello Theatre (50x43cm-20x17in) bears sig. 16-Dec-2 Pandolfini, Florence #100

PATINO, Anton (1957-) Spanish
£1097 $1733 €1700 Antifaz. s.i.d.1984 verso prov.exhib.lit. 17-Dec-2 Segre, Madrid #181/R

PATKO, Karoly (1895-1941) Hungarian
£20638 $32196 €29925 Shipbuilding in the Bay of Naples (84x96cm-33x38in) s. tempera panel. 13-Sep-2 Mu Terem Galeria, Budapest #32/R est:2500000 (H.F 8000000)
£21928 $34208 €32892 Landscape in Nagybanya, 1927 (80x65cm-31x26in) s.d.1927. 11-Sep-2 Kieselbach, Budapest #96/R (H.F 8500000)
£53095 $82828 €76988 Niobe, Niobidak (110x137cm-43x54in) s.d.1923 prov.exhib.lit. 12-Apr-3 Mu Terem Galeria, Budapest #81/R est:10000000 (H.F 19000000)
Works on paper
£5916 $9170 €8578 Vietri sul mare (48x71cm-19x28in) s. W/C. 9-Dec-2 Mu Terem Galeria, Budapest #26/R est:1200000 (H.F 2200000)

PATON, Donald (19/20th C) British
Works on paper
£520 $863 €754 By the loch side (25x35cm-10x14in) s. W/C. 13-Jun-3 Lyon & Turnbull, Edinburgh #20

PATON, Frank (1856-1909) British
Works on paper
£320 $496 €480 Portrait of a racehorse Garry Owen (33x46cm-13x18in) s.i.d.1909 W/C. 5-Oct-2 Finan Watkins & Co, Mere #198/R
£400 $664 €580 Whisky - portrait of a terrier (23x23cm-9x9in) s.d.1902. 10-Jun-3 Peter Francis, Wales #41/R
£1800 $2790 €2700 Rabbit with her young (46x66cm-18x26in) s.d.1901 W/C bodycol. 4-Dec-2 Christie's, Kensington #97/R est:2000-3000

PATON, Sir Joseph Noel (1821-1901) British
£10000 $16100 €15000 Evening (41x55cm-16x22in) mono. board prov.exhib. 20-Feb-3 Christie's, London #235/R est:15000
£12000 $19320 €18000 In Gethsemane (83x124cm-33x49in) mono.d.1868 prov.exhib.lit. 20-Feb-3 Christie's, London #298/R
Works on paper
£1600 $2656 €2400 Studies for Danube and Euxine, the lays of the Scottish cavaliers (40x56cm-16x22in) pencil. 12-Jun-3 Sotheby's, London #205/R est:700-1000

PATON, Thomas (20th C) British
£260 $406 €390 Busy harbour scene with figures and boats (19x24cm-7x9in) s. panel. 10-Sep-2 David Duggleby, Scarborough #359

PATON, Waller Hugh (1828-1895) British
£300 $456 €450 Lake District at dusk (41x61cm-16x24in) s. 29-Aug-2 Christie's, Kensington #266
£360 $587 €540 Lake District at dusk (38x53cm-15x21in) s. 14-Feb-3 Keys, Aylsham #664
£3600 $5616 €5400 Corn sheaves by the coast, moonlight (47x101cm-19x40in) mono.d.1860 s.verso. 10-Apr-3 Bonhams, Edinburgh #90/R est:3000-5000
£5500 $8525 €8250 Kincraig Point, Elie, moonlight (63x94cm-25x37in) s.d.1872 prov.exhib. 31-Oct-2 Christie's, London #70/R est:5000-8000
£12000 $18600 €18000 Autumn evening, Isle of Arran (66x137cm-26x54in) mono.d.1867 s.i.verso. 31-Oct-2 Christie's, London #76/R est:12000-18000
Works on paper
£250 $395 €375 Portrait of a Scottish lass (58x43cm-23x17in) monochrome crayon. 24-Apr-3 Richardson & Smith, Whitby #123
£250 $413 €363 Mountainous landscape (29x18cm-11x7in) s. pencil W/C. 3-Jul-3 Christie's, Kensington #69
£260 $406 €390 Wooer's Alley, Dunfermline (23x32cm-9x13in) s. W/C. 25-Mar-3 Bonhams, Knightsbridge #145
£280 $437 €420 Fishing at twilight (7x14cm-3x6in) mono.d.1867 W/C bodycol. 10-Apr-3 Bonhams, Edinburgh #98
£365 $569 €529 Sheep in a country landscape (27x35cm-11x14in) s.d.26th June 1851 W/C. 26-Mar-3 Walker's, Ottawa #54/R (C.D 850)
£500 $795 €750 Dawn (13x19cm-5x7in) s.i. W/C. 6-Mar-3 Christie's, Kensington #82/R
£600 $942 €900 Brook with cattle in the distance (18x27cm-7x11in) s. indis d. pencil W/C bodycol. 16-Apr-3 Christie's, Kensington #1023/R
£750 $1230 €1125 Sunset over the lake (24x35cm-9x14in) s.d.1878 pencil W/C bodycol. 5-Jun-3 Christie's, Kensington #910
£800 $1248 €1200 Gin Head, Fife (23x35cm-9x14in) s.d.1888 W/C. 17-Sep-2 Sotheby's, Olympia #27/R
£800 $1248 €1200 North Berwick (18x33cm-7x13in) s.i.d.21 June 1873 W/C. 14-Apr-3 Sotheby's, London #13/R
£920 $1435 €1380 Largo Bay (24x34cm-9x13in) s.i.d.26th September 1860 W/C htd white. 17-Oct-2 Bonhams, Edinburgh #196
£1000 $1560 €1500 Loch Gail Head. Anochar (15x23cm-6x9in) s. W/C two. 15-Oct-2 Gorringes, Lewes #2097/R
£1200 $1872 €1800 Looking towards the Island of Rhum (22x45cm-9x18in) s. W/C. 14-Apr-3 Sotheby's, London #15/R est:1000-1500
£1750 $2730 €2625 Castle Campbell (25x36cm-10x14in) s.i.d.1869 W/C. 14-Apr-3 Sotheby's, London #11/R est:1000-1500
£3200 $4992 €4800 Loch scene, moonlight, possibly Arran (32x56cm-13x22in) s.d.1880 W/C htd white. 10-Apr-3 Bonhams, Edinburgh #152/R est:2000-3000

PATOUX, Émile (1893-1985) Belgian
£290 $463 €420 Jeune hollandaise au jardin (85x70cm-33x28in) s. 17-Mar-3 Horta, Bruxelles #22
£497 $810 €750 Jeune femme nue a la plage (50x112cm-20x44in) s. 17-Feb-3 Horta, Bruxelles #484
£596 $972 €900 Pecheur ravaudant son filet (80x86cm-31x34in) s. 17-Feb-3 Horta, Bruxelles #483
Works on paper
£588 $947 €900 Portrait de femme dans un ovale (70x50cm-28x20in) s. pastel. 14-Jan-3 Vanderkindere, Brussels #93

PATRIARCA, Amato (1945-) Italian
£316 $494 €500 Village (40x30cm-16x12in) s. acrylic. 14-Sep-2 Meeting Art, Vercelli #335/R
£321 $503 €500 Benches (40x40cm-16x16in) s. i.verso acrylic. 23-Nov-2 Meeting Art, Vercelli #160/R

£327 $523 €500 Jeans (50x40cm-20x16in) s. acrylic. 4-Jan-3 Meeting Art, Vercelli #429
£327 $523 €500 Station (30x40cm-12x16in) s. i.verso acrylic. 4-Jan-3 Meeting Art, Vercelli #696
£340 $541 €500 Girl (40x40cm-16x16in) s. acrylic. 1-Mar-3 Meeting Art, Vercelli #397
£340 $541 €500 Moments (40x40cm-16x16in) s. acrylic. 1-Mar-3 Meeting Art, Vercelli #627
£475 $741 €750 Lilies (50x50cm-20x20in) s. acrylic. 14-Sep-2 Meeting Art, Vercelli #901/R
£523 $837 €800 Eros (60x40cm-24x16in) s. i.verso acrylic. 4-Jan-3 Meeting Art, Vercelli #655
£1154 $1788 €1800 Maria (80x60cm-31x24in) s. acrylic painted 1999. 4-Dec-2 Finarte, Milan #580/R
£1351 $2108 €2000 Eros (80x80cm-31x31in) s. acrylic painted 2003. 26-Mar-3 Finarte Semenzato, Milan #165/R
£1408 $2338 €2000 Panchina (80x80cm-31x31in) s. i.verso acrylic. 10-Jun-3 Finarte Semenzato, Milan #358/R est:2000-2400
£1923 $3019 €3000 Moments (120x120cm-47x47in) s. acrylic. 23-Nov-2 Meeting Art, Vercelli #428/R

PATRICK, Ann (1937-) British
£500 $815 €750 Farmhouse near Arbirlot (42x64cm-17x25in) 14-Feb-3 Lyon & Turnbull, Edinburgh #2
£1000 $1560 €1500 Bathers (24x19cm-9x7in) s. board with three works by same hand one by another five. 12-Sep-2 Sotheby's, Olympia #75/R est:500-700

PATRICK, James McIntosh (1907-1998) British
£3200 $4992 €4800 Abroath (24x29cm-9x11in) s. 17-Oct-2 Bonhams, Edinburgh #1/R est:2000-3000
£5000 $7950 €7500 Castle Campbell - highland castle with two mounted horsemen (30x40cm-12x16in) s.d.38. 29-Apr-3 Sworder & Son, Bishops Stortford #363/R est:2000-4000
£8500 $13515 €12750 Croft near Shuin Ferry, Loch Linnhe, Argyllshire (51x61cm-20x24in) s. prov. 6-Mar-3 Christie's, Kensington #227/R est:7000-10000
£9000 $13950 €13500 Bridge in Angus (44x59cm-17x23in) s.d.1941. 5-Dec-2 Bonhams, Edinburgh #89/R est:10000-15000
£9000 $14850 €13050 April snow, Craigowl, Angus (49x59cm-19x23in) s. s.i.d.1949 verso prov. 1-Jul-3 Bearnes, Exeter #539/R est:5000-7000
£11000 $17050 €16500 Midsummer, Carse of Gowrie, Perthshire, overlooking Mill Hill Farm (51x61cm-20x24in) s. exhib. 31-Oct-2 Christie's, London #163/R est:12000-18000
£14000 $22680 €21000 Tay from Kinfauns (63x76cm-25x30in) s.d.1966 exhib. 23-May-3 Lyon & Turnbull, Edinburgh #51/R est:10000-15000
£15000 $23400 €22500 At Dron, Carse of Gowrie (71x91cm-28x36in) s. 14-Apr-3 Sotheby's, London #179/R est:15000-20000

Works on paper
£400 $640 €580 Ford near Catterick, Yorkshire (22x28cm-9x11in) s.i. W/C. 17-May-3 Thomson Roddick & Medcalf, Edinburgh #653
£1300 $1989 €1950 Birch trees at Ballo (33x24cm-13x9in) s. s.i.d.1989 verso W/C. 22-Aug-2 Bonhams, Edinburgh #1120/R est:1500-2000
£1500 $2340 €2250 Holyrood Palace (37x56cm-15x22in) s. W/C exec.c.1940. 10-Apr-3 Bonhams, Edinburgh #116 est:1500-2000
£1800 $2808 €2700 Near Liff (38x55cm-15x22in) s. W/C exec.c.1965 exhib. 10-Apr-3 Bonhams, Edinburgh #16/R est:2000-3000
£1800 $2916 €2700 Tayside landscape (28x38cm-11x15in) s. W/C. 23-May-3 Lyon & Turnbull, Edinburgh #3/R est:800-1200
£2200 $3366 €3300 Ben Cruachan and Loch Awe from above Port Sonachan, Argyll (19x54cm-7x21in) s. ink W/C. 22-Aug-2 Bonhams, Edinburgh #1123/R est:1500-2000
£3400 $5304 €5100 Bye-road, Carse of Gowrie (53x75cm-21x30in) s. W/C prov. 10-Apr-3 Bonhams, Edinburgh #9/R est:2000-3000
£3800 $5928 €5700 On the road to Millhaven at Kirkmichael Farm, Longforgan, Carse of Gowrie (50x72cm-20x28in) s. W/C prov. 10-Apr-3 Bonhams, Edinburgh #15/R est:2000-3000

PATRIX, Michel (1917-) French
£360 $576 €500 Le charpentier V (46x38cm-18x15in) s. i.verso. 18-May-3 Charbonneaux, Paris #197
£719 $1151 €1000 Scene de port (73x92cm-29x36in) s. 14-May-3 Blanchet, Paris #137/R est:1500-2000

PATRU, Émile (20th C) French?
£279 $441 €419 Shepherd with flock in mountain village (33x41cm-13x16in) 29-Nov-2 Zofingen, Switzerland #3022 (S.FR 650)

PATTE, Albert (19th C) French
£3500 $5705 €5250 Still life of peaches and apples in a basket (80x98cm-31x39in) s. 29-Jan-3 Sotheby's, Olympia #341/R est:2500-3500

PATTEIN, Cesar (1850-1931) French
£497 $810 €750 L'artiste peignant un paysage (29x51cm-11x20in) s. 16-Feb-3 Mercier & Cie, Lille #284
£8000 $12720 €12000 Jeune garcon au pied blesse (65x91cm-26x36in) s.d.1899 prov. 18-Mar-3 Bonhams, New Bond Street #116/R est:7000-10000
£12510 $20016 €18140 Children playing (55x81cm-22x32in) s.d.1906. 18-May-3 Anders Antik, Landskrona #82 est:50000 (S.KR 160000)

PATTEN, Alfred Fowler (1829-1888) British
£1911 $2943 €3000 Idle mood (37x26cm-15x10in) mono. prov.exhib. 4-Sep-2 James Adam, Dublin #90/R est:1500-2000

PATTEN, Eric (20th C) British
£296 $491 €420 Aran (23x18cm-9x7in) board. 10-Jun-3 James Adam, Dublin #36/R

PATTEN, George (1801-1865) British

Miniatures
£1500 $2340 €2250 Naval officer wearing blue coat with gold edging gold buttons (6cm-2in) gold frame plaited hair verso oval. 5-Nov-2 Bonhams, New Bond Street #82/R est:1000-1500
£2000 $3180 €3000 Young girl, facing left in a white off the shoulder dress (6cm-2in) gold pendant frame coral beads plaited hair verso. 18-Mar-3 Christie's, Kensington #75 est:400-600

PATTEN, George (attrib) (1801-1865) British
£1987 $3140 €3100 Old bearded man tuning fiddle (66x56cm-26x22in) 12-Nov-2 Mealy's, Castlecomer #1042/R

PATTENDEN, Thomas (18/19th C) British

Works on paper
£12000 $19320 €18000 Foreign flowers, Dover (21x13cm-8x5in) i. W/C 113 leaves manuscript. 7-May-3 Sotheby's, London #24/R est:12000-15000

PATTERSON, Ambrose McCarthy (1877-1966) American
£6202 $9860 €9303 Black Rock (46x51cm-18x20in) s. painted c.1913-14 prov.exhib. 5-May-3 Sotheby's, Melbourne #178/R est:12000-18000 (A.D 16000)

PATTERSON, Keith (1925-1993) New Zealander

Works on paper
£732 $1120 €1098 Yellow boat, Dinghy, fishing net and shells (102x122cm-40x48in) s.d.90 mixed media. 21-Aug-2 Dunbar Sloane, Auckland #122/R est:2400-4000 (NZ.D 2400)

PATTERSON, Margaret Jordan (1867-1950) American

Prints
£2642 $4200 €3963 Nantucket, Main Street (18x26cm-7x10in) s. col woodcut exec.c.1918. 7-Mar-3 Skinner, Boston #102/R est:1200-1800

Works on paper
£355 $550 €533 Still life, flowers on a table (33x43cm-13x17in) W/C. 7-Dec-2 South Bay, Long Island #192/R
£1338 $2100 €2007 Venice nocturne (24x34cm-9x13in) s.d.1903 W/C gouache. 22-Nov-2 Skinner, Boston #299/R est:1500-2500
£2690 $4250 €4035 Along the river (33x48cm-13x19in) s.d.07 gouache prov. 24-Apr-3 Shannon's, Milford #8/R est:3000-5000

PATTERSON, Neil (1947-) Canadian
£533 $875 €773 Maclean Pond, sunset (45x60cm-18x24in) s.i. board. 9-Jun-3 Hodgins, Calgary #28/R est:1200-1500 (C.D 1200)
£978 $1604 €1418 Poppies (90x120cm-35x47in) i. 9-Jun-3 Hodgins, Calgary #317/R est:2500-3500 (C.D 2200)
£2076 $3301 €3114 Sunnyside (60x90cm-24x35in) s.i. 23-Mar-3 Hodgins, Calgary #71/R est:2000-3000 (C.D 4900)
£2889 $4738 €4189 Down in the valley (120x150cm-47x59in) s.i. 9-Jun-3 Hodgins, Calgary #320/R est:5500-7500 (C.D 6500)

PATTERSON, Robert (1898-?) American

Works on paper
£528 $850 €792 Couple at edge of pool, she with soda and cigarettes (46x43cm-18x17in) s.verso gouache. 20-Feb-3 Illustration House, New York #130/R

PATTERSON, Simon (1967-) British

Prints
£7500 $11700 €11250 The Great Bear (134x109cm-53x43in) s.d.1992 num.24/50 offset lithograph. 25-Mar-3 Sotheby's, London #192/R est:8000-12000

PATTI, A (20th C) ?
£250 $380 €375 Young beauty (81x61cm-32x24in) s. 29-Aug-2 Christie's, Kensington #195

PATTISON, Abbott Lawrence (1916-) American
£288 $450 €432 Landscape (76x102cm-30x40in) s. masonite. 10-Nov-2 Selkirks, St. Louis #902
£393 $625 €590 Landscape (102x76cm-40x30in) s. board painted c.1950. 2-Mar-3 Toomey, Oak Park #796/R

PATTISON, James William (1844-1915) American
£605 $950 €908 The mill (30x51cm-12x20in) s.d.1867. 22-Nov-2 Skinner, Boston #67/R est:400-600

PATTISON, Robert J (1838-1903) American
£18987 $30000 €28481 Windy day, New York Harbor (64x122cm-25x48in) s.d.1877 exhib. 24-Apr-3 Shannon's, Milford #144/R est:30000-50000

PATTON, Eric (?) Irish?
£514 $807 €750 Scottish coastline (40x50cm-16x20in) s. s.i.verso prov. 15-Apr-3 De Veres Art Auctions, Dublin #99b
£641 $1006 €1000 Headland (50x60cm-20x24in) i.verso board. 19-Nov-2 Hamilton Osborne King, Dublin #454
£696 $1079 €1100 Algarve Beach (41x51cm-16x20in) s. i.verso. 24-Sep-2 De Veres Art Auctions, Dublin #3 est:900-1200

PATTON, Katherine (20th C) American
£258 $400 €387 Wood interior (76x58cm-30x23in) s. 7-Dec-2 Harvey Clar, Oakland #1195

PATTY, William Arthur (1884-1960) American
£1355 $2100 €2033 New England landscape in winter (61x76cm-24x30in) s.d. 8-Dec-2 Toomey, Oak Park #680/R est:2500-4500

PATURSSON, Trondur (20th C) Danish
£604 $954 €906 Composition (81x100cm-32x39in) s. prov. 1-Apr-3 Rasmussen, Copenhagen #324 (D.KR 6500)

PATZELT, Andreas (1896-1980) Austrian
£629 $981 €1000 Portrait of beautiful woman (80x70cm-31x28in) s. lit. 20-Sep-2 Karlheinz Kaupp, Staufen #2079/R

PAU DE SAINT MARTIN, Alexandre (18th C) French
£347 $549 €500 Etude d'arbre mort (53x33cm-21x13in) s.d.1808 paper on canvas. 25-Apr-3 Beaussant & Lefèvre, Paris #34
£1573 $2422 €2500 Paysage de lac boise dans la campagne italienne avec des baigneurs (31x36cm-12x14in) panel. 25-Oct-2 Tajan, Paris #148 est:2400-3000
£1892 $2951 €2800 Landscapes with ruins and farmers (15x23cm-6x9in) panel pair. 26-Mar-3 Tajan, Paris #63

PAUDISS, Christoph (1618-1666) German
£38813 $60548 €58220 Kitchen still life (68x54cm-27x21in) panel. 28-Mar-3 Koller, Zurich #3033/R est:20000-30000 (S.FR 85000)

PAUELSEN, Erik (1749-1790) Danish
£1435 $2325 €2081 Norwegian fjord landscape (61x76cm-24x30in) prov. 26-May-3 Rasmussen, Copenhagen #1177/R est:15000-20000 (D.KR 15000)

PAUELSEN, Erik (circle) (1749-1790) Danish
£7097 $11000 €10646 Portrait of a lady, seated, playing with a small dog (129x94cm-51x37in) 2-Oct-2 Christie's, Rockefeller NY #119/R est:4000-6000

PAUL, Celia (1959-) British
£1500 $2445 €2250 My mother and God (157x91cm-62x36in) painted 1990. 3-Feb-3 Sotheby's, Olympia #23/R est:1500-2000
Works on paper
£300 $489 €450 Mother looking in the mirror (65x51cm-26x20in) chl executed 1984. 3-Feb-3 Sotheby's, Olympia #24/R

PAUL, Jeremy (1954-) British
£1400 $2170 €2100 Eagle catching a fish (43x64cm-17x25in) s. board. 6-Dec-2 Chrystals Auctions, Isle of Man #157 est:800-1000

PAUL, John (19th C) British
£2800 $4452 €4200 Log cart on a wooded track, with Norwich beyond (76x103cm-30x41in) 6-Mar-3 Christie's, Kensington #411/R est:3000-5000
£3800 $5966 €5700 City of London from the south bank of the Thames (54x109cm-21x43in) prov. 16-Dec-2 Sotheby's, London #55/R est:2000-3000
£4800 $7632 €7200 Westminster Bridge from the south looking towards Westminster Abbey (51x92cm-20x36in) s. 19-Mar-3 Sotheby's, London #76/R est:4000-6000

PAUL, John (attrib) (19th C) British
£800 $1312 €1200 River scene with boats and cattle in the foreground (66x56cm-26x22in) 4-Feb-3 Sworder & Son, Bishops Stortford #144/R
£1800 $2808 €2700 Old London Bridge (67x115cm-26x45in) 10-Sep-2 Bonhams, Knightsbridge #82/R est:2000-3000

PAUL, Joseph (1804-1887) British
£450 $720 €675 Country landscape with figures (50x45cm-20x18in) panel. 7-Jan-3 Bonhams, Knightsbridge #65/R
£520 $811 €780 Lane scene with cottage (28x23cm-11x9in) prov. 11-Apr-3 Keys, Aylsham #619/R
£550 $836 €825 Extensive Norfolk landscape with figures by cottages and watermill (94x76cm-37x30in) 16-Aug-2 Keys, Aylsham #658/R
£590 $985 €856 Norfolk wooded landscape with figures by cottage and mill (18x23cm-7x9in) 20-Jun-3 Keys, Aylsham #640/R
£650 $1007 €975 Back of the New Mills, Norwich (29x41cm-11x16in) panel. 30-Sep-2 Bonhams, Ipswich #472
£700 $1155 €1015 On the Wensum with Norwich Cathedral in the distance (76x63cm-30x25in) 1-Jul-3 Bonhams, Norwich #237/R
£780 $1271 €1170 Busy river landscape with numerous boats and figures unloading (43x53cm-17x21in) 14-Feb-3 Keys, Aylsham #648/R
£850 $1386 €1275 Norfolk landscape with figures in lane by a cottage (46x43cm-18x17in) 14-Feb-3 Keys, Aylsham #647/R
£1300 $2015 €1950 Pull's ferry, Norwich (35x46cm-14x18in) panel. 30-Sep-2 Bonhams, Ipswich #498/R est:1200-1800

PAUL, Maurice (1889-1965) Dutch
£704 $1134 €1000 Small mill (34x43cm-13x17in) s. 7-May-3 Vendue Huis, Gravenhage #566/R
£1210 $1888 €1900 Place Marie Jose a Ostende (49x59cm-19x23in) s. 6-Nov-2 Vendue Huis, Gravenhage #502/R est:2000-3000
£1210 $1888 €1900 View of park (49x59cm-19x23in) s. 6-Nov-2 Vendue Huis, Gravenhage #503/R est:2000-2500

PAUL, P I A (19/20th C) ?
£1600 $2592 €2400 Judgement of Paris (139x171cm-55x67in) s. 23-Jan-3 Christie's, Kensington #133/R est:1200-1500

PAUL, Sir John Dean (1775-1852) British
£3145 $4843 €5000 The Thames with Westminster bridge (52x92cm-20x36in) s. 26-Oct-2 Quittenbaum, Hamburg #37/R est:5200

PAUL, Sir John Dean (attrib) (1775-1852) British
£823 $1300 €1235 Crossing the river (61x84cm-24x33in) 5-Apr-3 Neal Auction Company, New Orleans #479/R
£10778 $18000 €15628 Old palace yard and Westminster house. Northumberland House, Charing Cross (71x91cm-28x36in) pair. 22-Jun-3 Freeman, Philadelphia #7/R est:10000-15000

PAUL, Sylvia (20th C) British
Works on paper
£280 $462 €406 Still life of flower in a vase with fruit and an ewer (43x35cm-17x14in) s. pastel gouache. 1-Jul-3 Bonhams, Norwich #343

PAULI, Georg (1855-1935) Swedish
£351 $554 €527 Landscape with house (30x34cm-12x13in) mono. cardboard. 30-Nov-2 Goteborg Auktionsverk, Sweden #605/R (S.KR 5000)
£355 $550 €533 Bridge by cottage (33x46cm-13x18in) s. 8-Dec-2 Uppsala Auktionskammare, Uppsala #141 (S.KR 5000)
£357 $556 €536 Roman shepherd (55x61cm-22x24in) s. 13-Sep-2 Lilla Bukowskis, Stockholm #312 (S.KR 5200)
£567 $879 €851 Sunbathing (15x21cm-6x8in) init. panel. 4-Dec-2 AB Stockholms Auktionsverk #1785/R (S.KR 8000)
£851 $1319 €1277 Landscape with two women bathing (62x50cm-24x20in) mono. s.d.1930 verso. 8-Dec-2 Uppsala Auktionskammare, Uppsala #194/R (S.KR 12000)
£1418 $2199 €2127 Woman sunbathing (107x64cm-42x25in) s.d.1911. 4-Dec-2 AB Stockholms Auktionsverk #1783/R est:20000-25000 (S.KR 20000)
£1472 $2296 €2208 Palada (59x71cm-23x28in) init. 5-Nov-2 Bukowskis, Stockholm #205/R est:30000-40000 (S.KR 21000)
£1702 $2638 €2553 Varberg's Fort (40x32cm-16x13in) panel sketch verso prov. 3-Dec-2 Bukowskis, Stockholm #358/R est:30000-40000 (S.KR 24000)
£1773 $2748 €2660 Green landscape (54x66cm-21x26in) s.d.98. 3-Dec-2 Bukowskis, Stockholm #199/R est:20000-25000 (S.KR 25000)

£7008 $10932 €10512 The deluge (83x104cm-33x41in) init. s.d.1914-17 verso prov. 5-Nov-2 Bukowskis, Stockholm #223/R est:100000-125000 (S.KR 100000)

PAULI, Hanna (1864-1940) Swedish
£1719 $2785 €2579 Interior (39x46cm-15x18in) s. 3-Feb-3 Lilla Bukowskis, Stockholm #830 est:4000-5000 (S.KR 24000)
£2828 $4638 €4101 Town in evening light (25x40cm-10x16in) s. 4-Jun-3 AB Stockholms Auktionsverk #2261/R est:15000-20000 (S.KR 36000)

PAULIN, Paul (19/20th C) French
Sculpture
£1268 $2104 €1800 Portrait de Renoir (31cm-12in) s.i. pat bronze Cast C.Valsuani. 11-Jun-3 Beaussant & Lefèvre, Paris #184/R est:1500-1800

PAULMAN, Joseph (19th C) British
£323 $510 €485 Harvesters resting by a river (41x30cm-16x12in) s. 18-Nov-2 Waddingtons, Toronto #103a/R (C.D 800)
£755 $1200 €1133 Driving sheep. Stroll by the pond (30x41cm-12x16in) one s. pair. 22-Mar-3 New Orleans Auction, New Orleans #102/R est:1500-2500
£1200 $1848 €1800 Returning home (91x71cm-36x28in) s. 5-Sep-2 Christie's, Kensington #166/R est:1200-1800

PAULSEN, Agnes (19th C) Danish
£1362 $2151 €2043 Still life of flowers in basket, and flowers on ledge (32x42cm-13x17in) one s.d.1871 pair. 30-Nov-2 Rasmussen, Havnen #2167/R est:10000-15000 (D.KR 16000)

PAULSEN, Fritz (1838-1898) German
£5500 $8524 €8250 Birthday present (102x86cm-40x34in) s.i. 3-Dec-2 Sotheby's, Olympia #256/R est:4000-6000

PAULSEN, Ingwer (1883-?) German
£1149 $1792 €1700 Halebull (40x60cm-16x24in) s. bears i. verso panel prov. 28-Mar-3 Ketterer, Hamburg #70/R est:1200-1300
£1195 $1852 €1900 Warft in spring (52x72cm-20x28in) canvas on panel. 2-Nov-2 Hans Stahl, Toestorf #82 est:1200
£1923 $2981 €3000 Halebull (39x78cm-15x31in) s. i. verso panel. 7-Dec-2 Hans Stahl, Hamburg #100/R est:1200

PAULSEN, John (1892-1972) Norwegian
£324 $506 €486 A dream (68x86cm-27x34in) s. painted 1939. 23-Sep-2 Blomqvist, Lysaker #1177 (N.KR 3800)

PAULSEN, Jon Boe (1958-) Norwegian
£260 $397 €390 Portrait of woman (56x46cm-22x18in) s. painted 1982. 26-Aug-2 Blomqvist, Lysaker #1298/R (N.KR 3000)

PAULSEN, Julius (1860-1940) Danish
£273 $422 €410 Portrait of woman (47x33cm-19x13in) s.d.1908. 28-Sep-2 Rasmussen, Havnen #2047 (D.KR 3200)
£298 $471 €447 Italian landscape with road. init.d.21 prov. 27-Nov-2 Museumsbygningen, Copenhagen #713 (D.KR 3500)
£596 $953 €894 Portrait of Pan playing the flute (89x64cm-35x25in) mono. 16-Mar-3 Hindemae, Ullerslev #735/R (D.KR 6400)
£605 $962 €908 Christ walking on water (27x22cm-11x9in) init. study for altar piece. 5-Mar-3 Rasmussen, Copenhagen #2001/R (D.KR 6500)
£745 $1184 €1118 Impressionist landscape (51x61cm-20x24in) init. 5-Mar-3 Rasmussen, Copenhagen #1912/R (D.KR 8000)
£775 $1178 €1163 View of the Seine (40x47cm-16x19in) init. 27-Aug-2 Rasmussen, Copenhagen #1704/R (D.KR 9000)
£807 $1259 €1211 View of Kolding fjord (28x39cm-11x15in) s.d.96 exhib. 5-Aug-2 Rasmussen, Vejle #197/R (D.KR 9500)
£840 $1335 €1260 Interior (53x55cm-21x22in) s.d.1907. 5-May-3 Rasmussen, Vejle #656/R (D.KR 9000)
£850 $1325 €1275 Herder boy in heather hills (40x48cm-16x19in) s. 5-Aug-2 Rasmussen, Vejle #98/R (D.KR 10000)
£909 $1473 €1364 Summer landscape with thatched farmhouse and rosebushes (47x60cm-19x24in) s.d.29. 21-May-3 Museumsbygningen, Copenhagen #66 (D.KR 9500)
£931 $1480 €1397 Model reading (30x25cm-12x10in) init. 5-Mar-3 Rasmussen, Copenhagen #1726/R (D.KR 10000)
£1034 $1571 €1551 Young women (17x23cm-7x9in) study. 27-Aug-2 Rasmussen, Copenhagen #1614/R est:12000-15000 (D.KR 12000)
£1073 $1695 €1610 Twilight landscape (41x60cm-16x24in) init.d.1910. 13-Nov-2 Kunsthallen, Copenhagen #55/R est:8000 (D.KR 12500)
£1447 $2286 €2171 Evening at Bakken with figures walking and sitting (30x26cm-12x10in) prov. 27-Nov-2 Museumsbygningen, Copenhagen #78/R est:5000 (D.KR 17000)
£1490 $2369 €2235 Pair of swans swimming (24x34cm-9x13in) init. 5-Mar-3 Rasmussen, Copenhagen #1856/R est:12000 (D.KR 16000)
£1723 $2618 €2585 Mother and baby (62x46cm-24x18in) s.d.1914. 27-Aug-2 Rasmussen, Copenhagen #1969/R est:25000 (D.KR 20000)
£1914 $3100 €2775 Reclining female model (22x33cm-9x13in) init. 26-May-3 Rasmussen, Copenhagen #1519/R est:5000-7000 (D.KR 20000)
£2167 $3380 €3251 Farmer working in cornfield (70x83cm-28x33in) s. exhib. 5-Aug-2 Rasmussen, Vejle #97/R est:25000 (D.KR 25500)
£2638 $4169 €3957 Double portrait of the artist's daughters (130x120cm-51x47in) s.d.1929 exhib.prov. 2-Dec-2 Rasmussen, Copenhagen #1796/R est:30000-40000 (D.KR 31000)
£3398 $5302 €5097 Interior scene with seated model (100x70cm-39x28in) s.d.1912 exhib. 5-Aug-2 Rasmussen, Vejle #72/R est:50000 (D.KR 40000)

PAULSEN, Oscar (1860-1932) Danish
£861 $1309 €1292 Southern European landscape with houses on a cliff (120x84cm-47x33in) s. 27-Aug-2 Rasmussen, Copenhagen #1661/R (D.KR 10000)

PAULSEN, Sophus (1883-1935) Danish
£396 $638 €594 Coastal landscape (39x68cm-15x27in) init.d.12/4 13. 22-Feb-3 Rasmussen, Havnen #2286 (D.KR 4400)

PAULUCCI, Enrico (1901-1999) Italian
£633 $987 €1000 Sea (18x24cm-7x9in) s. s.verso. 14-Sep-2 Meeting Art, Vercelli #943/R
£641 $1006 €1000 Sailing boats (18x24cm-7x9in) s. 23-Nov-2 Meeting Art, Vercelli #388/R
£680 $1082 €1000 Langhe (18x24cm-7x9in) s. painted 1998. 1-Mar-3 Meeting Art, Vercelli #525
£694 $1104 €1000 Sea (20x30cm-8x12in) s. 1-May-3 Meeting Art, Vercelli #528
£748 $1190 €1100 Sea (20x30cm-8x12in) s. 1-Mar-3 Meeting Art, Vercelli #750
£833 $1317 €1300 Untitled (20x30cm-8x12in) s. s.verso canvas on cardboard. 15-Nov-2 Farsetti, Prato #201/R
£903 $1435 €1300 Flowers (24x18cm-9x7in) s. 1-May-3 Meeting Art, Vercelli #301
£980 $1569 €1500 Lana (35x45cm-14x18in) s. 4-Jan-3 Meeting Art, Vercelli #62
£1282 $2013 €2000 Langa hills (35x45cm-14x18in) s. 23-Nov-2 Meeting Art, Vercelli #199/R
£1307 $2092 €2000 Still life (35x45cm-14x18in) s. 4-Jan-3 Meeting Art, Vercelli #207
£1319 $2098 €1900 Langhe (18x24cm-7x9in) s. board. 1-May-3 Meeting Art, Vercelli #55
£1548 $2446 €2400 Young De Pisis and Coco', the budgie (40x30cm-16x12in) s. prov. 18-Dec-2 Christie's, Rome #160
£1622 $2530 €2400 Beached boats (15x16cm-6x6in) s. board. 28-Mar-3 Farsetti, Prato #158/R
£1731 $2717 €2700 Sunset in Forio (34x50cm-13x20in) s.i.verso prov. 20-Nov-2 Pandolfini, Florence #23/R
£2432 $3795 €3600 Landscape in Siena (29x28cm-11x11in) s. board. 28-Mar-3 Farsetti, Prato #268/R
£2436 $3824 €3800 Boats (45x50cm-18x20in) s. painted c.1950. 19-Nov-2 Finarte, Milan #114/R
£2436 $3849 €3800 Monferrato (65x90cm-26x35in) s. painted 1967. 15-Nov-2 Farsetti, Prato #324/R
£2532 $3949 €4000 Roses and locust-trees (50x60cm-20x24in) s. s.i.verso. 14-Sep-2 Meeting Art, Vercelli #926/R
£2564 $4026 €4000 Changing huts (33x41cm-13x16in) s.i.d.1929 tempera paper prov.lit. 20-Nov-2 Pandolfini, Florence #10/R
£2703 $4216 €4000 Landscape (45x55cm-18x22in) s. 28-Mar-3 Farsetti, Prato #350/R
£4231 $6642 €6600 Night in the harbour (46x55cm-18x22in) s.d.46. 20-Nov-2 Pandolfini, Florence #24/R
£4762 $7571 €7000 Bay in Liguria (33x45cm-13x18in) s.d.1944. 1-Mar-3 Meeting Art, Vercelli #491
£4762 $7571 €7000 On the beach (55x75cm-22x30in) s. 1-Mar-3 Meeting Art, Vercelli #764
Works on paper
£316 $494 €500 Liguria (25x35cm-10x14in) s. wash. 14-Sep-2 Meeting Art, Vercelli #880/R
£340 $541 €500 Trees by the sea (24x33cm-9x13in) s. pastel. 1-Mar-3 Meeting Art, Vercelli #393
£347 $552 €500 Landscape (18x24cm-7x9in) s. pastel. 1-May-3 Meeting Art, Vercelli #538
£382 $607 €550 Landscape seen from above (21x31cm-8x12in) s. pastel. 1-May-3 Meeting Art, Vercelli #481
£476 $757 €700 Sailing boats (21x29cm-8x11in) s. pastel. 1-Mar-3 Meeting Art, Vercelli #398
£759 $1185 €1200 White house in the woods (32x43cm-13x17in) s. wash exec.1968. 14-Sep-2 Meeting Art, Vercelli #874/R
£1923 $3019 €3000 Pinewood onnto the sea (48x62cm-19x24in) s.d.56 mixed media card. 21-Nov-2 Finarte, Rome #241/R
£2436 $3824 €3800 Landscape in Liguria (46x60cm-18x24in) s. pastel. 10-Dec-2 Della Rocca, Turin #355/R

PAULUS, Leonhard (?) ?
£1235 $1914 €1853 Figures on steps of lakeside villa (100x74cm-39x29in) s. 3-Dec-2 Ritchie, Toronto #3094/R est:2500-4000 (C.D 3000)

PAULUS, Pierre (1881-1959) Belgian
£545 $855 €850 La recolte de bois (49x59cm-19x23in) s. 11-Dec-2 Hotel des Ventes Mosan, Brussels #249
£2179 $3422 €3400 La Sambre a Charleroi (40x50cm-16x20in) s. 10-Dec-2 Vanderkindere, Brussels #80/R est:2500-3500
£2800 $4648 €2800 Vue des terrils (32x40cm-13x16in) s.d.1947. 16-Jun-3 Horta, Bruxelles #91 est:3000-4000
£2821 $4428 €4400 Bord de la Sambre sous la neige (50x60cm-20x24in) s. 10-Dec-2 Vanderkindere, Brussels #10/R est:4000-6000
£2917 $4638 €4200 Usines pres de la Sambre en hiver (65x80cm-26x31in) s. 29-Apr-3 Campo & Campo, Antwerp #244/R est:6000-10000
£3673 $5841 €5400 Les remorqueurs (55x60cm-22x24in) s. s.i. verso. 19-Mar-3 Hotel des Ventes Mosan, Brussels #183/R est:4400-4600
£4459 $6955 €7000 Coucher de soleil sur la Sambre (50x60cm-20x24in) s. 11-Nov-2 Horta, Bruxelles #86 est:8500-14000
£4605 $7461 €7000 Autumn (65x55cm-26x22in) s. s.verso. 21-Jan-3 Christie's, Amsterdam #413/R est:3500-4500
£4698 $7564 €7000 Bord de Sambre industriel (40x50cm-16x20in) s.d.1936. 18-Feb-3 Vanderkindere, Brussels #16/R
£6731 $10567 €10500 La Sambre industrielle (110x125cm-43x49in) s. d.1931 verso. 19-Nov-2 Vanderkindere, Brussels #436/R est:10000-15000
£6962 $10861 €11000 Bord deSambre anime enneige (50x60cm-20x24in) s. 15-Oct-2 Horta, Bruxelles #110/R est:8500-13500
£13000 $21580 €13000 Remorqueurs en bord de Sambre (65x81cm-26x32in) s. 16-Jun-3 Horta, Bruxelles #89/R est:12000-15000

PAULY, Paul (1897-?) German
£423 $680 €600 Horses pulling cart in field (60x80cm-24x31in) s.i. 7-May-3 Michael Zeller, Lindau #867/R

PAUPARD, Marian (20th C) French
£360 $576 €500 Hier et aujourd'hui (100x81cm-39x32in) s. 18-May-3 Neret-Minet, Paris #187

PAUR, Jaroslav (1918-) Czechoslovakian
£863 $1398 €1251 City street (43x58cm-17x23in) s.d.84. 24-May-3 Dorotheum, Prague #138/R est:20000-30000 (C.KR 38000)

PAUS, Herbert Andrew (1880-1946) American
Works on paper
£311 $500 €467 Modern figures pausing near three crucifixes (10x46cm-4x18in) ink chl gouache W/C en grisaille. 20-Feb-3 Illustration House, New York #132/R
£404 $650 €606 Man proposing to seated charwoman (28x28cm-11x11in) s. ink gouache W/C. 20-Feb-3 Illustration House, New York #131/R
£745 $1200 €1118 Widening differential of wages between skilled male and menial females (58x20cm-23x8in) s. ink gouache W/C en grisaille exec.c.1935. 10-May-3 Illustration House, New York #102/R
£807 $1300 €1211 Aftermath of fight in hotel lobby (30x43cm-12x17in) s. ink gouache W/C exec.c.1930. 10-May-3 Illustration House, New York #101/R

PAUSER, Sergius (1896-?) Austrian
£256 $400 €384 Portrait of a man wearing glasses and a hat (51x41cm-20x16in) s. 10-Nov-2 Selkirks, St. Louis #567/R
Works on paper
£1154 $1823 €1800 Procession (25x36cm-10x14in) s.i.d.1926 chk W/C. 12-Nov-2 Dorotheum, Vienna #70/R est:2000-2800

PAUSINGER, Clemens von (1855-1936) German
Works on paper
£833 $1375 €1200 Portrait of an elegant lady dressed for winter (64x53cm-25x21in) s.i.indis.d. pastel oval. 1-Jul-3 Christie's, Amsterdam #147/R

PAUSINGER, Franz von (1839-1915) German
£1923 $3019 €3000 Billy-goat on the meadow (31x38cm-12x15in) mono.i. canvas on canvas. 21-Nov-2 Dorotheum, Vienna #141/R est:2000-3000
Works on paper
£1284 $2003 €1900 Deer (141x190cm-56x75in) s. chl canvas. 28-Mar-3 Dorotheum, Vienna #162/R est:1500-1700
£1923 $3019 €3000 Deer by mountain stream with oncoming storm (150x93cm-59x37in) s. chl dr. 21-Nov-2 Dorotheum, Vienna #394/R est:2200-2800

PAUTROT, Ferdinand (1832-1874) French
Sculpture
£962 $1471 €1500 Chien de meute (17x20cm-7x8in) s.d.1865 bronze. 23-Aug-2 Deauville, France #274/R
£1000 $1560 €1500 Partridge with chicks (26x21cm-10x8in) s.st.Beaux Arts brown pat bronze. 9-Apr-3 Sotheby's, London #186/R est:1000-1200

PAUW, Gabriel de (1924-2000) Belgian
£1384 $2145 €2200 Still life (100x120cm-39x47in) s. lit. 5-Oct-2 De Vuyst, Lokeren #97 est:2000-2500

PAUW, Jef de (1888-1930) Belgian
£274 $427 €400 Vase fleuri de roses (55x42cm-22x17in) s. 14-Apr-3 Horta, Bruxelles #436
£863 $1416 €1200 Landscape with farmhouses (18x22cm-7x9in) s. cardboard two. 3-Jun-3 Christie's, Amsterdam #293/R est:1200-1600
Works on paper
£479 $748 €700 Artiste dans son interieur (60x47cm-24x19in) s. mixed media. 14-Apr-3 Horta, Bruxelles #435

PAUW, Paul de (1910-1961) ?
£440 $682 €700 Jeune Africaine (67x50cm-26x20in) s. 1-Oct-2 Palais de Beaux Arts, Brussels #449

PAUW, René de (1887-1946) Belgian
£360 $576 €500 Le peintre dans son atelier (99x84cm-39x33in) s. board. 13-May-3 Vanderkindere, Brussels #51
£448 $717 €650 Night watch (76x76cm-30x30in) s. s.i.verso panel. 15-Mar-3 De Vuyst, Lokeren #97
£790 $1248 €1185 Hazy morning landscape (100x70cm-39x28in) s. 1-Apr-3 Rasmussen, Copenhagen #639/R (D.KR 8500)

PAUWELS, Andries (elder-attrib) (1600-1639) Flemish
£2568 $3750 €3852 Game birds and copper pot (38x46cm-15x18in) init. 3-Nov-1 North East Auctions, Portsmouth #1072/R est:3000-4000

PAUWELS, Ferdinand (1830-1904) Belgian
Works on paper
£2446 $3914 €3400 Catarina, Cornaro and King of Cyprus in San Marco, Venice (30x39cm-12x15in) s. W/C. 17-May-3 De Vuyst, Lokeren #285 est:750-850

PAUWELS, H J (1903-1987) Belgian
£285 $444 €450 Scene de rue orientale (74x57cm-29x22in) 16-Sep-2 Amberes, Antwerp #230
£1379 $2207 €2000 La Rade d'Anvers (110x140cm-43x55in) 17-Mar-3 Amberes, Antwerp #238

PAUWELS, Henri Joseph (1903-1983) Belgian
£288 $447 €450 Nature morte aux fleurs (71x101cm-28x40in) s. 3-Dec-2 Campo & Campo, Antwerp #236
£300 $468 €450 Outside the cottage (60x80cm-24x31in) s. 17-Sep-2 Bonhams, Knightsbridge #135/R

PAUWELS, Jos (1818-1876) Belgian
£360 $576 €500 Promenade sur l'etang (60x90cm-24x35in) s. 19-May-3 Horta, Bruxelles #330
£362 $594 €500 Tea time en plein air (30x40cm-12x16in) s. cardboard. 27-May-3 Campo & Campo, Antwerp #179
£380 $616 €570 Afternoon tea in the shade (51x61cm-20x24in) s. board. 23-Jan-3 Christie's, Kensington #247/R
£417 $663 €600 Jardin avec cage (51x67cm-20x26in) s. cardboard. 29-Apr-3 Campo & Campo, Antwerp #247
£432 $691 €600 Dejeuner champetre (63x88cm-25x35in) s. 19-May-3 Horta, Bruxelles #328
£443 $691 €700 Break time (50x65cm-20x26in) s. panel. 15-Oct-2 Dorotheum, Vienna #97/R
£443 $691 €700 Afternoon tea (50x61cm-20x24in) s. board. 15-Oct-2 Dorotheum, Vienna #107/R
£443 $691 €700 Lakeside picnic (60x80cm-24x31in) s.d.41 gouache. 15-Oct-2 Dorotheum, Vienna #109/R
£446 $687 €700 Sunny dining room with flowers on a table (70x94cm-28x37in) s. 3-Sep-2 Christie's, Amsterdam #393
£450 $702 €675 Lady at the piano (63x79cm-25x31in) s. board. 17-Sep-2 Sotheby's, Olympia #293/R
£450 $698 €675 Lettre (81x96cm-32x38in) s.i. 3-Dec-2 Sotheby's, Olympia #313/R
£450 $698 €675 Garden sunset (70x90cm-28x35in) s. 3-Dec-2 Sotheby's, Olympia #314/R
£464 $756 €700 Jeune femme soignant ses fleurs (60x80cm-24x31in) s. cardboard. 17-Feb-3 Horta, Bruxelles #332
£486 $773 €700 Chaton jouant au jardin (63x103cm-25x41in) s. panel. 29-Apr-3 Campo & Campo, Antwerp #246/R
£486 $802 €700 Red flowers on the tea table (61x80cm-24x31in) s. 1-Jul-3 Christie's, Amsterdam #278
£486 $802 €700 Afternoon tea with oranges (60x78cm-24x31in) s. 1-Jul-3 Christie's, Amsterdam #280
£500 $760 €750 Coffee on the terrace (70x98cm-28x39in) s. board. 29-Aug-2 Christie's, Kensington #168/R
£500 $790 €750 Amongst the sand dunes (61x97cm-24x38in) s. panel. 27-Nov-2 Hamptons Fine Art, Godalming #341
£504 $806 €700 Table de dejeuner au jardin (63x79cm-25x31in) s. 19-May-3 Horta, Bruxelles #329

£520 $842 €780 Summer breakfast (60x92cm-24x36in) s. 23-Jan-3 Christie's, Kensington #253/R
£521 $859 €750 Picnic in the garden (70x80cm-28x31in) s. 1-Jul-3 Christie's, Amsterdam #279/R
£521 $859 €750 Tea in the garden (97x102cm-38x40in) s. 1-Jul-3 Christie's, Amsterdam #281/R
£530 $864 €800 Canal a Bruges (56x72cm-22x28in) s. panel. 17-Feb-3 Horta, Bruxelles #334
£541 $843 €800 Baigneusse au parc (68x85cm-27x33in) s. cardboard. 25-Mar-3 Campo & Campo, Antwerp #155
£550 $891 €825 Afternoon siesta (69x84cm-27x33in) s. board. 23-Jan-3 Christie's, Kensington #251/R
£590 $939 €850 Femme lisante (65x88cm-26x35in) s. 29-Apr-3 Campo & Campo, Antwerp #249
£590 $974 €850 High tea at a pond with lillies (70x90cm-28x35in) s. 1-Jul-3 Christie's, Amsterdam #277/R
£596 $972 €900 Breakfast in the garden (48x71cm-19x28in) s. 28-Jan-3 Dorotheum, Vienna #75/R est:900-1400
£600 $948 €900 Tea time (80x100cm-31x39in) s. 14-Nov-2 Christie's, Kensington #236/R est:400-600
£600 $978 €900 Shaded spot for a meal (60x80cm-24x31in) s. 13-Feb-3 Christie's, Kensington #151/R
£621 $1000 €950 Table dressee au jardin (54x76cm-21x30in) s. cardboard. 20-Jan-3 Horta, Bruxelles #362
£650 $988 €975 Meal before the fountain (61x80cm-24x31in) s. board. 29-Aug-2 Christie's, Kensington #176/R
£650 $988 €975 Lecture (60x72cm-24x28in) s.i. board. 29-Aug-2 Christie's, Kensington #183/R
£658 $1066 €1000 Woman before an open window (94x103cm-37x41in) s. 21-Jan-3 Christie's, Amsterdam #428 est:800-1200
£700 $1141 €1050 Good read at the picnic (80x100cm-31x39in) s. 13-Feb-3 Christie's, Kensington #149/R
£700 $1141 €1050 Teatime siesta (64x97cm-25x38in) s. 13-Feb-3 Christie's, Kensington #152/R
£720 $1174 €1080 Meal amongst the summer blooms (60x89cm-24x35in) s. 13-Feb-3 Christie's, Kensington #150/R
£724 $1172 €1100 Woman in a garden (81x111cm-32x44in) s. board. 21-Jan-3 Christie's, Amsterdam #430/R est:900-1200
£743 $1159 €1100 Petit dejeuner dans le jardin (56x75cm-22x30in) s. 25-Mar-3 Campo & Campo, Antwerp #157
£789 $1279 €1200 Lady reading in the garden (84x93cm-33x37in) s. board. 21-Jan-3 Christie's, Amsterdam #427/R est:700-900
£800 $1264 €1200 Gathering apples (91x71cm-36x28in) s. 14-Nov-2 Christie's, Kensington #238/R
£800 $1304 €1160 Lady eating cherries (60x90cm-24x35in) s. 16-Jul-3 Sotheby's, Olympia #272/R
£833 $1325 €1200 Interieur avec une peinture de Renoir (64x84cm-25x33in) s. panel. 29-Apr-3 Campo & Campo, Antwerp #245
£850 $1343 €1275 Afternoon's yachting (71x100cm-28x39in) s. 14-Nov-2 Christie's, Kensington #237
£850 $1368 €1300 Jeune fille cueillant des roses (79x70cm-31x28in) s. cardboard. 20-Jan-3 Horta, Bruxelles #363
£850 $1377 €1275 Garden refreshments (61x91cm-24x36in) s. 23-Jan-3 Christie's, Kensington #249/R
£886 $1382 €1400 Table dressee au jardin (63x76cm-25x30in) s. cardboard. 15-Oct-2 Horta, Bruxelles #399
£927 $1511 €1400 Table du dejeuner (75x100cm-30x39in) s. 17-Feb-3 Horta, Bruxelles #333
£946 $1476 €1400 Le Minewater (72x90cm-28x35in) s. 25-Mar-3 Campo & Campo, Antwerp #156
£1200 $1968 €1800 Picnic by the waterlillies (60x100cm-24x39in) s. board. 5-Jun-3 Christie's, Kensington #820/R est:400-600
£1329 $2073 €2100 Interieur au Manet (94x95cm-37x37in) s. panel. 15-Oct-2 Horta, Bruxelles #398
£1500 $2340 €2250 Summer garden (58x78cm-23x31in) s. board. 17-Sep-2 Sotheby's, Olympia #292/R est:500-800
£1600 $2592 €2400 Afternoon nap (60x78cm-24x31in) s. 20-May-3 Sotheby's, Olympia #434/R est:400-600
£1645 $2664 €2500 Teatime in the garden (84x129cm-33x51in) s. 21-Jan-3 Christie's, Amsterdam #429/R est:900-1200
£2300 $3726 €3450 Tea on the veranda (66x76cm-26x30in) s. 20-May-3 Sotheby's, Olympia #432/R est:500-700
£2600 $4056 €3900 Al fresco (61x94cm-24x37in) s. pair. 26-Mar-3 Sotheby's, Olympia #276/R est:800-1200
£2600 $4212 €3900 Parasol (60x90cm-24x35in) s. 20-May-3 Sotheby's, Olympia #433/R est:500-700
£2800 $4368 €4200 Begging dog (59x88cm-23x35in) s. 26-Mar-3 Sotheby's, Olympia #277/R est:400-600
£3000 $4710 €4500 Friend for dessert (59x79cm-23x31in) s. board. 16-Apr-3 Christie's, Kensington #922/R est:400-600
£4500 $7335 €6525 Lady reading in the garden (61x83cm-24x33in) s. 16-Jul-3 Sotheby's, Olympia #274/R est:500-7000
£5000 $8150 €7250 Sweet scent of roses (76x100cm-30x39in) s. 16-Jul-3 Sotheby's, Olympia #273/R est:500-700

PAVAN, Angelo (1893-1945) Italian
£1135 $1838 €1600 Pescatori a Chioggia (22x27cm-9x11in) s. board. 22-May-3 Stadion, Trieste #336/R est:800-1200

PAVELIC, Myfanwy Spencer (1916-) Canadian
Works on paper
£807 $1291 €1211 Portrait of man (32x39cm-13x15in) s. ink wash executed 1978 prov. 15-May-3 Heffel, Vancouver #44 est:2000-3000 (C.D 1800)

PAVESI, Mario (1875-1928) Italian
£962 $1519 €1500 San Cristoforo on the Naviglio (30x40cm-12x16in) s. board. 15-Nov-2 Farsetti, Prato #562

PAVESI, Pietro (19th C) Italian
Works on paper
£2344 $3750 €3516 Mosque scene (53x36cm-21x14in) s. W/C. 17-May-3 Pook & Pook, Downington #99/R est:2000-3000

PAVEY, Mary (20th C) ?
£370 $577 €616 Black and yellow cloth (76x61cm-30x24in) s. i.d.1990 verso board. 13-Apr-3 Levis, Calgary #317/R (C.D 850)

PAVIAN SCHOOL (16th C) Italian
£13720 $22500 €20580 Madonna and Child surrounded by Saint Roch, Peter, Francis and Dominic (51x81cm-20x32in) panel. 29-May-3 Sotheby's, New York #109/R est:10000-15000

PAVIL, Elie Anatole (1873-1948) French
£1905 $3029 €2800 Une rue de la medina (61x46cm-24x18in) s. cardboard. 24-Mar-3 Rabourdin & Choppin de Janvry, Paris #281/R est:3000-3500
£1923 $3019 €3000 Au cabaret (54x65cm-21x26in) s. 11-Dec-2 Maigret, Paris #111/R est:3000-5000
£2800 $4452 €4200 Ruines de Creil (54x74cm-21x29in) s. exhib. 20-Mar-3 Sotheby's, Olympia #38/R est:2000-3000
Works on paper
£1139 $1800 €1800 Femme mettant ses bas (73x60cm-29x24in) s. pastel. 2-Dec-2 Cornette de St.Cyr, Paris #53

PAVLOS (1930-) Greek
Sculpture
£5417 $8613 €7800 Orange (78x50cm-31x20in) shredded paper plexiglas prov. 29-Apr-3 Artcurial Briest, Paris #354/R est:3500-4000
£9028 $14354 €13000 Appareil de photo (127x143cm-50x56in) shredded paper prov. 29-Apr-3 Artcurial Briest, Paris #353/R est:7500-9000
Works on paper
£782 $1244 €1150 Sock (46x28cm-18x11in) s.d.2002 verso collage panel. 24-Mar-3 Cornette de St.Cyr, Paris #157/R
£1132 $1766 €1800 Hemd, chemise (44x28cm-17x11in) s.d.1969 paper plexiglas. 11-Oct-2 Binoche, Paris #163
£1736 $2743 €2500 Chemise (45x28cm-18x11in) s.d.verso massicote colle paper on panel. 28-Apr-3 Cornette de St.Cyr, Paris #479/R est:800-1000
£1824 $2809 €2900 Chemise (45x29cm-18x11in) s.dd.1968 decoupage plexiglas. 26-Oct-2 Cornette de St.Cyr, Paris #62/R
£1918 $2992 €2800 Composition aux chemises (105x73cm-41x29in) s.d.1979 mixed media. 14-Apr-3 Horta, Bruxelles #223/R est:3000-4000
£3205 $4968 €5000 Salle de bain (200x142cm-79x56in) collage paper plexiglass. 7-Dec-2 Ketterer, Hamburg #731/R est:5000-7000

PAVLOVSKY, Vladmir (1884-1944) American
£1529 $2400 €2294 Showgirl (102x84cm-40x33in) s. 22-Nov-2 Skinner, Boston #182/R est:3000-5000
Works on paper
£239 $375 €359 Hillside town (37x48cm-15x19in) s. W/C. 22-Nov-2 Skinner, Boston #271/R
£265 $425 €384 Bali dancers (37x53cm-15x21in) s. i.verso W/C. 16-May-3 Skinner, Boston #186/R
£270 $425 €405 Purple mountains (35x51cm-14x20in) s. W/C. 22-Nov-2 Skinner, Boston #230/R
£406 $650 €589 Palm tree haven (37x52cm-15x20in) s. W/C. 16-May-3 Skinner, Boston #308/R
£692 $1100 €1038 Fishing scenes (40x57cm-16x22in) s. W/C double-sided set of four. 7-Mar-3 Skinner, Boston #462/R
£764 $1200 €1146 An afternoon in the city (38x52cm-15x20in) s. W/C. 22-Nov-2 Skinner, Boston #336/R est:1500-2000
£1000 $1600 €1450 View of the park (37x52cm-15x20in) s. W/C. 16-May-3 Skinner, Boston #319/R est:1500-2000

PAVY, Eugène (19th C) French
£11972 $17000 €17958 The lion (89x155cm-35x61in) 8-Aug-1 Barridorf, Portland #63/R est:15000-25000

PAVY, Philippe (1860-?) French
£1552 $2514 €2250 The gleaners (40x30cm-16x12in) s.d.1879. 25-May-3 Uppsala Auktionskammare, Uppsala #110/R est:6000-8000 (S.KR 20000)
£1931 $3013 €2800 Drawing room (61x46cm-24x18in) s.d.1884 prov. 26-Mar-3 Walker's, Ottawa #30/R est:8000-10000 (C.D 4500)

PAWLISZAK, Waclaw (1866-1904) Polish
£1698 $2649 €2700 Mounted Ukrainian cossacks playing music in the field (24x33cm-9x13in) s.d.1879 lit. 20-Sep-2 Karlheinz Kaupp, Staufen #1959/R est:2300

PAWLOWSKI, H (?) ?

£252 $392 €400 Danzig harbour (70x99cm-28x39in) i. 23-Sep-2 Dr Fritz Nagel, Stuttgart #7000/R

PAWLOWSKI, Jan (20th C) American

£318 $500 €477 Little Traverse Bay (41x51cm-16x20in) s.d.88. 20-Nov-2 Boos Gallery, Michigan #480/R

PAXSON, Edgar S (1852-1919) American

£6962 $11000 €10095 Indians in a canoe (46x28cm-18x11in) s. board. 26-Jul-3 Coeur d'Alene, Hayden #202/R est:10000-20000

£53797 $85000 €78006 Old guide (61x51cm-24x20in) s. 26-Jul-3 Coeur d'Alene, Hayden #95/R est:40000-60000

Works on paper

£9434 $15000 €14151 Blackfoot chief in headdress (51x38cm-20x15in) s.d.1915 i.verso W/C gouache pencil board. 5-Mar-3 Sotheby's, New York #122/R est:7000-10000

PAXTON, William McGregor (1869-1941) American

£1258 $2000 €1887 Portrait of a seated woman in a white dress (76x64cm-30x25in) s. board. 1-Mar-3 North East Auctions, Portsmouth #697/R est:2000-3000

PAYA, Emilio (1935-) Spanish

£1026 $1600 €1539 Paris street scene (38x46cm-15x18in) s. 29-Mar-3 Charlton Hall, Columbia #127/R est:1500-2000

PAYEN, G (19th C) French

£2405 $3752 €3800 Elegante au bord de la Seine (55x39cm-22x15in) s. 18-Oct-2 Rabourdin & Choppin de Janvry, Paris #36/R

£4557 $7109 €7200 Elegantes sur les grands boulevards (75x58cm-30x23in) s. 18-Oct-2 Rabourdin & Choppin de Janvry, Paris #38/R est:4000

PAYER, Ernst (1862-1937) Austrian

£1918 $2992 €2800 Putto with fruit basket (110x65cm-43x26in) s. 10-Apr-3 Dorotheum, Vienna #214/R est:1800-2400

PAYES, Eduardo (1938-) ?

£780 $1279 €1170 Venetian canal scene (45x54cm-18x21in) s. 2-Jun-3 David Duggleby, Scarborough #322/R

£1550 $2542 €2325 Busy Parisian street scene (45x54cm-18x21in) s. 2-Jun-3 David Duggleby, Scarborough #321/R est:1500-2000

PAYNE, Albert Henry (attrib) (1812-1902) British

£870 $1426 €1200 Paesaggio con mucche (44x63cm-17x25in) s.d.1840. 27-May-3 Finarte, Milan #113/R

PAYNE, Charles Johnson (1884-1967) British

£300 $477 €450 Bon Voyage - English gunner (34x43cm-13x17in) 7-Mar-3 Tennants, Leyburn #137

£300 $477 €450 A heilan lad (34x43cm-13x17in) s. 7-Mar-3 Tennants, Leyburn #142

£320 $509 €480 Wipers (34x43cm-13x17in) s. 7-Mar-3 Tennants, Leyburn #144

£320 $509 €480 Once upon a time (49x62cm-19x24in) s. 7-Mar-3 Tennants, Leyburn #145

£350 $557 €525 Snaffles - the glad throng that does laughing along (31x98cm-12x39in) 7-Mar-3 Tennants, Leyburn #121

£350 $557 €525 The bonny blue bonnets - frae over the border (43x44cm-17x17in) s. 7-Mar-3 Tennants, Leyburn #134

£400 $636 €600 Ubique means - RK (37x40cm-15x16in) s. 7-Mar-3 Tennants, Leyburn #141

£480 $763 €720 The gunner - good hunting! old sportsman (34x43cm-13x17in) 7-Mar-3 Tennants, Leyburn #139

£500 $795 €750 The gent in ratcatcher (35x39cm-14x15in) s. 7-Mar-3 Tennants, Leyburn #123

£500 $795 €750 A bona fide fox chaser (43x48cm-17x19in) s. 7-Mar-3 Tennants, Leyburn #127

£500 $795 €750 Merry England, and worth a guinea a minute (42x44cm-17x17in) s. 7-Mar-3 Tennants, Leyburn #130

£550 $875 €825 The D.R. (40x46cm-16x18in) 7-Mar-3 Tennants, Leyburn #133a

£600 $954 €900 Indian military (24x32cm-9x13in) s. ink crayon. 7-Mar-3 Tennants, Leyburn #148

£650 $1034 €975 Merry England, and worth a lakh a minute (43x48cm-17x19in) s. 7-Mar-3 Tennants, Leyburn #128

£650 $1034 €975 The huntsman (37x43cm-15x17in) s. 7-Mar-3 Tennants, Leyburn #129

£750 $1193 €1125 The sparrow catching sort (38x43cm-15x17in) s. 7-Mar-3 Tennants, Leyburn #126

£800 $1272 €1200 The stone-faced narrer-back (47x65cm-19x26in) 7-Mar-3 Tennants, Leyburn #124

£800 $1272 €1200 Solid and tall was the raspin wall (47x65cm-19x26in) 7-Mar-3 Tennants, Leyburn #124a

£850 $1352 €1275 A sight to take home and dream about (49x62cm-19x24in) s. 7-Mar-3 Tennants, Leyburn #122

Photographs

£1180 $1864 €1770 The informers (25x43cm-10x17in) s. photographic. 13-Nov-2 Halls, Shrewsbury #318 est:250-350

Works on paper

£520 $822 €780 Cavalree, an officer of the 17th, Duke of Cambridge's Own, Lancers (21x14cm-8x6in) s.i. W/C bodycol over pencil. 27-Nov-2 Bonhams, Knowle #93

£720 $1138 €1080 Horse Gunners, an officer of the Royal Horse Artillery (28x14cm-11x6in) s.i. W/C bodycol pencil. 27-Nov-2 Bonhams, Knowle #91

£820 $1296 €1230 The artist smoking a cigarette (26x12cm-10x5in) s.i.d.05 ink W/C over pencil. 27-Nov-2 Bonhams, Knowle #95/R

£840 $1327 €1260 The Hampshires, an officer in evening dress (24x16cm-9x6in) mono.i. ink W/C over pencil exec.c.1907-08. 27-Nov-2 Bonhams, Knowle #85/R

£880 $1390 €1320 The Royals, study of an officer (25x16cm-10x6in) mono.i. W/C ink over pencil. 27-Nov-2 Bonhams, Knowle #86/R

£920 $1454 €1380 The W I R, study of a Sergeant of the West India Regiment (26x15cm-10x6in) mono.i. W/C ink over pencil. 27-Nov-2 Bonhams, Knowle #87/R

£920 $1454 €1380 Royal Warwicks, study of an officer (34x25cm-13x10in) s.i. W/C bodycol over pencil. 27-Nov-2 Bonhams, Knowle #88/R

£920 $1454 €1380 Yer old pal Snaffles, with a bull terrier alongside (24x17cm-9x7in) i. ink W/C over pencil. 27-Nov-2 Bonhams, Knowle #94/R

£920 $1444 €1380 Jim the driver, study of a chauffeur (28x19cm-11x7in) s.i. pencil W/C paper laid down exec.c.1910. 15-Apr-3 Bonhams, Knowle #35/R

£940 $1476 €1410 The Ikonas, a mounted officer smoking a pipe (29x22cm-11x9in) s.i. pencil black ink exec.c.1908. 15-Apr-3 Bonhams, Knowle #36/R

£950 $1511 €1425 Where's the blighter gone? (21x25cm-8x10in) s.mono. W/C. 7-Mar-3 Tennants, Leyburn #147

£1050 $1659 €1575 Study of an officer of the Royal Marine Artillery (27x19cm-11x7in) s. W/C bodycol. 27-Nov-2 Bonhams, Knowle #89 est:500-800

£1050 $1649 €1575 Mounted infantry (29x21cm-11x8in) s.i. pencil black ink exec.c.1908. 15-Apr-3 Bonhams, Knowle #37/R est:800-1200

£1700 $2686 €2550 Field gunner, an officer of the Royal Field Artillery (34x25cm-13x10in) s.i. W/C bodycol over pencil sold with a companion. 27-Nov-2 Bonhams, Knowle #92/R est:1000-1500

£1800 $2934 €2610 Soldier wearing a kilt and military regalia (24x16cm-9x6in) s.i.verso pencil W/C htd white. 17-Jul-3 Tennants, Leyburn #770/R est:1000-1500

PAYNE, D (19th C) British

£1500 $2475 €2175 Portrait of Mary Edwrads, aged six (74x62cm-29x24in) s.d.1757. 2-Jul-3 Sotheby's, Olympia #46/R est:800-1200

PAYNE, David (19th C) British

£450 $747 €675 Haddon meadow, Derbyshire (30x50cm-12x20in) s. 10-Jun-3 Bonhams, Leeds #183

£820 $1337 €1230 Extensive wooded landscape with figures fishing cattle watering in distance (43x69cm-17x27in) s. 14-Feb-3 Keys, Aylsham #680/R

£1200 $1848 €1800 Scene on Sinfin Moor, near Derby (61x91cm-24x36in) s. 3-Sep-2 Gorringes, Lewes #2094 est:200-300

£1500 $2340 €2250 Solihull. Lichfield (51x41cm-20x16in) s.d.1885 s.i.d.verso pair. 13-Sep-2 Lyon & Turnbull, Edinburgh #61/R est:600-800

£2100 $3318 €3150 Summer Day, on the Derby Road, near Lenton Firs, Nottingham (55x45cm-22x18in) s. board. 27-Nov-2 Bonhams, Knowle #234 est:1500-2500

£2300 $3588 €3450 Derbyshire lane (63x105cm-25x41in) s. i.verso. 9-Oct-2 Woolley & Wallis, Salisbury #310/R est:2000-3000

£4800 $7488 €7200 Landscape with sheep crossing a bridge - near Melbourne, Derbyshire (61x92cm-24x36in) s. prov. 8-Oct-2 Sotheby's, Olympia #424/R est:3000-5000

PAYNE, E (?) ?

£500 $790 €750 Setters with the bag (46x56cm-18x22in) s. 28-Nov-2 Christie's, Kensington #349/R

PAYNE, Edgar (1882-1947) American

£258 $400 €387 French tuna boats, Concarneau, France (51x61cm-20x24in) s. oil serigraph. 29-Oct-2 John Moran, Pasadena #809

£1356 $2250 €1966 Autumn landscape (23x30cm-9x12in) s. board prov. 11-Jun-3 Butterfields, San Francisco #4199/R est:3000-5000

£2019 $3250 €3029 Colorado river landscape (15x20cm-6x8in) s. board. 18-Feb-3 John Moran, Pasadena #55a est:2000-3000

£3323 $5250 €4818 High Sierra (20x25cm-8x10in) s. board. 26-Jul-3 Coeur d'Alene, Hayden #175/R est:8000-12000
£3915 $6500 €5677 Indian pony, horse study (24x30cm-9x12in) s. canvas on board. 11-Jun-3 Butterfields, San Francisco #4325/R est:4000-6000
£4790 $8000 €6946 Near Bishop (29x39cm-11x15in) bears sig canvas on board. 18-Jun-3 Christie's, Los Angeles #65/R est:10000-15000
£5422 $9000 €7862 Portrait of a Navajo man (32x22cm-13x9in) s. canvasboard. 11-Jun-3 Butterfields, San Francisco #4324/R est:6000-8500
£5689 $9500 €8249 Mt. Lowe (30x40cm-12x16in) s. board prov. 18-Jun-3 Christie's, Los Angeles #27/R est:8000-12000
£6051 $9500 €9077 Sierra sunset (32x36cm-13x14in) s. 20-Nov-2 Christie's, Los Angeles #123/R est:8000-12000
£6832 $11000 €10248 High Sierras landscape (30x41cm-12x16in) s. board prov. 18-Feb-3 John Moran, Pasadena #38 est:10000-15000
£6832 $11000 €10248 Crashing waves on rocks (30x38cm-12x15in) s. board. 18-Feb-3 John Moran, Pasadena #42 est:3500-5500
£7229 $12000 €10482 Boulder Mountain, Sierras (29x38cm-11x15in) s. canvas on board exhib. 11-Jun-3 Butterfields, San Francisco #4317/R est:12000-16000
£8280 $13000 €12420 Sierra landscape (30x38cm-12x15in) s. canvas on board. 20-Nov-2 Christie's, Los Angeles #70/R est:12000-18000
£8434 $14000 €12229 Autumn hillside (41x51cm-16x20in) s. prov. 11-Jun-3 Butterfields, San Francisco #4243/R est:10000-15000
£8519 $13800 €12353 Red cliffs with Indian on horseback (33x41cm-13x16in) 23-May-3 Altermann Galleries, Santa Fe #158
£8917 $14000 €13376 After the first rain (36x46cm-14x18in) s. board prov. 19-Nov-2 Butterfields, San Francisco #8222/R est:12000-16000
£9554 $15000 €14331 Sierras in bloom (32x40cm-13x16in) s. prov. 19-Nov-2 Butterfields, San Francisco #8197/R est:10000-15000
£10559 $17000 €15839 Boats, Italy (30x36cm-12x14in) s. board prov. 18-Feb-3 John Moran, Pasadena #31 est:12000-18000
£10828 $17000 €16242 Fishing boats (41x51cm-16x20in) s. prov. 19-Nov-2 Butterfields, San Francisco #8271/R est:20000-30000
£10968 $17000 €16452 Venice sketch (30x36cm-12x14in) s. i.verso canvas on board prov. 29-Oct-2 John Moran, Pasadena #644a est:12000-18000
£11180 $18000 €16770 Chiogga sails (51x61cm-20x24in) s. canvas on canvas prov. 18-Feb-3 John Moran, Pasadena #119a est:20000-30000
£11321 $18000 €16982 Landscape in Switzerland (70x86cm-28x34in) s. prov. 5-Mar-3 Sotheby's, New York #22/R est:15000-20000
£12739 $20000 €19109 North Palisade, Upper Lodge Trail (41x51cm-16x20in) s. i.verso. 20-Nov-2 Christie's, Los Angeles #5/R est:20000-30000
£12739 $20000 €19109 Dana Point (71x86cm-28x34in) s. prov. 19-Nov-2 Butterfields, San Francisco #8268/R est:40000-60000
£17516 $27500 €26274 Fishing boats off shore (51x61cm-20x24in) s. i.stretcher prov. 19-Nov-2 Butterfields, San Francisco #8270/R est:25000-35000
£17742 $27500 €26613 Tuna boats, Brittany, France (51x61cm-20x24in) s. i.verso prov. 29-Oct-2 John Moran, Pasadena #644 est:30000-40000
£19108 $30000 €28662 Green hillside (66x86cm-26x34in) s. canvas on board prov. 19-Nov-2 Butterfields, San Francisco #8220/R est:25000-35000
£20700 $32500 €31050 Italian riviera near St Margarita (74x74cm-29x29in) s. i.verso prov. 19-Nov-2 Butterfields, San Francisco #8219/R est:30000-40000
£22156 $37000 €32126 San Gabriel foothills (51x61cm-20x24in) s. 18-Jun-3 Christie's, Los Angeles #6/R est:20000-30000
£24194 $37500 €36291 View at Murren (74x74cm-29x29in) s. i.verso prov. 29-Oct-2 John Moran, Pasadena #739 est:35000-45000
£26899 $42500 €39004 California mountains (84x102cm-33x40in) s. prov. 26-Jul-3 Coeur d'Alene, Hayden #136/R est:50000-75000
£27950 $45000 €41925 Red sails and blue nets (25x30cm-10x12in) s. 18-Feb-3 John Moran, Pasadena #64a est:25000-35000
£28662 $45000 €42993 Bishop Pass (41x51cm-16x20in) s. i.stretcher prov. 20-Nov-2 Christie's, Los Angeles #60/R est:40000-60000
£30573 $48000 €45860 Return of the fleet (71x87cm-28x34in) s. prov. 20-Nov-2 Christie's, Los Angeles #63/R est:40000-60000
£35928 $60000 €52096 Landscape -Fourth Lake, big pine High Sierras (64x76cm-25x30in) s. i.verso prov. 17-Jun-3 John Moran, Pasadena #44 est:70000-90000
£41935 $65000 €62903 Desert sky (51x61cm-20x24in) s. i.verso prov. 29-Oct-2 John Moran, Pasadena #643 est:70000-90000
£48387 $75000 €72581 Blue Canyon, Arizona (51x61cm-20x24in) s. i.verso prov. 29-Oct-2 John Moran, Pasadena #690 est:60000-80000
£51282 $80000 €76923 Navajo country (71x86cm-28x34in) s. prov.lit. 9-Nov-2 Santa Fe Art, Santa Fe #199/R est:100000-120000
£59880 $100000 €86826 Riders in Canyon de Chelly, Arizona (46x56cm-18x22in) i.verso prov. 17-Jun-3 John Moran, Pasadena #56 est:60000-80000
£196203 $310000 €284494 Navajo riders (81x102cm-32x40in) s. 26-Jul-3 Coeur d'Alene, Hayden #86/R est:150000-250000

Works on paper
£994 $1600 €1491 Aspens in landscape (18x23cm-7x9in) s. prov. 18-Feb-3 John Moran, Pasadena #132b est:1000-2000
£1582 $2500 €2294 Two Indians on horseback (30x23cm-12x9in) s. ink prov. 26-Jul-3 Coeur d'Alene, Hayden #60/R est:1500-2500
£3871 $6000 €5807 Breton fishing boats (8x10cm-3x4in) s.i. gouache. 29-Oct-2 John Moran, Pasadena #603 est:3000-5000
£8383 $14000 €12155 High Sierra landscape (20x28cm-8x11in) s. gouache on board. 17-Jun-3 John Moran, Pasadena #20 est:7000-9000
£20570 $32500 €29827 Scouting party (43x53cm-17x21in) s. mixed media prov. 26-Jul-3 Coeur d'Alene, Hayden #143/R est:10000-20000

PAYNE, Edgar and SMITH, Jack W (20th C) American
£4777 $7500 €7166 Oregon coast. Adriatic fishing boats. Mountain landscape (9x11cm-4x4in) one s. i.d.1922 verso one s. i.verso one i.verso board 3 prov. 19-Nov-2 Butterfields, San Francisco #8209/R est:6000-8000

PAYNE, Elsie Palmer (1884-1971) American
Sculpture
£1347 $2250 €1953 Pirate seated on rectangular sea chest (23x18x13cm-9x7x5in) s.d.1921 bronze. 17-Jun-3 John Moran, Pasadena #80a est:1200-1800

PAYNE, Frances Mallalieu (1885-1975) Australian
£1290 $1961 €1935 Portrait of a girl (29x24cm-11x9in) s. canvas on board. 28-Aug-2 Deutscher-Menzies, Melbourne #302/R est:3000-5000 (A.D 3600)

PAYNE, Henry Albert (1868-1940) British
Works on paper
£820 $1369 €1189 Watching the wild duck (34x40cm-13x16in) s.d.37 W/C. 24-Jun-3 Holloways, Banbury #479
£1000 $1670 €1450 Homeward (29x57cm-11x22in) W/C. 24-Jun-3 Holloways, Banbury #480 est:400-500
£3000 $4920 €4350 Valley of Humiliation (48x59cm-19x23in) indis sig.d.1923 black chk W/C htd white prov. 5-Jun-3 Christie's, London #144/R est:4000-6000

PAYNE, W (18/19th C) British
Works on paper
£300 $477 €450 River landscape with bridge and church (11x16cm-4x6in) W/C with another work two. 29-Apr-3 Henry Adams, Chichester #196

PAYNE, William (1760-1830) British
Works on paper
£250 $390 €375 Wooded river landscape with two figures on a footbridge (15x19cm-6x7in) W/C. 26-Mar-3 Hamptons Fine Art, Godalming #83
£475 $736 €750 View of the glacier from Montanvert near Chamouny (21x30cm-8x12in) s.d.1821 W/C paper on board. 27-Sep-2 Venator & Hansten, Koln #1334/R
£680 $1061 €1020 Binton Castle, Milford Haven (16x21cm-6x8in) W/C. 26-Mar-3 Woolley & Wallis, Salisbury #62/R
£800 $1248 €1160 Ferryboat. Figure before riverside cottages (13x17cm-5x7in) s. W/C pair. 27-Mar-3 Lane, Penzance #353
£1200 $1956 €1800 Extensive landscape with a stone bridge and a man upon horseback (30x40cm-12x16in) s. pen ink W/C. 29-Jan-3 Dreweatt Neate, Newbury #55 est:400-600
£1300 $2015 €1950 Cawsand bay (13x15cm-5x6in) s. W/C. 4-Oct-2 Mallams, Oxford #461/R est:100-150
£1600 $2656 €2400 Rustics at sunset (15x22cm-6x9in) W/C. 12-Jun-3 Bonhams, New Bond Street #658/R est:800-1200
£2300 $3588 €3450 Copper works between Redruth and Penzance. Pentilly upon the Tamar (13x17cm-5x7in) s. s.i.d.1791 verso W/C pen grey ink pair. 17-Oct-2 Lawrence, Crewkerne #381/R est:800-1200
£2400 $3984 €3600 Calstock on the Tamar (14x21cm-6x8in) s. W/C over pencil prov. 12-Jun-3 Sotheby's, London #130/R est:1000-1500
£2500 $3951 €3750 View of Totnes, Devon, taken from the banks of the River Dart (29x40cm-11x16in) i.verso pen ink W/C over pencil prov.exhib.lit. 28-Nov-2 Sotheby's, London #303/R est:2000-3000

PAZ, Manolo (1957-) Spanish
Sculpture
£4043 $6549 €5700 Untitled (121x34x46cm-48x13x18in) granite marbel incl wood base prov.exhib. 20-May-3 Segre, Madrid #168/R est:8400

PAZOTTI (19/20th C) ?
£3043 $4717 €4565 Constantinople, vue du Bosphore (54x81cm-21x32in) s. prov. 7-Dec-2 Galerie du Rhone, Sion #521/R est:2000-3000 (S.FR 7000)

Works on paper
£8784 $13703 €13000 View of the Bosphorus (54x81cm-21x32in) s. 28-Mar-3 Claude Aguttes, Neuilly #180/R

PEACAN, I T (19th C) Irish?
£1538 $2415 €2400 Young man seated in an interior, with bones on the floor (28x22cm-11x9in) s.d.1883. 19-Nov-2 Hamilton Osborne King, Dublin #576/R est:2500-3500

PEACOCK, George Edward (1806-1890) Australian
£2857 $4514 €4286 Parsley Bay, Port Jackson (14x19cm-6x7in) s.d.1852 i.verso board prov. 17-Nov-2 Sotheby's, Paddington #41/R est:6000-10000 (A.D 8000)
£3101 $4930 €4652 View of Port Jackson, Sydney, from Vaucluse (16x22cm-6x9in) i.indis.d. verso prov. 5-May-3 Sotheby's, Melbourne #310/R est:6000-8000 (A.D 8000)
£8000 $12720 €12000 Governor's house and fort Macquarrie Sydney. View in Middle Harbour, Port Jackson (16x21cm-6x8in) s. i.d.1848 verso board pair. 29-Apr-3 Bonhams, New Bond Street #6/R est:8000-12000
£48000 $77280 €72000 Sydney from Macquarie Street (39x84cm-15x33in) prov. 6-May-3 Christie's, Melbourne #108/R est:120000-170000 (A.D 120000)

PEACOCK, Ralph (1868-1946) British
£3600 $6012 €5220 Miss Edith Brignall (135x74cm-53x29in) s. 8-Jul-3 Bonhams, Knightsbridge #169a/R est:2500-3500

PEAK, Bob (1928-1992) American
Works on paper
£1923 $3000 €2885 Man with spiked glove, procession of spectators (56x43cm-22x17in) s. pastel. 9-Nov-2 Illustration House, New York #131/R est:4000-6000

PEAKE, Mervyn (1911-1968) British
£1800 $2808 €2700 Portrait of Sue French (51x41cm-20x16in) s.d.1957. 9-Oct-2 Woolley & Wallis, Salisbury #322/R est:300-500
Works on paper
£338 $561 €480 Cow and calf (23x28cm-9x11in) s.d.1956 pencil. 10-Jun-3 James Adam, Dublin #58/R
£500 $780 €750 Two nuns of Dubrovnik (25x35cm-10x14in) s. W/C grey wash prov. 26-Mar-3 Hamptons Fine Art, Godalming #109
£600 $936 €900 Untitled IV (22x21cm-9x8in) brush ink gouache. 27-Mar-3 Christie's, Kensington #293/R
£600 $936 €900 Political caricature (18x11cm-7x4in) pen ink sketch. 26-Mar-3 Hamptons Fine Art, Godalming #67
£680 $1061 €1020 Portrait of a girl, head and shoulders (28x44cm-11x17in) s.d.61 mixed media. 9-Oct-2 Woolley & Wallis, Salisbury #323/R
£700 $1085 €1050 Sleeping nude (20x24cm-8x9in) pencil exhib. 4-Dec-2 Christie's, Kensington #241
£750 $1163 €1125 Study of a nude. Old lady with cigarette (38x16cm-15x6in) s. pencil double-sided. 4-Dec-2 Christie's, Kensington #242/R
£750 $1170 €1125 Untitled I (22x14cm-9x6in) s. pencil prov. 27-Mar-3 Christie's, Kensington #297/R
£900 $1404 €1350 Untitled VI (23x24cm-9x9in) brush ink gouache prov. 27-Mar-3 Christie's, Kensington #286/R
£1200 $1872 €1800 Ithell colquhoun (30x24cm-12x9in) s.d.1939 pn ink prov. 27-Mar-3 Christie's, Kensington #289/R est:500-700
£1300 $2028 €1950 Study of three mythical figures (22x26cm-9x10in) s.d.84 pencil chl. 9-Oct-2 Woolley & Wallis, Salisbury #154/R est:300-500
£1300 $2028 €1950 Untitled VIII (26x20cm-10x8in) s. brush ink gouache prov. 27-Mar-3 Christie's, Kensington #290/R est:800-1200
£1800 $2808 €2700 Untitled VII (22x29cm-9x11in) s. brush black red ink double-sided. 27-Mar-3 Christie's, Kensington #294/R est:1000-1500

PEAKE, Robert (circle) (16/17th C) British
£6707 $11000 €10061 Portrait of a lady, said to be Anne of Denmark, half-length (57x43cm-22x17in) panel prov.exhib. 30-May-3 Christie's, Rockefeller NY #44/R est:5000-7000

PEALE, James (elder) (1749-1831) American
£32258 $50000 €48387 Portrait of a young child with peaches (76x64cm-30x25in) i.verso prov.lit. 2-Nov-2 North East Auctions, Portsmouth #609/R est:50000-80000
£129032 $200000 €193548 Fruits of autumn (39x56cm-15x22in) panel prov.exhib. 5-Dec-2 Christie's, Rockefeller NY #9/R est:250000-350000

PEALE, Mary Jane (1827-1902) American
£2215 $3500 €3323 Tuscan hat. Pilgrim daughter (69x56cm-27x22in) s.i.verso pair. 24-Apr-3 Shannon's, Milford #213/R est:800-1200

PEALE, Raphaelle (1774-1825) American
£593548 $920000 €890322 Still life with liqueur and fruit (34x49cm-13x19in) s.d.1814 panel prov.exhib. 5-Dec-2 Christie's, Rockefeller NY #20/R est:800000-1200000

PEALE, Rembrandt (1778-1860) American
£6169 $9500 €9254 Portrait of a lady (69x56cm-27x22in) s. oval prov. 24-Oct-2 Shannon's, Milford #150/R est:9000-12000
£8333 $13000 €12500 Portrait of Sarah Hepbourn (61x51cm-24x20in) s. 21-Sep-2 Pook & Pook, Downington #251/R est:7000-10000
£148387 $230000 €222581 Portrait of George Washington (91x73cm-36x29in) s. prov.lit. 4-Dec-2 Sotheby's, New York #118/R est:125000-175000
Prints
£3106 $5000 €4659 Portrait of George Washington (55x3cm-22x1in) lithograph prov. 16-Jan-3 Christie's, Rockefeller NY #1/R est:3000-4000

PEALE, Sarah Miriam (1800-1885) American
£688 $1100 €1032 Portrait of a young girl playing with a bird (76x64cm-30x25in) s. 17-May-3 Pook & Pook, Downington #235/R est:3000-5000

PEALE, Titian Ramsay (1799-1885) American
£58065 $90000 €87098 Five bobwhites at the Delaware water gap (56x69cm-22x27in) s.d.1868 prov.exhib. 5-Dec-2 Christie's, Rockefeller NY #2/R est:50000-70000

PEAN, René (1875-1945) French
Works on paper
£452 $714 €700 Colombine (46x32cm-18x13in) s. pastel. 19-Dec-2 Delvaux, Paris #31/R

PEARCE, Bryan (1929-) British
£1300 $2028 €1950 Bethesda, St Ives (46x35cm-18x14in) s. board. 7-Nov-2 Bonhams, Cornwall #858 est:800-1200
£1600 $2496 €2400 Snow on Man's Head and Clodgy (41x51cm-16x20in) s.i. d.1979 verso board. 17-Oct-2 David Lay, Penzance #1404/R est:1500-2000
£1600 $2496 €2400 Still life with jug (46x36cm-18x14in) s. board. 16-Oct-2 David Lay, Penzance #257/R est:800-1400
£2200 $3432 €3300 Fruit and Chianti (38x56cm-15x22in) s.i. d.1958 verso board. 17-Oct-2 David Lay, Penzance #1403/R est:1500-2000
Works on paper
£360 $558 €540 Godrevy lighthouse (74x107cm-29x42in) s. ink dr. 26-Sep-2 Lane, Penzance #7
£380 $593 €551 Smeaton's pier St. Ives (27x27cm-11x11in) s. ink. 27-Mar-3 Lane, Penzance #12
£440 $686 €638 St. Ives Harbour (29x42cm-11x17in) s. ink. 27-Mar-3 Lane, Penzance #13

PEARCE, Catherine (20th C) French?
£278 $453 €420 Tendresse (38x45cm-15x18in) s. 1-Feb-3 Claude Aguttes, Neuilly #310/R

PEARCE, Charles Sprague (1851-1914) American
£6289 $10000 €9434 In the poppy field (82x101cm-32x40in) s. prov. 5-Mar-3 Sotheby's, New York #55/R est:25000-35000

PEARCE, Edward Holroyd (1901-) British
£480 $773 €720 Suffolk shore (39x49cm-15x19in) s. board prov. 15-Jan-3 Cheffins Grain & Comins, Cambridge #438/R

PEARCE, William Houghton Sprague (19/20th C) American
£3165 $5000 €4748 Stream (81x81cm-32x32in) s. 24-Apr-3 Shannon's, Milford #166/R est:2500-3500

PEARCY, Frank William (?) British?
Works on paper
£360 $569 €522 View of Shoreham from the river (25x36cm-10x14in) s. W/C. 24-Apr-3 Scarborough Perry Fine Arts, Hove #648

PEARL, M P (20th C) American
£1039 $1600 €1559 Tunnel in the sky (86x117cm-34x46in) s. board painted c.1940. 8-Sep-2 Treadway Gallery, Cincinnati #748/R est:600-800

PEARLMUTTER, Stella (20th C) American
£301 $475 €452 Two ladies in garden (124x99cm-49x39in) s. 22-Apr-3 Arthur James, Florida #178

PEARLSTEIN, Philip (1924-) American
£2724 $4250 €4086 Back, standing female nude (76x66cm-30x26in) s. i.d.63 stretcher prov.exhib. 5-Nov-2 Doyle, New York #55/R est:6000-8000

PEARLSTEIN, Seymour (1923-) American
£323 $500 €485 Sam - reclining male (102x127cm-40x50in) s. prov. 25-Sep-2 Doyle, New York #56/R

PEARS, Charles (1873-1958) British
£650 $1053 €975 Swedish barquentine off the Old Man of Hoy, Orkney Islands (81x114cm-32x45in) s. 21-May-3 Christie's, Kensington #697/R
£1300 $1976 €1950 Lands End (48x74cm-19x29in) s. 14-Aug-2 Andrew Hartley, Ilkley #668/R est:1400-1800
£1750 $2730 €2625 Yacht, Maid of Malham by starlight (20x26cm-8x10in) s. board. 5-Nov-2 Bristol Auction Rooms #865/R est:100-200
£2000 $3040 €3000 Moonlight barque (102x127cm-40x50in) s. exhib. 15-Aug-2 Bonhams, New Bond Street #454/R est:2000-3000
Works on paper
£280 $437 €420 Eumaeus (31x31cm-12x12in) s.i. W/C gouache. 12-Sep-2 Sotheby's, Olympia #200/R
£750 $1170 €1125 Fleet lit up (37x37cm-15x15in) s. W/C gouache paper on board. 12-Sep-2 Sotheby's, Olympia #230/R
£1100 $1716 €1650 Fleet lit up (37x37cm-15x15in) W/C gouache paper on board. 12-Sep-2 Sotheby's, Olympia #229/R est:1200-1800

PEARS, Dion (20th C) British?
£320 $496 €480 Dragons racing to windward (71x97cm-28x38in) s. 31-Oct-2 Christie's, Kensington #416/R

PEARSE, Alfred (1856-1933) British
Works on paper
£1807 $2837 €2711 Portrait of HRH the Prince of Wales (34x24cm-13x9in) s.i.d.1920 W/C board. 25-Nov-2 Hodgins, Calgary #56/R est:5000-10000 (C.D 4500)

PEARSON, Alan (20th C) New Zealander?
£937 $1463 €1406 Captain Cook RN (45x36cm-18x14in) s.i.d.1978 verso. 8-Apr-3 Peter Webb, Auckland #150/R (NZ.D 2700)
£1625 $2599 €2356 Anthony Stones (12x90cm-5x35in) s.d.1969 i.verso. 13-May-3 Watson's, Christchurch #89/R (NZ.D 4500)

PEARSON, Cornelius (1805-1891) British
Works on paper
£360 $569 €522 Figures in a mountainous lakeland landscape (18x46cm-7x18in) s.d.1859 W/C. 23-Jul-3 Mallams, Oxford #108/R
£400 $616 €600 On the Dart, south Devon (30x41cm-12x16in) s.d.1868 W/C. 22-Oct-2 Sworder & Son, Bishops Stortford #700/R
£400 $656 €580 View probably in the Lake District, with figures in a ferry boat, fells beyond (23x33cm-9x13in) s.d.1853 W/C. 3-Jun-3 Capes Dunn, Manchester #65
£750 $1185 €1125 Contemplative moment beside a lake (20x50cm-8x20in) s.d.1860 W/C. 26-Nov-2 Bonhams, Knightsbridge #206a/R
£900 $1395 €1350 Figurers before a lake (30x48cm-12x19in) s.d.1853 W/C. 24-Sep-2 Bonhams, Knightsbridge #248/R
£1300 $2028 €1950 Scene between Barmouth and Dogelley. Scene near Capel Curig, North Wales (21x40cm-8x16in) s. one d.1870 W/C pair. 6-Nov-2 Bonhams, Chester #328 est:500-800

PEARSON, Cornelius and WAINEWRIGHT, Thomas Francis (19th C) British
Works on paper
£1100 $1826 €1650 Sheep in lakeland landscape (37x72cm-15x28in) s.d.1876 W/C. 12-Jun-3 Bonhams, New Bond Street #624/R est:1200-1800
£1400 $2310 €2030 Valley near Portmadoc (32x71cm-13x28in) s.i.d.1872 pencil W/C bodycol scratching out prov. 3-Jul-3 Christie's, Kensington #108/R est:1500-1800

PEARSON, Harry John (1872-1933) British
£260 $406 €390 Portrait of a young girl leaning against a wall (43x28cm-17x11in) s. 11-Apr-3 Keys, Aylsham #293
£600 $960 €900 Village street (20x25cm-8x10in) s. board. 11-Mar-3 Gorringes, Lewes #2346

PEARSON, Marguerite S (1898-1978) American
£897 $1400 €1346 May morning - an interior scene with two women (20x25cm-8x10in) s. board. 1-Aug-2 Eldred, East Dennis #818/R est:1200-1800
£1084 $1800 €1572 Autumn at Rockfort (51x61cm-20x24in) s. board prov. 11-Jun-3 Butterfields, San Francisco #4091c/R est:2000-3000
£2867 $4500 €4301 Andante (92x77cm-36x30in) s.d.1941. 22-Nov-2 Skinner, Boston #161/R est:6000-8000
£3019 $4800 €4529 Caller of 1816 (76x64cm-30x25in) s.i.d.1943. 4-Mar-3 Christie's, Rockefeller NY #47/R est:5000-7000
£4521 $6600 €6782 Still life with bottle (76x91cm-30x36in) s. exhib. 3-Nov-1 North East Auctions, Portsmouth #249/R

PEARSON, Peter (20th C) Irish
£676 $1054 €1000 Pigeon house from Killiney (39x48cm-15x19in) s.d.90. 26-Mar-3 James Adam, Dublin #42/R est:1000-1500

PEARSON, W A (19th C) British
Works on paper
£300 $486 €450 Nancy Lee at Queensborough (30x52cm-12x20in) s.i. W/C htd white. 21-Jan-3 Bonhams, New Bond Street #160/R

PEARSON, W H (19/20th C) British
Works on paper
£650 $988 €975 Across the bay (47x67cm-19x26in) s.i. W/C. 15-Aug-2 Bonhams, New Bond Street #279/R
£900 $1395 €1350 Turning into port (45x71cm-18x28in) s.i. W/C. 24-Sep-2 Anderson & Garland, Newcastle #328/R

PEARSON, William (19th C) American
£7595 $12000 €11393 View in New Hampshire (66x91cm-26x36in) s.d.1857 exhib. 24-Apr-3 Shannon's, Milford #115/R est:12000-18000

PEARSON, William Henry (19/20th C) British
Works on paper
£300 $468 €450 Fair weather down channel (32x52cm-13x20in) s.i. W/C. 10-Sep-2 David Duggleby, Scarborough #129

PEART, John (1945-) Australian
£232 $367 €348 Abstract (91x61cm-36x24in) board. 27-Nov-2 Deutscher-Menzies, Melbourne #190/R (A.D 650)

PEASE, David G (1932-) American
£881 $1400 €1322 Alabama jubilee (142x122cm-56x48in) s.i.d. masonite. 2-Mar-3 Toomey, Oak Park #817/R

PEBBLES, Frank M (1839-1928) American
£452 $700 €678 Monterey (41x61cm-16x24in) s. 29-Oct-2 John Moran, Pasadena #717

PECCHIO, Domenico (1712-1759) Italian
£9494 $15000 €15000 Landscape with figures (94x132cm-37x52in) 2-Dec-2 Finarte, Milan #180/R est:12000
£12414 $19738 €18000 Jacob meeting Rachel at the well (116x170cm-46x67in) 9-Mar-3 Semenzato, Venice #30/R
£13291 $20734 €21000 Lake landscape with shepherds (114x140cm-45x55in) 19-Oct-2 Semenzato, Venice #486/R est:18000-20000

PECCHIO, Domenico (attrib) (1712-1759) Italian
£17000 $26690 €25500 Washerwoman with peasants making music, amid their livestock. Peasants milking a cow, with figures (70x96cm-28x38in) pair. 10-Dec-2 Bonhams, New Bond Street #323/R est:8000-12000
£21000 $32760 €31500 Landscape with peasants by a river. Landscape with peasants treading grapes (74x94cm-29x37in) pair. 9-Apr-3 Christie's, London #106/R est:10000-15000

PECENKO, G (?) ?
Works on paper
£1277 $2068 €1800 Fishermen hauling in their nets (64x102cm-25x40in) 20-May-3 Mealy's, Castlecomer #1265/R est:1500-2000

PECHAUBES, Eugène (1890-1967) French
£651 $1022 €950 Courses, les sulkys (26x35cm-10x14in) s. 21-Apr-3 Rabourdin & Choppin de Janvry, Paris #115/R
£833 $1308 €1300 Moissons (53x65cm-21x26in) s. 15-Dec-2 Lombrail & Teucquam, Paris #5/R

PECHE, Dagobert (1887-1923) Austrian
Works on paper
£641 $994 €1000 Wallpaper design (56x59cm-22x23in) gouache. 5-Dec-2 Dorotheum, Graz #185/R

PECHE, Ernst (1885-1945) Austrian
£380 $635 €551 Tree with farm buildings beyond (54x46cm-21x18in) s. panel. 25-Jun-3 Bonhams, Bury St Edmunds #541

PECHEUX, Laurent (1729-1821) French
£33566 $56056 €48000 L'affliction d'Achille devant le depart de Briseis (110x135cm-43x53in) s.i.d.1778. 25-Jun-3 Sotheby's, Paris #46/R est:30000-40000

£74074 $120000 €111111 Diane and Endymion (262x152cm-103x60in) s.d.1761. 23-Jan-3 Sotheby's, New York #92/R est:150000-200000

PECHSTEIN, Max (1881-1955) German

£5696 $9000 €9000 Female nude (38x28cm-15x11in) s.i.d.1911 lithograph prov. 30-Nov-2 Villa Grisebach, Berlin #172/R est:15000-17000
£10127 $16000 €16000 Cornstooks (49x62cm-19x24in) s.d.1931 s.i.d. verso bodycol. 30-Nov-2 Villa Grisebach, Berlin #242/R est:18000-22000
£14493 $23768 €20000 Still life of flowers - red roses in dish (51x61cm-20x24in) s.d.1948 canvas on board prov.exhib. 29-May-3 Lempertz, Koln #849/R est:30000
£16667 $25833 €26000 Lotte sleeping (34x44cm-13x17in) init.d.1909 tempera prov. 6-Dec-2 Ketterer, Munich #41/R est:20000-30000
£17500 $29225 €25375 Aufholen des bootes - hauling the boats (32x48cm-13x19in) mono. s.i.verso canvasboard prov. 24-Jun-3 Sotheby's, London #187/R est:25000-35000
£24000 $37440 €36000 Vor der ausfahrt - Before leaving harbour (89x119cm-35x47in) s.d.1929 i.verso prov. 9-Oct-2 Sotheby's, London #35/R est:30000-40000
£40373 $65000 €60560 Calla (97x68cm-38x27in) s.d.1931 s.i.verso prov.exhib.lit. 7-May-3 Sotheby's, New York #360/R est:80000-120000
£42000 $65520 €63000 Kirschblute - Cherry blossom (80x100cm-31x39in) s.d.1929 i.verso prov. 9-Oct-2 Sotheby's, London #34/R est:30000-40000
£61594 $101014 €85000 Foggy morning, Bornholm (70x80cm-28x31in) s.d. s.i.d.1924 verso prov.exhib. 30-May-3 Villa Grisebach, Berlin #42/R est:90000-120000
£208861 $325823 €330000 Monterosso al Mare (99x95cm-39x37in) mono.d.1913 prov.lit. 18-Oct-2 Dr Fritz Nagel, Stuttgart #582/R est:360000
£240000 $374400 €360000 Sonnenuntergang - sunset (101x80cm-40x31in) s. painted 1922 prov.exhib. 9-Oct-2 Sotheby's, London #31/R est:250000-350000
£700000 $1141000 €1050000 Sommer (70x80cm-28x31in) mono.d.1910 prov.exhib. 3-Feb-3 Christie's, London #9/R est:70000-1000000

Prints

£1887 $2943 €3000 The wave II (25x26cm-10x10in) s.mono.d.1912 drypoint etching aquatint. 11-Oct-2 Winterberg, Heidelberg #1583/R est:4200
£1923 $3038 €3000 Shooting a bird for the feast (22x26cm-9x10in) s.d.1911 col woodcut. 14-Nov-2 Neumeister, Munich #665/R est:2000-2200
£1944 $3092 €2800 Two women (17x22cm-7x9in) mono.d. woodcut. 5-May-3 Ketterer, Munich #941/R est:1200-1500
£2013 $3140 €3200 Getandel (33x39cm-13x15in) s.d.1923 num.44/51 drypoint etching. 9-Oct-2 Sotheby's, London #506/R est:4000-5500
£2055 $3205 €3000 Acrobats III (22x27cm-9x11in) s. col woodcut. 11-Apr-3 Winterberg, Heidelberg #1464/R est:4400
£2055 $3205 €3000 After bathing (30x19cm-12x7in) s.d. etching drypoint. 11-Apr-3 Winterberg, Heidelberg #1468/R est:4200
£2500 $3875 €3750 Klohnende fischer (40x49cm-16x19in) s.num.41/51 col woodcut. 5-Dec-2 Sotheby's, London #167/R est:3500-4000
£2516 $3925 €4000 Fish head IV (22x20cm-9x8in) s.d.1911 woodcut. 11-Oct-2 Winterberg, Heidelberg #1578 est:4800
£2564 $4051 €4000 Rays of sunshine (50x38cm-20x15in) s.d.1923 W/C over lithograph. 14-Nov-2 Neumeister, Munich #668/R est:3000-3200
£2639 $4196 €3800 After swimming (30x19cm-12x7in) s.d. drypoint brush etching. 5-May-3 Ketterer, Munich #940/R est:1000-1500
£3333 $5467 €4600 Smoking Swiss man (50x40cm-20x16in) s. col woodcut. 29-May-3 Lempertz, Koln #861/R est:6000
£3380 $5611 €4800 Fishermen on the beach (50x32cm-20x13in) s.mono.i.d. col lithograph. 14-Jun-3 Hauswedell & Nolte, Hamburg #1499/R est:4000
£4000 $6240 €6000 Klohnende Fischer (40x49cm-16x19in) s.num.49/51 col woodcut. 10-Oct-2 Sotheby's, London #158/R est:5000-7000
£4225 $7014 €6000 Conversation (40x32cm-16x13in) s.d. col woodcut. 14-Jun-3 Hauswedell & Nolte, Hamburg #1507/R est:8000
£4892 $8023 €6800 Bright sunshine (52x37cm-20x15in) s.i.d. col lithograph. 6-Jun-3 Ketterer, Munich #66/R est:6500-7500
£5797 $9507 €8000 Carneval IV (28x38cm-11x15in) s.i.d. lithograph prov. 30-May-3 Villa Grisebach, Berlin #27/R est:8000-10000
£6056 $10054 €8600 Kneeling nude with dish (37x30cm-15x12in) mono.i. woodcut. 14-Jun-3 Hauswedell & Nolte, Hamburg #1503/R est:5000
£9615 $14904 €15000 Dance V (27x32cm-11x13in) s.i.d. col lithograph prov. 4-Dec-2 Lempertz, Koln #974/R est:12000
£11806 $18771 €17000 Head with necklace (35x21cm-14x8in) s.d. col lithograph. 5-May-3 Ketterer, Munich #939/R est:10000-15000
£11950 $18642 €19000 Im harem (37x49cm-15x19in) init.i.d.1909 lithograph. 9-Oct-2 Sotheby's, London #505/R est:20000-28000

Works on paper

£1087 $1783 €1500 Incoming boat (30x41cm-12x16in) s.d.1949 chk prov. 29-May-3 Lempertz, Koln #856/R
£1195 $1864 €1900 Two windmills (42x32cm-17x13in) mono. 11-Oct-2 Winterberg, Heidelberg #1577/R est:3800
£1449 $2377 €2000 Man's head (60x43cm-24x17in) s.d. Indian ink brush. 31-May-3 Villa Grisebach, Berlin #657/R est:2400-2800
£2536 $4159 €3500 Two islanders (20x26cm-8x10in) mono.d.1913 Indian ink. 31-May-3 Villa Grisebach, Berlin #178/R est:3000-4000
£2642 $4121 €4200 Alley with house and telegraph wires (46x56cm-18x22in) s.d.1917 brush col ink prov. 9-Oct-2 Sotheby's, London #135/R est:6000-9000
£2756 $4272 €4300 Woman wearing pearl necklace (47x36cm-19x14in) mono.d.1918 pencil w/C. 4-Dec-2 Lempertz, Koln #970/R est:5000
£2911 $4600 €4600 Landscape with farmstead (44x58cm-17x23in) s.d.1911 Indian ink brush. 30-Nov-2 Villa Grisebach, Berlin #237/R est:3500-4500
£3191 $5170 €4500 Peasants reaping (40x59cm-16x23in) s.d. Indian ink bodycol over pencil. 24-May-3 Van Ham, Cologne #455/R est:5000
£3261 $5348 €4500 Stone carriers (40x57cm-16x22in) s.d.1925 W/C col chks Indian ink prov. 29-May-3 Lempertz, Koln #852/R est:3500
£3333 $5167 €5200 Standing female nude (60x45cm-24x18in) mono.i.d.1910 Indian ink pen brush W/C. 4-Dec-2 Lempertz, Koln #968/R est:6500
£3623 $5942 €5000 Sunflowers in garden (34x26cm-13x10in) s.d.1948 pastel chk Indian ink brush prov. 29-May-3 Lempertz, Koln #854/R est:4000
£3803 $6313 €5400 Female nude (30x33cm-12x13in) mono.d. chk W/C. 14-Jun-3 Hauswedell & Nolte, Hamburg #1495/R est:8000
£3846 $5962 €6000 Nude X (39x40cm-15x16in) mono. i. verso Indian ink. 4-Dec-2 Lempertz, Koln #967/R est:5000
£4525 $7059 €7150 Neptune fountain, Florence (16x20cm-6x8in) mono. col chk graphite prov. 18-Oct-2 Dr Fritz Nagel, Stuttgart #580/R est:11800
£5063 $8000 €8000 Landscape with ducks (34x43cm-13x17in) mono.d.1918 chk W/C. 30-Nov-2 Bassenge, Berlin #6560/R est:10000
£5128 $7949 €8000 Sailing boat off the coast (20x30cm-8x12in) mono.d. col chk brush. 7-Dec-2 Hauswedell & Nolte, Hamburg #962/R est:6000
£5769 $8942 €9000 Nude (47x37cm-19x15in) mono.i.d. graphite W/C. 7-Dec-2 Hauswedell & Nolte, Hamburg #964/R est:10000
£5797 $9507 €8000 Boat (9x14cm-4x6in) s.i. verso pen col crayons postcard prov. 30-May-3 Villa Grisebach, Berlin #16/R est:7000-8000
£6159 $10101 €8500 Neptune fountain in Florence (16x20cm-6x8in) mono. col wax chk over pencil. 31-May-3 Villa Grisebach, Berlin #172/R est:8500-9500
£7051 $10929 €11000 Still life with elephant (38x54cm-15x21in) s.d.1947 W/C brush ink dr prov. 6-Dec-2 Ketterer, Munich #93/R est:11000-13000
£7639 $12146 €11000 Bathers (16x20cm-6x8in) mono.d. W/C over pencil. 5-May-3 Ketterer, Munich #942/R est:10000-15000
£7692 $11923 €12000 Mountain landscape - Lake Geneva (50x60cm-20x24in) s.d.1925 W/C. 4-Dec-2 Lempertz, Koln #973/R est:12000-14000
£8333 $12917 €13000 Sand dunes on the seashore (28x37cm-11x15in) s.d.1945 chk dr prov. 6-Dec-2 Ketterer, Munich #94/R est:14000-16000
£8333 $13667 €11500 Still life of flowers (14x9cm-6x4in) s.i. verso pen W/C postcard prov. 30-May-3 Villa Grisebach, Berlin #17/R est:8000-12000
£11538 $17885 €18000 Alley with house and telephone wires (46x57cm-18x22in) s.d.1917 brush col ink prov. 6-Dec-2 Ketterer, Munich #51/R est:15000-18000
£11538 $17885 €18000 Vineyard by Lake Geneva (48x58cm-19x23in) s.d.1925 W/C prov. 6-Dec-2 Ketterer, Munich #88/R est:18000-22000
£12658 $20000 €20000 Sunset on the Mole in Leba (50x65cm-20x26in) s.d.1935 gouache. 30-Nov-2 Villa Grisebach, Berlin #224/R est:18000-22000
£12692 $19673 €19800 House with thatched roof (29x42cm-11x17in) s.i.d.1935 chk board. 6-Dec-2 Michael Zeller, Lindau #879/R est:19800
£12975 $20500 €20500 Sunrise over the sea (60x77cm-24x30in) s.d.1944 W/C prov. 30-Nov-2 Villa Grisebach, Berlin #223/R est:25000-30000
£16000 $24640 €24000 Fischer - fishermen (52x42cm-20x17in) s.d.1922 W/C pencil prov. 22-Oct-2 Sotheby's, London #217/R est:8000-12000
£17610 $27472 €28000 Sitzende negerin art - seated black woman - nude (45x33cm-18x13in) mono. W/C over pencil executed c.1910. 9-Oct-2 Sotheby's, London #125/R est:40000-50000
£18987 $30000 €30000 Reclining figure (49x58cm-19x23in) s.d.1922 W/C over crayon prov. 29-Nov-2 Villa Grisebach, Berlin #37/R est:30000-40000
£27778 $44167 €40000 Seated female nude (37x28cm-15x11in) mono.d.18 W/C ink. 5-May-3 Ketterer, Munich #945/R est:10000-20000

PECHUEL-LOESCHE, William (1885-1959) German

£786 $1226 €1179 At the piano (100x125cm-39x49in) s.d.20. 6-Nov-2 Dobiaschofsky, Bern #875/R (S.FR 1800)

PECK, John (18/19th C) British

Works on paper

£250 $393 €375 View of Bangor ferry (31x43cm-12x17in) s.i.d.1808 verso W/C. 25-Nov-2 Bonhams, Chester #890

PECK, Sheldon (1797-1868) American

£4452 $6500 €6678 Portrait of a man in white stock and tie (76x61cm-30x24in) panel prov.lit. 3-Nov-1 North East Auctions, Portsmouth #741/R est:6000-9000
£11180 $18000 €16770 Portrait of a woman in ruffled bonnet and lace collar (24x16cm-9x6in) panel exhib.lit. 16-Jan-3 Christie's, Rockefeller NY #371/R est:20000-30000
£360248 $580000 €540372 Portrait of Frances Almira Millener and Fanny Root Millener (30x27cm-12x11in) panel prov.exhib. 16-Jan-3 Christie's, Rockefeller NY #356/R est:200000-400000

PECKARY, Karl (1848-1896) Austrian
Works on paper
£704 $1134 €1000 Crown Prince Rudolf (44x36cm-17x14in) s. W/C paper on board. 7-May-3 Dorotheum, Vienna #189/R

PECKHAM, Deacon Robert (attrib) (1785-1877) American
£10274 $15000 €15411 Portrait of a girl seated on a classical window seat (81x64cm-32x25in) panel lit. 3-Nov-1 North East Auctions, Portsmouth #779/R est:15000-20000
£13699 $20000 €20549 Portrait of a boy on a stool beside a cat (79x61cm-31x24in) panel lit. 3-Nov-1 North East Auctions, Portsmouth #778/R est:20000-25000

PECRON, G (?) ?
Sculpture
£1465 $2285 €2300 Buste de femme (62x30cm-24x12in) pat bronze. 10-Nov-2 Deauville, France #40/R

PECRUS, Charles (1826-1907) French
£1781 $2796 €2600 Artist at work (19x14cm-7x6in) s. panel. 15-Apr-3 Sotheby's, Amsterdam #75/R est:2000-3000
£1824 $2827 €2900 Reading (32x24cm-13x9in) s. panel. 6-Oct-2 Livinec, Gaudcheau & Jezequel, Rennes #73/R
£2000 $3200 €3000 Dancing lesson (31x39cm-12x15in) s.d.1869 panel. 7-Jan-3 Bonhams, Knightsbridge #251/R est:2000-3000
£2041 $3245 €3000 L'instant musical (28x36cm-11x14in) s.d.1860. 19-Mar-3 Hotel des Ventes Mosan, Brussels #178 est:3400-3600
£2283 $3562 €3425 Artist presenting his work (24x18cm-9x7in) s.s.d.61 panel. 28-Mar-3 Koller, Zurich #3140/R est:5000-7000 (S.FR 5000)
£4487 $6821 €7000 Sortie de la Touque entre Deauville et Trouville (31x25cm-12x10in) s. paper on cardboard lit. 16-Aug-2 Deauville, France #82/R est:6000

PECSI, Janos (19/20th C) Hungarian
£376 $584 €545 Budding roses (48x68cm-19x27in) s.d.1913 card. 9-Dec-2 Mu Terem Galeria, Budapest #50/R est:130000 (H.F 140000)

PECZELY, Anton (1891-?) Hungarian
£350 $532 €525 Amusing tale (61x80cm-24x31in) s. 29-Aug-2 Christie's, Kensington #45
£616 $962 €900 In bazaar (27x40cm-11x16in) s. board lit. 10-Apr-3 Allgauer, Kempten #2926/R
£1034 $1571 €1551 Arabian men on a terrace, town in background (60x80cm-24x31in) s. 27-Aug-2 Rasmussen, Copenhagen #1668/R est:12000-15000 (D.KR 12000)
£1233 $1923 €1800 Oriental market stall with figures (40x50cm-16x20in) s. 10-Apr-3 Allgauer, Kempten #2927/R est:1800

PEDDER, John (1850-1929) British
Works on paper
£300 $474 €450 Thames at Windsor (24x45cm-9x18in) s.d.1887 W/C. 26-Nov-2 Bonhams, Knightsbridge #245/R

PEDERROLI, P (19th C) Italian
£1769 $2812 €2600 Les seducteurs (87x65cm-34x26in) s.d.92. 24-Mar-3 Bernaerts, Antwerp #4a/R est:1250-1500

PEDERSEN, Carl-Henning (1913-1993) Danish
£974 $1509 €1461 Composition with bird (25x29cm-10x11in) painted 1944. 1-Oct-2 Rasmussen, Copenhagen #64/R (D.KR 11500)
£10161 $15749 €15242 Blue enchantment (96x89cm-38x35in) init.d.47 s.d.1947 stretcher lit.prov. 1-Oct-2 Rasmussen, Copenhagen #89/R est:125000-150000 (D.KR 120000)
£10963 $18308 €15896 Blue figure composition (120x80cm-47x31in) s.i.d.Juli 1997 verso. 17-Jun-3 Rasmussen, Copenhagen #7/R est:150000 (D.KR 115000)
£12797 $20347 €19196 Evening by the sea (47x59cm-19x23in) exhib.prov. 26-Feb-3 Kunsthallen, Copenhagen #31/R est:175000 (D.KR 140000)
£24493 $38209 €36740 White suns - composition (89x97cm-35x38in) s.verso painted 1948 exhib. 18-Sep-2 Kunsthallen, Copenhagen #64/R est:250000 (D.KR 290000)
Sculpture
£1317 $2054 €1976 Figure (27cm-11in) init.num.2/35 pat.bronze. 5-Aug-2 Rasmussen, Vejle #342/R est:10000-15000 (D.KR 15500)
Works on paper
£305 $509 €442 Composition with birds (29x21cm-11x8in) init.d.20-12-1998 Indian ink prov. 17-Jun-3 Rasmussen, Copenhagen #159 (D.KR 3200)
£343 $535 €515 Evening landscape (40x51cm-16x20in) init.d.1953 s.d.1953 verso W/C. 11-Nov-2 Rasmussen, Vejle #122/R (D.KR 4000)
£640 $1017 €960 Fantasy animal (21x28cm-8x11in) init.d.43 Indian ink. 26-Feb-3 Kunsthallen, Copenhagen #60 (D.KR 7000)
£746 $1187 €1119 Outburst by the threatened (77x56cm-30x22in) s.i.d.1987 W/C. 29-Apr-3 Kunsthallen, Copenhagen #23/R (D.KR 8000)
£1117 $1777 €1676 Fantasy animal (45x34cm-18x13in) init.d.1990 W/C. 10-Mar-3 Rasmussen, Vejle #721/R est:12000-15000 (D.KR 12000)
£1351 $2108 €2027 Bird in flight over town (35x46cm-14x18in) init.d.1957 W/C thin canvas. 18-Sep-2 Kunsthallen, Copenhagen #26/R est:18000 (D.KR 16000)
£1737 $2761 €2606 Fantasy creatures (28x40cm-11x16in) init.d.46 crayon exhib. 26-Feb-3 Kunsthallen, Copenhagen #1/R est:12000 (D.KR 19000)
£1862 $2961 €2793 Mask composition (50x38cm-20x15in) init.d.1953 W/C en grisaille. 10-Mar-3 Rasmussen, Vejle #772/R est:20000-25000 (D.KR 20000)
£1943 $3030 €2915 Creatures from heaven (28x35cm-11x14in) init.d.40 crayons. 18-Sep-2 Kunsthallen, Copenhagen #146/R est:25000 (D.KR 23000)
£1952 $3084 €2928 Composition with birds (29x22cm-11x9in) init.d.1941 s.verso W/C Indian ink back of wallpaper prov. 1-Apr-3 Rasmussen, Copenhagen #104/R est:20000 (D.KR 21000)
£2153 $3338 €3230 Fantasy creatures (78x56cm-31x22in) s.i.d.1974 W/C gouache exhib. 4-Dec-2 Kunsthallen, Copenhagen #36/R est:35000 (D.KR 25000)
£4064 $6300 €6096 Bird (23x37cm-9x15in) init.d.41 W/C chk prov.exhib.lit. 1-Oct-2 Rasmussen, Copenhagen #71/R est:30000-40000 (D.KR 48000)

PEDERSEN, Finn (1944-) Danish
£296 $459 €444 Figure composition (70x60cm-28x24in) s.d.80. 1-Oct-2 Rasmussen, Copenhagen #156 (D.KR 3500)
£297 $470 €446 Figure composition (73x50cm-29x20in) s.d.73. 1-Apr-3 Rasmussen, Copenhagen #249 (D.KR 3200)
£339 $525 €509 Red and black figure composition (65x54cm-26x21in) s.d.77. 1-Oct-2 Rasmussen, Copenhagen #251/R (D.KR 4000)
£347 $552 €500 Composition (80x65cm-31x26in) s.d.1994 verso. 29-Apr-3 Campo, Vlaamse Kaai #247
£350 $543 €525 Komposition (97x80cm-38x31in) s.verso. 5-Dec-2 Christie's, Kensington #238/R
£372 $587 €558 Big brother (61x72cm-24x28in) s.d.71 verso. 1-Apr-3 Rasmussen, Copenhagen #373/R (D.KR 4000)
£381 $591 €572 Midsummer Blues (100x81cm-39x32in) s.verso. 1-Oct-2 Rasmussen, Copenhagen #253/R (D.KR 4500)
£423 $656 €635 Dr Strangelove (100x80cm-39x31in) s.d.85 d.april 84 verso. 1-Oct-2 Rasmussen, Copenhagen #159/R (D.KR 5000)
£432 $691 €600 Composition (65x54cm-26x21in) s. s.d.94 verso. 17-May-3 De Vuyst, Lokeren #287
£540 $863 €750 Composition (73x60cm-29x24in) s. s.d.94 verso. 17-May-3 De Vuyst, Lokeren #286
£550 $853 €825 My castle in Italy (97x80cm-38x31in) s. s.i.verso. 5-Dec-2 Christie's, Kensington #236/R
£641 $1006 €1000 Faces (75x100cm-30x39in) s. 25-Nov-2 Glerum, Amsterdam #355/R
£972 $1546 €1400 Composition (100x130cm-39x51in) s.d.1988 verso. 29-Apr-3 Campo, Vlaamse Kaai #246/R
£1500 $2505 €2175 Untitled (96x129cm-38x51in) s.d.79. 24-Jun-3 Sotheby's, Olympia #88/R est:2000-3000

PEDERSEN, Holger Topp (1868-1938) Danish
£272 $424 €408 Coastal landscape with sailing vessels and birds in flight (66x153cm-26x60in) s.d.92. 5-Aug-2 Rasmussen, Vejle #2463 (D.KR 3200)

PEDERSEN, Hugo Vilfred (1870-1959) Danish
£259 $396 €389 Man with lantern (73x56cm-29x22in) s. 24-Aug-2 Rasmussen, Havnen #2040/R (D.KR 3000)
£279 $444 €419 Young man from the Island of Madura near Java (39x26cm-15x10in) s. 5-Mar-3 Rasmussen, Copenhagen #1807 (D.KR 3000)
£279 $444 €419 Shinto Priest from the Nikko Temple in Japan (40x27cm-16x11in) s. 5-Mar-3 Rasmussen, Copenhagen #1812/R (D.KR 3000)
£287 $465 €416 View towards an Indonesian village with houses, palmtrees and goat (70x100cm-28x39in) s. 26-May-3 Rasmussen, Copenhagen #1556/R (D.KR 3000)
£300 $475 €450 Woman from Java (41x31cm-16x12in) s.i. exhib. 13-Nov-2 Kunsthallen, Copenhagen #18 (D.KR 3500)
£326 $518 €489 Princess from the Mysore court (39x27cm-15x11in) s. 5-Mar-3 Rasmussen, Copenhagen #1814/R (D.KR 3500)
£350 $560 €525 Entrance to a temple (37x29cm-15x11in) s. 13-Jan-3 Rasmussen, Vejle #262/R (D.KR 4000)
£419 $666 €629 Hindu woman from Sumatra (39x26cm-15x10in) s. 5-Mar-3 Rasmussen, Copenhagen #1806 (D.KR 4500)
£482 $771 €723 Indian soldier on horseback, palace in background (42x33cm-17x13in) s. 13-Jan-3 Rasmussen, Vejle #264/R (D.KR 5500)

£484 $770 €726 Coastal landscape with figures (46x57cm-18x22in) s. 10-Mar-3 Rasmussen, Vejle #446 (D.KR 5200)
£559 $888 €839 Chinese street scene with rickshaw (55x73cm-22x29in) s. 5-Mar-3 Rasmussen, Copenhagen #1808/R (D.KR 6000)
£559 $888 €839 King Shamsuddin Altamash's grave in Kutab (62x39cm-24x15in) s. 5-Mar-3 Rasmussen, Copenhagen #1813/R (D.KR 6000)
£560 $857 €840 Bergen at night (95x108cm-37x43in) s.i.d.98. 24-Aug-2 Rasmussen, Havnen #2113/R (D.KR 6500)
£732 $1113 €1098 Still life of birds and vegetables (120x87cm-47x34in) s. 27-Aug-2 Rasmussen, Copenhagen #1820/R (D.KR 8500)
£1000 $1580 €1500 Figures on a bridge, south east Asia (69x102cm-27x40in) s. 15-Nov-2 Sotheby's, London #30/R est:1200-1800
£1258 $1950 €2000 Cannibal Borneo (39x26cm-15x10in) s.i. 29-Oct-2 Dorotheum, Vienna #147/R est:2200-2400
£1258 $1950 €2000 Portrait of noble woman from Siam (39x26cm-15x10in) s.i. verso. 29-Oct-2 Dorotheum, Vienna #148/R est:2200-2400
£1277 $2017 €1916 View of Bergen at night (94x108cm-37x43in) s.d.98. 2-Dec-2 Rasmussen, Copenhagen #1228/R est:20000 (D.KR 15000)
£1500 $2370 €2250 Rickshaw accident (170x121cm-67x48in) s. 14-Nov-2 Christie's, Kensington #283/R est:2000-3000
£25316 $40000 €37974 At the baths (89x119cm-35x47in) s. prov. 23-Apr-3 Christie's, Rockefeller NY #13/R est:30000-40000

PEDERSEN, Ole (1856-1898) Danish
£257 $401 €386 Coastal landscape, autumn (53x77cm-21x30in) s.d.94 exhib. 11-Nov-2 Rasmussen, Vejle #675/R (D.KR 3000)
£280 $445 €420 Landscape with cows and milkmaid (50x46cm-20x18in) s.d.85. 5-May-3 Rasmussen, Vejle #716/R (D.KR 3000)
£380 $593 €570 Southern town scene with donkey (45x55cm-18x22in) s. 23-Sep-2 Rasmussen, Vejle #189/R (D.KR 4500)

PEDERSEN, Thorolf (1858-1942) Danish
£343 $535 €515 Seascape with sailing ship (30x54cm-12x21in) s. 11-Nov-2 Rasmussen, Vejle #605/R (D.KR 4000)
£745 $1184 €1118 Interior scene with woman reading letter (52x46cm-20x18in) s.d.1888. 5-Mar-3 Rasmussen, Copenhagen #1556/R (D.KR 8000)

PEDERSEN, Viggo (1854-1926) Danish
£255 $403 €383 Fields by the sea (29x38cm-11x15in) s. 2-Dec-2 Rasmussen, Copenhagen #1252 (D.KR 3000)
£293 $465 €440 The road to Pescasolido (31x24cm-12x9in) s.i.d.1883. 26-Feb-3 Kunsthallen, Copenhagen #530 (D.KR 3200)
£299 $460 €449 Landscape with view towards church (36x45cm-14x18in) s.d.1905. 4-Sep-2 Kunsthallen, Copenhagen #174 (D.KR 3500)
£326 $518 €489 Summer morning (64x94cm-25x37in) s.d.1902 panel. 5-Mar-3 Rasmussen, Copenhagen #1622 (D.KR 3500)
£373 $593 €560 View across houses and trees near the sea (63x86cm-25x34in) s. 5-May-3 Rasmussen, Vejle #689/R (D.KR 4000)
£383 $620 €575 Glittering sea, Kullen (37x60cm-15x24in) s.d.1906 cardboard. 21-May-3 Museumsbygningen, Copenhagen #13 (D.KR 4000)
£383 $620 €555 Summer's day by the sea (47x72cm-19x28in) s. prov. 26-May-3 Rasmussen, Copenhagen #1414/R (D.KR 4000)
£386 $610 €579 Summer landscape with trees by water (41x61cm-16x24in) s. panel. 13-Nov-2 Kunsthallen, Copenhagen #44 (D.KR 4500)
£410 $631 €615 Evening sun over the Volterra, Italy (54x71cm-21x28in) s. 4-Sep-2 Kunsthallen, Copenhagen #44/R (D.KR 4800)
£420 $667 €630 Gravel grave at Skamstrup (27x48cm-11x19in) s. 29-Apr-3 Kunsthallen, Copenhagen #519 (D.KR 4500)
£448 $712 €672 Roskilde Cathedral (38x54cm-15x21in) s.d.1873. 5-May-3 Rasmussen, Vejle #463/R (D.KR 4800)
£465 $734 €698 Old farm at Fjellersborg (56x77cm-22x30in) s. 5-Apr-3 Rasmussen, Havnen #2016/R (D.KR 5000)
£468 $740 €702 Winter landscape with large tree and house, Dyssen, Skramstrup (45x63cm-18x25in) s. d.1884 verso. 27-Nov-2 Museumsbygningen, Copenhagen #73/R (D.KR 5500)
£524 $817 €786 Summer landscape with cattle by river, Denmark (58x83cm-23x33in) s. 23-Sep-2 Rasmussen, Vejle #78/R (D.KR 6200)
£593 $961 €890 Interior scene with women doing needlework (25x20cm-10x8in) init. 21-May-3 Museumsbygningen, Copenhagen #67 (D.KR 6200)
£595 $928 €893 Summer landscape with women and children picking elder flowers (42x52cm-17x20in) s.i.d.1889. 5-Aug-2 Rasmussen, Vejle #2280 (D.KR 7000)
£621 $1005 €932 Woman picking up cloth (31x25cm-12x10in) s.d.1887. 25-Jan-3 Rasmussen, Havnen #2083/R (D.KR 7000)
£745 $1184 €1118 Sunset over the ocean (45x63cm-18x25in) s. 10-Mar-3 Rasmussen, Vejle #335/R (D.KR 8000)
£766 $1210 €1149 Field near Sora with mountains in background (40x61cm-16x24in) s.i.d.Juli-August 1884 panel. 2-Dec-2 Rasmussen, Copenhagen #1478/R (D.KR 9000)
£780 $1271 €1131 Harvesting at sunset (32x41cm-13x16in) s. board. 16-Jul-3 Sotheby's, Olympia #142/R
£861 $1309 €1292 Silly summer landscape with trees and cattle (67x78cm-26x31in) s. cardboard. 28-Aug-2 Museumsbygningen, Copenhagen #100/R (D.KR 10000)
£1117 $1777 €1676 Interior scene with young woman having piano lesson (70x58cm-28x23in) s.d.1903. 10-Mar-3 Rasmussen, Vejle #42/R est:15000 (D.KR 12000)
£1244 $2015 €1804 Cliffs by the sea, Tidsvilde (124x152cm-49x60in) s.d.1901. 24-May-3 Rasmussen, Havnen #2164/R est:7000-10000 (D.KR 13000)
£1550 $2357 €2325 Women on a terrace in Sora (37x60cm-15x24in) s. panel. 27-Aug-2 Rasmussen, Copenhagen #1441/R est:10000-15000 (D.KR 18000)
£1712 $2756 €2568 Figures in rowing boat on small lake (72x87cm-28x34in) s.d.1884. 22-Feb-3 Rasmussen, Havnen #2058/R est:7000-10000 (D.KR 19000)
£1955 $3109 €2933 Landscape with harvesters, Frederikskilde near Tystrup Lake (58x89cm-23x35in) exhib. 5-Mar-3 Rasmussen, Copenhagen #1595/R est:20000-25000 (D.KR 21000)
£4307 $6546 €6461 Tea - two girlfriends drinking tea (53x56cm-21x22in) s.d.1916 exhib. 27-Aug-2 Rasmussen, Copenhagen #1506/R est:25000-35000 (D.KR 50000)
£6089 $9499 €9134 The baby is about to be washed (65x95cm-26x37in) s. exhib. 11-Nov-2 Rasmussen, Vejle #542/R est:80000 (D.KR 71000)

Works on paper
£426 $672 €639 The Annunciation (43x91cm-17x36in) i.verso crayon oil htd gold prov. 2-Dec-2 Rasmussen, Copenhagen #1779/R (D.KR 5000)

PEDERSEN, Vilhelm (1820-1859) Danish
£342 $550 €513 Winter afternoon chores (43x56cm-17x22in) prov. 19-Feb-3 Doyle, New York #43

PEDERSEN, Villy Daugaard (1915-1994) Danish
£296 $459 €444 Quartet (91x63cm-36x25in) s.d.1965 verso plywood exhib.prov. 1-Oct-2 Rasmussen, Copenhagen #181 (D.KR 3500)

PEDERSON, Hjalmar (1891-1977) Norwegian
£467 $719 €701 Landscape from Northern Norway (61x75cm-24x30in) s. 28-Oct-2 Blomqvist, Lysaker #1219 (N.KR 5500)

PEDON, Bartolomeo (1665-1732) Italian
£5696 $9000 €9000 Landscape covered in snow (58x72cm-23x28in) 27-Nov-2 Finarte, Milan #67/R est:9000-10000

PEDRETTI, Gian (1926-) Swiss

Sculpture
£1717 $2712 €2576 Hommage to Cezanne (78cm-31in) bronze. 29-Nov-2 Zofingen, Switzerland #2222/R est:5000 (S.FR 4000)
£1717 $2712 €2576 Rope dancer (44cm-17in) bronze. 29-Nov-2 Zofingen, Switzerland #2223/R est:5000 (S.FR 4000)

PEDRETTI, Turo (1896-1964) Swiss
£2830 $4528 €4245 December morning (49x60cm-19x24in) s.i.d. verso board. 17-Mar-3 Philippe Schuler, Zurich #4546/R est:5000-7000 (S.FR 6000)
£11354 $17825 €17031 Hommage a E L Kirchner (105x85cm-41x33in) s.i.d.1961 s.i. verso prov.exhib. 25-Nov-2 Sotheby's, Zurich #143/R est:15000-20000 (S.FR 26000)

Works on paper
£308 $459 €462 Washday (31x41cm-12x16in) mono. W/C. 25-Jun-2 Koller, Zurich #6710a (S.FR 700)
£386 $610 €579 Colourful mountain landscape (32x42cm-13x17in) mono. W/C. 29-Nov-2 Zofingen, Switzerland #3025 (S.FR 900)

PEEL, James (1811-1906) British
£375 $604 €563 Carting timber (23x38cm-9x15in) s. 9-May-3 Mallams, Oxford #128/R
£400 $620 €600 River landscape, with figures, boat and boat house (25x37cm-10x15in) s. 24-Sep-2 Anderson & Garland, Newcastle #427/R
£500 $790 €750 Coastal scene, a woman with a donkey on a pathway beside a bay with figures and boat (51x76cm-20x30in) s. 18-Dec-2 John Nicholson, Haslemere #1277/R
£806 $1274 €1209 Rydal Mere (41x66cm-16x26in) s. prov. 18-Nov-2 Waddingtons, Toronto #104/R est:1500-2000 (C.D 2000)
£823 $1276 €1235 Horse cart on a riverside track (51x86cm-20x34in) s.d.1882. 3-Dec-2 Ritchie, Toronto #3046/R est:2500-3000 (C.D 2000)
£3000 $4920 €4500 Figures on a track, near Huddersfield (36x53cm-14x21in) prov. 29-May-3 Christie's, Kensington #182/R est:4000-6000

PEEL, James (attrib) (1811-1906) British
£1500 $2325 €2250 Quiet retreat, fisherman carrying his rod (36x61cm-14x24in) 25-Sep-2 John Nicholson, Haslemere #1023/R est:1500-2000
£1800 $2952 €2700 Shepherd with his flock in a lake landscape (30x51cm-12x20in) s. 29-May-3 Christie's, Kensington #107/R est:2000-3000

PEEL, Paul (1861-1892) Canadian
£4221 $6500 €6332 Mother and child in an interior (30x41cm-12x16in) s. painted c.1888. 8-Sep-2 Treadway Gallery, Cincinnati #528/R est:10000-20000
£6584 $10206 €9876 Young child in a sailor suit (41x32cm-16x13in) s. 3-Dec-2 Joyner, Toronto #173/R est:6000-8000 (C.D 16000)
£6996 $10844 €10494 Une etude (46x38cm-18x15in) s.i.d.83 prov.lit. 3-Dec-2 Joyner, Toronto #38/R est:10000-15000 (C.D 17000)
£16461 $25514 €24692 Boy fishing in a village stream (56x35cm-22x14in) s.d.1884 indis i.verso prov.lit. 3-Dec-2 Joyner, Toronto #43/R est:50000-60000 (C.D 40000)
£22222 $36444 €33333 Pont-Aven, France (40x32cm-16x13in) s.d.1884 masonite prov. 27-May-3 Sotheby's, Toronto #76/R est:50000-70000 (C.D 50000)
£26210 $41411 €39315 Before the bath (27x20cm-11x8in) init. panel prov.lit. 18-Nov-2 Sotheby's, Toronto #53/R est:50000-70000 (C.D 65000)

PEELE, James (1847-1905) Australian
£357 $564 €536 Gathering firewood near the ford (45x29cm-18x11in) s.d.1896 board. 18-Nov-2 Joel, Victoria #375 est:1000-1200 (A.D 1000)
£392 $611 €588 Waterfall scene (75x43cm-30x17in) s.d.1901. 7-Nov-2 International Art Centre, Auckland #115/R est:1500-3000 (NZ.D 1250)
£421 $657 €632 George Sound after rain (35x60cm-14x24in) s. 27-Mar-3 International Art Centre, Auckland #154/R (NZ.D 1200)
£1404 $2189 €2106 Otira Gorge, West Coast (60x91cm-24x36in) s.d.1898. 27-Mar-3 International Art Centre, Auckland #122/R est:3000-5000 (NZ.D 4000)

PEELE, John Thomas (1822-1897) British
£3900 $6006 €5850 Mother and child feeding chickens in a farmyard (56x86cm-22x34in) s.d.1883. 3-Sep-2 Gorringes, Lewes #2197 est:2000-3000
£9740 $15000 €14610 Feeding the pets (102x119cm-40x47in) s.d.1852 prov. 24-Oct-2 Shannon's, Milford #104/R est:15000-20000

PEERBOOM, Alfons (1882-1958) German
£288 $447 €450 Interior (32x35cm-13x14in) s. 6-Dec-2 Michael Zeller, Lindau #881/R

PEERLESS, Tom (19/20th C) Australian
Works on paper
£281 $427 €422 Southern lake, scene (32x51cm-13x20in) s. W/C. 19-Aug-2 Joel, Victoria #325 (A.D 800)
£313 $489 €470 Lake Tarawera (34x59cm-13x23in) s.d.1884 W/C. 7-Nov-2 International Art Centre, Auckland #194 est:1500-2500 (NZ.D 1000)
£351 $533 €527 High mountain stream (42x60cm-17x24in) s. W/C. 19-Aug-2 Joel, Victoria #339 est:1500-2000 (A.D 1000)
£392 $611 €588 Southern alps (36x56cm-14x22in) s. W/C. 7-Nov-2 International Art Centre, Auckland #198 est:1400-1800 (NZ.D 1250)
£439 $684 €659 Southern lake scene with yacht (52x76cm-20x30in) s. W/C. 27-Mar-3 International Art Centre, Auckland #164/R (NZ.D 1250)
£985 $1438 €1478 Cleddau River, Milford Sounds (75x55cm-30x22in) s. W/C. 12-Sep-1 Watson's, Christchurch #45 est:7500-12500 (NZ.D 3300)

PEERSON, H (20th C) Continental
Works on paper
£828 $1275 €1300 Tending to the fire (32x38cm-13x15in) s.d.37 pencil W/C htd white. 3-Sep-2 Christie's, Amsterdam #191/R

PEETERS, Bonaventura (17th C) Flemish
£797 $1307 €1100 Marine a Zelande, navire hollandais au pavillon zelandais (43x71cm-17x28in) panel. 27-May-3 Campo & Campo, Antwerp #180
£11538 $17885 €18000 Dutch ships unloading on coast of America (53x80cm-21x31in) panel prov. 7-Dec-2 Ketterer, Hamburg #1/R est:9000-10000
£16547 $26475 €23000 Mediterranean harbour entrance with shipping on rough seas (91x180cm-36x71in) mono. 13-May-3 Sotheby's, Amsterdam #53/R est:25000-35000

PEETERS, Bonaventura (attrib) (17th C) Flemish
£1844 $2858 €2766 Shipwreck (44x70cm-17x28in) 3-Dec-2 Bukowskis, Stockholm #476/R est:20000-25000 (S.KR 26000)
£4717 $7358 €7500 Choppy waters in harbour entrance (116x165cm-46x65in) 23-Sep-2 Wiener Kunst Auktionen, Vienna #16/R est:9000-18000

PEETERS, Bonaventura I (1614-1652) Flemish
£4387 $6932 €6800 Marine pres de cote rocheuse (69x87cm-27x34in) copper. 18-Dec-2 Piasa, Paris #59/R
£35000 $58450 €50750 Frigates, smalschips and other shipping in a stiff breeze off a port (54x99cm-21x39in) init.d.1639 panel prov. 9-Jul-3 Christie's, London #45/R est:40000-60000
Works on paper
£8000 $13360 €11600 Capriccio view of a Mediterranean port (11x27cm-4x11in) s. bears i.verso pen brown ink wash over blk chk prov. 9-Jul-3 Sotheby's, London #100/R est:8000-12000

PEETERS, Bonaventura I (attrib) (1614-1652) Flemish
£10000 $15600 €15000 Coastal landscape with men-o-war in choppy seas outside a Mediterranean harbour (119x166cm-47x65in) 10-Apr-3 Christie's, Kensington #38/R est:10000-15000

PEETERS, Bonaventura I (circle) (1614-1652) Flemish
£7914 $12662 €11000 Shipping on the river Scheldt with Antwerp in the distance (54x98cm-21x39in) panel prov. 14-May-3 Christie's, Amsterdam #122/R est:7000-10000

PEETERS, Clara (1594-1657) Flemish
£11613 $18348 €18000 Still life of fruit and crystal vase (26x36cm-10x14in) s. board. 18-Dec-2 Ansorena, Madrid #90/R est:18000
£60000 $100200 €87000 Roses, tulips, carnation and other flowers in a stoneware vase with ornamental relieves (42x30cm-17x12in) s. panel prov.lit. 9-Jul-3 Christie's, London #60/R est:60000-80000

PEETERS, Clara (circle) (1594-1657) Flemish
£1214 $1919 €1821 Still life with fish, cheese, ale glass and flagons (66x55cm-26x22in) prov. 26-Nov-2 Sotheby's, Melbourne #162/R est:5000-8000 (A.D 3400)
£30380 $48000 €48000 Still life (18x14cm-7x6in) copper. 27-Nov-2 Finarte, Milan #118/R est:10000-15000

PEETERS, Hans J (1937-) American?
£2057 $3250 €2983 Peregrine pair (61x91cm-24x36in) s. board prov. 26-Jul-3 Coeur d'Alene, Hayden #10/R est:4000-6000

PEETERS, Jan (1624-1680) Flemish
£1572 $2453 €2500 Shipwreck on rocky coast (33x52cm-13x20in) panel lit. 20-Sep-2 Schloss Ahlden, Ahlden #1089/R est:2500

PEETERS, Jan (1912-1992) Dutch
Works on paper
£284 $460 €400 Still life in a garden (62x50cm-24x20in) s.d.76 W/C. 26-May-3 Glerum, Amsterdam #132/R

PEGOT-OGIER, Jean Bertrand (1877-1915) French
£1875 $3056 €2700 La plage a Quiberon, scene animee au chien (20x25cm-8x10in) s.i. cardboard. 19-Jul-3 Thierry & Lannon, Brest #159/R est:1000-1200
£2113 $3401 €3000 Laveuses sur le Scorff (32x41cm-13x16in) s.i. s.d.1914 verso board. 11-May-3 Thierry & Lannon, Brest #214/R est:3500-4000
£2564 $4026 €4000 Matin (35x46cm-14x18in) s.i. 15-Dec-2 Thierry & Lannon, Brest #182
£2746 $4422 €3900 Le muret de pierres dans la lande (70x60cm-28x24in) s. d.1912 verso. 11-May-3 Thierry & Lannon, Brest #213/R est:3000-4000
£2949 $4629 €4600 Jour de marche (46x63cm-18x25in) s.d.1915. 15-Dec-2 Thierry & Lannon, Brest #185
Works on paper
£308 $483 €480 Etude (27x17cm-11x7in) init. crayon dr. 15-Dec-2 Thierry & Lannon, Brest #42
£833 $1358 €1200 Femme de Hennebont en costume (28x23cm-11x9in) s.i.d.1913 W/C. 19-Jul-3 Thierry & Lannon, Brest #74
£951 $1531 €1350 Elegante sur la plage du Pouldu (25x33cm-10x13in) s.i. W/C chl. 11-May-3 Thierry & Lannon, Brest #74
£1119 $1868 €1600 Pardon a la Trinite pres de Concarneau (29x38cm-11x15in) s.i. W/C black crayon. 26-Jun-3 Tajan, Paris #54 est:250-350

PEGURIER, Auguste (1856-1936) French
Works on paper
£489 $817 €700 Tartanes sur la plage de la Ponche a St Tropez (32x24cm-13x9in) s. pastel. 26-Jun-3 Tajan, Paris #135

PEHRSON, Karl Axel (1921-) Swedish
£357 $567 €536 Blue symphony (67x84cm-26x33in) s.d.1962. 3-Mar-3 Lilla Bukowskis, Stockholm #686 (S.KR 4800)
£858 $1304 €1287 From Dunbrecke (60x73cm-24x29in) s. 16-Aug-2 Lilla Bukowskis, Stockholm #446 (S.KR 12500)
£1773 $2748 €2660 Sevenstar palm - landscape with exotic flowers and tree (66x80cm-26x31in) s. 8-Dec-2 Uppsala Auktionskammare, Uppsala #264/R est:25000-30000 (S.KR 25000)

£1901 $3004 €2852 Lirpa - exotic flowers in landscape (46x55cm-18x22in) s. 28-Apr-3 Bukowskis, Stockholm #266/R est:25000-30000 (S.KR 25000)
£2008 $3232 €3012 Trumpet lilies and other flowers (56x80cm-22x31in) s.d.66. 7-May-3 AB Stockholms Auktionsverk #689/R est:30000-40000 (S.KR 26000)
£2017 $3268 €2925 Near Negilgad (60x73cm-24x29in) s. acrylic. 25-May-3 Uppsala Auktionskammare, Uppsala #329/R est:20000-25000 (S.KR 26000)
£2102 $3280 €3153 Ejrin at Negalsor (42x72cm-17x28in) s. 5-Nov-2 Bukowskis, Stockholm #261a/R est:35000-40000 (S.KR 30000)
£3083 $4810 €4625 Beach flowers, Upper Oriro (41x54cm-16x21in) s. canvas on panel. 5-Nov-2 Bukowskis, Stockholm #260/R est:30000-35000 (S.KR 44000)
£3784 $5903 €5676 Beach flowers and shapes by Mefoitto river (64x52cm-25x20in) s. 5-Nov-2 Bukowskis, Stockholm #261/R est:50000-60000 (S.KR 54000)

PEIFFER-WATENPHUL, Max (1896-1976) German
£19149 $31021 €27000 Villa on Corfu (110x66cm-43x26in) mono.d.66 lit.exhib. 24-May-3 Van Ham, Cologne #462/R est:24000

PEIKOV, Ilia (1911-) Bulgarian
Sculpture
£1154 $1812 €1800 Bather (27x15x19cm-11x6x7in) init.i.d.1947 brown pat bronze. 21-Nov-2 Finarte, Rome #223/R

PEINADO, Francisco (1941-) Spanish
£962 $1519 €1500 Building (46x38cm-18x15in) s.i.d.1995 verso. 14-Nov-2 Arte, Seville #442a/R

PEINADO, Joaquin (1898-1975) Spanish
Works on paper
£288 $456 €450 Nude (21x13cm-8x5in) d.1992 verso pencil dr. 13-Nov-2 Ansorena, Madrid #430/R
£331 $540 €500 Nude (21x13cm-8x5in) pencil. 11-Feb-3 Segre, Madrid #369/R
£629 $981 €1000 Landscape in France (34x45cm-13x18in) s.d.58 W/C. 17-Sep-2 Segre, Madrid #148/R
£645 $1019 €1000 Thinking (41x32cm-16x13in) d.58 pencil dr. 18-Dec-2 Ansorena, Madrid #958/R
£1006 $1570 €1600 Erotic scene (29x18cm-11x7in) st.sig.verso W/C. 8-Oct-2 Ansorena, Madrid #536/R
£1258 $1937 €2000 View of San Francisco (28x38cm-11x15in) s.d.71 W/C. 28-Oct-2 Segre, Madrid #121/R
£1474 $2329 €2300 Still life (24x32cm-9x13in) s. col dr. 13-Nov-2 Ansorena, Madrid #440/R

PEINER, Werner (1897-1981) German
Works on paper
£288 $438 €450 Madonna with sleeping Child (57x39cm-22x15in) s. gouache lit. 11-Jul-2 Allgauer, Kempten #2367

PEIRCE, Waldo (1884-1970) American
£875 $1400 €1313 Flowers in kitchen (91x46cm-36x18in) s. 11-Jan-3 James Julia, Fairfield #152 est:3000-5000
£2817 $4000 €4226 Anna with flowers (58x91cm-23x36in) 8-Aug-1 Barridorf, Portland #13/R est:3000-6000
£5282 $7500 €7923 Through our window (130x89cm-51x35in) 8-Aug-1 Barridorf, Portland #119/R est:8000-12000
Works on paper
£3593 $6000 €5210 Ernest Hemingway and Waldo Peirce shark shooting off Florida's Tortugas (51x61cm-20x24in) s.i.d.1932 gouache prov. 21-Jun-3 Charlton Hall, Columbia #539/R est:3000-5000

PEIRE, Luc (1916-1994) Belgian
£1384 $2145 €2200 Graphie IXXC (32x90cm-13x35in) s.verso panel painted 1967. 5-Oct-2 De Vuyst, Lokeren #287/R est:2200-2800
£2949 $4629 €4600 Lhassa (35x70cm-14x28in) s. panel prov. 24-Nov-2 Laurence Calmels, Paris #206/R
£3774 $5811 €6000 Glacriss (73x100cm-29x39in) s.verso exhib. 22-Oct-2 Campo & Campo, Antwerp #214/R

PEISER, Kurt (1887-1962) Belgian
£374 $595 €550 Jeunes filles du port (20x26cm-8x10in) s. 18-Mar-3 Campo, Vlaamse Kaai #201
£538 $834 €850 Estacade (85x70cm-33x28in) s. 24-Sep-2 Galerie Moderne, Brussels #958
£577 $894 €900 Woman with vegetables (37x30cm-15x12in) s. panel. 7-Dec-2 De Vuyst, Lokeren #247
£833 $1308 €1300 Fish auction (38x28cm-15x11in) s. panel. 16-Dec-2 Bernaerts, Antwerp #810
£962 $1510 €1500 Femmes de pecheur (40x30cm-16x12in) s.d.1953 canvas on panel. 10-Dec-2 Vanderkindere, Brussels #82 est:400-600
£1013 $1580 €1600 Pecheurs tirant un eglefin (24x18cm-9x7in) s. panel. 16-Sep-2 Horta, Bruxelles #128
£1132 $1743 €1800 Vieux couple de dockers (57x65cm-22x26in) s. 22-Oct-2 Campo & Campo, Antwerp #215/R
£1603 $2484 €2500 Fisherwomen (70x60cm-28x24in) s. 7-Dec-2 De Vuyst, Lokeren #246/R est:2000-2400
£1655 $2647 €2300 La femme au chapeau vert (40x32cm-16x13in) s. cardboard. 13-May-3 Vanderkindere, Brussels #135/R est:1800-2200
£1944 $3092 €2800 La belle du quartier (56x73cm-22x29in) s. 29-Apr-3 Campo, Vlaamse Kaai #249/R est:2500-3000
£3038 $4739 €4800 Trois commeres au port de Bruxelles (89x70cm-35x28in) s. 16-Sep-2 Horta, Bruxelles #127/R est:5000-7500
Works on paper
£629 $969 €1000 Fillette (39x26cm-15x10in) s. pastel. 22-Oct-2 Campo, Vlaamse Kaai #585
£791 $1266 €1100 Still life of skull with hat and bottles with candles (54x43cm-21x17in) s. pastel. 17-May-3 De Vuyst, Lokeren #292/R
£1727 $2763 €2400 Poverty (73x53cm-29x21in) s. pastel. 17-May-3 De Vuyst, Lokeren #291/R est:2600-3000

PEITHNER VON LICHTENFELS, Eduard (1833-1913) Austrian
£1122 $1750 €1683 Panoramic landscape with figures and cattle (48x64cm-19x25in) s.d.1861 panel. 20-Oct-2 Jeffery Burchard, Florida #48/R
Works on paper
£521 $828 €750 Mountain landscape (36x51cm-14x20in) s. mixed media. 29-Apr-3 Wiener Kunst Auktionen, Vienna #535/R
£1195 $1852 €1900 Taormina coast (35x54cm-14x21in) s.i.d.8/1878 W/C pencil. 1-Oct-2 Dorotheum, Vienna #177/R est:1800-2000

PEIZEL, Bart (1887-1974) Dutch
£298 $483 €420 Portrait of a woman with a Japanese silk sash (60x50cm-24x20in) s.d.36 sold with silk sash. 26-May-3 Glerum, Amsterdam #73/R
£780 $1264 €1100 Reclining female nude (80x120cm-31x47in) prov. 26-May-3 Glerum, Amsterdam #115
£1151 $1888 €1600 Ligezicht, Amsterdam (50x60cm-20x24in) s. s.i.verso. 3-Jun-3 Christie's, Amsterdam #21/R est:1500-2000
Works on paper
£298 $483 €420 Ibiza (49x56cm-19x22in) s. i.verso W/C exec.1960. 26-May-3 Glerum, Amsterdam #5/R

PEKARY, Istvan (1905-1981) Hungarian
£2151 $3335 €3119 Tale harvest (51x80cm-20x31in) s.d.1964. 9-Dec-2 Mu Terem Galeria, Budapest #34/R est:550000 (H.F 800000)
£2580 $4024 €3741 Island of Ventotene (32x110cm-13x43in) s. 13-Sep-2 Mu Terem Galeria, Budapest #19/R est:550000 (H.F 1000000)
£3633 $5667 €5268 On the Italian church square (58x47cm-23x19in) s.d.59. 12-Apr-3 Mu Terem Galeria, Budapest #74/R est:480000 (H.F 1300000)
£4471 $6975 €6483 Fable burg (71x50cm-28x20in) s.d.1975. 12-Apr-3 Mu Terem Galeria, Budapest #27/R est:600000 (H.F 1600000)
Works on paper
£439 $684 €637 Scenery of the Roman Opera (25x34cm-10x13in) s.i.d.1942 W/C. 13-Sep-2 Mu Terem Galeria, Budapest #10/R est:120000 (H.F 170000)
£1032 $1610 €1496 Town by the seaside (20x28cm-8x11in) s.d.68 W/C. 13-Sep-2 Mu Terem Galeria, Budapest #11/R est:150000 (H.F 400000)

PELAEZ, Amelia (1897-1968) Cuban
£8333 $13000 €12500 Untitled, naturaleza muerta (63x48cm-25x19in) s.d.64. 14-Oct-2 Butterfields, San Francisco #2147/R est:10000-15000
£30573 $48000 €45860 Flowers (80x57cm-31x22in) s. painted 1930 prov.exhib. 20-Nov-2 Christie's, Rockefeller NY #79/R est:60000-80000
£36585 $60000 €54878 Sin titulo (36x30cm-14x12in) s. painted c.1950. 28-May-3 Christie's, Rockefeller NY #39/R est:40000-60000

PELAEZ, Mariano (1920-) Spanish
£379 $599 €550 Figures (24x30cm-9x12in) s. board. 1-Apr-3 Segre, Madrid #377/R
£822 $1282 €1200 Chat (81x100cm-32x39in) s. 8-Apr-3 Ansorena, Madrid #198/R

PELAYO FERNANDEZ, Eduardo (c.1850-?) Spanish
£2044 $3189 €3250 Warriors greeting monk (32x49cm-13x19in) s.i.d.1889 board. 23-Sep-2 Durán, Madrid #246/R

PELAYO, Orlando (1920-1990) Spanish
£448 $708 €650 Abstraction (27x35cm-11x14in) s. paper. 1-Apr-3 Segre, Madrid #384/R
£728 $1135 €1150 Composition (38x55cm-15x22in) s. 20-Oct-2 Chayette & Cheval, Paris #87

£943 $1453 €1500 Figure (44x62cm-17x24in) s. mixed media. 22-Oct-2 Durán, Madrid #186/R
£972 $1536 €1400 Jeune homme (43x30cm-17x12in) s. panel. 28-Apr-3 Cornette de St.Cyr, Paris #288
£1329 $2219 €1900 Mujer (27x35cm-11x14in) s. 25-Jun-3 Claude Aguttes, Neuilly #267/R est:1200-1400
£1821 $2969 €2750 J1 (38x54cm-15x21in) s.d.1956 i.verso. 11-Feb-3 Segre, Madrid #203/R
£2318 $3778 €3500 Mrs Nobody (55x46cm-22x18in) s. painted c.1970. 11-Feb-3 Segre, Madrid #207/R

Works on paper
£477 $773 €725 Figure (41x54cm-16x21in) s. gouache. 21-Jan-3 Durán, Madrid #65/R
£1097 $1733 €1700 Painter's study (22x32cm-9x13in) s.d. mixed media. 18-Dec-2 Ansorena, Madrid #183/R
£1129 $1784 €1750 Women (49x64cm-19x25in) s.d.1978 wax crayon. 17-Dec-2 Segre, Madrid #160/R
£1301 $2030 €1900 Composition (52x74cm-20x29in) s. gouache. 8-Apr-3 Ansorena, Madrid #259/R
£1509 $2355 €2400 Figures (50x70cm-20x28in) s. gouache. 23-Sep-2 Durán, Madrid #139/R

PELEGRI, Jose (20th C) Spanish
£308 $481 €450 Rural view (37x45cm-15x18in) s.d.56 cardboard. 8-Apr-3 Ansorena, Madrid #189/R

PELEZ, Fernand (1843-1913) French
£3595 $5788 €5500 Les jeunes archers nus (32x21cm-13x8in) s.d.78. 20-Jan-3 Horta, Bruxelles #91/R est:6000-8000

Works on paper
£1773 $2872 €2500 Jeune fille nue (144x59cm-57x23in) s. chl white chk. 23-May-3 Camard, Paris #13 est:900-1000

PELGROM, Jacobus (1811-1861) Dutch
£1118 $1812 €1700 View on a lake in a mountainous landscape. Shipping on a river (11x15cm-4x6in) s. panel. 21-Jan-3 Christie's, Amsterdam #115 est:1800-2200
£1439 $2302 €2000 Paysage fluvial Hollandais anime de personnage (17x26cm-7x10in) s. panel. 13-May-3 Palais de Beaux Arts, Brussels #346/R est:1200-2000

PELHAM, James II (1800-1874) British
£3800 $6118 €5700 Portrait of boy in brown hat (26x17cm-10x7in) pencil W/C oil prov. 20-Feb-3 Christie's, London #200/R

PELHAM, Thomas Kent (fl.1860-1891) British
£700 $1078 €1050 Far away thoughts (45x35cm-18x14in) s. 22-Oct-2 Bonhams, Bath #33
£750 $1170 €1125 Chat by the way (91x71cm-36x28in) s.i.verso. 7-Nov-2 Christie's, Kensington #212/R
£1000 $1550 €1500 Mother and child (92x71cm-36x28in) s. 3-Dec-2 Sotheby's, Olympia #58/R est:1000-2000
£1054 $1750 €1528 Portraits of women (41x30cm-16x12in) one s.d.1864 one init.d.1884. 11-Jun-3 Boos Gallery, Michigan #529/R est:3000-4000

PELISSIER-PEZOLT, Agnes (1901-1997) Swiss
£343 $542 €515 Still life with fruit and vessels (56x47cm-22x19in) s. 29-Nov-2 Zofingen, Switzerland #3026 (S.FR 800)

PELIZZARI, Gregory (1951-) American
£349 $548 €524 La baigneuse a Versaille (72x100cm-28x39in) s. 25-Nov-2 Germann, Zurich #779 (S.FR 800)

PELLAN, Alfred (1906-1988) Canadian
£8000 $13120 €12000 Affection (25x36cm-10x14in) s. panel prov. 3-Jun-3 Joyner, Toronto #250/R est:2000-2500 (C.D 18000)
£8969 $14350 €13454 Titre abstraction (46x30cm-18x12in) s. s.i.d.1939 verso prov.lit. 15-May-3 Heffel, Vancouver #65/R est:20000-25000 (C.D 20000)
£9274 $14653 €13911 Fleurs I (66x51cm-26x20in) s.d.78 acrylic prov. 18-Nov-2 Sotheby's, Toronto #76/R est:20000-30000 (C.D 23000)
£44444 $72889 €66666 Le couteau a pain ondule (91x63cm-36x25in) s.d.42 prov.exhib.lit. 27-May-3 Sotheby's, Toronto #145/R est:60000-80000 (C.D 100000)

Works on paper
£905 $1403 €1358 Lending a hand (44x39cm-17x15in) s.mixed media card. 3-Dec-2 Joyner, Toronto #226/R est:2000-3000 (C.D 2200)
£1157 $1817 €1736 Musicien-A- (58x38cm-23x15in) s.i.d.46 gouache prov. 24-Jul-2 Walker's, Ottawa #428/R est:3000-3500 (C.D 2800)
£8065 $12742 €12098 Bestiare 4E (51x66cm-20x26in) s.d.74 s.d.verso mixed media prov.lit. 18-Nov-2 Sotheby's, Toronto #142/R est:25000-30000 (C.D 20000)
£9778 $16036 €14667 Leda (32x27cm-13x11in) s. W/C ink. 3-Jun-3 Joyner, Toronto #72/R est:15000-18000 (C.D 22000)
£16000 $26240 €24000 Les treteaux (29x45cm-11x18in) s. mixed media executed 1958 prov.exhib.lit. 3-Jun-3 Joyner, Toronto #33/R est:40000-50000 (C.D 36000)

PELLAR, Hanns (1886-?) Austrian
£629 $981 €1000 Man (132x42cm-52x17in) i. 23-Sep-2 Dr Fritz Nagel, Stuttgart #6929/R
£2158 $3453 €3000 Women in park (112x115cm-44x45in) s.i. 15-May-3 Neumeister, Munich #328/R est:2500-2800
£4507 $7256 €6400 Mephisto (131x42cm-52x17in) s.i.d.1910 lit. 9-May-3 Schloss Ahlden, Ahlden #1548/R est:5200

PELLEGATA, Romeo (1870-1946) Italian
£884 $1406 €1300 Fishermen on Como Lake (24x35cm-9x14in) s.d.1911. 18-Mar-3 Finarte, Milan #180/R
£1224 $1947 €1800 Beach in Monterosso (29x39cm-11x15in) s.i. cardboard. 1-Mar-3 Meeting Art, Vercelli #278

PELLEGRIN, Honore (1800-1870) French

Works on paper
£1200 $1860 €1800 Brig Antiqua of Irvine, entering the port of Marseilles, 11 November 1845 (41x67cm-16x26in) s.i.d.1845 pen ink W/C. 31-Oct-2 Christie's, Kensington #364/R est:1500-2000

PELLEGRIN, Joseph Honore Maxime (1793-1869) American
£4934 $7500 €7401 Barque, Pilgrim, entering the port of Marseilles (46x61cm-18x24in) i. board. 17-Aug-2 North East Auctions, Portsmouth #974/R est:5000-7000

PELLEGRIN, Joseph Honore Maxime (attrib) (1793-1869) American

Works on paper
£4934 $7500 €7401 Brig, Belle of Camden, entering port of Marseilles (41x56cm-16x22in) i. W/C. 17-Aug-2 North East Auctions, Portsmouth #841/R est:7500-9500

PELLEGRIN, Louis (19th C) French

Works on paper
£1800 $2988 €2610 Spanish topsail schooner Victoria in two positions off Marseilles (39x57cm-15x22in) s.i.d.1852 pencil pen ink W/C. 12-Jun-3 Christie's, London #562/R est:1500-2000
£2600 $4316 €3770 Spanish three masted barque Balear heading into Marseilles (44x55cm-17x22in) i.d.1862-63 pencil pen ink W/C htd white. 12-Jun-3 Christie's, London #564/R est:1500-2000
£3000 $4980 €4350 Spanish barque Constancia approaching Marseilles with paddle steamer off her stern (43x60cm-17x24in) s.i.d.1855 pen ink W/C htd white. 12-Jun-3 Christie's, London #561/R est:1500-2500
£3500 $5810 €5075 Spanish brig Jaycee Ferrari approaching Marseilles with the pilot boat off her stern (46x57cm-18x22in) s.i.d.1856 pencil pen ink W/C. 12-Jun-3 Christie's, London #563/R est:2000-4000

PELLEGRINI, Alfred Heinrich (1881-1958) Swiss
£395 $624 €593 Portrait of a lady (100x75cm-39x30in) i. exhib. 26-Nov-2 Hans Widmer, St Gallen #1311 (S.FR 920)
£2358 $3821 €4175 Still life of flowers in tow vases (49x38cm-19x15in) s. board prov.exhib. 26-May-3 Sotheby's, Zurich #76/R est:7000-9000 (S.FR 5000)
£2620 $4114 €3930 Dead game (39x64cm-15x25in) mono.d.1937 exhib.lit. 25-Nov-2 Sotheby's, Zurich #57/R est:12000-13000 (S.FR 6000)
£2830 $4585 €5010 Fox pass in Wittnau (55x46cm-22x18in) mono.d.1942 exhib.prov. 26-May-3 Sotheby's, Zurich #79/R est:8000-12000 (S.FR 6000)
£3057 $4799 €4586 Faded peonies (34x43cm-13x17in) mono.d.1910 board exhib. 25-Nov-2 Sotheby's, Zurich #54/R est:8000-12000 (S.FR 7000)
£4367 $6856 €6551 Nude on divan (56x70cm-22x28in) s. prov.exhib.lit. 25-Nov-2 Sotheby's, Zurich #131/R est:10000-15000 (S.FR 10000)
£4481 $7259 €7932 Elsace landscape (68x87cm-27x34in) mono.d.1934 prov.exhib.lit. 26-May-3 Sotheby's, Zurich #137/R est:18000-25000 (S.FR 9500)
£4717 $7642 €8349 Hunting still life (66x93cm-26x37in) s.i.d.1938 prov.exhib.lit. 26-May-3 Sotheby's, Zurich #116/R est:20000-25000 (S.FR 10000)
£5240 $8227 €7860 Winter on the Schliersee - March snow (96x121cm-38x48in) s.d.1916 exhib.lit. 25-Nov-2 Sotheby's, Zurich #56/R est:35000-45000 (S.FR 12000)

£9607 $15083 €14411 Alpha and Omega - two people (200x160cm-79x63in) s.d.1927 exhib.lit. 25-Nov-2 Sotheby's, Zurich #55/R est:35000-45000 (S.FR 22000)

PELLEGRINI, Domenico (1759-1840) Italian
£688 $1100 €1032 Portrait of a woman wearing a red and blue dress holding a jewelry box (102x86cm-40x34in) s. 17-May-3 Pook & Pook, Downington #200c est:3000-4000

PELLEGRINI, Giovanni Antonio (1675-1741) Italian
£96552 $153517 €140000 Bacchanal. Offer to Pan (36x128cm-14x50in) pair prov. 9-Mar-3 Semenzato, Venice #45/R est:200000

PELLEGRINI, Giovanni Antonio (attrib) (1675-1741) Italian
£3500 $5845 €5075 Classical subject with a figure drawing his sword before a king (46x35cm-18x14in) 8-Jul-3 Sotheby's, Olympia #451/R est:4000-6000

Works on paper
£608 $949 €900 Scene de mariage (37x47cm-15x19in) pen wash htd gouache. 27-Mar-3 Maigret, Paris #50/R

PELLEGRINI, Giovanni Antonio (circle) (1675-1741) Italian
£5500 $8580 €8250 Rest on the flight into Egypt (94x126cm-37x50in) 10-Apr-3 Christie's, Kensington #262/R est:6000-8000

PELLEGRINI, Giovanni Antonio (studio) (1675-1741) Italian
£7500 $11775 €11250 Continence of Scipio (130x100cm-51x39in) prov. 10-Dec-2 Sotheby's, Olympia #391/R est:4000-6000
£14085 $23380 €20000 Rebecca at the well (121x97cm-48x38in) exhib.prov. 11-Jun-3 Dorotheum, Vienna #1/R est:5000-8000

PELLEGRINI, Riccardo (1863-1934) Italian
£751 $1232 €1089 Taking a walk. s.d.83. 4-Jun-3 Fischer, Luzern #2278/R est:1500-1800 (S.FR 1600)
£786 $1226 €1179 A stroll (21x42cm-8x17in) s. 20-Nov-2 Fischer, Luzern #2214/R est:1500-2000 (S.FR 1800)
£950 $1549 €1378 Admiring a statue (24x33cm-9x13in) s. board. 16-Jul-3 Sotheby's, Olympia #264/R
£1545 $2425 €2318 Spanish courtyard (46x34cm-18x13in) s.d.91 board prov. 10-Dec-2 Pinneys, Montreal #56 est:4000-6000 (C.D 3800)
£1844 $2987 €2600 Villaggio spagnolo (50x60cm-20x24in) s. 22-May-3 Stadion, Trieste #328/R est:3000-4000
£1974 $3197 €3000 Barque de pecheurs (33x42cm-13x17in) s.d.1881. 21-Jan-3 Galerie Moderne, Brussels #242/R est:1500-2000
£2174 $3565 €3000 Sole d'autunno (60x90cm-24x35in) s. s.i.verso. 27-May-3 Finarte, Milan #49/R est:3000-4000
£2642 $4068 €4200 Boats and fishermen (45x35cm-18x14in) s. 23-Oct-2 Finarte, Milan #135/R
£3459 $5327 €5500 Fishermen Island (60x98cm-24x39in) s.d.1897. 23-Oct-2 Finarte, Milan #170/R
£41667 $65417 €65000 La charmeuse de serpents (48x81cm-19x32in) s. canvas on cardboard. 16-Dec-2 Gros & Delettrez, Paris #75/R est:65000-80000

Works on paper
£903 $1427 €1400 Party (30x44cm-12x17in) s. W/C. 18-Dec-2 Finarte, Milan #138/R
£1032 $1631 €1600 Market scene (48x31cm-19x12in) s. W/C. 18-Dec-2 Finarte, Milan #195/R

PELLEJER, Guiomar (1974-) Spanish
£497 $810 €750 White woman, black head (84x62cm-33x24in) s.d.2000 oil mixed media. 11-Feb-3 Segre, Madrid #257/R

PELLERIN, Baptiste (16th C) French?
Works on paper
£6790 $11000 €10185 Triumph of a king in antique city (20x23cm-8x9in) chk pen ink wash. 22-Jan-3 Christie's, Rockefeller NY #59/R est:12000

PELLERIN, Patrice (20th C) French?
Works on paper
£317 $501 €460 Epervier (47x35cm-19x14in) s. Chinese ink. 7-Apr-3 Claude Aguttes, Neuilly #75/R

PELLET, Alphonse (19th C) French
£2903 $4500 €4355 In the seraglio (150x99cm-59x39in) s. 2-Nov-2 North East Auctions, Portsmouth #63/R est:8000-12000
£11392 $18000 €17088 Harem beauty (151x100cm-59x39in) s. 24-Apr-3 Sotheby's, New York #126/R est:20000-30000

PELLET, Marguerite (20th C) Swiss
£301 $484 €436 Still life of flowers, grapes and pears (47x60cm-19x24in) s.d.1955 panel. 7-May-3 Dobiaschofsky, Bern #876/R (S.FR 650)

PELLETIER, Joseph Laurent (1811-1892) French
Works on paper
£355 $592 €500 Cote mediterraneenne (33x55cm-13x22in) s. W/C. 23-Jun-3 Beaussant & Lefèvre, Paris #115
£1218 $1924 €1900 Moselle landscape with village (35x52cm-14x20in) s. w/c prov. 16-Nov-2 Lempertz, Koln #1376/R est:2000

PELLETIER, Pierre-Jacques (1869-1931) French
£950 $1558 €1425 Parisian boulevard (46x65cm-18x26in) s. 5-Jun-3 Christie's, Kensington #615/R
£1646 $2567 €2600 Landscape (44x75cm-17x30in) s. panel. 15-Oct-2 Dorotheum, Vienna #58/R est:1500-1800
Works on paper
£1392 $2158 €2200 Bord de riviere (49x80cm-19x31in) s. pastel. 29-Sep-2 Eric Pillon, Calais #49/R

PELLICCIOTTI, Tito (1872-1943) Italian
£449 $704 €700 Donkey and cows in the stable (16x18cm-6x7in) s. board. 16-Dec-2 Pandolfini, Florence #124/R
£577 $906 €900 Dogs and hare (16x40cm-6x16in) s.d.XII board. 16-Dec-2 Pandolfini, Florence #125/R
£1757 $2741 €2600 Back from the fields (24x30cm-9x12in) s. board. 28-Mar-3 Farsetti, Prato #720/R
£1757 $2741 €2600 Little donkeys (22x30cm-9x12in) s. board. 28-Mar-3 Farsetti, Prato #726/R
£1757 $2741 €2600 In the hen house (22x30cm-9x12in) s. cardboard. 28-Mar-3 Farsetti, Prato #733/R
£2642 $4068 €4200 Desert scene (35x86cm-14x34in) s. board. 23-Oct-2 Finarte, Milan #161/R est:3000-4000
£3019 $4649 €4800 Stable interior (38x89cm-15x35in) s. 23-Oct-2 Finarte, Milan #153/R

PELLICER, Rafael (1906-1963) Spanish
£1548 $2446 €2400 Still life with flowers and paper birds (38x32cm-15x13in) s. board painted c.1940. 17-Dec-2 Segre, Madrid #93/R
£4500 $7020 €6750 La chica del pericon (65x80cm-26x31in) s. s.i.verso. 17-Sep-2 Sotheby's, Olympia #287/R est:5000-7000

PELLINI, P (19/20th C) ?
£7194 $11799 €10000 Les quatre saisons (100x65cm-39x26in) s. set of four. 4-Jun-3 Marc Kohn, Paris #101/R est:13000-15000

PELLION, J Alphonse (fl.1817-20) ?
Works on paper
£3200 $4960 €4800 Voyage a Bathurst. Une vue de la Riviere de Coxe et du poste miliaire (23x30cm-9x12in) i. pencil grey wash set of three. 26-Sep-2 Christie's, London #89/R est:3000-5000
£3200 $4960 €4800 Une vue de Coxe passe. Voyage a Bathurst (23x30cm-9x12in) i. pencil chl three. 26-Sep-2 Christie's, London #90/R est:3000-5000
£3800 $5890 €5700 Coupang, Ile Timor, costums (30x39cm-12x15in) i. pen ink. 26-Sep-2 Christie's, London #50/R est:2000-3000
£4800 $7440 €7200 Voyage a Bathurst (23x30cm-9x12in) i. pencil wash sold with dr. by S. Leroys six. 26-Sep-2 Christie's, London #87/R est:3000-5000
£5500 $8525 €8250 Bateau pilote de Dielie (27x38cm-11x15in) i. pen ink W/C. 26-Sep-2 Christie's, London #60/R est:5000-7000
£6500 $10075 €9750 Government officials of Timor (36x27cm-14x11in) i. three W/C sold with an engraving. 26-Sep-2 Christie's, London #57/R est:6000-8000
£6500 $10075 €9750 Voyage a Bathursat, Tara, perva Jeunes Sauvages de la nouvelle galles du sud dans leur camp (30x23cm-12x9in) i. pen ink exhib. 26-Sep-2 Christie's, London #85/R est:3000-5000
£8000 $12400 €12000 Voyage a Bathurst, Hara-o Karadra (23x30cm-9x12in) i. pen ink sold with dr. by Sebastien Leroys five. 26-Sep-2 Christie's, London #86/R est:5000-8000
£10000 $15500 €15000 Coupang, Ile timor, vistite au Roi de Denca (29x37cm-11x15in) i. pen ink W/C exhib. 26-Sep-2 Christie's, London #46/R est:10000-15000
£10000 $15500 €15000 Coupang, Ile Timor, scene prise au Bazard (28x38cm-11x15in) mono.i. pen ink W/C exhib. 26-Sep-2 Christie's, London #47/R est:10000-15000
£10000 $15500 €15000 Coupang, Ile timor, vue prise dans les environs de la ville. i. pen ink W/C exhib. 26-Sep-2 Christie's, London #49/R est:10000-15000

£11000 $17050 €16500 Coupang, Ile Timor, divers travaux mecaniques (29x38cm-11x15in) i. pen ink W/C set of three. 26-Sep-2 Christie's, London #51/R est:10000-15000
£11500 $17825 €17250 Voyage a Bathurst. Jedat Nemare. Sauvages da le nouvelle galles du sud dans leur camp (24x30cm-9x12in) i. pen ink four. 26-Sep-2 Christie's, London #83/R est:3000-5000
£12000 $18600 €18000 Nouvelle Hollande, entrevue avec les sauvages de la presq'ile peron (26x34cm-10x13in) i. pencil paper on board. 26-Sep-2 Christie's, London #37/R est:5000-8000
£16000 $24800 €24000 Governor and officials arriving in Timor (27x38cm-11x15in) i. pen ink W/C. 26-Sep-2 Christie's, London #55/R est:15000-20000
£17000 $26350 €25500 Habitation de sir John Jameson. Une vue des bords de la nepean a Regent ville (25x30cm-10x12in) init. pencil wash two. 26-Sep-2 Christie's, London #88/R est:5000-8000
£22000 $34100 €33000 Marine, vue de la rade de Rio de Janerio (28x36cm-11x14in) i.d.1818 W/C gold paint. 26-Sep-2 Christie's, London #27/R est:10000-15000
£30000 $46500 €45000 Nouvelle Hollande, Etude des dunes and falaises de la presqu (29x37cm-11x15in) i. W/C exhib. 26-Sep-2 Christie's, London #35/R est:10000-15000
£42000 $65100 €63000 Baie des chiens-marines, observatoire de L'Uranie (36x48cm-14x19in) s.i. W/C prov.exhib.lit. 26-Sep-2 Christie's, London #34/R est:40000-60000
£55000 $85250 €82500 Le port Jackson - vu de l'observatoire de l'Uranie (24x59cm-9x23in) init.i. ink W/C on two joined sheets lit. 26-Sep-2 Christie's, London #79/R est:50000-70000
£62000 $96100 €93000 Une vue du port de Sidney prise de l'observatoire. Vue de la Rade de Sidney prise de l'observatoire (30x46cm-12x18in) i.d.13 Dec 1819 W/C htd white two. 26-Sep-2 Christie's, London #78/R est:60000-90000

PELLION, J Alphonse and TAUNAY, Adrien Aime (19th C) French
Works on paper
£6500 $10075 €9750 Croquis d'aiguade de Waigiou (29x41cm-11x16in) i. pencil pen ink set of four. 26-Sep-2 Christie's, London #68/R est:3000-5000

PELOUSE, Léon Germain (1838-1891) French
£250 $390 €375 Banks of a canal near Rockfort (61x76cm-24x30in) 17-Oct-2 David Lay, Penzance #1328
£750 $1215 €1125 Rocky river bed in a sunlit landscape (24x13cm-9x5in) s. panel. 23-Jan-3 Christie's, Kensington #176/R
£1338 $2221 €1900 Landscape in autumn with edge of river and peasant and cattle (55x75cm-22x30in) s. 14-Jun-3 Arnold, Frankfurt #829/R est:1600
£1667 $2717 €2400 Coucher de soleil sur la riviere en Bretagne (40x61cm-16x24in) s. 19-Jul-3 Thierry & Lannon, Brest #161/R est:2400-2600
£1800 $2736 €2700 Paysage de l'etang (38x55cm-15x22in) s. 29-Aug-2 Christie's, Kensington #211/R est:2000-3000
£1800 $2844 €2700 Sunlit wood (67x81cm-26x32in) 3-Apr-3 Christie's, Kensington #4/R
£1986 $3099 €2900 Landscape with water (41x61cm-16x24in) s. 10-Apr-3 Van Ham, Cologne #1640/R est:2800
£3103 $5027 €4499 Autumn scene with woman gathering faggots at edge of wood (64x90cm-25x35in) s. 25-May-3 Uppsala Auktionskammare, Uppsala #88/R est:30000-40000 (S.KR 40000)

PELOUSE, Léon Germain (attrib) (1838-1891) French
£300 $474 €450 Mother and child sitting on a grassy bank (22x35cm-9x14in) with sig. panel. 14-Nov-2 Christie's, Kensington #253

PELS, Albert (1910-1998) American
£292 $450 €438 Corner station (51x41cm-20x16in) s. 8-Sep-2 DeFina, Austinburg #346

PELT, Gottfried van (1873-1926) Dutch
£660 $1089 €950 Colourful bouquet (35x31cm-14x12in) s. cardboard. 1-Jul-3 Christie's, Amsterdam #176

PELTIER, Jean (20th C) French
£323 $500 €485 Paysage du Val D'Oise (53x74cm-21x29in) s. i.verso prov. 25-Sep-2 Doyle, New York #57/R

PELTIER, Marcel (20th C) French
£370 $596 €555 Landscape with stream and farmstead (54x65cm-21x26in) s. 7-May-3 Dobiaschofsky, Bern #877 (S.FR 800)

PELTON, Agnes (1881-1961) American
£2903 $4500 €4355 Smoke tree in bloom, June morning, Big Wash, Cathedral City, CA (46x61cm-18x24in) s.i.d. prov. 8-Dec-2 Toomey, Oak Park #703/R est:7000-9000
£3313 $5500 €4804 Spring comes to the desert (56x76cm-22x30in) s.d.34 prov. 11-Jun-3 Butterfields, San Francisco #4334/R est:6000-8000
£9554 $15000 €14331 Untitled, five women at a lily pond (71x122cm-28x48in) s.d.1920 lit. 19-Nov-2 Butterfields, San Francisco #8223/R est:30000-50000
Works on paper
£404 $650 €606 Farm landscape (23x51cm-9x20in) s. pastel. 18-Feb-3 John Moran, Pasadena #12a

PELUSO, Francesco (1836-?) Italian
£920 $1454 €1380 Lovesong. Sweetheart (31x20cm-12x8in) s. pair. 2-Dec-2 Bonhams, Bath #144/R

PELVO, Paavo (1947-) Finnish
£423 $680 €600 Figure (145x135cm-57x53in) s.d.87. 10-May-3 Bukowskis, Helsinki #243/R

PEMBA, George Mnyalaza Milwa (1912-2001) South African
£3267 $5261 €4901 Pennies from Heaven (40x47cm-16x19in) s.d.91. 12-May-3 Stephan Welz, Johannesburg #546/R est:30000-40000 (SA.R 38000)

PEMBERTON-SMITH, Freda (20th C) Canadian?
£246 $381 €369 Village church (25x35cm-10x14in) s. canvasboard. 24-Sep-2 Ritchie, Toronto #3157/R (C.D 600)

PENA Y MUNOZ, Maximino (1863-1940) Spanish
£1097 $1733 €1700 Village street (46x29cm-18x11in) s. 17-Dec-2 Segre, Madrid #57/R
£1284 $2003 €1900 Balcony with geraniums (42x32cm-17x13in) s. cardboard. 25-Mar-3 Durán, Madrid #103/R
Works on paper
£507 $791 €750 Girl with flowers (48x38cm-19x15in) s. pastel. 25-Mar-3 Durán, Madrid #37/R
£828 $1308 €1200 Portrait of woman (49x39cm-19x15in) s.pastel cardboard. 1-Apr-3 Segre, Madrid #356/R

PENA, Antonio de la (20th C) Spanish?
£461 $746 €700 Laguna, Castilla (30x71cm-12x28in) s.d.68 board. 21-Jan-3 Ansorena, Madrid #265/R

PENAGOS ZALABARDO, Rafael de (1889-1954) Spanish
Works on paper
£541 $843 €800 Maternity (43x30cm-17x12in) s. ink dr. 25-Mar-3 Durán, Madrid #56/R
£1097 $1733 €1700 Visit (21x23cm-8x9in) s. gouache. 18-Dec-2 Ansorena, Madrid #232/R

PENAGOS, Rafael (1941-) Colombian
Works on paper
£346 $540 €550 Meeting in the street (40x29cm-16x11in) s. pen dr. 23-Sep-2 Durán, Madrid #182/R

PENALBA, Alicia (1918-1982) Argentinian
Sculpture
£7639 $12069 €11000 Mistral (44x38x28cm-17x15x11in) s.num.1/7 green pat bronze marble socle Cast Valsuani prov.lit. 27-Apr-3 Perrin, Versailles #106/R est:10000-12000
£11644 $18164 €17000 Ancetre ailee (44x67x29cm-17x26x11in) st.sig. num.3/6 bronze exec.1962. 10-Apr-3 Finarte Semenzato, Rome #219/R est:22000
£14331 $22500 €21497 Contrepoint (26x38x69cm-10x15x27in) st.sig. num.3/6 brown pat bronze exec.1959 prov.lit. 19-Nov-2 Sotheby's, New York #87/R est:20000

PENCK, A R (1939-) German
£769 $1192 €1200 Man in motion - sea (31x40cm-12x16in) s. i. verso oil chk W/C. 7-Dec-2 Ketterer, Hamburg #681/R
£2319 $3803 €3200 KF 6 (78x106cm-31x42in) s.i.6 acrylic. 31-May-3 Villa Grisebach, Berlin #390/R est:4000-5000
£2536 $4159 €3500 Self portrait Berlin concept (50x40cm-20x16in) s. s.i. stretcher acrylic. 31-May-3 Villa Grisebach, Berlin #389/R est:3500-4000
£3473 $5521 €5000 Personnages (40x50cm-16x20in) s. prov. 29-Apr-3 Artcurial Briest, Paris #463/R est:4000-5000
£6028 $9766 €8500 Germany after the wall (99x200cm-39x79in) s. prov. 24-May-3 Van Ham, Cologne #464/R est:18500

£6329 $10000 €9494 Untitled (90x120cm-35x47in) s. 13-Nov-2 Sotheby's, New York #519/R
£7800 $13026 €11310 Reprasentanz (50x76cm-20x30in) s. painted 1985 prov. 27-Jun-3 Christie's, London #238/R est:7000-9000
£7801 $12638 €11000 Untitled (60x80cm-24x31in) s. 24-May-3 Van Ham, Cologne #465/R est:10000
£9615 $14904 €15000 Composition (100x80cm-39x31in) s. acrylic. 3-Dec-2 Lempertz, Koln #350/R est:15000
£18987 $30000 €30000 Evening in Hackney (130x280cm-51x110in) s. dispersion nettle painted 1983 prov. 29-Nov-2 Villa Grisebach, Berlin #92/R est:25000-30000
£53797 $85000 €80696 Systembild-end (145x150cm-57x59in) painted 1968 prov. 13-Nov-2 Sotheby's, New York #518/R est:70000-90000

Sculpture
£1700 $2635 €2550 Weibliches idol (12cm-5in) s.num.3/8 brown pat. bronze cast 1986 prov. 5-Dec-2 Christie's, Kensington #271/R est:1500-2000
£1884 $3090 €2600 Standard T - R (21x17x11cm-8x7x4in) mono.i. brown black pat.bronze Casst.Schmake Dusseldorf exhib. 28-May-3 Lempertz, Koln #327/R est:2500

Works on paper
£556 $878 €800 Untitled (42x59cm-17x23in) s. felt pen board. 26-Apr-3 Dr Lehr, Berlin #417/R
£1195 $1840 €1900 Abstract composition in red and brown (102x72cm-40x28in) s. mixed media board. 26-Oct-2 Dr Lehr, Berlin #430/R est:1000
£1799 $2950 €2500 Untitled (53x73cm-21x29in) s. gouache. 3-Jun-3 Christie's, Amsterdam #133/R est:3000-5000
£2029 $3328 €2800 The hand in the green woman (42x59cm-17x23in) s. col feltpen. 31-May-3 Villa Grisebach, Berlin #369/R est:3000-4000
£2456 $3905 €3610 Zeitlinie (36x48cm-14x19in) s. col pastel prov. 26-Feb-3 Artcurial Briest, Paris #381/R est:2500-4000

PENDER, Jack (1918-1998) British
£300 $468 €450 Mousehole Harbour (13x18cm-5x7in) s. board. 17-Oct-2 David Lay, Penzance #1238
£300 $468 €450 Boats (18x28cm-7x11in) s. board. 17-Oct-2 David Lay, Penzance #1239
£680 $1054 €1020 Punt with red sail (20x30cm-8x12in) s.d.94 board. 4-Dec-2 Christie's, Kensington #574/R
£1400 $2310 €2030 Mousehole Harbour (52x72cm-20x28in) s. board. 1-Jul-3 Bearnes, Exeter #522/R est:100-200
£2700 $4455 €3915 Evening (45x90cm-18x35in) s. s.i.verso board. 1-Jul-3 Bearnes, Exeter #521/R est:400-600

Works on paper
£375 $623 €544 Tom Bawcock's eve (41x48cm-16x19in) s.i.d.1978 mixed media. 10-Jun-3 David Lay, Penzance #69

PENDINI, Fulvio (1907-1975) Italian
£380 $592 €600 Still life (35x45cm-14x18in) s. 19-Oct-2 Semenzato, Venice #153/R
£1203 $1876 €1900 Composition (70x50cm-28x20in) s. painted 1957. 19-Oct-2 Semenzato, Venice #19/R

PENDINI, Ugo (1853-1895) Italian
£9500 $15485 €13775 Flower girl (67x48cm-26x19in) s. 16-Jul-3 Sotheby's, Olympia #243/R est:4000-6000

PENDL, Erwin (1875-1945) Austrian
Works on paper
£566 $877 €900 Karlskirche with car and horse drawn coach (15cm-6in circular) s. W/C. 1-Oct-2 Dorotheum, Vienna #288/R
£694 $1104 €1000 Peterskirche door in Vienna (27x16cm-11x6in) s. i. verso W/C. 29-Apr-3 Wiener Kunst Auktionen, Vienna #559/R
£759 $1200 €1200 Hoher Markt with fountain in Vienna (16x9cm-6x4in) s.i. W/C. 26-Nov-2 Wiener Kunst Auktionen, Vienna #146/R
£773 $1221 €1160 Old Burgtheater in Vienna (17x31cm-7x12in) s.i. W/C. 26-Nov-2 Hans Widmer, St Gallen #1313/R est:800-1800 (S.FR 1800)
£881 $1365 €1400 Molkerbastei with Dreimaderlhaus (23x17cm-9x7in) s.i. W/C. 1-Oct-2 Dorotheum, Vienna #279/R
£1006 $1560 €1600 Hofburg and Cafe Griensteidl (8x15cm-3x6in) s. W/C. 1-Oct-2 Dorotheum, Vienna #286/R est:1200-1500

PENDLEBURY, Laurence Scott (1914-) Australian
£286 $451 €429 Portrait of Nornie Gude (125x92cm-49x36in) s. board. 18-Nov-2 Joel, Victoria #315 (A.D 800)

PENE DU BOIS, Guy (1884-1958) American
£20968 $32500 €31452 Singer with fan (41x31cm-16x12in) s.d.12 prov. 4-Dec-2 Sotheby's, New York #71/R est:20000-30000
£98765 $160000 €148148 Pianist (30x41cm-12x16in) s. painted c.1912-14 prov.exhib.lit. 21-May-3 Sotheby's, New York #71/R est:100000-150000

Works on paper
£1958 $3250 €2839 Untitled (25x36cm-10x14in) gouache crayon. 13-Jun-3 Du Mouchelle, Detroit #2079/R est:800-1300
£4819 $8000 €6988 Seated couple with umbrella (20x28cm-8x11in) W/C. 13-Jun-3 Du Mouchelle, Detroit #2218/R est:800-1300

PENFOLD, Frank C (1849-1920) American
£1096 $1600 €1644 Northern New England seascape (25x51cm-10x20in) s. panel. 3-Nov-1 North East Auctions, Portsmouth #236/R
£3165 $5000 €4748 French peasant girl in a landscape (38x56cm-15x22in) s.d.1891 prov. 24-Apr-3 Shannon's, Milford #117/R est:5000-7000

PENFOLD, W J (19th C) British
£4400 $6864 €6600 Cattle and sheep resting by a tree stump. Farm horse and chickens (15x19cm-6x7in) s.d.1870 pair. 6-Nov-2 Bonhams, Chester #509/R est:1500-2500

PENGILLEY, Robert (1944-) Australian
£1434 $2179 €2151 Morning at Campbell's Cove (120x180cm-47x71in) s. 27-Aug-2 Goodman, Sydney #174/R est:4000-8000 (A.D 4000)

PENKOAT, Pierre (1945-) French
£344 $561 €520 Composition geometrique (55x33cm-22x13in) s. 1-Feb-3 Claude Aguttes, Neuilly #219/R
£443 $691 €700 Composition (21x27cm-8x11in) s. i.verso oil pastel cardboard. 20-Oct-2 Charbonneaux, Paris #82 est:450-500
£468 $748 €650 Le Mesnil (44x36cm-17x14in) s. oil collage panel. 18-May-3 Charbonneaux, Paris #198

Works on paper
£331 $540 €500 Composition cubiste (100x62cm-39x24in) s. gouache cardboard newspaper paper on isorel. 31-Jan-3 Charbonneaux, Paris #145/R
£510 $853 €730 Guitare et clarinette (42x53cm-17x21in) s. mixed media cardboard. 25-Jun-3 Claude Aguttes, Neuilly #232/R

PENLEY, Aaron Edwin (1807-1870) British
Works on paper
£850 $1420 €1233 Loch Awe in summer (49x99cm-19x39in) s. W/C. 9-Jul-3 George Kidner, Lymington #124/R

PENLEY, Edwin A (fl.1853-1890) British
Works on paper
£260 $411 €390 Wood gatherer by a lake (18x46cm-7x18in) mono.d.1865 W/C. 27-Apr-3 Lots Road, London #343

PENN, Irving (1917-) American
Photographs
£1840 $3000 €2760 Aaron Copeland, New York (22x19cm-9x7in) s. i.d.1946 verso gelatin silver print. 12-Feb-3 Christie's, Rockefeller NY #85/R est:4000-6000
£2000 $3200 €3000 Oliver Smith with Jane and Paul Bowles (24x19cm-9x7in) with sig. silver print. 15-May-3 Swann Galleries, New York #460/R est:4000-6000
£2454 $4000 €3681 Spencer Tracy, New York (24x20cm-9x8in) s.i.d.1948 gelatin silver print. 12-Feb-3 Christie's, Rockefeller NY #172/R est:5000-7000
£2532 $4000 €3798 Nude bathing in basin, New York (49x48cm-19x19in) s.i.d.1978/1992-93 platinum palladium print lit. 22-Apr-3 Christie's, Rockefeller NY #95/R est:5000-7000
£3165 $5000 €4748 Spencer Tracy, New York (24x20cm-9x8in) s.i.d.1948 gelatin silver print prov.lit. 22-Apr-3 Christie's, Rockefeller NY #175/R est:6000-8000
£3481 $5500 €5222 Two Asaro mudmen (26x26cm-10x10in) s.i.d.1970 photograph. 23-Apr-3 Sotheby's, New York #252/R est:3000-5000
£3571 $5500 €5357 Farmer with large basket and rope, Cuzco, Peru (20x18cm-8x7in) init.i.d.1948 verso gelatin silver print edition of 6 prov.lit. 25-Oct-2 Phillips, New York #26/R est:6000-8000
£3797 $6000 €5696 New Guinea man with painted on glasses (51x50cm-20x20in) s.i.d.1970-79 num.38/50 platinum palladium print prov.lit. 22-Apr-3 Christie's, Rockefeller NY #102/R est:5000-7000
£3896 $6000 €5844 Sculptor's model, Paris (41x30cm-16x12in) s.i.d.October 1976 num.21/30 verso platinum palladium print prov. 25-Oct-2 Phillips, New York #94/R est:6000-8000
£3896 $6000 €5844 Lily, imperial pink, New York (45x56cm-18x22in) s.i.d.num.16293 verso dye transfer print prov.lit. 25-Oct-2 Phillips, New York #151/R est:7000-10000
£3924 $6200 €5886 Nude no.55 (40x38cm-16x15in) s.i.verso num.55 gelatin silver print prov. 24-Apr-3 Phillips, New York #160/R est:5000-7000
£4114 $6500 €6171 Lion 3/4 view (48x60cm-19x24in) s.i.d.1986 toned selenium print. 23-Apr-3 Sotheby's, New York #254/R est:4000-6000

£4430 $7000 €6645 Two women both with nose rings, Nepal (49x49cm-19x19in) s.d.1967-72 num.5/15 platinum palladium print prov.lit. 22-Apr-3 Christie's, Rockefeller NY #100/R est:5000-7000
£4430 $7000 €6645 Scarred Dahomey girl (33x33cm-13x13in) s.i.d.1967/1984 num.20/21 platinum palladium print prov.lit. 22-Apr-3 Christie's, Rockefeller NY #101/R est:5000-7000
£4430 $7000 €6645 Sculptor's model (42x29cm-17x11in) s.i. num.4/35 platinum palladium print. 23-Apr-3 Sotheby's, New York #243/R est:6000-9000
£5696 $9000 €8544 Balenciaga mantle coat (55x44cm-22x17in) s.i.d.1950 selenium toned. 23-Apr-3 Sotheby's, New York #238/R est:10000-12000
£6329 $10000 €9494 Woman with umbrella (38x36cm-15x14in) s.i.d.1950/1984 gelatin silver print lit. 22-Apr-3 Christie's, Rockefeller NY #66/R est:8000-10000
£6494 $10000 €9741 Poppy, glowing embers, New York (42x54cm-17x21in) s.i.d.1968 num.15549 verso dye transfer print prov.lit. 25-Oct-2 Phillips, New York #149/R est:10000-15000
£6646 $10500 €9969 W. Somerset Maugham (50x50cm-20x20in) s.i.d.1962 num.P869 platinum palladium print prov.lit. 24-Apr-3 Phillips, New York #169/R est:8000-12000
£6962 $11000 €10443 Nude no.62 (40x38cm-16x15in) s.i. gelatin silver print prov.lit. 24-Apr-3 Phillips, New York #36/R est:5000-7000
£7143 $11000 €10715 Woman with umbrella, New York (39x47cm-15x19in) s.i.d.1950 photograph. 24-Oct-2 Sotheby's, New York #204/R est:10000-15000
£7792 $12000 €11688 Alfred Hitchock, New York (25x20cm-10x8in) i.d.May 23 1947 verso gelatin silver print edition of 21 prov.lit. 25-Oct-2 Phillips, New York #27/R est:18000-25000
£8228 $13000 €12342 Nude no.151 (47x45cm-19x18in) s.i.d.1976 num.36/38 platinum palladium print prov. 23-Apr-3 Sotheby's, New York #244/R est:6000-9000
£8442 $13000 €12663 Italian still life, New York (58x47cm-23x19in) s.i.d.Sept 1981 num.13969 verso dye transfer print prov.lit. 25-Oct-2 Phillips, New York #148/R est:9000-12000
£11039 $17000 €16559 Frozen foods, New York (66x53cm-26x21in) s.i.d.1977 num.14695 verso dye transfer print board prov.lit. 25-Oct-2 Phillips, New York #147/R est:15000-20000
£17722 $28000 €26583 Frozen foods, New York (55x44cm-22x17in) s.i.d.1977/1993 dye transfer print prov.lit. 22-Apr-3 Christie's, Rockefeller NY #78/R est:15000-25000
£19620 $31000 €29430 Girl behind bottle (47x45cm-19x18in) s.i.d.1978 platinum palladium print. 23-Apr-3 Sotheby's, New York #237/R est:20000-30000
£22152 $35000 €33228 Cuzco children, Peru (27x25cm-11x10in) s.i.d.1948-49 gelatin silver prints set of three lit. 22-Apr-3 Christie's, Rockefeller NY #123/R est:20000-30000

PENN, S (19/20th C) British?
£360 $562 €540 Dahlias in vases on a ledge. s.d.1898. 20-Sep-2 Moore Allen & Innocent, Cirencester #963

PENN, Stanley (20th C) British
£309 $500 €464 Lake Coomashagen, Glenbeigh (69x107cm-27x42in) s. i.verso. 24-Jan-3 Freeman, Philadelphia #173/R

PENN, William Charles (1877-1968) British
£1300 $2015 €1950 Half length portrait of young girl seated at a table holding a cupid figure (80x69cm-31x27in) s.d.1928. 4-Dec-2 Outhwaite & Litherland, Liverpool #317/R

PENNASILICO, Giuseppe (1861-1940) Italian
£2500 $3875 €3750 La marina (35x54cm-14x21in) indis i.verso board. 5-Dec-2 Christie's, Kensington #35/R est:2000-3000

PENNE, Olivier de (1831-1897) French
£1250 $2000 €1875 Hunt scene with two hounds chasing down a fox (25x20cm-10x8in) s. 17-May-3 Pook & Pook, Downington #175b/R est:1800-2500
£2483 $4022 €3600 Gundogs (47x37cm-19x15in) s. panel. 26-May-3 Bukowskis, Stockholm #253/R est:30000-35000 (S.KR 32000)
£5247 $8500 €7608 Waiting for master (28x23cm-11x9in) s. panel. 21-May-3 Doyle, New York #193/R est:5000-7000
£5806 $9000 €8709 Hunting dogs on a forest path (46x37cm-18x15in) s. panel. 30-Oct-2 Christie's, Rockefeller NY #125/R est:8000-12000
£7097 $11000 €10646 Huntmaster with his dogs on a forest trail (41x33cm-16x13in) s. panel prov.exhib. 30-Oct-2 Christie's, Rockefeller NY #124/R est:8000-12000
£7278 $11500 €11500 Le relais de chiens (24x33cm-9x13in) s. panel. 1-Dec-2 Peron, Melun #42
£10063 $16000 €15095 Packs of hunting hounds (27x21cm-11x8in) s. panel pair. 7-Mar-3 Skinner, Boston #240/R est:10000-15000
£28777 $46043 €40000 Sanglier au ferme (145x128cm-57x50in) s. 16-May-3 Beaussant & Lefèvre, Paris #44/R est:15000-18000
£28777 $46043 €40000 Cerf tenant les abois (151x128cm-59x50in) s. 16-May-3 Beaussant & Lefèvre, Paris #45/R est:15000-18000

Works on paper
£257 $405 €400 Chiens au terrier (18x25cm-7x10in) bears st.sig. black pencil htd W/C dr. 18-Nov-2 Tajan, Paris #115
£1835 $2900 €2900 Le depart pour la chasse a courre (19x27cm-7x11in) s. W/C. 1-Dec-2 Peron, Melun #10

PENNELL, Harry (19th C) British
£850 $1326 €1275 Edge of the cornfield (40x61cm-16x24in) s. i.verso. 25-Mar-3 Bonhams, Leeds #632
£1800 $2808 €2700 Near Bray (60x100cm-24x39in) s. s.i.verso. 8-Oct-2 Bonhams, Knightsbridge #184/R est:2000-3000
£2038 $3180 €2955 In the cornfield. At the well (41x61cm-16x24in) s.i. pair. 26-Mar-3 Walker's, Ottawa #66/R est:4000-5000 (C.D 4750)

PENNELL, Joseph (1860-1926) American
£3313 $5500 €4804 View of New York City in winter. New York Harbour (25x32cm-10x13in) one s. one s.indis.i. W/C gouache pair prov. 11-Jun-3 Butterfields, San Francisco #4045/R est:3000-5000

Works on paper
£549 $900 €796 Brooklyn Heights. Brooklyn (24x34cm-9x13in) mono.i. pencil double-sided. 5-Jun-3 Swann Galleries, New York #193/R
£645 $1000 €968 Snowy roofs (20x28cm-8x11in) s. i.verso W/C en grisaille. 29-Oct-2 John Moran, Pasadena #686b
£1154 $1800 €1731 Smoke screen (25x33cm-10x13in) s. gouache prov. 21-Sep-2 Rachel Davis, Shaker Heights #352/R est:1200-1800

PENNINGTON, Harper (1854-1920) American

Works on paper
£900 $1404 €1350 Portrait of Cope Whitehouse wearing Eastern dress (48x38cm-19x15in) s.d.1898 pastel dr. 25-Mar-3 Gorringes, Bexhill #1196/R
£1227 $2000 €1841 Beach scenes (13x20cm-5x8in) s. one d.92 gouache pair. 16-Feb-3 Jeffery Burchard, Florida #77

PENNINGTON, John (1773-1841) British
£330 $538 €495 Figures on a village street in winter (29x36cm-11x14in) s.i. 30-Jan-3 Lawrence, Crewkerne #683/R

PENNISI, Getulio (?) Italian
£1224 $1947 €1800 Mystic marriage of Saint Catherine (81x100cm-32x39in) s. 24-Mar-3 Finarte Semenzato, Rome #274/R

PENNOYER, Albert Shelton (1888-1957) American

Works on paper
£548 $850 €822 Afternoon in San Diego (53x33cm-21x13in) s. i.verso pastel. 29-Oct-2 John Moran, Pasadena #661

PENNY, Edward (attrib) (1714-1791) British
£1000 $1630 €1500 Portrait of a lady. Portrait of a gentleman (38x33cm-15x13in) pair painted oval. 29-Jan-3 Sotheby's, Olympia #5/R est:800-1200

PENNY, Edwin (1930-) British

Works on paper
£1100 $1738 €1595 Little owl (36x25cm-14x10in) s. W/C bodycol. 22-Jul-3 Bonhams, Knightsbridge #43/R est:1000-1500

PENNY, William Daniel (1834-1924) British
£550 $869 €825 Shipping scenes (15x23cm-6x9in) s. one d.1898 board pair. 12-Nov-2 Bonhams, Knightsbridge #298g/R
£1000 $1520 €1500 Shipping at anchor in a calm (28x46cm-11x18in) s.d.89 lit. 15-Aug-2 Bonhams, New Bond Street #333 est:1000-1500

PENONE, Giuseppe (1947-) Italian

Works on paper
£949 $1481 €1500 Plan (12x25cm-5x10in) s.i.verso pencil card. 19-Oct-2 Semenzato, Venice #52/R
£1905 $3029 €2800 Visage feuille (49x35cm-19x14in) s.d.1983 graphite prov. 24-Mar-3 Cornette de St.Cyr, Paris #196/R
£4218 $6706 €6200 Untitled (80x112cm-31x44in) s.d.1987 chlorophyll wood exhib. 24-Mar-3 Cornette de St.Cyr, Paris #197/R

PENOT, Albert Joseph (19th C) French
£1100 $1760 €1650 Half length study of a semi draped woman with flowers in her hair (58x40cm-23x16in) s. panel. 11-Mar-3 Bonhams, Knightsbridge #127/R est:1200-1800
£1829 $3000 €2652 Subtle glance (51x61cm-20x24in) s. 4-Jun-3 Doyle, New York #79/R est:3000-5000

PENOT, Jean Vallette (1710-1777) French
£12587 $21021 €18000 Trompe-l'oeil aux gravures et a l'assiette de cerises (62x50cm-24x20in) 27-Jun-3 Piasa, Paris #34/R est:18000-23000

PENROSE, Sir Roland (1900-1984) British
£17123 $26884 €25000 Union nocturne (41x30cm-16x12in) i.d.1936 verso panel. 15-Apr-3 Laurence Calmels, Paris #4395/R est:3000

PENSTONE, Constance (19th C) British
Works on paper
£322 $508 €483 Geese around the fountain (25x36cm-10x14in) s. W/C. 1-Apr-3 Stephan Welz, Johannesburg #161 (SA.R 4000)

PEPLOE, Samuel John (1871-1935) British
£4500 $7290 €6750 Comrie (12x21cm-5x8in) s. s.i.verso panel exhib. 23-May-3 Lyon & Turnbull, Edinburgh #60/R est:4000-6000
£9500 $15390 €14250 Tantallon Castle (33x40cm-13x16in) s.d.1909 verso panel prov. 23-May-3 Lyon & Turnbull, Edinburgh #87/R est:8000-12000
£10000 $16200 €15000 North Berwick (15x23cm-6x9in) s. s.i.verso panel prov.exhib. 23-May-3 Lyon & Turnbull, Edinburgh #59/R est:7000-9000
£34000 $53040 €51000 Iona (38x46cm-15x18in) s. panel. 14-Apr-3 Sotheby's, London #107/R est:30000-40000
£76000 $115520 €114000 Still life with jug, melon, grapes and apples (56x50cm-22x20in) s. board prov. 28-Aug-2 Sotheby's, London #1073/R est:60000-80000
£125000 $198750 €187500 Roses in a Chinese vase (51x41cm-20x16in) s. painted c.1923 prov.exhib. 6-Mar-3 Christie's, Kensington #205/R est:100000-150000
£160000 $249600 €240000 Still life with oranges and roses in an oriental vase (52x40cm-20x16in) s. prov. 14-Apr-3 Sotheby's, London #106/R est:150000-200000
£235000 $364250 €352500 Roses in a blue and white vase (51x41cm-20x16in) s. painted c.1925. 31-Oct-2 Christie's, London #128/R est:100000-150000
Works on paper
£6000 $9120 €9000 Girl with a boa (23x17cm-9x7in) s.i. red chk prov. 28-Aug-2 Sotheby's, London #1074/R est:3000-4000

PEPOON, Willis A (c.1860-1940) American
£563 $900 €816 Portrait of Peter Castor (64x76cm-25x30in) s.d.1903. 16-May-3 York Town, York #999

PEPPER, Beverly (1924-) American
Sculpture
£1154 $1800 €1731 Untitled (15cm-6in) s.i. steel. 14-Sep-2 Weschler, Washington #642/R est:1500-2500

PEPPER, Charles Hovey (1864-1950) American
Works on paper
£219 $350 €318 Mountain lake, sunset (24x34cm-9x13in) s. W/C gouache paper on board. 16-May-3 Skinner, Boston #247/R

PEPPER, George Douglas (1903-1962) Canadian
£173 $275 €251 Welcome to the sultan (25x30cm-10x12in) s. board. 1-May-3 Heffel, Vancouver #82/R (C.D 400)
£216 $344 €313 Night in Xauen (30x41cm-12x16in) s. canvasboard prov. 1-May-3 Heffel, Vancouver #79/R (C.D 500)
£448 $717 €672 French - poles, water and path (22x27cm-9x11in) i.verso board prov. 15-May-3 Heffel, Vancouver #62/R est:1200-1500 (C.D 1000)
£524 $828 €786 Ice forms, Ellesmere Island (61x102cm-24x40in) s.i. s.verso prov.exhib. 14-Nov-2 Heffel, Vancouver #111/R est:1500-2500 (C.D 1300)
£645 $1019 €968 Francois, Newfoundland (38x46cm-15x18in) s. i.verso canvasboard prov. 14-Nov-2 Heffel, Vancouver #112 est:1500-2000 (C.D 1600)
£673 $1076 €1010 Sky over Charlevoix (30x36cm-12x14in) i.verso board prov. 15-May-3 Heffel, Vancouver #61/R est:1500-2000 (C.D 1500)
£1210 $1911 €1815 Bylot Island (30x41cm-12x16in) s.i. verso canvasboard prov. 14-Nov-2 Heffel, Vancouver #110/R est:1500-2000 (C.D 3000)
£1233 $1973 €1850 Glacier ice forms, Davis Strait (30x41cm-12x16in) s. i.verso canvasboard prov. 15-May-3 Heffel, Vancouver #218/R est:2000-2500 (C.D 2750)
£1244 $2041 €1866 Winter landscape with river (22x30cm-9x12in) s. panel. 3-Jun-3 Joyner, Toronto #258/R est:3000-4000 (C.D 2800)
Works on paper
£173 $275 €251 Portrait of an Inuit man (38x28cm-15x11in) s. W/C prov. 1-May-3 Heffel, Vancouver #80/R (C.D 400)
£282 $446 €423 Arctic sketch (38x53cm-15x21in) s.i.verso W/C prov. 14-Nov-2 Heffel, Vancouver #145 (C.D 700)
£314 $502 €471 Morraine lake (30x40cm-12x16in) W/C prov. 15-May-3 Heffel, Vancouver #214 (C.D 700)
£314 $502 €471 Newfoundland coast (30x41cm-12x16in) s.d.1954 i.verso W/C prov. 15-May-3 Heffel, Vancouver #219 (C.D 700)

PER, Sophie (20th C) ?
£280 $442 €406 Bowl of summer flowers (8x8cm-3x3in) 22-Jul-3 Riddetts, Bournemouth #486

PERAIRE, Paul Emmanuel (1829-1893) French
£2817 $4676 €4000 Bain froid a la grande jatte (38x55cm-15x22in) s.i. 15-Jun-3 Anaf, Lyon #179/R est:4000-5000

PERALTA DEL CAMPO, Francisco (1837-1897) Spanish
£600 $936 €900 Portrait of Franciscan monk with a beard (49x37cm-19x15in) s.d.1866. 26-Mar-3 Sotheby's, Olympia #181/R
£1572 $2453 €2500 Soldier (25x20cm-10x8in) s. board. 23-Sep-2 Durán, Madrid #241/R

PERALTA, Pedro (1961-) Uruguayan
£288 $450 €432 Flying dream (60x80cm-24x31in) acrylic prov. 10-Oct-2 Galleria Y Remates, Montevideo #87/R

PERAUX, Lionel (1871-?) French
Works on paper
£2390 $3704 €3800 Venice (42x29cm-17x11in) s. W/C. 5-Oct-2 De Vuyst, Lokeren #288/R est:3000-4000

PERBOYRE, Paul Emile Léon (c.1826-1907) French
£313 $500 €454 Military men on horseback (53x64cm-21x25in) s. 17-May-3 CRN Auctions, Cambridge #28
£4808 $7548 €7500 Charge (66x49cm-26x19in) s. 16-Dec-2 Rabourdin & Choppin de Janvry, Paris #55/R est:15000

PERCEVAL, Celia (1949-) Australian
£297 $484 €446 Bleached light on the Cloncurry Hills, NQ (90x120cm-35x47in) s. board. 3-Feb-3 Lawson Menzies, Sydney #388 (A.D 820)
£326 $532 €489 Everlastings near Yalgoo (53x73cm-21x29in) s. paper. 3-Feb-3 Lawson Menzies, Sydney #347 (A.D 900)
£435 $709 €653 Banksia, blackboys and wild flowers, Kalbarri National Park (90x120cm-35x47in) s. board. 3-Feb-3 Lawson Menzies, Sydney #404 (A.D 1200)
£571 $903 €857 Late spring near Hatfield (61x64cm-24x25in) s.d.72. 18-Nov-2 Joel, Victoria #270 est:1500-1800 (A.D 1600)
£571 $903 €857 Rain on Regents Park (90x75cm-35x30in) s.d.72. 18-Nov-2 Joel, Victoria #364 est:2000-2500 (A.D 1600)

PERCEVAL, Don Louis (1908-1979) American
Works on paper
£1442 $2250 €2163 Two camping wagons (25x28cm-10x11in) s.d.31 gouache on paperboard prov. 9-Nov-2 Santa Fe Art, Santa Fe #242/R est:1500-2500
£1720 $2700 €2580 Rider on the plains (26x30cm-10x12in) s. W/C prov. 20-Nov-2 Christie's, Los Angeles #30/R est:2500-3500

PERCEVAL, John (1923-2000) Australian
£766 $1203 €1149 Mother of Romulus and Remus (58x76cm-23x30in) s. oil on paper. 15-Apr-3 Lawson Menzies, Sydney #185/R est:2500-3500 (A.D 2000)
£786 $1241 €1179 Orange angle (55x74cm-22x29in) s. oil on paper. 18-Nov-2 Joel, Victoria #385 est:1000-1500 (A.D 2200)
£1075 $1634 €1613 Angel (65x42cm-26x17in) s.d.1961 paper. 28-Aug-2 Deutscher-Menzies, Melbourne #179/R est:3500-5500 (A.D 3000)
£1362 $2070 €2043 Nude (66x42cm-26x17in) s. paper painted c.1961. 28-Aug-2 Deutscher-Menzies, Melbourne #178/R est:3500-5500 (A.D 3800)
£2107 $3308 €3161 Seascape (30x37cm-12x15in) s. s.d.84 verso oil model ship on canvas. 15-Apr-3 Lawson Menzies, Sydney #3/R est:5500-7500 (A.D 5500)
£2151 $3269 €3227 Nude and figure (65x41cm-26x16in) s.d.1961 paper. 28-Aug-2 Deutscher-Menzies, Melbourne #115/R est:6000-8000 (A.D 6000)
£2299 $3425 €3449 Colour painting (66x41cm-26x16in) s.d.62 oil on paper. 27-Aug-2 Christie's, Melbourne #321/R est:6000-10000 (A.D 6000)

£3571 $5536 €5357 Rabbit caught in a trap (36x45cm-14x18in) s. 29-Oct-2 Lawson Menzies, Sydney #34/R est:9000-15000 (A.D 10000)
£3584 $5448 €5376 Venice (53x68cm-21x27in) s.d.87 exhib. 28-Aug-2 Deutscher-Menzies, Melbourne #129/R est:10000-15000 (A.D 10000)
£4215 $6617 €6323 Flowers in a milk jug (45x35cm-18x14in) s. 15-Apr-3 Lawson Menzies, Sydney #2/R est:10000-15000 (A.D 11000)
£4732 $7192 €7098 Sunflowers to remember the famous (40x30cm-16x12in) s. s.i.verso linen. 28-Aug-2 Deutscher-Menzies, Melbourne #14/R est:10000-15000 (A.D 13200)
£6429 $10157 €9644 River Overgrowth (33x35cm-13x14in) s.d.58 board prov. 27-Nov-2 Deutscher-Menzies, Melbourne #46/R est:22000-28000 (A.D 18000)
£6911 $10919 €10021 Sunflowers (44x34cm-17x13in) s. s.i.verso. 22-Jul-3 Lawson Menzies, Sydney #119/R est:10000-15000 (A.D 17000)
£7117 $10890 €10676 Daisy bates at the you yangs (91x122cm-36x48in) s.d.90 i.verso prov. 25-Aug-2 Sotheby's, Paddington #17/R est:20000-30000 (A.D 20000)
£8765 $14375 €13148 Monk in the cornfield (76x101cm-30x40in) s.d.88 i.d.verso exhib. 4-Jun-3 Deutscher-Menzies, Melbourne #124/R est:25000-30000 (A.D 22000)
£8915 $14174 €13373 Angel in the mirror (66x56cm-26x22in) s.i.d.64/5 prov.exhib. 5-May-3 Sotheby's, Melbourne #156/R est:20000-30000 (A.D 23000)
£9562 $15681 €14343 French nun with fig leaves (76x102cm-30x40in) s.d.89 s.i.verso. 4-Jun-3 Deutscher-Menzies, Melbourne #87/R est:28000-35000 (A.D 24000)
£10078 $16023 €15117 Angel (56x44cm-22x17in) s.d.46-67 canvasboard. 5-May-3 Sotheby's, Melbourne #116/R est:18000-22000 (A.D 26000)
£10676 $16335 €16014 Card players at sunset (75x95cm-30x37in) s. painted c.1985 prov. 26-Aug-2 Sotheby's, Paddington #516/R est:18000-20000 (A.D 30000)
£12195 $19268 €17683 Sunflowers (61x50cm-24x20in) s. s.i.verso. 22-Jul-3 Lawson Menzies, Sydney #3/R est:15000-25000 (A.D 30000)
£12749 $20908 €19124 Snow on Two Chums Mine (81x101cm-32x40in) s. s.i.verso painted c.1980. 4-Jun-3 Deutscher-Menzies, Melbourne #47/R est:25000-35000 (A.D 32000)
£15326 $24061 €22989 Heath and warrle (80x100cm-31x39in) s.i. 15-Apr-3 Lawson Menzies, Sydney #36/R est:45000-65000 (A.D 40000)
£16279 $25884 €24419 Boat from Venice, at Williamstown (90x120cm-35x47in) s.d.89 s.i.d.89 verso exhib. 5-May-3 Sotheby's, Melbourne #145/R est:40000-60000 (A.D 42000)
£16370 $25046 €24555 Winter landscape, Gaffney's Creek (91x73cm-36x29in) s.d.58 oil on polystyrene panel prov. 26-Aug-2 Sotheby's, Paddington #562/R est:45000-65000 (A.D 46000)
£16370 $25046 €24555 Romantic landscape with horse and sulky (81x117cm-32x46in) s.d.69 s.i.d.verso prov. 25-Aug-2 Sotheby's, Paddington #65/R est:45000-60000 (A.D 46000)
£21429 $33643 €32144 Goat in a bayswater garden (91x92cm-36x36in) s.d.1956 board prov. 25-Nov-2 Christie's, Melbourne #72/R est:70000-90000 (A.D 60000)
£32520 $51382 €47154 Pleasure craft (90x152cm-35x60in) s. i.verso. 22-Jul-3 Lawson Menzies, Sydney #32/R est:80000-100000 (A.D 80000)
£34483 $51379 €51725 Tug boat in the floating dock, Williamstown (91x121cm-36x48in) s.d.68 s.i.d.verso prov.exhib.lit. 27-Aug-2 Christie's, Melbourne #31/R est:80000-100000 (A.D 90000)
£73171 $115610 €106098 London Bridge, Portsea 1957 (84x112cm-33x44in) s. prov.exhib. 22-Jul-3 Lawson Menzies, Sydney #35/R est:200000-300000 (A.D 180000)
£94306 $144288 €141459 Fisherman's sights, Williamstown (91x122cm-36x48in) s.d.1956 board prov.exhib. 26-Aug-2 Sotheby's, Paddington #519/R est:300000-500000 (A.D 265000)

Works on paper

£321 $508 €482 Portrait of Neil Douglas (32x43cm-13x17in) s.d.79 pencil prov. 27-Nov-2 Deutscher-Menzies, Melbourne #237/R est:1200-1400 (A.D 900)
£351 $533 €527 Flower lady (21x15cm-8x6in) init.d.87 pencil. 19-Aug-2 Joel, Victoria #168 est:1000-1500 (A.D 1000)
£357 $561 €536 Untitled (51x71cm-20x28in) s.d.83 ink prov. 25-Nov-2 Christie's, Melbourne #380 (A.D 1000)
£383 $602 €575 Cow beside a pond at sunset (26x35cm-10x14in) s, ink paper on board. 15-Apr-3 Lawson Menzies, Sydney #184/R est:1000-2000 (A.D 1000)
£386 $587 €579 Insects as decoration (21x16cm-8x6in) init.d.64 pencil. 19-Aug-2 Joel, Victoria #252 est:1000-1500 (A.D 1100)
£393 $621 €590 Female portrait (26x20cm-10x8in) s.d.74 pencil pen ink. 27-Nov-2 Deutscher-Menzies, Melbourne #171/R est:1200-1800 (A.D 1100)
£464 $733 €696 Female nude (29x20cm-11x8in) init.i.d.87 pencil. 27-Nov-2 Deutscher-Menzies, Melbourne #235/R est:1400-1600 (A.D 1300)
£464 $733 €696 Nude (27x20cm-11x8in) init.d.87 pencil. 27-Nov-2 Deutscher-Menzies, Melbourne #236/R est:1400-1600 (A.D 1300)
£536 $847 €804 Jack-in-the-box (29x20cm-11x8in) init.d.87 pencil. 27-Nov-2 Deutscher-Menzies, Melbourne #234/R est:1700-1900 (A.D 1500)
£536 $842 €804 Pond at sunset (26x35cm-10x14in) s.d.58 ink paper on board. 15-Apr-3 Lawson Menzies, Sydney #181/R est:1000-2000 (A.D 1400)
£561 $853 €842 American Angel landing on the moon (26x18cm-10x7in) s.i.d.67 pencil. 19-Aug-2 Joel, Victoria #173 est:1500-2500 (A.D 1600)
£571 $903 €857 Girl seated (67x42cm-26x17in) s. felt tip pen. 27-Nov-2 Deutscher-Menzies, Melbourne #170/R est:2000-3000 (A.D 1600)
£575 $856 €863 Animals at Murrumbeena (27x36cm-11x14in) s.d.Aug 46 chl prov. 27-Aug-2 Christie's, Melbourne #338 est:1500-2000 (A.D 1500)
£575 $902 €863 Pregnant nude (45x33cm-18x13in) s.d.49 pencil W/C. 15-Apr-3 Lawson Menzies, Sydney #179/R est:1200-1600 (A.D 1500)
£575 $902 €863 Pair of heads (27x18cm-11x7in) s.d.63 ink. 15-Apr-3 Lawson Menzies, Sydney #180/R est:900-1500 (A.D 1500)
£610 $964 €885 Ben and Julie in their garden (29x41cm-11x16in) s.d.88 W/C. 22-Jul-3 Lawson Menzies, Sydney #178/R est:800-1200 (A.D 1500)
£643 $1015 €965 Lovers (25x37cm-10x15in) s.d.48 ink wash. 27-Nov-2 Deutscher-Menzies, Melbourne #169/R est:2500-3500 (A.D 1800)
£690 $1083 €1035 Cows and trees (27x38cm-11x15in) s. pencil. 15-Apr-3 Lawson Menzies, Sydney #186/R est:2000-4000 (A.D 1800)
£773 $1221 €1121 Boat in the harbour (42x67cm-17x26in) s.d.60 ink. 22-Jul-3 Lawson Menzies, Sydney #176/R est:1500-2500 (A.D 1900)
£786 $1241 €1179 Two figures (26x33cm-10x13in) s.d.47 pencil. 27-Nov-2 Deutscher-Menzies, Melbourne #168/R est:2500-3500 (A.D 2200)
£894 $1413 €1296 Mustering the cattle (41x71cm-16x28in) s.d.72 pencil. 22-Jul-3 Lawson Menzies, Sydney #183/R est:2000-4000 (A.D 2200)
£1143 $1806 €1715 Albert Tucker (37x27cm-15x11in) s.i.d.26 Feb 60 ink. 27-Nov-2 Deutscher-Menzies, Melbourne #139/R est:3500-4500 (A.D 3200)
£1753 $2875 €2630 Mandy Pandy (47x55cm-19x22in) s.i.d.1950 conte prov. 4-Jun-3 Deutscher-Menzies, Melbourne #290/R est:3500-4500 (A.D 4400)
£1964 $3104 €2946 Nativity (36x41cm-14x16in) s.d.46 pencil prov. 27-Nov-2 Deutscher-Menzies, Melbourne #142/R est:5000-7000 (A.D 5500)
£5000 $7900 €7500 Fisherman with his catch (58x58cm-23x23in) s.d.1950 painted tiles. 26-Nov-2 Sotheby's, Melbourne #10/R est:15000-20000 (A.D 14000)

PERCEVAL, Matthew (1945-) Australian

£358 $545 €537 Spring blossoms (61x76cm-24x30in) s. 28-Aug-2 Deutscher-Menzies, Melbourne #439/R (A.D 1000)
£558 $914 €837 Bush landscape (122x91cm-48x36in) s.d.84 composition board. 4-Jun-3 Deutscher-Menzies, Melbourne #337/R (A.D 1400)
£714 $1129 €1071 Boats waiting offshore (151x120cm-59x47in) s. 18-Nov-2 Goodman, Sydney #135/R (A.D 2000)
£1214 $1918 €1821 Northern landscape (91x122cm-36x48in) s.d.84 board. 27-Nov-2 Deutscher-Menzies, Melbourne #185/R est:2000-3000 (A.D 3400)

PERCIER, Charles (1764-1838) French

Works on paper

£1543 $2500 €2315 Studies for platter (30x25cm-12x10in) i. chk ink wash. 21-Jan-3 Sotheby's, New York #132/R

PERCIVAL, Harold (1868-1914) British

Works on paper

£800 $1240 €1200 Mataura of London (29x44cm-11x17in) s.d.1891 W/C pair. 2-Oct-2 George Kidner, Lymington #114

PERCY, Arthur (1886-1976) Swedish

£310 $503 €450 Summer landscape from Alvaret, Oland (54x64cm-21x25in) s.d.1935. 25-May-3 Uppsala Auktionskammare, Uppsala #183 (S.KR 4000)
£496 $770 €744 Still life of roses in vase (35x27cm-14x11in) s.i.d.1932. 8-Dec-2 Uppsala Auktionskammare, Uppsala #254 (S.KR 7000)
£1472 $2296 €2208 Still life of flowers (55x37cm-22x15in) s.d.1945 panel. 6-Nov-2 AB Stockholms Auktionsverk #548/R est:12000-15000 (S.KR 21000)
£1472 $2296 €2208 White amaryllis (55x38cm-22x15in) s.d.1905 panel. 5-Nov-2 Bukowskis, Stockholm #52/R est:20000-25000 (S.KR 21000)
£1749 $2763 €2624 Ingrid, the artist's daughter in Paris (81x60cm-32x24in) s.i.d.1921 exhib. 28-Apr-3 Bukowskis, Stockholm #31/R est:25000-30000 (S.KR 23000)

£1939 $3142 €2812 Still life of flowers in French vase (47x37cm-19x15in) s.d.1920 panel. 25-May-3 Uppsala Auktionskammare, Uppsala #245/R est:20000-25000 (S.KR 25000)
£2053 $3244 €3080 Women bathing (65x81cm-26x32in) s.d.1916. 28-Apr-3 Bukowskis, Stockholm #19/R est:30000-35000 (S.KR 27000)
£2281 $3605 €3422 Still life of flowers and other objects against blue background (73x82cm-29x32in) s.d.1958. 28-Apr-3 Bukowskis, Stockholm #55/R est:40000-45000 (S.KR 30000)
£5323 $8411 €7985 Still life of flowers in vases (94x65cm-37x26in) s. 28-Apr-3 Bukowskis, Stockholm #63/R est:80000-100000 (S.KR 70000)

PERCY, F (19th C) British
£1200 $1908 €1800 Portrait of a horses head and two dogs (25x20cm-10x8in) s. panel. 19-Mar-3 John Nicholson, Haslemere #1171/R est:1200-1500
£3957 $6489 €5500 La caravane (34x84cm-13x33in) s. 4-Jun-3 Tajan, Paris #292/R est:5300-6300

PERCY, Sidney Richard (1821-1886) British
£1800 $2862 €2700 Highland road (20x30cm-8x12in) s.d.69. 6-Mar-3 Christie's, Kensington #74/R est:2000-3000
£3205 $5000 €4808 Highland loch with shepherds, maidens and cattle (51x97cm-20x38in) s. 20-Sep-2 New Orleans Auction, New Orleans #489/R est:12000-18000
£4000 $6320 €6000 On the Glaslyn, near Beddgelert, North Wales (13x22cm-5x9in) s.d.78 board. 26-Nov-2 Christie's, London #82/R est:5000-7000
£4500 $7155 €6750 Cader idris from the Mawddach (24x43cm-9x17in) s. i.on stretcher. 18-Mar-3 Bonhams, New Bond Street #60/R est:4000-6000
£4500 $7425 €6525 Figures and cattle in a mountain landscape (55x91cm-22x36in) s.d.1854. 2-Jul-3 Sotheby's, Olympia #341/R est:3000-5000
£7800 $12246 €11700 Lakeland landscape (21x46cm-8x18in) s. 19-Nov-2 Bonhams, Leeds #232/R est:3000-4000
£10357 $16364 €15536 Honester Grag, Cumberland (23x36cm-9x14in) s.d.70. 26-Nov-2 Sotheby's, Melbourne #211/R est:25000-35000 (A.D 29000)
£14839 $23000 €22259 Glen Dochrt, Perthshire (61x91cm-24x36in) s.d.1885 prov. 7-Dec-2 Neal Auction Company, New Orleans #285/R est:15000-25000
£15000 $24900 €22500 Autumn, Haslemere, Surrey (51x95cm-20x37in) s.d.66. 10-Jun-3 Christie's, London #134/R est:15000-20000
£28000 $46480 €42000 Lake in Wales (60x96cm-24x38in) s.d.1862. 10-Jun-3 Christie's, London #141/R est:30000-40000
£60000 $94200 €90000 Capel curig (61x102cm-24x40in) s.d.1873 prov. 19-Nov-2 Bonhams, New Bond Street #127/R est:60000-80000
£68000 $107440 €102000 Loch Coruisk, Isle of Skye (116x182cm-46x72in) s.d.1874 exhib. 2-Dec-2 Sotheby's, London #90/R est:70000-100000

PERCY, William (1820-1903) British
Works on paper
£597 $872 €896 Goose girl (52x37cm-20x15in) s. W/C. 12-Sep-1 Watson's, Christchurch #6 est:1500-2500 (NZ.D 2000)

PERDIKIDIS, Dimitri (1922-) Greek
£759 $1199 €1100 Composition II (50x63cm-20x25in) s.i.d.1965 verso oil collage canvas on board. 1-Apr-3 Segre, Madrid #330/R

PEREDA, Antonio de (1599-1669) Spanish
£135000 $225450 €195750 The Immaculate Conception (223x156cm-88x61in) prov.exhib. 10-Jul-3 Sotheby's, London #42/R est:20000-30000

PEREHUDOFF, Catherine (1958-) Canadian
Works on paper
£847 $1347 €1271 Spring colours (55x73cm-22x29in) s.d.1997 W/C. 23-Mar-3 Hodgins, Calgary #70/R est:750-1000 (C.D 2000)

PEREHUDOFF, William (1919-) Canadian
£258 $402 €387 Composition (56x75cm-22x30in) s.d.84 acrylic on paper. 25-Mar-3 Ritchie, Toronto #179/R (C.D 600)
£489 $802 €734 ACP 79-46 (57x77cm-22x30in) s. acrylic on paper prov. 3-Jun-3 Joyner, Toronto #499 est:500-700 (C.D 1100)
£652 $1017 €1088 AC87-44 (81x81cm-32x32in) s. i.d.1987 verso acrylic. 13-Apr-3 Levis, Calgary #318/R est:2500-3500 (C.D 1500)
£1205 $1904 €1808 AC 80 70 (79x178cm-31x70in) d.1980 acrylic. 1-Dec-2 Levis, Calgary #321/R (C.D 3000)
£3086 $4784 €4629 Untitled (180x132cm-71x52in) s. 3-Dec-2 Joyner, Toronto #188/R est:2500-3500 (C.D 7500)
Works on paper
£222 $364 €322 North of Saskatoon (36x51cm-14x20in) W/C. 1-Jun-3 Levis, Calgary #96/R (C.D 500)

PEREIRA, F V (20th C) Philippino
£1415 $2208 €2250 Children playing in the Philippines (50x40cm-20x16in) s.d.1957 cannvas on cardboard. 23-Sep-2 Durán, Madrid #127/R

PERELLI, Achille (1822-1891) American/Italian
Works on paper
£1923 $3000 €2885 Nature morte, red winged blackbird and robin (64x28cm-25x11in) s. W/C. 12-Oct-2 Neal Auction Company, New Orleans #485/R est:4000-6000
£2885 $4500 €4328 Nature morte, mallard or green headed duck (61x30cm-24x12in) s. W/C. 12-Oct-2 Neal Auction Company, New Orleans #486/R est:6000-9000

PERELLON, Celedonio (1926-) Spanish
£759 $1206 €1100 Nude (58x43cm-23x17in) s.d.94 canvas on board. 4-Mar-3 Ansorena, Madrid #277/R

PERELMANN, Iosif Yankelevich (1876-?) Russian
£5500 $8910 €8250 After the Easter vigil (92x64cm-36x25in) s.i.d.1907. 21-May-3 Sotheby's, London #127/R est:5000-7000

PEREPLETCHIKOFF, Vladimir Vassilievitch (1863-1918) Russian
£1500 $2354 €2250 Woodland meadow (19x26cm-7x10in) s. canvas on board lit. 20-Nov-2 Sotheby's, London #50/R est:2000-3000

PERETZ, David (1906-) French
£280 $440 €420 Lorier rose (55x46cm-22x18in) s.d.54 i.verso prov.exhib. 10-Dec-2 Rosebery Fine Art, London #624
£280 $440 €420 Floral study in blue and green (55x46cm-22x18in) s.d.54 prov. 10-Dec-2 Rosebery Fine Art, London #625/R
£280 $440 €420 Paysage aux gladiolles (55x46cm-22x18in) s.d.55 i.verso prov.exhib. 10-Dec-2 Rosebery Fine Art, London #628/R
£280 $440 €420 Panier de fruits (38x46cm-15x18in) s.d.55 i.verso prov. 10-Dec-2 Rosebery Fine Art, London #629/R
£360 $565 €540 Still life with apples in a bowl with grapes (46x55cm-18x22in) s.d.55 prov. 10-Dec-2 Rosebery Fine Art, London #626
£460 $722 €690 Poissons rouges au coq (54x73cm-21x29in) s.i.d.1955 i.verso prov.exhib. 10-Dec-2 Rosebery Fine Art, London #622
£600 $942 €900 Poissons Mediterranens (54x73cm-21x29in) s.i.d.54 i.verso prov.exhib. 10-Dec-2 Rosebery Fine Art, London #623

PEREZ AGUILERA, Miguel (1915-) Spanish
£292 $444 €450 Square (33x40cm-13x16in) s. painted 1961. 3-Jul-2 Castellana, Madrid #141/R
£390 $592 €600 Untitled (46x55cm-18x22in) s.d.1965. 3-Jul-2 Castellana, Madrid #148/R
£2404 $3798 €3750 Composition (118x89cm-46x35in) s.i.d.verso. 14-Nov-2 Arte, Seville #470/R est:3000

PEREZ ALCALA, Ricardo (1939-) Mexican
Works on paper
£319 $484 €463 Patio interior (30x22cm-12x9in) s.d.1942 W/C. 24-Jul-2 Louis Morton, Mexico #88/R (M.P 4800)

PEREZ DE VILLAAMIL, Genaro (1807-1854) Spanish
£6500 $10206 €9750 Paisaje romantico - romantic landscape (25x33cm-10x13in) s. copper. 19-Nov-2 Sotheby's, London #27/R est:5000-7000
£8974 $14179 €14000 Madrid view (19x15cm-7x6in) s.d.1835. 14-Nov-2 Arte, Seville #305/R
£140645 $222219 €218000 View of the Royal Palace in Madrid (45x77cm-18x30in) s.d.1854. 18-Dec-2 Ansorena, Madrid #86/R est:218000

PEREZ DEL PULGAR, Luis (19th C) Spanish
£1321 $2034 €2100 Still life with apples, pears and birds (43x54cm-17x21in) s. painted 1817. 28-Oct-2 Segre, Madrid #82/R est:2100

PEREZ GIL, Jose (1918-1998) Spanish
£321 $500 €465 Portrait of a man (51x61cm-20x24in) s. 30-Mar-3 Simpson's, Houston #481
£881 $1374 €1400 White suburbs (24x29cm-9x11in) s.i.verso board. 8-Oct-2 Ansorena, Madrid #448/R
£1517 $2412 €2200 White houses (46x54cm-18x21in) s.d.1973 s.i.d.verso. 4-Mar-3 Ansorena, Madrid #236/R

PEREZ MARTINEZ, Tomas (1911-) Spanish
£566 $883 €900 Huesca (92x73cm-36x29in) s. s.i.verso. 23-Sep-2 Durán, Madrid #83/R
£755 $1177 €1200 Costa Brava (73x91cm-29x36in) s. 23-Sep-2 Durán, Madrid #82/R

PEREZ SANZ, Antonio (1974-) Spanish
£258 $408 €400 Biar (65x73cm-26x29in) s.i. 17-Dec-2 Durán, Madrid #626/R

PEREZ TORCAL, Julio Pablo (1948-) Spanish
£364 $594 €550 Vegetable garden (54x65cm-21x26in) s.d.1973. 11-Feb-3 Segre, Madrid #197/R
£387 $612 €600 Woods (81x100cm-32x39in) s.d.74. 17-Dec-2 Durán, Madrid #37/R

PEREZ TORRES, Julio (1901-2001) Spanish
£1290 $2039 €2000 Guipuzcoa (46x55cm-18x22in) s.d.997. 18-Dec-2 Ansorena, Madrid #52/R

PEREZ VILLALTA, Guillermo (1948-) Spanish
£2384 $3886 €3600 Saint Lucy (70x50cm-28x20in) s.i.d.1984 acrylic card on board prov.exhib.lit. 11-Feb-3 Segre, Madrid #292/R
£2830 $4415 €4500 Acteon (70x100cm-28x39in) s.i.d.1981 acrylic pencil card exhib.lit. 17-Sep-2 Segre, Madrid #162/R

PEREZ Y VILLAGROSSA, Mariano Alonso (1857-1930) Spanish
£267 $417 €390 Waitress (60x50cm-24x20in) s.d.1917. 8-Apr-3 Ansorena, Madrid #151/R
£325 $474 €500 Waitress (60x50cm-24x20in) s.d.1917. 17-Jun-2 Ansorena, Madrid #340/R
£3930 $6131 €5895 Elegant figures (60x73cm-24x29in) s. panel. 6-Nov-2 Dobiaschofsky, Bern #881/R est:6000 (S.FR 9000)

PEREZ, Alonzo (fl.1893-1914) Spanish
£1795 $2800 €2693 Musical recital (28x20cm-11x8in) s. panel. 9-Oct-2 Doyle, New York #82/R est:3000-5000

PEREZ, Augusto (1929-) Italian
Sculpture
£2564 $4026 €4000 Study for monument to Louis XVI (58x32x18cm-23x13x7in) s. bronze exhib. exec.1967. 19-Nov-2 Finarte, Milan #141/R

PEREZ, Bartolomeo (circle) (1634-1693) Spanish
£5479 $8548 €8219 Still life of flowers (111x89cm-44x35in) 28-Mar-3 Koller, Zurich #3085/R est:14000-18000 (S.FR 12000)

PEREZ, Mario (1960-) Argentinian
£3185 $5000 €4778 Carousel (73x93cm-29x37in) s. s.i.d.1996 verso prov. 20-Nov-2 Christie's, Rockefeller NY #115/R

PEREZ, Raphael (1938-) Swiss/Venezuelan
£393 $617 €590 C A 0286 (30x30cm-12x12in) s.i.d.1998 verso acrylic. 23-Nov-2 Burkhard, Luzern #70/R (S.FR 900)
Sculpture
£1223 $1920 €1835 Untitled (185x15x9cm-73x6x4in) acrylic wood plexiglas. 23-Nov-2 Burkhard, Luzern #71/R est:1000-1500 (S.FR 2800)

PEREZ-DIEZ, Jose Luis (1931-1992) Spanish
£487 $711 €750 Motrico harbour (27x21cm-11x8in) s. s.i.verso cardboard. 17-Jun-2 Ansorena, Madrid #140/R

PEREZZOLI, Francesco (?-1772) Italian
£1486 $2319 €2200 Resting during the Flight to Egypt (32x23cm-13x9in) 26-Mar-3 Tajan, Paris #22/R

PERFALL, Erich Freiherr von (1882-1961) German
£261 $421 €400 Paysage ensoleille (80x100cm-31x39in) s. 14-Jan-3 Vanderkindere, Brussels #52

PERGER, Anton Chevalier de (1809-1876) Austrian
Works on paper
£480000 $772800 €720000 Agaric mushrooms (22x140cm-9x55in) W/C 117 manuscript prov. 7-May-3 Sotheby's, London #84/R est:6000-8000

PERIER, B A (fl.1836) British
Works on paper
£280 $437 €420 Little street (62x48cm-24x19in) s. W/C. 18-Sep-2 Cheffins Grain & Comins, Cambridge #496

PERIGAL, Arthur (jnr) (1816-1884) British
£1800 $2790 €2700 Cattle by a bridge (32x48cm-13x19in) s. 31-Oct-2 Christie's, London #67/R est:2000-3000

PERILLI, Achille (1927-) Italian
£1418 $2298 €2000 Scelta delle proporzioni (50x50cm-20x20in) s.d.83 s.i.d.verso prov. 26-May-3 Christie's, Milan #153/R est:2000-3000
£2863 $4181 €4295 La Pesa (70x99cm-28x39in) s.d. i. verso spray paper on panel. 17-Jun-2 Philippe Schuler, Zurich #4055/R est:2100-3500 (S.FR 6500)
£8865 $14362 €12500 La trappola (60x73cm-24x29in) s.d.62 s.i.d.verso prov.exhib. 26-May-3 Christie's, Milan #343/R est:6000-8000
£9804 $15686 €15000 Black rock (81x100cm-32x39in) s.i.d.1958 verso mixed media on canvas lit. 4-Jan-3 Meeting Art, Vercelli #628 est:10000
Works on paper
£633 $987 €1000 Nest (20x20cm-8x8in) s.d.2000 s.i.d.verso mixed media on canvas. 14-Sep-2 Meeting Art, Vercelli #285/R
£633 $987 €1000 Guiggia (20x20cm-8x8in) s.d.2000 mixed media on canvas. 14-Sep-2 Meeting Art, Vercelli #769/R
£641 $1006 €1000 Circus (20x20cm-8x8in) s.d.1999 mixed media on canvas. 23-Nov 2 Meeting Art, Vercelli #27/R
£694 $1104 €1000 Endo (20x20cm-8x8in) s.d.2000 mixcd media on canvas. 1-May-3 Meeting Art, Vercelli #42
£705 $1107 €1100 Sand (20x20cm-8x8in) s.d.2000 mixed media on canvas. 23-Nov-2 Meeting Art, Vercelli #274/R
£1090 $1711 €1700 Language practice (40x40cm-16x16in) s.d.2000 mixed media on canvas. 23-Nov-2 Meeting Art, Vercelli #95/R
£1613 $2548 €2500 All grey (73x50cm-29x20in) s.i.d.69 Chinese ink tempera card prov. 18-Dec-2 Christie's, Rome #199/R
£1667 $2650 €2400 Bruised beauty (50x50cm-20x20in) s.d.2000 mixed media on canvas. 1-May-3 Meeting Art, Vercelli #174
£2292 $3644 €3300 Back-up (50x40cm-20x16in) s.d.1970 mixed media on canvas. 1-May-3 Meeting Art, Vercelli #410
£2482 $4021 €3500 Eburneo (22x35cm-9x14in) s.d.58 mixed media panel. 26-May-3 Christie's, Milan #174/R est:3500-5000

PERIN-SALBREUX, Lie Louis (1753-1817) French
Miniatures
£1800 $2916 €2700 Young boy wearing black coat (5cm-2in) s. gilt mounted square wood frame. 22-May-3 Bonhams, New Bond Street #61/R est:1000-1500
£2065 $3262 €3200 Portrait de femme (6x5cm-2x2in) s. oval. 18-Dec-2 Beaussant & Lefèvre, Paris #10/R
£4200 $6594 €6300 Jean Baptiste Jacques Le Clerc (6cm-2in) s. cast gilt metal. 10-Dec-2 Christie's, London #82/R est:2500-3500

PERIN-SALBREUX, Lie Louis (attrib) (1753-1817) French
£709 $1121 €1100 Portrait d'homme en buste (19x16cm-7x6in) copper. 20-Dec-2 Tajan, Paris #135
Miniatures
£1935 $3058 €3000 Portrait d'homme (6x5cm-2x2in) oval. 18-Dec-2 Beaussant & Lefèvre, Paris #7/R

PERINCIOLI, Marcel (1911-) Swiss
Works on paper
£258 $407 €387 Abstract composition (21x28cm-8x11in) s.d.87 chk dr. 29-Nov-2 Zofingen, Switzerland #3029 (S.FR 600)

PERISCALLI, Piero (20th C) Italian
£1421 $2231 €2200 Sunset (143x113cm-56x44in) s. 16-Dec-2 Pandolfini, Florence #112/R est:2400

PERISSINOTTI, Lino (1897-1967) Italian
£1519 $2370 €2400 Urban landscape (35x42cm-14x17in) s. board. 19-Oct-2 Semenzato, Venice #7/R

PERJONS, Per Hilding (1911-1998) Swedish
£409 $650 €614 By the light of the open fire (55x46cm-22x18in) s. 2-Mar-3 Uppsala Auktionskammare, Uppsala #305 (S.KR 5500)

PERKINS, Christopher (1891-1968) British
£627 $978 €941 HurstCastle lighthouse, Dorset (18x20cm-7x8in) init. painted c.1961. 10-Nov-2 Dunbar Sloane, Auckland #82 est:2500-3500 (NZ.D 2000)
£3000 $4770 €4500 Lincolnshire (71x11cm-28x4in) s.d.44. 26-Feb-3 Sotheby's, Olympia #218/R est:800-1200

PERKINS, Granville (1830-1895) American
£1358 $2200 €1969 Fishing boats and other shipping on the Hudson with view of New York (31x46cm-12x18in) s. 29-Jul-3 Christie's, Rockefeller NY #152/R est:3000-5000
£3395 $5500 €4923 Schooner yacht in rough seas with other shipping in the distance (30x45cm-12x18in) s.d.1841. 29-Jul-3 Christie's, Rockefeller NY #156/R est:4000-6000
£3395 $5500 €4923 Isaac Edge's windmill, Jersey City, New Jersey (77x122cm-30x48in) s.d.1881. 29-Jul-3 Christie's, Rockefeller NY #159/R est:7000-10000

Works on paper

£563 $900 €845 Harbour scene with two men in a sailboat and dock (36x53cm-14x21in) s. W/C. 17-May-3 Pook & Pook, Downington #387/R est:1000-1200

PERKINS, Marcia (1946-) Canadian

£239 $373 €399 Untitled - self portrait (30x30cm-12x12in) s.d.1994 i.verso canvasboard prov. 13-Apr-3 Levis, Calgary #319/R (C.D 550)

PERKINS, Parker S (19/20th C) American

£321 $500 €482 Winterscape with tree and three houses (23x28cm-9x11in) s. i.verso. 15-Oct-2 Winter Associates, Plainville #227
£813 $1300 €1179 Surf on the rocks (64x76cm-25x30in) s. 17-May-3 CRN Auctions, Cambridge #10

PERKO, Anton (1833-1905) Austrian

Works on paper

£473 $738 €700 Monte Picino, Rome (24x17cm-9x7in) s.i.d.03 W/C. 28-Mar-3 Dorotheum, Vienna #235/R
£743 $1159 €1100 Sailing ships (33x24cm-13x9in) s. i.verso W/C. 28-Mar-3 Dorotheum, Vienna #294/R
£811 $1265 €1200 Mount Etna seen from sea (21x35cm-8x14in) si. W/C. 28-Mar-3 Dorotheum, Vienna #233/R

PERKOIS, Jacobus (1756-1804) Dutch

Works on paper

£294 $482 €450 Two peasant women (24x20cm-9x8in) s.d.1780 col crayon. 7-Feb-3 Piasa, Paris #167

PERLBERG, Friedrich (1848-1921) German

Works on paper

£432 $691 €600 Schloss Rumeli on the Bosphorus (28x41cm-11x16in) s. Indian ink brush htd white board. 13-May-3 Hartung & Hartung, Munich #4080/R
£1299 $1935 €2000 Klingenthor in Rothenburg (57x43cm-22x17in) s.i. W/C over pencil. 26-Jun-2 Neumeister, Munich #596/R
£1572 $2453 €2500 Santa Maria del Mar, Barcelona (63x49cm-25x19in) s. W/C painted c.1875. 23-Sep-2 Durán, Madrid #240/R
£4430 $7000 €6645 Jerusalem (68x99cm-27x39in) s. W/C. 27-Apr-3 Sotheby's, Tel Aviv #2/R est:8000-10000

PERLMAN, J (20th C) American

Sculpture

£1176 $1965 €1705 Composition AN (84x52cm-33x20in) mono.d. iron. 24-Jun-3 Koller, Zurich #185/R est:2000-3000 (S.FR 2600)

PERLMUTTER, Isaac (1866-1932) Czechoslovakian

£1677 $2616 €2432 Green hills (23x33cm-9x13in) s. canvas on board. 12-Apr-3 Mu Terem Galeria, Budapest #43/R est:280000 (H.F 600000)
£1882 $2918 €2823 Day in May (19x24cm-7x9in) s. board. 6-Dec-2 Kieselbach, Budapest #3 (H.F 700000)
£1956 $3052 €2934 Autumnal landscape (19x24cm-7x9in) s. panel. 11-Apr-3 Kieselbach, Budapest #53/R est:350000-700000 (H.F 700000)
£2689 $4168 €4034 In the room (24x15cm-9x6in) s. board. 6-Dec-2 Kieselbach, Budapest #23/R (H.F 1000000)
£3353 $5231 €5030 Boy in hat on sunlit field (18x23cm-7x9in) s. panel. 11-Apr-3 Kieselbach, Budapest #25/R est:650000-1200000 (H.F 1200000)
£3511 $5617 €5267 Breakfast (40x33cm-16x13in) s. cardboard. 16-May-3 Kieselbach, Budapest #45/R (H.F 1200000)
£6148 $9591 €8915 In the garden (55x69cm-22x27in) s. 12-Apr-3 Mu Terem Galeria, Budapest #76/R est:1200000 (H.F 2200000)
£7530 $11671 €10919 Vegetable market (42x32cm-17x13in) s. s.d.1906 verso panel card. 9-Dec-2 Mu Terem Galeria, Budapest #126/R est:1200000 (H.F 2800000)

PERLMUTTER, Jack (1920-) American

£273 $425 €410 Boardwalk with ferris wheel (81x91cm-32x36in) s. 14-Sep-2 Weschler, Washington #648/R

PERLOV, V (20th C) Russian

£2200 $3454 €3300 Horse's head (22x26cm-9x10in) s.d.1902 panel. 20-Nov-2 Sotheby's, London #56/R est:2000-3000

PERLROTT-CSABA (1880-1955) Hungarian

£4841 $7503 €7262 Still life of fruit (69x55cm-27x22in) s. 6-Dec-2 Kieselbach, Budapest #162/R (H.F 1800000)
£14189 $22135 €21284 Models (46x46cm-18x18in) 11-Sep-2 Kieselbach, Budapest #97/R (H.F 5500000)
£14791 $22926 €22187 Still life (59x47cm-23x19in) s. canvas on cardboard. 6-Dec-2 Kieselbach, Budapest #156/R (H.F 5500000)

PERLROTT-CSABA, Vilmos (1880-1955) Hungarian

£1614 $2501 €2421 Still life with a black statue, homage to Cezanne (49x59cm-19x23in) canvas on cardboard. 6-Dec-2 Kieselbach, Budapest #163/R (H.F 600000)
£2515 $3923 €3773 Shadowy garden in Szentendre (58x73cm-23x29in) s. board. 11-Apr-3 Kieselbach, Budapest #163/R est:600000-900000 (H.F 900000)
£4471 $6975 €6707 Fruit garden in Szentendre (67x86cm-26x34in) s. 11-Apr-3 Kieselbach, Budapest #135/R est:1400000-1600000 (H.F 1600000)
£4644 $7244 €6966 Mother with child (100x70cm-39x28in) tempera paper. 11-Sep-2 Kieselbach, Budapest #157/R (H.F 1800000)
£5160 $8049 €7740 Still life in Atelier (84x80cm-33x31in) s. 11-Sep-2 Kieselbach, Budapest #135/R (H.F 2000000)
£5589 $8719 €8104 Still life on a table (76x89cm-30x35in) 12-Apr-3 Mu Terem Galeria, Budapest #162/R est:1200000 (H.F 2000000)
£8255 $12878 €12383 View of Notre Dame (73x55cm-29x22in) s. 11-Sep-2 Kieselbach, Budapest #201/R (H.F 3200000)
£8606 $13339 €12479 Young lady with gladioli (100x71cm-39x28in) s. tempera. 9-Dec-2 Mu Terem Galeria, Budapest #175/R est:2600000 (H.F 3200000)
£9803 $15293 €14705 Town with trees, 1924 (76x76cm-30x30in) s. 11-Sep-2 Kieselbach, Budapest #146/R (H.F 3800000)
£11178 $17437 €16208 Street meandering through the bridge in a small city (81x65cm-32x26in) s. lit. 12-Apr-3 Mu Terem Galeria, Budapest #101/R est:3000000 (H.F 4000000)
£12287 $19659 €18431 Notre Dame in Paris (64x53cm-25x21in) s. 16-May-3 Kieselbach, Budapest #24/R (H.F 4200000)
£12899 $20122 €19349 Calvaria in Kecskemet (72x64cm-28x25in) s. 11-Sep-2 Kieselbach, Budapest #73/R (H.F 5000000)
£14042 $22467 €21063 Garden in Szentendre (73x57cm-29x22in) s. cardboard. 16-May-3 Kieselbach, Budapest #73/R (H.F 4800000)
£32180 $51488 €48270 Nagybanya (75x70cm-30x28in) s. 16-May-3 Kieselbach, Budapest #66/R (H.F 11000000)

Works on paper

£645 $1000 €935 Street in Locse (23x29cm-9x11in) s.d.920 pencil. 9-Dec-2 Mu Terem Galeria, Budapest #13/R est:180000 (H.F 240000)

PERLROTT-CSABA, Vilmos (attrib) (1880-1955) Hungarian

£5063 $8000 €8000 Paris, quais de Seine (42x49cm-17x19in) s.i.d. 2-Dec-2 Tajan, Paris #159/R

PERMAN, Louise E (1854-1921) British

£950 $1577 €1378 Still life of assorted roses on a table top (35x70cm-14x28in) s.d.1892. 13-Jun-3 Lyon & Turnbull, Edinburgh #11
£2300 $3496 €3450 Summer blooms (51x41cm-20x16in) s. 28-Aug-2 Sotheby's, London #1009/R est:2000-3000

PERMEKE (20th C) Belgian

£5517 $8828 €8000 Marine (49x59cm-19x23in) 17-Mar-3 Amberes, Antwerp #241/R

PERMEKE, C (1886-1952) Belgian

£3145 $4906 €5000 Marine (49x58cm-19x23in) 14-Oct-2 Amberes, Antwerp #185/R

PERMEKE, Constant (1886-1952) Belgian

£1702 $2843 €2400 Marine (36x21cm-14x8in) panel painted 1912-1913. 23-Jun-3 Amberes, Antwerp #116
£1871 $2993 €2600 Marine (26x35cm-10x14in) panel prov. 13-May-3 Palais de Beaux Arts, Brussels #117 est:1250-1750
£2158 $3540 €3000 Portrait of the artist's friend Jos Van Wassenhove (25x34cm-10x13in) s.d.14 board prov. 3-Jun-3 Christie's, Amsterdam #294/R est:3000-5000
£2821 $4372 €4400 Seascape (50x73cm-20x29in) s. panel. 7-Dec-2 De Vuyst, Lokeren #556/R est:4500-6000
£2821 $4428 €4400 Marine (55x64cm-22x25in) s. canvas on panel. 10-Dec-2 Vanderkindere, Brussels #30/R est:5000-7000
£3741 $5986 €5200 Paysage au crepusclule (61x75cm-24x30in) s. canvas laid down. 13-May-3 Palais de Beaux Arts, Brussels #115/R est:5000-7500
£3846 $5962 €6000 Landscape with farm in Latem (28x31cm-11x12in) mono. canvas on board. 7-Dec-2 De Vuyst, Lokeren #249/R est:2000-2400
£4828 $7724 €7000 Landscape with small bundles of straw (54x81cm-21x32in) s. 15-Mar-3 De Vuyst, Lokeren #546/R est:8000-9000
£7692 $11923 €12000 Boats in a harbour, Ostende (37x48cm-15x19in) s.d.1911 exhib. 3-Dec-2 Christie's, Amsterdam #229/R est:15000-20000
£11034 $17655 €16000 Seascape with fishing boats (100x130cm-39x51in) s. prov. 15-Mar-3 De Vuyst, Lokeren #541/R est:17000-20000
£11511 $18878 €16000 Landscape with farmhouses (49x70cm-19x28in) s. prov. 3-Jun-3 Christie's, Amsterdam #265/R est:12000-16000
£20833 $33125 €30000 La promenade (64x75cm-25x30in) s. 29-Apr-3 Campo, Vlaamse Kaai #250/R est:25000-30000

Sculpture

£5036 $8058 €7000 Femme agenouillee (44cm-17in) s.num.1/8 pat bronze. 13-May-3 Palais de Beaux Arts, Brussels #114/R est:4500-6000

£6115 $9784 €8500 Tete de Christ (41cm-16in) s. pat bronze prov. 13-May-3 Palais de Beaux Arts, Brussels #116/R est:3750-5000
Works on paper
£612 $978 €850 Fisherwoman with basket (22x15cm-9x6in) s. W/C exec.c.1919 prov.exhib. 17-May-3 De Vuyst, Lokeren #293
£1154 $1812 €1800 Nude sitting (26x20cm-10x8in) s. gouache pastel exhib. 25-Nov-2 Glerum, Amsterdam #131/R est:1200-2000
£2484 $3999 €3800 Autoportrait (29x21cm-11x8in) s.d.1910 pencil dr. 20-Jan-3 Horta, Bruxelles #159 est:4000-6000
£6507 $10151 €9500 Village fair (32x49cm-13x19in) s. mixed media exec.1920. 10-Apr-3 Finarte Semenzato, Rome #257/R
£37410 $61353 €52000 Mother and child (102x73cm-40x29in) s. pastel gouache W/C. 3-Jun-3 Christie's, Amsterdam #266/R est:30000-50000

PERMEKE, Hendrik Lodewyk (1849-1912) Belgian
£748 $1190 €1100 Village on the Scheldt with old windmill (32x54cm-13x21in) s. 24-Mar-3 Bernaerts, Antwerp #114/R est:1000-1500
£915 $1474 €1300 Ship in stormy weather (33x55cm-13x22in) s. 12-May-3 Bernaerts, Antwerp #198/R

PERMEKE, Paul (1918-1990) Belgian
£253 $395 €400 Vase de fleurs (65x50cm-26x20in) s. 15-Oct-2 Vanderkindere, Brussels #98
£266 $415 €420 Coucher de soleil (25x34cm-10x13in) s. panel. 15-Oct-2 Horta, Bruxelles #284
£288 $453 €450 Horse and wagon near a mill (50x60cm-20x24in) s. board. 25-Nov-2 Glerum, Amsterdam #39
£353 $546 €550 Vase fleuri (65x49cm-26x19in) s. paper. 9-Dec-2 Horta, Bruxelles #355
£377 $591 €550 La roulotte (30x40cm-12x16in) s. panel. 15-Apr-3 Galerie Moderne, Brussels #391
£408 $649 €600 Bord de mer (40x50cm-16x20in) s. panel. 18-Mar-3 Vanderkindere, Brussels #112
£442 $703 €650 Vue de village en Flandres (30x40cm-12x16in) s. 18-Mar-3 Vanderkindere, Brussels #109
£597 $926 €950 Fishing harbour (57x73cm-22x29in) s. panel painted c.1956. 5-Oct-2 De Vuyst, Lokeren #290
£701 $1093 €1100 Marche a Blankenberge (52x38cm-20x15in) s. 11-Nov-2 Horta, Bruxelles #612
£705 $1107 €1100 Street view (29x36cm-11x14in) s. 25-Nov-2 Glerum, Amsterdam #77
£710 $1121 €1100 Voiliers (65x50cm-26x20in) s. cardboard. 17-Dec-2 Galerie Moderne, Brussels #809
£769 $1192 €1200 Paysage enneige au crepuscule (60x80cm-24x31in) s. 9-Dec-2 Horta, Bruxelles #354
£1000 $1660 €1000 Coucher de soleil en hiver (30x40cm-12x16in) s. 16-Jun-3 Horta, Bruxelles #6
£1146 $1789 €1800 La petite terrasse (50x40cm-20x16in) s. 11-Nov-2 Horta, Bruxelles #613 est:1200-1900
£1519 $2370 €2400 Paysage enneige (70x100cm-28x39in) s. 15-Oct-2 Horta, Bruxelles #283

PERMOSER, Balthazar (style) (1651-1732) German
Sculpture
£11000 $17270 €16500 Figure of chronos (34cm-13in) boxwood lit. 10-Dec-2 Sotheby's, London #87/R est:6000-8000

PERNELLE, Ernest (1870-?) French
£1319 $2151 €1900 Le port de Treboul a maree basse (65x81cm-26x32in) s. 19-Jul-3 Thierry & Lannon, Brest #372 est:1500-2000

PERNES, Leo (19/20th C) ?
£1111 $1811 €1600 Le port de Lesconil (60x80cm-24x31in) s. 19-Jul-3 Thierry & Lannon, Brest #373 est:800-1200

PERNET, Jean Henry Alexandre (1763-?) French
Works on paper
£900 $1413 €1350 Capriccio of classical buildings with elegant ladies. Capriccio view of Trajan's Column (17x27cm-7x11in) s. pen ink W/C htd gum arabic pair. 13-Dec-2 Christie's, Kensington #316/R
£1701 $2704 €2500 Groupe de figures dans un paysage (26x39cm-10x15in) i. W/C pen ink. 24-Mar-3 Tajan, Paris #81/R
£4762 $7571 €7000 Projet de theatre (42x55cm-17x22in) s. pen ink sepia wash. 21-Mar-3 Rieunier, Bailly-Pommery, Mathias, Paris #45/R

PERNHARDT, Marcus (1828-1871) Austrian
£19858 $32170 €28000 View over Worther Lake (52x83cm-20x33in) s.indis.d. 22-May-3 Dorotheum, Vienna #15/R est:10000-15000

PERNOT, François Alexandre (1793-1865) French
£1282 $2026 €2000 Harbour (33x41cm-13x16in) s. board. 16-Nov-2 Lempertz, Koln #1550/R est:2200

PERNOT, Henri (19th C) French
Sculpture
£1800 $2862 €2700 Two infants (207cm-81in) s. alabaster marble column. 29-Apr-3 Sotheby's, Olympia #176/R est:2000-3000

PERRACHON, Andre (1827-1909) French
£1959 $3057 €2900 Bouquet (45x37cm-18x15in) s.d.1858. 26-Mar-3 Pierre Berge, Paris #18/R

PERRADON, Pierre Edmond (1893-1982) French
£291 $454 €460 Vienne-en-Bessin (39x56cm-15x22in) s. cardboard. 15-Sep-2 Etude Bailleul, Bayeux #211
£329 $513 €520 Village du Bessin (53x72cm-21x28in) s. cardboard. 15-Sep-2 Etude Bailleul, Bayeux #210

PERRET (?) ?
£1441 $2276 €2162 Landscapes (65x53cm-26x21in) s. oval pair. 5-Apr-3 Rasmussen, Havnen #2227/R est:10000-15000 (D.KR 15500)

PERRET, Aime (1847-1927) French
£9494 $15000 €14241 Waiting for the ferry (73x93cm-29x37in) s. 23-Apr-3 Christie's, Rockefeller NY #60/R est:10000-15000

PERRET, Charles (?-1911) French?
£2405 $3752 €3800 Roses (54x80cm-21x31in) s. 20-Oct-2 Anaf, Lyon #216/R est:3800-4000

PERRETT, John Douglas (1859-1937) New Zealander
£239 $349 €359 West arm manapouri (55x76cm-22x30in) s. 12-Sep-1 Watson's, Christchurch #121 (NZ.D 800)
£266 $416 €399 Lake Manapouri (34x49cm-13x19in) s. 5-Nov-2 Peter Webb, Auckland #146/R (NZ.D 850)
£531 $828 €797 South Island lake and mountain landscape (55x83cm-22x33in) s. 6-Aug-2 Peter Webb, Auckland #194/R est:2000-3000 (NZ.D 1800)
£1274 $2000 €1911 Mt. Cook in the moonlit landscape (79x136cm-31x54in) s. 10-Dec-2 Peter Webb, Auckland #62/R est:4000-6000 (NZ.D 4000)

PERRI, Frank (20th C) American
£252 $400 €378 Mexican town scene (61x76cm-24x30in) s.verso painted c.1940. 2-Mar-3 Toomey, Oak Park #629/R
£260 $400 €390 Day at the beach (61x76cm-24x30in) s. board painted c.1940. 8-Sep-2 Treadway Gallery, Cincinnati #699/R
£267 $425 €401 Mexican town scene (61x91cm-24x36in) s.verso painted c.1940. 2-Mar-3 Toomey, Oak Park #631/R
£306 $475 €459 Soulful gaze (91x114cm-36x45in) s. painted c.1960. 8-Dec-2 Toomey, Oak Park #768/R
£377 $600 €566 Mexican mother and child (76x61cm-30x24in) s.d. 2-Mar-3 Toomey, Oak Park #634/R

PERRICHON, Georges-Leon-Alfred (attrib) (?-1907) French
£300 $456 €450 Tending to the garden (29x42cm-11x17in) s. 29-Aug-2 Christie's, Kensington #76

PERRIE, Bertha Eversfield (1868-1921) American
£1006 $1600 €1509 Dock workers (31x41cm-12x16in) s. board. 7-Mar-3 Skinner, Boston #481/R est:300-500

PERRIER, Alexandre (1862-1936) Swiss
£349 $552 €524 Lac (26x20cm-10x8in) panel. 17-Nov-2 Koller, Geneva #1244 (S.FR 800)
£2183 $3450 €3275 Vue du lac (45x64cm-18x25in) s.d.1900 verso. 17-Nov-2 Koller, Geneva #1214/R (S.FR 5000)

PERRIER, François (1584-1650) French
Works on paper
£3662 $6079 €5200 Pope distributing alms (22x14cm-9x6in) wash pen over chk. 12-Jun-3 Hauswedell & Nolte, Hamburg #147/R est:2000

PERRIGARD, Hal Ross (1891-1960) Canadian
£203 $319 €305 Twin lights on Thatchers' Island (14x20cm-6x8in) s. i.verso board prov. 10-Dec-2 Pinneys, Montreal #11 (C.D 500)
£522 $814 €870 Twin lights on Thatchers Island, Cape Ann, Mass (15x20cm-6x8in) s. board. 13-Apr-3 Levis, Calgary #91/R est:1500-1700 (C.D 1200)
£732 $1149 €1098 Radiant trees beside an eastern township stream (41x61cm-16x24in) s. board. 10-Dec-2 Pinneys, Montreal #158 (C.D 1800)
£1235 $1914 €1853 Winter (30x40cm-12x16in) s. canvasboard. 3-Dec-2 Joyner, Toronto #321/R est:1500-1800 (C.D 3000)
£1647 $2602 €2471 Near Melbourne, Quebec (41x51cm-16x20in) d.1927 canvas on board. 1-Dec-2 Levis, Calgary #74/R est:3000-3500 (C.D 4100)
£2222 $3644 €3333 Golden days (45x60cm-18x24in) s. canvasboard. 3-Jun-3 Joyner, Toronto #237/R est:3000-4000 (C.D 5000)
£3333 $5467 €5000 Lobster shop, Rockport, Mass (42x50cm-17x20in) s.d.29. 3-Jun-3 Joyner, Toronto #328/R est:2500-3000 (C.D 7500)

PERRIN, Alfred Feyen (fl.1860-1911) British

£280 $454 €420 Portrait of a Spanish lady, bust length (41x32cm-16x13in) s. 23-Jan-3 Christie's, Kensington #23

PERRIN, Jean Charles Nicaise (1754-1831) French

Works on paper

£1541 $2403 €2280 Etude pour Notre-Dame des Gloires (34x23cm-13x9in) crayon chk prov.lit. 26-Mar-3 Piasa, Paris #84

PERRIN, Philippe (1964-) French

Sculpture

£6500 $10595 €9750 Couteau (335cm-132in) steel in two parts. 3-Feb-3 Sotheby's, Olympia #119/R est:5000-7000

PERRIN-MAXENCE, Henri (1872-1944) French

£567 $919 €800 Paysage du Crozant ou neige a Crozant (65x82cm-26x32in) s.d.1913. 23-May-3 Camard, Paris #81/R

PERRINE, Van Dearing (1869-1955) American

£419 $650 €629 Children running (18x25cm-7x10in) 25-Sep-2 Doyle, New York #62/R
£419 $650 €629 Children a wind (28x36cm-11x14in) s. 25-Sep-2 Doyle, New York #61/R
£1161 $1800 €1742 Girl reading in the garden (48x38cm-19x15in) canvas on board. 25-Sep-2 Doyle, New York #59/R est:2000-3000
£1752 $2750 €2628 Riverside play (66x56cm-26x22in) s. prov. 10-Dec-2 Doyle, New York #88/R est:5000-7000
£2070 $3250 €3105 Sunburst (107x89cm-42x35in) s. 10-Dec-2 Doyle, New York #91/R est:6000-8000
£2389 $3750 €3584 Children playing in a landscape (56x66cm-22x26in) s. prov. 10-Dec-2 Doyle, New York #87/R est:7000-9000

PERRON, Charles Clement Francis (1893-1958) French

£1400 $2268 €2100 Nue (24x19cm-9x7in) s. panel. 20-May-3 Sotheby's, Olympia #73/R est:500-700
£1479 $2381 €2100 Composition aux fruits et au pot de confiture (37x45cm-15x18in) s. panel. 11-May-3 Thierry & Lannon, Brest #388 est:1000-1200
£1538 $2415 €2400 Monnaie-du-pape (22x27cm-9x11in) s. panel. 15-Dec-2 Eric Pillon, Calais #147/R
£1600 $2592 €2400 Le pot blanc (19x24cm-7x9in) s. panel. 20-May-3 Sotheby's, Olympia #74/R est:400-600
£1600 $2592 €2400 Roses in a vase (19x24cm-7x9in) s. panel. 20-May-3 Sotheby's, Olympia #76/R est:300-500
£1700 $2754 €2550 Le pot jaune (19x24cm-7x9in) s. panel. 20-May-3 Sotheby's, Olympia #75/R est:400-600

PERRONEAU, Jean Baptiste (1715-1783) French

£4225 $6803 €6000 Karl von Hessen Kassel and his wife Louise (84x67cm-33x26in) lit. pair. 9-May-3 Schloss Ahlden, Ahlden #1334/R est:4500

Works on paper

£6329 $9873 €10000 Portrait du Comte de Rocheford. Portrait de la Comtesse de Rocheford (68x55cm-27x22in) s.d.1767 pastel pair exhib. 20-Oct-2 Anaf, Lyon #217/R est:10000-12000

PERROT, Ferdinand (1808-1841) French

£899 $1394 €1430 Sailing ship in the harbour in the evening (48x63cm-19x25in) s.d.1835. 29-Oct-2 Dorotheum, Vienna #248/R

PERROTT, James Stanford (1917-2001) Canadian

Works on paper

£361 $567 €542 Untitled - drilling in the foothills (27x36cm-11x14in) s. W/C. 25-Nov-2 Hodgins, Calgary #260/R (C.D 900)
£602 $946 €903 Untitled - Bragg Creek Farm (54x73cm-21x29in) s.d.1987 W/C. 25-Nov-2 Hodgins, Calgary #261/R (C.D 1500)
£847 $1347 €1271 Eden green hills (50x69cm-20x27in) s.d.1980 W/C. 23-Mar-3 Hodgins, Calgary #16/R est:1200-1800 (C.D 2000)

PERRY, Adelaide (1891-1973) Australian

£1760 $2834 €2552 Marigolds in a green jug (40x50cm-16x20in) s.d.1928 board. 12-May-3 Joel, Victoria #391 est:2000-3000 (A.D 4400)

PERRY, Lilla Cabot (1848-1933) American

£7547 $12000 €11321 Foot bridge - landscape (51x61cm-20x24in) s.d.1929 prov.exhib. 5-Mar-3 Sotheby's, New York #69/R est:12000-18000

PERRY, Robert Lee (?) American

£355 $550 €533 Three masted clipper ship under full sail (89x119cm-35x47in) s. panel. 28-Sep-2 Thomaston Place, Thomaston #59

PERSAC, Marie Adrien (1823-1873) American/French

Works on paper

£1000 $1590 €1500 Port at dusk (17x24cm-7x9in) s. W/C. 29-Apr-3 Bonhams, New Bond Street #191/R est:800-1200
£1000 $1590 €1500 River Loire at Saumur, France (6x10cm-2x4in) s. gouache. 29-Apr-3 Bonhams, New Bond Street #194/R
£1600 $2544 €2400 Skating on a frozen river (6x9cm-2x4in) gouache. 29-Apr-3 Bonhams, New Bond Street #190/R est:1000-1500
£1800 $2862 €2700 Figures on a track approaching a town (15x25cm-6x10in) s. gouache. 29-Apr-3 Bonhams, New Bond Street #192/R est:1000-1500
£1900 $3021 €2850 River Loire at Saumur, France (18x25cm-7x10in) s. gouache. 29-Apr-3 Bonhams, New Bond Street #188/R est:2000-3000
£1900 $3021 €2850 Horse drinking from a stream (27x36cm-11x14in) s. gouache. 29-Apr-3 Bonhams, New Bond Street #189/R est:2000-3000
£106707 $175000 €160061 Star Plantation, St Charles, La (43x84cm-17x33in) s. gouache exec.c.1861 prov. 8-Feb-3 Neal Auction Company, New Orleans #321/R est:75000-100000

PERSIAN SCHOOL, 16th C

Works on paper

£49296 $81831 €70000 Le miracle de la lune fendue (33x23cm-13x9in) illuminate manuscript lit. 13-Jun-3 Piasa, Paris #301/R est:8000-12000

PERSIAN SCHOOL, 19th C

Works on paper

£17000 $27030 €25500 Two birds perched in dense floral bouquet with butterflies (41x27cm-16x11in) gouache album page exec.c.1800. 30-Apr-3 Sotheby's, London #41/R est:6000-8000

PERSIN, Gustave Joseph (19th C) French

£759 $1185 €1200 Jeune femme au collier (35x26cm-14x10in) s.d.1861 panel. 15-Oct-2 Regis & Thiollet, Argentuil #190

PERSOGLIA, Franz von (1852-1912) Austrian

£600 $942 €900 Merry anglers (39x30cm-15x12in) s. panel. 16-Apr-3 Christie's, Kensington #767/R

PERSON, Henri (1876-1926) French

Works on paper

£1250 $1988 €1800 Antibes (32x41cm-13x16in) s. W/C pencil. 29-Apr-3 Artcurial Briest, Paris #33/R est:1500-1800

PERSON, Leroy (1907-1985) American

Sculpture

£3086 $5000 €4629 Elvis table (71x60x50cm-28x24x20in) crayon wood Elvis Presley trading cards prov. 27-Jan-3 Christie's, Rockefeller NY #94/R est:4000-6000

PERSSON, Folke (1905-1964) Swedish

£526 $831 €789 Harbour view with vessel (55x46cm-22x18in) s. 30-Nov-2 Goteborg Auktionsverk, Sweden #608/R (S.KR 7500)
£771 $1219 €1157 April light - view of the harbour (62x76cm-24x30in) s.d.52. 30-Nov-2 Goteborg Auktionsverk, Sweden #607/R (S.KR 11000)
£877 $1385 €1316 The building of bridges (52x65cm-20x26in) s. 30-Nov-2 Goteborg Auktionsverk, Sweden #609/R (S.KR 12500)
£1122 $1773 €1683 Coastal landscape with rowing boats and sailing boats, the skerries at Styrso (75x100cm-30x39in) s. 30-Nov-2 Goteborg Auktionsverk, Sweden #606/R est:10000 (S.KR 16000)

PERSSON, P A (1862-1914) Swedish

£1964 $3102 €2946 Spring landscape with woman walking by brook, Skane (74x109cm-29x43in) s,. 27-Nov-2 Falkkloos, Malmo #77551/R est:35000 (S.KR 28000)

PERSSON, Ragnar (1905-1993) Swedish

£384 $596 €576 Figures (36x13cm-14x5in) mono. panel. 29-Sep-2 Uppsala Auktionskammare, Uppsala #310 (S.KR 5500)
£423 $665 €635 Evening glow (22x27cm-9x11in) s. 16-Dec-2 Lilla Bukowskis, Stockholm #77 (S.KR 6000)
£504 $817 €731 Funeral procession (25x33cm-10x13in) mono. 25-May-3 Uppsala Auktionskammare, Uppsala #277/R (S.KR 6500)
£514 $802 €771 Five minutes (34x41cm-13x16in) s. 13-Sep-2 Lilla Bukowskis, Stockholm #250 (S.KR 7500)
£580 $922 €870 Woman with blue shawl (33x26cm-13x10in) mono.d.38 panel. 3-Mar-3 Lilla Bukowskis, Stockholm #660 (S.KR 7800)
£593 $931 €890 Interior scene with figure at table (33x42cm-13x17in) s. 16-Dec-2 Lilla Bukowskis, Stockholm #149 (S.KR 8400)
£669 $1064 €1004 The proposal (32x40cm-13x16in) mono. panel. 2-Mar-3 Uppsala Auktionskammare, Uppsala #43/R (S.KR 9000)

£743 $1182 €1115 Street scene (19x25cm-7x10in) s. 3-Mar-3 Lilla Bukowskis, Stockholm #309 (S.KR 10000)
£754 $1177 €1131 On the farmyard (38x49cm-15x19in) s. 13-Sep-2 Lilla Bukowskis, Stockholm #260/R (S.KR 11000)
£897 $1381 €1346 Barndance (31x41cm-12x16in) mono. s.verso panel. 27-Oct-2 Anders Antik, Landskrona #18/R (S.KR 13000)
£1064 $1649 €1596 Three men at kitchen table (27x34cm-11x13in) mono. panel. 8-Dec-2 Uppsala Auktionskammare, Uppsala #237/R est:10000-12000 (S.KR 15000)
£1065 $1682 €1598 The white shirt (77x90cm-30x35in) s.d.36 panel. 28-Apr-3 Bukowskis, Stockholm #175/R (S.KR 14000)
£1179 $1862 €1769 The parish meeting (27x40cm-11x16in) init. panel prov. 28-Apr-3 Bukowskis, Stockholm #174/R est:20000-25000 (S.KR 15500)
£1191 $1858 €1787 Southern street scene (44x25cm-17x10in) init. panel. 6-Nov-2 AB Stockholms Auktionsverk #609/R est:12000-15000 (S.KR 17000)
£1236 $1989 €1854 Bride and groom (33x41cm-13x16in) init. panel. 7-May-3 AB Stockholms Auktionsverk #887/R est:15000-18000 (S.KR 16000)
£1521 $2403 €2282 The workshop (46x56cm-18x22in) init. panel. 28-Apr-3 Bukowskis, Stockholm #176/R est:20000-25000 (S.KR 20000)
£1901 $3004 €2852 Spring washing (46x56cm-18x22in) init. painted 1958. 28-Apr-3 Bukowskis, Stockholm #173/R est:25000-30000 (S.KR 25000)

PERUVIAN SCHOOL, 17th C
£4878 $8000 €7317 Arcangel Gabriel (160x110cm-63x43in) painted c.1680 prov. 28-May-3 Christie's, Rockefeller NY #64/R est:15000-20000

PERUZZINI, Antonio Francesco (1668-?) Italian
£4828 $7676 €7000 Landscape with shepherd. Mountainous landscape with washerwomen (95x71cm-37x28in) pair oval. 9-Mar-3 Semenzato, Venice #6/R
£8228 $13000 €13000 Monks in landscape (74x100cm-29x39in) 27-Nov-2 Finarte, Milan #63/R est:15000-20000
£15385 $23846 €24000 River landscape with beggars. Landscape with travellers (73x97cm-29x38in) pair. 4-Dec-2 Christie's, Rome #456/R est:25000-35000
£23457 $38000 €35186 Castaways landing on the beach after the storm, a village beyond (115x175cm-45x69in) prov.exhib.lit. 24-Jan-3 Christie's, Rockefeller NY #155/R est:25000-35000

PERUZZINI, Domenico (1640-?) Italian
Prints
£3038 $4800 €4800 The bearing of the cross (10cm-4in circular) etching tondo. 29-Nov-2 Bassenge, Berlin #5227/R est:1500

PERUZZINI, Giovanni (attrib) (1629-1694) Italian
£9295 $14407 €14500 Landscape with bathers (116x145cm-46x57in) 6-Dec-2 Maigret, Paris #95/R est:17000

PESA, Giuseppe (1928-) Italian
£476 $757 €700 La scogliera (22x30cm-9x12in) canvas on panel. 28-Mar-3 Bolland & Marotz, Bremen #572/R

PESCE CASTRO, Cesar A (1891-?) Uruguayan
£701 $1100 €1052 Boats (24x35cm-9x14in) s.d.1928 cardboard. 20-Nov-2 Galleria Y Remates, Montevideo #46/R

PESCE, Gaetano (1939-) Italian
Sculpture
£2258 $3568 €3500 Windy house (35x60x84cm-14x24x33in) wood paper exec.1968 prov.lit. 18-Dec-2 Christie's, Rome #175/R
£2581 $4077 €4000 Elastic surface (65x65x15cm-26x26x6in) wood metal glass bulbs exec.1964 prov. 18-Dec-2 Christie's, Rome #177/R est:8000

PESCHKA, Anton (1885-1940) Austrian
£16456 $26000 €26000 Suburbs (63x75cm-25x30in) mono.d.18 mono.i.d. stretcher prov. 27-Nov-2 Dorotheum, Vienna #145/R est:12000-16000
Works on paper
£347 $549 €500 Rothenburg an der Tauber (50x35cm-20x14in) s.i.d.1927 pencil W/C. 24-Apr-3 Dorotheum, Vienna #61/R
£513 $810 €800 Landscape in northern Tyrol (19x28cm-7x11in) s.i.d.1937 W/C. 12-Nov-2 Dorotheum, Vienna #126/R
£612 $978 €850 Summer path (34x49cm-13x19in) s.d.1937. 14-May-3 Dorotheum, Linz #448
£795 $1295 €1200 Path in summer (34x49cm-13x19in) s.i.d.1937 chk W/C. 28-Jan-3 Dorotheum, Vienna #58/R
£1103 $1766 €1600 Country track near Langenlebern (36x49cm-14x19in) s.i.d.31 chk bister W/C paper on board. 11-Mar-3 Dorotheum, Vienna #61 est:1000-1400
£1111 $1756 €1600 Lainzer Tiergarten (35x50cm-14x20in) s.i.d.1933 bister chk W/C. 24-Apr-3 Dorotheum, Vienna #60/R est:1000-1500
£1528 $2414 €2200 By the ice lakes (35x50cm-14x20in) s.i.d.1923 pencil W/C. 24-Apr-3 Dorotheum, Vienna #62/R est:1000-1500
£2899 $4754 €4000 Nude back of young woman on a striped towel. s.d.1925 chl W/C. 27-May-3 Hassfurther, Vienna #58/R est:800-1200

PESKE, Jean (1870-1949) French
£1310 $2188 €1900 Le dejeuner du jeune enfant dans la cuisine (58x42cm-23x17in) s. 10-Jul-3 Artcurial Briest, Paris #175/R est:2000-3000
£1321 $2047 €2100 Vendee, Saint-Jean-de-Mont, les Bourines (38x54cm-15x21in) s. cardboard. 30-Oct-2 Artcurial Briest, Paris #324/R est:3000-4000
£1418 $2369 €2000 Laboureur dans sa ferme (46x33cm-18x13in) s. 17-Jun-3 Claude Boisgirard, Paris #108 est:1500-1800
£1572 $2437 €2500 La ferme a Saint-Jean-de-Mont, Vendee (38x55cm-15x22in) s. 30-Oct-2 Artcurial Briest, Paris #325/R est:3000-4000
£1573 $2438 €2500 Village de Provence (49x65cm-19x26in) s. cardboard. 4-Oct-2 Tajan, Paris #191 est:2000-3000
£2484 $4000 €3726 Rock and sea, Lavandou. Love in bloom, Bornies (36x25cm-14x10in) s. i. panel pair prov. 19-Feb-3 Doyle, New York #79 est:1500-2500
£3205 $5032 €5000 Bord de riviere (42x61cm-17x24in) s. 16-Dec-2 Rabourdin & Choppin de Janvry, Paris #68/R
£4114 $6377 €6500 Voilier et enfant sur la plage (45x55cm-18x22in) s. panel prov. 28-Sep-2 Christie's, Paris #12/R est:3800-5300
Works on paper
£306 $487 €450 Rochers en foret (48x63cm-19x25in) s. W/C gouache. 24-Mar-3 Coutau Begarie, Paris #193
£374 $595 €550 Musee Rodin (46x54cm-18x21in) s.i. gouache prov. 24-Mar-3 Coutau Begarie, Paris #189
£544 $865 €800 Pecheurs en bord de lac (60x49cm-24x19in) s. gouache prov. 24-Mar-3 Coutau Begarie, Paris #191/R
£701 $1093 €1100 Portrait de Jean (34x27cm-13x11in) s. pastel. 6-Nov-2 Claude Boisgirard, Paris #39/R
£701 $1093 €1100 Vieil arbre (31x39cm-12x15in) s. W/C. 6-Nov-2 Claude Boisgirard, Paris #40
£816 $1298 €1200 Paysage breton au moulin a vent (45x60cm-18x24in) s. gouache prov. 24-Mar-3 Coutau Begarie, Paris #190/R
£1701 $2704 €2500 Maternite (73x62cm-29x24in) s.d. pastel. 3-Mar-3 Claude Boisgirard, Paris #84/R est:2500-3000
£1773 $2961 €2500 Maternite (61x46cm-24x18in) s. pastel. 17-Jun-3 Claude Boisgirard, Paris #109/R est:2500-3000

PESNE, Antoine (attrib) (1683-1757) French
£1603 $2500 €2405 Portrait of an officer (79x64cm-31x25in) 18-Oct-2 Du Mouchelle, Detroit #2015/R est:3000-4000

PESNE, Antoine (style) (1683-1757) French
£6500 $10465 €9750 Portrait of a lady, as a shepherdess (96x81cm-38x32in) prov. 20-Feb-3 Christie's, Kensington #334/R est:3000-5000

PESNELLE, Charles Albert (19th C) French
£2200 $3586 €3300 Bathers (62x81cm-24x32in) s. 29-Jan-3 Sotheby's, Olympia #338/R est:2000-4000

PESSERS, Henriette (1899-?) Dutch
£592 $959 €900 Farmhouses (37x47cm-15x19in) s. plywood. 21-Jan-3 Christie's, Amsterdam #405

PESU, Daniel Johannes (1891-1956) Finnish
£258 $408 €400 Coastal landscape (57x68cm-22x27in) s.d.1943. 19-Dec-2 Hagelstam, Helsinki #909

PETAULASSIE, Isaacie (20th C) Canadian
Sculpture
£1565 $2442 €2610 Dancing bear (58x25x23cm-23x10x9in) green stone carving. 13-Apr-3 Levis, Calgary #62/R est:4000-5000 (C.D 3600)

PETER, Axel (1863-1942) Swedish
£567 $879 €851 Self portrait (59x45cm-23x18in) s.d.1892. 4-Dec-2 AB Stockholms Auktionsverk #1634/R (S.KR 8000)

PETER, Emanuel (1799-1873) Austrian
Miniatures
£1800 $2772 €2700 Lady with roses at her corsage (8cm-3in) s.i. gilt metal bezel oval exec.c.1830 after M M Daffinger. 24-Oct-2 Sotheby's, Olympia #43/R est:1500-2000
£2000 $3240 €3000 Lady wearing a white dress (7cm-3in) s. gilt mounted wood frame. 22-May-3 Bonhams, New Bond Street #123/R est:2000-3000
£5500 $8470 €8250 Lady with pearl necklace and earring (9cm-4in) s.d.1830 gilt metal bezel oval. 24-Oct-2 Sotheby's, Olympia #44/R est:1500-2000

Works on paper

£541 $843 €800 Portrait of blonde boy (14x10cm-6x4in) s. W/C oval. 28-Mar-3 Dorotheum, Vienna #209/R

PETER, Juliette (20th C) Australian

£424 $653 €636 Dark window (72x51cm-28x20in) s. board. 4-Sep-2 Dunbar Sloane, Wellington #14 est:800-1500 (NZ.D 1400)

PETER, Nori (?) Canadian

£247 $383 €371 Inuit sister and brother with husky pup (60x50cm-24x20in) s. acrylic on board. 3-Dec-2 Joyner, Toronto #471 (C.D 600)
£307 $476 €461 Feeding the family (41x51cm-16x20in) s. board. 24-Sep-2 Ritchie, Toronto #3228/R (C.D 750)

PETER, Victor (1840-1918) French

Sculpture

£1090 $1711 €1700 Lionceau de l'Atlas age de deux ans (24x29x12cm-9x11x5in) st.f.Susse brown green pat bronze. 24-Nov-2 Lesieur & Le Bars, Le Havre #140/R
£1115 $1784 €1550 Lionceau de l'Atlas age de deux ans (24x29cm-9x11in) s. green brown pat bronze Cast Susse. 18-May-3 Rabourdin & Choppin de Janvry, Paris #159 est:1600-1800

PETERDI, Gabor (1915-) American/Hungarian

£2096 $3270 €3039 Still life with painter's palette (79x99cm-31x39in) s. 12-Apr-3 Mu Terem Galeria, Budapest #22/R est:700000 (H.F 750000)
£3870 $6037 €5612 Still life with pipe (60x49cm-24x19in) s.d.34. 13-Sep-2 Mu Terem Galeria, Budapest #197/R est:600000 (H.F 1500000)

PETERELLE, Adolphe (1874-1947) French

£276 $436 €400 Visage (41x24cm-16x9in) s. 6-Apr-3 Herbette, Doullens #602/R
£288 $460 €400 Nu love (36x20cm-14x8in) s. chl estompe. 14-May-3 Blanchet, Paris #87
£340 $541 €500 Village (33x24cm-13x9in) s. 24-Mar-3 Coutau Begarie, Paris #207
£340 $541 €500 Verger (36x44cm-14x17in) s. 24-Mar-3 Coutau Begarie, Paris #206
£345 $545 €500 Baigneuse assise (73x50cm-29x20in) s. 6-Apr-3 Herbette, Doullens #600/R
£414 $654 €600 Femme assise (55x38cm-22x15in) s. 6-Apr-3 Herbette, Doullens #603/R
£690 $1090 €1000 Portrait de femme (39x29cm-15x11in) s. cardboard. 6-Apr-3 Herbette, Doullens #606/R
£863 $1381 €1200 Femme au collier (38x46cm-15x18in) s. exhib. 14-May-3 Blanchet, Paris #90/R
£957 $1599 €1350 Port de Provence (73x50cm-29x20in) s. exhib. 23-Jun-3 Claude Boisgirard, Paris #90

Works on paper

£255 $397 €400 Eve (33x14cm-13x6in) chl wash. 7-Nov-2 Chochon-Barre & Allardi, Paris #209
£286 $454 €420 Nu de dos (25x15cm-10x6in) s. pen wash. 24-Mar-3 Coutau Begarie, Paris #205/R
£360 $576 €500 Femme nue de dos au fruit (35x23cm-14x9in) s. sanguine chl exhib. 14-May-3 Blanchet, Paris #88/R

PETERS, Anna (1843-1926) German

£253 $400 €400 Still life of flowers (9x14cm-4x6in) i. verso postcard. 30-Nov-2 Bassenge, Berlin #6568
£452 $664 €700 Study of flowers (21x32cm-8x13in) s. 24-Jun-2 Dr Fritz Nagel, Stuttgart #6112/R
£685 $1068 €1000 Flowers (11x16cm-4x6in) s. board lit. 10-Apr-3 Allgauer, Kempten #2929/R
£968 $1423 €1500 Spring (14x10cm-6x4in) s. board. 20-Jun-2 Dr Fritz Nagel, Stuttgart #807/R est:1600
£2230 $3478 €3300 Flowers (46x34cm-18x13in) i. 31-Mar-3 Dr Fritz Nagel, Stuttgart #7102/R est:2500
£2302 $3776 €3200 Tree trunk bridge (36x31cm-14x12in) s. canvas on board. 6-Jun-3 Ketterer, Munich #10/R est:4000-5000
£2635 $4111 €3900 Kitchen interior with flowers on table (38x27cm-15x11in) s. canvas on board. 27-Mar-3 Dr Fritz Nagel, Stuttgart #854/R est:3900
£4088 $6377 €6500 Summer flowers (18x24cm-7x9in) s. board. 19-Sep-2 Dr Fritz Nagel, Stuttgart #980/R est:6800
£4487 $7045 €7000 Flowers in vase and plums on plate (75x57cm-30x22in) s. 21-Nov-2 Van Ham, Cologne #1861/R est:7000
£12658 $19620 €20000 Autumnal fruit still life (78x61cm-31x24in) s. 25-Sep-2 Neumeister, Munich #694/R est:12500
£19481 $29026 €30000 Still life of fruit and flowers (73x58cm-29x23in) s. 26-Jun-2 Neumeister, Munich #827/R est:18000

PETERS, Carl W (1897-1980) American

£274 $400 €411 Church (40x35cm-16x14in) s.i.verso canvasboard. 10-May-2 Skinner, Boston #158/R
£2125 $3400 €3188 Summer landscape with river (51x61cm-20x24in) s. s.verso. 11-Jan-3 James Julia, Fairfield #168 est:3000-5000
£2174 $3500 €3261 Cabins and stream in winter landscape (51x61cm-20x24in) bears another sig.verso. 18-Feb-3 John Moran, Pasadena #48a est:3000-5000
£2293 $3600 €3440 Winter landscape with village with multi-coloured buildings (46x53cm-18x21in) s. masonite. 19-Apr-3 James Julia, Fairfield #18/R est:2500-3500
£5063 $8000 €7595 Derelict - Gloucester (53x61cm-21x24in) prov.exhib. 24-Apr-3 Shannon's, Milford #89/R est:5000-7000

PETERS, Charles Rollo (1862-1928) American

£4321 $7000 €6265 Nocturnal reflections (48x64cm-19x25in) s.i.d.1916. 21-May-3 Doyle, New York #132/R est:6000-8000
£6051 $9500 €9077 San Luis Rey de Francia (74x99cm-29x39in) s. 19-Nov-2 Butterfields, San Francisco #8185/R est:10000-15000

PETERS, E (19th C) ?

£450 $698 €675 Man taking snuff (13x9cm-5x4in) s.i. panel. 25-Sep-2 John Nicholson, Haslemere #1037/R

PETERS, Harry T (jnr) (19th C) American

£3185 $5000 €4778 Family of golden pheasants (61x76cm-24x30in) i.d.1885 verso prov. 19-Nov-2 Butterfields, San Francisco #8012/R est:3000-5000

PETERS, Herbert (1925-) German?

Sculpture

£1223 $1957 €1700 Small pillar (40cm-16in) s.d. iron. 15-May-3 Neumeister, Munich #747/R est:400-600

Works on paper

£360 $576 €500 Composition (94x63cm-37x25in) mono.d. pencil. 15-May-3 Neumeister, Munich #748/R
£360 $576 €500 Figure (65x50cm-26x20in) s.d. pencil board. 15-May-3 Neumeister, Munich #751/R
£863 $1381 €1200 Sculptor's sketch (32x23cm-13x9in) mono.d.12.Nov. 70 pencil col pen bodycol. 15-May-3 Neumeister, Munich #749/R

PETERS, Matthew William (1742-1814) British

£6000 $9960 €9000 Two children with jay in a cage (90x71cm-35x28in) 12-Jun-3 Sotheby's, London #97/R est:6000-8000
£10323 $16000 €15485 Young lady in a white and pink dress, carrying flowers and fruit (79x89cm-31x35in) prov. 2-Oct-2 Christie's, Rockefeller NY #125/R est:8000-12000
£28000 $44520 €42000 Portrait of Lady Isabella Manners as a child (73x60cm-29x24in) prov.lit. 19-Mar-3 Sotheby's, London #53/R est:15000-20000

PETERS, Pieter Francis (1818-1903) Dutch

£4487 $6955 €7000 Lowenstein near Heilbronn in autumn (107x87cm-42x34in) s.d.1872. 5-Dec-2 Dr Fritz Nagel, Stuttgart #693/R est:4500

PETERS, Pietronella (1848-1924) German

£405 $632 €600 Wood (25x20cm-10x8in) s. bears sig. 27-Mar-3 Dr Fritz Nagel, Stuttgart #859/R
£4403 $6868 €7000 Doll's mother (30x30cm-12x12in) s. board. 19-Sep-2 Dr Fritz Nagel, Stuttgart #981/R est:8800

PETERS, Udo (1884-1964) German

£1709 $2700 €2700 Autumn landscape near Worpswede with small train station (43x55cm-17x22in) s.d.53 board. 29-Nov-2 Bolland & Marotz, Bremen #564/R est:2900
£2585 $4110 €3800 Sunlit farmstead in Worpswede (50x70cm-20x28in) s. board. 28-Mar-3 Bolland & Marotz, Bremen #364/R est:4400
£2585 $4110 €3800 Birches (53x69cm-21x27in) s. board. 28-Mar-3 Bolland & Marotz, Bremen #365/R est:4400
£3228 $5100 €5100 Landscape with houses (60x73cm-24x29in) s.d.54 board. 29-Nov-2 Bolland & Marotz, Bremen #563/R est:5600

PETERS, Wilhelm Otto (1851-1935) Norwegian

£354 $577 €531 Still life of roses (30x40cm-12x16in) s. 17-Feb-3 Blomqvist, Lysaker #1160 (N.KR 4000)
£2176 $3481 €3264 Young girl with goats (95x65cm-37x26in) s.d.26. 17-Mar-3 Blomqvist, Oslo #384/R est:30000-35000 (N.KR 25000)
£3122 $4871 €4683 Summer - three children in beached boat (66x94cm-26x37in) s.d.1926. 21-Oct-2 Blomqvist, Oslo #318/R est:30000-40000 (N.KR 36000)

PETERSEN, Albert (1875-1957) Danish

£772 $1204 €1158 Two fishermen talking by beached boat, women in background (115x180cm-45x71in) s. 11-Nov-2 Rasmussen, Vejle #525 (D.KR 9000)

£1021 $1614 €1532 Fishermen working on beach (114x176cm-45x69in) s.i. 2-Dec-2 Rasmussen, Copenhagen #1349/R est:10000 (D.KR 12000)

PETERSEN, Anna (1845-1910) Danish
£426 $672 €639 Field landscape with cattle and country road (26x35cm-10x14in) init.d.95 panel prov. 27-Nov-2 Museumsbygningen, Copenhagen #33/R (D.KR 5000)
£723 $1143 €1085 Portrait of man smoking pipe (55x47cm-22x19in) init.i.d.86 prov.lit. 27-Nov-2 Museumsbygningen, Copenhagen #31/R (D.KR 8500)
£2848 $4415 €4500 Moonlit lantern procession in small town (60x80cm-24x31in) s. 28-Sep-2 Hans Stahl, Hamburg #125/R est:2000
£6052 $9623 €9078 Girl from Brittany sorting plants in greenhouse (121x110cm-48x43in) s.i.d.84. 5-Mar-3 Rasmussen, Copenhagen #1594/R est:50000 (D.KR 65000)

PETERSEN, Armand (1891-1969) Swiss/French
Sculpture
£1824 $2846 €2700 Biche (15x19x9cm-6x7x4in) medaille pat bronze. 25-Mar-3 Chochon-Barre & Allardi, Paris #37/R est:2300-2500
£2258 $3568 €3500 Panthere assise (17cm-7in) s. brown pat bronze. 17-Dec-2 Rossini, Paris #57/R
£2770 $4322 €4100 Antilope (25x22x9cm-10x9x4in) medaille pat bronze Cast Biscieglia. 25-Mar-3 Chochon-Barre & Allardi, Paris #36/R est:4500-4800

PETERSEN, Carl Olof (1880-1939) Swedish
£1795 $2782 €2800 Trees (60x70cm-24x28in) s.i.d.1931 i. verso. 5-Dec-2 Neumeister, Munich #2855 est:300

PETERSEN, Edvard (1841-1911) Danish
£288 $464 €432 Hilly landscape (33x54cm-13x21in) mono. 22-Feb-3 Rasmussen, Havnen #2244 (D.KR 3200)
£431 $655 €647 Four oak trees near Sollerod (26x37cm-10x15in) init. panel. 27-Aug-2 Rasmussen, Copenhagen #1782/R (D.KR 5000)
£468 $740 €702 Coastal landscape with wood in background (27x55cm-11x22in) mono.d.1869. 30-Nov-2 Rasmussen, Havnen #2003/R (D.KR 5500)
£596 $941 €894 Landscape with stone bridge across river (38x55cm-15x22in) init.d.1867. 2-Dec-2 Rasmussen, Copenhagen #1480/R (D.KR 7000)
£1277 $2017 €1916 By a small brook - father and son near Esrum Lake (38x27cm-15x11in) mono.d.1886 exhib. 2-Dec-2 Rasmussen, Copenhagen #1759/R est:15000 (D.KR 15000)
£1397 $2221 €2096 Two boys by Dutch canal near Delft (28x43cm-11x17in) mono.d.79 exhib. 5-Mar-3 Rasmussen, Copenhagen #1874/R est:15000-20000 (D.KR 15000)
£1532 $2420 €2298 View across a fjord, possibly Frederikssund (68x113cm-27x44in) s.d.1897. 27-Nov-2 Museumsbygningen, Copenhagen #8/R est:15000-18000 (D.KR 18000)
£1769 $2813 €2654 The home-coming - the American steamer at Larsen's Plads (50x40cm-20x16in) init. study. 5-Mar-3 Rasmussen, Copenhagen #1918/R est:20000-25000 (D.KR 19000)
£6460 $9819 €9690 Young woman picking lilacs on a sunny day (81x60cm-32x24in) s.d.1910. 27-Aug-2 Rasmussen, Copenhagen #1493/R est:50000 (D.KR 75000)
£6699 $10852 €9714 The Forum in Rome with the Senate (70x100cm-28x39in) mono.i.d.1881. 26-May-3 Rasmussen, Copenhagen #1115/R est:75000-100000 (D.KR 70000)

PETERSEN, Elias (1859-1950) Danish
£468 $740 €702 Seascape off Sprogo (88x126cm-35x50in) s. 30-Nov-2 Rasmussen, Havnen #2048/R (D.KR 5500)

PETERSEN, Emmanuel Aage (1894-1948) Danish
£258 $393 €387 Vessel off Klampenborg (38x44cm-15x17in) init. 27-Aug-2 Rasmussen, Copenhagen #1731/R (D.KR 3000)
£297 $464 €446 Men of war in the Bay of Biscay (47x52cm-19x20in) init.i.d.22. 5-Aug-2 Rasmussen, Vejle #53/R (D.KR 3500)
£326 $519 €489 Coastal landscape with boats, Greenland (25x37cm-10x15in) init. 5-May-3 Rasmussen, Vejle #616/R (D.KR 3500)
£402 $651 €583 Landscape from Sukkertoppen at Greenland (26x40cm-10x16in) s.i.d.1929. 24-May-3 Rasmussen, Havnen #2124 (D.KR 4200)
£402 $651 €583 Fjord landscape with kayak (24x34cm-9x13in) init. 24-May-3 Rasmussen, Havnen #2136 (D.KR 4200)
£429 $682 €644 Coastal landscape with cliffs, Greenland (26x42cm-10x17in) s.i.d.1921. 5-May-3 Rasmussen, Vejle #614/R (D.KR 4600)
£440 $713 €638 Farm scene (21x35cm-8x14in) mono.d.1918. 24-May-3 Rasmussen, Havnen #2188 (D.KR 4600)
£459 $744 €666 Vessel in ice covered bay (50x82cm-20x32in) init. 24-May-3 Rasmussen, Havnen #2143 (D.KR 4800)
£510 $795 €765 Seascape from Greenland with view to mountains (33x55cm-13x22in) init. 5-Aug-2 Rasmussen, Vejle #62/R (D.KR 6000)
£519 $820 €779 Hunting polar bears (54x71cm-21x28in) s. 27-Nov-2 Falkkloos, Malmo #77814/R (S.KR 7400)
£526 $853 €763 Seascape with kayaks (33x55cm-13x22in) s.i. 24-May-3 Rasmussen, Havnen #2142/R (D.KR 5500)
£549 $856 €824 Fjord landscape with icebergs, Greenland (55x80cm-22x31in) init.i. 23-Sep-2 Rasmussen, Vejle #127/R (D.KR 6500)
£596 $953 €894 Settlement in Bay of Disco (30x41cm-12x16in) init. 16-Mar-3 Hindemae, Ullerslev #362/R (D.KR 6400)
£601 $949 €902 Seascape with icebergs - Klaushavn, Bay of Disco (60x80cm-24x31in) s. 13-Nov-2 Kunsthallen, Copenhagen #32/R (D.KR 7000)
£653 $1038 €980 Landscape from Greenland (39x58cm-15x23in) mono. 5-May-3 Rasmussen, Vejle #273 (D.KR 7000)
£678 $1072 €1017 Landscape from Klaushavn, Disco Bay (50x60cm-20x24in) s. 5-Apr-3 Rasmussen, Havnen #2007/R (D.KR 7300)
£681 $1056 €1022 Figures and houses, Greenland (60x90cm-24x35in) s. 28-Sep-2 Rasmussen, Havnen #3586/R (D.KR 8000)
£699 $1132 €1014 Landscape from Greenland (32x42cm-13x17in) s. 24-May-3 Rasmussen, Havnen #2007/R (D.KR 7300)
£709 $1127 €1064 Sunset over Ikeresak (52x31cm-20x12in) init. 5-May-3 Rasmussen, Vejle #618/R (D.KR 7600)
£750 $1207 €1125 Landscape with figures, houses, dogs and smoking hut for salmon, Greenland (60x76cm-24x30in) s,. 19-Jan-3 Hindemae, Ullerslev #7510/R (D.KR 8500)
£771 $1219 €1157 Landscape with figures, Greenland (70x100cm-28x39in) s. 5-Apr-3 Rasmussen, Havnen #2024/R (D.KR 8300)
£840 $1335 €1260 Archipelago, Egedes Minde (36x52cm-14x20in) init. 5-May-3 Rasmussen, Vejle #615/R (D.KR 9000)
£857 $1371 €1286 Mountain landscape with snow (74x116cm-29x46in) init. 16-Mar-3 Hindemae, Ullerslev #363/R (D.KR 9200)
£861 $1395 €1248 Seal hunters on the ice, Greenland (36x47cm-14x19in) s. 26-May-3 Rasmussen, Copenhagen #1362/R (D.KR 9000)
£861 $1395 €1248 The spring vessel, Greenland (33x46cm-13x18in) s. 26-May-3 Rasmussen, Copenhagen #1363/R (D.KR 9000)
£887 $1383 €1331 North of Cape Farewell, sunset (67x99cm-26x39in) init. 23-Sep-2 Rasmussen, Vejle #125/R (D.KR 10500)
£1073 $1706 €1610 Mountain landscape with figures, Greenland (24x24cm-9x9in) init. 5-May-3 Rasmussen, Vejle #617/R (D.KR 11500)
£1119 $1780 €1679 Sunset over the sea, Greenland (52x70cm-20x28in) s,. 29-Apr-3 Kunsthallen, Copenhagen #546/R est:15000 (D.KR 12000)
£1306 $2076 €1959 Midnight sun, Udsted, Rodebay (52x71cm-20x28in) init. 5-May-3 Rasmussen, Vejle #619/R est:3000-4000 (D.KR 14000)
£1539 $2447 €2309 Landscape from Greenland with hunters and their smoking hut (54x67cm-21x26in) s. 5-May-3 Rasmussen, Vejle #612/R est:10000 (D.KR 16500)
£1613 $2548 €2500 Frozen landscape (37x73cm-15x29in) s.i.d.1923. 19-Dec-2 Claude Aguttes, Neuilly #37/R
£1632 $2596 €2448 Landscape from Greenland (40x55cm-16x22in) init. 5-May-3 Rasmussen, Vejle #611/R est:8000 (D.KR 17500)
£1726 $2744 €2589 Eskimos looking out over the sea, Greenland (52x70cm-20x28in) s. 5-May-3 Rasmussen, Vejle #613/R est:8000 (D.KR 18500)
£1869 $2916 €2804 The inspection ship Heimdal at entrance to Copenhagen Harbour (100x140cm-39x55in) s. 5-Aug-2 Rasmussen, Vejle #60/R est:18000-20000 (D.KR 22000)
£3172 $5043 €4758 Fjord landscape with women's boat and figures, Greenland (93x115cm-37x45in) s. 5-May-3 Rasmussen, Vejle #621/R est:10000-15000 (D.KR 34000)
£3312 $5265 €4968 Eskimos looking at Northern lights (107x132cm-42x52in) s. prov. 5-May-3 Rasmussen, Vejle #620/R est:15000 (D.KR 35500)

PETERSEN, Gunther (1920-) German
£316 $500 €500 Bunch of lilac in glass vase (80x60cm-31x24in) s. 29-Nov-2 Bolland & Marotz, Bremen #812/R

PETERSEN, Hans Gyde (1862-1943) Danish
£272 $430 €408 Two boys at Skagen Strand (90x125cm-35x49in) s.i.d.1940. 2-Dec-2 Rasmussen, Copenhagen #1362/R (D.KR 3200)
£383 $594 €575 View of Rome with ruins (60x88cm-24x35in) s.i.d.1899. 28-Sep-2 Rasmussen, Havnen #2016/R (D.KR 4500)
£1702 $2689 €2553 View over Palatin towards Saint Peter's (59x88cm-23x35in) s.i.indis.d.189. exhib. 2-Dec-2 Rasmussen, Copenhagen #1542/R est:30000 (D.KR 20000)

PETERSEN, Heinrich Andreas (1834-1916) German
£2051 $3179 €3200 Hamburg Schooner - Mariquinha (50x66cm-20x26in) s.i. bears d.1851. 7-Dec-2 Ketterer, Hamburg #21/R est:3500-4000

PETERSEN, J (?) Danish?
£1519 $2354 €2400 Puppet show in peasant room (55x81cm-22x32in) s. 25-Sep-2 Neumeister, Munich #695/R est:1600

PETERSEN, Jakob (1774-1854) Danish
£1200 $1944 €1800 Brig Quay Side in three positions (55x76cm-22x30in) init.i.d.1876. 21-May-3 Christie's, Kensington #645/R est:1500-2500
£2500 $3875 €3750 British and Danish frigate under reduced sail in heavy seas (63x82cm-25x32in) s.d.1836. 31-Oct-2 Christie's, Kensington #497/R est:3000-5000

Works on paper
£775 $1178 €1163 Ship's portrait of the Royal Greenland ship Nordlys (48x64cm-19x25in) s. executed 1853 pencil W/C. 27-Aug-2 Rasmussen, Copenhagen #1986/R (D.KR 9000)
£1180 $1841 €1770 Minerva of Jersey sailing off a coast (44x58cm-17x23in) s. W/C pen ink. 26-Mar-3 Hamptons Fine Art, Godalming #105 est:800-1200
£2553 $4034 €3830 Ship's portrait Dronning Maria af Copenhagen (45x62cm-18x24in) s.i. pen W/C gouache. 2-Dec-2 Rasmussen, Copenhagen #1426/R est:30000-40000 (D.KR 30000)
£2553 $4034 €3830 Ship's portrait of Patrioten of Copenhagen (45x62cm-18x24in) s.i. pen W/C gouache. 2-Dec-2 Rasmussen, Copenhagen #1429/R est:30000-40000 (D.KR 30000)
£4934 $7500 €7401 The Nikolai of Newburyport (51x66cm-20x26in) s.i. W/C. 17-Aug-2 North East Auctions, Portsmouth #840/R est:8000-10000
£10526 $16000 €15789 Cronstadt of Boston, on Falsterbo Reef (48x66cm-19x26in) s.i. W/C. 17-Aug-2 North East Auctions, Portsmouth #978/R est:12000-15000

PETERSEN, Julius (1851-1911) Danish
£279 $444 €419 Mother and children walking at edge of forest (37x45cm-15x18in) s.d.73. 5-Mar-3 Rasmussen, Copenhagen #1895/R (D.KR 3000)

PETERSEN, Lorenz (1803-1870) German
£2010 $3256 €2915 Ship's portrait of the three master Syrla (46x64cm-18x25in) s.d.1850. 24-May-3 Rasmussen, Havnen #2214/R est:8000-10000 (D.KR 21000)

PETERSEN, Magnus Julius (1827-1917) Danish

Works on paper
£1464 $2226 €2196 The Nydam boat. The Nydam boat seen from two angles (40x24cm-16x9in) s. one d.63 pen Indian ink W/C pair. 28-Aug-2 Museumsbygningen, Copenhagen #79/R est:12000-15000 (D.KR 17000)

PETERSEN, Oscar (?) American?
£324 $525 €486 Gun boat warship (79x71cm-31x28in) 24-Jan-3 Douglas, South Deerfield #5

PETERSEN, Robert Storm (1882-1949) Danish
£476 $756 €714 Landscape in moonlight (31x48cm-12x19in) init. 5-May-3 Rasmussen, Vejle #45/R (D.KR 5100)

Works on paper
£280 $445 €420 The cafe - Matrosen's Lyst (26x34cm-10x13in) init. Indian ink. 29-Apr-3 Kunsthallen, Copenhagen #303/R (D.KR 3000)
£305 $509 €442 Should we not save a bit, Tibirius - No, there is a shortage of empty bottles (38x28cm-15x11in) s.d.22-9-46 Indian ink. 17-Jun-3 Rasmussen, Copenhagen #118 (D.KR 3200)
£343 $573 €497 Have you heard this one Sophokles, that they want to export Akkevit to England (37x27cm-15x11in) s.i.d.21-12-46 Indian ink. 17-Jun-3 Rasmussen, Copenhagen #173 (D.KR 3600)
£372 $587 €558 Men walking in a park (25x36cm-10x14in) s.i.d.1906 pencil. 1-Apr-3 Rasmussen, Copenhagen #514 (D.KR 4000)
£380 $586 €570 Man hanged (18x31cm-7x12in) s.d.1910 W/C crayon pencil. 23-Oct-2 Kunsthallen, Copenhagen #328/R (D.KR 4500)
£487 $799 €731 Negro Jackson has in a boxing match won over white man Jeffries (27x33cm-11x13in) s. Indian ink. 27-May-3 Museumsbygningen, Copenhagen #486/R (D.KR 5000)
£513 $816 €770 The merchant and the young lady (25x21cm-10x8in) s. Indian ink. 29-Apr-3 Kunsthallen, Copenhagen #305/R (D.KR 5500)
£522 $831 €783 I' going to try that when I get home (31x24cm-12x9in) s. Indian ink. 29-Apr-3 Kunsthallen, Copenhagen #304/R (D.KR 5600)
£929 $1468 €1394 Cain and Abel (17x13cm-7x5in) init.d.1911 W/C Indian ink. 1-Apr-3 Rasmussen, Copenhagen #40/R (D.KR 10000)
£1072 $1758 €1608 Danish classical books and nice bananas (19x27cm-7x11in) s. col pencil. 27-May-3 Museumsbygningen, Copenhagen #487/R (D.KR 11000)
£2367 $3645 €3551 Back yard missionary (24x30cm-9x12in) s.i.d.1912 W/C Indian ink. 23-Oct-2 Kunsthallen, Copenhagen #327/R est:12000 (D.KR 28000)

PETERSEN, Roland (1926-) American
£15823 $25000 €23735 Solitary figure (173x142cm-68x56in) s.d.1967. 22-Apr-3 Butterfields, San Francisco #6051/R est:20000-30000
£16026 $25000 €24039 American picnic (183x184cm-72x72in) s.d.1969 s.i.d.stretcher. 14-Oct-2 Butterfields, San Francisco #2069/R est:20000-30000

PETERSEN, Sophus (1837-1904) Danish
£603 $916 €905 A rose (12x16cm-5x6in) s.d.1883. 27-Aug-2 Rasmussen, Copenhagen #1799/R (D.KR 7000)

PETERSEN, Vilhelm (1812-1880) Danish
£431 $655 €647 River landscape, South Germany (19x25cm-7x10in) 27-Aug-2 Rasmussen, Copenhagen #1745/R (D.KR 5000)
£3319 $5244 €4979 Large wooden farm surrounded by mountains (29x43cm-11x17in) i.d.19 juli exhib. 2-Dec-2 Rasmussen, Copenhagen #1150/R est:40000 (D.KR 39000)
£3404 $5379 €5106 View from Tyrol with houses built on slopes, mountains in background (23x34cm-9x13in) i.verso painted 1850-1851 exhib. 2-Dec-2 Rasmussen, Copenhagen #1149/R est:40000 (D.KR 40000)

PETERSEN, Walter (1862-1950) German
£256 $397 €400 Bismarck (36x24cm-14x9in) mono.d.88. 5-Dec-2 Schopman, Hamburg #536

PETERSEN-ANGELN, Heinrich (1850-1906) German
£1635 $2535 €2600 Moonlight, Vlussingen (107x85cm-42x33in) s. i. stretcher. 29-Oct-2 Dorotheum, Vienna #21/R est:2500-2700

PETERSON, Ann (20th C) American

Works on paper
£304 $475 €456 Western landscape (49x65cm-19x26in) s.d.39 W/C exhib. 20-Sep-2 Sloan, North Bethesda #348/R

PETERSON, F (?) Scandinavian
£374 $558 €561 Flowers in vase (70x50cm-28x20in) i. 25-Jun-2 Koller, Zurich #6716 (S.FR 850)

PETERSON, Jane (1876-1965) American
£1935 $3000 €2903 Yellow lillies (64x76cm-25x30in) s. painted c.1930. 8-Dec-2 Toomey, Oak Park #683/R est:5500-7500
£2373 $3750 €3560 Blue and yellow (76x64cm-30x25in) s. 17-Nov-2 CRN Auctions, Cambridge #15/R
£3750 $6000 €5438 Purple petunias (46x46cm-18x18in) s. canvasboard. 16-May-3 Skinner, Boston #143/R est:2000-4000
£4487 $7000 €6731 Gloucester Harbour scene (41x30cm-16x12in) s. board prov. 1-Aug-2 Eldred, East Dennis #987/R est:10000-15000
£5389 $9000 €7814 San Giorgio, Venice (43x43cm-17x17in) board prov. 22-Jun-3 Freeman, Philadelphia #124/R est:10000-15000
£7792 $12000 €11688 Brittany village (53x71cm-21x28in) s. 24-Oct-2 Shannon's, Milford #58/R est:12000-18000
£8280 $13000 €12420 Street in Paris, Eglise St. Julien (61x46cm-24x18in) s. 10-Dec-2 Doyle, New York #48/R est:12000-18000
£13924 $22000 €20886 Boathouse (46x61cm-18x24in) s. prov. 24-Apr-3 Shannon's, Milford #36/R est:15000-20000
£14151 $22500 €21227 Sailboats by the pier (46x61cm-18x24in) s. W/C gouache chl prov. 5-Mar-3 Sotheby's, New York #42/R est:20000-30000
£15723 $25000 €23585 Palace Dario on the Grand Canal, Venice (46x46cm-18x18in) s.i. s.verso board prov. 5-Mar-3 Sotheby's, New York #19/R est:25000-35000
£32468 $50000 €48702 View of San Giorgio Maggiore from the Lagoon, Venice (46x61cm-18x24in) s. prov. 24-Oct-2 Shannon's, Milford #22/R est:50000-75000

Works on paper
£375 $600 €544 Daylight (23x30cm-9x12in) W/C. 16-May-3 Skinner, Boston #223/R
£441 $700 €662 Coastal cliffs (18x25cm-7x10in) s. W/C gouache. 7-Mar-3 Skinner, Boston #509/R
£472 $750 €708 Italian coastal view (18x25cm-7x10in) s. W/C gouache. 7-Mar-3 Skinner, Boston #436/R
£535 $850 €803 Gloucester beach scene (27x37cm-11x15in) s. W/C go. 7-Mar-3 Skinner, Boston #496/R
£892 $1400 €1338 Floral still life (58x43cm-23x17in) s. ink W/C. 23-Nov-2 Pook & Pook, Downington #570/R est:2000-3000
£1006 $1600 €1509 Blue morning glories (76x55cm-30x22in) s. s.i.verso W/C gouache paperboard. 7-Mar-3 Skinner, Boston #546/R est:2000-2500
£1563 $2500 €2345 Day at the beach (20x20cm-8x8in) s. W/C. 11-Jan-3 James Julia, Fairfield #482 est:1500-2000
£2201 $3500 €3302 San Giorgio, Venice (30x32cm-12x13in) s.i.verso W/C gouache chl exhib. 5-Mar-3 Sotheby's, New York #21/R est:7000-10000

£8025 $13000 €12038 Aiva (46x46cm-18x18in) s.i.d.Jan 1939 verso gouache prov. 21-May-3 Sotheby's, New York #146/R est:15000-25000
£8642 $14000 €12963 Chioggia sailboat (46x46cm-18x18in) s. i.verso gouache prov. 21-May-3 Sotheby's, New York #147/R est:15000-25000
£12579 $20000 €18869 Sailboat, Chioggia (46x46cm-18x18in) s.i.verso W/C gouache prov. 5-Mar-3 Sotheby's, New York #20/R est:15000-25000
£15432 $25000 €23148 Boats unloading by a dock, Venice (44x59cm-17x23in) gouache chl executed 1920 prov. 21-May-3 Sotheby's, New York #154/R est:25000-35000

PETERSON, Jo (20th C) American
£1032 $1600 €1548 Stretch of beach (43x58cm-17x23in) s. board painted c.1945. 8-Dec-2 Toomey, Oak Park #729/R est:2500-3500

PETERSSEN, Eilif (1852-1928) Norwegian
£2353 $3812 €3530 Portrait of Achille (53x44cm-21x17in) s.i.d.77 exhib. 26-May-3 Grev Wedels Plass, Oslo #89/R est:30000-40000 (N.KR 26000)
£7018 $11088 €10527 View from Ledaal with farm (71x109cm-28x43in) s.i.d.89 exhib. 17-Dec-2 Grev Wedels Plass, Oslo #178/R est:100000-150000 (N.KR 80000)
£8850 $13982 €13275 Judas Iskariot (56x46cm-22x18in) s.d.1877 lit. 28-Apr-3 Blomqvist, Oslo #331/R est:80000-100000 (N.KR 100000)
£10444 $16710 €15666 View towards the lagoons, Venice (68x55cm-27x22in) s.i.d.85. 17-Mar-3 Blomqvist, Oslo #326/R est:150000-250000 (N.KR 120000)

PETERSSON, Axel (1868-1925) Swedish
Sculpture
£1474 $2388 €2137 The concertina player (28cm-11in) with sig. wood. 26-May-3 Bukowskis, Stockholm #288/R est:20000-25000 (S.KR 19000)
£1560 $2418 €2340 Seated concertina player (21cm-8in) s.d.1919 partly painted wood. 3-Dec-2 Bukowskis, Stockholm #222/R est:20000-25000 (S.KR 22000)
£1964 $3221 €2848 Finger pulling (28x42cm-11x17in) s. carved wood. 4-Jun-3 AB Stockholms Auktionsverk #2388/R est:15000-20000 (S.KR 25000)
£2411 $3738 €3617 Milkmaid and cow (14cm-6in) s.d.1918 painted wood. 8-Dec-2 Uppsala Auktionskammare, Uppsala #355/R est:20000-25000 (S.KR 34000)
£2482 $3848 €3723 From The auction (34cm-13in) st.sig. wood four. 4-Dec-2 AB Stockholms Auktionsverk #1826/R est:40000-45000 (S.KR 35000)
£2837 $4397 €4256 Chess players (26x45cm-10x18in) partly painted wood. 3-Dec-2 Bukowskis, Stockholm #213/R est:40000-50000 (S.KR 40000)
£4034 $6535 €5849 The christening (26cm-10in) with sig.i. wood three parts. 26-May-3 Bukowskis, Stockholm #297a/R est:40000-60000 (S.KR 52000)
£5043 $8169 €7312 Jockey on horseback (45x49cm-18x19in) painted wood. 26-May-3 Bukowskis, Stockholm #297/R est:80000-100000 (S.KR 65000)
£5816 $9014 €8724 Full-blooded hore (28cm-11in) s. painted wood prov.exhib. 3-Dec-2 Bukowskis, Stockholm #221/R est:60000-70000 (S.KR 82000)
£7092 $10993 €10638 Enrolment of conscripts (29cm-11in) st.sig. partly painted wood. 3-Dec-2 Bukowskis, Stockholm #217/R est:80000-100000 (S.KR 100000)

PETERZANO, Simone (c.1590-?) Italian
Works on paper
£1100 $1705 €1650 St. Anthony (28x17cm-11x7in) brush ink htd white prov. 9-Dec-2 Bonhams, New Bond Street #47/R est:800-1000
£17284 $28000 €25926 Miracle of the mule (40x30cm-16x12in) i. chk pen ink wash prov. 22-Jan-3 Christie's, Rockefeller NY #9/R est:30000

PETHER (attrib) (18/19th C) British
£2600 $4264 €3900 Fire at Drury Lane; moonlit river landscape with St Paul's. 4-Feb-3 Lawrences, Bletchingley #1323/R est:800-1200

PETHER, Abraham (1756-1812) British
£1900 $2983 €2850 Wooded landscape with a fisherman by a stream (30x43cm-12x17in) s. 10-Dec-2 Bonhams, New Bond Street #116/R est:2000-3000
£8200 $13448 €12300 Figure on a bridge before a village at dusk (63x76cm-25x30in) s.d.1797. 29-May-3 Christie's, Kensington #72/R est:4000-6000

PETHER, Abraham (attrib) (1756-1812) British
£1300 $2002 €1950 Figures by a church in a moonlit lake landscape (30x41cm-12x16in) 5-Sep-2 Christie's, Kensington #122/R est:800-1200

PETHER, H (fl.1828-1865) British
£800 $1304 €1200 Rural landscape with figures on pathway and coastal fort to the left (46x30cm-18x12in) s.d.1847. 11-Feb-3 Fellows & Sons, Birmingham #6/R

PETHER, Henry (fl.1828-1865) British
£4861 $7000 €7292 Moonlit castle on riverbank (46x61cm-18x24in) prov. 15-Jan-3 Christie's, Rockefeller NY #126/R est:10000
£5000 $7800 €7500 Moonlight in Venice (61x92cm-24x36in) s. 17-Sep-2 Sotheby's, Olympia #145/R est:5000-7000
£10000 $15900 €15000 View of Windsor Castle under full moon from across the Thames (61x91cm-24x36in) s. painted c.1860. 30-Apr-3 Brightwells, Leominster #971/R est:10000-15000
£10000 $16600 €15000 Somerset House and the Thames by moonlight (61x91cm-24x36in) s. 12-Jun-3 Sotheby's, London #218/R est:5000-7000
£18000 $28620 €27000 Unloading cargo from the Grand Canal. Venice, by moonlight (60x90cm-24x35in) s. 19-Mar-3 Sotheby's, London #75/R est:18000-25000

PETHER, Henry (attrib) (fl.1828-1865) British
£1435 $2325 €2081 Harbour in moonlight (64x77cm-25x30in) s. 26-May-3 Rasmussen, Copenhagen #1369/R est:20000-25000 (D.KR 15000)

PETHER, Sebastian (1790-1844) British
£320 $496 €480 Castle ruins. 2-Nov-2 Hogben, Folkstone #247
£371 $590 €557 Moonlit castle (30x41cm-12x16in) 18-Mar-3 Maynards, Vancouver #1/R (C.D 875)
£400 $664 €580 Moonlit harbour with figures (37x67cm-15x26in) s. canvas on panel. 16-Jun-3 Waddingtons, Toronto #123/R est:1500-2000 (C.D 900)
£1650 $2690 €2393 River fishing by moonlight (35x44cm-14x17in) 21-Jul-3 Bonhams, Bath #52/R est:600-800
£2000 $3160 €3000 House on fire in a moonlit landscape (21x28cm-8x11in) s. panel. 28-Nov-2 Sotheby's, London #133 est:2000-3000
£7500 $12450 €11250 Coastal landscape with a volcano by moonlight (51x62cm-20x24in) s. indis d.1824. 10-Jun-3 Christie's, London #57/R est:4000-6000

PETHER, Sebastian (attrib) (1790-1844) British
£600 $978 €870 Moonlit estuary scene with figures unloading a boat (33x43cm-13x17in) panel prov. 21-Jul-3 Sotheby's, London #325 est:600-800
£958 $1600 €1389 Figures in a moonlit landscape (41x51cm-16x20in) 21-Jun-3 Selkirks, St. Louis #481/R est:1000-1500
£3000 $5010 €4350 Extensive river landscape with cattle on a bridge before a church ruins (71x91cm-28x36in) 17-Jun-3 Bonhams, New Bond Street #33/R est:3000-5000

PETHER, William (c.1731-1821) British
Prints
£3800 $5890 €5700 Philosopher giving a lecture on the Orrery (48x58cm-19x23in) mezzotint after Joseph Wright of Derby. 4-Dec-2 Bonhams, New Bond Street #113/R est:1000-1500

PETIET, Marie (1854-1893) French
£14557 $23000 €23000 Trois soeurs (109x80cm-43x31in) s.d.1879. 1-Dec-2 Anaf, Lyon #148/R est:28000

PETION, Françoise (20th C) French
Works on paper
£269 $423 €420 Jeune reveuse (15x15cm-6x6in) s. pastel. 15-Dec-2 Thierry & Lannon, Brest #246
£296 $476 €420 Meditation (32x26cm-13x10in) s. pastel. 11-May-3 Thierry & Lannon, Brest #274
£317 $510 €450 Jour de soleil en Bretagne (55x38cm-22x15in) s. pastel. 11-May-3 Thierry & Lannon, Brest #276
£361 $589 €520 Trois danseuses (30x40cm-12x16in) s. pastel. 19-Jul-3 Thierry & Lannon, Brest #228
£472 $770 €680 Retour de nuit (40x30cm-16x12in) s. pastel. 19-Jul-3 Thierry & Lannon, Brest #230

PETIT, Alfred (?-1895) French
£1346 $2113 €2100 Femme nue sur la greve (93x150cm-37x59in) s. 14-Dec-2 Herbette, Doullens #241/R est:1500
£2568 $4005 €3800 Nu au bord de plage (92x148cm-36x58in) s. 28-Mar-3 Claude Aguttes, Neuilly #77/R

PETIT, C (?) ?
£2532 $4000 €4000 L'heureuse famille (56x46cm-22x18in) s.i.d.1874 panel. 1-Dec-2 Peron, Melun #116

PETIT, Charles (19th C) French?
£1400 $2212 €2100 At play in the garden (20x14cm-8x6in) s. panel. 14-Nov-2 Christie's, Kensington #142/R est:1000-1500
£2313 $3678 €3400 Scene d'interieur a la ferme (50x40cm-20x16in) s.i. 19-Mar-3 Hotel des Ventes Mosan, Brussels #170 est:3200-3500

PETIT, Eugène (1839-1886) French
£1400 $2198 €2100 On the point (54x65cm-21x26in) s. 16-Apr-3 Christie's, Kensington #687/R est:1000-1500
£1800 $3006 €2700 Pointer hunting (38x46cm-15x18in) s. 18-Jun-3 Christie's, Kensington #25/R est:1500-2000
£2292 $3621 €3300 Vase de fleurs (65x54cm-26x21in) s. 23-Apr-3 Rabourdin & Choppin de Janvry, Paris #17/R
£2917 $4638 €4200 Blossom branches and peonies in a vase (73x60cm-29x24in) s. prov. 29-Apr-3 Christie's, Amsterdam #109/R est:4000-6000

PETIT, Eugène (attrib) (1839-1886) French
£676 $1054 €1000 Bouquet de coquelicots, bleuets et marguerites (100x81cm-39x32in) 28-Mar-3 Claude Aguttes, Neuilly #99/R

PETIT, Eugène Joseph (1845-?) French
£1481 $2104 €2400 Corvee d'eau (65x50cm-26x20in) s. 17-Mar-2 Galerie de Chartres, Chartres #148

PETIT, Louis (1794-?) French
£897 $1364 €1400 Houle de Cancale (31x55cm-12x22in) s. 17-Aug-2 Livinec, Gaudcheau & Jezequel, Rennes #38

PETIT, Paul (20th C) French
£276 $441 €400 Le Jardin du Luxembourg (50x65cm-20x26in) s. 12-Mar-3 Libert, Castor, Paris #152

PETIT, Pierre Joseph (18/19th C) French
£10764 $16792 €16900 Paysage italien anime (64x93cm-25x37in) s.d.1806. 6-Nov-2 Gioffredo, Nice #36/R
£12258 $19000 €18387 Italianate landscapes with travellers and shepherd and his flock (32x32cm-13x13in) s. copper oval pair prov. 2-Oct-2 Christie's, Rockefeller NY #176/R est:10000-15000

PETIT-GERARD, Pierre (1852-?) French
£437 $700 €634 On guard (21x27cm-8x11in) s.i. panel. 16-May-3 Skinner, Boston #14/R
£4795 $7527 €7000 Jour de nettoyage au camp (84x110cm-33x43in) s.d.1905 exhib. 15-Apr-3 Sotheby's, Amsterdam #61/R est:5000-7000

PETITBOIS, Agathon du (attrib) (19th C) French?
£8537 $14000 €12806 View of the Arno and Monte Pisani with the town of Fagnano in the distance (114x161cm-45x63in) indis sig.d.1822 prov. 29-May-3 Sotheby's, New York #146/R est:15000-20000

PETITI, Filiberto (1845-1924) Italian
£2564 $4026 €4000 Landscape with stream (55x73cm-22x29in) s. 10-Dec-2 Della Rocca, Turin #366/R
£3333 $5233 €5200 Marsh (77x150cm-30x59in) s. 10-Dec-2 Della Rocca, Turin #298/R

Works on paper
£400 $632 €580 Washerwoman (44x29cm-17x11in) s.i. W/C. 22-Jul-3 Bonhams, Knightsbridge #206/R
£513 $805 €800 Mountainous landscape with figures (49x33cm-19x13in) s. W/C cardboard. 10-Dec-2 Della Rocca, Turin #281/R
£680 $1082 €1000 Little lake in the woods (30x40cm-12x16in) s. W/C card. 1-Mar-3 Meeting Art, Vercelli #21

PETITJEAN (?) ?
£350 $553 €525 Fishing fleet in a French harbour (65x81cm-26x32in) s. 14-Nov-2 Christie's, Kensington #80

PETITJEAN, Edmond (1844-1925) French
£955 $1490 €1500 Bateaux pres des cotes (28x46cm-11x18in) st.sig. panel. 10-Nov-2 Eric Pillon, Calais #28/R
£2183 $3406 €3275 Summer landscape (46x65cm-18x26in) s. canvas on canvas prov. 9-Nov-2 Galerie Gloggner, Luzern #103/R est:5800-6500 (S.FR 5000)
£2446 $3914 €3400 Village anime en France (43x37cm-17x15in) s. 13-May-3 Galerie Moderne, Brussels #433/R est:1500-2000
£2620 $4087 €3930 Gothic church on village square (46x66cm-18x26in) s. prov. 20-Nov-2 Fischer, Luzern #1082/R est:4500-5500 (S.FR 6000)
£3200 $4992 €4800 On the quayside (14x22cm-6x9in) init. card. 26-Mar-3 Sotheby's, Olympia #258/R est:2000-4000
£3800 $5966 €5700 Port de mer (50x65cm-20x26in) s. 19-Nov-2 Sotheby's, London #100/R est:4000-6000
£4783 $7413 €7175 Marseilles harbour (89x130cm-35x51in) s. i. verso prov.exhib. 4-Dec-2 Koller, Zurich #106/R est:5000-10000 (S.FR 11000)
£5696 $8829 €9000 Bateaux au Treport (27x40cm-11x16in) s. panel. 28-Sep-2 Christie's, Paris #1/R est:3800-5300
£6111 $9717 €8800 Lavandieres au bord de la riviere (38x56cm-15x22in) s. 29-Apr-3 Artcurial Briest, Paris #196/R est:3500-4500
£6597 $10424 €9500 Lavandieres pres d'un pont (48x76cm-19x30in) s. 23-Apr-3 Rabourdin & Choppin de Janvry, Paris #48/R est:12000
£8544 $13244 €13500 Vue de Treport (46x65cm-18x26in) s. prov. 28-Sep-2 Christie's, Paris #2/R est:4500-7500
£8654 $13587 €13500 Port de Bordeaux (48x68cm-19x27in) s. i.verso. 13-Dec-2 Piasa, Paris #12/R

PETITJEAN, Hippolyte (1854-1929) French
£409 $638 €650 Escalier (21x14cm-8x6in) mono. cardboard painted c.1895 exhib. 11-Oct-2 Binoche, Paris #75/R
£17000 $26180 €25500 Nu au voile (82x47cm-32x19in) s. painted c.1890-92 prov. 22-Oct-2 Sotheby's, London #119/R est:20000-30000

Works on paper
£230 $373 €350 Portrait de femme (45x30cm-18x12in) studio st.d. chl estompe dr. 22-Jan-3 Tajan, Paris #70
£1800 $2934 €2700 Femme assise (46x55cm-18x22in) s.d.96 pastel. 3-Feb-3 Bonhams, New Bond Street #9/R est:2000-3000
£7547 $11774 €12000 Lettre (29x45cm-11x18in) s. W/C exec.c.1890. 11-Oct-2 Binoche, Paris #109/R est:15000-20000

PETITJEAN, Odette (20th C) French
£645 $1000 €968 Jours heureux (66x53cm-26x21in) s. i.on stretcher. 1-Oct-2 Arthur James, Florida #442

PETITOT, Jean (school) (17th C) French

Miniatures
£5600 $9352 €8120 Young nobleman in full armour (3cm-1in) jewelled gold openwork frame pendent oval exec.c.1680. 25-Jun-3 Sotheby's, Olympia #33/R est:1200-1800

PETITOT, Jean (snr) (1607-1691) French

Miniatures
£50000 $82000 €72500 Young lady called Marquise de Thianges, wearing a yellow silk dress (4cm-2in) enamel on gold oval. 3-Jun-3 Christie's, London #5/R est:10000-15000
£72000 $113040 €108000 Young lady in a low cut silk dress (5cm-2in) enamel on gold prov. 10-Dec-2 Christie's, London #30/R est:6000-8000

PETITPIERRE, Petra (1905-1959) Swiss

Works on paper
£826 $1289 €1239 Construction (20x35cm-8x14in) s.i.d.1953 mixed media. 16-Sep-2 Philippe Schuler, Zurich #3223/R (S.FR 1900)

PETLEY, Graham (?) British
£340 $534 €510 Tranquil water Maloon (30x36cm-12x14in) s. 19-Nov-2 Riddetts, Bournemouth #837

PETLEY, Roy (1951-) British
£400 $620 €600 Figures playing on a beach (35x45cm-14x18in) s. 4-Dec-2 Christie's, Kensington #404
£450 $702 €675 Norfolk landscape (30x46cm-12x18in) s. 27-Mar-3 Christie's, Kensington #499/R
£500 $795 €750 Norfolk Broads (24x34cm-9x13in) s. board. 4-May-3 Lots Road, London #348/R
£520 $827 €780 Figures on an open beach (30x51cm-12x20in) s. 29-Apr-3 Gorringes, Lewes #2337
£550 $902 €825 Beach scene (22x31cm-9x12in) s. b/. 3-Jun-3 Sotheby's, Olympia #178/R
£1600 $2624 €2400 Sunlit cafe, Tuileries (40x60cm-16x24in) s. board. 3-Jun-3 Sotheby's, Olympia #177/R est:1000-1500
£2600 $4056 €3900 Beach scene (29x45cm-11x18in) s. board. 12-Sep-2 Sotheby's, Olympia #68/R est:1500-2500

PETLEY-JONES, Llewellyn (1908-1986) Canadian
£236 $365 €354 Street scene (24x31cm-9x12in) s.d.54 i.verso canvas on panel prov. 24-Sep-2 Ritchie, Toronto #3219/R (C.D 575)
£267 $437 €387 Boathouses, Richmond (22x29cm-9x11in) s.i.d. 9-Jun-3 Hodgins, Calgary #427/R (C.D 600)
£282 $446 €423 Garden in the rain (21x26cm-8x10in) s.i.d.1939 init.verso prov.lit. 14-Nov-2 Heffel, Vancouver #103 (C.D 700)
£289 $474 €419 Mountains and cabin (40x50cm-16x20in) s. prov. 9-Jun-3 Hodgins, Calgary #37/R (C.D 650)
£400 $624 €600 Tow path at Twickenham (27x35cm-11x14in) s.d.70 i.verso. 17-Sep-2 Bonhams, Knightsbridge #26/R

£524 $828 €786 Montparnasse - spring morning (46x65cm-18x26in) s. s.i.verso prov. 14-Nov-2 Heffel, Vancouver #272/R est:1000-1500 (C.D 1300)
£645 $1019 €968 View from my studio (79x65cm-31x26in) s.d.55 i.verso prov. 18-Nov-2 Sotheby's, Toronto #70/R est:2000-2500 (C.D 1600)
£645 $1019 €968 Westminster, London, National Gallery. St. Martins in the Field, Trafalgar Square (30x41cm-12x16in) one s.d.54 s.i.verso pair prov. 18-Nov-2 Sotheby's, Toronto #158/R est:2000-2500 (C.D 1600)
£673 $1076 €1010 Maisons de Paris (46x55cm-18x22in) s.d.1956 i.verso prov. 15-May-3 Heffel, Vancouver #106/R est:1000-1500 (C.D 1500)
£711 $1166 €1067 Street scene (60x72cm-24x28in) s.d.55 prov. 27-May-3 Sotheby's, Toronto #178/R est:2000-2500 (C.D 1600)
£717 $1148 €1076 Hotel a la Gargonville (51x65cm-20x26in) s.d.1954 i.verso prov. 15-May-3 Heffel, Vancouver #228/R est:1000-1500 (C.D 1600)
£726 $1147 €1089 Place de la Concorde (46x55cm-18x22in) s.d.1956 i.verso prov. 14-Nov-2 Heffel, Vancouver #275/R est:1000-1500 (C.D 1800)
£766 $1210 €1149 Thames Bridge (36x51cm-14x20in) s. i.verso prov. 14-Nov-2 Heffel, Vancouver #276/R est:1000-1500 (C.D 1900)
£800 $1312 €1200 Du haut de la butte (80x60cm-31x24in) s.d.1955 prov. 27-May-3 Sotheby's, Toronto #116/R est:2000-2500 (C.D 1800)
£907 $1433 €1361 Coal Harbour (37x46cm-15x18in) s.i. s.verso prov. 14-Nov-2 Heffel, Vancouver #129 est:1000-1500 (C.D 2250)
£1111 $1822 €1667 Derby (41x51cm-16x20in) s.i.d.56 s.i.verso prov. 27-May-3 Sotheby's, Toronto #177/R est:2500-3000 (C.D 2500)
£1371 $2166 €2057 Place du Tertre (61x91cm-24x36in) s.d.55 prov. 18-Nov-2 Sotheby's, Toronto #162/R est:2500-3000 (C.D 3400)
Works on paper
£723 $1135 €1085 Demolition, raising the old power house (38x55cm-15x22in) s.i.d.1931 W/C exhib. 25-Nov-2 Hodgins, Calgary #289/R (C.D 1800)

PETR, Jaros (1859-1929) Czechoslovakian
£1032 $1630 €1548 Summer landscape (53x136cm-21x54in) s. 30-Nov-2 Dorotheum, Prague #73/R (C.KR 50000)

PETRELLA DA BOLOGNA, Vittorio (1886-1951) Italian
£340 $541 €500 Night scene in Venice (22x31cm-9x12in) s. board. 1-Mar-3 Meeting Art, Vercelli #118

PETRI, Erik (1880-?) Norwegian
£643 $1054 €932 Coastal landscape from Huk (57x85cm-22x33in) s. 2-Jun-3 Blomqvist, Oslo #105/R (N.KR 7000)

PETRI, Frederick Richard (1824-1857) American
Works on paper
£256 $400 €384 Reclining male nude (15x28cm-6x11in) pencil. 19-Oct-2 David Dike, Dallas #21/R

PETRICH, Ernst (1878-?) German
£255 $397 €400 Landscape with stream and village (26x35cm-10x14in) s. lit. 8-Nov-2 Auktionhaus Georg Rehm, Augsburg #8118
£764 $1192 €1200 River landscape with trees and boat (37x52cm-15x20in) s. lit. 8-Nov-2 Auktionhaus Georg Rehm, Augsburg #8117
Works on paper
£318 $497 €500 River landscape with houses and boats (32x43cm-13x17in) s. W/C lit. 8-Nov-2 Auktionhaus Georg Rehm, Augsburg #8119

PETRIDES, Konrad (1863-1943) Austrian
£380 $600 €600 Alpine landscape in Semmering, Austria (60x80cm-24x31in) s. 29-Nov-2 Bolland & Marotz, Bremen #755/R
£949 $1500 €1500 Daybreak (93x140cm-37x55in) s. 26-Nov-2 Wiener Kunst Auktionen, Vienna #67/R est:1500-2500

PETRIE, George (1790-1866) British
Works on paper
£3205 $4968 €5000 Lough Corrib Co Galway. Connemara Co Galway (15x22cm-6x9in) one s. W/C pair. 3-Dec-2 Bonhams & James Adam, Dublin #28/R est:3000-4000

PETRIE, Graham (1859-1940) British
Works on paper
£270 $448 €405 Venetian flower market (24x35cm-9x14in) s. W/C bodycol. 10-Jun-3 Sworder & Son, Bishops Stortford #479/R
£520 $827 €780 Hollyhocks (24x34cm-9x13in) s. W/C. 25-Feb-3 Bonhams, Knightsbridge #31/R

PETRIE, William McWhannel (1870-1937) British
£320 $522 €480 Portrait of a gentleman (76x61cm-30x24in) s. 1-Feb-3 Shapes, Edinburgh #317

PETRINI, Giuseppe Antonio (1677-1758) Italian
£3500 $5495 €5250 Assumption of the Virgin (69cm-27in circular) 10-Dec-2 Bonhams, New Bond Street #52/R est:4000-6000
£10063 $15597 €16000 St Peter (92x71cm-36x28in) 2-Oct-2 Dorotheum, Vienna #56/R est:16000-20000

PETRINI, Giuseppe Antonio (attrib) (1677-1758) Italian
£7382 $11885 €11000 Saint Joseph (125x91cm-49x36in) 18-Feb-3 Sotheby's, Amsterdam #266/R est:12000-15000

PETRINI, Giuseppe Antonio (circle) (1677-1758) Italian
£7200 $11160 €10800 Mythological scene, possibly Potiphar's wife accusing Joseph (203x140cm-80x55in) 31-Oct-2 Sotheby's, Olympia #86/R est:4000-6000

PETROCELLI, Achille (1861-?) Italian
£599 $964 €850 Peasant woman (23x16cm-9x6in) s. panel lit. 9-May-3 Schloss Ahlden, Ahlden #1478/R

PETROFF, Andre (1893-1975) Russian
£313 $500 €470 Scene with peasant woman in a courtyard (48x74cm-19x29in) s. 1-Jan-3 Nadeau, Windsor #149/R
£561 $853 €842 Street scene, Nice (53x48cm-21x19in) s.i.d.1925 board. 19-Aug-2 Joel, Victoria #310 est:1500-2000 (A.D 1600)

PETROFF, W (20th C) ?
£700 $1092 €1050 Interior of Hagia Sophia (52x36cm-20x14in) s.i. canvas on board pair. 17-Oct-2 Bonhams, Knightsbridge #483
£1019 $1590 €1600 Mosque interior (42x31cm-17x12in) s.i. board. 6-Nov-2 Hugo Ruef, Munich #1236/R est:450

PETROFF, Wladimir (20th C) French?
£1111 $1789 €1611 Man praying in Hagia Sophia (59x44cm-23x17in) s.i.d.1929 board. 7-May-3 Dobiaschofsky, Bern #881/R est:1900 (S.FR 2400)

PETROV-VODKIN, Kuzma (1878-1939) Russian
Works on paper
£7000 $11060 €10500 Male nude (62x46cm-24x18in) s.i.d.1910 chl htd chk paper on cardboard. 26-Nov-2 Christie's, Kensington #32/R est:4000-6000

PETROVA, Elena (1971-) Russian
£419 $663 €650 Still life with bells (45x38cm-18x15in) s. 17-Dec-2 Durán, Madrid #664/R

PETROVITS, Ladislaus Eugen (1839-1907) Austrian
£1370 $2137 €2000 Wood near Kubani in Bohmen (94x126cm-37x50in) s.d.1905. 10-Apr-3 Dorotheum, Vienna #2/R est:2400-2800
Works on paper
£439 $685 €650 Sawmill in Radmer (37x52cm-15x20in) s.i.d.August 1896 W/C. 28-Mar-3 Dorotheum, Vienna #303/R

PETRUOLO, Salvatore (1857-1946) Italian
£11392 $18000 €18000 Gran Canal (36x48cm-14x19in) s.d.92. 26-Nov-2 Christie's, Rome #281/R est:10000-15000

PETRUS, Marco (1960-) Italian
£7447 $12064 €10500 Soqquadro (180x120cm-71x47in) s.d.2000. 20-May-3 Porro, Milan #45/R est:7300-7500

PETTAFOR, Charles R (fl.1862-1900) British
£780 $1209 €1170 Shepherds with dogs and flock resting beneath old oaks (41x61cm-16x24in) mono.d.77. 30-Sep-2 Bonhams, Ipswich #517

PETTENKOFEN, August von (1822-1889) Austrian
£3526 $5535 €5500 Hungarian village with oxen (21x32cm-8x13in) panel prov.lit. 25-Nov-2 Hassfurther, Vienna #60/R est:3000-5000
Works on paper
£1486 $2319 €2200 Girl working in garden (34x24cm-13x9in) W/C. 28-Mar-3 Dorotheum, Vienna #226/R est:4000-5000
£2839 $4485 €4400 Paysage a la ferme et paysan sur son ane (11x28cm-4x11in) s.d. W/C. 17-Dec-2 Rossini, Paris #44/R

PETTER, Franz Xaver (1791-1866) Austrian
Works on paper
£1486 $2319 €2200 Female nude (44x29cm-17x11in) chl htd white. 28-Mar-3 Dorotheum, Vienna #116/R est:900-1000

PETTER, Theodor (1822-1872) Austrian
Works on paper
£473 $738 €700 Thoughtful figure (46x36cm-18x14in) chl htd white. 28-Mar-3 Dorotheum, Vienna #154/R

PETTERSEN, Arvid (1943-) Norwegian
£2768 $4374 €4152 Untitled - composition (200x200cm-79x79in) init.d.90 diptych. 2-Dec-2 Blomqvist, Oslo #495/R est:20000-25000 (N.KR 32000)

PETTERSON, Gunnar (1947-) Swedish
£526 $831 €789 Owls in stone quarry (73x100cm-29x39in) s. 27-Nov-2 Falkkloos, Malmo #77617/R (S.KR 7500)

PETTERSSON, Augusta (1852-1927) Swedish
Works on paper
£638 $989 €957 View of Rosendal's Palace, Djurgarden (48x64cm-19x25in) s. Indian ink wash. 3-Dec-2 Bukowskis, Stockholm #531/R (S.KR 9000)

PETTERSSON, Primus Mortimer (1895-1975) Swedish
Works on paper
£284 $440 €426 Froso Hospital, landscape with buildings (39x58cm-15x23in) mono. W/C. 8-Dec-2 Uppsala Auktionskammare, Uppsala #181 (S.KR 4000)

PETTET, William (1942-) American
£274 $425 €411 Untitled (244x86cm-96x34in) 7-Dec-2 Harvey Clar, Oakland #1259

PETTIBON, Raymond (1957-) American
£4687 $7500 €7031 Untitled - shooting ink (76x61cm-30x24in) s.d.91 panel prov. 16-May-3 Phillips, New York #103/R est:8000-10000
£6329 $10000 €9494 No title - accumulated sins are many (152x122cm-60x48in) painted 1988 prov. 12-Nov-2 Phillips, New York #191/R est:15000-20000

Works on paper
£1731 $2683 €2700 Vavoom (48x37cm-19x15in) Indian ink brush prov. 7-Dec-2 Ketterer, Hamburg #739/R est:3200-3400
£34000 $55760 €51000 Untitled (340x100cm-134x39in) ink W/C set of 10. 6-Feb-3 Christie's, London #706/R est:10000-15000

PETTIBONE, Richard (1938-) American
£10127 $16000 €15191 Perrer pot. Flowers lavender disaster (21x16cm-8x6in) s.i.d.1964 one s.i.d.on stretcher acrylic after Warhol. 13-Nov-2 Sotheby's, New York #129/R est:12000-18000
£28000 $46760 €40600 Roy Lichtenstein, in the car (18x23cm-7x9in) s.i.d.1969 acrylic. 24-Jun-3 Sotheby's, Olympia #56/R est:3000-4000

PETTIBONE, Shirley (20th C) American?
£509 $850 €738 Water surface with sawn (81x69cm-32x27in) 29-Jun-3 Butterfields, Los Angeles #7093/R

PETTIE, John (1839-1893) British
£8000 $12560 €12000 Portrait of William Pettie Watt (118x68cm-46x27in) s. 19-Nov-2 Bonhams, New Bond Street #145/R est:4000-6000
£175000 $281750 €262500 Chieftain's candlesticks (161x110cm-63x43in) s. s.i.on stretcher prov.exhib.lit. 20-Feb-3 Christie's, London #64/R est:100000

PETTINGALE, William (19/20th C) British
£310 $481 €465 Figures by stream (49x39cm-19x15in) canvas on board. 2-Oct-2 Bonhams, Knowle #92
£2100 $3255 €3150 View in Peak District, possibly Dovedale (76x63cm-30x25in) s. 2-Oct-2 Bonhams, Knowle #83 est:700-1000

PETTINGER, John Frederick (fl.1904-1934) British
£250 $390 €375 Church in Normandy (38x30cm-15x12in) s.d.1878 board exhib. 18-Sep-2 Cheffins Grain & Comins, Cambridge #493

PETTITT, Charles (19th C) British
£2500 $4075 €3750 Grange, Borrowdale, Cumberland (66x112cm-26x44in) s.d.1870 i.verso. 29-Jan-3 Sotheby's, Olympia #158/R est:1500-2500

PETTITT, Edwin Alfred (1840-1912) British
£1529 $2354 €2400 Figures in a wooded river landscape with Arundel Castle in background (97x148cm-38x58in) s.i.verso. 4-Sep-2 James Adam, Dublin #89 est:600-800

PETTITT, Joseph Paul (1812-1882) British
£340 $554 €510 Dollweddlan, North Wales (55x40cm-22x16in) s. 14-Feb-3 Bracketts, Tunbridge Wells #960/R
£850 $1326 €1275 Conway, North Wales (51x36cm-20x14in) s.d.69. 18-Oct-2 Keys, Aylsham #722/R
£949 $1500 €1424 Harbour landscape with figures and ships (51x97cm-20x38in) s.d.1865. 3-Apr-3 Boos Gallery, Michigan #236/R est:3000-5000
£2300 $3565 €3450 Morning express - coastal landscape with ruins and old man with dog (143x113cm-56x44in) s. indis d.1868. 1-Oct-2 Fellows & Sons, Birmingham #105/R est:2500-3500
£3333 $5400 €4700 Woodland scene with river pool and waterfall (92x133cm-36x52in) i.verso. 20-May-3 Mealy's, Castlecomer #986/R est:4000-6000

PETTS, John (?) British
£600 $930 €900 Rock Queen (76x33cm-30x13in) s. enamel on canvas. 3-Dec-2 Peter Francis, Wales #11/R

PETTY, George (20th C) American
Works on paper
£2795 $4500 €4193 Standing woman in peasant garb holding bucket (41x20cm-16x8in) s. gouache W/C en grisaille exec.c.1940. 10-May-3 Illustration House, New York #119/R est:5000-8000
£8974 $14000 €13461 Woman standing on point, speaking on telephone (53x36cm-21x14in) s. W/C gouache pastel. 9-Nov-2 Illustration House, New York #136/R est:12000-16000

PETUEL, Rudolf (1870-?) German
£1592 $2484 €2500 Dream - naked girl (56x44cm-22x17in) s. board. 6-Nov-2 Hugo Ruef, Munich #1235/R est:2000

PETYARRE, Gloria (1945-) Australian
£1423 $2248 €2063 Atnangkerre growth 1998 (120x90cm-47x35in) s.i. verso acrylic. 22-Jul-3 Lawson Menzies, Sydney #72/R est:4500-5500 (A.D 3500)

PETYARRE, Gloria Tamerre (1940-) Australian
£996 $1564 €1494 Alpite (90x60cm-35x24in) s. acrylic on linen. 15-Apr-3 Lawson Menzies, Sydney #110/R est:2000-3000 (A.D 2600)
£1916 $3008 €2874 Alpita - bush medicine 1999 (120x120cm-47x47in) i.verso acrylic on linen. 15-Apr-3 Lawson Menzies, Sydney #108/R est:3500-5500 (A.D 5000)
£2490 $3910 €3735 Bush medicine (147x91cm-58x36in) i.verso acrylic. 15-Apr-3 Lawson Menzies, Sydney #104/R est:5000-6000 (A.D 6500)
Works on paper
£1300 $2014 €1950 Leaves (122x91cm-48x36in) i.verso synthetic polymer paint linen prov. 3-Dec-2 Shapiro, Sydney #169/R est:3500-5000 (A.D 3600)

PETZHOLDT, Fritz (1805-1838) Danish
£3064 $4841 €4596 Trees near Charlottenlund and men making stone fence (57x49cm-22x19in) exhib.prov. 2-Dec-2 Rasmussen, Copenhagen #1297/R est:40000-50000 (D.KR 36000)
£6029 $9165 €9044 View of the town Anacapri (38x52cm-15x20in) prov. 27-Aug-2 Rasmussen, Copenhagen #1435/R est:20000-30000 (D.KR 70000)

PEVERELLI, Cesare (1922-2000) Italian
£353 $554 €550 Composition (26x46cm-10x18in) s.d.1953. 23-Nov-2 Meeting Art, Vercelli #305
£430 $680 €680 Abstrat composition (35x27cm-14x11in) s. 26-Nov-2 Camard, Paris #108
£1538 $2415 €2400 Souvenir amongst ancient pages (70x60cm-28x24in) s.d.1955. 23-Nov-2 Meeting Art, Vercelli #423/R

PEVERNAGIE, Erik (1939-) Belgian
£2532 $3949 €4000 You might think it is, but his is no chicken food (80x99cm-31x39in) s.i. oil sand metal. 18-Oct-2 Dr Fritz Nagel, Stuttgart #596/R est:2500
£3243 $5059 €4800 Would time be patient (73x92cm-29x36in) s. s.i. stretcher acrylic sand metal. 28-Mar-3 Ketterer, Hamburg #554/R est:4000-5000

Works on paper
£3270 $5036 €5200 Sisyphus climbing steep mountain (100x80cm-39x31in) s. mixed media on canvas. 22-Oct-2 Campo & Campo, Antwerp #217/R
£3526 $5465 €5500 I seek you (100x100cm-39x39in) s. mixed media canvas. 7-Dec-2 De Vuyst, Lokeren #252/R est:5000-6000

PEVERNAGIE, Louis (1904-1970) Belgian
£576 $921 €800 Composition (49x59cm-19x23in) s. 17-May-3 De Vuyst, Lokeren #294

PEYNET, Raymond (1908-1998) French
Works on paper
£276 $439 €400 La cigale et la fourmi (18x14cm-7x6in) s.d.41 gouache. 5-Mar-3 Doutrebente, Paris #88
£379 $603 €550 Fleuriste aux amoureux (29x21cm-11x8in) s.d.42 gouache. 5-Mar-3 Doutrebente, Paris #87/R

PEYNOT, Émile Edmond (1850-1932) French
Sculpture
£1799 $2878 €2500 L'Angelus (71cm-28in) s. brown pat bronze. 13-May-3 Vanderkindere, Brussels #149/R est:2000-3000
£4114 $6500 €6171 Figure of an Arab boy checking his weapons (65cm-26in) i. gilt bronze. 24-Apr-3 Christie's, Rockefeller NY #230/R est:8000-12000
£5000 $7700 €7500 Jeune Arabe verifiant (55cm-22in) i. pat bronze lit. 28-Oct-2 Sotheby's, Olympia #24/R est:3000-4000

PEYRAUD, Frank Charles (1858-1948) American
£3185 $5000 €4778 Last rays (66x76cm-26x30in) s.d.10. 22-Nov-2 Skinner, Boston #244/R est:4000-6000

PEYRON, Jean François Pierre (1744-1814) French
£1154 $1812 €1800 Jeune femme a la lyre (48x38cm-19x15in) d.1809. 19-Nov-2 Servarts Themis, Bruxelles #119/R

PEYROT, Arturo (1908-1993) Italian
£411 $641 €600 Landscape (15x8cm-6x3in) s.i. board. 8-Apr-3 Ansorena, Madrid #37/R

PEYROTTE, Alexis (1699-1769) French
Works on paper
£1538 $2415 €2400 Singe bonimenteur (27x28cm-11x11in) gouache. 13-Dec-2 Pierre Berge, Paris #44/R

PEYTON, Elizabeth (1965-) American
£22000 $36080 €33000 The Earl of Essex (31x23cm-12x9in) i. plaster on masonite prov. 6-Feb-3 Christie's, London #739/R est:22000-28000
£28481 $45000 €42722 Elizabeth I (30x23cm-12x9in) i. masonite prov. 14-Nov-2 Christie's, Rockefeller NY #327/R est:35000-45000
Works on paper
£10759 $17000 €16139 Savoy Tony Oct 1999 (31x23cm-12x9in) s.i.d.1999 verso W/C prov.exhib. 14-Nov-2 Christie's, Rockefeller NY #329/R est:10000-15000
£13291 $21000 €19937 Craig as Saint-Loup (30x23cm-12x9in) s.i.d.1997 verso W/C prov.exhib. 13-Nov-2 Sotheby's, New York #400/R est:15000-20000

PEZ, Aime (1808-1849) Belgian
£1052 $1662 €1578 Music making company (38x54cm-15x21in) s. panel. 27-Nov-2 Falkkloos, Malmo #77724/R est:18000 (S.KR 15000)

PEZANT, Aymar (1846-1916) French
£659 $1100 €956 Cattle watering (53x64cm-21x25in) s. 21-Jun-3 Selkirks, St. Louis #1036/R est:1000-1500
£886 $1382 €1400 Vaches au pre (19x27cm-7x11in) s. panel. 15-Sep-2 Etude Bailleul, Bayeux #98/R

PEZILLA, Mario (19/20th C) Italian
Works on paper
£1731 $2631 €2700 Au bar (35x26cm-14x10in) s. gouache pastel W/C crayon. 16-Aug-2 Deauville, France #48/R

PEZZATI, Pietro (1828-1890) Italian
£11565 $18388 €17000 Thread seller (53x32cm-21x13in) s.i.d.1875 board. 1-Mar-3 Meeting Art, Vercelli #272

PEZZO, Lucio del (1933-) Italian
£426 $689 €600 Acrobaleno (19x19cm-7x7in) s. s.i.verso oil wood on cork round prov. 26-May-3 Christie's, Milan #175/R
£811 $1265 €1200 Stones in time (34x49cm-13x19in) s.i.d.1964 tempera card. 26-Mar-3 Finarte Semenzato, Milan #78/R
£1528 $2429 €2200 Sidiki (75x60cm-30x24in) s. acrylic collage enamel board. 1-May-3 Meeting Art, Vercelli #231
£7092 $11489 €10000 Quadro con doppia scala cromatica (145x116cm-57x46in) s.d.65 s.i.d.verso panel. 26-May-3 Christie's, Milan #177/R est:10000-12000
Works on paper
£641 $1006 €1000 Still life (57x75cm-22x30in) s.i.d.1980 collage W/C card lit. 21-Nov-2 Finarte, Rome #156
£641 $1006 €1000 Microbilles (50x60cm-20x24in) s. i.verso collage enamel acrylic sand balls on panel. 23-Nov-2 Meeting Art, Vercelli #346/R
£769 $1192 €1200 Starry sky (58x38cm-23x15in) s. i.verso collage W/C. 5-Dec-2 Stadion, Trieste #690/R
£949 $1481 €1500 Metaphysica coreography (75x60cm-30x24in) s. collage acrylic board. 14-Sep-2 Meeting Art, Vercelli #814/R
£1042 $1656 €1500 Pearl blue (50x60cm-20x24in) s. s.i.verso collage acrylic panel. 1-May-3 Meeting Art, Vercelli #22
£1154 $1812 €1800 Geometry (75x60cm-30x24in) s. s.i.d.verso collage acrylic pigment panel. 23-Nov-2 Meeting Art, Vercelli #352/R
£1242 $1987 €1900 Pace-maker (60x75cm-24x30in) s. s.i.verso collage lacquer acrylic. 4-Jan-3 Meeting Art, Vercelli #392
£1560 $2528 €2200 Il rigo d'oro (60x49cm-24x19in) s.d.1965 s.i.d.verso mixed media collage paper on masonite. 26-May-3 Christie's, Milan #50 est:1000-1500

PFAFF, Judy (1946-) American/British
Prints
£1218 $1900 €1827 Double (183x81cm-72x32in) s.i.d.num.8/8 etching encaustic hand dye. 14-Oct-2 Butterfields, San Francisco #1328/R est:1000-2000
Works on paper
£417 $650 €626 Untitled (51x75cm-20x30in) s.d.93 mixed media. 5-Nov-2 Doyle, New York #39/R

PFAHLER, Karl Georg (1926-) German
£449 $696 €700 Untitled (16x12cm-6x5in) s.d.1962 oil chk feltpen. 7-Dec-2 Ketterer, Hamburg #469/R
£481 $745 €750 Untitled (19x13cm-7x5in) s.d.1962 oil chk feltpen collage ring binder paper. 7-Dec-2 Ketterer, Hamburg #470/R
£2276 $3596 €3300 Untitled (70x70cm-28x28in) s.d.1994 gouache feltpen col pen board prov. 2-Apr-3 Dr Fritz Nagel, Stuttgart #9522/R est:3000
£3453 $5663 €4800 Blue with silver grey (90x75cm-35x30in) s.d. verso acrylic prov. 6-Jun-3 Ketterer, Munich #146/R est:4800-5400
Works on paper
£513 $795 €800 Untitled (14x13cm-6x5in) s.d.1962 mixed media ringbinder paper. 7-Dec-2 Ketterer, Hamburg #467/R
£2069 $3269 €3000 Untitled (62x45cm-24x18in) s.d.1959 Indian ink. 2-Apr-3 Dr Fritz Nagel, Stuttgart #9523/R est:2600
£2069 $3269 €3000 Untitled (60x48cm-24x19in) s.d.1959 gouache Indian ink. 2-Apr-3 Dr Fritz Nagel, Stuttgart #9525/R est:3000
£20690 $32690 €30000 Untitled (63x45cm-25x18in) s.d.1959 collage Indian ink. 2-Apr-3 Dr Fritz Nagel, Stuttgart #9524/R est:3000

PFANNEKUCHEN, Ernst (1869-?) German
£3397 $5334 €5300 Fiesta di Redentore - nighttime gondola trip (80x157cm-31x62in) s.d.05. 21-Nov-2 Van Ham, Cologne #1863/R est:3000

PFANNSCHMIDT, Carl Gottfried (attrib) (1819-1887) German
£417 $654 €650 Portrait of woman wearing gold jewellery (31x25cm-12x10in) 23-Nov-2 Arnold, Frankfurt #833/R

PFAU, Conrad (1885-?) German
£316 $491 €500 Spring in the Jura mountains near Kallmunz (46x55cm-18x22in) s. 25-Sep-2 Neumeister, Munich #696/R
£506 $800 €800 Two ladies reading a letter (60x81cm-24x32in) s. 29-Nov-2 Bolland & Marotz, Bremen #813/R

PFEFFERKORN, Felix Samuel (1945-) German
£321 $497 €500 Bodensee (29x40cm-11x16in) mono. s.i. verso acrylic masonite. 7-Dec-2 Ketterer, Hamburg #630/R
£345 $545 €500 Sailing boats in Lindau harbour on the Bodensee (50x70cm-20x28in) mono. s.i.d.1975 verso board. 5-Apr-3 Hans Stahl, Hamburg #87
£579 $915 €840 Ski alpine (70x50cm-28x20in) mono. s.i. verso caparol on board. 5-Apr-3 Hans Stahl, Hamburg #86/R
£607 $959 €880 Regatta (70x50cm-28x20in) mono. s.i.d.1975 verso board. 5-Apr-3 Hans Stahl, Hamburg #88/R
£719 $1180 €1000 Still life with melon and fruit (51x41cm-20x16in) mono. s.verso acrylic panel. 5-Jun-3 Dorotheum, Salzburg #679/R

£863 $1416 €1200 Still life with covered table and fish on a plate (48x68cm-19x27in) s.d.1976 verso acrylic panel. 5-Jun-3 Dorotheum, Salzburg #650/R
£1282 $1987 €2000 Circus scene (99x50cm-39x20in) mono. s.d.1977 verso acrylic masonite. 7-Dec-2 Ketterer, Hamburg #632/R est:2200-2600
£1295 $2124 €1800 Casino (90x80cm-35x31in) mono. s.i.d.1979 verso acrylic panel. 5-Jun-3 Dorotheum, Salzburg #678/R est:2400-3000
£1295 $2124 €1800 Still life (78x98cm-31x39in) mono. s.i.d.1976 verso acrylic panel. 5-Jun-3 Dorotheum, Salzburg #680/R est:2400-3000
£1299 $1896 €2000 Female nude on sofa (100x50cm-39x20in) mono. s.i.verso oil mixed media board. 15-Jun-2 Hans Stahl, Hamburg #134/R
£1410 $2186 €2200 Sunflowers (100x50cm-39x20in) mono. s.i.d.1974 verso acrylic masonite. 7-Dec-2 Ketterer, Hamburg #631/R est:2200-2600
£5128 $7949 €8000 Pierre - the philosoph. Jacques - the actor. Robert - the piano player (101x155cm-40x61in) init. s.i.verso fibreboard triptych. 6-Dec-2 Ketterer, Munich #189/R est:9000-12000

PFEFFERLE, Erwin (1880-1962) German
£409 $638 €650 Landscape with meadows, water and trees (34x50cm-13x20in) s. prov.lit. 20-Sep-2 Karlheinz Kaupp, Staufen #1903
£692 $1079 €1100 Breisach fortress (35x40cm-14x16in) s. prov.lit. 20-Sep-2 Karlheinz Kaupp, Staufen #1895
Works on paper
£252 $392 €400 Young woman wearing white headscarf at window watering geraniums (27x21cm-11x8in) s.i. chl W/C prov.lit. 20-Sep-2 Karlheinz Kaupp, Staufen #2171
£566 $883 €900 Busy Staufen market (26x36cm-10x14in) gouache prov.lit. 20-Sep-2 Karlheinz Kaupp, Staufen #2199/R

PFEIFFER, Francois Joseph (elder) (1741-1807) German
Works on paper
£1656 $2583 €2600 Winter landscape with figures gathering wood (17x25cm-7x10in) mono. W/C. 5-Nov-2 Sotheby's, Amsterdam #168/R est:3000-4000

PFEIFFER, Gordon (1899-1983) Canadian
£224 $351 €336 Laurentian village in winter (28x33cm-11x13in) s. board. 10-Dec-2 Pinneys, Montreal #191 (C.D 550)
£343 $536 €497 October morning, North River (61x76cm-24x30in) s.i.d.1938 prov. 26-Mar-3 Walker's, Ottawa #246/R (C.D 800)

PFEIFFER, Johann Joachim I (1662-1701) German
Works on paper
£506 $800 €800 Traveller wearing hat (19x10cm-7x4in) brush. 29-Nov-2 Bassenge, Berlin #5427

PFEIFFER, Wilhelm (1822-1891) German
£1923 $2923 €3000 Man with dog surveying his field of corn (58x52cm-23x20in) s. 11-Jul-2 Hugo Ruef, Munich #773/R est:1200

PFEILER, Maximilian (18th C) German
£7000 $10990 €10500 Grapes, figs and other fruits on a ruined stone capital garden (73x60cm-29x24in) s. 10-Dec-2 Bonhams, New Bond Street #301/R est:7000-10000
£9091 $15182 €13000 Nature morte au plat de melon et raison, bouquet de fleurs et nappe brodee (65x49cm-26x19in) 25-Jun-3 Tajan, Paris #40/R est:10000-12000
£16352 $25182 €26000 Still life of fruit and biscuits in landscape (73x100cm-29x39in) s. 23-Oct-2 Finarte, Rome #523/R est:26000-28000
£16667 $26167 €26000 Nature morte aux coupes de fruits et biscuits (74x69cm-29x27in) mono. 14-Dec-2 Artcurial Briest, Paris #11/R est:15000

PFISTER, Albert (1884-1978) Swiss
£1938 $2830 €2907 Frauenwinkel in Pfaffikon (66x85cm-26x33in) s. i. verso. 17-Jun-2 Philippe Schuler, Zurich #4287/R est:4000-5000 (S.FR 4400)
£8584 $13562 €12876 Tangiers (61x58cm-24x23in) s.d.1912 prov. 26-Nov-2 Phillips, Zurich #30/R est:7000-9000 (S.FR 20000)

PFORR, Heinrich (1880-1970) German
£1310 $2083 €1900 Children in summer meadow (47x51cm-19x20in) s. 8-Mar-3 Arnold, Frankfurt #678/R est:800

PFORR, Johann Georg (attrib) (1745-1798) German
£7547 $11774 €12000 Hunting party resting by city walls (37x49cm-15x19in) panel. 19-Sep-2 Dr Fritz Nagel, Stuttgart #890/R est:14000

PFRUNDT, Georg (attrib) (1603-1663) German
Sculpture
£31000 $48670 €46500 Putti and monsters interwined (31cm-12in) ivory cup lit. 10-Dec-2 Sotheby's, London #72/R est:15000-20000

PFUND, Alois (1876-1946) Austrian
£360 $590 €500 Wilde Kaiser with mountain farm (80x100cm-31x39in) s.i. 5-Jun-3 Dorotheum, Salzburg #550/R
£392 $643 €600 Alpine hut in the high mountains (48x68cm-19x27in) s.i. 5-Feb-3 Neumeister, Munich #788/R
£432 $708 €600 Alpine pasture landscape with Herzogswand (60x80cm-24x31in) s.i. 5-Jun-3 Dorotheum, Salzburg #551/R
£490 $804 €750 Huntsman's hut by lake in the high mountains (50x70cm-20x28in) s.i.d.32 indis.i.verso. 5-Feb-3 Neumeister, Munich #787/R

PFYFFER, Niklaus (1836-1908) Swiss
£546 $852 €819 Blausee-Frutt (31x47cm-12x19in) i.d.90 aug canvas on board. 20-Nov-2 Fischer, Luzern #2217/R (S.FR 1250)
£755 $1208 €1133 Summer festival near Lucern. Reussbuhl landscape (14x16cm-6x6in) mono. panel pair. 17-Mar-3 Philippe Schuler, Zurich #4551 (S.FR 1600)

PHELPS, Stan (1949-) Canadian
£1610 $2560 €2415 Winter on 11a Street (80x90cm-31x35in) s.i.d.1980. 23-Mar-3 Hodgins, Calgary #102/R est:1000-1500 (C.D 3800)

PHELPS, William Preston (1848-1923) American
£897 $1400 €1346 Woodland scene (56x36cm-22x14in) s. 28-Mar-3 Eldred, East Dennis #796/R est:1500-2500
£1824 $2900 €2736 Autumn birches (35x50cm-14x20in) s. 7-Mar-3 Skinner, Boston #291/R est:1800-2200
£2435 $3750 €3653 Flowering orchard (36x51cm-14x20in) s. prov. 24-Oct-2 Shannon's, Milford #231/R est:2500-3500
£3067 $5000 €4601 Autumn landscape with mountain and lake (30x46cm-12x18in) s. i.stretcher. 2-Feb-3 Grogan, Boston #65 est:1000-5000
£4430 $7000 €6645 Cardinal amongst the blossoms (51x76cm-20x30in) s. 24-Apr-3 Shannon's, Milford #118/R est:3000-5000
£6013 $9500 €9020 The ice crust (41x61cm-16x24in) s.i.verso. 24-Apr-3 Shannon's, Milford #152/R est:8000-12000
£16456 $26000 €24684 Tillers of the soil (97x208cm-38x82in) s.i. prov.exhib. 24-Apr-3 Shannon's, Milford #110/R est:25000-35000

PHENEY, Robert Francis (20th C) New Zealander
Works on paper
£949 $1491 €1424 Pleasure boats off St Mary's Bay, Auckland (33x45cm-13x18in) s.d.1931 W/C. 25-Nov-2 Peter Webb, Auckland #12/R est:4000-6000 (NZ.D 3000)

PHILIBERT, Bernhard (1829-1894) French
£886 $1373 €1400 Les baigneuses pres du pont de pierre (35x27cm-14x11in) s. 29-Sep-2 Eric Pillon, Calais #105/R

PHILIP, John (?) British?
£1000 $1520 €1500 Spanish beauty (55x46cm-22x18in) s.d.1871 verso. 29-Aug-2 Christie's, Kensington #196/R est:1500-2000
£4000 $6200 €6000 Letter (34x26cm-13x10in) mono.d.1862. 6-Dec-2 Lyon & Turnbull, Edinburgh #100/R est:2500-3500

PHILIPP, Caesar (1859-?) German
£1410 $2214 €2200 Gypsy girl with a pipe (65x48cm-26x19in) s.d.1899. 10-Dec-2 Dorotheum, Vienna #81/R est:2500-2800

PHILIPP, Klaus (1932-) German
£1266 $1975 €2000 Horse racing (40x62cm-16x24in) s.i.d.1987 s.i.d. verso. 18-Oct-2 Dr Fritz Nagel, Stuttgart #586/R est:2000

PHILIPP, Kurt (1928-) Austrian
£540 $885 €750 View of Hohensalzburg Fortress and city from the Salzachufer (38x47cm-15x19in) s.d.1989 board. 5-Jun-3 Dorotheum, Salzburg #638/R

PHILIPP, Robert (1895-1981) American
£633 $1000 €950 On the lake (20x25cm-8x10in) s.verso prov. 24-Apr-3 Shannon's, Milford #186/R est:1000-1500
£950 $1500 €1425 Pensive mood (25x20cm-10x8in) s. s.d.1970 verso prov. 24-Apr-3 Shannon's, Milford #185/R est:1000-1500
£1401 $2200 €2102 Interior with boy seated at desk with open book (20x28cm-8x11in) s. masonite. 19-Apr-3 James Julia, Fairfield #304/R est:3000-4000
£1433 $2250 €2150 Nude stretching (41x30cm-16x12in) s. s.verso. 10-Dec-2 Doyle, New York #152/R est:4000-6000
£2160 $3500 €3132 Lost in thought (46x30cm-18x12in) s. s.d.73 verso. 21-May-3 Doyle, New York #143/R est:3000-4000
£2848 $4500 €4272 Green sweater (41x30cm-16x12in) s. s.verso prov. 24-Apr-3 Shannon's, Milford #188/R est:2000-3000
£3548 $5500 €5322 Street wisdom (64x76cm-25x30in) s.d. painted c.1938. 8-Dec-2 Toomey, Oak Park #757/R est:8000-12000

£3822 $6000 €5733 Friends (91x76cm-36x30in) s. i.verso. 10-Dec-2 Doyle, New York #151/R est:8000-10000
£4430 $7000 €6645 Young girl peeling apple (76x64cm-30x25in) s. s.i.verso prov. 24-Apr-3 Shannon's, Milford #187/R est:4000-6000

PHILIPPE, Jules (19th C) French
Works on paper
£380 $604 €570 Maiden with flowers and pearls (73x59cm-29x23in) s. pastel oval. 5-Mar-3 Bonhams, Bury St Edmunds #249/R

PHILIPPE, P (19/20th C) French
Sculpture
£1277 $2068 €1800 Female nude (60cm-24in) i. verso pat.bronze stone socle. 21-May-3 Dorotheum, Vienna #243/R est:2000-2500
£1300 $2054 €1950 Goddess of wine (54cm-21in) st.sig. bronze. 14-Nov-2 Christie's, Kensington #176/R est:1500-2000
£1800 $2844 €2700 Challenge (47cm-19in) bronze. 14-Nov-2 Christie's, Kensington #197/R est:2000-3000
£2922 $4266 €4500 Young woman dancing (55cm-22in) s. gilded bronze marble socle. 14-Jun-2 Auktionhaus Georg Rehm, Augsburg #6088/R est:150
£4000 $6280 €6000 Figure of a young woman holding a parrot (49cm-19in) s. bronze green veined marble base. 21-Nov-2 Tennants, Leyburn #871/R est:1500-2000

PHILIPPE, Paul (fl.1920-1929) French
Sculpture
£1884 $3090 €2600 Nu debout (66cm-26in) s. bronze marble base. 27-May-3 Campo, Vlaamse Kaai #188/R est:2000-2500
£8108 $12649 €12000 Danseuse russe (41cm-16in) s. ivory bronze onyx base exec.c.1925. 25-Mar-3 Campo & Campo, Antwerp #160/R est:12000-18000
£10500 $16695 €15750 Girl with parrot (49cm-19in) i. cold pat. bronze lit. 27-Feb-3 Sotheby's, Olympia #190/R est:5000-8000

PHILIPPE, Paul (19/20th C) French
£730 $1138 €1059 Brittany port activity (24x34cm-9x13in) s.i. 26-Mar-3 Walker's, Ottawa #22/R est:500-700 (C.D 1700)
£1111 $1811 €1600 Filets bleus, soleil couchant (46x55cm-18x22in) s. 19-Jul-3 Thierry & Lannon, Brest #162 est:1400-1600

PHILIPPEAU, Karel Frans (1825-1897) Dutch
£4403 $6780 €7000 Flowers for the baby (38x49cm-15x19in) s. panel. 23-Oct-2 Christie's, Amsterdam #31/R est:5000-7000
£8000 $12720 €12000 Figures in a courtyard (30x41cm-12x16in) s.d.1861 panel prov. 18-Mar-3 Bonhams, New Bond Street #1/R est:6000-8000
Works on paper
£900 $1422 €1350 Waiting for his return. Family meal (13x19cm-5x7in) s. W/C pair. 26-Nov-2 Bonhams, Knightsbridge #19/R

PHILIPPET, Léon (1843-1906) Belgian
£385 $604 €600 Maternite (20x18cm-8x7in) mono. panel. 11-Dec-2 Hotel des Ventes Mosan, Brussels #228
£417 $654 €650 Les barques a maree basse (35x46cm-14x18in) s. 11-Dec-2 Hotel des Ventes Mosan, Brussels #225
£641 $1006 €1000 La querelle (100x139cm-39x55in) s.d.1885. 11-Dec-2 Hotel des Ventes Mosan, Brussels #232b est:1000-1100
£4676 $7482 €6500 Fete villageoise en Italie (44x68cm-17x27in) s.d.79. 13-May-3 Palais de Beaux Arts, Brussels #118/R est:6700-8000

PHILIPPOT, Karl Ludwig (1801-1859) French
£2836 $4509 €4254 Portrait of Adolf Schwarzenberg with Order of the Golden Fleece (91x74cm-36x29in) s.d.1852. 8-Mar-3 Dorotheum, Prague #33/R est:50000-75000 (C.KR 130000)

PHILIPPOTEAUX, Henri Felix Emmanuel (1815-1884) French
Works on paper
£1149 $1792 €1700 Etudes d'hommes assis (21x26cm-8x10in) crayon htd gouache. 31-Mar-3 Piasa, Paris #102

PHILIPPOTEAUX, Paul Dominique (1846-1923) American
Works on paper
£755 $1162 €1200 Cavalier arabe (31x21cm-12x8in) s.i.d.1890 ink dr. 23-Oct-2 Rabourdin & Choppin de Janvry, Paris #162/R
£3333 $5233 €5200 Marchands de pasteques et melons (49x36cm-19x14in) s.i.d.1893 pen. 10-Dec-2 Tajan, Paris #226/R

PHILIPS, Richard (1681-1741) British
£18750 $30000 €28125 Persia (183x157cm-72x62in) oil pencil painted 1996 prov.exhib. 14-May-3 Sotheby's, New York #365/R est:20000-30000
Works on paper
£5625 $9000 €8438 Strawberry eater (51x41cm-20x16in) s.d.98 verso chl white chk prov. 14-May-3 Sotheby's, New York #363/R est:4000-6000

PHILIPS-WEBER, Marie (19/20th C) German
£538 $834 €850 Children playing in church yard (65x53cm-26x21in) s. board. 26-Sep-2 Neumeister, Munich #2813/R

PHILIPSEN, Sally (1879-1936) Danish
£296 $461 €444 View from Bakken (60x70cm-24x28in) s. 23-Sep-2 Rasmussen, Vejle #250/R (D.KR 3500)
£507 $791 €761 Seascape with vessels at sea and shore (48x62cm-19x24in) s. 23-Sep-2 Rasmussen, Vejle #120/R (D.KR 6000)

PHILIPSEN, Theodor (1840-1920) Danish
£259 $396 €389 Landscape with cow (12x23cm-5x9in) init. masonite. 24-Aug-2 Rasmussen, Havnen #2318 (D.KR 3000)
£631 $1015 €947 Landscape study with fence (26x35cm-10x14in) mono. 22-Feb-3 Rasmussen, Havnen #2123/R (D.KR 7000)
£851 $1345 €1277 Field landscape with cows (9x19cm-4x7in) mono. panel prov. 2-Dec-2 Rasmussen, Copenhagen #1312 (D.KR 10000)
£972 $1497 €1458 Southern street scene with musicians and children dancing (31x40cm-12x16in) mono.d.1875. 26-Oct-2 Rasmussen, Havnen #2057/R (D.KR 11500)
£1024 $1628 €1536 View towards village in autumn (36x61cm-14x24in) mono.d.76. 10-Mar-3 Rasmussen, Vejle #236/R (D.KR 11000)
£1397 $2221 €2096 Two musicians playing for three children dancing (29x38cm-11x15in) mono.d.1876. 5-Mar-3 Rasmussen, Copenhagen #1870/R est:15000-20000 (D.KR 15000)
£1458 $2274 €2187 Cattle at Saltholmen (39x50cm-15x20in) 11-Nov-2 Rasmussen, Vejle #489/R est:12000-15000 (D.KR 17000)
£4000 $6200 €6000 Fountains at Porta Furba (37x61cm-15x24in) s.verso i.d.1878 stretcher. 3-Dec-2 Sotheby's, Olympia #303/R est:4000-6000
£4976 $8061 €7464 River landscape from Voersaa in Vendsyssel, autumn (101x137cm-40x54in) painted 1899 exhib.lit. 21-May-3 Museumsbygningen, Copenhagen #53/R est:25000-35000 (D.KR 52000)
£5121 $8142 €7682 Cows and sheep at Saltholm (62x45cm-24x18in) mono. 5-Mar-3 Rasmussen, Copenhagen #1603/R est:15000-25000 (D.KR 55000)
Sculpture
£2834 $4505 €4251 Roman bull on large oval socle (40x50cm-16x20in) pat.bronze prov. 25-Feb-3 Rasmussen, Copenhagen #866/R est:25000 (D.KR 31000)
Works on paper
£270 $435 €405 Sheep at Saltholm (21x28cm-8x11in) mono. pastel. 26-Feb-3 Museumsbygningen, Copenhagen #95 (D.KR 3000)
£292 $455 €438 Cows at Saltholmen (12x24cm-5x9in) pen. 11-Nov-2 Rasmussen, Vejle #472/R (D.KR 3400)
£344 $558 €516 By the watering place (14x18cm-6x7in) pencil pen. 21-May-3 Museumsbygningen, Copenhagen #25 (D.KR 3600)
£446 $696 €669 Shepherd boy and sheep, approaching storm (31x39cm-12x15in) pastel. 11-Nov-2 Rasmussen, Vejle #482/R (D.KR 5200)
£553 $874 €830 From Trommesalen with cows and sheep in enclosure (20x27cm-8x11in) mono.d.1870 pen pencil exhib.prov. 2-Dec-2 Rasmussen, Copenhagen #1830 (D.KR 6500)
£2383 $3765 €3575 Cows. pencil Indian ink seven. 30-Nov-2 Rasmussen, Havnen #2215 est:2000 (D.KR 28000)

PHILIPSON, Robin (1916-1992) British
£2000 $3240 €3000 Flaying (91x63cm-36x25in) s.verso exhib. 23-May-3 Lyon & Turnbull, Edinburgh #33/R est:2000-3000
£2000 $3280 €3000 Kings on horseback (12x17cm-5x7in) s. panel exhib. 3-Jun-3 Sotheby's, Olympia #254/R est:800-1200
£2400 $3648 €3600 Whispering II (30x41cm-12x16in) s.verso. 28-Aug-2 Sotheby's, London #1039/R est:2000-3000
£2400 $3720 €3600 Prelude to a cock fight (46x102cm-18x40in) s.d.1978-79 overlap. 31-Oct-2 Christie's, London #192/R est:2000-3000
£2500 $3900 €3750 Cockfight, rose window (65x95cm-26x37in) prov.exhib. 10-Apr-3 Bonhams, Edinburgh #32/R est:2500-3500
£2600 $4134 €3900 Cock and hen I (48x58cm-19x23in) s.verso oil paper on board. 6-Mar-3 Christie's, Kensington #246/R est:1000-1500
£3000 $4560 €4500 Cock fight (68x81cm-27x32in) s. exhib. 28-Aug-2 Sotheby's, London #1022/R est:3000-5000
£3000 $4770 €4500 Woman observed (18x25cm-7x10in) board. 6-Mar-3 Christie's, Kensington #242/R est:1200-1800
£3000 $4770 €4500 In the afternoon (19x15cm-7x6in) s.verso board. 6-Mar-3 Christie's, Kensington #243/R est:1000-1500
£3000 $4770 €4500 Cock crowing (137x90cm-54x35in) s.d.1983-89 panel exhib. 6-Mar-3 Christie's, Kensington #245/R est:3000-5000
£3400 $5576 €5100 Fighting cocks (19x25cm-7x10in) s. board prov. 3-Jun-3 Sotheby's, Olympia #256/R est:1500-2000
£3600 $5472 €5400 Woman observed XIII (35x41cm-14x16in) board prov.exhib. 28-Aug-2 Sotheby's, London #1041/R est:2500-3500

£4500 $7380 €6750 Fighting cocks (19x26cm-7x10in) s. board prov. 3-Jun-3 Sotheby's, Olympia #255/R est:1500-2000
£5000 $7750 €7500 Compotier of fruit (61x30cm-24x12in) s.stretcher. 5-Dec-2 Bonhams, Edinburgh #13/R est:4000-6000
£5200 $7956 €7800 Iconostasis V (91x243cm-36x96in) s.i.on overlap s.stretcher. 22-Aug-2 Bonhams, Edinburgh #977/R est:6000-8000
£6500 $10075 €9750 Horses (71x92cm-28x36in) s.verso panel W/C collage. 31-Oct-2 Christie's, London #189/R est:7000-10000
£6500 $10725 €9425 Woman bathing in a summer pool (137x183cm-54x72in) s.d.56 exhib. 3-Jul-3 Christie's, Kensington #543/R est:4000-6000
£10000 $15300 €15000 November roses (75x75cm-30x30in) s.d.1983 board. 22-Aug-2 Bonhams, Edinburgh #970/R est:15000-20000
£15500 $23715 €23250 Byzantine interior (66x66cm-26x26in) s.on overlap. 22-Aug-2 Bonhams, Edinburgh #958/R est:7000-10000

Works on paper

£1000 $1560 €1500 Cocks fighting, red (35x44cm-14x17in) s. mixed media. 17-Sep-2 Sotheby's, Olympia #81/R est:1000-1500
£1250 $1950 €1875 Merry go round (17x20cm-7x8in) s.d.1986 verso W/C. 17-Oct-2 Bonhams, Edinburgh #73/R est:1000-1500
£1500 $2280 €2250 Girl approaches (19x19cm-7x7in) W/C gouache. 28-Aug-2 Sotheby's, London #1038/R est:1500-2000
£2000 $3120 €3000 Merry-go-round (20x17cm-8x7in) s.d.1986 verso W/C. 14-Apr-3 Sotheby's, London #181/R est:2000-3000
£2100 $3213 €3150 Gossips (20x20cm-8x8in) W/C gouache exhib. 22-Aug-2 Bonhams, Edinburgh #1098 est:800-1200
£2600 $4056 €3900 The eternal (68x68cm-27x27in) W/C. 10-Apr-3 Bonhams, Edinburgh #35/R est:2000-3000
£2700 $4185 €4050 Cock fight, yellow (57x60cm-22x24in) s. W/C gouache prov.exhib. 5-Dec-2 Bonhams, Edinburgh #7/R est:2500-4000
£3000 $4590 €4500 Arena Vill (19x34cm-7x13in) s.i.d.86 verso W/C. 22-Aug-2 Bonhams, Edinburgh #968 est:1200-1800
£3000 $4560 €4500 Nude and Ethiopian II. Nude and Ethiopian III (17x17cm-7x7in) s. W/C pair prov. 28-Aug-2 Sotheby's, London #1040/R est:2000-3000
£4000 $6120 €6000 Night (40x50cm-16x20in) s. W/C. 22-Aug-2 Bonhams, Edinburgh #974/R est:2000-3000
£5000 $7600 €7500 Zebra (78x136cm-31x54in) W/C exhib. 28-Aug-2 Sotheby's, London #1027/R est:5000-7000

PHILLIP, John (1817-1867) British

£500 $815 €750 Spanish dancer (30x25cm-12x10in) board. 12-Feb-3 Bonhams, Knightsbridge #63/R
£2000 $3280 €3000 Holy water (61x46cm-24x18in) mono.d.1857. 29-May-3 Christie's, Kensington #281/R est:2000-2500
£4600 $7038 €6900 Fiesta in Seville (75x154cm-30x61in) prov. 22-Aug-2 Bonhams, Edinburgh #1063/R est:7000-10000
£4800 $7488 €7200 Picking wild flowers (35x29cm-14x11in) s. 10-Apr-3 Bonhams, Edinburgh #126/R est:700-1000
£5200 $7904 €7800 Family in a cottage interior (47x60cm-19x24in) mono.d.1856 prov. 28-Aug-2 Sotheby's, London #910/R est:2000-3000
£11000 $16830 €16500 African princess enslaved (127x90cm-50x35in) 22-Aug-2 Bonhams, Edinburgh #1062/R est:7000-10000
£80000 $128800 €120000 Early career of Murillo (181x250cm-71x98in) mono.d.1865 s.i.d.verso prov.exhib.lit. 19-Feb-3 Christie's, London #8/R est:100000-200000

PHILLIP, John (attrib) (1817-1867) British

£385 $604 €600 Still life with two doves (45x62cm-18x24in) 19-Nov-2 Castellana, Madrid #26/R

PHILLIPE (20th C) ?

Sculpture

£6000 $9600 €9000 Female dancer (47cm-19in) s. cold pat. bronze. 15-May-3 Christie's, Kensington #465/R est:6000-8000

PHILLIPS, Ammi (1787-1865) American

£2963 $4800 €4296 Portrait of Polly Smith Husted (38x31cm-15x12in) masonite prov.lit. 22-May-3 Sotheby's, New York #759
£3000 $4800 €4500 Portrait. 1-Jan-3 Fallon, Copake #89
£4815 $7800 €6982 Portrait of a dark haired gentleman with pen and bible (76x63cm-30x25in) exhib. 22-May-3 Sotheby's, New York #765
£5556 $9000 €8056 Portrait of Mary Hoyt (102x84cm-40x33in) painted c.1836 prov.exhib.lit. 22-May-3 Sotheby's, New York #760

PHILLIPS, Ammi (attrib) (1787-1865) American

£769 $1200 €1154 Portrait of Samuel Hunt (74x66cm-29x26in) 9-Aug-2 Skinner, Bolton #476f

PHILLIPS, Barye (1924-) American

Works on paper

£1282 $2000 €1923 Standing woman defiantly overlooking shore town (43x30cm-17x12in) s. gouache. 9-Nov-2 Illustration House, New York #143/R est:1500-2500

PHILLIPS, Bert G (1868-1956) American

£5679 $9200 €8235 New Mexico landscape with lake (43x61cm-17x24in) board. 23-May-3 Altermann Galleries, Santa Fe #159
£12179 $19000 €18269 Springtime in Taos Pueblo (33x76cm-13x30in) s. prov.lit. 9-Nov-2 Santa Fe Art, Santa Fe #37/R est:25000-35000
£27623 $44750 €40053 Winter in Taos (86x102cm-34x40in) 23-May-3 Altermann Galleries, Santa Fe #160

Works on paper

£2244 $3500 €3366 Taxco, Mexico (36x25cm-14x10in) W/C. 9-Nov-2 Altermann Galleries, Santa Fe #106
£2244 $3500 €3366 Sunflowers (53x33cm-21x13in) gouache. 9-Nov-2 Altermann Galleries, Santa Fe #107

PHILLIPS, Clifford Holmead (1889-1975) American

£566 $883 €900 Crossroads (66x55cm-26x22in) s.mono.d.58. 21-Sep-2 Bolland & Marotz, Bremen #710/R
£755 $1177 €1200 Trees against blue sky (41x50cm-16x20in) s.mono.d.73 panel. 21-Sep-2 Bolland & Marotz, Bremen #711/R
£943 $1472 €1500 Two men's heads (36x50cm-14x20in) s. s.i.d. verso panel. 21-Sep-2 Bolland & Marotz, Bremen #709/R

PHILLIPS, Coles (1880-1927) American

Works on paper

£14103 $22000 €21155 Woman kneeling with scissors and yardstick (51x41cm-20x16in) s. W/C gouache. 9-Nov-2 Illustration House, New York #101/R est:18000-24000

PHILLIPS, Douglas (1926-) British

£340 $530 €510 Wind blown fields (24x24cm-9x9in) s. acrylic. 17-Oct-2 Bonhams, Edinburgh #33

PHILLIPS, Edith (?) British

£480 $768 €720 Still life of flowers and fruit (30x61cm-12x24in) s. board. 14-Mar-3 Gardiner & Houlgate, Bath #181/R

PHILLIPS, Gordon (1927-) American

£1282 $2000 €1923 On the way to water (66x86cm-26x34in) s. prov. 9-Nov-2 Santa Fe Art, Santa Fe #127/R est:8000-10000

PHILLIPS, James (?) ?

£241 $400 €349 Still life with gloves (51cm-20in) s. prov. 11-Jun-3 Boos Gallery, Michigan #351

PHILLIPS, James March (20th C) American

Works on paper

£778 $1300 €1128 Time for a rest, rider in shade in panoramic landscape (30x58cm-12x23in) W/C. 17-Jun-3 John Moran, Pasadena #82a est:800-1200

PHILLIPS, Joel (1960-) American

£2840 $4600 €4118 Tack room night (61x91cm-24x36in) 23-May-3 Altermann Galleries, Santa Fe #62
£4110 $6000 €6165 Courtyard poetry (71x84cm-28x33in) 18-May-2 Altermann Galleries, Santa Fe #148/R

PHILLIPS, John (fl.1832-1837) British

£2600 $4160 €3900 Prima Donna in the Character of Rosina (60x47cm-24x19in) mono.d.1865 i.verso prov. 8-Jan-3 George Kidner, Lymington #199/R est:3000-5000

PHILLIPS, John Campbell (1873-1949) American

£898 $1500 €1302 Wilmington Notch (51x64cm-20x25in) s.i.verso. 21-Jun-3 Charlton Hall, Columbia #297/R est:800-1200

PHILLIPS, Myfanwy (20th C) Canadian?

Works on paper

£258 $402 €387 Fourteen smiling people (98x86cm-39x34in) gouache prov. 25-Mar-3 Ritchie, Toronto #189 (C.D 600)

PHILLIPS, Peter (1939-) British

Works on paper

£1149 $1792 €1700 Glorious views (36x50cm-14x20in) pencil exec.1974. 26-Mar-3 Finarte Semenzato, Milan #77/R
£1216 $1897 €1800 Untitled (35x61cm-14x24in) s.d.1974 collage photograph. 26-Mar-3 Finarte Semenzato, Milan #72/R

PHILLIPS, Samuel George (c.1890-1965) American

£2395 $4000 €3473 Still life of flowers (51x41cm-20x16in) s. 22-Jun-3 Freeman, Philadelphia #157/R est:3000-5000

£3892 $6500 €5643 Covered bridge (63x56cm-25x22in) s. 22-Jun-3 Freeman, Philadelphia #147/R est:3000-5000

PHILLIPS, Thomas (1770-1845) British
£270 $451 €392 Kenilworth Castle, Leycester's buildings from the ford, summer landscape (48x38cm-19x15in) s.i. d.1880 verso. 10-Jul-3 Neales, Nottingham #458
£500 $815 €750 Portrait of a middle eastern boy (53x44cm-21x17in) 29-Jan-3 Sotheby's, Olympia #6/R

PHILLIPS, Walter Joseph (1884-1963) American/Canadian
Prints
£1406 $2221 €2109 Rushing River, lake of the woods (15x18cm-6x7in) d.1920 col woodblock. 1-Dec-2 Levis, Calgary #75/R est:3000-4000 (C.D 3500)
£1794 $2870 €2691 Howe Sound, BC (27x32cm-11x13in) s.i. col woodcut prov.lit. 15-May-3 Heffel, Vancouver #127/R est:4000-5000 (C.D 4000)
£2246 $3571 €3369 Mount Rundle (21x31cm-8x12in) s.i. col woodcut. 23-Mar-3 Hodgins, Calgary #33/R est:2000-3000 (C.D 5300)
£3614 $5675 €5421 Mamalilicoola, BC (31x36cm-12x14in) s.i.d.1928 num.63/100 col woodcut. 25-Nov-2 Hodgins, Calgary #63/R est:8000-10000 (C.D 9000)
£3815 $5990 €5723 York boat on Lake Winnipeg (26x35cm-10x14in) s.i. num.138/150 col woodcut. 25-Nov-2 Hodgins, Calgary #64/R est:8000-10000 (C.D 9500)
£4819 $7566 €7229 Summer idyll (46x31cm-18x12in) s.i. num.44/100 col woodcut. 25-Nov-2 Hodgins, Calgary #305/R est:9000-12000 (C.D 12000)
Works on paper
£800 $1304 €1200 Wild flowers (17x27cm-7x11in) s.indis.d.191 W/C. 30-Jan-3 Lawrence, Crewkerne #652/R
£1667 $2733 €2417 Enspik on the Linde (32x52cm-13x20in) s.i.d.1958 W/C. 9-Jun-3 Hodgins, Calgary #336/R est:4500-5500 (C.D 3750)
£1815 $2867 €2723 Twin River Farm, Chilliwack, BC (26x37cm-10x15in) s.d.1949 W/C. 14-Nov-2 Heffel, Vancouver #24/R est:5000-7000 (C.D 4500)
£1931 $3013 €2897 Vilas park, Madison, WIS (23x29cm-9x11in) s. i.verso W/C. 25-Mar-3 Ritchie, Toronto #77/R est:2500-3500 (C.D 4500)
£2610 $4098 €3915 San Jose Mission, San Antonio, Texas (38x47cm-15x19in) s.i.d.1955 W/C prov. 25-Nov-2 Hodgins, Calgary #351/R est:6000-8000 (C.D 6500)
£3012 $4729 €4518 Caledonian Hills, Ontario (40x44cm-16x17in) s.i.d.1958 W/C prov. 25-Nov-2 Hodgins, Calgary #106/R est:8000-10000 (C.D 7500)
£4260 $6816 €6390 Bow valley (38x53cm-15x21in) s.d.1952 i.verso W/C prov.lit. 15-May-3 Heffel, Vancouver #1/R est:10000-12000 (C.D 9500)

PHILOLAOS (20th C) ?
Sculpture
£25899 $42475 €36000 Arbre armoire (250cm-98in) stainless steel. 6-Jun-3 Rabourdin & Choppin de Janvry, Paris #99/R est:45000-50000

PHILP, James George (1816-1885) British
Works on paper
£800 $1312 €1200 Fishermen on the Cornish Coast with beached boats (43x86cm-17x34in) s.d.1860 W/C. 10-Feb-3 Robin Fenner, Tavistock #659/R

PHILPOT, Glyn (1884-1937) British
£800 $1232 €1200 Portrait of gentleman wearing glasses (102x89cm-40x35in) s. 24-Oct-2 Christie's, Kensington #220/R
£1600 $2496 €2400 Angels dancing in a drop of water (46x38cm-18x15in) init. 25-Mar-3 Bonhams, New Bond Street #104/R est:700-1000
£2400 $3792 €3600 Male model wearing sash (40x51cm-16x20in) init. 27-Nov-2 Sotheby's, Olympia #65/R est:1500-2000
£2500 $3900 €3750 Portrait of a young man (38x29cm-15x11in) canvasboard. 25-Mar-3 Bonhams, New Bond Street #44/R est:2500-3500
£25000 $38750 €37500 Dawn (113x142cm-44x56in) init. prov.exhib. 4-Dec-2 Sotheby's, London #24/R est:12000-18000
Works on paper
£350 $546 €525 Tree, North Africa (41x29cm-16x11in) init. pencil W/C. 27-Mar-3 Christie's, Kensington #353

PHIPPEN, George (1916-1966) American
£3526 $5500 €5289 Quarter horse (41x51cm-16x20in) 9-Nov-2 Altermann Galleries, Santa Fe #47
£3704 $6000 €5371 Christmas feast (38x48cm-15x19in) 23-May-3 Altermann Galleries, Santa Fe #34
£7099 $11500 €10294 A lick and a promise (61x91cm-24x36in) 23-May-3 Altermann Galleries, Santa Fe #35
£8333 $13000 €12500 On the pack trail (69x99cm-27x39in) s. prov.lit. 9-Nov-2 Santa Fe Art, Santa Fe #142/R est:10000-12000
£8519 $13800 €12353 White stallion (61x76cm-24x30in) 23-May-3 Altermann Galleries, Santa Fe #36
£21918 $32000 €32877 When there's time to talk (61x76cm-24x30in) 18-May-2 Altermann Galleries, Santa Fe #160/R
Sculpture
£5479 $8000 €8219 Wimpy P-1 (25cm-10in) one of 20 bronze. 18-May-2 Altermann Galleries, Santa Fe #161/R
Works on paper
£2724 $4250 €4086 Timid soul (28x36cm-11x14in) s.d.55 W/C on board prov.lit. 9-Nov-2 Santa Fe Art, Santa Fe #203/R est:3000-4000

PHIPPS, Edmund (fl.1884-1915) British
Works on paper
£340 $537 €510 Rainbow above castle ruins by a river (58x43cm-23x17in) s.d.1887 W/C. 26-Nov-2 Bonhams, Oxford #23

PHYSICK, Edward Gustavus (1822-1871) British
Sculpture
£3200 $4992 €4800 Bust of a young boy (38cm-15in) s.d.1865 white marble black marble socle. 9-Apr-3 Sotheby's, London #84/R est:2000-3000

PHYSICK, Robert (fl.1859-1866) British
£1800 $2862 €2700 Dog watching baby rabbits feeding (48x58cm-19x23in) s.d.1864. 29-Apr-3 Sworder & Son, Bishops Stortford #405/R est:800-1200
£6000 $9960 €9000 On guard (58x68cm-23x27in) s.d.1863. 12-Jun-3 Sotheby's, London #290/R est:6000-8000

PIACENZA, Carlo (1814-1887) Italian
£510 $811 €750 Under-growth (39x30cm-15x12in) s. board. 1-Mar-3 Meeting Art, Vercelli #115
£641 $1006 €1000 In the mountains (36x47cm-14x19in) s.d.1861. 16-Dec-2 Pandolfini, Florence #48/R
£943 $1453 €1500 Linen in the sun (46x34cm-18x13in) s.d.1886 cardboard. 28-Oct-2 Il Ponte, Milan #301/R

PIACESI, Walter (1929-) Italian
£1528 $2429 €2200 Advert (50x40cm-20x16in) s. s.i.verso board. 1-May-3 Meeting Art, Vercelli #550
Works on paper
£253 $395 €400 Untitled (20x20cm-8x8in) s.d.1974 W/C. 14-Sep-2 Meeting Art, Vercelli #847

PIAGGIO, Antonio (fl.1755-1779) Italian
Works on paper
£5556 $9000 €8334 Map of the Americas (46x70cm-18x28in) pen ink gouache gold leaf. 21-Jan-3 Sotheby's, New York #125/R est:6000

PIAN, Antonio de (1784-1851) Italian
£9507 $15306 €13500 Temple ruins on Venetian coast (79x109cm-31x43in) s. canvas on panel lit. 9-May-3 Schloss Ahlden, Ahlden #1328/R est:12500

PIANCA, Giuseppe Antonio (attrib) (1703-1757) Italian
£4878 $8000 €7317 Still life pears, apples and grapes in a bowl (72x138cm-28x54in) arched top. 29-May-3 Sotheby's, New York #50a est:10000-15000

PIANCASTELLI, Giovanni (1845-1926) Italian
£279 $444 €419 Portrait of Beatrice Cenci (64x48cm-25x19in) mono.d.1891 after Guido Reni. 5-Mar-3 Rasmussen, Copenhagen #1655/R (D.KR 3000)

PIANE, Giovanni Maria delle (attrib) (1660-1745) Italian
£1631 $2724 €2300 Portrait de jeune femme a la robe rouge (105x77cm-41x30in) 23-Jun-3 Beaussant & Lefèvre, Paris #259/R est:1500-2000

PIASECKI, Leszek (20th C) Austrian?
£566 $883 €900 Mongolian horsemen (70x90cm-28x35in) s. 19-Sep-2 Dr Fritz Nagel, Stuttgart #982/R

PIATTI, Antonio (1875-1962) Italian
£387 $612 €600 Portrait of lady (40x30cm-16x12in) s. 18-Dec-2 Finarte, Milan #180/R

PIATTOLI, Giuseppe (fl.1785-1807) Italian

Works on paper

£253 $400 €400 Monk introduced to the Pope (19x27cm-7x11in) pen ink W/C. 28-Nov-2 Tajan, Paris #121

£276 $441 €400 Saint Catherine's mystic marriage (34x25cm-13x10in) pencil dr. 17-Mar-3 Pandolfini, Florence #726

PIAUBERT, Jean (1900-2001) French

£845 $1318 €1250 Sans titre (19x24cm-7x9in) s. 31-Mar-3 Rossini, Paris #101/R

£952 $1514 €1400 Composition (60x73cm-24x29in) s. 24-Mar-3 Claude Boisgirard, Paris #109/R

£1042 $1656 €1500 Composition (81x100cm-32x39in) s. 29-Apr-3 Artcurial Briest, Paris #586/R est:1500-2000

PIAZZA, A (?) Italian

Sculpture

£8228 $13000 €12342 Figure of Cupid (107cm-42in) i. marble on onyx pedestal. 24-Apr-3 Christie's, Rockefeller NY #183/R est:8000-12000

PIAZZETTA, Giambattista (1682-1754) Italian

Works on paper

£6000 $10020 €8700 Two studies of hands resting on a board (18x27cm-7x11in) black white chk prov. 8-Jul-3 Christie's, London #45/R est:4000-6000

PIAZZETTA, Giambattista (attrib) (1682-1754) Italian

Works on paper

£1139 $1800 €1800 St Zeno tenant un plat avec un poisson (27x17cm-11x7in) red chk. 27-Nov-2 Christie's, Paris #100/R est:2000-3000

£1552 $2514 €2250 Head of man (25x18cm-10x7in) red chk prov. 26-May-3 Bukowskis, Stockholm #495/R est:25000-30000 (S.KR 20000)

PIAZZETTA, Giambattista (circle) (1682-1754) Italian

£8000 $12560 €12000 Mass of Saint Philip Neri (116x99cm-46x39in) prov. 10-Dec-2 Bonhams, New Bond Street #214/R est:8000-12000

£22069 $34869 €32000 Resurrection (181x135cm-71x53in) 5-Apr-3 Finarte Semenzato, Milan #74/R est:15000

PIAZZONI, Gottardo (1872-1945) American/Swiss

£2548 $4000 €3822 Marin county landscape (16x22cm-6x9in) s.d.07 canvasboard prov. 19-Nov-2 Butterfields, San Francisco #8177/R est:3000-5000

£2548 $4000 €3822 Through the trees (22x16cm-9x6in) s.d.25 i.d.25 verso canvasboard prov. 19-Nov-2 Butterfields, San Francisco #8178/R est:3000-5000

£3313 $5500 €4804 Boat house (15x23cm-6x9in) s. i.verso board prov. 11-Jun-3 Butterfields, San Francisco #4202/R est:4000-6000

PICABIA, Francis (1878-1953) French

£3500 $5565 €5250 La chevre (17x14cm-7x6in) s. cardboard painted c.1942. 20-Mar-3 Sotheby's, Olympia #199/R est:4000-6000

£7308 $11473 €11400 Le Loing a Moret (27x35cm-11x14in) s.d.1904 panel. 11-Dec-2 Artcurial Briest, Paris #526/R est:12000

£9317 $15000 €13976 Le Loing a Moret (27x35cm-11x14in) s.d.1904 panel. 7-May-3 Sotheby's, New York #174/R est:12000-15000

£9816 $16000 €14724 Effet de neige, bords de l'Yonne (38x46cm-15x18in) s.d.1906. 12-Feb-3 Sotheby's, New York #21/R est:20000-30000

£24679 $38747 €38500 Maternite bleue (103x82cm-41x32in) s. painted c.1935-36. 11-Dec-2 Artcurial Briest, Paris #534/R est:35000

£26398 $42500 €39597 Paysage avec bateaux (37x46cm-15x18in) s.d.1907. 7-May-3 Sotheby's, New York #160/R est:20000-30000

£40000 $65600 €60000 Pointe du port a Saint-Tropez (98x131cm-39x52in) s.d.1900 prov.exhib. 4-Feb-3 Christie's, London #239/R est:45000

£44872 $70449 €70000 Saint-Tropez (73x92cm-29x36in) s.d.1903. 13-Dec-2 Piasa, Paris #24/R est:60000

£50000 $83500 €72500 Le Mexicain (106x97cm-42x38in) s. board painted 1937 prov.exhib.lit. 24-Jun-3 Sotheby's, London #202/R est:40000-50000

£50544 $80365 €74300 Portrait d'Olga Picabia (73x60cm-29x24in) s. painted c.1935-1936 lit. 26-Feb-3 Artcurial Briest, Paris #302/R est:61000-91000

£57692 $90577 €90000 Negateur du hasard (92x73cm-36x29in) s.d.1946 cardboard prov.exhib.lit. 24-Nov-2 Laurence Calmels, Paris #209/R est:150000

£75862 $121379 €110000 Espagnole a l'eventail (104x75cm-41x30in) s. cardboard painted c.1925. 12-Mar-3 Libert, Castor, Paris #157/R est:40000-50000

£121795 $191218 €190000 Ergo (195x113cm-77x44in) s.d.1947 prov.exhib.lit. 24-Nov-2 Laurence Calmels, Paris #208/R est:200000

£128205 $200000 €192308 Halia (162x129cm-64x51in) s.i. painted c.1929 prov.exhib.lit. 7-Nov-2 Christie's, Rockefeller NY #332/R est:120000-160000

£243590 $382436 €380000 Femmes au bull-dog (106x76cm-42x30in) s. cardboard exhib.lit. 24-Nov-2 Laurence Calmels, Paris #207/R est:250000-350000

£1095890 $1720548 €1600000 Amoureux, apres la pluie (116x115cm-46x45in) s. ripolin prov.exhib.lit. 15-Apr-3 Laurence Calmels, Paris #4393/R est:500000-700000

Works on paper

£1282 $2013 €2000 Toilette (29x22cm-11x9in) s.d.45 verso W/C. 13-Dec-2 Piasa, Paris #251/R

£1600 $2544 €2400 La muse (22x16cm-9x6in) s. pencil W/C prov. 20-Mar-3 Sotheby's, Olympia #192/R est:2000-3000

£1728 $2454 €2800 Jeune homme et son chien (29x24cm-11x9in) s. graphite dr. 16-Mar-3 Eric Pillon, Calais #122/R

£2222 $3534 €3200 Portrait de Christine (28x21cm-11x8in) s.d.1946 wax crayon dr lit. 29-Apr-3 Artcurial Briest, Paris #98/R est:2500-3500

£2244 $3522 €3500 Figure feminine au singe (14x19cm-6x7in) s. crayon dr. 20-Nov-2 Claude Boisgirard, Paris #24/R

£2405 $3800 €3800 Voltige (21x27cm-8x11in) s. graphite dr lit. 29-Nov-2 Drouot Estimations, Paris #83/R

£2600 $4134 €3900 Portrait de femme (30x40cm-12x16in) s. chl gouache prov. 20-Mar-3 Sotheby's, Olympia #185/R est:1800-2500

£2685 $4322 €4000 Tete de femme (26x19cm-10x7in) s. graphite dr. 23-Feb-3 Mercier & Cie, Lille #46/R

£2800 $4452 €4200 Portrait de Leon-Pierre Quint (26x20cm-10x8in) s. pencil exec.c.1940-45 prov. 20-Mar-3 Sotheby's, Olympia #191/R est:2500-3500

£3125 $4969 €4500 Nu de trois quarts (21x16cm-8x6in) s. wax crayon dr lit. 29-Apr-3 Artcurial Briest, Paris #97 est:4000-6000

£3401 $5408 €5000 Espagnole a la coiffe (31x23cm-12x9in) s. crayon. 21-Mar-3 Rieunier, Bailly-Pommery, Mathias, Paris #107

£3453 $5525 €4800 Toreador (20x15cm-8x6in) s. ink prov. 15-May-3 Christie's, Paris #327/R est:600-800

£4138 $6911 €6000 Visage de femme (34x28cm-13x11in) s. Indian ink ink wash crayon dr. 10-Jul-3 Artcurial Briest, Paris #93/R est:6000-8000

£4762 $7571 €7000 Jeune femme de profil (23x17cm-9x7in) s. black pencil dr exec.c.1935-45 lit. 26-Feb-3 Artcurial Briest, Paris #62/R est:2000-3000

£5200 $8268 €7800 Transparence (29x22cm-11x9in) s. pencil exec.c.1940-45 prov. 20-Mar-3 Sotheby's, Olympia #184/R est:4000-5000

£5333 $8853 €7733 Seated nude (36x25cm-14x10in) s. gouache W/C ink paper on board. 16-Jun-3 Waddingtons, Toronto #265/R est:12000-14000 (C.D 12000)

£5500 $8745 €8250 Greta Garbo (26x20cm-10x8in) s. chl htd gouache prov. 20-Mar-3 Sotheby's, Olympia #186/R est:6000-8000

£5714 $9086 €8400 Couple assis (20x30cm-8x12in) s. W/C pencil exec.c.1926-27. 26-Feb-3 Artcurial Briest, Paris #61/R est:3000-4000

£6115 $9784 €8500 Nu de dos (26x21cm-10x8in) s. graphite estompe prov. 14-May-3 Blanchet, Paris #109/R est:7000-8000

£6748 $11000 €10122 La chouette (25x32cm-10x13in) s. W/C pencil executed c.1925-26 prov. 12-Feb-3 Sotheby's, New York #88/R est:10000-15000

£11000 $17490 €16500 Transparence (23x18cm-9x7in) s. pencil exec.c.1940 prov. 20-Mar-3 Sotheby's, Olympia #190/R est:4000-6000

£11180 $18000 €16770 Portriat d'homme (64x49cm-25x19in) s.d.1931 chl pen ink prov. 7-May-3 Sotheby's, New York #330/R est:10000-15000

£15000 $25050 €21750 Trois femmes nues (43x30cm-17x12in) s. W/C black crayon executed c.1941-45. 24-Jun-3 Sotheby's, London #226/R est:10000-12000

£20000 $32000 €29000 Pilar a la rose (61x49cm-24x19in) s. W/C graphite exec.c.1925. 12-Mar-3 Libert, Castor, Paris #156/R est:15000-20000

£28205 $44282 €44000 Deux femmes debout et profil d'homme (64x49cm-25x19in) s. Chinese ink prov.exhib. 24-Nov-2 Laurence Calmels, Paris #210/R est:25000

£90000 $146700 €135000 Homme debout (100x75cm-39x30in) s. gouache W/C cardboard exec.c.1926 prov.exhib.lit. 3-Feb-3 Christie's, London #160/R est:120000

PICARD, Biddy (?) British

£740 $1154 €1073 Blue and yellow still life (25x27cm-10x11in) s.d.2000 i.verso acrylic board. 27-Mar-3 Lane, Penzance #58

PICARD, Louis (1861-1940) French

£1266 $1975 €2000 In the studio (22x23cm-9x9in) s. board. 18-Oct-2 Dr Fritz Nagel, Stuttgart #585/R est:3300

£1310 $2097 €1900 Elegante dans une soiree (25x36cm-10x14in) s. panel. 12-Mar-3 Libert, Castor, Paris #158 est:600-800

£4000 $6680 €6000 Reclining female nude (73x91cm-29x36in) s. 18-Jun-3 Christie's, Kensington #128/R est:4000-6000

£4000 $6680 €6000 Sweet scent (94x55cm-37x22in) s. 18-Jun-3 Christie's, Kensington #131/R est:4000-6000

PICART LE DOUX (19/20th C) French

£1987 $3238 €3000 Vase de fleurs des champs (71x60cm-28x24in) s.d.42. 31-Jan-3 Rabourdin & Choppin de Janvry, Paris #101/R

£2365 $3689 €3500 Espagnol a la guitare (162x130cm-64x51in) s.d.1937. 28-Mar-3 Claude Aguttes, Neuilly #108

PICART LE DOUX, Charles (1881-1959) French

£316 $494 €500 Provence (53x65cm-21x26in) s. painted 1929. 20-Oct-2 Chayette & Cheval, Paris #66

£316 $500 €500 Mere et enfant (46x38cm-18x15in) s. 26-Nov-2 Palais de Beaux Arts, Brussels #196

£483 $772 €700 Nu dans l'atelier (81x60cm-32x24in) s.d.52 panel. 15-Mar-3 De Vuyst, Lokeren #251
£1062 $1731 €1593 Woman in board (60x73cm-24x29in) s.d.1912. 17-Feb-3 Blomqvist, Lysaker #1161 (N.KR 12000)
£2600 $4004 €3900 Portrait de jeune femme (73x60cm-29x24in) s. prov. 23-Oct-2 Sotheby's, Olympia #710/R est:1000-1500

PICART LEDOUX, Jean (1902-1982) French
£278 $439 €400 Paysage provencal (89x130cm-35x51in) s. 25-Apr-3 Piasa, Paris #163
£282 $454 €420 Le panier de pommes (38x46cm-15x18in) s. panel. 23-Feb-3 Lesieur & Le Bars, Le Havre #129
£621 $981 €900 Danseuse de cancan (40x32cm-16x13in) s. painted 1947. 4-Apr-3 Tajan, Paris #223

PICASSO (20th C) Spanish
Prints
£2436 $3776 €3800 Mere et enfant (56x47cm-22x19in) num.49/100 col engraving lit. 7-Dec-2 De Vuyst, Lokeren #253 est:3500-4000
Sculpture
£2128 $3447 €3000 Chouette (29cm-11in) Madoura 37/250 earthenware vase lit. 23-May-3 Camard, Paris #121/R est:2800-3300
£2837 $4596 €4000 Joueur de diaule (31x37cm-12x15in) num.50/200 rect earthenware plate yellow green white brown lit. 23-May-3 Camard, Paris #115/R est:4000-5000
£4823 $7813 €6800 Femme du barbu (37cm-15in) st.Madoura earthenware pitcher exhib.lit. 23-May-3 Camard, Paris #120/R est:7500-9000

PICASSO, Loulou (1958-) French
£1042 $1719 €1500 Untitled (47x65cm-19x26in) s.d.1982 oil gouache board. 3-Jul-3 Christie's, Paris #45/R est:400-600

PICASSO, Pablo (1881-1973) Spanish
£1154 $1812 €1800 Billet de Francs. s.d.49 on banknote. 24-Nov-2 Laurence Calmels, Paris #303/R
£2044 $3250 €3066 Viol II (51x51cm-20x20in) d.1933 drypoint aquatint one of 300. 30-Apr-3 Doyle, New York #264/R est:1000-1500
£2100 $3297 €3150 Enlevement II (49x45cm-19x18in) s.num.33/50 etching. 17-Apr-3 Christie's, Kensington #319/R est:2000-2500
£2516 $4000 €3774 Tetes et pierre (47x60cm-19x24in) s.num.29/50 lithograph. 2-May-3 Sotheby's, New York #290/R est:2000-3000
£7911 $12500 €12500 Autoportrait sous trois formes (30x37cm-12x15in) s. etching. 30-Nov-2 Villa Grisebach, Berlin #376/R est:5000-7000
£23077 $35769 €36000 La colombe (45x70cm-18x28in) s. lithograph. 7-Dec-2 Hauswedell & Nolte, Hamburg #1000/R est:45000
£23574 $37247 €35361 Francoise sur fond gris (63x47cm-25x19in) s.num.13/50 col lithograph lit. 28-Apr-3 Bukowskis, Stockholm #492/R est:250000-350000 (S.KR 310000)
£53000 $88510 €76850 Trois cartes a jouer (11x14cm-4x6in) board on panel painted 1914 prov.exhib.lit. 24-Jun-3 Sotheby's, London #150/R est:60000-80000
£63319 $98777 €94979 Taureau dans l'arene (20x25cm-8x10in) s. pastel. 6-Nov-2 Dobiaschofsky, Bern #884/R est:120000 (S.FR 145000)
£100000 $167000 €145000 Le transformateur (19x27cm-7x11in) s.d.10 Juin 53 prov.exhib.lit. 24-Jun-3 Sotheby's, London #174/R est:100000-150000
£128205 $200000 €192308 Bouteille, verre et pipe (49x31cm-19x12in) s. oil pencil painted 1914 prov.exhib.lit. 7-Nov-2 Christie's, Rockefeller NY #306/R est:100000-150000
£134615 $210000 €201923 Nature morte (16x22cm-6x9in) s.d.10.8.37 pencil. 6-Nov-2 Sotheby's, New York #322/R est:180000-250000
£140000 $229600 €210000 Peintre et modele (38x46cm-15x18in) s. d.65 verso prov.lit. 4-Feb-3 Christie's, London #318/R est:200000
£224359 $350000 €336539 Visage feminin, profil (55x46cm-22x18in) d.19.2.60 verso prov.lit. 7-Nov-2 Christie's, Rockefeller NY #348/R est:300000-400000
£260000 $434200 €390000 Grappe de raisin (27x22cm-11x9in) oil collage sawdust painted 1914 prov.exhib.lit. 23-Jun-3 Sotheby's, London #22/R est:200000-300000
£340000 $567800 €493000 Buste d'homme (97x65cm-38x26in) s.d.28.1.69 cardboard on panel prov.exhib.lit. 25-Jun-3 Christie's, London #205/R est:300000-500000
£400000 $668000 €580000 Le peintre at son modele (81x65cm-32x26in) s. i.d.64 verso prov.lit. 24-Jun-3 Christie's, London #75/R est:250000-350000
£512821 $800000 €769232 Deux bustes de profil (162x130cm-64x51in) d.22.5.72 verso prov.exhib.lit. 5-Nov-2 Sotheby's, New York #50/R est:1000000-1500000
£512821 $800000 €769232 Le peintre et son modele (97x130cm-38x51in) d.15.11.64 prov.exhib.lit. 7-Nov-2 Christie's, Rockefeller NY #337/R est:800000-1200000
£589744 $920000 €884616 Femme reposant (60x73cm-24x29in) s. painted 1940 prov.lit. 5-Nov-2 Sotheby's, New York #52/R est:600000-800000
£737180 $1150000 €1105770 Femme assise a la robe bleue (100x81cm-39x32in) d.13.3.49 verso prov. 5-Nov-2 Sotheby's, New York #41/R est:1500000-2000000
£880000 $1469600 €1276000 Femme assise dans un fauteuil, buste de Jacqueline (116x81cm-46x32in) d.64 prov.lit. 24-Jun-3 Christie's, London #71/R est:600000-800000
£1000000 $1670000 €1450000 L'Arlesienne (72x60cm-28x24in) s. oil ripolin painted 1937 prov.exhib.lit. 24-Jun-3 Christie's, London #69/R est:1000000-1500000
£1025641 $1600000 €1538462 Femme assise dans un fauteuil tresse - en gris (116x89cm-46x35in) d. d.11.12.53 verso prov. 5-Nov-2 Sotheby's, New York #44/R est:1800000-2500000
£1282051 $2000000 €1923077 Le fils de l'artiste en arlequin - Portrait of Paulo (35x27cm-14x11in) s.d.4 Mars 1924 exhib.lit. 5-Nov-2 Sotheby's, New York #61/R est:2000000-3000000
£1550000 $2526500 €2325000 Poireaux (80x130cm-31x51in) s. d.45 verso prov.exhib.lit. 3-Feb-3 Christie's, London #82/R est:2500000
£1600000 $2608000 €2400000 Femme assise dans un fauteuil (130x97cm-51x38in) s. painted 1941 prov.exhib.lit. 3-Feb-3 Christie's, London #80/R est:3000000
£1794872 $2800000 €2692308 Le repos - Marie Therese Walter (27x46cm-11x18in) s. i.d.17 Mai XXXII on stretcher prov.exhib.lit. 6-Nov-2 Christie's, Rockefeller NY #31/R est:2500000-3500000
£1900000 $3173000 €2850000 Courses de Taureaux (46x55cm-18x22in) s. painted Barcelona 1901 prov.exhib.lit. 23-Jun-3 Sotheby's, London #10/R est:1500000-2000000
£2115385 $3300000 €3173078 Mere aux enfants a l'orange (124x97cm-49x38in) d.25.1.51 verso panel prov.exhib.lit. 5-Nov-2 Sotheby's, New York #35/R est:3000000-5000000
£2550000 $4258500 €3825000 Le Baiser (130x96cm-51x38in) s. d.10.12.69.II verso prov.exhib.lit. 23-Jun-3 Sotheby's, London #26/R est:1200000-1800000
£4000000 $6520000 €6000000 Femme dans un fauteuil (92x73cm-36x29in) s.d.XXXII prov.exhib.lit. 3-Feb-3 Christie's, London #72/R est:4000000-6000000
Prints
£1720 $2700 €2580 Lysistrata, le festin (20x15cm-8x6in) s.num.150/37 etching. 23-Nov-2 Jackson's, Cedar Falls #269/R est:2750-3750
£1786 $2821 €2679 Portrait of Vollard II (35x25cm-14x10in) s. etching. 27-Nov-2 Deutscher-Menzies, Melbourne #264/R est:6000-8000 (A.D 5000)
£1887 $3000 €2831 Saltimbanque au repos (12x9cm-5x4in) etching drypoint edition of 250. 29-Apr-3 Christie's, Rockefeller NY #522/R est:4000-6000
£1887 $3000 €2831 Figure (24x14cm-9x6in) s. lithograph. 2-May-3 Sotheby's, New York #256/R est:3000-5000
£1887 $3000 €2831 Portrait d'Arthur Rimbaud (29x24cm-11x9in) s.i. lithograph edition of 104. 2-May-3 Sotheby's, New York #299 est:2500-3500
£1887 $3000 €2831 Peintre et modele (39x56cm-15x22in) s.num.5/50 etching aquatint. 2-May-3 Sotheby's, New York #309 est:2000-3000
£1887 $3000 €2831 Sculpteur et sculpture (38x28cm-15x11in) s.num.XII/XX aquatint. 1-May-3 Swann Galleries, New York #572/R est:4000-6000
£1887 $3000 €2831 Le peintre et la modele (27x38cm-11x15in) s.num.24/50 aquatint. 1-May-3 Swann Galleries, New York #573/R est:4000-6000
£1899 $3000 €2849 Studio (61x49cm-24x19in) s.i.num.6/6 lithograph. 28-Apr-3 Christie's, Rockefeller NY #108/R est:3000-4000
£1899 $3000 €2849 Tropical plants (62x47cm-24x19in) s.i.num.50 lithograph. 28-Apr-3 Christie's, Rockefeller NY #192/R est:1000-1500
£1899 $3000 €2849 Pike (44x59cm-17x23in) s.i.num.50 lithograph. 28-Apr-3 Christie's, Rockefeller NY #203/R est:3000-4000
£1899 $3000 €2849 Embroidered sweater (46x35cm-18x14in) s.i.num.50 lithograph. 28-Apr-3 Christie's, Rockefeller NY #222/R est:1000-1500
£1899 $3000 €2849 Woman's head (54x45cm-21x18in) s.i.num.50 lithograph. 28-Apr-3 Christie's, Rockefeller NY #223/R est:2000-3000
£1899 $3000 €2849 Two models (50x65cm-20x26in) s.i.num.50 lithograph. 28-Apr-3 Christie's, Rockefeller NY #244/R est:1200-1800
£1899 $3000 €2849 Faun and sailor or Mediterranean (14x9cm-6x4in) s.i.num.50 col lithograph. 28-Apr-3 Christie's, Rockefeller NY #274/R est:1000-1500
£1899 $3000 €2849 Flowers (60x46cm-24x18in) s.i.num.100 col lithograph. 28-Apr-3 Christie's, Rockefeller NY #322/R est:1000-1500
£1899 $3000 €2849 Profile of man looking to the left (61x45cm-24x18in) i. lithograph. 28-Apr-3 Christie's, Rockefeller NY #334/R est:2000-3000
£1899 $3000 €2849 Years of graphic works (59x46cm-23x18in) s.num.100 col lithograph. 28-Apr-3 Christie's, Rockefeller NY #348/R est:1800-2200
£1923 $3000 €2885 Buste d'homme (12x9cm-5x4in) drypoint edition of 250. 7-Nov-2 Swann Galleries, New York #768/R est:4000-6000
£1923 $3000 €2885 Femme nue couchee (5x16cm-2x6in) s. col lithograph edition of 1000. 7-Nov-2 Swann Galleries, New York #794/R est:2000-3000
£1923 $3038 €3000 Le repos du sculpteur III (19x27cm-7x11in) s. drypoint etching. 14-Nov-2 Neumeister, Munich #671/R est:3500-3800
£1923 $2981 €3000 Vallauris - 1956 Exhibition (66x54cm-26x21in) s. col linocut. 4-Dec-2 Lempertz, Koln #985/R est:4000

£1923 $2981 €3000 Coquillages et oiseaux (23x33cm-9x13in) s. lithograph. 7-Dec-2 Ketterer, Hamburg #325/R est:3600-3800
£1935 $3058 €3000 Affiche Vallauris (50x65cm-20x26in) s. num.20/50 col lithograph. 19-Dec-2 Delvaux, Paris #6/R
£1962 $3061 €3100 Papiers colles (58x45cm-23x18in) s. num.89/100 eau forte. 14-Sep-2 Meeting Art, Vercelli #200/R
£1963 $3200 €2945 Tete de femme stylisee (44x32cm-17x13in) s. num.22/50 lithograph exec.1945. 13-Feb-3 Christie's, Rockefeller NY #125/R
£1991 $3325 €2887 Femme au divan avec une jeune fille et un vieillard assis (32x22cm-13x9in) s. aquatint etching. 24-Jun-3 Koller, Zurich #474/R est:5000-7500 (S.FR 4400)
£2000 $3120 €3000 Trois mousquetaires saluant une femme au lit (25x32cm-10x13in) s.num.15/50 aquatint. 9-Oct-2 Christie's, London #76/R est:1200-1800
£2000 $3120 €3000 Vieux modele pour jeune odalisque (64x76cm-25x30in) st.sig.num.18/50 etching. 9-Oct-2 Christie's, London #104/R est:1800-2200
£2000 $3120 €3000 Odalisque au collier de chien (64x70cm-25x28in) st.sig.num.18/50 etching. 9-Oct-2 Christie's, London #164/R est:700-1000
£2000 $3120 €3000 Scene champetre, avec barbu couronne de fleurs par un putto, et femmes (31x36cm-12x14in) s.num.5/50 etching. 9-Oct-2 Christie's, London #226/R
£2000 $3100 €3000 Halte de comediens ambulants, avec Hibou, et Bouffon (49x45cm-19x18in) s.num.32/50 etching. 3-Dec-2 Christie's, London #197/R est:2000-3000
£2000 $3100 €3000 Fumeur d'opium (28x34cm-11x13in) s.num.43/50 etching. 3-Dec-2 Christie's, London #209/R est:2000-3000
£2000 $3120 €3000 Peintre et son modele (22x32cm-9x13in) s.num.17/50 aquatint etching. 25-Mar-3 Sotheby's, London #133/R est:1500-2000
£2000 $3120 €3000 Femme vu de dos (40x28cm-16x11in) s.num.XVIII/XXV etching. 25-Mar-3 Sotheby's, London #139/R est:2000-3000
£2000 $3120 €3000 Corrida (49x31cm-19x12in) s.num.17/50 lithograph. 25-Mar-3 Sotheby's, London #143/R est:1000-1500
£2000 $3120 €3000 Peintre et modele (32x47cm-13x19in) s.num.17/50 etching aquatint. 25-Mar-3 Sotheby's, London #145/R est:2000-3000
£2000 $3140 €3000 La celestine, fuite a l'aube (25x32cm-10x13in) s.num.33/50 etching. 17-Apr-3 Christie's, Kensington #309/R est:1500-2000
£2000 $3140 €3000 La celestine, fuite sous la lune (45x52cm-18x20in) s.num.29/50 aquatint. 17-Apr-3 Christie's, Kensington #311/R est:1500-2000
£2000 $3340 €2900 Artist and model (7x10cm-3x4in) s.num.17/50 etching. 30-Jun-3 Bonhams, New Bond Street #398/R est:700-1000
£2000 $3300 €2900 Toros en Vallauris (64x53cm-25x21in) s. blue linocut. 2-Jul-3 Christie's, London #329 est:1500-2500
£2013 $3200 €3020 Deux femmes (39x28cm-15x11in) s.num.44/50 aquatint. 3-Mar-3 Swann Galleries, New York #89/R est:4000-6000
£2013 $3200 €3020 Tete de femme de trois quarts (54x45cm-21x18in) s.num.17/50 lithograph. 29-Apr-3 Christie's, Rockefeller NY #540/R est:4000-5000
£2013 $3200 €3020 Le couple (22x17cm-9x7in) s.num.36/50 etching. 1-May-3 Swann Galleries, New York #558/R est:2000-3000
£2025 $3159 €3200 Toros Vallauris (80x65cm-31x26in) s. num.123/195 lithograph lit. 14-Sep-2 Meeting Art, Vercelli #240/R
£2025 $3200 €3200 Peace and joy (64x50cm-25x20in) s.num.71/200 lithograph. 1-Dec-2 Bukowskis, Helsinki #394/R est:1000-1300
£2025 $3200 €3038 Two small bulls (15x27cm-6x11in) i. lithograph. 28-Apr-3 Christie's, Rockefeller NY #10/R est:2000-3000
£2025 $3200 €3038 Side view of bull (29x42cm-11x17in) i. lithograph. 28-Apr-3 Christie's, Rockefeller NY #23/R est:2000-3000
£2025 $3200 €3038 Knife and the apple (25x27cm-10x11in) i. lithograph. 28-Apr-3 Christie's, Rockefeller NY #69/R est:1000-1500
£2025 $3200 €3038 Still life with glass and flowers (39x55cm-15x22in) s.i.num.6/6 lithograph. 28-Apr-3 Christie's, Rockefeller NY #78/R est:2500-3500
£2025 $3200 €3038 Vase of flowers with floral design carpet (46x58cm-18x23in) i. lithograph. 28-Apr-3 Christie's, Rockefeller NY #92/R est:2000-3000
£2025 $3200 €3038 Flying dove (53x59cm-21x23in) s.i.num.50 lithograph. 28-Apr-3 Christie's, Rockefeller NY #198/R est:2000-3000
£2025 $3200 €3038 Heads and stone (46x59cm-18x23in) s.i.num.50 lithograph. 28-Apr-3 Christie's, Rockefeller NY #201/R est:2000-3000
£2025 $3200 €3038 War and Peace (32x24cm-13x9in) s. lithograph black ochre. 28-Apr-3 Christie's, Rockefeller NY #236/R est:1000-1500
£2025 $3200 €3038 Figure and dove (50x65cm-20x26in) s.i.num.50 lithograph. 28-Apr-3 Christie's, Rockefeller NY #245/R est:1500-2000
£2029 $3328 €2800 Vallauris exhibition 1957 (63x53cm-25x21in) s. linocut. 31-May-3 Villa Grisebach, Berlin #896/R est:2000-2500
£2032 $3150 €3048 Le grand Hibou (72x54cm-28x21in) s.num.16/50 zinkograph. 1-Oct-2 Rasmussen, Copenhagen #137/R est:25000-35000 (D.KR 24000)
£2044 $3250 €3066 Buste d'homme (12x9cm-5x4in) s. drypoint edition of 250. 2-May-3 Sotheby's, New York #252/R est:2000-3000
£2051 $3200 €3077 Peintre et modele aux chevaux longs (39x28cm-15x11in) s.num.XXI/XX aquatint. 19-Sep-2 Swann Galleries, New York #665/R est:3000-5000
£2051 $3200 €3077 Vieil homme pensant a sa jeunesse, garcon sur un cheval et femmes (45x56cm-18x22in) s.num.5/50 etching. 5-Nov-2 Christie's, Rockefeller NY #262/R est:4000-6000
£2051 $3200 €3077 Cirque, ecuyere, femmes et spectateurs, dont un garagiste deguise (48x54cm-19x21in) s.num.22/50 etching. 5-Nov-2 Christie's, Rockefeller NY #273/R est:4000-6000
£2051 $3200 €3077 Caricature du General de Gaulle, et deux femmes (47x57cm-19x22in) s.num.22/50 aquatint drypoint. 5-Nov-2 Christie's, Rockefeller NY #274/R est:4000-6000
£2051 $3200 €3077 Char romain avec vieil athlete, ecuyere, odalisque et spectateur (45x54cm-18x21in) s.num.5/50 etching. 5-Nov-2 Christie's, Rockefeller NY #275/R est:4000-6000
£2051 $3200 €3077 Jeune femme montrant son sexe a deux courtisans (32x25cm-13x10in) s.num.29/50 etching. 5-Nov-2 Christie's, Rockefeller NY #295/R est:4000-6000
£2051 $3200 €3077 Peintre peignant sur son modele (56x64cm-22x25in) s.num.6/50 etching. 5-Nov-2 Christie's, Rockefeller NY #299/R est:4000-6000
£2051 $3200 €3077 Jacqueline, en Maja Nue, avec la celestine et deux mousquetaires (31x36cm-12x14in) s.num.32/50 aquatint. 5-Nov-2 Christie's, Rockefeller NY #301/R est:4000-6000
£2051 $3200 €3077 Couple pensant a une partie a trois (28x36cm-11x14in) s.num.33/50 drypoint. 5-Nov-2 Christie's, Rockefeller NY #302/R est:4000-6000
£2051 $3200 €3077 Deux femmes dont une sur une sellette, un hibou, et Don Quichotte (28x38cm-11x15in) s.num.29/50 etching. 5-Nov-2 Christie's, Rockefeller NY #305/R est:4000-6000
£2051 $3241 €3200 Untitled (28x39cm-11x15in) eau forte exec.1968 lit. 15-Nov-2 Farsetti, Prato #316/R
£2051 $3221 €3200 Danseur (64x53cm-25x21in) s. linocut. 13-Dec-2 Rossini, Paris #123
£2051 $3221 €3200 Bacchanale I (595x415cm-234x163in) s.i. lithograph. 12-Dec-2 Piasa, Paris #106/R
£2051 $3179 €3200 Shakespeare (22x17cm-9x7in) s.d.1965 lithograph. 7-Dec-2 Ketterer, Hamburg #326/R est:3400-3600
£2075 $3300 €3113 Scene d'interieur (21x27cm-8x11in) s. lithograph. 1-May-3 Swann Galleries, New York #549/R est:4000-6000
£2100 $3276 €3150 Femme au lit avec visiteurs en costume du XVIIe siecle (50x65cm-20x26in) st.sig.num.12/50 etching. 9-Oct-2 Christie's, London #168/R est:1000-1500
£2100 $3297 €3150 Gentilhomme et maja (33x25cm-13x10in) s.num.7/50 aquatint drypoint. 17-Apr-3 Christie's, Kensington #312/R est:2000-2500
£2100 $3297 €3150 Ecuyere, enfant, et jongleur avec ses ballons (28x35cm-11x14in) s.num.32/50 aquatint. 17-Apr-3 Christie's, Kensington #315/R est:2000-2500
£2100 $3297 €3150 Raphael et la fornarina V (56x64cm-22x25in) s.num.5/50 etching. 17-Apr-3 Christie's, Kensington #321/R est:2000-2500
£2100 $3465 €3045 Peintre et modele, ecuyere et bonhomme (32x42cm-13x17in) s.num.30/50 etching aquatint. 2-Jul-3 Christie's, London #330/R est:2000-3000
£2113 $3507 €3000 Deux femmes au miroir (38x28cm-15x11in) s.d. aquatint drypoint etching. 14-Jun-3 Hauswedell & Nolte, Hamburg #1527/R est:4000
£2113 $3507 €3000 Nu accoude (38x28cm-15x11in) s.d. aquatint etching. 14-Jun-3 Hauswedell & Nolte, Hamburg #1528/R est:4000
£2113 $3507 €3000 Sculpteur devant sa sellette, avec un spectateur barbu (38x27cm-15x11in) s.d. aquatint etching. 14-Jun-3 Hauswedell & Nolte, Hamburg #1529/R est:4000
£2138 $3400 €3207 Tete at pierre (47x61cm-19x24in) s.num.21/50 lithograph. 1-May-3 Swann Galleries, New York #557/R est:2500-3500
£2147 $3500 €3221 Circus (34x44cm-13x17in) s. drypoint exec.1933 one of 250. 13-Feb-3 Christie's, Rockefeller NY #124/R
£2147 $3500 €3221 Chevre (15x16cm-6x6in) s. num.46/50 etching exec.1952. 13-Feb-3 Christie's, Rockefeller NY #128/R
£2153 $3401 €3100 Exposition Vallauris (100x65cm-39x26in) s. col lithograph. 26-Apr-3 Cornette de St.Cyr, Paris #25/R est:3000-4000
£2158 $3453 €3000 Le bain (34x29cm-13x11in) etching edition of 250. 14-May-3 Blanchet, Paris #32a est:3500-4000
£2174 $3565 €3000 Scene biblique avec bouffon au chapeau (21x27cm-8x11in) s. etching echoppe. 31-May-3 Villa Grisebach, Berlin #306/R est:3500-4500
£2200 $3388 €3300 Autour d'El Greco et de Rembrandt portraits (22x32cm-9x13in) s.num.22/50 aquatint. 24-Oct-2 Christie's, Kensington #304/R est:2800-3200
£2200 $3388 €3300 Polichinelle avec une bicyclette d'acrobate (8x12cm-3x5in) s.num.7/50 etching. 24-Oct-2 Christie's, Kensington #307/R est:2000-3000
£2200 $3388 €3300 Faune et Bacchante, avec combat de faunes dans le Lointain (19x12cm-7x5in) s.num.33/50 etching. 24-Oct-2 Christie's, Kensington #310/R est:2800-3200

£2200 $3388 €3300 Superproduction hollywoodienne, avec spectateurs (21x27cm-8x11in) s.num.22/50 etching drypoint. 24-Oct-2 Christie's, Kensington #361/R est:2800-3200
£2200 $3432 €3300 Orage, enlevement, poursuite (37x47cm-15x19in) s.num.33/50 etching drypoint. 9-Oct-2 Christie's, London #51/R est:2000-3000
£2200 $3432 €3300 Peintre Cul-de-Jatte dans son atelier, avec un modele (38x45cm-15x18in) st.sig.num.12/50 etching. 9-Oct-2 Christie's, London #89/R est:800-1200
£2200 $3432 €3300 La peinture au cirque (33x48cm-13x19in) st.sig.num.12/50 etching. 9-Oct-2 Christie's, London #94/R est:1000-1500
£2200 $3432 €3300 La fete de la patronne, ces dames medisent de Degas (51x66cm-20x26in) st.sig.num.12/50 etching. 9-Oct-2 Christie's, London #129/R est:1200-1800
£2200 $3432 €3300 Degas et deux filles, dont une en cour de transformation en oeuvre d'Art (36x38cm-14x15in) st.sig.num.12/50 etching. 9-Oct-2 Christie's, London #130/R est:700-1000
£2200 $3432 €3300 Degas chez les filles, la note (50x65cm-20x26in) st.sig.num.12/50 etching. 9-Oct-2 Christie's, London #131/R est:1000-1500
£2200 $3432 €3300 Odalisque (33x25cm-13x10in) s.num.31/50 aquatint. 9-Oct-2 Christie's, London #162/R est:2000-3000
£2200 $3432 €3300 Danse du ventre devant homme impassible (41x48cm-16x19in) st.sig.num.18/50 etching. 9-Oct-2 Christie's, London #223/R est:700-1000
£2200 $3432 €3300 Maison close, bavardages, avec perroquet, Celestine et le portrait de Degas (51x65cm-20x26in) st.sig.num.12/50 etching. 9-Oct-2 Christie's, London #233/R est:1500-2500
£2200 $3410 €3300 Char romain monte par un athlete femini (45x54cm-18x21in) s.num.4/40 etching. 3-Dec-2 Christie's, London #186/R est:2800-3200
£2200 $3410 €3300 Don Quichotte rencontrant dulcinee (36x47cm-14x19in) s.num.31/50 aquatint. 3-Dec-2 Christie's, London #191/R est:2800-3200
£2200 $3410 €3300 Homme frise se balanccant (45x54cm-18x21in) s. num.22/50 aquatint. 3-Dec-2 Christie's, London #193/R est:2800-3200
£2200 $3410 €3300 Couple aux champs, avec un putto couronne de fleurs (49x45cm-19x18in) s.num.22/50 etching. 3-Dec-2 Christie's, London #196/R est:2800-3200
£2200 $3410 €3300 Vieillard assis avec femmes, et Danseuse (28x38cm-11x15in) s.num.6/50 etching. 3-Dec-2 Christie's, London #200/R est:2000-3000
£2200 $3410 €3300 Bacchantes et spectateurs, dont un au chapeau Rembranesque (33x45cm-13x18in) s.num.31/50 etching. 3-Dec-2 Christie's, London #202/R est:2000-3000
£2200 $3410 €3300 Jeune femme tirant la moustache d'un gentilhomme (41x33cm-16x13in) s.num.6/50 etching. 3-Dec-2 Christie's, London #206/R est:2800-3200
£2200 $3410 €3300 Celestine, client et petite maja nue sans visage (33x40cm-13x16in) s.num.31/50 aquatint. 3-Dec-2 Christie's, London #218/R est:2800-3200
£2200 $3454 €3300 Vieux peintre, modele et spectateur (32x25cm-13x10in) s.num.5/50 etching. 17-Apr-3 Christie's, Kensington #307/R est:2200-2600
£2200 $3454 €3300 Homme moyenageux au cirque (33x40cm-13x16in) s.num.22/50 etching. 17-Apr-3 Christie's, Kensington #326/R est:1500-2000
£2200 $3630 €3190 La danse des banderilles (50x66cm-20x26in) s.num.11/50 lithograph. 2-Jul-3 Christie's, London #197 est:2000-2500
£2200 $3630 €3190 La jeune artiste 2e etat (39x30cm-15x12in) s.num.38/50 lithograph. 2-Jul-3 Christie's, London #308/R est:2000-3000
£2200 $3630 €3190 Exposition Vallauris (63x53cm-25x21in) s.num.32/175 brown linocut. 2-Jul-3 Christie's, London #331/R est:1500-2500
£2200 $3630 €3190 Peintres aux champs, un dejeuner sur l'herbe impressionniste (21x27cm-8x11in) s.num.43/50 aquatint. 2-Jul-3 Christie's, London #334 est:1000-1500
£2201 $3500 €3302 Les banderilles (47x50cm-19x20in) s.num.27/50 lithograph. 29-Apr-3 Christie's, Rockefeller NY #537/R est:3500-4500
£2201 $3500 €3302 Trois figures se tenant debout (27x21cm-11x8in) drypoint. 1-May-3 Swann Galleries, New York #62/R est:4000-6000
£2215 $3500 €3500 Vieillard asis avec une femme, et danseuse (17x26cm-7x10in) s. etching. 30-Nov-2 Villa Grisebach, Berlin #371/R est:3500-4000
£2215 $3500 €3323 Portrait de poete Gongora, d'apres Velasquez (39x28cm-15x11in) s.i. aquatint. 22-Apr-3 Butterfields, San Francisco #2180/R est:4000-5000
£2215 $3500 €3323 Exposition ceramique - vallauris (64x53cm-25x21in) s.num.129/175 col linocut. 22-Apr-3 Butterfields, San Francisco #2185/R est:2000-3000
£2215 $3500 €3323 Woman's head (34x26cm-13x10in) s.i.num18/50 lithograph. 28-Apr-3 Christie's, Rockefeller NY #1/R est:2000-3000
£2215 $3500 €3323 Bullfight under a black sun (30x41cm-12x16in) i. lithograph. 28-Apr-3 Christie's, Rockefeller NY #21/R est:2000-3000
£2215 $3500 €3323 Owl with white background (63x42cm-25x17in) s.i.num.6/6 lithograph. 28-Apr-3 Christie's, Rockefeller NY #45/R est:4000-6000
£2215 $3500 €3323 Nude pose (54x38cm-21x15in) s.i.num.50 lithograph. 28-Apr-3 Christie's, Rockefeller NY #246/R est:1000-1500
£2215 $3500 €3323 Two nude models (58x37cm-23x15in) s.i.num.50 lithograph. 28-Apr-3 Christie's, Rockefeller NY #247/R est:1200-1800
£2215 $3500 €3323 Nu a la chaise (24x15cm-9x6in) s.i.num/50 col lithograph. 28-Apr-3 Christie's, Rockefeller NY #252/R est:1000-1500
£2215 $3500 €3323 Two squatting woman (43x54cm-17x21in) s.i.num.50 lithograph. 28-Apr-3 Christie's, Rockefeller NY #265/R est:2500-3500
£2215 $3500 €3323 Wounded toreador (36x47cm-14x19in) s.i.num.50 lithograph. 28-Apr-3 Christie's, Rockefeller NY #267/R est:1000-1500
£2215 $3500 €3323 Faun's dance (41x52cm-16x20in) s.i.num.200 lithograph. 28-Apr-3 Christie's, Rockefeller NY #281/R est:1200-1800
£2215 $3500 €3323 Picnic (26x32cm-10x13in) s.i.num.125 lithograph. 28-Apr-3 Christie's, Rockefeller NY #323/R est:500-800
£2215 $3500 €3323 Spanish woman (62x48cm-24x19in) i.num.141 lithograph. 28-Apr-3 Christie's, Rockefeller NY #328/R est:1800-2000
£2215 $3500 €3323 Picasso 1916 to 1961 (37x26cm-15x10in) i. lithograph. 28-Apr-3 Christie's, Rockefeller NY #329/R est:500-800
£2215 $3500 €3323 Head of young woman in profile looking to the right (61x45cm-24x18in) i. lithograph. 28-Apr-3 Christie's, Rockefeller NY #333/R est:2000-3000
£2240 $3405 €3360 L'atelier de l'artiste (22x32cm-9x13in) s.i. etching edition of 50 exhib.lit. 28-Aug-2 Deutscher-Menzies, Melbourne #289/R est:7000-10000 (A.D 6250)
£2244 $3500 €3366 L'atelier de Cannes (46x33cm-18x13in) s.i. lithograph. 19-Sep-2 Swann Galleries, New York #661/R est:5000-8000
£2244 $3500 €3366 Homme accoude et a demi agenouille sur une chaise devant une femme (37x31cm-15x12in) s.num.5/50 etching drypoint. 5-Nov-2 Christie's, Rockefeller NY #303/R est:3000-4000
£2244 $3478 €3500 Picasso - sculptures - dessins (61x52cm-24x20in) s. col lithograph col collotype exec.1958. 6-Dec-2 Ketterer, Munich #182/R est:3500-4500
£2244 $3522 €3500 Scene antique (460x367cm-181x144in) s.i. lithograph. 12-Dec-2 Piasa, Paris #105
£2255 $3518 €3383 Femme au bain (31x22cm-12x9in) s. one of 250 etching executed 1930. 21-Oct-2 Blomqvist, Oslo #502/R est:20000-25000 (N.KR 26000)
£2264 $3600 €3396 Peintre debout a son chevalet, avec une modele (39x28cm-15x11in) s.num.IV/XX aquatint. 3-Mar-3 Swann Galleries, New York #90/R est:3000-5000
£2264 $3600 €3396 Tete de homme au bouc (18x14cm-7x6in) s.num.34/100 etching. 1-May-3 Swann Galleries, New York #575/R est:4000-6000
£2297 $3584 €3400 Le Saltimbanque au repos (12x8cm-5x3in) drypoint etching. 28-Mar-3 Ketterer, Hamburg #563/R est:2200-2500
£2300 $3588 €3450 Le cirque de la vie observe par une petite fille (46x57cm-18x22in) st.sig.num.12/50 etching. 9-Oct-2 Christie's, London #35/R est:1000-1500
£2308 $3600 €3462 Sculpteur, sculpture de femme nue et homme barbu (39x28cm-15x11in) s.num.XII/XX aquatint. 7-Nov-2 Swann Galleries, New York #798/R est:3000-5000
£2308 $3600 €3462 Modele contemplant un groupe sculpte 1933 (29x36cm-11x14in) s. etching executed c.1933. 9-Nov-2 Sloan, North Bethesda #514/R est:4000-6000
£2308 $3577 €3600 Two figures (32x47cm-13x19in) s. eau forte aquatint. 4-Dec-2 Finarte, Milan #147/R
£2308 $3577 €3600 Sculpteur et sculpteur (38x28cm-15x11in) s.d. drypoint etching aquatint. 7-Dec-2 Hauswedell & Nolte, Hamburg #996/R est:3500
£2308 $3577 €3600 Tete d'homme barbu II (37x27cm-15x11in) s.i.d. aquatint etching. 7-Dec-2 Hauswedell & Nolte, Hamburg #997/R est:4000
£2317 $3730 €3476 La Colombe en Vol (54x58cm-21x23in) s.num.15/50 lithograph lit. 7-May-3 AB Stockholms Auktionsverk #1258/R est:20000-30000 (S.KR 30000)
£2358 $3750 €3537 347 series no 219 (14x22cm-6x9in) s.num.47/50 etching. 2-May-3 Sotheby's, New York #317/R est:2000-3000
£2358 $3750 €3537 Don Quichotte et sancho panca I (99x97cm-39x38in) s.d.1951 num.19/50 col lithograph. 30-Apr-3 Doyle, New York #266/R est:2000-3000
£2358 $3750 €3537 Main liees I (117x155cm-46x61in) s.d.1952 num.49/50 lithograph. 30-Apr-3 Doyle, New York #267/R est:1500-2500
£2358 $3750 €3537 347 series No.140 (56x74cm-22x29in) s.d.1968 num.24/50 etching. 30-Apr-3 Doyle, New York #273/R est:3000-4000
£2372 $3700 €3558 Danse des faunes (41x52cm-16x20in) s. col lithograph. 20-Sep-2 Sloan, North Bethesda #307/R est:2000-3000

£2400	$3696	€3600	Duel, avec un spectateur nu (6x11cm-2x4in) s.num.5/50 aquatint. 24-Oct-2 Christie's, Kensington #318/R est:2800-3200
£2400	$3744	€3600	Scene de cirque avec cheval aile, vue par un machiniste (64x70cm-25x28in) st.sig.num.12/50 etching. 9-Oct-2 Christie's, London #33/R est:1800-2200
£2400	$3744	€3600	Caballero a la pipe avec deux femmes, dont une masquee (41x48cm-16x19in) st.sig.num.12/50 etching. 9-Oct-2 Christie's, London #54/R est:1200-1800
£2400	$3744	€3600	La celestine presentant un gentilhomme a une jeune femme (25x32cm-10x13in) s.num.6/50 etching. 9-Oct-2 Christie's, London #70/R est:1000-2000
£2400	$3744	€3600	Celestine, Maja ou Olympia nue, avec Manet et Marcellin Desboutin (37x47cm-15x19in) s.num.6/50 aquatint. 9-Oct-2 Christie's, London #72/R est:1200-1800
£2400	$3744	€3600	Matin, pipe, femme et chocolat (33x40cm-13x16in) s.num.32/50 aquatint. 9-Oct-2 Christie's, London #74/R est:1200-1800
£2400	$3744	€3600	Peinture, autoportait-devinette, avec femme, putto et spectateurs (64x77cm-25x30in) st.sig.num.12/50 etching. 9-Oct-2 Christie's, London #92/R est:1500-2500
£2400	$3744	€3600	Le peintre et la femme (41x48cm-16x19in) st.sig.num.12/50 etching. 9-Oct-2 Christie's, London #95/R est:1000-1500
£2400	$3744	€3600	Fantaisie dans le genre du reve de fussli, avec voyeur sous le lit (45x55cm-18x22in) s.num.10/50 etching drypoint. 9-Oct-2 Christie's, London #114/R est:3000-4000
£2400	$3744	€3600	Vieil homme au chapeau tonkinois songeant (46x54cm-18x21in) s.num.5/50 etching. 9-Oct-2 Christie's, London #225/R est:2800-3200
£2400	$3744	€3600	Grosse prostituee, sorciere a la chouette et voyageur en sabots (28x35cm-11x14in) s.num.5/50 etching. 9-Oct-2 Christie's, London #244/R est:1200-1800
£2400	$3720	€3600	Cape et epee (28x33cm-11x13in) s.num.22/50 aquatint. 3-Dec-2 Christie's, London #189/R est:2800-3200
£2400	$3720	€3600	La celestine presentant ses deux pensionnaire a deux clients (25x32cm-10x13in) s.num.6/50 etching. 3-Dec-2 Christie's, London #190/R est:2800-3200
£2400	$3720	€3600	Ecrivain avec son Egerie (28x35cm-11x14in) s.num.5/50 etching. 3-Dec-2 Christie's, London #215/R est:2000-3000
£2400	$3720	€3600	Artiste peintre peignant une Venus au petit chien (33x40cm-13x16in) s.num.22/50 etching. 3-Dec-2 Christie's, London #216/R est:2000-3000
£2400	$3744	€3600	Scene de theatre (32x47cm-13x19in) s.num.10/50 aquatint. 25-Mar-3 Sotheby's, London #144/R est:1500-2000
£2400	$3768	€3600	Raphael et la fornarina XX (28x35cm-11x14in) s.num.33/50 etching. 17-Apr-3 Christie's, Kensington #325/R est:1500-2000
£2400	$3960	€3480	Le crapaud (51x66cm-20x26in) s. lithograph. 2-Jul-3 Christie's, London #164/R est:2500-3500
£2405	$3800	€3608	Cover project (53x70cm-21x28in) i. lithograph. 28-Apr-3 Christie's, Rockefeller NY #166/R est:1000-1500
£2405	$3800	€3608	Ines and her child (63x75cm-25x30in) s.i.num.6/6 lithograph. 28-Apr-3 Christie's, Rockefeller NY #51/R est:3000-4000
£2405	$3800	€3608	Small nude figure seated at the mirror (31x48cm-12x19in) s.i.num.50 lithograph. 28-Apr-3 Christie's, Rockefeller NY #85/R est:2000-3000
£2405	$3800	€3608	Seated nude in profile (48x60cm-19x24in) s.i.num.6/6 lithograph. 28-Apr-3 Christie's, Rockefeller NY #88/R est:2000-3000
£2405	$3800	€3608	Small pigeon (25x20cm-10x8in) i. lithograph. 28-Apr-3 Christie's, Rockefeller NY #179/R est:600-800
£2405	$3800	€3608	Lord and girl (64x49cm-25x19in) s.i.num.50 lithograph. 28-Apr-3 Christie's, Rockefeller NY #304/R est:1000-1500
£2405	$3800	€3608	Lord and the Dame (22x16cm-9x6in) i. lithograph. 28-Apr-3 Christie's, Rockefeller NY #308/R est:2000-3000
£2405	$3800	€3608	Football (48x62cm-19x24in) s.i.num.200 col lithograph. 28-Apr-3 Christie's, Rockefeller NY #327/R est:1200-1800
£2405	$3800	€3608	Young woman, full face (62x46cm-24x18in) i. lithograph. 28-Apr-3 Christie's, Rockefeller NY #339/R est:4000-6000
£2420	$3800	€3630	Untitled (25x22cm-10x9in) s. etching lithograph. 14-Dec-2 Weschler, Washington #800/R
£2425	$3856	€3638	Raphael et la fornarina XI. s.num.27/50 etching. 29-Apr-3 Kunsthallen, Copenhagen #349/R est:15000 (D.KR 26000)
£2425	$3856	€3638	Figure composition. s.num.27/50 etching. 29-Apr-3 Kunsthallen, Copenhagen #359/R est:15000 (D.KR 26000)
£2436	$3800	€3654	Grosse prostituee et homme au beret Rembranesque (32x25cm-13x10in) s.num.31/50 etching. 5-Nov-2 Christie's, Rockefeller NY #294/R est:4000-6000
£2436	$3824	€3800	Chez les filles: le client (267x210cm-105x83in) s.i. etching. 12-Dec-2 Piasa, Paris #109/R
£2439	$4000	€3537	Portrait of Dora Marr (71x53cm-28x21in) s. lithograph. 1-Jun-3 Wright, Chicago #128/R est:3500-4500
£2452	$3800	€3678	4 Mai (26x40cm-10x16in) s. etching. 25-Sep-2 Christie's, Rockefeller NY #176/R est:2500-3500
£2452	$3800	€3678	Deux femmes (58x44cm-23x17in) s.num.25/50 aquatint. 25-Sep-2 Christie's, Rockefeller NY #180/R est:3500-4500
£2454	$4000	€3681	Modele contemplant (34x45cm-13x18in) s. etching exec.1933 one of 250. 13-Feb-3 Christie's, Rockefeller NY #120/R
£2454	$4000	€3681	Deux hommes sculptes (45x34cm-18x13in) s. etching exec.1933 one of 250. 13-Feb-3 Christie's, Rockefeller NY #117/R
£2465	$4092	€3500	Peintre et modele aux cheveux longs (38x28cm-15x11in) s.d. aquatint etching. 14-Jun-3 Hauswedell & Nolte, Hamburg #1526/R est:4000
£2465	$4092	€3500	Philosophe discourant devant un notable avec femme nue a droite (24x25cm-9x10in) s.num. drypoint. 12-Jun-3 Piasa, Paris #156
£2468	$3900	€3900	Nu a la chaise (24x16cm-9x6in) s.i. col lithograph. 30-Nov-2 Bassenge, Berlin #6573/R est:4200
£2500	$3900	€3750	La fete de la patronne (51x67cm-20x26in) st.sig.num.12/50 etching. 9-Oct-2 Christie's, London #234/R est:1200-1800
£2500	$3900	€3750	Pourvu qu'on ait L'Ivresse (33x25cm-13x10in) s.num.31/50 etching. 9-Oct-2 Christie's, London #246/R est:1800-2200
£2500	$3900	€3750	Sable mouvant (38x28cm-15x11in) s.i. aquatint. 10-Oct-2 Sotheby's, London #76/R est:2000-2500
£2500	$3900	€3750	L'abreuvoir (12x18cm-5x7in) drypoint. 10-Oct-2 Sotheby's, London #80/R est:2000-2500
£2500	$3900	€3750	Untitled from 156 series (36x49cm-14x19in) st.sig.num.47/50 etching. 10-Oct-2 Sotheby's, London #85/R est:1500-2000
£2500	$4125	€3625	La maison tellier, l'arrive des clients (37x49cm-15x19in) st.sig.num.18/50 etching. 2-Jul-3 Christie's, London #190/R est:1000-1500
£2516	$3925	€4000	Affiche Toros Vallauris 1958 (80x65cm-31x26in) s.i.d.1958 num.122/195 col linocut. 11-Oct-2 Winterberg, Heidelberg #1612/R est:4800
£2516	$4000	€3774	Le repos du sculpture III (19x27cm-7x11in) bears sig. etching edition of 250. 29-Apr-3 Christie's, Rockefeller NY #528/R est:6000-8000
£2516	$4000	€3774	Peintre ramassant son pinceau (19x28cm-7x11in) s.num.75/99 etching. 2-May-3 Sotheby's, New York #255/R est:2000-3000
£2516	$4000	€3774	Vertumne poursuit pomone de son amour (31x22cm-12x9in) bears sig. etching. 2-May-3 Sotheby's, New York #258/R est:2000-3000
£2532	$4000	€4000	Deux femmes (38x28cm-15x11in) s. aquatint. 30-Nov-2 Villa Grisebach, Berlin #372/R est:4000-5000
£2532	$4000	€3798	Eight silhouettes (32x44cm-13x17in) s.i.num.50 lithograph. 28-Apr-3 Christie's, Rockefeller NY #25/R est:2500-3500
£2532	$4000	€3798	Bull's return (16x32cm-6x13in) i. lithograph. 28-Apr-3 Christie's, Rockefeller NY #175/R est:1000-1500
£2532	$4000	€3798	Woman's head with chignon (66x50cm-26x20in) s.i.num.50 lithograph. 28-Apr-3 Christie's, Rockefeller NY #224/R est:5000-7000
£2532	$4000	€3798	Cannes studio (48x35cm-19x14in) i.verso col lithograph. 28-Apr-3 Christie's, Rockefeller NY #270/R est:2000-3000
£2532	$4000	€3798	Vase with flowers (64x45cm-25x18in) s.i.num.50 col lithograph. 28-Apr-3 Christie's, Rockefeller NY #293/R est:2000-3000
£2564	$4000	€3846	Sculpteur et sculpture (39x28cm-15x11in) s.num.XIII/XX aquatint. 19-Sep-2 Swann Galleries, New York #667/R est:4000-6000
£2564	$4000	€3846	Deux femmes (39x28cm-15x11in) s.num.5/50 aquatint. 19-Sep-2 Swann Galleries, New York #668/R est:5000-8000
£2564	$4000	€3846	La toilette de la mere (51x33cm-20x13in) etching edition of 250. 5-Nov-2 Christie's, Rockefeller NY #213/R est:5000-7000
£2564	$4000	€3846	Sculpture d'un jeunne homme a la coupe (44x34cm-17x13in) s. etching edition 250. 5-Nov-2 Christie's, Rockefeller NY #225/R est:5000-7000
£2564	$4000	€3846	Homme en gilet afghan songeant aux amours d'un Mousquetaire (45x56cm-18x22in) s.num.22/50 etching. 5-Nov-2 Christie's, Rockefeller NY #266/R est:5000-7000
£2564	$4000	€3846	Homme nu assis en tailleur, et deux femmes (32x25cm-13x10in) s.num.6/50 aquatint drypoint. 5-Nov-2 Christie's, Rockefeller NY #287/R est:4000-6000
£2564	$4000	€3846	Jeune dame espagnole (33x22cm-13x9in) s.num.7/50 etching. 5-Nov-2 Christie's, Rockefeller NY #309/R est:4000-6000
£2564	$4000	€3846	Tetes et figures emmelees (28x20cm-11x8in) s. etching edition of 260. 7-Nov-2 Swann Galleries, New York #779a/R est:1500-2500
£2564	$4000	€3846	Sculpteur (39x28cm-15x11in) s.num.XII/XX aquatint. 7-Nov-2 Swann Galleries, New York #796/R est:3000-5000
£2568	$4005	€3800	Tete de femme: Madeleine (12x9cm-5x4in) drypoint etching. 28-Mar-3 Ketterer, Hamburg #561/R est:3500-4000
£2577	$4200	€3866	Tete de femme (12x9cm-5x4in) etching exec.1913 one of 250. 13-Feb-3 Christie's, Rockefeller NY #114/R
£2600	$4056	€3900	Ecuyeres et Jongleuse (55x71cm-22x28in) s.num.6/50 etching. 9-Oct-2 Christie's, London #26/R
£2600	$4056	€3900	Au cirque, halterophile (25x33cm-10x13in) s.num.30/50 etching. 9-Oct-2 Christie's, London #28/R est:1000-1500
£2600	$4056	€3900	Celestine et fille, avec deux hommes en costume (51x65cm-20x26in) st.sig.num.12/50 etching. 9-Oct-2 Christie's, London #57/R est:1000-1500
£2600	$4056	€3900	Raphael et la fornarina I (46x54cm-18x21in) s.num.33/50 etching. 9-Oct-2 Christie's, London #120/R est:1200-1800

£2600 $4056 €3900 Le cabinet particulier, Degas et une fille (33x25cm-13x10in) s.num.12/50 etching. 9-Oct-2 Christie's, London #123/R est:1000-1500
£2600 $4056 €3900 Degas revant, couple en Charette Sicilienne (51x66cm-20x26in) st.sig.num.12/50 etching. 9-Oct-2 Christie's, London #126/R est:1000-1500
£2600 $4056 €3900 Maison close, repos et bavardages (51x65cm-20x26in) st.sig.num.12/50 etching. 9-Oct-2 Christie's, London #243/R est:1200-1800
£2600 $4030 €3900 Femme faisant la Sieste, entouree de spectateurs (35x42cm-14x17in) s.num.29/50 etching. 3-Dec-2 Christie's, London #192/R est:2800-3200
£2600 $4030 €3900 Raphael et la Fornarina (28x35cm-11x14in) s.num.33/50 etching. 3-Dec-2 Christie's, London #213/R est:2000-3000
£2600 $4290 €3770 Sable mouvant (38x27cm-15x11in) s.num.XX/XX etching aquatint deluxe edition of 20. 1-Jul-3 Sotheby's, London #132/R est:2500-3000
£2600 $4290 €3770 Le peintre et son modele (23x33cm-9x13in) s.num.18/50 etching aquatint. 1-Jul-3 Sotheby's, London #136/R est:2500-3000
£2600 $4290 €3770 Toros en Vallauris (63x53cm-25x21in) s.num.49/185 col linocut. 2-Jul-3 Christie's, London #333/R est:1500-2500
£2602 $4059 €3903 Femme nue assise la tete appuyee sur la main (16x20cm-6x8in) s. one of 300 etching executed 1936. 21-Oct-2 Blomqvist, Oslo #501/R est:35000-45000 (N.KR 30000)
£2628 $4074 €4100 Paysage a Vallauris (51x65cm-20x26in) s.i.d.1953 lithograph. 7-Dec-2 Ketterer, Hamburg #322/R est:4000-5000
£2658 $4200 €4200 Etreinte (32x41cm-13x16in) s. etching aquatint. 30-Nov-2 Bassenge, Berlin #6570/R est:5500
£2658 $4200 €3987 August 8th 1947 composition (32x50cm-13x20in) s.i.num.50 lithograph black ochre. 28-Apr-3 Christie's, Rockefeller NY #93/R est:5000-8000
£2658 $4200 €3987 Big owl (67x54cm-26x21in) s.i.num.6/6 lithograph. 28-Apr-3 Christie's, Rockefeller NY #95/R est:2000-3000
£2658 $4200 €3987 Family (40x27cm-16x11in) s.i.num.50 lithograph. 28-Apr-3 Christie's, Rockefeller NY #226/R est:2000-3000
£2658 $4200 €3987 Troupe of actors (50x66cm-20x26in) s.i.num.50 lithograph. 28-Apr-3 Christie's, Rockefeller NY #241/R est:2000-3000
£2658 $4200 €3987 Two clowns (75x65cm-30x26in) s.i.num.50 lithograph. 28-Apr-3 Christie's, Rockefeller NY #256/R est:1200-1800
£2658 $4200 €3987 Noblewoman (64x49cm-25x19in) s.i.num.50 lithograph. 28-Apr-3 Christie's, Rockefeller NY #305/R est:2000-3000
£2663 $4154 €3995 Maternite (79x60cm-31x24in) s.num.51/200 collotype. 5-Nov-2 Bukowskis, Stockholm #624/R est:35000-40000 (S.KR 38000)
£2671 $4167 €3900 Au cirque (22x14cm-9x6in) drypoint etching. 11-Apr-3 Winterberg, Heidelberg #1487/R est:3800
£2692 $4200 €4038 Autour d'El Greco, portraits avec modele etendu, et bonhomme (38x46cm-15x18in) s.num.22/50 aquatint etching drypoint. 5-Nov-2 Christie's, Rockefeller NY #272/R est:4000-6000
£2692 $4200 €4038 Peintre, ou ecrivain, avec deux femmes (24x32cm-9x13in) s.num.31/50 aquatint. 5-Nov-2 Christie's, Rockefeller NY #291/R est:4000-6000
£2692 $4200 €4038 Repas du sculpteur un centaure 1933 (19x27cm-7x11in) s. etching executed c.1933. 9-Nov-2 Sloan, North Bethesda #515/R est:6000-8000
£2700 $4212 €4050 Portrait de mousquetaire vieillissant, au visage couperose (33x25cm-13x10in) s.num.32/50 etching. 9-Oct-2 Christie's, London #62/R est:2000-3000
£2700 $4212 €4050 Jeune prostitue et mousquetaire (35x28cm-14x11in) s.num.22/50 aquatint etching. 9-Oct-2 Christie's, London #71/R est:2000-3000
£2700 $4212 €4050 Femme aux trois profils (51x65cm-20x26in) st.sig.num.12/50 etching. 9-Oct-2 Christie's, London #169/R est:1200-1800
£2700 $4293 €4050 Les pauvres (23x18cm-9x7in) monochrome etching. 29-Apr-3 Rowley Fine Art, Newmarket #401/R est:2000-3000
£2710 $4200 €4065 Buste h'homme, from la suite des saltimbanques (26x21cm-10x8in) drypoint. 25-Sep-2 Christie's, Rockefeller NY #173/R est:4000-6000
£2754 $4516 €3800 Vallauris Exhibition 1956 (66x54cm-26x21in) s. col linocut. 31-May-3 Villa Grisebach, Berlin #300/R est:3000-4000
£2756 $4300 €4134 Homme devoilant une femme (36x29cm-14x11in) s. etching. 9-Nov-2 Sloan, North Bethesda #517/R est:4000-5000
£2761 $4500 €4142 Faunes et centaures (49x66cm-19x26in) s. num.42/50 lithograph exec.1947. 13-Feb-3 Christie's, Rockefeller NY #126/R
£2767 $4317 €4400 Accouplement I (20x28cm-8x11in) drypoint etching aquatint. 11-Oct-2 Winterberg, Heidelberg #1597/R est:4500
£2780 $4476 €4170 Femme nue assise et trois tetes barbues - Suite Vollard (13x18cm-5x7in) bears sig. etching burin aquatint lit. 7-May-3 AB Stockholms Auktionsverk #1257/R est:30000-40000 (S.KR 36000)
£2800 $4312 €4200 Trois femmes (42x31cm-17x12in) s.num.6/50 etching. 24-Oct-2 Christie's, Kensington #299/R est:3500-4500
£2800 $4368 €4200 Jeune femme et mousquetaire (25x33cm-10x13in) s.num.22/50 aquatint drypoint. 9-Oct-2 Christie's, London #58/R est:1200-1800
£2800 $4368 €4200 Barbu de profil (33x25cm-13x10in) s.num.5/50 etching. 9-Oct-2 Christie's, London #60/R est:1400-1800
£2800 $4368 €4200 La servante, des deux precedents (33x25cm-13x10in) s.num.7/50 etching. 9-Oct-2 Christie's, London #61/R est:1200-1800
£2800 $4368 €4200 Vieux corsaire a la retraite fumant sa pipe (37x32cm-15x13in) s.num.29/50 etching. 9-Oct-2 Christie's, London #63/R est:3500-4500
£2800 $4368 €4200 Vieux beau salutant tres bas un pupille de la celestine (25x33cm-10x13in) s.num.7/50 aquatint. 9-Oct-2 Christie's, London #73/R est:1200-1800
£2800 $4368 €4200 Cavalier en visite chez une fille, avec la celestine et un petit chien (25x33cm-10x13in) s.num.32/50 aquatint. 9-Oct-2 Christie's, London #75/R est:1800-2200
£2800 $4368 €4200 Peintre Rembranesque avec son modele (46x57cm-18x22in) s.num.22/50 etching. 9-Oct-2 Christie's, London #93/R est:2800-3200
£2800 $4368 €4200 Maja a la robe courte (32x25cm-13x10in) s.num.7/50 aquatint. 9-Oct-2 Christie's, London #161/R est:2000-3000
£2800 $4368 €4200 Groupe avec vieillard a la torche sur un ane amoureux (46x63cm-18x25in) s.num.22/50 etching. 9-Oct-2 Christie's, London #227/R est:3500-4500
£2800 $4368 €4200 Homme Rembranesque a la pipe et courtisane (36x28cm-14x11in) s.num.43/50 etching. 9-Oct-2 Christie's, London #229/R est:2000-3000
£2800 $4340 €4200 Jeaun seigneur fantoche avec un Reitre, et deux femmes nues (33x40cm-13x16in) s.num.32/50 etching. 3-Dec-2 Christie's, London #204/R est:3500-4500
£2800 $4340 €4200 Au jardin, Odalisque en Pantoufles au chapeau, avec des fleurs (31x45cm-12x18in) s.num.22/50 etching. 3-Dec-2 Christie's, London #207/R est:3500-4500
£2800 $4340 €4200 Raphael et la Fornarina (28x33cm-11x13in) s.num.22/50 etching. 3-Dec-2 Christie's, London #212/R est:3500-4500
£2800 $4340 €4200 Le Carmen des Carmen (40x30cm-16x12in) s.num.IX/XXX aquatint. 5-Dec-2 Sotheby's, London #173/R est:2000-2500
£2800 $4340 €4200 Le Carmen des Carmen (20x15cm-8x6in) s.num.IX/XXX drypoint. 5-Dec-2 Sotheby's, London #177/R est:1500-2000
£2800 $4396 €4200 Television (47x57cm-19x22in) s.num.22/50 aquatint etching. 17-Apr-3 Christie's, Kensington #305/R est:2800-3200
£2800 $4396 €4200 Ecyere, Bonhomme et mousquetaire (47x56cm-19x22in) s.num.29/50 drypoint aquatint. 17-Apr-3 Christie's, Kensington #306/R est:2800-3200
£2800 $4620 €4060 Au cirque (37x27cm-15x11in) drypoint edition of 250. 1-Jul-3 Sotheby's, London #114/R est:2000-3000
£2803 $4373 €4205 Le repos du sculpteur III (20x27cm-8x11in) s. etching lit. 5-Nov-2 Bukowskis, Stockholm #612/R est:40000-50000 (S.KR 40000)
£2803 $4373 €4205 Neuf tetes (32x23cm-13x9in) st.sig.num.31/50 etching drypoint lit. 5-Nov-2 Bukowskis, Stockholm #614/R est:40000-50000 (S.KR 40000)
£2803 $4373 €4205 Jeune fille aux grands cheveux (38x31cm-15x12in) s.num.25/50 lithograph lit. 5-Nov-2 Bukowskis, Stockholm #615/R est:35000-40000 (S.KR 40000)
£2817 $4676 €4000 Personnage assis et personnage couche (41x52cm-16x20in) s.num. lithograph edition of 50. 12-Jun-3 Piasa, Paris #154
£2817 $4676 €4000 Le torero blesse (36x47cm-14x19in) s.num. lithograph vellum edition of 50. 12-Jun-3 Piasa, Paris #155
£2821 $4400 €4232 La pique I (42x56cm-17x22in) s.num.67/50 lithograph. 7-Nov-2 Swann Galleries, New York #789/R est:4000-6000
£2830 $4500 €4245 Femme au bord de la mer (51x79cm-20x31in) s.d.1924 num.49/50 lithograph. 30-Apr-3 Doyle, New York #262/R est:2000-3000
£2848 $4500 €4272 Tete de femme de trois quarts (54x45cm-21x18in) s.num.15/50 lithograph. 22-Apr-3 Butterfields, San Francisco #2182/R est:5000-7000
£2848 $4500 €4272 Composition with skull (49x65cm-19x26in) i. lithograph. 28-Apr-3 Christie's, Rockefeller NY #30/R est:3000-4000
£2848 $4500 €4272 Centaur and Bacchante (48x55cm-19x22in) s.i.num.6/6 lithograph. 28-Apr-3 Christie's, Rockefeller NY #53/R est:3000-4000
£2848 $4500 €4272 White pigeon on black background (30x48cm-12x19in) s.i.num.65 lithograph. 28-Apr-3 Christie's, Rockefeller NY #56/R est:3000-4000
£2848 $4500 €4272 Young woman with triangle bodice (54x43cm-21x17in) s.i.num.6/6 lithograph. 28-Apr-3 Christie's, Rockefeller NY #90/R est:3000-4000
£2848 $4500 €4272 White bust on black (59x44cm-23x17in) s.num.50 lithograph. 28-Apr-3 Christie's, Rockefeller NY #168/R est:2500-3500

£2848	$4500	€4272	Dove in flight, black background (50x66cm-20x26in) s.i.num.50 lithograph. 28-Apr-3 Christie's, Rockefeller NY #197/R est:2000-3000
£2848	$4500	€4272	Reclining model (22x32cm-9x13in) s.num.25 lithograph. 28-Apr-3 Christie's, Rockefeller NY #235/R est:1500-2000
£2848	$4500	€4272	Tumbler's family (50x65cm-20x26in) s.i.num.50 lithograph. 28-Apr-3 Christie's, Rockefeller NY #240/R est:2000-3000
£2848	$4500	€4272	Clothed pose (55x38cm-22x15in) s.i.num.50 lithograph. 28-Apr-3 Christie's, Rockefeller NY #248/R est:2500-3500
£2848	$4500	€4272	Cannes studio (45x37cm-18x15in) s.i.num.50 lithograph. 28-Apr-3 Christie's, Rockefeller NY #259/R est:1000-1500
£2884	$4500	€4326	Les deux femmes nues (33x45cm-13x18in) s.verso lithograph. 14-Oct-2 Butterfields, San Francisco #1162/R est:6000-8000
£2885	$4500	€4328	Tete de jeune fille (44x32cm-17x13in) i. lithograph. 5-Nov-2 Christie's, Rockefeller NY #238/R est:4000-6000
£2885	$4500	€4328	Peintre au travail avec modele barbu et une spectatrice assise en tailleur (51x55cm-20x22in) bears sig.num.16/40 etching aquatint. 5-Nov-2 Christie's, Rockefeller NY #253/R est:2000-3000
£2885	$4500	€4328	Couple avec un amour, visiteurs, et spectateur (46x52cm-18x20in) s.num.5/50 etching aquatint. 5-Nov-2 Christie's, Rockefeller NY #284/R est:5000-7000
£2885	$4500	€4328	Peintre ou sculpteur pensant a une femme guerriere (35x28cm-14x11in) s.num.22/50 etching. 5-Nov-2 Christie's, Rockefeller NY #298/R est:4000-6000
£2885	$4500	€4328	Portrait d'une bourgeouise hollandaise coiffee d'un beguin (33x25cm-13x10in) s.num.7/50 etching. 5-Nov-2 Christie's, Rockefeller NY #310/R est:4000-6000
£2885	$4471	€4500	Sculpteur au travail (38x28cm-15x11in) s.d. aquatint etching. 7-Dec-2 Hauswedell & Nolte, Hamburg #995/R est:4000
£2945	$4800	€4418	Negre, negre, negre (51x38cm-20x15in) s.i. etching drypoint exec.1950. 13-Feb-3 Christie's, Rockefeller NY #127/R
£2958	$4910	€4200	Corrida (49x32cm-19x13in) s.num. lithograph vellum edition of 50. 12-Jun-3 Piasa, Paris #159
£2958	$4910	€4200	Portrait de famille V (45x59cm-18x23in) s.num. lithograph vellum edition of 50. 12-Jun-3 Piasa, Paris #160
£2972	$4755	€4458	Le repos du sculpteur devant un nu a la draperie (27x19cm-11x7in) s. etching lit. 17-Mar-3 Philippe Schuler, Zurich #4081/R est:7000-9000 (S.FR 6300)
£2987	$4750	€4481	347 series nos 145 and 176 (12x9cm-5x4in) s. one num.45/50 one num.4/50 aquatints pair. 2-May-3 Sotheby's, New York #316/R est:3500-4500
£3000	$4680	€4500	Crapaud (51x66cm-20x26in) lithograph. 9-Oct-2 Christie's, London #6/R est:3000-5000
£3000	$4680	€4500	Combat de gladiateurs, avec spectateurs, et en bas (45x57cm-18x22in) st.sig.num.12/50 etching. 9-Oct-2 Christie's, London #46/R est:1200-1800
£3000	$4680	€4500	Les trois mousquetaires, enlevement (28x34cm-11x13in) s.num.5/50 aquatint. 9-Oct-2 Christie's, London #52/R est:1200-1800
£3000	$4680	€4500	Mise en scene de la celestine (45x52cm-18x20in) s.num.22/50 etching. 9-Oct-2 Christie's, London #55/R est:2000-3000
£3000	$4680	€4500	Peintre et femme cueillant des fleurs (41x48cm-16x19in) st.sig.num.12/50 etching. 9-Oct-2 Christie's, London #97/R est:1200-1800
£3000	$4680	€4500	Les coulisses du tableau, odalisque et peintre (46x57cm-18x22in) st.sig.num.12/50 etching. 9-Oct-2 Christie's, London #103/R est:2000-3000
£3000	$4680	€4500	Maison close, medisances, avec profil de Degas au nez fronce (51x65cm-20x26in) st.sig.num.12/50 aquatint drypoint. 9-Oct-2 Christie's, London #232/R est:1500-2000
£3000	$4680	€4500	Prostituee et marins (35x28cm-14x11in) s.num.22/50 etching. 9-Oct-2 Christie's, London #245/R est:1800-2200
£3000	$4650	€4500	Prostituee et hommes vieillisants (35x28cm-14x11in) s.num.48/50 etching. 3-Dec-2 Christie's, London #194/R est:1200-1800
£3000	$4650	€4500	Danse du ventre dans le desert, avec spectateur bedonnant (28x38cm-11x15in) s.num.30/50 etching. 3-Dec-2 Christie's, London #199/R est:2800-3200
£3000	$4650	€4500	Femme a la fleur sur le transat (31x45cm-12x18in) s.num.6/50 etching. 3-Dec-2 Christie's, London #208/R est:2800-3200
£3000	$4650	€4500	Jeune femme at gentilhomme (33x40cm-13x16in) s.num.32/50 etching. 3-Dec-2 Christie's, London #214/R est:2000-3000
£3000	$4650	€4500	Le Carmen des Carmen (33x23cm-13x9in) s.num.IX/XXX col lithograph. 5-Dec-2 Sotheby's, London #178/R est:1500-2000
£3000	$4680	€4500	347 series - Untitled (22x28cm-9x11in) s.num.31/50 etching. 25-Mar-3 Sotheby's, London #134/R est:2000-2500
£3000	$4710	€4500	Jeune fille, celestine et petit maitre (25x32cm-10x13in) s.num.6/50 etching. 17-Apr-3 Christie's, Kensington #310/R est:1500-2000
£3000	$4950	€4350	Minotaure blesse VI (19x27cm-7x11in) s. etching from edition of50. 2-Jul-3 Christie's, London #157/R est:2500-3500
£3000	$4950	€4350	Peintre avec un modele barbu et une spectatrice (32x41cm-13x16in) s.num.32/50 etching. 2-Jul-3 Christie's, London #167/R est:2500-3500
£3000	$4950	€4350	Sculpteur, modele et deux spectateurs (32x42cm-13x17in) s.num.26/50 etching. 2-Jul-3 Christie's, London #168 est:2500-3500
£3000	$4950	€4350	Le pigeonneau (16x20cm-6x8in) s. brown linocut. 2-Jul-3 Christie's, London #302/R est:2000-3000
£3019	$4679	€4800	La chute d'icare (50x66cm-20x26in) s.num.86/125 engraving drypoint. 30-Oct-2 Artcurial Briest, Paris #545 est:1000-1500
£3038	$4800	€4557	Fat pigeon (38x51cm-15x20in) s.i.num6/6 lithograph. 28-Apr-3 Christie's, Rockefeller NY #57/R est:3000-4000
£3038	$4800	€4557	Bust of a young girl (50x42cm-20x17in) s.i.num.6/6 lithograph. 28-Apr-3 Christie's, Rockefeller NY #58/R est:4000-6000
£3038	$4800	€4557	Centaur dancing, black background (50x66cm-20x26in) s.i.num.6/6 lithograph. 28-Apr-3 Christie's, Rockefeller NY #105/R est:2000-3000
£3043	$4717	€4565	Minotaure vaincu (19x27cm-7x11in) s.i. etching lit. 9-Dec-2 Philippe Schuler, Zurich #3463/R est:8000-10000 (S.FR 7000)
£3045	$4750	€4568	Minotaure caressant une faune 1933 (29x36cm-11x14in) s. etching executed c.1933. 9-Nov-2 Sloan, North Bethesda #512/R est:10000-12000
£3050	$4940	€4300	Les mains liees III (46x61cm-18x24in) s. bears d.25 septembre 1952 lithograph. 24-May-3 Van Ham, Cologne #470/R est:4000
£3057	$4463	€4586	Jeune femme montrant son sexe a deux courtisans grotesques prosternes (19x15cm-7x6in) s. etching lit. 4-Jun-2 Germann, Zurich #446/R est:5000-6000 (S.FR 7000)
£3067	$5000	€4601	Repos du sculpteur (34x44cm-13x17in) s. etching exec.1933 one of 250. 13-Feb-3 Christie's, Rockefeller NY #119/R
£3067	$5000	€4601	Repos du sculpteur (34x44cm-13x17in) s. etching exec.1933 one of 250. 13-Feb-3 Christie's, Rockefeller NY #118/R
£3077	$4800	€4616	Jeune fille, regardee par une vielle femme et deux hommes dont un gitan (45x61cm-18x24in) s.num.22/50 aquatint etching drypoint. 5-Nov-2 Christie's, Rockefeller NY #269/R est:4000-6000
£3077	$4800	€4616	Femme sur un char romain attele a un cheval a demi humain (45x55cm-18x22in) s.num.8/50 etching. 5-Nov-2 Christie's, Rockefeller NY #276/R est:4000-6000
£3077	$4800	€4616	Peintre avec un modele a demi allonge (28x38cm-11x15in) s.num.5/50 aquatint. 5-Nov-2 Christie's, Rockefeller NY #306/R est:4000-6000
£3077	$4800	€4616	Oasis avec flutiste et danseurs (28x38cm-11x15in) s.num.22/50 etching. 5-Nov-2 Christie's, Rockefeller NY #307/R est:4000-6000
£3077	$4862	€4800	Minotaure vaincu (34x44cm-13x17in) s.d. drypoint etching. 14-Nov-2 Neumeister, Munich #672/R est:3800-4000
£3097	$4646	€4646	Toros vallauris (82x65cm-32x26in) s. col linocut. 25-Sep-2 Christie's, Rockefeller NY #181/R est:3500-4500
£3116	$5110	€4300	Le vol de la colombe (54x70cm-21x28in) s. lithograph. 29-May-3 Lempertz, Koln #865/R est:4500
£3125	$4938	€4500	Profil en trois couleurs (65x50cm-26x20in) s.num.4/50 col lithograph. 26-Apr-3 Cornette de St.Cyr, Paris #24/R est:4000-5000
£3145	$4906	€5000	Affiche Vallauris 1956 Exposition (86x66cm-34x26in) s.i. col linocut. 11-Oct-2 Winterberg, Heidelberg #1609/R est:2600
£3145	$5000	€4718	Scene antique (47x37cm-19x15in) s.num.25/50 lithograph. 29-Apr-3 Christie's, Rockefeller NY #543/R est:3000-4000
£3145	$5000	€4718	La colombe volant (56x76cm-22x30in) s.num.45/50 lithograph. 2-May-3 Sotheby's, New York #289/R est:3000-5000
£3145	$5000	€4718	Tete et profil (41x31cm-16x12in) s.num.29/50 aquatint etching. 2-May-3 Sotheby's, New York #302/R est:4000-6000
£3145	$5000	€4718	347 series no 51 (31x39cm-12x15in) s.num.5/50 aquatint etching drypoint. 2-May-3 Sotheby's, New York #312/R est:4000-6000
£3145	$5000	€4718	Magie quotidienne (56x81cm-22x32in) s.d.1968 etching one of 120. 30-Apr-3 Doyle, New York #272/R est:4000-6000
£3165	$5000	€4748	Woman with monkey (25x32cm-10x13in) s.i.num.25 lithograph. 28-Apr-3 Christie's, Rockefeller NY #234/R est:2000-3000
£3165	$5000	€4748	Diurnes (39x30cm-15x12in) s. num.3/100 linocut ochre brown executed c.1962. 12-Nov-2 Doyle, New York #327/R est:4000-6000
£3165	$5000	€4748	Black pitcher and the death's head (32x44cm-13x17in) s.num.50 lithograph. 28-Apr-3 Christie's, Rockefeller NY #29/R est:3000-4000
£3165	$5000	€4748	Composition (64x50cm-25x20in) s.i.num.6/6 lithograph. 28-Apr-3 Christie's, Rockefeller NY #110/R est:3000-5000
£3165	$5000	€4748	Profiles study (74x55cm-29x22in) s.i.num.6/6 lithograph. 28-Apr-3 Christie's, Rockefeller NY #115/R est:2000-3000
£3165	$5000	€4748	Flight of the dove (52x68cm-20x27in) s.i.num.50 lithograph. 28-Apr-3 Christie's, Rockefeller NY #199/R est:2000-3000
£3165	$5000	€4748	Three women and the Toreador (50x65cm-20x26in) s.i.num.50 lithograph. 28-Apr-3 Christie's, Rockefeller NY #242/R est:3000-4000
£3165	$5000	€4748	Painter and his model (49x65cm-19x26in) i. lithograph in greys olive black. 28-Apr-3 Christie's, Rockefeller NY #254/R est:5000-7000
£3165	$5000	€4748	Jacqueline's portrait (52x39cm-20x15in) s. col offset lithograph. 28-Apr-3 Christie's, Rockefeller NY #279/R est:6000-8000

£3200 $4992 €4800 Personnages masques et femme oiseau (34x45cm-13x18in) s. etching aquatint edition of 260. 9-Oct-2 Christie's, London #11/R est:3000-5000
£3200 $4992 €4800 Char Romain, avec ecuyere tombant, femme nue et spectateurs (48x57cm-19x22in) s.num.22/50 etching. 9-Oct-2 Christie's, London #30/R est:3500-4500
£3200 $4992 €4800 Autoportrait dedouble, Maja au pigeon (38x49cm-15x19in) st.sig.num.12/50 etching. 9-Oct-2 Christie's, London #41/R est:1800-2200
£3200 $4992 €4800 Vieux saltimbanque arrivant, avec sa roue cassee (32x40cm-13x16in) s.num.33/50 etching. 9-Oct-2 Christie's, London #44/R est:3000-5000
£3200 $4992 €4800 Spectacle de gladiateurs (48x57cm-19x22in) s.num.22/50 etching. 9-Oct-2 Christie's, London #45/R est:2000-3000
£3200 $4992 €4800 Client bedonnant chez la celestine (35x42cm-14x17in) s.num.30/50 etching. 9-Oct-2 Christie's, London #56/R est:2000-3000
£3200 $4992 €4800 Barbu au chapeau orne d'un grelot (32x25cm-13x10in) s.num.29/50 etching. 9-Oct-2 Christie's, London #64/R est:1800-2200
£3200 $4992 €4800 Artiste peintre au travail, avec un modele laid (36x28cm-14x11in) s.num.31/50 etching. 9-Oct-2 Christie's, London #98/R est:2000-3000
£3200 $4992 €4800 Raphael et la fornarina IX, le pape arrive (28x35cm-11x14in) s.num.5/50 etching. 9-Oct-2 Christie's, London #121/R est:1800-2200
£3200 $4992 €4800 Tete de femme (67x51cm-26x20in) lithograph. 9-Oct-2 Christie's, London #172/R est:2000-3000
£3200 $4992 €4800 Deux grosses femmes nues et un voyeur (28x35cm-11x14in) s.num.33/50 etching. 9-Oct-2 Christie's, London #222/R est:1800-2200
£3200 $4992 €4800 Homme Rembranesque assis chez les filles (28x35cm-11x14in) s.num.29/50 aquatint. 9-Oct-2 Christie's, London #230/R est:1800-2200
£3200 $4960 €4800 Peintre barbu en robe de chambre, avec deux femmes nues et un visteur (28x38cm-11x15in) s.num.22/50 aquatint. 3-Dec-2 Christie's, London #198/R est:2800-3200
£3200 $5024 €4800 Raphael et la fornarina VII (44x65cm-17x26in) s.num.5/50 etching. 17-Apr-3 Christie's, Kensington #322/R est:3000-4000
£3200 $5280 €4640 Sable mouvant (37x27cm-15x11in) s.num.XX/XX etching aquatint deluxe edition of 20. 1-Jul-3 Sotheby's, London #125/R est:2500-3000
£3200 $5280 €4640 Venus foraine (31x42cm-12x17in) s.num.27/50 etching drypoint. 2-Jul-3 Christie's, London #171/R est:3500-4500
£3200 $5280 €4640 Peintre au fauteuil, modele et spectatrice (23x33cm-9x13in) s.num.33/50 etching. 2-Jul-3 Christie's, London #326/R est:2500-3500
£3200 $5280 €4640 Venus foraine (32x42cm-13x17in) s.num.6/50 etching drypoint. 2-Jul-3 Christie's, London #328/R est:2000-3000
£3205 $5000 €4808 Minotaure contemplant une formeuse (41x53cm-16x21in) s. etching. 5-Nov-2 Christie's, Rockefeller NY #235/R est:6000-8000
£3205 $5000 €4808 Groupe avec femme a l'agneau, odalisque-ecuyere et autoportrait (45x63cm-18x25in) s.num.5/50 etching. 5-Nov-2 Christie's, Rockefeller NY #256/R est:5000-7000
£3205 $5000 €4808 Sur la plage, femme au miroir et deux baigneurs (56x65cm-22x26in) s.num.6/50 etching. 5-Nov-2 Christie's, Rockefeller NY #296/R est:4000-6000
£3205 $5000 €4808 Raphael et la fornarina, XIX, Pape sur son pot, avec tiare et manchon (28x35cm-11x14in) s.num.32/50 etching. 5-Nov-2 Christie's, Rockefeller NY #317/R est:4000-6000
£3205 $5000 €4808 Television, quaker, peau-rouge, ecuyere (32x40cm-13x16in) s.num.22/50 etching. 5-Nov-2 Christie's, Rockefeller NY #321/R est:5000-6000
£3205 $5064 €5000 Le repos du sculpteur devant un centaure et une femme (19x27cm-7x11in) s. drypoint etching. 14-Nov-2 Neumeister, Munich #670/R est:3800-4000
£3205 $4968 €5000 Couple (37x47cm-15x19in) s.d.68 num.36/70 etching. 6-Dec-2 Ketterer, Munich #140/R est:5000-6000
£3205 $4968 €5000 Tete de femme au beret, de profil (10x7cm-4x3in) s.num.7/150 dry point exec.1938 lit. 7-Dec-2 De Vuyst, Lokeren #554/R est:5500-6500
£3205 $4968 €5000 Rembrandt et femme au voile (28x19cm-11x7in) s. etching. 7-Dec-2 Hauswedell & Nolte, Hamburg #992/R est:6000
£3224 $5029 €4836 Bacchanale (47x56cm-19x22in) s.num.241/300 col aquatint c.1959. 5-Nov-2 Bukowskis, Stockholm #623/R est:40000-50000 (S.KR 46000)
£3239 $5377 €4600 Bacchanale (42x61cm-17x24in) s.num. lithograph edition of 50. 12-Jun-3 Piasa, Paris #157/R
£3243 $5059 €4800 Au cirque (22x14cm-9x6in) drypoint etching. 28-Mar-3 Ketterer, Hamburg #562/R est:2200-2500
£3354 $5500 €4863 Plate from the Vollard suite (28x18cm-11x7in) s. etching. 1-Jun-3 Wright, Chicago #127/R est:7000-9000
£3400 $5304 €5100 Femme en enfant sur un char romain avec une ecuyere acrobate (45x54cm-18x21in) s.num.33/50 drypoint. 9-Oct-2 Christie's, London #31/R est:2800-3200
£3400 $5304 €5100 Sculpteur, modele et sculpture assise (44x34cm-17x13in) s. etching from edition of 260. 9-Oct-2 Christie's, London #105/R est:3000-5000
£3400 $5304 €5100 Raphael et la fornarina XXXIV, avec voyeur au chapeau a deux cornes (28x35cm-11x14in) s.num.43/50 etching. 9-Oct-2 Christie's, London #122/R est:2800-3200
£3400 $5304 €5100 Degas aux bottines a elastiques et deux filles (50x65cm-20x26in) st.sig.num.12/50 etching. 9-Oct-2 Christie's, London #127/R est:1200-1800
£3400 $5304 €5100 Le trefle a quatre feuilles (64x77cm-25x30in) st.sig.num.12/50 etching. 9-Oct-2 Christie's, London #239/R est:800-1200
£3400 $5304 €5100 Toros en vallauris (65x52cm-26x20in) s.num.157/200 col linocut. 25-Mar-3 Sotheby's, London #141/R est:1500-2000
£3400 $5610 €4930 Peintre a son chevalet avec un modele (32x46cm-13x18in) s.num.18/50 drypoint aquatint. 2-Jul-3 Christie's, London #170/R est:2500-3500
£3459 $5500 €5189 Ropos de sculpteur (76x94cm-30x37in) d.1933 etching one of 300. 30-Apr-3 Doyle, New York #263/R est:2500-3500
£3475 $5595 €5213 Peintre et Modele tricontant (19x28cm-7x11in) s.num.99/99 etching lit. 7-May-3 AB Stockholms Auktionsverk #1256/R est:45000-50000 (S.KR 45000)
£3481 $5500 €5500 Jeune sculpteur grec avec sa sculpture: un homme et un ephebe (27x19cm-11x7in) s. etching. 30-Nov-2 Villa Grisebach, Berlin #375/R est:5000-7000
£3481 $5500 €5222 Owl in crayon (63x47cm-25x19in) s.i.num6/6 lithograph. 28-Apr-3 Christie's, Rockefeller NY #49/R est:4000-6000
£3481 $5500 €5222 Profile of a woman (54x30cm-21x12in) s.i.num.50 lithograph. 28-Apr-3 Christie's, Rockefeller NY #73/R est:3000-4000
£3481 $5500 €5222 Dove in flight (55x70cm-22x28in) s.i.num.50 lithograph. 28-Apr-3 Christie's, Rockefeller NY #200/R est:2000-3000
£3481 $5500 €5222 Jacqueline in profile (63x42cm-25x17in) s.i.num.50 lithograph. 28-Apr-3 Christie's, Rockefeller NY #284/R est:4000-6000
£3481 $5500 €5222 Bullfight (46x61cm-18x24in) s.i.num.50 col lithograph. 28-Apr-3 Christie's, Rockefeller NY #291/R est:1000-1500
£3498 $5527 €5247 Le verre sous la lampe (35x27cm-14x11in) s.num.7/50 col linocut prov.lit. 28-Apr-3 Bukowskis, Stockholm #499/R est:50000-60000 (S.KR 46000)
£3498 $5527 €5247 From - Series 347:75 (41x50cm-16x20in) s.num.31/50 etching lit. 28-Apr-3 Bukowskis, Stockholm #503/R est:35000-40000 (S.KR 46000)
£3500 $5460 €5250 Theatre ou television, cape et epee (46x52cm-18x20in) s.num.22/50 aquatint drypoint. 9-Oct-2 Christie's, London #49/R est:2800-3200
£3500 $5460 €5250 Celestine et fille, avec un chat et un jeune client (25x32cm-10x13in) s.num.5/50 aquatint. 9-Oct-2 Christie's, London #69/R est:2000-3000
£3500 $5460 €5250 Rembrandt et tetes de femme (50x38cm-20x15in) s. etching. 10-Oct-2 Sotheby's, London #77/R est:3000-4000
£3500 $5460 €5250 Tete de garcon (63x44cm-25x17in) s.num.17/50 linocut. 25-Mar-3 Sotheby's, London #140/R est:2500-3000
£3500 $5495 €5250 Echange de regards (28x34cm-11x13in) s.num.33/50 etching. 17-Apr-3 Christie's, Kensington #314/R est:1500-2000
£3526 $5500 €5289 Minotaure attaquant une amazone (34x45cm-13x18in) s. etching edition of 250. 5-Nov-2 Christie's, Rockefeller NY #230/R est:6000-8000
£3526 $5500 €5289 Odalisques avec deux hommes revant (58x45cm-23x18in) s.num.22/50 etching. 5-Nov-2 Christie's, Rockefeller NY #258/R est:5000-7000
£3526 $5500 €5289 Homme dans un fauteuil a boules et balustres songeant a l'amour (45x57cm-18x22in) s.num.22/50 etching. 5-Nov-2 Christie's, Rockefeller NY #265/R est:5000-8000
£3526 $5500 €5289 Television, course de chars a l'antique (45x56cm-18x22in) s.num.33/50 etching. 5-Nov-2 Christie's, Rockefeller NY #271/R est:3000-4000
£3526 $5500 €5289 En pensant a Goya, femmes en prison (47x56cm-19x22in) s.num.22/50 aquatint. 5-Nov-2 Christie's, Rockefeller NY #300/R est:6000-8000
£3526 $5500 €5289 Souvenirs d'enfance, fete de rue, avec bonhomme et el gigante (35x42cm-14x17in) s.num.29/50 aquatint. 5-Nov-2 Christie's, Rockefeller NY #289/R est:6000-8000
£3526 $5500 €5289 Vieux peintre Rembranesque peignant des bacchantes (33x45cm-13x18in) s.num.33/50 aquatint drypoint. 5-Nov-2 Christie's, Rockefeller NY #308/R est:4000-6000

£3526 $5500 €5289 Arbre dans la tempete, avec fuite vers une eglise (31x45cm-12x18in) s.num.22/50 aquatint drypoint. 5-Nov-2 Christie's, Rockefeller NY #311/R est:5000-7000

£3526 $5500 €5289 Artiste peintre avec un modele qui boude (36x47cm-14x19in) s.num.43/50 etching drypoint. 5-Nov-2 Christie's, Rockefeller NY #322/R est:4000-6000

£3526 $5500 €5289 Les coulisses du tableau, odalisque et peintre (45x57cm-18x22in) st.sig.num.25/50 etching drypoint. 5-Nov-2 Christie's, Rockefeller NY #323/R est:4000-6000

£3548 $5500 €5322 Jacqueline au bandeau (56x44cm-22x17in) s.num.33/50 col linocut. 25-Sep-2 Christie's, Rockefeller NY #179/R est:4000-6000

£3574 $5647 €5361 Tete de femme (31x24cm-12x9in) s.num.40/50 lithograph lit. 28-Apr-3 Bukowskis, Stockholm #489/R est:40000-50000 (S.KR 47000)

£3597 $5755 €5000 La toilette de la mere (23x18cm-9x7in) etching grattoir vellum edition of 250. 14-May-3 Blanchet, Paris #32/R est:5000-6000

£3600 $5544 €5400 Theatre autour de Rembrandt (29x35cm-11x14in) s.num.22/50 aquatint. 24-Oct-2 Christie's, Kensington #317/R est:4000-6000

£3600 $5616 €5400 Celestine, maja et deux gentilshommes (28x36cm-11x14in) s.num.22/50 aquatint. 9-Oct-2 Christie's, London #67/R est:3000-4000

£3600 $5616 €5400 Peintres aux champs, autour du XIXe siecle et de courbet (32x40cm-13x16in) s.num.29/50 aquatint. 9-Oct-2 Christie's, London #118/R est:2000-3000

£3600 $5616 €5400 Jeune femme laissant tomber sa robe (35x29cm-14x11in) s.num.22/50 aquatint. 9-Oct-2 Christie's, London #163/R est:1200-1800

£3600 $5580 €5400 Quatre hommes nus assis (32x26cm-13x10in) s. etching. 5-Dec-2 Sotheby's, London #174/R est:4000-6000

£3600 $5940 €5220 Deux femmes nues dans un arbre (38x30cm-15x12in) s.num.19/100 etching. 2-Jul-3 Christie's, London #161/R est:3000-5000

£3600 $5940 €5220 Sculpteur, modele et deux spectateurs (32x72cm-13x28in) s.num.43/50 etching. 2-Jul-3 Christie's, London #324/R est:2500-3500

£3644 $5685 €5466 Paloma (40x32cm-16x13in) s.num.27/50 lithograph 1948 lit. 6-Nov-2 AB Stockholms Auktionsverk #1042/R est:45000-50000 (S.KR 52000)

£3650 $5767 €5475 Mere et enfants (26x31cm-10x12in) s.num.6/50 etching aquatint lit. 28-Apr-3 Bukowskis, Stockholm #493/R est:40000-50000 (S.KR 48000)

£3671 $5800 €5800 Dans l'arene. Jeune homme achevant le minotaure (19x27cm-7x11in) s. etching. 30-Nov-2 Villa Grisebach, Berlin #378/R est:5000-7000

£3681 $6000 €5522 Minotaure caressant une femme (30x37cm-12x15in) s. etching exec.1933. 13-Feb-3 Christie's, Rockefeller NY #122/R

£3681 $6000 €5522 Diurnes (55x43cm-22x17in) s. col linocut exec.1962. 13-Feb-3 Christie's, Rockefeller NY #130/R

£3681 $6000 €5522 Mousquetaire (9x12cm-4x5in) s. aquatint pair. 13-Feb-3 Christie's, Rockefeller NY #152/R

£3718 $5800 €5577 Portrait d'un jeune homme a la coupe (37x30cm-15x12in) s. etching edition of 260. 18-Sep-2 Swann Galleries, New York #44/R est:7000-10000

£3774 $6000 €5661 Jeux de pages (32x42cm-13x17in) s.num.28/50 lithograph. 29-Apr-3 Christie's, Rockefeller NY #539/R est:3000-4000

£3774 $6000 €5661 347 series no 40 (22x32cm-9x13in) s.num.5/50 aquatint etching drypoint. 2-May-3 Sotheby's, New York #311/R est:4000-6000

£3774 $6000 €5661 156 series no 117 (37x49cm-15x19in) st.sig.i. drypoint scraper. 2-May-3 Sotheby's, New York #321 est:2000-3000

£3774 $6000 €5661 Sculpteurs, modeles at sclpturs (19x27cm-7x11in) s. etching. 1-May-3 Swann Galleries, New York #551/R est:8000-12000

£3774 $6000 €5661 Deux modeles se regardant (28x20cm-11x8in) s. etching. 1-May-3 Swann Galleries, New York #556/R est:8000-12000

£3774 $6000 €5661 Blues de Barcelone (58x84cm-23x33in) s.i.d.1963 etching aquatint. 30-Apr-3 Doyle, New York #271/R est:5000-7000

£3797 $6000 €6000 Sculpteur et son modele avec un groupe sculpte (20x27cm-8x11in) s. etching. 30-Nov-2 Villa Grisebach, Berlin #377/R est:5000-7000

£3797 $6000 €5696 Head of a young boy (32x24cm-13x9in) s.i.num 50 lithograph set of two. 28-Apr-3 Christie's, Rockefeller NY #8/R est:6000-10000

£3797 $6000 €5696 Page of bulls (32x44cm-13x17in) s. lithograph. 28-Apr-3 Christie's, Rockefeller NY #24/R est:3000-4000

£3797 $6000 €5696 Still life with fruit dish (47x61cm-19x24in) s.i.num.50 lithograph. 28-Apr-3 Christie's, Rockefeller NY #64/R est:5000-7000

£3797 $6000 €5696 Large profile (61x43cm-24x17in) s.i.num.6/6 lithograph. 28-Apr-3 Christie's, Rockefeller NY #76/R est:4000-6000

£3797 $6000 €5696 Woman on the beach (48x65cm-19x26in) s.i.num6/6 lithograph. 28-Apr-3 Christie's, Rockefeller NY #86/R est:2000-3000

£3797 $6000 €5696 Model and two figures (50x72cm-20x28in) s.i.num.50 lithograph. 28-Apr-3 Christie's, Rockefeller NY #249/R est:1200-1800

£3797 $6000 €5696 Painter and his model (50x64cm-20x25in) s.i.num.50 col lithograph. 28-Apr-3 Christie's, Rockefeller NY #253/R est:5000-7000

£3797 $6000 €5696 Three color profile (49x30cm-19x12in) s.i.num.50 col lithograph two. 28-Apr-3 Christie's, Rockefeller NY #278/R est:4000-6000

£3797 $6000 €5696 Picador II (21x27cm-8x11in) s.i.num.50 col lithograph two. 28-Apr-3 Christie's, Rockefeller NY #321/R est:2000-3000

£3800 $5928 €5700 Au cirque, acrobates, girafe, nageuses (46x57cm-18x22in) s.num.22/50 etching. 9-Oct-2 Christie's, London #25/R est:4000-6000

£3800 $5928 €5700 Autoportrait a la Canne, avec comedien en costume (61x50cm-24x20in) s.num.22/50 etching. 9-Oct-2 Christie's, London #29/R est:3500-4500

£3800 $5928 €5700 Homme allonge, avec deux femmes (55x43cm-22x17in) s.num.5/50 etching. 9-Oct-2 Christie's, London #40/R est:2800-3200

£3800 $5928 €5700 Peintre longiline avec des femmes, dont une petite pisseuse (57x65cm-22x26in) s.num.6/50 etching. 9-Oct-2 Christie's, London #99/R est:2800-3200

£3800 $5928 €5700 Le deux modeles nus (58x37cm-23x15in) s. lithograph. 9-Oct-2 Christie's, London #106/R est:3500-4500

£3800 $5928 €5700 Peintre en costume Espagnol peignant sur son modele (58x46cm-23x18in) s.num.6/50 etching. 9-Oct-2 Christie's, London #107/R est:4000-6000

£3800 $5928 €5700 Plaisanterie autour du bain turc, jeux, musique, et gateaux (51x65cm-20x26in) st.sig.num.12/50 etching. 9-Oct-2 Christie's, London #116/R est:1800-2200

£3800 $5928 €5700 La patronne faiseuse d'Anges, avec trois filles (50x65cm-20x26in) st.sig.num.12/50 etching. 9-Oct-2 Christie's, London #128/R est:1500-2500

£3800 $5966 €5700 Modele contemplant un groupe sculpte (34x44cm-13x17in) s. etching. 17-Apr-3 Christie's, Kensington #302/R est:4000-6000

£3800 $6270 €5510 Les deux Saltimbanques (12x9cm-5x4in) indis.sig. by another hand drypoint edition of 250. 1-Jul-3 Sotheby's, London #116/R est:3500-4500

£3800 $6270 €5510 Toros en vallauris (65x52cm-26x20in) s. col linocut edition of 100. 1-Jul-3 Sotheby's, London #128/R est:2000-3000

£3800 $6270 €5510 Homme frise se balancant, avec Odalisques, putto et Espagnol de profil (28x38cm-11x15in) s.num.26/50 aquatint. 2-Jul-3 Christie's, London #174/R est:4000-6000

£3800 $6270 €5510 Peintre neo-classique dans son atelier (42x57cm-17x22in) s.num.6/50 etching. 2-Jul-3 Christie's, London #325/R est:2800-3200

£3800 $6270 €5510 Toros Vallauris (65x53cm-26x21in) s.num.27/195 col linocut. 2-Jul-3 Christie's, London #332/R est:3000-5000

£3804 $6200 €5706 Trois graces (32x20cm-13x8in) s. num.100/100 etching. 13-Feb-3 Christie's, Rockefeller NY #115/R

£3819 $6035 €5500 Avant la pique (34x48cm-13x19in) s.num.42/50 linoleum. 26-Apr-3 Cornette de St.Cyr, Paris #28/R est:5000-6000

£3846 $6000 €5769 Modele et grande sculpture (45x34cm-18x13in) s. etching edition of 250. 5-Nov-2 Christie's, Rockefeller NY #226/R est:7000-9000

£3846 $6000 €5769 Patron et sa suite en visite a l'atelier du vieux peintre (36x47cm-14x19in) s.num.22/50 aquatint drypoint. 5-Nov-2 Christie's, Rockefeller NY #285/R est:5000-7000

£3846 $6000 €5769 Raphael et la fornarina, VIII, le Pape entre avec un sourire patelin (28x35cm-11x14in) s.num.33/50 etching. 5-Nov-2 Christie's, Rockefeller NY #314/R est:4000-6000

£3846 $6000 €5769 Raphael et la fornarina, X, le Pape a fait apporter son fauteuil (28x35cm-11x14in) s.num.31/50 etching. 5-Nov-2 Christie's, Rockefeller NY #315/R est:4000-6000

£3846 $6000 €5769 Le repos du sculpteur devant un nu a la draperie (27x20cm-11x8in) s. etching edition of 260. 7-Nov-2 Swann Galleries, New York #775/R est:8000-12000

£3846 $6000 €5769 Feuille d'etudes, trois profils de Marie Therese (28x20cm-11x8in) s. etching drypoint. 7-Nov-2 Swann Galleries, New York #777/R est:8000-12000

£3846 $6000 €5769 Picador II (20x26cm-8x10in) s.num.8/50 col lithograph. 7-Nov-2 Swann Galleries, New York #793/R est:8000-12000

£3861 $6216 €5792 La Colombe en Vol (51x70cm-20x28in) s.num.15/50 lithograph lit. 7-May-3 AB Stockholms Auktionsverk #1259/R est:40000-50000 (S.KR 50000)

£3871 $6000 €5807 Tete de femme (30x25cm-12x10in) dry point engraving. 2-Nov-2 North East Auctions, Portsmouth #110/R est:4000-6000

£3873 $6430 €5500 Peintre en costume Espagnol peignant sur son modele (42x31cm-17x12in) s.num. etching vellum edition of 75. 12-Jun-3 Piasa, Paris #152

£3913 $6065 €5870 Sculpteur et trois danseuses sculptees (22x31cm-9x12in) s. etching. 4-Dec-2 Koller, Zurich #399/R est:4000-5000 (S.FR 9000)

£3924 $6200 €6200 Vieux sculpteur et modele assoupi avec un group sculpte (19x26cm-7x10in) s. etching. 30-Nov-2 Villa Grisebach, Berlin #379/R est:5000-7000

£3974 $6240 €6200 Etreinte IV (346x424cm-136x167in) s.i. etching. 12-Dec-2 Piasa, Paris #113
£3988 $6500 €5982 Trois femmes nues pres d'une fenetre (45x34cm-18x13in) s. etching exec.1933 one of 250. 13-Feb-3 Christie's, Rockefeller NY #121/R
£3988 $6500 €5982 Calixte et Melibee (20x26cm-8x10in) s. etching two. 13-Feb-3 Christie's, Rockefeller NY #140/R
£3988 $6500 €5982 Maja et Celestine (21x15cm-8x6in) s.num.5/50 aquatint etching pair. 13-Feb-3 Christie's, Rockefeller NY #139/R
£3988 $6500 €5982 Celestine (9x12cm-4x5in) s. aquatint etching pair. 13-Feb-3 Christie's, Rockefeller NY #138/R
£3988 $6500 €5982 Jeune prostituee et vieillard (8x6cm-3x2in) s.num.7/50 etching pair. 13-Feb-3 Christie's, Rockefeller NY #151/R
£3988 $6500 €5982 Gros homme (21x27cm-8x11in) s. etching aquatint two. 13-Feb-3 Christie's, Rockefeller NY #155/R
£4000 $6240 €6000 Gamin se glissant dans un hammam un jour reserve aux femmes (63x80cm-25x31in) s.num.5/50 etching. 9-Oct-2 Christie's, London #240/R est:2800-3200
£4000 $6200 €6000 Collation en musique chez la celestine (45x56cm-18x22in) s.num.5/50 etching. 3-Dec-2 Christie's, London #187/R est:3500-4500
£4000 $6200 €6000 Jeune femme au chapeau pechant par pensee en louchant sur un prelat (45x56cm-18x22in) s.num.33/50 etching. 3-Dec-2 Christie's, London #188/R est:3500-4500
£4000 $6200 €6000 Vieil homme songeant a sa vie (66x46cm-26x18in) s.num.6/50 aquatint. 3-Dec-2 Christie's, London #195/R est:5000-8000
£4000 $6240 €6000 La collection de tableautins (49x65cm-19x26in) s.num.33/50 col lithograph. 25-Mar-3 Sotheby's, London #136/R est:2000-3000
£4000 $6240 €6000 La danse des faunes (41x52cm-16x20in) s.num.138/200 lithograph. 25-Mar-3 Sotheby's, London #138/R est:3000-3500
£4000 $6280 €6000 Coutisane au lit avec un visteur (57x64cm-22x25in) s.num.47/50 etching. 17-Apr-3 Christie's, Kensington #308/R est:2800-3200
£4000 $6280 €6000 Football (54x75cm-21x30in) s.num.92/200 col lithograph. 17-Apr-3 Christie's, Kensington #330/R est:1000-1500
£4000 $6680 €5800 Femme assise au chapeau et femme debout drapee (27x19cm-11x7in) s. etching edition of 250. 30-Jun-3 Bonhams, New Bond Street #396 est:4000-6000
£4000 $6600 €5800 Table des eaux-fortes (37x30cm-15x12in) s.num.87/66 etching. 1-Jul-3 Sotheby's, London #131/R est:2500-3000
£4025 $6400 €6038 Series 274.024 (31x41cm-12x16in) s.num.47/50 etching. 1-May-3 Swann Galleries, New York #574/R est:7000-10000
£4088 $6500 €6132 La modele nu (28x19cm-11x7in) s.num.52/110 etching. 29-Apr-3 Christie's, Rockefeller NY #526/R est:4000-6000
£4088 $6500 €6132 David and Bethsabee (65x50cm-26x20in) s.num.43/50 lithograph. 29-Apr-3 Christie's, Rockefeller NY #534/R est:8000-12000
£4088 $6500 €6132 Minotaure aveugle guide par une fillette (34x25cm-13x10in) s. etching engraving edition of 50. 2-May-3 Sotheby's, New York #274/R est:4000-6000
£4114 $6500 €6171 Exposition - vallauris (62x55cm-24x22in) s. linocut. 22-Apr-3 Butterfields, San Francisco #2183/R est:4000-6000
£4114 $6500 €6171 Profile on black background (53x36cm-21x14in) s.i.num.50 lithograph. 28-Apr-3 Christie's, Rockefeller NY #74/R est:4000-6000
£4114 $6500 €6171 Head of a young girl (40x30cm-16x12in) i. lithograph. 28-Apr-3 Christie's, Rockefeller NY #154/R est:5000-7000
£4114 $6500 €6171 Young artist (40x30cm-16x12in) s.i.num.50 lithograph two. 28-Apr-3 Christie's, Rockefeller NY #157/R est:4000-6000
£4114 $6500 €6171 Bull fight, picador (56x65cm-22x26in) s.i.num.50 lithograph. 28-Apr-3 Christie's, Rockefeller NY #178/R est:3000-4000
£4114 $6500 €6171 Rainbow dove (51x66cm-20x26in) col lithograph. 28-Apr-3 Christie's, Rockefeller NY #214/R est:3000-4000
£4114 $6500 €6171 Dancer (30x20cm-12x8in) s.i.num.50 col lithograph. 28-Apr-3 Christie's, Rockefeller NY #250/R est:1000-1500
£4114 $6500 €6171 Old painter's studio (33x53cm-13x21in) s.i.num.50 col lithograph. 28-Apr-3 Christie's, Rockefeller NY #251/R est:3000-4000
£4114 $6500 €6171 Woman of Algiers in their flat, 1st variation (28x35cm-11x14in) i. lithograph. 28-Apr-3 Christie's, Rockefeller NY #257/R est:5000-8000
£4114 $6500 €6171 Small bullfight (30x23cm-12x9in) s.i.num.50 col lithograph two. 28-Apr-3 Christie's, Rockefeller NY #290/R est:2000-3000
£4114 $6500 €6171 Bacchanal I and II (44x60cm-17x24in) s.i.num.50 lithograph two. 28-Apr-3 Christie's, Rockefeller NY #311/R est:2000-3000
£4167 $6500 €6251 L'atelier (48x60cm-19x24in) s.num.79/150 etching. 5-Nov-2 Christie's, Rockefeller NY #219/R est:7000-9000
£4167 $6500 €6251 La danse des faunes (50x66cm-20x26in) s.num.61/200 lithograph. 5-Nov-2 Christie's, Rockefeller NY #244/R est:4000-6000
£4167 $6500 €6251 Au cirque, groupe avec ecuyere et clown (61x50cm-24x20in) s.num.22/50 etching. 5-Nov-2 Christie's, Rockefeller NY #257/R est:5000-7000
£4167 $6500 €6251 Quatre hommes en costume Rembranesque (58x45cm-23x18in) s.num.5/50 etching. 5-Nov-2 Christie's, Rockefeller NY #261/R est:6000-8000
£4167 $6500 €6251 Cirque et catch (45x56cm-18x22in) s.num.27/50 etching. 5-Nov-2 Christie's, Rockefeller NY #267/R est:6000-8000
£4167 $6500 €6251 Autour de chef-d'oeuvre inconnu (56x65cm-22x26in) s.num.6/50 etching drypoint. 5-Nov-2 Christie's, Rockefeller NY #279/R est:5000-7000
£4167 $6500 €6251 Trois femmes passant le temps, avec spectateur severe (45x54cm-18x21in) s.num.5/50 etching. 5-Nov-2 Christie's, Rockefeller NY #280/R est:5000-7000
£4167 $6500 €6251 Autour de La Celestine (45x56cm-18x22in) s.num.22/50 etching. 5-Nov-2 Christie's, Rockefeller NY #281/R est:4000-6000
£4167 $6500 €6251 Visiteur Rembranesque chez une courtisane folatre (45x56cm-18x22in) s.num.6/50 etching. 5-Nov-2 Christie's, Rockefeller NY #282/R est:4000-6000
£4167 $6500 €6251 Portrait de Mousquetaire, triste (67x57cm-26x22in) s.num.5/50 aquatint. 5-Nov-2 Christie's, Rockefeller NY #290/R est:5000-7000
£4167 $6500 €6251 Raphael et la fornarina, XIII, dans son fauteuil, le Pape en tire la langue (28x35cm-11x14in) s.num.5/50 etching. 5-Nov-2 Christie's, Rockefeller NY #316/R est:4000-6000
£4167 $6500 €6251 Raphael et la fornarina, XXI, Michel Ange est cache sous le lit (58x35cm-23x14in) s.num.33/50 etching. 5-Nov-2 Christie's, Rockefeller NY #318/R est:4000-6000
£4167 $6500 €6251 Peintre, et modele qui se cache le visage (33x41cm-13x16in) s.num.22/50 etching. 5-Nov-2 Christie's, Rockefeller NY #320/R est:4000-6000
£4200 $6552 €6300 Au cirque, ecuyere, clown et Pierrot (48x57cm-19x22in) s.num.22/50 aquatint. 9-Oct-2 Christie's, London #36/R est:2000-3000
£4200 $6552 €6300 Mousquetaire de profil, avec combat a la lance autour d'une jeune femme (57x64cm-22x25in) s.num.5/50 aquatint. 9-Oct-2 Christie's, London #50/R est:3000-4000
£4200 $6552 €6300 La serenade (33x25cm-13x10in) s.num.7/50 aquatint sugar. 9-Oct-2 Christie's, London #59/R est:2000-3000
£4200 $6552 €6300 Couple et voyageuse (35x42cm-14x17in) s.num.22/50 etching. 9-Oct-2 Christie's, London #178/R est:2000-3000
£4200 $6552 €6300 Scene pastorale poussinesque sur le theme de Pan et Syrinx (56x65cm-22x26in) s.num.6/50 etching. 9-Oct-2 Christie's, London #112/R est:5000-7000
£4200 $6552 €6300 Les bleus de Barcelone (23x33cm-9x13in) s.num.36/75 etching aquatint. 10-Oct-2 Sotheby's, London #82/R est:3000-4000
£4200 $6552 €6300 Petit assis au miroir (31x49cm-12x19in) s.num.23/50 lithograph. 25-Mar-3 Sotheby's, London #128/R est:3000-4000
£4200 $6930 €6090 Minotaure aveugle guide par une fillette II (23x29cm-9x11in) etching edition of 300. 1-Jul-3 Sotheby's, London #121/R est:3000-3500
£4205 $6559 €6308 La pose habillee (55x38cm-22x15in) s.num.20/50 lithograph lit. 5-Nov-2 Bukowskis, Stockholm #617/R est:60000-80000 (S.KR 60000)
£4225 $7014 €6000 Picador et taureau I - la pique (30x41cm-12x16in) d. aquatint etching. 14-Jun-3 Hauswedell & Nolte, Hamburg #1525/R est:8000
£4294 $7000 €6441 Flutiste grec (9x12cm-4x5in) s. etching drypoint exec.1968 pair. 13-Feb-3 Christie's, Rockefeller NY #144/R
£4294 $7000 €6441 Couple d'amoureux (15x21cm-6x8in) s. num.5/50 etching exec.1968 pair. 13-Feb-3 Christie's, Rockefeller NY #154/R
£4392 $6851 €6500 Femmes sur la plage (49x65cm-19x26in) s. lithograph on of 50. 26-Mar-3 Finarte Semenzato, Milan #17/R
£4403 $6824 €7000 Le repos du sculpteur et le modele au masque (44x34cm-17x13in) s. engraving. 30-Oct-2 Artcurial Briest, Paris #548 est:5300-5800
£4403 $7000 €6605 Tete de femme, de profil (46x41cm-18x16in) drypoint one of 250 exec.1905. 5-Mar-3 Doyle, New York #123/R est:7000-9000
£4403 $7000 €6605 Le jeu du taureau (50x65cm-20x26in) s.num.34/50 lithograph. 2-May-3 Sotheby's, New York #291/R est:6000-8000
£4403 $7000 €6605 La fille au chapeau (64x49cm-25x19in) i.verso lithograph. 2-May-3 Sotheby's, New York #296/R est:4000-5000
£4403 $7000 €6605 Le repos du sculpteur devant un nu a la drapies (27x19cm-11x7in) s. etching. 1-May-3 Swann Galleries, New York #555/R est:8000-12000
£4423 $7032 €6635 Reclining sculptor in front of horses and the bull (19x26cm-7x10in) s. etching edition of 250 prov.lit. 4-Mar-3 Deutscher-Menzies, Melbourne #289/R est:8000-12000 (A.D 11500)
£4430 $7000 €6645 Repose de sculpteur devant des chevaux at un taureau (19x27cm-7x11in) s. etching one of 300 executed c.1933. 12-Nov-2 Doyle, New York #324/R est:8000-12000
£4430 $7000 €6645 From la suite vollard, femme assise et femme de dos (28x20cm-11x8in) s. etching. 22-Apr-3 Butterfields, San Francisco #2178/R est:6000-9000
£4430 $7000 €6645 Owl with chair (66x50cm-26x20in) s.i.num.6/6 lithograph. 28-Apr-3 Christie's, Rockefeller NY #46/R est:4000-6000
£4430 $7000 €6645 Black owl (63x48cm-25x19in) s.i.num.6/6 lithograph. 28-Apr-3 Christie's, Rockefeller NY #48/R est:6000-8000

£	$	€	Description
£4430	$7000	€6645	Composition with vase of flowers (46x60cm-18x24in) s.i.num.74 col lithograph. 28-Apr-3 Christie's, Rockefeller NY #65/R est:4000-6000
£4430	$7000	€6645	Smiling faun (66x54cm-26x21in) s.i.num.6/6 lithograph. 28-Apr-3 Christie's, Rockefeller NY #97/R est:4000-6000
£4430	$7000	€6645	Lobster (55x70cm-22x28in) s.i.num.6/6 lithograph. 28-Apr-3 Christie's, Rockefeller NY #148/R est:2500-3500
£4430	$7000	€6645	Portrait of young girl (39x29cm-15x11in) i. lithograph. 28-Apr-3 Christie's, Rockefeller NY #158/R est:7000-9000
£4430	$7000	€6645	Figure (65x50cm-26x20in) s.i.num.6/6 lithograph. 28-Apr-3 Christie's, Rockefeller NY #169/R est:4000-6000
£4430	$7000	€6645	Face of peace (26x20cm-10x8in) num.150 lithograph. 28-Apr-3 Christie's, Rockefeller NY #209/R est:1500-2000
£4430	$7000	€6645	Squatting woman with raised arm (43x59cm-17x23in) s.i.num.50 lithograph. 28-Apr-3 Christie's, Rockefeller NY #266/R est:2500-3500
£4460	$7315	€6200	Le repos du sculpteur II (19x27cm-7x11in) s.i.d.3 Avril XXXI-II etching. 6-Jun-3 Ketterer, Munich #119/R est:12000-16000
£4487	$7000	€6731	Le repos du sculpteur et le modele au masque (45x34cm-18x13in) s. etching edition of 250. 5-Nov-2 Christie's, Rockefeller NY #223/R est:8000-12000
£4487	$7000	€6731	Scene mythologique (45x54cm-18x21in) s.num.22/50 etching. 5-Nov-2 Christie's, Rockefeller NY #277/R est:5000-7000
£4487	$7000	€6731	Tournage, plan Americain (25x33cm-10x13in) s.num.7/50 aquatint etching. 5-Nov-2 Christie's, Rockefeller NY #288/R est:4000-6000
£4487	$7000	€6731	Baigneuse et putto flutiste, avec des hommes en tenue de plage (28x38cm-11x15in) s.num.22/50 etching aquatint. 5-Nov-2 Christie's, Rockefeller NY #304/R est:4000-6000
£4487	$7045	€7000	Repos du sculpteur et modele au masque (26x19cm-10x7in) s. eau forte exec.1933 lit. 21-Nov-2 Finarte, Rome #96/R
£4487	$7000	€6731	La celestine (21x17cm-8x7in) etchings aquatint edition of 350 twenty. 7-Nov-2 Swann Galleries, New York #800/R est:8000-12000
£4500	$7020	€6750	Peintre et modele, ecuyere et bonhomme (46x57cm-18x22in) s.num.22/50 aquatint. 9-Oct-2 Christie's, London #37/R est:2800-3200
£4500	$7020	€6750	Les deux femmes nues (33x44cm-13x17in) s. lithograph. 9-Oct-2 Christie's, London #160/R est:4000-6000
£4500	$7020	€6750	Notables espagnols visitant une maison close ornee d'une armure (57x64cm-22x25in) s.num.31/50 etching. 9-Oct-2 Christie's, London #242/R est:2800-3200
£4500	$7065	€6750	La femme au singe (38x49cm-15x19in) s.num.13/50 lithograph. 16-Dec-2 Sotheby's, London #87/R est:2500-3500
£4500	$7020	€6750	Henri-Dante Alberti dans l'argil de Picasso (32x27cm-13x11in) s.i. linocut printed black. 25-Mar-3 Sotheby's, London #131/R est:5000-7000
£4500	$7425	€6525	La famille de Saltimbanques (48x31cm-19x12in) indis.sig. by another hand drypoint edition of 250. 1-Jul-3 Sotheby's, London #115/R est:5000-7000
£4500	$7425	€6525	Scene familiale (40x53cm-16x21in) s.num.30/50 col linocut. 2-Jul-3 Christie's, London #169/R est:4500-5500
£4500	$7425	€6525	Les mains liees (47x61cm-19x24in) s.num.5/50 lithograph. 2-Jul-3 Christie's, London #309/R est:1000-1500
£4600	$7176	€6900	L'atelier, avec un hibou et un envoye officiel (45x55cm-18x22in) s.num.6/50 etching. 9-Oct-2 Christie's, London #96/R est:3500-4500
£4600	$7130	€6900	Femme aguichant un homme songeur (45x54cm-18x21in) s.num.33/50 etching. 3-Dec-2 Christie's, London #210/R est:2000-3000
£4600	$7176	€6900	Tete de femme de profil (29x25cm-11x10in) drypoint. 25-Mar-3 Sotheby's, London #125/R est:3000-4000
£4601	$7500	€6902	Jeune femme et vieux mari (8x6cm-3x2in) s.i. aquatint etching exec.1968 pair. 13-Feb-3 Christie's, Rockefeller NY #143/R
£4601	$7500	€6902	Grosse courtisane (19x11cm-7x4in) s.i. etching drypoint pair. 13-Feb-3 Christie's, Rockefeller NY #134/R
£4601	$7500	€6902	Gentilhomme espagnol et femme a barbe (32x20cm-13x8in) s. aquatint drypoint two. 13-Feb-3 Christie's, Rockefeller NY #150/R
£4601	$7500	€6902	Moine peintre (26x17cm-10x7in) s. etching exec.1968 two. 13-Feb-3 Christie's, Rockefeller NY #148/R
£4601	$7500	€6902	Femme acrobate (18x22cm-7x9in) s. etching two. 13-Feb-3 Christie's, Rockefeller NY #149/R
£4717	$7500	€7076	Profil en trois couleurs (52x33cm-20x13in) s.num.24/50 col lithograph. 29-Apr-3 Christie's, Rockefeller NY #544/R est:5000-7000
£4717	$7500	€7076	Gentilhomme en visite chez la Celestine. Peintre, modele et visiteur (6x12cm-2x5in) s. one num.30/50 one num.6/50 aquatint two. 29-Apr-3 Christie's, Rockefeller NY #556/R est:6000-8000
£4717	$7500	€7076	Une maja posant sur un piedestal. Celestine, maja et complice masculin (12x6cm-5x2in) s.num.7/50 aquatint two. 29-Apr-3 Christie's, Rockefeller NY #557/R est:6000-8000
£4717	$7500	€7076	Mousquetaire de profil, avec combat a la lance autour d'une jeune femme (41x49cm-16x19in) s.num.27/50 aquatint. 29-Apr-3 Christie's, Rockefeller NY #560/R est:5000-7000
£4717	$7500	€7076	Seranade a la flute. Homme a la pipe assis, maja et Celestine (15x22cm-6x9in) s. one num.22/50 one num.7/50 aquatint two. 29-Apr-3 Christie's, Rockefeller NY #566/R est:6000-8000
£4717	$7500	€7076	Couple posant pour un peintre en habit de cour. Polichinelle et nain (9x12cm-4x5in) s. one num.29/50 one num.5/50 etching two. 29-Apr-3 Christie's, Rockefeller NY #567/R est:5000-7000
£4717	$7500	€7076	Enlevement, I. Homme avec deux femmes nues (15x22cm-6x9in) s. one num.33/50 drypoint one num.32/50 mezzotint two. 29-Apr-3 Christie's, Rockefeller NY #568/R est:6000-8000
£4717	$7500	€7076	Deux nus assis (26x18cm-10x7in) s. etching. 2-May-3 Sotheby's, New York #259/R est:6000-8000
£4717	$7500	€7076	Deux modeles vetus (27x19cm-11x7in) s. etching edition of 310. 2-May-3 Sotheby's, New York #260/R est:6000-8000
£4717	$7500	€7076	Le repos du sculpteur (26x19cm-10x7in) s. etching edition of 310. 2-May-3 Sotheby's, New York #262/R est:6000-8000
£4717	$7500	€7076	347 series no 56 (28x39cm-11x15in) s.num.35/50 etching. 2-May-3 Sotheby's, New York #313/R est:3000-4000
£4717	$7500	€7076	Femme nue a la jambe pliee (31x22cm-12x9in) s. etching. 1-May-3 Swann Galleries, New York #550/R est:8000-12000
£4717	$7500	€7076	Le repos du sculpteur devant un centaure et une femme (19x27cm-7x11in) s. etching. 1-May-3 Swann Galleries, New York #552/R est:10000-15000
£4717	$7500	€7076	Sculpteur avec coupe et modele accroupi (27x19cm-11x7in) s. etching. 1-May-3 Swann Galleries, New York #553/R est:10000-15000
£4717	$7500	€7076	Danseurs et musicien (53x64cm-21x25in) s. col linoleum. 1-May-3 Swann Galleries, New York #566/R est:10000-15000
£4747	$7500	€7121	Minotaure, buveur et femmes (30x37cm-12x15in) etching one of 300 executed c.1933. 12-Nov-2 Doyle, New York #325/R est:5000-7000
£4747	$7500	€7121	Young nude woman resting (47x61cm-19x24in) s.i.num.6/6 lithograph. 28-Apr-3 Christie's, Rockefeller NY #87/R est:2000-3000
£4747	$7500	€7121	Musician faun no.5 (67x51cm-26x20in) s.i.num.6/6 lithograph. 28-Apr-3 Christie's, Rockefeller NY #101/R est:4000-6000
£4747	$7500	€7121	Figure (37x50cm-15x20in) s.i.num.50 lithograph. 28-Apr-3 Christie's, Rockefeller NY #112/R est:4000-6000
£4747	$7500	€7121	Figure (65x50cm-26x20in) s.i.num.6/6 lithograph. 28-Apr-3 Christie's, Rockefeller NY #113/R est:4000-6000
£4747	$7500	€7121	Head of Jacqueline (58x39cm-23x15in) i. lithograph. 28-Apr-3 Christie's, Rockefeller NY #325/R est:4000-6000
£4800	$7392	€7200	Vieil homme avec magicien evoquant trois odalisques (42x34cm-17x13in) s.num.22/50 etching. 24-Oct-2 Christie's, Kensington #298/R est:4000-6000
£4800	$7488	€7200	Retour aux sources, Picasso touriste a la Fuente de Canaletas (57x65cm-22x26in) s.num.22/50 etching. 9-Oct-2 Christie's, London #42/R est:5000-8000
£4800	$7488	€7200	Peintre avec couple et enfant (45x54cm-18x21in) s.num.29/50 etching. 9-Oct-2 Christie's, London #100/R est:6000-8000
£4800	$7488	€7200	Degas au double regard et sept baigneuses (46x57cm-18x22in) st.sig.num.12/50 drypoint. 9-Oct-2 Christie's, London #125/R est:1500-2500
£4800	$7488	€7200	Figure (66x50cm-26x20in) s.i. lithograph edition of 50. 9-Oct-2 Christie's, London #174/R est:4000-6000
£4800	$7488	€7200	Faune flutiste et bacchantes (26x32cm-10x13in) s.num.6/50 etching. 9-Oct-2 Christie's, London #192/R est:1200-1800
£4800	$7488	€7200	Vieil homme songeant a la peinture ancienne (61x50cm-24x20in) s.num.22/50 etching. 9-Oct-2 Christie's, London #221/R est:3500-4500
£4800	$7488	€7200	Demenagement, ou charrette revolutionnaire (45x54cm-18x21in) s.num.33/50 etching aquatint. 9-Oct-2 Christie's, London #241/R est:3000-5000
£4800	$7440	€7200	Le Carmen des Carmen (41x31cm-16x12in) s.num.IX/XXX aquatint. 5-Dec-2 Sotheby's, London #172/R est:2000-2500
£4800	$7920	€6960	Carnaval, clown et danseurs (64x52cm-25x20in) s.i. brown linocut. 1-Jul-3 Sotheby's, London #129/R est:4000-5000
£4800	$7920	€6960	Bande dessinee (41x31cm-16x12in) s.num.26/50 etching. 2-Jul-3 Christie's, London #173/R est:2200-2800
£4800	$7920	€6960	Portrait de famille ingresque IV (40x53cm-16x21in) s.num.33/50 col linocut. 2-Jul-3 Christie's, London #327/R est:3000-5000
£4808	$7500	€7212	Sculpteur avec coupe et modele accroupi (45x34cm-18x13in) s. etching edition of 250. 5-Nov-2 Christie's, Rockefeller NY #222/R est:7000-9000
£4808	$7500	€7212	La Vie en Rose (42x50cm-17x20in) s.num.5/50 etching. 5-Nov-2 Christie's, Rockefeller NY #283/R est:5000-7000

£4808 $7500 €7212 L'enterrement du Compte d'Orgaz, d'apres Picasso (45x52cm-18x20in) s.num.27/50 aquatint etching. 5-Nov-2 Christie's, Rockefeller NY #297/R est:5000-7000
£4808 $7500 €7212 Clin d'oeil au bain turc femmes faisant la sieste au soleil (45x54cm-18x21in) s.num.22/50 etching. 5-Nov-2 Christie's, Rockefeller NY #312/R est:4000-6000
£4808 $7500 €7212 Raphael et la fornarina, VI, enfin seuls (44x65cm-17x26in) s.num.32/50 etching. 5-Nov-2 Christie's, Rockefeller NY #313/R est:5000-7000
£4808 $7452 €7500 Danseur (74x60cm-29x24in) s. linocut one of 200. 7-Dec-2 Cornette de St.Cyr, Paris #8/R
£4808 $7500 €7212 Sculpteur avec coupe de modele accroupi (27x19cm-11x7in) s. etching edition of 260. 7-Nov-2 Swann Galleries, New York #771/R est:10000-15000
£4808 $7500 €7212 Le repos du sculpteur devant le petit torse (20x27cm-8x11in) s. etching edition of 260. 7-Nov-2 Swann Galleries, New York #773/R est:10000-15000
£4808 $7500 €7212 Rembrandt a la palette (28x20cm-11x8in) s. etching drypoint edition of 260. 7-Nov-2 Swann Galleries, New York #779/R est:8000-12000
£4808 $7500 €7212 Minotaure, une coupe a la main, et jeune femme (20x27cm-8x11in) s. etching edition of 260. 7-Nov-2 Swann Galleries, New York #776/R est:10000-15000
£4908 $8000 €7362 Raphael et la Fornarina (15x21cm-6x8in) s.i. etching pair. 13-Feb-3 Christie's, Rockefeller NY #153/R
£4908 $8000 €7362 Visiteur (15x21cm-6x8in) s. aquatint drypoint etching two. 13-Feb-3 Christie's, Rockefeller NY #145/R
£4943 $7810 €7415 Buste de femme (35x27cm-14x11in) s.num.14/50 linocut lit. 28-Apr-3 Bukowskis, Stockholm #498/R est:40000-50000 (S.KR 65000)
£5000 $7800 €7500 Trois femmes et le torero (50x65cm-20x26in) s.num.45/50 lithograph. 9-Oct-2 Christie's, London #4/R est:2000-3000
£5000 $7800 €7500 Minotaure endormi contemple par une femme (34x45cm-13x18in) s. etching edition of 260. 9-Oct-2 Christie's, London #12/R est:5000-7000
£5000 $7800 €7500 Enlevement III (50x46cm-20x18in) s.num.5/50 aquatint. 9-Oct-2 Christie's, London #48/R est:2000-3000
£5000 $7800 €7500 Peintre travaillant (38x50cm-15x20in) s.num.49/99 etching from set of 13. 9-Oct-2 Christie's, London #88/R est:2500-3500
£5000 $7800 €7500 Serenade au coucher du soleil dans un sous bois a la Monet (36x47cm-14x19in) s.num.22/50 aquatint. 9-Oct-2 Christie's, London #119/R est:4000-6000
£5000 $7800 €7500 Portrait de Dora Maar au Chignon (51x40cm-20x16in) st.sig.num.5/50 drypoint. 9-Oct-2 Christie's, London #170/R est:3500-4500
£5000 $7800 €7500 Les trois amies (61x47cm-24x19in) s.num.94/150 etching. 9-Oct-2 Christie's, London #190/R est:3000-5000
£5000 $7800 €7500 Vieillard fantasmant (45x57cm-18x22in) s.num.22/50 etching. 9-Oct-2 Christie's, London #228/R est:4000-6000
£5000 $7800 €7500 Spectacle, l'amour s'aventurant chez les femmes (64x77cm-25x30in) st.sig.num.18/50 etching. 9-Oct-2 Christie's, London #236/R est:3000-5000
£5000 $7750 €7500 Quatre portefaix apportant a un gentilhomme (45x54cm-18x21in) s.num.29/50 etching. 3-Dec-2 Christie's, London #211/R est:3500-4500
£5000 $7800 €7500 Les deux femmes nues (32x42cm-13x17in) s.num.45/50 lithograph. 25-Mar-3 Sotheby's, London #129/R est:3500-4500
£5000 $8250 €7250 Tete de fac, portrait de Marie Therese de face (31x22cm-12x9in) st.sig.num.34/50 etching drypoint aquatint. 1-Jul-3 Sotheby's, London #126/R est:3500-4500
£5000 $8250 €7250 Corrida, le picador (56x68cm-22x27in) s.num.42/50 lithograph. 2-Jul-3 Christie's, London #307/R est:4000-6000
£5031 $8000 €7547 Enlevement, a pied avec la Celestine. Mon Dieu, quel homme, qu'l est petit (6x8cm-2x3in) s.num.31/50 aquatint two. 29-Apr-3 Christie's, Rockefeller NY #561/R est:6000-8000
£5031 $8000 €7547 Vase de fleurs (66x51cm-26x20in) s.num.30/50 col lithograph. 1-May-3 Swann Galleries, New York #562/R est:6000-9000
£5063 $8000 €7595 Centaur and Bacchante with faun (50x65cm-20x26in) s.i.num6/6 lithograph. 28-Apr-3 Christie's, Rockefeller NY #54/R est:3000-4000
£5063 $8000 €7595 Head of young woman (60x44cm-24x17in) s.i.num.6/6 lithograph. 28-Apr-3 Christie's, Rockefeller NY #91/R est:4000-6000
£5063 $8000 €7595 Black figure (64x49cm-25x19in) s.i.num.6/6 lithograph. 28-Apr-3 Christie's, Rockefeller NY #109/R est:5000-7000
£5063 $8000 €7595 Figure (65x50cm-26x20in) s.i.num6/6 lithograph. 28-Apr-3 Christie's, Rockefeller NY #111/R est:4000-6000
£5063 $8000 €7595 Venus and love (75x36cm-30x14in) s.i.num.50 lithograph after Cranach. 28-Apr-3 Christie's, Rockefeller NY #191/R est:6000-8000
£5063 $8000 €7595 Knight and the page (37x27cm-15x11in) s.i.num.50 lithograph. 28-Apr-3 Christie's, Rockefeller NY #206/R est:2000-3000
£5128 $8000 €7692 Le repos du sculpteur (34x45cm-13x18in) s. etching edition of 300. 14-Oct-2 Butterfields, San Francisco #1159/R est:7000-10000
£5128 $8000 €7692 La famille du Saltimbanque (50x66cm-20x26in) s.num.18/50 lithograph. 14-Oct-2 Butterfields, San Francisco #1164/R est:4000-6000
£5128 $8000 €7692 Tete d'homme barbu, II (38x27cm-15x11in) s.num.X/XX aquatint. 19-Sep-2 Swann Galleries, New York #666/R est:6000-9000
£5128 $8000 €7692 Minotaure avegule guide par une fillette II (34x45cm-13x18in) s. etching edition of 250. 5-Nov-2 Christie's, Rockefeller NY #232/R est:6000-8000
£5128 $8000 €7692 Farol (38x48cm-15x19in) s.num.14/50 col linocut. 5-Nov-2 Christie's, Rockefeller NY #247/R est:10000-15000
£5128 $8000 €7692 Bande dessinee (58x45cm-23x18in) s.num.27/50 etching. 5-Nov-2 Christie's, Rockefeller NY #260/R est:7000-10000
£5128 $8000 €7692 Homme barbu songeant a une scene des Mille et une nuits (54x42cm-21x17in) s.num.5/50 etching. 5-Nov-2 Christie's, Rockefeller NY #263/R est:4000-6000
£5128 $8000 €7692 El arrastre, avec ecuyere et putto (45x57cm-18x22in) s.num.22/50 etching. 5-Nov-2 Christie's, Rockefeller NY #268/R est:7000-9000
£5128 $8000 €7692 Femme au lit revant, hommes et femmes (47x56cm-19x22in) s.num.8/50 aquatint etching. 5-Nov-2 Christie's, Rockefeller NY #270/R est:6000-8000
£5128 $8000 €7692 Reve de marin, des femmes dans chaque port (35x42cm-14x17in) s.num.22/50 etching. 5-Nov-2 Christie's, Rockefeller NY #278/R est:4000-6000
£5128 $8000 €7692 Raphael et la fornarina XXIII, Seuls, s'etreignant sur le sol (28x35cm-11x14in) s.num.6/50 etching. 5-Nov-2 Christie's, Rockefeller NY #319/R est:6000-8000
£5128 $7949 €8000 Femme au chapeau a fleurs et femme drapee dans une serviette (44x34cm-17x13in) s.d.XXXIV etching one of 260. 6-Dec-2 Ketterer, Munich #141/R est:10000-12000
£5128 $7949 €8000 Les faunes et la centauresse (49x64cm-19x25in) s.d. lithograph. 7-Dec-2 Hauswedell & Nolte, Hamburg #999/R est:10000
£5171 $8170 €7757 L'ecuyere et les clowns (51x69cm-20x27in) s.num.16/50 col lithograph prov.lit. 28-Apr-3 Bukowskis, Stockholm #495/R est:70000-90000 (S.KR 68000)
£5200 $8112 €7800 Les trois graces (40x26cm-16x10in) s.num.56/100 etching. 9-Oct-2 Christie's, London #189/R est:4000-6000
£5200 $8112 €7800 Frontispiece from Recordant el Doctor Revento (31x23cm-12x9in) s.num.81/180 drypoint. 9-Oct-2 Christie's, London #194/R est:2000-3000
£5200 $8112 €7800 Peintre a lavalliere dessinant son modele (64x77cm-25x30in) st.sig.num.12/50 etching. 9-Oct-2 Christie's, London #231/R est:3000-5000
£5200 $8580 €7540 La pose habillee (56x38cm-22x15in) s.num.45/50 lithograph. 2-Jul-3 Christie's, London #311/R est:4000-6000
£5215 $8500 €7823 Vieux copains (21x27cm-8x11in) s. etching aquatint two. 13-Feb-3 Christie's, Rockefeller NY #157/R
£5346 $8286 €8500 Portrait de Jacqueline (66x50cm-26x20in) s. col lithograph. 30-Oct-2 Artcurial Briest, Paris #546 est:5000-6000
£5346 $8500 €8019 Le repos du sculpteur devant des chevaux et un tareau (19x27cm-7x11in) s. etching edition of 250. 29-Apr-3 Christie's, Rockefeller NY #527/R est:8000-12000
£5346 $8500 €8019 Maja a la robe longue. Maja a la robe dechiree (12x6cm-5x2in) s. one num.7/50 one num.6/50 aquatint two. 29-Apr-3 Christie's, Rockefeller NY #558/R est:6000-8000
£5346 $8500 €8019 Femme au chapeau et a l'oeillet. Autour de Bain Turc d'Ingres (17x26cm-7x10in) s. one num.22/50 one num.31/50 etching two. 29-Apr-3 Christie's, Rockefeller NY #569/R est:6000-8000
£5346 $8500 €8019 Sculpteur, modele accroupi et tete sculptee (26x19cm-10x7in) s. etching edition of 310. 2-May-3 Sotheby's, New York #261/R est:6000-7000
£5346 $8500 €8019 Profil en trois couleurs (52x40cm-20x16in) s. col lithograph. 2-May-3 Sotheby's, New York #294/R est:4000-6000
£5346 $8500 €8019 El rapto de Jezabel pur quiron el centauro (50x35cm-20x14in) drypoint 1 of 106 impressions. 2-May-3 Sotheby's, New York #320 est:3000-5000
£5346 $8500 €8019 Sculteur et modele admirant une tete sculptee (27x19cm-11x7in) s. etching. 1-May-3 Swann Galleries, New York #554/R est:10000-15000
£5346 $8500 €8019 Le picador II (20x26cm-8x10in) s.num.5/50 col lithograph. 1-May-3 Swann Galleries, New York #569/R est:8000-12000

£5380 $8500 €8500 Trois femmes nues et une coupe d'anemones (36x29cm-14x11in) s. etching. 30-Nov-2 Villa Grisebach, Berlin #374/R est:5000-7000
£5380 $8500 €8500 Deux femmes au bain (28x20cm-11x8in) s. etching. 30-Nov-2 Villa Grisebach, Berlin #381/R est:7000-8000
£5380 $8500 €8070 Ines and her child (66x50cm-26x20in) s.i.num.6/6 lithograph. 28-Apr-3 Christie's, Rockefeller NY #52/R est:3000-4000
£5380 $8500 €8070 Black bull (41x60cm-16x24in) s.i.num.6/6 lithograph. 28-Apr-3 Christie's, Rockefeller NY #80/R est:3000-4000
£5380 $8500 €8070 Young woman (39x29cm-15x11in) i. lithograph. 28-Apr-3 Christie's, Rockefeller NY #155/R est:3000-5000
£5448 $8500 €8172 Modele nu et sculptures (45x34cm-18x13in) s. etching edition of 250. 14-Oct-2 Butterfields, San Francisco #1161/R est:8000-12000
£5449 $8500 €8174 Le repos du sculpteur (35x46cm-14x18in) s. etching edition of 250. 5-Nov-2 Christie's, Rockefeller NY #224/R est:7000-9000
£5449 $8500 €8174 Autoportrait transpose et dedouble revant au cirque (61x50cm-24x20in) s.num.22/50 etching drypoint. 5-Nov-2 Christie's, Rockefeller NY #259/R est:6000-8000
£5449 $8500 €8174 Jeune homme presentant un miroir, ou un portrait, a une femme (58x45cm-23x18in) s.num.8/50 etching drypoint. 5-Nov-2 Christie's, Rockefeller NY #264/R est:7000-10000
£5449 $8500 €8174 Jeune homme faisant sa declaration, en presence des autorites (36x47cm-14x19in) s.num.22/50 aquatint. 5-Nov-2 Christie's, Rockefeller NY #286/R est:5000-7000
£5449 $8500 €8174 Femme torero II (36x28cm-14x11in) s.num.220 etching exec.1934. 30-Mar-3 Susanin's, Chicago #6134/R est:10000-15000
£5479 $8548 €8000 Le peintre et son modele - au tabouret (42x47cm-17x19in) s.d. aquatint etching drypoint. 11-Apr-3 Winterberg, Heidelberg #1497/R est:9800
£5500 $8580 €8250 Taureau noir (50x66cm-20x26in) s.num.21/50 lithograph. 9-Oct-2 Christie's, London #2/R est:2000-3000
£5500 $8580 €8250 Variation sur le theme de Don Quichotte et Dulcinee (35x42cm-14x17in) s.num.22/50 aquatint. 9-Oct-2 Christie's, London #65/R est:2200-3200
£5500 $8580 €8250 Venus et l'Amour, dans le style Bon Sauvage (57x64cm-22x25in) s.num.5/50 etching. 9-Oct-2 Christie's, London #180/R est:2800-3200
£5500 $9075 €7975 Deux femmes sur la plage (65x50cm-26x20in) s.num.27/50 lithograph. 1-Jul-3 Sotheby's, London #119/R est:6000-8000
£5500 $9075 €7975 Portrait de Jacqueline (52x38cm-20x15in) s.num.65/100 col lithograph. 2-Jul-3 Christie's, London #163/R est:2000-3000
£5521 $9000 €8282 Minotaure vaincu (34x45cm-13x18in) s. etching one of 250. 13-Feb-3 Christie's, Rockefeller NY #123/R
£5521 $9000 €8282 Visiteur au nez bourbonien (37x27cm-15x11in) s.i. aquatint etching exec.1968 pair. 13-Feb-3 Christie's, Rockefeller NY #142/R
£5606 $8746 €8409 Tetes (64x53cm-25x21in) s.num.15/50 col linocut 1963 lit. 6-Nov-2 AB Stockholms Auktionsverk #1045/R est:80000-100000 (S.KR 80000)
£5696 $9000 €8544 Musician faun no.4 (68x27cm-27x11in) s.i.num.6/6 lithograph. 28-Apr-3 Christie's, Rockefeller NY #100/R est:4000-6000
£5696 $9000 €8544 Toad (50x64cm-20x25in) s.i.num.6/6 lithograph. 28-Apr-3 Christie's, Rockefeller NY #149/R est:2500-3500
£5696 $9000 €8544 Games and reading (48x63cm-19x25in) s.i.num.50 lithograph. 28-Apr-3 Christie's, Rockefeller NY #231/R est:4000-6000
£5696 $9000 €8544 Rehearsal (50x65cm-20x26in) s.i.num.50 lithograph. 28-Apr-3 Christie's, Rockefeller NY #243/R est:5000-7000
£5755 $9439 €8000 Le repos du sculpteur (19x26cm-7x10in) s.i.d.2 Avril XXXI-II etching. 6-Jun-3 Ketterer, Munich #116/R est:8000-10000
£5769 $9000 €8654 Sculpteur et modele debout (45x34cm-18x13in) s. etching. 14-Oct-2 Butterfields, San Francisco #1160/R est:8000-12000
£5769 $9000 €8654 Femmes se reposant (34x45cm-13x18in) s. drypoint edition of 250. 5-Nov-2 Christie's, Rockefeller NY #220/R est:9000-12000
£5769 $9000 €8654 Venus et l'amour, dans le style du XVI siecle (56x64cm-22x25in) s.num.6/50 etching. 5-Nov-2 Christie's, Rockefeller NY #292/R est:8000-10000
£5769 $9000 €8654 Sculpteur et modele admirant une tete sculptee (27x20cm-11x8in) s. etching edition of 260. 7-Nov-2 Swann Galleries, New York #774/R est:10000-15000
£5800 $9048 €8700 Clin d'oeil au bain turc, femmes prenant le soleil a la piscine (45x55cm-18x22in) s.num.22/50 etching. 9-Oct-2 Christie's, London #115/R est:5000-8000
£5828 $9500 €8742 Femme sur char romaine (28x39cm-11x15in) s.i. etching aquatint pair exec.1968. 13-Feb-3 Christie's, Rockefeller NY #132/R
£5828 $9500 €8742 Don Quichotte (15x21cm-6x8in) s. num.31/50 aquatint two. 13-Feb-3 Christie's, Rockefeller NY #146/R
£5828 $9500 €8742 Duel au soleil levant (15x22cm-6x9in) s.i. etching two. 13-Feb-3 Christie's, Rockefeller NY #147/R
£5828 $9500 €8742 Scene biblique (20x27cm-8x11in) s. etching aquatint two. 13-Feb-3 Christie's, Rockefeller NY #156/R
£5882 $9824 €8529 Les faunes et la centauresse (49x64cm-19x25in) s.i.d.26 janvier 1947 lithograph. 24-Jun-3 Koller, Zurich #473/R est:12000-18000 (S.FR 13000)
£5903 $9326 €8500 Les saltimbanques (60x33cm-24x13in) s.d. drypoint. 26-Apr-3 Cornette de St.Cyr, Paris #66/R est:5000-6000
£5946 $9276 €8800 Etude de profils (73x54cm-29x21in) s.d.1948 lithograph. 28-Mar-3 Ketterer, Hamburg #571/R est:8000-9000
£5975 $9500 €8963 Buste au fond etoile (66x50cm-26x20in) s.num.42/50 lithograph. 29-Apr-3 Christie's, Rockefeller NY #535/R est:12000-15000
£5975 $9500 €8963 Peintre peignant la nuque de son jeune modele. La Celestine, sa protegee (9x12cm-4x5in) s.num.15/50 aquatint two. 29-Apr-3 Christie's, Rockefeller NY #656/R est:6000-8000
£5975 $9500 €8963 Nu aux bottines. Homme Rembranesque, et deux femmes nues (22x15cm-9x6in) s. one num.47/50 one num.5/50 etching two. 29-Apr-3 Christie's, Rockefeller NY #570/R est:6000-8000
£5975 $9500 €8963 Femme nue assise en tailleur. Modele acrobatique et dissinateur (15x21cm-6x8in) s. one num.43/50 one num.7/50 etching two. 29-Apr-3 Christie's, Rockefeller NY #573/R est:7000-10000
£5975 $9500 €8963 347 series no 123 (49x33cm-19x13in) s.num.20/50 aquatint. 2-May-3 Sotheby's, New York #315/R est:6000-8000
£6000 $9360 €9000 Le repos du minotaure, champagne et amante (34x45cm-13x18in) s. etching edition of 260. 9-Oct-2 Christie's, London #9/R est:6000-8000
£6000 $9360 €9000 Le celestine presente sa pupille, avec un enfant au Rameau d'Olivier (36x47cm-14x19in) s.num.22/50 aquatint. 9-Oct-2 Christie's, London #68/R est:5000-8000
£6000 $9360 €9000 Ecce homo (66x56cm-26x22in) st.sig.num.12/50 etching after Rembrandt. 9-Oct-2 Christie's, London #90/R est:3000-5000
£6000 $9360 €9000 Le repos du sculpteur et le modele au masque (26x19cm-10x7in) s. etching. 10-Oct-2 Sotheby's, London #79/R est:4000-6000
£6000 $9360 €9000 Etreinte (42x57cm-17x22in) s.num.17/50 etching. 25-Mar-3 Sotheby's, London #132/R est:2000-3000
£6000 $9900 €8700 Corrida (51x66cm-20x26in) s.num.28/50 col lithograph prov. 2-Jul-3 Christie's, London #316/R est:2000-3000
£6000 $9900 €8700 L'aubade, avec femme dans un fauteuil (53x64cm-21x25in) s.num.3/50 col linocut. 2-Jul-3 Christie's, London #319/R est:7000-10000
£6013 $9500 €9020 Still life with fruit stand (25x36cm-10x14in) s.num. lithograph set of three. 28-Apr-3 Christie's, Rockefeller NY #6/R est:9000-12000
£6013 $9500 €9020 Fauns and the she centaur (50x65cm-20x26in) s.i.num.6/6 lithograph. 28-Apr-3 Christie's, Rockefeller NY #50/R est:4000-6000
£6013 $9500 €9020 Couple (49x64cm-19x25in) s.i.num.6/6 lithograph. 28-Apr-3 Christie's, Rockefeller NY #71/R est:5000-7000
£6013 $9500 €9020 Bull at play (48x64cm-19x25in) s.i.num.50 lithograph. 28-Apr-3 Christie's, Rockefeller NY #238/R est:2000-3000
£6013 $9500 €9020 Homage to Bacchus (49x64cm-19x25in) s.i.num.50 lithograph. 28-Apr-3 Christie's, Rockefeller NY #316/R est:3000-5000
£6024 $10000 €9036 Le pichet noir et la tete de mort (32x44cm-13x17in) s.i.num.20/50 lithograph prov.lit. 11-Jun-3 Phillips, New York #550/R est:3000-5000
£6041 $9545 €9062 Les trois amies (64x46cm-25x18in) s.num.108/150 etching. 1-Apr-3 Rasmussen, Copenhagen #62/R est:60000 (D.KR 65000)
£6071 $9471 €9107 Scene bachique au Mintotaure (30x37cm-12x15in) s. one of 250 etching executed 1933. 21-Oct-2 Blomqvist, Oslo #503/R est:80000-100000 (N.KR 70000)
£6090 $9500 €9135 Ecuyere et les clowns (49x65cm-19x26in) s. num.30/50 col lithograph. 20-Sep-2 Sloan, North Bethesda #306/R est:6000-8000
£6090 $9500 €9135 Deux modeles vetus (44x34cm-17x13in) s. etching edition of 250. 5-Nov-2 Christie's, Rockefeller NY #221/R est:6000-8000
£6090 $9500 €9135 Femme torero II (45x34cm-18x13in) s. etching edition of 250. 5-Nov-2 Christie's, Rockefeller NY #231/R est:10000-15000
£6090 $9500 €9135 La repetition (50x65cm-20x26in) s.num.5/50 lithograph. 5-Nov-2 Christie's, Rockefeller NY #243/R est:12000-15000
£6090 $9500 €9135 Tete de femme, de profil (29x25cm-11x10in) drypoint edition of 250. 7-Nov-2 Swann Galleries, New York #769/R est:7000-10000
£6135 $10000 €9203 Peintre devant sa toile (27x38cm-11x15in) s.i. aquatint pair. 13-Feb-3 Christie's, Rockefeller NY #131/R
£6135 $10000 €9203 Celestine (16x21cm-6x8in) s.i. aquatint etching two. 13-Feb-3 Christie's, Rockefeller NY #136/R
£6164 $9616 €9000 L'ecuyere et les clowns (50x69cm-20x27in) s.i.d. col lithograph. 11-Apr-3 Winterberg, Heidelberg #1492/R est:11800
£6200 $9672 €9300 La toilette de la mere (48x33cm-19x13in) etching drypoint. 9-Oct-2 Christie's, London #27/R est:4000-6000
£6250 $9875 €9000 Minotaure endormi comtemple par une femme (33x43cm-13x17in) d.18 mai 1933 etching edition of 260. 26-Apr-3 Cornette de St.Cyr, Paris #64/R est:5000-7000
£6289 $10000 €9434 Composition au vase de fleurs (45x60cm-18x24in) s.num.29/50 col lithograph. 29-Apr-3 Christie's, Rockefeller NY #533/R est:12000-16000
£6289 $10000 €9434 Polichinelle avec deux femmes. Le portrait (57x39cm-22x15in) s. one num.22/50 one num.5/50 etching two. 29-Apr-3 Christie's, Rockefeller NY #552/R est:6000-8000

£6289 $10000 €9434 La Celestine en action, le pigeon. La Celestine et sa creature (81x12cm-32x5in) s.num.33/50 one etching one aquatint two. 29-Apr-3 Christie's, Rockefeller NY #553/R est:6000-8000

£6289 $10000 €9434 Cape et epee, poursuite I. La Celestine, enlevement (17x21cm-7x8in) s. one num.33/50 one num.32/50 aquatint two. 29-Apr-3 Christie's, Rockefeller NY #554/R est:6000-8000

£6289 $10000 €9434 Grosse courtisane et vieux beau. Peintre peignant le sein de son modele (21x15cm-8x6in) s. one num.32/50 one num.5/50 etching two. 29-Apr-3 Christie's, Rockefeller NY #562/R est:7000-10000

£6289 $10000 €9434 Prostituee et Reitre. Grosse prostituee et Mousquetaire (21x15cm-8x6in) s. one num.6/50 one num.7/50 aquatint two. 29-Apr-3 Christie's, Rockefeller NY #563/R est:6000-8000

£6289 $10000 €9434 Picador, femme at cheval (64x53cm-25x21in) s. num2/50 col lithograph. 1-May-3 Swann Galleries, New York #565/R est:8000-12000

£6289 $10000 €9434 Fumeur (107x81cm-42x32in) s.d.1964 num.42/50 col aquatint. 30-Apr-3 Doyle, New York #271a/R est:5000-7000

£6329 $10000 €9494 Woman in the armchair (49x31cm-19x12in) s.i.num. col lithograph. 28-Apr-3 Christie's, Rockefeller NY #60/R est:5000-7000

£6329 $10000 €9494 Portrait of young girl (39x30cm-15x12in) i. lithograph. 28-Apr-3 Christie's, Rockefeller NY #159/R est:7000-9000

£6329 $10000 €9494 Paloma and her doll, white background (72x55cm-28x22in) s.i.num.50 lithograph. 28-Apr-3 Christie's, Rockefeller NY #219/R est:3000-5000

£6329 $10000 €9494 Dances (48x62cm-19x24in) s.i.num.50 lithograph. 28-Apr-3 Christie's, Rockefeller NY #237/R est:2000-3000

£6329 $10000 €9494 Little artist (65x50cm-26x20in) s.i.num/50 lithograph two. 28-Apr-3 Christie's, Rockefeller NY #255/R est:4000-6000

£6329 $10000 €9494 Girl with hat (65x50cm-26x20in) s.i.num.50 lithograph. 28-Apr-3 Christie's, Rockefeller NY #306/R est:3000-4000

£6338 $10521 €9000 Le repos du sculpteur devant le petit torse (19x27cm-7x11in) s.d. drypoint etching. 14-Jun-3 Hauswedell & Nolte, Hamburg #1523/R est:12000

£6410 $10000 €9615 Minotaure, une coupe a la main, et jeune femme (34x45cm-13x18in) s. etching edition of 250. 5-Nov-2 Christie's, Rockefeller NY #227/R est:10000-12000

£6410 $10000 €9615 Minotaure caressant une femme (34x45cm-13x18in) s. etching edition of 250. 5-Nov-2 Christie's, Rockefeller NY #228/R est:9000-12000

£6410 $10000 €9615 Tete de femme (47x37cm-19x15in) st.sig.num.25/50 drypoint. 5-Nov-2 Christie's, Rockefeller NY #233/R est:10000-15000

£6410 $10000 €9615 La repetition (50x5cm-20x2in) s. num.2/50 lithograph. 7-Nov-2 Swann Galleries, New York #785/R est:8000-12000

£6410 $9936 €10000 Le bain (34x29cm-13x11in) s.d. drypoint etching. 7-Dec-2 Hauswedell & Nolte, Hamburg #976/R est:10000

£6500 $10140 €9750 Taureau (32x44cm-13x17in) lithograph one of 18. 9-Oct-2 Christie's, London #1/R est:3000-5000

£6500 $10140 €9750 Marie Therese en femme torero (45x34cm-18x13in) s. etching. 9-Oct-2 Christie's, London #10/R est:8000-12000

£6500 $10140 €9750 Mousquetaire attable avec un jeune garcon, evoquant sa vie (50x65cm-20x26in) s.num.5/50 etching drypoint. 9-Oct-2 Christie's, London #53/R est:2800-3200

£6500 $10140 €9750 Les trois Graces (46x31cm-18x12in) s.num.1/100 etching. 25-Mar-3 Sotheby's, London #126/R est:3000-4000

£6500 $10725 €9425 Le repos du minotaure, champagne et amante (19x27cm-7x11in) s. etching from edition of 260. 2-Jul-3 Christie's, London #154/R est:6000-8000

£6500 $10725 €9425 Jeune femme au corsage a triangles (65x50cm-26x20in) s.num.42/50 lithograph. 2-Jul-3 Christie's, London #162/R est:5000-7000

£6522 $10109 €9783 Fumeur (42x32cm-17x13in) s. num.43/50 vernis mou. 4-Dec-2 Koller, Zurich #392/R est:5800-8000 (S.FR 15000)

£6748 $11000 €10122 Cavalier et valet (9x12cm-4x5in) s. etching aquatint two. 13-Feb-3 Christie's, Rockefeller NY #137/R

£6918 $11000 €10377 Marie-Therese en femme torero (30x24cm-12x9in) s. etching edition of 250. 29-Apr-3 Christie's, Rockefeller NY #530/R est:12000-18000

£6918 $11000 €10377 Mameluk enlevant une femme. Celestine, fille et vieux client (23x30cm-9x12in) s. one num.22/50 etching drypoint one num.5/50 aquatint two. 29-Apr-3 Christie's, Rockefeller NY #555/R est:6000-8000

£6918 $11000 €10377 Couple et petit valet encadres par une poriere. Amours ancillaires (12x9cm-5x4in) s. one num.31/50 one num.33/50 aquatint two. 29-Apr-3 Christie's, Rockefeller NY #564/R est:6000-8000

£6918 $11000 €10377 Tete de face, portrait de Marie-Therese de Face (31x23cm-12x9in) etching aquatint drypoint edition of 55. 2-May-3 Sotheby's, New York #277/R est:7000-10000

£6918 $11000 €10377 Au cabaret (23x30cm-9x12in) brown-black etching one of 108. 2-May-3 Sotheby's, New York #278/R est:8000-12000

£6918 $11000 €10377 Tete de femme au chapeau (16x10cm-6x4in) etching. 2-May-3 Sotheby's, New York #282/R est:6000-8000

£6918 $11000 €10377 Les deux femmes nues (32x44cm-13x17in) lithograph prov. 2-May-3 Sotheby's, New York #283/R est:4000-6000

£6918 $11000 €10377 347 series no 109 (29x35cm-11x14in) s.num.35/50 aquatint. 2-May-3 Sotheby's, New York #314/R est:5000-7000

£6962 $11000 €10443 Musician faun no.3 (66x54cm-26x21in) s.i.num.6/6 lithograph. 28-Apr-3 Christie's, Rockefeller NY #99/R est:4000-6000

£6962 $11000 €10443 Bull's head turned to the left. Bull's head turned to the right (65x50cm-26x20in) s.i.num.6/6 lithograph pair. 28-Apr-3 Christie's, Rockefeller NY #107/R est:2000-3000

£6962 $11000 €10443 Composed figure (65x50cm-26x20in) s.i.num.50 lithograph. 28-Apr-3 Christie's, Rockefeller NY #173/R est:6000-8000

£6962 $11000 €10443 Don Quixote and Sancho Panza I and II (47x39cm-19x15in) s.i.num.50 lithograph two. 28-Apr-3 Christie's, Rockefeller NY #211/R est:2000-3000

£6962 $11000 €10443 Portrait of woman (64x37cm-25x15in) s.i.num.50 lithograph. 28-Apr-3 Christie's, Rockefeller NY #263/R est:6000-8000

£6962 $11000 €10443 Shakespeare (22x18cm-9x7in) s.num.25 lithograph. 28-Apr-3 Christie's, Rockefeller NY #347/R est:1000-2000

£7000 $10920 €10500 Souvenirs, cirque avec El Gigante, et autoportrait en bebe-vieillard (65x47cm-26x19in) s.num.6/50 aquatint etching drypoint. 9-Oct-2 Christie's, London #39/R est:5000-8000

£7000 $10920 €10500 Huit silhouttes (33x44cm-13x17in) s.num.8/50 lithograph. 9-Oct-2 Christie's, London #159/R est:1000-1500

£7000 $10920 €10500 Rembrandt et femme au voile (50x38cm-20x15in) s. etching. 10-Oct-2 Sotheby's, London #81/R est:4000-6000

£7000 $11550 €10150 Picador, femme et cheval (64x53cm-25x21in) s.num.32/50 col linocut. 2-Jul-3 Christie's, London #166/R est:7000-10000

£7000 $11550 €10150 Figure (66x50cm-26x20in) s.num.31/50 lithograph. 2-Jul-3 Christie's, London #304/R est:4000-6000

£7042 $11690 €10000 Francoise au soleil (54x46cm-21x18in) s. lithograph. 14-Jun-3 Hauswedell & Nolte, Hamburg #1532/R est:15000

£7051 $11000 €10577 Variation autour de Don Quichotte et Dulcinee (50x60cm-20x24in) s.num.22/50 aquatint. 5-Nov-2 Christie's, Rockefeller NY #293/R est:8000-10000

£7051 $10929 €11000 Le repos du sculpteur, IV (19x27cm-7x11in) s.d. etching. 7-Dec-2 Hauswedell & Nolte, Hamburg #989/R est:12000

£7200 $11232 €10800 Tete de jeune femme tournee a droit (67x51cm-26x20in) lithograph. 9-Oct-2 Christie's, London #171/R est:2500-3500

£7362 $12000 €11043 Sexe a l'ancienne (41x49cm-16x19in) s. num.22/50 et aquatint exec.1968 pair. 13-Feb-3 Christie's, Rockefeller NY #141/R

£7362 $12000 €11043 Vieux faune (12x9cm-5x4in) s.i. etching pair. 13-Feb-3 Christie's, Rockefeller NY #135/R

£7362 $12000 €11043 Circus (9x12cm-4x5in) s.i. aquatint etching exec.1968 two. 13-Feb-3 Christie's, Rockefeller NY #133/R

£7394 $12275 €10500 Danse nocturne avec un hibou (53x64cm-21x25in) s.num. col engraving vellum on linoleum. 12-Jun-3 Piasa, Paris #158/R

£7500 $11625 €11250 Deux figures nues (51x44cm-20x17in) s.num.67 drypoint scraper. 3-Dec-2 Christie's, London #182/R est:8000-12000

£7547 $12000 €11321 Salome (40x35cm-16x14in) drypoint edition of 250. 29-Apr-3 Christie's, Rockefeller NY #524/R est:15000-20000

£7547 $12000 €11321 Buste au corsage a carreaux (55x44cm-22x17in) s.num.21/50 lithograph. 29-Apr-3 Christie's, Rockefeller NY #545/R est:15000-20000

£7547 $12000 €11321 Complications apres l'enlevement. Cavalier et son valet, Celestine et maja (25x29cm-10x11in) s. one num.6/50 one num.30/50 aquatint one with etching two. 29-Apr-3 Christie's, Rockefeller NY #559/R est:6000-8000

£7547 $12000 €11321 La sieste, couple. Homme Rembranesque a la pipe (15x21cm-6x8in) s. one num.22/50 one num.31/50 etching tow. 29-Apr-3 Christie's, Rockefeller NY #572/R est:5000-7000

£7547 $12000 €11321 Peintre devant une des Trois Graces de Raphael. Clin d'oeil a Valazquez (32x32cm-13x13in) s. one num.32/50 one num.15/50 etching two. 29-Apr-3 Christie's, Rockefeller NY #571/R est:6000-8000

£7547 $12000 €11321 Television, gymnastique au sol. Deux femmes batifolant sur un matelas (21x15cm-8x6in) s. one num.43/50 one num.5/50 etching two. 29-Apr-3 Christie's, Rockefeller NY #574/R est:6000-8000

£7547 $12000 €11321 Les trois femmes (18x13cm-7x5in) s. drypoint edition of 103. 2-May-3 Sotheby's, New York #254a/R est:15000-20000

£7547 $12000 €11321 Femme torero (49x69cm-19x27in) etching edition of 50. 2-May-3 Sotheby's, New York #272a/R est:8000-12000

£7547 $12000 €11321 Garcon et dormeuse (24x29cm-9x11in) s. etching aquatint edition of 310. 2-May-3 Sotheby's, New York #275/R est:15000-20000

£7595 $12000 €12000 La mere et les enfants (56x76cm-22x30in) s. lithograph exec.1953 one of 50. 29-Nov-2 Villa Grisebach, Berlin #86/R est:12000-15000

£7595 $12000 €11393 Head of young girl (27x21cm-11x8in) s.i.num lithograph set of four. 28-Apr-3 Christie's, Rockefeller NY #5/R est:12000-18000

£7595 $12000 €11393 Head of a young woman (30x22cm-12x9in) i. lithograph. 28-Apr-3 Christie's, Rockefeller NY #44/R est:5000-7000

£7595 $12000 €11393 Mother and children (48x74cm-19x29in) s.i.num.50 lithograph. 28-Apr-3 Christie's, Rockefeller NY #230/R est:4000-6000

£7595 $12000 €11393 Dance of the banderillas (50x66cm-20x26in) s.i.num.50 lithograph. 28-Apr-3 Christie's, Rockefeller NY #239/R est:2500-3500

£7595 $12000 €11393 Two women on the beach (48x62cm-19x24in) s.i.num.50 lithograph. 28-Apr-3 Christie's, Rockefeller NY #264/R est:3000-5000

£7692 $12000 €11538 David et Bethsabee (65x50cm-26x20in) s.num.35/50 lithograph. 5-Nov-2 Christie's, Rockefeller NY #239/R est:15000-20000

£7692 $12000 €11538 Tete de femme (75x62cm-30x24in) s.num.18/50 col linocut. 5-Nov-2 Christie's, Rockefeller NY #248/R est:6000-8000

£7692 $11923 €12000 Minotaure, buveur et femmes (30x37cm-12x15in) s.d. etching. 7-Dec-2 Hauswedell & Nolte, Hamburg #991/R est:14000

£7708 $12025 €11562 Sculpteur, modele accroupi et tete sculptee (27x19cm-11x7in) s. etching. 5-Nov-2 Bukowskis, Stockholm #610/R est:80000-100000 (S.KR 110000)

£7756 $12178 €12100 Dormeuse (270x350cm-106x138in) s.i. linocut. 12-Dec-2 Piasa, Paris #110/R

£7800 $12168 €11700 Paloma et sa poupee, fond blanc (76x57cm-30x22in) s.num.17/50 lithograph. 9-Oct-2 Christie's, London #182/R est:6000-8000

£8000 $12480 €12000 Menines et gentilshommes dans la Sierra (50x66cm-20x26in) s.num.43/50 aquatint. 9-Oct-2 Christie's, London #66/R est:2000-3000

£8000 $12400 €12000 Modele accroupi, sculpture de dos et tete barbue (27x19cm-11x7in) s.num.1/3 etching engraving. 5-Dec-2 Sotheby's, London #170/R est:8000-10000

£8176 $13000 €12264 Reveries d'opium. Raphael et la fornarina (17x21cm-7x8in) s. one num.5/50 one num.6/50 etching two. 29-Apr-3 Christie's, Rockefeller NY #576/R est:6000-8000

£8176 $13000 €12264 Homme assis aupres d'une femme se coiffant. Matamore endimanche (21x27cm-8x11in) s.num.22/50 one aquatint one etching two. 29-Apr-3 Christie's, Rockefeller NY #578/R est:6000-8000

£8176 $13000 €12264 Scene bachique au minotaure (29x36cm-11x14in) s. etching edition of 310. 2-May-3 Sotheby's, New York #269/R est:12000-16000

£8176 $13000 €12264 Femme torero (30x24cm-12x9in) s. etching edition of 50. 2-May-3 Sotheby's, New York #273/R est:10000-15000

£8176 $13000 €12264 Buste de femme a la chaise (25x14cm-10x6in) etching aquatint drypoint. 2-May-3 Sotheby's, New York #280/R est:6000-8000

£8228 $13000 €12342 Pan (66x51cm-26x20in) s.i.num.6/6 lithograph. 28-Apr-3 Christie's, Rockefeller NY #96/R est:4000-6000

£8228 $13000 €12342 Faun with branches (66x53cm-26x21in) s.i.num.6/6 lithograph. 28-Apr-3 Christie's, Rockefeller NY #98/R est:4000-6000

£8228 $13000 €12342 Head of young girl (40x30cm-16x12in) i. lithograph. 28-Apr-3 Christie's, Rockefeller NY #162/R est:6000-8000

£8228 $13000 €12342 Head on black background (70x55cm-28x22in) s.i.num.50 lithograph. 28-Apr-3 Christie's, Rockefeller NY #232/R est:6000-8000

£8333 $13000 €12500 L'homme a la guitare (24x18cm-9x7in) s.num.23/100 engraving. 5-Nov-2 Christie's, Rockefeller NY #216/R est:15000-20000

£8333 $12917 €13000 Le repos du sculpteur devant le petit torse (19x27cm-7x11in) s. etching. 7-Dec-2 Hauswedell & Nolte, Hamburg #986/R est:7000

£8500 $13175 €12750 David et Bethsabee (65x47cm-26x19in) s. lithograph. 5-Dec-2 Sotheby's, London #176/R est:7000-9000

£8500 $14025 €12325 Buste au fond etoile (65x50cm-26x20in) s.num.38/50 lithograph. 2-Jul-3 Christie's, London #305/R est:8000-12000

£8784 $13703 €13000 Les trois femmes (18x13cm-7x5in) drypoint etching. 28-Mar-3 Ketterer, Hamburg #564/R est:12000-15000

£8800 $13728 €13200 Jeune garcon revant, les femmes (68x57cm-27x22in) s.num.5/50 etching drypoint aquatint. 9-Oct-2 Christie's, London #220/R est:5000-8000

£8805 $14000 €13208 Ecuyere de cirque, homme Rembranesque. Peintre, modele au chapeau (28x39cm-11x15in) s.num.22/50 etching two. 29-Apr-3 Christie's, Rockefeller NY #575/R est:6000-8000

£8805 $14000 €13208 Raphael et la fornarina IV et XI (23x33cm-9x13in) s. one num.29/50 one num.33/50 etching two. 29-Apr-3 Christie's, Rockefeller NY #577/R est:6000-8000

£8861 $14000 €13292 Figure (74x56cm-29x22in) i. lithograph. 28-Apr-3 Christie's, Rockefeller NY #79/R est:5000-7000

£8861 $14000 €13292 Head of a young girl (30x23cm-12x9in) i.lithograph set of three. 28-Apr-3 Christie's, Rockefeller NY #7/R est:9000-12000

£8861 $14000 €13292 Woman with a necklace (59x40cm-23x16in) s.i.num.6/6 lithograph. 28-Apr-3 Christie's, Rockefeller NY #75/R est:4000-6000

£8861 $14000 €13292 Paloma and Claude (39x53cm-15x21in) i. lithograph. 28-Apr-3 Christie's, Rockefeller NY #193/R est:8000-12000

£9000 $14040 €13500 Scene bacchique au minotaure (34x45cm-13x18in) s. etching edition of 260. 9-Oct-2 Christie's, London #13/R est:10000-15000

£9000 $14850 €13050 Sculpteur et modele (36x29cm-14x11in) s. etching edition of 300. 1-Jul-3 Sotheby's, London #117/R est:10000-12000

£9125 $14418 €13688 Scene Bachique au minotaure - La suite Vollard (30x37cm-12x15in) s. etching lit. 28-Apr-3 Bukowskis, Stockholm #487/R est:100000-150000 (S.KR 120000)

£9155 $15197 €13000 Jacqueline au mouchoir noir (64x49cm-25x19in) s.d. lithograph. 14-Jun-3 Hauswedell & Nolte, Hamburg #1533/R est:15000

£9259 $14907 €13889 Sculpteur et rois dansueses sculptees (22x31cm-9x12in) s.i.d.2 mars 1934 etching lit. 7-May-3 Dobiaschofsky, Bern #1877/R est:24000 (S.FR 20000)

£9434 $15000 €14151 Figure composee (66x50cm-26x20in) s.num.35/50 lithograph. 29-Apr-3 Christie's, Rockefeller NY #536/R est:10000-15000

£9434 $15000 €14151 Peintre a la palette (64x53cm-25x21in) s.num.54/150 linocut. 29-Apr-3 Christie's, Rockefeller NY #549/R est:8000-10000

£9434 $15000 €14151 Femme se coiffant. Arlequin et personnages divers. s.num.22/50 one etching one aquatint two. 29-Apr-3 Christie's, Rockefeller NY #551/R est:6000-8000

£9434 $15000 €14151 Femme au chapeau a fleurs (35x27cm-14x11in) brown black linoleum cut. 2-May-3 Sotheby's, New York #301/R est:7000-10000

£9434 $15000 €14151 Jacqueline au bandeau (35x27cm-14x11in) s.num.10/50 brown black linoleum cut. 2-May-3 Sotheby's, New York #303/R est:15000-20000

£9434 $15000 €14151 Le dejeuner sur l'herbe (35x27cm-14x11in) s.num.47/50 col linoleum. 1-May-3 Swann Galleries, New York #570/R est:18000-22000

£9494 $15000 €14241 Francoise (61x48cm-24x19in) i. lithograph. 28-Apr-3 Christie's, Rockefeller NY #33/R est:5000-8000

£9494 $15000 €14241 Composed figure (66x50cm-26x20in) s.i.num.50 lithograph. 28-Apr-3 Christie's, Rockefeller NY #174/R est:4000-6000

£9500 $14820 €14250 Suenoy mentira de Franco (38x57cm-15x22in) s.num.125/150 etching aquatint two. 25-Mar-3 Sotheby's, London #135/R est:6000-8000

£9655 $16124 €14000 L'espagnole (62x44cm-24x17in) s.num.10/50 col linoleum. 9-Jul-3 Cornette de St.Cyr, Paris #98/R est:12000-15000

£9800 $15288 €14700 Minotaure, buveur et femme (18x24cm-7x9in) s. etching. 25-Mar-3 Sotheby's, London #127/R est:8000-10000

£10000 $16500 €14500 Tete de femme, Madeleine (12x9cm-5x4in) etching drypoint. 2-Jul-3 Christie's, London #301/R est:6000-8000

£10063 $16000 €15095 La toilette de la mere (24x18cm-9x7in) etching edition of 250 prov. 29-Apr-3 Christie's, Rockefeller NY #523/R est:10000-15000

£10063 $16000 €15095 Nature morte, guitare, clarinette et bouteille (10x15cm-4x6in) etching scraper two framed together prov. 29-Apr-3 Christie's, Rockefeller NY #525/R est:20000-30000

£10063 $16000 €15095 Le peintre sur la plage (47x82cm-19x32in) s.num.6/50 aquatint. 29-Apr-3 Christie's, Rockefeller NY #542/R est:15000-20000

£10127 $16000 €15191 Long haired young girl (44x32cm-17x13in) s.i.num. lithograph set of four. 28-Apr-3 Christie's, Rockefeller NY #11/R est:15000-20000

£10127 $16000 €15191 Owl with chair, ochre background (66x50cm-26x20in) s.i.num.6/6 col lithograph. 28-Apr-3 Christie's, Rockefeller NY #47/R est:6000-8000

£10127 $16000 €15191 Head of a young girl (40x29cm-16x11in) s.i.num.50 lithograph. 28-Apr-3 Christie's, Rockefeller NY #156/R est:5000-7000

£10127 $16000 €15191 Portrait of Madame X (77x52cm-30x20in) i. lithograph. 28-Apr-3 Christie's, Rockefeller NY #233/R est:4000-6000

£10161 $15851 €15242 Baccanale au Taureu Noir (52x64cm-20x25in) s.num.2/50 col linocut 1959 lit. 6-Nov-2 AB Stockholms Auktionsverk #1044/R est:100000-125000 (S.KR 145000)

£10256 $16000 €15384 Tete de jeune fille (40x30cm-16x12in) s.num.8/50 lithograph. 7-Nov-2 Swann Galleries, New York #783/R est:14000-16000

£10500 $16380 €15750 Le depart (56x60cm-22x24in) s.i. col lithograph. 9-Oct-2 Christie's, London #47/R est:5000-7000

£10512 $16398 €15768 Femme au chapeau sur fond raye, surnomme Dolores (41x31cm-16x12in) s.num.43/50 col aquatint. 5-Nov-2 Bukowskis, Stockholm #622/R est:100000-110000 (S.KR 150000)

£10577 $16606 €16500 Jeune homme coronne de feuillage (350x270cm-138x106in) s.i. linocut. 12-Dec-2 Piasa, Paris #111/R

£10759 $17000 €16139 Sleeping woman (50x65cm-20x26in) s.i.num.6/6 lithograph. 28-Apr-3 Christie's, Rockefeller NY #72/R est:5000-7000

£10759 $17000 €16139 Table with fish, black background (55x70cm-22x28in) i. lithograph set of three. 28-Apr-3 Christie's, Rockefeller NY #145/R est:9000-12000

£10759 $17000 €16139 Young woman (40x30cm-16x12in) s. lithograph two. 28-Apr-3 Christie's, Rockefeller NY #160/R est:8000-10000

£10759 $17000 €16139 Venus and love (65x35cm-26x14in) s.i.num.50 lithograph after Cranach. 28-Apr-3 Christie's, Rockefeller NY #189/R est:6000-8000

£10791 $17698 €15000 Four nude women and sculpted head (22x31cm-9x12in) s.i.d.10 mars XXXIV etching. 6-Jun-3 Ketterer, Munich #121/R est:12000-14000

£11111 $17556 €16000 Les vendangeurs (62x75cm-24x30in) s.num.44/50 col linoleum. 26-Apr-3 Cornette de St.Cyr, Paris #27/R est:8000-12000

£11321 $18000 €16982 Suenyo y Mentira de Franco (31x41cm-12x16in) s.num.128/150 etching aquatint pair. 2-May-3 Sotheby's, New York #279/R est:20000-30000

£11321 $18000 €16982 Buste de femme (65x49cm-26x19in) s.num.20/50 aquatint engraving. 2-May-3 Sotheby's, New York #292/R est:10000-15000

£11468 $19151 €16629 Le peintre sur la plage (47x83cm-19x33in) s.i. aquatint. 20-Jun-3 Kornfeld, Bern #128/R est:25000 (S.FR 25000)

£12025 $19000 €18038 Francoise (63x42cm-25x17in) i. lithograph. 28-Apr-3 Christie's, Rockefeller NY #32/R est:5000-8000
£12025 $19000 €18038 Francoise (59x49cm-23x19in) s.num.50 lithograph. 28-Apr-3 Christie's, Rockefeller NY #34/R est:5000-8000
£12025 $19000 €18038 Armchair woman no.2 (66x50cm-26x20in) i. lithograph. 28-Apr-3 Christie's, Rockefeller NY #128/R est:12000-15000
£12025 $19000 €18038 Lobsters and fish (74x103cm-29x41in) s.num.50 lithograph. 28-Apr-3 Christie's, Rockefeller NY #147/R est:10000-15000
£12025 $19000 €18038 Portrait of Mademoiselle Rosengart (62x46cm-24x18in) i. lithograph. 28-Apr-3 Christie's, Rockefeller NY #345/R est:8000-10000
£12579 $20000 €18869 Deux femmes (53x64cm-21x25in) s.num.2/50 col linocut. 29-Apr-3 Christie's, Rockefeller NY #546/R est:14000-18000
£12579 $20000 €18869 Jacqueline de profil a droite (56x44cm-22x17in) s.num.8/50 lithograph. 2-May-3 Sotheby's, New York #295/R est:20000-25000
£12658 $20000 €18987 Bust of a woman with white bodice (70x51cm-28x20in) s.i.num.50 lithograph. 28-Apr-3 Christie's, Rockefeller NY #299/R est:4000-6000
£12658 $20000 €18987 Jacqueline with black kerchief (63x74cm-25x29in) s.i.num.50 lithograph two. 28-Apr-3 Christie's, Rockefeller NY #302/R est:8000-10000
£12928 $20426 €19392 Apres la pique (53x64cm-21x25in) s.num.2/50 col linocut prov.lit. 28-Apr-3 Bukowskis, Stockholm #496/R est:150000-200000 (S.KR 170000)
£13000 $20150 €19500 Minotaure, une coupe a la main, et jeune femme (19x27cm-7x11in) s.num.1/3 etching engraving. 5-Dec-2 Sotheby's, London #171/R est:12000-15000
£13000 $21450 €18850 Le banderillero (54x67cm-21x26in) s.num.29/50 col lithograph. 2-Jul-3 Christie's, London #321/R est:7000-10000
£13208 $21000 €19812 Quatre femmes nues et tete sculptee (22x31cm-9x12in) s. etching engraving edition of 50. 2-May-3 Sotheby's, New York #272/R est:15000-20000
£13500 $21060 €20250 Les jeux et la lecture (51x66cm-20x26in) s. lithograph edition of 50. 9-Oct-2 Christie's, London #181/R est:10000-15000
£13836 $22000 €20754 Les jeux et la lecture (48x62cm-19x24in) s.num.23/50 lithograph. 29-Apr-3 Christie's, Rockefeller NY #541/R est:18000-22000
£13924 $22000 €20886 Francoise (62x48cm-24x19in) s.i.num.6/6 lithograph. 28-Apr-3 Christie's, Rockefeller NY #36/R est:5000-8000
£13924 $22000 €20886 Armchair woman no.1 (70x54cm-28x21in) i. lithograph. 28-Apr-3 Christie's, Rockefeller NY #118/R est:10000-15000
£13924 $22000 €20886 Head of Jacqueline (58x39cm-23x15in) i. lithograph. 28-Apr-3 Christie's, Rockefeller NY #326/R est:4000-6000
£14103 $22000 €21155 Scene bacchique au minotaure (34x45cm-13x18in) s. etching edition of 250. 5-Nov-2 Christie's, Rockefeller NY #229/R est:20000-25000
£14194 $22426 €22000 Francoise au noeud dans les cheveux (63x47cm-25x19in) s.num.37/50 lithograph lit. 17-Dec-2 Rossini, Paris #8/R
£15000 $23400 €22500 Francoise aux cheveux ondules (65x49cm-26x19in) s.num.21/50 lithograph. 9-Oct-2 Christie's, London #183/R est:12000-15000
£15190 $24000 €22785 Head of young girl (64x49cm-25x19in) i. lithograph. 28-Apr-3 Christie's, Rockefeller NY #152/R est:5000-7000
£15190 $24000 €22785 Still life with flower. Head of young girl (50x65cm-20x26in) s.i.num.50 lithograph set of three. 28-Apr-3 Christie's, Rockefeller NY #153/R est:10000-15000
£15190 $24000 €22785 Check cloth bodice (65x49cm-26x19in) s.i.num.50 lithograph. 28-Apr-3 Christie's, Rockefeller NY #182/R est:5000-8000
£15723 $25000 €23585 Les deux femmes (26x36cm-10x14in) lithograph prov. 2-May-3 Sotheby's, New York #284/R est:4000-6000
£15723 $25000 €23585 Figure au corsage (65x50cm-26x20in) s.num.33/50 col lithograph. 2-May-3 Sotheby's, New York #287/R est:30000-50000
£16000 $24960 €24000 Buste de profil (64x49cm-25x19in) s.num.6/50 lithograph. 10-Oct-2 Sotheby's, London #83/R est:12000-15000
£16000 $26400 €23200 Baccanale a l'acrobate (52x64cm-20x25in) s.num.43/50 col linocut. 2-Jul-3 Christie's, London #320/R est:12000-18000
£16456 $26000 €24684 Armchair woman no.1 (69x54cm-27x21in) i. lithograph. 28-Apr-3 Christie's, Rockefeller NY #124/R est:15000-20000
£16456 $26000 €24684 Armchair woman no.3 (66x50cm-26x20in) i. lithograph. 28-Apr-3 Christie's, Rockefeller NY #130/R est:12000-15000
£16456 $26000 €24684 Armchair woman no.3 (65x49cm-26x19in) i. lithograph. 28-Apr-3 Christie's, Rockefeller NY #131/R est:12000-15000
£16456 $26000 €24684 Head of young girl (64x49cm-25x19in) i. lithograph. 28-Apr-3 Christie's, Rockefeller NY #150/R est:5000-7000
£16456 $26000 €24684 Modern style bust (54x50cm-21x20in) s.i.num.50 lithograph. 28-Apr-3 Christie's, Rockefeller NY #172/R est:6000-8000
£16456 $26000 €24684 Youth (50x55cm-20x22in) s.num.50 lithograph two. 28-Apr-3 Christie's, Rockefeller NY #195/R est:12000-18000
£16456 $26000 €24684 Paloma and her doll, black background (70x55cm-28x22in) s.i. lithograph. 28-Apr-3 Christie's, Rockefeller NY #220/R est:4000-6000
£16667 $26000 €25001 Grande tete de femme (75x62cm-30x24in) s.num.44/50 col linocut. 5-Nov-2 Christie's, Rockefeller NY #251/R est:20000-30000
£16667 $26000 €25001 Grande tete de femme au chapeau (75x62cm-30x24in) s.num.28/50 col linocut. 5-Nov-2 Christie's, Rockefeller NY #252/R est:20000-30000
£17000 $26520 €25500 Pique II (62x75cm-24x30in) s.num.26/50 col linocut. 9-Oct-2 Christie's, London #15/R est:8000-12000
£17000 $26520 €25500 Pique, rouge et jaune (62x75cm-24x30in) s.num.38/50 col linocut. 9-Oct-2 Christie's, London #16/R est:14000-16000
£17500 $27300 €26250 L'Italienne (66x50cm-26x20in) s.num.41/50 lithograph. 9-Oct-2 Christie's, London #173/R est:16000-18000
£17722 $28000 €26583 Francoise (65x50cm-26x20in) s.i.num.6/6 lithograph. 28-Apr-3 Christie's, Rockefeller NY #37/R est:5000-8000
£17722 $28000 €26583 Francoise the sun woman (54x45cm-21x18in) s.i.num6/6 lithograph. 28-Apr-3 Christie's, Rockefeller NY #42/R est:4000-6000
£17722 $28000 €26583 Head of woman (63x45cm-25x18in) i. lithograph. 28-Apr-3 Christie's, Rockefeller NY #106/R est:6000-8000
£17722 $28000 €26583 Armchair woman no.4 (67x54cm-26x21in) i. lithograph. 28-Apr-3 Christie's, Rockefeller NY #132/R est:15000-20000
£17722 $28000 €26583 Italian woman (44x35cm-17x14in) s.i.num.50 lithograph two. 28-Apr-3 Christie's, Rockefeller NY #229/R est:12000-18000
£18000 $28080 €27000 Buste de femme au corsage blanc (77x57cm-30x22in) s.num.12/50 lithograph. 9-Oct-2 Christie's, London #186/R est:18000-22000
£18354 $29000 €27531 Bull (30x41cm-12x16in) s.i.num. lithograph set of four. 28-Apr-3 Christie's, Rockefeller NY #14/R est:15000-20000
£18987 $30000 €28481 Head of a young girl (65x50cm-26x20in) i.verso lithograph. 28-Apr-3 Christie's, Rockefeller NY #151/R est:5000-7000
£18987 $30000 €28481 Young girl inspired by Cranach (64x49cm-25x19in) s.num.25 lithograph two. 28-Apr-3 Christie's, Rockefeller NY #183/R est:10000-15000
£18987 $30000 €28481 Venus and love (64x35cm-25x14in) s.i.num.50 lithograph two. 28-Apr-3 Christie's, Rockefeller NY #190/R est:12000-18000
£18987 $30000 €28481 Woman at the mirror (39x52cm-15x20in) i. lithograph set of five. 28-Apr-3 Christie's, Rockefeller NY #204/R est:10000-15000
£19178 $29918 €28000 Portrait d'Andre Breton (15x10cm-6x4in) drypoint. 14-Apr-3 Laurence Calmels, Paris #4007/R est:12000
£20000 $31200 €30000 Minotaure caressant une dormeuse (34x45cm-13x18in) s. drypoint edition of 260. 9-Oct-2 Christie's, London #14/R est:20000-30000
£20000 $31200 €30000 Tete de femme no 5, portrait de Dora Maar (45x34cm-18x13in) col aquatint drypoint. 9-Oct-2 Christie's, London #177/R est:20000-30000
£20000 $31200 €30000 Femme au fauteuil no 1 (70x55cm-28x22in) s.num.2/50 lithograph. 9-Oct-2 Christie's, London #184/R est:20000-30000
£20000 $31000 €30000 Minotaure caressant une Dormeuse (34x44cm-13x17in) s. drypoint. 3-Dec-2 Christie's, London #183/R est:20000-30000
£20000 $33000 €29000 Minotaure caressant une dormeuse (30x37cm-12x15in) s. drypoint from edition of 260. 2-Jul-3 Christie's, London #159/R est:20000-30000
£20126 $32000 €30189 Faune devoilant une femme (32x42cm-13x17in) bears sig. etching aquatint edition of 250. 29-Apr-3 Christie's, Rockefeller NY #531/R est:40000-60000
£20139 $31819 €29000 Bachanale (65x75cm-26x30in) s.num.44/50 col linoleum. 26-Apr-3 Cornette de St.Cyr, Paris #31/R est:30000-40000
£20152 $31840 €30228 Tete de femme aux cheveux flous (61x45cm-24x18in) s.num.8/50 aquatint lit. 28-Apr-3 Bukowskis, Stockholm #491/R est:200000-250000 (S.KR 265000)
£20253 $32000 €30380 Armchair woman no.2 (70x55cm-28x22in) i. lithograph. 28-Apr-3 Christie's, Rockefeller NY #129/R est:15000-20000
£20253 $32000 €30380 Table with fish (54x69cm-21x27in) i. lithograph set of five. 28-Apr-3 Christie's, Rockefeller NY #144/R est:15000-20000
£20253 $32000 €30380 Check cloth bodice (65x50cm-26x20in) s.i.num.50 col lithograph. 28-Apr-3 Christie's, Rockefeller NY #181/R est:5000-8000
£20253 $32000 €30380 Bust with check cloth bodice (56x44cm-22x17in) s.i.num.50 lithograph two. 28-Apr-3 Christie's, Rockefeller NY #296/R est:8000-10000
£20440 $32500 €30660 La femme a la resille (66x50cm-26x20in) i.verso black lithograph. 2-May-3 Sotheby's, New York #288/R est:15000-20000
£20440 $32500 €30660 Faunes et chevre (53x63cm-21x25in) s. col linoleum cut. 2-May-3 Sotheby's, New York #298/R est:25000-35000
£20513 $32000 €30770 Picasso, son oeuvre, et son public (56x72cm-22x28in) s.num.5/50 etching. 5-Nov-2 Christie's, Rockefeller NY #255/R est:15000-20000
£20576 $31687 €30864 Deux femmes (53x64cm-21x25in) col linocut. 26-Oct-2 Heffel, Vancouver #35 est:30000-35000 (C.D 50000)
£21101 $35239 €30596 Faune devoilant une femme (31x42cm-12x17in) etching aquatint copperplate. 20-Jun-3 Kornfeld, Bern #127/R est:30000 (S.FR 46000)
£21519 $34000 €32279 Francoise with a bow in her hair (62x47cm-24x19in) s.i.num6/6 lithograph. 28-Apr-3 Christie's, Rockefeller NY #35/R est:5000-8000
£21519 $34000 €32279 Francoise (63x49cm-25x19in) s.i.num.6/6 lithograph. 28-Apr-3 Christie's, Rockefeller NY #38/R est:5000-8000
£21519 $34000 €32279 Francoise (61x46cm-24x18in) s.i.num.6/6 lithograph. 28-Apr-3 Christie's, Rockefeller NY #40/R est:6000-10000

£21519 $34000 €32279 Stylized figure (65x49cm-26x19in) s.i.num.6/6 lithograph set of three. 28-Apr-3 Christie's, Rockefeller NY #114/R est:4000-6000

£21519 $34000 €32279 Archair woman no.1 (70x55cm-28x22in) i. lithograph. 28-Apr-3 Christie's, Rockefeller NY #119/R est:15000-20000

£22013 $35000 €33020 Tete de femme no 5, portrait of Dora (30x24cm-12x9in) col aquatint drypoint one of 105. 2-May-3 Sotheby's, New York #306/R est:15000-20000

£22436 $35000 €33654 Buste de profil, portrait de Jacqueline (66x51cm-26x20in) s.num.i.verso lithograph set of three prov. 5-Nov-2 Christie's, Rockefeller NY #245/R est:40000-50000

£22785 $36000 €34178 Head of young girl (31x26cm-12x10in) s.num.50 lithograph set of six. 28-Apr-3 Christie's, Rockefeller NY #9/R est:25000-30000

£23585 $37500 €35378 Portrait de Francoise a la resille (43x33cm-17x13in) aquatint drypoint scraper one of 9 impressions. 2-May-3 Sotheby's, New York #308/R est:20000-30000

£24051 $38000 €36077 Armchair woman (70x54cm-28x21in) i. lithograph. 28-Apr-3 Christie's, Rockefeller NY #122/R est:15000-20000

£24684 $39000 €37026 Bust in profile (64x49cm-25x19in) s.i.num.50 lithograph two. 28-Apr-3 Christie's, Rockefeller NY #294/R est:8000-10000

£25316 $40000 €37974 Francoise with wavy hair (65x50cm-26x20in) s.i.num.6/6 lithograph. 28-Apr-3 Christie's, Rockefeller NY #41/R est:6000-10000

£25316 $40000 €37974 Armchair woman no.1 (70x55cm-28x22in) i. lithograph. 28-Apr-3 Christie's, Rockefeller NY #120/R est:15000-20000

£25316 $40000 €37974 Armchair woman (70x55cm-28x22in) i. lithograph. 28-Apr-3 Christie's, Rockefeller NY #133/R est:15000-20000

£25316 $40000 €37974 Young girl with striped bodice (65x49cm-26x19in) i. lithograph two. 28-Apr-3 Christie's, Rockefeller NY #164/R est:12000-18000

£25641 $40000 €38462 Tete de femme (5x62cm-2x24in) s.num.44/50 col linocut. 5-Nov-2 Christie's, Rockefeller NY #250/R est:25000-35000

£26087 $42783 €36000 Femme au fauteuil - No 3 (65x49cm-26x19in) lithograph. 30-May-3 Villa Grisebach, Berlin #61/R est:35000-45000

£26582 $42000 €39873 Armchair woman no.1 (70x55cm-28x22in) i. lithograph. 28-Apr-3 Christie's, Rockefeller NY #123/R est:15000-20000

£26582 $42000 €39873 Armchair woman no.1 (70x51cm-28x20in) s.i.num.50 lithograph. 28-Apr-3 Christie's, Rockefeller NY #126/R est:15000-20000

£27848 $44000 €41772 Armchair woman no.1 (59x55cm-23x22in) i. lithograph. 28-Apr-3 Christie's, Rockefeller NY #125/R est:15000-20000

£28000 $46200 €40600 Minotaure aveugle guide par une fillette dans la nuit (25x35cm-10x14in) s. aquatint from edition of 260 prov. 2-Jul-3 Christie's, London #158/R est:30000-50000

£28302 $45000 €42453 Minotaure aveugle guide par une fillette dans la nuit (25x34cm-10x13in) s. aquatint drypoint edition of 310. 2-May-3 Sotheby's, New York #276/R est:35000-50000

£28302 $45000 €42453 Figure au corsage raye (65x50cm-26x20in) col lithograph. 2-May-3 Sotheby's, New York #286/R est:30000-40000

£28302 $45000 €42453 Tete de femme (64x52cm-25x20in) s.num.12/50 linoleum cut. 2-May-3 Sotheby's, New York #300/R est:40000-60000

£28481 $45000 €42722 Armchair woman (66x50cm-26x20in) i. col lithograph. 28-Apr-3 Christie's, Rockefeller NY #117/R est:10000-15000

£28481 $45000 €42722 Armchair woman no.1 (70x54cm-28x21in) i. lithograph. 28-Apr-3 Christie's, Rockefeller NY #121/R est:15000-20000

£28481 $45000 €42722 Armchair woman (57x50cm-22x20in) i. lithograph. 28-Apr-3 Christie's, Rockefeller NY #138/R est:10000-15000

£28481 $45000 €42722 Armchair woman (70x55cm-28x22in) i. lithograph. 28-Apr-3 Christie's, Rockefeller NY #140/R est:15000-20000

£28931 $46000 €43397 Minotaure caressant une dormeuse (30x37cm-12x15in) s. drypoint edition of 310. 2-May-3 Sotheby's, New York #271/R est:25000-35000

£29000 $47850 €42050 Jacqueline (75x62cm-30x24in) s.num.23/50 col cut linoleum. 1-Jul-3 Sotheby's, London #124/R est:30000-40000

£29658 $46859 €44487 Faune devoilant une famme - La suite Vollard (32x42cm-13x17in) s. aquatint lit. 28-Apr-3 Bukowskis, Stockholm #490/R est:350000-450000 (S.KR 390000)

£30000 $46800 €45000 Femme au corsage a fleurs (66x50cm-26x20in) s.i. i.verso lithograph. 9-Oct-2 Christie's, London #187/R est:34000-38000

£30380 $48000 €45570 Francoise (63x49cm-25x19in) s.i.num.6/6 lithograph. 28-Apr-3 Christie's, Rockefeller NY #39/R est:6000-10000

£30380 $48000 €45570 Dove (54x70cm-21x28in) s.i.num.6/6 lithograph. 28-Apr-3 Christie's, Rockefeller NY #146/R est:15000-20000

£30380 $48000 €45570 Armchair woman (74x54cm-29x21in) i.lithograph two. 28-Apr-3 Christie's, Rockefeller NY #161/R est:20000-30000

£30380 $48000 €45570 Bust of a young girl (63x49cm-25x19in) i. lithograph two. 28-Apr-3 Christie's, Rockefeller NY #165/R est:12000-18000

£31447 $50000 €47171 Femme au fauteuil (76x56cm-30x22in) s.num.8/50 lithograph. 2-May-3 Sotheby's, New York #285/R est:40000-60000

£31646 $50000 €47469 Armchair woman (66x50cm-26x20in) i. lithograph. 28-Apr-3 Christie's, Rockefeller NY #139/R est:15000-20000

£31646 $50000 €47469 Armchair woman (70x54cm-28x21in) i. lithograph. 28-Apr-3 Christie's, Rockefeller NY #142/R est:15000-20000

£31646 $50000 €47469 Jacqueline reading (56x44cm-22x17in) s.i.num.50 lithograph set of three. 28-Apr-3 Christie's, Rockefeller NY #297/R est:12000-18000

£34591 $55000 €51887 Les metamorphoses (33x26cm-13x10in) s.num.23 etchings 60. 2-May-3 Sotheby's, New York #257/R est:80000-100000

£34591 $55000 €51887 Venus et l'amour d'apres Cranach (75x43cm-30x17in) st.sig.i. aquatint. 2-May-3 Sotheby's, New York #319/R est:30000-50000

£34810 $55000 €52215 Armchair woman no.4 (70x55cm-28x22in) i. lithograph. 28-Apr-3 Christie's, Rockefeller NY #134/R est:15000-20000

£34810 $55000 €52215 Bust with star spangled background (64x49cm-25x19in) i. three different col lithograph. 28-Apr-3 Christie's, Rockefeller NY #171/R est:15000-20000

£35443 $56000 €53165 Women of Algiers, 2nd variation (23x34cm-9x13in) i. lithograph three. 28-Apr-3 Christie's, Rockefeller NY #258/R est:15000-20000

£36709 $58000 €55064 Seated woman and sleeping woman (50x62cm-20x24in) s.i.num.6/6 lithograph set of three. 28-Apr-3 Christie's, Rockefeller NY #89/R est:6000-10000

£37975 $60000 €56963 Armchair woman no.4 (70x57cm-28x22in) i. lithograph. 28-Apr-3 Christie's, Rockefeller NY #135/R est:15000-20000

£37975 $60000 €56963 Armchair woman no.4 (70x55cm-28x22in) s.num.6/6 lithograph. 28-Apr-3 Christie's, Rockefeller NY #136/R est:15000-20000

£37975 $60000 €56963 Armchair woman no.4 (70x55cm-28x22in) i. lithograph. 28-Apr-3 Christie's, Rockefeller NY #137/R est:15000-20000

£37975 $60000 €56963 Armchair woman (70x55cm-28x22in) i. lithograph. 28-Apr-3 Christie's, Rockefeller NY #141/R est:15000-20000

£37975 $60000 €56963 Armchair woman (70x54cm-28x21in) i. lithograph. 28-Apr-3 Christie's, Rockefeller NY #143/R est:15000-20000

£37975 $60000 €56963 Francoise on grey background (65x49cm-26x19in) s.i.num.50 lithograph three. 28-Apr-3 Christie's, Rockefeller NY #202/R est:18000-22000

£38991 $65115 €56537 L'Egyptienne - torse de femme (83x47cm-33x19in) s.i. aquatint. 20-Jun-3 Kornfeld, Bern #129/R est:100000 (S.FR 85000)

£39130 $64174 €54000 Le repas frugal (46x38cm-18x15in) etching. 29-May-3 Lempertz, Koln #863/R est:50000

£40881 $65000 €61322 Le dejeuner sur l'herbe (53x64cm-21x25in) s.num.17/50 col linocut. 29-Apr-3 Christie's, Rockefeller NY #548/R est:70000-90000

£41139 $65000 €61709 Armchair woman (66x50cm-26x20in) i. col lithograph two. 28-Apr-3 Christie's, Rockefeller NY #116/R est:10000-15000

£44304 $70000 €66456 Two nude women (27x37cm-11x15in) s.i.num. lithograph set of 11. 28-Apr-3 Christie's, Rockefeller NY #12/R est:35000-45000

£45570 $72000 €68355 Woman with chignon. Portrait of Jacqueline. Right profile (56x44cm-22x17in) s.i.num lithograph three. 28-Apr-3 Christie's, Rockefeller NY #298/R est:12000-18000

£47468 $75000 €71202 Armchair woman no.1 (70x55cm-28x22in) i. black blue grey lithograph. 28-Apr-3 Christie's, Rockefeller NY #127/R est:15000-20000

£49367 $78000 €74051 Figure with striped bodice (65x50cm-26x20in) s.num.50 col lithograph three. 28-Apr-3 Christie's, Rockefeller NY #186/R est:15000-20000

£50633 $80000 €75950 David and Bathsheba (66x50cm-26x20in) s.i. lithograph set of eleven. 28-Apr-3 Christie's, Rockefeller NY #94/R est:50000-70000

£55000 $85250 €82500 Le repas frugal (62x47cm-24x19in) etching drypoint. 3-Dec-2 Christie's, London #179/R est:40000-60000

£56962 $90000 €85443 Woman with flower bodice (64x48cm-25x19in) s.i.num.50 lithograph set of four. 28-Apr-3 Christie's, Rockefeller NY #295/R est:12000-18000

£69620 $110000 €104430 Head of a young girl (49x39cm-19x15in) s.i.num6/6 lithograph set of eight. 28-Apr-3 Christie's, Rockefeller NY #59/R est:50000-70000

£70513 $110000 €105770 Le repas frugal (66x51cm-26x20in) etching edition of 250. 5-Nov-2 Christie's, Rockefeller NY #212/R est:100000-150000

£81761 $130000 €122642 Portrait de Jacqueline accoudee (73x62cm-29x24in) s. white linoleum cut one of five. 2-May-3 Sotheby's, New York #297/R est:50000-70000

£316456 $500000 €474684 Greenhaired woman. Woman with a hair net (65x51cm-26x20in) col lithograph set of eight. 28-Apr-3 Christie's, Rockefeller NY #185/R est:60000-80000

Sculpture

£1235 $1901 €1853 Untitled, young lady (29x14x20cm-11x6x8in) glazed ceramic pitcher exec.c.1951. 26-Oct-2 Heffel, Vancouver #36a est:4000-5000 (C.D 3000)

£1337 $2059 €2006 Cavalier et cheval (20x16x13cm-8x6x5in) glazed ceramic pitcher. 26-Oct-2 Heffel, Vancouver #34 est:4000-5000 (C.D 3250)

£1709 $2700 €2700 Femme (30cm-12in) faience. 2-Dec-2 Tajan, Paris #137/R

£1739 $2713 €2900 Four polychrome fish (32x39x4cm-13x15x2in) d.1947 num.63/200 ceramic plate. 13-Apr-3 Levis, Calgary #320/R est:3500-4500 (C.D 4000)

£1740 $2750 €2610 Small owl jug (27cm-11in) edition 500 col glazed terre de faience vase. 22-Apr-3 Butterfields, San Francisco #2192/R est:2000-3000

£1795 $2782 €2800 Turned pitcher: Yan black headband (28cm-11in) i.verso num.242/300 red earthenware clay exec.1963. 6-Dec-2 Ketterer, Munich #126/R est:2800-3000

£1796 $3000 €2604 Spanish pitcher (23x26cm-9x10in) i. earthenware clay lit. 22-Jun-3 Freeman, Philadelphia #62/R est:1000-1500

£1887 $3000 €2831 Visage no 144 (26x26cm-10x10in) i.num.36/150 col glazed terre de faience plate. 2-May-3 Sotheby's, New York #337/R est:2000-3000

£1918 $2992 €2800 Yan baandeau noir (27cm-11in) num.5/300 painted terracotta exec.1963 lit. 10-Apr-3 Finarte Semenzato, Rome #116/R

£1923 $3000 €2885 Face (25x25cm-10x10in) i.num.181/500 verso col glazed terre de faience plate. 14-Oct-2 Butterfields, San Francisco #1177/R est:2000-3000

£1923 $3000 €2885 Visage (30cm-12in) st. painted terre de faience vase edition of 500. 18-Sep-2 Swann Galleries, New York #88/R est:3000-5000

£1923 $2981 €3000 Turned pitcher: Woman (30cm-12in) i.verso white earthenware clay one of 100 exec.1955. 6-Dec-2 Ketterer, Munich #124/R est:3000-3500

£1987 $3080 €3100 Round dish: Face with hands (42x42cm-17x17in) i.verso num.17/100 white earthenware clay exec.1956. 6-Dec-2 Ketterer, Munich #125/R est:3200-3500

£2000 $3080 €3000 Lampe femme (27cm-11in) st. painted earthenware edition of 100. 23-Oct-2 Sotheby's, Olympia #722/R est:1800-2500

£2000 $3160 €3000 Visage 111 (25x25cm-10x10in) st.sig. glazed ceramic plate. 3-Apr-3 Christie's, Kensington #170/R

£2000 $3160 €2900 Hibou (38cm-15in) st.sig. faience oval lit. 4-Apr-3 Tajan, Paris #211/R

£2000 $3180 €3000 Deux danseurs (25x25cm-10x10in) st. glazed white earthenware plate edition of 450. 20-Mar-3 Sotheby's, Olympia #106/R est:1500-2000

£2000 $3180 €3000 Tete de chevre (25x25cm-10x10in) st. glazed white earthenware plate edition of 60. 20-Mar-3 Sotheby's, Olympia #112/R est:1000-1500

£2025 $3200 €3200 Cruchon hibou (26cm-10in) faience one of 500 exec.1955 lit. 26-Nov-2 Camard, Paris #72/R

£2057 $3250 €3086 Maroon black wood owl (30x15cm-12x6in) num.38/100 glazed terre de faience vase. 22-Apr-3 Butterfields, San Francisco #2189/R est:2000-3000

£2057 $3250 €3086 Blue fish (39cm-15in) num.174/200 partially glazed terre de faience oval dish. 22-Apr-3 Butterfields, San Francisco #2190/R est:3000-5000

£2071 $3252 €3107 Cavalier et cheval (22cm-9in) st.num.253/300 glazed ceramic pitcher. 25-Nov-2 Christie's, Melbourne #133/R est:3600-4400 (A.D 5800)

£2083 $3437 €3000 Tete de chevre de profil (41x41cm-16x16in) st.verso col terre de faience plate lit. 2-Jul-3 Artcurial Briest, Paris #675/R est:3000-4000

£2183 $3428 €3275 Visage grave noir (35x20cm-14x8in) painted ceramic vase lit. 25-Nov-2 Germann, Zurich #64/R est:4500-5500 (S.FR 5000)

£2200 $3432 €3300 Visage tourmente (42x42cm-17x17in) st.num.51/100 glazed ceramic plate lit. 9-Oct-2 Christie's, London #151/R est:2200-3200

£2200 $3476 €3300 Faune cavalier (43x43cm-17x17in) st.sig. ceramic plate. 3-Apr-3 Christie's, Kensington #164/R

£2200 $3476 €3300 Petits visages (25x25cm-10x10in) glazed ceramic plate. 3-Apr-3 Christie's, Kensington #172/R

£2244 $3522 €3500 Visage (31cm-12in) d.69 num.129/500 vase. 24-Nov-2 Laurence Calmels, Paris #304/R

£2321 $3644 €3482 Poisson (42x34cm-17x13in) st. glazed ceramic plate. 25-Nov-2 Christie's, Melbourne #136/R est:4000-6000 (A.D 6500)

£2390 $3800 €3585 Profile of Jacqueline (42x42cm-17x17in) st.i.num.38/100 verso terracotta plate. 29-Apr-3 Christie's, Rockefeller NY #582/R est:4000-5000

£2390 $3800 €3585 Visage aux feuilles (42x42cm-17x17in) num15/100 plate. 1-May-3 Swann Galleries, New York #560/R est:3000-5000

£2400 $3696 €3600 Profil de Jacqueline (18cm-7in) st.verso painted glazed white earthenware plaque edition of 500. 23-Oct-2 Sotheby's, Olympia #729/R est:1500-2000

£2400 $3792 €3600 Nature morte a la cuillere (33x33cm-13x13in) st.sig. glazed ceramic plate. 3-Apr-3 Christie's, Kensington #173/R

£2404 $3750 €3606 Diaulos player (32x39cm-13x15in) st.num.178/200 verso col glazed terre de faience dish. 14-Oct-2 Butterfields, San Francisco #1172/R est:3000-4000

£2414 $3814 €3500 Visage aux feuilles (42x42cm-17x17in) st.sig. num.10/100 faience lit. 4-Apr-3 Tajan, Paris #208/R

£2464 $4041 €3400 Bouteille gravee (44cm-17in) i. verso ceramic vase. 29-May-3 Lempertz, Koln #873/R est:4500

£2500 $3950 €3750 Visage a la grille (44x44cm-17x17in) st.sig. ceramic plate lit. 3-Apr-3 Christie's, Kensington #171

£2516 $4000 €3774 Visage (30cm-12in) col glazed terre de faience pitcher edition of 500. 2-May-3 Sotheby's, New York #330/R est:2000-3000

£2564 $4000 €3846 Visage de femme (33cm-13in) st.i.num.192/200 painted terre de faience pitcher. 18-Sep-2 Swann Galleries, New York #87/R est:5000-8000

£2564 $4026 €4000 Personnage (22x25cm-9x10in) num.170/300 vase. 24-Nov-2 Laurence Calmels, Paris #305/R

£2600 $4004 €3900 Corrida sur fond noir (31x39cm-12x15in) st. painted glazed white earthenware plate edition of 500. 23-Oct-2 Sotheby's, Olympia #749/R est:2500-3500

£2600 $4134 €3900 Visage no 202 (25x25cm-10x10in) i.num.485/500 glazed white earthenware plate. 20-Mar-3 Sotheby's, Olympia #118/R est:2500-3000

£2642 $4200 €3963 Flute player and cavaliers (37x37cm-15x15in) st.i.verso white ceramic dish edition of 100. 29-Apr-3 Christie's, Rockefeller NY #587/R est:3000-4000

£2673 $4250 €4010 Horloge a la langue (42x42cm-17x17in) st.i.num.27/100 terre de faience charger. 2-May-3 Sotheby's, New York #331/R est:2500-3500

£2673 $4250 €4010 Jacqueline au chevalet (42x42cm-17x17in) st.num.48/100 verso terre de faience charger. 2-May-3 Sotheby's, New York #333/R est:5000-7000

£2675 $4119 €4013 Woman's face (38x32x4cm-15x13x2in) painted glazed ceramic plate. 26-Oct-2 Heffel, Vancouver #36 est:5000-7000 (C.D 6500)

£2710 $4200 €4065 Four enlaced profiles (26x26cm-10x10in) col glazed ceramic plate. 25-Sep-2 Christie's, Rockefeller NY #188/R est:2500-3500

£2756 $4328 €4300 Chope visage (22cm-9in) num.86/300 faience exec.1959 lit. 11-Dec-2 Artcurial Briest, Paris #545/R

£2785 $4400 €4400 Femme au chapeau fleuri (33x25cm-13x10in) terracotta. 30-Nov-2 Bassenge, Berlin #6569/R est:3500

£2800 $4312 €4200 Assiette visage (25x25cm-10x10in) i.num.491/500 verso painted glazed white earthenware plate. 23-Oct-2 Sotheby's, Olympia #723/R est:2500-3000

£2800 $4368 €4200 Visage gris (39x39cm-15x15in) st. glazed ceramic plate edition of 500 lit. 9-Oct-2 Christie's, London #155/R est:3500-4500

£2800 $4424 €4200 Lampe femme (35cm-14in) st.sig. ceramic vase. 3-Apr-3 Christie's, Kensington #162/R

£2848 $4500 €4500 Hands with fish (32cm-13in) i.num.178/250 earthenware clay plate executed 1953. 26-Nov-2 Sotheby's, Amsterdam #196/R est:4500-5500

£2899 $4754 €4000 Wood owl (29cm-11in) i. ceramic. 31-May-3 Villa Grisebach, Berlin #303/R est:3000-4000

£2945 $4800 €4418 Wood owl (29cm-11in) s. num.78/500 glazed ceramic. 13-Feb-3 Christie's, Rockefeller NY #164/R

£2949 $4629 €4600 Cruchon hibou (27cm-11in) faience one of 500 lit. 11-Dec-2 Artcurial Briest, Paris #544/R

£2987 $4750 €4481 Vallauris (42x42cm-17x17in) st.num.92/100 and C-103 terre de faience charger. 2-May-3 Sotheby's, New York #332/R est:4000-6000

£3000 $4620 €4500 Tete de chevre de profil (31x51cm-12x20in) st.i. glazed white earthenware edition of 250. 23-Oct-2 Sotheby's, Olympia #719/R est:2500-3500

£3000 $4620 €4500 Femme aux cheveux flous (33x25cm-13x10in) st.num.19/100 verso painted terracotta tile. 23-Oct-2 Sotheby's, Olympia #744/R est:3000-4000

£3000 $4680 €4500 Masque (20x20cm-8x8in) st.num.134/250 glazed ceramic plaque lit. 9-Oct-2 Christie's, London #134/R est:800-1200

£3000 $4680 €4500 Femme aux cheveux flous (33x25x300cm-13x10x118in) st.num.88/100 terracotta tile lit. 9-Oct-2 Christie's, London #139/R est:3000-5000

£3000 $4680 €4500 Visage dans un ovale (40x40cm-16x16in) st.num.64/100 glazed ceramic plate lit. 9-Oct-2 Christie's, London #146/R est:2800-3200

£3000 $4650 €4500 Femme (30cm-12in) st.num.155/200 ceramic vase conceived 1955 lit. 5-Dec-2 Christie's, Kensington #162/R est:2500-3000

£3000 $4740 €4500 Hibou brillant (37cm-15in) st.sig. glazed ceramic plate lit. 3-Apr-3 Christie's, Kensington #169/R

£3000 $4770 €4500 Le barbu (31cm-12in) st.i. glazed white earthenware pitcher edition of 500 exhib. 20-Mar-3 Sotheby's, Olympia #120/R est:2000-3000

£3067 $5000 €4601 Femme assise (15cm-6in) i.d.65 num.1/3 hand blown glass. 12-Feb-3 Sotheby's, New York #100/R est:7000-9000

£3097 $4800 €4646 Corrida with figures (38x38cm-15x15in) col glazed ceramic plate executed c.1950. 25-Sep-2 Christie's, Rockefeller NY #189/R est:4000-6000

£3145 $5000 €4718 Scene de tauromachie (42x42cm-17x17in) st.num.61/200 col glazed terre de faience charger. 2-May-3 Sotheby's, New York #335/R est:4000-6000

£3200 $4992 €4800 Chouette (30x30cm-12x12in) s.num.223/500 glazed ceramic vase lit. 9-Oct-2 Christie's, London #80/R est:2000-3000

£3200 $4992 €4800 Chouette (30x30cm-12x12in) s.num.263/500 glazed ceramic vase lit. 9-Oct-2 Christie's, London #82/R est:4000-6000

£3200 $4992 €4800 Visage dans un ovale (39x39cm-15x15in) st.num.46/100 glazed ceramic plate lit. 9-Oct-2 Christie's, London #148/R est:3500-4000

£3200 $4992 €4800 Quatre visages (23x23cm-9x9in) st.num.45/300 ceramic pitcher lit. 9-Oct-2 Christie's, London #150/R est:1500-2000

£3200 $4992 €4800 Visage de faune toumente (42x42cm-17x17in) st.num.118/200 glazed ceramic plate lit. 9-Oct-2 Christie's, London #154/R est:2000-3000

£3200 $5216 €4800 Visage marron et bleu (31x38cm-12x15in) st.num.3/200 painted earthenware plate. 3-Feb-3 Bonhams, New Bond Street #77/R est:1000-1500

£3200 $5056 €4800 Mains aux poissons (32x32cm-13x13in) st.sig. glazed ceramic plate. 3-Apr-3 Christie's, Kensington #152/R

£3205 $5000 €4808 Jacqueline's profile (36x36cm-14x14in) st.num.7/100 glazed red ceramic plate. 5-Nov-2 Christie's, Rockefeller NY #331/R est:4000-6000

£3205 $4968 €5000 Pichet gothique aux oiseaux (28cm-11in) i. ceramic. 7-Dec-2 Quittenbaum, Munich #514/R est:5800

£3292 $5070 €4938 Bearded man's wife (38x20x20cm-15x8x8in) painted terracotta pitcher. 26-Oct-2 Heffel, Vancouver #33 est:6000-8000 (C.D 8000)

£3374 $5500 €5061 Femme (19cm-7in) i. hand blown glass. 12-Feb-3 Sotheby's, New York #101/R est:5000-7000

£3374 $5500 €5061 Pike (39cm-15in) s.i. glazed ceramic. 13-Feb-3 Christie's, Rockefeller NY #160/R

£3393 $5327 €5090 Tete de femme a la couronne de fleurs (33x25cm-13x10in) st.num.50/100 terracotta tile. 25-Nov-2 Christie's, Melbourne #134/R est:6000-8000 (A.D 9500)

£3400 $5304 €5100 Corrida (42x42cm-17x17in) st.d.11.3.53 edition of 200 glazed ceramic plate lit. 9-Oct-2 Christie's, London #17/R est:2500-3500

£3400 $5304 €5100 Scene de tauromachie (42x42cm-17x17in) st.d.11.6.59 num.87/100 glazed ceramic plate lit. 9-Oct-2 Christie's, London #19/R est:1500-2000

£3400 $5304 €5100 Colombe a la lucarne (39x39cm-15x15in) st.num.93/200 glazed ceramic plate lit. 9-Oct-2 Christie's, London #84/R est:2800-3200

£3400 $5304 €5100 Grand poisson (42x42cm-17x17in) st.num.65/100 ceramic plate lit. 9-Oct-2 Christie's, London #215/R est:1500-2000

£3400 $5304 €5100 Poisson bleu (39x39cm-15x15in) st.num.74/200 glazed ceramic plate lit. 9-Oct-2 Christie's, London #216/R est:2800-3200

£3459 $5500 €5189 Centaur (42x42cm-17x17in) st.i.verso white ceramic dish edition of 100. 29-Apr-3 Christie's, Rockefeller NY #586/R est:3000-4000

£3500 $5460 €5250 Picador et taureau (42x42cm-17x17in) st.num.69/100 glazed ceramic plate lit. 9-Oct-2 Christie's, London #20/R est:3000-5000

£3500 $5425 €5250 Colombe sur lit de paille (39cm-15in) st.num.175 partially glazed ceramic plate. 5-Dec-2 Christie's, Kensington #169/R est:2500-3500

£3500 $5425 €5250 Visage d'homme (31x31cm-12x12in) st.num.14/50 glazed ceramic plaque lit. 5-Dec-2 Christie's, Kensington #171/R est:3000-5000

£3500 $5565 €5250 Corrida (42x42cm-17x17in) st. glazed white earthenware plate edition of 200. 20-Mar-3 Sotheby's, Olympia #105/R est:2500-3500

£3600 $5616 €5400 Corrida verte (37x37cm-15x15in) st. glazed ceramic plate edition of 500 lit. 9-Oct-2 Christie's, London #18/R est:2500-3500

£3600 $5616 €5400 Joueur de flute (25x25cm-10x10in) st. glazed ceramic plate edition of 40 lit. 9-Oct-2 Christie's, London #153/R est:2800-3200

£3600 $5724 €5400 Femme (30cm-12in) st. glazed white earthenware jug edition of 100. 20-Mar-3 Sotheby's, Olympia #116/R est:1800-2500

£3623 $5942 €5000 Oiseau polychrome (30x37cm-12x15in) i. verso ceramic dish. 29-May-3 Lempertz, Koln #871/R est:4000

£3800 $5928 €5700 Colombe mate (37x37cm-15x15in) st. glazed ceramic plate edition of 450 exhib. 9-Oct-2 Christie's, London #83/R est:2000-3000

£3800 $5928 €5700 Visage (42x42cm-17x17in) st.d.17.1.65 num.6/100 ceramic plate lit. 9-Oct-2 Christie's, London #152/R est:2200-3200

£3800 $6004 €5700 Visage (39cm-15in) st.sig. num.52/100 glazed ceramic plate oval. 3-Apr-3 Christie's, Kensington #168/R

£3800 $6042 €5700 Femme du Barbu (37cm-15in) st.i. glazed white earthenware jug edition of 500 exhib. 20-Mar-3 Sotheby's, Olympia #121/R est:2000-3000

£3988 $6500 €5982 Wood owl (29cm-11in) st.sig. glazed ceramic. 13-Feb-3 Christie's, Rockefeller NY #163/R

£3988 $6500 €5982 Landscape (42cm-17in) s. num.88/200 glazed ceramic. 13-Feb-3 Christie's, Rockefeller NY #161/R

£4000 $6240 €6000 Faune cavalier (42x42cm-17x17in) s.num.27/100 ceramic plate lit. 9-Oct-2 Christie's, London #85/R est:2000-3000

£4000 $6240 €6000 Visage grave noir (37x37cm-15x15in) st. black ceramic vase edition of 100 lit. 9-Oct-2 Christie's, London #144/R est:2000-3000

£4000 $6240 €6000 Nature morte (37x37cm-15x15in) st. glazed ceramic plate edition of 400 lit. 9-Oct-2 Christie's, London #217/R est:3000-5000

£4000 $6200 €6000 Chouette (30cm-12in) st.num.94/500 partially glazed ceramic vase conceived 1968. 5-Dec-2 Christie's, Kensington #164/R est:3000-5000

£4000 $6320 €6000 Corrida aux figures (38x38cm-15x15in) st.sig. glazed ceramic plate. 3-Apr-3 Christie's, Kensington #156/R

£4000 $6320 €6000 Centaure (42x42cm-17x17in) st.sig. glazed ceramic plate. 3-Apr-3 Christie's, Kensington #154/R

£4000 $6320 €6000 Visage de faune (5x5cm-2x2in) st.sig. num.3/20 verso gold exhib. 3-Apr-3 Christie's, Kensington #176/R

£4088 $6500 €6132 Goat's head in profile (40x40cm-16x16in) st.i.verso col glazed ceramic plate edition of 100. 29-Apr-3 Christie's, Rockefeller NY #580/R est:4000-6000

£4088 $6500 €6132 Landscape (42x42cm-17x17in) st.num.71/200 verso col glazed ceramic dish. 29-Apr-3 Christie's, Rockefeller NY #583/R est:4000-6000

£4167 $6625 €6000 Chevre de profil (42x42cm-17x17in) ceramic plate. 29-Apr-3 Campo, Vlaamse Kaai #252 est:4500-5500

£4200 $6552 €6300 Cenature (42x42cm-17x17in) st.num.7/100 glazed ceramic plate lit,. 9-Oct-2 Christie's, London #78/R est:3500-4000

£4200 $6552 €6300 Profil de Jacqueline (18x18cm-7x7in) st. glazed ceramic plaque edition of 500 lit. 9-Oct-2 Christie's, London #136/R est:1000-1500

£4200 $6552 €6300 Assiette H and Assiette B, from service visage noir (24x24cm-9x9in) st. glazed ceramic plate edition of 100 pair lit. 9-Oct-2 Christie's, London #142/R est:1200-1800

£4348 $7000 €6522 Le Taureau (5x5cm-2x2in) st.num.8/20 23 carat gold conceived 1956 lit. 7-May-3 Sotheby's, New York #345a/R est:3000-5000

£4403 $7000 €6605 Vallauris (42x42cm-17x17in) st.verso white ceramic dish edition of 100. 29-Apr-3 Christie's, Rockefeller NY #585/R est:3000-4000

£4600 $7314 €6900 Tete de faune (9x4cm-4x2in) s. num.15/20 verso 23 carat gold medallion wooden box. 20-Mar-3 Sotheby's, Olympia #202/R est:5000-7000

£4800 $7488 €7200 Visage aux yeux rieurs (32x32cm-13x13in) st.num.252/350 glazed ceramic pitcher lit. 9-Oct-2 Christie's, London #149/R est:6000-10000

£4808 $7500 €7212 Bottle (44cm-17in) i.num.96/300 glazed painted ceramic vase. 5-Nov-2 Christie's, Rockefeller NY #328/R est:7000-9000

£5000 $7700 €7500 Ceil (3x5cm-1x2in) s.num.8/20 23 carat gold medallion. 23-Oct-2 Sotheby's, Olympia #780/R est:4000-6000

£5000 $7800 €7500 Joueur de flute (25x25cm-10x10in) st. glazed ceramic plate edition of 40 lit. 9-Oct-2 Christie's, London #143/R est:3500-4000

£5000 $7900 €7500 Tete de chevre de profil (51cm-20in) st.sig. glazed ceramic plate oval lit. 3-Apr-3 Christie's, Kensington #167/R

£5063 $8000 €8000 Jacqueline at the easel (42cm-17in) i.num.102/200 earthenware clay plate executed 1956. 26-Nov-2 Sotheby's, Amsterdam #195/R est:5500-7500

£5120 $8500 €7680 Le joueur de cymballes (15cm-6in) s.num.2009/1694 23 carat gold wooden base edition of 6 prov.lit. 11-Jun-3 Phillips, New York #301/R est:14000-18000

£5200 $8112 €7800 Visage (42x42cm-17x17in) st.num.60/100 glazed ceramic plate lit. 9-Oct-2 Christie's, London #156/R est:3000-5000

£5357 $8411 €8036 Visage (42x42cm-17x17in) st.num.78/100 glazed ceramic plate. 25-Nov-2 Christie's, Melbourne #135/R est:4000-6000 (A.D 15000)

£5556 $8667 €8334 Dish with face (42x42cm-17x17in) d.59 num.10/100 ceramic plate prov. 8-Apr-3 Peter Webb, Auckland #114/R est:15000-18000 (NZ.D 16000)

£6000 $9360 €9000 Visage de faune (5x5cm-2x2in) st.sig.num.3/20 yellow metal medallion exec.c.1967 lit. 9-Oct-2 Christie's, London #86/R est:4000-5000

£6000 $9480 €9000 Still life (37cm-15in) st.sig. glazed ceramic plate oval lit. 3-Apr-3 Christie's, Kensington #174/R

£6135 $10000 €9203 Bottle (43cm-17in) s. num.293/300 glazed ceramic. 13-Feb-3 Christie's, Rockefeller NY #162

£6289 $10000 €9434 Landscape (42x42cm-17x17in) st.num.158/200 verso col glazed ceramic dish. 29-Apr-3 Christie's, Rockefeller NY #581/R est:4000-6000

£6500 $10140 €9750 Hibou aux ailes deployees (42x42cm-17x17in) st.num.9/200 terracotta plate lit. 9-Oct-2 Christie's, London #77/R est:2200-3200

£6748 $11000 €10122 Femme nue debout (9cm-4in) brown pat. bronze st.f.Valsuani executed 1945 prov.lit. 12-Feb-3 Sotheby's, New York #65/R est:4000-6000

£6800 $10608 €10200 Chouette (30x30cm-12x12in) st.num.128/350 glazed ceramic vase lit. 9-Oct-2 Christie's, London #81/R est:4000-6000

£6897 $10897 €10000 Aztec vase with four faces (55cm-22in) i. num.18/50 ceramic vase. 2-Apr-3 Dr Fritz Nagel, Stuttgart #9529/R est:18000
£7000 $10920 €10500 Arene (31x31cm-12x12in) s.num.58/100 ceramic vase lit. 9-Oct-2 Christie's, London #21/R est:5000-7000
£7000 $10920 €10500 Hibou blanc sur fond rouge (48x48cm-19x19in) st.num.61/200 ceramic plate lit. 9-Oct-2 Christie's, London #79/R est:2500-3000
£7200 $11232 €10800 Faune cavalier (42x42cm-17x17in) st.num.61/100 glazed ceramic plate lit. 9-Oct-2 Christie's, London #87/R est:5000-8000
£7419 $11723 €11500 Vase ecossais (37x46cm-15x18in) num.11/25 faience exec.1956 lit. 19-Dec-2 Delvaux, Paris #61/R est:12000
£7453 $12000 €11180 Visage aux taches (41x41cm-16x16in) i.num.5/20 repoussed silver conceived 1956 lit. 7-May-3 Sotheby's, New York #346a/R est:15000-20000
£7547 $12000 €11321 Vase deux anses hautes (38cm-15in) col glazed terre de faience vase edition of 400. 2-May-3 Sotheby's, New York #329/R est:10000-15000
£7586 $12138 €11000 Dejeuner sur l'herbe (50x60cm-20x24in) painted ceramic exec.1964 lit. 11-Mar-3 Christie's, Paris #432/R
£7595 $12000 €11393 Fluffy haired woman (34x28cm-13x11in) num.53/100 terracotta rectangular plaque. 22-Apr-3 Butterfields, San Francisco #2194/R est:3500-4000
£7800 $12168 €11700 Jacqueline au chevalet (42x42cm-17x17in) st.num.113/200 glazed ceramic plate lit. 9-Oct-2 Christie's, London #138/R est:4000-7000
£7975 $13000 €11963 Sun God (20x20cm-8x8in) s.d.27/1/56 verso ceramic tile. 12-Feb-3 Sotheby's, New York #98/R est:12000-18000
£8000 $12480 €12000 Visage de femme (39cm-15in) st. glazed ceramic plate edition of 400 lit. 9-Oct-2 Christie's, London #135/R est:2800-3200
£8000 $12480 €12000 Femme de barbu (37cm-15in) st. glazed ceramic pitcher edition of 500 lit. 9-Oct-2 Christie's, London #141/R est:8000-10000
£8861 $14000 €13292 Large corrida bird (57cm-22in) num.10/25 glazed terre de faience vase. 22-Apr-3 Butterfields, San Francisco #2191/R est:10000-15000
£9434 $15000 €14151 Visages. i. brown pat bronze set of 3 lit. 27-Feb-3 Christie's, Rockefeller NY #71/R est:10000
£9615 $15000 €14423 Duex personnages au chien (27x22cm-11x9in) d.22/5/62 painted ceramic lit. 6-Nov-2 Sotheby's, New York #324/R est:18000-25000
£10692 $17000 €16038 Jacqueline at the easel (42x42cm-17x17in) st.i.num.65/200 col glazed ceramic dish. 29-Apr-3 Christie's, Rockefeller NY #584/R est:8000-10000
£11000 $16940 €16500 Vase de verre au visage (43cm-17in) s.d.1962 hand blown glass. 23-Oct-2 Sotheby's, Olympia #750/R est:12000-15000
£11180 $18000 €16770 Horloge aux chiffres (42x42cm-17x17in) i.num.14/20 repoussed silver conceived 1956 lit. 7-May-3 Sotheby's, New York #346/R est:20000-30000
£11268 $18704 €16000 Femme debout (8x3x3cm-3x1x1in) bronze. 14-Jun-3 Hauswedell & Nolte, Hamburg #1515/R est:16000
£11613 $18348 €18000 Jacqueline (40x23x17cm-16x9x7in) st.f.Madoura polychrome ceramic exec.1954 lit. 17-Dec-2 Segre, Madrid #95/R est:18000
£12000 $18960 €18000 Taureau (30cm-12in) st.sig. ceramic lit. 3-Apr-3 Christie's, Kensington #177/R est:18000
£12270 $20000 €18405 Tete de clown, fond bleu (20x20cm-8x8in) d.15.2.96 s.num.V painted ceramic prov.lit. 12-Feb-3 Sotheby's, New York #102/R est:10000-15000
£12658 $19747 €20000 Aztec vase with four faces (55cm-22in) i. num.18/50 ceramics. 18-Oct-2 Dr Fritz Nagel, Stuttgart #588/R est:23000
£12821 $20000 €19232 Tete en forme d'horloge (43cm-17in) i.num.1/2 cast silver conceived 1956 lit. 6-Nov-2 Sotheby's, New York #266/R est:20000-30000
£14907 $24000 €22361 Centaure phallique II (15cm-6in) i.num.3/10 23 karat gold conceived 1960 lit. 7-May-3 Sotheby's, New York #345/R est:15000-20000
£15000 $23400 €22500 Gros oiseau corrida (57cm-22in) st.num.20/25 glazed ceramic vase lit. 9-Oct-2 Christie's, London #24/R est:15000-20000
£15000 $23400 €22500 Vase gros oiseau vert (57x57cm-22x22in) st.num.9/25 glazed ceramic vase lit. 9-Oct-2 Christie's, London #145/R est:15000-20000
£15000 $24450 €22500 Tete en forme d'horloge (43x43cm-17x17in) i.num.9/20 cast silver lit,. 3-Feb-3 Bonhams, New Bond Street #76/R est:15000-20000
£15094 $24000 €22641 Aztec vase with four faces (57x27cm-22x11in) st.i.verso col glazed ceramic vase. 29-Apr-3 Christie's, Rockefeller NY #588/R est:20000-30000
£16000 $24640 €24000 Tete d'homme (30x25cm-12x10in) d.11.3.57 s.verso painted glazed white ceramic tile prov.lit. 23-Oct-2 Sotheby's, Olympia #725/R est:15000-20000
£16000 $26720 €23200 Faune cavalier (42cm-17in) i.num.11/20 silver plate conceived 1957 prov.lit. 24-Jun-3 Sotheby's, London #177/R est:15000-20000
£17000 $26520 €25500 Grand vase eccossais (37x37cm-15x15in) st.num.24/25 ceramic vase lit. 9-Oct-2 Christie's, London #157/R est:18000-22000
£18000 $28080 €27000 Taureau (30cm-12in) st.num.96/100 ceramic pitcher lit. 9-Oct-2 Christie's, London #23/R est:12000-18000
£18000 $29520 €27000 Vallauris (16x16cm-6x6in) s. num.2/2 silver. 4-Feb-3 Christie's, London #360/R
£18634 $30000 €27951 Joueur de flute et cavalier (37cm-15in) st.sig.num.7/20 silver repousse. 8-May-3 Christie's, Rockefeller NY #227/R est:18000-22000
£21000 $35070 €30450 Tete de faune (4cm-2in) engraved terracotta amulet executed c.1937 prov.exhib.lit. 24-Jun-3 Sotheby's, London #176/R est:12000-15000
£25000 $39000 €37500 Oiseau et poissons (49cm-19in) st.num.24/25 ceramic vase lit. 9-Oct-2 Christie's, London #219/R est:25000-30000
£26000 $43420 €37700 Cigare (11cm-4in) painted wood executed 1941 prov.lit. 24-Jun-3 Sotheby's, London #154/R est:18000-25000
£30000 $50100 €43500 Profil de Jacqueline (41x41cm-16x16in) s.d.22.1.56 num.1/20 silver. 25-Jun-3 Christie's, London #230/R est:18000-24000
£38000 $58900 €57000 Femme debout (26cm-10in) num.8/10 brown pat. bronze st.f.Valsuani cire perdue lit. 5-Dec-2 Christie's, Kensington #113/R est:20000-30000
£51282 $80000 €76923 Large vase with dancers (67cm-26in) s. red white engobe ceramic vase prov. 5-Nov-2 Christie's, Rockefeller NY #325/R est:50000-70000
£256410 $400000 €384615 Tete de femme, profil (29cm-11in) painted sheet metal executed 1961 prov.exhib. 6-Nov-2 Christie's, Rockefeller NY #52/R est:500000-700000
£288462 $450000 €432693 Bras (58cm-23in) d.15.3.59 num.5/6 brown pat. bronze st.f.Valsuani prov.lit. 6-Nov-2 Christie's, Rockefeller NY #40/R est:350000-450000
£3910257 $6100000 €5865386 La guenon et son petit (54cm-21in) d.10.51 num.4/6 brown pat. bronze st.f.C. Valsuani prov.exhib.lit. 6-Nov-2 Christie's, Rockefeller NY #42/R est:5000000-7000000

Works on paper

£1795 $2782 €2800 Fleurete (9x14cm-4x6in) ball-point pen dr prov. 5-Dec-2 Gros & Delettrez, Paris #97
£2244 $3545 €3500 Colombe volant - a l'arc en ciel (51x65cm-20x26in) s. num.33/200 col lithograph. 14-Nov-2 Neumeister, Munich #673/R est:2500-3000
£3459 $5327 €5500 Bulls and toreadors. s.i.d.66 dr. 22-Oct-2 Durán, Madrid #246/R
£3600 $5724 €5400 Esquisse pour ascher (35x26cm-14x10in) s.i. ballpoint pen prov. 20-Mar-3 Sotheby's, Olympia #97/R est:2000-3000
£3797 $6000 €6000 Marie-Therese agenouilee contemplant un groupe sculpte (30x36cm-12x14in) s. etching. 30-Nov-2 Villa Grisebach, Berlin #380/R est:5000-7000
£5660 $8717 €9000 Femmes a la colombe (25x20cm-10x8in) ink dr exec.1955 lit. 22-Oct-2 Campo & Campo, Antwerp #218/R est:7500
£5960 $9715 €9000 Smiling face (32x27cm-13x11in) felt-tip pen dr. 11-Feb-3 Segre, Madrid #247/R est:9000
£6410 $10000 €9615 Tete (16x16cm-6x6in) s.i.d.12.5.59 col crayon prov. 14-Oct-2 Butterfields, San Francisco #2017/R est:15000-20000
£6790 $11000 €9846 Tetes d'hommes (18x23cm-7x9in) ink book page prov. 21-May-3 Doyle, New York #33/R est:8000-12000
£8562 $13442 €12500 Portrait d'homme (30x25cm-12x10in) s.i.d. felt pen lit. 21-Apr-3 Rabourdin & Choppin de Janvry, Paris #108/R est:13000-15000
£9295 $14407 €14500 Pour Tania (30x25cm-12x10in) s.d.70 ink dr. 7-Dec-2 Cornette de St.Cyr, Paris #41a/R est:18000-20000
£9615 $15000 €14423 Faun with a staff (15x7cm-6x3in) s. pen purple ink personal cheque exec.c.1960. 18-Sep-2 Swann Galleries, New York #86/R est:7000-10000
£10855 $17585 €16500 Faune souriant (35x25cm-14x10in) s.i. blue crayon dr. 22-Jan-3 Tajan, Paris #164/R est:12000-15000
£10968 $17000 €16452 Le homme (19x9cm-7x4in) s.d.18.10.57 col wax crayon on terra cotta tile pair. 26-Sep-2 Christie's, Rockefeller NY #541/R est:10000-15000
£12270 $20000 €18405 Deux clowns et masque. col crayon pencil image sizes different prov.exhib. 12-Feb-3 Sotheby's, New York #71/R est:25000-35000
£12422 $20000 €18633 Etudes (35x25cm-14x10in) s.i. pen ink prov.exhib.lit. 8-May-3 Christie's, Rockefeller NY #102/R est:25000-35000
£12701 $19687 €19052 Dove of peace in flight with twig in his beak (19x15cm-7x6in) s. blue crayon executed 1950 exhib. 1-Oct-2 Rasmussen, Copenhagen #124/R est:150000-200000 (D.KR 150000)
£13000 $21320 €19500 Fille (20x9cm-8x4in) s.verso col crayon exec.1945 prov. 5-Feb-3 Sotheby's, London #251/R est:20000
£14000 $21560 €21000 Petit (31x21cm-12x8in) s.i. black crayon executed 1898 prov. 22-Oct-2 Sotheby's, London #132/R est:15000-20000

£18000 $28620 €27000 Tete (42x26cm-17x10in) s.i.d.4.4.63 wax crayon pencil prov. 20-Mar-3 Sotheby's, Olympia #98/R est:7000-9000

£18000 $30060 €27000 Taureau et cheval (34x44cm-13x17in) s. pen ink exec 1942 prov.lit. 26-Jun-3 Christie's, London #424/R est:10000-15000

£20000 $30800 €30000 Personnages sur la plage (26x42cm-10x17in) s.d.31-7-20 pencil prov. 22-Oct-2 Sotheby's, London #175/R est:20000-30000

£21739 $35000 €32609 Dora Maar de face (7x5cm-3x2in) gouache pen ink executed c.1936 prov. 7-May-3 Sotheby's, New York #355/R est:25000-35000

£21918 $34411 €32000 Landscape (29x18cm-11x7in) i.verso ink. 15-Apr-3 Laurence Calmels, Paris #4396/R est:60000

£24000 $40080 €36000 Nu assis dans un fauteuil (24x17cm-9x7in) pen ink exec 1923 prov. 26-Jun-3 Christie's, London #432/R est:20000-30000

£24359 $38000 €36539 Le visage de la paix (38x27cm-15x11in) s. chl executed 1952 prov.lit. 6-Nov-2 Sotheby's, New York #336/R est:20000-30000

£25641 $40513 €40000 Homme assis (50x63cm-20x25in) s.d.67 ink wash prov. 15-Nov-2 Laurence Calmels, Paris #26a/R est:80000

£26000 $43420 €39000 Fleurs et papillons (30x25cm-12x10in) s.i.d.28.12.63 wax crayon pencil prov. 26-Jun-3 Christie's, London #423/R est:12000-15000

£27000 $44280 €40500 Homme et femme endormie (23x29cm-9x11in) s. pencil prov.lit. 6-Feb-3 Christie's, London #442/R est:24000

£27950 $45000 €41925 Trois personnages (31x37cm-12x15in) s.d.20.6.70 pen ink ol. 7-May-3 Sotheby's, New York #352/R est:40000-60000

£30449 $47500 €45674 Nu au miroir (43x54cm-17x21in) s.d.6.12.71 brush ink wash lit. 6-Nov-2 Sotheby's, New York #251/R est:40000-60000

£32051 $50000 €48077 Femme nue (13x9cm-5x4in) bears sig pen ink col pencil on card executed c.1903 prov. 6-Nov-2 Sotheby's, New York #199/R est:60000-80000

£34266 $57224 €49000 Buste d'homme (39x31cm-15x12in) s.d.15.6.69.II col felt pen prov.lit. 30-Jun-3 Artcurial Briest, Paris #59/R est:50000-70000

£34965 $58392 €50000 Peintre et modeles (37x52cm-15x20in) s.d.31.8.68 ink wash prov.lit. 30-Jun-3 Pierre Berge, Paris #11/R est:50000-60000

£36000 $55440 €54000 Femme nue couchee et accoudee (26x34cm-10x13in) s. pen ink prov.lit. 22-Oct-2 Sotheby's, London #134/R est:25000-35000

£36000 $60120 €54000 Buste de femme (31x22cm-12x9in) s.d.16.9.71 col.crayon pencil prov.lit. 26-Jun-3 Christie's, London #425/R est:40000-60000

£37267 $60000 €55901 Nu avec deux personnages (37x52cm-15x20in) s.d.2.7.1967 ink wash prov.lit. 7-May-3 Sotheby's, New York #352a/R est:80000-100000

£38000 $58520 €57000 Etude pour l'aubade (21x26cm-8x10in) s.d.20 Mai 41 pencil prov.exhib. 22-Oct-2 Sotheby's, London #136/R est:25000-35000

£38000 $63460 €55100 Nu et homme (24x32cm-9x13in) d.27.1.54 col crayon p/. 24-Jun-3 Sotheby's, London #235/R est:40000-60000

£38462 $60000 €57693 Le peintre et son modele (28x54cm-11x21in) s.d.27.7.70 pen ink wash pencil prov.exhib.lit. 7-Nov-2 Christie's, Rockefeller NY #146/R est:60000-80000

£41304 $64022 €61956 Femme et magot (35x26cm-14x10in) s.d.18.12.53 Indian ink lit.prov. 9-Dec-2 Philippe Schuler, Zurich #3462/R est:100000-120000 (S.FR 95000)

£41667 $65000 €62501 Nu couche (31x24cm-12x9in) s.d.15.12.71 col wax crayon pencil prov.exhib. 7-Nov-2 Christie's, Rockefeller NY #154/R est:40000-60000

£42000 $68880 €63000 Guitare sur une table (16x12cm-6x5in) d.1922 gouache card prov.lit. 5-Feb-3 Sotheby's, London #157/R est:55000

£42000 $68880 €63000 Homme accoude sur table (32x25cm-13x10in) s. pencil exec.1914 prov.lit. 6-Feb-3 Christie's, London #441/R est:40000

£42000 $68880 €63000 Fleurs (19x16cm-7x6in) s. wax crayon exec.c.1960 prov. 6-Feb-3 Christie's, London #510/R est:24000

£44000 $72160 €66000 Buste de femme assise (31x23cm-12x9in) s.d.61 pencil prov.lit. 6-Feb-3 Christie's, London #503/R est:24000

£44872 $70000 €67308 Femme nues a la fleur (23x32cm-9x13in) s.d.16.4.71 pen black ink prov.exhib. 7-Nov-2 Christie's, Rockefeller NY #141/R est:80000-100000

£45000 $73800 €67500 Portrait d'homme. s.d.43 pen ink prov.exhib. 5-Feb-3 Sotheby's, London #172/R est:60000

£48077 $75000 €72116 Mousquetaire et courtisane (46x64cm-18x25in) s.d.26.2.68 chl red chk lit. 7-Nov-2 Christie's, Rockefeller NY #147/R est:120000-160000

£49054 $76524 €73581 Suerte de Varas (46x72cm-18x28in) s.d.1/6/60 Indian ink wash prov.exhib.lit. 5-Nov-2 Bukowskis, Stockholm #295/R est:700000-800000 (S.KR 700000)

£50000 $82000 €75000 Femmes nues et vieillards (23x32cm-9x13in) s.i.d.26 pen ink prov.exhib. 6-Feb-3 Christie's, London #508/R est:45000

£52795 $85000 €79193 Femme nue couchee sur la dos (37x32cm-15x13in) d.23.12.71 pencil oil pastel prov. 7-May-3 Sotheby's, New York #331/R est:60000-80000

£60000 $100200 €90000 Homme au mouton, mangeur de pasteque et flutiste (35x65cm-14x26in) s.d.20.1.67 brown crayon prov.exhib.lit. 26-Jun-3 Christie's, London #427/R est:60000-80000

£60000 $100200 €87000 Etreinte (12x19cm-5x7in) s. i.verso W/C brush ink executed 1901-02 prov.lit. 24-Jun-3 Sotheby's, London #229/R est:35000-45000

£60241 $100000 €87349 Tete d'homme (8x8cm-3x3in) ink. 13-Jun-3 Du Mouchelle, Detroit #2024/R est:5000-7000

£60870 $98000 €91305 Buste de femme (28x21cm-11x8in) s.d.3.1.70 col wax crayon pencil board prov.exhib.lit. 8-May-3 Christie's, Rockefeller NY #130/R est:60000-80000

£65000 $100100 €97500 Nu et profils (49x65cm-19x26in) s.d.9.3.67 pen ink wash prov.exhib.lit. 22-Oct-2 Sotheby's, London #135/R est:50000-70000

£65000 $108550 €94250 Nu couche (59x76cm-23x30in) s,i,d,18.8.72 pen ink prov.exhib.lit. 24-Jun-3 Sotheby's, London #253/R est:70000-90000

£70000 $114800 €105000 Portrait de jeune fille, probablement Martine Peloux (37x27cm-15x11in) s.i.d.58 pencil prov. 6-Feb-3 Christie's, London #497/R est:100000

£74890 $109339 €112335 Le bain de pieds de chien Dalmate (21x27cm-8x11in) i.d.26.1.60 i. verso Indian ink wash lit. three. 17-Jun-2 Philippe Schuler, Zurich #4056/R est:200000-250000 (S.FR 170000)

£80000 $133600 €120000 Composition (25x34cm-10x13in) pen ink pencil exec 1934 prov.exhib.lit. 26-Jun-3 Christie's, London #428/R est:80000-120000

£80745 $130000 €121118 Composition (41x51cm-16x20in) s.d.15 Juillet XXXIII W/C pen ink prov.lit. 7-May-3 Sotheby's, New York #337/R est:120000-180000

£85000 $141950 €127500 Course de taureaux (19x21cm-7x8in) st. verso pencil exec 1923 prov.exhib.lit. 26-Jun-3 Christie's, London #419/R est:60000-80000

£86957 $140000 €130436 Le Poete Alberto Lozano (22x14cm-9x6in) s. chl pastel executed 1901 prov.exhib.lit. 7-May-3 Sotheby's, New York #186/R est:80000-120000

£89744 $140000 €134616 Le peintre et son modele (22x32cm-9x13in) s.d.27.6.70 col wax crayon ink board prov.lit. 7-Nov-2 Christie's, Rockefeller NY #139/R est:120000-160000

£90000 $150300 €135000 Le peintre et son modele (32x49cm-13x19in) s.d.6.7.70 pencil exec 1970 prov.exhib.lit. 26-Jun-3 Christie's, London #426/R est:70000-100000

£90000 $150300 €135000 L'Homme a l'agneau et musicien (50x61cm-20x24in) s.d.9.1.67 wax crayon prov.lit. 26-Jun-3 Christie's, London #430/R est:100000-150000

£90062 $145000 €135093 Scene tauromachique (20x25cm-8x10in) s. pastel paper on card executed 1900 prov.exhib. 7-May-3 Sotheby's, New York #189/R est:120000-150000

£102564 $160000 €153846 Nu debout et nu couche (75x56cm-30x22in) s.d.3.9.67 gouache W/C pencil prov.exhib.lit. 6-Nov-2 Sotheby's, New York #213/R est:150000-200000

£105634 $175352 €150000 Modele a l'atelier (27x21cm-11x8in) s. W/C prov.lit. 12-Jun-3 Tajan, Paris #26/R est:200000-250000

£110000 $183700 €165000 Le peintre et son modele (32x49cm-13x19in) s.d. 6.7.70 pencil prov.exhib.lit. 26-Jun-3 Christie's, London #422/R est:100000-150000

£112179 $175000 €168269 Sylvette (31x24cm-12x9in) s.29.4.54 pencil prov.exhib.lit. 7-Nov-2 Christie's, Rockefeller NY #130/R est:80000-100000

£120000 $200400 €180000 Tete de femme (43x30cm-17x12in) s. pastel pencil exec 1941 prov.lit. 26-Jun-3 Christie's, London #429/R est:120000-150000

£124224 $200000 €186336 Femme nue et amour (44x31cm-17x12in) s.d.7.1.69 col wax crayon prov.exhib.lit. 8-May-3 Christie's, Rockefeller NY #125/R est:250000-350000

£125000 $192500 €187500 Nu couche (50x66cm-20x26in) s.d.18.8.69 col crayon pencil prov.exhib.lit. 22-Oct-2 Sotheby's, London #176/R est:80000-120000

£125000 $208750 €187500 Tete d'homme (90x63cm-35x25in) s.d.15.8.72 d.15.8.72 verso col.pencil prov.exhib.lit. 26-Jun-3 Christie's, London #431/R est:80000-120000

£135000 $221400 €202500 Nu couche (50x65cm-20x26in) s.i.d.69 pencil prov.lit. 6-Feb-3 Christie's, London #501/R est:160000

£136646 $220000 €204969 Le joueur de flute (26x33cm-10x13in) s.d.26 Octobre XXXII pen ink wash. 7-May-3 Sotheby's, New York #340/R est:80000-120000

£139241 $220000 €220000 Tete de femme (65x50cm-26x20in) s.d.43 Chinese ink oil lit. 30-Nov-2 Farsetti, Prato #716/R est:27000

£147436 $230000 €221154 Paysan de toledo (23x16cm-9x6in) s.i. pastel executed 1901 prov.exhib.lit. 6-Nov-2 Sotheby's, New York #197/R est:180000-250000

£155000 $254200 €232500 Nu couche sur le dos et joueur de flute de pan (24x32cm-9x13in) s.d.23 pen India ink prov.lit. 6-Feb-3 Christie's, London #438/R est:120000

£220000 $358600 €330000 Jeune femme au cafe courtisee par un pierrot (28x24cm-11x9in) s. pen ink exec.1903 prov. 3-Feb-3 Christie's, London #52/R est:180000

£224359 $350000 €336539 Bouquet de fleurs (63x47cm-25x19in) s.d.10 gouache prov.exhib.lit. 6-Nov-2 Christie's, Rockefeller NY #37/R est:400000-600000
£330000 $551100 €495000 Tete de femme au chapeau (35x27cm-14x11in) s.num.d.14.1.62 III wax crayon prov.exhib.lit. 26-Jun-3 Christie's, London #418/R est:80000-120000
£372671 $600000 €559007 Figures (49x61cm-19x24in) s.d.67 gouache W/C pen brush ink prov.exhib.lit. 6-May-3 Sotheby's, New York #33/R est:700000
£433566 $724056 €620000 Femme allongee (26x34cm-10x13in) s.d.28.12.38 Indian ink prov. 30-Jun-3 Artcurial Briest, Paris #57/R
£720000 $1202400 €1044000 Trois baigneuses, Juan-les-Pins (49x64cm-19x25in) s.d.1920 pastel prov.exhib.lit. 24-Jun-3 Christie's, London #67/R est:550000-750000

PICASSO, Pablo (after) (1881-1973) Spanish
Prints
£2536 $4159 €3500 Nature morte (33x41cm-13x16in) s. col etching aquatint pochoir. 31-May-3 Villa Grisebach, Berlin #304/R est:3000-4000
£4088 $6500 €6132 Composition with guitar and musical score III (25x11cm-10x4in) s.num.9/100 col pochoir exec.c.1920. 2-May-3 Sotheby's, New York #322/R est:2000-3000
£4808 $7500 €7212 Le cheval de cirque (30x43cm-12x17in) s. i.verso col lithograph. 18-Sep-2 Swann Galleries, New York #84/R est:4000-6000
£5660 $9000 €8490 La corrida (48x65cm-19x26in) s.num.51/200 col aquatint. 3-Mar-3 Swann Galleries, New York #88/R est:10000-15000
£5975 $9500 €8963 Le chapeau aux raisins (53x45cm-21x18in) s.num.146/350 col collotype. 3-Mar-3 Swann Galleries, New York #38/R est:5000-8000
£7547 $12000 €11321 Les demoiselles a'Avignon (50x47cm-20x19in) s.num.33/100 col lithograph executed c.1955. 3-Mar-3 Swann Galleries, New York #36/R est:10000-15000
£8500 $13260 €12750 Interieur rouge avec un transatlantique bleu (65x50cm-26x20in) s.num.208/300 col aquantint. 9-Oct-2 Christie's, London #108/R est:2000-2800
£8500 $13260 €12750 Nature morte au crane (58x76cm-23x30in) s.num.128/150 col aquantint exec.c.1960. 9-Oct-2 Christie's, London #110/R est:1000-1500
£10000 $16500 €14500 Corrida (48x65cm-19x26in) s.num.38/200 col aquatint. 2-Jul-3 Christie's, London #335/R est:3500-4500
£10000 $16500 €14500 Vollard et son chat (60x46cm-24x18in) s.num.90/200 col aquatint exec.c.1960. 2-Jul-3 Christie's, London #336/R est:1500-2500
£10000 $16500 €14500 Embrace (52x55cm-20x22in) s.num.68/125 col offset lithograph. 2-Jul-3 Christie's, London #338 est:4000-6000
£10000 $16500 €14500 Interieur rouge avec un transatlantique bleu (40x33cm-16x13in) s.num.136/300 col aquatint. 2-Jul-3 Christie's, London #339 est:3000-5000
£10063 $16000 €15095 Bacchanale (47x56cm-19x22in) s.num.241/300 col aquatint exec.c.1959. 2-May-3 Sotheby's, New York #323 est:6000-8000

PICAULT, C E (19/20th C) French
£974 $1500 €1461 Spring wooded landscape with stream (25x36cm-10x14in) s. panel. 7-Sep-2 Brunk, Ashville #157/R est:1000-2000

PICAULT, E (1839-1915) French
Sculpture
£976 $1600 €1415 Figure of a harlequin with mandolin (48cm-19in) s. bronze. 4-Jun-3 Doyle, New York #634 est:2500-3500

PICAULT, Émile (1839-1915) French
Sculpture
£1020 $1622 €1500 Winged Hermes (64cm-25in) s. green pat.bronze Cast.Boyer Fres a Paris. 24-Mar-3 Bernaerts, Antwerp #46/R est:1500-1800
£1088 $1731 €1600 Excelsior (60cm-24in) s. bronze. 18-Mar-3 Campo, Vlaamse Kaai #210/R est:1600-1800
£1190 $1893 €1750 Excelsior (75cm-30in) s. bronze. 24-Mar-3 Thierry & Lannon, Brest #37
£1295 $2072 €1800 Le penseur (73cm-29in) s. brown pat bronze sold with a red marble socle. 19-May-3 Horta, Bruxelles #41/R est:1800-2200
£1772 $2800 €2800 Elle porte la lumiere (93cm-37in) s.i. pat bronze. 29-Nov-2 Drouot Estimations, Paris #138/R
£1899 $2962 €3000 Source du Pactole (76cm-30in) s. green brown pat bronze. 21-Oct-2 Bernaerts, Antwerp #34/R est:5400-6200
£1915 $2968 €2873 La source du pactole (78cm-31in) s.i. pat.bronze. 4-Dec-2 AB Stockholms Auktionsverk #1829/R est:15000-20000 (S.KR 27000)
£1987 $3238 €3000 Joueur de tambourin (64cm-25in) s. pat bronze. 17-Feb-3 Horta, Bruxelles #88
£2200 $3476 €3300 Egyptian figure, King Menthuopis (73cm-29in) s. bronze st.f.GS. 13-Nov-2 Sotheby's, Olympia #120/R est:1500-2000
£2600 $4342 €3770 Ad lumen (4cm-2in) s. dark pat. bronze. 26-Jun-3 Mellors & Kirk, Nottingham #997/R est:2000-3000
£2767 $4289 €4400 Escholier (83x35cm-33x14in) st.sig. brown pat bronze lit. 5-Oct-2 De Vuyst, Lokeren #527/R est:4400-5000
£8000 $12560 €12000 Emperor valentian I with his Bearcubs (78x41x41cm-31x16x16in) s.i. dark brown pat. bronze. 10-Dec-2 Sotheby's, London #170/R est:4000-6000

PICCHI, Giorgio (1550-1599) Italian
Works on paper
£400 $628 €600 Scene of alms giving. Dying Saint celebrating mass (18x18cm-7x7in) black chk wash double-sided. 13-Dec-2 Christie's, Kensington #279

PICCINNI, Gennaro (1933-) Italian
£753 $1175 €1100 Tunnel (74x85cm-29x33in) s. board painted 1961 exhib. 10-Apr-3 Finarte Semenzato, Rome #133/R
£833 $1308 €1300 Kitchen interior (60x70cm-24x28in) s. s.i.verso board. 21-Nov-2 Finarte, Rome #194/R
£1026 $1590 €1600 Still life (93x62cm-37x24in) s.d.61 board. 4-Dec-2 Finarte, Milan #344

PICHETTE, James (1920-1996) French
£278 $439 €400 Composition (27x22cm-11x9in) s. s.d.verso. 28-Apr-3 Cornette de St.Cyr, Paris #482
£1600 $2608 €2400 Exaltation en rouge majeur (73x92cm-29x36in) s.d.52 s.i.d.verso prov. 3-Feb-3 Sotheby's, Olympia #83/R est:1000-1500

PICHHADZE, Meir (1955-) Israeli
£5696 $9000 €8544 Nude (77x79cm-30x31in) s. 27-Apr-3 Sotheby's, Tel Aviv #93/R est:4000-6000

PICHLER, Philomena (20th C) ?
£570 $889 €900 Simple pleasure - stay loose (150x125cm-59x49in) acrylic. 15-Oct-2 Dorotheum, Vienna #275/R

PICHLER, Rudolf (1874-1950) Austrian
Works on paper
£432 $708 €600 Village street in Stein with view of church (16x10cm-6x4in) s.i.indis.d. W/C mixed media. 5-Jun-3 Dorotheum, Salzburg #745/R

PICHON, Anna (19th C) French
£1698 $2615 €2700 Portrait de Madame Eyquem (143x100cm-56x39in) s.d.1847. 25-Oct-2 Tajan, Paris #159/R est:3000-4000
£4088 $6296 €6500 Portrait de Jean Eyquem devant un paysage (139x97cm-55x38in) s.d.1843. 25-Oct-2 Tajan, Paris #157/R est:4000-6000

PICHOT GIRONES, Ramon Antonio (1872-1925) Spanish
£2044 $3189 €3250 Melancholy (55x75cm-22x30in) s. cardboard. 23-Sep-2 Durán, Madrid #129/R
£5935 $9378 €9200 Paris at night (37x26cm-15x10in) s. 19-Dec-2 Claude Aguttes, Neuilly #175/R
£50000 $78500 €75000 Tres amigas - three friends (120x83cm-47x33in) s. gouache pastel canvas on board exhib. 19-Nov-2 Sotheby's, London #41/R est:25000-35000

PICILLO, Joseph (20th C) American
Works on paper
£359 $600 €521 Horse, 1981 (84x69cm-33x27in) s.i. chl. 29-Jun-3 Butterfields, Los Angeles #7079/R

PICK, Anton (1840-?) Austrian
£513 $805 €800 View of Villa d'Este (26x40cm-10x16in) s.d.1878. 13-Dec-2 Piasa, Paris #179
£1141 $1836 €1700 Wetterhorn, Switzerland (101x74cm-40x29in) s.d.1870 prov. 18-Feb-3 Sotheby's, Amsterdam #322/R est:1500-2000
£1224 $1947 €1800 Lake scene at dusk (69x105cm-27x41in) s. 25-Feb-3 Dorotheum, Vienna #25/R est:1600-2000
£1266 $1962 €2000 Lake Lugano (54x73cm-21x29in) s. i. stretcher. 25-Sep-2 Neumeister, Munich #697/R est:2000
£1419 $2213 €2129 Romantic landscape (68x105cm-27x41in) s. 11-Sep-2 Kieselbach, Budapest #56/R (H.F 550000)
£1548 $2415 €2322 Landscape in the Alps with lakelet (68x105cm-27x41in) s. 11-Sep-2 Kieselbach, Budapest #100/R (H.F 600000)

PICK, Seraphine (1964-) New Zealander
£1056 $1743 €1531 Untitled (38x30cm-15x12in) s.d.1993 verso. 1-Jul-3 Peter Webb, Auckland #55/R est:2500-3500 (NZ.D 3000)
£1688 $2617 €2532 Wound blossom (45x59cm-18x23in) s.d.2001 board. 4-Dec-2 Dunbar Sloane, Auckland #53/R est:4000-6000 (NZ.D 5250)

£3030 $4667 €4545 No generation without corruption (101x121cm-40x48in) s.d.2001. 4-Sep-2 Dunbar Sloane, Wellington #47/R est:9000-15000 (NZ.D 10000)

Prints

£1146 $1800 €1719 Portrait of a young woman (39x29cm-15x11in) s.d.1995. 10-Dec-2 Peter Webb, Auckland #15/R est:3000-4000 (NZ.D 3600)

PICK-MORINO, Edmund (1877-1958) Belgian

£385 $600 €578 Portrait of Pierre Monteaux (43x36cm-17x14in) i.verso lit. 31-Mar-3 Schrager Galleries, Milwaukee #1103/R
£641 $1013 €1000 River shore with trees (60x51cm-24x20in) s. 14-Nov-2 Neumeister, Munich #675/R

PICKARDT, Ernst (1876-1931) German

£988 $1531 €1482 Portrait of a fashionable woman (114x95cm-45x37in) s.d.1925. 3-Dec-2 Ritchie, Toronto #3093/R est:1200-1800 (C.D 2400)

PICKEN, George Alexander (1898-1971) American

£1165 $1700 €1748 Loading the coal barges, Queens (81x46cm-32x18in) s. 10-May-2 Skinner, Boston #306/R est:3500-5500

PICKERING, Henry (fl.1740-1771) British

£3000 $4680 €4500 Portrait of a lady half length (82x67cm-32x26in) s.d.1760. 26-Mar-3 Hamptons Fine Art, Godalming #137/R est:3000-5000
£3800 $6004 €5700 Edward Stanley of the Isle of Man, wearing a blue coat and holding a tricorn hat (76x63cm-30x25in) s.i.d.1753. 2-Dec-2 Bonhams, Bath #57/R est:1200-1800
£7500 $11850 €11250 Portrait of Susannah Holt, wife of John Chadwick (76x64cm-30x25in) i.d.1743 feigned oval prov.exhib. 26-Nov-2 Christie's, London #21/R est:4000-6000

PICKERING, Henry (attrib) (fl.1740-1771) British

£3000 $4740 €4500 Portrait of George Hill, Sergeant at law (74x62cm-29x24in) prov. 28-Nov-2 Sotheby's, London #162/R est:3000-5000

PICKERING, Joseph Langsdale (1845-1912) British

£500 $800 €750 Circular Road in Regents Park (18x25cm-7x10in) s. board. 11-Mar-3 Gorringes, Lewes #2409

PICKERSGILL, Frederick Richard (1820-1900) British

£9500 $15295 €14250 Mars and Venus crowned by Cupid (30x25cm-12x10in) init. panel prov.exhib. 20-Feb-3 Christie's, London #144/R est:10000

PICKERSGILL, Henry William (1782-1875) British

£1935 $3000 €2903 Portrait of a man said to be John Hill Hawkstone (37x35cm-15x14in) panel. 2-Oct-2 Christie's, Rockefeller NY #118/R est:1000-2000

PICKERSGILL, Henry William (attrib) (1782-1875) British

£1350 $2093 €2025 Light Company Officer, Coldstream Guards (61x48cm-24x19in) prov. 3-Oct-2 Heathcote Ball, Leicester #580/R
£2400 $3936 €3600 Portrait of Thomas Thynne, 2nd Marquis of Bath (128x103cm-50x41in) after Sir Thomas Lawrence. 29-May-3 Christie's, Kensington #54/R est:1500-2000

PICKERSGILL, Richard (fl.1818-1853) British

Works on paper

£1100 $1760 €1650 Red House Mill at Battersea with Nine Elms Mill in the distance (43x63cm-17x25in) s. W/C exhib. 11-Mar-3 Bonhams, New Bond Street #26/R est:1200-1800

PICKING, John (1939-) British

£288 $453 €450 Stepped landscape (50x40cm-20x16in) s.i.d.1995. 23-Nov-2 Meeting Art, Vercelli #410
£316 $494 €500 Remorse (60x70cm-24x28in) s.i.d.1990 verso. 14-Sep-2 Meeting Art, Vercelli #846
£327 $523 €500 River meditation (60x80cm-24x31in) s.i.d.1997 verso. 4-Jan-3 Meeting Art, Vercelli #35
£327 $523 €500 Olivesand objects (50x60cm-20x24in) s.i.d.1995 verso. 4-Jan-3 Meeting Art, Vercelli #700

PICO MARTI, Jose (1902-?) Spanish

£252 $392 €400 Mexican dance (81x81cm-32x32in) s.i.d.87 verso. 8-Oct-2 Ansorena, Madrid #605/R

PICOLLO, Giacomo (1905-?) Italian

£1218 $1888 €1900 Villa in Liguria (50x65cm-20x26in) s.d.38 board. 5-Dec-2 Stadion, Trieste #862/R

PICOLO Y LOPEZ, Manuel (1850-1892) Spanish

£1026 $1621 €1600 In the park (32x40cm-13x16in) s. 13-Nov-2 Ansorena, Madrid #284/R

PICON, Jose (1921-) Belgian

£348 $543 €550 Le jeune garcon et les citrons (76x61cm-30x24in) s. 16-Oct-2 Hotel des Ventes Mosan, Brussels #295

Works on paper

£340 $541 €500 Formes abstraites (73x55cm-29x22in) s. i.d.1991 verso pastel. 19-Mar-3 Hotel des Ventes Mosan, Brussels #344

PICOT, E (19/20th C) French

£1076 $1700 €1700 La bergerie (50x65cm-20x26in) s. 1-Dec-2 Peron, Melun #150

PICOU, Henri Pierre (1824-1895) French

£1731 $2683 €2700 Jeune bretonne et amour (41x34cm-16x13in) s.d.1889. 5-Dec-2 Gros & Delettrez, Paris #61/R
£3750 $6000 €5625 Angel of love (60x51cm-24x20in) s.d.1884. 14-May-3 Butterfields, San Francisco #1112/R est:6000-8000
£7813 $12500 €11720 Clipping of Cupid's wings (61x92cm-24x36in) s.d.1874. 14-May-3 Butterfields, San Francisco #1109/R est:8000-120000
£28481 $45000 €42722 Birth of Venus (76x98cm-30x39in) s.d.1874. 24-Apr-3 Sotheby's, New York #50/R est:50000-70000

PICQUE, Charles (1799-1869) Belgian

£506 $790 €800 Genevieve de Brabant (46x59cm-18x23in) s.d.1858 panel. 10-Sep-2 Vanderkindere, Brussels #362
£1905 $3029 €2800 Dame aux anges (126x97cm-50x38in) s. 18-Mar-3 Campo, Vlaamse Kaai #211/R est:2800-3300

PIDDING, Henry James (attrib) (1797-1864) British

£360 $562 €540 Still life of fish (36x31cm-14x12in) board. 18-Sep-2 Cheffins Grain & Comins, Cambridge #510/R

PIECHAUD, Guillaume (20th C) French?

Sculpture

£3813 $6253 €5300 Conversation. s. inox poli. 6-Jun-3 Rabourdin & Choppin de Janvry, Paris #68/R est:6000-7000

PIECK, Adri (1894-?) Dutch

£256 $403 €400 Heather (39x59cm-15x23in) s. 25-Nov-2 Glerum, Amsterdam #180
£482 $767 €700 Aan de plas, Maartensdijk (38x56cm-15x22in) s.i.verso. 10-Mar-3 Sotheby's, Amsterdam #321
£1379 $2193 €2000 Tree near a lake (50x35cm-20x14in) s. 10-Mar-3 Sotheby's, Amsterdam #322/R est:400-600

PIECK, Anton (1895-1987) Dutch

Works on paper

£423 $680 €600 Dominee Jens with lantern (17x17cm-7x7in) s. chl dr htd white lit. 7-May-3 Vendue Huis, Gravenhage #181/R
£5592 $9059 €8500 Antiquarian book seller (22x34cm-9x13in) s. pencil W/C htd white. 21-Jan-3 Christie's, Amsterdam #259/R est:6000-8000
£6289 $9686 €10000 Winterfun on the ice (31x41cm-12x16in) s. pencil W/C htd white. 23-Oct-2 Christie's, Amsterdam #70/R est:10000-15000

PIECK, Henri (1895-1972) Dutch

£423 $680 €600 Two figures by inn door (34x23cm-13x9in) s.d.14 panel. 7-May-3 Vendue Huis, Gravenhage #180

Works on paper

£1645 $2664 €2500 Les deux femmes (118x90cm-46x35in) s.i.d.14 mono.verso black chk pastel. 21-Jan-3 Christie's, Amsterdam #255/R est:3000-5000

PIEDMONTESE SCHOOL (16th C) Italian

£8000 $13360 €11600 Christ preaching before a classical temple (67x82cm-26x32in) panel marouflaged. 10-Jul-3 Sotheby's, London #153/R est:8000-12000

PIEDMONTESE SCHOOL (17th C) Italian

£8000 $12560 €12000 Portrait of a gentleman by a table in black costume, his young son by his side (198x118cm-78x46in) 10-Dec-2 Bonhams, New Bond Street #19/R est:8000-12000

PIEDMONTESE SCHOOL (18th C) Italian

£19595 $30568 €29000 Still lives of fruit on stone ledges (45x69cm-18x27in) set of 4. 25-Mar-3 Finarte Semenzato, Rome #113/R est:35000

PIELER, Franz Xaver (1879-1952) Austrian
£753 $1175 €1100 Flowers with butterfly (46x41cm-18x16in) s. panel. 10-Apr-3 Dorotheum, Vienna #257/R
£1064 $1649 €1596 Still life of flowers (39x28cm-15x11in) s. panel. 4-Dec-2 AB Stockholms Auktionsverk #1867/R est:18000-20000 (S.KR 15000)
£1224 $1947 €1800 Vast bunch of flowers (80x60cm-31x24in) s. panel. 25-Feb-3 Dorotheum, Vienna #184/R est:3000-3400
£1633 $2596 €2400 Summer flowers (23x18cm-9x7in) mono. panel. 19-Mar-3 Neumeister, Munich #694/R est:2200
£1646 $2600 €2600 Bunch of flowers in a vase (53x41cm-21x16in) s. panel. 28-Nov-2 Dorotheum, Vienna #84/R est:3000-3800
£2051 $3241 €3200 Still life of flowers and fruit (31x60cm-12x24in) s. 16-Nov-2 Lempertz, Koln #1551/R est:2000
£2532 $4000 €4000 Large still life of flowers with fruit and insects (61x53cm-24x21in) s. board. 28-Nov-2 Dorotheum, Vienna #32/R est:4500-5500
£3774 $5849 €6000 Still life with bird's nest (40x30cm-16x12in) s. panel. 29-Oct-2 Dorotheum, Vienna #90/R est:4500-5000
£4403 $6824 €7000 Still life of flowers (52x41cm-20x16in) s. panel. 29-Oct-2 Dorotheum, Vienna #107/R est:5000-5500

PIEMONTI, Lorenzo (1935-) Italian
£353 $554 €550 Three tenses (40x40cm-16x16in) s.i.d.1984 verso acrylic. 23-Nov-2 Meeting Art, Vercelli #310

PIENE, Otto (1928-) German
£633 $987 €1000 White gift (68x96cm-27x38in) s.i.d.1978 acrylic fire board. 18-Oct-2 Dr Fritz Nagel, Stuttgart #598/R
£780 $1264 €1100 Sky event (68x48cm-27x19in) s.i.d.92 gouache board. 24-May-3 Van Ham, Cologne #474
£2340 $3791 €3300 Untitled (144x96cm-57x38in) s.d.77/79 acrylic fire board. 24-May-3 Van Ham, Cologne #473/R est:4500
£8696 $14261 €12000 Fire flower (100x100cm-39x39in) s.i.d.65/72 verso oil smoke fire prov. 28-May-3 Lempertz, Koln #337/R est:12000
Sculpture
£5072 $8319 €7000 HI 2 (70x59cm-28x23in) steel lit. 28-May-3 Lempertz, Koln #334/R est:10000-12000
Works on paper
£321 $506 €500 Eye (42x37cm-17x15in) s. gouache Indian ink board. 14-Nov-2 Neumeister, Munich #856/R
£538 $839 €850 Blue II (11x14cm-4x6in) s.d.1963 fire gouache over Indian ink. 18-Oct-2 Dr Fritz Nagel, Stuttgart #597/R

PIEPENHAGEN, August (1791-1868) Polish
Works on paper
£1446 $2255 €2169 Landscape with castle ruin (23x30cm-9x12in) paint asphalt cardboard. 12-Oct-2 Dorotheum, Prague #174/R est:20000-30000 (C.KR 70000)

PIEPENHAGEN, August (attrib) (1791-1868) Polish
£1444 $2282 €2166 Sunset landscape (35x26cm-14x10in) mono. canvas on board. 30-Nov-2 Dorotheum, Prague #10/R est:50000-75000 (C.KR 70000)
£1816 $2942 €2724 In a forest (34x42cm-13x17in) 24-May-3 Dorotheum, Prague #44/R est:60000-90000 (C.KR 80000)

PIEPER, Carl (19th/20th C) ?
£632 $979 €948 Bouquet (53x71cm-21x28in) painted c.1900. 3-Dec-2 SOGA, Bratislava #159/R (SL.K 40000)

PIEPER, Christian (attrib) (1843-?) German
£1392 $2158 €2200 Young woman (120x60cm-47x24in) s.d.1887. 27-Sep-2 Weidler, Nurnberg #8920/R est:800

PIEPER, Hermann (1909-1964) Swiss
£322 $509 €483 Ball scene with friendly conversation (61x25cm-24x10in) masonite. 29-Nov-2 Zofingen, Switzerland #3031 (S.FR 750)
£699 $1090 €1049 Composition: on the beach (50x60cm-20x24in) panel. 6-Nov-2 Dobiaschofsky, Bern #887/R (S.FR 1600)
£787 $1267 €1181 Five women (26x34cm-10x13in) panel. 7-May-3 Dobiaschofsky, Bern #885/R (S.FR 1700)

PIEPER, Hugo J (20th C) American
£314 $500 €471 Shrimpers. s. painted c.1950. 2-Mar-3 Toomey, Oak Park #573/R

PIEPER, Nelda (20th C) American
£269 $450 €390 Impressionistic scene of three children standing near a lake with a Great Dane (61x91cm-24x36in) s. 21-Jun-3 Selkirks, St. Louis #169

PIER FRANCESCO (attrib) (15th C) Italian
£29000 $48430 €42050 Coronation of the Virgin, with Saints Bartholomew, Mary Magdalen, John the Baptist and female saint (74x47cm-29x19in) gold ground panel shaped top prov. 9-Jul-3 Christie's, London #73/R est:30000-50000

PIER FRANCESCO and SETTIGNANO, Desiderio da (studio) (15th C) Italian
£60377 $94189 €96000 Madonna with Child (43x36cm-17x14in) polychrome relief. 21-Sep-2 Semenzato, Venice #126/R est:75000-85000

PIERCE, Charles Franklin (1844-1920) American
£348 $550 €522 Resting cow (30x41cm-12x16in) s. 17-Nov-2 CRN Auctions, Cambridge #65/R

PIERCE, Diane (1939-) American
£1582 $2500 €2373 Whoopers and sandhill cranes arriving at Monte Vista (104x142cm-41x56in) s. prov. 3-Apr-3 Christie's, Rockefeller NY #201/R est:12000-18000

PIERCE, Joseph W (19th C) American
£1000 $1600 €1450 Sailing off Marblehead, Boston's north shore (43x66cm-17x26in) s.d.1872 board. 17-May-3 CRN Auctions, Cambridge #9

PIERLAIS, Count Hippolyte Cais de (19th C) French
£8129 $12844 €12600 Vue de Nice (52x75cm-20x30in) 17-Dec-2 Claude Boisgirard, Paris #10/R est:15000-18000

PIERNEEF, Jacob Hendrik (1886-1957) South African
£614 $958 €921 Sketch near Pretoria (10x25cm-4x10in) s.d.09 i.verso board. 15-Oct-2 Stephan Welz, Johannesburg #429 est:7000-10000 (SA.R 10000)
£1929 $3048 €2894 Cape Dutch house in between trees (44x34cm-17x13in) s.d.21. 1-Apr-3 Stephan Welz, Johannesburg #440/R est:25000-35000 (SA.R 24000)
£2050 $3198 €3075 Rustenburg kloof (45x55cm-18x22in) s. 11-Nov-2 Stephan Welz, Johannesburg #556/R est:40000-50000 (SA.R 32000)
£2408 $3876 €3612 Extensive landscape with a storm in the far distance (28x38cm-11x15in) s. board. 12-May-3 Stephan Welz, Johannesburg #452b/R est:20000-30000 (SA.R 28000)
£2562 $3997 €3843 Extensive landscape with trees (30x40cm-12x16in) s.d.1920 board. 11-Nov-2 Stephan Welz, Johannesburg #599/R est:30000-50000 (SA.R 40000)
£2764 $4312 €4146 Vanaf ebenlaejer se werf (28x39cm-11x15in) s.d.1927 i.verso panel. 15-Oct-2 Stephan Welz, Johannesburg #430/R est:40000-60000 (SA.R 45000)
£3095 $4984 €4643 Krokodilpoort by Nelspruit, Transvaal (29x39cm-11x15in) s.d.1940 s.i.verso board. 12-May-3 Stephan Welz, Johannesburg #480/R est:18000-24000 (SA.R 36000)
£3215 $5080 €4823 Miershope, S W A (44x54cm-17x21in) s.d.35. 1-Apr-3 Stephan Welz, Johannesburg #441/R est:40000-60000 (SA.R 40000)
£3831 $5709 €5747 Extensive landscape (45x60cm-18x24in) s.d.37 s.verso prov. 27-Aug-2 Christie's, Melbourne #105/R est:12000-16000 (A.D 10000)
£6879 $11075 €10319 Extensive landscape with a farmstead in the distance (39x54cm-15x21in) s.d.32. 12-May-3 Stephan Welz, Johannesburg #452a/R est:40000-60000 (SA.R 80000)
£7739 $12459 €11609 Pienaars River (44x59cm-17x23in) s.d.38. 12-May-3 Stephan Welz, Johannesburg #475/R est:90000-120000 (SA.R 90000)
£7739 $12459 €11609 Wild olive trees, Lowveld, North East Transvaal (44x59cm-17x23in) s.d.46 i.verso board. 12-May-3 Stephan Welz, Johannesburg #481/R est:60000-80000 (SA.R 90000)
Works on paper
£192 $300 €288 Extensive landscape with tree (11x9cm-4x4in) mono.i. pencil col crayon. 11-Nov-2 Stephan Welz, Johannesburg #213 (SA.R 3000)
£243 $380 €365 Sabie, eastern Transvaal (33x44cm-13x17in) s.i.d.1943 pencil. 11-Nov-2 Stephan Welz, Johannesburg #259 (SA.R 3800)
£258 $415 €387 Doringboom Bosveld 44 (20x34cm-8x13in) s.i.d.44 pencil. 12-May-3 Stephan Welz, Johannesburg #128 est:3000-5000 (SA.R 3000)
£301 $485 €452 Golden gate, Ovs (16x22cm-6x9in) s.i.d.1934 pencil W/C. 12-May-3 Stephan Welz, Johannesburg #118 est:2000-3000 (SA.R 3500)
£352 $550 €528 View of a house (12x20cm-5x8in) s.d.1918 laid down W/C over pencil. 11-Nov-2 Stephan Welz, Johannesburg #212 (SA.R 5500)

£361 $581 €542 Okahandja (24x34cm-9x13in) s.i.d.Spet 24 pencil W/C. 12-May-3 Stephan Welz, Johannesburg #117 est:3000-5000 (SA.R 4200)
£442 $699 €663 S.W.A (16x23cm-6x9in) s.d.1923 pencil W/C. 1-Apr-3 Stephan Welz, Johannesburg #438 est:4000-6000 (SA.R 5500)
£516 $831 €774 McGregor (25x35cm-10x14in) s.i. pencil gouache prov. 12-May-3 Stephan Welz, Johannesburg #91 est:4000-6000 (SA.R 6000)
£516 $831 €774 Quai des Marbriers, Brugge (24x32cm-9x13in) s.i.d.Nov 25 pencil W/C. 12-May-3 Stephan Welz, Johannesburg #104 est:4000-6000 (SA.R 6000)
£643 $1016 €965 Extensive landscape (29x48cm-11x19in) s.d.19 W/C. 1-Apr-3 Stephan Welz, Johannesburg #439 est:6000-8000 (SA.R 8000)
£705 $1099 €1058 Extensive landscape with a tree (37x52cm-15x20in) i.d.June 1952 pencil. 11-Nov-2 Stephan Welz, Johannesburg #559 (SA.R 11000)
£774 $1246 €1161 Rehoboth, S.W.A (17x26cm-7x10in) s.i.d.1924 pencil W/C. 12-May-3 Stephan Welz, Johannesburg #304 est:7000-9000 (SA.R 9000)
£817 $1315 €1226 Extensive landscape with a tree (44x59cm-17x23in) s. chl. 12-May-3 Stephan Welz, Johannesburg #149 est:5000-8000 (SA.R 9500)
£1025 $1599 €1538 Extensive Bushveld landscape (20x27cm-8x11in) s.d.1920 W/C. 11-Nov-2 Stephan Welz, Johannesburg #551/R est:8000-12000 (SA.R 16000)

PIERON, Henry (19th C) Belgian
£376 $616 €545 River landscape (47x75cm-19x30in) s.d.1877. 4-Jun-3 Fischer, Luzern #2281/R (S.FR 800)
£475 $741 €750 Souvenir de l'Escaut a Anvers (40x92cm-16x36in) s. 15-Oct-2 Horta, Bruxelles #372

PIERRAKOS, Alkis (1920-) ?
£1418 $2369 €2000 Portrait de Madame Rousseau (90x110cm-35x43in) s.d. 23-Jun-3 Delvaux, Paris #158/R est:2000-3000
£1418 $2369 €2000 Batisses (55x45cm-22x18in) s. painted c.1960. 23-Jun-3 Delvaux, Paris #159 est:2000-3000
£1511 $2417 €2100 Composition (73x60cm-29x24in) s.d.58. 14-May-3 Blanchet, Paris #181/R est:2200-2500
£1844 $3079 €2600 Collines (65x92cm-26x36in) s.d. prov.exhib. 23-Jun-3 Delvaux, Paris #157/R est:1500-2000
£2000 $3160 €3000 Yellow rose (65x54cm-26x21in) 1-Apr-3 Bonhams, New Bond Street #94 est:1200-1800

PIERRE and GILLES (20th C) French
£9494 $15000 €14241 Prince des tenebres (121x93cm-48x37in) s.i.d.97 acrylic over photograph prov.exhib. 13-Nov-2 Sotheby's, New York #508/R est:20000-25000

Photographs
£4514 $7448 €6500 La licorne (22x46cm-9x18in) C-print lit. 3-Jul-3 Christie's, Paris #100/R est:3000-5000
£5063 $8000 €7595 Le bateau (57x47cm-22x19in) s.i.d.1986 hand painted chromogenic col print prov.exhib. 24-Apr-3 Phillips, New York #57/R est:8000-12000
£11076 $17500 €16614 Les flammes - Violetta sanchez (69x85cm-27x33in) s.i.d.83 hand painted photograph prov.lit. 12-Nov-2 Phillips, New York #206/R est:15000-20000
£11392 $18000 €17088 Pascaline (25x50cm-10x20in) s.i.d.84 hand col coupler print prov. 14-Nov-2 Christie's, Rockefeller NY #457/R est:15000-20000
£14557 $23000 €21836 La princesse et le paon, Sophiya (102x102cm-40x40in) s.i.d.verso hand col chromogenic col print prov.exhib.lit. 24-Apr-3 Phillips, New York #58/R est:25000-35000
£15584 $24000 €23376 Sainte Marie Madeleine, Sophie Blondy (109x92cm-43x36in) s.verso col chromogenic print aluminum prov.exhib.lit. 25-Oct-2 Phillips, New York #56/R est:25000-35000
£15584 $24000 €23376 Sainte Lucie, Bernadette Jurkowski (101x85cm-40x33in) s.verso col chromogenic print aluminum prov.exhib.lit. 25-Oct-2 Phillips, New York #57/R est:25000-35000
£20253 $32000 €30380 Le petit mendiant - Tomah (125x107cm-49x42in) s.i.d.1992 hand painted col photograph prov.exhib.lit. 12-Nov-2 Phillips, New York #203/R est:25000-35000
£25000 $40000 €37500 Blond Venus - Julie Delpy (99x74cm-39x29in) col photograph executed 1992 prov.lit. 14-May-3 Sotheby's, New York #342/R est:40000-60000
£26250 $42000 €39375 Le buveur d'absinthe (132x107cm-52x42in) s.i.d.97 hand col coupler print prov.exhib.lit. 15-May-3 Christie's, Rockefeller NY #409/R est:25000-35000

Works on paper
£13924 $22000 €22000 Le danseur exotique (120x76cm-47x30in) overpainted photo on aluminium prov.lit. 27-Nov-2 Dorotheum, Vienna #117/R est:28000-32000

PIERRE, Arthur (1866-1938) Belgian

Sculpture
£1379 $2207 €2000 Dancers (67x35cm-26x14in) s. green pat bronze marble base. 15-Mar-3 De Vuyst, Lokeren #252 est:1500-1750

PIERRE, Gustave René (1875-?) French
£262 $414 €393 Portrait of Pierre (44x38cm-17x15in) s. indis.i.stretcher. 18-Nov-2 Waddingtons, Toronto #222/R (C.D 650)

PIERRE, Jean Baptiste Marie (1713-1789) French
£23077 $36231 €36000 Renaud et Armide (39x53cm-15x21in) paper on canvas. 20-Nov-2 Libert, Castor, Paris #72/R est:8000-10000

PIERRI, Duilio (1954-) Latin American
£3049 $5000 €4574 Bosque otonal (150x150cm-59x59in) s.i.d.1998 verso prov.exhib. 28-May-3 Christie's, Rockefeller NY #143/R est:5000-7000

PIERSON, Jack (1960-) American
£710 $1100 €1065 Billy Holiday, Berlin 1954 (35x28cm-14x11in) s.i.d.16 Oct 92 graphite oilstick prov. 26-Sep-2 Christie's, Rockefeller NY #829/R est:2000-3000

Photographs
£4000 $6560 €6000 The roses we brought Daniel (66x101cm-26x40in) s.i.d.1993 num.3/5 verso cibachrome print prov. 7-Feb-3 Sotheby's, London #121/R est:3000-4000

Sculpture
£84375 $135000 €126563 Stardust (488cm-192in) found metal plastic objects with neon prov.exhib.lit. 15-May-3 Phillips, New York #42/R est:40000-60000

Works on paper
£1392 $2200 €2088 You got what you deserved (36x28cm-14x11in) s.d.6 Dec 1991 graphite prov. 12-Nov-2 Phillips, New York #222/R est:1500-2000

PIET, Fernand (1869-1942) French
£541 $843 €800 Liseuse en noir (24x32cm-9x13in) st.sig. cardboard. 28-Mar-3 Charbonneaux, Paris #127
£646 $1028 €950 Jeune fille a la couture (30x23cm-12x9in) s. cardboard. 27-Feb-3 Chochon-Barre & Allardi, Paris #192/R
£823 $1300 €1300 Nu allonge endormi (40x52cm-16x20in) st.sig. cardboard. 27-Nov-2 Blanchet, Paris #32/R

Works on paper
£263 $427 €400 Femme pensive sur fond bleu (17x13cm-7x5in) st. W/C exec.c.1895-1900 exhib. 22-Jan-3 Tajan, Paris #99
£272 $433 €400 Jeune fille en rose (14x12cm-6x5in) s. W/C. 27-Feb-3 Chochon-Barre & Allardi, Paris #150/R

PIETERCELIE, Alfred (1879-1955) Belgian
£316 $494 €500 Vase fleuri devant une fenetre (70x70cm-28x28in) s.d.1934. 15-Oct-2 Horta, Bruxelles #348
£355 $561 €550 Les peupliers (70x80cm-28x31in) s. 17-Dec-2 Palais de Beaux Arts, Brussels #595
£419 $663 €650 Paysage de bruyere (40x50cm-16x20in) s. 17-Dec-2 Palais de Beaux Arts, Brussels #594
£621 $981 €900 Chemin de la ferme (80x110cm-31x43in) s.d.1918. 1-Apr-3 Palais de Beaux Arts, Brussels #571

PIETERS, Dick (1941-) Dutch
£1986 $3217 €2800 Drowning person (16x42cm-6x17in) init. panel prov.exhib. 26-May-3 Glerum, Amsterdam #257/R est:1200-1600

PIETERS, Evert (1856-1932) Dutch
£353 $546 €550 Vaches dans un paysage hollandais (40x60cm-16x24in) s. 3-Dec-2 Campo & Campo, Antwerp #238
£615 $959 €923 Pecheur (16x12cm-6x5in) s. panel. 10-Sep-2 Iegor de Saint Hippolyte, Montreal #93 (C.D 1500)
£1107 $1726 €1661 La fermiere (16x12cm-6x5in) s. panel. 10-Sep-2 Iegor de Saint Hippolyte, Montreal #92/R (C.D 2700)
£1233 $1923 €1800 Farm in Laren (60x80cm-24x31in) s. 14-Apr-3 Glerum, Amsterdam #79/R est:1800-2200
£1595 $2600 €2393 Portrait of a peasant woman (30x28cm-12x11in) 14-Feb-3 Du Mouchelle, Detroit #2091/R est:2000-4000
£1644 $2564 €2400 Corn makers in front of a farm and a haystack (70x50cm-28x20in) s. 14-Apr-3 Glerum, Amsterdam #78/R est:3000-5000
£2436 $3776 €3800 De archivaris aan zijn werktafel (90x136cm-35x54in) s. 3-Dec-2 Campo & Campo, Antwerp #239/R est:4000-5000
£2532 $3949 €4000 Seated pipe smoker (40x30cm-16x12in) s. panel. 21-Oct-2 Bernaerts, Antwerp #729/R est:3000-4000

£2632	$4263	€4000	Blaricum (80x150cm-31x59in) s. 21-Jan-3 Christie's, Amsterdam #319/R est:4000-6000
£4452	$6990	€6500	In the kitchen. Shell fisher (16x12cm-6x5in) s. panel pair. 15-Apr-3 Sotheby's, Amsterdam #133/R est:4000-6000
£4687	$7500	€6796	Peeling potatoes (60x50cm-24x20in) s. 16-May-3 Skinner, Boston #26/R est:4000-6000
£5263	$7842	€7895	Femme a l'enfant (61x76cm-24x30in) s. 26-Jun-2 Iegor de Saint Hippolyte, Montreal #70/R (C.D 12000)

PIETERSZEN, Abraham van der Wayen (1817-1880) Dutch

£1019	$1569	€1600	Spinnekopmolen in a meadow (40x51cm-16x20in) s.d.40 panel. 3-Sep-2 Christie's, Amsterdam #111/R est:4000-6000

PIETERSZEN, Abraham van der Wayen (attrib) (1817-1880) Dutch

£769	$1208	€1200	River landscape in summer with hay makers and river boats (61x81cm-24x32in) indis.s.d.1857. 10-Dec-2 Dorotheum, Vienna #52/R

PIETILA, Tuulikki (1917-) Finnish

£1392	$2200	€2200	Testaccio (39x32cm-15x13in) s.d.59 board. 1-Dec-2 Bukowskis, Helsinki #344/R est:1300-1500

PIETRO DI MINIATO (1366-c.1450) Italian

£116129	$183484	€180000	Saint Francis receiving the stigmata. Jesus' christening (98x90cm-39x35in) tempera board triptych. 19-Dec-2 Semenzato, Venice #23/R est:200000

PIETRO, Piccoli (20th C) Italian?

£1881	$2934	€2822	Composizione Con Barche (40x60cm-16x24in) s. 7-Nov-2 International Art Centre, Auckland #174/R est:8000-10000 (NZ.D 6000)

PIETTE, Ludovic (1826-1877) French

£1757	$2741	€2600	Paysan se reposant sous les arbres en fleurs (21x30cm-8x12in) s. panel. 31-Mar-3 Rossini, Paris #54
Works on paper			
£2532	$3949	€4000	Lavandieres pres du village (27x53cm-11x21in) s. gouache. 18-Oct-2 Rabourdin & Choppin de Janvry, Paris #42/R

PIFFARD, Harold (fl.1895-1899) British

£500	$780	€750	Double characters (64x77cm-25x30in) s. 10-Sep-2 Sworder & Son, Bishops Stortford #742/R
£4800	$8016	€7200	Sultan's favourite (77x64cm-30x25in) s. 18-Jun-3 Christie's, Kensington #193/R est:4000-6000
£5200	$8112	€7800	Family heirlooms. Breach of promise (64x77cm-25x30in) s. pair. 10-Sep-2 Sworder & Son, Bishops Stortford #741/R est:1500-2000

PIFFARD, Jeanne (1892-1971) French

Sculpture			
£1392	$2200	€2200	Lion (33x65cm-13x26in) s. brown red plaster. 27-Nov-2 Camard, Paris #167/R
£2025	$3200	€3200	Buffle (23x45cm-9x18in) s. green pat bronze wooden sole. 27-Nov-2 Camard, Paris #166/R

PIGA, Bernard (1934-) French

£364	$594	€550	Atelier de peintre (80x80cm-31x31in) s. 3-Feb-3 Cornette de St.Cyr, Paris #502

PIGAGE, Werner von (1888-1959) German

£316	$500	€500	Studio with female nude sitting on a sofa (72x51cm-28x20in) s.d.1912 board. 30-Nov-2 Berlinghof, Heidelberg #359

PIGALLE, Jean Baptiste (1714-1785) French

Sculpture			
£2564	$4026	€4000	Mercure attachant ses talonnieres (55cm-22in) brown pat bronze lit. 13-Dec-2 Pierre Berge, Paris #132/R
£19231	$29808	€30000	Portrait d'Antoine Ferrein (67x32x26cm-26x13x10in) marble exec.1771 exhib.lit. 9-Dec-2 Rabourdin & Choppin de Janvry, Paris #23/R est:60000
£118910	$184311	€185500	Portrait de l'Abbe Nollet (64x35x28cm-25x14x11in) bronze exec.c.1760 lit. 9-Dec-2 Rabourdin & Choppin de Janvry, Paris #22/R est:60000

PIGHILLS, Joseph (1902-1984) British

£260	$403	€390	Wycoller in snow (30x43cm-12x17in) s. i.verso acrylic. 4-Dec-2 Andrew Hartley, Ilkley #1125

PIGNATELLI, Ercole (1935-) Italian

£1622	$2530	€2400	Solarium (24x30cm-9x12in) s. painted 1974. 26-Mar-3 Finarte Semenzato, Milan #102
£1773	$2872	€2500	Il panettone (101x83cm-40x33in) st. s.d.1965-66 verso exhib. 26-May-3 Christie's, Milan #134/R est:2500-3500
Works on paper			
£317	$526	€450	Dinosauro (10x17cm-4x7in) s.d.31.12.1972 pen. 10-Jun-3 Finarte Semenzato, Milan #283
£962	$1404	€1500	Panettone (101x83cm-40x33in) s.d.1965-66 mixed media on canvas. 5-Jun-2 Il Ponte, Milan #167

PIGNATELLI, Luca (1962-) Italian

£3846	$5962	€6000	Recognition (40x60cm-16x24in) s.i.d.2001. 4-Dec-2 Finarte, Milan #506/R est:2400
£6690	$11106	€9500	New York (80x60cm-31x24in) s.i.d.2001 verso. 10-Jun-3 Finarte Semenzato, Milan #346/R est:5500-6500
Works on paper			
£759	$1200	€1200	New York (42x29cm-17x11in) s.d.2001 verso mixed media paper on canvas. 29-Nov-2 Farsetti, Prato #30
£5282	$8768	€7500	New York (73x60cm-29x24in) s. s.i.d.1998 verso mixed media canvas. 10-Jun-3 Finarte Semenzato, Milan #360/R est:400-500
£6419	$10014	€9500	Aphrodites (80x60cm-31x24in) s.i.d.2000-01 verso mixed media fabric. 26-Mar-3 Finarte Semenzato, Milan #148/R

PIGNON, Edouard (1905-1993) French

£1560	$2606	€2200	Rendez vous Antibes nu bleu rose (46x88cm-18x35in) s.d. acrylic. 18-Jun-3 Charbonneaux, Paris #76/R est:3000-4000
£1700	$2771	€2550	Les baigneuses (55x37cm-22x15in) s.d.59. 3-Feb-3 Sotheby's, Olympia #210/R est:1500-2000
£1871	$2974	€2750	Pecheurs en bord de mer (25x41cm-10x16in) s.d.46. 26-Feb-3 Artcurial Briest, Paris #90/R est:900-1200
£2000	$3260	€3000	Divers (55x38cm-22x15in) s. s.d.60 verso. 3-Feb-3 Sotheby's, Olympia #211/R est:2000-3000
£2013	$3119	€3200	Paysage de sanary (55x38cm-22x15in) s.d.55. 30-Oct-2 Artcurial Briest, Paris #488/R est:3000-4000
£2128	$3553	€3000	Les gymnastes (64x81cm-25x32in) s.d.82. 20-Jun-3 Piasa, Paris #176/R est:1800-2500
£2516	$3899	€4000	Cueillette du jasmin (38x46cm-15x18in) s.d.55. 30-Oct-2 Artcurial Briest, Paris #487/R est:4000-6000
£2830	$4387	€4500	Combat de coqs (50x61cm-20x24in) s.d.59 i.d.1959 verso. 30-Oct-2 Artcurial Briest, Paris #489/R est:4000-6000
£3165	$5065	€4400	Baigneurs sur les rochers (55x38cm-22x15in) s.d. 18-May-3 Eric Pillon, Calais #230/R
£3404	$5515	€4800	La bataille bleue (50x61cm-20x24in) d.63 i.d.stretcher prov. 26-May-3 Christie's, Milan #324/R est:2000-2500
£3500	$5845	€5075	Paysans a l'olivier (44x59cm-17x23in) s.d.1950. 24-Jun-3 Sotheby's, Olympia #89/R est:2000-3000
£4082	$6490	€6000	Bateaux a Ostende (26x35cm-10x14in) s.d.47 prov. 26-Feb-3 Artcurial Briest, Paris #540/R est:600-800
£4167	$6583	€6000	Le petit bleu de la mer (61x81cm-24x32in) s.d. i.d.verso prov. 27-Apr-3 Perrin, Versailles #65/R est:6000-8000
Works on paper			
£353	$554	€550	Oiseau (35x53cm-14x21in) s.d.59 Chinese ink wash. 11-Dec-2 Fraysse & Associes, Paris #18
£506	$790	€800	Combat de coqs (41x53cm-16x21in) s.d.1958 drawing. 20-Oct-2 Claude Boisgirard, Paris #79
£601	$938	€950	Dans l'atelier du peintre (20x25cm-8x10in) s.d.1970 pastel ink wash. 20-Oct-2 Claude Boisgirard, Paris #80/R
£641	$1006	€1000	Combat de coqs (32x44cm-13x17in) s.d.1959 wax crayon. 23-Nov-2 Meeting Art, Vercelli #281/R
£676	$1054	€1000	Combat de coqs (53x69cm-21x27in) s.d.69 gouache exhib.lit. 28-Mar-3 Farsetti, Prato #357/R
£881	$1365	€1400	Sans titre (56x77cm-22x30in) s.d.64 W/C prov. 30-Oct-2 Artcurial Briest, Paris #726
£884	$1406	€1300	Paysage de Sanary (50x65cm-20x26in) s.d.58 W/C. 26-Feb-3 Artcurial Briest, Paris #541
£943	$1462	€1500	Nu (55x77cm-22x30in) s.d.80 gouache prov. 30-Oct-2 Artcurial Briest, Paris #727 est:1500-2000
£1026	$1610	€1600	Combat de coqs (36x53cm-14x21in) s.d.59 pastel col crayon. 24-Nov-2 Laurence Calmels, Paris #211/R
£1103	$1754	€1600	Nus feminins (73x55cm-29x22in) s.d.75 W/C. 7-Mar-3 Claude Aguttes, Neuilly #9/R
£1132	$1755	€1800	Les collines (46x63cm-18x25in) s.d.56 W/C. 4-Oct-2 Tajan, Paris #198 est:1000-1500
£1146	$1789	€1800	Nus aux parasols rouges (31x39cm-12x15in) s.d.1980 W/C gouache. 10-Nov-2 Eric Pillon, Calais #261/R
£1224	$1947	€1800	Tete de guerrier (55x75cm-22x30in) s.d.1967 W/C. 24-Mar-3 Cornette de St.Cyr, Paris #21/R
£1307	$2144	€2000	Travailleurs de la terre (46x61cm-18x24in) s.d.1952 gouache. 9-Feb-3 Anaf, Lyon #211/R
£1633	$2596	€2400	Les Oliviers (56x76cm-22x30in) s.d.58 W/C prov. 26-Feb-3 Artcurial Briest, Paris #542/R est:1800-2200
£1783	$2782	€2800	Table dans la cuisine (21x27cm-8x11in) s.d.1938 gouache W/C. 10-Nov-2 Eric Pillon, Calais #262/R
£1923	$3019	€3000	Cueillette du jasmin (47x62cm-19x24in) s.d.52 gouache W/C. 24-Nov-2 Laurence Calmels, Paris #212/R
£1946	$3134	€2900	Femme allongee (48x64cm-19x25in) s.d.1975 W/C. 23-Feb-3 Mercier & Cie, Lille #98/R
£2177	$3461	€3200	Monteurs electriciens (64x49cm-25x19in) s.d.1959 gouache paper on canvas. 24-Mar-3 Cornette de St.Cyr, Paris #20/R

PIGNONI, Simone (1614-1698) Italian
£5031 $7799 €8000 Esther before Ahasver (65x81cm-26x32in) 2-Oct-2 Dorotheum, Vienna #38/R est:8000-12000
£6329 $9873 €10000 Martyr (70x57cm-28x22in) 19-Oct-2 Semenzato, Venice #494/R est:12000-15000
£10563 $17535 €15000 Madonna col Bambino, San Giovannino e Sant'Antonio da Padova (80x65cm-31x26in) 11-Jun-3 Dorotheum, Vienna #28/R est:15000-20000

PIGNONI, Simone (attrib) (1614-1698) Italian
£878 $1370 €1300 Portrait of lady (58x48cm-23x19in) prov. 27-Mar-3 Dorotheum, Vienna #351/R

PIGNONI, Simone (circle) (1614-1698) Italian
£60000 $93000 €90000 Saint Catherine of Alexandria tended by putti (166x196cm-65x77in) canvas on board. 30-Oct-2 Christie's, Kensington #130/R est:3000-5000

PIGOT, R St Leger (fl.1864-1871) British
£1524 $2500 €2210 Portrait of a soldier (130x99cm-51x39in) 31-May-3 Harvey Clar, Oakland #1262

PIGOTT, Charles (1863-c.1940) British
Works on paper
£280 $434 €420 Rural landscape with sheep grazing (46x33cm-18x13in) s. W/C. 1-Oct-2 Fellows & Sons, Birmingham #153/R

PIGOTT, Marjorie (1904-1990) Canadian
Works on paper
£248 $389 €372 Migration (56x46cm-22x18in) s. W/C. 24-Jul-2 Walker's, Ottawa #266/R (C.D 600)

PIGOTT, Walter Henry (c.1810-1901) British
Works on paper
£344 $550 €499 Approaching the storm (39x59cm-15x23in) s.d.73 W/C. 16-May-3 Skinner, Boston #41/R

PIGUENIT, William Charles (1836-1914) Australian
£1600 $2576 €2320 Mount barker (22x38cm-9x15in) s. 12-May-3 Joel, Victoria #383 est:2500-3000 (A.D 4000)
£6071 $9593 €9107 St. Pauls dome from South Esk, Tasmania (61x91cm-24x36in) s.d.1881 prov.exhib.lit. 17-Nov-2 Sotheby's, Paddington #66/R est:25000-35000 (A.D 17000)
£9562 $15681 €14343 River scene with cattle, Tasmania (50x75cm-20x30in) s. 4-Jun-3 Deutscher-Menzies, Melbourne #79/R est:20000-30000 (A.D 24000)
£14947 $22868 €22421 Lake St. Claire, the Source of the river Derwent, Tasmania (78x128cm-31x50in) s. canvas on board prov.exhib. 26-Aug-2 Sotheby's, Paddington #533/R est:50000-60000 (A.D 42000)
£22901 $36183 €34352 On the break-o-day plains, Tasmania (74x125cm-29x49in) s. exhib. 2-Apr-3 Christie's, Melbourne #28/R est:60000-80000 (A.D 60000)

PIGUET, Jean Louis (1944-) Swiss
£417 $671 €626 Summer garden (64x80cm-25x31in) s.d.88 panel. 7-May-3 Dobiaschofsky, Bern #886/R (S.FR 900)
£741 $1193 €1074 Garden landscape in summer (93x92cm-37x36in) s.d.83. 9-May-3 Dobiaschofsky, Bern #207/R (S.FR 1600)

PIKE, Sidney (fl.1880-1901) British
£720 $1116 €1080 Highland landscapes with cattle (28x43cm-11x17in) s.d.99 board pair. 3-Oct-2 Heathcote Ball, Leicester #596/R
£800 $1248 €1200 Rye (23x33cm-9x13in) s.i.d.1919. 9-Oct-2 Woolley & Wallis, Salisbury #85/R

PIKE, William H (1846-1908) British
Works on paper
£450 $734 €675 Coastal village (28x48cm-11x19in) s. W/C. 13-Feb-3 David Lay, Penzance #98

PIKE, William H (attrib) (1846-1908) British
Works on paper
£420 $672 €630 Kynance Cove, Lizard, Cornwall (32x60cm-13x24in) s.d.1870 W/C. 11-Mar-3 Bonhams, Oxford #47

PIKELNY, Robert (1904-) Polish
£680 $1082 €1000 Nature morte au poisson (54x65cm-21x26in) isorel. 3-Mar-3 Claude Boisgirard, Paris #85
£680 $1082 €1000 Nature morte dans l'atelier (54x73cm-21x29in) panel. 3-Mar-3 Claude Boisgirard, Paris #86
£1497 $2380 €2200 Le ventriloque (55x77cm-22x30in) s. panel. 3-Mar-3 Claude Boisgirard, Paris #87/R est:2200-2500

PIKESLEY, Richard (1951-) British
£300 $456 €450 Etruscan horseman and flowers (46x46cm-18x18in) s. 16-Aug-2 Keys, Aylsham #467

PILET, Léon (1839-1916) French
Sculpture
£1424 $2250 €2136 Bust of a young queen (76x43cm-30x17in) polychrome spelter. 15-Nov-2 Du Mouchelle, Detroit #2132/R est:1500-2000
£2179 $3422 €3400 Diane chasseresse (87cm-34in) s. brown pat bronze. 19-Nov-2 Vanderkindere, Brussels #140/R est:2000-3000

PILHAN, M (19/20th C) French?
Works on paper
£2019 $3250 €3029 Children collecting money falling from the heavens (117x81cm-46x32in) s. ink gouache W/C exec.c.1905. 10-May-3 Illustration House, New York #1/R est:2500-3500

PILHS, Hans (1903-) ?
£833 $1317 €1200 Flowers (48x38cm-19x15in) s. 24-Apr-3 Dorotheum, Vienna #188/R

PILKINGTON, Audrey (1922-) British
Works on paper
£520 $868 €754 Portrait of John Minton (63x50cm-25x20in) s. gouache. 17-Jun-3 Bonhams, Knightsbridge #112/R

PILKINGTON, George W (1879-1958) South African
£362 $572 €543 Aquarium Reef, St James, SA (55x75cm-22x30in) s.d.50 i.verso. 1-Apr-3 Stephan Welz, Johannesburg #174 est:2500-4000 (SA.R 4500)

PILLEAU, Henry (1815-1899) British
£1000 $1630 €1500 Eastern town square (30x24cm-12x9in) indis sig. 29-Jan-3 Sotheby's, Olympia #155/R est:1000-1500
Works on paper
£280 $437 €420 View of a Mediterranean town. Coastal scene (11x19cm-4x7in) mono. W/C pair frame as one. 25-Mar-3 Bonhams, Knightsbridge #229/R
£1500 $2339 €2250 Fort city of Valleta, Malta (28x54cm-11x21in) mono. pencil W/C htd bodycol. 19-Sep-2 Christie's, Kensington #124/R est:500-700

PILLEMENT, Jean (1728-1808) French
£2327 $3770 €3374 Elegant party of monkeys - Political satire (32x37cm-13x15in) cardboard. 26-May-3 Bukowskis, Stockholm #461/R est:15000-18000 (S.KR 30000)
£13415 $22000 €20123 Wooded, hilly landscape with peasants, goats and sheep near a ruined castle (55x75cm-22x30in) prov. 29-May-3 Sotheby's, New York #56/R est:25000-35000
£15094 $23547 €24000 Promeneurs pres d'un lac. Laveuses au bord d'une riviere (33x45cm-13x18in) one s. pair. 10-Oct-2 Ribeyre & Baron, Paris #30/R est:6000-9000
£24051 $38000 €38000 Paysage rocheux avec bergers se reposant (31x42cm-12x17in) s.indis.d. metal. 27-Nov-2 Christie's, Paris #42/R est:30000-50000
£47436 $74949 €74000 Wooded landscape with herders (100x152cm-39x60in) s. 16-Nov-2 Lempertz, Koln #1068/R est:70000
£64748 $106187 €90000 Paysanne se promenant dans la campagne portugaise (54x85cm-21x33in) s.d.1791. 5-Jun-3 Fraysse & Associes, Paris #13/R est:40000-60000
Works on paper
£755 $1170 €1200 Paysages animes (14x21cm-6x8in) s.d.1792 pierre noire stump pair. 29-Oct-2 Artcurial Briest, Paris #15
£900 $1404 €1350 Fishing boats on a river in pastoral landscape (19x29cm-7x11in) s.d.1792 black chk. 9-Apr-3 Bonhams, New Bond Street #131
£1000 $1570 €1500 Mill near a bridge (22x32cm-9x13in) s. black chk. 11-Dec-2 Sotheby's, Olympia #190/R est:1000-1500
£1268 $2104 €1800 Chaumiere avec deux villages. Pote d'une petite ville (14x22cm-6x9in) s. one d.1774 pierre noire col wash pair. 13-Jun-3 Rossini, Paris #66/R est:900-1100

£1400 $2198 €2100 Two washerwomen by a mountain stream (25x32cm-10x13in) init.d.1802 black chk. 11-Dec-2 Sotheby's, Olympia #179/R est:1000-1500
£2568 $4005 €3800 Mountainous river landscape with fortress on cliff (32x44cm-13x17in) pastel en grisaille prov. 27-Mar-3 Dorotheum, Vienna #29/R est:2000-3000
£2837 $4738 €4000 Paysage animes (29x39cm-11x15in) one s.d.1792 black crayon pair. 19-Jun-3 Piasa, Paris #130 est:4000
£6173 $10000 €9260 Travellers on road in wooded landscape (44x66cm-17x26in) s.d. pastel. 21-Jan-3 Sotheby's, New York #119/R est:15000
£7407 $12000 €11111 Rustics and animals on path (42x35cm-17x14in) s. pastel. 21-Jan-3 Sotheby's, New York #120/R est:8000
£22378 $37371 €32000 Paysans et leur troupeau pres d'une riviere (55x82cm-22x32in) s.d.1779 pastel. 25-Jun-3 Tajan, Paris #79/R est:12000-15000

PILLEMENT, Jean (attrib) (1728-1808) French
Works on paper
£1392 $2172 €2200 Paysage avec bergers (48x65cm-19x26in) s.d.1793 pastel. 20-Oct-2 Mercier & Cie, Lille #275 est:1400-1600

PILLEN, Rudi (1931-) Belgian
£414 $662 €600 Female nude (54x38cm-21x15in) s.d.71 canvas on panel. 15-Mar-3 De Vuyst, Lokeren #353
Works on paper
£360 $576 €500 Composition with women (45x100cm-18x39in) s.d.72 mixed media panel. 17-May-3 De Vuyst, Lokeren #296

PILLET, Edgar (1912-1996) French
£1410 $2214 €2200 Fertilite (65x81cm-26x32in) s.d.1953 s.i.d.verso prov. 15-Dec-2 Perrin, Versailles #20/R
Works on paper
£742 $1172 €1150 Serie des creuset (38x43cm-15x17in) s. mixed media. 18-Dec-2 Digard, Paris #200
£1290 $2039 €2000 Creuset (115x82cm-45x32in) i.d.64 s.verso mixed media. 18-Dec-2 Digard, Paris #245/R

PILLHOFER, Josef (1921-) Austrian
£506 $790 €800 Sketch for sculpture (40x31cm-16x12in) s. Indian ink brush. 15-Oct-2 Dorotheum, Vienna #141/R
Sculpture
£5797 $9507 €8000 Gegretschte Figur (65cm-26in) mono.num.2/8 green pat bronze exec.1968 prov. 27-May-3 Hassfurther, Vienna #59/R est:6000-8000
£10811 $16865 €16000 Sculpture (107cm-42in) mono. num.P1/8 green pat.bronze wooden socle. 25-Mar-3 Wiener Kunst Auktionen, Vienna #3/R est:16000-28000
Works on paper
£621 $993 €900 Standing figure (43x30cm-17x12in) s.d.1956 chl gouache. 11-Mar-3 Dorotheum, Vienna #143/R

PILLIN, Polia (1905-1992) American
Works on paper
£2083 $3250 €3125 Wash day (30x38cm-12x15in) s.d.38 W/C prov. 9-Nov-2 Santa Fe Art, Santa Fe #222/R est:5000-6000

PILNY, Otto (1866-1936) Swiss
£1223 $1907 €1835 In the Egyptian desert (45x55cm-18x22in) s.i.d.1901. 6-Nov-2 Dobiaschofsky, Bern #888/R est:3800 (S.FR 2800)
£3493 $5450 €5240 Evening desert landscape (54x65cm-21x26in) s.i.d.1901. 6-Nov-2 Dobiaschofsky, Bern #889/R est:9000 (S.FR 8000)
£3548 $5216 €5500 Sale of slave girls in desert (66x93cm-26x37in) s.d.1904. 20-Jun-2 Dr Fritz Nagel, Stuttgart #806/R est:6000
£4167 $6458 €6500 Slave trade in the desert (66x93cm-26x37in) s.d.1904. 5-Dec-2 Dr Fritz Nagel, Stuttgart #694/R est:3000
£14155 $22082 €21233 Arabs in desert (119x180cm-47x71in) s.d.1910 prov. 28-Mar-3 Koller, Zurich #3131/R est:40000-60000 (S.FR 31000)
£18455 $28605 €27683 Oriental figures in the desert (119x180cm-47x71in) s.d.1910 prov. 3-Oct-2 Koller, Zurich #3086/R est:40000-60000 (S.FR 43000)
£20000 $33400 €30000 Rest in the desert (121x181cm-48x71in) s. prov. 19-Jun-3 Christie's, London #11/R est:30000-40000
£29032 $45000 €43548 Slave market (121x180cm-48x71in) s.d.1914. 30-Oct-2 Christie's, Rockefeller NY #87/R est:50000-70000

PILO, Carl Gustaf (1712-1792) Swedish
£3404 $5277 €5106 Portrait of gentleman, possibly Johan Tobias Sergel (76x60cm-30x24in) prov.exhib. 3-Dec-2 Bukowskis, Stockholm #402/R est:60000-80000 (S.KR 48000)
£15504 $23566 €23256 Portrait of Queen Louise in her Coronation outfit (143x116cm-56x46in) 27-Aug-2 Rasmussen, Copenhagen #1407/R est:200000 (D.KR 180000)

PILO, Carl Gustaf (attrib) (1712-1792) Swedish
£3273 $4975 €4910 Portrait of Adam Gottlob Moltke (76x63cm-30x25in) i. 28-Aug-2 Museumsbygningen, Copenhagen #15/R est:20000-30000 (D.KR 38000)

PILOPOVIC, Ivan (?) Yugoslavian
£300 $468 €435 Broomfield Road London (22x33cm-9x13in) s. board. 27-Mar-3 Lane, Penzance #218
£300 $468 €435 Eottere Venice - canal side cafe (22x28cm-9x11in) s. board. 27-Mar-3 Lane, Penzance #219

PILOT, Robert Wakeham (1898-1967) Canadian
£1210 $1911 €1815 Ack-ack emplacement, Witley camp, England (20x27cm-8x11in) s. s.i.d.1942 verso panel prov. 18-Nov-2 Sotheby's, Toronto #43/R est:3500-5000 (C.D 3000)
£1345 $2152 €2018 Toledo, Spain (15x22cm-6x9in) s.i.d.1927 s.verso panel prov. 15-May-3 Heffel, Vancouver #19/R est:3500-4500 (C.D 3000)
£1717 $2678 €2490 Mont St. Sauveur, Quebec (20x27cm-8x11in) s.i.d.1938 panel prov. 26-Mar-3 Walker's, Ottawa #235/R est:5000-7000 (C.D 4000)
£1815 $2867 €2723 Sunlit pond near Gravetye (19x27cm-7x11in) s. board prov. 14-Nov-2 Heffel, Vancouver #259/R est:3500-4500 (C.D 4500)
£2117 $3345 €3176 Canal bridge (14x18cm-6x7in) s. i.d.1915 verso panel. 18-Nov-2 Sotheby's, Toronto #169/R est:5000-7000 (C.D 5250)
£2621 $4141 €3932 Quebec city in winter (20x25cm-8x10in) panel prov.lit. 18-Nov-2 Sotheby's, Toronto #81/R est:5000-7000 (C.D 6500)
£3226 $5097 €4839 Rue d'auteil, Quebec (21x27cm-8x11in) s. s.i.d.Mar 14 62 prov.lit. 18-Nov-2 Sotheby's, Toronto #166/R est:7000-9000 (C.D 8000)
£3292 $5103 €4938 Gondola wharf, Venice (20x26cm-8x10in) s. panel painted 1957. 3-Dec-2 Joyner, Toronto #306/R est:3000-4000 (C.D 8000)
£3363 $5381 €5045 Street in Perce, PQ (31x43cm-12x17in) s. s.i.verso panel prov. 15-May-3 Heffel, Vancouver #16/R est:8000-10000 (C.D 7500)
£3629 $5734 €5444 Devil River, Mt. Tremblant (32x42cm-13x17in) s.i.d.1943 panel prov.exhib. 14-Nov-2 Heffel, Vancouver #170/R est:9000-12000 (C.D 9000)
£4444 $7289 €6666 St. Francois, Ile d'Orleans (33x45cm-13x18in) s.d.35 board prov. 3-Jun-3 Joyner, Toronto #34/R est:8000-10000 (C.D 10000)
£5645 $8919 €8468 Greenock Presbyterian Kirk, St. Andrews-by-the-sea, Nova Scotia (41x51cm-16x20in) s. prov. 18-Nov-2 Sotheby's, Toronto #69/R est:7000-9000 (C.D 14000)
£5778 $9476 €8667 Yarmouth, N.S (48x61cm-19x24in) s. i.on stretcher verso prov. 27-May-3 Sotheby's, Toronto #166/R est:12000-15000 (C.D 13000)
£6278 $10045 €9417 Quebec farm (46x61cm-18x24in) s. prov. 15-May-3 Heffel, Vancouver #14/R est:14000-18000 (C.D 14000)
£6667 $10933 €10001 Place d'armes, Quebec (40x50cm-16x20in) s. prov. 3-Jun-3 Joyner, Toronto #42/R est:15000-20000 (C.D 15000)
£6996 $10844 €10494 Autumn's splendour (55x70cm-22x28in) s.d.62 prov. 3-Dec-2 Joyner, Toronto #47/R est:15000-20000 (C.D 17000)
£7623 $12197 €11435 Three sisters (46x61cm-18x24in) s.d.1930 prov. 15-May-3 Heffel, Vancouver #13/R est:14000-18000 (C.D 17000)
£9053 $14033 €13580 Dufferin Terrace, Quebec (45x55cm-18x22in) s. prov. 3-Dec-2 Joyner, Toronto #142/R est:15000-20000 (C.D 22000)
£9778 $16036 €14667 Springtime St. Sauveur (56x71cm-22x28in) s. prov. 27-May-3 Sotheby's, Toronto #163/R est:15000-20000 (C.D 22000)
£9877 $15309 €14816 Snow cart, Levis, PQ (40x50cm-16x20in) s. painted 1966. 3-Dec-2 Joyner, Toronto #159/R est:15000-20000 (C.D 24000)
£10081 $15927 €15122 Quebec (32x43cm-13x17in) s.i.d.1952 s.verso panel prov. 14-Nov-2 Heffel, Vancouver #55/R est:15000-20000 (C.D 25000)
£13333 $21867 €20000 Wharf, Sillery Quebec (45x55cm-18x22in) s. prov. 27-May-3 Sotheby's, Toronto #167/R est:30000-35000 (C.D 30000)
£14444 $23689 €21666 Sunset, Chambly (56x71cm-22x28in) s. prov. 27-May-3 Sotheby's, Toronto #74/R est:30000-40000 (C.D 32500)
£32922 $51029 €49383 View of Quebec from Levis (60x80cm-24x31in) s.d.47 lit. 3-Dec-2 Joyner, Toronto #25/R est:75000-100000 (C.D 80000)
Works on paper
£311 $510 €451 Nursing a young boy (30x24cm-12x9in) chl. 9-Jun-3 Hodgins, Calgary #163/R (C.D 700)
£472 $736 €708 Church (25x19cm-10x7in) s. pencil. 25-Mar-3 Iegor de Saint Hippolyte, Montreal #108 (C.D 1100)

PILOTY, Karl Theodor von (1824-1886) German
£1633 $2596 €2400 Mark Anthony's speech at the burial of Julius Caesar in Rome (99x146cm-39x57in) 19-Mar-3 Neumeister, Munich #695/R est:2500

PILS, Edouard Aime (1823-1850) French
£1268 $2104 €1800 Moutons, coq et poule (50x3cm-20x1in) s. 11-Jun-3 Beaussant & Lefèvre, Paris #118/R est:1000-1500

PILS, Isidore (1813-1875) French
£2419 $3750 €3629 Seated Arab (27x26cm-11x10in) prov. 29-Oct-2 Sotheby's, New York #27/R est:3000-5000
£3226 $5000 €4839 Lamentation (25x30cm-10x12in) s. 29-Oct-2 Sotheby's, New York #31/R est:1500-2000
Works on paper
£258 $400 €387 Chapel of San Benedetto (21x23cm-8x9in) i. pencil W/C prov. 29-Oct-2 Sotheby's, New York #32/R
£580 $900 €870 Men shoeing horses (23x34cm-9x13in) s.i. W/C pencil. 29-Oct-2 Sotheby's, New York #28/R est:700-1000
£645 $1000 €968 Study of St. Andrew for the cathedral of St. Eustache (43x28cm-17x11in) i. pencil red chk. 29-Oct-2 Sotheby's, New York #34/R est:700-1000
£1081 $1686 €1600 Zouave a l'epee (25x17cm-10x7in) crayon stump. 26-Mar-3 Piasa, Paris #111/R
£1451 $2250 €2177 Arab chief on horseback (33x41cm-13x16in) prov. 29-Oct-2 Sotheby's, New York #25/R est:700-1000
£1451 $2250 €2177 Military encampment (38x30cm-15x12in) s.i.d.1871 pencil W/C wash htd white. 29-Oct-2 Sotheby's, New York #30/R est:1000-1500
£1554 $2424 €2300 Sculpteur dans son atelier (26x18cm-10x7in) s.d.1870 W/C over crayon. 27-Mar-3 Maigret, Paris #125/R
£2581 $4000 €3872 Two Zoaves at battle (22x35cm-9x14in) s.d.1860 pencil gouache wash. 29-Oct-2 Sotheby's, New York #29/R est:1500-2000
£3226 $5000 €4839 Studies of Mohamed (31x48cm-12x19in) s.d.2 Dec 1861 pencil gouache chk. 29-Oct-2 Sotheby's, New York #26/R est:700-1000
£4838 $7500 €7257 Young man reading (33x27cm-13x11in) s. pencil gouache W/C. 29-Oct-2 Sotheby's, New York #33/R est:1200-1800

PILSBURY, Harry Clifford (1870-?) British
£500 $785 €750 View of Ludlow (40x50cm-16x20in) s.d.1906 canvas on board. 21-Nov-2 Tennants, Leyburn #827/R

PILSBURY, Wilmot (1840-1908) British
Works on paper
£320 $509 €480 Cattle grazing by a river, a house beyond (24x37cm-9x15in) s.d.1889 W/C. 27-Feb-3 Bonhams, Chester #412
£360 $572 €540 Stream (18x27cm-7x11in) s.d.1874 W/C. 5-Mar-3 Bonhams, Bury St Edmunds #278
£360 $576 €540 Farmyard with hayricks and ducks to foreground (25x35cm-10x14in) s.d.1883 W/C. 13-Mar-3 Morphets, Harrogate #603
£480 $749 €720 Stream (21x29cm-8x11in) s.d.1876 pencil W/C htd white. 17-Oct-2 Christie's, Kensington #58
£800 $1264 €1200 Cattle beside a pond with farmhouse beyond (48x74cm-19x29in) s.d.1901 W/C. 13-Nov-2 Halls, Shrewsbury #340/R
£1100 $1760 €1650 Farmyard (25x36cm-10x14in) s.d.1884 W/C. 11-Mar-3 Bonhams, New Bond Street #73/R est:1000-1500

PILTZ, Otto (1846-1910) German
£29032 $45000 €43548 In the Bavarian beergarden (78x114cm-31x45in) s.d.75. 29-Oct-2 Sotheby's, New York #130/R est:40000-50000

PILZ, Otto (1876-1934) German
Sculpture
£1509 $2355 €2400 Pipe playing Satyr (29cm-11in) s. brown green pat.bronze. 20-Sep-2 Schloss Ahlden, Ahlden #631/R est:2800

PIMENTEL, Vincente (1948-) French
Works on paper
£580 $951 €800 Untitled (105x75cm-41x30in) s.d.1999 pigment W/C. 27-May-3 Tajan, Paris #44/R

PIMM, William Edwin (1863-1952) British
£2000 $3080 €3000 Feeding the pigeons in the park (97x127cm-38x50in) s. 5-Sep-2 Christie's, Kensington #266/R est:2000-3000

PINA, A (1887-1966) Italian
Sculpture
£1772 $2765 €2800 Homme accroupi s'etirant les bras (19x37x25cm-7x15x10in) st.f.Valsuani brown pat bronze. 18-Oct-2 Rabourdin & Choppin de Janvry, Paris #69

PINA, Adria (1959-) Spanish
Works on paper
£353 $557 €550 Package. s.d.1996 W/C acrylic oil board. 14-Nov-2 Arte, Seville #440/R

PINA, Alfredo (1887-1966) Italian
Sculpture
£1667 $2633 €2600 Beethoven (26cm-10in) s.st.f.Pannini brown pat bronze. 18-Nov-2 Sotheby's, Paris #414/R
£2778 $4389 €4000 Young man drinking (64cm-25in) s. bronze. 23-Apr-3 Rabourdin & Choppin de Janvry, Paris #94/R
£3500 $5460 €5250 Homme a genoux sur un rocher (44cm-17in) s. brown pat bronze. 5-Nov-2 Sotheby's, London #205/R est:3500-5000
£3600 $5652 €5400 Kneeling woman (54cm-21in) s. white marble. 10-Dec-2 Sotheby's, London #158/R est:4000-6000
£4167 $6583 €6000 Head of Beethoven (55cm-22in) s. pat bronze. 25-Apr-3 Piasa, Paris #31/R
£5493 $9118 €7800 Nu assis (60cm-24in) s.d.1924 medaille pat bronze st.f. 18-Jun-3 Anaf, Lyon #105/R est:6000-7000
£6000 $9360 €9000 Man kneeling on a rock (90cm-35in) s. green pat bronze. 9-Apr-3 Sotheby's, London #212/R est:7000-10000
£7000 $10920 €10500 Tired work horse (36x70cm-14x28in) s.st.f.Meroni Radice brown pat bronze. 9-Apr-3 Sotheby's, London #224/R est:7000-10000
£7500 $12525 €10875 Bust of Ludwig van Beethoven (62cm-24in) s. dk brown green pat bronze incl base st.f.Montagutelli. 8-Jul-3 Sotheby's, London #231/R est:8000-12000
£7746 $12859 €11000 Couple s'embrassant (48x57cm-19x22in) s.num.23 green pat bronze. 13-Jun-3 Rabourdin & Choppin de Janvry, Paris #129/R est:5200-5500
£20000 $31200 €30000 Icarus (46x82x51cm-18x32x20in) s. black Belgian marble lit. 9-Apr-3 Sotheby's, London #226/R est:20000-30000
£22000 $34320 €33000 Leffort supreme, or, Thais et Alexandre (29x97x38cm-11x38x15in) s.i.num.V black brown pat bronze col marble base st.f.A.Valsuani. 5-Nov-2 Sotheby's, London #207/R est:12000-18000

PINAL, Fernand (1881-1958) French
£520 $848 €780 Boat and figures. s. 1-Feb-3 Hogben, Folkstone #156

PINAR MOYA, Eduardo (19th C) Spanish
£581 $917 €900 Behind the Escorial (87x45cm-34x18in) s.d.93. 17-Dec-2 Durán, Madrid #109/R

PINAZO MARTINEZ, Jose Ignacio (1879-1933) Spanish
£3974 $6477 €6000 Portrait of woman with shawl (74x85cm-29x33in) s. 11-Feb-3 Segre, Madrid #126/R

PINCEMIN, Jean-Pierre (1944-) French
£577 $894 €900 Untitled (62x45cm-24x18in) s.d.1985 paper prov. 7-Dec-2 Cornette de St.Cyr, Paris #123/R
£903 $1426 €1300 Sans titre (28x27cm-11x11in) s.d. acrylic cardboard. 27-Apr-3 Perrin, Versailles #119/R
£2653 $4218 €3900 Peinture (43x32cm-17x13in) paper painted c.1980. 24-Mar-3 Cornette de St.Cyr, Paris #182/R
£3655 $5848 €5300 Composition (130x140cm-51x55in) s.d.1979 verso. 15-Mar-3 De Vuyst, Lokeren #254/R est:5000-6000
£7383 $11886 €11000 Untitled (222x160cm-87x63in) prov. 23-Feb-3 Mercier & Cie, Lille #147/R est:13000
£8333 $13750 €12000 Composition (200x280cm-79x110in) s.d.75 exhib. 1-Jul-3 Artcurial Briest, Paris #551/R est:12000-15000
£13462 $21135 €21000 Untitled (210x150cm-83x59in) s.d.1983 verso. 11-Dec-2 Artcurial Briest, Paris #748/R est:18000
Works on paper
£1395 $2217 €2050 Nu rouge (56x37cm-22x15in) s.i.verso gouache. 26-Feb-3 Artcurial Briest, Paris #566 est:800-1200
£7372 $11574 €11500 Untitled (112x92cm-44x36in) s.d.1989 verso mixed media cardboard on canvas prov. 11-Dec-2 Artcurial Briest, Paris #749/R est:15000

PINCHART, Émile Auguste (1842-1924) French
£4630 $7500 €6714 Lost in thought (56x38cm-22x15in) init. 21-May-3 Doyle, New York #218/R est:5000-7000
£4800 $8016 €7200 Water carrier (45x33cm-18x13in) s. 18-Jun-3 Christie's, Kensington #112/R est:4000-6000

PINCHON, Robert Antoine (1886-1943) French
£4895 $8175 €7000 Riviere animee, l'automne (51x73cm-20x29in) s. 26-Jun-3 Tajan, Paris #248/R est:4600-6000
£5000 $7850 €7800 Peniches sur la Seine (33x61cm-13x24in) s. 13-Dec-2 Piasa, Paris #245/R
£5035 $8409 €7200 Vue de la Seine a Rouen (38x65cm-15x26in) s. 26-Jun-3 Tajan, Paris #245/R est:7500-9000
£9494 $14715 €15000 Port de Saint Tropez (59x76cm-23x30in) s. prov.exhib. 28-Sep-2 Christie's, Paris #21/R est:2200-3000
£11486 $17919 €17000 Le vieux bassin de Dieppe (47x65cm-19x26in) s. 25-Mar-3 Chochon-Barre & Allardi, Paris #181/R est:13000-15000
£14110 $23000 €21165 Port de St Tropez (59x73cm-23x29in) s. prov.exhib. 12-Feb-3 Sotheby's, New York #47/R est:20000-30000

Works on paper
£278 $441 €400 Vue de village (18x20cm-7x8in) s. col crayon dr. 29-Apr-3 Artcurial Briest, Paris #18

PINCI-GRAZI (fl.1880-1920) Italian
£3750 $6000 €5625 Seranade (46x60cm-18x24in) s.i.d.1919. 14-May-3 Butterfields, San Francisco #1055/R est:4000-6000

PINDER, Douglas H (?) British
Works on paper
£280 $456 €420 Pentire point (36x48cm-14x19in) s. W/C. 13-Feb-3 David Lay, Penzance #172
£450 $702 €675 Polperro (54x67cm-21x26in) s.i. gouache W/C over pencil. 10-Oct-2 Rupert Toovey, Partridge Green #1500/R

PINEDA, Jose (1837-1907) Spanish
£3500 $5460 €5250 View of Tangier (23x14cm-9x6in) s.i. panel. 26-Mar-3 Sotheby's, Olympia #227/R est:2500-3500
Works on paper
£1000 $1660 €1450 Spanish barque Reusense if Tarragona amidst other shipping at sea (44x63cm-17x25in) s.i.d.1886 pen ink W/C htd white. 12-Jun-3 Christie's, London #565/R est:800-1200
£1500 $2490 €2175 Spanish polacra schooner Francisqueta (48x64cm-19x25in) s.i.d.1889 pencil pen ink W/C htd white. 12-Jun-3 Christie's, London #560/R est:1000-1500
£1600 $2656 €2320 Spanish brigantine Aurora in coastal waters (41x60cm-16x24in) s.i.d.1869 pencil pen ink W/C htd white. 12-Jun-3 Christie's, London #552/R est:1000-1500
£1800 $2988 €2610 Spanish paddle gunboat Lepanto at anchor (28x43cm-11x17in) s.i.d.1878 pencil pen ink W/C. 12-Jun-3 Christie's, London #537/R est:800-1200
£1900 $3154 €2755 Spanish brig Guillermo Juan under sail in the Mediterranean (49x69cm-19x27in) s.i.d.1875 pen ink W/C htd white. 12-Jun-3 Christie's, London #567/R est:1000-1500
£2000 $3320 €2900 American clipper Sweepstakes in two positions (49x69cm-19x27in) s.d.1880 pen ink W/C htd bodycol. 12-Jun-3 Christie's, London #548/R est:1500-2500
£2200 $3652 €3190 Spanish polacca barque Frasquita flying her number off the Spanish coast (46x63cm-18x25in) s.i.d.1871 pencil pen ink W/C htd white. 12-Jun-3 Christie's, London #557/R est:1500-2000
£2600 $4316 €3770 Spanish barque Teresa in full sail off the coast (41x52cm-16x20in) s.i.d.1881 pencil pen ink W/C htd white. 12-Jun-3 Christie's, London #555/R est:1500-2500
£2600 $4316 €3770 Polacca schooner Maria amidst small craft off the Spanish coast (43x60cm-17x24in) s.i. indis d. pencil pen ink W/C. 12-Jun-3 Christie's, London #558/R est:1500-2500
£2800 $4648 €4060 Spanish three masted barque Anibal with a pilot cutter off her stern (47x64cm-19x25in) s.i.d.1870 pencil pen ink W/C htd white. 12-Jun-3 Christie's, London #559/R est:1000-1500

PINEDA, Jose (attrib) (1837-1907) Spanish
Works on paper
£800 $1328 €1160 Spanish xebec Jabal at the entrance to the harbour, possibly Port Mahon (46x67cm-18x26in) indis i. pencil pen ink W/C. 12-Jun-3 Christie's, London #569/R
£1500 $2490 €2175 Polacra Goleta, N. Carlota (46x65cm-18x26in) i. pencil W/C scratching out. 12-Jun-3 Christie's, London #554/R est:800-1200
£1700 $2822 €2465 Spanish barque Atenas running inshore with a lighthouse off her port bow (56x87cm-22x34in) i. pencil pen ink W/C bodycol. 12-Jun-3 Christie's, London #556/R est:800-1200

PINEDA-MONTON, Miguel (?) Spanish
£10897 $17109 €17000 Bacchus triumphing (165x224cm-65x88in) s. 13-Dec-2 Rossini, Paris #173/R est:9000

PINEL DE GRANDCHAMP, Louis-Émile (1831-1894) French
£3526 $5535 €5500 Cimetiere d'Eyup a Constantinople (62x46cm-24x18in) s. 16-Dec-2 Millon & Associes, Paris #133/R est:4500-5500

PINELLI, Bartolomeo (1781-1835) Italian
£324 $518 €450 Young peasant woman with three small children praying at cross (15x19cm-6x7in) s.i.d.1829 W/C Indian in. 17-May-3 Lempertz, Koln #1328/R
Works on paper
£316 $500 €500 Une famille de Ciociani pleurant leurs defunts (18x23cm-7x9in) s.i.d.1813 black chk W/C. 27-Nov-2 Christie's, Paris #112/R
£1600 $2624 €2400 Achilles and Hector (49x51cm-19x20in) s.i.d.1807 pen ink wash. 5-Jun-3 Christie's, Kensington #885 est:300-500
£2400 $3936 €3600 Zeus and Venus (42x58cm-17x23in) pen ink wash. 5-Jun-3 Christie's, Kensington #884/R est:300-500

PINELLI, Pino (1938-) Italian
Works on paper
£321 $503 €500 Painting (57x76cm-22x30in) s.i.d.1992 mixed media collage card. 23-Nov-2 Meeting Art, Vercelli #311
£347 $552 €500 Interior (57x76cm-22x30in) s.d.1992 verso mixed media. 1-May-3 Meeting Art, Vercelli #183

PINGRET, Edouard Henri Theophile (1788-1875) French
£3846 $6423 €5500 Portrait d'Hippolyte de la porte a son bureau (43x32cm-17x13in) s.d.183. 25-Jun-3 Tajan, Paris #75/R est:6000-8000
£27972 $46713 €40000 Vue du Chateau de Caulaincourt pres de Saint-Quentin (53x68cm-21x27in) s.d.1814. 25-Jun-3 Sotheby's, Paris #65/R est:12000-15000

PINGRET, Edouard Henri Theophile (attrib) (1788-1875) French
£755 $1162 €1200 Jeune bergere (54x41cm-21x16in) s. 25-Oct-2 Tajan, Paris #156

PINK, Lutka (1916-) ?
£1146 $1789 €1800 Repos dans le jardin (48x54cm-19x21in) s. painted c.1941. 6-Nov-2 Claude Boisgirard, Paris #44/R est:2500-3000

PINKER, Stanley (1924-) South African
£1768 $2794 €2652 Bather (46x76cm-18x30in) s. 1-Apr-3 Stephan Welz, Johannesburg #495/R est:25000-35000 (SA.R 22000)

PINO (?) ?
£12987 $20000 €19481 Homeward bound II (76x91cm-30x36in) 25-Oct-2 Morris & Whiteside, Hilton Head Island #1 est:20000-22000
£12987 $20000 €19481 The diary (76x102cm-30x40in) 25-Oct-2 Morris & Whiteside, Hilton Head Island #3 est:20000-25000
£15823 $25000 €22943 Longing for (102x112cm-40x44in) s. 26-Jul-3 Coeur d'Alene, Hayden #170/R est:30000-50000

PINOLE Y RODRIGUEZ, Nicanor (1877-1978) Spanish
£15094 $23547 €24000 Portrait of Melquiades Alvarez (97x96cm-38x38in) s. painted 1929 lit. 23-Sep-2 Durán, Madrid #207/R est:24000
Works on paper
£570 $918 €850 Landscape (16x23cm-6x9in) s. W/C. 18-Feb-3 Durán, Madrid #108/R
£1935 $3058 €3000 Portrait of D Melquiades Alvarez (60x30cm-24x12in) s. chl dr. 17-Dec-2 Durán, Madrid #174/R
£2083 $3292 €3250 In the cafe (42x50cm-17x20in) s. wash dr. 19-Nov-2 Durán, Madrid #206/R

PINOT, Albert (1875-1962) Belgian
£258 $408 €400 Bouquet de fleurs dans un vase (55x46cm-22x18in) s. 17-Dec-2 Palais de Beaux Arts, Brussels #597
£268 $417 €420 Bord d'etang en ete (50x65cm-20x26in) s. sold with a book. 11-Nov-2 Horta, Bruxelles #476
£514 $801 €750 Remorqueur a Asnieres (30x45cm-12x18in) s.d.1907 panel. 14-Apr-3 Horta, Bruxelles #349
£3459 $5362 €5500 Summer bouquet (92x73cm-36x29in) s. 5-Oct-2 De Vuyst, Lokeren #552/R est:7000-8000

PINTALDI, Cristiano (1970-) Italian
£2394 $3975 €3400 Ufo (60x80cm-24x31in) s.i.d.1998. 10-Jun-3 Finarte Semenzato, Milan #347/R est:3000-3600
Works on paper
£1026 $1590 €1600 Untitled (26x35cm-10x14in) init.d.1997 verso mixed media polyester. 4-Dec-2 Finarte, Milan #512/R

PINTO, Angelo (1908-1994) American
Works on paper
£732 $1200 €1061 Still life (23x28cm-9x11in) s.i.d.1966 W/C paperboard prov. 1-Jun-3 Wright, Chicago #233/R est:700-900
£926 $1500 €1389 Red waterlilies (33x38cm-13x15in) s. W/C pencil exhib. 24-Jan-3 Freeman, Philadelphia #117/R est:1500-2500

PINTO, Biagio (1911-1989) American
£494 $800 €741 Two heads (25x33cm-10x13in) s.i.verso oil pastel. 24-Jan-3 Freeman, Philadelphia #119/R

PINTURICCHIO (studio) (15th C) Italian
£12587 $21021 €18000 Vierge a l'Enfant avec les Saints Jean Baptiste, Sebastien, Pierre et Paul (46x33cm-18x13in) panel exec.c.1500. 25-Jun-3 Pierre Berge, Paris #14/R est:6000-8000

PINTURICCHIO, Bernardino (circle) (1454-1513) Italian
£6500 $10855 €9425 Madonna and Child (39x29cm-15x11in) panel. 11-Jul-3 Christie's, Kensington #235/R est:6000-8000

PIOCHE, Michel Louis (attrib) (1764-?) French
Sculpture
£20513 $31795 €32000 Jeune femme accoudee sur urne funeraire (30x23x17cm-12x9x7in) i. terracotta lit. 9-Dec-2 Rabourdin & Choppin de Janvry, Paris #91/R est:7000
£28846 $44712 €45000 Vestale pleurant (35x30x18cm-14x12x7in) terracotta. 9-Dec-2 Rabourdin & Choppin de Janvry, Paris #92/R est:9000

PIOLA, Domenico (17/18th C) Italian
£20979 $35035 €30000 Putti portant des vases de fleurs (168x47cm-66x19in) pair. 25-Jun-3 Pierre Berge, Paris #9/R est:30000-45000
Prints
£3038 $4800 €4800 Old man with beard (15x10cm-6x4in) etching. 29-Nov-2 Bassenge, Berlin #5228/R est:4000
Works on paper
£2025 $3200 €3200 Le repos pendant la fuite en Egypte (28x42cm-11x17in) i. black chk pen brown ink brown wash. 27-Nov-2 Christie's, Paris #77/R est:2000-3000
£3200 $5344 €4640 Christ healing a cripple (43x30cm-17x12in) pen brown ink wash over blk chk. 9-Jul-3 Sotheby's, London #44/R est:2500-3500

PIOLA, Domenico (elder) (1627-1703) Italian
£55556 $90000 €83334 Assumption of the Virgin (91x61cm-36x24in) prov.exhib. 23-Jan-3 Sotheby's, New York #29/R est:70000-90000
Works on paper
£699 $1000 €1049 Annunciation (27x20cm-11x8in) pen brown ink grey wash. 23-Jan-3 Swann Galleries, New York #101/R est:2000-3000
£1800 $2826 €2700 Two music making putti perched on an ionic column, their score held up by a monkey in a hat (18x22cm-7x9in) pen ink wash corner made up. 11-Dec-2 Sotheby's, Olympia #59/R est:1500-2000
£2365 $3689 €3500 Mac (39x27cm-15x11in) i. pen ink wash. 27-Mar-3 Christie's, Paris #13/R
£4392 $6851 €6500 Two putti holding garland (20x24cm-8x9in) chk pen ink wash. 27-Mar-3 Christie's, Paris #12/R

PIOLA, Paolo Gerolamo (1666-1724) Italian
£44872 $69551 €70000 Magdalene buying ointments for Jesus (135x203cm-53x80in) octagonal. 4-Dec-2 Christie's, Rome #430/R est:50000-80000
Works on paper
£839 $1200 €1259 Abraham's sacrifice (13x10cm-5x4in) brush ink white gouache. 23-Jan-3 Swann Galleries, New York #112/R est:700-1000
£950 $1587 €1378 Noli me Tangere (26x20cm-10x8in) i. black white chk oval prov. 8-Jul-3 Christie's, London #14/R

PIOLA, Paolo Gerolamo (attrib) (1666-1724) Italian
Works on paper
£1400 $2338 €2030 Design for a funerary (28x10cm-11x4in) i. pen ink brown wash over black chk. 9-Jul-3 Bonhams, Knightsbridge #57/R est:500-700
£3043 $4717 €4565 Christening of Christ (43x29cm-17x11in) i. Indian ink brush over pen htd white. 9-Dec-2 Philippe Schuler, Zurich #4174/R est:2000-2500 (S.FR 7000)

PIOLA, Paolo Gerolamo (circle) (1666-1724) Italian
£5000 $7850 €7500 Joseph interpreting the dreams of Pharaoh's butler and baker (101x117cm-40x46in) 13-Dec-2 Christie's, Kensington #253/R est:4000-6000

PIOMBO, Sebastiano del (style) (1485-1547) Italian
£8500 $13260 €12750 Portrait of Pope Clement VII (56x46cm-22x18in) i. panel. 10-Apr-3 Christie's, Kensington #221/R est:3000-5000

PIOT, Adolphe (1850-1910) French
£1505 $2423 €2258 Young woman (71x53cm-28x21in) s. canvas on board. 12-May-3 Stephan Welz, Johannesburg #422/R est:8000-12000 (SA.R 17500)
£1687 $2750 €2531 Cherry girl (46x41cm-18x16in) 14-Feb-3 Du Mouchelle, Detroit #21/R est:3000-4000
£2800 $4676 €4200 Pensive beauty (65x50cm-26x20in) s. 18-Jun-3 Christie's, Kensington #104a/R est:3000-5000
£6014 $9864 €8300 L'album Japonais (66x51cm-26x20in) s. painted c.1910. 27-May-3 Artcurial Briest, Paris #95/R est:10000-12000
£6159 $10101 €8500 La jeune femme accoudee (65x50cm-26x20in) s. painted c.1899. 27-May-3 Artcurial Briest, Paris #99/R est:10000-12000
£7742 $12000 €11613 Young girl with holly berries in her hair (46x37cm-18x15in) s. canvas on board. 30-Oct-2 Christie's, Rockefeller NY #157/R est:12000-16000

PIOTROWSKI, Antoni (1853-1924) Polish
£1074 $1750 €1611 Portrait of a young peasant girls (30x41cm-12x16in) s. board. 1-Feb-3 Thomaston Place, Thomaston #114

PIPAL, Viktor (1887-1971) Austrian
£833 $1317 €1300 End of the line, Neuwaldegg, Vienna (48x61cm-19x24in) s. 12-Nov-2 Dorotheum, Vienna #139/R
£1392 $2200 €2200 Gersthof in spring (74x95cm-29x37in) s. 26-Nov-2 Wiener Kunst Auktionen, Vienna #118/R est:2200-4000
£2308 $3646 €3600 Viennese suburb, Gehardusgasse (48x61cm-19x24in) s. 12-Nov-2 Dorotheum, Vienna #136/R est:2600-3600
Works on paper
£348 $543 €550 Beethovenstatte, Eroicagasse (21x27cm-8x11in) s.i. verso Indian ink W/C board. 15-Oct-2 Dorotheum, Vienna #119
£348 $543 €550 Guest house garden in Grinzingerstrasse (21x26cm-8x10in) s. chk W/C gouache board. 15-Oct-2 Dorotheum, Vienna #120
£377 $588 €550 Roses in blue vase (43x33cm-17x13in) s. chk W/C. 8-Apr-3 Dorotheum, Vienna #153
£563 $918 €850 View of Greiner street in Nussdorf (27x36cm-11x14in) s. pastel. 28-Jan-3 Dorotheum, Vienna #126/R
£586 $938 €850 Gumpoldskirchen (29x43cm-11x17in) s. W/C gouache. 11-Mar-3 Dorotheum, Vienna #100/R
£1761 $2712 €2800 Thoughtful smoker (74x54cm-29x21in) s. 22-Oct-2 Wiener Kunst Auktionen, Vienna #1127/R est:1000-2400

PIPER, Edward (1938-1990) British
Works on paper
£250 $390 €375 Study of two nudes (48x31cm-19x12in) s. pencil W/C. 9-Oct-2 Woolley & Wallis, Salisbury #38/R
£300 $468 €450 Sketch of two nudes (41x31cm-16x12in) s.d.84 pen ink. 9-Oct-2 Woolley & Wallis, Salisbury #37/R

PIPER, John (1903-1992) British
£4200 $6468 €6300 Village on a river, Mareuil (51x61cm-20x24in) s. prov. 5-Sep-2 Christie's, Kensington #736/R est:4000-6000
£4800 $7632 €7200 Reilhac, Dordogne I (57x76cm-22x30in) s. gouache prov. 26-Feb-3 Sotheby's, Olympia #310/R est:2500-3500
£6000 $9420 €9000 House at Ventnor, Isle of Wight (25x35cm-10x14in) prov. 22-Nov-2 Christie's, London #50/R est:5000-7000
£7500 $11849 €11250 Ruined cottage (63x76cm-25x30in) s. 27-Nov-2 Sotheby's, Olympia #181/R est:2000-3000
£16000 $26240 €24000 Rievaulx (15x20cm-6x8in) s. s.i.verso canvas on panel prov. 6-Jun-3 Christie's, London #55/R est:6000-8000
£80000 $131200 €116000 Rocky Valley, North Wales (91x122cm-36x48in) s. painted 1948 prov.lit. 4-Jun-3 Sotheby's, London #36/R est:12000-18000
Prints
£2400 $3768 €3600 Huish Episcopi (78x56cm-31x22in) s.num.9/100 col screenprint. 17-Apr-3 Christie's, Kensington #127/R est:1200-1600
£2800 $4676 €4060 Abstract composition (67x50cm-26x20in) s.i. col autolithograph on lithographic cartridge. 30-Jun-3 Bonhams, New Bond Street #399/R est:2000-3000
£4800 $7392 €7200 Nursery frieze (46x121cm-18x48in) two lithograph. 24-Oct-2 Christie's, Kensington #109/R est:2800-3200
Works on paper
£440 $686 €660 Cartoon faces, abstract (40x27cm-16x11in) s. W/C. 10-Sep-2 David Duggleby, Scarborough #243
£520 $832 €780 Harbour scene with lighthouse (29x40cm-11x16in) s.d.44 gouache. 11-Mar-3 David Duggleby, Scarborough #108
£650 $1034 €975 Interior set design (88x57cm-35x22in) s.d.1962 gouache on tracing. 26-Feb-3 Sotheby's, Olympia #372/R
£750 $1170 €1125 Santa croce (22x31cm-9x12in) s.i.d.27.2.61 col crayon. 15-Oct-2 Bonhams, Knightsbridge #9/R
£800 $1240 €1200 Church interior, Wiltshire (20x25cm-8x10in) chl pen brush black ink. 4-Dec-2 Christie's, Kensington #335/R
£1050 $1638 €1575 Abstract landscape (33x51cm-13x20in) s. ink wash W/C. 17-Sep-2 Goldings, Lincolnshire #703/R
£1100 $1705 €1650 Dryhope town (22x35cm-9x14in) i.d.17 X 75 pencil col crayon. 4-Dec-2 Christie's, Kensington #348/R est:600-800
£1200 $1872 €1800 Carennac - studies from Romanesque sculptures (34x52cm-13x20in) s.i. W/C ink pencil prov. 12-Sep-2 Sotheby's, Olympia #54/R est:800-1200

£1200	$1860	€1800	MacLellan's Castle, Kirkcudbright (22x35cm-9x14in) i. pen black ink W/C bodycol. 4-Dec-2 Christie's, Kensington #347/R est:800-1200
£1200	$1860	€1800	Hermitage (22x35cm-9x14in) i.d.10 X 75 pen black ink col crayon. 4-Dec-2 Christie's, Kensington #349/R est:500-700
£1200	$1896	€1800	Clifton Campville, Staffs (22x35cm-9x14in) i.d.76 pencil col crayon. 27-Nov-2 Sotheby's, Olympia #38/R est:600-800
£1200	$1896	€1800	Edlington, Northumberland (22x35cm-9x14in) i.d.78 pencil col crayon. 27-Nov-2 Sotheby's, Olympia #39/R est:600-800
£1200	$1896	€1800	Edlington (22x35cm-9x14in) i.d.76 pencil col crayon. 27-Nov-2 Sotheby's, Olympia #41/R est:600-800
£1300	$2002	€1950	Donzy Le Pre Tympanum (39x60cm-15x24in) s.i.d.70 brush ink bodycol. 5-Sep-2 Christie's, Kensington #666/R est:800-1200
£1300	$2028	€1950	Lincoln - studies from Romanesque sculptures (30x53cm-12x21in) s. ink oil pencil prov. 12-Sep-2 Sotheby's, Olympia #55/R est:1000-1500
£1300	$2028	€1950	Woodland (14x19cm-6x7in) s. W/C pen. 15-Oct-2 Bonhams, Knightsbridge #118/R est:1200-1800
£1500	$2369	€2250	Vienna (21x35cm-8x14in) i. brown ink wash after Claude Lorraine. 27-Nov-2 Sotheby's, Olympia #40/R est:600-800
£1500	$2340	€2250	Monument silhouettes (45x74cm-18x29in) W/C pastel collage. 27-Mar-3 Christie's, Kensington #624/R est:1500-2000
£1600	$2624	€2400	Abstract with green, blue and black (20x30cm-8x12in) s. W/C. 5-Feb-3 Goldings, Lincolnshire #285
£1800	$2790	€2700	Kiss of Judas, Pamplona Cathedral (39x50cm-15x20in) i.d.18.Xi.80 pen ink wax resist prov. 3-Dec-2 Bonhams, New Bond Street #85/R est:2000-3000
£1800	$2844	€2700	Design for a church window, St Andrews, Plymouth (76x50cm-30x20in) s.i.d.1967 verso ink W/C gouache collage prov. 27-Nov-2 Sotheby's, Olympia #178/R est:2000-3000
£1900	$3001	€2850	Design for window, St Andrew's, Plymouth (77x47cm-30x19in) s.i.d.1965 verso ink W/C gouache collage prov. 27-Nov-2 Sotheby's, Olympia #179/R est:2000-3000
£2000	$3240	€3000	Welsh Chapel (12x16cm-5x6in) pen ink W/C prov. 20-May-3 Sotheby's, Olympia #138/R est:600-900
£2000	$3340	€2900	Buoys and boats, Portsall (34x52cm-13x20in) s.i. i.verso W/C ink. 18-Jun-3 Rupert Toovey, Partridge Green #150/R est:2000-3000
£2100	$3276	€3150	Red-roofed house (21x21cm-8x8in) s. collage wash prov.exhib. 9-Apr-3 Cheffins Grain & Comins, Cambridge #655/R est:2000-3000
£2200	$3432	€3300	Design for stained glass window (124x70cm-49x28in) s.i. brush ink gouache collage. 27-Mar-3 Christie's, Kensington #649/R est:2500-3500
£2200	$3674	€3190	Woodland landscape (20x23cm-8x9in) s.d.17 iii 67 mixed media. 24-Jun-3 Bonhams, New Bond Street #71/R est:1000-1500
£2300	$3633	€3450	Cartoon for baptistery window at Coventry Cathedral (121x51cm-48x20in) init. W/C gouache collage prov. 27-Nov-2 Sotheby's, Olympia #293/R est:1000-1500
£2300	$3795	€3335	Brittany landscape (11x31cm-4x12in) s. W/C bodycol pen ink executed 1953 prov. 3-Jul-3 Christie's, Kensington #720/R est:1200-1800
£2400	$3720	€3600	Green field (18x31cm-7x12in) s. brush black ink W/C bodycol col crayon. 4-Dec-2 Christie's, Kensington #336/R est:1500-2000
£2500	$4125	€3625	Double Welsh landscape (40x58cm-16x23in) s. pen brush col ink crayon prov. 3-Jul-3 Christie's, Kensington #722/R est:2500-3500
£2600	$4290	€3770	Christ appearing to St Thomas (38x56cm-15x22in) s.i.d.80 gouache col chks. 3-Jul-3 Christie's, Kensington #521/R est:2000-3000
£2600	$4290	€3770	Trajan's forum III (53x35cm-21x14in) s. pastel bodycol prov.lit. 3-Jul-3 Christie's, Kensington #717/R est:3000-5000
£2800	$4592	€4200	Figure study (51x36cm-20x14in) s. ink wash. 3-Jun-3 Sotheby's, Olympia #239/R est:600-800
£3200	$4960	€4800	Low tide, La Trinite, Brittany (35x52cm-14x20in) s.i. crayon W/C bodycol. 4-Dec-2 Christie's, Kensington #338/R est:2500-3500
£3200	$5344	€4640	Street, Isle of Wight (19x25cm-7x10in) s. gouache chk black ink. 24-Jun-3 Bonhams, New Bond Street #73/R est:1200-1800
£3200	$5280	€4640	Port Bene (27x36cm-11x14in) s. indis i. pencil gouache. 3-Jul-3 Christie's, Kensington #721/R est:2000-3000
£3293	$5500	€4775	Field road at Weston, Portland (35x53cm-14x21in) s. W/C ink wax crayon executed 1954 prov.lit. 22-Jun-3 Freeman, Philadelphia #47/R est:4000-6000
£3500	$5390	€5250	Ivy on the wall, Portesham, Dorset (35x53cm-14x21in) s.i.d.1954 verso crayon brush ink W/C prov. 5-Sep-2 Christie's, Kensington #665/R est:2500-3500
£3500	$5845	€5075	Neuville sur l'Oeully between Amiens and Rouen (37x56cm-15x22in) s.i.d.30.viii.74 W/C wax resist. 24-Jun-3 Bonhams, New Bond Street #67/R est:1500-2500
£3800	$5890	€5700	Pembrokeshire, distant prospect (35x53cm-14x21in) s.d.4.VII.64 s.i.verso col crayon brush col ink W/C bodycol. 4-Dec-2 Christie's, Kensington #351/R est:3000-5000
£3800	$6232	€5700	Kirby Muxlote Castel (19x27cm-7x11in) s. s.i.d.1981 verso ink W/C gouache pastel prov. 3-Jun-3 Sotheby's, Olympia #251/R est:2000-3000
£4000	$6240	€6000	Two views of Seaton Delaval, Northumberland (16x43cm-6x17in) s. pencil ink W/C pair prov. 12-Sep-2 Sotheby's, Olympia #56/R est:1000-1500
£4000	$6200	€6000	Tisbury II (35x53cm-14x21in) s.indis.i.d.4.5.66 pen brush black ink W/C bodycol prov. 4-Dec-2 Christie's, Kensington #350/R est:2500-3500
£4000	$6240	€6000	Abbeville, St. Wolfrun (56x39cm-22x15in) s.i.d.74 brush ink crayon bodycol. 27-Mar-3 Christie's, Kensington #626/R est:3200-3800
£4000	$6560	€6000	Bedfield (34x52cm-13x20in) s.i.d.25.4.65 pen ink W/C bodycol. 6-Jun-3 Christie's, London #166/R est:2000-3000
£4000	$6600	€5800	Palazzo Vendremin Calergi, Venice (36x53cm-14x21in) s.i. pen brush ink bodycol. 3-Jul-3 Christie's, Kensington #718/R est:3000-5000
£4100	$6478	€5945	Lincolnshire church - Haltham on Bain VII (28x36cm-11x14in) s.i. pen ink W/C htd bodycol. 23-Jul-3 Mallams, Oxford #102/R est:1500-2000
£4200	$6594	€6300	Old mine working, Luckett, Cornwall (33x51cm-13x20in) s.i.d.18.6.63 W/C bodycol brush ink col crayon prov. 21-Nov-2 Christie's, London #130/R est:3000-5000
£4200	$6594	€6300	Stone gate, Pirtland (35x48cm-14x19in) s. W/C bodycol brush ink col crayon prov. 21-Nov-2 Christie's, London #131/R est:3000-5000
£4200	$6636	€6300	Foliate head (50x60cm-20x24in) col ink gouache blue chk collage. 27-Nov-2 Sotheby's, Olympia #183/R est:1000-1500
£4400	$7348	€6380	Woman with sunflower (55x75cm-22x30in) s. mixed media. 24-Jun-3 Bonhams, New Bond Street #70/R est:3000-5000
£4500	$7380	€6750	Bullslaughter Bay, Pembroke (15x23cm-6x9in) s.i. pen ink W/C bodycol prov. 6-Jun-3 Christie's, London #164/R est:2500-3500
£4500	$7425	€6525	Double hill top town (57x75cm-22x30in) s. pen brush ink crayon bodycol. 3-Jul-3 Christie's, Kensington #715/R est:4500-5500
£4800	$7536	€7200	Village street with church in background (36x53cm-14x21in) s. gouache. 20-Nov-2 Sotheby's, Olympia #75/R est:1500-2000
£5000	$8200	€7500	Douriez (34x53cm-13x21in) s.i. pen ink W/C bodycol col crayon prov. 6-Jun-3 Christie's, London #163/R est:5000-7000
£5000	$8200	€7500	Oedipus Rex (38x55cm-15x22in) s. pen brush ink W/C bodycol collage executed 1945 prov.exhib.lit. 6-Jun-3 Christie's, London #165/R est:6000-8000
£5500	$9020	€8250	Venice palazzo (29x39cm-11x15in) s. W/C bodycol pen ink exhib. 6-Jun-3 Christie's, London #135/R est:4000-6000
£5800	$8990	€8700	Lewknor, Oxon. (24x34cm-9x13in) s.i.d.1961 pen ink W/C gouache prov. 3-Dec-2 Bonhams, New Bond Street #82/R est:3000-5000
£6000	$9360	€9000	English church yard (33x41cm-13x16in) i. pen ink W/C gouache. 25-Mar-3 Bonhams, New Bond Street #98/R est:3500-4500
£6000	$9840	€9000	Church (46x60cm-18x24in) s. W/C ink pastel. 3-Jun-3 Sotheby's, Olympia #250/R est:2500-3500
£6000	$10020	€8700	Garden in the Chilterns (45x60cm-18x24in) s. mixed media prov. 24-Jun-3 Bonhams, New Bond Street #68/R est:4000-6000
£6500	$10205	€9750	South midlands landscape (53x75cm-21x30in) s. W/C bodycol brush ink prov. 21-Nov-2 Christie's, London #128/R est:4000-6000
£6800	$10540	€10200	Ivychurch (38x56cm-15x22in) s. W/C pen ink W/C htd white prov. 3-Dec-2 Bonhams, New Bond Street #83/R est:3000-5000
£7000	$10990	€10500	Shanklin, Isle of Wight (37x51cm-15x20in) s. pencil W/C bodycol brush ink executed c.1954 prov. 21-Nov-2 Christie's, London #127/R est:6000-8000
£8000	$12560	€12000	Design for a stage back drop (41x51cm-16x20in) s. W/C bodycol pen col crayon prov. 21-Nov-2 Christie's, London #129/R est:10000-15000
£8000	$12400	€12000	Death in Venice (54x102cm-21x40in) s. gouache W/C col chk prov. 4-Dec-2 Sotheby's, London #38/R est:3000-5000
£8500	$13176	€12750	Ship (47x38cm-19x15in) s. pen black ink W/C gouache. 4-Dec-2 Sotheby's, London #36/R est:4000-6000
£16000	$24960	€24000	Cornish coast (38x51cm-15x20in) s. pen ink W/C gouache bodycol prov. 9-Oct-2 Woolley & Wallis, Salisbury #181/R est:3000-5000

PIPER, Raymond (1923-) British

Works on paper

£250	$388	€375	Mourne mountains near Kilkeel (25x36cm-10x14in) s.d.1949 W/C. 2-Oct-2 John Ross, Belfast #249

£	$	€	Description
£2534	$3979	€3700	Orchid study - Epipactis Kelleborine (51x32cm-20x13in) s. W/C prov. 15-Apr-3 De Veres Art Auctions, Dublin #275 est:4000-5000

PIPINS, Tom (19th C) British
Works on paper

£	$	€	Description
£1000	$1550	€1500	His Majesty's yacht Royal Sovereign conveying Louis XVIII. Royal barge approaching his yacht (56x84cm-22x33in) s. W/C two. 31-Oct-2 Christie's, Kensington #312/R est:1500-2000

PIPPAL, Hans Robert (1915-1999) Austrian

£	$	€	Description
£288	$447	€450	Portrait of young woman (51x43cm-20x17in) oil chk. 6-Dec-2 Michael Zeller, Lindau #884/R
£417	$646	€650	Portrait of young woman (65x50cm-26x20in) s.d.1957. 6-Dec-2 Michael Zeller, Lindau #889/R
£615	$954	€960	Birds in cage with flowers and candle in candlestick (48x59cm-19x23in) s.i. oil chk. 6-Dec-2 Michael Zeller, Lindau #887/R
£873	$1362	€1310	Avenue Notre Dame (46x60cm-18x24in) s.i. pastel. 6-Nov-2 Dobiaschofsky, Bern #891/R (S.FR 2000)
£886	$1382	€1400	Vienna, Salmannsdorf (38x52cm-15x20in) s.i. oil chk. 15-Oct-2 Dorotheum, Vienna #101/R
£897	$1391	€1400	Constance harbour (50x61cm-20x24in) s.i. oil chk. 6-Dec-2 Michael Zeller, Lindau #890/R
£1048	$1635	€1572	Avenue de l'Opera with Palais Garnier (24x33cm-9x13in) s.i.d.53. 6-Nov-2 Dobiaschofsky, Bern #890/R est:1900 (S.FR 2400)

Works on paper

£	$	€	Description
£795	$1295	€1200	Village street in Morbisch, Burgenland (32x25cm-13x10in) s. pastel. 28-Jan-3 Dorotheum, Vienna #106/R est:1400-2000
£833	$1267	€1300	Boulevard with well-dressed figures (62x48cm-24x19in) s.i. mixed media lit. 11-Jul-2 Allgauer, Kempten #2368/R
£1060	$1727	€1600	Avenue in Schonbrunn (33x25cm-13x10in) s. pastel. 28-Jan-3 Dorotheum, Vienna #102/R est:1400-2000
£1266	$1975	€2000	Vienna, Freyung (23x26cm-9x10in) s.i. W/C bodycol. 15-Oct-2 Dorotheum, Vienna #168/R est:1400-1800

PIPPEL, Otto (1878-1960) German

£	$	€	Description
£345	$545	€500	View from Grossglockner road of Sonnenwelleck (46x42cm-18x17in) s. 5-Apr-3 Quittenbaum, Hamburg #104/R
£487	$740	€750	Winter landscape (79x100cm-31x39in) s. 6-Jul-2 Berlinghof, Heidelberg #234/R
£541	$843	€800	Hay harvest (50x60cm-20x24in) s. 26-Mar-3 Hugo Ruef, Munich #192
£637	$981	€1000	Titisee in the Black Forest (80x100cm-31x39in) s. 5-Sep-2 Arnold, Frankfurt #835
£645	$1019	€968	Blick vom Schwarzenkopf auf Zugspitze und ins Hollental (80x70cm-31x28in) s. s.i.verso. 18-Nov-2 Waddingtons, Toronto #258/R (C.D 1600)
£711	$1180	€1031	Blick von Eckbauer auf die alpspitze (81x70cm-32x28in) s. 16-Jun-3 Waddingtons, Toronto #295/R est:1500-2000 (C.D 1600)
£736	$1200	€1104	Spring alpine landscape with snow on the mountains beyond (81x102cm-32x40in) s. 16-Feb-3 Butterfields, San Francisco #2038
£743	$1159	€1100	Cows in water (42x62cm-17x24in) s. panel. 26-Mar-3 Hugo Ruef, Munich #193
£753	$1175	€1100	Village with church in extensive landscape (60x70cm-24x28in) s. 10-Apr-3 Van Ham, Cologne #1645
£755	$1177	€1200	Summer landscape (66x85cm-26x33in) s. 19-Sep-2 Dr Fritz Nagel, Stuttgart #983/R
£823	$1300	€1300	Gossau lake (66x86cm-26x34in) s. lit. 29-Nov-2 Schloss Ahlden, Ahlden #1369/R
£839	$1233	€1300	Mountain landscape (82x70cm-32x28in) s. 20-Jun-2 Dr Fritz Nagel, Stuttgart #810/R
£925	$1378	€1388	Harvest on Kugleralm (50x62cm-20x24in) s. 25-Jun-2 Koller, Zurich #6678/R est:3000-5000 (S.FR 2100)
£1074	$1741	€1611	Blick ins Raintal (100x90cm-39x35in) s. 3-Feb-3 Lilla Bukowskis, Stockholm #645 est:14000-16000 (S.KR 15000)
£1139	$1800	€1800	Mountain landscape (72x82cm-28x32in) s. lit. 29-Nov-2 Schloss Ahlden, Ahlden #1393/R est:1400
£1156	$1918	€1676	Fohnstimung am herzogstand (100x90cm-39x35in) s. s.i.on stretcher. 16-Jun-3 Waddingtons, Toronto #296/R est:2500-3000 (C.D 2600)
£1218	$1912	€1900	Early spring on the Luneburg Heide (110x101cm-43x40in) s. s.i. verso. 21-Nov-2 Van Ham, Cologne #1864/R est:3000
£1410	$2214	€2200	Evening gathering in salon (80x70cm-31x28in) s. 21-Nov-2 Van Ham, Cologne #1865 est:1500
£1419	$2086	€2200	Monastery garden in Italy (70x60cm-28x24in) s. i. verso. 20-Jun-2 Dr Fritz Nagel, Stuttgart #809/R est:1900
£1793	$2851	€2600	Summer (81x100cm-32x39in) s. s.i. verso. 8-Mar-3 Arnold, Frankfurt #681/R est:3000
£1899	$3000	€3000	Forest path with oxen wagon piled high (111x101cm-44x40in) s. 29-Nov-2 Bolland & Marotz, Bremen #814/R est:3300
£1972	$3175	€2800	Cattle returning home (55x80cm-22x31in) s.i. 7-May-3 Michael Zeller, Lindau #878/R est:2800
£2215	$3500	€3323	Late fall landscape with snow covered mountains (76x97cm-30x38in) s. 5-Apr-3 DeFina, Austinburg #1319 est:2000-3000
£2516	$3925	€4000	Harvest on the Kugleralm (50x62cm-20x24in) s. lit. 20-Sep-2 Karlheinz Kaupp, Staufen #1938/R est:4000
£2793	$4441	€4190	Summer's day at Wurmsee (50x64cm-20x25in) s. 5-Mar-3 Rasmussen, Copenhagen #2050/R est:30000-40000 (D.KR 30000)
£3185	$4968	€5000	Summer on the Chiemsee (95x113cm-37x44in) s. 6-Nov-2 Hugo Ruef, Munich #1237/R est:3900
£3237	$5180	€4500	Bodensee hotel interior (42x47cm-17x19in) s. 15-May-3 Neumeister, Munich #331/R est:1000-1200
£3380	$5442	€4800	Mountain valley, Allgau (60x48cm-24x19in) s.i. 7-May-3 Michael Zeller, Lindau #879/R est:4800
£5986	$9637	€8500	Horse racing (81x70cm-32x28in) s.i. canvas on masonite lit. 9-May-3 Schloss Ahlden, Ahlden #1527/R est:9500
£8861	$14000	€14000	Beer garden (80x71cm-31x28in) s. 30-Nov-2 Bassenge, Berlin #6576/R est:18000

Works on paper

£	$	€	Description
£506	$800	€800	Study for 'Salome' (60x44cm-24x17in) s.i. pastel lit. 29-Nov-2 Schloss Ahlden, Ahlden #1418/R

PIPPICH, Carl (1862-1932) Austrian
Works on paper

£	$	€	Description
£473	$738	€700	Road in Bruges (16x18cm-6x7in) s.i. bears d. W/C. 28-Mar-3 Dorotheum, Vienna #287/R
£503	$780	€800	Sirk Ecke (14x14cm-6x6in) s.d.927 W/C. 1-Oct-2 Dorotheum, Vienna #275/R
£608	$949	€900	Freihaus on the market place in Vienna (23x28cm-9x11in) s.i.d.916 W/C bodycol. 28-Mar-3 Dorotheum, Vienna #283/R
£608	$949	€900	Maria am Gstade, doorway (42x29cm-17x11in) s.d.921 W/C. 28-Mar-3 Dorotheum, Vienna #319/R

PIPPIG, Heiko (1951-) German

£	$	€	Description
£1392	$2172	€2200	Standing male nude (137x98cm-54x39in) 15-Oct-2 Dorotheum, Vienna #208/R est:2200-3000

PIRA, Gioacchino la (19th C) Italian
Works on paper

£	$	€	Description
£2775	$4052	€4163	Sorrento (59x90cm-23x35in) s. gouache board. 17-Jun-2 Philippe Schuler, Zurich #4806/R est:2500-3000 (S.FR 6300)

PIRA, la (19th C) Italian
Works on paper

£	$	€	Description
£2083	$3250	€3125	View of Procida (41x61cm-16x24in) s. W/C. 18-Sep-2 Alderfer's, Hatfield #249/R est:1000-1500

PIRANDELLO, Fausto (1899-1975) Italian

£	$	€	Description
£7092	$11489	€10000	Ritratto di Picci (42x31cm-17x12in) s. panel. 26-May-3 Christie's, Milan #253/R est:10000-15000
£10638	$17234	€15000	Composizione con fondo rosso (50x70cm-20x28in) s. board prov. 26-May-3 Christie's, Milan #357/R est:16000-20000
£11218	$17612	€17500	Still life (61x50cm-24x20in) s. board. 19-Nov-2 Finarte, Milan #217/R est:16000-18000
£12766	$20681	€18000	Paessagio d'Anticoli (42x61cm-17x24in) s. s.i.d.1944 verso panel prov. 26-May-3 Christie's, Milan #255/R est:18000-24000
£13475	$21830	€19000	Wheelbarrow (45x75cm-18x30in) s. s.i.verso panel painted 1942-43 prov. 26-May-3 Christie's, Milan #256/R est:15000-20000

Works on paper

£	$	€	Description
£1277	$2068	€1800	Gruppo di bagnanti (22x28cm-9x11in) s. pastel. 26-May-3 Christie's, Milan #40 est:1500-2000
£2260	$3526	€3300	Bathers (28x22cm-11x9in) s. pastel lit. 10-Apr-3 Finarte Semenzato, Rome #79/R

PIRANESI, Giovan Battista (1720-1778) Italian
Prints

£	$	€	Description
£2100	$3276	€3150	Waterfall at Tivoli (47x71cm-19x28in) etching. 10-Oct-2 Sotheby's, London #205/R est:1000-1200
£3000	$4650	€4500	Vedute di Roma. etching. 5-Dec-2 Sotheby's, London #27/R est:3500-4500
£4730	$7378	€7000	Drawbridges (71x50cm-28x20in) s. etching lit. 25-Mar-3 Wiener Kunst Auktionen, Vienna #102/R est:10000-15000
£15000	$24750	€21750	Differentes vues de quelques restes de trois grands edifices (52x73cm-20x29in) 20 etchings and frontispiece by Francesco Piranesi. 2-Jul-3 Christie's, London #34/R est:15000-20000
£28000	$46200	€40600	Carceri d'Invenzione (56x80cm-22x31in) etchings set of 16 exec.c.1749-61 with two solander boxes. 2-Jul-3 Christie's, London #36/R est:30000-50000
£35000	$57750	€50750	Various views (56x82cm-22x32in) etchings 83 album. 1-Jul-3 Sotheby's, London #38/R est:35000-40000
£37000	$61050	€53650	Vedute di Roma (79x54cm-31x21in) etchings 68 album. 1-Jul-3 Sotheby's, London #34/R est:30000-40000
£70000	$115500	€101500	Carceri d'Invenzione (55x41cm-22x16in) etchings set of 14 prov. 2-Jul-3 Christie's, London #35/R est:80000-120000

Works on paper

£	$	€	Description
£3800	$6346	€5510	Standing figure turning to the left (10x4cm-4x2in) red chk double-sided corner made up. 8-Jul-3 Christie's, London #44/R est:2000-3000
£28369	$47376	€40000	Etude d'homme vu de dos (15x12cm-6x5in) pen brown ink sanguine prov. 19-Jun-3 Piasa, Paris #24/R est:20000-30000

PIRAUD (19th C) Italian?
£15000 $25050 €21750 River town scene with a fisherman in foreground and figures beyond (36x29cm-14x11in) s. board. 8-Jul-3 Sotheby's, Olympia #497/R est:5000-7000

PIRCHAN, Emil (snr) (1844-1929) Austrian
£1800 $2880 €2700 Woman bathing in a wooded pool (123x72cm-48x28in) s. 7-Jan-3 Bonhams, Knightsbridge #95c/R est:2000-3000

PIRE, Ferdinand (1943-) Belgian
£408 $649 €600 La Naissance du Monde. s.d.95 graphite htd gold. 18-Mar-3 Galerie Moderne, Brussels #94/R

PIRE, Marcel (1913-1981) Belgian
£258 $408 €400 Bouquet champetre (100x900cm-39x354in) s. 17-Dec-2 Palais de Beaux Arts, Brussels #600
£548 $866 €850 La fauche (90x130cm-35x51in) s. 17-Dec-2 Palais de Beaux Arts, Brussels #599
£637 $994 €1000 Vase fleuri de glaieuls (90x80cm-35x31in) s.d.1961. 11-Nov-2 Horta, Bruxelles #693

PIRIA, Maria Olga (1927-) Uruguayan
£385 $604 €600 Untitled (25x40cm-10x16in) s. paper on board. 16-Dec-2 Castellana, Madrid #918/R
£385 $604 €600 Untitled (27x41cm-11x16in) s. paper on board. 16-Dec-2 Castellana, Madrid #931/R
£449 $704 €700 Untitled (33x43cm-13x17in) s. 16-Dec-2 Castellana, Madrid #990/R
£577 $900 €866 Puerto (39x47cm-15x19in) s.d.1955 cardboard. 30-Jul-2 Galleria Y Remates, Montevideo #19/R

PIRIE, Sir George (1863-1946) British
£2000 $3180 €3000 Three dogs at a cauldron (69x62cm-27x24in) s. exhib. 6-Mar-3 Christie's, Kensington #123/R est:2000-3000
£2761 $4500 €4142 Clumber spaniel with pheasant (35x45cm-14x18in) s. 11-Feb-3 Bonhams & Doyles, New York #165/R est:5000-7000

PIRMEZ, Charles (19th C) French
£1892 $2951 €2800 Furie espagnole (96x160cm-38x63in) s. 25-Mar-3 Campo & Campo, Antwerp #161/R est:4000-6000

PIROGOV, Nikolai Vasilievich (1872-1913) Russian
Works on paper
£3000 $4860 €4500 Covered sledge (28x27cm-11x11in) s.d.1908 gouache on card. 21-May-3 Sotheby's, London #125/R est:1500-2000

PIRON, Jose (1916-) Belgian
£696 $1086 €1100 Long de l'Escaut a Tournai (68x81cm-27x32in) s. panel. 16-Sep-2 Horta, Bruxelles #416

PIRON, Laurent (19th C) Belgian
£362 $594 €500 Vaches a l'abreuvoir (25x35cm-10x14in) s. canvas on panel. 27-May-3 Campo & Campo, Antwerp #184

PIRON, Léon (1899-1962) Belgian
£7097 $11213 €11000 Paysage en Flandres (80x100cm-31x39in) s. 17-Dec-2 Galerie Moderne, Brussels #799 est:15000

PISA, Alberto (1864-1931) Italian
Works on paper
£380 $604 €570 Girl gathering lemons (28x20cm-11x8in) s. W/C. 29-Apr-3 Gorringes, Lewes #2314
£500 $770 €750 View of Sorrento, Italy (60x44cm-24x17in) s. W/C. 22-Oct-2 Bonhams, Knightsbridge #213/R

PISANI, Vettor (1938-) Italian
Works on paper
£321 $497 €500 Rabbit on monocycle (49x34cm-19x13in) s. wac crayon pastel. 4-Dec-2 Finarte, Milan #553

PISANO, Edouardo (1912-) Spanish
£321 $503 €500 Still life of fruit (46x55cm-18x22in) s. oil gouache cardboard. 15-Dec-2 Eric Pillon, Calais #194/R
£1379 $2179 €2000 Model (61x50cm-24x20in) s. prov. 1-Apr-3 Segre, Madrid #307/R

PISANO, Giovanni (1875-1954) Italian
£476 $757 €700 Grazing (24x35cm-9x14in) s. board. 1-Mar-3 Meeting Art, Vercelli #142
£1020 $1622 €1500 Dawn (40x60cm-16x24in) s. 1-Mar-3 Meeting Art, Vercelli #111
£1020 $1622 €1500 Man from Sardinia on horseback (50x37cm-20x15in) s. 1-Mar-3 Meeting Art, Vercelli #81

PISANO, Sam (20th C) Spanish?
£878 $1370 €1300 Party (43x60cm-17x24in) s. 25-Mar-3 Durán, Madrid #725/R

PISCHINGER, Carl (1823-1886) Austrian
£1027 $1603 €1500 Well guarded! (29x23cm-11x9in) s. panel. 10-Apr-3 Dorotheum, Vienna #79 est:1600-1800

PISECKI, Josef (1878-1954) Czechoslovakian
£619 $978 €929 Dubrovnik (85x95cm-33x37in) s.indis.d. 30-Nov-2 Dorotheum, Prague #108/R (C.KR 30000)

PISEMSKY, Alexei A (1859-1909) Russian
Works on paper
£775 $1247 €1100 Winter landscape (13x20cm-5x8in) s. W/C. 10-May-3 Bukowskis, Helsinki #386/R

PISIS, Filippo de (1896-1956) Italian
£2600 $4108 €3900 Saint-Francois (45x22cm-18x9in) panel. 3-Apr-3 Christie's, Kensington #100/R
£2600 $4108 €3900 Eucharistie (44x22cm-17x9in) panel. 3-Apr-3 Christie's, Kensington #98/R
£3205 $5032 €5000 Still life (16x21cm-6x8in) s.d.1936 tempera card. 19-Nov-2 Finarte, Milan #276/R
£3800 $6004 €5700 Figures devant temple (44x21cm-17x8in) panel. 3-Apr-3 Christie's, Kensington #95/R
£4200 $6636 €6300 Peau de tigre (21x44cm-8x17in) panel. 3-Apr-3 Christie's, Kensington #90/R
£4392 $6851 €6500 Still life with mushrooms (20x20cm-8x8in) s.d.1942. 26-Mar-3 Finarte Semenzato, Milan #354/R
£5674 $9191 €8000 Natura morta con uva e pera (24x24cm-9x9in) s.d.42 faesite. 26-May-3 Christie's, Milan #123/R est:5000-7000
£6129 $9684 €9500 Glass with flowers (24x18cm-9x7in) s.d.53 masonite prov. 18-Dec-2 Christie's, Rome #166/R
£8511 $13787 €12000 Flowers in a bottle (50x33cm-20x13in) s.d.26 prov. 26-May-3 Christie's, Milan #372/R est:15000-20000
£10127 $16000 €16000 Boy in the studt (65x45cm-26x18in) s.d.1948 tempera cardboard. 30-Nov-2 Farsetti, Prato #641/R est:18000
£10256 $16103 €16000 Still life with bottle (42x31cm-17x12in) s.d.1946. 20-Nov-2 Pandolfini, Florence #40/R est:17000
£12258 $19368 €19000 Still life with fruit bowl and cutlery (35x54cm-14x21in) s.d.45. 18-Dec-2 Christie's, Rome #247/R est:24000
£12258 $19368 €19000 Fighter (42x34cm-17x13in) s.d.33 prov.lit. 18-Dec-2 Christie's, Rome #257/R est:20000
£13514 $21081 €20000 Still life in the studio (62x48cm-24x19in) s.d.40 masonite. 26-Mar-3 Finarte Semenzato, Milan #342/R
£15190 $24000 €24000 Still life (50x40cm-20x16in) s.d.1948. 30-Nov-2 Farsetti, Prato #689/R est:30000
£15484 $24465 €24000 Abbot (85x71cm-33x28in) s.d.40 prov.lit. 18-Dec-2 Christie's, Rome #231/R est:35000
£15827 $25324 €22000 Paesaggio (50x70cm-20x28in) s.d. prov.lit. 15-May-3 Neumeister, Munich #333/R est:20000-25000
£16216 $25297 €24000 Marine still life (45x57cm-18x22in) s. cardboard. 26-Mar-3 Finarte Semenzato, Milan #334/R
£16456 $26000 €26000 Painter's study (51x53cm-20x21in) s.d.51 board. 30-Nov-2 Farsetti, Prato #640/R est:35000
£16456 $26000 €26000 Flowers (70x50cm-28x20in) s. s.d.49 verso. 30-Nov-2 Farsetti, Prato #701/R est:30000
£17949 $27821 €28000 Vase of flowers (50x40cm-20x16in) s.d.47. 4-Dec-2 Finarte, Milan #320/R est:24000
£18243 $28459 €27000 Still life with books (38x46cm-15x18in) s.d.30. 26-Mar-3 Finarte Semenzato, Milan #324/R
£19355 $30581 €30000 Paris (74x50cm-29x20in) s.d.47 prov. 18-Dec-2 Christie's, Rome #251/R
£22152 $35000 €35000 Barbaria delle Tole, Venice (65x50cm-26x20in) i.verso. 30-Nov-2 Farsetti, Prato #633/R est:32000
£22785 $36000 €36000 Flowers (50x34cm-20x13in) s.d.1927 cardboard on canvas exhib.lit. 30-Nov-2 Farsetti, Prato #696/R est:40000
£26000 $40300 €39000 Cannes (76x60cm-30x24in) s.d.32 prov. 5-Dec-2 Christie's, Kensington #135/R est:15000-20000
£49367 $78000 €78000 Flowers on table (81x65cm-32x26in) s.d.42 lit. 30-Nov-2 Farsetti, Prato #730/R est:90000
£51282 $80513 €80000 Laid table (70x100cm-28x39in) s.i.d.39 prov.exhib.lit. 21-Nov-2 Finarte, Rome #295/R est:65000-75000
£82278 $130000 €130000 Flowers (96x83cm-38x33in) s.d.1940 exhib.lit. 30-Nov-2 Farsetti, Prato #700/R est:140000
Works on paper
£780 $1264 €1100 Ritratto (21x17cm-8x7in) s. pencil prov. 26-May-3 Christie's, Milan #100
£1026 $1590 €1600 Traveller (15x11cm-6x4in) s.d.45 W/C. 5-Dec-2 Stadion, Trieste #881/R
£1056 $1754 €1500 Nudo disteso (20x27cm-8x11in) pencil. 10-Jun-3 Finarte Semenzato, Milan #176/R est:1400-1600
£1100 $1738 €1650 Peasant woman (27x10cm-11x4in) s.d.32 col crayon prov. 3-Apr-3 Christie's, Kensington #103/R
£1111 $1767 €1600 Yellow nude (21x27cm-8x11in) s. pastel W/C. 1-May-3 Meeting Art, Vercelli #318

£1731 $2683 €2700 Paris street (27x36cm-11x14in) s. W/C. 5-Dec-2 Stadion, Trieste #880/R
£2083 $3312 €3000 Two figures in interior (22x21cm-9x8in) s. W/C. 1-May-3 Meeting Art, Vercelli #516
£4487 $7045 €7000 Still life with bottle (49x35cm-19x14in) s. W/C exec.1940. 19-Nov-2 Finarte, Milan #60/R est:7500

PISIS, Filippo de (attrib) (1896-1956) Italian
£611 $954 €917 Still life with fan, glass and letter (39x67cm-15x26in) i.d.47 board. 20-Nov-2 Fischer, Luzern #2218/R (S.FR 1400)

PISSARRO, Camille (1830-1903) French
£32000 $53440 €46400 Paysage avec troupeau de Mountons et meules (10x18cm-4x7in) s. panel painted c.1863 prov. 24-Jun-3 Sotheby's, London #106/R est:15000-20000
£131410 $205000 €197115 La gardeuse de vache (33x41cm-13x16in) s.d.1874 i.on stretcher oil paper on canvas prov.exhib.lit. 7-Nov-2 Christie's, Rockefeller NY #211/R est:250000-350000
£173077 $270000 €259616 Paysage d'automne, pres Lou-Veciennes (50x55cm-20x22in) s. prov.exhib. 6-Nov-2 Sotheby's, New York #130/R est:300000-400000
£205128 $320000 €307692 Femme nue vue de dos (41x33cm-16x13in) s.d.95 prov.exhib.lit. 5-Nov-2 Sotheby's, New York #58/R est:300000-400000
£205128 $320000 €307692 Le port du Havre (54x65cm-21x26in) painted 1903 prov.exhib.lit. 7-Nov-2 Christie's, Rockefeller NY #254/R est:300000-400000
£260000 $434200 €377000 Bazincourt, soleil couchant, effet de neige (32x41cm-13x16in) s.d.1892 prov.exhib.lit. 24-Jun-3 Sotheby's, London #114/R est:120000-180000
£435897 $680000 €653846 Les mathurins, Pontoise (73x59cm-29x23in) s.d.1877 prov.exhib.lit. 6-Nov-2 Christie's, Rockefeller NY #11/R est:700000-900000
£641026 $1000000 €961539 Le cours la reine a Rouen, matin, soleil (65x81cm-26x32in) s.d.98 prov.exhib.lit. 6-Nov-2 Christie's, Rockefeller NY #23/R est:1000000-1500000
£720000 $1173600 €1080000 Paysanne et enfant, Eragny (65x54cm-26x21in) s.d.93 prov.exhib.lit. 3-Feb-3 Christie's, London #55/R est:600000
£745342 $1200000 €1118013 Meules de foin dans le pre, Eragny (73x92cm-29x36in) s.d.96 prov.exhib.lit. 6-May-3 Sotheby's, New York #2/R est:1000000-1500000
£1602564 $2500000 €2403846 La route par la neige, Louveciennes (43x65cm-17x26in) s. painted c.1872 prov.exhib.lit. 6-Nov-2 Christie's, Rockefeller NY #4/R est:1500000-2000000
£3105590 $5000000 €4658385 Route de Rocquencourt (51x77cm-20x30in) s.d.1871 prov.exhib. 6-May-3 Sotheby's, New York #7/R est:3000000-5000000

Prints
£1887 $3000 €2831 Portrait le Lucien Pissarro (18x15cm-7x6in) etching. 1-May-3 Swann Galleries, New York #102/R est:4000-6000
£2365 $3690 €3500 Paysage a Osny (11x15cm-4x6in) drypoint exec.1887. 31-Mar-3 Tajan, Paris #372/R
£2692 $4200 €4038 Porteuses de fagots (27x35cm-11x14in) lithograph. 7-Nov-2 Swann Galleries, New York #471/R est:4000-6000
£2817 $4000 €4226 Paris, Le Pont Neuf (20x28cm-8x11in) s. etching. 8-Aug-1 Barridorf, Portland #83/R est:4000-6000
£2949 $4600 €4424 Portrait de Jeanne Pissarro (33x26cm-13x10in) i.verso lithograph exec.c.1895. 7-Nov-2 Swann Galleries, New York #469/R est:6000-9000
£3590 $5600 €5385 Convalescence, Lucien Pissarro (32x23cm-13x9in) st.init.i.num.2/11 lithograph exec.c.1897. 7-Nov-2 Swann Galleries, New York #473/R est:7000-10000
£3899 $6044 €6200 Le marche a Pontoise (44x31cm-17x12in) s. black lithograph. 30-Oct-2 Artcurial Briest, Paris #551/R est:2300-2500
£5769 $9000 €8654 Rue Saint Lazare, Paris (21x14cm-8x6in) i. lithograph. 7-Nov-2 Swann Galleries, New York #472/R est:6000-9000
£9615 $15000 €14423 Camille Pissarro, par lui-meme (19x18cm-7x7in) st.init.i. etching drypoint. 7-Nov-2 Swann Galleries, New York #462/R est:20000-30000
£10898 $17109 €17000 Paysage sous-bois a l'Hermitage - Pontoise (22x27cm-9x11in) s. aquatint. 22-Nov-2 Tajan, Paris #371/R est:4600-6000

Works on paper
£449 $704 €700 Etude de chevreau (7x8cm-3x3in) st.mono. crayon. 21-Nov-2 Neret-Minet, Paris #14
£449 $704 €700 Etude de fillette (7x6cm-3x2in) st.sig. crayon. 21-Nov-2 Neret-Minet, Paris #15
£878 $1370 €1300 Promeneur (16x19cm-6x7in) s. dr. 27-Mar-3 Maigret, Paris #262/R
£1538 $2415 €2400 Homme de ferme aupres de deux chevaux (20x18cm-8x7in) mono. crayon dr. 13-Dec-2 Piasa, Paris #266/R
£1824 $2827 €2900 Etudes d'hommes couches (13x21cm-5x8in) st.mono. crayon dr prov. 30-Oct-2 Coutau Begarie, Paris #38/R est:750-800
£2152 $3335 €3400 Cheval a la charrette de paille (17x22cm-7x9in) init. pencil exec.c.1870. 28-Sep-2 Christie's, Paris #3/R est:1200-1800
£2390 $3800 €3585 Etude de Rachel etendue sur un lit (9x15cm-4x6in) st.init. pencil W/C brush wash exec.c.1888 prov. 27-Feb-3 Christie's, Rockefeller NY #17/R
£3165 $5000 €5000 Cow in meadow - Eragny (8x14cm-3x6in) mono. chk. 30-Nov-2 Villa Grisebach, Berlin #106/R est:3000-5000
£3226 $5000 €4839 Trois figures (25x19cm-10x7in) init. chl red pencil. 26-Sep-2 Christie's, Rockefeller NY #505/R est:6000-8000
£3919 $6113 €5800 Laboureur et chevaux atteles (7x11cm-3x4in) init. crayon pastel dr prov. 26-Mar-3 Tajan, Paris #8/R
£4839 $7500 €7259 La Roche-Goyon (23x31cm-9x12in) init. pencil paper on board prov. 26-Sep-2 Christie's, Rockefeller NY #514/R est:6000-8000
£5000 $7700 €7500 Paysanne accroupie (29x24cm-11x9in) init. chl exec.c.1890-95 prov. 23-Oct-2 Sotheby's, Olympia #612/R est:3000-5000
£5161 $8000 €7742 Les arbres (22x35cm-9x14in) init. pencil prov. 26-Sep-2 Christie's, Rockefeller NY #502/R est:8000-10000
£5417 $8613 €7800 Caracas. Etude de personnages au bord d'une riviere (25x28cm-10x11in) init. graphite dr double-sided. 29-Apr-3 Artcurial Briest, Paris #25/R est:8000-10000
£6000 $9240 €9000 La Roche-Guyon (29x44cm-11x17in) s.i.d.1889 pencil htd chk prov. 23-Oct-2 Sotheby's, Olympia #609/R est:6000-8000
£7097 $11213 €11000 Recolte en Bretagne (12x20cm-5x8in) mono. graphite W/C dr. 18-Dec-2 Digard, Paris #108/R est:15000
£7278 $11282 €11500 Paysan (23x18cm-9x7in) init. chl W/C exec.c.1880 prov. 28-Sep-2 Christie's, Paris #4/R est:1500-2200
£7692 $12000 €11538 La maison du peintre Ludovic Piette (22x27cm-9x11in) artist st. pencil. 18-Sep-2 Swann Galleries, New York #3/R est:12000-18000
£10000 $15900 €15000 All Saints' Church, Beulah Hill (16x21cm-6x8in) init. W/C over pencil exec.c.1870-71 prov. 20-Mar-3 Sotheby's, Olympia #3/R est:6000-8000
£11392 $18000 €18000 Landscape (20x26cm-8x10in) s.d.1884 chk. 30-Nov-2 Villa Grisebach, Berlin #105/R est:7000-9000
£12821 $20000 €19232 Portrait of Ludovic Rodo Pissarro (18x20cm-7x8in) init. India ink executed c.1891-92 prov. 6-Nov-2 Sotheby's, New York #104/R est:15000-20000
£14000 $21560 €21000 Paysanne et enfant (21x17cm-8x7in) init. W/C black crayon executed c.1890. 22-Oct-2 Sotheby's, London #124/R est:10000-15000
£14000 $22960 €21000 Paysannes travaillant aux champs (20x31cm-8x12in) s. crayon brush ink chk exec.c.1880 prov. 5-Feb-3 Sotheby's, London #208/R est:10000
£17949 $28000 €26924 Chelsea, Londres (18x13cm-7x5in) i.d.1890 W/C over pencil paper on board prov.exhib. 7-Nov-2 Christie's, Rockefeller NY #156/R est:15000-20000
£22222 $31556 €36000 Moissons a Montfoucault (22x26cm-9x10in) s.d.1879 pastel. 16-Mar-3 Eric Pillon, Calais #106/R
£36859 $57500 €55289 Paysage a Saint Charles (29x19cm-11x7in) s. pastel pencil canvas on board prov.lit. 6-Nov-2 Sotheby's, New York #120/R est:50000-70000
£55000 $91850 €79750 La vachere, matin, soleil (20x27cm-8x11in) s.d.1887 gouache pencil prov.lit. 24-Jun-3 Sotheby's, London #217/R est:40000-60000
£80000 $133600 €120000 Femme etendant du linge, Eragny (24x16cm-9x6in) s.d.1890 gouache W/C pencil prov. 26-Jun-3 Christie's, London #361/R est:70000-100000
£112179 $175000 €168269 Portrait de Monsieur Louis Estruc (46x38cm-18x15in) s. pastel paper on canvas executed c.1874 prov.lit. 6-Nov-2 Sotheby's, New York #107/R est:120000-180000
£115385 $180000 €173078 Les deux faneuses (60x46cm-24x18in) init. chl brown chk executed c.1880-82 prov.exhib.lit. 5-Nov-2 Sotheby's, New York #11/R est:180000-250000
£140000 $233800 €203000 Les gardeuses de vaches (30x23cm-12x9in) s.d.1883 gouache W/C chl prov.exhib.lit. 24-Jun-3 Christie's, London #47/R est:140000-180000
£141026 $220000 €211539 Bords de l'oise (30x63cm-12x25in) s.d.1890 gouache pencil silk on paper mounted on board prov.exhib. 6-Nov-2 Sotheby's, New York #119/R est:250000-350000
£217391 $350000 €326087 Jeune paysanne a sa toilette (33x25cm-13x10in) s.d.1888 gouache on linen prov.exhib.lit. 8-May-3 Christie's, Rockefeller NY #140/R est:350000-450000

PISSARRO, Camille (attrib) (1830-1903) French
Works on paper
£3521 $5845 €5000 Londres (14x17cm-6x7in) bears sig.i. W/C prov.exhib. 11-Jun-3 Beaussant & Lefèvre, Paris #186/R est:6000-8000

PISSARRO, Claude (1935-) French
£732 $1200 €1098 Winding road (23x33cm-9x13in) s. i.stretcher. 5-Feb-3 Doyle, New York #37/R est:1500-2500
£915 $1500 €1373 Houses in a landscape (28x33cm-11x13in) s. board. 5-Feb-3 Doyle, New York #36/R est:1500-2500
£2761 $4500 €4142 Le petit fils (46x53cm-18x21in) painted c.1980. 14-Feb-3 Du Mouchelle, Detroit #2010/R est:5000-7000
£4516 $7000 €6774 La port de Dieppe (65x81cm-26x32in) s. s.i.verso. 26-Sep-2 Christie's, Rockefeller NY #585/R est:5000-7000
Works on paper
£1509 $2400 €2264 Paysage fluvial (25x37cm-10x15in) s. s.i.verso pastel prov. 27-Feb-3 Christie's, Rockefeller NY #55/R
£4800 $7824 €7200 Neige a Nortre-Dame, Paris (37x51cm-15x20in) s. pastel. 3-Feb-3 Bonhams, New Bond Street #7/R est:3000-5000

PISSARRO, L (?) French
£1600 $2480 €2400 Still lifes a bowl of flowers and fruit (29x22cm-11x9in) s. pair. 25-Sep-2 John Nicholson, Haslemere #1059/R

PISSARRO, Lucien (1863-1944) British/French
£7200 $11592 €10800 La Frette (23x30cm-9x12in) panel painted 1924 prov. 9-May-3 Mallams, Oxford #118/R est:4000-6000
£9500 $14725 €14250 Riggs, Brough (53x65cm-21x26in) mono.d.1914 exhib.lit. 3-Dec-2 Bonhams, New Bond Street #22/R est:10000-15000
£18000 $29520 €27000 Rue Carnot, Bormes (52x65cm-20x26in) mono.d.1927 i.on stretcher prov.exhib.lit. 6-Jun-3 Christie's, London #18/R est:20000-30000
£18000 $29520 €27000 Compas Rocks, Dartmouth (44x53cm-17x21in) mono.d.1922 i.on stretcher. 6-Jun-3 Christie's, London #19/R est:18000-25000
£21293 $33855 €31300 Estuary Dartmouth (55x46cm-22x18in) mono.d.1922 i.verso prov. 26-Feb-3 Artcurial Briest, Paris #167/R est:15000-18000
£22000 $36080 €33000 Nut tree (65x51cm-26x20in) mono. painted May 1938 prov.lit. 6-Jun-3 Christie's, London #22/R est:20000-30000
£26000 $42640 €37700 Tunstal, the Estuary (45x54cm-18x21in) mono.d.1922 prov.exhib.lit. 4-Jun-3 Sotheby's, London #20/R est:18000-25000
Works on paper
£1700 $2652 €2550 Summer landscape, Blackpool, Devon (4x13cm-2x5in) mono.d.1921 pen ink col crayon prov. 27-Mar-3 Christie's, Kensington #304/R est:800-1200
£2200 $3432 €3300 White City from Wormwood Scrubs (10x13cm-4x5in) mono.d.1911 pencil col crayon htd white. 27-Mar-3 Christie's, Kensington #302/R est:1500-2000
£3500 $5460 €5250 Reynoldston, Pembroke (23x28cm-9x11in) mono.d.1932 pencil W/C. 27-Mar-3 Christie's, Kensington #301/R est:2500-3500

PISSARRO, Ludovic Rodo (1878-1952) French
£568 $829 €852 Le final (45x81cm-18x32in) s. 4-Jun-2 Germann, Zurich #816 (S.FR 1300)
£833 $1375 €1200 Rue sous la neige (53x44cm-21x17in) s. 1-Jul-3 Rossini, Paris #118/R
£1266 $1849 €1950 Street scene in a French town (33x38cm-13x15in) s. prov. 15-Jun-2 Hans Stahl, Hamburg #107/R
£1634 $2680 €2500 Jeune femme a la bague verte (73x60cm-29x24in) s. 7-Feb-3 Oger, Dumont, Paris #126
Works on paper
£481 $750 €722 La bal (20x25cm-8x10in) s. W/C. 22-Sep-2 Susanin's, Chicago #5021/R

PISSARRO, Orovida (1893-1968) British
Works on paper
£8000 $12480 €12000 Three ladies with Siamese kitten (56x66cm-22x26in) s.d.1932 W/C gouache exhib. 25-Mar-3 Bonhams, New Bond Street #53/R est:1500-2000

PISSARRO, Paul Émile (1884-1972) French
£1863 $3000 €2795 Foret de Lyon (56x46cm-22x18in) s. s.i.verso prov. 19-Feb-3 Doyle, New York #22 est:2000-3000
£2564 $4000 €3846 La pointe de l'iste clecy (61x46cm-24x18in) 18-Oct-2 Du Mouchelle, Detroit #2074/R est:2000-3000
£2716 $3857 €4400 Petit moulin (40x61cm-16x24in) s. 16-Mar-3 Eric Pillon, Calais #220/R
£2759 $4358 €4000 Bouquet de fleurs blanches et rouges (55x46cm-22x18in) s. 4-Apr-3 Tajan, Paris #152/R
£2901 $4120 €4700 Bords de l'Orne (54x65cm-21x26in) s. 16-Mar-3 Eric Pillon, Calais #219/R
Works on paper
£769 $1208 €1200 Chaumiere en campagne (23x28cm-9x11in) s. W/C chl. 15-Dec-2 Thierry & Lannon, Brest #44

PISTOLETTO, Michelangelo (1933-) Italian
Prints
£1923 $2981 €3000 Self-portrait (100x70cm-39x28in) s.verso serigraph. 4-Dec-2 Finarte, Milan #148
£2150 $3333 €3225 Maria (100x100cm-39x39in) s.num.4/24 col silkscreen. 5-Dec-2 Sotheby's, London #222/R est:2000-3000
£4387 $6932 €6800 Pegs (100x70cm-39x28in) s.num.verso serigraph on steel. 18-Dec-2 Christie's, Rome #192/R est:3000
£7746 $12859 €11000 Il telefono (70x100cm-28x39in) s. verso num.43/60 serigraph clear steel mirror. 10-Jun-3 Finarte Semenzato, Milan #223/R est:10000-12000
£32000 $49920 €48000 Concerto - quadro no.3 (120x150cm-47x59in) s.i.verso silkscreen on stainless steel executed 1974 prov. 21-Oct-2 Sotheby's, London #38/R est:35000-45000
£43871 $69316 €68000 Parrot at the zoo (230x120cm-91x47in) s.i.d.1961-62 verso serigraph on steel. 18-Dec-2 Christie's, Rome #311/R est:70000

PITA, Gerardo (1950-) ?
Works on paper
£759 $1199 €1100 Window (61x48cm-24x19in) s. pencil chl. 1-Apr-3 Segre, Madrid #232/R
£828 $1308 €1200 Old lady (56x46cm-22x18in) s. pencil dr. 1-Apr-3 Segre, Madrid #233/R
£1793 $2833 €2600 Boots 76 (75x79cm-30x31in) s.d.1976 graphite dr prov. 1-Apr-3 Segre, Madrid #234/R

PITCHFORTH, Roland Vivian (1895-1982) British
£800 $1240 €1200 Estuary, Essex (60x74cm-24x29in) s.d.1937. 30-Sep-2 Bonhams, Ipswich #378/R
Works on paper
£280 $440 €420 Off the coast (30x44cm-12x17in) s. W/C. 15-Apr-3 Bonhams, Knightsbridge #67
£300 $489 €450 Man and dog on a beach at low tide (42x55cm-17x22in) s. W/C. 30-Jan-3 Lawrence, Crewkerne #672
£350 $550 €525 Natal National Park (30x48cm-12x19in) s.d.47 W/C. 13-Dec-2 Keys, Aylsham #428
£360 $594 €522 Mist over the Stour (45x59cm-18x23in) s. W/C. 1-Jul-3 Bonhams, Norwich #158
£380 $635 €551 Europa Point, Gibraltar (28x44cm-11x17in) s. W/C. 17-Jun-3 Bonhams, Knightsbridge #18/R
£2200 $3498 €3300 Marine lake, Southport. s.i. W/C five various sizes. 26-Feb-3 Sotheby's, Olympia #176/R est:2500-3500

PITL, Nicholas R (1932-2001) American
£260 $400 €390 Cattle drive to Tuscon, nighthawkers tending to beddin' down the herd (24x36cm-9x14in) s. 9-Sep-2 Schrager Galleries, Milwaukee #1293/R
£292 $450 €438 Indian Chief (16x20cm-6x8in) s. acrylic masonite. 9-Sep-2 Schrager Galleries, Milwaukee #1280/R
£311 $500 €467 Opening day - ring neck pheasant, 1983 (74x127cm-29x50in) s. 20-Jan-3 Schrager Galleries, Milwaukee #1136
£311 $500 €467 Mountain man's long journey (51x61cm-20x24in) s, acrylic board. 20-Jan-3 Schrager Galleries, Milwaukee #1226
£325 $500 €488 Canadian geese in the spring (5x7cm-2x3in) s. acrylic W/C. 9-Sep-2 Schrager Galleries, Milwaukee #1294/R
£373 $600 €560 Mallards in the California gold (61x91cm-24x36in) s. s.d.1981 stretcher. 20-Jan-3 Schrager Galleries, Milwaukee #1138
£649 $1000 €974 Rainbow trout with royal coachman fly (6x8cm-2x3in) s.d.1981 i.verso acrylic W/C. 9-Sep-2 Schrager Galleries, Milwaukee #1290/R
£2435 $3750 €3653 Cochise's fair warning (24x48cm-9x19in) s.d.80 exhib. masonite. 9-Sep-2 Schrager Galleries, Milwaukee #1281/R
Works on paper
£260 $400 €390 Rodeo Bronc, twist'in 'n turn'in (22x16cm-9x6in) s. sepia ink col pencil. 9-Sep-2 Schrager Galleries, Milwaukee #1282/R

PITLOO, Antonio Sminck (1791-1837) Dutch
£6000 $9540 €9000 Ischia and Capri seen from the Neapolitan Coast (21x27cm-8x11in) s. board. 20-Mar-3 Christie's, Kensington #64/R est:4000-6000
£12238 $20437 €17500 Sorrente (22x33cm-9x13in) mono.i. 27-Jun-3 Claude Aguttes, Neuilly #26/R est:10000-12000
£68966 $108966 €100000 Naples from Mergellina beach (35x48cm-14x19in) s.d.1829 prov.exhib.lit. 3-Apr-3 Porro, Milan #46/R est:150000

PITNER, Franz (1826-1892) Austrian
Works on paper
£300 $492 €450 Portrait of a young girl, seated, playing with her toys (18x16cm-7x6in) s.d.1855 pencil W/C. 5-Jun-3 Christie's, Kensington #856/R
£372 $580 €550 Peasant scene (37x42cm-15x17in) s.d.862 W/C. 28-Mar-3 Dorotheum, Vienna #215/R

PITRA, Margot (?) ?
Sculpture
£1667 $2617 €2600 Grenouille (36cm-14in) num.1/8 bronze. 15-Dec-2 Mercier & Cie, Lille #258
£3020 $4862 €4500 Songeuse (45cm-18in) num.1/8 bronze. 23-Feb-3 Mercier & Cie, Lille #225/R

PITT, William (19th C) British
£780 $1209 €1170 Boscastle, Cornwall (23x17cm-9x7in) init. s.d.1868 i. verso. 2-Oct-2 Bonhams, Knowle #61
£1200 $1872 €1800 On the St Germans, Cornwall (61x117cm-24x46in) i.d.1867 verso. 26-Mar-3 Woolley & Wallis, Salisbury #165/R est:600-800
£1300 $2028 €1950 Roadside inn, Shropshire (22x36cm-9x14in) s.d.1853 i.verso. 8-Oct-2 Bonhams, Knightsbridge #276/R est:300-500
£2200 $3564 €3300 On the Salcombe river, Devon (21x44cm-8x17in) s.i.d.1869 verso. 20-May-3 Sotheby's, Olympia #234/R est:800-1200
£3000 $4890 €4350 Creek off the Dart, Devon (60x120cm-24x47in) mono.d.1874. 21-Jul-3 Bonhams, Bath #54/R est:4000-6000

PITTAR, J F Barry (1880-1948) British
Works on paper
£850 $1318 €1275 Grand Canal, Venice (53x74cm-21x29in) s. W/C. 6-Dec-2 Chrystals Auctions, Isle of Man #166

PITTMAN, Hobson (c.1899-1972) American
£1355 $2100 €2033 Late afternoon (61x76cm-24x30in) s. 8-Dec-2 Freeman, Philadelphia #151/R est:2000-3000
£1935 $3000 €2903 Pennsylvania landscape with cat on front porch (61x76cm-24x30in) s. 8-Dec-2 Freeman, Philadelphia #158/R est:2000-3000
Works on paper
£958 $1600 €1389 Mixed flowers (31x47cm-12x19in) s. pastel. 22-Jun-3 Freeman, Philadelphia #146/R est:600-1000
£1317 $2200 €1910 Floral still life (49x32cm-19x13in) s. pastel. 22-Jun-3 Freeman, Philadelphia #154/R est:600-1000
£1410 $2200 €2115 Floral still life on shelf (61x48cm-24x19in) s.i. pastel. 5-Nov-2 Arthur James, Florida #381
£1410 $2200 €2115 Roses (33x43cm-13x17in) s.i. pastel. 5-Nov-2 Arthur James, Florida #382

PITTMAN, Lari (1952-) American
£2658 $4200 €3987 Life, liberty and the pursuit of happiness (76x56cm-30x22in) acrylic ink painted 1985 prov. 12-Nov-2 Phillips, New York #211/R est:4000-6000
£18987 $30000 €28481 Thankfully, you will have taught me freedom within constraints (163x241cm-64x95in) acrylic alkyd spray enamel on panel painted 1999 prov. 14-Nov-2 Christie's, Rockefeller NY #344/R est:50000-70000
£28125 $45000 €42188 Regenerative and needy (208x168cm-82x66in) acrylic enamel panel painted 1991 prov.exhib. 15-May-3 Christie's, Rockefeller NY #343/R est:40000-60000

PITTMAN, Osmund (1874-1958) British
£310 $493 €465 Trees and shadows (49x74cm-19x29in) mono. 4-Mar-3 Bristol Auction Rooms #314/R

PITTO, Giacomo (1872-?) Italian
£800 $1280 €1200 Young woman with a basket in a market (50x68cm-20x27in) s. 7-Jan-3 Bonhams, Knightsbridge #204/R
£900 $1422 €1350 Market scene (60x80cm-24x31in) s. 12-Nov-2 Bonhams, Knightsbridge #141/R

PITTO, Guiseppe (1857-1928) Italian
£1400 $2226 €2100 Fruit market (48x69cm-19x27in) s. 29-Apr-3 Gorringes, Lewes #2302

PITTONI, Giovanni Battista (younger) (1687-1767) Italian
£22759 $35959 €33000 David by the Arc (91x130cm-36x51in) prov.exhib.lit. 5-Apr-3 Finarte Semenzato, Milan #152/R est:35000-45000
£49383 $80000 €74075 Holy Family (93x116cm-37x46in) prov.lit. 23-Jan-3 Sotheby's, New York #44/R est:80000-120000
£59451 $97500 €89177 Allegory of time and beauty (63x81cm-25x32in) 29-May-3 Sotheby's, New York #108/R est:60000-80000

PITTS, Joseph (fl.1830-1870) British
Sculpture
£1400 $2268 €2100 Bust of Lord Nelson (24cm-9in) i.verso parian exec.c.1853 after Whichelo. 21-May-3 Christie's, Kensington #38/R est:400-600

PITZ, Henry C (1895-1974) American
Works on paper
£466 $750 €699 Medicine man standing near rock formation (33x23cm-13x9in) s. pen ink. 20-Feb-3 Illustration House, New York #134/R
£559 $900 €839 Man approaches woman with black cat (28x20cm-11x8in) s.d.1928 pen ink. 20-Feb-3 Illustration House, New York #135/R

PITZNER, Max Joseph (1855-1912) German
£1090 $1711 €1700 Girl with geese meeting mounted soldiers by river (17x22cm-7x9in) s.i. panel. 23-Nov-2 Arnold, Frankfurt #836/R est:800
£1218 $1900 €1827 Rustic scene (23x43cm-9x17in) s.d.1882. 9-Oct-2 Doyle, New York #83 est:800-1200

PIXIS, Theodor (1831-1907) German
£29932 $47592 €44000 Arrival of travelling theatre at village tavern (111x140cm-44x55in) s.d.1876. 19-Mar-3 Neumeister, Munich #698/R est:45000

PIZA, Arthur (1928-) Brazilian
Works on paper
£2692 $4227 €4200 Mosaique en bois (70x65cm-28x26in) s. mixed media panel prov.exhib. 24-Nov-2 Laurence Calmels, Paris #213/R

PIZZANELLI, Ferruccio (1884-?) Italian
£609 $956 €950 Huts at the seaside (35x43cm-14x17in) s. card. 10-Dec-2 Della Rocca, Turin #350

PIZZI CANNELLA, Piero (1955-) Italian
£1268 $2104 €1800 Untitled (70x70cm-28x28in) s.verso. 10-Jun-3 Finarte Semenzato, Milan #257/R est:1500-1700
£1282 $1987 €2000 Blind (73x52cm-29x20in) s.d.197 verso tempera card. 5-Dec-2 Stadion, Trieste #806/R
£1538 $2385 €2400 Impression (28x63cm-11x25in) s.d.1989 oil mixed media board. 5-Dec-2 Stadion, Trieste #808/R
£4167 $6542 €6500 North-North West (80x110cm-31x43in) s.d.1994 verso. 21-Nov-2 Finarte, Rome #280
Works on paper
£523 $837 €800 Living at sea (42x31cm-17x12in) s.i. mixed media. 4-Jan-3 Meeting Art, Vercelli #461
£1373 $2196 €2100 View (103x73cm-41x29in) s.i.d.1989 mixed media collage cardboard. 4-Jan-3 Meeting Art, Vercelli #582
£1667 $2617 €2600 Untitled (160x120cm-63x47in) d.1992 mixed media. 20-Nov-2 Pandolfini, Florence #151/R

PIZZINATO, Armando (1910-) Italian
£1646 $2567 €2600 Amongst fruit trees (100x70cm-39x28in) s. 19-Oct-2 Semenzato, Venice #10/R
£2025 $3159 €3200 Landscape in the lagoon (48x78cm-19x31in) s.d.1960. 19-Oct-2 Semenzato, Venice #31/R

PLA Y GALLARDO, Cecilio (1860-1934) Spanish
£855 $1386 €1300 Portrait of woman (44x42cm-17x17in) s.d.1905. 21-Jan-3 Ansorena, Madrid #152/R
£943 $1472 €1500 Portrait of gentleman (80x54cm-31x21in) s.d.1893 oval. 23-Sep-2 Durán, Madrid #113/R
£1026 $1621 €1600 In the cafe (11x14cm-4x6in) s. board. 19-Nov-2 Durán, Madrid #176/R
£1090 $1722 €1700 Head of man (32x28cm-13x11in) s. 19-Nov-2 Durán, Madrid #177/R
£1218 $1924 €1900 Lady in a cafe (11x14cm-4x6in) s. cardboard. 19-Nov-2 Durán, Madrid #175/R
£1258 $1962 €2000 Portrait of lady (80x54cm-31x21in) s.d.1893 oval. 23-Sep-2 Durán, Madrid #114/R
£16552 $26483 €24000 Crisis in New York (86x145cm-34x57in) s. double-sided. 11-Mar-3 Castellana, Madrid #62/R est:37500
£20000 $31400 €30000 Personajes en la playa - children on the beach (14x30cm-6x12in) s.i. canvasboard painted c.1925 prov.exhib. 19-Nov-2 Sotheby's, London #15/R est:20000-25000
£34000 $53380 €51000 Junto al pabellon de las arenas, sobre el mar, Valencia - swimming lagoon, Valencia Beach (14x24cm-6x9in) s. board painted c.1923 exhib. 19-Nov-2 Sotheby's, London #14/R est:25000-35000
Works on paper
£298 $486 €450 Garden and fountain (16x14cm-6x6in) s.d.20 pencil dr. 11-Feb-3 Segre, Madrid #147/R
£621 $981 €900 Portuguese landscape (6x11cm-2x4in) s. W/C. 1-Apr-3 Segre, Madrid #362/R
£715 $1166 €1080 Leiria, Portugal (7x13cm-3x5in) s.i. W/C. 11-Feb-3 Segre, Madrid #148/R

PLA Y RUBIO, Alberto (1867-1929) Spanish
£4000 $6320 €6000 Fishing boat with children on the shore (27x35cm-11x14in) s. board. 3-Apr-3 Christie's, Kensington #23/R
£4839 $7645 €7500 Idyll amongst orange trees (40x54cm-16x21in) s.d.1924. 18-Dec-2 Ansorena, Madrid #74/R
£4934 $7993 €7500 Peasant women (39x65cm-15x26in) s. 21-Jan-3 Ansorena, Madrid #185/R
£5128 $8103 €8000 Beach (24x34cm-9x13in) s. board. 13-Nov-2 Ansorena, Madrid #127/R

PLAGEMANN, Augusta (1799-1888) Swedish
£982 $1610 €1424 Wild berries on cabbage leaf - still life (25x36cm-10x14in) init. metal. 4-Jun-3 AB Stockholms Auktionsverk #2195/R (S.KR 12500)

PLAGEMANN, Carl (1805-1868) Swedish
£1206 $1869 €1809 Portrait of Christoffer Columbus holding a globe (100x74cm-39x29in) s.d.1860. 4-Dec-2 AB Stockholms Auktionsverk #1588/R est:20000-25000 (S.KR 17000)

PLAMONDON, Antoine Sebastian (1804-1895) Canadian
£528 $830 €792 Portrait d'un pretre (30x24cm-12x9in) s. 12-Dec-2 Iegor de Saint Hippolyte, Montreal #78b (C.D 1300)

PLANAS DORIA, Francisco (1879-1955) Spanish
£710 $1121 €1100 Landscape with trees and house (45x70cm-18x28in) s. board. 18-Dec-2 Ansorena, Madrid #49/R

PLANAS GALLES, Jaime (1926-) Spanish
£1007 $1621 €1500 Dancers (95x109cm-37x43in) s. 18-Feb-3 Durán, Madrid #149/R

PLANCKNER, Lonny von (1863-?) German
£880 $1373 €1320 Paysage Alpine en hiver (51x63cm-20x25in) s. 9-Oct-2 Woolley & Wallis, Salisbury #356/R

PLANELLS, Angel (1902-1989) Spanish
£16438 $25644 €24000 Wounded will's sleep (25x28cm-10x11in) s.d.1929 oil collage panel. 14-Apr-3 Laurence Calmels, Paris #4011/R est:8000

PLANER, Josef (20th C) Austrian
£612 $973 €900 Abundant fruit and flower still life (50x116cm-20x46in) s. 25-Feb-3 Dorotheum, Vienna #141/R

PLANGG, Warner R (20th C) American
Sculpture
£884 $1396 €1326 Open season (33x41x25cm-13x16x10in) bronze. 1-Dec-2 Levis, Calgary #78/R est:3000-4000 (C.D 2200)

PLANQUETTE, Felix (1873-1964) French
£1195 $1864 €1900 Peasant woman with cattle in the evening (29x40cm-11x16in) s. prov.lit. 20-Sep-2 Karlheinz Kaupp, Staufen #2066/R est:1900
£1656 $2699 €2500 Troupeau s'abreuvant au lever du jour (50x65cm-20x26in) s. 16-Feb-3 Mercier & Cie, Lille #239/R est:2800-3200

PLANSON, Andre (1898-1981) French
£700 $1078 €1050 La marne au printemps (55x81cm-22x32in) s.d.52 i.d.stretcher. 23-Oct-2 Sotheby's, Olympia #794/R
£903 $1426 €1300 Fete au bord de la Marne (41x72cm-16x28in) s. 23-Apr-3 Rabourdin & Choppin de Janvry, Paris #37/R
£1154 $1812 €1800 Inondations a Bezons (60x73cm-24x29in) s. 15-Dec-2 Eric Pillon, Calais #174/R
£1233 $1936 €1800 Saint Cyr sur Morin (46x55cm-18x22in) s.d.63. 21-Apr-3 Rabourdin & Choppin de Janvry, Paris #93/R est:1800-2000
£1538 $2415 €2400 Cannotage (54x65cm-21x26in) s.d. 11-Dec-2 Maigret, Paris #104/R est:2000-2500
£1736 $2743 €2500 Paysage de Seine a Paris (38x56cm-15x22in) s.i.d.verso. 23-Apr-3 Rabourdin & Choppin de Janvry, Paris #49/R
£3525 $5781 €4900 Baigneuse au miroir (92x64cm-36x25in) s.d. 4-Jun-3 Marc Kohn, Paris #49/R est:5000-6000

PLANT, Hollins H (?) ?
£1829 $2579 €3000 Heading home (71x91cm-28x36in) s. 7-Feb-2 Woodwards, Cork #237

PLANTE, Ada May (1875-1950) Australian
£1036 $1699 €1554 Portrait of Mr Malcolm Pratt (56x45cm-22x18in) s. canvas on board exhib. 4-Jun-3 Deutscher-Menzies, Melbourne #309/R est:3000-4000 (A.D 2600)

PLANTEY, Madeleine (19/20th C) French
£549 $900 €824 Ballerinas (23x25cm-9x10in) s. board two. 5-Feb-3 Doyle, New York #42/R

PLAS, Hans van der (1925-1991) Dutch
£510 $795 €800 Clown (34x28cm-13x11in) s. panel. 5-Nov-2 Vendu Notarishuis, Rotterdam #25

PLAS, Nicholaas van der (1954-) Dutch
£335 $539 €475 Donkey rides on the beach (23x29cm-9x11in) s. panel. 7-May-3 Vendue Huis, Gravenhage #114/R
£387 $624 €550 Duindigt horse race (23x29cm-9x11in) s. panel. 7-May-3 Vendue Huis, Gravenhage #112
£387 $624 €550 Beach scene with Katwijk church in the background (23x17cm-9x7in) s. panel. 7-May-3 Vendue Huis, Gravenhage #113/R
£528 $850 €750 Fun on the ice in Katwijk on the Rijn (38x58cm-15x23in) s. 7-May-3 Vendue Huis, Gravenhage #26
£563 $907 €800 Children playing on the beach (28x48cm-11x19in) s. panel. 7-May-3 Vendue Huis, Gravenhage #69
£625 $1031 €900 Playing in the surf (30x40cm-12x16in) s. i.verso. 1-Jul-3 Christie's, Amsterdam #332/R
£667 $1107 €967 Children on the beach (18x20cm-7x8in) s. panel. 16-Jun-3 Waddingtons, Toronto #220/R est:700-900 (C.D 1500)
£775 $1247 €1100 Children playing on the beach (39x49cm-15x19in) s. panel. 7-May-3 Vendue Huis, Gravenhage #63
£972 $1604 €1400 At the beach (30x49cm-12x19in) s. plywood. 1-Jul-3 Christie's, Amsterdam #330/R
£1491 $2400 €2237 Children on the beach (38x48cm-15x19in) s. panel. 20-Jan-3 Arthur James, Florida #498

PLASKETT, Joe (1918-) Canadian
£1033 $1622 €1550 Heritage of France (48x99cm-19x39in) s.i.d.61 s.d.verso prov. 24-Jul-2 Walker's, Ottawa #216/R est:2500-3000 (C.D 2500)
Works on paper
£239 $373 €399 Untitled - Davis Hill and Philippe Donati in the studio (48x63cm-19x25in) s.d.1963 pastel prov. 13-Apr-3 Levis, Calgary #577/R (C.D 550)
£248 $389 €372 Barges on the Seine, Paris (48x64cm-19x25in) s.d.66 pastel prov. 24-Jul-2 Walker's, Ottawa #260/R (C.D 600)
£348 $543 €580 Untitled - French landscape (48x63cm-19x25in) s.d.1961 pastel prov. 13-Apr-3 Levis, Calgary #578/R (C.D 800)
£593 $943 €890 Sunset on the Valais (49x64cm-19x25in) s.i. pastel prov. 23-Mar-3 Hodgins, Calgary #114/R est:800-1200 (C.D 1400)
£1008 $1593 €1512 View from dufferin terrace (46x61cm-18x24in) s.d.1968 pastel prov. 18-Nov-2 Sotheby's, Toronto #104/R est:1500-2000 (C.D 2500)

PLASSAN, Antoine-Émile (1817-1903) French
£446 $687 €700 Summer landscape with goats (29x19cm-11x7in) s. board. 5-Sep-2 Arnold, Frankfurt #836/R

PLASSCHAERT, Richard W (1941-) American
£285 $450 €428 Great blue heron (53x65cm-21x26in) s. board prov.exhib. 3-Apr-3 Christie's, Rockefeller NY #208/R
£641 $1000 €929 Wood ducks (61x51cm-24x20in) oil acrylic on board. 13-Oct-2 Cobbs, Peterborough #442

PLATE, Carl Olaf (1909-1977) Australian
£320 $515 €464 Dancing water birds (59x44cm-23x17in) s. board. 12-May-3 Joel, Victoria #321 (A.D 800)
£333 $530 €500 Destructive paradox, the gesture (91x72cm-36x28in) s.i.verso. 4-Mar-3 Deutscher-Menzies, Melbourne #261/R (A.D 870)
£376 $598 €564 Threaded segments (90x121cm-35x48in) s.d.65-67 i.verso oil rope. 23-Mar-3 Goodman, Sydney #48 (A.D 1000)
£610 $964 €885 Untitled (45x63cm-18x25in) s.d.1965 board exhib. 22-Jul-3 Lawson Menzies, Sydney #171/R est:2000-3000 (A.D 1500)

PLATER-ZYBERK, K (19/20th C) ?
£5183 $8500 €7515 View on the lake (120x145cm-47x57in) s. 4-Jun-3 Christie's, Rockefeller NY #237/R est:5000-7000

PLATT, John Edgar (attrib) (1886-1967) British
£580 $957 €841 Ships un dry dock (66x102cm-26x40in) s.d.55. 1-Jul-3 Bonhams, Norwich #333

PLATTEEL, Jean (fl.1839-1867) Belgian
£1019 $1590 €1600 Game seller (56x46cm-22x18in) mono. 6-Nov-2 Vendue Huis, Gravenhage #403/R est:1500-2000

PLATTEMONTAGNE, Nicolas de (c.1631-1706) French
Works on paper
£4808 $7452 €7500 Religieux agenouille (23x23cm-9x9in) i. sanguine prov. 4-Dec-2 Piasa, Paris #54/R

PLATTNER, Karl (1919-1987) Austrian
£8013 $12580 €12500 Boy in a chair (29x24cm-11x9in) s.d.82 tempera cardboard. 19-Nov-2 Finarte, Milan #31/R est:10000-12000
Works on paper
£1871 $2993 €2600 Reclining figure (56x78cm-22x31in) s.d. pencil col pen. 15-May-3 Neumeister, Munich #334/R est:800-1000
£3000 $4650 €4500 Zwei frauen (47x33cm-19x13in) s.d.1952 pen ink W/C. 5-Dec-2 Christie's, Kensington #188/R est:1000-1500
£3716 $5797 €5500 Figures at window (15x46cm-6x18in) s.d.1967 Chinese ink w tempera. 26-Mar-3 Finarte Semenzato, Milan #236/R
£12162 $18973 €18000 Landscape (47x70cm-19x28in) s.d.67 mixed media board. 26-Mar-3 Finarte Semenzato, Milan #289/R

£16667 $26167 €26000 Figure with flowers (34x49cm-13x19in) s.d.1965 mixed media board. 21-Nov-2 Finarte, Rome #285/R

PLATZ, Ernst Heinrich (1867-1940) German

Works on paper

£437 $725 €620 Reminder of Alex v Wagner's drawing class (21x35cm-8x14in) s.i.d. s. verso pencil. 12-Jun-3 Hauswedell & Nolte, Hamburg #382/R

£1088 $1731 €1600 Mountain wood. Saas Fee (29x40cm-11x16in) s.i.d.1895 and 1904 W/C bodycol two. 20-Mar-3 Neumeister, Munich #2510 est:200

PLATZER, Johann Georg (1704-1761) Austrian

£13514 $21081 €20000 Music making party drinking wine (21x30cm-8x12in) copper one of pair prov. 27-Mar-3 Dorotheum, Vienna #270/R est:25000-35000

£14865 $23189 €22000 Drawing up a marriage agreement (21x30cm-8x12in) copper one of pair. 27-Mar-3 Dorotheum, Vienna #271/R est:25000-35000

£94340 $146226 €150000 Sacrifice of Jephta's daughter. Joseph sold by his brothers (23x30cm-9x12in) metal prov. two. 2-Oct-2 Dorotheum, Vienna #247/R est:140000-230000

£175000 $274750 €262500 Young couple and huntsman in woodland garden. Old man, his wife and her lover in interior (27x21cm-11x8in) s. copper two. 11-Dec-2 Christie's, London #73/R est:60000-80000

PLATZER, Johann Georg (attrib) (1704-1761) Austrian

£1226 $1962 €1839 Allegory of Architecture (39x53cm-15x21in) copper. 17-Mar-3 Philippe Schuler, Zurich #8659 est:2500-3000 (S.FR 2600)

PLATZODER, Ludwig (1898-1976) German

£445 $695 €650 Still life with bottle, glass and fruit (25x20cm-10x8in) s.s. panel. 9-Apr-3 Neumeister, Munich #726/R

£878 $1370 €1300 Still life with apples and dish (20x24cm-8x9in) s. board. 26-Mar-3 Hugo Ruef, Munich #194

PLAVINSKY, Dimitri (1937-) Russian

Works on paper

£22000 $34540 €33000 Wall of appearances (72x99cm-28x39in) init.d.62 mixed media panel. 20-Nov-2 Sotheby's, London #194/R est:10000-15000

PLAYER, F da Ponte (fl.1880-1882) British

Works on paper

£480 $749 €720 Cliffs at Saltwick, Yorkshire (66x46cm-26x18in) s. W/C. 10-Sep-2 David Duggleby, Scarborough #275

PLAZEAU, Alfred (1875-1918) French

£5660 $9000 €8490 Enlevee par l'amour (368x168cm-145x66in) s. 5-Mar-3 Christie's, Rockefeller NY #65/R est:7000-9000

PLAZZOTTA, Enzo (1921-1981) Italian

Sculpture

£1600 $2528 €2400 Galloping horse (26x31cm-10x12in) bronze oblong marble base edition 7/9 exec.c.1969. 28-Nov-2 Martel Maides, Guernsey #88/R est:350-450

£1800 $2808 €2700 Red Rum on the rails (38cm-15in) num.1/12 brown pat. bronze st.f. 6-Nov-2 Sotheby's, Olympia #176/R est:2000-3000

£2200 $3630 €3190 Anthony Dowell (42cm-17in) s.num.8/12 dark brown pat. bronze lit. 3-Jul-3 Christie's, Kensington #428/R est:1500-2000

£3797 $6000 €6000 Sur les pointes (82cm-32in) num.6/9 brown pat bronze prov. 27-Nov-2 Blanchet, Paris #114/R

£4500 $7020 €6750 Nureyev (58cm-23in) brown pat. bronze lit. 25-Mar-3 Bonhams, New Bond Street #62/R est:5000-7000

£7500 $11775 €11250 Nureyev (27cm-11in) num.5/12 18 caret yellow gold cast 1979 prov.lit. 22-Nov-2 Christie's, London #47/R est:8000-12000

PLE, Henri Honore (1853-1922) French

Sculpture

£2276 $3641 €3300 Inspiration du poete (84cm-33in) s.i. brown pat bronze. 13-Mar-3 Artcurial Briest, Paris #208/R

PLEIFF, Norbert (20th C) French

£594 $938 €920 A consommer avec moderation (48x63cm-19x25in) s.d.1983 acrylic collage cardboard. 18-Dec-2 Digard, Paris #223

PLEISSNER, Ogden M (1905-1983) American

£2452 $3800 €3678 Edge of the pasture (20x25cm-8x10in) s. canvas on masonite. 3-Dec-2 Christie's, Rockefeller NY #606/R est:2500-3500

£12346 $20000 €18519 Arno, Florence (62x102cm-24x40in) s. painted 1949 prov.exhib.lit. 21-May-3 Sotheby's, New York #175/R est:15000-25000

£37736 $60000 €56604 Vermont farm with view of Mt Equinox and the Manchester valley (66x97cm-26x38in) prov. 1-Mar-3 North East Auctions, Portsmouth #499/R est:40000-60000

Works on paper

£3459 $5500 €5189 Fishing boats, Coasta Caparica (18x25cm-7x10in) s. i.verso W/C. 4-Mar-3 Christie's, Rockefeller NY #84/R est:4000-6000

£3648 $5800 €5472 Narrow Street, Avignon (48x72cm-19x28in) s. i.verso W/C gouache exhib. 4-Mar-3 Christie's, Rockefeller NY #85/R est:4000-6000

£5096 $8000 €7644 Bomber revetments at Adak (29x39cm-11x15in) s.verso W/C. 22-Nov-2 Skinner, Boston #333/R est:6000-8000

£5732 $9000 €8598 Church, Old Lyme (37x52cm-15x20in) s. W/C. 22-Nov-2 Skinner, Boston #273/R est:12000-18000

£7643 $12000 €11465 Quarry (45x58cm-18x23in) s. W/C. 22-Nov-2 Skinner, Boston #356/R est:4000-6000

£7792 $12000 €11688 Casting a line (36x53cm-14x21in) s. W/C prov. 24-Oct-2 Shannon's, Milford #10/R est:12000-18000

£12903 $20000 €19355 At the Point of Rocks (43x62cm-17x24in) s. i.v, W/C. 5-Dec-2 Christie's, Rockefeller NY #148/R est:30000-50000

£22152 $35000 €32120 Setting out the decoys (46x69cm-18x27in) s. W/C. 26-Jul-3 Coeur d'Alene, Hayden #200/R est:25000-45000

£24193 $37500 €36290 Venetian fishermen (53x96cm-21x38in) s. W/C prov.exhib. 4-Dec-2 Sotheby's, New York #50/R est:30000-40000

£29221 $45000 €43832 Duckblind (46x69cm-18x27in) W/C. 25-Oct-2 Morris & Whiteside, Hilton Head Island #63 est:30000-40000

PLENSA, Jaume (1955-) Spanish

Sculpture

£1986 $3217 €2800 Untitled (35x26cm-14x10in) iron plaster. 20-May-3 Segre, Madrid #192/R est:3300

PLESSEN, Willy von (1868-?) German

£314 $491 €500 Peasant woman in village square (66x81cm-26x32in) s. lit. 20-Sep-2 Schloss Ahlden, Ahlden #1253/R

PLESSI, Fabrizio (1940-) Italian

£2581 $4077 €4000 Water report (60x80cm-24x31in) s.d.72 s.i.d.verso prov. 18-Dec-2 Christie's, Rome #88/R

PLESSIS, Enslin du (1894-1978) South African

£295 $460 €443 English landscape with church (31x38cm-12x15in) s. board exhib. 15-Oct-2 Stephan Welz, Johannesburg #175 est:2200-2800 (SA.R 4800)

£602 $969 €903 Three bottles (43x36cm-17x14in) s. i.verso canvasboard. 12-May-3 Stephan Welz, Johannesburg #379 est:3000-4000 (SA.R 7000)

PLESSNER, Rudolf (1889-?) German

£3165 $5000 €5000 View of Viennese Opera House (65x93cm-26x37in) s. 28-Nov-2 Dorotheum, Vienna #143/R est:4000-5000

PLETSER, George (1871-1942) Dutch

£310 $499 €440 View of Maasbrug in Rotterdam (45x50cm-18x20in) s. 6-May-3 Vendu Notarishuis, Rotterdam #151/R

PLEUER, Hermann (1863-1911) German

£692 $1079 €1100 Female nude in wood (47x36cm-19x14in) board. 19-Sep-2 Dr Fritz Nagel, Stuttgart #985/R

£903 $1328 €1400 Late autumn landscape (41x51cm-16x20in) canvas on board. 20-Jun-2 Dr Fritz Nagel, Stuttgart #812/R

£1006 $1570 €1600 Portrait of Hermann Tafel (54x41cm-21x16in) s.d.08 board lit. 19-Sep-2 Dr Fritz Nagel, Stuttgart #984/R

£1548 $2276 €2400 Black Forest near Schweigmatt (42x54cm-17x21in) s.d.06 i. verso canvas on panel. 20-Jun-2 Dr Fritz Nagel, Stuttgart #811/R est:3000

PLEYSIER, Ary (1809-1879) Dutch

£1056 $1700 €1821 European fishing scene (20x28cm-8x11in) s. prov. 9-May-3 Eldred, East Dennis #764/R est:1500-2500

£2439 $4000 €3537 Sailboat on rough seas by a windmill (31x47cm-12x19in) indis.sig. panel. 4-Jun-3 Christie's, Rockefeller NY #232/R

PLIMER, Andrew (1763-1837) British

Miniatures

£1300 $2015 €1950 Gentleman in a striped waistcoat and white stock (7cm-3in) gold frame oval. 1-Oct-2 Bonhams, New Bond Street #222/R est:600-800

£1900 $2964 €2850 Young gentleman wearing pale green coat white waistcoat frilled cravat (7cm-3in) gilt mounted papier- mache frame oval. 5-Nov-2 Bonhams, New Bond Street #73/R est:1500-2000
£2000 $3120 €3000 Hon Guy Carleton wearing double-breasted brown coat white cravat (5cm-2in) gold bracelet mount rec. prov. 5-Nov-2 Bonhams, New Bond Street #58/R est:2000-3000
£2500 $3925 €3750 Young gentleman in a brown coat (6cm-2in) silver gilt frame oval. 10-Dec-2 Christie's, London #72/R est:1500-2500
£2800 $4676 €4060 Gentleman in a grey coat (6cm-2in) gilt metal frame oval exec.c.1795. 25-Jun-3 Sotheby's, Olympia #11/R est:800-1200
£5000 $7800 €7500 Young girl possibly artist's daughter wearing short sleeved low cut dress (7cm-3in) gold frame plaited hair verso oval. 5-Nov-2 Bonhams, New Bond Street #79/R est:5000-7000
£5000 $7850 €7500 Young gentleman wearing a brown coat (6cm-2in) gilt metal frame oval prov. 10-Dec-2 Christie's, London #125/R est:2000-3000
£7000 $10990 €10500 Young lady wearing a white dress (6cm-2in) gilt metal oval prov.lit. 10-Dec-2 Christie's, London #69/R est:3000-5000
£7500 $11775 €11250 Young lady in a white dress (8cm-3in) silver gilt frame oval. 10-Dec-2 Christie's, London #178/R est:3000-5000

PLIMER, Andrew (style) (1763-1837) British
Miniatures
£5000 $7850 €7500 Young man with curly brown hair, wearing a blue jacket (7x6cm-3x2in) lock of hair. 21-Nov-2 Tennants, Leyburn #552/R est:400-600

PLIMER, Nathaniel (c.1751-c.1822) British
Miniatures
£5000 $8100 €7500 Lady wearing pale yellow dress (5cm-2in) gold frame engraved border. 22-May-3 Bonhams, New Bond Street #77/R est:1400-1600
£9500 $14820 €14250 Lady wearing decollete white dress with frilled collar yellow ribbon waistband (9cm-4in) gold frame paste border oval prov.lit. 5-Nov-2 Bonhams, New Bond Street #59/R est:7000-9000

PLISSON, Henri (1908-) French
£545 $855 €850 Voiliers sur l'Aven (38x46cm-15x18in) s. 15-Dec-2 Thierry & Lannon, Brest #408
£687 $1100 €1031 Boats on a beach (64x77cm-25x30in) s. 16-Mar-3 Butterfields, San Francisco #1019 est:1000-1500

PLOMTEUX, Leopold (1920-) Belgian
£417 $654 €650 Vue de San Miguel, Mexico (59x49cm-23x19in) s. i.verso. 11-Dec-2 Hotel des Ventes Mosan, Brussels #325
£510 $811 €750 Composition (81x122cm-32x48in) s.d.80 panel. 18-Mar-3 Galerie Moderne, Brussels #514/R
£1277 $2132 €1800 Abstraction (122x153cm-48x60in) s.d.71 panel. 18-Jun-3 Hotel des Ventes Mosan, Brussels #303 est:1800-2200
£1887 $2906 €3000 Composition (61x61cm-24x24in) s. panel. 22-Oct-2 Campo, Vlaamse Kaai #591
Works on paper
£3270 $5036 €5200 Composition (26x35cm-10x14in) W/C. 22-Oct-2 Campo, Vlaamse Kaai #593

PLOOS VAN AMSTEL, Cornelis (1726-1798) Dutch
Works on paper
£350 $546 €550 Winter scene (10x13cm-4x5in) init.i.verso brush grey brown wash prov. 5-Nov-2 Sotheby's, Amsterdam #139/R

PLOSKY, Jonas (1940-) British
£250 $413 €363 Yr Eifl - Lleyn Peninsula (41x58cm-16x23in) s. board. 3-Jul-3 Christie's, Kensington #669/R
£350 $578 €508 Pebbles (51x63cm-20x25in) s.d.1980 s.d.verso board. 3-Jul-3 Christie's, Kensington #670
£350 $578 €508 Out and about - Blaenau Ffestiniog (41x58cm-16x23in) s. s.i.verso board. 3-Jul-3 Christie's, Kensington #671/R
£400 $624 €600 Quarrymen's cottages, Blaenau Ffestiniog (61x107cm-24x42in) s. board. 27-Mar-3 Christie's, Kensington #617/R
£420 $693 €609 Kids and cats (41x58cm-16x23in) s. s.verso board. 3-Jul-3 Christie's, Kensington #672/R
£550 $853 €825 Grey Area, blaenau ffestiniog (51x71cm-20x28in) s. board. 4-Dec-2 Christie's, Kensington #550/R
£550 $853 €825 Red jersey (46x58cm-18x23in) s. board. 4-Dec-2 Christie's, Kensington #553/R
£650 $1007 €975 Dog watch (51x71cm-20x28in) s. board. 4-Dec-2 Christie's, Kensington #547/R
£650 $1034 €975 Message (60x50cm-24x20in) s.d.1972 board. 26-Feb-3 Sotheby's, Olympia #373/R
£700 $1085 €1050 Passing sails (56x102cm-22x40in) s. board. 4-Dec-2 Christie's, Kensington #554/R
£800 $1248 €1200 Grey shades - Blaenau ffestiniog (50x60cm-20x24in) s. i.verso board. 11-Sep-2 Bonhams, Newport #388
£800 $1240 €1200 Looking out to sea (56x102cm-22x40in) s. board. 4-Dec-2 Christie's, Kensington #551/R

PLUCKEBAUM, Carl (attrib) (1880-1952) German
£1169 $1742 €1800 Spring landscape with singing putto (50x40cm-20x16in) i. masonite. 26-Jun-2 Neumeister, Munich #832/R

PLUCKEBAUM, Meta (1876-1945) German
£548 $855 €800 Kitten (50x40cm-20x16in) s. masonite. 10-Apr-3 Van Ham, Cologne #1647

PLUCKEN-BUTZKE, Jeanette (?) ?
£503 $800 €755 Untitled, still life of apples, bowl and pitcher (58x48cm-23x19in) 28-Feb-3 Douglas, South Deerfield #16/R

PLUM, Poul August (1815-1876) Danish
£467 $729 €701 Fishermen looking out to sea by fisherman's cottage (60x73cm-24x29in) s. 5-Aug-2 Rasmussen, Vejle #249/R (D.KR 5500)

PLUMCAKE (20th C) Italian
Works on paper
£272 $433 €400 Atlantis (41x41cm-16x16in) s.i.d.1987 spray paint. 1-Mar-3 Meeting Art, Vercelli #305

PLUMIER, Edmond Theodore (1694-1733) Flemish
£1497 $2380 €2200 La fuite en Egypte (88x72cm-35x28in) 19-Mar-3 Hotel des Ventes Mosan, Brussels #142 est:1200-1600

PLUMMER, W H (1839-?) American
£1316 $2000 €1974 Point Judith Light, Rhode Island (20x46cm-8x18in) s.d.1884 board. 17-Aug-2 North East Auctions, Portsmouth #972/R est:1000-1400

PLUMMER, William Henry (1839-?) American
£223 $350 €335 Landscape with tree (46x20cm-18x8in) s.d.1892 wood panel. 23-Nov-2 Jackson's, Cedar Falls #308/R
£1154 $1800 €1731 Shore scene with fishing shacks, dories and schooners off shore (18x41cm-7x16in) s. 1-Aug-2 Eldred, East Dennis #142/R est:500-800

PLUMOT, Andre (1829-1906) Belgian
£11538 $18115 €18000 Bergere et chevres devant l'etable dans un paysage montagneux (96x72cm-38x28in) 16-Dec-2 Amberes, Antwerp #283/R

PLUMOT, Andre (attrib) (1829-1906) Belgian
£321 $503 €500 Etude d'une vache (20x26cm-8x10in) mono. cardboard. 16-Dec-2 Amberes, Antwerp #242

PLUMP, Berta (1853-?) German
£1549 $2494 €2200 Still life with azaleas (54x75cm-21x30in) s. lit. 9-May-3 Schloss Ahlden, Ahlden #1507/R est:2200

PO, Giacomo del (1652-1726) Italian
£6000 $9360 €9000 Saint Januarius (23x17cm-9x7in) copper. 9-Apr-3 Christie's, London #108/R est:6000-8000
£10000 $16700 €14500 Adoration of the shepherds (124x109cm-49x43in) prov.lit. 9-Jul-3 Christie's, London #97/R est:10000-15000

PO, Giacomo del (attrib) (1652-1726) Italian
£5488 $9000 €8232 Tobit burying the dead (59x72cm-23x28in) 29-May-3 Sotheby's, New York #103/R est:12000-16000

POCHINI, V (20th C) Italian?
Sculpture
£1081 $1686 €1600 Bust of girl (52cm-20in) s. alabaster. 27-Mar-3 Dr Fritz Nagel, Stuttgart #992/R est:1500
£1456 $2256 €2300 Mademoiselle de la Valliere (50x40cm-20x16in) alabaster exec.c.1900. 27-Sep-2 Rabourdin & Choppin de Janvry, Paris #114/R est:2300-2500

POCHVALSKI, Kazimierz (1855-1940) Polish
£1656 $2600 €2484 Still life with hare, pheasants and vegetables (47x71cm-19x28in) s.d.1919 prov. 14-Dec-2 Weschler, Washington #633/R est:2000-3000

POCK, Alexander (1871-1950) Austrian

£1154 $1823 €1800 Lieutenant on horseback (37x33cm-15x13in) s. board. 12-Nov-2 Dorotheum, Vienna #28/R est:1600-2600

POCKELS, C (19th C) German

£1964 $3104 €2946 Portrait of Leonora Baroness St. Davids (55x44cm-22x17in) s.d.1871 oval. 26-Nov-2 Sotheby's, Melbourne #183/R est:1500-2500 (A.D 5500)

POCOCK, N (1740-1821) British

Works on paper

£850 $1326 €1275 Figure with horse and cart crossing bridge and country house in background (53x33cm-21x13in) i. 17-Sep-2 Gorringes, Bexhill #1289

POCOCK, Nicholas (1740-1821) British

Works on paper

£580 $916 €870 Pulteney Bridge, bath (13x20cm-5x8in) i. W/C. 2-Dec-2 Bonhams, Bath #3/R

£781 $1250 €1172 Hauling a boat ashore (38x53cm-15x21in) s.d.1792 W/C. 11-Jan-3 James Julia, Fairfield #39a est:2000-4000

£1000 $1630 €1500 Galleon on a stormy sea, watched by three figures upon a rock. Cattle watering (26x40cm-10x16in) s.d.1793 W/C two. 29-Jan-3 Dreweatt Neate, Newbury #100/R est:700-900

£1300 $2106 €1950 Frigate on the Severn, with Gloucester Cathedral off her port beam (23x37cm-9x15in) s.d.1790 pencil W/C bodycol. 21-May-3 Christie's, Kensington #363/R est:500-700

£1400 $2184 €2100 Shipping entering and leaving harbour off Tenby (32x42cm-13x17in) s.d.1788 W/C. 11-Sep-2 Bonhams, Newport #194 est:1500-2000

£2000 $3240 €3000 Dutch shipping off a fortified town (13x19cm-5x7in) s.d.1793 pen grey ink W/C. 21-May-3 Christie's, Kensington #362/R est:600-800

£2800 $4424 €4200 Stoke Gifford near Bristol, seat of the Duke of Beaufort (54x78cm-21x31in) s. W/C over pencil. 28-Nov-2 Sotheby's, London #251/R est:3000-5000

£3200 $5088 €4800 H.M.S Vanguard and H.M.S Alexander off Toulon (33x48cm-13x19in) W/C over pencil htd bodycol. 19-Mar-3 Sotheby's, London #182/R est:2000-3000

POCOCK, Nicholas (attrib) (1740-1821) British

£2400 $3696 €3600 Sailing ships in a breeze (23x33cm-9x13in) 25-Oct-2 Gorringes, Lewes #893

Works on paper

£270 $421 €405 Figures near a bridge with a church beyond (16x24cm-6x9in) W/C. 9-Oct-2 Woolley & Wallis, Salisbury #52/R

£280 $445 €420 Opening shots of the battle of the Nile with H.M.S Goliath coming around the French line (42x51cm-17x20in) W/C. 29-Apr-3 Bonhams, Knightsbridge #175/R

£650 $929 €975 Mornin. Evening, British men o'war off coast (19x25cm-7x10in) i.verso pen pencil ink W/C oval two. 11-Apr-2 Mellors & Kirk, Nottingham #519

£1300 $2002 €1950 Bristol harbour (20x28cm-8x11in) pen ink W/C. 25-Oct-2 Gorringes, Lewes #879

£2100 $3402 €3150 St. Mary Redcliffe and the harbour from the prince St. Bridge, Bristol (20x30cm-8x12in) pen ink W/C. 22-Jan-3 Bonhams, New Bond Street #330/R est:2000-3000

PODCHERNIKOFF, Alexis M (1886-1933) American/Russian

£478 $750 €717 Mountain river landscape with figures (25x36cm-10x14in) s. 20-Nov-2 Boos Gallery, Michigan #532

£1497 $2500 €2171 Wooded sunset landscape (23x30cm-9x12in) s. 17-Jun-3 John Moran, Pasadena #20a est:1000-1500

£1863 $3000 €2795 Cattle watering in wooded landscape (36x43cm-14x17in) s. board. 18-Feb-3 John Moran, Pasadena #34 est:2000-3000

£2070 $3250 €3105 Women by a stream in a forest clearing (71x56cm-28x22in) s. prov. 19-Nov-2 Butterfields, San Francisco #8160/R est:3000-5000

£2795 $4500 €4193 Cattle watering in wooded landscape (41x51cm-16x20in) s. board. 18-Feb-3 John Moran, Pasadena #147 est:2500-3500

£2861 $4750 €4148 Figures on a path at a forest clearing (56x71cm-22x28in) s. prov. 11-Jun-3 Butterfields, San Francisco #4178/R est:3000-5000

£3614 $6000 €5240 Woman by a stream in forest clearing (71x56cm-28x22in) s. prov. 11-Jun-3 Butterfields, San Francisco #4179/R est:3000-5000

£3822 $6000 €5733 Pastoral landscape near Santa Barbara (76x102cm-30x40in) s. prov. 19-Nov-2 Butterfields, San Francisco #8161/R est:6000-8000

£4192 $7000 €6078 Eucalyptus coastal landscape (71x56cm-28x22in) s. 17-Jun-3 John Moran, Pasadena #57 est:6000-9000

PODESTA, August (1813-1858) German

£1401 $2186 €2200 Mountain landscape (32x44cm-13x17in) s. 6-Nov-2 Hugo Ruef, Munich #1239/R est:1500

PODESTA, August (attrib) (1813-1858) German

£377 $589 €600 Evening in high mountain valley (32x38cm-13x15in) lit. 20-Sep-2 Schloss Ahlden, Ahlden #1227/R

PODESTA, Giampiero (1943-) Italian

£1923 $2981 €3000 Packaging of Eros (27x20cm-11x8in) s.i.d.2001 set of 5 panel. 4-Dec-2 Finarte, Milan #551/R est:3000

PODESVA, Frantisek (1893-1979) Czechoslovakian

£310 $483 €465 Market at Solan (67x101cm-26x40in) s. 12-Oct-2 Dorotheum, Prague #129/R (C.KR 15000)

PODLASHUC, Alexander (1930-) South African

£281 $445 €422 Still life of peppers, onions and leeks (64x49cm-25x19in) s.d.95. 1-Apr-3 Stephan Welz, Johannesburg #235 est:2000-3000 (SA.R 3500)

POEL, Egbert van der (1621-1664) Dutch

£1132 $1743 €1800 La vendeuse de beignets (19x17cm-7x7in) s. panel. 25-Oct-2 Tajan, Paris #56/R est:2000-3000

£2128 $3553 €3000 Scene de cour de ferme (39x37cm-15x15in) panel. 18-Jun-3 Tajan, Paris #69 est:3000-4000

£3597 $5755 €5000 Boors gathered around a bonfire at night (41x34cm-16x13in) s. panel. 14-May-3 Christie's, Amsterdam #137/R est:4000-6000

£5031 $7799 €8000 Riverside farm with figures and boat (47x64cm-19x25in) panel. 2-Oct-2 Dorotheum, Vienna #351/R est:7000-9000

£5431 $8798 €7875 Outside a farmhouse (57x75cm-22x30in) panel. 26-May-3 Bukowskis, Stockholm #440/R est:80000-100000 (S.KR 70000)

£8500 $13260 €12750 Villagers putting out a cottage fire at night (32x39cm-13x15in) s. panel prov. 9-Apr-3 Christie's, London #38/R est:8000-12000

£9000 $13950 €13500 Visit to the wet nurse (32x42cm-13x17in) init.d.1657 panel. 31-Oct-2 Sotheby's, Olympia #49/R est:5000-7000

POEL, Egbert van der (attrib) (1621-1664) Dutch

£886 $1382 €1400 Sodoma burning (13x18cm-5x7in) copper. 20-Oct-2 Anaf, Lyon #220

£3205 $5032 €5000 Landscape with sand dunes (33x25cm-13x10in) panel. 21-Nov-2 Dorotheum, Vienna #16/R est:3500-4500

POELENBURGH, Cornelis van (1586-1667) Dutch

£3459 $5396 €5500 Kallisto and Juno (44x56cm-17x22in) panel. 19-Sep-2 Dr Fritz Nagel, Stuttgart #891/R est:2000

£3871 $6000 €5807 Bathsheba at her toilet (30x24cm-12x9in) init. panel. 2-Oct-2 Christie's, Rockefeller NY #158/R est:8000-12000

£4114 $6377 €6500 Women bathers by water (21x27cm-8x11in) panel. 25-Sep-2 Neumeister, Munich #508/R est:10000

£5000 $8350 €7250 Southern landscape with two figures bathing near ruins (19x25cm-7x10in) oak panel. 10-Jul-3 Sotheby's, London #143/R est:6000-8000

£14815 $24000 €22223 Danae (26x34cm-10x13in) panel prov.lit. 24-Jan-3 Christie's, Rockefeller NY #8/R est:25000-35000

£46296 $75000 €69444 Joseph sold into slavery (35x45cm-14x18in) copper prov. 24-Jan-3 Christie's, Rockefeller NY #9/R est:50000-70000

Works on paper

£417 $654 €650 Ruines (19x29cm-7x11in) pen ink wash. 13-Dec-2 Rossini, Paris #128

POELENBURGH, Cornelis van (circle) (1586-1667) Dutch

£5396 $8633 €7500 Nymphs bathing in classical landscape near grotto (34x44cm-13x17in) mono. copper. 13-May-3 Sotheby's, Amsterdam #35/R est:8000-8250

POELL, Alfred (attrib) (1867-1929) Austrian

£1538 $2415 €2400 Holl-Turm-Eger (25x29cm-10x11in) d.24 board. 21-Nov-2 Dorotheum, Vienna #202/R est:2000-2800

POEPPEL, Rudolph (attrib) (1823-1889) German

£348 $540 €550 Castelbell near Latsch in Vintschgau (24x35cm-9x14in) bears sig. i. verso. 26-Sep-2 Neumeister, Munich #2818/R

POERTZEL, Otto (1876-?) German

Sculpture

£1026 $1590 €1600 Amazon (48cm-19in) s. black pat bronze with marble base. 4-Dec-2 Neumeister, Munich #28/R est:1500

£1039 $1548 €1600 Female abduction (55cm-22in) s. brown pat.bronze. 26-Jun-2 Neumeister, Munich #37/R
£1154 $1788 €1800 L'enlevement (74cm-29in) s. brown pat bronze. 9-Dec-2 Horta, Bruxelles #180 est:1800-2000
£1538 $2385 €2400 Belly dancer (48cm-19in) i. bronze marble socle. 5-Dec-2 Schopman, Hamburg #388 est:700

POETZELBERGER, Robert (1856-1930) Austrian
£453 $706 €720 Figure inside old church (40x45cm-16x18in) s.d.1903 i. verso. 9-Oct-2 Michael Zeller, Lindau #871/R

POGANY, Willy (1882-1956) American
£1042 $1646 €1500 Elisabeth Schwarzkopf (92x71cm-36x28in) s. 24-Apr-3 Dorotheum, Vienna #123/R est:1600-2000

POGEDAIEFF, George (1899-1971) Russian
£567 $948 €800 Nature morte aux asperges (33x46cm-13x18in) s. panel. 17-Jun-3 Claude Boisgirard, Paris #111/R
£4200 $6804 €6300 Still life with vase of lilies and apples (61x38cm-24x15in) s. board. 21-May-3 Sotheby's, London #203/R est:3000-4000
Works on paper
£2600 $4082 €3900 Visions of Biblical times in Egypt (46x61cm-18x24in) s.d.36 mixed media paper on card pair. 20-Nov-2 Sotheby's, London #177/R est:2400-2800
£2800 $4396 €4200 Visions of Biblical times in Egypt (46x61cm-18x24in) s.d.36 mixed media paper on card pair. 20-Nov-2 Sotheby's, London #178/R est:2400-2800
£3200 $5184 €4800 Costume designs for biblical productions (50x65cm-20x26in) s.d.1936 gouache on card three. 21-May-3 Sotheby's, London #164/R est:2500-3500
£6500 $10206 €9750 Polovtsian dances from Prince Igor (42x44cm-17x17in) init. chl W/C gold silver paint. 20-Nov-2 Sotheby's, London #179/R est:2000-3000

POGGENBEEK, Geo (1853-1903) Dutch
£475 $741 €750 French landscape with white house (14x22cm-6x9in) s. studio st. 21-Oct-2 Glerum, Amsterdam #173/R
Works on paper
£949 $1500 €1500 Eenden aan de waterkant (23x42cm-9x17in) s. W/C. 2-Dec-2 Amberes, Antwerp #1353

POGGI, Raphael (fl.1863-1879) French
£3000 $4800 €4500 Venus and Cupid (137x191cm-54x75in) s.d.1869. 11-Mar-3 Bonhams, Knightsbridge #136/R est:3000-5000
£8461 $13369 €13200 L'offrande (163x130cm-64x51in) s.d.1866. 18-Nov-2 Tajan, Paris #20/R est:7000-8000
£9500 $14915 €14250 Roman dance (61x49cm-24x19in) s. panel. 21-Nov-2 Christie's, Kensington #166/R est:6000-8000

POGGIOLI, Marcel Dominique (attrib) (1882-?) French
£10127 $16000 €16000 Scene africaine (160x470cm-63x185in) 29-Nov-2 Coutau Begarie, Paris #20

POGNA, Giuseppe (1845-1907) Italian
£641 $994 €1000 Riverbank (16x29cm-6x11in) s. cardboard. 5-Dec-2 Stadion, Trieste #701/R

POGOLOTTI, Marcelo (1902-1988) Cuban
Works on paper
£14024 $23000 €21036 Cronometraje-Boceto (33x51cm-13x20in) i.verso ink exec.c.1934 prov.exhib. 28-May-3 Christie's, Rockefeller NY #25/R est:12000-16000

POHJOLA, Gunnar (1927-) Finnish
£576 $921 €800 Talvilento (28x40cm-11x16in) s.d.1974. 17-May-3 Hagelstam, Helsinki #177/R

POHL, Adolf Josef (1872-?) Austrian
Sculpture
£2148 $3458 €3200 Dressing his wound during the Bosnian Campaign. s.d.1878 brown pat. bronze prov. 18-Feb-3 Sotheby's, Amsterdam #304/R est:3500-4500
£4026 $6482 €6000 Soldier from the Austro-prussian war (99cm-39in) s.d.1866 brown pat. bronze prov. 18-Feb-3 Sotheby's, Amsterdam #303/R est:3500-5500

POHLE, Hermann (1831-1901) German
£1987 $3080 €3100 Mountain landscape with wooden bridge (86x67cm-34x26in) s.i.d.1857 prov. 7-Dec-2 Ketterer, Hamburg #84/R est:2200-2400

POINDEXTER, James Thomas (1832-1891) American
£366 $600 €549 Portrait of a young girl (66x41cm-26x16in) s.d.1886. 8-Feb-3 Neal Auction Company, New Orleans #323

POINGDESTRE, Charles H (?-1905) British
£680 $1034 €1020 Wooded landscape (38x64cm-15x25in) s.d.1879 board. 28-Aug-2 Brightwells, Leominster #1099/R
£1200 $1920 €1800 Women washing laundry on a Mediterranean hillside (45x70cm-18x28in) s.i.d.63. 11-Mar-3 Bonhams, Knightsbridge #236/R est:1200-1800

POINT, Armand (1860-1932) French
£323 $510 €500 Femme nue allongee au paon (33x46cm-13x18in) 17-Dec-2 Gioffredo, Nice #24/R
£1139 $1800 €1800 Mosquee, Tunisie (18x12cm-7x5in) s. panel. 28-Nov-2 Piasa, Paris #5/R
£4516 $7135 €7000 Paysage, vu du pont Charraud (65x81cm-26x32in) s. 19-Dec-2 Claude Aguttes, Neuilly #156/R est:8500
£5674 $9191 €8000 Salome (82x117cm-32x46in) s. 26-May-3 Joron-Derem, Paris #84/R est:10000-15000
Works on paper
£414 $646 €650 Nu endormi (28x43cm-11x17in) s.d.1891 chl dr. 10-Nov-2 Eric Pillon, Calais #13/R

POINT, Rudolf (1927-) German
£287 $447 €450 Chiemsee with view of Fraueninsel (30x40cm-12x16in) s. panel. 8-Nov-2 Auktionhaus Georg Rehm, Augsburg #8120/R

POINTELIN, Auguste (1839-1933) French
£347 $552 €500 Clairiere dans le Jura (23x37cm-9x15in) s. 30-Apr-3 Tajan, Paris #87
Works on paper
£729 $1159 €1050 Clairiere dans le Jura (27x41cm-11x16in) sd.89 pastel pair. 30-Apr-3 Tajan, Paris #88

POIRIER, Anne and Patrick (1942-) French
Photographs
£1875 $3000 €2813 Fragilty (170x110cm-67x43in) cibachrome mounted on aluminum executed 1994 prov.lit. 16-May-3 Phillips, New York #231/R est:3000-4000
Works on paper
£1111 $1833 €1600 Du regard des statues (33x73cm-13x29in) s. gouache ink leaf lit. 3-Jul-3 Christie's, Paris #50/R est:800-1200

POIRIER, Jacques (1942-) Canadian
£494 $765 €741 Coin paisible au printemps (50x60cm-20x24in) s. 3-Dec-2 Joyner, Toronto #248/R est:1500-2000 (C.D 1200)
£703 $1110 €1055 Rapides en automne (76x102cm-30x40in) 1-Dec-2 Levis, Calgary #79/R est:2000-2500 (C.D 1750)
£741 $1148 €1112 Jeux d'ombres (60x75cm-24x30in) s. 3-Dec-2 Joyner, Toronto #285/R est:1500-1800 (C.D 1800)
£773 $1205 €1121 Hilltop panorama (76x102cm-30x40in) s. s.verso. 26-Mar-3 Walker's, Ottawa #236/R est:1500-2000 (C.D 1800)
£826 $1289 €1378 Route en Montagune (76x91cm-30x36in) s. s.i.verso. 13-Apr-3 Levis, Calgary #93 est:2000-2500 (C.D 1900)

POIRIER, Narcisse (1883-1983) Canadian
£215 $335 €323 Le moulin Cartier (23x30cm-9x12in) s.d.46 cardboard on canvas. 25-Mar-3 Iegor de Saint Hippolyte, Montreal #109 (C.D 500)
£226 $349 €339 Cabane a sucre a St Hilaire (30x40cm-12x16in) s. cardboard. 22-Oct-2 Iegor de Saint Hippolyte, Montreal #83 (C.D 550)
£329 $507 €494 Cabane a sucre a St Canut, P Quebec (30x40cm-12x16in) s. cardboard. 22-Oct-2 Iegor de Saint Hippolyte, Montreal #82 (C.D 800)

POITEVIN, Georges le (1912-1992) French
£1132 $1743 €1800 Port dE bougie (46x55cm-18x22in) s. lit. 23-Oct-2 Rabourdin & Choppin de Janvry, Paris #207/R est:1800-2000

POITRAS, Jane Ash (1951-) Canadian
Works on paper
£402 $635 €603 Peyote miracle (13x33cm-5x13in) d.1991 mixed media panel. 1-Dec-2 Levis, Calgary #325/R (C.D 1000)

POKORNY, Jaroslav (1904-) Hungarian?
£284 $414 €426 Bunch of lilac (60x81cm-24x32in) painted c.1920. 4-Jun-2 SOGA, Bratislava #214/R est:18000 (SL.K 18000)

POKORNY, Richard (1907-) Austrian
Works on paper
£377 $585 €600 Haarhof from Seitzergasse (34x24cm-13x9in) s. W/C. 1-Oct-2 Dorotheum, Vienna #294/R
£377 $585 €600 Kahlenbergerdorfel (32x25cm-13x10in) s.d.43 W/C. 1-Oct-2 Dorotheum, Vienna #316/R
£377 $585 €600 Wigandgasse corner in Vienna (35x25cm-14x10in) s. gouache. 1-Oct-2 Dorotheum, Vienna #317/R
£440 $682 €700 Farmstead in Scharding (21x33cm-8x13in) i. verso W/C. 1-Oct-2 Dorotheum, Vienna #349/R
£692 $1072 €1100 Ruprechtskirche in Vienna (34x24cm-13x9in) s. gouache. 1-Oct-2 Dorotheum, Vienna #318/R
£943 $1462 €1500 Kartnerthor (24x35cm-9x14in) s.i. W/C. 1-Oct-2 Dorotheum, Vienna #284/R
£1195 $1852 €1900 Vienna I, Singerstrasse (30x21cm-12x8in) s. gouache. 1-Oct-2 Dorotheum, Vienna #259 est:1200-1400
£1284 $2003 €1900 The Opera in Vienna (24x35cm-9x14in) s. W/C. 28-Mar-3 Dorotheum, Vienna #317/R est:2000-2500

POL, Arend van de (1886-1956) Dutch
£350 $546 €550 Landscape with cows resting (58x38cm-23x15in) s. 5-Nov-2 Vendu Notarishuis, Rotterdam #277/R
£411 $641 €600 Flock of sheep near a pen (45x60cm-18x24in) s. 14-Apr-3 Glerum, Amsterdam #121
£445 $695 €650 Cows under willows at a ditch (45x60cm-18x24in) s. 14-Apr-3 Glerum, Amsterdam #122
£915 $1474 €1300 Cows in the meadow (59x43cm-23x17in) s. 7-May-3 Vendue Huis, Gravenhage #73/R

POLACK, Salomon (attrib) (1757-1839) British
Miniatures
£1400 $2170 €2100 Grenadier Company officer (7cm-3in) gold frame oval. 1-Oct-2 Bonhams, New Bond Street #217/R est:500-700

POLAK, Flora (19th C) ?
£2734 $4374 €3800 Jeune femme assoupie avec une brebis (35x45cm-14x18in) s.d.1851 panel. 19-May-3 Horta, Bruxelles #154/R est:4000-5000

POLASEK, Albin (1879-1965) Czechoslovakian
Sculpture
£3145 $5000 €4718 Table top fountain (49cm-19in) i. weathered pat. bronze prov. 5-Mar-3 Sotheby's, New York #75/R est:5000-10000
£3822 $6000 €5733 Bust of Charles F McKim (46cm-18in) s. bronze with marble base. 20-Nov-2 Boos Gallery, Michigan #441/R est:6000-8000

POLASTRI, Constantin (1933-) ?
£261 $407 €392 Seated female nude (27x22cm-11x9in) s.d.1985 panel. 16-Sep-2 Philippe Schuler, Zurich #3396 (S.FR 600)
£1739 $2696 €2609 Harbour in Tessin (73x92cm-29x36in) s. 9-Dec-2 Philippe Schuler, Zurich #3834/R est:3000-3500 (S.FR 4000)

POLDERMAN, Hugo (1886-1977) Dutch
£638 $1034 €900 Wooden bridge over the river in the forest (46x60cm-18x24in) s. 26-May-3 Glerum, Amsterdam #112/R

POLEDNE, Franz (1873-1932) Austrian
Works on paper
£676 $1054 €1000 Country school (60x66cm-24x26in) s. W/C gouache. 28-Mar-3 Dorotheum, Vienna #268/R
£1899 $3000 €3000 Stephansplatz in Vienna (27x23cm-11x9in) s.i.d.1915 W/C. 28-Nov-2 Dorotheum, Vienna #65/R est:3000-3500

POLENOV (19/20th C) Russian
£1151 $1888 €1600 The first snow (41x58cm-16x23in) s. 5-Jun-3 Hagelstam, Helsinki #889 est:1700

POLEO, Hector (1918-) Venezuelan
£9554 $15000 €14331 Head of girl (66x56cm-26x22in) s. painted c.1964. 20-Nov-2 Christie's, Rockefeller NY #125/R
£12195 $20000 €18293 Maternidad (46x56cm-18x22in) s.d.36 prov.exhib. 28-May-3 Christie's, Rockefeller NY #75/R est:30000-40000
£19817 $32500 €28735 Paisaje andino (60x50cm-24x20in) s.d.43 burlap prov. 27-May-3 Sotheby's, New York #44
£50955 $80000 €76433 Homeless (88x72cm-35x28in) s.d.1947 prov.lit. 19-Nov-2 Sotheby's, New York #31/R est:100000

POLESELLO, Eugenio (1895-?) Italian
£387 $612 €600 Still life (44x59cm-17x23in) 18-Dec-2 Finarte, Milan #247

POLI (20th C) French
Works on paper
£460 $718 €690 Golfing character (34x24cm-13x9in) s.i.d.1930 pencil col crayon. 26-Mar-3 Hamptons Fine Art, Godalming #89

POLI, Fabio de (1947-) Italian
£256 $403 €400 Face (120x70cm-47x28in) s. vinyl. 23-Nov-2 Meeting Art, Vercelli #24
£348 $543 €550 Red armchair (120x80cm-47x31in) s. vinyl. 14-Sep-2 Meeting Art, Vercelli #898/R
£1899 $3000 €3000 Flying cards (100x70cm-39x28in) s. s.i.verso vinyl. 29-Nov-2 Farsetti, Prato #298/R

POLI, Gherardo (1676-1739) Italian
£17949 $27821 €28000 Figures by elegant buildings (45x73cm-18x29in) pair. 4-Dec-2 Christie's, Rome #451/R est:12000-18000
£24000 $40080 €34800 Architectural capriccio with elegant company in carriages, mountainous coastline beyond (62x140cm-24x55in) prov. 9-Jul-3 Christie's, London #102/R est:20000-30000

POLI, Gherardo and Giuseppe (circle) (18th C) Italian
£53000 $83210 €79500 Piazza Santa Croce Florence, looking north, with the festa del calcio (56x153cm-22x60in) i. 13-Dec-2 Christie's, Kensington #277/R est:10000-15000

POLIAKOFF, Nicolas (1899-1976) Russian
£637 $994 €1000 Nu allonge (33x46cm-13x18in) s. paper on canvas. 10-Nov-2 Eric Pillon, Calais #241/R
£637 $994 €1000 Portrait de femme a l'eventail (61x46cm-24x18in) s. paper on canvas. 10-Nov-2 Eric Pillon, Calais #260/R
£637 $994 €1000 Portrait de femme (61x46cm-24x18in) s. paper on canvas. 10-Nov-2 Eric Pillon, Calais #258/R
£709 $1184 €1000 Pont Neuf (65x50cm-26x20in) s. 17-Jun-3 Claude Boisgirard, Paris #112/R est:1000-1500

POLIAKOFF, Serge (1906-1969) Russian
£5742 $9072 €8900 Pont de la Concorde (36x45cm-14x18in) s. cardboard exhib. 18-Dec-2 Digard, Paris #160/R
£12179 $19122 €19000 Composition monochrome (51x61cm-20x24in) s. s.i.d.1940 verso panel prov.exhib. 24-Nov-2 Laurence Calmels, Paris #217/R
£23448 $37048 €34000 Composition vert monochrome (65x81cm-26x32in) s. painted c.1965-66 prov. 2-Apr-3 Christie's, Paris #22/R est:36000
£25338 $39527 €38007 Composition No.XI (72x59cm-28x23in) s. painted 1954 prov. 18-Sep-2 Kunsthallen, Copenhagen #15/R est:400000 (D.KR 300000)
£26000 $43420 €37700 Composition rouge, jaune et noir (46x37cm-18x15in) s. prov. 26-Jun-3 Sotheby's, London #191/R est:20000-30000
£30769 $48308 €48000 Composition polychrome (61x50cm-24x20in) s.d.1946 s.i.d.verso prov.exhib.lit. 24-Nov-2 Laurence Calmels, Paris #216/R est:60000
£32000 $52480 €48000 Composition abstraite (73x60cm-29x24in) s. prov. 7-Feb-3 Sotheby's, London #232/R est:35000-45000
£33333 $54000 €47000 Untitled (33x41cm-13x16in) mono. s.verso prov. 26-May-3 Christie's, Milan #371/R est:20000-30000
£35443 $55291 €56000 Composition bleu, vert, rouge (65x81cm-26x32in) s. 31-Jul-2 Tajan, Paris #56/R est:60000-80000
£36232 $59420 €50000 Composition (73x60cm-29x24in) s. prov. 30-May-3 Villa Grisebach, Berlin #73/R est:50000-70000
£41284 $68945 €59862 Composition abstraite (81x60cm-32x24in) s. prov. 20-Jun-3 Kornfeld, Bern #130/R est:80000 (S.FR 90000)
£43590 $68436 €68000 Composition rouge brun orange (81x65cm-32x26in) s. s.verso prov.exhib. 24-Nov-2 Laurence Calmels, Paris #218/R est:60000
£44928 $73683 €62000 Composition (65x81cm-26x32in) s. prov. 27-May-3 Tajan, Paris #11/R est:60000-80000
£45000 $75150 €65250 Composition (100x81cm-39x32in) s. prov. 27-Jun-3 Christie's, London #146/R est:50000-70000
£50000 $78500 €78000 Composition jaune, rouge, noir, blanc (92x73cm-36x29in) s. painted 1968 prov. 24-Nov-2 Laurence Calmels, Paris #219/R est:60000
£51724 $81724 €75000 Composition bleu et jaune (81x65cm-32x26in) s. painted 1955 prov. 2-Apr-3 Christie's, Paris #12/R est:90000
£56000 $91840 €84000 Composition noir vert bleu rouge (130x97cm-51x38in) s. prov.exhib.lit. 7-Feb-3 Sotheby's, London #221/R est:70000-90000
£57692 $89423 €90000 Composition abstraite (81x65cm-32x26in) s. painted 1950 prov.exhib. 4-Dec-2 Lempertz, Koln #34/R est:90000-120000
£65219 $106959 €90000 Composition (54x80cm-21x31in) s.d.1954 prov. 27-May-3 Tajan, Paris #7/R est:90000-120000
£67308 $105673 €105000 Composition (81x100cm-32x39in) s. painted 1964 prov.exhib.lit. 24-Nov-2 Laurence Calmels, Paris #220/R est:120000
£89744 $140897 €140000 Composition rouge (81x100cm-32x39in) s. painted 1961 prov.lit. 11-Dec-2 Artcurial Briest, Paris #716/R est:200000
£98718 $154987 €154000 Composition (97x130cm-38x51in) s. painted 1967 prov.exhib. 24-Nov-2 Laurence Calmels, Paris #221/R est:120000
£100000 $167000 €150000 Composition (89x116cm-35x46in) s. painted 1952-1954 prov.exhib.lit. 26-Jun-3 Christie's, London #13/R est:100000-150000
£102564 $161026 €160000 Composition bleu, rouge, jaune (89x116cm-35x46in) s. prov.exhib. 24-Nov-2 Laurence Calmels, Paris #215/R est:120000
£110000 $180400 €165000 Composition rouge, jaune et gris sur fond noir (130x89cm-51x35in) s. painted 1956 exhib.lit. 6-Feb-3 Sotheby's, London #21/R

£124138 $196138 €180000 Composition abstraite (162x130cm-64x51in) s.i.d.66 oil tempera prov.exhib.lit. 2-Apr-3 Christie's, Paris #28/R est:120000-180000
£198718 $311987 €310000 Composition (116x81cm-46x32in) s. painted 1954 prov.exhib.lit. 24-Nov-2 Laurence Calmels, Paris #214/R est:200000
£220690 $348690 €320000 Composition abstraite (162x130cm-64x51in) s. painted 1969 prov.exhib. 2-Apr-3 Christie's, Paris #18/R est:120000-180000

Prints

£1899 $3000 €3000 Composition in orange, red and black (19x11cm-7x4in) etching. 27-Nov-2 Dorotheum, Vienna #58/R est:3000-4000
£1923 $2981 €3000 Composition lie de vin et bleue (62x79cm-24x31in) s. num.64/75 col lithograph exec.1966. 7-Dec-2 Cornette de St.Cyr, Paris #20/R
£1923 $2981 €3000 Composition bleue, noire et jaune (55x41cm-22x16in) s. col lithograph. 4-Dec-2 Lempertz, Koln #1003/R est:3000
£2051 $3179 €3200 Composition orange (50x66cm-20x26in) s.num.57/95 col lithograph exec.1956. 6-Dec-2 Ketterer, Munich #150/R est:3200-3500
£2075 $3217 €3300 Composition bleue, jaune et grise (55x70cm-22x28in) s.i. col lithograph edition of 100. 30-Oct-2 Artcurial Briest, Paris #554 est:2200-2500
£2081 $3476 €3017 Composition in green, orange and burgundy (48x63cm-19x25in) s. lithograph. 24-Jun-3 Koller, Zurich #479/R est:3800-4800 (S.FR 4600)
£2158 $3453 €3000 Composition in red, yellow, grey and blue (57x44cm-22x17in) s. col lithograph. 15-May-3 Neumeister, Munich #508/R est:750-850
£2172 $3627 €3149 Composition in yellow, blue and red (65x97cm-26x38in) s. lithograph. 24-Jun-3 Koller, Zurich #482 est:4800-6800 (S.FR 4800)
£2215 $3500 €3500 Composition in burgundy red and orange (47x61cm-19x24in) s.i. col lithograph. 30-Nov-2 Villa Grisebach, Berlin #365/R est:3000-4000
£2262 $3778 €3280 Composition in grey, blue and red (47x62cm-19x24in) s.i. aquatint burin copper. 24-Jun-3 Koller, Zurich #484/R est:5800-7800 (S.FR 5000)
£2383 $3717 €3575 Composition grise, rouge et jaune (50x69cm-20x27in) s.num.72/100 col lithograph 1960 lit. 6-Nov-2 AB Stockholms Auktionsverk #1050/R est:30000-35000 (S.KR 34000)
£2405 $3800 €3800 Composition in red and blue (61x45cm-24x18in) s.i. lithograph. 27-Nov-2 Dorotheum, Vienna #59/R est:3800-4000
£2436 $3776 €3800 Composition bleue (64x49cm-25x19in) s.i num.10/49 col lithograph. 7-Dec-2 Ketterer, Hamburg #329/R est:3500-4500
£2464 $4041 €3400 Composition orange et verte (61x45cm-24x18in) s. col lithograph. 29-May-3 Lempertz, Koln #878/R est:3000
£2471 $3978 €3707 Composition orange et vert (60x45cm-24x18in) s. col lithograph lit. 7-May-3 AB Stockholms Auktionsverk #1265/R est:25000-30000 (S.KR 32000)
£2523 $3936 €3785 Composition grise, rouge et jaune (50x69cm-20x27in) s.num.54/100 col lithograph 1960 lit. 6-Nov-2 AB Stockholms Auktionsverk #1051/R est:35000-40000 (S.KR 36000)
£2564 $3974 €4000 Composition orange et verte (61x45cm-24x18in) s. col lithograph. 4-Dec-2 Lempertz, Koln #1004/R est:3500
£2620 $3825 €3930 Composition in red, grey and black (54x40cm-21x16in) s. col etching aquatint lit. 4-Jun-2 Germann, Zurich #447/R est:5000-7000 (S.FR 6000)
£2695 $4366 €3800 Composition in brown and red (63x49cm-25x19in) s.d. etching aquatint. 24-May-3 Van Ham, Cologne #480/R est:4000
£2756 $4272 €4300 Composition rouge, grise et noire (76x56cm-30x22in) s.i. col lithograph exec.1960. 6-Dec-2 Ketterer, Munich #149/R est:3500-3800
£2821 $4372 €4400 Composition in yellow, green, blue and red (56x38cm-22x15in) s.num.XVI/XXX col lithograph exec.1956. 7-Dec-2 Van Ham, Cologne #419/R est:4650
£2987 $4750 €4481 Composition bleue, rouge et noire (87x65cm-34x26in) s.num.48/80 col lithograph. 2-May-3 Sotheby's, New York #339/R est:3000-5000
£3165 $5000 €5000 Composition in Burgundy red, yellow, black (45x60cm-18x24in) s. lithograph. 27-Nov-2 Dorotheum, Vienna #56/R est:4800-5200
£3167 $5290 €4592 Composition in blue (96x64cm-38x25in) s. lithograph. 24-Jun-3 Koller, Zurich #483/R est:5800-7800 (S.FR 7000)
£3205 $4968 €5000 Composition in orange and green (70x50cm-28x20in) s.num.277/300 col lithograph exec.1964. 7-Dec-2 Van Ham, Cologne #421/R est:3700
£3398 $5470 €5097 Composition verte, bleu, rouge et jaune (49x64cm-19x25in) s.num.31/75 col etching aquatint lit. 7-May-3 AB Stockholms Auktionsverk #1267/R est:30000-40000 (S.KR 44000)
£3526 $5465 €5500 Composition bleue (39x54cm-15x21in) s.num.42/100 col aquatint exec.1958. 6-Dec-2 Ketterer, Munich #147/R est:3800-4000
£3526 $5465 €5500 Composition grise, rouge et verte (44x59cm-17x23in) s. col lithograph. 4-Dec-2 Lempertz, Koln #1001/R est:5500
£4402 $7086 €6603 Composition bleue (96x64cm-38x25in) s.num.64/80 col lithograph lit. 7-May-3 AB Stockholms Auktionsverk #1269/R est:40000-50000 (S.KR 57000)

Works on paper

£3846 $5962 €6000 Composition abstraite (9x14cm-4x6in) init. green chk gouache exec.c.1946 prov. 6-Dec-2 Ketterer, Munich #151/R est:6000-7000
£5500 $8470 €8250 Composition (33x24cm-13x9in) s. gouache executed 1965 prov.exhib. 23-Oct-2 Christie's, London #109/R est:5000-7000
£5660 $8774 €9000 Composition bleue (26x19cm-10x7in) s. i.verso gouache. 30-Oct-2 Artcurial Briest, Paris #432/R est:10000-15000
£6038 $9298 €9600 Composition bleue (21x14cm-8x6in) s.i. gouache. 26-Oct-2 Cornette de St.Cyr, Paris #4/R
£7051 $11071 €11000 Composition (70x53cm-28x21in) s. gouache over lithograph prov.exhib. 24-Nov-2 Laurence Calmels, Paris #227/R
£8333 $13083 €13000 Untitled (69x52cm-27x20in) s.i. gouache over lithograph prov.exhib. 24-Nov-2 Laurence Calmels, Paris #225/R
£9655 $15255 €14000 Forme rouge noir et blanc (63x48cm-25x19in) s. gouache exec.1968 prov.exhib. 2-Apr-3 Christie's, Paris #39/R est:9000
£9804 $16078 €15000 Composition fond rouge (54x39cm-21x15in) s. gouache prov. 9-Feb-3 Anaf, Lyon #213/R est:16000
£10000 $16700 €14500 Composition (47x63cm-19x25in) s. gouache on card prov. 27-Jun-3 Christie's, London #127/R est:10000-15000
£10000 $16700 €14500 Composition (45x60cm-18x24in) s. gouache executed c.1959 prov. 27-Jun-3 Christie's, London #128/R est:10000-15000
£10345 $16345 €15000 Composition grise (48x64cm-19x25in) s. gouache paper on cardboard exec.1964. 2-Apr-3 Christie's, Paris #40/R est:20000
£10345 $16345 €15000 Sur fond bleu, tache rouge et blanc (65x50cm-26x20in) s.i. gouache tempera exec.1966 prov.exhib. 2-Apr-3 Christie's, Paris #38/R est:12000
£11007 $18052 €15300 Composition (63x48cm-25x19in) s. gouache exec.c.1964. 4-Jun-3 Marc Kohn, Paris #67/R est:15000-18000
£11724 $18524 €17000 Composition jaune et blanc (63x47cm-25x19in) s. gouache cardboard exec.1960 prov. 2-Apr-3 Christie's, Paris #11/R est:18000
£12414 $19614 €18000 Composition (63x48cm-25x19in) s.d.53 gouache prov.exhib. 2-Apr-3 Christie's, Paris #10/R est:18000
£12687 $20172 €18650 Composition rouge et noire sur fond blanc (48x63cm-19x25in) s. gouache prov. 26-Feb-3 Artcurial Briest, Paris #464/R est:11000-12000
£14000 $23380 €20300 Composition (61x46cm-24x18in) s. gouache prov. 27-Jun-3 Christie's, London #126/R est:10000-15000
£14744 $22853 €23000 Untitled (64x49cm-25x19in) s. gouache airbrush col chk over pencil exec.1946 double-sided. 6-Dec-2 Ketterer, Munich #153/R est:22000-25000
£17722 $28000 €28000 Composition bleu, gris et rouge (63x48cm-25x19in) s. gouache. 27-Nov-2 Dorotheum, Vienna #55/R est:28000-30000
£17949 $28179 €28000 Composition jaune et vert (47x62cm-19x24in) s. gouache prov. 24-Nov-2 Laurence Calmels, Paris #226/R est:15000
£26923 $42269 €42000 Composition abstraite (49x63cm-19x25in) s. gouache prov. 24-Nov-2 Laurence Calmels, Paris #223/R est:20000
£28696 $44478 €43044 Composition abstraite 5 (60x44cm-24x17in) s.i.d.1957 verso gouache prov. 4-Dec-2 Koller, Zurich #47/R est:65000-80000 (S.FR 66000)
£29817 $49794 €43235 Composition abstraite (61x46cm-24x18in) s. gouache prov. 20-Jun-3 Kornfeld, Bern #131/R est:50000 (S.FR 65000)
£31674 $52896 €45927 Abstract composition (63x47cm-25x19in) s. gouache prov.exhib.lit. 24-Jun-3 Koller, Zurich #144/R est:70000-120000 (S.FR 70000)
£32051 $50321 €50000 Composition gris, noir, bleu, rouge (62x94cm-24x37in) s. gouache cardboard diptych prov.exhib. 24-Nov-2 Laurence Calmels, Paris #224/R est:30000
£32692 $51327 €51000 Composition abstraite (48x63cm-19x25in) s. gouache prov. 24-Nov-2 Laurence Calmels, Paris #228/R
£33333 $52333 €52000 Composition rouge, jaune, bleu, mauve (94x62cm-37x24in) s.d.64 gouache cardboard diptych prov.exhib. 24-Nov-2 Laurence Calmels, Paris #222/R est:30000
£35897 $56359 €56000 Composition vert, bleu, rouge, jaune (93x62cm-37x24in) gouache cardboard diptych prov.exhib. 24-Nov-2 Laurence Calmels, Paris #229/R
£39744 $62397 €62000 Composition jaune, vert, brun-rouge (62x94cm-24x37in) s. gouache cardboard diptych prov.exhib. 24-Nov-2 Laurence Calmels, Paris #230/R

POLIDORI, Robert (1951-) Canadian

Photographs

£2675 $4200 €4013 Grand Central, New York City (61x76cm-24x30in) s.verso fujicol crystal archive print. 21-Apr-3 Phillips, New York #31/R est:5000-7000

£3896 $6000 €5844 Ancien vestibule de l'appartement de Mme Adelaide (76x102cm-30x40in) i.verso col chromogenic print plexiglas prov.exhib.lit. 25-Oct-2 Phillips, New York #202/R est:5000-7000

POLIDORO DA CARAVAGGIO (1492-1543) Italian

£40000 $62400 €60000 Adoration of the shepherds (157x87cm-62x34in) panel arched top prov. 9-Apr-3 Christie's, London #90/R est:20000-30000

POLIDORO DA CARAVAGGIO (attrib) (1492-1543) Italian

Works on paper

£1329 $1900 €1994 Frieze of figures before altar (15x34cm-6x13in) i. pen ink prov. 22-Jan-3 Doyle, New York #6/R

POLITTI, Leo (1908-) American

Works on paper

£252 $400 €378 Dancing children (23x20cm-9x8in) s.d. W/C pencil. 2-Mar-3 Toomey, Oak Park #632/R

POLKE, Sigmar (1941-) German

£4167 $6458 €6500 Untitled (70x100cm-28x39in) s.d.85 acrylic gouache gold bronze board. 3-Dec-2 Lempertz, Koln #362/R est:8000
£26000 $43420 €37700 Untitled (55x40cm-22x16in) s.d.94 on stretcher acrylic varnish. 27-Jun-3 Christie's, London #232/R est:15000-20000
£40625 $65000 €60938 Untitled (67x98cm-26x39in) s.d.77 acrylic paper prov. 15-May-3 Christie's, Rockefeller NY #158/R est:35000-45000
£56250 $90000 €84375 Untitled (99x137cm-39x54in) acrylic enamel paper prov. 15-May-3 Christie's, Rockefeller NY #157/R est:50000-70000
£150000 $240000 €225000 Untitled (126x150cm-50x59in) s.d.1993 verso synthetic resin tablecloth prov. 13-May-3 Sotheby's, New York #41/R est:180000-220000
£165000 $275550 €247500 Candle before the mirror (180x150cm-71x59in) init.verso init.d.82 stretcher oil acrylic on fabric prov.exhib. 25-Jun-3 Sotheby's, London #17/R est:180000-250000
£190000 $311600 €285000 Laterna magica - zyklus (219x406cm-86x160in) lacquer on transparent synthetic fabric on five panels. 5-Feb-3 Christie's, London #20/R est:200000-300000

Photographs

£2273 $3500 €3410 Untitled (51x61cm-20x24in) s.d.88 gelatin silver print board on board prov. 25-Oct-2 Phillips, New York #153/R est:5000-7000
£29000 $44660 €43500 Freundinnen (56x72cm-22x28in) s.d.67 black white photograph and pencil prov.exhib. 22-Oct-2 Sotheby's, London #334/R est:10000-15000

Prints

£2564 $3974 €4000 Friends I (48x61cm-19x24in) s.i.d.1967 num53/150 offset lithograph board. 3-Dec-2 Lempertz, Koln #365/R est:4200
£3165 $4905 €5000 Friends I (46x59cm-18x23in) s.i.d.num.18/150 offset. 28-Sep-2 Ketterer, Hamburg #673/R est:2000-2200
£3188 $5229 €4400 Untitled (70x100cm-28x39in) s.d.92 col offset lithograph Indian ink board. 28-May-3 Lempertz, Koln #348/R est:4800
£3774 $6000 €5661 Freudinnen (46x59cm-18x23in) s.d.num.21/150 offset lithograph. 29-Apr-3 Christie's, Rockefeller NY #703/R est:2500-3500
£7500 $11550 €11250 S.H oder die Liebe Zum Stoff (100x70cm-39x28in) s.i.d.2000 primer silkscreen on tablecloth. 23-Oct-2 Christie's, London #154/R est:8000-12000

Works on paper

£411 $654 €617 Heute Morgen (17x24cm-7x9in) s.d.11.11.93 pencil. 26-Feb-3 Kunsthallen, Copenhagen #186/R (D.KR 4500)
£603 $959 €905 Keine Zeichnung (24x17cm-9x7in) s. Indian ink. 26-Feb-3 Kunsthallen, Copenhagen #187/R (D.KR 6600)
£1282 $1987 €2000 Untitled (22x32cm-9x13in) s.d.98 Indian ink feltpen. 3-Dec-2 Lempertz, Koln #364/R est:2000
£6159 $10101 €8500 Untitled - heron (21x15cm-8x6in) s.d.69 W/C squared notepad paper. 28-May-3 Lempertz, Koln #343/R est:8000
£7051 $10929 €11000 Untitled (70x99cm-28x39in) gouache board. 3-Dec-2 Lempertz, Koln #361/R est:14000
£11000 $18370 €15950 Untitled (70x99cm-28x39in) gouache executed c.1980 prov. 27-Jun-3 Christie's, London #240/R est:12000-16000
£18000 $30060 €26100 Untitled (69x99cm-27x39in) init. gouache executed 1983 prov.lit. 27-Jun-3 Christie's, London #239/R est:15000-20000
£22436 $34776 €35000 Untitled (70x100cm-28x39in) gouache prov. 3-Dec-2 Lempertz, Koln #359/R est:35000-40000
£235000 $385400 €352500 Fur den dritten stand bleiben nur noch die krumel (280x350cm-110x138in) synthetic sealing wax on polyester fabric executed 1997 prov.exhi. 5-Feb-3 Christie's, London #18/R est:300000-400000

POLKORAB, Stefan (1896-1951) Czechoslovakian

£553 $856 €830 By bridge (74x57cm-29x22in) cardboard painted c.1935. 3-Dec-2 SOGA, Bratislava #18/R (SL.K 35000)

POLL, Hugo (1867-1931) Hungarian

£2838 $4427 €4115 Fishing barques (79x100cm-31x39in) s. 13-Sep-2 Mu Terem Galeria, Budapest #14/R est:500000 (H.F 1100000)

Works on paper

£387 $604 €561 At the market (23x30cm-9x12in) s. pastel. 13-Sep-2 Mu Terem Galeria, Budapest #176/R est:120000 (H.F 150000)
£450 $702 €675 Exterior luncheon scene (24x31cm-9x12in) s.d.19 pastel. 17-Oct-2 Christie's, Kensington #169/R
£503 $785 €729 On the waterside (22x29cm-9x11in) s. pastel. 12-Apr-3 Mu Terem Galeria, Budapest #199/R est:140000 (H.F 180000)
£516 $805 €748 Ladies on 'High Stand' (50x35cm-20x14in) s. pastel. 13-Sep-2 Mu Terem Galeria, Budapest #175/R est:180000 (H.F 200000)
£671 $1046 €1007 Wind blown clouds in Bretagne (38x59cm-15x23in) s. pastel. 11-Apr-3 Kieselbach, Budapest #12/R est:220000-240000 (H.F 240000)

POLLACK, Don (20th C) American

£2545 $4250 €3690 Untitled no.91 (140x183cm-55x72in) 29-Jun-3 Butterfields, Los Angeles #7081/R est:400-600

POLLACK, Hans (1891-1968) Austrian

£396 $633 €550 Storm clouds (35x40cm-14x16in) s. bears d.194 i. verso oil egg tempera board. 14-May-3 Dorotheum, Klagenfurt #16/R

Works on paper

£288 $460 €400 Steyr (40x46cm-16x18in) s.d.1963 Indian ink. 14-May-3 Dorotheum, Linz #453

POLLAK, August (1838-?) Austrian

£2264 $3509 €3600 Young travelling musician (44x81cm-17x32in) s. 29-Oct-2 Dorotheum, Vienna #73/R est:1800-2200
£3873 $6236 €5500 Erzherzog Karl Ludwig (136x97cm-54x38in) s. 7-May-3 Dorotheum, Vienna #235/R est:2500-4000

POLLAND, Donald Jack (1932-) American

Sculpture

£1923 $3000 €2885 Ambush at Rock canyon (28x79x119cm-11x31x47in) i. num.2/25 bronze prov.lit. 9-Nov-2 Santa Fe Art, Santa Fe #247/R est:3000-4000

POLLARD, J (1797-1867) British

Prints

£4194 $6626 €6500 Royal Mails preparing to start. aquatint. 20-Dec-2 Ribeyre & Baron, Paris #12/R

POLLARD, James (attrib) (1797-1867) British

£1600 $2656 €2320 London to Reading mail coach passing the Bolt-In-Tun General Coach Office (25x36cm-10x14in) 12-Jun-3 Christie's, Kensington #101/R est:1000-1500
£2481 $3920 €3722 Coaching scene (30x36cm-12x14in) s. 15-Nov-2 Naón & Cia, Buenos Aires #70/R

POLLARD, James (style) (1797-1867) British

£34247 $50000 €51371 Royal Mails in the yard of the Swan with Two Necks (43x61cm-17x24in) 3-Nov-1 North East Auctions, Portsmouth #1177/R

POLLENTINE, Alfred (fl.1861-1880) British

£400 $652 €600 Grand Canal, Venice (29x23cm-11x9in) s. s.i.verso. 13-Feb-3 Mellors & Kirk, Nottingham #795/R
£650 $1014 €975 S Pietro de Castello, Venice (40x61cm-16x24in) s. i.verso. 18-Sep-2 Dreweatt Neate, Newbury #159
£800 $1264 €1200 Grand Canal, Venice (41x30cm-16x12in) s.i.verso. 14-Nov-2 Christie's, Kensington #48/R
£807 $1300 €1211 Harbour scene with the convent at St Michele, Venice (38x56cm-15x22in) s. 22-Feb-3 Pook & Pook, Downington #113/R
£815 $1272 €1223 The Rialto (41x61cm-16x24in) s. s.i.verso. 25-Mar-3 Iegor de Saint Hippolyte, Montreal #110 (C.D 1900)
£1100 $1782 €1650 St Pietro de Castello, Venice (51x76cm-20x30in) s. 23-Jan-3 Christie's, Kensington #149/R est:800-1200
£1200 $2004 €1740 On the Grand Canal, Venice (29x49cm-11x19in) s.d.84. 17-Jun-3 Bonhams, New Bond Street #84/R est:1200-1800
£1400 $2282 €2030 Grand Canal with the Doge's Palace (30x51cm-12x20in) s.d.77. 16-Jul-3 Sotheby's, Olympia #10/R est:600-900
£1452 $2294 €2178 Grand Canal, Venice (41x61cm-16x24in) s.d.89 s.i.verso. 18-Nov-2 Waddingtons, Toronto #122/R est:3000-5000 (C.D 3600)
£1500 $2460 €2250 On the Grand Canal towards Santa Maria Della Salute, Venice (53x43cm-21x17in) s. i.verso. 5-Jun-3 Christie's, Kensington #707/R est:1500-2000
£1565 $2442 €2348 Venice (51x76cm-20x30in) s. 16-Sep-2 Philippe Schuler, Zurich #3490/R est:3500-4000 (S.FR 3600)
£1600 $2496 €2400 Grand Canal, Venice (48x74cm-19x29in) s. i.verso. 11-Apr-3 Keys, Aylsham #513/R est:1500-2000
£4286 $6771 €6429 Venice by moonlight (31x51cm-12x20in) s. i.on stretcher. 26-Nov-2 Sotheby's, Melbourne #215/R est:8000-12000 (A.D 12000)

£8228 $13000 €12342 Bragozzi in the Bacino of San Marco with Piazza San Marco beyond. View of Santa Maria della salute (30x50cm-12x20in) s.d.76 set of three painted 1876-82. 23-Apr-3 Christie's, Rockefeller NY #90/R est:10000-15000
£11000 $17270 €16500 Grand Canal looking towards Santa Maria del 'Salute, Venice (76x127cm-30x50in) s.d.84 i.verso prov. 16-Dec-2 Sotheby's, London #78/R est:12000-18000

Works on paper
£1300 $2119 €1950 Venice (60x96cm-24x38in) s.d.80 W/C gum arabic. 29-Jan-3 Dreweatt Neate, Newbury #95/R est:1000-1500

POLLET, Joseph (1897-1979) American
£409 $650 €614 Acrobats in New York (46x36cm-18x14in) 1-Mar-3 North East Auctions, Portsmouth #737/R
£610 $1000 €885 Prelude to spring (76x102cm-30x40in) s. prov. 1-Jun-3 Wright, Chicago #218/R est:2000-3000

POLLET, Jules (1870-1941) Belgian
£4088 $6377 €6500 Resting writer (163x109cm-64x43in) s.d.1921. 20-Sep-2 Millon & Associes, Paris #41/R est:12000-18000

POLLEY, Frederick (1875-1958) American
£884 $1406 €1300 Cheval a l'ecurie (51x61cm-20x24in) s. 21-Mar-3 Rieunier, Bailly-Pommery, Mathias, Paris #115

POLLI, Felice (1793-1859) Italian
Works on paper
£3125 $4750 €4688 British brig, Jupiter (41x58cm-16x23in) s.i.d. W/C. 17-Aug-2 North East Auctions, Portsmouth #1054/R est:4000-6000

POLLINI, Sophie (20th C) French
Works on paper
£1209 $1970 €1825 Nacre rose (146x97cm-57x38in) s.verso mixed media canvas. 1-Feb-3 Claude Aguttes, Neuilly #336 est:1900-2100

POLLITT, Albert (fl.1889-1920) British
Works on paper
£320 $506 €480 Travellers on a country track (25x35cm-10x14in) s. W/C over pencil. 27-Nov-2 Bonhams, Knowle #182
£320 $525 €480 River landscape with farmer and sheep crossing stone bridge (21x30cm-8x12in) s.d.1916 W/C. 4-Jun-3 Bonhams, Chester #282
£430 $684 €645 Penmaenback, North Wales (25x40cm-10x16in) s.d.1913 W/C. 27-Feb-3 Greenslade Hunt, Taunton #1256
£520 $806 €780 Walkers by the coast (29x62cm-11x24in) s.d.1904 W/C. 25-Sep-2 Peter Wilson, Nantwich #131
£600 $978 €870 Little Budworth, near Chester, Lleder Valley, North Wales (25x35cm-10x14in) s.d.1920 W/C pair. 16-Jul-3 Sotheby's, Olympia #50/R
£1000 $1670 €1450 Landscape with cottages (29x43cm-11x17in) s.d.1920 W/C sold with a companion. 17-Jun-3 Gildings, Market Harborough #457/R est:1000-1500

POLLOCK, Fred (1937-) British
Works on paper
£350 $571 €525 Blue, yellow, green and black (77x115cm-30x45in) s.d.87 W/C oil. 3-Feb-3 Sotheby's, Olympia #120/R

POLLOCK, Jackson (1912-1956) American
£2937500 $4700000 €4406250 Number 17 (57x72cm-22x28in) s.d.49 enamel aluminium paint paper on board prov.exhib.lit. 13-May-3 Sotheby's, New York #19/R est:5000000-7000000

Prints
£4487 $7000 €6731 Composition in red (20x16cm-8x6in) i.d.1950 i.verso red screenprint. 7-Nov-2 Swann Galleries, New York #803/R est:7000-10000
£8000 $12400 €12000 Untitled (70x56cm-28x22in) s.d.1951 num.4/30 screenprint. 3-Dec-2 Christie's, London #220 est:5000-7000

Works on paper
£10000 $16000 €15000 Untitled (22x21cm-9x8in) yellow brown pencil executed c.1939-40 prov.exhib.lit. 14-May-3 Sotheby's, New York #131/R est:18000-22000
£15625 $25000 €23438 Untitled (23x21cm-9x8in) red blue pencil executed c.1939-40 prov.exhib.lit. 14-May-3 Sotheby's, New York #130/R est:20000-25000
£88608 $140000 €132912 Untitled (30x41cm-12x16in) s.d.38 black ink pencil prov.lit. 13-Nov-2 Sotheby's, New York #210/R est:100000-150000
£350000 $574000 €525000 Untitled (48x152cm-19x60in) s.d.44 gouache masonite prov.exhib.lit. 6-Feb-3 Sotheby's, London #8/R est:450000

POLLONI, Silvio (1888-1972) Italian
£449 $704 €700 Flowers (50x35cm-20x14in) s.d.56 board. 16-Dec-2 Pandolfini, Florence #347/R

POLONSKY, Arthur (1925-) American
Works on paper
£629 $1000 €944 Female figures (52x40cm-20x16in) s. one d.1953 graphite pair. 7-Mar-3 Skinner, Boston #603/R

POLONYI, Karol (1894-1946) Czechoslovakian
£410 $635 €615 Tatras mountains (70x103cm-28x41in) painted c.1935. 1-Oct-2 SOGA, Bratislava #5/R est:26000 (SL.K 26000)
£945 $1465 €1418 Gerlach Peak (103x146cm-41x57in) painted c.1935. 1-Oct-2 SOGA, Bratislava #4/R est:38000 (SL.K 60000)

POLOS, Theodore C (1901-1976) American
£281 $450 €422 Still life with orange background (107x75cm-42x30in) s. 16-Mar-3 Butterfields, San Francisco #1099

POLS, D (19th C) Belgian
£3600 $5904 €5400 Dutch street scene with figures (25x36cm-10x14in) init.d.57 panel. 4-Feb-3 Sworder & Son, Bishops Stortford #93/R est:3000-3500

POLYA, Ivan (1889-1939) Hungarian
£2236 $3487 €3242 Picnic (100x97cm-39x38in) s. 12-Apr-3 Mu Terem Galeria, Budapest #181/R est:650000 (H.F 800000)

POLYA, Tibor (1886-?) Hungarian
£3218 $5149 €4827 Autumn rain on the boulevard (50x60cm-20x24in) s. cardboard. 16-May-3 Kieselbach, Budapest #15/R (H.F 1100000)

POLYCARPE, G (20th C) Haitian
£271 $425 €407 Enchanted jungle (61x51cm-24x20in) s. 23-Nov-2 Jackson's, Cedar Falls #299/R

POMA, Silvio (1840-1932) Italian
£1419 $2243 €2200 Lake landscape (22x33cm-9x13in) s. board. 18-Dec-2 Finarte, Milan #16
£8176 $12591 €13000 Lake landscape with boats and figures (13x25cm-5x10in) s. board. 28-Oct-2 Il Ponte, Milan #278/R est:6000
£22695 $35177 €34043 Lake landscape, possibly from Lake Como (60x94cm-24x37in) s. 4-Dec-2 AB Stockholms Auktionsverk #1902/R est:50000-60000 (S.KR 320000)

POMARDI, Simone (1760-1830) Italian
Works on paper
£1900 $2964 €2850 Couple seated in the foreground of a boulder strewn landscape with waterfall (51x66cm-20x26in) s.d.1795 W/C gouache over pen ink. 9-Apr-3 Bonhams, New Bond Street #125/R est:800-1200
£3226 $5097 €5000 Capriccio. Ruins with figures (52x73cm-20x29in) one s.d.1796 gouache pair. 20-Dec-2 Ribeyre & Baron, Paris #28/R

POMEROY, Frederick William (1856-1924) British
Sculpture
£12000 $18600 €18000 Perseus, holding aloft the head of Medussa (50cm-20in) s.i. brown pat bronze square base. 29-Oct-2 Bonhams, New Bond Street #179/R est:13000-15000

POMI, Alessandro (1890-1976) Italian
£2516 $3899 €4000 Portrait of young beauty (50x35cm-20x14in) s. panel. 29-Oct-2 Dorotheum, Vienna #68/R est:4200-4400

POMMAYRAC, Pierre Paul de (attrib) (1807-1880) French
Miniatures
£1284 $2003 €1900 Portrait d'homme en redingote verte (13x10cm-5x4in) s. 26-Mar-3 Pierre Berge, Paris #70/R

POMMER, Hans (19/20th C) German
£1872 $2958 €2808 Girl seated holding straw hat by the sea (75x100cm-30x39in) s. 2-Dec-2 Rasmussen, Copenhagen #1434/R est:15000 (D.KR 22000)

POMMEREULLE, Daniel (1937-) French
Works on paper
£629 $975 €1000 Composition au pastel (150x270cm-59x106in) s. mixed media. 4-Oct-2 Tajan, Paris #200

POMODORO, Arnaldo (1926-) Italian
Sculpture
£1026 $1590 €1600 Radar (7x11cm-3x4in) st.sig. num.31/50 silver pat.bronze wooden socle. 3-Dec-2 Lempertz, Koln #380/R est:2000
£1100 $1738 €1650 Poems. s. gold pat bronze. 3-Apr-3 Christie's, Kensington #208/R
£1329 $2073 €2100 Sphere (12x8x8cm-5x3x3in) s. num.XVII/XXX gold bronze exec.1990. 14-Sep-2 Meeting Art, Vercelli #796a
£1603 $2516 €2500 Totem (23cm-9in) s.i. silver. 23-Nov-2 Meeting Art, Vercelli #39/R
£1781 $2778 €2600 Rotating (14cm-6in) s. num.17/70 bronze. 10-Apr-3 Finarte Semenzato, Rome #216/R
£3597 $5755 €5000 Composition cubique (27cm-11in) s.d.77 um.13/30 gold pat bronze. 19-May-3 Horta, Bruxelles #146/R est:5000-7000
£3800 $5890 €5700 Sfera (7cm-3in) s.d.68 num.1/2 brass prov. 5-Dec-2 Christie's, Kensington #205/R est:4000-6000
£4943 $7810 €7415 Lastra per Opera Grafica (76x59x4cm-30x23x2in) s.d.75 wall sculpture lead black pat.bronze iron wood. 28-Apr-3 Bukowskis, Stockholm #1019/R est:80000-100000 (S.KR 65000)
£5556 $8889 €8500 Composition (24x32x8cm-9x13x3in) s.d.2000 num.2/3 gilt pat bronze. 4-Jan-3 Meeting Art, Vercelli #601 est:8000
£5806 $9174 €9000 Shape X (30x30x30cm-12x12x12in) s.i.d.1968 num.2/2 steel plexiglas prov. 18-Dec-2 Christie's, Rome #195/R est:8000
£11348 $18383 €16000 Untitled (45x49cm-18x19in) s.d.69 num.5/6 base steel bronze. 26-May-3 Christie's, Milan #236/R est:14000-18000
£12821 $20000 €19232 Colpo d'Ala, a Boccioni (44x42cm-17x17in) s.num.5/6 bronze. 14-Oct-2 Butterfields, San Francisco #2095/R est:15000-20000
£12964 $20224 €19446 Foglio N (33x70x41cm-13x28x16in) s.d.66 num.2/B polished bronze. 5-Nov-2 Bukowskis, Stockholm #349/R est:100000-125000 (S.KR 185000)
£14000 $22960 €21000 Foglio no.2B (37x79x41cm-15x31x16in) s.i.num.N2-1/2 d.66 golden brown pat.bronze prov.exhib.lit. 6-Feb-3 Christie's, London #658/R est:10000-15000
£37500 $60000 €56250 Sfera - rotante primo (30cm-12in) s.i.d.1966 num.2/22 gold pat. bronze prov. 14-May-3 Sotheby's, New York #118/R est:15000-20000
£70000 $109200 €105000 Radar no.1 (200x98x79cm-79x39x31in) s.d.61 on bronze base prov. 21-Oct-2 Sotheby's, London #56/R est:80000-120000
£110000 $169400 €165000 Disco III (105cm-41in) s.num.66-02 polished bronze executed 1966 prov.lit. 22-Oct-2 Christie's, London #27/R est:70000-100000
Works on paper
£11000 $18370 €15950 Situazione vegetale no 3 (62x102cm-24x40in) s.d.57 s.i.d.1957 verso silver mixed media canvas board prov. 26-Jun-3 Sotheby's, London #217/R est:6000-8000

POMODORO, Gio (1930-) Italian
£1277 $2068 €1800 Immagini (24x18cm-9x7in) s.i.d.56 prov. 26-May-3 Christie's, Milan #327/R est:2000-2500
Sculpture
£2179 $3182 €3400 Tree and sun (44x30x43cm-17x12x17in) init.num12/12 bronze. 5-Jun-2 Il Ponte, Milan #112/R est:4000-5000
£4774 $7543 €7400 Fracture (22x34cm-9x13in) polished bronze exec.1962 prov.exhib. 18-Dec-2 Christie's, Rome #178/R est:8000
£6944 $11181 €10069 Sole produttore (94x94x2cm-37x37x1in) s.i.d.74 black pat.bronze. 7-May-3 Dobiaschofsky, Bern #2353/R est:19000 (S.FR 15000)
£8462 $12354 €13200 Door and sun (65x32x32cm-26x13x13in) black marble. 5-Jun-2 Il Ponte, Milan #111/R est:12000-14000

POMPA, Gaetano (1928-) Italian
£1844 $2987 €2600 Mutmassungen sulle isole Borromee (45x60cm-18x24in) s.i.d.1991 oil Indian ink. 26-May-3 Christie's, Milan #83 est:1500-2000
£4397 $7123 €6200 Mutmassungen su Das Urtier (50x70cm-20x28in) s.i.d.1984 i.d.verso oil Indian ink prov. 26-May-3 Christie's, Milan #179/R est:1800-2200
£5128 $8051 €8000 Italian landscape (60x100cm-24x39in) s.d.1986 s.i.d.verso. 21-Nov-2 Finarte, Rome #245/R
Sculpture
£2270 $3677 €3200 Untitled (84cm-33in) s.d.87 bronze. 26-May-3 Christie's, Milan #116/R est:1000-1500

POMPE, Walter (attrib) (1707-1777) Flemish
Sculpture
£1795 $2818 €2800 Virgin and child (56cm-22in) terracotta. 16-Dec-2 Bernaerts, Antwerp #194/R est:2000-2500

POMPEY, Francisco (1887-1974) Spanish
£304 $481 €475 Avila (65x81cm-26x32in) s.i.d.1934 verso. 14-Nov-2 Arte, Seville #392/R

POMPON, François (1855-1933) French
Sculpture
£2778 $4583 €4000 Poule (5x6x4cm-2x2x2in) s.st.f.Valsuani silver pat bronze. 2-Jul-3 Artcurial Briest, Paris #631/R est:1500-2000
£4167 $6458 €6500 Panthere prete a bondir (21x15x7cm-8x6x3in) s. black pat bronze exec.1927 lit. 7-Dec-2 Martinot & Savignat, Pontoise #101/R
£6329 $9873 €10000 Ours blanc (21x41cm-8x16in) exec.1930 biscuit de Sevres. 18-Oct-2 Rabourdin & Choppin de Janvry, Paris #63/R
£10458 $17150 €16000 Grue couronnee en marche (28cm-11in) s.st.f.Valsuani black pat bronze lit. 9-Feb-3 Anaf, Lyon #88/R est:15000
£10563 $17535 €15000 Dromadaire (15x23x6cm-6x9x2in) s.st.f.C.Valsuani brown pat bronze exhib.lit. 11-Jun-3 Beaussant & Lefèvre, Paris #185/R est:7000-9000
£15823 $25000 €25000 Coq dormant (22x16x11cm-9x6x4in) s.st.f.Hebrard black pat bronze lit. 26-Nov-2 Tajan, Paris #7/R est:25000-30000
£23718 $36763 €37000 Jeune oie marchant (25x22x14cm-10x9x6in) st.sig. pat bronze lit. 7-Dec-2 Martinot & Savignat, Pontoise #104/R est:30000
£25641 $39744 €40000 Ours brun (10x14x5cm-4x6x2in) s. black pat bronze exec.1918-26 lit. 7-Dec-2 Martinot & Savignat, Pontoise #109/R est:50000
£25641 $39744 €40000 Tourterelle (23x9x9cm-9x4x4in) s. brown pat bronze exec.1919 lit. 7-Dec-2 Martinot & Savignat, Pontoise #108/R est:40000
£30496 $49404 €43000 Ours brun (10cm-4in) s. brown green pat bronze st.f.A A Hebrard cire perdue lit. 23-May-3 Camard, Paris #42/R est:30500-38000
£55405 $86432 €82000 Panthere noire (59x22cm-23x9in) s.st.f.C. Valsuani medaille brown black pat bronze exhib.lit. 31-Mar-3 Rossini, Paris #46/R

PONC, Joan (1927-1984) Spanish
Works on paper
£346 $540 €550 Magi (10x44cm-4x17in) s.i.d.1950 ink wash. 17-Sep-2 Segre, Madrid #159/R

PONCE DE LEON, Fidelio (1896-1957) Cuban
£9146 $15000 €13719 Sin titulo (51x39cm-20x15in) s.d.937 prov. 28-May-3 Christie's, Rockefeller NY #82/R est:18000-22000

PONCELET, Maurice Georges (1897-1978) French
£665 $1050 €1050 Les saltimbanques (115x153cm-45x60in) s.d.1937. 27-Nov-2 Lemoine & Ferrando, Paris #107

PONCELET, Thierry (1946-) Belgian
£320 $506 €480 Scholar (92x71cm-36x28in) s. 12-Nov-2 Bonhams, Knightsbridge #199/R
£2987 $4750 €4481 Young family (63x71cm-25x28in) s. 30-Apr-3 Sotheby's, New York #566/R est:4000-6000

PONCET, Antoine (1928-) Swiss
Sculpture
£1026 $1600 €1539 Gobe-reflets (22x18cm-9x7in) polished bronze num.3/6 with base prov. 5-Nov-2 Doyle, New York #21/R est:600-800
£2600 $4134 €3900 Douce corolle (26cm-10in) s.num.4/6 bronze with base st.f.Fonderia Tesconi prov. 20-Mar-3 Sotheby's, Olympia #196/R
£2778 $4583 €4000 Aux ecoutes (40cm-16in) mono.num.4/6 gold pat bronze black marble socle prov.lit. 1-Jul-3 Artcurial Briest, Paris #783/R est:3000-4000

PONCET, Francois Marie (1736-1797) French
Sculpture
£15248 $25465 €21500 Buste de Voltaire (77x60cm-30x24in) white marble lit. 23-Jun-3 Beaussant & Lefèvre, Paris #349/R est:8000-12000

PONCHIN, Louis (19th C) French
£3205 $5000 €4808 Return from school in Provence (122x173cm-48x68in) s.d. 14-Sep-2 Selkirks, St. Louis #720/R est:5000-6000

PONDER, Richard (?) ?
£530 $853 €795 Yacht basin at night (76x61cm-30x24in) s. 7-May-3 Dunbar Sloane, Auckland #55/R (NZ.D 1500)

PONDICK, Rona (1952-) American
Sculpture
£2532 $4000 €3798 Angel (75x51x51cm-30x20x20in) 5 pillows, wax plastic nylon executed 1987-88 prov.exhib. 12-Nov-2 Phillips, New York #229/R est:5000-7000

PONGRATZ, Peter (1940-) German
£3481 $5396 €5500 Sarajevo II (150x250cm-59x98in) s.d.93 s.i.d. verso acrylic. 24-Sep-2 Wiener Kunst Auktionen, Vienna #254/R est:7000-12000

PONKKONEN, Maila (1943-) Finnish
£288 $472 €400 Shoes (19x23cm-7x9in) s.d.1974. 5-Jun-3 Hagelstam, Helsinki #841
£313 $498 €460 Hazy landscape (38x46cm-15x18in) s.d.1991. 24-Mar-3 Bukowskis, Helsinki #247/R

PONOMAREW, Serge (20th C) Russian
£319 $533 €450 Le sous-bois (41x33cm-16x13in) s. 17-Jun-3 Claude Boisgirard, Paris #113
£340 $541 €500 Nu (55x38cm-22x15in) s. 3-Mar-3 Claude Boisgirard, Paris #89

PONS, Jean (1913-) French
£577 $906 €900 Untitled (51x39cm-20x15in) s. s.d.73 verso. 24-Nov-2 Laurence Calmels, Paris #231/R
£641 $1006 €1000 Untitled (51x39cm-20x15in) s.d.57 s.d.verso. 24-Nov-2 Laurence Calmels, Paris #232/R

PONS, Louis (1927-) ?
Works on paper
£256 $397 €400 Couple enlace dans la foret (67x51cm-26x20in) s.d. Chinese ink dr. 9-Dec-2 Beaussant & Lefèvre, Paris #8
£256 $397 €400 Foret (51x67cm-20x26in) s.d.1968 Chinese ink dr. 9-Dec-2 Beaussant & Lefèvre, Paris #7
£556 $884 €800 La belle nina no 9 (48x29cm-19x11in) s.d.73 verso collage panel prov. 29-Apr-3 Artcurial Briest, Paris #617

PONS-ARNAU, Francisco (1886-1955) Spanish
£2027 $3162 €3000 Woman from Valencia (107x85cm-42x33in) s.d1920. 25-Mar-3 Durán, Madrid #164/R
£2452 $3800 €3678 Le femme a la sortie (99x66cm-39x26in) s. 26-Sep-2 Christie's, Rockefeller NY #559/R est:3000-5000
£3034 $4825 €4400 Dark night (100x81cm-39x32in) s. 4-Mar-3 Ansorena, Madrid #179/R
£7801 $12638 €11000 Paisaje de Guardarrama (120x101cm-47x40in) s. 20-May-3 Segre, Madrid #95/R est:8000

PONSEN, Tunis (1891-1968) American
£1506 $2500 €2184 Harbour scene (51x61cm-20x24in) s. 11-Jun-3 Boos Gallery, Michigan #502/R est:4000-6000
Works on paper
£419 $650 €629 Chicago skyline (28x41cm-11x16in) s. W/C exec.c.1920. 8-Dec-2 Toomey, Oak Park #701/R

PONSIOEN, Johannes Bernardus (1900-1969) Dutch
£493 $794 €700 Still life with small plant and apples (33x23cm-13x9in) s. cardboard. 7-May-3 Vendue Huis, Gravenhage #575/R
£915 $1474 €1300 Portrait (35x28cm-14x11in) s. 7-May-3 Vendue Huis, Gravenhage #572
£1079 $1770 €1500 Still life with brown bottle, wooden spoon and an egg on pewter plate (39x45cm-15x18in) s. canvasboard prov. 3-Jun-3 Christie's, Amsterdam #212/R est:1500-2000
£1268 $2041 €1800 Still life wih mackerel and blue bottle (34x44cm-13x17in) s. 7-May-3 Vendue Huis, Gravenhage #574/R est:700-900
£5282 $8504 €7500 Strawberries and stone bottle (38x48cm-15x19in) s. 7-May-3 Vendue Huis, Gravenhage #573/R est:600-800

PONSON, Aime (1850-?) French
£839 $1325 €1300 Interieur d'atelier (45x37cm-18x15in) s. pair. 19-Dec-2 Claude Aguttes, Neuilly #221a/R

PONSON, Luc Raphael (1835-1904) French
£962 $1490 €1500 Grand Canal, Doges Palace and Santa Maria della Salute (62x87cm-24x34in) s. canvas on board. 6-Dec-2 Michael Zeller, Lindau #891/R
£2740 $4274 €4000 View of Grand Canal with Doges Palace and Santa Maria della Salute (62x87cm-24x34in) s. canvas on board. 10-Apr-3 Dorotheum, Vienna #187/R est:3800-4200
£3099 $5144 €4400 Vue presumee du Tonkin (40x61cm-16x24in) s. 13-Jun-3 Rabourdin & Choppin de Janvry, Paris #90/R est:4000-5000

PONSONELLI, Giacomo Antonio (attrib) (1654-1735) Italian
Sculpture
£35000 $54950 €52500 Bust of a gentleman (211cm-83in) white marble col marble column lit. 10-Dec-2 Sotheby's, London #126/R est:40000-60000

PONTEN, Julia (1880-?) German
Works on paper
£318 $497 €500 Munich (32x44cm-13x17in) s.d.1911. 5-Nov-2 Hartung & Hartung, Munich #5198/R

PONTHUS-CINIER, Antoine (attrib) (1812-1885) French
£4231 $6685 €6600 Venise, Notre Dame de la Salute vue de la Piazzeta (35x45cm-14x18in) bears sig. cardboard. 18-Nov-2 Tajan, Paris #1/R est:7000-8000

PONTI, Pino (1905-) Italian
£1026 $1610 €1600 Road in landscape (63x49cm-25x19in) s.d.1941 tempera paper. 19-Nov-2 Finarte, Milan #36/R

PONTING, Herbert G (1871-1935) American
Photographs
£2600 $4082 €3900 Freezing of the sea (75x60cm-30x24in) i.num.39 blue toned carbon print. 19-Nov-2 Christie's, Kensington #41/R est:1500-2000
£2800 $4536 €4200 Midnight in the Antarctic summer (54x74cm-21x29in) st. blue toned carbon print card. 22-May-3 Sotheby's, London #61/R est:1000-1500
£3600 $5832 €5400 Midnight sun (59x75cm-23x30in) st. blue toned carbon print card. 22-May-3 Sotheby's, London #62/R est:1500-2000
£4000 $6480 €6000 Hut at Cape Evans looking over to the Barne Glacier at noon (76x60cm-30x24in) st. blue toned carbon print card lit. 22-May-3 Sotheby's, London #59/R est:3000-5000
£5000 $8100 €7500 Cavern in an iceberg (76x55cm-30x22in) s.i.mount carbon print. 21-May-3 Christie's, London #109/R est:4000-6000

PONTOY, Henri Jean (1888-1968) French
£637 $981 €1000 Simbana (55x46cm-22x18in) s. i.d.verso. 3-Sep-2 Christie's, Amsterdam #216/R
£1235 $1753 €2000 Vue de Marrakech (26x34cm-10x13in) s. cardboard double-sided. 17-Mar-2 Galerie de Chartres, Chartres #151
£1439 $2360 €2000 Scene familiale dans un village de Guinee (37x37cm-15x15in) s. paper. 4-Jun-3 Tajan, Paris #298/R est:1200-1500
£2051 $3221 €3200 Scene de marche (38x56cm-15x22in) s. 16-Dec-2 Gros & Delettrez, Paris #32 est:2000-3000
£3038 $4800 €4800 Marocaine a l'amphore (26x34cm-10x13in) s. panel. 29-Nov-2 Drouot Estimations, Paris #35
£3145 $4843 €5000 Embarquement (41x33cm-16x13in) s. 23-Oct-2 Rabourdin & Choppin de Janvry, Paris #183/R
£3718 $5837 €5800 Scene de fete devant les remparts des Oudaias, Rabat (23x32cm-9x13in) s. panel. 16-Dec-2 Gros & Delettrez, Paris #72/R est:3000-4500
£4677 $7670 €6500 Les trois porteuses d'eau (61x92cm-24x36in) s. isorel. 4-Jun-3 Tajan, Paris #297/R est:4500-6000
£7194 $11799 €10000 Souq a fes (65x80cm-26x31in) s. 4-Jun-3 Tajan, Paris #295/R est:6000-8000
£8273 $13568 €11500 Femmes dans la palmeraie (131x97cm-52x38in) s. 4-Jun-3 Tajan, Paris #299/R est:7500-9000
Works on paper
£449 $704 €700 Porteuse d'eau (35x57cm-14x22in) gouache. 16-Dec-2 Gros & Delettrez, Paris #23/R
£641 $1006 €1000 Porteuses au village, Cameroun (2x44cm-1x17in) gouache. 16-Dec-2 Gros & Delettrez, Paris #21/R
£641 $1006 €1000 Ma case de Fonta-Djallon, Guinee (37x45cm-15x18in) s. i.verso gouache. 16-Dec-2 Gros & Delettrez, Paris #22/R
£641 $1006 €1000 Village de Foumbay (37x48cm-15x19in) s. i.verso gouache. 16-Dec-2 Gros & Delettrez, Paris #25/R
£833 $1308 €1300 Village du Cameroun (44x53cm-17x21in) s. gouache. 16-Dec-2 Gros & Delettrez, Paris #18/R
£833 $1308 €1300 Village de Leinde (36x45cm-14x18in) s. i.verso gouache. 16-Dec-2 Gros & Delettrez, Paris #19/R
£863 $1381 €1200 Vue de Saint-Louis-des-Invalides (44x53cm-17x21in) s. gouache W/C. 18-May-3 Eric Pillon, Calais #98/R
£962 $1510 €1500 Femmes a Bororo, Leinde pres de Gorora (36x44cm-14x17in) s. i.verso W/C gouache. 16-Dec-2 Gros & Delettrez, Paris #24/R est:1200-1500
£1090 $1711 €1700 A l'ombre du baobab (37x45cm-15x18in) s. W/C gouache. 16-Dec-2 Gros & Delettrez, Paris #28/R est:1200-1500
£1282 $2013 €2000 La case pres des flamboyants (65x50cm-26x20in) gouache mixed media. 16-Dec-2 Gros & Delettrez, Paris #20/R est:2000-3000

£1282 $2013 €2000 Casbah dans l'Atlas (44x54cm-17x21in) gouache. 16-Dec-2 Gros & Delettrez, Paris #33 est:2800-3000
£1769 $2812 €2600 Femme au bord de l'oued devant la casbah (35x45cm-14x18in) s. gouache. 24-Mar-3 Rabourdin & Choppin de Janvry, Paris #248/R est:2300-2600
£1859 $2919 €2900 Au bord de l'oued a Zagora (37x46cm-15x18in) s. i.verso gouache. 16-Dec-2 Gros & Delettrez, Paris #4/R est:1200-1800
£1923 $3019 €3000 Vue de Zagora (37x44cm-15x17in) s. i.verso gouache. 16-Dec-2 Gros & Delettrez, Paris #8/R est:900-1200
£1923 $3019 €3000 Oued Reraira (33x41cm-13x16in) s. i.verso gouache. 16-Dec-2 Gros & Delettrez, Paris #9/R est:1200-2300
£1923 $3019 €3000 Atlas vue de l'oued (30x44cm-12x17in) s. i.verso gouache. 16-Dec-2 Gros & Delettrez, Paris #16/R est:900-1200
£1987 $3120 €3100 Vue de Targa (36x45cm-14x18in) gouache. 16-Dec-2 Gros & Delettrez, Paris #12/R est:1200-1800
£2051 $3221 €3200 Sous les remparts de la ville (53x57cm-21x22in) gouache. 16-Dec-2 Gros & Delettrez, Paris #2/R est:1200-1800
£2158 $3540 €3000 Promeneurs aux abords des remparts de Marrakech (33x44cm-13x17in) s. gouache. 4-Jun-3 Tajan, Paris #296/R est:1500-1800
£2207 $3531 €3200 La mosquee Doukala a Marrakech (46x59cm-18x23in) s.i. chl gouache. 12-Mar-3 E & Eve, Paris #89/R est:1000-1500
£2244 $3522 €3500 Vallee du Gheris (40x49cm-16x19in) s.i. gouache. 16-Dec-2 Gros & Delettrez, Paris #13/R est:900-1200
£2244 $3522 €3500 Vallee du Gheris (42x52cm-17x20in) s.i. gouache. 16-Dec-2 Gros & Delettrez, Paris #14/R est:1200-1800
£2308 $3623 €3600 Environs de Marrakech (44x52cm-17x20in) s. gouache. 16-Dec-2 Gros & Delettrez, Paris #7/R est:1200-1500
£2308 $3623 €3600 Devant la casbah (37x46cm-15x18in) s.i. gouache. 16-Dec-2 Gros & Delettrez, Paris #10/R est:2300-3000
£2518 $4130 €3500 Porteuses d'eau a Foumbay (37x46cm-15x18in) s.i. W/C gouache cardboard. 4-Jun-3 Tajan, Paris #300/R est:1200-1500
£2564 $4026 €4000 Casbah d'Aremt (38x45cm-15x18in) s.i. gouache. 16-Dec-2 Gros & Delettrez, Paris #11/R est:2300-3000
£2564 $4026 €4000 Casbah Targa, Tafilaret (38x45cm-15x18in) s.i. gouache. 16-Dec-2 Gros & Delettrez, Paris #15/R est:900-1200
£3077 $4831 €4800 Casbah du sud marocain (42x50cm-17x20in) s.d.31 gouache. 16-Dec-2 Gros & Delettrez, Paris #1/R est:2300-3000
£3333 $5233 €5200 Portrait de jeune marocaine (32x24cm-13x9in) s. chl sanguine. 10-Dec-2 Tajan, Paris #215/R

PONTREMOLI, Enrico (1914-) Italian
£258 $400 €387 Bowl of fruit (33x46cm-13x18in) s. i.stretcher. 25-Sep-2 Doyle, New York #96/R

PONZA, Giuseppe (20th C) Italian
£1408 $2310 €2042 Market (31x41cm-12x16in) s. pavatex. 4-Jun-3 Fischer, Luzern #1097/R est:3000-4000 (S.FR 3000)

POOL, J (?) ?
£850 $1335 €1275 Landscape with river (65x91cm-26x36in) 11-Dec-2 Rupert Toovey, Partridge Green #50/R

POOLE, Abram (c.1882-1920) American
£621 $1000 €932 Autumn landscape (36x51cm-14x20in) s.d.10/02/09 prov. 18-Feb-3 John Moran, Pasadena #166

POOLE, Charles E (19th C) British
Works on paper
£600 $1002 €870 Seascape with merchant ship to foreground (64x89cm-25x35in) s.i.verso W/C. 24-Jun-3 Neal & Fletcher, Woodbridge #337

POOLE, George (?) British?
£717 $1176 €1040 Nora Poole reading (68x74cm-27x29in) s. 3-Jun-3 Lawson Menzies, Sydney #1003 (A.D 1800)

POOLE, James (1804-1886) British
Works on paper
£2400 $3744 €3480 Zermatt and the Matterhorn (25x36cm-10x14in) s. W/C bodycol htd white. 27-Mar-3 Neales, Nottingham #952/R est:600-800

POOLE, Paul Falconer (1807-1879) British
£320 $515 €464 Girl selling apples (39x3cm-15x1in) s.d.1867. 12-May-3 Joel, Victoria #396 (A.D 800)
£680 $1061 €1020 Mother and child on a farm track (15x21cm-6x8in) init. panel. 6-Nov-2 Bonhams, Chester #465
£2600 $4056 €3900 Portrait of a lady in a Greek landscape (45x35cm-18x14in) 15-Oct-2 Sotheby's, London #39/R est:3000-4000
£9500 $15010 €14250 Laurence Stern and Maria (91x70cm-36x28in) d.1839 panel prov. 26-Nov-2 Christie's, London #51/R est:8000-12000
£13000 $20930 €19500 Ferdinand declaring his love for Miranda (69x46cm-27x18in) s.i. prov. 20-Feb-3 Christie's, London #226/R est:15000
£20313 $32500 €30470 Song of the Troubadours (138x189cm-54x74in) s.d.54 exhib. 14-May-3 Butterfields, San Francisco #1146/R est:25000-35000
£68000 $109480 €102000 Conspiracy of Sebastian and Antonio (91x102cm-36x40in) s.d.1856 part of triptych prov.exhib.lit. 20-Feb-3 Christie's, London #225/R est:80000

POOLE-SMITH, Leslie (19/20th C) ?
£1655 $2632 €2400 La lecon de piano (122x96cm-48x38in) s. 4-Mar-3 Palais de Beaux Arts, Brussels #392 est:2600-3500

POOLEY, Thomas (1646-1723) Irish
£32000 $50560 €48000 Portrait of William Tighe (121x98cm-48x39in) 28-Nov-2 Sotheby's, London #151/R est:12000-18000

POONS, Larry (1937-) American
£3043 $4748 €5075 Ores (223x81cm-88x32in) s. i.d.1980 verso acrylic prov. 13-Apr-3 Levis, Calgary #322/R est:10000-15000 (C.D 7000)

POOR, Henry Varnum (1888-1970) American
£3727 $6000 €5591 California landscape (46x53cm-18x21in) s. canvas on canvas. 18-Feb-3 John Moran, Pasadena #40b est:3500-5000
£4430 $7000 €6645 Gray day (81x97cm-32x38in) s. painted 1933 prov.lit. 24-Apr-3 Shannon's, Milford #97/R est:7000-9000

POORE, Henry Rankin (1859-1940) American
£833 $1300 €1250 Colonial man reading (33x23cm-13x9in) s. oil pencil en grisaille board. 9-Nov-2 Illustration House, New York #93/R

POORTEN, Jacobus Johannes van (1841-1914) German
£1560 $2528 €2200 Woodland glade with deer (70x105cm-28x41in) s.d.87. 22-May-3 Dorotheum, Vienna #28/R est:3000-4000

POORTVLIET, Rien (1932-1995) Dutch
£1379 $2193 €2000 Wild zwijn (38x25cm-15x10in) s. 10-Mar-3 Sotheby's, Amsterdam #359/R est:2000-3000
£3448 $5482 €5000 Study of birds (50x60cm-20x24in) s.d.79 prov. 10-Mar-3 Sotheby's, Amsterdam #364/R est:1500-2000
Works on paper
£318 $497 €500 Deer (61x32cm-24x13in) s. Indian ink. 5-Nov-2 Vendu Notarishuis, Rotterdam #245/R

POOSCH, Max von (1872-1960) Austrian
£556 $883 €800 Untitled (31x44cm-12x17in) s.d.42 masonite. 29-Apr-3 Wiener Kunst Auktionen, Vienna #628/R

POOT, Rik (1924-) Belgian
Sculpture
£2621 $4193 €3800 Horse lying down (13x19cm-5x7in) mono. silver. 15-Mar-3 De Vuyst, Lokeren #256 est:4000-5000

POOTOOGOOK, Elijah (1943-) North American
Sculpture
£1630 $2543 €2719 Caribou (57x69x43cm-22x27x17in) green stone carving. 13-Apr-3 Levis, Calgary #63/R est:4000-5000 (C.D 3750)

POPE, Alexander (1849-1924) American
£1258 $2000 €1887 Still life with daffodils (56x41cm-22x16in) s. 7-Mar-3 Skinner, Boston #589/R est:400-500
£35714 $55000 €53571 Waiting for his master (66x46cm-26x18in) s.d.05 prov. 24-Oct-2 Shannon's, Milford #108/R est:40000-60000
Sculpture
£10692 $17000 €16038 Pheasant and game bag after the hunt (76x58cm-30x23in) s. polychrome wood on panel. 4-Mar-3 Christie's, Rockefeller NY #33/R est:10000-15000
£10692 $17000 €16038 Mallard and game bag after the hunt (76x58cm-30x23in) s. polychrome wood on panel. 4-Mar-3 Christie's, Rockefeller NY #34/R est:10000-15000

POPE, Henry (1843-1908) British
Works on paper
£300 $468 €450 River landscape with figures (33x1067cm-13x420in) s. W/C. 16-Oct-2 Brightwells, Leominster #1178
£340 $530 €510 Humphries boatbuilder (22x17cm-9x7in) s.i. pencil W/C scratching. 17-Oct-2 Christie's, Kensington #97
£350 $546 €525 Gate house, Kenilworth (35x51cm-14x20in) s. W/C. 10-Apr-3 Tennants, Leyburn #844

POPE, Nicholas (1949-) British
Works on paper
£252 $390 €400 Untitled (140x57cm-55x22in) chl exec.1987 prov. 5-Oct-2 De Vuyst, Lokeren #295
£314 $487 €500 Untitled (134x100cm-53x39in) chl exec.1987 prov. 5-Oct-2 De Vuyst, Lokeren #296

POPE, Perpetua (?) ?
£300 $462 €450 Port Cam, Loch Alsh (71x91cm-28x36in) s. exhib. 5-Sep-2 Christie's, Kensington #566/R
£450 $702 €675 White poppies (45x60cm-18x24in) s. 13-Sep-2 Lyon & Turnbull, Edinburgh #7/R
£600 $936 €900 Ditch with ferns (60x75cm-24x30in) s. 13-Sep-2 Lyon & Turnbull, Edinburgh #87/R
£780 $1248 €1131 Flowers (70x51cm-28x20in) s. 17-May-3 Thomson Roddick & Medcalf, Edinburgh #649/R

POPELIN, Claudius (1825-1892) French
Works on paper
£2483 $3948 €3600 Projet d'un email pour le portrait de Napoleon III (31x22cm-12x9in) s. pencil dr sold with a book. 5-Mar-3 Oger, Dumont, Paris #25/R est:500-600

POPHILLAT, Jean Pierre (1937-) French
£449 $704 €700 Vase de fleurs (61x50cm-24x20in) s. 15-Dec-2 Eric Pillon, Calais #260/R

POPOVA, Liubov (1889-1924) Russian
Works on paper
£5449 $8446 €8500 Cubist-futuristic nude (26x20cm-10x8in) pencil prov.lit. 4-Dec-2 Lempertz, Koln #1005/R est:9000-10000
£8681 $13803 €12500 L'histoire du pop et de son ouvrier balda (56x44cm-22x17in) gouache exhib. 29-Apr-3 Artcurial Briest, Paris #100/R est:12000-15000
£12319 $20203 €17000 Space craft composition (17x15cm-7x6in) bears cyrillic mono. gouache prov.lit. 29-May-3 Lempertz, Koln #879/R est:9000-12000
£13291 $20734 €21000 Romeo masque (61x41cm-24x16in) s. gouache. 20-Oct-2 Claude Boisgirard, Paris #32/R est:25000-30000

POPOVIC, Vladimir (1939-) Czechoslovakian
£395 $612 €593 Bratislava (50x101cm-20x40in) painted c.1975. 3-Dec-2 SOGA, Bratislava #288/R (SL.K 25000)
Works on paper
£425 $604 €638 Lips (86x60cm-34x24in) mixed media plywood exec.1993. 26-Mar-2 SOGA, Bratislava #283/R (SL.K 27000)
£709 $1006 €1064 Concrete sonate II (97x97cm-38x38in) mixed media canvas exec.1986-87. 26-Mar-2 SOGA, Bratislava #282/R (SL.K 45000)

POPPE, Michel Jean (1883-1976) Belgian
Sculpture
£1034 $1634 €1500 Baigneuse et enfant sur le rocher (37cm-15in) s. white marble. 2-Apr-3 Vanderkindere, Brussels #563/R est:1250-1750

POPPEL, Peter van (1945-) Dutch
£1583 $2596 €2200 De eerste pornograaf (17x10cm-7x4in) init.d.70 s.i.verso panel. 3-Jun-3 Christie's, Amsterdam #305/R est:1800-2200

POPPELMAN, Peter (1866-?) German
Sculpture
£2055 $3205 €3000 Female nude getting washed (46cm-18in) i. bronze. 10-Apr-3 Van Ham, Cologne #1113/R est:4000

POPPER, Isidor (1816-1884) German
£1899 $3000 €3000 In the village school (78x66cm-31x26in) s.d.1871. 29-Nov-2 Bolland & Marotz, Bremen #756/R est:3200

POR, Bertalan (1880-?) Hungarian
Works on paper
£391 $610 €587 Plan of a fresco (22x27cm-9x11in) s. pencil. 11-Apr-3 Kieselbach, Budapest #105/R est:140000 (H.F 140000)

PORAY, Stanislaus (1888-1948) American
£307 $500 €461 Vermont autumnal landscape with barn (46x56cm-18x22in) s. 16-Feb-3 Jeffery Burchard, Florida #42
£1398 $2250 €2097 Farm in a river landscape (25x28cm-10x11in) s. prov. 18-Feb-3 John Moran, Pasadena #60 est:3000-5000

PORCAR RIPOLLES, Juan Bautista (1888-1974) Spanish
£6415 $9943 €10200 Seascape (34x41cm-13x16in) s.d.19947. 7-Oct-2 Ansorena, Madrid #67/R

PORCEL, Georges (1931-) Algerian
£360 $562 €540 Still life (61x50cm-24x20in) prov. 26-Mar-3 Woolley & Wallis, Salisbury #181/R

PORCEL, Guillermo (1911-) Spanish
£855 $1386 €1300 Beltrana beach, Majorca (63x53cm-25x21in) s. s.i.verso. 21-Jan-3 Ansorena, Madrid #57/R

PORCELLIS, Jan (16/17th C) Dutch
£6369 $9936 €10000 Shipping in stormy seas (55x100cm-22x39in) mono. prov.exhib.lit. 5-Nov-2 Sotheby's, Amsterdam #83/R est:12000-18000
£10000 $15700 €15000 Coastal scene with fishing pink hauled up on the beach (21x29cm-8x11in) panel prov. 12-Dec-2 Sotheby's, London #166/R est:7000-10000
£154321 $250000 €231482 Seascape with fishermen in a rowboat and other sailing vessels in a choppy sea (32x39cm-13x15in) init. panel prov.lit. 23-Jan-3 Sotheby's, New York #13/R est:150000-200000

PORDENONE, Giovanni Antonio (1483-1576) Italian
Works on paper
£23148 $37500 €34722 Two figures studies (9x6cm-4x2in) chk pair prov.exhib.lit. 21-Jan-3 Sotheby's, New York #21/R est:30000
£26452 $41000 €39678 Study of Poseidon and galloping horse (15x18cm-6x7in) s. pen ink htd white prov.lit. 2-Nov-2 North East Auctions, Portsmouth #109/R est:2500-5000

POREAU, Oswald (1877-1955) Belgian
£258 $408 €400 Paysage a Barchon (30x40cm-12x16in) s.d.1927 panel. 17-Dec-2 Palais de Beaux Arts, Brussels #604
£298 $486 €450 Chemin creux avec moulin (46x38cm-18x15in) s.d.1941. 17-Feb-3 Horta, Bruxelles #379
£348 $543 €550 Paysage. s.d.1941 panel. 10-Sep-2 Vanderkindere, Brussels #328
£353 $546 €550 Peniche halee sur l'Escaut (38x46cm-15x18in) s.d.1942 panel. 9-Dec-2 Horta, Bruxelles #472
£481 $755 €750 Travaux maritimes (43x36cm-17x14in) s.i.d.13-IX-1922 s.verso. 19-Nov-2 Vanderkindere, Brussels #61
£523 $842 €800 Champs de trefles a Dion le Mont (32x40cm-13x16in) d.8 aout 35 panel. 20-Jan-3 Horta, Bruxelles #3
£552 $883 €800 Kerhostin (37x46cm-15x18in) s.1937 s.i.d.1937 verso panel. 15-Mar-3 De Vuyst, Lokeren #259
£884 $1406 €1300 Reflets sur la mer, le Dibon Finistere (70x90cm-28x35in) s.d.1947. 18-Mar-3 Galerie Moderne, Brussels #510/R

PORET, Alicia (1902-1984) Russian
£8000 $12960 €12000 Still life with apple and glass (39x50cm-15x20in) s.d.1922 verso board. 21-May-3 Sotheby's, London #182/R est:8000-10000

PORET, Xavier de (1894-1975) Swiss
Works on paper
£239 $371 €359 Becasses en vol (31x24cm-12x9in) s. chl pastel. 7-Dec-2 Galerie du Rhone, Sion #426 (S.FR 550)
£349 $545 €524 Mickey (35x26cm-14x10in) mono.i. col crayon dr. 8-Nov-2 Dobiaschofsky, Bern #58/R (S.FR 800)
£1454 $2166 €2181 Horse with dog in meadow (38x63cm-15x25in) s. chl. 25-Jun-2 Koller, Zurich #6577/R est:1000-1500 (S.FR 3300)
£1517 $2428 €2200 Royaumont (64x50cm-25x20in) s. chl pastel. 11-Mar-3 Christie's, Paris #257/R
£1517 $2428 €2200 Hibou et souris (26x17cm-10x7in) s. crayon. 11-Mar-3 Christie's, Paris #261/R
£2203 $3282 €3305 Hunting still life with hare and dove (94x61cm-37x24in) s. chl. 25-Jun-2 Koller, Zurich #6580/R est:1000-1500 (S.FR 5000)
£16552 $26483 €24000 Grand chene a Royaumont (66x50cm-26x20in) s.d.1962 chl pastel. 11-Mar-3 Christie's, Paris #256/R

PORET, Xavier de (attrib) (1894-1975) Swiss
Works on paper
£345 $548 €500 Biches et faons couches (38x56cm-15x22in) chl col crayon double-sided. 8-Mar-3 Peron, Melun #21
£690 $1097 €1000 Perdrix (51x73cm-20x29in) W/C chl col crayon. 8-Mar-3 Peron, Melun #20

PORGES, Clara (1879-?) Swiss
£786 $1148 €1179 Peonies (26x21cm-10x8in) s. panel prov. 4-Jun-2 Germann, Zurich #102/R (S.FR 1800)
£1397 $2040 €2096 Silsersee (40x50cm-16x20in) prov. 4-Jun-2 Germann, Zurich #105 est:1500-2000 (S.FR 3200)
£9607 $14026 €14411 Engadine landscape (105x101cm-41x40in) s. prov. 4-Jun-2 Germann, Zurich #45/R est:10000-12000 (S.FR 22000)
Works on paper
£262 $383 €393 Uetliberg (25x32cm-10x13in) s. W/C prov. 4-Jun-2 Germann, Zurich #107 (S.FR 600)
£386 $610 €579 Mediterranean coastal landscape with view of pine grove (37x51cm-15x20in) s. W/C. 29-Nov-2 Zofingen, Switzerland #3033 (S.FR 900)

£873 $1275 €1310 Morcote. Flower twig (49x39cm-19x15in) s.d.1957 W/C two prov. 4-Jun-2 Germann, Zurich #104/R (S.FR 2000)
£1226 $1962 €1839 Mountain landscape with lake and snowy mountains (53x75cm-21x30in) s. W/C. 17-Mar-3 Philippe Schuler, Zurich #4358/R est:2000-3000 (S.FR 2600)
£1397 $2040 €2096 Soglio with Bondasca mountains (43x33cm-17x13in) s. W/C. 4-Jun-2 Germann, Zurich #106/R est:2500-3000 (S.FR 3200)
£1572 $2295 €2358 Firenze. Alassio coast (34x51cm-13x20in) s. one i.d.1951 W/C two prov. 4-Jun-2 Germann, Zurich #103/R est:2000-3000 (S.FR 3600)
£1747 $2742 €2621 Lago di Cavloccia and Monte del Forno - Engadin (75x56cm-30x22in) s. W/C. 25-Nov-2 Germann, Zurich #143/R est:4000-5000 (S.FR 4000)

PORILA, Evert (1886-1941) Finnish
Sculpture
£1079 $1727 €1500 Mannerheim (56cm-22in) s.d.1940 bronze. 17-May-3 Hagelstam, Helsinki #13/R est:1000

PORSCHE, Otto Maria (1858-1931) German
£828 $1292 €1300 Flora (140x146cm-55x57in) s. 6-Nov-2 Hugo Ruef, Munich #1240

PORSON, Henriette (20th C) French
Works on paper
£296 $476 €420 Canots de peche au mouillage (30x23cm-12x9in) s. pastel chk. 11-May-3 Thierry & Lannon, Brest #300
£317 $510 €450 Bretonne de dos sur le chemin du bourg (30x23cm-12x9in) s. pastel. 11-May-3 Thierry & Lannon, Brest #302
£387 $624 €550 Lever de soleil sur la lande (25x34cm-10x13in) s.d.1962 pastel. 11-May-3 Thierry & Lannon, Brest #301

PORTA, Enrique (?) Spanish
£252 $392 €400 Still life (40x55cm-16x22in) s. s.verso. 23-Sep-2 Durán, Madrid #570/R
£283 $442 €450 Landscape (27x41cm-11x16in) s. 23-Sep-2 Durán, Madrid #607/R

PORTA, Guglielmo della (c.1514-1577) Italian
Works on paper
£7500 $12525 €10875 Classical armour decorated with amorous couples and Neptune with Hippocampi (25x17cm-10x7in) i.verso pen ink prov. 8-Jul-3 Christie's, London #22/R est:8000-12000

PORTA, Marco (1956-) Italian
Sculpture
£1418 $2298 €2000 I cercatori di quiete (147x40x40cm-58x16x16in) crystal marble resin water salt. 20-May-3 Porro, Milan #46/R est:2500-2700

PORTAELS, Jean François (1818-1895) Belgian
£321 $497 €500 Diseuse de bonne aventure (43x33cm-17x13in) s. panel. 3-Dec-2 Campo & Campo, Antwerp #245
£336 $540 €500 Portrait de jeune fille (47x37cm-19x15in) s. panel. 18-Feb-3 Vanderkindere, Brussels #223
£696 $1086 €1100 Sous-bois (31x48cm-12x19in) s.d.1880 canvas on panel. 16-Sep-2 Horta, Bruxelles #360
£1361 $2163 €2000 L'orientale (60x50cm-24x20in) s. 18-Mar-3 Campo, Vlaamse Kaai #212 est:600-700
£5036 $8259 €7000 La Moabite (73x60cm-29x24in) s.i. 3-Jun-3 Tajan, Paris #45/R est:8000-12000

PORTAIL, Jacques Andre (1695-1759) French
Works on paper
£6731 $10433 €10500 Vieillard disant le Benedicite (28x35cm-11x14in) crayon sanguine. 4-Dec-2 Piasa, Paris #74/R

PORTATIUS, Hans Heinrich (1902-1986) German
£475 $741 €750 Seaview (50x72cm-20x28in) s. verso. 18-Oct-2 Dr Fritz Nagel, Stuttgart #296/R

PORTEN, C (19/20th C) ?
£2051 $3221 €3200 Rotterdam harbour (74x100cm-29x39in) s. 10-Dec-2 Dorotheum, Vienna #19/R est:2000-2400

PORTENEUVE, Alfred and SUBES, Raymond (20th C) ?
Sculpture
£10791 $17698 €15000 Untitled (184x263cm-72x104in) black metal prov.lit. 6-Jun-3 Rabourdin & Choppin de Janvry, Paris #154/R est:16000-18000

PORTER, Charles E (1847-1923) American
£3438 $5500 €4985 Floral still life (18x28cm-7x11in) s. 17-May-3 CRN Auctions, Cambridge #31

PORTER, Daniel (19/20th C) British
£600 $924 €900 Angler on a quiet stretcher of the river. Canal boat on a river (25x35cm-10x14in) s. oil paper on canvas pair. 24-Oct-2 Christie's, Kensington #140/R

PORTER, David (1780-1843) American
£287 $450 €431 Happy woman No.1 - people of the beach (109x86cm-43x34in) s.d.1958 s.i.verso. 20-Nov-2 Boos Gallery, Michigan #426/R

PORTER, Eliot (1901-1990) American
Photographs
£9740 $15000 €14610 Selected early landscapes (20x19cm-8x7in) photograph two. 22-Oct-2 Sotheby's, New York #174/R est:3000-5000

PORTER, Fairfield (1907-1975) American
£3767 $5500 €5651 Raymond family skiff (15x23cm-6x9in) canvasboard prov.lit. 3-Nov-1 North East Auctions, Portsmouth #749/R
£11321 $18000 €16982 View of the Barred Island (46x91cm-18x36in) s. masonite prov.lit. 4-Mar-3 Christie's, Rockefeller NY #117/R est:20000-30000
£22581 $35000 €33872 Landscape (33x56cm-13x22in) s. masonite. 4-Dec-2 Sotheby's, New York #88/R est:20000-30000
Works on paper
£4110 $6000 €6165 Southampton (46x53cm-18x21in) W/C exec.c.1965 prov.lit. 3-Nov-1 North East Auctions, Portsmouth #750/R

PORTER, George (1795-1856) British?
Works on paper
£2400 $3720 €3600 Architectural orders, Corinthian, Doric and Ionic (52x36cm-20x14in) s. pencil pen black ink two W/C three prov. 4-Dec-2 Christie's, Kensington #122/R est:1200-1800

PORTER, Liliana (1941-) Argentinian
£7643 $12000 €11465 Untitled (130x180cm-51x71in) s.verso acrylic painted 1979 prov. 20-Nov-2 Christie's, Rockefeller NY #49/R est:14000-16000

PORTEUS, Edgar (fl.1868-1878) British
£2100 $3255 €3150 Cottage interior (51x61cm-20x24in) s.d.1871 verso. 1-Oct-2 Capes Dunn, Manchester #768/R

PORTIELJE, Edward Antoon (1861-1949) Belgian
£353 $546 €550 Vue sur un paysage hollandais (10x15cm-4x6in) s. cardboard. 3-Dec-2 Campo & Campo, Antwerp #249
£353 $546 €550 Deux petits vases aux fleurs (16x13cm-6x5in) s. panel. 3-Dec-2 Campo & Campo, Antwerp #250
£966 $1545 €1400 View of harbour (9x15cm-4x6in) s. canvas on board. 15-Mar-3 De Vuyst, Lokeren #260/R
£986 $1587 €1400 Animated beach view (8x16cm-3x6in) s. panel. 12-May-3 Bernaerts, Antwerp #195/R
£1014 $1581 €1500 Fille nue (120x70cm-47x28in) s. 25-Mar-3 Campo & Campo, Antwerp #166 est:1600-1800
£1088 $1731 €1600 Tea time (15x19cm-6x7in) s. panel. 24-Mar-3 Bernaerts, Antwerp #11/R est:200-2200
£1282 $2013 €2000 Pierrot assis dans un interieur pres d'une lampe (65x77cm-26x30in) 16-Dec-2 Amberes, Antwerp #284
£1361 $2163 €2000 Egmond aan Zee, Holland (13x23cm-5x9in) board. 24-Mar-3 Bernaerts, Antwerp #270/R est:2000-3000
£3846 $5962 €6000 Deux femmes zelandaises avec un enfant (19x27cm-7x11in) s. panel exhib. 3-Dec-2 Campo & Campo, Antwerp #251/R est:3000-3500
£9220 $15397 €13000 Interior with two Zeeland girls (51x65cm-20x26in) s. 23-Jun-3 Bernaerts, Antwerp #131/R est:12500-15000
£10638 $17766 €15000 Card game (58x75cm-23x30in) s. 23-Jun-3 Bernaerts, Antwerp #132/R est:15000-20000
£11321 $17547 €18000 On the look-out (55x47cm-22x19in) s. 5-Oct-2 De Vuyst, Lokeren #434/R est:20000-24000
£11538 $17885 €18000 Deux dames zelandaises faisant de la dentelle aux fuseaux (62x77cm-24x30in) s. 3-Dec-2 Campo & Campo, Antwerp #247/R est:16000-18000
£12025 $18759 €19000 Good news (64x50cm-25x20in) s. 21-Oct-2 Bernaerts, Antwerp #92/R est:10000-15000
£12739 $19873 €20000 Jeune Zelandaise soufflant des bulles de savon (73x56cm-29x22in) s. 11-Nov-2 Horta, Bruxelles #164/R est:28000-35000
£17266 $27626 €24000 Tea group (65x92cm-26x36in) s. 17-May-3 Lempertz, Koln #1462/R est:26000
£18987 $29620 €30000 Jeune hollandaise a la lecture (82x72cm-32x28in) s.d.1898. 16-Sep-2 Horta, Bruxelles #102/R est:32000-38000

PORTIELJE, Gerard (1856-1929) Belgian
£1538 $2415 €2400 Paysanne au bonnet rouge (24x17cm-9x7in) s. panel. 10-Dec-2 Campo, Vlaamse Kaai #427/R est:1800-2400
£2051 $3179 €3200 Portrait d'une vieille femme (24x18cm-9x7in) s. panel. 3-Dec-2 Campo & Campo, Antwerp #252/R est:2500-3500
£2051 $3179 €3200 Portrait d'un veneur (24x18cm-9x7in) s. panel. 3-Dec-2 Campo & Campo, Antwerp #253/R est:2500-3500
£3378 $5270 €5000 Le cure (22x16cm-9x6in) s. panel. 25-Mar-3 Campo & Campo, Antwerp #167/R est:5250-5750
£4676 $7482 €6500 Pares le classe (36x28cm-14x11in) s. panel. 13-May-3 Galerie Moderne, Brussels #428/R est:10000-12000
£13889 $22083 €20000 Squandered supper (32x22cm-13x9in) s.d.1879 i.verso panel. 29-Apr-3 Christie's, Amsterdam #34/R est:7000-9000
£22436 $34776 €35000 Joueurs de cartes dans l'auberge (44x54cm-17x21in) s.i. 3-Dec-2 Campo & Campo, Antwerp #254/R est:30000-40000
£27660 $46191 €39000 The cheat (47x58cm-19x23in) s. 23-Jun-3 Bernaerts, Antwerp #134/R est:30000-35000
Works on paper
£321 $497 €500 La discussion tranquille dans l'auberge (30x31cm-12x12in) s. dr. 3-Dec-2 Campo & Campo, Antwerp #255
£696 $1079 €1100 Scene de cabaret. s. dr. 24-Sep-2 Galerie Moderne, Brussels #706/R
£863 $1381 €1200 Three against one (42x49cm-17x19in) s. pencil dr exec.1910. 17-May-3 De Vuyst, Lokeren #299/R

PORTIELJE, Jon Frederik Pieter (1829-1908) Belgian/Dutch
£5063 $7899 €8000 Woman with green parrot (103x78cm-41x31in) s. 21-Oct-2 Bernaerts, Antwerp #93/R est:12000-14000
£7194 $11511 €10000 Rosary (59x48cm-23x19in) s.i. panel. 17-May-3 De Vuyst, Lokeren #433/R est:10000-12000
£15190 $24000 €22785 Dreaming of love (80x61cm-31x24in) s.i. prov. 24-Apr-3 Sotheby's, New York #141/R est:18000-25000

PORTIER, Francis (1876-1961) Swiss
£349 $552 €524 Portrait de Valaisan (63x51cm-25x20in) s.i. 17-Nov-2 Koller, Geneva #1330 (S.FR 800)

PORTINARI, Candido (1903-1962) Brazilian
£23885 $37500 €35828 Portrait of Madame Arthur Rubinstein (73x60cm-29x24in) s.d.1940 prov.lit. 19-Nov-2 Sotheby's, New York #30/R est:25000

PORTOCARRERO, René (1912-1986) Cuban
£9146 $15000 €13719 Retrato un azul. Mujer de Carnaval, Josefine Baker (41x52cm-16x20in) s.i.d.66 verso one s.d.66 one s. two prov.exhib. 28-May-3 Christie's, Rockefeller NY #126/R est:10000-15000
Works on paper
£4140 $6500 €6210 Portrait of woman (70x49cm-28x19in) s.d.70 gouache prov. 20-Nov-2 Christie's, Rockefeller NY #147/R
£4676 $7669 €6500 Woman and pigeon (75x55cm-30x22in) s. gouache prov. 3-Jun-3 Christie's, Amsterdam #310/R est:7000-9000
£11465 $18000 €17198 Still life with flowers and fruit (56x38cm-22x15in) s.d.1946 pastel prov. 20-Nov-2 Christie's, Rockefeller NY #20/R est:12000-16000

PORTOCARRERO, René (attrib) (1912-1986) Cuban
£4367 $6812 €6551 Portrait of a woman wearing a hat (76x55cm-30x22in) s. mixed media. 6-Nov-2 Dobiaschofsky, Bern #893/R est:2800 (S.FR 10000)

PORTUGUESE SCHOOL, 17th C
Sculpture
£10044 $15668 €15066 Ecce homo (55cm-22in) ivory wooden socle. 20-Nov-2 Fischer, Luzern #1333/R est:8000-10000 (S.FR 23000)

PORZANO, Giacomo (1925-) Italian
£414 $662 €600 Young Pasqua (35x26cm-14x10in) s. painted 1966 prov. 11-Mar-3 Babuino, Rome #132/R

POSCHINGER, Hermann (1886-?) German
Works on paper
£385 $604 €600 Turracherhohe - Schwarzsee (39x43cm-15x17in) s.i. W/C htd white. 20-Nov-2 Dorotheum, Klagenfurt #58

POSCHINGER, Richard von (1839-1915) German
£1150 $1886 €1725 Young girls picking flowers by a parkway between woods (41x58cm-16x23in) s. 5-Feb-3 John Nicholson, Haslemere #1069 est:1000-1500
£1258 $1962 €2000 Peasant with cows (36x51cm-14x20in) s. board. 21-Sep-2 Bolland & Marotz, Bremen #540/R est:2600
£1731 $2683 €2700 Boat by shore of Starnberg lake (28x51cm-11x20in) s. canvas on board prov. 7-Dec-2 Ketterer, Hamburg #99/R est:2500-3000
£2690 $4277 €3900 Pre-alpine landscape in summer with cart on track (103x156cm-41x61in) s. 8-Mar-3 Arnold, Frankfurt #686/R est:2400
£3481 $5396 €5500 Two peasant girls in vegetable garden (47x62cm-19x24in) s. board. 25-Sep-2 Neumeister, Munich #699/R est:4200
£5414 $8446 €8500 View of Oberzeismering on the Starnberger See (52x90cm-20x35in) lit. 8-Nov-2 Auktionhaus Georg Rehm, Augsburg #8124 est:12500

POSE, Eduard Wilhelm (1812-1878) German
£1164 $1816 €1700 In Appenin (38x47cm-15x19in) board. 11-Apr-3 Winterberg, Heidelberg #519/R est:1850

POSEN, Stephen (1939-) American
£5400 $8856 €8100 Three cornered orange (193x229cm-76x90in) s.overlap s.i.d.1972 stretcher prov.1972. 7-Feb-3 Sotheby's, London #284/R est:6000-8000

POSENAER, Jozef Karel Frans (1876-1935) Belgian
£314 $484 €500 Canards pres de l'etang (50x32cm-20x13in) s. 22-Oct-2 Campo, Vlaamse Kaai #253
£346 $533 €550 Le Volmolen a Lierre (60x50cm-24x20in) s. 22-Oct-2 Campo, Vlaamse Kaai #597
£660 $1049 €950 Paysage (76x100cm-30x39in) s. 29-Apr-3 Campo & Campo, Antwerp #255
£886 $1382 €1400 Beach view at Domburg (17x22cm-7x9in) s. board. 21-Oct-2 Bernaerts, Antwerp #518/R

POSILLIPO SCHOOL (19th C) Italian
£7692 $11231 €12000 View of Naples Bay (27x121cm-11x48in) 5-Jun-2 Il Ponte, Milan #264/R est:3500-4500

POSSART, Felix (1837-1928) German
£2019 $3250 €3029 Alhembre interior scene (64x41cm-25x16in) s. s.i.stretcher. 20-Jan-3 Arthur James, Florida #628

POSSENTI, Antonio (1933-) Italian
£545 $856 €850 Fish (9x49cm-4x19in) s. board. 16-Dec-2 Pandolfini, Florence #363
£625 $994 €900 Sailor (18x13cm-7x5in) s. board painted 1995. 1-May-3 Meeting Art, Vercelli #319
£696 $1086 €1100 Untitled (30x20cm-12x8in) s. cardboard on canvas. 14-Sep-2 Meeting Art, Vercelli #930/R
£705 $1107 €1100 Fish, apple and flowers (15x20cm-6x8in) s. board. 16-Dec-2 Pandolfini, Florence #362/R
£791 $1234 €1250 If I dream of butterflies (30x20cm-12x8in) s. s.verso cardboard on canvas. 14-Sep-2 Meeting Art, Vercelli #870/R
£890 $1389 €1300 Puppet maker (50x35cm-20x14in) s. cardboard. 10-Apr-3 Finarte Semenzato, Rome #153
£1044 $1629 €1650 Giverny flowers (30cm-12in circular) s. 14-Sep-2 Meeting Art, Vercelli #862/R
£1156 $1839 €1700 Untitled (50x35cm-20x14in) s. paper. 1-Mar-3 Meeting Art, Vercelli #472
£1378 $2164 €2150 Mushrooms in the woods (40x30cm-16x12in) s. s.i.verso. 23-Nov-2 Meeting Art, Vercelli #227/R
£1410 $2214 €2200 Planes flying (30x40cm-12x16in) s. cardboard on canvas. 23-Nov-2 Meeting Art, Vercelli #462/R
£1644 $2564 €2400 Still life (29x48cm-11x19in) s. cardboard on canvas. 10-Apr-3 Finarte Semenzato, Rome #143/R
£1731 $2717 €2700 Composition (48x38cm-19x15in) s. card. 16-Dec-2 Pandolfini, Florence #343/R
£1806 $2871 €2600 Untitled (40x30cm-16x12in) s.s.verso. 1-May-3 Meeting Art, Vercelli #549
£1962 $3061 €3100 Untitled (47x37cm-19x15in) s. board. 14-Sep-2 Meeting Art, Vercelli #972/R
£2179 $3422 €3400 Tower (50x40cm-20x16in) s. cardboard on canvas. 21-Nov-2 Finarte, Rome #238/R
£2973 $4638 €4400 In the garden (40x50cm-16x20in) s. s.i.verso board. 28-Mar-3 Farsetti, Prato #743/R
£3108 $4849 €4600 Sailor dance (39x50cm-15x20in) s. s.i.verso board. 28-Mar-3 Farsetti, Prato #761/R
Works on paper
£359 $575 €550 Venus (35x25cm-14x10in) s. mixed media paper on canvas exec.1999. 4-Jan-3 Meeting Art, Vercelli #432

POSSIN, Rudolf (1861-1922) German
£1911 $2943 €3000 Volendam girls in an interior (80x100cm-31x39in) s. 3-Sep-2 Christie's, Amsterdam #181/R est:4000-6000
£2025 $3159 €3200 Volendam interior (80x102cm-31x40in) s. 21-Oct-2 Glerum, Amsterdam #78/R est:1000-2000

POSSOZ, Miley (?) ?
Works on paper
£1321 $2060 €2100 Portrait de femme a l'oiseau (41x31cm-16x12in) s. W/C. 9-Oct-2 Lombrail & Teucquam, Paris #16/R

POST, George (1906-) American
Works on paper
£427 $700 €641 Summer garden. s. W/C. 31-May-3 Harvey Clar, Oakland #1212b

POST, Gerardus Arnoldus Johannes (1826-1879) Dutch
£637 $994 €1000 Small village on canal with small boat and figures (24x32cm-9x13in) s. panel. 6-Nov-2 Vendue Huis, Gravenhage #385

POST, Gerardus Arnoldus Johannes (attrib) (1826-1879) Dutch
£701 $1093 €1100 Landscape with figures on a path (28x38cm-11x15in) panel. 6-Nov-2 Vendue Huis, Gravenhage #386/R

POST, Howard (20th C) ?
Works on paper
£458 $701 €687 Corriente herd (63x48cm-25x19in) pastel oil. 24-Aug-2 Heffel, Vancouver #24 (C.D 1100)

POST, William Merritt (1856-1935) American
£2532 $4000 €3798 Autumnal wooded river landscape (56x71cm-22x28in) s. 17-Nov-2 Jeffery Burchard, Florida #91/R
£3247 $5000 €4871 Brook in November (41x66cm-16x26in) s. prov. 24-Oct-2 Shannon's, Milford #173/R est:4000-6000
£4747 $7500 €7121 Autumn landscape (71x102cm-28x40in) s. prov. 24-Apr-3 Shannon's, Milford #57/R est:5000-7000
Works on paper
£478 $750 €717 Winter landscape (20x25cm-8x10in) s. W/C gouache. 22-Nov-2 Skinner, Boston #286/R

POST-IMPRESSIONIST FRENCH SCHOOL
£8273 $13237 €11500 Les grands arbres, matinee ensoleille (92x73cm-36x29in) 14-May-3 Blanchet, Paris #78/R est:4000-5000

POSTEL, Jules (1867-1955) Belgian
£556 $894 €850 Port de peche (40x50cm-16x20in) s. 14-Jan-3 Vanderkindere, Brussels #153

POSTEMSKI, Sava Vassilievitch (1825-?) Russian
£4930 $7937 €7000 Gathering grapes (84x62cm-33x24in) s. 10-May-3 Bukowskis, Helsinki #376/R est:1500-1800

POSTIGLIONE, Luca (1876-1936) Italian
£3270 $5036 €5200 Pulcinella (88x38cm-35x15in) indis.s. 23-Oct-2 Finarte, Milan #157/R
£4600 $7176 €6900 Secret (87x61cm-34x24in) indis.sig. s.verso. 17-Sep-2 Sotheby's, Olympia #277/R est:3000-5000
£5000 $7950 €7500 La Donna della vendemmia (93x60cm-37x24in) s. 20-Mar-3 Christie's, Kensington #59/R est:4000-6000

POSTMA, Cornelius (1903-1977) Dutch
Works on paper
£308 $486 €480 Surrealist composition - glove (27x20cm-11x8in) s.d.1936 gouache prov. 14-Nov-2 Neumeister, Munich #678/R

POSTMA, Gerrit (1819-1894) Dutch
£550 $897 €798 Water carriers in the Roman campania (48x82cm-19x32in) s.d.1864. 16-Jul-3 James Thompson, Kirby Lonsdale #151/R

POT, Hendrick Gerritsz (attrib) (1585-1657) Dutch
£1000 $1570 €1500 Figures in an interior (49x37cm-19x15in) mono. panel. 13-Dec-2 Christie's, Kensington #26/R est:1500-2000

POT, Hendrick Gerritsz (circle) (1585-1657) Dutch
£5500 $8635 €8250 Portrait of a gentleman, aged 46 in a black coat and white ruff (17x12cm-7x5in) i.d.1634 copper oval. 13-Dec-2 Christie's, Kensington #20/R est:3000-4000

POTAMIANOU, Artemis (1975-) Greek
£1375 $2200 €1994 Urban sign II (110x110cm-43x43in) s.d.2000 verso oil varnish acrylic. 13-May-3 Sotheby's, Tel Aviv #76/R est:2200-2800

POTEMONT, Adolphe Theodore (1828-1883) French
£2548 $4000 €3822 La place Saint George (28x22cm-11x9in) s.d.1886. 10-Dec-2 Doyle, New York #210/R est:5000-7000
£7200 $11736 €10440 Place St. Georges, Paris (70x55cm-28x22in) s.d.1876. 16-Jul-3 Sotheby's, Olympia #207/R est:4000-6000

POTET, Loys (1866-?) French
Sculpture
£1132 $1766 €1800 Boy with panther (56cm-22in) s. bronze. 23-Sep-2 Wiener Kunst Auktionen, Vienna #74/R est:700-1400

POTHAST, Bernard (1882-1966) Dutch/Belgian
£5806 $9000 €8709 Motherly love (76x64cm-30x25in) s. 7-Dec-2 Neal Auction Company, New Orleans #279/R est:12000-18000
£6500 $10335 €9750 Sewing lesson (51x61cm-20x24in) s. prov. 18-Mar-3 Bonhams, New Bond Street #18/R est:5000-7000
£6918 $10654 €11000 Happy family (50x60cm-20x24in) s. 22-Oct-2 Sotheby's, Amsterdam #107/R est:7000-9000
£7556 $12542 €10956 New toy (56x46cm-22x18in) s. prov. 16-Jun-3 Waddingtons, Toronto #253/R est:15000-20000 (C.D 17000)
£8333 $13250 €12000 Mealtime for baby (51x61cm-20x24in) s. 29-Apr-3 Christie's, Amsterdam #148/R est:12000-16000
£8383 $14000 €12155 Mother and children (41x51cm-16x20in) s. prov. 22-Jun-3 Freeman, Philadelphia #13/R est:8000-12000
£9500 $14915 €14250 Blowing bubbles (65x76cm-26x30in) s. 21-Nov-2 Christie's, Kensington #28/R est:10000-15000
£16000 $25120 €24000 Motherhood (65x78cm-26x31in) s. 21-Nov-2 Christie's, Kensington #29/R est:10000-15000

POTHAST, Willem Frederik Alfons (1877-1917) Dutch
Works on paper
£701 $1079 €1100 Moonlit dune landscape (23x32cm-9x13in) s.d.99 W/C brush black ink col pencil. 3-Sep-2 Christie's, Amsterdam #357/R

POTHOVEN, Hendrik (1726-1807) Dutch
Works on paper
£1497 $2380 €2200 Westermarkt (35x31cm-14x12in) s.i. W/C over crayon. 24-Mar-3 Tajan, Paris #16/R

POTIER, Antoine Julien (1796-1865) French
£943 $1472 €1500 Portrait d'homme assis tenat un livre (81x65cm-32x26in) s.d.1838. 8-Oct-2 Christie's, Paris #29/R

POTRONAT, Lucien (1889-?) French
£581 $900 €872 S. (46x56cm-18x22in) 16-Jul-2 Arthur James, Florida #54
£2200 $3454 €3300 Cote d'Azur, la Napoule, environs. Cote d'Azur, le Chemin Creux (45x54cm-18x21in) s. i.verso pair. 10-Dec-2 Rosebery Fine Art, London #563/R est:200-400

POTSCH, Igo (1884-1939) Austrian
£1646 $2567 €2600 Church interior, Klosterneuburg (125x96cm-49x38in) s.d.22 panel. 15-Oct-2 Dorotheum, Vienna #46/R est:1400-2200

POTT, Laslett John (1837-1898) British
£515 $803 €747 Lady Jane Grey on the way to the Tower of London (25x36cm-10x14in) s.i. prov. 26-Mar-3 Walker's, Ottawa #77/R est:900-1200 (C.D 1200)
£2100 $3423 €3150 Shrimper's tale (44x34cm-17x13in) s.d.1894. 29-Jan-3 Sotheby's, Olympia #125/R est:1500-2500
£6000 $9960 €9000 Departure (90x128cm-35x50in) s.d.96. 12-Jun-3 Sotheby's, London #262/R est:6000-8000
£17000 $26520 €25500 Plan of campaign (86x112cm-34x44in) s. 7-Nov-2 Christie's, Kensington #242/R est:4000-6000

POTTENGER, Mary L (20th C) American
£404 $650 €606 Floral still life (61x56cm-24x22in) s. board. 18-Feb-3 John Moran, Pasadena #19

POTTER, Beatrix (1866-1943) British
Works on paper
£6000 $9900 €8700 Study of a house mouse (8x10cm-3x4in) d.87 pencil W/C htd white. 3-Jul-3 Christie's, Kensington #235/R est:2000-3000

POTTER, Charles (1878-?) British
£260 $426 €390 Shepherd with his flock in autumnal wooded landscape (19x29cm-7x11in) s. board. 10-Feb-3 David Duggleby, Scarborough #593/R

POTTER, George (?) Irish
£2055 $3205 €3000 Sandycove Station (69x59cm-27x23in) s. board. 8-Apr-3 James Adam, Dublin #80/R est:2200-2500

POTTER, Mary (1900-1981) British
£1600 $2624 €2400 Three jugs. Mere with swan, Thorpeness (17x26cm-7x10in) pencil W/C two prov. 6-Jun-3 Christie's, London #88/R est:600-800

£2000 $3180 €3000 Three flints (75x64cm-30x25in) s.i.d.79 verso board prov.exhib. 26-Feb-3 Sotheby's, Olympia #338/R est:2000-3000
£2800 $4452 €4200 Building (60x101cm-24x40in) board prov. 26-Feb-3 Sotheby's, Olympia #340/R est:2000-3000
£4000 $6360 €6000 Mauve and ochre (44x75cm-17x30in) i.on overlap. 26-Feb-3 Sotheby's, Olympia #339/R est:4000-6000
£4000 $6240 €6000 Greenhouse (76x51cm-30x20in) init. prov. 25-Mar-3 Bonhams, New Bond Street #93/R est:2000-3000
£5500 $8580 €8250 Rough sea at Aldeburgh (61x51cm-24x20in) prov.exhib. 25-Mar-3 Bonhams, New Bond Street #92/R est:1500-2500
£6000 $9840 €9000 Birds 2 (61x76cm-24x30in) i.verso prov. 3-Jun-3 Sotheby's, Olympia #227/R est:6000-8000

Works on paper

£400 $660 €580 Studio (12x15cm-5x6in) W/C prov. 3-Jul-3 Christie's, Kensington #274
£620 $1011 €899 Study for the swans (24x30cm-9x12in) W/C exhib. 15-Jul-3 Bonhams, Knightsbridge #139/R

POTTER, Paulus (1625-1654) Dutch

£4225 $6803 €6000 Young herdress milling (102x110cm-40x43in) s.d.1649. 10-May-3 Berlinghof, Heidelberg #295/R est:6000

POTTER, Paulus (attrib) (1625-1654) Dutch

Works on paper

£283 $442 €450 Head of cow lying down (15x19cm-6x7in) chk pencil. 11-Oct-2 Winterberg, Heidelberg #302

POTTER, Paulus (circle) (1625-1654) Dutch

£7547 $11698 €12000 Portrait of four dogs (79x91cm-31x36in) 2-Oct-2 Dorotheum, Vienna #150/R est:12000-16000

POTTER, Pieter Symonsz (1597-1652) Dutch

£3413 $5530 €4949 Interior scene with figures at an inn (49x38cm-19x15in) s.d.1648 panel. 26-May-3 Bukowskis, Stockholm #414/R est:40000-50000 (S.KR 44000)

POTTHAST, Edward Henry (1857-1927) American

£833 $1300 €1250 Rocky coast (30x41cm-12x16in) s. board. 20-Oct-2 Susanin's, Chicago #5004/R
£833 $1300 €1250 Mountain landscape (36x48cm-14x19in) s. board. 20-Oct-2 Susanin's, Chicago #5005/R
£2315 $3750 €3357 Forest interior (41x30cm-16x12in) s. board. 21-May-3 Doyle, New York #139/R est:7000-10000
£2922 $4500 €4383 Long Island sand dune (13x18cm-5x7in) s.i.verso canvasboard. 24-Oct-2 Shannon's, Milford #230/R est:3000-5000
£12739 $20000 €19109 Lake Louise, British Columbia (30x41cm-12x16in) s. s.i.verso canvasboard. 20-Nov-2 Christie's, Los Angeles #69/R est:20000-30000
£24193 $37500 €36290 Nude (51x41cm-20x16in) s. prov. 4-Dec-2 Sotheby's, New York #34/R est:20000-30000
£35484 $55000 €53226 Bathing boy (30x41cm-12x16in) s. board prov. 5-Dec-2 Christie's, Rockefeller NY #102/R est:60000-80000
£148387 $230000 €222581 Manhattan Beach (30x41cm-12x16in) s. canvasboard prov.exhib. 5-Dec-2 Christie's, Rockefeller NY #79/R est:200000-300000

POTTHAST, Edward Henry (attrib) (1857-1927) American

£264 $425 €396 Desert landscape (61x71cm-24x28in) s.d.1923 s.i.d.verso board. 10-May-3 Susanin's, Chicago #5015

POTTHOF, Hans (1911-) Swiss

£3275 $4782 €4913 Untitled (52x60cm-20x24in) s. paper on aluminium. 4-Jun-2 Germann, Zurich #817/R est:2500-3000 (S.FR 7500)
£5240 $8227 €7860 Landscape in southern France (46x65cm-18x26in) s. 23-Nov-2 Burkhard, Luzern #202/R est:11000-13000 (S.FR 12000)

Works on paper

£786 $1234 €1179 Midi a Vallet (33x60cm-13x24in) s.d.1960 pencil prov. sold with four others. 23-Nov-2 Burkhard, Luzern #199/R (S.FR 1800)
£961 $1499 €1442 Tavern. Street. Table (21x29cm-8x11in) s.i. pencil three. 6-Nov-2 Dobiaschofsky, Bern #1828 (S.FR 2200)
£1135 $1783 €1703 French impressions. s.i. pencil six prov. 23-Nov-2 Burkhard, Luzern #201/R est:600-800 (S.FR 2600)

POTTIER, Gaston (20th C) French

£347 $566 €500 Chapelle de Kerinec a Poulland (48x41cm-19x16in) s. panel. 19-Jul-3 Thierry & Lannon, Brest #377
£660 $1075 €950 Le Pardon de Ste Anne La Palud (24x33cm-9x13in) s. 19-Jul-3 Thierry & Lannon, Brest #378
£972 $1585 €1400 Port anime (60x90cm-24x35in) board. 19-Jul-3 Thierry & Lannon, Brest #9hc

POTTS, John Joseph (19th C) British

Works on paper

£400 $624 €600 Lady Palmer's cottage (30x41cm-12x16in) mono.d.1884 W/C. 20-Sep-2 Richardson & Smith, Whitby #138

POTVIN, Jules (?) Belgian?

£737 $1157 €1150 Cour d'estaminet anime (67x55cm-26x22in) s. 19-Nov-2 Vanderkindere, Brussels #37

POU, Ramon (c.1862-1947) ?

£500 $830 €725 Steam yacht at anchor in coastal waters (17x27cm-7x11in) s. oil on card. 12-Jun-3 Christie's, London #542/R
£700 $1162 €1015 Spanish steamer Villa de Puller lying at anchor (59x39cm-23x15in) s.d.1949. 12-Jun-3 Christie's, London #541/R

Works on paper

£1500 $2490 €2175 Spanish brigantine Catalina at sea (32x49cm-13x19in) s.i. pencil pen ink W/C bodycol. 12-Jun-3 Christie's, London #550/R est:1000-1500

POUCETTE (1935-) French

£3767 $5914 €5500 Regard de l'oeil (55x46cm-22x18in) s.d.1954 oil collage panel. 15-Apr-3 Laurence Calmels, Paris #4224/R

POUGHEON, Eugène Robert (1886-1955) French

£1457 $2375 €2200 Femmes a la fontain (65x81cm-26x32in) s. 16-Feb-3 Mercier & Cie, Lille #279/R est:1200-1500

POUGNY, Jean (1894-1956) French

£3145 $4874 €5000 Personnages dans un jardin (11x22cm-4x9in) s. panel lit. 30-Oct-2 Artcurial Briest, Paris #66/R est:5000-6000
£4717 $7311 €7500 Interieur (19x28cm-7x11in) s. exhib. 30-Oct-2 Artcurial Briest, Paris #65/R est:8000-10000
£5449 $8554 €8500 Moulin Rouge (14x15cm-6x6in) s. painted 1944. 10-Dec-2 Piasa, Paris #58/R est:3000-4000
£7000 $11340 €10500 Still life with fish and shrimps (24x33cm-9x13in) s. 21-May-3 Sotheby's, London #185/R est:5000-7000
£55975 $86761 €89000 Nature morte a la trompette et a la raquette de tennis (72x100cm-28x39in) s. painted c.1924-25 lit. 30-Oct-2 Artcurial Briest, Paris #64/R est:6000-8000
£76389 $121457 €110000 La fenetre ouverte, Cote d'Azur (100x65cm-39x26in) prov.exhib.lit. 29-Apr-3 Artcurial Briest, Paris #248/R est:30000-40000
£83333 $137500 €120000 Violoniste (129x96cm-51x38in) s.d.1925 prov.exhib.lit. 2-Jul-3 Artcurial Briest, Paris #707/R est:50000-60000

Works on paper

£1887 $2925 €3000 Montmartre, scene de rue (44x61cm-17x24in) st.sig. pastel crayon. 30-Oct-2 Artcurial Briest, Paris #67/R est:3000-4000

POUJOL, Pierre Louis Marius (1858-?) French

£1429 $2086 €2200 Reclining female nude in landscape (38x56cm-15x22in) s.d.1894. 17-Jun-2 Ansorena, Madrid #332/R

POULAKAS, Ioannis (1864-1942) Greek

£4000 $6200 €6000 Young angler (60x45cm-24x18in) s. 2-Oct-2 Sotheby's, London #82/R

POULSEN, Georg (1911-) Danish

£374 $583 €561 Town scene II (47x66cm-19x26in) s. exhib. 5-Aug-2 Rasmussen, Vejle #303/R (D.KR 4400)

POULSEN, Gudrun (1918-) Danish

£1355 $2100 €2033 Still life of jug and bowl (82x72cm-32x28in) init. 1-Oct-2 Rasmussen, Copenhagen #315/R est:8000 (D.KR 16000)

POULSEN, Margrethe Svenn (1877-1922) Danish

£1115 $1762 €1673 Model study with nude women (180x190cm-71x75in) painted c.1925. 1-Apr-3 Rasmussen, Copenhagen #604/R est:8000 (D.KR 12000)

POULTON, James (19th C) British

£1400 $2268 €2100 Grapes, plums, peaches, pear, pineapple, chilli, melon and a basket (63x76cm-25x30in) s. 23-Jan-3 Christie's, Kensington #181/R est:800-1200

POUMEYROL, Jean-Marie (1945-) French

£4808 $7548 €7500 Tea time (73x100cm-29x39in) s. acrylic panel painted 1979 lit. 15-Dec-2 Eric Pillon, Calais #209/R

POURBUS, Frans (younger-attrib) (1570-1622) Flemish

£4403 $6824 €7000 Portrait of gentleman (105x82cm-41x32in) panel. 2-Oct-2 Dorotheum, Vienna #375/R est:6000-9000

POURBUS, Frans (younger-circle) (1570-1622) Flemish
£11986 $18699 €17500 Portrait of Heinrich Krufft of Cologne. Portrait of Maria Krufft (99x72cm-39x28in) d.1604 panel two. 11-Apr-3 Winterberg, Heidelberg #153/R est:22000

POURBUS, Frans (younger-style) (1570-1622) Flemish
£8600 $13416 €12900 Daughters of France (48x59cm-19x23in) panel. 17-Oct-2 Lawrence, Crewkerne #452/R est:5000-8000

POUSETTE-DART, Richard (1916-1992) American
£25000 $40000 €36250 Yellow centre (76x102cm-30x40in) s.d.67. 16-May-3 Skinner, Boston #372/R est:10000-15000
£126582 $200000 €189873 Number 1, 1951 (109x218cm-43x86in) s. verso painted 1951-52 prov.exhib. 14-Nov-2 Christie's, Rockefeller NY #123/R est:200000-300000
Works on paper
£11250 $18000 €16875 Untitled (15x23cm-6x9in) W/C ink paperboard executed 1946 prov. 14-May-3 Sotheby's, New York #102/R est:15000-20000

POUSSIN, Nicolas (1594-1665) French
Works on paper
£12838 $20027 €19000 Untitled. pen ink prov.lit. album. 26-Mar-3 Piasa, Paris #40/R

POUSSIN, Nicolas (attrib) (1594-1665) French
Works on paper
£1006 $1570 €1600 Figure studies (7x10cm-3x4in) pen. 19-Sep-2 Dr Fritz Nagel, Stuttgart #827/R est:2000

POUSSIN, Nicolas (style) (1594-1665) French
£6133 $9444 €9750 L'adoration des bergers (151x180cm-59x71in) 25-Oct-2 Tajan, Paris #105/R est:9000-12000
£15190 $24000 €24000 Moise enfant foulant aux pieds la couronne de Pharaon (95x126cm-37x50in) prov. 27-Nov-2 Christie's, Paris #23/R est:8000-12000

POUWELSEN, Martinus (1806-1891) Dutch
£2468 $3677 €3800 Mountain landscape (74x94cm-29x37in) s.d.1839. 26-Jun-2 Neumeister, Munich #833/R est:4000

POUWELSEN, Willem (1801-1873) Dutch
£1401 $2186 €2200 Shady landscape with farm and figures (44x58cm-17x23in) s. panel. 6-Nov-2 Vendue Huis, Gravenhage #450/R est:2500-3000

POVORINA, Alexandra (1885-1963) Russian/German
£1772 $2800 €2800 Still life with blue book (60x70cm-24x28in) s.d.1931. 30-Nov-2 Arnold, Frankfurt #440/R est:2000

POVORINA-AHLERS-HESTERMANN, Alexandra (1888-1963) Russian
£1026 $1590 €1600 Radiation (54x65cm-21x26in) oil sand. 7-Dec-2 Hauswedell & Nolte, Hamburg #1008/R est:1500
£1538 $2385 €2400 Still life with bottle (45x54cm-18x21in) mono. 7-Dec-2 Hauswedell & Nolte, Hamburg #1007/R est:2000
£2051 $3179 €3200 Women in wash place (57x69cm-22x27in) s.d. cloth. 7-Dec-2 Hauswedell & Nolte, Hamburg #1006/R est:3000
£2535 $4208 €3600 Still life of flowers (41x32cm-16x13in) s.d. board. 14-Jun-3 Hauswedell & Nolte, Hamburg #1542/R est:2500

POWDITCH, Peter (1942-) Australian
Works on paper
£543 $863 €815 Two pieces (59x39cm-23x15in) s. i.d.68 verso synthetic polymer board. 5-May-3 Sotheby's, Melbourne #250 (A.D 1400)

POWELL, Ace (1912-) American
£482 $800 €699 Abandoned cabin (46x61cm-18x24in) s. canvasboard. 14-Jun-3 Jackson's, Cedar Falls #428/R
£2690 $4250 €3901 Sunset and evening glow (46x71cm-18x28in) s. prov. 26-Jul-3 Coeur d'Alene, Hayden #13/R est:2500-4500

POWELL, Anna Maria (19th C) British
£550 $853 €825 Dutch skaters on a frozen river (27x42cm-11x17in) s.d.1810 verso panel. 6-Oct-2 Lots Road, London #351

POWELL, C M (1775-1824) British
£1750 $2713 €2625 Shipping off the coast (22x31cm-9x12in) s. 1-Nov-2 Moore Allen & Innocent, Cirencester #477/R est:800-1200

POWELL, Charles Martin (1775-1824) British
£1500 $2430 €2250 End of the day (25x33cm-10x13in) s. panel. 21-May-3 Christie's, Kensington #544/R est:1000-1500
£5500 $9185 €7975 Dutch man-o-war and other shipping off the coast (82x108cm-32x43in) mono.d.1816. 18-Jun-3 Sotheby's, Olympia #14/R est:6000-9000
£6500 $10530 €9750 Busy channel (29x37cm-11x15in) s.d.1805 panel. 22-Jan-3 Bonhams, New Bond Street #398/R est:5000-8000
£6800 $10608 €10200 Fishing boats and merchantman at sea (25x35cm-10x14in) s. panel. 10-Apr-3 Tennants, Leyburn #946/R est:3000-4000
£10000 $15900 €15000 British man of war and Dutch barges (67x93cm-26x37in) mono. 19-Mar-3 Sotheby's, London #1/R est:10000-15000

POWELL, Charles Martin (attrib) (1775-1824) British
£1500 $2370 €2250 Frigate with fishing boats off a Dutch coast in choppy seas (44x58cm-17x23in) 7-Apr-3 Bonhams, Bath #84/R est:1500-2500
£1600 $2592 €2400 Dutch barge and other shipping off the coast (21x28cm-8x11in) panel. 23-May-3 Lyon & Turnbull, Edinburgh #21/R est:1500-2000
£2500 $3900 €3750 Merchantmen, barges and traders in a channel (63x76cm-25x30in) 10-Sep-2 Bonhams, Knightsbridge #266/R est:800-1200

POWELL, Joseph (1780-1834) British
Works on paper
£400 $632 €600 Farmstead by a church with horses watering at a pond (44x59cm-17x23in) s. W/C. 2-Dec-2 Bonhams, Bath #6/R
£7500 $12225 €11250 Bridgnorth, Shropshire (21x32cm-8x13in) W/C. 29-Jan-3 Sotheby's, Olympia #52/R est:1000-1500

POWELL, Lucien Whiting (1846-1930) American
£321 $500 €482 Grand Canal (23x38cm-9x15in) s. board. 22-Sep-2 Jeffery Burchard, Florida #6
£1282 $2000 €1923 View of the Grand Canal at sunset (66x81cm-26x32in) s.d.1930. 14-Sep-2 Weschler, Washington #620/R est:2000-4000
£1534 $2500 €2301 Grand Canyon of the Yellowstone (46x76cm-18x30in) s. 16-Feb-3 Jeffery Burchard, Florida #34
£3185 $5000 €4778 Grand Canyon (61x91cm-24x36in) s. 14-Dec-2 Weschler, Washington #670/R est:3000-5000
Works on paper
£272 $425 €408 At the Soukh (28x46cm-11x18in) s. W/C. 20-Sep-2 Freeman, Philadelphia #30/R
£513 $800 €770 River landscape at dusk (44x62cm-17x24in) s. W/C gouache paper on board. 14-Sep-2 Weschler, Washington #621/R

POWELL, Mary (fl.1900-1925) British
£400 $632 €600 Dawn (43x58cm-17x23in) mono. 18-Dec-2 John Nicholson, Haslemere #1148
£700 $1106 €1050 Christmas roses (33x51cm-13x20in) 18-Dec-2 John Nicholson, Haslemere #1149
£750 $1185 €1125 Corner of stately house (64x38cm-25x15in) 18-Dec-2 John Nicholson, Haslemere #1145
£800 $1264 €1200 Long corridor (43x56cm-17x22in) mono. 18-Dec-2 John Nicholson, Haslemere #1146
Works on paper
£1050 $1659 €1575 Cedars, Victoria Road, Acocks Green, Birmingham (28x18cm-11x7in) W/C. 18-Dec-2 John Nicholson, Haslemere #1144 est:600-900

POWELL, Moila (1895-1994) British
Works on paper
£481 $755 €750 Fallen gum tree, Australia (34x47cm-13x19in) init. W/C gouache crayon prov. 19-Nov-2 Whyte's, Dublin #155
£577 $906 €900 By the pond (50x37cm-20x15in) init. W/C crayon gouache prov. 19-Nov-2 Whyte's, Dublin #157
£833 $1308 €1300 Red Warratah, Undalia, South Australia (33x52cm-13x20in) init. W/C gouache crayon prov. 19-Nov-2 Whyte's, Dublin #156/R

POWELL, Sir Francis (1833-1914) British
Works on paper
£560 $862 €840 Figures in a Scottish parkland landscape with country house (50x78cm-20x31in) s. W/C. 22-Oct-2 Bonhams, Bath #196
£1100 $1837 €1595 Ailsa Craig (77x132cm-30x52in) s.d.1880 i.verso W/C prov. 17-Jun-3 Rosebery Fine Art, London #476 est:800-1200
£1125 $1778 €1688 Gilmpse of the sea (69x51cm-27x20in) s. W/C exhib. 1-Apr-3 Stephan Welz, Johannesburg #412 est:4000-6000 (SA.R 14000)

POWELL, W E (19/20th C) British
Works on paper
£760 $1170 €1140 Ducks in flight amongst reeds (30x43cm-12x17in) s.verso W/C. 6-Sep-2 Biddle & Webb, Birmingham #98

POWELL, William E (19/20th C) British
Works on paper
£650 $1027 €975 Geese on a beach (24x34cm-9x13in) s.d.1928 W/C gum arabic. 28-Nov-2 Bonhams, Knightsbridge #53/R
£850 $1343 €1275 Shell ducks and stone curlews on a beach (24x34cm-9x13in) s.d.1928 W/C gum arabic. 28-Nov-2 Bonhams, Knightsbridge #52/R

POWER, Cyril (1872-1951) British
Prints
£2400 $3984 €3600 The Trio (20x18cm-8x7in) s.i. num.4/60 col. lino-cut. 12-Jun-3 Scarborough Perry Fine Arts, Hove #2400
£8500 $13260 €12750 Speed trial (20x37cm-8x15in) s.i. col linocut. 31-Mar-3 Bonhams, New Bond Street #385/R est:1500-2000

POWER, H S (1878-1951) New Zealander
£1400 $2226 €2100 Farmer following a two-horse plough team across a field within a landscape (22x37cm-9x15in) s. board. 19-Mar-3 Rupert Toovey, Partridge Green #150/R est:700-1000

POWER, Harold Septimus (1878-1951) New Zealander
£251 $381 €377 By the canal (28x37cm-11x15in) s. board. 27-Aug-2 Goodman, Sydney #187 (A.D 700)
£575 $856 €863 Ploughing the fields (19x27cm-7x11in) s. canvas on board. 27-Aug-2 Christie's, Melbourne #324 est:1500-2500 (A.D 1500)
£1000 $1580 €1500 Hauling logs (38x49cm-15x19in) s. 18-Nov-2 Joel, Victoria #399 est:4000-6000 (A.D 2800)
£1004 $1525 €1506 Beach scene (16x21cm-6x8in) s. canvas on board. 28-Aug-2 Deutscher-Menzies, Melbourne #301/R est:3000-4000 (A.D 2800)
£1846 $2935 €2769 Farmyard scene (63x76cm-25x30in) s. 4-Mar-3 Deutscher-Menzies, Melbourne #235/R est:5000-8000 (A.D 4800)
£2500 $3950 €3750 Rough rider (49x38cm-19x15in) s. 18-Nov-2 Joel, Victoria #314 est:7000-8000 (A.D 7000)
£2642 $4175 €3831 Draught horses (32x42cm-13x17in) s. board. 22-Jul-3 Lawson Menzies, Sydney #78/R est:3000-5000 (A.D 6500)
£2682 $4211 €4023 Dairy maid (53x73cm-21x29in) s. board. 15-Apr-3 Lawson Menzies, Sydney #52/R est:5000-7000 (A.D 7000)
£3681 $6000 €5522 Irish setter (63x76cm-25x30in) s. 11-Feb-3 Bonhams & Doyles, New York #252/R est:6000-8000
£6050 $9256 €9075 Horses after toil (86x110cm-34x43in) s. painted c.1930 prov. 26-Aug-2 Sotheby's, Paddington #544/R est:22000-28000 (A.D 17000)
Works on paper
£448 $721 €650 Ploughing team (26x30cm-10x12in) s. W/C. 12-May-3 Joel, Victoria #349 est:1400-1800 (A.D 1120)
£714 $1129 €1071 Ploughing with Polly and Jack (31x41cm-12x16in) s. W/C. 18-Nov-2 Joel, Victoria #219/R est:2000-2500 (A.D 2000)

POWER, Ralph E (20th C) American
Works on paper
£479 $800 €695 Lumber schooner unloading in harbour (46x53cm-18x21in) s.d.1935 W/C exhib. 17-Jun-3 John Moran, Pasadena #120

POWERS, Hiram (1805-1873) American
Sculpture
£7547 $12000 €11321 Loule's hand (12cm-5in) i. marble conceived 1839 lit. 5-Mar-3 Sotheby's, New York #25/R est:12000-18000
£46296 $75000 €69444 Proserpine (57cm-22in) i. marble executed c.1849. 22-May-3 Christie's, Rockefeller NY #50/R est:50000-70000

POWERS, Ken (?) American
Works on paper
£256 $400 €384 Fishermen with canoe on river (41x51cm-16x20in) gouache. 18-Sep-2 Alderfer's, Hatfield #265

POWERS, Richard M (1921-1996) American
Works on paper
£1180 $1900 €1770 Single man and machines on desolate planet (33x20cm-13x8in) s. gouache. 10-May-3 Illustration House, New York #167/R est:2000-3000

POWNALL, George Hyde (c.1876-1932) Australian
£382 $603 €573 Bulldog (19x14cm-7x6in) s. board. 1-Apr-3 Lawson Menzies, Sydney #451 (A.D 1000)

POY DALMAU, Emilio (1876-1933) Spanish
£329 $533 €500 Peasant man (37x22cm-15x9in) s. 21-Jan-3 Ansorena, Madrid #140/R

POYET, Leonard (1798-1873) French
£2100 $3339 €3150 Portrait of William, Anne and Emily Burkinyoung (46x51cm-18x20in) s. 29-Apr-3 Gorringes, Lewes #2155

POYNTER, Ambrose (1796-1886) British
Works on paper
£300 $474 €450 St Leon, Northern France (24x17cm-9x7in) W/C. 26-Nov-2 Bonhams, Knightsbridge #228/R

POYNTER, Sir Edward John (1836-1919) British
£2700 $4482 €4050 Study of fruit (22x27cm-9x11in) i.verso prov. 12-Jun-3 Sotheby's, London #236/R est:2500-3000
£100000 $161000 €150000 Prodigal's return (120x91cm-47x36in) mono.d.1869 prov.exhib.lit. 19-Feb-3 Christie's, London #29/R est:150000-220000
Works on paper
£480 $792 €696 Study of an arm for 'Michelangelo and Phidias' (23x28cm-9x11in) studio st. black white chk. 3-Jul-3 Christie's, Kensington #159
£667 $1107 €967 Figure studies (32x23cm-13x9in) mono. chl htd white prov. 16-Jun-3 Waddingtons, Toronto #32/R est:1500-2000 (C.D 1500)
£900 $1404 €1350 Apse of the lecture theatre, South Kensington (9x13cm-4x5in) mono. pastel two. 17-Oct-2 Christie's, Kensington #34/R
£950 $1530 €1425 Figure and drapery studies (35x26cm-14x10in) one i. one d.1869 chk pair prov.exhib. 20-Feb-3 Christie's, London #167/R
£9000 $14490 €13500 Mercy: the prodigal son (16x12cm-6x5in) mono.d.1868 pencil W/C gum arabic arched top prov.exhib.lit. 20-Feb-3 Christie's, London #164/R

POZIER, Jacinte (1844-1915) French
£2817 $4535 €4000 Rochers du Bois d'Amour a Pont Aven (55x81cm-22x32in) s.i.d.1901 verso. 11-May-3 Thierry & Lannon, Brest #216/R est:3200-3500

POZZATI, Concetto (1935-) Italian
£1046 $1673 €1600 Guard (50x60cm-20x24in) s.i.d.1999 verso acrylic enamel. 4-Jan-3 Meeting Art, Vercelli #626
£1203 $1876 €1900 Painting guardian (40x50cm-16x20in) s.i.d.1999 acrylic enamel. 14-Sep-2 Meeting Art, Vercelli #756/R
£1275 $2039 €1950 Orange guard (50x60cm-20x24in) s.i.d.1999 verso acrylic enamel. 4-Jan-3 Meeting Art, Vercelli #78
£6646 $10500 €10500 Still life in pink (175x200cm-69x79in) s.i.d.68/69 oil collage mirror. 29-Nov-2 Farsetti, Prato #466/R est:8800
Works on paper
£1154 $1788 €1800 Memory (70x80cm-28x31in) s.verso collage mixed media on canvas. 5-Dec-2 Stadion, Trieste #726/R

POZZI, Ennio (1893-1972) Italian
£1266 $1975 €2000 Hut in the wood (70x86cm-28x34in) s.d.1949. 19-Oct-2 Semenzato, Venice #24/R

POZZI, Walter (1911-1989) Italian
£272 $433 €400 Inn (20x15cm-8x6in) s. tempera cardboard on canvas. 1-Mar-3 Meeting Art, Vercelli #670

POZZO, Ugo (1900-1981) Italian
£340 $541 €500 Panther (40x50cm-16x20in) s. tempera cardboard. 1-Mar-3 Meeting Art, Vercelli #411
£385 $596 €600 Figure (34x24cm-13x9in) s. tempera pencil paper. 4-Dec-2 Finarte, Milan #189/R
Works on paper
£1282 $1987 €2000 Composition (70x50cm-28x20in) s. collage mixed media card. 4-Dec-2 Finarte, Milan #289/R est:2400

PRABHA, B (20th C) Indian
£2176 $3590 €3155 Fisherwoman (63x51cm-25x20in) s.d. prov. 6-Jul-3 Christie's, Hong Kong #99/R est:30000-40000 (HK.D 28000)

PRACHENSKY, Markus (1932-) Austrian
£3041 $4743 €4500 Solitude (69x50cm-27x20in) s.d.64 col Indian ink. 25-Mar-3 Wiener Kunst Auktionen, Vienna #5/R est:4000-6000
£7971 $13072 €11000 California revisited (130x100cm-51x39in) s.d.01 acrylic. 27-May-3 Wiener Kunst Auktionen, Vienna #216/R est:8000-12000
£10811 $16865 €16000 Umbria 13-1986 (130x120cm-51x47in) s.d.86 s.d. verso i.d.stretcher acrylic. 25-Mar-3 Wiener Kunst Auktionen, Vienna #6/R est:14000-22000
£13475 $21830 €19000 Rechberg (130x99cm-51x39in) s.d.66 acrylic prov. 20-May-3 Dorotheum, Vienna #195/R est:14000-17000

Works on paper

£2138 $3293 €3400 Umbria red (76x56cm-30x22in) s.d.1988 s.i.d. verso Indian ink. 26-Oct-2 Dr Lehr, Berlin #434/R est:3400
£2215 $3434 €3500 Red on white (65x48cm-26x19in) s. W/C. 24-Sep-2 Wiener Kunst Auktionen, Vienna #209/R est:3000-4500
£2532 $4000 €4000 Berlin (69x48cm-27x19in) s.d.63 W/C. 27-Nov-2 Dorotheum, Vienna #236/R est:2800-3400
£2778 $4417 €4000 Lada, Luras, Bilela (56x77cm-22x30in) s.d.94 col Indian ink. 29-Apr-3 Wiener Kunst Auktionen, Vienna #500/R est:2600-4000
£3165 $4905 €5000 Vienna III (70x50cm-28x20in) s.d.67 W/C. 24-Sep-2 Wiener Kunst Auktionen, Vienna #217/R est:4300-7000
£3165 $4905 €5000 Liechtenstein (48x65cm-19x26in) s. W/C. 24-Sep-2 Wiener Kunst Auktionen, Vienna #220/R est:4500-6500
£3819 $6035 €5500 Untitled (76x56cm-30x22in) s.d.97 Indian ink. 24-Apr-3 Dorotheum, Vienna #302/R est:2600-3400
£4965 $8043 €7000 Red and blue (50x70cm-20x28in) s.d.65 s.d. verso brush Indian ink. 20-May-3 Dorotheum, Vienna #198/R est:4000-6000
£4965 $8043 €7000 Puglia Marina (56x76cm-22x30in) s.d.77 col Indian ink paper on board. 20-May-3 Dorotheum, Vienna #235/R est:3000-4000

PRACHENSKY, Theodor (1888-1970) Austrian
Works on paper
£694 $1104 €1000 Flowers in turquoise vase (46x54cm-18x21in) s.d.57 W/C. 29-Apr-3 Wiener Kunst Auktionen, Vienna #621/R

PRACHENSKY, Wilhelm Nikolaus (1898-1956) Austrian
£12025 $19000 €19000 Landscape (70x49cm-28x19in) mono. board. 27-Nov-2 Dorotheum, Vienna #187/R est:17000-20000
Works on paper
£1812 $2971 €2500 Flowers (29x20cm-11x8in) s.d.55 pencil w. 27-May-3 Wiener Kunst Auktionen, Vienna #95/R est:2500-5000
£2174 $3565 €3000 Flowers (29x20cm-11x8in) s.d.55 pencil W/C. 27-May-3 Wiener Kunst Auktionen, Vienna #94/R est:2500-5000
£2695 $4366 €3800 Farmsteads (29x29cm-11x11in) i. mixed media board. 20-May-3 Dorotheum, Vienna #129/R est:3800-5000
£2899 $4754 €4000 Flowers (20x29cm-8x11in) s. pencil W/C. 27-May-3 Wiener Kunst Auktionen, Vienna #96/R est:2500-5000

PRADA, Carlo (1884-1960) Italian
£645 $1019 €1000 View of Como Lake (30x39cm-12x15in) s. board. 18-Dec-2 Finarte, Milan #163/R

PRADES, A F de (fl.1844-1883) British
£260 $406 €390 Portrait of Prince, property of Lord Cardigan (58x46cm-23x18in) i. board. 8-Apr-3 Bonhams, Knightsbridge #79/R
£620 $967 €930 Morning ride (29x45cm-11x18in) with sig. 26-Mar-3 Sotheby's, Olympia #93/R

PRADES, Alfred F de (fl.1844-1883) British
£6800 $10744 €10200 Jockey's enclosure (46x70cm-18x28in) 27-Nov-2 Christie's, London #9/R

PRADIER, Jean Jacques (1792-1852) French/Swiss
Sculpture
£2405 $3800 €3800 Phryne (54x18cm-21x7in) s. pat bronze Cast Susse. 27-Nov-2 Lemoine & Ferrando, Paris #168/R est:3800-4500
£2800 $4368 €4200 Birth of cupid (12x22cm-5x9in) two tone gilt bronze green brown pat bronze lit. 5-Nov-2 Sotheby's, London #183/R est:3000-5000
£2800 $4676 €4060 Phryne (54cm-21in) s.i. rich brown pat bronze Cast Susse F. 8-Jul-3 Sotheby's, London #195/R est:3000-5000
£4200 $7014 €6090 Standing Sappho (45cm-18in) s.d.1848 dk brown pat bronze st.f.VP. 8-Jul-3 Sotheby's, London #194/R est:3000-5000

PRADIER, Raoul (1929-) French
£250 $403 €375 Les irises (73x54cm-29x21in) s.d.61 board prov. 18-Feb-3 Bonhams, Knightsbridge #121/R

PRADILLA Y ORTIZ, Francisco (1848-1921) Spanish
£450 $734 €675 Head of a boy (37x30cm-15x12in) i.verso. 13-Feb-3 Christie's, Kensington #57
£2466 $3847 €3600 Coastal view (19x28cm-7x11in) s. board. 8-Apr-3 Ansorena, Madrid #237/R
£2690 $4250 €3901 Washing day (18x28cm-7x11in) s.d.1873 panel. 5-Apr-3 DeFina, Austinburg #1284 est:1500-2500
£14000 $21700 €21000 Preparatory study for Juana la Loca (44x58cm-17x23in) s.i.d.1876 i.verso. 4-Dec-2 Christie's, London #22/R est:12000-18000
£19388 $30827 €28500 Carnival souvenir in Rome (33x22cm-13x9in) s. i.d.1883 verso panel. 23-Mar-3 Herbette, Doullens #8/R

PRADILLA, Francisco (1840-1921) Spanish
Works on paper
£6000 $9420 €9000 Ninas Napolitanas - Neapolitan girls (54x37cm-21x15in) s.d.1875 W/C pencil pair. 19-Nov-2 Sotheby's, London #74/R est:6000-8000

PRAED, Michael J (1941-) British
£250 $408 €375 Corner of the harbour (38x46cm-15x18in) s. i.verso board. 13-Feb-3 David Lay, Penzance #371
£290 $452 €435 Inlet, St Mary's, Isles of Scilly (25x43cm-10x17in) s. i.verso board. 17-Oct-2 David Lay, Penzance #1103
£450 $702 €675 Harbour (41x33cm-16x13in) s. i.verso board. 17-Oct-2 David Lay, Penzance #1413

PRAEGER, Sophia Rosamund (1867-1954) British
Works on paper
£650 $949 €975 By the Bay of Donegal (33x18cm-13x7in) s. waxed moulded plaster. 12-Jun-2 John Ross, Belfast #22
£700 $1022 €1050 Wind from the East (33x18cm-13x7in) s. wax moulded plaster. 12-Jun-2 John Ross, Belfast #21

PRAGNELL, Bartley R (1907-1966) Canadian
£283 $441 €471 Untitled - Portrait of a woman in grey (48x36cm-19x14in) s. board prov. 13-Apr-3 Levis, Calgary #95/R (C.D 650)
£304 $475 €508 Checked table (37x53cm-15x21in) s.d.1951 canvasboard prov. 13-Apr-3 Levis, Calgary #94/R (C.D 700)

PRAGUE SCHOOL (17th C) Czechoslovakian
£7432 $11595 €11000 Danae (98x147cm-39x58in) prov. 27-Mar-3 Dorotheum, Vienna #414/R est:4000-7000

PRAGUE SCHOOL (18th C) Czechoslovakian
£23226 $36697 €36000 Capriccios (47x70cm-19x28in) s. pair. 18-Dec-2 Piasa, Paris #51/R est:15000

PRAMPOLINI, Alessandro (1823-1865) Italian
£283 $436 €450 Wheat amongst rocks (22x29cm-9x11in) indis.sig. s.i.verso cardboard. 28-Oct-2 Il Ponte, Milan #269

PRAMPOLINI, Enrico (1894-1956) Italian
£6081 $9486 €9000 Forms and forces in the space (18x11cm-7x4in) s.d.34 tempera paper exhib. 26-Mar-3 Finarte Semenzato, Milan #244/R
£28443 $47500 €41242 Composition (81x100cm-32x39in) s.i. indis d. masonite exhib. 22-Jun-3 Freeman, Philadelphia #48/R est:8000-10000
Works on paper
£833 $1308 €1300 Bather (24x31cm-9x12in) s. mixed media. 20-Nov-2 Pandolfini, Florence #6
£1096 $1710 €1600 Study of woman (23x19cm-9x7in) init.d.44 Chinese ink pencil card. 10-Apr-3 Finarte Semenzato, Rome #276/R

PRAMPOLINI, Hiero (1913-1973) Italian
£878 $1370 €1300 Abstract composition (65x50cm-26x20in) s.d.58 prov. 26-Mar-3 Finarte Semenzato, Milan #110/R

PRAMPOLINI, Luigi (1892-?) Italian
Works on paper
£833 $1317 €1300 Figure (20x14cm-8x6in) pencil col crayon double-sided exec.c.1947-48. 15-Nov-2 Farsetti, Prato #121

PRANCE, Bertram (1889-?) British
£320 $531 €464 Trees in a landscape (23x28cm-9x11in) s. board. 12-Jun-3 Gorringes, Lewes #1691

PRANG, Y (?) ?
£1277 $1979 €1916 Bedouin on horseback looking out (100x80cm-39x31in) s. 4-Dec-2 AB Stockholms Auktionsverk #1881/R est:15000-20000 (S.KR 18000)

PRANGETTI, D (19th C) Italian
Works on paper
£300 $467 €450 Pantheon, Rome (13x20cm-5x8in) s. pencil W/C. 19-Sep-2 Christie's, Kensington #95

PRANGEY, Emile (1832-?) French
£3020 $4862 €4500 Combat sur la route de Paris (75x100cm-30x39in) s. 18-Feb-3 Vanderkindere, Brussels #20/R

PRANTL, Karl (1923-) Austrian
Sculpture
£4808 $7596 €7500 Stone for meditation (30x49x13cm-12x19x5in) marble. 14-Nov-2 Neumeister, Munich #859/R est:7000-8000

PRASCHL, Stefan (1910-1994) Austrian
Works on paper
£625 $987 €900 Black panther with flowing eyes (48x34cm-19x13in) s. mixed media. 24-Apr-3 Dorotheum, Vienna #179/R

PRASSINOS, Mario (1916-1985) Turkish
£881 $1365 €1400 Composition (21x16cm-8x6in) s.d.57 prov. 30-Oct-2 Artcurial Briest, Paris #730
£2138 $3314 €3400 La trouee (73x92cm-29x36in) s.i.d.22 juillet - 6 aout 81 verso. 30-Oct-2 Artcurial Briest, Paris #729/R est:2200-3000
£3000 $4740 €4500 Untitled (40x60cm-16x24in) 1-Apr-3 Bonhams, New Bond Street #92 est:2800-4000

PRATA DA CARAVAGGIO, Francesco (c.1500-1575) Italian
£30864 $50000 €46296 Holy Family in a landscape (43x34cm-17x13in) panel prov. 24-Jan-3 Christie's, Rockefeller NY #29/R est:30000-50000

PRATELLA, A (19/20th C) Italian
£8200 $12956 €11890 Fishing fleet in the Bay of Naples (30x48cm-12x19in) s. 23-Jul-3 Wintertons, Lichfield #482/R est:1800-2000

PRATELLA, Ada (1901-1929) Italian
£270 $422 €400 Seascape (15x27cm-6x11in) s. board. 28-Mar-3 Farsetti, Prato #663
Works on paper
£308 $486 €480 Marine with sailing boats (17x12cm-7x5in) s. W/C. 15-Nov-2 Farsetti, Prato #565

PRATELLA, Attilio (1856-1949) Italian
£2436 $3776 €3800 Girls in the field (17x28cm-7x11in) s. board. 5-Dec-2 Stadion, Trieste #743/R
£3774 $5811 €6000 Naples beach (16x28cm-6x11in) s. 23-Oct-2 Finarte, Milan #21/R est:6000-7000
£5975 $9201 €9500 Capri (36x27cm-14x11in) s. 23-Oct-2 Finarte, Milan #46/R est:10000-12000
£6149 $9592 €9100 On the beach (23x35cm-9x14in) s. board. 28-Mar-3 Farsetti, Prato #674/R
£7595 $12000 €12000 Marine (45x55cm-18x22in) s. 26-Nov-2 Christie's, Rome #242/R est:15000
£8228 $13000 €12342 Une place de Paris (45x90cm-18x35in) s.i. prov.exhib. 23-Apr-3 Christie's, Rockefeller NY #94/R est:12000-16000
£10870 $17826 €15000 Giardini comunali a Napoli (27x36cm-11x14in) s. panel. 27-May-3 Finarte, Milan #27/R est:12000-13000
£11348 $17589 €17022 Picnic on the heights above Naples (25x36cm-10x14in) s.i. 4-Dec-2 AB Stockholms Auktionsverk #1895/R est:30000-35000 (S.KR 160000)
£13889 $22083 €20000 Naples Bay (52x64cm-20x25in) s. prov. 30-Apr-3 Tajan, Paris #101/R est:15000
£14000 $21980 €21000 Capo di Monte, Napoli (35x21cm-14x8in) s.d.1907 panel. 21-Nov-2 Christie's, Kensington #133/R est:4000-6000
£18987 $30000 €30000 Naples seen from Posillipo (37x69cm-15x27in) s.d.919 cardboard. 26-Nov-2 Christie's, Rome #240/R est:38000
Works on paper
£4762 $7571 €7000 Treed avenue (47x20cm-19x8in) s. pastel. 1-Mar-3 Meeting Art, Vercelli #271
£8228 $13000 €13000 Naples (32x55cm-13x22in) s. W/C card. 26-Nov-2 Christie's, Rome #241/R

PRATELLA, Attilio (attrib) (1856-1949) Italian
£5063 $8000 €8000 Vomero Street with figures (21x36cm-8x14in) s. board. 26-Nov-2 Christie's, Rome #164/R est:8000-12000

PRATELLA, Fausto (1888-1948) Italian
£1449 $2377 €2000 Velieri nel porto (18x24cm-7x9in) s. panel. 27-May-3 Finarte, Milan #12/R est:1000-1200
£1824 $2809 €2900 Marine (32x42cm-13x17in) s. board. 23-Oct-2 Finarte, Milan #23/R
£4500 $7515 €6750 Fishing boats mooring at dusk (70x99cm-28x39in) s. 18-Jun-3 Christie's, Kensington #142/R est:5000-7000

PRATERE, Henri de (1815-1890) Belgian
£1572 $2453 €2500 Hunting party (73x102cm-29x40in) s. 19-Sep-2 Dr Fritz Nagel, Stuttgart #986/R est:3000

PRATS Y VELASCO, Francisco (19th C) Spanish
£1730 $2698 €2750 Portrait of lady (84x68cm-33x27in) s.d.1838. 23-Sep-2 Durán, Madrid #164/R

PRATT, Christopher (1935-) Canadian
£9073 $14335 €13610 Portrait of Donna (30x25cm-12x10in) s.i.d.1976 board prov. 14-Nov-2 Heffel, Vancouver #180/R est:13000-16000 (C.D 22500)
Prints
£1864 $2964 €2796 Railway (64x75cm-25x30in) s.i.d.1978 col serigraph. 23-Mar-3 Hodgins, Calgary #44/R est:2000-2500 (C.D 4400)

PRATT, Claude (1860-c.1935) British
£2500 $3900 €3750 Figures on a street in Algiers (87x69cm-34x27in) s. 15-Oct-2 Sotheby's, London #209/R est:3000-5000
Works on paper
£280 $442 €406 Watched kettle (29x44cm-11x17in) s.d.1898 W/C. 22-Jul-3 Bonhams, Knightsbridge #199/R
£620 $1004 €930 Husband and wife taking breakfast (31x22cm-12x9in) s.d.1915 W/C. 21-Jan-3 Bonhams, Knightsbridge #14/R

PRATT, Douglas Fieldew (1900-1972) Australian
£872 $1238 €1308 Pelorous sound (66x88cm-26x35in) s. board prov. 21-Nov-1 Watson's, Christchurch #19/R est:3000-6000 (NZ.D 3000)

PRATT, H L (19th C) British
£1200 $1872 €1800 Portrait of a fighting cock (28x23cm-11x9in) s. pair. 10-Sep-2 Louis Taylor, Stoke on Trent #1144/R

PRATT, Henry Cheever (1803-1880) American
£2293 $3600 €3440 Portraits of Henry Foxcroft Esq and his wife Abigail Foxcroft Hammond (64x76cm-25x30in) one s.d.1826 verso one s.stretcher pair prov. 22-Nov-2 Eldred, East Dennis #850/R est:4000-6000
£3774 $6000 €5661 Gentleman in his library (25x20cm-10x8in) s.i.d.1842 panel prov. 5-Mar-3 Christie's, Rockefeller NY #92/R est:2000-3000
£32258 $50000 €48387 View in the Canyon of the Coppermines, Santa Rita, New Mexico (76x112cm-30x44in) prov.exhib.lit. 5-Dec-2 Christie's, Rockefeller NY #153/R est:60000-80000

PRATT, Henry Lark (1805-1873) British
£600 $1002 €870 Derby from the River Derwent (65x93cm-26x37in) s.d.1855. 26-Jun-3 Mellors & Kirk, Nottingham #925

PRATT, Hilton L (fl.1867-1873) British
£1050 $1722 €1575 Crossing the brook (23x40cm-9x16in) s.d.1872 board. 29-May-3 Christie's, Kensington #128/R est:500-800

PRATT, Jonathan (1835-1911) British
£800 $1304 €1160 News from abroad (60x50cm-24x20in) s.d.1871. 21-Jul-3 Bonhams, Bath #85/R
£4500 $7110 €6750 James Watt's workshop (42x51cm-17x20in) s.d.1889 s.i.d.verso prov. 26-Nov-2 Christie's, London #151/R est:2000-3000

PRATT, Mary Frances (1935-) Canadian
£4435 $7008 €6653 Jack Brown - 35 (36x61cm-14x24in) s.d.1971 i.verso board. 14-Nov-2 Heffel, Vancouver #99/R est:5000-7000 (C.D 11000)
£8065 $12742 €12098 Silver fish on crimson foil (47x60cm-19x24in) s.d.87 masonite prov.exhib.lit. 18-Nov-2 Sotheby's, Toronto #28/R est:20000-25000 (C.D 20000)
£11290 $17839 €16935 Blue grapes and yellow apple (55x68cm-22x27in) s.d.84 masonite sold with postcard poster prov.exhib.lit. 18-Nov-2 Sotheby's, Toronto #141/R est:20000-25000 (C.D 28000)
Prints
£1864 $2964 €2796 Through the window, bright (35x49cm-14x19in) s.d.1997 col serigraph. 23-Mar-3 Hodgins, Calgary #9/R est:2000-2500 (C.D 4400)

PRATT, William (1855-1936) British
£280 $434 €420 Drying nets, Fife coast (30x45cm-12x18in) s. 5-Dec-2 Bonhams, Edinburgh #60
£600 $984 €900 Cattle watering by an estuary (58x89cm-23x35in) s.d.80. 29-May-3 Christie's, Kensington #91/R
£700 $1113 €1050 Waterfall (81x66cm-32x26in) s. 5-Mar-3 Bonhams, Bury St Edmunds #416
£900 $1431 €1350 Figures holding banners gathered in a town square (30x41cm-12x16in) s.d.1892. 29-Apr-3 Gorringes, Lewes #2060
£1146 $1766 €1800 An old lady seated by a fireside (41x29cm-16x11in) 4-Sep-2 James Adam, Dublin #86 est:1500-2500
£1450 $2291 €2175 Way to the fold with Ayrshire cattle (68x101cm-27x40in) s.d.1935. 2-Dec-2 Bonhams, Bath #97 est:1500-2500
£1450 $2248 €2175 Seaward thoughts (40x29cm-16x11in) s.d. 26-Sep-2 Locke & England, Leamington Spa #273 est:1500-2500
£1700 $2652 €2550 Harbour at sunset (60x39cm-24x15in) s.d.83 board. 14-Apr-3 Sotheby's, London #90/R est:1500-2000
£2200 $3432 €3300 Crofter's wife (40x51cm-16x20in) s.d.1929. 14-Apr-3 Sotheby's, London #53/R est:1500-2000
£7000 $10640 €10500 Collecting the catch (68x102cm-27x40in) s.d.1933. 28-Aug-2 Sotheby's, London #996/R est:7000-10000

PRAX, Valentine (1899-1981) French
£1042 $1656 €1500 Allegorie aux marins (44x62cm-17x24in) s. 29-Apr-3 Artcurial Briest, Paris #249/R est:1500-2000
£1195 $1900 €1793 Nu couche (65x81cm-26x32in) s. prov. 27-Feb-3 Christie's, Rockefeller NY #104/R
£1439 $2302 €2000 Nature morte au violon (81x100cm-32x39in) 16-May-3 Lombrail & Teucquam, Paris #146/R
£1511 $2417 €2100 Le couple (100x81cm-39x32in) 16-May-3 Lombrail & Teucquam, Paris #147/R
£1655 $2648 €2400 Still life (50x65cm-20x26in) s. 15-Mar-3 De Vuyst, Lokeren #474/R est:2500-3500
£2229 $3478 €3500 Nature morte a la Volaille (81x100cm-32x39in) s.d.1926. 6-Nov-2 Claude Boisgirard, Paris #47 est:3500-4000
£2381 $3786 €3500 Invitation au voyage (65x81cm-26x32in) s. 24-Mar-3 Claude Boisgirard, Paris #63/R
£3472 $5729 €5000 Nu a la cheminee (117x81cm-46x32in) s. painted c.1920 prov. 2-Jul-3 Artcurial Briest, Paris #671/R est:5000-7000
£3537 $5624 €5200 Vase de fleurs (100x86cm-39x34in) s. 3-Mar-3 Claude Boisgirard, Paris #90/R est:6000-8000
£4403 $6824 €7000 Nu a la cheminee (117x81cm-46x32in) s. painted c.1920 prov. 30-Oct-2 Artcurial Briest, Paris #68/R est:7000-10000
£5328 $8311 €7992 Deux femmes au terrasse (80x116cm-31x46in) s.d.1925. 20-Nov-2 Fischer, Luzern #1104/R est:15000-18000 (S.FR 12200)
£5769 $9058 €9000 Jeune fille assise (100x81cm-39x32in) s. 22-Nov-2 Millon & Associes, Paris #117/R
Works on paper
£473 $738 €700 Vie de la ferme (38x41cm-15x16in) s. dr. 28-Mar-3 Claude Aguttes, Neuilly #142

PREAULX, Michel François (fl.1796-1827) French
Works on paper
£2979 $4974 €4200 La cote de Fanaraka d'Europe (32x91cm-13x36in) s.i.d.juillet 1813 pencil grey wash prov. 23-Jun-3 Beaussant & Lefèvre, Paris #82/R est:1000-1200
£8042 $13430 €11500 Vue du kiosk de la Vallee du Grand Seigneur, puis la papeterie (22x37cm-9x15in) i.d.24 juin 1814 W/C. 27-Jun-3 Claude Aguttes, Neuilly #107/R est:10000-12000
£8392 $14014 €12000 Vue du Bosphore (28x43cm-11x17in) W/C. 27-Jun-3 Claude Aguttes, Neuilly #106/R est:10000-12000
£8741 $14598 €12500 Vue du Kief de Sultanie sur le Boshphore, Cote d'Asie (22x37cm-9x15in) s.i.d.3 juillet 1814 W/C. 27-Jun-3 Claude Aguttes, Neuilly #105/R est:10000-12000

PRECLIK, Vladimir (1929-) Czechoslovakian
Sculpture
£1238 $1956 €1857 Rose (195cm-77in) s.d.77 wood polychrome paint guiding. 30-Nov-2 Dorotheum, Prague #212/R est:60000-90000 (C.KR 60000)

PREDA, Ambrogio (1839-1906) Italian
£6332 $9878 €9498 Monte Bre and Lugano (73x111cm-29x44in) s. 8-Nov-2 Dobiaschofsky, Bern #25/R est:20000 (S.FR 14500)

PREECE, Patricia (1900-1971) British
£900 $1476 €1350 Still life with flowers (51x40cm-20x16in) s. panel. 3-Jun-3 Sotheby's, Olympia #91/R

PREEN, Hugo von (1854-?) Austrian
Works on paper
£321 $506 €500 Aschach an der Donau (29x42cm-11x17in) mono. W/C. 18-Nov-2 Dorotheum, Linz #447/R

PREGARTBAUER, Louis (1899-1971) Austrian
Works on paper
£382 $603 €550 Strolling in Vienna (41x53cm-16x21in) s. chl pastel. 24-Apr-3 Dorotheum, Vienna #138/R
£385 $608 €600 Aschach power station (49x75cm-19x30in) s. pastel. 12-Nov-2 Dorotheum, Vienna #205/R
£449 $709 €700 San Sebastian, Spain (44x59cm-17x23in) bears s. pastel. 12-Nov-2 Dorotheum, Vienna #215/R

PREGEL, Alexandra Nicholaevna (1907-1984) Russian
£2700 $4374 €4050 Plant and Manhattan skyline (45x56cm-18x22in) board. 21-May-3 Sotheby's, London #222/R est:3000-4000

PREGO, Manuel (1915-1986) Spanish
£4897 $7786 €7100 Washerwomen (73x60cm-29x24in) s. 4-Mar-3 Ansorena, Madrid #240/R
Works on paper
£903 $1427 €1400 Still life (65x50cm-26x20in) s.d.83 mixed media. 17-Dec-2 Durán, Madrid #167/R

PREHN, A (19th C) ?
£559 $888 €839 The hencoop ladder (63x31cm-25x12in) s. 5-Mar-3 Rasmussen, Copenhagen #1920/R (D.KR 6000)

PREISLER, J M (18th C) Danish?
Prints
£2412 $3666 €3618 Frederik V on horseback (88x62cm-35x24in) copperplate after J Saly lit. 27-Aug-2 Rasmussen, Copenhagen #2110/R est:12000-15000 (D.KR 28000)

PREISLER, Jan (1872-1918) Czechoslovakian
£943 $1462 €1500 Peniche (29x37cm-11x15in) mono. oil wax pastel cardboard prov. 30-Oct-2 Artcurial Briest, Paris #70 est:1500-2000

PREISS, F (1882-1943) German
Sculpture
£1900 $3002 €2850 Figure of a nude female (21cm-8in) i. bronze. 14-Nov-2 Christie's, Kensington #297/R est:1000-1500
£3000 $4740 €4500 Hoop girl (20cm-8in) bronze ivory. 14-Nov-2 Christie's, Kensington #282/R est:1800-2200
£3800 $6080 €5700 Hoop girl. Sonny boy (21cm-8in) bronze pair lit. 15-May-3 Christie's, Kensington #454/R est:4000-6000
£8500 $13515 €12750 Young bathing beauty reclining on a rock, with red swimming cap (10cm-4in) s. ivory gold painted bronze black slate base. 18-Mar-3 Fellows & Sons, Birmingham #234/R est:4000-6000
£18000 $28800 €27000 Autumn dancer (37cm-15in) s. cold pat. bronze st.f. lit. 15-May-3 Christie's, Kensington #460/R est:18000-22000

PREISS, Ferdinand (1882-1943) German
Sculpture
£1484 $2181 €2300 Vanity (22cm-9in) i. verso bronze ivory marble socle. 20-Jun-2 Dr Fritz Nagel, Stuttgart #204/R est:3900
£3700 $5809 €5550 Young woman partly disrobed (21cm-8in) s. gilt bronze green alabaster base. 21-Nov-2 Tennants, Leyburn #874/R est:2000-3000
£5500 $8800 €8250 Sunshade girl (23cm-9in) i. cold pat. bronze ivory lit. 15-May-3 Christie's, Kensington #458/R est:6000-8000
£6175 $9633 €9263 Two women scantily dressed (22cm-9in) gilt and pat.bronze incl. green marble socle pair. 11-Nov-2 Rasmussen, Vejle #745/R est:80000-100000 (D.KR 72000)
£6200 $9858 €9300 Moth girl (41cm-16in) bronze ivory. 27-Feb-3 Sotheby's, Olympia #195 est:3500-4500
£7600 $12160 €11400 Dancer (36cm-14in) s. cold pat. bronze lit. 15-May-3 Christie's, Kensington #457/R est:8000-12000
£7742 $12000 €11613 Torch dancer (32x30cm-13x12in) st.sig. ivory cold painted bronze resin with onyx base c.1925. 6-Dec-2 Sotheby's, New York #159/R est:15000-20000
£9000 $14310 €13500 Lighter than air, young woman holding a glass ball (35cm-14in) bronze ivory. 27-Feb-3 Sotheby's, Olympia #196/R est:9000-12000

PREISSLER, Georg Martin (1700-1754) German
Works on paper
£811 $1265 €1200 Portrait of man (27x18cm-11x7in) s.d.1736 crayon htd W/C. 27-Mar-3 Maigret, Paris #109/R

PREISSLER, Johann Justin (1698-1771) German
Works on paper
£420 $600 €630 Juno asking Jupiter to calm the storm unleashed by Aeolos to destroy the fleet (27x32cm-11x13in) black chk htd white. 23-Jan-3 Swann Galleries, New York #339/R

PREISWERK, Theophil (1846-1919) Swiss
£305 $500 €442 Boys swimming (27x49cm-11x19in) s. canvas on board. 4-Jun-3 Fischer, Luzern #2284/R (S.FR 650)

PREITSCHOFF, Jakob (1786-1833) Austrian
£274 $430 €400 Christ on Mount of Olives (54x40cm-21x16in) s. panel. 16-Apr-3 Dorotheum, Salzburg #56/R

PREKAS, Paris (1926-1999) Greek
£1600 $2528 €2400 View of Kalavryta (45x57cm-18x22in) 1-Apr-3 Bonhams, New Bond Street #67 est:1000-2000

PRELLER, Alexis (1911-1975) South African

£276 $431 €414 Portrait of a boy in a shawl (9x6cm-4x2in) board. 15-Oct-2 Stephan Welz, Johannesburg #469 est:3000-4000 (SA.R 4500)
£369 $575 €554 Portrait of a woman with a yellow face (19x15cm-7x6in) s. board. 15-Oct-2 Stephan Welz, Johannesburg #471/R est:6000-9000 (SA.R 6000)
£860 $1342 €1290 Portrait of a girl wearing bangles (21x17cm-8x7in) s. board. 15-Oct-2 Stephan Welz, Johannesburg #470/R est:6000-9000 (SA.R 14000)
£1032 $1661 €1548 Arms (64x59cm-25x23in) s.d.45. 12-May-3 Stephan Welz, Johannesburg #587/R est:12000-16000 (SA.R 12000)
£1307 $2105 €1961 Portrait of African woman (40x37cm-16x15in) s.d.38. 7-May-3 Dunbar Sloane, Auckland #61/R est:2000-3000 (NZ.D 3700)
£1548 $2492 €2322 Still life with mangoes (35x45cm-14x18in) s.d.63 board. 12-May-3 Stephan Welz, Johannesburg #558/R est:20000-30000 (SA.R 18000)
£2050 $3198 €3075 Still life with mangoes (24x30cm-9x12in) s.d.52 canvas on board. 11-Nov-2 Stephan Welz, Johannesburg #471/R est:35000-50000 (SA.R 32000)
£2580 $4153 €3870 Sunflowers (43x61cm-17x24in) s.d.46. 12-May-3 Stephan Welz, Johannesburg #568/R est:25000-35000 (SA.R 30000)
£5125 $7995 €7688 Helios (167x182cm-66x72in) s.d.65 prov.exhib. 11-Nov-2 Stephan Welz, Johannesburg #514/R est:60000-90000 (SA.R 80000)
£9930 $15490 €14895 Snail, Mahe (44x40cm-17x16in) s.d.49 canvas on board. 11-Nov-2 Stephan Welz, Johannesburg #473/R est:40000-60000 (SA.R 155000)
£12038 $19381 €18057 Hay cart (25x30cm-10x12in) s.d.52 canvas on board exhib. 12-May-3 Stephan Welz, Johannesburg #489/R est:60000-90000 (SA.R 140000)

Works on paper

£352 $550 €528 Preliminary sketch for Wounded Sculpture (89x100cm-35x39in) pencil col crayon paint dabs. 11-Nov-2 Stephan Welz, Johannesburg #486 (SA.R 5500)
£1608 $2540 €2412 African woman (16x11cm-6x4in) s. painted ceramic tile. 1-Apr-3 Stephan Welz, Johannesburg #469/R est:10000-15000 (SA.R 20000)

PRELLER, Friedrich Johann Christian Ernst (1804-1878) German

Works on paper

£475 $750 €750 Self portrait (38x58cm-15x23in) mono.i.d.1855 pencil. 29-Nov-2 Bassenge, Berlin #6020/R
£576 $944 €800 Italian river landscape (30x46cm-12x18in) mono.i.d.1875 pencil. 4-Jun-3 Reiss & Sohn, Konigstein #279/R
£612 $1003 €850 Muskau Park (24x35cm-9x14in) mono.i. Septbe 1849 W/C sepia board. 4-Jun-3 Reiss & Sohn, Konigstein #278/R
£737 $1077 €1150 Study of rocks, Studesnas, Norway (18x26cm-7x10in) s.i. pencil sepia wash. 4-Jun-2 Karl & Faber, Munich #121/R

PRELLER, J (19th C) German

£1299 $1896 €2000 Spring landscape with figures and animals (58x79cm-23x31in) s. 15-Jun-2 Hans Stahl, Hamburg #155/R

PRELOG, Drago J (1939-) Yugoslavian

£2128 $3447 €3000 The letter G (120x150cm-47x59in) s.d.1980 acylic. 20-May-3 Dorotheum, Vienna #243/R est:3200-5000

Works on paper

£316 $494 €500 On the day of honour for Alfred (31x48cm-12x19in) s.i.d.3.12.1981 Indian ink collage bodycol. 15-Oct-2 Dorotheum, Vienna #243/R

PREM, Heimrad (1934-1978) German

£1859 $2714 €2900 Untitled (71x81cm-28x32in) oil material. 4-Jun-2 Karl & Faber, Munich #389/R est:4500
£2244 $3276 €3500 Two 'one eyes' (60x60cm-24x24in) s.d.76 oil pigment ed. 4-Jun-2 Karl & Faber, Munich #388/R est:6000-7000
£2842 $4406 €4263 Composition (53x33cm-21x13in) s.verso masonite painted c.1961. 4-Dec-2 Kunsthallen, Copenhagen #115/R est:30000 (D.KR 33000)
£3717 $5874 €5576 Juwelensucher - composition (80x90cm-31x35in) s.d.63 lit. 1-Apr-3 Rasmussen, Copenhagen #180/R est:50000 (D.KR 40000)

Works on paper

£684 $1081 €1026 Untitled (41x58cm-16x23in) s.d.65 gouache. 28-Apr-3 Bukowskis, Stockholm #322/R (S.KR 9000)
£759 $1177 €1200 Nameless brood (42x28cm-17x11in) s.d. i. verso gouache over biro chk. 28-Sep-2 Ketterer, Hamburg #623/R
£1394 $2203 €2091 Erotic figure composition with woman on yellow background (42x59cm-17x23in) s.d.66 mixed media gouache W/C pencil prov. 1-Apr-3 Rasmussen, Copenhagen #245/R est:15000-18000 (D.KR 15000)

PREMAZZI, Ludwig (1814-1891) Russian

Works on paper

£840 $1328 €1260 Coastal landscape, Krim (25x36cm-10x14in) s. gouache. 16-Nov-2 Crafoord, Lund #64/R est:4000 (S.KR 12000)

PRENDERGAST, Charles E (1863-1948) American

£27778 $45000 €41667 Bounding deer (34x49cm-13x19in) init.i. tempera gold leaf on gessoed panel painted c.1915 prov.exhib. 21-May-3 Sotheby's, New York #29/R est:60000-80000

Works on paper

£4403 $7000 €6605 Grenoble (20x25cm-8x10in) init. W/C crayon prov.exhib.lit. 4-Mar-3 Christie's, Rockefeller NY #57/R est:4000-6000

PRENDERGAST, Maurice (1859-1924) American

£98765 $160000 €148148 Point, Gloucester (45x54cm-18x21in) s. prov.exhib.lit. 21-May-3 Sotheby's, New York #57/R est:200000-300000
£148148 $240000 €222222 East Boston ferry (37x32cm-15x13in) s. panel prov.exhib.lit. 21-May-3 Sotheby's, New York #20/R est:100000-150000
£197531 $320000 €296297 In the park (30x29cm-12x11in) s. W/C pencil executed c.1900-03 prov.exhib.lit. 21-May-3 Sotheby's, New York #65/R est:100000-150000
£216049 $350000 €324074 Luxembourg gardens (27x35cm-11x14in) s. panel painted c.1907 prov.exhib.lit. 21-May-3 Sotheby's, New York #21/R est:200000-300000

Prints

£20440 $32500 €30660 Lady with pigeons (22x15cm-9x6in) col monotype exec.c.1895-97 prov.exhib. 2-May-3 Sotheby's, New York #61/R est:25000-35000
£40881 $65000 €61322 Park promenade (22x16cm-9x6in) col monotype prov.exhib. 2-May-3 Sotheby's, New York #62/R est:60000-80000
£42169 $70000 €61145 Beach scene (25x20cm-10x8in) col monotype. 13-Jun-3 Du Mouchelle, Detroit #2021/R est:8000-12000

Works on paper

£10494 $17000 €15741 Nude model with drapery. Standing female nude (32x24cm-13x9in) W/C black chk pencil double-sided executed c.1912-15 prov.exhib. 21-May-3 Sotheby's, New York #99/R est:8000-12000
£24096 $40000 €34939 Fete (20x15cm-8x6in) W/C. 13-Jun-3 Du Mouchelle, Detroit #2020/R est:15000-20000
£24691 $40000 €37037 View of Venice (39x56cm-15x22in) s.i. W/C panel executed c.1911-12 prov.exhib.lit. 21-May-3 Sotheby's, New York #66/R est:60000-80000
£37419 $58000 €56129 Country road, New Hampshire (25x36cm-10x14in) s. W/C over pencil paper on board prov.exhib.lit. 3-Dec-2 Phillips, New York #68/R est:45000-65000
£61728 $100000 €92592 Road to the shore (28x37cm-11x15in) s. W/C pencil prov. 22-May-3 Christie's, Rockefeller NY #47/R est:100000-150000
£154321 $250000 €231482 Montparnasse (35x51cm-14x20in) s. W/C prov.exhib.lit. 21-May-3 Sotheby's, New York #53/R est:300000-500000
£322581 $500000 €483872 Venetian palaces on the Grand Canal (36x53cm-14x21in) s.i.d.1898 W/C. 4-Dec-2 Sotheby's, New York #15/R est:700000-900000
£540123 $875000 €810185 Handkerchief Point (36x53cm-14x21in) s.d.1896 i.verso W/C pencil prov.exhib.lit. 21-May-3 Sotheby's, New York #25/R est:100000-150000

PRENDERGAST, Peter (1946-) British

£720 $1159 €1044 Tal-Y-Bont (10x11cm-4x4in) s.d.1995 verso board. 19-Feb-3 Peter Wilson, Nantwich #57/R

PRENTICE, J R (19th C) British

£291 $413 €437 Sunset Holy Island (40x59cm-16x23in) prov. 21-Nov-1 Watson's, Christchurch #46/R (NZ.D 1000)

PRENTICE, Levi Wells (1851-1935) American

£11950 $19000 €17925 Strawberries (14x22cm-6x9in) s. prov. 5-Mar-3 Sotheby's, New York #11/R est:12000-18000
£12025 $19000 €18038 Cherries in a basket (20x25cm-8x10in) s. prov. 24-Apr-3 Shannon's, Milford #44/R est:8000-12000
£14815 $24000 €22223 Apples under a tree (25x20cm-10x8in) s. s.verso prov. 22-May-3 Christie's, Rockefeller NY #6/R est:25000-35000
£16049 $26000 €24074 Harvest of apples (29x48cm-11x19in) s. prov. 22-May-3 Christie's, Rockefeller NY #1/R est:25000-35000
£16129 $25000 €24194 Basket of apples (23x30cm-9x12in) s. prov. 4-Dec-2 Sotheby's, New York #134/R est:15000-25000
£20645 $32000 €30968 Raquette Lake (44x74cm-17x29in) s.d.1883 prov.exhib. 5-Dec-2 Christie's, Rockefeller NY #10/R est:40000-60000
£24193 $37500 €36290 Basket of apples (26x30cm-10x12in) s. prov. 4-Dec-2 Sotheby's, New York #135/R est:15000-25000

£26582 $42000 €39873 Apples in a basket (30x46cm-12x18in) s. 24-Apr-3 Shannon's, Milford #78/R est:40000-60000
£27097 $42000 €40646 Adirondack camp, after the hunt (43x83cm-17x33in) s.d.1879 canvas masonite prov.exhib. 5-Dec-2 Christie's, Rockefeller NY #49/R est:40000-60000

PRENTZEL, Hans (1880-1956) German
£321 $497 €500 Sunlit late summer landscape (65x104cm-26x41in) s. lit. 6-Dec-2 Karlheinz Kaupp, Staufen #2159/R
£440 $687 €700 Quiet corner (70x60cm-28x24in) s. s.i. verso lit. 20-Sep-2 Karlheinz Kaupp, Staufen #1921

PRESSET, Henri (1928-) Swiss
£1266 $2000 €2000 Summer flowers with fruit (121x91cm-48x36in) s. 29-Nov-2 Schloss Ahlden, Ahlden #1218/R est:2400

PRESSMANE, Joseph (1904-1967) French
£404 $638 €606 Coin de foret (40x17cm-16x7in) s. panel prov. 18-Nov-2 Waddingtons, Toronto #232/R (C.D 1000)
£709 $1107 €1050 Nature morte aux fleurs (46x38cm-18x15in) s. 26-Mar-3 Millon & Associes, Paris #107/R
£1572 $2437 €2500 Vue de Paris, la Seine (46x33cm-18x13in) s. 30-Oct-2 Artcurial Briest, Paris #73/R est:2700-3500
Works on paper
£440 $717 €660 La cle (36x20cm-14x8in) s. gouache prov. 3-Feb-3 Bonhams, New Bond Street #59/R

PRESTON, Henry (fl.1898-1901) British
Works on paper
£250 $408 €375 Windsor Castle from across the Thames (48x72cm-19x28in) s.d.1889 W/C. 17-Feb-3 Bonhams, Bath #201

PRESTON, Margaret Rose (1875-1963) Australian
£6000 $9660 €9000 Still life (48x58cm-19x23in) painted c.1900 prov. 6-May-3 Christie's, Melbourne #113/R est:15000-20000 (A.D 15000)
£6513 $9705 €9770 Studio window (80x59cm-31x23in) init.d.06 prov.exhib. 27-Aug-2 Christie's, Melbourne #98/R est:12000-15000 (A.D 17000)
Prints
£2286 $3611 €3429 Flowers in a jug (29x21cm-11x8in) s. woodblock print executed c.1929. 26-Nov-2 Sotheby's, Melbourne #77/R est:5500-7500 (A.D 6400)
£7308 $11619 €10962 Bridge from North Shore (19x23cm-7x9in) s.i.num. hand col woodcut edition 4 exec.c.1932 lit. 4-Mar-3 Deutscher-Menzies, Melbourne #272/R est:8000-10000 (A.D 19000)
Works on paper
£2000 $3220 €2900 Portrait of a child (15x13cm-6x5in) init. mixed media. 12-May-3 Joel, Victoria #347 est:5000-6000 (A.D 5000)

PRESTOPINO, Gregorio (1907-) American
£1946 $3250 €2822 Nude, late Sunday (122x136cm-48x54in) s. exhib. 22-Jun-3 Freeman, Philadelphia #155/R est:3000-5000
Works on paper
£455 $700 €683 New York river scene (28x43cm-11x17in) s. W/C exec.c.1940. 8-Sep-2 Treadway Gallery, Cincinnati #701/R

PRETI, Gregorio (1603-1672) Italian
£25641 $39744 €40000 Christ and the tribute (121x171cm-48x67in) 4-Dec-2 Christie's, Rome #475/R est:40000-60000

PRETI, Gregorio (attrib) (1603-1672) Italian
£14744 $22853 €23000 Prodigal son coming back (120x179cm-47x70in) exhib. 4-Dec-2 Christie's, Rome #428/R est:20000-30000

PRETI, Mattia (1613-1699) Italian
£37037 $60000 €55556 Saint Luke painting the Virgin (64x47cm-25x19in) 23-Jan-3 Sotheby's, New York #28/R est:40000-60000
£110345 $174345 €160000 Saint Anthony visiting Saint Paul the hermit (151x128cm-59x50in) 5-Apr-3 Finarte Semenzato, Milan #95/R est:120000-160000

PRETI, Mattia (attrib) (1613-1699) Italian
£4255 $6894 €6000 Ecce Homo (217x168cm-85x66in) lit. 20-May-3 Babuino, Rome #43/R est:4000-5000
Works on paper
£2200 $3674 €3190 Pool at Bethesda. Venus and Adonis (36x42cm-14x17in) i.verso pen ink red chk wash double-sided. 9-Jul-3 Bonhams, Knightsbridge #40/R est:2500-3000

PRETI, Mattia (circle) (1613-1699) Italian
£16000 $26720 €23200 Bacchanale (136x208cm-54x82in) 9-Jul-3 Bonhams, New Bond Street #129/R est:20000-30000

PREUSS, Rudolf (1879-?) Austrian
£1761 $2835 €2500 Country path (71x102cm-28x40in) s.d.1915 i. stretcher lit. 9-May-3 Schloss Ahlden, Ahlden #1513/R est:2800
Works on paper
£473 $738 €700 Riva from Lido, Lake Garda (20x29cm-8x11in) s.d.Mai 1903 W/C. 28-Mar-3 Dorotheum, Vienna #272/R
£541 $843 €800 Durnstein, Wachau (18x25cm-7x10in) s.i.d.28.6.06 W/C. 28-Mar-3 Dorotheum, Vienna #274/R

PREVERT, Jacques (1900-1977) French
Works on paper
£385 $596 €600 Portrait de famille (26x19cm-10x7in) s. collage. 7-Dec-2 De Vuyst, Lokeren #257
£943 $1462 €1500 Pont neuf (32x24cm-13x9in) s.i.d.71 collage photos chromos magazine page prov. 30-Oct-2 Artcurial Briest, Paris #259/R est:1500-1800
£1090 $1711 €1700 Printemps (23x18cm-9x7in) init.d.72 collage. 11-Dec-2 Maigret, Paris #108/R est:500-800
£1132 $1755 €1800 Sans titre (32x24cm-13x9in) s. collage magazine photos exec.c.1970. 30-Oct-2 Artcurial Briest, Paris #257/R est:2000-2500
£1321 $2047 €2100 Sans titre (30x22cm-12x9in) s. collage engravings chromos exec.c.1970 prov. 30-Oct-2 Artcurial Briest, Paris #258 est:1500-2000
£1418 $2369 €2000 Composition (56x15cm-22x6in) s.i. collage. 18-Jun-3 Pierre Berge, Paris #78/R est:1200-1500
£1465 $2285 €2300 Femme Toucan (24x18cm-9x7in) i.d.1976 collage. 7-Nov-2 Chochon-Barre & Allardi, Paris #213

PREVIATI, Gaetano (1852-1920) Italian
£1935 $3058 €3000 Portrait of Achille Cova (32x24cm-13x9in) cardboard on board. 18-Dec-2 Finarte, Milan #128/R
£2264 $3487 €3600 Christ's head (26x36cm-10x14in) s. on leather. 23-Oct-2 Finarte, Milan #124/R
Works on paper
£755 $1177 €1200 Female nude (12x28cm-5x11in) Indian ink board. 22-Sep-2 Semenzato, Venice #103/R

PREVITALI, Andrea (circle) (1470-1528) Italian
£5500 $9185 €7975 Portrait of a young man, head and shoulders wearing black (22x16cm-9x6in) panel. 8-Jul-3 Sotheby's, Olympia #321/R est:3000-4000

PREVOST, A (19/20th C) French
Works on paper
£2000 $3100 €3000 Dolphins (36x30cm-14x12in) one i. pen ink two. 26-Sep-2 Christie's, London #98/R est:1000-2000

PREVOST, Antoine (1930-) Canadian
Works on paper
£267 $437 €401 Les bonnes dames (27x35cm-11x14in) s. W/C prov. 3-Jun-3 Joyner, Toronto #405/R (C.D 600)
£356 $583 €534 Le Grand Pin (37x50cm-15x20in) s. W/C prov. 3-Jun-3 Joyner, Toronto #343/R (C.D 800)

PREVOST, Marguerite (19/20th C) French
£629 $969 €1000 Cour du musee du Bardo (64x105cm-25x41in) s.i.d.1949. 23-Oct-2 Rabourdin & Choppin de Janvry, Paris #174/R

PREVOT-VALERI, Andre (1890-1930) French
£550 $847 €825 Tranquil river landscape with cattle grazing near trees (28x36cm-11x14in) st.sig. board. 23-Oct-2 Hamptons Fine Art, Godalming #123/R
£608 $948 €960 Le troupeau pres de l'eglise (54x84cm-21x33in) s. 15-Sep-2 Etude Bailleul, Bayeux #66/R
£680 $1047 €1020 French cattle market (28x35cm-11x14in) st.sig. board. 23-Oct-2 Hamptons Fine Art, Godalming #126/R
£731 $1162 €1060 Paysage aux trois vaches a la mare (33x55cm-13x22in) s. 10-Mar-3 Thierry & Lannon, Brest #130/R

PREY, Barbara Ernst (?) American
Works on paper
£332 $525 €498 Marshal Point light fog (13x18cm-5x7in) W/C. 26-Apr-3 Thomaston Place, Thomaston #696a

PREYER, Emilie (1849-1930) German
£16456 $25671 €26000 Nature morte aux fruits (31x37cm-12x15in) s.d.1872. 16-Oct-2 Hotel des Ventes Mosan, Brussels #154/R est:15000-20000

PREYER, Ernest (1842-1917) German
£935 $1496 €1300 View from Monte Mario towards Rome (36x52cm-14x20in) s.d.1867 canvas on board. 17-May-3 Hagelstam, Helsinki #26/R

PREYER, Johann Wilhelm (1803-1889) German
£50000 $83500 €75000 Grapes, oysters, hazelnut and champagne flute on a draped table (36x33cm-14x13in) s.d.1858. 19-Jun-3 Christie's, London #46/R est:20000-30000

PREYER, Johann Wilhelm (attrib) (1803-1889) German
£7051 $11000 €10577 Still life with goblet, fruit and nuts (33x43cm-13x17in) 28-Mar-3 Eldred, East Dennis #682/R est:15000-25000

PREYER, Paul (1847-1931) German
£3288 $5129 €4800 Still life with full wine glass, bottle and fruit (45x36cm-18x14in) s. 10-Apr-3 Van Ham, Cologne #1651/R est:3000

PREZIOSI, Amadeo (1816-1882) Italian
Works on paper
£1400 $2226 €2100 Turkish infantryman (27x19cm-11x7in) s.i. W/C set of three. 29-Apr-3 Bonhams, New Bond Street #80/R est:1000-1500
£3742 $5912 €5800 View of the Bosphorus (24x35cm-9x14in) s.d.1853 W/C prov. 19-Dec-2 Claude Aguttes, Neuilly #139/R est:8000
£4500 $7290 €6525 View of Smyrna (28x46cm-11x18in) s. W/C. 29-Jul-3 Henry Adams, Chichester #530/R est:500-1000
£5000 $7800 €7500 View across the Golden Horn, Constantinople (40x57cm-16x22in) s.d.1854 pen ink W/C over pencil. 15-Oct-2 Sotheby's, London #76/R est:5000-7000
£5500 $8910 €7975 View of Constantinople (25x42cm-10x17in) s.d.1871 W/C. 29-Jul-3 Henry Adams, Chichester #532/R est:500-1000
£6200 $10044 €8990 View of Constantinople (43x60cm-17x24in) s. W/C. 29-Jul-3 Henry Adams, Chichester #533/R est:2000-3000
£6500 $10530 €9425 The Jewish quarter, Smyrna (29x45cm-11x18in) s. W/C. 29-Jul-3 Henry Adams, Chichester #531/R est:500-1000

PRIANICHNIKOFF, Ivan (1841-1909) Russian
Works on paper
£2000 $3240 €3000 Soldiers returning home (15x27cm-6x11in) s. W/C over pencil htd white. 21-May-3 Sotheby's, London #97/R est:1000-2000
£7500 $12150 €11250 Studies of a Tavrik woman (30x21cm-12x8in) init. W/C htd gouache. 21-May-3 Sotheby's, London #17/R est:4500-5500

PRICE, Edward (19th C) British
£2100 $3276 €3150 Salmon stream, Norway. Borgen, Norway. pair. 20-Sep-2 Moore Allen & Innocent, Cirencester #1011/R est:2000-2500

PRICE, Frank Corbyn (1862-?) British
Works on paper
£300 $468 €450 Fallen leaf (25x17cm-10x7in) s. W/C. 9-Oct-2 Woolley & Wallis, Salisbury #99/R

PRICE, Gary (1958-) American
Sculpture
£9091 $14000 €13637 Candice (117cm-46in) bronze. 25-Oct-2 Morris & Whiteside, Hilton Head Island #18a est:13000-15000

PRICE, Herbert H (20th C) American
£269 $450 €390 Santa Ana train station (25x36cm-10x14in) s.d.40 masonite prov. 17-Jun-3 John Moran, Pasadena #2

PRICE, J (?) ?
£1000 $1630 €1450 Portrait of a child with a basket of flowers (75x62cm-30x24in) s.d.1740. 17-Jul-3 Tennants, Leyburn #790a/R est:500-800

PRICE, Ken (1935-) American
Sculpture
£14241 $22500 €21362 Untitled. glazed ceramic in three parts prov. 13-Nov-2 Sotheby's, New York #120/R est:6000-8000

PRICE, Norman Mills (1877-1951) American
£2484 $4000 €3726 Sailors pulled aboard from rough sea (30x51cm-12x20in) s. board. 10-May-3 Illustration House, New York #44/R est:4000-6000
Works on paper
£404 $650 €606 Men in sombreros on horse (38x23cm-15x9in) s. pen ink. 20-Feb-3 Illustration House, New York #137/R
£617 $957 €926 Chicago fire 1871 - rush for life over Randolph Street Bridge (14x21cm-6x8in) s. pen ink W/C. 3-Dec-2 Ritchie, Toronto #3115/R est:2500-4000 (C.D 1500)

PRICE, Peter (?) British?
£274 $420 €411 Sailboats in a French port (25x39cm-10x15in) s. board. 21-Aug-2 Dunbar Sloane, Auckland #5/R (NZ.D 900)
£408 $636 €612 Day at the beach (28x40cm-11x16in) s. board. 7-Nov-2 International Art Centre, Auckland #191/R est:800-1500 (NZ.D 1300)

PRICE, William Henry (1864-1940) American
£2545 $4250 €3690 Sunlight on Sierra slopes (74x84cm-29x33in) s. i.verso. 17-Jun-3 John Moran, Pasadena #151 est:4000-6000

PRICE, Winchell Addison (1907-) Canadian
£738 $1143 €1107 Haymaking (51x76cm-20x30in) s. board. 24-Sep-2 Ritchie, Toronto #3155/R est:700-1000 (C.D 1800)

PRIEBE, Karl (1914-1976) American
Works on paper
£401 $650 €581 Figure holding bird's egg. Priebe Junior the Fourth (46x38cm-18x15in) s.d.1950 i.verso W/C htd white board double-sided. 21-May-3 Doyle, New York #155/R
£475 $750 €713 Young girl with birds in her hair (61x30cm-24x12in) s.d.1944 W/C gouache board prov. 2-Apr-3 Doyle, New York #55/R

PRIECHENFRIED, Alois (1867-1953) German
£1226 $1900 €1839 Portrait of a Jewish man (25x20cm-10x8in) s. 7-Dec-2 Selkirks, St. Louis #734 est:800-1200
£1397 $2180 €2096 Chess game (24x32cm-9x13in) s. 6-Nov-2 Dobiaschofsky, Bern #896/R est:5000 (S.FR 3200)

PRIECHENFRIED, G Kalla (20th C) German
£5200 $8164 €7800 Cellist (46x34cm-18x13in) s. 19-Nov-2 Bonhams, New Bond Street #40/R est:2000-3000
£5500 $8635 €8250 Forbidden fruit (45x35cm-18x14in) s. 19-Nov-2 Bonhams, New Bond Street #39/R est:6000-8000

PRIEM, Paul (1868-?) German
£472 $726 €750 Still life of flowers (50x41cm-20x16in) s. panel. 26-Oct-2 Dr Lehr, Berlin #435/R

PRIEST, Alfred (1810-1850) British
£2800 $4340 €4200 Figures in a boat, in a river landscape (49x71cm-19x28in) 30-Sep-2 Bonhams, Ipswich #478/R est:2000-3000

PRIESTLEY, Edward (19th C) British
£420 $668 €630 Blackberry Dell, Yorkshire (76x51cm-30x20in) s. i.verso. 6-Mar-3 Christie's, Kensington #467/R

PRIESTLEY, Glenn (20th C) Canadian
£1116 $1741 €1674 Self portrait (61x51cm-24x20in) s.d.83 masonite sold with 9 studies. 25-Mar-3 Ritchie, Toronto #138/R est:1500-2000 (C.D 2600)

PRIESTMAN, Arnold (1854-1925) British
£260 $406 €390 Coastal landscape (34x53cm-13x21in) s.d.1902. 9-Oct-2 Woolley & Wallis, Salisbury #262/R

PRIESTMAN, Bertram (1868-1951) British
£400 $624 €600 Landscape with man loading a cart (20x26cm-8x10in) init.d.13 panel. 6-Nov-2 Bonhams, Chester #489
£450 $725 €675 Walberswick Marshes (31x39cm-12x15in) board prov. 15-Jan-3 Cheffins Grain & Comins, Cambridge #430/R
£590 $974 €856 Two-masted steam vessel in an estuary (15x23cm-6x9in) s.d.91 board. 3-Jul-3 Ewbank, Send #314/R
£700 $1113 €1050 Lake with hills beyond (28x25cm-11x10in) init.d.10 panel. 29-Apr-3 Gorringes, Lewes #2110
£800 $1232 €1200 Dordrecht (33x41cm-13x16in) s. board. 3-Sep-2 Gorringes, Lewes #2304
£800 $1256 €1200 Manningtree, Essex (71x91cm-28x36in) exhib. 19-Nov-2 Bonhams, Leeds #159
£800 $1328 €1160 Storm clouds over the meadow (47x56cm-19x22in) s. prov. 16-Jun-3 Waddingtons, Toronto #132/R est:2000-3000 (C.D 1800)
£900 $1431 €1350 Winter landscape with horse and cart. Coastal scene with sailing boats (20x25cm-8x10in) board pair. 18-Mar-3 Lawrences, Bletchingley #1461/R
£980 $1529 €1470 Yorkshire river landscape. Limestone outcrop in the Dales (19x25cm-7x10in) init.d.15. 25-Mar-3 Bonhams, Leeds #617/R
£1000 $1560 €1500 By the Stour - the Barbican Bridge (31x42cm-12x17in) i. board exhib. 12-Sep-2 Sotheby's, Olympia #99/R est:1000-1500
£1067 $1771 €1547 Sluice (61x92cm-24x36in) s. 16-Jun-3 Waddingtons, Toronto #129/R est:2400-2600 (C.D 2400)
£1150 $1898 €1668 River landscape (26x35cm-10x14in) init.d.25 board prov. 1-Jul-3 Bonhams, Norwich #329 est:700-1000

£1200 $1860 €1800 Cattle on the marshes, Walberswick (30x61cm-12x24in) init.d.11 i.verso cardboard. 30-Sep-2 Bonhams, Ipswich #436/R est:1200-1600

£2200 $3454 €3300 Brecon Beacons (124x185cm-49x73in) s. 20-Nov-2 Sotheby's, Olympia #1/R est:3000-5000

£2900 $4553 €4350 River estuary with shipping by a quayside (51x76cm-20x30in) s.d.09. 19-Nov-2 Bonhams, Leeds #158/R est:2500-3500

PRIETO, F (20th C) Spanish

£561 $853 €842 De la Vida Jitana - gypsy life (88x93cm-35x37in) s.d.1925. 19-Aug-2 Joel, Victoria #186/R est:1000-1500 (A.D 1600)

PRIETO, Gregorio (1899-1992) Spanish

£1513 $2451 €2300 Garden (23x18cm-9x7in) s. board. 21-Jan-3 Ansorena, Madrid #67/R

£10968 $17329 €17000 Mills in Majorca (88x68cm-35x27in) s. cardboard. 17-Dec-2 Durán, Madrid #205/R est:5000

PRIEUR, Barthelemy (attrib) (1540-1611) French

Sculpture

£43357 $72406 €62000 Jeune femme se coiffant (14cm-6in) brown pat bronze lit. 25-Jun-3 Sotheby's, Paris #26/R est:45000-60000

PRIEUR-BARDIN, François L (1870-1936) French

£29371 $49049 €42000 Le souk (62x92cm-24x36in) s.d.1901. 27-Jun-3 Claude Aguttes, Neuilly #130/R est:40000-50000

PRIKING, Franz (1927-1979) French

£862 $1440 €1250 Bouquet (51x40cm-20x16in) s. paper on canvas. 9-Jul-3 Cornette de St.Cyr, Paris #190/R

£946 $1476 €1400 Paysage (39x49cm-15x19in) s. 28-Mar-3 Claude Aguttes, Neuilly #110

£1277 $2068 €1800 Barques (50x65cm-20x26in) s. paper on canvas. 21-May-3 Cornette de St.Cyr, Paris #98/R est:2000-3000

£1724 $2724 €2500 Compotier, cavalier et cheval (54x65cm-21x26in) s. 4-Apr-3 Tajan, Paris #235

£3061 $4867 €4500 Vase de fleurs (66x55cm-26x22in) s. 21-Mar-3 Rieunier, Bailly-Pommery, Mathias, Paris #128/R

Works on paper

£276 $439 €400 Nu allonge (31x48cm-12x19in) s. W/C gouache. 5-Mar-3 Doutrebente, Paris #36

£297 $464 €470 Bouquet de fleurs (50x32cm-20x13in) s. W/C. 20-Oct-2 Chayette & Cheval, Paris #8

£316 $500 €500 Pont (50x32cm-20x13in) s. W/C. 27-Nov-2 Blanchet, Paris #98/R

£414 $654 €600 Ecce Homo (65x50cm-26x20in) s. W/C. 4-Apr-3 Tajan, Paris #236

£420 $701 €600 Portrait de clown (31x49cm-12x19in) s. W/C. 26-Jun-3 Tajan, Paris #106

£570 $889 €900 Paysage de Provence (32x49cm-13x19in) s. W/C. 20-Oct-2 Charbonneaux, Paris #85 est:1000

£696 $1086 €1100 Peniches a quai (32x50cm-13x20in) s. W/C. 20-Oct-2 Charbonneaux, Paris #84 est:1000

£774 $1223 €1200 Coupe de fleurs (53x74cm-21x29in) s. W/C ink prov. 19-Dec-2 Claude Aguttes, Neuilly #198/R

PRIMATICCIO, Francesco (1504-1570) French

Works on paper

£27778 $45000 €41667 Mymphs bathing (22x29cm-9x11in) chk. 21-Jan-3 Sotheby's, New York #24/R est:65000

PRIMITIVE SCHOOL, 19th C

£5449 $8609 €8500 Young girl standing in landscape holding flowers (112x92cm-44x36in) 12-Nov-2 Mealy's, Castlecomer #1318/R est:7000

PRINA, Andre Julien (1886-1941) Italian

Works on paper

£461 $720 €692 Paysage de campagne (34x48cm-13x19in) studio st. pastel paper on canvas. 11-Nov-2 Stephan Welz, Johannesburg #435/R (SA.R 7200)

£516 $831 €774 Village sous le Neige (42x56cm-17x22in) s. mixed media. 12-May-3 Stephan Welz, Johannesburg #428 est:6000-9000 (SA.R 6000)

£577 $899 €866 La femme au chapeau vert (52x36cm-20x14in) studio st. pencil pastel paper on canvas. 11-Nov-2 Stephan Welz, Johannesburg #437/R (SA.R 9000)

PRINCE EUGENE LOUIS JOSEPH NAPOLEON (19th C) French

Works on paper

£979 $1635 €1400 L'Empereur Napoleon III et l'Imperatrice debarquent d'un navire (28x37cm-11x15in) s.i.d.1866 ink dr. 25-Jun-3 Piasa, Paris #7/R

PRINCE, Richard (1949-) Canadian

£11875 $19000 €17813 Was that a girl (61x46cm-24x18in) s.i.d.1989 verso acrylic silkscreen ink on canvas. 14-May-3 Sotheby's, New York #446/R est:6000-8000

£23750 $38000 €35625 Untitled - a girl walks (229x147cm-90x58in) s.d.1995 on overlap acrylic silkscreen prov.exhib. 16-May-3 Phillips, New York #120/R est:35000-45000

£56962 $90000 €85443 Untitled - How to tell (142x244cm-56x96in) s.i.d.1989 acrylic silkscreen ink canvas diptych prov. 14-Nov-2 Christie's, Rockefeller NY #389/R est:100000-150000

Photographs

£2000 $3080 €3000 Joke, girlfriend, cowboy (77x103cm-30x41in) s.d.2001 verso col photograph. 23-Oct-2 Christie's, London #241/R est:2500-3500

£2078 $3200 €3117 Untitled (60x40cm-24x16in) s.d.94 num.25/25 verso ilfochrome cibachrome print prov. 25-Oct-2 Phillips, New York #140/R est:1200-1800

£4430 $7000 €6645 Cowgirl (61x51cm-24x20in) s. num.1/5 verso ektachrome print exec.1994. 13-Nov-2 Sotheby's, New York #456/R

£5440 $8378 €8650 Rolex (51x61cm-20x24in) s. num.5/10 col photograph. 26-Oct-2 Cornette de St.Cyr, Paris #165/R

£7500 $12000 €11250 Untitled (104x83cm-41x33in) s.verso photocollage set of six frame as one executed 1999 prov. 16-May-3 Phillips, New York #221/R est:15000-20000

£7595 $12000 €11393 Point zero (142x122cm-56x48in) s.d.1987 chromogenic col print prov.lit. 24-Apr-3 Phillips, New York #49/R est:10000-15000

£12658 $20000 €18987 Untitled - every time i meet (157x122cm-62x48in) silkscreen acrylic on canvas executed 1995 prov. 12-Nov-2 Phillips, New York #180/R est:25000-35000

£16000 $26720 €23200 Cowboys and girlfriends. s.i.d.1992 num.V init.verso col photos 14 portfolio box prov. 26-Jun-3 Sotheby's, London #121/R est:20000-30000

£18987 $30000 €28481 Cowboys and girlfriends (50x61cm-20x24in) s.d.1992 num. init.v ektacolor print set of 14 prov. 12-Nov-2 Phillips, New York #178/R est:30000-40000

£22115 $34500 €33173 Untitled - Cindy Sherman and Richard Prince (39x58cm-15x23in) s. verso chromagenic colour diptych lit. 21-Oct-2 Swann Galleries, New York #319/R est:60000-90000

£24051 $38000 €36077 Untitled - fashion (61x51cm-24x20in) s.d.1982-84 num.2/2 ektacolor print prov.exhib. 14-Nov-2 Christie's, Rockefeller NY #449/R est:30000-40000

£30000 $49200 €45000 Untitled - man's hand with watch (98x147cm-39x58in) s.i.d.1980 verso num.1/1 ektacolour print foamcore prov. 6-Feb-3 Christie's, London #751/R est:20000-30000

£32812 $52500 €49218 Cowboys and girl friends (61x51cm-24x20in) s.d.1992 num. 14 col photograph. 14-May-3 Sotheby's, New York #447/R est:25000-35000

£38000 $63460 €55100 Untitled - fashion (40x58cm-16x23in) s.i.d.83-84 verso ektacolor print prov.lit. 27-Jun-3 Christie's, London #250/R est:25000-35000

£40625 $65000 €60938 Untitled (102x69cm-40x27in) s.d.1980 ektacolor print prov.exhib. 15-May-3 Christie's, Rockefeller NY #363/R est:50000-70000

£41667 $65000 €62501 Untitled - man's hand with cigarette (102x152cm-40x60in) ektacolor photograph executed 1980 prov. 11-Nov-2 Phillips, New York #7/R est:40000-60000

£83333 $130000 €125000 Untitled - cowboy (155x104cm-61x41in) s.d.1994 ektacolor photograph prov. 11-Nov-2 Phillips, New York #4/R est:100000-150000

£93750 $150000 €140625 Four women looking inthe same direction (51x61cm-20x24in) s.d.1977 verso ektacolor prints set of 4. 14-May-3 Christie's, Rockefeller NY #3/R est:80000-120000

£101266 $160000 €151899 Untitled - cowboys (122x183cm-48x72in) s.d.1993 verso ektacolor print prov.exhib.lit. 13-Nov-2 Christie's, Rockefeller NY #3/R est:120000-180000

Prints

£2708 $4279 €3900 Sans titre (59x40cm-23x16in) s.num.23/40 verso col photo. 28-Apr-3 Cornette de St.Cyr, Paris #489/R est:2500-3000

PRINCE, Richard and SHERMAN, Cindy (20th C) Canadian/American
Photographs
£82278 $130000 €123417 Untitled - double portrait (51x61cm-20x24in) s.num.1/10 col coupler prints two prov.exhib.lit. 13-Nov-2 Christie's, Rockefeller NY #71/R est:100000-150000

PRINCESS BEATRICE OF BATTENBERG (1858-1944) German
Works on paper
£1900 $2964 €2850 Balmoral Castle (23x34cm-9x13in) s. W/C prov. 14-Apr-3 Sotheby's, London #10/R est:1000-1500

PRINCESS CLEMENTINE OF ORLEANS (1817-1907) French
Works on paper
£411 $650 €650 Aria Gonzala trouvant son fils apres le combat (26x36cm-10x14in) s.i.d.1838 W/C gouache. 27-Nov-2 Christie's, Paris #227/R
£475 $750 €750 Les tours en ruine du chateau de Montlhery (25x31cm-10x12in) s.i.d.1838 W/C gouache. 27-Nov-2 Christie's, Paris #225/R
£506 $800 €800 Une avenue du parc au chateau de Neuilly (25x21cm-10x8in) s.i.d.juin 1838 W/C gouache. 27-Nov-2 Christie's, Paris #229/R
£1081 $1686 €1600 View of Saint-Valery. View of castle. Cliffs in Scotland. View of Mont Richard Castle. s.i. graphite W/C gouache grattage set of 4. 27-Mar-3 Christie's, Paris #160/R
£1139 $1800 €1800 Une vue de parc de Champlatreux (15x27cm-6x11in) i.d.Aout 1838 graphite W/C gouache. 27-Nov-2 Christie's, Paris #224/R est:1000-1500
£3481 $5500 €5500 Une vue de Paris depuis Saint Cloud (24x35cm-9x14in) s.i.d.1839 W/C gouache. 27-Nov-2 Christie's, Paris #223/R est:2000-3000

PRINCESS HENRY OF BATTENBURG (19th C) German?
£420 $651 €630 Balmoral Castle in landscape (25x36cm-10x14in) s. prov. 3-Dec-2 Peter Francis, Wales #45/R

PRINCESS MARIE (1865-1909) Danish/British
Works on paper
£279 $444 €419 One green and one yellow pumpkin (38x55cm-15x22in) s. pen W/C. 5-Mar-3 Rasmussen, Copenhagen #2112/R (D.KR 3000)
£279 $444 €419 Yellow mushrooms (29x54cm-11x21in) s. pencil W/C. 5-Mar-3 Rasmussen, Copenhagen #2113/R (D.KR 3000)
£380 $593 €570 Branch of lemons (49x67cm-19x26in) s. W/C. 23-Sep-2 Rasmussen, Vejle #151/R (D.KR 4500)

PRINCESS VICTORIA MELITA (1876-1936) German
£710 $1043 €1100 Still life of carnations with jug (46x61cm-18x24in) s.d.1908. 20-Jun-2 Dr Fritz Nagel, Stuttgart #829/R

PRINCETEAU, René (1844-1914) French
£3696 $5728 €5544 Little duck (59x73cm-23x29in) s. prov. 9-Dec-2 Philippe Schuler, Zurich #3927/R est:5700-8500 (S.FR 8500)

PRINET, René-Xavier (1861-1946) French
£282 $468 €400 La porte maure (32x23cm-13x9in) panel. 11-Jun-3 Beaussant & Lefèvre, Paris #171
£317 $526 €450 Sucrerie de Flavy-le-Martel (19x24cm-7x9in) bears studio st.verso panel. 11-Jun-3 Beaussant & Lefèvre, Paris #177
£352 $585 €500 Le chateau (15x24cm-6x9in) bears studio st.verso panel. 11-Jun-3 Beaussant & Lefèvre, Paris #140
£352 $585 €500 L'abbaye d'Ourscamp, Oise (19x24cm-7x9in) s. bears studio st.verso panel. 11-Jun-3 Beaussant & Lefèvre, Paris #176
£352 $585 €500 Le retour du blesse (27x35cm-11x14in) bears studio st.verso panel. 11-Jun-3 Beaussant & Lefèvre, Paris #183
£387 $643 €550 Cabourg (14x19cm-6x7in) bears studio st.verso panel. 11-Jun-3 Beaussant & Lefèvre, Paris #122
£423 $701 €600 Chateau de prives, Isere (19x24cm-7x9in) bears studio st.verso panel. 11-Jun-3 Beaussant & Lefèvre, Paris #134
£423 $701 €600 Suaucourt, les tomates (18x24cm-7x9in) bears studio st.verso panel. 11-Jun-3 Beaussant & Lefèvre, Paris #136
£423 $701 €600 Nu de dos dans un interieur (20x14cm-8x6in) bears studio st.verso panel. 11-Jun-3 Beaussant & Lefèvre, Paris #144
£423 $701 €600 Femme nue au drap blanc (20x12cm-8x5in) bears studio st.verso panel. 11-Jun-3 Beaussant & Lefèvre, Paris #147
£423 $701 €600 Interieur d'eglise (55x46cm-22x18in) bears studio st.verso panel exhib. 11-Jun-3 Beaussant & Lefèvre, Paris #178
£458 $760 €650 Digue devant le casino, Cabourg (14x19cm-6x7in) bears studio st.verso panel. 11-Jun-3 Beaussant & Lefèvre, Paris #124
£493 $818 €700 Vue de Coublevie, Isere (50x59cm-20x23in) s. bears studio st.verso cardboard. 11-Jun-3 Beaussant & Lefèvre, Paris #135
£528 $877 €750 Etude pour l'offrande, Bourbonne (35x26cm-14x10in) bears studio st.verso panel painted c.1935. 11-Jun-3 Beaussant & Lefèvre, Paris #158
£563 $935 €800 La violoniste (18x18cm-7x7in) bears studio st.verso panel. 11-Jun-3 Beaussant & Lefèvre, Paris #154
£633 $981 €1000 Pommone (20x27cm-8x11in) s. panel. 29-Sep-2 Eric Pillon, Calais #76/R
£634 $1052 €900 L'heure du diner (26x29cm-10x11in) bears studio st.verso panel. 11-Jun-3 Beaussant & Lefèvre, Paris #160
£634 $1052 €900 L'eglise de Ribecourt (19x24cm-7x9in) s. bears studio st.verso cardboard. 11-Jun-3 Beaussant & Lefèvre, Paris #179/R
£704 $1169 €1000 La halte (80x100cm-31x39in) s. 11-Jun-3 Beaussant & Lefèvre, Paris #174/R
£775 $1286 €1100 La pendule portique (20x14cm-8x6in) s.i. panel. 11-Jun-3 Beaussant & Lefèvre, Paris #161
£775 $1286 €1100 Le lit, Suaucourt, etude pour le lever (35x26cm-14x10in) bears studio st.verso panel exec.c.1903. 11-Jun-3 Beaussant & Lefèvre, Paris #163
£791 $1250 €1250 Refectoire (76x65cm-30x26in) s. 29-Nov-2 Drouot Estimations, Paris #52
£915 $1520 €1300 Femme etendue sur la plage, etude (20x33cm-8x13in) bears studio st.verso panel. 11-Jun-3 Beaussant & Lefèvre, Paris #128
£915 $1520 €1300 Suaucourt (13x20cm-5x8in) bears studio st.verso panel. 11-Jun-3 Beaussant & Lefèvre, Paris #139
£1056 $1754 €1500 Suaucourt, mon lit (14x20cm-6x8in) bears studio st.verso panel. 11-Jun-3 Beaussant & Lefèvre, Paris #138 est:200
£1056 $1754 €1500 Femme assis dans un canape jaune (27x32cm-11x13in) bears studio st.verso panel. 11-Jun-3 Beaussant & Lefèvre, Paris #156 est:1000-1200
£1056 $1754 €1500 Nu au drape devant une porte maure (20x13cm-8x5in) bears studio st.verso panel. 11-Jun-3 Beaussant & Lefèvre, Paris #170/R est:400-500
£1127 $1870 €1600 Etude pour blanche et noire (48x38cm-19x15in) chl estompe white chk dr. 11-Jun-3 Beaussant & Lefèvre, Paris #168 est:600-800
£1197 $1987 €1700 Etude pour Tradition ou les visiteurs (27x27cm-11x11in) bears studio st.verso panel painted c.1915. 11-Jun-3 Beaussant & Lefèvre, Paris #172/R est:1000-1200
£1268 $2104 €1800 Cabourg, couple sur la plage (14x20cm-6x8in) bears studio st.verso panel. 11-Jun-3 Beaussant & Lefèvre, Paris #126 est:1000-1200
£1268 $2104 €1800 Portrait de jeune fille a la charlotte (15x12cm-6x5in) panel. 11-Jun-3 Beaussant & Lefèvre, Paris #153/R est:300-400
£1338 $2221 €1900 Le bonnet rouge (21x34cm-8x13in) bears studio st.verso panel. 11-Jun-3 Beaussant & Lefèvre, Paris #125/R est:1000-1200
£1620 $2689 €2300 Couple au crepuscule (26x35cm-10x14in) s. painted c.1921 lit. 11-Jun-3 Beaussant & Lefèvre, Paris #123/R est:1200-1500
£1761 $2923 €2500 Bain dans la vague (22x35cm-9x14in) bears studio st.verso panel. 11-Jun-3 Beaussant & Lefèvre, Paris #143 est:1000-1200
£2465 $4092 €3500 Etude pour la pecheuse de crevettes a Cabourg (26x29cm-10x11in) bears studio st.verso panel painted c.1920 lit. 11-Jun-3 Beaussant & Lefèvre, Paris #131/R est:2500-3000
£2606 $4325 €3700 Etude pour baigneuse a Cabourg (26x35cm-10x14in) bears studio st. verso panel. 11-Jun-3 Beaussant & Lefèvre, Paris #121/R est:1200-1800
£2676 $4442 €3800 Etude pour avant l'orage, Cabourg (24x18cm-9x7in) bears studio st.verso panel lit. 11-Jun-3 Beaussant & Lefèvre, Paris #129/R est:2000-2200
£2958 $4910 €4200 Le bouquet (20x14cm-8x6in) bears studio st.verso panel. 11-Jun-3 Beaussant & Lefèvre, Paris #162 est:300-400
£3028 $5027 €4300 La femme en brun (26x35cm-10x14in) bears studio st.verso panel exec.c.1907. 11-Jun-3 Beaussant & Lefèvre, Paris #155/R est:2000-2500
£3380 $5611 €4800 Cavaliers sur la plage. Etude de personnages dans une taverne (21x35cm-8x14in) bears studio st.verso panel double-sided. 11-Jun-3 Beaussant & Lefèvre, Paris #127/R est:2000-2200
£3380 $5611 €4800 Etude pour la lecon de geographie (27x27cm-11x11in) bears studio st.verso panel painted c.1911. 11-Jun-3 Beaussant & Lefèvre, Paris #169/R est:1200-1500
£3521 $5845 €5000 Etude pour la plage, Cabourg (26x35cm-10x14in) bears studio st.verso panel. 11-Jun-3 Beaussant & Lefèvre, Paris #130/R est:1800-2200
£3662 $6079 €5200 Etude pour blanche et noire (35x27cm-14x11in) bears studio st.verso panel. 11-Jun-3 Beaussant & Lefèvre, Paris #167/R est:2000-2500
£11620 $19289 €16500 Etude pour la digue, ou coup de vent (29x41cm-11x16in) bears studio st.verso panel lit. 11-Jun-3 Beaussant & Lefèvre, Paris #132/R est:3000-3500

Works on paper
£317 $526 €450 Etude pour la cantatrice sur la scene (39x49cm-15x19in) chl estompe white chk dr exec.c.1925. 11-Jun-3 Beaussant & Lefèvre, Paris #149/R
£352 $585 €500 Chevaux sur la plage (39x49cm-15x19in) chl estompe white chk dr. 11-Jun-3 Beaussant & Lefèvre, Paris #145/R

£423 $701 €600 Cabourg, sur la plage (39x49cm-15x19in) chl estompe white chk dr. 11-Jun-3 Beaussant & Lefèvre, Paris #141/R
£423 $701 €600 Etude de fillette marchant (23x17cm-9x7in) chl dr. 11-Jun-3 Beaussant & Lefèvre, Paris #159
£458 $760 €650 Jeune garcon sur la digue regardant un voilier devant St Malo (39x59cm-15x23in) chl estompe dr. 11-Jun-3 Beaussant & Lefèvre, Paris #142
£563 $935 €800 Etude pour Tradition ou les visiteirs (61x40cm-24x16in) chl estompe dr. 11-Jun-3 Beaussant & Lefèvre, Paris #173
£704 $1169 €1000 Etude pour la mare devant le casino (38x58cm-15x23in) chl dr lit. 11-Jun-3 Beaussant & Lefèvre, Paris #133/R
£775 $1286 €1100 Etude pour le parachute sur la plage (38x58cm-15x23in) chl estompe dr lit. 11-Jun-3 Beaussant & Lefèvre, Paris #137/R
£845 $1403 €1200 Etude pour la mounou noire (30x54cm-12x21in) chl estompe dr lit. 11-Jun-3 Beaussant & Lefèvre, Paris #151/R
£845 $1403 €1200 La violoncelliste (49x39cm-19x15in) chl estompe dr. 11-Jun-3 Beaussant & Lefèvre, Paris #157/R
£915 $1520 €1300 Ane de bat (20x25cm-8x10in) s. black crayon dr. 11-Jun-3 Beaussant & Lefèvre, Paris #166

PRINGLE, John Balfour (1815-1885) British
£658 $1000 €987 Canadian bark passing the Ailsa Craig (48x76cm-19x30in) s.d.1867 lit. 17-Aug-2 North East Auctions, Portsmouth #1169/R

PRINNER, Anton (1902-1983) French
Sculpture
£3774 $5887 €6000 Guerre d'Espagne (27x77x17cm-11x30x7in) s.st.f.Bocquel num.4/8 brown pat bronze. 11-Oct-2 Binoche, Paris #167/R est:5000-8000
£8741 $14598 €12500 Fille a la natte. s.num.2/8 brown pat bronze. 25-Jun-3 Claude Aguttes, Neuilly #198/R est:12200-15250
Works on paper
£252 $392 €400 Symbole (29x22cm-11x9in) s.d.1948 chl. 11-Oct-2 Binoche, Paris #138

PRINS, Ferdinand de (1859-1908) Belgian
£1026 $1590 €1600 Paturage a Duffel (81x104cm-32x41in) s.d. s.i.verso. 9-Dec-2 Horta, Bruxelles #53 est:1500-2000

PRINS, Johannes Huibert (1757-1806) Dutch
£4430 $6867 €7000 View of the Montelbeanstoren, Amsterdam (46x55cm-18x22in) s.d.1789 prov. 24-Sep-2 Christie's, Amsterdam #129/R est:7000-10000
Works on paper
£850 $1335 €1275 Village street with three peasants by a well (18x23cm-7x9in) s.d. chk pen wash framing lines prov. 13-Dec-2 Christie's, Kensington #307/R

PRINS, Pierre (1838-1913) French
Works on paper
£263 $427 €400 Arbre dans un champ (20x31cm-8x12in) s. pastel. 22-Jan-3 Tajan, Paris #66/R
£385 $604 €600 Vase de roses (26x33cm-10x13in) s. pastel. 15-Dec-2 Eric Pillon, Calais #148/R
£578 $919 €850 Lac de Fluelen (35x51cm-14x20in) s. pastel. 24-Mar-3 Coutau Begarie, Paris #197/R
£1398 $2335 €2000 Le village (31x44cm-12x17in) s. pastel. 30-Jun-3 Pierre Berge, Paris #15/R est:2000-3000

PRINSEP, Valentine Cameron (1838-1904) British
£49000 $78890 €73500 On the Lido, Venice (151x56cm-59x22in) init. prov.exhib. 20-Feb-3 Christie's, London #294/R est:30000
£72000 $115920 €108000 Festa di Lido (150x187cm-59x74in) prov.exhib.lit. 20-Feb-3 Christie's, London #293/R est:80000

PRINTZ, Lars (1889-1968) Norwegian
£305 $479 €458 Scene from the Garden of Eden. s. panel. 25-Nov-2 Blomqvist, Lysaker #1220 (N.KR 3500)

PRINZ, A Emil (19th C) ?
£446 $700 €669 Cows in pasture (51x71cm-20x28in) s. 14-Dec-2 CRN Auctions, Cambridge #109/R

PRINZ, Bernhard (1953-) German
Photographs
£2639 $4354 €3800 Nadine (173x118cm-68x46in) C-print prov.exhib. 3-Jul-3 Christie's, Paris #92/R est:4000-6000
£6597 $10885 €9500 Alba, Aurore et equivalent feminin pour Albrecht (126x360cm-50x142in) C-print triptych prov.exhib. 3-Jul-3 Christie's, Paris #93/R est:7000-9000

PRINZ, Christian August (1819-1867) Norwegian
£4163 $6494 €6245 Fighting for the catch (110x145cm-43x57in) s.i.d.1861. 21-Oct-2 Blomqvist, Oslo #321/R est:45000-50000 (N.KR 48000)

PRINZ, Karl Ludwig (1875-1944) Austrian
£513 $810 €800 Durnstein. Castelbell ruins, south Tyrol (22x27cm-9x11in) s. canvas on panel tempera board two. 12-Nov-2 Dorotheum, Vienna #23/R
£540 $863 €750 Grundlsee, Salzkammergut (49x60cm-19x24in) s. i. verso. 14-May-3 Dorotheum, Linz #369/R
£949 $1500 €1424 Oversized, sunset in the Alps (168x191cm-66x75in) s. 17-Nov-2 CRN Auctions, Cambridge #61/R
£949 $1500 €1424 Oversized, village at the foot of the Alps (168x203cm-66x80in) s. 17-Nov-2 CRN Auctions, Cambridge #62/R
£962 $1519 €1500 Rax, Preinerwand seen from above (61x50cm-24x20in) s. exhib. board. 12-Nov-2 Dorotheum, Vienna #113/R est:2000-2800
£962 $1519 €1500 Dolomites on sunny winter day (61x50cm-24x20in) s. board exhib. 12-Nov-2 Dorotheum, Vienna #114/R est:2000-2800
£1266 $1975 €2000 Durnstein (37x50cm-15x20in) s. panel. 15-Oct-2 Dorotheum, Vienna #82/R est:900-1300
£1362 $2207 €2043 Usti nad Labem town (102x132cm-40x52in) s. 24-May-3 Dorotheum, Prague #47/R est:60000-90000 (C.KR 60000)
£1517 $2428 €2200 Drei Zinnen, Dolomites (68x98cm-27x39in) s. board prov. 11-Mar-3 Dorotheum, Vienna #20/R est:2600-3600
£3797 $6000 €6000 Rax and Schneeberg in winter (90x112cm-35x44in) s. 26-Nov-2 Wiener Kunst Auktionen, Vienna #70/R est:6000-8000
Works on paper
£513 $810 €800 Karntner landscape - Rosental (63x80cm-25x31in) s. gouache tempera. 12-Nov-2 Dorotheum, Vienna #80/R

PRIOR, William Matthew (1806-1873) American
£813 $1300 €1220 Portrait of a gentleman (28x23cm-11x9in) i. board oval. 17-May-3 Pook & Pook, Downington #90a/R est:1000-1500
£2813 $4500 €4220 Portrait of a young gentleman wearing a black coat and yellow vest (33x25cm-13x10in) panel. 17-May-3 Pook & Pook, Downington #389/R est:3000-5000

PRIOR, William Matthew (attrib) (1806-1873) American
£373 $600 €560 Portrait of George Washington reverse. glass. 16-Jan-3 Skinner, Bolton #859/R
£1647 $2700 €2388 Portrait of a gentleman, wearing black cravat and jacket (58x48cm-23x19in) board. 8-Jun-3 Skinner, Boston #239 est:1500-2500
£15854 $26000 €22988 Portrait of Albert Coman Smith with his toys (69x56cm-27x22in) i.verso. 8-Jun-3 Skinner, Boston #79/R est:4000-6000

PRIOU, Gaston (20th C) French
£3608 $5628 €5700 Untitled (155x225cm-61x89in) isorel polychrome lacquer panel exec.c.1925. 20-Oct-2 Mercier & Cie, Lille #134/R est:1500-1800

PRISTON, Francine (20th C) French
£345 $548 €500 Vision, imagination (73x54cm-29x21in) s. 10-Mar-3 Millon & Associes, Paris #298
£414 $658 €600 Hesitation du doute (91x64cm-36x25in) s. 10-Mar-3 Millon & Associes, Paris #299

PRITCHARD, Edward F D (1809-1905) British
£900 $1476 €1350 Sheep in a meadow (44x57cm-17x22in) framed oval. 29-May-3 Christie's, Kensington #163/R est:1000-1500

PRITCHARD, G Thompson (1878-1962) American
£833 $1300 €1250 Sunrise on the Maine coast (61x74cm-24x29in) s. board. 30-Mar-3 Susanin's, Chicago #6059/R
£968 $1500 €1452 Landscape, wooded stream (58x81cm-23x32in) s. prov. 29-Oct-2 John Moran, Pasadena #658 est:1000-2000
£968 $1500 €1452 Figures, horse cart and ship (64x76cm-25x30in) s. prov. 29-Oct-2 John Moran, Pasadena #659 est:1000-2000
£1198 $2000 €1737 Boats in fortress harbour (61x71cm-24x28in) s. prov. 17-Jun-3 John Moran, Pasadena #144 est:2000-3000
£1452 $2250 €2178 Tall sail ship in moderate seas (64x76cm-25x30in) s. prov. 29-Oct-2 John Moran, Pasadena #657 est:2000-3000

PRITCHARD, Gwilym (1931-) British
£250 $388 €375 Farm in Angelsey (23x63cm-9x25in) s.d.59 board prov.exhib. 4-Dec-2 Christie's, Kensington #556/R
£750 $1185 €1125 Cottage (36x46cm-14x18in) s. 27-Nov-2 Sotheby's, Olympia #141/R
£900 $1476 €1350 View of Angelsey (61x106cm-24x42in) s. board. 3-Jun-3 Sotheby's, Olympia #291/R

PRITCHARD, J Ambrose (1858-1905) American
Works on paper
£660 $1050 €990 View of cove with wild flower field. Ocean cove with sail boat (48x64cm-19x25in) W/C pastel pair. 3-May-3 Van Blarcom, South Natick #89/R

PRITCHARD, Thomas (fl.1866-1877) British
Works on paper
£300 $477 €450 Farmyard scene (34x52cm-13x20in) s.d.1866 W/C. 5-Mar-3 Bonhams, Bury St Edmunds #252

PRITCHETT, Edward (fl.1828-1864) British
£1200 $1956 €1800 Venetian scene (17x22cm-7x9in) board. 12-Feb-3 Bonhams, Knightsbridge #118/R est:1200-1800
£1800 $2934 €2700 View of the church San Georgio Maggiore (46x67cm-18x26in) s.d.1839. 29-Jan-3 Sotheby's, Olympia #164/R est:1000-1500
£2100 $3423 €3150 Rialto Bridge (24x35cm-9x14in) board. 29-Jan-3 Sotheby's, Olympia #163/R est:1500-2000
£3000 $4770 €4500 View across the Grand Canal from the old customs house, Venice (18x25cm-7x10in) 19-Mar-3 Sotheby's, London #236/R est:3000-5000
£3000 $4980 €4500 Riva degli Schiavoni, Venice (30x25cm-12x10in) 10-Jun-3 Christie's, London #75/R est:3000-4000
£3500 $5530 €5250 Figures in the Piazzetta, Venice, San Salute beyond (30x25cm-12x10in) 26-Nov-2 Christie's, London #171/R est:4000-6000
£4000 $6320 €6000 View of the Molo, with Ducal Palace to the right (30x48cm-12x19in) 26-Nov-2 Christie's, London #169/R est:5000-7000
£4878 $8000 €7317 View of the Doge's Palace from the Dogana, Venice (17x23cm-7x9in) panel. 29-May-3 Sotheby's, New York #150/R est:5000-7000
£6000 $9540 €9000 Dogana and Santa Maria della Salute, Venice. Doge's Palace from Dogana, Venice (30x46cm-12x18in) s. pair prov. 18-Mar-3 Bonhams, New Bond Street #55/R est:6000-8000
£9000 $14220 €13500 Venice - view of the Piazzetta, San Marco (51x44cm-20x17in) s. 26-Nov-2 Christie's, London #174/R est:10000-15000
Works on paper
£850 $1326 €1275 Venice from the Doges Palace (28x42cm-11x17in) W/C. 8-Oct-2 Sotheby's, Olympia #411/R
£2800 $4396 €4200 Piazzetta, Venice, with figures in the La Santa Maria Della Salute (24x39cm-9x15in) W/C. 21-Nov-2 Tennants, Leyburn #649/R est:2000-3000

PRITCHETT, Edward (attrib) (fl.1828-1864) British
£5200 $8216 €7800 View of Santa Maria Della Salute and the Dogana from the mint, Venice (57x74cm-22x29in) prov. 28-Nov-2 Sotheby's, London #127/R est:3000-5000
£6000 $9120 €9000 Piazetta, Venice (28x43cm-11x17in) 16-Aug-2 Keys, Aylsham #646/R

PRITCHETT, F (?) ?
£550 $858 €825 At Scheusmingen, Holland (36x26cm-14x10in) mono. panel. 10-Sep-2 Bonhams, Knightsbridge #218/R

PRITCHETT, Robert Taylor (1828-1907) British
Works on paper
£600 $948 €900 Sioux Indian outside a general store (12x12cm-5x5in) i. W/C over pencil htd bodycol. 15-Nov-2 Sotheby's, London #71/R

PRITZELWITZ, Johanne von (19th C) German
Works on paper
£290 $450 €435 Portrait of a gentleman (33x25cm-13x10in) s. W/C. 28-Sep-2 Charlton Hall, Columbia #575/R

PRIVATO, Cosimo (1899-1971) Italian
£300 $475 €450 Gondola in Venice (47x69cm-19x27in) board. 29-Nov-2 Zofingen, Switzerland #2523 (S.FR 700)

PROBSTHAYN, Carl (1770-1818) Danish
£5587 $8883 €8381 Albert and Nicolaus Rubens (195x153cm-77x60in) after painting by Rubens in 1625. 5-Mar-3 Rasmussen, Copenhagen #1586/R est:60000-80000 (D.KR 60000)

PROCACCINI, Camillo (1546-1629) Italian
Prints
£2308 $3600 €3462 Rest on the Flight into Egypt (18x26cm-7x10in) etching exec.c.1587. 6-Nov-2 Swann Galleries, New York #58/R est:2500-3500
Works on paper
£1000 $1570 €1500 David and Bathsheba (13x13cm-5x5in) red chk squared in black chk prov. 11-Dec-2 Sotheby's, Olympia #113/R est:500-700
£20062 $32500 €30093 Rape of Persephone (20x18cm-8x7in) red black chk prov.exhib.lit. 21-Jan-3 Sotheby's, New York #12/R est:40000-60000

PROCACCINI, Ercole (16/17th C) Italian
Works on paper
£3200 $5344 €4640 David with the head of Goliath (13x10cm-5x4in) red chk. 9-Jul-3 Sotheby's, London #43/R est:1500-2000

PROCACCINI, Ercole (younger-attrib) (1596-1676) Italian
£6849 $10685 €10274 Maria Magdalena washing Christ's feet (108x81cm-43x32in) 28-Mar-3 Koller, Zurich #3046/R est:10000-15000 (S.FR 15000)

PROCACCINI, Giulio Cesare (1570-1625) Italian
£147925 $230762 €235200 Holy Family (97x68cm-38x27in) 21-Sep-2 Semenzato, Venice #145/R
£290000 $484300 €420500 The judgement of Paris (53x118cm-21x46in) prov.lit. 10-Jul-3 Sotheby's, London #36/R est:80000-120000

PROCHASKA, Emil (1874-1948) Swiss
£262 $409 €393 Trees in meadow (75x54cm-30x21in) s. exhib. 6-Nov-2 Dobiaschofsky, Bern #898/R (S.FR 600)

PROCHAZKA, Antonin (1882-1945) Czechoslovakian
Works on paper
£1033 $1611 €1550 Cubistic head (30x17cm-12x7in) mono. pencil dr. 12-Oct-2 Dorotheum, Prague #239/R (C.KR 50000)

PROCHAZKA, Franz Xaver (1749-1815) Czechoslovakian
£3054 $4856 €4581 Landscape with river and ruins (13x24cm-5x9in) s.d.1804 board. 8-Mar-3 Dorotheum, Prague #1/R est:30000-45000 (C.KR 140000)

PROCHAZKA, Iaro (1886-1947) Czechoslovakian
£320 $522 €480 Winter landscape with a river and farm buildings beyond (61x91cm-24x36in) indis sig. 29-Jan-3 Dreweatt Neate, Newbury #145

PROCHAZKA, Josef (1909-) ?
£698 $1110 €1047 Footbridge over a stream (65x85cm-26x33in) s. board. 8-Mar-3 Dorotheum, Prague #116/R est:10000-15000 (C.KR 32000)
£1200 $1908 €1800 Stream (100x120cm-39x47in) s. 8-Mar-3 Dorotheum, Prague #68/R est:30000-45000 (C.KR 55000)

PROCHAZKA, Oldrich (1903-) Czechoslovakian
£347 $538 €521 Allegory of autumn (67x97cm-26x38in) painted 1930. 3-Dec-2 SOGA, Bratislava #213/R (SL.K 22000)

PROCHAZKOVA, Linka (1884-1960) Czechoslovakian
£2836 $4509 €4254 Allegory of spring (72x59cm-28x23in) s.d.34 board. 8-Mar-3 Dorotheum, Prague #144/R est:80000-120000 (C.KR 130000)
£3927 $6243 €5891 Still life with blue bouquet (72x86cm-28x34in) s.d.30 board. 8-Mar-3 Dorotheum, Prague #128/R est:150000-230000 (C.KR 180000)

PROCHOWNIK, Walter (?) ?
Works on paper
£206 $319 €309 Abstract composition (36x51cm-14x20in) s. mixed media on canvas. 3-Dec-2 Ritchie, Toronto #3117/R (C.D 500)

PROCOFIEFF, N (19th C) Russian
Works on paper
£1923 $3019 €3000 Grand pont sur la Neva (12x28cm-5x11in) s. W/C. 13-Dec-2 Rossini, Paris #142/R est:1800-2300

PROCOPIO, Pino (1954-) Italian
£380 $592 €600 Jockey (30x40cm-12x16in) s.d.1993. 14-Sep-2 Meeting Art, Vercelli #844
£685 $1068 €1000 Hunters (40x50cm-16x20in) s. 10-Apr-3 Finarte Semenzato, Rome #211

PROCTER, Burt (1901-1980) American
£3822 $6000 €5733 Cowboys on horseback (51x76cm-20x30in) s. masonite prov. 19-Nov-2 Butterfields, San Francisco #8103/R est:5000-7000
£4167 $6500 €6251 Cowboy resting, night (51x81cm-20x32in) s. masonite prov. 14-Sep-2 Weschler, Washington #635/R est:6000-8000
£7229 $12000 €10482 Low tide (61x81cm-24x32in) s. 11-Jun-3 Butterfields, San Francisco #4313/R est:7000-9000

PROCTER, Dod (1892-1972) British
£2300 $3818 €3335 Corner of my sitting room (89x61cm-35x24in) 10-Jun-3 David Lay, Penzance #414 est:2000-2500
£2400 $3936 €3600 Flower still life (59x41cm-23x16in) s. board exhib. 3-Jun-3 Sotheby's, Olympia #82/R est:2000-3000
£4000 $6200 €6000 Portrait of a tribal woman (76x61cm-30x24in) s. 4-Dec-2 Christie's, Kensington #420/R est:4000-6000
£4000 $6520 €6000 Portrait of a lady with blue bird in the sky (76x51cm-30x20in) prov. 28-Jan-3 Peter Francis, Wales #8/R est:4000-6000
£4200 $6552 €6300 Jamaican girl (51x41cm-20x16in) 12-Sep-2 Sotheby's, Olympia #81/R est:1500-2000
£8500 $14025 €12325 Burmese children on the Irrawaddy (41x41cm-16x16in) s. panel. 3-Jul-3 Christie's, Kensington #426/R est:3000-5000

PROCTOR, Adam E (1864-1913) British
£1200 $1872 €1800 In a garden (38x27cm-15x11in) s. 26-Mar-3 Hamptons Fine Art, Godalming #143 est:200-300
£3200 $5344 €4640 Turning the hay (24x34cm-9x13in) s. 25-Jun-3 Cheffins, Cambridge #772/R est:2000-3000

PROCTOR, Alexander Phimister (1862-1950) American
Sculpture
£2078 $3200 €3117 Fawn (16cm-6in) s.d.1893 num.RT95 brown pat bronze prov. 4-Sep-2 Christie's, Rockefeller NY #355/R est:4000-6000
£6962 $11000 €10443 Fate (18cm-7in) i. reddish brown pat. prov.lit. 3-Apr-3 Christie's, Rockefeller NY #154/R est:2000-3000
£9063 $14500 €13595 Prowling panther (91cm-36in) s. dark golden brown pat bronze st.f.Roman Bronze Works. 15-Mar-3 Selkirks, St. Louis #112/R est:4000-6000
£44304 $70000 €64241 The Q Street buffalo (33x46cm-13x18in) s.d.1912 bronze st.f.Gorhm. 26-Jul-3 Coeur d'Alene, Hayden #94/R est:20000-30000
£48438 $77500 €72657 Bucking Bronco! (74cm-29in) s.i. bronze. 16-May-3 Du Mouchelle, Detroit #2032/R est:40000-60000

PROCTOR, Althea Mary (1879-1966) Australian
Prints
£2107 $3308 €3161 Rose (22x21cm-9x8in) mono. hand col woodblock. 15-Apr-3 Lawson Menzies, Sydney #268/R est:2000-3000 (A.D 5500)
£2313 $3539 €3470 Swing (22x25cm-9x10in) s.i.num.32 hand col woodcut executed 1925 prov. 26-Aug-2 Sotheby's, Paddington #577/R est:7000-10000 (A.D 6500)
Works on paper
£268 $421 €402 Dancer (31x26cm-12x10in) s. pencil. 15-Apr-3 Lawson Menzies, Sydney #142/R (A.D 700)
£285 $436 €428 Ballerina (35x27cm-14x11in) s. pencil pastel prov. 26-Aug-2 Sotheby's, Paddington #708 (A.D 800)
£620 $986 €930 Portrait of a young lady holding a fan (38x35cm-15x14in) s. W/C pencil. 29-Apr-3 Bonhams, New Bond Street #17/R
£3461 $5504 €5192 Lovers (27x54cm-11x21in) s.d.1911 W/C fan shape prov. 4-Mar-3 Deutscher-Menzies, Melbourne #121/R est:9000-12000 (A.D 9000)

PROCTOR, Robert Field (1879-1931) New Zealander
£561 $876 €842 Village archway (52x42cm-20x17in) s. lit. 27-Mar-3 International Art Centre, Auckland #148/R (NZ.D 1600)

PROEBES (19th C) ?
Sculpture
£976 $1600 €1415 Figure of a blacksmith (36cm-14in) s. bronze executed c.1838. 4-Jun-3 Doyle, New York #708 est:1000-1500

PROEHL, Paul (19/20th C) American
£471 $750 €707 Shoot if you must, but spare your country's flag (76x76cm-30x30in) s. 7-Mar-3 Jackson's, Cedar Falls #626/R

PROENCA, Pedro (1962-) Portuguese?
£476 $757 €700 Rimus remedius (61x50cm-24x20in) s.i.d.1988 verso acrylic prov. 24-Mar-3 Cornette de St.Cyr, Paris #147/R

PROIETTI, Norberto (1927-) Italian
£382 $607 €550 Trimming (18x25cm-7x10in) s. acrylic over dr paper on canvas. 1-May-3 Meeting Art, Vercelli #562
£2051 $3241 €3200 Structure (30x20cm-12x8in) s. s.i.verso board. 15-Nov-2 Farsetti, Prato #31/R
£2244 $3522 €3500 Stairs (40x20cm-16x8in) s. board. 23-Nov-2 Meeting Art, Vercelli #153/R
£2680 $4288 €4100 Convent covered in snow (38x18cm-15x7in) s. board. 4-Jan-3 Meeting Art, Vercelli #725

PROKOFIEV, N (19th C) Russian
Works on paper
£2200 $3564 €3300 View of the River Neva (13x28cm-5x11in) s.d.97 W/C. 21-May-3 Sotheby's, London #9/R est:2000-3000
£3500 $5670 €5250 Marine scene (26x35cm-10x14in) s.i.d.94 W/C htd white. 21-May-3 Sotheby's, London #32/R est:2000-3000

PROKOP, Stefan (1941-1987) Czechoslovakian
Works on paper
£551 $805 €827 Maternity III (59x45cm-23x18in) pencil. 4-Jun-2 SOGA, Bratislava #265/R est:35000 (SL.K 35000)

PROLSS, Friedrich Anton Otto (1855-?) German
£1603 $2436 €2500 Pdeasant girl asleep by oven (40x30cm-16x12in) s. panel. 11-Jul-2 Hugo Ruef, Munich #781/R est:2500

PRONK, Cornelis (1691-1759) Dutch
Works on paper
£7643 $11924 €12000 Church and ruins of Rijnsburg, seen from the north east (28x46cm-11x18in) s.i.d.1753 pen black ink black grey wash prov.lit. 5-Nov-2 Sotheby's, Amsterdam #127/R est:5000-7000

PROOST, Alfons (1880-1957) Belgian
£540 $863 €750 Winter scene (31x48cm-12x19in) s. 17-May-3 De Vuyst, Lokeren #301
£633 $987 €1000 Enfants jouant dans les vagues (28x38cm-11x15in) s. panel. 16-Sep-2 Horta, Bruxelles #46
£2759 $4414 €4000 View of park (75x84cm-30x33in) s. s.d.1927 verso. 15-Mar-3 De Vuyst, Lokeren #532/R est:4000-5000

PROOST, Frans (1866-1941) Belgian
£900 $1458 €1350 Still life of sweet peas in a green vase (43x53cm-17x21in) s. canvas on panel. 21-May-3 Bonhams, Knightsbridge #180/R

PROOYEN, Albert Jurardus van (1834-1898) Dutch
£446 $687 €700 Allegory on summer and winter (22x13cm-9x5in) s. panel pair. 3-Sep-2 Christie's, Amsterdam #102
£769 $1169 €1200 Enjoying the ice (21x35cm-8x14in) s. panel. 17-Aug-2 Hans Stahl, Toestorf #50/R
£845 $1361 €1200 Coastal view at dusk (32x48cm-13x19in) s. panel. 7-May-3 Vendue Huis, Gravenhage #399/R
£955 $1471 €1500 Haybarge on the Ij, Amsterdam in the distance (38x58cm-15x23in) s. panel with another work by same hand two. 3-Sep-2 Christie's, Amsterdam #282/R est:1500-2000

PROSALENTIS, Emilios (1859-1926) Greek
£4000 $6320 €6000 Erectheion (47x37cm-19x15in) 1-Apr-3 Bonhams, New Bond Street #5 est:4000-6000
£4000 $6320 €6000 Boy in sailor suit (38x28cm-15x11in) 1-Apr-3 Bonhams, New Bond Street #18 est:4000-6000
£30000 $46500 €45000 Tallship in high seas (84x109cm-33x43in) s. 2-Oct-2 Sotheby's, London #21/R est:20000-30000
Works on paper
£600 $936 €900 Parthenon (22x31cm-9x12in) s. W/C. 15-Oct-2 Sotheby's, London #20/R
£600 $936 €900 Acropolis (22x32cm-9x13in) s. W/C. 15-Oct-2 Sotheby's, London #21/R
£600 $936 €900 Classical column near the Acropolis, Athens (31x22cm-12x9in) s. W/C. 15-Oct-2 Sotheby's, London #55/R
£6000 $9300 €9000 Ships at sea (31x42cm-12x17in) s. W/C pair. 2-Oct-2 Sotheby's, London #79/R est:4000-6000

PROSALENTIS, Spyros (1830-1895) Greek
Works on paper
£650 $1014 €975 Port (22x36cm-9x14in) s.i.indis.d.902 W/C. 15-Oct-2 Sotheby's, London #54/R

PROSDOCINI, Alberto (1852-1925) Italian
Works on paper
£629 $975 €1000 Venice, sailing ships by Magazini dei Sali (27x42cm-11x17in) s.i. W/C. 1-Oct-2 Dorotheum, Vienna #203/R
£1200 $1908 €1800 Il ponte dei Sospiri, Venezia (30x49cm-12x19in) s. W/C. 20-Mar-3 Christie's, Kensington #41/R est:1500-2000

PROSPERI, Liberio (19/20th C) British
Works on paper
£1450 $2320 €2175 Portrait of a polo player in red striped cap; an illustration for Vanity Fair (42x27cm-17x11in) s.d.1893 W/C htd white. 11-Mar-3 Bonhams, Oxford #43/R est:200-300

PROSSALENDIS, Pavlo (1857-1894) Greek
£12000 $18600 €18000 Oriental beauty (93x63cm-37x25in) s.d.92. 2-Oct-2 Sotheby's, London #11 est:15000-20000

PROSSER, George Frederick (fl.1828-1868) British
Works on paper
£3300 $5148 €4950 View of Winchester, Winton from SE (44x77cm-17x30in) s.i. pencil W/C. 18-Sep-2 Dreweatt Neate, Newbury #68/R est:2500-3500

PROST, Maurice (1894-1967) French
Sculpture
£2200 $3564 €3300 Lioness (32cm-13in) s. brown pat. bronze cire perdue. 20-May-3 Sotheby's, Olympia #119/R est:2000-3000
£7092 $11489 €10000 Panthere se lechant (32x60cm-13x24in) s. artist st. brown pat bronze. 23-May-3 Camard, Paris #101/R est:10000-12000

PROTITCH, Svetla (20th C) Bulgarian
Works on paper
£318 $497 €500 Portrait (50x24cm-20x9in) gouache. 10-Nov-2 Eric Pillon, Calais #259/R

PROTTI, Alfredo (1882-1949) Italian
£13462 $20865 €21000 Female nude (94x74cm-37x29in) s. 4-Dec-2 Finarte, Rome #795/R est:20000

PROUD, Geoffrey (1946-) Australian
£429 $669 €644 Firemen, engine (53x55cm-21x22in) i.verso paper composition board prov. 11-Nov-2 Deutscher-Menzies, Melbourne #135/R (A.D 1200)
£538 $817 €807 Abstract landscape (115x120cm-45x47in) s. 27-Aug-2 Goodman, Sydney #74 (A.D 1500)
£571 $891 €857 Falling water (58x57cm-23x22in) s.d.86 i.verso composition board. 11-Nov-2 Deutscher-Menzies, Melbourne #179/R (A.D 1600)
£928 $1448 €1392 Waterlillies (106x106cm-42x42in) s. 11-Nov-2 Deutscher-Menzies, Melbourne #178/R est:3000-5000 (A.D 2600)
£1138 $1798 €1650 Still life with oysters (105x120cm-41x47in) s.d.88 s.i.d.verso. 22-Jul-3 Lawson Menzies, Sydney #201/R est:3000-5000 (A.D 2800)
Works on paper
£286 $446 €429 Through the window (61x61cm-24x24in) s.d.83 synthetic polymer paint pastel composition board. 11-Nov-2 Deutscher-Menzies, Melbourne #192 (A.D 800)
£464 $724 €696 Pinball (66x55cm-26x22in) s.d.66 synthetic polymer paint pastel composition board. 11-Nov-2 Deutscher-Menzies, Melbourne #137/R (A.D 1300)
£534 $844 €926 Sailor boy (107x74cm-42x29in) s.d.79 mixed media perspex. 1-Apr-3 Goodman, Sydney #5 (A.D 1400)
£571 $891 €857 Dry cleaner (63x55cm-25x22in) i.verso synthetic polymer paint W/C composition board. 11-Nov-2 Deutscher-Menzies, Melbourne #136/R (A.D 1600)
£575 $902 €863 Violets (60x60cm-24x24in) s.d.84 pastel oil. 15-Apr-3 Lawson Menzies, Sydney #170/R est:1500-3000 (A.D 1500)

PROUDFOOT, James (1908-) British
£250 $390 €375 Swimming pool (35x46cm-14x18in) s.d.38. 27-Mar-3 Christie's, Kensington #453

PROUDFOOT, William (19th C) British?
£1700 $2652 €2550 Spearing trout at the head of Glenalmond (89x69cm-35x27in) arched top. 28-Mar-3 Bonhams, Edinburgh #167/R est:2000-3000

PROUT, John Skinner (1806-1876) British
Works on paper
£280 $434 €420 Figures outside a church with houses beyond (38x53cm-15x21in) s.d.1876 W/C. 31-Oct-2 Duke & Son, Dorchester #131/R
£300 $474 €435 Mount Oilatus, Lucerne (20x30cm-8x12in) s. W/C. 24-Jul-3 John Nicholson, Haslemere #1053/R
£400 $664 €600 Continental street scene with figures (52x38cm-20x15in) s. pencil W/C htd white. 10-Jun-3 Bonhams, Leeds #79
£419 $650 €629 English mansion and grounds (41x33cm-16x13in) s. W/C. 16-Jul-2 Arthur James, Florida #337
£600 $924 €900 View of the back of a continental cathedral (34x25cm-13x10in) s.d.1892 W/C. 22-Oct-2 Bonhams, Knightsbridge #22/R
£857 $1354 €1286 Cow pastures, New South Wales (20x36cm-8x14in) s. W/C. 26-Nov-2 Sotheby's, Melbourne #160 est:1500-2000 (A.D 2400)
£2321 $3668 €3482 On the Derwent (23x34cm-9x13in) s. W/C gouache executed c.1848 prov. 17-Nov-2 Sotheby's, Paddington #43/R est:6000-10000 (A.D 6500)
£7143 $11286 €10715 Break o'day plains, Tasmania (26x37cm-10x15in) s. W/C gouache prov. 26-Nov-2 Sotheby's, Melbourne #y/R est:12000-18000 (A.D 20000)

PROUT, Margaret Fisher (1875-1963) British
£400 $652 €580 In the garden (56x43cm-22x17in) s.d.1953 board. 21-Jul-3 Bonhams, Bath #34/R
£600 $966 €900 Still life of fruit and flowers (76x63cm-30x25in) s. board. 14-Jan-3 Bonhams, Knightsbridge #81/R
£600 $942 €900 View of Bosham (57x86cm-22x34in) s.d.1947 board. 15-Apr-3 Bonhams, Knightsbridge #141/R
£850 $1309 €1275 Farm by Hastings (63x76cm-25x30in) s. board exhib. 5-Sep-2 Christie's, Kensington #644
£900 $1485 €1305 View of Bosham, West Sussex (51x76cm-20x30in) s. board exhib. 3-Jul-3 Christie's, Kensington #450/R
£2300 $3633 €3450 Reclining nude (51x61cm-20x24in) s.d.1937 board prov. 27-Nov-2 Sotheby's, Olympia #135/R est:2000-3000
£2800 $4424 €4200 Soda fountain, Battersea Park (47x58cm-19x23in) s.d.1925. 27-Nov-2 Sotheby's, Olympia #144/R est:3000-5000

PROUT, Samuel (1783-1852) British
Works on paper
£250 $388 €375 West entrance of Lichfield Cathedral (30x24cm-12x9in) s.i.d.1811 pencil pen brown ink wash. 4-Dec-2 Christie's, Kensington #119
£270 $440 €405 Ademach on the Rhine (29x22cm-11x9in) W/C. 28-Jan-3 Henry Adams, Chichester #397
£280 $456 €420 Lisieux, Normandy (32x22cm-13x9in) W/C. 28-Jan-3 Henry Adams, Chichester #396
£300 $477 €450 Devon village (15x22cm-6x9in) W/C. 4-Mar-3 Bearnes, Exeter #350/R
£305 $497 €460 Ledford Vale, Devonshire (10x15cm-4x6in) s.i.verso monochrome wash. 28-Jan-3 James Adam, Dublin #24
£311 $516 €451 Market day (28x41cm-11x16in) s. W/C. 16-Jun-3 Waddingtons, Toronto #82/R (C.D 700)
£360 $572 €540 Figure studies (22x12cm-9x5in) W/C pencil. 30-Apr-3 Hampton & Littlewood, Exeter #420/R
£380 $600 €551 Interior of the cathedral at Chartres (41x26cm-16x10in) s. W/C. 22-Jul-3 Sworder & Son, Bishops Stortford #321/R
£413 $649 €620 Figures in a courtyard (33x23cm-13x9in) s. W/C. 24-Jul-2 Walker's, Ottawa #16/R est:1500-2000 (C.D 1000)
£480 $758 €696 Church doorway and congregation (37x27cm-15x11in) s. W/C. 22-Jul-3 Sworder & Son, Bishops Stortford #319/R
£520 $863 €780 Fishing boats on the Devon coast (19x35cm-7x14in) s. W/C prov. 10-Jun-3 Sworder & Son, Bishops Stortford #482/R
£550 $852 €825 Figures by a medieval church (36x26cm-14x10in) s. W/C. 3-Dec-2 Sotheby's, Olympia #29/R
£600 $948 €900 Venetian scene (40x27cm-16x11in) s. W/C. 27-Nov-2 Bonhams, Brooks & Langlois, Jersey #78
£600 $948 €870 Entrance to Chartres Cathedral with groups of figures (76x54cm-30x21in) s.d.1828 W/C prov. 22-Jul-3 Sworder & Son, Bishops Stortford #322/R
£700 $1085 €1050 Fisher folk with their boats on the beach (18x26cm-7x10in) s. W/C. 25-Sep-2 John Nicholson, Haslemere #908/R
£700 $1113 €1050 Cathedral interior (43x30cm-17x12in) mono. W/C. 29-Apr-3 Gorringes, Lewes #2229
£720 $1159 €1080 River landscape with peasants near a cottage (20x28cm-8x11in) s.i.verso W/C. 9-May-3 Mallams, Oxford #53/R
£760 $1201 €1102 Continental street with figures by a shop and cathedral beyond (41x29cm-16x11in) W/C prov. 22-Jul-3 Sworder & Son, Bishops Stortford #320/R
£769 $1192 €1200 Constantine Arch (53x42cm-21x17in) init. W/C. 4-Dec-2 Finarte, Rome #714
£800 $1264 €1200 Dusseldorf (33x22cm-13x9in) s. W/C htd white. 26-Nov-2 Bonhams, Knightsbridge #177/R
£900 $1395 €1350 Fisherfolk on the shore (40x53cm-16x21in) init. pencil W/C prov. 4-Dec-2 Christie's, Kensington #64
£1500 $2325 €2250 Street scene, Strasbourg (46x30cm-18x12in) W/C. 6-Dec-2 Chrystals Auctions, Isle of Man #254n est:1200-1800
£2800 $4648 €4200 By the water front, Strasbourg. Continental view (36x26cm-14x10in) s. W/C htd white two. 12-Jun-3 Bonhams, New Bond Street #648/R est:3000-4000
£3600 $5976 €5400 Rue Gros Horloge, Rouen. Continental street (55x43cm-22x17in) s. W/C over pen ink pair. 12-Jun-3 Bonhams, New Bond Street #642/R est:3000-5000
£5500 $9020 €7975 Riva Degli Schiavone, Venice (26x37cm-10x15in) i. pencil htd white prov. 5-Jun-3 Christie's, London #103/R est:1000-1500
£12000 $18960 €18000 Towns of France, Belgium and Germany, Netherlands (43x29cm-17x11in) pencil dr. album prov.lit. 28-Nov-2 Sotheby's, London #326/R est:12000-18000

PROUT, Samuel Gillespie (1822-1911) British
Works on paper
£320 $493 €480 Doge's palace from the Dogana, Venice (22x33cm-9x13in) W/C htd white. 22-Oct-2 Bonhams, Knightsbridge #44/R
£650 $1021 €975 Courtyard scene, France (50x35cm-20x14in) s. pencil W/C scratching out. 16-Apr-3 Christie's, Kensington #986/R

PROUT, Samuel Gillespie (attrib) (1822-1911) British
Works on paper
£480 $782 €720 Ducal Palace, Venice (25x36cm-10x14in) i. pencil W/C htd white. 29-Jan-3 Dreweatt Neate, Newbury #64

PROUVE, Victor (1858-1943) French
£12180 $19244 €19000 Le triomphe de Monsieur Corbin (167x523cm-66x206in) s.d.1927 prov.lit. 18-Nov-2 Tajan, Paris #182/R est:22000-30000
Works on paper
£2564 $4051 €4000 Amoureux (94x66cm-37x26in) s.d.97 pastel chl. 18-Nov-2 Sotheby's, Paris #91/R est:6000

PROVINO, Salvatore (1943-) Italian
£272 $433 €400 Sculpture (22x33cm-9x13in) s. 1-Mar-3 Meeting Art, Vercelli #597
£316 $494 €500 Winner (40x30cm-16x12in) s. 14-Sep-2 Meeting Art, Vercelli #713
£316 $494 €500 Lava (40x30cm-16x12in) s. painted 1992. 14-Sep-2 Meeting Art, Vercelli #724/R
£340 $541 €500 Body (22x27cm-9x11in) s. s.verso. 1-Mar-3 Meeting Art, Vercelli #338
£340 $541 €500 Landscape (40x60cm-16x24in) s. paper on canvas. 1-Mar-3 Meeting Art, Vercelli #390
£359 $575 €550 Transparences (33x22cm-13x9in) s. s.verso. 4-Jan-3 Meeting Art, Vercelli #318
£408 $649 €600 Zolfara (40x60cm-16x24in) s. paper on canvas. 1-Mar-3 Meeting Art, Vercelli #576
£438 $701 €670 Symphony (22x27cm-9x11in) s. s.verso. 4-Jan-3 Meeting Art, Vercelli #550
£475 $741 €750 Object (40x50cm-16x20in) s. s.i.d.1992 verso lit. 14-Sep-2 Meeting Art, Vercelli #70/R
£475 $741 €750 Sea transparences (50x40cm-20x16in) s. painted 2000. 14-Sep-2 Meeting Art, Vercelli #743/R
£506 $790 €800 Light refraction (50x70cm-20x28in) s. s.i.d.1991 verso. 14-Sep-2 Meeting Art, Vercelli #762/R
£521 $828 €750 Pieta' (55x38cm-22x15in) s. s.verso. 1-May-3 Meeting Art, Vercelli #164
£523 $837 €800 Stromboli (40x50cm-16x20in) s. s.i.d.1996 verso. 4-Jan-3 Meeting Art, Vercelli #63
£654 $1046 €1000 Autumn (50x60cm-20x24in) s. s.i.d.1998 verso. 4-Jan-3 Meeting Art, Vercelli #80
£694 $1104 €1000 Body in the ashes (50x70cm-20x28in) s. painted 1992. 1-May-3 Meeting Art, Vercelli #57
£949 $1481 €1500 Night scene (80x60cm-31x24in) s. s.i.d.1999 verso. 14-Sep-2 Meeting Art, Vercelli #777/R
£1088 $1731 €1600 Rythms (60x50cm-24x20in) s. painted 1992. 1-Mar-3 Meeting Art, Vercelli #370
£1088 $1731 €1600 Graffiti on the rocks (60x80cm-24x31in) s. lit. 1-Mar-3 Meeting Art, Vercelli #763
£1242 $1987 €1900 Submerged garden (70x100cm-28x39in) s. 4-Jan-3 Meeting Art, Vercelli #611
£1307 $2092 €2000 Water breathing (100x100cm-39x39in) s. s.i.d.2000 verso. 4-Jan-3 Meeting Art, Vercelli #94
£1393 $2229 €2020 For a new town (70x50cm-28x20in) s.d.1975. 11-Mar-3 Babuino, Rome #169/R
£1736 $2760 €2500 Ship (60x80cm-24x31in) s. painted 1999. 1-May-3 Meeting Art, Vercelli #167
£1875 $2981 €2700 Sun stone (100x100cm-39x39in) s. s.i.verso. 1-May-3 Meeting Art, Vercelli #469
£1961 $3137 €3000 Lands with snow and shadows (100x100cm-39x39in) s. s.i.verso. 4-Jan-3 Meeting Art, Vercelli #402
£2115 $3321 €3300 Deep Mediterranean (200x100cm-79x39in) s. s.i.d.2000 verso lit. 23-Nov-2 Meeting Art, Vercelli #358/R

PROVIS, Alfred (19th C) British
£1000 $1590 €1500 On the sunlit stairs (28x23cm-11x9in) s.d.1855. 6-Mar-3 Christie's, Kensington #607/R est:1000-1500
£1333 $2213 €1933 Her firstborn (37x52cm-15x20in) s. indis d.1869. 16-Jun-3 Waddingtons, Toronto #159/R est:5000-7000 (C.D 3000)
£1410 $2144 €2200 Playmates sharing their meal (21x25cm-8x10in) s.d.1871 lit. 11-Jul-2 Allgauer, Kempten #2654/R
£1500 $2445 €2250 Children with pet rabbit in an interior (18x25cm-7x10in) s.d.1879. 14-Feb-3 Keys, Aylsham #732/R est:1500-2000
£1800 $2934 €2610 Breton girl selling her hair (33x51cm-13x20in) s.d1855 exhib. 21-Jul-3 Bonhams, Bath #83/R est:2000-3000
£4000 $6320 €6000 Wiltshire forge (36x61cm-14x24in) s.d.1854. 7-Apr-3 Bonhams, Bath #134/R est:4000-6000

PROVOST, Jan (15/16th C) Flemish
£185185 $300000 €277778 Nativity (51x38cm-20x15in) panel prov.exhib.lit. 23-Jan-3 Sotheby's, New York #34/R est:300000-500000

PROVOT, Andre (1899-1985) French
£380 $600 €600 Rue orientaliste animee (46x61cm-18x24in) s.d.26. 1-Dec-2 Livinec, Gaudcheau & Jezequel, Rennes #48/R

PROVOT, J A (?) French
£423 $680 €600 Bretonnes en profil de confiture (38x46cm-15x18in) s.d.21. 11-May-3 Thierry & Lannon, Brest #389

PROWETT, James C (?-1946) British
£480 $749 €720 Bring the cattle home (24x32cm-9x13in) s. board. 17-Sep-2 Sotheby's, Olympia #34/R
£915 $1500 €1373 Figures in a landscape (41x51cm-16x20in) s. 5-Feb-3 Doyle, New York #48/R est:1500-2000

PROWSE, Ruth (1883-1967) South African
£3376 $5334 €5064 Bo-Kaap, Cape Town (23x33cm-9x13in) mono. board. 1-Apr-3 Stephan Welz, Johannesburg #435/R est:9000-12000 (SA.R 42000)

PRUCHA, Gustav (1875-1952) Austrian
£425 $697 €650 Dutch coastal landscape (55x68cm-22x27in) s. 29-Mar-3 Dannenberg, Berlin #638/R
£600 $972 €900 Winter wedding (51x71cm-20x28in) s. 23-Jan-3 Christie's, Kensington #129/R
£683 $1100 €1025 Midday rest in the wheat field (64x91cm-25x36in) s. 20-Jan-3 Arthur James, Florida #631
£2188 $3500 €3282 Sleigh ride (69x56cm-27x22in) s. 14-May-3 Butterfields, San Francisco #1090/R est:3000-5000

PRUD'HOMME, Marcel (20th C) French
£1887 $2906 €3000 Scenes de rue dans la ville arabe (46x65cm-18x26in) s. pair. 23-Oct-2 Rabourdin & Choppin de Janvry, Paris #265/R

PRUD'HON, Jean (1778-?) French
Works on paper
£380 $631 €540 Dancers on frieze (7x69cm-3x27in) brush. 12-Jun-3 Hauswedell & Nolte, Hamburg #384/R

PRUDHON, Pierre Paul (1758-1823) French
£2907 $4767 €4215 Scene from Atala (33x40cm-13x16in) bears indis sig. panel. 4-Jun-3 AB Stockholms Auktionsverk #2520/R est:20000-25000 (S.KR 37000)
Works on paper
£1154 $1788 €1800 Enfant tenant un arc (9x7cm-4x3in) crayon htd chk. 4-Dec-2 Piasa, Paris #176/R
£2778 $4500 €4167 Design for mirror (25x29cm-10x11in) pen ink prov.exhib.lit. 21-Jan-3 Sotheby's, New York #127/R est:7000
£3077 $4769 €4800 Clotho la fileuse (22x12cm-9x5in) pierre noire htd white prov.lit. 4-Dec-2 Piasa, Paris #178/R est:12200
£8784 $13703 €13000 Parques et Charite (17x42cm-7x17in) crayon prov.lit. 26-Mar-3 Pierre Berge, Paris #17/R est:13000

PRUKNER, Stefan (1931-) Czechoslovakian
£315 $447 €473 Erotica (84x76cm-33x30in) painted 1971. 26-Mar-2 SOGA, Bratislava #251/R (SL.K 20000)
£473 $671 €710 Erotic composition (34x24cm-13x9in) plywood painted c.1997. 26-Mar-2 SOGA, Bratislava #252/R (SL.K 30000)

PRUNA, Pedro (1904-1977) Spanish
£4321 $6136 €7000 Vase de tulipes (100x73cm-39x29in) s.d.1967. 16-Mar-3 Eric Pillon, Calais #138/R
£9517 $15037 €13800 Arlequin (44x36cm-17x14in) s.d.1925. 1-Apr-3 Segre, Madrid #135/R est:13800
£10000 $15900 €14500 Annunciation (116x89cm-46x35in) s.d.42. 4-Mar-3 Ansorena, Madrid #171/R
£13000 $20410 €19500 Mujer con panuelo rojo - woman with a red head scarf (92x73cm-36x29in) prov.exhib. 19-Nov-2 Sotheby's, London #71/R est:8000-12000
£18947 $30695 €28800 Woman in profile (92x73cm-36x29in) s. 21-Jan-3 Ansorena, Madrid #292/R est:28000
Works on paper
£516 $815 €800 Couple (21x15cm-8x6in) s.d.1927 W/C ink. 19-Dec-2 Delvaux, Paris #21/R
£699 $1168 €1000 Couple de danseurs (36x27cm-14x11in) s.d.1943 W/C. 26-Jun-3 Tajan, Paris #126

PRUNKEIT, Emil (19/20th C) German
£2152 $3400 €3400 Waiting for departure (35x27cm-14x11in) s. 29-Nov-2 Schloss Ahlden, Ahlden #1353/R est:3600

PRUNNIER, Ant (19th C) French
£586 $833 €950 Amour au champs (49x59cm-19x23in) s.i.d.1883 oval. 17-Mar-2 Galerie de Chartres, Chartres #121

PRUSEY, F (?) Belgian?
£2308 $3577 €3600 Le gouter au jardin (57x74cm-22x29in) s. 9-Dec-2 Horta, Bruxelles #138 est:5000-7500

PRUSS, Zglinicki von (19th C) ?
£548 $855 €800 The egg of Columbus (72x54cm-28x21in) s.d.80 i. verso. 9-Apr-3 Neumeister, Munich #728/R

PRUSSEN, Clemens (20th C) German
£719 $1151 €1000 Eifel landscape with Nurburg (60x80cm-24x31in) s. 17-May-3 Lempertz, Koln #1465

PRUVOST, Pierre (1921-) French
£288 $460 €400 Square a Cannes (33x41cm-13x16in) s. i.verso panel. 14-May-3 Blanchet, Paris #136/R

PRYCE, Willis (?) British
£300 $477 €450 Guy's Cliffe from the lake (29x36cm-11x14in) s. board. 27-Feb-3 Locke & England, Leamington Spa #138/R

PRYDE, James (1869-1941) British
£1300 $2055 €1950 Monument (36x26cm-14x10in) s. i.stretcher prov. 27-Nov-2 Sotheby's, Olympia #53/R est:1000-1500
£3500 $5390 €5250 Homage to Desiderio (63x76cm-25x30in) prov. 5-Sep-2 Christie's, Kensington #563/R est:2000-3000
£3500 $5425 €5250 Corner (46x35cm-18x14in) s. prov. 31-Oct-2 Christie's, London #117/R est:4000-6000
Works on paper
£280 $442 €406 Waterfront scene (15x11cm-6x4in) s. W/C pencil. 22-Jul-3 Sotheby's, Olympia #276/R est:200-400

PRYLLERET, P de (19th C) French
£655 $1022 €983 Lake landscape with rowing boat (80x67cm-31x26in) s. 20-Nov-2 Fischer, Luzern #2221/R est:1500-1800 (S.FR 1500)

PRYN, Harald (1891-1968) Danish
£255 $403 €383 Winter landscape (67x100cm-26x39in) s.i. 30-Nov-2 Rasmussen, Havnen #2204 (D.KR 3000)
£270 $422 €405 Winter landscape from a village (70x100cm-28x39in) s. 11-Aug-2 Hindemae, Ullerslev #7700/R (D.KR 3200)
£279 $444 €419 Winter landscape (50x70cm-20x28in) s. 10-Mar-3 Rasmussen, Vejle #530 (D.KR 3000)
£338 $527 €507 Wooded landscape with river (86x105cm-34x41in) s.i.d.1958. 22-Sep-2 Hindemae, Ullerslev #7238/R (D.KR 4000)
£343 $535 €515 Snow-covered landscape with trees and houses by road (80x110cm-31x43in) s. 11-Nov-2 Rasmussen, Vejle #486 (D.KR 4000)
£343 $535 €515 Winter landscape with road (72x100cm-28x39in) s. 11-Nov-2 Rasmussen, Vejle #487 (D.KR 4000)
£383 $620 €555 Winter landscape, Slagslunde (71x100cm-28x39in) s.i. 24-May-3 Rasmussen, Havnen #2149 (D.KR 4000)
£414 $633 €621 Winter landscape with river (70x100cm-28x39in) s.i. 24-Aug-2 Rasmussen, Havnen #2110 (D.KR 4800)
£466 $742 €699 Winter landscape with road (50x71cm-20x28in) s. 5-May-3 Rasmussen, Vejle #665/R (D.KR 5000)
£493 $778 €740 Winter landscape (70x100cm-28x39in) s. 5-Apr-3 Rasmussen, Havnen #2053 (D.KR 5300)
£511 $807 €767 Road through village in winter (70x100cm-28x39in) s. 2-Dec-2 Rasmussen, Copenhagen #1566/R (D.KR 6000)
£559 $888 €839 Sunny winter's day in the village (70x97cm-28x38in) s.i. 5-Mar-3 Rasmussen, Copenhagen #1883 (D.KR 6000)
£596 $941 €894 Winter's day in Kajerod (70x96cm-28x38in) s.i.d.1950. 2-Dec-2 Rasmussen, Copenhagen #1564/R (D.KR 7000)
£605 $962 €908 Spring day in Troldeskogen at Herlufsholm (80x102cm-31x40in) s.i.d.53. 5-Mar-3 Rasmussen, Copenhagen #1905/R (D.KR 6500)
£788 $1261 €1182 Winter landscape with country road near Orholm (102x152cm-40x60in) s.d.1922. 13-Jan-3 Rasmussen, Vejle #120/R (D.KR 9000)
£975 $1550 €1463 Snow filled lane (69x94cm-27x37in) s. 18-Mar-3 Maynards, Vancouver #19/R est:2500-3500 (C.D 2300)
£1013 $1600 €1600 Winter landscape (50x70cm-20x28in) s. lit. 29-Nov-2 Schloss Ahlden, Ahlden #1290/R est:1400
£1064 $1649 €1596 Winter landscape (70x100cm-28x39in) s. 4-Dec-2 AB Stockholms Auktionsverk #1906/R est:10000-12000 (S.KR 15000)
£2516 $3874 €4000 Snowy landscape (70x100cm-28x39in) s. 23-Oct-2 Finarte, Milan #49/R

PSAIER, Pietro (20th C) American
£420 $701 €609 Coca cola high ball (100x59cm-39x23in) i.verso. 25-Jun-3 Cheffins, Cambridge #811

PSEUDO BOLTRAFFIO (16th C) Italian?
£35000 $54600 €52500 Madonna and Child with Saints Romanus and Ptolomaeus and two donors (80x101cm-31x40in) panel prov. 9-Apr-3 Christie's, London #87/R est:30000-50000

PSEUDO FARDELLA (17th C) Italian
£11189 $18685 €16000 Bouquet de fleurs, poissons, champignons, sur un entablement (36x57cm-14x22in) panel. 25-Jun-3 Pierre Berge, Paris #28/R est:8000-12000
£19000 $31730 €27550 Grapes, pears, apples and roses on a white cloth. Pomegranates and fig on forest floor (73x99cm-29x39in) pair. 9-Jul-3 Christie's, London #84/R est:15000-20000

PSEUDO PACCHIA (16th C) Italian?
Works on paper
£4013 $6500 €6020 Studies (29x22cm-11x9in) chk pen ink prov. 22-Jan-3 Christie's, Rockefeller NY #6/R

PSEUDO PIER FRANCESCO FIORENTINO (fl.c.1460-1500) Italian
£51613 $81548 €80000 Madonna adoring the Child (66x48cm-26x19in) tempera board. 19-Dec-2 Semenzato, Venice #27/R est:85000
£52469 $85000 €78704 Madonna and Child with angels (76x46cm-30x18in) tempera panel prov.exhib.lit. 23-Jan-3 Sotheby's, New York #150/R est:80000

PSEUDO ROESTRAETEN (17th C) ?
£6475 $10360 €9000 Silver jug and a teapot, watch, golden chain on a draped table (117x102cm-46x40in) i. 14-May-3 Christie's, Amsterdam #194/R est:6000-8000

PSEUDO ROESTRAETEN (circle) (17th C) ?
£30000 $46800 €45000 Trompe l'oeil depiction of an illuminated book (44x54cm-17x21in) panel. 10-Apr-3 Christie's, Kensington #145/R est:2500-3500

PSEUDO SIMONS (17th C) Flemish
£19000 $29830 €28500 Lobster, crab on a pewter plate, grapes, figs, bottle of wine on a stone ledge (56x96cm-22x38in) 13-Dec-2 Christie's, Kensington #104/R est:12000-18000

PSEUDO SONJE (attrib) (17th C) Dutch
£1419 $2200 €2129 Figures on a path by a river, a town beyond (47x63cm-19x25in) panel. 2-Oct-2 Christie's, Rockefeller NY #114/R est:4000-6000

PU HUA (1830-1911) Chinese
Works on paper
£290 $475 €400 Small bird with plum branches and bamboo (41x57cm-16x22in) i. seals Indian ink painted with other artists. 30-May-3 Dr Fritz Nagel, Stuttgart #1137/R

PU RU (1896-1963) Chinese
Works on paper
£764 $1192 €1200 Landscape (133x16cm-52x6in) s.i. Indian ink col paper hanging scroll. 8-Nov-2 Dr Fritz Nagel, Stuttgart #1207/R
£2176 $3590 €3155 Gibbons (18x50cm-7x20in) s.i.d.1941 ink fan. 6-Jul-3 Christie's, Hong Kong #356/R est:25000-30000 (HK.D 28000)
£2439 $3854 €3659 Poems in Xing Shu (12x5cm-5x2in) s.i.d.1947 forty-four leaves album. 28-Apr-3 Sotheby's, Hong Kong #635/R est:30000-50000 (HK.D 30000)
£3252 $5138 €4878 Monk (60x29cm-24x11in) s.i. ink hanging scroll. 28-Apr-3 Sotheby's, Hong Kong #664/R est:40000-60000 (HK.D 40000)
£3497 $5769 €5071 Zhong Kui (78x35cm-31x14in) s.i. ink scroll. 6-Jul-3 Christie's, Hong Kong #308/R est:50000-60000 (HK.D 45000)

PU RU and QI BAISHI (19/20th C) Chinese
Works on paper
£2020 $3333 €2929 Scholar under a willow tree (90x42cm-35x17in) s.i. ink scroll. 6-Jul-3 Christie's, Hong Kong #309/R est:30000-40000 (HK.D 26000)

PU RU and ZHANG DAQIAN (20th C) Chinese
Works on paper
£5285 $8350 €7928 Chinese opera figure (21x22cm-8x9in) s.i. ink col hanging scroll. 28-Apr-3 Sotheby's, Hong Kong #565/R est:40000-60000 (HK.D 65000)
£19512 $30829 €29268 Peach blossoms (16x94cm-6x37in) s.i.d.1934 ink col handscrolls pair. 28-Apr-3 Sotheby's, Hong Kong #638/R est:80000-100000 (HK.D 240000)
£36585 $57805 €54878 Bird, flower and bird (26x38cm-10x15in) s.i.d.1946 ink col two. 28-Apr-3 Sotheby's, Hong Kong #546/R est:450000-600000 (HK.D 450000)

PUCCI, Silvio (1892-1961) Italian
£449 $704 €700 Little farm (50x60cm-20x24in) sd.43. 16-Dec-2 Pandolfini, Florence #292/R
£513 $805 €800 Vase de fleurs (45x35cm-18x14in) s. 16-Dec-2 Pandolfini, Florence #246
£513 $805 €800 Vase de fleurs (50x40cm-20x16in) s. 16-Dec-2 Pandolfini, Florence #245
£541 $843 €800 Flowers (40x30cm-16x12in) s. 28-Mar-3 Farsetti, Prato #642/R
£1892 $2951 €2800 Still life (40x49cm-16x19in) s. painted 1933. 28-Mar-3 Farsetti, Prato #752/R

PUCCINI, Mario (1869-1920) Italian
£7595 $12000 €12000 Still life with green vase (27x29cm-11x11in) s. i.verso cardboard prov. 26-Nov-2 Christie's, Rome #198/R est:18000

PUDLICH, Robert (1905-1962) German
£1377 $2258 €1900 Little dancers (34x21cm-13x8in) s. 29-May-3 Lempertz, Koln #880/R est:1800

PUEL, Gaston (20th C) French
Sculpture
£1233 $1936 €1800 Hommage a Fourier (13x36cm-5x14in) box objects. 15-Apr-3 Laurence Calmels, Paris #4234/R

PUENTE, Carlos (?) Spanish?
£513 $800 €770 Cityscape (81x81cm-32x32in) s. 22-Sep-2 Susanin's, Chicago #5082/R

PUEYRREDON, Prilidiano (1823-1870) Argentinian
£148734 $235000 €223101 Peasant scene (102x128cm-40x50in) s.d.1865 prov. 15-Nov-2 Naón & Cia, Buenos Aires #1/R

PUGET, Francois (1651-1707) French
Works on paper
£705 $1093 €1100 Portrait de Pierre Puget (37x28cm-15x11in) i. sanguine. 4-Dec-2 Piasa, Paris #60

PUGET, Pierre (1620-1694) French
Works on paper
£46296 $75000 €69444 Study of Bucephalus (36x26cm-14x10in) i. chk htd white prov.lit. 21-Jan-3 Sotheby's, New York #62/R est:40000

PUGET, Pierre (attrib) (1620-1694) French
£4516 $7135 €7000 Fuite en Egypte (72x95cm-28x37in) 18-Dec-2 Piasa, Paris #76/R
£10976 $18000 €16464 Mediterranean ports with shipping (25x44cm-10x17in) pair prov. 30-May-3 Christie's, Rockefeller NY #51/R est:20000-30000

PUGGAARD, Bolette (1798-1847) Danish
£287 $465 €416 Swiss landscape (55x65cm-22x26in) s.d.1830. 26-May-3 Rasmussen, Copenhagen #1268 (D.KR 3000)

PUGH, Bryan (20th C) Australian
Works on paper
£420 $663 €609 Reclining nude. s. graphite. 7-Apr-3 Australian Art Auctions, Sydney #141 (A.D 1100)

PUGH, Clifton Ernest (1924-1990) Australian
£1143 $1771 €1715 On the edge of the Salt Pans, Cottles Bridge, Victoria (67x90cm-26x35in) s.d.Feb 60 board. 29-Oct-2 Lawson Menzies, Sydney #100/R est:3000-5000 (A.D 3200)
£2400 $3864 €3600 Upside down Suzie (121x91cm-48x36in) s.d.83 board. 6-May-3 Christie's, Melbourne #220/R est:6000-8000 (A.D 6000)
£2500 $3925 €3750 Nude Suzi (121x90cm-48x35in) s.d.29.3.83 board. 25-Nov-2 Christie's, Melbourne #214/R est:8000-10000 (A.D 7000)
£2598 $3975 €3897 Autumn mist (120x136cm-47x54in) s.d.Mar 77 board prov. 25-Aug-2 Sotheby's, Paddington #118/R est:9000-12000 (A.D 7300)
£2857 $4429 €4286 Eros suit I (91x121cm-36x48in) composition board. 29-Oct-2 Lawson Menzies, Sydney #49/R est:12000-14000 (A.D 8000)
£3000 $4830 €4500 Portrait of Esther (122x88cm-48x35in) s.d.1956 board lit. 6-May-3 Christie's, Melbourne #363/R est:8000-12000 (A.D 7500)
£3654 $5809 €5481 Magpies (60x74cm-24x29in) s. composition board. 4-Mar-3 Deutscher-Menzies, Melbourne #60/R est:9000-12000 (A.D 9500)
£4270 $6534 €6405 Lizard and butterfly (68x91cm-27x36in) s.d.Dec 57 board. 26-Aug-2 Sotheby's, Paddington #537/R est:18000-28000 (A.D 12000)
£4400 $7084 €6600 Dance of the crows (68x91cm-27x36in) s.d.57 prov. 6-May-3 Christie's, Melbourne #117/R est:14000-18000 (A.D 11000)
£5385 $8562 €8078 Flight of a magpie (91x122cm-36x48in) s.d.Aug 29/83 composition board. 4-Mar-3 Deutscher-Menzies, Melbourne #156/R est:10000-15000 (A.D 14000)
£5694 $8712 €8541 And waited (91x122cm-36x48in) s.d.79 i.verso board prov. 26-Aug-2 Sotheby's, Paddington #637/R est:8000-10000 (A.D 16000)
£6504 $10276 €9431 Bull riding (135x90cm-53x35in) s. i.verso board prov. 22-Jul-3 Lawson Menzies, Sydney #42/R est:20000-25000 (A.D 16000)
£7829 $11979 €11744 Autumn black of the waterhole (121x90cm-48x35in) s.d.76 feb board prov.exhib. 25-Aug-2 Sotheby's, Paddington #125/R est:9000-12000 (A.D 22000)
£17347 $26369 €26021 On a chicken farm (91x122cm-36x48in) s.d.Oct.1960 s.i.verso composition board prov.exhib.lit. 28-Aug-2 Deutscher-Menzies, Melbourne #113/R est:35000-45000 (A.D 48400)

Works on paper
£323 $490 €485 Point Arkwright (55x74cm-22x29in) s.i.d.13-1-89 gouache. 28-Aug-2 Deutscher-Menzies, Melbourne #341/R (A.D 900)
£498 $782 €747 Loading the pack saddles (36x49cm-14x19in) s. W/C gouache prov. 15-Apr-3 Lawson Menzies, Sydney #220/R est:1000-1500 (A.D 1300)
£502 $763 €753 Landscape (54x73cm-21x29in) s.d.5-12-79 gouache W/C. 28-Aug-2 Deutscher-Menzies, Melbourne #262/R (A.D 1400)
£536 $799 €804 8am - 10am-6pm (78x56cm-31x22in) s.d.26.3.74 gouache. 27-Aug-2 Christie's, Melbourne #339 est:1500-2500 (A.D 1400)
£560 $902 €812 Outback (54x74cm-21x29in) s.d.7/6/80 mixed media. 12-May-3 Joel, Victoria #248 est:1500-2000 (A.D 1400)
£577 $917 €866 Clearing (56x75cm-22x30in) s.d.26.1.79 gouache paper on board. 4-Mar-3 Deutscher-Menzies, Melbourne #271/R (A.D 1500)
£637 $1045 €956 Landscape (54x73cm-21x29in) s.d.23-07-86 gouache. 4-Jun-3 Deutscher-Menzies, Melbourne #325/R (A.D 1600)
£637 $1045 €956 Landscape (51x73cm-20x29in) s.d.29-7-86 gouache. 4-Jun-3 Deutscher-Menzies, Melbourne #326/R (A.D 1600)
£717 $1090 €1076 Reclining nude (68x97cm-27x38in) s.d.Jan 1970 chl pastel. 28-Aug-2 Deutscher-Menzies, Melbourne #340/R (A.D 2000)
£1395 $2219 €2093 Landscape with cockatoos (55x77cm-22x30in) s.d.83 gouache two. 5-May-3 Sotheby's, Melbourne #348/R est:2500-3500 (A.D 3600)

PUGH, David (1946-1994) Canadian
£763 $1213 €1145 Bragg creek (68x90cm-27x35in) s.d.1980. 23-Mar-3 Hodgins, Calgary #73/R est:1500-2000 (C.D 1800)
£870 $1357 €1450 Blue cumulus (97x122cm-38x48in) s. s.i.d.1992 verso. 13-Apr-3 Levis, Calgary #97/R est:2500-3000 (C.D 2000)
£1156 $1895 €1676 Evening rays (95x120cm-37x47in) s.i.d.1992. 9-Jun-3 Hodgins, Calgary #190/R est:2500-3500 (C.D 2600)
£1244 $2041 €1804 Mt. Kidd (100x120cm-39x47in) s.i.d.1990. 9-Jun-3 Hodgins, Calgary #39/R est:2500-3500 (C.D 2800)

PUGIN, Augustus Charles (1769-1832) French
Works on paper
£800 $1336 €1160 Hall of Queens College, Cambridge (19x29cm-7x11in) W/C. 24-Jun-3 Bonhams, Knightsbridge #73/R
£17308 $26827 €27000 Vue de la bibliotheque de Cassiobury (20x28cm-8x11in) s.d.1816 W/C gouache. 6-Dec-2 Millon & Associes, Paris #35/R est:23000

PUGIN, Augustus Welby Northmore (1812-1852) British
Works on paper
£350 $574 €525 Lantern studies (30x19cm-12x7in) s.d.1830 pencil. 5-Jun-3 Christie's, Kensington #882

PUHONNY, Victor (1838-1909) Polish
£538 $850 €850 Forest path with view of houses in a settlement on forest edge (32x21cm-13x8in) 30-Nov-2 Berlinghof, Heidelberg #361
£1486 $2319 €2200 View of Strasbourg across river meadows (16x29cm-6x11in) s.d.188 panel. 27-Mar-3 Dr Fritz Nagel, Stuttgart #863/R
£1887 $2925 €3000 Forest interior (73x51cm-29x20in) s. 29-Oct-2 Dorotheum, Vienna #222/R est:2000-2400

PUHONNY, Victor (attrib) (1838-1909) Polish
£323 $474 €500 Woodland path flooded with sun (31x20cm-12x8in) s. 24-Jun-2 Dr Fritz Nagel, Stuttgart #5959/R

PUIG Y SAURET, Salvador (1875-1944) South American
£513 $800 €770 Anciano (62x50cm-24x20in) s.i.d.7-1900. 30-Jul-2 Galleria Y Remates, Montevideo #32/R

PUIG, August (1929-1999) Spanish
Works on paper
£631 $984 €947 Head (34x23cm-13x9in) s. mixed media. 6-Nov-2 AB Stockholms Auktionsverk #938/R (S.KR 9000)
£1277 $2068 €1800 Face (38x28cm-15x11in) s.i.d.1952 W/C gouache. 24-May-3 Van Ham, Cologne #492/R est:2400

PUIG, Magi (1966-) Spanish
£514 $801 €750 Gold (116x116cm-46x46in) s. 8-Apr-3 Ansorena, Madrid #274/R

PUIG, Vicente (?) ?
£1600 $2576 €2400 Masquerade (77x60cm-30x24in) s.d.1924. 18-Feb-3 Bonhams, Knightsbridge #175/R est:1000-1500

PUIG-RODA, Gabriel (1865-1919) Spanish
£1923 $3038 €3000 Charity (35x16cm-14x6in) s. board. 19-Nov-2 Durán, Madrid #228/R
Works on paper
£3097 $4893 €4800 Mosquetaire (51x37cm-20x15in) s. W/C. 18-Dec-2 Ansorena, Madrid #235/R

PUIGAUDEAU, Fernand du (1866-1930) French
£1667 $2717 €2400 Bords de la Loire, meditation (17x22cm-7x9in) s.verso panel painted c.1910. 19-Jul-3 Thierry & Lannon, Brest #164/R est:1800-2200
£2500 $3875 €3750 Rue du Bourg du Batz (38x29cm-15x11in) s. board lit. 5-Dec-2 Christie's, Kensington #32/R est:3000-5000
£3000 $4620 €4500 Crepuscule dans le Golfe du Morbihan (65x81cm-26x32in) s.d.25 prov.lit. 23-Oct-2 Sotheby's, Olympia #632/R est:3000-5000
£3000 $4770 €4500 Vue de Samois (21x30cm-8x12in) s. panel. 20-Mar-3 Sotheby's, Olympia #43/R est:3500-4000
£4236 $6905 €6100 Vue de Clisson (13x18cm-5x7in) s. panel. 19-Jul-3 Thierry & Lannon, Brest #165/R est:4300-4500
£4908 $8000 €7362 Coucher de soleil en briere (27x35cm-11x14in) s. panel. 12-Feb-3 Sotheby's, New York #19/R est:12000-15000
£5031 $7799 €8000 Effect de vagues sur les rochers (54x65cm-21x26in) s.d.15 prov.lit. 4-Oct-2 Tajan, Paris #203 est:5000-6000
£6832 $11000 €10248 Crepuscule dans le golfe du Morbihan (59x73cm-23x29in) s. lit. 7-May-3 Sotheby's, New York #395/R est:15000-20000
£10063 $16000 €15095 Enfants sur la dune (27x35cm-11x14in) s. prov.exhib. 27-Feb-3 Christie's, Rockefeller NY #14/R est:15000
£10897 $16564 €17000 Jardin fleuri (65x81cm-26x32in) s. 16-Aug-2 Deauville, France #93/R est:23000
£11392 $17658 €18000 Moulin pres de guerande (128x101cm-50x40in) s. lit. 29-Sep-2 Eric Pillon, Calais #194/R
£11950 $19000 €17925 Coucher de soleil (60x73cm-24x29in) s. exhib. 27-Feb-3 Christie's, Rockefeller NY #15/R est:18000
£12676 $20408 €18000 Le moulin a vent a Guerande (60x73cm-24x29in) s. 11-May-3 Thierry & Lannon, Brest #218/R est:20000-22000
£12883 $21000 €19325 Briere au clair de lune (65x81cm-26x32in) s. 12-Feb-3 Sotheby's, New York #49/R est:25000-30000
£13000 $20150 €19500 Le chemin du jardin de Kervadu (54x74cm-21x29in) s. lit. 5-Dec-2 Christie's, Kensington #29/R est:7000-10000
£13000 $20150 €19500 Pont de pendille (46x61cm-18x24in) s.d.25 lit. 5-Dec-2 Christie's, Kensington #30/R est:6000-8000
£14110 $23000 €21165 Moulin de La Mass (65x81cm-26x32in) s. 12-Feb-3 Sotheby's, New York #15/R est:25000-35000
£15094 $24000 €22641 Manege la nuit (46x55cm-18x22in) s. prov.exhib.lit. 27-Feb-3 Christie's, Rockefeller NY #13/R est:28000
£16149 $26000 €24224 Paysage de la grande briere (60x74cm-24x29in) s. painted c.1924-26 prov.exhib. 7-May-3 Sotheby's, New York #169/R est:25000-35000
£18000 $27900 €27000 Place de village (60x73cm-24x29in) s. lit. 5-Dec-2 Christie's, Kensington #31/R est:7000-10000
£26923 $42000 €40385 Voile sur un etang (65x81cm-26x32in) s. 7-Nov-2 Christie's, Rockefeller NY #258/R est:28000-35000
Works on paper
£1586 $2649 €2300 Barque en briere, soleil couchant (31x47cm-12x19in) s. pastel col crayon dr. 10-Jul-3 Artcurial Briest, Paris #18/R est:2500-3000

PUIGDENGOLAS BARELLA, Jose (1906-1987) Spanish
£4516 $7135 €7000 Landscape in Majorca (47x55cm-19x22in) s. 18-Dec-2 Ansorena, Madrid #71/R est:6500

PUJOL DE GUASTAVINO, Clement (1850-1905) French
£14516 $22935 €22500 Juggler (47x73cm-19x29in) s. 18-Dec-2 Castellana, Madrid #13/R est:12000
£20958 $35000 €30389 Esteemed visitor (92x65cm-36x26in) s. panel. 22-Jun-3 Freeman, Philadelphia #39/R est:7000-10000
£22013 $33899 €35000 Choosing the swor (89x66cm-35x26in) s. board. 22-Oct-2 Durán, Madrid #275/R est:30000

PUJOL, Casimir Paul (1848-?) French
Works on paper
£260 $411 €390 Spanish dancer (20x58cm-8x23in) s. fan shaped. 13-Nov-2 Halls, Shrewsbury #373

PUJOLA, Ramon Estalella (1893-1986) Spanish
£542 $900 €786 Spanish street scene (41x33cm-16x13in) s. board. 14-Jun-3 Jackson's, Cedar Falls #372/R

PULACINI, Franco (1934-) Italian
Works on paper
£3041 $4743 €4500 Appearances (85x43cm-33x17in) s.d.1992 assemblage. 26-Mar-3 Finarte Semenzato, Milan #130/R

PULE, John (20th C) New Zealander?
£1625 $2617 €2438 Victorious spirit (61x46cm-24x18in) s.d.2000 oil ink. 7-May-3 Dunbar Sloane, Auckland #25/R est:4500-6500 (NZ.D 4600)

PULGA, Bruno (1922-) Italian
£577 $912 €900 Landscape (50x65cm-20x26in) painted 1963. 15-Nov-2 Farsetti, Prato #226
£1161 $1835 €1800 Painting 9 (82x65cm-32x26in) s.d.1974. 18-Dec-2 Christie's, Rome #94/R
£1548 $2446 €2400 Painting 1 (100x81cm-39x32in) s.d.1973 verso. 18-Dec-2 Christie's, Rome #103

PULIDO, Ramon (1868-?) Spanish
£592 $959 €900 Virgin (55x42cm-22x17in) s. 21-Jan-3 Durán, Madrid #70/R

PULIGO, Domenico (attrib) (1492-1527) Italian
£14612 $22795 €21918 Madonna with Christ and Infant St John (86x61cm-34x24in) panel. 28-Mar-3 Koller, Zurich #3012/R est:25000-35000 (S.FR 32000)

PULINCKX, Louis (1843-1910) Belgian
£550 $891 €825 First snow (36x51cm-14x20in) s.d.1881 i.d.verso. 23-Jan-3 Christie's, Kensington #165
£2532 $3949 €4000 Impressionist landscape with children (102x152cm-40x60in) s. 21-Oct-2 Bernaerts, Antwerp #26/R est:6900-8600

PULLER, John Anthony (fl.1821-1867) British
£1000 $1590 €1500 Ford, cattle by a river and figures resting (20x25cm-8x10in) 19-Mar-3 John Nicholson, Haslemere #1158 est:800-1000
£1800 $2916 €2700 Feeding the rabbits (25x20cm-10x8in) s. 20-May-3 Sotheby's, Olympia #253/R est:1200-1800

PULLICINO, Giorgio (19th C) ?
£10000 $15900 €15000 Grand harbour from Ras Hanzir. Grand harbour from Ricasoli Point (25x36cm-10x14in) panel pair. 29-Apr-3 Bonhams, New Bond Street #158/R est:10000-15000

PULLINEN, Laila (1933-) Finnish
Works on paper
£443 $700 €700 Woman (82x57cm-32x22in) s.d.1971 Indian ink. 30-Nov-2 Hagelstam, Helsinki #176/R

PULM, Peter (20th C) German
£503 $785 €800 Sea in evening light (60x80cm-24x31in) s. lit. 20-Sep-2 Karlheinz Kaupp, Staufen #1857/R

PULZONE, Scipione (1550-1598) Italian
£13793 $21793 €20000 Portrait of Clelia Farnese (48x37cm-19x15in) 3-Apr-3 Porro, Milan #2/R est:35000
£14198 $23000 €21297 Archangel Gabriel (27x18cm-11x7in) en grisaille prov. 21-Jan-3 Sotheby's, New York #15/R est:20000-30000
£41379 $65379 €60000 Portrait of princess Orsini (115x86cm-45x34in) 3-Apr-3 Porro, Milan #3/R est:90000

PUMMIL, Robert (1936-) American
£1775 $2875 €2574 Rain or shine (41x51cm-16x20in) 23-May-3 Altermann Galleries, Santa Fe #2
£2372 $3700 €3558 Bone tired (61x76cm-24x30in) s. prov. 9-Nov-2 Santa Fe Art, Santa Fe #129/R est:3000-5000

£3549 $5750 €5146 Wyoming riders (51x76cm-20x30in) 23-May-3 Altermann Galleries, Santa Fe #3
£5479 $8000 €8219 Package from the east (76x122cm-30x48in) 18-May-2 Altermann Galleries, Santa Fe #136/R
£6507 $9500 €9761 Troopers warning (76x102cm-30x40in) 18-May-2 Altermann Galleries, Santa Fe #135/R

PUMPIN, Fritz (1901-1972) Swiss
£1135 $1794 €1703 Early spring landscape (60x73cm-24x29in) s. i.d.1960 verso. 14-Nov-2 Stuker, Bern #466 est:3000-3500 (S.FR 2600)

PUNJAB SCHOOL (19th C) Indian
Works on paper
£5000 $7950 €7500 Portrait of Maharaja Ranjit Singh (18x13cm-7x5in) gouache gold exec.c.1840. 2-May-3 Christie's, Kensington #503/R est:5000-7000

PUPINI, Biagio (16th C) Italian
Works on paper
£4392 $6851 €6500 Marriage of the Virgin (28x33cm-11x13in) i. pen ink wash htd white prov. 27-Mar-3 Christie's, Paris #3/R

PURGAU, Franz Michael Siegmund von (elder-attrib) (1677-1754) Austrian
£5704 $9184 €8500 Forest floor with a kingfisher and frog (40x58cm-16x23in) 18-Feb-3 Sotheby's, Amsterdam #262/R est:1800-2200

PURIFICATO, Domenico (1915-1984) Italian
£1923 $3019 €3000 Landscape (60x80cm-24x31in) s. prov. 20-Nov-2 Pandolfini, Florence #70/R
£1935 $3058 €3000 Meeting in the woods (60x50cm-24x20in) s. 18-Dec-2 Christie's, Rome #180
£2244 $3522 €3500 Seashore in Ostia (47x62cm-19x24in) s. s.i.d.48 verso. 20-Nov-2 Pandolfini, Florence #72/R
£2258 $3568 €3500 Horses (50x60cm-20x24in) s.d.70. 18-Dec-2 Christie's, Rome #221
£2466 $3847 €3600 Woman with white cloth (40x30cm-16x12in) s. 10-Apr-3 Finarte Semenzato, Rome #127
£2979 $4826 €4200 Fiori con bicchiere (50x40cm-20x16in) s. s.i.d.1965 verso. 26-May-3 Christie's, Milan #124/R est:2200-2800
£3191 $5170 €4500 Amanti (100x70cm-39x28in) s.d.63 exhib. 26-May-3 Christie's, Milan #133/R est:3500-4500

PURRMANN, Hans (1880-1966) German
£12950 $20719 €18000 Landscape near Casis (38x45cm-15x18in) s. prov. 15-May-3 Neumeister, Munich #338/R est:18000-20000
£16667 $25833 €26000 Fano, Porta Augustea (38x46cm-15x18in) prov.lit. 4-Dec-2 Lempertz, Koln #1010/R est:28000-32000
£17606 $28345 €25000 Purrmann's house in Langenargen (54x66cm-21x26in) 7-May-3 Michael Zeller, Lindau #890/R est:25000
£31646 $49367 €50000 Woman wearing blue pullover (89x73cm-35x29in) s. i. verso exhib. 18-Oct-2 Dr Fritz Nagel, Stuttgart #599/R est:65000
£42029 $68928 €58000 Still life of flowers with gladioli, zinnia (81x65cm-32x26in) s. prov. 29-May-3 Lempertz, Koln #886/R est:40000-45000
£56410 $87436 €88000 Harbour - Porto d'Ischia (61x50cm-24x20in) s. prov.exhib. 4-Dec-2 Lempertz, Koln #1011/R est:40000-60000
£74236 $115808 €111354 Florence (73x92cm-29x36in) s. prov. 20-Nov-2 Fischer, Luzern #1189/R est:170000-190000 (S.FR 170000)
Works on paper
£3333 $5467 €4600 Still life of flowers (26x41cm-10x16in) s. W/C gouache over pencil prov. 29-May-3 Lempertz, Koln #890/R est:3000
£5449 $8446 €8500 Autumnal valley (47x62cm-19x24in) s. W/C bodycol. 4-Dec-2 Lempertz, Koln #1012/R est:10000-12000

PURRMANN, Karl (1877-1966) German
£321 $497 €500 Castle interior - Ludwigsburg (55x70cm-22x28in) i. 9-Dec-2 Dr Fritz Nagel, Stuttgart #6965/R
£325 $484 €500 Alexander room in Wurzburg Castle (55x75cm-22x30in) s.d.1941 exhib. 28-Jun-2 Sigalas, Stuttgart #855/R

PURSER, Sarah (1848-1943) British
£1449 $2377 €2000 Head of a young man (41x30cm-16x12in) 28-May-3 Bonhams & James Adam, Dublin #28/R est:2000-3000
£2600 $4160 €3900 Autumnal field. Field on a stormy day (15x22cm-6x9in) board two. 15-May-3 Christie's, Kensington #217/R est:600-800
£22436 $35224 €35000 Portrait of a woman with flowers in her lap (90x60cm-35x24in) prov. 19-Nov-2 Hamilton Osborne King, Dublin #468/R est:30000-40000

PURSER, William (attrib) (c.1790-c.1852) British
Works on paper
£709 $1184 €1000 Le temple de Zeus a Menea (27x37cm-11x15in) pencil W/C. 23-Jun-3 Beaussant & Lefèvre, Paris #81

PURTON, Arthur (attrib) (19th C) British?
£559 $888 €839 Autumn landscape (46x61cm-18x24in) indis.sig. 5-Mar-3 Rasmussen, Copenhagen #1626 (D.KR 6000)

PURVES-SMITH, Peter (1913-1949) Australian
Works on paper
£12903 $19613 €19355 Street in Pimlico (46x38cm-18x15in) s.d.1939 W/C gouache prov.lit. 28-Aug-2 Deutscher-Menzies, Melbourne #36/R est:30000-40000 (A.D 36000)

PURVIS, Tom (1888-1959) British
£250 $395 €375 Design for the Scottish Institute of Structural engineers (102x150cm-40x59in) board. 18-Dec-2 Mallams, Oxford #640/R
Works on paper
£2000 $3120 €2900 East Coast Resort L.N.E.R - painting for a poster (74x123cm-29x48in) s. gouache on card. 27-Mar-3 Lane, Penzance #270/R est:2000-3000

PURYEAR, Martin (1941-) American
Sculpture
£265823 $420000 €398735 Divide (269x33x28cm-106x13x11in) red cedar and pine executed 1988 prov.exhib. 12-Nov-2 Sotheby's, New York #53/R est:350000-450000

PURYGIN, Leonid (1951-1995) Russian
£13000 $21060 €19500 Lenya Purygin from life (58x134cm-23x53in) s.d.1982 triptych prov. 21-May-3 Sotheby's, London #230/R est:10000-15000
Sculpture
£3500 $5494 €5250 She butterfly (31cm-12in) init.d.1988 gilt bronze prov.lit. 20-Nov-2 Sotheby's, London #196/R est:3500-4500
£3500 $5494 €5250 Him - self portrait (35cm-14in) init.d.1988 silvered bronze prov.lit. 20-Nov-2 Sotheby's, London #197/R est:3500-4500

PUSA, Unto (1913-1973) Finnish
£680 $1082 €1000 Pond (46x38cm-18x15in) s. 27-Feb-3 Hagelstam, Helsinki #1031
£690 $1090 €1000 Sahkokentta - composition (52x130cm-20x51in) s. 3-Apr-3 Hagelstam, Helsinki #834/R
£949 $1500 €1500 Mountain landscape (41x82cm-16x32in) s. 1-Dec-2 Bukowskis, Helsinki #346/R est:1300-1500
£1013 $1600 €1600 Concrete composition (98x60cm-39x24in) lit. 1-Dec-2 Bukowskis, Helsinki #345/R est:700-1000
£1056 $1701 €1500 Tree trunk II (73x92cm-29x36in) s.d.56. 10-May-3 Bukowskis, Helsinki #213/R est:1700-2000
£1242 $2037 €1900 The old saw (60x47cm-24x19in) s.d.68. 9-Feb-3 Bukowskis, Helsinki #339/R est:2200
£2394 $3855 €3400 Project for wall painting at Fiskartorpet (52x160cm-20x63in) s.d.68. 10-May-3 Bukowskis, Helsinki #256/R est:2000-2500
Works on paper
£317 $501 €460 Factory (37x43cm-15x17in) s. pastel. 3-Apr-3 Hagelstam, Helsinki #835

PUSHMAN, Hovsep (1877-1966) American
£12739 $20000 €19109 Wife of the shiek (89x63cm-35x25in) s. s.i.verso board prov.exhib. 20-Nov-2 Christie's, Los Angeles #114/R est:20000-30000
£19355 $30000 €29033 Sunbeam (94x117cm-37x46in) s. prov. 4-Dec-2 Sotheby's, New York #35/R est:30000-50000
£30645 $47500 €45968 Page from Omar Khayyam (114x74cm-45x29in) s. panel prov. 4-Dec-2 Sotheby's, New York #28/R est:20000-30000
£31847 $50000 €47771 Youth (122x91cm-48x36in) s. prov.exhib.lit. 19-Nov-2 Butterfields, San Francisco #8058/R est:60000-70000

PUSHWAGNER (1940-) Norwegian
£424 $649 €636 Conductor (110x172cm-43x68in) s. panel. 26-Aug-2 Blomqvist, Lysaker #1306/R (N.KR 4900)

PUSOLE, Pierluigi (1963-) Italian
£1277 $2068 €1800 Pane e pesci (40x70cm-16x28in) s.i.verso two prov. 26-May-3 Christie's, Milan #84/R est:2000-3000
£2340 $3791 €3300 Levitomobili rai quattro (80x80cm-31x31in) s. acrylic. 20-May-3 Porro, Milan #47/R est:3500-3800
£2692 $4227 €4200 Sony-hal 9005-RAI 4 (127x203cm-50x80in) s. 20-Nov-2 Pandolfini, Florence #155/R est:3500
£3378 $5270 €5000 Levitobarca pac quattro (100x120cm-39x47in) s.i. s.i.verso. 26-Mar-3 Finarte Semenzato, Milan #150/R
£3974 $6160 €6200 Televisions (60x60cm-24x24in) s.d.1987 verso acrylic set of 8. 4-Dec-2 Finarte, Milan #569/R est:7000
Works on paper
£1218 $1912 €1900 Rai Four Vision (50x80cm-20x31in) s.d.1994 verso mixed media on canvas. 21-Nov-2 Finarte, Rome #248/R
£1528 $2429 €2200 I am God (67x98cm-26x39in) init. mixed media paper on canvas. 1-May-3 Meeting Art, Vercelli #207

PUTHOD, Dolores (1934-) Italian
£340 $541 €500 Comparing (80x70cm-31x28in) s. painted 1995. 1-Mar-3 Meeting Art, Vercelli #560
£475 $741 €750 Colza (60x120cm-24x47in) s. s.i.d.1994 verso. 14-Sep-2 Meeting Art, Vercelli #499

PUTHUFF, Hanson Duvall (1875-1972) American
£1019 $1600 €1529 California landscape on a clear day (30x41cm-12x16in) masonite prov. 19-Nov-2 Butterfields, San Francisco #8234/R est:3000-5000
£1370 $2000 €2055 Restless tide (61x76cm-24x30in) s. 17-Jun-2 Schrager Galleries, Milwaukee #1168/R
£1741 $2750 €2612 View of the old bridge. 16-Nov-2 Harvey Clar, Oakland #1253
£1911 $3000 €2867 Landscape with large tree in the foreground, Hemet, California (30x41cm-12x16in) s. canvasboard prov. 19-Nov-2 Butterfields, San Francisco #8235/R est:3000-5000
£1923 $3000 €2885 View of the old bridge. 21-Sep-2 Harvey Clar, Oakland #1508
£2548 $4000 €3822 Rocky coast on a calm day (30x41cm-12x16in) init. masonite prov. 19-Nov-2 Butterfields, San Francisco #8233/R est:3000-5000
£3915 $6500 €5677 Mountains near La Crescenta (30x40cm-12x16in) s. i.verso canvasboard prov. 11-Jun-3 Butterfields, San Francisco #4250/R est:5000-7000
£4194 $6500 €6291 Clouds and sunshine (30x41cm-12x16in) s. i.verso prov. 29-Oct-2 John Moran, Pasadena #640b est:6000-8000
£4217 $7000 €6115 Evening star (30x40cm-12x16in) s. canvasboard prov. 11-Jun-3 Butterfields, San Francisco #4251/R est:7000-10000
£4375 $7000 €6344 Near La Canada (46x61cm-18x24in) s. i.verso. 16-May-3 Skinner, Boston #250/R est:7000-9000
£7742 $12000 €11613 November morning, near the Salinas River San Benito County, Calif (36x51cm-14x20in) s. 29-Oct-2 John Moran, Pasadena #640a est:12000-18000
£11465 $18000 €17198 Tender autumn (61x76cm-24x30in) s. i.verso prov. 19-Nov-2 Butterfields, San Francisco #8221/R est:20000-30000
£15528 $25000 €23292 Beach road (20x24cm-8x9in) s. i.stretcher prov. 18-Feb-3 John Moran, Pasadena #62 est:20000-25000
£19355 $30000 €29033 Above the heights (66x76cm-26x30in) s. prov. 29-Oct-2 John Moran, Pasadena #633 est:30000-50000
£22293 $35000 €33440 Hills, rock ribbed (61x76cm-24x30in) s. i.verso prov. 19-Nov-2 Butterfields, San Francisco #8200/R est:20000-25000
£22293 $35000 €33440 View of the California coast with a painter in the foreground (46x62cm-18x24in) prov. 19-Nov-2 Butterfields, San Francisco #8201/R est:5000-7000

PUTNAM, Arthur (1873-1930) American
Sculpture
£2229 $3500 €3344 Bear (12cm-5in) s.st.f.Gorham brown pat bronze. 19-Nov-2 Butterfields, San Francisco #8262/R est:3000-5000
£4819 $8000 €6988 Lion (33cm-13in) i. brown pat bronze prov. 11-Jun-3 Butterfields, San Francisco #4295/R est:10000-12000
£9581 $16000 €13892 Lovers, nuzzling pumas (20cm-8in) i.d.04 brown pat. bronze. 18-Jun-3 Christie's, Los Angeles #83/R est:6000-8000

PUTNAM, Wallace (1899-1989) American
£1982 $3250 €2874 Three edge of the ocean (127x152cm-50x60in) prov. 1-Jun-3 Wright, Chicago #236/R est:700-900

PUTTEN, Jasper van der (1944-) Dutch
£1519 $2400 €2400 Lobby (20x17cm-8x7in) s.d.September 1997 s.i.verso panel. 26-Nov-2 Sotheby's, Amsterdam #83/R est:1000-1500

PUTTER, Pieter de (1600-1659) Dutch
£1783 $2782 €2800 Still life with fish and birds on a wooden ledge (39x48cm-15x19in) s. panel prov. 5-Nov-2 Sotheby's, Amsterdam #75/R est:3000-5000

PUTTMAN, Donald (1926-) American
£385 $600 €578 East meets west (76x102cm-30x40in) s. board prov. 9-Nov-2 Santa Fe Art, Santa Fe #245/R

PUTTNER, Josef Carl Berthold (1821-1881) Austrian
£1497 $2380 €2200 Fishing family with boat in front of still coast (27x44cm-11x17in) s.d.1874. 25-Feb-3 Dorotheum, Vienna #145/R est:2200-2400
£1600 $2480 €2400 Fleets of European ironclads lying in the Mediterranean harbour (75x138cm-30x54in) indis i.d. 31-Oct-2 Christie's, Kensington #502/R est:2000-3000
£4114 $6500 €6500 Harbour view with figures (79x119cm-31x47in) s.d.1874. 28-Nov-2 Dorotheum, Vienna #199/R est:5000-6500

PUTTNER, Walther (1872-1953) German
£529 $788 €794 Man (30x26cm-12x10in) s.d.04. 25-Jun-2 Koller, Zurich #6674 (S.FR 1200)

PUTZ, Leo (1869-1940) German
£5128 $7949 €8000 Gallant scene (58x51cm-23x20in) s. panel painted 1922 prov. 6-Dec-2 Ketterer, Munich #35/R est:10000-12000
£8442 $13000 €12663 Rio dancer (48x61cm-19x24in) s. board painted c.1931. 8-Sep-2 Treadway Gallery, Cincinnati #691/R est:15000-20000
£10072 $16518 €14000 House by water (50x60cm-20x24in) s. prov. 6-Jun-3 Ketterer, Munich #14/R est:12000-14000
£17000 $27880 €25500 Wintersonne - winter sun (85x76cm-33x30in) s.i.d.1913. 3-Jun-3 Sotheby's, London #115/R est:20000-30000
£28369 $45957 €40000 Carnival walk (49x63cm-19x25in) s.d.31 board prov.exhib. 20-May-3 Dorotheum, Vienna #27/R est:38000-45000

PUTZHOFEN-ESTERS, Heinrich (20th C) German
£616 $962 €900 Beilstein on the Moselle lit by setting sun (49x60cm-19x24in) s. 10-Apr-3 Van Ham, Cologne #1652

PUTZHOFEN-HAMBUCHEN, Paul (19/20th C) German
£1644 $2564 €2400 Eifel landscape (94x104cm-37x41in) s. canvas on panel. 10-Apr-3 Van Ham, Cologne #1654/R est:1800

PUVIS DE CHAVANNES (1824-1898) French
Works on paper
£355 $592 €500 Etude d'homme assis (29x21cm-11x8in) st.init. blk crayon. 20-Jun-3 Piasa, Paris #74

PUVIS DE CHAVANNES, Edouard (19/20th C) French
£641 $1006 €1000 Chaumiere (47x57cm-19x22in) panel. 16-Dec-2 Millon & Associes, Paris #127

PUVIS DE CHAVANNES, Pierre (1824-1898) French
£4392 $6851 €6500 Jeune homme de profil en habit militaire (42x34cm-17x13in) s.i. 28-Mar-3 Delvaux, Paris #13/R est:5000
£6159 $10101 €8500 L'enfance de Sainte Genevieve (34x41cm-13x16in) s. prov. 31-May-3 Villa Grisebach, Berlin #102/R est:4000-6000
Works on paper
£355 $592 €500 Etude d'homme de profil (23x15cm-9x6in) st.init. blk crayon. 20-Jun-3 Piasa, Paris #75
£390 $651 €550 Pere et fils (30x18cm-12x7in) st.init. blk crayon. 20-Jun-3 Piasa, Paris #77
£426 $711 €600 Etude d'homme debout (24x16cm-9x6in) st.init. blk crayon. 20-Jun-3 Piasa, Paris #76
£743 $1159 €1100 Jeune homme en buste (28x22cm-11x9in) s.d.1859 chl oval. 28-Mar-3 Delvaux, Paris #10/R
£949 $1500 €1500 Jeune homme agenouille (31x23cm-12x9in) pierre noire chk. 28-Nov-2 Tajan, Paris #203/R
£1554 $2424 €2300 Portrait de jeune homme (31x23cm-12x9in) chl pastel. 28-Mar-3 Delvaux, Paris #11/R
£1622 $2530 €2400 Jeune homme de profil (33x24cm-13x9in) s.i.d.1880 graphite. 28-Mar-3 Delvaux, Paris #12/R
£2482 $4145 €3500 La lecture (36x25cm-14x10in) s.i. blk crayon. 20-Jun-3 Piasa, Paris #73/R est:1500-2000
£3000 $4650 €4500 Le violoniste. Paysage de montagne (33x23cm-13x9in) init. chl htd white prov. 5-Dec-2 Christie's, Kensington #4/R est:1500-2000

PUVIS DE CHAVANNES, Pierre (attrib) (1824-1898) French
£10791 $17266 €15000 Scene from Roman antiquity (48x23cm-19x9in) i. 17-May-3 Lempertz, Koln #1466/R est:5000

PUVREZ, Henri (1893-1971) Belgian
Sculpture
£3526 $5465 €5500 Sleeping girl (23cm-9in) s.d.27 grey marble. 3-Dec-2 Christie's, Amsterdam #47/R est:2000-3000
£5517 $8828 €8000 Suzanna and the Gruijsaards (127x84cm-50x33in) s. blue stone exec.1940 lit. 15-Mar-3 De Vuyst, Lokeren #465/R est:7500-8500

PUY, Jean (1876-1960) French
£1042 $1656 €1500 La digue a Doelan (27x34cm-11x13in) s.i.d.47 oil gouache pencil paper on canvas. 29-Apr-3 Artcurial Briest, Paris #160 est:800-1000
£1761 $2730 €2800 Bouquet de fleurs mauves et jaunes (44x29cm-17x11in) s. paper on canvas. 30-Oct-2 Artcurial Briest, Paris #326 est:2000-3000
£1887 $2925 €3000 Nature morte au rouget (34x26cm-13x10in) s.d.14 panel prov. 30-Oct-2 Coutau Begarie, Paris #117/R
£1962 $3100 €3100 Vase de fleurs (33x46cm-13x18in) s. 27-Nov-2 Blanchet, Paris #41/R

£3423 $5512 €5135 Garden with bushes, trees and house in background (52x62cm-20x24in) init. 26-Feb-3 Museumsbygningen, Copenhagen #122/R est:25000-30000 (D.KR 38000)
£3704 $6000 €5371 Fleurs dans un vase (46x38cm-18x15in) s. prov. 21-May-3 Doyle, New York #11/R est:3000-4000
£6757 $10541 €10000 Neige pres des Aravis (65x50cm-26x20in) s. paper on cardboard prov.exhib.lit. 30-Mar-3 Anaf, Lyon #215/R
£7042 $11690 €10000 Femme au hamac (97x130cm-38x51in) s. prov.exhib.lit. 15-Jun-3 Anaf, Lyon #183/R est:12000-15000
£11149 $17392 €16500 Navire aux sabls d'Olonne (54x72cm-21x28in) s.d.45 masonite prov. 30-Mar-3 Anaf, Lyon #214/R
£23226 $36697 €36000 Barques a Colliure (60x73cm-24x29in) s. 19-Dec-2 Claude Aguttes, Neuilly #169/R est:8000

Works on paper
£1268 $2041 €1800 Belle-Isle (36x48cm-14x19in) s. pastel. 11-May-3 Thierry & Lannon, Brest #78 est:1800-2000

PUYBAREAU, Annie (1955-) French
£1235 $2000 €1791 Tentes a Trouville (46x56cm-18x22in) s. i.overlap. 21-May-3 Doyle, New York #252/R est:3000-4000
£1420 $2300 €2059 Bassin du jardin des plantes (51x61cm-20x24in) s. i.overlap. 21-May-3 Doyle, New York #251/R est:3000-4000

PUYENBROECK, Gregoor van (1906-1982) Belgian
£270 $422 €400 Nature morte au potiche orientale at au vase de fleurs (65x80cm-26x31in) s. 25-Mar-3 Campo & Campo, Antwerp #236
£377 $589 €600 Promeneurs dans un parc (89x99cm-35x39in) 14-Oct-2 Amberes, Antwerp #218

PUYENBROECK, Hortensy van (?) Belgian?
£278 $439 €400 Dame devant un trois-mats dans le port (88x113cm-35x44in) 28-Apr-3 Amberes, Antwerp #328

PUYENBROECK, Jan van (1887-1972) Belgian
£306 $487 €450 Autoportrait (36x26cm-14x10in) panel. 18-Mar-3 Campo, Vlaamse Kaai #272

PUYENBROECK, Vital van (1906-) Belgian
£566 $883 €900 Still life with parrots (35x40cm-14x16in) s.d.1966. 23-Sep-2 Bernaerts, Antwerp #137/R

PUYET, Jose (1922-) Spanish
£704 $1134 €1000 Spanish couple in Belle Epoch ball gown (99x79cm-39x31in) s. s.d.1974 verso. 10-May-3 Hans Stahl, Toestorf #56/R
£759 $1199 €1100 Venus (33x80cm-13x31in) s. 1-Apr-3 Segre, Madrid #379/R
£759 $1199 €1100 Woman seen from the back (65x54cm-26x21in) s. 1-Apr-3 Segre, Madrid #375/R
£800 $1328 €1160 Noche de gala (79x63cm-31x25in) s. i.d.1968 verso. 16-Jun-3 Waddingtons, Toronto #351/R est:2000-3000 (C.D 1800)
£833 $1308 €1300 Young woman with fan (82x65cm-32x26in) s. 21-Nov-2 Van Ham, Cologne #1870/R
£839 $1325 €1300 Lady (46x38cm-18x15in) s. s.i.verso. 17-Dec-2 Durán, Madrid #5/R
£903 $1427 €1400 Young man (45x35cm-18x14in) s. s.i.verso. 17-Dec-2 Durán, Madrid #59/R
£1603 $2532 €2500 Gypsy woman with fan (92x72cm-36x28in) s. 19-Nov-2 Durán, Madrid #201/R
£1774 $2803 €2750 Chrysalides (81x65cm-32x26in) s. s.i.d.1988 verso. 17-Dec-2 Durán, Madrid #203/R
£3548 $5606 €5500 Ladies (81x65cm-32x26in) s. s.i.verso. 17-Dec-2 Durán, Madrid #204/R
£3947 $6395 €6000 Young woman by the river (32x80cm-13x31in) s. 21-Jan-3 Durán, Madrid #61/R
£6452 $10194 €10000 After the meal (65x81cm-26x32in) s. s.i.verso. 17-Dec-2 Durán, Madrid #219/R est:800

PUYROCHE-WAGNER, Elise (1828-1895) German
Works on paper
£6203 $9614 €9800 Natures mortes aux fleurs et fruits voisinant avec un nid et une perruche (59x42cm-23x17in) one s.d.1857 one s. gouache pair. 27-Sep-2 Rabourdin & Choppin de Janvry, Paris #161/R est:10000-10500

PWERLE, Louis (c.1938-) Australian
Works on paper
£440 $708 €660 Young fella way (122x92cm-48x36in) with sig. synthetic polymer paint on canvas prov. 6-May-3 Christie's, Melbourne #316 est:800-1200 (A.D 1100)

PYE, Patrick (1929-) Irish
£833 $1308 €1300 Carpenter's inventory (25x24cm-10x9in) s.d.1969 i.verso board prov. 19-Nov-2 Whyte's, Dublin #1/R
£2051 $3221 €3200 Elegy, Passion, Entombment (61x152cm-24x60in) s.d.1974 board prov.exhib.lit. triptych. 19-Nov-2 Whyte's, Dublin #31/R est:4000-5000

PYE, William (fl.1881-1908) British
Works on paper
£250 $390 €375 Sunset, Myrlon on Swale, Yorkshire (52x42cm-20x17in) s.d.1911 pencil W/C. 27-Mar-3 Christie's, Kensington #94
£1800 $2988 €2700 Study in Weymouth Harbor, Dorset (37x77cm-15x30in) s. W/C exhib. 12-Jun-3 Bonhams, New Bond Street #656/R est:1000-1500

PYK, Madeleine (1934-) Swedish
£339 $532 €492 Pearly gate. 15-Dec-2 Anders Antik, Landskrona #1225 (S.KR 4800)
£494 $820 €716 Hommage a Velasquez (46x41cm-18x16in) s. 16-Jun-3 Lilla Bukowskis, Stockholm #1080 (S.KR 6400)
£549 $856 €824 Untitled (81x81cm-32x32in) s. 13-Sep-2 Lilla Bukowskis, Stockholm #577 (S.KR 8000)
£550 $875 €825 Morocco (38x36cm-15x14in) s. exhib. 3-Mar-3 Lilla Bukowskis, Stockholm #357 (S.KR 7400)
£556 $923 €806 Family group (65x98cm-26x39in) s. 16-Jun-3 Lilla Bukowskis, Stockholm #46 (S.KR 7200)
£573 $928 €860 Figure composition (40x70cm-16x28in) s. 3-Feb-3 Lilla Bukowskis, Stockholm #745 (S.KR 8000)
£631 $997 €947 Chameleon (81x96cm-32x38in) s. 30-Nov-2 Goteborg Auktionsverk, Sweden #611/R (S.KR 9000)
£755 $1148 €1133 Cafe, Valbonne (66x48cm-26x19in) s. 16-Aug-2 Lilla Bukowskis, Stockholm #918 (S.KR 11000)
£1059 $1662 €1589 Town in Provence (67x49cm-26x19in) s.d.92. 16-Dec-2 Lilla Bukowskis, Stockholm #821 est:10000-12000 (S.KR 15000)
£1329 $2127 €1927 Outing (95x64cm-37x25in) s. 18-May-3 Anders Antik, Landskrona #52 est:12000 (S.KR 17000)
£1699 $2735 €2549 At Cafe de Terasse (67x49cm-26x19in) s. 7-May-3 AB Stockholms Auktionsverk #862/R est:20000-25000 (S.KR 22000)
£1825 $2884 €2738 On holiday, Coignac (67x48cm-26x19in) s. 28-Apr-3 Bukowskis, Stockholm #295/R est:25000-28000 (S.KR 24000)
£1901 $3004 €2852 Cafe des Pyrenees (95x95cm-37x37in) s. 28-Apr-3 Bukowskis, Stockholm #294/R est:20000-22000 (S.KR 25000)
£2057 $3188 €3086 Summer (68x49cm-27x19in) s. 8-Dec-2 Uppsala Auktionskammare, Uppsala #268/R est:30000-40000 (S.KR 29000)
£2453 $3826 €3680 Stockholm (93x129cm-37x51in) s. 5-Nov-2 Bukowskis, Stockholm #273/R est:25000-30000 (S.KR 35000)
£3552 $5719 €5328 An outing (69x50cm-27x20in) s,. 7-May-3 AB Stockholms Auktionsverk #861/R est:20000-25000 (S.KR 46000)
£5043 $8169 €7312 The Creation (195x250cm-77x98in) s. 25-May-3 Uppsala Auktionskammare, Uppsala #309/R est:40000-50000 (S.KR 65000)

PYKE, Guelda (1905-1994) Australian
Works on paper
£338 $555 €507 Racing yachts (40x44cm-16x17in) mixed media collage card prov. 4-Jun-3 Deutscher-Menzies, Melbourne #379/R (A.D 850)

PYLE, Howard (1853-1911) American
£10241 $17000 €14849 Magic flute (44x30cm-17x12in) s. canvasboard prov.lit. 11-Jun-3 Butterfields, San Francisco #4100/R est:10000-15000
£12346 $20000 €18519 Villon - the singer fate fashioned to her liking (65x41cm-26x16in) s. i.verso prov.lit. 21-May-3 Sotheby's, New York #229/R est:25000-35000
£23148 $37500 €34722 Guarded by rough English soldiers (63x41cm-25x16in) s. prov.lit. 21-May-3 Sotheby's, New York #230/R est:20000-30000
£58642 $95000 €87963 La Salle christening the country Louisiana (61x41cm-24x16in) s. i.verso prov.lit. 21-May-3 Sotheby's, New York #228/R est:60000-80000

PYNACKER, Adam (attrib) (1622-1673) Dutch
£2315 $3727 €3473 Hunter resting (39x53cm-15x21in) 7-May-3 Dobiaschofsky, Bern #895/R est:2600 (S.FR 5000)
£2419 $3750 €3629 Italianate landscape with peasants and their cattle (33x48cm-13x19in) panel prov. 7-Dec-2 Neal Auction Company, New Orleans #112/R est:2000-3000

Works on paper
£1678 $2400 €2517 Early morning landscape study (35x24cm-14x9in) brush ink wash. 23-Jan-3 Swann Galleries, New York #199/R est:1500-2500

PYNACKER, Adam (circle) (1622-1673) Dutch
£5096 $7949 €8000 Italianate mountain landscape with a shepherd and shepherdess resting (100x133cm-39x52in) 6-Nov-2 Christie's, Amsterdam #76/R est:10000-15000

PYNAS, Jan (attrib) (1583-1631) Dutch
£962 $1490 €1500 Fuite en Egypte (22x29cm-9x11in) copper. 3-Dec-2 Campo & Campo, Antwerp #259 est:2000-3000

£2703 $4216 €4000 Scene de jugement de prisonniers (38x60cm-15x24in) panel. 26-Mar-3 Tajan, Paris #112/R est:6000
£4585 $7153 €6878 Figures along river bank (61x99cm-24x39in) 6-Nov-2 Dobiaschofsky, Bern #900/R est:7500 (S.FR 10500)

PYNE, Charles (1842-?) British

Works on paper

£350 $574 €525 View of Windsor Castle from Datchet Lock (28x42cm-11x17in) s.d.1864 W/C. 3-Jun-3 Bonhams, Oxford #11
£360 $601 €522 Playing in the woods (34x48cm-13x19in) s.d.1910 W/C. 24-Jun-3 Bonhams, Knightsbridge #172/R

PYNE, Ganesh (1937-) Indian

£10101 $16667 €14646 Monkey prince (51x47cm-20x19in) s.d. tempera board. 6-Jul-3 Christie's, Hong Kong #93/R est:100000-150000 (HK.D 130000)

Works on paper

£2720 $4487 €3944 Fairy tale character (36x36cm-14x14in) s.d.2002 mixed media. 6-Jul-3 Christie's, Hong Kong #94/R est:40000-60000 (HK.D 35000)

PYNE, George (1800-1884) British

Works on paper

£620 $1035 €899 Exeter Collage Oxford (15x20cm-6x8in) s.d.1840 pencil W/C htd white. 26-Jun-3 Mellors & Kirk, Nottingham #812/R
£680 $1102 €1020 View of Magdalene Collage tower from Christ Church meadow, Oxford (14x20cm-6x8in) s.d.1871 W/C. 20-May-3 Sotheby's, Olympia #4/R est:300-500
£700 $1092 €1050 View in the High Street, Oxford (17x25cm-7x10in) s.d.1848 W/C. 17-Sep-2 Bonhams, Oxford #10/R
£2200 $3652 €3190 Interior of a library in a house, possibly in Oxford (20x30cm-8x12in) pencil W/C. 10-Jun-3 Mellors & Kirk, Nottingham #774/R est:200-400
£2800 $4620 €4060 Interior of a drawing room. Interior of a dining room (36x55cm-14x22in) pencil W/C gum arabic htd body col one arched prov. 3-Jul-3 Christie's, Kensington #36/R est:2000-3000

PYNE, James Baker (1800-1870) British

£450 $702 €675 Italianate landscape (47x64cm-19x25in) s. 18-Sep-2 Dreweatt Neate, Newbury #103
£800 $1328 €1200 Continental landscape (35x29cm-14x11in) s.d.1840. 10-Jun-3 Bonhams, Knightsbridge #301/R
£875 $1400 €1269 View of Loch Lomond (61x107cm-24x42in) s. 17-May-3 CRN Auctions, Cambridge #12
£1100 $1749 €1650 Figures walking on a country lane. Loading haycart (24x37cm-9x15in) one init. paper on panel pair. 18-Mar-3 Bonhams, New Bond Street #37/R est:1000-1500
£1200 $1908 €1800 Figure seated beside a windmill, Sandwich, on the Kent Coast (25x38cm-10x15in) s.d.1844. 18-Mar-3 Bonhams, New Bond Street #36/R est:1000-1500
£1800 $2934 €2700 Landscape with cattle, sheep and goats in the foreground, Arundel castle beyond (50x15cm-20x6in) 28-Jan-3 Henry Adams, Chichester #441/R est:2000-3000
£2500 $3900 €3750 Figures by an Italianate lake (56x86cm-22x34in) s. 7-Nov-2 Christie's, Kensington #175/R est:3000-5000
£4000 $6280 €6000 Lake Garda (48x66cm-19x26in) s.d.1897. 19-Nov-2 Bonhams, New Bond Street #113/R est:4000-5000
£35000 $55300 €52500 View of the Custom House from the Thames (122x103cm-48x41in) s.d.1850. 26-Nov-2 Christie's, London #175/R est:40000-60000

Works on paper

£400 $656 €600 L. (30x46cm-12x18in) I. W/C. 7-Feb-3 Biddle & Webb, Birmingham #100
£900 $1404 €1350 Hauling in the nets (37x68cm-15x27in) s.d.61 W/C. 25-Mar-3 Bonhams, Knightsbridge #209/R
£1500 $2385 €2250 Figures on the shore near Dover (22x31cm-9x12in) W/C over pencil htd bodycol stopping out prov. 19-Mar-3 Sotheby's, London #155/R est:800-1200

PYNE, Robert Lorraine (19th C) American

£353 $550 €530 Sunset (23x36cm-9x14in) s.d.1888. 20-Sep-2 Sloan, North Bethesda #492/R

PYNE, Thomas (1843-1935) British

£400 $628 €600 Landscape with figures walking (20x33cm-8x13in) s.d.1881. 11-Dec-2 Rupert Toovey, Partridge Green #11/R
£456 $712 €684 English rural scene (37x52cm-15x20in) s.verso. 27-Mar-3 International Art Centre, Auckland #182 (NZ.D 1300)

Works on paper

£260 $406 €390 Flatford Mill (33x53cm-13x21in) s.d.1891 W/C. 11-Nov-2 Trembath Welch, Great Dunmow #462
£400 $660 €580 Manningtree, Essex (33x52cm-13x20in) s.d.1898 pencil W/C. 3-Jul-3 Christie's, Kensington #66
£530 $790 €795 Cattle grazing in a river landscape (23x33cm-9x13in) s.d.1899 pair. 27-Jun-2 Greenslade Hunt, Taunton #704
£900 $1404 €1350 Bridge and cattle at Flatford. In pasture green (23x33cm-9x13in) s.d.1897 W/C board. 6-Nov-2 Bonhams, Chester #441

PYNE, William Henry (1769-1843) British

Works on paper

£480 $802 €696 Road to Aberystwyth (19x26cm-7x10in) s. W/C. 24-Jun-3 Bonhams, Knightsbridge #31/R
£1800 $2826 €2700 Unionists, three paupers. I'll tell you my business. youth and folly (13x14cm-5x6in) i.verso pencil pen ink W/C set of three. 21-Nov-2 Christie's, London #34/R est:2000-3000

PYNENBORG, Jaques (?) ?

£420 $655 €630 Poultry in a barn (28x38cm-11x15in) s. 11-Apr-3 Keys, Aylsham #635

QI BAISHI (1863-1957) Chinese

Works on paper

£1304 $2139 €1800 Chrysanthemum and bees (18cm-7in) s. seal i. verso Indian ink col paper on silk fan painting. 30-May-3 Dr Fritz Nagel, Stuttgart #1170/R est:1000
£1739 $2852 €2400 Crow on rock (136x33cm-54x13in) s. seals Indian ink col hanging scroll. 30-May-3 Dr Fritz Nagel, Stuttgart #1144/R est:700-1000
£2293 $3577 €3600 Frogs and frogspawn (108x34cm-43x13in) s.i. Indian ink paper hanging scroll. 8-Nov-2 Dr Fritz Nagel, Stuttgart #1193/R est:3000
£3087 $5063 €4260 Crabs (68x33cm-27x13in) s.d.1948 Indian ink seals hanging scroll. 30-May-3 Dr Fritz Nagel, Stuttgart #1132/R est:1200-1800
£3252 $5138 €4878 Crabs (33x37cm-13x15in) seal ink prov.exhib. 28-Apr-3 Sotheby's, Hong Kong #628/R est:50000-70000 (HK.D 40000)
£3822 $5962 €6000 Chrysanthemums and crab (111x34cm-44x13in) s.i.d.1948 Indian ink col hanging scroll. 8-Nov-2 Dr Fritz Nagel, Stuttgart #1194/R est:3500
£5051 $8333 €7324 Hibiscus (131x46cm-52x18in) s.i.d.1925 ink scroll. 6-Jul-3 Christie's, Hong Kong #372/R est:70000-90000 (HK.D 65000)
£5439 $8974 €7887 Plum blossom and bird (133x34cm-52x13in) s.i. ink scroll. 6-Jul-3 Christie's, Hong Kong #249/R est:70000-90000 (HK.D 70000)
£6216 $10256 €9013 Grapes and insects (135x33cm-53x13in) s. ink scroll. 6-Jul-3 Christie's, Hong Kong #371/R est:60000-80000 (HK.D 80000)
£6341 $10020 €9512 Frolicking fish (20x30cm-8x12in) s. ink hanging scroll. 28-Apr-3 Sotheby's, Hong Kong #600/R est:60000-80000 (HK.D 78000)
£6993 $11538 €10140 Bodhidharma (17x16cm-7x6in) s. gold blue ground scroll. 6-Jul-3 Christie's, Hong Kong #246/R est:100000-120000 (HK.D 90000)
£7770 $12821 €11267 Eagle (105x33cm-41x13in) s. ink scroll. 6-Jul-3 Christie's, Hong Kong #370/R est:100000-150000 (HK.D 100000)
£8943 $14130 €13415 Cicadas (23x23cm-9x9in) s. ink col. 28-Apr-3 Sotheby's, Hong Kong #627/R est:30000-50000 (HK.D 110000)
£8943 $14130 €13415 Chrysanthemum (80x34cm-31x13in) s.i.d.1930 ink col. 28-Apr-3 Sotheby's, Hong Kong #637/R est:120000-125000 (HK.D 110000)
£8943 $14130 €13415 Inscription dedicated to the exhibition held by Qiu Shiming (22x34cm-9x13in) s.i.d.1943 ink. 28-Apr-3 Sotheby's, Hong Kong #655/R est:80000-100000 (HK.D 110000)
£10163 $16057 €15245 Shrimps (33x95cm-13x37in) s. ink. 28-Apr-3 Sotheby's, Hong Kong #599/R est:400000-600000 (HK.D 125000)
£10878 $17949 €15773 Fish, prawn and crab (123x30cm-48x12in) s.i. ink scroll. 6-Jul-3 Christie's, Hong Kong #245/R est:80000-100000 (HK.D 140000)
£10878 $17949 €15773 Silkworms (104x34cm-41x13in) s.i. ink scroll. 6-Jul-3 Christie's, Hong Kong #251/R est:70000-90000 (HK.D 140000)
£12432 $20513 €18026 Shrimp (100x33cm-39x13in) s.i. ink scroll. 6-Jul-3 Christie's, Hong Kong #250/R est:50000-70000 (HK.D 160000)
£13008 $20553 €19512 Pear and bee (23x23cm-9x9in) s. ink col. 28-Apr-3 Sotheby's, Hong Kong #626/R est:25000-35000 (HK.D 160000)
£13986 $23077 €20280 Chicken and fish (139x69cm-55x27in) s.i. ink scroll. 6-Jul-3 Christie's, Hong Kong #247/R est:120000-150000 (HK.D 180000)
£24390 $38537 €36585 Chrysanthemum (136x33cm-54x13in) s.i. ink col hanging scroll exhib. 28-Apr-3 Sotheby's, Hong Kong #633/R est:250000-300000 (HK.D 300000)

£26016 $41106 €39024 Beauty XI SHI (83x35cm-33x14in) s.i. ink col. 28-Apr-3 Sotheby's, Hong Kong #662/R est:180000-250000 (HK.D 320000)
£44715 $70650 €67073 Butterflies dancing in the air (51x36cm-20x14in) s. ink col hanging scroll prov.exhib. 28-Apr-3 Sotheby's, Hong Kong #602/R est:25000-35000 (HK.D 550000)
£101626 $160569 €152439 Sailing boats (154x42cm-61x17in) s.i. ink col hanging scroll exhib. 28-Apr-3 Sotheby's, Hong Kong #591/R est:300000-400000 (HK.D 1250000)

QIAN SONGYAN (1898-1985) Chinese
Works on paper
£616 $1010 €850 Landscape (46x33cm-18x13in) s.d.1979 seals Indian ink col hanging scroll. 30-May-3 Dr Fritz Nagel, Stuttgart #1247/R

QIANG GUOZHONG (17/18th C) Chinese
Works on paper
£5439 $8974 €7887 Welcoming the Imperial procession (49x108cm-19x43in) s. ink col silk handscroll. 6-Jul-3 Christie's, Hong Kong #473/R est:50000-60000 (HK.D 70000)

QING DYNASTY, Chinese
£12195 $19268 €18293 Buddhist figure in a garden with pine trees and flowers (92x92cm-36x36in) bears seal i.d. rice paper. 27-Apr-3 Sotheby's, Hong Kong #319/R est:150000-200000 (HK.D 150000)

QING DYNASTY, 18th/19th C Chinese
£14388 $23022 €20000 Un homme jouant de la flute (65x57cm-26x22in) reverse painting on mirrored glass. 15-May-3 Christie's, Paris #1/R est:8000-10000

QINNUAYUAK, Lucy (1915-1982) North American
Works on paper
£225 $352 €338 Man waiting a seal (43x26cm-17x10in) s.i.d.1964 col stencil. 25-Mar-3 Ritchie, Toronto #196/R (C.D 525)

QUADAL, Martin Ferdinand (1736-1811) Austrian
£15723 $25000 €23585 Faithful companions (91x117cm-36x46in) 30-Apr-3 Sotheby's, New York #548/R est:25000-35000

QUADAL, Martin Ferdinand (circle) (1736-1811) Austrian
£14000 $23380 €20300 Two dogs and two cats in a landscape with flowers (81x132cm-32x52in) exhib. 11-Jul-3 Christie's, Kensington #144/R est:10000-15000

QUADRONE, Giovanni Battista (1844-1898) Italian
Works on paper
£340 $541 €500 Angry esquire (17x9cm-7x4in) pencil. 1-Mar-3 Meeting Art, Vercelli #124

QUAGLIA, Carlo (1907-1970) Italian
£449 $704 €700 Roman Forum (19x14cm-7x6in) s. board painted 1968. 21-Nov-2 Finarte, Rome #53/R
£510 $811 €750 Statue in a garden (35x25cm-14x10in) s. masonite. 1-Mar-3 Meeting Art, Vercelli #721
£638 $1034 €900 Foro romano (35x25cm-14x10in) s.i.d.1968 masonite. 26-May-3 Christie's, Milan #85
£1419 $2243 €2200 San Giovanni e Paolo (45x60cm-18x24in) s. board prov.exhib. 18-Dec-2 Christie's, Rome #75/R
£2115 $3321 €3300 Beach in Liguria (45x60cm-18x24in) s. s.i.verso board painted 1954. 21-Nov-2 Finarte, Rome #334/R

QUAGLIA, Ferdinando (1780-1853) Italian
Miniatures
£2600 $4212 €3900 Young boy, wearing dark green coat over white shirt (5cm-2in) s. gilt metal frame. 22-May-3 Bonhams, New Bond Street #55/R est:600-800

QUAGLINO, Massimo (1899-1982) Italian
£321 $503 €500 Church (28x37cm-11x15in) s. board. 10-Dec-2 Della Rocca, Turin #348/R
£510 $811 €750 Landscape in Piemonte (29x39cm-11x15in) s.d.1945 board. 1-Mar-3 Meeting Art, Vercelli #94

QUAGLIO, Domenico (younger) (1787-1837) German
Works on paper
£705 $1093 €1100 Interior of a Gothic church (10x15cm-4x6in) indis.i. W/C over pencil. 4-Dec-2 Neumeister, Munich #546/R

QUAGLIO, Franz (1844-1920) German
£1000 $1630 €1500 Rest from the journey (16x26cm-6x10in) s.d.1885 panel. 12-Feb-3 Bonhams, Knightsbridge #59/R est:1000-1200
£1043 $1617 €1565 Elegant woman on horseback. Elegant man on horseback (21x16cm-8x6in) s. panel pair. 9-Dec-2 Philippe Schuler, Zurich #3928/R est:2000-2500 (S.FR 2400)
£1282 $1987 €2000 Horsemen in the mountains (18x14cm-7x6in) s.d.1892. 5-Dec-2 Dr Fritz Nagel, Stuttgart #695/R est:2000
£1923 $2981 €3000 Hunter on a horse in rococo time with his love reaching for a rose (27x21cm-11x8in) s.i. panel. 4-Dec-2 Neumeister, Munich #854/R est:2500
£2000 $3240 €3000 Cavalier. Cavliere (21x15cm-8x6in) s. panel two. 20-May-3 Sotheby's, Olympia #381/R est:2000-3000

QUARTLEY, Arthur (1839-1886) American
£2548 $4000 €3822 Pier near the beach at Narragansett, Rhode Island (39x69cm-15x27in) s.d.1877 i.verso prov. 19-Nov-2 Butterfields, San Francisco #8003/R est:4000-6000
£2848 $4500 €4272 Fishing fleet (41x58cm-16x23in) s. prov. 24-Apr-3 Shannon's, Milford #71/R est:3000-5000

QUARTO, Andrea (1959-) Italian
£316 $494 €500 True light (50x40cm-20x16in) s. i.verso painted 2000. 14-Sep-2 Meeting Art, Vercelli #864/R
£327 $523 €500 Oasis (50x60cm-20x24in) s. i.verso. 4-Jan-3 Meeting Art, Vercelli #77
£340 $541 €500 Oasis (40x50cm-16x20in) s. i.verso. 1-Mar-3 Meeting Art, Vercelli #714
£521 $828 €750 Oasis (60x70cm-24x28in) s. painted 2001. 1-May-3 Meeting Art, Vercelli #561
£556 $889 €850 Fantasy landscape (60x70cm-24x28in) s. i.verso. 4-Jan-3 Meeting Art, Vercelli #720
£556 $883 €800 Oasis (60x50cm-24x20in) s. i.verso. 1-May-3 Meeting Art, Vercelli #83
£850 $1352 €1250 Source of life (70x50cm-28x20in) s. 1-Mar-3 Meeting Art, Vercelli #473

QUARTREMAIN, William Wells (fl.1906-1908) British
Works on paper
£370 $618 €537 Punting on the Avon (16x26cm-6x10in) s.d.1921 W/C over pencil. 24-Jun-3 Bonhams, Knowle #14
£420 $651 €630 Cottages in Station Road, Salford Priors (130x195cm-51x77in) s. W/C. 27-Sep-2 Bigwood, Stratford on Avon #315/R
£425 $672 €638 Thatched Warwickshire cottage, with figures at a door and summer flowers (23x17cm-9x7in) s. W/C. 20-Dec-2 Bigwood, Stratford on Avon #221/R
£650 $1027 €975 Holy Trinity Church. Anne Hathaway's cottage (9x13cm-4x5in) s. W/C pair. 20-Dec-2 Bigwood, Stratford on Avon #219/R
£850 $1318 €1275 Wimpstone Bridge, Wimpstone near Stratford-upon-Avon (18x28cm-7x11in) s. W/C. 27-Sep-2 Bigwood, Stratford on Avon #316/R
£1250 $1938 €1875 Down river view at Severn Meadows below Old Mill Bridge, Stratford-upon-Avon (23x37cm-9x15in) s. W/C. 27-Sep-2 Bigwood, Stratford on Avon #317/R est:800-1000
£1400 $2170 €2100 View of Peacock Gardens, Warwick Castle from conservatory (28x45cm-11x18in) s.d.1911 W/C. 27-Sep-2 Bigwood, Stratford on Avon #318/R est:1400-1600
£4000 $6320 €6000 West Gate, Warwick, winter snowy view (37x63cm-15x25in) W/C. 20-Dec-2 Bigwood, Stratford on Avon #220/R est:2500-3000

QUAST, Jan Zacharias (1814-1891) Austrian
Works on paper
£351 $548 €527 Portrait of girl with bonnet (14x14cm-6x6in) s. pencil dr W/C. 12-Oct-2 Dorotheum, Prague #165/R (C.KR 17000)

QUAST, Pieter (1606-1647) Dutch
£3957 $6331 €5500 Kortegaardje, soldiers and peasants round fire in barn (43x62cm-17x24in) s. panel. 13-May-3 Sotheby's, Amsterdam #66/R est:6000-8000
£4936 $7799 €7700 Head operation (19x28cm-7x11in) mono. copper. 16-Nov-2 Lempertz, Koln #1073/R est:4000

QUAST, Pieter (attrib) (1606-1647) Dutch
£641 $994 €1000 Peasants reading (19x22cm-7x9in) panel. 5-Dec-2 Dr Fritz Nagel, Stuttgart #626/R

£2172 $3519 €3149 Couple flirting (38x29cm-15x11in) panel. 26-May-3 Bukowskis, Stockholm #415/R est:20000-25000 (S.KR 28000)
Works on paper
£290 $461 €420 Dutch man in an interior (16x15cm-6x6in) pencil. 10-Mar-3 Sotheby's, Amsterdam #34

QUATAL, Anton (18th C) German
£5031 $7799 €8000 Large river landscape with horsemen (70x100cm-28x39in) s. 2-Oct-2 Dorotheum, Vienna #233/R est:10000-15000

QUAYLE, Alec C (?) British
Works on paper
£280 $434 €420 Castletown (36x48cm-14x19in) s. W/C. 6-Dec-2 Chrystals Auctions, Isle of Man #210
£300 $465 €450 Sulby River (36x48cm-14x19in) s. W/C. 6-Dec-2 Chrystals Auctions, Isle of Man #208

QUAYLE, E Christian (fl.1894-1921) British
£500 $775 €750 Fishing trawlers at the harbour mouth (35x23cm-14x9in) s. 31-Oct-2 Christie's, Kensington #543/R
£560 $868 €840 Feeding chickens. Cottage garden (41x30cm-16x12in) s. pair. 6-Dec-2 Chrystals Auctions, Isle of Man #459
Works on paper
£500 $820 €750 Market scene, Douglas. Church yard (25x17cm-10x7in) s. W/C pair. 4-Jun-3 Bonhams, Chester #298
£750 $1118 €1125 Douglas Harbour (25x33cm-10x13in) s. W/C. 28-Jun-2 Chrystals Auctions, Isle of Man #151
£900 $1341 €1350 Happy Valley, Onchan (41x58cm-16x23in) s. W/C. 28-Jun-2 Chrystals Auctions, Isle of Man #160
£900 $1341 €1350 Low tide in small Manx harbour (41x66cm-16x26in) s. W/C. 28-Jun-2 Chrystals Auctions, Isle of Man #164

QUAYTMAN, Harvey (1937-2002) American
£1261 $1968 €1892 Pirate - pyrite (71x71cm-28x28in) s.i.d.1988 acrylic. 6-Nov-2 AB Stockholms Auktionsverk #820 est:12000-15000 (S.KR 18000)

QUECK, R Alfred (1878-1932) German
£2102 $3279 €3300 Winter landscape with sheep (121x202cm-48x80in) s.d.08 lit. 7-Nov-2 Allgauer, Kempten #2927/R est:4000

QUEEN ALEXANDRA (1844-1925) British/Danish
Works on paper
£280 $442 €406 View of a hilltop castle (13x21cm-5x8in) s.d.1870 W/C. 22-Jul-3 Bonhams, Knightsbridge #165/R

QUEEN OF THE NETHERLANDS, Wilhelmina (1880-1962) Dutch
£15789 $25579 €24000 Avnd aan het Bygdinmeer, Noorwegen (40x59cm-16x23in) init. painted c.1932. 21-Jan-3 Christie's, Amsterdam #191/R est:4000-6000
Works on paper
£3125 $5156 €4500 Trees in a mountainous landscape (50x62cm-20x24in) W/C. 1-Jul-3 Christie's, Amsterdam #164/R est:800-1200

QUEEN VICTORIA (attrib) (1819-1901) British
Works on paper
£700 $1078 €1050 Sketch of an Italian town (13x19cm-5x7in) pencil wash. 8-Sep-2 Lots Road, London #347

QUEEN, James W (19th C) American
Works on paper
£6410 $10000 €9615 Mount Vernon, the Seat of the late Gen G Washington (41x51cm-16x20in) i.d.Jan 1 1820 W/C ink dr. 21-Sep-2 Pook & Pook, Downington #30/R est:4000-6000

QUELLINUS, Artus (elder-circle) (1609-1668) Flemish
Sculpture
£8000 $12400 €12000 Group of the Virgin and Child (26cm-10in) 30-Oct-2 Sotheby's, London #70/R est:8000-12000

QUELLINUS, Artus (younger-attrib) (c.1625-1700) Flemish
Sculpture
£16000 $24800 €24000 Figure of an angel (137cm-54in) wood lit. 30-Oct-2 Sotheby's, London #56/R est:10000-15000

QUELLINUS, Erasmus (17th C) Flemish
£1773 $2961 €2500 Cincinnatus recevant les envoyes du senat (31x31cm-12x12in) mono. 18-Jun-3 Tajan, Paris #87/R est:3000-4000
£8974 $14179 €14000 Madonna with child sitting in garden (65x51cm-26x20in) s.d.1646 prov. 16-Nov-2 Lempertz, Koln #1074/R est:15000

QUELLINUS, Erasmus (attrib) (17th C) Flemish
£6643 $11094 €9500 Flore au l'allegorie du printemps (117x92cm-46x36in) 27-Jun-3 Piasa, Paris #40/R est:12000-15000

QUELLINUS, Erasmus II (1607-1678) Flemish
Works on paper
£446 $696 €700 Design for a tympanum with gambolling putti (10x32cm-4x13in) black chk. 5-Nov-2 Sotheby's, Amsterdam #155/R

QUELLINUS, Erasmus II (circle) (1607-1678) Flemish
£16000 $26720 €23200 Judgement of Solomon, Conversion of Saint Paul (50x66cm-20x26in) copper pair after Sir Peter Paul Rubens. 11-Jul-3 Christie's, Kensington #53/R est:8000-12000

QUELLINUS, Erasmus II and VERBRUGGEN, Gaspar Pieter (attrib) (17th C) Flemish
£8500 $13260 €12750 Garland of tulips, daffodils and other flower on a stone cartouche, with the Holy Family (91x66cm-36x26in) prov. 9-Apr-3 Christie's, London #25/R est:8000-12000

QUELLINUS, Jan Erasmus (1634-1715) Flemish
Works on paper
£2315 $3750 €3473 Apparition of the Madonna and Child (12x9cm-5x4in) pen ink wash over chk prov. 21-Jan-3 Sotheby's, New York #147/R est:3500

QUELLINUS, Jan Erasmus (attrib) (1634-1715) Flemish
£23488 $37816 €35000 Solomon sacrificing offerings before the ark of the covenant (120x201cm-47x79in) i. 18-Feb-3 Sotheby's, Amsterdam #757/R est:10000-15000

QUELVEE, François Albert (1884-1967) French
£486 $773 €700 Paysage de Provence (32x40cm-13x16in) s. 29-Apr-3 Artcurial Briest, Paris #161

QUENCE, Raymond (1932-) French
£710 $1100 €1065 St. Aygulf (64x81cm-25x32in) s. s.i.verso prov. 16-Jul-2 Arthur James, Florida #141
£968 $1500 €1452 Sur les bords du leff (81x102cm-32x40in) s. s.i.verso prov. 16-Jul-2 Arthur James, Florida #142

QUENNEVILLE, Chantal (1897-1959) French?
£900 $1431 €1350 Le dejeuner (61x50cm-24x20in) s. prov. 20-Mar-3 Sotheby's, Olympia #31/R

QUENTIN, Bernard (1923-) French
£278 $439 €400 Bataille (50x94cm-20x37in) s. panel. 28-Apr-3 Cornette de St.Cyr, Paris #491
£348 $540 €550 Art (216x120cm-85x47in) s. acrylic cardboard. 28-Sep-2 Cornette de St.Cyr, Paris #396/R
£417 $658 €600 Le passage du temps (100x92cm-39x36in) s. acrylic dechire paper on moquette canvas. 28-Apr-3 Cornette de St.Cyr, Paris #492
£609 $956 €950 Untitled (56x63cm-22x25in) s.d.1950. 15-Dec-2 Perrin, Versailles #21/R
Works on paper
£283 $442 €450 Composition blanche (100x195cm-39x77in) s.d.1957. 11-Oct-2 Binoche, Paris #136
£306 $487 €450 Tonnerre (152x162cm-60x64in) s.d.1989 mixed media fabric. 24-Mar-3 Claude Boisgirard, Paris #145
£345 $545 €500 Untitled (32x50cm-13x20in) s. ink gouache. 4-Apr-3 Tajan, Paris #280
£513 $805 €800 Untitled (72x51cm-28x20in) s.d.1961 mixed media collage panel. 15-Dec-2 Perrin, Versailles #24

QUENTIN, Laurence (20th C) French
Works on paper
£432 $691 €600 Anis et les etoiles (110x110cm-43x43in) s. mixed media canvas. 18-May-3 Neret-Minet, Paris #159/R

QUERALT, Jaume (1949-) Spanish
Works on paper
£805 $1297 €1200 View from the balcony (38x54cm-15x21in) s. pastel. 18-Feb-3 Durán, Madrid #145/R

QUERCIA, Federico (19th C) Italian
Works on paper
£800 $1248 €1200 Portrait of a young girl (105x70cm-41x28in) s.i. pastel. 26-Mar-3 Sotheby's, Olympia #190/R

QUERE, Paul (20th C) French?
Works on paper
£568 $909 €790 L'ancrage d'or (76x92cm-30x36in) s.verso mixed media wood panel. 18-May-3 Neret-Minet, Paris #122

QUERE, René (1932-) French
£472 $770 €680 Cote Bretonne (46x56cm-18x22in) s. 19-Jul-3 Thierry & Lannon, Brest #235
£486 $792 €700 Petit port Breton (16x27cm-6x11in) s. isorel. 19-Jul-3 Thierry & Lannon, Brest #234
Works on paper
£521 $849 €750 Ramassage du goemon devant Notre Dame de la Joie (30x23cm-12x9in) s. gouache. 19-Jul-3 Thierry & Lannon, Brest #233

QUERENA, Luigi (1820-c.1890) Italian
£22000 $34540 €33000 Figures before a palazzo on a Venetian backwater with San Giorgio Maggiore beyond (51x64cm-20x25in) s.d.1860. 16-Apr-3 Christie's, Kensington #574/R est:4000-6000

QUERFURT, August (1696-1761) German
£1800 $2790 €2700 Riding party departing in a mountainous landscape (23x30cm-9x12in) panel. 30-Oct-2 Bonhams, New Bond Street #24/R est:2000-3000
£5068 $7905 €7500 Cavalry engagements between Turkish and Imperial troops (28x46cm-11x18in) pair. 27-Mar-3 Dorotheum, Vienna #310/R est:3000-5000
£8176 $12673 €13000 Cavalry engagement (41x56cm-16x22in) prov. 2-Oct-2 Dorotheum, Vienna #234/R est:9000-12000
£8917 $13911 €14000 Soldiers and horsemen halted and resting at a military encampment (82x111cm-32x44in) mono. 5-Nov-2 Sotheby's, Amsterdam #334/R est:6000-8000

QUERFURT, August (attrib) (1696-1761) German
£1014 $1581 €1500 Cavalry engagement in landscape (27x35cm-11x14in) panel. 27-Mar-3 Dorotheum, Vienna #311/R est:1200-1600
£1299 $1935 €2000 Cavalry battle against Turks (19x26cm-7x10in) panel pair. 26-Jun-2 Neumeister, Munich #650/R est:3000
£1724 $2741 €2500 Conversation (29x38cm-11x15in) copper. 8-Mar-3 Arnold, Frankfurt #688 est:3000
£2027 $3162 €3000 Peasants resting in field before haycart (36x41cm-14x16in) prov. 27-Mar-3 Dorotheum, Vienna #413/R est:3000-5000
£3333 $5167 €5000 Battle scene (32x39cm-13x15in) copper. 3-Dec-2 Bukowskis, Stockholm #498/R est:20000-25000 (S.KR 47000)
£3688 $5716 €5532 Army camp (35x48cm-14x19in) copper. 3-Dec-2 Bukowskis, Stockholm #497/R est:50000-60000 (S.KR 52000)
£5499 $9018 €7974 Battle scene (37x51cm-15x20in) bears later mono.PW. 4-Jun-3 AB Stockholms Auktionsverk #2566/R est:30000-35000 (S.KR 70000)

QUERNER, Curt (1904-1976) German
£818 $1259 €1300 Portrait study of Erhard Frommhold (40x29cm-16x11in) i. verso panel. 26-Oct-2 Dr Lehr, Berlin #437/R
£5346 $8233 €8500 Karsdorf on March evening (47x80cm-19x31in) s.i. verso. 26-Oct-2 Dr Lehr, Berlin #436/R est:8000
Works on paper
£252 $387 €400 Seated female nude (50x35cm-20x14in) s. i. verso graphite board. 26-Oct-2 Dr Lehr, Berlin #446/R
£278 $439 €400 Standing female nude (64x25cm-25x10in) s.d.29.3.62 graphite col pen board. 26-Apr-3 Dr Lehr, Berlin #426
£313 $494 €450 Crawling female nude (35x51cm-14x20in) s.d.12.9.71 i. verso graphite. 26-Apr-3 Dr Lehr, Berlin #427/R
£314 $484 €500 Kneeling female nude (48x32cm-19x13in) s.d.12.10.69 i. verso graphite board. 26-Oct-2 Dr Lehr, Berlin #445
£409 $630 €650 Seated peasant woman (66x48cm-26x19in) s.d.21.7.59 i. verso W/C. 26-Oct-2 Dr Lehr, Berlin #441/R
£440 $678 €700 Nude (66x48cm-26x19in) s.d.7.3.58 i. verso W/C board. 26-Oct-2 Dr Lehr, Berlin #440/R
£486 $768 €700 Crouching female nude (47x36cm-19x14in) s. i. verso W/C board. 26-Apr-3 Dr Lehr, Berlin #425/R
£556 $878 €800 Standing female nude (72x25cm-28x10in) s.d.1966 W/C board. 26-Apr-3 Dr Lehr, Berlin #424
£791 $1250 €1250 Standing female nude with arms raised (72x22cm-28x9in) s.d.12.12.65 i. verso W/C. 29-Nov-2 Villa Grisebach, Berlin #859/R
£818 $1259 €1300 Standing female nude (66x31cm-26x12in) s.d.5.8.64 w/C. 26-Oct-2 Dr Lehr, Berlin #443/R
£1107 $1705 €1760 Norwegian bay in snow (11x24cm-4x9in) s.d.15.12.43 W/C htd bodycol board. 26-Oct-2 Dr Lehr, Berlin #438/R est:1600
£1111 $1756 €1600 Trees in Diebels Gut (61x48cm-24x19in) s.d.11.2.68 W/C board. 26-Apr-3 Dr Lehr, Berlin #422/R est:2000
£1132 $1743 €1800 Naked peasant girl (72x50cm-28x20in) i. verso W/C board. 26-Oct-2 Dr Lehr, Berlin #439/R est:1200
£1384 $2131 €2200 Landscape - Schumanns Gut in Bornchen (48x67cm-19x26in) s.d.12.4.64 i. verso W/C. 26-Oct-2 Dr Lehr, Berlin #442/R est:1500

QUERZOLI, Alvaro (1955-) Brazilian
£288 $453 €450 Jesus (36x36cm-14x14in) s.d.2000 masonite. 23-Nov-2 Meeting Art, Vercelli #190

QUESADA GILABERT, Julio (1918-) Spanish
Works on paper
£445 $695 €650 Landscape with house (29x46cm-11x18in) s.d.86 W/C. 8-Apr-3 Ansorena, Madrid #611

QUESADA, Marietta (20th C) Spanish?
Works on paper
£353 $557 €550 Landscape (48x40cm-19x16in) s. mixed media. 19-Nov-2 Durán, Madrid #79/R

QUESNE, Fernand le (1856-?) French
£863 $1381 €1200 Souvenir du torrent (30x40cm-12x16in) s.d.1894. 13-May-3 Palais de Beaux Arts, Brussels #192

QUESNEL, Augustin I (1595-1661) French
Prints
£2848 $4500 €4500 Man playing guitar and dancing girl with tambourine (22x28cm-9x11in) etching. 29-Nov-2 Bassenge, Berlin #5230/R est:3000

QUESNET, Eugène (1816-1899) French
£851 $1421 €1200 Portrait de femme (117x90cm-46x35in) s. 23-Jun-3 Beaussant & Lefèvre, Paris #283/R

QUETGLAS, Matias (1946-) Spanish
£3311 $5397 €5000 Leaves (46x55cm-18x22in) s.d.1976 s.i.verso tempera board prov.exhib. 11-Feb-3 Segre, Madrid #201/R

QUICK, Richard (fl.1882-1889) British
£364 $560 €546 Smithy (17x27cm-7x11in) s.i.verso board. 4-Sep-2 Dunbar Sloane, Wellington #87/R est:1200-1800 (NZ.D 1200)

QUIDLEY, Peter (20th C) American
£287 $450 €431 Beach dune with fence (51x61cm-20x24in) s. 22-Nov-2 Eldred, East Dennis #1016

QUIESSE, Claude (1938-) French
£673 $1057 €1050 Pecheur (61x46cm-24x18in) s. 24-Nov-2 Lesieur & Le Bars, Le Havre #145/R
£1056 $1701 €1500 Les haleurs (81x99cm-32x39in) s. 12-May-3 Lesieur & Le Bars, Le Havre #81/R

QUIGLEY, Edward B (1895-?) American
Photographs
£2110 $3250 €3165 Light abstraction (34x27cm-13x11in) photograph. 22-Oct-2 Sotheby's, New York #161/R est:4000-6000

QUILICHINI, Andree (20th C) French
£448 $713 €650 Seule (74x100cm-29x39in) s. 10-Mar-3 Millon & Associes, Paris #295
£552 $877 €800 Pourtant (82x100cm-32x39in) s. 10-Mar-3 Millon & Associes, Paris #296

QUILLIARD, Pierre Antoine (attrib) (1701-1733) French
£1935 $3058 €3000 Scene de jeu dans un parc (64x109cm-25x43in) 19-Dec-2 Delvaux, Paris #94/R
Works on paper
£1351 $2108 €2000 Scene de genre (19x27cm-7x11in) crayon chk oval prov. 26-Mar-3 Piasa, Paris #77/R

QUILLIVIC, Raymond (1942-) French
Works on paper
£313 $509 €450 Les Plomarc'h, l'entree du port (25x17cm-10x7in) s. gouache. 19-Jul-3 Thierry & Lannon, Brest #239
£321 $503 €500 Douarnenez (46x38cm-18x15in) s. 15-Dec-2 Thierry & Lannon, Brest #254
£333 $543 €480 Le lavoir aux Plomarc'h (25x17cm-10x7in) s. gouache. 19-Jul-3 Thierry & Lannon, Brest #236

£333 $543 €480 Beuzec, la roch de Cortel Ar Cor (36x28cm-14x11in) s. gouache. 19-Jul-3 Thierry & Lannon, Brest #238

QUINAURT, Charles Louis François (1788-c.1848) French
£943 $1453 €1500 Le Tibre (21x26cm-8x10in) s. 27-Oct-2 Muizon & Le Coent, Paris #25/R

QUINAUX, Joseph (1822-1895) Belgian
£605 $944 €950 Le pont pres de la ferme (39x59cm-15x23in) s. 11-Nov-2 Horta, Bruxelles #567
£1130 $1763 €1695 Landscape with cows (68x98cm-27x39in) s.d.1871. 16-Sep-2 Philippe Schuler, Zurich #3491/R est:2500-3000 (S.FR 2600)

QUINET, Mig (1908-2001) Belgian
£1772 $2800 €2800 Opus printanier (140x130cm-55x51in) s.d.1963 verso. 26-Nov-2 Palais de Beaux Arts, Brussels #254/R est:2000-3000

QUINKHARD, Jan Maurits (1688-1772) Dutch
£3822 $5962 €6000 Portrait of a gentleman wearing a black coat (30x22cm-12x9in) s.d.1735 panel exhib.lit. 5-Nov-2 Sotheby's, Amsterdam #68/R est:3000-5000

QUINLAN, Will J (1877-?) American
£382 $600 €573 Forehead, Mt. Mansfield, Vt (20x25cm-8x10in) s.d.1931 board. 14-Dec-2 CRN Auctions, Cambridge #35/R

QUINN, Marc (1964-) British
Sculpture
£7595 $12000 €11393 Beached (80x225cm-31x89in) RTV rubber 74-30 polyurethane executed 1998 prov.exhib. 14-Nov-2 Christie's, Rockefeller NY #350/R est:15000-20000
Works on paper
£1772 $2800 €2658 Blind leading the blind (75x56cm-30x22in) s.d.95 paper collage graphite prov. 12-Nov-2 Phillips, New York #242/R est:2000-3000

QUINN, William (20th C) American
£256 $400 €384 Still life with rhubarb (61x76cm-24x30in) s. 10-Nov-2 Selkirks, St. Louis #921/R

QUINQUAND, Anna (1890-1984) French
Sculpture
£6076 $9478 €9600 La femme du Foutah Djallon (45cm-18in) d.1930 brown pat bronze f.Susse Freres Paris. 20-Oct-2 Galerie de Chartres, Chartres #364 est:3800-4600
£6731 $10567 €10500 Femme du Fouta Djallon (42cm-17in) s. stone htd gold silver. 20-Nov-2 Claude Boisgirard, Paris #61/R est:8000-10000
Works on paper
£475 $741 €750 Femme, foutah-djallon (20x20cm-8x8in) s.i. chl chk. 20-Oct-2 Charbonneaux, Paris #41

QUINQUELA MARTIN, Benito (1890-1977) Argentinian
£9063 $13775 €13595 Chico en la playa (53x43cm-21x17in) s. 3-Jul-2 Naón & Cia, Buenos Aires #18/R est:2000-2500

QUINTANILLA, Luis (1893-1978) Spanish
£774 $1223 €1200 Still life with basket (66x55cm-26x22in) s. 18-Dec-2 Ansorena, Madrid #197/R

QUINTE, Lothar (1923-2000) German
£538 $839 €850 Untitled (41x57cm-16x22in) s.d.1980 tempera. 18-Oct-2 Dr Fritz Nagel, Stuttgart #298/R
£2564 $3974 €4000 Diagonal slit picture (54x62cm-21x24in) s.d.1966 verso acrylic. 7-Dec-2 Ketterer, Hamburg #554/R est:4500-5000

QUINTERO, Daniel (1940-) Spanish
Works on paper
£2317 $3800 €3476 Muchacho en la cama (114x102cm-45x40in) s.d.71 chl paper on wood prov. 28-May-3 Christie's, Rockefeller NY #148/R est:1000-1500

QUINTON, Alfred Robert (1853-1934) British
Works on paper
£300 $489 €450 Houses of Parliament from Lambeth Bridge (24x17cm-9x7in) s. W/C over pencil htd white. 11-Feb-3 Bonhams, Knowle #46
£600 $936 €900 Bredwardine bridge on the Wye, Hereford (39x58cm-15x23in) s. pencil W/C exhib. 27-Mar-3 Christie's, Kensington #118/R
£850 $1385 €1275 Church gate, Welford-on-Avon (17x25cm-7x10in) s. W/C. 29-Jan-3 Sotheby's, Olympia #124/R est:300-500
£850 $1394 €1275 Rock streams running through villages (15x10cm-6x4in) s. pair. 5-Feb-3 John Nicholson, Haslemere #1003

QUINTON, Clement (1851-?) French
£370 $596 €555 Two cows on track (49x65cm-19x26in) s. 7-May-3 Dobiaschofsky, Bern #897/R (S.FR 800)
£534 $828 €850 Labour au soleil couchant (97x105cm-38x41in) s.d.1905. 4-Oct-2 Tajan, Paris #206
£1200 $1896 €1800 Rest at the canal (48x65cm-19x26in) s. 14-Nov-2 Christie's, Kensington #83/R est:1000-1500
£1899 $3000 €3000 La sortie de la bergerie (54x65cm-21x26in) s. 1-Dec-2 Peron, Melun #147

QUINTON, J (19th C) British?
£500 $780 €750 Study of a bay hunter standing in profile, in a stable (44x59cm-17x23in) s.d.1883. 23-Apr-3 Rupert Toovey, Partridge Green #167/R
£1350 $2200 €2025 Charlie (20x25cm-8x10in) s.i.verso. 11-Feb-3 Bonhams & Doyles, New York #107/R est:1500-2000

QUIROS, Antonio (1918-1984) Spanish
Works on paper
£692 $1065 €1100 Composition (33x52cm-13x20in) s. mm. 22-Oct-2 Durán, Madrid #137/R

QUISPEL, Matthys (1805-1858) Dutch
Works on paper
£816 $1298 €1200 Paysans et troupeau dans un paysage fluvial (27x38cm-11x15in) s. pen ink. 28-Feb-3 Beaussant & Lefèvre, Paris #38/R

QUIST, Carl Gustaf (1787-1822) Swedish
£5120 $8295 €7424 Landscapes with goldfinch and red-backed shrike (30x19cm-12x7in) i.verso panel pair exhib.prov. 26-May-3 Bukowskis, Stockholm #364/R est:30000-40000 (S.KR 66000)

QUISTDORFF, Victor (1883-1953) Danish
£259 $396 €389 Vessels in harbour (36x48cm-14x19in) s.i.d.1927 panel double-sided. 24-Aug-2 Rasmussen, Havnen #2241 (D.KR 3000)
£306 $496 €444 Harbour scene with figures (37x49cm-15x19in) s. 24-May-3 Rasmussen, Havnen #2112 (D.KR 3200)
£344 $558 €499 Seascape with freight ship (41x60cm-16x24in) s.d.1939 panel. 24-May-3 Rasmussen, Havnen #2111 (D.KR 3600)
£429 $626 €660 Rusty steam ship in dock (16x21cm-6x8in) s.indis.d. cardboard. 15-Jun-2 Hans Stahl, Hamburg #254/R
£440 $713 €638 Ship's portrait of Vivi Danmark (45x68cm-18x27in) s.d.1941. 24-May-3 Rasmussen, Havnen #2014/R (D.KR 4600)
£659 $1028 €989 Winter's day at Hojbro Plads with figures and tram (33x26cm-13x10in) s.d.1931. 23-Sep-2 Rasmussen, Vejle #269/R (D.KR 7800)
£957 $1550 €1388 English battle ship Hood at anchor off New York (34x47cm-13x19in) s.i.d.1943. 26-May-3 Rasmussen, Copenhagen #1349/R (D.KR 10000)

QUISTGAARD, Jens H and SORENSEN, Soren (20th C) Danish
£459 $716 €689 Kitchen interior with mother and two children (100x80cm-39x31in) s.d.1930. 5-Aug-2 Rasmussen, Vejle #94/R (D.KR 5400)

QUITTELIER, Henri (1884-1980) Belgian
£253 $395 €400 Moissonneurs surpris par l'orage (80x100cm-31x39in) s. panel. 15-Oct-2 Vanderkindere, Brussels #236
£316 $494 €500 Madeleine lisant (45x55cm-18x22in) s.d.1946. 15-Oct-2 Vanderkindere, Brussels #224
£316 $494 €500 Auto portrait au chapeaux (75x61cm-30x24in) s. 15-Oct-2 Vanderkindere, Brussels #246/R
£316 $494 €500 Famille heuruese (90x111cm-35x44in) s.d.1921 cardboard. 15-Oct-2 Vanderkindere, Brussels #249
£336 $540 €500 Printemps au Kamerdelle (45x55cm-18x22in) s.d.1929 panel. 18-Feb-3 Vanderkindere, Brussels #106
£348 $543 €550 Grimbergen (75x61cm-30x24in) s. 15-Oct-2 Vanderkindere, Brussels #241
£403 $648 €600 Soir de kermesse (26x49cm-10x19in) s. d.1920 verso. 18-Feb-3 Vanderkindere, Brussels #264
£696 $1086 €1100 Paysage lacustre (54x74cm-21x29in) s.d.1925. 15-Oct-2 Vanderkindere, Brussels #234
£709 $1184 €1000 La chevauchee fantastique (93x145cm-37x57in) s. i.verso. 18-Jun-3 Hotel des Ventes Mosan, Brussels #198
£886 $1382 €1400 Ars Conga-Vita Brevis (87x108cm-34x43in) s.d.1923 cardboard. 15-Oct-2 Vanderkindere, Brussels #231

QUITTON, Edovard (1842-1934) Belgian
£3797 $5924 €6000 Painter at the farm (41x66cm-16x26in) s. 21-Oct-2 Bernaerts, Antwerp #81/R est:2000-2500
£6000 $10020 €8700 In the palmhouse (80x65cm-31x26in) s.i.d.1890 panel. 17-Jun-3 Bonhams, New Bond Street #6/R est:7000-10000

QUIVIERES, Augustin Marcotte de (1854-1907) French
£700 $1092 €1050 Lady and parasol (21x16cm-8x6in) s.d.1879 panel. 17-Sep-2 Rosebery Fine Art, London #668/R

QUIZET, Alphonse (1885-1955) French
£699 $1168 €1000 Pechine sur le canal (38x46cm-15x18in) s. isorel. 26-Jun-3 Tajan, Paris #293
£949 $1481 €1500 Rue de village animee (38x46cm-15x18in) s. panel. 20-Oct-2 Chayette & Cheval, Paris #68
£980 $1548 €1470 Rainy November day in Montmartre (44x34cm-17x13in) s. board. 15-Nov-2 Rowley Fine Art, Newmarket #384/R
£1034 $1655 €1500 Rue animee (72x59cm-28x23in) s. 12-Mar-3 Libert, Castor, Paris #163 est:3000-3500
£1034 $1655 €1500 Remparts de Verneuil (65x81cm-26x32in) s. prov.exhib. 12-Mar-3 Libert, Castor, Paris #165 est:3000-3500
£1582 $2500 €2500 Eglise (73x92cm-29x36in) s. masonite. 27-Nov-2 Blanchet, Paris #116
£1724 $2759 €2500 Paysage anime (54x81cm-21x32in) s. 12-Mar-3 Libert, Castor, Paris #164/R est:3000-3500
£1806 $2853 €2600 Rue de village (60x73cm-24x29in) 25-Apr-3 Piasa, Paris #184/R
£2200 $3388 €3300 Roses blanches, vase fond vert (55x46cm-22x18in) s. board exhib. 23-Oct-2 Sotheby's, Olympia #635/R est:2000-3000
£5172 $8276 €7500 15-17 rue des Lilas, Paris (77x96cm-30x38in) s. 12-Mar-3 Libert, Castor, Paris #162/R est:3000-3500

QUOST, Ernest (1844-1931) French
£473 $738 €700 Jetee de fleurs (20x39cm-8x15in) mono. panel. 25-Mar-3 Chochon-Barre & Allardi, Paris #186
£480 $749 €720 Paysage, with figures in the foreground (21x16cm-8x6in) panel. 17-Sep-2 Rosebery Fine Art, London #663/R
£2564 $3897 €4000 Vase de fleurs (91x74cm-36x29in) s. 10-Jul-2 Rabourdin & Choppin de Janvry, Paris #13/R est:4600-4800

R S (?) ?
£9929 $15390 €14894 Exotic landscape with animals and figures (85x170cm-33x67in) init.d.1861. 3-Dec-2 Bukowskis, Stockholm #321/R est:40000-50000 (S.KR 140000)

RAAB, Georg (1821-1885) Austrian
Miniatures
£1800 $2916 €2700 Young lady, called Marie von Wedel (9cm-4in) s.i. gilt metal. 22-May-3 Bonhams, New Bond Street #122/R est:1500-2500

RAAB, Hendrik (1903-1983) Dutch
£255 $397 €400 Still life with cauliflower, copper bowl and jug (34x49cm-13x19in) s. 6-Nov-2 Vendue Huis, Gravenhage #60/R

RAADAL, Erik (1905-1941) Danish
£1691 $2604 €2537 Landscape from Gronhoj (50x80cm-20x31in) init.d.40 exhib.lit. 23-Oct-2 Kunsthallen, Copenhagen #7/R est:25000 (D.KR 20000)
£1691 $2604 €2537 Heath landscape (61x81cm-24x32in) init.d.39 exhib.lit. 23-Oct-2 Kunsthallen, Copenhagen #24/R est:25000 (D.KR 20000)

RAADSIG, Peter (1806-1882) Danish
£478 $775 €717 Political meeting at an inn (31x48cm-12x19in) study. 21-May-3 Museumsbygningen, Copenhagen #65 (D.KR 5000)
£605 $962 €908 Landscape from Kjoldnesholm (40x66cm-16x26in) mono.i.d.1855. 10-Mar-3 Rasmussen, Vejle #310 (D.KR 6500)
£1702 $2689 €2553 Monks working on a terrace near Albaner Lake (37x55cm-15x22in) 2-Dec-2 Rasmussen, Copenhagen #1485/R est:20000-25000 (D.KR 20000)
£1862 $2961 €2793 Figures by well (49x67cm-19x26in) 10-Mar-3 Rasmussen, Vejle #199/R est:20000-30000 (D.KR 20000)

RAAPHORST, Cornelis (1875-1954) Dutch
£1911 $2981 €3000 Kittens playing. s. panel. 6-Nov-2 Vendue Huis, Gravenhage #560/R est:2500-3500
£2038 $3139 €3200 Playful kittens (40x50cm-16x20in) s. 3-Sep-2 Christie's, Amsterdam #241/R est:3000-5000
£2038 $3180 €3200 Two kittens with a feather and cushion (23x28cm-9x11in) s. 5-Nov-2 Vendu Notarishuis, Rotterdam #234/R est:2500-3000
£2548 $3975 €4000 Four kittens playing on an Oriental carpet (39x49cm-15x19in) 5-Nov-2 Vendu Notarishuis, Rotterdam #87/R est:4000-5000
£3082 $4808 €4500 Kittens on music sheets (40x50cm-16x20in) s. 14-Apr-3 Glerum, Amsterdam #154/R est:2000-3000
£3600 $5832 €5400 Kittens playing (60x80cm-24x31in) s. 20-May-3 Sotheby's, Olympia #390/R est:4000-6000
£3904 $6090 €5700 Six kittens playing on books (50x60cm-20x24in) s. 14-Apr-3 Glerum, Amsterdam #159/R est:3000-5000
£4114 $6418 €6500 Five kittens near a fish bowl (50x70cm-20x28in) s. 21-Oct-2 Glerum, Amsterdam #209/R est:6500-7500
£5263 $8526 €8000 Two kittens sleeping on a pillow (24x30cm-9x12in) s. 21-Jan-3 Christie's, Amsterdam #178/R est:1500-2000

RAAPHORST, W (1870-1963) Dutch
£253 $395 €380 Still life of poppies in water glass (36x30cm-14x12in) s. 23-Sep-2 Rasmussen, Vejle #138/R (D.KR 3000)

RAATIKAINEN, Olavi (20th C) Finnish
£1223 $2006 €1700 Washerwomen (60x50cm-24x20in) s.d.1965. 5-Jun-3 Hagelstam, Helsinki #1003/R est:1500

RAATIKAINEN, Orvo (1914-2000) Finnish
£1438 $2358 €2200 Boy fishing (70x55cm-28x22in) s. 9-Feb-3 Bukowskis, Helsinki #340/R est:1200

RABA, Manuel (1928-1983) Spanish
Works on paper
£2303 $3730 €3500 Composition (60x72cm-24x28in) s. mixed media. 21-Jan-3 Durán, Madrid #137/R

RABARAMA (1969-) Italian
£769 $1208 €1200 Orange symphony (50x50cm-20x20in) s.d.1995 board. 23-Nov-2 Meeting Art, Vercelli #28/R
Sculpture
£4167 $6542 €6500 Transport (51x40cm-20x16in) i.verso num.7/8 painted bronze. 23-Nov-2 Meeting Art, Vercelli #93/R

RABER, Robert M (20th C) American
£307 $500 €461 Autumn days (81x102cm-32x40in) s.d.20 i.d.1923 verso. 2-Feb-3 Grogan, Boston #58

RABES, Max (1868-1944) Austrian
£306 $493 €459 Landscape with cliffs (38x24cm-15x9in) s.d.20.12.86 cardboard. 22-Feb-3 Rasmussen, Havnen #2346 (D.KR 3400)
£2113 $3401 €3000 Souk with minaret and figures (139x110cm-55x43in) s. 7-May-3 Michael Zeller, Lindau #892/R est:3000
£6000 $9360 €9000 Bridges of Thebes (39x54cm-15x21in) s. 26-Mar-3 Sotheby's, Olympia #232/R est:6000-8000
£8805 $13736 €14000 By the fire - Biskra (100x126cm-39x50in) s. i. stretcher lit. 20-Sep-2 Schloss Ahlden, Ahlden #1211/R est:12000

RABINE, Oskar (1928-) Russian
£993 $1619 €1500 Self-portrait (97x124cm-38x49in) s.d.1978. 3-Feb-3 Cornette de St.Cyr, Paris #330/R
£1572 $2452 €2358 Violin in snowy sheet (81x65cm-32x26in) s.d.1989 oil material collage. 20-Nov-2 Fischer, Luzern #1133/R est:3200-4000 (S.FR 3600)
£2215 $3434 €3500 La ferme (59x92cm-23x36in) s. 28-Sep-2 Cornette de St.Cyr, Paris #185/R est:3500-4000
£2756 $4328 €4300 Nord-sud (81x100cm-32x39in) s.d. 24-Nov-2 Chayette & Cheval, Paris #313/R est:3500-5000
Works on paper
£833 $1325 €1200 Nature morte a l'icone (41x50cm-16x20in) s.d.70 ink black felt pen graphite dr. 29-Apr-3 Artcurial Briest, Paris #320
£903 $1435 €1300 Moscou (43x32cm-17x13in) s.d.66 black felt pen dr. 29-Apr-3 Artcurial Briest, Paris #318 est:1200-1500

RABUZIN, Ivan (1919-) Yugoslavian
£3846 $5962 €6000 Saulovec - hilly landscape (81x112cm-32x44in) mono.i.d.1961. 4-Dec-2 Lempertz, Koln #1017/R est:6000-7000

RACE, G (19th C) British
£1350 $2160 €2025 Steamships, Lynbrook. Cold finder. Cold Seeker (25x43cm-10x17in) s.d.1898 set of three. 14-Mar-3 Gardiner & Houlgate, Bath #226/R est:1500-2000

RACHOU, Henri (1856-?) French
£813 $1300 €1220 Barge on canal. Spring trees. House along a river (15x23cm-6x9in) s. panel three. 8-Jan-3 Doyle, New York #44/R est:800-1200

RACITI, Mario (1934-) Italian
£1090 $1711 €1700 Presences-absences (70x100cm-28x39in) s.d.71 s.i.d.verso. 20-Nov-2 Pandolfini, Florence #122/R
£1197 $1987 €1700 Mister (100x70cm-39x28in) s.i.d.2001 verso. 10-Jun-3 Finarte Semenzato, Milan #258/R est:1300-1500

RACKHAM, Arthur (1867-1939) British
Works on paper
£600 $936 €900 Sussex lane (31x22cm-12x9in) s.d.1888 pencil W/C. 27-Mar-3 Christie's, Kensington #131/R
£1500 $2325 €2250 Kensington Gardens (18x25cm-7x10in) init. pen black ink W/C. 4-Dec-2 Christie's, Kensington #151/R est:1500-2000
£2200 $3652 €3300 River Arun at Amberley, Sussex (23x18cm-9x7in) s. W/C prov. 12-Jun-3 Bonhams, New Bond Street #701/R est:800-1200
£4545 $7000 €6818 Salmon's enemies (30x25cm-12x10in) s. ink W/C prov. 24-Oct-2 Shannon's, Milford #125/R est:6000-8000
£16352 $26000 €24528 Wandering trees (30x23cm-12x9in) s.i.d.1912 pen ink W/C. 5-May-3 Butterfields, San Francisco #93/R est:12000-15000

RACKHAM, W Leslie (1864-1944) British
Works on paper
£260 $429 €377 Whitlingham Reach, Norwich (7x15cm-3x6in) init. W/C. 1-Jul-3 Bonhams, Norwich #65
£300 $489 €450 Yachts passing on a cornerof the Norfolk Broads (13x30cm-5x12in) s. W/C. 14-Feb-3 Keys, Aylsham #561/R
£300 $468 €450 Rice's farm, River Thurne (18x25cm-7x10in) s. W/C. 11-Apr-3 Keys, Aylsham #552/R
£340 $517 €510 Horning Ferry (18x25cm-7x10in) s.i. W/C. 16-Aug-2 Keys, Aylsham #562
£400 $668 €580 At Horning Ferry (20x36cm-8x14in) s. W/C. 20-Jun-3 Keys, Aylsham #592

RACKUS, Richard (1922-) American
£1032 $1600 €1548 Path to the lake (64x76cm-25x30in) s. i.verso prov. 29-Oct-2 John Moran, Pasadena #768 est:2000-3000

RACLE, Paul (1932-) Swiss
£306 $446 €459 Figure (38x46cm-15x18in) s. 4-Jun-2 Germann, Zurich #819 (S.FR 700)
£306 $480 €459 Surrealist composition (100x70cm-39x28in) s.d.1986. 25-Nov-2 Germann, Zurich #791 (S.FR 700)
£352 $515 €528 Lake Thun (89x99cm-35x39in) s.d.1977 i. verso masonite. 17-Jun-2 Philippe Schuler, Zurich #7438 (S.FR 800)
£393 $617 €590 Surreal woman (116x90cm-46x35in) s.d.1976. 25-Nov-2 Germann, Zurich #793 (S.FR 900)
£396 $579 €594 Surreal composition (70x60cm-28x24in) s.d.1978 panel. 17-Jun-2 Philippe Schuler, Zurich #7439 (S.FR 900)
£437 $681 €656 Winter landscape with village (100x120cm-39x47in) s.d.85. 6-Nov-2 Dobiaschofsky, Bern #901/R (S.FR 1000)
£441 $643 €662 Surreal composition (119x85cm-47x33in) s.d.1976. 17-Jun-2 Philippe Schuler, Zurich #7437 (S.FR 1000)
£611 $893 €917 Mutantoskop (161x120cm-63x47in) s.d.1967. 4-Jun-2 Germann, Zurich #820 (S.FR 1400)

RACOFF, Rotislaw (1904-) Russian
£311 $500 €467 Bridge over cityscape (36x28cm-14x11in) s.d.64 masonite. 20-Jan-3 Schrager Galleries, Milwaukee #1126
£780 $1209 €1170 Barges at quay on the Seine (37x28cm-15x11in) s. d.1952 verso panel. 8-Dec-2 Uppsala Auktionskammare, Uppsala #197/R (S.KR 11000)

RACZYNSKI, Athanasius Graf von (attrib) (1788-1874) German
Works on paper
£411 $638 €650 Land surveyor studying map in landscape with ruins (26x32cm-10x13in) brush pen. 25-Sep-2 Neumeister, Munich #427/R

RADA, Vlastimil (1895-1962) Czechoslovakian
Works on paper
£454 $709 €681 Neighbourly conversation (27x36cm-11x14in) s.d. Indian ink dr W/C. 12-Oct-2 Dorotheum, Prague #273 (C.KR 22000)

RADCLYFFE, Charles Walter (1817-1903) British
£540 $853 €810 Maple Durham (74x51cm-29x20in) s. 17-Dec-2 Gorringes, Lewes #1419

RADDA, Madame (1891-1967) French
£449 $704 €700 Bowl with fruit and flowers (55x65cm-22x26in) s. 25-Nov-2 Glerum, Amsterdam #136

RADECKER, Antoon (1887-1960) Dutch
Sculpture
£2014 $3304 €2800 Abraham (34cm-13in) s. stone prov. 3-Jun-3 Christie's, Amsterdam #160/R est:1800-2200

RADECKER, John (1885-1956) Dutch
Sculpture
£10791 $17698 €15000 Mask (37cm-15in) init. bronze on wood base conceived c.1923-24. 3-Jun-3 Christie's, Amsterdam #161/R est:15000-20000

RADECKER, Max (1914-) Dutch
Works on paper
£1154 $1812 €1800 Port de la peche - La Rochelle (49x64cm-19x25in) s. gouache. 25-Nov-2 Glerum, Amsterdam #149/R est:650-850

RADEMACHER, Niels Gronbeck (1812-1885) Danish
£617 $901 €950 Extensive wooded landscape with small figures and animals (47x63cm-19x25in) mono. i.verso. 15-Jun-2 Hans Stahl, Hamburg #156/R
£8613 $13092 €12920 Portrait of Christian Ulrich Wedege Jensen, aged 3 1/2 (125x78cm-49x31in) with d.12 august 1854 i.verso. 27-Aug-2 Rasmussen, Copenhagen #1402/R est:100000 (D.KR 100000)

RADEMAKER, Abraham (1675-1735) Dutch
Works on paper
£449 $709 €700 Personnages a l'entree d'une grotte (13cm-5in circular) s. gouache. 18-Nov-2 Sotheby's, Paris #10/R
£4730 $7378 €7000 View of Dutch harbour (21x31cm-8x12in) s.i. chk pen ink pair. 27-Mar-3 Christie's, Paris #151/R

RADEMAKER, Hermanus Everhardus (1820-1885) Dutch
£1484 $2181 €2300 Extensive landscape with castle ruins (54x71cm-21x28in) s. bears d.18. 20-Jun-2 Dr Fritz Nagel, Stuttgart #815/R est:1300

RADERSCHEIDT, Anton (1892-1970) German
£769 $1192 €1200 Gereon church (51x65cm-20x26in) s.d.56 acrylic paper on board. 7-Dec-2 Van Ham, Cologne #429/R
£11348 $18383 €16000 Still life of flowers (28x19cm-11x7in) s.d. masonite exhib.lit. 24-May-3 Van Ham, Cologne #493/R est:18000

RADFORD, Edward (1831-1920) British
Works on paper
£400 $628 €600 Study of lady reading a book (29x21cm-11x8in) W/C over pencil. 21-Nov-2 Tennants, Leyburn #693
£1200 $1884 €1800 Nausicaa (41x26cm-16x10in) indi.s.d. W/C. 21-Nov-2 Tennants, Leyburn #692/R est:400-600

RADICE, Mario (1900-1987) Italian
£2979 $4826 €4200 A.N.F.G. (30x30cm-12x12in) s.i.d.20-3-1971. 26-May-3 Christie's, Milan #81/R est:3000-4000
£3205 $5032 €5000 M.I.L (20x30cm-8x12in) s. painted 1972. 23-Nov-2 Meeting Art, Vercelli #350/R
£7639 $12146 €11000 Geometry (80x70cm-31x28in) s. 1-May-3 Meeting Art, Vercelli #455 est:10000
£8163 $12980 €12000 P.R.O.G.4C.R.A. (59x59cm-23x23in) s. s.i.d.1974 verso. 1-Mar-3 Meeting Art, Vercelli #646

RADIMSKY, Vaclav (1867-1946) Czechoslovakian
£1091 $1734 €1637 Polabi landscape (47x72cm-19x28in) s. board. 8-Mar-3 Dorotheum, Prague #90/R est:50000-75000 (C.KR 50000)
£1300 $2015 €1950 Sunlit river landscape (51x70cm-20x28in) s. 5-Dec-2 Christie's, Kensington #37/R est:1500-2500
£1476 $2390 €2214 Winter in Elbe district (50x70cm-20x28in) s. board. 24-May-3 Dorotheum, Prague #72/R est:50000-75000 (C.KR 65000)
£3165 $5000 €5000 Soir orageux (66x97cm-26x38in) s. i. verso board. 27-Nov-2 Dorotheum, Vienna #138/R est:5500-7500
£3741 $5949 €5500 Paysage printanier (57x74cm-22x29in) s. 3-Mar-3 Claude Boisgirard, Paris #94/R est:3000-3500

RADL, Anton (1774-1852) German
Works on paper
£385 $604 €600 Schneidwall in Frankfut am Main (52x66cm-20x26in) gouache. 23-Nov-2 Arnold, Frankfurt #848

RADLER, Max (1904-1971) German
£4487 $6551 €7000 Untermuhle, Zeitz (60x70cm-24x28in) canvas on panel. 4-Jun-2 Karl & Faber, Munich #396/R est:13000-14000
£20000 $31200 €30000 Station SD/2 (84x64cm-33x25in) s.d.1933 s.i.d. prov.exhib. 9-Oct-2 Sotheby's, London #40/R est:15000-20000

RADZIWILL, Franz (1895-1983) German
£4167 $6458 €6500 Three heads - woman and two men wearing hats (41x49cm-16x19in) board on panel prov. 4-Dec-2 Lempertz, Koln #1018/R est:10000-15000
£5769 $8942 €9000 Interior with vase and jug (58x51cm-23x20in) board on panel prov. 4-Dec-2 Lempertz, Koln #1019/R est:10000-15000
£34810 $55000 €55000 Within 24 hours (85x91cm-33x36in) s. i.verso canvas on panel painted 1947 prov.exhib.lit. 29-Nov-2 Villa Grisebach, Berlin #60/R est:40000-60000

£86957 $142609 €120000 River landscape (77x100cm-30x39in) s.d.1934 canvas on panel prov.exhib.lit. 30-May-3 Villa Grisebach, Berlin #47/R est:1000-150000

Works on paper

£1266 $2000 €2000 Man's portrait (25x24cm-10x9in) mono. W/C Indian ink board. 30-Nov-2 Villa Grisebach, Berlin #294/R est:3000-4000
£1474 $2285 €2300 Still life with white jug and dish (10x15cm-4x6in) s.d. gouache. 7-Dec-2 Hauswedell & Nolte, Hamburg #1012/R est:3000
£4500 $6930 €6750 Femme au bouquet de fleurs (47x34cm-19x13in) init. W/C over pencil. 23-Oct-2 Sotheby's, Olympia #673/R est:5000-7000
£5449 $8446 €8500 Figures round table (37x49cm-15x19in) mono.d.23 W/C pencil. 4-Dec-2 Lempertz, Koln #1020/R est:8000-10000

RAE, Barbara (1943-) British

£600 $936 €900 Derelict glasshouse, Springburn (60x88cm-24x35in) s.d.85 acrylic collage card. 17-Oct-2 Bonhams, Edinburgh #107

Works on paper

£550 $853 €825 Creel box, Dornie Harbour (76x79cm-30x31in) mixed media. 4-Oct-2 Mallams, Oxford #540
£620 $967 €930 Summer, Istan (45x53cm-18x21in) s. mixed media. 17-Oct-2 Bonhams, Edinburgh #52

RAE, Fiona (1963-) British

£7500 $12000 €11250 Untitled - orange, pink and white (122x366cm-48x144in) painted 1995. 16-May-3 Phillips, New York #119/R est:8000-12000

RAE, Henrietta (1859-1928) British

£7500 $12075 €11250 Garland (38x34cm-15x13in) s. prov.exhib.lit. 20-Feb-3 Christie's, London #130/R
£15000 $24150 €22500 Bacchante (127x63cm-50x25in) s.d.1885 prov.exhib.lit. 20-Feb-3 Christie's, London #286/R est:30000

RAE, Iso (fl.1880-1920) Australian

£351 $533 €527 Portrait of a lady (64x53cm-25x21in) s. 19-Aug-2 Joel, Victoria #302 est:1000-1500 (A.D 1000)

RAE, John (1882-?) American

Works on paper

£244 $400 €354 Summer foliage (12x11cm-5x4in) s. W/C gouache. 5-Jun-3 Swann Galleries, New York #203/R

RAEBURN, Agnes (?-1955) British

£450 $738 €675 Blue pool (46x37cm-18x15in) s. panel. 5-Jun-3 Christie's, Kensington #672
£535 $850 €803 Fontain Bleau (36x46cm-14x18in) s. panel painted c.1910 exhib. 2-Mar-3 Toomey, Oak Park #593/R

RAEBURN, Sir Henry (1756-1823) British

£3500 $5810 €5250 Portrait of Dr Colin Lauder of Fountainhall (74x61cm-29x24in) 12-Jun-3 Sotheby's, London #74/R est:4000-6000
£5000 $8300 €7500 Portrait of Adam Rolland of Gask (88x68cm-35x27in) prov.lit. 12-Jun-3 Sotheby's, London #75/R est:5000-7000
£17284 $28000 €25926 Portrait of gentleman (92x71cm-36x28in) 23-Jan-3 Sotheby's, New York #208/R est:20000
£20000 $31800 €30000 Portrait of John Rennie (75x62cm-30x24in) prov. 20-Mar-3 Sotheby's, London #477/R est:15000-20000
£38000 $63080 €57000 Portrait of Commander Hugh Clapperton, wearing blue coat (75x62cm-30x24in) prov.lit. 12-Jun-3 Sotheby's, London #80/R est:20000-30000

RAEBURN, Sir Henry (attrib) (1756-1823) British

£2600 $4160 €3900 Portrait of John Grant (76x64cm-30x25in) 11-Mar-3 Gorringes, Lewes #2369/R est:1000-1500

RAEBURN, Sir Henry (circle) (1756-1823) British

£6500 $10335 €9750 Portrait of a gentleman in black coat and breeches (123x102cm-48x40in) i. 6-Mar-3 Christie's, Kensington #11/R est:3000-5000

RAEBURN, Sir Henry (style) (1756-1823) British

£12000 $18480 €18000 Portrait of two brothers in red costume, a wooded landscape beyond (76x63cm-30x25in) prov. 23-Oct-2 Hamptons Fine Art, Godalming #200/R est:2500-3500

RAEDECKER, Michael (1963-) American

£6013 $9500 €9020 Surface (66x81cm-26x32in) s.d.2000 oil acrylic thread yarn on canvas prov. 12-Nov-2 Phillips, New York #185/R est:10000-15000
£53125 $85000 €79688 Down (102x300cm-40x118in) s.i.d.2001 acrylic thread prov.exhib. 15-May-3 Christie's, Rockefeller NY #336/R est:40000-60000

RAEMDONCK, Dis van (1901-1971) Belgian

£705 $1107 €1100 Oude tjalk (85x100cm-33x39in) s. 16-Dec-2 Bernaerts, Antwerp #327/R

RAEMDONCK, George van (1888-1966) Dutch

£242 $384 €350 Horse in a field (70x112cm-28x44in) s. indis d. 10-Mar-3 Sotheby's, Amsterdam #313

RAETZ, Markus (1941-) Swiss

Works on paper

£1485 $2316 €2228 Intertwined snakes (15x23cm-6x9in) W/C. 8-Nov-2 Dobiaschofsky, Bern #279/R est:4500 (S.FR 3400)
£1747 $2742 €2621 Untitled (17x25cm-7x10in) mono.i. mixed media. 23-Nov-2 Burkhard, Luzern #234/R est:3500-4000 (S.FR 4000)
£2271 $3565 €3407 Untitled (21x29cm-8x11in) mono. pencil w/C. 23-Nov-2 Burkhard, Luzern #236/R est:4000-5000 (S.FR 5200)
£5895 $9255 €8843 Out of shape and flat (43x61cm-17x24in) mono. W/C paste. 23-Nov-2 Burkhard, Luzern #235/R est:7000-8000 (S.FR 13500)

RAFFAELLI, Jean François (1850-1924) French

£6294 $10510 €9000 Faubourgs Parisiens (31x39cm-12x15in) s. cardboard exhib. 25-Jun-3 Sotheby's, Paris #100/R est:6000-9000
£9000 $14130 €13500 Sur les quais (20x35cm-8x14in) s. panel. 19-Nov-2 Sotheby's, London #164/R est:4000-6000
£12658 $20000 €20000 Homme dans les champs (83x61cm-33x24in) s. cardboard on canvas. 27-Nov-2 Marc Kohn, Paris #5/R est:20000-25000
£12903 $20000 €19355 Le chiffonnier (23x9cm-9x4in) s. panel. 30-Oct-2 Christie's, Rockefeller NY #141/R est:25000-35000
£15000 $23550 €22500 Le chiffonier (55x38cm-22x15in) s.d.79 panel exhib. 19-Nov-2 Sotheby's, London #163/R est:15000-20000
£19444 $32083 €28000 L'apres-midi a la plage, la Panne, Belgique (54x81cm-21x32in) s. paper on canvas prov.exhib. 2-Jul-3 Artcurial Briest, Paris #634/R est:30000-40000

Works on paper

£5755 $9439 €8000 Le buveur d'absinthe (36x61cm-14x24in) s. mixed media varnish. 5-Jun-3 Fraysse & Associes, Paris #27/R est:6000-8000
£26923 $42269 €42000 Saint-Germain-des-Pres (69x79cm-27x31in) s. pastel on canvas. 13-Dec-2 Piasa, Paris #5/R

RAFFALT, Ignaz (1800-1857) Austrian

£3191 $5170 €4500 Courting of the hunters (36x50cm-14x20in) s.d.1840 panel. 22-May-3 Dorotheum, Vienna #20/R est:4500-5500

RAFFALT, Ignaz (attrib) (1800-1857) Austrian

£288 $453 €450 Village street at dusk (21x26cm-8x10in) panel. 21-Nov-2 Van Ham, Cologne #1873
£1361 $2163 €2000 Idyllic river landscape with figures (15x21cm-6x8in) 25-Feb-3 Dorotheum, Vienna #36/R est:2000-2500
£2064 $3220 €3096 House on the lakeside (21x37cm-8x15in) s. board. 11-Sep-2 Kieselbach, Budapest #57/R (H.F 800000)

RAFFET, Auguste-Marie (1804-1860) French

£1773 $2961 €2500 Etude d'armures (27x29cm-11x11in) st.verso paper on canvas. 23-Jun-3 Beaussant & Lefèvre, Paris #320/R est:2500-3000

Works on paper

£340 $557 €520 Elegantes sevillanes (35x25cm-14x10in) i. W/C gouache over crayon prov. 7-Feb-3 Piasa, Paris #174
£664 $950 €996 Gypsy woman (31x30cm-12x12in) i. pastel. 22-Jan-3 Doyle, New York #59
£1419 $2200 €2129 Two studies of an Albanian guardsman. Shop in Smyrna (18x24cm-7x9in) i. i.verso pencil W/C double-sided prov.exhib. 29-Oct-2 Sotheby's, New York #17/R est:600-800

RAFFIN, Andre (1927-) French

£411 $642 €650 Automne (54x65cm-21x26in) s.i.d.1984 verso. 20-Oct-2 Charbonneaux, Paris #152 est:500-600
£436 $702 €650 Le Havre vu de Villerville (54x65cm-21x26in) s. 23-Feb-3 Lesieur & Le Bars, Le Havre #131
£705 $1107 €1100 Plage de Villerville (54x65cm-21x26in) s. 24-Nov-2 Lesieur & Le Bars, Le Havre #146
£1115 $1784 €1550 Nice, le promenade des Anglais devant l'Hotel Negresco (75x92cm-30x36in) s. 18-May-3 Eric Pillon, Calais #247/R

Works on paper

£321 $503 €500 Apres le bain (48x64cm-19x25in) s.d. i.verso pastel. 16-Dec-2 Charbonneaux, Paris #188/R

RAFFLER, Max (1902-1988) German

Works on paper

£260 $379 €400 Woodland (33x24cm-13x9in) s. mixed media. 14-Jun-2 Auktionhaus Georg Rehm, Augsburg #8123/R
£299 $476 €440 Kloster Andechs (29x40cm-11x16in) s.i. w/C. 20-Mar-3 Neumeister, Munich #2511/R
£519 $774 €800 Children (40x29cm-16x11in) s. W/C over pencil. 27-Jun-2 Neumeister, Munich #2618

RAFFY LE PERSAN, Jean (1920-) French
£685 $1075 €1000 Joueurs de boules a la plage (22x30cm-9x12in) s.d.93 panel. 21-Apr-3 Rabourdin & Choppin de Janvry, Paris #203

RAFN, Christian (1740-1825) Danish
£861 $1309 €1292 Portrait of young noble lady (37x26cm-15x10in) s. panel. 27-Aug-2 Rasmussen, Copenhagen #1567/R (D.KR 10000)

RAFOLS CULLERES, Alberto (1892-) Spanish
Works on paper
£270 $437 €410 Girl in the field (19x24cm-7x9in) s.i. col dr. 21-Jan-3 Ansorena, Madrid #803/R

RAFTERY, Ted (1938-) Canadian
£244 $401 €354 Wet snow (41x51cm-16x20in) 1-Jun-3 Levis, Calgary #110/R (C.D 550)
£543 $848 €906 Turnbull Creek Lake, Bragg Creek (61x76cm-24x30in) s. s.i.d.1980 verso prov. 13-Apr-3 Levis, Calgary #98/R est:1500-2000 (C.D 1250)
£622 $1020 €902 Peyto Lake (45x60cm-18x24in) s.i.d.1991. 9-Jun-3 Hodgins, Calgary #365/R est:1000-1400 (C.D 1400)
£723 $1142 €1085 Home farm (61x91cm-24x36in) d.1984. 1-Dec-2 Levis, Calgary #80/R est:1500-2000 (C.D 1800)
£763 $1198 €1145 Alpine zone, Peyto Glacier (60x90cm-24x35in) s.i.d.1985. 25-Nov-2 Hodgins, Calgary #329/R est:2000-2500 (C.D 1900)
£803 $1261 €1205 Fog bank, Smith-Dorrien Trail (60x90cm-24x35in) s.i.d.1985. 25-Nov-2 Hodgins, Calgary #44/R est:2000-2500 (C.D 2000)

RAGGI, Antonio (elder-circle) (1624-1686) Italian
Sculpture
£9259 $15000 €13889 Charity (35cm-14in) terracotta exec.c.1653 lit. 23-Jan-3 Sotheby's, New York #177/R est:20000

RAGGIO, Giuseppe (1823-1916) Italian
£1411 $2300 €2117 Herd at dusk (63x100cm-25x39in) s.d.1869 prov. 12-Feb-3 Iegor de Saint Hippolyte, Montreal #152/R (C.D 3500)
£1532 $2498 €2298 Return of the herd (63x100cm-25x39in) prov. 12-Feb-3 Iegor de Saint Hippolyte, Montreal #153 (C.D 3800)

RAGIONE, Raffaele (1851-1925) Italian
£2885 $4529 €4500 Elegantes, Avenue du Bois (14x22cm-6x9in) s. cardboard. 16-Dec-2 Rabourdin & Choppin de Janvry, Paris #101/R
£4430 $7000 €7000 Paris, women at Parc Monceau (19x24cm-7x9in) s. 26-Nov-2 Christie's, Rome #158/R est:9000
£4717 $7264 €7500 Mother and daughter at Monceau Park (34x29cm-13x11in) s. cardboard. 23-Oct-2 Finarte, Milan #45/R est:7000-9000
£7742 $12232 €12000 Games in the park (22x31cm-9x12in) s. cardboard. 18-Dec-2 Finarte, Milan #7/R est:14000

RAGIONE, Raffaele (attrib) (1851-1925) Italian
£3797 $6000 €6000 Girls at Parc Monceau (25x37cm-10x15in) s. canvas on cardboard. 26-Nov-2 Christie's, Rome #159/R

RAGLESS, Maxwell Richard (1901-1981) Australian
£350 $546 €525 Road in Northern Territory (61x76cm-24x30in) s. board. 10-Apr-3 Tennants, Leyburn #1133
£391 $599 €587 Country town (51x76cm-20x30in) s. board painted c.1970. 26-Aug-2 Sotheby's, Paddington #634 est:1000-2000 (A.D 1100)
£854 $1307 €1281 Mount Rose, Central Australia (49x91cm-19x36in) s. board painted c.1961 prov. 26-Aug-2 Sotheby's, Paddington #622 est:1000-2000 (A.D 2400)

RAGN-JENSEN, Leif (1911-1993) Danish
£279 $444 €419 Vindrossel (16x26cm-6x10in) s.d.1975. 10-Mar-3 Rasmussen, Vejle #549 (D.KR 3000)
£298 $474 €447 Landscape with birds in flight (30x46cm-12x18in) s. 10-Mar-3 Rasmussen, Vejle #551 (D.KR 3200)
£372 $592 €558 Swans in flight (32x45cm-13x18in) s.d.1949. 10-Mar-3 Rasmussen, Vejle #550 (D.KR 4000)
£372 $592 €558 Pair of pheasants (26x31cm-10x12in) s.d.1976. 10-Mar-3 Rasmussen, Vejle #552 (D.KR 4000)
£403 $629 €605 Winter landscape with pheasants (30x45cm-12x18in) s.d.1972. 11-Nov-2 Rasmussen, Vejle #490 (D.KR 4700)
£472 $736 €708 Autumn landscape (30x45cm-12x18in) s.i.d.1973. 11-Nov-2 Rasmussen, Vejle #491 (D.KR 5500)
£482 $771 €723 Landscape with mallards in flight (30x50cm-12x20in) s.d.1976. 13-Jan-3 Rasmussen, Vejle #36/R (D.KR 5500)
£701 $1121 €1052 Landscape with partridge (30x50cm-12x20in) s.d.1976. 13-Jan-3 Rasmussen, Vejle #34/R (D.KR 8000)
£701 $1121 €1052 Landscape with pheasants (30x50cm-12x20in) s.d.1976. 13-Jan-3 Rasmussen, Vejle #35/R (D.KR 8000)

RAGOT, Andre (1894-?) French
Works on paper
£272 $433 €400 Village sur la route d'Hebron (35x51cm-14x20in) s. i.verso W/C. 24-Mar-3 Rabourdin & Choppin de Janvry, Paris #39
£272 $433 €400 Beyrouth vue de Ramleh (33x49cm-13x19in) s. i.verso W/C. 24-Mar-3 Rabourdin & Choppin de Janvry, Paris #40/R
£272 $433 €400 Beyrouth le Djebel sanin (32x49cm-13x19in) s. i.verso W/C. 24-Mar-3 Rabourdin & Choppin de Janvry, Paris #43
£408 $649 €600 Route de Djedeide (27x41cm 11x16in) s. i.verso W/C. 24-Mar-3 Rabourdin & Choppin de Janvry, Paris #44
£476 $757 €700 Les teinturiers de Kachan (27x40cm-11x16in) s. i.verso wax crayon W/C. 24-Mar-3 Rabourdin & Choppin de Janvry, Paris #37/R

RAGOT, Jules (19th C) French
£360 $576 €500 Nature morte aux fleurs et aux fruits (74x107cm-29x42in) s. 13-May-3 Vanderkindere, Brussels #250
£475 $741 €750 Bouquet de lys sur un entablement (60x40cm-24x16in) s. painted c.1900. 15-Oct-2 Vanderkindere, Brussels #117
£478 $750 €717 Still life with roses (41x27cm-16x11in) s. canvasboard. 22-Nov-2 Skinner, Boston #51/R
£538 $834 €850 Nature morte aux roses (100x65cm-39x26in) s. 24-Sep-2 Galerie Moderne, Brussels #840
£1020 $1622 €1500 Trophee de chasse (100x60cm-39x24in) s. pair. 18-Mar-3 Galerie Moderne, Brussels #271 est:1500-2000
£1099 $1550 €1649 Flower arrangement (58x38cm-23x15in) s. board. 12-Feb-2 Lincoln, Orange #485
£4000 $6360 €6000 Le vendeur des journaux (121x76cm-48x30in) s. 20-Mar-3 Christie's, Kensington #129/R est:4000-6000

RAHLEJEV, Marie de (20th C) Russian
£270 $422 €400 House on the Volga (65x80cm-26x31in) s. 26-Mar-3 Hugo Ruef, Munich #314/R

RAHM, Johannes (20th C) Swiss?
£1310 $2044 €1965 Schaffhausen (46x27cm-18x11in) s. board. 20-Nov-2 Fischer, Luzern #1292/R est:3000-4000 (S.FR 3000)

RAHN, Johann Caspar (1769-1840) Swiss
£429 $678 €644 View of Glarner Alps from small Linthal (55x77cm-22x30in) s. 29-Nov-2 Zofingen, Switzerland #2357 (S.FR 1000)
£1528 $2400 €2292 Bridge over gorge (48x67cm-19x26in) s.d.1806. 25-Nov-2 Sotheby's, Zurich #12/R est:4000-6000 (S.FR 3500)
£2838 $4456 €4257 Two peasants on lakeshore (54x76cm-21x30in) s. 25-Nov-2 Sotheby's, Zurich #13/R est:7000-9000 (S.FR 6500)

RAHON, Alice (1916-1987) French
£6849 $10753 €10000 Paysage esquimau (33x41cm-13x16in) s.i. s.i.d.1945 verso prov. 15-Apr-3 Laurence Calmels, Paris #4397/R est:2500
£10191 $16000 €15287 Canaries (76x57cm-30x22in) s.d.46 oil sand. 20-Nov-2 Christie's, Rockefeller NY #85/R est:15000-20000
Works on paper
£1134 $1768 €1701 Sin titulo (31x43cm-12x17in) s. mixed media wood. 17-Oct-2 Louis Morton, Mexico #158/R est:18000-20000 (M.P 18000)
£4110 $6452 €6000 Femme qui neige (25x20cm-10x8in) s.d.45 s.i.d.verso mixed media canvas on cardboard. 15-Apr-3 Laurence Calmels, Paris #4398/R est:2000

RAILLARD, Jacques (c.1692-1754) French
£516 $815 €800 Portrait de Charles Cesar Poirier (55x45cm-22x18in) 18-Dec-2 Piasa, Paris #86

RAILTON, Frederick John (fl.1846-1866) British
£800 $1248 €1200 Woodland scenes with figures (23x50cm-9x20in) s. 17-Sep-2 Sotheby's, Olympia #164/R

RAIMONDI, Aldo (1902-1998) Italian
Works on paper
£353 $554 €550 Little calf (17x22cm-7x9in) s. W/C. 19-Nov-2 Finarte, Milan #23
£472 $731 €750 Little donkey (50x70cm-20x28in) s.d.1959 W/C. 29-Oct-2 Finarte, Milan #412
£710 $1121 €1100 Farm (44x64cm-17x25in) s.d.1952 W/C. 18-Dec-2 Finarte, Milan #41
£1154 $1788 €1800 Cows in the stable (37x53cm-15x21in) s. W/C. 4-Dec-2 Finarte, Rome #710/R
£1282 $2013 €2000 Milan in the 19th Century (49x34cm-19x13in) s.i. W/C card. 19-Nov-2 Finarte, Milan #111/R
£1634 $2614 €2500 Stable (70x98cm-28x39in) s.d.1957 W/C card. 4-Jan-3 Meeting Art, Vercelli #215
£1667 $2583 €2600 Horses (49x69cm-19x27in) s.d.1945 W/C. 4-Dec-2 Finarte, Rome #705/R
£1923 $3019 €3000 Spring flowers (100x70cm-39x28in) s.d.1964 W/C paper on card. 23-Nov-2 Meeting Art, Vercelli #470/R

RAIMONDI, Marcantonio (c.1480-c.1527) Italian
Prints
£3205 $5000 €4808 Climbers (26x23cm-10x9in) engraving. 6-Nov-2 Swann Galleries, New York #44/R est:2500-3500
Works on paper
£3716 $5797 €5500 Hercules between Vice and Virtue (17x18cm-7x7in) chk pen ink prov.lit. 27-Mar-3 Christie's, Paris #53/R
£4500 $7515 €6525 Flying angel, after Rapheal. Mountainous landscape beyond (11x19cm-4x7in) pen ink sd. prov. 8-Jul-3 Christie's, London #5/R est:4000-6000

RAIMONDI, Marcantonio (attrib) (c.1480-c.1527) Italian
Works on paper
£9355 $14500 €14033 Sculpture of a female figure (20x10cm-8x4in) brown ink exhib. 2-Nov-2 North East Auctions, Portsmouth #108/R est:12000-18000

RAIMONDI, Roberto (1877-1961) Italian
Works on paper
£506 $800 €800 Rome, Fabricio Bridge (48x68cm-19x27in) s. W/C card. 26-Nov-2 Christie's, Rome #63
£745 $1200 €1118 Interior genre scene with cardinals (51x74cm-20x29in) s. 19-Jan-3 Jeffery Burchard, Florida #71a/R
£1156 $1918 €1676 Eternal gallant. Interesting lecture (56x38cm-22x15in) s.i. W/C pair. 16-Jun-3 Waddingtons, Toronto #326/R est:2000-3000 (C.D 2600)

RAINBIRD, Victor Noble (1889-1936) British
Works on paper
£144 $222 €216 Ashore on the French coast (26x38cm-10x15in) W/C. 26-Oct-2 Heffel, Vancouver #37 (C.D 350)
£144 $222 €216 Madonna and Child (37x25cm-15x10in) W/C. 26-Oct-2 Heffel, Vancouver #38 (C.D 350)
£144 $222 €216 Morning in the bay (27x39cm-11x15in) W/C. 26-Oct-2 Heffel, Vancouver #39 (C.D 350)
£144 $222 €216 Newbiggin, Northumberland (25x37cm-10x15in) W/C. 26-Oct-2 Heffel, Vancouver #40 (C.D 350)
£144 $222 €216 On the Tyne from harbour view (26x38cm-10x15in) W/C. 26-Oct-2 Heffel, Vancouver #41 (C.D 350)
£144 $222 €216 People at Cullercoats Bay (27x38cm-11x15in) W/C. 26-Oct-2 Heffel, Vancouver #42 (C.D 350)
£195 $301 €293 Harbour mouth, North Shields (16x25cm-6x10in) W/C. 26-Oct-2 Heffel, Vancouver #44 (C.D 475)
£226 $348 €339 Tyne from North Shields (18x25cm-7x10in) W/C. 26-Oct-2 Heffel, Vancouver #45 (C.D 550)
£250 $418 €363 Old Evreux (26x16cm-10x6in) s.i. W/C. 17-Jun-3 Anderson & Garland, Newcastle #226
£260 $403 €390 View of Dutch girls coming from boats (17x27cm-7x11in) s. W/C. 3-Dec-2 Sworder & Son, Bishops Stortford #968/R
£280 $456 €420 French flower seller (35x21cm-14x8in) pencil W/C. 13-Feb-3 Mellors & Kirk, Nottingham #769
£300 $489 €450 French fisherfolk (34x23cm-13x9in) s.i. pencil W/C htd white. 13-Feb-3 Mellors & Kirk, Nottingham #768/R
£300 $501 €435 La grosse horloge Rouen (35x24cm-14x9in) s.i. W/C. 17-Jun-3 Anderson & Garland, Newcastle #228/R
£320 $534 €464 Figures seated in the sunshine outside a cafe (37x26cm-15x10in) s. W/C. 17-Jun-3 Anderson & Garland, Newcastle #224
£320 $534 €464 Evreux (25x16cm-10x6in) s.i. W/C. 17-Jun-3 Anderson & Garland, Newcastle #227
£330 $511 €495 Urban Dutch canal scene (19x34cm-7x13in) s. W/C. 24-Sep-2 Anderson & Garland, Newcastle #282/R
£340 $527 €510 Autumn, Belgium (35x26cm-14x10in) s.i. W/C. 24-Sep-2 Anderson & Garland, Newcastle #280
£400 $620 €600 Beached sailing ship in the Durham coast (22x28cm-9x11in) s. W/C. 24-Sep-2 Anderson & Garland, Newcastle #285

RAINER, Arnulf (1929-) Austrian
£1064 $1723 €1500 Fight in the cellar (18x24cm-7x9in) i. oil chk pencil on photo prov. 20-May-3 Dorotheum, Vienna #237/R est:1500-1700
£1250 $1988 €1800 Ferner Rauch (20x27cm-8x11in) s.i. oil photo aluminum prov. 29-Apr-3 Artcurial Briest, Paris #517/R est:1200-1500
£2174 $3565 €3000 Untitled (34x25cm-13x10in) s. overpainting paper on board. 28-May-3 Lempertz, Koln #352/R est:2900
£2536 $4159 €3500 Untitled (31x44cm-12x17in) s. col oil chks pencil transparent foil. 31-May-3 Villa Grisebach, Berlin #341/R est:3500
£2734 $4374 €3800 Mexico - over painting (52x45cm-20x18in) s.i.d. oil chk Indian ink wash over photo. 15-May-3 Neumeister, Munich #510/R est:3500-4000
£3797 $6000 €6000 Body painting (59x50cm-23x20in) s.i.d.71 s.i. verso oil chk pencil on photo. 27-Nov-2 Dorotheum, Vienna #92/R est:6000-9000
£5674 $9191 €8000 Ludwig Uhland, death mask series (60x50cm-24x20in) mono. oil chk scratching on photo. 20-May-3 Dorotheum, Vienna #242/R est:10000-13000
£5696 $9000 €9000 Hour - distress (29x42cm-11x17in) bears s.i.d.68 oil oil chk graphite on ultraphan. 27-Nov-2 Dorotheum, Vienna #87/R est:9000-10000
£6329 $9810 €10000 Hirschkafer (60x50cm-24x20in) s.i. oil mixed media on photograph exhib. 24-Sep-2 Wiener Kunst Auktionen, Vienna #238/R est:10000-15000
£6383 $10340 €9000 Composition (50x61cm-20x24in) s.i. oil chk oil on photo prov. 20-May-3 Dorotheum, Vienna #65/R est:10000-12000
£6383 $10340 €9000 Motherhood (60x46cm-24x18in) s.i. oil chk feltpen wash on photo. 20-May-3 Dorotheum, Vienna #66/R est:9000-11000
£7092 $11489 €10000 Van Gogh as (58x46cm-23x18in) mono.i. oil on photo prov. 20-May-3 Dorotheum, Vienna #75/R est:11000-13000
£12658 $19620 €20000 Eddy (49x69cm-19x27in) s.i.d.58 oil chk graphite Indian ink exhib. 24-Sep-2 Wiener Kunst Auktionen, Vienna #232/R est:18000-25000
£12658 $20000 €20000 Striped fly eater (92x65cm-36x26in) s.i.d.Feb 66 oil chk graphite on offset lithograph. 27-Nov-2 Dorotheum, Vienna #73/R est:20000-28000
£13462 $21135 €21000 Finger painting (73x51cm-29x20in) s. cardboard on board painted 1984. 21-Nov-2 Finarte, Rome #319/R est:20000-22000
£22152 $34335 €35000 Vertical object (70x100cm-28x39in) s.d.52 oil chk board. 24-Sep-2 Wiener Kunst Auktionen, Vienna #221/R est:35000-50000
£31915 $51702 €45000 Green on white (49x99cm-19x39in) prov. 20-May-3 Dorotheum, Vienna #50/R est:45000-70000
£33333 $54667 €46000 Untitled (56x65cm-22x26in) s. s.d. stretcher prov.exhib. 30-May-3 Villa Grisebach, Berlin #71/R est:10000-12000
Works on paper
£1203 $1900 €1900 Berlin concert (18x24cm-7x9in) s.mono. wax chk Indian ink graphite on photo. 27-Nov-2 Dorotheum, Vienna #247/R est:1900-2400
£1348 $2183 €1900 Berlin concert (18x24cm-7x9in) s.mono. wax chk Indian ink graphite on photo. 20-May-3 Dorotheum, Vienna #241/R est:1900-2400
£2695 $4366 €3800 Sitting position (18x23cm-7x9in) mono.i. mixed media on photo prov. 20-May-3 Dorotheum, Vienna #234/R est:2200-2800
£2885 $4471 €4500 Untitled (61x51cm-24x20in) s. gouache oil wax crayon photograph exec.1980. 7-Dec-2 Van Ham, Cologne #430/R est:5000
£3797 $6000 €6000 Composition (43x61cm-17x24in) s.d.52 pencil exhib. 27-Nov-2 Dorotheum, Vienna #227/R est:6500-9000
£5380 $8500 €8500 Zig-zag profile (42x30cm-17x12in) s.i. oil chk pencil board. 27-Nov-2 Dorotheum, Vienna #105/R est:8000-9000
£44304 $68671 €70000 My world with twenty (76x105cm-30x41in) s.d.1950 pencil transparent paper exhib. 24-Sep-2 Wiener Kunst Auktionen, Vienna #218/R est:60000-120000

RAINER, P (?) ?
£305 $433 €458 Cherubs (38x49cm-15x19in) s.d.1850 prov. 21-Nov-1 Watson's, Christchurch #63/R (NZ.D 1050)

RAINEY, William (1852-1936) British
Works on paper
£550 $864 €825 Dutch woman and boy (33x43cm-13x17in) i.verso W/C. 10-Dec-2 Rosebery Fine Art, London #721/R

RAISHO, Nakajima (1796-1871) Japanese
Works on paper
£506 $800 €800 Untitled. ink paper on kakemono. 29-Nov-2 Tajan, Paris #111

RAITTILA, Tapani (1921-) Finnish
£453 $697 €720 Southern landscape (29x39cm-11x15in) s.i.d.1958. 27-Oct-2 Bukowskis, Helsinki #260/R
Works on paper
£475 $779 €660 The doll (31x34cm-12x13in) s.d.1968 mixed media. 4-Jun-3 Bukowskis, Helsinki #398/R

RAJLICH, Thomas (1940-) Czechoslovakian
Works on paper
£3237 $5309 €4500 Untitled (105x95cm-41x37in) s.d.85 verso pencil oil on canvas prov. 3-Jun-3 Christie's, Amsterdam #371/R est:3000-5000

RAKOCZI, Basil (1908-1979) British
Works on paper
£900 $1422 €1305 Horsemen (40x53cm-16x21in) s. gouache. 28-Jul-3 David Duggleby, Scarborough #215/R
£1800 $2880 €2700 On the beach (48x58cm-19x23in) s. pen brush black ink W/C. 15-May-3 Christie's, Kensington #222/R est:500-700

RAKOWSKI, Mecislas de (1887-1947) Belgian
£318 $497 €500 Namur, vu de la citadelle (27x35cm-11x14in) s.d.1938 panel. 11-Nov-2 Horta, Bruxelles #517
£345 $545 €500 Mirage de barques (60x40cm-24x16in) s. 2-Apr-3 Vanderkindere, Brussels #529/R
£350 $546 €550 Peniches a quai (27x35cm-11x14in) s.d.1934 panel. 11-Nov-2 Horta, Bruxelles #516
£690 $1090 €1000 Le port d'Ostende (33x24cm-13x9in) s.d.1924 panel pair. 2-Apr-3 Vanderkindere, Brussels #543
£1329 $2073 €2100 Peniches au port de Bruxelles (55x65cm-22x26in) s.d.1938. 15-Oct-2 Horta, Bruxelles #43

RALEIGH, Charles Sidney (1830-1925) American
£10510 $16500 €15765 Portrait of American bark Western Belle (66x91cm-26x36in) s.d.1887. 22-Nov-2 Eldred, East Dennis #846a/R est:15000-18000

RALLI, Theodore Jacques (1852-1909) Greek
£10000 $15800 €15000 Mosque entrance (30x26cm-12x10in) 1-Apr-3 Bonhams, New Bond Street #16 est:10000-15000
£10500 $16275 €15750 After the bath (31cm-12in circular) s.d.80 vellum. 2-Oct-2 Sotheby's, London #4/R est:6000-8000
£32911 $52000 €52000 Oriental woman in a dream (142x112cm-56x44in) s. lit. 29-Nov-2 Schloss Ahlden, Ahlden #1362/R est:28000
£95000 $147250 €142500 After the service (66x100cm-26x39in) s. prov. 2-Oct-2 Sotheby's, London #15a/R est:60000-80000
Works on paper
£1079 $1770 €1500 A la fontaine (59x37cm-23x15in) s. W/C. 5-Jun-3 Fraysse & Associes, Paris #26 est:1000-1200

RAMAH, Henri (1887-1947) Belgian
£966 $1545 €1400 Christ jaune (92x70cm-36x28in) prov.exhib.lit. 15-Mar-3 De Vuyst, Lokeren #266/R
£2276 $3641 €3300 Portrait of Mister Furnemont (125x112cm-49x44in) s.d.1925 prov.exhib.lit. 15-Mar-3 De Vuyst, Lokeren #264/R est:3800-4400

RAMASSO, Marco (1964-) Italian
£980 $1569 €1500 Hope messenger (40x50cm-16x20in) s. lit. 4-Jan-3 Meeting Art, Vercelli #709

RAMBERG, Arthur von (1819-1875) Austrian
£1218 $1912 €1900 Country boys (77x117cm-30x46in) s.i. 22-Nov-2 Karrenbauer, Konstanz #1860 est:1900
£2293 $3531 €3600 Portrait of boy in summer landscape (151x100cm-59x39in) s.d.1868. 5-Sep-2 Arnold, Frankfurt #844/R est:2000
£2813 $4500 €4220 Grandfather's labour of love (76x62cm-30x24in) s. 14-May-3 Butterfields, San Francisco #1086/R est:3000-5000

RAMBERG, August (19/20th C) ?
£479 $753 €700 Passenger ship, AMS Traun in front of Durnstein (65x90cm-26x35in) s.d.919. 16-Apr-3 Dorotheum, Salzburg #130/R

RAMBERG, Johann Heinrich (1763-1840) German
Works on paper
£353 $557 €550 Actress dressed as Athene (31cm-12in circular) pen sepia wash htd white prov. 16-Nov-2 Lempertz, Koln #1272

RAMBERG, Ulf (1935-) Swedish
£1977 $3124 €2966 Painting number 9 (60x218cm-24x86in) mono.d.december 61-februari 62 verso triptych lit. 28-Apr-3 Bukowskis, Stockholm #922/R est:14000-16000 (S.KR 26000)
Works on paper
£608 $961 €912 Hugskott - erotic fantasy (23x78cm-9x31in) s.verso W/C three in one frame executed 1965-66. 28-Apr-3 Bukowskis, Stockholm #923/R (S.KR 8000)
£1472 $2296 €2208 During the 3rd World War (152x86cm-60x34in) mixed media collage exhib.lit. 5-Nov-2 Bukowskis, Stockholm #342/R est:35000-40000 (S.KR 21000)

RAMBO, Jules (20th C) Belgian
£822 $1282 €1200 Compositions florales (39x48cm-15x19in) s. three. 14-Apr-3 Horta, Bruxelles #458
£3767 $5877 €5500 Songerie (66x86cm-26x34in) s.d.1925. 14-Apr-3 Horta, Bruxelles #452 est:1200-1400

RAMBOUX, Johann Anton Alban (attrib) (1790-1866) German
£374 $595 €550 Christ porte au tombeau (40x32cm-16x13in) 28-Feb-3 Beaussant & Lefèvre, Paris #36

RAMENGHI, Bartolomeo (elder-attrib) (1484-1542) Italian
£2778 $4500 €4167 Pentecost (23x43cm-9x17in) i. paper prov. 21-Jan-3 Sotheby's, New York #31/R est:7000
£39419 $61493 €58340 Saint Catherine's marriage (92x75cm-36x30in) panel. 26-Mar-3 Tajan, Paris #6/R
Works on paper
£7407 $12000 €11111 Holy Family (30x22cm-12x9in) chk htd white. 21-Jan-3 Sotheby's, New York #26/R est:15000

RAMENGHI, Bartolomeo (elder-style) (1484-1542) Italian
£5500 $9185 €7975 The Holy Family with Saint Catherine (60x47cm-24x19in) panel. 8-Jul-3 Sotheby's, Olympia #310/R est:6000-8000

RAMEY, Claude (1754-1838) French
Sculpture
£3846 $5962 €6000 Portrait de Demartinecourt (17x17cm-7x7in) d.1788 terracotta relief. 9-Dec-2 Raboudin & Choppin de Janvry, Paris #109/R

RAMIREZ, Martin (1895-1963) Mexican
Works on paper
£10494 $17000 €15741 Untitled - horse and rider (63x60cm-25x24in) crayon W/C prov.exhib. 27-Jan-3 Christie's, Rockefeller NY #16/R est:15000-25000
£37037 $60000 €55556 Untitled - double train (125x94cm-49x37in) bears d.Oct 1954 W/C graphite crayon collage. 27-Jan-3 Christie's, Rockefeller NY #13/R est:25000-35000
£49383 $80000 €74075 Alamentosa (204x88cm-80x35in) col pencil collage W/C executed c.1953 prov.exhib. 27-Jan-3 Christie's, Rockefeller NY #12/R est:55000-80000

RAMOS ARTAL, Manuel (1855-1900) Spanish
£566 $883 €900 Landscape with houses (22x41cm-9x16in) s. 17-Sep-2 Segre, Madrid #80/R
£609 $956 €950 Landscape in northern Spain (30x55cm-12x22in) s.d.1889. 21-Nov-2 Van Ham, Cologne #1451/R
£710 $1121 €1100 Landscape with river (31x18cm-12x7in) s. board. 17-Dec-2 Segre, Madrid #37/R
£769 $1215 €1200 Landscape (19x40cm-7x16in) s.d.1901 board. 19-Nov-2 Durán, Madrid #154/R
£1218 $1924 €1900 Train (20x40cm-8x16in) s. board. 19-Nov-2 Durán, Madrid #153/R
£2083 $3292 €3250 Landscapes (30x15cm-12x6in) s.d.1887 board pair. 14-Nov-2 Arte, Seville #340/R

RAMOS, Maximo (1880-1944) Spanish?
Works on paper
£597 $920 €950 Poet (37x21cm-15x8in) s. ink dr. 22-Oct-2 Durán, Madrid #680/R

RAMOS, Mel (1935-) American
£58228 $92000 €87342 Peek-a-boo, platinum no.2 (112x81cm-44x32in) s.i.d.1964 acrylic prov.lit. 14-Nov-2 Christie's, Rockefeller NY #146/R est:40000-60000
£68750 $110000 €103125 Camilla 2 (182x130cm-72x51in) s. painted 1963 prov.exhib.lit. 14-May-3 Christie's, Rockefeller NY #20/R est:100000-150000
£106250 $170000 €159375 Ketsup Kween (152x120cm-60x47in) s.i.d.1965 prov.exhib.lit. 15-May-3 Christie's, Rockefeller NY #125/R est:100000-150000
Works on paper
£3097 $4893 €4800 Nude and antilope (33x43cm-13x17in) s.d.70 pencil prov. 18-Dec-2 Christie's, Rome #116/R

RAMOSA, E (20th C) Italian
Sculpture
£1419 $2243 €2200 Rainbow (45x45x45cm-18x18x18in) s.d.1970 plexiglas0. 18-Dec-2 Christie's, Rome #197/R

RAMPASO, Luciano (1934-) Italian
£253 $400 €380 Marchande de fleurs (51x61cm-20x24in) s.i. 2-Apr-3 Doyle, New York #58/R
£316 $500 €474 Salute (38x56cm-15x22in) s. 2-Apr-3 Doyle, New York #57/R
£417 $650 €626 Venice, fin de jour (38x56cm-15x22in) s. s.i.verso. 9-Oct-2 Doyle, New York #84
£457 $750 €686 Boulevard St. Michel (46x33cm-18x13in) s. s.i.on overlap. 5-Feb-3 Doyle, New York #79/R
£497 $800 €746 Madeleine (51x61cm-20x24in) s. s.i.verso. 19-Feb-3 Doyle, New York #57
£732 $1200 €1098 Montmartre- place de Tertre (61x51cm-24x20in) s. s.i.on overlap. 5-Feb-3 Doyle, New York #80/R est:800-1200
£1173 $1900 €1701 Grand Canal (51x61cm-20x24in) s. 21-May-3 Doyle, New York #257/R est:2500-3500

RAMPIN, Saverio (1930-) Italian
£443 $691 €700 Natural moment (60x50cm-24x20in) s.d.1958. 19-Oct-2 Semenzato, Venice #42/R
£1139 $1777 €1800 Natural moments (80x60cm-31x24in) s.i.d.1957. 19-Oct-2 Semenzato, Venice #112/R

RAMSAY, Allan (1713-1784) British
£58000 $96280 €87000 Portrait of John Prideaux Basset, in pink van Dyck dress, whippet at his side (151x98cm-59x39in) s. prov.lit. 10-Jun-3 Christie's, London #34/R est:50000-80000

RAMSAY, Allan (fl.1880-1920) British
£680 $1061 €1020 Waterhead, Glen Lethnot (35x52cm-14x20in) s.d.1901 s.i.verso. 17-Oct-2 Bonhams, Edinburgh #251

RAMSAY, Dennis (1925-) British
£323 $500 €485 Higher the plum tree, the richer the plum (25x20cm-10x8in) s.i. masonite. 28-Sep-2 Charlton Hall, Columbia #535
£326 $515 €473 Red wine and lemons (29x21cm-11x8in) s.d.MVIM board. 18-Nov-2 Goodman, Sydney #93 (A.D 910)
£3077 $4892 €4616 Still life with lilium (70x91cm-28x36in) s.d. i.d.4/7/99 verso oil tempera board exhib. 4-Mar-3 Deutscher-Menzies, Melbourne #130/R est:9000-12000 (A.D 8000)

RAMSAY, Hugh (1877-1906) Australian
£11494 $17126 €17241 Young girl in hat with fan (33x23cm-13x9in) mono. s.verso prov.lit. 27-Aug-2 Christie's, Melbourne #48/R est:30000-40000 (A.D 30000)

RAMSAY, James (1786-1854) British
£1235 $1901 €1853 Caroline 7 1/2, Ellen 5 1/2 (44x36cm-17x14in) 26-Oct-2 Heffel, Vancouver #47 est:2000-3000 (C.D 3000)
£1500 $2445 €2250 Portrait of the Hon. Master Henry Clifford (46x36cm-18x14in) i.d.August 1 1833 verso board. 29-Jan-3 Dreweatt Neate, Newbury #172 est:1800-2200

RAMSDELL, Fred Winthrop (1865-1915) American
£260 $400 €390 Fish beach, Monhegan Island Maine (20x25cm-8x10in) s. board. 27-Oct-2 Grogan, Boston #64

RAMSEY, Milne (1847-1915) American
£1006 $1600 €1509 Summer landscape with figure (23x33cm-9x13in) s. 7-Mar-3 Jackson's, Cedar Falls #622/R est:2500-4500
£4375 $7000 €6563 Still life of a bottle of wine, goblets and fruit (58x48cm-23x19in) s. 17-May-3 Pook & Pook, Downington #214/R est:8000-12000
£4545 $7000 €6818 Still life with wine glass and orange (30x41cm-12x16in) s.d.1865. 24-Oct-2 Shannon's, Milford #100/R est:6000-8000
Works on paper
£685 $1000 €1028 Clouds over salt flats (23x36cm-9x14in) W/C. 3-Nov-1 North East Auctions, Portsmouth #277

RAMUS, Aubrey (?) ?
£280 $448 €420 Cottage in a landscape (50x76cm-20x30in) s. 11-Mar-3 Bonhams, Knightsbridge #224
£300 $501 €435 Evening in the highlands (18x51cm-7x20in) s. board. 26-Jun-3 Mellors & Kirk, Nottingham #916
£500 $800 €750 Cattle watering in a highland landscape (50x75cm-20x30in) s. 7-Jan-3 Bonhams, Knightsbridge #228/R

RANCILLAC, Bernard (1931-) French
£5208 $8281 €7500 Stuff, Smith (89x116cm-35x46in) s.i.d.1917 verso acrylic. 29-Apr-3 Artcurial Briest, Paris #387/R est:8000-10000

RANCOULET, Ernest (19th C) French
Sculpture
£3797 $6000 €5696 Triumphator - two putti (107cm-42in) i. bronze. 24-Apr-3 Christie's, Rockefeller NY #331/R est:5000-7000

RANDALL, Asa Grant (1869-?) American
£791 $1250 €1187 Salisbury marshes (56x76cm-22x30in) board. 30-Nov-2 Thomaston Place, Thomaston #114

RANDELL, Friedrich (attrib) (1808-1886) German
£7042 $11338 €10000 Portrait of Prince Albrecht on horseback (57x45cm-22x18in) lit. 9-May-3 Schloss Ahlden, Ahlden #1361/R est:9500

RANDERSON, Glenda (?) ?
£654 $961 €981 Rag doll returned (64x49cm-25x19in) s. linen prov. 19-Jun-2 Watson's, Christchurch #64/R est:4500-7000 (NZ.D 2000)
£654 $961 €981 Gosho Ningyo III (49x30cm-19x12in) s.d.94 linen prov. 19-Jun-2 Watson's, Christchurch #65/R est:3500-5500 (NZ.D 2000)

RANDS, Angus Bernard (1922-1985) British
Works on paper
£300 $474 €450 Village street, East Keswick (36x53cm-14x21in) s. W/C. 24-Apr-3 Richardson & Smith, Whitby #4
£350 $550 €525 Royal pump room, Harrogate (49x71cm-19x28in) s. W/C. 19-Nov-2 Bonhams, Leeds #86

RANFT, Richard (1862-1931) Swiss
£282 $462 €409 Roman festivities (29x40cm-11x16in) s.d.1900 board. 4-Jun-3 Fischer, Luzern #2287/R (S.FR 600)
£524 $765 €786 Personaggi (27x34cm-11x13in) s. 4-Jun-2 Germann, Zurich #822 (S.FR 1200)
Works on paper
£387 $643 €550 Les tulipes a Hyde Park. Paysage (325x505cm-128x199in) s.i. pastel double-sided. 16-Jun-3 Oger, Dumont, Paris #10
£2695 $4501 €3800 Le bal (46x36cm-18x14in) s. pastel. 20-Jun-3 Rieunier, Paris #43/R est:1000

RANFTL, Johann Matthias (1805-1854) Austrian
£5975 $9261 €9500 Madonna with Infant Christ, St Mark Evangelista, Ursula and virgins (134x196cm-53x77in) prov. 2-Oct-2 Dorotheum, Vienna #398/R est:5500-7000

RANGER, Henry Ward (1858-1916) American
£2808 $4100 €4212 Under the bridge (30x36cm-12x14in) s. board. 3-Nov-1 North East Auctions, Portsmouth #271/R
£3185 $5000 €4778 Verdant landscape under cloudy skies (71x91cm-28x36in) s.d.1910 prov. 19-Nov-2 Butterfields, San Francisco #8044/R est:4000-6000
£3247 $5000 €4871 Forest in autumn (30x41cm-12x16in) s. board. 4-Sep-2 Christie's, Rockefeller NY #339/R est:2500-3500
£8696 $14000 €13044 Men building a stone wall in a pastoral Connecticut landscape (28x36cm-11x14in) s.indis.d.1900 prov. 18-Feb-3 John Moran, Pasadena #61 est:9000-12000

RANIERI, Robert (1930-) American
£494 $800 €741 Discovery of the goddess (152x135cm-60x53in) s.d.61. 24-Jan-3 New Orleans Auction, New Orleans #1065/R

RANK, William (20th C) American
£466 $750 €699 Ship theorem with an American flag (38x48cm-15x19in) s. velvet. 22-Feb-3 Pook & Pook, Downington #108/R

RANKEN, William Bruce Ellis (1881-1941) British
£500 $825 €725 Salon de la Paix, Versailles (76x53cm-30x21in) init.d.1927 s.i.verso board prov. 3-Jul-3 Christie's, Kensington #586

RANKIN, Andrew Scott (1868-1942) British
Works on paper
£798 $1300 €1197 Christmas wait (26x16cm-10x6in) s. W/C. 11-Feb-3 Bonhams & Doyles, New York #188/R est:800-1200

RANKIN, David (1946-) Australian
£321 $501 €482 Mildura landscape scrub (35x61cm-14x24in) s.d.85 i.verso. 11-Nov-2 Deutscher-Menzies, Melbourne #173/R (A.D 900)
£393 $613 €590 Blue landscape (65x52cm-26x20in) s.d.81 paper. 11-Nov-2 Deutscher-Menzies, Melbourne #170/R (A.D 1100)
£491 $747 €737 Children II (85x64cm-33x25in) i. s.d.75 verso acrylic. 19-Aug-2 Joel, Victoria #279 est:1500-2000 (A.D 1400)
£571 $891 €857 Landscape (67x52cm-26x20in) s.d.81 paper. 11-Nov-2 Deutscher-Menzies, Melbourne #171/R (A.D 1600)
£643 $1003 €965 Ritual at night I (60x44cm-24x17in) s.d.87 paper. 11-Nov-2 Deutscher-Menzies, Melbourne #182/R (A.D 1800)
£714 $1114 €1071 Ritual at night II (60x44cm-24x17in) s.d.87 paper. 11-Nov-2 Deutscher-Menzies, Melbourne #183/R (A.D 2000)
£928 $1448 €1392 Bay landscape (71x89cm-28x35in) s.d.84 i.verso composition board. 11-Nov-2 Deutscher-Menzies, Melbourne #115/R est:3000-4000 (A.D 2600)
£928 $1448 €1392 Lilli pilli (68x95cm-27x37in) s.i.d.67 i.d.1967-8 verso composition board. 11-Nov-2 Deutscher-Menzies, Melbourne #126/R est:3000-4000 (A.D 2600)
£956 $1568 €1434 Yellow hillside (76x91cm-30x36in) s.d.85 prov. 4-Jun-3 Deutscher-Menzies, Melbourne #359/R (A.D 2400)
£1286 $2031 €1929 Husband and wife (101x160cm-40x63in) s. i.d.95 verso triptych. 27-Nov-2 Deutscher-Menzies, Melbourne #137/R est:5000-8000 (A.D 3600)

£1423 $2178 €2135 Wall marking II (101x77cm-40x30in) s.d.95 prov. 25-Aug-2 Sotheby's, Paddington #112/R est:4000-6000 (A.D 4000)
£1423 $2178 €2135 Prophecy of dry bones (101x74cm-40x29in) s.d.94 i.verso prov. 25-Aug-2 Sotheby's, Paddington #229/R est:4000-6000 (A.D 4000)
£1714 $2674 €2571 Cottlesbridge ridge (91x76cm-36x30in) s.d.85 composition board. 11-Nov-2 Deutscher-Menzies, Melbourne #157/R est:3000-4000 (A.D 4800)
£1992 $3267 €2988 Light on the Judean hills II (91x121cm-36x48in) s.d.89 s.i.d.89 verso. 4-Jun-3 Deutscher-Menzies, Melbourne #358/R est:3500-5500 (A.D 5000)
£2135 $3267 €3203 Summer coast II (197x91cm-78x36in) s.d.94 i.verso prov. 25-Aug-2 Sotheby's, Paddington #230/R est:6000-8000 (A.D 6000)
£2135 $3267 €3203 Witness (138x198cm-54x78in) s.d.95 prov. 25-Aug-2 Sotheby's, Paddington #247/R est:6000-8000 (A.D 6000)
£2491 $3811 €3737 Golgotha (122x273cm-48x107in) s.d.1990 triptych panel. 25-Aug-2 Sotheby's, Paddington #161/R est:4000-6000 (A.D 7000)
£2847 $4356 €4271 Mungo nocturn (212x126cm-83x50in) s. s.i.d.88 verso prov. 25-Aug-2 Sotheby's, Paddington #231/R est:8000-12000 (A.D 8000)
£2907 $4622 €4361 Golden hills (121x151cm-48x59in) s.d.89 i.verso. 5-May-3 Sotheby's, Melbourne #360/R est:8000-12000 (A.D 7500)
£3295 $5238 €4943 Hillside in summer (106x167cm-42x66in) s.d.87 s.i.d.verso. 5-May-3 Sotheby's, Melbourne #200 est:5000-8000 (A.D 8500)
£3393 $5361 €5090 Husband and wife, there is that day (180x130cm-71x51in) s.d.93. 27-Nov-2 Deutscher-Menzies, Melbourne #127/R est:7000-9000 (A.D 9500)
£3571 $5571 €5357 Ridge after rain (121x182cm-48x72in) s.d.89 s.i.d.89 verso. 11-Nov-2 Deutscher-Menzies, Melbourne #81/R est:6000-8000 (A.D 10000)
£3584 $5448 €5376 Road to Attotonilco II (122x173cm-48x68in) s.i.d.97 verso. 28-Aug-2 Deutscher-Menzies, Melbourne #349/R est:4000-6000 (A.D 10000)
£3831 $5709 €5747 Husband and wife diptych (136x187cm-54x74in) s. i.d.95 verso oil paper on linen. 27-Aug-2 Christie's, Melbourne #68/R est:10000-15000 (A.D 10000)
£3831 $5709 €5747 Knowing or not knowing (243x136cm-96x54in) s.d.88 s.i.d.verso acrylic paper on linen. 27-Aug-2 Christie's, Melbourne #152/R est:9000-12000 (A.D 10000)
£6071 $9471 €9107 Pier, Grays Point (225x209cm-89x82in) s.d.83. 11-Nov-2 Deutscher-Menzies, Melbourne #39/R est:15000-20000 (A.D 17000)

Works on paper

£480 $773 €720 Hillside (57x74cm-22x29in) s.d.91 W/C. 6-May-3 Christie's, Melbourne #380 est:1000-1500 (A.D 1200)
£480 $773 €696 Liebela (23x27cm-9x11in) mixed media. 12-May-3 Joel, Victoria #274 est:1000-1500 (A.D 1200)
£536 $836 €804 Landscape (46x59cm-18x23in) s.d.84 W/C. 11-Nov-2 Deutscher-Menzies, Melbourne #172/R (A.D 1500)
£600 $966 €870 Untitled (44x59cm-17x23in) s.d.84 W/C. 12-May-3 Joel, Victoria #295 est:1000-1500 (A.D 1500)
£786 $1241 €1179 Dona Nobis pacem (92x87cm-36x34in) s. i.d.2000 verso synthetic polymer on canvas. 27-Nov-2 Deutscher-Menzies, Melbourne #195/R est:3000-5000 (A.D 2200)
£1643 $2563 €2465 Headland and bay (123x92cm-48x36in) s.d.88 s.i.d.88 verso synthetic polymer paint canvas. 11-Nov-2 Deutscher-Menzies, Melbourne #71/R est:4000-6000 (A.D 4600)
£3214 $5078 €4821 Jerusalem Golgotha (96x193cm-38x76in) s.d.91 s.i.d.verso synthetic polymer triptych. 27-Nov-2 Deutscher-Menzies, Melbourne #134/R est:6000-8000 (A.D 9000)
£4651 $7395 €6977 Mungo, walls of China (138x168cm-54x66in) s.d.87 s.i.d.verso prov. 5-May-3 Sotheby's, Melbourne #240/R est:7000-10000 (A.D 12000)

RANKIN, George James (1864-1937) British

Works on paper

£400 $632 €600 Sparrow hawk (35x25cm-14x10in) s. W/C. 28-Nov-2 Bonhams, Knightsbridge #30/R

RANKLEY, Alfred (1819-1872) British

£10000 $15800 €15000 Home revisited as a long parted mother with child plays fondley with her tears (94x72cm-37x28in) s.d.1854 verso exhib. 2-Dec-2 Sotheby's, London #98/R est:10000-15000

RANKLEY, Alfred (attrib) (1819-1872) British

£1400 $2184 €2100 Letter (41x33cm-16x13in) oval. 26-Mar-3 Sotheby's, Olympia #56/R est:800-1200

RANNEY, W (?) American

Works on paper

£1392 $2200 €2088 Bird in the Chinese tradition (28x41cm-11x16in) s. W/C. 26-Apr-3 Thomaston Place, Thomaston #352

RANUCCI, Lucio (1924-) Italian

£256 $400 €384 Merry go round (76x81cm-30x32in) s.d.1971. 9-Oct-2 Doyle, New York #86

RANVIER-CHARTIER, Lucie (1867-1932) French

£440 $678 €700 Personnage devant une porte (26x19cm-10x7in) s. cardboard. 23-Oct-2 Rabourdin & Choppin de Janvry, Paris #131

RANZA, G (19th C) Italian

Works on paper

£1013 $1600 €1520 Italian coastal landscape (74x91cm-29x36in) s. W/C. 30-Nov-2 Thomaston Place, Thomaston #102

RANZONI, Gustav (1826-1900) Austrian

£513 $779 €800 Girl by stream (37x49cm-15x19in) mono. 11-Jul-2 Hugo Ruef, Munich #785/R
£1560 $2418 €2340 Watering the cattle (73x120cm-29x47in) s.d.871. 4-Dec-2 AB Stockholms Auktionsverk #1863/R est:15000-20000 (S.KR 22000)

RAON, Jean (attrib) (1630-1707) French

Sculpture

£22436 $34776 €35000 Bustes allegoriques (44x27cm-17x11in) white marble pair lit. 9-Dec-2 Rabourdin & Choppin de Janvry, Paris #2/R est:45000

RAOUX, Albert (19th C) French

£8511 $13191 €12767 Allegory of the art of sculpture (206x252cm-81x99in) s.d.1860. 4-Dec-2 AB Stockholms Auktionsverk #1869/R est:80000-100000 (S.KR 120000)

RAOUX, Jean (1677-1734) French

£2027 $3162 €3000 Achille decouvert parmi les filles de Lycomede (60x74cm-24x29in) 26-Mar-3 Tajan, Paris #91/R

Works on paper

£353 $557 €550 Etude de main de femme (16x25cm-6x10in) sanguine. 15-Nov-2 Drouot Estimations, Paris #57

RAOUX, Jean (attrib) (1677-1734) French

£2759 $4414 €4000 Femme au fourneau (74x59cm-29x23in) 12-Mar-3 E & Eve, Paris #63/R est:3200-3800

RAPETTI, Alfredo (1961-) Italian

£1702 $2757 €2400 Untitled (100x200cm-39x79in) s.d.2002 two arcylic two parts. 20-May-3 Porro, Milan #48/R est:3000-3200

RAPETTI, Ottavio Giovanni (1849-?) Italian

£2893 $4455 €4600 Polenta (125x135cm-49x53in) s.d.1886. 23-Oct-2 Finarte, Milan #17/R est:4000-5000

RAPHAEL (after) (1483-1520) Italian

£6517 $10557 €9450 The Holy Family (105x85cm-41x33in) panel. 26-May-3 Bukowskis, Stockholm #372/R est:50000-60000 (S.KR 84000)

RAPHAEL (attrib) (1483-1520) Italian

Works on paper

£92593 $150000 €138890 Cupid and Psyche (18x25cm-7x10in) i. chk prov. 21-Jan-3 Sotheby's, New York #27/R est:70000

RAPHAEL (circle) (1483-1520) Italian

£42000 $65940 €63000 Holy Family (40x29cm-16x11in) panel prov.exhib.lit. 11-Dec-2 Christie's, London #87/R est:20000-30000

RAPHAEL (school) (1483-1520) Italian

Works on paper

£5000 $8350 €7250 Three dancing maidens. Three women holding a lyre (42x29cm-17x11in) i. chk pen ink double-sided. 8-Jul-3 Christie's, London #4/R est:5000-8000

RAPHAEL (studio) (1483-1520) Italian
Works on paper
£9000 $15030 €13050 Pagan sacrifice with figures bringing rams to an altar (19x23cm-7x9in) chk pen ink prov. 8-Jul-3 Christie's, London #2/R est:2000-3000

RAPHAEL (style) (1483-1520) Italian
£6000 $10020 €8700 Madonna and Child (59x48cm-23x19in) 11-Jul-3 Christie's, Kensington #204/R est:1500-2500
£6475 $10360 €9000 Madonna with carnation (30x24cm-12x9in) 17-May-3 Lempertz, Koln #1112/R est:10000
£18000 $28260 €27000 Holy Family with the infant St John the Baptist (35x26cm-14x10in) copper prov.lit. 12-Dec-2 Sotheby's, London #109/R est:10000-15000

RAPHAEL, Joseph (1869-1950) American
£816 $1298 €1200 Petite fille jouant (20x26cm-8x10in) s. canvas on cardboard. 26-Feb-3 Artcurial Briest, Paris #164
£816 $1298 €1200 Fillette a la fenetre (21x24cm-8x9in) s. canvas on cardboard. 26-Feb-3 Artcurial Briest, Paris #165
£1463 $2326 €2150 Portrait de jeune fille (45x36cm-18x14in) s. canvas on cardboard. 26-Feb-3 Artcurial Briest, Paris #162/R est:1500-1800
£2096 $3500 €3039 Woman in red wearing vest and cowboy hat (61x25cm-24x10in) s. 17-Jun-3 John Moran, Pasadena #61a est:4000-6000
£2229 $3500 €3344 Old Tower, Amsterdam (22x27cm-9x11in) s.i. i.verso panel. 19-Nov-2 Butterfields, San Francisco #8187/R est:3000-3500
£2244 $3478 €3500 Groene Rei, Brugge, Belgium (22x35cm-9x14in) s. s.i.d.1932 verso cardboard. 3-Dec-2 Christie's, Amsterdam #215/R est:3000-4000
£2516 $3899 €4000 Portrait de fillette (63x48cm-25x19in) s. prov. 30-Oct-2 Artcurial Briest, Paris #152 est:4500-5000
£2619 $4164 €3850 Paysage de Belgique (13x22cm-5x9in) s. panel. 26-Feb-3 Artcurial Briest, Paris #163 est:900-1000
£4790 $8000 €6946 Mother and child in interior (56x43cm-22x17in) s. board prov. 17-Jun-3 John Moran, Pasadena #64 est:9000-12000
£6832 $11000 €10248 Nuremberg, cityscape (43x36cm-17x14in) s. i.verso prov. 18-Feb-3 John Moran, Pasadena #50a est:14000-18000
£10778 $18000 €15628 Artist self portrait (51x41cm-20x16in) s.i. 17-Jun-3 John Moran, Pasadena #61 est:8000-12000
£14970 $25000 €21707 Country road with houses and barn (51x71cm-20x28in) s. prov. 17-Jun-3 John Moran, Pasadena #50 est:30000-50000
£22590 $37500 €32756 Chateau in the woods (67x75cm-26x30in) s. prov. 11-Jun-3 Butterfields, San Francisco #4205/R est:40000-60000
£35032 $55000 €52548 Peacocks with a chateau in the background (72x109cm-28x43in) s. i.verso prov. 19-Nov-2 Butterfields, San Francisco #8198/R est:50000-70000
£116129 $180000 €174194 Figures in a garden (79x94cm-31x37in) s. prov. 29-Oct-2 John Moran, Pasadena #670 est:200000-300000

RAPIN, Aimee (1869-1956) Swiss
Works on paper
£371 $586 €557 Man's portrait (60x48cm-24x19in) s.d.1919 pastel board. 14-Nov-2 Stuker, Bern #469 (S.FR 850)

RAPISARDI, Michele (1822-1886) Italian
£3521 $5669 €5000 Portrait of lady (103x97cm-41x38in) 11-May-3 Finarte, Venice #11/R

RAPOTEC, Stanislaus (1913-1997) Australian
£651 $970 €977 Moon II (107x92cm-42x36in) s.i.d.70 board. 27-Aug-2 Christie's, Melbourne #307/R est:1500-2000 (A.D 1700)
£923 $1468 €1385 Sunflowers (63x49cm-25x19in) s. composition board lit. 4-Mar-3 Deutscher-Menzies, Melbourne #192/R est:2500-3000 (A.D 2400)
£4789 $7136 €7184 Abstract (150x121cm-59x48in) s.d.61 board prov. 27-Aug-2 Christie's, Melbourne #164/R est:4000-6000 (A.D 12500)
£5747 $9023 €8621 Untitled (75x100cm-30x39in) s.d.60 board. 15-Apr-3 Lawson Menzies, Sydney #41/R est:12000-15000 (A.D 15000)
£6513 $9705 €9770 Disturbance No.10 (182x120cm-72x47in) s.d.61 s.i.verso board exhib. 27-Aug-2 Christie's, Melbourne #214/R est:6000-8000 (A.D 17000)
Works on paper
£1500 $2340 €2250 Mine shaft (73x58cm-29x23in) s. synthetic polymer paint. 11-Nov-2 Deutscher-Menzies, Melbourne #86/R est:2000-3000 (A.D 4200)
£3077 $4892 €4616 Glen Coe (137x137cm-54x54in) s.d.69 mixed media composition board. 4-Mar-3 Deutscher-Menzies, Melbourne #168/R est:9000-12000 (A.D 8000)

RAPP, Alex (1869-1927) Finnish
£405 $632 €640 Frozen lake (40x66cm-16x26in) s,. 12-Sep-2 Hagelstam, Helsinki #955/R
£465 $717 €740 Sunny winter's day (53x45cm-21x18in) s.d.08. 27-Oct-2 Bukowskis, Helsinki #261/R

RAPP, Ginette (1928-1998) French?
£250 $390 €375 Grand Briere (112x160cm-44x63in) s. 20-Oct-2 Lots Road, London #331
£300 $483 €450 Montmartre in the snow (81x65cm-32x26in) s. 18-Feb-3 Bonhams, Knightsbridge #41
£350 $567 €508 Plage, boat and figures (25x33cm-10x13in) s. 23-May-3 Dee Atkinson & Harrison, Driffield #650

RAPPARD, Anton Gerhard Alexander van (1858-1892) Dutch
£3459 $5327 €5500 Workman at a bench (90x50cm-35x20in) painted 1885 prov.exhib.lit. 22-Oct-2 Sotheby's, Amsterdam #223/R est:5000-7000
£8805 $13560 €14000 View of the Ruimzicht brickyard, Jutphaas (50x90cm-20x35in) s. painted 1885 prov.exhib.lit. 22-Oct-2 Sotheby's, Amsterdam #222/R est:15000-20000
Works on paper
£382 $589 €600 Still life with a jug (36x44cm-14x17in) s.d.02 W/C. 3-Sep-2 Christie's, Amsterdam #263
£1529 $2385 €2400 Farmer working (32x24cm-13x9in) s. chl pastel. 6-Nov-2 Vendue Huis, Gravenhage #109/R est:800-1000

RAPPINI, Vittorio (1877-1939) Italian
Works on paper
£3100 $5053 €4650 Woman with rababa. Gathering roses for perfume making (33x23cm-13x9in) s. W/C pair. 29-Jan-3 Sotheby's, Olympia #311/R est:2000-3000

RASCH, Heinrich (1840-1913) German
£1500 $2505 €2175 Gossiping fishwives (35x58cm-14x23in) s.i. 18-Jun-3 Sotheby's, Olympia #60/R est:1500-2000

RASCH-NAGELE, Lilo (1914-1978) German
£1871 $2750 €2900 Portrait of young woman entitled ' l'heure bleu' (60x41cm-24x16in) s.d.1963 i. verso panel. 20-Jun-2 Dr Fritz Nagel, Stuttgart #816/R est:3000

RASCHEN, Carl Martin (1882-1962) American
£385 $600 €578 Rural landscape with country road and barns (51x66cm-20x26in) s. 1-Aug-2 Eldred, East Dennis #341/R

RASCHEN, Henry (1854-1937) German/American
£4717 $7500 €7076 Apaches scouting in mountains, sunset (76x102cm-30x40in) s. prov. 5-Mar-3 Sotheby's, New York #125/R est:10000-15000
£5346 $8500 €8019 Ambush, sunset on the Colorado (66x117cm-26x46in) s. prov. 4-Mar-3 Christie's, Rockefeller NY #32/R est:10000-15000
£5625 $9000 €8156 Sentry (76x102cm-30x40in) s. 17-May-3 CRN Auctions, Cambridge #26

RASCHKA, Robert (1847-?) Rumanian
Works on paper
£1622 $2530 €2400 Old Hof theatre and Hof (24x29cm-9x11in) s. W/C. 28-Mar-3 Dorotheum, Vienna #346/R est:3000-3500

RASCO, Stephen (1924-) American
£481 $750 €722 Gulls (61x46cm-24x18in) board. 19-Oct-2 David Dike, Dallas #182/R

RASEK, Karel (1861-1918) Czechoslovakian
£284 $440 €426 Countryside (48x51cm-19x20in) painted c.1880. 3-Dec-2 SOGA, Bratislava #211/R (SL.K 18000)

RASENBERGER, Alfred (1885-1949) German
£256 $403 €400 Eifel village at dusk (60x80cm-24x31in) s. 21-Nov-2 Van Ham, Cologne #1875
£414 $658 €600 River in winter with punt and horse cart (30x40cm-12x16in) s. panel. 8-Mar-3 Arnold, Frankfurt #693
£448 $713 €650 Boat on river in winter with village beyond (30x41cm-12x16in) s. panel. 8-Mar-3 Arnold, Frankfurt #692/R
£1014 $1581 €1500 Catching fish in winter on the Altrhein (93x78cm-37x31in) s. lit. 28-Mar-3 Karrenbauer, Konstanz #1774/R est:800

RASENBERGER, Gernot (1943-) German
£253 $400 €400 Figures walking on frozen backwater of the lower Rhine (23x18cm-9x7in) s.i. 29-Nov-2 Schloss Ahlden, Ahlden #1311/R
£348 $550 €550 Paris at night (24x19cm-9x7in) s.i.d.98. 29-Nov-2 Schloss Ahlden, Ahlden #1312/R
£506 $800 €800 Dusseldorf city centre on winter evening (30x30cm-12x12in) s.d.98. 29-Nov-2 Schloss Ahlden, Ahlden #1299/R

£633 $1000 €1000 Winter landscape with trees by river (20x42cm-8x17in) s. 29-Nov-2 Schloss Ahlden, Ahlden #1310/R

RASER, J Heyl (1824-1901) American
£270 $425 €405 Riverside farm (23x32cm-9x13in) s. 22-Nov-2 Skinner, Boston #65/R
£2404 $3750 €3606 Still life of cut flowers in glass on a table (23x30cm-9x12in) s. board. 18-Sep-2 Alderfer's, Hatfield #341/R est:3000-5000

RASETTI, Georges (19th C) French
£256 $403 €400 Paysage de campagne (36x46cm-14x18in) s. 15-Dec-2 Thierry & Lannon, Brest #189

RASIN, Stenka (?) Russian
£510 $785 €800 Guest in rowing party (108x193cm-43x76in) after Repin. 5-Sep-2 Arnold, Frankfurt #845

RASKIN, Joseph (1897-1981) American
£1154 $1800 €1731 Village in landscape (61x76cm-24x30in) s. 9-Nov-2 Sloan, North Bethesda #611/R est:2000-3000

RASMUSSEN, A (19/20th C) Danish
£266 $431 €399 Seascape in rough seas (37x55cm-15x22in) s. 25-Jan-3 Rasmussen, Havnen #2034 (D.KR 3000)
£468 $740 €702 Norwegian fjord landscape (47x66cm-19x26in) s. 2-Dec-2 Rasmussen, Copenhagen #1584/R (D.KR 5500)

RASMUSSEN, Carl (1831-1903) Danish
£756 $1217 €1134 Coastal landscape with schooner (33x51cm-13x20in) s.d.1870 masonite. 11-May-3 Hindemae, Ullerslev #664/R (D.KR 8000)
£887 $1436 €1331 Fishermen at the straight (20x33cm-8x13in) init.d.1884. 25-Jan-3 Rasmussen, Havnen #2182 (D.KR 10000)
£1605 $2503 €2408 Landscape from Isefjorden (74x111cm-29x44in) s.i.d.1869. 23-Sep-2 Rasmussen, Vejle #99/R est:15000 (D.KR 19000)

RASMUSSEN, Daniel (20th C) American
Works on paper
£580 $900 €870 Dancer and cat. Bellerina (29x40cm-11x16in) s.d.48 pencil black wash ink double-sided. 29-Oct-2 Sotheby's, New York #275/R est:500-700

RASMUSSEN, Erik (20th C) Danish
£560 $890 €840 Sunbather (150x120cm-59x47in) s. on stretcher. 29-Apr-3 Kunsthallen, Copenhagen #185/R (D.KR 6000)

RASMUSSEN, Georg Anton (1842-1914) Norwegian
£1295 $2072 €1800 Norwegian fjord landscape (40x75cm-16x30in) s. 17-May-3 Lempertz, Koln #1468/R est:2000
£2000 $3260 €2900 Strandhugg - by the shore (37x55cm-15x22in) 16-Jul-3 Sotheby's, Olympia #216/R est:2000-3000
£2244 $3478 €3500 Norwegian fjord landscape (75x127cm-30x50in) s. prov. 7-Dec-2 Ketterer, Hamburg #150/R est:4000-5000
£2342 $3653 €3513 Sun, summer and boat on the fjord (23x25cm-9x10in) s. panel. 21-Oct-2 Blomqvist, Oslo #329/R est:30000-35000 (N.KR 27000)
£3333 $5300 €4800 Fishermen by Norwegian coast (37x68cm-15x27in) s.dd.82. 30-Apr-3 Tajan, Paris #109/R
£3481 $5430 €5500 Extensive Norwegian fjord landscape (75x125cm-30x49in) s. lit. 14-Sep-2 Bergmann, Erlangen #742/R est:5500
£4602 $7271 €6903 Calm summer's day by the fjord (76x125cm-30x49in) s. 28-Apr-3 Blomqvist, Oslo #334/R est:60000-80000 (N.KR 52000)
£5918 $9469 €8877 Fjord landscape with figures and boat on the shore (44x61cm-17x24in) s/d/68. 17-Mar-3 Blomqvist, Oslo #368/R est:70000-80000 (N.KR 68000)

RASMUSSEN, I E C (1841-1893) Danish
£420 $667 €630 Landscape with cabin (24x34cm-9x13in) init. i.stretcher. 5-May-3 Rasmussen, Vejle #464/R (D.KR 4500)
£559 $888 €839 Coastal landscape with approaching storm (19x30cm-7x12in) init.d.67 panel. 5-Mar-3 Rasmussen, Copenhagen #2014/R (D.KR 6000)
£596 $941 €894 Coastal landscape with storm approaching (27x43cm-11x17in) init.d.12 Mai 1862. 2-Dec-2 Rasmussen, Copenhagen #1408/R (D.KR 7000)
£931 $1480 €1397 Coastal landscape with sailing vessels (33x49cm-13x19in) init.d.85. 10-Mar-3 Rasmussen, Vejle #479/R (D.KR 10000)
£957 $1550 €1388 Seascape with sailing ship (18x25cm-7x10in) init. panel. 26-May-3 Rasmussen, Copenhagen #1351/R (D.KR 10000)
£1313 $2102 €1970 Landscape with man on skies hunting grouse at sunset, Greenland (27x40cm-11x16in) s.d.1877. 13-Jan-3 Rasmussen, Vejle #123/R est:15000 (D.KR 15000)
£1340 $2170 €1943 Landscape from Aero towards Svendborgsund (50x77cm-20x30in) s. 26-May-3 Rasmussen, Copenhagen #1401/R est:15000 (D.KR 14000)

RASMUSSEN, Ida (19th C) Danish
£628 $1031 €911 Still life of blue flowers (12x23cm-5x9in) s.d.1858 panel. 4-Jun-3 AB Stockholms Auktionsverk #2399/R (S.KR 8000)
£943 $1546 €1367 Still life of roses (16x23cm-6x9in) s.d.61 panel. 4-Jun-3 AB Stockholms Auktionsverk #2398/R (S.KR 12000)
£1021 $1675 €1480 Still life of flowers and palette (18x25cm-7x10in) s.d.76 panel. 4-Jun-3 AB Stockholms Auktionsverk #2400/R (S.KR 13000)

RASMUSSEN, Jens Erik Carl (1841-1893) Danish
£2756 $4189 €4134 Moonlight off Greenland (40x74cm-16x29in) s. 27-Aug-2 Rasmussen, Copenhagen #1725/R est:25000 (D.KR 32000)
£3790 $5761 €5685 Full speed down a mountain, Greenland - man on skies (41x52cm-16x20in) s.d.1878. 27-Aug-2 Rasmussen, Copenhagen #1921/R est:20000 (D.KR 44000)

RASMUSSEN, N P (1847-1918) Danish
£383 $620 €555 Pigeon (30x39cm-12x15in) mono.d.3 Febr 1907. 26-May-3 Rasmussen, Copenhagen #1389/R (D.KR 4000)
£468 $740 €702 Bird (28x16cm-11x6in) mono.i.d.23 juli 1909. 2-Dec-2 Rasmussen, Copenhagen #1324/R (D.KR 5500)

RASMUSSEN, Niels Peter (1847-1918) Danish
£420 $685 €630 Bird study (35x24cm-14x9in) s.d.1891. 2-Feb-3 Lots Road, London #333/R

RASMUSSEN, Tonning (1936-) Danish
£689 $1068 €1034 Picture from Waterloo-Plein, Amsterdam (60x73cm-24x29in) s.d.1969 verso. 4-Dec-2 Kunsthallen, Copenhagen #20/R (D.KR 8000)
£1097 $1744 €1646 Dutch picture II (73x92cm-29x36in) s.d.1970 verso. 26-Feb-3 Kunsthallen, Copenhagen #92/R est:10000 (D.KR 12000)

RASPANTI, Bruno (1938-) Italian
Sculpture
£962 $1404 €1500 Camera (80x63x30cm-31x25x12in) bronze. 5-Jun-2 Il Ponte, Milan #123/R

RASSENFOSSE, Armand (1862-1934) Belgian
£4082 $6490 €6000 Les bas mauves (36x25cm-14x10in) mono. board. 19-Mar-3 Hotel des Ventes Mosan, Brussels #314/R est:7000-9000
£8333 $12917 €13000 Jeune femme devant une fenetre (44x34cm-17x13in) s.d.1906 cardboard exhib. 9-Dec-2 Horta, Bruxelles #167/R est:10000-12000

Works on paper
£256 $390 €400 Nu perspectif. mono. dr. 27-Aug-2 Galerie Moderne, Brussels #88
£355 $592 €500 Tete de hiercheuse (30x23cm-12x9in) studio st. mixed media. 18-Jun-3 Hotel des Ventes Mosan, Brussels #228
£390 $651 €550 Modele nu, de dos (41x26cm-16x10in) s. mixed media. 18-Jun-3 Hotel des Ventes Mosan, Brussels #257
£897 $1409 €1400 La belle et le sultan (30x20cm-12x8in) mono. mixed media. 11-Dec-2 Hotel des Ventes Mosan, Brussels #279
£4231 $6642 €6600 Jeune fille a sa toilette (39x31cm-15x12in) s.d.1915 chl pastel. 10-Dec-2 Vanderkindere, Brussels #35/R est:1250-1750

RASTRUP, Lars (1862-1949) Danish
£301 $458 €452 Portrait of girl wearing red suit (69x49cm-27x19in) s.i. verso. 27-Aug-2 Rasmussen, Copenhagen #1599/R (D.KR 3500)
£391 $626 €587 Coastal landscape with figures in dinghy (18x38cm-7x15in) s.d.15. 16-Mar-3 Hindemae, Ullerslev #537/R (D.KR 4200)
£474 $720 €711 The day's work is ended (150x105cm-59x41in) init.d.1913. 27-Aug-2 Rasmussen, Copenhagen #1625/R (D.KR 5500)
£901 $1405 €1352 Clear winter's day with two school children on road (51x68cm-20x27in) s.d.1905. 11-Nov-2 Rasmussen, Vejle #661/R (D.KR 10500)

RATH, Hildegard (1909-) American/German
£613 $950 €920 Spring on Stratton mountain (66x79cm-26x31in) s. s.i.on stretcher. 1-Oct-2 Arthur James, Florida #26

RATHBONE, John (1750-1807) British
£360 $587 €540 Upland river landscape with figures, ruin and mountains (35x42cm-14x17in) 17-Feb-3 Bonhams, Bath #38
£500 $815 €750 Figures resting on a country path with a house above a gorge in the distance (25x34cm-10x13in) panel. 12-Feb-3 Bonhams, Knightsbridge #39/R

£1000 $1550 €1500 Milkmaids and livestock in a wooded valley (21x27cm-8x11in) panel. 26-Sep-2 Mellors & Kirk, Nottingham #687/R est:1000-1500

Works on paper

£1000 $1640 €1500 River Dee, Chester (28x42cm-11x17in) i.d. bodycol. 4-Feb-3 Bonhams, Leeds #225 est:600-900

RATHBONE, John (attrib) (1750-1807) British

£280 $437 €420 Lakeland landscape with oarsmen (18x23cm-7x9in) panel. 6-Nov-2 Bonhams, Chester #430
£500 $825 €725 Landscape at sunset (40x59cm-16x23in) canvas on board. 2-Jul-3 Sotheby's, Olympia #83/R

RATHMELL, Thomas (1912-1990) British

£500 $780 €750 Landscape with figures (59x76cm-23x30in) s.i.verso. 11-Sep-2 Bonhams, Newport #406

RATHSMAN, Siri (1895-1974) Swedish

Works on paper

£624 $985 €936 Landscape (63x47cm-25x19in) s. chk. 28-Apr-3 Bukowskis, Stockholm #255/R (S.KR 8200)

RATINCKX, Jos (1860-1937) Belgian

Works on paper

£327 $526 €500 L'alchimiste (42x30cm-17x12in) s. W/C. 14-Jan-3 Vanderkindere, Brussels #8

RATTERMAN, Walter G (1887-1944) American

£2019 $3250 €3029 Couple stepping away from crowed dance floor (74x97cm-29x38in) s. 10-May-3 Illustration House, New York #97/R est:1800-2400

RATTERMAN, Walter G (attrib) (1887-1944) American

£870 $1400 €1305 Couple seated on garden bench (81x61cm-32x24in) s.d.1928. 20-Feb-3 Illustration House, New York #139/R est:1500-2000
£1429 $2300 €2144 Woman hypnotized outside of African hut (81x64cm-32x25in) s. en grisaille. 20-Feb-3 Illustration House, New York #140/R est:1600-2400

RATTNER, Abraham (1895-1978) American

£2545 $4250 €3690 Tabletop still life of mixed fruits (60x73cm-24x29in) s. s.on stretcher. 22-Jun-3 Freeman, Philadelphia #130/R est:2000-3000

RATTRAY, Alexander Wellwood (1849-1902) American

£472 $736 €684 Idyllic riverscape (36x53cm-14x21in) s. 26-Mar-3 Walker's, Ottawa #76/R est:1200-1600 (C.D 1100)
£550 $858 €825 On the coast (30x40cm-12x16in) s. 17-Oct-2 Bonhams, Edinburgh #176
£635 $965 €990 Late autumn in the Scottish highlands (27x17cm-11x7in) s. panel two. 17-Aug-2 Hans Stahl, Toestorf #60/R
£1100 $1705 €1650 Collecting sticks (26x17cm-10x7in) s. panel. 5-Dec-2 Bonhams, Edinburgh #31 est:1000-1500

RATY, Albert (1889-1970) Belgian

£252 $387 €400 Pont de Liege a Bouillon (50x57cm-20x22in) 22-Oct-2 Galerie Moderne, Brussels #1656
£696 $1086 €1100 Village ardennais (20x28cm-8x11in) indis.s. 16-Sep-2 Horta, Bruxelles #62
£851 $1421 €1200 Vue de Saint-Hubert (38x46cm-15x18in) s. board. 18-Jun-3 Hotel des Ventes Mosan, Brussels #241
£1307 $2105 €2000 Les amanites tues mouches (33x40cm-13x16in) s. canvas on panel. 20-Jan-3 Horta, Bruxelles #243 est:2000-3000
£1899 $2962 €3000 Paysage des Ardennes (48x59cm-19x23in) s. 20-Oct-2 Charbonneaux, Paris #153/R est:4000-4500
£2532 $3949 €4000 Maison en Ardennes (40x47cm-16x19in) s. 15-Oct-2 Horta, Bruxelles #135/R
£2866 $4471 €4500 Petit pont sur la Semois (49x56cm-19x22in) s. 11-Nov-2 Horta, Bruxelles #108/R est:4000-6000
£6369 $9936 €10000 Lueur dans une maisons sous la neige (60x80cm-24x31in) s. 11-Nov-2 Horta, Bruxelles #107/R est:10000-14000

RAU, Emil (1858-1937) German

£650 $1027 €975 Welcome visitor (72x90cm-28x35in) s.d.1890. 14-Nov-2 Christie's, Kensington #282/R
£1149 $1792 €1700 Alpine couple in kitchen (25x21cm-10x8in) s. 28-Mar-3 Ketterer, Hamburg #81/R est:1800-2000
£1818 $2709 €2800 Hunter (37x24cm-15x9in) s.d.02. 26-Jun-2 Neumeister, Munich #834/R est:2250

RAUB, Charles Francisque (19/20th C) French

£1000 $1600 €1450 Farmyard (54x73cm-21x29in) s. 16-May-3 Skinner, Boston #343/R est:3000-5000

RAUCH, Ferdinand (1813-1852) Austrian

£961 $1499 €1442 Jockey on brown race horse (46x58cm-18x23in) s. bears d. 20-Nov-2 Fischer, Luzern #1149/R est:2200-2800 (S.FR 2200)

RAUCH, Neo (1960-) German

£71875 $115000 €107813 Lokal (140x100cm-55x39in) s.i.d.98 prov. 15-May-3 Phillips, New York #38/R est:50000-70000
£106250 $170000 €159375 Gegenlicht - black light (250x200cm-98x79in) s.d.00 prov.exhib. 15-May-3 Phillips, New York #5/R est:100000-150000

RAUCHINGER, Heinrich (attrib) (1858-1942) Polish

£1646 $2567 €2600 In the nursery (179x141cm-70x56in) i. 15-Oct-2 Dorotheum, Vienna #14/R est:2000-2800

RAUDNITZ, Albert (1814-1899) German

£3500 $5565 €5250 Important letter (100x70cm-39x28in) s. panel. 20-Mar-3 Christie's, Kensington #103/R est:4000-6000
£17000 $28390 €25500 Preliminaries of peace (85x61cm-33x24in) s.d.88. 18-Jun-3 Christie's, Kensington #91/R est:15000-20000

RAUFER-REDWITZ, Anton (1871-1965) German

£755 $1170 €1200 Still life with grapes (55x68cm-22x27in) s. 29-Oct-2 Dorotheum, Vienna #165/R
£890 $1389 €1300 Still life with basket of grapes, melon, plums and jugs (73x100cm-29x39in) s. 10-Apr-3 Dorotheum, Vienna #36/R est:1300-1500
£1333 $2213 €1933 Still life of fruit, porcelain vase and brass chalice (55x68cm-22x27in) s. 16-Jun-3 Waddingtons, Toronto #300/R est:3000-3500 (C.D 3000)

RAUGHT, John Willard (1857-1931) American

£897 $1400 €1346 Stand of trees (23x18cm-9x7in) s.d.1906 board. 18-Sep-2 Alderfer's, Hatfield #338/R

RAUH, Caspar Walter (1912-1983) German

Works on paper

£1457 $2375 €2200 Death of the writer (42x65cm-17x26in) s.i.d. Indian ink over pencil. 14-Feb-3 Paul Kieffer, Pforzhiem #7239 est:750

RAULINO, Tobias (1787-1838) German

Works on paper

£1892 $2951 €2800 Heiligenstadt (16x24cm-6x9in) s. W/C. 28-Mar-3 Dorotheum, Vienna #221/R est:2000-2500

RAUMANN, Joseph (1908-) Hungarian

£528 $850 €750 Bassin a Honfleur (40x32cm-16x13in) s. isorel. 12-May-3 Lesieur & Le Bars, Le Havre #82/R

RAUPP, Friedrich (1871-1949) German

£274 $427 €400 Beach scene with fishermen talking (36x49cm-14x19in) s.d.09 lit. 10-Apr-3 Allgauer, Kempten #2951/R
£955 $1490 €1500 Summer morning on the Chiemsee (58x73cm-23x29in) s. 6-Nov-2 Hugo Ruef, Munich #1242/R

RAUPP, Karl (1837-1918) German

£3165 $5000 €4748 Storm on the Cheimsee (41x101cm-16x40in) s.d.1883. 1-Apr-3 Christie's, Rockefeller NY #208/R est:6000-8000
£3378 $5270 €5000 Bather by river (41x60cm-16x24in) s. 27-Mar-3 Dr Fritz Nagel, Stuttgart #861/R est:2200
£11702 $18138 €17553 An outing to the sea (73x133cm-29x52in) s. 3-Dec-2 Bukowskis, Stockholm #187/R est:60000-80000 (S.KR 165000)

RAUSCH, Leonhard (1813-1895) German

£2048 $3257 €3072 Street scene from Berchtesgaden (97x127cm-38x50in) s. 5-Mar-3 Rasmussen, Copenhagen #1787/R est:20000 (D.KR 22000)

RAUSCHENBERG, Robert (1925-) American

£53125 $85000 €79688 Territorial rites - shiner (155x133cm-61x52in) s.d.86 acrylic metal hardware stainless steel prov.exhib. 14-May-3 Sotheby's, New York #240/R est:60000-80000
£55000 $88000 €82500 Untitled (124x246cm-49x97in) s.d.89 acrylic copper prov.exhib. 15-May-3 Christie's, Rockefeller NY #194/R est:70000-90000
£56250 $90000 €84375 Scripture II (328x154cm-129x61in) s.d.74 acrylic sand graphite collage fabric laminated paper exhib. 14-May-3 Sotheby's, New York #193/R est:20000-30000
£569620 $900000 €854430 Wanderlust (76x63cm-30x25in) s.d.1957 on stretcher oil graphite collage on canvas. 12-Nov-2 Sotheby's, New York #38/R est:1000000-1500000

£632911 $1000000 €949367 Nettle (215x100cm-85x39in) oil paper collage on canvas attached metal chain executed 1960. 13-Nov-2 Christie's, Rockefeller NY #60/R est:1200000-1800000

Prints

£1840 $3000 €2760 Pledge (79x58cm-31x23in) s.d.1968 col lithograph. 13-Feb-3 Christie's, Rockefeller NY #332/R
£1935 $3000 €2903 Passport, from Ten ffrom Leo Castelli (51x51cm-20x20in) incised sig.num.76/100 col screenprint. 25-Sep-2 Christie's, Rockefeller NY #373/R est:1400-2800
£2390 $3800 €3585 Landmark (105x71cm-41x28in) s.d.num.39/40 col lithograph. 29-Apr-3 Christie's, Rockefeller NY #720/R est:2200-2800
£2400 $3960 €3480 Glint (109x115cm-43x45in) s.d.num.11/37 collage. 2-Jul-3 Christie's, London #342 est:1800-2200
£2516 $4000 €3774 Suburban (72x49cm-28x19in) s.d.num.14/25 lithograph. 29-Apr-3 Christie's, Rockefeller NY #708/R est:4000-6000
£2516 $4000 €3774 Guardian (107x76cm-42x30in) s.d.num.25/44 col lithograph. 29-Apr-3 Christie's, Rockefeller NY #719/R est:2000-3000
£3019 $4800 €4529 Rank (41x40cm-16x16in) s.i.d. lithograph. 29-Apr-3 Christie's, Rockefeller NY #711/R est:2500-3500
£5660 $9000 €8490 Local means (82x110cm-32x43in) s.d.num.2/11 col lithograph. 29-Apr-3 Christie's, Rockefeller NY #722/R est:7000-9000
£5975 $9500 €8963 Kip-up (105x76cm-41x30in) s.d.num.22/23 lithograph. 29-Apr-3 Christie's, Rockefeller NY #713/R est:6000-8000
£10063 $16000 €15095 Stuntman I. Stuntman II. Stuntman III (46x36cm-18x14in) s.d. num.22/37, 22/35 and 22/36 col lithograph set of 3. 29-Apr-3 Christie's, Rockefeller NY #710/R est:12000-15000
£13836 $22000 €20754 License (101x71cm-40x28in) s.d.num.10/16 col lithograph prov. 29-Apr-3 Christie's, Rockefeller NY #709/R est:25000-35000
£15723 $25000 €23585 Shades (35x35cm-14x14in) s.num.3/24 lithograph plexiglas aluminum light bulb set of 6 prov. 29-Apr-3 Christie's, Rockefeller NY #712/R est:14000-16000

Sculpture

£1087 $1783 €1500 Ballot - from bones and unions (220x75cm-87x30in) s.i.d. verso rope plastic. 28-May-3 Lempertz, Koln #357/R est:1500
£1761 $2800 €2642 Tibetan locks, mountaineer (12x12x4cm-5x5x2in) s.num.9/21 steel wall relief col photo screenprint. 29-Apr-3 Christie's, Rockefeller NY #724/R est:3000-4000
£6289 $10000 €9434 Sling-shots lit no 5 (215x97x32cm-85x38x13in) s.num.15/25 col lithograph wood box mylar sailcloth. 2-May-3 Sotheby's, New York #573/R est:25000-35000
£37975 $60000 €56963 Untitled - shiner series (246x131x25cm-97x52x10in) s.d.87 acrylic objects mirrored aluminum prov.exhib. 13-Nov-2 Sotheby's, New York #279/R est:50000-70000

Works on paper

£922 $1494 €1300 Monuments (50x35cm-20x14in) s.d.75 collage pencil board. 26-May-3 Christie's, Milan #13/R
£3145 $5000 €4718 Howl (102x67cm-40x26in) s.d. collage silk medallion mirror. 2-May-3 Sotheby's, New York #571/R est:3000-4000
£4610 $7145 €6915 Red heart (90x67cm-35x26in) s.d.82 mixed media on panel in plexiglas box. 8-Dec-2 Uppsala Auktionskammare, Uppsala #285/R est:60000-80000 (S.KR 65000)
£6329 $10000 €9494 Light no.3 (80x67cm-31x26in) s. collage ink silk ribbon executed 1982. 12-Nov-2 Phillips, New York #117/R est:12000-18000
£10063 $16000 €15095 Samarkand stitches. s.embroidered tag num.46 screenprint fabric set of seven. 2-May-3 Sotheby's, New York #574/R est:7000-9000
£12000 $20040 €17400 Shrub (54x54cm-21x21in) s.d.79 solvent transfer fabric collage prov. 26-Jun-3 Sotheby's, London #152/R est:10000-15000
£13000 $21320 €19500 Untitled (77x58cm-30x23in) s.d.80 solvent transfer acrylic fabric collage prov. 6-Feb-3 Christie's, London #677/R est:12000-16000
£25316 $40000 €37974 Jones diner (116x76cm-46x30in) s.d.95 solvent transfer pencil prov.exhib. 13-Nov-2 Sotheby's, New York #339/R est:40000-60000
£26563 $42500 €39845 Beth Elohim Collage (37x29cm-15x11in) s.i.d.1966 solvent transfer gouache pencil tape prov. 14-May-3 Sotheby's, New York #184/R est:50000-70000
£47468 $75000 €71202 Hangout - anagram (153x245cm-60x96in) solvent transfer on paper executed 1995 prov.exhib. 13-Nov-2 Sotheby's, New York #334/R est:80000-120000
£56250 $90000 €84375 Untitled (57x76cm-22x30in) s.d.68 solvent transfer acrylic W/C pencil on paper prov. 14-May-3 Sotheby's, New York #185/R est:70000-90000
£62500 $100000 €93750 Cloister series rush II (248x40cm-98x16in) s.i.d.80 verso fabric paper collage oil silkscreen prov. 16-May-3 Phillips, New York #153/R est:100000-150000
£75949 $120000 €113924 Xantone sedan (188x244cm-74x96in) s.i.d.79 verso solvent transfer acrylic collage on wood prov. 13-Nov-2 Sotheby's, New York #281/R est:120000-180000

RAUSCHNABEL, William F (20th C) American?

£261 $425 €392 Bay Ranch (30x36cm-12x14in) s. i.verso canvasboard. 16-Feb-3 Butterfields, San Francisco #2112

RAUSENBERGER, Eline (1944-) Belgian

Works on paper

£352 $567 €500 Red light district (71x81cm-28x32in) s. gouache. 12-May-3 Bernaerts, Antwerp #702

RAUTH, Otto (1862-1922) German

£1795 $2818 €2800 Man playing for girl (65x81cm-26x32in) s. 21-Nov-2 Van Ham, Cologne #1879/R est:1500

RAUTIAINEN, Johan Hjalmar (?) Finnish

£323 $510 €500 Still life (33x33cm-13x13in) s. 19-Dec-2 Hagelstam, Helsinki #880

RAVA, Giovanni (1874-1944) Italian

£645 $1019 €1000 Peasant women (31x22cm-12x9in) s. board. 18-Dec-2 Finarte, Milan #142/R

RAVAL, Rasik Durgashanker (1928-1980) Indian

£320 $506 €464 Horses (92x123cm-36x48in) s.d.1964. 22-Jul-3 Sotheby's, Olympia #300/R

RAVANNE, Léon Gustave (1854-1904) French

£699 $1090 €1049 Coastal scene in evening (33x46cm-13x18in) s.i.d.1890. 6-Nov-2 Dobiaschofsky, Bern #903/R (S.FR 1600)

RAVEEL, Roger (1921-) Belgian

£2590 $4144 €3600 Nude and square (18x23cm-7x9in) s. acrylic pencil. 17-May-3 De Vuyst, Lokeren #305/R est:2200-2600
£9615 $14904 €15000 Kasteelbomen (77x100cm-30x39in) s.d.65 i.on stretcher. 3-Dec-2 Christie's, Amsterdam #341/R est:15000-20000
£14103 $21859 €22000 Silma in vondelpark (80x100cm-31x39in) s.d.3.8.70. 3-Dec-2 Christie's, Amsterdam #340/R est:18000-22000

RAVEL DE MALVAL, Edouard (19th C) French

£1458 $2304 €2100 Descente de Croix (210x176cm-83x69in) exhib. 25-Apr-3 Beaussant & Lefèvre, Paris #33/R est:1800-2200

RAVEL, Daniel (1915-) French

£417 $663 €600 Transparence (54x80cm-21x31in) s. painted c.1955. 29-Apr-3 Artcurial Briest, Paris #619

RAVEL, Edouard-John E (1847-1920) Swiss

£437 $690 €656 Femme et enfant devant un miroir (26x20cm-10x8in) s. canvas on panel. 17-Nov-2 Koller, Geneva #1224 (S.FR 1000)
£786 $1242 €1179 Vieux paysan (56x29cm-22x11in) s. cardboard. 17-Nov-2 Koller, Geneva #1223/R (S.FR 1800)

Works on paper

£349 $545 €524 Cow herd (29x38cm-11x15in) s.d.1901 W/C prov. 9-Nov-2 Galerie Glogner, Luzern #107/R (S.FR 800)
£1310 $2057 €1965 Pique nique a la montagne (27x37cm-11x15in) mono. pencil Indian ink. 25-Nov-2 Sotheby's, Zurich #17/R est:3000-5000 (S.FR 3000)
£17391 $26957 €26087 Ronde des enfants a Evolene (51x43cm-20x17in) s.d.86 W/C prov. 7-Dec-2 Galerie du Rhone, Sion #459/R est:40000-60000 (S.FR 40000)

RAVEL, Maurice (20th C) French

£456 $735 €680 Interieur d'atelier (73x92cm-29x36in) s. 23-Feb-3 Mercier & Cie, Lille #179

RAVEN, John Samuel (1829-1877) British

£2848 $4500 €4500 View of the Hohen Goll with Hintersee in foreground (82x122cm-32x48in) s. 28-Nov-2 Dorotheum, Vienna #211/R est:4500-8000

RAVEN-HILL, Leonard (1867-1942) British

Works on paper

£226 $349 €339 Irruption des soldats (28x18cm-11x7in) s. gouache. 22-Oct-2 Iegor de Saint Hippolyte, Montreal #84 (C.D 550)

RAVENNA, Juti (1897-1972) Italian

£5696 $9000 €9000 Still life (39x52cm-15x20in) s.d.1924 board. 30-Nov-2 Farsetti, Prato #755/R est:3500

RAVENSTEIN, Paul von (1854-1938) German
£962 $1490 €1500 Meadow landscape (68x87cm-27x34in) s.d.1910 lit. 6-Dec-2 Karlheinz Kaupp, Staufen #2341/R est:1500
£1310 $2044 €1965 River landscape (87x69cm-34x27in) s.d.1899 prov. 20-Nov-2 Fischer, Luzern #1183/R est:2500-3000 (S.FR 3000)

RAVENSWAAY, Jan van (1789-1869) Dutch
£1572 $2421 €2500 In de holm te Westerbork in de provincie Drenthe (24x31cm-9x12in) init. s.i.verso panel. 23-Oct-2 Christie's, Amsterdam #63/R est:3000-5000
£1761 $2712 €2800 Panoramic view of a river landscape with cows in the foreland (21x35cm-8x14in) init. panel. 23-Oct-2 Christie's, Amsterdam #32/R est:2500-3500
Works on paper
£473 $738 €700 Sheep resting (18x30cm-7x12in) s. ochre. 28-Mar-3 Dorotheum, Vienna #66/R

RAVERAT, Gwendolen (1885-1957) British
£280 $437 €420 Mill at Newnham, Cambridge (30x41cm-12x16in) i. s.verso board prov. 18-Sep-2 Cheffins Grain & Comins, Cambridge #545/R
Works on paper
£420 $664 €609 Quant a moi j'adore les beautes de la nature (14x11cm-6x4in) i. pen ink W/C. 22-Jul-3 Sworder & Son, Bishops Stortford #345/R
£520 $822 €754 Baby. Gossip (13x19cm-5x7in) s.i. W/C two. 22-Jul-3 Sworder & Son, Bishops Stortford #343/R
£820 $1296 €1189 Philosopher. Elizabeth, the artist's daughter (7x8cm-3x3in) i. pen ink wash two. 22-Jul-3 Sworder & Son, Bishops Stortford #344/R

RAVESTEYN, Dirck de Quade van (fl.1589-1619) Dutch
£21795 $34436 €34000 Religious scenes (56x33cm-22x13in) copper triptych. 13-Nov-2 Marc Kohn, Paris #7/R est:30000-40000

RAVESTEYN, Hubert van (1638-1691) Dutch
£450 $702 €675 Card game (33x24cm-13x9in) mono. panel. 10-Apr-3 Tennants, Leyburn #926/R
£5000 $7850 €7500 Man in a interior drinking beer. Peasant in an interior eating mussels (19x17cm-7x7in) panel pair prov. 13-Dec-2 Christie's, Kensington #151/R est:6000-8000

RAVESTEYN, Jan Anthonisz van (1570-1657) Dutch
£10191 $15898 €16000 Portrait of a lady, half length, lemon in her right hand (70x61cm-28x24in) panel prov. 6-Nov-2 Christie's, Amsterdam #62/R est:7000-10000

RAVESTEYN, Nicolas van I (1613-1693) Dutch
£4054 $6324 €6000 Cavalry engagement near bridge (26x46cm-10x18in) s. panel. 27-Mar-3 Dorotheum, Vienna #316/R est:4000-7000

RAVET, Victor (1840-1895) Belgian
£737 $1157 €1150 La preparation du repas (24x15cm-9x6in) s. panel. 19-Nov-2 Vanderkindere, Brussels #21/R

RAVIER, Auguste François (1814-1895) French
£1000 $1570 €1500 Paysage avec un tour (24x29cm-9x11in) s. prov. 16-Dec-2 Sotheby's, London #81 est:1000-1500
£1346 $2113 €2100 Paysage a l'etang (24x29cm-9x11in) st.sig. W/C. 13-Dec-2 Piasa, Paris #226
£1474 $2315 €2300 Paysage (30x25cm-12x10in) s. cardboard. 13-Dec-2 Piasa, Paris #223/R
£1709 $2666 €2700 Sous-bois (32x22cm-13x9in) s. canvas on cardboard. 20-Oct-2 Anaf, Lyon #221 est:1500-1800
£1895 $3108 €2900 Jardin, remparts de Cremieu (35x25cm-14x10in) indis.sig. i.verso cardboard. 9-Feb-3 Anaf, Lyon #216/R
Works on paper
£288 $453 €450 Allee (33x22cm-13x9in) studio st. pen W/C dr. 13-Dec-2 Piasa, Paris #229
£309 $479 €464 Sunset (23x29cm-9x11in) s. W/C. 3-Dec-2 Ritchie, Toronto #3068/R est:800-1200 (C.D 750)
£314 $491 €500 Chemin pres de Morestel (16x19cm-6x7in) mono. Indian ink dr. 14-Oct-2 Blache, Grenoble #108
£314 $491 €500 Effet de nuages (15x9cm-6x4in) W/C. 14-Oct-2 Blache, Grenoble #110
£321 $500 €510 La tour des remparts de Cremieu (9x11cm-4x4in) pencil ink wash dr. 14-Oct-2 Blache, Grenoble #107
£380 $600 €600 Falaise (38x49cm-15x19in) st.sig. W/C dr double-sided. 1-Dec-2 Anaf, Lyon #150
£391 $606 €587 Bend in the river (25x33cm-10x13in) s. W/C. 3-Dec-2 Ritchie, Toronto #3069/R est:1000-1500 (C.D 950)
£412 $638 €618 Late autumn landscape with farm in distance (26x37cm-10x15in) s. W/C. 3-Dec-2 Ritchie, Toronto #3070/R est:1200-1800 (C.D 1000)
£622 $1033 €902 Landscape at dusk (27x37cm-11x15in) s. W/C. 10-Jun-3 Ritchie, Toronto #108 est:600-900 (C.D 1400)
£641 $1006 €1000 Paysage (20x28cm-8x11in) s. W/C. 13-Dec-2 Piasa, Paris #224
£711 $1180 €1031 Lengthening shadows (27x37cm-11x15in) W/C. 10-Jun-3 Ritchie, Toronto #110/R est:800-1200 (C.D 1600)
£756 $1254 €1096 Evening on the river (23x30cm-9x12in) s. W/C. 10-Jun-3 Ritchie, Toronto #109/R est:700-1000 (C.D 1700)
£756 $1254 €1096 Tranquil river view (25x33cm-10x13in) s. W/C. 10-Jun-3 Ritchie, Toronto #111 est:700-900 (C.D 1700)
£1026 $1610 €1600 Etang de la Liva pres Morestel (21x26cm-8x10in) studio st. W/C. 13-Dec-2 Piasa, Paris #228
£1081 $1686 €1600 Paysage au crepuscule (14x20cm-6x8in) s. W/C gouache over crayon. 26-Mar-3 Piasa, Paris #119
£1329 $2100 €2100 Paysage au soleil couchant (29x42cm-11x17in) s. W/C. 28-Nov-2 Tajan, Paris #154/R
£1346 $2113 €2100 Escalier au-dessus du precipice (29x21cm-11x8in) s. W/C. 13-Dec-2 Piasa, Paris #227/R
£1346 $2113 €2100 Paysage au couchant (23x29cm-9x11in) s. W/C. 13-Dec-2 Piasa, Paris #225
£1891 $2969 €2950 Riviere e sous-bois (43x28cm-17x11in) s. W/C. 13-Dec-2 Piasa, Paris #230

RAVIER, Auguste François (attrib) (1814-1895) French
£348 $539 €522 Paysage avant l'orage (22x32cm-9x13in) s. panel. 7-Dec-2 Galerie du Rhone, Sion #113 (S.FR 800)

RAVILIOUS, Eric (1903-1942) British
Works on paper
£30000 $49200 €45000 New year snow (46x54cm-18x21in) s. pencil pen ink W/C executed 1935 exhib.lit. 6-Jun-3 Christie's, London #91/R est:10000-15000

RAVN, Lars (1959-) Danish
£635 $984 €953 Large flower (130x97cm-51x38in) s.d.1991. 1-Oct-2 Rasmussen, Copenhagen #234/R (D.KR 7500)

RAWLINGS, Leo (1918-1990) British
Works on paper
£2000 $3180 €3000 Interior of a prison hut, Changi, Singapore (23x27cm-9x11in) s. W/C prov. 29-Apr-3 Bonhams, New Bond Street #29/R est:2000-3000
£3000 $4770 €4500 Extensive view of Changi jail Pow camp (23x28cm-9x11in) indis sig.i. W/C prov. 29-Apr-3 Bonhams, New Bond Street #30/R est:2000-3000
£3200 $5088 €4800 Prisoners working on the aerodrome at Changi (28x46cm-11x18in) s.i.d.1944 W/C prov. 29-Apr-3 Bonhams, New Bond Street #28/R est:2000-3000
£20000 $31800 €30000 To and the dawn came up like thunder (34x49cm-13x19in) s.i. W/C bodycol set of 192. 29-Apr-3 Bonhams, New Bond Street #26/R est:20000-30000

RAWORTH, William Henry (1820-1905) Australian
Works on paper
£470 $734 €705 Lake Wakatipu (37x87cm-15x34in) s.d.1877 W/C. 7-Nov-2 International Art Centre, Auckland #129/R est:1500-2500 (NZ.D 1500)
£500 $810 €750 Lake Pkaki, Otago, New Zealand (33x56cm-13x22in) s.i. W/C. 20-May-3 Sotheby's, Olympia #184/R
£650 $1040 €943 Early settlers (34x65cm-13x26in) s. W/C. 13-May-3 Watson's, Christchurch #45/R (NZ.D 1800)
£799 $1135 €1199 Lake Pukaki (34x61cm-13x24in) s.i. W/C prov. 21-Nov-1 Watson's, Christchurch #49/R est:3000-5000 (NZ.D 2750)

RAWSON, Carl W (1884-1970) American
£348 $543 €580 Untitled - Summer cove (40x51cm-16x20in) s.d.1929 board prov. 13-Apr-3 Levis, Calgary #213/R (C.D 800)
£573 $900 €860 Autumn hills (41x51cm-16x20in) s. board. 23-Nov-2 Jackson's, Cedar Falls #75/R

RAY, Charles (1953-) American
Photographs
£44304 $70000 €66456 All my clothes (23x152cm-9x60in) sixteen kodachrome photographs mounted on board executed 1973. 13-Nov-2 Christie's, Rockefeller NY #74/R est:100000-150000

£75949 $120000 €113924 Untitled (69x100cm-27x39in) gelatin silver print mounted on board executed 1973 prov.exhib. 13-Nov-2 Christie's, Rockefeller NY #69/R est:150000-200000

RAY, Gary (20th C) American
£745 $1200 €1118 Ventura coastal (28x36cm-11x14in) s. board. 18-Feb-3 John Moran, Pasadena #130
£1242 $2000 €1863 Montecito landscape (51x61cm-20x24in) s. 18-Feb-3 John Moran, Pasadena #131 est:2000-3000
£1356 $2250 €1966 Carpinteria Bluffs (46x61cm-18x24in) s. i.verso. 11-Jun-3 Butterfields, San Francisco #4346/R est:3000-5000
£1656 $2750 €2401 Santa Barbara coast, looking south from Carpenteria (51x61cm-20x24in) s. 11-Jun-3 Butterfields, San Francisco #4345/R est:3000-5000

RAY, Jules le (19/20th C) French
£1389 $2264 €2000 Doelan, la criee, pecheur et Bretonnes aux paniers de poissons (52x78cm-20x31in) s. 19-Jul-3 Thierry & Lannon, Brest #148/R est:1400-1600
£1875 $3056 €2700 Retour de peche sur le port de Doelan (60x73cm-24x29in) s. painted c.1927. 19-Jul-3 Thierry & Lannon, Brest #147/R est:1400-1600
£4366 $7030 €6200 Vue de Quimperle - Bretonnes sur le pont (50x64cm-20x25in) s. 11-May-3 Thierry & Lannon, Brest #198/R est:6000-6500

RAY, Ruth (1919-1977) American
£2532 $4000 €3798 Ancient past future world (61x76cm-24x30in) s.d.1944 prov. 24-Apr-3 Shannon's, Milford #84/R est:4000-6000

RAY, Stuart (1916-1985) British
£380 $589 €570 Leicester Square (24x30cm-9x12in) board. 4-Dec-2 Christie's, Kensington #414

RAYA-SORKINE (1936-) French
£976 $1600 €1415 En promenada (74x58cm-29x23in) s. s.i.d.1992 verso. 4-Jun-3 Doyle, New York #15 est:2000-3000
£1034 $1728 €1500 Bouquet rouge (70x80cm-28x31in) s. i.verso. 9-Jul-3 Cornette de St.Cyr, Paris #198/R est:1500-1800
£1384 $2145 €2200 Le cirque, clowns musiciens (50x61cm-20x24in) s.d.1967. 30-Oct-2 Artcurial Briest, Paris #412 est:1500-2500
£1603 $2516 €2500 Sagesse devant Notre-Dame (73x60cm-29x24in) s. s.i.verso cardboard. 12-Dec-2 Rabourdin & Choppin de Janvry, Paris #142/R
£1689 $2635 €2500 Voyage de la Bretonne (55x46cm-22x18in) s. s.i.verso. 26-Mar-3 Millon & Associes, Paris #139/R est:2500
£2230 $3478 €3300 Femme enceinte (73x54cm-29x21in) s. s.i.verso. 26-Mar-3 Millon & Associes, Paris #140/R
£2756 $4328 €4300 Maries de Venise (46x55cm-18x22in) s. s.i.d.1952 verso. 12-Dec-2 Rabourdin & Choppin de Janvry, Paris #141/R

RAYBAUD, Alexandre (?) French?
£1644 $2564 €2400 Nature morte a l'ombrelle japonaise (70x119cm-28x47in) s. 8-Apr-3 Gioffredo, Nice #50/R

RAYBORG, B A (19th C) American
£1019 $1600 €1529 Visit from the doctor (102x140cm-40x55in) s. 28-Jul-2 Butterfields, San Francisco #3021 est:600-800

RAYLICH, Thomas (1940-) Dutch
£633 $1000 €1000 Untitled (20x20cm-8x8in) s.d.82 verso oil pencil prov. 26-Nov-2 Sotheby's, Amsterdam #284/R est:450-650

RAYMOND, Marie (1908-1988) French
£577 $906 €900 Terre verte (46x55cm-18x22in) s. 24-Nov-2 Laurence Calmels, Paris #233/R
£578 $919 €850 Composition (38x46cm-15x18in) s. panel painted c.1950. 26-Feb-3 Artcurial Briest, Paris #466
£647 $1036 €900 Composition abstraite (17x59cm-7x23in) s. isorel. 14-May-3 Blanchet, Paris #178
£823 $1300 €1300 Composition abstraite (50x61cm-20x24in) s. painted c.1957. 27-Nov-2 Lemoine & Ferrando, Paris #110/R
£1923 $3019 €3000 Untitled (73x54cm-29x21in) s. prov.exhib. 24-Nov-2 Laurence Calmels, Paris #235/R
£2449 $3894 €3600 Composition (130x81cm-51x32in) s. painted c.1950. 26-Feb-3 Artcurial Briest, Paris #465/R est:2300-2800
£2885 $4529 €4500 Untitled (49x60cm-19x24in) s. prov.exhib. 24-Nov-2 Laurence Calmels, Paris #234/R

RAYMOND, Maurice (20th C) ?
£402 $635 €603 Still life with grapes (36x46cm-14x18in) d.1941 canvasboard. 1-Dec-2 Levis, Calgary #81/R (C.D 1000)

RAYNAUD, Jean Pierre (1939-) French
Sculpture
£3265 $5192 €4800 Vitrail (81x57cm-32x22in) metal wood prov. 26-Feb-3 Artcurial Briest, Paris #416/R est:5000-6000
£9375 $14907 €13500 Coin (100x75x75cm-39x30x30in) assemblage polyester enamelled steel lit. 29-Apr-3 Artcurial Briest, Paris #375/R est:15000-18000
Works on paper
£7143 $11357 €10500 Carrelage 5 (79x63cm-31x25in) s.i.verso mixed media exec.1974 exhib.lit. 24-Mar-3 Cornette de St.Cyr, Paris #42/R est:7000
£9524 $15143 €14000 Drapeau libre (62x154cm-24x61in) s.d.1987 verso flag mixed media exhib. 24-Mar-3 Cornette de St.Cyr, Paris #43/R est:15000
£15972 $26354 €23000 Bleu, blanc, rouge (178x193cm-70x76in) s.i.d.87 verso fabric tiles panel exhib. 1-Jul-3 Artcurial Briest, Paris #534/R est:23000-30000
£19231 $30192 €30000 Psycho-objet 27B2 (122x183cm-48x72in) s.i.d.1966 assemblage paint panel prov.exhib.lit. 11-Dec-2 Artcurial Briest, Paris #734a/R est:40000

RAYNER, Gordon (20th C) Canadian
£402 $635 €603 Another Egypt (48x196cm-19x77in) d.1969 acrylic. 1-Dec-2 Levis, Calgary #326/R (C.D 1000)

RAYNER, Henry Hewitt (1903-1957) Australian
£224 $327 €336 Yellow chrysanthemums (56x43cm-22x17in) s. board. 12-Sep-1 Watson's, Christchurch #32/R est:1000-2000 (NZ.D 750)
£239 $349 €359 Brighton Beach (28x48cm-11x19in) board. 12-Sep-1 Watson's, Christchurch #28 (NZ.D 800)
£478 $697 €717 Brighton Beach (45x55cm-18x22in) s.d.1933 board. 12-Sep-1 Watson's, Christchurch #26/R est:1000-3000 (NZ.D 1600)
£507 $741 €761 An English beach (43x55cm-17x22in) s.d.1952 board. 12-Sep-1 Watson's, Christchurch #27 est:1000-3000 (NZ.D 1700)
£821 $1198 €1232 Yacht race (32x46cm-13x18in) s. board. 12-Sep-1 Watson's, Christchurch #30/R est:1000-3000 (NZ.D 2750)
£970 $1416 €1455 My last portrait of Sir Walter Sickert (58x38cm-23x15in) s. board. 12-Sep-1 Watson's, Christchurch #31/R est:1000-3000 (NZ.D 3250)
£1164 $1700 €1746 French beach (38x52cm-15x20in) s. 12-Sep-1 Watson's, Christchurch #29/R est:1000-3000 (NZ.D 3900)

RAYNER, Louise (1832-1924) British
Works on paper
£1800 $2754 €2700 Children playing in a graveyard, Edinburgh Castle behind (23x23cm-9x9in) s. W/C gouache. 22-Aug-2 Bonhams, Edinburgh #1113/R est:2000-3000
£2148 $3458 €3200 Cathedral interior (50x38cm-20x15in) s. i.d.1868 verso W/C htd bdycol. 18-Feb-3 Whyte's, Dublin #204/R est:2000-3000
£8000 $12720 €12000 View of York (35x26cm-14x10in) s. W/C. 19-Mar-3 Sotheby's, London #229/R est:8000-12000
£13000 $20150 €19500 Canongate Tolbooth looking up the Royal Mile (35x25cm-14x10in) s. pencil W/C prov. 31-Oct-2 Christie's, London #62/R est:8000-12000

RAYNER, Margaret (fl.1866-1895) British
Works on paper
£222 $364 €322 Children playing on the church grounds (39x29cm-15x11in) s. W/C gouache. 9-Jun-3 Hodgins, Calgary #168/R (C.D 500)

RAYNER, Samuel (?-1874) British
Works on paper
£320 $496 €480 Old watermill (132x104cm-52x41in) s.d.1866 W/C bodycol. 26-Sep-2 Lane, Penzance #178
£360 $562 €540 Ecclesiastical interior with monks by monumental effigies and a font (36x52cm-14x20in) mono.d.58 W/C. 6-Nov-2 Bonhams, Chester #442
£400 $624 €600 Church interior (43x60cm-17x24in) W/C htd bodycol. 17-Sep-2 Sotheby's, Olympia #128/R
£700 $1148 €1050 Interior of the chapel Haddon Hall (43x58cm-17x23in) mono. W/C. 2-Jun-3 David Duggleby, Scarborough #255/R
£900 $1422 €1350 Faest at Haddon Hall (55x71cm-22x28in) mono.d.64 W/C bodycol. 1-Dec-2 Lots Road, London #335

RAYSSE, Martial (1936-) French
£5248 $8765 €7400 Coin decoupe (22x16cm-9x6in) s.d.verso acrylic collage prov. 23-Jun-3 Claude Boisgirard, Paris #161/R est:3500-4000
Sculpture
£3125 $4969 €4500 Sans titre (18x24x21cm-7x9x8in) s.i.d.1972 verso wood stone paper mache photo prov.exhib. 29-Apr-3 Artcurial Briest, Paris #352/R est:3500-4000

Works on paper

£1156 $1804 €1734 Dessin No.4 (32x40cm-13x16in) s.i.d.76 verso gouache prov.exhib. 6-Nov-2 AB Stockholms Auktionsverk #944/R est:12000-15000 (S.KR 16500)

£12000 $19680 €18000 Loco bello, image X (133x200cm-52x79in) pastel tempera mixed media board plexiglass box prov.exhib. 7-Feb-3 Sotheby's, London #213/R est:8000-10000

RAZA, Sayed Haider (1922-) Indian

£800 $1248 €1200 Abstract (46x61cm-18x24in) s.i.d.Mai 1965 paper prov. 17-Oct-2 Bonhams, Knightsbridge #547/R

£4662 $7692 €6760 Janama bhoomi (50x50cm-20x20in) s.d.02 s.i.d.2002 verso acrylic. 6-Jul-3 Christie's, Hong Kong #88/R est:65000-85000 (HK.D 60000)

£6605 $10897 €9577 Feuillaison (55x46cm-22x18in) s.d.70 i.d.verso. 6-Jul-3 Christie's, Hong Kong #87/R est:80000-100000 (HK.D 85000)

Works on paper

£1400 $2184 €2100 Indo-Pharma (22x32cm-9x13in) W/C prov. 17-Oct-2 Bonhams, Knightsbridge #546/R est:1500-2000

£1855 $2931 €2783 Eglise jaune (48x63cm-19x25in) s.d.56 mixed media masonite prov. 18-Nov-2 Waddingtons, Toronto #264/R est:1000-1500 (C.D 4600)

RAZUMOV, Konstantin (1974-) Russian

£250 $388 €375 In the child's room (35x27cm-14x11in) s. 29-Sep-2 John Nicholson, Haslemere #96

£260 $403 €390 Young girl with dolls (35x27cm-14x11in) s. 8-Dec-2 John Nicholson, Haslemere #178

£280 $434 €420 Drinking tea (33x24cm-13x9in) s. 8-Dec-2 John Nicholson, Haslemere #111/R

£300 $465 €450 Svetlana (35x27cm-14x11in) s. 29-Sep-2 John Nicholson, Haslemere #55

£300 $465 €450 Getting ready to a ballet play (24x35cm-9x14in) s. 29-Sep-2 John Nicholson, Haslemere #95/R

£300 $465 €450 Before the play (33x24cm-13x9in) s. 29-Sep-2 John Nicholson, Haslemere #161

£350 $543 €525 Girl with a violin (33x41cm-13x16in) s. 29-Sep-2 John Nicholson, Haslemere #97

£350 $543 €525 Little girl with her toy (33x24cm-13x9in) s. 29-Sep-2 John Nicholson, Haslemere #134/R

£350 $543 €525 We are drawing (33x24cm-13x9in) s. 29-Sep-2 John Nicholson, Haslemere #190

£350 $543 €525 Nu (46x33cm-18x13in) s. 29-Sep-2 John Nicholson, Haslemere #199

£500 $775 €750 Girl with a toy bear (33x24cm-13x9in) s. 8-Dec-2 John Nicholson, Haslemere #3/R

£500 $775 €750 Girl with a violin (35x22cm-14x9in) s. 8-Dec-2 John Nicholson, Haslemere #85

£500 $775 €750 Motherhood (50x40cm-20x16in) s. 29-Sep-2 John Nicholson, Haslemere #98

£500 $775 €750 While drawing (22x27cm-9x11in) s. 29-Sep-2 John Nicholson, Haslemere #133/R

£608 $949 €900 Tea time (50x35cm-20x14in) s. 25-Mar-3 Durán, Madrid #747/R

£650 $1007 €975 Little ballerina (22x27cm-9x11in) s. 8-Dec-2 John Nicholson, Haslemere #1/R

£750 $1163 €1125 Playing cards (55x38cm-22x15in) s. 8-Dec-2 John Nicholson, Haslemere #82

£850 $1318 €1275 Ballerina in a ballet suit (65x50cm-26x20in) s. 29-Sep-2 John Nicholson, Haslemere #130/R

£900 $1395 €1350 Last preparation (30x30cm-12x12in) s. 8-Dec-2 John Nicholson, Haslemere #78/R

£900 $1395 €1350 Etude of a woman's figure (41x27cm-16x11in) s. 8-Dec-2 John Nicholson, Haslemere #83/R

£900 $1395 €1350 Girl in a hat (35x27cm-14x11in) s. 29-Sep-2 John Nicholson, Haslemere #129/R

£1000 $1550 €1500 Girl with dolla (50x33cm-20x13in) s. 8-Dec-2 John Nicholson, Haslemere #79/R

£1200 $1860 €1800 After bathing (46x55cm-18x22in) s. 29-Sep-2 John Nicholson, Haslemere #159/R

£1355 $2141 €2100 Clothes for my dolls (55x46cm-22x18in) s. 17-Dec-2 Durán, Madrid #665/R

£1400 $2170 €2100 Playful dog, it's my time (55x46cm-22x18in) s. 29-Sep-2 John Nicholson, Haslemere #94/R

£1500 $2325 €2250 Picnic (60x73cm-24x29in) s. 8-Dec-2 John Nicholson, Haslemere #4/R

£1600 $2480 €2400 My favourite toys (61x50cm-24x20in) s. 29-Sep-2 John Nicholson, Haslemere #135/R

£1700 $2635 €2550 On the terrace of Ritz Hotel, Madrid (50x61cm-20x24in) s. 8-Dec-2 John Nicholson, Haslemere #77/R

£1700 $2635 €2550 Near the mirror (55x46cm-22x18in) s. 29-Sep-2 John Nicholson, Haslemere #92/R

£1900 $2945 €2850 Girls and kittens (55x46cm-22x18in) s. 8-Dec-2 John Nicholson, Haslemere #130

£2000 $3100 €3000 Portrait of a pretty girl (35x27cm-14x11in) s. 8-Dec-2 John Nicholson, Haslemere #2/R

£2000 $3100 €3000 Morning bath (61x50cm-24x20in) s. 8-Dec-2 John Nicholson, Haslemere #81/R

£2200 $3410 €3300 On the shore with my dogs (61x50cm-24x20in) s. 8-Dec-2 John Nicholson, Haslemere #127/R

£2200 $3410 €3300 Two ballerinas (65x54cm-26x21in) s. 8-Dec-2 John Nicholson, Haslemere #128/R

£2200 $3410 €3300 Morning (61x50cm-24x20in) s. 29-Sep-2 John Nicholson, Haslemere #99

£2300 $3565 €3450 Portrait of a girl (46x38cm-18x15in) s. 8-Dec-2 John Nicholson, Haslemere #129/R

£2300 $3565 €3450 Near the window (55x38cm-22x15in) s. 29-Sep-2 John Nicholson, Haslemere #132/R

£3300 $5115 €4950 Morning (46x38cm-18x15in) s. 8-Dec-2 John Nicholson, Haslemere #80/R

£4000 $6200 €6000 During the introduction (50x61cm-20x24in) s. 29-Sep-2 John Nicholson, Haslemere #128/R

RE, Primo (20th C) Italian

£256 $400 €384 Venice (61x71cm-24x28in) s. 22-Sep-2 Susanin's, Chicago #5088/R

REA, Constance (19/20th C) British

£2100 $3339 €3150 An Arcadian Idyll (69x90cm-27x35in) 26-Feb-3 Sotheby's, Olympia #221/R est:2000-3000

READ, Catherine (1723-1778) British

£2500 $4150 €3750 Portrait of Elizabeth Dashwood, later Duchess of Manchester (60x49cm-24x19in) oval. 12-Jun-3 Sotheby's, London #62/R est:3000-4000

Works on paper

£4200 $6930 €6090 Portrait of Stephen Fox, Lord Holland. Portrait of Caroline, Lady Holland (56x45cm-22x18in) one i. pastel pair. 2-Jul-3 Sotheby's, Olympia #163/R est:2000-3000

READ, Charles Carter (fl.1882-1907) British

£650 $1040 €975 Luccombe, Isle of Wight (30x51cm-12x20in) s. 7-Jan-3 Bonhams, Knightsbridge #227i/R

READ, Edward (18/19th C) British

£500 $760 €750 Unintended intrusion (46x38cm-18x15in) s.d.1903 panel. 29-Aug-2 Christie's, Kensington #151

READ, George A (fl.1876-?) British

£300 $468 €450 Still life of a French partridge with a blue and white jug and fruit in a basket (25x28cm-10x11in) init.d.1871 i.verso board. 9-Apr-3 Cheffins Grain & Comins, Cambridge #702/R

READ, Harry Hope (fl.1907-1928) British

Works on paper

£260 $416 €390 Ladies at Hastings beach (18x28cm-7x11in) ini.,d.1923 pencil. 11-Mar-3 Gorringes, Lewes #2446

READ, John (?) British

£330 $528 €495 Suspense (56x70cm-22x28in) after Sir Edwin Henry Landseer. 15-May-3 Lawrence, Crewkerne #920

READ, Samuel (1816-1883) British

Works on paper

£3000 $4740 €4500 Entrance to the banqueting hall, Greenwich (60x44cm-24x17in) s.d.1843 W/C. 26-Nov-2 Bonhams, Knightsbridge #173/R est:600-800

READ, William (18/19th C) British

£950 $1473 €1425 Haymaker (62x43cm-24x17in) s. 25-Sep-2 Hamptons Fine Art, Godalming #375/R

READY, William James Durant (1823-1873) British

£460 $699 €690 Shipping on the coast with fisherfolk (17x28cm-7x11in) init. artist's board. 4-Jul-2 Mellors & Kirk, Nottingham #823

REAL DEL SARTE, M (1888-1954) French

£320 $499 €480 Still life of flowers in an albarello (55x46cm-22x18in) s. 13-Sep-2 Jacobs & Hunt, Petersfield #184/R

REAL, Daniel (1877-1931) French

£566 $872 €900 Rue de village orientale (38x46cm-15x18in) s. panel. 23-Oct-2 Rabourdin & Choppin de Janvry, Paris #242/R

REAL, Rafael del (1932-) Spanish

£577 $912 €900 Cattle in landscape (89x116cm-35x46in) s. s.i.verso. 19-Nov-2 Durán, Madrid #80/R

REAM, C P (1837-1917) American
£1227 $2000 €1841 Raspberries in landscape (46x38cm-18x15in) s. panel. 1-Feb-3 Thomaston Place, Thomaston #46

REAM, Carducius Plantagenet (1837-1917) American
£875 $1400 €1269 Still life with fruits and nuts (16x31cm-6x12in) s. board. 16-May-3 Skinner, Boston #84/R est:1800-2200
£1104 $1700 €1656 Plums on a silver plate (20x25cm-8x10in) s. prov. 24-Oct-2 Shannon's, Milford #213/R
£2108 $3500 €3057 Still life with peaches (46x56cm-18x22in) s. prov. 11-Jun-3 Butterfields, San Francisco #4023/R est:4000-6000
£2500 $4000 €3625 Still life with champagne and fruit (25x20cm-10x8in) s. board. 16-May-3 Skinner, Boston #90/R est:4000-6000
£2848 $4500 €4272 Still life with grapes (46x66cm-18x26in) s. 24-Apr-3 Shannon's, Milford #112/R est:5000-7000
£3503 $5500 €5255 Still life with peaches (31x38cm-12x15in) s. 22-Nov-2 Skinner, Boston #98/R est:4000-6000

REAM, Morston C (1840-1898) American
£5063 $8000 €7595 Still life with wine glass, fruit and nuts (28x36cm-11x14in) s. prov. 24-Apr-3 Shannon's, Milford #45/R est:6000-8000

REASER, Wilbur Aaron (1860-1942) American
Works on paper
£1084 $1800 €1572 Isle of Capri (64x112cm-25x44in) i.verso pastel. 14-Jun-3 Jackson's, Cedar Falls #14/R est:2000-3000

REAUGH, Charles Franklin (1860-1945) American
Works on paper
£2673 $4250 €4010 Longhorn in a Texas landscape (3x6cm-1x2in) s. pastel paperboard exec.c.1900. 4-May-3 Treadway Gallery, Cincinnati #562/R est:2500-3500

REBAY, Hilla (1890-1967) American/French
Works on paper
£854 $1400 €1238 Cotton club (27x21cm-11x8in) s.i. pencil W/C. 5-Jun-3 Swann Galleries, New York #204/R
£1220 $2000 €1769 Untitled (25x20cm-10x8in) s.d.1913 W/C prov. 1-Jun-3 Wright, Chicago #151/R est:1000-1500

REBECCA, Biagio (1735-1808) British/Italian
£250 $418 €363 Landscape with river and figures (24x32cm-9x13in) 17-Jun-3 Bristol Auction Rooms #536

REBELL, Joseph (1787-1828) Austrian
£20000 $31600 €29000 View of Ischia (44x59cm-17x23in) s.d.1813 lit. 3-Apr-3 Porro, Milan #45/R est:40000
Works on paper
£1772 $2800 €2800 Classical landscape with temple and figures (37x50cm-15x20in) s.d.1809 pen wash chk. 29-Nov-2 Bassenge, Berlin #6026 est:1400
£2027 $3162 €3000 Boats on Lake Como (28x41cm-11x16in) s.d.1810 W/C. 28-Mar-3 Dorotheum, Vienna #174/R est:4000-4500

REBEYROLLE, Paul (1926-) French
£1266 $2000 €2000 Untitled (28x36cm-11x14in) s.d.1959 paper. 27-Nov-2 Tajan, Paris #3/R
Works on paper
£1049 $1752 €1500 Belier (33x25cm-13x10in) s.d. blue crayon prov. 26-Jun-3 Tajan, Paris #168/R est:1200-1500

REBOLLEDO CORREA, Benito (1880-1964) Chilean
£1282 $2026 €2000 Boy with jug (53x42cm-21x17in) s. 19-Nov-2 Durán, Madrid #186/R

REBOURGEON, L (?) ?
£800 $1264 €1200 Dishing craft drying their sails on the lagoon, Venice (55x68cm-22x27in) s. 14-Nov-2 Christie's, Kensington #204/R

REBOUSSIN, Roger Andre Fernand (1881-1965) French
£261 $421 €400 Renard et papillon (33x41cm-13x16in) s.d.1924. 16-Jan-3 Muizon & Le Coent, Paris #1

REBRY, Gaston (1933-) Canadian
£242 $377 €363 Shawanigan (40x50cm-16x20in) s. 30-Jul-2 Iegor de Saint Hippolyte, Montreal #125 (C.D 600)
£267 $437 €401 Winter stillness (30x40cm-12x16in) s. 3-Jun-3 Joyner, Toronto #590 (C.D 600)
£329 $510 €494 Winter sunset (40x50cm-16x20in) s. 3-Dec-2 Joyner, Toronto #435 (C.D 800)
£412 $638 €618 Gatineau, P Que (40x50cm-16x20in) s. 3-Dec-2 Joyner, Toronto #263/R est:1000-1500 (C.D 1000)
£435 $679 €653 L'ete au lac Long (40x61cm-16x24in) s. s.i.d.1985 verso. 30-Jul-2 Iegor de Saint Hippolyte, Montreal #126 (C.D 1080)
£442 $694 €663 Maison de grand pere (45x60cm-18x24in) s.i.d.1983. 25-Nov-2 Hodgins, Calgary #35/R (C.D 1100)
£556 $911 €806 Dawn at island lake (46x61cm-18x24in) 1-Jun-3 Levis, Calgary #112/R est:1500-1800 (C.D 1250)
£667 $1093 €1001 Le Grand Rocher (50x40cm-20x16in) s. 3-Jun-3 Joyner, Toronto #387/R est:1000-1200 (C.D 1500)
£823 $1276 €1235 Fin d'aout, Mauricie, P. Que (60x75cm-24x30in) s. painted 1989 prov. 3-Dec-2 Joyner, Toronto #301/R est:2000-2500 (C.D 2000)
£1152 $1786 €1728 Doux hiver (100x75cm-39x30in) s. 3-Dec-2 Joyner, Toronto #323/R est:2500-3000 (C.D 2800)
£1630 $2543 €2719 Tourbillon (101x76cm-40x30in) s. s.i.verso prov. 13-Apr-3 Levis, Calgary #99/R est:4000-4500 (C.D 3750)

RECALCATI, Antonio (1938-) Italian
£641 $994 €1000 Untitled (80x70cm-31x28in) s.d.1962 verso. 4-Dec-2 Finarte, Milan #309
£1111 $1756 €1600 More (100x80cm-39x31in) s.i.d.verso acrylic. 27-Apr-3 Perrin, Versailles #66 est:800-1000
£1164 $1816 €1700 Moments (102x76cm-40x30in) s.verso. 10-Apr-3 Finarte Semenzato, Rome #235/R
£1709 $2649 €2700 Sans titre (200x300cm-79x118in) prov. 28-Sep-2 Cornette de St.Cyr, Paris #407/R est:3000-4000
Works on paper
£513 $795 €800 Figures and waves (70x50cm-28x20in) s.i.d.1967 verso mixed media on canvas. 5-Dec-2 Stadion, Trieste #718/R

RECCHI, Giovanni Paolo (attrib) (c.1600-1683) Italian
£2400 $3768 €3600 Crucifixion of saint peter (40x50cm-16x20in) 10-Dec-2 Bonhams, New Bond Street #285/R est:2500-3500

RECCO, Elena (attrib) (17th C) Italian
£3873 $6430 €5500 Still life with mushrooms (48x61cm-19x24in) one of pair. 11-Jun-3 Dorotheum, Vienna #9/R est:5000-7000
£4225 $7014 €6000 Still life with pears (48x61cm-19x24in) one of pair. 11-Jun-3 Dorotheum, Vienna #10/R est:5000-7000

RECCO, Giovan Battista (1630-1675) Italian
£17610 $27296 €28000 Still life with fruit and game birds (72x48cm-28x19in) prov.lit. 2-Oct-2 Dorotheum, Vienna #37/R est:28000-35000

RECCO, Giuseppe (1634-1695) Italian
£40848 $66991 €59230 Still life of flowers and musical instruments (80x110cm-31x43in) prov. 4-Jun-3 AB Stockholms Auktionsverk #2542/R est:300000-400000 (S.KR 520000)

RECHER, Peter Emil (1879-1948) German
£382 $596 €600 Morcote on Lake Lugano (57x45cm-22x18in) s. 6-Nov-2 Hugo Ruef, Munich #1245/R

RECHLIN, Karl (1804-1882) German
£1132 $1766 €1800 Old soldier telling children about his adventures (50x74cm-20x29in) s.i.d.3/58. 19-Sep-2 Dr Fritz Nagel, Stuttgart #987/R

RECIPON, Georges (1860-1920) French
Sculpture
£1500 $2445 €2250 Allegorical group of a woman with a lion (80cm-31in) s.i. gilt bronze. 11-Feb-3 Sotheby's, Olympia #340/R est:1500-2500
£2200 $3432 €3300 Good luck charm (15cm-6in) s.i. gilt silvered bronze st.f.Susse. 9-Apr-3 Sotheby's, London #133/R est:1500-2000

RECKELBUS, Louis (1864-1958) Belgian
£1019 $1590 €1600 Canal a Dixmude (54x75cm-21x30in) s. mixed media cardboard. 11-Nov-2 Horta, Bruxelles #712 est:1000-1500
Works on paper
£1800 $2790 €2700 Cottage and a haystack (37x56cm-15x22in) s. gouache on card. 5-Dec-2 Christie's, Kensington #87/R est:2000-3000
£2025 $3200 €3200 Vieux chateau, vue du chateau de Zottegem (75x109cm-30x43in) s. 26-Nov-2 Palais de Beaux Arts, Brussels #144/R est:2300-3500

RECKHARD, Gardner Arnold (1858-1908) American
£400 $640 €600 River landscape at sunset (9x14cm-4x6in) s. board. 13-May-3 Bonhams, Knightsbridge #126/R

RECKLESS, Stanley Lawrence (attrib) (1892-?) American
£705 $1100 €1058 Impressionist landscape (15x10cm-6x4in) board prov. 18-Sep-2 Alderfer's, Hatfield #330/R

RECKNAGEL, Otto (1845-1926) German
£373 $596 €570 Head of stag of ten points (39x28cm-15x11in) s.i. canvas on board lit. 10-Jan-3 Allgauer, Kempten #1734/R

RECKNAGL, Theodor (19th C) German
£1300 $2002 €1950 Oriental beauty (58x49cm-23x19in) s.d.1901. 24-Oct-2 Christie's, Kensington #184/R est:1500-2000

REDDY, Krishna (1925-) Indian
£696 $1079 €1100 Personnage dans une ville (110x58cm-43x23in) s.d. panel. 28-Sep-2 Cornette de St.Cyr, Paris #186

REDEL, Eike (1951-) German
£417 $646 €650 Tiger (80x60cm-31x24in) s. panel. 5-Dec-2 Schopman, Hamburg #591
£559 $906 €850 Der jager - the hunter (32x63cm-13x25in) s.i.verso panel. 21-Jan-3 Christie's, Amsterdam #419
£950 $1501 €1425 Two tigers bathing (80x140cm-31x55in) s.d.2000. 14-Nov-2 Christie's, Kensington #225/R

REDER, Bernard (1897-1963) Israeli
£2400 $3816 €3600 Bride with red glove (130x109cm-51x43in) s.d.1958 prov. 20-Mar-3 Sotheby's, Olympia #208/R est:2500-3500

REDER, Christian (attrib) (1656-1729) German
£2000 $3120 €3000 Riding school, with a town beyond (50x66cm-20x26in) 9-Apr-3 Bonhams, New Bond Street #61/R est:1500-2000

REDER-BROILI, Franz (1854-1918) German
£545 $855 €850 Gulf of Sorrento (24x37cm-9x15in) s. 21-Nov-2 Van Ham, Cologne #1880

REDFIELD, Edward (1869-1965) American
£9063 $14500 €13595 Monhegan winter (28x36cm-11x14in) s. 11-Jan-3 James Julia, Fairfield #89a est:20000-30000
£19355 $30000 €29033 Town of St. Nazaire on the Mediterranean (60x83cm-24x33in) s.i.d.90 prov.exhib.lit. 5-Dec-2 Christie's, Rockefeller NY #89/R est:25000-35000
£20958 $35000 €30389 Flock in a snowy field (66x81cm-26x32in) bears sig indis d. lit. 22-Jun-3 Freeman, Philadelphia #162/R est:30000-50000
£35484 $55000 €53226 Winter afternoon (56x47cm-22x19in) s. painted c.1903. 5-Dec-2 Christie's, Rockefeller NY #93/R est:60000-80000
£62112 $100000 €93168 Winter landscape with meandering brook, trees and a house (66x81cm-26x32in) s.i. prov.exhib. 22-Feb-3 Pook & Pook, Downington #94/R est:40000-60000
£188679 $300000 €283019 Winter solitude (66x81cm-26x32in) i. s.on stretcher painted c.1920 prov.lit. 5-Mar-3 Sotheby's, New York #71/R est:40000-60000
£245161 $380000 €367742 Spring at point Pleasant on the Delaware River (96x127cm-38x50in) s.d.1926 prov.exhib.lit. 5-Dec-2 Christie's, Rockefeller NY #91/R est:250000-350000

Works on paper
£282 $446 €423 Red barn (30x41cm-12x16in) s. W/C prov. 18-Nov-2 Waddingtons, Toronto #9/R (C.D 700)

REDGATE, Arthur W (fl.1880-1906) British
£300 $501 €435 Spring blossom (20x38cm-8x15in) s. board. 18-Jun-3 Andrew Hartley, Ilkley #1150
£657 $1051 €986 Landscape with swans on lake (30x45cm-12x18in) s. 13-Jan-3 Rasmussen, Vejle #258/R (D.KR 7500)
£750 $1155 €1125 Feeding the bonfire (51x76cm-20x30in) s. i.verso. 5-Sep-2 Christie's, Kensington #207/R
£1200 $1848 €1800 Pastures new (61x51cm-24x20in) s. 5-Sep-2 Christie's, Kensington #208/R est:1200-1800

REDGRAVE, Richard (1804-1888) British
£85000 $136850 €127500 Seamstress (64x77cm-25x30in) s.d.1846 i.verso prov.exhib.lit. 20-Feb-3 Christie's, London #110/R est:50000

REDLICH-VISZEG, Gustav von (20th C) Austrian
£369 $595 €550 Celebration of a marriage (129x90cm-51x35in) s. 18-Feb-3 Sotheby's, Amsterdam #325/R

REDMOND, Granville (1871-1935) American
£1774 $2750 €2661 Landscape - dunes and cliffs (10x13cm-4x5in) init. canvasboard prov. 29-Oct-2 John Moran, Pasadena #604 est:4000-6000
£1935 $3000 €2903 California landscape with poppies (5x5cm-2x2in) init. canvasboard prov. 29-Oct-2 John Moran, Pasadena #603a est:4000-6000
£1958 $3250 €2839 High desert in bloom (8x13cm-3x5in) bears init. canvasboard. 11-Jun-3 Butterfields, San Francisco #4249/R est:3000-5000
£4459 $7000 €6689 Fishing on the Seine (24x36cm-9x14in) s. 20-Nov-2 Christie's, Los Angeles #88/R est:4000-6000
£8125 $13000 €12188 Moonrise (15x30cm-6x12in) s. 11-Jan-3 Harvey Clar, Oakland #1436
£12903 $20000 €19355 Twilight (61x92cm-24x36in) s. prov. 4-Dec-2 Sotheby's, New York #141/R est:25000-35000
£19108 $30000 €28662 Field of poppies with snowcapped mountains in the distance (28x36cm-11x14in) i.verso masonite. 19-Nov-2 Butterfields, San Francisco #8196/R est:25000-35000
£20958 $35000 €30389 Landscape with poppies and lupin (18x25cm-7x10in) s.d.1914 canvasboard prov. 18-Jun-3 Christie's, Los Angeles #79/R est:30000-50000
£47771 $75000 €71657 San Mateo Hills with the Oakland Hills beyond (41x51cm-16x20in) s.d.1914 prov. 19-Nov-2 Butterfields, San Francisco #8218/R est:40000-60000
£48193 $80000 €69880 California landscape with poppies and lupines (41x51cm-16x20in) s. prov. 11-Jun-3 Butterfields, San Francisco #4234/R est:60000-80000
£119760 $200000 €173652 Haystacks, California (51x66cm-20x26in) s.d.1913 prov. 18-Jun-3 Christie's, Los Angeles #8/R est:80000-120000

REDMORE, Edward King (1860-1941) British
£280 $456 €420 Fishing vessels in stormy seas (36x43cm-14x17in) s. 7-Feb-3 Dee Atkinson & Harrison, Driffield #685
£280 $456 €420 Fishing vessels by the cliffs (36x43cm-14x17in) s. 7-Feb-3 Dee Atkinson & Harrison, Driffield #686
£320 $518 €464 Fishing boat in rough seas (33x41cm-13x16in) s. 23-May-3 Dee Atkinson & Harrison, Driffield #612/R
£650 $1027 €975 Fishing boats in rough seas, windmill in the distance (25cm-10in circular) s. panel. 29-Nov-2 Dee Atkinson & Harrison, Driffield #796/R
£1000 $1670 €1450 Shipping running down the north-East Coast (41x66cm-16x26in) s. 8-Jul-3 Bonhams, Knightsbridge #175/R est:1000-1500
£1600 $2432 €2400 Small merchant traders drying their sails offshore (24x39cm-9x15in) mono. 15-Aug-2 Bonhams, New Bond Street #330/R est:1200-1800

REDMORE, Edward King (attrib) (1860-1941) British
£600 $1002 €870 Dutch man-o-war with sailing barges in the foreground (29x44cm-11x17in) init.d.1876 canvas on board. 18-Jun-3 Sotheby's, Olympia #72/R

REDMORE, Henry (1820-1887) British
£1300 $2119 €1950 Vessel floundering on the rocks (23x48cm-9x19in) s. board. 7-Feb-3 Dee Atkinson & Harrison, Driffield #704/R est:800-1200
£1500 $2355 €2250 Seascape with figures on a life raft in the foreground (26x45cm-10x18in) s. indis d.1870. 19-Nov-2 Bonhams, Leeds #184/R est:1500-2500
£2300 $3726 €3450 Shipping off Dover (20x30cm-8x12in) s. indis d. 22-Jan-3 Bonhams, New Bond Street #369/R est:2000-3000
£2300 $3841 €3335 Shipping at anchor (33x49cm-13x19in) s.d.1880 board. 18-Jun-3 Sotheby's, Olympia #64/R est:2000-3000
£3000 $4710 €4500 Figures and fishing boats in a calm off the Humber estuary (28x46cm-11x18in) s. 19-Nov-2 Bonhams, Leeds #181/R est:3000-4000
£3500 $5495 €5250 Coastal scene with figures hauling in nets (21x31cm-8x12in) s. 19-Nov-2 Bonhams, Leeds #183/R est:1500-2500
£3600 $5616 €5400 Fishing smacks in choppy seas outside Scarborough harbour (30x45cm-12x18in) s. 10-Sep-2 David Duggleby, Scarborough #372/R est:4000-6000
£3800 $5890 €5700 Running home (20x37cm-8x15in) s.d.1881. 31-Oct-2 Christie's, Kensington #523/R est:2000-3000
£3800 $6156 €5700 Stranding (47x76cm-19x30in) s.d.1874. 21-May-3 Christie's, Kensington #557/R est:3000-5000
£4100 $6396 €6150 Shipping in a heavy swell, Whitby harbour beyond (25x38cm-10x15in) s. 10-Sep-2 David Duggleby, Scarborough #382 est:3000-4000
£5000 $7750 €7500 Reducing sail at the entrance to Whitby Harbour. Fishing fleet retuning to Scarborough (37x57cm-15x22in) s. panel pair. 31-Oct-2 Christie's, Kensington #522/R est:6000-8000
£5000 $7850 €7500 Seascape with fishing boats and figures, possibly off the Humber estuary (21x31cm-8x12in) s. indis d.1861. 19-Nov-2 Bonhams, Leeds #182/R est:2500-3000
£5000 $8000 €7500 Fishing boats near a wrecked frigate (62x97cm-24x38in) s.d.1883. 15-May-3 Lawrence, Crewkerne #971/R est:2000-3000
£5800 $8990 €8700 Merchant brig and smaller traffic off Scarborough (36x60cm-14x24in) init.d.1865. 31-Oct-2 Christie's, Kensington #520/R est:3000-5000
£6000 $9480 €8700 Harbour at dusk (55x100cm-22x39in) s.d.1872. 28-Jul-3 David Duggleby, Scarborough #270/R est:6000-8000
£6500 $10530 €9750 Barges shortening sail offshore (38x60cm-15x24in) s.d.1861. 21-May-3 Christie's, Kensington #556/R est:3000-5000

£7000 $11620 €10500 Heavy squall of the coast of Scarborough (76x122cm-30x48in) s.d.1861. 12-Jun-3 Sotheby's, London #235b/R est:7000-10000
£7400 $11470 €11100 Low tide at Margate (36x61cm-14x24in) s.d.1865. 31-Oct-2 Christie's, Kensington #521/R est:3000-5000
£8000 $12960 €12000 Schooner and fishing vessels in a calm. Dutch fishing barges (20x30cm-8x12in) s. one d.1862 pair. 21-May-3 Christie's, Kensington #558/R est:7000-10000
£8200 $13612 €12300 Passing storm. Gathering storm (20x33cm-8x13in) s.d.1869-70 panel pair. 12-Jun-3 Sotheby's, London #230/R est:6000-8000
£11000 $17380 €16500 Fishing vessels heading out to sea. Fishing vessels and a merchant ship in choppy seas (35x56cm-14x22in) s.d.1866 pair. 2-Dec-2 Sotheby's, London #36/R est:10000-15000
£11000 $17930 €15950 Fishing boats and a steam packet entering Whitby Harbour (61x101cm-24x40in) s.d.1881. 17-Jul-3 Tennants, Leyburn #813/R est:10000-15000
£12500 $20875 €18125 Wreck buoy (62x103cm-24x41in) s.d.1877 i.verso. 18-Jun-3 Sotheby's, Olympia #74/R est:10000-15000

REDMORE, Henry (attrib) (1820-1887) British
£878 $1369 €1317 Ships anchored in an estuary (12x38cm-5x15in) board. 10-Nov-2 Dunbar Sloane, Auckland #21 est:3000-5000 (NZ.D 2800)
£1900 $3002 €2850 Shipping in a calm (34x48cm-13x19in) bears sig. 27-Nov-2 Hamptons Fine Art, Godalming #338 est:1800-2500
£4658 $7313 €6987 Seascapes (20x30cm-8x12in) one with sig.d.1863 pair. 16-Dec-2 Lilla Bukowskis, Stockholm #494 est:15000-18000 (S.KR 66000)

REDON, Gaston (1853-1921) French
Works on paper
£6790 $11000 €10185 Fantastic town (25x32cm-10x13in) s.d.96 pen ink. 22-Jan-3 Christie's, Rockefeller NY #114/R est:3000

REDON, Georges (19/20th C) French
£637 $994 €1000 Fillette au manchon (45x38cm-18x15in) s. s.d1932 verso panel. 7-Nov-2 Chochon-Barre & Allardi, Paris #216/R
Works on paper
£287 $447 €450 Scene galante (26x33cm-10x13in) s. pastel oval. 7-Nov-2 Chochon-Barre & Allardi, Paris #215

REDON, Odilon (1840-1916) French
£20513 $32000 €30770 La naissance de Venus (46x37cm-18x15in) s. prov.exhib.lit. 7-Nov-2 Christie's, Rockefeller NY #239/R est:50000-70000
£21795 $34000 €32693 Les bouleaux en automme (25x32cm-10x13in) s. oil paper on board prov.exhib.lit. 7-Nov-2 Christie's, Rockefeller NY #212/R est:40000-60000
£30000 $50100 €43500 La chrysalide (35x26cm-14x10in) s. prov.exhib. 25-Jun-3 Christie's, London #104/R est:40000-60000
£146853 $245245 €210000 Barque mystique (42x37cm-17x15in) s. detrempe cardboard painted c.1897 prov.lit. 30-Jun-3 Pierre Berge, Paris #61/R est:200000-230000
Prints
£2254 $3741 €3200 Un masque sonne le glas funebre (26x19cm-10x7in) s. lithograph. 14-Jun-3 Hauswedell & Nolte, Hamburg #1545/R est:3500
£2390 $3800 €3585 Gnome (27x22cm-11x9in) lithograph. 1-May-3 Swann Galleries, New York #340/R est:2000-3000
£2949 $4600 €4424 La sulamite (24x19cm-9x7in) s.i. col lithograph edition of 15. 7-Nov-2 Swann Galleries, New York #477a/R est:6000-9000
£3270 $5200 €4905 Ari (21x12cm-8x5in) i. lithograph. 1-May-3 Swann Galleries, New York #345/R est:10000-15000
£3774 $6000 €5661 Tete d'enfant avec fleurs (25x21cm-10x8in) num.29/35 lithograph. 2-May-3 Sotheby's, New York #345/R est:8000-12000
£5282 $8768 €7500 Profil de lumiere (34x24cm-13x9in) s. lithograph. 14-Jun-3 Hauswedell & Nolte, Hamburg #1547/R est:10000
£8805 $14000 €13208 Tete d'enfant avec fleurs (32x25cm-13x10in) lithograph on chine volant exhib. 1-May-3 Swann Galleries, New York #344/R est:12000-18000
£11538 $18000 €17307 A Edgar Poe, Paris, G Fischbacher (32x45cm-13x18in) lithograph edition of 50 set of 6. 5-Nov-2 Christie's, Rockefeller NY #19/R est:15000-20000
Works on paper
£7372 $11647 €11500 Mystere (15x13cm-6x5in) s. crayon htd white exhib. 15-Nov-2 Laurence Calmels, Paris #26b/R est:12000
£18000 $30060 €26100 Tete de femme (30x25cm-12x10in) s. pencil chl prov.lit. 24-Jun-3 Sotheby's, London #221/R est:20000-30000
£19231 $30000 €28847 Crucifixion (53x28cm-21x11in) s. chl prov.exhib.lit. 7-Nov-2 Christie's, Rockefeller NY #120/R est:35000-45000
£25641 $40000 €38462 Ophelie (37x46cm-15x18in) s. chl prov.exhib.lit. 7-Nov-2 Christie's, Rockefeller NY #119/R est:80000-100000
£30000 $50100 €45000 Carnet de dessins l dit 'du pays basque' (11x18cm-4x7in) pencil executed 1862-1863 album prov.exhib.lit. 26-Jun-3 Christie's, London #357/R est:30000-40000
£57692 $90000 €86538 Mercure (42x37cm-17x15in) s. chl graphite paper on board exhib.lit. 7-Nov-2 Christie's, Rockefeller NY #116/R est:80000-100000
£75000 $125250 €108750 Profil feminin (43x37cm-17x15in) s. chl prov.exhib.lit. 24-Jun-3 Christie's, London #40/R est:60000-90000
£76923 $120000 €115385 Le crucifix (49x37cm-19x15in) s. pastel black chk paper on board exhib.lit. 7-Nov-2 Christie's, Rockefeller NY #118/R est:250000-350000
£95000 $158650 €137750 Le chevalier mystique, le Sphinx (115x89cm-45x35in) s. chl black brown pastel htd white chk exec.c.1892 prov.exhib.li. 24-Jun-3 Christie's, London #41/R est:90000-120000
£108974 $170000 €163461 Centaure lisant (48x38cm-19x15in) s. chl prov.exhib.lit. 7-Nov-2 Christie's, Rockefeller NY #115/R est:120000-160000
£281690 $467606 €400000 Vase de fleurs (82x64cm-32x25in) s. pastel prov.exhib.lit. 12-Jun-3 Tajan, Paris #9/R est:500000-600000

REDONDELA, Agustin (1922-) Spanish
£3045 $4811 €4750 Village in the valley (27x35cm-11x14in) s. board. 19-Nov-2 Durán, Madrid #226/R
£3448 $5517 €5000 Meeting (27x35cm-11x14in) s. board. 11-Mar-3 Castellana, Madrid #64/R
£4138 $6538 €6000 Village people (27x35cm-11x14in) s. s.i.d.2001 verso board. 1-Apr-3 Segre, Madrid #336/R
£5975 $9201 €9500 Market (27x35cm-11x14in) s. s.i.d.01 verso board. 22-Oct-2 Durán, Madrid #199/R est:9000
£8966 $14345 €13000 Landscape (46x55cm-18x22in) s.d.68. 11-Mar-3 Castellana, Madrid #357/R est:6000
Works on paper
£811 $1265 €1200 Little shop (17x25cm-7x10in) s.d.1983 W/C. 25-Mar-3 Durán, Madrid #150/R
£1548 $2446 €2400 Church (48x33cm-19x13in) s. W/C. 18-Dec-2 Ansorena, Madrid #233/R

REDOUTE, Pierre Joseph (1759-1840) French
Works on paper
£11111 $18000 €16667 Tradescantia erecta (46x34cm-18x13in) s. W/C pencil on vellum prov. 23-Jan-3 Sotheby's, New York #82/R est:20000-30000
£17284 $28000 €25926 Allium ampeloprasum (48x35cm-19x14in) s. W/C pencil on vellum prov. 23-Jan-3 Sotheby's, New York #83/R est:30000-40000
£19753 $32000 €29630 Gladiolus inclinatus. Ixia longifora (47x34cm-19x13in) s. one i. W/C panel on vellum pair prov. 23-Jan-3 Sotheby's, New York #81/R est:25000-35000
£23457 $38000 €35186 Veltheimia Capensis (46x34cm-18x13in) s. W/C prov. 23-Jan-3 Sotheby's, New York #84/R est:30000-50000
£27778 $45000 €41667 Amaryllis atamasco (48x34cm-19x13in) s. W/C pencil on vellum prov. 23-Jan-3 Sotheby's, New York #80/R est:15000-20000
£35802 $58000 €53703 Bouquet with violas, carnations, jasmine and a poppy (21x15cm-8x6in) s. W/C bodycol vellum. 22-Jan-3 Christie's, Rockefeller NY #80/R est:16000
£40000 $66800 €58000 Caribbean New World pancratius lily (48x34cm-19x13in) s. W/C vellum. 9-Jul-3 Sotheby's, London #117/R est:40000-60000
£135802 $220000 €203703 Hemerocallis fulva day lilly (48x34cm-19x13in) s. W/C prov. 23-Jan-3 Sotheby's, New York #79/R est:50000-70000
£148148 $240000 €222222 Globba nutans (46x34cm-18x13in) s. indis i. W/C pencil on vellum prov. 23-Jan-3 Sotheby's, New York #85/R est:50000-70000

REDOUTE, Pierre Joseph (attrib) (1759-1840) French
Works on paper
£348 $550 €550 Etudes de champignons (37x22cm-15x9in) bears sig. crayon pen W/C. 29-Nov-2 Coutau Begarie, Paris #92

REDPATH, Anne (1895-1965) British
£3500 $5425 €5250 Golden teapot (51x61cm-20x24in) s. board prov. 31-Oct-2 Christie's, London #178/R est:4000-6000
£5000 $7750 €7500 Still life with flowers, wine glasses and fruit (71x91cm-28x36in) s. prov. 31-Oct-2 Christie's, London #177/R est:7000-10000
£6500 $10075 €9750 Fruit on an ashet (29x39cm-11x15in) s. panel. 5-Dec-2 Bonhams, Edinburgh #92/R est:7000-10000
£7000 $10850 €10500 Mushrooms and aubergines (42x66cm-17x26in) s. board exhib. 31-Oct-2 Christie's, London #176/R est:8000-12000
£9000 $13950 €13500 White cineraria (76x63cm-30x25in) s. board exhib. 31-Oct-2 Christie's, London #175/R est:10000-15000
£13000 $20280 €19500 San Nicolo (61x51cm-24x20in) s. prov. 14-Apr-3 Sotheby's, London #172/R est:8000-12000
£19000 $30780 €28500 Still life of roses (42x48cm-17x19in) s. board. 23-May-3 Lyon & Turnbull, Edinburgh #92/R est:4000-6000
£25000 $38000 €37500 Seaside town (63x76cm-25x30in) s. prov. 28-Aug-2 Sotheby's, London #1057/R est:12000-18000
£46000 $71760 €69000 Daisies (53x44cm-21x17in) s. i.verso board prov. 14-Apr-3 Sotheby's, London #169/R est:20000-30000
£78000 $121680 €117000 Prelude to spring (76x85cm-30x33in) s. prov.exhib. 14-Apr-3 Sotheby's, London #170/R est:20000-30000

Works on paper
£1800 $2754 €2700 Border houses (13x22cm-5x9in) W/C gouache prov. 22-Aug-2 Bonhams, Edinburgh #1155/R est:1200-1500
£2000 $3160 €3000 Still life of flowers (47x38cm-19x15in) s. ink gouache wash. 27-Nov-2 Sotheby's, Olympia #1/R est:800-1200
£3800 $5814 €5700 Jane and a China cat (45x35cm-18x14in) s. W/C gouache over pencil exhib. 22-Aug-2 Bonhams, Edinburgh #1040/R est:4000-6000
£4000 $6080 €6000 Palms (57x77cm-22x30in) s. W/C gouache over pencil. 28-Aug-2 Sotheby's, London #1028/R est:4000-6000
£4800 $7680 €7200 Still life study of a vase of lilies (56x61cm-22x24in) s. gouache. 8-Jan-3 Brightwells, Leominster #1094/R est:500-600
£5800 $8990 €8700 Still life with white (70x56cm-28x22in) s. W/C. 6-Dec-2 Lyon & Turnbull, Edinburgh #60/R est:4000-6000
£6200 $9486 €9300 Old house, Portugal (22x31cm-9x12in) s. gouache over pencil. 22-Aug-2 Bonhams, Edinburgh #1152/R est:1500-2000
£7000 $10850 €10500 Still life with jug and plate (49x49cm-19x19in) s. black crayon W/C. 31-Oct-2 Christie's, London #179/R est:3000-5000

REDPATH, Norma (1928-) Australian
Sculpture
£1395 $2219 €2093 Untitled (13x14cm-5x6in) init.d.67 bronze. 5-May-3 Sotheby's, Melbourne #188/R est:4000-6000 (A.D 3600)

REDWORTH, William (19th C) British
£520 $848 €754 Lancelot (43x54cm-17x21in) s.i.d.Nov 1902 i.board verso. 16-Jul-3 Sotheby's, Olympia #71/R

REE, Anita (1885-1933) German
Works on paper
£1275 $2090 €1950 Cacti in front of wall (41x31cm-16x12in) mono. mixed media oil tempera Indian ink board. 8-Feb-3 Hans Stahl, Hamburg #138/R est:2200

REEB, David (1952-) Israeli
£1513 $2390 €2270 Sea road, Haifa (99x69cm-39x27in) s.d.1988 card on canvas. 27-Apr-3 Sotheby's, Tel Aviv #96/R est:3000-5000

REED, David (1946-) American
£3165 $5000 €4748 No 140 (69x110cm-27x43in) s.i.d.1975 verso acrylic diptych prov. 12-Nov-2 Phillips, New York #140/R est:6000-8000
£5625 $9000 €8438 Untitled no.151 (71x49cm-28x19in) s.i.d.1979 on overlap acrylic on canvas in two parts prov. 14-May-3 Sotheby's, New York #435/R est:5000-7000

REED, Doel (1894-1985) American
Prints
£1763 $2750 €2645 Picuris Pueblo, winter (25x41cm-10x16in) s. etching aquatint prov.lit. 9-Nov-2 Santa Fe Art, Santa Fe #232/R est:1500-2500

REED, Joseph (1822-1877) British
Works on paper
£260 $411 €390 Haymaking on a summer's day (31x48cm-12x19in) s. W/C. 26-Nov-2 Bonhams, Knightsbridge #113
£380 $604 €570 Fishermen beside a Highland loch (29x65cm-11x26in) s.d.1872 W/C. 25-Feb-3 Bonhams, Knightsbridge #188/R

REED, Marjorie (1915-1997) American
£449 $700 €674 Canyon trail (13x18cm-5x7in) s. canvas on board prov. 9-Nov-2 Santa Fe Art, Santa Fe #72/R
£516 $800 €774 Artist painting in forest interior (51x41cm-20x16in) s. canvasboard. 29-Oct-2 John Moran, Pasadena #777
£812 $1300 €1218 Bringin in a bunch (41x51cm-16x20in) s. canvasboard. 16-Mar-3 Butterfields, San Francisco #1057 est:1500-2000
£886 $1400 €1285 West apache pass, summer storm (23x30cm-9x12in) s. board prov. 26-Jul-3 Coeur d'Alene, Hayden #43/R est:1000-1500
£1557 $2600 €2258 Oh mamal (41x51cm-16x20in) s. 18-Jun-3 Christie's, Los Angeles #34/R est:2500-3500
£2019 $3250 €3029 Old Round Rock Trading Post (76x102cm-30x40in) s. prov. 18-Feb-3 John Moran, Pasadena #152 est:2500-3500
£3293 $5500 €4775 Mission San Antonio de Padua (122x183cm-48x72in) s. i.verso. 17-Jun-3 John Moran, Pasadena #173 est:3500-4500
£10759 $17000 €15601 All aboard (76x102cm-30x40in) s. prov. 26-Jul-3 Coeur d'Alene, Hayden #214/R est:8000-12000

REED, William (1908-) New Zealander
£2070 $3250 €3105 Canterbury landscape with autumn trees and cottages before a mountain range (69x118cm-27x46in) s. board. 10-Dec-2 Peter Webb, Auckland #78/R est:8000-12000 (NZ.D 6500)

REED, William J (20th C) New Zealander
£877 $1368 €1316 Shell (45x58cm-18x23in) s. board. 27-Mar-3 International Art Centre, Auckland #54/R (NZ.D 2500)
£1404 $2189 €2106 Rower boy, Otago (33x26cm-13x10in) s. board prov. 27-Mar-3 International Art Centre, Auckland #36/R est:5000-7000 (NZ.D 4000)
£3135 $4890 €4703 Fisherman's jetty, Southland (62x42cm-24x17in) s. board prov.exhib. 7-Nov-2 International Art Centre, Auckland #19/R est:10000-15000 (NZ.D 10000)
£3509 $5474 €5264 Mariners Bay (43x58cm-17x23in) s. board prov.exhib. 27-Mar-3 International Art Centre, Auckland #35/R est:10000-15000 (NZ.D 10000)
Works on paper
£1332 $2078 €1998 Self portrait with shells (27x39cm-11x15in) s. mixed media. 7-Nov-2 International Art Centre, Auckland #20/R est:4000-7000 (NZ.D 4250)

REEDE, Johan van (1921-) Dutch
£293 $457 €460 Hairdresser's (50x39cm-20x15in) s. 5-Nov-2 Vendu Notarishuis, Rotterdam #127/R

REEDER, Dixon (1912-1970) American
£1282 $2000 €1923 Flora in Paris (41x30cm-16x12in) canvasboard. 19-Oct-2 David Dike, Dallas #145a/R est:750-1500
£1474 $2300 €2211 Three kings (20x18cm-8x7in) canvasboard. 19-Oct-2 David Dike, Dallas #145/R est:1500-3000

REEDY, Leonard Howard (1899-1956) American
£1883 $2900 €2825 Shootout (61x76cm-24x30in) s. painted c.1935. 8-Sep-2 Treadway Gallery, Cincinnati #600/R est:2500-4500
Works on paper
£368 $600 €552 Wolves and buffalo (20x28cm-8x11in) s. pencil W/C. 16-Feb-3 Butterfields, San Francisco #2108
£488 $800 €708 Untitled (33x43cm-13x17in) s. pair. 7-Jun-3 Susanin's, Chicago #5038/R
£577 $900 €866 Untitled (18x28cm-7x11in) W/C. 19-Oct-2 David Dike, Dallas #197/R

REEKERS, Johannes (1790-1858) Dutch
£2420 $3776 €3800 Interior with tea drinking party near a cabinet (49x40cm-19x16in) s.d.1813 panel. 5-Nov-2 Vendu Notarishuis, Rotterdam #89 est:1000-1500
Works on paper
£786 $1219 €1250 Bouquet (36x23cm-14x9in) s. W/C. 4-Nov-2 Glerum, Amsterdam #91/R

REEKERS, Johannes (jnr) (1824-1895) Dutch
£2917 $4813 €4200 Still life with various fruit and flowers (59x45cm-23x18in) s.d.51 panel. 1-Jul-3 Christie's, Amsterdam #35/R est:4000-6000

REEP, Edward (1918-) American
Works on paper
£1406 $2250 €2109 Figures (27x19cm-11x7in) W/C gouache. 14-Mar-3 Du Mouchelle, Detroit #2009/R est:3000-4000

REES, Lloyd Frederick (1895-1988) Australian
£2174 $3435 €3261 Pink roses in a glass vase (37x27cm-15x11in) s. painted c.1935. 18-Nov-2 Goodman, Sydney #138/R est:7000-12000 (A.D 6090)
£2500 $3925 €3750 May morning Bathurst 2 (24x34cm-9x13in) init.d.76 paper prov. 25-Nov-2 Christie's, Melbourne #200/R est:8000-12000 (A.D 7000)
£3846 $6115 €5769 Sydney harbour (19x31cm-7x12in) s.d.60 canvas on board. 4-Mar-3 Deutscher-Menzies, Melbourne #96/R est:9000-12000 (A.D 10000)
£6429 $10157 €9644 West Pennant Hills (28x35cm-11x14in) s. board. 18-Nov-2 Goodman, Sydney #142/R est:18000-28000 (A.D 18000)
£8397 $13267 €12596 Summer morning, North Ryde (46x61cm-18x24in) s.d.50 i.verso prov. 7-Apr-3 Shapiro, Sydney #439/R est:10000-15000 (A.D 22000)
£8462 $13454 €12693 Towards the city, Sydney (30x45cm-12x18in) s.d.56 canvas on board. 4-Mar-3 Deutscher-Menzies, Melbourne #110/R est:20000-30000 (A.D 22000)
£8929 $14018 €13394 Shoalhaven yachts (19x30cm-7x12in) s.d.57 board prov.lit. 25-Nov-2 Christie's, Melbourne #2/R est:18000-25000 (A.D 25000)

£11494 $18046 €17241 Untitled 1957 - possibly the reef, Werri Beach (51x61cm-20x24in) s. prov.exhib. 15-Apr-3 Lawson Menzies, Sydney #38/R est:30000-40000 (A.D 30000)
£13953 $22186 €20930 Yellow broom in flower (31x41cm-12x16in) s.d.56 i.verso panel. 5-May-3 Sotheby's, Melbourne #111/R est:28000-38000 (A.D 36000)
£14504 $22916 €21756 Cornish fishing village (29x37cm-11x15in) s.d.23 prov.exhib.lit. 2-Apr-3 Christie's, Melbourne #4/R est:18000-25000 (A.D 38000)
£17438 $26680 €26157 Sydney dream (121x137cm-48x54in) init.d.87 prov. 26-Aug-2 Sotheby's, Paddington #529/R est:65000-85000 (A.D 49000)
£19643 $31035 €29465 Dusk, Illawarra coast (93x123cm-37x48in) s.d.79 i.verso prov. 27-Nov-2 Deutscher-Menzies, Melbourne #44/R est:65000-85000 (A.D 55000)
£19920 $32669 €28884 Summer at Richmond, Tasmania (61x91cm-24x36in) s.d.69 composition board prov.lit. 4-Jun-3 Deutscher-Menzies, Melbourne #39/R est:50000-70000 (A.D 50000)
£28470 $43559 €42705 Woolwich (49x60cm-19x24in) s.d.57 prov. 25-Aug-2 Sotheby's, Paddington #3/R est:40000-60000 (A.D 80000)
£28571 $45143 €42857 Sydney opera house, from Dawes Point (89x150cm-35x59in) s.d.81 prov.lit. 17-Nov-2 Sotheby's, Paddington #36/R est:100000-150000 (A.D 80000)
£68000 $109480 €102000 Tuscany (88x108cm-35x43in) s.d57-63-72 prov. 6-May-3 Christie's, Melbourne #37/R est:140000-180000 (A.D 170000)

Works on paper
£429 $677 €644 Landscape (11x14cm-4x6in) s. pencil. 26-Nov-2 Sotheby's, Melbourne #144 est:1200-1800 (A.D 1200)
£500 $790 €750 Church on a hill (12x10cm-5x4in) init. pencil. 26-Nov-2 Sotheby's, Melbourne #138 est:1200-1800 (A.D 1400)
£1220 $1927 €1769 Country scene (12x17cm-5x7in) s.d.1933 pencil. 22-Jul-3 Lawson Menzies, Sydney #167/R est:3000-5000 (A.D 3000)
£1357 $2131 €2036 Interior St Paul's Cathedral (32x20cm-13x8in) init.d.69 ink prov.exhib. 25-Nov-2 Christie's, Melbourne #396/R est:3000-5000 (A.D 3800)
£1829 $2891 €2652 Cliff face (38x45cm-15x18in) s.d.1966 chl pencil wash. 22-Jul-3 Lawson Menzies, Sydney #169/R est:5000-7000 (A.D 4500)
£2313 $3539 €3470 Italy (33x43cm-13x17in) s.d.66 ink W/C. 25-Aug-2 Sotheby's, Paddington #202/R est:5000-7000 (A.D 6500)
£2500 $3925 €3750 Elizabeth Street entrance, Central Station, Sydney (17x23cm-7x9in) ink exec.c.1922 prov. 25-Nov-2 Christie's, Melbourne #373/R est:5000-7000 (A.D 7000)
£3101 $4930 €4652 Boats in the bay (37x55cm-15x22in) s.d.81 W/C pastel oil exhib. 5-May-3 Sotheby's, Melbourne #195/R est:8000-12000 (A.D 8000)
£3125 $4938 €4688 Tingira, Berry's Bay, Sydney Harbour (15x21cm-6x8in) pencil executed c.1933 prov. 26-Nov-2 Sotheby's, Melbourne #85/R est:7000-10000 (A.D 8750)
£3559 $5445 €5339 Illawarra House (17x29cm-7x11in) s.d.1943 pencil prov. 26-Aug-2 Sotheby's, Paddington #652/R est:3000-5000 (A.D 10000)

REES, Otto van (1884-1957) Dutch
£7051 $10929 €11000 Family (132x156cm-52x61in) s. painted c.1935 prov. 3-Dec-2 Christie's, Amsterdam #320/R est:12000-16000
£17986 $29496 €25000 Nature morte - still life (33x28cm-13x11in) s. oil collage on canvas painted c.1916-17 prov.lit. 3-Jun-3 Christie's, Amsterdam #250/R est:10000-15000

Works on paper
£449 $704 €700 Portrait d'un adolescent (51x41cm-20x16in) studio st. mixed media. 10-Dec-2 Campo, Vlaamse Kaai #544
£1026 $1590 €1600 Cubist composition (24x15cm-9x6in) gouache prov. 3-Dec-2 Christie's, Amsterdam #321/R est:1000-1500
£1090 $1689 €1700 Nude with still life (17x12cm-7x5in) gouache set of three prov. 3-Dec-2 Christie's, Amsterdam #323/R est:1000-1500
£1218 $1888 €1900 Nude torso (29x22cm-11x9in) gouache prov. 3-Dec-2 Christie's, Amsterdam #322/R est:1000-1500

REEVE-FOWKES, Amy C (1886-1968) British
Works on paper
£420 $689 €630 Autumn glory (69x94cm-27x37in) s. pencil W/C htd white. 5-Jun-3 Christie's, Kensington #902/R

REEVES, Joseph Mason (jnr) (1898-1974) American
£435 $700 €653 Reclining nude on colourful drape (41x51cm-16x20in) s. prov. 18-Feb-3 John Moran, Pasadena #182
£452 $700 €678 Sam McGee (36x30cm-14x12in) s. i.verso prov. 29-Oct-2 John Moran, Pasadena #652
£452 $700 €678 Negro woman wearing red bandana (43x36cm-17x14in) s. prov. 29-Oct-2 John Moran, Pasadena #653
£613 $950 €920 Swimsuit model in blue (81x58cm-32x23in) s. prov. 29-Oct-2 John Moran, Pasadena #760
£683 $1100 €1025 Man in blue overalls (46x36cm-18x14in) s. prov. 18-Feb-3 John Moran, Pasadena #146c
£1032 $1600 €1548 Cowboy in ten gallon hat (41x33cm-16x13in) s. prov. 29-Oct-2 John Moran, Pasadena #707 est:1000-2000
£1032 $1600 €1548 Ballerina (61x51cm-24x20in) s. prov. 29-Oct-2 John Moran, Pasadena #761 est:1500-2500
£1242 $2000 €1863 Portrait of a Negro man in a floppy hat (36x30cm-14x12in) estate st. prov. 18-Feb-3 John Moran, Pasadena #146b est:800-1200
£1452 $2250 €2178 Vera (43x61cm-17x24in) s. prov. 29-Oct-2 John Moran, Pasadena #651 est:1500-2000
£1553 $2500 €2330 Portrait of Miss Elizabeth Sutton (99x89cm-39x35in) s. prov.exhib. 18-Feb-3 John Moran, Pasadena #146a est:3000-5000
£2581 $4000 €3872 Portrait of American Indian brave (76x64cm-30x25in) s. prov. 29-Oct-2 John Moran, Pasadena #703 est:3000-5000

REEVES, Mary (fl.1880-1906) British
Works on paper
£320 $506 €464 Fishing fleet in a cove (32x52cm-13x20in) s.d.1888 W/C. 28-Jul-3 David Duggleby, Scarborough #242

REFREGIER, Anton (1905-1979) American/Russian
£2404 $3750 €3606 Miners descending in elevator (53x43cm-21x17in) s. casein masonite lit. 9-Nov-2 Illustration House, New York #185/R est:4000-6000

REGAGNON, Albert (20th C) French
£237 $375 €356 Rocky stream (20x25cm-8x10in) s.d.1921. 16-Nov-2 New Orleans Auction, New Orleans #307/R
£1032 $1600 €1548 Au bord de la riviere (23x32cm-9x13in) s. panel. 2-Oct-2 Christie's, Rockefeller NY #767/R est:1000-1500

REGEMORTER, Ignatius Josephus van (1785-1873) Flemish
£750 $1200 €1125 River landscape with a fisherman casting his net (41x39cm-16x15in) s. panel. 13-May-3 Bonhams, Knightsbridge #155/R

REGENSBURG, Sophy Pollak (1885-1974) American
£290 $450 €435 Pink vase (23x30cm-9x12in) s.d.1957 i.on stretcher. 29-Oct-2 Doyle, New York #64

REGGIANI, Mauro (1897-1980) Italian
£3741 $5949 €5500 Composition 2 (60x50cm-24x20in) s.i.d.1969 verso. 1-Mar-3 Meeting Art, Vercelli #372
£9615 $14904 €15000 Composition (89x116cm-35x46in) s. painted 1953. 4-Dec-2 Finarte, Milan #298/R est:18000

Works on paper
£1736 $2760 €2500 Abstract composition (41x33cm-16x13in) s. collae card. 1-May-3 Meeting Art, Vercelli #193

REGGIANINI, Vittorio (1858-1939) Italian
£6000 $9420 €9000 Beat friends (35x27cm-14x11in) s. 19-Nov-2 Bonhams, New Bond Street #89 est:6000-8000
£22152 $35000 €33228 Elegant lady in pink (94x57cm-37x22in) s. prov. 24-Apr-3 Sotheby's, New York #71/R est:35000-45000
£24000 $40080 €36000 In the music room (71x55cm-28x22in) s. 19-Jun-3 Christie's, London #25/R est:30000-40000

REGGIO, Gianni (1898-1961) Italian
Works on paper
£1370 $2137 €2000 Maternity (98x98cm-39x39in) s. exhib. 10-Apr-3 Finarte Semenzato, Rome #122/R

REGHENZI, Piercarla (1921-) Italian
£443 $691 €700 Wind on the sea (100x70cm-39x28in) s. s.i.d.1957 verso. 19-Oct-2 Semenzato, Venice #127/R

REGILD, Carsten (1941-1992) Swedish
Works on paper
£1296 $2022 €1944 Riff raff (190x190cm-75x75in) s. mixed media collage. 5-Nov-2 Bukowskis, Stockholm #367/R est:20000-25000 (S.KR 18500)

REGNAULT, Baron Jean Baptiste (1754-1829) French
£4028 $6364 €5800 Enee et Anchise (22x17cm-9x7in) panel prov. 25-Apr-3 Beaussant & Lefèvre, Paris #29/R

Works on paper
£1818 $2600 €2727 Plato at the deathbed of Socrates (14x19cm-6x7in) brush ink wash htd white. 23-Jan-3 Swann Galleries, New York #300/R est:800-1200

REGNAULT, Baron Jean Baptiste (attrib) (1754-1829) French
£774 $1223 €1200 Tete de Saint Jean Baptiste (46x38cm-18x15in) 18-Dec-2 Piasa, Paris #103

Works on paper
£833 $1292 €1300 Pan et Syrinx (28x25cm-11x10in) mono. pen ink wash over sanguine. 4-Dec-2 Piasa, Paris #109

REGNAULT, Baron Jean Baptiste (style) (1754-1829) French
£5245 $8759 €7500 Psyche endormie enlevee par Zephir (72x92cm-28x36in) 25-Jun-3 Sotheby's, Paris #56/R est:8000-12000

REGNAULT, Georges (1898-1979) French
£823 $1300 €1300 La Seine et le Pont Marie (65x50cm-26x20in) s. 2-Dec-2 Tajan, Paris #82

REGNAULT, Henri (1843-1871) French
£2642 $4094 €4200 Auto-portrait (55x46cm-22x18in) s. 30-Oct-2 Coutau Begarie, Paris #70/R
£3526 $5571 €5500 Judith et Holopherne (45x54cm-18x21in) painted c.1867-69. 18-Nov-2 Sotheby's, Paris #56/R

REGNAULT, Henri (attrib) (1843-1871) French
£480 $749 €720 Portrait of a North African man holding a pipe (30x22cm-12x9in) 10-Sep-2 Bonhams, Knightsbridge #78/R

REGNIER, Nicolas (attrib) (1590-1667) Flemish
£8228 $12013 €13000 Fortune teller (93x129cm-37x51in) 21-May-2 Thomas Adams, Dublin #281
£8316 $12891 €13140 David (61x50cm-24x20in) 27-Sep-2 Rabourdin & Choppin de Janvry, Paris #150/R est:15000-16000

REGNIER, Nicolas (circle) (1590-1667) Flemish
£30822 $48390 €45000 Goddess Diana with hunting horn (98x83cm-39x33in) 16-Apr-3 Dorotheum, Salzburg #10/R est:5000-7000

REGO, Paula (1935-) Portuguese
Works on paper
£300 $468 €450 Seated child holding a rabbit and a monkey (21x21cm-8x8in) s.d.84 pen black ink wash. 17-Sep-2 Rosebery Fine Art, London #685

REGOS, Polykleitos (1903-1984) Greek
£2400 $3792 €3600 Meltemi, Skopelos (39x39cm-15x15in) 1-Apr-3 Bonhams, New Bond Street #60 est:2000-3000
£2800 $4424 €4200 Paraportiani church, Myconos olive grove (20x23cm-8x9in) 1-Apr-3 Bonhams, New Bond Street #56 est:1800-2200

REGOYOS, Dario de (1857-1913) Spanish
Works on paper
£20690 $32897 €30000 Dance (46x71cm-18x28in) s. pastel. 4-Mar-3 Ansorena, Madrid #173/R

REGT, Pieter de (1877-1960) Dutch
£637 $981 €1000 Aan de wind, sailing boats in a breeze (40x80cm-16x31in) s. 3-Sep-2 Christie's, Amsterdam #327/R
£637 $994 €1000 Winter scene with stranded boat (34x49cm-13x19in) s. 6-Nov-2 Vendue Huis, Gravenhage #30/R
£764 $1192 €1200 Farm (43x58cm-17x23in) s. 6-Nov-2 Vendue Huis, Gravenhage #4/R

REGTEREN ALTENA, Marie E van (1868-1958) Dutch
£1911 $2943 €3000 Still life with flowers and illustrated books (65x75cm-26x30in) init. 3-Sep-2 Christie's, Amsterdam #350/R est:1200-1600

REGTERS, Tibout (1710-1768) Dutch
£2420 $3776 €3800 Portrait of Herr Kustner, merchant (34x28cm-13x11in) s.d.1763 panel. 6-Nov-2 Hugo Ruef, Munich #954/R est:1500

REGUERA, Alberto (1961-) Spanish
£728 $1187 €1100 Landscape (73x93cm-29x37in) s.i.d.1992 verso oil mixed media. 11-Feb-3 Segre, Madrid #254/R

REHFISCH, Alison (1900-1975) Australian
£1214 $1919 €1821 Rich pastures (50x59cm-20x23in) s. canvas on board. 18-Nov-2 Goodman, Sydney #119 est:3000-5000 (A.D 3400)
£1226 $1925 €1839 Still life (38x30cm-15x12in) s. 15-Apr-3 Lawson Menzies, Sydney #68/R est:4000-6000 (A.D 3200)
£1423 $2248 €2063 Great valley (30x34cm-12x13in) s. canvas on board. 22-Jul-3 Lawson Menzies, Sydney #110/R est:4000-5000 (A.D 3500)
£1456 $2286 €2184 Cottage scene (31x35cm-12x14in) s. board. 15-Apr-3 Lawson Menzies, Sydney #167/R est:4000-5000 (A.D 3800)
£1564 $2471 €2709 Farmhouse in landscape (36x47cm-14x19in) hessian. 1-Apr-3 Goodman, Sydney #31/R est:3000-6000 (A.D 4100)
£1714 $2657 €2571 Ace of hearts (30x31cm-12x12in) s.i.verso canvasboard. 29-Oct-2 Lawson Menzies, Sydney #113/R est:2000-4000 (A.D 4800)
£1792 $2724 €2688 Farmhouse and trees (41x51cm-16x20in) s. hessian. 28-Aug-2 Deutscher-Menzies, Melbourne #167/R est:6000-8000 (A.D 5000)
£1857 $2916 €2786 Brick kiln (41x52cm-16x20in) hessian prov.exhib. 25-Nov-2 Christie's, Melbourne #398/R est:3000-5000 (A.D 5200)
£2107 $3308 €3161 Blue white flowers (29x24cm-11x9in) s. board painted c.1930 exhib. 15-Apr-3 Lawson Menzies, Sydney #21/R est:6000-7000 (A.D 5500)
£2107 $3308 €3161 Untitled - Lake Macquarie (46x61cm-18x24in) s. board exhib. 15-Apr-3 Lawson Menzies, Sydney #69/R est:5000-7000 (A.D 5500)

REHM, Helmut (1911-) Austrian
£1667 $2650 €2400 Inn valley landscape from Vomperberg (56x71cm-22x28in) s.d.1939. 29-Apr-3 Wiener Kunst Auktionen, Vienna #620/R est:2000-4000

REHN, Frank Knox Morton (1848-1914) American
£802 $1300 €1163 Sunset river landscape (41x71cm-16x28in) s. indis.i.stretcher. 21-May-3 Doyle, New York #82/R
£1019 $1600 €1529 West beach, Beverly, Massachusetts (64x76cm-25x30in) s. 10-Dec-2 Doyle, New York #46/R est:3000-5000

REHNBERG, Hakan (1953-) Swedish
£2205 $3484 €3308 Untitled (75x66cm-30x26in) s.d.2001 verso oil acrylic glass prov. 28-Apr-3 Bukowskis, Stockholm #886/R est:10000-15000 (S.KR 29000)
£2662 $4205 €3993 Untitled (75x65cm-30x26in) s.d.2000 verso oil acrylic glass prov. 28-Apr-3 Bukowskis, Stockholm #887/R est:10000-15000 (S.KR 35000)
£2738 $4325 €4107 Untitled (170x150cm-67x59in) s.d.1999 verso oil on acrylic glass prov. 28-Apr-3 Bukowskis, Stockholm #960/R est:25000-30000 (S.KR 36000)
£2857 $4600 €4286 Variation - triptych (100x139cm-39x55in) s.i.d.1986 verso oil pencil steel panel. 7-May-3 AB Stockholms Auktionsverk #951/R est:40000-60000 (S.KR 37000)
£3118 $4926 €4677 Untitled (75x62cm-30x24in) s.d.1994 verso oil on acrylic glass prov. 28-Apr-3 Bukowskis, Stockholm #960a/R est:25000-30000 (S.KR 41000)
£4555 $7106 €6833 Painting in two parts (150x100cm-59x39in) s.d.1990 oil over pencil steel panel diptych prov. 6-Nov-2 AB Stockholms Auktionsverk #801/R est:60000-70000 (S.KR 65000)

REICH AN DER STOLPE, Siegfried (1912-) German
£449 $696 €700 Orion (13x45cm-5x18in) s. board prov. 3-Dec-2 Christie's, Amsterdam #105/R
£506 $800 €800 Composition (33x45cm-13x18in) board. 30-Nov-2 Arnold, Frankfurt #455/R

REICH, Adolf (1887-1963) Austrian
£444 $701 €666 Refreshing interlude (48x32cm-19x13in) s. 18-Nov-2 Waddingtons, Toronto #26/R (C.D 1100)
£2025 $3200 €3200 Waiting room (57x73cm-22x29in) s.indis.d. board. 26-Nov-2 Christie's, Rome #80

REICH, Albert (1881-1942) German
Works on paper
£329 $513 €480 Soldiers resting in Piazza Vittorio Emanuele in Udine (38x29cm-15x11in) s.i. W/C htd bodycol over pencil. 11-Apr-3 Winterberg, Heidelberg #1541

REICH, Josef (19/20th C) ?
£550 $897 €825 Still life of china and apples on a table (54x70cm-21x28in) s.d.1912. 12-Feb-3 Bonhams, Knightsbridge #278/R

REICH, Paul (1925-) German
Sculpture
£1013 $1580 €1600 Untitled (48cm-19in) bronze plexiglas. 18-Oct-2 Dr Fritz Nagel, Stuttgart #299/R est:1200

REICHART, Carl (?) ?
Works on paper
£450 $752 €653 On the Venetian lagoon (26x57cm-10x22in) s.d.1877 W/C. 24-Jun-3 Bonhams, Knightsbridge #2/R

REICHART, Joseph Francis (20th C) American
£774 $1200 €1161 Winter landscape (25x36cm-10x14in) s. board. 25-Sep-2 Doyle, New York #71/R

REICHEK, Jesse (1916-) American
£881 $1400 €1277 Abstract composition (51x86cm-20x34in) s.d. prov. 4-May-3 Treadway Gallery, Cincinnati #643/R
£881 $1400 €1277 Abstract composition (51x86cm-20x34in) s.d. prov. 4-May-3 Treadway Gallery, Cincinnati #644/R

REICHEL, Hans (1892-1958) German
Works on paper
£937 $1547 €1350 Composition (18x12cm-7x5in) mono.d. W/C. 1-Jul-3 Rossini, Paris #41/R
£1348 $2183 €1900 Carte de voeux (13x10cm-5x4in) mono.i. W/C exec.c.1948. 23-May-3 Binoche, Paris #14 est:800-1000
£2319 $3803 €3200 Composition (21x33cm-8x13in) mono.i.d.1953 W/C Indian ink brush over pencil paper on board. 31-May-3 Villa Grisebach, Berlin #667/R est:1800-2200
£2535 $4082 €3600 Night poetry (18x27cm-7x11in) s.d.1941 mixed media linen lit. 9-May-3 Schloss Ahlden, Ahlden #1564/R est:3600
£2619 $4164 €3850 Sans titre (29x23cm-11x9in) mono.d.1949 W/C ink. 26-Feb-3 Artcurial Briest, Paris #68/R est:2500-3000
£2848 $4500 €4500 Chemin sans issue (28x21cm-11x8in) mono.d.1952 W/C pen exhib. 26-Nov-2 Camard, Paris #101/R est:5000
£3514 $5481 €5200 Sans titre (19x28cm-7x11in) mono.d. W/C gouache. 31-Mar-3 Rossini, Paris #98/R
£4082 $6490 €6000 Composition (25x18cm-10x7in) mono.d.55 W/C Indian ink. 26-Feb-3 Artcurial Briest, Paris #69/R est:2500-3000
£4088 $6377 €6500 Sea snails (18x27cm-7x11in) init.d.1940 W/C pastel prov. 9-Oct-2 Sotheby's, London #225/R est:6000-9000

REICHERT, Carl (1836-1918) Austrian
£897 $1409 €1400 Portrait of dog (19x13cm-7x5in) s. panel. 21-Nov-2 Van Ham, Cologne #1881/R
£1026 $1590 €1600 Young cats (26x21cm-10x8in) s. panel lit. 7-Dec-2 Bergmann, Erlangen #816/R est:2000
£1166 $1900 €1749 Kitten with bees (18x15cm-7x6in) panel. 2-Feb-3 Grogan, Boston #28 est:800-1200
£1918 $2992 €2800 Cat with kittens and horse with foal (31x24cm-12x9in) s. 10-Apr-3 Van Ham, Cologne #1662/R est:1800
£3741 $5949 €5500 Two dogs (15x24cm-6x9in) s. paper on panel. 19-Mar-3 Neumeister, Munich #702/R est:3000
£6135 $10000 €9203 Hunter's companions (40x51cm-16x20in) s.d.77. 11-Feb-3 Bonhams & Doyles, New York #154/R est:10000-15000
Works on paper
£503 $800 €755 Little white kitten (26x18cm-10x7in) s. pencil W/C on card. 5-Mar-3 Christie's, Rockefeller NY #63/R

REICHERT, Willy (?) German?
£616 $962 €900 Moroccan rider (145x200cm-57x79in) s.d.86. 9-Apr-3 Neumeister, Munich #730/R

REICHLE, Paul (1900-1981) German
£483 $763 €700 Composition 1969 (55x69cm-22x27in) s.d.1969 s.i.d. verso masonite. 2-Apr-3 Dr Fritz Nagel, Stuttgart #9196/R

REICHLEN, Jean (1846-1913) Swiss
£1687 $2750 €2531 View of Freiburg, Switzerland (80x104cm-31x41in) s.d.1889. 16-Feb-3 Butterfields, San Francisco #2039 est:3000-5000
£1703 $2657 €2555 Mountain landscape with hut (33x43cm-13x17in) s.d.1908. 8-Nov-2 Dobiaschofsky, Bern #51/R est:2900 (S.FR 3900)

REID, Alec (19/20th C) British
Works on paper
£320 $499 €480 Gas, crumper and wizzbang, with the ruins of Hulloch in the distance (46x60cm-18x24in) s.i. chk bodycol. 18-Sep-2 Cheffins Grain & Comins, Cambridge #494

REID, Eileen (1894-1981) Irish
£2564 $4026 €4000 Head and shoulders of a young man (61x51cm-24x20in) i.d.1923/24 verso prov.exhib. 19-Nov-2 Whyte's, Dublin #55/R est:4000-6000

REID, George Agnew (1860-1947) Canadian
£1515 $2409 €2197 Figure in a landscape (30x46cm-12x18in) s.d.1904 prov. 1-May-3 Heffel, Vancouver #89/R est:4000-6000 (C.D 3500)
£2675 $4146 €4013 Gardener's barrow (30x24cm-12x9in) s.d.89. 3-Dec-2 Joyner, Toronto #385 est:800-1000 (C.D 6500)
£2823 $4460 €4235 On the banks of the Don (76x84cm-30x33in) s.d.1940 prov.exhib.lit. 18-Nov-2 Sotheby's, Toronto #182/R est:4000-6000 (C.D 7000)
£3111 $5102 €4667 Indian trail (62x75cm-24x30in) s.d.1939. 3-Jun-3 Joyner, Toronto #221/R est:4000-5000 (C.D 7000)
£17284 $26790 €25926 Children picking flowers (26x36cm-10x14in) s.d.91. 3-Dec-2 Joyner, Toronto #379 est:1500-2000 (C.D 42000)
£31111 $51022 €46667 In the cellar window (76x101cm-30x40in) s.d.1914 prov.exhib. 27-May-3 Sotheby's, Toronto #40/R est:15000-20000 (C.D 70000)
Works on paper
£978 $1604 €1467 Street singer (30x23cm-12x9in) s.d.1887 W/C. 3-Jun-3 Joyner, Toronto #379/R est:1500-1800 (C.D 2200)

REID, George Ogilvy (1851-1928) British
£1500 $2340 €2250 Confidence (77x64cm-30x25in) s. 10-Sep-2 Bonhams, Knightsbridge #95/R est:1500-2500
Works on paper
£700 $1085 €1050 Pawning the titles (25x36cm-10x14in) s.d.87 W/C. 5-Dec-2 Bonhams, Edinburgh #117/R

REID, Henry C (20th C) British
£260 $380 €390 Head of the Lough (20x28cm-8x11in) mono.d.verso board. 12-Jun-2 John Ross, Belfast #58
£300 $465 €450 Autumn day, Maam Cross (23x20cm-9x8in) mono.d.2001 verso board. 4-Dec-2 John Ross, Belfast #85

REID, Irene Hoffar (1908-1994) Canadian
£390 $592 €585 Boats at a Wharfe - Canoe Cover (88x39cm-35x15in) 4-Jul-2 Heffel, Vancouver #19 (C.D 900)

REID, Jane Brewster (1862-1966) American
Works on paper
£273 $425 €396 Country home (15x30cm-6x12in) s. W/C. 28-Mar-3 Eldred, East Dennis #298
£531 $850 €770 Stone Alley, Nantucket (23x16cm-9x6in) W/C graphite. 16-May-3 Skinner, Boston #205/R

REID, John Robertson (1851-1926) British
£380 $608 €570 Study of a fisherman (23x13cm-9x5in) panel. 11-Mar-3 Gorringes, Lewes #2469
£540 $842 €810 Market scene in Northern France (44x59cm-17x23in) 6-Nov-2 Bonhams, Chester #434
£700 $1162 €1015 An angler on a river bank (35x53cm-14x21in) s. 12-Jun-3 Christie's, Kensington #169/R
£1100 $1705 €1650 Chat by the canal, Amsterdam (25x35cm-10x14in) s.d.94. 5-Dec-2 Bonhams, Edinburgh #128 est:1200-1800
£2300 $3496 €3450 Leaving Fowey (25x35cm-10x14in) s.d.1911. 15-Aug-2 Bonhams, New Bond Street #449/R est:800-1200
£5000 $7750 €7500 When the flowing tide comes in, Looe, Cornwall (76x63cm-30x25in) s.d.89 i.verso. 31-Oct-2 Christie's, London #90/R est:5000-8000
£10000 $16100 €15000 Hiding the deserter (104x93cm-41x37in) s. 20-Feb-3 Christie's, London #348/R est:20000
Works on paper
£720 $1181 €1080 By the harvest field (21x43cm-8x17in) pencil W/C htd white. 4-Feb-3 Bonhams, Leeds #268
£1300 $2015 €1950 Dutch canal (25x35cm-10x14in) s.d.07 gouache. 5-Dec-2 Bonhams, Edinburgh #62 est:1000-1500

REID, John Robertson (attrib) (1851-1926) British
Works on paper
£320 $509 €480 Fishing boats in a harbour at low tide (25x30cm-10x12in) init. W/C. 29-Apr-3 Gorringes, Lewes #2119

REID, Mary Augusta Hiester (1854-1921) Canadian
£905 $1403 €1358 Forest path (36x26cm-14x10in) s.d.1886. 3-Dec-2 Joyner, Toronto #320/R est:2500-3000 (C.D 2200)

REID, Nano (1905-1981) Irish
£900 $1395 €1350 Portrait of a young girl (35x25cm-14x10in) board. 4-Dec-2 John Ross, Belfast #139
£1208 $1945 €1800 Head of a young girl wearing a red hat (33x30cm-13x12in) canvas on board painted c.1938. 18-Feb-3 Whyte's, Dublin #68/R est:2000-3000
£3243 $5059 €4800 Gweedore, Co. Donegal (29x38cm-11x15in) s. canvasboard. 26-Mar-3 James Adam, Dublin #70/R est:2000-3000
£3611 $5742 €5200 Portrait (64x76cm-25x30in) s. 29-Apr-3 Whyte's, Dublin #67/R est:3000-5000
£3623 $5942 €5000 Geranium on a window sill (46x36cm-18x14in) s. 28-May-3 Bonhams & James Adam, Dublin #79/R est:2000-3000
£3800 $6080 €5700 Where Oengus Og magnificently dwells (59x74cm-23x29in) s. board prov.exhib. 16-May-3 Sotheby's, London #118/R est:1800-2500

£6000 $9600 €9000 Remote corner (37x68cm-15x27in) s. board prov. 16-May-3 Sotheby's, London #120/R est:3000-5000
Works on paper
£1370 $2151 €2000 Glengarrif (27x36cm-11x14in) s. W/C. 15-Apr-3 De Veres Art Auctions, Dublin #106/R est:1800-2000

REID, Robert (1862-1929) American
£3438 $5500 €5157 Summer landscape (41x51cm-16x20in) s. 11-Jan-3 James Julia, Fairfield #195 est:4000-6000

REID, Robert Payton (1859-1945) British
£300 $498 €435 View from Slindon, West Sussex (40x61cm-16x24in) s. i.verso. 13-Jun-3 Lyon & Turnbull, Edinburgh #121
£420 $685 €630 View of an alpine valley (63x77cm-25x30in) 14-Feb-3 Lyon & Turnbull, Edinburgh #59
£1300 $2119 €1950 Dordrecht (22x35cm-9x14in) 14-Feb-3 Lyon & Turnbull, Edinburgh #28
£2700 $4293 €4050 In the garden (61x91cm-24x36in) indis sig. 6-Mar-3 Christie's, Kensington #131/R est:3000-5000

REID, Sir George (1841-1913) British
£1600 $2480 €2400 Boys at Boddam harbour (34x26cm-13x10in) bears sig.i.verso panel. 5-Dec-2 Bonhams, Edinburgh #15/R est:1500-2000
£2000 $3040 €3000 Still life of Christmas roses (29x47cm-11x19in) mono.d.1886. 28-Aug-2 Sotheby's, London #1018/R est:2000-3000

REID, Sir George (attrib) (1841-1913) British
£320 $499 €480 Young boys on a quayside (36x28cm-14x11in) bears i.verso paper. 17-Sep-2 Bonhams, Sevenoaks #194/R

REID, Stephen (1873-1948) British
£978 $1623 €1418 Vagabonds (72x91cm-28x36in) s.d.28. 10-Jun-3 Ritchie, Toronto #79/R est:4000-6000 (C.D 2200)

REID, William Bernard (19/20th C) British
£400 $616 €600 Bowl of mixed fruit, a vase of summer flowers, scissors and reel of cotton (61x52cm-24x20in) s. 24-Oct-2 Christie's, Kensington #61/R

REID, William Ronald (1920-1998) Canadian
Sculpture
£149194 $235726 €223791 Killer whale (112x74x50cm-44x29x20in) s.d.1984 num.3/9 dark green pat. bronze prov.lit. 14-Nov-2 Heffel, Vancouver #172/R est:275000-325000 (C.D 370000)

REIDY, Lilla (?) Australian
£1500 $2370 €2250 Native campsite (45x70cm-18x28in) s. canvas on board prov.exhib.lit. 17-Nov-2 Sotheby's, Paddington #14/R est:4000-6000 (A.D 4200)

REIFFEL, Charles (1862-1942) American
£1078 $1800 €1563 Landscape (30x33cm-12x13in) s. masonite on panel prov. 17-Jun-3 John Moran, Pasadena #119 est:2000-3000
£9639 $16000 €13977 Springtime in the hills (41x42cm-16x17in) s. canvas on board exhib. 11-Jun-3 Butterfields, San Francisco #4239/R est:15000-20000
Works on paper
£1290 $2000 €1935 Pennsylvania woodlands (33x33cm-13x13in) s. crayon pencil exhib. 29-Oct-2 John Moran, Pasadena #673 est:1800-2200

REIFFENSTEIN, Carl Theodore (1820-1893) German
Works on paper
£256 $403 €400 River landscape with ruins and fishermen (10x15cm-4x6in) s. W/C. 23-Nov-2 Arnold, Frankfurt #845

REIGER, Albert (?) ?
£552 $900 €828 Landscape (119x84cm-47x33in) 14-Feb-3 Du Mouchelle, Detroit #2116/R

REIGL, Judit (1923-) Hungarian
£37671 $59144 €55000 Ils ont soif insatiable de l'infini (109x97cm-43x38in) s.d.1950 exhib.lit. 15-Apr-3 Laurence Calmels, Paris #4399/R est:12000

REIGNER, Leopold (20th C) French
£784 $1263 €1200 La conversation (89x64cm-35x25in) s.d.1954 cardboard double-sided. 14-Jan-3 Vanderkindere, Brussels #19

REILLE, Karl (1886-1975) French
Works on paper
£994 $1520 €1550 Debuche (7x15cm-3x6in) mono. W/C. 23-Aug-2 Deauville, France #146/R
£1486 $2319 €2200 Lads a l'entrainement a Chantilly (20x28cm-8x11in) mono.d.1903 ink W/C. 25-Mar-3 Chochon-Barre & Allardi, Paris #187/R est:2200-2400
£1538 $2354 €2400 Depart. s. W/C. 23-Aug-2 Deauville, France #147
£1784 $2926 €2587 Hunting scene (39x44cm-15x17in) s. gouache. 4-Jun-3 Fischer, Luzern #2547/R est:4000-6000 (S.FR 3800)
£2075 $3238 €3300 Bas l'eau (31x48cm-12x19in) s. W/C. 11-Oct-2 Pierre Berge, Paris #21/R
£2276 $3482 €3550 Aigles a Chantilly (30x42cm-12x17in) W/C. 23-Aug-2 Deauville, France #148/R
£2581 $4077 €4000 Boar hunting (30x47cm-12x19in) s.d.1925 W/C gouache. 23-Dec-2 Claude Aguttes, Neuilly #60
£2695 $4501 €3800 Scene de chasse a courre (31x48cm-12x19in) s. gouache. 20-Jun-3 Piasa, Paris #49/R est:4000-4500
£2979 $4974 €4200 La halte (23x27cm-9x11in) s. gouache. 20-Jun-3 Piasa, Paris #48/R est:3000-4000

REILLY, Frank Joseph (1906-1967) American
£1026 $1600 €1539 Benjamin Franklin's printing and bookshop, with men (66x102cm-26x40in) s. 18-Sep-2 Alderfer's, Hatfield #266/R est:3000-4000
£1433 $2250 €2150 Outside Ben Franlin's printer and books (66x102cm-26x40in) s. prov. 10-Dec-2 Doyle, New York #157/R est:2500-3500

REILLY, James (1956-) American
£4516 $7000 €6774 Unresolved (183x152cm-72x60in) s.i.d.1998 verso prov. 26-Sep-2 Christie's, Rockefeller NY #878/R est:6000-8000

REILLY, Michael (1898-?) British
£270 $421 €405 Hyde park Corner, London (51x38cm-20x15in) s. canvas on board. 2-Aug-2 Biddle & Webb, Birmingham #378

REIMER, Christine (20th C) Canadian
£1144 $1819 €1716 Royal Victoria yacht club (90x90cm-35x35in) s.i.d.1992 acrylic. 23-Mar-3 Hodgins, Calgary #77/R est:1000-1400 (C.D 2700)

REIMERS, H (19th C) ?
£706 $1074 €1059 The schooner N M Harboe of Skielkior (47x64cm-19x25in) indis.sig. 28-Aug-2 Museumsbygningen, Copenhagen #46/R (D.KR 8200)

REIMERS, Heinrich (1824-1900) German
Works on paper
£4317 $6906 €6000 Ship's portrait of the barque Iris (45x75cm-18x30in) s. W/C. 17-May-3 Hagelstam, Helsinki #75/R est:2000

REINA, Giuseppe (1829-1905) Italian
£748 $1190 €1100 Kitchen interior with woman (23x32cm-9x13in) s. 18-Mar-3 Finarte, Milan #164/R
£1290 $2039 €2000 By the fire (35x46cm-14x18in) s. cardboard. 18-Dec-2 Finarte, Milan #245/R

REINAGLE, Philip (1749-1833) British
£3822 $6000 €5733 Shepherd with cows and sheep (71x89cm-28x35in) 13-Dec-2 Du Mouchelle, Detroit #2045/R est:3000-4000

REINAGLE, Philip (circle) (1749-1833) British
£9500 $15770 €14250 Cockerel and chickens in a wooded landscape (86x117cm-34x46in) prov. 10-Jun-3 Christie's, London #60/R est:8000-12000

REINAGLE, Ramsay Richard (1775-1862) British
£2300 $3611 €3450 Portrait of Mrs Gardiner, wife of Captain Gardiner (35x57cm-14x22in) indis.i.d.96 prov.exhib. 15-Apr-3 Bonhams, Knowle #121/R est:2000-3000
£6494 $10000 €9741 Learning to ride (71x91cm-28x36in) s. 4-Sep-2 Christie's, Rockefeller NY #380/R est:5000-8000

REINAGLE, Ramsay Richard (attrib) (1775-1862) British
£450 $720 €675 Deer by a waterfall (46x35cm-18x14in) 7-Jan-3 Bonhams, Knightsbridge #139/R
£480 $758 €720 Cattle sheep and drover on a lane (36x46cm-14x18in) 2-Dec-2 Gorringes, Lewes #2685
£884 $1406 €1300 Extensive landscape with traveller in front of ruin (21x27cm-8x11in) panel. 25-Feb-3 Dorotheum, Vienna #9
£1020 $1622 €1500 Landscape with horse and cart (21x27cm-8x11in) panel. 25-Feb-3 Dorotheum, Vienna #8/R est:1300-1800
£1687 $2750 €2531 Greyhound in landscape (23x31cm-9x12in) board. 11-Feb-3 Bonhams & Doyles, New York #113 est:1000-1500

REINAGLE, Ramsay Richard and WATTS, Frederick W (18/19th C) British
£4000 $6240 €6000 Wooded path near Southampton (56x86cm-22x34in) s. 17-Oct-2 David Lay, Penzance #1474/R est:5000-8000

REINBERG, Johan (1823-1896) Finnish
£839 $1325 €1300 Bullfinches (26x37cm-10x15in) s.d.1895. 19-Dec-2 Hagelstam, Helsinki #822/R

REINER, Imre (1900-) ?
£553 $857 €830 Composition (23x33cm-9x13in) s.i.d.1962 tempera W/C. 4-Dec-2 Koller, Zurich #197/R est:2000-3000 (S.FR 1270)

REINGANUM, Victor (1907-1995) British
£400 $668 €580 Three figures (41x51cm-16x20in) s.d.1953 paper prov. 17-Jun-3 Bonhams, Knightsbridge #180/R

REINHARD, Josef (1749-1824) Swiss
£1048 $1635 €1572 Portrait of Jakob Rieter (60x48cm-24x19in) panel. 20-Nov-2 Fischer, Luzern #1229/R est:2500-3000 (S.FR 2400)
£1174 $1925 €1702 Portrait of young couple with son (77x65cm-30x26in) 4-Jun-3 Fischer, Luzern #1210/R est:2000-2500 (S.FR 2500)

REINHARD, Ken (1936-) Australian
£463 $708 €695 Course it's only an illustration (44x60cm-17x24in) s.d.65 oil pencil on board. 25-Aug-2 Sotheby's, Paddington #221/R est:1000-2000 (A.D 1300)

REINHARDT, Ad (1913-1967) American
£50000 $80000 €75000 Number 4 (129x53cm-51x21in) s.d.46 prov.exhib. 15-May-3 Christie's, Rockefeller NY #108/R est:70000-90000
£68750 $110000 €103125 Abstract triptych, blue (121x43cm-48x17in) s. s.d.1953 verso oil acrylic prov.exhib.lit. 15-May-3 Christie's, Rockefeller NY #109/R est:200000-300000
£93750 $150000 €140625 Number 17 (127x51cm-50x20in) s.d.verso painted 1953 prov. 15-May-3 Phillips, New York #24/R est:200000-300000
£200000 $328000 €300000 Abstract painting - green (91x61cm-36x24in) painted 1952 prov. 6-Feb-3 Sotheby's, London #9/R est:300000
Works on paper
£3750 $6000 €5625 Untitled (13x17cm-5x7in) init. black ink W/C executed c.1943 prov. 14-May-3 Sotheby's, New York #101/R est:6000-8000
£10625 $17000 €15938 Untitled (10x13cm-4x5in) s.d.43 W/C paperboard prov. 14-May-3 Sotheby's, New York #100/R est:6000-8000

REINHARDT, Carl August (1818-1877) German
£1164 $1816 €1700 Cows on alpine meadow (63x104cm-25x41in) 10-Apr-3 Dorotheum, Vienna #174/R est:2600-2800

REINHARDT, Louis (?-1870) German
£689 $1047 €1034 Still life of lobster, grapes and wine (58x88cm-23x35in) s.i. 27-Aug-2 Rasmussen, Copenhagen #1804/R (D.KR 8000)

REINHARDT, Siegfried (1925-1984) American
£353 $550 €530 Flaming smug pot (46x36cm-18x14in) s.d.1951 acrylic masonite. 10-Nov-2 Selkirks, St. Louis #941
£769 $1200 €1154 Reflection (61x30cm-24x12in) s.d.1950 board. 10-Nov-2 Selkirks, St. Louis #940
£962 $1500 €1443 Christ is born (61x30cm-24x12in) s.d.1943 masonite. 10-Nov-2 Selkirks, St. Louis #935/R est:400-600
£1000 $1600 €1450 Boy and the hawk (36x46cm-14x18in) s.d. masonite prov. 17-May-3 Selkirks, St. Louis #411/R est:600-900
£1090 $1700 €1635 Woman and monkey (58x28cm-23x11in) s.i.d.1949 verso masonite. 10-Nov-2 Selkirks, St. Louis #939/R est:600-800
£1750 $2800 €2538 Cage (53x61cm-21x24in) s.d. masonite prov. 17-May-3 Selkirks, St. Louis #412/R est:800-1200
£3365 $5250 €5048 Figures and animals in an artist's studio (89x119cm-35x47in) s.d.1951 masonite. 10-Nov-2 Selkirks, St. Louis #942/R est:800-1200
Works on paper
£548 $850 €822 Mural study (25x25cm-10x10in) s.d. mixed media board. 8-Dec-2 Toomey, Oak Park #834/R

REINHART, Johann Christian (1761-1847) German
Works on paper
£9259 $15000 €13889 Landscape with satyr spying on bathing nymph (78x110cm-31x43in) chk pen ink wash prov.lit. 21-Jan-3 Sotheby's, New York #173/R est:20000

REINHART, Johann Christian (attrib) (1761-1847) German
Works on paper
£897 $1418 €1400 Forest clearing (21x18cm-8x7in) sepia brush htd white. 16-Nov-2 Lempertz, Koln #1384

REINHART, Lea (1877-1970) Austrian
£926 $1491 €1389 Still life with works of art (21x27cm-8x11in) s. panel. 7-May-3 Dobiaschofsky, Bern #904/R est:2200 (S.FR 2000)
£1088 $1731 €1600 Still life with porcelain objects (21x26cm-8x10in) s. panel. 25-Feb-3 Dorotheum, Vienna #70/R est:1200-1400

REINHART, Sigmund (?) ?
£250 $380 €375 Figures before Continental buildings by moonlight (30x43cm-12x17in) s. 16-Aug-2 Keys, Aylsham #414

REINHOLD, Franz (1816-1893) Austrian
£1944 $3092 €2800 Wooded landscape (31x25cm-12x10in) s. board. 29-Apr-3 Wiener Kunst Auktionen, Vienna #532/R est:1000-1500

REINHOLD, Friedrich (younger) (1814-1881) Austrian
£705 $1100 €1058 Untitled (33x43cm-13x17in) panel. 18-Oct-2 Du Mouchelle, Detroit #2020/R

REINHOLD, Heinrich (1788-1825) Austrian
Works on paper
£1389 $2208 €2000 Berchtesgaden, road to Konigssee (30x43cm-12x17in) i. pencil. 5-May-3 Ketterer, Munich #272/R est:700-900
£11511 $18878 €16000 Compositions. Indian ink pencil wash or circle 29. 4-Jun-3 Reiss & Sohn, Konigstein #281/R est:1000

REINHOLD, Heinrich (attrib) (1788-1825) Austrian
Works on paper
£570 $900 €900 Houses in Roman Campagna (31x46cm-12x18in) pencil. 29-Nov-2 Bassenge, Berlin #6031/R

REINICKE, René (1860-1926) German
Works on paper
£377 $588 €550 The visit (36x30cm-14x12in) s. gouache. 10-Apr-3 Van Ham, Cologne #1665
£411 $641 €600 In the salon (33x24cm-13x9in) mono.d.06 gouache. 10-Apr-3 Van Ham, Cologne #1664
£582 $908 €850 Young woman trying on hat in front of mirror (34x26cm-13x10in) s. WC paper on board. 10-Apr-3 Van Ham, Cologne #1663/R

REINIGER, Otto (1863-1909) German
£645 $948 €1000 Stream at dusk (42x27cm-17x11in) canvas on board. 20-Jun-2 Dr Fritz Nagel, Stuttgart #817/R
£881 $1374 €1400 Small lake (30x46cm-12x18in) board. 19-Sep-2 Dr Fritz Nagel, Stuttgart #988/R

REINIKE, Charles Henry (1906-1983) American
Works on paper
£549 $900 €796 Cabin and horses on the bayou (33x48cm-13x19in) s. W/C. 7-Jun-3 Neal Auction Company, New Orleans #401 est:700-1000
£696 $1100 €1044 Cabin on the Bayou (25x36cm-10x14in) s. W/C. 5-Apr-3 Neal Auction Company, New Orleans #336
£696 $1100 €1044 Shrimp boat in the marsh (25x36cm-10x14in) s. W/C. 5-Apr-3 Neal Auction Company, New Orleans #335

REINITZ, Maximilian (1872-1935) Austrian
£13924 $22000 €22000 Towers, houses, water (53x42cm-21x17in) s.d.21 prov. 27-Nov-2 Dorotheum, Vienna #148/R est:7000-12000

REISER, Carl (1877-1950) German
£392 $643 €600 Village in the mountains (70x89cm-28x35in) s.d.29. 5-Feb-3 Neumeister, Munich #799/R
£654 $1072 €1000 Village in the mountains (50x100cm-20x39in) s. 5-Feb-3 Neumeister, Munich #800
£980 $1608 €1500 Part of a snow-covered mountain village (59x73cm-23x29in) s.d.12. 5-Feb-3 Neumeister, Munich #801 est:750
£1014 $1581 €1500 Waxenstein in winter (80x95cm-31x37in) s. 26-Mar-3 Hugo Ruef, Munich #210 est:1500
£1830 $3001 €2800 Mountain landscape in winter (32x40cm-13x16in) s. d.1945 verso board. 5-Feb-3 Neumeister, Munich #798/R est:600
£2041 $3245 €3000 Still life of flowers including roses, lilies and others (103x74cm-41x29in) s.d.23 oval. 19-Mar-3 Neumeister, Munich #703 est:2200
£2041 $3245 €3000 Partenkirchen with Zugspitze (44x100cm-17x39in) s.d.43. 19-Mar-3 Neumeister, Munich #704/R est:2500
£2109 $3353 €3100 Peonies in jug (100x90cm-39x35in) s. 19-Mar-3 Neumeister, Munich #706 est:1800
£4777 $7452 €7500 Marienplatz in Garmisch in winter (80x100cm-31x39in) s.d.25. 6-Nov-2 Hugo Ruef, Munich #1250/R est:1500

Works on paper
£411 $638 €650 Mountain landscape (39x50cm-15x20in) s. bears d.1930. 27-Sep-2 Weidler, Nurnberg #8949/R

REISMAN, Ori (1924-1991) Israeli
£6962 $11000 €10443 Nude in interior (31x20cm-12x8in) s.d.53 oil on card. 27-Apr-3 Sotheby's, Tel Aviv #92/R est:5000-7000
£15823 $25000 €23735 Jaffa harbour (60x73cm-24x29in) s.d.1950 verso. 27-Apr-3 Sotheby's, Tel Aviv #91/R est:28000-35000

REISS, Fritz (1857-1916) German
£327 $523 €500 Cow at the water in the forest (67x51cm-26x20in) s.d.96 lit. 10-Jan-3 Allgauer, Kempten #1735/R

REITER, Erwin (1933-) Austrian
Works on paper
£283 $439 €450 Untitled (56x42cm-22x17in) s.d.66 felt-tip pen. 30-Oct-2 Dorotheum, Vienna #196

REITER, Johann Baptist (1813-1890) Austrian
£22642 $35094 €36000 Lute player (141x125cm-56x49in) copy after Orazio Gentileschi prov.exhib.lit. 2-Oct-2 Dorotheum, Vienna #50/R est:20000-25000

RELINK, Karel (1880-1945) Czechoslovakian
£409 $662 €614 Lady with hat (67x47cm-26x19in) s.i. board. 24-May-3 Dorotheum, Prague #100/R est:15000-23000 (C.KR 18000)

REMBOLD, Marc (1918-2002) Swiss
£2620 $4114 €3930 Light in colour (140x120cm-55x47in) s. s.i.d.14 juillet 1999 verso. 25-Nov-2 Germann, Zurich #124/R est:3000-5000 (S.FR 6000)

REMBRANDT (1606-1669) Dutch
£6200000 $10354001 €8990000 Self-portrait with shaded eyes (71x55cm-28x22in) s.d.1634 panel prov.exhib.lit. 10-Jul-3 Sotheby's, London #19/R est:4000000-6000000

Prints
£1887 $3000 €2831 Baptism of the Eunuch (18x21cm-7x8in) etching. 1-May-3 Swann Galleries, New York #17/R est:2500-3500
£1887 $3000 €2831 Agony in the garden (11x8cm-4x3in) etching. 1-May-3 Swann Galleries, New York #32/R est:2000-3000
£1887 $3000 €2831 Death of the Virgin (41x31cm-16x12in) etching drypoint. 1-May-3 Swann Galleries, New York #255/R est:4000-6000
£1887 $3000 €2831 Christ at Emmaus (21x16cm-8x6in) etching. 1-May-3 Swann Galleries, New York #272/R est:3000-5000
£1887 $3000 €2831 Peter and John healing the cripple at the gate of the temple (18x22cm-7x9in) etching drypoint. 1-May-3 Swann Galleries, New York #281/R est:2000-3000
£1899 $3000 €3000 Prodigal Son (16x14cm-6x6in) etching. 29-Nov-2 Bassenge, Berlin #5451 est:1500
£1899 $3000 €3000 Woman outdoors with feet in water (16x8cm-6x3in) etching. 29-Nov-2 Bassenge, Berlin #5458/R est:3000
£1899 $3000 €3000 La negresse couchee (8x16cm-3x6in) etching. 29-Nov-2 Bassenge, Berlin #5459/R est:4000
£1923 $3000 €2885 Beggar leaning on a stick (9x5cm-4x2in) etching exec.c.1630. 6-Nov-2 Swann Galleries, New York #66/R est:4000-6000
£1963 $3200 €2945 Death of the Virgin (40x31cm-16x12in) etching drypoint exec.1639. 13-Feb-3 Christie's, Rockefeller NY #172/R
£1988 $3200 €2982 Strolling musicians (13x10cm-5x4in) etching executed c.1635. 22-Feb-3 Brunk, Ashville #324/R
£2000 $3100 €3000 Christ and the woman of Samaria (12x16cm-5x6in) etching arched. 5-Dec-2 Sotheby's, London #49/R est:3000-4000
£2000 $3120 €3000 Jan Asselyn, painter (22x17cm-9x7in) etching executed c.1647. 25-Mar-3 Sotheby's, London #36/R est:2500-3000
£2000 $3340 €2900 Death of the Virgin (41x30cm-16x12in) etching. 30-Jun-3 Bonhams, New Bond Street #97/R est:1000-1500
£2000 $3300 €2900 Jan Lutma, goldsmith (19x15cm-7x6in) etching. 1-Jul-3 Sotheby's, London #52/R est:1800-2200
£2013 $3200 €3020 Christ and the woman of Samaria among ruins (12x10cm-5x4in) etching drypoint. 1-May-3 Swann Galleries, New York #243/R est:3000-5000
£2051 $3200 €3077 Rest on the flight (9x6cm-4x2in) etching exec.c.1644. 7-Nov-2 Swann Galleries, New York #340/R est:2000-3000
£2051 $3241 €3200 Les baigneurs. etching. 14-Nov-2 Libert, Castor, Paris #34 est:2250
£2069 $3269 €3000 Persian man (11x8cm-4x3in) etching. 4-Apr-3 Venator & Hansten, Koln #1605/R est:3900
£2100 $3255 €3150 Artist mother with her hands on her chest (9x6cm-4x2in) etching. 5-Dec-2 Sotheby's, London #55/R est:1000-1500
£2179 $3444 €3400 Three Oriental figures. eau forte exec.1641. 13-Nov-2 Piasa, Paris #94/R
£2179 $3400 €3269 Peter and John healing the cripple at the gate of the temple (18x22cm-7x9in) etching drypoint. 7-Nov-2 Swann Galleries, New York #371/R est:2500-3500
£2200 $3432 €3300 Self portrait drawing at the window (16x13cm-6x5in) etching. 10-Oct-2 Sotheby's, London #210/R est:800-1000
£2200 $3410 €3300 Abraham caressing Isaac (11x8cm-4x3in) etching executed c.1637. 5-Dec-2 Sotheby's, London #47/R est:2000-3000
£2200 $3432 €3300 Beggar seated on a bank (11x6cm-4x2in) etching. 25-Mar-3 Sotheby's, London #38/R est:1000-1200
£2200 $3630 €3190 Self portrait with Saskia (10x9cm-4x4in) etching. 1-Jul-3 Sotheby's, London #39/R est:1500-2000
£2244 $3500 €3366 Mort de la vierge (42x31cm-17x12in) etching executed c.1639. 9-Nov-2 Sloan, North Bethesda #518/R est:6000-8000
£2244 $3545 €3500 Jesus Christ au milieu des docteurs. etching. 14-Nov-2 Libert, Castor, Paris #29 est:3800
£2244 $3545 €3500 Vieillard a grande barbe. etching. 14-Nov-2 Libert, Castor, Paris #43 est:4500
£2264 $3600 €3396 Virgin and Child with the cat and snake (10x15cm-4x6in) etching. 1-May-3 Swann Galleries, New York #26/R est:2000-3000
£2264 $3600 €3396 Christ seated disputing with the doctors (10x14cm-4x6in) etching. 1-May-3 Swann Galleries, New York #27/R est:2500-3500
£2264 $3600 €3396 Begger man and begger woman conversing (8x7cm-3x3in) etching. 1-May-3 Swann Galleries, New York #39/R est:1500-2500
£2264 $3600 €3396 Pancake woman (11x8cm-4x3in) etching drypoint. 1-May-3 Swann Galleries, New York #247/R est:2000-3000
£2264 $3600 €3396 Christ at Emmaus (21x16cm-8x6in) etching. 1-May-3 Swann Galleries, New York #275/R est:3000-5000
£2300 $3565 €3450 Artist drawing from the model. Etching executed c.1639. 5-Dec-2 Sotheby's, London #58/R est:1000-1200
£2308 $3600 €3462 Self portrait in a cap and scarf (14x10cm-6x4in) etching. 7-Nov-2 Swann Galleries, New York #304/R est:4000-6000
£2308 $3600 €3462 Woman bathing her feet at a brook (16x8cm-6x3in) etching. 7-Nov-2 Swann Galleries, New York #368/R est:3000-5000
£2340 $3628 €3510 Self portrait with Saska (10x9cm-4x4in) etching lit. 3-Dec-2 Bukowskis, Stockholm #555/R est:12000-15000 (S.KR 33000)
£2390 $3800 €3585 Abraham caressing Isaac (12x9cm-5x4in) etching. 1-May-3 Swann Galleries, New York #253/R est:3000-5000
£2400 $3744 €3600 Return of the Prodigal Son (15x13cm-6x5in) etching. 25-Mar-3 Sotheby's, London #37/R est:2000-2500
£2400 $3960 €3480 Raising of Lazarus (36x25cm-14x10in) etching exec.c.1632. 1-Jul-3 Sotheby's, London #47/R est:1000-1200
£2402 $3747 €3603 Jan Utenbogaert (27x22cm-11x9in) etching drypoint. 20-Nov-2 Fischer, Luzern #2443/R est:2500-3500 (S.FR 5500)
£2404 $3750 €3606 Abraham and Isaac (16x13cm-6x5in) etching burin. 14-Oct-2 Butterfields, San Francisco #1072/R est:1000-1500
£2405 $3728 €3800 Taking down from the cross (21x16cm-8x6in) drypoint etching. 27-Sep-2 Venator & Hansten, Koln #1096/R est:4500
£2411 $3738 €3617 Young man in velvet hat - possibly Ferdinand Bol (10x8cm-4x3in) etching lit. 3-Dec-2 Bukowskis, Stockholm #558/R est:15000-20000 (S.KR 34000)
£2436 $3800 €3654 Presentation in the temple (22x29cm-9x11in) etching drypoint exec.c.1640. 7-Nov-2 Swann Galleries, New York #327/R est:5000-8000
£2436 $3800 €3654 Star of the Kings (9x14cm-4x6in) etching drypoint exec.c.1651. 7-Nov-2 Swann Galleries, New York #352/R est:5000-8000
£2436 $3800 €3654 Goldsmith (8x6cm-3x2in) etching drypoint. 7-Nov-2 Swann Galleries, New York #364/R est:5000-8000
£2436 $3800 €3654 Polander leaning on a stick (8x4cm-3x2in) etching exec.c.1632. 6-Nov-2 Swann Galleries, New York #71/R est:5000-8000
£2500 $3900 €3700 Abraham Francen (16x21cm-6x8in) eau forte drypoint. 31-Mar-3 Piasa, Paris #170
£2500 $4125 €3625 Raising of Lazarus (15x11cm-6x4in) etching. 1-Jul-3 Sotheby's, London #44/R est:2000-3000
£2516 $4000 €3774 Joseph and Potiphar's wife (9x11cm-4x4in) etching drypoint. 1-May-3 Swann Galleries, New York #242/R est:2000-3000
£2516 $4000 €3774 Preesentation in the temple (21x29cm-8x11in) etching drypoint executed c.1640. 1-May-3 Swann Galleries, New York #257/R est:3000-5000
£2560 $4250 €3712 Return of the Prodigal son (15x13cm-6x5in) etching drypoint. 13-Jun-3 Du Mouchelle, Detroit #2117/R est:1200-2200
£2564 $4000 €3846 Joseph telling his dreams (11x8cm-4x3in) etching. 14-Oct-2 Butterfields, San Francisco #1073/R est:1000-1500
£2564 $4000 €3846 Student at a table by candlelight (15x14cm-6x6in) etching exec.c.1642. 7-Nov-2 Swann Galleries, New York #321/R est:2000-3000
£2642 $4200 €3963 Landscape with a cow (10x13cm-4x5in) etching. 1-May-3 Swann Galleries, New York #83/R est:4000-6000
£2642 $4200 €3963 Jan Uytenbogaert (23x19cm-9x7in) etching drypoint. 1-May-3 Swann Galleries, New York #248/R est:4000-6000
£2642 $4200 €3963 Abraham and Isaac (16x13cm-6x5in) etching. 1-May-3 Swann Galleries, New York #265/R est:2000-3000
£2692 $4200 €4038 Descent from the cross (53x41cm-21x16in) etching engraving. 7-Nov-2 Swann Galleries, New York #306/R est:5000-8000
£2700 $4185 €4050 Man making water (9x5cm-4x2in) etching. 3-Dec-2 Christie's, London #75/R est:2500-3500
£2700 $4185 €4050 Joseph telling his dreams (11x8cm-4x3in) etching. 5-Dec-2 Sotheby's, London #48/R est:3000-3500
£2767 $4400 €4151 Strolling musicians (14x11cm-6x4in) etching. 1-May-3 Swann Galleries, New York #52/R est:4000-6000
£2767 $4400 €4151 Old man with beard, fur cap and velvet cloak (15x13cm-6x5in) etching drypoint. 1-May-3 Swann Galleries, New York #237/R est:2500-3500

£2800 $4340 €4200 Quacksalver (7x3cm-3x1in) etching. 5-Dec-2 Sotheby's, London #46/R est:2500-3500
£2800 $4368 €4200 Studies of the head of Saskia and others (15x12cm-6x5in) etching. 25-Mar-3 Sotheby's, London #42/R est:1500-2000
£2830 $4500 €4245 Christ and the woman of Samaria among ruins (12x10cm-5x4in) etching drypoint. 1-May-3 Swann Galleries, New York #12/R est:5000-8000
£2893 $4600 €4340 Pancake woman (11x8cm-4x3in) etching. 1-May-3 Swann Galleries, New York #49/R est:3000-5000
£2893 $4600 €4340 Nude woman seated on a mound (18x16cm-7x6in) etching. 1-May-3 Swann Galleries, New York #66/R est:2000-3000
£2893 $4600 €4340 Presentation in the temple (21x29cm-8x11in) etching drypoint executed c.1640. 1-May-3 Swann Galleries, New York #256/R est:3000-5000
£2949 $4600 €4424 Beggar with a wooden leg (11x6cm-4x2in) etching drypoint exec.c.1630. 6-Nov-2 Swann Galleries, New York #67/R est:6000-9000
£3000 $4680 €4500 Abraham Francen, apothecary (16x21cm-6x8in) etching executed c.1657. 25-Mar-3 Sotheby's, London #30/R est:1800-2200
£3000 $4950 €4350 Self portrait drawing at a window (16x13cm-6x5in) i.verso etching. 1-Jul-3 Sotheby's, London #40/R est:1500-2000
£3000 $4950 €4350 Christ healing the sick (28x39cm-11x15in) i. etching drypoint engraving. 2-Jul-3 Christie's, London #37/R est:3200-5000
£3012 $5000 €4367 Untitled (15x10cm-6x4in) etching drypoint. 13-Jun-3 Du Mouchelle, Detroit #2115/R est:1500-2500
£3077 $4800 €4616 Christ at Emmaus (10x8cm-4x3in) etching drypoint. 7-Nov-2 Swann Galleries, New York #309/R est:6000-9000
£3077 $4800 €4616 Christ disputing with the doctors (13x22cm-5x9in) etching. 7-Nov-2 Swann Galleries, New York #354/R est:6000-9000
£3077 $4800 €4616 Christ at Emmaus (11x8cm-4x3in) etching. 6-Nov-2 Swann Galleries, New York #75/R est:6000-9000
£3077 $4800 €4616 Three heads of women, one asleep (14x10cm-6x4in) etching. 6-Nov-2 Swann Galleries, New York #81/R est:5000-8000
£3145 $5000 €4718 Return of the Prodigal Son (16x14cm-6x6in) etching drypoint. 1-May-3 Swann Galleries, New York #33/R est:7000-10000
£3145 $5000 €4718 Raising of Lazarus (37x26cm-15x10in) etching engraving drypoint. 1-May-3 Swann Galleries, New York #238/R est:3000-5000
£3145 $5000 €4718 Clement de Jonghe, printseller (21x16cm-8x6in) etching. 1-May-3 Swann Galleries, New York #270/R est:5000-8000
£3200 $4960 €4800 Strolling musicians (14x12cm-6x5in) etching executed c.1635. 3-Dec-2 Christie's, London #73/R est:2500-3500
£3200 $4960 €4800 Peter and John healing the cripple at the gate of the temple (18x22cm-7x9in) etching. 5-Dec-2 Sotheby's, London #50/R est:2000-2500
£3205 $5000 €4808 Strolling musicians (14x12cm-6x5in) etching exec.c.1634. 7-Nov-2 Swann Galleries, New York #317/R est:6000-9000
£3205 $5000 €4808 Samuel Menasseh Ben Israel (15x11cm-6x4in) etching. 6-Nov-2 Swann Galleries, New York #79/R est:7000-10000
£3270 $5200 €4905 Abraham and Isaac (16x13cm-6x5in) etching. 1-May-3 Swann Galleries, New York #22/R est:3000-5000
£3270 $5200 €4905 Student at a table by candlelight (15x13cm-6x5in) etching. 1-May-3 Swann Galleries, New York #58/R est:3000-5000
£3333 $5200 €5000 Jan Cornelis Sylvius, preacher (17x14cm-7x6in) etching engraving. 7-Nov-2 Swann Galleries, New York #294/R est:4000-6000
£3333 $5200 €5000 Christ driving the money changers from the temple (14x17cm-6x7in) etching drypoint. 7-Nov-2 Swann Galleries, New York #310/R est:3000-5000
£3333 $5200 €5000 Jan Uytenbogaert, preacher of the Remonstrants (23x19cm-9x7in) etching drypoint. 7-Nov-2 Swann Galleries, New York #316/R est:4000-6000
£3333 $5200 €5000 Old man shading his eyes with his hand (14x11cm-6x4in) etching exec.c.1638. 7-Nov-2 Swann Galleries, New York #322/R est:4000-6000
£3333 $5200 €5000 Death of the Virgin (41x31cm-16x12in) etching drypoint. 7-Nov-2 Swann Galleries, New York #323/R est:5000-8000
£3333 $5200 €5000 Beggars receiving alms at a door (17x13cm-7x5in) etching. 7-Nov-2 Swann Galleries, New York #350/R est:3000-5000
£3374 $5500 €5061 Death of the Virgin (41x31cm-16x12in) etching drypoint exec.1639. 13-Feb-3 Christie's, Rockefeller NY #173/R
£3396 $5400 €5094 Self portrait in a flat cap and embroidered dress (8x6cm-3x2in) etching. 1-May-3 Swann Galleries, New York #3/R est:4000-6000
£3400 $5610 €4930 Descent from the cross (53x41cm-21x16in) etching. 1-Jul-3 Sotheby's, London #48/R est:1000-1500
£3462 $5400 €5193 Raising of Lazarus (37x26cm-15x10in) etching engraving drypoint exec.c.1632. 7-Nov-2 Swann Galleries, New York #302/R est:2000-3000
£3500 $5775 €5075 Beggars receiving alms at the door (17x13cm-7x5in) i. etching exec.c.1630. 2-Jul-3 Christie's, London #40/R est:1600-2600
£3571 $5643 €5357 Joseph telling his dreams (12x8cm-5x3in) etching. 26-Nov-2 Sotheby's, Melbourne #247/R est:10000-12000 (A.D 10000)
£3600 $5580 €5400 Naked woman seated on a mound (18x16cm-7x6in) etching executed c.1631 sold with another. 5-Dec-2 Sotheby's, London #32/R est:3600-4600
£3648 $5800 €5472 Descent from the cross (53x41cm-21x16in) etching engraving. 1-May-3 Swann Galleries, New York #240/R est:4000-6000
£3774 $6000 €5661 Angel appearing to the shepherds (26x22cm-10x9in) etching engraving drypoint. 1-May-3 Swann Galleries, New York #10/R est:4000-6000
£3774 $6000 €5661 Virgin and Child in the clouds (17x11cm-7x4in) etching drypoint. 1-May-3 Swann Galleries, New York #19/R est:6000-9000
£3774 $6000 €5661 Blind fiddler (8x5cm-3x2in) etching drypoint. 1-May-3 Swann Galleries, New York #43/R est:5000-8000
£3774 $6000 €5661 Beggers receiving alms at a door (16x13cm-6x5in) etching. 1-May 3 Swann Galleries, New York #60/R est:5000-8000
£3774 $6000 €5661 Joseph's coat brought to Jacob (11x8cm-4x3in) etching executed c.1633. 1-May-3 Swann Galleries, New York #241/R est:2500-3500
£3774 $6000 €5661 Sheet studies, head of Saskia and others (15x12cm-6x5in) etching. 1-May-3 Swann Galleries, New York #251/R est:6000-9000
£3774 $6000 €5661 Self portrait in a velvet cap with plume (13x10cm-5x4in) etching. 1-May-3 Swann Galleries, New York #254/R est:4000-6000
£3800 $5928 €5700 Huge man seated on the ground with one leg extended (10x17cm-4x7in) etching. 25-Mar-3 Sotheby's, London #32/R est:2500-3500
£3846 $6000 €5769 Christ and the woman of Samaria among ruins (12x11cm-5x4in) etching. 14-Oct-2 Butterfields, San Francisco #1075/R est:4000-6000
£3846 $6000 €5769 Return of the Prodigal Son (16x14cm-6x6in) etching drypoint. 7-Nov-2 Swann Galleries, New York #319/R est:7000-10000
£3846 $6000 €5769 Man in a coat and fur cap leaning against a bank (11x8cm-4x3in) etching exec.c.1630. 6-Nov-2 Swann Galleries, New York #68/R est:8000-12000
£3846 $6077 €6000 Le transport de Jesus Christ au tombeau. etching. 14-Nov-2 Libert, Castor, Paris #32 est:9000
£4000 $6200 €6000 Christ and the woman of Samaria (12x16cm-5x6in) etching arched. 5-Dec-2 Sotheby's, London #43/R est:5000-8000
£4000 $6600 €5800 Jan Uytenbogaert, the goldweigher (25x20cm-10x8in) etching. 1-Jul-3 Sotheby's, London #45/R est:3000-4000
£4088 $6500 €6132 Christ crucified between the two thieves (14x10cm-6x4in) etching drypoint. 1-May-3 Swann Galleries, New York #18/R est:3000-5000
£4138 $6538 €6000 Abraham cuddling Isaac (12x9cm-5x4in) etching. 4-Apr-3 Venator & Hansten, Koln #1602 est:9000
£4167 $6583 €6500 La Sainte Famille au chat. etching. 14-Nov-2 Libert, Castor, Paris #28/R est:3800
£4200 $6510 €6300 Woman reading (12x10cm-5x4in) etching. 5-Dec-2 Sotheby's, London #52/R est:1500-2000
£4200 $6510 €6300 Woman reading (12x10cm-5x4in) etching. 4-Dec-2 Bonhams, New Bond Street #68/R est:1800-2000
£4403 $7000 €6605 Jan Uytenbogaert - the goldweighter (25x20cm-10x8in) etching drypoint. 1-May-3 Swann Galleries, New York #96/R est:3000-5000
£4459 $6957 €6600 Circoncision (21x16cm-8x6in) eau forte. 31-Mar-3 Piasa, Paris #169/R
£4487 $7000 €6731 Joseph and Potiphar's wife (9x12cm-4x5in) etching drypoint. 7-Nov-2 Swann Galleries, New York #307/R est:4000-6000
£4487 $7000 €6731 Jan Uytenbogaert, the goldweigher (25x20cm-10x8in) etching drypoint. 7-Nov-2 Swann Galleries, New York #324/R est:4000-6000
£4487 $7000 €6731 Return of the Prodigal Son (16x14cm-6x6in) etching drypoint. 6-Nov-2 Swann Galleries, New York #78/R est:7000-10000
£4487 $7090 €7000 Tobie aveugle. etching. 14-Nov-2 Libert, Castor, Paris #27 est:6000
£4500 $7515 €6525 Young man in a velvet cap with books beside him (9x8cm-4x3in) etching. 30-Jun-3 Bonhams, New Bond Street #99/R est:5000-7000
£4600 $7590 €6670 Cornelis Claesz Anslo, preacher (18x15cm-7x6in) etching. 1-Jul-3 Sotheby's, London #41/R est:2000-3000
£4717 $7500 €7076 Old man with a divided fur cap (15x14cm-6x6in) etching drypoint. 1-May-3 Swann Galleries, New York #97/R est:7000-10000
£4717 $7500 €7076 Jan Asselyn, painter (22x17cm-9x7in) etching engraving drypoint. 1-May-3 Swann Galleries, New York #101/R est:10000-15000
£4717 $7500 €7076 Clement de Jongh, paintseller (21x16cm-8x6in) etching drypoint. 1-May-3 Swann Galleries, New York #103/R est:5000-8000
£4717 $7500 €7076 Three heads of women (14x10cm-6x4in) etching. 1-May-3 Swann Galleries, New York #110/R est:10000-15000
£4717 $7500 €7076 Return of the Prodigal Son (16x14cm-6x6in) etching drypoint. 1-May-3 Swann Galleries, New York #250/R est:7000-10000
£4717 $7500 €7076 Faust (21x16cm-8x6in) etching drypoint executed c.1652. 1-May-3 Swann Galleries, New York #271/R est:10000-15000
£4808 $7500 €7212 Three heads of women (13x11cm-5x4in) etching exec.c.1637. 6-Nov-2 Swann Galleries, New York #82/R est:5000-8000
£5000 $7750 €7500 Abraham casting out Hagar and Ishmael (13x10cm-5x4in) etching drypoint. 3-Dec-2 Christie's, London #66/R est:5000-7000
£5031 $8000 €7547 Self portrait in a cap and scarf (14x10cm-6x4in) etching. 1-May-3 Swann Galleries, New York #1/R est:5000-8000
£5128 $8000 €7692 Bearded man in a velvet cap with a jewel clasp (10x8cm-4x3in) s.d.1637etching. 7-Nov-2 Swann Galleries, New York #320/R est:4000-6000
£5128 $8000 €7692 Abraham and Isaac (16x13cm-6x5in) etching. 7-Nov-2 Swann Galleries, New York #341/R est:7000-10000

£5128 $8103 €8000 Jeune fille au panier. etching. 14-Nov-2 Libert, Castor, Paris #44 est:6500
£5449 $8500 €8174 Head of Saskia and others (15x12cm-6x5in) etching. 6-Nov-2 Swann Galleries, New York #80/R est:6000-9000
£5449 $8609 €8500 Descente de croix, effet de nuit. etching drypoint. 14-Nov-2 Libert, Castor, Paris #31 est:6500
£5660 $9000 €8490 Holy Family (9x7cm-4x3in) etching drypoint. 1-May-3 Swann Galleries, New York #7/R est:8000-12000
£5828 $9500 €8742 Goldweigher (26x21cm-10x8in) etching drypoint exec.c.1639 prov. 13-Feb-3 Christie's, Rockefeller NY #174/R
£6013 $9500 €9020 Death appearing to a wedded couple from an open grave (11x8cm-4x3in) etching. 22-Apr-3 Butterfields, San Francisco #2082/R est:4500-6500
£6090 $9500 €9135 Old man with beard, fur cap and velvet cloak (15x13cm-6x5in) etching drypoint. 7-Nov-2 Swann Galleries, New York #301/R est:5000-8000
£6090 $9500 €9135 Christ and the woman of Samaria among ruins (12x11cm-5x4in) etching drypoint. 7-Nov-2 Swann Galleries, New York #308/R est:8000-12000
£6090 $9500 €9135 Man at a desk wearing a cross and chain (16x10cm-6x4in) etching. 7-Nov-2 Swann Galleries, New York #331/R est:8000-12000
£6090 $9500 €9135 Faust (21x16cm-8x6in) etching drypoint exec.c.1652. 7-Nov-2 Swann Galleries, New York #355/R est:7000-10000
£6090 $9500 €9135 Rat catcher (14x13cm-6x5in) etching drypoint. 6-Nov-2 Swann Galleries, New York #72/R est:6000-9000
£6092 $9748 €9138 The artist Jan Asselijn (22x17cm-9x7in) s. etching drypoint executed c.1647. 17-Mar-3 Blomqvist, Oslo #418/R est:35000-45000 (N.KR 70000)
£6410 $10000 €9615 Great Jewish bride (22x17cm-9x7in) etching drypoint. 6-Nov-2 Swann Galleries, New York #77/R est:10000-15000
£6410 $10000 €9615 Virgin and Child in the clouds (17x11cm-7x4in) etching drypoint. 6-Nov-2 Swann Galleries, New York #83/R est:6000-9000
£7000 $10850 €10500 Artist's mother seated at a table (15x13cm-6x5in) etching executed c.1631 prov. 3-Dec-2 Christie's, London #77/R est:8000-12000
£7000 $10850 €10500 Diana at the bath (18x16cm-7x6in) etching executed c.1633. 5-Dec-2 Sotheby's, London #34/R est:8000-12000
£7000 $10850 €10500 Beggars receiving alms at the door of a house (16x13cm-6x5in) etching. 5-Dec-2 Sotheby's, London #39/R est:7000-9000
£7000 $10850 €10500 Landscape with farm buildings and a sketching (13x21cm-5x8in) etching. 4-Dec-2 Bonhams, New Bond Street #65/R est:4000-6000
£7500 $11625 €11250 Triumph of Mordecal (17x21cm-7x8in) etching executed c.1641. 5-Dec-2 Sotheby's, London #42/R est:6000-8000
£7500 $11625 €11250 Studies of the heads of Saskia and others (15x12cm-6x5in) etching. 5-Dec-2 Sotheby's, London #44/R est:4000-5000
£7800 $12090 €11700 Sleeping herdsman (8x6cm-3x2in) etching executed 1644. 5-Dec-2 Sotheby's, London #37/R est:7000-10000
£7800 $12090 €11700 Three heads of women , one asleep (14x9cm-6x4in) etching. 5-Dec-2 Sotheby's, London #45/R est:6000-8000
£8176 $13000 €12264 Christ preaching (15x21cm-6x8in) etching drypoint. 1-May-3 Swann Galleries, New York #25/R est:10000-15000
£8333 $13000 €12500 Clement de Jonghe, printseller (21x17cm-8x7in) etching drypoint. 6-Nov-2 Swann Galleries, New York #88/R est:8000-12000
£8333 $12917 €13000 Self portrait leaning on stone sill (20x16cm-8x6in) etching. 5-Dec-2 Dr Fritz Nagel, Stuttgart #577/R est:12000
£8500 $13260 €12750 Sheet of studies (10x10cm-4x4in) etching executed c.1632. 25-Mar-3 Sotheby's, London #33/R est:6000-7000
£8805 $14000 €13208 Raising of Lazarus (37x26cm-15x10in) etching engraving drypoint. 1-May-3 Swann Galleries, New York #8/R est:5000-8000
£9000 $15030 €13050 Triumph of Mordecai (18x22cm-7x9in) etching drypoint exec.c.1641. 30-Jun-3 Bonhams, New Bond Street #94/R est:10000-15000
£9434 $15000 €14151 Christ healing the sick (28x39cm-11x15in) etching engraving drypoint. 1-May-3 Swann Galleries, New York #20/R est:20000-30000
£9434 $15000 €14151 Beared man in a velvet cap (9x8cm-4x3in) etching. 1-May-3 Swann Galleries, New York #95/R est:5000-8000
£9434 $15000 €14151 Return of the prodigal son (41x36cm-16x14in) d.1636 etching. 30-Apr-3 Doyle, New York #287/R est:6000-8000
£9615 $15000 €14423 Joseph's coat brought to Jacob (11x8cm-4x3in) etching drypoint exec.c.1633. 6-Nov-2 Swann Galleries, New York #74/R est:12000-18000
£9859 $16366 €14000 Christ preaching - La petite tombe (16x21cm-6x8in) etching drypoint. 12-Jun-3 Hauswedell & Nolte, Hamburg #151/R est:12000
£10256 $16000 €15384 Abraham entertaining the angels (16x13cm-6x5in) etching drypoint. 6-Nov-2 Swann Galleries, New York #90/R est:10000-15000
£10897 $17000 €16346 Blind fiddler (8x6cm-3x2in) etching drypoint. 6-Nov-2 Swann Galleries, New York #69/R est:8000-12000
£10897 $17218 €17000 Le sacrifice d'Abraham. etching drypoint. 14-Nov-2 Libert, Castor, Paris #26/R est:9500
£11538 $18000 €17307 Christ healing the sick (28x39cm-11x15in) etching engraving drypoint exec.c.1643-49. 6-Nov-2 Swann Galleries, New York #84/R est:15000-20000
£12658 $20000 €20000 Prodigal son (16x14cm-6x6in) etching. 29-Nov-2 Bassenge, Berlin #5450/R est:12000
£12821 $20256 €20000 La barque a la voile. etching. 14-Nov-2 Libert, Castor, Paris #40 est:12000
£13836 $22000 €20754 Jan Cornelis Sylvins, preacher (28x19cm-11x7in) etching drypoint. 1-May-3 Swann Galleries, New York #99/R est:6000-9000
£14000 $21700 €21000 Angel appearing to the shepherds (26x22cm-10x9in) etching. 5-Dec-2 Sotheby's, London #38/R est:10000-14000
£14103 $22000 €21155 Abraham's sacrifice (16x13cm-6x5in) etching drypoint. 6-Nov-2 Swann Galleries, New York #89/R est:20000-30000
£14103 $22282 €22000 L'obelisque. etching drypoint. 14-Nov-2 Libert, Castor, Paris #39/R est:13000
£14744 $23295 €23000 Le moulin de Rembrandt. etching. 14-Nov-2 Libert, Castor, Paris #41/R est:25000
£15000 $23250 €22500 Angel appearing to the shepherds (26x22cm-10x9in) etching. 5-Dec-2 Sotheby's, London #35/R est:12000-18000
£16000 $24800 €24000 Lieven Willemsz van Coppenol, writing master (34x29cm-13x11in) etching. 5-Dec-2 Sotheby's, London #36/R est:15000-20000
£16352 $26000 €24528 Self portrait in a velvet cap with plume (13x10cm-5x4in) etching. 1-May-3 Swann Galleries, New York #2/R est:20000-30000
£16500 $25575 €24750 Self portrait in a cap and scarf (13x10cm-5x4in) etching. 5-Dec-2 Sotheby's, London #40/R est:5000-7000
£18868 $30000 €28302 Descent from the cross by torchlight (21x16cm-8x6in) etching drypoint. 1-May-3 Swann Galleries, New York #29/R est:40000-60000
£19231 $30385 €30000 Jesus au milieu de ses disciples. etching. 14-Nov-2 Libert, Castor, Paris #33/R est:22500
£19231 $30385 €30000 Le chasseur. drypoint etching. 14-Nov-2 Libert, Castor, Paris #38/R est:11500
£20000 $31000 €30000 Abraham's sacrifice (16x13cm-6x5in) etching drypoint. 3-Dec-2 Christie's, London #64/R est:20000-30000
£20126 $32000 €30189 Faust (21x16cm-8x6in) etching drypoint. 1-May-3 Swann Galleries, New York #34/R est:20000-30000
£20513 $32000 €30770 Descent from the cross (53x41cm-21x16in) etching engraving. 6-Nov-2 Swann Galleries, New York #73/R est:12000-18000
£21795 $34436 €34000 Jean Lutma. etching drypoint. 14-Nov-2 Libert, Castor, Paris #42 est:10000
£25000 $41250 €36250 Good Samaritan (24x20cm-9x8in) etching. 1-Jul-3 Sotheby's, London #46/R est:30000-40000
£25157 $40000 €37736 Ephraim bonus, Jewish physician (22x18cm-9x7in) etching drypoint. 1-May-3 Swann Galleries, New York #100/R est:30000-40000
£28205 $44000 €42308 Self portrait drawing at a window (16x13cm-6x5in) etching engraving drypoint. 6-Nov-2 Swann Galleries, New York #87/R est:30000-50000
£30769 $48615 €48000 Negresse couchee. etching drypoint engraving. 14-Nov-2 Libert, Castor, Paris #36/R est:25000
£32051 $50641 €50000 Femme au bain. etching drypoint. 14-Nov-2 Libert, Castor, Paris #35/R est:30000
£42000 $65100 €63000 Receuil de quatre vingt cinq estampes originales par Rembrandt (45x32cm-18x13in) album prints. 3-Dec-2 Christie's, London #78/R est:15000-20000

Works on paper

£113208 $175472 €180000 Jonathan helping David (20x16cm-8x6in) ink lit. 7-Oct-2 Ansorena, Madrid #22/R est:180000
£165000 $275550 €239250 Seated man with long hair, hands folded (13x10cm-5x4in) black chk framing lines. 8-Jul-3 Christie's, London #100/R est:15000-20000

REMBRANDT (after) (1606-1669) Dutch

£12821 $20256 €20000 Prophets Elias and Elischa (39x31cm-15x12in) panel prov. 16-Nov-2 Lempertz, Koln #1078/R est:10000

Sculpture

£38000 $59280 €57000 Jeune cerf et sa biche amoureuse - Mother and baby deer (23x24x15cm-9x9x6in) s.num.3 bronze st.f. A.A. Hebrard. 7-Nov-2 Christie's, London #59/R est:35000-50000

REMBRANDT (circle) (1606-1669) Dutch

£37037 $60000 €55556 Portrait of old man (66x53cm-26x21in) ex. 23-Jan-3 Sotheby's, New York #137/R est:30000

Works on paper

£3704 $6000 €5556 Banishment of Hagar (19x27cm-7x11in) pen ink wash prov.lit. 22-Jan-3 Christie's, Rockefeller NY #91/R

REMBRANDT (school) (1606-1669) Dutch

£13669 $21871 €19000 Portrait of young man wearing fantasy costume and beret (54x47cm-21x19in) panel. 13-May-3 Sotheby's, Amsterdam #62/R est:20000-30000
£80000 $133600 €116000 An old woman weighing gold coins (87x73cm-34x29in) bears sig.d.1647 panel prov. 10-Jul-3 Sotheby's, London #18/R est:30000-40000

REMBRANDT (style) (1606-1669) Dutch
£544 $865 €800 Dispute outside tavern (39x39cm-15x15in) panel. 28-Mar-3 Bolland & Marotz, Bremen #412/R
£5500 $8580 €8250 Elijah visited by an Angel (90x108cm-35x43in) prov.lit. 10-Apr-3 Christie's, Kensington #41/R est:6000-8000
£10000 $15700 €15000 Tronic of an old man (61x51cm-24x20in) prov. 13-Dec-2 Christie's, Kensington #19/R est:3000-5000
£16000 $24960 €24000 Young man in Oriental costume (70x56cm-28x22in) 19-Sep-2 Christie's, Kensington #33/R est:1000-1500

REMENICK, Seymour (1923-) American
£417 $650 €626 Boats at harbour (20x38cm-8x15in) s. panel. 20-Sep-2 Freeman, Philadelphia #84/R
£417 $650 €626 Amongst the trees (41x51cm-16x20in) s. 20-Sep-2 Freeman, Philadelphia #114/R
£518 $850 €777 Fishing boats at dock (61x81cm-24x32in) s. 5-Feb-3 Doyle, New York #47/R
£525 $850 €788 Docks, Cape May (25x36cm-10x14in) prov. 24-Jan-3 Freeman, Philadelphia #205/R

REMINGTON, Frederic (1861-1909) American
£43210 $70000 €64815 Field drill for the Prussian infantry (21x36cm-8x14in) s. prov.lit. 22-May-3 Christie's, Rockefeller NY #25/R est:40000-60000
£74074 $120000 €111111 He made his magazine gun blaze until empty (102x69cm-40x27in) s. en grisaille painted c.1900 prov.lit. 21-May-3 Sotheby's, New York #225/R est:150000-200000
£96774 $150000 €145161 Waiting - study of a cow pony (61x51cm-24x20in) s. painted c.1896 prov.lit. 4-Dec-2 Sotheby's, New York #148/R est:150000-250000
£419355 $650000 €629033 Comanche brave, Fort Reno, Indian territory (61x51cm-24x20in) s.i.d.88 prov.exhib.lit. 5-Dec-2 Christie's, Rockefeller NY #179/R est:600000-800000
£1096774 $1700000 €1645161 Scare in a pack train (69x110cm-27x43in) s.d.1908 prov.lit. 5-Dec-2 Christie's, Rockefeller NY #171/R est:2000000-3000000

Sculpture
£1046 $1715 €1600 Trapper on horse back (73cm-29in) bronze. 8-Feb-3 Hans Stahl, Hamburg #471 est:1700
£4208 $6648 €6312 The mountain man (71cm-28in) s. pat.bronze. 30-Nov-2 Goteborg Auktionsverk, Sweden #228/R est:60000 (S.KR 60000)
£27778 $45000 €40278 Rattlesnake (61cm-24in) s.i.65 blk pat bronze f.Roman Bronze Works NY prov. 21-May-3 Doyle, New York #134/R est:60000-80000
£31447 $50000 €47171 Bronco buster (57cm-22in) s.i.num.171 brown black pat bronze. 7-Mar-3 Skinner, Boston #348/R est:50000-60000
£40881 $65000 €61322 Bronco buster (22cm-9in) s.num.189 brown pat bronze st.f.Roman Bronze Works exec.c.1895. 4-May-3 Treadway Gallery, Cincinnati #559/R est:60000-80000
£48387 $75000 €72581 Bronco buster (58cm-23in) i. dark brown pat. bronze prov.lit. 5-Dec-2 Christie's, Rockefeller NY #170/R est:60000-80000
£148148 $240000 €222222 Scalp (67cm-26in) i. dark brown pat. bronze i.f.Henry Bonnard prov.lit. 22-May-3 Christie's, Rockefeller NY #89/R est:200000-300000
£209877 $340000 €314816 Mountain man (72cm-28in) i. dark brown pat. bronze i.f.Roman prov.lit. 22-May-3 Christie's, Rockefeller NY #86/R est:180000-240000

Works on paper
£4614 $7475 €6690 Cavalry man on horseback (8x10cm-3x4in) India ink. 23-May-3 Altermann Galleries, Santa Fe #97
£8176 $13000 €12264 Head of a cavalry trooper (29x22cm-11x9in) s.i. W/C pencil prov. 5-Mar-3 Sotheby's, New York #124/R est:8000-12000
£13924 $22000 €20190 Bit of rough road (33x48cm-13x19in) s. ink wash prov.lit. 26-Jul-3 Coeur d'Alene, Hayden #160/R est:10000-20000
£16049 $26000 €24074 Kiowa buck starting a race (36x37cm-14x15in) s.i. ink gouache prov.lit. 22-May-3 Christie's, Rockefeller NY #21/R est:40000-60000
£21605 $35000 €32408 Indian scout at Fort Reno (38x37cm-15x15in) s.i. ink g, prov.lit. 22-May-3 Christie's, Rockefeller NY #84/R est:40000-60000
£21605 $35000 €32408 Dispatch bearer troop B, United States Scouts (25x25cm-10x10in) s.i. ink wash on board prov.lit. 22-May-3 Christie's, Rockefeller NY #91/R est:30000-50000
£37037 $60000 €55556 Cheyenne type (38x28cm-15x11in) s. ink wash board prov.lit. 22-May-3 Christie's, Rockefeller NY #92/R est:30000-50000
£69620 $110000 €100949 Friendly scout signaling the main column (53x36cm-21x14in) s. ink wash lit. 26-Jul-3 Coeur d'Alene, Hayden #181/R est:95000-125000
£119863 $175000 €179795 You know this thing, chief? The Indian nodded slightly (48x69cm-19x27in) gouache. 18-May-2 Altermann Galleries, Santa Fe #50/R

REMINGTON, Frederic (attrib) (1861-1909) American

Works on paper
£813 $1276 €1220 Scout (25x19cm-10x7in) s. W/C prov. 10-Dec-2 Pinneys, Montreal #49 est:2500-3500 (C.D 2000)

REMINGTON, Mary (1910-) British
£450 $738 €675 Honesty in the lustre pot (34x32cm-13x13in) s. board. 3-Jun-3 Sotheby's, Olympia #190/R

REMOND, Jean (1872-1913) French
£710 $1100 €1065 Safely on shore (22x27cm-9x11in) s.d.1901 card. 2-Oct-2 Christie's, Rockefeller NY #795/R est:1000-1500

REMOND, Jean Charles Joseph (attrib) (1795-1875) French
£909 $1518 €1300 Paysage montagneux anime de personnages (29x40cm-11x16in) paper on canvas. 27-Jun-3 Piasa, Paris #107
£1049 $1752 €1500 Paysage de falaises (24x35cm-9x14in) paper on cardboard. 27-Jun-3 Piasa, Paris #113 est:1200-1500

REMSEY, Jeno (1885-1960) Hungarian
£380 $619 €551 Figure washing in an interior (100x70cm-39x28in) s. 15-Jul-3 Bonhams, Knightsbridge #117/R
£2580 $4024 €3741 Parisian coffee house (117x148cm-46x58in) s.d.963. 13-Sep-2 Mu Terem Galeria, Budapest #180/R est:480000 (H.F 1000000)

REMY, Gio (19th C) Italian?
£469 $751 €680 Girl with cavalier (51x37cm-20x15in) s.d.68. 18-May-3 Anders Antik, Landskrona #132 (S.KR 6000)

REN XUN (1835-1893) Chinese

Works on paper
£4715 $7450 €7073 Lady playing the pipe (20x55cm-8x22in) s.i. ink col fan painting. 28-Apr-3 Sotheby's, Hong Kong #577/R est:35000-50000 (HK.D 58000)

REN YI (1840-1895) Chinese

Works on paper
£4274 $7051 €6197 Mandarin ducks (129x32cm-51x13in) s.i. ink scroll. 6-Jul-3 Christie's, Hong Kong #301/R est:60000-80000 (HK.D 55000)
£5439 $8974 €7887 Returning home (40x80cm-16x31in) s.i. ink scroll. 6-Jul-3 Christie's, Hong Kong #302/R est:40000-50000 (HK.D 70000)
£12432 $20513 €18026 Wisteria and bird (163x45cm-64x18in) s.i. ink scroll. 6-Jul-3 Christie's, Hong Kong #300/R est:80000-100000 (HK.D 160000)
£113821 $179837 €170732 Autumn feast (41x190cm-16x75in) s.i.d.1875 ink col handscroll satin. 28-Apr-3 Sotheby's, Hong Kong #578/R est:250000-350000 (HK.D 1400000)

REN YU (1853-1901) Chinese

Works on paper
£4472 $7065 €6708 Home coming (29x252cm-11x99in) s.i.d.1892 ink handscroll. 28-Apr-3 Sotheby's, Hong Kong #653/R est:60000-80000 (HK.D 55000)

RENARD, Edward (?) ?

Works on paper
£280 $454 €420 Quayside of the Zatteri, Venice (17x25cm-7x10in) s. W/C. 21-Jan-3 Bonhams, Knightsbridge #282/R

RENARD, Fernand (1912-) French
£481 $750 €722 Pink flowers in a glass vase (36x25cm-14x10in) s. 9-Oct-2 Doyle, New York #88
£513 $800 €770 Verre, oeuf et jeu de cartes (41x33cm-16x13in) s. prov. 9-Oct-2 Doyle, New York #87
£545 $850 €818 Vase of flowers and white berries (46x33cm-18x13in) s. 9-Oct-2 Doyle, New York #90
£609 $950 €914 Still life with wildflowers and shell (61x38cm-24x15in) s. 9-Oct-2 Doyle, New York #89
£769 $1200 €1154 Currants, gooseberries and cherries (25x36cm-10x14in) one s. pair. 9-Oct-2 Doyle, New York #91
£833 $1300 €1250 Still life with eggs, cards and blackberries (74x61cm-29x24in) s. 9-Oct-2 Doyle, New York #92
£1000 $1580 €1500 Sweetcorn, egg and chillies on stone ledge (37x55cm-15x22in) s. 4-Apr-3 Moore Allen & Innocent, Cirencester #658/R est:1000-1200
£1146 $1800 €1719 Still life with fruit and flowers upon a table (20x26cm-8x10in) s. 10-Dec-2 Doyle, New York #254/R est:2500-3500
£2070 $3250 €3105 White primroses no.16 (22x18cm-9x7in) s. 10-Dec-2 Doyle, New York #253/R est:3000-4000

RENARD, Fredericus Theodorus (1778-?) Dutch
£3957 $6331 €5500 Amsterdam: view of the De Duif church on Prinsengraft (39x50cm-15x20in) panel. 13-May-3 Sotheby's, Amsterdam #90/R est:6000-8000

RENARD, Mary (19th C) French
£285 $444 €450 Paysage aux meules (38x55cm-15x22in) s.d.1892. 15-Sep-2 Etude Bailleul, Bayeux #177

RENARD, Stephen J (1947-) British
£2600 $4212 €3900 Lulworth and Britannia in a stiff breeze (38x51cm-15x20in) s. 21-May-3 Christie's, Kensington #501/R est:2500-3500
£2600 $4212 €3900 Leander and Julnar off Norris Castle (38x50cm-15x20in) s. s.i.d.2002 stretcher. 21-May-3 Christie's, Kensington #504/R est:2500-3000
£3800 $6156 €5700 Westward and Britannia in a stiff breeze off Norris Castle (38x51cm-15x20in) s. 21-May-3 Christie's, Kensington #503/R est:2500-3500
£5500 $8635 €8250 Endeavour, Shamrock V and Britannia racing in the Solent (50x75cm-20x30in) s. 16-Dec-2 Sotheby's, Olympia #179/R est:6000-8000
£11000 $17820 €16500 White Heather III, Candida and Shamrock V racing off Yarmouth (81x107cm-32x42in) s. 21-May-3 Christie's, Kensington #502/R est:10000-20000
£13580 $22000 €19691 Yankee racing Britannia and Endeavor off the Royal yacht squadron (74x125cm-29x49in) s.i.on stretcher. 29-Jul-3 Christie's, Rockefeller NY #184/R est:25000-35000
£15000 $23550 €22500 Reliance overhauling Shamrock III off Newport Rhode Island (76x127cm-30x50in) s. i.on stretcher. 16-Dec-2 Sotheby's, Olympia #174/R est:15000-20000
£18000 $30060 €26100 Britannia and Vigilant in the Solent off Cowes (102x152cm-40x60in) s. 18-Jun-3 Sotheby's, Olympia #135/R est:20000-30000

RENARDT, J (19th C) German
£1762 $2626 €2643 Winter landscape with hunter (55x75cm-22x30in) s.d.1895. 25-Jun-2 Koller, Zurich #6462 est:800-1600 (S.FR 4000)

RENAUDIN, Alfred (1866-1944) French
£1258 $2000 €1887 Chantegrille (73x102cm-29x40in) s.i.d.1934. 7-Mar-3 Skinner, Boston #532/R est:2000-2500
£3688 $5974 €5200 Le haut de la rue Lepic (50x73cm-20x29in) st.sig. s.verso. 23-May-3 Camard, Paris #70/R est:5300-6000
£4085 $6780 €5800 Peintre dans le parc du chateau (24x35cm-9x14in) s.d.88. 11-Jun-3 Beaussant & Lefèvre, Paris #194/R est:1500-2000

RENAULD, R (19th C) ?
£258 $393 €387 Coastal landscape with village in the hills (33x46cm-13x18in) s.d.84. 27-Aug-2 Rasmussen, Copenhagen #1711/R (D.KR 3000)

RENAULT, Luigi P (attrib) (1845-c.1910) Italian
Works on paper
£600 $972 €900 Severn entering the port of Leghorn (41x56cm-16x22in) i. pencil pen ink W/C. 21-May-3 Christie's, Kensington #427/R

RENAULT-DES-GRAVIERS, Victor J (?-1905) French
£700 $1134 €1050 Still life with flowers and fruit (54x73cm-21x29in) s. 20-May-3 Sotheby's, Olympia #375/R

RENCK, Ernst Emil (1841-1912) German
£377 $589 €600 Flowering cherry trees (23x33cm-9x13in) s. canvas on board. 19-Sep-2 Dr Fritz Nagel, Stuttgart #989/R

RENDELL, Joseph Frederick Percy (1872-1955) British
£250 $393 €375 Street scene (49x60cm-19x24in) s. 15-Dec-2 Lots Road, London #357

RENDL, Georg (20th C) ?
£481 $755 €750 Summer landscape (40x55cm-16x22in) mono.d.67. 21-Nov-2 Dorotheum, Vienna #281/R

RENDON, Manuel (1894-1980) Ecuadorian/French
£11465 $18000 €17198 Untitled (92x65cm-36x26in) s. painted c.1950 prov. 20-Nov-2 Christie's, Rockefeller NY #84/R est:25000-30000

RENE, Jean Jacques (1943-) French
£4051 $6400 €6400 Femme devant la mer (46x38cm-18x15in) s. 27-Nov-2 Blanchet, Paris #99/R est:1200
Works on paper
£349 $562 €520 Femmes au cafe (18x16cm-7x6in) s. W/C. 23-Feb-3 Lesieur & Le Bars, Le Havre #133
£436 $702 €650 Rosalie a Fecamp (17x15cm-7x6in) s. W/C. 23-Feb-3 Lesieur & Le Bars, Le Havre #132
£548 $860 €800 Les tentes sur la plage a Trouville (19x26cm-7x10in) s. W/C. 21-Apr-3 Rabourdin & Choppin de Janvry, Paris #150

RENESON, Chet (20th C) American
Works on paper
£1582 $2500 €2294 Morning hunt (38x66cm-15x26in) s. W/C. 26-Jul-3 Coeur d'Alene, Hayden #229/R est:3000-5000
£2025 $3200 €3038 Bad luck wind (43x69cm-17x27in) s.d.75 W/C gouache prov. 3-Apr-3 Christie's, Rockefeller NY #188/R est:2000-3000

RENESSE, Constantin van (1626-1680) Dutch
£6090 $9622 €9500 Portrait of bearded man (46x36cm-18x14in) mono. panel. 16-Nov-2 Lempertz, Koln #1079/R est:8000

RENGER-PATZSCH, Albert (1897-1966) German
Photographs
£1899 $3000 €3000 Pelecyphora Aselliformis (23x17cm-9x7in) i. verso silver gelatin. 28-Nov-2 Villa Grisebach, Berlin #1350/R est:300-4000
£1899 $3000 €3000 Mesembrianthum Pseudotruncatellum (17x23cm-7x9in) i. verso silver gelatin. 28-Nov-2 Villa Grisebach, Berlin #1351/R est:300-4000
£2013 $3119 €3200 Beech tree (38x28cm-15x11in) i. verso gelatin silver. 2-Nov-2 Lempertz, Koln #337/R est:2300-2600
£2215 $3500 €3500 On the Wall, Lubeck (27x38cm-11x15in) i. verso silver gelatin lit.exhib. 28-Nov-2 Villa Grisebach, Berlin #1353/R est:4000-6000
£2215 $3500 €3500 Fishermen on banks of the Rhine, Duisburg (27x38cm-11x15in) silver gelatin. 28-Nov-2 Villa Grisebach, Berlin #1354/R est:4000-6000
£2390 $3704 €3800 Thorn bushes in the snow (28x37cm-11x15in) i. gelatin silver. 2-Nov-2 Lempertz, Koln #81/R est:2600
£2532 $4000 €3798 Faltung (22x16cm-9x6in) i.verso gelatin silver print prov.lit. 24-Apr-3 Phillips, New York #103/R est:4000-6000
£2704 $4192 €4300 Mantel Pavian (23x17cm-9x7in) i. silver gelatine. 31-Oct-2 Van Ham, Cologne #254/R est:4300
£2808 $4381 €4100 Paprika (22x16cm-9x6in) i. verso gelatin. 12-Apr-3 Lempertz, Koln #176/R est:2800
£3191 $5170 €4500 Building (22x16cm-9x6in) bears i.d. silver gelatin agfa-brovira. 23-May-3 Van Ham, Cologne #188/R est:2800
£3291 $5200 €4937 Haus der jugend (23x17cm-9x7in) gelatin silver print prov. 24-Apr-3 Phillips, New York #105/R est:3000-5000
£4247 $6625 €6200 Wood (22x16cm-9x6in) i. gelatin silver lit. 12-Apr-3 Lempertz, Koln #180/R est:4000
£4430 $7000 €6645 Cranes in front of Lubeck (17x23cm-7x9in) gelatin silver print prov. 24-Apr-3 Phillips, New York #123/R est:7000-9000

RENGETSU, Otagaki (1791-1875) Japanese
Works on paper
£3200 $5344 €4640 Kyusu and two tea bowls with a poem (33x45cm-13x18in) s. ink hanging scroll. 18-Jun-3 Christie's, London #295/R est:2000-3000

RENI, Guido (1575-1642) Italian
£629 $975 €1000 Saint Sebastian (40x32cm-16x13in) 1-Oct-2 Palais de Beaux Arts, Brussels #416
£20000 $31400 €30000 Penitent Magdalen (55x47cm-22x19in) prov.lit. 11-Dec-2 Christie's, London #112/R est:20000-30000
£24000 $40080 €34800 Madonna and Child seated on a cloud (31x19cm-12x7in) prov.lit. 8-Jul-3 Christie's, London #32/R est:15000-20000
Works on paper
£9000 $15030 €13050 Study of praying man (27x20cm-11x8in) black white chk prov. 8-Jul-3 Christie's, London #33/R est:5000-8000
£10494 $17000 €15741 Assumption of the Virgin (14x23cm-6x9in) chk pen ink htd white prov. 21-Jan-3 Sotheby's, New York #168/R est:12000

RENI, Guido (after) (1575-1642) Italian
£7500 $11699 €11250 Aurora (89x176cm-35x69in) 19-Sep-2 Christie's, Kensington #225/R est:2000-3000
£8954 $14506 €13431 The Penitent Magdalene (83x71cm-33x28in) 3-Feb-3 Lilla Bukowskis, Stockholm #977 est:15000-20000 (S.KR 125000)
Sculpture
£10323 $16310 €16000 Seneca (47cm-19in) black pat bronze marble base lit. 17-Dec-2 Sotheby's, Paris #22/R est:15000

RENI, Guido (circle) (1575-1642) Italian
£5769 $9115 €9000 St Cecilia at the organ (74x60cm-29x24in) 16-Nov-2 Lempertz, Koln #1080/R est:9000

£6500 $10205 €9750 Head of a man (50x43cm-20x17in) prov. 13-Dec-2 Christie's, Kensington #236/R est:3000-5000

RENI, Guido (style) (1575-1642) Italian

£5000 $7850 €7500 Agony in the garden (58x45cm-23x18in) 10-Dec-2 Sotheby's, Olympia #316/R est:4000-6000
£7317 $12000 €10976 Head of a bearded Saint (62x51cm-24x20in) 29-May-3 Sotheby's, New York #130/R est:4000-6000
£7547 $11698 €12000 Sleeping cupid (71x91cm-28x36in) 18th C. 2-Oct-2 Dorotheum, Vienna #280/R est:3000-5000
£9434 $14717 €15000 Victorious Samson (125x93cm-49x37in) 20-Sep-2 Millon & Associes, Paris #655/R est:16000-25000
£18710 $29561 €29000 Saint John the Baptist (48x60cm-19x24in) 18-Dec-2 Ferri, Paris #19

RENIE, Jean Emile (attrib) (1835-1910) French

£993 $1658 €1400 France, suite de quatre vues de Villers (13x21cm-5x8in) i.d.15 juillet 1875 verso. 23-Jun-3 Beaussant & Lefèvre, Paris #163

RENISON, William (fl.1920`s) British

£650 $1034 €975 Dawn, Vorlich from Strathearn (74x91cm-29x36in) s. board prov. 6-Mar-3 Christie's, Kensington #140/R

RENNIE, George Melvin (1874-1953) British

£350 $553 €525 Loch Avon and Benillac, Dhu, Cairngorm (46x61cm-18x24in) s. s.i.on stretcher. 14-Nov-2 Bonhams, Edinburgh #332
£380 $600 €570 On Ben Macdhui (46x61cm-18x24in) s. s.i. on stretcher. 14-Nov-2 Bonhams, Edinburgh #318
£550 $842 €825 Duntulm Castle, Skye (49x75cm-19x30in) s. 22-Aug-2 Bonhams, Edinburgh #1170
£600 $948 €900 Arran (44x60cm-17x24in) 1-Apr-3 Patersons, Paisley #525
£667 $1027 €1001 Glen Muick, near Ballater (33x44cm-13x17in) s. 4-Sep-2 Dunbar Sloane, Wellington #86/R est:1200-1800 (NZ.D 2200)

RENNIE, Helen Sewell (20th C) American

£427 $700 €619 Untitled - musicians (58x71cm-23x28in) s. 1-Jun-3 Wright, Chicago #173/R

RENOIR, Joseph Alexandre (1811-1855) French

Sculpture

£60000 $94200 €90000 La reine Berenice consacre sa chevelure au dieu Mars - Queen Berenice offering her hair to Mars (200cm-79in) s.d.1854 white marble exhib.lit. 10-Dec-2 Sotheby's, London #178/R est:70000-100000

RENOIR, Pierre Auguste (1841-1919) French

£543 $907 €787 Femme nue assise (19x14cm-7x6in) vernis mou. 24-Jun-3 Koller, Zurich #489 (S.FR 1200)
£10645 $16819 €16500 Fruits sur un drape (6x9cm-2x4in) canvas on panel lit. 18-Dec-2 Beaussant & Lefèvre, Paris #44/R est:3000
£16000 $26720 €23200 Les poissons (11x16cm-4x6in) mono. 25-Jun-3 Christie's, London #131/R est:12000-16000
£19651 $30655 €29477 Nature morte aux tomates (13x16cm-5x6in) s. 6-Nov-2 Dobiaschofsky, Bern #906/R est:60000 (S.FR 45000)
£23077 $35769 €36000 Paysage aux arbres (12x16cm-5x6in) st.sig. canvas on panel lit. 9-Dec-2 Beaussant & Lefèvre, Paris #85/R est:24000-28000
£30000 $50100 €43500 Etudes, tetes et maisons (14x21cm-6x8in) lit. 24-Jun-3 Sotheby's, London #122/R est:30000-40000
£30406 $47433 €45000 Buste de Coco et maison blanche (14x21cm-6x8in) prov.lit. 26-Mar-3 Tajan, Paris #12/R
£32000 $53440 €46400 Cannes (103x2cm-41x1in) st.sig painted 1892 prov.lit. 24-Jun-3 Sotheby's, London #101/R est:18000-25000
£35000 $57400 €52500 Jeune femme debout (34x23cm-13x9in) s.painted 1895 prov.lit. 5-Feb-3 Sotheby's, London #110/R est:60000
£45000 $73800 €67500 Portrait de femme (22x18cm-9x7in) st.sig. prov. 5-Feb-3 Sotheby's, London #107/R est:60000
£51282 $80000 €76923 Fort Carre et phare d'antibes (20x32cm-8x13in) st.sig. painted 1916 prov.lit. 7-Nov-2 Christie's, Rockefeller NY #219/R est:90000-120000
£55000 $91850 €79750 Route a Cagnes (21x30cm-8x12in) st.sig prov. 25-Jun-3 Christie's, London #103/R est:50000-70000
£55000 $91850 €79750 Etude de Gabrielle (30x28cm-12x11in) painted 1905-08 prov.exhib.lit. 24-Jun-3 Sotheby's, London #119/R est:60000-80000
£58000 $95120 €87000 Anemones et roses (25x18cm-10x7in) st.sig. prov.lit. 5-Feb-3 Sotheby's, London #108/R est:85000
£82192 $128219 €120000 Paysage des Collettes (20x30cm-8x12in) s. 8-Apr-3 Gioffredo, Nice #62/R
£90000 $150300 €130500 Fleurs (34x28cm-13x11in) s. painted 1908 prov. 25-Jun-3 Christie's, London #105/R est:80000-100000
£96273 $155000 €144410 Bouquet de fleurs (60x50cm-24x20in) s.d.Juin 1858 prov.lit. 8-May-3 Christie's, Rockefeller NY #138/R est:120000-160000
£99379 $160000 €149069 Portrait de Gabrielle (27x22cm-11x9in) s. prov. 7-May-3 Sotheby's, New York #114/R est:180000-250000
£102564 $160000 €153846 Port de la Rochelle (21x32cm-8x13in) s. painted 1896 prov.exhib.lit. 7-Nov-2 Christie's, Rockefeller NY #160/R est:150000-200000
£105590 $170000 €158385 Nature morte aux peches (21x38cm-8x15in) s. prov.lit. 7-May-3 Sotheby's, New York #121/R est:150000-200000
£116129 $183484 €180000 Femme a la robe noire (33x19cm-13x7in) st.mono. 18-Dec-2 Ferri, Paris #103/R
£120000 $196800 €180000 Portrait de Lucienne (37x32cm-15x13in) s. painted 1918 prov. 4-Feb-3 Christie's, London #224/R est:160000
£140000 $233800 €203000 Vase de roses et orange (34x25cm-13x10in) s. painted 1910 prov. 25-Jun-3 Christie's, London #111/R est:160000-220000
£140000 $233800 €203000 Nymphe couchee (25x32cm-10x13in) s. painted c.1880 prov.exhib. 24-Jun-3 Sotheby's, London #110/R est:90000-120000
£141026 $220000 €211539 Bord de riviere, rameur dans une barque (33x41cm-13x16in) st.sig. prov.lit. 7-Nov-2 Christie's, Rockefeller NY #205/R est:200000-300000
£146853 $245245 €210000 Les oliviers de Cagnes (32x54cm-13x21in) s. prov.lit. 30-Jun-3 Artcurial Briest, Paris #46/R
£181249 $290000 €271874 Roses au vase bleu (34x25cm-13x10in) s. prov.exhib. 14-May-3 Butterfields, San Francisco #1133/R est:220000-260000
£223602 $360000 €335403 Jeune fille au chapeau fleuri (55x46cm-22x18in) s. painted c.1900-05 prov.exhib. 8-May-3 Christie's, Rockefeller NY #158/R est:300000-400000
£240000 $400800 €348000 La coiffure de l'enfant (30x30cm-12x12in) st.sig prov. 25-Jun-3 Christie's, London #133/R est:250000-350000
£260870 $420000 €391305 Portrait D'Helen Bellon (34x29cm-13x11in) s. painted 1908 prov.exhib.lit. 7-May-3 Sotheby's, New York #112/R est:200000-300000
£335404 $540000 €503106 Baie d'Alger (51x65cm-20x26in) s.d.81 prov.exhib.lit. 7-May-3 Christie's, Rockefeller NY #18/R est:500000-700000
£384615 $600000 €576923 Reunion autour d'un bateau (51x62cm-20x24in) s.d.1862 prov.exhib.lit. 5-Nov-2 Sotheby's, New York #9/R est:800000-1200000
£443662 $736479 €630000 Le bain (33x38cm-13x15in) s. prov.lit. 11-Jun-3 Beaussant & Lefèvre, Paris #191/R est:150000-200000
£581560 $971206 €820000 Baigneuse assise endormie (55x46cm-22x18in) s. prov.exhib.lit. 20-Jun-3 Piasa, Paris #17/R est:800000-1200000
£683230 $1100000 €1024845 Jeune fille dans un jardin, Cagnes (46x55cm-18x22in) s. painted 1903-05 prov. 7-May-3 Christie's, Rockefeller NY #10/R est:1000000-1500000
£705128 $1100000 €1057692 Portrait d'Edmond Maitre - le liseur (22x29cm-9x11in) s. painted 1871 prov.exhib.lit. 5-Nov-2 Sotheby's, New York #1/R est:700000-900000
£931677 $1500000 €1397516 Gabrielle et Coco jouant aux dominos (52x46cm-20x18in) s. painted c.1905-06 prov.exhib.lit. 6-May-3 Sotheby's, New York #12/R est:1200000-1600000
£950000 $1586500 €1377500 Portrait de Madame Adrien Mithouard (81x66cm-32x26in) s.d.92 prov.exhib. 24-Jun-3 Christie's, London #53/R est:1200000-1600000
£2400000 $3912000 €3600000 Canotiers a Argenteuil (50x61cm-20x24in) s. painted 1873 prov.exhib.lit. 3-Feb-3 Christie's, London #60/R est:3500000
£13043479 $21000000 €19565219 Dans les roses, Madame Leon Clapisson (100x81cm-39x32in) s.d.82 prov.exhib. 6-May-3 Sotheby's, New York #18/R est:20000000-30000000

Prints

£1923 $3000 €2885 Femme nue assise (19x15cm-7x6in) soft ground etching. 7-Nov-2 Swann Galleries, New York #483/R est:2000-3000
£2083 $3312 €3000 Etude pour une baigneuse (22x16cm-9x6in) drypoint. 5-May-3 Ketterer, Munich #46/R est:700-900
£2162 $3373 €3200 Louis Valtat (30x24cm-12x9in) s. lithograph. 28-Mar-3 Ketterer, Hamburg #105/R est:2500-3500
£2201 $3500 €3302 Etude pour un baigneuse (56x43cm-22x17in) st.sig.d.1906 etching drypoint one of 1000. 30-Apr-3 Doyle, New York #290/R est:1500-2000
£2432 $3795 €3600 Baigneuse assise (22x13cm-9x5in) vernis mou. 28-Mar-3 Ketterer, Hamburg #88/R est:1800-2200
£2500 $3900 €3700 Odalisque (8x12cm-3x5in) s. lithograph. 28-Mar-3 Ketterer, Hamburg #103/R est:1200-1500
£2516 $4000 €3774 Le petite garcon au port-plume (29x40cm-11x16in) lithograph exec.c.1910. 2-May-3 Sotheby's, New York #348/R est:3000-8000
£2516 $4000 €3774 Etude pour une baigneuse (22x17cm-9x7in) drypoint. 1-May-3 Swann Galleries, New York #70/R est:3000-5000
£2642 $4200 €3963 Les laveuses (46x61cm-18x24in) lithograph executed c.1912. 1-May-3 Swann Galleries, New York #355/R est:3000-5000
£3194 $5079 €4600 Les laveuses, 1re pensee (46x61cm-18x24in) lithograph. 5-May-3 Ketterer, Munich #51/R est:2500-3500
£3205 $5000 €4808 Maternite, grande planche (66x50cm-26x20in) col lithograph. 14-Oct-2 Butterfields, San Francisco #1182/R est:3000-5000
£3243 $5059 €4800 L'enfant au biscuit - Jean Renoir (32x27cm-13x11in) lithograph. 28-Mar-3 Ketterer, Hamburg #101/R est:2500-3500
£3472 $5521 €5000 L'enfant au biscuit - Jean Renoir (32x26cm-13x10in) lithograph. 5-May-3 Ketterer, Munich #54/R est:3000-4000
£3526 $5571 €5500 Baigneuse assise. print exec.c.1897. 13-Nov-2 Piasa, Paris #266
£3718 $5837 €5800 Maternite (490x490cm-193x193in) lithograph. 12-Dec-2 Piasa, Paris #128
£4167 $6625 €6000 Maternite, grande planche (50x48cm-20x19in) s. lithograph. 5-May-3 Ketterer, Munich #49/R est:1500-2000

£4514 $7177 €6500 Le petit garcon au porte plume - Claude Renoir ecrivant (29x40cm-11x16in) lithograph. 5-May-3 Ketterer, Munich #45/R est:5000-7000
£4595 $7168 €6800 La danse a la campage, 2e planche (22x14cm-9x6in) vernis mou. 28-Mar-3 Ketterer, Hamburg #83/R est:4500-5500
£4690 $7503 €6800 La danse a la campagne (22x13cm-9x5in) s. print vellum. 12-Mar-3 Libert, Castor, Paris #21/R est:4000-4500
£4730 $7378 €7000 Le petit garcon au porte plume - Claude Renoir ecrivant (30x40cm-12x16in) lithograph. 28-Mar-3 Ketterer, Hamburg #113/R est:3500-4500
£4861 $7729 €7000 Pierre Renoir, de face (28x23cm-11x9in) s.i. lithograph. 5-May-3 Ketterer, Munich #44/R est:4000-5000
£5031 $8000 €7547 Danse a la campagne, 2eme planche (56x36cm-22x14in) soft ground etching executed c.1890. 30-Apr-3 Doyle, New York #288/R est:7000-10000
£5093 $8199 €7640 L'enfant au biscuit (31x26cm-12x10in) col lithograph. 7-May-3 Dobiaschofsky, Bern #1895/R est:7500 (S.FR 11000)
£5128 $8000 €7692 La danse a la campagne (33x25cm-13x10in) st.sig. soft ground etching exec.c.1890. 5-Nov-2 Christie's, Rockefeller NY #20/R est:6000-8000
£5346 $8286 €8500 La danse a la campagne (32x25cm-13x10in) s. vellum exec.c.1890. 30-Oct-2 Artcurial Briest, Paris #555/R est:6000-6500
£6597 $10490 €9500 L'enfant au biscuit - Jean REnoir (32x27cm-13x11in) col lithograph. 5-May-3 Ketterer, Munich #53/R est:4500-5500
£6800 $11220 €9860 Enfant au biscuit (61x47cm-24x19in) col lithograph. 1-Jul-3 Sotheby's, London #142/R est:7000-9000
£7051 $11141 €11000 Femme nue assise. drypoint sold with other prints by Cezanne Pissarro Guillaumin. 13-Nov-2 Piasa, Paris #267/R
£7095 $11068 €10500 L'enfant au biscuit - Jean Renoir (32x27cm-13x11in) col lithograph. 28-Mar-3 Ketterer, Hamburg #102/R est:5000-6000
£7362 $12000 €11043 Untitled (33x25cm-13x10in) lithograph set of 12. 13-Feb-3 Christie's, Rockefeller NY #177/R est:7000
£7372 $11574 €11500 Les enfants jouant a la balle (600x510cm-236x201in) lithograph. 12-Dec-2 Piasa, Paris #126/R
£7722 $12432 €11583 Le chapeau epingle - Iere planche (60x49cm-24x19in) s.d.1897 lithograph printed in green lit. 7-May-3 AB Stockholms Auktionsverk #1271/R est:80000-100000 (S.KR 100000)
£9032 $14271 €14000 Jeune femme en buste. lithograph exec.1892 lit. 19-Dec-2 Claude Aguttes, Neuilly #153/R est:7500
£11806 $18771 €17000 L'enfant au biscuit - Jean Renoir (32x27cm-13x11in) s. col lithograph. 5-May-3 Ketterer, Munich #52/R est:9000-12000
£14744 $23295 €23000 Le chapeau epingle et la baigneuse. lithograph. 14-Nov-2 Libert, Castor, Paris #129/R est:8000
£26606 $44431 €38579 Le chapeau epingle (61x49cm-24x19in) s.i. col lithograph. 20-Jun-3 Kornfeld, Bern #132/R est:40000 (S.FR 58000)
£31159 $51101 €43000 Le chapeau epingle (62x49cm-24x19in) s. col lithograph. 30-May-3 Villa Grisebach, Berlin #4/R est:45000-55000
£35000 $54250 €52500 Le chapeau epingle (71x59cm-28x23in) col lithograph. 3-Dec-2 Christie's, London #229/R est:30000-40000

Sculpture
£1795 $2818 €2800 Coco de profil (22x22cm-9x9in) brown black pat bronze relief. 15-Dec-2 Eric Pillon, Calais #111/R
£2200 $3410 €3300 Tete de Coco (22x22cm-9x9in) s. black pat. bronze st.f.C.Valsuani. 5-Dec-2 Christie's, Kensington #5/R est:3000-4000
£3226 $5000 €4839 Tete de coco (21x21cm-8x8in) st.sig.num.21/30 brown pat. bronze prov.lit. 26-Sep-2 Christie's, Rockefeller NY #536/R est:5000-7000
£8500 $13430 €12750 Etude pou maternite (25cm-10in) s.st.f.Tivernon num.EA1/4 brown pat bronze. 3-Apr-3 Christie's, Kensington #5/R
£18868 $30000 €28302 Petit forgeron (32cm-13in) st.sig.st.f.Rudier num.2 black green pat bronze prov.lit. 27-Feb-3 Christie's, Rockefeller NY #10/R est:20000
£33654 $52500 €50481 Femme nue assise et guir lande de fleurs (23x23cm-9x9in) init. painted ceramic plate executed c.1905-06 prov. 6-Nov-2 Sotheby's, New York #139/R est:25000-35000

Works on paper
£3871 $6000 €5807 Etude pour le portrait d'une jeune fille (16x11cm-6x4in) pencil white gouache wash prov. 26-Sep-2 Christie's, Rockefeller NY #503/R est:3000-5000
£9804 $16078 €15000 Femme portat un panier (99x38cm-39x15in) s. crayon dr exhib. 9-Feb-3 Anaf, Lyon #219/R est:13000
£12411 $20727 €17500 Bord de mer Mediterraneen (13x25cm-5x10in) init. W/C. 20-Jun-3 Piasa, Paris #18/R est:15000-20000
£12821 $20000 €19232 Paysage de Cagnes (19x20cm-7x8in) init. W/C executed c.1896-1908 prov.exhib.lit. 7-Nov-2 Christie's, Rockefeller NY #158/R est:15000-20000
£16000 $26720 €24000 Esquisse pour Oedipe Roi (28x29cm-11x11in) st.sig. sanguine htd white exec c.1895 prov. 26-Jun-3 Christie's, London #353/R est:10000-15000
£16026 $25000 €24039 Deux figures (30x21cm-12x8in) s. sanguine prov.exhib.lit. 6-Nov-2 Sotheby's, New York #134/R est:15000-20000
£32000 $49280 €48000 Paysage a essoyes (14x24cm-6x9in) s. W/C prov.lit. 22-Oct-2 Sotheby's, London #104/R est:22000-28000
£95000 $154850 €142500 Nana, Pauline et les autres (29x43cm-11x17in) s. W/C over pencil executed c.1877 prov. 3-Feb-3 Bonhams, New Bond Street #5/R est:30000-50000

RENOTTE, Paul (1906-1966) Belgian
£380 $592 €600 Composition cubiste (99x65cm-39x26in) s.d.1960 panel. 16-Sep-2 Horta, Bruxelles #487

RENOU, Antoine (attrib) (1731-1806) French
£3846 $5846 €6000 Le concert (100x81cm-39x32in) 10-Jul-2 Rabourdin & Choppin de Janvry, Paris #95/R est:5300-5500

RENOUARD, Baron (20th C) French
£543 $885 €820 Composition (65x92cm-26x36in) s.d.1960. 1-Feb-3 Claude Aguttes, Neuilly #229

RENOUART, Georges (19/20th C) ?
£1200 $1968 €1800 Bustling Parisian boulevard (51x65cm-20x26in) s. set of three. 5-Jun-3 Christie's, Kensington #818/R est:700-1000

RENOUF, Émile (1845-1894) French
£705 $1100 €1058 Fisherwoman and daughter (76x63cm-30x25in) s.d.81. 20-Sep-2 Sloan, North Bethesda #416/R est:1000-2000

RENOUX, Andre (1939-) French
£298 $486 €450 Paris, rue de Rivoli (22x35cm-9x14in) s. s.i.verso. 31-Jan-3 Charbonneaux, Paris #153
£319 $533 €450 Paris, le theatre de l'atelier (27x22cm-11x9in) s. 18-Jun-3 Charbonneaux, Paris #101

RENOUX, Charles (1795-1846) French
£2238 $3737 €3200 L'entree du couvent de Sciano (21x30cm-8x12in) s.d.1821. 25-Jun-3 Sotheby's, Paris #61/R est:2000-3000

RENOUX, Jules Ernest (1863-1932) French
£900 $1368 €1350 Quai des Tuileries, Pont de Carrousel. Quai de Louvre (26x41cm-10x16in) s. panel pair. 29-Aug-2 Christie's, Kensington #121/R

RENQVIST, Torsten (1924-) Swedish
£841 $1312 €1262 House facades (22x27cm-9x11in) init.d.51. 5-Nov-2 Bukowskis, Stockholm #253/R (S.KR 12000)
£1156 $1804 €1734 Landscape (28x36cm-11x14in) init.d.48. 5-Nov-2 Bukowskis, Stockholm #254/R est:8000-10000 (S.KR 16500)

RENSBURG, Eugène (1872-1956) Dutch
£395 $639 €600 Harbour scene with city beyond (28x48cm-11x19in) s.d.1897 exhib. 21-Jan-3 Christie's, Amsterdam #292

RENSHAW, A (19th C) British
Works on paper
£550 $836 €825 Portrait of a lady (46x36cm-18x14in) W/C bodycol oval. 4-Jul-2 Duke & Son, Dorchester #70/R

RENSHAW, Alice (fl.1880-1890) British
£520 $868 €754 Portrait of a young woman wearing a straw hat (34x29cm-13x11in) indis sig. 17-Jun-3 Anderson & Garland, Newcastle #407/R
Works on paper
£800 $1296 €1200 Young elegance (35x25cm-14x10in) s. W/C htd gouache. 21-May-3 Bonhams, Knightsbridge #138

RENSON, Roland (1943-) Belgian
£890 $1389 €1300 Attelage dans un chemin ensoleille (138x100cm-54x39in) s. 14-Apr-3 Horta, Bruxelles #376

RENSON, Victoria (20th C) British?
£280 $442 €406 Flowers. 22-Jul-3 Riddetts, Bournemouth #485

RENTEL, Max (1850-?) German
£346 $540 €550 Interior with candles (35x26cm-14x10in) s. panel. 21-Sep-2 Bolland & Marotz, Bremen #549/R
£1127 $1814 €1600 Still life with apples and bottle (75x60cm-30x24in) s. lit. 9-May-3 Schloss Ahlden, Ahlden #1352/R est:1400

RENTERIA, Horacio (1912-1972) Mexican
£3119 $4928 €4679 Girl in the kitchen (59x44cm-23x17in) s. 28-Nov-2 Louis Morton, Mexico #273/R (M.P 50000)

RENTON, Joan (1935-) British
£300 $498 €435 Still life of vase and flowers (52x74cm-20x29in) s. board. 13-Jun-3 Lyon & Turnbull, Edinburgh #122

RENTON, John (fl.1798-1840) British
Works on paper
£360 $554 €540 Monumental figure (9x7cm-4x3in) pencil W/C. 22-Oct-2 Bonhams, Knightsbridge #174/R

RENUCCI, Renuccio (1880-1947) Italian
£748 $1190 €1100 Ships in Livorno harbour (34x50cm-13x20in) s. 18-Mar-3 Finarte, Milan #201/R
£962 $1510 €1500 Seascape (25x40cm-10x16in) s. board. 16-Dec-2 Pandolfini, Florence #320/R
£1014 $1664 €1400 Ritorno dall pesca. Tramonto (30x40cm-12x16in) s.i.verso panel. 27-May-3 Finarte, Milan #157/R est:800-1000

RENVALL, Essi (1911-1979) Finnish
Works on paper
£816 $1298 €1200 Marja-Liisa Varia (61x48cm-24x19in) s. mixed media. 24-Mar-3 Bukowskis, Helsinki #256/R

RENZULLI, Franco (1924-) Italian
£254 $391 €381 Surrealistic composition (90x70cm-35x28in) s.d.70 masonite. 26-Oct-2 Rasmussen, Havnen #2244 (D.KR 3000)
£254 $391 €381 Surrealistic composition (70x90cm-28x35in) s.d.71 masonite. 26-Oct-2 Rasmussen, Havnen #2245 (D.KR 3000)

REOL, Marie Marguerite (1880-1963) French
£329 $520 €520 Bouquet et pommes (81x65cm-32x26in) s. 1-Dec-2 Livinec, Gaudcheau & Jezequel, Rennes #66/R
£481 $755 €750 Bouquet de roses (33x41cm-13x16in) s.d.1934. 15-Dec-2 Thierry & Lannon, Brest #411
£1181 $1924 €1700 Bouquet de fleurs (64x80cm-25x31in) s. 19-Jul-3 Thierry & Lannon, Brest #169/R est:1000-1200
Works on paper
£1408 $2268 €2000 La fleuriste au parapluie (92x71cm-36x28in) s. pastel. 11-May-3 Thierry & Lannon, Brest #79/R est:1800-2200

REPENTIGNY, Halin de (20th C) Canadian
£289 $474 €419 Hart River trapping cabin (55x70cm-22x28in) s.i.d.1992. 9-Jun-3 Hodgins, Calgary #67/R (C.D 650)
£289 $474 €419 Reflectons on Bear Creek, Yukon (75x100cm-30x39in) s.i.d.1991. 9-Jun-3 Hodgins, Calgary #270/R (C.D 650)

REPIN, Ilia (1844-1930) Russian
£3521 $5669 €5000 Portrait of Lidya Brodski (39x32cm-15x13in) s.i.d.1909. 10-May-3 Bukowskis, Helsinki #407/R est:5000-7000
£8108 $12649 €12000 Man in blue tunic (19x13cm-7x5in) mono.d. i. verso canvas on board. 28-Mar-3 Ketterer, Hamburg #114/R est:12000-15000
£9000 $14580 €13500 Sketch of the terrorist attack in 1916 on King Albert I of Belgium (46x68cm-18x27in) s.d.1930. 21-May-3 Sotheby's, London #57/R est:4000-6000
£13732 $22109 €19500 Bearded man wearing peaked cap (55x43cm-22x17in) s.d.1913 study. 10-May-3 Bukowskis, Helsinki #409/R est:20000-22000
Works on paper
£503 $780 €800 Figure study (9x8cm-4x3in) s.d.1898 Indian ink over pencil. 1-Oct-2 Dorotheum, Vienna #152/R
£1408 $2268 €2000 Landscape with farmhouse (14x23cm-6x9in) s. W/C. 10-May-3 Bukowskis, Helsinki #406/R est:2500-3000
£1549 $2494 €2200 Man with beard (35x28cm-14x11in) s.d.30 March 1870 pencil. 10-May-3 Bukowskis, Helsinki #408/R est:1500-2000
£2152 $3400 €3400 Young man (36x24cm-14x9in) s. Indian ink. 1-Dec-2 Bukowskis, Helsinki #271/R est:1500-2000
£2436 $3800 €3654 Portraits of an elderly woman and man (51x41cm-20x16in) init. pastel pair. 12-Oct-2 Neal Auction Company, New Orleans #289/R est:4000-6000
£2837 $4738 €4000 Cafe de Paris (13x20cm-5x8in) s. graphite. 17-Jun-3 Claude Boisgirard, Paris #115 est:4000-5000
£6690 $10771 €9500 Woman reading (26x36cm-10x14in) s. W/C. 10-May-3 Bukowskis, Helsinki #398/R est:6000-8000

REPIN, Ilia (attrib) (1844-1930) Russian
£3401 $5408 €5000 Portrait of woman (96x76cm-38x30in) s.cyrillic d.1874. 19-Mar-3 Neumeister, Munich #707/R est:4000
£6803 $10816 €10000 Woman's portrait (117x89cm-46x35in) s.d.1875. 19-Mar-3 Neumeister, Munich #708/R est:3000

REPIN, Yuri Ilich (1877-1954) Russian
£882 $1447 €1350 Winter's night (49x42cm-19x17in) s. 9-Feb-3 Bukowskis, Helsinki #428/R
£1108 $1728 €1750 Man and horse (63x46cm-25x18in) s. 12-Sep-2 Hagelstam, Helsinki #930/R est:2000

REPPEN, John Richard (1933-1964) Canadian
£386 $603 €579 Rediscovered world (68x61cm-27x24in) s.d.63 s.i.d.verso mixed media on board prov. 25-Mar-3 Ritchie, Toronto #193/R est:800-1000 (C.D 900)

REQUICHOT, Bernard (1929-1961) French
£2431 $3840 €3500 Traces graphiques (90x60cm-35x24in) oil isorel lacquer prov. 27-Apr-3 Perrin, Versailles #122/R est:3500-4500

RESCALLI, Don Angelo (1884-c.1956) Italian
£1088 $1731 €1600 Morning in Susa Valley (14x17cm-6x7in) s.d.1929 board. 18-Mar-3 Finarte, Milan #191/R
£1304 $2139 €1800 Autumn in Val di Susa (23x33cm-9x13in) s. s.i.verso panel. 27-May-3 Finarte, Milan #9/R est:1500-1800
£2194 $3466 €3400 Hemil farm in Susa (25x30cm-10x12in) s.i.verso board. 18-Dec-2 Finarte, Milan #144/R
£2536 $4159 €3500 Nevicata in Val di Susa (42x33cm-17x13in) s. panel. 27-May-3 Finarte, Milan #21/R est:2000-2400
£5660 $8717 €9000 Landscape with two figures and bell tower (54x45cm-21x18in) s. 23-Oct-2 Finarte, Milan #169/R est:12000-13000
£9434 $14528 €15000 Pax (89x69cm-35x27in) s.d.1920 prov. 23-Oct-2 Finarte, Milan #168/R est:15000-16000

RESCH, Ernst (1807-1864) German
£2051 $3179 €3200 Portrait of a lady in early Victorian interior (54x43cm-21x17in) s.d.1834. 4-Dec-2 Neumeister, Munich #861/R est:4000

RESCHI, Pandolfo (attrib) (1643-1699) Polish
£6289 $9748 €10000 Stag hunt in mountain landscape (73x98cm-29x39in) 2-Oct-2 Dorotheum, Vienna #67/R est:10000-14000

RESCHREITER, Rudolf (1868-?) German
Works on paper
£514 $801 €750 Obergrainau and the Waxenstein (49x34cm-19x13in) s.i. gouache. 9-Apr-3 Neumeister, Munich #542
£962 $1462 €1500 View from summit of foothills (48x34cm-19x13in) s. gouache lit. 11-Jul-2 Allgauer, Kempten #2370/R

RESEN-STEENSTRUP, J (1868-1921) Danish
£357 $565 €536 Horses in field (69x126cm-27x50in) mono.d.16. 30-Nov-2 Rasmussen, Havnen #2259 (D.KR 4200)

RESNICK, Milton (1917-) American
£3963 $6500 €5746 Bondo (102x76cm-40x30in) s.i.d.1982 board. 1-Jun-3 Wright, Chicago #274/R est:7000-9000

RESTOUT, Jean (younger-attrib) (1692-1768) French
£2517 $4204 €3600 Saint Paul guerissant les malades de son ombre (88x65cm-35x26in) prov.lit. 27-Jun-3 Piasa, Paris #79/R est:4000-6000
Works on paper
£1899 $3000 €3000 Enfant satyre (46x27cm-18x11in) crayon. 28-Nov-2 Tajan, Paris #30 est:3000

RESTOUT, Jean Bernard (attrib) (1732-1797) French
£7343 $12262 €10500 Loth et ses filles (104x137cm-41x54in) 27-Jun-3 Piasa, Paris #69/R est:8000-10000

RETH, Alfred (1884-1966) French
£420 $701 €600 Les maisons (27x34cm-11x13in) s. 26-Jun-3 Tajan, Paris #270/R
£420 $701 €600 La route (27x35cm-11x14in) s. prov.exhib. 26-Jun-3 Tajan, Paris #271
£629 $975 €1000 Paysage urbain (54x65cm-21x26in) s. oil collage. 30-Oct-2 Artcurial Briest, Paris #399
£2885 $4529 €4500 Composition (46x56cm-18x22in) oil sand panel. 24-Nov-2 Laurence Calmels, Paris #236/R
£4327 $6750 €6491 Figures in a landscape (81x65cm-32x26in) s. 20-Sep-2 Sloan, North Bethesda #373/R est:6000-8000
Works on paper
£367 $584 €540 Scene de cafe (17x22cm-7x9in) st.sig. graphite dr. 26-Feb-3 Artcurial Briest, Paris #77
£531 $844 €780 La cueillette (20x26cm-8x10in) st.sig. blue ink dr. 26-Feb-3 Artcurial Briest, Paris #76
£552 $922 €800 Personnages (71x54cm-28x21in) s.d.1946 graphite dr. 10-Jul-3 Artcurial Briest, Paris #82
£645 $1019 €1000 Composition abstraite (63x48cm-25x19in) s.d.52 graphite sand dr. 18-Dec-2 Digard, Paris #216/R
£1513 $2452 €2300 Au bord de la Seine (46x54cm-18x21in) s. gouache matiere cardboard. 22-Jan-3 Tajan, Paris #195 est:2500-3000

RETH, Caspar von (1858-1913) German
£1342 $2161 €2000 Two hunting dogs (59x73cm-23x29in) s.i.d.1892. 18-Feb-3 Sotheby's, Amsterdam #970/R est:700-900

£1781 $2778 €2600 Hunting dogs (38x48cm-15x19in) s.d.1891 two. 10-Apr-3 Van Ham, Cologne #166/R est:2500

RETHEL, Alfred (1816-1859) German
£1026 $1621 €1600 Scene from Tyrolean fight for freedom 1809 (15x10cm-6x4in) s. d.3. Januar 1839 verso panel. 16-Nov-2 Lempertz, Koln #1560/R est:1800

RETS, Jean (1910-1998) Belgian
£1064 $1777 €1500 Danseuses aux Folies-Bergeres (46x38cm-18x15in) s. panel. 18-Jun-3 Hotel des Ventes Mosan, Brussels #291 est:1500-2000
Works on paper
£443 $691 €700 Composition abstraite (28x38cm-11x15in) s. s.d.1982 verso mixed media. 16-Oct-2 Hotel des Ventes Mosan, Brussels #293
£949 $1481 €1500 Les quatres elements (18x18cm-7x7in) s. gouache four in one frame. 16-Oct-2 Hotel des Ventes Mosan, Brussels #287/R est:2500-3000

RETT, Gustav (1889-1969) German
£6209 $9935 €9500 View of Engelhalde in Kempten (140x241cm-55x95in) s.d.37 lit. 10-Jan-3 Allgauer, Kempten #1736/R est:5000

RETTICH, Karl Lorenz (1841-1904) German
£1346 $2127 €2100 On the Riviera near Bordighera (40x60cm-16x24in) s. 16-Nov-2 Lempertz, Koln #1561 est:2000

RETTIG, Heinrich (1859-1921) German
£2676 $4308 €3800 Big city boulevard in the evening (60x90cm-24x35in) s.i.d.1911 lit. 9-May-3 Schloss Ahlden, Ahlden #1518/R est:3800

REUMERT, Niels (1949-) Danish
£933 $1483 €1400 Dream with time slaves (135x160cm-53x63in) s.d.87 verso. 29-Apr-3 Kunsthallen, Copenhagen #119/R (D.KR 10000)
£1016 $1575 €1524 Composition (100x155cm-39x61in) indis.i. s.d.1990 verso prov. 1-Oct-2 Rasmussen, Copenhagen #178/R est:12000-15000 (D.KR 12000)

REUMONTE, Anton (18th C) Dutch
£2115 $3321 €3300 Portrait d'un jeune musicien. Portrait d'une jeune musicienne (81x65cm-32x26in) s.d.1777 verso pair. 19-Nov-2 Vanderkindere, Brussels #103/R est:2000-3000

REUSCH, Helga Ring (1865-1944) Norwegian
£10860 $17593 €16290 Boy on bare rock-face (55x48cm-22x19in) s.d.1886. 26-May-3 Grev Wedels Plass, Oslo #45/R est:60000-80000 (N.KR 120000)

REUSCH, Joseph (1887-1976) German
Works on paper
£897 $1409 €1400 Young beauty with Tunis beyond (81x67cm-32x26in) s.d.1924 pastel board. 21-Nov-2 Van Ham, Cologne #1884/R

REUTER, Elisabeth (1853-1903) German
£359 $590 €550 Lubeck harbour (55x38cm-22x15in) s.d.97 canvas on panel. 29-Mar-3 Dannenberg, Berlin #639/R

REUTER, Erich Fritz (1911-1997) German
Sculpture
£2848 $4500 €4500 Francesca da Rimini - lovers (25cm-10in) mono.d.71 silver Cast.Barth Rinteln. 30-Nov-2 Villa Grisebach, Berlin #411/R est:3500-4500

REUTER, Helmut (1913-1985) German
£680 $1115 €1020 Unloading the catch (50x41cm-20x16in) s. 5-Jun-3 Christie's, Kensington #752/R

REUTER, Werner (20th C) German
£440 $687 €700 Still life with fish and water bowl (49x62cm-19x24in) s. panel. 21-Sep-2 Bolland & Marotz, Bremen #646/R

REUTERSWARD, Carl Fredrik (1934-) Swedish
£439 $668 €659 The Peking opera-Brown-Selhing 1984-85 (92x73cm-36x29in) s. 16-Aug-2 Lilla Bukowskis, Stockholm #23 (S.KR 6400)
£849 $1410 €1231 The Kobe-Cat for the Peking Opera (99x99cm-39x39in) s. painted 1984-85. 16-Jun-3 Lilla Bukowskis, Stockholm #535 (S.KR 11000)
£1390 $2238 €2085 The caprice of nature (116x126cm-46x50in) s. acrylic triptych. 7-May-3 AB Stockholms Auktionsverk #998/R est:20000-25000 (S.KR 18000)
£1822 $2842 €2733 Red billiards (73x66cm-29x26in) s.verso. 6-Nov-2 AB Stockholms Auktionsverk #612/R est:15000-18000 (S.KR 26000)
£2890 $4566 €4335 A wonderful day (40x107cm-16x42in) s. varnish tempera painted 1960-61. 28-Apr-3 Bukowskis, Stockholm #246d/R est:25000-30000 (S.KR 38000)
Sculpture
£1552 $2514 €2250 Non violence (16x26cm-6x10in) s.num.35/99 dark pat.bronze marble. 25-May-3 Uppsala Auktionskammare, Uppsala #387/R est:20000-25000 (S.KR 20000)
£2803 $4373 €4205 Non violence (26cm-10in) s.num.34/99 dark pat.bronze on granite base. 5-Nov-2 Bukowskis, Stockholm #233/R est:30000-40000 (S.KR 40000)
Works on paper
£272 $440 €394 Composition (22x30cm-9x12in) mono. d.1984 verso mixed media. 25-May-3 Uppsala Auktionskammare, Uppsala #303 (S.KR 3500)
£340 $564 €493 Study for the Peking Opera (96x65cm-38x26in) s. mixed media. 16-Jun-3 Lilla Bukowskis, Stockholm #673 (S.KR 4400)
£965 $1554 €1448 Herr von Hancken (153x87cm-60x34in) s. gouache. 7-May-3 AB Stockholms Auktionsverk #1096/R (S.KR 12500)
£1081 $1741 €1622 Viscountess von Hancken (153x78cm-60x31in) s. gouache. 7-May-3 AB Stockholms Auktionsverk #1097/R est:12000-15000 (S.KR 14000)

REUTERSWARD, Oscar (1915-2002) Swedish
£477 $753 €716 Impossible figure (60x73cm-24x29in) s. 27-Nov-2 Falkkloos, Malmo #77595/R (S.KR 6800)
Sculpture
£1429 $2300 €2144 Obelisque (118cm-46in) s. polished brass incl. iron base. 7-May-3 AB Stockholms Auktionsverk #799/R est:10000-12000 (S.KR 18500)
£2172 $3389 €3258 Striving cylinders (270cm-106in) s. stainless black circular bottom dish. 6-Nov-2 AB Stockholms Auktionsverk #619/R est:30000-40000 (S.KR 31000)
Works on paper
£494 $781 €741 Everlasting loop with four impossible crossings (55x38cm-22x15in) s. W/C executed c.1960. 28-Apr-3 Bukowskis, Stockholm #271/R (S.KR 6500)

REUTHER, Wolf (1917-) ?
£255 $397 €400 Crucifixion group (27x16cm-11x6in) s. verso. 6-Nov-2 Hugo Ruef, Munich #1251
£1351 $2108 €2000 Women carrying water (130x80cm-51x31in) s. 26-Mar-3 Hugo Ruef, Munich #316/R est:1500
Works on paper
£382 $596 €600 Woman with cat (67x47cm-26x19in) s.d.45 W/C sold with book. 6-Nov-2 Hugo Ruef, Munich #1405/R

REVEL, Paul Jean (1922-1983) French
£276 $461 €400 Composition (73x100cm-29x39in) s. 9-Jul-3 Millon & Associes, Paris #322
£276 $461 €400 Composition (100x82cm-39x32in) s. 9-Jul-3 Millon & Associes, Paris #324
£310 $518 €450 Composition (100x82cm-39x32in) s. 9-Jul-3 Millon & Associes, Paris #325
£310 $518 €450 Composition (82x100cm-32x39in) s. 9-Jul-3 Millon & Associes, Paris #327
£310 $518 €450 Composition (82x100cm-32x39in) s. d.76 verso. 9-Jul-3 Millon & Associes, Paris #328
£310 $518 €450 Composition (400x82cm-157x32in) s. 9-Jul-3 Millon & Associes, Paris #329
£310 $518 €450 Diptyque (130x65cm-51x26in) s. paper on canvas diptych. 9-Jul-3 Millon & Associes, Paris #331
£345 $576 €500 Composition (80x115cm-31x45in) s. 9-Jul-3 Millon & Associes, Paris #330
£345 $576 €500 Composition (92x130cm-36x51in) s.d.60 exhib. 9-Jul-3 Millon & Associes, Paris #333
£400 $640 €600 Reflection (81x130cm-32x51in) s.d.59. 14-Mar-3 Gardiner & Houlgate, Bath #20/R
£414 $691 €600 Composition (145x115cm-57x45in) s.d.69. 9-Jul-3 Millon & Associes, Paris #335
£428 $714 €620 Composition (93cm-37in circular) s.d.62 contre-plaque. 9-Jul-3 Millon & Associes, Paris #317
£483 $806 €700 Allegresse (130x80cm-51x31in) s.d.58. 9-Jul-3 Millon & Associes, Paris #332/R
£483 $806 €700 Composition (92x130cm-36x51in) s. 9-Jul-3 Millon & Associes, Paris #334

REVERE, Paul (after) (1735-1818) American
Prints
£4658 $7500 €6987 The bloody massacre perpetrated in King Street, Boston (19x22cm-7x9in) hand col engraving. 16-Jan-3 Sotheby's, New York #4/R est:2000-3000

REVERON, Armando (1889-1954) Venezuelan
£89172 $140000 €133758 Portrait of lady with monkey (110x92cm-43x36in) s. burlap on canvas painted c.1933-37 prov. 20-Nov-2 Christie's, Rockefeller NY #14/R est:120000-160000

REVESZ, Imre (1859-1945) Hungarian
£2555 $3960 €3833 Spring celebration (140x100cm-55x39in) s. 6-Dec-2 Kieselbach, Budapest #114/R (H.F 950000)
£8255 $12878 €12383 Wooers, 1881 (92x70cm-36x28in) s.d.1881. 11-Sep-2 Kieselbach, Budapest #87/R (H.F 3200000)

REVILLA, Carlos (1940-) Peruvian
£3125 $4969 €4500 Elle cachait ses soupirs dans la nuit (100x120cm-39x47in) s.d.1975. 29-Apr-3 Campo, Vlaamse Kaai #260/R est:2500-3000

REVILLE, H Whittaker (fl.1881-1903) British
£800 $1264 €1200 Liver chestnut hunter in a stable (46x61cm-18x24in) s. 28-Nov-2 Christie's, Kensington #126/R
£3050 $4819 €4575 On the scent through open country (13x22cm-5x9in) s. panel four. 7-Apr-3 David Duggleby, Scarborough #385 est:2500-3500

REVOIL, Pierre (1776-1842) French
Works on paper
£11859 $18619 €18500 Jeanne d'Arrc prisonniere a Rouen (49x69cm-19x27in) mono.i. pen ink W/C. 13-Dec-2 Pierre Berge, Paris #34/R est:8000

REVOL, Michel (19/20th C) French
£1519 $2400 €2400 Roses tremieres (160x100cm-63x39in) s.d.1900. 1-Dec-2 Anaf, Lyon #152 est:2200-2500

REVOLD, Axel (1887-1962) Norwegian
£937 $1452 €1406 Landscape (40x48cm-16x19in) s. masonite. 28-Sep-2 Rasmussen, Havnen #2072 (D.KR 11000)
£1305 $2089 €1958 House in the skerries (100x120cm-39x47in) s. 17-Mar-3 Blomqvist, Oslo #389/R est:35000-45000 (N.KR 15000)
£1593 $2517 €2390 Landscape from Soon (76x68cm-30x27in) s. prov.exhib. 28-Apr-3 Blomqvist, Oslo #356/R est:25000-35000 (N.KR 18000)
£2212 $3496 €3318 Cagnes (45x37cm-18x15in) s. panel prov.exhib. 28-Apr-3 Blomqvist, Oslo #355/R est:30000-35000 (N.KR 25000)
£2478 $3915 €3717 Landscape with farm from Haagaa in Sel (80x100cm-31x39in) s. prov.exhib. 28-Apr-3 Blomqvist, Oslo #366/R est:35000-45000 (N.KR 28000)
£5204 $8118 €7806 Night (114x146cm-45x57in) s. i.stretcher painted 1927 prov.exhib.lit. 21-Oct-2 Blomqvist, Oslo #366/R est:70000-90000 (N.KR 60000)

REVOLD, Axel (attrib) (1887-1962) Norwegian
£606 $927 €909 Decoration sketch for The Exchange in Bergen (85x62cm-33x24in) prov. 26-Aug-2 Blomqvist, Lysaker #1471/R (N.KR 7000)

REX, Jytte (20th C) Danish?
£345 $534 €518 Composition (155x155cm-61x61in) s.d.91 paper. 4-Dec-2 Kunsthallen, Copenhagen #294 (D.KR 4000)

REY, Alphonse (1863-1938) French
Works on paper
£296 $421 €480 Promenade en Haute-Provence (25x53cm-10x21in) s. W/C. 17-Mar-2 Galerie de Chartres, Chartres #122
£346 $491 €560 Martigues (25x52cm-10x20in) s.i. W/C. 17-Mar-2 Galerie de Chartres, Chartres #123
£1020 $1622 €1500 Caravane au coucher du soleil (24x50cm-9x20in) s.i. W/C. 24-Mar-3 Rabourdin & Choppin de Janvry, Paris #198/R est:1500-1800
£1447 $2228 €2300 Notre-Dame d'Afrique, Alger (27x47cm-11x19in) s. W/C. 23-Oct-2 Rabourdin & Choppin de Janvry, Paris #172/R
£2893 $4455 €4600 Villas mauresques et balcon (25x110cm-10x43in) s. W/C triptych. 23-Oct-2 Rabourdin & Choppin de Janvry, Paris #175/R

REY, Etienne (1789-1867) French
Works on paper
£709 $1184 €1000 Tombeau dit de Saint Luc a Thebes, en Beotie (17x24cm-7x9in) W/C prov. 23-Jun-3 Beaussant & Lefèvre, Paris #100

REY, Paul Henri (1904-1981) French?
Sculpture
£2128 $3553 €3000 Couple debout (172cm-68in) wood. 20-Jun-3 Piasa, Paris #204/R est:1500-2000
£3077 $4831 €4800 Femme debout, bras sur la tete (140x44cm-55x17in) s. wood. 11-Dec-2 Piasa, Paris #38/R est:2000-2500

REYES FERREIRA, Jesus (1882-1977) Mexican
£742 $1187 €1076 Payaso (75x55cm-30x22in) s. tempura China paper. 15-May-3 Louis Morton, Mexico #168/R (M.P 12000)
£1008 $1572 €1512 Cristo (75x50cm-30x20in) s. tempera. 17-Oct-2 Louis Morton, Mexico #14/R est:18000-20000 (M.P 16000)

REYLANDER-BOHME, Ottilie (1882-1965) German
£1258 $1962 €2000 Young mother with child (76x5cm-30x2in) s. panel. 21-Sep-2 Bolland & Marotz, Bremen #391/R est:2200

REYMANN, J (19/20th C) French
£1862 $2961 €2700 Coming out from Fondouk (40x31cm-16x12in) s. board. 4-Mar-3 Ansorena, Madrid #187/R

REYMERSWAELE, Marinus van (circle) (1493-1567) Dutch
£15000 $23550 €22500 Two tax gathers (111x84cm-44x33in) panel prov. 13-Dec-2 Christie's, Kensington #1/R est:7000-10000

REYMOND, Carlos (1884-1970) French
£390 $651 €550 Femme lisant (54x65cm-21x26in) s. 23-Jun-3 Claude Boisgirard, Paris #95

REYNA, Antonio Maria de (1859-1937) Spanish
£1655 $2615 €2400 Portrait of peasant woman (23x15cm-9x6in) s. 1-Apr-3 Segre, Madrid #125/R
£1655 $2615 €2400 Portrait of lady (23x15cm-9x6in) s. 1-Apr-3 Segre, Madrid #124/R
£2903 $4587 €4500 Venetian canal (15x20cm-6x8in) s. 18-Dec-2 Finarte, Milan #58/R est:5000
£4605 $7461 €7000 Flag holder (50x40cm-20x16in) s. 21-Jan-3 Durán, Madrid #149/R
£7692 $12000 €11538 Venetian canal scene with bridges and boats (36x76cm-14x30in) s. 21-Sep-2 Nadeau, Windsor #202/R est:6000-9000
£7742 $12000 €11613 Venetian backwater (35x75cm-14x30in) s.i. prov. 30-Oct-2 Christie's, Rockefeller NY #214/R est:12000-16000
£11321 $17660 €18000 Gran Canal (25x50cm-10x20in) s. 23-Sep-2 Durán, Madrid #266/R
£12903 $20387 €20000 Canal in Venice (35x75cm-14x30in) s.i. 17-Dec-2 Durán, Madrid #210/R est:16000
£16026 $25160 €25000 Tivoli beach (34x74cm-13x29in) s. 19-Nov-2 Castellana, Madrid #70/R est:9000
£16552 $26152 €24000 Canl and church in Venice (35x74cm-14x29in) s. prov.lit. 1-Apr-3 Segre, Madrid #126/R est:21000
£17296 $26981 €27500 View of Venice (34x70cm-13x28in) s. 23-Sep-2 Durán, Madrid #253/R
£18000 $29160 €27000 La Guideecca, Venice (32x72cm-13x28in) s. 20-May-3 Sotheby's, Olympia #426/R est:3000-4000
£18065 $28000 €27098 View towards Saint Marks Square, Venice (35x75cm-14x30in) s.i. 30-Oct-2 Christie's, Rockefeller NY #73/R est:30000-40000
£20833 $32708 €32500 View of Venice (35x75cm-14x30in) s. 19-Nov-2 Castellana, Madrid #497/R est:9000
£34591 $53962 €55000 Rialto Bridge (34x70cm-13x28in) s. 23-Sep-2 Durán, Madrid #252/R

REYNAUD, François (1825-1909) French
£1772 $2765 €2800 Enfant jouant avec un chien (55x41cm-22x16in) s. 16-Oct-2 Fraysse & Associes, Paris #53 est:1500-2000
£1772 $2765 €2800 Enfants jouant sur des marches (56x34cm-22x13in) s. panel. 16-Oct-2 Fraysse & Associes, Paris #54/R est:1200-1500
£1799 $2878 €2500 Jeux d'enfants (56x34cm-22x13in) s. wood. 14-May-3 Blanchet, Paris #53

REYNAUD, Marius Gustave (1860-1935) French
£1235 $1753 €2000 Port de Honfleur (43x55cm-17x22in) s. 16-Mar-3 Eric Pillon, Calais #168/R

REYNI, Ingalvur av (1920-) Icelandic
£1397 $2221 €2096 Harbour scene with houses from Midvag (73x100cm-29x39in) s.d.70. 10-Mar-3 Rasmussen, Vejle #641/R est:15000-20000 (D.KR 15000)
£1630 $2542 €2445 Composition (85x66cm-33x26in) s.d.89. 11-Nov-2 Rasmussen, Vejle #78/R est:10000 (D.KR 19000)

REYNIER, Gustave (1885-?) French
£8500 $13260 €12750 Sword dance (65x48cm-26x19in) s. 15-Oct-2 Sotheby's, London #183/R est:10000-15000

REYNOLDS, Alan (1926-) British

£640 $1011 €960 Bluebell thicket - 47 (61x51cm-24x20in) s. 4-Apr-3 Moore Allen & Innocent, Cirencester #653
£2200 $3410 €3300 Ascending III (102x76cm-40x30in) s.i.d.70 verso oil relief. 3-Dec-2 Bonhams, New Bond Street #109/R est:1200-1800
£3800 $6232 €5510 Legend in early autumn (33x42cm-13x17in) s.i.d.55. 4-Jun-3 Sotheby's, London #69/R est:3000-4000
£4000 $6240 €6000 Untitled abstract (29x39cm-11x15in) s.d.51/52 board prov. 25-Mar-3 Bonhams, New Bond Street #131/R est:3000-5000
£6200 $9858 €9300 Composition with ovoid - green, rose, orange and black (81x77cm-32x30in) s.i.d.30/4/62 verso board prov. 26-Feb-3 Sotheby's, Olympia #385/R est:3000-5000
£6800 $10608 €10200 Composition pastoral (100x125cm-39x49in) s.d.53 verso board prov. 25-Mar-3 Bonhams, New Bond Street #135/R est:8000-12000
£17000 $27880 €25500 Sunrise - the hillside (82x104cm-32x41in) s.i.d.1956 verso board prov. 6-Jun-3 Christie's, London #186/R est:10000-15000
£32000 $52480 €46400 Cheveley Well, Suffolk (101x76cm-40x30in) s.d.52 board prov.exhib.lit. 4-Jun-3 Sotheby's, London #32/R est:12000-18000

Works on paper

£1250 $1938 €1875 Village, brown and green (17x25cm-7x10in) s.d.52 W/C grey wash. 1-Nov-2 Moore Allen & Innocent, Cirencester #235/R est:300-500
£1400 $2184 €2100 Poem - yellow, brown and black (27x23cm-11x9in) s. W/C prov. 25-Mar-3 Bonhams, New Bond Street #130/R est:1200-1800
£1500 $2340 €2250 Movement in October (17x30cm-7x12in) s.d.58 brush ink W/C. 27-Mar-3 Christie's, Kensington #627/R est:800-1200
£1700 $2839 €2465 Kentish hopfield (37x27cm-15x11in) W/C prov. 24-Jun-3 Bonhams, New Bond Street #113/R est:800-1200
£2000 $3080 €3000 Evening (34x43cm-13x17in) s.d.56 W/C bodycol. 22-Oct-2 Bonhams, Bath #239 est:400-600
£2800 $4620 €4060 In winter (21x32cm-8x13in) W/C bodycol prov. 3-Jul-3 Christie's, Kensington #668/R est:1500-2500
£2950 $4868 €4278 Autumn landscape, Shoreham (32x48cm-13x19in) s.d.52 W/C brush ink prov. 3-Jul-3 Christie's, Kensington #666/R est:1500-2500
£3200 $5280 €4640 Village (47x63cm-19x25in) s.d.57 pen ink W/C prov. 3-Jul-3 Christie's, Kensington #664/R est:2500-3500
£3500 $5740 €5250 Hillside I (48x58cm-19x23in) s.d.57 W/C bodycol prov.exhib. 6-Jun-3 Christie's, London #124/R est:2000-3000
£4500 $7020 €6750 Nocturne, early October (50x61cm-20x24in) s.i.d.55 W/C htd white prov. 25-Mar-3 Bonhams, New Bond Street #133/R est:3000-5000
£4800 $7392 €7200 November (48x61cm-19x24in) d.55/56 brush ink W/C bodycol prov. 5-Sep-2 Christie's, Kensington #672/R est:2000-3000
£5500 $8470 €8250 Poem in the orchard (38x62cm-15x24in) pen ink W/C bodycol prov. 5-Sep-2 Christie's, Kensington #674/R est:2000-3000

REYNOLDS, Charles H (1902-1963) American

£404 $650 €606 Nocturnal covered wagons in canyon (41x51cm-16x20in) s. prov. 18-Feb-3 John Moran, Pasadena #168
£1282 $2000 €1923 Early morning in Palo Duro (36x46cm-14x18in) s. i.verso canvas on board prov. 9-Nov-2 Santa Fe Art, Santa Fe #65/R est:2000-4000

REYNOLDS, Dorothy (19/20th C) British

Works on paper

£3500 $5390 €5250 Portrait of a young lady, Heilda Priestman (86x68cm-34x27in) indis.sig.indis.d. pastel. 9-Sep-2 Bonhams, Ipswich #117 est:800-1200

REYNOLDS, F (19th C) British

£1166 $1900 €1749 Two terriers (34x45cm-13x18in) mono.i. 11-Feb-3 Bonhams & Doyles, New York #181 est:1500-2000

REYNOLDS, Frank (?-1895) British

Works on paper

£360 $583 €522 Caught in the slips (16x26cm-6x10in) s. W/C htd white. 29-Jul-3 Henry Adams, Chichester #474

REYNOLDS, Frank (1876-1953) British

Works on paper

£450 $702 €675 Dance at the Moulin Rouge (31x21cm-12x8in) s. pencil bodycol. 25-Mar-3 Bonhams, Knightsbridge #58/R

REYNOLDS, Frederick George (1880-1932) Australian

£2105 $3200 €3158 Princess Bridge, Melbourne (86x147cm-34x58in) s.d.1915. 19-Aug-2 Joel, Victoria #263 est:6000-8000 (A.D 6000)

REYNOLDS, G (?) ?

£401 $578 €650 Hunting scene (46x76cm-18x30in) s. 25-Apr-2 Woodwards, Cork #245

REYNOLDS, James (1926-) American

£4167 $6500 €6251 Near Wilcox (46x61cm-18x24in) 9-Nov-2 Altermann Galleries, Santa Fe #197
£8861 $14000 €12848 H-Box Country (46x61cm-18x24in) s.d.1975 board. 26-Jul-3 Coeur d'Alene, Hayden #167/R est:5000-10000
£17123 $25000 €25685 Cold night watch (46x61cm-18x24in) 18-May-2 Altermann Galleries, Santa Fe #134/R
£26899 $42500 €39004 Catch pens (71x102cm-28x40in) s. lit. 26-Jul-3 Coeur d'Alene, Hayden #163/R est:35000-55000

REYNOLDS, John (20th C) New Zealander

Works on paper

£526 $821 €789 Diptych (50x130cm-20x51in) s.d.1986 mixed media. 27-Mar-3 International Art Centre, Auckland #68/R (NZ.D 1500)

REYNOLDS, Samuel William (attrib) (19th C) British

£600 $936 €900 Girl at window (51x41cm-20x16in) 26-Mar-3 Hamptons Fine Art, Godalming #158/R

REYNOLDS, Sir Joshua (1723-1792) British

£5000 $8300 €7500 Portrait of an officer (74x62cm-29x24in) prov. 12-Jun-3 Sotheby's, London #70/R est:6000-8000
£8000 $12640 €12000 Portrait of Miss Mary Powis wearing white dress (77x63cm-30x25in) feigned oval prov.lit. 26-Nov-2 Christie's, London #32/R est:10000-15000
£8387 $13000 €12581 Portrait of Major General Stringer Lawrence (76x63cm-30x25in) prov.exhib.lit. 2-Oct-2 Christie's, Rockefeller NY #126/R est:4000-6000
£18000 $28440 €27000 Portrait of Henry Mervyn of Stoke Damerell and his wife (76x63cm-30x25in) one s. pair prov.lit. 26-Nov-2 Christie's, London #31/R est:20000-30000
£40000 $63200 €60000 Portrait of John Townshend (75x62cm-30x24in) prov.exhib.lit. 28-Nov-2 Sotheby's, London #173/R est:20000-30000
£45000 $74700 €67500 Portrait of a lady in a blue dress. leaning on a ledge (76x63cm-30x25in) prov.exhib.lit. 10-Jun-3 Christie's, London #35/R est:30000-50000
£2400000 $3984000 €3600000 Portrait of Mary Wordsworth, Lady Kent, seated in a landscape (127x102cm-50x40in) 12-Jun-3 Sotheby's, London #7/R est:300000-500000

Works on paper

£1103 $1754 €1600 Boy's portrait (24x24cm-9x9in) mono. chl chk. 8-Mar-3 Arnold, Frankfurt #696/R est:1400
£180000 $298800 €270000 Portrait of the artist aged seventeen (41x26cm-16x10in) black white chk stump. 12-Jun-3 Sotheby's, London #1/R est:60000-80000

REYNOLDS, Sir Joshua (circle) (1723-1792) British

£9000 $14760 €13500 Portrait of Mrs Hargreave (76x63cm-30x25in) prov.exhib. 29-May-3 Christie's, Kensington #39/R est:2000-3000

REYNOLDS, Sir Joshua (studio) (1723-1792) British

£4500 $7111 €6750 Portrait of Charles Fitzroy, 1st Baron Southampton (88x70cm-35x28in) 28-Nov-2 Sotheby's, London #172/R est:5000-7000
£5195 $8000 €7793 Portrait of George III (228x141cm-90x56in) 23-Oct-2 Doyle, New York #66/R est:7000-10000
£6000 $9960 €9000 Portrait of George III. Queen Charlotte (240x147cm-94x58in) pair. 12-Jun-3 Sotheby's, London #58/R est:5000-7000

REYNTJENS, Henrich Engelbert (1817-1900) Dutch

£1447 $2345 €2200 Reading the letter (64x83cm-25x33in) s. panel. 21-Jan-3 Christie's, Amsterdam #109/R est:2500-3500
£1572 $2421 €2500 Farewell (27x20cm-11x8in) s.i. panel. 22-Oct-2 Sotheby's, Amsterdam #59/R est:2000-3000
£2500 $4050 €3800 Caught during his nap (55x68cm-22x27in) indis sig. 21-Jan-3 Christie's, Amsterdam #75/R est:2000-3000
£5605 $8744 €8800 Notary visitor and the reading of the testament (34x58cm-13x23in) panel. 5-Nov-2 Vendu Notarishuis, Rotterdam #218/R est:8000-10000

REYSSCHOOT, Peter Jan van (1702-1772) Flemish

£3500 $5565 €5250 Portrait of Sir John Coton, holding a porte-crayon in his hand (80x65cm-31x26in) prov.lit. 19-Mar-3 Sotheby's, London #46/R est:4000-6000

REYSSCHOOT, Peter Jan van (attrib) (1702-1772) Flemish
£2200 $3410 €3300 Dete champetre with ladies seated by a tree and figures from the commedia dell'arte (66x53cm-26x21in) 30-Oct-2 Christie's, Kensington #86/R est:2000-3000

REZEK, Ivo (1898-1979) Yugoslavian
Works on paper
£982 $1561 €1473 Female nude (29x37cm-11x15in) s.i.d.924 pencil. 8-Mar-3 Dorotheum, Prague #242/R est:8000-12000 (C.KR 45000)

REZEK, Ivo (attrib) (1898-1979) Yugoslavian
£2400 $3815 €3600 Girl nude (80x65cm-31x26in) 8-Mar-3 Dorotheum, Prague #152/R est:50000-75000 (C.KR 110000)

REZIA, Felice A (fl.1866-1902) British
£360 $572 €540 Milan Cathedral interior (46x30cm-18x12in) s.d.1886. 29-Apr-3 Gorringes, Lewes #2189
£450 $693 €675 Near Verona, Italy (16x32cm-6x13in) s.d.1906 i.verso board. 24-Oct-2 Christie's, Kensington #74/R
£550 $891 €825 Figures by a bridge, a continental town (25x20cm-10x8in) s. panel. 23-Jan-3 Christie's, Kensington #163/R
£600 $936 €900 Lago Maggiore. Abbeville (47x21cm-19x8in) s.indis.d. board pair. 18-Sep-2 Dreweatt Neate, Newbury #172
£1000 $1570 €1500 Street sellers at the quay, a Continental town (35x30cm-14x12in) s.d.1883 pair. 16-Apr-3 Christie's, Kensington #579/R est:1200-1800
£1500 $2310 €2250 Chiavenia. Chartres (41x30cm-16x12in) s.d.1894 pair. 24-Oct-2 Christie's, Kensington #136/R est:1500-2000
£1800 $2880 €2700 Street scene in Bruge (77x51cm-30x20in) s.d.1901 pair. 13-May-3 Bonhams, Knightsbridge #167/R est:1800-2000

REZNICEK, Ferdinand von (1868-1909) German
£272 $433 €400 Young woman wearing negligee (36x31cm-14x12in) mono. board. 28-Mar-3 Bolland & Marotz, Bremen #518/R

REZVANI, Serge (1928-) French
£962 $1510 €1500 Jungle verte (189x340cm-74x134in) s.d.66 prov.exhib. 24-Nov-2 Laurence Calmels, Paris #238/R
£2564 $4026 €4000 Mask (120x60cm-47x24in) s.d.1962. 24-Nov-2 Laurence Calmels, Paris #237/R
Sculpture
£4808 $7548 €7500 Untitled (169x310cm-67x122in) s.verso wood. 20-Nov-2 Binoche, Paris #45/R est:10000-10500

RHAYE, Yves (1936-1995) Belgian
£310 $497 €450 Composition (70x80cm-28x31in) s. 15-Mar-3 De Vuyst, Lokeren #272
£345 $552 €500 Composition (110x110cm-43x43in) s. 15-Mar-3 De Vuyst, Lokeren #271
£577 $894 €900 Composition (100x100cm-39x39in) s. 7-Dec-2 De Vuyst, Lokeren #263
£694 $1104 €1000 Composition (150x120cm-59x47in) s. 29-Apr-3 Campo, Vlaamse Kaai #261
£755 $1170 €1200 Composition (150x150cm-59x59in) s. 5-Oct-2 De Vuyst, Lokeren #306
Sculpture
£2264 $3487 €3600 Torso (51cm-20in) terracotta. 22-Oct-2 Campo, Vlaamse Kaai #603

RHEAD, Louis John (1857-1926) British/American
Works on paper
£696 $1100 €1044 Sirens. Scene from the story 'Little Seamaid' (41x30cm-16x12in) one s. pen ink one s. i.verso pen ink board two. 2-Apr-3 Doyle, New York #59/R

RHEAM, Henry Meynell (1859-1920) British
Works on paper
£750 $1155 €1125 Portrait of a young girl looking out to sea (35x27cm-14x11in) init. W/C. 22-Oct-2 Bonhams, Knightsbridge #204/R
£880 $1373 €1320 Fishing boats at St. Ives (24x57cm-9x22in) s.i.d.1919 pencil W/C htd bodycol. 17-Oct-2 Christie's, Kensington #56/R
£1422 $2361 €2062 By the river, Helston (51x60cm-20x24in) s. W/C. 16-Jun-3 Waddingtons, Toronto #96/R est:2000-3000 (C.D 3200)
£1850 $3016 €2775 Girl in pink (35x27cm-14x11in) init.d.1911 W/C. 28-Jan-3 Bristol Auction Rooms #527/R est:2000-2500
£2000 $3100 €3000 Preparing the nets, Mullion (48x76cm-19x30in) W/C. 26-Sep-2 Lane, Penzance #135/R est:2000-3000

RHEAUME, Jeanne (1915-2000) Canadian
£403 $657 €605 Red flowers (51x61cm-20x24in) prov. 12-Feb-3 Iegor de Saint Hippolyte, Montreal #154 (C.D 1000)

RHEE, Seund Ja (1918-) Korean
£705 $1107 €1100 Chemin des Antipodes (46x55cm-18x22in) s.d.81 s.i.d.verso acrylic. 24-Nov-2 Laurence Calmels, Paris #243/R
£769 $1208 €1200 Montagne et mer (65x50cm-26x20in) s.d.79 acrylic. 24-Nov-2 Laurence Calmels, Paris #244/R
£791 $1266 €1100 Composition (55x38cm-22x15in) s.d. 18-May-3 Eric Pillon, Calais #270/R
£1923 $3019 €3000 Untitled (73x60cm-29x24in) s.d.69 s.i.d.verso. 24-Nov-2 Laurence Calmels, Paris #245/R
£2051 $3221 €3200 Debut de ceremonie 3 (49x60cm-19x24in) s.d.60. 24-Nov-2 Laurence Calmels, Paris #250/R
£2057 $3435 €2900 Composition (55x38cm-22x15in) s.d. prov. 23-Jun-3 Claude Boisgirard, Paris #151/R est:3000-3500
£2244 $3522 €3500 Gratte-ciel sur la lune (49x64cm-19x25in) s.d.63 s.i.d.verso. 24-Nov-2 Laurence Calmels, Paris #247/R
£2244 $3522 €3500 Adolescence (65x46cm-26x18in) s.d.61 prov. 24-Nov-2 Laurence Calmels, Paris #246/R
£2244 $3522 €3500 Untitled (49x61cm-19x24in) s. 24-Nov-2 Laurence Calmels, Paris #248/R
£2244 $3522 €3500 Intemporel Aout (73x60cm-29x24in) s.d.75 panel. 24-Nov-2 Laurence Calmels, Paris #249/R
Works on paper
£962 $1510 €1500 Untitled (15x31cm-6x12in) s.d.60 gouache. 24-Nov-2 Laurence Calmels, Paris #240/R
£1154 $1812 €1800 Untitled (24x33cm-9x13in) s.d.60 gouache. 24-Nov-2 Laurence Calmels, Paris #241/R
£2244 $3522 €3500 Untitled (30x41cm-12x16in) s.d.60 gouache. 24-Nov-2 Laurence Calmels, Paris #242/R

RHEIN, Fritz (1873-1948) German
£2391 $3922 €3300 Garden (66x81cm-26x32in) s. exhib. 31-May-3 Villa Grisebach, Berlin #127/R est:3000-3500

RHEINER, Louis (1863-1924) Swiss
£279 $441 €419 Landscape with female nude on a towel on the beach (60x73cm-24x29in) s.d.19. 26-Nov-2 Hans Widmer, St Gallen #1317 (S.FR 650)
£284 $448 €426 Paysage en Cote d'Azur (24x32cm-9x13in) s.i. 17-Nov-2 Koller, Geneva #1235 (S.FR 650)
£371 $579 €557 Boy sitting down with wine bottle and bread (28x23cm-11x9in) mono. 6-Nov-2 Dobiaschofsky, Bern #3615 (S.FR 850)
£371 $586 €557 Juan-Les-Pins (55x46cm-22x18in) s. 17-Nov-2 Koller, Geneva #1306 (S.FR 850)
£480 $759 €720 Champ de coquelicots (80x40cm-31x16in) s.d.1892 cardboard. 17-Nov-2 Koller, Geneva #1207 (S.FR 1100)

RHEINERT, Adolf (1880-1958) German
£445 $695 €650 Rees beach on the lower Rhine (40x50cm-16x20in) s. 10-Apr-3 Van Ham, Cologne #1671

RHIJNNEN, Johannes van (1859-1927) Dutch
£886 $1382 €1400 Fisherman on a boat on a polder canal (60x39cm-24x15in) s. 21-Oct-2 Glerum, Amsterdam #20/R
£1053 $1705 €1600 Polder landscape with a fisherman in a rowing boat. Study of a river landscape (46x57cm-18x22in) s. two. 21-Jan-3 Christie's, Amsterdam #177 est:600-800

RHINE SCHOOL (15th C) German
Works on paper
£89506 $145000 €134259 Raising of Lazarus (19x17cm-7x7in) init. pen ink vellum. 21-Jan-3 Sotheby's, New York #57/R est:30000

RHO, Camillo (1872-1946) Italian
£340 $541 €500 Portrait of man (60x48cm-24x19in) s. 1-Mar-3 Meeting Art, Vercelli #223

RHODES, Carol (1959-) British
£800 $1336 €1160 Forest (41x47cm-16x19in) s.i.d.1999 verso board exhib. 24-Jun-3 Sotheby's, Olympia #113/R
£1000 $1630 €1500 Airport (41x48cm-16x19in) s. i.d.1995 verso board prov. 3-Feb-3 Sotheby's, Olympia #32/R est:800-1200

RHODES, Daniel (1911-1989) American
£764 $1200 €1146 Stormy weather. Still life (46x61cm-18x24in) s. masonite painted c.1934 double-sided painted by artist's wife. 23-Nov-2 Jackson's, Cedar Falls #104/R
£1084 $1800 €1572 Female nude (71x56cm-28x22in) s. masonite. 14-Jun-3 Jackson's, Cedar Falls #34 est:500-750
£1145 $1900 €1660 Landscape with aspens. Mountain landscape (41x51cm-16x20in) s. one board one masonite pair. 14-Jun-3 Jackson's, Cedar Falls #31/R est:600-900

RHODES, Joseph (1782-1854) British
£600 $936 €900 Still life of a butterfly and fruits on a ledge (63x76cm-25x30in) indis sig. 8-Oct-2 Bonhams, Knightsbridge #41/R
£800 $1256 €1200 River landscape with figures beside a path. Woodland gorge (25x38cm-10x15in) one s.indis d.1810 pair. 19-Nov-2 Bonhams, Leeds #237
£2500 $4125 €3625 River landscape with bathers and boat. River landscape with boat and rocky outcrop beyond (24x36cm-9x14in) one s.d.1811 panel pair. 2-Jul-3 Sotheby's, Olympia #95/R est:3000-5000

RHONSTAD, Eric (1909-) Swedish
£371 $563 €557 Winter landscape (63x80cm-25x31in) s.d.1950 panel. 16-Aug-2 Lilla Bukowskis, Stockholm #1025 (S.KR 5400)

RHYS, Oliver (fl.1876-1895) British
£645 $1019 €968 Fishing village, evening (61x46cm-24x18in) s.d.1882 prov. 18-Nov-2 Waddingtons, Toronto #101/R (C.D 1600)
£900 $1476 €1350 Siren (23x30cm-9x12in) s. panel. 29-May-3 Christie's, Kensington #246/R
£1266 $2000 €2000 Seated lady with red shawl reading (44x35cm-17x14in) s.d.1883. 27-Nov-2 James Adam, Dublin #82/R est:2000-3000
£3354 $5500 €5031 Seated muse (91x61cm-36x24in) s. 5-Feb-3 Christie's, Rockefeller NY #174/R est:6000-8000
£3963 $6500 €5945 Mother and child curling twine (91x70cm-36x28in) s. 5-Feb-3 Christie's, Rockefeller NY #175/R est:7000-9000
£4600 $7314 €6900 Venetian backwater (76x127cm-30x50in) s.d.1888. 6-Mar-3 Christie's, Kensington #575/R est:5000-7000
£5000 $7700 €7500 Budgerigar (46x36cm-18x14in) s. 5-Sep-2 Christie's, Kensington #330/R est:2500-3500

RIAB, Boris (1898-1975) American/Russian
Prints
£5172 $8224 €7500 Pointers a l'arret (22x31cm-9x12in) col prints pair. 10-Mar-3 Coutau Begarie, Paris #88

RIAN, Johannes (1891-1981) Norwegian
£263 $416 €395 Farmyard in winter (32x41cm-13x16in) s. i.verso panel. 17-Dec-2 Grev Wedels Plass, Oslo #265 (N.KR 3000)
£276 $420 €414 Composition (27x23cm-11x9in) cardboard. 31-Aug-2 Grev Wedels Plass, Oslo #70 (N.KR 3200)
£310 $505 €465 Portrait of young lady (65x47cm-26x19in) s. 17-Feb-3 Blomqvist, Lysaker #1173 (N.KR 3500)
£328 $498 €492 Composition with prism (25x20cm-10x8in) s. cardboard. 31-Aug-2 Grev Wedels Plass, Oslo #90 (N.KR 3800)
£329 $503 €494 Negress (41x32cm-16x13in) s. panel. 26-Aug-2 Blomqvist, Lysaker #1316 (N.KR 3800)
£341 $532 €512 Old farm (21x33cm-8x13in) s. 23-Sep-2 Blomqvist, Lysaker #1188 (N.KR 4000)
£380 $577 €570 Palette (44x29cm-17x11in) s. wood. 31-Aug-2 Grev Wedels Plass, Oslo #96 (N.KR 4400)
£432 $721 €626 Self-portrait (50x35cm-20x14in) init. cardboard. 18-Jun-3 Grev Wedels Plass, Oslo #209/R (N.KR 5000)
£442 $721 €663 Torpo stave church (54x46cm-21x18in) s.d.1932 panel. 17-Feb-3 Blomqvist, Lysaker #1174 (N.KR 5000)
£1735 $2706 €2603 Florence (33x40cm-13x16in) s.i.d.1934 panel. 21-Oct-2 Blomqvist, Oslo #394/R est:12000-15000 (N.KR 20000)
£1735 $2706 €2603 Interior scene with man and easel (47x38cm-19x15in) s. panel. 21-Oct-2 Blomqvist, Oslo #395/R est:25000-35000 (N.KR 20000)
£1812 $2754 €2718 Game of cards (21x30cm-8x12in) s. pencil W/C paper on panel. 31-Aug-2 Grev Wedels Plass, Oslo #93/R est:15000 (N.KR 21000)
£2336 $3690 €3504 Interior scene with woman (33x41cm-13x16in) s.i.d.1934 panel. 2-Dec-2 Blomqvist, Oslo #420/R est:30000-40000 (N.KR 27000)
£3620 $5864 €5430 From Torremolinos with men and donkeys (38x46cm-15x18in) s. s.i.d.1957 verso panel. 26-May-3 Grev Wedels Plass, Oslo #80/R est:50000-70000 (N.KR 40000)
£4040 $6626 €5858 Man in studio (60x50cm-24x20in) s. 2-Jun-3 Blomqvist, Oslo #201/R est:20000-25000 (N.KR 44000)
£4325 $6834 €6488 The sailor (48x57cm-19x22in) s. 2-Dec-2 Blomqvist, Oslo #437/R est:60000-70000 (N.KR 50000)
£4526 $7241 €6789 Blue lady (46x38cm-18x15in) s. paper on panel. 17-Mar-3 Blomqvist, Oslo #422/R est:35000-45000 (N.KR 52000)
£5672 $8905 €8508 Siracuse, Sicily (46x55cm-18x22in) s. s.i.d.1951 verso lit. 21-Nov-2 Grev Wedels Plass, Oslo #79/R est:70000-90000 (N.KR 65000)
£5800 $9512 €8700 Kunstnerens atelier - artist's studio (46x38cm-18x15in) s. board prov. 3-Jun-3 Sotheby's, London #273/R est:4500-6000
£5882 $9529 €8823 Composition (110x100cm-43x39in) s.d.78 lit. 26-May-3 Grev Wedels Plass, Oslo #22/R est:80000-100000 (N.KR 65000)
£5965 $9425 €8948 Out in the room (101x81cm-40x32in) s.d.72 i.stretcher. 17-Dec-2 Grev Wedels Plass, Oslo #266/R est:50000-70000 (N.KR 68000)
£15611 $25601 €22636 Pink and black I (90x100cm-35x39in) i.stretcher exhib. 2-Jun-3 Blomqvist, Oslo #203/R est:180000-200000 (N.KR 170000)
Prints
£2368 $3742 €3552 Head of woman (33x28cm-13x11in) s.num.1/1 etching. 17-Dec-2 Grev Wedels Plass, Oslo #41/R est:8000-10000 (N.KR 27000)

Works on paper
£259 $393 €389 Seated nude (29x20cm-11x8in) s.indis.i.d.1949 pencil. 31-Aug-2 Grev Wedels Plass, Oslo #76 (N.KR 3000)
£273 $426 €410 Composition (21x15cm-8x6in) s. W/C painted 1970. 23-Sep-2 Blomqvist, Lysaker #1189 (N.KR 3200)
£293 $446 €440 Woman (28x20cm-11x8in) s.d.1956 mixed media. 31-Aug-2 Grev Wedels Plass, Oslo #73/R (N.KR 3400)
£294 $490 €426 Saint Francis preaching to the birds (21x17cm-8x7in) s.d.1934 i.verso W/C varnish paper on cardboard exhib. 18-Jun-3 Grev Wedels Plass, Oslo #210 (N.KR 3400)
£345 $525 €518 Nude seen from behind (30x19cm-12x7in) init.d.1949 mixed media. 31-Aug-2 Grev Wedels Plass, Oslo #95 (N.KR 4000)
£414 $630 €621 Seated nude (29x22cm-11x9in) init.indis.i. W/C. 31-Aug-2 Grev Wedels Plass, Oslo #94 (N.KR 4800)
£431 $656 €647 Seated boy (18x13cm-7x5in) s.d.1950 mixed media paper on panel. 31-Aug-2 Grev Wedels Plass, Oslo #92/R (N.KR 5000)
£485 $742 €728 Composition (28x29cm-11x11in) s. W/C executed 1977. 26-Aug-2 Blomqvist, Lysaker #1317 (N.KR 5600)
£561 $852 €842 Spanish girl (17x12cm-7x5in) s. i.verso mixed media. 31-Aug-2 Grev Wedels Plass, Oslo #84/R (N.KR 6500)
£561 $852 €842 Seated boy (17x13cm-7x5in) s.d.1942 mixed media. 31-Aug-2 Grev Wedels Plass, Oslo #91 (N.KR 6500)
£604 $918 €906 Coastal landscape with man seated (25x35cm-10x14in) s.d.1941 W/C. 31-Aug-2 Grev Wedels Plass, Oslo #89/R (N.KR 7000)
£683 $1065 €1025 Still life of flowers (45x31cm-18x12in) s. W/C. 23-Sep-2 Blomqvist, Lysaker #1192/R (N.KR 8000)
£690 $1049 €1035 From a window (26x20cm-10x8in) s.d.1948 mixed media. 31-Aug-2 Grev Wedels Plass, Oslo #81/R (N.KR 8000)
£1079 $1639 €1619 Boy with bowl of fruit (25x19cm-10x7in) s.d.1950 mixed media. 31-Aug-2 Grev Wedels Plass, Oslo #82/R (N.KR 12500)
£1337 $2033 €2006 Woman and sailor with concertina (26x23cm-10x9in) s.d.1951 mixed media. 31-Aug-2 Grev Wedels Plass, Oslo #80 est:6000-8000 (N.KR 15500)
£1706 $2662 €2559 Seated woman holding cat on her lap (25x18cm-10x7in) s. W/C. 23-Sep-2 Blomqvist, Lysaker #1191/R est:12000-15000 (N.KR 20000)
£1877 $2928 €2816 Outside the window. Sailor. Man in room with dish. s. W/C three in one frame. 23-Sep-2 Blomqvist, Lysaker #1193/R est:20000-22000 (N.KR 22000)

RIANCHO GOMEZ DE MORA, Agustin (1841-1929) Spanish
£621 $981 €900 Landscape (28x38cm-11x15in) s. oil chl cardboard. 1-Apr-3 Segre, Madrid #143/R
£3165 $4937 €5000 Chasseur a la barque (35x51cm-14x20in) s.d.1873 panel. 20-Oct-2 Galerie de Chartres, Chartres #135 est:7000-12000

RIBA-ROVIRA, François (1913-) Spanish
Works on paper
£314 $491 €500 Nude (45x36cm-18x14in) s. pencil dr. 17-Sep-2 Segre, Madrid #236/R

RIBARZ, Rudolf (attrib) (1848-1904) Austrian
£750 $1155 €1125 Italian town with figures on a riverbank (30x43cm-12x17in) s. board. 3-Sep-2 Gorringes, Lewes #2211

RIBAS MONTENEGRO, Federico (1890-1952) Spanish
Works on paper
£503 $775 €800 Women from Seville (56x37cm-22x15in) s. mixed media. 22-Oct-2 Durán, Madrid #601/R
£839 $1325 €1300 Figures (50x38cm-20x15in) s. gouache. 17-Dec-2 Durán, Madrid #101/R

RIBAUPIERRE, François de (1886-1981) Swiss
£742 $1158 €1113 Portrait of a lady from Wallis (42x32cm-17x13in) mono. paper on board. 8-Nov-2 Dobiaschofsky, Bern #86/R (S.FR 1700)
Works on paper
£1888 $2984 €2832 Portrait of a Wallis girl (33x32cm-13x13in) mono. pastel chk. 26-Nov-2 Hans Widmer, St Gallen #1318/R est:1400-2800 (S.FR 4400)
£4292 $6781 €6438 Profile portrait of girl from Wallis in national costume (29x28cm-11x11in) mono. pastel. 29-Nov-2 Zofingen, Switzerland #3040/R est:6500 (S.FR 10000)
£6481 $10435 €9397 Jeune fille valaisanne (33x31cm-13x12in) mono. pastel. 9-May-3 Dobiaschofsky, Bern #179/R est:7500 (S.FR 14000)

RIBCOWSKY, Dey de (1880-1936) American/Bulgarian
£968 $1500 €1452 Sunset marine (51x76cm-20x30in) s. painted c.1920. 8-Dec-2 Toomey, Oak Park #674/R est:2000-3000
£1129 $1750 €1694 Panoramic sunset Venice canal scene (43x124cm-17x49in) s.d.23. 29-Oct-2 John Moran, Pasadena #694 est:2500-3500

RIBEIRO, Alceu (1919-) Uruguayan
£256 $400 €384 Street (44x54cm-17x21in) cardboard. 17-Oct-2 Galleria Y Remates, Montevideo #60
£321 $500 €482 Calle de Mallorca (55x65cm-22x26in) s. 30-Jul-2 Galleria Y Remates, Montevideo #52/R
£449 $704 €700 Montevideo harbour. s.d.63 double-sided. 16-Dec-2 Castellana, Madrid #377/R
£513 $800 €770 Quinta de Mendizabal (52x65cm-20x26in) s. 30-Jul-2 Galleria Y Remates, Montevideo #51
£605 $950 €908 Still life with bottle (51x46cm-20x18in) s. 20-Nov-2 Galleria Y Remates, Montevideo #27
£609 $950 €914 Composicion con barco (62x44cm-24x17in) s. board. 30-Jul-2 Galleria Y Remates, Montevideo #92/R
£929 $1450 €1394 Composicion con lampara (70x50cm-28x20in) s. board. 30-Jul-2 Galleria Y Remates, Montevideo #91/R

RIBEIRO, Edgardo (1921-) Uruguayan
£481 $750 €722 Paris (61x50cm-24x20in) s.d.68. 10-Oct-2 Galleria Y Remates, Montevideo #28/R
£769 $1200 €1154 Puerto (49x69cm-19x27in) s.d.50. 30-Jul-2 Galleria Y Remates, Montevideo #54/R

RIBEMONT-DESSAIGNES, Georges (1884-1974) French
£7372 $11574 €11500 Paysage (65x77cm-26x30in) init. cardboard prov. 24-Nov-2 Laurence Calmels, Paris #251/R est:6000
£68493 $106849 €100000 Grand musicien (75x57cm-30x22in) mono.i. cardboard exhib. 14-Apr-3 Laurence Calmels, Paris #4030/R est:90000
Works on paper
£25342 $39788 €37000 Petit desert (47x61cm-19x24in) mono.i. ink prov.exhib. 15-Apr-3 Laurence Calmels, Paris #4400/R est:20000

RIBER, Asger (1897-?) Danish
£321 $501 €482 Landscape from Fano with girl by dunes (73x98cm-29x39in) s. 23-Sep-2 Rasmussen, Vejle #2153 (D.KR 3800)

RIBER, Peder (19/20th C) Danish
£438 $701 €657 Girl from Fanoe wearing national costume seated in the dunes (60x70cm-24x28in) s.d.1910. 13-Jan-3 Rasmussen, Vejle #237/R (D.KR 5000)

RIBERA (?) Spanish
£5128 $8103 €8000 Saint Jerome at the mouth of a cave (109x92cm-43x36in) 12-Nov-2 Mealy's, Castlecomer #1046

RIBERA GOMEZ, Francisco (20th C) Spanish
£503 $785 €800 Family portrait (108x120cm-43x47in) s.d.MCMLVIII. 23-Sep-2 Durán, Madrid #58/R

RIBERA Y FIEVE, Carlos Luis de (1815-1891) Spanish
Works on paper
£346 $533 €550 Nudes (60x45cm-24x18in) dr. 22-Oct-2 Durán, Madrid #1315
£409 $630 €650 Nudes (61x45cm-24x18in) dr. 22-Oct-2 Durán, Madrid #1314

RIBERA, Francisco (1907-1990) Spanish
£650 $1040 €975 Bailarinaen reposo (39x47cm-15x19in) s. board. 11-Mar-3 Bonhams, Knightsbridge #191/R
£1290 $2039 €2000 Shawl (70x58cm-28x23in) s.d.MCMLXII s.i.d.verso. 17-Dec-2 Durán, Madrid #196/R
£2436 $3849 €3800 Hunting party (54x81cm-21x32in) s. 13-Nov-2 Ansorena, Madrid #174/R
£3871 $6116 €6000 Shape and colour (90x72cm-35x28in) s.d.MCMLXII s.i.d.verso. 17-Dec-2 Durán, Madrid #193/R
£5705 $9185 €8500 Back from hunting (54x82cm-21x32in) s.d.MCMLII. 18-Feb-3 Durán, Madrid #180/R

RIBERA, J (19th C) Spanish
£306 $477 €459 Coastal landscape with sailing boat and fishermen (60x100cm-24x39in) s. 5-Aug-2 Rasmussen, Vejle #52/R (D.KR 3600)

RIBERA, Jusepe de (1588-1656) Spanish
£5696 $9000 €9000 Saint Gerolamo (61x47cm-24x19in) 2-Dec-2 Finarte, Milan #152/R est:7000
Prints
£7595 $12000 €12000 Small grotesque head (14x11cm-6x4in) etching. 29-Nov-2 Bassenge, Berlin #5231/R est:6000

RIBERA, Jusepe de (attrib) (1588-1656) Spanish
£8936 $14119 €13404 Portrait of man holding paper with geometric figures (75x58cm-30x23in) prov. 2-Dec-2 Rasmussen, Copenhagen #1651/R est:60000-80000 (D.KR 105000)
£11872 $18521 €17808 St Peter (113x82cm-44x32in) 28-Mar-3 Koller, Zurich #3048/R est:20000-30000 (S.FR 26000)

RIBERA, Jusepe de (circle) (1588-1656) Spanish
£8974 $13910 €14000 Bearded old man in three-quarter profile sitting in front of a book (75x67cm-30x26in) canvas on canvas. 4-Dec-2 Neumeister, Munich #633/R est:1200

RIBERA, Jusepe de (studio) (1588-1656) Spanish
£9000 $13950 €13500 Saint Phillip (61x50cm-24x20in) 30-Oct-2 Christie's, Kensington #126/R est:10000-15000

RIBERA, Pierre (1867-1932) French
£4196 $7007 €6000 La sortie du Sultan (50x61cm-20x24in) s. lit. 27-Jun-3 Claude Aguttes, Neuilly #146/R est:5000-6000
£25915 $42500 €37577 Jour de marche a San Gabriel, Mexique (61x130cm-24x51in) s.i.d.1905 prov.exhib. 27-May-3 Sotheby's, New York #47

RIBERA, Pierre (attrib) (1867-1932) French
Works on paper
£903 $1400 €1355 Standing academy nude with additional studies of head and arms (61x47cm-24x19in) s. chl htd white. 29-Oct-2 Sotheby's, New York #83/R est:400-600

RIBERA, Roman (1848-1935) Spanish
£4167 $6583 €6500 Inn scene (73x100cm-29x39in) s. 13-Nov-2 Ansorena, Madrid #104/R est:3600
£7000 $10990 €10500 An attentive audience (100x71cm-39x28in) s. 19-Nov-2 Bonhams, New Bond Street #85/R est:7000-10000
£8500 $13345 €12750 Rehearsal (86x86cm-34x34in) s. 21-Nov-2 Christie's, Kensington #185/R est:6000-8000

RIBES COLL, Juan (1946-) Spanish
£855 $1386 €1300 Red flowers (46x65cm-18x26in) s.d.01 s.d.verso. 21-Jan-3 Durán, Madrid #68/R

RIBLET, Fernand (1873-1944) Italian
£1218 $1924 €1900 Landscape in Brittany (59x72cm-23x28in) s. 15-Nov-2 Farsetti, Prato #524/R

RIBOLI, Joseph (20th C) American?
£355 $550 €533 Conch shell on arm of weathered Adirondack chair at the beach (43x53cm-17x21in) s. 28-Sep-2 Thomaston Place, Thomaston #159

RIBOT, Germain Theodore (1845-1893) French
£962 $1510 €1500 Vase de fleurs (61x50cm-24x20in) s. 24-Nov-2 Lesieur & Le Bars, Le Havre #154
£4000 $6280 €6000 Still life with eggs, plums and a lemon on a draped ledge (19x25cm-7x10in) s. prov. 21-Nov-2 Christie's, Kensington #86/R est:5000-7000

RIBOT, Theodule (1823-1891) French
£2244 $3500 €3366 Chef in his kitchen (46x30cm-18x12in) s. panel. 14-Sep-2 Selkirks, St. Louis #722/R est:5000-7000
£10959 $17205 €16000 Still life with oysters (46x54cm-18x21in) s. 15-Apr-3 Sotheby's, Amsterdam #232/R est:10000-15000

RIBOUD, Marc (20th C) ?
Photographs
£2761 $4500 €4142 Painter of the Eiffel Tower, Paris (53x35cm-21x14in) s.num.6/50 gelatin silver print. 12-Feb-3 Christie's, Rockefeller NY #260/R est:5000-7000

RICARD, J (19th C) French
£386 $602 €610 Paysage (65x92cm-26x36in) s. 15-Sep-2 Feletin, Province #104

RICARD, Louis Gustave (1823-1873) French
£250 $410 €375 Waif warming herself by the stove (27x22cm-11x9in) mono. panel. 5-Jun-3 Christie's, Kensington #597

RICARD, Louis Gustave (attrib) (1823-1873) French
£1554 $2424 €2300 Autoportrait presume de l'artiste (55x46cm-22x18in) 25-Mar-3 Chochon-Barre & Allardi, Paris #26/R est:2500-3000

RICARD, Mahne (20th C) French?
Works on paper
£753 $1183 €1100 Swan and figures (28x39cm-11x15in) s.d.1955 W/C gouache. 15-Apr-3 Laurence Calmels, Paris #4222/R

RICARD-CORDINGLEY, Georges (1873-1939) French
£577 $906 €900 Marine au soleil couchant (27x35cm-11x14in) s. 15-Dec-2 Eric Pillon, Calais #14/R
£1090 $1711 €1700 Marine (31x40cm-12x16in) s. panel. 15-Dec-2 Eric Pillon, Calais #15/R

RICCARDI, Luigi (1808-1877) French?
£16026 $24840 €25000 Napoleon leaving for Saint Helen. Napoleon's rests arriving in Paris (77x101cm-30x40in) s.d. pair. 4-Dec-2 Finarte, Rome #797/R est:27000

RICCI, Arturo (1854-1919) Italian
£60000 $100200 €90000 An afternoon's entertainment (68x93cm-27x37in) s. prov. 19-Jun-3 Christie's, London #41/R est:70000-90000

RICCI, Dante (1879-1957) Italian
£8228 $13000 €13000 Navona Square, Rome (122x210cm-48x83in) s.i.d.1911 exhib. 26-Nov-2 Christie's, Rome #222/R

RICCI, Giulia (1976-) Italian
Works on paper
£638 $1034 €900 Pesci in padella (160x127cm-63x50in) collage. 20-May-3 Porro, Milan #50/R est:1100-1300

RICCI, Marco (1676-1729) Italian
£12821 $19872 €20000 River landscape with ruined bridge (200x172cm-79x68in) 4-Dec-2 Christie's, Rome #465/R
£21887 $34143 €34800 Classical capriccio (77x135cm-30x53in) 22-Sep-2 Semenzato, Venice #300/R est:40000-50000
Works on paper
£16000 $25120 €24000 Landscape with travellers on a road and buildings and mountains beyond (30x44cm-12x17in) gouache on kidskin. 11-Dec-2 Sotheby's, Olympia #207/R est:10000-15000
£24691 $40000 €37037 Capriccio of square with fountain (30x44cm-12x17in) gouache kidskin. 21-Jan-3 Sotheby's, New York #73/R est:20000

RICCI, Marco (attrib) (1676-1729) Italian
£1216 $1897 €1800 Landscape with herders resting. 26-Mar-3 Hugo Ruef, Munich #15/R est:1800
Works on paper
£1600 $2656 €2320 View of Raby Castle from the deer park with two figures in the shade of trees (28x43cm-11x17in) i. gouache. 16-Jun-3 Duke & Son, Dorchester #128/R est:1000-2000
£2800 $4676 €4060 River view in the Veneto (18x25cm-7x10in) pen brown ink grey wash blk chk. 9-Jul-3 Sotheby's, London #73/R est:1500-2000

RICCI, Marco (circle) (1676-1729) Italian
£37736 $58868 €60000 Architectural capricci with ruins of classical monuments. tempera set of six. 20-Sep-2 Millon & Associes, Paris #383/R est:70000-100000

RICCI, Marco (style) (1676-1729) Italian
£8621 $13707 €12500 Paysage avec berger et troupeau pres d'un gue (63x85cm-25x33in) 7-Mar-3 Rabourdin & Choppin de Janvry, Paris #54/R est:12000-15000

RICCI, Pio (?-1919) Italian
£2452 $3604 €3800 Beautiful model (47x33cm-19x13in) s. 20-Jun-2 Dr Fritz Nagel, Stuttgart #818/R est:6800
£3125 $5000 €4688 If music be the food of love (35x23cm-14x9in) s.indis.d.187. 14-May-3 Butterfields, San Francisco #1050/R est:3000-5000
£8500 $14195 €12750 Entertaining the guests (57x84cm-22x33in) s. 18-Jun-3 Christie's, Kensington #146/R est:10000-15000

RICCI, Sebastiano (1659-1734) Italian
£18000 $30060 €26100 Sermon on the Mount (43x60cm-17x24in) prov.lit. 10-Jul-3 Sotheby's, London #175/R est:20000-30000
Works on paper
£3800 $5966 €5700 Mocking of Christ (26x20cm-10x8in) pen ink wash over black chk prov. 11-Dec-2 Sotheby's, Olympia #122/R est:1000-1500

RICCI, Sebastiano (attrib) (1659-1734) Italian
Works on paper
£633 $1000 €1000 Moines assistant a la messe (27x17cm-11x7in) pen ink wash. 28-Nov-2 Tajan, Paris #38/R
£641 $994 €1000 Communion des apotres (22x14cm-9x6in) i. crayon. 4-Dec-2 Piasa, Paris #13

RICCI, Sebastiano (school) (1659-1734) Italian
£5660 $8717 €9000 Bacchanal (48x65cm-19x26in) 23-Oct-2 Finarte, Rome #518/R est:9000-10000

RICCI, Sebastiano (studio) (1659-1734) Italian
£9500 $15865 €13775 Christ and the Woman of Samaria (85x70cm-33x28in) prov.exhib.lit. 8-Jul-3 Sotheby's, Olympia #452/R est:6000-8000

RICCI, Sebastiano (style) (1659-1734) Italian
£12000 $20040 €17400 Angelica and Medoro (99x117cm-39x46in) 10-Jul-3 Sotheby's, London #177/R est:12000-18000

RICCIARDI (?) Italian
£4591 $7070 €7300 Carpet and fabric seller (150x100cm-59x39in) s.i.d.1936. 23-Oct-2 Rabourdin & Choppin de Janvry, Paris #264/R est:8000

RICCIARDI, Caesar A (1892-1988) American
£577 $900 €866 Autumn landscape (61x91cm-24x36in) s.d.53. 20-Sep-2 Freeman, Philadelphia #79/R
£609 $950 €914 River landscape (61x91cm-24x36in) s.d.66. 20-Sep-2 Freeman, Philadelphia #92/R
£833 $1300 €1250 Pennsylvania landscape with waterfall and red barn (61x76cm-24x30in) s.d.50. 18-Sep-2 Alderfer's, Hatfield #339/R
£1852 $3000 €2685 Boats at twilight (64x76cm-25x30in) s.d.1930. 21-May-3 Doyle, New York #103/R est:2000-3000

RICCIARDI, Oscar (1864-1935) Italian
£377 $600 €566 Italian market place (34x24cm-13x9in) s. indis.i.verso. 7-Mar-3 Skinner, Boston #522/R
£507 $791 €761 Street scene from Naples (31x24cm-12x9in) s. 23-Sep-2 Rasmussen, Vejle #218/R (D.KR 6000)
£550 $864 €825 Fishermen off the Capri Coast (27x42cm-11x17in) s. board. 16-Apr-3 Christie's, Kensington #593/R
£600 $936 €900 Italian market scene (38x25cm-15x10in) s. pair. 12-Sep-2 Bonhams, Edinburgh #342
£600 $960 €900 Rainy market day (29x21cm-11x8in) board. 11-Mar-3 Bonhams, Knightsbridge #44/R
£725 $1188 €1000 Marina con barca (15x20cm-6x8in) s. panel. 27-May-3 Finarte, Milan #128/R
£950 $1558 €1425 Continental market (37x22cm-15x9in) s. panel. 5-Jun-3 Christie's, Kensington #714/R
£1195 $1840 €1900 Market at Porta Capuana (30x24cm-12x9in) s. board. 23-Oct-2 Finarte, Milan #194/R
£1500 $2340 €2250 Busy market square in Naples (19x9cm-7x4in) s.i. panel sold with two others by the same hand. 17-Sep-2 Rosebery Fine Art, London #694 est:1800-2500
£1500 $2370 €2250 Market day, Naples. Vegetable market, Naples (33x18cm-13x7in) s.i. panel pair. 14-Nov-2 Christie's, Kensington #141/R est:1500-2500
£2200 $3498 €3300 Um mercato Napoletano (35x60cm-14x24in) s. 20-Mar-3 Christie's, Kensington #63/R est:1500-2000
£2200 $3586 €3190 Neapolitan view (61x40cm-24x16in) s.i. 16-Jul-3 Sotheby's, Olympia #225/R est:800-1200
£2200 $3586 €3190 Neapolitan view (61x40cm-24x16in) s.i. 16-Jul-3 Sotheby's, Olympia #227/R est:800-1200
£2585 $4110 €3800 Fabric seller in the East (30x47cm-12x19in) s. board. 18-Mar-3 Finarte, Milan #63/R
£2721 $4327 €4000 Coming back (23x55cm-9x22in) s. board. 18-Mar-3 Finarte, Milan #64/R

RICCIO, Andrea (1470-1532) Italian
Sculpture
£8228 $13000 €13000 Satyr (19cm-7in) gilt pat bronze lit. 29-Nov-2 Semenzato, Venice #521/R est:23000
£3000000 $4710000 €4500000 Bust of the Virgin and child (64cm-25in) terracotta prov.exhib.lit. 10-Dec-2 Sotheby's, London #42/R est:1800000-2500000

RICCIOLINI, Niccolo (1687-?) Italian
Works on paper
£2963 $4800 €4445 Worker falling from scaffolding (22x20cm-9x8in) i. chk pen ink wash. 22-Jan-3 Christie's, Rockefeller NY #41/R

RICCIOLINI, Niccolo (attrib) (1687-?) Italian
Works on paper
£524 $750 €786 Male academy (53x37cm-21x15in) black chk. 23-Jan-3 Swann Galleries, New York #122/R
£1030 $1597 €1545 Sacrifice of Elias. Isiah and the angel (29x22cm-11x9in) i. pen wash pair. 3-Oct-2 Koller, Zurich #3061 est:4000-7000 (S.FR 2400)

RICE, Anne Estelle (1879-1959) American
£900 $1476 €1350 Landscape (46x31cm-18x12in) s. 3-Jun-3 Sotheby's, Olympia #40/R
£3000 $4920 €4500 Beached boats (33x41cm-13x16in) board. 3-Jun-3 Sotheby's, Olympia #39/R est:3000-5000
£3800 $5814 €5700 Tabletop still life (44x54cm-17x21in) init. canvasboard prov. 22-Aug-2 Bonhams, Edinburgh #1184/R est:3000-5000
£3800 $5890 €5700 White cottage with boats. Cottage by a harbour (32x41cm-13x16in) board pair prov. 31-Oct-2 Christie's, London #168/R est:4000-6000

RICE, Henry Webster (1853-1934) American
Works on paper
£346 $550 €519 Chickens feeding before a country cottage (34x48cm-13x19in) s. W/C gouache paperboard. 7-Mar-3 Skinner, Boston #440/R
£480 $700 €720 Rocky bluff (33x50cm-13x20in) s. W/C. 10-May-2 Skinner, Boston #164/R
£1465 $2300 €2198 Summer garden, Castine, Maine (52x35cm-20x14in) s.d.1889 W/C. 22-Nov-2 Skinner, Boston #68/R est:300-500

RICE, Marion (20th C) American
£323 $500 €485 Figures beside lily pond (61x76cm-24x30in) s. 1-Oct-2 Arthur James, Florida #119
£419 $650 €629 Mother and daughter by lily pond (76x91cm-30x36in) s. 1-Oct-2 Arthur James, Florida #120

RICE-PEREIRA, Irene (1907-1971) American
£2532 $4000 €3798 Untitled (91x127cm-36x50in) s. 22-Apr-3 Butterfields, San Francisco #6064/R est:5000-7000
£2805 $4600 €4067 Movement in space (85x106cm-33x42in) s. i.d.verso. 5-Jun-3 Swann Galleries, New York #197/R est:1500-2500
Works on paper
£244 $400 €354 Descent of power or form (94x62cm-37x24in) s.i.d. chl pastel W/C. 5-Jun-3 Swann Galleries, New York #199/R
£258 $400 €387 Untitled (43x58cm-17x23in) s.i.d.53 ink gouache. 25-Sep-2 Doyle, New York #58/R
£290 $475 €421 Abstract movement (30x20cm-12x8in) s. W/C gouache on 2 pieces of card stock exec.c.1960. 5-Jun-3 Swann Galleries, New York #198/R
£335 $550 €486 Exercise in space (23x11cm-9x4in) s. pen ink gouache exec.c.1965 sold with another by the same hand. 5-Jun-3 Swann Galleries, New York #200/R
£343 $542 €515 Bathers (91x61cm-36x24in) s. mixed media paper on masonite. 18-Nov-2 Waddingtons, Toronto #7/R (C.D 850)
£457 $750 €663 Abstract composition (23x15cm-9x6in) s. gouache exec.c.1966 sold with a book. 5-Jun-3 Swann Galleries, New York #201/R

RICH, A N (19/20th C) British
Works on paper
£280 $426 €420 On the Medway (28x51cm-11x20in) s.d.1893 i.verso W/C. 14-Aug-2 Andrew Hartley, Ilkley #584

RICH, Graham D (1946-) British
£260 $426 €390 Balcony window (20x25cm-8x10in) s.i.d.2000verso wood. 2-Jun-3 David Duggleby, Scarborough #339

RICH, James Rogers (1847-1910) American
£1562 $2500 €2265 Sphinx (45x60cm-18x24in) s.d.1895 prov. 16-May-3 Skinner, Boston #354/R est:500-700

RICH, John Hubbard (1876-1954) American
£6051 $9500 €9077 Portrait of a young woman (77x63cm-30x25in) s. prov. 19-Nov-2 Butterfields, San Francisco #8264/R est:6000-8000

RICHARD, Achille (20th C) French
£278 $453 €400 Nature morte au vase en faience (35x22cm-14x9in) s. 19-Jul-3 Thierry & Lannon, Brest #381

RICHARD, Alexandre Louis Marie Theodore (1782-1859) French
£2838 $4427 €4200 Paysage de riviere anime de baigneurs (31x28cm-12x11in) mono. 28-Mar-3 Piasa, Paris #61/R

RICHARD, Alexandre Louis Marie Theodore (attrib) (1782-1859) French
£1026 $1610 €1600 Pecheurs au bord de lac (23x31cm-9x12in) bears sig.d.1841. 25-Nov-2 Rieunier, Bailly-Pommery, Mathias, Paris #3/R

RICHARD, Alfred Pierre (?-1884) French
Sculpture
£2069 $3310 €3000 Colombine a l'eventail (60cm-24in) s. 17-Mar-3 Horta, Bruxelles #154 est:3500-4500

RICHARD, Durando Togo (1910-) ?
£2318 $3778 €3500 Jeune femme au tambourin (61x49cm-24x19in) s. 31-Jan-3 Rabourdin & Choppin de Janvry, Paris #147/R

RICHARD, Edna Vergon (1890-1985) American
£274 $425 €411 Still life (76x76cm-30x30in) s. painted c.1935. 8-Dec-2 Toomey, Oak Park #618/R

RICHARD, Edouard (1883-?) French
£417 $679 €600 Les marins sur le quai (18x24cm-7x9in) s. panel. 19-Jul-3 Thierry & Lannon, Brest #383
£451 $736 €650 Les marins aux paniers (18x24cm-7x9in) s. panel. 19-Jul-3 Thierry & Lannon, Brest #382
£556 $906 €800 Pardon de Notre Dame de la joie a St Guenole (37x57cm-15x22in) s. panel. 19-Jul-3 Thierry & Lannon, Brest #171/R
£590 $962 €850 Bretonnes en discussion devant l'eglise (27x35cm-11x14in) s. panel. 19-Jul-3 Thierry & Lannon, Brest #170

RICHARD, Herve (20th C) French
Works on paper
£321 $506 €500 Trois-mats longeant la coste (32x23cm-13x9in) s. W/C. 12-Nov-2 Thierry & Lannon, Brest #87/R

RICHARD, Leonard (1945-) Norwegian
£2249 $3554 €3374 Mysterious happenings (60x146cm-24x57in) init.d.89 s.d.1988 stretcher exhib. 2-Dec-2 Blomqvist, Oslo #476/R est:40000-60000 (N.KR 26000)
Works on paper
£5724 $8930 €8586 The sunny wall I and II (135x91cm-53x36in) s.d.29 IV 86 stretcher collage oil panel exhib. 21-Oct-2 Blomqvist, Oslo #417/R est:40000-60000 (N.KR 66000)

RICHARD, Maurice (20th C) Swiss
£346 $537 €519 Still life with fish (73x50cm-29x20in) s. 24-Sep-2 Koller, Zurich #6739 (S.FR 800)

RICHARD, René (1895-1982) Canadian
£494 $760 €741 Montagne (25x30cm-10x12in) s. isorel. 22-Oct-2 Iegor de Saint Hippolyte, Montreal #85 (C.D 1200)
£605 $986 €908 Riverbank (24x29cm-9x11in) s. panel. 12-Feb-3 Iegor de Saint Hippolyte, Montreal #155 (C.D 1500)
£968 $1510 €1452 Paysage du Manitoba (20x25cm-8x10in) s. s.i.d.1933 verso isorel. 30-Jul-2 Iegor de Saint Hippolyte, Montreal #127 (C.D 2400)
£1033 $1622 €1550 Baie St. Paul, Quebec (41x51cm-16x20in) s. board. 24-Jul-2 Walker's, Ottawa #237/R est:2500-3000 (C.D 2500)
£1067 $1749 €1601 Baie St. Paul, Que (22x30cm-9x12in) s. panel. 3-Jun-3 Joyner, Toronto #284/R est:1200-1500 (C.D 2400)
£1129 $1840 €1694 Charlevoix scene (33x28cm-13x11in) s. 12-Feb-3 Iegor de Saint Hippolyte, Montreal #156 (C.D 2800)
£1140 $1699 €1710 Les eboulements (41x51cm-16x20in) s. isorel. 26-Jun-2 Iegor de Saint Hippolyte, Montreal #76 (C.D 2600)
£1756 $2757 €2634 Barns in a Quebec landscape (41x51cm-16x20in) s. board. 24-Jul-2 Walker's, Ottawa #236/R est:2500-3000 (C.D 4250)
£2311 $3790 €3467 Near Baie St. Paul (54x69cm-21x27in) s. board. 3-Jun-3 Joyner, Toronto #165/R est:4000-6000 (C.D 5200)
£2479 $3893 €3719 Scene Du Nord (81x86cm-32x34in) s.i. s.verso board. 24-Jul-2 Walker's, Ottawa #422/R est:7000-8000 (C.D 6000)
£2621 $4141 €3932 Maison Joe Simard, de Sorel a Baie St. Paul (53x66cm-21x26in) s.i.d.1960 board prov. 14-Nov-2 Heffel, Vancouver #166/R est:7000-9000 (C.D 6500)
£3226 $5097 €4839 Est de la baie ungava, Chutes de Riviere, Korok (61x80cm-24x31in) s. i.d.1953 verso board prov. 14-Nov-2 Heffel, Vancouver #243/R est:8500-9500 (C.D 8000)

RICHARDE, Ludvig (1862-1929) Swedish
£391 $625 €567 Seascape (37x96cm-15x38in) s.d.95. 18-May-3 Anders Antik, Landskrona #17 (S.KR 5000)
£849 $1316 €1350 Sailing boat and fishermen (23x39cm-9x15in) s.d.87. 6-Oct-2 Bukowskis, Helsinki #344/R

RICHARDS, Ceri (1903-1971) British
£5000 $8350 €7250 Cathedrale Engloutie (151x61cm-59x24in) s.d.60. 24-Jun-3 Bonhams, New Bond Street #104/R est:5000-7000

£6000 $9300 €9000 Rape of the Sabines (32x41cm-13x16in) s.d.48. 4-Dec-2 Sotheby's, London #66/R est:6000-8000
£7000 $10990 €10500 Musique de Cathedrale Engbutie (126x100cm-50x39in) s.d.62 stretcher prov. 20-Nov-2 Sotheby's, Olympia #78/R est:2000-3000
£8000 $12480 €12000 La cathedrale engloute (76x76cm-30x30in) s.i.d.1960 oil collage on board prov.exhib. 27-Mar-3 Christie's, Kensington #656/R est:4000-6000
£70000 $114800 €101500 Music room, composition in red and black (102x91cm-40x36in) s.d.51 prov.lit. 4-Jun-3 Sotheby's, London #33/R est:15000-20000

Works on paper

£550 $886 €825 Garden with bridge (48x67cm-19x26in) s.d. June 30/59 pen ink. 14-Jan-3 Bonhams, Knightsbridge #13/R
£1300 $2028 €1950 La cathedrale engloute (16x13cm-6x5in) s.d.60 pen ink W/C. 27-Mar-3 Christie's, Kensington #655/R est:600-800
£1400 $2184 €2100 Embrace (20x33cm-8x13in) s.d.1947 pen black ink crayon. 27-Mar-3 Christie's, Kensington #574/R est:700-1000
£1600 $2480 €2400 Homage to Dylan Thomas (39x56cm-15x22in) s.d.54 pen brush black ink prov. 4-Dec-2 Christie's, Kensington #328/R est:1500-2000
£2200 $3498 €3300 Pianist (37x54cm-15x21in) s.d.54 W/C. 26-Feb-3 Sotheby's, Olympia #165/R est:1500-2000
£3600 $5724 €5400 Prometheus (36x46cm-14x18in) s.d.July 30 pen ink W/C prov. 26-Feb-3 Sotheby's, Olympia #175/R est:2000-3000
£4500 $7155 €6750 Pianist 3 (33x49cm-13x19in) s.d.58 ink W/C prov. 26-Feb-3 Sotheby's, Olympia #180/R est:2500-3500
£6500 $10660 €9750 Girls at a piano (37x49cm-15x19in) s.d.1943 pen ink crayon W/C bodycol. 6-Jun-3 Christie's, London #104/R est:4000-6000

RICHARDS, Charles (1906-1992) American

£321 $500 €482 Picnic (30x33cm-12x13in) s.d.71. 12-Oct-2 Neal Auction Company, New Orleans #1384a
£519 $850 €753 Donna bath series II (71x56cm-28x22in) i.d.July 1988. 7-Jun-3 Neal Auction Company, New Orleans #416/R
£732 $1200 €1098 Crabs (23x28cm-9x11in) s. canvas on masonite prov. 8-Feb-3 Neal Auction Company, New Orleans #394
£839 $1300 €1259 Reclining nude (46x61cm-18x24in) s. 7-Dec-2 Neal Auction Company, New Orleans #500/R
£1341 $2200 €2012 Pass Christian, Mississippi (33x46cm-13x18in) s. prov. 8-Feb-3 Neal Auction Company, New Orleans #392/R est:1500-2500
£2885 $4500 €4328 Morning call, French quarter (43x61cm-17x24in) s. prov. 12-Oct-2 Neal Auction Company, New Orleans #657/R est:2000-3000

RICHARDS, Frank (1863-1935) British

£480 $730 €720 Mediterranean port with hills beyond (33x48cm-13x19in) i.verso board prov. 4-Jul-2 Duke & Son, Dorchester #252/R
£6000 $9300 €9000 Lizard lighthouse (68x88cm-27x35in) s. i.on stretcher. 3-Dec-2 Bonhams, New Bond Street #23/R est:5000-8000

Works on paper

£260 $406 €390 River scene at sunset with ducks (23x28cm-9x11in) s. W/C. 2-Aug-2 Biddle & Webb, Birmingham #323
£2200 $3410 €3300 Young girl seated on a chair before a Newlyn cottage window (46x30cm-18x12in) s.d.1890 W/C. 26-Sep-2 Lane, Penzance #282 est:1500-2000

RICHARDS, Frederick Thompson (1864-1921) American

£3247 $5000 €4871 Life cover magazine, Christmas 1904 (48x38cm-19x15in) s. canvasboard prov. 24-Oct-2 Shannon's, Milford #123/R est:5000-7000

RICHARDS, Frederick de Berg (1822-1903) American

£6013 $9500 €9020 Sailing along the coast (46x91cm-18x36in) s. 24-Apr-3 Shannon's, Milford #157/R est:10000-15000

RICHARDS, John Inigo (?-1810) British

£300 $495 €435 Drover with cattle in a landscape (12x19cm-5x7in) card. 2-Jul-3 Sotheby's, Olympia #81/R
£3000 $4680 €4500 Maid of the mill (30x36cm-12x14in) panel prov. 26-Mar-3 Hamptons Fine Art, Godalming #161/R est:3000-4000

Works on paper

£360 $594 €522 Country landscape with wood choppers in the foreground (20x25cm-8x10in) mono.d.1800 W/C. 3-Jul-3 Duke & Son, Dorchester #158

RICHARDS, John Inigo (circle) (?-1810) British

£13000 $20540 €19500 Wooded landscape with figures, ruins and harbour in distance (93x136cm-37x54in) prov. 26-Nov-2 Christie's, London #52/R est:6000-8000

RICHARDS, L (19th C) British

£720 $1152 €1080 Haymaking scene on the Arun, Sussex (29x39cm-11x15in) s. 15-May-3 Lawrence, Crewkerne #995

RICHARDS, Lucy Currier (20th C) American

Sculpture

£3774 $6000 €5661 Decorative sundial (32cm-13in) i. brown pat. bronze i.f.Roman. 4-Mar-3 Christie's, Rockefeller NY #38/R est:4000-6000

RICHARDS, R P (1840-1877) British

£650 $1034 €975 River landscape (25x41cm-10x16in) s. panel. 19-Mar-3 John Nicholson, Haslemere #1178

RICHARDS, Thomas Miles (jnr) (19th C) British

Works on paper

£300 $474 €435 Bowness, Windermere (24x35cm-9x14in) i. W/C htd white. 22-Jul-3 Bonhams, Knightsbridge #94/R

RICHARDS, W (19th C) British

£577 $900 €866 Fisherfolk with the day's catch (30x51cm-12x20in) s. pair. 14-Sep-2 Selkirks, St. Louis #202

RICHARDS, William (?) ?

£289 $454 €434 Unloading the catch (51x74cm-20x29in) s. 24-Jul-2 Walker's, Ottawa #23/R (C.D 700)

RICHARDS, William Trost (1833-1905) American

£1290 $2000 €1935 Lofoten Island with mountains and heavy sea (8x13cm-3x5in) s. oil on card. 2-Nov-2 North East Auctions, Portsmouth #7/R
£1419 $2200 €2129 Mullen Cove, Cornwall (13x25cm-5x10in) s.i.verso. 2-Nov-2 North East Auctions, Portsmouth #9/R
£1806 $2800 €2709 Spring landscapes (8x15cm-3x6in) i. oil on card two. 2-Nov-2 North East Auctions, Portsmouth #10/R
£1871 $2900 €2807 Harbor with city in background (8x13cm-3x5in) i. oil on card. 2-Nov-2 North East Auctions, Portsmouth #8/R
£2903 $4500 €4355 From my room window, Briefond Hotel. Vesteraalen Island. Breaking surf (8x13cm-3x5in) i. oil on card set of three. 2-Nov-2 North East Auctions, Portsmouth #6/R
£3892 $6500 €5643 Two boaters on a lake (14x23cm-6x9in) panel prov. 18-Jun-3 Christie's, Los Angeles #21/R est:8000-12000
£4430 $7000 €6645 Vesuvius in winter (20x41cm-8x16in) s.d.93 i.verso board. 24-Apr-3 Shannon's, Milford #100/R est:5000-7000
£4459 $7000 €6689 Breaking waves (14x23cm-6x9in) s. panel prov. 19-Nov-2 Butterfields, San Francisco #8005/R est:6000-8000
£6329 $10000 €9494 Sunset over the cliffs (13x23cm-5x9in) s.d.98 panel prov. 24-Apr-3 Shannon's, Milford #156/R est:8000-12000
£7143 $11000 €10715 Breaking waves (18x30cm-7x12in) s. board. 24-Oct-2 Shannon's, Milford #89/R est:6000-8000
£7742 $12000 €11613 Seascape. Landscape in Callender, Scotland (13x23cm-5x9in) s. panel two. 2-Nov-2 North East Auctions, Portsmouth #11/R
£9877 $16000 €14816 Harbor at Monhegan (14x23cm-6x9in) init.i.verso board prov. 21-May-3 Sotheby's, New York #181/R est:8000-12000
£10317 $16300 €15476 Whiteface mountain, summer (25x41cm-10x16in) s. panel on masonite prov. 24-Apr-3 Shannon's, Milford #40/R est:20000-30000
£12025 $19000 €18038 Whiteface mountain, Spring (25x38cm-10x15in) s. canvasboard prov. 24-Apr-3 Shannon's, Milford #134/R est:15000-25000
£12903 $20000 €19355 On the shore (57x43cm-22x17in) s.d.89 prov. 4-Dec-2 Sotheby's, New York #137/R est:25000-35000
£19355 $30000 €29033 Roxborough baptist church (30x42cm-12x17in) s. indis d.1861 prov. 4-Dec-2 Sotheby's, New York #105/R est:30000-50000
£27420 $42500 €41130 Leverington cemetery (36x51cm-14x20in) s.d.1861 prov. 4-Dec-2 Sotheby's, New York #104/R est:30000-50000
£27742 $43000 €41613 Beach scene, foggy day (15x43cm-6x17in) s.d.1885 board prov. 2-Nov-2 North East Auctions, Portsmouth #18/R
£29032 $45000 €43548 Seascapes (22x41cm-9x16in) s.d.1900 board pair. 4-Dec-2 Sotheby's, New York #122/R est:12000-18000
£40123 $65000 €60185 Break in the storm (43x69cm-17x27in) s.d.03. 21-May-3 Sotheby's, New York #195/R est:60000-80000
£51613 $80000 €77420 Flora (19x15cm-7x6in) s.d.1859 panel. 4-Dec-2 Sotheby's, New York #108/R est:15000-20000
£72327 $115000 €108491 Sunlit waves (71x122cm-28x48in) s.d.03. 7-Mar-3 Skinner, Boston #333/R est:175000-275000

Works on paper

£1161 $1800 €1742 Land's End (34x41cm-13x16in) indis.i. W/C prov. 3-Dec-2 Christie's, Rockefeller NY #600/R est:2000-3000
£1461 $2250 €2192 Adirondack Lake (15x23cm-6x9in) s. W/C prov. 24-Oct-2 Shannon's, Milford #197/R est:1200-1800
£2848 $4500 €4272 Rocky coast (38x64cm-15x25in) s.d.97. 24-Apr-3 Shannon's, Milford #102/R est:5000-7000
£4403 $7000 €6605 Pulpit Rock, Nahant (15x13cm-6x5in) init.i.d.76 W/C. 5-Mar-3 Christie's, Rockefeller NY #89/R est:2500-3500
£4717 $7500 €7076 Along the coast. Sailboats by the coast. Rocky shore. Ruins on the coast (16x24cm-6x9in) s. W/C pencil set of four prov. 5-Mar-3 Christie's, Rockefeller NY #90/R est:5000-7000

£19108 $30000 €28662 Moonlight, twin lights in the distance, possibly Thatcher Island (58x94cm-23x37in) s.d.1878 W/C gouache. 22-Nov-2 Skinner, Boston #125/R est:20000-40000
£22581 $35000 €33872 Gull rock, Newport (23x35cm-9x14in) s.d.1876 W/C gouache prov.exhib.lit. 3-Dec-2 Phillips, New York #36/R est:30000-50000
£30864 $50000 €46296 Seascape (28x41cm-11x16in) s.d.1874 W/C gouache prov. 21-May-3 Sotheby's, New York #189/R est:20000-30000

RICHARDS, William Trost (attrib) (1833-1905) American
£577 $900 €866 Off shore wind (30x56cm-12x22in) bears sig. 20-Sep-2 Freeman, Philadelphia #113/R

RICHARDSON, Anne Worsham (20th C) American
Works on paper
£1097 $1700 €1646 Red cardinal in pine (36x25cm-14x10in) s.d.1947 W/C artist board. 28-Sep-2 Charlton Hall, Columbia #617/R est:2000-3000

RICHARDSON, Constance Coleman (1905-) American
£542 $850 €813 Morning in the wild country (46x81cm-18x32in) s.d.1958 board. 20-Nov-2 Boos Gallery, Michigan #412/R

RICHARDSON, Edward (1810-1874) British
Works on paper
£560 $874 €840 On the Rhine (22x31cm-9x12in) s.d.1856 W/C bodycol. 6-Nov-2 Bonhams, Chester #393
£750 $1163 €1125 Busy Victorian street scene with ruined tower in foreground (22x32cm-9x13in) s.d.1867 W/C. 24-Sep-2 Anderson & Garland, Newcastle #366/R

RICHARDSON, Francis Henry (1859-1934) American
£542 $850 €813 Open pasture, winter (26x34cm-10x13in) s. board. 22-Nov-2 Skinner, Boston #288/R

RICHARDSON, Frederic Stuart (1855-1934) British
£1230 $1918 €1845 Retour des pecheurs (61x101cm-24x40in) s. 10-Sep-2 Iegor de Saint Hippolyte, Montreal #97 (C.D 3000)
Works on paper
£550 $897 €825 River in full spate (50x75cm-20x30in) s. W/C. 29-Jan-3 Sotheby's, Olympia #150/R
£600 $972 €900 Evening view, possibly Whitby (36x45cm-14x18in) s. W/C. 21-Jan-3 Bonhams, Knightsbridge #231/R
£620 $967 €930 Farm along Egton Road (23x34cm-9x13in) s.i.verso W/C. 10-Sep-2 David Duggleby, Scarborough #191
£1050 $1638 €1575 Shrimping on the Yorkshire coast (30x48cm-12x19in) s. W/C. 20-Sep-2 Richardson & Smith, Whitby #107 est:900-1200
£1500 $2340 €2250 Whitby Harbour (36x45cm-14x18in) s. W/C bodycol htd white on board. 25-Mar-3 Bonhams, Leeds #506/R est:1500-2000

RICHARDSON, H Linley (1878-1947) New Zealander
Works on paper
£398 $625 €597 Portrait of a Maori woman (38x28cm-15x11in) s. chl dr. 10-Dec-2 Peter Webb, Auckland #99/R est:1200-1800 (NZ.D 1250)

RICHARDSON, Henry Burdon (1826-1874) British
Works on paper
£360 $572 €540 Vessels off a jetty (21x32cm-8x13in) W/C over pencil. 5-Mar-3 Bonhams, Bury St Edmunds #262

RICHARDSON, John Frederick (1906-1998) American
£274 $425 €411 Bluffs along the Mississipi (76x102cm-30x40in) s. acrylic painted c.1960. 8-Dec-2 Toomey, Oak Park #783/R
£645 $1000 €968 Oak Creek Canyon (66x91cm-26x36in) s. acrylic painted c.1960. 8-Dec-2 Toomey, Oak Park #785/R
£710 $1100 €1065 Rock formations, Arizona (56x86cm-22x34in) s. painted c.1960. 8-Dec-2 Toomey, Oak Park #782/R
£764 $1200 €1146 Town in winter (81x112cm-32x44in) s. 14-Dec-2 Charlton Hall, Columbia #491/R est:400-600
£968 $1500 €1452 Starved rock state park (76x102cm-30x40in) s. acrylic painted c.1960. 8-Dec-2 Toomey, Oak Park #784/R est:1500-2500

RICHARDSON, Jonathan (snr-attrib) (1665-1745) British
£1000 $1580 €1500 Portrait of William Harvey (76x64cm-30x25in) 17-Dec-2 Gorringes, Lewes #1426/R

RICHARDSON, Ray (1964-) British
£1500 $2325 €2250 Someone is ripping me off (35x35cm-14x14in) s. i.d.1995-96 on overlap. 3-Dec-2 Bonhams, New Bond Street #129/R est:2000-3000

RICHARDSON, Sir Albert (1880-1964) British
Works on paper
£400 $632 €600 Visiting day, Ham House (27x37cm-11x15in) init.d.1955 W/C. 27-Nov-2 Sotheby's, Olympia #246/R

RICHARDSON, Theodore J (1855-1914) American
£656 $1050 €984 Alaskan valley glacier and river inlet (43x25cm-17x10in) s. 16-May-3 York Town, York #958
Works on paper
£290 $450 €435 View of steamship before a glacier in Alaska. W/C. 3-Nov-2 Van Blarcom, South Natick #101
£4605 $7000 €6908 Coastal view of Sitka, Alaska, with schooner and canoes (38x53cm-15x21in) s. W/C exec.c.1884 lit. 17-Aug-2 North East Auctions, Portsmouth #837/R est:7000-10000

RICHARDSON, Thomas Miles (jnr) (1813-1890) British
£1450 $2262 €2175 Scottish landscape (32x55cm-13x22in) s. 25-Mar-3 Gildings, Market Harborough #388 est:1500-2000
Works on paper
£360 $590 €540 Castle of Baden (27x37cm-11x15in) init.i.d.1846 bodycol wash. 4-Jun-3 Bonhams, Chester #425
£500 $810 €725 Coastal landscape with figures on a cliff top path (24x36cm-9x14in) s.d.1879 W/C. 20-May-3 Dreweatt Neate, Newbury #230/R
£580 $899 €870 Busy cottage, Jesmond Dene, Newcastle (21x34cm-8x13in) i.indis.d.183 col wash Chinese white. 24-Sep-2 Anderson & Garland, Newcastle #385/R
£620 $1035 €899 Schiehallion, from Loch Rannock, Perthshire (15x22cm-6x9in) init.d.1886 W/C. 25-Jun-3 Bonhams, Bury St Edmunds #479/R
£680 $1061 €1020 Weymouth Castle (20x32cm-8x13in) init. W/C. 6-Nov-2 Bonhams, Chester #392
£750 $1155 €1125 Among the Borromean Islands (15x23cm-6x9in) s.d.1884 W/C. 22-Oct-2 Bonhams, Knightsbridge #45/R
£1250 $1950 €1875 Entrance to Glencoe (11x29cm-4x11in) s. W/C white htd sold with a companion. 10-Apr-3 Bonhams, Edinburgh #168 est:600-800
£1300 $2158 €1950 Travelers on a Continental track (34x67cm-13x26in) s.d.1888 W/C htd white. 12-Jun-3 Bonhams, New Bond Street #626a/R est:1000-1500
£1750 $2923 €2538 Mt. Giuliano, Sicily (41x62cm-16x24in) s. indis d. W/C. 17-Jun-3 Anderson & Garland, Newcastle #320a/R est:1800-2400
£2500 $4100 €3750 St. Guilono, Sicily (43x60cm-17x24in) s.d.1859 W/C. 4-Jun-3 Bonhams, Chester #426/R est:1800-2500
£2800 $4592 €4200 Genoa (34x68cm-13x27in) s.d.1860 W/C htd white. 4-Feb-3 Bonhams, Leeds #297 est:2000-3000
£5800 $9512 €8700 Shooting part in the Highlands (62x90cm-24x35in) s.d.1853 W/C. 4-Jun-3 Bonhams, Chester #423/R est:2000-3000
£7500 $11625 €11250 Foot of Loch Katrine, Perthshire (77x111cm-30x44in) s.d.1880 pencil W/C htd white prov. 31-Oct-2 Christie's, London #75/R est:8000-12000
£12097 $19113 €18146 Edinburgh from the Grassmarket (67x98cm-26x39in) init.d.1869 W/C htd white. 18-Nov-2 Waddingtons, Toronto #78/R est:10000-15000 (C.D 30000)

RICHARDSON, Thomas Miles (jnr-attrib) (1813-1890) British
Works on paper
£300 $474 €450 Loch Awe (15x25cm-6x10in) W/C scratching out. 2-Dec-2 Bonhams, Bath #9
£600 $948 €900 Continental view of figures on a pathway overlooking a bay (20x30cm-8x12in) W/C. 18-Dec-2 Mallams, Oxford #542/R

RICHARDSON, Thomas Miles (snr) (1784-1848) British
Works on paper
£420 $664 €630 Stone quarry near Keswick, with a group of figures in the foreground (30x45cm-12x18in) init.i.d.1840 W/C over pencil htd white. 2-Dec-2 Bonhams, Bath #7
£460 $713 €690 Dunstanffnage castle, Lismore in the distance (22x34cm-9x13in) init.i.d.1836 col wash. 24-Sep-2 Anderson & Garland, Newcastle #381
£550 $875 €825 Robinson Place, Langdale (23x34cm-9x13in) s.i. W/C over pencil htd bodycol. 19-Mar-3 Sotheby's, London #175

RICHARDSON, Thomas Miles (snr-attrib) (1784-1848) British
Works on paper
£380 $635 €551 Father and daughter fishing from a river bank (22x32cm-9x13in) indis sig. W/C. 17-Jun-3 Anderson & Garland, Newcastle #275

RICHARDSON, Zetta Behne (1873-1964) American
£219 $350 €329 Portrait of a lady with roses (114x75cm-45x30in) s.d.1898. 18-May-3 Butterfields, Los Angeles #7042

RICHARDT, Ferdinand (1819-1895) Danish
£250 $400 €363 Figures before a great house with kennel and dogs (28x37cm-11x15in) s.i.d.1878 canvasboard. 16-May-3 Skinner, Boston #40/R
£1288 $2034 €1932 The fire at Frederiksborg Palace in 18?? (26x39cm-10x15in) 13-Nov-2 Kunsthallen, Copenhagen #108/R est:10000 (D.KR 15000)
£1550 $2357 €2325 Branch of white fruit blossom against black background (22x26cm-9x10in) s.d.1868. 27-Aug-2 Rasmussen, Copenhagen #1798/R est:6000-8000 (D.KR 18000)
£2207 $3554 €3311 Summer's day at Vorgaard (60x84cm-24x33in) s.d.1846. 22-Feb-3 Rasmussen, Havnen #2111/R est:10000-15000 (D.KR 24500)
£31869 $48441 €47804 Niagara Falls seen from the ferry to Canada on a summer's day (93x158cm-37x62in) s.d.1865 exhib. 27-Aug-2 Rasmussen, Copenhagen #1433/R est:250000-350000 (D.KR 370000)

RICHARDT, Ferdinand (attrib) (1819-1895) Danish
£378 $609 €567 Regensgarden (17x20cm-7x8in) s.verso painted c.1840 prov. 26-Feb-3 Museumsbygningen, Copenhagen #25 (D.KR 4200)
£478 $775 €693 Lovenborg near Holbaek (25x32cm-10x13in) study. 26-May-3 Rasmussen, Copenhagen #1293/R (D.KR 5000)

RICHE, I S J le (attrib) (18th C) French
£1000 $1550 €1500 Hyacinths in a glass vase on a marble ledge (35x32cm-14x13in) canvas on panel. 30-Oct-2 Bonhams, New Bond Street #6/R est:1000-1500

RICHENBERG, Robert (1917-) American
£641 $1000 €962 Modern abstract in grey, green and orange (140x135cm-55x53in) s.d.1958 verso impasto. 1-Aug-2 Eldred, East Dennis #1087/R

RICHERT, Charles Henry (1880-?) American
£270 $425 €405 Summer landscape (25x35cm-10x14in) s. board. 22-Nov-2 Skinner, Boston #251/R
Works on paper
£346 $550 €519 Blue mountain (38x51cm-15x20in) s. W/C chl. 29-Apr-3 Doyle, New York #34

RICHES, Charles M (19/20th C) British
£340 $561 €493 English fisherman (24x40cm-9x16in) s. 6-Jul-3 Lots Road, London #342

RICHET, Léon (1847-1907) French
£696 $1100 €1044 Woods (33x41cm-13x16in) panel. 15-Nov-2 Du Mouchelle, Detroit #2118/R
£2128 $3447 €3000 Pond landscape with rowing boat (40x61cm-16x24in) s. 22-May-3 Dorotheum, Vienna #146/R est:3600-4000
£2229 $3500 €3344 Landscape with lone figure walking down a country road (28x38cm-11x15in) s. panel. 23-Nov-2 Pook & Pook, Downington #372/R est:3500-4500
£2979 $4706 €4469 Portrait of the actress Sarah Bernhardt (62x49cm-24x19in) s. 2-Dec-2 Rasmussen, Copenhagen #1201/R est:30000-50000 (D.KR 35000)
£3165 $5000 €5000 La ramasseuse de fagots (68x42cm-27x17in) s.d.76. 1-Dec-2 Peron, Melun #124
£3247 $5000 €4871 Figure in a wooded landscape at sunset (38x61cm-15x24in) s. 4-Sep-2 Christie's, Rockefeller NY #331/R est:8000-12000
£3425 $5342 €5138 Landscape with pond and fisherman (46x34cm-18x13in) s. 28-Mar-3 Koller, Zurich #3138/R est:4000-6000 (S.FR 7500)
£3481 $5396 €5500 Barque sur la riviere (50x65cm-20x26in) s. 29-Sep-2 Eric Pillon, Calais #43/R
£3963 $6500 €5746 Pond with lonely figure (48x64cm-19x25in) s. 7-Jun-3 Neal Auction Company, New Orleans #112/R est:7000-10000
£4200 $6594 €6300 Tranquil lake landscape at dusk (82x145cm-32x57in) s. 21-Nov-2 Christie's, Kensington #8/R est:4000-6000
£4747 $7500 €7500 Mare en foret de Fontainebleau (51x73cm-20x29in) s. 1-Dec-2 Peron, Melun #55
£6849 $10753 €10000 Farm in a summer landscape (41x64cm-16x25in) s.d.72 panel. 15-Apr-3 Sotheby's, Amsterdam #57/R est:6000-8000
£6962 $11000 €10443 Pecheurs au bord d'un lac (45x25cm-18x10in) s. prov. 23-Apr-3 Christie's, Rockefeller NY #68/R est:10000-15000
£9494 $15000 €14241 Pool in a wooded landscape (66x52cm-26x20in) s. 23-Apr-3 Christie's, Rockefeller NY #64/R est:10000-15000

RICHIER, Germaine (1904-1959) French
Sculpture
£2857 $4543 €4200 Femme-coq I (12cm-5in) s. pat bronze Cast Valsuani exhib.lit. 21-Mar-3 Rieunier, Bailly-Pommery, Mathias, Paris #143
£8333 $13750 €12000 Guerrier no 2 (38x9x18cm-15x4x7in) s.num.4/8 pat bronze prov.exhib.lit. 1-Jul-3 Artcurial Briest, Paris #496/R est:12000-15000
£14000 $21560 €21000 L'araignee II, petit (13x7x7cm-5x3x3in) s.num.6/8 bronze i.f.L. Thinot conceived 1946 prov.lit. 22-Oct-2 Sotheby's, London #417/R est:10000-15000
£20253 $32000 €32000 Untitled (60cm-24in) d.1953 lead slate glass. 27-Nov-2 Marc Kohn, Paris #33/R est:35000-50000
£21000 $32340 €31500 Le sablier I (21x17x17cm-8x7x7in) s.num.8/8 i.f L.Thinot prov.lit. 22-Oct-2 Sotheby's, London #407/R est:12000-15000
£25000 $38500 €37500 Don Quichotte a la Lance (36x20x17cm-14x8x7in) s. bronze conceived 1949 prov.lit. 22-Oct-2 Sotheby's, London #408/R est:25000-35000
£27000 $44280 €40500 Le cheval a six tetes, petit (35x30x42cm-14x12x17in) s.num.8/8 gold bronze st.f.L Thinot prov.lit. 7-Feb-3 Sotheby's, London #236/R est:35000-45000
£30000 $46200 €45000 L'araignee I (50x34x17cm-20x13x7in) num.3/8 bronze conceived 1946 prov.exhib.lit. 22-Oct-2 Sotheby's, London #418/R est:20000-30000
£45000 $69300 €67500 Le cheval a six tetes, petit (35x30x42cm-14x12x17in) s.num.3/8 bronze conceived 1952 prov.exhib.lit. 22-Oct-2 Sotheby's, London #399/R est:35000-45000
£80000 $131200 €120000 Grand cheval a six tetes (102x110x48cm-40x43x19in) st.sig.st.f.Thinot num.HC1 bronze prov.lit. 6-Feb-3 Sotheby's, London #24/R est:120000
£100000 $154000 €150000 L'hydre (79x28x32cm-31x11x13in) s.num.6/8 bronze st.f.Valsuani prov.exhib.lit. 22-Oct-2 Sotheby's, London #411/R est:60000-80000
£110000 $169400 €165000 La mante, moyenne (69x16x37cm-27x6x15in) s.num.1/8 bronze st.f.Valsuani conceived 1946 prov.exhib.lit. 22-Oct-2 Sotheby's, London #393/R est:70000-90000
£170000 $261800 €255000 La fourmi (104x94x55cm-41x37x22in) s.num.5/6 bronze i.f.L.Thinot conceived 1953 prov.lit. 22-Oct-2 Sotheby's, London #439/R est:150000-200000

RICHIER, Ligier (attrib) (1500-1566) French
Works on paper
£2848 $4500 €4500 Un soldat attaque par trois hommes. Un homme taillant un morceau de bois (20x29cm-8x11in) i. pen brown ink double-sided prov.lit. 27-Nov-2 Christie's, Paris #125/R est:5000-7000

RICHIR, Herman (1866-1942) Belgian
£353 $554 €550 Jardin de lar rue de Vincotte (25x20cm-10x8in) s. panel. 19-Nov-2 Galerie Moderne, Brussels #208/R
£476 $757 €700 Nature morte aux fleurs (43x36cm-17x14in) s. 18-Mar-3 Vanderkindere, Brussels #104
Works on paper
£475 $741 €750 Imperia (40x32cm-16x13in) s. pastel cardboard. 15-Oct-2 Horta, Bruxelles #370
£863 $1381 €1200 Elegante au miroir (39x29cm-15x11in) s. pastel. 13-May-3 Palais de Beaux Arts, Brussels #120/R

RICHLER, Franz (19th C) ?
£300 $489 €450 Figures and cattle in a landscape (36x47cm-14x19in) i.d.1820. 12-Feb-3 Bonhams, Knightsbridge #21d

RICHMOND, D K (20th C) ?
Works on paper
£762 $1166 €1143 Spring in the west country (39x28cm-15x11in) init. W/C. 21-Aug-2 Dunbar Sloane, Auckland #93/R est:3700-5000 (NZ.D 2500)

RICHMOND, Dorothy Kate (1861-1935) New Zealander
£608 $948 €912 Feeding the pigs (37x39cm-15x15in) board. 17-Sep-2 Peter Webb, Auckland #172/R est:2000-4000 (NZ.D 2000)

£6897 $10759 €10346 Lady of the lilies (64x47cm-25x19in) s.d.1900. 7-Nov-2 International Art Centre, Auckland #58/R est:20000-30000 (NZ.D 22000)

Works on paper

£320 $454 €480 Homestead garden (34x51cm-13x20in) s. W/C prov. 21-Nov-1 Watson's, Christchurch #53/R (NZ.D 1100)
£606 $933 €909 Rural landscape (24x34cm-9x13in) s.d.1927 W/C. 4-Sep-2 Dunbar Sloane, Wellington #64 est:2000-3000 (NZ.D 2000)
£1060 $1707 €1590 Farm scene with grazing sheep (22x27cm-9x11in) s.d.26 W/C. 7-May-3 Dunbar Sloane, Auckland #34/R (NZ.D 3000)

RICHMOND, George (1809-1896) British

£22000 $34760 €33000 Self portrait (60x49cm-24x19in) prov.exhib. 28-Nov-2 Sotheby's, London #191/R est:8000-12000
£26000 $41080 €39000 Portrait of Beilby Richard Lawley, 2nd Baron Wenlock on terrace (236x145cm-93x57in) s.d.1870 prov.exhib.lit. 26-Nov-2 Christie's, London #180/R est:20000-30000

Works on paper

£250 $418 €363 Head study, possibly of George Eliot (33x26cm-13x10in) pencil white chk. 25-Jun-3 Cheffins, Cambridge #692
£650 $1014 €975 Portrait of Anne Sapte, nee Walker (32x24cm-13x9in) s.d.1836 W/C. 5-Nov-2 Bonhams, New Bond Street #97/R
£650 $1014 €975 Portrait of a young gentleman seated (39x31cm-15x12in) W/C htd white. 5-Nov-2 Bonhams, New Bond Street #98/R
£806 $1250 €1209 Portraits of Mr Hedley Vicars and Mrs Elizabeth Vicars (33x24cm-13x9in) one s. pencil W/C htd white pair corners cut. 29-Oct-2 Sotheby's, New York #122/R est:2500-3500
£900 $1431 €1350 Portrait of a young man (31x21cm-12x8in) W/C over pen htd bodycol prov. 19-Mar-3 Sotheby's, London #122/R
£950 $1482 €1425 Portrait of a young fusilier officer (34x25cm-13x10in) s.d.1836. 5-Nov-2 Bonhams, New Bond Street #96/R
£1013 $1600 €1520 Portrait of a young lady in a white dress with blue sash, on a terrace (51x40cm-20x16in) s.i.d.1859 pencil W/C htd white prov. 24-Apr-3 Sotheby's, New York #181/R est:1000-1500
£1200 $1872 €1800 Portrait of lady (48x32cm-19x13in) W/C. 5-Nov-2 Bonhams, New Bond Street #95/R est:1200-1800
£1550 $2542 €2325 Portrait of a young lady in a white dress with red paisley shawl (56x41cm-22x16in) W/C htd white. 4-Feb-3 Bonhams, Leeds #272 est:1200-1800
£1600 $2528 €2400 Portrait of Colonel Cust. Portrait of a gentleman, member of the Cust family (59x45cm-23x18in) s. col chks pair. 28-Nov-2 Sotheby's, London #221/R est:1000-1500
£2000 $3120 €3000 Portrait of Mr V Woodcock (29x24cm-11x9in) s.i.indis d. W/C prov.exhib. 5-Nov-2 Bonhams, New Bond Street #93/R est:2000-3000
£2200 $3608 €3190 Portrait of a young boy (34x25cm-13x10in) s.d.1842 pencil W/C htd white. 5-Jun-3 Christie's, London #137/R est:2000-3000
£3548 $5500 €5322 Portrait of William Benson. Seated gentleman (59x45cm-23x18in) s.d.1855 pencil black white chk two prov. 29-Oct-2 Sotheby's, New York #124/R est:2000-3000

RICHMOND, Leonard (1889-1965) British

£300 $498 €435 St Malo beach (51x61cm-20x24in) 10-Jun-3 David Lay, Penzance #26
£400 $660 €580 River Barle (49x59cm-19x23in) s. i.on stretcher. 1-Jul-3 Bearnes, Exeter #535/R
£581 $900 €872 River, Menton, France (41x51cm-16x20in) s. canvasboard. 21-Jul-2 Jeffery Burchard, Florida #24a/R
£700 $1092 €1015 River Wey, Guildford, Surrey (51x61cm-20x24in) s. i.verso. 27-Mar-3 Lane, Penzance #253

Works on paper

£260 $408 €390 River and bridge in a mountain landscape (46x61cm-18x24in) s. pastel. 10-Dec-2 Lane, Penzance #307
£320 $502 €480 Potminster Beach St. Ives (46x61cm-18x24in) pastel. 10-Dec-2 Lane, Penzance #306

RICHMOND, Sir William Blake (1842-1921) British

£320 $499 €480 On the slopes of Subasio, near Carceri (37x61cm-15x24in) init. panel exhib. 8-Apr-3 Bonhams, Knightsbridge #185/R
£350 $553 €525 Spello, Italy (39x30cm-15x12in) s.verso panel. 1-Dec-2 Lots Road, London #351
£480 $787 €720 On the slopes of Subasio, near Carceri (38x62cm-15x24in) init. panel exhib. 29-May-3 Christie's, Kensington #208/R
£12000 $19320 €18000 Perseus and Andromeda (91x70cm-36x28in) panel prov.exhib.lit. 20-Feb-3 Christie's, London #143/R est:25000

Works on paper

£250 $388 €375 Male nude swooping through the air (25x20cm-10x8in) red chk over pencil. 9-Dec-2 Bonhams, New Bond Street #3
£260 $421 €390 Study of hands (16x23cm-6x9in) s.i.d.March 12 1862 pencil. 21-May-3 Bonhams, Knightsbridge #252
£419 $650 €629 Rebecca at the well (28x23cm-11x9in) i.verso dr. 2-Nov-2 North East Auctions, Portsmouth #399

RICHMOND, Thomas (snr) (1771-1837) British

Miniatures

£1100 $1727 €1650 Naval officer (7cm-3in) s.d.1808 gilt metal frame oval. 10-Dec-2 Christie's, London #177/R est:1000-1500

RICHOMME, Jules (1818-1903) French

£2830 $4387 €4500 Young love (32x44cm-13x17in) s. panel. 29-Oct-2 Dorotheum, Vienna #160/R est:1600-1800

RICHTER, Aurel (1870-1957) Hungarian

£2025 $3200 €3038 Barnstorming (44x32cm-17x13in) s. 1-Apr-3 Christie's, Rockefeller NY #210/R est:1500-2500

RICHTER, Bruno (1872-?) German

Works on paper

£449 $704 €700 On the Bab-Souika in Tunis (37x48cm-15x19in) s.d.1901 W/C. 21-Nov-2 Van Ham, Cologne #1885

RICHTER, Edouard Frederic Wilhelm (1844-1913) French

£32258 $50000 €48387 In the harem (94x74cm-37x29in) s.i. 30-Oct-2 Christie's, Rockefeller NY #80/R est:30000-40000

RICHTER, Erica (1869-?) German

£1266 $2000 €2000 Harvest time (71x103cm-28x41in) s. panel lit. 29-Nov-2 Schloss Ahlden, Ahlden #1396/R est:2500

RICHTER, Gerhard (1932-) German

£2308 $3577 €3600 Black-red-gold (21x7cm-8x3in) s.d.98 board on paper. 7-Dec-2 Van Ham, Cologne #444/R est:3500
£2319 $3803 €3200 Untitled - black, red, gold (21x7cm-8x3in) s.i.d.98 paper on board. 31-May-3 Villa Grisebach, Berlin #402/R est:4000-5000
£2464 $4041 €3400 Black, red, gold (21x7cm-8x3in) s.i.d.98 paper. 28-May-3 Lempertz, Koln #359/R est:3500
£3548 $5606 €5500 Untitled (39x39cm-15x15in) s.d.71 paper prov. 18-Dec-2 Christie's, Rome #121/R
£4000 $6160 €6000 Untitled (10x15cm-4x6in) s.d.16.3.89 oil on photograph prov. 22-Oct-2 Sotheby's, London #335/R est:4000-6000
£4430 $7000 €6645 Schwarz, rot, gold (36x36cm-14x14in) s.d.99 verso acrylic on gloss prov.lit. 14-Nov-2 Christie's, Rockefeller NY #109/R est:8000-12000
£6200 $10354 €8990 Vermalung - braun (27x39cm-11x15in) s.d.72 verso prov.lit. 27-Jun-3 Christie's, London #233/R est:6000-8000
£6329 $10000 €9494 Untitled - from 128 photographs of painting (15x22cm-6x9in) s.d.1998 oil gelatin silver print. 14-Nov-2 Christie's, Rockefeller NY #195/R est:15000-20000
£6962 $11000 €10443 Untitled (10x15cm-4x6in) s.d.88 oilpaint over photograph prov. 13-Nov-2 Sotheby's, New York #533/R est:10000-15000
£7609 $12478 €10500 Composition - brown (27x40cm-11x16in) s.i.d.1972 verso. 28-May-3 Lempertz, Koln #358/R est:7000
£8000 $13360 €11600 Vermalung - braun (27x39cm-11x15in) s.d.72 verso prov.lit. 27-Jun-3 Christie's, London #234/R est:7000-9000
£10145 $16637 €14000 Varmalung (26x39cm-10x15in) s.d.1972 verso. 27-May-3 Tajan, Paris #22/R est:14000-16000
£11613 $18348 €18000 Paper Fuji (30x41cm-12x16in) s.i.d.1996 paper prov. 18-Dec-2 Christie's, Rome #240/R
£12658 $20000 €20000 From: red-blue-yellow (26x53cm-10x21in) s.i.d.73 64 exhib. 30-Nov-2 Villa Grisebach, Berlin #463/R est:16000-18000
£13750 $22000 €20625 Rot blau gelb - red, blue and green (26x53cm-10x21in) s.d.73 verso prov.lit. 16-May-3 Phillips, New York #140/R est:18000-25000
£14000 $23380 €20300 Kerze 1 (90x90cm-35x35in) s.d.1989 oil offset lithograph on card lit. 26-Jun-3 Sotheby's, London #251/R est:12000-15000
£14557 $23000 €23000 From: red-blue-yellow (26x53cm-10x21in) s.i.d.73 63 verso exhib. 30-Nov-2 Villa Grisebach, Berlin #462/R est:16000-18000
£16000 $26240 €24000 Vermalung braun (27x40cm-11x16in) s.d.72 prov.exhib.lit. 7-Feb-3 Sotheby's, London #156/R est:5000-7000
£19000 $31160 €28500 Grun-blau-rot (30x40cm-12x16in) s.i.d.93 prov.lit. 6-Feb-3 Christie's, London #717/R est:18000-22000
£20000 $33400 €29000 Untitled (30x42cm-12x17in) d.11 Oktober 1996 oil Fuji photograph paper prov. 27-Jun-3 Christie's, London #231/R est:15000-20000
£25316 $40000 €37974 Abstraktes bild (61x86cm-24x34in) s.d.8.3.86 oil graphite prov.exhib. 14-Nov-2 Christie's, Rockefeller NY #193/R est:50000-70000
£25316 $40000 €37974 Grun-blau-rot (30x40cm-12x16in) s.d.93 verso prov.lit. 14-Nov-2 Christie's, Rockefeller NY #201/R est:40000-50000
£30000 $46200 €45000 Vermalung - grau (40x32cm-16x13in) s.d.69 225/6 prov.lit. 22-Oct-2 Sotheby's, London #337/R est:30000-40000
£30000 $50100 €43500 Kerze II (60x62cm-24x24in) s.d.89 s.d.verso oil offset print prov.lit. 27-Jun-3 Christie's, London #235/R est:20000-30000
£33000 $55110 €47850 Abstraktes bild (51x71cm-20x28in) s.d.1986 prov.lit. 26-Jun-3 Sotheby's, London #250/R est:25000-35000

£45000 $69300 €67500 Overholland, Amsterdam (61x86cm-24x34in) s.d.1983 oil on paper prov.exhib. 23-Oct-2 Christie's, London #156/R est:35000-55000
£50000 $83500 €72500 Abstrakte bilder (78x52cm-31x20in) s.d.1979 one num.448/2 one num.448/4 verso two prov.exhib.lit. 26-Jun-3 Sotheby's, London #139/R est:50000-70000
£50633 $80000 €75950 Abstrakes bild (40x49cm-16x19in) s.d.1992 prov. 14-Nov-2 Christie's, Rockefeller NY #197/R est:50000-70000
£57500 $92000 €86250 Abstraktes bild - Abstract (62x82cm-24x32in) s.d.1992 verso prov.lit. 16-May-3 Phillips, New York #142/R est:100000-150000
£80000 $131200 €120000 Abstraktes bild (72x101cm-28x40in) s.d.1988 verso prov.exhib.lit. 7-Feb-3 Sotheby's, London #160/R est:50000-70000
£107595 $170000 €161393 Untitled (100x120cm-39x47in) s.d.1985 paper exhib. 13-Nov-2 Sotheby's, New York #526/R est:125000-175000
£110000 $180400 €165000 Abstraktes bild (72x62cm-28x24in) s.d.1988 verso prov.lit. 7-Feb-3 Sotheby's, London #182/R est:70000-90000
£130000 $213200 €195000 Abstraktes bild (62x82cm-24x32in) s.d.1989 verso prov.lit. 7-Feb-3 Sotheby's, London #261/R est:120000-150000
£160000 $246400 €240000 Lawrence of Arabia (70x50cm-28x20in) s.d.1971 prov. 22-Oct-2 Sotheby's, London #336/R est:100000-150000
£185897 $288141 €290000 Teyde landscape, sketch (60x80cm-24x31in) s.i.d.1971 prov.exhib. 3-Dec-2 Lempertz, Koln #388/R est:250000
£200000 $320000 €300000 Arizona (65x80cm-26x31in) s.i.d.1984 verso prov.lit. 13-May-3 Sotheby's, New York #37/R est:200000-300000
£200000 $334000 €300000 Abstraktes bild (70x100cm-28x39in) s.d.1984 i.verso prov.exhib.lit. 25-Jun-3 Sotheby's, London #16/R est:130000-160000
£218750 $350000 €328125 Study for clouds (40x80cm-16x31in) s.i.d.1970 verso prov.lit. 15-May-3 Christie's, Rockefeller NY #160/R est:300000-400000
£253165 $400000 €379748 Untitled (200x149cm-79x59in) s.i.d.1979 i.on stretcher prov.lit. 12-Nov-2 Sotheby's, New York #28/R est:600000-800000
£270000 $450900 €405000 Kleine Kanarische Landschaft (48x58cm-19x23in) s.d.7.71 i.verso prov.lit. 25-Jun-3 Sotheby's, London #18/R est:200000-300000
£325000 $520000 €487500 Abstract composition 818-2 (71x61cm-28x24in) s.i.d.1994 verso prov.exhib.lit. 15-May-3 Christie's, Rockefeller NY #174/R est:250000-350000
£341772 $540000 €512658 Untitled (201x160cm-79x63in) s.i.d.1986 verso prov. 13-Nov-2 Christie's, Rockefeller NY #67/R est:400000-600000
£350000 $574000 €525000 Villa (65x90cm-26x35in) s.d.1972 prov. 5-Feb-3 Christie's, London #17/R est:400000-600000
£350000 $584500 €525000 Abstraktes Bild (145x150cm-57x59in) s.d.1991 verso panel prov.lit. 26-Jun-3 Christie's, London #26/R est:300000-400000
£400000 $656000 €600000 Cythera skizze (100x140cm-39x55in) s.i.d.1986 verso prov.lit. 6-Feb-3 Sotheby's, London #15/R est:600000
£480000 $801600 €720000 Waldstuck - Chile (174x124cm-69x49in) s.i.d. d.69 verso prov.exhib.lit. 26-Jun-3 Christie's, London #25/R est:500000-700000
£500000 $820000 €750000 Tote - Dead (100x150cm-39x59in) painted 1963 prov.exhib.lit. 6-Feb-3 Sotheby's, London #31/R est:800000
£600000 $984000 €900000 Abstract composition (200x160cm-79x63in) s.d.1986 i.verso prov.lit. 6-Feb-3 Sotheby's, London #3/R est:600000
£601266 $950000 €901899 Abstraktes bild (175x250cm-69x98in) painted 1992 prov.exhib.lit. 13-Nov-2 Christie's, Rockefeller NY #59/R est:700000-900000
£700000 $1169000 €1050000 Wald - 3 (340x260cm-134x102in) s.d.1990 verso prov.exhib.lit. 26-Jun-3 Christie's, London #30/R est:700000-1000000
£750000 $1200000 €1125000 Vesuv - Vesuvius (66x95cm-26x37in) s.d.1976 oil on wood prov.exhib.lit. 15-May-3 Phillips, New York #16/R est:1800000-2500000
£1125000 $1800000 €1687500 Davos S (70x100cm-28x39in) s.verso painted 1981 prov.exhib.lit. 13-May-3 Sotheby's, New York #8/R est:2000000-3000000
£1265823 $2000000 €1898735 Blue (300x300cm-118x118in) s. d.1988 verso prov.exhib.lit. 12-Nov-2 Sotheby's, New York #27/R est:1000000-1500000
£1300000 $2132000 €1950000 Clouds (200x300cm-79x118in) s. i.d.1970 verso prov.exhib.lit. 6-Feb-3 Sotheby's, London #12/R est:1800000
£1312500 $2100000 €1968750 Laacher meadow (87x122cm-34x48in) s.i.d.1987 verso prov.exhib.lit. 14-May-3 Christie's, Rockefeller NY #9/R est:2500000-3000000
£1858974 $2900000 €2788461 Troisdorf (85x120cm-33x47in) s.i.d.1985 prov.exhib.lit. 11-Nov-2 Phillips, New York #26/R est:2500000-3500000
£1875000 $3000000 €2812500 Abstract composition (250x400cm-98x157in) s.i.d.1987 verso prov.exhib.lit. 14-May-3 Christie's, Rockefeller NY #44/R est:2000000-3000000

Photographs

£2642 $4200 €3963 Untitled, from 128 details from a picture (15x22cm-6x9in) s.i.d.verso gelatin silver print oil. 29-Apr-3 Christie's, Rockefeller NY #726/R est:5000-7000
£5937 $9500 €8906 Domecke - cathedral corner (78x55cm-31x22in) s.d.1998 num.60 verso cibachrome mounted on plexiglass prov.lit. 16-May-3 Phillips, New York #185/R est:10000-15000
£7595 $12000 €11393 Domecke (78x56cm-31x22in) s.d.1998 num.8/60 verso cibachrome print mounted plexiglas. 14-Nov-2 Christie's, Rockefeller NY #108/R est:15000-20000
£7692 $11923 €12000 Cathedral corner (78x55cm-31x22in) s.i.d.1998 cibachrome. 3-Dec-2 Lempertz, Koln #393/R est:15000
£9375 $15000 €14063 Onkel Rudi - uncle Rudy (87x50cm-34x20in) s.num60 verso cibachrome executed 2000 prov.lit. 16-May-3 Phillips, New York #186/R est:10000-15000
£13924 $22000 €20886 Ravine (75x54cm-30x21in) s.d.97 num.28/45 cibachrome mounted between plexiglas prov.lit. 14-Nov-2 Christie's, Rockefeller NY #107/R est:15000-20000
£14000 $22960 €21000 Ravine (75x54cm-30x21in) s.d.97 num.31/45 verso cibachrome print prov.lit. 6-Feb-3 Christie's, London #715/R est:10000-15000
£15190 $24000 €22785 Onkel Rudi (87x50cm-34x20in) s.num.65/80 verso cibachrome print mounted on dibond executed 2000. 14-Nov-2 Christie's, Rockefeller NY #110/R est:10000-15000
£33228 $52500 €49842 Kerze (89x93cm-35x37in) s. offset lithograph crayon exec.1988. 13-Nov-2 Sotheby's, New York #516/R est:25000-35000

Prints

£1911 $3000 €2867 Auto (37x46cm-15x18in) s.d.1969 num.7/120 offset col lithograph. 21-Nov-2 Swann Galleries, New York #164/R est:2500-3500
£2057 $3250 €3086 Seestuck II (60x46cm-24x18in) s.d.1970 offset lithograph. 22-Apr-3 Butterfields, San Francisco #2348/R est:2500-3000
£2057 $3250 €3086 Wolke (44x44cm-17x17in) s.num.67/150 offset lithograph. 22-Apr-3 Butterfields, San Francisco #2349/R est:2000-3000
£2293 $3600 €3440 Bahnhof Hannover (48x59cm-19x23in) s.i.d.1967 offset col lithograph. 21-Nov-2 Swann Galleries, New York #159/R est:3000-5000
£12000 $19800 €17400 Orchids (29x33cm-11x13in) s.d.num.7/24 verso offset print plexiglass. 1-Jul-3 Sotheby's, London #208/R est:4000-5000
£13836 $22000 €20754 Kerze (90x95cm-35x37in) s. col offset lithograph edition of 250. 29-Apr-3 Christie's, Rockefeller NY #727/R est:15000-20000
£56962 $90000 €85443 Betty (98x62cm-39x24in) s.i.d.1991 offset lithograph prov.lit. 13-Nov-2 Sotheby's, New York #443/R est:60000-80000
£96875 $155000 €145313 Betty (95x66cm-37x26in) s.i.d.1991 verso offset lithograph board prov.lit. 15-May-3 Christie's, Rockefeller NY #161/R est:80000-120000

Sculpture

£5000 $8000 €7500 Kugelobjekt I (18x13x5cm-7x5x2in) s.d.1970 num.2/30 verso box construction wood glass prov.lit. 14-May-3 Sotheby's, New York #414/R est:8000-12000

Works on paper

£8974 $13910 €14000 Untitled (21x30cm-8x12in) s.d.VII. 91 Indian ink W/C. 6-Dec-2 Hauswedell & Nolte, Hamburg #302/R est:12000
£23438 $37500 €35157 Kerze (89x93cm-35x37in) s. black crayon offset lithograph executed 1988 prov. 14-May-3 Sotheby's, New York #415/R est:25000-35000

RICHTER, Gottfried (1904-) German

£314 $484 €500 View from Alexander Square skyscraper towards Friedrichshain (30x59cm-12x23in) mono. panel. 26-Oct-2 Dr Lehr, Berlin #452/R

RICHTER, Hans (1888-1975) German

£2096 $3291 €3144 Dymo XXVI (100x65cm-39x26in) mono.d.1970 s.i. verso oil collage. 25-Nov-2 Germann, Zurich #74/R est:5000-6000 (S.FR 4800)
£18261 $28304 €27392 Dada head (18x13cm-7x5in) mono.d.18 canvas on panel prov.exhib.lit. 4-Dec-2 Koller, Zurich #117/R est:28000-35000 (S.FR 42000)

Works on paper

£1026 $1497 €1600 Dada head (40x30cm-16x12in) s.d.62 mixed media prov. 5-Jun-2 Il Ponte, Milan #150

RICHTER, Hans Theo (1902-1969) German

Works on paper

£314 $484 €500 Karl Rade (25x24cm-10x9in) s. chk. 26-Oct-2 Dr Lehr, Berlin #453/R

RICHTER, Henry James (1772-1857) German

£400 $668 €580 Tight shoe, study of three figures in a house with onlookers. 11-Jul-3 Moore Allen & Innocent, Cirencester #791

RICHTER, Henry James (attrib) (1772-1857) German

£720 $1123 €1080 Brigands espying a coach on a country road (94x124cm-37x49in) 17-Oct-2 Lawrence, Crewkerne #453/R

RICHTER, Henry Leopold (1870-1960) American
£1347 $2250 €1953 San Pedro coast line (61x76cm-24x30in) i. 17-Jun-3 John Moran, Pasadena #67 est:3000-5000
£1647 $2750 €2388 Eucalyptus coastal, Santa Monica (61x76cm-24x30in) s.i.d.June 1933 prov. 17-Jun-3 John Moran, Pasadena #150 est:3000-5000

RICHTER, Herbert Davis (1874-1955) British
£320 $506 €480 Pink and white carnations in a vase (41x50cm-16x20in) s. 14-Nov-2 Christie's, Kensington #77/R
£370 $603 €555 Still life study of mixed flowers, and Oriental porcelain (49x42cm-19x17in) i.verso. 28-Jan-3 Henry Adams, Chichester #446/R
£480 $778 €720 Urn of flowers and candelabra (75x50cm-30x20in) s. 23-Jan-3 Bonhams, Edinburgh #332
£500 $780 €750 Still life of daffodils (41x32cm-16x13in) s. panel. 12-Sep-2 Sotheby's, Olympia #73/R
£500 $825 €725 Still life with poppies and wine (51x41cm-20x16in) s.d.34 board. 3-Jul-3 Christie's, Kensington #483/R
£640 $1005 €960 Coloured flowers in a glass vase (53x43cm-21x17in) s. 15-Apr-3 Bonhams, Knowle #119
£700 $1092 €1050 Still life of azaleas and rhododendrons in an urn (76x49cm-30x19in) s. 26-Mar-3 Hamptons Fine Art, Godalming #171
£1000 $1620 €1500 White roses and lilac on a ledge (74x61cm-29x24in) s.d.1911. 23-Jan-3 Christie's, Kensington #204/R est:1000-1500
Works on paper
£420 $697 €609 Still life of flowers in a jug (43x56cm-17x22in) s.d.34 W/C. 12-Jun-3 Gorringes, Lewes #1644
£550 $858 €825 Still life in a vase (46x54cm-18x21in) s. pencil W/C. 27-Mar-3 Christie's, Kensington #351/R

RICHTER, J (?) ?
£1863 $3000 €2795 Dog with basket. Dog with newspaper (30x23cm-12x9in) one s. one bears s. pair. 20-Jan-3 Arthur James, Florida #630

RICHTER, Johan Anton (1665-1745) Swedish
£33951 $55000 €50927 Venice, the Piazza San Marco looking north from the Piazzetta (53x81cm-21x32in) prov. 24-Jan-3 Christie's, Rockefeller NY #164/R est:40000-60000
£90000 $141300 €135000 Entrance to the Grand canal, Venice (58x94cm-23x37in) 10-Dec-2 Bonhams, New Bond Street #311/R est:20000-30000

RICHTER, Johann Carl August (1785-1853) German
Prints
£2885 $4471 €4500 Bad Doberan (28x41cm-11x16in) etching. 6-Dec-2 Bassenge, Berlin #7568/R est:750

RICHTER, Johann Carl August (attrib) (1785-1853) German
Works on paper
£8333 $13167 €13000 Mountain landscape with figures (53x72cm-21x28in) gouache. 16-Nov-2 Lempertz, Koln #1387/R est:14000

RICHTER, Leopold (1896-?) German
£378 $627 €548 Tropical fruits (47x33cm-19x13in) init.d.66 oil paper on board. 16-Jun-3 Waddingtons, Toronto #287/R (C.D 850)

RICHTER, Ludwig Adrian (1803-1884) German
Works on paper
£308 $449 €480 Sleeping children with angel (19x13cm-7x5in) pencil. 4-Jun-2 Karl & Faber, Munich #123
£641 $994 €1000 Children with angel (17x9cm-7x4in) pencil board. 7-Dec-2 Ketterer, Hamburg #71/R
£741 $1193 €1112 Young girl peeling potatoes (9x7cm-4x3in) s.i. pencil. 7-May-3 Dobiaschofsky, Bern #1172/R (S.FR 1600)
£1282 $2026 €2000 Romantic greeting - composition (31x22cm-12x9in) pencil W/C prov. 16-Nov-2 Lempertz, Koln #1388/R est:2000
£1507 $2351 €2200 Jakob and Rahel (22x28cm-9x11in) mono.d. pencil. 11-Apr-3 Winterberg, Heidelberg #536/R est:2750
£8500 $14195 €12325 Der lenz ist angekommen - spring is coming, children at a cottage gate watching returning stocks (18x15cm-7x6in) black lead pen ink wash W/C. 8-Jul-3 Christie's, London #114/R est:4000-6000
£9500 $15865 €13775 Shepherd and shepherdess with their flock. Cattle and herdsman on a road (20x27cm-8x11in) s.i.d.1874 black chk pen ink wash two prov. 8-Jul-3 Christie's, London #115/R est:3500-4500

RICHTER, Walter (20th C) German?
£551 $854 €827 Autumn mountains (58x78cm-23x31in) painted c.1900. 1-Oct-2 SOGA, Bratislava #168/R est:25000 (SL.K 35000)

RICHTER, Wilhelm (1824-1892) Austrian
£464 $724 €696 Yellow horse (50x70cm-20x28in) s. 11-Sep-2 Kieselbach, Budapest #205/R (H.F 180000)
£1935 $3018 €2903 Fox hunting (53x66cm-21x26in) s. 11-Sep-2 Kieselbach, Budapest #24/R (H.F 750000)
£2064 $3220 €3096 Fox hunting, 1870 (50x63cm-20x25in) s.d.1870. 11-Sep-2 Kieselbach, Budapest #22/R (H.F 800000)
£2580 $4024 €3870 Jockey in blue waistcoat, 1887 (60x76cm-24x30in) s. 11-Sep-2 Kieselbach, Budapest #26/R (H.F 1000000)

RICHTER-LUSSNITZ, Georg (1891-1938) German
£1795 $2782 €2800 Children in autumnal heath (70x100cm-28x39in) s.d.1918 i. verso. 5-Dec-2 Neumeister, Munich #2858/R est:1200

RICHTERICH, Marco (1929-) Swiss
£279 $441 €419 Small town in southern France (100x100cm-39x39in) s.i.d.1965. 29-Nov-2 Zofingen, Switzerland #3041 (S.FR 650)

RICHTERS, Marius (1878-1955) Dutch
£552 $877 €800 River landscape (30x41cm-12x16in) s. canvas on board. 10-Mar-3 Sotheby's, Amsterdam #308
£592 $959 €900 Treuwilg bij Bergsteijn (97x76cm-38x30in) s.d.1921 prov. 21-Jan-3 Christie's, Amsterdam #329
£704 $1134 €1000 Woman at dressing-table (111x92cm-44x36in) s. 6-May-3 Vendu Notarishuis, Rotterdam #77

RICKETTS, Charles Robert (fl.1868-1874) British
Works on paper
£390 $616 €566 Cutter yachts, Royal southern yacht club, June 1877 (31x45cm-12x18in) s.i. W/C. 22-Jul-3 Bristol Auction Rooms #396/R
£707 $1138 €1061 Royal Thames Yacht Club Regatta, Thames Estuary (35x64cm-14x25in) s.d.1879 W/C gouache. 7-May-3 Dunbar Sloane, Auckland #65/R (NZ.D 2000)

RICKETTS, William (1899-1993) Australian
Sculpture
£1346 $2100 €2019 Aborigine men (36cm-14in) terracotta bookends. 8-Apr-3 Christie's, Melbourne #114/R est:2000-3000 (A.D 3500)
£1538 $2400 €2307 Aborigine seated (33cm-13in) terracotta. 8-Apr-3 Christie's, Melbourne #112/R est:1800-2000 (A.D 4000)

RICKEY, George (1907-2002) American
Sculpture
£2516 $3874 €4000 Single line (22x48x400cm-9x19x157in) steel wooden socle. 26-Oct-2 Dr Lehr, Berlin #460/R est:3600
£5769 $8942 €9000 Three triangles with spirals (22cm-9in) s.d.1973 num.2/3 gilded stainless steel wire. 3-Dec-2 Christie's, Amsterdam #60/R est:4000-6000
£8917 $14000 €13376 Three open parallelepipeds (26cm-10in) s.num. stainless steel 1 from edition of 3 prov. 19-Nov-2 Wright, Chicago #226/R est:15000-20000
£12319 $20203 €17000 Two open rectangles III (78cm-31in) s.d.1978. 31-May-3 Villa Grisebach, Berlin #342/R est:15000-20000
£12658 $20000 €20000 One vertical one horizontal line (64cm-25in) s.i.d.1979 steel wooden socle. 30-Nov-2 Villa Grisebach, Berlin #428/R est:20000-25000
£12903 $20000 €19355 Two lines oblique down (94x58x15cm-37x23x6in) s.d.1999 stainless steel prov. 26-Sep-2 Christie's, Rockefeller NY #707/R est:30000-40000
£28125 $45000 €42188 Column (157x30x15cm-62x12x6in) s.d.1987 num.2/3 stainless steel prov.lit. 15-May-3 Christie's, Rockefeller NY #186/R est:20000-30000
£44304 $70000 €66456 Two open triangles up IV (120x135cm-47x53in) s.d.1984 num.2/3 stainless steel prov. 14-Nov-2 Christie's, Rockefeller NY #158/R est:30000-40000

RICKLY, Jessie Beard (1895-1975) American
£1299 $2000 €1949 Grocer, St Genevieve (91x76cm-36x30in) s. board painted c.1940. 8-Sep-2 Treadway Gallery, Cincinnati #705/R est:1500-2500

RICKMAN, Philip (1891-1982) British
Works on paper
£274 $425 €411 Pheasants at flight (41x36cm-16x14in) s. gouache. 28-Sep-2 Charlton Hall, Columbia #543/R
£285 $450 €428 Partridge sunning (24x31cm-9x12in) s. W/C gouache prov. 3-Apr-3 Christie's, Rockefeller NY #220/R
£300 $465 €450 Pheasants in a field (25x32cm-10x13in) s. W/C. 25-Sep-2 Hamptons Fine Art, Godalming #131
£300 $489 €450 Grouse in winter plumage in flight (36x51cm-14x20in) s. gouache. 28-Jan-3 Gorringes, Lewes #1719
£300 $468 €450 Smews (7x12cm-3x5in) s.d.1960 W/C on linen. 6-Nov-2 Sotheby's, Olympia #126/R

£300 $489 €435 Black grouse in a Highland setting (25x33cm-10x13in) s. W/C gouache sketch verso. 17-Jul-3 Thomson, Roddick & Medcalf, Carlisle #68/R
£355 $550 €533 Mallards at flight (41x36cm-16x14in) s. gouache. 28-Sep-2 Charlton Hall, Columbia #542/R
£450 $711 €675 Magpies on a branch (41x30cm-16x12in) s.d.1978 bodycol W/C. 28-Nov-2 Christie's, Kensington #20/R
£500 $790 €750 Great spotted woodpecker. Bullfinch on blackthorn (27x18cm-11x7in) s. i.verso pencil W/C htd white pair. 28-Nov-2 Christie's, Kensington #42
£500 $790 €750 Coal tits (37x28cm-15x11in) s.d.1960 bodycol exhib. 28-Nov-2 Bonhams, Knightsbridge #13/R
£503 $800 €755 Pheasants in a wood (38x56cm-15x22in) s.d.1956 W/C. 30-Apr-3 Sotheby's, New York #568/R
£550 $858 €825 Lapwings (27x36cm-11x14in) s.i.d.1924 W/C bodycol. 10-Apr-3 Tennants, Leyburn #879
£550 $913 €798 Ptarmigan shooting downhill (36x51cm-14x20in) s. W/C col chk htd white. 12-Jun-3 Christie's, Kensington #143/R
£550 $913 €798 Pheasant in flight (18x27cm-7x11in) s. W/C bodycol. 12-Jun-3 Christie's, Kensington #144/R
£600 $948 €900 Hesitation - pied wagtails (28x40cm-11x16in) bodycol exhib. 28-Nov-2 Bonhams, Knightsbridge #12/R
£650 $1027 €975 Grey wagtails (28x39cm-11x15in) s.d.1962 W/C bodycol exhib. 28-Nov-2 Bonhams, Knightsbridge #11/R
£700 $1169 €1015 Mallard alighting (48x64cm-19x25in) s.d.1920 W/C. 20-Jun-3 Keys, Aylsham #512
£900 $1422 €1305 Male and female teal, dropping in to the reeds (37x52cm-15x20in) s. bodycol. 22-Jul-3 Bonhams, Knightsbridge #54/R
£1350 $2147 €2025 Capercaillie in flight over moorland (36x48cm-14x19in) W/C. 19-Mar-3 Brightwells, Leominster #1135/R est:500-700

RICKS, Douglas (1954-) American
£2885 $4500 €4328 Watcher in the woods (81x107cm-32x42in) egg tempera. 9-Nov-2 Altermann Galleries, Santa Fe #25
£3013 $4700 €4520 Teton camp (61x91cm-24x36in) 9-Nov-2 Altermann Galleries, Santa Fe #28

RICKS, James (fl.1868-1894) British
£260 $406 €390 Head of a bulldog (25x20cm-10x8in) s. 9-Oct-2 Woolley & Wallis, Salisbury #358/R

RICO Y CEJUDO, Jose (1864-?) Spanish
£10256 $16205 €16000 In the kitchen (111x91cm-44x36in) s. 14-Nov-2 Arte, Seville #381/R
£15603 $25277 €22000 Los Novilleros (150x150cm-59x59in) s.d.1936. 20-May-3 Segre, Madrid #96/R est:15000

RICO Y ORTEGA, Martin (1833-1908) Spanish
£2262 $3665 €3393 Man with basket near well (27x18cm-11x7in) s.d.86 panel. 26-May-3 Grev Wedels Plass, Oslo #96/R est:10000 (N.KR 25000)
£22152 $35000 €33228 Family fishing by a river (33x46cm-13x18in) s. 23-Apr-3 Christie's, Rockefeller NY #74/R est:12000-16000
£25806 $40774 €40000 View of Venice (70x44cm-28x17in) s. 17-Dec-2 Durán, Madrid #232/R est:32500
£31690 $45000 €47535 Sunny day in Venice (66x51cm-26x20in) 8-Aug-1 Barridorf, Portland #168/R est:50000-75000
Works on paper
£1336 $2084 €1950 River landscape (25x44cm-10x17in) s. W/C. 8-Apr-3 Ansorena, Madrid #415/R
£2628 $4153 €4100 Washerwomen in France (19x40cm-7x16in) s. W/C. 13-Nov-2 Ansorena, Madrid #187/R

RICOEUR, Nicolas (18th C) French
£4575 $7503 €7000 Fleurs dans un vase (51x41cm-20x16in) panel prov. 9-Feb-3 Anaf, Lyon #220/R

RICOIS, François Edme (1795-1881) French
£3846 $5962 €6000 Vue du chateau de Montalet (50x66cm-20x26in) s.indis.d. 6-Dec-2 Maigret, Paris #94/R est:8000

RICOIS, François Edme (attrib) (1795-1881) French
£759 $1177 €1200 Vue de Beauvais (35x48cm-14x19in) paper on canvas. 29-Sep-2 Eric Pillon, Calais #56/R

RIDDEL, James (1858-1928) British
£222 $350 €333 Haystacks by a roadside pasture (30x41cm-12x16in) s. 18-Nov-2 Waddingtons, Toronto #172/R (C.D 550)
£1850 $2886 €2775 Farm near Longforgan (60x45cm-24x18in) s. 10-Apr-3 Bonhams, Edinburgh #161 est:1200-1800

RIDDER, Marieke de (20th C) Belgian
£462 $725 €720 Catwalk (80x100cm-31x39in) s.indis.d. 25-Nov-2 Glerum, Amsterdam #258

RIDEL, Leopold (19/20th C) French
Works on paper
£1064 $1777 €1500 La tour des Vents a Athenes (40x29cm-16x11in) s.i. pencil W/C. 23-Jun-3 Beaussant & Lefèvre, Paris #98/R est:300-400

RIDEOUT, Philip H (fl.1880-1912) British
£444 $701 €666 Royal Mail coaching scene, winter. Hunt scene (17x36cm-7x14in) s.d.1896 board pair. 18-Nov-2 Waddingtons, Toronto #88/R (C.D 1100)
£2000 $3160 €3000 Coaching scenes (30x50cm-12x20in) s.d.1888 pair. 28-Nov-2 Bonhams, Knightsbridge #98 est:2000-3000

RIDEOUT, Philip H (attrib) (fl.1880-1912) British
£260 $400 €390 Hunt (22x42cm-9x17in) bears sig. card. 22-Oct-2 Bonhams, Bath #224

RIDER, Arthur G (1886-1975) American
£633 $1000 €950 Villa scene (28x30cm-11x12in) s. board. 5-Apr-3 Susanin's, Chicago #5013/R
£633 $1000 €950 Two fishing boats (28x30cm-11x12in) s. board. 5-Apr-3 Susanin's, Chicago #5014/R
£1887 $3000 €2831 Spanish terrace (12x13cm-5x5in) s. board painted c.1921. 4-May-3 Treadway Gallery, Cincinnati #580/R est:4000-6000
£5988 $10000 €8683 Taxco landscape (43x55cm-17x22in) s. 18-Jun-3 Christie's, Los Angeles #1/R est:12000-18000
£6289 $10000 €9434 Valencia, Spain (11x13cm-4x5in) s. board painted c.1921. 4-May-3 Treadway Gallery, Cincinnati #579/R est:10000-20000
Works on paper
£1613 $2500 €2420 Spanish courtyard (38x30cm-15x12in) s. i.verso W/C prov. 29-Oct-2 John Moran, Pasadena #689 est:2000-3000

RIDER, H Orne (1860-?) American
£982 $1600 €1473 Early afternoon sunlight, Provincetown (64x76cm-25x30in) s.d.1938 s.i.d.verso. 2-Feb-3 Grogan, Boston #64 est:300-900

RIDGE, Hugh E (?) British
£250 $415 €363 Winter landscape (64x76cm-25x30in) s. 10-Jun-3 David Lay, Penzance #189

RIDGEWELL, John (1937-) British
£340 $568 €493 Townscape with acquaduct (86x111cm-34x44in) 17-Jun-3 Bonhams, Knightsbridge #118/R

RIDINGER, Johann Elias (1698-1767) German
Prints
£8724 $14046 €13000 Riding school (66x48cm-26x19in) copper engraving portfolio. 18-Feb-3 Sotheby's, Amsterdam #1010/R est:10000-15000
£10067 $16207 €15000 Verschiedene sonderbare thiere (47x33cm-19x13in) 18 copper engravings portfolio. 18-Feb-3 Sotheby's, Amsterdam #609/R est:1500-2000
Works on paper
£316 $500 €500 Two wolves in wood (16x9cm-6x4in) mono.d.1735 pen. 29-Nov-2 Bassenge, Berlin #5735
£559 $800 €839 Effects of gluttony (31x27cm-12x11in) brush ink wash. 23-Jan-3 Swann Galleries, New York #337/R

RIDINGER, Johann Elias (attrib) (1698-1767) German
Works on paper
£1678 $2400 €2517 Boar hunt (25x35cm-10x14in) pen ink wash. 23-Jan-3 Swann Galleries, New York #338/R est:1800-2200

RIDLEY, Matthew White (1837-1888) British
£800 $1264 €1200 Old pond (30x51cm-12x20in) s. 2-Dec-2 Gorringes, Lewes #2748

RIDOLA, Mario (1890-?) Italian
£23022 $37756 €32000 Beaute a la fenetre du harem (125x95cm-49x37in) s. lit. 4-Jun-3 Tajan, Paris #308/R est:25000-35000

RIDOLFI, Claudio (1570-1644) Italian
£5128 $7949 €8000 Pieta' with angels (34x29cm-13x11in) slate. 4-Dec-2 Finarte, Rome #948/R est:7000

RIDOLFI, Claudio (attrib) (1570-1644) Italian
£16352 $25346 €26000 Christ bearing the cross with donor (102x66cm-40x26in) 2-Oct-2 Dorotheum, Vienna #259/R est:8000-12000

RIDOUT, P H (?) British?
£700 $1085 €1050 York to Leeds mail coach brought to a halt by a foxhunt (28x44cm-11x17in) s. one indis.d. board pair. 24-Sep-2 Anderson & Garland, Newcastle #517

RIECKE, George (1848-1924) ?
£1258 $2000 €1887 Barnyard fowl (25x36cm-10x14in) s. i.verso. 29-Apr-3 Doyle, New York #35 est:1000-1500
£2656 $4250 €3851 Haying (56x92cm-22x36in) s.d.1875. 16-May-3 Skinner, Boston #61/R est:4500-5500

RIECKE, Johann George Lodewyck (1817-1898) Dutch
£641 $1000 €962 Two cows resting in a landscape (25x36cm-10x14in) s. 14-Sep-2 Weschler, Washington #573/R

RIEDEL, August (attrib) (1799-1883) German
£2611 $4074 €4100 Mother and sleeping children on a southern beach (70x87cm-28x34in) lit. 7-Nov-2 Allgauer, Kempten #2938/R est:7000

RIEDEL, Felix (1878-1980) Austrian
Works on paper
£439 $685 €650 Griechengasse (21x18cm-8x7in) s.i. W/C. 28-Mar-3 Dorotheum, Vienna #350/R
£473 $738 €700 Staphanskirche, Kapistrankanzel (20x17cm-8x7in) s.i. W/C. 28-Mar-3 Dorotheum, Vienna #351/R

RIEDEL, Johann Anton (1736-1816) German
£1486 $2319 €2200 The lamentation (68x43cm-27x17in) s. 27-Mar-3 Dorotheum, Vienna #262/R est:1500-2000

RIEDEL, Wilhelm (1832-1876) German
£314 $487 €500 Italian landscape (21x44cm-8x17in) i. verso paper. 29-Oct-2 Dorotheum, Vienna #97/R

RIEDER, E (19th C) ?
£2044 $3250 €3066 Recital (99x74cm-39x29in) s. 18-Mar-3 Arthur James, Florida #368

RIEDER, Marcel (1852-1942) French
£897 $1409 €1400 Femme au claire de lune (33x41cm-13x16in) 13-Dec-2 Piasa, Paris #181

RIEDL, Fritz (1923-) Austrian
£1772 $2800 €2800 Portrait of Joanna Thul (121x75cm-48x30in) prov. 27-Nov-2 Dorotheum, Vienna #199/R est:3200-4500

RIEDL, Jaroslav (1893-?) Czechoslovakian
£497 $810 €750 Village (41x53cm-16x21in) s.d.1932. 28-Jan-3 Dorotheum, Vienna #62/R

RIEDMULLER, Franz Xaver (1829-1901) German
£641 $994 €1000 Bodensee idyll with farmstead (69x102cm-27x40in) s. 6-Dec-2 Michael Zeller, Lindau #902/R
£4610 $7468 €6500 Sunny day by the sea (69x102cm-27x40in) s.d.1881. 22-May-3 Dorotheum, Vienna #89/R est:4500-5500

RIEFENSTAHL, Leni (1902-) German
Photographs
£2532 $4000 €4000 Under water view of plunge into water (28x22cm-11x9in) s.d.1936 verso lit.exhib. 28-Nov-2 Villa Grisebach, Berlin #1360/R est:2500-3500

RIEFSTAHL, Erich (1862-1920) German
£1410 $2200 €2115 Summer luncheon (81x102cm-32x40in) s.i.d.1902 verso. 9-Oct-2 Doyle, New York #95 est:3000-5000

RIEGEN, Nicolaas (1827-1889) Dutch
£828 $1308 €1200 Ships in harbour entrance (20x25cm-8x10in) mono. panel lit. 5-Apr-3 Hans Stahl, Hamburg #171/R
£1793 $2994 €2600 La rentree au port un jour de tempete (65x96cm-26x38in) s.d.1871. 9-Jul-3 Millon & Associes, Paris #119/R est:1000-1200
£2038 $3139 €3200 Sailing barge from Marken on the Ij, Amsterdam (31x48cm-12x19in) s. prov. 3-Sep-2 Christie's, Amsterdam #294/R est:3500-4500
£2200 $3454 €3300 Dutch estuary scene with man-o-war (50x80cm-20x31in) s. 16-Dec-2 Sotheby's, Olympia #70/R est:2000-3000
£2201 $3390 €3500 Sailing vessels off the coast (19x29cm-7x11in) s. panel. 22-Oct-2 Sotheby's, Amsterdam #16/R est:4000-6000
£2420 $3727 €3800 Barges moored in a calm, steamship in the distance (44x67cm-17x26in) s. prov. 3-Sep-2 Christie's, Amsterdam #289/R est:4000-6000
£2500 $3900 €3750 Ships unloading at a jetty (20x31cm-8x12in) s.indis.d. 26-Mar-3 Woolley & Wallis, Salisbury #210/R est:2000-3000
£2877 $4488 €4200 Ships on choppy sea (43x66cm-17x26in) s.d.1866 panel. 14-Apr-3 Glerum, Amsterdam #20/R est:5000-6000
£4140 $6459 €6500 Boat on calm water at sunset (42x66cm-17x26in) s. 6-Nov-2 Vendue Huis, Gravenhage #379/R est:7000-9000
£5346 $8233 €8500 Sailing vessels in an estuary (29x38cm-11x15in) s. panel. 23-Oct-2 Christie's, Amsterdam #1/R est:2500-3500
£10417 $16563 €15000 Calm, fishermen inspecting their catch (27x44cm-11x17in) s. panel. 29-Apr-3 Christie's, Amsterdam #83/R est:10000-15000

RIEGER, Albert (1834-1905) Austrian
£411 $645 €600 Hunter by mountain stream (26x37cm-10x15in) s. 16-Apr-3 Dorotheum, Salzburg #88/R
£1757 $2741 €2600 Zell am See (34x56cm-13x22in) s.i. panel. 28-Mar-3 Ketterer, Hamburg #116/R est:3000-3500
£2138 $3314 €3400 Lake landscape in autumn (55x68cm-22x27in) s. 29-Oct-2 Dorotheum, Vienna #14/R est:2500-2800
£2516 $3925 €4000 Alpine view. Mountainous landscape (39x63cm-15x25in) board pair. 20-Sep-2 Semenzato, Venice #225/R
£3927 $6243 €5891 Mountain waterfall at Fernleihen in Grossglockner area (142x97cm-56x38in) s. bears d. 8-Mar-3 Dorotheum, Prague #3/R est:180000-270000 (C.KR 180000)
£5164 $8469 €7488 Stormy seas of Dutch coast (48x42cm-19x17in) s.d.1866 panel. 4-Jun-3 Fischer, Luzern #138/R est:3500-4500 (S.FR 11000)

RIEHL, A (19th C) German
£823 $1275 €1235 What has mother brought? (40x33cm-16x13in) 24-Sep-2 Koller, Zurich #6551/R (S.FR 1900)
£952 $1476 €1428 First a kiss (41x33cm-16x13in) 24-Sep-2 Koller, Zurich #6549/R (S.FR 2200)

RIEMERSCHMID, Richard (1868-1957) German
Works on paper
£608 $936 €912 Untitled - children dancing (40x48cm-16x19in) s. mixed media board. 3-Sep-2 Shapiro, Sydney #404/R est:1800-2500 (A.D 1700)

RIENKS, Leni (1914-) Dutch
£284 $460 €400 Two Indonesian dolls (80x60cm-31x24in) s. 26-May-3 Glerum, Amsterdam #99/R

RIEPENHAUSEN, Franz (1786-1831) German
£4054 $6324 €6000 Adoration (78x59cm-31x23in) 27-Mar-3 Dorotheum, Vienna #437/R est:6000-8000

RIERA FERRARI, Joan (?) Spanish
Works on paper
£974 $1481 €1500 Untitled (116x90cm-46x35in) s. mixed media on canvas. 3-Jul-2 Castellana, Madrid #149/R

RIESAU, Vic (20th C) American
£311 $500 €467 Just restin (30x41cm-12x16in) s. i.verso prov. 18-Feb-3 John Moran, Pasadena #185

RIESCH, Cesare (1906-) Italian
£321 $503 €500 Along the Mugnone (21x13cm-8x5in) board. 16-Dec-2 Pandolfini, Florence #283/R

RIESS, Paul (1857-1933) German
£409 $638 €650 Shepherd with flock in forest clearing (30x33cm-12x13in) lit. 20-Sep-2 Karlheinz Kaupp, Staufen #1995
£838 $1332 €1257 Seascape with steamship and rowing boats off coastal cliffs (40x65cm-16x26in) s.i. 5-Mar-3 Rasmussen, Copenhagen #1995/R (D.KR 9000)

RIET, Willy van (1882-1927) Belgian
£481 $745 €750 Portrait de dame portant un chale mauve (135x85cm-53x33in) s. 3-Dec-2 Campo & Campo, Antwerp #325
£700 $1092 €1050 Betrayal (32x45cm-13x18in) s. panel. 10-Sep-2 Bonhams, Knightsbridge #254/R

RIETH, Paul (1871-1925) German
£1509 $2355 €2400 Dancing (55x86cm-22x34in) bears sig. board on canvas. 21-Sep-2 Bolland & Marotz, Bremen #553/R est:2400

RIETSCHEL, Otto (1822-1887) German
£1972 $3273 €2800 Two small sellers (132x99cm-52x39in) s.d.1870. 14-Jun-3 Arnold, Frankfurt #843/R est:1200

RIETSCHOOF, Hendrik (circle) (1687-1746) Dutch
£3086 $5000 €4629 Shipping in stiff breeze (89x74cm-35x29in) init. 21-Jan-3 Christie's, Rockefeller NY #366/R

RIETSCHOOF, Jan Claes (1652-1719) Dutch
£87241 $140458 €129990 Dutch ship of the line Westvriesland and other shipping in the roads of Hoorn (152x225cm-60x89in) mono. prov.lit. 18-Feb-3 Sotheby's, Amsterdam #236/R est:45000-55000
Works on paper
£1911 $2981 €3000 River landscape with fishing boats and village beyond (10x9cm-4x4in) bears sig.verso pen black ink grey wash prov. 5-Nov-2 Sotheby's, Amsterdam #106/R est:4000-5000

RIETSCHOOF, Jan Claes (attrib) (1652-1719) Dutch
£15000 $25050 €21750 Dutch two decker and other shipping at anchor along a quayside (93x127cm-37x50in) i. 10-Jul-3 Sotheby's, London #146/R est:15000-20000

RIETTI, Arturo (1863-1942) Italian
£314 $484 €500 Chinese man laughing (22x32cm-9x13in) s.d.1940 i.verso cardboard. 28-Oct-2 Il Ponte, Milan #206/R
£440 $678 €700 Chinese (30x22cm-12x9in) s.d.1941 cardboard on canvas. 28-Oct-2 Il Ponte, Milan #190/R
£692 $1065 €1100 Cafe (10x16cm-4x6in) s.d.1935 board. 28-Oct-2 Il Ponte, Milan #217/R
£692 $1065 €1100 Melancholy (26x18cm-10x7in) s. board. 28-Oct-2 Il Ponte, Milan #230
£818 $1259 €1300 Hotel Europa (35x24cm-14x9in) s. board. 28-Oct-2 Il Ponte, Milan #184
£881 $1356 €1400 Venice, La Salute (45x30cm-18x12in) s. cardboard. 28-Oct-2 Il Ponte, Milan #200/R
Works on paper
£1447 $2228 €2300 Portrait of woman with hat (49x39cm-19x15in) s. pastel. 28-Oct-2 Il Ponte, Milan #212/R
£2128 $3447 €3000 Lo sguardo (71x57cm-28x22in) s.d.1904 mixed media board. 22-May-3 Stadion, Trieste #304/R est:3000-4000

RIEU, Gilles (20th C) French
£2069 $3455 €3000 Sans titre (75x95cm-30x37in) s.d.2002 verso acrylic. 10-Jul-3 Artcurial Briest, Paris #345 est:1000-1500

RIGALT Y FARRIOLS, Luis (1814-1894) Spanish
£8387 $13252 €13000 Montserrat mountains (62x98cm-24x39in) i.verso. 18-Dec-2 Ansorena, Madrid #364/R est:12000

RIGAUD, Hyacinthe (after) (1659-1743) French
£10638 $16489 €15957 King Ludvig XIV of France (240x157cm-94x62in) 3-Dec-2 Bukowskis, Stockholm #510/R est:70000-80000 (S.KR 150000)

RIGAUD, Hyacinthe (attrib) (1659-1743) French
£1690 $2806 €2400 Portrait of Cardinal Andre Hercule de Fleury (101x81cm-40x32in) prov. 11-Jun-3 Dorotheum, Vienna #176/R est:1800-2500

RIGAUD, Hyacinthe (circle) (1659-1743) French
£8805 $13648 €14000 Portrait of King Louis XIV (130x97cm-51x38in) 2-Oct-2 Dorotheum, Vienna #321/R est:7000-10000

RIGAUD, Hyacinthe (studio) (1659-1743) French
£16250 $26000 €24375 Portrait of nobleman, possibly Stanislas Lezszczynski-Duc de Lorraine (141x112cm-56x44in) 14-May-3 Doyle, New York #67/R est:20000-30000
£20980 $35036 €30000 Portrait en pied de Chretien de Lamoignon (195x117cm-77x46in) prov.exhib.lit. 25-Jun-3 Tajan, Paris #51/R est:30000-40000

RIGAUD, Jean (1912-1999) French
£306 $500 €459 Village roof tops (33x46cm-13x18in) s. i.verso. 16-Feb-3 Butterfields, San Francisco #2071
£1007 $1612 €1400 Plage et falaises a Veules-les-roses (38x55cm-15x22in) s.i.d.verso. 18-May-3 Eric Pillon, Calais #240/R
£1027 $1613 €1500 La plage, Hossegor (38x46cm-15x18in) s.d.1952. 21-Apr-3 Rabourdin & Choppin de Janvry, Paris #103 est:1500-1800
£1384 $2145 €2200 Vue de Camaret (46x56cm-18x22in) s.d.51. 4-Oct-2 Tajan, Paris #211 est:1800-2000
£1592 $2484 €2500 Rivage de l'Ile d'Yeu (32x45cm-13x18in) s.d.83 verso. 7-Nov-2 Chochon-Barre & Allardi, Paris #218
£3694 $5763 €5800 Port Joinville (60x80cm-24x31in) s. 7-Nov-2 Chochon-Barre & Allardi, Paris #219/R

RIGAUX, Albert (1950-) Belgian
£353 $546 €550 Jeux de plage (30x40cm-12x16in) s. 9-Dec-2 Horta, Bruxelles #253
£651 $1015 €950 Enfants a la mer du Nord (46x55cm-18x22in) s. 14-Apr-3 Horta, Bruxelles #299

RIGAUX, Jack (1931-) Canadian
Works on paper
£222 $364 €322 Still life with violin (90x60cm-35x24in) s.d.1983 gouache. 9-Jun-3 Hodgins, Calgary #431/R (C.D 500)

RIGBY, Cuthbert (1850-1935) British
Works on paper
£380 $608 €570 Rocky coastal scene (50x74cm-20x29in) s. W/C. 11-Mar-3 David Duggleby, Scarborough #81/R

RIGBY, John Thomas (1922-) Australian
£894 $1413 €1296 Hide and seek (90x38cm-35x15in) s.d.61 i.verso tempera on board exhib. 22-Jul-3 Lawson Menzies, Sydney #109/R est:1500-2000 (A.D 2200)

RIGET, Karl Age (1933-2001) Danish
£429 $716 €622 Blue figure of room (115x80cm-45x31in) s.d.1965 verso. 17-Jun-3 Rasmussen, Copenhagen #117/R (D.KR 4500)
£572 $955 €829 Composition (80x80cm-31x31in) init.d.79 s.verso. 17-Jun-3 Rasmussen, Copenhagen #201 (D.KR 6000)
£933 $1483 €1400 Composition (150x50cm-59x20in) s. panel. 29-Apr-3 Kunsthallen, Copenhagen #135/R (D.KR 10000)
£1097 $1744 €1646 Composition (150x50cm-59x20in) s. panel. 26-Feb-3 Kunsthallen, Copenhagen #194/R est:12000 (D.KR 12000)
£4182 $6608 €6273 Geometric composition (200x350cm-79x138in) s.d.92. 1-Apr-3 Rasmussen, Copenhagen #185/R est:50000 (D.KR 45000)

RIGG, Ernest Higgins (1868-1947) British
£260 $403 €390 An old barge, sunset (51x69cm-20x27in) s. board. 26-Sep-2 Lane, Penzance #161
£280 $437 €420 River Esk (25x38cm-10x15in) i.verso board. 20-Sep-2 Richardson & Smith, Whitby #172
£320 $496 €480 Willows cottage, Devon (81x99cm-32x39in) s. board. 26-Sep-2 Lane, Penzance #158
£350 $571 €525 Sheep in a moor landscape (28x38cm-11x15in) s. board. 30-Jan-3 Richardson & Smith, Whitby #555
£380 $600 €570 Tree-lined landscape (30x46cm-12x18in) s. board. 24-Apr-3 Richardson & Smith, Whitby #185/R
£500 $790 €750 Peaceful evening (23x33cm-9x13in) s. board i.verso. 24-Apr-3 Richardson & Smith, Whitby #195/R
£550 $919 €798 Flowers in a glass vase (41x31cm-16x12in) s. 17-Jun-3 Rosebery Fine Art, London #605/R
£1000 $1560 €1500 Harvester with dog in landscape. Sheep in landscape (25x33cm-10x13in) s. pair. 18-Oct-2 Keys, Aylsham #780 est:280-320
£1200 $1884 €1800 Landscape with cattle (31x39cm-12x15in) s. canvasboard. 21-Nov-2 Tennants, Leyburn #817 est:600-800
£1300 $2015 €1950 Peatgate Moors, Yorkshire, evening light, shepherd on horseback (74x99cm-29x39in) s. board. 26-Sep-2 Lane, Penzance #159 est:300-400
£1600 $2496 €2400 Coastal landscape at sunset with ducks and haystack (30x38cm-12x15in) s. board. 15-Oct-2 Gorringes, Lewes #2154/R est:700-1000
£4100 $6355 €6150 Young mothers (74x99cm-29x39in) s. board. 26-Sep-2 Lane, Penzance #160/R est:1000-1500
£5400 $8802 €8100 Young girl in a summer garden (41x33cm-16x13in) s. 29-Jan-3 Sotheby's, Olympia #230/R est:6000-9000

RIGG, Jack (1927-) British
£320 $534 €464 Quiet waters (33x43cm-13x17in) s. board. 26-Jun-3 Richardson & Smith, Whitby #639
£400 $652 €600 Whitby looking from Sandsend (20x38cm-8x15in) s. board. 7-Feb-3 Dee Atkinson & Harrison, Driffield #698
£480 $782 €720 Sail o' Steam, the Olympic sister ship to the Titanic (33x43cm-13x17in) s.d.1985 board. 7-Feb-3 Dee Atkinson & Harrison, Driffield #697
£620 $973 €930 Off Abersoch, North Wales (15x10cm-6x4in) 26-Jul-2 Dee Atkinson & Harrison, Driffield #670/R
£700 $1106 €1050 Drying the nets (25x43cm-10x17in) s.d.1989. 29-Nov-2 Dee Atkinson & Harrison, Driffield #826/R

RIGGS, Robert (1896-1970) American
Prints
£2083 $3250 €3125 One punch knockout (37x49cm-15x19in) s.i. lithograph executed c.1934. 12-Sep-2 Freeman, Philadelphia #202/R est:2000-3000
Works on paper
£545 $850 €818 Beasts of Burden (28x41cm-11x16in) s.i. W/C crayon. 20-Sep-2 Freeman, Philadelphia #28/R

RIGHETTI, F (1738-1819) Italian
Sculpture
£2900 $4524 €4350 Greek academic seated in an empire chair (28x23x13cm-11x9x5in) i. bronze with base. 17-Sep-2 Bonhams, Leeds #23/R est:300-500

RIGHETTI, Guido (1875-1958) Italian
Sculpture
£1221 $2002 €1770 Three goats (30cm-12in) i.d.1917 pat.bronze. 4-Jun-3 Fischer, Luzern #1370/R est:2500-3000 (S.FR 2600)
£1899 $2962 €3000 Deux antilopes africaines (27x31x19cm-11x12x7in) s. brown red pat bronze Cast Blanchet Landowski. 20-Oct-2 Mercier & Cie, Lille #126/R est:3000-3500
£1918 $3011 €2800 Ours polaire assis (16x21x17cm-6x8x7in) num.4/8 red brown pat bronze Cast Chapon. 21-Apr-3 Rabourdin & Choppin de Janvry, Paris #48/R est:2800-3800

RIGHI, Frederico (1908-1986) Italian
£417 $646 €650 Carnations on the table (51x74cm-20x29in) s. board. 5-Dec-2 Stadion, Trieste #679

RIGHINI, Sigismund (1870-1937) German
£2575 $4069 €3863 Morning (36x39cm-14x15in) mono.i.d.1911 verso canvas on board. 28-Nov-2 Christie's, Zurich #49/R est:4000-6000 (S.FR 6000)
£3433 $5425 €5150 Bergstrasse with winter trees (16x27cm-6x11in) mono.i.d.1909 verso board. 26-Nov-2 Phillips, Zurich #63/R est:8000-12000 (S.FR 8000)
Works on paper
£2165 $3355 €3248 Portrait of Rudolf Koller, Arnold Boeklin and Gottfried Keller (55x68cm-22x27in) mono. pastel prov. 24-Sep-2 Koller, Zurich #6640/R est:6000-9000 (S.FR 5000)

RIGOLOT, Albert (1862-1932) French
£1667 $2617 €2600 Meadow near waters edge (31x46cm-12x18in) s. 10-Dec-2 Dorotheum, Vienna #3/R est:2200-2600
£2500 $4175 €3750 French river landscape (41x75cm-16x30in) s. 18-Jun-3 Christie's, Kensington #5/R est:3000-4000
£2790 $4408 €4185 Landscape (30x46cm-12x18in) s. prov. 3-Apr-3 Heffel, Vancouver #78/R est:7000-8000 (C.D 6500)
£3500 $5565 €5250 Meandering river (65x100cm-26x39in) s. 20-Mar-3 Christie's, Kensington #10/R est:4000-6000
£3800 $6194 €5510 Soleil couchant, Vallee de la Somme (73x100cm-29x39in) s. 16-Jul-3 Sotheby's, Olympia #231/R est:2000-3000
£5190 $8096 €8200 Rue de Bou Saada (81x60cm-32x24in) s.i.d.1896. 20-Oct-2 Galerie de Chartres, Chartres #116 est:3000-4000

RIGON, Auguste Maillet (c.1855-1884) French
£493 $818 €700 Chasseurs a tir en sous-bois (27x39cm-11x15in) s. paper. 11-Jun-3 Beaussant & Lefèvre, Paris #94

RIIS, Bendik (1911-1988) Norwegian
£436 $685 €654 Spring thaw in birch wood with brook running (16x22cm-6x9in) s. panel. 25-Nov-2 Blomqvist, Lysaker #1224 (N.KR 5000)

RIKET, Léon (1876-1938) Belgian
£347 $549 €500 Sous-bois (49x68cm-19x27in) 28-Apr-3 Amberes, Antwerp #305
£503 $775 €800 Sous-bois avec femme et vaches (50x70cm-20x28in) s. 22-Oct-2 Campo & Campo, Antwerp #222
£543 $891 €750 Maison pres de la foret (70x100cm-28x39in) s. 27-May-3 Campo & Campo, Antwerp #191
£1918 $2992 €2800 La cueillette des coux (56x70cm-22x28in) s. 14-Apr-3 Horta, Bruxelles #107/R est:3000-4000

RILEY, Bridget (1931-1984) British
£68750 $110000 €103125 In attendance (165x228cm-65x90in) oil on linen painted 1993 prov.exhib. 15-May-3 Phillips, New York #31/R est:40000-60000
£170000 $278800 €255000 Orient 3 (216x292cm-85x115in) s.i.d.1970 verso acrylic prov.exhib.lit. 6-Feb-3 Sotheby's, London #2/R est:200000
Prints
£1692 $2691 €2538 Untitled (57x83cm-22x33in) s.d.num.59/75 col screenprint. 4-Mar-3 Deutscher-Menzies, Melbourne #212/R est:3000-5000 (A.D 4400)
£1715 $2709 €2573 Untitled (57x83cm-22x33in) s.d.1978 num.64/75 col screenprint. 27-Nov-2 Deutscher-Menzies, Melbourne #260/R est:2500-4500 (A.D 4800)
£2000 $3220 €3000 Untitled (57x84cm-22x33in) s.d.1978 num.58/75 col silkscreen. 6-May-3 Christie's, Melbourne #337/R est:5000-7000 (A.D 5000)
£2138 $3400 €3207 Elapse (102x64cm-40x25in) s.i.d.1982 col screenprint. 4-Mar-3 Swann Galleries, New York #546/R est:1500-2500
£2201 $3500 €3302 Elapse (103x64cm-41x25in) s.i.d. col screenprint edition of 260. 29-Apr-3 Christie's, Rockefeller NY #728/R est:3000-4000
£2500 $3875 €3750 Coloured greys (74x70cm-29x28in) s.i.d.1972 num.23/125 col screenprint. 2-Oct-2 Christie's, Kensington #156/R est:800-1200
£2500 $3875 €3750 Coloured greys (70x73cm-28x29in) s.i.d.1972 num.41/125 col screenprint. 2-Oct-2 Christie's, Kensington #157/R est:800-1200
£2600 $4056 €3900 Untitled (76x76cm-30x30in) s.i.d.1968 col silkscreen. 25-Mar-3 Sotheby's, London #197/R est:1500-2000
£2800 $4368 €4200 Untitled (76x76cm-30x30in) s.i.d.1968 col silkscreen. 25-Mar-3 Sotheby's, London #198/R est:1500-2000
£2822 $4600 €4233 Fragment 8 (63x81cm-25x32in) s.verso num.14/75 screenprint. 13-Feb-3 Christie's, Rockefeller NY #340/R
£3000 $4680 €4500 Elapse (102x64cm-40x25in) s.i.d.1982 col silkscreen. 25-Mar-3 Sotheby's, London #200/R est:2000-3000
£10063 $16000 €15095 Nineteen greys (198x196cm-78x77in) s.i.d.1968 col screenprints. 30-Apr-3 Doyle, New York #291/R est:800-1200
Works on paper
£5000 $7700 €7500 November 16 bassacs (27x33cm-11x13in) s.i.d.87 gouache prov. 22-Oct-2 Sotheby's, London #475/R est:3000-4000
£5000 $7800 €7500 January 20 study (27x33cm-11x13in) s.i.d.88 gouache. 25-Mar-3 Bonhams, New Bond Street #146/R est:5000-7000
£7000 $11690 €10150 Series 12, cerise turquoise olive, sequence study (22x96cm-9x38in) s.i.d.73 verso gouache pencil graph paper prov. 26-Jun-3 Sotheby's, London #130/R est:7000-10000
£7424 $11655 €11136 Three colour study (69x63cm-27x25in) s.i.d.1975 gouache prov. 25-Nov-2 Germann, Zurich #55/R est:12000-18000 (S.FR 17000)
£9319 $14165 €13979 Turquoise, blue, yellow, red, with black and white (93x65cm-37x26in) s.i.d.81 gouache prov. 28-Aug-2 Deutscher-Menzies, Melbourne #292/R est:8000-12000 (A.D 26000)
£9500 $15580 €14250 Study for a painting (77x54cm-30x21in) s.i.d.85 pencil bodycol prov. 6-Jun-3 Christie's, London #201/R est:10000-15000
£11354 $17825 €17031 Study following entice (119x69cm-47x27in) s.i.d.1975 gouache prov. 25-Nov-2 Germann, Zurich #56/R est:18000-23000 (S.FR 26000)

RILEY, Harold (1934-) British
£850 $1352 €1275 Steps, Brindle Heath, Salford (48x38cm-19x15in) i.verso board. 18-Mar-3 Capes Dunn, Manchester #431
£1400 $2170 €2100 Man carrying suitcase (20x13cm-8x5in) s.d.72 panel. 1-Oct-2 Capes Dunn, Manchester #718
£1600 $2528 €2400 Public lavatories (26x31cm-10x12in) s. board. 27-Nov-2 Peter Wilson, Nantwich #79 est:1000-1500
£2300 $3588 €3450 Steps, Salford (102x76cm-40x30in) s. s.i.verso board. 6-Nov-2 Bonhams, Chester #362 est:900-1200
Works on paper
£300 $477 €450 Landscape with mine workings beyond (20x13cm-8x5in) mono. pen black ink crayon. 18-Mar-3 Capes Dunn, Manchester #428
£380 $604 €570 Monks Hall Museum, spring (23x30cm-9x12in) s. 18-Mar-3 Capes Dunn, Manchester #405
£410 $652 €615 Young girl (18x15cm-7x6in) s. pen col ink white chk. 18-Mar-3 Capes Dunn, Manchester #427
£420 $668 €630 View of Ordsall, Salford (18x18cm-7x7in) s.i.d.1960 pencil grey wash col chk. 18-Mar-3 Capes Dunn, Manchester #425
£460 $718 €690 Old man in Chimney Pot Park (22x18cm-9x7in) s.i. s.i.verso chl col chk. 6-Nov-2 Bonhams, Chester #366
£560 $874 €840 View of Macclesfield from the Buxton Road (18x30cm-7x12in) s.d.69 pencil W/C bodycol. 6-Nov-2 Bonhams, Chester #363
£620 $967 €930 Eller St, Salford (17x24cm-7x9in) s. i.d.61 pencil W/C bodycol. 6-Nov-2 Bonhams, Chester #364
£850 $1394 €1233 Urban scene with roof tops and snow covered steps in the foreground (36x48cm-14x19in) s.d.62 mixed media. 3-Jun-3 Capes Dunn, Manchester #32/R
£1000 $1620 €1450 Baby in a cot upon a chair (17x10cm-7x4in) s.d.71 chk. 29-Jul-3 Capes Dunn, Manchester #5
£1100 $1804 €1595 Girl in a red coat seated on a chair clutching a teddy bear (46x28cm-18x11in) s.i.d.1970 pastel. 3-Jun-3 Capes Dunn, Manchester #31/R

RILEY, John (1646-1691) British
£3200 $5280 €4640 Portrait of a gentleman (119x94cm-47x37in) 2-Jul-3 Sotheby's, Olympia #16/R est:3000-5000
£10000 $15800 €15000 Portrait of Anne Sherard, Lady Brownlow (126x101cm-50x40in) prov. 28-Nov-2 Sotheby's, London #149/R est:8000-12000

RILEY, John (attrib) (1646-1691) British
£1800 $2808 €2700 Portrait of Mary Ibbetson (76x62cm-30x24in) painted cartouche. 17-Sep-2 Sotheby's, Olympia #93/R est:2000-3000

RILEY, Kenneth (1919-) American

£3247 $5000 €4871 Crow fair (13x13cm-5x5in) acrylic. 25-Oct-2 Morris & Whiteside, Hilton Head Island #21 est:5500-6000
£15401 $24950 €22331 Brothers (76x51cm-30x20in) 23-May-3 Altermann Galleries, Santa Fe #103
£15401 $24950 €22331 The white captive (23x43cm-9x17in) 23-May-3 Altermann Galleries, Santa Fe #104
£20779 $32000 €31169 Starting line (64x122cm-25x48in) 25-Oct-2 Morris & Whiteside, Hilton Head Island #22 est:35000-40000
£32468 $50000 €48702 Thunder bird (122x91cm-48x36in) 25-Oct-2 Morris & Whiteside, Hilton Head Island #19 est:55000-65000
£44304 $70000 €64241 Crow chiefs visit the Minnetarees (91x152cm-36x60in) s. exhib.lit. 26-Jul-3 Coeur d'Alene, Hayden #142/R est:75000-125000
£44521 $65000 €66782 Canyon scout (102x86cm-40x34in) 18-May-2 Altermann Galleries, Santa Fe #87/R

RILEY, Michael (1960-) Australian

Prints

£1549 $2400 €2324 Untitled, from the cloud series, boomerang (85x120cm-33x47in) s.d.2001 ink jet print exhib.lit. 3-Dec-2 Shapiro, Sydney #53 est:1800-2000 (A.D 4290)

RIMBERT, René (1896-1991) French

£10345 $16345 €15000 Petit paysage aux affiches (30x19cm-12x7in) s.i.d.1969 panel prov.lit. 4-Apr-3 Tajan, Paris #100/R

RIMINGTON, Alexander Wallace (c.1854-1918) British

Works on paper

£340 $544 €510 View of a Continental church (51x33cm-20x13in) s. W/C. 11-Mar-3 Gorringes, Lewes #2394

RIMMINGTON, Edith (1902-1986) British

Works on paper

£1500 $2355 €2250 Still life with fish (76x101cm-30x40in) s. 15-Apr-3 Bonhams, Knightsbridge #32/R est:1500-2000

RIMMINGTON, Eric (1926-) British

£300 $480 €450 Spa, Scarborough, two girls standing on a slipway (80x54cm-31x21in) s. board. 13-May-3 Bonhams, Oxford #275

RIMOLDI, Pietro Adamo (1869-?) Italian

£1097 $1733 €1700 Naviglio Grande, Milan (30x55cm-12x22in) s. board. 18-Dec-2 Finarte, Milan #23

RINALDI (?) Italian?

£861 $1309 €1292 Monk enjoying a glass of wine (48x34cm-19x13in) s.i. i.d.1914 verso. 27-Aug-2 Rasmussen, Copenhagen #1970/R (D.KR 10000)

Sculpture

£2278 $3736 €3303 Nymph and faun (34cm-13in) white marble. 4-Jun-3 AB Stockholms Auktionsverk #2397/R est:30000-40000 (S.KR 29000)

RINALDI, Rinaldo (1793-1873) Italian

£1274 $1987 €2000 Tailor mending clothes in his studio (37x32cm-15x13in) s. prov. 5-Nov-2 Sotheby's, Amsterdam #115/R est:2000-3000

Sculpture

£26000 $40560 €39000 Eve and Abel (251x105cm-99x41in) s.i.d.1870 white marble base prov.lit. 9-Apr-3 Sotheby's, London #83/R est:12000-18000

RINCON, Vicente (1893-1958) Spanish

£322 $522 €490 Still life with onions and fish (29x43cm-11x17in) s.indis.d. 21-Jan-3 Ansorena, Madrid #861/R
£493 $769 €720 Seascape (60x100cm-24x39in) s. 8-Apr-3 Ansorena, Madrid #32/R

RINDISBACHER, Peter (1806-1834) Swiss

Works on paper

£42683 $67012 €64025 Hunting the bison (23x36cm-9x14in) s.d.1825 i.verso. 10-Dec-2 Pinneys, Montreal #149 est:80000-120000 (C.D 105000)
£50813 $79776 €76220 Hunting the bison (23x36cm-9x14in) s.d.1825 i.verso. 10-Dec-2 Pinneys, Montreal #150 est:80000-120000 (C.D 125000)

RINDY, Dell M (20th C) American?

£609 $950 €914 Untitled landscape (43x51cm-17x20in) s. 29-Mar-3 Charlton Hall, Columbia #646/R

RING, Hermann Tom (circle) (1521-1595) German

£5449 $8609 €8500 Portrait of young woman (47x32cm-19x13in) d.1593 panel. 16-Nov-2 Lempertz, Koln #1082/R est:9000

RING, Laurits Andersen (1854-1933) Danish

£448 $698 €672 Landscape with houses and church (46x34cm-18x13in) s. 23-Sep-2 Rasmussen, Vejle #2003 (D.KR 5300)
£485 $771 €728 Landscape with Hove Mill, Sejro Bay (16x24cm-6x9in) s.d.29. 5-May-3 Rasmussen, Vejle #465/R (D.KR 5200)
£652 $1036 €978 Portrait of woman (24x18cm-9x7in) s. s.indis.i.d.1886 verso exhib. 10-Mar-3 Rasmussen, Vejle #418/R (D.KR 7000)
£680 $1060 €1020 Gyde (32x20cm-13x8in) s. 5-Aug-2 Rasmussen, Vejle #248/R (D.KR 8000)
£1238 $1907 €1857 Winter - road through village (25x20cm-10x8in) s.d.1911. 4-Sep-2 Kunsthallen, Copenhagen #138/R est:15000 (D.KR 14500)
£1306 $2076 €1959 Hazy landscape with angler by river (19x29cm-7x11in) s.d.05. 5-May-3 Rasmussen, Vejle #459/R est:6000-8000 (D.KR 14000)
£1447 $2286 €2171 Autumn landscape with farm (20x30cm-8x12in) s. 2-Dec-2 Rasmussen, Copenhagen #1298/R est:10000 (D.KR 17000)
£1583 $2517 €2375 Coastal landscape with marram grass (47x70cm-19x28in) s. 5-Mar-3 Rasmussen, Copenhagen #1505/R est:30000-40000 (D.KR 17000)
£2010 $3256 €3015 Village street scene in summer (25x34cm-10x13in) s.d.96 i.verso. 21-May-3 Museumsbygningen, Copenhagen #56/R est:15000-18000 (D.KR 21000)
£2010 $3256 €3015 Village street scene with butcher selling meat (19x27cm-7x11in) s.d.99 i.verso canvas on board. 21-May-3 Museumsbygningen, Copenhagen #59/R est:10000-12000 (D.KR 21000)
£2316 $3612 €3474 Early spring, Melby (41x45cm-16x18in) s.d.1901 exhib. 11-Nov-2 Rasmussen, Vejle #485/R est:25000 (D.KR 27000)
£3234 $5110 €4851 Cottage interior with man reading newspaper and wife knitting (44x53cm-17x21in) 2-Dec-2 Rasmussen, Copenhagen #1573/R est:30000 (D.KR 38000)
£3923 $6356 €5885 Street scene, St Jorgensbjerg (29x20cm-11x8in) s.d.1919 prov. 21-May-3 Museumsbygningen, Copenhagen #62/R est:20000-25000 (D.KR 41000)
£4019 $6511 €6029 Village street with thatched houses, winter (81x101cm-32x40in) s.d.1908. 21-May-3 Museumsbygningen, Copenhagen #63/R est:30000-35000 (D.KR 42000)
£4255 $6723 €6383 Portrait of the artist H A Brendekilde (51x37cm-20x15in) s.d.1882. 2-Dec-2 Rasmussen, Copenhagen #1273/R est:50000 (D.KR 50000)
£7464 $12092 €11196 Railway crossing by the village Ring (45x60cm-18x24in) s.d.90 prov.lit. 21-May-3 Museumsbygningen, Copenhagen #54/R est:30000-40000 (D.KR 78000)
£8511 $13447 €12767 The Cathedral seen from road near Sjordvilla, Roskilde (80x58cm-31x23in) s.d.1928 exhib.prov. 2-Dec-2 Rasmussen, Copenhagen #1157/R est:75000 (D.KR 100000)

Works on paper

£429 $669 €644 Man walking carrying a spade (27x19cm-11x7in) pastel. 11-Nov-2 Rasmussen, Vejle #484/R (D.KR 5000)

RING, Laurits Andersen (attrib) (1854-1933) Danish

£335 $543 €503 Street scene, Rigensgade seen from Ostervold (22x30cm-9x12in) 21-May-3 Museumsbygningen, Copenhagen #55 (D.KR 3500)
£746 $1187 €1119 Landscape with Vesuvius (18x20cm-7x8in) indis sig. canvas on panel. 29-Apr-3 Kunsthallen, Copenhagen #528/R (D.KR 8000)
£1077 $1637 €1616 Street scene, Palermo (19x27cm-7x11in) s.d.1900 prov. 28-Aug-2 Museumsbygningen, Copenhagen #56/R est:10000 (D.KR 12500)

RING, Ole (1902-1972) Danish

£320 $509 €480 Parisian street scene, evening (61x73cm-24x29in) s.i.d.1925. 26-Feb-3 Kunsthallen, Copenhagen #331 (D.KR 3500)
£383 $620 €555 Horses behind a thatched farm (21x31cm-8x12in) s. 26-May-3 Rasmussen, Copenhagen #1476/R (D.KR 4000)
£574 $930 €832 On the outskirts of town (24x33cm-9x13in) s. 26-May-3 Rasmussen, Copenhagen #1477/R (D.KR 6000)
£598 $921 €897 Landscape from Stroby Ladeplads (44x60cm-17x24in) s. 4-Sep-2 Kunsthallen, Copenhagen #111/R (D.KR 7000)
£681 $1076 €1022 Landscape from Naestved (42x52cm-17x20in) s.d.1944. 30-Nov-2 Rasmussen, Havnen #2075 (D.KR 8000)
£773 $1221 €1160 Street in Sakskobing, winter (21x32cm-8x13in) s.d.1963. 13-Nov-2 Kunsthallen, Copenhagen #20/R (D.KR 9000)
£947 $1440 €1421 Thatched house by village pond. Hilly landscape (14x22cm-6x9in) s. one d.1955 two. 27-Aug-2 Rasmussen, Copenhagen #1912/R (D.KR 11000)
£1042 $1729 €1511 Winter's day in St Magleby (38x47cm-15x19in) s. 12-Jun-3 Kunsthallen, Copenhagen #352/R (D.KR 11000)
£1196 $1938 €1734 Summer's day by village pond (50x75cm-20x30in) s. 24-May-3 Rasmussen, Havnen #2030/R est:10000-15000 (D.KR 12500)
£1210 $1925 €1815 Saint Morten's church, Maestved (43x53cm-17x21in) s.d.1944. 5-Mar-3 Rasmussen, Copenhagen #1936/R est:15000 (D.KR 13000)

£1490 $2369 €2235 Village houses by pond (43x70cm-17x28in) s.d.1945. 5-Mar-3 Rasmussen, Copenhagen #2038/R est:20000 (D.KR 16000)
£1914 $3100 €2775 Twilight - near Stranden with Nikolaj Church in background (51x62cm-20x24in) s. 26-May-3 Rasmussen, Copenhagen #1134/R est:20000-25000 (D.KR 20000)
£1914 $3100 €2775 Winter's day in Hoje Taastrup village (41x56cm-16x22in) s. 26-May-3 Rasmussen, Copenhagen #1215/R est:20000-25000 (D.KR 20000)
£6518 $10363 €9777 Winter's day, Kirkestreade, Koge (68x91cm-27x36in) s. 5-Mar-3 Rasmussen, Copenhagen #1606/R est:20000-25000 (D.KR 70000)
£19139 $31005 €27752 Summer's day at Nyhavn, Copenhagen (45x66cm-18x26in) s.d.1948. 26-May-3 Rasmussen, Copenhagen #1135/R est:200000 (D.KR 200000)

RING, Thomas (1892-1983) German
Works on paper
£633 $1000 €1000 Linear composition (32x22cm-13x9in) mono.d.21 pen. 30-Nov-2 Bassenge, Berlin #6586/R

RINGEL, Franz (1940-) Austrian
£1931 $3090 €2800 Obituary (41x55cm-16x22in) s.d.98 acrylic pencil oil chk. 11-Mar-3 Dorotheum, Vienna #278/R est:3000-4000
£4965 $8043 €7000 Portrait of Viktor Matejka (100x70cm-39x28in) s. acrylic prov. 20-May-3 Dorotheum, Vienna #244/R est:8000-12000
£5696 $9000 €9000 Maria in night-shirt (170x129cm-67x51in) s.d.92 i. verso acrylic graphite prov. 27-Nov-2 Dorotheum, Vienna #333/R est:9000-13000
Works on paper
£475 $741 €750 Untitled (31x22cm-12x9in) s.d.2000 s.d. verso mixed media. 15-Oct-2 Dorotheum, Vienna #273/R
£759 $1185 €1200 Untitled (55x42cm-22x17in) s.d.90 pencil col pen. 15-Oct-2 Dorotheum, Vienna #288/R
£795 $1295 €1200 Journey to Petuschki (21x15cm-8x6in) s.i.d.99 mixed media. 28-Jan-3 Dorotheum, Vienna #297/R
£1795 $2836 €2800 Untitled out of the self portrait cycle (100x69cm-39x27in) s.d.86 mixed media. 12-Nov-2 Dorotheum, Vienna #262/R est:2800-3600
£2152 $3400 €3400 Untitled (62x62cm-24x24in) s.d.72 mixed media. 27-Nov-2 Dorotheum, Vienna #280/R est:3600-5000
£2639 $4169 €3800 Woman sitting on sofa (78x85cm-31x33in) s.d.84 mixed media. 24-Apr-3 Dorotheum, Vienna #247/R est:3800-5000
£2778 $4417 €4000 Untitled (60x71cm-24x28in) s.d.67 mixed media. 29-Apr-3 Wiener Kunst Auktionen, Vienna #452/R est:4500-7500
£3472 $5521 €5000 Untitled (56x75cm-22x30in) s.d.74. 29-Apr-3 Wiener Kunst Auktionen, Vienna #491/R est:5000-7000

RINGEL, Max (19/20th C) German?
£357 $543 €550 Reclining female nude (92x177cm-36x70in) s. 5-Jul-2 Weidler, Nurnberg #8726/R

RINGNER, Enoch (1870-1967) Swedish
£390 $617 €585 Interior from a shoemaker's workshop (69x56cm-27x22in) s.d.1914. 5-Apr-3 Rasmussen, Havnen #2051/R (D.KR 4200)

RINGQVIST, Bernt (1917-1966) Swedish
Works on paper
£425 $705 €616 Vessel in moonlight (34x30cm-13x12in) s.d.40 mixed media panel prov. 16-Jun-3 Lilla Bukowskis, Stockholm #272 (S.KR 5500)

RINK, Paulus Philippus (1861-1903) Dutch
£12102 $18879 €19000 By the meadow (61x90cm-24x35in) s.d.1899 s.verso. 6-Nov-2 Vendue Huis, Gravenhage #565/R est:7000-10000

RINK, William (20th C) British?
£360 $565 €540 Fisherfolk on the shore before barges at dusk (51x102cm-20x40in) indis sig. 16-Apr-3 Christie's, Kensington #918/R

RIOCREUX, Alfred (19th C) French
Works on paper
£348 $550 €550 Etude d'azalee (29x20cm-11x8in) s.i.d.1876 W/C gouache. 27-Nov-2 Christie's, Paris #290/R
£372 $580 €550 Etudes de plantes (60x44cm-24x17in) s. W/C gouache htd white. 27-Mar-3 Christie's, Paris #209/R

RIOPELLE, Jean-Paul (1923-2002) Canadian
£6584 $10206 €9876 Nouvelles impressions no.99 (22x16cm-9x6in) init. painted 1977. 3-Dec-2 Joyner, Toronto #121/R est:20000-25000 (C.D 16000)
£7631 $12056 €11447 Chateau II (36x28cm-14x11in) d.1977. 1-Dec-2 Levis, Calgary #328/R (C.D 19000)
£15217 $23587 €22826 Les oies sur la ville (160x240cm-63x94in) s. stretcher mixed media collage prov.exhib. 4-Dec-2 Koller, Zurich #194/R est:60000-90000 (S.FR 35000)
£16000 $26240 €24000 Canoe Place (50x60cm-20x24in) s.d.60 prov. 3-Jun-3 Joyner, Toronto #82/R est:25000-35000 (C.D 36000)
£20423 $33901 €29000 Sans titre (100x81cm-39x32in) s.d.62 paint. 18-Jun-3 Anaf, Lyon #69/R est:30000-40000
£20492 $31967 €30738 P M 15 (38x46cm-15x18in) s.d.60 prov. 10-Sep-2 Iegor de Saint Hippolyte, Montreal #98/R (C.D 50000)
£22000 $36740 €31900 Composition (60x46cm-24x18in) s. prov. 26-Jun-3 Sotheby's, London #182/R est:20000-30000
£22358 $35102 €33537 Cascade (74x96cm-29x38in) s. 12-Dec-2 Iegor de Saint Hippolyte, Montreal #80/R (C.D 55000)
£22634 $35082 €33951 Untitled (45x54cm-18x21in) s.d.59 prov. 3-Dec-2 Joyner, Toronto #104/R est:60000-70000 (C.D 55000)
£24444 $40089 €36666 L'oiseau des neiges (99x72cm-39x28in) s.i.d.1962 verso prov.exhib. 27-May-3 Sotheby's, Toronto #91/R est:60000-80000 (C.D 55000)
£28170 $46762 €40000 Composition (61x73cm-24x29in) s.d.58 prov.exhib. 12-Jun-3 Tajan, Paris #41/R est:50000-60000
£32110 $53624 €46560 Nios (64x80cm-25x31in) s. s.i.d.1959 stretcher prov. 20-Jun-3 Kornfeld, Bern #133/R est:70000 (S.FR 70000)
£32258 $50968 €48387 L'ombre d'un grand oiseau (63x76cm-25x30in) s. prov.lit. 18-Nov-2 Sotheby's, Toronto #77/R est:100000-120000 (C.D 80000)
£33333 $54667 €50000 Composition (68x84cm-27x33in) s. prov. 27-May-3 Sotheby's, Toronto #187/R est:70000-90000 (C.D 75000)
£33632 $53812 €50448 Composition (65x81cm-26x32in) s. i.d.1960 verso prov.lit. 15-May-3 Heffel, Vancouver #132/R est:70000-80000 (C.D 75000)
£34000 $55760 €51000 Bivouac (97x130cm-38x51in) s. prov.exhib. 7-Feb-3 Sotheby's, London #231/R est:25000-35000
£34722 $54861 €50000 Composition (54x81cm-21x32in) s.d. prov. 27-Apr-3 Perrin, Versailles #31/R est:50000-55000
£35000 $57400 €52500 Composition (89x116cm-35x46in) s. painted 1959-60 prov. 6-Feb-3 Christie's, London #619/R est:35000-45000
£35874 $57399 €53811 Itineraire (89x117cm-35x46in) s.i.1958 verso prov.exhib.lit. 15-May-3 Heffel, Vancouver #59/R est:80000-100000 (C.D 80000)
£36601 $58562 €56000 Habite le vent (81x65cm-32x26in) s.d.1961. 4-Jan-3 Meeting Art, Vercelli #408 est:30000
£49383 $76543 €74075 Untitled (72x99cm-28x39in) s. painted 1962 prov.exhib.lit. 3-Dec-2 Joyner, Toronto #77/R est:100000-125000 (C.D 120000)
£55072 $90318 €76000 Composition (60x73cm-24x29in) s. s.d.1955 verso prov. 27-May-3 Tajan, Paris #8/R est:50000-60000
£65625 $105000 €98438 Puits de lumiere (100x81cm-39x32in) s. s.d.56 verso prov. 15-May-3 Christie's, Rockefeller NY #139/R est:70000-90000
£110000 $180400 €165000 Untitled (114x146cm-45x57in) painted 1953 prov.exhib.lit. 5-Feb-3 Christie's, London #32/R est:100000-150000
£150000 $250500 €225000 Untitled (88x130cm-35x51in) s.d.53 prov.exhib.lit. 25-Jun-3 Sotheby's, London #31/R est:150000-200000
Works on paper
£4167 $6583 €6000 Composition (79x58cm-31x23in) gouache exec.c.1955 prov. 28-Apr-3 Cornette de St.Cyr, Paris #496/R est:6000-8000
£5500 $8525 €8250 Untitled (25x32cm-10x13in) s.d.47 pen ink col ink paper on card. 5-Dec-2 Christie's, Kensington #178/R est:2500-3500
£6061 $9636 €8788 Untitled, superbagneres (44x55cm-17x22in) s.d.1964 W/C gouache ink prov. 1-May-3 Heffel, Vancouver #91/R est:12000-15000 (C.D 14000)
£7586 $11986 €11000 Untitled (45x37cm-18x15in) s.d.53 Chinese ink ink. 2-Apr-3 Christie's, Paris #26/R est:6000
£10090 $16143 €15135 Composition (51x66cm-20x26in) s.d.1958 gouache paper on canvas prov.lit. 15-May-3 Heffel, Vancouver #77/R est:20000-30000 (C.D 22500)
£11523 $17860 €17285 Foret musicale (25x34cm-10x13in) s.d.48 W/C ink prov. 3-Dec-2 Joyner, Toronto #61/R est:25000-30000 (C.D 28000)
£12329 $19356 €18000 Untitled (17x13cm-7x5in) s.d.46 W/C ink. 15-Apr-3 Laurence Calmels, Paris #4401/R est:20000
£13014 $20432 €19000 Untitled (24x31cm-9x12in) s.d.47 W/C ink exhib. 15-Apr-3 Laurence Calmels, Paris #4402/R est:20000
£36017 $57267 €54026 Composition (149x133cm-59x52in) s. gouache paper on board exhib. 23-Mar-3 Hodgins, Calgary #95/R est:100000-125000 (C.D 85000)

RIORDON, Eric (1906-1948) Canadian
£410 $635 €615 Little red cottage, Ste-Adele (41x51cm-16x20in) s. 24-Sep-2 Iegor de Saint Hippolyte, Montreal #109 (C.D 1000)
£697 $1080 €1046 October day St Sauveur (30x41cm-12x16in) s. panel prov. 24-Sep-2 Ritchie, Toronto #3170/R (C.D 1700)
£889 $1458 €1334 Winter landscape with cabin (30x40cm-12x16in) s. prov. 3-Jun-3 Joyner, Toronto #162/R est:2000-3000 (C.D 2000)
£1152 $1786 €1728 Cache River Country, Que, winter (30x40cm-12x16in) s. board prov. 3-Dec-2 Joyner, Toronto #160/R est:2000-3000 (C.D 2800)
£1152 $1786 €1728 Sunny winter's day (30x40cm-12x16in) s. 3-Dec-2 Joyner, Toronto #293/R est:2000-3000 (C.D 2800)
£1333 $2187 €2000 Early spring (40x50cm-16x20in) s. board prov. 3-Jun-3 Joyner, Toronto #184/R est:3000-4000 (C.D 3000)

RIOS, Luigi da (1844-1892) Italian

£18239 $28088 €29000 Maternity (150x110cm-59x43in) s.d.1880 lit. 23-Oct-2 Finarte, Milan #173/R est:30000-35000

RIOS, Ricardo de los (attrib) (1846-1929) Spanish

£559 $888 €839 Sculpture in the park (64x44cm-25x17in) indis.sig. 5-Mar-3 Rasmussen, Copenhagen #2023/R (D.KR 6000)

RIOU, Edouard (1833-1900) French

£245 $387 €368 Hunters in landscape (15x24cm-6x9in) s. panel. 16-Nov-2 Crafoord, Lund #9/R (S.KR 3500)

Works on paper

£3901 $6514 €5500 Inauguration du canal de Suez (25x33cm-10x13in) s. W/C gouache. 23-Jun-3 Beaussant & Lefèvre, Paris #112/R est:1500-2000

RIOU, Louis (1893-1958) French

£1282 $1987 €2000 Vue d'Alger (73x54cm-29x21in) s. 5-Dec-2 Gros & Delettrez, Paris #45

Works on paper

£881 $1356 €1400 Port d'Alger (36x52cm-14x20in) s. gouache. 23-Oct-2 Rabourdin & Choppin de Janvry, Paris #206/R

RIOULT, Louis Edouard (1790-1855) French

£2158 $3540 €3000 Portrait d'un Turc (47x37cm-19x15in) s.d.1825. 4-Jun-3 Tajan, Paris #306/R est:3000-4000

RIP, Willem C (1856-1922) Dutch

£350 $550 €525 Figure on a pastoral track (30x23cm-12x9in) s. panel. 16-Apr-3 Christie's, Kensington #744/R
£764 $1260 €1100 Polder landscape at dawn (42x61cm-17x24in) 1-Jul-3 Christie's, Amsterdam #120/R
£884 $1406 €1300 Dutch landscape lit by evening sun (31x49cm-12x19in) s. i. verso. 19-Mar-3 Neumeister, Munich #710/R est:1500
£1519 $2370 €2400 Wijk near Duurstede (26x35cm-10x14in) s. i.verso panel. 21-Oct-2 Glerum, Amsterdam #69/R est:1200-1800
£2113 $3401 €3000 Mill on canal with boat (46x65cm-18x26in) s. 7-May-3 Vendue Huis, Gravenhage #460/R est:3000-4000

Works on paper

£446 $687 €700 Angler in a polder landscape at dusk (24x34cm-9x13in) s. black chk W/C gouache. 3-Sep-2 Christie's, Amsterdam #172
£520 $868 €754 Dutch river landscape with windmills (31x57cm-12x22in) s. W/C. 23-Jun-3 Bonhams, Bath #19
£1274 $1987 €2000 Village on the water (49x64cm-19x25in) s. W/C. 6-Nov-2 Vendue Huis, Gravenhage #544/R est:2000-2500

RIPA, Erme (?) Italian?

£377 $589 €600 Cottage (35x45cm-14x18in) s.d.46 tempera board. 20-Sep-2 Semenzato, Venice #577

RIPLEY, Aiden Lassell (1896-1969) American

£2656 $4250 €3984 Panoramic spring landscape (61x91cm-24x36in) s. 11-Jan-3 James Julia, Fairfield #270 est:5000-8000

Works on paper

£382 $600 €573 Self portrait (58x37cm-23x15in) s.d.29 chl. 22-Nov-2 Skinner, Boston #156/R
£688 $1100 €1032 River (36x51cm-14x20in) s. W/C. 11-Jan-3 James Julia, Fairfield #271 est:3000-5000
£1863 $3000 €2795 Two farm workers (36x51cm-14x20in) s. i.verso W/C. 18-Feb-3 Arthur James, Florida #445
£5696 $9000 €8259 Winter grouse (23x33cm-9x13in) s. W/C. 26-Jul-3 Coeur d'Alene, Hayden #11/R est:5000-10000
£10526 $16000 €15789 Hunting scene at Sunnyhill Farm. s.d.1939 W/C. 30-Aug-2 Thomaston Place, Thomaston #40
£11538 $18000 €16730 Good retrieve (64x79cm-25x31in) s.d.1939 W/C. 13-Oct-2 Cobbs, Peterborough #504a
£15753 $23000 €23630 Cock and hen pheasant (46x74cm-18x29in) s. W/C. 3-Nov-1 North East Auctions, Portsmouth #743/R est:12000-18000

RIPOLLES, Juan (1932-) Spanish

£1384 $2131 €2200 Interior with two figures (54x65cm-21x26in) s.d.1979. 28-Oct-2 Segre, Madrid #175/R
£1517 $2397 €2200 Woman with fan (61x50cm-24x20in) s.d.1993 s.d.verso. 1-Apr-3 Segre, Madrid #340/R

RIPPEL, Morris (b.1930) American

£14722 $23850 €21347 Spirit of the basketmakers (46x76cm-18x30in) egg tempera. 23-May-3 Altermann Galleries, Santa Fe #176

Works on paper

£25316 $40000 €36708 Ranch house on the Rio Grande (33x56cm-13x22in) s. W/C. 26-Jul-3 Coeur d'Alene, Hayden #186/R est:8000-12000

RIPPINGILLE, Edward Villiers (1798-1859) British

£280 $437 €420 Spectators (13x24cm-5x9in) s.d.1826 panel. 8-Apr-3 Bonhams, Knightsbridge #206/R

RIPPL-RONAI, Jozsef (1861-1927) Hungarian

£18164 $28336 €26338 Lady in hat and in fur coat (51x40cm-20x16in) pastel board. 12-Apr-3 Mu Terem Galeria, Budapest #185/R est:5500000 (H.F 6500000)
£24508 $38232 €36762 Woman in Paris with purple scarf (37x30cm-15x12in) 11-Sep-2 Kieselbach, Budapest #130/R (H.F 9500000)
£30957 $48293 €46436 Uncle Fulop, 1915 (52x75cm-20x30in) s.d.1915 cardboard. 11-Sep-2 Kieselbach, Budapest #216/R (H.F 12000000)
£61915 $96587 €89777 Woman's head with red bun (41x32cm-16x13in) s.d.1891 exhib.lit. 13-Sep-2 Mu Terem Galeria, Budapest #73/R est:7500000 (H.F 24000000)
£61915 $96587 €89777 Young woman in a red hat (69x48cm-27x19in) s. cardboard prov.exhib. 13-Sep-2 Mu Terem Galeria, Budapest #154/R est:14000000 (H.F 24000000)
£112949 $175071 €169424 Picnic in the garden of the Roman villa (70x100cm-28x39in) s. cardboard. 6-Dec-2 Kieselbach, Budapest #75/R (H.F 42000000)
£162079 $252843 €243119 Saarga zongoraszoba II (71x103cm-28x41in) s.d.1909 board. 11-Apr-3 Kieselbach, Budapest #43/R est:25000000-58000000 (H.F 58000000)

Works on paper

£861 $1334 €1292 Drinking coffee (28x45cm-11x18in) s. W/C. 6-Dec-2 Kieselbach, Budapest #1/R (H.F 320000)
£1806 $2817 €2709 My grandmother, 1895 (23x36cm-9x14in) s. pastel. 11-Sep-2 Kieselbach, Budapest #4/R (H.F 700000)
£2689 $4168 €4034 Portrait of the Kossuth devoted uncle (37x29cm-15x11in) s. pastel. 6-Dec-2 Kieselbach, Budapest #153/R (H.F 1000000)
£4500 $7380 €6750 In the cafe (16x21cm-6x8in) s.i.d.1915 pencil col crayon. 3-Jun-3 Sotheby's, London #99/R est:4000-6000
£4751 $7411 €6889 Woman sleeping (37x29cm-15x11in) s. pastel exhib. 12-Apr-3 Mu Terem Galeria, Budapest #174/R est:1500000 (H.F 1700000)
£5110 $7920 €7665 Rakoczi - celebration in Kassa (20x29cm-8x11in) s. pastel. 6-Dec-2 Kieselbach, Budapest #22/R (H.F 1900000)
£5379 $8337 €8069 Twilight (40x50cm-16x20in) s. pastel. 6-Dec-2 Kieselbach, Budapest #122/R (H.F 2000000)
£5916 $9170 €8874 Lake Balation (24x30cm-9x12in) s. pastel. 6-Dec-2 Kieselbach, Budapest #12/R (H.F 2200000)
£7825 $12206 €11346 French soldiers (18x25cm-7x10in) s. pastel. 12-Apr-3 Mu Terem Galeria, Budapest #196/R est:850000 (H.F 2800000)
£9501 $14822 €14252 Landscape in Somogy with golden grain (41x51cm-16x20in) s.d.919 pastel. 11-Apr-3 Kieselbach, Budapest #202/R est:3200000-3400000 (H.F 3400000)
£14791 $22926 €22187 Self portrait in a red cap (51x41cm-20x16in) s. pastel. 6-Dec-2 Kieselbach, Budapest #166/R (H.F 5500000)
£15479 $24147 €22445 Self-portrait with pipe (52x42cm-20x17in) s.d.1922 pastel. 13-Sep-2 Mu Terem Galeria, Budapest #199/R est:5500000 (H.F 6000000)
£16769 $26159 €25154 Girl in blue background (27x39cm-11x15in) s. pastel. 11-Sep-2 Kieselbach, Budapest #209/R (H.F 6500000)
£21928 $34208 €32892 Larazine with parrot (37x29cm-15x11in) s. pastel. 11-Sep-2 Kieselbach, Budapest #174/R (H.F 8500000)
£22356 $34875 €33534 Girl in blue dress (50x40cm-20x16in) s. pastel. 11-Apr-3 Kieselbach, Budapest #194/R est:3800000-8000000 (H.F 8000000)
£22859 $35431 €34289 Portrait of a girl with a red scarf (51x41cm-20x16in) s. pastel. 6-Dec-2 Kieselbach, Budapest #64/R (H.F 8500000)
£24203 $37515 €36305 Actress, Rozsi Ilosval (52x42cm-20x17in) s. pastel. 6-Dec-2 Kieselbach, Budapest #152/R (H.F 9000000)
£87763 $140421 €131645 Embroidering women (42x51cm-17x20in) s. pastel exec.c.1894. 16-May-3 Kieselbach, Budapest #46/R (H.F 30000000)

RIQUER E INGLADA, Alejandro de (1856-1920) Spanish

Works on paper

£878 $1370 €1300 Modernist woman (30x22cm-12x9in) s.d.1897 W/C. 25-Mar-3 Durán, Madrid #699/R

RISAGER, Robert (20th C) Danish

£253 $395 €380 Figure group I (63x78cm-25x31in) s.d.53. 18-Sep-2 Kunsthallen, Copenhagen #150 (D.KR 3000)

RISBERG, Harald (1917-1996) Norwegian

£263 $416 €395 Fishing village in Lofoten (50x61cm-20x24in) s.d.50 panel. 17-Dec-2 Grev Wedels Plass, Oslo #267 (N.KR 3000)

RISBERG, Roger (1956-) Swedish?

£494 $781 €741 Carolean dreams (50x50cm-20x20in) mono. s.d.1991 verso. 28-Apr-3 Bukowskis, Stockholm #932/R (S.KR 6500)

RISLEY, Tom (1947-) Australian
£415 $648 €719 Still life with golden yellow (90x90cm-35x35in) s.verso wood acrylic board prov. 31-Mar-3 Goodman, Sydney #158/R (A.D 1100)
Sculpture
£3960 $6178 €6861 Untitled (206cm-81in) s. painted welded steel prov. 31-Mar-3 Goodman, Sydney #168/R (A.D 10500)

RISPOLI, Giuseppe (20th C) Italian
£250 $380 €375 Naples street market (34x51cm-13x20in) s. canvas on board. 29-Aug-2 Christie's, Kensington #186

RISSA (1938-) German
Works on paper
£1489 $2413 €2100 The sleeper (63x54cm-25x21in) s.i.d.93 Indian ink gouache board. 24-May-3 Van Ham, Cologne #503 est:2600

RISSALA, Kaapo (1900-1971) Finnish
£290 $459 €450 Washerwomen (85x65cm-33x26in) s.d.1929. 19-Dec-2 Hagelstam, Helsinki #811
£828 $1308 €1200 Helsinki (110x140cm-43x55in) s.d.1942-44. 3-Apr-3 Hagelstam, Helsinki #1045

RISSANEN, Juho (1873-1950) Finnish
£1646 $2600 €2600 Park landscape (60x46cm-24x18in) s.d.1914. 1-Dec-2 Bukowskis, Helsinki #147/R est:1500-1800
£2590 $4144 €3600 Self-portrait (45x35cm-18x14in) s.d.1910 canvas on board. 17-May-3 Hagelstam, Helsinki #139/R est:4000
£3669 $6017 €5100 Cleaning the whortleberries (95x70cm-37x28in) s.d.1916. 4-Jun-3 Bukowskis, Helsinki #404/R est:3500
Works on paper
£1677 $2650 €2600 Father (20x26cm-8x10in) s. W/C. 19-Dec-2 Hagelstam, Helsinki #900/R est:200
£1835 $2863 €2900 Teacher hitting small boy with birch rod (105x95cm-41x37in) s.d.1934 mixed media. 12-Sep-2 Hagelstam, Helsinki #957/R est:1800
£3239 $5215 €4600 Harvest time (57x20cm-22x8in) s.d.31 W/C. 10-May-3 Bukowskis, Helsinki #85/R est:2000-2500

RISUENO, Joaquin (1957-) Spanish
£1507 $2351 €2200 Landscape (50x61cm-20x24in) s.d.1996 verso. 8-Apr-3 Ansorena, Madrid #253/R

RITCHIE, John (fl.1841-1875) British
£4800 $7392 €7200 Hide and seek (46x44cm-18x17in) init. arched top panel. 5-Sep-2 Christie's, Kensington #324/R est:3000-5000
£5000 $8300 €7500 Shadow on the tree (35x30cm-14x12in) prov.exhib. 10-Jun-3 Christie's, London #123/R est:6000-8000
£22000 $35420 €33000 Vestry meeting (45x60cm-18x24in) init. prov.exhib.lit. 20-Feb-3 Christie's, London #117/R est:30000

RITCHIE, Maxine (1949-) Australian?
£1316 $2000 €1974 Eclips (63x84cm-25x33in) s. acrylic canvas on board. 19-Aug-2 Joel, Victoria #183 est:3000-5000 (A.D 3750)
Works on paper
£1214 $1918 €1821 Snowballs (74x94cm-29x37in) s. synthetic polymer canvas on board. 27-Nov-2 Deutscher-Menzies, Melbourne #158/R est:3000-4000 (A.D 3400)
£1398 $2124 €2097 Frangipani, from the Aura Series I (61x83cm-24x33in) s. synthetic polymer paint canvas on board. 28-Aug-2 Deutscher-Menzies, Melbourne #260/R est:4000-5000 (A.D 3900)

RITCHIE, Ross (1941-) New Zealander
£704 $1162 €1021 Jack mackerel (44x60cm-17x24in) s.d.1988 prov. 1-Jul-3 Peter Webb, Auckland #92/R est:3500-5500 (NZ.D 2000)

RITHMANN, J C (18th C) German
£943 $1472 €1500 Man's portrait (85x69cm-33x27in) i.d.1754 verso. 19-Sep-2 Dr Fritz Nagel, Stuttgart #892/R
£1887 $2943 €3000 Six children (102x238cm-40x94in) 19-Sep-2 Dr Fritz Nagel, Stuttgart #894/R est:3000

RITMAN, Lieke (20th C) ?
Works on paper
£320 $499 €480 Beach huts (76x76cm-30x30in) s.d.1984 mixed media. 16-Oct-2 David Lay, Penzance #281/R

RITMAN, Louis (1889-1963) American/Russian
£1032 $1600 €1548 Village trees (66x61cm-26x24in) s. prov. 3-Dec-2 Christie's, Rockefeller NY #598/R est:2500-3500
£1132 $1800 €1698 Tree mood (53x81cm-21x32in) prov. 5-Mar-3 Christie's, Rockefeller NY #80/R est:2000-3000
£1195 $1900 €1793 Country road (46x37cm-18x15in) s. panel prov. 5-Mar-3 Christie's, Rockefeller NY #82/R est:2000-3000
£1299 $2000 €1949 La ferme (54x64cm-21x25in) s. 4-Sep-2 Christie's, Rockefeller NY #340/R est:3000-5000
£1557 $2600 €2258 Reaching for the sky (54x64cm-21x25in) s. canvas on masonite prov. 18-Jun-3 Christie's, Los Angeles #44/R est:3000-5000
£29940 $50000 €43413 Girl on balcony (93x74cm-37x29in) s. prov. 18-Jun-3 Christie's, Los Angeles #11/R est:40000-60000
£61728 $100000 €92592 Reminiscence (65x81cm-26x32in) s. prov. 22-May-3 Christie's, Rockefeller NY #45/R est:120000-180000
£62893 $100000 €94340 In the flower garden, Frieseke's garden, Giverny (28x24cm-11x9in) s. painted c.1916. 4-May-3 Treadway Gallery, Cincinnati #531/R est:140000-180000
£197531 $320000 €296297 Day in July (92x92cm-36x36in) s.d.1918 prov.exhib.lit. 22-May-3 Christie's, Rockefeller NY #42/R est:300000-500000

RITSCHEL, William (1864-1949) American
£3145 $5000 €4718 Harbour view with fisherfolk (56x74cm-22x29in) s. 7-Mar-3 Skinner, Boston #497/R est:2500-4500
£9494 $15000 €14241 Fishing boats (56x84cm-22x33in) s. prov. 24-Apr-3 Shannon's, Milford #4/R est:15000-25000
£50955 $80000 €76433 Wind carved cypresses, point Lobos (76x91cm-30x36in) s. 19-Nov-2 Butterfields, San Francisco #8204/R est:60000-80000
Works on paper
£3012 $5000 €4367 Dutch harbour scene (44x70cm-17x28in) s. pencil W/C paperboard. 11-Jun-3 Butterfields, San Francisco #4207/R est:3000-5000
£3025 $4750 €4538 Storm approaching Tahiti (51x66cm-20x26in) s. pencil W/C prov.exhib.lit. 19-Nov-2 Butterfields, San Francisco #8237/R est:4000-6000
£4217 $7000 €6115 Beaching the boat (65x86cm-26x34in) s. gouache paper on board prov. 11-Jun-3 Butterfields, San Francisco #4206/R est:3000-5000

RITSCHL, Otto (1885-1976) German
£1076 $1668 €1700 Composition (80x60cm-31x24in) s.d.1968/33 i. verso. 28-Sep-2 Ketterer, Hamburg #515/R est:1600-1800
£1812 $2971 €2500 Composition 56/14 (52x39cm-20x15in) s.d.56 s.i. verso masonite prov. 28-May-3 Lempertz, Koln #371/R est:4000
£2536 $4159 €3500 Composition (65x80cm-26x31in) s.d.56 s.i. verso prov. 28-May-3 Lempertz, Koln #372/R est:6000
£3901 $6319 €5500 Composition 1964/21 (130x97cm-51x38in) s.d.64l. 20-May-3 Dorotheum, Vienna #55/R est:6000-7000
£8511 $13787 €12000 Mykorandos (76x55cm-30x22in) s.d.27 oil tempera. 20-May-3 Dorotheum, Vienna #25/R est:14000-24000
£9615 $14904 €15000 Composition 65/15 (130x97cm-51x38in) s.d.1965 i.verso prov. 6-Dec-2 Ketterer, Munich #162/R est:15000-17000

RITSEMA, Coba (1876-1961) Dutch
£380 $592 €600 Flower garden (31x47cm-12x19in) s. 21-Oct-2 Glerum, Amsterdam #81
£475 $741 €750 Still life with Biedermeier bouquet (75x90cm-30x35in) s. 21-Oct-2 Glerum, Amsterdam #56
£4717 $7264 €7500 Still life with flowers (33x40cm-13x16in) s. 22-Oct-2 Sotheby's, Amsterdam #117/R est:5000-7000

RITT, Augustin (1765-1799) Russian
Miniatures
£1400 $2240 €2100 Portrait of a lady with bejeweled headdress and fur trimmed robes (5x3cm-2x1in) s.d.1795 W/C on ivory. 11-Mar-3 Gorringes, Lewes #2270 est:1500-2000

RITTENBERG, Henry R (attrib) (1879-1969) American
£759 $1200 €1139 Still life of vase of peonies (76x69cm-30x27in) 26-Apr-3 Thomaston Place, Thomaston #112

RITTER, Anne Gregory (1868-1929) American
£535 $850 €803 French harbour (28x33cm-11x13in) s.d. canvas on board. 2-Mar-3 Toomey, Oak Park #553/R

RITTER, Caspar (1861-1923) German
£787 $1267 €1181 Young boy in front of wooden chalet (34x25cm-13x10in) s.d.21 panel. 7-May-3 Dobiaschofsky, Bern #913/R est:2500 (S.FR 1700)

RITTER, Chris (1906-1976) American
Works on paper
£274 $450 €397 Summer tree (51x64cm-20x25in) s.d.1941 W/C prov. 1-Jun-3 Wright, Chicago #219/R

RITTER, Leo (19/20th C) ?
£371 $605 €560 Naissance de Venus (20x40cm-8x16in) on porcelain after C Chaplin. 13-Feb-3 Muizon & Le Coent, Paris #1

RITTER, Wilhelm Georg (1850-1926) German
£1844 $2987 €2600 View over the rooftops of Nurnberg (58x44cm-23x17in) s. 22-May-3 Dorotheum, Vienna #94/R est:2800-3400

RITTS, Herb (1952-) American
Photographs
£2500 $4050 €3750 Richard Gere, San Bernardino (43x33cm-17x13in) s.i.d.verso silver print edition 15/25 lit. 22-May-3 Sotheby's, London #196/R est:3000-5000
£2597 $4000 €3896 Waterfall IV, Hollywood (49x38cm-19x15in) s.i.d.1988 num.6/25 verso platinum print prov.lit. 25-Oct-2 Phillips, New York #173/R est:5000-7000
£2600 $4212 €3900 Rachel with shark, Hollywood (46x31cm-18x12in) s.i.d.num.17/25 verso silver print. 22-May-3 Sotheby's, London #195/R est:2000-3000
£4430 $7000 €6645 Body shop, Fred with Tires, Hollywood (48x39cm-19x15in) s.d.1984 num.3/25 gelatin silver print. 22-Apr-3 Butterfields, San Francisco #2493/R est:5000-7000
£10759 $17000 €16139 Versace dress, back view, el mirage (56x47cm-22x19in) s.i.d.1990 num.10/25 gelatin silver print lit. 22-Apr-3 Christie's, Rockefeller NY #113/R est:15000-20000

RITTUN, Thorstein (1929-) Norwegian
£736 $1126 €1104 Green landscape (74x90cm-29x35in) s. 26-Aug-2 Blomqvist, Lysaker #1320 (N.KR 8500)
£952 $1457 €1428 Flower seller (46x61cm-18x24in) s. painted 1954. 26-Aug-2 Blomqvist, Lysaker #1319/R (N.KR 11000)
£1096 $1732 €1644 Marsh marigolds (100x66cm-39x26in) s.d.92 s.i.stretcher exhib. 17-Dec-2 Grev Wedels Plass, Oslo #268/R (N.KR 12500)

RITZENHOFEN, Hubert (1879-1961) Dutch
£1389 $2292 €2000 Katwijk, awaiting the return (80x116cm-31x46in) 1-Jul-3 Christie's, Amsterdam #71 est:1000-1500

RITZMANN, Jakob (1894-?) Swiss
£472 $746 €708 Boy with cat in calf stall (38x65cm-15x26in) 29-Nov-2 Zofingen, Switzerland #3043 (S.FR 1100)

RITZOW, Charlotte (1971-) German
Works on paper
£321 $503 €500 Behind bars (50x80cm-20x31in) s. s.verso mixed media on canvas exec.2002. 23-Nov-2 Meeting Art, Vercelli #10
£411 $642 €650 Posing (60x50cm-24x20in) s. mixed media on canvas exec.2001. 14-Sep-2 Meeting Art, Vercelli #865/R

RIVA, Egidio (1866-1946) Italian
£306 $487 €450 Rio San Bravasio, Venice (18x24cm-7x9in) s. board. 18-Mar-3 Finarte, Milan #211

RIVA, Giovanni (1890-1973) Italian
Works on paper
£340 $541 €500 Model (30x24cm-12x9in) s.d.1927 pastel card. 1-Mar-3 Meeting Art, Vercelli #230

RIVALZ, Antoine (1667-1735) French
£26452 $41794 €41000 Cleopatre (77x63cm-30x25in) 18-Dec-2 Piasa, Paris #66/R est:10000

RIVALZ, Antoine (attrib) (1667-1735) French
Works on paper
£621 $993 €900 Etude de trois personnages (16x23cm-6x9in) ink wash. 12-Mar-3 E & Eve, Paris #29

RIVAROLI, Giuseppe (1885-1943) Italian
£942 $1545 €1300 Nudo femminile con bambini (24x31cm-9x12in) s.d.1921 panel. 27-May-3 Finarte, Milan #51/R est:1300-1600
£1392 $2200 €2200 Night party (83x104cm-33x41in) 26-Nov-2 Christie's, Rome #95/R
£1538 $2431 €2400 Mythological scene (54x61cm-21x24in) s. 15-Nov-2 Farsetti, Prato #515

RIVAS Y OLIVER, Antonio (19th C) Spanish
£779 $1138 €1200 Coastal view (17x29cm-7x11in) s. board. 17-Jun-2 Ansorena, Madrid #380/R

RIVAS, Antonio (19th C) Italian
£8500 $13260 €12750 Odalisque (29x47cm-11x19in) s.i. panel prov. 15-Oct-2 Sotheby's, London #185/R est:10000-15000

RIVERA, Diego (1886-1957) Mexican
£28662 $45000 €42993 Portrait of man (46x38cm-18x15in) s.d.1911 prov. 19-Nov-2 Sotheby's, New York #76/R est:50000
£136986 $215068 €200000 Cheminee (73x59cm-29x23in) s.d. oil crayon double-sided. 15-Apr-3 Laurence Calmels, Paris #4403/R est:150000
£165605 $260000 €248408 Woman selling corn (67x50cm-26x20in) s.d.26 prov.exhib.lit. 20-Nov-2 Christie's, Rockefeller NY #15/R est:400000-600000
£197452 $310000 €296178 Portrait of man (82x46cm-32x18in) painted 1916 exhib.lit. 19-Nov-2 Sotheby's, New York #9/R est:450000
£229299 $360000 €343949 Still life (81x54cm-32x21in) init.d.16 s.d.verso prov. 19-Nov-2 Sotheby's, New York #7/R est:550000
Prints
£4088 $6500 €6132 Boy and dog (42x30cm-17x12in) s.d.num.40 lithograph edition of 100. 2-May-3 Sotheby's, New York #42/R est:5000-7000
£7547 $12000 €11321 Sleep (41x30cm-16x12in) s.d.num.61 lithograph edition of 100. 2-May-3 Sotheby's, New York #41/R est:8000-12000
Works on paper
£1410 $2200 €2115 Mask at the Huejozzingo Carnival (38x28cm-15x11in) s. pencil dr prov. 10-Nov-2 Selkirks, St. Louis #631/R est:2000-2500
£2564 $4000 €3846 Untitled, mountain landscape (16x23cm-6x9in) s.indis.d.1929 W/C pencil prov. 14-Oct-2 Butterfields, San Francisco #2130/R est:6000-8000
£2994 $5000 €4341 Autorretrato con Espejos (23x23cm-9x9in) s.d.1951 conte crayon pencil. 21-Jun-3 Charlton Hall, Columbia #514/R est:5000-8000
£3049 $5000 €4421 Untitled - man with boy (36x25cm-14x10in) s.d.34 chl on rice paper prov. 1-Jun-3 Wright, Chicago #112/R est:5000-7000
£3205 $5000 €4808 Untitled, mountain landscape (15x22cm-6x9in) s.d.29 W/C pencil prov. 14-Oct-2 Butterfields, San Francisco #2131/R est:7000-9000
£3205 $5000 €4808 Untitled, portrait of a young girl with shawl (38x25cm-15x10in) s. chl prov. 14-Oct-2 Butterfields, San Francisco #2134/R est:6000-8000
£3369 $5457 €4750 El Mecapalero (35x27cm-14x11in) s. pencil sketch prov. 20-May-3 Segre, Madrid #124/R est:6000
£3463 $5403 €5195 Cantero (39x27cm-15x11in) s.d.Agosto 1955 chl rice paper. 17-Oct-2 Louis Morton, Mexico #61/R est:60000-65000 (M.P 55000)
£3463 $5403 €5195 Albanil haciendo ladrillos (39x27cm-15x11in) s.d.Agosto 1955 chl rice paper. 17-Oct-2 Louis Morton, Mexico #107/R est:60000-65000 (M.P 55000)
£3711 $5937 €5381 Tree of life (61x33cm-24x13in) s. W/C. 15-May-3 Louis Morton, Mexico #105a (M.P 60000)
£3711 $5937 €5381 Cantero (24x18cm-9x7in) s. chl rice paper. 15-May-3 Louis Morton, Mexico #55/R est:60000-65000 (M.P 60000)
£4329 $6926 €6277 Escena revolucionaria (31x24cm-12x9in) s. Indian ink. 15-May-3 Louis Morton, Mexico #115/R est:80000-90000 (M.P 70000)
£4573 $7500 €6631 Untitled - man with shovel (38x25cm-15x10in) s. ink prov. 1-Jun-3 Wright, Chicago #111/R est:9000-12000
£5257 $8411 €7623 Indio tomando una siesta (23x14cm-9x6in) s. W/C. 15-May-3 Louis Morton, Mexico #113/R est:95000-100000 (M.P 85000)
£5566 $8905 €8071 Choza (11x18cm-4x7in) s. W/C chl. 15-May-3 Louis Morton, Mexico #63/R est:100000-120000 (M.P 90000)
£6098 $10000 €9147 Obrero (39x27cm-15x11in) s. W/C pencil painted c.1940 prov. 28-May-3 Christie's, Rockefeller NY #80/R est:6000-8000
£9554 $15000 €14331 Coloured dancer (39x27cm-15x11in) s. gouache exec.c.1939 prov. 19-Nov-2 Sotheby's, New York #117/R est:22000
£12739 $20000 €19109 Women bathing in the river (21x16cm-8x6in) s.d.49 W/C pencil prov. 20-Nov-2 Christie's, Rockefeller NY #69/R
£13415 $22000 €19452 Untitled - man with rug (38x25cm-15x10in) s.d.1941 gouache prov. 1-Jun-3 Wright, Chicago #113/R est:10000-15000
£15244 $25000 €22104 Mujer Cargando una canasta (28x38cm-11x15in) s. W/C rice paper exec.c.1935 prov. 27-May-3 Sotheby's, New York #143
£15924 $25000 €23886 Woman with flowers (46x58cm-18x23in) s. ink prov. 19-Nov-2 Sotheby's, New York #85/R est:30000
£17073 $28000 €24756 Mujer Cargando a su hijo (38x27cm-15x11in) s.d.44 W/C rice paper prov.lit. 27-May-3 Sotheby's, New York #97
£22293 $35000 €33440 Man with shovel (28x39cm-11x15in) s. ink prov. 19-Nov-2 Sotheby's, New York #118/R est:15000
£23171 $38000 €34757 Rumbo al mercado (28x38cm-11x15in) s.d.1948 W/C ink rice paper prov.lit. 28-May-3 Christie's, Rockefeller NY #104/R est:30000-40000
£24204 $38000 €36306 Working scene (28x38cm-11x15in) s.d.34 W/C chl rice paper prov. 20-Nov-2 Christie's, Rockefeller NY #12/R est:25000-35000

£25915 $42500 €37577 Dos hombres (38x27cm-15x11in) s. W/C rice paper exec.c.1935 prov. 27-May-3 Sotheby's, New York #6
£25915 $42500 €37577 Dos hombres con mula (38x27cm-15x11in) s. W/C rice paper exhib.1935 prov. 27-May-3 Sotheby's, New York #7
£30488 $50000 €44208 El picapedrero (39x28cm-15x11in) s.d.44 W/C Indian ink rice paper prov. 27-May-3 Sotheby's, New York #39
£30488 $50000 €44208 El picapedrero (39x28cm-15x11in) s.d.44 W/C Indian ink rice paper prov. 27-May-3 Sotheby's, New York #40
£30573 $48000 €45860 Stone cutter (28x39cm-11x15in) s. Chinese ink exec.c.1930 prov. 20-Nov-2 Christie's, Rockefeller NY #72/R est:20000-25000
£102740 $160274 €150000 Vases communicantes (93x121cm-37x48in) s.d.38 gouache paper on canvas exhib.lit. 14-Apr-3 Laurence Calmels, Paris #4033/R est:40000

RIVERA, Diego (attrib) (1886-1957) Mexican
Works on paper
£854 $1400 €1281 Portrait of Al Rose (30x23cm-12x9in) chl prov. 8-Feb-3 Neal Auction Company, New Orleans #1031 est:1000-1500

RIVERA, Jose de (1904-) American
Sculpture
£2516 $4000 €3774 Construction no 174 (24cm-9in) i.d.1976 brass black base. 7-Mar-3 Skinner, Boston #626/R est:4000-6000

RIVERA, Manuel (1927-1995) Spanish
£14000 $21560 €21000 Metamorfosis (82x254cm-32x100in) s. s.i.d.1963 verso metal paint on wood prov.exhib. 23-Oct-2 Christie's, London #126/R est:7000-9000
Sculpture
£11000 $18040 €16500 Espejismo (89x130cm-35x51in) s. s.i.d.1965 verso metal paint wood prov.exhib. 6-Feb-3 Christie's, London #627/R est:8000-12000
£12346 $20000 €17902 Metamorphosis (71x94cm-28x37in) s. wire wire netting. 21-May-3 Doyle, New York #15/R est:18000-25000
£17000 $26180 €25500 Metamorfosis coco (102x75cm-40x30in) s.i.d.1962 wire mesh suspended frame. 23-Oct-2 Christie's, London #120/R est:5000-7000
Works on paper
£1100 $1738 €1650 Untitled (62x44cm-24x17in) s. s.i.d.1961 verso pen brush ink prov. 3-Apr-3 Christie's, Kensington #213/R
£1300 $2054 €1950 Untitled (70x49cm-28x19in) s. s.i.d.1960 verso pen brush ink prov. 3-Apr-3 Christie's, Kensington #215/R
£1300 $2054 €1950 Untitled (44x62cm-17x24in) s.i. pen brush ink prov. 3-Apr-3 Christie's, Kensington #214/R

RIVERS, Elizabeth (1903-1964) British
£316 $491 €500 Out of bedlam. 24-Sep-2 De Veres Art Auctions, Dublin #186
£1419 $2214 €2100 Still life study of a pot of tulips (38x30cm-15x12in) s.d.1931. 26-Mar-3 James Adam, Dublin #71/R est:2000-3000
Works on paper
£365 $566 €570 Portrait of a young boy (28x25cm-11x10in) s. pencil. 3-Dec-2 Bonhams & James Adam, Dublin #146/R
£486 $773 €700 Aran fishermen sorting nets (46x38cm-18x15in) pencil dr. prov. 29-Apr-3 Whyte's, Dublin #5/R

RIVERS, Larry (1923-2002) American
£417 $650 €626 Two models. init. oil pastel. 19-Oct-2 Harvey Clar, Oakland #1434
£9375 $15000 €14063 Red webster (28x35cm-11x14in) s.d.65 oil pencil wood construction paper on board prov. 14-May-3 Sotheby's, New York #183/R est:15000-20000
£15625 $25000 €23438 Arab king Hussein at the U.N (122x112cm-48x44in) s. i.d.60 verso prov. 14-May-3 Sotheby's, New York #192/R est:20000-30000
£18065 $28000 €27098 Throwaway dress - New York to Nairobi (117x198cm-46x78in) oil burlap collage shaped canvas painted 1967 prov.exhib.lit. 26-Sep-2 Christie's, Rockefeller NY #765/R est:20000-30000
£34810 $55000 €52215 Nine French bank notes (80x58cm-31x23in) oil pencil col crayon printed paper prov. 13-Nov-2 Sotheby's, New York #204/R est:15000-20000
£78125 $125000 €117188 Me II (294x474cm-116x187in) oil collage prov.lit. 15-May-3 Christie's, Rockefeller NY #117/R est:80000-120000
£88608 $140000 €132912 French money (89x151cm-35x59in) s. painted 1965 prov. 12-Nov-2 Phillips, New York #128/R est:120000-180000
£93750 $150000 €140625 Family (208x183cm-82x72in) s.i.verso painted 1954-55 prov.exhib.lit. 15-May-3 Phillips, New York #26/R est:120000-180000
£137500 $220000 €206250 Dutch masters II (107x127cm-42x50in) s.i.d.63 verso prov.exhib.lit. 13-May-3 Sotheby's, New York #14/R est:300000-400000
£225000 $360000 €337500 Accident (208x230cm-82x91in) painted 1957 prov.exhib.lit. 14-May-3 Christie's, Rockefeller NY #41/R est:200000-300000
Prints
£1887 $3000 €2831 Dutch masters (36x36cm-14x14in) s.num.1/10 offset lithograph. 4-Mar-3 Swann Galleries, New York #548/R est:2000-3000
£1887 $3000 €2831 Golden tales (137x101cm-54x40in) s.d.num.19/35 col lithograph. 29-Apr-3 Christie's, Rockefeller NY #731/R est:3500-4500
£2013 $3200 €3020 On the phone (82x122cm-32x48in) s.d.82 num.PP 2/2 col lithograph screenprint. 29-Apr-3 Christie's, Rockefeller NY #730/R est:1500-2000
£2830 $4500 €4245 Jack of spades (108x76cm-43x30in) s.d.num.21/35 col lithograph. 2-May-3 Sotheby's, New York #578/R est:5000-7000
£3481 $5500 €5222 Blue collar holiday (120x97cm-47x38in) s.d.1990 num.87/100 silkscreen lithograph. 22-Apr-3 Butterfields, San Francisco #2351/R est:5000-7000
£4194 $6500 €6291 French money (57x79cm-22x31in) s.d.1963 num.5/32 col lithograph. 25-Sep-2 Christie's, Rockefeller NY #380/R est:2500-3500
£6289 $10000 €9434 Bike girl (30x40cm-12x16in) s.d.num.II 4/8 lithograph. 29-Apr-3 Christie's, Rockefeller NY #729/R est:3000-4000
Works on paper
£4375 $7000 €6563 Spanish (41x51cm-16x20in) s. pencil col crayon fabric staples paper collage on board prov. 14-May-3 Sotheby's, New York #182/R est:6000-8000
£4487 $7000 €6731 Study for Boston Massacre III (102x81cm-40x32in) s. spray enamel col crayon graphite collage paperboard prov. 14-Oct-2 Butterfields, San Francisco #2057/R est:7000-9000
£5128 $7949 €8000 That girl is in many parts - Portrait of B Goldsmith (40x50cm-16x20in) mixed media. 6-Dec-2 Hauswedell & Nolte, Hamburg #315/R est:9000
£10000 $15400 €15000 Dutch masters (40x36cm-16x14in) s.d.62 pencil pastel paper on cardboard. 22-Oct-2 Sotheby's, London #459/R est:5000-7000

RIVERS, Larry (attrib) (1923-2002) American
£301 $475 €452 Two models. oil pastel. 16-Nov-2 Harvey Clar, Oakland #1211

RIVERS, Leopold (1852-1905) British
£2390 $3681 €3800 Landscape with herds (71x107cm-28x42in) s.d.1872. 23-Oct-2 Finarte, Milan #12/R est:2000-3000
Works on paper
£400 $632 €600 Horse and cart crossing a bridge (20x28cm-8x11in) s. W/C. 2-Dec-2 Gorringes, Lewes #2632
£571 $903 €857 Outside the village inn, The Ostrich (32x54cm-13x21in) s. W/C. 26-Nov-2 Sotheby's, Melbourne #227/R est:1000-1500 (A.D 1600)
£760 $1216 €1140 Near Hartlepool. On the Durham coast, mending nets (25x35cm-10x14in) s. W/C pair. 11-Mar-3 David Duggleby, Scarborough #16/R

RIVES, Leida (1915-1989) ?
£526 $820 €789 Composition (90x50cm-35x20in) s. 6-Nov-2 AB Stockholms Auktionsverk #564/R (S.KR 7500)
£1051 $1640 €1577 Spiral lying down (61x96cm-24x38in) s. panel. 6-Nov-2 AB Stockholms Auktionsverk #696/R est:10000-15000 (S.KR 15000)

RIVET, Rick (1949-) Canadian
£890 $1415 €1335 Cougar mask series (90x93cm-35x37in) s.i.d.1994 acrylic. 23-Mar-3 Hodgins, Calgary #111/R est:1400-1800 (C.D 2100)

RIVIERE, Adriaan de la (1857-1941) Dutch
£634 $1020 €900 Farmer's wife at the water hole (43x33cm-17x13in) s. 6-May-3 Vendu Notarishuis, Rotterdam #99
£637 $994 €1000 Market scene (26x36cm-10x14in) s.i. 6-Nov-2 Vendue Huis, Gravenhage #504
£764 $1192 €1200 Market scene (20x30cm-8x12in) s. board. 6-Nov-2 Vendue Huis, Gravenhage #505/R

RIVIERE, Briton (1840-1920) British
£32000 $53120 €48000 Rus in urbe (66x51cm-26x20in) mono.d.90 prov.exhib.lit. 12-Jun-3 Sotheby's, London #259/R est:20000-30000
£95000 $152950 €142500 Requiescat (66x93cm-26x37in) mono.d.1889 prov.exhib.lit. 19-Feb-3 Christie's, London #39/R est:80000-120000
Works on paper
£500 $825 €725 Wounded lioness (45x61cm-18x24in) mono. blk chk htd white. 2-Jul-3 Sotheby's, Olympia #355/R
£15000 $24150 €22500 Study of dog (70x53cm-28x21in) mono. chk prov. 20-Feb-3 Christie's, London #85/R est:5000

RIVIERE, Denis (20th C) ?
£662 $1079 €1000 Untitled (97x130cm-38x51in) s.verso painted c.1975. 3-Feb-3 Cornette de St.Cyr, Paris #512

RIVIERE, Henri (1864-1951) French
Prints
£2051 $3220 €3200 Paysanne et sa vache - Saint Briac (23x35cm-9x14in) col etching panel. 22-Nov-2 Tajan, Paris #145/R est:2400-3000
£2838 $4427 €4200 Pecheurs en mer (35x52cm-14x20in) col engraving exec.1891. 31-Mar-3 Tajan, Paris #380
£3851 $6008 €5700 Depart des sardiniers a Treboul (23x35cm-9x14in) col engraving exec.1893. 31-Mar-3 Tajan, Paris #383/R
£5270 $8222 €7800 Mer, etude de vagues (23x34cm-9x13in) col engraving exec.1892. 31-Mar-3 Tajan, Paris #382/R
Works on paper
£1319 $2151 €1900 Loguivy, rochers et arbustes en bord de mer (41x26cm-16x10in) s.i.d.juillet 1905 W/C. 19-Jul-3 Thierry & Lannon, Brest #75/R est:2000-2200
£3590 $5636 €5600 Pins japonisants (24x34cm-9x13in) W/C. 15-Dec-2 Thierry & Lannon, Brest #66

RIVIERE, Pierre (1904-1949) French
Works on paper
£316 $494 €500 Une tirelire pour Toto (76x53cm-30x21in) s. W/C. 15-Sep-2 Etude Bailleul, Bayeux #75
£342 $533 €540 Le Bougie-Bougie (71x44cm-28x17in) s. W/C. 15-Sep-2 Etude Bailleul, Bayeux #77/R
£494 $770 €780 Je me sens dans tes bras si petite (71x44cm-28x17in) s. W/C. 15-Sep-2 Etude Bailleul, Bayeux #74/R

RIVIERE, Theodore (1857-1912) French
Sculpture
£1282 $2013 €2000 Centurion et Messaline (36cm-14in) s.st.f.Susse brown pat bronze. 11-Dec-2 Piasa, Paris #35

RIVOIRE, François (1842-1919) French
Works on paper
£473 $738 €700 Still life of carnations (56x37cm-22x15in) s. W/C. 28-Mar-3 Dorotheum, Vienna #243/R
£748 $1190 €1100 Nature morte (21x34cm-8x13in) s. W/C. 24-Mar-3 Tajan, Paris #185
£2069 $3290 €3000 Nature morte au bouquet de roses et cerises (47x62cm-19x24in) s. W/C. 6-Mar-3 Artcurial Briest, Paris #17/R
£5000 $7901 €7800 Le buisson de roses (70x54cm-28x21in) s.d.1872 gouache. 18-Nov-2 Tajan, Paris #31/R est:6800-9000

RIVOIRE, Raymond (1884-1966) French
Sculpture
£4516 $7000 €6774 Femme et levrier (39x39cm-15x15in) st.sig. gilded bronze with marble base executed c.1925. 6-Dec-2 Sotheby's, New York #166/R est:5000-7000

RIX, Julian (1850-1903) American
£362 $550 €543 Woods with waterfall (36x23cm-14x9in) board. 16-Aug-2 Du Mouchelle, Detroit #2078/R
£510 $800 €765 Lakeside cottage (25x31cm-10x12in) s. 22-Nov-2 Skinner, Boston #64/R
£685 $1000 €1028 Woodland scene with brook (25x36cm-10x14in) s.d.97 board. 3-Nov-1 North East Auctions, Portsmouth #282
£11465 $18000 €17198 New Jersey landscape with town in distance (117x137cm-46x54in) s. 10-Dec-2 Doyle, New York #113/R est:6000-8000
Works on paper
£267 $425 €401 Autumn landscape with distant village (35x25cm-14x10in) s. W/C. 7-Mar-3 Skinner, Boston #268/R

RIZEK, Emil (1901-1985) Austrian
£795 $1295 €1200 Coastal landscape with dunes (66x80cm-26x31in) s.i.d.verso. 28-Jan-3 Dorotheum, Vienna #147/R

RIZVI, Jacqueline (1944-) British
Works on paper
£1000 $1640 €1500 Still life of a teapot with cups and saucers (65x40cm-26x16in) init.d.86 W/C. 3-Jun-3 Sotheby's, Olympia #157/R est:1000-1500

RIZZARDINI, Cecilio (19th C) Italian
£1724 $2741 €2500 Supper in Emmaus (54x71cm-21x28in) mono. 5-Mar-3 Sotheby's, Milan #220 est:3500

RIZZO, Pippo (1897-1964) Italian
£685 $1068 €1000 Beach in the summer (29x39cm-11x15in) s. s.i.verso board. 10-Apr-3 Finarte Semenzato, Rome #156/R
£2179 $3422 €3400 Cane flower (100x70cm-39x28in) s.d.59 board exhib. 21-Nov-2 Finarte, Rome #243/R

ROALLIER, Christian (19th C) French
£1474 $2300 €2211 Afternoon pleasures (81x71cm-32x28in) s. prov. 14-Sep-2 Selkirks, St. Louis #721/R est:3000-4000

ROBATHIN, Max (1882-?) Austrian
£255 $397 €400 Still life with Madonna and child with candles and flowers (120x63cm-47x25in) s. panel. 6-Nov-2 Hugo Ruef, Munich #1253

ROBB, Charles (studio) (19th C) American
Sculpture
£48077 $75000 €72116 Indian princess (196cm-77in) col painted polychrome exec.c.1890 prov.exhib. 21-Sep-2 Pook & Pook, Downington #135/R est:75000-100000

ROBB, Mary Emma (?-1924) British
Works on paper
£500 $745 €750 Still life of white tulips in a vase (33x33cm-13x13in) W/C. 27-Jun-2 Greenslade Hunt, Taunton #712/R

ROBB, William George (1872-1940) British
£360 $569 €540 In the garden (27x49cm-11x19in) s. 27-Nov-2 Sotheby's, Olympia #46/R
£380 $619 €551 Figures in classical garden (32x38cm-13x15in) board oval. 15-Jul-3 Bonhams, Knightsbridge #136/R
£1100 $1737 €1650 Fete champetre (34x126cm-13x50in) s. 27-Nov-2 Sotheby's, Olympia #48/R est:600-800

ROBBE (?) ?
£6289 $9811 €10000 Berger au repos avec son troupeau (84x124cm-33x49in) 14-Oct-2 Amberes, Antwerp #186

ROBBE, Henri (1807-1899) Belgian
£5696 $9000 €9000 Still life of flowers and fruit (37x45cm-15x18in) s. lit. 29-Nov-2 Schloss Ahlden, Ahlden #1174/R est:8500

ROBBE, Joe (?) ?
£420 $664 €630 Sheep, goats and ducks (49x59cm-19x23in) s. 27-Nov-2 Bonhams, Brooks & Langlois, Jersey #89/R

ROBBE, Louis (1806-1887) Belgian
£272 $433 €400 Cheval au paturage (30x38cm-12x15in) s. panel. 18-Mar-3 Campo, Vlaamse Kaai #216
£647 $1036 €900 Interieur de la bergerie (27x41cm-11x16in) s. 13-May-3 Vanderkindere, Brussels #166
£705 $1107 €1100 Vache au pre (36x49cm-14x19in) mono. 10-Dec-2 Vanderkindere, Brussels #17/R
£833 $1292 €1300 La remise paysanne animee (26x41cm-10x16in) s. i.verso. 9-Dec-2 Horta, Bruxelles #47
£1172 $1876 €1700 Landscape with cows and sheep (34x54cm-13x21in) s. 15-Mar-3 De Vuyst, Lokeren #276/R est:2000-2500
£1192 $1943 €1800 Vaches et veau (34x50cm-13x20in) s. 17-Feb-3 Horta, Bruxelles #183
£1519 $2370 €2400 Bouc et moutons dan sun paysage (50x47cm-20x19in) s. paper on canvas. 16-Sep-2 Horta, Bruxelles #193
£2207 $3531 €3200 Landscape with cows (57x80cm-22x31in) s. 15-Mar-3 De Vuyst, Lokeren #275/R est:4000-4600
£2222 $3200 €3333 Hound in landscape (72x96cm-28x38in) s. 15-Jan-3 Christie's, Rockefeller NY #164/R
£3028 $4875 €4300 Sheep in meadow (65x88cm-26x35in) s. panel lit. 9-May-3 Schloss Ahlden, Ahlden #1442/R est:4800
£6962 $11000 €11000 Vaches et moutons au paturage (75x102cm-30x40in) s. 26-Nov-2 Palais de Beaux Arts, Brussels #146/R est:10000-15000

ROBBIA, Giovanni della (fl.1510-1520) Italian
Sculpture
£25806 $40774 €40000 Roman emperor (65x65cm-26x26in) polychrome relief wood. 17-Dec-2 Tajan, Paris #98/R est:60000

ROBBIA, Giovanni della (studio) (fl.1510-1520) Italian
Sculpture
£10127 $16000 €16000 Basket of fruit (15x38cm-6x15in) polychrome terracotta. 28-Nov-2 Semenzato, Venice #140/R est:12000
£18987 $30000 €30000 Baskets of fruit (27cm-11in) polychrome terracotta pair. 28-Nov-2 Semenzato, Venice #141/R est:32000

ROBBIA, Luca della (younger) (15/16th C) Italian

Sculpture

£87248 $140470 €130000 Bust of woman (53cm-21in) painted terracotta prov. 19-Feb-3 Semenzato, Venice #61/R est:65000

£161290 $254839 €250000 Madonna and Child with Saints (38x28cm-15x11in) marble relief lit. 19-Dec-2 Semenzato, Venice #45/R est:350000

ROBBIA, della (studio) (15/16th C) Italian

Sculpture

£12751 $20528 €19000 Angel Annunciate, holding a lily in his hand (82cm-32in) glazed terracotta head in fragments. 18-Feb-3 Sotheby's, Amsterdam #192/R est:1500-2500

ROBBINS, Ellen (1828-1905) American

Works on paper

£255 $400 €383 Still life with red and white roses (35x60cm-14x24in) s.d.1884 W/C. 22-Nov-2 Skinner, Boston #102/R

ROBELLAZ, Emile (1844-1882) Swiss

£699 $1104 €1049 Admonestation (31x24cm-12x9in) s.d.75 panel. 17-Nov-2 Koller, Geneva #1228/R (S.FR 1600)

£962 $1500 €1443 Rehearsal (25x20cm-10x8in) s. panel. 30-Mar-3 Susanin's, Chicago #6065/R est:1200-1600

ROBERT, Albert (19th C) ?

£696 $1086 €1100 Portrait de gentilhomme (136x108cm-54x43in) s.d.1853. 16-Sep-2 Horta, Bruxelles #456

ROBERT, Alexandre (1817-1890) Belgian

£436 $702 €650 Moine en priere (27x20cm-11x8in) s. panel. 18-Feb-3 Vanderkindere, Brussels #42

£724 $1144 €1050 Portrait du comte de Hainaut. s. panel. 2-Apr-3 Vanderkindere, Brussels #183/R

ROBERT, Eugène (?-1912) French

Sculpture

£1154 $1788 €1800 Maria d'Etrurie (66x36cm-26x14in) s. white marble gilt pat bronze. 6-Dec-2 Maigret, Paris #190/R

ROBERT, Henry (1881-1961) French

£2160 $3542 €3132 Pon St Jean a Fribourg (46x55cm-18x22in) s. d.1939 verso. 4-Jun-3 Fischer, Luzern #2293/R est:1800-2500 (S.FR 4600)

Works on paper

£3843 $5995 €5765 Fillette d'Evolene (50x35cm-20x14in) s. i.verso W/C over pencil. 8-Nov-2 Dobiaschofsky, Bern #84/R est:5500 (S.FR 8800)

ROBERT, Hubert (1733-1808) French

£10000 $15600 €15000 Landscape with a horseman pausing by a fountain (14cm-6in circular) panel prov. 9-Apr-3 Christie's, London #78/R est:15000-20000

£18519 $30000 €27779 Landscape with antique ruins (40x64cm-16x25in) 23-Jan-3 Sotheby's, New York #249/R est:40000

£18519 $30000 €27779 Landscape with ruins by river (40x64cm-16x25in) 23-Jan-3 Sotheby's, New York #248/R est:40000

£30488 $50000 €45732 Dessinateur (67x55cm-26x22in) prov.exhib. 30-May-3 Christie's, Rockefeller NY #50/R est:50000-70000

£174194 $275226 €270000 Vue de la cascade et du temple de Vesta a Tivoli (172x98cm-68x39in) prov. 18-Dec-2 Piasa, Paris #64/R est:180000-200000

£185185 $300000 €277778 Maison pres du lac (242x192cm-95x76in) s.i. prov.exhib.lit. 24-Jan-3 Christie's, Rockefeller NY #126/R est:300000-500000

Works on paper

£440 $682 €700 Barques au milieu d'une colonnade (23x17cm-9x7in) i. pierre noire. 29-Oct-2 Artcurial Briest, Paris #16/R

£629 $975 €1000 Little temple (21x15cm-8x6in) pierre noire double-sided. 29-Oct-2 Artcurial Briest, Paris #17/R

£979 $1635 €1400 Vue de la villa et de l'escalier de Caprarola (18x23cm-7x9in) pierre noire prov. 25-Jun-3 Artcurial Briest, Paris #507 est:1500-1800

£1013 $1600 €1600 Figures sous un pont (34x67cm-13x26in) pierre noire. 28-Nov-2 Tajan, Paris #91

£1049 $1752 €1500 Paniers et selle dans une grange (23x18cm-9x7in) pierre noire prov. 25-Jun-3 Artcurial Briest, Paris #506/R est:1500-1800

£1130 $1752 €1695 Capriccio au temple (23x32cm-9x13in) sanguine prov. 7-Dec-2 Galerie du Rhone, Sion #503/R est:2500-3000 (S.FR 2600)

£3147 $5255 €4500 La statue (34x26cm-13x10in) s.d.25 avril 1771 sanguine prov. 25-Jun-3 Artcurial Briest, Paris #503/R est:4500-5000

£3459 $5396 €5500 Huit croquis. pen sanguine was 8 in one frame. 11-Oct-2 Pierre Berge, Paris #4/R

£3846 $6038 €6000 Transport d'une statue de Jupiter (34x43cm-13x17in) s. W/C over pen prov. 21-Nov-2 Neret-Minet, Paris #63/R est:6000-8000

£5000 $8350 €7250 Group of figures around a fire at night (12x21cm-5x8in) s. black chk pen ink prov. 8-Jul-3 Christie's, London #70/R est:3000-5000

£5380 $8500 €8500 Une porte monumentale avec d'autel et de fontaine. Fenetres et une porte (25x14cm-10x6in) s.i.d.1763 black chk pen brown ink brown wash pair. 27-Nov-2 Christie's, Paris #190/R est:8000-12000

£7500 $12525 €10875 Le seau d'eau - Woman on a pontoon (35x28cm-14x11in) red chk prov.lit. 8-Jul-3 Christie's, London #81/R est:7000-10000

£8500 $14195 €12325 Steps by a bridge with figures mooring a small boat (37x29cm-15x11in) red chk prov. 8-Jul-3 Christie's, London #82/R est:5000-7000

£11189 $18685 €16000 Etudes de personnages (45x33cm-18x13in) sanguine nine in one frame prov. 27-Jun-3 Claude Aguttes, Neuilly #11/R est:8000-10000

£11566 $18390 €17000 Pecheurs sur un quai (27x30cm-11x12in) i. pen ink W/C over crayon. 24-Mar-3 Tajan, Paris #38/R est:10000

£13462 $21269 €21000 Figures dans un escalier antique (48x40cm-19x16in) i. sanguine. 15-Nov-2 Beaussant & Lefèvre, Paris #21/R est:10000-12000

£14685 $24524 €21000 Etudes de personnages (45x33cm-18x13in) sanguine four in one frame prov. 27-Jun-3 Claude Aguttes, Neuilly #10/R est:8000-10000

£17008 $27043 €25000 Couple et lavandiere dans le jardin de la Villa d'Este (28x36cm-11x14in) W/C sanguine htd pen ink gouache exhib. 24-Mar-3 Tajan, Paris #40/R est:10000

£19136 $31000 €28704 Temple of the Sibyl in Tivoli (31x44cm-12x17in) pen ink W/C over chk prov.lit. 21-Jan-3 Sotheby's, New York #85/R est:35000

£21768 $34613 €32000 Composition architecturale inspiree de la Villa Madama (23x31cm-9x12in) s.d.1773 W/C pen ink over sanguine. 24-Mar-3 Tajan, Paris #39/R est:10000

£31646 $50000 €50000 Femmes et enfants au lavoir au pied d'une villa (31x42cm-12x17in) s. i.verso pen ink wash W/C. 28-Nov-2 Tajan, Paris #89/R est:30000-40000

ROBERT, Hubert (attrib) (1733-1808) French

£8248 $13527 €11960 Classical landscape with temple ruins and figures (67x47cm-26x19in) 4-Jun-3 AB Stockholms Auktionsverk #2552/R est:30000-40000 (S.KR 105000)

ROBERT, Hubert (circle) (1733-1808) French

£7000 $10920 €10500 Capriccio of classical ruins with three men conversing at the steps of a temple, landscape beyond (98x75cm-39x30in) 9-Apr-3 Christie's, London #77/R est:8000-12000

£11189 $18686 €16000 Dessinateur devant la cascade et le Temple de Tivoli Parc (98x74cm-39x29in) oval pair. 25-Jun-3 Tajan, Paris #71/R est:12000-15000

Works on paper

£15385 $22000 €23078 Capriccios of Roman ruins (57x71cm-22x28in) W/C oval set of 4. 22-Jan-3 Doyle, New York #47/R est:30000

ROBERT, Hubert (studio) (1733-1808) French

£30380 $47392 €48000 Ravitaillement des prisoniers a Saint-Lazare (35x28cm-14x11in) bears mono. paperon panel oval. 18-Oct-2 Raboundin & Choppin de Janvry, Paris #143/R

ROBERT, Hubert (style) (1733-1808) French

£4088 $6296 €6500 Lavandieres et pecheur aux pieds d'une cascade. Barques sur un canal (125x144cm-49x57in) pair. 25-Oct-2 Tajan, Paris #130/R est:4500-6000

ROBERT, Leopold (1850-1935) Belgian

£3038 $4739 €4800 Vue de la ville de Dinant (183x226cm-72x89in) s.d.1898. 16-Sep-2 Horta, Bruxelles #172

ROBERT, Leopold-Louis (1794-1835) French

£9259 $14907 €13426 Paysanne de la campagne romaine (63x50cm-25x20in) s.i.d.1820. 9-May-3 Dobiaschofsky, Bern #32/R est:17000 (S.FR 20000)

£14151 $22925 €20519 Two brigands and young woman in mountain landscape (61x50cm-24x20in) s.d.1831. 26-May-3 Sotheby's, Zurich #33/R est:30000-35000 (S.FR 30000)

Works on paper

£278 $447 €403 Students fighting (24x35cm-9x14in) pencil. 7-May-3 Dobiaschofsky, Bern #1173 (S.FR 600)

£556 $894 €806 Two eastern figures (45x39cm-18x15in) s.d.1822 chl htd. 7-May-3 Dobiaschofsky, Bern #918/R (S.FR 1200)

ROBERT, Leopold-Louis (after) (1794-1835) French
£4367 $6900 €6551 Halte des moissonneurs (120x210cm-47x83in) 17-Nov-2 Koller, Geneva #1217/R est:25000 (S.FR 10000)

ROBERT, Leopold-Louis (attrib) (1794-1835) French
£1852 $2981 €2685 Injured robber (46x38cm-18x15in) mono.d.1833. 7-May-3 Dobiaschofsky, Bern #919/R est:4500 (S.FR 4000)

ROBERT, Louis Remy (1811-1882) French
Photographs
£2400 $3888 €3600 Study of statuary at Versailles (33x26cm-13x10in) waxed paper negative exec.c.1850 prov. 22-May-3 Sotheby's, London #42/R est:2000-3000
£3800 $6156 €5700 Courtyard of the Manufactory, Sevres (21x17cm-8x7in) waxed paper negative exec.c.1850 prov. 22-May-3 Sotheby's, London #40/R est:2000-3000
£4000 $6480 €6000 Study of a plough (37x27cm-15x11in) waxed paper negative exec.c.1850 prov. 22-May-3 Sotheby's, London #39/R est:2000-3000
£4800 $7776 €7200 Seated figure at the Manufactory, Sevres (27x34cm-11x13in) waxed paper negative exec.c.1850 prov. 22-May-3 Sotheby's, London #37/R est:2000-3000

ROBERT, Marcel (1906-) Belgian?
Works on paper
£359 $579 €550 Portrait d'un jeune garcon (29x22cm-11x9in) s.d.1936 W/C. 14-Jan-3 Vanderkindere, Brussels #64

ROBERT, Marius Hubert (19/20th C) French
£242 $382 €363 Lake view and snow capped mountain (71x53cm-28x21in) s. 18-Nov-2 Waddingtons, Toronto #226/R (C.D 600)
£321 $503 €500 Cote d'Azur (46x60cm-18x24in) s. 13-Dec-2 Piasa, Paris #138
£764 $1192 €1200 Vue de menton (46x61cm-18x24in) s. 10-Nov-2 Eric Pillon, Calais #6/R

ROBERT, Nicolas (1614-1685) French
Works on paper
£4895 $8175 €7000 Aechmea (43x30cm-17x12in) W/C gouache gold vellum. 25-Jun-3 Sotheby's, Paris #5/R est:8000-12000

ROBERT, Paul (?) ?
£1803 $2848 €2705 Woodland path in spring (41x32cm-16x13in) s. prov.lit. 26-Nov-2 Phillips, Zurich #72/R est:1500-2500 (S.FR 4200)

ROBERT, Philippe (1881-1930) Swiss
£566 $906 €849 Landscape (25x39cm-10x15in) s.d. board. 17-Mar-3 Philippe Schuler, Zurich #8474 (S.FR 1200)
£602 $969 €873 A la montagne (24x40cm-9x16in) s.d.1917 i.verso masonite. 9-May-3 Dobiaschofsky, Bern #82/R (S.FR 1300)

ROBERT, Theophile (1879-1954) Swiss
£437 $681 €656 Lake shore (30x50cm-12x20in) s. board. 6-Nov-2 Dobiaschofsky, Bern #913/R (S.FR 1000)
£802 $1283 €1203 Paysage (55x62cm-22x24in) s. 17-Mar-3 Philippe Schuler, Zurich #4554 (S.FR 1700)
£917 $1431 €1376 Baie de la Tene (46x55cm-18x22in) s. 6-Nov-2 Dobiaschofsky, Bern #912/R (S.FR 2100)
£1296 $2087 €1879 L'allee du jardin (60x70cm-24x28in) mono. i.verso exhib. 9-May-3 Dobiaschofsky, Bern #203/R est:3600 (S.FR 2800)
£1852 $2981 €2685 Chemin entre des murs (55x62cm-22x24in) s. exhib. 9-May-3 Dobiaschofsky, Bern #145/R est:5000 (S.FR 4000)
Works on paper
£602 $969 €873 Still life with apples and pear near a window (21x28cm-8x11in) s. gouache. 9-May-3 Dobiaschofsky, Bern #138/R (S.FR 1300)

ROBERT-FLEURY, Tony (1837-1912) French
£633 $981 €1000 Jeune femme a la coiffe (27x37cm-11x15in) s. panel. 29-Sep-2 Eric Pillon, Calais #86/R
Works on paper
£532 $888 €750 Henri de Navarre enfant et son chien (17x10cm-7x4in) s.d.1832 W/C gouache black crayon. 18-Jun-3 Piasa, Paris #18

ROBERTI, Albert (1811-1864) Belgian
£1560 $2528 €2200 La visite au nouveau-ne (90x72cm-35x28in) 26-May-3 Amberes, Antwerp #60
Works on paper
£580 $945 €841 Recital (29x43cm-11x17in) s.i. W/C. 16-Jul-3 Sotheby's, Olympia #195/R

ROBERTO, Luigi (1845-1910) Italian
Works on paper
£800 $1304 €1160 Schooner in open seas (38x59cm-15x23in) s. gouache two. 21-Jul-3 Bonhams, Bath #18/R
£850 $1352 €1275 Naples, ship portraits of a schooner in rough and calm weather (43x63cm-17x25in) one s.d.1889 W/C two. 6-Mar-3 Bonhams, Cornwall #712/R
£850 $1420 €1233 Britannia in the Bay of Naples (32x58cm-13x23in) s.i.d.1888 gouache. 18-Jun-3 Sotheby's, Olympia #49/R
£880 $1434 €1276 Transitional schooner off a headland (38x59cm-15x23in) s. gouache two. 21-Jul-3 Bonhams, Bath #17/R
£1600 $2592 €2400 Greve Frijs under full sail in the Med and under reduced sail in a swell (41x62cm-16x24in) s.i. bodycol pair. 21-May-3 Christie's, Kensington #431/R est:1200-1800

ROBERTS, Benjamin (fl.1847-1872) British
£350 $546 €525 Still life of plums with a cabbage white (16x21cm-6x8in) s.d.62 board arched top. 26-Mar-3 Sotheby's, Olympia #106/R

ROBERTS, Bonita (1947-) American
Works on paper
£1429 $2200 €2144 Study for ballerina (53x41cm-21x16in) pastel. 25-Oct-2 Morris & Whiteside, Hilton Head Island #4
£2055 $3000 €3083 Lydia with pots of pansies (51x81cm-20x32in) pastel. 18-May-2 Altermann Galleries, Santa Fe #245/R

ROBERTS, Bruce Elliott (20th C) American
£833 $1300 €1250 Bound for the island (46x61cm-18x24in) s.d.1975 s.i.verso prov. 5-Nov-2 Arthur James, Florida #458

ROBERTS, David (1796-1864) British
£238 $379 €357 Interior of cathedral with religious procession (45x29cm-18x11in) panel. 4-Mar-3 Dales, Durban #10 (SA.R 3000)
£1000 $1600 €1500 Monks in Saint Etienne-du-Mont Cathedral (20x25cm-8x10in) s.d.1843 panel. 12-Jan-3 William Jenack, New York #445
£1410 $2200 €2115 Edinburgh (30x36cm-12x14in) s.d.1842. 30-Mar-3 Simpson's, Houston #461
£4900 $7644 €7350 View of Edinburgh and Arthur's Seat from the south (28x59cm-11x23in) s.d.1838. 28-Mar-3 Bonhams, Edinburgh #134/R est:7000-10000
£19000 $29640 €28500 Ruins of St. Andrews Cathedral (45x35cm-18x14in) s.d.1830 panel prov.lit. 14-Apr-3 Sotheby's, London #4/R est:12000-18000
£30000 $48300 €45000 Entrance to the Firth of Forth (49x120cm-19x47in) s.d.1852 prov.exhib.lit. 20-Feb-3 Christie's, London #256/R est:60000
Prints
£2300 $3588 €3450 Approach of the Simoon - Desert of Gizech (35x26cm-14x10in) col lithograph gum arabic. 31-Mar-3 Bonhams, New Bond Street #98/R est:1000-1500
Works on paper
£766 $1249 €1149 Altar boys before altar (23x15cm-9x6in) s.d.1855 W/C. 12-Feb-3 Iegor de Saint Hippolyte, Montreal #158/R (C.D 1900)
£880 $1452 €1276 Cathedral with figures (43x29cm-17x11in) s.d.1851 W/C. 1-Jul-3 Peter Webb, Auckland #119/R est:2500-3500 (NZ.D 2500)
£1000 $1590 €1500 Dying chieftain (17x12cm-7x5in) s. W/C over pencil htd bodycol scratching out prov. 19-Mar-3 Sotheby's, London #126/R est:1200-1800
£1400 $2142 €2100 Halt at Wady Araba, Idumea, Jordan (15x23cm-6x9in) i.d.March 4 W/C bodycol. 22-Aug-2 Bonhams, Edinburgh #1111/R est:1500-2000
£2000 $3080 €3000 Descent upon the valley of the Jordan (32x48cm-13x19in) W/C. 7-Sep-2 Shapes, Edinburgh #401 est:2000-3000
£2200 $3432 €3300 Entrance of Albaycin, Granada (15x11cm-6x4in) pencil W/C. 17-Oct-2 Christie's, Kensington #128/R est:2000-3000
£2600 $4264 €3770 Capitol viewed across the Tiber, Rome (24x33cm-9x13in) s.d.1854 pencil W/C htd white prov.exhib. 5-Jun-3 Christie's, London #158/R est:3000-5000
£5000 $8300 €7500 Interior of the church of St. Sauveur, Caen (29x22cm-11x9in) s. pen ink W/C over pencil htd bodycol prov.lit. 12-Jun-3 Sotheby's, London #168/R est:4000-6000
£7000 $10990 €10500 View of Luxor, Egypt (16x24cm-6x9in) s.i. pencil W/C htd bodycol prov.exhib. 21-Nov-2 Christie's, London #64/R est:8000-12000
£7200 $11448 €10800 Temple at Tafa in Nubia (16x24cm-6x9in) s.i. W/C over pencil htd white. 19-Mar-3 Sotheby's, London #215/R est:4000-6000
£9000 $14220 €13500 Great gateway leading to the temple of Karnak, Thebes (38x30cm-15x12in) indis sig.i. W/C over pencil htd bodycol prov. 28-Nov-2 Sotheby's, London #325/R est:10000-15000

£9000 $14940 €13500 Pompey's Pillar, Alexandria (15x23cm-6x9in) s. W/C over pencil htd bodycol prov. 12-Jun-3 Sotheby's, London #165/R est:10000-15000
£13000 $21580 €19500 Siout, upper Egypt (24x34cm-9x13in) s.i. W/C over pencil htd bodycol prov. 12-Jun-3 Sotheby's, London #164/R est:15000-20000
£20000 $28600 €30000 Street in Cairo (20x15cm-8x6in) s. pencil W/C htd white prov.exhib.lit. 22-Jan-3 Christie's, London #66/R est:20000
£28000 $44240 €42000 Statues of Memnon in the plains of Thebes (33x49cm-13x19in) s.i. W/C over pencil htd bodycol. 28-Nov-2 Sotheby's, London #17/R est:30000-40000
£28000 $46480 €42000 Convent of St. Catherine, Mount Sinai (15x23cm-6x9in) i. W/C over pencil htd bodycol. 12-Jun-3 Sotheby's, London #167/R est:8000-12000
£45000 $73800 €65250 Petra (23x33cm-9x13in) s.i.d.March 7 1839 pencil W/C htd white. 5-Jun-3 Christie's, London #157/R est:15000-20000
£48000 $79680 €72000 On the banks of the Jordan (23x32cm-9x13in) s. W/C over pencil htd bodycol prov. 12-Jun-3 Sotheby's, London #166/R est:10000-15000

ROBERTS, David (attrib) (1796-1864) British
£600 $930 €900 Church interior scene with figures (28x22cm-11x9in) bears sig.d.1853 indis.i.verso panel. 1-Nov-2 Moore Allen & Innocent, Cirencester #429

ROBERTS, David (circle) (1796-1864) British
£6790 $11000 €10185 View of Jerusalem (48x62cm-19x24in) 23-Jan-3 Sotheby's, New York #156/R est:20000

ROBERTS, Dorothy M (fl.1935-1940) British
£270 $451 €392 Spring flowers (48x38cm-19x15in) s. exhib. 20-Jun-3 Keys, Aylsham #860

ROBERTS, Edwin (1840-1917) British
£1100 $1738 €1650 Young Italian couple in an interior (41x31cm-16x12in) s. 12-Nov-2 Bonhams, Knightsbridge #47/R est:1200-1800
£2500 $3975 €3750 Picking flowers (61x46cm-24x18in) s. 6-Mar-3 Christie's, Kensington #614/R est:3000-5000
£2516 $3874 €4000 Coming home (46x36cm-18x14in) s. prov. 23-Oct-2 Christie's, Amsterdam #46/R est:4000-6000
£3500 $5390 €5250 Rustic courtship (91x71cm-36x28in) s. prov. 5-Sep-2 Christie's, Kensington #283/R est:4000-6000
£5800 $8990 €8700 Double or quits (193x157cm-76x62in) s. i.verso. 26-Sep-2 Lane, Penzance #200/R est:6000-8000
£6000 $9480 €9000 The new toy (86x74cm-34x29in) s. prov. 26-Nov-2 Christie's, London #100/R est:6000-10000
£10000 $15900 €15000 Little fishes (62x46cm-24x18in) s. 18-Mar-3 Bonhams, New Bond Street #66/R est:6000-8000
£10887 $17202 €16331 The duet. The shop (46x36cm-18x14in) s. s.i.verso pair prov. 18-Nov-2 Waddingtons, Toronto #118/R est:4000-6000 (C.D 27000)
£24000 $37920 €36000 Rule Brittania! A merry crew (71x92cm-28x36in) s. s.i.verso. 26-Nov-2 Christie's, London #99/R est:6000-10000

ROBERTS, Elizabeth W (1871-1927) American
£1491 $2400 €2237 Autumn landscape in mountains (61x91cm-24x36in) s. 18-Feb-3 Arthur James, Florida #450

ROBERTS, Ellis (1860-1930) British
£10500 $16590 €15750 Portrait of Edith, Lady Cunard in a white dress (146x100cm-57x39in) s.d.97 prov. 26-Nov-2 Christie's, London #179/R est:7000-10000

ROBERTS, Gary Lynn (1953-) American
£3082 $4500 €4623 No immediate danger (61x76cm-24x30in) 18-May-2 Altermann Galleries, Santa Fe #149/R
£4181 $6522 €6272 Hunter's challenge (102x76cm-40x30in) 9-Nov-2 Altermann Galleries, Santa Fe #35
£4259 $6900 €6176 Crossing (76x102cm-30x40in) 23-May-3 Altermann Galleries, Santa Fe #53

ROBERTS, Glenda (20th C) New Zealander
£643 $997 €965 Eighteenth century Maori kite (83x103cm-33x41in) s. acrylic lacquer. 4-Dec-2 Dunbar Sloane, Auckland #26/R (NZ.D 2000)

Works on paper
£274 $420 €411 View from Mt. Eden (54x70cm-21x28in) s. gouache. 21-Aug-2 Dunbar Sloane, Auckland #65/R (NZ.D 900)
£455 $700 €683 Shona's red teapot (63x76cm-25x30in) s. gouache. 4-Sep-2 Dunbar Sloane, Wellington #69/R est:1500-1800 (NZ.D 1500)

ROBERTS, H (?) ?
£2500 $4000 €3750 Mending the bellows (44x35cm-17x14in) s. board. 11-Mar-3 Bonhams, Knightsbridge #276/R est:1500-2000

ROBERTS, Henry Benjamin (1831-1915) British
£1200 $1872 €1800 Quiet moment (25x20cm-10x8in) s. 8-Oct-2 Bonhams, Knightsbridge #216/R est:600-800

Works on paper
£500 $805 €725 Dull blade (21x30cm-8x12in) s.d.1878 W/C exhib. 7-May-3 Gorringes, Bexhill #899

ROBERTS, Hilda (1901-1982) British

Works on paper
£506 $785 €800 Reading the news in a Paris park (18x25cm-7x10in) s. W/C. 24-Sep-2 De Veres Art Auctions, Dublin #124

ROBERTS, James (fl.1858-1876) British

Works on paper
£1300 $2119 €1950 His Grace the Archbishop of York's Palace at Bishopthorpe (28x47cm-11x19in) s.d.1777 pencil W/C prov. 29-Jan-3 Dreweatt Neate, Newbury #98/R

ROBERTS, Lucille D (1927-) American
£272 $425 €408 Vase of flowers by an open window (81x60cm-32x24in) s. acrylic masonite. 20-Sep-2 Sloan, North Bethesda #458/R

ROBERTS, R (19th C) British
£412 $650 €618 Ragged boy (41x30cm-16x12in) s.d.1861 exhib. 16-Nov-2 New Orleans Auction, New Orleans #965

ROBERTS, Ray (20th C) American
£3312 $5200 €4968 Arch at Point Lobos (51x61cm-20x24in) s. i.verso canvas on wood prov.exhib. 20-Nov-2 Christie's, Los Angeles #91/R est:6000-8000

ROBERTS, S (?) ?
£500 $780 €750 Receiving a valentine (13x10cm-5x4in) s.d.1824 sold with another. 7-Nov-2 Amersham Auction Rooms, UK #191/R

ROBERTS, Thomas Keith (1909-1998) Canadian
£369 $572 €554 Road to Elliot Lake (41x56cm-16x22in) s. board. 24-Sep-2 Ritchie, Toronto #3173/R (C.D 900)
£533 $875 €800 Blue boat at cap a L'Aigle (30x60cm-12x24in) s. board prov. 3-Jun-3 Joyner, Toronto #581 est:1500-2000 (C.D 1200)
£595 $976 €893 Red maple (30x41cm-12x16in) s. s.i.verso board. 6-Feb-3 Heffel, Vancouver #043/R (C.D 1500)
£656 $1016 €984 View of trout lake (41x51cm-16x20in) s. board. 24-Sep-2 Ritchie, Toronto #3174 (C.D 1600)
£658 $1021 €987 Parliament buildings (50x65cm-20x26in) s. board. 3-Dec-2 Joyner, Toronto #182/R est:2000-2500 (C.D 1600)
£720 $1159 €1044 Shadows St. Hilair (45x60cm-18x24in) s. board. 12-May-3 Joel, Victoria #331 est:1400-1800 (A.D 1800)
£741 $1148 €1112 Maytime in Madawasks Valley (40x60cm-16x24in) s. board prov. 3-Dec-2 Joyner, Toronto #388 est:1200-1500 (C.D 1800)
£744 $1168 €1116 Old water tower at Barry's Bay (41x56cm-16x22in) s.i. s.verso board. 24-Jul-2 Walker's, Ottawa #232/R est:1200-1600 (C.D 1800)
£782 $1212 €1173 Poplar pool (40x50cm-16x20in) s. board prov. 3-Dec-2 Joyner, Toronto #463 est:800-1200 (C.D 1900)
£823 $1276 €1235 Woodland pool (40x50cm-16x20in) s. board prov. 3-Dec-2 Joyner, Toronto #475 est:800-1200 (C.D 2000)
£893 $1464 €1340 Winter village (36x51cm-14x20in) s. board. 6-Feb-3 Heffel, Vancouver #044/R (C.D 2250)
£894 $1404 €1341 Summer, La Malbaie (40x61cm-16x24in) s. board prov. 10-Dec-2 Pinneys, Montreal #170 est:1200-1800 (C.D 2200)
£978 $1604 €1467 St. Octave station (35x50cm-14x20in) s. board. 3-Jun-3 Joyner, Toronto #290/R est:1200-1500 (C.D 2200)
£1082 $1645 €1623 Persephone (36x51cm-14x20in) board. 4-Jul-2 Heffel, Vancouver #24 est:1500-2000 (C.D 2500)
£1235 $1914 €1853 St. Pascal Station (45x65cm-18x26in) s. board. 3-Dec-2 Joyner, Toronto #287/R est:1500-2000 (C.D 3000)
£1310 $2071 €1965 Hasting Mill (41x61cm-16x24in) s.i. s.verso board. 14-Nov-2 Heffel, Vancouver #90 est:1800-2200 (C.D 3250)
£1399 $2169 €2099 Cutting wheat, near Inglewood (45x60cm-18x24in) s. prov. 3-Dec-2 Joyner, Toronto #231/R est:1500-2000 (C.D 3400)
£1511 $2478 €2267 Mill in October (50x65cm-20x26in) s. board prov. 3-Jun-3 Joyner, Toronto #302/R est:2000-3000 (C.D 3400)
£1564 $2424 €2346 Atlantic storm - Cap de rosiers (40x55cm-16x22in) s. board prov. 3-Dec-2 Joyner, Toronto #362 est:1000-1500 (C.D 3800)
£1613 $2548 €2420 St. Octave view (51x66cm-20x26in) s.i.d.1980 board. 14-Nov-2 Heffel, Vancouver #157/R est:2500-3500 (C.D 4000)
£1732 $2753 €2511 White house (36x61cm-14x24in) s. board. 1-May-3 Heffel, Vancouver #92/R est:2000-2500 (C.D 4000)
£1778 $2916 €2667 Gathering hay, cap-a-l'aigle (40x60cm-16x24in) s. board prov. 3-Jun-3 Joyner, Toronto #264/R est:1800-2200 (C.D 4000)

£1815 $2867 €2723 Late winter sunlight, Paris, Ontario (51x76cm-20x30in) s. masonite prov. 18-Nov-2 Sotheby's, Toronto #130/R est:3000-4000 (C.D 4500)

Works on paper

£363 $573 €545 Summer morning, Bridgetown (30x41cm-12x16in) s. W/C. 14-Nov-2 Heffel, Vancouver #134 est:1000-1200 (C.D 900)
£484 $765 €726 Roslin Mill (29x44cm-11x17in) s.i.verso W/C. 14-Nov-2 Heffel, Vancouver #115 est:1000-1200 (C.D 1200)
£489 $802 €734 Cove reflections (29x43cm-11x17in) s. W/C prov. 3-Jun-3 Joyner, Toronto #523 est:600-800 (C.D 1100)

ROBERTS, Thomas Sautelle (attrib) (1760-1826) British

£4000 $6320 €6000 Landscape with figures and a mule on a path, waterfall and mountains beyond (82x117cm-32x46in) 28-Nov-2 Sotheby's, London #123/R est:5000-8000

ROBERTS, Thomas William (1856-1931) Australian

£4270 $6534 €6405 Snow drops - Miss Lola Playfair (38x24cm-15x9in) board painted 1893 prov. 26-Aug-2 Sotheby's, Paddington #534/R est:18000-22000 (A.D 12000)
£7143 $11214 €10715 Coughlan portrait (75x62cm-30x24in) s.d.19 prov.lit. 25-Nov-2 Christie's, Melbourne #92/R est:20000-30000 (A.D 20000)
£7857 $12336 €11786 Portrait of a lady (24x19cm-9x7in) i. canvas on board prov.lit. 25-Nov-2 Christie's, Melbourne #77/R est:14000-18000 (A.D 22000)
£9286 $14671 €13929 Pool of London (16x24cm-6x9in) init. canvas on board prov. 27-Nov-2 Deutscher-Menzies, Melbourne #59/R est:16000-20000 (A.D 26000)
£14176 $22257 €21264 Untitled - possibly Jephthah's daughter (51x41cm-20x16in) s. painted c.1881-84 prov.lit. 15-Apr-3 Lawson Menzies, Sydney #43/R est:40000-60000 (A.D 37000)

Works on paper

£11429 $18057 €17144 Portrait of Olive Bird (39x43cm-15x17in) s.d.1900 pastel prov.lit. 27-Nov-2 Deutscher-Menzies, Melbourne #48/R est:35000-45000 (A.D 32000)

ROBERTS, Will (1910-2000) British

£580 $899 €870 River bank, Cookham (20x25cm-8x10in) s.d.1983 board. 3-Dec-2 Peter Francis, Wales #17/R
£1100 $1694 €1650 Figures on beach (25x20cm-10x8in) s. board. 22-Oct-2 Peter Francis, Wales #51
£1100 $1694 €1650 Still life (36x30cm-14x12in) s.i.verso board. 22-Oct-2 Peter Francis, Wales #50/R
£1300 $2015 €1950 Two workers (20x25cm-8x10in) s.d.1989 verso board. 3-Dec-2 Peter Francis, Wales #19/R est:800-1200
£1400 $2170 €2100 Farmer (23x20cm-9x8in) s.d.88 verso board. 3-Dec-2 Peter Francis, Wales #18/R est:800-1200
£1500 $2325 €2250 Cockle pickers (23x28cm-9x11in) s.d.1989 i.verso. 3-Dec-2 Peter Francis, Wales #20/R est:1000-1500
£1700 $2771 €2550 Farm Road, Tynywaun (41x51cm-16x20in) s.d.1989 lit. 28-Jan-3 Peter Francis, Wales #26/R est:1200-1600
£2000 $3080 €3000 Farm (66x76cm-26x30in) s. board. 22-Oct-2 Peter Francis, Wales #48/R
£3000 $4620 €4500 Man with barrow. i. board. 22-Oct-2 Peter Francis, Wales #49/R

ROBERTS, William (1895-1980) British

£14500 $22475 €21750 Pussy-cats (63x76cm-25x30in) s.d.1976 exhib. 3-Dec-2 Bonhams, New Bond Street #89/R est:10000-15000
£32800 $52808 €49200 Swimming lesson (51x41cm-20x16in) s. prov.exhib. 6-May-3 Christie's, Melbourne #95/R est:45000-65000 (A.D 82000)
£40000 $65600 €60000 Punting on the Cherwell (51x41cm-20x16in) s. prov.exhib. 6-Jun-3 Christie's, London #153/R est:20000-30000

Works on paper

£2400 $3720 €3600 Pussy-cats (15x17cm-6x7in) s.d.76 W/C pencil. 3-Dec-2 Bonhams, New Bond Street #90/R est:1500-2500
£2800 $4312 €4200 Good old days (14x24cm-6x9in) s. pencil W/C exec.c.1936. 5-Sep-2 Christie's, Kensington #604/R est:2500-3500
£3000 $4770 €4500 On the beach (14x19cm-6x7in) s.d.77 W/C squared for transfer. 26-Feb-3 Sotheby's, Olympia #179/R est:3000-5000
£4200 $6510 €6300 Trooping of the Colour (30x46cm-12x18in) pencil prov.exhib. 4-Dec-2 Christie's, Kensington #286/R est:4000-6000
£5000 $7750 €7500 Christ driving the moneychangers from the temple (20x23cm-8x9in) s. W/C over pencil. 3-Dec-2 Bonhams, New Bond Street #88/R est:5000-7000
£9000 $14760 €13500 Couple reclining by the Thames (35x53cm-14x21in) pencil W/C prov.exhib. 6-Jun-3 Christie's, London #152/R est:5000-8000
£9500 $15580 €14250 Plough (35x53cm-14x21in) s. crayon W/C executed 1944-45 prov.exhib. 6-Jun-3 Christie's, London #151/R est:7000-10000
£18000 $29520 €27000 Study for the cockneys (37x37cm-15x15in) pencil pen ink W/C part squared for transfer prov. 6-Jun-3 Christie's, London #35/R est:12000-18000

ROBERTS, William Goodridge (1904-1974) Canadian

£331 $519 €497 Boy in a parka (41x30cm-16x12in) s. 24-Jul-2 Walker's, Ottawa #214/R (C.D 800)
£363 $592 €545 Piedmont 1950 (18x23cm-7x9in) s. board on canvas. 12-Feb-3 Iegor de Saint Hippolyte, Montreal #159 (C.D 900)
£363 $592 €545 Piedmont June 1946 (18x23cm-7x9in) s.d. board on canvas. 12-Feb-3 Iegor de Saint Hippolyte, Montreal #160 (C.D 900)
£1345 $2152 €2018 Laurentian field in autumn (30x41cm-12x16in) s. board prov. 15-May-3 Heffel, Vancouver #221/R est:3000-4000 (C.D 3000)
£1481 $2296 €2222 Still life with oranges (37x45cm-15x18in) s. board. 3-Dec-2 Joyner, Toronto #282/R est:4000-5000 (C.D 3600)
£1512 $2389 €2268 Still life (41x51cm-16x20in) s. board prov. 18-Nov-2 Sotheby's, Toronto #129/R est:3000-3500 (C.D 3750)
£1613 $2548 €2420 Summer day, Eastern townships (46x72cm-18x28in) s.i.d.1948-49 board prov. 14-Nov-2 Heffel, Vancouver #219/R est:2500-3500 (C.D 4000)
£1689 $2770 €2534 Bay of Fundy, Grand Manan (50x60cm-20x24in) s. board prov. 3-Jun-3 Joyner, Toronto #210/R est:4000-6000 (C.D 3800)
£1956 $3207 €2934 Landscape, 1948 (49x60cm-19x24in) s. canvasboard prov. 3-Jun-3 Joyner, Toronto #350/R est:2000-3000 (C.D 4400)
£2222 $3644 €3333 Dried berries, blue and yellow cloths (50x60cm-20x24in) s. board prov. 3-Jun-3 Joyner, Toronto #200/R est:6000-8000 (C.D 5000)
£2469 $3827 €3704 Bright day, Georgian Bay (50x60cm-20x24in) s. board prov. 3-Dec-2 Joyner, Toronto #138/R est:8000-12000 (C.D 6000)
£2621 $4141 €3932 Near St. Jovite, Quebec (56x72cm-22x28in) s. i.verso prov.lit. 14-Nov-2 Heffel, Vancouver #234/R est:3500-4500 (C.D 6500)
£2675 $4146 €4013 Still life with fruit and green flowers vase (50x60cm-20x24in) s. board. 3-Dec-2 Joyner, Toronto #177/R est:5000-7000 (C.D 6500)
£2691 $4305 €4037 Red cloth and striped jug (30x41cm-12x16in) s. i.verso board prov. 15-May-3 Heffel, Vancouver #69/R est:7000-9000 (C.D 6000)
£2691 $4305 €4037 Georgian Bay (51x61cm-20x24in) s. board prov. 15-May-3 Heffel, Vancouver #209/R est:4000-6000 (C.D 6000)
£3200 $5248 €4800 Blue water, Georgian Bay (60x90cm-24x35in) s. board prov. 3-Jun-3 Joyner, Toronto #176/R est:6000-8000 (C.D 7200)
£3292 $5103 €4938 Barn, fence and tree (72x90cm-28x35in) s. board prov. 3-Dec-2 Joyner, Toronto #214/R est:10000-15000 (C.D 8000)
£3433 $5356 €4978 Looking out the window (71x56cm-28x22in) s.i.d.59 board prov. 26-Mar-3 Walker's, Ottawa #243/R est:6000-8000 (C.D 8000)
£3863 $6026 €5795 Still life with Buddha (64x81cm-25x32in) s. masonite. 25-Mar-3 Ritchie, Toronto #114/R est:10000-15000 (C.D 9000)
£4000 $6560 €6000 Pine trees and water, Georgian Bay (73x91cm-29x36in) s. masonite prov. 27-May-3 Sotheby's, Toronto #133/R est:10000-15000 (C.D 9000)
£4016 $6345 €6024 Summer landscape (81x112cm-32x44in) hardboard. 1-Dec-2 Levis, Calgary #82/R est:12000-15000 (C.D 10000)
£4115 $6379 €6173 Still life (50x40cm-20x16in) s. canvasboard prov. 3-Dec-2 Joyner, Toronto #175/R est:5000-6000 (C.D 10000)
£6278 $10045 €9417 Laurentian landscape (81x114cm-32x45in) s. i.d.1953 verso board prov.lit. 15-May-3 Heffel, Vancouver #110/R est:12000-16000 (C.D 14000)
£7258 $11468 €10887 Self portrait (122x81cm-48x32in) s. masonite prov.lit. 18-Nov-2 Sotheby's, Toronto #106/R est:18000-20000 (C.D 18000)

Works on paper

£206 $317 €309 Nu feminin (37x19cm-15x7in) s. chl W/C. 22-Oct-2 Iegor de Saint Hippolyte, Montreal #87 (C.D 500)
£207 $322 €344 Untitled - Group of men at a party (25x20cm-10x8in) s. graphite. 13-Apr-3 Levis, Calgary #582 (C.D 475)
£2000 $3280 €3000 Clearing, Laurentians (61x91cm-24x36in) s.i.d.1960 verso masonite. 27-May-3 Sotheby's, Toronto #64/R est:5000-7000 (C.D 4500)

ROBERTS, Winifred Russell (fl.1893-1907) British

£800 $1232 €1200 Setters on a moorland (56x79cm-22x31in) s. 23-Oct-2 Hamptons Fine Art, Godalming #160/R

Works on paper

£300 $477 €450 Rural landscape with trees in blossom (33x30cm-13x12in) s. W/C. 7-Mar-3 Biddle & Webb, Birmingham #211

ROBERTS-JONES, Ivor (1916-1966) British

Sculpture

£900 $1485 €1305 Portrait of Augustus John (19cm-7in) num.3/20 dark brown pat. bronze. 3-Jul-3 Christie's, Kensington #597/R

Works on paper

£420 $668 €630 Leopard (26x33cm-10x13in) init.d.60 pencil two. 26-Feb-3 Sotheby's, Olympia #120/R

ROBERTSON, Anderson B (?) British
£260 $424 €390 Carter (75x96cm-30x38in) 14-Feb-3 Lyon & Turnbull, Edinburgh #91

ROBERTSON, Andrew (1777-1845) British
Miniatures
£1800 $2808 €2700 Gentleman said to be Thomas Moore wearing dark grey coat black collar (9cm-4in) mono.d.1830 i.verso gilt mount brown leather case oval. 5-Nov-2 Bonhams, New Bond Street #122/R est:1000-1500
£2000 $3120 €3000 Lady wearing crimson velvet coat lined with white satin over blue dress (8cm-3in) s.d.1817 verso gilt mount oval prov. 5-Nov-2 Bonhams, New Bond Street #118/R est:1200-1800
£2800 $4368 €4200 Portrait of Captain Edward John Johnston seated with an Irish Water Spaniel (16cm-6in) gilded frame rec. prov. 5-Nov-2 Bonhams, New Bond Street #159/R est:3000-5000
£4200 $6552 €6300 Lady wearing pale grey dress with blue buttons gold coloured belt (8cm-3in) mono.d.1812 i.verso gilt mount card verso oval prov. 5-Nov-2 Bonhams, New Bond Street #119/R est:1000-1500
Works on paper
£387 $600 €581 Portrait of a gentleman with a top hat (48x33cm-19x13in) s.d.1839 W/C gouache prov. 29-Oct-2 Sotheby's, New York #129/R

ROBERTSON, Beatrice Hagarty (?) Canadian
£222 $364 €322 Nasturtiums (33x40cm-13x16in) s.i. board. 9-Jun-3 Hodgins, Calgary #389/R (C.D 500)
£309 $478 €464 Flowers by a lake (42x30cm-17x12in) indis sig. 3-Dec-2 Joyner, Toronto #479 (C.D 750)

ROBERTSON, Charles (1760-1821) Irish
Miniatures
£2200 $3454 €3300 Young lady wearing a blue bordered white dress (7cm-3in) init. gold frame with seed pearls oval. 10-Dec-2 Christie's, London #124/R est:2000-3000
£2600 $4056 €3900 Lady wearing white dress with high frilled collar pearl armbands (6cm-2in) gold frame blue enamel border with white spots hair verso oval. 5-Nov-2 Bonhams, New Bond Street #57/R est:2500-3500

ROBERTSON, Charles (1844-1891) British
Works on paper
£1200 $1920 €1800 Past repair (25x17cm-10x7in) s. W/C bodycol. 15-May-3 Lawrence, Crewkerne #832/R est:600-900
£1300 $2106 €1950 Signal station, Dover, Kent (18x26cm-7x10in) s. W/C htd white. 22-Jan-3 Bonhams, New Bond Street #358/R est:1000-1500

ROBERTSON, Charles Kay (fl.1888-1931) British
£550 $847 €825 Portrait of a girl, in a blue coat (66x48cm-26x19in) s.d.1910. 5-Sep-2 Christie's, Kensington #75

ROBERTSON, David T (1879-1952) British
Works on paper
£270 $419 €405 Horse-cart on a track at evening (22x36cm-9x14in) s. W/C. 24-Sep-2 Anderson & Garland, Newcastle #377
£280 $434 €420 Ploughman and team (27x38cm-11x15in) s. W/C. 24-Sep-2 Anderson & Garland, Newcastle #378/R
£320 $506 €480 Ploughing on a blustery day (19x27cm-7x11in) s. W/C. 12-Nov-2 Bonhams, Oxford #217
£360 $601 €522 Portrait of a girl reading in an armchair (39x29cm-15x11in) s.d.1907 W/C. 17-Jun-3 Anderson & Garland, Newcastle #211/R

ROBERTSON, Eric Harold Macbeth (1887-1941) British
Works on paper
£320 $522 €480 Male and female nude in stylised landscape (34x26cm-13x10in) s. W/C. 1-Feb-3 Shapes, Edinburgh #371
£1290 $2000 €1935 Male nude. Artist and his model (18x23cm-7x9in) s.i.d.1911 pencil two. 29-Oct-2 Sotheby's, New York #295/R est:600-800

ROBERTSON, George Edward (1864-?) British
£12000 $19920 €18000 Love letter (136x115cm-54x45in) s. 10-Jun-3 Christie's, London #104/R est:7000-10000

ROBERTSON, J (?) British
£1016 $1626 €1473 Woman by water pump (68x46cm-27x18in) s. 18-May-3 Anders Antik, Landskrona #113 (S.KR 13000)

ROBERTSON, James Downie (1931-) British
£780 $1201 €1170 Garden at Sanolo Point, winter (80x110cm-31x43in) board. 23-Oct-2 Hamptons Fine Art, Godalming #148/R
£820 $1279 €1230 At anchor, Crinan harbour (30x40cm-12x16in) s.d.61. 10-Oct-2 Bonhams, Edinburgh #323
£850 $1343 €1275 Equinox (40x40cm-16x16in) s. board prov. 27-Nov-2 Sotheby's, Olympia #308/R
Works on paper
£1800 $2844 €2700 Regatta (80x110cm-31x43in) s. gouache prov. 27-Nov-2 Sotheby's, Olympia #307/R est:1500-2000

ROBERTSON, John Tazewell (1905-) American
£755 $1200 €1133 New York cityscape from Central Park (36x46cm-14x18in) s.d.1932 board. 22-Mar-3 New Orleans Auction, New Orleans #1150/R est:3000-5000

ROBERTSON, Percy (1868-?) British
Works on paper
£350 $543 €525 Edinburgh by moonlight (25x20cm-10x8in) s.d.1902 W/C. 5-Dec-2 Bonhams, Edinburgh #79
£400 $652 €600 Blakeney (23x33cm-9x13in) W/C. 14-Feb-3 Keys, Aylsham #470
£800 $1240 €1200 Blakeney, Norfolk. Beach scene (30x46cm-12x18in) one s. i.verso W/C two. 3-Dec-2 Sotheby's, Olympia #176/R
£920 $1426 €1380 Westminster Abbey. London Bridge. Stable Inn, Holborn (20x25cm-8x10in) one s.i. W/C gouache three. 3-Dec-2 Sotheby's, Olympia #175/R est:800-1200
£950 $1472 €1425 Trafalgar Square. St James's Palace. People's Folly, Edinburgh (23x17cm-9x7in) one s. W/C gouache three. 3-Dec-2 Sotheby's, Olympia #173/R est:800-1200
£1000 $1560 €1500 No 8 Hanover Square (27x19cm-11x7in) init. W/C. 9-Oct-2 Woolley & Wallis, Salisbury #81/R est:400-600

ROBERTSON, Sarah Margaret (1891-1948) Canadian
£2691 $4305 €4037 Woman with doves in a Canadian landscape (51x61cm-20x24in) init. prov. 15-May-3 Heffel, Vancouver #197/R est:6000-8000 (C.D 6000)
Works on paper
£386 $603 €560 Apple tree (25x36cm-10x14in) s.d.28 W/C prov. 26-Mar-3 Walker's, Ottawa #463 est:500-700 (C.D 900)
£2667 $4373 €4001 Cab stand, Dominion Square, Montreal (26x32cm-10x13in) W/C ink prov. 3-Jun-3 Joyner, Toronto #181/R est:4000-5000 (C.D 6000)

ROBERTSON, Struan (fl.1903-1938) British
Works on paper
£280 $451 €406 Rural landscape with faggot-gatherers (9x13cm-4x5in) s. pastel. 7-May-3 Gorringes, Bexhill #889
£780 $1256 €1131 Farmyard scene with ducks on a pond and chicken being fed (9x13cm-4x5in) s. pastel. 7-May-3 Gorringes, Bexhill #888

ROBERTSON, Suze (1856-1922) Dutch
£278 $458 €400 Back alley (42x27cm-17x11in) s. panel. 1-Jul-3 Christie's, Amsterdam #220
£1266 $1975 €2000 Small courtyard (42x28cm-17x11in) s. 21-Oct-2 Glerum, Amsterdam #118/R est:2000-3000
Works on paper
£764 $1215 €1100 Head of a boy (27x23cm-11x9in) s. pastel exhib. 29-Apr-3 Christie's, Amsterdam #168/R est:1200-1600

ROBERTSON, Walford Graham (1867-1948) British
£900 $1396 €1350 Portrait of a lady (61x51cm-24x20in) mono.d.1897. 3-Dec-2 Sotheby's, Olympia #189/R est:1000-1500
£1800 $2790 €2700 Little girl and flowers (120x60cm-47x24in) s.i.d.1912. 3-Dec-2 Sotheby's, Olympia #188/R est:2000-3000
Works on paper
£260 $406 €390 Dead dreams, lady in violet and green beside a cavernous void (38x42cm-15x17in) s.d.1907 W/C. 18-Sep-2 Dreweatt Neate, Newbury #43/R

ROBERTSON, Walter (?-1801) British
Miniatures
£2000 $3280 €2900 Margaret Batton, wearing a white dress (6cm-2in) init, gold frame prov. 3-Jun-3 Christie's, London #143/R est:2000-3000

ROBERTSON-SWANN, Ron (1941-) Australian

Sculpture

£2321 $3621 €3482 Jacob's dream (106x97x57cm-42x38x22in) baked automotive paint steel. 11-Nov-2 Deutscher-Menzies, Melbourne #59/R est:6000-9000 (A.D 6500)

ROBERTY, Andre Felix (1887-1963) French

£342 $538 €500 Le port de Saint-Tropez (50x65cm-20x26in) s. 21-Apr-3 Rabourdin & Choppin de Janvry, Paris #105

£452 $714 €700 Nu etendu (33x46cm-13x18in) mono. 18-Dec-2 Rieunier, Bailly-Pommery, Mathias, Paris #47/R

£957 $1550 €1388 Reclining nude model (33x46cm-13x18in) mono. 26-May-3 Rasmussen, Copenhagen #1518/R (D.KR 10000)

ROBICHAUD, Louis (1963-) Canadian

£538 $861 €807 Byward market (41x76cm-16x30in) s. 15-May-3 Heffel, Vancouver #194/R est:2000-3000 (C.D 1200)

ROBIE, Jean Baptiste (1821-1910) Belgian

£1410 $2186 €2200 Les roses (37x28cm-15x11in) s. cardboard. 9-Dec-2 Horta, Bruxelles #304 est:1000-1500

£2532 $4000 €3798 Floral still life (38x112cm-15x44in) s. 24-Apr-3 Shannon's, Milford #169/R est:4000-6000

£16129 $25000 €24194 Still life with Japanese vase and flowers (77x56cm-30x22in) s. panel prov. 29-Oct-2 Sotheby's, New York #39/R est:30000-40000

£32258 $50000 €48387 Bouquet of roses and other flowers in a glass goblet with a Chinese lacquer box (49x37cm-19x15in) s.d.1891 panel exhib. 30-Oct-2 Christie's, Rockefeller NY #111/R est:20000-30000

ROBIE, Jean Baptiste (attrib) (1821-1910) Belgian

£1090 $1711 €1700 Vase de fleurs (32x26cm-13x10in) s. panel. 19-Nov-2 Servarts Themis, Bruxelles #122

ROBINET, Gustave Paul (elder) (1845-1932) French

£838 $1332 €1257 Coastal landscape with rocks in summer (42x70cm-17x28in) s.i.d.1871. 5-Mar-3 Rasmussen, Copenhagen #2011/R (D.KR 9000)

£3200 $5152 €4800 Dutch scene (61x94cm-24x37in) s.d.1878. 6-May-3 Christie's, Melbourne #339/R est:7000-10000 (A.D 8000)

ROBINS, Thomas Sewell (1814-1880) British

Works on paper

£280 $434 €420 Rocky gorge (36x58cm-14x23in) s.d.1860 W/C. 3-Dec-2 Sotheby's, Olympia #51/R

£800 $1248 €1200 Shipping in stormy sea (48x66cm-19x26in) s. W/C. 17-Sep-2 Sotheby's, Olympia #133/R

£1605 $2600 €2327 Blackwall frigate getting underway in the downs (32x46cm-13x18in) s.d.1851 pencil W/C htd white. 29-Jul-3 Christie's, Rockefeller NY #107/R est:3000-5000

£2900 $4553 €4350 On the Scheldt with fishing boats (43x67cm-17x26in) init.d.58 W/C. 16-Dec-2 Sotheby's, Olympia #62/R est:1000-2000

£3800 $6156 €5700 French egg boat entering Southampton (29x44cm-11x17in) s.d.1846 W/C scratching out htd white. 22-Jan-3 Bonhams, New Bond Street #347/R est:1000-2000

£6600 $10824 €9900 Fishing boats and merchantmen in an estuary (39x61cm-15x24in) s.d.1837 pencil W/C. 4-Feb-3 Bonhams, Leeds #221 est:3000-5000

ROBINS, Thomas Sewell (attrib) (1814-1880) British

Works on paper

£400 $620 €600 On the coast at Genoa (15x22cm-6x9in) pencil W/C. 31-Oct-2 Christie's, Kensington #310/R

ROBINSON (20th C) ?

£1161 $1800 €1742 Passage to India (61x91cm-24x36in) s. 7-Dec-2 Selkirks, St. Louis #738 est:1000-1500

ROBINSON, Albert Henry (1881-1956) Canadian

£1235 $1914 €1853 Under full sail (14x20cm-6x8in) s. board. 3-Dec-2 Joyner, Toronto #198/R est:3000-5000 (C.D 3000)

£2033 $3191 €3050 Quebec vu du fleuve (21x27cm-8x11in) s. s.d. verso panel. 12-Dec-2 Iegor de Saint Hippolyte, Montreal #89 (C.D 5000)

£2133 $3499 €3200 Old gate, St. Malo, Brittany (21x26cm-8x10in) s.i.d.1912 panel. 3-Jun-3 Joyner, Toronto #174/R est:6000-8000 (C.D 4800)

£3427 $5415 €5141 Nice (22x27cm-9x11in) s. panel prov. 14-Nov-2 Heffel, Vancouver #151/R est:7000-9000 (C.D 8500)

£6098 $9573 €9147 Winter scene (20x25cm-8x10in) s. panel. 12-Dec-2 Iegor de Saint Hippolyte, Montreal #90 (C.D 15000)

£8969 $14350 €13454 Village on the St. Lawrence in winter (22x27cm-9x11in) s. panel prov. 15-May-3 Heffel, Vancouver #119/R est:12000-15000 (C.D 20000)

£17778 $29156 €26667 Quebec village in winter (28x33cm-11x13in) s. i.verso panel. 27-May-3 Sotheby's, Toronto #15/R est:20000-30000 (C.D 40000)

Works on paper

£1333 $2187 €2000 Untitled. s.i.d. mixed media set of six various sizes. 3-Jun-3 Joyner, Toronto #528 est:2500-3500 (C.D 3000)

ROBINSON, Alexander (1867-1952) American

Works on paper

£329 $510 €494 Autumn day in Flanders (46x57cm-18x22in) s.d.1901 i.verso W/C. 3-Dec-2 Ritchie, Toronto #3107/R (C.D 800)

ROBINSON, Annie (20th C) Irish

£298 $483 €420 West of Ireland scene with two women looking out to sea (41x51cm-16x20in) s. 20-May-3 Mealy's, Castlecomer #1319/R

Works on paper

£469 $746 €680 West of Ireland scene with figures by a cottage (39x50cm-15x20in) s. 4-Mar-3 Mealy's, Castlecomer #1230/R

ROBINSON, Charles (1870-1937) British

Works on paper

£289 $479 €419 Quality at bath in Beau Nash's day (18x67cm-7x26in) d.Nov 1933 verso W/C gouache prov. 16-Jun-3 Waddingtons, Toronto #34/R (C.D 650)

ROBINSON, Chas Dorman (1847-1933) American

£2866 $4500 €4299 Iceberg (46x76cm-18x30in) s.d.1881 prov. 20-Nov-2 Christie's, Los Angeles #125/R est:4000-6000

£6051 $9500 €9077 Views of San Francisco Bay (23x23cm-9x9in) s. board pair prov. 19-Nov-2 Butterfields, San Francisco #8143/R est:3000-5000

ROBINSON, Clifford Feard (1917-1992) Canadian

Works on paper

£381 $606 €572 B.C. mill (29x36cm-11x14in) init. chl. 23-Mar-3 Hodgins, Calgary #116/R (C.D 900)

ROBINSON, Dorothy Napangardi (1956-) Australian

Works on paper

£939 $1455 €1409 Wild bush plum (121x90cm-48x35in) s.verso synthetic polymer paint linen. 3-Dec-2 Shapiro, Sydney #199/R est:3000-5000 (A.D 2600)

ROBINSON, Florence Vincent (1874-?) American

Works on paper

£242 $382 €363 Figures on the beach (19x28cm-7x11in) s. W/C. 18-Nov-2 Waddingtons, Toronto #8/R (C.D 600)

ROBINSON, Frederick Cayley (1862-1927) British

£30000 $49800 €45000 Winter's evening (99x77cm-39x30in) s.d.1918 exhib.lit. 10-Jun-3 Christie's, London #85/R est:30000-50000

ROBINSON, G (19th C) British

£676 $1088 €1014 Ship's portrait - sail with steam (63x97cm-25x38in) s.d.1878. 22-Feb-3 Rasmussen, Havnen #2170 (D.KR 7500)

ROBINSON, George Crosland (fl.1882-1901) British

£338 $527 €507 Slumber (100x46cm-39x18in) canvas on board exhib. 15-Oct-2 Stephan Welz, Johannesburg #417 est:4000-6000 (SA.R 5500)

£400 $644 €580 Portrait of a young girl (61x43cm-24x17in) s. i.verso painted c.1890. 12-May-3 Joel, Victoria #272 est:1000-1500 (A.D 1000)

ROBINSON, Gregory (fl.1907-1934) British

Works on paper

£360 $576 €540 Steamship in stormy seas (28x38cm-11x15in) s. htd white. 14-Mar-3 Gardiner & Houlgate, Bath #68/R

£450 $684 €675 Pelican - which became Drake's Golden Hind (26x37cm-10x15in) s. W/C bodycol. 15-Aug-2 Bonhams, New Bond Street #244

ROBINSON, Hal (1875-1933) American

£1911 $3000 €2867 Swimming hole (64x76cm-25x30in) s. 10-Dec-2 Doyle, New York #78/R est:1500-2500

£2395 $4000 €3473 Apple picking (36x51cm-14x20in) s. 22-Jun-3 Freeman, Philadelphia #84/R est:1500-2500

ROBINSON, J (18th C) British
£285 $433 €428 Rowing out on choppy waters (49x91cm-19x36in) init.d.1875. 29-Aug-2 Christie's, Kensington #95

ROBINSON, Margaret Frances (1908-) American
£1026 $1600 €1539 French quarter courtyard (36x28cm-14x11in) s. board. 12-Oct-2 Neal Auction Company, New Orleans #630/R est:1800-2500

ROBINSON, Markey (1918-1999) Irish
£380 $555 €570 Donegal (10x13cm-4x5in) s.verso board. 12-Jun-2 John Ross, Belfast #197
£385 $585 €600 Yachting (15x28cm-6x11in) s. card. 27-Aug-2 Thomas Adams, Dublin #3
£514 $853 €730 Two seated figures (9x9cm-4x4in) board prov. 10-Jun-3 James Adam, Dublin #211/R
£610 $866 €1000 North Africa (6x11cm-2x4in) s. board. 5-Mar-2 Thomas Adams, Dublin #374
£611 $954 €960 Cottages and a figure (30x61cm-12x24in) s. card. 5-Nov-2 Thomas Adams, Dublin #311
£641 $974 €1000 Swallows in flight (33x51cm-13x20in) s. card. 27-Aug-2 Thomas Adams, Dublin #1
£669 $1043 €1050 Female nude (43x18cm-17x7in) s. card. 5-Nov-2 Thomas Adams, Dublin #310
£673 $1043 €1050 Italian scene (48x29cm-19x11in) init. board. 3-Dec-2 Bonhams & James Adam, Dublin #141/R
£696 $1079 €1100 Still life with eggs and pot (13x24cm-5x9in) s. board. 25-Sep-2 James Adam, Dublin #48/R
£705 $1093 €1100 Female nude, in an interior (51x33cm-20x13in) s. oil on card. 3-Dec-2 Thomas Adams, Dublin #381
£732 $1039 €1200 Sailing boats (10x12cm-4x5in) s. card. 5-Mar-2 Thomas Adams, Dublin #314
£736 $1053 €1200 Celtic warriors (13x14cm-5x6in) s. card. 9-Apr-2 Thomas Adams, Dublin #369
£801 $1170 €1250 Gable End cottage (22x52cm-9x20in) s. card. 10-Jun-2 Thomas Adams, Dublin #305
£801 $1242 €1250 Village with church spine (33x51cm-13x20in) s. oil on card. 3-Dec-2 Thomas Adams, Dublin #382
£846 $1345 €1269 What's behind the green door (10x21cm-4x8in) s. composition board. 4-Mar-3 Deutscher-Menzies, Melbourne #182/R (A.D 2200)
£915 $1299 €1500 Still life of fruit on a table (35x50cm-14x20in) card. 5-Mar-2 Thomas Adams, Dublin #389
£962 $1510 €1500 Grey day. Shoreline (17x20cm-7x8in) s. i.verso board prov. pair. 19-Nov-2 Whyte's, Dublin #12 est:1800-2200
£1000 $1600 €1500 Waiting (8x31cm-3x12in) s. board. 15-May-3 Christie's, Kensington #203/R est:400-600
£1037 $1472 €1700 Two figures (21x13cm-8x5in) s. card. 5-Mar-2 Thomas Adams, Dublin #316
£1067 $1515 €1750 Woman at window (20x13cm-8x5in) s. card. 5-Mar-2 Thomas Adams, Dublin #315
£1173 $1665 €1900 Spinning outside the cottage (51x69cm-20x27in) s. 29-Mar-2 Woodwards, Cork #161
£1227 $1755 €2000 Shawlie walking in village street (33x56cm-13x22in) s. card. 9-Apr-2 Thomas Adams, Dublin #326
£1250 $2063 €1800 Rural cottages (50x63cm-20x25in) 7-Jul-3 Hamilton Osborne King, Dublin #201/R est:1400-1800
£1275 $2053 €1900 Quiet stroll (17x25cm-7x10in) s. board. 18-Feb-3 Whyte's, Dublin #224/R est:1200-1500
£1338 $2221 €1900 Mountain eagle (50x31cm-20x12in) s. board. 10-Jun-3 James Adam, Dublin #193/R
£1384 $2158 €2200 Solitary shawlie by a cottage (15x50cm-6x20in) s. board. 17-Sep-2 Whyte's, Dublin #217 est:1500-1800
£1400 $2170 €2100 Gathering firewood (30x76cm-12x30in) board. 4-Dec-2 John Ross, Belfast #173 est:1500-1800
£1461 $2324 €2192 Fishing village (24x31cm-9x12in) s. board. 4-Mar-3 Deutscher-Menzies, Melbourne #180/R est:4000-6000 (A.D 3800)
£1477 $2377 €2200 Village scene (19x43cm-7x17in) s. board. 18-Feb-3 Whyte's, Dublin #172/R est:2000-3000
£1585 $2235 €2600 Figure on a country lane (15x28cm-6x11in) s. 7-Feb-2 Woodwards, Cork #249
£1667 $2733 €2300 Figures in a cornfield (14x40cm-6x16in) s. board. 28-May-3 Bonhams & James Adam, Dublin #78/R est:1800-2200
£1690 $2806 €2400 Coastal scene with sailing boats and figures (53x50cm-21x20in) s. panel. 10-Jun-3 James Adam, Dublin #26/R est:400-600
£1800 $2790 €2700 Cottages by the sea (21x70cm-8x28in) s. acrylic on board. 4-Dec-2 Christie's, Kensington #546/R est:1200-1800
£1806 $2871 €2600 Looking out to sea (23x36cm-9x14in) s. board. 29-Apr-3 Whyte's, Dublin #154/R est:2000-3000
£2019 $3210 €3029 Landscape with houses (24x30cm-9x12in) s. oil gouache board. 4-Mar-3 Deutscher-Menzies, Melbourne #181/R est:4000-6000 (A.D 5250)
£2123 $3312 €3100 Figures in a coastal village landscape (22x60cm-9x24in) s. board. 8-Apr-3 James Adam, Dublin #115/R est:1200-1800
£2327 $3630 €3700 Sailboats at dusk (51x64cm-20x25in) s. board. 17-Sep-2 Whyte's, Dublin #35/R est:3000-4000
£2500 $3975 €3750 Harbour, Roundstone, Connemara (50x55cm-20x22in) s. board. 5-Mar-3 John Ross, Belfast #136 est:1500-2000
£2778 $4417 €4000 East of the sun. West of the moon (37x13cm-15x5in) init. oil on plywood pair prov. 29-Apr-3 Whyte's, Dublin #10/R est:2000-3000
£3000 $4770 €4500 Cottages, Connemara (45x89cm-18x35in) s. board. 5-Mar-3 John Ross, Belfast #65 est:2000-2500
£3056 $4858 €4400 Shawlie and cottage (33x56cm-13x22in) s. board. 29-Apr-3 Whyte's, Dublin #234/R est:2500-3500
£3200 $4960 €4800 Figures on a Spanish beach (64x48cm-25x19in) s.verso board. 2-Oct-2 John Ross, Belfast #156 est:4000-5000
£3718 $5837 €5800 Going down to the harbour (33x57cm-13x22in) s. board. 19-Nov-2 Whyte's, Dublin #122/R est:4000-6000
£4027 $6483 €6000 Woman and child entering a village (36x57cm-14x22in) s. gouache board prov. 18-Feb-3 Whyte's, Dublin #122/R est:5000-7000
£4700 $6862 €7050 Shepherd (46x91cm-18x36in) s. board painted c.1958. 12-Jun-2 John Ross, Belfast #228 est:5000-7000
£4843 $7555 €7700 Bathers (36x51cm-14x20in) s. panel. 17-Sep-2 Whyte's, Dublin #166/R est:5000-7000
£5556 $8833 €8000 Coastal landscape with figures looking out to sea (61x91cm-24x36in) s. board prov. 29-Apr-3 Whyte's, Dublin #150/R est:8000-10000
£5660 $8830 €9000 Village of Rugapa, Malorca (61x104cm-24x41in) s.i.verso hardboard. 17-Sep-2 Whyte's, Dublin #167/R est:9000-10000
£5769 $9058 €9000 McDand's shop (66x97cm-26x38in) s. board exhib. 19-Nov-2 Whyte's, Dublin #114/R est:10000-12000
£6090 $9561 €9500 Achill (76x102cm-30x40in) s. canvasboard prov. 19-Nov-2 Whyte's, Dublin #125/R est:10000-12000

Works on paper
£290 $450 €435 Lake by the trees (15x28cm-6x11in) s. mixed media. 4-Dec-2 John Ross, Belfast #187
£300 $465 €450 Trees and landscape (17x12cm-7x5in) s. mixed media. 4-Dec-2 John Ross, Belfast #58
£350 $511 €525 Figures by the trees (25x30cm-10x12in) s. mixed media. 12-Jun-2 John Ross, Belfast #8
£380 $589 €570 Woodlands, France (18x28cm-7x11in) s. mixed media. 2-Oct-2 John Ross, Belfast #18
£380 $589 €570 Forest (20x36cm-8x14in) s. mixed media. 2-Oct-2 John Ross, Belfast #122
£420 $651 €630 Galway cottage (13x38cm-5x15in) s. mixed media. 2-Oct-2 John Ross, Belfast #183
£450 $657 €675 Watching the boats, Galway (13x25cm-5x10in) s. mixed media. 12-Jun-2 John Ross, Belfast #196
£450 $698 €675 Still life (23x38cm-9x15in) s. mixed media. 2-Oct-2 John Ross, Belfast #134
£479 $753 €700 Coastal landscape (16x42cm-6x17in) s. gouache. 15-Apr-3 De Veres Art Auctions, Dublin #17
£480 $744 €720 French street scene (30x15cm-12x6in) s. mixed media. 2-Oct-2 John Ross, Belfast #100
£493 $818 €700 Cottages in landscape (10x21cm-4x8in) s. gouache. 10-Jun-3 James Adam, Dublin #219/R
£500 $775 €750 Still life (36x25cm-14x10in) s. mixed media. 2-Oct-2 John Ross, Belfast #209
£550 $853 €825 Stroll by the cottage (24x35cm-9x14in) s. mixed media. 4-Dec-2 John Ross, Belfast #32
£600 $954 €900 Boats at Kilronan, Aran (20x33cm-8x13in) s. mixed media. 5-Mar-3 John Ross, Belfast #4
£641 $1006 €1000 Still life with bottles and green fruit (33x22cm-13x9in) s. gouache board. 19-Nov-2 Whyte's, Dublin #235/R
£650 $1007 €975 Galway cottages (22x40cm-9x16in) s. mixed media. 4-Dec-2 John Ross, Belfast #98
£680 $1081 €1020 In the field (15x40cm-6x16in) s. mixed media. 5-Mar-3 John Ross, Belfast #16
£800 $1240 €1200 Clown (71x50cm-28x20in) s. gouache. 4-Dec-2 John Ross, Belfast #11
£833 $1308 €1300 Tahitian maiden (44x30cm-17x12in) s. gouache board prov. 19-Nov-2 Whyte's, Dublin #236/R
£950 $1511 €1425 Kapallo (15x71cm-6x28in) s. mixed media. 5-Mar-3 John Ross, Belfast #90
£972 $1546 €1400 Desert outpost, North Africa (28x39cm-11x15in) s. gouache on board. 29-Apr-3 Whyte's, Dublin #228/R est:1500-2000
£1013 $1570 €1600 Fish on the quayside (25x40cm-10x16in) s. gouache on board. 25-Sep-2 James Adam, Dublin #146 est:1200-1500
£1062 $1667 €1550 Still life and seascape (31x22cm-12x9in) s. gouache. 15-Apr-3 De Veres Art Auctions, Dublin #1/R est:900-1200
£1100 $1749 €1650 Port, North Africa (15x73cm-6x29in) s. mixed media. 5-Mar-3 John Ross, Belfast #103/R est:600-800
£1164 $1828 €1700 Tree lined coastal landscape with buildings (31x50cm-12x20in) s. gouache. 15-Apr-3 De Veres Art Auctions, Dublin #35 est:1000-1500
£1200 $1860 €1800 North Africa (61x101cm-24x40in) s. mixed media. 4-Dec-2 John Ross, Belfast #263 est:1000-1500
£1218 $1912 €1900 Pine sky, Connemara. Green sky, Connemara (25x32cm-10x13in) s. gouache board pair. 19-Nov-2 Whyte's, Dublin #127 est:1500-1800
£1300 $2067 €1950 Copenhagen (15x71cm-6x28in) s. mixed media. 5-Mar-3 John Ross, Belfast #48 est:600-800
£1370 $2137 €2000 Figures and boats by the sea. s. gouache. 8-Apr-3 James Adam, Dublin #54/R est:400-600
£1463 $2078 €2400 Still life of jugs and fruit. s. gouache. 5-Mar-2 Thomas Adams, Dublin #390
£1507 $2366 €2200 Returning home (31x50cm-12x20in) s. gouache. 15-Apr-3 De Veres Art Auctions, Dublin #30/R est:1000-1500
£1507 $2366 €2200 Returning home (31x50cm-12x20in) s. gouache. 15-Apr-3 De Veres Art Auctions, Dublin #44 est:1000-1500
£1538 $2415 €2400 Village (20x44cm-8x17in) s. gouache board. 19-Nov-2 Whyte's, Dublin #9/R est:1800-2200

£1538 $2415 €2400 Watching the boats (14x29cm-6x11in) s. gouache board. 19-Nov-2 Whyte's, Dublin #126/R est:1200-1500
£1538 $2415 €2400 Sailing boats (32x50cm-13x20in) s. 19-Nov-2 Hamilton Osborne King, Dublin #439 est:1500-3000
£1538 $2415 €2400 Men meeting (50x75cm-20x30in) s. gouache. 19-Nov-2 Hamilton Osborne King, Dublin #440 est:1000-2500
£1600 $2480 €2400 Three shawlies (81x51cm-32x20in) s. mixed media. 2-Oct-2 John Ross, Belfast #60 est:2000-2500
£1615 $2342 €2600 Nude bathers (30x48cm-12x19in) s. gouache. 3-May-2 Woodwards, Cork #243
£1635 $2551 €2600 Still life with teapot and eggs (46x58cm-18x23in) s. gouache board. 17-Sep-2 Whyte's, Dublin #179 est:1800-2200
£1635 $2551 €2600 Mourne mountains (30x46cm-12x18in) s. i.verso gouache board. 17-Sep-2 Whyte's, Dublin #180 est:2500-3500
£1700 $2703 €2550 Green door (38x63cm-15x25in) s. mixed media. 5-Mar-3 John Ross, Belfast #241 est:1500-1800
£1900 $3021 €2850 Figures in woodlands (50x61cm-20x24in) s. mixed media. 5-Mar-3 John Ross, Belfast #12 est:2200-2500
£1944 $3092 €2800 Traveler women. Shawlies (29x11cm-11x4in) s. W/C gouache pair. 29-Apr-3 Whyte's, Dublin #155/R est:3000-4000
£2013 $3242 €3000 Women of achill (30x51cm-12x20in) s. gouache board prov. 18-Feb-3 Whyte's, Dublin #171/R est:2500-3500
£2025 $3139 €3200 Figures on a roadway in Western Village (25x96cm-10x38in) s. gouache on board. 24-Sep-2 De Veres Art Auctions, Dublin #184/R est:2000-3000
£2500 $3975 €3600 Still life with carafe and goblet (33x48cm-13x19in) s. gouache on board. 29-Apr-3 Whyte's, Dublin #157/R est:2500-3500
£2778 $4417 €4000 Artist daughter at study (36x25cm-14x10in) s. W/C. 29-Apr-3 Whyte's, Dublin #153/R est:3000-4000
£2953 $4754 €4400 Song birds (56x36cm-22x14in) s. gouache card prov. 18-Feb-3 Whyte's, Dublin #64/R est:3000-4000
£2953 $4754 €4400 Potato gatherers (39x56cm-15x22in) s. gouache card. 18-Feb-3 Whyte's, Dublin #119/R est:4000-6000
£3356 $5403 €5000 Waiting for the boats (51x99cm-20x39in) s. gouache card. 18-Feb-3 Whyte's, Dublin #167/R est:4000-5000
£3396 $5298 €5400 Still life with blue jug (53x33cm-21x13in) s. gouache board. 17-Sep-2 Whyte's, Dublin #174/R est:3000-4000
£3767 $5914 €5500 Two figures in a mountain landscape (51x69cm-20x27in) s. gouache. 15-Apr-3 De Veres Art Auctions, Dublin #189/R est:3000-4000
£6711 $10805 €10000 Green boats at the quay (69x105cm-27x41in) s. gouache board. 18-Feb-3 Whyte's, Dublin #124/R est:10000-12000

ROBINSON, Peter (1966-) New Zealander
£1007 $1571 €1511 Boy am I scared eh! (44x38cm-17x15in) s.i. acrylic paper. 8-Apr-3 Peter Webb, Auckland #26/R (NZ.D 2900)
£1064 $1660 €1596 Say Mouldy like in cheese (86x111cm-34x44in) acrylic on paper. 17-Sep-2 Peter Webb, Auckland #108/R est:4000-6000 (NZ.D 3500)
£1212 $1867 €1818 Untitled (65x50cm-26x20in) s.d.1999 acrylic on paper prov. 4-Sep-2 Dunbar Sloane, Wellington #23/R est:2000-3000 (NZ.D 4000)
£1250 $1950 €1875 Untitled (63x49cm-25x19in) s.d.1999 paper. 8-Apr-3 Peter Webb, Auckland #27/R est:3500-4500 (NZ.D 3600)
£2727 $4200 €4091 Cowie's great escape plan (113x110cm-44x43in) s.i.d.1995 oil stick acrylic on paper. 4-Sep-2 Dunbar Sloane, Wellington #29/R est:7000-10000 (NZ.D 9000)
£4502 $6977 €6753 Huh (180x147cm-71x58in) s.d.1997 verso. 4-Dec-2 Dunbar Sloane, Auckland #4/R est:15000-22000 (NZ.D 14000)
£8333 $13000 €12500 Untitled (45x378cm-18x149in) s.verso acrylic. 8-Apr-3 Peter Webb, Auckland #31/R est:10000-15000 (NZ.D 24000)

ROBINSON, Peter Frederick (1776-1858) British
Works on paper
£1600 $2624 €2320 Fountains Abbey, Yorkshire (34x26cm-13x10in) s.i.d.1805 pencil W/C prov. 5-Jun-3 Christie's, London #98/R est:800-1200

ROBINSON, Theodore (1852-1896) American
£161290 $250000 €241935 Springtime (43x55cm-17x22in) s. prov. 5-Dec-2 Christie's, Rockefeller NY #36/R est:200000-300000
£1172840 $1900000 €1759260 Boats at a landing (46x56cm-18x22in) painted 1894. 21-May-3 Sotheby's, New York #24/R est:400000-600000

ROBINSON, Thomas (?-1810) British
£800 $1264 €1200 Portrait of an Irish gentleman (71x59cm-28x23in) s.d.1800. 1-Dec-2 Lots Road, London #331/R
£3437 $5500 €4984 Cattle (61x102cm-24x40in) s.d.1875. 16-May-3 Skinner, Boston #69/R est:4000-6000

ROBINSON, William (19th C) British
£3000 $4770 €4500 Pet rabbits (53x43cm-21x17in) s.d.1879. 6-Mar-3 Christie's, Kensington #609/R est:2000-3000
£11470 $17434 €17205 Farmyard construction with self portrait (53x62cm-21x24in) s. painted c.1982-83 prov.exhib. 28-Aug-2 Deutscher-Menzies, Melbourne #40/R est:50000-60000 (A.D 32000)
£19124 $31363 €28686 Chooks and ducks, Birkdale (61x76cm-24x30in) s. painted c.1978 prov.exhib. 4-Jun-3 Deutscher-Menzies, Melbourne #29/R est:70000-90000 (A.D 48000)
£32692 $51981 €49038 Beechmont landscape with moon (94x119cm-37x47in) s. i.verso prov.exhib.lit. 4-Mar-3 Deutscher-Menzies, Melbourne #30/R est:90000-120000 (A.D 85000)
£39841 $65339 €59762 Birkdale farm (131x193cm-52x76in) s. prov. 4-Jun-3 Deutscher-Menzies, Melbourne #24/R est:130000-150000 (A.D 100000)
£48387 $73548 €72581 Landscape with heavenly bodies (142x198cm-56x78in) s. i.verso painted c.1988 prov.exhib. 28-Aug-2 Deutscher-Menzies, Melbourne #29/R est:120000-150000 (A.D 135000)
£76923 $122308 €115385 Bright sea, Springbrook (152x228cm-60x90in) s.d.2000 prov.lit. 4-Mar-3 Deutscher-Menzies, Melbourne #34/R est:250000-300000 (A.D 200000)
Works on paper
£2933 $4546 €4400 Untitled, the farm (55x76cm-22x30in) s. pencil. 3-Dec-2 Shapiro, Sydney #115/R est:10000-15000 (A.D 8100)
£8602 $13075 €12903 Tallanbanna (54x74cm-21x29in) s.i.d.2000 pastel prov. 28-Aug-2 Deutscher-Menzies, Melbourne #20/R est:28000-35000 (A.D 24000)
£8765 $14375 €13148 Evening rainforest (54x74cm-21x29in) s.i.d. pastel prov. 4-Jun-3 Deutscher-Menzies, Melbourne #59/R est:28000-35000 (A.D 22000)

ROBINSON, William Francis (1936-) Australian
£6513 $9705 €9770 Hibiscus and persimmons (96x80cm-38x31in) s. canvas on board. 27-Aug-2 Christie's, Melbourne #162/R est:3000-5000 (A.D 17000)
£8929 $14107 €13394 Farm construction I (26x39cm-10x15in) s. i.verso. 26-Nov-2 Sotheby's, Melbourne #43/R est:18000-28000 (A.D 25000)
£16071 $25232 €24107 Landscape with two creeks (64x83cm-25x33in) s. i.verso prov. 25-Nov-2 Christie's, Melbourne #59/R est:45000-65000 (A.D 45000)
£25000 $39500 €37500 Landscape with morning cloud (76x101cm-30x40in) s. prov. 26-Nov-2 Sotheby's, Melbourne #3/R est:80000-100000 (A.D 70000)
£28736 $42816 €43104 Bush landscape with sunbeams (93x119cm-37x47in) s. i.verso. 27-Aug-2 Christie's, Melbourne #28/R est:100000-120000 (A.D 75000)
£43750 $69125 €65625 Artist, his wife, cows and goats (94x111cm-37x44in) s. prov. 26-Nov-2 Sotheby's, Melbourne #20/R est:80000-100000 (A.D 122500)
£56940 $87117 €85410 Box construction with cow, goat and chooks (123x181cm-48x71in) s. painted 1983 prov.exhib. 25-Aug-2 Sotheby's, Paddington #7/R est:140000-180000 (A.D 160000)
£71174 $108897 €106761 Approaching storm, Springbrook (127x183cm-50x72in) s.d.96 prov. 25-Aug-2 Sotheby's, Paddington #25/R est:250000-350000 (A.D 200000)
Sculpture
£7143 $11214 €10715 Beach ceramic (50cm-20in) s. glazed ceramic. 25-Nov-2 Christie's, Melbourne #19/R est:10000-15000 (A.D 20000)
Works on paper
£4982 $7623 €7473 Rain and sunlight numbinbah (25x35cm-10x14in) s.d.96 pastel. 25-Aug-2 Sotheby's, Paddington #232/R est:14000-18000 (A.D 14000)
£5747 $8563 €8621 Farmyard (51x66cm-20x26in) s.d.81 ink prov. 27-Aug-2 Christie's, Melbourne #65/R est:14000-18000 (A.D 15000)
£6513 $10226 €9770 Girl's bedroom (73x54cm-29x21in) s. mixed media executed c.1976 prov. 15-Apr-3 Lawson Menzies, Sydney #19/R est:10000-15000 (A.D 17000)
£7663 $11418 €11495 Farmyard scene (55x75cm-22x30in) s. pencil prov. 27-Aug-2 Christie's, Melbourne #53/R est:14000-18000 (A.D 20000)
£9286 $14671 €13929 Cows and ducks (57x80cm-22x31in) s.d.80 pastel. 26-Nov-2 Sotheby's, Melbourne #25/R est:30000-40000 (A.D 26000)

ROBINSON, William Heath (1872-1944) British
Works on paper
£600 $936 €900 Twelfth Night, act 1, scene 5 (53x28cm-21x11in) s. W/C pencil bodycol laid down. 17-Oct-2 Lawrence, Crewkerne #423/R
£650 $1007 €975 Father stork (38x28cm-15x11in) mono. pencil pen black ink. 4-Dec-2 Christie's, Kensington #137/R
£900 $1413 €1350 Compressed billiards for maisonettes (38x29cm-15x11in) s. pen ink over pencil. 21-Nov-2 Tennants, Leyburn #701/R
£2200 $3454 €3300 Intelligent way of overcoming a difficult problem (41x30cm-16x12in) s.i. pen ink. 21-Nov-2 Tennants, Leyburn #702/R est:2000-2500

ROBINSON, William S (1861-1945) American
£1529 $2400 €2294 Autumn, Lyme, Connecticut (20x25cm-8x10in) s. i.d.October 22, 1924 verso board prov. 20-Nov-2 Christie's, Los Angeles #34/R est:3000-5000
£5844 $9000 €8766 Summer landscape (76x102cm-30x40in) 25-Oct-2 Morris & Whiteside, Hilton Head Island #143 est:9000-12000

ROBINSON, William T (1852-?) American
£252 $400 €378 Indian encampment (25x41cm-10x16in) s. painted c.1880. 2-Mar-3 Toomey, Oak Park #587/R
£368 $600 €552 Sunset river (36x56cm-14x22in) s. 2-Feb-3 Grogan, Boston #56

ROBISON, Jessie Howe (20th C) American
£6090 $9500 €9135 Portrait of Julian Martinez (76x64cm-30x25in) s. prov. 9-Nov-2 Santa Fe Art, Santa Fe #38/R est:8000-12000

ROBJENT, Richard (1937-) British
Works on paper
£1100 $1704 €1650 Winter day - partridges (56x76cm-22x30in) s.d.1934 W/C prov. 3-Dec-2 Sotheby's, Olympia #202/R est:1000-1500

ROBLEDANO TORRES, Jose (1884-1974) Spanish
£449 $709 €700 Small lake (61x41cm-24x16in) s. cardboard. 13-Nov-2 Ansorena, Madrid #256/R

ROBLES, Roger (20th C) American
£764 $1200 €1146 Portrait of Esther Lederer wearing a black dress (91x84cm-36x33in) s.i.d.1977. 24-Nov-2 Butterfields, San Francisco #2633/R est:800-1000

ROBLEY, Major Horatio Gordon (1840-1930) British
Works on paper
£295 $460 €443 Kiki is worn at the neck upright or by an arm looking down (8x13cm-3x5in) init.i. verso ink dr. 8-Apr-3 Peter Webb, Auckland #22/R (NZ.D 850)
£347 $542 €521 Not to be seen ever again a carved Maori chief, and seagoing war canoe (8x13cm-3x5in) i.verso ink dr. 8-Apr-3 Peter Webb, Auckland #23/R (NZ.D 1000)
£4737 $7389 €7106 Paikia, Maori Chief of Thames (18x26cm-7x10in) W/C. 27-Mar-3 International Art Centre, Auckland #94/R est:4000-6000 (NZ.D 13500)

ROBLIN, Richard (1940-) Canadian
£944 $1473 €1416 Sans titre (156x248cm-61x98in) s. acrylic. 25-Mar-3 Iegor de Saint Hippolyte, Montreal #123 (C.D 2200)

ROBOZ, Zsuzsi (20th C) British/Hungarian
Works on paper
£300 $474 €450 Portrait of actor Tom Courtney (66x41cm-26x16in) s. black chk exec.c.1960. 6-Apr-3 Lots Road, London #357

ROBSON, George Fennel (1788-1833) British
Works on paper
£660 $1049 €990 Northam Castle, on the Tweed (18x25cm-7x10in) W/C prov. 27-Feb-3 Bonhams, Chester #381
£1500 $2400 €2250 View of Durham Cathedral from Prebends Bridge (6x11cm-2x4in) W/C. 11-Mar-3 Bonhams, New Bond Street #32/R est:600-900
£1750 $2870 €2625 Skye (31x43cm-12x17in) i. pencil W/C. 4-Feb-3 Bonhams, Leeds #219
£3000 $4830 €4500 Loch Avon (49x85cm-19x33in) W/C lit. 7-May-3 Sotheby's, London #190/R est:3000-4000

ROCA, Junn (1948-) American
£870 $1400 €1305 Early October, Bishop (30x41cm-12x16in) s. i.verso masonite. 18-Feb-3 John Moran, Pasadena #122 est:1000-2000
£968 $1500 €1452 LA street scenes (18x23cm-7x9in) s. board two. 29-Oct-2 John Moran, Pasadena #674 est:1500-2000
£1198 $2000 €1737 Los Angeles Theatre Historic District (41x30cm-16x12in) s. i.verso canvasboard. 17-Jun-3 John Moran, Pasadena #128a est:1500-2500
£1242 $2000 €1863 Old Rialto theater, Broadway St, LA (36x36cm-14x14in) s. i.verso canvasboard. 18-Feb-3 John Moran, Pasadena #120 est:2000-3000
£1647 $2750 €2388 Landscape, California spring 03 (41x51cm-16x20in) s. i.verso canvasboard. 17-Jun-3 John Moran, Pasadena #129 est:2000-3000
£2174 $3500 €3261 Santiago Park, Orange County (51x41cm-20x16in) s. i.verso canvas on birch panel. 18-Feb-3 John Moran, Pasadena #121 est:2000-3000
£2258 $3500 €3387 El Pueblo de Los Angles, Olvera street, LA (36x36cm-14x14in) s. i.verso board. 29-Oct-2 John Moran, Pasadena #675 est:1500-2500
£2395 $4000 €3473 L.A street scene (51x41cm-20x16in) s. i.verso canvas on board. 17-Jun-3 John Moran, Pasadena #128 est:2000-3000

ROCCA, Davide la (1970-) Italian
Works on paper
£385 $596 €600 Untitled (50x65cm-20x26in) s. mixed media card exec.1999. 4-Dec-2 Finarte, Milan #497

ROCCA, Michele (1670-1751) Italian
£40288 $64460 €56000 Rinaldo and Armida (53x67cm-21x26in) prov. 13-May-3 Christie's, Amsterdam #46/R est:15000-20000

ROCCA, Michele (attrib) (1670-1751) Italian
£1418 $2369 €2000 Diane et endymion (43x29cm-17x11in) 18-Jun-3 Tajan, Paris #20 est:2000-3000

ROCCATAGLIATA, Niccolo (attrib) (16/17th C) Italian
Sculpture
£16552 $26483 €24000 Putti (64x24cm-25x9in) bronze pair prov. 17-Mar-3 Pandolfini, Florence #745/R est:25000

ROCCHI, Fortunato (1822-1909) Italian
Works on paper
£1090 $1711 €1700 Horses (33x56cm-13x22in) s.i. W/C pair. 16-Dec-2 Pandolfini, Florence #78

ROCCHI, Francesco de (1902-1978) Italian
£2564 $4026 €4000 Venetian lagoon (50x60cm-20x24in) s.d.1966. 19-Nov-2 Finarte, Milan #287/R
£3205 $5032 €5000 Garden (40x50cm-16x20in) s.d.1976. 19-Nov-2 Finarte, Milan #256/R
£4167 $6542 €6500 Interior with red flowers (80x60cm-31x24in) s.d.1976 s.i.d.verso. 19-Nov-2 Finarte, Milan #116/R est:5000
£5743 $8959 €8500 Still life of fruit and fish (55x70cm-22x28in) s.d.27 board exhib.lit. 26-Mar-3 Finarte Semenzato, Milan #304/R
£8333 $13250 €12000 Venice (50x60cm-20x24in) s.i.d.1943 board lit. 1-May-3 Meeting Art, Vercelli #353 est:12000

ROCCO, Sophie (20th C) French?
£1007 $1612 €1400 Le grand saut (130x97cm-51x38in) s. acrylic tempera. 18-May-3 Neret-Minet, Paris #149/R

ROCHARD, I (20th C) French
Sculpture
£1400 $2212 €2100 Panther (23cm-9in) s. bronze. 14-Nov-2 Christie's, Kensington #247/R est:1000-1500

ROCHARD, Irenee (1906-1984) French
Sculpture
£1122 $1716 €1750 Sybille (19x22cm-7x9in) s. bronze. 23-Aug-2 Deauville, France #290/R
£1603 $2484 €2500 Canard a sa toilette (27x15x15cm-11x6x6in) s. brown pat bronze exec.c.1930. 7-Dec-2 Martinot & Savignat, Pontoise #126/R

ROCHART, Simon Jacques (1788-1872) French
Miniatures
£1800 $2862 €2700 Child wearing a fur cap (6cm-2in) s.d.1817 red leather case. 6-Mar-3 Sotheby's, Olympia #8/R est:500-700
£22000 $34320 €33000 Arthur Wellesley, 1st Duke of Wellington wearing scarlet uniform (8cm-3in) s.d.1815 ormolu frame base with hook for medal oval prov.exhib. 5-Nov-2 Bonhams, New Bond Street #113/R est:6000-8000

ROCHAT, Willy (1920-) Swiss
£2800 $4340 €4200 La plage a la jetee (28x80cm-11x31in) s. s.i.on stretcher. 5-Dec-2 Christie's, Kensington #131/R est:2000-3000

ROCHE, Alexander (1861-1921) British
£360 $569 €540 Corfe Castle (25x32cm-10x13in) i.verso panel. 19-Dec-2 Bonhams, Edinburgh #313
£680 $1054 €1020 Street scene (33x25cm-13x10in) s. board. 3-Dec-2 Sotheby's, Olympia #203/R

ROCHE, Graeme (?) ?
£1643 $2563 €2465 Retirement (61x66cm-24x26in) s.d.74. 11-Nov-2 Deutscher-Menzies, Melbourne #92/R est:3000-4000 (A.D 4600)

ROCHE, Manuel (20th C) French?
Works on paper
£483 $772 €700 Elegante de dos (40x27cm-16x11in) s. chl col crayon chk. 12-Mar-3 Libert, Castor, Paris #167

ROCHE, Serge (1898-1988) French
Sculpture
£17568 $27405 €26000 Palmier (185cm-73in) s. stucco pair lit. 25-Mar-3 Claude Aguttes, Neuilly #258/R est:12000

ROCHEFOUCAULD, Antoine de la (1862-1960) French
£817 $1267 €1300 L'annonciation (204x330cm-80x130in) s.i.verso. 4-Oct-2 Tajan, Paris #213 est:1000-1500
£9500 $15865 €13775 Riviere au printemps, cimaise (33x40cm-13x16in) mono.d.1920 canvasboard. 24-Jun-3 Sotheby's, London #115/R est:7000-9000

ROCHEGROSSE, Georges (1859-1938) French
£563 $935 €800 Homme a la barbe rousse (46x38cm-18x15in) s. 11-Jun-3 Beaussant & Lefèvre, Paris #198/R
£828 $1292 €1300 Etude pour David et Goliath (41x32cm-16x13in) 7-Nov-2 Chochon-Barre & Allardi, Paris #220/R
£1582 $2468 €2500 Episode de la conquete de Rome (100x80cm-39x31in) s. en grisaille. 20-Oct-2 Chayette & Cheval, Paris #21
£2215 $3434 €3500 Le bain Oriental (31x26cm-12x10in) s. panel. 29-Sep-2 Eric Pillon, Calais #10/R
£4000 $6280 €6000 Arab guard (33x23cm-13x9in) s. panel. 21-Nov-2 Christie's, Kensington #198/R est:4000-6000
£4430 $6867 €7000 Confidence (81x65cm-32x26in) s.d.1919. 29-Sep-2 Eric Pillon, Calais #12/R
£12102 $19000 €18153 Resting by the fountain (92x73cm-36x29in) s.d.1916. 21-Nov-2 Sotheby's, New York #181/R est:10000-15000
£15000 $23400 €22500 La toilette (76x110cm-30x43in) s.d.1921 prov. 15-Oct-2 Sotheby's, London #172/R est:15000-20000
£32051 $50321 €50000 La toilette au harem (81x110cm-32x43in) s.d.1921. 16-Dec-2 Gros & Delettrez, Paris #121/R est:50000-60000
Works on paper
£878 $1370 €1300 Reves (34x23cm-13x9in) s. W/C Chinese ink. 25-Mar-3 Claude Aguttes, Neuilly #94/R

ROCHELT AMANN, Juan Jose (1881-1953) Spanish
£5806 $9174 €9000 View of Durango (50x60cm-20x24in) s.d.1917. 18-Dec-2 Ansorena, Madrid #81/R est:9000
Works on paper
£276 $439 €400 Landscape (19x23cm-7x9in) s. W/C. 4-Mar-3 Ansorena, Madrid #654/R

ROCHER, Ernest (1871-1938) French
£282 $437 €440 Flowers (28x24cm-11x9in) s.i. 7-Dec-2 De Vuyst, Lokeren #269

ROCHER, Georges (1927-) French
£633 $1000 €950 Anemones (66x53cm-26x21in) s. prov. sold with letter. 2-Apr-3 Doyle, New York #60/R

ROCHI, Alonso (1898-?) Spanish
£795 $1295 €1200 Peonies (81x65cm-32x26in) s. 11-Feb-3 Segre, Madrid #122/R

ROCHOLL, Theodor (1854-1933) German
£577 $906 €900 Battle scene (52x95cm-20x37in) s.d.98 canvas on panel. 21-Nov-2 Van Ham, Cologne #1888/R

ROCHUSSEN, Charles (1814-1894) Dutch
£1911 $2981 €3000 Falcon hunt with Jacoba van Beijeren (26x36cm-10x14in) mono.d.79 panel. 5-Nov-2 Vendu Notarishuis, Rotterdam #30/R est:3000-4000
£4403 $6780 €7000 Chasse au faucon, an elegant company during a falcon hunt (24x33cm-9x13in) init.d.60 panel lit. 23-Oct-2 Christie's, Amsterdam #106/R est:9000-14000
£6250 $9938 €9000 Stadholder William III inspecting the troups at Hinderschans (66x102cm-26x40in) init.d.73 prov.exhib.lit. 29-Apr-3 Christie's, Amsterdam #79/R est:10000-15000
Works on paper
£282 $454 €400 Riders on drawbridge (25x32cm-10x13in) s.d.42 pencil dr ink. 7-May-3 Vendue Huis, Gravenhage #518/R
£548 $855 €800 Seventeenth century rider reading, with his horse near a well (28x22cm-11x9in) mono.d.85 W/C. 14-Apr-3 Glerum, Amsterdam #49/R
£955 $1490 €1500 Landscape with shepherd and horsewoman (15x24cm-6x9in) mono. W/C. 6-Nov-2 Vendue Huis, Gravenhage #455 est:1500-2000

ROCHUSSEN, Charles (attrib) (1814-1894) Dutch
Works on paper
£2420 $3776 €3800 Elegant company seated at a table in a wooded landscape (34x46cm-13x18in) bears sig. pen black ink brown grey wash black chk. 5-Nov-2 Sotheby's, Amsterdam #182/R est:2500-3500

ROCK, Geoffrey (1923-) Canadian
£2218 $3504 €3327 Back of the Princeton Hotel, Vancouver (51x76cm-20x30in) s.i.d.1981 s.verso board. 14-Nov-2 Heffel, Vancouver #220 est:900-1200 (C.D 5500)

ROCKBURNE, Dorothea (1934-) Canadian
Works on paper
£503 $800 €755 Curve (74x56cm-29x22in) s.i.d.91 chl col chk. 5-Mar-3 Doyle, New York #109/R

ROCKLINE, Vera (1896-1934) American
£414 $654 €600 Flowers in a vase (61x50cm-24x20in) s. 4-Apr-3 Tajan, Paris #221
£689 $1089 €1000 Vase of roses in lounge (61x50cm-24x20in) s. 4-Apr-3 Tajan, Paris #222
£1757 $2741 €2600 Nu allonge de dos (54x73cm-21x29in) s. 26-Mar-3 Millon & Associes, Paris #66/R
Works on paper
£306 $487 €450 Nu (40x27cm-16x11in) s. graphite dr. 26-Feb-3 Artcurial Briest, Paris #96

ROCKMAN, Alexis (1962-) American
Works on paper
£1800 $2934 €2700 Pig (81x102cm-32x40in) s.d.96 verso enviotex soil refuse oil on wood prov. 3-Feb-3 Sotheby's, Olympia #167/R est:2000-3000

ROCKMORE, Noel (1928-1995) American
£645 $1000 €968 Signe gemeni (102x76cm-40x30in) s.d.69 prov. 7-Dec-2 Neal Auction Company, New Orleans #498 est:1200-1800
£1935 $3000 €2903 Fats Houston (127x97cm-50x38in) s.d.June 15 prov. 7-Dec-2 Neal Auction Company, New Orleans #499/R est:3000-5000
£1982 $3250 €2874 Babe Stovall. s.d.64 masonite prov. 7-Jun-3 Neal Auction Company, New Orleans #419/R est:5000-7000
£2215 $3500 €3323 Ruthie, the duck girl (76x38cm-30x15in) s.i.d.69 masonite prov. 5-Apr-3 Neal Auction Company, New Orleans #362/R est:3500-5500
£2287 $3750 €3431 Nocturnal banquet (183x102cm-72x40in) s.d.Jan/Feb 64. 8-Feb-3 Neal Auction Company, New Orleans #400/R est:3000-5000
£2532 $4000 €3798 Ernest 'Kid Punch' Miller (97x76cm-38x30in) s.i.d.64 prov. 5-Apr-3 Neal Auction Company, New Orleans #363/R est:4000-6000
£3226 $5000 €4839 Interior with two figures (102x127cm-40x50in) s.d.1948 prov. 7-Dec-2 Neal Auction Company, New Orleans #497/R est:5000-8000
£5793 $9500 €8690 Dan Leyrer (102x76cm-40x30in) s.d.66 acrylic prov. 8-Feb-3 Neal Auction Company, New Orleans #401/R est:2500-3500
Works on paper
£221 $350 €332 Gospel tent (28x36cm-11x14in) s.i.d.78 W/C ink prov. 5-Apr-3 Neal Auction Company, New Orleans #365
£288 $450 €432 Untitled (76x56cm-30x22in) s.i.d.93-4 W/C mixed media. 12-Oct-2 Neal Auction Company, New Orleans #1396
£305 $500 €442 Sister Gertrude Morgan painting (28x36cm-11x14in) s.i. W/C prov. 7-Jun-3 Neal Auction Company, New Orleans #420
£443 $700 €665 Papa John (36x28cm-14x11in) s.i.d.63 W/C prov. 5-Apr-3 Neal Auction Company, New Orleans #371

ROCKSTUHL, Alois Gustav (1798-1877) Russian
Miniatures
£9500 $14915 €14250 Tsar Alexander II, standing with holding gloves, landscape beyond (10x6cm-4x2in) s.d.1864 gilt wood frame rec. 10-Dec-2 Christie's, London #265/R est:6000-8000

ROCKWELL, Augustus (attrib) (1822-1882) American

£438 $700 €657 Rocky coastline with sailboats (13x25cm-5x10in) panel. 12-Jan-3 William Jenack, New York #337
£469 $750 €704 Fishing village (13x25cm-5x10in) panel. 12-Jan-3 William Jenack, New York #312

ROCKWELL, Norman (1894-1978) American

£5696 $9000 €8259 New day (28x23cm-11x9in) s. board prov. 26-Jul-3 Coeur d'Alene, Hayden #146/R est:8000-12000
£8805 $14000 €13208 Pollution (34x27cm-13x11in) s. oil posterboard prov.lit. 4-Mar-3 Christie's, Rockefeller NY #100/R est:12000-18000
£51613 $80000 €77420 Harmony (53x48cm-21x19in) s. lit. 4-Dec-2 Sotheby's, New York #174/R est:25000-35000
£64516 $100000 €96774 Runaway pants - boy chasing dog with pants (69x61cm-27x24in) s. prov.lit. 4-Dec-2 Sotheby's, New York #165/R est:100000-150000
£77419 $120000 €116129 Boy with puppies (67x59cm-26x23in) s. prov.lit. 5-Dec-2 Christie's, Rockefeller NY #211/R est:150000-250000
£116129 $180000 €174194 Boy and dog snuggled in blanket (84x66cm-33x26in) s. prov.lit. 4-Dec-2 Sotheby's, New York #169/R est:150000-200000
£122581 $190000 €183872 Sea captain with young boy (86x76cm-34x30in) s. prov.lit. 4-Dec-2 Sotheby's, New York #170/R est:200000-300000
£160494 $260000 €240741 Echoes of romance (122x81cm-48x32in) s. painted 1936 lit. 22-May-3 Christie's, Rockefeller NY #64/R est:300000-500000
£483871 $750000 €725807 Framed (108x83cm-43x33in) s. painted 1946 prov.lit. 4-Dec-2 Sotheby's, New York #164/R est:800000-1200000

Works on paper

£1592 $2500 €2388 Portrait of Captain David S Garland (39x30cm-15x12in) s.i. chl prov. 19-Nov-2 Butterfields, San Francisco #8060/R est:3000-5000
£20645 $32000 €30968 Make Christmas dreams come true (34x41cm-13x16in) s. conte crayon prov.lit. 5-Dec-2 Christie's, Rockefeller NY #218/R est:25000-35000
£28662 $45000 €42993 Father and boy, rocket ship (56x51cm-22x20in) s.i.d.1961 graphite board prov.lit. 20-Nov-2 Christie's, Los Angeles #104/R est:20000-30000
£109677 $170000 €164516 Study for framed (104x81cm-41x32in) s. pencil chl executed 1946 prov.lit. 4-Dec-2 Sotheby's, New York #166/R est:175000-225000

RODA, Leonardo (1868-1933) Italian

£952 $1514 €1400 Wood with figures (32x48cm-13x19in) s. board. 18-Mar-3 Finarte, Milan #42/R
£1097 $1733 €1700 Landscape with cows (18x25cm-7x10in) s. cardboard. 18-Dec-2 Finarte, Milan #150/R
£1224 $1947 €1800 Madonna (22x31cm-9x12in) s. cardboard. 1-Mar-3 Meeting Art, Vercelli #279
£1290 $2039 €2000 Mountain lake (33x48cm-13x19in) s.d.918 cardboard. 18-Dec-2 Finarte, Milan #123/R
£1548 $2446 €2400 Dawn at Tredil (32x47cm-13x19in) s.d.1914 board. 18-Dec-2 Finarte, Milan #124/R
£1548 $2446 €2400 Landscape with figure (23x47cm-9x19in) s. cardboard. 18-Dec-2 Finarte, Milan #151/R
£1701 $2704 €2500 Alpine view (23x47cm-9x19in) s. cardboard. 1-Mar-3 Meeting Art, Vercelli #267
£2065 $3262 €3200 Mount Cervino (32x24cm-13x9in) s.d.1919 cardboard. 18-Dec-2 Finarte, Milan #11/R
£2348 $3663 €3522 Pre alpine landscape with woman and cows (70x100cm-28x39in) s. 16-Sep-2 Philippe Schuler, Zurich #3521/R est:3500-4000 (S.FR 5400)
£4762 $7571 €7000 Village by Mount Cervino (42x140cm-17x55in) s. 1-Mar-3 Meeting Art, Vercelli #235
£6159 $10101 €8500 Paessaggio montano col Cervino (140x100cm-55x39in) s. 27-May-3 Finarte, Milan #1/R est:6000-7000

RODARD, P (19/20th C) French?

£1295 $2124 €1800 Kairouan (33x33cm-13x13in) s.i.d.1913 cardboard. 4-Jun-3 Tajan, Paris #309/R est:1800-2000

RODCHENKO, Alexander (1891-1956) Russian

Photographs

£1829 $3000 €2744 Vladimir Mayakovsky (28x13cm-11x5in) i.d.verso silver print exec.c.1950. 10-Feb-3 Swann Galleries, New York #33/R est:4000-6000
£2215 $3500 €3500 Radio station (22x14cm-9x6in) i. verso silver gelatin lit.exhib. 28-Nov-2 Villa Grisebach, Berlin #1371/R est:3000-5000
£3797 $6000 €5696 Moscow Zoo, children at the zoo (16x19cm-6x7in) gelatin silver print lit. 22-Apr-3 Christie's, Rockefeller NY #149/R est:15000-20000
£6013 $9500 €9020 Rhythmic gymnastics, on the red square (29x38cm-11x15in) init.d.1938 gelatin silver print prov.lit. 24-Apr-3 Phillips, New York #107/R est:10000-15000
£41139 $65000 €61709 Sokolniki Park, Winter, hockey (29x24cm-11x9in) gelatin silver print lit. 22-Apr-3 Christie's, Rockefeller NY #147/R est:90000-120000

RODE, Christian Bernhard (1727-1797) German

£2817 $4676 €4000 Washing of the Feet (77x155cm-30x61in) 11-Jun-3 Dorotheum, Vienna #165/R est:4000-6000

RODE, Edmund (19th C) German

£2800 $4564 €4200 Boy with a wooden sword. Girl with a rabbit (31x21cm-12x8in) s. pair. 29-Jan-3 Sotheby's, Olympia #271/R est:3000-4000

RODE, Ingeborg Marta (1865-1932) Danish

£972 $1497 €1458 Girl combing her doll's hair (126x87cm-50x34in) s.d.1897. 26-Oct-2 Rasmussen, Havnen #2045/R (D.KR 11500)

RODECK, Karl (1841-1909) Dutch

£1042 $1719 €1500 Returning to the village at dusk (67x117cm-26x46in) s. prov. 1-Jul-3 Christie's, Amsterdam #186/R est:1500-2000

RODEN, John (20th C) American

Sculpture

£2563 $4100 €3716 Caryatids (173cm-68in) bronze exec.c.1954. 17-May-3 Selkirks, St. Louis #416/R est:1500-2000

RODER, Endre (1933-) British/Hungarian

£1000 $1580 €1500 Linzi and Liz (102x127cm-40x50in) s. i.verso prov. 27-Nov-2 Sotheby's, Olympia #316/R est:1000-1500

RODER, Julius Sigismund (1824-1860) German

£1948 $2844 €3000 Icy winter day in Berlin with mother and child (104x76cm-41x30in) s.d.1859 lit. 15-Jun-2 Hans Stahl, Hamburg #137

RODHE, Lennart (1916-) Swedish

£463 $769 €671 Pattern for Schiva I (20x29cm-8x11in) s. acrylic. 16-Jun-3 Lilla Bukowskis, Stockholm #936 (S.KR 6000)
£2453 $3826 €3680 By the sea (51x21cm-20x8in) mono. 6-Nov-2 AB Stockholms Auktionsverk #704/R est:35000-40000 (S.KR 35000)
£5606 $8746 €8409 Women (65x65cm-26x26in) mono. s.d.1989 verso exhib. 6-Nov-2 AB Stockholms Auktionsverk #555/R est:80000-100000 (S.KR 80000)
£11583 $18649 €17375 Tattered mollusc (48x28cm-19x11in) mono.d.48. 7-May-3 AB Stockholms Auktionsverk #949/R est:150000-200000 (S.KR 150000)
£20077 $32324 €30116 Laadspel II - box game (71x71cm-28x28in) mono. tempera prov.lit. 7-May-3 AB Stockholms Auktionsverk #915/R est:125000-150000 (S.KR 260000)

Works on paper

£386 $622 €579 Untitled (29x23cm-11x9in) mono. mixed media prov. 7-May-3 AB Stockholms Auktionsverk #917/R (S.KR 5000)
£398 $621 €597 Untitled (20x14cm-8x6in) s.d.58. 13-Sep-2 Lilla Bukowskis, Stockholm #307 (S.KR 5800)
£456 $721 €684 Septimus Severus triumphal arch, Rome (26x20cm-10x8in) mono.d.24-11-53 mixed media. 28-Apr-3 Bukowskis, Stockholm #251a/R (S.KR 6000)
£684 $1081 €1026 Untitled (11x9cm-4x4in) mono. gouache. 28-Apr-3 Bukowskis, Stockholm #250/R (S.KR 9000)
£849 $1368 €1274 Untitled (28x20cm-11x8in) mono.d.29.4.59 pastel prov. 7-May-3 AB Stockholms Auktionsverk #916/R (S.KR 11000)

RODIGUE, Marie (19/20th C) French

£4200 $6552 €6300 At his mercy (25x32cm-10x13in) s.verso. 15-Oct-2 Sotheby's, London #197/R est:5000-7000

RODIN, Auguste (1840-1917) French

Prints

£5769 $9058 €9000 Les amours conduisant le monde (200x252cm-79x99in) drypoint. 12-Dec-2 Piasa, Paris #129/R

Sculpture

£1800 $2790 €2700 Portrait de Madame Druet (15cm-6in) d.1984 num.III/IV bronze st.f.Delval. 5-Dec-2 Christie's, Kensington #7/R est:2000-3000
£2452 $3800 €3678 Main (7cm-3in) s. green pat. bronze. 26-Sep-2 Christie's, Rockefeller NY #522/R est:3000-4000
£3544 $5600 €5600 Buste de Suzon. s. pat bronze Cast Cie des Bronzes Bruxelles. 26-Nov-2 Palais de Beaux Arts, Brussels #189/R est:5500-7500
£4808 $7500 €7212 Petit main gauche (8cm-3in) s. red brown pat bronze exec.c.1900. 18-Sep-2 Swann Galleries, New York #6/R est:5000-8000

£4908	$8000	€7362	Suzon (33cm-13in) i. bisque de sevres conceived 1872 prov.lit. 12-Feb-3 Sotheby's, New York #1/R est:10000-15000
£6897	$11034	€10000	Suzon (31x14cm-12x6in) s.i. brown pat bronze marble base exec.1872 lit. 15-Mar-3 De Vuyst, Lokeren #409/R est:9000-10000
£7000	$11690	€10150	Suzon (25cm-10in) s. golden brown pat. bronze i.f.ALC prov.lit. 25-Jun-3 Christie's, London #123/R est:8000-12000
£7453	$12000	€11180	Suzon (30cm-12in) i. brown pat. bronze lit. 7-May-3 Sotheby's, New York #104/R est:15000-20000
£8333	$13000	€12500	Vase les centaures (30cm-12in) i. glazed ceramic executed 1907 prov.lit. 6-Nov-2 Sotheby's, New York #136/R est:15000-20000
£8633	$13813	€12000	Le desespoir, dit de la porte (18cm-7in) s.st.f.A.Rudier bronze exec.c.1890 lit. 14-May-3 Blanchet, Paris #77/R est:10000-12000
£9434	$15000	€14151	Cri (26cm-10in) st.sig.st.f.Rudier green black pat bronze prov.lit. 27-Feb-3 Christie's, Rockefeller NY #9/R est:20000
£9500	$14630	€14250	Torse masculin (22cm-9in) i.num.9 bronze i.f.Rodin prov. 22-Oct-2 Sotheby's, London #128/R est:12000-16000
£9500	$14820	€14250	Bust of Albert Ernest Carrier-Belleuse (37cm-15in) s. bears mono.CB Sevres biscuit lit. 5-Nov-2 Sotheby's, London #156/R est:4000-6000
£10256	$16000	€15384	Tete de Jean d'Aire (30cm-12in) s. brown pat. bronze i.f Georges Rudier prov.lit. 7-Nov-2 Christie's, Rockefeller NY #235/R est:20000-30000
£11111	$17111	€16667	Buste de Victor Hugo (39x99cm-15x39in) s.num.5/12 black green pat bronze st.f.Georges Rudier prov.lit. 22-Oct-2 Iegor de Saint Hippolyte, Montreal #91/R (C.D 27000)
£13462	$21000	€20193	Suzon (25cm-10in) i. brown pat. bronze conceived 1872. 6-Nov-2 Sotheby's, New York #101/R est:15000-20000
£13836	$22000	€20754	Defense, tete (15cm-6in) s.st.f.Rudier brown green pat bronze lit. 27-Feb-3 Christie's, Rockefeller NY #8/R est:24000
£14000	$23380	€20300	Bust of Suzon (60cm-24in) s.i. silvered gilt bronze incl red marble base st.f.Bruxelles. 8-Jul-3 Sotheby's, London #201/R est:15000-20000
£14286	$23000	€21429	La faunesse - le petite Bretonne (23cm-9in) i.num.10 brown green pat. bronze i.f.G Rudier prov.lit. 7-May-3 Sotheby's, New York #120/R est:30000-40000
£16000	$26240	€24000	Buste de femme (33cm-13in) i. painted terracotta lit. 5-Feb-3 Sotheby's, London #111/R est:20000
£16000	$26240	€24000	Fatigue (50cm-20in) st.sig.st.f.Godard num.6/8 bronze prov.lit. 5-Feb-3 Sotheby's, London #112/R est:25000
£17949	$28000	€26924	Le vieil arbre (39cm-15in) i.num.4/8 black pat. bronze st.f.Georges Rudier cast 1987 lit. 6-Nov-2 Sotheby's, New York #135/R est:30000-40000
£18987	$30000	€28481	Movement in dance A (31cm-12in) s.num.12 dark brown pat. bronze. 22-Apr-3 Butterfields, San Francisco #6008/R est:25000-35000
£19000	$31160	€28500	Masque de l'homme au nez casse (25cm-10in) s.st.f.Rudier bronze prov.lit. 5-Feb-3 Sotheby's, London #128/R est:25000
£25000	$41000	€37500	Buste de Camille Claudel (27cm-11in) s.st.f.Rudier black green pat bronze prov.lit. 4-Feb-3 Christie's, London #248/R est:35000
£27244	$42500	€40866	Etude pour Pierre de Wiessant, sans bras ni tete (63cm-25in) i. brown pat. bronze i.f.Georges Rudier cast 1952 prov.lit. 6-Nov-2 Sotheby's, New York #103/R est:40000-60000
£35000	$58450	€50750	L'eternel printemps, second etat, 4eme reduction (25cm-10in) s. green pat. bronze i.f.F Barbedienne lit. 25-Jun-3 Christie's, London #121/R est:35000-45000
£37267	$60000	€55901	Le baiser (25cm-10in) i. brown pat. bronze st.f.F.Barbedienne prov.lit. 7-May-3 Sotheby's, New York #116/R est:40000-60000
£38194	$63021	€55000	L'eternal printemps (24x33cm-9x13in) s.num.72909 gold pat bronze st.f.F.Barbedienne lit. 2-Jul-3 Artcurial Briest, Paris #628/R est:30000-40000
£40278	$63639	€58000	Baiser (25x16x15cm-10x6x6in) s. brown pat bronze Cast Barbedienne. 23-Apr-3 Rabourdin & Choppin de Janvry, Paris #53/R est:50000
£49689	$80000	€74534	Tete de Jean de Fiennes (32cm-13in) i.num.7/8 black pat. bronze i.f.E Godard prov. 7-May-3 Sotheby's, New York #224/R est:15000-20000
£51282	$80000	€76923	Masque de l'homme au nez casse (25cm-10in) s. black pat. bronze st.f.Alexis Rudier conceived 1863-64 prov. 7-Nov-2 Christie's, Rockefeller NY #228/R est:40000-60000
£57692	$90000	€86538	La jeune mere (39cm-15in) s. brown green pat. bronze i.f.Georges Rudier prov.lit. 7-Nov-2 Christie's, Rockefeller NY #214/R est:50000-70000
£58000	$96860	€84100	La jeunesse triomphante (52cm-20in) s.num.19 dark brown pat. bronze st.f.Epreuve Thiebaut prov.lit. 25-Jun-3 Christie's, London #110/R est:50000-70000
£63830	$106596	€90000	Le baiser (39cm-15in) s. num.7275 num.28 blk pat bronze st.f.Barbedienne. 20-Jun-3 Piasa, Paris #15/R est:80000-100000
£65000	$106600	€97500	Age d'Airain (65cm-26in) s.st.f.Rudier green black pat bronze lit. 4-Feb-3 Christie's, London #208/R est:70000
£68000	$111520	€102000	Helene von Nostitz, nee Hindenburg (22cm-9in) s. silver prov.exhib. 4-Feb-3 Christie's, London #217/R est:24000
£73718	$115737	€115000	Jeunesse triomphante (50x43x38cm-20x17x15in) s.st.f.Thiebaut Freres brown pat bronze exec.1894 lit. 10-Dec-2 Artcurial Briest, Paris #471a/R est:100000-120000
£76923	$120000	€115385	Etude d'une femme assise - Cybele (50cm-20in) i.num.4/12 green pat. bronze i.f.Alexis Rudier cast 1953 prov.exhib. 6-Nov-2 Sotheby's, New York #127/R est:120000-180000
£77640	$125000	€116460	Le baiser (40cm-16in) s. gold pat. bronze cast 1898-19 lit. 8-May-3 Christie's, Rockefeller NY #146/R est:70000-90000
£80000	$133600	€116000	Le penseur (37cm-15in) s. green brown pat. bronze st.f.Alexis Rudier prov.lit. 25-Jun-3 Christie's, London #106/R est:80000-120000
£80420	$134301	€115000	Le Baiser (39cm-15in) s. num.61113 brn pat bronze st.f.Barbedienne lit. 30-Jun-3 Artcurial Briest, Paris #43/R est:75000-100000
£90000	$147600	€135000	Andrieus d'Andres (43cm-17in) s.st.f.Rudier bronze exec.1886 prov.lit. 5-Feb-3 Sotheby's, London #129/R est:60000
£93168	$150000	€139752	Le baiser du fantome a la jeune fille (26x60x24cm-10x24x9in) s. green brown pat. bronze cast c.1911-15 prov.lit. 8-May-3 Christie's, Rockefeller NY #153/R est:150000-200000
£95000	$155800	€142500	Baiser (59cm-23in) s.st.f.Barbedienne bronze prov.lit. 5-Feb-3 Sotheby's, London #116/R est:90000
£96154	$150000	€144231	Faunesse debout (59cm-23in) i. brown green pat. bronze i.f. Georges Rudier cast 1952-54 prov. 6-Nov-2 Sotheby's, New York #105/R est:150000-200000
£105000	$172200	€157500	Cariatide tombee portant sa pierre (43cm-17in) s.st.f.Rudier bronze prov.lit. 5-Feb-3 Sotheby's, London #130/R est:40000
£217391	$350000	€326087	Eternel printemps (66cm-26in) s.st.f.Barbedienne brown black pat bronze prov.lit. 7-May-3 Christie's, Rockefeller NY #2/R est:350000-450000
£307692	$480000	€461538	Eve au rocher (75cm-30in) s. brown pat. bronze cast c.1900 prov.lit. 6-Nov-2 Christie's, Rockefeller NY #7/R est:500000-800000
£435897	$680000	€653846	L'eternel printemps, premier etat, taille originale (67cm-26in) s. brown green pat. bronze st.f.Rodin prov.lit. 6-Nov-2 Christie's, Rockefeller NY #2/R est:700000-900000
£448718	$700000	€673077	Femme accroupie (87cm-34in) i. brown pat. bronze st.f.Georges Rudier executed 1970 prov.lit. 6-Nov-2 Sotheby's, New York #108/R est:300000-400000
£512821	$800000	€769232	Le baiser du fantome a la jeune fille (30x58x27cm-12x23x11in) i.sig. white marble conceived c.1892 prov.exhib.lit. 6-Nov-2 Christie's, Rockefeller NY #14/R est:400000-600000
£1250000	$1950000	€1875000	La grande ombre (193x100cm-76x39in) s.i. green pat. bronze cast 1925-27 prov.exhib.lit. 6-Nov-2 Christie's, Rockefeller NY #10/R est:1400000-1800000

Works on paper

£1892	$2951	€2800	Femme accroupie se tenant la tete (21x34cm-8x13in) s. crayon stump. 26-Mar-3 Piasa, Paris #124/R
£3121	$5211	€4400	La Fortune (32x24cm-13x9in) s.i. lead pencil drawing W/C. 20-Jun-3 Piasa, Paris #107/R est:2800-3000
£3899	$6044	€6200	Les deux amies (31x24cm-12x9in) mono. graphite W/C prov. 30-Oct-2 Artcurial Briest, Paris #195/R est:3000-4000
£4487	$7000	€6731	Nu vue de dos (32x24cm-13x9in) s. pencil wash prov. 6-Nov-2 Sotheby's, New York #116/R est:10000-15000
£10559	$17000	€15839	Danseuse (31x20cm-12x8in) s. W/C pencil prov.exhib. 8-May-3 Christie's, Rockefeller NY #114/R est:15000-20000
£11000	$16940	€16500	Femme nue, debout (49x31cm-19x12in) s. W/C gouache pencil prov. 22-Oct-2 Sotheby's, London #123/R est:10000-12000
£11392	$18000	€18000	Pleiade (25x32cm-10x13in) s.i. W/C pencil paper on paper prov. 29-Nov-2 Villa Grisebach, Berlin #35/R est:10000-15000
£11950	$19000	€17925	Etudes pour 'La ronde' (7x9cm-3x4in) pencil brush wash exhib. 27-Feb-3 Christie's, Rockefeller NY #7/R est:3500
£17610	$27472	€28000	Standing female nude with hands folded on chest (49x32cm-19x13in) wash pencil. 11-Oct-2 Winterberg, Heidelberg #677/R est:34000

RODIN, Auguste (after) (1840-1917) French

Sculpture

£4573	$7500	€6631	La luxure (64x38x41cm-25x15x16in) s. bronze i.f.Alexis Rudier prov. 1-Jun-3 Wright, Chicago #101/R est:10000-15000
£7927	$13000	€11494	Le baiser (64x38x43cm-25x15x17in) s. bronze st.f.Alexis Rudier prov. 1-Jun-3 Wright, Chicago #103/R est:10000-15000
£27848	$43443	€44000	L'eternal printemps (25x32cm-10x13in) green pat bronze f.Barbedienne. 20-Oct-2 Galerie de Chartres, Chartres #160 est:18000-25000
£55696	$86886	€88000	Le baiser. s. num.62900 pat bronze f.Barbedienne. 20-Oct-2 Galerie de Chartres, Chartres #159 est:22000-30000

RODIN, Auguste (attrib) (1840-1917) French
Works on paper
£962 $1500 €1443 Two nude models. W/C. 21-Sep-2 Harvey Clar, Oakland #1430

RODRIGUEZ DE LOSADA, Jose Maria (1826-1896) Spanish
£1118 $1812 €1700 Portrait of man (42x29cm-17x11in) s. board. 21-Jan-3 Ansorena, Madrid #154/R
£2897 $4606 €4200 Last Supper (110x84cm-43x33in) 4-Mar-3 Ansorena, Madrid #42/R

RODRIGUEZ LOZANO, Manuel (1896-1974) Mexican
£8280 $13000 €12420 Untitled (80x100cm-31x39in) s.d.53. 20-Nov-2 Christie's, Rockefeller NY #129/R est:15000-20000

RODRIGUEZ SAN CLEMENT, Francisco (1861-1956) Spanish
£677 $1050 €1016 Figures on a beach (51x61cm-20x24in) s. 7-Dec-2 Selkirks, St. Louis #742 est:2000-3000
£724 $1172 €1100 Baile flamenco (48x36cm-19x14in) s. 21-Jan-3 Christie's, Amsterdam #105/R est:1000-1500

RODRIGUEZ SANCHEZ CLEMENT, Francisco (1893-1968) Spanish
£795 $1295 €1200 Portrait of lady with shawl (50x39cm-20x15in) s. 11-Feb-3 Segre, Madrid #361/R
£823 $1275 €1300 Flamenco dancer (46x58cm-18x23in) s. 28-Sep-2 Hans Stahl, Hamburg #98/R
£872 $1405 €1300 Dance (24x32cm-9x13in) s. canvas on cardboard. 18-Feb-3 Durán, Madrid #198/R
£878 $1370 €1300 Flamenco (28x38cm-11x15in) s. 25-Mar-3 Durán, Madrid #77/R
£946 $1476 €1400 Mending the nets (22x32cm-9x13in) s. canvas on board. 25-Mar-3 Durán, Madrid #185/R
£1218 $1924 €1900 Dance (52x39cm-20x15in) s. 14-Nov-2 Arte, Seville #410/R
£1520 $2372 €2250 Flamenco dancer (73x60cm-29x24in) s. 25-Mar-3 Durán, Madrid #710/R
£1603 $2532 €2500 Woman in Andalucia (66x82cm-26x32in) s. 14-Nov-2 Arte, Seville #409/R
£1730 $2698 €2750 Bull fight (33x41cm-13x16in) s. board. 23-Sep-2 Durán, Madrid #190/R
£3716 $5797 €5500 Meeting (66x82cm-26x32in) s. 25-Mar-3 Durán, Madrid #128/R

RODRIGUEZ, Alfred C (1862-1890) American
£955 $1500 €1433 Figures on a beach (30x51cm-12x20in) s. prov. 19-Nov-2 Butterfields, San Francisco #8142/R est:3000-5000

RODRIGUEZ, Alfredo (1954-) American
£1018 $1700 €1476 Sioux chief (76x51cm-30x20in) s.d.1973. 21-Jun-3 Selkirks, St. Louis #184/R est:2000-3000
£4491 $7500 €6512 Land of the brave (102x76cm-40x30in) s. 21-Jun-3 Selkirks, St. Louis #185/R est:10000-15000

RODRIGUEZ, M (19th C) ?
£1154 $1823 €1800 Gypsy toasting (48x32cm-19x13in) s. on porcelain. 14-Nov-2 Arte, Seville #319/R

RODRIGUEZ, Mariano (1912-1990) Cuban
Works on paper
£6707 $11000 €10061 Tres mujeres. Sin titulo. Cabeza (27x35cm-11x14in) one s.d.42 W/C two W/C exec.c.1940 one exhib. three prov. 28-May-3 Christie's, Rockefeller NY #88/R est:12000-16000
£7317 $12000 €10976 Sin titulo. Sin tutulo. Florero (57x76cm-22x30in) one s.d.49 W/C one ink one s. W/C crayon ink three prov. 28-May-3 Christie's, Rockefeller NY #97/R est:15000-20000

RODRIGUEZ, Nacho (20th C) Spanish
£385 $608 €600 Untitled (147x114cm-58x45in) s.d.2001 verso. 13-Nov-2 Ansorena, Madrid #70/R

RODRIGUEZ, Victor (1970-) Mexican
£7927 $13000 €11494 Red belle de jour (198x147cm-78x58in) acrylic s.i.d.Feb 28/0 verso prov.exhib. 27-May-3 Sotheby's, New York #63

RODWAY, Florence (1881-1971) Australian
Works on paper
£2768 $4373 €4152 Nude girl (97x67cm-38x26in) s. pastel. 18-Nov-2 Goodman, Sydney #125/R est:6000-9000 (A.D 7750)

ROE CLARAMUNT, Juan (1913-) Spanish
£346 $540 €550 Carousel (60x70cm-24x28in) s. exhib. 23-Sep-2 Durán, Madrid #601/R

ROE, Clarence (1850-1909) British
£340 $568 €493 Entrance to the port of Scarborough (29x44cm-11x17in) s. board. 17-Jun-3 Anderson & Garland, Newcastle #383
£400 $620 €600 Ducks in a Highland landscape (58x89cm-23x35in) s. 4-Dec-2 Andrew Hartley, Ilkley #1251
£400 $628 €600 Landscape with river (61x91cm-24x36in) s. 10-Dec-2 Capes Dunn, Manchester #845
£420 $689 €630 On the Mint - a river landscape with waterfall (61x91cm-24x36in) s.i.d.1886. 4-Feb-3 Bonhams, Chester #674
£440 $700 €660 Heart of the forest, Windsor (51x76cm-20x30in) s. s.i.verso. 27-Feb-3 Bonhams, Chester #464
£450 $684 €675 Extensive lakeland landscape with sheep in foreground (53x86cm-21x34in) s. 16-Aug-2 Keys, Aylsham #683
£450 $707 €675 Coast at Whitby (61x91cm-24x36in) s. 10-Dec-2 Capes Dunn, Manchester #844
£700 $1134 €1050 Buttermere (61x92cm-24x36in) s.i. 20-May-3 Sotheby's, Olympia #229/R
£886 $1382 €1400 Near Aberfoyle (60x91cm-24x36in) s. 15-Oct-2 Mealy's, Castlecomer #241/R
£1150 $1817 €1725 Ari Bahn and Balloch Grodich, Perthshire (61x91cm-24x36in) s. s.i.d.Oct 1882. 7-Apr-3 Bonhams, Bath #91/R est:800-1200
£1200 $1896 €1800 Lake and mountains landscape with cattle watering (61x91cm-24x36in) s. 28-Nov-2 Morphets, Harrogate #564/R est:1200-1800

ROE, Fred (1864-1947) British
£360 $562 €540 Sun Inn, Ipswich - with two children playing in the street before the inn (42x46cm-17x18in) s. 6-Nov-2 Bonhams, Chester #486
£370 $562 €555 Young girl seated reading beneath a blossom tree (38x48cm-15x19in) s. 16-Aug-2 Keys, Aylsham #426
£380 $635 €551 Sun Inn, Ipswich, since demolished (43x46cm-17x18in) s.d.1899 i.verso. 24-Jun-3 Bonhams, Knowle #73
£500 $780 €750 Timbered inn on a bridge, with river and swans (49x75cm-19x30in) s.indis.d. 8-Apr-3 Bonhams, Knightsbridge #209/R
£1200 $1992 €1740 Joan of Arc (43x58cm-17x23in) s. 10-Jun-3 David Lay, Penzance #437/R est:1500-2500
£3500 $5845 €5075 Ghost story (44x60cm-17x24in) s.d.1898. 17-Jun-3 Anderson & Garland, Newcastle #477/R est:2500-3500

ROE, Robert Ernest (fl.1860-1880) British
£850 $1318 €1275 Unloading the cargo (26x35cm-10x14in) s. board. 31-Oct-2 Christie's, Kensington #501/R
£1450 $2407 €2175 East Hartlepool (35x61cm-14x24in) board. 10-Jun-3 Bonhams, Leeds #175/R est:800-1200
£2400 $3984 €3600 Loading a ship from pier (58x88cm-23x35in) s. 10-Jun-3 Bonhams, Leeds #176/R est:2000-2500
£2707 $4250 €4061 Staiths near Whitby (114x94cm-45x37in) s. 23-Nov-2 Jackson's, Cedar Falls #16/R est:3000-5000
£3075 $4797 €4613 Lighters in Blackwall Reach (73x99cm-29x39in) s.indis.d. s.i.verso exhib. 11-Nov-2 Stephan Welz, Johannesburg #413/R est:25000-35000 (SA.R 48000)
Works on paper
£410 $640 €615 Coming into harbour (28x43cm-11x17in) s. pencil W/C. 27-Mar-3 Christie's, Kensington #161
£1800 $2880 €2700 Whitby, unloading the catch (52x77cm-20x30in) s. W/C htd white. 13-Mar-3 Morphets, Harrogate #611/R est:1500-2000
£3000 $4860 €4350 Shipping off Scarborough (32x53cm-13x21in) one s.i. W/C pair. 29-Jul-3 Holloways, Banbury #341/R est:700-900

ROE, Robert Henry (1822-1905) British
£922 $1429 €1383 Fox hunting ducks (78x127cm-31x50in) s.d.65. 8-Dec-2 Uppsala Auktionskammare, Uppsala #77/R (S.KR 13000)

ROE, Robert Henry (attrib) (1822-1905) British
£850 $1343 €1275 Stags on a mountain (61x86cm-24x34in) with sig,. 28-Nov-2 Christie's, Kensington #58/R

ROEBER, Philip (1913-) American
£306 $475 €459 Untitled (178x84cm-70x33in) s.d.1961. 7-Dec-2 Harvey Clar, Oakland #1252
£323 $500 €485 Untitled (244x86cm-96x34in) s.d.1961. 7-Dec-2 Harvey Clar, Oakland #1254
£323 $500 €485 Untitled (239x84cm-94x33in) s.d.1961. 7-Dec-2 Harvey Clar, Oakland #1256

ROED, Holger Peter (1846-1874) Danish
£357 $557 €536 Scene with two Vikings with spear and harp (46x36cm-18x14in) init. 5-Aug-2 Rasmussen, Vejle #263/R (D.KR 4200)

ROED, Jorgen (1808-1888) Danish
£258 $393 €387 Portrait of old man (31x25cm-12x10in) s. 28-Aug-2 Museumsbygningen, Copenhagen #91 (D.KR 3000)
£345 $528 €518 Portrait of an Italian (27x23cm-11x9in) mono.d.1861 prov. 24-Aug-2 Rasmussen, Havnen #2302 (D.KR 4000)
£687 $1085 €1031 From Helsingborg with Oresund in background (16x23cm-6x9in) cardboard. 13-Nov-2 Kunsthallen, Copenhagen #101 (D.KR 8000)

£698 $1110 €1047 Glimmingehus in Skaane (16x23cm-6x9in) 5-Mar-3 Rasmussen, Copenhagen #1817/R (D.KR 7500)
£914 $1453 €1371 Portrait of the artist P C Skovgaard (12x10cm-5x4in) canvas on panel painted c.1855. 26-Feb-3 Kunsthallen, Copenhagen #551/R (D.KR 10000)
£4270 $6576 €6405 Street in Florence (33x39cm-13x15in) unfinished study paper prov.exhib. 4-Sep-2 Kunsthallen, Copenhagen #2/R est:30000 (D.KR 50000)
£4842 $7698 €7263 Portrait of Sophie Philipsen. Portrait of Aaon Philipsen (29x23cm-11x9in) one s.indis.d.7.5.1861, second attributed to Roed two prov. 5-Mar-3 Rasmussen, Copenhagen #1547/R est:20000-25000 (D.KR 52000)

ROED, Jorgen (attrib) (1808-1888) Danish
£266 $431 €399 Portrait of Susanne Kobke, nee Ryder (16x14cm-6x6in) 25-Jan-3 Rasmussen, Havnen #2270 (D.KR 3000)

ROEDE, Jan (1914-) Dutch
£1792 $2795 €3104 Portrait Hussum (100x81cm-39x32in) s. prov. 31-Mar-3 Goodman, Sydney #193/R (A.D 4750)
£2302 $3776 €3200 Untitled (55x46cm-22x18in) s.d.63. 3-Jun-3 Christie's, Amsterdam #315/R est:2000-3000
£2885 $4471 €4500 Rije, rije, rije, een wagentje (46x55cm-18x22in) s.d.66. 3-Dec-2 Christie's, Amsterdam #141/R est:4500-6000
£3165 $5000 €5000 Kooitje op een berg (45x54cm-18x21in) s.d.56 prov. 26-Nov-2 Sotheby's, Amsterdam #257/R est:5000-6000

ROEDEG, I (20th C) ?
Works on paper
£3314 $5104 €4971 Woman bringing offerings to temple (37x56cm-15x22in) d. 11.5.37 wash pen ink W/C prov.exhib.lit. 27-Oct-2 Christie's, Hong Kong #24/R est:45000-55000 (HK.D 40000)

ROEDER, Emy (1890-1971) German
Works on paper
£652 $1070 €900 Goats (30x40cm-12x16in) mono. chl board prov. 29-May-3 Lempertz, Koln #895/R

ROEDERSTEIN, Ottilie Wilhelmine (1859-1937) Swiss
£352 $585 €500 Portrait of Ernst Levi, Frankfurt am Main (50x33cm-20x13in) mono.d.1930. 14-Jun-3 Arnold, Frankfurt #847/R
£370 $596 €555 Portrait of man (60x46cm-24x18in) mono.d.1928. 7-May-3 Dobiaschofsky, Bern #920/R (S.FR 800)
£370 $596 €555 Portrait of woman (60x46cm-24x18in) mono.d.1928. 7-May-3 Dobiaschofsky, Bern #921/R (S.FR 800)
£1135 $1771 €1703 Still life of flowers (54x41cm-21x16in) mono. 6-Nov-2 Dobiaschofsky, Bern #916/R est:3500 (S.FR 2600)

ROEDIG, Johann Christian (1751-1802) Dutch
£7500 $11775 €11250 Peaches and a bee on a pewter platter on a marble ledge, in a wooded landscape (36x29cm-14x11in) s. panel prov. 13-Dec-2 Christie's, Kensington #136/R est:7000-10000
£34615 $54692 €54000 Still life of fruit and flowers (78x59cm-31x23in) s. panel. 16-Nov-2 Lempertz, Koln #1084/R est:17000

ROEGGE, Wilhelm (jnr) (1870-1947) German
£252 $392 €400 Wooden hallway (45x35cm-18x14in) s.i.d.1920. 9-Oct-2 Michael Zeller, Lindau #884
£506 $785 €800 Cellist on summer terrace in Franken (24x27cm-9x11in) s. panel. 26-Sep-2 Neumeister, Munich #2825
£1282 $1987 €2000 Archivist homeward bound in snowy old city square (25x18cm-10x7in) s. i.verso panel. 4-Dec-2 Neumeister, Munich #866/R est:750
£2254 $3628 €3200 Four old men in discussion on summer afternoon (23x35cm-9x14in) s. panel. 7-May-3 Michael Zeller, Lindau #902/R est:400

ROEGGE, Wilhelm (snr) (1829-1908) German
£2108 $3500 €3057 Baptism (66x107cm-26x42in) 13-Jun-3 Du Mouchelle, Detroit #2037/R est:6000-8000
£2201 $3390 €3500 Die politische Zeitung (48x59cm-19x23in) s. s.i.on stretcher. 23-Oct-2 Christie's, Amsterdam #23/R est:4000-6000

ROEKENS, Paulette van (1896-?) American
£1401 $2200 €2102 Still life of a pitcher of flowers besides a Buddha figure (33x30cm-13x12in) s.d.29. 23-Nov-2 Pook & Pook, Downington #301/R est:1500-2500
£1548 $2400 €2322 Little girl with pink (41x51cm-16x20in) s. 8-Dec-2 Freeman, Philadelphia #173/R est:3000-5000
£5484 $8500 €8226 Mirror (30x36cm-12x14in) s. i.d.stretcher. 8-Dec-2 Freeman, Philadelphia #141/R est:3000-5000
£6731 $10500 €10097 Beach scene with sunbathers (20x30cm-8x12in) s.d.1927 artist board. 15-Oct-2 Winter Associates, Plainville #100 est:5000-7000
£14194 $22000 €21291 Village in winter (63x76cm-25x30in) s.indis.d.25. 8-Dec-2 Freeman, Philadelphia #128/R est:4000-6000

ROELAND, Jannes (1935-) Dutch
£2518 $4129 €3500 Envelope (70x70cm-28x28in) s. painted c.1967 lit. 3-Jun-3 Christie's, Amsterdam #374/R est:3000-5000

ROELOFS, Albert (1877-1920) Dutch
£2830 $4358 €4500 Elegant lady at a writing desk (18x14cm-7x6in) canvas on board painted 1914 prov.lit. 22-Oct-2 Sotheby's, Amsterdam #203/R est:5000-7000
£4717 $7264 €7500 Portrait of a boy (37x55cm-15x22in) s. panel prov.lit. 22-Oct-2 Sotheby's, Amsterdam #204/R est:8000-12000
£4861 $7729 €7000 Precious flowers (27x19cm-11x7in) s. panel. 29-Apr-3 Christie's, Amsterdam #167/R est:6000-8000
£34591 $53270 €55000 AtelierJOOL (62x83cm-24x33in) s. prov.exhib.lit. 22-Oct-2 Sotheby's, Amsterdam #201/R est:60000-80000

ROELOFS, W (1822-1897) Dutch
£1408 $2268 €2000 Polder landscape with cattle and rowers (30x40cm-12x16in) panel. 6-May-3 Vendu Notarishuis, Rotterdam #57 est:2000-2500

ROELOFS, Willem (1822-1897) Dutch
£566 $877 €900 Landscape (15x24cm-6x9in) s. studio st. paper on panel prov. 5-Oct-2 De Vuyst, Lokeren #309
£2639 $4354 €3800 Drachenfels by the Rhine (24x43cm-9x17in) i. paper on panel prov.exhib.lit. 1-Jul-3 Christie's, Amsterdam #191/R est:600-800
£2639 $4354 €3800 Watering cows (19x34cm-7x13in) s. 1-Jul-3 Christie's, Amsterdam #192/R est:1500-2000
£2961 $4796 €4500 Farmhouses in Aalden, Drenthe (22x39cm-9x15in) s.i. canvas on panel. 21-Jan-3 Christie's, Amsterdam #318/R est:5000-7000
£3822 $5885 €6000 Panoramic summer landscape with harvesters (47x61cm-19x24in) s.d.1845 canvas on plywood. 3-Sep-2 Christie's, Amsterdam #170/R est:7000-9000
£3916 $6500 €5678 Cattle by canal (69x91cm-27x36in) s. 13-Jun-3 Du Mouchelle, Detroit #2114/R est:5000-7000
£9554 $15000 €14331 Cattle by canal (69x91cm-27x36in) 13-Dec-2 Du Mouchelle, Detroit #2082/R est:18000-22000
£11644 $18281 €17000 Painter at work (36x26cm-14x10in) s. canvas on panel. 15-Apr-3 Sotheby's, Amsterdam #218/R est:15000-20000
£11806 $18771 €17000 Apres midi a Gouda (29x44cm-11x17in) s. init.i.verso canvas on panel. 29-Apr-3 Christie's, Amsterdam #121/R est:10000-15000
£13014 $20432 €19000 View of Glen Sligichan, Isle De Skye, Scotland (28x44cm-11x17in) s.i. i.verso canvas on panel. 15-Apr-3 Sotheby's, Amsterdam #124/R est:4000-6000
£23899 $36805 €38000 Watering cows (63x96cm-25x38in) s. 22-Oct-2 Sotheby's, Amsterdam #219/R est:38000-45000
£40881 $62956 €65000 Watering cows (25x39cm-10x15in) s.d.1881 prov.exhib. 22-Oct-2 Sotheby's, Amsterdam #208/R est:25000-35000
Works on paper
£552 $877 €800 Peasant on a horse drawn cart in a landscape (20x4cm-8x2in) s. W/C. 10-Mar-3 Sotheby's, Amsterdam #178
£11465 $18000 €17198 Cows watering in the early morning (12x20cm-5x8in) s. indis i.verso W/C htd white. 10-Dec-2 Doyle, New York #192/R est:5000-7000
£11972 $19275 €17000 Sunny day with farmer's wife on country path (32x48cm-13x19in) s. W/C. 7-May-3 Vendue Huis, Gravenhage #444/R est:2000-2500

ROELOFS, Willem Elisa (1874-1940) Dutch
£382 $596 €600 Still life with flowers and vases (29x43cm-11x17in) s. 6-Nov-2 Vendue Huis, Gravenhage #122/R
£1300 $2132 €1950 Lone fisherman (41x70cm-16x28in) s. 5-Jun-3 Christie's, Kensington #626/R est:700-1000
Works on paper
£395 $639 €600 Still life with fish (45x72cm-18x28in) s.d.03 W/C htd white. 21-Jan-3 Christie's, Amsterdam #284

ROERICH, Nikolai Konstantinovitch (1874-1947) American/Russian
£24000 $37680 €36000 Cliff dwellings (50x76cm-20x30in) mono. tempera. 20-Nov-2 Sotheby's, London #98/R est:18000-25000
Works on paper
£4895 $8175 €7000 Le chateau de Gengis Khan (21x27cm-8x11in) mono. i.verso gouache prov.lit. 26-Jun-3 Tajan, Paris #104/R est:8000-12000

ROESCH, Kurt (1905-) American
£599 $1000 €869 Insects (58x84cm-23x33in) s. i.on stretcher. 29-Jun-3 Butterfields, Los Angeles #7048/R est:1000-1500

ROESELER, August (1866-1934) German
£260 $434 €377 Bilious man in a red waistcoat (25x25cm-10x10in) s.d.1922 panel. 17-Jun-3 Rosebery Fine Art, London #499

ROESEN, Severin (fl.1848-1872) American/German
£26235 $42500 €39353 Still life of fruit (67x79cm-26x31in) painted c.1851 prov.exhib. 21-May-3 Sotheby's, New York #102/R est:60000-80000
£27778 $45000 €41667 Still life with fruit (51x41cm-20x16in) s. painted c.1855 prov. 21-May-3 Sotheby's, New York #202/R est:30000-50000

ROESSINGH, Louis Albert (1873-1951) Dutch/Belgian
£1296 $2087 €1944 Small boy in red hat (37x29cm-15x11in) s.d.1923. 7-May-3 Dobiaschofsky, Bern #922/R est:3500 (S.FR 2800)
£2878 $4604 €4000 Still life of flowers in front of Japanese print (42x34cm-17x13in) s. panel. 17-May-3 De Vuyst, Lokeren #313 est:440-480

ROESSLER, G (1861-1925) German
£419 $616 €650 Man with pipe (24x18cm-9x7in) s. 24-Jun-2 Dr Fritz Nagel, Stuttgart #6033/R

ROESSLER, Georg (1861-1925) German
£411 $641 €600 Rendezvous in the wood (45x36cm-18x14in) s.d.1896. 10-Apr-3 Van Ham, Cologne #1676
£563 $855 €845 Portrait of man and woman (21x16cm-8x6in) panel pair. 16-Aug-2 Lilla Bukowskis, Stockholm #264 (S.KR 8200)

ROESTENBURG, Martinus Wouterus (1909-1966) Dutch
£329 $533 €500 Farmhouse in a landscape (40x50cm-16x20in) s. 21-Jan-3 Christie's, Amsterdam #458

ROESTRATEN, Pieter Gerritsz van (1630-1700) Dutch
£8387 $13252 €13000 Vanity (64x50cm-25x20in) exhib. 18-Dec-2 Piasa, Paris #45/R est:15000

ROESTRATEN, Pieter Gerritsz van (attrib) (1630-1700) Dutch
£11000 $17270 €16500 Still life of lobsters, oysters, bread, fruit, bottle of wine and glass (64x76cm-25x30in) prov. 12-Dec-2 Sotheby's, London #152/R est:8000-12000

ROETING, Julius Amatus (1822-1896) German
£2260 $3526 €3300 Portrait of Max Volkhart (115x90cm-45x35in) s.d.1881. 10-Apr-3 Van Ham, Cologne #1679/R est:1800

ROFFE, William John (fl.1845-1889) British
£400 $624 €600 River landscape at sunset (76x63cm-30x25in) s.d.1865. 9-Oct-2 Woolley & Wallis, Salisbury #248/R
Works on paper
£250 $390 €375 Village hall at Crail (24x34cm-9x13in) s.d.91 pencil W/C scratching out. 17-Oct-2 Christie's, Kensington #40

ROFFIAEN, Jean François (1820-1898) Belgian
£450 $729 €675 Cattle grazing before a mountain lake (37x56cm-15x22in) s.d.1856. 23-Jan-3 Christie's, Kensington #148/R
£645 $1019 €1000 Au bord du lac de Lugano (18x29cm-7x11in) s. panel. 17-Dec-2 Rossini, Paris #120
£962 $1490 €1500 Extensive landscape with grazing cows (24x33cm-9x13in) s. indis.i.verso panel. 4-Dec-2 Neumeister, Munich #868/R est:1800
£1400 $2324 €1400 Locarno du Val Maggio (20x31cm-8x12in) panel. 16-Jun-3 Horta, Bruxelles #71
£1911 $2981 €3000 Vue de Neuhaus (24x34cm-9x13in) s. s.i.verso panel. 11-Nov-2 Horta, Bruxelles #184 est:2500-3700
£2000 $3320 €2000 L'entree de la vallee du Rhone (32x41cm-13x16in) s. 16-Jun-3 Horta, Bruxelles #70 est:2000-3000
£2179 $3378 €3400 Troupeau traversant le village de Meyringen (47x65cm-19x26in) s.d.1852. 9-Dec-2 Horta, Bruxelles #212/R est:3500-5500
£2532 $4000 €4000 Des hauteurs de Brientz, la vallee de Meyringen et la plubtenstock (25x36cm-10x14in) s.i.verso panel. 26-Nov-2 Palais de Beaux Arts, Brussels #364/R est:2000-3000
£3165 $5065 €4400 Paysage montagneux avec riviere anime de personnages (49x42cm-19x17in) s.d.1873. 13-May-3 Palais de Beaux Arts, Brussels #127/R est:5000-7000
£3205 $5032 €5000 Paysage anime (63x73cm-25x29in) s.d.1842. 10-Dec-2 Vanderkindere, Brussels #25/R est:5000-7000
£12500 $19376 €18750 Alpine lake scenes (71x117cm-28x46in) stamp verso two. 3-Dec-2 Sotheby's, Olympia #247/R est:7000-10000

ROGAN, J H (19th C) ?
£745 $1184 €1118 Italian street scene with figures (79x64cm-31x25in) s. 10-Mar-3 Rasmussen, Vejle #192/R (D.KR 8000)

ROGER, Emili Bosch (1894-1980) Spanish
£3846 $6038 €6000 Barcelona harbour (51x62cm-20x24in) s. 16-Dec-2 Castellana, Madrid #797/R
£7660 $12409 €10800 Teatro Arnau en El Paralelo, Barcelona (60x73cm-24x29in) s. 20-May-3 Segre, Madrid #117/R est:10800
Works on paper
£303 $490 €460 Urban landscape (38x26cm-15x10in) s. W/C felt-tip pen. 21-Jan-3 Ansorena, Madrid #831/R

ROGER, Suzanne (1898-1986) French
£1076 $1700 €1700 Paix (130x162cm-51x64in) s. 2-Dec-2 Tajan, Paris #148
£2778 $4583 €4000 Le palmier (100x65cm-39x26in) s. prov. 2-Jul-3 Artcurial Briest, Paris #674/R est:4000-6000

ROGERS, Frank Whiting (1854-?) American
£1274 $2000 €1911 Portrait of a collie (36x41cm-14x16in) s. 22-Nov-2 Skinner, Boston #94/R est:800-1200

ROGERS, Howard (1932-) American
£4259 $6900 €6176 Into the shadows (71x107cm-28x42in) 23-May-3 Altermann Galleries, Santa Fe #147

ROGERS, John (1829-1904) American
Works on paper
£283 $450 €425 Hillside farm (49x68cm-19x27in) s. W/C exhib. 7-Mar-3 Skinner, Boston #449/R

ROGERS, Raymond M (?) ?
£350 $550 €525 Boys fishing (59x75cm-23x30in) s. 15-Dec-2 Lots Road, London #355

ROGERS, Wendell (20th C) American
£224 $350 €336 Clam shacks (51x76cm-20x30in) s. 1-Aug-2 Eldred, East Dennis #377i

ROGERS, William (19th C) British
£1500 $2280 €2250 Pastoral scene with figures (25x36cm-10x14in) init. board. 14-Aug-2 Andrew Hartley, Ilkley #670/R est:1500-2000

ROGERS, William P (fl.1842-1872) British
Works on paper
£1181 $1877 €1700 Female fishmonger and travelling merchant (43x36cm-17x14in) s.d.1869 W/C over pencil. 29-Apr-3 Whyte's, Dublin #180/R est:1000-1500

ROGGE, Emy (1866-?) German
£1076 $1700 €1700 Farmhouse in Worpswede (80x60cm-31x24in) s. 29-Nov-2 Bolland & Marotz, Bremen #565/R est:700

ROGGER, Roger van (1914-1983) American
£2439 $4000 €3537 Interior (104x89cm-41x35in) s.d.48 prov. 1-Jun-3 Wright, Chicago #154/R est:2500-3500

ROGHMAN, Roeland (1597-1686) Dutch
Works on paper
£7006 $10930 €11000 Group of tall trees before a panoramic landscape (18x29cm-7x11in) pen brown ink grey wash prov.exhib.lit. 5-Nov-2 Sotheby's, Amsterdam #58/R est:8000-12000

ROGHMAN, Roeland (attrib) (1597-1686) Dutch
Works on paper
£1266 $2000 €2000 Rocky landscape with wooden bridge over waterfall (19x24cm-7x9in) Indian ink brush. 29-Nov-2 Bassenge, Berlin #5469/R est:3000

ROGIER, Camille (attrib) (19th C) French
Works on paper
£256 $397 €400 Oriental dans sa boutique (24x19cm-9x7in) W/C over crayon. 4-Dec-2 Piasa, Paris #160

ROGINSKY, Michel (1931-) Russian
£662 $1079 €1000 Bottles (62x101cm-24x40in) mono.d.78 acrylic board lit. 28-Jan-3 Dorotheum, Vienna #205/R

ROGNONI, Franco (1913-1999) Italian
£729 $1159 €1050 Look at the city (16x22cm-6x9in) s. cardboard on canvas. 1-May-3 Meeting Art, Vercelli #540

£1361 $2163 €2000 Selene (55x46cm-22x18in) s.d.1972. 1-Mar-3 Meeting Art, Vercelli #555
£1474 $2315 €2300 Town (55x46cm-22x18in) s. s.i.d.1998 verso. 23-Nov-2 Meeting Art, Vercelli #354/R
£1689 $2635 €2500 Red knight (55x46cm-22x18in) s.d.70 s.i.d.verso. 26-Mar-3 Finarte Semenzato, Milan #256/R
£1935 $3058 €3000 Night scene (55x45cm-22x18in) s.d.68 prov. 18-Dec-2 Christie's, Rome #84/R
£2254 $3741 €3200 Grand Hotel Bellevue et du Parc (54x73cm-21x29in) s.d.68 s.i.d.verso. 10-Jun-3 Finarte Semenzato, Milan #185/R est:2800-3000

Works on paper
£327 $523 €500 Little mermaid (28x22cm-11x9in) s. mixed media paper on canvas. 4-Jan-3 Meeting Art, Vercelli #651
£382 $607 €550 Figure (29x21cm-11x8in) s. Chinese ink W/C. 1-May-3 Meeting Art, Vercelli #280
£986 $1637 €1400 Figura femminile (41x33cm-16x13in) s. mixed media cardboard. 10-Jun-3 Finarte Semenzato, Milan #192/R est:1200-1600
£1042 $1656 €1500 Ancient village (55x46cm-22x18in) s. mixed media paper on canvas. 1-May-3 Meeting Art, Vercelli #339

ROGUIER, Henri Victor (1758-?) French
Sculpture
£25641 $39744 €40000 Abraham, marquis Duquesne (32x12x12cm-13x5x5in) terracotta prov.lit. 9-Dec-2 Rabourdin & Choppin de Janvry, Paris #98/R est:9000

ROGY, Georges (1897-1981) Belgian
£278 $434 €440 Vase de Bruxelles fleuri (40x50cm-16x20in) s.d.30. 15-Oct-2 Horta, Bruxelles #449
£1020 $1622 €1500 Les nouvelles du matin (75x59cm-30x23in) s. lit. 24-Mar-3 Bernaerts, Antwerp #166/R est:1500-2000

ROH, Franz (1890-1965) German
Works on paper
£822 $1282 €1200 Composition (23x16cm-9x6in) collage. 11-Apr-3 Winterberg, Heidelberg #1556

ROHDE, C (19th C) ?
£566 $883 €900 Poultry yard (14x28cm-6x11in) i. 23-Sep-2 Dr Fritz Nagel, Stuttgart #6935/R

ROHDE, Carl (1840-1891) German
£1389 $2292 €2000 Roses in a vase (39x32cm-15x13in) s. 1-Jul-3 Christie's, Amsterdam #40/R est:2000-3000

ROHDE, Fredrik (1816-1886) Danish
£326 $508 €489 The artist P A Plum and his family on terrace (44x40cm-17x16in) s.d.1876. 11-Nov-2 Rasmussen, Vejle #692/R (D.KR 3800)
£390 $592 €600 Monk in southern monastery garden (24x33cm-9x13in) s.d.1873 board. 6-Jul-2 Berlinghof, Heidelberg #240/R
£431 $698 €625 Hunter on woodland path in winter (37x40cm-15x16in) s.d.1875. 26-May-3 Rasmussen, Copenhagen #1287/R (D.KR 4500)
£596 $941 €894 Danish summer landscape (16x31cm-6x12in) s. 2-Dec-2 Rasmussen, Copenhagen #1299/R (D.KR 7000)
£596 $941 €894 Winter landscape with stag by lake (37x45cm-15x18in) s.d.1874. 2-Dec-2 Rasmussen, Copenhagen #1554/R (D.KR 7000)
£775 $1178 €1163 Monastery garden near Lake Garda (18x20cm-7x8in) init.d.1849 panel. 27-Aug-2 Rasmussen, Copenhagen #1659/R (D.KR 9000)
£1213 $1928 €1820 The market in Riva by Lago di Garda (36x51cm-14x20in) s. 29-Apr-3 Kunsthallen, Copenhagen #523/R est:20000 (D.KR 13000)
£2010 $3256 €2915 Figures in Italian village by water (36x50cm-14x20in) s.d.1865. 26-May-3 Rasmussen, Copenhagen #1320/R est:15000-20000 (D.KR 21000)
£2392 $3876 €3468 Winter landscape with frozen lakes (90x130cm-35x51in) mono.indis.d.18.2. 26-May-3 Rasmussen, Copenhagen #1149/R est:30000-40000 (D.KR 25000)

ROHDE, Johan (1856-1935) Danish
£254 $391 €381 Palatine Mountain, Rome (30x36cm-12x14in) s. cardboard. 26-Oct-2 Rasmussen, Havnen #2150/R (D.KR 3000)
£254 $391 €381 Ruins at Palatine in Rome (31x36cm-12x14in) s. cardboard. 26-Oct-2 Rasmussen, Havnen #2151/R (D.KR 3000)
£337 $546 €506 Landscape from Fano (29x36cm-11x14in) s.d.1912. 25-Jan-3 Rasmussen, Havnen #2144 (D.KR 3800)
£338 $521 €507 Capuchin Monastery, Sorento (31x36cm-12x14in) s. cardboard. 26-Oct-2 Rasmussen, Havnen #2149/R (D.KR 4000)
£517 $786 €776 Town prospect from Randers with houses and boats by water (51x63cm-20x25in) s. 28-Aug-2 Museumsbygningen, Copenhagen #72/R (D.KR 6000)
£559 $888 €839 Coastal landscape with vessels (47x63cm-19x25in) init.d.1910. 10-Mar-3 Rasmussen, Vejle #80 (D.KR 6000)
£643 $1003 €965 Venetian canal scene (51x61cm-20x24in) s. exhib. 11-Nov-2 Rasmussen, Vejle #592/R (D.KR 7500)
£746 $1187 €1119 Interior scene with small boy doing homework (75x63cm-30x25in) s.d.1922. 5-May-3 Rasmussen, Vejle #650/R (D.KR 8000)
£957 $1550 €1388 Beached boats, Fano (51x63cm-20x25in) s.d.1925. 26-May-3 Rasmussen, Copenhagen #1402/R (D.KR 10000)
£1164 $1851 €1746 Three boats at Fano beach (48x60cm-19x24in) s.d.1924. 10-Mar-3 Rasmussen, Vejle #74/R est:8000-10000 (D.KR 12500)

ROHL, Karl Peter (1890-1975) German
Works on paper
£1282 $1987 €2000 Abstract composition (50x31cm-20x12in) s.d.1924 Indian ink gouache. 4-Dec-2 Lempertz, Koln #1025/R est:2500
£1522 $2496 €2100 Geometric composition (28x24cm-11x9in) s.i.d.1922 paper collage. 29-May-3 Lempertz, Koln #896/R est:1800

ROHL, Maria (1801-1875) Swedish
Works on paper
£384 $599 €576 Portrait of Empress Eugenie of France (66x44cm-26x17in) s.i.d.1856 after Winterhalter. 13-Sep-2 Lilla Bukowskis, Stockholm #623 (S.KR 5600)

ROHLFS, Christian (1849-1938) German
£3205 $5064 €5000 Anenomes (31x54cm-12x21in) mono.d.26 tempera board. 14-Nov-2 Neumeister, Munich #682/R est:7500-8000
£6731 $10433 €10500 Thuring landscape (25x40cm-10x16in) s. prov. 4-Dec-2 Lempertz, Koln #1028/R est:15000-20000
£6884 $11290 €9500 Squatting negro (70x55cm-28x22in) mono.d.28 tempera chl prov.exhib. 29-May-3 Lempertz, Koln #903/R est:12000-15000
£8696 $14261 €12000 Roses (37x47cm-15x19in) s.i.d.89 prov.exhib. 31-May-3 Villa Grisebach, Berlin #117/R est:12000-15000
£9810 $15500 €15500 Summer landscape (58x76cm-23x30in) mono.d.02 prov.exhib.lit. 30-Nov-2 Villa Grisebach, Berlin #121/R est:25000-30000
£10345 $16345 €15000 Bridge in Tessin (56x78cm-22x31in) mono.d.1932 tempera prov. 2-Apr-3 Dr Fritz Nagel, Stuttgart #9540/R est:15000
£13043 $20217 €19565 Landscape (51x65cm-20x26in) prov. 4-Dec-2 Koller, Zurich #102/R est:35000-45000 (S.FR 30000)
£16667 $25833 €26000 Early Alpine landscape - Bavaria (50x70cm-20x28in) prov. 4-Dec-2 Lempertz, Koln #1029/R est:25000-30000
£24359 $37756 €38000 Lady's slipper and red flower in a glass (50x67cm-20x26in) mono.d.20 tempera board prov. 7-Dec-2 Van Ham, Cologne #455/R est:38000
£25949 $41000 €41000 Man and Woman (80x60cm-31x24in) mono.d.27 oil tempera prov.exhib. 29-Nov-2 Villa Grisebach, Berlin #48/R est:50000-60000

Prints
£4348 $7130 €6000 Three heads (36x26cm-14x10in) s.i. woodcut. 31-May-3 Villa Grisebach, Berlin #191/R est:5500-6500
£5217 $8557 €7200 Conversation (33x22cm-13x9in) s.i. gouache on woodcut. 31-May-3 Villa Grisebach, Berlin #193/R est:6000-8000

Works on paper
£435 $713 €600 Farmsteads (13x17cm-5x7in) chk. 29-May-3 Lempertz, Koln #902/R
£563 $935 €800 Sketch sheet (16x10cm-6x4in) mono. Indian ink. 14-Jun-3 Hauswedell & Nolte, Hamburg #1559/R
£704 $1169 €1000 November storm (44x46cm-17x18in) mono. i. verso Indian ink brush W/C gouache. 14-Jun-3 Hauswedell & Nolte, Hamburg #1558/R
£1408 $2338 €2000 Male nude (62x46cm-24x18in) mono.d Indian ink W/C. 14-Jun-3 Hauswedell & Nolte, Hamburg #1555/R est:1800
£1884 $3090 €2600 Poppy heads (16x24cm-6x9in) mono.d.32 water tempera chk. 31-May-3 Villa Grisebach, Berlin #670/R est:2000-2500
£1900 $2945 €2850 Behinderter soldat (59x46cm-23x18in) init.d.19 brush ink bodycol. 5-Dec-2 Christie's, Kensington #110/R est:2000-3000
£2115 $3321 €3300 Lake in the high mountains (22x30cm-9x12in) mono.d.1920 pastel. 23-Nov-2 Arnold, Frankfurt #853/R est:2000
£2174 $3565 €3000 Timeless autumn (25x37cm-10x15in) water tempera ink pen. 31-May-3 Villa Grisebach, Berlin #260/R est:4000-5000
£2308 $3577 €3600 King with pipe (25x13cm-10x5in) s. Indian ink W/C prov. 4-Dec-2 Lempertz, Koln #1030/R est:3200
£2536 $4159 €3500 Yellow iris (32x20cm-13x8in) mono.d32 water tempera blue pen. 31-May-3 Villa Grisebach, Berlin #259/R est:4000-5000
£3261 $5348 €4500 Holstein landscape (19x26cm-7x10in) W/C Indian ink. 31-May-3 Villa Grisebach, Berlin #261/R est:4000-5000
£5208 $8281 €7500 Horse grazing (26x19cm-10x7in) mono.d. W/C pen double-sided. 5-May-3 Ketterer, Munich #948/R est:4000-6000
£6338 $10521 €9000 Red flowers (64x49cm-25x19in) mono.d. W/C gouache. 14-Jun-3 Hauswedell & Nolte, Hamburg #1556/R est:12000
£6475 $10619 €9000 The Alps (56x80cm-22x31in) mono. mono.i. verso water temper pigment Indian ink crayon. 6-Jun-3 Ketterer, Munich #68/R est:18000-24000

£6522 $10696 €9000 Cosmeen (38x28cm-15x11in) mono.d.34 chk water tempera. 31-May-3 Villa Grisebach, Berlin #166/R est:9000-12000
£6757 $10541 €10000 Kohlrabi (35x51cm-14x20in) mono.d.1923 water tempera Indian ink prov. 28-Mar-3 Ketterer, Hamburg #600/R est:10000-15000
£7246 $11884 €10000 Penitent figure (66x47cm-26x19in) mono. W/C Indian ink prov. 31-May-3 Villa Grisebach, Berlin #245/R est:10000-15000
£10000 $15500 €15000 Blute (46x59cm-18x23in) indis sig. pastel. 5-Dec-2 Christie's, Kensington #144/R est:10000-15000
£10127 $16000 €16000 Pine tree (55x39cm-22x15in) mono.d.20 i.verso water tempera prov. 29-Nov-2 Villa Grisebach, Berlin #45/R est:9000-12000
£13208 $20604 €21000 Artischockenbluten - artichoke flowers (44x59cm-17x23in) mono.i. water tempera executed c.1936-37 prov. 9-Oct-2 Sotheby's, London #129/R est:30000-40000
£13768 $22580 €19000 Flower (48x33cm-19x13in) mono.d.32 W/C chk prov. 29-May-3 Lempertz, Koln #906/R est:20000-22000
£20290 $33275 €28000 Sunflowers (57x39cm-22x15in) mono.d.31 watertempera prov. 29-May-3 Lempertz, Koln #905/R est:28000-30000
£21739 $35652 €30000 Red tulips (68x49cm-27x19in) mono.d.25 water tempera crayon paper on board prov. 30-May-3 Villa Grisebach, Berlin #59/R est:30000-40000
£26582 $42000 €42000 Peasant house (47x60cm-19x24in) mono.d.22 water tempera black brush paper on cardboard prov. 29-Nov-2 Villa Grisebach, Berlin #47/R est:30000-45000

ROHLING, Carl (1849-1922) German
£519 $820 €779 Gluck bei der Konigin (77x57cm-30x22in) s. 27-Nov-2 Falkkloos, Malmo #78320/R (S.KR 7400)

ROHMEYER, Wilhelm Heinrich (1882-1936) German
£475 $750 €750 Field work in Fischerhude (45x64cm-18x25in) s. board. 29-Nov-2 Bolland & Marotz, Bremen #566/R

ROHNER, Georges (1913-2000) French
£510 $785 €800 Boats, Locquemau (27x46cm-11x18in) s.d.48 prov. 3-Sep-2 Christie's, Amsterdam #338/R
£1019 $1590 €1600 Paysage avec maison (40x55cm-16x22in) 8-Nov-2 Pierre Berge, Paris #3
£2414 $4031 €3500 Nature morte aux poires et au vase (60x81cm-24x32in) s.d.49. 10-Jul-3 Artcurial Briest, Paris #228/R est:1500-1800
£2518 $4029 €3500 Paris, la Seine et l'Institut (54x81cm-21x32in) s. 18-May-3 Eric Pillon, Calais #15/R
£3503 $5465 €5500 Forum et Curie (81x65cm-32x26in) s. 10-Nov-2 Eric Pillon, Calais #189/R

ROHRHIRSCH, Karl (1875-1954) German
£318 $497 €500 Ramsau (16x28cm-6x11in) s. panel. 6-Nov-2 Hugo Ruef, Munich #1254
£1223 $1932 €1835 Post coach in Bavaria (14x18cm-6x7in) s.i. panel. 14-Nov-2 Stuker, Bern #483 est:1200-1500 (S.FR 2800)

ROHRICHT, Wolf (1886-1953) German
£313 $500 €470 Winter landscape (86x66cm-34x26in) s.d.21.2.45. 18-May-3 Butterfields, Los Angeles #7018

ROHRS, Marie (1820-?) German
£3797 $6000 €6000 Italien girl with tambourine (75x63cm-30x25in) s.d.1864. 28-Nov-2 Dorotheum, Vienna #116/R est:4500-5500

ROHSAL, Luis (fl.1844-1878) German
£704 $1134 €1000 Graubunden Alps (42x58cm-17x23in) mono. lit. 9-May-3 Schloss Ahlden, Ahlden #1419/R

ROIDOT, Henri (1877-1960) Belgian
£255 $397 €400 Arbres au printemps (14x19cm-6x7in) s. panel. 11-Nov-2 Horta, Bruxelles #717
£364 $594 €550 Attelage au tonneau (22x30cm-9x12in) s. cardboard. 17-Feb-3 Horta, Bruxelles #331
£397 $648 €600 Brabancons aux champs (22x30cm-9x12in) s. cardboard. 17-Feb-3 Horta, Bruxelles #357
£411 $641 €600 Vieux saules (45x60cm-18x24in) s. panel. 14-Apr-3 Horta, Bruxelles #31
£586 $938 €850 Pond (19x31cm-7x12in) s. panel. 15-Mar-3 De Vuyst, Lokeren #278
£645 $1019 €1000 La ferme ensoleillee (60x80cm-24x31in) s. 17-Dec-2 Palais de Beaux Arts, Brussels #608/R
£651 $1015 €950 Petite mare aux canards (50x60cm-20x24in) s. 14-Apr-3 Horta, Bruxelles #30
£1224 $1947 €1800 Hiver (100x150cm-39x59in) s. panel. 18-Mar-3 Campo, Vlaamse Kaai #217 est:1000-1200
£1226 $1937 €1900 Vacher et troupeau dans un paysage (60x80cm-24x31in) s. 17-Dec-2 Palais de Beaux Arts, Brussels #609/R est:1900-2900
£1258 $1937 €2000 Verger (60x80cm-24x31in) s. 22-Oct-2 Galerie Moderne, Brussels #1714/R

ROIG GUTIERREZ, Francisco (1882-1958) Spanish
£1027 $1603 €1500 View of Calas Cobas (31x39cm-12x15in) s. cardboard. 8-Apr-3 Ansorena, Madrid #257/R

ROIG Y SOLER, Juan (1852-1909) Spanish
£10526 $17053 €16000 Street with balconies (36x25cm-14x10in) s. board. 21-Jan-3 Ansorena, Madrid #172/R est:12000
£12500 $20250 €19000 Coastal village (50x32cm-20x13in) s. 21-Jan-3 Ansorena, Madrid #167/R est:17500

ROILOS, Georgios (1867-1928) Greek
£2600 $4108 €3900 Greek Easter (70x54cm-28x21in) 1-Apr-3 Bonhams, New Bond Street #7 est:1000-1500

ROJO, Vicente (1932-) Mexican/Spanish
£1637 $2554 €2456 Sin titulo (50x40cm-20x16in) s. 17-Oct-2 Louis Morton, Mexico #138/R est:30000-35000 (M.P 26000)

Works on paper
£1259 $1965 €1889 Geometria 3 (55x38cm-22x15in) s.d.1964 mixed media prov. 17-Oct-2 Louis Morton, Mexico #19/R est:24000-26000 (M.P 20000)

ROLAND, Philippe Laurent (1746-1816) French

Sculpture
£16026 $24840 €25000 Portrait d'Augustin Pajou (30x30cm-12x12in) s.d.1802 pat bronze relief exhib.lit. 9-Dec-2 Rabourdin & Choppin de Janvry, Paris #24/R est:3000
£64103 $99359 €100000 Portrait de madame Roland (78x48x26cm-31x19x10in) terracotta exec.c.1788 lit. 9-Dec-2 Rabourdin & Choppin de Janvry, Paris #53/R

ROLANDO, Charles (1844-1893) Australian
£961 $1470 €1442 Bush Creek (60x90cm-24x35in) s. 25-Aug-2 Sotheby's, Paddington #193/R est:2000-3000 (A.D 2700)
£1964 $3104 €2946 Sequestered Sot, Watts River (51x76cm-20x30in) s. prov.exhib. 26-Nov-2 Sotheby's, Melbourne #122/R est:7000-10000 (A.D 5500)

ROLANDO, Rosa (1897-1962) Mexican
£15924 $25000 €23886 Bride from Tehuantepec (77x61cm-30x24in) s. painted c.1950. 19-Nov-2 Sotheby's, New York #2/R est:20000

ROLDAN, Enrique (19th C) Spanish
£517 $817 €750 Alcazar, Seville (14x10cm-6x4in) s. board. 7-Apr-3 Castellana, Madrid #2/R

ROLDAN, Modesto (1926-) Spanish?
£357 $521 €550 Portrait of Giovanna Tornavoni (50x39cm-20x15in) s.i.d.94 acrylic cardboard. 17-Jun-2 Ansorena, Madrid #100

ROLFE, H L (19th C) British
£850 $1292 €1275 Otters playing with a salmon (45x30cm-18x12in) s.d.1890. 13-Aug-2 Gildings, Market Harborough #253/R

ROLFSEN, Alf (1895-1979) Norwegian
£1298 $2050 €1947 The death of Balder (72x102cm-28x40in) s. 2-Dec-2 Blomqvist, Oslo #435/R est:18000-20000 (N.KR 15000)
£1305 $2089 €1958 Forest worker (103x124cm-41x49in) s. sketch panel prov. 17-Mar-3 Blomqvist, Oslo #426/R est:20000-30000 (N.KR 15000)

Works on paper
£1316 $2079 €1974 Sketch for Vestre Crematorium (68x66cm-27x26in) init.d.Mai 1936 mixed media panel. 17-Dec-2 Grev Wedels Plass, Oslo #269 est:3000 (N.KR 15000)

ROLING, Gerard Victor Alphons (1904-1981) Dutch
£1235 $2000 €1791 Floral still life (51x41cm-20x16in) init. i.verso masonite. 21-May-3 Doyle, New York #236/R est:4000-6000
£10791 $17698 €15000 Plums in a dish (21x29cm-8x11in) init. s.i.verso board prov. 3-Jun-3 Christie's, Amsterdam #211/R est:6000-8000

ROLL, Alfred Philippe (1846-1919) French
£1582 $2468 €2500 Interieur de bergerie (65x92cm-26x36in) s.d.84. 20-Oct-2 Galerie de Chartres, Chartres #117 est:2500-3000

ROLLA, Adolfo Giuseppe (1899-1967) Italian
£2564 $4026 €4000 Stream (100x130cm-39x51in) s.d.1946. 10-Dec-2 Della Rocca, Turin #310/R

ROLLAND, Antoni Vidal (1889-1970) Spanish

£452	$714	€700	Dancer (73x60cm-29x24in) s. 18-Dec-2 Ansorena, Madrid #338/R

ROLLAND, Auguste (1797-1859) French

Works on paper

£1154	$1788	€1800	Bateau (80x80cm-31x31in) pastel oval. 8-Dec-2 Teitgen, Nancy #119

ROLLE, A (19th C) ?

Sculpture

£861	$1334	€1292	Le Dieu Pan enlacant une femme nue en un enfant (47cm-19in) s. terracotta after Clodion. 24-Sep-2 Iegor de Saint Hippolyte, Montreal #221 (C.D 2100)

ROLLER, Alfred (1864-1935) Austrian

Works on paper

£570	$889	€900	Mountain landscape (64x45cm-25x18in) s.d.1892 mixed media paper on canvas. 15-Oct-2 Dorotheum, Vienna #9/R

ROLLER, Mileva (1886-1949) Austrian?

Works on paper

£347	$549	€500	Allegory (13x20cm-5x8in) mixed media transparent paper on board. 24-Apr-3 Dorotheum, Vienna #9/R

ROLLIN, J (19th C) French

£582	$903	€920	Mountain lake (105x78cm-41x31in) s. 27-Sep-2 Weidler, Nurnberg #8858/R
£1154	$1788	€1800	Ugleisee - Holstein, Switzerland (75x100cm-30x39in) s. 5-Dec-2 Schopman, Hamburg #541 est:1600

ROLLINS, Tim and K O S (20th C) American

£4114	$6500	€6171	Scarlet letter (274x36cm-108x14in) acrylic W/C chl on printed book pages executed 1987-88 prov. 12-Nov-2 Phillips, New York #249/R est:8000-10000

Works on paper

£301	$500	€452	Untitled (20x6cm-8x2in) s.d.89 gouache ink prov. 11-Jun-3 Phillips, New York #357/R
£3041	$4743	€4500	A Midsummer Night's Dream VII - after Shakespeare (107x122cm-42x48in) s.i.d. verso collage W/C paper on typograph prov. 28-Mar-3 Ketterer, Hamburg #603/R est:4500-5000

ROLLINS, Warren E (1861-1962) American

£870	$1400	€1305	Landscape (23x20cm-9x8in) s. board. 18-Feb-3 John Moran, Pasadena #1 est:700-900
£1154	$1800	€1731	Santa Fe River, New Mexico (28x43cm-11x17in) s. s.i.verso prov.lit. 9-Nov-2 Santa Fe Art, Santa Fe #134/R est:3000-5000
£1433	$2250	€2150	Western landscape (25x49cm-10x19in) s. i.verso prov. 19-Nov-2 Butterfields, San Francisco #8102/R est:3000-5000
£1442	$2250	€2163	Sangre de Christo (28x46cm-11x18in) s. s.i.on stretcher prov.lit. 9-Nov-2 Santa Fe Art, Santa Fe #136/R est:3000-5000
£1592	$2500	€2388	Desert landscape. Arroyo, Santa Fe (31x44cm-12x17in) s. one canvas on board pair prov. 19-Nov-2 Butterfields, San Francisco #8101/R est:3000-5000
£2244	$3500	€3366	An old timer - Santa Fe, New Mexico (33x51cm-13x20in) s. s.i.verso prov.lit. 9-Nov-2 Santa Fe Art, Santa Fe #135/R est:3000-5000
£16129	$25000	€24194	Pueblo pottery maker and pots (71x91cm-28x36in) s. prov. 29-Oct-2 John Moran, Pasadena #702 est:12000-18000

Works on paper

£581	$900	€872	Desert sage (23x33cm-9x13in) s. conte crayon exec.c.1910 prov. 8-Dec-2 Toomey, Oak Park #715/R

ROLLOF, Ulf (1961-) Swedish

£245	$383	€368	From the serie Red paintings (100x62cm-39x24in) pigment wax eggshell masonite. 5-Nov-2 Bukowskis, Stockholm #462/R (S.KR 3500)

Works on paper

£280	$437	€420	Untitled (75x60cm-30x24in) s.d.91 verso paper pigment latex beeswax. 5-Nov-2 Bukowskis, Stockholm #483/R (S.KR 4000)
£456	$721	€684	Untitled (75x99cm-30x39in) s.d.87 verso mixed media on latex. 28-Apr-3 Bukowskis, Stockholm #958/R (S.KR 6000)

ROLPH, John A (1799-1862) British/American

Works on paper

£3026	$4600	€4539	Scenes of shipboard travel (43x41cm-17x16in) sepia W/C set of five lit. 17-Aug-2 North East Auctions, Portsmouth #924/R

ROLSHOVEN, Julius (1858-1930) American

£1000	$1600	€1500	Mother and child (46x38cm-18x15in) s. 15-Mar-3 Eldred, East Dennis #479/R
£1562	$2500	€2265	Ancestral devotion (96x117cm-38x46in) s. i.verso. 16-May-3 Skinner, Boston #138/R est:4000-6000

ROM, Henrik (1887-1919) Norwegian

£303	$464	€455	Boy standing (99x60cm-39x24in) s. painted c.1913. 26-Aug-2 Blomqvist, Lysaker #1324/R (N.KR 3500)
£929	$1468	€1394	Girl wearing orange dress and white hat (100x80cm-39x31in) painted c.1920. 1-Apr-3 Rasmussen, Copenhagen #55/R (D.KR 10000)

ROMAGNONI, Bepi (1930-1964) Italian

£5743	$8959	€8500	Tale (100x100cm-39x39in) s.d.61. 26-Mar-3 Finarte Semenzato, Milan #283/R

Works on paper

£1026	$1497	€1600	Anatomy (70x100cm-28x39in) s.d.59 mixed media. 5-Jun-2 Il Ponte, Milan #29
£1418	$2298	€2000	Racconto (49x69cm-19x27in) s.d.3/62 s.verso mixed media collage prov. 26-May-3 Christie's, Milan #110/R est:2000-3000

ROMAKO, Anton (1832-1889) Austrian

£9494	$15000	€15000	Swans in lake with village beyond (32x42cm-13x17in) s. panel. 26-Nov-2 Wiener Kunst Auktionen, Vienna #60/R est:15000-25000

ROMAN SCHOOL (16th C) Italian

£8974	$14179	€14000	Laokoon (37x22cm-15x9in) pen sepia chk. 16-Nov-2 Lempertz, Koln #1273/R est:2600

Miniatures

£4730	$7378	€7000	Portrait of young woman with pearl necklace (8x5cm-3x2in) copper. 31-Mar-3 Finarte Semenzato, Milan #274/R

Works on paper

£6790	$11000	€10185	Perseus holding the head of Medusa. Triton and nymph (15x29cm-6x11in) pen ink htd white double-sided prov. 21-Jan-3 Sotheby's, New York #23/R est:18000

ROMAN SCHOOL (17th C) Italian

£6000	$10020	€8700	Madonna and Child (97x73cm-38x29in) 10-Jul-3 Sotheby's, London #167/R est:6000-8000
£6081	$9486	€9000	Still life of flowers and fruit (88x126cm-35x50in) 31-Mar-3 Finarte Semenzato, Milan #472/R
£6604	$10170	€10500	Allegory of Hearing (74x62cm-29x24in) 23-Oct-2 Finarte, Rome #474/R est:5500-6500
£6962	$11000	€11000	Still life of flowers (73x58cm-29x23in) 2-Dec-2 Finarte, Milan #80/R est:10000
£7500	$11775	€11250	Saint Jerome, reading (88x73cm-35x29in) 12-Dec-2 Sotheby's, London #182/R est:8000-12000
£8387	$13000	€12581	Equestrian portrait of Roman Emperor Servius Sulpicius Galba (145x115cm-57x45in) i. 2-Oct-2 Christie's, Rockefeller NY #140/R est:4000-6000
£8500	$13260	€12750	Jupiter and Juno with cherubs (54x46cm-21x18in) prov. 8-Oct-2 Sotheby's, Olympia #375/R est:6000-8000
£9494	$15000	€15000	Landscape with Saint Francis (49x66cm-19x26in) 2-Dec-2 Finarte, Milan #181 est:20000
£10000	$15700	€15000	Christ healing the sick at the pool of Bethseda (137x97cm-54x38in) 10-Dec-2 Sotheby's, Olympia #322/R est:3000-5000
£15108	$24173	€21000	Armageddon (92x82cm-36x32in) 13-May-3 Sotheby's, Amsterdam #75/R est:10000-15000
£15854	$26000	€23781	Venus and Adonis (63x77cm-25x30in) 29-May-3 Sotheby's, New York #64/R est:15000-20000
£32407	$52500	€48611	Still life with pears, grapes and pomegranates. Still life with grapes and figs (97x72cm-38x28in) pair. 23-Jan-3 Sotheby's, New York #245/R est:60000

ROMAN SCHOOL (18th C) Italian

£5272	$8225	€8330	Abundance (98x74cm-39x29in) 15-Oct-2 Babuino, Rome #88/R
£5500	$8635	€8250	Still life of roses and carnations and other flowers, in a glass vase resting on a stone ledge (59x78cm-23x31in) 10-Dec-2 Sotheby's, Olympia #381/R est:3000-5000
£5696	$9000	€9000	Vase of flowers (60x50cm-24x20in) 27-Nov-2 Finarte, Milan #22
£5912	$9164	€9400	Proserpina's kidnapping (121x96cm-48x38in) 29-Oct-2 Finarte, Milan #477/R est:5000-6000
£6056	$9751	€8600	Putti with flowers (78x89cm-31x35in) 10-May-3 Berlinghof, Heidelberg #169/R est:7200

£13931 $22011 €20200 Madonna and Child (103x82cm-41x32in) 1-Apr-3 Babuino, Rome #105/R
£25000 $39250 €37500 Basilica of Saint Peter, Rome (71x111cm-28x44in) i.verso. 12-Dec-2 Sotheby's, London #223/R est:25000-35000
£85443 $135000 €135000 Vase with roses and other flowers. Vase with fruit (73x98cm-29x39in) pair. 27-Nov-2 Christie's, Paris #60/R est:60000-80000
Works on paper
£3704 $6000 €5556 Head of boy (31x25cm-12x10in) chk prov. 22-Jan-3 Christie's, Rockefeller NY #30/R

ROMAN SCHOOL (19th C) Italian
£10544 $16449 €16660 Roman countryside (35x25cm-14x10in) pair. 15-Oct-2 Babuino, Rome #266/R

ROMAN, Gyorgy (1903-1981) Hungarian
£1183 $1834 €1775 Flowery garden (70x100cm-28x39in) s. cardboard. 6-Dec-2 Kieselbach, Budapest #143/R (H.F 440000)
£3633 $5667 €5450 Kecskekompozicio lakassal (110x125cm-43x49in) board. 11-Apr-3 Kieselbach, Budapest #164/R est:1300000 (H.F 1300000)
£12371 $19174 €17938 Fun-fair at Nagybanya (101x120cm-40x47in) lit. 9-Dec-2 Mu Terem Galeria, Budapest #64/R est:3000000 (H.F 4600000)

ROMANELLI (?) Italian
Sculpture
£1646 $2567 €2600 Romaine se tenant debout pres d'une cruche (80cm-31in) marble. 16-Sep-2 Amberes, Antwerp #423/R

ROMANELLI DE CERQUEIRA, Armando (?) Spanish?
£359 $579 €550 Untitled (80x80cm-31x31in) s. 14-Jan-3 Castellana, Madrid #84/R

ROMANELLI, Giovanni Francesco (1610-1662) Italian
£15000 $25050 €21750 Annunciation (77x102cm-30x40in) prov.lit. 9-Jul-3 Christie's, London #95/R est:15000-20000

ROMANELLI, Pasquale (1812-1887) Italian
Sculpture
£25000 $41750 €36250 Raphael with his muse Fornarina (185cm-73in) s. white marble incl verde antico revolving column. 8-Jul-3 Sotheby's, London #220/R est:30000-40000

ROMANELLI, Raffaelo (1856-1920) Italian
Sculpture
£8861 $14000 €13292 Figure of a maiden with bird (126cm-50in) i. marble. 24-Apr-3 Christie's, Rockefeller NY #340/R est:15000-25000

ROMANI, Juana (1869-1924) Italian
£1627 $2635 €2359 Mother and child at a theatre scene (46x30cm-18x12in) init. panel. 26-May-3 Rasmussen, Copenhagen #1484/R est:20000 (D.KR 17000)

ROMANIDIS, Konstantin (1884-1972) Greek
£5000 $7750 €7500 Seascape (39x56cm-15x22in) s. board. 2-Oct-2 Sotheby's, London #81/R est:4000
£6000 $9300 €9000 Naval battle (35x55cm-14x22in) s. 2-Oct-2 Sotheby's, London #20/R est:4000-6000
£12500 $19375 €18750 Navarrino battle (37x65cm-15x26in) s. board. 2-Oct-2 Sotheby's, London #19/R est:5000-7000

ROMANO, Antoniazzo (fl.1460-1508) Italian
£80000 $133600 €116000 Saint Francis of Assisis (160x60cm-63x24in) i. tempera canvas on panel prov.exhib.lit. 9-Jul-3 Christie's, London #78/R est:100000-150000
£240506 $380000 €380000 Madonna and Child (47x31cm-19x12in) i.verso tempera board lit. 29-Nov-2 Semenzato, Venice #490/R est:100000-120000

ROMANO, Daniela (1947-) Italian
£321 $503 €500 Seduction (40x30cm-16x12in) s. s.i.verso. 23-Nov-2 Meeting Art, Vercelli #438
Works on paper
£327 $523 €500 Dancers (50x70cm-20x28in) s. W/C over chk card on canvas lit. 4-Jan-3 Meeting Art, Vercelli #666

ROMANO, Giulio (1499-1546) Italian
Works on paper
£1300 $2041 €1950 Death of Cleopatra (12x26cm-5x10in) bears i. pen ink prov.exhib. 11-Dec-2 Sotheby's, Olympia #7/R est:1500-2000
£4321 $7000 €6482 Priestess leading sacrificial goat (13x9cm-5x4in) i. pen ink prov. 22-Jan-3 Christie's, Rockefeller NY #16/R est:8000

ROMANO, Giulio (after) (1499-1546) Italian
£9000 $14040 €13500 Capture of Carthagena (101x135cm-40x53in) 10-Apr-3 Christie's, Kensington #199/R est:4000-6000

ROMANO, Giulio (circle) (1499-1546) Italian
Works on paper
£5556 $9000 €8334 Design for tapestry, putti playing under a pergola (41x95cm-16x37in) pen brown ink wash htd white two joined sheets prov.exhib.lit. 21-Jan-3 Sotheby's, New York #9/R est:10000-15000

ROMANO, Giulio (style) (1499-1546) Italian
Works on paper
£5500 $9185 €7975 Head of an old man in profile. Fragment of a decorative detail (24x18cm-9x7in) blk chk htd white chk recto red chk verso double-sided. 9-Jul-3 Sotheby's, London #6/R est:3000-4000

ROMANO, Umberto (1905-1984) American
£414 $650 €621 Prodigal returns (76x64cm-30x25in) s. 22-Nov-2 Skinner, Boston #197/R

ROMANY, Adele (attrib) (1769-1846) French
£3125 $5000 €4688 Portrait of a girl (117x90cm-46x35in) 14-May-3 Doyle, New York #78/R est:5000-7000

ROMBALD, F (20th C) ?
£646 $1028 €950 Putti musicians by lake (67x98cm-26x39in) s. 1-Mar-3 Stadion, Trieste #189

ROMBAUX, Egide (1865-1942) Belgian
Sculpture
£20253 $31595 €32000 Bacchanale (99x60cm-39x24in) s. Carrara marble. 16-Sep-2 Horta, Bruxelles #116/R est:18500-25000

ROMBOUTS, Gillis (1630-1678) Dutch
£5000 $7750 €7500 Wooded landscape with huntsmen and other figures (37x52cm-15x20in) init. panel. 31-Oct-2 Sotheby's, Olympia #66/R est:5000-7000
£9395 $15127 €14000 Landscape with cattle on a woodland path (34x47cm-13x19in) mono. mono.verso prov.exhib.lit. 18-Feb-3 Sotheby's, Amsterdam #221/R est:4000-6000

ROMBOUTS, Theodor (attrib) (1597-1637) Flemish
£13720 $22500 €20580 Continence of Scipio (117x147cm-46x58in) 29-May-3 Sotheby's, New York #35/R est:10000-15000

ROMBOUTS, Theodor (circle) (1597-1637) Flemish
£6289 $9686 €10000 Men smoking (111x162cm-44x64in) 22-Oct-2 Wiener Kunst Auktionen, Vienna #1061/R est:5000-13000
£6500 $10140 €9750 Three men smoking and drinking at a table in an interior (110x162cm-43x64in) 10-Apr-3 Christie's, Kensington #70/R est:6000-8000

ROMERO BARRERA, Emilio (20th C) Spanish
£493 $799 €750 Market (113x95cm-44x37in) s. s.i.verso. 21-Jan-3 Ansorena, Madrid #251/R

ROMERO DE TORRES, Julio (1879-1930) Spanish
£44521 $69452 €65000 Portrait of lady (65x50cm-26x20in) s.verso. 8-Apr-3 Ansorena, Madrid #117/R est:60000
£500000 $785000 €750000 Rivalidad - rivalry (170x140cm-67x55in) s. s.verso tempera painted c.1925-26 prov.exhib.lit. 19-Nov-2 Sotheby's, London #52/R est:200000-300000

ROMERO RESSENDI, Baldomero (1922-1977) Spanish
£1824 $2845 €2900 Dancer (55x46cm-22x18in) s. 8-Oct-2 Ansorena, Madrid #271/R
£2264 $3532 €3600 Still life with teapot (62x50cm-24x20in) s. 8-Oct-2 Ansorena, Madrid #317/R
£2390 $3681 €3800 Self-portrait (62x50cm-24x20in) s.d.1966. 28-Oct-2 Segre, Madrid #84/R
£3718 $5874 €5800 Goyan cats (61x50cm-24x20in) s. pair. 13-Nov-2 Ansorena, Madrid #108/R

ROMERO Y LOPEZ, Jose Maria (c.1815-1880) Spanish
£4088 $6296 €6500 Portrait of boy with lamb (123x105cm-48x41in) oval. 28-Oct-2 Segre, Madrid #70/R

ROMERO, Carlos Orozco (1898-1984) Mexican
£4487 $7000 €6731 Paisaje (113x79cm-44x31in) s. 12-Apr-3 Weschler, Washington #596/R est:10000-15000
£5353 $8350 €8030 Tehuano (65x50cm-26x20in) s. 17-Oct-2 Louis Morton, Mexico #95/R est:95000-100000 (M.P 85000)
£11465 $18000 €17198 Desert landscape (90x30cm-35x12in) s. painted c.1960 prov. 20-Nov-2 Christie's, Rockefeller NY #82/R est:25000-30000

ROMERO, Juan (1932-) Spanish
£1090 $1722 €1700 Meteor on the motorway (56x47cm-22x19in) s.d.1995 acrylic. 14-Nov-2 Arte, Seville #445/R

ROMEYN, Willem (1624-1694) Dutch
£1258 $1962 €2000 Mountain landscape with cows and goats (37x47cm-15x19in) s. 19-Sep-2 Dr Fritz Nagel, Stuttgart #895/R est:2000
£10191 $15898 €16000 Cow, goats and sheep in a meadow (66x90cm-26x35in) s. exhib.lit. 5-Nov-2 Sotheby's, Amsterdam #147/R est:7000-10000

ROMEYN, Willem (attrib) (1624-1694) Dutch
£786 $1288 €1140 Landscape with sheep and cattle (40x50cm-16x20in) 4-Jun-3 AB Stockholms Auktionsverk #2563/R (S.KR 10000)

ROMIEUX, Osmond (19th C) French
Works on paper
£460 $731 €690 Guayaquil, Ecuador (25x41cm-10x16in) i. pencil. 29-Apr-3 Bonhams, New Bond Street #222/R

ROMIJN, Gust (1922-) Dutch
£863 $1416 €1200 Untitled (80x100cm-31x39in) s.d.50 s.d.verso prov. 3-Jun-3 Christie's, Amsterdam #82/R est:1500-2000

ROMITI, Gino (1881-1967) Italian
£288 $449 €432 Landscape at dusk (34x45cm-13x18in) s. panel. 13-Sep-2 Lilla Bukowskis, Stockholm #175 (S.KR 4200)
£510 $811 €750 Antignano (30x40cm-12x16in) s. s.i.verso masonite. 1-Mar-3 Meeting Art, Vercelli #93
Works on paper
£395 $640 €600 L'ondee (35x22cm-14x9in) s.d.1912 gouache. 22-Jan-3 Tajan, Paris #34

ROMITI, Sergio (1928-) Italian
£545 $855 €850 Untitled (10x8cm-4x3in) s.d.1959 tempera cardboard. 19-Nov-2 Finarte, Milan #134/R
£3846 $6038 €6000 Untitled (54x74cm-21x29in) s.d.1953. 19-Nov-2 Finarte, Milan #90/R
£4808 $7548 €7500 Untitled (65x60cm-26x24in) painted 1958. 19-Nov-2 Finarte, Milan #233/R

ROMMELAERE, Émile (1873-1961) Belgian
£387 $612 €600 View of Bruges (65x80cm-26x31in) s. 17-Dec-2 Galerie Moderne, Brussels #793
£443 $691 €700 Beguinage at Brugge (40x44cm-16x17in) s. 21-Oct-2 Bernaerts, Antwerp #509/R
£609 $926 €950 Vue de Bruges (65x80cm-26x31in) s. 27-Aug-2 Galerie Moderne, Brussels #312

ROMNEY, George (1734-1802) British
£2273 $3250 €3410 Portrait of Sir Henry watkins Dashwood (76x65cm-30x26in) 22-Jan-3 Doyle, New York #158/R
£4200 $6720 €6300 Harry Burrard (76x63cm-30x25in) prov. 8-Jan-3 George Kidner, Lymington #186/R est:3000-5000
£11000 $17380 €16500 Portrait of Emma Hamilton (43x36cm-17x14in) exhib. 28-Nov-2 Sotheby's, London #181/R est:10000-15000
£15000 $23700 €22500 Reclining female nude (63x76cm-25x30in) prov. 28-Nov-2 Sotheby's, London #182/R est:15000-20000
£15000 $23700 €22500 Portrait of the Hon. Robert Banks Jenkinson (77x65cm-30x26in) prov.lit. 26-Nov-2 Christie's, London #35a/R est:8000-12000
£25000 $39500 €37500 Portrait of Lord George Lennox (76x64cm-30x25in) prov.exhib.lit. 28-Nov-2 Sotheby's, London #10/R est:30000-40000
£46296 $75000 €69444 Portrait of Mr William Hayley (77x63cm-30x25in) prov. 23-Jan-3 Sotheby's, New York #8/R est:30000-50000
£80000 $132800 €120000 Serena in contemplation (74x62cm-29x24in) prov.lit. 12-Jun-3 Sotheby's, London #22/R est:40000-60000
£100000 $166000 €150000 Portrait of Mary Moser, holding a palette and brush, before a ledge (76x64cm-30x25in) prov. 10-Jun-3 Christie's, London #36/R est:20000-30000
Works on paper
£559 $800 €839 Study for Howard visiting the prisoners (16x19cm-6x7in) pencil. 23-Jan-3 Swann Galleries, New York #393/R
£1081 $1686 €1600 Homme, tete tournee (30x23cm-12x9in) pen ink. 31-Mar-3 Piasa, Paris #121
£1300 $2015 €1950 Male figure drawing a sword (37x24cm-15x9in) brush ink over pencil. 9-Dec-2 Bonhams, New Bond Street #88/R est:700-1000
£1800 $2988 €2700 Studies of a woman dancing (19x15cm-7x6in) pen ink. 12-Jun-3 Sotheby's, London #118/R est:2000-3000
£3800 $5966 €5700 Serena, stydy of a seated woman reading (34x26cm-13x10in) pencil prov. 21-Nov-2 Christie's, London #3/R est:4000-6000
£6000 $9420 €9000 Study for the misses hill (33x27cm-13x11in) pencil pen brush ink prov. 21-Nov-2 Christie's, London #5/R est:7000-10000
£22000 $31460 €33000 Mother holding her child (25x16cm-10x6in) pencil ink wash prov.exhib.lit. 22-Jan-3 Christie's, London #11/R est:25000

ROMNEY, George (attrib) (1734-1802) British
£1613 $2548 €2420 Mother and child holding a pet bird (36x30cm-14x12in) 18-Nov-2 Waddingtons, Toronto #138/R est:4000-4500 (C.D 4000)
£2000 $3220 €2900 Portrait of John Askew of Whitehaven (71x59cm-28x23in) canvas on board. 12-May-3 Joel, Victoria #330/R est:5000-7000 (A.D 5000)
£3500 $5775 €5075 Portrait of William Wilson Carus (74x61cm-29x24in) prov.lit. 2-Jul-3 Sotheby's, Olympia #29/R est:3000-5000

RON, Eduard de (1811-1858) German
Works on paper
£1646 $2551 €2600 Carl Prinz von Bayern in uniform (20x17cm-8x7in) s.d.1845 W/C htd white. 25-Sep-2 Neumeister, Munich #430/R est:1500

RON, Lior (1971-) Israeli
£806 $1257 €1209 Lambretta (92x66cm-36x26in) s. acrylic. 6-Nov-2 AB Stockholms Auktionsverk #923/R (S.KR 11500)
£1158 $1865 €1737 Licking honey off the wings of a butterfly (126x155cm-50x61in) s. acrylic. 7-May-3 AB Stockholms Auktionsverk #1095/R est:25000-30000 (S.KR 15000)

RONALD, William S (1926-1998) Canadian
£216 $344 €313 Abstract (41x58cm-16x23in) s. paper. 1-May-3 Heffel, Vancouver #94/R (C.D 500)
£494 $765 €741 Zen black (90x90cm-35x35in) s.d.85 acrylic. 3-Dec-2 Joyner, Toronto #295/R est:1000-1500 (C.D 1200)
£2444 $4009 €3666 Sabu (119x82cm-47x32in) s.d.95 acrylic prov. 27-May-3 Sotheby's, Toronto #184/R est:4000-6000 (C.D 5500)
£3427 $5415 €5141 Evening in Paris (122x91cm-48x36in) s. prov.lit. 18-Nov-2 Sotheby's, Toronto #174/R est:3000-3500 (C.D 8500)
Works on paper
£397 $651 €596 Untitled (46x61cm-18x24in) s.d.1970 W/C ink. 6-Feb-3 Heffel, Vancouver #045/R (C.D 1000)

RONAY, Erno (1899-?) Czechoslovakian
£819 $1311 €1229 Pigtailed girl in front of a Paravan (81x72cm-32x28in) s.d.29. 16-May-3 Kieselbach, Budapest #8/R (H.F 280000)

RONAY, J L (19th C) Hungarian?
£1218 $1900 €1827 Telling the truth by the cards (76x64cm-30x25in) s. 18-Sep-2 Alderfer's, Hatfield #252 est:2000-3000

RONCALLI, Cristoforo (1552-1626) Italian
Works on paper
£750 $1185 €1125 Madonna and Child enthroned and flanked by Saints (18x17cm-7x7in) pen ink. 15-Nov-2 Rowley Fine Art, Newmarket #354/R

RONCALLI, Cristoforo (attrib) (1552-1626) Italian
Works on paper
£420 $600 €630 Statue of a Roman Emperor (28x13cm-11x5in) red chk. 23-Jan-3 Swann Galleries, New York #49/R
£709 $1184 €1000 Figure d'apotre (25x18cm-10x7in) black crayon white chk. 19-Jun-3 Piasa, Paris #4 est:1000-1200

RONDA, Omar (1947-) Italian
Works on paper
£1042 $1656 €1500 Frozen (50x50cm-20x20in) s.i.d.2002 verso plastic lit. 1-May-3 Meeting Art, Vercelli #402

RONDAS, Willi (1907-1975) British/Belgian
£283 $439 €450 Negociations, hommage a Monsieur Kissinger (50x40cm-20x16in) s.d. 4-Oct-2 Tajan, Paris #215
£521 $828 €750 Untitled (53x72cm-21x28in) s.d.71 cardboard. 5-May-3 Bernaerts, Antwerp #225/R
£1319 $2098 €1900 Villes Belges (97x323cm-38x127in) s.d.1972. 5-May-3 Bernaerts, Antwerp #228/R

RONDE, Philippe (1815-1883) German
£1972 $3175 €2800 Sleeping child (41x30cm-16x12in) s. lit. 9-May-3 Schloss Ahlden, Ahlden #1386/R est:2500

RONDEL, Frederick (1826-1892) American
£1419 $2200 €2129 Meadow (16x29cm-6x11in) s. s.i.d.1855 verso board. 3-Dec-2 Christie's, Rockefeller NY #585/R est:1200-1800

RONDEL, Georgette (?) Irish
Works on paper
£1090 $1711 €1700 Woman seated at piano (32x18cm-13x7in) s.d.1941 gouache board. 19-Nov-2 Whyte's, Dublin #36/R est:1000-1200

RONDEL, Henri (1857-1919) French
£3000 $4860 €4500 Young beauty (74x61cm-29x24in) s. 23-Jan-3 Christie's, Kensington #37/R est:800-1200

RONDEL, Henri (attrib) (1857-1919) French
£577 $900 €866 Sleeping beauty (23x46cm-9x18in) init. sold with another by L Ferstel. 9-Oct-2 Doyle, New York #96

RONDINONE, Ugo (1963-) French
£42500 $68000 €63750 Zehnterseptemberneunzehn hundertachtundneuzig (220cm-87in circular) s.i.d.1998 acrylic prov. 16-May-3 Phillips, New York #114/R est:40000-60000

RONDO, Julio (20th C) German?
£506 $800 €800 Landscape near Reutlingen (120x110cm-47x43in) s.d.1998 verso acrylic behind glass panel. 30-Nov-2 Arnold, Frankfurt #472/R
£823 $1300 €1300 T R a young woman (120x100cm-47x39in) s.d.1999 verso acrylic behind glass panel. 30-Nov-2 Arnold, Frankfurt #471/R

RONEK, Jaroslav (1892-?) Czechoslovakian
£621 $993 €950 Two steam locomotives (49x69cm-19x27in) s. board lit. 10-Jan-3 Allgauer, Kempten #1740/R
£705 $1093 €1100 Steam trains in station (77x100cm-30x39in) s. 6-Dec-2 Michael Zeller, Lindau #903/R
£950 $1558 €1425 Steam locomotive leaving the station (48x69cm-19x27in) s. board. 5-Jun-3 Christie's, Kensington #822/R

RONEY, Harold (1899-1986) American
£1282 $2000 €1923 Haystacks in autumn (36x41cm-14x16in) board. 19-Oct-2 David Dike, Dallas #260/R est:2000-4000

RONGET, Elisabeth (20th C) French
£461 $770 €650 Personnage a la mandoline (35x27cm-14x11in) s. 17-Jun-3 Claude Boisgirard, Paris #118/R
£872 $1405 €1300 Nature morte aux pommes (50x61cm-20x24in) s.d.1935. 23-Feb-3 Lesieur & Le Bars, Le Havre #136

RONIG, Ludwig Ernst (1885-1960) German
£705 $1093 €1100 Red stream (48x38cm-19x15in) s. 7-Dec-2 Van Ham, Cologne #457/R
£870 $1426 €1200 Growing (84x64cm-33x25in) s.d.56 s.i. stretcher exhib. 29-May-3 Lempertz, Koln #909/R

RONMY, Guillaume Frederic (1786-1854) French
£4196 $7007 €6000 Le port de Naples (25x33cm-10x13in) s.d. 27-Jun-3 Claude Aguttes, Neuilly #27/R est:10000-15000

RONNBERG, Hanna (1862-1946) Finnish
£4317 $6906 €6000 Light-house (47x35cm-19x14in) s.d.1899. 17-May-3 Hagelstam, Helsinki #119/R est:7000

RONNE, Paul (1884-1964) Danish
£250 $395 €375 Sun-lit hall interior with a vase of flowers on a chest (47x37cm-19x15in) s. 14-Nov-2 Christie's, Kensington #74

RONNE, Svend (1868-1938) Danish
£1378 $2095 €2067 Young couple at Charlottenborg exhibition (48x38cm-19x15in) s.d.1893. 27-Aug-2 Rasmussen, Copenhagen #1498/R est:12000-15000 (D.KR 16000)

RONNER, Alice (1857-1906) Belgian
£577 $906 €900 Nature morte aux fleurs et objets (31x25cm-12x10in) s.d.96 panel. 10-Dec-2 Vanderkindere, Brussels #6

RONNER, Henriette (1821-1909) Dutch
£347 $552 €500 Le perroquet blanc. s. 29-Apr-3 Campo, Vlaamse Kaai #269
£352 $567 €500 Circus dogs (8x11cm-3x4in) s.verso paper. 12-May-3 Bernaerts, Antwerp #623
£696 $1086 €1100 Hare hunting (26x37cm-10x15in) s. paper. 21-Oct-2 Glerum, Amsterdam #155/R
£696 $1086 €1100 Pug dog (25x20cm-10x8in) bears sig. panel. 21-Oct-2 Glerum, Amsterdam #222
£1026 $1621 €1600 Circus dogs (9x14cm-4x6in) s.verso cardboard. 18-Nov-2 Bernaerts, Antwerp #54 est:1500-1800
£1249 $2023 €1874 Kittens (21x26cm-8x10in) s.d.97 canvas on board. 24-May-3 Dorotheum, Prague #21/R est:30000-45000 (C.KR 55000)
£1341 $2200 €1944 Play time (27x35cm-11x14in) s. panel prov. 4-Jun-3 Christie's, Rockefeller NY #242/R est:3000-4000
£1379 $2193 €2000 Peaceful moment (21x35cm-8x14in) s. paper on panel exhib. 10-Mar-3 Sotheby's, Amsterdam #135/R est:1200-1500
£2241 $3564 €3250 Inspecting the catch (36x27cm-14x11in) s. panel. 10-Mar-3 Sotheby's, Amsterdam #145/R est:3500-4500
£2436 $3824 €3800 Chien attele (19x15cm-7x6in) s. panel. 19-Nov-2 Servarts Themis, Bruxelles #121/R
£2483 $3948 €3600 Intruder (19x16cm-7x6in) s. panel. 10-Mar-3 Sotheby's, Amsterdam #88 est:1800-2200
£2639 $4354 €3800 Prince Charles dog (36x51cm-14x20in) bears mono. paper on panel prov. 1-Jul-3 Christie's, Amsterdam #550/R est:3500-4500
£3082 $4839 €4500 Dog (60x48cm-24x19in) s.d.94. 15-Apr-3 Sotheby's, Amsterdam #39/R est:4000-6000
£4000 $6640 €5800 An attentive look (39x29cm-15x11in) s.d.1875 panel. 12-Jun-3 Christie's, Kensington #264/R est:4000-6000
£4294 $7000 €6441 Playful pups (27x38cm-11x15in) s. panel. 11-Feb-3 Bonhams & Doyles, New York #151 est:7000-9000
£5346 $8233 €8500 Playfull gesture (19x23cm-7x9in) s.d.1903 oil paper on panel. 23-Oct-2 Christie's, Amsterdam #33/R est:5000-7000
£6250 $10313 €9000 Sleeping kittens (32x32cm-13x13in) s.d.96 panel. 1-Jul-3 Christie's, Amsterdam #545/R est:10000-15000
£6849 $10753 €10000 Watchful mother (41x32cm-16x13in) s.d.1845 panel. 15-Apr-3 Sotheby's, Amsterdam #43/R est:8000-10000
£10500 $16380 €15750 Three kittens playing (24x32cm-9x13in) with sig. oil sketch panel. 26-Mar-3 Sotheby's, Olympia #249/R est:3000-5000
£11258 $18351 €17000 Le petit ramasseur de moules (69x90cm-27x35in) s. 16-Feb-3 Mercier & Cie, Lille #227/R est:1000-1500
£16000 $26720 €24000 Cairn terrier and her puppies (45x33cm-18x13in) s. panel prov. 19-Jun-3 Christie's, London #59/R est:20000-30000
£19718 $31746 €28000 Parasites (33x45cm-13x18in) s. panel prov.exhib.lit. 7-May-3 Vendue Huis, Gravenhage #357/R est:20000-25000
£21477 $34577 €32000 Chatte et ses petits (23x28cm-9x11in) s. panel. 18-Feb-3 Galerie Moderne, Brussels #377/R est:10000-12000
£23899 $36805 €38000 Violin lesson (20x30cm-8x12in) s. panel. 22-Oct-2 Sotheby's, Amsterdam #162/R est:50000-60000
£24528 $37774 €39000 Playful kittens (23x19cm-9x7in) s.d.93 panel. 22-Oct-2 Sotheby's, Amsterdam #165/R est:20000-30000
£27465 $45592 €39000 Chats a l'eventail (33x45cm-13x18in) s. panel exhib. 13-Jun-3 Rabourdin & Choppin de Janvry, Paris #83/R est:23000-25000
£36000 $60120 €54000 Proud mother (33x45cm-13x18in) s. panel prov. 19-Jun-3 Christie's, London #60/R est:25000-35000
£36111 $57417 €52000 Purring with content (32x40cm-13x16in) s.d.94 panel prov.exhib.lit. 29-Apr-3 Christie's, Amsterdam #208/R est:35000-45000
£41667 $66250 €60000 Verstoorde theevisite (34x46cm-13x18in) s.d.97. 29-Apr-3 Christie's, Amsterdam #187/R est:30000-50000
£41667 $66250 €60000 Katjesspel (48x60cm-19x24in) s. prov. 29-Apr-3 Christie's, Amsterdam #197/R est:40000-60000
£44025 $67799 €70000 Three curious kittens (24x32cm-9x13in) s.d.93 panel. 22-Oct-2 Sotheby's, Amsterdam #153/R est:40000-60000
£51572 $79421 €82000 Playing time (32x45cm-13x18in) s. panel. 22-Oct-2 Sotheby's, Amsterdam #130/R est:25000-35000
£58000 $91060 €87000 Mother's pride (33x45cm-13x18in) s. panel. 19-Nov-2 Sotheby's, London #167/R est:20000-30000
Works on paper
£426 $711 €600 Etude de chats (13x17cm-5x7in) mono.d.1886 pen. 18-Jun-3 Hotel des Ventes Mosan, Brussels #180
£461 $746 €700 Chats. mono. 21-Jan-3 Galerie Moderne, Brussels #140/R
£3082 $4839 €4500 Proud mother (15x25cm-6x10in) s.d.99 W/C. 15-Apr-3 Sotheby's, Amsterdam #49/R est:4000-6000
£4452 $6990 €6500 Intruder (53x70cm-21x28in) s. W/C. 15-Apr-3 Sotheby's, Amsterdam #80/R est:5000-7000
£5346 $8233 €8500 Hide and seek (39x57cm-15x22in) s. W/C. 22-Oct-2 Sotheby's, Amsterdam #23/R est:5000-7000
£8219 $12904 €12000 Lunch time (34x51cm-13x20in) s. W/C. 15-Apr-3 Sotheby's, Amsterdam #51/R est:5000-7000
£8805 $13560 €14000 Favourite (26x33cm-10x13in) s.d.98 W/C. 22-Oct-2 Sotheby's, Amsterdam #46/R est:8000-12000

RONNQUIST, Lotten (1864-1912) Swedish
£1164 $1885 €1688 Boy in Apulien (49x73cm-19x29in) s.d.92. 26-May-3 Bukowskis, Stockholm #65/R est:20000-25000 (S.KR 15000)
£1629 $2639 €2362 Magpies in Harnosand, winter (129x49cm-51x19in) 26-May-3 Bukowskis, Stockholm #110/R est:25000-30000 (S.KR 21000)
£1702 $2638 €2553 Young girl and boy on road to town (150x120cm-59x47in) s.d.90. 8-Dec-2 Uppsala Auktionskammare, Uppsala #86/R est:30000-40000 (S.KR 24000)
£1807 $2963 €2620 Winter landscape with cat and two mice (56x49cm-22x19in) 4-Jun-3 AB Stockholms Auktionsverk #2146/R est:10000-15000 (S.KR 23000)
£2638 $4273 €3825 Snow-covered branches with bullfinches (65x49cm-26x19in) 26-May-3 Bukowskis, Stockholm #111/R est:15000-20000 (S.KR 34000)

RONTANI, Gian Franco (1926-) Italian
£316 $494 €500 Nature lady (120x100cm-47x39in) s. s.verso lit. 14-Sep-2 Meeting Art, Vercelli #920/R

RONTINI, Alessandro (1854-?) Italian
£25157 $38742 €40000 In the garden (36x24cm-14x9in) s. 23-Oct-2 Finarte, Milan #77/R est:70000-80000

ROOBJEE, Pjeroo (1945-) Belgian
£1806 $2871 €2600 Brave huismoeder in een rapenveld bedreigd door sneldalende matras (120x100cm-47x39in) s.d.1969. 29-Apr-3 Campo & Campo, Antwerp #258/R est:1750-2250

ROOGE, Charles van (?) ?
£260 $411 €390 Musical interlude (64x49cm-25x19in) s. 12-Nov-2 Bonhams, Knightsbridge #202/R

ROOJEN, Joost van (1928-) Dutch
Works on paper
£1392 $2200 €2200 Vier uit de serie van elf (20x16cm-8x6in) s.d.8-66 W/C pencil set of four. 26-Nov-2 Sotheby's, Amsterdam #64/R est:2500-3500

ROOK, Edward F (1870-1960) American
£1173 $1900 €1701 Santa Maria de Los Angeles de Churubusco (66x91cm-26x36in) s. prov.exhib. 21-May-3 Doyle, New York #9191/R est:3000-5000

ROOKE, Thomas Matthew (1842-1942) British
Works on paper
£500 $770 €750 Side street, St Jacques, Lisieux (44x19cm-17x7in) s.i.d.1891 W/C. 22-Oct-2 Bonhams, Knightsbridge #64/R

ROOKER, Michael Angelo (1743-1801) British
£8000 $12640 €12000 View of Castle Hill, Oxford (42x60cm-17x24in) s. exhib. 28-Nov-2 Sotheby's, London #139/R est:8000-12000
Works on paper
£1800 $2916 €2700 Wincheslsea Castle, Sussex (25x24cm-10x9in) s. pencil W/C. 23-Jan-3 Christie's, Kensington #320/R est:800-1200
£2600 $4264 €3900 Queen Elizabeth's dressing room, Kenilworth Castle (28x37cm-11x15in) s.i.d.1793 pen ink wash. 4-Feb-3 Bonhams, Leeds #251 est:800-1200
£6500 $10660 €9425 Builwas Abbey, Shropshire (23x28cm-9x11in) s. i.verso pencil W/C prov. 5-Jun-3 Christie's, London #83/R est:3000-5000

ROOKER, Michael Angelo (attrib) (1743-1801) British
Works on paper
£260 $404 €390 Castle Acre Monastery, Norfolk (35x46cm-14x18in) i.verso W/C over pencil. 3-Dec-2 Sotheby's, Olympia #20/R

ROONEY, J P (1947-) British
£320 $496 €480 Fishing village, West of Ireland (61x91cm-24x36in) s. board. 2-Oct-2 John Ross, Belfast #109
£380 $589 €570 Mending the boats, Galway (51x61cm-20x24in) s. board. 2-Oct-2 John Ross, Belfast #78
£380 $589 €570 Out for a stroll (51x61cm-20x24in) s. board. 2-Oct-2 John Ross, Belfast #260
£400 $620 €600 Fishing village, West of Ireland (15x122cm-6x48in) s. board. 2-Oct-2 John Ross, Belfast #76
£650 $949 €975 Mending the boats, West of Ireland (46x61cm-18x24in) s. board. 12-Jun-2 John Ross, Belfast #50
Works on paper
£300 $465 €450 Heroes of the seaboard (36x76cm-14x30in) s. mixed media. 2-Oct-2 John Ross, Belfast #39

ROONEY, Mick (1944-) British
£3800 $6346 €5510 Gardeners (78x127cm-31x50in) acrylic W/C prov. 24-Jun-3 Bonhams, New Bond Street #126/R est:3000-5000
Works on paper
£1500 $2385 €2250 Two figures with a canary (38x56cm-15x22in) init.d.00 gouache. 26-Feb-3 Sotheby's, Olympia #382/R est:800-1200

ROONEY, Robert (1937-) Australian
Works on paper
£3036 $4675 €4554 Cereal bird beaks II (228x137cm-90x54in) s. i.d.1969 verso synthetic polymer on canvas. 8-Sep-2 Sotheby's, Melbourne #53/R est:2500-3500 (A.D 8500)
£5000 $7700 €7500 Silly symphony 6 (140x183cm-55x72in) s.d.1988 verso liquitex on canvas prov. 8-Sep-2 Sotheby's, Melbourne #56/R est:3000-5000 (A.D 14000)
£7857 $12100 €11786 Juke box jungle (122x198cm-48x78in) s. i.d.1985 verso synthetic polymer on canvas. 8-Sep-2 Sotheby's, Melbourne #72/R est:2000-3000 (A.D 22000)

ROOS, Alexander (1895-1973) ?
£561 $875 €842 Graveyard (51x61cm-20x24in) 6-Nov-2 AB Stockholms Auktionsverk #606/R (S.KR 8000)

ROOS, Cajetan (1690-1770) Italian
£2075 $3238 €3300 Extensive hilly landscape with cows, goats and figures (63x85cm-25x33in) s.d.1768. 19-Sep-2 Dr Fritz Nagel, Stuttgart #896/R est:3000
£2767 $4262 €4400 Landscape with animals and shepherds (77x100cm-30x39in) 23-Oct-2 Finarte, Rome #507
£2800 $4676 €4060 Landscape with a drover, cattle and goats before a waterfall and ruins (72x99cm-28x39in) 8-Jul-3 Sotheby's, Olympia #423/R est:3000-4000
£5000 $7750 €7500 River landscape with shepherds and their flocks resting (127x102cm-50x40in) indis.sig.d.172. 31-Oct-2 Sotheby's, Olympia #139/R est:5000-7000

ROOS, Erik (20th C) Swiss?
Works on paper
£437 $686 €656 Landscape (20x24cm-8x9in) s.i.d.1978 col pen pencil prov. 23-Nov-2 Burkhard, Luzern #103/R (S.FR 1000)

ROOS, Jacob (1682-?) Italian
£3648 $5654 €5800 Herder with cattle in arcadian landscape (62x78cm-24x31in) 2-Nov-2 Hans Stahl, Toestorf #119/R est:4500
£10046 $15671 €15069 Cattle by river. Three herders with herds (85x96cm-33x38in) i. verso pair. 28-Mar-3 Koller, Zurich #3089/R est:25000-35000 (S.FR 22000)

ROOS, Johann Heinrich (1631-1685) German
£5414 $8446 €8500 Italianate landscape with a blacksmith and children playing before his workshop (37x46cm-15x18in) s.d.1678 prov.lit. 5-Nov-2 Sotheby's, Amsterdam #332/R est:7000-10000
£6081 $9486 €9000 Horseman and dog resting in Roman Campagna (30x39cm-12x15in) s.d. 27-Mar-3 Dorotheum, Vienna #236/R est:8000-10000
£15000 $23550 €22500 Southern landscape with a drover and shepherdess with their flocks beside a fountain (53x56cm-21x22in) s.d.1665 prov. 10-Dec-2 Sotheby's, Olympia #371/R est:4000-6000
Works on paper
£550 $853 €825 Studies of sheep and a goat (183x229cm-72x90in) s.i. black chk laid down. 30-Oct-2 Bonhams, New Bond Street #212/R
£552 $850 €828 Three herdsman in a landscape taming a bull (305x387cm-120x152in) s. red chk. 4-Sep-2 Christie's, Rockefeller NY #278/R est:1000-1500

ROOS, Johann Melchior (attrib) (1659-1731) German
£2968 $4689 €4600 Pastoral scene (57x78cm-22x31in) 19-Dec-2 Delvaux, Paris #88/R est:3000
£5769 $9058 €9000 Paysages de riviere animes de bergers (76x62cm-30x24in) pair oval. 14-Dec-2 Artcurial Briest, Paris #23/R est:12000

ROOS, Joseph (1726-1805) Austrian
£1935 $3058 €3000 Patre et troupeau (36x47cm-14x19in) s. 18-Dec-2 Piasa, Paris #62/R

ROOS, Philipp Peter (1657-1706) German
£2600 $4342 €3770 Italianate landscape with a shepherd and his animals (95x133cm-37x52in) 8-Jul-3 Sotheby's, Olympia #424/R est:2500-3500
£2903 $4587 €4500 Paysan. Troupeau (72x60cm-28x24in) pair. 20-Dec-2 Tajan, Paris #97/R est:6000
£5000 $7800 €7500 Cowherd and livestock in a Roman campagna (156x217cm-61x85in) 23-Sep-2 Bonhams, Bayswater #435 est:7000-9000
£12766 $19787 €19149 Italian landscape with herders and cattle (120x168cm-47x66in) 3-Dec-2 Bukowskis, Stockholm #483/R est:100000-150000 (S.KR 180000)
£13793 $21931 €20000 Landscapes in Lazio with shepherds and herds (110x138cm-43x54in) pair. 7-Mar-3 Semenzato, Venice #532/R est:24000
£18621 $29607 €27000 Landscape with shepherd and herd (95x132cm-37x52in) 4-Mar-3 Ansorena, Madrid #66/R

ROOS, Philipp Peter (attrib) (1657-1706) German
£1644 $2564 €2400 Campagna landscape with herder and cattle (71x101cm-28x40in) 10-Apr-3 Van Ham, Cologne #1258/R est:5000
£1852 $2981 €2778 Pastoral scene (73x59cm-29x23in) 7-May-3 Dobiaschofsky, Bern #924/R est:5000 (S.FR 4000)
£2897 $4634 €4200 Landscape with shepherd (72x91cm-28x36in) 17-Mar-3 Pandolfini, Florence #633/R est:4000
£3262 $5057 €4893 Mountain landscape with herders and animals (97x73cm-38x29in) prov. 8-Dec-2 Uppsala Auktionskammare, Uppsala #22/R est:30000-40000 (S.KR 46000)
£15190 $24000 €24000 Pastoral landscape (170x244cm-67x96in) prov. 30-Nov-2 Hagelstam, Helsinki #29/R est:16000

ROOS, Philipp Peter (style) (1657-1706) German
£1266 $1962 €2000 Shepherd with flock in the campagna (38x56cm-15x22in) 18th C lit. 28-Sep-2 Hans Stahl, Hamburg #217 est:2000

ROOS, Theodor (1638-1698) German
£2878 $4604 €4000 Italianate landscape with a shepherd resting with cattle (48x42cm-19x17in) s.d.1669. 14-May-3 Christie's, Amsterdam #152/R est:4000-6000

ROOS, William (1808-1878) British
£400 $628 €600 Portrait of a lady said to be Hannah Jones of Llangefni (57x49cm-22x19in) s.d.1878 arched top. 20-Nov-2 Sotheby's, Olympia #58/R

ROOSDORP, A (?) Dutch
£323 $474 €500 Dutch town (24x18cm-9x7in) s. 24-Jun-2 Dr Fritz Nagel, Stuttgart #6048/R

ROOSE, Charles van (1883-1960) Belgian
£347 $552 €500 Nature morte aux fleurs (62x45cm-24x18in) s. 29-Apr-3 Campo & Campo, Antwerp #326
£1290 $2039 €2000 Nu de dos (55x45cm-22x18in) s. 17-Dec-2 Galerie Moderne, Brussels #687/R
£1456 $2271 €2300 Nu assis (82x60cm-32x24in) s. 15-Oct-2 Vanderkindere, Brussels #104 est:1400-1800

ROOSENBOOM, Albert (1845-1875) Belgian
£1074 $1729 €1600 Arrosage des plantes (24x19cm-9x7in) s. panel. 24-Feb-3 Bernaerts, Antwerp #163a
£1141 $1837 €1700 Lecture. L'enfant et le pantin (24x19cm-9x7in) pair. 18-Feb-3 Vanderkindere, Brussels #74
£1859 $2919 €2900 Jeunes enfants au jardin. La lecture (24x19cm-9x7in) s. pair. 19-Nov-2 Vanderkindere, Brussels #528 est:1250-1750
£2734 $4374 €3800 Fillette chez la modiste. Jeune garcon a la mer du Nord (30x22cm-12x9in) panel pair. 19-May-3 Horta, Bruxelles #198/R est:4000-6000
£3125 $4969 €4500 Wonderful toys (27x21cm-11x8in) s. 29-Apr-3 Christie's, Amsterdam #29/R est:5000-7000

ROOSENBOOM, Margaretha (1843-1896) Dutch
£9434 $14528 €15000 Still life with flowers on a forest floor (25x33cm-10x13in) s. panel. 22-Oct-2 Sotheby's, Amsterdam #11/R est:6000-8000

Works on paper
£15094 $23245 €24000 Still life with peonies in a vase (52x34cm-20x13in) s. W/C htd white. 22-Oct-2 Sotheby's, Amsterdam #187/R est:12000-15000

ROOSENBOOM, Nicolaas Johannes (1805-1880) Dutch
£1019 $1600 €1529 Windmills along a canal (8x12cm-3x5in) s. panel. 10-Dec-2 Doyle, New York #187/R est:3000-5000
£1958 $3270 €2800 Pecheurs tirant leurs filets en Hollande (21x41cm-8x16in) s.d.1870 panel. 26-Jun-3 Tajan, Paris #195/R est:3000-4000
£3296 $5208 €4944 Winter landscape with figures by lake, mill and houses in background (19x25cm-7x10in) s. panel. 27-Nov-2 Falkkloos, Malmo #77639/R est:20000 (S.KR 47000)
£4403 $6780 €7000 Winter landscape with skaters on the ice (25x33cm-10x13in) s. panel exhib. 22-Oct-2 Sotheby's, Amsterdam #38/R est:5000-7000
£4717 $7264 €7500 Skaters near a bridge (36x47cm-14x19in) s. 22-Oct-2 Sotheby's, Amsterdam #41/R est:8000-12000
£5500 $8635 €8250 Skaters on a frozen river (21x29cm-8x11in) s. panel prov. 21-Nov-2 Christie's, Kensington #97/R est:6000-8000
£11000 $17270 €16500 Skaters on a frozen river (24x34cm-9x13in) s. panel. 21-Nov-2 Christie's, Kensington #98/R est:7000-10000
£16438 $25644 €24000 Winter pleasures near Dordrecht (35x49cm-14x19in) s. panel. 10-Apr-3 Schopman, Hamburg #591/R est:8500

ROOSKENS, Anton (1906-1976) Dutch
£526 $853 €800 Still life (65x77cm-26x30in) executed c.1935. 21-Jan-3 Christie's, Amsterdam #380
£547 $853 €948 Abstract (16x20cm-6x8in) s.d.73 oil wood prov. 31-Mar-3 Goodman, Sydney #176/R (A.D 1450)
£5128 $7949 €8000 Totem (122x61cm-48x24in) s.i.verso board painted c.1956 prov.exhib. 3-Dec-2 Christie's, Amsterdam #268/R est:8000-10000
£5755 $9439 €8000 Provo girl (69x59cm-27x23in) s.d.63 s.i.d.verso. 3-Jun-3 Christie's, Amsterdam #348/R est:8000-12000
£6013 $9500 €9500 Het gesprek (60x75cm-24x30in) s.d.68 s.i.verso 26-Nov-2 Sotheby's, Amsterdam #226/R est:9000-12000
£9615 $14904 €15000 Figuren met gele wolk (97x75cm-35x30in) s.d.1970 i.verso. 3-Dec-2 Christie's, Amsterdam #270/R est:12000-14000
£11511 $18878 €16000 Figure with bird (130x100cm-51x39in) s.d.73 i.d.verso. 3-Jun-3 Christie's, Amsterdam #334/R est:18000-25000
£11538 $17885 €18000 De droom - the dream (97x130cm-38x51in) s.d.75 i.verso prov. 3-Dec-2 Christie's, Amsterdam #259/R est:18000-22000
£25180 $41295 €35000 Untitled (53x64cm-21x25in) s. painted c.1950 prov. 3-Jun-3 Christie's, Amsterdam #314/R est:18000-22000

Works on paper
£1439 $2360 €2000 Untitled (32x49cm-13x19in) s.d.60 pastel col gouache. 3-Jun-3 Christie's, Amsterdam #78/R est:2000-3000
£1603 $2484 €2500 Untitled (28x38cm-11x15in) s.d.67 gouache wax crayon pencil. 3-Dec-2 Christie's, Amsterdam #110/R est:2000-3000
£1795 $2782 €2800 Abstract composition (26x46cm-10x18in) s. gouache executed c.1962. 3-Dec-2 Christie's, Amsterdam #108/R est:2800-3500
£2734 $4483 €3800 Figures (31x43cm-12x17in) s. black chk gouache prov. 3-Jun-3 Christie's, Amsterdam #302/R est:4000-6000
£2985 $4746 €4478 Fantasy animal (49x64cm-19x25in) init. gouache. 29-Apr-3 Kunsthallen, Copenhagen #22/R est:35000 (D.KR 32000)
£4220 $6542 €6330 Fantasy animal (43x62cm-17x24in) s.d.50 gouache. 4-Dec-2 Kunsthallen, Copenhagen #98/R est:60000 (D.KR 49000)

ROOSVAAL-KALLSTENIUS, Gerda (1864-1939) Swedish
£535 $851 €803 Portrait of my daughter (65x58cm-26x23in) s.d.1923. 3-Mar-3 Lilla Bukowskis, Stockholm #429 (S.KR 7200)
£4823 $7475 €7235 Small girl on beach promenade (70x93cm-28x37in) s.i.d.94. 4-Dec-2 AB Stockholms Auktionsverk #1577/R est:50000-60000 (S.KR 68000)
£7070 $11595 €10252 On the way to the ball at Karlberg (161x109cm-63x43in) s.d.91. 4-Jun-3 AB Stockholms Auktionsverk #2189/R est:50000-60000 (S.KR 90000)

ROOT, John (18th C) British?
£1900 $3116 €2850 Rhinoceros and camel (24x38cm-9x15in) panel. 4-Feb-3 Sworder & Son, Bishops Stortford #153/R est:800-1200

ROOTIUS, Jan Albertsz (1624-1666) Dutch
£7051 $11071 €11000 Portrait of woman holding pocket watch (120x91cm-47x36in) prov. 21-Nov-2 Van Ham, Cologne #1414/R est:12000

ROOTIUS, Jan Albertsz (attrib) (1624-1666) Dutch
£12230 $19568 €17000 Portrait of a young lady, aged 24, wearing black dress (110x85cm-43x33in) i.d.1661 panel. 14-May-3 Christie's, Amsterdam #169/R est:8000-12000

ROOVER, Carlo de (1900-1986) Belgian
£264 $412 €420 Paradise (200x150cm-79x59in) s.d.1969 verso exhib. 23-Sep-2 Bernaerts, Antwerp #427/R
£302 $486 €450 Portrait of the artist's wife (100x60cm-39x24in) s. 24-Feb-3 Bernaerts, Antwerp #876/R
£314 $491 €500 Portrait of Paula Vanderpoorten (81x65cm-32x26in) 23-Sep-2 Bernaerts, Antwerp #213/R
£314 $491 €500 Amazon (127x99cm-50x39in) s.d.37 exhib. 23-Sep-2 Bernaerts, Antwerp #414/R
£316 $494 €500 Pleureuses (150x120cm-59x47in) s. painted 1966. 21-Oct-2 Bernaerts, Antwerp #323/R
£346 $540 €550 Nausicaa (78x98cm-31x39in) s.d.1937. 23-Sep-2 Bernaerts, Antwerp #415/R
£348 $543 €550 Dansritme (44x62cm-17x24in) s. 21-Oct-2 Bernaerts, Antwerp #308/R
£476 $757 €700 Returning home (115x150cm-45x59in) s.d. verso. 24-Mar-3 Bernaerts, Antwerp #441/R
£506 $790 €800 Gestalten (183x100cm-72x39in) s.d.1947 verso. 21-Oct-2 Bernaerts, Antwerp #317/R
£818 $1275 €1300 Dorische zuilen (67x54cm-26x21in) s.d.1935. 23-Sep-2 Bernaerts, Antwerp #417/R
£952 $1514 €1400 Reclining nude (80x128cm-31x50in) s. d. verso panel. 24-Mar-3 Bernaerts, Antwerp #443/R est:600-800
£3378 $5270 €5000 Trois graces (81x65cm-32x26in) s. exhib. 26-Mar-3 Millon & Associes, Paris #141/R est:3000

ROOVER, Prosper de (1899-1974) Belgian
£346 $540 €550 Figures at the bank of the river Schelde (76x112cm-30x44in) s. 23-Sep-2 Bernaerts, Antwerp #38/R
£377 $589 €600 Fishing boat at the river Schelde at dusk (76x112cm-30x44in) s. 23-Sep-2 Bernaerts, Antwerp #40/R

ROOYEN, Gabriel van (1752-1817) Dutch
£667 $1033 €1001 Portrait of lady (54x44cm-21x17in) s.d.1798 panel. 4-Dec-2 AB Stockholms Auktionsverk #2000/R (S.KR 9400)

ROPE, George Thomas (1846-1929) British
£380 $589 €570 Study of a bay horse (24x32cm-9x13in) board. 30-Sep-2 Bonhams, Ipswich #512
£800 $1240 €1200 Cottage by the pond at dusk (36x51cm-14x20in) s. 30-Sep-2 Bonhams, Ipswich #445
£800 $1240 €1200 Harrowing before a farmstead (35x51cm-14x20in) s. 30-Sep-2 Bonhams, Ipswich #446

ROPES, Joseph (1812-1885) American
£774 $1200 €1161 Figure with a dog (76x64cm-30x25in) s.i.stretcher painted c.1844. 8-Dec-2 Toomey, Oak Park #630/R

ROPP, Hubert (1894-1985) American
£2903 $4500 €4355 Conductor (136x101cm-54x40in) s. prov. 29-Oct-2 Sotheby's, New York #272/R est:600-800

ROPS, Felicien (1833-1898) Belgian
£290 $463 €420 Maturite (19x15cm-7x6in) mono. lit. 15-Mar-3 De Vuyst, Lokeren #279
£1333 $2213 €1933 La chasse a la femelle (30x22cm-12x9in) painted c.1887 sold with a book prov. 16-Jun-3 Waddingtons, Toronto #23/R est:1500-2000 (C.D 3000)
£2244 $3522 €3500 Plage animee (26x40cm-10x16in) mono. panel. 16-Dec-2 Rabourdin & Choppin de Janvry, Paris #113/R
£2302 $3683 €3200 Promenade sur la plage a Essonnes (30x46cm-12x18in) s. canvas on cardboard. 19-May-3 Horta, Bruxelles #234/R est:3000-5000
£5449 $8282 €8500 Busy street scene at night (44x47cm-17x19in) s. canvas on canvas lit. 11-Jul-2 Allgauer, Kempten #2664/R est:630
£10791 $17266 €15000 Quatre elegantes jouant au croquet sur la Plage de Heyst (20x27cm-8x11in) mono. panel. 13-May-3 Galerie Moderne, Brussels #309/R est:10000-15000

Works on paper
£279 $443 €410 Viol de soldats (11x8cm-4x3in) Indian ink. 19-Mar-3 Hotel des Ventes Mosan, Brussels #182
£306 $487 €450 L'etreinte (10x7cm-4x3in) Indian ink. 19-Mar-3 Hotel des Ventes Mosan, Brussels #180
£403 $648 €600 Lapin (13x8cm-5x3in) mono. ink. 18-Feb-3 Vanderkindere, Brussels #23
£680 $1082 €1000 Untitled (18x13cm-7x5in) mono.i.d.84 mixed media. 19-Mar-3 Hotel des Ventes Mosan, Brussels #171
£769 $1208 €1200 Gardien de galerie (18x11cm-7x4in) i. Chinese ink. 16-Dec-2 Rabourdin & Choppin de Janvry, Paris #16/R
£1795 $2818 €2800 Telemaque. fils du Lys (18x9cm-7x4in) mono. chl dr. 16-Dec-2 Rabourdin & Choppin de Janvry, Paris #15/R
£2100 $3277 €3150 Portrait of old woman (30x21cm-12x8in) mono.i.d.Sept. 1873 pencil chl. 28-Mar-3 Koller, Zurich #3170/R est:5000-8000 (S.FR 4600)
£2516 $3899 €4000 Femme a l'eventail assise sur la plage (19x13cm-7x5in) mono.i.d.76 pen Indian ink dr pencil prov. 5-Oct-2 De Vuyst, Lokeren #310/R est:2200-2800
£5674 $9191 €8000 Etude pour le frontispice le Roman d'une nuit par Catulle Mendes (25x16cm-10x6in) s. crayon stumping out. 23-May-3 Camard, Paris #21/R est:9000-10000
£10127 $16000 €16000 La femme et la folie dominant le monde (15x24cm-6x9in) s. dr prov.exhib.lit. 26-Nov-2 Palais de Beaux Arts, Brussels #365/R est:10000-15000
£50633 $80000 €80000 Hommage a Paon (30x21cm-12x8in) chl chk dr lit. 26-Nov-2 Camard, Paris #17/R est:10000

ROQUEPLAN, Camille (1803-1855) French
£1481 $2104 €2400 Lecture dans le jardin (38x29cm-15x11in) s.d.1851. 16-Mar-3 Eric Pillon, Calais #25/R

ROQUEPLO, Florence (?) French
Works on paper
£1821 $2969 €2750 Elevation (100x100cm-39x39in) s.verso mixed media canvas. 1-Feb-3 Claude Aguttes, Neuilly #290/R est:2800-3000

RORBYE, Martinus (1803-1848) Danish
£1914 $3100 €2775 Seated Italian woman with basket on her head (28x20cm-11x8in) init.i. 26-May-3 Rasmussen, Copenhagen #1332/R est:25000 (D.KR 20000)
£6052 $9623 €9078 Italian woman and child seated at church door (27x20cm-11x8in) d.1834. 10-Mar-3 Rasmussen, Vejle #173/R est:75000-100000 (D.KR 65000)
£14354 $23254 €21531 Two young shepherds at the Roman Campagna (22x29cm-9x11in) i.d.1835 study prov.exhib.lit. 21-May-3 Museumsbygningen, Copenhagen #37/R est:100000-150000 (D.KR 150000)
£21053 $34105 €30527 A Nubian seated smoking a cigarette (57x46cm-22x18in) s.d.1846. 26-May-3 Rasmussen, Copenhagen #1124/R est:300000 (D.KR 220000)
£102128 $161362 €153192 Young scholar reading (39x28cm-15x11in) init.i.d.1836 sold with print by Ballin, same subject. 2-Dec-2 Rasmussen, Copenhagen #1153/R est:1200000 (D.KR 1200000)

Works on paper
£818 $1244 €1227 Shepherd boy resting with sheep by the sea (18x20cm-7x8in) with sig. i.verso pencil W/C. 28-Aug-2 Museumsbygningen, Copenhagen #18/R (D.KR 9500)
£946 $1523 €1419 Villa Mitis, Palatinus Rome (21x13cm-8x5in) pencil W/C - basket on socle verso. 26-Feb-3 Museumsbygningen, Copenhagen #108/R (D.KR 10500)
£1583 $2517 €2375 Boats in the Bay of Naples (17x34cm-7x13in) i.verso pen. 5-Mar-3 Rasmussen, Copenhagen #2084/R est:15000-20000 (D.KR 17000)

RORKE, Edward A (1856-1905) American
£3247 $5000 €4871 Wash day (61x51cm-24x20in) s. painted c.1885 prov. 24-Oct-2 Shannon's, Milford #149/R est:5000-7000

RORUP, Viggo (1903-1971) Danish
£317 $503 €476 Still life of flowers in vase (65x54cm-26x21in) s.d.63. 10-Mar-3 Rasmussen, Vejle #579 (D.KR 3400)

ROS Y GUELL, Antonio (1873-1957) Spanish
£651 $1015 €950 Seascape (40x50cm-16x20in) s. board. 8-Apr-3 Ansorena, Madrid #21/R

ROS, Frans (?) ?
£426 $711 €600 Interior of the Saint Gummar church in Lier (93x68cm-37x27in) s. 23-Jun-3 Bernaerts, Antwerp #144/R
£676 $1054 €1000 Eglise Saint-Guimares a Lierre (75x80cm-30x31in) s. 25-Mar-3 Campo & Campo, Antwerp #180
£680 $1082 €1000 Interior of Saint Gommaire church in Lier (68x59cm-27x23in) s. 24-Mar-3 Bernaerts, Antwerp #638/R est:1000-1250
£1392 $2172 €2200 Interior of the Saint Gummar church in Lier (85x75cm-33x30in) s. 21-Oct-2 Bernaerts, Antwerp #576/R est:1000-1200

ROSA, Fabian de la (1869-1937) Philippino
£7042 $10845 €10563 Pasay beach, Manila (25x34cm-10x13in) s.d.1927 board. 27-Oct-2 Christie's, Hong Kong #70/R est:55000-85000 (HK.D 85000)

ROSA, Herve and Richard di (20th C) French
Sculpture
£1042 $1656 €1500 Monsieur Plat dit Victor (210cm-83in) s.d.83 oil metal lit. 29-Apr-3 Artcurial Briest, Paris #408/R est:2000-2500

ROSA, Herve di (1959-) French
£625 $987 €900 Raymond Raymond, Dr Tube, Monsieur Vert (75x56cm-30x22in) s.d. acrylic. 28-Apr-3 Cornette de St.Cyr, Paris #380/R
£862 $1440 €1250 Bouquet (65x50cm-26x20in) s.i.d. 9-Jul-3 Cornette de St.Cyr, Paris #276/R
£1389 $2292 €2000 Projet pour le carton d'invitation au defile femme printemps-ete (31x62cm-12x24in) s.d.84. 3-Jul-3 Christie's, Paris #42/R est:1500-2000
£1392 $2158 €2200 La cauchemar de Rene (80x80cm-31x31in) s.i. acrylic. 28-Sep-2 Cornette de St.Cyr, Paris #291 est:2200-3000
£2107 $3245 €3350 Atelier du peintre (78x58cm-31x23in) s.d.1989 paint. 26-Oct-2 Cornette de St.Cyr, Paris #107/R
£2704 $4165 €4300 Trois figures (101x101cm-40x40in) s.d.1992 paint. 26-Oct-2 Cornette de St.Cyr, Paris #108/R

Works on paper
£1887 $2925 €3000 Je l'aurai (149x119cm-59x47in) s.d. gouache prov. 30-Oct-2 Artcurial Briest, Paris #667a est:3000-4000
£2885 $4529 €4500 Ethiopien fin (29x21cm-11x8in) lacquer exec.1998. 10-Dec-2 Piasa, Paris #159

ROSA, Martin la (1972-) Argentinian
£8917 $14000 €13376 What is left of time (129x150cm-51x59in) s. s.i.verso painted 2000. 19-Nov-2 Sotheby's, New York #151/R est:18000

ROSA, Raffaele de (1940-) Italian
£327 $523 €500 Invented knight (40x24cm-16x9in) s. i.verso. 4-Jan-3 Meeting Art, Vercelli #30

£327 $523 €500 Knight (25x35cm-10x14in) s. 4-Jan-3 Meeting Art, Vercelli #688
£340 $541 €500 Knight (40x40cm-16x16in) s. 1-Mar-3 Meeting Art, Vercelli #529
£481 $755 €750 Pinocchio (40x60cm-16x24in) s. oil mixed media board. 23-Nov-2 Meeting Art, Vercelli #146/R
£481 $755 €750 Toyland (50x50cm-20x20in) s. 23-Nov-2 Meeting Art, Vercelli #156/R

ROSA, Richard di (1963-) French
Sculpture
£962 $1510 €1500 Chef d'orchestre (97x35x42cm-38x14x17in) s.d.1994 painted wood metal exhib. 15-Dec-2 Perrin, Versailles #139/R
£1042 $1646 €1500 Le percutioniste (82x60x40cm-32x24x16in) s.d. painted wood metal exhib. 27-Apr-3 Perrin, Versailles #129/R est:1500-2000
£1186 $1862 €1850 Contrebasse (153x65x44cm-60x26x17in) s.d.1994 painted wood metal exhib. 15-Dec-2 Perrin, Versailles #140/R
£1215 $1920 €1750 Le cactus (105cm-41in) s.num.4/8 polychrome resin. 27-Apr-3 Perrin, Versailles #130/R est:3000-4000
£1282 $2013 €2000 Trompetiste (129x46x70cm-51x18x28in) s.d.1994 painted wood metal exhib. 15-Dec-2 Perrin, Versailles #142/R
£1410 $2214 €2200 Dizzy gillespie (112x52x67cm-44x20x26in) s.d.1994 painted wood metal exhib. 15-Dec-2 Perrin, Versailles #143/R
£1538 $2415 €2400 Poule chantant avec micro (62x50x50cm-24x20x20in) s.d.1994 painted wood metal exhib. 15-Dec-2 Perrin, Versailles #145/R
£1701 $2704 €2500 Cactus (105cm-41in) s. num.3/8 resin. 24-Mar-3 Cornette de St.Cyr, Paris #141/R

ROSA, Salvator (1615-1673) Italian
£58621 $92621 €85000 Coral fishing (52x87cm-20x34in) init. exhib.lit. 3-Apr-3 Porro, Milan #16/R est:120000
Works on paper
£699 $1000 €1049 Landscape with Saint Jerome (22x16cm-9x6in) pen brown ink. 23-Jan-3 Swann Galleries, New York #81/R est:1500-2500
£3217 $4600 €4826 Standing woman seen from behind (14x7cm-6x3in) pen ink red chk. 23-Jan-3 Swann Galleries, New York #79/R est:4000-6000
£24324 $37946 €36000 Etude de dragon (19x20cm-7x8in) i. pen ink prov. 31-Mar-3 Piasa, Paris #28/R est:6000

ROSA, Salvator (circle) (1615-1673) Italian
£12000 $18840 €18000 Fishermen mooring their boat beneath a castle on a rocky outcrop. River landscape with fishermen (61x74cm-24x29in) pair. 10-Dec-2 Bonhams, New Bond Street #59/R est:12000-18000
£22378 $37371 €32000 Bergers et troupeaux se reposant dans un paysage de la campagne Italienne (72x135cm-28x53in) bears mono. 25-Jun-3 Tajan, Paris #8/R est:6000-8000

ROSA, Salvator (style) (1615-1673) Italian
£5000 $7850 €7500 Rocky landscape with anglers by a stream (135x98cm-53x39in) 13-Dec-2 Christie's, Kensington #242/R est:5000-8000

ROSAI, Ottone (1895-1957) Italian
£5811 $9065 €8600 Man with umbrella (41x28cm-16x11in) s. board painted c.1956. 28-Mar-3 Farsetti, Prato #759/R
£8228 $13000 €13000 Seated woman (30x20cm-12x8in) s.d.45 exhib.lit. 30-Nov-2 Farsetti, Prato #692/R
£9434 $15095 €13680 Tuscan landscape (50x70cm-20x28in) s. cardboard on canvas. 11-Mar-3 Babuino, Rome #283/R
£10323 $16310 €16000 Men at table (64x50cm-25x20in) s. s.verso prov. 18-Dec-2 Christie's, Rome #228/R est:20000
£13291 $21000 €21000 Landscape (40x50cm-16x20in) s.d.1945 cardboard. 30-Nov-2 Farsetti, Prato #690/R est:20000
£13291 $21000 €21000 Landscape (40x50cm-16x20in) s.d.42. 30-Nov-2 Farsetti, Prato #723/R est:28000
£13462 $21135 €21000 Street in Florence (65x50cm-26x20in) s. 20-Nov-2 Pandolfini, Florence #41/R est:17000
£15541 $24243 €23000 Three men and mountain (50x65cm-20x26in) s. painted 1955. 26-Mar-3 Finarte Semenzato, Milan #320/R
£17230 $26878 €25500 Flowers (70x50cm-28x20in) s. painted c.1954. 28-Mar-3 Farsetti, Prato #773/R est:25000
£20253 $32000 €32000 Tulipes (50x40cm-20x16in) painted 1942 exhib.lit. 30-Nov-2 Farsetti, Prato #638/R est:35000
£25316 $40000 €40000 Landscape (65x54cm-26x21in) s.d.40 exhib.lit. 30-Nov-2 Farsetti, Prato #697/R est:45000
£107595 $170000 €170000 Wind house (61x47cm-24x19in) s.d.22 cardboard on masonite exhib.lit. 30-Nov-2 Farsetti, Prato #732/R est:21000
Works on paper
£704 $1169 €1000 L'ubriaco (19x14cm-7x6in) mono. Indian ink exhib. 10-Jun-3 Finarte Semenzato, Milan #194/R
£1233 $1923 €1800 Landscape with church (27x22cm-11x9in) s. graphite. 10-Apr-3 Finarte Semenzato, Rome #104/R
£2568 $4005 €3800 Landscape (35x31cm-14x12in) s. W/C card exec.1955. 26-Mar-3 Finarte Semenzato, Milan #262/R
£2658 $4200 €4200 Men at table (33x47cm-13x19in) s. chl dr. 30-Nov-2 Farsetti, Prato #619/R

ROSAIRE, Arthur Dominique (1879-1922) Canadian
£535 $829 €803 Trees (12x17cm-5x7in) s.d.15 panel. 3-Dec-2 Joyner, Toronto #369 est:1000-1500 (C.D 1300)

ROSARIO (?) Italian?
Sculpture
£3548 $5500 €5322 Figure of a young girl holding a playful cat (94cm-37in) bronze. 7-Dec-2 Selkirks, St. Louis #564/R est:4000-5000

ROSATI, Giulio (1858-1917) Italian
£2724 $4250 €4086 Figures in an elegant interior (51x38cm-20x15in) s. panel. 9-Oct-2 Doyle, New York #97/R est:2500-3500
Works on paper
£4000 $6240 €6000 Merchant (36x52cm-14x20in) s. W/C. 15-Oct-2 Sotheby's, London #258/R est:8000-12000
£4355 $6750 €6533 An important purchase (36x48cm-14x19in) s. W/C. 7-Dec-2 Neal Auction Company, New Orleans #306/R est:3000-5000
£4800 $7488 €7200 Horseman stopping at a desert, North Africa (38x54cm-15x21in) s. W/C over pencil htd bodycol. 15-Oct-2 Sotheby's, London #264/R est:5000-7000
£5200 $8268 €7800 Choosing the right weapon (35x53cm-14x21in) s.i. pencil W/C bodycol. 20-Mar-3 Christie's, Kensington #189/R est:4000-6000
£5247 $8500 €7608 Contemplating a new purchase (53x36cm-21x14in) s. W/C. 21-May-3 Doyle, New York #188/R est:5000-7000
£22535 $32000 €33803 Rug merchants (56x36cm-22x14in) W/C. 8-Aug-1 Barridorf, Portland #106/R est:12000-18000

ROSCH, Carl (1884-?) German
£687 $1085 €1031 Landscape near to the artist's studio (38x46cm-15x18in) mono.d.37. 26-Nov-2 Hans Widmer, St Gallen #1321/R est:800-2200 (S.FR 1600)
£693 $1074 €1040 Going home (34x44cm-13x17in) mono. board. 24-Sep-2 Koller, Zurich #6688 (S.FR 1600)
£1747 $2725 €2621 Four women in the fields (26x34cm-10x13in) mono.d.65 s.d.1966 verso board. 6-Nov-2 Hans Widmer, St Gallen #31/R est:2800-4200 (S.FR 4000)
£1834 $2861 €2751 Red field (44x55cm-17x22in) mono.d.61 board. 6-Nov-2 Hans Widmer, St Gallen #132/R est:1500-3500 (S.FR 4200)
£1921 $2997 €2882 Three peasant women (42x54cm-17x21in) mono. board. 6-Nov-2 Hans Widmer, St Gallen #94/R est:2500-3800 (S.FR 4400)
Works on paper
£300 $475 €450 Still life with smoked fish (28x36cm-11x14in) mono.d.27 W/C chl. 26-Nov-2 Hans Widmer, St Gallen #1322 (S.FR 700)
£346 $537 €519 Women working in field (23x30cm-9x12in) s.d.42 chk W/C. 24-Sep-2 Koller, Zurich #6690 (S.FR 800)
£399 $631 €599 Homecoming farming women (14x20cm-6x8in) mono.d.60 W/C chl. 26-Nov-2 Hans Widmer, St Gallen #1323 (S.FR 930)
£515 $814 €773 Farming women on the field (15x23cm-6x9in) mono.d.25 W/C pencil. 26-Nov-2 Hans Widmer, St Gallen #1324 (S.FR 1200)
£536 $848 €804 Ploughing farmer with ox and cart (17x26cm-7x10in) mono.d.41 chl W/C. 26-Nov-2 Hans Widmer, St Gallen #1325 (S.FR 1250)

ROSCOE, S G Williams (1852-c.1922) British
Works on paper
£244 $405 €354 On the River Spean, Tulloch, Scotland (35x51cm-14x20in) s.d.55 i.verso W/C. 16-Jun-3 Waddingtons, Toronto #63/R (C.D 550)

ROSE, George Herbert (1882-?) British
£400 $624 €600 River scene with moored sailing craft and buildings (15x20cm-6x8in) s. w/C. 7-Nov-2 Amersham Auction Rooms, UK #216

ROSE, Guy (1867-1925) American
£165606 $260000 €248409 Twin Lakes, the eastern Sierras near Bridgeport (60x73cm-24x29in) s. canvas on board prov.lit. 19-Nov-2 Butterfields, San Francisco #8205/R est:250000-350000
£419355 $650000 €629033 Sunshine and firelight (79x48cm-31x19in) s. prov. 29-Oct-2 John Moran, Pasadena #636 est:300000-400000

ROSE, H Randolph (fl.1880-1907) British
Works on paper
£420 $651 €630 Young Lancelot (48x71cm-19x28in) s. W/C. 24-Sep-2 Bonhams, Knightsbridge #167/R

ROSE, Iver (1899-1972) American
Prints
£2516 $4000 €3774 Bread line (38x43cm-15x17in) s.i.num.54/85 lithograph exec.c.1930. 3-May-3 Rachel Davis, Shaker Heights #107/R est:3000-5000

ROSE, Jean-Baptiste de la (elder-attrib) (1612-1687) French
£4516 $7135 €7000 Pique-nique sous les arbres. Scene d'hiver devant un port (32x44cm-13x17in) panel pair oval. 19-Dec-2 Delvaux, Paris #86/R

ROSE, Joe (?) ?
£300 $477 €450 Life of Einstein. 18-Mar-3 Bonhams, Knightsbridge #186
£300 $477 €450 Samson and Deliah. 18-Mar-3 Bonhams, Knightsbridge #187

ROSE, Julius (1828-1911) German
£391 $650 €567 Landscape with figures (53x71cm-21x28in) s. 11-Jun-3 Boos Gallery, Michigan #520/R
£566 $906 €849 Landscape with pond, fisherman and view of fortress (18x29cm-7x11in) s.d.83. 17-Mar-3 Philippe Schuler, Zurich #4637/R (S.FR 1200)
£659 $1042 €989 Fishing boats at the Adriatic seacoast (37x48cm-15x19in) s. 27-Nov-2 Falkkloos, Malmo #77895/R (S.KR 9400)
£759 $1200 €1200 Mountain landscape with anglers at a mountain torrent (69x102cm-27x40in) s. 29-Nov-2 Sigalas, Stuttgart #1125
£1384 $2158 €2200 Landscape with children (39x53cm-15x21in) s. lit. 20-Sep-2 Schloss Ahlden, Ahlden #1223/R est:1900
£2013 $3140 €3200 Boats at anchor (58x37cm-23x15in) s. lit. 20-Sep-2 Schloss Ahlden, Ahlden #1116/R est:2600

ROSE, Knut (1936-2002) Norwegian
£2715 $4398 €4073 Figures (56x48cm-22x19in) s.d.1981 s.d.verso. 26-May-3 Grev Wedels Plass, Oslo #40/R est:40000-60000 (N.KR 30000)

ROSE, Manuel (1872-1961) Uruguayan
£2628 $4100 €3942 Paisaje (73x63cm-29x25in) s.d.XXV cardboard. 30-Jul-2 Galleria Y Remates, Montevideo #73/R est:3500-4500
£12500 $20000 €18750 Sarandi battle (138x206cm-54x81in) 5-Jan-3 Galleria Y Remates, Montevideo #125/R est:24000

ROSE, Samuel (1941-) American
£403 $650 €605 Surreal interior (81x46cm-32x18in) s. board painted c.1969. 10-May-3 Skinner, Boston #528/R

ROSE, Ted (20th C) American?
Works on paper
£377 $600 €566 Winter, San Juan, Durango (48x26cm-19x10in) s.d.85 W/C. 7-Mar-3 Skinner, Boston #454/R
£574 $900 €861 Train scenes (35x51cm-14x20in) s.d.87 W/C two. 22-Nov-2 Skinner, Boston #332/R est:1000-1500

ROSE, William S (1810-1873) British
£650 $1027 €943 Evening after thunder storm at the Thames, Wargrave. s.i. verso. 24-Jul-3 John Nicholson, Haslemere #1197/R
£685 $1083 €1028 In the Fraser Country (34x51cm-13x20in) s. prov. 18-Nov-2 Waddingtons, Toronto #106/R (C.D 1700)

ROSE-INNES, Alexander (1915-1996) South African
£522 $814 €783 Dwelling (63x69cm-25x27in) s. board. 15-Oct-2 Stephan Welz, Johannesburg #486/R est:9000-12000 (SA.R 8500)
£643 $1016 €965 Three doves resting on rooftop (45x60cm-18x24in) s. board. 1-Apr-3 Stephan Welz, Johannesburg #479/R est:6000-9000 (SA.R 8000)
£683 $1080 €1025 Woman at her dressing. Nude mother and child on a beach (39x25cm-15x10in) s. board double-sided. 1-Apr-3 Stephan Welz, Johannesburg #478 est:6000-9000 (SA.R 8500)
£1075 $1730 €1613 Figures and children on a beach under a cloudy sky (35x50cm-14x20in) s. 12-May-3 Stephan Welz, Johannesburg #462/R est:10000-15000 (SA.R 12500)
Works on paper
£516 $831 €774 Cottages, Arniston (34x51cm-13x20in) s. pastel. 12-May-3 Stephan Welz, Johannesburg #193 est:4000-6000 (SA.R 6000)

ROSEL, Johann Gottlob Samuel (1768-1843) German
Works on paper
£414 $654 €600 Landscape with house and waterfall (18x16cm-7x6in) s.d.1797 W/C. 1-Apr-3 Segre, Madrid #28/R

ROSELAND, Harry (1868-1950) American
£2244 $3500 €3366 Spelling game (30x25cm-12x10in) s.d.89. 12-Oct-2 Neal Auction Company, New Orleans #397/R est:3000-5000
£13208 $21000 €19812 Fortune teller (51x76cm-20x30in) s. painted c.1910. 4-May-3 Treadway Gallery, Cincinnati #512/R est:10000-20000

ROSELL, Alexander (1859-1922) British
£280 $442 €420 Dutch woman sewing in an interior (25x33cm-10x13in) s. 14-Nov-2 Christie's, Kensington #84
£500 $835 €725 Cavalier and a waiting maid at the supper table (46x60cm-18x24in) s.d.1904. 23-Jun-3 Bonhams, Bath #108
£620 $973 €930 Women in a sunlit Dutch interior (25x33cm-10x13in) s. 15-Apr-3 Bonhams, Knowle #115
£700 $1106 €1050 Gleaner (69x51cm-27x20in) s. 13-Nov-2 Halls, Shrewsbury #390/R
£800 $1312 €1200 Frozen frolics (66x50cm-26x20in) s.d.96 canvas on board. 29-May-3 Christie's, Kensington #265/R
£900 $1503 €1305 Carol singers (53x43cm-21x17in) s.d.1890. 9-Jul-3 Edgar Horn, Eastbourne #310/R
£950 $1539 €1378 Time to depart, rustic interior scene with door ajar and fisherman's farewell (66x52cm-26x20in) s. 22-May-3 Wintertons, Lichfield #564/R
£988 $1551 €1482 Ice track (69x51cm-27x20in) s.d.96. 16-Dec-2 Lilla Bukowskis, Stockholm #7/R est:12000-15000 (S.KR 14000)
£1600 $2496 €2400 In a tangle. Recruit (37x30cm-15x12in) s. pair. 8-Oct-2 Bonhams, Knightsbridge #66/R est:1200-1800
£2400 $3840 €3600 Presents for grandma (55x75cm-22x30in) indis sig.d. 13-May-3 Bonhams, Knightsbridge #307/R est:2000-3000
£2500 $4100 €3750 Playtime (56x76cm-22x30in) s.d.1910. 4-Jun-3 Bonhams, Chester #345/R est:1800-2400

ROSELLI, Carlo (1939-) Italian
£316 $494 €500 Courtship (30x30cm-12x12in) s. 14-Sep-2 Meeting Art, Vercelli #249
£347 $552 €500 Roman sunset (18x30cm-7x12in) s. 1-May-3 Meeting Art, Vercelli #104
£348 $543 €550 Card game (30x30cm-12x12in) s. painted 2002. 14-Sep-2 Meeting Art, Vercelli #320/R
£348 $543 €550 Lovers (30x30cm-12x12in) s. 14-Sep-2 Meeting Art, Vercelli #861/R
£359 $575 €550 Strolling in Via del Corso (30x35cm-12x14in) s. 4-Jan-3 Meeting Art, Vercelli #498
£382 $607 €550 Rome seen from the hills (25x35cm-10x14in) s. painted 2002. 1-May-3 Meeting Art, Vercelli #298
£385 $604 €600 Crowd (40x25cm-16x10in) s. 23-Nov-2 Meeting Art, Vercelli #183/R
£425 $680 €650 Hyppodrome (25x45cm-10x18in) s. 4-Jan-3 Meeting Art, Vercelli #64
£510 $811 €750 Day at the hyppodrome (25x35cm-10x14in) s. painted 2002. 1-Mar-3 Meeting Art, Vercelli #748
£538 $839 €850 Crowd in Via del Corso (25x45cm-10x18in) s. painted 2002 lit. 14-Sep-2 Meeting Art, Vercelli #921/R
£694 $1104 €1000 Card game (50x50cm-20x20in) s. painted 2001. 1-May-3 Meeting Art, Vercelli #286
£694 $1104 €1000 Hyppodrome spectators (50x50cm-20x20in) s. acrylic. 1-May-3 Meeting Art, Vercelli #514
£719 $1150 €1100 Rome roofs (30x70cm-12x28in) s. 4-Jan-3 Meeting Art, Vercelli #212
£748 $1190 €1100 Snooker (25x45cm-10x18in) s. painted 2002. 1-Mar-3 Meeting Art, Vercelli #537
£1111 $1778 €1700 Snooker game (50x80cm-20x31in) s. 4-Jan-3 Meeting Art, Vercelli #195
£1800 $2772 €2700 Rooftops of Rome (50x80cm-20x31in) s. s.i.d.1997 verso prov. 23-Oct-2 Sotheby's, Olympia #808/R est:1500-2000
£1923 $3019 €3000 Snookers (80x100cm-31x39in) s. 23-Nov-2 Meeting Art, Vercelli #477/R

ROSELLO, Joaquin Luque (1866-?) Spanish
£377 $589 €600 Girl and doll (73x55cm-29x22in) s. 8-Oct-2 Ansorena, Madrid #453/R

ROSELLO, Joaquin Luque (attrib) (1866-?) Spanish
£1410 $2200 €2115 Woman on the beach (8x152cm-3x60in) 30-Mar-3 Susanin's, Chicago #6016/R est:2000-4000

ROSEN, Ernest (1877-1926) American
£1603 $2484 €2500 Sleeping beauty (41x61cm-16x24in) s. cardboard. 3-Dec-2 Christie's, Amsterdam #32/R est:3000-5000

ROSEN, Georg von (1843-1923) Swedish
Works on paper
£587 $952 €881 Shoemaker's bazaar, Sioot (30x27cm-12x11in) mono.d.1877 W/C. 3-Feb-3 Lilla Bukowskis, Stockholm #25 (S.KR 8200)
£2302 $3776 €3200 L'entree du bazar (29x26cm-11x10in) mono.i.d.1877 W/C lit. 4-Jun-3 Tajan, Paris #197/R est:3000-4000

ROSEN, Konstantin (19/20th C) Russian
£3830 $6051 €5745 Winter's day in the woods (136x109cm-54x43in) s.d.1909. 2-Dec-2 Rasmussen, Copenhagen #1558/R est:40000 (D.KR 45000)

ROSEN, Sven Olof (1908-1982) Swedish
£1673 $2643 €2510 The vegetable stall (81x100cm-32x39in) s.i.d.37. 28-Apr-3 Bukowskis, Stockholm #206/R est:30000-40000 (S.KR 22000)

ROSENBERG, Edward (1858-1934) Swedish
£586 $938 €850 Coastal landscape (47x77cm-19x30in) s.d.91. 18-May-3 Anders Antik, Landskrona #150c (S.KR 7500)
£922 $1429 €1383 Green landscape with woman and child (47x71cm-19x28in) s.d.1882. 4-Dec-2 AB Stockholms Auktionsverk #1593/R (S.KR 13000)

ROSENBERG, F (19th C) German?
£903 $1400 €1355 Street scene in Pont Aven (38x23cm-15x9in) s.d.1885. 7-Dec-2 Selkirks, St. Louis #227/R est:1500-1800

ROSENBERG, Gustaf Valdemar (1891-1919) Finnish
£1439 $2302 €2000 Portrait of Ture Jansson (31x26cm-12x10in) board exhib. 17-May-3 Hagelstam, Helsinki #138/R est:2000
Works on paper
£313 $498 €460 Fetsi (36x24cm-14x9in) gouache. 24-Mar-3 Bukowskis, Helsinki #259/R

ROSENBERGER, Raphael (19th C) Austrian
£3226 $5000 €4839 Woman waiting in the library (64x81cm-25x32in) s. panel. 2-Oct-2 Christie's, Rockefeller NY #82/R est:2000-3000

ROSENGREN, Jean (1894-1965) Swedish
£245 $387 €368 View towards Lund with Hoje river in foreground (66x100cm-26x39in) s. 16-Nov-2 Crafoord, Lund #80/R (S.KR 3500)

ROSENHAUER, Theodor (1901-1996) German
£6329 $10000 €10000 Assisi (58x85cm-23x33in) s. 30-Nov-2 Villa Grisebach, Berlin #353/R est:12000-15000
£6962 $11000 €11000 Cockerel (47x37cm-19x15in) mono. 30-Nov-2 Villa Grisebach, Berlin #354/R est:7000-9000

ROSENKRANTZ, Anna (19/20th C) Danish
£298 $462 €447 Interior from Liselund (29x39cm-11x15in) s.i.d.1919. 28-Sep-2 Rasmussen, Havnen #2083/R (D.KR 3500)
£399 $646 €599 Interior (33x31cm-13x12in) s.d.1920. 25-Jan-3 Rasmussen, Havnen #2058/R (D.KR 4500)
£700 $1099 €1050 Liselund interior (30x38cm-12x15in) s.i.d.1919. 16-Apr-3 Christie's, Kensington #707/R

ROSENKRANZ (?) ?
£1572 $2452 €2358 Portrait of a member of the Freiburg clergy (105x78cm-41x31in) s.d.1800. 20-Nov-2 Fischer, Luzern #1228/R est:3800-4500 (S.FR 3600)

ROSENQUIST, James (1933-) American
£27778 $45833 €40000 Target II (121x121cm-48x48in) s.d.1996 verso acrylic prov. 1-Jul-3 Artcurial Briest, Paris #524a/R est:40000-60000
£28125 $45000 €42188 Defense by design (122x122cm-48x48in) s.d.1996 overlap s.d.verso canvas on panel prov. 14-May-3 Sotheby's, New York #253/R est:30000-40000
£28125 $45000 €42188 Red rod (122x122cm-48x48in) s.i.d.1996 overlap canvas on panel prov. 14-May-3 Sotheby's, New York #254/R est:40000-60000
£31646 $50000 €47469 Gift wrapped doll No.25 (152x152cm-60x60in) painted 1993 prov. 13-Nov-2 Sotheby's, New York #251/R est:40000-60000
£82000 $134480 €123000 Untitled (160x213cm-63x84in) s.d.1984 overlap board. 7-Feb-3 Sotheby's, London #175/R est:40000-60000
Prints
£1763 $2750 €2645 Night transitions (135x88cm-53x35in) s.i.d.num.4/4 col lithograph. 14-Oct-2 Butterfields, San Francisco #1344/R est:3000-4000
£1772 $2800 €2800 Where the water goes (261x147cm-103x58in) s.d.1989 lithograph collage lit. 27-Nov-2 Tajan, Paris #136/R
£1807 $3000 €2711 Industrial cottage (69x126cm-27x50in) s.i.d.1978-80 col lithograph edition of 100 prov. 11-Jun-3 Phillips, New York #540/R est:1000-2000
£2201 $3500 €3302 Roll down (97x73cm-38x29in) s.d.num.3/29 col lithograph. 2-May-3 Sotheby's, New York #579/R est:2000-3000
£5031 $8000 €7547 Space dust (169x267cm-67x105in) s.i.d.num.3/56 col lithograph pressed paper pulp. 2-May-3 Sotheby's, New York #581/R est:10000-15000
£6013 $9500 €9020 From welcome to the water planet, sky hole (27x149cm-11x59in) s.i.d.1989 num.15/56 col lithograph paper pulp collage. 22-Apr-3 Butterfields, San Francisco #2354/R est:10000-14000
£13836 $22000 €20754 House of fire (138x304cm-54x120in) s.i.d.num.3/54 col lithograph col pressed paper. 2-May-3 Sotheby's, New York #582/R est:15000-20000
Works on paper
£8861 $14000 €13292 Grisaille star pale and star pale (107x77cm-42x30in) s.i.d.1974 ink pencil W/C acrylic in two sheets prov. 13-Nov-2 Sotheby's, New York #333/R est:15000-20000
£13514 $21081 €20000 Sieve (77x190cm-30x75in) s.i.d.1974 pencil pastel acrylic paper on canvas. 26-Mar-3 Finarte Semenzato, Milan #287/R

ROSENSTAND, Emil (1852-1932) German
Works on paper
£3212 $4947 €4818 Girl with mirror (50x37cm-20x15in) s.d.1901 gouache exhib. 26-Oct-2 Rasmussen, Havnen #2016/R est:10000-15000 (D.KR 38000)
£8612 $13952 €12487 Young girl in front of mirror (50x37cm-20x15in) s.d.1901 pastel W/C exhib. 26-May-3 Rasmussen, Copenhagen #1157/R est:75000 (D.KR 90000)

ROSENSTAND, Vilhelm (1838-1915) Danish
£270 $422 €405 Old peasant woman (23x17cm-9x7in) i.verso. 23-Sep-2 Rasmussen, Vejle #154/R (D.KR 3200)
£397 $607 €596 Italian woman holding a jug (29x21cm-11x8in) mono.d.80. 24-Aug-2 Rasmussen, Havnen #2057/R (D.KR 4600)
£560 $897 €840 Portrait of Ludvig Holberg (61x50cm-24x20in) init.d.92. 13-Jan-3 Rasmussen, Vejle #232/R (D.KR 6400)
£936 $1479 €1404 Italian street scene with figures (31x28cm-12x11in) with sig. verso cardboard. 27-Nov-2 Museumsbygningen, Copenhagen #9 (D.KR 11000)
£2201 $3566 €3191 Cottage interior with man playing the violin for girl and her grandmother (51x67cm-20x26in) s.d.1869. 26-May-3 Rasmussen, Copenhagen #1106/R est:25000-30000 (D.KR 23000)
£4190 $6662 €6285 Tordenskjold's valet Kold by the body of his fallen Master (126x190cm-50x75in) s.d.1894 exhib. 5-Mar-3 Rasmussen, Copenhagen #1587/R est:50000 (D.KR 45000)

ROSENSTOCK, Isidore (1880-1956) French
Works on paper
£280 $445 €420 View of a villa with flowers and fines (56x75cm-22x30in) s. W/C. 18-Mar-3 Sworder & Son, Bishops Stortford #407/R
£600 $978 €900 Roses in a vase (55cm-22in circular) W/C. 29-Jan-3 Sotheby's, Olympia #307/R
£2878 $4719 €4000 Promeneurs pres de la fontaine (38x56cm-15x22in) s. W/C gouache. 4-Jun-3 Tajan, Paris #199/R est:4000-4500

ROSENTHAL, August (1820-?) German
£818 $1275 €1300 Small chapel in morning light (51x56cm-20x22in) s. one of pair. 19-Sep-2 Dr Fritz Nagel, Stuttgart #992/R
£881 $1374 €1400 Evening light on pond (51x56cm-20x22in) s.i. one of pair. 19-Sep-2 Dr Fritz Nagel, Stuttgart #991/R

ROSENTHAL, Doris (20th C) American
£475 $750 €689 Two boys (28x38cm-11x15in) prov. 5-Apr-3 DeFina, Austinburg #1330a

ROSENTHAL, Harry (20th C) ?
Sculpture
£4780 $7409 €7600 Creer un rythme (120cm-47in) mono. num.2/6 polished bronze Cast De Andreisse. 7-Oct-2 Claude Aguttes, Neuilly #182/R

ROSENTHAL, Joe (1921-) Canadian
Photographs
£1763 $2750 €2645 Flag raising on Iwo Jima (22x17cm-9x7in) s.verso gelatin silver print. 14-Oct-2 Butterfields, San Francisco #1526/R est:2500-3500
£1875 $3000 €2813 Raising of Old Glory on Iwo Jima (25x20cm-10x8in) with sig.i. platinum print. 15-May-3 Swann Galleries, New York #473/R est:1500-2500

ROSES, Gerard (20th C) German
£472 $746 €680 Deux personnages devant une fenetre (87x99cm-34x39in) s.d. cardboard. 28-Apr-3 Cornette de St.Cyr, Paris #499
£590 $933 €850 Trois femmes (140x89cm-55x35in) s. oil collage cardboard. 28-Apr-3 Cornette de St.Cyr, Paris #500

ROSIER, Amedee (1831-1898) French
£755 $1200 €1133 Market scene (20x30cm-8x12in) s. panel painted c.1890. 2-Mar-3 Toomey, Oak Park #710/R

£1397 $2180 €2096 Evening in Constantinople (17x27cm-7x11in) s. panel. 6-Nov-2 Dobiaschofsky, Bern #924/R est:4500 (S.FR 3200)
£1441 $2248 €2162 Venice in evening (17x27cm-7x11in) s. panel. 6-Nov-2 Dobiaschofsky, Bern #923/R est:4000 (S.FR 3300)
£2120 $3286 €3350 Venise, le Grand Canal (15x24cm-6x9in) s. panel. 29-Sep-2 Eric Pillon, Calais #2/R
Works on paper
£1064 $1777 €1500 Eglise de la Salute a Venise (21x27cm-8x11in) s. pencil W/C. 23-Jun-3 Beaussant & Lefèvre, Paris #95 est:300-400

ROSIER, J (19/20th C) ?
£1538 $2338 €2400 Maria della Salute, Venice (80x60cm-31x24in) s. 11-Jul-2 Hugo Ruef, Munich #794 est:600

ROSIER, Jean Guillaume (1858-1931) Belgian
£2500 $3925 €3750 Santa Maria della Salute, Venice (82x61cm-32x24in) s. 21-Nov-2 Christie's, Kensington #175/R est:2000-3000

ROSIERSE, Johannes (1818-1901) Dutch
£750 $1170 €1125 Figures at a stall by candlelight (46x36cm-18x14in) s. panel. 26-Mar-3 Hamptons Fine Art, Godalming #123
£949 $1481 €1500 Jeux d'enfants a la lueur de la chandelle (41x33cm-16x13in) s. panel. 16-Sep-2 Horta, Bruxelles #437
£2866 $4500 €4299 Night market (51x38cm-20x15in) s. panel. 10-Dec-2 Doyle, New York #175/R est:5000-7000
£3567 $5564 €5600 Interior with mother and two children by an oil lamp (37x29cm-15x11in) s. panel. 5-Nov-2 Vendu Notarishuis, Rotterdam #168/R est:5000-7000
£3800 $5966 €5700 Candlelit market (50x38cm-20x15in) s. 19-Nov-2 Bonhams, New Bond Street #3/R est:2000-3000

ROSIGNOLI, Vincenzo (1856-1920) Italian
Sculpture
£2115 $3279 €3300 At the source (62x27x25cm-24x11x10in) s.d.180 terracotta. 4-Dec-2 Finarte, Rome #523/R

ROSLIN, Alexander (1718-1793) Swedish
£8544 $13329 €13500 Tableau representant buste en bronze de feu l'abbe Gougenot (76x66cm-30x26in) prov.exhib.lit. 18-Oct-2 Rabourdin & Choppin de Janvry, Paris #137/R est:10000-12000
£13830 $21436 €20745 Portrait of Martin Pierre Foache. s.d.1772 prov.exhib.lit. 3-Dec-2 Bukowskis, Stockholm #407/R est:200000-250000 (S.KR 195000)
£20171 $32676 €29248 Baron Christoffer Bogislaus Zibet (65x55cm-26x22in) s.i.d.1784 prov.exhib.lit. 26-May-3 Bukowskis, Stockholm #362/R est:250000-300000 (S.KR 260000)
£78555 $128830 €113905 Portrait of the Italian Princess Maria Felice Colonna in palace interior (130x104cm-51x41in) s.i. prov.lit. 4-Jun-3 AB Stockholms Auktionsverk #2211/R est:1000000-1200000 (S.KR 1000000)

ROSLIN, Alexander (after) (1718-1793) Swedish
£12057 $18688 €18086 Portrait of Countess Maria Fjodorovna of Russia (80x64cm-31x25in) 3-Dec-2 Bukowskis, Stockholm #406/R est:30000-35000 (S.KR 170000)

ROSLIN, Alexander (studio) (1718-1793) Swedish
£13924 $21722 €22000 Portrait of the Queen Catherine of Russia (84x66cm-33x26in) 18-Oct-2 Rabourdin & Choppin de Janvry, Paris #140/R

ROSLIN, Marie Suzanne (1734-1772) French
Works on paper
£12588 $21022 €18000 Portrait de Marie Joseph Peyre architecte du Roi (63x55cm-25x22in) s.d.1771 pastel exhib. 25-Jun-3 Tajan, Paris #59/R est:20000-25000

ROSNAY, Arnaud de (20th C) French?
Photographs
£2110 $3250 €3165 Marisa Berenson (41x51cm-16x20in) i.verso photograph prov.lit. 24-Oct-2 Sotheby's, New York #208/R est:2000-4000

ROSNAY, Gaetan de (1914-) French
£818 $1267 €1300 Scieur de long (80x110cm-31x43in) s.d.1949. 6-Oct-2 Livinec, Gaudcheau & Jezequel, Rennes #28

ROSOFSKY, Seymour (1925-1981) American
£516 $800 €774 San Gregorio, Italy (61x91cm-24x36in) s.i.d. 8-Dec-2 Toomey, Oak Park #820/R

ROSOMAN, Leonard (1913-) British
£1100 $1804 €1650 Balloons over Djakarta fair, Indonesia. Floating landscape (13x11cm-5x4in) s.d.1969 pen ink W/C two. 6-Jun-3 Christie's, London #84/R est:500-800
Works on paper
£300 $477 €450 Dancing girl and a little boy in a Paris street (24x16cm-9x6in) s.i. pen black ink brown wash. 18-Mar-3 Rosebery Fine Art, London #815/R
£460 $731 €690 Lovers and a jealous onlooker (17x30cm-7x12in) s. pen black ink W/C. 18-Mar-3 Rosebery Fine Art, London #814/R
£550 $897 €825 Portrait of Nicholas Benby (40x49cm-16x19in) s. gouache. 28-Jan-3 Henry Adams, Chichester #470/R
£550 $858 €825 Sun loungers on the seashore (27x25cm-11x10in) s. W/C bodycol. 27-Mar-3 Christie's, Kensington #612/R
£1400 $2212 €2030 Street scene (25x35cm-10x14in) s.i.d.1959 gouache collage. 22-Jul-3 Sotheby's, Olympia #272/R est:1000-2000

ROSS, Alexander (1918-) American
£14375 $23000 €21563 Untitled (77x213cm-30x84in) s.d.98 verso prov. 16-May-3 Phillips, New York #115/R est:8000-12000

ROSS, Christian Meyer (1843-1904) Norwegian
£2618 $4110 €3927 Young girl seated with fan (41x32cm-16x13in) s.d.78 i.verso panel. 21-Nov-2 Grev Wedels Plass, Oslo #23/R est:30000-40000 (N.KR 30000)

ROSS, Cyril Joshua (1891-1973) British
£500 $820 €750 Marguerites (49x39cm-19x15in) s. s.i.d.1960 verso board. 3-Jun-3 Sotheby's, Olympia #92/R

ROSS, James (18/19th C) British
£2500 $3975 €3750 John Churchill, 1st duke of Marlborough at battle scene, possibly Blenheim (25x31cm-10x12in) s. prov. 6-Mar-3 Christie's, Kensington #510/R est:3000-5000
£8000 $13280 €12000 Hunting party in an extensive landscape (62x175cm-24x69in) 12-Jun-3 Sotheby's, London #91/R est:10000-15000

ROSS, John (19/20th C) British
£400 $620 €600 Clipper under sail on a choppy sea (104x69cm-41x27in) s. 1-Oct-2 Fellows & Sons, Birmingham #24/R

ROSS, Joseph Halford (1866-?) British
Works on paper
£350 $550 €525 Cottage garden in bloom (51x75cm-20x30in) s. W/C gouache paperboard. 22-Nov-2 Skinner, Boston #18/R
£900 $1431 €1350 View from fort Chambray, Gozo, Malta (38x58cm-15x23in) s. W/C. 29-Apr-3 Bonhams, New Bond Street #163/R

ROSS, Mary Herrick (20th C) American
£2229 $3500 €3344 Rocky coastline (41x51cm-16x20in) s.d.1917 prov. 19-Nov-2 Butterfields, San Francisco #8206/R est:4000-6000
£2388 $3750 €3582 Waves on a rocky shore with mountains in the distance (41x51cm-16x20in) s.d.1918 prov. 19-Nov-2 Butterfields, San Francisco #8207/R est:4000-6000

ROSS, Sir William Charles (1794-1860) British
Miniatures
£1000 $1600 €1500 Young lady holding a blue book, with a landscape background (18x13cm-7x5in) s.d.1837 ormolu frame rec. 13-May-3 Christie's, Kensington #87/R est:800-1200
£1000 $1640 €1450 Randolph, 9th Earl of Galloway (5x4cm-2x2in) silver gilt frame octagonal prov. 3-Jun-3 Christie's, London #209/R est:1000-1500
£1200 $1908 €1800 Young lady wearing decollete blue dress (8cm-3in) s.d.1838 verso gold frame. 4-Mar-3 Bonhams, New Bond Street #191/R est:900-1100
£1800 $2808 €2700 William West wearing brown coat (8cm-3in) gold frame oval. 5-Nov-2 Bonhams, New Bond Street #120/R est:1800-2200
£4000 $6240 €6000 Lady Augusta Margaret FitzClarence wearing white dress with pale blue trim (17cm-7in) s.d.1844 verso ormolu frame set in leather travelling case rec. p. 5-Nov-2 Bonhams, New Bond Street #160/R est:4000-5000
£18000 $28080 €27000 Portrait of Queen Victoria aged 18 wearing low cut cerise dress (4cm-2in) s.i.verso set in gold bracelet beaded surround oval prov. 5-Nov-2 Bonhams, New Bond Street #166/R est:5000-7000

Works on paper
£2500 $3925 €3750 Portrait of Lady Caroline Lennox, wearing a light blue dress (19x15cm-7x6in) i. col pencil W/C htd white. 21-Nov-2 Christie's, London #11/R est:2000-3000

ROSS, Thomas (attrib) (1829-1896) American
£1957 $3250 €2838 Looking south-west from Masonic and Geary Street, San Fransisco (31x51cm-12x20in) 11-Jun-3 Butterfields, San Francisco #4182/R est:6000-10000

ROSSANO, Federico (1835-1912) Italian
£443 $691 €700 Tete de gavroche a la cigarette (33x24cm-13x9in) s. 15-Oct-2 Vanderkindere, Brussels #29
£700 $1085 €1050 River scene, figures in a rowing boat beyond (25x35cm-10x14in) s.d.1877 board. 31-Oct-2 Greenslade Hunt, Taunton #631/R
£1800 $2862 €2700 Boating party on the river (27x36cm-11x14in) panel. 20-Mar-3 Christie's, Kensington #70/R est:1500-2000
£17687 $28122 €26000 Landscape with cows and peasant man (73x64cm-29x25in) s.d.1874 prov. 18-Mar-3 Finarte, Milan #94/R

ROSSARO, Edgardo (1882-1972) Italian
£408 $649 €600 Fishing at dusk (45x70cm-18x28in) s.d.1938 board. 1-Mar-3 Meeting Art, Vercelli #176
£674 $1091 €950 Sassolungo dal Pordoi. Nevicata in montagna (19x28cm-7x11in) s. board pair. 22-May-3 Stadion, Trieste #262/R

ROSSE, Franz (1858-1900) German
Sculpture
£1164 $1885 €1688 Oriental dancer with trumpet (50cm-20in) s.d.88 brown pat.bronze incl. socle. 25-May-3 Uppsala Auktionskammare, Uppsala #393/R est:8000-10000 (S.KR 15000)

ROSSE, Susan Penelope (1652-1700) British
Miniatures
£1100 $1716 €1650 Lady wearing decollete red dress with frilled white underslip (6cm-2in) vellum set in fishskin travelling case green velvet lining oval. 5-Nov-2 Bonhams, New Bond Street #26/R est:1200-1500

ROSSE, Susan Penelope (attrib) (1652-1700) British
Miniatures
£3500 $5495 €5250 King Charles II wearing decorated armour (8cm-3in) vellum on card rectangular. 10-Dec-2 Christie's, London #46/R est:2000-3000

ROSSEAU, Percival (1859-1937) American
£32258 $50000 €48387 Bay and Beau (67x81cm-26x32in) s.d.1919 i.on stretcher prov. 4-Dec-2 Sotheby's, New York #160/R est:20000-30000

ROSSEELS, Jacques (1828-1912) Flemish
£1013 $1580 €1600 Heathland at Wechelderzande with ox-cart and farmer's wife (62x43cm-24x17in) s. 21-Oct-2 Bernaerts, Antwerp #25/R est:1500-1800
£1509 $2355 €2400 Landscape with sloop and figure (43x66cm-17x26in) s. panel. 23-Sep-2 Bernaerts, Antwerp #20/R est:2500-3000

ROSSELL, Peter (1964-) Danish
£840 $1335 €1260 Red alert (200x120cm-79x47in) s.d.1992 acrylic. 29-Apr-3 Kunsthallen, Copenhagen #115/R (D.KR 9000)

ROSSELLI, Bernardo (fl.1532-1569) Italian
£52564 $83051 €82000 Saint John the Baptist's birth (80x45cm-31x18in) tempera board el. 16-Nov-2 Farsetti, Prato #332/R est:70000-80000

ROSSELLI, Matteo (attrib) (1578-1650) Italian
£31111 $51644 €45111 Annunciation (35x54cm-14x21in) copper. 10-Jun-3 Ritchie, Toronto #178/R est:10000-15000 (C.D 70000)

ROSSELLO, Mario (1927-) Italian
£333 $523 €520 Objects and landscape (50x60cm-20x24in) s.d.1978. 23-Nov-2 Meeting Art, Vercelli #258/R

ROSSERT, Paul (1851-1918) French
£8000 $13280 €11600 Elegant ladies and children playing on the beach (49x91cm-19x36in) s. 16-Jun-3 Waddingtons, Toronto #283/R est:18000-20000 (C.D 18000)

Works on paper
£252 $387 €400 Dimanche au jardin du Luxembourg (30x42cm-12x17in) s. W/C. 22-Oct-2 Campo, Vlaamse Kaai #605

ROSSET, Joseph (c.1703-1786) French
Sculpture
£2113 $3507 €3000 Buste de Voltaire (17cm-7in) ivory wood socle. 16-Jun-3 Anaf, Lyon #39/R est:2200-2800

ROSSET, Joseph (attrib) (c.1703-1786) French
Sculpture
£1314 $2063 €2050 Jean Jacques Rousseau (8cm-3in) s.i.d.1782 ivory wooden base. 16-Dec-2 Rabourdin & Choppin de Janvry, Paris #284/R

ROSSET-GRANGER, Paul Edouard (1853-?) French
£1392 $2200 €2200 La lecture (33x23cm-13x9in) s.d.85 panel. 26-Nov-2 Palais de Beaux Arts, Brussels #145/R est:1500-2000

ROSSETTI, Antonio (1819-?) Italian
Sculpture
£33000 $51480 €49500 Reading girl (213cm-84in) s.i.d.1873 white marble base lit. 5-Nov-2 Sotheby's, London #162/R est:12000-18000

ROSSETTI, Dante Gabriel (1828-1882) British
Works on paper
£12000 $19920 €18000 Angel with a censer (48x48cm-19x19in) pencil black chk W/C paper on card. 12-Jun-3 Sotheby's, London #200/R est:1000-1500
£22000 $36080 €31900 Cat's cradle (27x21cm-11x8in) pencil pen ink prov.lit. 5-Jun-3 Christie's, London #117a/R est:15000-20000
£170000 $282200 €255000 Alexa Wilding (72x60cm-28x24in) mono.d.1866 col chks exhib.lit. 12-Jun-3 Sotheby's, London #31/R est:200000-300000

ROSSI, Alberto (1858-1936) Italian
£1154 $1812 €1800 Marine with boats (31x41cm-12x16in) s.d.1914 board. 10-Dec-2 Della Rocca, Turin #318/R

ROSSI, Alexander M (fl.1870-1905) British
£1795 $2836 €2800 Young lady seated by beach (33x24cm-13x9in) s. 12-Nov-2 Mealy's, Castlecomer #1035
£2200 $3586 €3300 Urchin boy seated studying a photograph (54x44cm-21x17in) s. 28-Jan-3 Bristol Auction Rooms #549/R est:1000-1500
£2994 $5000 €4341 Waiting (55x67cm-22x26in) s. 22-Jun-3 Freeman, Philadelphia #45/R est:5000-8000
£12000 $19920 €18000 Expectation (35x27cm-14x11in) s. 10-Jun-3 Christie's, London #84/R est:6000-10000

ROSSI, Alexander M (attrib) (fl.1870-1905) British
£20000 $32200 €30000 Ship ahoy (76x53cm-30x21in) prov.exhib. 20-Feb-3 Christie's, London #201/R est:10000

ROSSI, Attilio (1909-) Italian
£1127 $1870 €1600 Il barcone (50x73cm-20x29in) s.d.1960. 10-Jun-3 Finarte Semenzato, Milan #312 est:500-800
Works on paper
£521 $828 €750 Study of nude (65x50cm-26x20in) s. W/C chl Chinese ink paper on canvas. 1-May-3 Meeting Art, Vercelli #564

ROSSI, Carlo (1921-) British
£320 $499 €480 Facades, Venice (27x14cm-11x6in) s. paper. 17-Oct-2 Bonhams, Edinburgh #49
£516 $800 €774 Music in the park (46x38cm-18x15in) s. 1-Oct-2 Arthur James, Florida #172

ROSSI, Dino (1904-) Italian
£680 $1082 €1000 Boulevard in Paris (37x51cm-15x20in) s. masonite. 18-Mar-3 Finarte, Milan #236/R

ROSSI, Giacomo (1748-1817) Italian
Works on paper
£2113 $3401 €3000 Tre scene dall'antico (18x23cm-7x9in) pen brown ink brown grey W/C blue paper three. 12-May-3 Sotheby's, Milan #56/R est:3000-4000

ROSSI, Gino (1884-1947) Italian
£42581 $67277 €66000 Hills in Brittany (24x34cm-9x13in) cardboard painted 1910 prov.exhib.lit. 18-Dec-2 Christie's, Rome #279/R est:80000
£48387 $76452 €75000 Port in Brittany (24x34cm-9x13in) cardboard painted 1910 prov.exhib.lit. 18-Dec-2 Christie's, Rome #278/R est:100000

ROSSI, Giovan Battista (attrib) (fl.1749-1782) Italian
£4054 $6324 €6000 The Immaculate Conception, flanked by Archangel Michael and St Andrew (61x49cm-24x19in) prov. 27-Mar-3 Dorotheum, Vienna #48/R est:6000-10000

ROSSI, Lucius (1846-1913) French
£1500 $2505 €2175 Portrait of a girl wearing a feathered hat (36x26cm-14x10in) s. panel. 8-Jul-3 Bonhams, Knightsbridge #155/R est:1500-2000
£8406 $13786 €11600 La Parisienne (88x67cm-35x26in) s. painted c.1900. 27-May-3 Artcurial Briest, Paris #101/R est:12000-15000
Works on paper
£314 $515 €480 Colin-maillard (36x51cm-14x20in) s.d.1904 W/C. 7-Feb-3 Oger, Dumont, Paris #33/R
£476 $757 €700 Romantic stroll (30x20cm-12x8in) s. W/C. 18-Mar-3 Finarte, Milan #70/R
£680 $1082 €1000 Divertissements galants (36x51cm-14x20in) W/C pair. 24-Mar-3 Coutau Begarie, Paris #113/R

ROSSI, Luigi (1853-1923) Swiss
£2000 $3300 €2900 Young fig seller (39x29cm-15x11in) s. 1-Jul-3 Bearnes, Exeter #511/R est:600-900
Works on paper
£1759 $2832 €2551 Farmer with scythe (34x26cm-13x10in) s. W/C over pencil. 9-May-3 Dobiaschofsky, Bern #191/R est:1600 (S.FR 3800)

ROSSI, Nicholas (18/19th C) ?
Miniatures
£2200 $3388 €3300 Count Alexei Ivanovich Vasiliev (8cm-3in circular) s. gilt metal bezel exec.c.1800. 24-Oct-2 Sotheby's, Olympia #24/R est:800-1200

ROSSI, Nuzio (1626-1651) Italian
£16000 $26720 €23200 Sculptor burnishing a statuette (129x95cm-51x37in) 9-Jul-3 Christie's, London #83/R est:15000-20000

ROSSITER, Anthony (?) ?
£500 $810 €725 Stubble field, impasto (76x51cm-30x20in) init. board exhib. 29-Jul-3 Holloways, Banbury #370/R

ROSSITER, Charles (1827-?) British
£350 $546 €525 Sound advice (35x51cm-14x20in) s. 7-Nov-2 Bonhams, Cornwall #851
£1700 $2788 €2550 Newhaven fish women (51x41cm-20x16in) s. 7-Feb-3 Honiton Galleries, Honiton #257/R est:200-300

ROSSITER, Thomas Pritchard (1817-1871) American
£48387 $75000 €72581 House on the Hudson (61x86cm-24x34in) init.d.1852 prov. 3-Dec-2 Phillips, New York #13/R est:75000-125000

ROSSITER, Wayne (20th C) American
£6211 $10000 €9317 Untitled (73x46cm-29x18in) s. teak three panel dressing screen. 18-Feb-3 John Moran, Pasadena #79a est:3000-4000

ROSSLER, Rudolf (1864-1934) Austrian
£1145 $1809 €1718 Untitled, naked girl playing with a cat (57x37cm-22x15in) s. 7-Apr-3 Shapiro, Sydney #531 est:3000-5000 (A.D 3000)

ROSSO, Medardo (1858-1928) Italian
Sculpture
£1200 $1956 €1740 Gavroche (49cm-19in) brown black bronze marble plinth. 15-Jul-3 Sotheby's, Olympia #124/R est:1200-1500
£2830 $4500 €4245 Gavroche (31cm-12in) green pat bronze. 27-Feb-3 Christie's, Rockefeller NY #128/R est:3000
£6098 $10000 €8842 La rieuse (53x18x23cm-21x7x9in) s. bronze marble base prov. 1-Jun-3 Wright, Chicago #105/R est:6000-7000
£160000 $262400 €240000 Golden age (43cm-17in) wax over plaster exec.c.1898 prov.lit. 5-Feb-3 Sotheby's, London #109/R est:150000

ROSSUM DU CHATTEL, Fredericus Jacobus van (1856-1917) Dutch
£2083 $3437 €3000 Sheep on a sandy path by a bridge (49x79cm-19x31in) s.d.96. 1-Jul-3 Christie's, Amsterdam #89/R est:3000-4000
£2581 $4000 €3872 Canal scene with barge and house (51x36cm-20x14in) s. 2-Nov-2 North East Auctions, Portsmouth #79/R est:4000-6000
£3082 $4839 €4500 View of Loenen Aan de Vecht (57x40cm-22x16in) s. 15-Apr-3 Sotheby's, Amsterdam #135/R est:4000-6000
£4717 $7264 €7500 Fisherman in a polder landscape (57x40cm-22x16in) s. prov. 22-Oct-2 Sotheby's, Amsterdam #114/R est:7000-9000
£5137 $8065 €7500 Unloading the freight (51x37cm-20x15in) s. 15-Apr-3 Sotheby's, Amsterdam #251/R est:8000-12000
Works on paper
£1645 $2664 €2500 Autumn river landscape (34x50cm-13x20in) s. s.i.verso W/C htd white. 21-Jan-3 Christie's, Amsterdam #179/R est:1200-1600
£2516 $3874 €4000 River landscape at dusk (75x54cm-30x21in) s. W/C. 22-Oct-2 Sotheby's, Amsterdam #127/R est:4000-6000

ROSSUM, Jacobus Willem van (1881-1963) Dutch
£955 $1490 €1500 Roosting chickens (38x62cm-15x24in) s. panel. 5-Nov-2 Vendu Notarishuis, Rotterdam #172/R est:1000-1500

ROSSUM, Jan van (1630-1673) Dutch
£1401 $2186 €2200 Portrait of Francois van Diest, aged 14 (43x32cm-17x13in) s.d.1666 panel prov.exhib.lit. 5-Nov-2 Sotheby's, Amsterdam #153/R est:2000-3000

ROSTRUP-BOYESEN, P (1882-1952) Danish
£423 $651 €635 Nature morte - Sunday dinner (50x60cm-20x24in) mono. 23-Oct-2 Kunsthallen, Copenhagen #75 (D.KR 5000)

ROSTRUP-BOYESEN, Peter (1882-1952) Danish
£254 $394 €381 French street musician (64x41cm-25x16in) mono. panel. 1-Oct-2 Rasmussen, Copenhagen #305 (D.KR 3000)
£426 $672 €639 Circus Bech Olsen (50x56cm-20x22in) mono. 2-Dec-2 Rasmussen, Copenhagen #1328/R (D.KR 5000)
£478 $775 €693 Coastal landscape (60x80cm-24x31in) mono. 24-May-3 Rasmussen, Havnen #4160 (D.KR 5000)
£489 $763 €734 Still life of flowers in vase (62x51cm-24x20in) mono. 11-Nov-2 Rasmussen, Vejle #17/R (D.KR 5700)
£743 $1175 €1115 Still life of flowers in vase, pears and jug (71x54cm-28x21in) init. exhib. 1-Apr-3 Rasmussen, Copenhagen #88/R (D.KR 8000)

ROSZAK, Theodore (1907-1981) American
£2134 $3500 €3094 Figure in blue hat (30x28cm-12x11in) board prov. 1-Jun-3 Wright, Chicago #208/R est:4000-5000
Works on paper
£1218 $1900 €1827 Golden bough - study for sculpture (28x37cm-11x15in) s.d.1954 pen ink W/C prov. 5-Nov-2 Doyle, New York #26/R est:1000-1500
£2070 $3250 €3105 Study for invocation III (44x24cm-17x9in) s. ink exec.c.1950 prov. 19-Nov-2 Wright, Chicago #154/R est:2000-3000

ROTA, Aldo (1941-) Italian
£1042 $1656 €1500 Untitled (60x60cm-24x24in) s.i.d.2003 verso acrylic mixed media. 1-May-3 Meeting Art, Vercelli #178
£2083 $3312 €3000 Composition 10 (100x80cm-39x31in) s.i.d.2003 verso acrylic mixed media. 1-May-3 Meeting Art, Vercelli #428

ROTARI, Pietro (1707-1762) Italian
£10345 $16552 €15000 Portrait of woman with red jacket (45x35cm-18x14in) 17-Mar-3 Pandolfini, Florence #703/R
£80247 $130000 €120371 Young girl hiding behind a muff (45x35cm-18x14in) prov. 24-Jan-3 Christie's, Rockefeller NY #68/R est:70000-100000

ROTARI, Pietro (attrib) (1707-1762) Italian
£1132 $1743 €1800 Portrait de femme a la boucle d'oreille (48x37cm-19x15in) 25-Oct-2 Tajan, Paris #32 est:1500-1800

ROTARI, Pietro (circle) (1707-1762) Italian
£5063 $8000 €8000 Portrait of Princess Maria Antoia (40x33cm-16x13in) 2-Dec-2 Finarte, Milan #118

ROTELLA, Mimmo (1918-) Italian
£590 $933 €850 Erotellique (41x59cm-16x23in) s.i. acrylic photo. 28-Apr-3 Cornette de St.Cyr, Paris #501/R
£3125 $4969 €4500 Marilyn (100x100cm-39x39in) s.i.d.1995 over serigraph. 1-May-3 Meeting Art, Vercelli #404
£6731 $10567 €10500 Sun (58x55cm-23x22in) s. paint decollage on tin painted 1990. 21-Nov-2 Finarte, Rome #344/R
£9434 $14623 €15000 Sans titre (300x150cm-118x59in) s.d. acrylic torn poster prov. 30-Oct-2 Artcurial Briest, Paris #455/R est:18000-22000
Prints
£5000 $8150 €7500 Still life (136x95cm-54x37in) s.d.66 s.i.d.verso col silkscreen paper on canvas. 3-Feb-3 Sotheby's, Olympia #86/R est:5000-7000
£16000 $26080 €24000 Jacqueline Kennedy (83x121cm-33x48in) s.d.63 silkscreen on canvas prov. 3-Feb-3 Sotheby's, Olympia #91/R est:2500-3500
Works on paper
£795 $1295 €1200 Sans titre (54x81cm-21x32in) s.d. photograph collage on canvas. 31-Jan-3 Charbonneaux, Paris #156
£926 $1473 €1335 Composition (24x13cm-9x5in) s. torn poster. 29-Apr-3 Artcurial Briest, Paris #548/R est:2000-2500
£949 $1481 €1500 Doll (19x25cm-7x10in) s.d.1974 effacage card. 14-Sep-2 Meeting Art, Vercelli #708/R
£962 $1510 €1500 Untitled (22x20cm-9x8in) s.d.1974 mixed media collage. 20-Nov-2 Pandolfini, Florence #111/R
£1307 $2092 €2000 Suspended in the air (25x23cm-10x9in) s. s.i.d.1974 verso effacage cardboard on canvas. 4-Jan-3 Meeting Art, Vercelli #409

£1361 $2163 €2000 Waiting (26x16cm-10x6in) s.d.1973 effacage paper on canvas. 1-Mar-3 Meeting Art, Vercelli #632
£1528 $2429 €2200 Satanic (25x18cm-10x7in) s.d.1972 collage card. 1-May-3 Meeting Art, Vercelli #413
£1736 $2865 €2500 Quasi geografica (18x12cm-7x5in) s.d.56 s.i.d.verso torn poster wood. 1-Jul-3 Artcurial Briest, Paris #826/R est:1500-2000
£1899 $3000 €3000 West-East (36x30cm-14x12in) s. i.d.89 verso decollage. 29-Nov-2 Farsetti, Prato #95/R
£2102 $3280 €3153 Untitled (22x16cm-9x6in) s.i.d.8 dic.60 collage. 5-Nov-2 Bukowskis, Stockholm #314/R est:25000-30000 (S.KR 30000)
£2500 $3900 €3700 Untitled (32x25cm-13x10in) s. decollage. 28-Mar-3 Farsetti, Prato #275/R
£2658 $4200 €4200 Goddess (60x50cm-24x20in) s. i.verso decollage acrylic on canvas. 29-Nov-2 Farsetti, Prato #232/R
£2721 $4327 €4000 Untitled (88x48cm-35x19in) s. decollage paper on canvas. 1-Mar-3 Meeting Art, Vercelli #631
£2848 $4500 €4500 Pression (70x50cm-28x20in) s.d.91 decollage on canvas. 29-Nov-2 Farsetti, Prato #276/R est:2700
£3191 $5170 €4500 Milano (17x15cm-7x6in) s.d.59 s.verso collage cardboard on canvas lit. 26-May-3 Christie's, Milan #109/R est:5000-7000
£4114 $6500 €6500 Untitled (84x51cm-33x20in) s.d.1969 torn posters prov. 27-Nov-2 Tajan, Paris #26/R est:7500-9000
£4255 $6894 €6000 Intervento su quattro (70x50cm-28x20in) s.d.90 s.i.d.verso decollage canvas prov. 26-May-3 Christie's, Milan #117/R est:2500-3500
£4255 $6894 €6000 Indicazione rosso-blu (70x50cm-28x20in) s.d.90 s.i.d.verso decollage canvas prov. 26-May-3 Christie's, Milan #118/R est:2500-3500
£4861 $8021 €7000 Onna (33x41cm-13x16in) s. s.i.verso torn poster on canvas exhib. 1-Jul-3 Artcurial Briest, Paris #528/R est:6000-8000
£5063 $7899 €8000 Mixed (36x46cm-14x18in) s.d.1957 decollage on canvas. 14-Sep-2 Meeting Art, Vercelli #787/R est:5000
£6757 $10541 €10000 The end (54x74cm-21x29in) s. decollage on canvas exec.1991 exhib.lit. 28-Mar-3 Farsetti, Prato #162/R est:12000
£6757 $10541 €10000 Mad (74x54cm-29x21in) s.d.1991 decollage paint on canvas. 28-Mar-3 Farsetti, Prato #343/R est:12000
£6774 $10703 €10500 Homage to Walt Disney (43x36cm-17x14in) s.d.61 i.verso decollage prov.lit. 18-Dec-2 Christie's, Rome #297/R est:15000
£10638 $17234 €15000 Il dramma piu grande del secolo (90x84cm-35x33in) s. s.i. verso decollage canvas prov. 20-May-3 Dorotheum, Vienna #76/R est:16000-18000
£11348 $18383 €16000 Il processo (100x101cm-39x40in) s.i.d. verso decollage prov.lit. 24-May-3 Van Ham, Cologne #508/R est:18000
£21290 $33639 €33000 Collage (100x120cm-39x47in) s.i.d.1958 verso collage glue on canvas prov. 18-Dec-2 Christie's, Rome #241/R est:25000
£42000 $68880 €63000 Classico and moderno (137x92cm-54x36in) s. s.i.d.62 verso decollage prov.lit. 7-Feb-3 Sotheby's, London #198/R est:40000-60000
£115000 $179400 €172500 Caltiki il mostro immortale (196x140cm-77x55in) s.d.61 s.i.d.verso decollage on canvas prov.exhib.lit. 21-Oct-2 Sotheby's, London #57/R est:40000-50000

ROTH, Bjorn (1961-) German
£1310 $1913 €1965 Travelling provisions - still life (105x120cm-41x47in) s. s.i.d.1988-89 verso. 4-Jun-2 Germann, Zurich #88/R est:2000-3000 (S.FR 3000)

ROTH, Dieter (1930-1998) German
£786 $1148 €1179 Flowers (37x25cm-15x10in) s.i.d.1997 mixed medai over col offset. 4-Jun-2 Germann, Zurich #827 (S.FR 1800)
£2628 $4074 €4100 Postcard (64x95cm-25x37in) s.i.d. plastic acrylic on serigraph photo on board prov. 3-Dec-2 Lempertz, Koln #402/R est:2500
£5696 $8829 €9000 Still life of flowers No 5 (65x55cm-26x22in) s.i.d.Okt 77 paper on panel. 24-Sep-2 Wiener Kunst Auktionen, Vienna #269/R est:6500-9000
£11304 $17522 €16956 Untitled (195x65cm-77x26in) oil pen pencil kelko five. 4-Dec-2 Koller, Zurich #178/R est:25000-40000 (S.FR 26000)
£12766 $20681 €18000 Garden gnome (38x22cm-15x9in) oil plaster chocolate prov. 24-May-3 Van Ham, Cologne #515/R est:2500
Prints
£2340 $3791 €3300 Graphic with cocoa (70x100cm-28x39in) s.d. col silkcut cocoa board. 24-May-3 Van Ham, Cologne #513/R est:2500
Sculpture
£3205 $4968 €5000 Motorbiker (1x17x11cm-0x7x4in) s.d.69 acrylic tin. 3-Dec-2 Lempertz, Koln #404/R est:3000
£3478 $5704 €4800 In the sea (8x20x22cm-3x8x9in) s.i.d.70 tin toy sugar cardboard box. 28-May-3 Lempertz, Koln #378/R est:2500
£3623 $5942 €5000 By the sea (26x11x17cm-10x4x7in) s.i.d. wood sugar flag. 28-May-3 Lempertz, Koln #377/R est:3000
£4855 $7962 €6700 On the Rhine (33x35x5cm-13x14x2in) s.d.69 chocolate iron box. 28-May-3 Lempertz, Koln #376/R est:3800
Works on paper
£288 $447 €450 Bulb - flower, flower - bulb (28x22cm-11x9in) i. pen. 6-Dec-2 Hauswedell & Nolte, Hamburg #325/R
£393 $574 €590 Rose (23x33cm-9x13in) s.i.d.1978/1979 pencil. 4-Jun-2 Germann, Zurich #87/R (S.FR 900)
£962 $1490 €1500 Punch glass (20x10cm-8x4in) s. verso brush pen bodycol. 6-Dec-2 Hauswedell & Nolte, Hamburg #324/R est:2000
£993 $1609 €1400 Bats (49x64cm-19x25in) s.d.78/79 graphite board. 24-May-3 Van Ham, Cologne #512/R
£1042 $1719 €1500 Nuage, et creme chocolat (76x101cm-30x40in) s.d.71 creme au chocolat. 1-Jul-3 Artcurial Briest, Paris #820/R est:1500-2000
£1923 $2981 €3000 Little sunset (42x31cm-17x12in) sausage board plastic bag. 3-Dec-2 Lempertz, Koln #401/R est:2000
£1987 $3080 €3100 Small landscape (30x42cm-12x17in) s.i. melted cheese sandpaper board plastic bag. 3-Dec-2 Lempertz, Koln #403/R est:2000
£2308 $3577 €3600 Composition with blocks (31x47cm-12x19in) W/C gouache. 6-Dec-2 Hauswedell & Nolte, Hamburg #323/R est:1400
£10044 $15769 €15066 Large feather on hat and others (50x70cm-20x28in) s.i.d.76 mixed media collage oil panel on board prov. 23-Nov-2 Burkhard, Luzern #223/R est:18000-24000 (S.FR 23000)

ROTH, Dieter and PAGE, Robin (20th C) German/British
Sculpture
£4783 $7843 €6600 Ears itch pong wad (58x41x4cm-23x16x2in) s.i.d.71 verso cheese boxes glass wood metal lit. 28-May-3 Lempertz, Koln #379/R est:4500

ROTH, Emil (1904-) Austrian
£728 $1187 €1100 Bird mountain (50x60cm-20x24in) s. masonite. 28-Jan-3 Dorotheum, Vienna #141/R

ROTH, Helene (1887-?) Swiss
£352 $525 €528 Still life of flowers with tulips (60x55cm-24x22in) mono. 25-Jun-2 Koller, Zurich #6589 (S.FR 800)

ROTH, Imre (1814-?) Hungarian
£3750 $6000 €5625 Still life with flowers and grapes (74x56cm-29x22in) s. panel. 14-May-3 Butterfields, San Francisco #1091/R est:6000-8000

ROTH, Philipp (1841-1921) German
£449 $696 €700 Cows by water (21x32cm-8x13in) s. board. 5-Dec-2 Neumeister, Munich #2859/R
£1000 $1630 €1450 Landscape by lake chiemsee (44x39cm-17x15in) s.d.74. 16-Jul-3 Sotheby's, Olympia #194/R est:1000-1500
£2821 $4372 €4400 Farm buildings between trees on the river bank (28x55cm-11x22in) s.d.99. 4-Dec-2 Neumeister, Munich #867/R est:4000
Works on paper
£253 $392 €400 Dachauer Moor landscape (36x50cm-14x20in) s.d.97 chl W/C lit. 27-Sep-2 Karrenbauer, Konstanz #1669
£394 $634 €591 Cows grazing in meadow (24x38cm-9x15in) s.d.1904. 7-May-3 Dobiaschofsky, Bern #927/R (S.FR 850)
£463 $745 €695 Landscape with farmstead (24x29cm-9x11in) s.i.d.3.Aug 65 W/C over pencil. 7-May-3 Dobiaschofsky, Bern #926/R (S.FR 1000)

ROTH, Toni (1899-1971) German
£476 $757 €700 Autumn flowers in vase (53x39cm-21x15in) s. lit. 21-Mar-3 Auktionhaus Georg Rehm, Augsburg #8077/R

ROTH, Willi (1908-1952) Swiss
Works on paper
£509 $820 €764 St albastor, Basle (40x29cm-16x11in) s.d.44 i. verso W/C bodycol. 7-May-3 Dobiaschofsky, Bern #928 (S.FR 1100)

ROTHAUG, Alexander (1870-1946) Austrian
£316 $494 €500 Mountain landscape with mountain climber (18x16cm-7x6in) s. board. 15-Oct-2 Dorotheum, Vienna #23/R
£5797 $9507 €8000 Hunting centaur (57x88cm-22x35in) s. tempera. 27-May-3 Wiener Kunst Auktionen, Vienna #38/R est:8000-16000

ROTHAUG, Leopold (1868-1959) Austrian
£497 $810 €750 Morning (61x34cm-24x13in) s. board. 28-Jan-3 Dorotheum, Vienna #39/R
£577 $912 €900 Poplars on riverside (30x24cm-12x9in) s.d.1925 board. 12-Nov-2 Dorotheum, Vienna #34/R
£600 $978 €900 Summer stroll (28x23cm-11x9in) s.d.1918 board. 13-Feb-3 Christie's, Kensington #210/R

ROTHENBERG, Susan (1945-) American
£21875 $35000 €32813 Head with arm - yellow (99x152cm-39x60in) s.i.d.1996-97 verso prov. 14-May-3 Sotheby's, New York #372/R est:40000-60000
Works on paper
£5000 $8000 €7500 Untitled (79x56cm-31x22in) s.d.1982 verso pencil prov. 14-May-3 Sotheby's, New York #371/R est:8000-12000

ROTHENSTEIN, Michael (1908-1994) British

Works on paper

£1500 $2385 €2250 Sawn log (26x33cm-10x13in) s.d.1942 ink W/C two prov.exhib. 26-Feb-3 Sotheby's, Olympia #121/R est:800-1200

ROTHENSTEIN, Sir William (1872-1945) British

£300 $477 €450 Portrait of a Catholic priest in Biretta (44x34cm-17x13in) 26-Feb-3 Sotheby's, Olympia #111/R
£360 $572 €540 Portrait of Joan Waters (60x50cm-24x20in) 26-Feb-3 Sotheby's, Olympia #112/R
£550 $875 €825 Portrait of a lady in a headscarf (76x51cm-30x20in) 26-Feb-3 Sotheby's, Olympia #107/R
£550 $875 €825 Ruins at Bouillion (76x102cm-30x40in) 18-Mar-3 Rosebery Fine Art, London #826/R
£600 $954 €900 Portrait of a lady (53x43cm-21x17in) 26-Feb-3 Sotheby's, Olympia #110/R
£650 $1034 €975 Portrait of Sir William Croft Murray (53x43cm-21x17in) 26-Feb-3 Sotheby's, Olympia #109/R
£900 $1431 €1350 In the garden, Iles farm (61x76cm-24x30in) 26-Feb-3 Sotheby's, Olympia #103/R est:1000-1500
£900 $1431 €1350 Sunlit view of the barn at Lles farm (76x102cm-30x40in) 26-Feb-3 Sotheby's, Olympia #104/R est:1000-1500
£1000 $1590 €1500 Nude with mirror (56x68cm-22x27in) 26-Feb-3 Sotheby's, Olympia #106/R est:800-1200
£1200 $1908 €1800 Abbey church of St. Seine l'abbaye, by moonlight (82x100cm-32x39in) init.i. painted 1906 exhib.lit. 26-Feb-3 Sotheby's, Olympia #74/R est:800-1200
£1200 $1908 €1800 Haystacks with barn, Iles farm, Far Oakridge, Gloucestershire (83x91cm-33x36in) painted c.1933 exhib. 26-Feb-3 Sotheby's, Olympia #96/R est:800-1200
£1300 $2067 €1950 Sheffield seamstresses (61x76cm-24x30in) 26-Feb-3 Sotheby's, Olympia #105/R est:1000-1500
£1400 $2226 €2100 Iles farm (64x76cm-25x30in) 26-Feb-3 Sotheby's, Olympia #95/R est:1500-2000
£1600 $2544 €2400 Portrait of Sir Henry Wood (51x41cm-20x16in) 26-Feb-3 Sotheby's, Olympia #108/R est:600-800
£2000 $3180 €3000 Haystacks in the sunlight (76x101cm-30x40in) painted c.1930. 26-Feb-3 Sotheby's, Olympia #94/R est:800-1200
£2400 $3816 €3600 Ghats at Benares (71x91cm-28x36in) painted 1910-11. 26-Feb-3 Sotheby's, Olympia #69/R est:1500-2000
£2400 $3816 €3600 Morris dancer from Bampton, Oxfordshire (76x51cm-30x20in) 26-Feb-3 Sotheby's, Olympia #97/R est:2500-3500
£2800 $4452 €4200 Portrait of a student at his easel (67x59cm-26x23in) painted 1935. 26-Feb-3 Sotheby's, Olympia #92/R est:3000-4000
£3500 $5565 €5250 Mother and child (99x63cm-39x25in) s.d.1901. 26-Feb-3 Sotheby's, Olympia #65/R est:800-1200
£4500 $7155 €6750 Woman in a black bonnet (61x38cm-24x15in) s.i. exhib. 26-Feb-3 Sotheby's, Olympia #27/R est:5000-7000
£13669 $21871 €19000 Femme assise dans un interieur (92x73cm-36x29in) s. 15-May-3 Christie's, Paris #330/R est:4000-6000
£29000 $46110 €43500 Portrait of Max Beerbohm (81x46cm-32x18in) init.d.1900 exhib.lit. 26-Feb-3 Sotheby's, Olympia #53/R est:10000-15000

Works on paper

£320 $499 €480 Cottage in a rural landscape (30x49cm-12x19in) s.i. pastel. 15-Oct-2 Bonhams, Knightsbridge #105a
£350 $557 €525 Open air painter (22x34cm-9x13in) black white chk. 26-Feb-3 Sotheby's, Olympia #23/R
£360 $572 €540 Red stone Castle (42x40cm-17x16in) init.d.1932 pastel. 26-Feb-3 Sotheby's, Olympia #99/R
£450 $715 €675 In the wings. Model in the studio (37x24cm-15x9in) chl white chk dr. two. 26-Feb-3 Sotheby's, Olympia #14/R
£450 $715 €675 Violinist (37x24cm-15x9in) i. chl white chk. 26-Feb-3 Sotheby's, Olympia #15/R
£450 $715 €675 Woman reading (37x24cm-15x9in) chl white chk. 26-Feb-3 Sotheby's, Olympia #21/R
£450 $715 €675 Finished (36x23cm-14x9in) i.d.Oct 15/90 chl white chk. 26-Feb-3 Sotheby's, Olympia #22/R
£450 $715 €675 Ajanta (44x28cm-17x11in) init.i.d.1910 chl. 26-Feb-3 Sotheby's, Olympia #67/R
£480 $763 €720 Figure seated by the fire, possibly Phil May (37x24cm-15x9in) chl white chk sold with a drawing. 26-Feb-3 Sotheby's, Olympia #13/R
£550 $875 €825 Farm buildings, Gloucestershire (42x40cm-17x16in) s.d.1931 pastel. 26-Feb-3 Sotheby's, Olympia #98/R
£650 $1034 €975 Portrait of Algernon Charles Swinbure (18x12cm-7x5in) col chk. 26-Feb-3 Sotheby's, Olympia #33/R
£700 $1127 €1050 Portrait of Walter de la Mere (22x16cm-9x6in) init.i.d.1920 chl. 14-Jan-3 Bonhams, Knightsbridge #79/R
£750 $1193 €1125 Caricatures of himself and Thomas Hardy (33x40cm-13x16in) s.i. 26-Feb-3 Sotheby's, Olympia #28/R
£900 $1431 €1350 Portrait of Gervals (37x25cm-15x10in) s. chl white chk sold with a portrait by same hand. 26-Feb-3 Sotheby's, Olympia #18/R est:1000-1500
£900 $1431 €1350 Posthumous portrait of Paul Verlaine (19x18cm-7x7in) s.i.d.March 23 18 red chk. 26-Feb-3 Sotheby's, Olympia #25/R est:1000-1500
£900 $1431 €1350 Posthumous portrait of Rodin (20x18cm-8x7in) init.i.d.1918 red chk. 26-Feb-3 Sotheby's, Olympia #26/R est:1000-1500
£1000 $1590 €1500 Aftermath of World War I (51x35cm-20x14in) init.d.1919 gouache pastel. 26-Feb-3 Sotheby's, Olympia #78/R est:600-800
£1200 $1908 €1800 Phil May (37x24cm-15x9in) s.d.Oct 6/90 sold with a tracing. 26-Feb-3 Sotheby's, Olympia #12/R est:800-1200
£1300 $2067 €1950 Portrait of Laurence Housman (33x23cm-13x9in) pencil. 26-Feb-3 Sotheby's, Olympia #31/R est:800-1200
£1700 $2703 €2550 Philip Wilson Steer (25x16cm-10x6in) lithograph chk exhib.lit. 26-Feb-3 Sotheby's, Olympia #35/R est:700-900
£1700 $2703 €2550 Self portrait (30x25cm-12x10in) col chk. 26-Feb-3 Sotheby's, Olympia #102/R est:500-700
£2000 $3180 €3000 Mother and child (21x18cm-8x7in) init.d.1902 chl pastel two. 26-Feb-3 Sotheby's, Olympia #64/R est:200-300
£2400 $3816 €3600 Jewish man reading by candlelight (32x36cm-13x14in) red conte sold with four dr. 26-Feb-3 Sotheby's, Olympia #66/R est:800-1200
£7000 $11130 €10500 Portrait of Augustus John (22x16cm-9x6in) init. col chk. 26-Feb-3 Sotheby's, Olympia #59/R est:5000-7000

ROTHKO, Mark (1903-1970) American

£47468 $75000 €71202 Portrait of Joe Liss (51x41cm-20x16in) s. painted 1939 prov.exhib.lit. 14-Nov-2 Christie's, Rockefeller NY #119/R est:80000-120000
£375000 $600000 €562500 Untitled (122x103cm-48x41in) tempera on paper painted 1969 prov.exhib. 15-May-3 Phillips, New York #21/R est:800000-1200000
£387500 $620000 €581250 White over orange (75x55cm-30x22in) s.d.1959 verso paper on canvas prov.exhib. 13-May-3 Sotheby's, New York #18/R est:800000-1000000
£531250 $850000 €796875 Grays in yellow (60x48cm-24x19in) s.d.1960 verso paper on canvas prov. 13-May-3 Sotheby's, New York #10/R est:450000-550000
£696203 $1100000 €1044305 No. 18 (141x117cm-56x46in) s.d.1947 verso i.d.on stretcher prov.exhib.lit. 13-Nov-2 Christie's, Rockefeller NY #15/R est:1000000-1500000
£950000 $1558000 €1425000 Untitled (132x103cm-52x41in) paper on canvas painted 1969 prov. 6-Feb-3 Sotheby's, London #6/R est:1200000
£3750000 $6000000 €5625000 Brown and black in reds (231x152cm-91x60in) s.d.1957 verso prov.exhib.lit. 14-May-3 Christie's, Rockefeller NY #35/R est:6000000-8000000
£9125001 $14600000 €13687502 White and black on wine (267x422cm-105x166in) s.verso painted 1958 prov.exhib.lit. 14-May-3 Christie's, Rockefeller NY #13/R est:8000000-12000000

ROTHSTEIN, Arthur (1915-1985) American

Photographs

£1875 $3000 €2813 Dust storm, Cimarron County, Oklahoma (20x20cm-8x8in) s. silver print. 15-May-3 Swann Galleries, New York #475/R est:1500-2000

ROTHSTEN, A V (19th C) Swedish

£1411 $2216 €2117 Landscape from Kolmaarden (89x132cm-35x52in) s.d.1884 after Alfred Wahlberg. 16-Dec-2 Lilla Bukowskis, Stockholm #896 est:15000-20000 (S.KR 20000)

ROTHSTEN, Carl Abraham (1826-1877) Swedish

£419 $650 €629 Landscape with buildings by water (70x85cm-28x33in) indis.sig. 29-Sep-2 Uppsala Auktionskammare, Uppsala #272 (S.KR 6000)
£494 $776 €741 Landscape from Alvkarleby (50x71cm-20x28in) s. 16-Dec-2 Lilla Bukowskis, Stockholm #6 (S.KR 7000)
£5106 $8374 €7404 View of Stockholm (63x95cm-25x37in) s.d.1856. 4-Jun-3 AB Stockholms Auktionsverk #2117/R est:40000-45000 (S.KR 65000)

ROTHWELL, Richard (1800-1868) British

£2482 $4021 €3500 Young Diana the huntress (43cm-17in circular) s.d.1851. 20-May-3 Mealy's, Castlecomer #1259/R est:3000-4000

ROTIG, Georges Frederic (1873-1961) French

£745 $1200 €1118 Dog in hilly wooded landscape (46x38cm-18x15in) s.d.57. 20-Jan-3 Arthur James, Florida #808
£1471 $2412 €2250 Cerf et biche a l'eau (60x80cm-24x31in) s.d.31. 7-Feb-3 Oger, Dumont, Paris #128
£1503 $2465 €2300 Cerf et biche (45x53cm-18x21in) s.d.1912. 7-Feb-3 Oger, Dumont, Paris #127
£2483 $3998 €3700 Cerf et biches (33x45cm-13x18in) s.d.03. 23-Feb-3 Lesieur & Le Bars, Le Havre #137/R
£2975 $4611 €4700 Cerf et biche en foret de Fontainebleau (33x41cm-13x16in) s.d.1927. 29-Sep-2 Eric Pillon, Calais #46/R

£3205 $5032 €5000 Compagnie de sangliers dans un sous-bois (60x82cm-24x32in) s.d.1945. 14-Dec-2 Herbette, Doullens #240/R est:3500
£3333 $4733 €5400 Cerfs et bichesa l'oree du bois (60x81cm-24x32in) s. 16-Mar-3 Eric Pillon, Calais #92/R
£3704 $5963 €5556 Bear family (150x200cm-59x79in) s.d.11. 7-May-3 Dobiaschofsky, Bern #932/R est:12000 (S.FR 8000)

Works on paper
£288 $441 €450 Marais de Sologne (12x15cm-5x6in) s.d.1920 gouache. 23-Aug-2 Deauville, France #151
£577 $883 €900 Combat de cerfs (9x13cm-4x5in) gouache. 23-Aug-2 Deauville, France #152
£680 $1082 €1000 Etudes de gibier (43x33cm-17x13in) s. pastel. 23-Mar-3 Herbette, Doullens #10/R
£1090 $1667 €1700 Famille de chevreuils (9x12cm-4x5in) s. gouache. 23-Aug-2 Deauville, France #150/R

ROTTA, Silvio Giulio (1853-1913) Italian
Works on paper
£453 $706 €720 Two figures (10x8cm-4x3in) s. Indian ink pastel board. 22-Sep-2 Semenzato, Venice #112/R

ROTTEKEN, Carl Johann Friedrich Adolf (1831-1900) German
£1370 $2151 €2000 Smithy in woodland clearing (83x117cm-33x46in) s.d.1883 canvas on panel. 16-Apr-3 Dorotheum, Salzburg #116/R est:3000-4000

ROTTENHAMMER, Dominicus (attrib) (1622-?) German
Works on paper
£943 $1472 €1500 Venus washing (15x29cm-6x11in) i. wash pen ochre. 11-Oct-2 Winterberg, Heidelberg #320/R

ROTTENHAMMER, Hans (16/17th C) German
£15000 $23550 €22500 Immaculate conception (31x23cm-12x9in) copper. 12-Dec-2 Sotheby's, London #113/R est:8000-12000

Works on paper
£5903 $9385 €8500 Whitsun wonder (14x17cm-6x7in) pen wash prov. 5-May-3 Ketterer, Munich #211/R est:2000-3000
£15278 $24292 €22000 Snake worship (23x15cm-9x6in) mono.i.d.1599 pen wash lit. 5-May-3 Ketterer, Munich #212/R est:2500-3500

ROTTENHAMMER, Hans (attrib) (16/17th C) German
Works on paper
£556 $883 €800 Satyr with nymph with Venus approaching on clouds (20x32cm-8x13in) i. pen wash. 5-May-3 Ketterer, Munich #208/R
£1181 $1877 €1700 Madonna with child and small John (17x16cm-7x6in) pen wash. 5-May-3 Ketterer, Munich #209/R
£15278 $24292 €22000 Neptune and Minerva with muse playing music (13x15cm-5x6in) i. pen wash over pencil paper on board prov. 5-May-3 Ketterer, Munich #210/R est:5000-6000

ROTTENHAMMER, Hans (style) (16/17th C) German
£5500 $8580 €8250 Garden of Eden (66x74cm-26x29in) 10-Apr-3 Christie's, Kensington #17/R est:6000-8000

ROTTENHAMMER, Johann (attrib) (1564-1625) German
Works on paper
£2564 $3974 €4000 Christ calling souls in Purgatory (23x13cm-9x5in) pen ink wash sanguine. 4-Dec-2 Piasa, Paris #34/R

ROTTER, Leonard (20th C) ?
£454 $736 €681 Prague viewed from seminary garden (65x85cm-26x33in) s.d.1959. 24-May-3 Dorotheum, Prague #84/R est:15000-23000 (C.KR 20000)

ROTTER-PETERS, Ernestine (1899-1975) Austrian
£2885 $4558 €4500 St Francis (70x100cm-28x39in) s. board. 12-Nov-2 Dorotheum, Vienna #158/R est:4500-6000

ROTTMANN, Carl (1798-1850) German
Works on paper
£880 $1399 €1320 Field workers returning home in a mountain landscape (14x35cm-6x14in) s.i. pencil W/C. 18-Mar-3 Rosebery Fine Art, London #910/R

ROTTMANN, Carl (attrib) (1798-1850) German
£2302 $3683 €3200 Scicilian landscape near Palermo (20x28cm-8x11in) canvas on board. 17-May-3 Lempertz, Koln #1473/R est:2000

ROTTMANN, Leopold (1812-1881) German
£1582 $2500 €2500 Konigssee with view of St Bartholoma and Watzmann chain (46x66cm-18x26in) s. 29-Nov-2 Bassenge, Berlin #6042/R est:3500
£7143 $10643 €11000 Stream in the high mountains (25x36cm-10x14in) s. i. verso board. 26-Jun-2 Neumeister, Munich #838/R est:8000

Works on paper
£1899 $3000 €3000 Lake landscape near Brixlegg, Tyrol (36x55cm-14x22in) mono. d.April 70 verso W/C. 29-Nov-2 Bassenge, Berlin #6043 est:3000

ROTTMANN, Mozart (1874-?) Hungarian
£1200 $1920 €1800 Goddess Flora (119x88cm-47x35in) s. 11-Mar-3 Bonhams, Knightsbridge #137/R est:1200-1800
£1374 $2171 €2061 Untitled, slave trader with two nude girls (100x71cm-39x28in) s. prov. 7-Apr-3 Shapiro, Sydney #554 est:5000-7000 (A.D 3600)
£2013 $3119 €3200 In the tavern (60x80cm-24x31in) s. 29-Oct-2 Dorotheum, Vienna #278/R est:3200-3400

ROTTONARA, Franz Angelo (1848-?) Austrian
Works on paper
£387 $569 €600 Castle interior (60x85cm-24x33in) s. bodycol over W/C quartered. 20-Jun-2 Dr Fritz Nagel, Stuttgart #680/R

ROUAN, François (1943-) French
Works on paper
£884 $1406 €1300 Coquille (13x20cm-5x8in) i.d.1994 s.verso wax prov. 26-Feb-3 Artcurial Briest, Paris #567/R

ROUAULT, Georges (1871-1958) French
£6329 $10000 €10000 Christ on the cross (65x49cm-26x19in) s. col aquatint. 30-Nov-2 Villa Grisebach, Berlin #201/R est:8000-15000
£7362 $12000 €11043 Mastuvu (10x23cm-4x9in) s. indis d.1932 oil pen ink paper on canvas lit. 12-Feb-3 Sotheby's, New York #105/R est:15000-20000
£7692 $12000 €11538 Le pere ubu chantre (52x37cm-20x15in) oil paper on canvas painted c.1917 lit. 7-Nov-2 Christie's, Rockefeller NY #352/R est:25000-35000
£7911 $12263 €12500 Etude pour Passion (10x20cm-4x8in) st.mono. paper on canvas painted c.1934-36 lit. 28-Sep-2 Cornette de St.Cyr, Paris #187/R est:10000-12000
£11538 $18000 €17307 J'irai droit au ciel V Madame X (31x19cm-12x7in) oil paper on canvas painted 1912-13 prov.lit. 7-Nov-2 Christie's, Rockefeller NY #312/R est:20000-30000
£12179 $19122 €19000 Christ solitaire (30x42cm-12x17in) 13-Dec-2 Piasa, Paris #27/R est:22000
£16149 $26000 €24224 Benigne (28x16cm-11x6in) s. estate st.verso oil paper on canvas prov. 7-May-3 Sotheby's, New York #226/R est:10000-15000
£46474 $72500 €69711 Paysage biblique (30x43cm-12x17in) painted c.1950-51 prov. 6-Nov-2 Sotheby's, New York #347/R est:70000-90000
£80128 $125000 €120192 Acrobate XIV - Lutteur (104x73cm-41x29in) s.d.1913 oil gouache paper on canvas prov.lit. 7-Nov-2 Christie's, Rockefeller NY #291/R est:200000-300000

Prints
£2138 $3400 €3207 Le baie de trepasses (62x45cm-24x18in) s.num.46/175 col aquatint. 4-Mar-3 Swann Galleries, New York #568/R est:2500-3500
£2297 $3584 €3400 Nu de profil (31x21cm-12x8in) mono.d.1936 col aquatint etching. 28-Mar-3 Ketterer, Hamburg #612/R est:2800-3400
£2390 $3800 €3585 Christ de profil (31x21cm-12x8in) col aquatint. 1-May-3 Swann Galleries, New York #594/R est:4000-6000
£2454 $4000 €3681 Pierrot noir (31x20cm-12x8in) col aquatint one of 270 exec.1930. 13-Feb-3 Christie's, Rockefeller NY #180/R
£2500 $3875 €3750 Tristes Os (44x33cm-17x13in) aquatint. 3-Dec-2 Christie's, London #225/R est:2800-3200
£2500 $4125 €3625 Miserere, qui ne se grime pas (56x43cm-22x17in) aquatint edition of 450. 1-Jul-3 Sotheby's, London #143/R est:3000-4000
£2564 $4000 €3846 Amer citron (32x22cm-13x9in) col aquatint edition of 280. 7-Nov-2 Swann Galleries, New York #808/R est:4000-6000
£2821 $4400 €4232 La sybille de cumes (53x38cm-21x15in) s.num.XVIII/XX col lithograph exec.c.1928. 7-Nov-2 Swann Galleries, New York #805/R est:3000-5000
£3006 $4750 €4509 Qui ne se grime pas? (56x43cm-22x17in) Heliogravure aquatint drypoint executed c.1923. 12-Nov-2 Doyle, New York #353/R est:4000-6000
£3125 $4969 €4500 Nu de profil (31x21cm-12x8in) mono.d. col aquatint. 5-May-3 Ketterer, Munich #55/R est:2800-3400
£3239 $5377 €4600 Amazone (30x23cm-12x9in) s.d. col aquatint etching. 14-Jun-3 Hauswedell & Nolte, Hamburg #1562/R est:5000

£3333 $5233 €5200 Automne (435x570cm-171x224in) lithograph. 12-Dec-2 Piasa, Paris #140/R

£6289 $10000 €9434 Le Christ en croix (65x50cm-26x20in) s.num.65/175 col aquatint. 1-May-3 Swann Galleries, New York #593/R est:15000-20000

£10577 $16606 €16500 Les fleurs du mal (312x212cm-123x83in) aquatint. 12-Dec-2 Piasa, Paris #137/R

£19231 $30000 €28847 Cirque de l'etoile filante, Paris, Ambroise Vollard (46x36cm-18x14in) col aquatints 17 i. wood engravings 82 wrapper album. 5-Nov-2 Christie's, Rockefeller NY #339/R est:40000-60000

£23148 $37269 €34722 Andre Suares: Passion. s. folio of 17 col lithographs 82 woodcuts 17 illustrations. 7-May-3 Dobiaschofsky, Bern #2207/R est:60000 (S.FR 50000)

Works on paper

£252 $390 €400 Nu debout (20x40cm-8x16in) s. chl. 3-Nov-2 Feletin, Province #138

£272 $433 €400 Vue de Notre Dame de Paris (49x61cm-19x24in) s. W/C. 19-Mar-3 Hotel des Ventes Mosan, Brussels #235/R

£6447 $10445 €9800 Nu a la toilette (27x29cm-11x11in) W/C prov. 22-Jan-3 Tajan, Paris #101/R est:12000-15000

£7931 $13245 €11500 Paysage d'inondation (20x24cm-8x9in) s.d. gouache ink wash prov. 9-Jul-3 Cornette de St.Cyr, Paris #194/R est:10000-12000

£9000 $14760 €13500 Village entre les arbres (19x31cm-7x12in) brush ink W/C chl gouache exec.c.1913 prov.lit. 5-Feb-3 Sotheby's, London #263/R est:15000

£10063 $15597 €16000 Nu se coiffant (35x26cm-14x10in) i.verso W/C exec.c.1911 prov.lit. 30-Oct-2 Artcurial Briest, Paris #212/R est:15000-18000

£12500 $20875 €18125 Professeur momine (30x18cm-12x7in) i.verso col crayon gouache wash executed c.1910-14 prov.lit. 24-Jun-3 Sotheby's, London #271/R est:10000-15000

£16026 $25000 €24039 Juge (20x13cm-8x5in) W/C prov.exhib.lit. 6-Nov-2 Sotheby's, New York #221/R est:25000-35000

£19231 $30000 €28847 Christ en croix (24x21cm-9x8in) studio st. bears another sig.verso gouache W/C sold with photo. 18-Sep-2 Swann Galleries, New York #56/R est:30000-50000

£134615 $210000 €201923 Filles (69x52cm-27x20in) s.d.1906 W/C gouache board on panel lit. 7-Nov-2 Christie's, Rockefeller NY #127/R est:200000-300000

ROUAULT, Georges Dominique (1904-) French

£569 $900 €900 Plae de la Concorde (46x55cm-18x22in) s. 2-Dec-2 Tajan, Paris #80

£741 $1052 €1200 Paris, Conciergerie (55x38cm-22x15in) s. 16-Mar-3 Eric Pillon, Calais #203/R

Works on paper

£304 $474 €450 Quai de la Seine a Paris (31x44cm-12x17in) s. W/C. 28-Mar-3 Claude Aguttes, Neuilly #147

ROUAULT, Isabelle (19/20th C) ?

£276 $461 €400 Vase de fleurs (74x61cm-29x24in) s. 9-Jul-3 Millon & Associes, Paris #145

ROUBAL, Franz (1884-1967) Austrian

£552 $883 €800 St Francis intervening (60x67cm-24x26in) s.d.1946. 11-Mar-3 Dorotheum, Vienna #82/R

£769 $1192 €1200 Peasant returning home (36x48cm-14x19in) s.d.1953 board. 5-Dec-2 Dorotheum, Graz #50/R

ROUBAUD, Franz (1856-1928) Russian

£2402 $3507 €3603 Cossack in winter landscape (62x37cm-24x15in) s.d.1892. 4-Jun-2 Germann, Zurich #99/R est:4000-6000 (S.FR 5500)

£3034 $4794 €4400 Caucasian cavalry man with flag (40x23cm-16x9in) s. canvas on board. 5-Apr-3 Hans Stahl, Hamburg #20/R est:1200

£6410 $10000 €9615 Russian Cossack (36x28cm-14x11in) board. 20-Sep-2 Du Mouchelle, Detroit #2013/R est:2500-3500

£7500 $12150 €11250 Cossack leading his horse (35x64cm-14x25in) s.d.1915. 21-May-3 Sotheby's, London #43/R est:4000-6000

£8000 $12960 €12000 Mounted Cossack on a mountain pass (62x37cm-24x15in) s.d.1892. 21-May-3 Sotheby's, London #46/R est:2500-3500

£8176 $12591 €13000 Cossacks on the move (51x71cm-20x28in) s. 23-Oct-2 Christie's, Amsterdam #50/R est:5000-7000

£9000 $14580 €13500 Caucasian warrior chief on horseback (36x58cm-14x23in) s. panel. 21-May-3 Sotheby's, London #42/R est:8000-10000

£9500 $15390 €14250 Lone Caucasian warrior on horseback (41x26cm-16x10in) s. panel. 21-May-3 Sotheby's, London #45/R est:4000-6000

£11465 $17885 €18000 Tscherkess men on horses taking wagons across river (59x81cm-23x32in) s. 6-Nov-2 Hugo Ruef, Munich #1256/R est:6000

£12500 $19875 €18000 Tcherkess falconer (48x35cm-19x14in) s. 29-Apr-3 Christie's, Amsterdam #92/R est:8000-12000

£15132 $24513 €23000 Kozaks crossing the river (53x69cm-21x27in) 21-Jan-3 Christie's, Amsterdam #43/R est:2500-3500

£16139 $25016 €25500 La retraite des cosaques (180x128cm-71x50in) s. 29-Sep-2 Eric Pillon, Calais #69/R

£19231 $30000 €28847 Untitled, men on galloping horses (107x15cm-42x6in) 20-Sep-2 Du Mouchelle, Detroit #2012/R est:10000-15000

£20833 $32500 €31250 Wild Cossack division (58x102cm-23x40in) s. 20-Sep-2 Du Mouchelle, Detroit #2017/R est:15000-20000

Works on paper

£324 $518 €450 Market in Eriwan, Armenia (13x22cm-5x9in) d.16 7ber 83 pencil prov. 17-May-3 Lempertz, Koln #1332

£10000 $15700 €15000 Crossing the river (49x68cm-19x27in) s. gouache W/C. 20-Nov-2 Sotheby's, London #33/R est:2000-3000

£15000 $24300 €22500 At the circus (64x42cm-25x17in) s.d.1906 gouache. 21-May-3 Sotheby's, London #165/R est:5000-7000

ROUBILLE, Auguste (1872-1955) French

Works on paper

£288 $453 €450 Femme au sac (38x20cm-15x8in) s.d.1911 chl col crayon. 20-Nov-2 Claude Boisgirard, Paris #25/R

ROUBOS, Leon (1959-) Australian

£1400 $2254 €2100 Pedestrian crossing (135x179cm-53x70in) s.d.1998 prov. 6-May-3 Christie's, Melbourne #324a est:1500-2500 (A.D 3500)

ROUBTZOFF, Alexandre (1884-1949) French?

£1361 $2163 €2000 Le Belvedere, Tunis (18x28cm-7x11in) s.i.d.1917 canvas on cardboard. 24-Mar-3 Rabourdin & Choppin de Janvry, Paris #113/R est:2000-2500

£1701 $2704 €2500 Une rue de la medina, Tunis (27x17cm-11x7in) s.i.d.1914 canvas on cardboard. 24-Mar-3 Rabourdin & Choppin de Janvry, Paris #106/R est:2500-3000

£1701 $2704 €2500 Rue animee a Sfax (27x18cm-11x7in) s.i.d.1919 canvas on cardboard. 24-Mar-3 Rabourdin & Choppin de Janvry, Paris #114/R est:2000-2500

£2041 $3245 €3000 Juan les Pins (21x29cm-8x11in) s.i.d.sept.1932 canvas on cardboard. 24-Mar-3 Rabourdin & Choppin de Janvry, Paris #122/R est:2500-3000

£2109 $3353 €3100 Le souk des etoffes (27x17cm-11x7in) s.d.1914 i.verso canvas on cardboard. 24-Mar-3 Rabourdin & Choppin de Janvry, Paris #108/R est:2500-3000

£2177 $3461 €3200 Cordoue (27x20cm-11x8in) s.i.d.1922 canvas on cardboard. 24-Mar-3 Rabourdin & Choppin de Janvry, Paris #116/R est:1800-2000

£3205 $5032 €5000 Tunis (20x29cm-8x11in) s.d.1918 canvas on cardboard. 10-Dec-2 Tajan, Paris #220/R

£3205 $5032 €5000 Medenine (17x27cm-7x11in) s.i.d.1918 canvas on cardboard. 10-Dec-2 Tajan, Paris #219/R

£3333 $5233 €5200 Bizerte (19x28cm-7x11in) s.d.1918 canvas on cardboard. 10-Dec-2 Tajan, Paris #221/R est:4000

£3401 $5408 €5000 Une rue animee a El Kef (17x27cm-7x11in) s.i.d.1915 canvas on cardboard. 24-Mar-3 Rabourdin & Choppin de Janvry, Paris #109/R est:2500-3000

£3718 $5838 €5800 Tunis (27x18cm-11x7in) s.i.d.1918 canvas on cardboard. 10-Dec-2 Tajan, Paris #222/R est:4000

£5986 $9518 €8800 Une rue devant la minaret (30x39cm-12x15in) s.i.d.1915 canvas on cardboard. 24-Mar-3 Rabourdin & Choppin de Janvry, Paris #111/R est:3000-4000

£6259 $9951 €9200 Devant la mosquee (18x28cm-7x11in) s.i.d.1915 canvas on cardboard. 24-Mar-3 Rabourdin & Choppin de Janvry, Paris #112/R est:2500-3000

£31973 $50837 €47000 La jeune fille pensive, Mahouba (97x79cm-38x31in) s.i.d.1915. 24-Mar-3 Rabourdin & Choppin de Janvry, Paris #110/R est:35000-40000

Works on paper

£1905 $3029 €2800 Orchestre de musiciens Arabes (48x63cm-19x25in) s.i.d.1933 chl htd W/C dr. 24-Mar-3 Rabourdin & Choppin de Janvry, Paris #103/R est:2800-3200

£2041 $3245 €3000 Scene de cafe, Tunis (39x49cm-15x19in) s.i.d.16 juillet 1929 black pencil col crayon dr. 24-Mar-3 Rabourdin & Choppin de Janvry, Paris #104/R est:3000-4000

£2041 $3245 €3000 Interieur eclaire a Nabeul le soir (49x31cm-19x12in) s.i.d.novembre 1928 chl col crayon dr. 24-Mar-3 Rabourdin & Choppin de Janvry, Paris #105/R est:3000-3500

£2381 $3786 €3500 Vue de Tunis a travers le balcon (63x47cm-25x19in) s.i.d.novembre 1929 pencil W/C dr. 24-Mar-3 Rabourdin & Choppin de Janvry, Paris #107/R est:3000-4000

£2692 $4227 €4200 Bashir ouvrier tunisien (53x44cm-21x17in) s.i.d.1944 W/C. 10-Dec-2 Tajan, Paris #223/R est:6000

ROUBY, Alfred (1849-1909) French
£1579 $2399 €2369 Still life of flowers (120x70cm-47x28in) s. 16-Aug-2 Lilla Bukowskis, Stockholm #266 est:16000-18000 (S.KR 23000)

ROUGE, Frederic (1867-1950) Swiss
Works on paper
£611 $954 €917 Devil in the desert (48x70cm-19x28in) s. col chk. 6-Nov-2 Dobiaschofsky, Bern #927/R (S.FR 1400)

ROUGELET, Benedict (1834-1894) French
Sculpture
£2600 $4030 €3900 Standing cherub holding a tambourine (60cm-24in) s. pat bronze circular red marble base exec.c.1880. 1-Oct-2 Christie's, London #244/R est:2500-3500

ROUGEMONT, Guy de (1935-) French
£2027 $3162 €3000 Or (150x197cm-59x78in) s.d.67 acrylic. 26-Mar-3 Millon & Associes, Paris #148/R
Sculpture
£1944 $3208 €2800 Les couverts d'harlequin (33x56x34cm-13x22x13in) s.num.195/200 cutlery 118 pieces Jagua casket. 1-Jul-3 Artcurial Briest, Paris #864/R est:3000-4000
Works on paper
£278 $441 €400 Poursuite de la lumiere, bleu (76x56cm-30x22in) s. col wax pastel. 29-Apr-3 Artcurial Briest, Paris #588
£448 $717 €650 Landscape (35x50cm-14x20in) s.i.d.64 W/C ink. 11-Mar-3 Christie's, Paris #430/R

ROUGHSEY, Dick (1924-1985) Australian
£286 $443 €429 Marnbill and Gin-Gin making fish traps (37x45cm-15x18in) s.d.79 board. 29-Oct-2 Lawson Menzies, Sydney #284 (A.D 800)
Works on paper
£894 $1413 €1296 Return from the hunt (44x60cm-17x24in) s.d.80 synthetic polymer. 22-Jul-3 Lawson Menzies, Sydney #107/R (A.D 2200)
£1949 $3022 €2924 Collecting oysters (30x40cm-12x16in) synthetic polymer paint board exhib. 3-Dec-2 Shapiro, Sydney #231/R est:3500-5000 (A.D 5400)

ROULET, Henry (1915-) Swiss
£694 $1118 €1006 Le petit train (33x55cm-13x22in) s. 9-May-3 Dobiaschofsky, Bern #212/R (S.FR 1500)

ROULIN, Felix (1931-) Belgian
Sculpture
£1931 $3090 €2800 Composition (200x54cm-79x21in) copper iron exec.c.1965 exhib. 15-Mar-3 De Vuyst, Lokeren #280/R est:3000-4000

ROULLET, Gaston (1847-1925) French
£3395 $5262 €5093 Indian encampment on the plains (46x81cm-18x32in) s. indis i. prov. 3-Dec-2 Joyner, Toronto #512 est:3000-4000 (C.D 8250)
Works on paper
£503 $800 €755 Breton coastal scene with lighthouse (36x43cm-14x17in) s. W/C. 22-Mar-3 New Orleans Auction, New Orleans #1158/R
£1042 $1698 €1500 Port d'Audierne a maree basse (25x37cm-10x15in) W/C. 19-Jul-3 Thierry & Lannon, Brest #77/R est:1200-1500
£1798 $2949 €2500 Mosquee de Sidi-Bou-Said (43x29cm-17x11in) s.i. W/C. 4-Jun-3 Tajan, Paris #198/R est:2000-2500

ROUNDS, George L (20th C) American
£323 $500 €485 Spring landscape (69x51cm-27x20in) s. painted c.1920. 8-Dec-2 Toomey, Oak Park #638/R

ROUNTREE, Harry (1878-1950) British
Works on paper
£360 $601 €522 Portrait of a Pekinese dog (30x41cm-12x16in) s. pastel. 20-Jun-3 Keys, Aylsham #315/R

ROUQUET, Jean Andre (1701-1758) French
Miniatures
£5500 $8910 €8250 Portrait of a nobleman, wearing ochre and scarlet robes (9cm-4in) s. shaped gilt metal frame. 22-May-3 Bonhams, New Bond Street #20/R est:2000-3000

ROUSAUD, Aristide (1868-1946) French
Sculpture
£1481 $2400 €2222 Egyptian revival figure of Cleopatra (66cm-26in) s. gold pat. bronze and marble with carved celluloid hands face. 25-Jan-3 Skinner, Boston #862/R

ROUSE, Frank (?) British
Works on paper
£950 $1539 €1378 Whitby Harbour with fishing boats (50x29cm-20x11in) s. W/C. 29-Jul-3 Holloways, Banbury #342

ROUSE, Robert William Arthur (fl.1883-1927) British
£580 $928 €870 Fishing boats in the estuary at low tide (28x46cm-11x18in) s. board. 14-Mar-3 Gardiner & Houlgate, Bath #161/R
£1400 $2184 €2100 Cattle resting in a meadow. Cattle watering in a meadow (46x91cm-18x36in) s.d.90. 7-Nov-2 Christie's, Kensington #151/R est:1500-2000

ROUSSE, Charles (attrib) (fl.1870-1890) British
Works on paper
£500 $770 €750 Estuary town, perhaps Whitby (26x37cm-10x15in) W/C pair. 22-Oct-2 Sworder & Son, Bishops Stortford #601/R

ROUSSE, Frank (fl.1897-1915) British
£440 $704 €660 Landing the fish (27x37cm-11x15in) s. i.verso. 11-Mar-3 David Duggleby, Scarborough #96
£540 $864 €810 Fishing boats (27x37cm-11x15in) s. i.verso. 11-Mar-3 David Duggleby, Scarborough #97
£850 $1360 €1275 Fishing fleet in Whitby Harbour with the Abbey in background (54x29cm-21x11in) s. 11-Mar-3 David Duggleby, Scarborough #43/R
Works on paper
£280 $440 €420 Harbour scene with figures (31x22cm-12x9in) s. W/C. 21-Nov-2 Tennants, Leyburn #661
£280 $454 €406 English sea front (23x33cm-9x13in) s. W/C. 1-Aug-3 Dee Atkinson & Harrison, Driffield #648
£300 $468 €450 Busy street scene with figures, horse and cart and cathedral (29x19cm-11x7in) s.d.1894 W/C. 10-Sep-2 David Duggleby, Scarborough #280/R
£300 $474 €450 Coastal study, near Whitby (23x33cm-9x13in) s. W/C. 24-Apr-3 Richardson & Smith, Whitby #187
£300 $501 €435 Ugthorpe Mill (23x33cm-9x13in) s. W/C. 26-Jun-3 Richardson & Smith, Whitby #557
£400 $620 €600 Fisherfolk on a beach (29x50cm-11x20in) s. W/C. 24-Sep-2 Bonhams, Knightsbridge #8/R
£420 $659 €630 Whitby harbour with a fisherman in a cobble in the foreground (19x36cm-7x14in) s.d.97 pencil W/C htd white. 19-Nov-2 Bonhams, Leeds #92
£440 $730 €660 Whitby Harbour in the abbey and St. Mary's church (24x34cm-9x13in) s. W/C. 10-Jun-3 Bonhams, Leeds #97
£480 $768 €720 Fishermen on the quayside (31x22cm-12x9in) s. W/C. 11-Mar-3 David Duggleby, Scarborough #78/R
£620 $967 €930 Fishergirl looking out to sea (26x41cm-10x16in) s. W/C. 10-Sep-2 David Duggleby, Scarborough #145
£650 $1014 €975 Whitby harbour (33x51cm-13x20in) s. W/C. 28-Mar-3 Dee Atkinson & Harrison, Driffield #672/R
£660 $1030 €990 Fishing boats moored by a quayside with figures (24x30cm-9x12in) s. W/C. 10-Sep-2 David Duggleby, Scarborough #116/R
£700 $1120 €1050 Whitby harbour east side (20x37cm-8x15in) s.d.97 W/C. 11-Mar-3 David Duggleby, Scarborough #84/R
£850 $1343 €1275 Whitby Harbour showing the Angel Hotel (36x53cm-14x21in) s.d.03 W/C. 24-Apr-3 Richardson & Smith, Whitby #145/R
£900 $1395 €1350 Fishermen in the harbour (28x46cm-11x18in) s. W/C. 25-Sep-2 Peter Wilson, Nantwich #109/R
£900 $1395 €1350 Fishing boats in the harbour (30x41cm-12x16in) s. W/C. 25-Sep-2 Peter Wilson, Nantwich #111/R
£900 $1422 €1350 Fishing boat moored in Whitby harbour (39x23cm-15x9in) s.d. W/C. 27-Nov-2 Peter Wilson, Nantwich #105/R
£920 $1454 €1380 Quayside, Whitby (15x25cm-6x10in) s. W/C. 24-Apr-3 Richardson & Smith, Whitby #236
£1000 $1560 €1500 Herring boats setting sail from Whitby harbour (29x43cm-11x17in) s. W/C. 10-Sep-2 David Duggleby, Scarborough #164 est:1000-1200
£1020 $1591 €1530 Fishing fleet, Scarborough (40x28cm-16x11in) s.d.98 W/C. 10-Sep-2 David Duggleby, Scarborough #102 est:700-1000
£1020 $1591 €1530 Fisherfolk sorting the catch on Pier Road, Whitby (25x44cm-10x17in) s. W/C. 10-Sep-2 David Duggleby, Scarborough #218 est:500-700
£1150 $1840 €1725 Fishing smacks by the quayside, Whitby (30x41cm-12x16in) s. W/C. 11-Mar-3 David Duggleby, Scarborough #82/R est:1200-1800
£1300 $2106 €1885 Whitby Sands (28x46cm-11x18in) s. W/C. 22-May-3 Richardson & Smith, Whitby #465

£1350 $2106 €2025 Putting out to sea. Unloading catch from beached fishing boats (26x44cm-10x17in) s. W/C pair. 10-Sep-2 David Duggleby, Scarborough #80/R est:1500-2000
£1400 $2170 €2100 Fisherfolk on market day (30x42cm-12x17in) s. W/C. 25-Sep-2 Peter Wilson, Nantwich #110/R est:1000-1500
£1450 $2248 €2175 Coastal town scene (29x54cm-11x21in) s. W/C. 25-Sep-2 Peter Wilson, Nantwich #132/R est:1000-1500
£1550 $2449 €2325 Whitby Harbour scenes (23x18cm-9x7in) one s. W/C pair. 24-Apr-3 Richardson & Smith, Whitby #231 est:1500-2000
£1600 $2496 €2400 View towards Tate Hill pier with fishing vessels (20x33cm-8x13in) s.d.1899 W/C. 10-Sep-2 David Duggleby, Scarborough #115/R est:1500-2000

ROUSSEAU, Adrien (19th C) French
£854 $1350 €1350 Paysanne abdl. mare (54x65cm-21x26in) s. 29-Nov-2 Drouot Estimations, Paris #51

ROUSSEAU, Albert (1908-1982) Canadian
£218 $340 €327 Ballerine (40x30cm-16x12in) s. isorel. 30-Jul-2 Iegor de Saint Hippolyte, Montreal #156 (C.D 540)
£387 $604 €581 Arbres (23x30cm-9x12in) s. cardboard. 30-Jul-2 Iegor de Saint Hippolyte, Montreal #149 (C.D 960)
£403 $657 €605 Journee hivernale (23x33cm-9x13in) s. i. verso. 12-Feb-3 Iegor de Saint Hippolyte, Montreal #163 (C.D 1000)
£514 $792 €771 Cartier Latin, Quebec (40x15cm-16x6in) s. i.verso. 22-Oct-2 Iegor de Saint Hippolyte, Montreal #92 (C.D 1250)
£528 $830 €792 Une rue a Quebec (30x41cm-12x16in) s. 10-Dec-2 Pinneys, Montreal #17 (C.D 1300)
£570 $850 €855 Maisons (40x51cm-16x20in) s. 26-Jun-2 Iegor de Saint Hippolyte, Montreal #80 (C.D 1300)
£597 $919 €896 Maison a la retraite (30x40cm-12x16in) s. cardboard. 22-Oct-2 Iegor de Saint Hippolyte, Montreal #93 (C.D 1450)
£610 $957 €915 Baie St Paul (41x51cm-16x20in) s. i.verso. 10-Dec-2 Pinneys, Montreal #137 (C.D 1500)
£677 $1057 €1016 St Urbain (23x30cm-9x12in) s. 30-Jul-2 Iegor de Saint Hippolyte, Montreal #150 (C.D 1680)
£738 $1151 €1107 Vieux chemin Ste Anne (46x61cm-18x24in) s. 10-Sep-2 Iegor de Saint Hippolyte, Montreal #103 (C.D 1800)
£741 $1141 €1112 Maisons (40x50cm-16x20in) s. cardboard. 22-Oct-2 Iegor de Saint Hippolyte, Montreal #94 (C.D 1800)
£1116 $1741 €1674 Houses in winter (40x56cm-16x22in) s. 25-Mar-3 Iegor de Saint Hippolyte, Montreal #124 (C.D 2600)
£1148 $1790 €1722 Charlevoix (46x61cm-18x24in) s. 10-Sep-2 Iegor de Saint Hippolyte, Montreal #102 (C.D 2800)
£1210 $1887 €1815 Au pied de Cap-Diamant (38x76cm-15x30in) s. i.verso. 30-Jul-2 Iegor de Saint Hippolyte, Montreal #148 (C.D 3000)
£1230 $1918 €1845 Montmagny, Qc (51x61cm-20x24in) s. 10-Sep-2 Iegor de Saint Hippolyte, Montreal #101 (C.D 3000)

Works on paper
£197 $294 €296 Arriere Coure (47x60cm-19x24in) s. W/C. 26-Jun-2 Iegor de Saint Hippolyte, Montreal #79/R (C.D 450)
£203 $319 €305 La vieille maison (38x56cm-15x22in) s. W/C. 12-Dec-2 Iegor de Saint Hippolyte, Montreal #92 (C.D 500)
£247 $380 €371 Nouvelle-Orleans (33x48cm-13x19in) s.d.1972 ink W/C. 22-Oct-2 Iegor de Saint Hippolyte, Montreal #95 (C.D 600)
£339 $528 €509 Paysage (37x54cm-15x21in) s. W/C. 30-Jul-2 Iegor de Saint Hippolyte, Montreal #152 (C.D 840)

ROUSSEAU, Camille (?) French?
£818 $1259 €1300 Beach scene (51x77cm-20x30in) s. canvas on board. 22-Oct-2 Durán, Madrid #682/R

ROUSSEAU, Helen (1896-1992) American
£2560 $4250 €3712 Rooftop view (61x76cm-24x30in) s. board. 11-Jun-3 Butterfields, San Francisco #4303/R est:3000-5000

ROUSSEAU, Henri (attrib) (19th C) French
£12329 $19233 €18000 Monastere sur la colline (18x27cm-7x11in) i. 14-Apr-3 Laurence Calmels, Paris #4001/R est:600

ROUSSEAU, Henri Emilien (1875-1933) French
£321 $500 €482 Morning (38x48cm-15x19in) s. 22-Sep-2 Susanin's, Chicago #5118/R
£385 $604 €600 Berger et son troupeau (23x33cm-9x13in) s. panel. 13-Dec-2 Piasa, Paris #66
£577 $906 €900 Cheval s'abreuvant (12x7cm-5x3in) s. panel. 16-Dec-2 Gros & Delettrez, Paris #310
£629 $981 €1000 Afrique du Nord, cheval s'abreuvant (12x7cm-5x3in) s. panel prov. 10-Oct-2 Ribeyre & Baron, Paris #60
£1603 $2516 €2500 Berger et son troupeau (38x55cm-15x22in) s.d.19. 13-Dec-2 Piasa, Paris #244/R
£2500 $3875 €3750 Outside the mosque (33x24cm-13x9in) s. board. 5-Dec-2 Christie's, Kensington #62/R est:2500-3500
£3800 $5928 €5700 Mounted standard bearer (20x16cm-8x6in) s. panel. 15-Oct-2 Sotheby's, London #190/R est:1500-2000

Works on paper
£9494 $15000 €15000 Caid et escorte (60x49cm-24x19in) s. W/C gouache. 28-Nov-2 Piasa, Paris #13/R est:15000-18000

ROUSSEAU, Henri Julien Felix (1844-1910) French
£31035 $49035 €45000 Promeneur dans la campagne avec fabrique de charbon de bois (17x33cm-7x13in) s. prov.exhib. 4-Apr-3 Tajan, Paris #101/R est:46000-55000

Works on paper
£4225 $7014 €6000 Interieur d'un debit de boisson (17x22cm-7x9in) s. pencil. 13-Jun-3 Rabourdin & Choppin de Janvry, Paris #135/R est:9000-10000

ROUSSEAU, J R (?) French
£2564 $4000 €3846 The crossing (43x53cm-17x21in) 20-Sep-2 Du Mouchelle, Detroit #2015/R est:3000-5000
£3500 $5845 €5250 Polish caravan (43x53cm-17x21in) s. 18-Jun-3 Christie's, Kensington #78/R est:4000-6000

ROUSSEAU, Jean Jacques (1861-1911) French
Works on paper
£317 $500 €500 Pecheurs au bord de fleuve (25x21cm-10x8in) W/C. 28-Nov-2 Tajan, Paris #200

ROUSSEAU, Philippe (1816-1887) French
£1519 $2370 €2400 Rouge gorge et peches (27x36cm-11x14in) s. panel. 20-Oct-2 Galerie de Chartres, Chartres #118 est:800-1200
£2436 $3849 €3800 Canard colvert, coq, tasse, miche de pain et verre (73x60cm-29x24in) s.d.72. 18-Nov-2 Tajan, Paris #33/R est:3000-4000
£2564 $4051 €4000 Ecureuil (24x32cm-9x13in) s. panel. 18-Nov-2 Sotheby's, Paris #53/R
£3147 $5255 €4500 Peches et rouge-gorge (28x36cm-11x14in) s. panel. 25-Jun-3 Sotheby's, Paris #75/R est:5000-7000

Works on paper
£2278 $3736 €3303 La Bruyere-Un coin de l'atelier (37x51cm-15x20in) s. W/C. 4-Jun-3 AB Stockholms Auktionsverk #2500/R est:25000-30000 (S.KR 29000)

ROUSSEAU, Theodore (1812-1867) French
£2308 $3577 €3600 Plaine aux abords de la foret de Fotainebleau (12x23cm-5x9in) mono. panel. 4-Dec-2 Libert, Castor, Paris #68/R
£9615 $15096 €15000 Paysage fluvial (27x40cm-11x16in) mono. paper on canvas. 16-Dec-2 Rabourdin & Choppin de Janvry, Paris #58/R est:5000
£9722 $16042 €14000 Paysage anime (27x41cm-11x16in) s. lit. 2-Jul-3 Artcurial Briest, Paris #627/R est:15000-20000
£20645 $32000 €30968 Coucher de soleil (25x33cm-10x13in) s. panel. 30-Oct-2 Christie's, Rockefeller NY #21/R est:30000-40000
£25316 $40000 €37974 Une chaumiere dans la Berry (23x32cm-9x13in) s. panel prov.lit. 24-Apr-3 Sotheby's, New York #30/R est:50000-70000
£53797 $85000 €80696 Bords de L'Oise (41x64cm-16x25in) s. panel lit. 24-Apr-3 Sotheby's, New York #14/R est:50000-70000

Works on paper
£2095 $3268 €3100 Arbre au cours d'eau (9x14cm-4x6in) st.mono. pen brown ink. 31-Mar-3 Rossini, Paris #23/R
£2986 $4748 €4300 Hilly landscape with trees (21x30cm-8x12in) mono. pen over pencil. 5-May-3 Ketterer, Munich #337/R est:1000-1200
£3300 $5116 €4950 View of cottages (26x36cm-10x14in) studio st. pencil prov. 3-Dec-2 Sotheby's, Olympia #259/R est:1000-1500
£7484 $11900 €11000 Paysage (12x15cm-5x6in) studio st. pen ink prov. 24-Mar-3 Tajan, Paris #162/R
£13924 $22000 €20886 Femme et enfant au bord d'un lac (22x34cm-9x13in) s. W/C htd white prov.lit. 24-Apr-3 Sotheby's, New York #29/R est:25000-35000

ROUSSEAU, Theodore (attrib) (1812-1867) French
£1154 $1800 €1731 Landscape at dusk (28x41cm-11x16in) bears sig. panel. 9-Oct-2 Doyle, New York #98 est:800-1200
£18239 $28088 €29000 Landscape with angler on bridge (41x63cm-16x25in) board. 28-Oct-2 Il Ponte, Milan #241/R est:2200

ROUSSEAU, Victor (1865-1954) Belgian
Sculpture
£949 $1500 €1424 Seated man with dog (2x29cm-1x11in) s. brown pat, bronze black metal base. 24-Apr-3 Sotheby's, New York #176/R est:3000-4000
£1154 $1812 €1800 La famille (36cm-14in) s. terracotta. 10-Dec-2 Vanderkindere, Brussels #149/R est:2000-3000
£1164 $1816 €1700 Jeune femme nue accoudee a un rocher (37cm-15in) s. dark pat bronze. 14-Apr-3 Horta, Bruxelles #95 est:2500-3500
£1295 $2072 €1800 Leda et le Cygne (22cm-9in) s. green pat bronze. 13-May-3 Vanderkindere, Brussels #157/R est:1250-1750
£1875 $2850 €2813 Instructum laborem (100cm-39in) s.i. brown pat bronze. 3-Jul-2 Naón & Cia, Buenos Aires #568 est:3200-3600

£4838	$7500	€7257	Man contemplating mask of Beethoven (41cm-16in) s. brown pat. bronze marble base prov.exhib. 29-Oct-2 Sotheby's, New York #215/R est:8000-12000
ROUSSEAUX, Fernand (1892-1971) Belgian			
£476	$757	€700	Le Bassin de la Sambre (75x90cm-30x35in) s. 18-Mar-3 Galerie Moderne, Brussels #512
ROUSSEL, A (19th C) French?			
£1549	$2494	€2200	Fishing women on the beach (66x89cm-26x35in) s.d.1859. 12-May-3 Bernaerts, Antwerp #204/R est:2000-3000
ROUSSEL, Charles-Emanuel-Joseph (1861-1936) French			
£641	$1006	€1000	Paysage (18x28cm-7x11in) s. panel painted 1920. 15-Dec-2 Eric Pillon, Calais #10/R
£705	$1107	€1100	Petite maison sur la lande (17x27cm-7x11in) s. panel painted 1904. 15-Dec-2 Eric Pillon, Calais #9/R
£719	$1151	€1000	Marche aux boeufs a Castelnau (9x14cm-4x6in) studio st.verso panel. 18-May-3 Eric Pillon, Calais #10/R
£769	$1208	€1200	Marche aux boeufs a Castelnau (9x14cm-4x6in) studio st. panel. 15-Dec-2 Eric Pillon, Calais #5/R
£769	$1208	€1200	Bateaux en mer au claire de lune (18x11cm-7x4in) s. panel. 15-Dec-2 Eric Pillon, Calais #13/R
£833	$1308	€1300	Scene de plage (8x13cm-3x5in) s. panel. 15-Dec-2 Eric Pillon, Calais #8/R
£897	$1409	€1400	Bord de riviere (35x27cm-14x11in) s. 15-Dec-2 Eric Pillon, Calais #6/R
£1154	$1812	€1800	Berck le matin (10x14cm-4x6in) s. panel. 15-Dec-2 Eric Pillon, Calais #4/R
£2230	$3568	€3100	Femmes et enfants assis sur la plage (8x14cm-3x6in) s. panel. 18-May-3 Eric Pillon, Calais #9/R
£3269	$5133	€5100	Bateaux en mer (33x46cm-13x18in) s. 15-Dec-2 Eric Pillon, Calais #3/R
£3846	$6038	€6000	Femmes et enfants sur la plage (8x14cm-3x6in) s. panel. 15-Dec-2 Eric Pillon, Calais #2/R
ROUSSEL, Ker Xavier (1867-1944) French			
£5743	$8959	€8500	Scene antique (65x81cm-26x32in) 26-Mar-3 Millon & Associes, Paris #79/R est:9000
£7643	$11924	€12000	Apres-midi des faunes (79x100cm-31x39in) s. panel. 10-Nov-2 Eric Pillon, Calais #43/R
Prints			
£1923	$3019	€3000	Deux femmes dans un paysage (220x385cm-87x152in) s. lithograph. 12-Dec-2 Piasa, Paris #144/R
£2564	$4000	€3846	L'education du chien (58x41cm-23x16in) s.num.76 col lithograph edition of 100. 5-Nov-2 Christie's, Rockefeller NY #21/R est:5000-8000
£4487	$7045	€7000	Deux baigneuses (250x410cm-98x161in) s. lithograph. 12-Dec-2 Piasa, Paris #145/R
£5449	$8554	€8500	Paysages (215x320cm-85x126in) s. lithograph 6 plates. 12-Dec-2 Piasa, Paris #142
Works on paper			
£256	$397	€400	Nus de profil (32x37cm-13x15in) init. chl dr prov. 9-Dec-2 Beaussant & Lefèvre, Paris #91
£269	$417	€420	Etude pour le Palais des Nations, Geneve (30x46cm-12x18in) bears sig. chl stump dr prov. 9-Dec-2 Beaussant & Lefèvre, Paris #100
£288	$447	€450	Repos du modele (37x49cm-15x19in) bears sig. chl stump dr prov. 9-Dec-2 Beaussant & Lefèvre, Paris #94
£288	$447	€450	Tour en ruines (29x46cm-11x18in) bears sig. pastel prov. 9-Dec-2 Beaussant & Lefèvre, Paris #87
£321	$497	€500	Modele nu assis (30x22cm-12x9in) bears sig. chl stup dr prov. 9-Dec-2 Beaussant & Lefèvre, Paris #95
£353	$546	€550	Scene mythologique (40x50cm-16x20in) init. chl dr prov. 9-Dec-2 Beaussant & Lefèvre, Paris #90
£385	$596	€600	Clocher derriere les remparts (29x46cm-11x18in) init. chl htd pastel dr prov. 9-Dec-2 Beaussant & Lefèvre, Paris #88
£417	$646	€650	Saint Jean-Baptiste (20x18cm-8x7in) init. sanguine dr prov. 9-Dec-2 Beaussant & Lefèvre, Paris #103
£449	$696	€700	Modele assis (31x23cm-12x9in) init. pastel prov. 9-Dec-2 Beaussant & Lefèvre, Paris #86/R
£513	$795	€800	Etude pour jardin (44x32cm-17x13in) init. chl stump dr prov. 9-Dec-2 Beaussant & Lefèvre, Paris #97/R
£566	$883	€900	Nu (23x30cm-9x12in) mono. chl prov. 11-Oct-2 Binoche, Paris #119
£577	$894	€900	Etude pour jardin (45x33cm-18x13in) bears sig. chl stump dr prov. 9-Dec-2 Beaussant & Lefèvre, Paris #98/R
£833	$1317	€1200	Sous-bois (44x67cm-17x26in) s. chl stump. 25-Apr-3 Piasa, Paris #36
£839	$1401	€1200	Etude du nu (36x26cm-14x10in) s. pastel chl. 26-Jun-3 Tajan, Paris #115
£3050	$5093	€4300	Arbres d'hiver (30x46cm-12x18in) s. pastel prov. 23-Jun-3 Claude Boisgirard, Paris #62/R est:3000-4000
£3846	$6038	€6000	Idylle (15x21cm-6x8in) pastel exec.1941 prov.exhib. 10-Dec-2 Piasa, Paris #259 est:2000
£5128	$8051	€8000	Surprise (22x33cm-9x13in) pastel prov.exhib. 10-Dec-2 Piasa, Paris #258/R
ROUSSEL, Pierre (1927-1995) French			
£600	$936	€900	Olivier et Jacques (94x76cm-37x30in) s. 11-Apr-3 Keys, Aylsham #493
ROUSSEL, Theodore (1847-1926) British			
£550	$902	€825	Fowey, Cornwall (26x35cm-10x14in) panel. 3-Jun-3 Sotheby's, Olympia #25/R
£1000	$1640	€1500	Garden at Belfield House (26x35cm-10x14in) 3-Jun-3 Sotheby's, Olympia #30/R est:1200-1800
Prints			
£2051	$3200	€3077	Anemonies (12x8cm-5x3in) s.i. col aquatint etching edition of 17. 7-Nov-2 Swann Galleries, New York #488/R est:4000-6000
ROUSSELET, Gilles (1610-1686) French			
Works on paper			
£696	$1100	€1100	Reclining male nude in landscape (16x21cm-6x8in) ochre. 29-Nov-2 Bassenge, Berlin #5474/R
ROUSSELET, Louis (1845-1929) French			
Photographs			
£60000	$97200	€90000	Voyage dans l'Inde. i. albumen prints 155 in two albums prov.lit. 21-May-3 Christie's, London #96/R est:60000-80000
ROUSSET, Jules (1840-?) French			
£774	$1200	€1161	Portrait of a man (53x38cm-21x15in) s.d.1871 oil chl prov. 29-Oct-2 Sotheby's, New York #63/R est:800-1000
ROUSSIL, Robert (1925-) Canadian			
Sculpture			
£2275	$3548	€3413	Untitled (114cm-45in) s. wood. 25-Mar-3 Iegor de Saint Hippolyte, Montreal #125/R (C.D 5300)
ROUSSOFF, Alexandre Nicolaievitch (1844-1928) Russian			
£1373	$2251	€2100	Venice (61x38cm-24x15in) s. 9-Feb-3 Bukowskis, Helsinki #429/R est:1000
Works on paper			
£505	$798	€758	Venetian scene with gondolas (60x39cm-24x15in) s. W/C. 27-Nov-2 Falkkloos, Malmo #77821/R (S.KR 7200)
£600	$936	€900	Figures conversing on a street in Cairo (34x19cm-13x7in) s. W/C over pencil htd bodycol. 15-Oct-2 Sotheby's, London #230/R
£1000	$1560	€1500	Cairo, Egypt (35x23cm-14x9in) s.i.d.1891 pencil W/C prov. 19-Sep-2 Christie's, Kensington #139/R est:500-700
ROUX, Carl (1826-1894) German			
£1189	$1737	€1784	Farmstead with cows and herder (40x76cm-16x30in) s. 17-Jun-2 Philippe Schuler, Zurich #4360/R est:3000-5000 (S.FR 2700)
ROUX, Constantin le (?-1909) French			
Works on paper			
£481	$750	€722	Homme dans u cafe (45x58cm-18x23in) s. chl exec.c.1900. 19-Sep-2 Swann Galleries, New York #735/R
ROUX, Eugene le (?) ?			
£2000	$3200	€3000	Connisseur (54x36cm-21x14in) s. 11-Mar-3 Bonhams, Knightsbridge #316/R est:2000-3000
ROUX, Francois (1927-) French?			
£243	$380	€365	Rocky outcrop with rain showers in the distance (59x71cm-23x28in) s.d.65 board. 11-Nov-2 Stephan Welz, Johannesburg #595 (SA.R 3800)
ROUX, Georges (?-1929) French			
£3336	$5404	€4837	Woman reading (72x53cm-28x21in) s.d.1884. 25-May-3 Uppsala Auktionskammare, Uppsala #95/R est:25000-30000 (S.KR 43000)
ROUX, Hippolyte (1852-?) French			
£475	$741	€750	Cosmos dans un vase chinois (35x23cm-14x9in) s. panel. 20-Oct-2 Galerie de Chartres, Chartres #119
ROUX, Louis (1817-1903) French			
Works on paper			
£346	$533	€550	Brick vu sous deux angles (23x29cm-9x11in) s. W/C gouache. 27-Oct-2 Lesieur & Le Bars, Le Havre #191
£1700	$2822	€2465	Spanish brigantine Nicolas amidst Mediterranean craft (45x63cm-18x25in) s.i. pencil pen ink W/C htd white. 12-Jun-3 Christie's, London #566/R est:1000-1500

£1900 $3154 €2755 Spanish trading xebec Antonieta off Marseilles (44x60cm-17x24in) s.i.d.1885 pen ink W/C htd white. 12-Jun-3 Christie's, London #570/R est:1500-2000
£2000 $3320 €2900 Spanish xebec Libertad in the Mediterranean (32x50cm-13x20in) s.i.d.1886 pencil pen ink W/C htd bodycol. 12-Jun-3 Christie's, London #571/R est:1500-2500
£2600 $4316 €3770 Spanish trading schooner Roberto heading into Marseilles (46x65cm-18x26in) s.i. pencil pen ink W/C. 12-Jun-3 Christie's, London #568/R est:1500-2500
£2949 $4571 €4600 Hamburg bark - Justine Helene (50x72cm-20x28in) s.i.d.1888 W/C bodycol over pen lit. 7-Dec-2 Ketterer, Hamburg #20/R est:2000-2500

ROUX, Oswald (1880-1960) Austrian
£2252 $3670 €3400 Worshippers (82x116cm-32x46in) s. panel. 28-Jan-3 Dorotheum, Vienna #54/R est:3300-4000

ROUX, Paul (?-1918) French
Works on paper
£248 $400 €372 Fountains la Nonnes (51x36cm-20x14in) s.i. W/C. 19-Jan-3 Jeffery Burchard, Florida #134/R
£350 $546 €550 Clairefontaine (66x99cm-26x39in) s. pastel cardboard. 6-Nov-2 Gioffredo, Nice #59/R

ROUX, Tony Georges (1894-1928) French
£6803 $10816 €10000 Portrait of lady with stick and hat (200x155cm-79x61in) s. 18-Mar-3 Finarte, Milan #16/R

ROUXEL, Jacques (20th C) French?
Works on paper
£276 $436 €400 Shadok (25x32cm-10x13in) s.i.d.90 gouache. 7-Apr-3 Claude Aguttes, Neuilly #183/R

ROVEA, Giorgio (19th C) Italian
£25926 $42000 €38889 Still life of fruit (80x61cm-31x24in) s. 23-Jan-3 Sotheby's, New York #243/R est:35000

ROVERE, Giovanni Mauro della (1575-1640) Italian
Works on paper
£6790 $11000 €10185 Luxury (28x20cm-11x8in) pen ink wash over chk htd white. 21-Jan-3 Sotheby's, New York #69/R est:5000

ROVERO, G (?) ?
£400 $624 €600 Baptism of Christ (55x88cm-22x35in) s. 10-Sep-2 Bonhams, Knightsbridge #278/R

ROVERS, Jos (1893-1976) Dutch
£590 $974 €850 Still life with rhododendrons in a pitcher (80x80cm-31x31in) s. 1-Jul-3 Christie's, Amsterdam #326
£694 $1146 €1000 Still life with grapes in a bowl (80x65cm-31x26in) s. 1-Jul-3 Christie's, Amsterdam #321
£694 $1146 €1000 Nude in a blue chair (64x50cm-25x20in) s. 1-Jul-3 Christie's, Amsterdam #325/R
£3819 $6302 €5500 Salome (95x150cm-37x59in) s. 1-Jul-3 Christie's, Amsterdam #320/R est:2000-3000

ROWAN, Marian Ellis (1848-1922) Australian
£321 $508 €482 Helianthus (43x26cm-17x10in) s. board. 18-Nov-2 Joel, Victoria #360 est:1200-1500 (A.D 900)
Works on paper
£383 $602 €575 Flower study (36x25cm-14x10in) gouache. 15-Apr-3 Lawson Menzies, Sydney #216/R est:1200-1800 (A.D 1000)
£383 $602 €575 Flower study (36x25cm-14x10in) gouache. 15-Apr-3 Lawson Menzies, Sydney #217/R est:1200-1800 (A.D 1000)
£457 $750 €686 Pine branches with caterpillar (53x38cm-21x15in) s. W/C gouache htd white paper on board. 5-Feb-3 Doyle, New York #55/R
£465 $740 €698 Christmas bush (51x34cm-20x13in) s. W/C. 5-May-3 Sotheby's, Melbourne #274 (A.D 1200)
£714 $1107 €1071 Mabenaria (53x36cm-21x14in) s. gouache. 29-Oct-2 Lawson Menzies, Sydney #120/R (A.D 2000)
£1000 $1610 €1500 Caterpillars (48x34cm-19x13in) gouache. 6-May-3 Christie's, Melbourne #394/R est:2500-3500 (A.D 2500)
£1071 $1650 €1607 Sweet pitcher plant (53x38cm-21x15in) s. gouache. 3-Sep-2 Shapiro, Sydney #357/R est:3000-5000 (A.D 3000)
£1116 $1829 €1674 Flannel flowers (49x34cm-19x13in) s.d. W/C bodycol. 4-Jun-3 Deutscher-Menzies, Melbourne #327/R est:3000-4000 (A.D 2800)
£1143 $1760 €1715 Native tree - Indian bean tree (54x38cm-21x15in) s. gouache. 3-Sep-2 Shapiro, Sydney #353/R est:3000-5000 (A.D 3200)
£1240 $1972 €1860 Flannel flowers (54x36cm-21x14in) s. W/C. 5-May-3 Sotheby's, Melbourne #304/R est:3000-5000 (A.D 3200)
£1429 $2214 €2144 Floral leaved orchid (53x36cm-21x14in) s. gouache. 29-Oct-2 Lawson Menzies, Sydney #121/R est:4000-6000 (A.D 4000)
£1533 $2406 €2300 Red cedar (53x63cm-21x25in) s. gouache. 15-Apr-3 Lawson Menzies, Sydney #211/R est:4000-6000 (A.D 4000)
£1533 $2406 €2300 Three flowers (53x38cm-21x15in) s. gouache. 15-Apr-3 Lawson Menzies, Sydney #212/R est:4000-6000 (A.D 4000)

ROWBOTHAM, Charles (1856-1921) British
Works on paper
£400 $624 €600 Children and cattle at water's edge (25x43cm-10x17in) s. W/C. 25-Mar-3 Gorringes, Bexhill #1211
£400 $624 €600 Italian lake scene with figures and horse-drawn cart (15x31cm-6x12in) s.d.1903 W/C bodycol. 10-Apr-3 Tennants, Leyburn #861
£447 $707 €648 Lago di Mergazzo (20x47cm-8x19in) s.d. W/C. 22-Jul-3 Lawson Menzies, Sydney #292/R est:1200-1500 (A.D 1100)
£450 $702 €675 Italian lake scene (12x19cm-5x7in) s. pencil W/C. 26-Mar-3 Sotheby's, Olympia #81/R
£460 $736 €690 Walberswick, Suffolk (30x59cm-12x23in) s.i.d.1886 W/C. 11-Mar-3 Bonhams, Oxford #32
£520 $842 €780 Father and children outside a cottage (32x23cm-13x9in) s. W/C. 21-Jan-3 Bonhams, Knightsbridge #161/R
£550 $852 €825 Capri (12x19cm-5x7in) s.d.1906 W/C bodycol. 3-Dec-2 Sotheby's, Olympia #71/R
£550 $902 €825 Figures on a track beside a lake (23x18cm-9x7in) s.d.1881 pencil W/C htd white. 5-Jun-3 Christie's, Kensington #911/R
£580 $951 €870 Castel a Mare, Sicily (13x19cm-5x7in) s. pencil W/C bodycol. 5-Jun-3 Christie's, Kensington #940/R
£680 $1068 €1020 View of Ischia, Bay of Naples (16x21cm-6x8in) s.i. pencil W/C htd white. 16-Apr-3 Christie's, Kensington #1080/R
£680 $1068 €1020 Figures with a donkey resting by the steps overlooking the bay (16x21cm-6x8in) s.i. pencil W/C htd white. 16-Apr-3 Christie's, Kensington #1084/R
£700 $1092 €1050 Figures on a coastal path with a goat (15x28cm-6x11in) s. pencil W/C htd white. 17-Oct-2 Christie's, Kensington #101/R
£700 $1092 €1050 Alizo on lake D'Orta, Italy (12x19cm-5x7in) s. W/C. 9-Oct-2 Woolley & Wallis, Salisbury #108/R
£700 $1085 €1050 Lake Lago, northern Italy (12x19cm-5x7in) s. pencil W/C htd white. 4-Dec-2 Christie's, Kensington #84/R
£800 $1240 €1200 Continental landscape with figures and goats on a path (14x27cm-6x11in) s. pencil W/C htd white. 4-Dec-2 Christie's, Kensington #81/R
£800 $1240 €1200 Children resting by a coastal path beside the Bay of Naples (16x30cm-6x12in) s. pencil W/C htd white. 4-Dec-2 Christie's, Kensington #82/R
£800 $1248 €1200 Italian sea view with figures and goat in foreground (15x28cm-6x11in) s.d.1905 W/C. 10-Apr-3 Brightwells, Leominster #931
£800 $1320 €1160 Cannero, Lake Maggiore (23x48cm-9x19in) s. W/C bodycol. 3-Jul-3 Duke & Son, Dorchester #131/R
£800 $1320 €1160 Walberswick, Suffolk (30x59cm-12x23in) s.i.d.1886 W/C. 1-Jul-3 Bonhams, Norwich #107/R
£825 $1295 €1238 Veege, Switzerland (12x18cm-5x7in) s. W/C. 21-Nov-2 Clevedon Sale Rooms #213
£850 $1403 €1233 At Syracuse (23x48cm-9x19in) s. W/C bodycol. 3-Jul-3 Duke & Son, Dorchester #132
£900 $1413 €1350 Splatz Castle, Lake Thun, Switzerland (12x19cm-5x7in) s. W/C. 21-Nov-2 Clevedon Sale Rooms #212/R
£900 $1440 €1350 At the quay (28x40cm-11x16in) bears studio st.verso W/C. 11-Mar-3 Bonhams, New Bond Street #86/R
£1000 $1550 €1500 Figures on a path in a coastal landscape (26x68cm-10x27in) s.d.1893 pencil W/C htd white. 4-Dec-2 Christie's, Kensington #83/R est:1000-1500
£1000 $1670 €1450 On the Italian coast (24x19cm-9x7in) s.d.1891 pencil W/C htd white. 26-Jun-3 Mellors & Kirk, Nottingham #828/R est:800-1000
£1100 $1727 €1650 Bay of Spezia (12x18cm-5x7in) s. W/C. 21-Nov-2 Clevedon Sale Rooms #214 est:500-750
£1100 $1760 €1650 Walking beside a river, Switzerland (24x18cm-9x7in) s.i.d.1884 W/C bodycol. 11-Mar-3 Bonhams, New Bond Street #84/R est:800-1200
£1100 $1837 €1595 Weggis with Mount Pilatus in the distance. Lake Lucerne, Switzerland (13x18cm-5x7in) s.d.1916 W/C bodycol pair. 24-Jun-3 Bonhams, Knightsbridge #54/R est:800-12000
£1500 $2340 €2250 Near Grindelwald, Bernese Oberland. Switzerland, the Junfrau, Switzerland (13x18cm-5x7in) s. W/C bodycol pair. 5-Nov-2 Bonhams, New Bond Street #18/R est:1500-2000
£1800 $2808 €2700 Quay, Savona, Northern Italy (17x30cm-7x12in) s. pencil W/C gum arabic htd white. 17-Oct-2 Christie's, Kensington #100/R est:1000-1500
£1900 $2964 €2850 Figures coming from market on the Italian Coast (14x27cm-6x11in) s. pencil W/C htd white. 17-Oct-2 Christie's, Kensington #103/R est:1000-1500

£2000 $3120 €3000 Salerno, the Bay of Naples, Italy (13x19cm-5x7in) s. i.verso W/C bodycol. 5-Nov-2 Bonhams, New Bond Street #8/R est:800-1200
£2500 $3900 €3750 Italian peasants resting on a stone terrace path overlooking a bay (41x59cm-16x23in) s.d.1902 pencil W/C. 17-Oct-2 Christie's, Kensington #102/R est:2500-3500

ROWBOTHAM, Claude (1864-1949) British
Works on paper
£250 $408 €363 Isola pescatori, Lake Maggiore (19x13cm-7x5in) s. W/C gouache. 17-Jul-3 Tennants, Leyburn #724

ROWBOTHAM, Thomas Charles Leeson (1823-1875) British
£8861 $14000 €14000 View of Benares (77x134cm-30x53in) s.i.d.1872 tempera card on panel. 26-Nov-2 Christie's, Rome #226/R est:6000-9000
Works on paper
£340 $537 €510 Alpine scene depicting horse and cart with figures along a mountain trail (8x10cm-3x4in) init.d.1869 W/C. 24-Apr-3 Richardson & Smith, Whitby #118/R
£400 $648 €600 Fisherfolk on the beach (16x45cm-6x18in) s.d.1859 W/C. 21-May-3 Bonhams, Knightsbridge #205/R
£520 $822 €780 Italian alpine landscape with figure and a cart (16x23cm-6x9in) s.d.1872 W/C bodycol. 7-Apr-3 Bonhams, Bath #4
£520 $868 €754 On the lake of Como (16x29cm-6x11in) s.d.1875 i.verso W/C. 17-Jun-3 Anderson & Garland, Newcastle #192/R
£1000 $1560 €1500 Coast of Italy (20x48cm-8x19in) s.d.1860 pencil W/C htd white scratching out. 17-Oct-2 Christie's, Kensington #96/R est:1200-1800

ROWBOTHAM, Thomas Charles Leeson (attrib) (1823-1875) British
Works on paper
£280 $465 €420 View of Heideleberg and the Neckar (64x88cm-25x35in) W/C. 10-Jun-3 Sworder & Son, Bishops Stortford #516/R
£450 $701 €675 View of a small alpine town with lake beyond (44x70cm-17x28in) s.d.1876 pencil W/C htd white. 19-Sep-2 Christie's, Kensington #131

ROWBOTHAM, Thomas Leeson (snr) (1783-1853) British
£600 $948 €900 Construction of East Pier, Whitby (23x33cm-9x13in) s.i.d.1848. 24-Apr-3 Richardson & Smith, Whitby #135/R

ROWDEN, Thomas (1842-1926) British
Works on paper
£266 $421 €399 Highland landscape with sheep (21x40cm-8x16in) s. W/C. 30-Nov-2 Goteborg Auktionsverk, Sweden #219/R (S.KR 3800)
£340 $568 €493 Cattle watering (23x51cm-9x20in) s.d.99. 18-Jun-3 Andrew Hartley, Ilkley #1001
£410 $668 €615 Cattle grazing (23x38cm-9x15in) i. W/C. 29-Jan-3 Brightwells, Leominster #841
£444 $738 €644 Highland cattle watering (53x37cm-21x15in) s. W/C. 16-Jun-3 Waddingtons, Toronto #64 est:700-900 (C.D 1000)
£520 $811 €780 Downs, Budleigh Salteron, with cattle grazing (19x38cm-7x15in) s. W/C. 6-Nov-2 Bonhams, Chester #472
£520 $848 €780 Cattle watering (25x48cm-10x19in) s.d.1888 W/C. 13-Feb-3 David Lay, Penzance #354
£550 $919 €798 Moorland scene with cattle (20x36cm-8x14in) s. W/C. 20-Jun-3 Keys, Aylsham #492/R
£580 $945 €870 Cattle on Dartmoor (40x75cm-16x30in) s.d.86 W/C. 29-Jan-3 Sotheby's, Olympia #149/R
£580 $945 €870 Sheep resting by a river (23x48cm-9x19in) s.d.1888 W/C. 13-Feb-3 David Lay, Penzance #353/R
£600 $936 €900 Perronporth near Newquay, Cornwall (31x55cm-12x22in) s. W/C. 6-Nov-2 Bonhams, Chester #471
£600 $978 €900 Rural scenes (13x23cm-5x9in) s.d.87 W/C pair. 7-Feb-3 Dee Atkinson & Harrison, Driffield #746
£700 $1085 €1050 The Lyd, Dartmoor, moorland landscape (22x51cm-9x20in) s.d.94 W/C. 1-Nov-2 Moore Allen & Innocent, Cirencester #193/R
£760 $1201 €1140 Dartmoor ponies beside a steam (22x52cm-9x20in) s. W/C htd white. 7-Apr-3 Bonhams, Bath #25/R
£800 $1248 €1200 Cattle by a Devon stream (36x51cm-14x20in) s.d.1886 W/C. 17-Oct-2 David Lay, Penzance #1207/R
£800 $1232 €1200 Dartmoor, South Devon, sheep and cattle in a landscape (23x54cm-9x21in) s.d.92 W/C. 22-Oct-2 Bonhams, Bath #215
£1000 $1540 €1500 Ponies on Dartmoor (45x76cm-18x30in) s.d.1900 W/C. 22-Oct-2 Bonhams, Knightsbridge #54/R est:1000-1500

ROWE, E Arthur (1863-1922) British
Works on paper
£260 $413 €390 Fountain in an ornamental garden (37x24cm-15x9in) s. W/C. 18-Mar-3 Rosebery Fine Art, London #722
£440 $713 €660 Mediterranean coastal landscape scene depicting a town, mountains beyond (24x25cm-9x10in) s.d.1905 W/C. 23-Jan-3 Ambrose, Loughton #805/R
£1274 $2000 €1911 Salisbury from the meadows (30x46cm-12x18in) s.d.93 i.d.Sep 1893 verso W/C on board. 10-Dec-2 Doyle, New York #165/R est:3000-4000
£1600 $2496 €2400 Quiet read at Melbourne (29x44cm-11x17in) s.d.94 W/C. 8-Oct-2 Sotheby's, Olympia #422 est:2000-3000

ROWE, Sydney Grant (1861-1928) British
£556 $917 €800 In the hayfield (38x54cm-15x21in) s. s.i.verso exhib. 1-Jul-3 Christie's, Amsterdam #44
£1950 $3081 €2925 Shepherd, sheep and a dog in a country lane (60x90cm-24x35in) s. 2-Dec-2 Bonhams, Bath #136/R est:1200-1800
£2300 $3634 €3450 Cattle in an orchard (60x90cm-24x35in) s. 2-Dec-2 Bonhams, Bath #135/R est:1200-1800

ROWELL, John Thomas (1894-1973) Australian
£320 $515 €464 Cane fields (28x39cm-11x15in) s. 12-May-3 Joel, Victoria #359 (A.D 800)
£321 $508 €482 Under the old river gums (48x58cm-19x23in) board. 18-Nov-2 Joel, Victoria #397 est:800-1200 (A.D 900)
£4800 $7728 €6960 Mornington (24x39cm-9x15in) s. 12-May-3 Joel, Victoria #279/R est:7000-9000 (A.D 12000)
£4800 $7728 €6960 Holiday time (22x29cm-9x11in) s. 12-May-3 Joel, Victoria #292/R est:7000-9000 (A.D 12000)

ROWLAND, Stanley J (20th C) American
£2963 $4800 €4445 Day of racing (114x170cm-45x67in) s.d.1930 board. 21-Jan-3 Christie's, Rockefeller NY #397/R

ROWLAND, William (20th C) British
£350 $557 €525 Holmes winter, horse racing scenes (14x30cm-6x12in) s. panel pair. 2-Mar-3 Lots Road, London #351
£500 $790 €750 Over the fence. Final furlong (15x29cm-6x11in) s. board pair. 28-Nov-2 Christie's, Kensington #193/R

ROWLANDSON, George Derville (1861-?) British
£3026 $4901 €4388 Hunting party with dogs (36x46cm-14x18in) mono. 26-May-3 Bukowskis, Stockholm #230/R est:25000-30000 (S.KR 39000)
£4000 $6320 €6000 Highwaymen (51x76cm-20x30in) s. 2-Dec-2 Sotheby's, London #19/R est:4000-6000

ROWLANDSON, Thomas (1756-1827) British
Works on paper
£260 $434 €377 Jealous husband (27x20cm-11x8in) pen ink W/C. 25-Jun-3 Bonhams, Bury St Edmunds #476
£400 $668 €580 Mother and child with a lamb (20x16cm-8x6in) pen ink W/C. 25-Jun-3 Bonhams, Bury St Edmunds #472/R
£400 $668 €580 Female figures, a composition (14x22cm-6x9in) s. pen ink W/C. 25-Jun-3 Bonhams, Bury St Edmunds #473/R
£400 $660 €580 Job and his comforters (14x14cm-6x6in) indis.i. pen ink. 2-Jul-3 Sotheby's, Olympia #170/R
£440 $686 €660 Manor house (16x22cm-6x9in) pencil red ink. 25-Mar-3 Bonhams, Knightsbridge #71/R
£480 $754 €720 Man on horseback in a village street (14x23cm-6x9in) pen ink W/C prov. 19-Nov-2 Bonhams, Leeds #54
£500 $776 €750 Gentle emetic (16x12cm-6x5in) i. ink W/C. 3-Dec-2 Sotheby's, Olympia #25/R
£550 $847 €825 Destitute (30x24cm-12x9in) s. W/C. 23-Oct-2 Hamptons Fine Art, Godalming #85/R
£600 $948 €900 Distressed mariners (23x21cm-9x8in) s.i. pen ink W/C over pencil. 28-Nov-2 Sotheby's, London #272
£600 $954 €900 Fine wine (18x15cm-7x6in) s. ink wash dr. 30-Apr-3 Halls, Shrewsbury #255/R
£750 $1185 €1125 Disgruntled squire setting off on his pony (16x13cm-6x5in) W/C over pen ink. 26-Nov-2 Bonhams, Knightsbridge #42/R
£750 $1238 €1088 Horseman at an inn (14x22cm-6x9in) pen grey brown ink W/C over pencil. 2-Jul-3 Sotheby's, Olympia #168/R
£780 $1248 €1170 Susannah and the elders (23x28cm-9x11in) pen black ink grey wash prov. 11-Mar-3 Bonhams, New Bond Street #16/R
£800 $1320 €1160 Travellers outside an inn (14x23cm-6x9in) pen brown ink W/C over pencil. 2-Jul-3 Sotheby's, Olympia #169/R
£820 $1361 €1189 Tumblers (15x13cm-6x5in) W/C. 10-Jun-3 Louis Taylor, Stoke on Trent #948
£850 $1394 €1275 Stonebreaker (16x12cm-6x5in) pencil pen ink col wash. 6-Jun-3 Christie's, London #98/R
£850 $1352 €1275 Judgement of Paris (10x15cm-4x6in) pen ink W/C. 29-Apr-3 Gorringes, Lewes #2219
£900 $1431 €1350 At the coopers (17x12cm-7x5in) pen sepia ink wash over pencil. 19-Mar-3 Sotheby's, London #136/R
£900 $1440 €1350 Wagon at the village inn (17x23cm-7x9in) pen ink prov. 11-Mar-3 Bonhams, New Bond Street #20/R
£950 $1492 €1425 Figures outside an inn on the banks of the River Ouse, York (23x36cm-9x14in) i. pencil W/C prov. 19-Nov-2 Bonhams, Leeds #53

£950	$1473	€1425	Greenwich Hospital and One Tree Hill Greenwich Park (16x9cm-6x4in) s.i. pencil pen black ink W/C. 4-Dec-2 Christie's, Kensington #114
£1000	$1590	€1500	Close shave (13x13cm-5x5in) pen ink W/C. 29-Apr-3 Gorringes, Lewes #2210
£1200	$1932	€1800	Two young gentlemen quarreling outside Grant's Bagnio (14x22cm-6x9in) s. pencil ink pen W/C prov. 20-Feb-3 Christie's, London #191/R
£1200	$1920	€1800	Bring up the ladies (13x21cm-5x8in) W/C over pen ink prov. 11-Mar-3 Bonhams, New Bond Street #18/R est:1200-1800
£1200	$1908	€1800	Death and the maiden (13x20cm-5x8in) s. pen ink W/C. 29-Apr-3 Gorringes, Lewes #2213
£1300	$2067	€1950	Reverendissimo viro - Wm Huntingdon (18x15cm-7x6in) i. pen ink W/C. 29-Apr-3 Gorringes, Lewes #2215
£1350	$2160	€2025	Tax man (17x14cm-7x6in) pen ink wash. 11-Mar-3 Bonhams, Oxford #35 est:1000-1200
£1500	$2325	€2250	At the fishmonger (28x23cm-11x9in) pencil pen ink W/C prov. 4-Dec-2 Christie's, Kensington #128/R est:800-1200
£1500	$2385	€2250	Ladies and a gentleman conversing (21x16cm-8x6in) pen ink W/C over pencil. 19-Mar-3 Sotheby's, London #137/R est:1200-1800
£1500	$2385	€2250	Conducted tour (30x23cm-12x9in) pen ink W/C. 29-Apr-3 Gorringes, Lewes #2222
£1600	$2544	€2400	Cottage near Launcetown, Cornwall (13x20cm-5x8in) s.d.1803 ink wash dr. 30-Apr-3 Halls, Shrewsbury #256/R est:1000-1500
£1700	$2669	€2550	Gentleman admiring female musicians playing at his window (24x15cm-9x6in) s. pen col ink W/C over pencil prov. 16-Dec-2 Sotheby's, London #62/R est:2000-3000
£1800	$2808	€2700	Blue stocking club (10x18cm-4x7in) with sig. pencil pen ink W/C prov. 17-Oct-2 Christie's, Kensington #43/R est:2000-3000
£1800	$2826	€2700	Glutton. Invalid (22x16cm-9x6in) one s.d.1818 one with sig.d. pencil pen W/C two in one frame. 21-Nov-2 Christie's, London #19/R est:1500-2000
£1800	$2844	€2700	Ceremonious and fashionable meeting, Rome (14x23cm-6x9in) i.verso pen ink W/C over pencil prov. 28-Nov-2 Sotheby's, London #268/R est:2000-3000
£1800	$2880	€2700	Outside the village tavern (15x24cm-6x9in) W/C over pen ink. 11-Mar-3 Bonhams, New Bond Street #34/R est:2000-3000
£1900	$3021	€2850	Field preaching (30x20cm-12x8in) pen ink W/C. 29-Apr-3 Gorringes, Lewes #2211
£1900	$3021	€2850	Recruits (15x23cm-6x9in) s.i. pen ink W/C. 29-Apr-3 Gorringes, Lewes #2212
£1900	$3021	€2850	Every age has its comforts - gin and snuff (28x23cm-11x9in) s.d.1823 pen ink W/C. 29-Apr-3 Gorringes, Lewes #2220
£1900	$3021	€2850	Music at home (15x23cm-6x9in) pen ink W/C. 29-Apr-3 Gorringes, Lewes #2223
£2000	$3220	€3000	Dr Syntax obtruding (12x21cm-5x8in) i. pencil pen ink W/C prov. 20-Feb-3 Christie's, London #193/R
£2000	$3180	€3000	Tripe and trollebobs (18x23cm-7x9in) s. pen ink W/C. 29-Apr-3 Gorringes, Lewes #2221
£2100	$3339	€3150	Evolution of man (18x15cm-7x6in) pen ink W/C. 29-Apr-3 Gorringes, Lewes #2216
£2100	$3339	€3150	Dr Syntax admires the buxom daughter (8x13cm-3x5in) s. pen ink W/C. 29-Apr-3 Gorringes, Lewes #2218
£2200	$3498	€3300	Figures on a track approaching St. Cullum's Church, Cornwall (17x24cm-7x9in) pen ink W/C over pencil prov. 19-Mar-3 Sotheby's, London #134/R est:1500-2000
£2200	$3520	€3300	Fisherman and his family (22x28cm-9x11in) W/C over pen ink. 11-Mar-3 Bonhams, New Bond Street #33/R est:2000-3000
£2200	$3520	€3300	Village violinist (15x24cm-6x9in) s.d.1820 W/C. 11-Mar-3 Bonhams, New Bond Street #45/R est:2500-3500
£2200	$3652	€3300	Soldiers and their families crossing a stream (23x28cm-9x11in) pen ink W/C over pencil. 12-Jun-3 Sotheby's, London #122/R est:2500-3500
£2200	$3630	€3190	Posting in Ireland (13x22cm-5x9in) i. pen ink W/C over pencil. 2-Jul-3 Sotheby's, Olympia #167/R est:1200-1800
£2300	$3611	€3450	Shepherd with his flock before a cottage, beside a river (19x27cm-7x11in) pencil pen ink W/C. 21-Nov-2 Christie's, London #17/R est:1200-1800
£2400	$3720	€3600	Drowsy boy and watchful cat (20x27cm-8x11in) s.i.d.1819 pencil pen ink W/C. 4-Dec-2 Christie's, Kensington #127/R est:1500-2000
£2400	$3936	€3480	View of Oxford Castle (22x31cm-9x12in) i. pencil pen ink W/C prov. 5-Jun-3 Christie's, London #16/R est:2000-3000
£2500	$4025	€3750	Lucretia (18x14cm-7x6in) s.i. pencil pen ink W/C after Andrea del Sarto prov. 20-Feb-3 Christie's, London #189/R
£2500	$4150	€3750	Old man and his pregnant woman (29x23cm-11x9in) pen ink W/C over pencil. 12-Jun-3 Sotheby's, London #119/R est:1500-2000
£2500	$3975	€3750	Eye on the will (28x23cm-11x9in) s. pen ink W/C. 29-Apr-3 Gorringes, Lewes #2214
£2800	$4508	€4200	Temptation (24x20cm-9x8in) i. pencil pen ink W/C prov. 20-Feb-3 Christie's, London #197/R
£2800	$4452	€4200	Horse traders (26x42cm-10x17in) s. pen ink W/C over pencil prov. 19-Mar-3 Sotheby's, London #133/R est:2000-3000
£2800	$4452	€4200	Libraries and schools from Exeter College gardens (20x30cm-8x12in) ink wash dr. 30-Apr-3 Halls, Shrewsbury #254/R est:2000-3000
£2800	$4648	€4200	Skating party (14x23cm-6x9in) pen ink W/C over pencil prov. 12-Jun-3 Sotheby's, London #121/R est:3000-4000
£2800	$4592	€4200	Harvesters (19x30cm-7x12in) pencil pen ink W/C. 6-Jun-3 Christie's, London #97/R est:1200-1800
£2800	$4592	€4060	Woolpack Inn, Hungerford, Berkshire (23x33cm-9x13in) pencil pen ink col wash prov.exhib. 5-Jun-3 Christie's, London #12/R est:3000-5000
£3000	$4830	€4500	Three graces (20x16cm-8x6in) pencil pen ink W/C prov. 20-Feb-3 Christie's, London #185/R
£3000	$4830	€4500	Capsizing the launch (10x21cm-4x8in) pen ink W/C prov. 20-Feb-3 Christie's, London #199/R
£3000	$4770	€4500	Art of kissing (25x21cm-10x8in) pen ink W/C over pencil prov. 19-Mar-3 Sotheby's, London #150/R est:1500-2000
£3000	$4770	€4500	Congress of Clergymen (25x20cm-10x8in) s. pen ink W/C. 29-Apr-3 Gorringes, Lewes #2224
£3200	$5152	€4800	Fortune teller (29x22cm-11x9in) s. pencil pen ink W/C prov. 20-Feb-3 Christie's, London #196/R
£3200	$5312	€4800	Fashionably dressed gentleman (29x19cm-11x7in) s. pen ink. 12-Jun-3 Bonhams, New Bond Street #638/R est:1000-1500
£3400	$5406	€5100	Ballad singer (11x17cm-4x7in) pen ink W/C. 19-Mar-3 Sotheby's, London #179/R est:1500-2000
£3400	$5406	€5100	Darning the sock (25x20cm-10x8in) s. pen ink W/C. 29-Apr-3 Gorringes, Lewes #2217
£3500	$5810	€5250	Artificial flower makers (21x28cm-8x11in) i. pen ink W/C over pencil. 12-Jun-3 Sotheby's, London #123/R est:4000-6000
£3500	$5740	€5250	Saunder's wonderful troupe of performers (15x23cm-6x9in) i. pen ink W/C. 6-Jun-3 Christie's, London #96/R est:2000-3000
£3800	$6232	€5510	Careless servant (25x21cm-10x8in) pencil pen ink prov. 5-Jun-3 Christie's, London #3/R est:3000-5000
£4000	$6320	€6000	Lady under a tree (23x18cm-9x7in) pen ink W/C over pencil. 28-Nov-2 Sotheby's, London #271/R est:3000-5000
£4000	$6440	€6000	Women bathing in stream (26x22cm-10x9in) pencil pen ink W/C prov. 20-Feb-3 Christie's, London #186/R est:7000
£4000	$6560	€5800	Post (22x33cm-9x13in) pencil ink W/C prov. 5-Jun-3 Christie's, London #9/R est:2500-3500
£4200	$6888	€6090	View of Hillford on the river Fal, Cornwall (29x44cm-11x17in) pencil pen W/C prov. 5-Jun-3 Christie's, London #8/R est:4000-6000
£4500	$7245	€6750	Richardson's show (14x21cm-6x8in) pencil pen ink W/C prov.lit. 20-Feb-3 Christie's, London #187/R
£4500	$7245	€6750	Stolen kiss (15x24cm-6x9in) pencil pen ink W/C prov. 20-Feb-3 Christie's, London #192/R
£4800	$6864	€7200	Sunrise and sunset (14x10cm-6x4in) i. pencil pen W/C prov.exhib. 22-Jan-3 Christie's, London #12/R
£4800	$7728	€7200	Barrow women basting the beadle (26x22cm-10x9in) i. pencil pen ink W/C. 20-Feb-3 Christie's, London #195/R
£5200	$8372	€7800	Recruiting day (20x27cm-8x11in) i. pencil pen ink W/C prov. 20-Feb-3 Christie's, London #198/R
£5200	$8268	€7800	Market, Covent Garden from the south (14x23cm-6x9in) pen ink W/C over pencil. 19-Mar-3 Sotheby's, London #132/R est:3000-5000
£5500	$8580	€8250	Potmender pushing his barrow, Kingswear, Devon (18x28cm-7x11in) W/C over pen ink. 5-Nov-2 Bonhams, New Bond Street #30/R est:4000-6000
£5500	$9020	€7975	Mrs Bundle in a rage (18x47cm-7x19in) i. pencil pen W/C prov. 5-Jun-3 Christie's, London #14/R est:2500-3500
£6000	$9660	€9000	Study of girl in profile (17x14cm-7x6in) s. pencil pen ink W/C prov. 20-Feb-3 Christie's, London #190/R
£6500	$10465	€9750	Devotees (33x74cm-13x29in) s.d.1820 pencil pen ink W/C prov. 20-Feb-3 Christie's, London #194/R
£8000	$12880	€12000	Cuckhold's lover (23x35cm-9x14in) i. pencil pen ink W/C prov. 20-Feb-3 Christie's, London #188/R
£9000	$14310	€13500	Dr Syntax at the auction (25x41cm-10x16in) i. pen ink W/C executed c.1820. 29-Apr-3 Gorringes, Lewes #2225
£9000	$14760	€13050	Dinner in the kitchens (28x43cm-11x17in) pencil exhib. 5-Jun-3 Christie's, London #7/R est:10000-15000
£18000	$28260	€27000	Happy family - or the married man (25x30cm-10x12in) pencil pen prov.exhib.lit. 21-Nov-2 Christie's, London #16/R est:20000-30000

ROWLANDSON, Thomas (attrib) (1756-1827) British

Works on paper

£250	$398	€375	At the door of the Old Ship Inn (27x21cm-11x8in) pen ink W/C. 18-Mar-3 Rosebery Fine Art, London #822/R
£1100	$1716	€1650	Suiters (18x30cm-7x12in) s.d.1805 W/C. 20-Sep-2 Richardson & Smith, Whitby #136 est:1000-1500

ROWLEY, William (attrib) (18th C) British

£750	$1223	€1125	Menai Strait and Bridgenorth, Wales (58x79cm-23x31in) i. panel. 29-Jan-3 Sotheby's, Olympia #13/R est:500-700

ROWNTREE, Harry (19/20th C) British

£450	$747	€653	Pekinese (38x48cm-15x19in) s. 12-Jun-3 Christie's, Kensington #308/R

Works on paper
£400 $636 €600 Sparrows on a jasmine branch (25x38cm-10x15in) s. gouache. 30-Apr-3 Halls, Shrewsbury #214/R

ROWNTREE, Kenneth (1915-1997) British
£350 $543 €525 Homage to Verlaine (40x50cm-16x20in) board. 1-Oct-2 Bonhams, Leeds #309
£480 $744 €720 Fresians at Acomb (61x61cm-24x24in) board. 1-Oct-2 Bonhams, Leeds #311
£550 $875 €825 Farmyard by a country lane (41x61cm-16x24in) init. 5-Mar-3 Bonhams, Bury St Edmunds #397
£650 $1007 €975 Lights over the Tyne, Corbridge (40x51cm-16x20in) board exhib. 1-Oct-2 Bonhams, Leeds #312
£840 $1302 €1260 Moving girl by a Northern sea (60x61cm-24x24in) s.i.verso panel. 1-Oct-2 Bonhams, Leeds #313/R
£1100 $1716 €1650 Allotments at Gisors (46x61cm-18x24in) s.d.39. 15-Oct-2 Bonhams, Knightsbridge #112/R est:1200-1500
£1900 $3135 €2755 Venice, evening (63x76cm-25x30in) s.d.62 board prov. 3-Jul-3 Christie's, Kensington #691/R est:1000-1500
Works on paper
£410 $636 €615 Table in a dark garden (61x61cm-24x24in) mixed media. 1-Oct-2 Bonhams, Leeds #310

ROWORTH, Edward (1880-1964) British
£215 $335 €323 False Bay coast (60x75cm-24x30in) s. s.i.d.1961 verso board. 15-Oct-2 Stephan Welz, Johannesburg #426 est:3500-5000 (SA.R 3500)
£222 $363 €333 View of mountains and river valley (62x75cm-24x30in) s. 4-Feb-3 Dales, Durban #16 (SA.R 3000)
£246 $383 €369 Showery weather, Kuils river (61x85cm-24x33in) s. s.i.verso board. 15-Oct-2 Stephan Welz, Johannesburg #428 est:4000-6000 (SA.R 4000)
£256 $400 €384 Silver lining of the cloud (49x74cm-19x29in) s.i. 11-Nov-2 Stephan Welz, Johannesburg #257 (SA.R 4000)
£258 $415 €387 View of a house with two cyresses and a figure (26x37cm-10x15in) s. panel on board. 12-May-3 Stephan Welz, Johannesburg #188 est:1800-2400 (SA.R 3000)
£275 $443 €413 River beneath a mountainous landscape (59x74cm-23x29in) s. 12-May-3 Stephan Welz, Johannesburg #162 est:1800-2400 (SA.R 3200)
£295 $460 €443 Western Cape landscape (39x57cm-15x22in) s. board. 15-Oct-2 Stephan Welz, Johannesburg #171 est:2000-3000 (SA.R 4800)
£320 $500 €480 Winter in the Hex river valley (80x101cm-31x40in) s. s.i.verso board. 11-Nov-2 Stephan Welz, Johannesburg #596 (SA.R 5000)
£322 $508 €483 View of the mountains (85x60cm-33x24in) s.d.1947 panel. 1-Apr-3 Stephan Welz, Johannesburg #175 est:4000-6000 (SA.R 4000)
£333 $520 €500 Dante (121x90cm-48x35in) s. canvas on board. 11-Nov-2 Stephan Welz, Johannesburg #258 (SA.R 5200)
£361 $581 €542 Landscape with a tree (49x38cm-19x15in) indis sig. 12-May-3 Stephan Welz, Johannesburg #66 est:3000-5000 (SA.R 4200)
£361 $581 €542 Gleam between showers from north Ridge Road (49x75cm-19x30in) s.i. 12-May-3 Stephan Welz, Johannesburg #172 est:2000-4000 (SA.R 4200)
£413 $664 €620 Cape Dutch House (49x75cm-19x30in) s. indis d.1945 board. 12-May-3 Stephan Welz, Johannesburg #202 est:3500-4500 (SA.R 4800)
£418 $652 €627 Rainbow after the storm (60x85cm-24x33in) s. board. 15-Oct-2 Stephan Welz, Johannesburg #427 est:4000-6000 (SA.R 6800)
£577 $899 €866 Autumn morning, Shaw's mountain near Hermanus (69x89cm-27x35in) s.d.1961 s.i.d.1961 verso board. 11-Nov-2 Stephan Welz, Johannesburg #594 (SA.R 9000)

ROY, G B (19th C) French
£1159 $1901 €1600 Cherichetti che cantano (87x69cm-34x27in) s. 27-May-3 Finarte, Milan #122/R est:1400-1600

ROY, Jamini (1887-1972) Indian
£2000 $3180 €3000 Gopini (137x102cm-54x40in) 1-May-3 Bonhams, Knightsbridge #160 est:2000-3000
Works on paper
£1000 $1590 €1500 Elephants (34x44cm-13x17in) s. gouache card. 2-May-3 Christie's, Kensington #576/R est:1500-2000
£2000 $3120 €3000 Gopini (79x62cm-31x24in) s. gouache board. 17-Oct-2 Bonhams, Knightsbridge #542/R est:2500-3500
£2200 $3432 €3300 Gopini (85x51cm-33x20in) s. gouache board. 17-Oct-2 Bonhams, Knightsbridge #543/R est:2500-3500
£5439 $8974 €7887 Santhal girl. Deer (39x25cm-15x10in) s. gouache card pair. 6-Jul-3 Christie's, Hong Kong #71/R est:40000-60000 (HK.D 70000)

ROY, Jean Baptiste de (1759-1839) Belgian
£3600 $5616 €5400 Dutch landscape with drover and sheep (37x54cm-15x21in) s.d.1807 panel. 26-Mar-3 Sotheby's, Olympia #187/R est:3000-5000

ROY, Louis George Eleonor (1862-1907) French
Works on paper
£694 $1132 €1000 Jeune Breton au pied de l'arbre (26x30cm-10x12in) s. W/C. 19-Jul-3 Thierry & Lannon, Brest #78

ROY, Suhas (1936-) Indian
Works on paper
£1000 $1560 €1500 Radha (28x38cm-11x15in) s.d.2002 mixed media rice paper. 17-Oct-2 Bonhams, Knightsbridge #586/R est:1000-1400

ROYBET, Ferdinand (1840-1920) French
£1027 $1500 €1541 Jugadores de Dados (41x33cm-16x13in) s. panel prov. 17-Jun-2 Schrager Galleries, Milwaukee #1194/R
£1397 $2180 €2096 Portrait of young woman with white collar (42x35cm-17x14in) mono. 20-Nov-2 Fischer, Luzern #1120/R est:4000-4500 (S.FR 3200)
£2548 $3975 €4000 Velasquez peignant l'infante, Marguerite d'Espagne (61x37cm-24x15in) s. panel. 11-Nov-2 Horta, Bruxelles #241/R est:5000-7500
£3871 $6000 €5807 Visit to the music shop (59x73cm-23x29in) s. panel. 3-Dec-2 Christie's, Rockefeller NY #637/R est:6000-8000
£5806 $9000 €8709 Dashing cavalier (55x44cm-22x17in) s.d.1871 panel prov.exhib.lit. 30-Oct-2 Christie's, Rockefeller NY #145/R est:12000-16000
£7742 $12000 €11613 Recital (48x46cm-19x18in) s. panel. 30-Oct-2 Christie's, Rockefeller NY #143/R est:10000-15000

ROYBET, Ferdinand (attrib) (1840-1920) French
£282 $462 €409 Musketeer (36x27cm-14x11in) bears sig. 4-Jun-3 Fischer, Luzern #2297/R (S.FR 600)

ROYCE, Bianca Conti (?) American
£256 $400 €384 Old ranch house, Stoneybrook. board. 21-Sep-2 Harvey Clar, Oakland #1493

ROYEN, Willem Frederik van (1645-1723) German
£13580 $22000 €20370 Still life of grapes and peaches on marble ledge (41x29cm-16x11in) s.d.1714 copper. 23-Jan-3 Sotheby's, New York #202/R est:20000
Works on paper
£419 $650 €629 Fanciful bird in a landscape (41x25cm-16x10in) black chk pen brown ink W/C. 2-Oct-2 Christie's, Rockefeller NY #184/R

ROYER, Jacob S (1883-?) American
£419 $650 €629 Still life of peaches (41x51cm-16x20in) painted c.1928. 8-Dec-2 Toomey, Oak Park #646/R

ROYER, Leon Jules Alphonse le (1858-1939) French
£1772 $2800 €2658 Vessel on a choppy sea off the coast of Normandy (30x38cm-12x15in) s. 16-Nov-2 New Orleans Auction, New Orleans #316/R est:3000-5000

ROYER, Philippe (20th C) French
£373 $593 €560 Composition (78x97cm-31x38in) mono. acrylic. 29-Apr-3 Kunsthallen, Copenhagen #107 (D.KR 4000)

ROYERE, Jean (1902-1981) French
Sculpture
£9748 $15013 €15500 Ondulation (22cm-9in) welded iron marble base lit. 27-Oct-2 Muizon & Le Coent, Paris #116/R

ROYERS, W (?) ?
£580 $945 €870 Sailing vessels on a choppy sea (75x48cm-30x19in) s. 11-Feb-3 Fellows & Sons, Birmingham #56/R

ROYLE, Herbert (1870-1958) British
£800 $1240 €1200 Loch Torridon (48x58cm-19x23in) s. board. 4-Dec-2 Andrew Hartley, Ilkley #1248
£900 $1404 €1350 Drinking pool, Sulby, Isle of Man (61x41cm-24x16in) s.i.verso canvas on panel. 10-Apr-3 Tennants, Leyburn #1005/R
£1050 $1722 €1575 Morning breeze, Halsall moss (24x35cm-9x14in) s. board. 4-Feb-3 Bonhams, Leeds #403 est:800-1200
£1150 $1783 €1725 Scottish loch scene (28x38cm-11x15in) s. board. 4-Dec-2 Andrew Hartley, Ilkley #1252/R est:1200-1800
£1450 $2378 €2175 Gathering clouds, Loch Tarbert (30x40cm-12x16in) s. board. 4-Feb-3 Bonhams, Leeds #402 est:700-900

£1500 $2505 €2175 Drinking pool (23x28cm-9x11in) s. 18-Jun-3 Andrew Hartley, Ilkley #1195/R est:1500-2000
£1800 $2808 €2700 Cottage at Beamsley Beacon (28x38cm-11x15in) s. board. 9-Oct-2 Andrew Hartley, Ilkley #766/R est:1800-2500
£2200 $3608 €3300 Winter landscape with the river Wharfe above Low Mills, Addingham church in the distance (25x46cm-10x18in) s. 4-Feb-3 Bonhams, Leeds #401 est:1500-2000
£3000 $4680 €4500 Haymaking Addingham moorside (51x61cm-20x24in) s. 9-Oct-2 Andrew Hartley, Ilkley #768 est:1200-1800
£3000 $4710 €4500 Bluebell wood, Beamsley Hall, Bolton Abbey (38x34cm-15x13in) s. i.verso board prov. 21-Nov-2 Tennants, Leyburn #837/R est:600-800
£3000 $4650 €4500 Autumn at Bolton Abbey (48x58cm-19x23in) s. i.verso board. 4-Dec-2 Andrew Hartley, Ilkley #1238/R est:3000-4000
£3000 $4650 €4500 Nesfield Dene (51x61cm-20x24in) s. 4-Dec-2 Andrew Hartley, Ilkley #1258/R est:3000-4000
£3600 $5472 €5400 Moorland scene with figure, horse and cart (28x38cm-11x15in) s. board. 14-Aug-2 Andrew Hartley, Ilkley #693/R est:2000-3000
£3600 $5904 €5400 Bridge over the Lochart, Killin (61x66cm-24x26in) s. board. 4-Feb-3 Bonhams, Leeds #400 est:2500-3000
£4000 $6520 €5800 View on the wharfe (41x61cm-16x24in) s.i. 17-Jul-3 Tennants, Leyburn #858/R est:3000-4000
£5000 $7850 €7500 Wharfedale from Langshawe bank (51x76cm-20x30in) s. 21-Nov-2 Tennants, Leyburn #838/R est:3000-4000
£5000 $7750 €7500 Tree felling (48x58cm-19x23in) s. 4-Dec-2 Andrew Hartley, Ilkley #1237/R est:6000-8000
£5500 $9020 €8250 Haymaking (18x24cm-7x9in) s. board. 4-Feb-3 Bonhams, Leeds #404 est:1500-2000
£6000 $9360 €9000 Haymaking at Nesfield, Ilkley (48x58cm-19x23in) s. 9-Oct-2 Andrew Hartley, Ilkley #770/R est:6000-8000
£6000 $9420 €9000 Sunlit farmyard scene, possibly a scene at Nessfield (50x60cm-20x24in) s. board. 19-Nov-2 Bonhams, Leeds #162/R est:4000-5000
£6000 $9420 €9000 Mountain landscape North Harris (51x61cm-20x24in) s. indis i. prov. 21-Nov-2 Tennants, Leyburn #836/R est:2000-3000
£6200 $9734 €9300 Dales landscape with figures cutting timber (34x51cm-13x20in) s. board. 19-Nov-2 Bonhams, Leeds #163/R est:1800-2500
£7600 $11932 €11400 Topcliffe, River Swale, North Yorkshire (49x59cm-19x23in) s.i.verso board. 19-Nov-2 Bonhams, Leeds #164/R est:3000-4000
£8000 $13280 €12000 Figures cutting timber at Bolton Abbey, Wharfedale (51x61cm-20x24in) s. 10-Jun-3 Bonhams, Leeds #213/R est:8000-10000
£9000 $14040 €13500 Burnsall village, Wharfedale (48x58cm-19x23in) s. 9-Oct-2 Andrew Hartley, Ilkley #767/R est:5000-7000
£9000 $14760 €13500 Haymaking in the Wharfe Valley (51x61cm-20x24in) 4-Feb-3 Bonhams, Leeds #405 est:3000-5000
£9000 $14760 €13500 Picking bluebells in the woods near Nessfield (59x49cm-23x19in) s. 4-Feb-3 Bonhams, Leeds #406 est:3000-5000
£10000 $15700 €15000 Sunlit river landscape with cattle watering in the foreground, near Bolton Abbey (76x63cm-30x25in) s. 19-Nov-2 Bonhams, Leeds #161/R est:3000-4000
£11200 $18368 €16800 Snow scene above Nessfield, Ilkley (51x61cm-20x24in) s. 4-Feb-3 Bonhams, Leeds #407 est:6000-8000
£12500 $19625 €18750 Harbour scene (71x107cm-28x42in) s. 16-Dec-2 Sotheby's, Olympia #168/R est:1500-2000

ROYLE, Herbert (attrib) (1870-1958) British
£380 $597 €570 Woodland scene with figures beside a pond (51x61cm-20x24in) bears sig. 19-Nov-2 Bonhams, Leeds #165

ROYLE, Stanley (1888-1961) British
£1600 $2496 €2400 West-way, Ravenglass, Cumberland (30x40cm-12x16in) s.d.20 i.verso board. 25-Mar-3 Bonhams, Leeds #571/R est:1200-1800
£5000 $7800 €7500 Feeding the geese (51x61cm-20x24in) s. 25-Mar-3 Bonhams, Leeds #572/R est:5000-7000

Works on paper
£320 $499 €480 Open moorland scene with figure and sheep in lane (23x33cm-9x13in) s. W/C. 11-Apr-3 Keys, Aylsham #441
£854 $1340 €1281 Snow fantasy (23x30cm-9x12in) s. pastel prov. 10-Dec-2 Pinneys, Montreal #166 est:900-1200 (C.D 2100)
£4600 $7498 €6670 In the potato fields Ecclesfield, early evening (46x71cm-18x28in) s.d.1913 i.verso W/C gouache. 17-Jul-3 Tennants, Leyburn #747/R est:3000-5000

ROYO (20th C) Spanish?
£2200 $3410 €3300 Girl with sun hat and parasol (45x26cm-18x10in) s. 24-Sep-2 Anderson & Garland, Newcastle #404/R est:1500-2500
£2400 $3720 €3600 Girl in a pink dress (45x26cm-18x10in) s. 24-Sep-2 Anderson & Garland, Newcastle #402/R est:1200-2200
£2400 $3720 €3600 Girl with flowers in her hair (45x26cm-18x10in) s. 24-Sep-2 Anderson & Garland, Newcastle #405/R est:1000-1800
£4600 $7130 €6900 Girl with yellow umbrella (67x59cm-26x23in) s. 24-Sep-2 Anderson & Garland, Newcastle #403/R est:3000-5000

ROZ, Andre (1897-?) French
£3537 $5624 €5200 Fete de village (46x65cm-18x26in) s. isorel. 2-Mar-3 Lombrail & Teucquam, Paris #183/R

ROZANOVA, Olga (1886-1918) Russian

Works on paper
£629 $981 €1000 Suprematist landscape - harbour (26x36cm-10x14in) s.cyrillic pencil. 21-Sep-2 Bolland & Marotz, Bremen #772/R

ROZEN, George (1895-1973) American
£1739 $2800 €2609 Rio Kid leaping onto gun-wielding cowboy on horseback (53x38cm-21x15in) canvasboard painted c.1940. 10-May-3 Illustration House, New York #171/R est:2500-3500

ROZEN, Jerome (20th C) American
£1603 $2500 €2405 Aircraft carrier sunk by German warplanes, crew clinging to wreckage (76x56cm-30x22in) s. 9-Nov-2 Illustration House, New York #32/R est:3000-4500

ROZIER, Dominique Hubert (1840-1901) French
£929 $1459 €1450 Musique et fleurs (67x140cm-26x55in) s. painted with L Ruel. 16-Dec-2 Eric Coutrier, Paris #44/R
£1139 $1800 €1800 Bouquet de fleurs (80x65cm-31x26in) 27-Nov-2 Camard, Paris #22
£2365 $3689 €3500 Bouquet de roses (60x73cm-24x29in) s. 28-Mar-3 Claude Aguttes, Neuilly #96/R

ROZIER, Jules (1821-1882) French
£775 $1286 €1100 Bord de riviere anime (31x15cm-12x6in) s. panel. 13-Jun-3 Rabourdin & Choppin de Janvry, Paris #133
£1127 $1814 €1600 Seine shore with fishing boat (26x41cm-10x16in) s.d.1861 panel. 10-May-3 Berlinghof, Heidelberg #304/R est:1500
£1522 $2359 €2283 Winter landscape with cart and dog (24x33cm-9x13in) s/. 9-Dec-2 Philippe Schuler, Zurich #3930/R est:3000-4000 (S.FR 3500)
£2532 $4000 €4000 Troupeau pres de ruiseau (25x41cm-10x16in) s.d.1863 panel. 2-Dec-2 Tajan, Paris #5

ROZSDA, Endre (1918-1999) French?
£2397 $3764 €3500 Untitled (38x46cm-15x18in) s. 15-Apr-3 Laurence Calmels, Paris #4405/R

Works on paper
£822 $1290 €1200 Nu feminin allonge (25x38cm-10x15in) s. graphite. 15-Apr-3 Laurence Calmels, Paris #4404/R

RUBBIANI, Felice (attrib) (1677-1752) Italian
£14744 $22853 €23000 Still lives with fruit (68x89cm-27x35in) pair. 4-Dec-2 Christie's, Rome #460/R est:25000-35000

RUBBO, Anthony Dattilo (1870-1955) Australian
£643 $1016 €965 Bottle and glass in Sydney Harbour (36x25cm-14x10in) s. 18-Nov-2 Joel, Victoria #381/R est:3000-4000 (A.D 1800)
£1615 $2568 €2423 Bottle and glass in Sydney harbour (28x38cm-11x15in) s. 4-Mar-3 Deutscher-Menzies, Melbourne #244/R est:3000-4000 (A.D 4200)

RUBENS (after) (1577-1640) Flemish
£6522 $10696 €9000 La bataille des Amazones (135x201cm-53x79in) 27-May-3 Palais de Beaux Arts, Brussels #302/R est:10000-15000

RUBENS (circle) (1577-1640) Flemish
£6790 $11000 €10185 Portrait of cleric thought to be Padre de Buzzara (65x77cm-26x30in) panel prov.exhib. 23-Jan-3 Sotheby's, New York #135/R est:15000
£7000 $11690 €10150 Garden of Love (73x104cm-29x41in) panel. 9-Jul-3 Bonhams, New Bond Street #60/R est:7000-10000
£20000 $31400 €30000 Victory of eucharistic truth over Heresy (63x84cm-25x33in) copper. 13-Dec-2 Christie's, Kensington #51/R est:4000-6000
£30000 $50100 €43500 Portrait of a young girl and boy believed to be Rubens' children, Albert and Clara Serena (49x64cm-19x25in) panel prov. 8-Jul-3 Sotheby's, Olympia #332/R est:3000-5000

RUBENS (school) (1577-1640) Flemish
£9155 $15197 €13000 Putto with hourglass - allegory of transitoriness (87x57cm-34x22in) 11-Jun-3 Dorotheum, Vienna #117/R est:2500-4500

RUBENS (studio) (1577-1640) Flemish
£5517 $8772 €8000 Ecce Homo (40x53cm-16x21in) copper. 9-Mar-3 Semenzato, Venice #9/R
£7547 $11774 €12000 La vierge et l'enfant (130x110cm-51x43in) 14-Oct-2 Amberes, Antwerp #126/R

£37162 $57973 €55000 The lion hunt (217x344cm-85x135in) prov. 27-Mar-3 Dorotheum, Vienna #402/R est:10000-15000

RUBENS (style) (1577-1640) Flemish

£9615 $15192 €15000 Judith and Holofernes (106x75cm-42x30in) panel. 16-Nov-2 Lempertz, Koln #1087/R est:16000
£10000 $15600 €15000 Minerrva protecting Pax from Mars (242x293cm-95x115in) 9-Apr-3 Bonhams, New Bond Street #27/R est:4000-5000
£10274 $16027 €15000 Epic scenes (55x73cm-22x29in) metal pair. 8-Apr-3 Ansorena, Madrid #81/R est:8000
£16768 $27500 €25152 Venus surrounded by a garland of flowers and putti and Helana fourment. Garland of flowers and putti (180x100cm-71x39in) panel pair. 29-May-3 Sotheby's, New York #34/R est:10000-15000

RUBENS, Arnold Frans (attrib) (1687-1719) Flemish

£1420 $2243 €2200 Battle scene (21x27cm-8x11in) panel. 20-Dec-2 Tajan, Paris #72/R est:2000

RUBENS, Sir Peter Paul (1577-1640) Flemish

£14744 $22853 €23000 Portrait de Neron (65x50cm-26x20in) i. panel prov.lit. 6-Dec-2 Maigret, Paris #83/R est:30000-40000
£130000 $217100 €188500 Portrait of a Capuchin monk, head and shoulders, wearing a chain (53x45cm-21x18in) panel prov.lit. 10-Jul-3 Sotheby's, London #14/R est:60000-80000

Works on paper

£150000 $250500 €217500 Nude youth in the pose of the Spinario (28x19cm-11x7in) i. black white chk lit. 8-Jul-3 Christie's, London #96/R est:150000-200000

RUBIN (?) ?

£15000 $24000 €22500 Still life Ha'Aretz (43x74cm-17x29in) s. 11-Jan-3 Harvey Clar, Oakland #1428

RUBIN, Frank (20th C) ?

£1056 $1647 €1584 M II - 1982 (81x100cm-32x39in) exhib. 18-Sep-2 Kunsthallen, Copenhagen #230/R est:8000 (D.KR 12500)

RUBIN, Reuven (1893-1974) Israeli

£10000 $15500 €15000 Flowers in vase (41x33cm-16x13in) s. prov. 4-Dec-2 Koller, Zurich #109/R est:25000-35000 (S.FR 23000)
£10127 $16000 €15191 Flowers at the window (35x30cm-14x12in) s.d.1947 on stretcher prov. 27-Apr-3 Sotheby's, Tel Aviv #29/R est:16000-20000
£10127 $16000 €15191 African violets (51x41cm-20x16in) s. prov. 27-Apr-3 Sotheby's, Tel Aviv #30/R est:20000-30000
£15190 $24000 €22785 Landscape in Galilee (41x51cm-16x20in) s. s.i.d.1961 on stretcher. 27-Apr-3 Sotheby's, Tel Aviv #35/R est:25000-35000
£25211 $39830 €37817 Autumn bouquet (66x81cm-26x32in) s. s.d.1944. 27-Apr-3 Sotheby's, Tel Aviv #14/R est:40000-60000
£27848 $44000 €41772 Landscape (66x81cm-26x32in) s. s.i.stretcher. 27-Apr-3 Sotheby's, Tel Aviv #15/R est:40000-60000
£35000 $57050 €52500 Still life with pomegranates (93x74cm-37x29in) s. i.on stretcher verso. 3-Feb-3 Bonhams, New Bond Street #81/R est:50000-70000
£43038 $68000 €64557 Mount of olives (66x81cm-26x32in) s. painted 1930. 27-Apr-3 Sotheby's, Tel Aviv #36/R est:60000-80000

Works on paper

£645 $1019 €968 Flutist (16x11cm-6x4in) s. pen ink W/C wash. 18-Nov-2 Waddingtons, Toronto #265/R (C.D 1600)
£860 $1384 €1290 Sword fight (28x38cm-11x15in) s. pen brush ink crayon. 12-May-3 Stephan Welz, Johannesburg #29 est:4000-6000 (SA.R 10000)
£1911 $2981 €3000 Angel (53x40cm-21x16in) s. Chinese ink dr. 10-Nov-2 Eric Pillon, Calais #166/R
£2143 $3385 €3215 Artist at his easel (16x12cm-6x5in) s. s.i.d.1943 W/C pen ink paper on card. 27-Apr-3 Sotheby's, Tel Aviv #6/R est:2000-3000
£2756 $4272 €4300 Scene hebraique (30x42cm-12x17in) s.d.1948 pen W/C. 5-Dec-2 Gros & Delettrez, Paris #99/R
£2821 $4372 €4400 Scene hebraique (30x42cm-12x17in) s.d.1948 pen W/C. 5-Dec-2 Gros & Delettrez, Paris #100
£4088 $6500 €6132 Camel with rider (50x71cm-20x28in) s. pen brush ink htd gouache paper on board prov. 27-Feb-3 Christie's, Rockefeller NY #81/R
£7563 $11950 €11345 Jacob's dream (49x64cm-19x25in) s.d.1972 pastel ink prov. 27-Apr-3 Sotheby's, Tel Aviv #57/R est:12000-18000

RUBIN, Victor (1950-) Australian

£1149 $1805 €1724 Luna Park, Sydney (90x121cm-35x48in) s. board. 15-Apr-3 Lawson Menzies, Sydney #259/R est:3000-5000 (A.D 3000)
£1195 $1960 €1793 Cafe Avro round the zoo (91x122cm-36x48in) s. i.d.9th April-15 March verso composition board. 4-Jun-3 Deutscher-Menzies, Melbourne #278/R est:4000-6000 (A.D 3000)
£1357 $2117 €2036 Drift (167x197cm-66x78in) s.d.88 s.i.d.1988 verso. 11-Nov-2 Deutscher-Menzies, Melbourne #101/R est:4000-6000 (A.D 3800)

Works on paper

£1545 $2441 €2240 Sydney suite (122x91cm-48x36in) s. mixed media collage. 22-Jul-3 Lawson Menzies, Sydney #8/R est:4000-6000 (A.D 3800)

RUBINO, Edoardo (1871-1954) Italian

Sculpture

£8000 $13360 €11600 Bust of a woman (40cm-16in) s. dk brown pat bronze. 8-Jul-3 Sotheby's, London #227/R est:2500-3500

RUBIO, Louis (1795-1882) Italian

£3472 $5590 €5208 Fortune teller (65x54cm-26x21in) s. 7-May-3 Dobiaschofsky, Bern #935/R est:7500 (S.FR 7500)
£6115 $9784 €8500 Italian landscape with young musician (60x48cm-24x19in) s. 17-May-3 De Vuyst, Lokeren #419/R est:6000-6500

RUBOVICS, Markus (1867-1947) Hungarian

£1816 $2834 €2724 Sailing boats on Lake Balaton (100x150cm-39x59in) s. 11-Apr-3 Kieselbach, Budapest #201/R est:240000-650000 (H.F 650000)

RUCH, Jakob (1868-?) Swiss

£386 $610 €579 Mountain landscape with farm buildings (55x46cm-22x18in) s.d.96. 26-Nov-2 Hans Widmer, St Gallen #1327 (S.FR 900)
£1092 $1703 €1638 Glarn mountain landscape with goats in autumn (120x70cm-47x28in) s.d.04 exhib. 20-Nov-2 Fischer, Luzern #1276/R est:2500-3500 (S.FR 2500)

RUCKER, Robert (1932-2000) American

Works on paper

£224 $350 €336 Louisiana bayou landscape (15x23cm-6x9in) s. W/C. 12-Oct-2 Neal Auction Company, New Orleans #1414
£288 $450 €432 Louisiana swamp, moss laden cypress trees (23x15cm-9x6in) s. W/C. 12-Oct-2 Neal Auction Company, New Orleans #1413

RUCKRIEM, Ulrich (1938-) German

Sculpture

£2899 $4754 €4000 Untitled (180cm-71in) steel. 28-May-3 Lempertz, Koln #380/R est:5000
£5797 $9507 €8000 Head (40x30x30cm-16x12x12in) sandstone prov. 28-May-3 Lempertz, Koln #381/R est:9000
£7246 $11884 €10000 Untitled (67x54x40cm-26x21x16in) basalt prov. 28-May-3 Lempertz, Koln #382/R est:12000

RUCKSTUHL, Xaver (1911-1979) German

Sculpture

£1310 $2044 €1965 Untitled (44cm-17in) mono.indis.i.d.73 pat bronze prov. 9-Nov-2 Galerie Gloggner, Luzern #110/R est:1000-1200 (S.FR 3000)

RUDBERG, Gustav (1915-1994) Swedish

£386 $641 €560 Backafall, Hven (19x39cm-7x15in) s. panel. 16-Jun-3 Lilla Bukowskis, Stockholm #68 (S.KR 5000)
£401 $650 €602 The beach, Hven (64x48cm-25x19in) s,. 3-Feb-3 Lilla Bukowskis, Stockholm #710 (S.KR 5600)
£412 $626 €618 Southern landscape (42x61cm-17x24in) s. canvas on panel. 16-Aug-2 Lilla Bukowskis, Stockholm #739 (S.KR 6000)
£412 $642 €618 Prince Eugen's oak (97x97cm-38x38in) s. 13-Sep-2 Lilla Bukowskis, Stockholm #890 (S.KR 6000)
£446 $709 €669 By an old farm, Hven (70x82cm-28x32in) s. 3-Mar-3 Lilla Bukowskis, Stockholm #326 (S.KR 6000)
£483 $743 €725 Spring in Vacluse (74x88cm-29x35in) s. d.1969 verso. 27-Oct-2 Anders Antik, Landskrona #32/R (S.KR 7000)
£549 $835 €824 Juryman's house on a grey day at Hven (75x96cm-30x38in) s. 16-Aug-2 Lilla Bukowskis, Stockholm #596 (S.KR 8000)
£638 $989 €957 View of the sea at Hven (59x79cm-23x31in) s. d.58 verso. 8-Dec-2 Uppsala Auktionskammare, Uppsala #224/R (S.KR 9000)
£709 $1099 €1064 Landscape from Hven (116x140cm-46x55in) s.d.64. 8-Dec-2 Uppsala Auktionskammare, Uppsala #221/R (S.KR 10000)
£710 $1179 €1030 Landscape from Kyrkbacken, Hven (44x92cm-17x36in) s. 16-Jun-3 Lilla Bukowskis, Stockholm #67 (S.KR 9200)
£776 $1257 €1125 Namdemansgarden, Hven (67x72cm-26x28in) s. d.1970 verso. 25-May-3 Uppsala Auktionskammare, Uppsala #284 (S.KR 10000)
£888 $1474 €1288 The beach at Hven (56x65cm-22x26in) s. 16-Jun-3 Lilla Bukowskis, Stockholm #991 (S.KR 11500)
£895 $1451 €1343 Coastal bay (49x92cm-19x36in) s. 3-Feb-3 Lilla Bukowskis, Stockholm #709 (S.KR 12500)
£917 $1440 €1376 Hazy sunshine, Ibiza (76x67cm-30x26in) s. 16-Dec-2 Lilla Bukowskis, Stockholm #211 (S.KR 13000)
£1003 $1625 €1505 Hven Harbour (70x68cm-28x27in) s. 3-Feb-3 Lilla Bukowskis, Stockholm #63 (S.KR 14000)
£1051 $1640 €1577 Morning haze, Hven (60x90cm-24x35in) s. 6-Nov-2 AB Stockholms Auktionsverk #588/R est:20000-25000 (S.KR 15000)
£1051 $1640 €1577 Landscape, Hven (75x75cm-30x30in) init. 5-Nov-2 Bukowskis, Stockholm #134/R est:15000-20000 (S.KR 15000)

£1063 $1658 €1595 The beach at Hven (59x67cm-23x26in) s,. 13-Sep-2 Lilla Bukowskis, Stockholm #303 est:18000-20000 (S.KR 15500)
£1121 $1749 €1682 Oresund and half of Hven (70x73cm-28x29in) s. 5-Nov-2 Bukowskis, Stockholm #133/R est:18000-20000 (S.KR 16000)
£1158 $1865 €1737 Coastal landscape from Hven (49x60cm-19x24in) s. 7-May-3 AB Stockholms Auktionsverk #859/R est:15000-20000 (S.KR 15000)
£1402 $2186 €2103 Landscape with farm, Hven (78x118cm-31x46in) init. panel. 6-Nov-2 AB Stockholms Auktionsverk #586/R est:35000-40000 (S.KR 20000)
£1655 $2549 €2483 Vessel at anchor under Hven's cliffs (43x64cm-17x25in) s. d.1984 verso. 27-Oct-2 Anders Antik, Landskrona #17/R est:20000-25000 (S.KR 24000)
£1655 $2549 €2483 Coastal landscape, Kyrkbacken (70x72cm-28x28in) s. 27-Oct-2 Anders Antik, Landskrona #31/R est:15000-20000 (S.KR 24000)
£1752 $2733 €2628 Summer landscape from Hven (74x96cm-29x38in) s. d.1987 verso. 6-Nov-2 AB Stockholms Auktionsverk #535/R est:35000-40000 (S.KR 25000)
£1892 $2952 €2838 Sailing boat, Hven (71x68cm-28x27in) s. 6-Nov-2 AB Stockholms Auktionsverk #599/R est:20000-25000 (S.KR 27000)
£1892 $2952 €2838 Vessel in Sundet, Hven (75x81cm-30x32in) s. 5-Nov-2 Bukowskis, Stockholm #250/R est:25000-30000 (S.KR 27000)
£1977 $3124 €2966 Norreborg's Harbour, Hven (49x75cm-19x30in) s. 28-Apr-3 Bukowskis, Stockholm #219a/R est:20000-25000 (S.KR 26000)
£2053 $3244 €3080 Heavy rain clouds, Hven (65x94cm-26x37in) s. 28-Apr-3 Bukowskis, Stockholm #221/R est:15000-18000 (S.KR 27000)
£2102 $3280 €3153 Landscape, Kyrkbacken, Hven (60x100cm-24x39in) s. 6-Nov-2 AB Stockholms Auktionsverk #534/R est:35000-40000 (S.KR 30000)
£2281 $3605 €3422 Kyrckbacken, Hven (72x78cm-28x31in) s. 28-Apr-3 Bukowskis, Stockholm #218/R est:25000-30000 (S.KR 30000)
£2593 $4045 €3890 Landscape from Hven (96x96cm-38x38in) s. d.1974 verso. 6-Nov-2 AB Stockholms Auktionsverk #594/R est:35000-40000 (S.KR 37000)
£2593 $4045 €3890 After the rain, Hven (73x63cm-29x25in) s. 5-Nov-2 Bukowskis, Stockholm #248/R est:25000-30000 (S.KR 37000)
£2593 $4045 €3890 Vessel at Hven (66x95cm-26x37in) s. 5-Nov-2 Bukowskis, Stockholm #249/R est:20000-25000 (S.KR 37000)
£2703 $4351 €4055 Vessel off Hven (85x58cm-33x23in) S. 7-May-3 AB Stockholms Auktionsverk #857/R est:15000-20000 (S.KR 35000)
£4411 $6969 €6617 Norreborg, Hven (95x65cm-37x26in) s. 28-Apr-3 Bukowskis, Stockholm #220/R est:50000-60000 (S.KR 58000)

Works on paper

£841 $1312 €1262 Vessels and sailing boats (41x52cm-16x20in) s. W/C. 6-Nov-2 AB Stockholms Auktionsverk #595/R (S.KR 12000)

RUDD, Agnes J (fl.1880-1938) British

Works on paper

£290 $450 €435 Harvest moon, Wells (47x59cm-19x23in) s. W/C exhib. 1-Oct-2 Bristol Auction Rooms #419/R

RUDDER, J de (?) Belgian?

Sculpture

£1139 $1777 €1800 Dame au cobra. brown pat.bronze marble socle. 16-Sep-2 Amberes, Antwerp #413

RUDE, François (1784-1855) French

Sculpture

£2400 $3744 €3600 Neapolitan fisherboy (24x25cm-9x10in) s.num.90460 bob. st.f.F Barbedienne. 9-Apr-3 Sotheby's, London #145/R est:2000-3000
£3548 $5500 €5322 Head of a Gaul (37cm-15in) black pat. bronze prov.exhib. 29-Oct-2 Sotheby's, New York #238/R est:3000-5000
£6000 $10020 €8700 Bust of the old warrior (60cm-24in) s. terracotta. 8-Jul-3 Sotheby's, London #204/R est:6000-8000

RUDE, Olaf (1886-1957) Danish

£392 $623 €588 Portrait of the artist Axel P Jensen (63x47cm-25x19in) s. 29-Apr-3 Kunsthallen, Copenhagen #243 (D.KR 4200)
£572 $955 €829 Standing female nude (61x50cm-24x20in) s.d.07. 17-Jun-3 Rasmussen, Copenhagen #220/R (D.KR 6000)
£652 $1036 €978 Portrait of Johanne Krause, Henrik Pontoppidan's daughter (57x45cm-22x18in) s. d.1913 verso prov. 10-Mar-3 Rasmussen, Vejle #570/R (D.KR 7000)
£667 $1114 €967 Wooded landscape (50x64cm-20x25in) s.d.32. 17-Jun-3 Rasmussen, Copenhagen #72/R (D.KR 7000)
£1208 $1909 €1812 Interior scene with woman knitting (55x65cm-22x26in) s.d.32 study. 1-Apr-3 Rasmussen, Copenhagen #527/R est:15000-20000 (D.KR 13000)
£1651 $2559 €2477 Still life with oranges in bowl (38x50cm-15x20in) s. painted 1937/38. 1-Oct-2 Rasmussen, Copenhagen #311/R est:10000 (D.KR 19500)
£1679 $2670 €2519 Storm and rain (70x80cm-28x31in) s.d.29. 29-Apr-3 Kunsthallen, Copenhagen #250/R est:20000 (D.KR 18000)
£2045 $3230 €3068 Landscape with house in background (54x65cm-21x26in) s. 1-Apr-3 Rasmussen, Copenhagen #34/R est:20000 (D.KR 22000)
£2052 $3263 €3078 Interior from my studio with view across Allinge (70x80cm-28x31in) s. exhib. 29-Apr-3 Kunsthallen, Copenhagen #218/R est:25000 (D.KR 22000)
£2052 $3263 €3078 Landscape from Bornholm (70x80cm-28x31in) s.d.23. 5-May-3 Rasmussen, Vejle #31/R est:20000-30000 (D.KR 22000)
£2138 $3377 €3207 Wide landscape (64x92cm-25x36in) s. 1-Apr-3 Rasmussen, Copenhagen #103/R est:25000 (D.KR 23000)
£2383 $3980 €3455 Evening after a rainy day (89x130cm-35x51in) s.d.1930-35 exhib. 17-Jun-3 Rasmussen, Copenhagen #79/R est:30000-40000 (D.KR 25000)
£2788 $4405 €4182 Dance (31x25cm-12x10in) veneer prov.lit. 1-Apr-3 Rasmussen, Copenhagen #5/R est:40000 (D.KR 30000)
£2974 $4699 €4461 Interior scene with view across the sea at Gudhjem (65x92cm-26x36in) s. 1-Apr-3 Rasmussen, Copenhagen #79/R est:30000-40000 (D.KR 32000)
£3051 $5094 €4424 Figures by the sea with sailing boats on the water (65x92cm-26x36in) s/. 17-Jun-3 Rasmussen, Copenhagen #94/R est:20000-25000 (D.KR 32000)
£3622 $6050 €5252 The mirror - still life (97x73cm-38x29in) s. 17-Jun-3 Rasmussen, Copenhagen #88/R est:40000 (D.KR 38000)
£3717 $5874 €5576 Houses in Allinge (61x80cm-24x31in) s.d.22 prov.exhib.lit. 1-Apr-3 Rasmussen, Copenhagen #14/R est:25000-35000 (D.KR 40000)
£4234 $6562 €6351 Nature morte - square table with jug (105x86cm-41x34in) s.d.23 prov.exhib.lit. 1-Oct-2 Rasmussen, Copenhagen #135a est:60000-80000 (D.KR 50000)
£4296 $6831 €6444 Clearing in the woods, Bornholm (89x116cm-35x46in) s.d.33. 26-Feb-3 Kunsthallen, Copenhagen #305/R est:40000 (D.KR 47000)
£4647 $7342 €6971 Cubist still life with blue jug (52x52cm-20x20in) s. painted c.1919-20. 1-Apr-3 Rasmussen, Copenhagen #35/R est:25000 (D.KR 50000)
£16729 $26431 €25094 Dance wearing pink dress against green background (90x69cm-35x27in) s.d.17 prov. 1-Apr-3 Rasmussen, Copenhagen #2/R est:125000-150000 (D.KR 180000)

Works on paper

£383 $605 €575 Flaeskedalen, landscape from Bornholm (45x60cm-18x24in) s.i.d.27-6-38 W/C pencil. 27-Nov-2 Museumsbygningen, Copenhagen #557/R (D.KR 4500)
£423 $651 €635 Woman on horseback (13x23cm-5x9in) s.d.13 Indian ink. 23-Oct-2 Kunsthallen, Copenhagen #6 (D.KR 5000)

RUDELL, Carl (1852-1920) German

Works on paper

£897 $1418 €1400 Garden wall in Blankenheim, Eifel (41x31cm-16x12in) s.d.Sept 1910 W/C board. 16-Nov-2 Lempertz, Koln #1392
£962 $1510 €1500 View of St Kunibert over Rhine (25x34cm-10x13in) s. W/C. 21-Nov-2 Van Ham, Cologne #1891/R est:2000
£1268 $2041 €1800 Village in winter (38x50cm-15x20in) s.d.1925 W/C chl lit. 9-May-3 Schloss Ahlden, Ahlden #1438/R est:2400
£1690 $2721 €2400 Skaters in Volksgarten, Southern Cologne (15x22cm-6x9in) s. i. verso W/C lit. 9-May-3 Schloss Ahlden, Ahlden #1488/R est:2800
£2734 $4374 €3800 Cologne with St Maria Lys Church and Malakoff tower (38x48cm-15x19in) s.d.38 W/C. 17-May-3 Lempertz, Koln #1335/R est:2000
£6115 $9784 €8500 Cologne (49x69cm-19x27in) s. W/C exhib. 17-May-3 Lempertz, Koln #1334/R est:9000

RUDISUHLI, Eduard (1875-1938) Swiss

£324 $522 €486 Young woman in park (39x55cm-15x22in) s. board. 7-May-3 Dobiaschofsky, Bern #3548 (S.FR 700)
£324 $522 €486 Autumn meadow landscape (40x55cm-16x22in) s. board. 7-May-3 Dobiaschofsky, Bern #3549 (S.FR 700)
£370 $596 €555 Landscape with villa (40x53cm-16x21in) s. board. 7-May-3 Dobiaschofsky, Bern #936/R (S.FR 800)
£957 $1483 €1436 Holy Grove (105x150cm-41x59in) s.i. 9-Dec-2 Philippe Schuler, Zurich #8751 (S.FR 2200)

RUDISUHLI, Hermann (1864-1944) Swiss

£385 $562 €600 Trees against cloudy skies (46x75cm-18x30in) s. board. 4-Jun-2 Karl & Faber, Munich #403

£420 $685 €630 Autumnal landscape (57x76cm-22x30in) s.d.1904 board. 13-Feb-3 Christie's, Kensington #181
£577 $912 €900 Man playing lyre on rock in sea with bird (50x39cm-20x15in) s. i. verso board. 16-Nov-2 Quittenbaum, Munich #446/R
£779 $1161 €1200 Autumn landscape (63x90cm-25x35in) s.i.d.1910 panel. 27-Jun-2 Neumeister, Munich #2811/R
£1942 $3108 €2700 Late summer landscape with peasants harvesting hay (66x80cm-26x31in) s. panel prov. 17-May-3 Lempertz, Koln #1476/R est:3000

RUDNAY, Gyula (1878-1957) Hungarian
£877 $1368 €1316 Hilly landscape (58x70cm-23x28in) s. 11-Sep-2 Kieselbach, Budapest #147/R (H.F 340000)
£894 $1395 €1341 Scene (55x69cm-22x27in) 11-Apr-3 Kieselbach, Budapest #108/R est:320000 (H.F 320000)
£1022 $1584 €1533 Small town with riders (40x50cm-16x20in) s. 6-Dec-2 Kieselbach, Budapest #84/R (H.F 380000)
£1183 $1834 €1775 At the market place (41x51cm-16x20in) s. 6-Dec-2 Kieselbach, Budapest #161/R (H.F 440000)
£1290 $2012 €1935 Scene - brother sells Joseph (86x72cm-34x28in) s. 11-Sep-2 Kieselbach, Budapest #134/R (H.F 500000)
£1397 $2180 €2026 Hilly landscape with riders (40x50cm-16x20in) s. 12-Apr-3 Mu Terem Galeria, Budapest #132/R est:350000 (H.F 500000)
£1479 $2293 €2219 Clouds of smoke (40x50cm-16x20in) s. 6-Dec-2 Kieselbach, Budapest #6/R (H.F 550000)
£1935 $3018 €2903 Mother with child (100x75cm-39x30in) s. 11-Sep-2 Kieselbach, Budapest #185/R (H.F 750000)
£2487 $3979 €3731 Lovers under a tree (50x60cm-20x24in) s. 16-May-3 Kieselbach, Budapest #82/R (H.F 850000)
£2689 $4168 €3899 Edge of the woods at Babony (54x42cm-21x17in) s.d.1920. 9-Dec-2 Mu Terem Galeria, Budapest #136/R est:440000 (H.F 1000000)

RUDOLPH, Harold (1850-1884) American
£1024 $1587 €1536 Shoemaker (23x19cm-9x7in) painted c.1880. 1-Oct-2 SOGA, Bratislava #152/R est:25000 (SL.K 65000)

RUDOLPH, Wilhelm (1889-?) German
£1509 $2325 €2400 Summer landscape with peasant in fields (49x59cm-19x23in) mono. verso board. 26-Oct-2 Dr Lehr, Berlin #465/R est:2000
£1528 $2414 €2200 Harvest landscape in high summer (50x75cm-20x30in) mono. masonite. 26-Apr-3 Dr Lehr, Berlin #441/R est:2000

RUDOLPHI, A (?) ?
£286 $418 €429 Still life with peaches and strawberries (30x40cm-12x16in) s. 17-Jun-2 Philippe Schuler, Zurich #7356 (S.FR 650)

RUDZKA-CYBISOWA, Hanna (1897-1988) Polish
Works on paper
£1701 $2704 €2500 Nature morte au givier (41x31cm-16x12in) s.i.indis.d. gouache. 3-Mar-3 Claude Boisgirard, Paris #95 est:3000-3500

RUE, Louis-Felix de la (1731-1765) French
Works on paper
£385 $596 €600 Putti building palace (10x27cm-4x11in) pen ink W/C. 4-Dec-2 Christie's, Rome #397
£886 $1400 €1400 Satyres et femmes presentant des offrandes a un couple de dieux (21x27cm-8x11in) black chk pen brown ink brown wash prov. 27-Nov-2 Christie's, Paris #178/R
£3165 $4937 €5000 Triomphe de Flore. Triomphe de Bacchus (35x50cm-14x20in) pen Chinese ink W/C dr pair prov. 18-Oct-2 Rabourdin & Choppin de Janvry, Paris #95/R

RUE, Philibert Benoit de la (1718-1780) French
Works on paper
£2215 $3500 €3500 Batailles de cavaliers (8x39cm-3x15in) pen ink W/C wash pair. 28-Nov-2 Tajan, Paris #51/R est:1200

RUEDA, Gerardo (1926-) Spanish
£862 $1379 €1250 Multiple (30x30cm-12x12in) i. board. 11-Mar-3 Castellana, Madrid #22/R
£4110 $6411 €6000 Two houses (29x34cm-11x13in) s.d.48. 8-Apr-3 Ansorena, Madrid #264/R
£5137 $8014 €7500 Composition (24x81cm-9x32in) s. 8-Apr-3 Ansorena, Madrid #263/R
Works on paper
£927 $1511 €1400 Abstraction (22x49cm-9x19in) s.d.1957 W/C wax crayon prov. 11-Feb-3 Segre, Madrid #220/R
£943 $1472 €1500 Untitled (25x18cm-10x7in) s.d.1990 collage. 17-Sep-2 Segre, Madrid #167/R

RUEFF, A (19th C) Austrian
£1447 $2228 €2300 Scene de rue (26x35cm-10x14in) s. panel. 23-Oct-2 Rabourdin & Choppin de Janvry, Paris #86/R

RUEGG, Ernst Georg (1883-1948) Swiss
£437 $686 €656 Landscape in spring (44x59cm-17x23in) s. s.i.d.1931 verso. 25-Nov-2 Sotheby's, Zurich #118/R (S.FR 1000)

RUELAS, Julio (1870-1907) Mexican
Works on paper
£936 $1478 €1404 French elederly people (5x29cm-2x11in) s.d.1901 ink. 28-Nov-2 Louis Morton, Mexico #266 est:20000 (M.P 15000)

RUELLAN, Andree (1905-) American
£1935 $3000 €2903 At the circus (33x46cm-13x18in) s. painted c.1940. 8-Dec-2 Toomey, Oak Park #771/R est:3500-5500

RUELLAN, Joseph Alexandre (1864-?) French
£552 $877 €800 Eglise St Michel a Quimperle (46x38cm-18x15in) 4-Mar-3 Livinec, Gaudcheau & Jezequel, Rennes #59

RUETER, Georg (1875-1966) Dutch
£314 $484 €500 Still life of flowers and fruit (30x40cm-12x16in) s. 22-Oct-2 Campo & Campo, Antwerp #228

RUFF, Emma (1884-?) French
£1511 $2417 €2100 Parc anime a Paris (32x41cm-13x16in) s. pair. 13-May-3 Vanderkindere, Brussels #251 est:1500-2500
£2516 $3899 €4000 Young girl in armchair (79x100cm-31x39in) mono. prov. 30-Oct-2 Coutau Begarie, Paris #104/R est:5000-6000

RUFF, George (fl.1880s) British
£280 $442 €420 Figures in a cottage garden (46x61cm-18x24in) s.d.1883. 2-Dec-2 Gorringes, Lewes #2677

RUFF, Thomas (1958-) German
Photographs
£2100 $3423 €3150 Portrait Blaue Augen (51x40cm-20x16in) init.i.d.1991 verso c-print prov.lit. 3-Feb-3 Sotheby's, Olympia #1/R est:2000-3000
£2187 $3500 €3281 Haus no.102 (50x61cm-20x24in) s.d.1989-98 num.15/20 c-print prov. 14-May-3 Sotheby's, New York #390/R est:4000-6000
£2400 $3936 €3600 Haus nr 61 (50x61cm-20x24in) s.d.1989/98 num.5/20 verso cibachrome print prov.lit. 7-Feb-3 Sotheby's, London #121a/R est:3000-4000
£5500 $8470 €8250 Haus Nr.7 II (236x188cm-93x74in) s. d.num.verso chromagenic col print mounted diasec face prov.lit. 23-Oct-2 Christie's, London #199/R est:7000-9000
£6500 $10660 €9750 Double self portrait (29x40cm-11x16in) init.i.d.1992 i.verso cibachrome print prov.lit. 7-Feb-3 Sotheby's, London #103/R est:4000-6000
£11250 $18000 €16875 Nudes FJ 23 (122x139cm-48x55in) s.d.2000 num.5 verso c-print prov.lit. 16-May-3 Phillips, New York #125/R est:12000-18000
£12000 $19680 €18000 Portrat, A Koschkarow (201x157cm-79x62in) s.d.1999 num.2/4 verso cibachrome print prov.lit. 7-Feb-3 Sotheby's, London #125/R est:10000-15000
£12658 $20000 €18987 Nudes 194 (127x100cm-50x39in) chromogenic colorprint mounted with diasec face executed 1999. 14-Nov-2 Christie's, Rockefeller NY #418/R est:20000-25000
£13125 $21000 €19688 Portrait - J Roing (209x165cm-82x65in) s.d.1988 verso num.2/3 chromogenic col print mounted with diasec frame. 15-May-3 Christie's, Rockefeller NY #353/R est:15000-20000
£13924 $22000 €20886 Nacht 19 II (190x190cm-75x75in) s.d.1995 num.2/2 chromogenic colorprint diasec face. 14-Nov-2 Christie's, Rockefeller NY #417/R est:20000-30000
£14500 $22330 €21750 Haus Nr 12 lll a (124x185cm-49x73in) s.d.1989 verso cibachrome print lit. 22-Oct-2 Sotheby's, London #308/R est:12000-15000
£15000 $24600 €22500 Portrat, A Vollmann (201x157cm-79x62in) s.d.1998 num.1/4 cibachrome print prov.lit. 7-Feb-3 Sotheby's, London #124/R est:10000-15000
£17000 $27880 €25500 Nudes pus 10 (135x120cm-53x47in) s.d.2000 num.1/5 verso laserchrome diasec print lit. 7-Feb-3 Sotheby's, London #120/R est:15000-20000
£18987 $30000 €28481 Portrait of Caroline Keever (208x164cm-82x65in) s.i.d.1989 c.print prov. 13-Nov-2 Sotheby's, New York #453/R est:20000-30000
£18987 $30000 €28481 Ruppert (206x160cm-81x63in) s.d.1988 c-print prov. 13-Nov-2 Sotheby's, New York #138/R est:20000-30000

£21875 $35000 €32813 Nudes wr 28 (127x100cm-50x39in) s.d.2000 num.2/5 chromogenic col print mounted with diasec face. 15-May-3 Christie's, Rockefeller NY #355/R est:22000-28000
£22000 $36740 €31900 Nude ft04 (165x120cm-65x47in) s.d.2001 num.1/5 c-print prov.lit. 27-Jun-3 Christie's, London #262/R est:15000-20000
£22000 $36740 €31900 Portrat, T Djordjadze (161x120cm-63x47in) s.d.1999 num.2/4 verso cibachrome print prov.lit. 26-Jun-3 Sotheby's, London #116/R est:10000-15000
£23000 $35420 €34500 12H 06M /-75 (201x134cm-79x53in) s. i.d.1991 col couple print prov.exhib.lit. 22-Oct-2 Sotheby's, London #304/R est:25000-35000
£23734 $37500 €35601 Nudes inn06 (147x114cm-58x45in) s.d.2000 num.1/5 laserchrome diasec prov. 13-Nov-2 Sotheby's, New York #440/R est:25000-35000
£23750 $38000 €35625 Nude laz 04 (130x100cm-51x39in) s.d.2000 chromogenic col print mounted with diasec face. 15-May-3 Christie's, Rockefeller NY #354/R est:25000-35000
£25000 $41750 €36250 Nudes Pl 08 (100x145cm-39x57in) s.d.2001 num.2/5 verso laserchrome print laminated diasec prov. 26-Jun-3 Sotheby's, London #122/R est:15000-20000
£26000 $43420 €37700 Portrat, A Giese (161x120cm-63x47in) s.d.1990 num.4/4 verso cibachrome print prov.lit. 26-Jun-3 Sotheby's, London #117/R est:12000-15000
£37500 $60000 €56250 19h 36m/-35 (260x188cm-102x74in) s.i.d.1992 num.1/2 chromogenic print mounted with diasec face. 15-May-3 Christie's, Rockefeller NY #352/R est:35000-45000
£38000 $63460 €55100 14h 30m - 50 (258x185cm-102x73in) s.i.d.1990 num.2/2 verso c-print prov.lit. 27-Jun-3 Christie's, London #263/R est:25000-35000

Prints
£2405 $3800 €3608 Night photo (76x76cm-30x30in) s.d.1993 verso num.35/45 colour print. 16-Nov-2 New Orleans Auction, New Orleans #1398/R est:3000-5000
£38750 $62000 €58125 Substrat 11 (240x187cm-94x74in) s.i.d.2001 num.3 inkjet on paper mounted with diasec prov.exhib. 15-May-3 Phillips, New York #2/R est:40000-60000

RUFFALO, Gasper J (1908-) American
£390 $600 €585 Sailing the high seas (79x91cm-31x36in) s. board painted c.1940. 8-Sep-2 Treadway Gallery, Cincinnati #569/R

RUFFI, Gianni (1938-) Italian
£609 $962 €950 Small sea (43x60cm-17x24in) board painted 1965. 12-Nov-2 Babuino, Rome #290/R

RUFS, F (20th C) ?
£3000 $5010 €4500 Woodland bather (79x58cm-31x23in) s. 18-Jun-3 Christie's, Kensington #119/R est:3000-5000

RUGE, Rohwedder (19/20th C) German
£681 $1076 €1022 Morning in Skagen (80x122cm-31x48in) s. exhib. 2-Dec-2 Rasmussen, Copenhagen #1378/R (D.KR 8000)

RUGENDAS, Georg Philipp (attrib) (17/18th C) German
£548 $806 €850 Wounded soldier receiving care on battlefield (28x34cm-11x13in) panel. 20-Jun-2 Dr Fritz Nagel, Stuttgart #728/R
£1146 $1789 €1800 Riders in romantic setting (61x82cm-24x32in) 8-Nov-2 Auktionhaus Georg Rehm, Augsburg #8143/R est:2500
£1274 $1987 €2000 Cavalry battle (48x74cm-19x29in) 8-Nov-2 Auktionhaus Georg Rehm, Augsburg #8144/R est:2500

RUGENDAS, Georg Philipp I (1666-1742) German
£1408 $2310 €2042 Cavalry battle (49x71cm-19x28in) 4-Jun-3 Fischer, Luzern #1116/R est:3500-4000 (S.FR 3000)

RUGENDAS, Georg Philipp I (attrib) (1666-1742) German
Works on paper
£265 $432 €400 Cavalry battle (27x34cm-11x13in) Indian ink wash. 14-Feb-3 Paul Kieffer, Pforzhiem #7248
£348 $539 €522 Riders after battle (10x15cm-4x6in) wash Indian ink. 9-Dec-2 Philippe Schuler, Zurich #4184 (S.FR 800)

RUGENDAS, Johann Moritz (1802-1858) German
£21341 $35000 €30944 Vue de Lima (26x36cm-10x14in) mono. canvas on board painted c.1843. 27-May-3 Sotheby's, New York #48
£22866 $37500 €33156 India Mexicana Banandose en el Rio (46x37cm-18x15in) s.d.1834 prov.exhib.lit. 27-May-3 Sotheby's, New York #136
£26452 $38884 €41000 Mexican peasants (51x62cm-20x24in) mono.d.18. 20-Jun-2 Dr Fritz Nagel, Stuttgart #819/R est:4500
£35000 $55300 €52500 View of the Bay of Valparaiso, Chile (64x92cm-25x36in) prov.lit. 15-Nov-2 Sotheby's, London #95/R est:40000-60000
£60976 $100000 €88415 La danse (50x62cm-20x24in) s.d.1850. 27-May-3 Sotheby's, New York #50
£70000 $110600 €105000 Figures by a river, Lima beyond (55x88cm-22x35in) prov.lit. 15-Nov-2 Sotheby's, London #90/R est:40000-60000
£96000 $151680 €144000 Plaza Mayor, Lima (68x92cm-27x36in) prov.lit. 15-Nov-2 Sotheby's, London #88/R est:50000-70000
Works on paper
£1500 $2369 €2250 Lady lying in a hammock at Miraflores, Lima (28x21cm-11x8in) s.i. pencil. 15-Nov-2 Sotheby's, London #89/R est:800-1200

RUGGERI, Piero (1930-) Italian
£897 $1409 €1400 Figure and landscape (50x40cm-20x16in) s. painted 1972. 19-Nov-2 Finarte, Milan #88
£1181 $1877 €1700 Figure (90x70cm-35x28in) s. painted 1970-71. 1-May-3 Meeting Art, Vercelli #445
£1282 $2013 €2000 Hussard in yellow (100x80cm-39x31in) s. s.i.d.1971 verso. 23-Nov-2 Meeting Art, Vercelli #72/R
£1410 $2214 €2200 Napoleon (120x80cm-47x31in) s. 23-Nov-2 Meeting Art, Vercelli #339/R
£1449 $2289 €2260 Paint (30x25cm-12x10in) board painted 1960. 12-Nov-2 Babuino, Rome #94/R

RUGGIERO, Pasquale (1851-1916) Italian
£2146 $3391 €3219 Net repairers on the beach of Naples (32x46cm-13x18in) s.i. 29-Nov-2 Zofingen, Switzerland #2535/R est:4500 (S.FR 5000)
£2837 $4596 €4000 View of Naples (32x46cm-13x18in) s.i. 22-May-3 Dorotheum, Vienna #12/R est:5000-6000

RUHM, Gerhard (1930-) Austrian
Works on paper
£696 $1100 €1100 Drawing (43x61cm-17x24in) s.d.13.10.71 pencil. 27-Nov-2 Dorotheum, Vienna #291/R
£1519 $2354 €2400 Perception (70x49cm-28x19in) collage mixed media. 24-Sep-2 Wiener Kunst Auktionen, Vienna #261/R est:2000-3000

RUHTENBERG, Cornelis (1923-) American/Latvian
£1195 $1840 €1900 Sick girl (37x61cm-15x24in) s.d.1947 i. verso panel. 26-Oct-2 Dr Lehr, Berlin #467/R

RUIFROK, Wilhelmus (20th C) New Zealander
£3343 $5216 €5015 Mound of Humankind (128x182cm-50x72in) s.i.d.1988. 17-Sep-2 Peter Webb, Auckland #113/R est:20000-30000 (NZ.D 11000)

RUIN, Ingrid (1881-1956) Finnish
£1111 $1822 €1700 Girl on stones on the beach (68x41cm-27x16in) s. 9-Feb-3 Bukowskis, Helsinki #344/R est:1500
Sculpture
£949 $1481 €1500 The ring (26cm-10in) s.d.1910 bronze. 15-Sep-2 Bukowskis, Helsinki #148/R

RUIPEREZ, Luis (1832-1867) Spanish
£3200 $5088 €4800 Bookshop (34x29cm-13x11in) s.d.1861 panel prov. 20-Mar-3 Christie's, Kensington #91/R est:3500-4500

RUITER DE WITT, Maria de (1947-) Dutch
£5828 $9615 €8451 Tribute to Ni Pollok (130x130cm-51x51in) s.d. 6-Jul-3 Christie's, Hong Kong #16/R est:48000-65000 (HK.D 75000)

RUITH, Horace van (1839-1923) British
£1282 $1987 €2000 Man in rags playing flute with dog (35x41cm-14x16in) s. panel lit. 6-Dec-2 Karlheinz Kaupp, Staufen #2305/R est:2400

RUIZ BALERDI, Rafael (1934-1992) Spanish
Works on paper
£563 $918 €850 Untitled (35x48cm-14x19in) s. ink. 11-Feb-3 Segre, Madrid #298/R

RUIZ DE LA CASA (20th C) Spanish?
£336 $540 €500 Aranjuez (50x60cm-20x24in) s. s.i.d.1990. 18-Feb-3 Durán, Madrid #591/R

RUIZ FERRANDIS, Francisco (1909-) Spanish
£296 $480 €450 Valencian carnations (55x46cm-22x18in) s. s.i.verso. 21-Jan-3 Ansorena, Madrid #859/R

RUIZ LUNA, Justo (1865-1926) Spanish
£1923 $3038 €3000 Coastal landscape (64x78cm-25x31in) s. 13-Nov-2 Ansorena, Madrid #184/R

£4027 $6483 €6000 Serrallo Guard (69x46cm-27x18in) s. 18-Feb-3 Durán, Madrid #232/R

RUIZ MORALES, Francisco (19th C) Spanish
Works on paper
£1689 $2635 €2500 View of Granada (63x42cm-25x17in) s. W/C. 25-Mar-3 Durán, Madrid #704/R

RUIZ, Antonio (1897-1964) Mexican
£111317 $178108 €161410 Ensayo de titeres (29x20cm-11x8in) s.d.1935 tempera board. 15-May-3 Louis Morton, Mexico #83/R est:450000-800000 (M.P 1800000)
£178344 $280000 €267516 Main speaker (31x22cm-12x9in) canvas on board painted 1939 prov.exhib.lit. 19-Nov-2 Sotheby's, New York #3/R est:300000

RUIZ, Cristobal (20th C) Spanish
£774 $1223 €1200 Vase with coloured leaves (59x45cm-23x18in) s. board. 18-Dec-2 Ansorena, Madrid #198/R

RUIZ-PIPO, Manolo (1929-1998) Spanish
£274 $427 €400 Montmartre et portrait de femme (26x34cm-10x13in) s. 13-Apr-3 Feletin, Province #145
£1538 $2385 €2400 Les enfants du Paradis (116x80cm-46x31in) s.d.1956. 6-Dec-2 Rieunier, Bailly-Pommery, Mathias, Paris #95/R

RUKAVINA, Robert (1914-1977) American
£287 $450 €431 Large crowd at the State Fair (61x76cm-24x30in) 20-Nov-2 Boos Gallery, Michigan #395/R
£1019 $1600 €1529 Crowd of African Americans with boy holding US flag (51x61cm-20x24in) s.d.1963. 20-Nov-2 Boos Gallery, Michigan #392/R est:500-700

RUL, Henri (1862-1942) Belgian
£288 $453 €450 Fagne (48x68cm-19x27in) 25-Nov-2 Amberes, Antwerp #193
£513 $805 €800 Paysage hivernal (63x85cm-25x33in) 25-Nov-2 Amberes, Antwerp #194
£755 $1162 €1200 Paysage au fosse (33x25cm-13x10in) s. 22-Oct-2 Campo, Vlaamse Kaai #607
£897 $1409 €1400 Pies dans la foret (54x70cm-21x28in) 25-Nov-2 Amberes, Antwerp #192

RULLENS, Jules (1850-?) Belgian
£278 $453 €420 Interieur flamand (65x48cm-26x19in) s. 17-Feb-3 Horta, Bruxelles #300

RUMEAU, Jean Claude (18/19th C) French
Works on paper
£17931 $28510 €26000 Le reveil de la Belle au bois dormant (38x46cm-15x18in) s.d.1810 gouache exhib. 5-Mar-3 Oger, Dumont, Paris #27/R

RUMENAPF, Ludwig (19/20th C) German?
£417 $654 €650 Young Berber 1913 (70x54cm-28x21in) s.i. i. verso board. 23-Nov-2 Arnold, Frankfurt #855

RUMMELSPACHER, Joseph (1852-1921) German
£500 $820 €750 Down at the rocky shore (66x96cm-26x38in) s. i.verso. 5-Jun-3 Christie's, Kensington #696/R

RUMOHR, Knut (1916-2002) Norwegian
£255 $392 €383 Formations (22x28cm-9x11in) s. tempera painted 1974. 28-Oct-2 Blomqvist, Lysaker #1248/R (N.KR 3000)
£272 $418 €408 Composition (36x27cm-14x11in) s. tempera painted 1963. 28-Oct-2 Blomqvist, Lysaker #1247 (N.KR 3200)
£351 $554 €527 Study I (39x49cm-15x19in) s.d.77 i.verso. 17-Dec-2 Grev Wedels Plass, Oslo #271 (N.KR 4000)
£542 $879 €813 Composition (50x65cm-20x26in) s. tempera. 27-Jan-3 Blomqvist, Lysaker #1206/R (N.KR 6000)
£1062 $1678 €1593 Landscape from Faroe Islands (100x80cm-39x31in) s.d.70 i. stretcher tempera. 28-Apr-3 Blomqvist, Oslo #383/R (N.KR 12000)
£1298 $2050 €1947 Composition (50x65cm-20x26in) s.d.80 tempera. 2-Dec-2 Blomqvist, Oslo #453/R est:15000-18000 (N.KR 15000)
£1930 $3049 €2895 Composition (80x100cm-31x39in) s.d.64 i.verso. 17-Dec-2 Grev Wedels Plass, Oslo #270/R est:10000-15000 (N.KR 22000)
£2437 $3899 €3656 Vase on patterned tablecloth (125x100cm-49x39in) s.d.86 exhib. 17-Mar-3 Blomqvist, Oslo #436/R est:25000-40000 (N.KR 28000)
£3287 $5194 €4931 Stones (52x67cm-20x26in) s.d.1962 tempera exhib. 2-Dec-2 Blomqvist, Oslo #455/R est:15000-18000 (N.KR 38000)

RUMP, Godfred (1816-1880) Danish
£253 $395 €380 Landscape with large stones, Jylland (39x44cm-15x17in) 23-Sep-2 Rasmussen, Vejle #68/R (D.KR 3000)
£335 $543 €486 Wooded landscape with lake, summer (37x55cm-15x22in) s.d.1873. 26-May-3 Rasmussen, Copenhagen #1534 (D.KR 3500)
£403 $629 €605 Coastal landscape with sailing ship at moonlight (72x85cm-28x33in) s.d.1878. 11-Nov-2 Rasmussen, Vejle #633/R (D.KR 4700)
£6029 $9165 €9044 Farmers by a marl pit (63x78cm-25x31in) painted 1837 exhib. 27-Aug-2 Rasmussen, Copenhagen #1495/R est:60000 (D.KR 70000)

RUMPF, Gernot (1941-) German
Sculpture
£1367 $2242 €1900 House of love (18x31x9cm-7x12x4in) brown pat.bronze. 4-Jun-3 Reiss & Sohn, Konigstein #624/R est:1500
£1582 $2500 €2500 Portraits of Herzog von Urbino and wife Battista Sforza (60x47x47cm-24x19x19in) col pat.bronze. 30-Nov-2 Arnold, Frankfurt #477/R est:4000

RUMPF, Philipp (1821-1896) German
£602 $969 €873 Portrait of young woman wearing white shawl (18x14cm-7x6in) mono. copperplate. 7-May-3 Dobiaschofsky, Bern #938/R (S.FR 1300)
£800 $1264 €1200 Waiting (24x19cm-9x7in) s. 2-Dec-2 Bonhams, Bath #156/R

RUMPLER, Franz (1848-1922) Austrian
£3165 $5000 €5000 Figures strolling in garden (18x13cm-7x5in) s. panel. 26-Nov-2 Wiener Kunst Auktionen, Vienna #36/R est:5000-7000

RUMYANTSVEV, Nikolai (1937-) Russian
£250 $380 €375 Model near the screen (46x28cm-18x11in) s. 14-Jul-2 John Nicholson, Haslemere #109

RUND, Franz (1883-1962) Austrian
£471 $750 €707 Still life with fruit and flowers (74x102cm-29x40in) s. 7-Mar-3 Jackson's, Cedar Falls #529/R

RUNDLE, J S (19th C) British
Works on paper
£1250 $1988 €1813 Muscat (16x29cm-6x11in) pen ink W/C executed c.1839 with two other W/C three. 29-Apr-3 Henry Adams, Chichester #185

RUNDT, Carl Ludwig (1802-1868) German
£18000 $28260 €27000 Rom panorama - panoramic of Rome (27x53cm-11x21in) s.d.57. 19-Nov-2 Sotheby's, London #106/R est:20000-30000

RUNEBERG, Ludvig Michael (20th C) Finnish
Works on paper
£719 $1180 €1000 Sund (21x30cm-8x12in) mixed media lit. 5-Jun-3 Hagelstam, Helsinki #893

RUNEBERG, Walter (1838-1920) Finnish
£943 $1453 €1500 Coastal landscape (38x46cm-15x18in) 27-Oct-2 Bukowskis, Helsinki #264/R est:350
£1195 $1840 €1900 Oyster gatherers in Brittany (32x41cm-13x16in) 27-Oct-2 Bukowskis, Helsinki #263/R est:350
Sculpture
£1321 $2034 €2100 Girl (50cm-20in) s. plaster. 27-Oct-2 Bukowskis, Helsinki #130/R est:300
£8576 $13379 €12864 Lex (92x73x34cm-36x29x13in) s. pat.bronze st.f.Gruet sold with sandstone socle. 11-Nov-2 Rasmussen, Vejle #712/R est:80000-100000 (D.KR 100000)

RUNGE, Julius Friedrich Ludwig (1843-1922) German
£705 $1093 €1100 Breakers near the Genoa lighthouse with cloudy skies and rocky coast (92x141cm-36x56in) s. 4-Dec-2 Neumeister, Munich #871

RUNGIUS, Carl (1869-1959) American/German
£2690 $4250 €4035 Challenged (18x13cm-7x5in) s.d.1919 board. 17-Nov-2 CRN Auctions, Cambridge #8/R
£4114 $6500 €5965 Mountain landscape (23x28cm-9x11in) s. 26-Jul-3 Coeur d'Alene, Hayden #79/R est:8000-12000
£7333 $12027 €11000 Sunlit lake in the Rockies (22x27cm-9x11in) s. canvas on board. 3-Jun-3 Joyner, Toronto #154/R est:8000-12000 (C.D 16500)
£10730 $16953 €16095 Mount Rundle (23x30cm-9x12in) s. s.i.d.1946 verso prov. 3-Apr-3 Heffel, Vancouver #80/R est:20000-25000 (C.D 25000)
£22152 $35000 €33228 Study for Big Horn ram's head (32x39cm-13x15in) s. board prov. 3-Apr-3 Christie's, Rockefeller NY #131/R est:7000-10000

£25316 $40000 €37974 Missouri prong horn antelope (41x36cm-16x14in) s. board prov. 3-Apr-3 Christie's, Rockefeller NY #146/R est:7000-10000
£37809 $61250 €54823 In the Yukon Territory 1919 (46x61cm-18x24in) 23-May-3 Altermann Galleries, Santa Fe #78
£117284 $190000 €175926 Mighty elk (77x107cm-30x42in) s. 21-May-3 Sotheby's, New York #220/R est:150000-250000
£139241 $220000 €201899 Visit to the lily pond (64x76cm-25x30in) s. prov. 26-Jul-3 Coeur d'Alene, Hayden #115/R est:100000-150000
£335484 $520000 €503226 Alaskan brown bear out of the shadows (152x190cm-60x75in) s. painted 1918 prov.exhib.lit. 5-Dec-2 Christie's, Rockefeller NY #185/R est:300000-500000

Prints
£1889 $3098 €2739 Old prospector (16x21cm-6x8in) s. etching aquatint. 9-Jun-3 Hodgins, Calgary #305/R est:2500-3500 (C.D 4250)
£3111 $5102 €4511 Alaskan wilderness (20x28cm-8x11in) s. etching aquatint. 9-Jun-3 Hodgins, Calgary #303/R est:3000-4000 (C.D 7000)
£3797 $6000 €5506 Morning mist (15x20cm-6x8in) s. etching lit. 26-Jul-3 Coeur d'Alene, Hayden #185/R est:3000-5000

Sculpture
£52469 $85000 €78704 Big-horn sheep (42cm-17in) i. reddish brown pat. bronze lit. 22-May-3 Christie's, Rockefeller NY #18/R est:50000-70000

Works on paper
£6013 $9500 €9020 Running antelope (39x55cm-15x22in) s. graphite executed 1897 prov.lit. 3-Apr-3 Christie's, Rockefeller NY #145/R est:2000-3000
£6962 $11000 €10443 Study of four antelope heads (39x55cm-15x22in) s. graphite prov.lit. 3-Apr-3 Christie's, Rockefeller NY #144/R est:2000-3000

RUOFF, Fritz (1906-) German

Works on paper
£641 $994 €1000 Miniature: divided circle (11x11cm-4x4in) s. s.i.d.7/1964 verso W/C lit. 6-Dec-2 Karlheinz Kaupp, Staufen #2296/R
£1154 $1788 €1800 Composition (27x26cm-11x10in) s. collage gouache lit. 6-Dec-2 Karlheinz Kaupp, Staufen #2298/R est:1800

RUOKOKOSKI, Jalmari (1886-1936) Finnish
£331 $543 €460 The child (46x38cm-18x15in) s.d.1923. 4-Jun-3 Bukowskis, Helsinki #406/R
£465 $717 €740 Landscape (44x48cm-17x19in) s.d.1934. 24-Oct-2 Hagelstam, Helsinki #912
£509 $785 €810 Flowers (55x38cm-22x15in) s.d.1922. 24-Oct-2 Hagelstam, Helsinki #843/R
£566 $872 €900 Landscape (46x55cm-18x22in) s.d.1922. 24-Oct-2 Hagelstam, Helsinki #911
£719 $1180 €1000 Landscape (43x62cm-17x24in) s. 5-Jun-3 Hagelstam, Helsinki #849/R
£774 $1223 €1200 Potato field (30x40cm-12x16in) s.d.1916. 19-Dec-2 Hagelstam, Helsinki #853/R
£850 $1352 €1250 Roses (51x60cm-20x24in) s. 27-Feb-3 Hagelstam, Helsinki #896/R
£881 $1356 €1400 By the hole in the ice (50x71cm-20x28in) 27-Oct-2 Bukowskis, Helsinki #265/R
£915 $1501 €1400 Pine on beach (46x55cm-18x22in) s.d.1920. 9-Feb-3 Bukowskis, Helsinki #346/R
£1076 $1700 €1700 Still life of fish (83x85cm-33x33in) s.d.1926. 1-Dec-2 Bukowskis, Helsinki #149/R est:2000-2500
£1139 $1800 €1800 Girl with red cheeks (50x37cm-20x15in) s.i.d.1913 lit. 30-Nov-2 Hagelstam, Helsinki #85/R est:2500
£1266 $2000 €2000 Still life of birds (74x100cm-29x39in) s.d.1933. 1-Dec-2 Bukowskis, Helsinki #148/R est:2200-2500
£1392 $2200 €2200 Women bathing (55x60cm-22x24in) s.d.1917. 30-Nov-2 Hagelstam, Helsinki #84/R est:2500
£3310 $5230 €4800 Sleeping (78x46cm-31x18in) s. 3-Apr-3 Hagelstam, Helsinki #1015/R est:1500

Works on paper
£252 $387 €400 Roses (33x24cm-13x9in) s.d.1915 W/C. 27-Oct-2 Bukowskis, Helsinki #268/R

RUOPPOLO, Gian Battista (1629-1693) Italian
£64748 $103597 €90000 Still life of fruit in basket on stone ledge (74x111cm-29x44in) 13-May-3 Sotheby's, Amsterdam #79/R est:40000-60000

RUOPPOLO, Gian Battista (attrib) (1629-1693) Italian
£45161 $70000 €67742 Celery in a basket, watermelon on a plate, and apples on a ledge (131x93cm-52x37in) prov.lit. 2-Oct-2 Christie's, Rockefeller NY #149/R est:20000-30000

RUOT (1939-) ?
£1747 $2742 €2621 Allegro (80x80cm-31x31in) s. 25-Nov-2 Germann, Zurich #101/R est:4000-5000 (S.FR 4000)

RUPERTI, Madya (1903-1981) Swiss/Russian
£694 $1097 €1000 Sailing ship and moon (55x38cm-22x15in) s.d.50. 24-Apr-3 Dorotheum, Vienna #165/R

Works on paper
£365 $576 €548 Abstract composition (13x24cm-5x9in) mono.d.62 collage. 29-Nov-2 Zofingen, Switzerland #3052 (S.FR 850)
£513 $810 €800 Untitled (33x24cm-13x9in) mono.d.71 material collage. 12-Nov-2 Dorotheum, Vienna #227/R
£641 $1013 €1000 Untitled (63x50cm-25x20in) s.d.62 gouache. 12-Nov-2 Dorotheum, Vienna #197/R
£769 $1215 €1200 Untitled (62x49cm-24x19in) s.d.62 oil gouache. 12-Nov-2 Dorotheum, Vienna #204/R

RUPPERSBERG, Allen (1944-) American

Works on paper
£1218 $1900 €1827 Searching for passion and sex (7x25cm-3x10in) s.d.1979 pencil dr. three in one frame. 30-Mar-3 Butterfields, Los Angeles #1452/R est:2000-3000

RUPPERT, Friedrich Karl Leopold (1878-1939) German
£1282 $1987 €2000 Still life with apples, old bottles and jug (65x80cm-26x31in) s.d.1914. 6-Dec-2 Michael Zeller, Lindau #905/R

RUPPERT, Otto von (1841-?) German
£788 $1229 €1150 Weissenburg in Elsace (25x19cm-10x7in) s. s.i.d. verso panel. 11-Apr-3 Winterberg, Heidelberg #549/R
£1146 $1800 €1719 Tightrope walker (26x35cm-10x14in) s. panel. 22-Nov-2 Skinner, Boston #34/R est:2000-4000

RURIER, E (19th C) Belgian
£1747 $2725 €2621 Fish market in Ostend (25x39cm-10x15in) s. i. verso panel. 6-Nov-2 Dobiaschofsky, Bern #934/R est:1500 (S.FR 4000)

RUSCA, Carlo Francesco (1696-1769) Swiss
£1573 $2422 €2500 Portrait d'un acteur de theatre en Don Quichotte (49x38cm-19x15in) s.d.1737. 25-Oct-2 Tajan, Paris #40/R est:3000-4000

RUSCH, Mabel (19/20th C) American
£299 $500 €434 Sao Paolo (51x61cm-20x24in) s.i.d.27. 22-Jun-3 Jeffery Burchard, Florida #77/R

RUSCHA, Edward (1937-) American
£22785 $36000 €34178 Safe (51x76cm-20x30in) s.d.1990 acrylic prov. 13-Nov-2 Sotheby's, New York #123/R est:20000-25000
£34810 $55000 €52215 City boy (76x102cm-30x40in) s.d.1990 acrylic on paper prov. 12-Nov-2 Phillips, New York #124/R est:40000-60000
£46875 $75000 €70313 Dish (102x152cm-40x60in) s.d.1985 acrylic pigment paper prov. 15-May-3 Christie's, Rockefeller NY #183/R est:30000-40000
£60000 $98400 €90000 Production (51x61cm-20x24in) i. s.d.1972 on stretcher prov.exhib. 6-Feb-3 Sotheby's, London #1/R est:70000
£91772 $145000 €137658 Glass of milk, falling (51x61cm-20x24in) s. i.d.1967 on stretcher prov.exhib. 13-Nov-2 Sotheby's, New York #119/R est:150000-200000
£126582 $200000 €189873 Days of the week (56x203cm-22x80in) s. i.d.1979 on stretcher prov. 13-Nov-2 Sotheby's, New York #239/R est:175000-225000
£164557 $260000 €246836 Spasm (152x137cm-60x54in) s.d.1987 s.i.d.on stretcher acrylic prov.exhib. 14-Nov-2 Christie's, Rockefeller NY #190/R est:250000-350000
£175000 $280000 €262500 Era ends (163x163cm-64x64in) s.i.d.86 verso oil enamel prov. 14-May-3 Christie's, Rockefeller NY #17/R est:200000-300000
£180000 $295200 €270000 Who am I ? (56x203cm-22x80in) i. s.i.d.1979 on stretcher acrylic prov.exhib.lit. 6-Feb-3 Sotheby's, London #40/R est:150000
£240506 $380000 €360759 Ghost ship (163x163cm-64x64in) s.d.1986 verso s.i.d.on stretcher oil enamel prov.exhib. 12-Nov-2 Sotheby's, New York #63/R est:350000-450000
£250000 $400000 €375000 Heaven (150x370cm-59x146in) s.d.86 verso prov.exhib. 13-May-3 Sotheby's, New York #36/R est:250000-350000
£284810 $450000 €427215 That was then this is now (107x244cm-42x96in) s.d.1989 s.i.d.on stretcher prov. 13-Nov-2 Sotheby's, New York #128/R est:250000-350000
£303797 $480000 €455696 Cold beer beautiful girls (213x152cm-84x60in) s.d.93 verso s.i.d.on stretcher acrylic on canvas prov.exhib. 13-Nov-2 Christie's, Rockefeller NY #39/R est:400000-600000
£307692 $480000 €461538 Peach (76x74cm-30x29in) s.d.1964 prov. 11-Nov-2 Phillips, New York #11/R est:400000-600000
£822785 $1300000 €1234178 War surplus (180x169cm-71x67in) painted 1962 prov.exhib.lit. 13-Nov-2 Christie's, Rockefeller NY #18/R est:1500000-2000000
£1012658 $1600000 €1518987 Desire (152x140cm-60x55in) s.i.d.1969 on stretcher s.d.verso prov.exhib.lit. 13-Nov-2 Christie's, Rockefeller NY #29/R est:1000000-1500000

Photographs

£9494 $15000 €14241 Four parking lots, Church of Chris. Pierce Collage. Fashion Square. Unidentified (51x41cm-20x16in) s.num.33/35 black white photographs prov. 13-Nov-2 Sotheby's, New York #241/R est:12000-18000

£18987 $30000 €28481 The end (28x36cm-11x14in) num.ru61-ru64 four holograms executed 1997. 14-Nov-2 Christie's, Rockefeller NY #105/R est:35000-45000

£37500 $60000 €56250 Parking lots (50x40cm-20x16in) init. num.5/35 verso gelatin silver print set of 30 prov.lit. 15-May-3 Christie's, Rockefeller NY #204/R est:60000-80000

£44304 $70000 €66456 Gasoline station 1962 (49x58cm-19x23in) num.9/25 ten gelatin silver prints on board prov.lit. 14-Nov-2 Christie's, Rockefeller NY #106/R est:60000-80000

Prints

£1763 $2750 €2645 Fruit-metrecal Hollywood (37x107cm-15x42in) s.d.num.48/85 organic silkscreen. 14-Oct-2 Butterfields, San Francisco #1348/R est:1500-2000

£1899 $3000 €2849 Sin (48x67cm-19x26in) s.d.1970 num.46/150 col lithograph. 22-Apr-3 Butterfields, San Francisco #2358/R est:4000-6000

£2044 $3250 €3066 V, W A C 185 (92x69cm-36x27in) s.d.num.20/35 black lithograph. 2-May-3 Sotheby's, New York #588/R est:2000-3000

£2166 $3400 €3249 Us (60x82cm-24x32in) s.d.1994 mixografia. 21-Nov-2 Swann Galleries, New York #188/R est:3000-5000

£2258 $3500 €3387 OOO (51x71cm-20x28in) s.d.1970 num.73/90 col lithograph. 25-Sep-2 Christie's, Rockefeller NY #385/R est:1400-1800

£2500 $4125 €3625 Fruit-Metrecal Hollywood (26x96cm-10x38in) s.d.num.49/85 col screenprint. 2-Jul-3 Christie's, London #351/R est:3000-5000

£2516 $4000 €3774 Coyote (114x86cm-45x34in) s.d.num.5/30 lithograph. 29-Apr-3 Christie's, Rockefeller NY #739/R est:3500-4500

£2830 $4500 €4245 Sin (33x55cm-13x22in) s.d.num.105/150 col screenprint. 29-Apr-3 Christie's, Rockefeller NY #736/R est:4000-6000

£3006 $4750 €4509 Now (153x102cm-60x40in) s.d.1990 num.35/60 lithograph. 22-Apr-3 Butterfields, San Francisco #2360/R est:3500-4000

£3797 $6000 €5696 Cheese mold standard with olive (65x102cm-26x40in) s.d.1969 num.129/150 col silkscreen. 22-Apr-3 Butterfields, San Francisco #2357/R est:7000-9000

£5346 $8500 €8019 Cheese mold standard with olive (50x94cm-20x37in) s.i.d. col screenprint. 29-Apr-3 Christie's, Rockefeller NY #735/R est:8000-10000

£5975 $9500 €8963 Evil (50x75cm-20x30in) s.d.num.17/30 verso col screenprint wood veneer. 2-May-3 Sotheby's, New York #586/R est:6000-8000

£6918 $11000 €10377 Adios (24x56cm-9x22in) s.d.num.6/20 col lithograph. 29-Apr-3 Christie's, Rockefeller NY #733/R est:2500-3000

£6918 $11000 €10377 Mocha standard (50x94cm-20x37in) s.d.num.10/100 col screenprint. 29-Apr-3 Christie's, Rockefeller NY #734/R est:8000-12000

£9615 $15000 €14423 Hollywood (44x113cm-17x44in) s.d.num.57/100 col screenprint. 5-Nov-2 Christie's, Rockefeller NY #483/R est:15000-20000

£10063 $16000 €15095 Hollywood with observatory (6x74cm-2x29in) s.d.num.3/17 col lithograph. 29-Apr-3 Christie's, Rockefeller NY #732/R est:10000-15000

£10256 $16000 €15384 Hollywood (45x113cm-18x44in) s.d.num.53/100 silkscreen. 14-Oct-2 Butterfields, San Francisco #1347/R est:15000-20000

£16667 $26000 €25001 Standard station (65x102cm-26x40in) s.d.num.30/50 col screenprint. 5-Nov-2 Christie's, Rockefeller NY #482/R est:20000-30000

Sculpture

£5000 $8000 €7500 Me (20x13x3cm-8x5x1in) s.d.2001 acrylic clothbound first edition book prov. 14-May-3 Sotheby's, New York #209/R est:8000-12000

Works on paper

£14063 $22500 €21095 Dynamo (28x38cm-11x15in) s.d.89 dry pigment acrylic on paper prov. 14-May-3 Sotheby's, New York #200/R est:12000-18000

£15823 $25000 €23735 Last thing I need in a pair of binoculars (58x74cm-23x29in) s.d.1982 gouache pastel. 13-Nov-2 Sotheby's, New York #284/R est:20000-30000

£18987 $30000 €28481 Very true (57x76cm-22x30in) pastel executed 1973 prov. 13-Nov-2 Sotheby's, New York #285/R est:20000-30000

£28000 $46760 €40600 Sheets with whisky stains (36x58cm-14x23in) s.d.1973 W/C pencil prov. 26-Jun-3 Sotheby's, London #133/R est:15000-20000

£28125 $45000 €42188 Wolf (25x29cm-10x11in) s.d.64 pastel wax crayon ink graphite prov. 15-May-3 Christie's, Rockefeller NY #129/R est:70000

£113924 $180000 €170886 Blank (22x20cm-9x8in) s.d.1963 verso gouache on board prov. 14-Nov-2 Christie's, Rockefeller NY #133/R est:70000-90000

RUSCHE WOLTERS, Ursula (1914-2003) German

£1367 $2187 €1900 Perachora (120x85cm-47x33in) s.i.d. stretcher exhib. 15-May-3 Neumeister, Munich #777/R est:1800-2000

Works on paper

£540 $863 €750 Mythological scene - Sirens (96x69cm-38x27in) s.mono.d. W/C Indian ink brush bodycol. 15-May-3 Neumeister, Munich #778/R

RUSCHI, Francesco (attrib) (17th C) Italian

£7372 $11426 €11500 Justice and Wealth (71x106cm-28x42in) 5-Dec-2 Stadion, Trieste #655/R est:15000

RUSDAL, Torstein (1887-1971) Norwegian

£256 $399 €384 Coastal landscape (56x75cm-22x30in) s. panel painted 1959. 23-Sep-2 Blomqvist, Lysaker #102 (N.KR 3000)

RUSHBURY, Sir Henry (1889-1968) British

Works on paper

£260 $406 €390 High Bridge, Lincoln (30x24cm-12x9in) s. pencil chl W/C. 25-Mar-3 Gildings, Market Harborough #396

£280 $437 €420 Italian town (28x36cm-11x14in) s. pencil dr. 26-Mar-3 Woolley & Wallis, Salisbury #46/R

£380 $593 €570 Mullion Cove with figures on the quay (28x41cm-11x16in) s.d.1927 pen W/C. 7-Nov-2 Bonhams, Cornwall #801/R

£650 $1073 €943 Santa Maria della Salute, Venice (37x43cm-15x17in) s.i.d.1931 pencil W/C bodycol. 3-Jul-3 Christie's, Kensington #148/R

£1050 $1638 €1575 Godmanchester. The Common, St Ives (45x25cm-18x10in) s.i. one d.1934 W/C pencil pair. 17-Oct-2 Lawrence, Crewkerne #432/R est:600-900

RUSHTON, William Charles (1860-1921) British

£380 $593 €570 Sunlight and shadow, Beckfoot, Bingley (38x54cm-15x21in) s.indis.d.79 i.verso. 10-Apr-3 Tennants, Leyburn #982

£500 $780 €750 River landscape (51x76cm-20x30in) s.d.1887. 17-Sep-2 Sotheby's, Olympia #6/R

£550 $853 €825 Woodland, spring time Bolton woods (30x46cm-12x18in) s.i.verso. 30-Oct-2 Wingetts, Wrexham #216/R

RUSINOL, Santiago (1861-1931) Spanish

£17763 $28776 €27000 Boat keeper (81x151cm-32x59in) s. 21-Jan-3 Ansorena, Madrid #168/R est:24000

£160000 $251200 €240000 Casa de pescadors, Mallorca - Fisherman's house, Majorca (89x129cm-35x51in) s. painted 1905 prov.exhib.lit. 19-Nov-2 Sotheby's, London #10/R est:130000-180000

RUSKIN, John (1819-1900) British

Works on paper

£1400 $2212 €2100 Study of a gothic capital Wooded landscape (20x24cm-8x9in) W/C over pencil htd white prov. 28-Nov-2 Sotheby's, London #265/R est:1500-2000

£2200 $3410 €3300 Le Puy, France (31x23cm-12x9in) pencil htd bodycol. 3-Dec-2 Sotheby's, Olympia #44/R est:2000-3000

£2800 $4592 €4060 Northern facade of the monastery of S Giovanni a Carbonara, Naples, Italy (30x46cm-12x18in) i. pencil pen ink wash prov.exhib.lit. 5-Jun-3 Christie's, London #106/R est:3000-5000

£4200 $6888 €6090 Ruined belfry (46x32cm-18x13in) i. pencil blue grey wash prov. 5-Jun-3 Christie's, London #107/R est:2000-3000

£4600 $7314 €6900 Alpine scene, Switzerland (13x25cm-5x10in) s. W/C. 29-Apr-3 Gorringes, Lewes #2227

RUSPINI, R (19/20th C) Italian

£2532 $4000 €4000 Naples Bay (29x62cm-11x24in) s. i.verso. 26-Nov-2 Christie's, Rome #16/R

RUSS, C B (19th C) American

£417 $650 €626 Estuary (30x51cm-12x20in) s.d.1876 panel. 9-Nov-2 Sloan, North Bethesda #597/R

£1321 $2100 €1982 On the lake (66x122cm-26x48in) s.d.1877. 7-Mar-3 Skinner, Boston #273/R est:3000-5000

RUSS, Franz (younger) (1844-1906) Austrian

£565 $920 €848 Little girls eating apples (33x24cm-13x9in) s.i.d.1887 panel. 12-Feb-3 Iegor de Saint Hippolyte, Montreal #167 (C.D 1400)

£6013 $9500 €9500 Oriental beauty (100x74cm-39x29in) s.d.1868. 28-Nov-2 Dorotheum, Vienna #97/R est:4500-5500

RUSS, Robert (1847-1922) Austrian

£1900 $2888 €2850 Children playing by a torrent (131x89cm-52x35in) s.d.1874. 29-Aug-2 Christie's, Kensington #101/R est:1000-1500

£2465 $3968 €3500 Waidhofen (25x30cm-10x12in) s.d.1869. 10-May-3 Hans Stahl, Toestorf #17/R est:3300

£5696 $9000 €9000 Wooded landscape with figure (40x50cm-16x20in) s.d.1910 canvas on board. 28-Nov-2 Dorotheum, Vienna #14/R est:11000-13000
£10759 $17000 €17000 Southern garden landscape (19x29cm-7x11in) s. 28-Nov-2 Dorotheum, Vienna #176/R est:18000-22000
£24113 $39064 €34000 Mill in sunlight (60x80cm-24x31in) s. 22-May-3 Dorotheum, Vienna #44/R est:34000-45000
Works on paper
£943 $1462 €1500 Mountain stream (40x28cm-16x11in) s. mixed media. 1-Oct-2 Dorotheum, Vienna #249/R est:3000-3500

RUSSE, K (20th C) German/Austrian
£1500 $2505 €2250 Wildflowers in a vase with a plate of cherries, china figurine and a tea services on draped table (100x80cm-39x31in) s. 18-Jun-3 Christie's, Kensington #31/R est:1800-2200

RUSSELL, Andrew J (1830-1902) American
Photographs
£2452 $3800 €3678 Green river valley, looking down the river (23x28cm-9x11in) num.25 albumen print. 5-Dec-2 Swann Galleries, New York #365/R est:1800-2200

RUSSELL, Charles M (1864-1926) American
£60127 $95000 €87184 Red Crow - Chief of the Bloods (28x25cm-11x10in) s. 26-Jul-3 Coeur d'Alene, Hayden #106/R est:40000-60000
£82278 $130000 €119303 Buck deer (38x48cm-15x19in) s.d.1910 prov. 26-Jul-3 Coeur d'Alene, Hayden #65/R est:100000-175000
£221519 $350000 €321203 Kindergarten or storyteller (25x30cm-10x12in) s. board prov.lit. 26-Jul-3 Coeur d'Alene, Hayden #83/R est:100000-150000
Prints
£3006 $4750 €4359 Caught with the goods (23x33cm-9x13in) with sig. print. 26-Jul-3 Coeur d'Alene, Hayden #1/R est:1500-2500
Sculpture
£1401 $2200 €2102 Climbing Bighorn (10cm-4in) mono.d.1924 num.20/30 bronze prov. 14-Dec-2 Weschler, Washington #674/R est:2000-3000
£2848 $4500 €4130 Offering to the sun Gods (23cm-9in) bronze prov.exhib.lit. 26-Jul-3 Coeur d'Alene, Hayden #23/R est:5000-8000
£2885 $4500 €4328 Indian chief (15cm-6in) bronze. 9-Nov-2 Altermann Galleries, Santa Fe #92
£3082 $4500 €4623 Watcher of the plains (28cm-11in) one of 100 bronze. 18-May-2 Altermann Galleries, Santa Fe #48/R
£3082 $4500 €4623 Antelope (13x18cm-5x7in) num.23/30 bronze. 18-May-2 Altermann Galleries, Santa Fe #49/R
£6329 $10000 €9177 Range father (15cm-6in) bronze st.f.Roman prov.lit. 26-Jul-3 Coeur d'Alene, Hayden #140/R est:10000-15000
£13608 $21500 €19732 Oh! mother, whats is it? (10x23cm-4x9in) bronze st.f.Calif lit. 26-Jul-3 Coeur d'Alene, Hayden #165/R est:15000-25000
£28846 $45000 €43269 Medicine man (18x15x13cm-7x6x5in) bronze prov.lit. 9-Nov-2 Santa Fe Art, Santa Fe #156/R est:50000-75000
£41139 $65000 €59652 Smoking with the spirit of the buffalo (10cm-4in) bronze st.f.B Zoppo prov.lit. 26-Jul-3 Coeur d'Alene, Hayden #67/R est:20000-35000
Works on paper
£3481 $5500 €5222 Mounted plainsman shooting antelope (11x18cm-4x7in) init. graphite ink. 3-Apr-3 Christie's, Rockefeller NY #142/R est:2000-3000
£17405 $27500 €25237 Trapper's fracas outside the walls of ft. union (33x53cm-13x21in) s. pen ink prov.lit. 26-Jul-3 Coeur d'Alene, Hayden #125/R est:30000-50000
£19475 $31550 €28239 Hunting scene on Menu (15x10cm-6x4in) W/C. 23-May-3 Altermann Galleries, Santa Fe #79
£20570 $32500 €29827 Portrait of a Blackfoot (25x20cm-10x8in) s.d.1900 W/C prov. 26-Jul-3 Coeur d'Alene, Hayden #182/R est:25000-45000
£22152 $35000 €32120 Trails plowed under (25x30cm-10x12in) s. pen ink prov.lit. 26-Jul-3 Coeur d'Alene, Hayden #39/R est:15000-25000
£28481 $45000 €41297 Letter to friend Joe (23x41cm-9x16in) s. W/C pen ink prov.exhib.lit. 26-Jul-3 Coeur d'Alene, Hayden #118/R est:30000-50000
£30063 $47500 €43591 First American news writer (48x36cm-19x14in) s.d.1910 pen ink lit. 26-Jul-3 Coeur d'Alene, Hayden #159/R est:40000-60000
£31080 $49000 €45066 Thurston held Mona somewhat tighter than he need to have done (38x33cm-15x13in) s. W/C prov.exhib.lit. 26-Jul-3 Coeur d'Alene, Hayden #176/R est:75000-150000
£34810 $55000 €50475 War party (20x30cm-8x12in) s.d. W/C. 26-Jul-3 Coeur d'Alene, Hayden #198/R est:25000-50000
£53797 $85000 €78006 Meeting of Sacajawea and her relatives of the Shoshone Tribe (33x58cm-13x23in) s. pen ink prov.exhib.lit. 26-Jul-3 Coeur d'Alene, Hayden #93/R est:40000-60000
£69620 $110000 €100949 Elk in lake McDonald (33x3cm-13x1in) s.d.1906 W/C lit. 26-Jul-3 Coeur d'Alene, Hayden #49/R est:60000-90000
£585443 $925000 €848892 Trail of the iron horse (43x69cm-17x27in) s. W/C prov.exhib.lit. 26-Jul-3 Coeur d'Alene, Hayden #129/R est:600000-900000

RUSSELL, Charles M (after) (1864-1926) American
Sculpture
£10692 $17000 €16038 Changing outfits (30x85cm-12x33in) i. brown pat. bronze i.f.Roman prov.lit. 5-Mar-3 Sotheby's, New York #123/R est:8000-12000

RUSSELL, Deborah (1951-) Australian
£500 $770 €750 Untitled (50x45cm-20x18in) s. i.d.94 verso oil on linen. 8-Sep-2 Sotheby's, Melbourne #85 est:1500-2500 (A.D 1400)
£537 $817 €806 Cyprus (35x30cm-14x12in) s.d.98 verso. 28-Aug-2 Deutscher-Menzies, Melbourne #155/R (A.D 1500)
£537 $817 €806 Dead tree (35x30cm-14x12in) s.d.98 verso. 28-Aug-2 Deutscher-Menzies, Melbourne #156/R (A.D 1500)

RUSSELL, Edward J (1835-1906) American
Works on paper
£335 $550 €486 Portrait of a three masted American bark (53x76cm-21x30in) s.d.1902 W/C gouache pen ink. 8-Jun-3 Skinner, Boston #77

RUSSELL, Geoffrey (20th C) Australian
£226 $353 €393 Dei and adversity (122x124cm-48x49in) s.verso oil plywood. 31-Mar-3 Goodman, Sydney #173d/R (A.D 600)

RUSSELL, Geoffrey Robert (1902-?) British
£260 $424 €390 Place de Morlaix, Paris (48x38cm-19x15in) s. prov. 30-Jan-3 Lawrence, Crewkerne #744

RUSSELL, George (1867-1935) Irish
£1500 $2445 €2250 Extensive mountain and lakeland landscape (56x91cm-22x36in) mono. 14-Feb-3 Keys, Aylsham #729 est:1000-1500
£2600 $4160 €3900 Dancing in the moonlight (36x46cm-14x18in) 15-May-3 Christie's, Kensington #215/R est:1000-1500
£6711 $10805 €10000 Children in the forest (41x56cm-16x22in) prov. 18-Feb-3 Whyte's, Dublin #78/R est:8000-10000
£7246 $11884 €10000 Woman and child in a rock pool (41x54cm-16x21in) mono. 28-May-3 Bonhams & James Adam, Dublin #85/R est:10000-14000
£7971 $13072 €11000 Windy day on the beach (40x53cm-16x21in) mono. 28-May-3 Bonhams & James Adam, Dublin #154/R est:8000-10000
£9434 $14717 €15000 Gazing over the Lough (53x81cm-21x32in) mono. 17-Sep-2 Whyte's, Dublin #63/R est:8000-10000
£12025 $18639 €19000 Two girls by a stream (56x41cm-22x16in) mono. 24-Sep-2 De Veres Art Auctions, Dublin #17/R est:10000-15000
Works on paper
£897 $1409 €1400 Portrait of Dudley Digges, actor (46x37cm-18x15in) init. pastel brown paper. 19-Nov-2 Whyte's, Dublin #86/R

RUSSELL, George D (19th C) American
£2405 $3800 €3608 Yosemite Valley (51x61cm-20x24in) s.d.1840 exhib. 17-Nov-2 CRN Auctions, Cambridge #36/R

RUSSELL, George Horne (1861-1933) Canadian
£246 $381 €369 Old Nova Scotia fisherman (32x20cm-13x8in) s. i.verso board prov. 24-Sep-2 Ritchie, Toronto #3128/R (C.D 600)
£617 $957 €926 Ploughing the fields, Nova Scotia (36x50cm-14x20in) s. 3-Dec-2 Joyner, Toronto #125/R est:1500-1800 (C.D 1500)
£978 $1604 €1467 Ploughing the fields (27x35cm-11x14in) s. 3-Jun-3 Joyner, Toronto #529 est:2000-3000 (C.D 2200)
£1811 $2807 €2717 Montreal Harbour (50x70cm-20x28in) s. 3-Dec-2 Joyner, Toronto #135/R est:2500-3000 (C.D 4400)
Works on paper
£1235 $1914 €1853 Calves (50x63cm-20x25in) s. 3-Dec-2 Joyner, Toronto #276/R est:2000-2500 (C.D 3000)

RUSSELL, Gyrth (1892-1970) Canadian
£680 $1061 €1020 Mannin Bay, Connemara (18x39cm-7x15in) s. s.i.verso. 11-Sep-2 Bonhams, Newport #339
£720 $1123 €1080 Harbour scene with figures and boats at a quay (36x46cm-14x18in) s. 11-Sep-2 Bonhams, Newport #340
£3200 $5088 €4800 French harbour (34x45cm-13x18in) s. 26-Feb-3 Sotheby's, Olympia #272/R est:2500-3500
£4800 $7872 €7200 Polperro (67x100cm-26x39in) s.i. board. 6-Jun-3 Christie's, London #11/R est:4000-6000

RUSSELL, J B (19/20th C) British
£450 $702 €675 Still life of dead game (40x60cm-16x24in) s. i.verso. 14-Apr-3 Hamilton Osborne King, Dublin #1475

RUSSELL, Janette Catherine (fl.1868-1894) British
Works on paper
£600 $942 €900 Portrait of a young girl (34x27cm-13x11in) s.d.1878 i.verso W/C. 16-Dec-2 Bonhams, Bury St Edmunds #402/R

RUSSELL, John (1745-1806) British
Miniatures
£6500 $10530 €9750 Lady wearing white dress with cream waistband (8cm-3in) gold frame. 22-May-3 Bonhams, New Bond Street #114/R est:3000-5000
Works on paper
£371 $579 €557 Portrait of a gentleman (39x33cm-15x13in) pastel chk prov. 9-Nov-2 Galerie Gloggner, Luzern #112/R (S.FR 850)
£1300 $2015 €1950 Portrait of Benjamin Thompson (10x8cm-4x3in) pastel. 30-Oct-2 Mallams, Oxford #711/R
£3500 $5565 €5250 Portrait of Miss Courtney (60x44cm-24x17in) pastel. 19-Mar-3 Sotheby's, London #120/R est:3000-5000
£3600 $5652 €5400 Portrait of a young boy in a red coat and white collar, with a spaniel (60x44cm-24x17in) pastel arched top. 21-Nov-2 Christie's, London #9/R est:4000-6000
£4878 $8000 €7317 Portrait of a gentleman, half-length, in a blue coat (75x57cm-30x22in) s. pastel paper on board exhib. 30-May-3 Christie's, Rockefeller NY #46/R est:8000-12000
£6962 $10861 €11000 Portrait of Samuel Walker-Parker seated by a tree. Catherine Parker (100x76cm-39x30in) s.d.1798 pastel pair. 15-Oct-2 Mealy's, Castlecomer #459/R est:5000-7000
£10800 $17064 €16200 Portrait of Miss E and Miss L Earle with a lamb (74x62cm-29x24in) s. pastel prov.exhib.lit. 28-Nov-2 Sotheby's, London #213/R est:8000-12000

RUSSELL, John (attrib) (1745-1806) British
Works on paper
£550 $875 €798 Portrait of James Gurney (25x22cm-10x9in) pastel. 29-Apr-3 Henry Adams, Chichester #216
£800 $1248 €1200 Prudence (57x42cm-22x17in) pastel. 19-Sep-2 Christie's, Kensington #11/R
£1000 $1560 €1500 Portrait of lady with feathered black hat thought to be the Duchess of Devonshire (59x43cm-23x17in) pastel. 17-Oct-2 Christie's, Kensington #11/R est:1000-1500

RUSSELL, John (fl.1869-1918) British
£540 $875 €810 Dove on a window ledge by a still life of fruit (90x69cm-35x27in) 23-Jan-3 Bonhams, Edinburgh #310
£1603 $2500 €2405 Farmyard scene with a Jack Russell terrier, pigeons and hen (81x122cm-32x48in) s. 14-Sep-2 Selkirks, St. Louis #203/R est:3000-4000

RUSSELL, John B (19/20th C) British
£3000 $4560 €4500 Day's catch. Salmon on the bank (35x61cm-14x24in) s. board pair. 28-Aug-2 Sotheby's, London #809/R est:3000-4000

RUSSELL, John Bucknell (1819-1893) British
£1500 $2340 €2250 Yellow trout (26x46cm-10x18in) s. i.verso. 14-Apr-3 Sotheby's, London #46/R est:1000-1500
£7500 $11850 €11250 Three salmon on rocky riverbank (63x76cm-25x30in) s. 27-Nov-2 Christie's, London #37/R est:6000-8000

RUSSELL, John Peter (1859-1930) Australian
Works on paper
£5338 $8167 €8007 Races at Saint Tropez (26x36cm-10x14in) s.i. W/C executed 1910. 26-Aug-2 Sotheby's, Paddington #542/R est:20000-30000 (A.D 15000)

RUSSELL, Mary E (1947-) American
£974 $1500 €1461 Cranberries and Chinese dish (20x25cm-8x10in) 25-Oct-2 Morris & Whiteside, Hilton Head Island #135 est:1800-2000

RUSSELL, Sir Walter Westley (1867-1949) British
£7500 $11850 €11250 Firelight (76x102cm-30x40in) indis.sig. 26-Nov-2 Christie's, London #155/R est:8000-12000

RUSSELL, Ulisa (20th C) ?
£769 $1215 €1200 Playing the guitar (82x65cm-32x26in) s. 19-Nov-2 Durán, Madrid #142/R

RUSSIAN SCHOOL
£5755 $9209 €8000 Beaute Orientale (73x51cm-29x20in) s. 13-May-3 Palais de Beaux Arts, Brussels #196/R est:8500-10000

RUSSIAN SCHOOL, 17th C
£8000 $12560 €12000 Portrait of Tsar Mikhail Fedorovich (94x69cm-37x27in) 20-Nov-2 Sotheby's, London #8/R est:8000-12000

RUSSIAN SCHOOL, 19th C
£4861 $7729 €7000 Landscape with sea (44x77cm-17x30in) 30-Apr-3 Tajan, Paris #77/R
£8000 $13360 €12000 Preparing for battle (68x100cm-27x39in) mono,. 18-Jun-3 Christie's, Kensington #79/R est:2000-3000
£8904 $13890 €13000 Gypsy girl (49x42cm-19x17in) bears sig. paper on board oval. 10-Apr-3 Van Ham, Cologne #1683/R est:6000
£9500 $14914 €14250 Italian coast scene (61x91cm-24x36in) 20-Nov-2 Sotheby's, London #41/R est:10000-15000
£11390 $18680 €16516 Portrait of Count Ernest Munich (67x52cm-26x20in) i.verso. 4-Jun-3 AB Stockholms Auktionsverk #2504/R est:20000-25000 (S.KR 145000)
£15625 $25000 €23438 View of Kasbeck, Caucasus and Darial Pass, Caucasus (44x63cm-17x25in) i.verso board pair. 14-May-3 Butterfields, San Francisco #1101/R est:3000-5000
£18000 $28260 €27000 Russian Uhlans on manoeuvres (99x155cm-39x61in) 19-Nov-2 Bonhams, New Bond Street #44/R est:4000-6000
£22000 $35640 €33000 Beggars outside the church (81x133cm-32x52in) indis sig. 21-May-3 Sotheby's, London #54 est:1000-2000
Prints
£155159 $251358 €224981 Description of Sacred Coronation of Emperor Alexander II and Empress Maria (90x67cm-35x26in) folio of lithographs lit. 26-May-3 Bukowskis, Stockholm #515/R est:125000-150000 (S.KR 2000000)

RUSSIAN SCHOOL, 20th C
£6759 $10814 €9800 Wall of Complaints (47x61cm-19x24in) bears sig. cardboard. 12-Mar-3 Rabourdin & Choppin de Janvry, Paris #73/R
Works on paper
£540 $863 €750 Sketch for ballet costume (23x15cm-9x6in) st.sig.cyrillic gouache pencil board. 15-May-3 Neumeister, Munich #344/R

RUSSO, Mario (1925-2000) Italian
£1233 $1923 €1800 Girl (118x62cm-46x24in) s. s.i.verso exhib. 10-Apr-3 Finarte Semenzato, Rome #161/R

RUSSOLO, Luigi (1885-1947) Italian
£3900 $6435 €5655 Nocturne landscape (23x29cm-9x11in) s. board. 1-Jul-3 Bearnes, Exeter #524/R est:2000-3000

RUST, Johan Adolph (1828-1915) Dutch
£1557 $2491 €2336 Harbour in Dutch city (17x23cm-7x9in) s. panel. 17-Mar-3 Philippe Schuler, Zurich #4638/R est:2000-2500 (S.FR 3300)
£1800 $2808 €2700 Hay barge (15x23cm-6x9in) s. panel. 10-Sep-2 Bonhams, Knightsbridge #236/R est:2000-3000
£2390 $3681 €3800 Sunny river landscape with figures on a path (40x60cm-16x24in) s. 22-Oct-2 Sotheby's, Amsterdam #19/R est:4000-6000

RUSTH, Ian (1950-) Swedish
£526 $831 €789 Danish bathing place (40x45cm-16x18in) s. panel. 30-Nov-2 Goteborg Auktionsverk, Sweden #616/R (S.KR 7500)

RUSTI, Olav (1850-1920) Norwegian
£1104 $1699 €1656 Fjord landscape with small holding and man (28x46cm-11x18in) s. painted 1886. 28-Oct-2 Blomqvist, Lysaker #1252/R est:12000-15000 (N.KR 13000)

RUSTIN, Jean (1928-) French
£5396 $8849 €7500 Portrait of a man (64x54cm-25x21in) s.d.90 s.d.verso. 3-Jun-3 Christie's, Amsterdam #219/R est:4000-6000

RUSTIN, Jean (attrib) (1928-) French
Works on paper
£387 $612 €600 Composition (37x28cm-15x11in) gouache. 18-Dec-2 Digard, Paris #225

RUSZKOWSKI, Zdzislaw (1907-1990) Polish
£1000 $1550 €1500 Standing female (112x71cm-44x28in) s. sold with two W/C by same hand. 3-Dec-2 Bonhams, Knightsbridge #92/R est:800-1000
£2800 $4340 €4200 Still life (53x67cm-21x26in) s. exhib.lit. 4-Dec-2 Christie's, Kensington #591/R est:600-800
£4200 $6510 €6300 Irish Coast, Stradbally, County Waterford (59x86cm-23x34in) s. exhib.lit. 4-Dec-2 Christie's, Kensington #563/R est:1000-1500
£5800 $9570 €8410 Surreal landscape (55x81cm-22x32in) s. 3-Jul-3 Christie's, Kensington #710/R est:800-1200

RUTGERS, Abraham (17th C) Dutch
Works on paper
£676 $1054 €1000 Paysage montagneux pres d'un estuaire (15x19cm-6x7in) crayon wash. 31-Mar-3 Piasa, Paris #26

RUTHART, Karl Andreas (attrib) (1630-1703) German
£1646 $2567 €2600 L'hallali du daim (51x38cm-20x15in) panel. 20-Oct-2 Galerie de Chartres, Chartres #79 est:2300-3000

RUTHART, Karl Andreas (circle) (1630-1703) German
£4697 $7563 €7000 Wild boar hunt (104x187cm-41x74in) 18-Feb-3 Sotheby's, Amsterdam #243/R est:3500-4500

RUTHERFORD, Charles Adrian (20th C) American
£373 $600 €560 Still life of grapes in a basket (41x76cm-16x30in) s. 19-Jan-3 Jeffery Burchard, Florida #65/R

RUTHERFORD, Harry (1903-) British
£600 $984 €870 View of the Seine river bridge in summer (51x61cm-20x24in) s. board. 3-Jun-3 Capes Dunn, Manchester #28

RUTHERSTON, Albert (1881-1953) British
£900 $1431 €1350 The Rothenstein children at Vaucottes sur mer (48x76cm-19x30in) s.i.d.1910 sold with two painting. 26-Feb-3 Sotheby's, Olympia #73/R est:1000-1500

RUTHS, Valentin (1825-1905) German
£423 $651 €635 Landscape (33x52cm-13x20in) with sig. panel. 26-Oct-2 Rasmussen, Havnen #2202 (D.KR 5000)
£481 $745 €750 Heringsdorf (19x25cm-7x10in) i.d.78 verso board. 5-Dec-2 Schopman, Hamburg #640
£704 $1169 €1000 Sorengo in autumn (32x43cm-13x17in) mono. panel. 12-Jun-3 Hauswedell & Nolte, Hamburg #393/R
£704 $1169 €1000 Landscape (35x54cm-14x21in) s. board. 12-Jun-3 Hauswedell & Nolte, Hamburg #392/R
£897 $1417 €1300 River landscape (37x53cm-15x21in) s. board. 5-Apr-3 Hans Stahl, Hamburg #136/R
£1623 $2370 €2500 Friedrichsruh with angler by the steam and farmer in the distance (34x47cm-13x19in) s.d.1885 panel prov. 15-Jun-2 Hans Stahl, Hamburg #208/R
Works on paper
£2436 $3776 €3800 Spring (84x61cm-33x24in) s.i. chk htd white. 7-Dec-2 Hauswedell & Nolte, Hamburg #1018/R est:4500
£2436 $3776 €3800 Winter (85x61cm-33x24in) s.i. chk htd white. 7-Dec-2 Hauswedell & Nolte, Hamburg #1019/R est:4500

RUTHVEN, Jerry (1947-) American
£2740 $4000 €4110 Hill country floral (51x102cm-20x40in) 18-May-2 Altermann Galleries, Santa Fe #212/R

RUTHVEN, John (20th C) American
Works on paper
£6329 $10000 €9494 Great horned owl (56x81cm-22x32in) s. W/C. 3-Apr-3 Boos Gallery, Michigan #219/R est:12000-15000

RUTTKAY-NEDECKY, Viliam (1892-1967) Czechoslovakian
£299 $425 €449 Piper (74x60cm-29x24in) painted c.1930. 26-Mar-2 SOGA, Bratislava #74/R (SL.K 19000)
£505 $783 €758 Shepherd with pipe (67x50cm-26x20in) painted c.1935. 3-Dec-2 SOGA, Bratislava #37/R (SL.K 32000)

RUTZ, Ulrich Johann (1859-1926) German
Works on paper
£6550 $10284 €9825 Mountain peasants with cattle (19x127cm-7x50in) W/C silver gold bronze. 25-Nov-2 Sotheby's, Zurich #36/R est:1500-25000 (S.FR 15000)

RUUTSALO, Eino (1921-2001) Finnish
Works on paper
£453 $697 €720 The brain of the war (46x52cm-18x20in) s.d.90 collage. 27-Oct-2 Bukowskis, Helsinki #270/R

RUYSCH, Aletta van (1860-1930) Dutch
£528 $850 €750 Farm family at table (29x34cm-11x13in) s. panel. 7-May-3 Vendue Huis, Gravenhage #71/R

RUYSCH, Rachel (1664-1750) Dutch
£600000 $942000 €900000 Still life of roses, poppies and other flowers in a glass vase (48x39cm-19x15in) s.d.1716 prov. 12-Dec-2 Sotheby's, London #42/R est:300000-400000

RUYSCH, Rachel (after) (1664-1750) Dutch
£12000 $18840 €18000 Tulips, carnations and other flowers in a glass vase on a ledge. Forest floor with fruit (88x67cm-35x26in) pair. 10-Dec-2 Bonhams, New Bond Street #114/R est:12000-18000

RUYSCH, Rachel (circle) (1664-1750) Dutch
£7500 $11700 €11250 Roses, carnations and other flowers in a glass vase on a stone ledge (67x51cm-26x20in) 10-Apr-3 Christie's, Kensington #130/R est:7000-10000

RUYSDAEL, Jacob van (1628-1682) Dutch
£67686 $105590 €101529 Farmstead in winter landscape under cloudy sky (28x33cm-11x13in) s. lit.prov. 20-Nov-2 Fischer, Luzern #1044/R est:150000-180000 (S.FR 155000)

RUYSDAEL, Jacob van (circle) (1628-1682) Dutch
£2581 $4000 €3872 Wooded landscape on a rocky hill with a waterfall (33x38cm-13x15in) mono. panel prov. 7-Dec-2 Neal Auction Company, New Orleans #159/R

RUYSDAEL, Jacob van (style) (1628-1682) Dutch
£1549 $2494 €2200 River landscape (61x91cm-24x36in) 12-May-3 Bernaerts, Antwerp #200/R est:2000-3000
£4697 $7563 €7000 Landscape with figures by a boat at the edge of a river, cottage beyond (53x68cm-21x27in) mono. prov.exhib. 18-Feb-3 Sotheby's, Amsterdam #226/R est:6000-8000

RUYSDAEL, Salomon van (1600-1670) Dutch
£13000 $20280 €19500 Philip and the Eunch (77x97cm-30x38in) init.d.1630 prov.lit. 9-Apr-3 Christie's, London #51/R est:15000-20000
£260000 $408200 €390000 River landscape with cattle ferry (57x81cm-22x32in) s.d.1656 panel prov.exhib.lit. 12-Dec-2 Sotheby's, London #28/R est:150000-250000
£300000 $501000 €435000 River landscape with the pellecussenpoort neat Utrecht, five cattle wading in foreground (74x60cm-29x24in) s.d.1663 panel prov.exhib.lit. 9-Jul-3 Christie's, London #47/R est:300000-400000

RUYSSEVELT, Jozef van (1941-1985) Belgian
Works on paper
£1006 $1550 €1600 Interieur (54x72cm-21x28in) s.d.1981 gouache. 22-Oct-2 Campo, Vlaamse Kaai #665

RUYTEN, Jan Michael (1813-1881) Belgian
£1875 $3000 €2813 River landscape with ships moored to the shore and figures (20x25cm-8x10in) s.d.1852 panel. 14-May-3 Butterfields, San Francisco #1066/R est:3000-5000
£3022 $4835 €4200 Having fun on the ice outside Flemish city (25x33cm-10x13in) s.d.1850 panel prov. 17-May-3 Lempertz, Koln #1478/R est:5000
£10131 $16614 €15500 Marche aux volailles (49x60cm-19x24in) s.d.1874. 9-Feb-3 Anaf, Lyon #246/R est:12000
£10897 $17109 €17000 Vue du port anime de Gorcum, Hollande (43x52cm-17x20in) s. d.1876 verso panel. 19-Nov-2 Vanderkindere, Brussels #445/R est:6000-8000
£12821 $20128 €20000 Marche anime sur la Grand Place d'Anvers (44x54cm-17x21in) s. d.1877 verso panel. 19-Nov-2 Vanderkindere, Brussels #441/R est:6000-8000
Works on paper
£2201 $3390 €3500 Figures on the ice near a Dutch town (27x38cm-11x15in) s.d.57 W/C. 22-Oct-2 Sotheby's, Amsterdam #24/R est:3000-5000

RUYTER, Lisa (1968-) German?
£7500 $12000 €11250 Heartbreak Ridge (122x91cm-48x36in) s.d.2001 acrylic prov. 16-May-3 Phillips, New York #109/R est:12000-18000
£11000 $18040 €16500 Branches of the tree (112x152cm-44x60in) s.i.d.1999 verso acrylic prov. 6-Feb-3 Christie's, London #754/R est:7000-9000
£12500 $20000 €18750 Untitled (183x244cm-72x96in) acrylic painted 1998 prov. 14-May-3 Sotheby's, New York #324/R est:20000-30000

RUYTINX, Alfred (1871-?) Belgian
£3000 $4770 €4500 Mixed summer flowers in a blue vase on a table (95x115cm-37x45in) s. 20-Mar-3 Christie's, Kensington #37/R est:2000-3000

RUZICKA, Dr Drahomir Josef (1870-1960) American
Photographs
£1899 $3000 €2849 Penn Station (34x27cm-13x11in) s.i.d. warm toned. 23-Apr-3 Sotheby's, New York #59/R est:3500-5000
£1948 $3000 €2922 Penn Station (34x27cm-13x11in) s.i.d.1915 photograph. 24-Oct-2 Sotheby's, New York #80/R est:4000-6000
£3896 $6000 €5844 Penn Station (41x33cm-16x13in) s.i.d.1941 photograph. 24-Oct-2 Sotheby's, New York #79/R est:5000-7000
£4430 $7000 €6645 Pennsylvania station, New York (35x25cm-14x10in) s. photograph exhib. 25-Apr-3 Phillips, New York #208/R est:1500-2500

RUZICKA-LAUTENSCHLAGER, Hans (1862-1933) Austrian
£331 $540 €500 Piazza d'Erbe, Verona (53x42cm-21x17in) s.d.1927. 28-Jan-3 Dorotheum, Vienna #26/R

RYAG, Vary (20th C) ?
£3425 $5377 €5000 Bataille navale (32x38cm-13x15in) mono.d.1903 panel double-sided. 15-Apr-3 Laurence Calmels, Paris #4225/R

RYAN, Adrian (1920-1998) British
£340 $530 €493 Rio Sam Barnabe Venice (23x25cm-9x10in) s. card. 27-Mar-3 Lane, Penzance #149
Works on paper
£400 $664 €580 Road to Sheffield (20x23cm-8x9in) s. mixed media. 10-Jun-3 David Lay, Penzance #304

RYAN, John (?) ?
£1258 $1962 €2000 From the garden (56x61cm-22x24in) s. exhib. 17-Sep-2 Whyte's, Dublin #106/R est:2000-3000
£1509 $2355 €2400 Asgard returns (28x38cm-11x15in) s. s.i.verso board. 17-Sep-2 Whyte's, Dublin #187/R est:1200-1500

RYAN, Thomas (1864-1927) New Zealander
Works on paper
£526 $821 €789 In Western Bay, Lake Taupo (43x27cm-17x11in) s.d.1921 W/C. 27-Mar-3 International Art Centre, Auckland #110/R (NZ.D 1500)
£842 $1314 €1263 Approaching storm, Lake Taupo (30x50cm-12x20in) s.d.1919 W/C. 27-Mar-3 International Art Centre, Auckland #111/R (NZ.D 2400)

RYAN, Thomas (1929-) Irish
£577 $929 €860 Twelve Bens near Roundstone, Connemara (20x30cm-8x12in) s. i.verso canvas on board prov. 18-Feb-3 Whyte's, Dublin #210/R
£690 $1146 €980 Twelve Bens near Roundstone (20x29cm-8x11in) s. 10-Jun-3 James Adam, Dublin #254/R
£1071 $1629 €1650 Fish on white plate. s. board. 2-Jul-2 Thomas Adams, Dublin #421
£1164 $1828 €1700 Rose and quill (14x19cm-6x7in) s. 15-Apr-3 De Veres Art Auctions, Dublin #264/R est:1400-1800
£1342 $2161 €2000 St Peter's Church, Drogheda (30x23cm-12x9in) s. board prov. 18-Feb-3 Whyte's, Dublin #27/R est:2000-2500
£1364 $2073 €2100 Road near home (46x36cm-18x14in) s. 2-Jul-2 Thomas Adams, Dublin #354
£1667 $2650 €2400 Western landscape (41x61cm-16x24in) s. i.d.1980 verso. 29-Apr-3 Whyte's, Dublin #23/R est:1500-2000
£1899 $2943 €3000 Summer day at home (19x24cm-7x9in) s. board. 25-Sep-2 James Adam, Dublin #119/R est:1200-1800
£2222 $3533 €3200 View of Muckish mountain from the Dunfanaghy direction (51x64cm-20x25in) s. i.d.1970 verso. 29-Apr-3 Whyte's, Dublin #198/R est:2000-3000
£2308 $3577 €3600 Naul Church (50x60cm-20x24in) s.d.1973 i.verso. 3-Dec-2 Bonhams & James Adam, Dublin #112/R est:2500-3500
£2361 $3754 €3400 Geraniums and Buddha (25x30cm-10x12in) s. d.1983 verso. 29-Apr-3 Whyte's, Dublin #104/R est:2000-3000
£2400 $3840 €3600 Still life (20x25cm-8x10in) s. canvasboard. 16-May-3 Sotheby's, London #129/R est:1000-1500
£2432 $3795 €3600 Roses (50x39cm-20x15in) s. i.d.1968 verso. 26-Mar-3 James Adam, Dublin #132/R est:3000-5000
£2436 $3776 €3800 Georgian interior with figures (50x60cm-20x24in) s.d.1974 i.verso. 3-Dec-2 Bonhams & James Adam, Dublin #113/R est:2500-3500
£2564 $3974 €4000 Turf shed (49x60cm-19x24in) s.d.1973 board. 3-Dec-2 Bonhams & James Adam, Dublin #111/R est:4000-6000
£2949 $4571 €4600 Three Irish sailors (32x40cm-13x16in) s. canvasboard. 3-Dec-2 Bonhams & James Adam, Dublin #37/R est:1800-2500
£4000 $6400 €6000 Codicil (35x46cm-14x18in) s. s.i.verso board exhib. 15-May-3 Christie's, London #98/R est:4000-6000
£6500 $10400 €9750 Ryan's garden (51x61cm-20x24in) s. s.i.verso board. 15-May-3 Christie's, London #96/R est:8000
Works on paper
£464 $756 €700 Walking in sun, Crete (15x11cm-6x4in) s. 29-Jan-3 Woodwards, Cork #196

RYAN, Tom (1922-) American
£1242 $2000 €1863 Cowboy pointing gun at viewer (56x43cm-22x17in) s. 10-May-3 Illustration House, New York #181/R est:2000-3000
£2740 $4000 €4110 Pioneer home (41x51cm-16x20in) 18-May-2 Altermann Galleries, Santa Fe #128/R
£35616 $52000 €53424 The heritage (61x76cm-24x30in) 18-May-2 Altermann Galleries, Santa Fe #122/R
£41096 $60000 €61644 Big enough (61x91cm-24x36in) 18-May-2 Altermann Galleries, Santa Fe #121/R
£50685 $74000 €76028 Ghost town (61x76cm-24x30in) 18-May-2 Altermann Galleries, Santa Fe #123/R
Works on paper
£2877 $4200 €4316 6666 Chuck wagon (20x41cm-8x16in) pencil. 18-May-2 Altermann Galleries, Santa Fe #126/R
£2949 $4600 €4424 Passing by (15x20cm-6x8in) gouache. 9-Nov-2 Altermann Galleries, Santa Fe #50
£3425 $5000 €5138 Henry 6666 ranch (48x43cm-19x17in) pastel. 18-May-2 Altermann Galleries, Santa Fe #124/R
£6164 $9000 €9246 Patching his saddle (38x30cm-15x12in) mixed media. 18-May-2 Altermann Galleries, Santa Fe #125/R
£6744 $10925 €9779 Torn chaps (41x25cm-16x10in) pencil dr. 23-May-3 Altermann Galleries, Santa Fe #7/R

RYBACK, Issachar (1897-1935) Russian
£7000 $11130 €10500 Fleurs des champs (92x63cm-36x25in) s. s.i.verso. 20-Mar-3 Sotheby's, Olympia #157/R est:6000-8000

RYBCOWSKY, Dey de (1880-1936) Polish
£952 $1514 €1400 Sunset (61x102cm-24x40in) 25-Feb-3 Dorotheum, Vienna #105/R

RYBKOWSKI, Tadeusz (1848-1926) Polish
£1266 $2000 €2000 Campement de cosaques (25x40cm-10x16in) s. panel. 2-Dec-2 Tajan, Paris #4

RYBNIKOW, M (19/20th C) ?
£455 $677 €700 Turkish village with mosque and figures (32x42cm-13x17in) indis.s. 28-Jun-2 Sigalas, Stuttgart #841/R

RYCHTER-MAY, A (?) ?
Works on paper
£260 $406 €390 Jerusalem (28x19cm-11x7in) s.i. W/C. 25-Mar-3 Bonhams, Knightsbridge #244/R

RYCK, Pieter Cornelisz van (attrib) (1568-c.1628) Dutch
£7534 $11829 €11000 La preparation du poisson (133x187cm-52x74in) exhib. 15-Apr-3 Galerie Moderne, Brussels #337/R est:10000-15000

RYCKAERT, David (style) (16/17th C) Flemish
£8974 $14090 €14000 Kitchen interiors with figures. pair. 19-Nov-2 Servarts Themis, Bruxelles #230/R est:7000

RYCKAERT, David III (1612-1661) Flemish
£2365 $3689 €3500 Scene d'auberge (50x71cm-20x28in) 30-Mar-3 Anaf, Lyon #418/R
£5921 $9592 €9000 Inn interior with figures and still life (41x52cm-16x20in) mono. board. 21-Jan-3 Ansorena, Madrid #92/R est:9000

RYCKAERT, David III (attrib) (1612-1661) Flemish
£2918 $4611 €4377 In the chemist's kitchen (60x87cm-24x34in) canvas on canvas. 29-Nov-2 Zofingen, Switzerland #2359/R est:8500 (S.FR 6800)

RYCKAERT, Marten (1587-1631) Flemish
£16129 $25484 €25000 Flemish landscapes (8x19cm-3x7in) copper pair. 18-Dec-2 Tajan, Paris #13/R est:12000
£18000 $28080 €27000 Wooded landscape with travellers and a cart (32x46cm-13x18in) panel. 9-Apr-3 Christie's, London #20/R est:10000-15000
£22000 $34540 €33000 Wooded river landscape with sportsmen shooting duck (71x101cm-28x40in) panel prov. 11-Dec-2 Christie's, London #20/R est:25000-35000
£50000 $83500 €72500 Extensive Italianate landscape with goatherds, shepherd and their flocks (98x139cm-39x55in) s.d.1625 prov. 9-Jul-3 Christie's, London #14/R est:50000-70000
£52000 $81640 €78000 Classical landscape with the satyr's family (56x88cm-22x35in) panel exhib. 12-Dec-2 Sotheby's, London #3/R est:60000-80000

RYCKAERT, Marten (circle) (1587-1631) Flemish
£6000 $9420 €9000 Village landscape with an avenue of trees (49x71cm-19x28in) panel. 13-Dec-2 Christie's, Kensington #22/R est:4000-6000

RYCKHALS, Frans (1600-1647) Dutch
£1592 $2484 €2500 Barn interior with a kitchen still life, with a goat and sheep (32x38cm-13x15in) mono. panel prov. 5-Nov-2 Sotheby's, Amsterdam #73/R est:3000-5000

RYDBERG, Gustaf (1835-1933) Swedish
£388 $609 €582 Autumn landscape with rippling brook (36x26cm-14x10in) s. 16-Dec-2 Lilla Bukowskis, Stockholm #123 (S.KR 5500)
£824 $1335 €1236 Landscape with figures and cattle by mill (39x61cm-15x24in) 3-Feb-3 Lilla Bukowskis, Stockholm #484 (S.KR 11500)
£912 $1440 €1368 Cliffs on the Riviera (38x62cm-15x24in) mono.d.1902 prov.lit. 27-Nov-2 Falkkloos, Malmo #77567/R (S.KR 13000)
£1552 $2514 €2250 Summer landscape with man by road (31x40cm-12x16in) init. canvas on board. 26-May-3 Bukowskis, Stockholm #8/R est:12000-15000 (S.KR 20000)
£1560 $2418 €2340 Mill by waterway (43x68cm-17x27in) s. canvas on panel. 3-Dec-2 Bukowskis, Stockholm #293/R est:20000-25000 (S.KR 22000)
£1862 $3017 €2793 Winter landscape with man on horseback (50x65cm-20x26in) s.d.1891. 3-Feb-3 Lilla Bukowskis, Stockholm #748 est:12000-15000 (S.KR 26000)
£3366 $5318 €5049 Winter landscape with stags in the snow (44x70cm-17x28in) s.d.1872. 27-Nov-2 Falkkloos, Malmo #77680/R est:40000 (S.KR 48000)
£4348 $6870 €6522 Coastal landscape with sailing boats, buildings and figures by jetty, evening (55x85cm-22x33in) s.d.1866. 27-Nov-2 Falkkloos, Malmo #77645/R est:80000 (S.KR 62000)

RYDER, Albert Pinkham (attrib) (1847-1917) American
£1338 $2100 €2007 Landscape (41x30cm-16x12in) panel painted c.1900. 13-Dec-2 Du Mouchelle, Detroit #1036/R est:3000-5000

RYDER, Chauncey F (1868-1949) American
£414 $650 €621 Sunlit marshy pond lined with trees in a summer setting (46x61cm-18x24in) s. board. 19-Apr-3 James Julia, Fairfield #404/R
£2244 $3500 €3366 Morrisville, landscape (30x41cm-12x16in) masonite. 18-Oct-2 Du Mouchelle, Detroit #2076/R est:3000-4000
£2358 $3750 €3537 Day in the fog (56x71cm-22x28in) s. 7-Mar-3 Skinner, Boston #416/R est:1500-2500
£2532 $4000 €3798 On the canal, Venice (36x25cm-14x10in) s. 24-Apr-3 Shannon's, Milford #50/R est:4000-6000
£2564 $4000 €3846 Landscape (30x41cm-12x16in) 18-Oct-2 Du Mouchelle, Detroit #2075/R est:3000-4000
£4088 $6500 €6132 November (51x61cm-20x24in) s. prov. 4-Mar-3 Christie's, Rockefeller NY #3/R est:4000-6000
£6024 $10000 €8735 Amherst Road (30x41cm-12x16in) s. 11-Jun-3 Butterfields, San Francisco #4068/R est:5000-7000

Works on paper
£503 $800 €755 Landscape (46x56cm-18x22in) s. W/C. 7-Mar-3 Skinner, Boston #384/R

RYDER, Platt Powell (1821-1896) American
£563 $900 €845 Young Indian girl in an interior by the hearth (30x25cm-12x10in) s. board. 15-Mar-3 Jeffery Burchard, Florida #52/R

RYDER, Susan (1944-) British
£400 $660 €580 Crossword (45x36cm-18x14in) i.verso board. 1-Jul-3 Bonhams, Norwich #293
£650 $1053 €975 Interior scene with yellow armchair (60x45cm-24x18in) s. board. 20-May-3 Bonhams, Knightsbridge #178/R
£750 $1253 €1088 Drawing room at Rode (106x90cm-42x35in) s. 23-Jun-3 Bonhams, Bath #88

RYGGEN, Hans (1894-1956) Norwegian
£467 $719 €701 Hanna reading (52x63cm-20x25in) s. panel painted 1956 exhib. 28-Oct-2 Blomqvist, Lysaker #1255/R (N.KR 5500)
£509 $784 €764 Reading (66x69cm-26x27in) s. painted 1952. 28-Oct-2 Blomqvist, Lysaker #1254/R (N.KR 6000)
£640 $998 €960 Woman winding wool (73x60cm-29x24in) s. panel painted 1949. 23-Sep-2 Blomqvist, Lysaker #1203 (N.KR 7500)
£806 $1242 €1209 Man in garden (75x90cm-30x35in) s. panel exhib. 28-Oct-2 Blomqvist, Lysaker #1256 (N.KR 9500)
£1648 $2571 €2472 Field of poppies in sunshine (88x114cm-35x45in) s.d.1946 panel exhib. 21-Oct-2 Blomqvist, Oslo #365/R est:12000-15000 (N.KR 19000)
£1995 $3112 €2993 Hanna with blanket (88x114cm-35x45in) s.d.1947 panel exhib. 21-Oct-2 Blomqvist, Oslo #368/R est:12000-15000 (N.KR 23000)

RYLAARSDAM, Jan (1911-) Dutch
£562 $888 €843 Street scene (71x91cm-28x36in) d.1964. 1-Dec-2 Levis, Calgary #229/R (C.D 1400)
£789 $1279 €1200 Het Kolkje, Amsterdam (36x27cm-14x11in) s. black chk pastel. 21-Jan-3 Christie's, Amsterdam #303/R est:700-1200
£1056 $1701 €1500 Cafe Tabac (39x29cm-15x11in) s. 7-May-3 Vendue Huis, Gravenhage #514 est:800-1000
£1274 $1987 €2000 Three chairs (38x58cm-15x23in) s. 6-Nov-2 Vendue Huis, Gravenhage #94/R est:500-700
£1538 $2415 €2400 Flower girls (59x38cm-23x15in) s. 25-Nov-2 Glerum, Amsterdam #61/R est:1500-2000
£2051 $3221 €3200 Market scene (29x39cm-11x15in) s. 25-Nov-2 Glerum, Amsterdam #110 est:1500-2000
£2222 $3667 €3200 Flower girl (77x61cm-30x24in) s. 1-Jul-3 Christie's, Amsterdam #398/R est:1800-2200
£3333 $5500 €4800 Encounter (80x60cm-31x24in) s. 1-Jul-3 Christie's, Amsterdam #374/R est:1800-2200

Works on paper
£217 $339 €363 Lezender oude man (72x53cm-28x21in) s. i.verso mixed media. 13-Apr-3 Levis, Calgary #214/R (C.D 500)
£362 $586 €550 Meeting in a bar (36x27cm-14x11in) s. pastel gouache. 21-Jan-3 Christie's, Amsterdam #392
£592 $959 €900 Victoria Hotel Amsterdam (28x29cm-11x11in) s. black chk ink gouache. 21-Jan-3 Christie's, Amsterdam #393
£658 $1066 €1000 Amsterdam canal (26x38cm-10x15in) s. black chk pastel. 21-Jan-3 Christie's, Amsterdam #297/R est:700-1500
£789 $1279 €1200 Leidseplein, Amsterdam (20x28cm-8x11in) s.i. W/C gouache pen ink sold with a print three. 21-Jan-3 Christie's, Amsterdam #298 est:400-600

RYLAND, Henry (1856-1924) British
£460 $750 €690 Hayfield (36x56cm-14x22in) s. 2-Feb-3 Grogan, Boston #23

Works on paper
£518 $850 €777 Classical maiden with birds (36x20cm-14x8in) s. W/C gouache paper on board. 5-Feb-3 Doyle, New York #66/R
£2300 $3749 €3450 Almond blossom (51x39cm-20x15in) s. W/C. 29-Jan-3 Sotheby's, Olympia #142/R est:1000-1500

RYLANDER, Hans Chr (1939-) Danish
£406 $630 €609 Jugglers (65x75cm-26x30in) s.d.1971 verso. 1-Oct-2 Rasmussen, Copenhagen #242 (D.KR 4800)
£2974 $4699 €4461 The lust's obscure goal (241x325cm-95x128in) init. s.d.1989-90 verso. 1-Apr-3 Rasmussen, Copenhagen #209/R est:30000-40000 (D.KR 32000)

RYLE, Arthur Johnston (1857-1915) British
£550 $858 €825 Summer at the mill pond (34x52cm-13x20in) s. 15-Oct-2 Bearnes, Exeter #427/R

RYLEY, Charles Reuben (1752-1798) British

Works on paper
£250 $388 €375 Devils vanquished, possibly a scene from John milton's Comus (17x10cm-7x4in) s. pen ink wash. 9-Dec-2 Bonhams, New Bond Street #22/R

RYMAN, Robert (1930-) American
£31646 $50000 €47469 Untitled (22x22cm-9x9in) s.d.60 verso prov.exhib. 13-Nov-2 Sotheby's, New York #109/R est:80000-120000
£36250 $58000 €54375 Versions X (42x38cm-17x15in) s.i.d.91 oil fiberglass wax paper prov.exhib. 15-May-3 Christie's, Rockefeller NY #319/R est:40000-60000
£56250 $90000 €84375 Untitled (47x47cm-19x19in) s.d.69 acrylic polymer fiberglass panel prov. 15-May-3 Phillips, New York #9/R est:50000-70000
£75000 $120000 €112500 Untitled (20x20cm-8x8in) s. on linen prov. 13-May-3 Sotheby's, New York #4/R est:90000-120000
£75949 $120000 €113924 Untitled (23x23cm-9x9in) s. oil on linen painted 1962 prov. 13-Nov-2 Christie's, Rockefeller NY #10/R est:150000-200000
£143750 $230000 €215625 Instructor (131x121cm-52x48in) s.i.d.85 oil enamel fiberboard aluminum brackets prov.exhib. 15-May-3 Phillips, New York #11/R est:350000-450000
£215190 $340000 €322785 Untitled (26x26cm-10x10in) s.d.1965 on overlap prov.lit. 13-Nov-2 Christie's, Rockefeller NY #53/R est:200000-300000

Sculpture
£41139 $65000 €61709 Boundry no.3 (58x58x8cm-23x23x3in) s.d.1990 num.9.10.11.12 verso encaustic black cherry wood prov.exhib. 13-Nov-2 Sotheby's, New York #306/R est:80000-120000

RYOJO (19th C) Japanese

Sculpture
£1183 $1858 €1775 Old man with rabbits (31cm-12in) s. ivory. 25-Nov-2 Stephan Welz, Johannesburg #171/R est:20000-30000 (SA.R 18000)

RYOTT, James Russell (fl.1810-1860) British
£1000 $1620 €1500 Racehorse Silvertail standing in an extensive landscape (81x108cm-32x43in) s.i.indisd.1833. 23-Jan-3 Christie's, Kensington #69/R est:1000-1500

RYSBRACK, Pieter (1655-1729) Flemish
£3734 $5563 €5750 Still life of fish and crustacae (61x109cm-24x43in) s.d. 28-Jun-2 Woodwards, Cork #198
£7693 $12847 €11000 Vue d'une forteresse pres d'une riviere (42x55cm-17x22in) s.indis.d.172. 25-Jun-3 Tajan, Paris #22/R est:6000-8000

RYSBRAECK, Gerard (1696-1773) Flemish
£6452 $10194 €10000 Still life with pheasant and artichoke. Still life with duck and celery (65x80cm-26x31in) one s. pair. 18-Dec-2 Piasa, Paris #32/R est:15000

RYSEN, Warnard van (1625-?) Dutch
£5096 $7949 €8000 Nymphs bathing and a washerwoman near ruins in a southern landscape (21x29cm-8x11in) panel prov.lit. 5-Nov-2 Sotheby's, Amsterdam #141/R est:8000-12000

RYSSEL, Louis van (1873-1962) French
£1701 $2704 €2500 Coo et le violon (47x55cm-19x22in) s.d.07. 24-Mar-3 Coutau Begarie, Paris #196/R

RYSSELBERGHE, Theo van (1862-1926) Belgian
£465 $725 €698 Porticoes house in landscape (76x91cm-30x36in) s. 21-Sep-2 Nadeau, Windsor #360/R
£1646 $2567 €2600 Composition aux muguets (32x37cm-13x15in) s. lit. 16-Sep-2 Horta, Bruxelles #191
£7692 $11923 €12000 Portrait d'Elisabeth van Rysselberghe se reposant (41x33cm-16x13in) mono.i.d.1909 i.d.1908 lit. 7-Dec-2 De Vuyst, Lokeren #542/R est:13000-15000
£9434 $14623 €15000 Marguerites (50x61cm-20x24in) mono.d.08 lit. 5-Oct-2 De Vuyst, Lokeren #444/R
£1538462 $2400000 €2307693 Voiliers sur l'escault (68x90cm-27x35in) mono.d.1892 canvas on painted liner prov.exhib.lit. 5-Nov-2 Sotheby's, New York #4/R est:1000000-1500000

Works on paper
£297 $475 €431 Grecian urn in a lush landscape (29x22cm-11x9in) studio st. graphite gouache. 16-May-3 Skinner, Boston #170/R
£701 $1093 €1100 Le maigre de forges (54x19cm-21x7in) s.d.1893 mixed media. 11-Nov-2 Horta, Bruxelles #23
£1399 $2336 €2000 Arbres au bord de la falaise (41x32cm-16x13in) studio st. chl dr. 26-Jun-3 Tajan, Paris #7/R est:2000-3000
£2276 $3641 €3300 Violinist (26x31cm-10x12in) mono.i.d.1918 pencil dr lit. 15-Mar-3 De Vuyst, Lokeren #355/R est:3000-3600
£6500 $10660 €9750 Etude pour promenade (62x37cm-24x15in) studio st. chl pencil exec.c.1901 prov. 5-Feb-3 Sotheby's, London #210/R est:12000

RYSWYCK, Edward van (1871-1936) Belgian
£417 $654 €650 Still life with roses (20x50cm-8x20in) s. 16-Dec-2 Bernaerts, Antwerp #315/R
£563 $907 €800 Flowers in a ginger pot (45x53cm-18x21in) s. 7-May-3 Vendue Huis, Gravenhage #156
£822 $1290 €1200 Nature morte au vase (32x43cm-13x17in) 15-Apr-3 Galerie Moderne, Brussels #346
£2278 $3554 €3600 Still life with tulips and peonies (70x100cm-28x39in) s. 21-Oct-2 Bernaerts, Antwerp #108/R est:2000-3000
£8228 $13000 €12342 Pink rose and irises on a stone ledge (91x71cm-36x28in) s. prov. 23-Apr-3 Christie's, Rockefeller NY #97/R est:12000-16000

RYSWYCK, T van (?) Belgian?
Sculpture
£2390 $3728 €3800 Biche (47cm-19in) green pat.bronze. 14-Oct-2 Amberes, Antwerp #391/R
£11321 $17660 €18000 Deux dromodaires (47x64cm-19x25in) brown pat.bronze Cast.Batardy. 14-Oct-2 Amberes, Antwerp #392/R

RYSWYCK, Theodor van (1811-1849) Belgian
Sculpture
£1739 $2852 €2400 Deux martins-pecheurs (20cm-8in) s. bronze st.f.Batardy BXL cire perdu. 27-May-3 Campo, Vlaamse Kaai #251/R est:750-1000

RYSWYCK, Thierry van (20th C) Belgian
Sculpture
£3448 $5517 €5000 Two cubs (23x33cm-9x13in) s.i. brown pat bronze wood base prov. 15-Mar-3 De Vuyst, Lokeren #534/R est:4500-5000
£4967 $8096 €7500 Tigre en marche (34cm-13in) s.st.f.Susse pat bronze. 17-Feb-3 Horta, Bruxelles #131/R

RYUKOSAI, Jokei (fl.1777-1809) Japanese
Works on paper
£2642 $4200 €3963 Treasury of Loyal Retainers (117x15cm-46x6in) s. ink col hanging scroll. 24-Mar-3 Christie's, Rockefeller NY #34/R est:2000-3000

RZEZNIK, Marion Michael (1899-1979) American/Polish
£241 $400 €349 Horrors of war (91x66cm-36x26in) 14-Jun-3 Jackson's, Cedar Falls #374/R
£452 $750 €655 Angels (66x147cm-26x58in) pair. 14-Jun-3 Jackson's, Cedar Falls #438/R
£512 $850 €742 Transfiguration of Christ (272x193cm-107x76in) 14-Jun-3 Jackson's, Cedar Falls #354/R
£542 $900 €786 St Cecilia (147x91cm-58x36in) 14-Jun-3 Jackson's, Cedar Falls #358/R
£602 $1000 €873 Mythological heroic allegory of love (137x91cm-54x36in) 14-Jun-3 Jackson's, Cedar Falls #200/R
£1024 $1700 €1485 Immaculate conception (427x239cm-168x94in) 14-Jun-3 Jackson's, Cedar Falls #433/R est:1000-1500
£1205 $2000 €1747 Lord Almighty (302x152cm-119x60in) 14-Jun-3 Jackson's, Cedar Falls #434/R est:750-1000
£3373 $5600 €4891 Immaculate conception (279x173cm-110x68in) 14-Jun-3 Jackson's, Cedar Falls #356/R est:750-1000
£3735 $6200 €5416 Holy Trinity (307x216cm-121x85in) 14-Jun-3 Jackson's, Cedar Falls #357/R est:750-1000

SAABYE, Carl Anton (1807-1878) Danish
£441 $710 €662 Mountain village with woman by well (41x36cm-16x14in) s.d.15 april 1840. 19-Jan-3 Hindemae, Ullerslev #7286/R (D.KR 5000)

SAABYE, Svend (1913-) Danish
£279 $441 €419 Composition with sun (55x80cm-22x31in) s. 1-Apr-3 Rasmussen, Copenhagen #648 (D.KR 3000)
£304 $469 €456 Interior (69x88cm-27x35in) s. 23-Oct-2 Kunsthallen, Copenhagen #458 (D.KR 3600)
£343 $542 €515 Landscape from Sofienberg, Nyborg (55x70cm-22x28in) s. 17-Nov-2 Hindemae, Ullerslev #7542/R (D.KR 4000)
£428 $681 €642 Autumn evening, Langeso-Stenlose (110x150cm-43x59in) s. painted 1941-43. 10-Mar-3 Rasmussen, Vejle #617/R (D.KR 4600)
£433 $676 €650 Back garden in evening (62x83cm-24x33in) s.i.d.1942 verso. 5-Aug-2 Rasmussen, Vejle #2230 (D.KR 5100)
£446 $705 €669 Harvesting scene (81x100cm-32x39in) s. 17-Nov-2 Hindemae, Ullerslev #7541/R (D.KR 5200)
£1351 $2108 €2027 Composition (100x130cm-39x51in) s. 22-Sep-2 Hindemae, Ullerslev #7622/R est:10000-12000 (D.KR 16000)

SAAF, Erik (1856-1934) Swedish
£420 $664 €630 Coastal landscape from Torekow, Skaane (58x92cm-23x36in) s.d.85. 16-Nov-2 Crafoord, Lund #83/R (S.KR 6000)
£2250 $3645 €3263 The vegetable garden (49x40cm-19x16in) init. prov. 26-May-3 Bukowskis, Stockholm #5/R est:12000-15000 (S.KR 29000)

SAAL, Georg (1818-1870) German
£552 $872 €800 Tavern scenes (37x49cm-15x19in) s. two lit. 5-Apr-3 Geble, Radolfzell #721/R

SAAR, Betye (1926-) American
£3045 $4750 €4568 My last buffalo (34x28cm-13x11in) s.d.1973 mixed media bone beads plexiglas case prov. 14-Oct-2 Butterfields, San Francisco #2105/R est:4000-6000

SAARINEN, Yrjo (1899-1958) Finnish
£1266 $2000 €2000 Asti Vermanen painting (61x46cm-24x18in) s.d.1947 lit. 30-Nov-2 Hagelstam, Helsinki #154/R est:2400
£1646 $2600 €2600 Rocky landscape (54x65cm-21x26in) s.d.1944 board. 1-Dec-2 Bukowskis, Helsinki #152/R est:2500-3000
£2658 $4200 €4200 Landscape from Nukarinkoski (65x81cm-26x32in) s.d.1947. 1-Dec-2 Bukowskis, Helsinki #151/R est:2700-3000

SAARTO, Marja (1942-) Finnish
£775 $1247 €1100 Dance (93x97cm-37x38in) s.d.90. 10-May-3 Bukowskis, Helsinki #233/R

SABATELLI, Luigi (1772-1850) Italian
Works on paper
£411 $638 €650 Scene from the life of Don Rodrigo (34x52cm-13x20in) s.i.d.1831 pen. 25-Sep-2 Neumeister, Munich #432/R
£1282 $1987 €2000 Moses. battle scene (54x76cm-21x30in) pencil pen ink double-sided. 4-Dec-2 Christie's, Rome #411a

£5069 $8060 €7300 Dante and Virgil in hell, surrounded by studies of the damned (36x48cm-14x19in) s.i. pen sepia sketches verso. 5-May-3 Ketterer, Munich #421/R est:500-700

SABATER Y MUR, Jose (1875-?) Spanish
£323 $510 €500 Garden (100x81cm-39x32in) s. 18-Dec-2 Ansorena, Madrid #23/R

SABATER, Daniel (1888-1951) Spanish
£408 $649 €600 This makes me laugh (40x32cm-16x13in) s.i. 24-Mar-3 Claude Boisgirard, Paris #192
£833 $1317 €1300 Landscape (38x58cm-15x23in) s. s.i.d.1948 verso. 19-Nov-2 Durán, Madrid #143/R
£873 $1380 €1310 Viva tu madre (46x55cm-18x22in) s.i.d.1931. 14-Nov-2 Stuker, Bern #496 est:1800-2400 (S.FR 2000)
£1329 $2219 €1900 La barque (60x75cm-24x30in) s. 26-Jun-3 Tajan, Paris #315/R est:1200-1500
£3000 $4710 €4500 La maja morerna - Spanish maja (65x921cm-26x363in) s.i. 19-Nov-2 Sotheby's, London #65/R est:6000-8000

SABATIER, Roland (1942-) French
£2532 $4000 €4000 Multiplication hyperthestine (134x109cm-53x43in) s.i.d.1966 acrylic ink oil prov. 27-Nov-2 Tajan, Paris #103/R

SABATINI, Raphael (1898-?) American
£516 $800 €774 City canyons (91x61cm-36x24in) s. i.verso oil tempera canvas on board. 8-Dec-2 Freeman, Philadelphia #124/R
Works on paper
£247 $400 €371 Abstract cathedral (61x41cm-24x16in) s. W/C. 24-Jan-3 Freeman, Philadelphia #111/R

SABBAGH, Georges (1887-1951) French
£433 $662 €650 Female nude (73x60cm-29x24in) s. painted 1926. 26-Aug-2 Blomqvist, Lysaker #1113 (N.KR 5000)
£563 $907 €800 Baigneuse (45x36cm-18x14in) s.d.1991 s.i.verso. 7-May-3 Vendue Huis, Gravenhage #552
£645 $1019 €1000 Bord du lac de Geneve (92x73cm-36x29in) st.sig. cardboard. 19-Dec-2 Bondu, Paris #15
£961 $1510 €1500 Felouques au bord du Nil (31x39cm-12x15in) s. cardboard. 10-Dec-2 Tajan, Paris #231/R
£1571 $2466 €2450 Paysage de Bretagne (54x73cm-21x29in) s.d.1927 panel. 16-Dec-2 Chochon-Barre & Allardi, Paris #93/R est:2600-2800

SABBATINI, Lorenzo (after) (c.1530-1577) Italian
£14634 $24000 €21951 Holy Family with St Catherine of Alexandria (82x64cm-32x25in) panel. 5-Feb-3 Christie's, Rockefeller NY #283/R est:7000-10000

SABOOTIN, S (19th C) ?
£1800 $2988 €2700 Woman in a harem (36x53cm-14x21in) s. panel. 10-Jun-3 Bonhams, Knightsbridge #146/R est:800-1200

SABORIT, Enrique (19th C) Spanish
£1007 $1621 €1500 Landscape with mansion (45x70cm-18x28in) s. 18-Feb-3 Durán, Madrid #187/R
£1074 $1729 €1600 Washerwoman at river (45x70cm-18x28in) s. 18-Feb-3 Durán, Madrid #186/R

SABOURAUD, Émile (1900-1996) French
£449 $704 €700 Nature morte au masque et aux pichets (33x41cm-13x16in) s. painted c.1960. 16-Dec-2 Charbonneaux, Paris #288
£545 $855 €850 L'etang a bievre (72x75cm-28x30in) s. prov. 16-Dec-2 Charbonneaux, Paris #287
£552 $877 €800 Vase de fleurs (55x46cm-22x18in) s. 9-Mar-3 Feletin, Province #87
£638 $1034 €900 Jeune femme aux bas noirs (54x65cm-21x26in) s. 25-May-3 Feletin, Province #107
£641 $1006 €1000 Nature morte sur table (73x50cm-29x20in) s. 22-Nov-2 Millon & Associes, Paris #101
£690 $1097 €1000 Vue de village (60x81cm-24x32in) s. 9-Mar-3 Feletin, Province #92
£759 $1206 €1100 Village a Neuville pres de Dieppe (46x55cm-18x22in) s. s.d.1959 verso. 9-Mar-3 Feletin, Province #107
£1079 $1727 €1500 Le jardin de la villa (50x61cm-20x24in) s. 18-May-3 Eric Pillon, Calais #131/R

SABY, Bernard (1925-1975) French?
£2639 $4196 €3800 Sans titre (147x114cm-58x45in) s.d.1961 prov.exhib. 29-Apr-3 Artcurial Briest, Paris #589/R est:4000-6000

SACCHI, Andrea (attrib) (1599-1661) Italian
Works on paper
£1600 $2512 €2400 Sacrifice of Noah (30x40cm-12x16in) red chk prov. 11-Dec-2 Sotheby's, Olympia #98/R est:400-600

SACCOMANDI, Sergio (20th C) Italian
£327 $523 €500 I don't know God but I am known by Him and this is my hope (110x92cm-43x36in) s.d.1970 board. 4-Jan-3 Meeting Art, Vercelli #607

SACHAROFF, Olga (1889-1969) Russian
£11972 $19873 €17000 Vase de fleurs (41x33cm-16x13in) s. cardboard. 15-Jun-3 Anaf, Lyon #184/R est:17000-20000
£29032 $45871 €45000 Les amoureux (73x92cm-29x36in) s. 17-Dec-2 Rossini, Paris #121/R
£48077 $74519 €75000 Danspartij - dancing (65x81cm-26x32in) s. s.verso. 3-Dec-2 Christie's, Amsterdam #188/R est:12000-16000

SACHERI, Giuseppe (1863-1950) Italian
£1565 $2442 €2348 Coastal landscape with pines (46x57cm-18x22in) s. paper. 16-Sep-2 Philippe Schuler, Zurich #3522/R est:2000-2500 (S.FR 3600)

SACHS, Benno (1868-1939) Austrian
£380 $592 €600 Roccocco couple in lakeside park (24x13cm-9x5in) s. panel lit. 14-Sep-2 Bergmann, Erlangen #787/R
£380 $592 €600 Roccocco couple on castle terrace (24x13cm-9x5in) s. panel lit. 14-Sep-2 Bergmann, Erlangen #788/R

SACHS, Michael (1837-1893) German
£641 $994 €1000 Summer meadows with stream, half hidden farmsteads and windmill (25x36cm-10x14in) s. 6-Dec-2 Michael Zeller, Lindau #907/R

SACHS, Tom (1966-) American
£4514 $7448 €6500 Pandaba (61x61cm-24x24in) s.i.d.1998 acrylic felt-pen resin collage on canvas prov.exhib. 3-Jul-3 Christie's, Paris #24/R est:6000-8000
Sculpture
£3000 $4920 €4500 Hello Kitty (23x17x14cm-9x7x6in) s.i.d.2000 paper foam core ink glue cellotape prov.exhib.lit. 6-Feb-3 Christie's, London #747/R est:5000-7000
£3472 $5729 €5000 R2D2 Brickee (60x47x13cm-24x19x5in) s.i.d.2000 verso oil ink serigraph board ironed on prov. 3-Jul-3 Christie's, Paris #25/R est:7000-9000
£3797 $6000 €5696 Spartan 357 magnum kit (28x20x20cm-11x8x8in) s.d.1998 gun police barriers box executed 1998. 12-Nov-2 Phillips, New York #164/R est:8000-12000
£5556 $9167 €8000 Clock (48x50x15cm-19x20x6in) s.i.d.1998 verso painted wood metal Coca-cola bottles prov.exhib. 3-Jul-3 Christie's, Paris #23/R est:8000-12000
Works on paper
£8750 $14000 €13125 Falling (91x91cm-36x36in) duct tape on plywood executed 1996 prov.exhib. 16-May-3 Phillips, New York #101/R est:4000-6000

SACRE, Émile (1844-1882) Belgian
£1844 $2987 €2600 Dame avec un chien (45x34cm-18x13in) panel. 26-May-3 Amberes, Antwerp #61

SACRISTAN, Ricardo (1921-1981) Spanish
Works on paper
£331 $526 €480 Bilbao harbour (57x78cm-22x31in) s. W/C. 4-Mar-3 Ansorena, Madrid #658/R
£483 $768 €700 View of harbour (49x68cm-19x27in) s. W/C. 4-Mar-3 Ansorena, Madrid #661/R

SADAHIDE, Hashimoto (1807-1873) Japanese
Prints
£2000 $3340 €2900 View of the trading floor in a foreign building in Yokohama (37x77cm-15x30in) s. triptych. 18-Jun-3 Christie's, London #229/R est:2000-2500
£4000 $6680 €5800 Western traders transporting merchandise at Yokohama. s. pentaptych. 18-Jun-3 Christie's, London #228/R est:4000-4500
£10897 $17000 €16346 Western traders transporting merchandise at Yokohama (36x25cm-14x10in) s. col print pentaptych. 25-Mar-3 Christie's, Rockefeller NY #348/R est:12000-15000

SADALI, Ahmad (1924-1987) Indonesian
£3730 $6154 €5409 Abstract (80x60cm-31x24in) s.d.64. 6-Jul-3 Christie's, Hong Kong #51/R est:50000-70000 (HK.D 48000)
£5439 $8974 €7887 Self portrait (84x65cm-33x26in) s. acrylic. 6-Jul-3 Christie's, Hong Kong #49/R est:50000-70000 (HK.D 70000)

SADD, William Harvey (1862-1954) Canadian
Works on paper
£578 $948 €838 Untitled - alpine campers (36x58cm-14x23in) W/C. 1-Jun-3 Levis, Calgary #115/R est:2000-2200 (C.D 1300)

SADEE, Philippe (1837-1904) Dutch
£4514 $7177 €6500 Harvesting potatoes (39x70cm-15x28in) s. oil paper on panel lit. 29-Apr-3 Christie's, Amsterdam #125/R est:6000-8000
£11950 $18403 €19000 Shrimper on the beach (29x45cm-11x18in) s. panel. 22-Oct-2 Sotheby's, Amsterdam #224/R est:15000-20000
£18056 $28708 €26000 Anticipating the return (71x57cm-28x22in) s. prov. 29-Apr-3 Christie's, Amsterdam #132/R est:10000-15000

SADEQUAIN (1930-1987) Indian
£2000 $3120 €3000 Upward (127x97cm-50x38in) s. 17-Oct-2 Bonhams, Knightsbridge #598/R est:2000-3000
£2600 $4056 €3900 Abstract (193x93cm-76x37in) 17-Oct-2 Bonhams, Knightsbridge #596/R est:3000-5000
£2600 $4056 €3900 Abstract (93x193cm-37x76in) 17-Oct-2 Bonhams, Knightsbridge #597/R est:3000-5000
£3000 $4680 €4500 Organic form (94x193cm-37x76in) 17-Oct-2 Bonhams, Knightsbridge #595/R est:3000-5000
Works on paper
£600 $936 €900 Abstract form (49x65cm-19x26in) s. ink W/C. 17-Oct-2 Bonhams, Knightsbridge #632/R

SADKOWSKI, Alex (1934-) Swiss
£961 $1508 €1442 Old man with rabbit (100x81cm-39x32in) s.d.1964 lit. 25-Nov-2 Germann, Zurich #800/R est:1500-2000 (S.FR 2200)

SADKOWSKI, E von (20th C) German?
£1507 $2366 €2200 Still life of flowers with butterflies (75x65cm-30x26in) i. 16-Apr-3 Dorotheum, Salzburg #86/R est:2000-2600

SADLER, Kate (fl.1880-94) British
Works on paper
£280 $434 €420 Still life of roses (15x20cm-6x8in) s. mixed media. 2-Oct-2 John Ross, Belfast #187

SADLER, Walter Dendy (1854-1923) British
£650 $1079 €975 In the days of Isaac Walton (55x40cm-22x16in) s. 10-Jun-3 Bonhams, Knightsbridge #299/R
£4200 $6846 €6300 Little laundress (45x34cm-18x13in) s.d.79 exhib. 29-Jan-3 Sotheby's, Olympia #218/R est:4000-6000

SADLER, William (18/19th C) British
£12414 $19738 €18000 Seven Churches, Glendalough (49x72cm-19x28in) panel. 4-Mar-3 Mealy's, Castlecomer #1185/R est:18000-22000

SADLER, William (jnr) (1782-1839) British
£769 $1208 €1200 Southern wooded river landscape with figures by a hermits cave (42x28cm-17x11in) panel. 19-Nov-2 Hamilton Osborne King, Dublin #458
£1456 $2256 €2300 Salmon leap (21x31cm-8x12in) board. 25-Sep-2 James Adam, Dublin #84/R est:2000-3000
£2609 $4278 €3600 Shipping in stormy seas by a lighthouse (21x30cm-8x12in) board. 28-May-3 Bonhams & James Adam, Dublin #27/R est:3000-5000
£5797 $9507 €8000 Street scene, possibly Blarney , Co Cork (32x50cm-13x20in) panel. 28-May-3 Bonhams & James Adam, Dublin #16/R est:8000-12000
£10256 $15897 €16000 House of Lords, Portico of Parliment House from Collage Street, Dublin (21x32cm-8x13in) board prov. 3-Dec-2 Bonhams & James Adam, Dublin #27/R est:8000-12000

SADLER, William (jnr-attrib) (1782-1839) British
£1400 $2240 €2100 Exercise in Phoenix park, Dublin. Shipping in Dublin Bay, near Poolbeg lighthouse (10x18cm-4x7in) panel pair. 15-May-3 Christie's, Kensington #133/R est:1000-1500
£4800 $7680 €7200 Killarney capriccio (56x82cm-22x32in) panel. 15-May-3 Christie's, Kensington #131/R est:3000-5000

SADUN, Piero (1919-1974) Italian
Works on paper
£641 $1006 €1000 Untitled (50x70cm-20x28in) s.d.67 mixed media. 21-Nov-2 Finarte, Rome #154/R

SAEC, Rene le (1935-1999) French
£266 $420 €420 Chantier de bateaux (60x81cm-24x32in) s. acrylic. 1-Dec-2 Livinec, Gaudcheau & Jezequel, Rennes #58
£285 $450 €450 Regate (50x75cm-20x30in) s.d.83 acrylic. 1-Dec-2 Livinec, Gaudcheau & Jezequel, Rennes #55
£304 $480 €480 Crepuscule (33x46cm-13x18in) s.d.87 acrylic. 1-Dec-2 Livinec, Gaudcheau & Jezequel, Rennes #53
£304 $480 €480 Regate (36x90cm-14x35in) s. acrylic panel. 1-Dec-2 Livinec, Gaudcheau & Jezequel, Rennes #58d
£316 $500 €500 Coiffes bretonnes (48x62cm-19x24in) s. acrylic. 1-Dec-2 Livinec, Gaudcheau & Jezequel, Rennes #58c

SAEDELEER, Valerius de (1867-1941) Belgian
£4828 $7724 €7000 Summer landscape with mill (27x36cm-11x14in) prov. 15-Mar-3 De Vuyst, Lokeren #432/R est:6500-7500
£7547 $11623 €12000 Paysage vallonne (24x61cm-9x24in) s. 22-Oct-2 Campo & Campo, Antwerp #77/R est:15000

SAEGHER, Rodolphe de (1871-1941) Belgian
£1274 $1987 €2000 Vue de fjord en Norvege (35x25cm-14x10in) s.d.1897. 11-Nov-2 Horta, Bruxelles #188 est:3000-4000
Works on paper
£276 $441 €400 Children in front of the farm (22x28cm-9x11in) s. W/C. 15-Mar-3 De Vuyst, Lokeren #98

SAENE, Maurice van (1919-2000) Belgian
£897 $1391 €1400 Seascape (27x36cm-11x14in) s. paper on panel. 7-Dec-2 De Vuyst, Lokeren #371
Works on paper
£818 $1267 €1300 Seascape (47x62cm-19x24in) s. pastel. 5-Oct-2 De Vuyst, Lokeren #389/R

SAENZ DE LA CALZADA, Luis (1910-1994) Spanish
Works on paper
£968 $1529 €1500 Surrealist head (31x23cm-12x9in) s. ink pencil dr exhib.lit. 17-Dec-2 Segre, Madrid #140/R

SAETTI, Bruno (1902-1984) Italian
£676 $1054 €1000 Red sun in Venice (12x16cm-5x6in) s. cardboard. 26-Mar-3 Finarte Semenzato, Milan #104/R
£3041 $4743 €4500 Still life (50x70cm-20x28in) s. acrylic. 26-Mar-3 Finarte Semenzato, Milan #127/R
£6129 $9500 €9194 Alfresco mosaico (53x72cm-21x28in) s.d.65 s.i.d.verso oil sand tile on canvas. 26-Sep-2 Christie's, Rockefeller NY #729/R est:6000-8000
Works on paper
£7092 $11489 €10000 Composition of fruit and trumpet (60x60cm-24x24in) s. s.d.80 verso fresco canvas prov. 26-May-3 Christie's, Milan #120/R est:10000-12000

SAEYS, Jakob Ferdinand (1658-1725) Flemish
£5595 $9343 €8000 Fete devant la facade d'un palais Renaissance (56x83cm-22x33in) s.d.1683. 25-Jun-3 Tajan, Paris #36/R est:8000-10000

SAEYS, Jakob Ferdinand (circle) (1658-1725) Flemish
£7000 $10850 €10500 Capriccio of a classical palace with elegant company and falconers (79x110cm-31x43in) 30-Oct-2 Christie's, Kensington #56/R est:7000-10000
£7500 $12525 €10875 Palace capriccio scene with elegant figures (63x75cm-25x30in) 8-Jul-3 Sotheby's, Olympia #402/R est:6000-8000

SAEYS, Jakob Ferdinand (style) (1658-1725) Flemish
£10067 $16207 €15000 Architectural capricci with the story of the Prodigal Son (82x104cm-32x41in) pair. 18-Feb-3 Sotheby's, Amsterdam #259/R est:3000-5000

SAEZ, Fernando (1921-) Spanish
£1007 $1621 €1500 Composition (104x87cm-41x34in) s. 18-Feb-3 Durán, Madrid #156/R

SAFARAN, Aluev (1051-) ?
£288 $472 €400 Horse (76x91cm-30x36in) s.i.verso. 5-Jun-3 Dorotheum, Salzburg #716/R

SAFARIK, Jan (1886-?) Czechoslovakian
Works on paper
£436 $694 €654 Place de la Concorde in Paris (28x47cm-11x19in) s.i. w/C. 8-Mar-3 Dorotheum, Prague #238/R est:12000-18000 (C.KR 20000)

SAFFARO, Lucio (1929-) Italian
£748 $1190 €1100 Opus CCXXXIII (60x50cm-24x20in) 1-Mar-3 Stadion, Trieste #413

SAFFORD, M A (19th C) American
£503 $800 €755 On the Intervale (24x39cm-9x15in) prov. 7-Mar-3 Skinner, Boston #292/R

SAFI, Ibrahim (1898-1983) Turkish
£608 $949 €900 Bosfor (34x43cm-13x17in) 26-Mar-3 Hugo Ruef, Munich #370

SAFI, J (20th C) Turkish
£256 $390 €400 Girl wearing turban (42x33cm-17x13in) s. board. 11-Jul-2 Hugo Ruef, Munich #800/R
£449 $682 €700 Turkish coast (34x43cm-13x17in) s. board. 11-Jul-2 Hugo Ruef, Munich #797
£2866 $4471 €4500 Burgos (34x43cm-13x17in) s. board. 6-Nov-2 Hugo Ruef, Munich #1264 est:300
£3185 $4968 €5000 Place de la Republique in Paris (50x60cm-20x24in) s. 6-Nov-2 Hugo Ruef, Munich #1261/R est:500
£3503 $5465 €5500 Bosfor (34x43cm-13x17in) s. 6-Nov-2 Hugo Ruef, Munich #1265 est:300
£5096 $7949 €8000 Southern coastal landscape (50x70cm-20x28in) s. 6-Nov-2 Hugo Ruef, Munich #1262/R est:500
£5414 $8446 €8500 Istanbul (50x63cm-20x25in) s. 6-Nov-2 Hugo Ruef, Munich #1263/R est:500

SAFTLEVEN, Cornelis (1607-1681) Dutch
£3237 $5180 €4500 Open landscape with a herdsman, goats and a cow on a track (39x52cm-15x20in) s.d.1639 panel. 14-May-3 Christie's, Amsterdam #124/R est:3500-5500
£4103 $6482 €6400 Bergere et troupeau dans un paysage (39x64cm-15x25in) panel. 12-Nov-2 Palais de Beaux Arts, Brussels #69/R est:4500-6000
£19108 $29809 €30000 Farmstead near a stream, with a horse, sheep and goat (73x105cm-29x41in) panel prov.exhib.lit. 5-Nov-2 Sotheby's, Amsterdam #20/R est:25000-35000
Works on paper
£563 $907 €800 Village street (9x14cm-4x6in) brown pen. 12-May-3 Glerum, Amsterdam #71/R
£938 $1425 €1407 Cabeza de perro (25x37cm-10x15in) s. chl dr. 3-Jul-2 Naón & Cia, Buenos Aires #103 est:1500-1800
£2548 $3975 €4000 Sleeping dog (10x14cm-4x6in) mono. black chk grey wash prov.lit. 5-Nov-2 Sotheby's, Amsterdam #75/R est:1200-1800

SAFTLEVEN, Cornelis (attrib) (1607-1681) Dutch
£4655 $7541 €6750 Figures dancing and making music (42x38cm-17x15in) panel. 26-May-3 Bukowskis, Stockholm #413/R est:40000-50000 (S.KR 60000)
£5696 $9000 €9000 River landscape with dealers (33x42cm-13x17in) mono. canvas on canvas. 30-Nov-2 Berlinghof, Heidelberg #346/R est:9800

SAFTLEVEN, Herman (1609-1685) Dutch
£5200 $8684 €7540 Wooded landscape with figures, goats and view to village and church beyond (20x26cm-8x10in) init. panel. 9-Jul-3 Bonhams, New Bond Street #17/R est:3000-5000
£16561 $25834 €26000 Rhenish river landscape capriccio with moored boats (29x36cm-11x14in) mono.d.1676 i.d.verso. 5-Nov-2 Sotheby's, Amsterdam #227/R est:20000-30000
£17568 $27405 €26000 Rhine landscape (18x25cm-7x10in) panel. 27-Mar-3 Dorotheum, Vienna #157/R est:30000-40000
£20946 $33933 €30372 Rhine landscape with boats and figures (29x38cm-11x15in) mono.d.1670 panel prov. 25-May-3 Uppsala Auktionskammare, Uppsala #50/R est:150000-200000 (S.KR 270000)
£28025 $43720 €44000 Rhenish landscape with peasants dancing around a maypole (38x46cm-15x18in) indis.sig.d.1682 prov.lit. 6-Nov-2 Christie's, Amsterdam #60/R est:30000-50000

SAFTLEVEN, Herman (attrib) (1609-1685) Dutch
£828 $1316 €1200 Landscape with river (21x30cm-8x12in) panel. 8-Mar-3 Arnold, Frankfurt #703/R
£915 $1520 €1300 Landscape (19x18cm-7x7in) panel. 11-Jun-3 Dorotheum, Vienna #364/R
£3774 $5849 €6000 Rhine landscape (24x31cm-9x12in) panel prov. 2-Oct-2 Dorotheum, Vienna #332/R est:6000-9000
Works on paper
£2113 $3507 €3000 Travellers on path by farmstead (15x29cm-6x11in) chk wash. 12-Jun-3 Hauswedell & Nolte, Hamburg #161/R est:1000

SAGE, Henry James (1868-1953) British
Works on paper
£450 $702 €675 Bramley high street (20x33cm-8x13in) W/C. 10-Sep-2 Clarke Gammon, Guildford #39
£500 $780 €750 Spire Hollen, Priorsfield Road, Godalming (28x51cm-11x20in) s. W/C. 10-Sep-2 Clarke Gammon, Guildford #38/R

SAGE, Kay (1898-1963) American
£26027 $40603 €38000 Untitled (76x102cm-30x40in) s.d.41. 14-Apr-3 Laurence Calmels, Paris #4082/R est:15000

SAGER, Xavier (20th C) French
£276 $450 €414 Trayas (48x61cm-19x24in) s. panel. 2-Feb-3 Simpson's, Houston #309

SAGER-NELSON, Olof (1868-1896) Swedish
£5275 $8546 €7649 Small girl in the green grass (33x40cm-13x16in) s.d.89 lit. 26-May-3 Bukowskis, Stockholm #8a/R est:20000-25000 (S.KR 68000)
£19639 $32207 €28477 Bleke Avenue, Gaarda (25x25cm-10x10in) s.d.93. 4-Jun-3 AB Stockholms Auktionsverk #2282/R est:80000-100000 (S.KR 250000)

SAGLIER, Giovanni (17th C) Italian
£15823 $25000 €25000 Vase of flowers (115x82cm-45x32in) 27-Nov-2 Finarte, Milan #85/R

SAGLIO, Eduardo (1867-?) French
£845 $1403 €1200 Plage de Cabourg (12x18cm-5x7in) init. panel pair. 11-Jun-3 Beaussant & Lefèvre, Paris #190

SAGRESTANI, Giovanni Camillo (attrib) (1660-1731) Italian
Works on paper
£650 $1086 €943 Vision of the sacred chalice held by angels to St. Catherine of Siena (36x25cm-14x10in) black white chk. 9-Jul-3 Bonhams, Knightsbridge #52/R

SAHLIN, Gillis (1901-1984) Swedish?
£760 $1202 €1140 Abraham's Sacrifice (26x23cm-10x9in) s.d.26. 28-Apr-3 Bukowskis, Stockholm #28/R (S.KR 10000)

SAHLSTEN, Anna (1859-1931) Finnish
£6329 $10000 €10000 Small boy (70x45cm-28x18in) s.d.1899 lit.exhib. 30-Nov-2 Hagelstam, Helsinki #92/R est:7500
£8544 $13500 €13500 Woman having a cup of coffee (66x60cm-26x24in) s.d.1895. 30-Nov-2 Hagelstam, Helsinki #93/R est:8000

SAILO, Jyrki (1913-1980) Finnish
Sculpture
£1139 $1800 €1800 Mannerheim on horseback (55x60cm-22x24in) s. brown pat.plaster. 30-Nov-2 Hagelstam, Helsinki #6/R est:650

SAIN, Edouard Alexandre (1830-1910) French
£1027 $1603 €1500 Head of girl (33x25cm-13x10in) s. i. verso. 10-Apr-3 Dorotheum, Vienna #116/R est:1200-1800
£7911 $12342 €12500 Pecheurs de moules du Bourg d'Ault, Somme (147x112cm-58x44in) s.d. exhib.lit. 20-Oct-2 Mercier & Cie, Lille #322/R est:12000-15000

SAIN, Paul Jean Marie (1853-1908) French
£570 $900 €900 Woodland stream in autumn (59x69cm-23x27in) s.lit. 29-Nov-2 Sigalas, Stuttgart #1126/R
£1375 $2200 €1994 Le Havre vue prise du cap de la Heve (38x53cm-15x21in) i. 17-May-3 New Orleans Auction, New Orleans #458/R est:2500-4000
£7692 $12846 €11000 Bord de mer a Houlgate (22x33cm-9x13in) s. panel. 27-Jun-3 Claude Aguttes, Neuilly #38/R est:10000-12000

SAINDON, G (19th C) ?
Works on paper
£1000 $1560 €1500 Constantinople (23x35cm-9x14in) s. W/C gouache. 15-Oct-2 Sotheby's, London #98/R est:600-800

SAINSBURY, Jonathan (1951-) British
Works on paper
£250 $380 €375 Grouse in a moorland landscape (36x49cm-14x19in) s.d.84 W/C. 13-Aug-2 Gildings, Market Harborough #243

SAINT CLAIR, Norman (1863-1912) American
Works on paper
£2097 $3250 €3146 Landscape (48x38cm-19x15in) s. W/C. 29-Oct-2 John Moran, Pasadena #686 est:700-1000

ST JOHN, Edwin (19th C) British
Works on paper
£300 $456 €450 North Italian mountainous lake scene (34x60cm-13x24in) s. W/C. 10-Jul-2 Peter Wilson, Nantwich #85/R
£310 $502 €450 Extensive Highland landscape (49x76cm-19x30in) s. W/C. 29-Jul-3 Henry Adams, Chichester #470

ST JOHN, Susan Hely (1833-1913) American
£1534 $2500 €2301 Portrait of a young girl (43x53cm-17x21in) s.d.1885. 2-Feb-3 Simpson's, Houston #276

ST JOHN, Terry (1934-) American
£475 $750 €713 Mount Diablo No.4. board. 16-Nov-2 Harvey Clar, Oakland #1265

ST JOHN-JONES, Herbert (fl.1905-1923) British
£900 $1494 €1305 Favourite beagle (23x35cm-9x14in) s. 12-Jun-3 Christie's, Kensington #261/R
£2200 $3674 €3190 Seaweed a hunter in a loose box (39x49cm-15x19in) s.d.1925 s.i.verso set of three. 26-Jun-3 Mellors & Kirk, Nottingham #898/R est:800-1200

SAINT PAULL, Alex (20th C) ?
£2966 $4745 €4300 Elegante au chapeau, Renee Albouy (81x107cm-32x42in) s. oil gouache. 12-Mar-3 Libert, Castor, Paris #175/R est:1000-1200

SAINT PAULL, Alex (attrib) (20th C) ?
£897 $1434 €1300 Portrait de Gerard Albouy a la colombe (100x73cm-39x29in) s. s.i.verso. 12-Mar-3 Libert, Castor, Paris #174/R
£966 $1545 €1400 Elegante en buste (73x92cm-29x36in) s. 12-Mar-3 Libert, Castor, Paris #173 est:1500-2000

SAINT, Daniel (1778-1847) French
Miniatures
£1622 $2530 €2400 Geographe assis (21x15cm-8x6in) lit. 26-Mar-3 Pierre Berge, Paris #68/R
£5532 $8962 €7800 L'Imperatrice Josephine (5x3cm-2x1in) s. ivory gold surround. 21-May-3 Piasa, Paris #344/R est:4000-5000

SAINT-AUBIN, Augustin de (1736-1807) French
Works on paper
£3062 $4868 €4500 Marchande de broderie (12x7cm-5x3in) pen ink wash prov. 24-Mar-3 Tajan, Paris #105/R

SAINT-AUBIN, Augustin de and Charles Germain de (attrib) (18th C) French
Works on paper
£993 $1609 €1400 Portrait presume de Louis XVI (25x19cm-10x7in) ink wash W/C pencil. 21-May-3 Piasa, Paris #359/R

SAINT-AUBIN, Charles Germain de (1721-1786) French
Works on paper
£641 $1013 €1000 Etude pour initiales (33x26cm-13x10in) pierre noire. 15-Nov-2 Beaussant & Lefèvre, Paris #15/R

SAINT-AUBIN, Gabriel de (1724-1780) French
Prints
£6090 $9622 €9500 Les quatre vases. etching. 14-Nov-2 Libert, Castor, Paris #45/R est:3000
Works on paper
£2703 $4216 €4000 Projet de pavillon (27x36cm-11x14in) W/C pen ink prov.exhib.lit. 31-Mar-3 Piasa, Paris #54/R
£3378 $5270 €5000 Officier sur des marches (17x13cm-7x5in) chk wash brush ink. 27-Mar-3 Christie's, Paris #101/R
£3514 $5481 €5200 Main chaude (10x16cm-4x6in) pen ink wash prov.lit. 31-Mar-3 Piasa, Paris #44/R

SAINT-AUBIN, Gabriel de (attrib) (1724-1780) French
£793 $1158 €1190 Le dejeuner (26x22cm-10x9in) study panel. 17-Jun-2 Philippe Schuler, Zurich #7357 (S.FR 1800)
£5807 $9175 €9000 Scene de peste (53x69cm-21x27in) 18-Dec-2 Tajan, Paris #50/R est:12000

SAINT-CHARLES, Joseph (1868-1945) Canadian
£222 $364 €333 St. Sauveur des monts (22x31cm 9x12in) s. 3-Jun-3 Joyner, Toronto #558 (C.D 500)
£378 $619 €567 Woodcock (40x30cm-16x12in) s. board. 3-Jun-3 Joyner, Toronto #402/R est:1000-1500 (C.D 850)
Works on paper
£206 $317 €309 Portrait d'Irene Letourneux fille de Ida Decarie (61x51cm-24x20in) pastel. 22-Oct-2 Iegor de Saint Hippolyte, Montreal #98 (C.D 500)

SAINT-DALMAS, Francis Emeric de (fl.1872-1885) British
Works on paper
£1350 $2241 €1958 Beach at Port du Moulin, Sark (48x36cm-19x14in) init. W/C. 12-Jun-3 Martel Maides, Guernsey #35/R est:800-1200

SAINT-DELIS, Henri de (1878-1949) French
£3310 $5297 €4800 Barque de peche (27x32cm-11x13in) s. 12-Mar-3 Libert, Castor, Paris #172 est:800-1000
Works on paper
£430 $671 €680 Jetee du port de Honfleur par gros temps (32x45cm-13x18in) s. ink dr. 15-Sep-2 Etude Bailleul, Bayeux #124/R
£1154 $1754 €1800 Honfleur (25x32cm-10x13in) s. W/C. 16-Aug-2 Deauville, France #14/R
£1370 $2151 €2000 Le marche Sainte-Catherine a Honfleur (26x21cm-10x8in) s. W/C. 21-Apr-3 Rabourdin & Choppin de Janvry, Paris #110/R est:2000-2500
£1603 $2436 €2500 Honfleur (25x32cm-10x13in) s. W/C. 16-Aug-2 Deauville, France #12/R
£1871 $2974 €2750 La lieutenance a Honfleur (23x30cm-9x12in) s. W/C pencil. 26-Feb-3 Artcurial Briest, Paris #31/R est:2500-3000
£3185 $5000 €4650 Les quais a Honfleur (30x48cm-12x19in) s. W/C. 21-Apr-3 Rabourdin & Choppin de Janvry, Paris #109/R est:4500-5000
£3425 $5377 €5000 Barques sur le lac Leman (48x58cm-19x23in) s. W/C. 21-Apr-3 Rabourdin & Choppin de Janvry, Paris #111/R est:5000-6000

SAINT-DELIS, René de (1877-1958) French
£417 $654 €650 Cote rocheuse (32x40cm-13x16in) s.d.1904. 24-Nov-2 Lesieur & Le Bars, Le Havre #156
Works on paper
£513 $805 €800 Barques a Etretat (45x60cm-18x24in) s. wax crayon. 24-Nov-2 Lesieur & Le Bars, Le Havre #157

SAINT-EDME, Ludovic Alfred de (1820-?) French
Works on paper
£496 $829 €700 Personnage grec dans des ruines (20x14cm-8x6in) s.i.d.1865 pencil W/C. 23-Jun-3 Beaussant & Lefèvre, Paris #69

SAINT-EVRE, Gillot (1791-1858) French
£1719 $2750 €2579 Jeanne d'Arc devant Charles VII (74x93cm-29x37in) s.d.1860. 14-May-3 Butterfields, San Francisco #1125/R est:3000-5000

SAINT-GAUDENS, Augustus (1848-1907) American
Sculpture
£9032 $14000 €13548 Jules Basrien Lepage (37x27cm-15x11in) s.i. brown pat. bronze prov.exhib. 29-Oct-2 Sotheby's, New York #259/R est:3000-5000
£18868 $30000 €28302 William Evarts Beaman in his fourth year (72x67cm-28x26in) mono. bronze mounted on panel prov.lit. 4-Mar-3 Christie's, Rockefeller NY #50/R est:12000-18000
£70988 $115000 €106482 Puritan - Deacon Samuel Chapin (77cm-30in) i. weathered green pat. bronze prov.lit. 21-May-3 Sotheby's, New York #183/R est:50000-75000

SAINT-HILAIRE, Louis (1860-1922) French
£341 $539 €512 Still life with day's catch (69x48cm-27x19in) d.1896. 1-Dec-2 Levis, Calgary #84/R (C.D 850)

SAINT-HILAIRE, Louis (attrib) (1860-1922) French
£391 $607 €587 Desert caravan (22x41cm-9x16in) s. panel. 9-Dec-2 Philippe Schuler, Zurich #8674 (S.FR 900)

SAINT-IGNY, Jean de (c.1600-c.1649) French
Works on paper
£1543 $2500 €2315 Head of bearded saint looking down (18x13cm-7x5in) chk. 21-Jan-3 Sotheby's, New York #67/R est:4000
£7432 $11595 €11000 Deux couples elegantes accompagnes de pages dans un paysage (18x32cm-7x13in) chk. 27-Mar-3 Christie's, Paris #45/R est:30000

SAINT-JEAN, Paul (1842-1875) French
£11392 $18000 €17088 La reveuse (120x93cm-47x37in) s. prov. 23-Apr-3 Christie's, Rockefeller NY #136/R est:18000-25000

SAINT-JEAN, Simon (1808-1860) French
£1644 $2564 €2400 Bouquet de fleurs (93x73cm-37x29in) 8-Apr-3 Gioffredo, Nice #169
£2994 $4670 €4700 Bouquet de fleurs (93x73cm-37x29in) 6-Nov-2 Gioffredo, Nice #58/R
£4747 $7405 €7500 Still life with roses (23x32cm-9x13in) s.d.1848 board. 21-Oct-2 Glerum, Amsterdam #129/R est:5000-8000
£14194 $22000 €21291 Still life with roses (76x60cm-30x24in) s.d.1858. 29-Oct-2 Sotheby's, New York #37/R est:20000-30000
£15484 $24000 €23226 Bouquet of roses, daisies and violets with a butterfly on a mossy bank (49x62cm-19x24in) s.d.1850 prov.exhib.lit. 30-Oct-2 Christie's, Rockefeller NY #108/R est:25000-35000

SAINT-LANNE, Georges (19th C) French
£3400 $5542 €5100 Visitor (80x99cm-31x39in) s. 29-Jan-3 Sotheby's, Olympia #340/R est:3000-4000

SAINT-LANNE, Georges (attrib) (19th C) French
£710 $1121 €1100 Jeune femme cousant (56x79cm-22x31in) 18-Dec-2 Rieunier, Bailly-Pommery, Mathias, Paris #53

SAINT-LOUIS (?) French
Sculpture
£5245 $8759 €7500 Saint en armure (230cm-91in) wood two. 25-Jun-3 Artcurial Briest, Paris #53/R est:7500-9000

SAINT-MARCEAUX, René (1845-1915) French
Sculpture
£4483 $7172 €6500 Arlequin (68cm-27in) s.d.1879 brown pat.bronze Cast.Barbedienne. 17-Mar-3 Horta, Bruxelles #131/R est:5000-7000
£4843 $7506 €7700 Baiser (65cm-26in) s.d.1883 pat terracotta. 30-Oct-2 Coutau Begarie, Paris #126/R est:1500-1800

SAINT-MARCEL, Edme de (1819-1890) French
Works on paper
£314 $487 €500 Deux fauves (23x32cm-9x13in) s. pen Chinese ink. 30-Oct-2 Coutau Begarie, Paris #37/R

SAINT-NON, L'Abbe de (1727-1791) French
Works on paper
£325 $500 €488 Assumption of St Catherine of Alexandria (134x134cm-53x53in) i. pen black ink brown wash after Mattia Preti. 4-Sep-2 Christie's, Rockefeller NY #271/R

SAINT-OURS, Jean-Pierre (1752-1809) Swiss
Works on paper
£8333 $13083 €13000 Habitants d'Alba Longa (56x93cm-22x37in) pen ink wash htd gouache. 13-Dec-2 Pierre Berge, Paris #20/R est:12000

SAINT-OURS, Jean-Pierre (attrib) (1752-1809) Swiss
Works on paper
£2230 $3478 €3300 Etude (35x20cm-14x8in) pierre noire htd white double-sided. 27-Mar-3 Maigret, Paris #68/R

SAINT-PHALLE, Niki de (1930-2002) French
£3205 $4968 €5000 Chere Erica (50x61cm-20x24in) s.i. acrylic felt-tip ballpoint collage cardboard painted 1968. 6-Dec-2 Ketterer, Munich #195/R est:3500-4500
£3974 $6279 €6200 Tir (73x55cm-29x22in) on plaster. 15-Nov-2 Laurence Calmels, Paris #23/R est:2500
Sculpture
£1986 $3316 €2800 L'obelisque (18cm-7in) num.10/10 paint resin. 18-Jun-3 Pierre Berge, Paris #68/R est:2000-3000
£6552 $10483 €9500 Nana soleil (33x20cm-13x8in) st.sig. num.46/150 resin. 15-Mar-3 De Vuyst, Lokeren #502/R est:12000-13000
£7051 $11071 €11000 Vase Nana (35cm-14in) s. num.80/150 polyester resin. 13-Dec-2 Piasa, Paris #271/R est:6000
£7595 $11848 €12000 Nana soleil (35x20x19cm-14x8x7in) s.d.2001 num.118/150 polyester polychrome resin. 20-Oct-2 Charbonneaux, Paris #193/R est:11500-14000
£7692 $11692 €12000 Nana de Berlin (27x30x35cm-11x12x14in) st.sig. num.317/500 polyester resin. 16-Aug-2 Deauville, France #69/R est:13000
£7708 $12025 €11562 Nana - vase (48cm-19in) s.d.127/150 polychrome painted polyester. 6-Nov-2 AB Stockholms Auktionsverk #732/R est:80000-100000 (S.KR 110000)
£8000 $13360 €11600 Vache vase (54x63cm-21x25in) sig.num.6/10 painted resin on a metal base executed 1992 prov. 27-Jun-3 Christie's, London #170/R est:6000-8000
£9825 $15426 €14738 The couple (31x20cm-12x8in) s. num.45/150 resin. 23-Nov-2 Burkhard, Luzern #120/R est:20000-24000 (S.FR 22500)
£12821 $19872 €20000 Untitled - Nana pregnant (13cm-5in) col plaster prov. 3-Dec-2 Lempertz, Koln #410/R est:50000
£14000 $21560 €21000 Le poete et sa muse (57x21x14cm-22x8x6in) ac on plaster executed c.1975 prov. 22-Oct-2 Sotheby's, London #357/R est:15000-20000
£15000 $24000 €22500 Collaboration (91x76x8cm-36x30x3in) s. fiberglass painted polyester prov.exhib.lit. 15-May-3 Christie's, Rockefeller NY #187/R est:30000-40000
£16312 $26426 €23000 Black column (95x37x40cm-37x15x16in) i. painted polyester. 24-May-3 Van Ham, Cologne #518/R est:22400
£20000 $30800 €30000 Monkey and child (117x88cm-46x35in) painted polyester executed 1996 prov.lit. 23-Oct-2 Christie's, London #116/R est:20000-30000
£20126 $31195 €32000 Josephine Baker (52x37x37cm-20x15x15in) s.num.7/8 polyester paint aluminum socle. 30-Oct-2 Artcurial Briest, Paris #449/R est:30000-40000
£20833 $34375 €30000 Bouddha (52x33x31cm-20x13x12in) s.num.4/8 verso paint resin prov. 1-Jul-3 Artcurial Briest, Paris #537/R est:35000-40000
£28125 $45000 €42188 Nana (127x102x18cm-50x40x7in) s.verso fiberglass painted polyester executed c.1970. 14-May-3 Sotheby's, New York #340/R est:30000-40000
£28481 $45000 €42722 Do you like my new dress (100x60x7cm-39x24x3in) sig. fiberglass painted polyester executed 1997 prov.exhib.lit. 14-Nov-2 Christie's, Rockefeller NY #184/R est:20000-30000
£32051 $49679 €50000 Chat (125x140x70cm-49x55x28in) s.st.f.Haligon glass painted polyester. 4-Dec-2 Pierre Berge, Paris #119/R est:20000
£32653 $51918 €48000 Fauteuil serpent (182x90x90cm-72x35x35in) s. num.14/20 painted resin exec.1991. 24-Mar-3 Cornette de St.Cyr, Paris #63/R est:40000
£40000 $65600 €60000 Nana pregnant - Last night I had a dream (142x127cm-56x50in) painted polyester exhib.lit. 6-Feb-3 Christie's, London #672/R est:40000-60000
£110759 $175000 €166139 Les baigneuses (274x284x304cm-108x112x120in) s.num. polychromed polyester fiberglass executed 1984 prov.exhib. 12-Nov-2 Phillips, New York #134/R est:200000-300000

Works on paper
£426 $711 €600 Par avion (26x36cm-10x14in) collage. 18-Jun-3 Pierre Berge, Paris #69
£886 $1373 €1400 Mechant-mechant (41x42cm-16x17in) s.num. painted wood jigsaw 250 pieces. 28-Sep-2 Cornette de St.Cyr, Paris #411
£993 $1658 €1400 Love Nikita (26x21cm-10x8in) s. collage. 18-Jun-3 Pierre Berge, Paris #73/R
£1277 $2132 €1800 Gemeaux et scorpion (29x21cm-11x8in) col crayon. 18-Jun-3 Pierre Berge, Paris #75/R est:1000-1200
£1550 $2403 €2325 Composition (21x30cm-8x12in) s.i. W/C crayon collage. 4-Dec-2 Kunsthallen, Copenhagen #87/R est:25000 (D.KR 18000)
£1915 $3198 €2700 Crabes, balance, belier (29x21cm-11x8in) col crayon. 18-Jun-3 Pierre Berge, Paris #72/R est:1000-1200
£3019 $4649 €4800 Indian (21x27cm-8x11in) mixed media prov. 26-Oct-2 Cornette de St.Cyr, Paris #42/R
£3974 $6160 €6200 Mort (49x64cm-19x25in) s.d.1993 gouache W/C ink prov. 7-Dec-2 Cornette de St.Cyr, Paris #107/R est:8000
£4025 $6239 €6400 L'ermite (49x31cm-19x12in) s.d.93 col dr W/C. 5-Oct-2 De Vuyst, Lokeren #589/R est:7000-8000
£4964 $7942 €6900 Composition (21x29cm-8x11in) s.i. mixed media. 14-May-3 Blanchet, Paris #190/R est:5000-6000
£10000 $15500 €15000 L'ange protecteur (70x73cm-28x29in) s. gouache W/C maquette prov.lit. 4-Dec-2 Koller, Zurich #200/R est:22000-30000 (S.FR 23000)

SAINT-PHALLE, Niki de and TINGUELY, Jean (20th C) French/Swiss
Sculpture
£9615 $15096 €15000 Dancing nana (44cm-17in) paint polyester socle editon of 150. 16-Dec-2 Charbonneaux, Paris #319/R est:12000-14000

SAINT-PIERRE, Gaston Casimir (1833-1916) French
£600 $942 €900 Femmes a l'interieur (36x28cm-14x11in) s.d.1871. 16-Apr-3 Christie's, Kensington #790/R
£7610 $11796 €12100 L'orientale servant (70x37cm-28x15in) s. 6-Oct-2 Feletin, Province #106/R

SAINTHILL, Loudon (1919-1969) Australian
Works on paper
£643 $990 €965 Dancer with mandolin (47x37cm-19x15in) s.i. W/C gouache pen ink. 3-Sep-2 Shapiro, Sydney #351 est:1000-1500 (A.D 1800)

SAINTIN, Henri (1846-1899) French
£255 $397 €400 Rochers a Erquy (12x22cm-5x9in) s. panel. 7-Nov-2 Chochon-Barre & Allardi, Paris #227
£308 $477 €480 Duck pond by farmstead (29x55cm-11x22in) s.i.d.1885. 5-Dec-2 Neumeister, Munich #2863/R
£321 $503 €500 Le Donjon du chateau (15x23cm-6x9in) s. panel. 16-Dec-2 Chochon-Barre & Allardi, Paris #96
£504 $806 €700 Paysage (37x54cm-15x21in) s. 14-May-3 Blanchet, Paris #96
£769 $1208 €1200 Riviere du Val Saint-Germain (16x24cm-6x9in) s.i.d.86 cardboard pair. 10-Dec-2 Renaud, Paris #19
£1282 $2013 €2000 Campement (38x56cm-15x22in) s. prov. 13-Dec-2 Piasa, Paris #208

SAINTIN, Jules Émile (1829-1894) French
£4088 $6500 €6132 Jeune fille pensive sur un balcon (62x43cm-24x17in) s.d.1880. 5-Mar-3 Christie's, Rockefeller NY #61/R est:8000-12000
£7500 $12525 €11250 L'elegante au livre d'estampes Japonaises (62x44cm-24x17in) s.d.1879. 18-Jun-3 Christie's, Kensington #107/R est:8000-10000

SAINTON, Charles Prosper (1861-1914) British
Works on paper
£764 $1207 €1146 Four winds (73x130cm-29x51in) s. W/C. 1-Apr-3 Stephan Welz, Johannesburg #414/R est:7000-10000 (SA.R 9500)

SAINZ DE MORALES, Gumersindo (1900-1976) Spanish
Works on paper
£301 $476 €470 View of the Seine in Paris (48x59cm-19x23in) s. W/C. 13-Nov-2 Ansorena, Madrid #202/R

SAITO, Kiyoshi (1907-) Japanese
Prints
£2215 $3500 €3323 Red flower (53x41cm-21x16in) s.i.d.1952 num.15/30 col woodcut. 22-Apr-3 Butterfields, San Francisco #2213/R est:3000-5000
£2243 $3500 €3365 Cats (55x66cm-22x26in) s.i.d.num.6/80 col woodcut. 14-Oct-2 Butterfields, San Francisco #1193/R est:4000-6000

SAIVE, Jean Baptiste de (1540-1624) Flemish
£11392 $18000 €18000 Scene de cuisine devant un fete de palais dans un interieur du Renaissance (154x240cm-61x94in) 2-Dec-2 Amberes, Antwerp #1328

SAIVE, Jean Baptiste de (circle) (1540-1624) Flemish
£6000 $9660 €9000 Street market (98x138cm-39x54in) panel. 20-Feb-3 Christie's, Kensington #1/R est:3000-5000

SAKHAROVA, Olga Nikolaevna (1879-1967) Russian
£3500 $5670 €5250 Flowers in a vase (42x31cm-17x12in) s. board. 21-May-3 Sotheby's, London #210/R est:2500-3500

SAKLIKOVSKAYA, Sofia (1899-1975) Russian
Works on paper
£5000 $8100 €7500 Reveling table, from the series old and new ways of life (40x30cm-16x12in) init. W/C pencil ink. 21-May-3 Sotheby's, London #181/R est:4000-6000
£6000 $9720 €9000 Country village scene, from the series old and new ways of life (44x40cm-17x16in) init. W/C pencil ink. 21-May-3 Sotheby's, London #179/R est:5000-7000

SAKURADA, Haruyosi (20th C) ?
£439 $685 €650 Surrealist composition (55x46cm-22x18in) s. 25-Mar-3 Durán, Madrid #1197/R

SALA LLORENS, Josep (1928-) Spanish
£1415 $2208 €2250 Landscape (37x45cm-15x18in) s. 23-Sep-2 Durán, Madrid #117/R est:1500

SALA Y FRANCES, Emilio (1850-1910) Spanish
£1282 $2026 €2000 Landscape (35x47cm-14x19in) s. 19-Nov-2 Durán, Madrid #189/R
£3396 $5230 €5400 Rural scene (42x55cm-17x22in) s. 28-Oct-2 Segre, Madrid #92/R
£8333 $13167 €13000 Portrait of lady (200x100cm-79x39in) s.i.d.184. 13-Nov-2 Ansorena, Madrid #113/R est:12000
£10063 $15698 €16000 Francisco Tarega, guitar player (90x115cm-35x45in) s.d.92. 23-Sep-2 Durán, Madrid #213/R est:7000

SALA, Eugène de (1899-1987) Danish
£260 $413 €390 Still life study of a jug and basket of fruit (48x58cm-19x23in) s. board. 27-Feb-3 Richardson & Smith, Whitby #460
£465 $734 €698 Composition with four women (95x182cm-37x72in) s. 1-Apr-3 Rasmussen, Copenhagen #372 (D.KR 5000)
£621 $1005 €900 Self-portrait with brush (100x70cm-39x28in) s. panel. 25-May-3 Uppsala Auktionskammare, Uppsala #232/R (S.KR 8000)
£677 $1050 €1016 Still life of jug, dish and oranges (48x70cm-19x28in) s. artist's board. 1-Oct-2 Rasmussen, Copenhagen #321/R (D.KR 8000)
£681 $1076 €1022 Composition (31x23cm-12x9in) s. cardboard. 27-Nov-2 Museumsbygningen, Copenhagen #572/R (D.KR 8000)
£762 $1181 €1143 Portrait of woman (46x46cm-18x18in) s. 1-Oct-2 Rasmussen, Copenhagen #280/R (D.KR 9000)
£927 $1538 €1344 Interior scene with woman and blue vase (122x102cm-48x40in) s. 16-Jun-3 Lilla Bukowskis, Stockholm #152 (S.KR 12000)
£2286 $3544 €3429 Visage - cubist portrait (84x70cm-33x28in) s. painted 1924 exhib. 1-Oct-2 Rasmussen, Copenhagen #37/R est:35000-40000 (D.KR 27000)

SALA, Giuseppe (17/18th C) Italian
Works on paper
£903 $1435 €1300 Sketch for decoration (23x19cm-9x7in) i. pen wash prov. 5-May-3 Ketterer, Munich #414/R

SALA, Paolo (1859-1929) Italian
£1419 $2243 €2200 Seascape (20x28cm-8x11in) s. cardboard. 18-Dec-2 Finarte, Milan #17/R est:2000
£1667 $2617 €2600 Mountainous landscape (24x34cm-9x13in) s. board. 10-Dec-2 Della Rocca, Turin #300/R
Works on paper
£456 $720 €684 Canal scene, Venice (44x27cm-17x11in) s. W/C. 30-Nov-2 Goteborg Auktionsverk, Sweden #220/R (S.KR 6500)
£976 $1600 €1464 Evening at Venice (38x53cm-15x21in) s. W/C. 9-Feb-3 William Jenack, New York #43 est:600-800
£3800 $6004 €5510 Broad sanctuary, London (52x21cm-20x8in) s. W/C. 22-Jul-3 Bristol Auction Rooms #351/R est:800-1200

SALABERRY, A de (?) ?
Works on paper
£7051 $10929 €11000 Sainfoin (39x54cm-15x21in) s.d.1912 W/C. 4-Dec-2 Libert, Castor, Paris #36/R est:1800

SALABET, Jean (20th C) French
£444 $738 €644 Near the Hotel de Ville in spring (27x35cm-11x14in) s.i. 10-Jun-3 Ritchie, Toronto #119/R est:1500-2000 (C.D 1000)
£717 $1090 €1076 Place de la Concord (26x33cm-10x13in) s. 27-Aug-2 Goodman, Sydney #255/R (A.D 2000)
£755 $1200 €1133 Street scene of the Champs Elysees (46x53cm-18x21in) s. 1-Mar-3 North East Auctions, Portsmouth #698/R
£843 $1400 €1222 Paris street scene (61x76cm-24x30in) s.d.1952. 11-Jun-3 Boos Gallery, Michigan #590/R est:1000-1500
£2000 $3180 €3000 Les promenades par nuit (28x36cm-11x14in) s. board. 20-Mar-3 Christie's, Kensington #25/R est:1000-1500
£2000 $3180 €3000 L'equipage en route a Paris (32x41cm-13x16in) s. board. 20-Mar-3 Christie's, Kensington #26/R est:1000-1500
Works on paper
£600 $930 €900 Outside the theatre (21x29cm-8x11in) s. gouache. 3-Dec-2 Sotheby's, Olympia #309/R

SALANSON, Eugenie Marie (19th C) French
£2564 $4026 €4000 Jeune italienne a la fontaine (60x44cm-24x17in) s. 10-Dec-2 Renaud, Paris #7/R

SALAS, M (?) Spanish
£789 $1279 €1200 Village in Morocco (40x50cm-16x20in) s. 21-Jan-3 Durán, Madrid #688/R

SALAT, Jean (19/20th C) French?
Works on paper
£256 $403 €400 Les musiciennes (55x45cm-22x18in) s.d.1880 pencil pastel htd gouache. 16-Dec-2 Gros & Delettrez, Paris #421

SALATHE, Friedrich (1793-1860) French
Works on paper
£472 $731 €750 Trees (22x30cm-9x12in) i. verso pen over pencil. 1-Oct-2 Dorotheum, Vienna #83/R

SALAZAR, Lodovico S (1924-) Mexican
£409 $622 €630 Times Square, New York (90x60cm-35x24in) s. 6-Jul-2 Berlinghof, Heidelberg #241/R

SALAZAR, Luis (1956-) ?
£1139 $1777 €1800 Composition abstraite (150x200cm-59x79in) s.d.1991 acrylic. 16-Oct-2 Hotel des Ventes Mosan, Brussels #310 est:2000-2500

SALCEDO, Doris (1958-) Colombian
Sculpture
£34375 $55000 €51563 Untitled (80x41x43cm-31x16x17in) cement steel wood executed 1995 prov.exhib. 15-May-3 Christie's, Rockefeller NY #305/R est:40000-60000

SALCES Y GUTIERREZ, Manuel (1861-1932) Spanish
£548 $866 €850 Landscape (41x32cm-16x13in) s. canvas on cardboard. 18-Dec-2 Ansorena, Madrid #25/R

SALCES, Manuel (19th C) Spanish
£523 $842 €800 Landscape (17x8cm-7x3in) s. canvas on board. 14-Jan-3 Castellana, Madrid #16/R
£524 $765 €786 Puerto de Escudo (28x36cm-11x14in) s. 4-Jun-2 Germann, Zurich #832 (S.FR 1200)

SALEH, Raden (c.1814-1880) Javanese
£31483 $48484 €47225 Last embrace of foes - Bedouin horseman attacked by a lion (33x51cm-13x20in) init.d.1844 prov.lit. 27-Oct-2 Christie's, Hong Kong #37/R est:320000-400000 (HK.D 380000)

SALEM, Aly Ben (1910-2001) Swedish?
Works on paper
£388 $628 €563 Female head with animals (34x26cm-13x10in) s. mixed media panel. 25-May-3 Uppsala Auktionskammare, Uppsala #292 (S.KR 5000)

SALEMANN, Georg (c.1670-1729) Danish
£1266 $2000 €2000 Vincent Gidon Henri Marquis de Cheussis (11x8cm-4x3in) ivory prov. 26-Nov-2 Wiener Kunst Auktionen, Vienna #4/R est:2000-5000

SALEMME, Antonio (1892-1995) American
£385 $600 €578 Loe tide, Rockport (33x43cm-13x17in) s.d.1941 s.i.d.1938 verso. 20-Sep-2 Sloan, North Bethesda #444/R

SALES, Francisco (1905-1976) Spanish
£521 $823 €750 Roofs (50x64cm-20x25in) s. cardboard. 25-Apr-3 Piasa, Paris #215/R
£590 $933 €850 Composition (73x54cm-29x21in) s.d.73. 25-Apr-3 Piasa, Paris #220
£590 $933 €850 Autumn leaves (50x65cm-20x26in) s.d.59. 25-Apr-3 Piasa, Paris #219
£833 $1308 €1300 Village (54x73cm-21x29in) s.d.65. 13-Dec-2 Piasa, Paris #275/R
£1111 $1756 €1600 Doves (40x80cm-16x31in) s.d.68. 25-Apr-3 Piasa, Paris #217/R est:1200
Works on paper
£382 $603 €550 Still life with lemons (29x43cm-11x17in) s.d.69 gouache oil. 25-Apr-3 Piasa, Paris #218

SALESIO (?) French?
Sculpture
£3800 $6004 €5700 Female figure (46cm-18in) s. gilt bronze. 14-Nov-2 Christie's, Kensington #301/R est:3000-4000

SALGADO COSME, Demetrio (1915-) Spanish
£709 $1149 €1000 Nino de espaldas (48x34cm-19x13in) s.d.1974 paper. 20-May-3 Segre, Madrid #139/R

SALGADO, Sebastiao (1944-) ?
Photographs
£2500 $4050 €3750 Brasil, Serra Pelada Goldmine (30x44cm-12x17in) st. s.i.d.verso silver print prov.lit. 22-May-3 Sotheby's, London #211/R est:1500-2000
£2800 $4536 €4200 Brasil, Serra Pelada Goldmine (30x44cm-12x17in) st. s.i.d.verso silver print prov.lit. 22-May-3 Sotheby's, London #210/R est:1500-2000
£3000 $4860 €4500 Brasil, Serra Pelada Goldmine (44x30cm-17x12in) st. s.i.d.verso silver print prov.lit. 22-May-3 Sotheby's, London #209/R est:1500-2000
£4000 $6480 €6000 Brasil, Serra Pelada Goldmine (44x30cm-17x12in) st. s.i.d.verso silver print prov.lit. 22-May-3 Sotheby's, London #208/R est:2000-3000

SALIETTI, Alberto (1892-1961) Italian
£1373 $2196 €2100 Mountainous landscape (24x30cm-9x12in) s. cardboard. 4-Jan-3 Meeting Art, Vercelli #495
£1923 $2808 €3000 Portrait in the studio (90x75cm-35x30in) s.d.1926 board exhib. 5-Jun-2 Il Ponte, Milan #86
£1923 $2808 €3000 Angels' flight (65x84cm-26x33in) s. board. 5-Jun-2 Il Ponte, Milan #88 est:3000
£2564 $3744 €4000 Portrait of lady (90x75cm-35x30in) s.d.1927 board. 5-Jun-2 Il Ponte, Milan #83/R
£14865 $23189 €22000 Interior with girl and vase of flowers (79x60cm-31x24in) s.d.1921 cardboard. 26-Mar-3 Finarte Semenzato, Milan #297/R

SALIGER, Ivo (1894-1975) Austrian
£256 $405 €400 Seated female nude (60x80cm-24x31in) s. panel. 18-Nov-2 Dorotheum, Linz #335/R
£556 $878 €800 Female nude by lake (68x90cm-27x35in) s. 24-Apr-3 Dorotheum, Vienna #113/R
£694 $1104 €1000 Girl's portrait (81x61cm-32x24in) s. 29-Apr-3 Wiener Kunst Auktionen, Vienna #591/R

SALIGO, Charles Louis (1804-1874) Belgian
£12821 $20256 €20000 Portrait of a lady (180x111cm-71x44in) s.d.1859. 18-Nov-2 Bernaerts, Antwerp #53/R est:20000-30000

SALIMBENI, Arcangelo (16th C) Italian
Works on paper
£3000 $5010 €4350 Virgin of the immaculate conception (15x11cm-6x4in) pen brown ink wash exhib. 9-Jul-3 Sotheby's, London #22/R est:1000-1500

SALIMBENI, Ventura (1568-1613) Italian
£13000 $21710 €18850 Madonna and Child (75x61cm-30x24in) 9-Jul-3 Christie's, London #92/R est:12000-18000
Works on paper
£3846 $5962 €6000 Annunciation (23x19cm-9x7in) pencil ink W/C. 4-Dec-2 Christie's, Rome #405/R est:2000-3000

SALIN, R (?) ?
£466 $742 €699 Park landscape with mothers and children (50x70cm-20x28in) s. 5-May-3 Rasmussen, Vejle #668/R (D.KR 5000)

SALINAS Y TERUEL, Augustin (1862-1915) Spanish
£507 $791 €750 Italia peasant women (14x21cm-6x8in) s. board. 25-Mar-3 Durán, Madrid #35/R
£1316 $2132 €2000 Capri (23x37cm-9x15in) s. 21-Jan-3 Durán, Madrid #147/R
£3208 $4940 €5100 Palermo Bay (24x49cm-9x19in) s. 23-Oct-2 Finarte, Milan #8/R est:4500-5500
£20440 $31887 €32500 Washerwomen (23x40cm-9x16in) s. board. 23-Sep-2 Durán, Madrid #254/R

SALINAS, Baruj (1935-) Cuban
£2138 $3377 €3207 AnimaMotrix (133x150cm-52x59in) s. d.Feb.77 verso exhib. 1-Apr-3 Rasmussen, Copenhagen #198/R est:30000-40000 (D.KR 23000)

SALINAS, Pablo (1871-1946) Spanish
£7609 $12478 €10500 Partita a scacchi (24x35cm-9x14in) s. panel. 27-May-3 Finarte, Milan #93/R est:12000-13000
£23270 $36069 €37000 Celebrating (42x62cm-17x24in) board. 7-Oct-2 Ansorena, Madrid #63/R est:37000
£39007 $63191 €55000 A la bacia de oro (40x66cm-16x26in) s.i. 22-May-3 Stadion, Trieste #331/R est:16000-22000

SALINAS, Porfirio (1910-1972) American
£1558 $2400 €2337 Texas bluebonnets (15x23cm-6x9in) s. canvas laid down painted c.1950. 8-Sep-2 Treadway Gallery, Cincinnati #584/R est:1500-2500

£2308 $3600 €3462 Hill country autumn (41x51cm-16x20in) 9-Nov-2 Altermann Galleries, Santa Fe #202
£2877 $4200 €4316 Autumn hill country landscape (41x51cm-16x20in) 18-May-2 Altermann Galleries, Santa Fe #191/R
£4194 $6500 €6291 Seventy five miles south of El Paso, Texas (41x51cm-16x20in) s.d. prov. 8-Dec-2 Toomey, Oak Park #705/R est:7000-9000
£4795 $7000 €7193 Hill country landscape (64x76cm-25x30in) 18-May-2 Altermann Galleries, Santa Fe #192/R

SALINI, Tommaso (1575-1625) Italian
£18868 $29245 €30000 San Rocco (110x146cm-43x57in) 2-Oct-2 Dorotheum, Vienna #33/R est:30000-40000

SALIOU, Herve (20th C) French
Sculpture
£1338 $2154 €1900 Le Taureau (26x16cm-10x6in) num.6/8 blue pat.bronze Susse Fondeur. 11-May-3 Thierry & Lannon, Brest #43/R est:1500-1800

SALISBURY, Frank O (1874-1962) British
£260 $413 €390 H.M. The Queen (56x44cm-22x17in) s. 25-Feb-3 John Taylors, Louth #452
£420 $701 €609 Portrait of a sailor boy (49x39cm-19x15in) 19-Jun-3 Lane, Penzance #147
£750 $1170 €1125 Waterlilies (91x71cm-36x28in) s. 27-Mar-3 Christie's, Kensington #606/R
£780 $1217 €1170 Portrait of James Macarthur as Bishop of Bombay (140x117cm-55x46in) s.d.1919. 26-Mar-3 Woolley & Wallis, Salisbury #141/R
£1300 $2119 €1950 Portrait of Mrs Grinling (82x69cm-32x27in) s.d.1924 exhib. 29-Jan-3 Sotheby's, Olympia #229/R est:1000-1500
£1300 $2119 €1950 Lilium, delphinium and boccania (91x71cm-36x28in) s. s.i.verso. 13-Feb-3 Christie's, Kensington #247/R est:800-1200
£1608 $2540 €2412 St Stevens Tower Westminster (73x61cm-29x24in) s. 1-Apr-3 Stephan Welz, Johannesburg #415 est:4000-6000 (SA.R 20000)
£2400 $3912 €3480 Portrait of a girl in a white dress (91x63cm-36x25in) mono. 16-Jul-3 Sotheby's, Olympia #119/R est:1000-1500

SALKELD, Cecil (1908-1968) British
£769 $1208 €1200 Stylised portrait of Mrs Campbell (32x24cm-13x9in) panel prov. 19-Nov-2 Hamilton Osborne King, Dublin #436/R
£2703 $4216 €4000 Connemara (39x50cm-15x20in) s. board. 26-Mar-3 James Adam, Dublin #109/R est:4000-6000
£2754 $4516 €3800 Portrait of a medical gentleman (91x71cm-36x28in) s. 28-May-3 Bonhams & James Adam, Dublin #173/R est:2500-3500
Works on paper
£1384 $2158 €2200 Crippled man on path (61x46cm-24x18in) s.d.1935 gouache. 17-Sep-2 Whyte's, Dublin #29 est:2000-30000
£2308 $3623 €3600 Figure composition - an allegory of temptation (30x23cm-12x9in) mono.i.d.1923 verso W/C gouache gold ink. 19-Nov-2 Whyte's, Dublin #32/R est:2500-3500

SALKELD, Cecil (attrib) (1908-1968) British
£1507 $2366 €2200 Traveller family (55x78cm-22x31in) board. 15-Apr-3 De Veres Art Auctions, Dublin #238/R est:1500-2000

SALLAERT, Anthonie (1590-1657) Flemish
£8537 $14000 €12806 Glorification of the Name of Jesus (36x25cm-14x10in) panel prov.exhib. 30-May-3 Christie's, Rockefeller NY #29/R est:8000-12000
Works on paper
£777 $1212 €1150 Adam and Eve (30x19cm-12x7in) wash htd gouache. 27-Mar-3 Maigret, Paris #41/R

SALLAERT, Anthonie (attrib) (1590-1657) Flemish
Works on paper
£244 $400 €354 Madonna and Child with Saint peter (13x18cm-5x7in) W/C gouache. 7-Jun-3 Neal Auction Company, New Orleans #114

SALLBERG, Harald (1895-1963) Swedish
£1028 $1594 €1542 View towards Kungsholmen from Langholmen (49x62cm-19x24in) s.d.1907. 3-Dec-2 Bukowskis, Stockholm #13/R est:10000-12000 (S.KR 14500)

SALLE, David (1952-) American
£13000 $21320 €19500 I fear I fall (147x107cm-58x42in) acrylic oil prov. 7-Feb-3 Sotheby's, London #185/R est:12000-15000
£18000 $30060 €26100 Girl with pie (81x102cm-32x40in) acrylic oil painted 1997 prov.exhib. 27-Jun-3 Christie's, London #243/R est:8000-12000
£21875 $35000 €32813 Untitled (152x107cm-60x42in) acrylic painted 1983 prov. 14-May-3 Sotheby's, New York #442/R est:40000-60000
£22152 $35000 €33228 Postoral artichoke (163x244cm-64x96in) acrylic painted 1999 prov. 13-Nov-2 Sotheby's, New York #144/R est:40000-60000
£50000 $80000 €75000 Making the bed (305x239cm-120x94in) oil acrylic wood on canvas dipytch prov.exhib. 15-May-3 Christie's, Rockefeller NY #378/R est:80000-120000
Works on paper
£6500 $10010 €9750 Untitled (57x76cm-22x30in) s.i.d.1987 gouache prov. 22 Oct-2 Sotheby's, London #330/R est:5000-7000

SALLI, Aares (1914-) Finnish
£289 $446 €460 Landscape (65x55cm-26x22in) s. 24-Oct-2 Hagelstam, Helsinki #940
£327 $519 €480 Birches on the beach (74x48cm-29x19in) s.d.1972. 24-Mar-3 Bukowskis, Helsinki #271/R
£377 $581 €600 Winter (81x65cm-32x26in) s. 24-Oct-2 Hagelstam, Helsinki #1034

SALLINEN, Tyko (1879-1955) Finnish
£380 $592 €600 Town (40x50cm-16x20in) i.verso. 15-Sep-2 Bukowskis, Helsinki #276/R
£597 $920 €950 Landscape (55x74cm-22x29in) s.d.1946. 24-Oct-2 Hagelstam, Helsinki #827
£654 $1072 €1000 The ridge (54x65cm-21x26in) s.d.50. 9-Feb-3 Bukowskis, Helsinki #347/R
£1429 $2271 €2100 Landscape (34x42cm-13x17in) s. 27-Feb-3 Hagelstam, Helsinki #864/R est:1800
£2785 $4400 €4400 Stony beach (65x66cm-26x26in) s.d.08. 1-Dec-2 Bukowskis, Helsinki #153/R est:3300-3500
Works on paper
£258 $408 €400 Windmill in the skerries (31x44cm-12x17in) s.d.1941 W/C. 19-Dec-2 Hagelstam, Helsinki #879/R
£484 $765 €750 Mountain village (37x29cm-15x11in) s.d.1921 W/C. 19-Dec-2 Hagelstam, Helsinki #827/R
£863 $1416 €1200 Tyomies - the Newspaper editor Merilainen (45x34cm-18x13in) s. mixed media exhib. 4-Jun-3 Bukowskis, Helsinki #416/R

SALMI, Max (1931-1995) Finnish
£472 $726 €750 Light mountain (35x53cm-14x21in) s.d.1973. 24-Oct-2 Hagelstam, Helsinki #1009
£504 $826 €700 Portrait (70x50cm-28x20in) s.d.1970. 5-Jun-3 Hagelstam, Helsinki #844
£538 $839 €850 Korento (69x48cm-27x19in) s.d.1971. 12-Sep-2 Hagelstam, Helsinki #991
£557 $869 €880 Nude (45x34cm-18x13in) s.d.1964. 12-Sep-2 Hagelstam, Helsinki #917/R
£563 $907 €800 The fisherman's house (50x50cm-20x20in) s.d.73 board. 10-May-3 Bukowskis, Helsinki #259/R
£613 $968 €950 Cactus (48x30cm-19x12in) s.d.1964. 19-Dec-2 Hagelstam, Helsinki #840
£621 $1018 €950 In deep thought (69x49cm-27x19in) s.d.75. 9-Feb-3 Bukowskis, Helsinki #348/R
£755 $1162 €1200 Resting (50x50cm-20x20in) s.d.1969. 24-Oct-2 Hagelstam, Helsinki #1048
£791 $1234 €1250 Evening (60x53cm-24x21in) s.d.1959. 12-Sep-2 Hagelstam, Helsinki #886
£845 $1361 €1200 Landscape (50x50cm-20x20in) BOARD. 10-May-3 Bukowskis, Helsinki #257/R
£1013 $1600 €1600 Target (40x45cm-16x18in) s.d.70 board exhib. 1-Dec-2 Bukowskis, Helsinki #349/R est:1800-2000
£1013 $1600 €1600 Blue mill (70x49cm-28x19in) s.d.74 board. 1-Dec-2 Bukowskis, Helsinki #350/R est:1000-1300
£1056 $1701 €1500 Shape (50x50cm-20x20in) s.d.70 and 72 board. 10-May-3 Bukowskis, Helsinki #240/R est:1500-1800
£1079 $1727 €1500 Model reading (50x48cm-20x19in) s.d.1968 board. 17-May-3 Hagelstam, Helsinki #197/R est:1200
£1197 $1927 €1700 Figure (50x50cm-20x20in) board. 10-May-3 Bukowskis, Helsinki #241/R est:1200-1500
£2183 $3515 €3100 Juggler (70x50cm-28x20in) s.d.81 board. 10-May-3 Bukowskis, Helsinki #234/R est:1800-2000

SALMINEN, Juho (1892-1945) Finnish
£277 $426 €440 View from Paris (36x44cm-14x17in) s.d.28 exhib. 27-Oct-2 Bukowskis, Helsinki #272/R
£354 $562 €520 Still life of bottle, jug and dish (51x64cm-20x25in) s.d.1925. 27-Feb-3 Hagelstam, Helsinki #847/R
£365 $562 €580 Still life (59x66cm-23x26in) s.d.31. 27-Oct-2 Bukowskis, Helsinki #271/R

SALMON, John (?) British
Works on paper
£250 $398 €375 Old Gillingham Fort, Medway (36x53cm-14x21in) s.i.d.1886 W/C. 30-Apr-3 Halls, Shrewsbury #260/R

SALMON, John Cuthbert (attrib) (1844-1917) British
Works on paper
£300 $477 €450 Fishermen in a choppy sea (22x30cm-9x12in) W/C. 4-Mar-3 Bearnes, Exeter #339

SALMON, Robert (1775-1844) American
£25926 $42000 €37593 Small fishing cove in the region of the Clyde estuary, Scotland (28x44cm-11x17in) init. i.verso panel prov. 29-Jul-3 Christie's, Rockefeller NY #127/R est:45000-55000
£50000 $83000 €75000 English vessel off the Liverpool waterfront on the River Mersey (41x64cm-16x25in) init. prov. 12-Jun-3 Sotheby's, London #27/R est:60000-80000
£67901 $110000 €101852 Fifth rate ship of the line on the river Mersey (68x110cm-27x43in) s.d.1808. 21-Jan-3 Christie's, Rockefeller NY #375/R est:180000

SALMOND, Kathleen (1895-1946) New Zealander
Works on paper
£261 $384 €392 Lake and mountain scene (22x18cm-9x7in) s. W/C prov. 19-Jun-2 Watson's, Christchurch #31/R (NZ.D 800)

SALMSON, Esther (1877-1966) Swedish
Works on paper
£350 $567 €525 View of Visby (69x58cm-27x23in) s.i.d.1917 chl pastel. 23-Jan-3 Christie's, Kensington #356/R

SALMSON, Hugo (1844-1894) Swedish
£1335 $2190 €1936 Girl with doll (100x70cm-39x28in) s. 4-Jun-3 AB Stockholms Auktionsverk #2150/R est:20000-25000 (S.KR 17000)
£1532 $2512 €2221 Girl from Rettvik (43x34cm-17x13in) s.d.1868. 4-Jun-3 AB Stockholms Auktionsverk #2232/R est:20000-25000 (S.KR 19500)
£5674 $8794 €8511 The small hill - young girl seated holding flowers (118x80cm-46x31in) s. exhib.lit. 3-Dec-2 Bukowskis, Stockholm #170/R est:80000-100000 (S.KR 80000)
£7070 $11595 €10252 Young mother holding small child in Russian interior (100x60cm-39x24in) s. 4-Jun-3 AB Stockholms Auktionsverk #2280/R est:90000-100000 (S.KR 90000)

SALMSON, Jean Jules (1823-1902) French
Sculpture
£1000 $1560 €1500 Pandora (47cm-19in) s. brown pat bronze. 5-Nov-2 Sotheby's, London #188/R est:1200-1800
£3500 $5390 €5250 Arab figures (41cm-16in) cold painted bronze pair lit. 28-Oct-2 Sotheby's, Olympia #25/R est:2000-3000

SALOKIVI, Santeri (1886-1940) Finnish
£272 $433 €400 Bonfire (42x58cm-17x23in) i.verso painted c.1906-08. 27-Feb-3 Hagelstam, Helsinki #836
£506 $790 €800 View from Rome (32x24cm-13x9in) s. 15-Sep-2 Bukowskis, Helsinki #277/R
£1203 $1900 €1900 Landscape from the South of France (30x21cm-12x8in) s.i.d.20 board. 1-Dec-2 Bukowskis, Helsinki #160/R est:1500-1800
£1408 $2268 €2000 Morning landscape (35x30cm-14x12in) s. cardboard. 10-May-3 Bukowskis, Helsinki #82/R est:2400-2600
£1761 $2835 €2500 Archipelago, Dragsfjard (38x46cm-15x18in) s.d.29. 10-May-3 Bukowskis, Helsinki #39/R est:2000-2500
£2086 $3422 €2900 Fishermen (42x49cm-17x19in) s. painted c.1939. 5-Jun-3 Hagelstam, Helsinki #964/R est:3000
£2254 $3628 €3200 By the sauna on the beach (46x63cm-18x25in) s.i. 10-May-3 Bukowskis, Helsinki #166/R est:4000-5000
£2278 $3600 €3600 By the gate at home (55x70cm-22x28in) s.d.1924. 1-Dec-2 Bukowskis, Helsinki #159/R est:5000-6000
£2381 $3786 €3500 Aabo (32x40cm-13x16in) s.d.1915. 27-Feb-3 Hagelstam, Helsinki #802 est:4000
£2465 $3968 €3500 Village scene, Cancale (46x55cm-18x22in) s.i.d.25. 10-May-3 Bukowskis, Helsinki #73/R est:3500-4000
£2518 $4029 €3500 Reflections (41x54cm-16x21in) s.d.1912 canvas on board. 17-May-3 Hagelstam, Helsinki #157/R
£2532 $4000 €4000 Coastal breakers (48x71cm-19x28in) s.d.29. 1-Dec-2 Bukowskis, Helsinki #161/R est:4000-4500
£2590 $4144 €3600 Nadendal - with figures (47x40cm-19x16in) s. board. 17-May-3 Hagelstam, Helsinki #156/R
£2722 $4246 €4300 Aura river (31x40cm-12x16in) s. 12-Sep-2 Hagelstam, Helsinki #908/R est:4700
£3291 $5200 €5200 Sunny summer's day (48x68cm-19x27in) s.d.34. 1-Dec-2 Bukowskis, Helsinki #158/R est:6000-7000
£3803 $6123 €5400 Reclining female model (37x45cm-15x18in) s.d.21. 10-May-3 Bukowskis, Helsinki #47/R est:3500-4000
£4304 $6800 €6800 Notre Dame de Paris (63x89cm-25x35in) s.i.d.39 exhib. 1-Dec-2 Bukowskis, Helsinki #155/R est:7000-8000
£4930 $7937 €7000 View from Aabo (44x60cm-17x24in) s. board. 10-May-3 Bukowskis, Helsinki #117/R est:5500-6500
£5127 $8100 €8100 View of the sea at Aaland (48x92cm-19x36in) s.d.1907. 30-Nov-2 Hagelstam, Helsinki #135/R est:7000
£5696 $9000 €9000 Park scene from Paris (22x31cm-9x12in) s.i.d.1919 board. 30-Nov-2 Hagelstam, Helsinki #134/R est:8000

SALOME (1954-) German
£2754 $4516 €3800 Frozen pond (100x140cm-39x55in) s.d.96 s.i.d.96 verso acrylic. 31-May-3 Villa Grisebach, Berlin #392/R est:4000-6000
£3986 $6536 €5500 Artists (160x141cm-63x56in) s.d.79 s.i.d.79 verso acrylic. 31-May-3 Villa Grisebach, Berlin #394/R est:5000-7000
£4430 $7000 €7000 Waterlily pond (160x200cm-63x79in) s.d.94 s.i.d. verso acrylic cotton. 30-Nov-2 Villa Grisebach, Berlin #475/R est:7000-9000
£4430 $7000 €7000 Waterlilies (160x200cm-63x79in) s.d.94 s.i.d. verso acrylic cotton. 30-Nov-2 Villa Grisebach, Berlin #476/R est:7000-9000
£5072 $8319 €7000 Waterlilies (160x200cm-63x79in) s. s.i.d.94 verso acrylic cotton. 31-May-3 Villa Grisebach, Berlin #397/R est:7000-9000
£5072 $8319 €7000 Swimmers (160x200cm-63x79in) s.d.94 s.i.d.94 verso acrylic cotton. 31-May-3 Villa Grisebach, Berlin #398/R est:7000-9000
£5072 $8319 €7000 Waterlilies (160x200cm-63x79in) s.d.94 s.i.d. verso acrylic. 28-May-3 Lempertz, Koln #386/R est:7000-9000
£5435 $8913 €7500 Swimmers (160x200cm-63x79in) s.d.94 s.i.d. verso acrylic. 28-May-3 Lempertz, Koln #385/R est:7000-9000
£6329 $10000 €10000 Spring. Summer. Autumn. Winter (100x100cm-39x39in) s.d.97 s.i.d. verso four. 30-Nov-2 Villa Grisebach, Berlin #474/R est:1000-15000
Works on paper
£949 $1500 €1500 Nude (100x70cm-39x28in) s.i.d.85 gouache. 29-Nov-2 Villa Grisebach, Berlin #872/R est:1500-2000

SALOMONS, Edward (1827-1906) British
Works on paper
£850 $1326 €1275 Canal, Utrecht (20x14cm-8x6in) init.d.90 W/C exhib. 5-Nov-2 Bonhams, New Bond Street #139/R

SALONEN, Risto (1945-2001) Finnish
Works on paper
£6013 $9500 €9500 At the gallery (25x31cm-10x12in) s.d.1993 mixed media. 30-Nov-2 Hagelstam, Helsinki #172/R est:840

SALONEN, Wille (20th C) Finnish
£392 $643 €600 Summer's day (69x85cm-27x33in) s. 9-Feb-3 Bukowskis, Helsinki #350/R
£784 $1286 €1200 Green summer landscape (88x114cm-35x45in) s.d.53. 9-Feb-3 Bukowskis, Helsinki #351/R

SALOSMAA, Aarno (1941-) Finnish
£253 $395 €400 Composition (42x49cm-17x19in) s.d.1974. 12-Sep-2 Hagelstam, Helsinki #998
£289 $448 €460 Composition (24x26cm-9x10in) s.d.70. 6-Oct-2 Bukowskis, Helsinki #272/R
£313 $498 €460 Composition (41x36cm-16x14in) s.d.81. 24-Mar-3 Bukowskis, Helsinki #278/R
£704 $1134 €1000 Relief (62x52cm-24x20in) s.d.72. 10-May-3 Bukowskis, Helsinki #244/R

SALOUN, Ladislav (1870-1946) Czechoslovakian
Sculpture
£2497 $4045 €3621 Messalina. marble polychrome. 24-May-3 Dorotheum, Prague #257/R est:40000-60000 (C.KR 110000)

SALT, James (19th C) British
£301 $500 €436 Venetian harbour scene (46x81cm-18x32in) s. 11-Jun-3 Boos Gallery, Michigan #558
£1900 $3097 €2850 Capriccio view of Venice (46x81cm-18x32in) s. 29-Jan-3 Sotheby's, Olympia #165/R est:1200-1800
£3000 $4680 €4500 Venetian capriccios (35x61cm-14x24in) s. pair. 7-Nov-2 Christie's, Kensington #174 est:1000-1500

SALT, James (attrib) (19th C) British
£1000 $1580 €1450 Italian capriccio river scenes (35x60cm-14x24in) bears sig pair. 22-Jul-3 Sworder & Son, Bishops Stortford #353/R est:300-500

SALT, John (1937-) British
£15823 $25000 €23735 Albuquerque wreck yard - Sandia auto electric (122x183cm-48x72in) s.d.72 verso prov. 13-Nov-2 Sotheby's, New York #258/R est:25000-35000

SALTER, John William (19th C) British
Works on paper
£600 $966 €900 Coastal view and lady reading a book while sheltering beneath parasol (23x36cm-9x14in) s.d.1862 W/C. 9-May-3 Mallams, Oxford #11/R
£660 $1089 €957 Bradley manor, Newton Abbot (25x36cm-10x14in) s.d.1868 W/C. 1-Jul-3 Bearnes, Exeter #435/R
£900 $1431 €1350 St. Michael's chapel, Torquay (24x30cm-9x12in) s.d.1885 s.i.verso W/C. 4-Mar-3 Bearnes, Exeter #380/R
£940 $1495 €1410 Torbay (21x46cm-8x18in) s.d.1869 W/C. 4-Mar-3 Bearnes, Exeter #379/R

SALTER, William (1804-1875) British
£1115 $1750 €1673 Reclining female and 2 Bacchantes (46x53cm-18x21in) 13-Dec-2 Du Mouchelle, Detroit #2046/R est:2000-3000
£4000 $6160 €6000 Portrait of General Sir Arthur Clifton (240x148cm-94x58in) i. 5-Sep-2 Christie's, Kensington #64/R est:2000-4000

SALTFLEET, Frank (c.1860-1937) British
Works on paper
£550 $875 €825 Summer garden (32x48cm-13x19in) s.d.1915 W/C. 5-Mar-3 Bonhams, Bury St Edmunds #312/R
£900 $1467 €1350 Whitby Harbour (33x48cm-13x19in) s. W/C. 28-Jan-3 Gorringes, Lewes #1580/R

SALTI, Giulio (1899-1984) Italian
£676 $1054 €1000 Beach resort in Lerici (34x49cm-13x19in) s. i.verso. 28-Mar-3 Farsetti, Prato #484/R
£743 $1159 €1100 Maternity (58x47cm-23x19in) s. board. 28-Mar-3 Farsetti, Prato #753/R
£811 $1265 €1200 Fruit in the sun (57x46cm-22x18in) s. board. 28-Mar-3 Farsetti, Prato #768/R
£878 $1370 €1300 Afternoon on the beach (34x51cm-13x20in) s. cardboard. 28-Mar-3 Farsetti, Prato #479/R
£1351 $2108 €2000 Herring (40x50cm-16x20in) s. board. 28-Mar-3 Farsetti, Prato #629/R

SALTMER, Florence A (fl.1882-1908) British
£6000 $9960 €9000 By the millpond (51x76cm-20x30in) s.d.1898. 10-Jun-3 Christie's, London #114/R est:5000-8000

SALTO, Axel (1889-1961) Danish
£1532 $2420 €2298 Landscape with vulcano and antelopes (154x247cm-61x97in) s. panel. 30-Nov-2 Rasmussen, Havnen #2187/R est:10000 (D.KR 18000)
Works on paper
£380 $586 €570 Sketch for a large jug (56x42cm-22x17in) s.d.19/8-54 Indian ink. 23-Oct-2 Kunsthallen, Copenhagen #87/R (D.KR 4500)

SALTOFT, Edvard Anders (1883-1939) Danish
Works on paper
£558 $881 €837 Portrait of Knud Rasmussen (100x80cm-39x31in) s. pastel. 5-Apr-3 Rasmussen, Havnen #3500/R (D.KR 6000)

SALTZMANN, Carl (1847-1923) German
£9000 $14580 €13500 Kaiser's yacht Hohenzollern under escort on a summer cruise (70x120cm-28x47in) s.d.1904. 21-May-3 Christie's, Kensington #671/R est:4000-6000
Works on paper
£1234 $1950 €1851 Three master at sea (27x45cm-11x18in) s. gouache. 2-Dec-2 Rasmussen, Copenhagen #1417/R est:15000 (D.KR 14500)

SALUCCI, Alessandro (circle) (17th C) Italian
£9790 $14000 €14685 Finding of Moses. Arrival of the Queen of Sheba (60x88cm-24x35in) pair. 22-Jan-3 Doyle, New York #88/R est:12000

SALUCCI, Roger Francois (20th C) French?
£305 $497 €460 Un mariage de raison (40x30cm-16x12in) s.d.99 acrylic canvas on cardboard. 1-Feb-3 Claude Aguttes, Neuilly #108

SALVA-SIMBOR, Gonzalo (1845-1923) Spanish
£1208 $1945 €1800 Portrait of woman (54x39cm-21x15in) s. 18-Feb-3 Durán, Madrid #191/R

SALVADO, Jacinto (1892-1983) Spanish
£705 $1107 €1100 Abstract composition (81x54cm-32x21in) s.d.1950. 16-Dec-2 Pandolfini, Florence #373

SALVADOR GOMEZ, Vicente (1637-1680) Spanish
Works on paper
£4747 $7500 €7500 L'Enfant Jesus apparaissant a St Antoine de Padoue (18x13cm-7x5in) i. pen brown ink. 27-Nov-2 Christie's, Paris #124/R est:6000-8000

SALVADORI, Aldo (1905-) Italian
£3514 $5481 €5200 Seated nude (100x70cm-39x28in) s. painted 1970. 26-Mar-3 Finarte Semenzato, Milan #303/R
£4487 $7045 €7000 Woman (50x60cm-20x24in) s. s.i.d.1975 verso. 19-Nov-2 Finarte, Milan #102

SALVESTRINI, Bartolomeo (attrib) (?-c.1630) Italian
Works on paper
£1519 $2400 €2400 Jeune homme portant un plat (40x24cm-16x9in) black chk. 27-Nov-2 Christie's, Paris #58/R est:2500-3500

SALVIATI, Francesco (circle) (1510-1563) Italian
£35000 $58450 €50750 Adoration of the Magi (52x180cm-20x71in) panel. 9-Jul-3 Christie's, London #107/R est:15000-20000
Works on paper
£8000 $13360 €11600 Roman soldiers attacking a temple within city walls (32x26cm-13x10in) i. verso pen brown ink wash blk chk exhib. 9-Jul-3 Sotheby's, London #1/R est:8000-12000

SALVINI, Innocente (1889-?) Italian
£316 $491 €500 Serotha valley and Zimba (60x50cm-24x20in) s.d.32 i. verso. 28-Sep-2 Hans Stahl, Hamburg #31

SALVINO, Andrea (1969-) Italian
£1026 $1590 €1600 Socially antagonist subject (70x60cm-28x24in) s.d.2000 verso acrylic. 4-Dec-2 Finarte, Milan #450/R

SALVO (1947-) Italian
£2288 $3660 €3500 Coffee pot (40x30cm-16x12in) s.i. masonite. 4-Jan-3 Meeting Art, Vercelli #509
£2292 $3644 €3300 Portrait of woman (40x30cm-16x12in) s.d.1982. 1-May-3 Meeting Art, Vercelli #412
£2308 $3623 €3600 Snack (45x35cm-18x14in) s.i.verso. 23-Nov-2 Meeting Art, Vercelli #235/R
£2361 $3754 €3400 December (35x25cm-14x10in) s.i.verso. 1-May-3 Meeting Art, Vercelli #190
£2532 $3949 €4000 Alberobello (36x46cm-14x18in) s.verso masonite. 14-Sep-2 Meeting Art, Vercelli #789/R
£2614 $4183 €4000 Minaret (35x25cm-14x10in) s.i.d.1991 verso. 4-Jan-3 Meeting Art, Vercelli #738
£3404 $5515 €4800 Un giorno (50x40cm-20x16in) s.i.d.91. 26-May-3 Christie's, Milan #135/R est:4000-6000
£4082 $6490 €6000 San Nicola Arcella (30x40cm-12x16in) i. s.verso. 1-Mar-3 Meeting Art, Vercelli #620
£4255 $6894 €6000 Marina (24x38cm-9x15in) s.i.d.1986 verso prov. 26-May-3 Christie's, Milan #232/R est:6000-8000
£4487 $6955 €7000 Trees (46x29cm-18x11in) s.d.1986 verso board. 4-Dec-2 Finarte, Milan #480/R est:7000
£4516 $7135 €7000 January (50x50cm-20x20in) s.i. 18-Dec-2 Christie's, Rome #253/R est:10000
£5449 $8446 €8500 Saint George and the dragon (64x64cm-25x25in) s.verso polychrome ceramic painted 2002. 4-Dec-2 Finarte, Milan #484/R est:12000
£9028 $14354 €13000 Village (100x80cm-39x31in) s.i.verso. 1-May-3 Meeting Art, Vercelli #596 est:12000
£11392 $17772 €18000 Tough battles (100x150cm-39x59in) s.i.d.1998. 14-Sep-2 Meeting Art, Vercelli #832/R est:15000
£15000 $23400 €22500 Interno con funzioni straordinarie (150x100cm-59x39in) s. i.d.30-1-90 verso prov.exhib. 21-Oct-2 Sotheby's, London #65/R est:12000-15000
Works on paper
£272 $433 €400 Still life (25x30cm-10x12in) s.d.2001 Chinese ink paper on canvas. 1-Mar-3 Meeting Art, Vercelli #417
£316 $494 €500 Landscape (20x30cm-8x12in) s. mixed media card. 14-Sep-2 Meeting Art, Vercelli #758/R
£833 $1308 €1300 Minarets (60x40cm-24x16in) s. mixed media. 21-Nov-2 Finarte, Rome #160/R
£1042 $1656 €1500 The most beautiful dream (40x30cm-16x12in) s.i. mixed media paper on canvas. 1-May-3 Meeting Art, Vercelli #24

SALZER, Friedrich (1827-1876) German
£7051 $11071 €11000 View of city of Esslingen with Frauen church (65x91cm-26x36in) s. 21-Nov-2 Dorotheum, Vienna #132/R est:2600-3400

SALZMANN, Gottfried (1943-) Austrian
Works on paper
£285 $450 €450 New York (29x26cm-11x10in) bears sig.d.15.09.1984 W/C. 30-Nov-2 Arnold, Frankfurt #483/R
£1218 $1888 €1900 New York (60x28cm-24x11in) s.d.2001 W/C bodycol Indian ink. 7-Dec-2 Ketterer, Hamburg #757/R est:2400-2600
£1379 $2207 €2000 New York (46x29cm-18x11in) s. mixed media. 11-Mar-3 Dorotheum, Vienna #161/R est:1300-1900

SALZMANN, Uschka (1943-) Swiss
£529 $788 €794 Untitled (140x100cm-55x39in) s.d. acrylic. 25-Jun-2 Koller, Zurich #6092 (S.FR 1200)

SAMACCHINI, Orazio (1532-1577) Italian
Works on paper
£1203 $1864 €1900 Flagellation of Christ (30x22cm-12x9in) i. verso pen wash. 27-Sep-2 Venator & Hansten, Koln #1126 est:480

SAMARAS, Lucas (1936-) American/Greek
Photographs
£3571 $5500 €5357 Photo transformation (11x9cm-4x4in) d.7/21/76 num.28249 verso polaroid SX-70 print emulsion prov. 25-Oct-2 Phillips, New York #146/R est:3000-5000
Sculpture
£15625 $25000 €23438 Box no.131 (32x61x62cm-13x24x24in) jewelry box with glass beads stone acrylic col pencil prov. 14-May-3 Sotheby's, New York #212/R est:25000-35000
Works on paper
£1600 $2480 €2400 Untitled (32x23cm-13x9in) pastel executed 2 September 1974 prov.exhib. 5-Dec-2 Christie's, Kensington #216/R est:2000-3000

SAMARTINO, Edoardo (1901-1992) Italian
£413 $644 €620 Portrait of woman in green dress (33x24cm-13x9in) s. masonite. 16-Sep-2 Philippe Schuler, Zurich #6487 (S.FR 950)

SAMBA, Cheri (1956-) Zairean
£621 $1037 €900 Crise politique (65x81cm-26x32in) s.d. acrylic. 9-Jul-3 Cornette de St.Cyr, Paris #342

SAMBERGER, Leo (1861-1949) German
Works on paper
£273 $406 €420 Portrait of Walter Zmmermann (62x50cm-24x20in) s.d.26 mixed media grisaille board. 26-Jun-2 Neumeister, Munich #598

SAMBO, Edgardo Cappelletti (1882-1966) Italian
£461 $747 €650 Temporale imminente (47x62cm-19x24in) s. board. 22-May-3 Stadion, Trieste #378/R

SAMBROOK, Russell (20th C) American?
£1366 $2200 €2049 Intrepid hunter boy and dog startled by frog (76x64cm-30x25in) s. 19-Feb-3 Illustration House, New York #210/R est:2500-4000

SAMERJAN, George E (1915-) American
Works on paper
£274 $450 €397 How green is my valley (51x71cm-20x28in) s. W/C. 31-May-3 Harvey Clar, Oakland #1182

SAMMONS, Carl (1888-1968) American
£590 $950 €885 Moonlight, Carmel by the sea (15x20cm-6x8in) s. i.verso canvasboard prov. 18-Feb-3 John Moran, Pasadena #2b
£659 $1100 €956 Carmel by the sea (15x20cm-6x8in) i.verso canvasboard. 17-Jun-3 John Moran, Pasadena #10 est:1500-2000
£839 $1300 €1259 Landscape (30x41cm-12x16in) s. canvasboard prov. 29-Oct-2 John Moran, Pasadena #727
£1118 $1800 €1677 Crashing surf (30x41cm-12x16in) s. prov. 18-Feb-3 John Moran, Pasadena #135 est:2000-3000
£1154 $1800 €1731 High Sierras. board. 21-Sep-2 Harvey Clar, Oakland #1523
£1198 $2000 €1737 Yosemite Valley (27x34cm-11x13in) i.verso canvasboard. 18-Jun-3 Christie's, Los Angeles #54/R est:2500-3500
£1415 $2250 €2123 Mt. Ritter (51x76cm-20x30in) s. 8-Mar-3 Harvey Clar, Oakland #1389
£1415 $2250 €2123 Mattole River (51x66cm-20x26in) 8-Mar-3 Harvey Clar, Oakland #1390
£1592 $2500 €2388 Mammoth lake region, High Sierra (61x76cm-24x30in) s. i.verso prov. 19-Nov-2 Butterfields, San Francisco #8297/R est:3000-5000
£1592 $2500 €2388 Evening shadows, Palm Springs (30x41cm-12x16in) s. i.verso canvasboard prov. 19-Nov-2 Butterfields, San Francisco #8322/R est:3000-5000
£1774 $2750 €2661 Verbenas and encelia near Indio, California (30x41cm-12x16in) s. i.verso canvasboard prov. 29-Oct-2 John Moran, Pasadena #749 est:1500-2500
£2108 $3500 €3057 Ocotillo, desert mallow and encelia (51x66cm-20x26in) s. prov. 11-Jun-3 Butterfields, San Francisco #4336/R est:4000-6000
£2258 $3500 €3387 Carmel by the sea (51x66cm-20x26in) s. i.verso prov. 29-Oct-2 John Moran, Pasadena #781 est:3000-5000
£2358 $3750 €3537 Mattole River (61x76cm-24x30in) s. panel. 8-Mar-3 Harvey Clar, Oakland #1391
£2545 $4250 €3690 Landscape, smoke trees and desert kavender La Quinta Canyon (25x66cm-10x26in) s. i.on stretcher. 17-Jun-3 John Moran, Pasadena #36 est:2500-3500
£2695 $4500 €3908 Smoke trees and wild flowers, Palm Springs, California (30x40cm-12x16in) s. i.verso canvasboard. 18-Jun-3 Christie's, Los Angeles #16/R est:3000-5000
£2795 $4500 €4193 River landscape (30x41cm-12x16in) s. canvasboard. 18-Feb-3 John Moran, Pasadena #160 est:1500-2500
£3293 $5500 €4775 Coastal Mendocino Point (41x51cm-16x20in) s. i.verso canvasboard prov. 17-Jun-3 John Moran, Pasadena #31 est:3000-4000
£3593 $6000 €5210 Carmel coast (30x41cm-12x16in) s. i.verso canvasboard. 18-Jun-3 Christie's, Los Angeles #97/R est:3000-5000
Works on paper
£1613 $2500 €2420 Flower fields landscape (23x33cm-9x13in) s.d.1928 pastel. 29-Oct-2 John Moran, Pasadena #610a est:1500-2500

SAMOKICH, Nicolai (1860-1944) Russian
£4234 $6648 €6139 Military force. 15-Dec-2 Anders Antik, Landskrona #214 est:25000-30000 (S.KR 60000)

SAMPLE, Paul (1896-1974) American
£2358 $3750 €3537 Vermont farm (41x48cm-16x19in) s. painted c.1940. 2-Mar-3 Toomey, Oak Park #643/R est:3000-5000
£3797 $6000 €5696 Town in winter. s. board. 16-Nov-2 Harvey Clar, Oakland #1391
£4221 $6500 €6332 New England town (23x36cm-9x14in) s. painted c.1940. 8-Sep-2 Treadway Gallery, Cincinnati #564/R est:7000-9000
Works on paper
£581 $900 €872 Native boy (28x20cm-11x8in) s. W/C. 7-Dec-2 Neal Auction Company, New Orleans #863/R est:300-500
£736 $1200 €1104 Portrait of an old man (51x41cm-20x16in) s. W/C. 16-Feb-3 Butterfields, San Francisco #2098
£5625 $9000 €8156 Field (32x50cm-13x20in) s. W/C. 16-May-3 Skinner, Boston #257/R est:3000-5000

SAMUEL, Charles (1862-?) Belgian
Sculpture
£1656 $2583 €2600 Est ce qu'on enterre Uylenspiegel l'esprit, Nele, le coeur de la mere Flandre (58x55cm-23x22in) s.st.f.J. Petermann brown pat bronze red marble socle. 11-Nov-2 Horta, Bruxelles #98 est:3000-3750

SAMUEL, Richard (?-1787) British
£516 $800 €774 Portrait of John Oseland Esq (76x64cm-30x25in) i. 2-Nov-2 North East Auctions, Portsmouth #1023/R

SAMUELSON, Bruce (1946-) American
£340 $550 €510 No.2 (198x152cm-78x60in) s.d.78 verso exhib. 24-Jan-3 Freeman, Philadelphia #176/R
£387 $600 €581 Torso no 1 (193x163cm-76x64in) s.i.d.1976 verso. 8-Dec-2 Freeman, Philadelphia #190/R
Works on paper
£387 $600 €581 Untitled (56x71cm-22x28in) s.d.74 pastel over pencil. 8-Dec-2 Freeman, Philadelphia #197/R

SAMUELSON, Kenneth (1936-) Canadian
Works on paper
£593 $943 €890 Steveston Wharf (22x33cm-9x13in) s.i. W/C. 23-Mar-3 Hodgins, Calgary #45/R est:300-500 (C.D 1400)

SAMUELSON, Ulrik (1935-) Swedish
£456 $721 €684 Stockholm's sea (63x73cm-25x29in) s. 28-Apr-3 Bukowskis, Stockholm #985/R (S.KR 6000)
£760 $1202 €1140 Sundbyholm XIV (125x135cm-49x53in) s. init.d.1965 verso. 28-Apr-3 Bukowskis, Stockholm #984/R (S.KR 10000)
£1467 $2362 €2201 Picture (44x37cm-17x15in) s.d.1965 verso oil on glass. 7-May-3 AB Stockholms Auktionsverk #1013/R est:20000-25000 (S.KR 19000)
£2242 $3498 €3363 Adieu (116x92cm-46x36in) init. exhib. 6-Nov-2 AB Stockholms Auktionsverk #903/R est:30000-40000 (S.KR 32000)

SAN JOSE, Francisco (1919-1981) Spanish
£252 $392 €400 Cabalgata (54x66cm-21x26in) s.d.71. 8-Oct-2 Ansorena, Madrid #416/R
£516 $815 €800 Landscape (24x33cm-9x13in) s.d.63 board. 18-Dec-2 Ansorena, Madrid #7/R
£839 $1325 €1300 Carts (50x61cm-20x24in) s.d.57 canvas on cardboard. 18-Dec-2 Ansorena, Madrid #53/R
Works on paper
£270 $422 €400 Donkey (32x47cm-13x19in) s. dr. 25-Mar-3 Durán, Madrid #112/R

£993 $1619 €1500 Market seller (31x22cm-12x9in) s. ink wash. 11-Feb-3 Segre, Madrid #151/R
£1517 $2397 €2200 Chorrillo Fountain, La Olmeda (52x73cm-20x29in) s.d.1979 gouache cardboard. 1-Apr-3 Segre, Madrid #165/R

SAN JUAN TARRES, Bernardo (1915-1979) Spanish
£597 $920 €950 Jug and grapes (49x34cm-19x13in) s. board. 28-Oct-2 Segre, Madrid #236/R

SAN-YU (1901-1966) Chinese
£46620 $76923 €67599 Kneeling horse (41x66cm-16x26in) s. painted c.1930 lit. 6-Jul-3 Christie's, Hong Kong #136/R est:550000-750000 (HK.D 600000)
£108780 $179487 €157731 Cat and mouse (50x80cm-20x31in) s. lit. 6-Jul-3 Christie's, Hong Kong #137/R est:1200000-1400000 (HK.D 1400000)
Works on paper
£645 $1019 €1000 Femme aux lunettes assise (45x28cm-18x11in) black ink wash. 17-Dec-2 Rossini, Paris #47
£903 $1427 €1400 Nu feminin aux bras tendus (44x27cm-17x11in) s. black ink wash. 17-Dec-2 Rossini, Paris #46
£3108 $5128 €4507 Portrait of ladies (43x27cm-17x11in) s. chl ink dr three. 6-Jul-3 Christie's, Hong Kong #165/R est:50000-70000 (HK.D 40000)

SANBORN, Percy A (1849-1929) American
£949 $1500 €1424 Boy fishing streamside (58x79cm-23x31in) s. 30-Nov-2 Thomaston Place, Thomaston #29

SANCHA, Carlos (20th C) Spanish
£1500 $2340 €2250 Portrait of Susan Rawnsley (103x83cm-41x33in) s.d.1950 with dress and robe she wore. 8-Oct-2 Sotheby's, Olympia #392/R est:1000-1500

SANCHA, Francisco (1874-1937) Spanish
Works on paper
£596 $972 €900 This life is not to get old (47x72cm-19x28in) s.i.d.1923 gouache pastel. 11-Feb-3 Segre, Madrid #169/R
£629 $1025 €950 Seal tamer (49x64cm-19x25in) s.i.d.1923 gouache pastel. 11-Feb-3 Segre, Madrid #170/R

SANCHES, Harriet de (20th C) American
£409 $650 €614 On the rooftop, New York (30x20cm-12x8in) s. 7-Mar-3 Skinner, Boston #621/R
£4430 $7000 €6645 On the street of New York (51x41cm-20x16in) s. prov. 24-Apr-3 Shannon's, Milford #211/R est:4000-6000

SANCHEZ BLANCO, Pedro (1833-1902) Spanish
£592 $959 €900 Onions, garlic and radishes (28x30cm-11x12in) s.d.1879. 21-Jan-3 Durán, Madrid #703/R
£592 $959 €900 Saint Isidro's cakes (28x30cm-11x12in) s. s.d.1880 verso. 21-Jan-3 Durán, Madrid #702/R

SANCHEZ COELLO, Alonso (circle) (c.1531-1588) Spanish
£8108 $12649 €12000 Portrait of military leader, probably Duke Charles II of Lorraine (71x59cm-28x23in) 27-Mar-3 Dorotheum, Vienna #294/R est:12000-15000

SANCHEZ COELLO, Alonso (studio) (c.1531-1588) Spanish
£9655 $15352 €14000 Portrait de femme (110x88cm-43x35in) 4-Mar-3 Livinec, Gaudcheau & Jezequel, Rennes #38/R

SANCHEZ CORTES, Antonio (?) Spanish
Works on paper
£252 $387 €400 Nude (22x33cm-9x13in) s. W/C. 22-Oct-2 Durán, Madrid #640/R

SANCHEZ LAREDO, Miguel (1969-) Spanish
£484 $765 €750 Still life (73x92cm-29x36in) s.d.2001. 17-Dec-2 Durán, Madrid #93/R
Works on paper
£306 $484 €475 Still life (73x54cm-29x21in) s.d.2001. 17-Dec-2 Durán, Madrid #86/R

SANCHEZ NAVARRO, Vicente (?) Spanish
£263 $426 €400 Celebration (27x35cm-11x14in) s. 21-Jan-3 Durán, Madrid #706/R

SANCHEZ SALVADOR (20th C) Spanish?
Works on paper
£755 $1162 €1200 Facade (27x44cm-11x17in) s. wash dr set of 3. 22-Oct-2 Durán, Madrid #127/R

SANCHEZ SOLA, Eduardo (1869-1949) Spanish
£5778 $9591 €8378 Mischief (95x122cm-37x48in) s. 16-Jun-3 Waddingtons, Toronto #353/R est:7000-9000 (C.D 13000)
Works on paper
£303 $490 €460 Seascape (44x55cm-17x22in) s.i. W/C. 21-Jan-3 Ansorena, Madrid #13/R

SANCHEZ, Emilio (1921-) Cuban
£962 $1500 €1443 Moroccan building (121x182cm-48x72in) s.artist's symbol prov. 14-Sep-2 Weschler, Washington #658/R est:3000-5000
Works on paper
£305 $500 €442 Casita del sol (43x104cm-17x41in) init. mixed media on board prov. 1-Jun-3 Wright, Chicago #245/R

SANCHEZ, Enrique (1938-) Colombian
£1328 $2019 €1926 Atardecer sobre el Valle de Mexico (40x65cm-16x26in) s. 24-Jul-2 Louis Morton, Mexico #58/R est:25000-30000 (M.P 20000)

SANCHEZ, Pepi (1932-) Spanish
£385 $608 €600 Girl in pink (41x33cm-16x13in) s.d.64 board. 19-Nov-2 Durán, Madrid #195/R
£496 $804 €700 Nina (41x33cm-16x13in) s.d.1964 panel. 20-May-3 Segre, Madrid #290/R
£517 $817 €750 Girl with folded arms (41x33cm-16x13in) s.d.1962 board. 1-Apr-3 Segre, Madrid #376/R
£570 $918 €850 Girl sewing (41x33cm-16x13in) s. board. 18-Feb-3 Durán, Madrid #79/R
£581 $917 €900 Boy with pink ribbon (41x33cm-16x13in) s. board. 17-Dec-2 Durán, Madrid #154/R

SANCHEZ, Tomas (1948-) Cuban
£12195 $20000 €18293 Paisaje (64x48cm-25x19in) s.d.79 acrylic paper on canvas prov. 28-May-3 Christie's, Rockefeller NY #123/R est:25000-30000
£22293 $35000 €33440 Lagoon fishermen (56x76cm-22x30in) s.d.90 tempera paper on canvas prov. 19-Nov-2 Sotheby's, New York #50/R est:45000
£25915 $42500 €37577 La lluvia y la cascada (61x46cm-24x18in) s.d.01 s.i.d.2001 verso acrylic. 27-May-3 Sotheby's, New York #41
£35032 $55000 €52548 Stormy evening (56x71cm-22x28in) s.d.90 s.i.d.verso prov.lit. 19-Nov-2 Sotheby's, New York #37/R est:45000
£36585 $60000 €54878 Contemplando al contemplador (60x50cm-24x20in) s.d.01 s.i.d.01 verso acrylic. 28-May-3 Christie's, Rockefeller NY #33/R est:35000-45000

SANCHEZ, Trino (1968-) Venezuelan
£5096 $8000 €7644 Temples to live in (150x120cm-59x47in) s.d.97 i.verso prov. 20-Nov-2 Christie's, Rockefeller NY #117
£7006 $11000 €10509 Red circus (120x150cm-47x59in) s. i.verso painted 1997 prov. 20-Nov-2 Christie's, Rockefeller NY #118/R est:10000-15000

SANCHEZ-PERRIER, Emilio (1855-1907) Spanish
£4076 $6520 €6114 Man in boat on the river (28x23cm-11x9in) s. 11-Jan-3 James Julia, Fairfield #117b est:4000-6000
£4839 $7500 €7259 River landscape at dusk (34x61cm-13x24in) s.i. panel. 3-Dec-2 Christie's, Rockefeller NY #648/R est:7000-9000
£6962 $11000 €10443 River landscape (61x46cm-24x18in) with sig. 23-Apr-3 Christie's, Rockefeller NY #83/R est:12000-16000
£9375 $14250 €14063 Octubre en Andalucia (32x43cm-13x17in) board. 3-Jul-2 Naón & Cia, Buenos Aires #17/R est:15000-18000
£11000 $17490 €16500 Venetian boathouse (36x54cm-14x21in) s.i.d.85 panel. 18-Mar-3 Bonhams, New Bond Street #74/R est:12000-18000

SANCHO, Jose (1924-) Spanish
£1579 $2558 €2400 Still life with basket of pomegranates (81x100cm-32x39in) s. 21-Jan-3 Ansorena, Madrid #851/R

SAND, George (1804-1876) French
Works on paper
£1456 $2300 €2300 Deux enfants dans un paysage (11x15cm-4x6in) i.verso W/C htd gouache. 28-Nov-2 Tajan, Paris #196

SAND, Lennart (1946-) Swedish
£674 $1044 €1011 Winter landscape with fox (75x96cm-30x38in) s.d.83. 8-Dec-2 Uppsala Auktionskammare, Uppsala #188/R (S.KR 9500)
£1571 $2577 €2278 Bullfinches in winter landscape (81x64cm-32x25in) s.d.02. 4-Jun-3 AB Stockholms Auktionsverk #2313/R est:8000-10000 (S.KR 20000)
£2095 $3393 €3038 Winter landscape with wolves in snow (150x230cm-59x91in) s.d.86. 25-May-3 Uppsala Auktionskammare, Uppsala #184/R est:18000-20000 (S.KR 27000)

SANDALINAS, Joan (1903-1991) Spanish

£252 $387 €400 Bather (34x24cm-13x9in) s. paper. 28-Oct-2 Segre, Madrid #234/R
£314 $484 €500 Dandy (36x26cm-14x10in) s.i.d.1976 verso paper. 28-Oct-2 Segre, Madrid #239/R
£660 $1017 €1050 Family (46x37cm-18x15in) s. s.i.verso board. 28-Oct-2 Segre, Madrid #235/R
£690 $1097 €1000 Self-portrait (40x29cm-16x11in) s.i.d.1926 cardboard. 4-Mar-3 Ansorena, Madrid #202/R
£1034 $1645 €1500 Market (41x49cm-16x19in) s. board. 4-Mar-3 Ansorena, Madrid #215/R
£1039 $1517 €1600 Surrealist figure (52x42cm-20x17in) s. board. 17-Jun-2 Ansorena, Madrid #78/R
£1419 $2243 €2200 Woman, boat and plane (51x40cm-20x16in) s. board. 18-Dec-2 Ansorena, Madrid #196/R

Works on paper

£379 $603 €550 Painter (20x16cm-8x6in) s. W/C. 4-Mar-3 Ansorena, Madrid #656/R
£379 $603 €550 Study (20x15cm-8x6in) s. W/C. 4-Mar-3 Ansorena, Madrid #657/R
£421 $682 €640 Volley-ball players (26x4cm-10x2in) s. 21-Jan-3 Ansorena, Madrid #2/R
£422 $616 €650 At the bar (13x10cm-5x4in) s. gouache. 17-Jun-2 Ansorena, Madrid #304/R
£452 $714 €700 Man reading (34x27cm-13x11in) s. W/C. 18-Dec-2 Ansorena, Madrid #253
£484 $765 €750 Painter (37x26cm-15x10in) s. W/C. 18-Dec-2 Ansorena, Madrid #254
£621 $987 €900 Landscape (24x32cm-9x13in) s. W/C. 4-Mar-3 Ansorena, Madrid #684/R
£897 $1426 €1300 Sailor (34x24cm-13x9in) s. W/C. 4-Mar-3 Ansorena, Madrid #695/R

SANDBACK, Fred (1943-) American

Works on paper

£2128 $3447 €3000 Untitled (28x38cm-11x15in) s.d.92 pencil. 20-May-3 Dorotheum, Vienna #272/R est:3000-3200

SANDBERG, Armid (1876-1927) Finnish

£352 $542 €560 Southern harbour (40x52cm-16x20in) s.d.1919. 27-Oct-2 Bukowskis, Helsinki #273/R

SANDBERG, Einar (1876-1947) Norwegian

£918 $1506 €1331 Winter landscape with road in snow (46x56cm-18x22in) s.d.31 i.verso. 2-Jun-3 Blomqvist, Oslo #189/R (N.KR 10000)

SANDBERG, Johan Gustaf (1782-1854) Swedish

£284 $440 €426 Portrait of gentleman, possibly August Bergman (47x38cm-19x15in) s.d.1840. 8-Dec-2 Uppsala Auktionskammare, Uppsala #39 (S.KR 4000)
£1862 $2961 €2700 Christ in the Olive Grove (46x72cm-18x28in) s.d.1842. 7-Mar-3 Semenzato, Venice #159/R

SANDBERG, Ragnar (1902-1972) Swedish

£1331 $2077 €1997 Street in Stenungsund (39x30cm-15x12in) init.d.26. 6-Nov-2 AB Stockholms Auktionsverk #744/R est:25000-30000 (S.KR 19000)
£2239 $3605 €3359 Still life of fruit (31x65cm-12x26in) init. 7-May-3 AB Stockholms Auktionsverk #783/R est:35000-40000 (S.KR 29000)
£3243 $5222 €4865 Self-portrait (35x28cm-14x11in) init.d.38. 7-May-3 AB Stockholms Auktionsverk #833/R est:12000-15000 (S.KR 42000)
£3644 $5685 €5466 Via del Ordine (30x25cm-12x10in) init.d.63 panel exhib. 6-Nov-2 AB Stockholms Auktionsverk #545/R est:30000-35000 (S.KR 52000)
£5046 $7871 €7569 The lock, Orust (39x48cm-15x19in) init.d.34. 6-Nov-2 AB Stockholms Auktionsverk #739/R est:80000-100000 (S.KR 72000)
£6950 $11189 €10425 Stone masons (36x61cm-14x24in) init. panel exhib.prov. 7-May-3 AB Stockholms Auktionsverk #678/R est:40000-50000 (S.KR 90000)
£6996 $11054 €10494 Summer's day in the country (29x46cm-11x18in) init.d.39 canvas on panel. 28-Apr-3 Bukowskis, Stockholm #104/R est:120000-130000 (S.KR 92000)
£7008 $10932 €10512 Summer evening at Lilla Bommens Harbour (45x70cm-18x28in) init.d.42. 5-Nov-2 Bukowskis, Stockholm #165a/R est:100000-120000 (S.KR 100000)
£7008 $10932 €10512 Hising Bridge, Lilla Bommen (39x55cm-15x22in) init.i.d.1937-38 prov.exhib. 5-Nov-2 Bukowskis, Stockholm #185/R est:100000-125000 (S.KR 100000)
£8108 $13054 €12162 Man and seagulls (42x23cm-17x9in) init. panel. 7-May-3 AB Stockholms Auktionsverk #786/R est:80000-100000 (S.KR 105000)
£9110 $14212 €13665 Seaside promenade (28x44cm-11x17in) init.d.44. 6-Nov-2 AB Stockholms Auktionsverk #544/R est:125000-150000 (S.KR 130000)
£14068 $22228 €21102 Spring morning, Lilla Bommen (37x45cm-15x18in) init. painted 1941. 28-Apr-3 Bukowskis, Stockholm #103/R est:120000-130000 (S.KR 185000)
£14672 $23622 €22008 The ferry station in Les Sablettes (23x33cm-9x13in) init. tempera panel. 7-May-3 AB Stockholms Auktionsverk #899/R est:125000-150000 (S.KR 190000)
£15767 $24597 €23651 Football players (33x43cm-13x17in) init.i.d.38 exhib.lit. 6-Nov-2 AB Stockholms Auktionsverk #603/R est:250000-300000 (S.KR 225000)
£18533 $29838 €27800 In the hammock (39x48cm-15x19in) init.d.35. 7-May-3 AB Stockholms Auktionsverk #817/R est:150000-175000 (S.KR 240000)
£19622 $30610 €29433 Thawing - street scene from Drottningtorvet in Gothenburg (52x75cm-20x30in) init.d.39 prov.exhib.lit. 6-Nov-2 AB Stockholms Auktionsverk #712/R est:300000-350000 (S.KR 280000)
£26616 $42053 €39924 American launch (43x98cm-17x39in) init. 28-Apr-3 Bukowskis, Stockholm #116/R est:200000-250000 (S.KR 350000)

Works on paper

£1014 $1581 €1521 Composition with head and black bird (27x35cm-11x14in) init. crayon prov. 18-Sep-2 Kunsthallen, Copenhagen #93/R est:12000 (D.KR 12000)
£1825 $2884 €2738 German troop train (27x34cm-11x13in) init.i.d.40 pastel. 28-Apr-3 Bukowskis, Stockholm #113/R est:30000-35000 (S.KR 24000)
£2394 $3854 €3591 Stylish fruit - cover for Art Review (34x25cm-13x10in) init.d.42 gouache. 7-May-3 AB Stockholms Auktionsverk #832/R est:15000-20000 (S.KR 31000)
£2738 $4325 €4107 Man and seagull (28x36cm-11x14in) init. chk chl paper on canvas. 28-Apr-3 Bukowskis, Stockholm #100/R est:25000-30000 (S.KR 36000)
£7336 $11811 €11004 Lilla Bommen (29x36cm-11x14in) s.d.1945 gouache exhib. 7-May-3 AB Stockholms Auktionsverk #914/R est:70000-80000 (S.KR 95000)

SANDBY, Paul (1730-1809) British

Works on paper

£262 $371 €393 Melton, Surrey (36x53cm-14x21in) pen wash. 21-Nov-1 Watson's, Christchurch #160/R (NZ.D 900)
£420 $600 €630 Coastal scene with two houses (15x28cm-6x11in) i. brush ink wash. 23-Jan-3 Swann Galleries, New York #392/R
£550 $886 €825 Child with doll (13x9cm-5x4in) i. pencil prov. 15-Jan-3 Cheffins Grain & Comins, Cambridge #366/R
£680 $1095 €1020 Coachman (16x8cm-6x3in) pencil chl prov. 15-Jan-3 Cheffins Grain & Comins, Cambridge #360/R
£800 $1248 €1200 Italianate landscape with figure in the foreground (23x30cm-9x12in) s. pencil W/C. 19-Sep-2 Christie's, Kensington #126/R
£889 $1476 €1289 Castle ruins (30x46cm-12x18in) s.d.1799 W/C gouache. 16-Jun-3 Waddingtons, Toronto #78/R est:800-1200 (C.D 2000)
£1600 $2512 €2400 Seated girl with a doll (8x6cm-3x2in) pencil brown wash prov. 21-Nov-2 Christie's, London #6/R est:1000-1500
£1600 $2608 €2400 Castle in the Highlands (17x26cm-7x10in) pencil W/C prov. 13-Feb-3 Mellors & Kirk, Nottingham #766/R est:300-400
£2812 $4500 €4077 River landscape with ferry and ruined tower (16x27cm-6x11in) gouache paper on board. 16-May-3 Skinner, Boston #39/R est:2000-3000
£5000 $7150 €7500 View down valley towards distant buildings (15x18cm-6x7in) pen ink W/C prov.exhib.lit. 22-Jan-3 Christie's, London #6/R
£6000 $8580 €9000 Old grey horse tethered to tree (17x21cm-7x8in) pencil ink W/C prov.exhib. 22-Jan-3 Christie's, London #5/R
£6500 $10205 €9750 Riverside landscape (37x51cm-15x20in) init.d.1792 pencil W/C htd bodycol prov. 21-Nov-2 Christie's, London #27/R est:6000-8000
£7000 $11060 €10500 Aysgarth Falls, Yorkshire (31x44cm-12x17in) s. gouache. 28-Nov-2 Sotheby's, London #285/R est:6000-8000
£7000 $11620 €10500 Figures by the entrance to a castle (38x51cm-15x20in) pen ink wash over pencil. 12-Jun-3 Sotheby's, London #125/R est:5000-7000
£8500 $13940 €12325 View of Rackett Lodge, Wandsworth, London (17x27cm-7x11in) i. pencil pen ink W/C prov. 5-Jun-3 Christie's, London #36/R est:8000-12000
£13000 $21320 €18850 Extensive river landscape with travellers and donkeys crossing a bridge with a fortified castle (77x103cm-30x41in) s.d.1805 W/C bodycol. 5-Jun-3 Christie's, London #26/R est:15000-20000
£24000 $34320 €36000 Woolwich from the Conduit Hill (32x47cm-13x19in) s.i. pencil W/C bodycol prov. 22-Jan-3 Christie's, London #4/R est:35000

£24000 $38400 €36000 Ross Castle, Killarney (63x89cm-25x35in) pencil bodycol prov.exhib. 15-May-3 Christie's, London #1/R est:30000

SANDBY, Paul (attrib) (1730-1809) British
Works on paper
£450 $734 €675 Craig Toraphen and the Lin of Tumel (26x29cm-10x11in) bears sig.d.1757 verso gouache W/C. 30-Jan-3 Lawrence, Crewkerne #616

SANDELS, Gosta (1877-1919) Swedish
£12355 $19892 €18533 Girl under the rowan berry tree (100x72cm-39x28in) s.d.1914 verso prov.exhib.lit. 7-May-3 AB Stockholms Auktionsverk #726/R est:160000-180000 (S.KR 160000)

SANDER, August (1876-1964) German
£3459 $5362 €5500 Painter - Prof Robert Seuffert (16x10cm-6x4in) silver gelatine prov. 31-Oct-2 Van Ham, Cologne #287/R est:3600
Photographs
£2128 $3447 €3000 Kappenstein family, Kuchhausen. silver gelatin. 23-May-3 Van Ham, Cologne #196/R est:3200
£2201 $3412 €3500 Confirmation of Heinrich Gerhard Hundhausen, Leuscheid (28x22cm-11x9in) silver gelatine. 31-Oct-2 Van Ham, Cologne #286/R est:3000

SANDER, Ludwig (1906-1975) American
£873 $1371 €1310 Athabascan I (80x90cm-31x35in) s.d.1971 verso prov. 25-Nov-2 Germann, Zurich #93/R est:2000-4000 (S.FR 2000)
£2287 $3750 €3316 Pensacola IV (61x56cm-24x22in) s. prov.exhib.lit. 1-Jun-3 Wright, Chicago #288/R est:2000-3000

SANDER, Sherry Salari (1941-) American
Sculpture
£2740 $4000 €4110 Crossing the divide (226cm-89in) bronze. 18-May-2 Altermann Galleries, Santa Fe #220/R

SANDER, Zilfer (20th C) American
£1299 $2000 €1949 Village scene (99x69cm-39x27in) s.d.1923 prov. 24-Oct-2 Shannon's, Milford #109/R est:2500-3500

SANDERS, Christopher (1905-1991) British
£700 $1092 €1050 Yachts in Poole harbour (51x61cm-20x24in) s. s.i.verso. 17-Sep-2 Bonhams, Knightsbridge #17/R

SANDERS, George (1774-1846) British
£6000 $9780 €8700 Portrait of Elizabeth King (89x68cm-35x27in) prov. 21-Jul-3 Sotheby's, London #170/R est:3000-5000
£6500 $10595 €9425 Portrait of Lady Rowley, daughter of Sir Richard King, BT (93x68cm-37x27in) 21-Jul-3 Sotheby's, London #315/R est:3000-4000
£13000 $21190 €18850 Portrait of Admiral Sir Charles Rowley, BT., G.C.B., G.C.H., K.M.T. (89x68cm-35x27in) prov. 21-Jul-3 Sotheby's, London #171/R est:3000-5000
£22000 $35860 €31900 Portrait of Elizabeth Sophia Rowley (228x137cm-90x54in) prov. 21-Jul-3 Sotheby's, London #476 est:8000-12000
Miniatures
£1500 $2340 €2250 John Fane, Lord Burghersh wearing white trimmed grey doublet (8cm-3in) gilt mount octagonal. 5-Nov-2 Bonhams, New Bond Street #124/R est:1500-1800

SANDERS, Har (1929-) Dutch
£605 $944 €950 Swing bottle (98x118cm-39x46in) s.i.d.68. 5-Nov-2 Vendu Notarishuis, Rotterdam #142/R est:1000-1500

SANDERSON, Robert (fl.1858-1908) British
£740 $1199 €1110 Poacher. Paddy at home (23x19cm-9x7in) s. pair. 23-Jan-3 Bonhams, Edinburgh #316
£1800 $2862 €2700 News from the front (35x46cm-14x18in) s.d.1901 panel exhib. 6-Mar-3 Christie's, Kensington #117/R est:2000-3000
£2400 $3744 €3600 Poacher. Daddy at home (25x20cm-10x8in) one s two. 14-Apr-3 Sotheby's, London #68/R est:1500-2000
£3000 $4770 €4500 Playtime (74x56cm-29x22in) s. 6-Mar-3 Christie's, Kensington #538/R est:3000-5000

SANDERSON, Robert (attrib) (fl.1858-1908) British
£1900 $2964 €2850 Edinburgh Castle from the South East (74x62cm-29x24in) 28-Mar-3 Bonhams, Edinburgh #170 est:1200-1500

SANDERSON-WELLS, John (1872-1955) British
£650 $1079 €975 Cavalier (24x17cm-9x7in) s. board. 10-Jun-3 Bonhams, Knightsbridge #87/R
£900 $1467 €1305 Bethrothal (27x37cm-11x15in) s. panel. 16-Jul-3 Sotheby's, Olympia #82/R
£1500 $2370 €2250 Approaching the covert (21x28cm-8x11in) board prov. 28-Nov-2 Christie's, Kensington #95/R est:1500-2000
£1800 $2844 €2700 Stag hunt (27x38cm-11x15in) s. panel. 28-Nov-2 Christie's, Kensington #94/R est:2000-3000
£5031 $8000 €7547 Hunting party (39x60cm-15x24in) s. prov. pair. 30-Apr-3 Sotheby's, New York #556/R est:10000-15000
£8000 $12960 €11600 Coach and horses outside an inn. Companion picture (40x60cm-16x24in) s. pair. 29-Jul-3 Henry Adams, Chichester #611/R est:4000-6000
Works on paper
£300 $468 €450 Meet (33x28cm-13x11in) s. W/C. 9-Oct-2 Woolley & Wallis, Salisbury #13/R
£580 $905 €870 Fishing vessel in harbour (25x37cm-10x15in) s. W/C. 9-Oct-2 Woolley & Wallis, Salisbury #14/R
£650 $1066 €975 Riding at Rotten Row, Hyde Park (19x30cm-7x12in) s. W/C on board. 3-Jun-3 Bonhams, Knightsbridge #31/R

SANDHAM, Henry (1842-1910) Canadian
£438 $700 €657 Night watch (33x23cm-13x9in) s. panel. 12-Jan-3 William Jenack, New York #224
Works on paper
£288 $447 €432 Flock of birds over a meadow (32x47cm-13x19in) s. W/C prov. 3-Dec-2 Joyner, Toronto #426 (C.D 700)
£307 $476 €461 Boating on the St Lawrence (22x34cm-9x13in) s.d.1882 W/C prov. 24-Sep-2 Ritchie, Toronto #3094/R (C.D 750)
£610 $1000 €915 Flower garden (51x69cm-20x27in) s.d.1908 W/C. 8-Feb-3 Neal Auction Company, New Orleans #390/R
£2444 $4009 €3666 Tobogganing (34x20cm-13x8in) s.i. W/C ink prov. 27-May-3 Sotheby's, Toronto #32/R est:3000-5000 (C.D 5500)

SANDHOLT, Marie (1872-1942) Danish
£355 $547 €533 White painted farmhouse in garden with flowers (39x59cm-15x23in) mono.d.1899. 26-Oct-2 Rasmussen, Havnen #2005 (D.KR 4200)

SANDLE, Michael (1936-) British/German
Sculpture
£1500 $2325 €2250 Drummer (32cm-13in) s.num.I/VIII dark brown pat. bronze. 4-Dec-2 Christie's, Kensington #507/R est:1000-1500

SANDOZ, Claude (1946-) Swiss
Works on paper
£261 $404 €392 Composition with figures and ghosts (29x39cm-11x15in) mono.d.1981 mixed media. 9-Dec-2 Philippe Schuler, Zurich #3594 (S.FR 600)
£371 $542 €557 Untitled (69x98cm-27x39in) mono.d.1974 mixed media. 4-Jun-2 Germann, Zurich #833 (S.FR 850)
£371 $542 €557 Untitled (69x98cm-27x39in) mono.d.1974 mixed emdia. 4-Jun-2 Germann, Zurich #834 (S.FR 850)
£371 $542 €557 Untitled (69x98cm-27x39in) mono.d.1974 mixed media. 4-Jun-2 Germann, Zurich #835 (S.FR 850)

SANDOZ, Edouard-Marcel (1881-1971) Swiss
£321 $497 €500 Meknes (24x15cm-9x6in) s. a. prov. 7-Dec-2 Martinot & Savignat, Pontoise #45/R
£390 $632 €550 Rochers (16x24cm-6x9in) panel. 23-May-3 Camard, Paris #49
£390 $632 €550 Mer calme (16x24cm-6x9in) s. panel. 23-May-3 Camard, Paris #55
£426 $689 €600 Montalban (16x24cm-6x9in) i.d.sept 1922 panel. 23-May-3 Camard, Paris #50
£426 $689 €600 Petite chapelle sur une falaise (16x24cm-6x9in) s. panel. 23-May-3 Camard, Paris #54
£556 $917 €800 Canards sur un ilot du bassin au Denantou (54x72cm-21x28in) s.d.1951. 1-Jul-3 Claude Aguttes, Neuilly #113/R
Sculpture
£1042 $1719 €1500 Lapin assis (8cm-3in) s. brown pat bronze Cast Susses lit. 1-Jul-3 Rossini, Paris #56/R
£1583 $2500 €2500 Crapaud a l'arret (5x11cm-2x4in) s. stone lit. 26-Nov-2 Tajan, Paris #60/R
£2176 $3503 €3155 Lapin bijou (5cm-2in) s. st.f.Susse green black pat bronze lit. 9-May-3 Dobiaschofsky, Bern #174/R est:3800 (S.FR 4700)
£2436 $3776 €3800 Chat de Siam assis (15x6cm-6x2in) i. silver pat bronze lit. 7-Dec-2 Martinot & Savignat, Pontoise #118/R
£2703 $4216 €4000 Lapin tete tournee (7x4x6cm-3x2x2in) s.st.f.Susse brown pat bronze lit. 28-Mar-3 Delvaux, Paris #61/R est:5000
£2848 $4500 €4500 Fennec assis (19cm-7in) st.f.Susse brown pat bronze. 29-Nov-2 Drouot Estimations, Paris #135/R
£2885 $4471 €4500 Chat assis (13cm-5in) s. silver pat bronze lit. 7-Dec-2 Martinot & Savignat, Pontoise #120/R

£3061 $4867 €4500 Singe assis (18x12cm-7x5in) st.f.Susse silver pat bronze green marble book-ends pair lit. 28-Feb-3 Tajan, Paris #26/R est:1000-1200
£3141 $4869 €4900 Oiseau bleu (14x6x6cm-6x2x2in) s. brown pat bronze lit. 7-Dec-2 Martinot & Savignat, Pontoise #122/R
£3205 $4968 €5000 Fennec assis (13x15cm-5x6in) s. st.f.Susse verso brown pat bronze. 7-Dec-2 Martinot & Savignat, Pontoise #123/R
£4138 $6621 €6000 Perruche (14x24x7cm-6x9x3in) s. num.1113R marble. 11-Mar-3 Christie's, Paris #431/R
£6115 $9784 €8500 Fennec assis (29cm-11in) s. brown pat.bronze lit. 19-May-3 Tajan, Paris #47/R est:5000-6000
£13291 $21000 €21000 Poisson geant ajoure (35x37cm-14x15in) s. pat bronze lit. 26-Nov-2 Tajan, Paris #58/R est:22000-25000
£16987 $26670 €26500 Lily (44x14x16cm-17x6x6in) s.st.f.C. Valsuani brown pat bronze exhib.lit. 11-Dec-2 Maigret, Paris #227/R est:10000-15000

Works on paper

£993 $1609 €1400 Petit voilier (16x24cm-6x9in) s. pochade. 23-May-3 Camard, Paris #48

SANDQVIST, Rolf (1919-) Finnish

£528 $850 €750 Composition (62x88cm-24x35in) S.D.1988. 10-May-3 Bukowskis, Helsinki #249/R

SANDRI, Eric (20th C) Belgian?

Sculpture

£3333 $5233 €5200 Jeune asiatique (82cm-32in) s. num.1/8 green pat bronze Cast Ducros. 15-Dec-2 Mercier & Cie, Lille #257/R

SANDROCK, Leonhard (1867-1945) German

£1410 $2186 €2200 Old windmill on the bank of a river with small harbour town (125x105cm-49x41in) s. 4-Dec-2 Neumeister, Munich #874/R est:1500
£1793 $2851 €2600 Winter flood - Hamburg (80x115cm-31x45in) s. 8-Mar-3 Arnold, Frankfurt #706/R est:2000
£4167 $6458 €6500 Hamburg harbour (55x65cm-22x26in) s. board. 5-Dec-2 Schopman, Hamburg #669 est:7000

SANDRUCCI, Giovanni (1828-1897) Italian

£1646 $2600 €2600 Grapes (77x46cm-30x18in) s. s.i.verso. 26-Nov-2 Christie's, Rome #61/R est:1900

SANDS, Frederick (?) ?

£500 $780 €750 Mont Orgueil Castle (34x44cm-13x17in) s. board. 26-Mar-3 Bonhams & Langlois, Jersey #183/R
£1100 $1738 €1650 Suza (61x90cm-24x35in) s. s.i.verso. 27-Nov-2 Bonhams, Brooks & Langlois, Jersey #91/R est:2000-3000
£2800 $4424 €4200 St Ouen's Bay, no 12 (92x122cm-36x48in) s.i.stretcher s.verso. 27-Nov-2 Bonhams, Brooks & Langlois, Jersey #76/R est:1500-2000

Works on paper

£600 $948 €900 Italian fountain (59x39cm-23x15in) s. W/C. 27-Nov-2 Bonhams, Brooks & Langlois, Jersey #83/R
£700 $1092 €1050 Sirmdine, Lake Garda (42x59cm-17x23in) s. d.75 verso W/C. 26-Mar-3 Bonhams & Langlois, Jersey #181
£950 $1482 €1425 Sand dunes (39x54cm-15x21in) s. W/C. 26-Mar-3 Bonhams & Langlois, Jersey #182/R
£1100 $1716 €1650 Yellow flower (60x36cm-24x14in) s. W/C. 26-Mar-3 Bonhams & Langlois, Jersey #180/R
£1150 $1817 €1725 North coast of Jersey (37x56cm-15x22in) s. W/C. 27-Nov-2 Bonhams, Brooks & Langlois, Jersey #85/R est:700-1000

SANDYS, Anthony (1806-1883) British

£320 $528 €464 Boats near a drainage mill (20x30cm-8x12in) board lit. 1-Jul-3 Bonhams, Norwich #239/R

SANDYS, Emma (1834-1877) British

£3500 $5565 €5250 Revealing her hand (35x25cm-14x10in) board. 6-Mar-3 Christie's, Kensington #553/R est:3000-5000
£4500 $7470 €6750 Preparing for the ball (62x44cm-24x17in) mono.d.1867 prov.exhib. 10-Jun-3 Christie's, London #105/R est:3000-5000
£9000 $14490 €13500 Garland (43x33cm-17x13in) mono.d.1870 board prov.exhib. 20-Feb-3 Christie's, London #129/R est:12000

Works on paper

£900 $1476 €1305 Portrait of Marguerite Ince, aged six (29x34cm-11x13in) mono.i. black white red chk prov.exhib. 5-Jun-3 Christie's, London #133/R

SANDYS, Frederick (1832-1904) British

£28000 $45080 €42000 At vespers (61x50cm-24x20in) s.i. panel prov.exhib.lit. 20-Feb-3 Christie's, London #239/R est:60000
£115000 $185150 €172500 Love's shadow (41x32cm-16x13in) panel prov.exhib.lit. 20-Feb-3 Christie's, London #91/R est:80000

Works on paper

£260 $408 €390 Portrait of a gentleman (25x18cm-10x7in) init.d.1881 red chk. 13-Dec-2 Keys, Aylsham #634/R
£3200 $4928 €4800 Portrait of Mr Simms Reeve, bust length. Portrait of his wife Anne (53x42cm-21x17in) black white red chk pair. 9-Sep-2 Bonhams, Ipswich #116/R est:1000-2000

SANDYS, Winifred (fl.1903-1914) British

Works on paper

£1000 $1640 €1450 Portrait of Percy Wood, in Indian dress (28x23cm-11x9in) i. pencil pastel after Anthony Frederick Sandys. 5-Jun-3 Christie's, London #134/R est:1200-1800

SANDYS-LUMSDAINE, Leesa (1936-) British

£350 $546 €525 Going to the post (45x61cm-18x24in) s.i.d.58 board. 6-Nov-2 Sotheby's, Olympia #100/R

SANDZEN, Birger (1871-1954) American/Swedish

£7097 $11000 €10646 Lone pine tree (38x43cm-15x17in) canvas on board prov. 29-Oct-2 John Moran, Pasadena #644b est:12000-18000
£10390 $16000 €15585 Autumn chord, Smoky River, Kansas (33x30cm-13x12in) s. s.i.d.1932 verso board prov. 24-Oct-2 Shannon's, Milford #49/R est:12000-18000
£10897 $17000 €16346 Brightly coloured mountain landscape (30x46cm-12x18in) s. 10-Nov-2 Selkirks, St. Louis #955/R est:10000-15000
£14744 $23000 €22116 Pines by the lake, Estes Park, Colorado (25x30cm-10x12in) s. s.i.d.1927 verso panel. 10-Nov-2 Selkirks, St. Louis #954/R est:15000-20000
£15823 $25000 €22943 Southwestern landscape (43x58cm-17x23in) s. prov. 26-Jul-3 Coeur d'Alene, Hayden #124/R est:30000-50000
£16467 $27500 €23877 Pines and rocks - study manitou (25x36cm-10x14in) s.i.verso board prov. 17-Jun-3 John Moran, Pasadena #103/R est:20000-25000
£19461 $32500 €28218 Moonrise in the mountains, Manitou, Colorado (28x36cm-11x14in) s.i.verso board prov. 17-Jun-3 John Moran, Pasadena #95 est:20000-25000
£20958 $35000 €30389 Still life with summer flowers (63x76cm-25x30in) s. canvas on board. 18-Jun-3 Christie's, Los Angeles #78/R est:25000-35000
£24691 $40000 €37037 Wild horse Creek, Graham County, Kansas (61x86cm-24x34in) s. s.i.verso panel. 21-May-3 Sotheby's, New York #174/R est:50000-70000
£30645 $47500 €45968 Western landscape (61x92cm-24x36in) s. prov.exhib. 4-Dec-2 Sotheby's, New York #142/R est:40000-60000
£49383 $80000 €74075 Lone pine, Pike's Peak, Colorado (91x122cm-36x48in) s.d.1923 prov.exhib. 21-May-3 Sotheby's, New York #173/R est:100000-150000

Works on paper

£1946 $3250 €2822 River landscape (25x36cm-10x14in) s. W/C prov. 17-Jun-3 John Moran, Pasadena #103a est:3000-5000
£2532 $4000 €3671 Moonrise over the prairie saline county, Kansas (36x51cm-14x20in) s. chl prov. 26-Jul-3 Coeur d'Alene, Hayden #184/R est:5000-10000
£2949 $4600 €4424 Untitled (18x25cm-7x10in) W/C. 19-Oct-2 David Dike, Dallas #139/R est:3000-6000
£3459 $5500 €5189 Silent stream (28x38cm-11x15in) s. W/C exec.c.1930. 2-Mar-3 Toomey, Oak Park #616/R est:3000-5000

SANEJOUAND, Jean Michel (1934-) French

£3333 $5300 €4800 Sans titre (50x65cm-20x26in) s.d.29/4/80 verso acrylic. 29-Apr-3 Artcurial Briest, Paris #521/R est:800-1200

SANFILIPPO, Antonio (1923-1980) Italian

£1795 $2818 €2800 Untitled (38x61cm-15x24in) s. 21-Nov-2 Finarte, Rome #315/R

SANGER, M (?) American?

£881 $1400 €1322 Meditation (64x99cm-25x39in) s. 8-Mar-3 Harvey Clar, Oakland #1199

SANGSTER, Hendrick Alexander (1825-1901) Dutch

£634 $1020 €900 Portrait of a man (78x60cm-31x24in) s. oval. 7-May-3 Vendue Huis, Gravenhage #361/R

SANJUAN TARRE, Bernardo (1915-1974) Spanish

Works on paper

£295 $466 €460 Still life (68x98cm-27x39in) s. W/C. 13-Nov-2 Ansorena, Madrid #223/R

SANO di PIETRO (style) (1406-1481) Italian
£6835 $10935 €9500 Madonna with Child (37x27cm-15x11in) tempera gold prov. 17-May-3 Lempertz, Koln #118/R est:5000

SANON, Roosvelt (1952-) Haitian
£319 $497 €500 Wood (51x40cm-20x16in) s.d.1982. 5-Nov-2 Tajan, Paris #79/R

SANPAOLO, Ettore (1852-1910) Italian
£641 $1006 €1000 Male nude (106x67cm-42x26in) s. 16-Dec-2 Pandolfini, Florence #34

SANQUEST, Frank (?) Irish?
£247 $351 €400 Monument and Dun Mhuire, Grand Parade, Cork (48x58cm-19x23in) s. 29-Mar-2 Woodwards, Cork #160

SANQUIRICO, Alessandro (1777-1849) Italian
Works on paper
£1200 $1860 €1800 Stage design for the Scala Theatre in Milan of the interior of the Grande Sala de Ballo (29x38cm-11x15in) pen ink wash prov.exhib. 9-Dec-2 Bonhams, New Bond Street #16/R est:600-800

SANS HUGUET, Francisco (1926-) Spanish
£340 $530 €540 Street in Paris (50x65cm-20x26in) s. 8-Oct-2 Ansorena, Madrid #420/R

SANSALVADORE, Piero (1892-1955) Italian
£360 $587 €540 Suspension Bridge, Glasgow (20x25cm-8x10in) 14-Feb-3 Lyon & Turnbull, Edinburgh #54

SANSIL, Walter E (19/20th C) ?
£417 $650 €626 Public garden, Venice (30x51cm-12x20in) painted c.1900. 11-Apr-3 Du Mouchelle, Detroit #2135/R

SANSOM, Gareth Laurence (1939-) Australian
£426 $673 €639 Adrian's dream house (81x101cm-32x40in) s.i.d.1979 verso enamel collage on board. 27-Nov-2 Deutscher-Menzies, Melbourne #167/R est:1000-2000 (A.D 1190)

SANSOVINO, Jacopo (after) (1486-1570) Italian
Sculpture
£6993 $11678 €10000 Jupiter (51cm-20in) black pat bronze prov.exhib.lit. 25-Jun-3 Sotheby's, Paris #6/R est:10000-15000

SANT, James (1820-1916) British
£7000 $11130 €10500 Moonlit beauty (76x63cm-30x25in) with sig. prov. 6-Mar-3 Christie's, Kensington #556/R est:4000-6000
£18000 $28980 €27000 Morning, it's the lark! (76x63cm-30x25in) mono. oval prov. 20-Feb-3 Christie's, London #51/R est:20000
£18000 $28980 €27000 Morning, it's the lark! (219x121cm-86x48in) arched top prov.exhib.lit. 20-Feb-3 Christie's, London #52/R est:50000
£65000 $102700 €97500 Portrait of the Misses Wilson of Tranby Croft, one seated in a garden (185x112cm-73x44in) mono. prov.exhib.lit. 27-Nov-2 Christie's, London #18/R est:60000-100000

SANT, James (attrib) (1820-1916) British
£577 $900 €866 Portrait of a young boy (51x41cm-20x16in) 12-Apr-3 Weschler, Washington #501/R est:700-900

SANTA COLOMA, Emmanuel de (1826-1886) French
Works on paper
£601 $950 €950 Napoleon en campagne (50x65cm-20x26in) s. gouache en grisaille. 27-Nov-2 Lemoine & Ferrando, Paris #73/R

SANTA MARIA, Andres de (1860-1945) Colombian
£3066 $4967 €4446 Jesus walking on water (41x52cm-16x20in) panel prov. 24-May-3 Galerie Gloggner, Luzern #21/R est:5800-6500 (S.FR 6500)

SANTA MARIA, Marceliano (1866-1952) Spanish
£1216 $1897 €1800 Portrait of lady (73x63cm-29x25in) s. 25-Mar-3 Durán, Madrid #144/R
£1809 $2931 €2750 Portrait of lady (93x74cm-37x29in) s. 21-Jan-3 Durán, Madrid #97/R
£1809 $2931 €2750 Portrait of young woman (75x65cm-30x26in) s. 21-Jan-3 Durán, Madrid #98/R
£9211 $14921 €14000 Rural view (44x51cm-17x20in) s. 21-Jan-3 Ansorena, Madrid #175/R est:14000
£11484 $18145 €17800 Stream (55x60cm-22x24in) s. exhib.lit. 18-Dec-2 Ansorena, Madrid #165/R est:16800
£12579 $19623 €20000 Landscape with river (81x98cm-32x39in) s. 17-Sep-2 Segre, Madrid #104b/R est:10800

SANTACROCE, Girolamo da (style) (16th C) Italian
£6115 $9784 €8500 Madonna and Child with the infant Saint John the Baptist (38x32cm-15x13in) panel. 14-May-3 Christie's, Amsterdam #167/R est:8000-10000

SANTASUSAGNA, Ernest (1900-1964) Spanish
£872 $1405 €1300 Young lady at balcony (114x146cm-45x57in) s. 18-Feb-3 Durán, Madrid #214/R

SANTI, Andriolo di Pagano de (?-1375) Italian
Sculpture
£22148 $35658 €33000 Madonna and Child enthroned (78x49cm-31x19in) stone relief. 19-Feb-3 Semenzato, Venice #50/R est:48000

SANTIAGO, Carlos de (1875-1951) South American
£912 $1450 €1368 View of Montevideo harbour (60x120cm-24x47in) s. 2-Mar-3 Galleria Y Remates, Montevideo #109/R
£1125 $1800 €1688 View of Montevideo (60x120cm-24x47in) s. 5-Jan-3 Galleria Y Remates, Montevideo #41
£1313 $2100 €1970 Punta Ballena (81x111cm-32x44in) s.d.904. 5-Jan-3 Galleria Y Remates, Montevideo #42/R

SANTIYAN Y VELASCO, Carlo (1819-1875) Spanish?
£1410 $2214 €2200 Portrait of Duke Franz V von Modena (126x92cm-50x36in) s.d.1862. 21-Nov-2 Dorotheum, Vienna #111/R est:4400-5100

SANTOMASO, Giuseppe (1907-1990) Italian
£3205 $5032 €5000 Nude (50x64cm-20x25in) s.d.1945. 23-Nov-2 Meeting Art, Vercelli #212/R
£7424 $10838 €11136 Untitled - Timbri 12 (60x50cm-24x20in) s. s. verso prov. 4-Jun-2 Germann, Zurich #25/R est:18000-22000 (S.FR 17000)
£9494 $15000 €15000 Forms (67x67cm-26x26in) s.d.61 oil Indian ink. 30-Nov-2 Villa Grisebach, Berlin #410/R est:8000-10000
£13768 $22580 €19000 Untitled (66x67cm-26x26in) s.d.61 oil Indian ink board prov. 28-May-3 Lempertz, Koln #387/R est:10000
£18590 $28814 €29000 Suite friulana No 9 (116x89cm-46x35in) i. stretcher. 6-Dec-2 Hauswedell & Nolte, Hamburg #337/R est:30000
£30323 $47910 €47000 Granary in winter (120x80cm-47x31in) s.d.52 exhib.lit. 18-Dec-2 Christie's, Rome #282/R est:60000
Works on paper
£2479 $4139 €3595 Composition (57x63cm-22x25in) s. W/C collage. 17-Jun-3 Rasmussen, Copenhagen #57/R est:12000-15000 (D.KR 26000)
£3049 $5000 €4421 I Basti (69x69cm-27x27in) s. gouache prov.exhib. 1-Jun-3 Wright, Chicago #276/R est:1000-1500
£3165 $4937 €5000 Capriccio (27x24cm-11x9in) s. mixed media board on canvas prov. 18-Oct-2 Dr Fritz Nagel, Stuttgart #633/R est:4800
£4808 $7548 €7500 Curious (46x38cm-18x15in) s. mixed media collage on canvas. 23-Nov-2 Meeting Art, Vercelli #335/R
£10256 $16103 €16000 Red in brown (92x73cm-36x29in) s.d.1969 mixed media on canvas lit. 19-Nov-2 Finarte, Milan #171/R est:14000-16000

SANTONJA, Elena (1932-) Spanish
£514 $801 €750 Landscape in Llanes (36x45cm-14x18in) s. board. 8-Apr-3 Ansorena, Madrid #33/R

SANTONOCITO, Michele (20th C) Italian
£475 $741 €750 Composition (80x60cm-31x24in) board. 19-Oct-2 Semenzato, Venice #152/R

SANTORO, Francesco Raffaello (1844-1927) Italian
£483 $764 €725 Italian village scene (86x50cm-34x20in) s. canvas on masonite. 18-Nov-2 Waddingtons, Toronto #279/R (C.D 1200)

SANTORO, Rubens (1859-1942) Italian
£10000 $15700 €15000 Palace guard (18x11cm-7x4in) s. panel. 19-Nov-2 Bonhams, New Bond Street #91/R est:10000-15000
£10884 $17306 €16000 Houses in Ischia (63x86cm-25x34in) s. 1-Mar-3 Meeting Art, Vercelli #74 est:15000
£12766 $20681 €18000 View of Venice (66x51cm-26x20in) s. 22-May-3 Dorotheum, Vienna #81/R est:18000-22000
£14500 $23055 €21750 Gondolas at the entrance to the Grand Canal (31x22cm-12x9in) s. 18-Mar-3 Bonhams, New Bond Street #83/R est:15000-20000
£24000 $37680 €36000 St. Mariua canal, Venice (33x25cm-13x10in) s. panel. 19-Nov-2 Bonhams, New Bond Street #99/R est:20000-30000
£25316 $40000 €37974 Morning walk along the Amalfi coast (34x55cm-13x22in) s.d.81. 23-Apr-3 Christie's, Rockefeller NY #24/R est:40000-60000
£26000 $41340 €39000 Women walking beside a Venetian Canal (39x30cm-15x12in) s. prov. 18-Mar-3 Bonhams, New Bond Street #84/R est:20000-30000
£26582 $42000 €42000 Marine in Posillipo (38x64cm-15x25in) s.d.87. 26-Nov-2 Christie's, Rome #225/R est:18000-25000

£32000 $50240 €48000 St. Apostoli canal, Venice (33x25cm-13x10in) s. panel. 19-Nov-2 Bonhams, New Bond Street #101/R est:20000-30000
£34177 $54000 €54000 Landscape in Sarno (127x96cm-50x38in) s. 26-Nov-2 Christie's, Rome #280/R est:50000-60000
£35000 $55650 €52500 Woman carrying water beside a Venetian canal (40x28cm-16x11in) s. prov. 18-Mar-3 Bonhams, New Bond Street #78/R est:15000-20000
£48000 $76320 €72000 Gondolas on a Venetian backwater (40x29cm-16x11in) s. 18-Mar-3 Bonhams, New Bond Street #77/R est:20000-30000
£62000 $97340 €93000 Santa Maria della Salute, Venice (49x36cm-19x14in) s. 19-Nov-2 Bonhams, New Bond Street #95/R est:30000-50000

SANTOS VIANA, Antonio (1942-) Spanish
£263 $426 €400 Landscape (50x84cm-20x33in) s.d.61 board. 21-Jan-3 Ansorena, Madrid #329/R
£395 $639 €600 Toledo (65x100cm-26x39in) s.d.75 board. 21-Jan-3 Durán, Madrid #643/R

SANTOS, Angeles (1912-) Spanish
£299 $460 €475 Landscape (27x35cm-11x14in) s. cardboard. 22-Oct-2 Durán, Madrid #1298

SANTOS, Fermin (1915-1997) Spanish
£314 $491 €500 Landscape (33x41cm-13x16in) s. s.i.verso. 23-Sep-2 Durán, Madrid #685/R
£642 $1001 €950 Madrid seen from the farm (65x81cm-26x32in) s. s.i.verso. 25-Mar-3 Durán, Madrid #711/R
£679 $1046 €1080 Basket with flowers (55x73cm-22x29in) s. 28-Oct-2 Segre, Madrid #85/R
£774 $1223 €1200 Landscape in the countryside around Madrid (60x73cm-24x29in) s.verso. 18-Dec-2 Ansorena, Madrid #54/R

SANTOS, Manuel Gonzalez (1875-1949) Spanish
£4200 $6510 €6300 Feeding the doves (56x82cm-22x32in) s.i. 3-Dec-2 Sotheby's, Olympia #286/R est:4000-6000

SANTOSUOSSO, Francesco (1960-) Italian
Works on paper
£545 $845 €850 Bovisa (43x70cm-17x28in) s.i.d.2001 verso mixed media board exhib.lit. 4-Dec-2 Finarte, Milan #581/R

SANTRY, Terence John (1910-1990) Australian
£1964 $3045 €2946 View from the Botanic Gardens (53x90cm-21x35in) s. 29-Oct-2 Lawson Menzies, Sydney #64/R est:4000-5000 (A.D 5500)
Works on paper
£326 $511 €489 Reclining nude (32x50cm-13x20in) s. chl. 15-Apr-3 Lawson Menzies, Sydney #192/R (A.D 850)

SANTVOORT, Dirck van (attrib) (1610-1680) Dutch
£132867 $190000 €199301 Portrait of Dirck Alewijn (107x75cm-42x30in) panel prov.exhib. 22-Jan-3 Doyle, New York #119/R est:35000

SANUY, Juan (19th C) Uruguayan
Works on paper
£655 $1042 €950 Elegant lady (45x29cm-18x11in) s.d.1899 W/C. 4-Mar-3 Ansorena, Madrid #691/R

SANVISENS, Ramon (1917-1987) Spanish
£862 $1379 €1250 Landscape (30x42cm-12x17in) s. board. 11-Mar-3 Castellana, Madrid #5/R

SANVITALE, Giovanni (1935-) Italian
£1150 $1886 €1725 Rabbits (28x48cm-11x19in) s. panel. 4-Jun-3 Bonhams, Chester #410/R est:500-800

SANYAL, Gopal (1933-) Indian
Works on paper
£700 $1092 €1050 Couple (55x38cm-22x15in) s.d. pen ink W/C. 17-Oct-2 Bonhams, Knightsbridge #544/R

SANZ MAGALLON, Jose Luis (1926-2000) Spanish
£710 $1121 €1100 Landscape (38x61cm-15x24in) s. 18-Dec-2 Ansorena, Madrid #30/R
£1250 $2025 €1900 The Thames (38x61cm-15x24in) s. s.verso. 21-Jan-3 Durán, Madrid #130/R

SANZ, Eduardo (1928-) Spanish
£743 $1159 €1100 Mass (64x50cm-25x20in) s. board. 25-Mar-3 Durán, Madrid #175/R

SAOLI, Winston (1950-1995) South African
£559 $900 €839 African images (80x132cm-31x52in) s.d.95. 12-May-3 Stephan Welz, Johannesburg #555 est:6000-8000 (SA.R 6500)
Works on paper
£269 $420 €404 Mother's agony, Mother Africa the agony (56x81cm-22x32in) s. i.verso mixed media. 11-Nov-2 Stephan Welz, Johannesburg #181 (SA.R 4200)

SAPORITI, Rinaldo (1840-1913) Italian
£507 $832 €700 Barche sulla riva (50x70cm-20x28in) s. board. 27-May-3 Finarte, Milan #105/R

SAPP, Allen (1929-) Canadian
£181 $287 €272 Mountain river (46x36cm-18x14in) s. board. 14-Nov-2 Heffel, Vancouver #203 (C.D 450)
£207 $324 €311 Habitants in the sleigh (10x15cm-4x6in) s. 24-Jul-2 Walker's, Ottawa #263/R (C.D 500)
£261 $412 €392 Indian grandmother (18x13cm-7x5in) canvasboard. 1-Dec-2 Levis, Calgary #89/R (C.D 650)
£281 $447 €407 Be night soon (18x13cm-7x5in) s. s.d.Nov.27/74 verso acrylic prov. 1-May-3 Heffel, Vancouver #96/R (C.D 650)
£356 $583 €534 Mamma making a bannock (22x30cm-9x12in) s. acrylic prov. 3-Jun-3 Joyner, Toronto #498 (C.D 800)
£368 $585 €534 Another load finished (30x25cm-12x10in) s. acrylic. 1-May-3 Heffel, Vancouver #95/R (C.D 850)
£482 $761 €723 Lady holding baby in a moss bag (25x30cm-10x12in) acrylic. 1-Dec-2 Levis, Calgary #88/R (C.D 1200)
£519 $826 €753 Eating outside at Sweetgrass Reserve (41x51cm-16x20in) s. acrylic. 1-May-3 Heffel, Vancouver #97/R (C.D 1200)
£622 $1020 €902 Good feeling after hard day's work (25x30cm-10x12in) s.i.d.1980 acrylic. 9-Jun-3 Hodgins, Calgary #341/R est:1000-1500 (C.D 1400)
£643 $1015 €965 Barn, Onion Lake reserve (46x61cm-18x24in) d.1969 acrylic. 1-Dec-2 Levis, Calgary #86/R (C.D 1600)
£643 $1015 €965 Looking at the horse (41x30cm-16x12in) d.1976 acrylic. 1-Dec-2 Levis, Calgary #87/R (C.D 1600)
£683 $1072 €1025 Threshing oats at red pheasant reserve (60x85cm-24x33in) s. acrylic. 25-Nov-2 Hodgins, Calgary #428/R est:2500-3000 (C.D 1700)
£711 $1166 €1067 He's taking snow into the house (45x60cm-18x24in) s. acrylic prov. 3-Jun-3 Joyner, Toronto #280/R est:1000-1500 (C.D 1600)
£711 $1166 €1031 View from a hay wagon (50x40cm-20x16in) s. acrylic. 9-Jun-3 Hodgins, Calgary #186/R est:1750-2250 (C.D 1600)
£800 $1312 €1160 Nice day to slide (40x50cm-16x20in) s. acrylic. 9-Jun-3 Hodgins, Calgary #185/R est:2000-2500 (C.D 1800)
£803 $1261 €1205 Little Pine Reserve dance hall (60x90cm-24x35in) s.i.d.1971 acrylic. 25-Nov-2 Hodgins, Calgary #348/R est:2500-3000 (C.D 2000)
£843 $1324 €1265 Men gathered behind the house (60x75cm-24x30in) s. acrylic. 25-Nov-2 Hodgins, Calgary #269/R est:2500-3000 (C.D 2100)
£848 $1323 €1414 Chickens like Bannock and oats (41x30cm-16x12in) s. acrylic. 13-Apr-3 Levis, Calgary #103 est:1500-2000 (C.D 1950)
£1000 $1560 €1668 Have been away all day (46x61cm-18x24in) s. i.d.1976 verso acrylic. 13-Apr-3 Levis, Calgary #102 est:2000-2500 (C.D 2300)
£1044 $1639 €1566 Her husband is giving her a prairie chicken to cook (45x60cm-18x24in) s. acrylic exhib. 25-Nov-2 Hodgins, Calgary #391/R est:2200-2500 (C.D 2600)
£1084 $1702 €1626 Dad has to work but the kids get to play (60x75cm-24x30in) s. acrylic. 25-Nov-2 Hodgins, Calgary #19/R est:2500-3000 (C.D 2700)
£1111 $1822 €1611 Dad's warming up (40x50cm-16x20in) s. acrylic. 9-Jun-3 Hodgins, Calgary #298/R est:2000-2500 (C.D 2500)
£1130 $1763 €1885 Untitled - Getting ready for dinner (61x91cm-24x36in) s. acrylic prov. 13-Apr-3 Levis, Calgary #101 est:3000-3500 (C.D 2600)
£1205 $1892 €1808 Visiting her older sister (45x60cm-18x24in) s.i. acrylic. 25-Nov-2 Hodgins, Calgary #20/R est:2000-2500 (C.D 3000)
£1261 $1967 €2103 Untitled - Pow cow (60x91cm-24x36in) s. acrylic. 13-Apr-3 Levis, Calgary #100/R est:3000-3500 (C.D 2900)
£1285 $2018 €1928 Children playing in the yard (60x60cm-24x24in) s. acrylic. 25-Nov-2 Hodgins, Calgary #346/R est:2000-2500 (C.D 3200)
£1289 $2114 €1869 My brother's harness (75x120cm-30x47in) s.i. acrylic. 9-Jun-3 Hodgins, Calgary #299/R est:3000-4000 (C.D 2900)
£1325 $2094 €1988 Nokum mending blanket (46x61cm-18x24in) d.1990 acrylic. 1-Dec-2 Levis, Calgary #85/R est:2000-3000 (C.D 3300)
£1333 $2187 €1933 Telling his Lil' brother to come home (50x40cm-20x16in) s. acrylic. 9-Jun-3 Hodgins, Calgary #385/R est:2000-2500 (C.D 3000)
£1406 $2207 €2109 Not so cold today for working (45x60cm-18x24in) s.i. acrylic. 25-Nov-2 Hodgins, Calgary #121/R est:2000-2500 (C.D 3500)
£1600 $2624 €2400 Coming home from work (60x90cm-24x35in) s. acrylic. 3-Jun-3 Joyner, Toronto #148/R est:2500-3000 (C.D 3600)
£1647 $2585 €2471 Log hauling on a crisp winter day (75x120cm-30x47in) s. acrylic. 25-Nov-2 Hodgins, Calgary #80/R est:4000-5000 (C.D 4100)
£1737 $2762 €2606 He's chopping firewood (50x60cm-20x24in) s.i. acrylic. 23-Mar-3 Hodgins, Calgary #28/R est:2000-2800 (C.D 4100)
£1864 $2964 €2796 Going to visit (60x75cm-24x30in) s.i.d.1978 acrylic prov. 23-Mar-3 Hodgins, Calgary #12/R est:2500-3500 (C.D 4400)
£2242 $3587 €3363 Two teams went together (61x91cm-24x36in) s.i.verso. 15-May-3 Heffel, Vancouver #101/R est:2000-3000 (C.D 5000)

SAQOJOFF, Dan (20th C) ?
£2323 $3670 €3600 Deux visages. s. paper. 19-Dec-2 Bondu, Paris #16

SARAZIN DE BELMONT, Louise Josephine (1790-1870) French
£1899 $3000 €3000 Paysage de la campagne italienne (48x61cm-19x24in) 1-Dec-2 Anaf, Lyon #155
£6643 $11094 €9500 Vue de Saint-Jean de Luz (24x41cm-9x16in) s.i.d.1830 paper on cardboard. 25-Jun-3 Sotheby's, Paris #63/R est:3000-4000

SARAZIN, Jean Philippe (?-c.1795) French
£1987 $3080 €3100 Paysage d'Italie a la cascade (29x35cm-11x14in) i.d.1772 verso panel. 6-Dec-2 Rieunier, Bailly-Pommery, Mathias, Paris #47/R
Works on paper
£227 $350 €341 Landscape with arched bridge spanning a stream (207x154cm-81x61in) i. black chk pen ink W/C prov.exhib. 4-Sep-2 Christie's, Rockefeller NY #273/R

SARAZIN, Jean Philippe (attrib) (?-c.1795) French
£661 $985 €992 Small pond in wooded landscape (75x92cm-30x36in) 25-Jun-2 Koller, Zurich #6437/R (S.FR 1500)

SARDA LADICO, Francisco (1877-1912) Spanish
£3161 $4995 €4900 Soldiers (82x118cm-32x46in) s. 18-Dec-2 Ansorena, Madrid #156/R

SARDESAI, N R (?) ?
Works on paper
£1800 $2808 €2700 Kabuliwala (37x25cm-15x10in) s. W/C. 17-Oct-2 Bonhams, Knightsbridge #566/R est:1800-2400

SARDI, Jean (1947-) French
£690 $1097 €1000 Port du sud (46x55cm-18x22in) s. 7-Mar-3 Rabourdin & Choppin de Janvry, Paris #27
£1667 $2650 €2400 Cassis (60x81cm-24x32in) s. 29-Apr-3 Artcurial Briest, Paris #317 est:2000-2500

SARESTONIEMI, Reidar (1925-1981) Finnish
£823 $1284 €1300 Reindeer (48x63cm-19x25in) s. pastel. 12-Sep-2 Hagelstam, Helsinki #809
£6962 $11000 €11000 Bog-myrtle (73x100cm-29x39in) s.d.63. 1-Dec-2 Bukowskis, Helsinki #359/R est:8500-10000
£27848 $44000 €44000 Reindeer (120x150cm-47x59in) s.d.72. 1-Dec-2 Bukowskis, Helsinki #358/R est:28000-32000
Works on paper
£1709 $2700 €2700 Winter's day in Lapland (49x64cm-19x25in) s.d.81 pastel. 1-Dec-2 Bukowskis, Helsinki #360/R est:1500-1700
£2152 $3400 €3400 Reindeer (50x65cm-20x26in) s.d.1975 mixed media. 30-Nov-2 Hagelstam, Helsinki #174/R est:1700

SARGENT, John Singer (1856-1925) British/American
£26235 $42500 €39353 Seascape (28x21cm-11x8in) painted 1875 prov. 21-May-3 Sotheby's, New York #143/R est:30000-50000
£26415 $42000 €39623 David in Saul's Camp (44x64cm-17x25in) en grisaille prov. 4-Mar-3 Christie's, Rockefeller NY #46/R est:15000-25000
£140000 $232400 €210000 Gassed (27x69cm-11x27in) s.i. painted 1918-19 prov.exhib.lit. 11-Jun-3 Christie's, London #23/R est:100000-150000
£306452 $475000 €459678 Madame Errazuriz (48x39cm-19x15in) painted c.1883-84 prov.lit. 4-Dec-2 Sotheby's, New York #40/R est:600000-800000
£1290323 $2000000 €1935485 Jacques Barenton (57x46cm-22x18in) s.d.1883 prov.exhib.lit. 4-Dec-2 Sotheby's, New York #32/R est:1000000-1500000
Sculpture
£22013 $35000 €33020 Study for conflict between Victory and death (31cm-12in) init. dark brown pat. bronze prov.exhib.lit. 5-Mar-3 Sotheby's, New York #60/R est:10000-15000
Works on paper
£21605 $35000 €32408 Tyrol (25x36cm-10x14in) W/C executed 1914 prov.exhib. 21-May-3 Sotheby's, New York #142/R est:20000-30000
£31447 $48428 €50000 Stream (37x53cm-15x21in) s. mixed media prov.lit. 28-Oct-2 Il Ponte, Milan #255/R est:40000
£52469 $85000 €78704 Corfu (36x50cm-14x20in) W/C pencil executed c.1909 prov.exhib.lit. 21-May-3 Sotheby's, New York #58/R est:120000-160000
£61728 $100000 €92592 Base of a palace (36x51cm-14x20in) W/C pencil exhib. 22-May-3 Christie's, Rockefeller NY #37/R est:100000-150000
£166667 $270000 €250001 Vase fountain, pocantico (53x40cm-21x16in) W/C pencil prov.exhib.lit. 21-May-3 Sotheby's, New York #140/R est:200000-300000

SARGENT, John Singer (attrib) (1856-1925) British/American
£342 $500 €513 Winter traveler in woodlands (30x25cm-12x10in) oak panel prov. 3-Nov-1 North East Auctions, Portsmouth #275

SARGENT, Louis August (1881-?) British
£568 $886 €852 Portrait of young sailor (70x53cm-28x21in) s. 6-Nov-2 Dobiaschofsky, Bern #941/R (S.FR 1300)
£600 $1002 €870 Rocky coastline (45x54cm-18x21in) s. board. 17-Jun-3 Bonhams, Knightsbridge #67

SARGENT, Paul Turner (1880-1946) American
£241 $400 €349 In the Smoky mountains (36x43cm-14x17in) s.d.1927 board. 11-Jun-3 Boos Gallery, Michigan #580/R
£260 $400 €390 Campfire stories (36x25cm-14x10in) s.verso board painted c.1918. 8-Sep-2 Treadway Gallery, Cincinnati #556/R
£292 $450 €438 Portrait of a girl (43x36cm-17x14in) board painted c.1918. 8-Sep-2 Treadway Gallery, Cincinnati #646/R
£308 $475 €462 Illinois farm (25x33cm-10x13in) board painted c.1918. 8-Sep-2 Treadway Gallery, Cincinnati #614/R
£325 $500 €488 Autumn hillside (25x33cm-10x13in) board painted c.1918. 8-Sep-2 Treadway Gallery, Cincinnati #612/R
£419 $650 €629 Illinois landscape (23x30cm-9x12in) s. painted c.1920. 8-Dec-2 Toomey, Oak Park #675/R
£419 $650 €629 Gladys James (46x36cm-18x14in) s. board painted c.1918. 8-Dec-2 Toomey, Oak Park #730/R
£422 $650 €633 Green meadow (25x33cm-10x13in) s.verso board painted c.1918. 8-Sep-2 Treadway Gallery, Cincinnati #634/R
£519 $800 €779 Sunset (30x41cm-12x16in) s. board painted c.1918. 8-Sep-2 Treadway Gallery, Cincinnati #601/R
£535 $850 €803 Rainbow (25x36cm-10x14in) board painted c.1925. 2-Mar-3 Toomey, Oak Park #568/R
£548 $850 €822 Cloud filled sky (23x30cm-9x12in) canvas on board painted c.1918. 8-Dec-2 Toomey, Oak Park #719/R
£629 $1000 €944 California landscape (51x61cm-20x24in) s.d. 2-Mar-3 Toomey, Oak Park #566/R
£714 $1100 €1071 Approaching storm (30x41cm-12x16in) s. board painted c.1925. 8-Sep-2 Treadway Gallery, Cincinnati #622/R
£714 $1100 €1071 Sunlight and shadows (20x28cm-8x11in) painted c.1918. 8-Sep-2 Treadway Gallery, Cincinnati #643/R
£779 $1200 €1169 Riverbend (25x33cm-10x13in) s.verso board painted c.1918. 8-Sep-2 Treadway Gallery, Cincinnati #638/R
£1234 $1900 €1851 First snow (61x76cm-24x30in) s.d.1930. 8-Sep-2 Treadway Gallery, Cincinnati #640/R est:2000-3000
£1509 $2400 €2264 Sunny autumn day (51x36cm-20x14in) painted c.1918. 2-Mar-3 Toomey, Oak Park #571/R est:2000-3000
£1806 $2800 €2709 Wildflowers (30x41cm-12x16in) s.d. 8-Dec-2 Toomey, Oak Park #699/R est:2000-3000
£2358 $3750 €3537 Day at the lake (30x20cm-12x8in) s.d. 4-May-3 Treadway Gallery, Cincinnati #577/R est:5000-7000

SARGENT, Walter (1868-1927) American
£955 $1500 €1433 Northern landscape with mountain (41x51cm-16x20in) s. 20-Nov-2 Boos Gallery, Michigan #533/R est:3000-5000

SARKANY, Julius (1887-?) Hungarian
£1923 $3019 €3000 Hungarian gypsy girl (53x42cm-21x17in) s. 10-Dec-2 Dorotheum, Vienna #89/R est:3000-4000

SARKIS, Zabunyan (20th C) ?
Works on paper
£764 $1215 €1100 Etre seul (100x65cm-39x26in) mixed media photo collage prov.exhib.lit. 29-Apr-3 Artcurial Briest, Paris #465/R

SARKISIAN, Sarkis (1909-1977) American
£362 $550 €543 Renaissance girl (51x41cm-20x16in) 16-Aug-2 Du Mouchelle, Detroit #2115/R
£438 $700 €657 Judy (53x46cm-21x18in) board. 16-May-3 Du Mouchelle, Detroit #2218/R
£663 $1100 €961 Portrait of a clown (41x30cm-16x12in) board. 13-Jun-3 Du Mouchelle, Detroit #2186/R
£769 $1200 €1154 Untitled, lady with a bird (61x46cm-24x18in) board. 20-Sep-2 Du Mouchelle, Detroit #2183/R est:1400-1600
£783 $1300 €1135 Woman in turban (51x36cm-20x14in) 13-Jun-3 Du Mouchelle, Detroit #2184/R
£5696 $9000 €8544 Woman seated at a table in an interior (112x102cm-44x40in) s. prov. 3-Apr-3 Boos Gallery, Michigan #258a/R est:10000-15000

SARMENTO, Juliao (1948-) Portuguese
£34000 $55760 €51000 Savanah no 442 (256x188cm-101x74in) s.i.d.26/10/85 verso acrylic mixed media prov.exhib. 7-Feb-3 Sotheby's, London #157/R est:7000-10000
Sculpture
£11250 $18000 €16875 Dentro 1 (165x198x198cm-65x78x78in) wood polyester resin fiberglass fabric construction executed 1998. 14-May-3 Sotheby's, New York #367/R est:25000-35000
Works on paper
£2027 $3162 €3000 Untitled (70x50cm-28x20in) s.i.d.1988 mixed media acrylic. 28-Mar-3 Ketterer, Hamburg #619/R est:3500-4000

£11250 $18000 €16875 Am i a man or a woman (125x150cm-49x59in) mixed media on canvas executed 2000 prov. 14-May-3 Sotheby's, New York #366/R est:15000-20000

£22000 $36740 €31900 Purloined letter (189x210cm-74x83in) s.i.d.1989 verso mixed media on canvas prov.exhib.lit. 27-Jun-3 Christie's, London #255/R est:10000-15000

SARNARI, Franco (1933-) Italian

£1438 $2244 €2100 Still life 2 (40x50cm-16x20in) s. 10-Apr-3 Finarte Semenzato, Rome #238/R

SARNOFF, Arthur (1912-2000) American

£1688 $2700 €2532 Valley watch (51x61cm-20x24in) s.i.verso. 11-Jan-3 James Julia, Fairfield #216 est:3500-5000

£1938 $3100 €2907 East of Mecker (61x91cm-24x36in) s. s.i.verso board. 11-Jan-3 James Julia, Fairfield #217 est:4000-6000

£2672 $4275 €4008 Scouting party (61x76cm-24x30in) s.i.verso. 11-Jan-3 James Julia, Fairfield #215 est:4500-6500

£3526 $5500 €5289 Wild mustangs (61x76cm-24x30in) s. prov. 9-Nov-2 Santa Fe Art, Santa Fe #126/R est:5000-7000

Works on paper

£559 $900 €839 Pensive woman on busy Asian street (41x56cm-16x22in) W/C gouache. 20-Feb-3 Illustration House, New York #149/R

SAROYAN, William (1908-1981) American

Works on paper

£736 $1200 €1104 Wednesday January 19 1966 Fresno 2 (56x77cm-22x30in) s.i.d.1966 W/C. 16-Feb-3 Butterfields, San Francisco #2125

£759 $1200 €1139 I saw you this morning 50 years later (76x105cm-30x41in) s.i.d.1963 W/C. 22-Apr-3 Butterfields, San Francisco #6063/R est:2500-3500

SARQUELLA, Josep (1928-) Spanish

£510 $836 €780 Market day (53x72cm-21x28in) 5-Feb-3 Arte, Seville #766/R

SARRA, Manlio (1910-) Italian

£245 $378 €390 Cat (47x33cm-19x13in) s. tempera paper. 28-Oct-2 Il Ponte, Milan #169

£252 $387 €400 Workman back at home (53x45cm-21x18in) s. 28-Oct-2 Il Ponte, Milan #166/R

£252 $387 €400 FRom my study (50x40cm-20x16in) s. 28-Oct-2 Il Ponte, Milan #185

SARRABAT, Daniel II (1666-1748) French

£1761 $2712 €2800 La cene (97x130cm-38x51in) 25-Oct-2 Tajan, Paris #101/R est:3000-4000

SARRI, Sergio (1938-) Italian

£458 $732 €700 Exercise at the rings (100x100cm-39x39in) s.d.1972. 4-Jan-3 Meeting Art, Vercelli #326

£458 $732 €700 Massages (120x120cm-47x47in) s.d.1971. 4-Jan-3 Meeting Art, Vercelli #349

£532 $862 €750 Il grande custode (120x140cm-47x55in) s.d.1970 verso acrylic exhib. 22-May-3 Stadion, Trieste #211/R

£660 $1049 €950 Sonograph (120x100cm-47x39in) s.i.d.1974. 1-May-3 Meeting Art, Vercelli #49

SARTAIN, William (1843-1924) American

£833 $1300 €1250 Shadows by an archway (36x25cm-14x10in) s. 20-Sep-2 Freeman, Philadelphia #107/R est:200-300

£10494 $17000 €15216 Meadows at Mannasquan, New Jersey (56x81cm-22x32in) s. 21-May-3 Doyle, New York #63/R est:4000-6000

SARTELLE, Herbert (1885-1955) American

£613 $950 €920 Eucalyptus landscape (61x76cm-24x30in) s. painted c.1930 prov. 8-Dec-2 Toomey, Oak Park #708/R

£710 $1100 €1065 Foothill landscape (71x91cm-28x36in) s. 29-Oct-2 John Moran, Pasadena #748

£955 $1500 €1433 Carmel coast inlet (63x76cm-25x30in) s. 19-Nov-2 Butterfields, San Francisco #8288/R est:3000-5000

SARTHOU, Maurice (1911-) French

£252 $400 €378 Abstract landscape (79x86cm-31x34in) 1-Mar-3 Thomaston Place, Thomaston #24

£283 $450 €425 Abstract landscape (48x51cm-19x20in) s. 1-Mar-3 Thomaston Place, Thomaston #28

SARTO, Andrea del (attrib) (1487-1530) Italian

£13836 $21447 €22000 Jospeh of Arimathea holding Christ's body (73x58cm-29x23in) panel prov.lit. 2-Oct-2 Dorotheum, Vienna #32/R est:15000-20000

SARTO, Andrea del (circle) (1487-1530) Italian

£5031 $7799 €8000 Madonna with Child (107x83cm-42x33in) 2-Oct-2 Dorotheum, Vienna #20/R est:8000-12000

£5500 $8635 €8250 Virgin (51x36cm-20x14in) oil gesso transferred to panel. 10-Dec-2 Bonhams, New Bond Street #20/R est:3000-4000

£7860 $12262 €11790 Judith and the head of Holofernes (84x71cm-33x28in) panel. 6-Nov-2 Dobiaschofsky, Bern #943/R est:12000 (S.FR 18000)

SARTO, Lucia (?) Italian?

£260 $403 €390 Nudo (69x48cm-27x19in) s. 6-Dec-2 Chrystals Auctions, Isle of Man #254y

SARTORE, Hugo (1935-) Uruguayan

£333 $520 €500 Couple (46x61cm-18x24in) s.d.68. 10-Oct-2 Galleria Y Remates, Montevideo #100

SARTORELLI, Carlo (1896-1956) Italian

£645 $1019 €1000 Cypress (46x33cm-18x13in) s. cardboard. 18-Dec-2 Finarte, Milan #51

SARTORELLI, Francesco (1856-1939) Italian

£300 $471 €450 Paesaggio Firmato (18x41cm-7x16in) i.verso panel. 16-Apr-3 Christie's, Kensington #591/R

£1911 $2981 €3000 Girls in a sunny garden (68x98cm-27x39in) s. board. 6-Nov-2 Vendue Huis, Gravenhage #526/R est:2000-3000

SARTORIO, Giulio Aristide (1861-1932) Italian

£2532 $3949 €4000 Anastasiella (52x42cm-20x17in) s.i. 19-Oct-2 Semenzato, Venice #159/R

Works on paper

£774 $1200 €1161 Allegorical sea figure and bodies (27x20cm-11x8in) pencil black ink chk prov.exhib. 29-Oct-2 Sotheby's, New York #117/R est:600-800

£6000 $9540 €9000 Tiber beyond the Porta San Paola (28x61cm-11x24in) s. pencil pastel. 20-Mar-3 Christie's, Kensington #80/R est:1000-1500

SARTORIUS, C J (fl.1810-1821) British

£2402 $3747 €3603 English frigate chasing a French frigate in a gale (54x77cm-21x30in) indis.s.d.1808 canvas on canvas prov. 9-Nov-2 Galerie Gloggner, Luzern #114/R est:1200-1500 (S.FR 5500)

£5000 $8100 €7500 English and French frigates in pursuit off a rocky coastline (54x77cm-21x30in) s.d.1808 prov. 21-May-3 Christie's, Kensington #549/R est:4000-6000

SARTORIUS, Francis (elder) (1734-1804) British

£820 $1353 €1189 Gone away (20x25cm-8x10in) s. 1-Jul-3 Bonhams, Norwich #208/R

£4200 $6972 €6300 Dolly, chesnut raceshorse, with jockey up, racecourse beyond (61x74cm-24x29in) s. 12-Jun-3 Sotheby's, London #85/R est:4000-6000

£6000 $9480 €9000 Sir Patrick Blake's Sir Anthony held by a groom in landscape (61x74cm-24x29in) s.d.1770. 27-Nov-2 Christie's, London #8/R

£7600 $12616 €11400 Red Rose, bay hunter, hold by a groom, with hound in a landscape (62x72cm-24x28in) s.i. 12-Jun-3 Sotheby's, London #84/R est:3000-5000

£8500 $14025 €12325 Goldfinger (61x73cm-24x29in) s.d.1770 i.verso. 2-Jul-3 Sotheby's, Olympia #147/R est:4000-6000

SARTORIUS, Francis (younger) (1777-?) British

£950 $1482 €1425 Ships in distress at the cliff foot (29x45cm-11x18in) s.d. panel pair. 10-Sep-2 David Duggleby, Scarborough #288

SARTORIUS, John Francis (c.1775-1831) British

£2600 $4264 €3900 Dead game in an interior - woodcock, snipe and rabbit (50x60cm-20x24in) s.d.1862. 3-Jun-3 Bonhams, Knightsbridge #26/R est:2500-3500

SARTORIUS, John Nott (1759-1828) British

£2200 $3608 €3300 Meteor (31x35cm-12x14in) i. 3-Jun-3 Bonhams, Knightsbridge #59/R est:2000-3000

£14000 $22120 €21000 Groom holding a lady and gentleman's hunters in a landscape. 28-Nov-2 Bonhams, Knightsbridge #106/R est:5000-8000

SARTORIUS, John Nott (attrib) (1759-1828) British

£920 $1500 €1380 Two greyhounds coursing a hare (27x60cm-11x24in) board. 11-Feb-3 Bonhams & Doyles, New York #90 est:1000-1500

£4321 $7000 €6265 Hunting scenes (36x46cm-14x18in) three bears sig indis d. five. 21-May-3 Doyle, New York #168/R est:6000-8000

SARTORIUS, Virginie de (1828-?) Belgian
£1277 $2132 €1800 Nature morte aux fleurs (31x40cm-12x16in) s.d.1875 panel. 18-Jun-3 Hotel des Ventes Mosan, Brussels #173 est:1400-1600
£2449 $3894 €3600 Adoration de la Vierge a l'enfant (90x70cm-35x28in) s.d.1863. 19-Mar-3 Hotel des Ventes Mosan, Brussels #196 est:4000-5000

SARTORIUS, William (18th C) British
£18000 $30060 €26100 Peaches in basket with various dead game, hare and fishes and vegetables (139x154cm-55x61in) s. 9-Jul-3 Bonhams, New Bond Street #24/R est:8000-12000

SASSE, Art (20th C) ?
Photographs
£3250 $5200 €4875 Einstein's birthday joke (22x16cm-9x6in) silver print. 15-May-3 Swann Galleries, New York #334/R est:1500-2500

SASSE, Richard (1774-1849) British
Photographs
£6962 $11000 €10443 5502 (106x160cm-42x63in) s.i.d.1996 num.5502 verso col coupler print mounted on plexiglas. 14-Nov-2 Christie's, Rockefeller NY #431/R est:10000-15000

SASSENBROUCK, Achille van (1886-1979) Belgian
£497 $810 €750 Vue de la rue des Princes (67x60cm-26x24in) panel. 17-Feb-3 Amberes, Antwerp #252
£566 $872 €900 Interieur (90x80cm-35x31in) s. 22-Oct-2 Campo, Vlaamse Kaai #666
£578 $919 €850 Vue sur les champs de ble et Lisseweghe au loin (64x71cm-25x28in) s. 18-Mar-3 Campo, Vlaamse Kaai #275/R
£818 $1267 €1300 Ruins of the Beguinage of Diksmuide (60x73cm-24x29in) s.d.1919. 5-Oct-2 De Vuyst, Lokeren #391
£1006 $1550 €1600 Trois hommes devant la rade d'Anvers (120x160cm-47x63in) s. 22-Oct-2 Campo & Campo, Antwerp #314
£1111 $1767 €1600 Nature morte (120x90cm-47x35in) s. 29-Apr-3 Campo & Campo, Antwerp #328/R est:800-1000
£1258 $1950 €2000 Fishing boats in Ostend (79x89cm-31x35in) s.d.1930. 5-Oct-2 De Vuyst, Lokeren #390/R est:2000-2400
£1296 $1841 €2100 Bouquinistes (83x54cm-33x21in) s. 17-Mar-2 Galerie de Chartres, Chartres #154

SASSI, Pietro (1834-1905) Italian
£3846 $5962 €6000 Capannelle. Roman countryside (15x24cm-6x9in) s. board pair. 4-Dec-2 Finarte, Rome #755/R

SASSOFERRATO (1609-1685) Italian
£1887 $2925 €3000 Putti amongst clouds (28x21cm-11x8in) canvas on board pair. 7-Oct-2 Ansorena, Madrid #20/R
£19000 $31730 €27550 The Virgin in Prayer (48x37cm-19x15in) 10-Jul-3 Sotheby's, London #168/R est:10000-15000
£20062 $32500 €30093 Head of the Madonna (49x37cm-19x15in) prov. 23-Jan-3 Sotheby's, New York #149/R est:30000
£43210 $70000 €64815 Holy Family (76x65cm-30x26in) prov. 24-Jan-3 Christie's, Rockefeller NY #151/R est:60000-80000
£49655 $78455 €72000 Crucifixion (98x73cm-39x29in) 5-Apr-3 Finarte Semenzato, Milan #68/R est:20000

SASSOFERRATO (attrib) (1609-1685) Italian
£6090 $9622 €9500 Madonna with sleeping child (74x62cm-29x24in) prov. 16-Nov-2 Lempertz, Koln #1093/R est:8000
£6338 $10204 €9000 Madonna and Child (69x45cm-27x18in) 11-May-3 Finarte, Venice #30/R est:10000
£8000 $12560 €12000 Madonna at prayer (51x39cm-20x15in) prov.lit. 12-Dec-2 Sotheby's, London #116/R est:8000-12000

SASSOFERRATO (studio) (1609-1685) Italian
£12785 $19945 €19178 Maria praying (48x36cm-19x14in) prov. 28-Mar-3 Koller, Zurich #3040/R est:7000-10000 (S.FR 28000)

SASSOFERRATO (style) (1609-1685) Italian
£2885 $4471 €4500 Madonna praying (47x36cm-19x14in) prov. 4-Dec-2 Christie's, Rome #333

SASSU, Aligi (1912-2000) Italian
£2128 $3447 €3000 Uccello di rovo (12x19cm-5x7in) s. s.d.1985 verso canvasboard. 22-May-3 Stadion, Trieste #274/R est:3000-4000
£3462 $5435 €5400 Man and horse (18x24cm-7x9in) s. cardboard on canvas. 20-Nov-2 Pandolfini, Florence #80/R
£4430 $6911 €7000 Toreador (30x24cm-12x9in) s. s.verso cardboard. 14-Sep-2 Meeting Art, Vercelli #982/R
£4730 $7378 €7000 Jockeys at start (30x40cm-12x16in) s. s.i.d.1959 verso. 26-Mar-3 Finarte Semenzato, Milan #319/R
£5319 $8617 €7500 Figure (38x22cm-15x9in) s. cardboard prov.exhib. 26-May-3 Christie's, Milan #309/R est:7000-10000
£7092 $11489 €10000 Il noce, Zorzino (53x73cm-21x29in) s. s.i.d.1943 verso prov. 26-May-3 Christie's, Milan #121/R est:8000-12000
£7092 $11489 €10000 La moglie del poeta (35x22cm-14x9in) s. s.i.d.1945 verso canvas on board. 26-May-3 Christie's, Milan #132/R est:5000-7000
£14103 $22141 €22000 Cyclop (50x70cm-20x28in) s.i.d.1987 verso. 19-Nov-2 Finarte, Milan #201/R est:19000-23000
£16312 $26426 €23000 Cavalli e Mefistofele (50x60cm-20x24in) s. prov.exhib. 26-May-3 Christie's, Milan #139/R est:10000-15000
Works on paper
£513 $805 €800 Andromedes (11x16cm-4x6in) s.i. gouache card exec.1985. 21-Nov-2 Finarte, Rome #22/R
£1042 $1656 €1500 Horse and knight (14x22cm-6x9in) s.i. W/C. 1-May-3 Meeting Art, Vercelli #63
£1176 $1882 €1800 Landscape wit trees (66x45cm-26x18in) s. ink W/C lit. 4-Jan-3 Meeting Art, Vercelli #658
£2692 $4227 €4200 Figures (70x50cm-28x20in) s. mixed media. 21-Nov-2 Finarte, Rome #146/R

SATO, Ado (1936-) ?
£253 $392 €400 Still life (61x92cm-24x36in) s.d.75 verso. 28-Sep-2 Cornette de St.Cyr, Paris #214
£577 $906 €900 Pyramids (50x50cm-20x20in) s.d.1977 verso prov. 24-Nov-2 Laurence Calmels, Paris #2/R
£1026 $1610 €1600 Couv N I (65x92cm-26x36in) s.i.d.1975 verso prov. 24-Nov-2 Laurence Calmels, Paris #3/R
£1154 $1812 €1800 Souvenir de l'ete dernier (100x64cm-39x25in) s.i.d.1978 s.d.verso prov. 24-Nov-2 Laurence Calmels, Paris #1/R
Works on paper
£385 $604 €600 Quatre coins de metal (61x61cm-24x24in) s.d.1987 verso mixed media paper on board prov. 24-Nov-2 Laurence Calmels, Paris #4/R

SATO, Key (1906-1978) Japanese
£818 $1267 €1300 Abime (73x60cm-29x24in) s. 7-Oct-2 Claude Aguttes, Neuilly #162
£962 $1510 €1500 Signe du passe (55x46cm-22x18in) s.d.71 paper on canvas. 24-Nov-2 Laurence Calmels, Paris #257/R
£962 $1510 €1500 Signe du passe (55x46cm-22x18in) s.d.71 paper on canvas. 24-Nov-2 Laurence Calmels, Paris #256/R
£1115 $1739 €1750 Oracle au fond de la mer (55x46cm-22x18in) s.d.1971 i.verso. 10-Nov-2 Eric Pillon, Calais #235/R
£1282 $2013 €2000 Untitled (46x55cm-18x22in) s.d.63. 24-Nov-2 Laurence Calmels, Paris #255/R
£1410 $2214 €2200 Pierre de flame (61x73cm-24x29in) s.d.1964 s.i.d.verso. 15-Dec-2 Perrin, Versailles #26/R
£1795 $2818 €2800 Rouille du ciel (73x60cm-29x24in) s.d.62 s.i.d.verso. 24-Nov-2 Laurence Calmels, Paris #258/R
£2158 $3453 €3000 La mer figee (92x73cm-36x29in) s.d. i.verso. 18-May-3 Eric Pillon, Calais #267/R
Works on paper
£513 $805 €800 Untitled (32x24cm-13x9in) s.d.74 gouache. 24-Nov-2 Laurence Calmels, Paris #253/R
£577 $906 €900 Untitled (30x40cm-12x16in) s. gouache. 24-Nov-2 Laurence Calmels, Paris #252/R
£705 $1107 €1100 Untitled (34x27cm-13x11in) s.d.71 gouache. 24-Nov-2 Laurence Calmels, Paris #254/R
£1633 $2596 €2400 Carte de voeux (18x28cm-7x11in) s.d.1975 W/C ink. 26-Feb-3 Artcurial Briest, Paris #568 est:100-150

SATRE, August (1879-1926) American
£750 $1200 €1088 Downtown Boston (51x38cm-20x15in) s.indis.d. 17-May-3 CRN Auctions, Cambridge #47

SATTERLEE, Walter (1844-1908) American
Works on paper
£441 $700 €662 Ornithologist (48x32cm-19x13in) s. W/C gouache. 7-Mar-3 Skinner, Boston #313/R

SATTLER, Hubert (1817-1904) Austrian
£481 $755 €750 View of promenade and housing on the river (20x30cm-8x12in) s. board. 10-Dec-2 Dorotheum, Vienna #117/R
£543 $880 €787 Landscape from Linderhof. Lake landscape (12x17cm-5x7in) one s. panel two. 25-May-3 Uppsala Auktionskammare, Uppsala #142/R (S.KR 7000)
£641 $1006 €1000 View of Interlaken and Jungfrau (17x24cm-7x9in) mono. i.verso board. 10-Dec-2 Dorotheum, Vienna #159/R
£641 $1006 €1000 View of Switzerland (23x31cm-9x12in) s. i.verso board. 10-Dec-2 Dorotheum, Vienna #246/R
£1164 $1816 €1700 Jungfrau seen from Eisenflut (24x32cm-9x13in) mono. i. verso board. 10-Apr-3 Dorotheum, Vienna #236/R est:1700-1900
£3165 $5000 €5000 View of Prague (58x42cm-23x17in) s. 28-Nov-2 Dorotheum, Vienna #37/R est:4000-5000

SATTLER, Hubert (attrib) (1817-1904) Austrian
£1203 $1864 €1900 Mexican landscape (24x38cm-9x15in) i.d.1875 panel. 28-Sep-2 Hans Stahl, Hamburg #32/R est:1700

SAUDEMONT, Émile (1898-?) French
£256 $403 €400 Paquebot a Brest (38x56cm-15x22in) s. 15-Dec-2 Thierry & Lannon, Brest #415

SAUER, Walter (1889-1972) Belgian
£1655 $2648 €2400 Still life (40x50cm-16x20in) mono.d.15 lit. 15-Mar-3 De Vuyst, Lokeren #537/R est:2500-3500
£13014 $20432 €19000 Le coffret noir (53x45cm-21x18in) mono. oil silver leaf col crayon. 15-Apr-3 Galerie Moderne, Brussels #362/R est:10000-12000

Works on paper
£915 $1473 €1400 Timidite (36x28cm-14x11in) mono. pencil dr. 20-Jan-3 Horta, Bruxelles #400
£1300 $2028 €1950 Female nude (46x34cm-18x13in) mono.d.1918 pencil. 26-Mar-3 Sotheby's, Olympia #241/R est:400-600
£2759 $4414 €4000 Jeune femme nue se baignant (51x40cm-20x16in) s.mono.d.1918 pencil. 17-Mar-3 Horta, Bruxelles #189/R est:3500-4500
£4051 $6319 €6400 Jeune femme au pagne (56x41cm-22x16in) s.d.1917 mixed media. 16-Sep-2 Horta, Bruxelles #167
£5063 $7899 €8000 Jeune femme au turban (48x15cm-19x6in) s.d.1919 mixed media. 16-Sep-2 Horta, Bruxelles #168

SAUERBRUCH, Hans (1910-) German
£288 $453 €450 Still life with fruit (38x54cm-15x21in) s.d.1982 board lit. 22-Nov-2 Karrenbauer, Konstanz #1865

Works on paper
£385 $604 €600 Market (17x41cm-7x16in) s. W/C. 22-Nov-2 Karrenbauer, Konstanz #1867
£641 $974 €1000 Busy market (40x50cm-16x20in) s. W/C htd white. 31-Aug-2 Geble, Radolfzell #694/R
£833 $1308 €1300 Constance (39x31cm-15x12in) s. mixed media. 22-Nov-2 Karrenbauer, Konstanz #1866

SAUERWEID, Nicolas Alexandrovitch (1836-1866) Russian

Works on paper
£1100 $1793 €1650 Nicholas in a horse drawn brichka (17x24cm-7x9in) W/C two. 29-Jan-3 Sotheby's, Olympia #275/R est:400-600

SAUERWEIN, Frank P (1871-1910) American
£2188 $3500 €3282 Farmhouse in summer meadow (20x30cm-8x12in) s.d.1908 board. 11-Jan-3 Harvey Clar, Oakland #1437

Works on paper
£11218 $17500 €16827 Southern Ute reservation, Colorado (36x23cm-14x9in) s.i.d.98 W/C gouache prov.lit. 9-Nov-2 Santa Fe Art, Santa Fe #81/R est:10000-15000

SAUKKONEN, Immanuel (1909-1970) Finnish
£314 $484 €500 Winter's day (65x82cm-26x32in) s. 27-Oct-2 Bukowskis, Helsinki #274/R

SAUKKONEN, Teemu (1954-) Finnish
£845 $1361 €1200 Sunset (65x95cm-26x37in) s.verso board. 10-May-3 Bukowskis, Helsinki #231/R

SAULO, Georges Ernest (1865-?) French

Sculpture
£1603 $2500 €2405 Bust of Napoleon (41x25x18cm-16x10x7in) s.st.f.Susse Fres pat bronze. 12-Oct-2 Neal Auction Company, New Orleans #247/R est:3000-5000

SAUNDERS, Charles L (?-1915) British
£1258 $2000 €1887 Punters on a river by a cottage (61x95cm-24x37in) s. 5-Mar-3 Christie's, Rockefeller NY #70/R est:1000-1500

SAUNDERS, George Lethbridge (1807-1863) British

Miniatures
£3200 $4992 €4800 Lady wearing rust coloured dress with blue trim and matching waistband (9cm-4in) gilt frame octagonal. 5-Nov-2 Bonhams, New Bond Street #125/R est:1800-2200

SAUNDERS, Michelle (20th C) British
£350 $546 €525 Low waters, Runswick Bay (51x61cm-20x24in) s. 25-Mar-3 Bonhams, Leeds #584

SAUNDERS, Norman (1906-1988) American
£8974 $14000 €13461 Woman breaking out of jail (51x38cm-20x15in) s.d.1950 board lit. 9-Nov-2 Illustration House, New York #145/R est:14000-18000

SAUNIER, Noel (1847-1890) French
£641 $1006 €1000 Promenade en bord d'etang (32x46cm-13x18in) s. 11-Dec-2 Maigret, Paris #100/R

SAUR, Hans Michael (1692-1745) German
£873 $1362 €1310 Meeting by the golden gate (116x94cm-46x37in) s.d.1745. 20-Nov-2 Fischer, Luzern #2227/R est:2000-3000 (S.FR 2000)

SAUR, P (19th C) German
£480 $739 €720 Artist (39x32cm-15x13in) s.d.1883. 8-Sep-2 Lots Road, London #331

SAURA PACHECO, Fulgencio (1905-1988) Spanish
£287 $448 €425 Fountain, Aranjuez (100x70cm-39x28in) s.i. s.i.d.1960 verso. 25-Mar-3 Durán, Madrid #618/R

SAURA, Antonio (1930-1998) Spanish
£1955 $3109 €2933 Foule - composition (33x23cm-13x9in) mono.d.73 exhib. 10-Mar-3 Rasmussen, Vejle #742/R est:20000-30000 (D.KR 21000)
£11724 $18759 €17000 Dog (30x40cm-12x16in) s.d.85 board. 11-Mar-3 Castellana, Madrid #359/R est:12000
£16216 $26108 €24324 Crucifixion (62x90cm-24x35in) s.d.60 tempera paper on panel and canvas prov. 7-May-3 AB Stockholms Auktionsverk #1121/R est:160000-180000 (S.KR 210000)
£17579 $27071 €27950 Goya's dog (74x109cm-29x43in) s.d.1992 acrylic paper. 26-Oct-2 Cornette de St.Cyr, Paris #13/R
£26027 $40863 €38000 Untitled (46x61cm-18x24in) s.d.1950 verso. 15-Apr-3 Laurence Calmels, Paris #4407/R est:20000
£42308 $66423 €66000 Chien de Goya I (97x130cm-38x51in) s. painted 1981 prov. 15-Dec-2 Perrin, Versailles #98/R est:50000
£50000 $82000 €75000 Brigitte Bardot (129x97cm-51x38in) s.i.d.63 prov. 6-Feb-3 Christie's, London #635/R est:50000-70000
£60000 $98400 €90000 Pica (130x97cm-51x38in) s.d.63 s.i.d.on stretcher prov.exhib. 5-Feb-3 Christie's, London #31/R est:60000-80000
£75000 $123000 €112500 Infanta (162x130cm-64x51in) s.d.62 prov.exhib.lit. 6-Feb-3 Sotheby's, London #27/R est:120000

Works on paper
£1673 $2643 €2510 Figure compositions. s.i.indis.d. Indian ink nine in one frame. 1-Apr-3 Rasmussen, Copenhagen #141/R est:30000 (D.KR 18000)
£1899 $3000 €3000 Personnage (20x26cm-8x10in) s.d.77 ink W/C collage on cardboard. 26-Nov-2 Sotheby's, Amsterdam #256/R est:3000-5000
£2516 $3975 €3900 Lady (40x30cm-16x12in) s.d.1975 ink. 17-Dec-2 Segre, Madrid #166/R
£3673 $5841 €5400 Sans titre (33x24cm-13x9in) s.d.26-4-83 ink gouache. 26-Feb-3 Artcurial Briest, Paris #431/R est:2000-3000
£3797 $6000 €6000 Cure (31x21cm-12x8in) s. s.d.77 oil ink prov. 26-Nov-2 Sotheby's, Amsterdam #243/R est:4000-6000
£4300 $6794 €6450 Poeme-objet (48x65cm-19x26in) s.d.1959 pen brush ink collage prov. 3-Apr-3 Christie's, Kensington #197/R
£5168 $8010 €7752 Composition (67x48cm-26x19in) s.d.5-7-58 collage. 4-Dec-2 Kunsthallen, Copenhagen #85/R est:40000 (D.KR 60000)
£5512 $8544 €8268 Composition no.13 (70x50cm-28x20in) s.d.56-57-58 collage Indian ink. 4-Dec-2 Kunsthallen, Copenhagen #170/R est:40000 (D.KR 64000)

SAURFELT, Leonard (1840-?) French
£2848 $4500 €4500 Par ordre du Roy (93x73cm-37x29in) s.d.1884. 1-Dec-2 Peron, Melun #137b

SAUSMAREZ, Maurice de (1915-1969) British
£550 $869 €825 Mountainous landscape (48x74cm-19x29in) s.d.66. 18-Dec-2 Mallams, Oxford #657/R

SAUTER, Aloys (1952-) ?
£1586 $2507 €2300 Chat (65x54cm-26x21in) s.d.1934. 4-Apr-3 Tajan, Paris #10/R

SAUTER, Rudolph (1895-1977) British

Works on paper
£340 $530 €510 New York (23x29cm-9x11in) s. pastel. 10-Apr-3 Tennants, Leyburn #837

SAUTEUR, Claude le (1926-) Canadian
£333 $547 €483 Lueur d'un jour nouveau (25x30cm-10x12in) s.i.d.1980. 9-Jun-3 Hodgins, Calgary #333/R (C.D 750)
£532 $830 €798 La grange de Stanislas (25x30cm-10x12in) s.d.77. 30-Jul-2 Iegor de Saint Hippolyte, Montreal #96 (C.D 1320)
£629 $981 €944 Arbres en automne (20x25cm-8x10in) s.d.1979. 30-Jul-2 Iegor de Saint Hippolyte, Montreal #95 (C.D 1560)
£726 $1183 €1089 Trois a table (20x25cm-8x10in) s.d.82 s.i.d. verso. 12-Feb-3 Iegor de Saint Hippolyte, Montreal #123b (C.D 1800)

SAUTIN, René (1881-1968) French
£1088 $1731 €1600 Automne sur la Seine (38x46cm-15x18in) s. i.verso. 24-Mar-3 Coutau Begarie, Paris #249/R

SAUTTER, Walter (1911-1991) Swiss
£328 $514 €492 Riva degli Schiavoni - Venezia (63x84cm-25x33in) mono.d.1964. 25-Nov-2 Germann, Zurich #803 (S.FR 750)

SAUVAGE, François Phillippe (19th C) French
£1143 $1760 €1715 Untitled - reading the news (25x19cm-10x7in) s. board. 3-Sep-2 Shapiro, Sydney #437/R est:3000-5000 (A.D 3200)

SAUVAGE, Georges (fl.1874-1913) French
£355 $592 €500 Etude de main et de pied (40x33cm-16x13in) i.verso. 23-Jun-3 Beaussant & Lefèvre, Paris #164

SAUVAGE, Pieter Joseph (1744-1818) Flemish
Miniatures
£1100 $1782 €1650 Gentleman in profile (4cm-2in) en grisaille cicular. 22-May-3 Bonhams, New Bond Street #31/R est:600-800
£1489 $2413 €2100 Madame Royale (6cm-2in circular) s. grisaille ivory gilded brass frame prov. 21-May-3 Piasa, Paris #317/R est:2000-3000

SAUVAGE, Pieter Joseph (circle) (1744-1818) Flemish
£6098 $10000 €9147 Disporting Putti, a feigned bas-relief (56x173cm-22x68in) en grisaille. 30-May-3 Christie's, Rockefeller NY #7/R est:8000-12000

SAUVAGE, Raymond (20th C) French
£385 $604 €600 Regates aux voiles rouges (54x65cm-21x26in) s. 15-Dec-2 Thierry & Lannon, Brest #250

SAUVAIGE, Marcel Louis (?-1927) French
£694 $1132 €1000 Camaret, barques au clair de lune (56x76cm-22x30in) s. cardboard. 19-Jul-3 Thierry & Lannon, Brest #172/R

SAUZAY, Adrien Jacques (1841-1928) French
£453 $689 €680 Interior scene with woman and children (40x31cm-16x12in) s. panel. 16-Aug-2 Lilla Bukowskis, Stockholm #240 (S.KR 6600)
£650 $1027 €975 Rowing boat moored on a riverbank (36x61cm-14x24in) s. 2-Dec-2 Gorringes, Lewes #2768
£886 $1400 €1400 Village au bord de l'eau (31x50cm-12x20in) s.i. panel. 29-Nov-2 Drouot Estimations, Paris #42
£2405 $3800 €3800 Maisons au bord de l'eau, printemps (39x62cm-15x24in) s. 1-Dec-2 Peron, Melun #142
£2848 $4443 €4500 Bords de riviere (36x63cm-14x25in) s. 20-Oct-2 Mercier & Cie, Lille #298/R est:4500-5000

SAVAGE, Anne (1896-1971) Canadian
£2469 $3827 €3704 Birches, Lake Wonish (22x30cm-9x12in) init.verso panel painted c.1935 prov. 3-Dec-2 Joyner, Toronto #2/R est:3000-4000 (C.D 6000)
£2667 $4373 €4001 St. Octave de metis (68x120cm-27x47in) s.verso panel painted c.1935 prov. 27-May-3 Sotheby's, Toronto #3/R est:5000-7000 (C.D 6000)
£3111 $5102 €4667 Laurentians (30x35cm-12x14in) init. panel prov. 3-Jun-3 Joyner, Toronto #180/R est:7000-9000 (C.D 7000)
£3111 $5102 €4667 Spring, Lake Wonish, PQ (22x30cm-9x12in) s. panel prov. 3-Jun-3 Joyner, Toronto #201/R est:6000-8000 (C.D 7000)
£4444 $7289 €6666 Rural homes in winter (30x35cm-12x14in) s. panel. 3-Jun-3 Joyner, Toronto #3/R est:5000-7000 (C.D 10000)

SAVAGE, Cedric (1901-1969) New Zealander
£336 $540 €504 Forest Trek with horse and rider (62x50cm-24x20in) s.d.1940 board. 7-May-3 Dunbar Sloane, Auckland #32/R (NZ.D 950)
£737 $1149 €1106 Woolloomooloo Alley (34x44cm-13x17in) s. board. 27-Mar-3 International Art Centre, Auckland #123/R (NZ.D 2100)
£752 $1174 €1128 Coastal scene with Baches. s. board. 7-Nov-2 International Art Centre, Auckland #138/R est:1500-2500 (NZ.D 2400)
£909 $1400 €1364 Still life (43x52cm-17x20in) s. canvas on board. 4-Sep-2 Dunbar Sloane, Wellington #9/R est:2000-4000 (NZ.D 3000)
£1136 $1750 €1704 Boat sheds, Titahi Bay (32x42cm-13x17in) s. board. 4-Sep-2 Dunbar Sloane, Wellington #117 est:1500-2500 (NZ.D 3750)
£1232 $2033 €1786 Old fortress above Naphlion, Greece (41x59cm-16x23in) s. board. 1-Jul-3 Peter Webb, Auckland #81/R est:3500-5000 (NZ.D 3500)
£1608 $2492 €2412 Fishing boats at Mediterranean port (50x68cm-20x27in) s. 4-Dec-2 Dunbar Sloane, Auckland #11/R est:5000-8000 (NZ.D 5000)
Works on paper
£606 $933 €909 South End - Titahi Bay (31x41cm-12x16in) s. W/C. 4-Sep-2 Dunbar Sloane, Wellington #120 est:1500-2500 (NZ.D 2000)

SAVAGE, Edward (after) (1761-1817) American
£6129 $9500 €9194 The Washington family (71x91cm-28x36in) 2-Nov-2 North East Auctions, Portsmouth #629/R est:5000-8000

SAVARY, Robert (1920-) French
£1619 $2590 €2250 La plage (81x100cm-32x39in) s. 14-May-3 Blanchet, Paris #129/R est:800-1000

SAVATER, Juan Carlos (1953-) Spanish
£1548 $2446 €2400 Cave (161x130cm-63x51in) s.i.d.1984 verso exhib.lit. 17-Dec-2 Segre, Madrid #188/R

SAVELLI, Angelo (1911-1995) Italian
£570 $889 €900 Marina (46x50cm-18x20in) s. s.i.d.1949 verso. 19-Oct-2 Semenzato, Venice #124/R

SAVERFELT, Leonard (attrib) (19th C) American?
£688 $1100 €1032 Market day (64x53cm-25x21in) s. 15-Mar-3 Eldred, East Dennis #408/R

SAVERY, Hans (elder) (1564-1622) Dutch
£10811 $16865 €16000 Ships in tempest (50x92cm-20x36in) panel lit. 27-Mar-3 Dorotheum, Vienna #214/R est:7000-10000

SAVERY, Roeland (1576-1639) Dutch
£50314 $77987 €80000 Landscape with cows, stags and water flow by waterfall (45x64cm-18x25in) s.d.1623 panel prov. 2-Oct-2 Dorotheum, Vienna #162/R est:80000-100000
£61151 $97842 €85000 Wooded river landscape with deer, goats and lizards by a waterfall and cattle (56x86cm-22x34in) s. panel prov.lit. 14-May-3 Christie's, Amsterdam #174/R est:30000-40000
Works on paper
£1007 $1621 €1500 Etude de hiboux (24x19cm-9x7in) pierre noire htd white. 18-Feb-3 Vanderkindere, Brussels #101
£4966 $7895 €7200 Le jardin d'Eden (40x31cm-16x12in) brush painted with studio. 5-Mar-3 Doutrebente, Paris #17/R est:7000-8000

SAVERY, Roeland (studio) (1576-1639) Dutch
£12000 $20040 €17400 River landscape with deer and other animals and birds beside a waterfall (104x81cm-41x32in) 10-Jul-3 Sotheby's, London #141/R est:15000-20000

SAVERYS, Albert (1886-1964) Belgian
£1007 $1612 €1400 Heron et cruche sur une table (76x101cm-30x40in) s. 13-May-3 Palais de Beaux Arts, Brussels #129/R
£2069 $3310 €3000 Vue de jardin et d'une maison (79x99cm-31x39in) 17-Mar-3 Amberes, Antwerp #244/R
£2083 $3312 €3000 Paysage expressionniste de la Lys (65x80cm-26x31in) s. 29-Apr-3 Campo & Campo, Antwerp #262/R est:4000-6000
£2138 $3293 €3400 Etude de pintade (60x80cm-24x31in) s. lit. 22-Oct-2 Campo & Campo, Antwerp #231/R
£2483 $3972 €3600 La lys en automne (40x50cm-16x20in) s. panel. 17-Mar-3 Horta, Bruxelles #137/R est:3000-4000
£3165 $5000 €5000 Chemin de campagne en hiver (40x50cm-16x20in) s. panel. 26-Nov-2 Palais de Beaux Arts, Brussels #367/R est:5000-7500
£3165 $5000 €5000 Vue du pont de Moret (40x50cm-16x20in) s. panel. 26-Nov-2 Palais de Beaux Arts, Brussels #368/R est:5000-7000
£3472 $5521 €5000 Vase de fleurs (80x60cm-31x24in) s. panel. 29-Apr-3 Campo, Vlaamse Kaai #272/R est:5000-6000
£4430 $6911 €7000 Patineurs pres du pont a bascule (60x60cm-24x24in) s. 16-Sep-2 Horta, Bruxelles #151/R
£4483 $7083 €6500 Paysage sous la neige (57x77cm-22x30in) s. 2-Apr-3 Vanderkindere, Brussels #531/R est:5000-7500
£4676 $7482 €6500 La Lys en ete (93x120cm-37x47in) s.verso. 19-May-3 Horta, Bruxelles #131 est:6000-8000
£4676 $7482 €6500 Bouquet de fleurs dans un vase (60x50cm-24x20in) s. panel. 13-May-3 Palais de Beaux Arts, Brussels #131/R est:6200-8700
£5063 $8000 €8000 Village au bord de l'eau (60x80cm-24x31in) s. panel. 26-Nov-2 Palais de Beaux Arts, Brussels #149/R est:8000-10000
£6250 $9938 €9000 Paysage a la Lys (90x120cm-35x47in) s. 29-Apr-3 Campo & Campo, Antwerp #263/R est:18000-22000
£6552 $10483 €9500 Pecheur au bord de la Lys avec moulin et vaches (60x80cm-24x31in) s. 17-Mar-3 Horta, Bruxelles #136/R est:10000-12000
£6962 $11000 €11000 Vue de la Lys en hiver (79x99cm-31x39in) s. 26-Nov-2 Palais de Beaux Arts, Brussels #369/R est:10000-15000
£8228 $13000 €13000 Paysage d'hiver avec patineurs (30x40cm-12x16in) s. panel. 26-Nov-2 Palais de Beaux Arts, Brussels #148/R est:10000-15000
£11348 $18950 €16000 Maisons en bord de Lys (85x100cm-33x39in) s. 17-Jun-3 Palais de Beaux Arts, Brussels #622/R est:12500-15000
£11392 $18000 €18000 Soleil d'hiver sur la Lys (90x100cm-35x39in) s. 26-Nov-2 Palais de Beaux Arts, Brussels #150/R est:20000-30000

Works on paper
£683 $1094 €950 Farmer picking (50x59cm-20x23in) s. wash exec.c.1925. 17-May-3 De Vuyst, Lokeren #322
£1006 $1550 €1600 Vue ensoleillee de Villefranche (48x67cm-19x26in) s. pastel. 22-Oct-2 Campo & Campo, Antwerp #229/R
£1007 $1612 €1400 Along the Leie (48x66cm-19x26in) s. W/C. 17-May-3 De Vuyst, Lokeren #321/R
£1905 $3029 €2800 Village en automne (50x60cm-20x24in) s. W/C. 18-Mar-3 Vanderkindere, Brussels #105/R est:2000-3000

SAVIGNAC, Louis de (1734-?) Italian
Works on paper
£1519 $2400 €2279 Figures dancing in a landscape. Figures strolling near the steps of a palace (62x58cm-24x23in) s. bodycol board two. 1-Apr-3 Christie's, Rockefeller NY #390/R est:1500-2000

SAVIGNY, Jean Paul (1933-) French
£292 $475 €420 Les arbres en fleurs (30x41cm-12x16in) s. 19-Jul-3 Thierry & Lannon, Brest #386
£577 $906 €900 Moulin a Pont-Aven (50x61cm-20x24in) s. 15-Dec-2 Thierry & Lannon, Brest #258
£704 $1134 €1000 Paysage d'automne a la chaumiere (53x65cm-21x26in) s. 11-May-3 Thierry & Lannon, Brest #280

SAVILLE, Jenny (1970-) British
£280000 $467600 €420000 Untitled (204x183cm-80x72in) i.verso exc.c.1990 prov.exhib. 25-Jun-3 Sotheby's, London #5/R est:300000-400000

SAVIN, Maurice (1894-1973) French
£516 $815 €800 Paysage de la Drome (50x65cm-20x26in) s. i.verso. 19-Dec-2 Claude Aguttes, Neuilly #191/R
£696 $1086 €1100 Paysage de la Manche (46x55cm-18x22in) s. s.i.verso. 20-Oct-2 Chayette & Cheval, Paris #72
£823 $1275 €1300 Nu allonge et endormi (46x55cm-18x22in) s. 29-Sep-2 Eric Pillon, Calais #211/R
£949 $1481 €1500 Champ en Normandie (54x73cm-21x29in) s. s.i. verso. 20-Oct-2 Claude Boisgirard, Paris #84/R est:1500-2000
£1026 $1610 €1600 Dans le jardin (60x73cm-24x29in) s. 15-Dec-2 Eric Pillon, Calais #134/R
£1295 $2072 €1800 Table sur la terrasse devant les vignes (46x55cm-18x22in) s.d.60. 14-May-3 Blanchet, Paris #92/R est:1500-1800
£6369 $9936 €10000 Baigneuses (146x114cm-57x45in) s. 10-Nov-2 Eric Pillon, Calais #181/R
£11465 $17885 €18000 Ete (130x195cm-51x77in) s. painted 1929. 10-Nov-2 Eric Pillon, Calais #177/R
Works on paper
£319 $533 €450 Elegantes au cafe (41x34cm-16x13in) s. gouache. 20-Jun-3 Piasa, Paris #167/R

SAVINI, Alfonso (1836-1908) Italian
£2500 $3925 €3750 Ardent suitor (15x12cm-6x5in) s. panel prov. 21-Nov-2 Christie's, Kensington #65/R est:2500-3500

SAVIO, Francesco Lo (1935-1963) Italian
Prints
£8511 $13787 €12000 Visione prospettiva frontale per progetto di un metallo monocromatico (43x78cm-17x31in) s.i.d.1961 blueprint glossy paper prov.lit. 26-May-3 Christie's, Milan #223/R est:12000-14000
Works on paper
£1026 $1610 €1600 Space-light (9x16cm-4x6in) s. pencil. 21-Nov-2 Finarte, Rome #117/R
£11348 $18383 €16000 Filto: depotenziamento cromatico and dinamica d'assorbimento (46x53cm-18x21in) transparent paper board prov.exhib. 26-May-3 Christie's, Milan #106/R est:9000-12000

SAVIO, John (1902-1938) Norwegian
Prints
£2251 $3444 €3377 Coffee rest II (21x30cm-8x12in) s.num.22/50 hand col woodcut. 26-Aug-2 Blomqvist, Lysaker #1342/R est:16000-18000 (N.KR 26000)

SAVORGNANI, C (19th C) Italian
£1184 $1800 €1776 Still life of vegetables (33x51cm-13x20in) 16-Aug-2 Du Mouchelle, Detroit #2167/R est:1200-1600

SAVREUX, Maurice (1884-1971) French
£1103 $1842 €1600 Paysage du Midi (50x65cm-20x26in) s. isorel. 10-Jul-3 Artcurial Briest, Paris #173/R est:1500-2000

SAVRY, Hendrick (1823-1907) Dutch
£833 $1375 €1200 Flower nursery (26x75cm-10x30in) s.d.1942 verso board. 1-Jul-3 Christie's, Amsterdam #125

SAVVAS, Nike (1964-) Australian
£307 $481 €461 Untitled 2000 (36x36cm-14x14in) s.verso acrylic. 15-Apr-3 Lawson Menzies, Sydney #9/R (A.D 800)
£307 $481 €461 Untitled 2000 (36x36cm-14x14in) s. verso acrylic. 15-Apr-3 Lawson Menzies, Sydney #10/R (A.D 800)

SAVY, Max (1918-) French?
£513 $805 €800 Retour au village a a tombee du jour (20x50cm-8x20in) s. 15-Dec-2 Eric Pillon, Calais #232/R

SAWREY, Hugh (1923-1999) Australian
£536 $846 €804 Sleeping drover (29x39cm-11x15in) s. 18-Nov-2 Goodman, Sydney #56 (A.D 1500)
£637 $1045 €924 Roebuck shearer (28x33cm-11x13in) s. board. 3-Jun-3 Lawson Menzies, Sydney #708 (A.D 1600)
£766 $1203 €1149 Rousabout (36x30cm-14x12in) s. 15-Apr-3 Lawson Menzies, Sydney #203/R est:1500-2500 (A.D 2000)
£840 $1327 €1260 Ready for the muster (13x13cm-5x5in) s. board. 7-Apr-3 Australian Art Auctions, Sydney #139/R (A.D 2200)
£916 $1447 €1374 Stockman (12x12cm-5x5in) s. board. 7-Apr-3 Australian Art Auctions, Sydney #101/R (A.D 2400)
£920 $1444 €1380 Gentleman of the tribe (35x30cm-14x12in) s. 15-Apr-3 Lawson Menzies, Sydney #204/R est:1500-2500 (A.D 2400)
£1140 $1733 €1710 Tilbooroo horses (23x29cm-9x11in) s. board. 19-Aug-2 Joel, Victoria #306 est:1800-2500 (A.D 3250)
£1143 $1806 €1715 Drover's horses, Western Queensland (30x35cm-12x14in) s. s.i.on stretcher. 27-Nov-2 Deutscher-Menzies, Melbourne #182/R est:2500-3500 (A.D 3200)
£1214 $1919 €1821 Little church on the Rise, lockyer (28x33cm-11x13in) s. s.i.verso. 18-Nov-2 Joel, Victoria #361 est:2000-2500 (A.D 3400)
£1602 $2532 €2777 Station folk (19x24cm-7x9in) s. board. 1-Apr-3 Goodman, Sydney #103 est:2000-3000 (A.D 4200)
£1829 $2891 €2652 Stingy Jones, shearing team, WQ (30x34cm-12x13in) s. 22-Jul-3 Lawson Menzies, Sydney #135/R est:3000-4000 (A.D 4500)
£1938 $3081 €2907 When Dad comes riding home; boundary riders series (29x34cm-11x13in) s. s.i.verso board. 5-May-3 Sotheby's, Melbourne #248 est:800-1200 (A.D 5000)
£1971 $2996 €2957 Island boats and village (58x73cm-23x29in) s. 27-Aug-2 Goodman, Sydney #166/R est:4500-6500 (A.D 5500)
£2107 $3308 €3161 Approaching the Finke River Mission, NT (50x60cm-20x24in) s. board. 15-Apr-3 Lawson Menzies, Sydney #196/R est:6000-9000 (A.D 5500)
£2236 $3533 €3242 At the finish (40x50cm-16x20in) s. 22-Jul-3 Lawson Menzies, Sydney #137/R est:5000-6000 (A.D 5500)
£2289 $3617 €3966 Shearers picnic, along the Wollen river (49x59cm-19x23in) s. 1-Apr-3 Goodman, Sydney #23 est:6000-9000 (A.D 6000)
£2589 $4091 €3884 Camp by no.10 Bore, W. QLD (48x59cm-19x23in) s. s.verso board. 18-Nov-2 Joel, Victoria #150 est:4000-6000 (A.D 7250)
£2857 $4514 €4286 The Overlander (56x76cm-22x30in) s. s.i.verso prov. 27-Nov-2 Deutscher-Menzies, Melbourne #181a/R est:9000-12000 (A.D 8000)
£2863 $4523 €4295 Steading the load (36x33cm-14x13in) s. paper. 7-Apr-3 Australian Art Auctions, Sydney #102/R (A.D 7500)
£2993 $4669 €4490 Cow time (51x61cm-20x24in) s. 21-Oct-2 Australian Art Auctions, Sydney #86/R (A.D 8500)
£3036 $4796 €4554 Boundary Rider's missus, W QLD (49x59cm-19x23in) s. s.i.verso board. 18-Nov-2 Joel, Victoria #238 est:4000-6000 (A.D 8500)
£3149 $4975 €4724 Break of day (36x33cm-14x13in) s. paper. 7-Apr-3 Australian Art Auctions, Sydney #140/R (A.D 8250)
£3226 $4903 €4839 Cattlemen (51x61cm-20x24in) s. s.i.verso. 28-Aug-2 Deutscher-Menzies, Melbourne #432/R est:3000-5000 (A.D 9000)
£3243 $5124 €5618 Fight in the lane (50x60cm-20x24in) s. 1-Apr-3 Goodman, Sydney #32/R est:6000-9000 (A.D 8500)
£3659 $5780 €5306 Country wedding (49x59cm-19x23in) s. s.i.verso board. 22-Jul-3 Lawson Menzies, Sydney #2/R est:8000-10000 (A.D 9000)
£3984 $6534 €5976 Attack on the wagon train (75x100cm-30x39in) s. s.i.verso composition board. 4-Jun-3 Deutscher-Menzies, Melbourne #299/R est:8000-12000 (A.D 10000)
£4472 $7065 €6484 Boiling up - the cattle camp (73x98cm-29x39in) s. prov. 22-Jul-3 Lawson Menzies, Sydney #136/R est:7500-10000 (A.D 11000)
£4577 $7141 €6866 Plainsman, N W Queensland (77x102cm-30x40in) s. 21-Oct-2 Australian Art Auctions, Sydney #110 (A.D 13000)
£4626 $7078 €6939 Camp by the Broncho Yard, Dimantina Lakes Station (74x99cm-29x39in) s. i.verso. 25-Aug-2 Sotheby's, Paddington #124/R est:8000-12000 (A.D 13000)
£4651 $7395 €6977 Cattle rustlers, Poddy-Dogers roost (48x74cm-19x29in) s. i.verso board. 5-May-3 Sotheby's, Melbourne #349/R est:8000-12000 (A.D 12000)

£5364 $8421 €8046 Commercial traveller, Darkie Dywer Kogan Creek Hotel, South West Queensland (49x59cm-19x23in) s. 15-Apr-3 Lawson Menzies, Sydney #198/R est:7500-8500 (A.D 14000)
£5426 $8628 €8139 Holding the floor (51x60cm-20x24in) s. s.i.verso. 5-May-3 Sotheby's, Melbourne #298/R est:8000-12000 (A.D 14000)

SAWYER, Clifton Howard (1896-1966) American
£1118 $1800 €1677 Old barn, probably stables in south Pasadena (76x102cm-30x40in) s. i.verso. 18-Feb-3 John Moran, Pasadena #117b est:1500-2500

SAWYER, Philip Ayer (1877-1949) American
£308 $475 €462 Clearwater, Florida (51x61cm-20x24in) s.d.1945 board. 8-Sep-2 Treadway Gallery, Cincinnati #657/R

SAWYER, William (1820-1889) Canadian
£2361 $3682 €3423 Indian encampment at night (15x25cm-6x10in) s.d.1847 board prov. 26-Mar-3 Walker's, Ottawa #476/R est:700-1000 (C.D 5500)

SAWYIER, Paul (1865-1917) American
£30645 $47500 €45968 Landscape (51x61cm-20x24in) s. prov. 29-Oct-2 John Moran, Pasadena #650 est:5000-8000

SAXON, Charles (1920-1088) American
Works on paper
£621 $1000 €932 Couple in separate beds while their alteregos argue (30x33cm-12x13in) s. W/C pencil. 20-Feb-3 Illustration House, New York #150/R est:1200-1800

SAXTON, John Gordon (attrib) (1860-1907) American
£956 $1500 €1434 Sailing off of Egg Rock, Nahant (36x56cm-14x22in) init.d.87. 22-Nov-2 Skinner, Boston #128/R est:3000-5000

SAYAGO, Adolfo (1963-) Uruguayan
£563 $900 €845 Night dying out (100x100cm-39x39in) s.d.2001. 5-Jan-3 Galleria Y Remates, Montevideo #123/R
£1258 $2000 €1887 Pedrera (80x120cm-31x47in) s. 2-Mar-3 Galleria Y Remates, Montevideo #106/R

SAYER, George (19th C) British
£300 $480 €450 Our best friend (25x28cm-10x11in) s.d.1849 panel. 13-Mar-3 Duke & Son, Dorchester #286/R

SAYERS, R (19th C) British
£7800 $13026 €11310 Portrait of Mary Jane Heycock, standing in a landscape (86x71cm-34x28in) 24-Jun-3 Neal & Fletcher, Woodbridge #379/R est:1000-1500

SAYERS, Reuben (1815-1888) British
£520 $822 €780 Adoration of the Holy Child (69x48cm-27x19in) s. after Raphael. 18-Dec-2 Mallams, Oxford #685/R
Works on paper
£246 $381 €369 Homme grondant son chien (38x33cm-15x13in) s.d.1850 chl white chk. 24-Sep-2 Iegor de Saint Hippolyte, Montreal #113 (C.D 600)

SAYRE, Fred Grayson (1879-1938) American
£645 $1000 €968 Figure in Pal Canyon landscape (76x64cm-30x25in) s. masonite. 29-Oct-2 John Moran, Pasadena #783
£2548 $4000 €3822 Lure of desert trails (51x62cm-20x24in) s. i.verso. 19-Nov-2 Butterfields, San Francisco #8320/R est:4000-6000

SCACCIATI, Andrea (circle) (1642-1704) Italian
£9459 $14757 €14000 Still life of flowers (70x97cm-28x38in) prov. 27-Mar-3 Dorotheum, Vienna #35/R est:8000-12000

SCAGLIA, Michele (1859-1918) Italian
£769 $1208 €1200 Moving (55x38cm-22x15in) s. cardboard. 10-Dec-2 Della Rocca, Turin #314/R

SCAIOLA, Giuseppe (1951-) Italian
£261 $418 €400 Palm trees (40x30cm-16x12in) s.i.d.1988 verso acrylic sand. 4-Jan-3 Meeting Art, Vercelli #324
£261 $418 €400 Wave (30x40cm-12x16in) s.i.d.1986 verso acrylic sand. 4-Jan-3 Meeting Art, Vercelli #566
£374 $595 €550 To understand misteries (50x50cm-20x20in) s.i.d.1983 acrylic. 1-Mar-3 Meeting Art, Vercelli #323
£694 $1104 €1000 Golden land (50x70cm-20x28in) s.i.d.2002 acrylic. 1-May-3 Meeting Art, Vercelli #225
£1389 $2208 €2000 Nature course (120x80cm-47x31in) s.i.d.2001 verso acrylic. 1-May-3 Meeting Art, Vercelli #436

SCALBERT, Jules (1851-?) French
£6200 $9610 €9300 Three graces dancing with a faun (65x81cm-26x32in) s. 3-Dec-2 Sotheby's, Olympia #278/R est:5000-8000

SCALELLA, Jules (1895-?) American
£340 $550 €510 Tide is coming in (41x51cm-16x20in) masonite. 24-Jan-3 Freeman, Philadelphia #244/R

SCALVINI, Roberto (?) Italian
£385 $596 €600 La vieille ville (61x50cm-24x20in) s. 8-Dec-2 Feletin, Province #170
£385 $596 €600 Scene champetre (60x81cm-24x32in) s. 8-Dec-2 Feletin, Province #171

SCANAVINO, Emilio (1922-1986) Italian
£443 $691 €700 Shape (22x22cm-9x9in) acrylic. 14-Sep-2 Meeting Art, Vercelli #706/R
£949 $1481 €1500 Wool (58x34cm-23x13in) acrylic. 14-Sep-2 Meeting Art, Vercelli #790/R
£962 $1510 €1500 Alphabet (26x39cm-10x15in) acrylic. 23-Nov-2 Meeting Art, Vercelli #270/R
£1795 $2818 €2800 Littl emoon (30x37cm-12x15in) s.d.1966 oil acrylic cardboard. 23-Nov-2 Meeting Art, Vercelli #64/R
£2027 $3162 €3000 Untitled (49x63cm-19x25in) s. acrylic paper. 26-Mar-3 Finarte Semenzato, Milan #69/R
£2245 $3569 €3300 Thread (73x51cm-29x20in) s. acrylic card. 1-Mar-3 Meeting Art, Vercelli #660
£4397 $7123 €6200 Piccolo teatro (46x55cm-18x22in) s. s.i.d.1963 verso prov.exhib. 26-May-3 Christie's, Milan #341/R est:5000-7000
£6081 $9486 €9000 Landscape (70x100cm-28x39in) s.d.1960 paper on canvas. 26-Mar-3 Finarte Semenzato, Milan #254/R
£8228 $12835 €13000 Grub (150x100cm-59x39in) s. s.i.d.1967 verso lit. 14-Sep-2 Meeting Art, Vercelli #835/R est:10000
£9804 $15686 €15000 Bonded shape (150x150cm-59x59in) s.i.d.1966. 4-Jan-3 Meeting Art, Vercelli #404 est:15000
£12821 $20128 €20000 Plot with circle (100x100cm-39x39in) s. painted 1975. 23-Nov-2 Meeting Art, Vercelli #108/R est:15000
£14379 $23007 €22000 Endless alphabet (112x146cm-44x57in) s. painted 1980. 4-Jan-3 Meeting Art, Vercelli #624
Works on paper
£458 $760 €650 Untitled (40x40cm-16x16in) s.d.65 Indian ink pencil prov. 10-Jun-3 Finarte Semenzato, Milan #236/R
£878 $1370 €1300 Composition (21x29cm-8x11in) s.d.1961 chl. 26-Mar-3 Finarte Semenzato, Milan #237/R
£1026 $1610 €1600 Obligation of silence (34x23cm-13x9in) s. s.i.d.1966 verso mixed media collage card. 21-Nov-2 Finarte, Rome #65/R
£1538 $2385 €2400 White penetration (51x51cm-20x20in) s. mixed media card. 5-Dec-2 Stadion, Trieste #730/R
£1795 $2818 €2800 In two times (35x50cm-14x20in) s.d.65 mixed media card. 21-Nov-2 Finarte, Rome #261/R

SCANDELLARI, Giacomo (attrib) (18th C) Italian
Sculpture
£4000 $6680 €5800 Roundel with the Holy Family (24x24cm-9x9in) init. terracotta round. 8-Jul-3 Sotheby's, London #133/R est:4000-6000

SCANLAN, Robert Richard (c.1801-1876) Irish
Works on paper
£577 $906 €900 Off to market (36x66cm-14x26in) 19-Nov-2 Hamilton Osborne King, Dublin #471

SCARANO, Marcello (1901-1962) Italian
£385 $596 €600 Biblical scene (31x28cm-12x11in) s.i. paper. 5-Dec-2 Stadion, Trieste #744/R

SCARBOROUGH, F W (fl.1896-1939) British
Works on paper
£2675 $4200 €4013 Lower Pool, London (51x33cm-20x13in) s. W/C. 26-Jul-2 Eldred, East Dennis #520/R est:4000-6000

SCARBOROUGH, Frederick W (fl.1896-1939) British
Works on paper
£380 $600 €570 Fishing boat off a pier (19x25cm-7x10in) s. W/C htd white. 27-Nov-2 Hamptons Fine Art, Godalming #167
£460 $750 €690 Lowestoft trawler entering harbour (41x36cm-16x14in) s. 28-Jan-3 Gorringes, Lewes #1650
£460 $731 €690 Lowestoft fishing fleet in port (24x34cm-9x13in) s. W/C. 4-Mar-3 Bonhams, Knightsbridge #261
£800 $1240 €1200 Autumn morn, Fife (25x35cm-10x14in) s. pencil W/C htd white. 31-Oct-2 Christie's, Kensington #382/R

£2500 $3875 €3750 Off Rotherhithe, Pool of London (36x23cm-14x9in) s.i. W/C. 3-Oct-2 Ewbank, Send #460/R est:2000-3000
£3600 $5616 €5400 Busy harbour scene with shipping. Scottish fishing port (35x50cm-14x20in) s. W/C pair. 6-Nov-2 Bonhams, Chester #396/R est:1800-2400
£4000 $6080 €6000 Limehouse reach, London (51x40cm-20x16in) s. W/C bodycol. 15-Aug-2 Bonhams, New Bond Street #440/R est:4000-6000
£4400 $7348 €6380 Sunset over Limehouse Reach, London (34x75cm-13x30in) s.i. W/C. 18-Jun-3 Sotheby's, Olympia #106/R est:2000-3000
£4400 $7348 €6380 Pool of London (28x65cm-11x26in) s. W/C. 18-Jun-3 Sotheby's, Olympia #107/R est:2000-3000
£5800 $9048 €8700 Sunset, port of London (38x58cm-15x23in) s. W/C. 28-Mar-3 Dee Atkinson & Harrison, Driffield #720/R est:2000-3000

SCARBROUGH, Frank William (fl.1896-1939) British
£3427 $5415 €5141 Pool of London (41x62cm-16x24in) s. 18-Nov-2 Waddingtons, Toronto #148/R est:7000-9000 (C.D 8500)
Works on paper
£340 $558 €510 Fishing boats in a calm (24x34cm-9x13in) s. W/C. 4-Jun-3 Bonhams, Chester #331
£645 $1019 €968 East lighthouse, Whitby (24x33cm-9x13in) s.i. W/C. 18-Nov-2 Waddingtons, Toronto #76/R (C.D 1600)
£1899 $2981 €2849 Woolwich, London (35x26cm-14x10in) s.i. W/C. 25-Nov-2 Peter Webb, Auckland #54/R est:6000-8000 (NZ.D 6000)
£2000 $3240 €3000 Woolwich Reach, London (34x50cm-13x20in) i. W/C htd white. 22-Jan-3 Bonhams, New Bond Street #342/R est:2000-3000
£2100 $3444 €3150 Blackwall Reach (17x25cm-7x10in) s.i. W/C. 4-Feb-3 Sworder & Son, Bishops Stortford #164/R est:800-1200
£2300 $3726 €3450 Harbour, Boulogne-sur-mer (24x34cm-9x13in) s.i. W/C htd white. 22-Jan-3 Bonhams, New Bond Street #344/R est:1000-1500
£2400 $3720 €3600 Shipping on the river Thames, with London Bridge beyond (16x24cm-6x9in) s.i. W/C htd white. 4-Dec-2 Christie's, Kensington #59/R est:2500-3500
£2500 $3925 €3750 River barges at sunset (49x73cm-19x29in) s. W/C. 16-Dec-2 Sotheby's, Olympia #129/R est:1500-2000
£2600 $4134 €3900 Blackfriars Bridge, London (24x34cm-9x13in) s.i. W/C. 29-Apr-3 Sworder & Son, Bishops Stortford #355/R est:300-400
£4000 $6080 €6000 Unloading Lowestoft trawlers. Misty morning Whitby (42x29cm-17x11in) s. W/C htd white pair. 15-Aug-2 Bonhams, New Bond Street #432/R est:3000-5000
£5400 $8478 €8100 Lower pool, London (34x52cm-13x20in) s.i. W/C. 16-Dec-2 Sotheby's, Olympia #130/R est:2500-3500

SCARLETT, Rolph (1889-1984) American
£11465 $18000 €17198 Untitled, geometric abstract (102x132cm-40x52in) s. prov. 19-Nov-2 Butterfields, San Francisco #8072/R est:3000-5000
£12346 $20000 €18519 Abstraction (132x99cm-52x39in) s. painted c.1940 prov.exhib. 21-May-3 Sotheby's, New York #90/R est:4000-6000
Works on paper
£412 $638 €618 Abstract composition (26x32cm-10x13in) s. gouache. 3-Dec-2 Ritchie, Toronto #3119/R est:800-1200 (C.D 1000)
£472 $750 €708 Configurations in space (25x20cm-10x8in) s. W/C exec.c.1952. 2-Mar-3 Toomey, Oak Park #798/R
£503 $800 €755 Yellow star (13x15cm-5x6in) s.verso gouache graphite exec.c.1941. 2-Mar-3 Toomey, Oak Park #795/R

SCARLETT, S (19th C) American/British
£11644 $17000 €17466 Views of Niagara falls with figures (51x76cm-20x30in) s. verso pair lit. 3-Nov-1 North East Auctions, Portsmouth #707/R est:7000-10000

SCARPA, Gino (1924-) Italian
Sculpture
£1146 $1800 €1719 Portrait of a African woman (25cm-10in) s. brown pat. bronze. 14-Dec-2 Weschler, Washington #722/R

SCARPITTA, Antonio (20th C) American?
Works on paper
£4346 $6867 €6780 Untitled (20x30cm-8x12in) mixed media on canvas exec.1958. 12-Nov-2 Babuino, Rome #185/R

SCARPITTA, Salvatore (1919-) American
£7051 $11071 €11000 Remembering Harlem (70x90cm-28x35in) s.d.55 exhib. 21-Nov-2 Finarte, Rome #371/R est:11000-12000
Sculpture
£23438 $37500 €35157 Sal's red hauler special (112x274x123cm-44x108x48in) i.d.1967 racing car prov.exhib. 14-May-3 Sotheby's, New York #314/R est:18000-25000

SCARVELLI, Spyridon (1868-1942) Greek
£1300 $2067 €1950 On the Nile, Cairo (17x30cm-7x12in) s. one i. pair. 29-Apr-3 Bonhams, New Bond Street #128/R est:1000-1500
Works on paper
£800 $1272 €1200 Fishing boats at sea (32x18cm-13x7in) s. W/C. 29-Apr-3 Bonhams, New Bond Street #125/R
£1069 $1647 €1700 Chamelier au Caire (23x34cm-9x13in) s.i. W/C. 23-Oct-2 Rabourdin & Choppin de Janvry, Paris #126/R
£1100 $1749 €1650 Dhows on the Nile, Egypt (15x28cm-6x11in) s. W/C pair. 29-Apr-3 Bonhams, New Bond Street #127/R est:1200-1800
£1400 $2226 €2100 Pyramids at Giza, Egypt (32x49cm-13x19in) s. W/C. 29-Apr-3 Bonhams, New Bond Street #126/R est:1200-1800
£1600 $2496 €2400 Citadel at Corfu (17x33cm-7x13in) s. W/C over pencil htd bodycol. 15-Oct-2 Sotheby's, London #47/R est:1000-1500
£4800 $7488 €7200 Pontikonissi, Corfu (34x56cm-13x22in) s. W/C over pencil htd bodycol. 15-Oct-2 Sotheby's, London #46/R est:2000-3000
£6000 $9360 €9000 Fortress of Garitza, Corfu. Village of Benitza, Corfu (29x49cm-11x19in) s. W/C over pencil htd bodycol pair. 15-Oct-2 Sotheby's, London #45/R est:3000-4000

SCATTOLA, Ferruccio (1873-1950) Italian
£1565 $2488 €2300 Saint Mark's (27x40cm-11x16in) s. 18-Mar-3 Finarte, Milan #73/R
£1585 $2472 €2520 Rialto (24x34cm-9x13in) board. 22-Sep-2 Semenzato, Venice #108/R est:700-1000

SCAUFLAIRE, Edgar (1893-1960) Belgian
£256 $403 €400 Nature morte a la pipe (30x24cm-12x9in) s.d.1949 cardboard. 11-Dec-2 Hotel des Ventes Mosan, Brussels #265
£298 $497 €420 Etre chez soi (98x73cm-39x29in) s.d.60 panel. 18-Jun-3 Hotel des Ventes Mosan, Brussels #278
£417 $646 €650 L'homme arbre (32x24cm-13x9in) mono. panel. 9-Dec-2 Horta, Bruxelles #281
£426 $711 €600 La confession (50x35cm-20x14in) s.verso panel. 18-Jun-3 Hotel des Ventes Mosan, Brussels #260
£443 $691 €700 Jeune femme au bouquet bleu (50x35cm-20x14in) s. cardboard. 16-Sep-2 Horta, Bruxelles #408
£506 $790 €800 La ferme et le cheval blanc (22x31cm-9x12in) s. cardboard. 16-Oct-2 Hotel des Ventes Mosan, Brussels #178
£759 $1185 €1200 Nature morte au buste (75x100cm-30x39in) s.d.1943 panel prov.exhib.lit. 16-Oct-2 Hotel des Ventes Mosan, Brussels #184/R
£2115 $3279 €3300 Matelot (47x62cm-19x24in) s.d.1928 pastel. 7-Dec-2 De Vuyst, Lokeren #283/R est:3000-3600
£2446 $3914 €3400 Paysage avec champs et fermes (91x107cm-36x42in) s.d.43 panel. 13-May-3 Palais de Beaux Arts, Brussels #134/R est:3300-3750
Works on paper
£321 $503 €500 Sirene (25x33cm-10x13in) s.d.1942 graphite ink lit. 11-Dec-2 Hotel des Ventes Mosan, Brussels #277
£390 $651 €550 Pierrot, Arlequin et Colombine (35x26cm-14x10in) s.d.1948 lead pencil. 18-Jun-3 Hotel des Ventes Mosan, Brussels #246
£601 $938 €950 Amies (49x34cm-19x13in) s.d.39. 15-Oct-2 Horta, Bruxelles #65
£612 $978 €850 Deux femmes tenant chacune une fleur (50x37cm-20x15in) s. chl. 13-May-3 Palais de Beaux Arts, Brussels #307
£1439 $2302 €2000 Couple nu enlace (55x46cm-22x18in) s.d.1926 mixed media. 19-May-3 Horta, Bruxelles #89 est:2200-2800
£3309 $5295 €4600 Deux femmes et deux hommes autour d'un vase de fleurs (59x78cm-23x31in) s.d.1929 pencil dr. 13-May-3 Palais de Beaux Arts, Brussels #132/R est:4500-6200
£4082 $6490 €6000 Portrait de la femme de l'artiste aux seins nus (67x46cm-26x18in) s.d.1925 pastel. 19-Mar-3 Hotel des Ventes Mosan, Brussels #286/R est:4500-5500

SCHAAP, Hendrik (1878-1955) Dutch
£478 $736 €750 Crowded Rotterdam market (27x36cm-11x14in) s. cardboard. 3-Sep-2 Christie's, Amsterdam #394

SCHABRATZKY, Josef (fl.1880-1919) Austrian
Works on paper
£314 $487 €500 Old Eisgrubl (24x30cm-9x12in) s.i.d.98 W/C. 1-Oct-2 Dorotheum, Vienna #290/R

SCHACHAMAYER, Elise (19/20th C) German
£1781 $2796 €2600 Extensive landscape: on the way home (47x77cm-19x30in) s.d.1887. 16-Apr-3 Dorotheum, Salzburg #152/R est:3600-4500

SCHACHENMANN, Albert (attrib) (1916-1996) Swiss
£322 $509 €483 Winter landscape with trees (92x66cm-36x26in) board. 26-Nov-2 Hans Widmer, St Gallen #1337 (S.FR 750)

SCHACHNER, Therese (1890-c.1930) Austrian
£432 $691 €600 Forest clearing (68x50cm-27x20in) s. board. 14-May-3 Dorotheum, Klagenfurt #17/R
£833 $1292 €1300 In the evening (48x48cm-19x19in) s. board. 5-Dec-2 Dorotheum, Graz #51/R

SCHACHT, Wilhelm (1872-?) German
£535 $823 €850 Hilly summer landscape (71x100cm-28x39in) s. 23-Oct-2 Neumeister, Munich #740/R

SCHACK, Sophus (1811-1864) Danish
£1914 $3100 €2775 Merry soldiers, episode from 1864 (47x63cm-19x25in) s. prov. 26-May-3 Rasmussen, Copenhagen #1200/R est:25000 (D.KR 20000)

SCHADE, Karl Martin (1862-1954) Austrian
£288 $460 €400 Sunset (70x93cm-28x37in) s. 14-May-3 Dorotheum, Linz #407/R
£351 $554 €527 River in winter (80x120cm-31x47in) s. 30-Nov-2 Dorotheum, Prague #87 (C.KR 17000)
£552 $883 €800 Erika hill (80x110cm-31x43in) i. 11-Mar-3 Dorotheum, Vienna #42/R

SCHADL, Janos (1892-1944) Hungarian
Works on paper
£1258 $1962 €1887 Head of boy (44x27cm-17x11in) s.d.921 Indian ink. 11-Apr-3 Kieselbach, Budapest #190/R est:450000 (H.F 450000)

SCHAEFELS, Lucas (1824-1885) Belgian
£5000 $8000 €7500 Still life of fruit and a goblet upon a draped stone ledge (79x128cm-31x50in) s. 15-May-3 Lawrence, Crewkerne #927/R est:5000-7000

SCHAEFER, Carl Fellman (1903-1995) Canadian
£3292 $5103 €4938 Firewood (52x72cm-20x28in) s.d.41 board exhib. 3-Dec-2 Joyner, Toronto #146/R est:8000-10000 (C.D 8000)
Works on paper
£301 $476 €452 Church, Hanover (13x15cm-5x6in) d.1924 ink. 1-Dec-2 Levis, Calgary #92/R (C.D 750)
£341 $536 €512 Old Jack Pine, Pickerel River (18x18cm-7x7in) s.i.d.1926 ink. 25-Nov-2 Hodgins, Calgary #113/R (C.D 850)
£482 $761 €723 Oat field from Pinnacle Hill, Waterloo (25x36cm-10x14in) d.1969 W/C. 1-Dec-2 Levis, Calgary #91/R (C.D 1200)
£601 $937 €902 View of Bomber Station from new site officers billets, Middleton (29x38cm-11x15in) init.i.d.3.21.44 ink wash. 25-Mar-3 Ritchie, Toronto #153/R est:1200-1500 (C.D 1400)
£617 $957 €926 Field and woodlot on the Huron Road, Waterloo County (27x37cm-11x15in) s.d.20.VII 71 W/C. 3-Dec-2 Joyner, Toronto #94/R est:2000-3000 (C.D 1500)
£700 $1084 €1050 Billet in the castle, R.A.F Castle Archdale, Northern Ireland (24x34cm-9x13in) init.d.23/8/44 ink brush dr. 3-Dec-2 Joyner, Toronto #368 est:1000-1500 (C.D 1700)
£756 $1239 €1134 Low water, Lake Kushog, Haliburton, version II (27x37cm-11x15in) s.d.10.4.76 W/C. 3-Jun-3 Joyner, Toronto #244/R est:1500-2000 (C.D 1700)
£800 $1312 €1200 Firewood (51x71cm-20x28in) s.d.41 chl prov.lit. 3-Jun-3 Joyner, Toronto #294/R est:2000-3000 (C.D 1800)
£807 $1291 €1211 Fields, Doon (28x38cm-11x15in) s.d.18 August 1953 i.verso W/C prov.exhib. 15-May-3 Heffel, Vancouver #220/R est:2000-2500 (C.D 1800)
£807 $1291 €1211 Back of our houses, Hanover (28x38cm-11x15in) init. i.d.1942 verso ink wash prov. 15-May-3 Heffel, Vancouver #229/R est:2000-3000 (C.D 1800)
£950 $1492 €1425 Spring at Green Lake, West Guilford (28x38cm-11x15in) s.i.d.79 s.d.verso prov. 24-Jul-2 Walker's, Ottawa #219/R est:1200-1600 (C.D 2300)
£1109 $1752 €1664 Budding poplars, Heck's Lake near the big East River, Algonquin (28x38cm-11x15in) s.d.1954 s.i.d.verso W/C. 14-Nov-2 Heffel, Vancouver #194/R est:2500-3000 (C.D 2750)

SCHAEFERS, Karin (1942-) German
£556 $900 €834 The poet (61x76cm-24x30in) s. 24-Jan-3 Freeman, Philadelphia #224/R
£1090 $1700 €1635 Favourite spot (51x61cm-20x24in) s. 20-Sep-2 Sloan, North Bethesda #423/R est:2000-2500

SCHAEFFEL-DINARD, E (19th C) German?
£283 $449 €425 Sheep in stable (30x42cm-12x17in) s. 2-Mar-3 Uppsala Auktionskammare, Uppsala #310 (S.KR 3800)

SCHAEFFER, August (1833-1916) Austrian
£890 $1398 €1300 Ausseerberge (26x48cm-10x19in) paper. 16-Apr-3 Dorotheum, Salzburg #67/R
£1096 $1710 €1600 Winter river landscape (32x24cm-13x9in) s. 10-Apr-3 Van Ham, Cologne #1685/R est:2200
£1139 $1766 €1800 Coastal landscape (80x63cm-31x25in) s.d.876. 25-Sep-2 Neumeister, Munich #706/R est:3000

SCHAEFFER, David (20th C) British
Sculpture
£3006 $4750 €4359 Royal elk (102cm 40in) bronze. 26-Jul-3 Coeur d'Alene, Hayden #195/R est:3000-5000

SCHAEFFER, Ilse (1884-?) German
£540 $885 €750 Amaryllis in vase (62x45cm-24x18in) s. painted c.1920/25 panel. 5-Jun-3 Dorotheum, Salzburg #489/R

SCHAEFLEIN, Wilfrid (20th C) German
Works on paper
£625 $987 €900 The helpless Prime Minister! (31x25cm-12x10in) s.i.d.34/1 collage board. 26-Apr-3 Dr Lehr, Berlin #453/R

SCHAEFLER, Fritz (1888-1954) German
Works on paper
£1346 $2087 €2100 Female nude (55x50cm-22x20in) i.verso W/C over pencil exec.c.1923 prov. 6-Dec-2 Ketterer, Munich #79/R est:2000-2500

SCHAEKEN, Leo (19/20th C) Belgian
Works on paper
£336 $540 €500 Portrait de jeune fille (60x50cm-24x20in) s. pastel. 18-Feb-3 Vanderkindere, Brussels #43

SCHAEP, Henri Adolphe (1826-1870) Dutch
£897 $1400 €1346 Shipwreck (46x53cm-18x21in) s.d.1859. 9-Oct-2 Doyle, New York #101
£1301 $2030 €1900 Scene in font of an inn with riders and figures (24x33cm-9x13in) s.d.51 panel prov. 14-Apr-3 Glerum, Amsterdam #14/R est:3000-5000
£2308 $3600 €3462 Seascape with becalmed sloops and figures rowing skiff (28x36cm-11x14in) s. 21-Sep-2 Nadeau, Windsor #137/R est:3000-4000
£2313 $3678 €3400 Le naufrage (40x51cm-16x20in) s. 18-Mar-3 Galerie Moderne, Brussels #557/R est:3000-4000
£3416 $5500 €5124 Rescue at sea (61x84cm-24x33in) s.indisd.1855. 19-Feb-3 Doyle, New York #6 est:2000-3000
£4000 $6280 €6000 Gathering outside a Dutch hostelry (45x54cm-18x21in) s.d.47 panel. 21-Nov-2 Christie's, Kensington #100/R est:3000-5000
£12821 $19872 €20000 Le depart du trois-mats, sous escorte, sur fond de ville (62x82cm-24x32in) s.d.1853. 9-Dec-2 Horta, Bruxelles #93/R est:10000-15000

SCHAEPKENS, Theodor (1810-1883) Dutch
£458 $737 €700 Pecheurs en Hollande (29x41cm-11x16in) mono. panel. 14-Jan-3 Vanderkindere, Brussels #33
£481 $745 €750 Couple de chiens (21x27cm-8x11in) s. 9-Dec-2 Horta, Bruxelles #421
£504 $806 €700 Deux chiens (21x27cm-8x11in) s. panel. 13-May-3 Vanderkindere, Brussels #128

SCHAFER, Dirk (1864-1941) Dutch
Works on paper
£250 $400 €375 Indian procession with elephants by a city gate (32x45cm-13x18in) s.d.1914 pastel. 15-May-3 Lawrence, Crewkerne #847

SCHAFER, Frederick Ferdinand (1839-1927) American
£1000 $1600 €1500 High Sierra waterfall (53x32cm-21x13in) s. board. 16-Mar-3 Butterfields, San Francisco #1027 est:1500-2500
£1741 $2750 €2612 Bridal Veil Fall in Yosemite Valley, Ca. s. 5-Apr-3 Harvey Clar, Oakland #1503
£1958 $3250 €2839 Straits of San Juan de Fuca and the Olympic Mountains (51x91cm-20x36in) s. 11-Jun-3 Butterfields, San Francisco #4168/R est:4000-6000
£2108 $3500 €3057 On Boulder Creek, Santa Cruz Mountains, California (51x91cm-20x36in) s. i.verso prov. 11-Jun-3 Butterfields, San Francisco #4169/R est:4000-6000
£2564 $4000 €3846 Encampment near the Sierras (51x91cm-20x36in) s. prov.lit. 9-Nov-2 Santa Fe Art, Santa Fe #163/R est:4000-6000
£2711 $4500 €3931 Mt Tamalpais, California (76x51cm-30x20in) s. prov. 11-Jun-3 Butterfields, San Francisco #4171/R est:3000-5000
£4819 $8000 €6988 Cypress Point, midway point between Carmel and Monterey (51x91cm-20x36in) s. prov. 11-Jun-3 Butterfields, San Francisco #4170/R est:4000-6000

SCHAFER, Heinrich Hermann (1815-1884) German

£280 $445 €420 St. Lorient, Rouen, Normandy (29x24cm-11x9in) s. indis sig.d. s.i.verso. 27-Feb-3 Bonhams, Chester #475
£500 $795 €750 Continental town scene (24x19cm-9x7in) s.indis d.1887. 27-Feb-3 Bonhams, Chester #365

SCHAFER, Henry Thomas (1854-1915) British

£290 $467 €435 Nuremburg, Bavaria (28x18cm-11x7in) s.i.verso. 9-May-3 Mallams, Oxford #129/R
£361 $581 €542 Plague of her (88x47cm-35x19in) s. 12-May-3 Stephan Welz, Johannesburg #31 est:3000-5000 (SA.R 4200)
£400 $624 €600 Figures on the street of a continental town (30x25cm-12x10in) s.d.1878. 26-Mar-3 Hamptons Fine Art, Godalming #229
£500 $800 €750 Goslar, Germany. Convent de Croiser, France (23x18cm-9x7in) mono.i.indis.d. verso pair. 11-Mar-3 Bonhams, Oxford #75
£550 $858 €825 In a continental town (41x30cm-16x12in) mono.d.1885. 26-Mar-3 Hamptons Fine Art, Godalming #230
£582 $942 €820 Chartres, France (40x29cm-16x11in) s. 21-May-3 James Adam, Dublin #64
£600 $978 €900 Portrait of a lady in a pink satin dress, standing on a veranda (91x70cm-36x28in) s.d.11/79. 29-Jan-3 Sotheby's, Olympia #73/R est:400-600
£600 $984 €900 Fecamp, Normandy (25x20cm-10x8in) s. i.verso. 29-May-3 Christie's, Kensington #202/R
£601 $938 €950 Busy Continental street scene with cathedral (38x30cm-15x12in) 15-Oct-2 Mealy's, Castlecomer #354/R
£650 $1066 €975 Qudebec sur Seine, France (30x26cm-12x10in) s.d.1875 s.i.verso. 5-Jun-3 Christie's, Kensington #719/R
£700 $1148 €1050 Bamberg, Bavaria (41x30cm-16x12in) mono.d.1889 i.verso. 4-Feb-3 Sworder & Son, Bishops Stortford #120/R
£700 $1162 €1015 Rue du bar, Rouen, Normandy (40x30cm-16x12in) s. s.i.verso. 13-Jun-3 Lyon & Turnbull, Edinburgh #29
£800 $1264 €1200 Nuremberg, Germany. Fecamp, Normandy (23x17cm-9x7in) mono.d.1881 panel pair. 14-Nov-2 Christie's, Kensington #58/R
£800 $1312 €1200 Frankfurt, Germany (42x30cm-17x12in) mono.d.1883 i.verso. 29-May-3 Christie's, Kensington #201/R
£900 $1467 €1350 Continental town scenes (34x11cm-13x4in) s.d.79 board pair arched top. 29-Jan-3 Sotheby's, Olympia #156/R est:1000-1500
£980 $1509 €1470 Nuremberg, Germany (29x24cm-11x9in) mono.d.1899 s.i.verso. 22-Oct-2 Bonhams, Bath #56
£1000 $1630 €1450 Continental townscape with figures (40x29cm-16x11in) s.d.77 pair. 21-Jul-3 Bonhams, Bath #95/R est:800-1200
£1067 $1771 €1547 Continental town scenes (41x30cm-16x12in) mono.d.1883 pair. 16-Jun-3 Waddingtons, Toronto #128/R est:3000-5000 (C.D 2400)
£1100 $1716 €1650 Bamburg, Bavaria (39x29cm-15x11in) s.i.verso. 8-Oct-2 Bonhams, Knightsbridge #63/R est:800-1200
£1100 $1672 €1650 Fecamp (41x30cm-16x12in) s.i. 4-Jul-2 Mellors & Kirk, Nottingham #868/R est:250-350
£1141 $1837 €1700 Cathedral interior (46x35cm-18x14in) s. 18-Feb-3 Durán, Madrid #63/R
£1200 $1896 €1800 Nuremburg, Germany. Fecamp, Normandy (23x15cm-9x6in) s.d.1881 panel pair. 18-Dec-2 Mallams, Oxford #648/R est:1200-1800
£1300 $2028 €1950 Evreux, Normandy (51x76cm-20x30in) s.d.1873 i.verso. 17-Sep-2 Sotheby's, Olympia #174/R est:1000-2000
£1300 $2028 €1950 Continental street scenes with figures (41x30cm-16x12in) mono.d.1886 pair. 26-Mar-3 Hamptons Fine Art, Godalming #228 est:700-1000
£1400 $2240 €2100 St. Wilfrans, Abbeville, Antwerp (41x30cm-16x12in) s.d.1890 pair. 13-May-3 Bonhams, Knightsbridge #299/R est:1200-1800
£1911 $3000 €2867 Procession in the Capilla Del Condestable, Burgos, Spain (112x86cm-44x34in) s. prov. 10-Dec-2 Doyle, New York #180/R est:4000-6000
£2000 $3260 €2900 Continental town square with a monument (40x30cm-16x12in) s.d.1873 pair. 21-Jul-3 Bonhams, Bath #96/R est:2000-2500
£2100 $3255 €3150 Gottingen, Germany. Rheims, France (30x25cm-12x10in) s.i.verso pair. 4-Oct-2 Mallams, Oxford #569/R est:800-1200
£2200 $3586 €3300 Dortrecht, Holland. Abbeville, Normandy (40x31cm-16x12in) s.d.1884 pair. 29-Jan-3 Sotheby's, Olympia #154/R est:1500-2000
£2800 $4396 €4200 Chartres, France. Frankfort on Maine, Germany (41x30cm-16x12in) mono.d.1885 s.i.verso pair. 16-Apr-3 Christie's, Kensington #578/R est:2000-3000
£4362 $7023 €6500 Burgos cathedral (112x86cm-44x34in) s. 18-Feb-3 Durán, Madrid #235/R

Works on paper

£345 $552 €500 View of Antwerp, Belgium (25x20cm-10x8in) s.i. W/C. 12-Mar-3 James Adam, Dublin #169/R
£448 $700 €672 North Ambulatory, Westminster Abbey (64x46cm-25x18in) s. W/C. 21-Sep-2 Pook & Pook, Downington #496
£450 $707 €675 Strassburg, street scene with figures in the foreground (46x35cm-18x14in) s.i. pencil W/C htd white. 19-Nov-2 Bonhams, Leeds #33
£800 $1248 €1200 Nuremberg, St Sebaid. Caudebec, France (41x29cm-16x11in) s.i. pencil red crayon W/C pair. 19-Sep-2 Christie's, Kensington #133
£940 $1513 €1400 Batalha convent, Portugal (47x35cm-19x14in) s. W/C. 18-Feb-3 Durán, Madrid #64/R
£943 $1453 €1500 San Miguel, Jerez de la Frontera (47x35cm-19x14in) s.i. W/C. 22-Oct-2 Durán, Madrid #253/R
£1069 $1647 €1700 Burgos cathedral (47x35cm-19x14in) s.i. W/C. 22-Oct-2 Durán, Madrid #252/R
£1730 $2664 €2750 Interior of Burgos cathedral (63x45cm-25x18in) s.i. W/C. 22-Oct-2 Durán, Madrid #251/R

SCHAFER, Herman (19th C) German

£1900 $3078 €2850 Ulm, Germany. Antwerp, Belgium (41x30cm-16x12in) mono.d.1889 pair. 20-May-3 Sotheby's, Olympia #252/R est:1500-2000

SCHAFFER, Adalbert (1815-1871) Hungarian

£1218 $1888 €1900 Still life of flowers with roses in a Delft vase and coin-covered tankard (36x29cm-14x11in) s.indis.d. panel. 4-Dec-2 Neumeister, Munich #877/R est:2000

SCHAFFER, H (19th C) German

£290 $461 €435 Venetian waterway with gondola (76x76cm-30x30in) s. 18-Mar-3 Bonhams, Knowle #276

SCHAFFER, Henri (19th C) ?

£500 $795 €750 Market day in a continental town (41x30cm-16x12in) s. 30-Apr-3 Halls, Shrewsbury #273/R

SCHAGEN, Gerbrand Frederik van (1880-1968) Dutch

£263 $426 €400 Figures in a sunlit village square, possible Blaricum (30x41cm-12x16in) s. 21-Jan-3 Christie's, Amsterdam #273
£345 $548 €500 Boats in a canal with farmhouse in the distance (40x60cm-16x24in) s. 10-Mar-3 Sotheby's, Amsterdam #214
£395 $639 €600 Farmer at work in a kitchen garden (40x60cm-16x24in) s. 21-Jan-3 Christie's, Amsterdam #278
£610 $1001 €885 Landscape with cattle (28x43cm-11x17in) bears sig. 4-Jun-3 Fischer, Luzern #2339/R (S.FR 1300)

SCHAIK, Willem Henri van (1876-1938) Dutch

£643 $1015 €965 Windmill on the polder (58x81cm-23x32in) 1-Dec-2 Levis, Calgary #230/R (C.D 1600)

SCHALCK, Ernst (1827-1865) German

£1500 $2505 €2250 At the picture gallery (61x76cm-24x30in) s.d.1863. 18-Jun-3 Christie's, Kensington #98/R est:2000-3000

SCHALCKEN, Godfried (1643-1706) Dutch

£3185 $4968 €5000 Portrait of Matthijs pompe (24x19cm-9x7in) panel shaped prov.exhib.lit. 5-Nov-2 Sotheby's, Amsterdam #67/R est:6000-8000

SCHALDACH, William J (1896-1982) American

Works on paper

£962 $1500 €1395 Bobwhite quail (46x48cm-18x19in) i. W/C. 13-Oct-2 Cobbs, Peterborough #468

SCHALIN, Greta (1897-1993) Finnish

£633 $1000 €1000 Flowers (69x59cm-27x23in) s.d.1988. 1-Dec-2 Bukowskis, Helsinki #164/R
£710 $1121 €1100 Flowers (46x55cm-18x22in) s.d.1979. 19-Dec-2 Hagelstam, Helsinki #837
£719 $1180 €1000 Still life of flowers (46x55cm-18x22in) s.d.1982. 4-Jun-3 Bukowskis, Helsinki #421/R
£775 $1247 €1100 Flowers (41x49cm-16x19in) s.d.74 board. 10-May-3 Bukowskis, Helsinki #70/R
£854 $1333 €1350 Flowers (40x51cm-16x20in) s.d.1943. 12-Sep-2 Hagelstam, Helsinki #808/R
£863 $1416 €1200 Flowers (50x40cm-20x16in) s. 5-Jun-3 Hagelstam, Helsinki #983/R
£935 $1534 €1300 Still life of flowers (46x55cm-18x22in) s.d.1979. 4-Jun-3 Bukowskis, Helsinki #420/R
£1132 $1755 €1800 Flowers in vase (33x27cm-13x11in) s.d.37. 6-Oct-2 Bukowskis, Helsinki #273/R est:600
£1266 $2000 €2000 Still life of flowers (50x40cm-20x16in) s.d.48 board. 1-Dec-2 Bukowskis, Helsinki #163/R est:2000-2500
£1646 $2600 €2600 Still life of flowers (82x65cm-32x26in) s.d.56. 1-Dec-2 Bukowskis, Helsinki #162/R est:2500-2800

Works on paper

£576 $921 €800 Flowers (36x27cm-14x11in) s. W/C. 17-May-3 Hagelstam, Helsinki #60/R

SCHAMBERG, Morton Livingston (1881-1918) American

£20062 $32500 €30093 Abstraction (19x27cm-7x11in) s. panel prov. 21-May-3 Sotheby's, New York #40/R est:10000-15000

Works on paper

£15723 $25000 €23585 Composition (14x22cm-6x9in) s. pastel executed c.1916 exhib. 5-Mar-3 Sotheby's, New York #80/R est:12000-18000

SCHAMPHELEER, Edmond de (1824-1899) Belgian
£379 $599 €550 Paturage au bord de l'eau (31x48cm-12x19in) s. panel. 1-Apr-3 Palais de Beaux Arts, Brussels #522
£440 $682 €700 Chaumiere, Limbourg (26x43cm-10x17in) s. s.i.verso. 5-Oct-2 De Vuyst, Lokeren #102
£478 $745 €750 Bord de riviere (62x92cm-24x36in) s. 11-Nov-2 Horta, Bruxelles #499
£506 $785 €800 Matin a Wetteren (22x37cm-9x15in) s.d.1879 panel. 24-Sep-2 Galerie Moderne, Brussels #847
£605 $944 €950 Peniches sur la Durme (25x33cm-10x13in) s. panel. 11-Nov-2 Horta, Bruxelles #500
£720 $1138 €1080 Dutch landscape with figures, windmill, pond and estuary (50x100cm-20x39in) s.d.1872. 2-Dec-2 Bonhams, Bath #114
£1456 $2271 €2300 Le dejeuner dans les bles (65x82cm-26x32in) s. 10-Sep-2 Vanderkindere, Brussels #412/R est:1750-2500
£1769 $2812 €2600 Retour au village du vacher et de son troupeau (64x90cm-25x35in) s.d.1856. 18-Mar-3 Vanderkindere, Brussels #9 est:1500-2500
£1899 $3000 €3000 Pres de Dordrecht (29x48cm-11x19in) s.d.1885 panel exhib. 1-Dec-2 Peron, Melun #11
£2229 $3433 €3500 Vue de Dordrecht (49x101cm-19x40in) s.d.1872 s.i.stretcher. 3-Sep-2 Christie's, Amsterdam #147/R est:2000-3000

SCHANTZ, Philip von (1928-1998) Swedish
£2032 $3170 €3048 Autumn (24x33cm-9x13in) init.d.92 prov. 5-Nov-2 Bukowskis, Stockholm #138/R est:15000-20000 (S.KR 29000)
£2738 $4325 €4107 Still life of by Vaddo canal (73x92cm-29x36in) init.d.90 s.verso. 28-Apr-3 Bukowskis, Stockholm #267/R est:40000-50000 (S.KR 36000)
£3366 $5318 €5049 Winter (80x100cm-31x39in) init.d.89. 30-Nov-2 Goteborg Auktionsverk, Sweden #625/R est:40000 (S.KR 48000)
£4909 $7756 €7364 Three vessels in landscape (120x150cm-47x59in) init.d.88. 30-Nov-2 Goteborg Auktionsverk, Sweden #624/R est:75000 (S.KR 70000)
£15417 $24050 €23126 Bowl full of blueberries (73x60cm-29x24in) init.d.76. 5-Nov-2 Bukowskis, Stockholm #139/R est:100000-150000 (S.KR 220000)

Works on paper
£2205 $3484 €3308 By Vaddo canal (76x56cm-30x22in) s.d.88 W/C exhib. 28-Apr-3 Bukowskis, Stockholm #268/R est:20000-25000 (S.KR 29000)
£2453 $3826 €3680 Vaado canal (57x75cm-22x30in) s.d.90 gouache prov. 6-Nov-2 AB Stockholms Auktionsverk #597/R est:40000-50000 (S.KR 35000)

SCHANZ, Heinz (1927-) German
Works on paper
£1069 $1668 €1700 Untitled (21x15cm-8x6in) s.d.1957 col wax chk pencil. 11-Oct-2 Winterberg, Heidelberg #1677/R est:1950

SCHANZENBACHER, Nellie (20th C) American
£387 $600 €581 Young girl and baby (102x76cm-40x30in) s. painted c.1940. 8-Dec-2 Toomey, Oak Park #745/R

SCHAPER, Friedrich (1869-1956) German
£385 $596 €600 Hamburg harbour (43x55cm-17x22in) s.d.1949 board on panel prov. 7-Dec-2 Ketterer, Hamburg #45/R
£532 $777 €820 Meadow with calf (27x43cm-11x17in) i.indis.d. cardboard. 15-Jun-2 Hans Stahl, Hamburg #209/R
£1266 $1962 €2000 Landscape (32x41cm-13x16in) s.d.25 board. 28-Sep-2 Hans Stahl, Hamburg #177/R est:1800

SCHAPERKOTTER, Gerardus Johannes (1914-) Dutch
£1223 $2006 €1700 Aan zee - on the beach (52x71cm-20x28in) s.d.65 board. 3-Jun-3 Christie's, Amsterdam #394/R est:600-800
£1583 $2596 €2200 Zoneiland (100x50cm-39x20in) s.d.70 lit. 3-Jun-3 Christie's, Amsterdam #391/R est:2500-3500
£1583 $2596 €2200 Poezie (80x100cm-31x39in) s.d.67. 3-Jun-3 Christie's, Amsterdam #392/R est:1200-1600
£1583 $2596 €2200 Landschap in blauw (80x100cm-31x39in) s.d.70. 3-Jun-3 Christie's, Amsterdam #393/R est:1200-1600

SCHAPOSCHNIKOV, Andrei A (1906-1986) Russian
£2523 $3936 €3785 Musical composition (50x40cm-20x16in) s.d.26 verso prov. 5-Nov-2 Bukowskis, Stockholm #286/R est:12000-15000 (S.KR 36000)

SCHAR, Arnold (1893-1957) ?
£755 $1177 €1200 Scene in the park (52x46cm-20x18in) s.d.1927. 20-Sep-2 Schloss Ahlden, Ahlden #1292/R

SCHARER, Hans (1927-1997) Swiss
£873 $1371 €1310 Untitled (35x25cm-14x10in) s.d.75 board. 23-Nov-2 Burkhard, Luzern #230/R (S.FR 2000)
£2096 $3291 €3144 Small Madonna (73x42cm-29x17in) s.d.74 oil mortar collage on panel pavatex. 23-Nov-2 Burkhard, Luzern #243/R est:3000-4000 (S.FR 4800)

Sculpture
£721 $1131 €1082 Ursula (30x24x6cm-12x9x2in) s.d.73 oil mortar collage on panel pavatex. 23-Nov-2 Burkhard, Luzern #242/R (S.FR 1650)

Works on paper
£437 $686 €656 Untitled (29x21cm-11x8in) s.d.79 w/C. 23-Nov-2 Burkhard, Luzern #240/R (S.FR 1000)
£590 $926 €885 Untitled (42x50cm-17x20in) s.d.73 W/C. 23-Nov-2 Burkhard, Luzern #228/R (S.FR 1350)
£699 $1097 €1049 Untitled (43x50cm-17x20in) s.d.73 w/C. 23-Nov-2 Burkhard, Luzern #231/R (S.FR 1600)
£1085 $1758 €1573 Untitled (40x51cm-16x20in) s.d.70 W/C gouache bodycol prov. 24-May-3 Galerie Gloggner, Luzern #95/R est:2600-2800 (S.FR 2300)

SCHARER, Hans and WALKER, Aldo (20th C) Swiss
Works on paper
£611 $960 €917 Untitled (85x97cm-33x38in) s.d.87 mixed media. 23-Nov-2 Burkhard, Luzern #229/R (S.FR 1400)

SCHARF, Kenny (1958-) American
£1763 $2750 €2645 Lemon lick grape (67x53cm-26x21in) s.i.d.98 verso acrylic oil prov. 14-Oct-2 Butterfields, San Francisco #2115/R est:2500-3500
£5063 $8000 €7595 Past is new (151x126cm-59x50in) s.d.1990 verso acrylic oil silkscreen ink prov. 13-Nov-2 Sotheby's, New York #564/R

Works on paper
£903 $1400 €1355 Fred bird (63x76cm-25x30in) s. i.d.82 verso acrylic on appliance prov. 26-Sep-2 Christie's, Rockefeller NY #816/R est:3000-5000

SCHARFF, Dollie C (20th C) American
£506 $800 €759 Pointers in a marsh (76x127cm-30x50in) s. 2-Apr-3 Doyle, New York #61/R

SCHARFF, Erwin (1887-1955) German
Sculpture
£2817 $4676 €4000 Youth fighting with swordfish (20x20x7cm-8x8x3in) bronze. 14-Jun-3 Hauswedell & Nolte, Hamburg #1571/R est:4000

SCHARFF, William (1886-1959) Danish
£286 $478 €415 Man with lamp (85x75cm-33x30in) paper on panel painted c.1928 prov. 17-Jun-3 Rasmussen, Copenhagen #221/R (D.KR 3000)
£402 $651 €583 The daily bread (75x100cm-30x39in) s.d.1937. 24-May-3 Rasmussen, Havnen #4272/R (D.KR 4200)
£477 $796 €692 Moor-woman (65x62cm-26x24in) s. sketch plywood painted c.1926 prov. 17-Jun-3 Rasmussen, Copenhagen #223/R (D.KR 5000)
£490 $755 €735 Large cat on table (45x54cm-18x21in) s. panel exhib. 23-Oct-2 Kunsthallen, Copenhagen #42 (D.KR 5800)
£697 $1101 €1046 Three chickens (27x51cm-11x20in) s. paper on panel. 1-Apr-3 Rasmussen, Copenhagen #574 (D.KR 7500)
£1268 $1953 €1902 Two calves (121x87cm-48x34in) init.d.17 exhib.lit. 23-Oct-2 Kunsthallen, Copenhagen #66/R est:15000 (D.KR 15000)
£1716 $2866 €2488 The Golden Bird (145x210cm-57x83in) s. indis.d.1928. 17-Jun-3 Rasmussen, Copenhagen #96/R est:18000 (D.KR 18000)
£1737 $2761 €2606 Street scene with figures and two trams, Town Hall Square (60x71cm-24x28in) init.d.09 exhib.lit. 26-Feb-3 Kunsthallen, Copenhagen #236/R est:6000 (D.KR 19000)
£1809 $2804 €2714 Pine forest (100x80cm-39x31in) s.d.1940. 4-Dec-2 Kunsthallen, Copenhagen #365/R est:15000 (D.KR 21000)
£4647 $7342 €6971 Study of pines (125x110cm-49x43in) init.d.12 exhib.prov. 1-Apr-3 Rasmussen, Copenhagen #21/R est:30000-50000 (D.KR 50000)

SCHARL, J (19/20th C) German?
£1800 $2862 €2700 Rabbi's blessing (80x61cm-31x24in) s.i. after Moritz Daniel Oppenheim. 29-Apr-3 Bonhams, New Bond Street #85/R est:2000-3000

SCHARL, Josef (1896-1954) German
£8696 $14261 €12000 Boy (63x49cm-25x19in) s.d.1930. 31-May-3 Villa Grisebach, Berlin #201/R est:12000-15000

Works on paper
£281 $438 €410 Spring trees (32x38cm-13x15in) s.i.d. Indian ink. 11-Apr-3 Winterberg, Heidelberg #1600
£295 $457 €460 Star lines in the night sky (31x38cm-12x15in) s.i.d. Indian ink brush. 7-Dec-2 Hauswedell & Nolte, Hamburg #1021/R
£342 $534 €500 Sleeping man - Bowery, New York (31x46cm-12x18in) s.i.d. Indian ink brush. 11-Apr-3 Winterberg, Heidelberg #1598/R
£428 $667 €680 Reclining female nude (30x45cm-12x18in) s.i.d.1952 pencil. 11-Oct-2 Winterberg, Heidelberg #1681/R
£434 $677 €690 Female nude (30x45cm-12x18in) s.i.d.1952 pencil. 11-Oct-2 Winterberg, Heidelberg #1680/R
£513 $795 €800 Albert Einstein (33x30cm-13x12in) s.d.Febr. 14, 1951 pen prov. 4-Dec-2 Lempertz, Koln #1041/R

SCHARL, Ludwig (1929-) German
£764 $1192 €1200 Mother with son - both in sailor outfits (143x90cm-56x35in) s.d.1954 verso double-sided. 6-Nov-2 Hugo Ruef, Munich #1285/R
£1401 $2186 €2200 Variety (161x78cm-63x31in) s.d.1957 verso. 6-Nov-2 Hugo Ruef, Munich #1286/R est:1500

SCHARY, Saul (1904-1978) American
£290 $450 €435 Self portrait (51x41cm-20x16in) s. i.stretcher prov. 25-Sep-2 Doyle, New York #75/R

SCHATTANEK, Karl (1884-1967) Austrian
£468 $767 €650 South Tyrol landscape with Alps (44x49cm-17x19in) s. i.verso board. 5-Jun-3 Dorotheum, Salzburg #552/R

SCHATTENSTEIN, Nicolaus (1877-1954) Russian
£408 $649 €600 Farmer resting (80x60cm-31x24in) s. 25-Feb-3 Dorotheum, Vienna #209/R
£1509 $2400 €2264 Portrait of a woman. Portrait of a gentleman (117x89cm-46x35in) s. pair. 18-Mar-3 Doyle, New York #48/R

SCHATZ, Arnold (1929-) German
£385 $596 €600 Two wild boar in winter wood (100x90cm-39x35in) s. i. verso. 5-Dec-2 Neumeister, Munich #2865
£390 $581 €600 Wild ducks flying up from pond (60x90cm-24x35in) s. 27-Jun-2 Neumeister, Munich #2814/R
£545 $845 €850 Fox in winter wood (70x80cm-28x31in) s. i. verso. 5-Dec-2 Neumeister, Munich #2864/R

SCHATZ, Manfred (1925-) German
£1169 $1742 €1800 Pheasant in winter wood (60x80cm-24x31in) s. 27-Jun-2 Neumeister, Munich #2813/R est:800
£1274 $1987 €2000 Fox in winter (60x90cm-24x35in) s. 6-Nov-2 Hugo Ruef, Munich #1287 est:1200
£3165 $5000 €4589 Sunrise (30x46cm-12x18in) s. prov. 26-Jul-3 Coeur d'Alene, Hayden #233/R est:6000-9000
£5063 $8000 €7341 Free and easy (51x69cm-20x27in) s. prov. 26-Jul-3 Coeur d'Alene, Hayden #88/R est:10000-20000

SCHATZ, Otto Rudolf (1901-1961) Austrian
£360 $576 €500 Erotic scene (15x14cm-6x6in) col pencil board. 14-May-3 Dorotheum, Klagenfurt #71/R
£556 $883 €800 Female nude in cafe (23x16cm-9x6in) mono. W/C pen. 29-Apr-3 Wiener Kunst Auktionen, Vienna #605/R
£2115 $3321 €3300 Sailing boats on the Adria (35x49cm-14x19in) mono. panel. 25-Nov-2 Hassfurther, Vienna #63 est:800-1000
£8974 $14090 €14000 New York, Wall Street (83x65cm-33x26in) s. 25-Nov-2 Hassfurther, Vienna #62/R est:8000-12000

Works on paper
£417 $663 €600 Seated woman (45x27cm-18x11in) mono. mixed media. 29-Apr-3 Wiener Kunst Auktionen, Vienna #606/R
£818 $1275 €1300 Nude (42x34cm-17x13in) mixed media. 23-Sep-2 Dr Fritz Nagel, Stuttgart #9005/R
£1474 $2315 €2300 Woman wearing underwear seated (46x30cm-18x12in) mono.d.22/X pencil. 25-Nov-2 Hassfurther, Vienna #64 est:600-900
£2536 $4159 €3500 Still life of flowers (42x56cm-17x22in) mono. W/C. 27-May-3 Wiener Kunst Auktionen, Vienna #71/R est:1500-3000
£3526 $5535 €5500 Standing female nude (45x29cm-18x11in) mono.d. chl col pen oil. 25-Nov-2 Hassfurther, Vienna #65/R est:1000-1100

SCHAUER, Otto (1923-1985) German
£962 $1519 €1500 Charrettes (92x73cm-36x29in) s. prov. 15-Nov-2 Laurence Calmels, Paris #9a/R
£962 $1519 €1500 Clos II (54x64cm-21x25in) s.d.1962 prov. 15-Nov-2 Laurence Calmels, Paris #7a/R
£2244 $3545 €3500 Lampe au jardin (116x89cm-46x35in) s. s.i.d.1960 verso prov. 15-Nov-2 Laurence Calmels, Paris #6a/R

SCHAUMAN, Sigrid (1877-1979) Finnish
£2158 $3453 €3000 Potted plant (46x38cm-18x15in) s. painted c.1954 exhib. 17-May-3 Hagelstam, Helsinki #163/R
£2278 $3600 €3600 Mountain village (35x24cm-14x9in) s. cardboard. 30-Nov-2 Hagelstam, Helsinki #153/R est:4000
£3418 $5400 €5400 Southern landscape in summer (35x24cm-14x9in) s. cardboard. 30-Nov-2 Hagelstam, Helsinki #152/R est:4000
£3957 $6331 €5500 Rome (40x30cm-16x12in) s. board. 17-May-3 Hagelstam, Helsinki #164/R
£6906 $11050 €9600 Aagatan in Borgaa, street scene (46x38cm-18x15in) s. exhib. 17-May-3 Hagelstam, Helsinki #165/R
£6962 $11000 €11000 Villa Aurelia (34x44cm-13x17in) s. board. 1-Dec-2 Bukowskis, Helsinki #165/R est:4000-5000

SCHAWINSKY, Xanti (1904-1979) Italian
£371 $579 €557 Untitled (49x26cm-19x10in) s.d.1961 acrylic. 6-Nov-2 Dobiaschofsky, Bern #3631/R (S.FR 850)

SCHAYCHIS, Ernesto (fl.1567-1631) Italian
£5656 $9276 €8201 Saint Francis - head study (48x29cm-19x11in) paper on panel lit. 4-Jun-3 AB Stockholms Auktionsverk #2515/R est:70000-90000 (S.KR 72000)

SCHEDRIN, Sylvester Feodosievich (1791-1830) Russian
£206897 $326897 €300000 View of Mergellina (48x72cm-19x28in) s.d.1826 prov.exhib.lit. 3-Apr-3 Porro, Milan #49/R est:200000

SCHEEL, Signe (attrib) (1860-1942) Norwegian
£435 $696 €653 Village individual (46x43cm-18x17in) panel. 17-Mar-3 Blomqvist, Oslo #379/R (N.KR 5000)

SCHEELE, Hugo (1881-?) German
£800 $1256 €1200 Picking lemons, Corfu (22x34cm-9x13in) s.i.d.1914 oil on card. 16-Apr-3 Christie's, Kensington #921/R

SCHEERBOOM, Andries (1832-1880) Dutch
£1739 $2800 €2609 Interior scene with the new baby (36x46cm-14x18in) s.indis.d. 20-Jan-3 Arthur James, Florida #691
£2108 $3500 €3057 Mother and children at seashore (91x71cm-36x28in) 13-Jun-3 Du Mouchelle, Detroit #2031/R est:4000-8000
£2390 $3681 €3800 Elegant couple in an interior (26x33cm-10x13in) s. panel. 22-Oct-2 Sotheby's, Amsterdam #36/R est:4000-6000

SCHEERES, Hendricus Johannes (1829-1864) Dutch
£510 $800 €765 In the shop of the sword maker (23x17cm-9x7in) s.d.63 panel. 22-Nov-2 Skinner, Boston #37/R
£530 $864 €800 Cartographe (15x14cm-6x6in) s.d.1846 panel. 17-Feb-3 Horta, Bruxelles #427
£828 $1292 €1300 Interior with lady (15x18cm-6x7in) s.d.55 panel. 6-Nov-2 Vendue Huis, Gravenhage #457/R
£2500 $3975 €3750 Cavalier writing a letter. Young girl reading a letter (28x23cm-11x9in) s. panel pair. 20-Mar-3 Christie's, Kensington #161/R est:3000-5000

SCHEFFEL, Johan Hendrik (1690-1781) Swedish
£1862 $3016 €2700 Portrait of man, possibly Georg Wilhelm von Scheven (77x64cm-30x25in) prov.lit. 26-May-3 Bukowskis, Stockholm #356/R est:15000-18000 (S.KR 24000)

SCHEFFEL, Johan Hendrik (attrib) (1690-1781) Swedish
£1418 $2199 €2127 Portrait of Baron Ture Gustaf Klinckowstrom (71x56cm-28x22in) prov.lit. 3-Dec-2 Bukowskis, Stockholm #400/R est:25000-35000 (S.KR 20000)
£2837 $4397 €4256 Portrait of Count Gustaf Fredrik von Rosen (80x64cm-31x25in) 4-Dec-2 AB Stockholms Auktionsverk #1611/R est:20000-25000 (S.KR 40000)

SCHEFFER, F (fl.1701-1711) British?
£22000 $34760 €33000 Portrait of Sir John Shaw with his second wife, Sarah and children from first marriage (193x265cm-76x104in) prov. 26-Nov-2 Christie's, London #16/R est:20000-30000
£80000 $126400 €120000 Portrait of Sir John Shaw with his second wife, Sarah and their children (244x366cm-96x144in) d.1709 prov. 26-Nov-2 Christie's, London #17/R est:30000-50000

SCHEFFER, Jean Gabriel (1797-1876) Swiss
£565 $876 €848 Femme d'Albano (27x35cm-11x14in) s. init.verso. 7-Dec-2 Galerie du Rhone, Sion #337/R (S.FR 1300)

SCHEFFLER, Thomas Christian (1700-1756) German
£1452 $2251 €2178 Rest on flight to Egypt (42x33cm-17x13in) painted c.1750. 3-Dec-2 SOGA, Bratislava #134/R est:89000 (SL.K 92000)

SCHEIBE, Richard (1879-1964) German

Sculpture

£	$	€	
£2532	$4000	€4000	Memorial for Oranierkirche, Biebrich am Rhein (36cm-14in) mono. brown pat.bronze Cast.H.Noack Berlin. 30-Nov-2 Villa Grisebach, Berlin #349/R est:4500-6500
£3448	$5448	€5000	Standing boy (34cm-13in) mono.d.1928 brown pat.bronze. 2-Apr-3 Dr Fritz Nagel, Stuttgart #9210/R est:1200
£5634	$9352	€8000	Seated girl - nymph (32x25x25cm-13x10x10in) s. bronze. 14-Jun-3 Hauswedell & Nolte, Hamburg #1572/R est:4000

SCHEIBER, Hugo (1873-1950) Hungarian

£	$	€	
£582	$908	€850	Woman with children (51x43cm-20x17in) s. board. 11-Apr-3 Sigalas, Stuttgart #457
£699	$1090	€1049	Tramp in landscape (49x34cm-19x13in) s. tempera. 11-Apr-3 Kieselbach, Budapest #73/R est:250000 (H.F 250000)
£966	$1545	€1400	Circus scene (56x46cm-22x18in) s. cardboard. 12-Mar-3 Rabourdin & Choppin de Janvry, Paris #115/R
£1129	$1751	€1637	Portrait of a man possibly Ronai Viktor (44x30cm-17x12in) s. canvas on card. 9-Dec-2 Mu Terem Galeria, Budapest #210/R est:280000 (H.F 420000)
£1419	$2213	€2129	Vajdahunyad castle in Budapest, 1912 (45x29cm-18x11in) s. cardboard. 11-Sep-2 Kieselbach, Budapest #171/R (H.F 550000)
£1935	$3018	€2903	Lady with hat (66x49cm-26x19in) s. tempera panel. 11-Sep-2 Kieselbach, Budapest #21o/R (H.F 750000)
£2151	$3335	€3227	Music hall dancer (64x52cm-25x20in) s. tempera on paper. 6-Dec-2 Kieselbach, Budapest #194/R (H.F 800000)
£2794	$4359	€4051	Woman with necklace (62x44cm-24x17in) s. tempera. 12-Apr-3 Mu Terem Galeria, Budapest #115/R est:960000 (H.F 1000000)
£3096	$4829	€4489	Expressive landscape (47x73cm-19x29in) s. cardboard. 13-Sep-2 Mu Terem Galeria, Budapest #75/R est:850000 (H.F 1200000)
£3633	$5667	€5268	In the bar (59x43cm-23x17in) s. tempera. 12-Apr-3 Mu Terem Galeria, Budapest #154/R est:800000 (H.F 1300000)
£4751	$7411	€6889	Rainy city (30x40cm-12x16in) s. board. 12-Apr-3 Mu Terem Galeria, Budapest #209/R est:1100000 (H.F 1700000)
£5755	$9439	€8000	Path through park and housing enclosure (70x49cm-28x19in) s. chipboard on board. 5-Jun-3 Dorotheum, Salzburg #479/R est:10000-13000
£5916	$9170	€8578	City traffic (43x55cm-17x22in) s. card exhib. 9-Dec-2 Mu Terem Galeria, Budapest #211/R est:1100000 (H.F 2200000)
£6148	$9591	€9222	Model by studio window (48x59cm-19x23in) s. 11-Apr-3 Kieselbach, Budapest #200/R est:1400000-2200000 (H.F 2200000)
£29254	$46807	€43881	Athletic championship (78x95cm-31x37in) s. 16-May-3 Kieselbach, Budapest #81/R (H.F 10000000)

Works on paper

£	$	€	
£503	$785	€800	Three girls (56x37cm-22x15in) s. pastel chl sketch verso lit. 20-Sep-2 Karlheinz Kaupp, Staufen #2218/R
£538	$834	€807	In the park (40x29cm-16x11in) s. pencil. 6-Dec-2 Kieselbach, Budapest #192/R (H.F 200000)
£774	$1207	€1161	Sailing boat (49x36cm-19x14in) s. mixed media. 11-Sep-2 Kieselbach, Budapest #58/R (H.F 300000)
£861	$1334	€1292	Man in hat (60x43cm-24x17in) s. mixed media. 6-Dec-2 Kieselbach, Budapest #104/R (H.F 320000)
£936	$1498	€1404	Dancer (43x30cm-17x12in) s. chl. 16-May-3 Kieselbach, Budapest #1/R (H.F 320000)
£966	$1545	€1400	Auto-portrait a la pipe (31x20cm-12x8in) s. W/C chl. 12-Mar-3 Rabourdin & Choppin de Janvry, Paris #153/R
£1062	$1657	€1593	Tramp on the road (63x48cm-25x19in) mixed media. 11-Apr-3 Kieselbach, Budapest #123/R est:380000 (H.F 380000)
£1118	$1744	€1677	Still life of flowers in green vase (67x47cm-26x19in) s. mixed media. 11-Apr-3 Kieselbach, Budapest #60/R est:380000-400000 (H.F 400000)
£1238	$1932	€1857	Suburb (41x57cm-16x22in) s. mixed media. 11-Sep-2 Kieselbach, Budapest #183/R (H.F 480000)
£1284	$2003	€1900	Portrait of bearded man (62x50cm-24x20in) s. W/C. 31-Mar-3 Finarte Semenzato, Milan #40/R
£1285	$2005	€1928	Dancer woman with fan (63x47cm-25x19in) s. mixed media. 11-Apr-3 Kieselbach, Budapest #34/R est:420000-460000 (H.F 460000)
£1345	$2084	€2018	In the cafe (37x40cm-15x16in) s. chl. 6-Dec-2 Kieselbach, Budapest #31/R (H.F 500000)
£1345	$2084	€2018	Man in a hat (70x50cm-28x20in) s. mixed media. 6-Dec-2 Kieselbach, Budapest #51/R (H.F 500000)
£1345	$2084	€2018	Man in hat (52x43cm-20x17in) s. mixed media. 6-Dec-2 Kieselbach, Budapest #73/R (H.F 500000)
£1397	$2180	€2096	Street detail (57x42cm-22x17in) s. mixed media. 11-Apr-3 Kieselbach, Budapest #51/R est:400000-500000 (H.F 500000)
£1537	$2398	€2306	Veiled vamps (50x40cm-20x16in) s. mixed media. 11-Apr-3 Kieselbach, Budapest #74/R est:500000-550000 (H.F 550000)
£1548	$2415	€2322	Clown (57x39cm-22x15in) s. mixed media. 11-Sep-2 Kieselbach, Budapest #45/R (H.F 600000)
£1677	$2616	€2516	Meeting (64x48cm-25x19in) s. mixed media. 11-Sep-2 Kieselbach, Budapest #181/R (H.F 650000)
£1677	$2616	€2432	Wanderer returning (60x69cm-24x27in) s. mixed media. 12-Apr-3 Mu Terem Galeria, Budapest #208/R est:380000 (H.F 600000)
£1806	$2817	€2619	Girlfriends (36x48cm-14x19in) s. mixed media. 13-Sep-2 Mu Terem Galeria, Budapest #95/R est:420000 (H.F 700000)
£1816	$2834	€2724	Coach (37x32cm-15x13in) s. pastel. 11-Apr-3 Kieselbach, Budapest #191/R est:400000-650000 (H.F 650000)
£1882	$2918	€2823	Music hall (67x55cm-26x22in) s. mixed media. 6-Dec-2 Kieselbach, Budapest #32/R (H.F 700000)
£1956	$3052	€2934	Dancer woman (66x48cm-26x19in) s. mixed media. 11-Apr-3 Kieselbach, Budapest #4/R est:220000-700000 (H.F 700000)
£2096	$3270	€3144	Evening boulevard with automobiles (57x45cm-22x18in) s. mixed media. 11-Apr-3 Kieselbach, Budapest #165/R est:240000-750000 (H.F 750000)
£2487	$3979	€3731	Dancer with a guitar (65x51cm-26x20in) s. mixed media. 16-May-3 Kieselbach, Budapest #12/R (H.F 850000)
£2689	$4168	€4034	Budapest (33x48cm-13x19in) mixed media pair. 6-Dec-2 Kieselbach, Budapest #96/R (H.F 1000000)
£2689	$4168	€4034	Girls (59x42cm-23x17in) s. mixed media. 6-Dec-2 Kieselbach, Budapest #105/R (H.F 1000000)
£3074	$4795	€4457	Dancer (69x50cm-27x20in) s. pastel mixed media. 12-Apr-3 Mu Terem Galeria, Budapest #103/R est:750000 (H.F 1100000)
£3612	$5634	€5418	In the bar (66x54cm-26x21in) s. mixed media. 11-Sep-2 Kieselbach, Budapest #46/R (H.F 1400000)
£4192	$6539	€6288	Town park (70x50cm-28x20in) s. mixed media. 11-Apr-3 Kieselbach, Budapest #166/R est:850000-1500000 (H.F 1500000)
£5589	$8719	€8104	Rail bridge (57x43cm-22x17in) s. chl. 12-Apr-3 Mu Terem Galeria, Budapest #116/R est:1800000 (H.F 2000000)
£6185	$9587	€9278	In the bar (68x60cm-27x24in) s. mixed media. 6-Dec-2 Kieselbach, Budapest #52/R (H.F 2300000)
£7021	$11234	€10532	Promenade (47x43cm-19x17in) s. mixed media. 16-May-3 Kieselbach, Budapest #27/R (H.F 2400000)
£7223	$11268	€10835	Dance show (46x66cm-18x26in) s. mixed media. 11-Sep-2 Kieselbach, Budapest #61/R (H.F 2800000)
£7530	$11671	€10919	Boats under the bridge (65x85cm-26x33in) s. pastel prov. 9-Dec-2 Mu Terem Galeria, Budapest #27/R est:1800000 (H.F 2800000)
£8068	$12505	€11699	Three dancers (52x66cm-20x26in) s. mixed media lit. 9-Dec-2 Mu Terem Galeria, Budapest #134/R est:1600000 (H.F 3000000)

SCHEIBER, Hugo (attrib) (1873-1950) Hungarian

£	$	€	
£755	$1177	€1200	Accordion player at night (51x45cm-20x18in) s. board. 21-Sep-2 Bolland & Marotz, Bremen #773/R

Works on paper

£	$	€	
£1299	$2013	€1949	Three women in cafe (63x48cm-25x19in) s. pencil pastel. 24-Sep-2 Koller, Zurich #6765/R est:2000-3000 (S.FR 3000)

SCHEIBL, Hubert (1951-) Austrian

£	$	€	
£764	$1207	€1100	Dog's paws (50x38cm-20x15in) s.d.1988 verso. 24-Apr-3 Dorotheum, Vienna #268/R
£833	$1317	€1200	Untitled (44x41cm-17x16in) s.d.1988 verso collage oil board paper on masonite. 24-Apr-3 Dorotheum, Vienna #267/R
£3797	$5886	€6000	Pleasure of the yellow knot (200x150cm-79x59in) s.i.d.83 verso. 24-Sep-2 Wiener Kunst Auktionen, Vienna #291/R est:6000-10000

SCHEIDL, Roman (1949-) Austrian

£	$	€	
£633	$981	€1000	Untitled (50x65cm-20x26in) s.d.93 alkorel Indian ink molino. 24-Sep-2 Wiener Kunst Auktionen, Vienna #330/R
£3797	$5886	€6000	Between two ages (122x168cm-48x66in) s. i.d.1986 verso lit. 24-Sep-2 Wiener Kunst Auktionen, Vienna #259/R est:6000-10000

Works on paper

£	$	€	
£411	$642	€650	Untitled (75x55cm-30x22in) s. d.29.2.88 verso Indian ink brush W/C. 15-Oct-2 Dorotheum, Vienna #255/R

SCHEIER, Edwin (1910-) American

£	$	€	
£774	$1200	€1161	Cote d'Azur (51x61cm-20x24in) s. painted c.1940. 8-Dec-2 Toomey, Oak Park #663/R

SCHEIL, Hans (1896-1988) German

£	$	€	
£696	$1100	€1100	Two nudes (80x65cm-31x26in) s. i.d.1960 verso. 30-Nov-2 Arnold, Frankfurt #499/R

SCHEINHAMMER, Otto (1897-1982) German

£	$	€	
£638	$1034	€900	Voldendam quay (65x75cm-26x30in) s. exhib. 26-May-3 Glerum, Amsterdam #33/R
£764	$1192	€1200	Landscape with mountain stream (76x66cm-30x26in) s. 8-Nov-2 Auktionhaus Georg Rehm, Augsburg #8146/R

SCHEINS, Karl Ludwig (1808-1879) German

£	$	€	
£1027	$1603	€1500	Winter wooded landscape (39x53cm-15x21in) s. 10-Apr-3 Van Ham, Cologne #1686/R est:1600
£2500	$3975	€3750	Winter's walk (88x122cm-35x48in) s. 20-Mar-3 Christie's, Kensington #176/R est:3000-5000

SCHEIRING, Leopold (1884-?) Austrian

£	$	€	
£625	$987	€900	Single tree in mountain landscape (29x24cm-11x9in) s. board. 24-Apr-3 Dorotheum, Vienna #53/R

Works on paper
£449 $709 €700 Seefeld with Reitherspitze (23x31cm-9x12in) s.i.d.1919 W/C. 18-Nov-2 Dorotheum, Linz #451/R
£513 $810 €800 Natters with rosskopf (23x31cm-9x12in) s.d.1919 W/C. 18-Nov-2 Dorotheum, Linz #452/R

SCHELCK, Maurice (1906-1978) Belgian
£252 $387 €400 Paysage (50x60cm-20x24in) s. panel. 22-Oct-2 Campo, Vlaamse Kaai #611
£503 $775 €800 Nature morte aux pommes (50x70cm-20x28in) s. panel. 22-Oct-2 Campo, Vlaamse Kaai #610
£863 $1381 €1200 Paysage de neige avec moulin (101x101cm-40x40in) s. 13-May-3 Palais de Beaux Arts, Brussels #136/R
£886 $1400 €1400 Formes melodieuses (102x77cm-40x30in) mono. prov. 26-Nov-2 Palais de Beaux Arts, Brussels #257/R
£2075 $3217 €3300 Landscape with red light (80x100cm-31x39in) s. panel. 5-Oct-2 De Vuyst, Lokeren #313/R est:3500-4500

SCHELFHOUT, A (1787-1870) Dutch
£2658 $4120 €4200 Enjoying the ice (30x44cm-12x17in) i. 27-Sep-2 Dr Fritz Nagel, Leipzig #3997/R est:6500

SCHELFHOUT, Andreas (1787-1870) Dutch
£3145 $5000 €4718 Skating (23x30cm-9x12in) s. panel. 7-Mar-3 Skinner, Boston #217/R est:10000-15000
£3819 $6073 €5500 Deux silhouettes (21x29cm-8x11in) s. panel. 30-Apr-3 Tajan, Paris #54/R
£4577 $7370 €6500 Landscape with two figures on the edge of the water (12x16cm-5x6in) s. panel. 7-May-3 Vendue Huis, Gravenhage #383/R est:7000-9000
£7000 $11130 €10500 Dutch boats moored on a river beside a windmill (16x22cm-6x9in) s. panel. 18-Mar-3 Bonhams, New Bond Street #13/R est:5000-7000
£10191 $15898 €16000 Beach view with fishermen and small groups of figures (22x29cm-9x11in) s. panel. 6-Nov-2 Vendue Huis, Gravenhage #416/R est:20000-30000
£10274 $16130 €15000 Steamship at sea (13x18cm-5x7in) s.d.53 panel. 15-Apr-3 Sotheby's, Amsterdam #22/R est:8000-12000
£11465 $17656 €18000 Panoramic wooded landscape in summer (80x93cm-31x37in) s. prov. 3-Sep-2 Christie's, Amsterdam #125/R est:12000-16000
£14584 $23188 €21000 Scene de patinage (48x68cm-19x27in) s. 30-Apr-3 Tajan, Paris #55/R
£18440 $29872 €26000 Winter landscape with skaters (24x34cm-9x13in) s.d.1839 panel. 22-May-3 Dorotheum, Vienna #55/R est:25000-35000
£19444 $30917 €28000 Calm, sailing vessels at anchor on the Merwede river with Dordrecht beyond (27x36cm-11x14in) s.d.1845 panel. 29-Apr-3 Christie's, Amsterdam #20/R est:15000-20000
£20833 $33125 €30000 Preparing for the falcon hunt at the royal palace Het Loo (85x112cm-33x44in) s. panel prov. 29-Apr-3 Christie's, Amsterdam #206/R est:30000-50000
£21519 $34000 €34000 Winters day in Holland (23x35cm-9x14in) s.d.67 panel. 28-Nov-2 Dorotheum, Vienna #64/R est:30000-40000
£21722 $35190 €31497 Winter landscape with skaters on frozen canal (40x51cm-16x20in) s. panel prov. 25-May-3 Uppsala Auktionskammare, Uppsala #57/R est:150000-200000 (S.KR 280000)
£72000 $118080 €108000 Winter landscape with skaters on a frozen river (41x53cm-16x21in) s.d.1841 prov. 3-Jun-3 Sotheby's, London #145/R est:20000-30000
£107639 $171146 €155000 Summer in Holland - panoramic view of a village in the dunes (38x51cm-15x20in) s.d.1842 panel prov.exhib.lit. 29-Apr-3 Christie's, Amsterdam #194/R est:60000-80000

Works on paper
£550 $853 €825 Dutch winter landscape with skaters (39x52cm-15x20in) W/C. 6-Oct-2 Lots Road, London #339
£1370 $2151 €2000 Ships on the Merwede near Dordrecht (14x20cm-6x8in) s. W/C. 15-Apr-3 Sotheby's, Amsterdam #50/R est:2000-3000

SCHELFHOUT, Andreas (attrib) (1787-1870) Dutch
£1132 $1766 €1800 Winter landscape with ice skaters (22x27cm-9x11in) s.d.68 panel prov. 19-Sep-2 Dr Fritz Nagel, Stuttgart #994/R est:1200
£2183 $3450 €3275 Animated winter landscape (29x36cm-11x14in) panel. 14-Nov-2 Stuker, Bern #497 est:6000-8000 (S.FR 5000)

SCHELL, L (19th C) German
£1000 $1560 €1500 Figures in a landscape (19x43cm-7x17in) s. 15-Oct-2 Bearnes, Exeter #413/R est:1000-1500

SCHELL, Sherill (1877-1964) American
Photographs
£3247 $5000 €4871 Portrait of Rupert Brooke (23x19cm-9x7in) gelatin silver print prov.lit. 25-Oct-2 Phillips, New York #74/R est:1000-5000
£9740 $15000 €14610 Wall Street, New York (35x27cm-14x11in) i. photograph prov. 22-Oct-2 Sotheby's, New York #55/R est:7000-10000

SCHELL, Susan Gertrude (1891-1970) American
£962 $1500 €1443 Protected, mountainous landscape with village (41x36cm-16x14in) 18-Sep-2 Alderfer's, Hatfield #362/R est:1000-1500

SCHELLENBERG, Johann Rudolf (1740-1806) German
£802 $1170 €1250 Peasant woman carrying wood. Traveller resting (18x14cm-7x6in) panel two. 4-Jun-2 Karl & Faber, Munich #40

SCHELLER, Emil (1880-1942) ?
£262 $414 €393 Icy pleasures (70x55cm-28x22in) s. 14-Nov-2 Stuker, Bern #498 (S.FR 600)

SCHELLI, Jakob Rudolf (1895-1962) Swiss
£269 $392 €404 Summer landscape with village. Still life with flowers (58x45cm-23x18in) s. double-sided. 17-Jun-2 Philippe Schuler, Zurich #7442 (S.FR 610)

SCHELLINCKS, Daniel (1627-1701) Dutch
£18868 $29245 €30000 Elegant company crossing river by ferry (47x63cm-19x25in) prov. 2-Oct-2 Dorotheum, Vienna #125/R est:30000-40000

SCHELLINKS, Willem (1627-1678) Dutch
£16000 $24960 €24000 Landscape with figures and animals crossing river in a ferry (100x154cm-39x61in) prov.exhib. 10-Apr-3 Sotheby's, London #65/R est:15000

SCHELLINKS, Willem (attrib) (1627-1678) Dutch
£4459 $6955 €7000 Wooded landscape with a shepherd and his flock, a church beyond (52x79cm-20x31in) panel. 6-Nov-2 Christie's, Amsterdam #20/R est:8000-12000

SCHELLNAST, Karl (1892-1968) Austrian
£1573 $2500 €2360 Still life with fruit (75x100cm-30x39in) s.d.24. 7-Mar-3 Skinner, Boston #255/R est:2000-4000

SCHELTEMA, J H (1861-1938) Dutch
£1912 $3136 €2868 Gippsland cattle, early morning (40x56cm-16x22in) s. 4-Jun-3 Deutscher-Menzies, Melbourne #331/R est:5000-7000 (A.D 4800)
£5578 $9147 €8367 Horses in a landscape (71x101cm-28x40in) s. 4-Jun-3 Deutscher-Menzies, Melbourne #144/R est:15000-20000 (A.D 14000)

SCHELTEMA, Jan Hendrik (1861-1938) Dutch
£659 $1048 €989 Highland scene (31x46cm-12x18in) s. prov. 5-May-3 Sotheby's, Melbourne #287 (A.D 1700)
£1123 $1707 €1685 Hazy afternoon (24x54cm-9x21in) s. canvas on board. 19-Aug-2 Joel, Victoria #148 est:2000-3000 (A.D 3200)
£1254 $1907 €1881 Cattle grazing (24x54cm-9x21in) s. canvas on board. 27-Aug-2 Goodman, Sydney #105/R est:2800-3800 (A.D 3500)
£2099 $3317 €3149 Untitled, horses in a field (53x76cm-21x30in) s. canvas on board. 7-Apr-3 Shapiro, Sydney #453 est:5000-7000 (A.D 5500)
£4982 $7623 €7473 Bullock team in the forest of Canungra, Queensland (70x105cm-28x41in) s. prov. 25-Aug-2 Sotheby's, Paddington #242/R est:10000-15000 (A.D 14000)
£7634 $12061 €11451 Cattle grazing in a summer pastoral (70x100cm-28x39in) s. 2-Apr-3 Christie's, Melbourne #10/R est:8000-12000 (A.D 20000)
£42857 $67714 €64286 Morley's track Fernshaw (100x150cm-39x59in) s. prov. 18-Nov-2 Goodman, Sydney #159/R est:130000-230000 (A.D 120000)

SCHENAU, Johann Eleazar (1737-1806) German
£9146 $15000 €13262 Apollo and Hyacinthus (234x142cm-92x56in) s.d.1803. 4-Jun-3 Christie's, Rockefeller NY #204/R est:20000-30000

SCHENCK, August Friedrich Albrecht (1828-1901) Danish
£873 $1380 €1310 Shepherd with sheep in mountain landscape (35x65cm-14x26in) s.d.1839. 14-Nov-2 Stuker, Bern #499 est:5000-7000 (S.FR 2000)
£1027 $1500 €1541 Sheep on a snowy mountainside (41x28cm-16x11in) s. 3-Nov-1 North East Auctions, Portsmouth #235/R

SCHENCK, William (?) ?
£3194 $5175 €4631 Waco (97x97cm-38x38in) acrylic. 23-May-3 Altermann Galleries, Santa Fe #146

SCHENDEL, Bernardus van (1649-1709) Dutch
£1800 $3006 €2610 Interior with a marriage scene (58x69cm-23x27in) bears init. 8-Jul-3 Sotheby's, Olympia #379/R est:1500-2500

SCHENDEL, Mira (1919-1988) Brazilian

£5488 $9000 €8232 Sem titulo (47x23cm-19x9in) s.d.64 oil crayon paper three prov. 28-May-3 Christie's, Rockefeller NY #46/R est:6000-9000

Works on paper

£2927 $4800 €4391 Sem titulo (65x95cm-26x37in) gouache oil stick exec.1960 prov. 28-May-3 Christie's, Rockefeller NY #160/R est:4000-6000
£3659 $6000 €5489 Sem titulo (48x66cm-19x26in) s.d.1964 W/C chl prov. two. 28-May-3 Christie's, Rockefeller NY #45/R est:5000-7000
£4268 $7000 €6402 Sem titulo (47x23cm-19x9in) s.i.d.1964 graphite two prov. 28-May-3 Christie's, Rockefeller NY #165/R est:4000-6000
£4459 $7000 €6689 Untitled (46x23cm-18x9in) s.d.78 col crayon sticker graphite gouache set of 3 prov. 20-Nov-2 Christie's, Rockefeller NY #51/R

SCHENDEL, Petrus van (1806-1870) Belgian

£10072 $16115 €14000 Evening market (38x32cm-15x13in) indis.s. panel lit. 17-May-3 De Vuyst, Lokeren #423/R est:8000-10000
£15723 $24214 €25000 Saying Grace (55x42cm-22x17in) s.d.1837 panel prov. 22-Oct-2 Sotheby's, Amsterdam #181/R est:25000-35000
£16500 $25905 €24750 Young market girl by candlelight (31x26cm-12x10in) s. panel. 19-Nov-2 Bonhams, New Bond Street #17/R est:10000-15000
£22013 $33899 €35000 Divine inspiration (54x44cm-21x17in) s.d.1844 panel. 23-Oct-2 Christie's, Amsterdam #100/R est:25000-35000
£31447 $48428 €50000 Vegetable seller by candle light (51x40cm-20x16in) s.d.1849 panel prov.exhib. 22-Oct-2 Sotheby's, Amsterdam #152/R est:30000-50000
£40000 $62000 €60000 Fruit seller (75x63cm-30x25in) s.d.1841 panel prov. 4-Dec-2 Christie's, London #47/R est:50000-70000
£95000 $149150 €142500 Market by moonlight (57x42cm-22x17in) s. panel prov. 19-Nov-2 Sotheby's, London #134/R est:40000-60000
£109677 $170000 €164516 Night market (69x52cm-27x20in) s. panel prov. 30-Oct-2 Christie's, Rockefeller NY #1/R est:100000-150000

SCHENER, Mihaly (1923-) Hungarian

£980 $1529 €1421 Abstract levels with figures (40x60cm-16x24in) s. cardboard. 13-Sep-2 Mu Terem Galeria, Budapest #130/R est:240000 (H.F 380000)
£1291 $2001 €1872 Carnival in Venice in front of the Goge Palace (80x100cm-31x39in) s. s.i.d.1995 verso panel. 9-Dec-2 Mu Terem Galeria, Budapest #105/R est:280000 (H.F 480000)

SCHENK, Karl (1905-1973) Swiss

£368 $570 €552 Young bull (63x78cm-25x31in) s. pavatex. 24-Sep-2 Koller, Zurich #6663 (S.FR 850)
£1065 $1714 €1544 Girl with white paper bag (49x40cm-19x16in) panel. 9-May-3 Dobiaschofsky, Bern #122/R (S.FR 2300)
£1572 $2452 €2358 Girl with doll in a doll's pram (40x52cm-16x20in) s. i.verso panel. 8-Nov-2 Dobiaschofsky, Bern #197/R est:3000 (S.FR 3600)
£1747 $2725 €2621 Two boys with paper hats (76x68cm-30x27in) s. i.verso panel. 8-Nov-2 Dobiaschofsky, Bern #198/R est:5000 (S.FR 4000)

Works on paper

£284 $443 €426 Portrait of little girl (50x38cm-20x15in) s.i. pencil. 6-Nov-2 Dobiaschofsky, Bern #1863/R (S.FR 650)

SCHENKEL, Jan Jacob (1829-1900) Dutch

£2564 $4000 €3846 Cathedral interior with figures (51x38cm-20x15in) s. panel. 18-Sep-2 Boos Gallery, Michigan #277/R est:6000-8000

SCHENKER, Jacques Matthias (1854-1927) German

£645 $948 €1000 Snow covered mountain landscape (61x85cm-24x33in) s. 20-Jun-2 Dr Fritz Nagel, Stuttgart #821/R
£1923 $2981 €3000 Stormy seas off Normandy coast (78x141cm-31x56in) s.i. 5-Dec-2 Dr Fritz Nagel, Stuttgart #697/R est:1750

SCHERBAN, Alexander (1886-1964) Austrian

£480 $749 €720 Aufstieg zum silvrettahorn (60x65cm-24x26in) s.d.1932 s.i.verso board. 26-Mar-3 Sotheby's, Olympia #273/R

SCHERBRING, Carl (1859-1899) German

£350 $546 €550 Idyllic backyard with farmer's wife feeding hens (59x73cm-23x29in) s.i.d.97 lit. 7-Nov-2 Allgauer, Kempten #2947/R
£473 $738 €700 Isar meadows (43x57cm-17x22in) s. 26-Mar-3 Hugo Ruef, Munich #223

SCHERER, Hermann (1893-1927) Swiss

Works on paper

£438 $653 €657 Sertig valley near Davos (33x43cm-13x17in) chl. 25-Jun-2 Koller, Zurich #6611 (S.FR 995)

SCHERER, Joseph (attrib) (1814-1891) German

£2245 $3569 €3300 Portrait of African princess (31x25cm-12x10in) i.d.1846 verso paper. 20-Mar-3 Neumeister, Munich #2731/R est:250

SCHERER, Sean (1968-) American?

£2187 $3500 €3281 File-phile. Phenol (60x60cm-24x24in) pair painted 1990-91 prov. 16-May-3 Phillips, New York #195/R est:4000-6000

SCHERFIG, Hans (1905-1979) Danish

£1183 $1822 €1775 Hippopotamus (31x47cm-12x19in) tempera plywood. 23-Oct-2 Kunsthallen, Copenhagen #129/R est:8000 (D.KR 14000)
£1378 $2136 €2067 Three flamingos (17x25cm-7x10in) s.d.1958 tempera masonite exhib. 4-Dec-2 Kunsthallen, Copenhagen #300/R est:10000 (D.KR 16000)
£1394 $2203 €2091 Love game with animals and figures (178x193cm-70x76in) init. 1-Apr-3 Rasmussen, Copenhagen #645/R est:10000 (D.KR 15000)
£1737 $2761 €2606 Breakfast out of doors (100x136cm-39x54in) init. 26-Feb-3 Kunsthallen, Copenhagen #353/R est:25000 (D.KR 19000)
£1817 $2799 €2726 Tapir with young (16x18cm-6x7in) s.d.1964 masonite. 23-Oct-2 Kunsthallen, Copenhagen #1/R est:8000 (D.KR 21500)
£1863 $2887 €2795 Hyacinths and goldfish (61x57cm-24x22in) s. lit.prov. 1-Oct-2 Rasmussen, Copenhagen #318/R est:25000 (D.KR 22000)
£2536 $3905 €3804 Giraffes and zebras on the savannah (40x52cm-16x20in) s. masonite painted 1934. 23-Oct-2 Kunsthallen, Copenhagen #59/R est:25000 (D.KR 30000)
£2669 $4458 €3870 Still life of fruit, bowls and bottle (68x59cm-27x23in) s.d.1927. 17-Jun-3 Rasmussen, Copenhagen #90/R est:30000 (D.KR 28000)
£3532 $5580 €5298 Mother and child - rhino and young in jungle (26x29cm-10x11in) s.d.59 tempera masonite. 1-Apr-3 Rasmussen, Copenhagen #92/R est:18000 (D.KR 38000)
£6764 $10755 €10146 Jungle picture with elephants (43x60cm-17x24in) s.d.1958 masonite. 26-Feb-3 Kunsthallen, Copenhagen #233/R est:40000 (D.KR 74000)

Works on paper

£335 $529 €503 Palace scene (43x30cm-17x12in) s.i.d.1959 gouache prov. 1-Apr-3 Rasmussen, Copenhagen #540 (D.KR 3600)

SCHERMAN, Tony (1950-) Canadian

Works on paper

£800 $1304 €1200 Two phyllo (61x76cm-24x30in) s.i.d.1978 on overlap encaustic on canvas prov. 3-Feb-3 Sotheby's, Olympia #178/R
£1411 $2230 €2117 Wolf child (99x70cm-39x28in) s.i.d.1982 mixed media prov. 14-Nov-2 Heffel, Vancouver #72/R est:3000-3500 (C.D 3500)
£6278 $10045 €9417 Untitled - comforts of food (76x152cm-30x60in) s.d.1988 verso prov.lit. 15-May-3 Heffel, Vancouver #201/R est:15000-18000 (C.D 14000)

SCHERMANN, H (?) German?

£414 $638 €650 Frankfurt am Main (80x101cm-31x40in) s. 5-Sep-2 Arnold, Frankfurt #854

SCHERMER, Cornelis (1824-1915) Dutch

£590 $974 €850 Huzaar in action (20x16cm-8x6in) s.d.70 panel. 1-Jul-3 Christie's, Amsterdam #553/R

SCHERPEREEL, Koen (1961-1997) Belgian

Works on paper

£566 $877 €900 Head (59x48cm-23x19in) s.d.90 pastel acrylic. 5-Oct-2 De Vuyst, Lokeren #316/R
£705 $1093 €1100 Head (59x48cm-23x19in) s.d.90 mixed media. 7-Dec-2 De Vuyst, Lokeren #285/R

SCHERRES, Alfred (1864-1924) German

£577 $906 €900 Fishing boats at quayside (36x47cm-14x19in) s. i.d.1905 verso board. 23-Nov-2 Arnold, Frankfurt #862/R
£2675 $4173 €4200 October snow (90x150cm-35x59in) s. 6-Nov-2 Hugo Ruef, Munich #1288/R est:2000

SCHERRES, Carl (1833-1923) German

£1139 $1800 €1800 Ostsee from the dunes (72x93cm-28x37in) mono. 29-Nov-2 Bassenge, Berlin #6049/R est:1800

SCHERREWITZ, Johan (1868-1951) Dutch

£559 $906 €850 Brown horse (30x36cm-12x14in) s. cardboard on plywood. 21-Jan-3 Christie's, Amsterdam #158
£1333 $2213 €1933 To the stable (39x49cm-15x19in) s. panel. 16-Jun-3 Waddingtons, Toronto #247/R est:3000-5000 (C.D 3000)
£1373 $2142 €1991 Milkmaid (41x51cm-16x20in) s. prov. 26-Mar-3 Walker's, Ottawa #6/R est:2500-3500 (C.D 3200)
£2178 $3398 €3267 Barn interior with animals and washer woman (79x98cm-31x39in) s. 11-Nov-2 Stephan Welz, Johannesburg #445/R est:18000-24000 (SA.R 34000)

£2479 $3893 €3719 Cattle drinking (51x41cm-20x16in) s.i. prov. 24-Jul-2 Walker's, Ottawa #2/R est:5000-7000 (C.D 6000)

£2500 $3975 €3750 Milking time (51x36cm-20x14in) s. board. 29-Apr-3 Gorringes, Lewes #2050

£2778 $4583 €4000 Daily duties (80x101cm-31x40in) s. 1-Jul-3 Christie's, Amsterdam #100/R est:2500-3500

£3125 $4969 €4500 Farmer at work (50x65cm-20x26in) s. 29-Apr-3 Christie's, Amsterdam #146/R est:3000-5000

£3333 $5500 €4800 Peat wagon (71x100cm-28x39in) s. 1-Jul-3 Christie's, Amsterdam #87/R est:4000-6000

£3526 $5500 €5289 Landscape with sheep (64x48cm-25x19in) 30-Mar-3 Susanin's, Chicago #6052/R est:3000-5000

£4721 $7365 €6845 Activity in a Dutch farmyard (61x86cm-24x34in) s. prov. 26-Mar-3 Walker's, Ottawa #7/R est:12000-15000 (C.D 11000)

£6918 $10654 €11000 Shellfisher on the beach, Noordwijk (35x60cm-14x24in) s. s.i.verso. 22-Oct-2 Sotheby's, Amsterdam #99/R est:6000-8000

£13014 $20432 €19000 Unloading the catch (31x49cm-12x19in) s. 15-Apr-3 Sotheby's, Amsterdam #207/R est:15000-20000

£25000 $39750 €36000 Gathering nets (32x42cm-13x17in) s. plywood. 29-Apr-3 Christie's, Amsterdam #166/R est:20000-30000

SCHETKY, John Christian (1778-1874) British

£450 $702 €675 Mr William Garnham Luard discharges from R N Collage (36x56cm-14x22in) i. s.verso. 11-Apr-3 Keys, Aylsham #805

£1800 $3006 €2610 Khedive's disaster, a troop ship in distress being rescued by the Royal Yacht Squadron (54x79cm-21x31in) 18-Jun-3 Sotheby's, Olympia #23/R est:2000-3000

£86000 $130720 €129000 Bombardment of Algiers, 27th August 1816 (91x168cm-36x66in) s.d.1841 prov.lit. 15-Aug-2 Bonhams, New Bond Street #391/R est:60000-80000

SCHEUBEL, Johann Joseph III (1733-1801) German

£671 $1081 €1000 Portrait of a nobleman wearing a blue coat (88x72cm-35x28in) i.d.1786. 18-Feb-3 Sotheby's, Amsterdam #346/R est:400-500

SCHEUCHZER, Wilhelm (1803-1866) Swiss

£4110 $6411 €6165 Glarnerland - Mollis against Glarnisch (78x107cm-31x42in) s. 28-Mar-3 Koller, Zurich #3151/R est:9000-14000 (S.FR 9000)

Works on paper

£352 $515 €528 Mountain lake (19x25cm-7x10in) s. W/C. 17-Jun-2 Philippe Schuler, Zurich #4817/R (S.FR 800)

£2208 $3290 €3400 Gasteig with Prater Insel near Munich (18x25cm-7x10in) i.d.1858 W/C over pencil. 26-Jun-2 Neumeister, Munich #599/R est:2000

SCHEUCHZER, Wilhelm (attrib) (1803-1866) Swiss

Works on paper

£705 $1093 €1100 Windberg Abbey. Haibach ruins (20x27cm-8x11in) i.d.1859/1860 two. 4-Dec-2 Neumeister, Munich #549/R

£1410 $2186 €2200 Views of Upper Bavaria. three i. one d.1860 four. 4-Dec-2 Neumeister, Munich #548/R est:1500

SCHEUERER, Julius (1859-1913) German

£445 $695 €650 Poultry by water trough (15x39cm-6x15in) s. board. 9-Apr-3 Neumeister, Munich #738/R

£461 $746 €700 Balzender Auerhahn (21x40cm-8x16in) s.i. board. 21-Jan-3 Christie's, Amsterdam #119/R

£641 $1000 €962 Ducks at pond's edge (18x25cm-7x10in) s. panel. 9-Oct-2 Doyle, New York #103

£1233 $1923 €1800 Ducks and peacock by water (8x21cm-3x8in) s. panel. 10-Apr-3 Van Ham, Cologne #1688/R est:2300

£1282 $2000 €1923 Ducks and hens in a landscape (41x61cm-16x24in) s.d.1911. 9-Oct-2 Doyle, New York #102 est:2000-3000

SCHEUERER, Otto (1862-1934) German

£258 $379 €400 Ducks in reeds (16x22cm-6x9in) s.i. panel. 20-Jun-2 Dr Fritz Nagel, Stuttgart #822/R

£304 $474 €450 Pheasant and hens (18x26cm-7x10in) s. board. 26-Mar-3 Hugo Ruef, Munich #224

£759 $1206 €1100 Poultry with peacock (22x33cm-9x13in) s.i. 8-Mar-3 Arnold, Frankfurt #708/R

£1027 $1603 €1500 Poultry (37x49cm-15x19in) s.i. board. 10-Apr-3 Dorotheum, Vienna #251 est:3000-3500

SCHEUERLE, Joe (1873-1948) American

Works on paper

£538 $850 €807 Chief Iron Tail, Ogalala (28x20cm-11x8in) s.d.1916 W/C. 3-Apr-3 Boos Gallery, Michigan #221/R

SCHEUERMANN, Carl Georg (1803-1859) Danish

£3445 $5237 €5168 Hilly landscape with houses, Jylland (71x103cm-28x41in) with sig.d.1840 verso. 27-Aug-2 Rasmussen, Copenhagen #1410/R est:40000 (D.KR 40000)

SCHEUREN, Caspar Johann Nepomuk (1810-1887) German

£1646 $2600 €2600 Rhein landscape with farm buildings and figures (56x80cm-22x31in) s. 29-Nov-2 Bolland & Marotz, Bremen #766/R est:1800

£2055 $3205 €3000 Soldiers sheltering in tower in winter landscape (36x28cm-14x11in) s.d.1839. 10-Apr-3 Van Ham, Cologne #1689/R est:4200

Works on paper

£478 $745 €750 Moonlit lakeside fishing hut (15x23cm-6x9in) s.d.1863 W/C pen board. 5-Nov-2 Hartung & Hartung, Munich #5125/R

£519 $795 €779 Das Schloss am Meere von Uhland (46x56cm-18x22in) s.d.1858 W/C gouache prov. 26-Aug-2 Blomqvist, Lysaker #1344/R (N.KR 6000)

£828 $1292 €1300 Fairytales (19x14cm-7x6in) i.d.1864 W/C htd gold pen. 5-Nov-2 Hartung & Hartung, Munich #5127/R

£1304 $2022 €1956 Returning to the monastery (49x63cm-19x25in) s.d.1867 W/C Indian ink. 9-Dec-2 Philippe Schuler, Zurich #4191/R est:4000-5000 (S.FR 3000)

SCHEUREN, Caspar Johann Nepomuk (attrib) (1810-1887) German

£1076 $1668 €1700 Winter landscape (26x32cm-10x13in) i. panel. 25-Sep-2 Neumeister, Munich #709/R est:1400

SCHEYERER, Franz (1770-1839) Austrian

£4088 $6336 €6500 Italian landscape by moonlight (58x73cm-23x29in) s.d.1803. 2-Oct-2 Dorotheum, Vienna #227/R est:3800-4500

£17610 $27296 €28000 Ruin of Weitenegg Castle and Weitenbache, lower Austria (103x140cm-41x55in) prov. 2-Oct-2 Dorotheum, Vienna #208/R est:18000-25000

SCHIANCHI, Federico (1858-1919) Italian

Works on paper

£700 $1134 €1050 Bay of Naples (18x51cm-7x20in) s. pencil W/C bodycol. 23-Jan-3 Christie's, Kensington #325/R

SCHIATTZ-JENSEN, N F (20th C) Swedish

£441 $656 €662 Peasant woman at spinning wheel (55x39cm-22x15in) s.d.1925. 25-Jun-2 Koller, Zurich #6704 (S.FR 1000)

SCHIAVONE, Andrea (1522-1563) Italian

£18000 $28080 €27000 Lamentation (115x95cm-45x37in) 10-Apr-3 Christie's, Kensington #220/R est:3000-5000

Prints

£3797 $6000 €6000 Mystic marriage of St Catherine (31x23cm-12x9in) woodcut. 29-Nov-2 Bassenge, Berlin #5219/R est:6000

SCHIAVONI, Felice (attrib) (1803-1881) Italian

£2174 $3565 €3000 Ritratto di donna seduta con ventaglio (118x90cm-46x35in) 27-May-3 Finarte, Milan #91/R est:4000-5000

SCHIAVONI, Giovanni (1804-1848) Italian

£6757 $10541 €10000 Sleeping child (80x101cm-31x40in) s.d.1843. 27-Mar-3 Dorotheum, Vienna #368/R est:6000-9000

SCHIAVONI, Natale (1777-1858) Italian

£2590 $4144 €3600 Female nude (102x81cm-40x32in) s.d.1851. 14-May-3 Dorotheum, Linz #350/R est:3000-3800

£3846 $6000 €5769 Lute playing girl (81x66cm-32x26in) 11-Apr-3 Du Mouchelle, Detroit #2257/R est:1500-2500

SCHIBIG, Philippe (1940-) Swiss

Works on paper

£377 $611 €547 Untitled (35x32cm-14x13in) s.d.78 biro prov. 24-May-3 Galerie Gloggner, Luzern #97/R (S.FR 800)

£377 $611 €547 Untitled (35x29cm-14x11in) s.d.78 biro prov. 24-May-3 Galerie Gloggner, Luzern #98/R (S.FR 800)

SCHICHT, W L (?) German

£349 $542 €524 Still life of fruit and flowers (66x105cm-26x41in) s. 29-Sep-2 Uppsala Auktionskammare, Uppsala #213 (S.KR 5000)

SCHICK, Carl (1826-1873) German

£769 $1208 €1200 Children playing in street. Italian village spring (45x35cm-18x14in) s.d.1915 two. 21-Nov-2 Van Ham, Cologne #1895/R

SCHICK, Christian Gottlieb (1776-1812) German

£1100 $1738 €1650 Rhineland landscape (20x29cm-8x11in) s. panel. 2-Dec-2 Bonhams, Bath #163/R est:1200-1800

SCHICK, Jakob (attrib) (15/16th C) German
£2703 $4216 €4000 Altar panel (75x40cm-30x16in) gilded relief. 27-Mar-3 Dr Fritz Nagel, Stuttgart #970/R est:3000

SCHICKHARDT, K (1866-1933) German
£645 $948 €1000 At lake Boden (86x130cm-34x51in) s. 24-Jun-2 Dr Fritz Nagel, Stuttgart #5906/R

SCHICKHARDT, Karl (1866-1933) German
£321 $497 €500 Swabian Alb landscape (29x42cm-11x17in) s. panel lit. 6-Dec-2 Karlheinz Kaupp, Staufen #2270

SCHIDER, Fritz (1846-1907) Austrian
£422 $629 €650 Doctor visiting sick patient (37x46cm-15x18in) 26-Jun-2 Neumeister, Munich #842/R

SCHIEBECK, W (20th C) German
Works on paper
£1603 $2484 €2500 Orpheus (16x11cm-6x4in) s.d.1920 W/C. 5-Dec-2 Dr Fritz Nagel, Stuttgart #698/R est:1200

SCHIEDGES, Peter Paulus (1812-1876) Dutch
£338 $544 €480 Woman reading in meadow (45x32cm-18x13in) s. canvas on board. 7-May-3 Michael Zeller, Lindau #915/R
£700 $1085 €1050 Paddle tug and barges on a Dutch estuary (25x35cm-10x14in) s. panel. 31-Oct-2 Christie's, Kensington #507/R
£828 $1292 €1300 Sailing boat on turbulent sea (13x19cm-5x7in) s. panel. 6-Nov-2 Vendue Huis, Gravenhage #378/R
£886 $1382 €1400 Etang au moulin (47x37cm-19x15in) s. 15-Oct-2 Horta, Bruxelles #420
£1210 $1888 €1900 Boat in the surf (32x43cm-13x17in) s. 6-Nov-2 Vendue Huis, Gravenhage #378a est:2000-3000
£1974 $3197 €3000 Washing by the river (107x82cm-42x32in) s. 21-Jan-3 Christie's, Amsterdam #172/R est:3000-5000
£2215 $3434 €3500 Shipping in the harbour of Batavia (38x74cm-15x29in) s.d.1855. 24-Sep-2 Christie's, Amsterdam #170/R est:900-1100
£5031 $7748 €8000 Sailing vessels in a calm (26x35cm-10x14in) s.d.59 panel prov. 22-Oct-2 Sotheby's, Amsterdam #57/R est:7000-9000
£17610 $27119 €28000 Figures on Scheveningen beach (28x43cm-11x17in) s.d.58 panel. 22-Oct-2 Sotheby's, Amsterdam #145/R est:25000-35000
Works on paper
£1210 $1864 €1900 Windmill in polder landscape (46x68cm-18x27in) s. pencil W/C htd white. 3-Sep-2 Christie's, Amsterdam #166/R est:1500-2000

SCHIEDGES, Peter Paulus (younger) (1860-1922) Dutch
Works on paper
£285 $444 €450 Polder landscape with pigs by a stream (35x53cm-14x21in) s. gouache prov. 21-Oct-2 Glerum, Amsterdam #66/R

SCHIELE, Egon (1890-1918) Austrian
£11300000 $18871000 €16950000 Krumau landscape, town and river (110x141cm-43x56in) s.d.1916 s.i.stretcher oil tempera col.chk. prov.exhib.lit. 23-Jun-3 Sotheby's, London #6/R est:5000000-7000000
Prints
£2083 $3312 €3000 Portrait of Franz Hauer (13x11cm-5x4in) st.sig. drypoint. 5-May-3 Ketterer, Munich #949/R est:800-1200
£2516 $3925 €4000 Worries (52x32cm-20x13in) st.sig.d.1914 drypoint etching. 23-Sep-2 Dr Fritz Nagel, Stuttgart #9004/R est:6000
£2628 $4126 €4100 Portrait of Arthur Roessler (25x32cm-10x13in) drypoint etching lit. 25-Nov-2 Hassfurther, Vienna #16/R est:2500-3000
£5063 $8000 €8000 Crouching figure (47x31cm-19x12in) etching. 27-Nov-2 Dorotheum, Vienna #3/R est:8000-10000
£5696 $9000 €9000 Worries (47x31cm-19x12in) etching. 27-Nov-2 Dorotheum, Vienna #4/R est:8000-10000
£6731 $10567 €10500 Troubles (48x31cm-19x12in) drypoint etching lit. 25-Nov-2 Hassfurther, Vienna #15/R est:2500-3500
Sculpture
£1139 $1766 €1800 Self portrait (28x17x21cm-11x7x8in) brown pat.bronze Cast.Venturi Art. 28-Sep-2 Ketterer, Hamburg #70/R est:1900-2000
Works on paper
£13043 $21391 €18000 Girl standing, seen from the back, in lilac dress and red shoes (14x9cm-6x4in) mono.d.09 W/C col pencil postcard prov.lit. 27-May-3 Wiener Kunst Auktionen, Vienna #65/R est:15000-30000
£21014 $34464 €29000 Study of his sister Gerti (47x32cm-19x13in) s.d.1909 pencil prov.exhib. 29-May-3 Lempertz, Koln #916/R est:10000-12000
£22000 $36740 €31900 Stehender frauenakt, masturbierend - standing nude woman, masturbating (46x29cm-18x11in) s.d.1913 pencil prov.exhib.lit. 24-Jun-3 Sotheby's, London #263/R est:25000-35000
£32051 $50000 €48077 Stehender akt (46x29cm-18x11in) black conte crayon executed 1918 prov.exhib.lit. 7-Nov-2 Christie's, Rockefeller NY #129/R est:35000-45000
£51282 $80513 €80000 Friends (30x46cm-12x18in) s.d.1917 chk lit.prov. 25-Nov-2 Hassfurther, Vienna #14/R est:80000-100000
£57971 $95072 €80000 Friends (30x46cm-12x18in) s.d.1917 black chk prov.lit. 27-May-3 Hassfurther, Vienna #15/R est:80000-90000
£87097 $135000 €130646 Russian prisoner-of-war with fur hat (43x31cm-17x12in) s.i.d.1915 i.verso pencil prov.exhib.lit. 4-Nov-2 Phillips, New York #14/R est:100000-150000
£95000 $158650 €137750 Selbstbildnis mit erhobenem linken Arm und rotem Mund (40x29cm-16x11in) s. chl red crayon pencil exec.1909 prov.exhib.lit. 24-Jun-3 Christie's, London #34/R est:60000-80000
£193548 $300000 €290322 Akt - nude (41x29cm-16x11in) s.d.1913 W/C black crayon prov.exhib.lit. 4-Nov-2 Phillips, New York #11/R est:350000-450000
£394495 $658807 €572018 Girl with umbrella (46x30cm-18x12in) s.d.1916 W/C bodycol over pencil prov. 20-Jun-3 Kornfeld, Bern #134/R est:500000 (S.FR 860000)
£420000 $701400 €609000 Sitzender weiblicher Akt. Stehender mannlicher Akt (48x32cm-19x13in) s.d.1914 gouache W/C pencil double-sided prov.lit. 24-Jun-3 Christie's, London #62/R est:400000-600000
£460432 $755108 €640000 Woman with red muff and wearing orange dress (44x29cm-17x11in) s.d.1911 W/C gouache opaque white over pencil prov. 6-Jun-3 Ketterer, Munich #26/R est:150000-250000

SCHIER, Franz (1852-1922) German
£2245 $3569 €3300 Japanese woman in kimono holding fan (68x58cm-27x23in) lit. 19-Mar-3 Neumeister, Munich #720/R est:1500

SCHIERTZ, Franz Wilhelm (1813-1887) German
£1754 $2772 €2631 Sailing vessel and pilot boat by Lindesnes (37x53cm-15x21in) s.d.1844 indis.i.verso. 17-Dec-2 Grev Wedels Plass, Oslo #182/R est:20000-30000 (N.KR 20000)

SCHIESS, Ernst Traugott (1872-1919) Swiss
£573 $836 €860 Portrait of young woman wearing hat. Still life study (40x33cm-16x13in) board double-sided. 17-Jun-2 Philippe Schuler, Zurich #4290/R (S.FR 1300)
£611 $960 €917 Algerian women (41x31cm-16x12in) s. verso board exhib. 25-Nov-2 Germann, Zurich #144/R (S.FR 1400)
£699 $1097 €1049 Oriental scene (45x31cm-18x12in) s.d.1917. 25-Nov-2 Sotheby's, Zurich #70/R (S.FR 1600)

SCHIESS, Hans Rudolf (1904-1978) Swiss
£558 $882 €837 Untitled (40x32cm-16x13in) s. s.d.1972 verso. 26-Nov-2 Hans Widmer, St Gallen #1341/R (S.FR 1300)
£1509 $2445 €2672 Composition (92x73cm-36x29in) prov. 26-May-3 Sotheby's, Zurich #146/R est:2000-4000 (S.FR 3200)

SCHIESS, Traugott (1834-1869) Swiss
£463 $745 €695 Lake in the afternoon (33x40cm-13x16in) 7-May-3 Dobiaschofsky, Bern #948/R (S.FR 1000)
£497 $800 €746 Three figures in a valley (56x81cm-22x32in) s. 20-Jan-3 Arthur James, Florida #632

SCHIESTL, Matthaus (1869-1939) German
£577 $906 €900 Angel of the Annunciation before the shepherds (40x50cm-16x20in) s.d.1897 board. 21-Nov-2 Dorotheum, Vienna #205/R

SCHIESTL-ARDING, Albert (20th C) ?
£1026 $1590 €1600 Still life of flowers (110x89cm-43x35in) mono. panel lit. 6-Dec-2 Karlheinz Kaupp, Staufen #2291 est:900

SCHIFANO, Mario (1934-1998) Italian
£742 $1166 €1113 Acerbo (40x40cm-16x16in) prov. 25-Nov-2 Germann, Zurich #806 est:1300-1600 (S.FR 1700)
£830 $1211 €1245 1 x 100 information (50x50cm-20x20in) s.i.d. 1985/86 acrylic enamel prov. 4-Jun-2 Germann, Zurich #839 (S.FR 1900)
£833 $1325 €1200 Untitled (30x20cm-12x8in) s.verso enamel. 1-May-3 Meeting Art, Vercelli #227
£873 $1275 €1310 1 x 100 information (50x50cm-20x20in) s.i.d.1985/86 verso acrylic enamel prov. 4-Jun-2 Germann, Zurich #837 (S.FR 2000)
£873 $1275 €1310 1 x 100 information (50x50cm-20x20in) s.i.d.1985/86 verso acrylic enamel prov. 4-Jun-2 Germann, Zurich #838 (S.FR 2000)
£1042 $1656 €1500 Untitled (20x30cm-8x12in) s.verso enamel sand. 1-May-3 Meeting Art, Vercelli #21
£1076 $1678 €1700 The making of Rio de Janeiro (52x64cm-20x25in) s.verso enaamel acrylic painted 1996. 14-Sep-2 Meeting Art, Vercelli #355/R
£1090 $1689 €1700 Untitled (35x50cm-14x20in) s.verso enamel painted 1996. 4-Dec-2 Finarte, Milan #563/R
£1266 $1988 €1899 Untitled (84x65cm-33x26in) s. verso acrylic. 23-Nov-2 Burkhard, Luzern #136/R est:3000-4000 (S.FR 2900)
£1329 $2073 €2100 The making of Rio de Janeiro (52x64cm-20x25in) s.verso enamel acrylic. 14-Sep-2 Meeting Art, Vercelli #742/R

£1346 $2113 €2100 Untitled (40x50cm-16x20in) s.verso aniline. 20-Nov-2 Pandolfini, Florence #131/R est:2400
£1438 $2301 €2200 Making of Rio de Janeiro (52x64cm-20x25in) s.verso enamel acrylic. 4-Jan-3 Meeting Art, Vercelli #395
£1702 $2757 €2400 Rettili (50x50cm-20x20in) s.d.1996 verso enamel canvas. 22-May-3 Stadion, Trieste #275/R est:1200-1600
£1731 $2717 €2700 Untitled (30x20cm-12x8in) s. enamel painted 1997. 23-Nov-2 Meeting Art, Vercelli #316/R
£2115 $3342 €3300 Tree (40x50cm-16x20in) s. enamel painted 1974. 15-Nov-2 Farsetti, Prato #323/R
£2397 $3740 €3500 Untitled (60x75cm-24x30in) s.verso enamel. 10-Apr-3 Finarte Semenzato, Rome #304/R
£2564 $4026 €4000 Untitled (60x80cm-24x31in) s.d.1996 enamel. 19-Nov-2 Finarte, Milan #86/R
£3109 $4881 €4850 Botanical (70x70cm-28x28in) s.i.d.1988 enamel acrylic. 23-Nov-2 Meeting Art, Vercelli #106/R
£3205 $4968 €5000 Television sets (70x70cm-28x28in) s. enamel serigraph. 4-Dec-2 Finarte, Milan #516/R est:6000
£3333 $5300 €4800 Untitled (70x100cm-28x39in) s.verso enamel acrylic. 1-May-3 Meeting Art, Vercelli #214
£3404 $5515 €4800 Untitled (100x96cm-39x38in) s. enamel painted 1979-80. 26-May-3 Christie's, Milan #146/R est:4000-6000
£3526 $5535 €5500 Untitled (110x97cm-43x38in) s. enamel. 21-Nov-2 Finarte, Rome #349
£3688 $5974 €5200 Untitled (75x100cm-30x39in) s. enamel. 26-May-3 Christie's, Milan #147/R est:3500-5000
£3718 $5874 €5800 Flowers (100x70cm-39x28in) s. enamel acrylic painted 1995. 15-Nov-2 Farsetti, Prato #101/R est:6300
£3846 $6038 €6000 Untitled (80x100cm-31x39in) s. acrylic enamel painted 1990. 23-Nov-2 Meeting Art, Vercelli #325/R
£4103 $6566 €5950 Clouds (100x70cm-39x28in) painted c.1970. 11-Mar-3 Babuino, Rome #9a/R
£4146 $6467 €6550 Anemic landscape (90x110cm-35x43in) 15-Oct-2 Babuino, Rome #300/R
£4167 $6625 €6000 Anaemic landscape (60x80cm-24x31in) s. enamel. 1-May-3 Meeting Art, Vercelli #453
£4269 $6830 €6190 Window (100x70cm-39x28in) painted c.1970. 11-Mar-3 Babuino, Rome #10a/R
£4487 $7045 €7000 Untitled (100x100cm-39x39in) s. enamel. 19-Nov-2 Finarte, Milan #72/R
£4487 $6955 €7000 TV (80x120cm-31x47in) s. enamel painted 1974. 4-Dec-2 Finarte, Milan #303/R est:10000
£4487 $6955 €7000 Tree (105x100cm-41x39in) s. enamel. 4-Dec-2 Finarte, Milan #307/R est:8000
£4808 $7548 €7500 Monochrome (50x68cm-20x27in) s.d.61 enamel wax pastel. 19-Nov-2 Finarte, Milan #123/R est:4200-5000
£4808 $7548 €7500 Untitled (121x102cm-48x40in) s. enamel. 19-Nov-2 Finarte, Milan #175/R
£5128 $8051 €8000 Futuristic people (70x100cm-28x39in) s. enamel. 21-Nov-2 Finarte, Rome #312/R est:7000
£5579 $8927 €8090 Untitled (75x110cm-30x43in) s.verso enamel painted 1973. 11-Mar-3 Babuino, Rome #305/R
£5769 $9058 €9000 Re-visiting the futurism (100x100cm-39x39in) s. enamel paper on canvas. 19-Nov-2 Finarte, Milan #282/R est:6500-8000
£5769 $9058 €9000 Window (185x130cm-73x51in) s. enamel painted 1979-80. 21-Nov-2 Finarte, Rome #269/R
£6410 $9936 €10000 Untitled (160x140cm-63x55in) s.verso enamel. 4-Dec-2 Finarte, Milan #488/R est:12000
£7595 $11848 €12000 Untitled (200x100cm-79x39in) s. enamel painted 1980. 14-Sep-2 Meeting Art, Vercelli #820/R est:10000
£8333 $13083 €13000 Fish (180x95cm-71x37in) s. enamel collage paper on canvas. 19-Nov-2 Finarte, Milan #257/R
£9615 $15096 €15000 Milan (120x122cm-47x48in) s.verso enamel paper prov. 19-Nov-2 Finarte, Milan #223/R est:11000-14000
£9615 $14904 €15000 Palm tree (200x100cm-79x39in) s. enamel. 4-Dec-2 Finarte, Milan #313/R est:11000
£10897 $16891 €17000 My sun (130x160cm-51x63in) s.i.verso enamel prov. 4-Dec-2 Finarte, Milan #493/R est:14000
£37671 $58767 €55000 Landscape (200x300cm-79x118in) enamel. 10-Apr-3 Finarte Semenzato, Rome #258/R est:70000

Works on paper

£769 $1208 €1200 Composition (100x70cm-39x28in) s. mixed media collage. 19-Nov-2 Finarte, Milan #164
£784 $1255 €1200 Untitled (100x70cm-39x28in) s. mixed media collage. 4-Jan-3 Meeting Art, Vercelli #597
£786 $1148 €1179 Composition (100x60cm-39x24in) s. mixed media collage prov. 4-Jun-2 Germann, Zurich #836 (S.FR 1800)
£1226 $1937 €1900 Untitled (100x70cm-39x28in) s. mixed media. 18-Dec-2 Christie's, Rome #66/R
£1282 $2013 €2000 Untitled (100x70cm-39x28in) s. mixed media collage. 19-Nov-2 Finarte, Milan #64/R
£1282 $2013 €2000 Untitled (100x70cm-39x28in) s. mixed media. 19-Nov-2 Finarte, Milan #63/R
£1282 $1987 €2000 Untitled (100x70cm-39x28in) s. mixed media. 4-Dec-2 Finarte, Milan #218/R est:2600
£1361 $2123 €2150 Composition (100x70cm-39x28in) s. mixed media exec.1979. 14-Sep-2 Meeting Art, Vercelli #40
£1418 $2298 €2000 1 x 100 informazione (50x50cm-20x20in) mixed media canvas prov. 22-May-3 Stadion, Trieste #208/R est:1600-2200
£1538 $2415 €2400 Landscape (20x30cm-8x12in) s. mixed media collage exec.1990. 21-Nov-2 Finarte, Rome #236/R
£1761 $2923 €2500 Untitled (100x70cm-39x28in) s. collage mixed media. 10-Jun-3 Finarte Semenzato, Milan #272/R est:2500-3000
£2027 $3162 €3000 Untitled (100x70cm-39x28in) s. mixed media. 26-Mar-3 Finarte Semenzato, Milan #74/R
£2129 $3364 €3300 Untitled (100x70cm-39x28in) s. collage felt-tip pen pencil prov. 18-Dec-2 Christie's, Rome #65/R
£2564 $3974 €4000 Untitled (100x70cm-39x28in) s. mixed media collage. 4-Dec-2 Finarte, Milan #467/R
£2603 $4060 €3800 Untitled (70x19cm-28x7in) s. mixed media collage exec.1995. 10-Apr-3 Finarte Semenzato, Rome #140/R
£2658 $4200 €4200 Tree (40x50cm-16x20in) s. enamel painted 1974. 29-Nov-2 Farsetti, Prato #429/R
£2885 $4529 €4500 Untitled (100x70cm-39x28in) s. mixed media collage. 19-Nov-2 Finarte, Milan #265/R
£4359 $6844 €6800 Natural (84x114cm-33x45in) s.i.verso. 23-Nov-2 Meeting Art, Vercelli #341/R
£4610 $7468 €6500 Compagni Compagni (53x79cm-21x31in) s. plexiglass collage photo paper on masonite exec.1968 lit. 26-May-3 Christie's, Milan #32/R est:5000-7000
£4730 $7378 €7000 Untitled (100x70cm-39x28in) s. mixed media enamel collage. 26-Mar-3 Finarte Semenzato, Milan #197/R
£4730 $7378 €7000 Coca Cola (100x70cm-39x28in) s.d.1962 mixed media collage enamel. 26-Mar-3 Finarte Semenzato, Milan #203/R
£4730 $7378 €7000 Coca Cola (100x70cm-39x28in) s.d.1962 mixed media enamel collage. 26-Mar-3 Finarte Semenzato, Milan #208/R
£4747 $7500 €7500 Futuristic (78x120cm-31x47in) s. enamel. 29-Nov-2 Farsetti, Prato #302/R
£10127 $16000 €16000 Palm tree (206x119cm-81x47in) s. enamel. 29-Nov-2 Farsetti, Prato #479/R est:8800
£10645 $16819 €16500 En plein air (100x139cm-39x55in) s. enamel pencil wax crayon prov. 18-Dec-2 Christie's, Rome #238/R est:20000
£18354 $29000 €29000 Anemic landscape (200x320cm-79x126in) s.verso enamel. 29-Nov-2 Farsetti, Prato #535/R est:20000

SCHIFF, Lesley (1951-) American

Prints

£3000 $4890 €4500 One point two (62x54cm-24x21in) laser light on paper executed 1997. 3-Feb-3 Sotheby's, Olympia #153/R est:3000-4000

SCHIFF, Robert (1869-1935) Austrian

£2152 $3400 €3400 Portrait of small girl (153x86cm-60x34in) s.d.1912. 27-Nov-2 Dorotheum, Vienna #123/R est:4000-6000

SCHIFFER, Anton (1811-1876) Austrian

£6028 $9766 €8500 View of Orts church in Ramsau, Berchtesgaden (20x26cm-8x10in) s. i.verso board. 22-May-3 Dorotheum, Vienna #24/R est:6500-7000

SCHIFFERDECKER, Heinz (1889-1924) German

£541 $845 €850 Bunch of summer flowers in a blue vase (58x47cm-23x19in) s. board lit. 7-Nov-2 Allgauer, Kempten #2949/R

SCHIFFERLE, Claudia (1955-) Swiss

£2183 $3188 €3275 Still life (163x158cm-64x62in) s.i.d.1982 verso acrylic varnish. 4-Jun-2 Germann, Zurich #47/R est:5500-7500 (S.FR 5000)

Works on paper

£306 $446 €459 Untitled (33x29cm-13x11in) s.d.1984 verso chl. 4-Jun-2 Germann, Zurich #841 (S.FR 700)

SCHILBACH, Johann Heinrich (1798-1851) German

£19231 $30385 €30000 Mountain landscape near Berchtesgaden (45x59cm-18x23in) s.d.1847. 16-Nov-2 Lempertz, Koln #1573/R est:35000

SCHILL, Emil (1870-1958) Swiss

£437 $681 €656 Mountain road in Metchtal (32x37cm-13x15in) s.d.1922 panel prov. 9-Nov-2 Galerie Gloggner, Luzern #117/R (S.FR 1000)

SCHILLE, Alice (1969-1955) American

Works on paper

£312 $500 €452 Hillside town (52x45cm-20x18in) s. W/C gouache. 16-May-3 Skinner, Boston #307/R
£1763 $2750 €2645 Red bridge (13x15cm-5x6in) s. W/C exec.c.1930. 18-Sep-2 Alderfer's, Hatfield #263 est:2000-4000
£2083 $3250 €3125 Horseback riding, New Mexico (13x15cm-5x6in) s. W/C exec.c.1919-1920. 18-Sep-2 Alderfer's, Hatfield #262/R est:2000-4000

SCHILLEROVA, Gabriela (1924-1993) Czechoslovakian

£442 $685 €663 Blue bouquet (95x77cm-37x30in) painted 1979. 3-Dec-2 SOGA, Bratislava #256/R (SL.K 28000)

SCHILY-KOPPERS, Julia (1855-?) German

£1384 $2158 €2200 Portrait of boy (56x45cm-22x18in) s. 9-Oct-2 Michael Zeller, Lindau #895/R est:2200

SCHIMMEL, Wilhelm (1817-1890) American/German
Sculpture
£1751 $2750 €2627 Figure of a rooster (8cm-3in) painted black yellow red with a green plinth prov. 23-Nov-2 Pook & Pook, Downington #324/R est:800-1000
£3185 $5000 €4778 Spread winged eagle (13x20cm-5x8in) polychrome carving prov. 23-Nov-2 Pook & Pook, Downington #95/R est:3000-5000

SCHIMMELPHFENNIG, Oswalt (19th C) German
Sculpture
£6000 $9780 €9000 Butterfly girl (64cm-25in) s.d.1897 pat bronze red marble base st.f.Gladenbeck and Sohn. 11-Feb-3 Christie's, Kensington #253/R est:5000-7000

SCHINDLER, Emil Jakob (1842-1892) Austrian
£1370 $2151 €2000 Rocks in landscape (18x28cm-7x11in) s. bears d.873 board. 16-Apr-3 Dorotheum, Salzburg #149/R est:2000-3000
Works on paper
£472 $731 €750 Dutch landscape with windmills (18x12cm-7x5in) i. Indian ink. 1-Oct-2 Dorotheum, Vienna #90/R

SCHINDLER, Emil Jakob (attrib) (1842-1892) Austrian
£3205 $4968 €5000 Spring walk through wood (22x28cm-9x11in) 5-Dec-2 Dr Fritz Nagel, Stuttgart #699/R est:1900

SCHINK, W (19th C) German
£1646 $2551 €2600 Grandfather with grandson by window (40x31cm-16x12in) s.d.1860. 25-Sep-2 Neumeister, Munich #710/R est:2800

SCHINKEL, Karl Friedrich (1781-1841) German
Prints
£39873 $63000 €63000 Gothic church in oak grove (49x34cm-19x13in) lithograph. 29-Nov-2 Bassenge, Berlin #5238/R est:20000
Works on paper
£9877 $16000 €14816 Elevation and plan of the facade of a building (24x23cm-9x9in) s.d.1840 pen ink W/C over pencil. 21-Jan-3 Sotheby's, New York #126/R est:30000
£25926 $42000 €38889 Pediment of doric building. Study (36x27cm-14x11in) s.d.1836 chk W/C two. 22-Jan-3 Christie's, Rockefeller NY #118/R est:10000

SCHINKEL, Susanne (1811-?) German
Works on paper
£704 $1169 €1000 Portrait of Elisabeth Schinkel (18x17cm-7x7in) pencil. 12-Jun-3 Hauswedell & Nolte, Hamburg #396/R

SCHINNAGL, Maximilian Joseph (1697-1762) German
£3774 $5849 €6000 Mountainous river landscape with figures (45x64cm-18x25in) lit. 2-Oct-2 Dorotheum, Vienna #262/R est:6000-9000

SCHIOLER, Inge (1908-1971) Swedish
£1822 $2842 €2733 Cliffs no.7 (19x24cm-7x9in) s. 6-Nov-2 AB Stockholms Auktionsverk #710/R est:30000-40000 (S.KR 26000)
£1964 $3102 €2946 Coastal landscape (26x24cm-10x9in) s. 30-Nov-2 Goteborg Auktionsverk, Sweden #628/R est:30000 (S.KR 28000)
£2102 $3280 €3153 Cliffs no.5 (19x24cm-7x9in) s.d.1968. 6-Nov-2 AB Stockholms Auktionsverk #711/R est:30000-40000 (S.KR 30000)
£2453 $3826 €3680 Evening landscape (38x46cm-15x18in) s. 6-Nov-2 AB Stockholms Auktionsverk #607/R est:40000-50000 (S.KR 35000)
£2662 $4205 €3993 The yellow cliff (26x32cm-10x13in) s.d.1960. 28-Apr-3 Bukowskis, Stockholm #106/R est:50000-55000 (S.KR 35000)
£2803 $4373 €4205 Vesterhavet - seascape (22x23cm-9x9in) s. 6-Nov-2 AB Stockholms Auktionsverk #740/R est:40000-50000 (S.KR 40000)
£2814 $4446 €4221 Blue water (22x24cm-9x9in) s. 28-Apr-3 Bukowskis, Stockholm #109/R est:25000-30000 (S.KR 37000)
£3498 $5527 €5247 Beach huts (19x24cm-7x9in) s. 28-Apr-3 Bukowskis, Stockholm #107/R est:40000-50000 (S.KR 46000)
£4765 $7434 €7148 Beach by Sundet (50x55cm-20x22in) s.d.1968. 5-Nov-2 Bukowskis, Stockholm #103/R est:80000-100000 (S.KR 68000)
£4867 $7690 €7301 Narrow channel (33x22cm-13x9in) s.d.1960. 28-Apr-3 Bukowskis, Stockholm #98/R est:30000-35000 (S.KR 64000)
£5046 $7871 €7569 Silver birches in spring (55x65cm-22x26in) s.d.56 panel. 5-Nov-2 Bukowskis, Stockholm #52a/R est:100000-125000 (S.KR 72000)
£5551 $8771 €8327 Boats by the shore (38x42cm-15x17in) s.d.1959. 28-Apr-3 Bukowskis, Stockholm #97/R est:50000-60000 (S.KR 73000)
£6307 $9839 €9461 Hill by beach, Southern Koster (50x55cm-20x22in) s.d.1961. 5-Nov-2 Bukowskis, Stockholm #105/R est:100000-125000 (S.KR 90000)
£8409 $13118 €12614 Coastal landscape from Kostersundet (37x42cm-15x17in) s.d.1960. 6-Nov-2 AB Stockholms Auktionsverk #600/R est:80000-100000 (S.KR 120000)
£8745 $13817 €13118 Coastal landscape from Bastuviken, Koster (51x56cm-20x22in) s.d.1966. 28-Apr-3 Bukowskis, Stockholm #204/R est:115000-125000 (S.KR 115000)
£9653 $15541 €14480 Summer landscape, Koster (58x65cm-23x26in) s. 7-May-3 AB Stockholms Auktionsverk #847/R est:150000-175000 (S.KR 125000)
£9811 $15305 €14717 Skogsridaa - landscape with trees (73x65cm-29x26in) s.d.1960 exhib. 5-Nov-2 Bukowskis, Stockholm #191/R est:150000-175000 (S.KR 140000)
£10425 $16784 €15638 Coastal landscape, Kostervik with boat houses (56x62cm-22x24in) s.d.1967. 7-May-3 AB Stockholms Auktionsverk #680/R est:125000-150000 (S.KR 135000)
£10811 $17405 €16217 House by the sea (46x50cm-18x20in) s.d.1960. 7-May-3 AB Stockholms Auktionsverk #756/R est:80000-100000 (S.KR 140000)
£16118 $25144 €24177 Autumn day - Sydkoster (66x73cm-26x29in) s.d.1965. 6-Nov-2 AB Stockholms Auktionsverk #527/R est:125000-150000 (S.KR 230000)
£21236 $34189 €31854 Punts at anchor, Langestrand, Koster (72x72cm-28x28in) s.d.1959. 7-May-3 AB Stockholms Auktionsverk #662/R est:150000-175000 (S.KR 275000)
Works on paper
£494 $776 €741 Tree, St Jorgen (42x33cm-17x13in) s. pastel. 16-Dec-2 Lilla Bukowskis, Stockholm #525 (S.KR 7000)
£617 $975 €926 At the foot of Billingen (46x38cm-18x15in) s. pastel. 30-Nov-2 Goteborg Auktionsverk, Sweden #627/R (S.KR 8800)
£701 $1093 €1052 Sunlit landscape - Sydkoster (37x45cm-15x18in) s.d.1961 pastel exhib. 6-Nov-2 AB Stockholms Auktionsverk #525/R (S.KR 10000)
£1004 $1666 €1456 Flowers (36x44cm-14x17in) s. gouache. 16-Jun-3 Lilla Bukowskis, Stockholm #79 est:18000-20000 (S.KR 13000)

SCHIOTT, August (1823-1895) Danish
£359 $552 €539 Mountain landscape, Austria (38x60cm-15x24in) s. 4-Sep-2 Kunsthallen, Copenhagen #77 (D.KR 4200)
£1088 $1731 €1600 Woodland glade in sunlight (63x100cm-25x39in) s.indis.d. 25-Feb-3 Dorotheum, Vienna #196/R est:1700-1900

SCHIOTTZ-JENSEN, N F (1855-1941) Danish
£315 $504 €473 Oxen and cart on heath, Jylland (29x40cm-11x16in) init.d.August 1876. 13-Jan-3 Rasmussen, Vejle #39/R (D.KR 3600)
£420 $667 €630 Two Italian street musicians (72x48cm-28x19in) s.d.1891. 5-May-3 Rasmussen, Vejle #559 (D.KR 4500)
£468 $740 €702 Italian girl with jug by fountain (44x35cm-17x14in) s.d.1914. 2-Dec-2 Rasmussen, Copenhagen #1613/R (D.KR 5500)
£510 $795 €765 Southern landscape with woman by fountain (27x23cm-11x9in) s/. 5-Aug-2 Rasmussen, Vejle #233/R (D.KR 6000)
£683 $1052 €1025 Italian woman in landscape (39x34cm-15x13in) s. 4-Sep-2 Kunsthallen, Copenhagen #91/R (D.KR 8000)
£689 $1047 €1034 Italian woman on the way to market (41x29cm-16x11in) s. 27-Aug-2 Rasmussen, Copenhagen #1663/R (D.KR 8000)
£1397 $2221 €2096 Man riding on donkey, woman and boy walking, Italy (52x70cm-20x28in) s. 10-Mar-3 Rasmussen, Vejle #201/R est:15000-18000 (D.KR 15000)

SCHIOTTZ-JENSEN, Niels F (1855-1941) Danish
£1359 $2121 €2039 Italian women by town's fountain (44x50cm-17x20in) s. 5-Aug-2 Rasmussen, Vejle #127/R est:10000 (D.KR 16000)
£1872 $2958 €2808 Young Italian girl leaning on a wall, basket of fruit by her side (37x28cm-15x11in) init. prov. 27-Nov-2 Museumsbygningen, Copenhagen #39/R est:25000 (D.KR 22000)
£2400 $3912 €3480 On the beach (68x54cm-27x21in) s.d.1919. 16-Jul-3 Sotheby's, Olympia #249/R est:2500-3500
£3483 $5434 €5225 Jens, the road worker gets a visit from girl coming with a dram (56x76cm-22x30in) s.d.1882. 5-Aug-2 Rasmussen, Vejle #250/R est:30000 (D.KR 41000)
£3724 $5922 €5586 Two Italian women and small boy eated watermelons on terrace (68x100cm-27x39in) s.i.d.1891. 5-Mar-3 Rasmussen, Copenhagen #1567/R est:50000 (D.KR 40000)

SCHIPPERHEYN, Peter Marinus (1955-) Australian
Sculpture
£2500 $3900 €3750 Paura dell intimita (58x46x30cm-23x18x12in) mono. exec.c.1988. 11-Nov-2 Deutscher-Menzies, Melbourne #113/R est:8000-12000 (A.D 7000)

SCHIPPERS, Joseph (1868-1950) Belgian

£423 $680 €600 Stormy weather at sea (41x67cm-16x26in) s.d.1948 verso. 12-May-3 Bernaerts, Antwerp #694
£451 $718 €650 La mere du Nord en tempete (28x37cm-11x15in) s.d.1928 panel. 29-Apr-3 Campo & Campo, Antwerp #787
£473 $738 €700 Renard dans un paysage enneige au couchant du soleil (55x100cm-22x39in) s. 25-Mar-3 Campo & Campo, Antwerp #183
£759 $1185 €1200 Marina at stormy weather (55x74cm-22x29in) s.d.1937. 21-Oct-2 Bernaerts, Antwerp #631
£2025 $3159 €3200 Marine at sunset (95x130cm-37x51in) s.d.1916. 21-Oct-2 Bernaerts, Antwerp #7/R est:3000-4000
£2158 $3453 €3000 L'envol des canards (72x120cm-28x47in) s. 19-May-3 Horta, Bruxelles #54 est:2500-3500
£2830 $4415 €4500 Chimpanze (35x25cm-14x10in) panel. 14-Oct-2 Amberes, Antwerp #187

SCHIPPERUS, Pieter Adrianus (1840-1929) Dutch

£896 $1425 €1300 Cows in a landscape (15x23cm-6x9in) s. canvas on panel. 10-Mar-3 Sotheby's, Amsterdam #107/R est:1200-1500
£1042 $1719 €1500 Tranquil village (40x53cm-16x21in) s. canvas on board. 1-Jul-3 Christie's, Amsterdam #105/R est:1500-2000
£3289 $5329 €5000 Goldberg at the Rotterdam docks (94x77cm-37x30in) s. 21-Jan-3 Christie's, Amsterdam #350/R est:5000-7000
£5263 $8526 €8000 Old plantation on the Maas, Rotterdam (70x118cm-28x46in) s. 21-Jan-3 Christie's, Amsterdam #345/R est:8000-12000

Works on paper

£563 $907 €800 Forest in winter with woodgather. Woodgatherers in forest (42x31cm-17x12in) s. one gouache two. 7-May-3 Vendue Huis, Gravenhage #465/R
£739 $1190 €1050 Forest view with wood cutter and tree wagon (41x57cm-16x22in) s. mixed media. 6-May-3 Vendu Notarishuis, Rotterdam #52/R

SCHIRM, Carl Cowen (1852-1928) German

£679 $1100 €1019 On the banks of the Oder River, Breslau, Poland (41x48cm-16x19in) s.i.verso board. 24-Jan-3 New Orleans Auction, New Orleans #1282/R est:1000-1500
£845 $1403 €1200 Mill near Soldau (71x96cm-28x38in) s. 14-Jun-3 Arnold, Frankfurt #855/R

SCHIRMANN, S (20th C) ?

£1603 $2452 €2500 Chasse en Baviere (80x93cm-31x37in) s.d.1946. 23-Aug-2 Deauville, France #208

SCHIRMER, August Wilhelm (1802-1866) German

Works on paper

£414 $646 €650 Vaison (27x26cm-11x10in) s.i. W/C over pencil. 5-Nov-2 Hartung & Hartung, Munich #5130

SCHIRMER, Johann Wilhelm (1807-1863) German

£3247 $4838 €5000 MOUntain landscape with the prophet Elias by waterfall (47x39cm-19x15in) mono. 26-Jun-2 Neumeister, Munich #843/R est:4000
£22000 $34100 €33000 View of Civitella, Italy (30x51cm-12x20in) i. oil on paper prov. 4-Dec-2 Christie's, London #74/R est:7000-9000
£46763 $74820 €65000 Swiss alpine landscape with Jungfrau (69x87cm-27x34in) exhib.prov.lit. 17-May-3 Lempertz, Koln #1480/R est:40000-45000

Works on paper

£404 $630 €590 Italian landscape (12x19cm-5x7in) i. pencil. 11-Apr-3 Winterberg, Heidelberg #553
£719 $1122 €1050 Campagna landscape with seated travellers (25x35cm-10x14in) pencil htd white sketch verso. 11-Apr-3 Winterberg, Heidelberg #552

SCHIRMER, Johann Wilhelm (attrib) (1807-1863) German

£918 $1432 €1450 Extensive Italian landscape in evening (17x42cm-7x17in) i. verso board lit. 14-Sep-2 Bergmann, Erlangen #739/R
£8974 $14090 €14000 Figures and horses pulling cart in landscape with bridge over dried up river bed (71x94cm-28x37in) 23-Nov-2 Arnold, Frankfurt #865/R est:3000

Works on paper

£897 $1418 €1400 Landscape near Tivoli (44x62cm-17x24in) d.14 Juni 1840 i. verso pen. 16-Nov-2 Lempertz, Koln #1398

SCHIRREN, Ferdinand (1872-1944) Belgian

£1310 $2097 €1900 Nature morte aux chrysanthemes (58x58cm-23x23in) s.d.44. 17-Mar-3 Horta, Bruxelles #138 est:2500-3500

Works on paper

£641 $1006 €1000 Vases aux petales de fleurs. s. W/C. 19-Nov-2 Galerie Moderne, Brussels #179/R
£1206 $2013 €1700 Maternite (69x57cm-27x22in) s. pastel. 18-Jun-3 Hotel des Ventes Mosan, Brussels #204 est:800-1000
£1987 $3120 €3100 La lecon de piano (72x93cm-28x37in) s.d.1915 chl. 19-Nov-2 Vanderkindere, Brussels #432 est:1250-1750
£2051 $3221 €3200 Maternite (73x84cm-29x33in) s. chl dr. 19-Nov-2 Vanderkindere, Brussels #435 est:1250-1750
£2734 $4374 €3800 Nude seated (83x61cm-33x24in) s.d.1910 chl dr. 17-May-3 De Vuyst, Lokeren #325/R est:3300-3800

SCHIVE, Jacob Oxholm (1847-1912) Norwegian

£716 $1160 €1074 Winter landscape with birds in field (77x133cm-30x52in) s. 3-Feb-3 Lilla Bukowskis, Stockholm #725 (S.KR 10000)

SCHIVERT, Victor (1863-?) Rumanian

£1667 $2583 €2600 Tavern with cavalier and young woman at a table (53x63cm-21x25in) s.i. canvas on canvas. 4-Dec-2 Neumeister, Munich #880 est:1000

SCHIWETZ, Edward M (1898-1984) American

Works on paper

£1603 $2500 €2405 Ft Davis ruins (33x43cm-13x17in) mixed media executed c.1960. 19-Oct-2 David Dike, Dallas #223/R est:1500-3000
£3045 $4750 €4568 Old Fort Brown (18x41cm-7x16in) mixed media. 19-Oct-2 David Dike, Dallas #224/R est:4000-6000

SCHJERFBECK, Helene (1862-1946) Finnish

£395 $627 €580 Ex libris Einar Reuter (12x8cm-5x3in) 27-Feb-3 Hagelstam, Helsinki #890
£2848 $4500 €4500 The confirmation candidate (62x44cm-24x17in) s.num.57/70 lithograph. 1-Dec-2 Bukowskis, Helsinki #174/R est:3500-4000
£7595 $12000 €12000 Nun (56x46cm-22x18in) s.d.79. 1-Dec-2 Bukowskis, Helsinki #166/R est:12000-15000
£15823 $25000 €25000 Head of Christ (45x37cm-18x15in) s. canvas on board exhib.lit. 1-Dec-2 Bukowskis, Helsinki #171/R est:25000-27000
£26582 $42000 €42000 The girl in Florence (54x32cm-21x13in) s.d.94 prov.lit. 1-Dec-2 Bukowskis, Helsinki #169/R est:42000-45000
£180000 $300600 €261000 Karin (46x29cm-18x11in) init. canvas on board painted 1928 prov.exhib.lit. 25-Jun-3 Christie's, London #149/R est:180000-220000
£190000 $311600 €285000 Stubborn girl (42x43cm-17x17in) init. painted 1938-39 prov.exhib.lit. 4-Feb-3 Christie's, London #315/R est:160000
£250000 $410000 €375000 Tanssiaiskengat balskorna - dancing shoes (20x26cm-8x10in) init.d.83 prov.exhib.lit. 3-Jun-3 Sotheby's, London #214/R est:250000-350000
£316456 $500000 €500000 Hjordis (47x37cm-19x15in) s. exhib. 1-Dec-2 Bukowskis, Helsinki #168/R est:500000-550000
£485916 $782324 €690000 Self-portrait, light and shade (36x34cm-14x13in) s.d.45 oil chl prov.exhib.lit. 10-May-3 Bukowskis, Helsinki #154/R est:400000-500000
£600000 $978000 €900000 Alarm (74x62cm-29x24in) init. painted 1935 prov.exhib.lit. 3-Feb-3 Christie's, London #85/R est:800000

Prints

£2948 $4776 €4275 The picture book (27x41cm-11x16in) s.num.55/90 lithograph. 26-May-3 Bukowskis, Stockholm #206/R est:30000-35000 (S.KR 38000)
£3879 $6284 €5625 The convalescence (36x55cm-14x22in) s. col lithograph exec.c.1938-39. 26-May-3 Bukowskis, Stockholm #208/R est:50000-60000 (S.KR 50000)
£5190 $8200 €8200 The convalescent (48x83cm-19x33in) s.num.5/30 col lithograph. 1-Dec-2 Bukowskis, Helsinki #173/R est:7000-7500
£6362 $10306 €9225 The satin shoe (37x42cm-15x17in) s.num.38/50 col lithograph. 26-May-3 Bukowskis, Stockholm #207/R est:50000-60000 (S.KR 82000)

Works on paper

£2911 $4600 €4600 Girl from the loom (30x22cm-12x9in) s. pencil W/C executed c.1915. 30-Nov-2 Hagelstam, Helsinki #104/R est:5000
£3546 $5496 €5319 Study for In front of the mirror (26x23cm-10x9in) init. chl executed c.1937 exhib.lit. 3-Dec-2 Bukowskis, Stockholm #313a/R est:50000-70000 (S.KR 50000)
£3597 $5755 €5000 Tree trunks, birch wood (23x28cm-9x11in) pencil sketch. 17-May-3 Hagelstam, Helsinki #52/R est:5000
£3662 $5896 €5200 Portrait study (22x18cm-9x7in) s. s.d.29 verso dr. 10-May-3 Bukowskis, Helsinki #155/R est:4000-5000
£6646 $10500 €10500 A picture postcard from Ekenas with Happy Christmas (21x31cm-8x12in) s. mixed media. 1-Dec-2 Bukowskis, Helsinki #167/R est:5000-6000
£11392 $18000 €18000 Birch trunks (17x22cm-7x9in) s. W/C gouache. 1-Dec-2 Bukowskis, Helsinki #172/R est:7000-8000
£26582 $42000 €42000 Girl with red lips (26x24cm-10x9in) s. W/C. 1-Dec-2 Bukowskis, Helsinki #170/R est:20000-25000

£28704 $46501 €41621 Young girl (43x35cm-17x14in) init.i. mixed media exec.c.after 1938 prov. 26-May-3 Bukowskis, Stockholm #276/R est:450000-500000 (S.KR 370000)
£35211 $56690 €50000 Two women (26x33cm-10x13in) s. W/C pencil. 10-May-3 Bukowskis, Helsinki #169/R est:25000-30000
£95000 $155800 €142500 Mother from the alarm (35x29cm-14x11in) init. W/C chl exec.1935 prov.lit. 4-Feb-3 Christie's, London #316/R est:120000
£240000 $393600 €360000 Sininauhainen tytto, flick med blatt band - girl with a blue ribbon (46x34cm-18x13in) indis sig. W/C gouache pastel paper on card prov.exhib.lit. 3-Jun-3 Sotheby's, London #216/R est:150000-200000

SCHLAGETER, Karl (1894-?) Swiss
£349 $545 €524 Harbour (42x71cm-17x28in) s.d.1956. 20-Nov-2 Fischer, Luzern #2231/R (S.FR 800)
£409 $630 €650 Mother and child (98x78cm-39x31in) s.d.1928 panel. 26-Oct-2 Quittenbaum, Hamburg #116/R
£570 $889 €900 Three female nudes in river landscape (70x100cm-28x39in) s. 18-Oct-2 Dr Fritz Nagel, Stuttgart #310/R

SCHLEEH, Hans (1928-) Canadian
Sculpture
£645 $1019 €968 Composition (52cm-20in) s. grey stone prov. 18-Nov-2 Sotheby's, Toronto #41/R est:2000-3000 (C.D 1600)
£1067 $1749 €1601 Embrace (46cm-18in) s. stone slate base prov. 27-May-3 Sotheby's, Toronto #83/R est:3000-4000 (C.D 2400)

SCHLEGEL, Friedrich August (1828-?) German
Works on paper
£629 $900 €944 River landscape (15x23cm-6x9in) s. W/C. 23-Jan-3 Swann Galleries, New York #383/R

SCHLEGEL, Herbert Rolf (1889-1972) German
£256 $374 €400 Female nude (60x60cm-24x24in) mono. 4-Jun-2 Karl & Faber, Munich #410

SCHLEICH, Anton (1809-1851) German
Works on paper
£436 $689 €680 Meeting on a bridge (17x24cm-7x9in) s.d.1843 Indian ink brush over pencil wash board. 15-Nov-2 Reiss & Sohn, Konigstein #364/R

SCHLEICH, Eduard (elder) (1812-1874) German
£616 $962 €900 Morning mist on the mountains (15x21cm-6x8in) s. panel. 9-Apr-3 Neumeister, Munich #741
£962 $1490 €1500 Extensive lower alpine landscape (23x30cm-9x12in) panel. 5-Dec-2 Dr Fritz Nagel, Stuttgart #700/R est:1000
£1161 $1707 €1800 Extensive landscape with town (23x30cm-9x12in) panel. 20-Jun-2 Dr Fritz Nagel, Stuttgart #823/R est:2500
£1795 $2782 €2800 Extensive landscape with course of a river in distance (22x40cm-9x16in) canvas on canvas. 4-Dec-2 Neumeister, Munich #882/R est:1200
£1885 $3092 €2733 Alpine landscape (43x35cm-17x14in) s. panel. 4-Jun-3 AB Stockholms Auktionsverk #2440/R est:30000-40000 (S.KR 24000)
£2042 $3288 €2900 Meadow landscape with avenue of trees and peasant woman with horse (8x26cm-3x10in) panel. 10-May-3 Hans Stahl, Toestorf #20 est:2700
£2051 $3179 €3200 Dutch landscape at dusk with windmill near water (19x42cm-7x17in) s. 4-Dec-2 Neumeister, Munich #881/R est:2500

SCHLEICH, Eduard (elder-attrib) (1812-1874) German
£641 $974 €1000 Starnberger lake viewed through shining light (15x21cm-6x8in) panel. 11-Jul-2 Allgauer, Kempten #2675/R

SCHLEICH, Eduard (elder-circle) (1812-1874) German
£325 $484 €500 Autumn in Ramsau (31x22cm-12x9in) i. panel. 26-Jun-2 Neumeister, Munich #845/R

SCHLEICH, Eduard (younger) (1853-1893) German
£1329 $2060 €2100 Horse drawn cart on country track (20x29cm-8x11in) s. canvas on board. 25-Sep-2 Neumeister, Munich #711/R est:2500
£1859 $2881 €2900 Extensive Isar landscape with boat and figures (24x34cm-9x13in) mono. d.1886 lit. 7-Dec-2 Bergmann, Erlangen #805/R est:3200

SCHLEICH, Eduard (younger-attrib) (1853-1893) German
£584 $871 €900 Lower alpine landscape (13x41cm-5x16in) i. panel. 26-Jun-2 Neumeister, Munich #846/R
£633 $981 €1000 Meadow path (35x48cm-14x19in) s. bears d. 25-Sep-2 Neumeister, Munich #712/R

SCHLEICH, Franz Xaver (1869-1911) Austrian
Works on paper
£574 $896 €850 Himmelpfortgasse (45x33cm-18x13in) s.d.1904 W/C. 28-Mar-3 Dorotheum, Vienna #336/R

SCHLEICH, Robert (1845-1934) German
£823 $1275 €1300 Harvesting hay in pre-alpine landscape (7x8cm-3x3in) s. panel. 25-Sep-2 Neumeister, Munich #713/R
£1169 $1742 €1800 Autumnal wooded landscape with cows (17x25cm-7x10in) s. board. 26-Jun-2 Neumeister, Munich #847/R
£1300 $2067 €1950 Haymaking scene (6x7cm-2x3in) s. panel. 27-Feb-3 Greenslade Hunt, Taunton #1293/R est:1500-2500
£1549 $2494 €2200 Figures in landscape (9x25cm-4x10in) s. panel lit. 9-May-3 Schloss Ahlden, Ahlden #1417/R est:1900
£2534 $3953 €3700 Ice pleasures (11x13cm-4x5in) s. panel. 10-Apr-3 Van Ham, Cologne #1691/R est:2800
£3205 $4968 €5000 Hay making in the lower Alps with oxen, horses and fully laden carts (14x27cm-6x11in) s.d.1885 panel. 4-Dec-2 Neumeister, Munich #883/R est:2000

SCHLEICHER, Carl (19th C) Austrian
£305 $500 €442 Watchmaker (20x15cm-8x6in) s. indis i.verso panel. 4-Jun-3 Doyle, New York #84
£705 $1107 €1100 Portraits of old men (12x9cm-5x4in) s. panel. 21-Nov-2 Van Ham, Cologne #1896/R
£818 $1259 €1300 Card game (40x50cm-16x20in) s. 22-Oct-2 Wiener Kunst Auktionen, Vienna #1101/R
£2278 $3554 €3600 Inn scenes (20x16cm-8x6in) s. panel pair. 16-Sep-2 Horta, Bruxelles #85

SCHLEISNER, C A (1810-1882) Danish
£372 $592 €558 Interior scene with small boy not wanting to take his medicine (45x35cm-18x14in) 5-Mar-3 Rasmussen, Copenhagen #1721/R (D.KR 4000)
£419 $666 €629 Two monks in discussion in a monastery (39x31cm-15x12in) s. 5-Mar-3 Rasmussen, Copenhagen #1720/R (D.KR 4500)
£681 $1076 €1022 Fishermen enjoying a glass of wine (25x36cm-10x14in) s.d.1861. 2-Dec-2 Rasmussen, Copenhagen #1700/R (D.KR 8000)
£1171 $1886 €1757 Interior from an inn with two sailors and a sleeping negro (45x37cm-18x15in) s. 26-Feb-3 Museumsbygningen, Copenhagen #11/R est:6000 (D.KR 13000)

SCHLEISNER, Christian Andreas (1810-1882) Danish
£512 $789 €768 Two children gathering firewood in winter forest (25x22cm-10x9in) s. 4-Sep-2 Kunsthallen, Copenhagen #61/R (D.KR 6000)
£630 $1009 €945 Interior scene with man around table (25x33cm-10x13in) s.d.1869. 13-Jan-3 Rasmussen, Vejle #235/R (D.KR 7200)
£850 $1325 €1275 Danish summer landscape with woman knitting and watching butterfly (42x36cm-17x14in) s.d.1860. 5-Aug-2 Rasmussen, Vejle #242/R (D.KR 10000)
£1818 $2709 €2800 Tyrolean boy (32x24cm-13x9in) s.d.1843. 26-Jun-2 Neumeister, Munich #848/R est:1250
£2239 $3404 €3359 Interior scene with fisherman's family - grandparents watching children playing skittles (50x69cm-20x27in) s.d.1854. 27-Aug-2 Rasmussen, Copenhagen #1499/R est:15000-20000 (D.KR 26000)

SCHLEMMER, Oskar (1888-1943) German
£9929 $16085 €14000 Sunlit house (32x44cm-13x17in) s.d.1911 oil tempera board prov. 20-May-3 Dorotheum, Vienna #7/R est:15000-20000
£24638 $40406 €34000 Head in profile (14x5cm-6x2in) tempera canvas on board prov. 30-May-3 Villa Grisebach, Berlin #49/R est:20000-25000
£81761 $127547 €130000 Sitzende nach rechts - Seated woman facing right (56x19cm-22x7in) oil on olpapier executed 1936 prov.exhib.lit. 9-Oct-2 Sotheby's, London #335/R est:130000-200000
£125786 $196226 €200000 Sitzende und zwei figuren - Seated woman and two figures (60x45cm-24x18in) s.i.d.1936 verso prov.exhib.lit. 8-Oct-2 Sotheby's, London #33/R est:240000-320000
£251572 $392453 €400000 Blaue treppe - Blue steps (65x48cm-26x19in) d.2766 prov.exhib.lit. 8-Oct-2 Sotheby's, London #28/R est:300000-400000
Prints
£2885 $4471 €4500 Head (20x14cm-8x6in) s. lithograph. 7-Dec-2 Hauswedell & Nolte, Hamburg #1024/R est:5000
£3239 $5377 €4600 Figure plan (33x22cm-13x9in) s. lithograph. 14-Jun-3 Hauswedell & Nolte, Hamburg #1573/R est:4500
£4173 $6843 €5800 Figure H2 - Figure from the side (36x24cm-14x9in) s.d. lithograph. 6-Jun-3 Ketterer, Munich #59/R est:5800-6500
Works on paper
£3623 $5942 €5000 Forest study (24x34cm-9x13in) i. verso W/C over pencil prov. 31-May-3 Villa Grisebach, Berlin #199/R est:4000-5000

£5380 $8392 €8500 Boys head with light on forehead and chest (12x9cm-5x4in) ink wash prov.lit. 18-Oct-2 Dr Fritz Nagel, Stuttgart #606/R est:9500
£14241 $22500 €22500 Profile to the left (33x24cm-13x9in) i.d.27 pencil paper on cardboard. 29-Nov-2 Villa Grisebach, Berlin #71/R est:25000-30000
£238994 $372830 €380000 Konzentrische madchen gruppe - Concentric group of girls (55x44cm-22x17in) W/C gouache pencil executed 1928 prov.exhib.lit. 8-Oct-2 Sotheby's, London #22/R est:240000-320000

SCHLEMNINGER, Max (20th C) Danish?
£681 $1076 €1022 Interior scene with nude model (100x75cm-39x30in) s. 30-Nov-2 Rasmussen, Havnen #2161/R (D.KR 8000)

SCHLENK, H (?) ?
£1500 $2355 €2250 Off to the ball (71x49cm-28x19in) s.i. panel. 16-Apr-3 Christie's, Kensington #863/R est:800-1200

SCHLESINGER, Felix (1833-1910) German
£1146 $1800 €1719 Boy with pipe (25x20cm-10x8in) s. panel. 10-Dec-2 Doyle, New York #179/R est:3000-5000
£1593 $2517 €2390 The sausage thief (32x40cm-13x16in) s.d.53. 28-Apr-3 Blomqvist, Oslo #316/R est:25000-35000 (N.KR 18000)
£2800 $4592 €4200 Time for a good smoke (25x20cm-10x8in) s. panel. 5-Jun-3 Christie's, Kensington #618/R est:2000-3000
£8387 $13000 €12581 Old basket weaver (60x76cm-24x30in) s. prov. 3-Dec-2 Christie's, Rockefeller NY #636/R est:8000-12000
£10044 $15668 €15066 Blonde girl feeding rabbit (17x14cm-7x6in) s. panel. 20-Nov-2 Fischer, Luzern #1157/R est:24000-30000 (S.FR 23000)
£10127 $16000 €15191 Family interior (36x49cm-14x19in) s. panel. 24-Apr-3 Sotheby's, New York #136/R est:10000-15000
£14103 $22141 €22000 Dog training (48x34cm-19x13in) s. 21-Nov-2 Van Ham, Cologne #1897/R est:35000

SCHLESINGER, Henri-Guillaume (1814-1893) French
£2329 $3750 €3494 Portrait of a young woman (74x58cm-29x23in) s.d.1873 oval. 19-Feb-3 Doyle, New York #25/R est:6000-8000
Works on paper
£321 $503 €500 Ne suis-je pas belle (47x50cm-19x20in) s. chl W/C. 24-Nov-2 Chayette & Cheval, Paris #236b
£353 $554 €550 Enfin un matin apparurent les murs de la ville Sainte, Jerusalem (31x46cm-12x18in) s. chl W/C. 24-Nov-2 Chayette & Cheval, Paris #236a
£385 $604 €600 Mur des lamentations (38x44cm-15x17in) s. chl. 24-Nov-2 Chayette & Cheval, Paris #236c

SCHLESINGER, Johann (attrib) (1768-1848) German
£599 $994 €850 Portrait of Leonard Heyl (42x34cm-17x13in) i.verso. 14-Jun-3 Arnold, Frankfurt #857/R
£704 $1169 €1000 Portrait of Katherina Heyl, born Vollmer (42x35cm-17x14in) i.verso. 14-Jun-3 Arnold, Frankfurt #858/R

SCHLESINGER, Karl (1825-1893) Swiss
£1396 $2262 €2024 Landscape with women resting (33x40cm-13x16in) s.i.d.1864 prov. 25-May-3 Uppsala Auktionskammare, Uppsala #61/R est:12000-15000 (S.KR 18000)

SCHLESINGER, Karl (attrib) (1825-1893) Swiss
£1646 $2551 €2469 At the dressing table (60x50cm-24x20in) bears sig prov. 3-Dec-2 Ritchie, Toronto #3090/R est:2000-2500 (C.D 4000)

SCHLESINGER, M (19/20th C) ?
Works on paper
£550 $858 €825 Portrait of Richard Sickert (30x20cm-12x8in) chl executed c.1903 prov. 12-Sep-2 Sotheby's, Olympia #60/R

SCHLESINGER, Mark (1949-) American
£510 $800 €765 Trace (153x142cm-60x56in) 21-Nov-2 Swann Galleries, New York #190/R

SCHLETTE, Emma (1847-1912) German
£372 $580 €550 Lake landscape with mountains beyond (42x100cm-17x39in) i. verso. 31-Mar-3 Dr Fritz Nagel, Stuttgart #7083/R
£372 $580 €550 Lower alpine landscape (41x100cm-16x39in) i. verso. 31-Mar-3 Dr Fritz Nagel, Stuttgart #7084/R

SCHLETTE, Engelina Helena (1875-1954) Dutch
Works on paper
£955 $1490 €1500 Lady with mirror (85x68cm-33x27in) s. pastel. 6-Nov-2 Vendue Huis, Gravenhage #104 est:1800-2200

SCHLEU, Michael (1961-) Swedish?
Works on paper
£309 $497 €464 The dream (35x46cm-14x18in) s.d.00 verso beeswax oil on cotton cloth. 7-May-3 AB Stockholms Auktionsverk #1056/R (S.KR 4000)

SCHLICHTER, Rudolf (1890-1955) German
£2051 $2995 €3200 Life and death (100x74cm-39x29in) s.d.1940 board. 4-Jun-2 Karl & Faber, Munich #411/R est:7000-8000
Works on paper
£252 $392 €400 In the harem (16x14cm-6x6in) s.i. pen brush ink prov. 9-Oct-2 Sotheby's, London #252/R
£316 $500 €500 One man trips another on a staircase (49x36cm-19x14in) s. pen dr. 30-Nov-2 Geble, Radolfzell #732
£755 $1177 €1200 Alpine landscape. Hohenzollern Alp (37x45cm-15x18in) s.i.d.34 pencil two prov. 9-Oct-2 Sotheby's, London #245/R est:2000-3000
£1195 $1864 €1900 Sumpfvogel - marsh bird (50x65cm-20x26in) s.i.d.1938 pen ink prov. 9-Oct-2 Sotheby's, London #212/R est:2800-3500
£1761 $2747 €2800 Nailing to the cross (51x73cm-20x29in) s.i.d.1939 pen ink prov. 9-Oct-2 Sotheby's, London #240/R est:4200-5200
£1761 $2747 €2800 Danube Valley. Black forest slopes (51x66cm-20x26in) s.i.d.1939 pen ink two prov. 9-Oct-2 Sotheby's, London #246/R est:4000-6000
£1772 $2800 €2800 The collector (64x50cm-25x20in) s. feltpen. 30-Nov-2 Villa Grisebach, Berlin #282/R est:3000-4000
£1887 $2943 €3000 Apocalypse - whore of Babylon (64x50cm-25x20in) s.i.d.1948 pen brush ink prov. 9-Oct-2 Sotheby's, London #217/R est:4500-6500
£2201 $3434 €3500 Siegfried;s journey on the Rhine. Fasolt and Fafner. s.i.d.1934 one s.i.verso pen ink two. 9-Oct-2 Sotheby's, London #238/R est:5000-7000
£2201 $3434 €3500 Mountain landscape. Hohenzollern (51x64cm-20x25in) s.i.d.1939 pen ink prov. 9-Oct-2 Sotheby's, London #247/R est:5000-7000
£3019 $4709 €4800 Apocalypse - four riders (64x50cm-25x20in) s.i.d.1948 pen ink prov. 9-Oct-2 Sotheby's, London #216/R est:4500-6500
£3145 $4906 €5000 Untitled (73x51cm-29x20in) s.d.1943 pen ink prov. 9-Oct-2 Sotheby's, London #237/R est:3000-4000
£3165 $5000 €5000 Big city vision (54x42cm-21x17in) s. gouache over pencil sketch verso. 30-Nov-2 Villa Grisebach, Berlin #272/R est:5000-7000
£3459 $5396 €5500 Portrait of Ernst Junger (65x50cm-26x20in) s.i.d.1937 pencil prov. 9-Oct-2 Sotheby's, London #248/R est:4000-6000
£3774 $5887 €6000 Save yourselves, those who can (72x51cm-28x20in) s.i.d.June 39 pen ink prov. 9-Oct-2 Sotheby's, London #244/R est:4000-6000
£5769 $8942 €9000 Maid (77x56cm-30x22in) s.i.d.1929 W/C pencil. 4-Dec-2 Lempertz, Koln #1045/R est:8000-10000

SCHLICHTING CARLSEN, Carl (1852-1903) Danish
£391 $622 €587 Landscape from Funkedammen (64x94cm-25x37in) s.d.81 exhib. 10-Mar-3 Rasmussen, Vejle #289/R (D.KR 4200)
£426 $672 €639 Wooded landscape with brook, spring (33x24cm-13x9in) s.d.76. 2-Dec-2 Rasmussen, Copenhagen #1251/R (D.KR 5000)
£512 $814 €768 Landscape with road, Hellebaek (48x66cm-19x26in) s.d.1901 exhib. 10-Mar-3 Rasmussen, Vejle #129 (D.KR 5500)
£553 $874 €830 Coastal landscape, North Sjaelland (66x107cm-26x42in) s.d.1900. 2-Dec-2 Rasmussen, Copenhagen #1282/R (D.KR 6500)
£813 $1318 €1179 By Funkedammen in September (64x93cm-25x37in) s.d.81 exhib. 26-May-3 Rasmussen, Copenhagen #1509/R (D.KR 8500)
£986 $1539 €1479 Wooded landscape with woman by river (60x90cm-24x35in) s. 11-Nov-2 Rasmussen, Vejle #651/R (D.KR 11500)

SCHLICK, Benst (19th C) Italian
Works on paper
£3448 $5448 €5000 Carmine church, Naples (23x16cm-9x6in) s. i.verso W/C. 3-Apr-3 Porro, Milan #50/R est:8000

SCHLIEBEN, Caroline von (19th C) German
Works on paper
£1006 $1550 €1600 White satllion (36x47cm-14x19in) s. W/C. 28-Oct-2 Il Ponte, Milan #43/R

SCHLIECKER, August Eduard (1833-1911) German
£1635 $2551 €2600 Old city street with figures (35x27cm-14x11in) s. 19-Sep-2 Dr Fritz Nagel, Stuttgart #996/R est:900
Works on paper
£353 $546 €550 Lauenburg (26x22cm-10x9in) s. W/C. 5-Dec-2 Schopman, Hamburg #643

SCHLIMARSKI, Heinrich Hans (1859-1913) Austrian
Works on paper
£2000 $3340 €3000 Sailor's girl (150x97cm-59x38in) indis sig. pastel. 18-Jun-3 Christie's, Kensington #139/R est:2000-3000

SCHLITT, Heinrich (1849-1923) German
£1830 $3001 €2800 Gnome and cricket on floor of forest with mushrooms (20x30cm-8x12in) s. panel. 5-Feb-3 Neumeister, Munich #811/R est:700

SCHLOBACH, Willy (1865-1951) Belgian
£538 $834 €850 Summer flowers in vase (61x73cm-24x29in) mono. 27-Sep-2 Karrenbauer, Konstanz #1672
£1076 $1668 €1700 Trees on lake shore near Nonnenhorn (77x91cm-30x36in) mono. lit. 27-Sep-2 Karrenbauer, Konstanz #1671 est:850
£2270 $3790 €3200 Marina with trees near the border (75x90cm-30x35in) 23-Jun-3 Bernaerts, Antwerp #179/R est:3000-4000
£2500 $3975 €3750 Summer flowers in a vase (61x74cm-24x29in) mono. 20-Mar-3 Christie's, Kensington #30/R est:3000-5000
£41139 $65000 €65000 Vue des falaises anglaises a l'aube (61x70cm-24x28in) mono.d.07 exhib. 26-Nov-2 Palais de Beaux Arts, Brussels #372/R est:30000-50000

SCHLOBACH, Willy (attrib) (1865-1951) Belgian
£1724 $2759 €2500 Pecheuses de crevettes (55x82cm-22x32in) painted c.1880-85 prov. 15-Mar-3 De Vuyst, Lokeren #286/R est:2700-3000

SCHLOEMANN, Eduard (1888-1940) German
£400 $648 €600 At the shore (65x82cm-26x32in) s.d.1919. 23-Jan-3 Christie's, Kensington #87

SCHLOESSER, Carl (1832-1914) German
£566 $883 €900 Landscape (43x61cm-17x24in) s. 23-Sep-2 Durán, Madrid #87/R
£1282 $2013 €2000 Grandfather playing the accordion (46x37cm-18x15in) s. panel. 16-Dec-2 Bernaerts, Antwerp #45/R est:2000-2200
£2878 $4604 €4000 Woman thinking (72x54cm-28x21in) s. 17-May-3 Lempertz, Koln #1482/R est:4000

SCHLOGL, Josef von (1851-?) Austrian
£705 $1072 €1100 Lake Garda (24x35cm-9x14in) s.d.1897 panel. 31-Aug-2 Geble, Radolfzell #660/R
£949 $1500 €1500 Procession in mountain valley (36x29cm-14x11in) s.d.1905 panel. 29-Nov-2 Bassenge, Berlin #6054 est:1200
£2800 $4676 €4200 Lake Lugano (46x54cm-18x21in) s. panel. 18-Jun-3 Christie's, Kensington #165/R est:3000-5000

SCHLOSSER, Bernhard (1802-1859) German
£2009 $3134 €3014 Young bird lover (109x66cm-43x26in) s.d.1891. 6-Nov-2 Dobiaschofsky, Bern #950/R est:6500 (S.FR 4600)

SCHLOSSER, Gerard (1931-) French
£3459 $5362 €5500 Il ne parlera jamais (162x130cm-64x51in) s.i.d.verso prov. 30-Oct-2 Artcurial Briest, Paris #483/R est:5000-7000
£5479 $8603 €8000 Pres de Brest (150x150cm-59x59in) s.d.1990 i.verso acrylic. 21-Apr-3 Rabourdin & Choppin de Janvry, Paris #209/R est:9500-10000
£13087 $21070 €19500 Deuxieme balade (200x200cm-79x79in) s.i.d.1999 verso. 23-Feb-3 Mercier & Cie, Lille #169/R
£15278 $24292 €22000 On est bien la (190x190cm-75x75in) s.d.1973 verso acrylic lit. 29-Apr-3 Artcurial Briest, Paris #381/R est:12000-15000
£17361 $27605 €25000 Il ne vient pas (113x145cm-44x57in) s.i.d.1970 verso acrylic. 29-Apr-3 Artcurial Briest, Paris #380/R est:20000-25000

SCHLOSSER, Leopold Ludwig (?-1836) German
Works on paper
£493 $818 €700 Gothic ruins on Oybin (10x13cm-4x5in) s. W/C. 12-Jun-3 Hauswedell & Nolte, Hamburg #398/R

SCHMAEDEL, Max von (1856-?) German
£800 $1304 €1200 Girls in a garden (99x79cm-39x31in) 28-Jan-3 Gorringes, Lewes #1655/R

SCHMALIX, Hubert (1952-) Austrian
£759 $1200 €1200 Untitled (60x42cm-24x17in) s.d.83 acrylic. 27-Nov-2 Dorotheum, Vienna #293/R
£823 $1300 €1300 Trees (57x76cm-22x30in) s.d.76 verso. 27-Nov-2 Dorotheum, Vienna #294/R
£4167 $6625 €6000 Life and death (230x86cm-91x34in) s.d.1983. 29-Apr-3 Wiener Kunst Auktionen, Vienna #472/R est:5000-8000
£6623 $10795 €10000 Crossing (140x287cm-55x113in) s.d.1982 verso. 28-Jan-3 Dorotheum, Vienna #247/R est:11000-16000
£9220 $14936 €13000 North wind - south wind (290x390cm-114x154in) 20-May-3 Dorotheum, Vienna #267/R est:15000-20000
Works on paper
£705 $1093 €1100 Face (61x45cm-24x18in) s.d.85 W/C. 5-Dec-2 Dorotheum, Graz #128/R
£823 $1275 €1300 Bent over person (62x44cm-24x17in) s.d.82 mixed media. 24-Sep-2 Wiener Kunst Auktionen, Vienna #295/R
£833 $1325 €1200 Yellow face (59x42cm-23x17in) gouache. 29-Apr-3 Wiener Kunst Auktionen, Vienna #480/R

SCHMALZ, Herbert Gustave (1856-1935) British
£900 $1467 €1350 Firoza (23x18cm-9x7in) s.i. 29-Jan-3 Sotheby's, Olympia #127/R est:1000-1500

SCHMEDES-WURTH, Ottilie von (19/20th C) Austrian
£1507 $2351 €2200 Sarajevo (55x45cm-22x18in) s.d.1898. 10-Apr-3 Dorotheum, Vienna #71/R est:1200-1500

SCHMEDINGEN, Alfred (1871-?) German
£359 $564 €560 Ducks by stream (18x37cm-7x15in) s. panel. 23-Nov-2 Arnold, Frankfurt #866

SCHMEIDLER, Carl Gottlob (1772-1838) German
Miniatures
£1800 $2952 €2610 Young lady in gold bordered pale yellow dress (7cm-3in) s. gold frame oval. 3-Jun-3 Christie's, London #248/R est:2000-3000

SCHMID, Carl (1837-1871) Austrian
£2721 $4327 €4000 Portrait of young girl in summer landscape (60x46cm-24x18in) s.d.1846. 28-Mar-3 Bolland & Marotz, Bremen #527 est:1100

SCHMID, David Alois (attrib) (1791-1861) Swiss
Works on paper
£1485 $2346 €2228 Nafels and Mollis with Todi, Glarnisch and Vrenelisgartli (25x37cm-10x15in) W/C over pencil. 14-Nov-2 Stuker, Bern #9319 est:2500-3500 (S.FR 3400)
£2183 $3450 €3275 Weesen with Leistkamm (26x38cm-10x15in) W/C over pencil. 14-Nov-2 Stuker, Bern #9320 est:2000-3000 (S.FR 5000)

SCHMID, Erich (1908-1984) Austrian
£355 $592 €500 Fillette au vase de fleurs jaunes (46x55cm-18x22in) s.d. 23-Jun-3 Delvaux, Paris #180

SCHMID, Henri (1924-) Swiss
£401 $642 €602 Untitled (100x65cm-39x26in) s.d. double-sided. 17-Mar-3 Philippe Schuler, Zurich #4558 (S.FR 850)
£437 $686 €656 Otto-Charles Banninger in studio (70x61cm-28x24in) s.d.1972. 25-Nov-2 Germann, Zurich #808 (S.FR 1000)
£849 $1358 €1274 Interior with fruit still life (100x92cm-39x36in) s.d. 17-Mar-3 Philippe Schuler, Zurich #4557 (S.FR 1800)

SCHMID, Mathias (1835-1923) Austrian
£962 $1490 €1500 Young girl and lad at the table (24x19cm-9x7in) i. canvas on canvas. 4-Dec-2 Neumeister, Munich #884/R est:1200
£1700 $2635 €2550 Pleasant dreams (52x69cm-20x27in) s. i.on stretcher. 26-Sep-2 Mellors & Kirk, Nottingham #707/R est:1000-1500
£14423 $21058 €22500 Paznau lovers in high mountain landscape (87x63cm-34x25in) s. 4-Jun-2 Karl & Faber, Munich #131/R est:10000-12000

SCHMID, Richard (1934-) American
£2108 $3500 €3057 The Freak House, Riverview Park, Chicago (20x30cm-8x12in) s. i.verso masonite. 11-Jun-3 Butterfields, San Francisco #4138/R est:4000-6000
£2358 $3750 €3537 Low tide - Monhegan Island (41x51cm-16x20in) s. s.i.verso. 7-Mar-3 Jackson's, Cedar Falls #634/R est:4000-7000
£3437 $5500 €4984 Portrait of Cheryl Carlson (41x30cm-16x12in) s. masonite sold with a letter. 16-May-3 Skinner, Boston #148/R est:2500-3500
£4777 $7500 €7166 Nude (46x30cm-18x12in) s. s.i.d.1965 verso. 23-Nov-2 Jackson's, Cedar Falls #85/R est:7500-10000
£5324 $8625 €7720 Dingle Bay cliffs (18x33cm-7x13in) 23-May-3 Altermann Galleries, Santa Fe #204
£10648 $17250 €15440 Buckhorn steam (25x41cm-10x16in) board. 23-May-3 Altermann Galleries, Santa Fe #201

SCHMID, Wilhelm (1892-1971) Swiss
£644 $1017 €966 Bunch of flowers in a vase (46x40cm-18x16in) s. 26-Nov-2 Hans Widmer, St Gallen #1348 est:1000-2000 (S.FR 1500)
£1266 $2000 €1899 Bunch of flowers in stone jug (46x33cm-18x13in) s. 26-Nov-2 Hans Widmer, St Gallen #1347/R est:2600-3800 (S.FR 2950)
£2620 $4087 €3930 Landscape with pruned trees (60x81cm-24x32in) s. s.i. verso board. 6-Nov-2 Hans Widmer, St Gallen #23/R est:3500-5800 (S.FR 6000)

SCHMIDLIN, Aja Iskander (1932-) Swiss
£262 $411 €393 Untitled (81x65cm-32x26in) s.d.1979. 25-Nov-2 Germann, Zurich #810 (S.FR 600)

SCHMIDT, Albert (1883-1970) Swiss
£394 $634 €591 Still life of flowers including roses (46x33cm-18x13in) s.d.64 panel. 7-May-3 Dobiaschofsky, Bern #954/R (S.FR 850)
£742 $1158 €1113 Sheep in wood (35x47cm-14x19in) paper. 6-Nov-2 Dobiaschofsky, Bern #951/R (S.FR 1700)
£801 $1250 €1202 Autumn landscape with ducks (41x51cm-16x20in) s. prov.lit. 9-Nov-2 Santa Fe Art, Santa Fe #186/R est:2000-4000
Works on paper
£577 $900 €866 Windy day, Santa Fe (30x48cm-12x19in) pastel prov.lit. 9-Nov-2 Santa Fe Art, Santa Fe #236/R est:2000-5000

SCHMIDT, Albert H (1885-1957) American
£2436 $3800 €3654 Northern New Mexico landscape (51x71cm-20x28in) s. 30-Mar-3 Susanin's, Chicago #6154/R est:5000-7000

SCHMIDT, Albrecht (1870-1945) Danish
£422 $659 €633 Large waves (66x85cm-26x33in) init.i.d.1916. 23-Sep-2 Rasmussen, Vejle #123/R (D.KR 5000)

SCHMIDT, Alexander (1842-1903) Danish
£313 $488 €470 Landscape with old woman on country road (39x50cm-15x20in) s.d.80. 23-Sep-2 Rasmussen, Vejle #100/R (D.KR 3700)

SCHMIDT, Allan (1923-1989) Danish
£257 $401 €386 Fruit of life (65x82cm-26x32in) prov. 11-Nov-2 Rasmussen, Vejle #95/R (D.KR 3000)

SCHMIDT, Anina (19th C) German?
£766 $1240 €1111 Lake landscape, Walternsee in Tyrol (30x41cm-12x16in) s.i. 26-May-3 Rasmussen, Copenhagen #1343/R (D.KR 8000)

SCHMIDT, Carl (1885-1969) American
£2419 $3750 €3629 High Sierras (76x91cm-30x36in) s. painted c.1930 prov. 8-Dec-2 Toomey, Oak Park #713/R est:4500-6500

SCHMIDT, Christian (1835-?) German
£2254 $3628 €3200 Still life with roses, butterfly and insects on woodland floor (54x66cm-21x26in) s.d.1871. 7-May-3 Michael Zeller, Lindau #918/R est:3200
£3226 $5000 €4839 Still life with wine, bottles and a cigar (45x41cm-18x16in) s. prov. 29-Oct-2 Sotheby's, New York #19/R est:8000-12000

SCHMIDT, Eduard (1806-1862) German
£3288 $5162 €4800 Windmill in a winter landscape (45x57cm-18x22in) s. s.i.verso. 15-Apr-3 Sotheby's, Amsterdam #88/R est:4000-6000
£3648 $5691 €5800 Harbour in morning light (59x42cm-23x17in) s. lit. 20-Sep-2 Schloss Ahlden, Ahlden #1118/R est:5800

SCHMIDT, Eduard Allan (19th C) German
£250 $418 €363 Path through the wood and a hedgerow (12x20cm-5x8in) board. 24-Jun-3 Rowley Fine Art, Newmarket #359
£600 $954 €900 View of hedgerow and fields (9x8cm-4x3in) s.d.1892 panel. 29-Apr-3 Rowley Fine Art, Newmarket #427

SCHMIDT, F (?) ?
£1226 $1937 €1900 Belle hetaire (21x13cm-8x5in) s. paper on board. 19-Dec-2 Claude Aguttes, Neuilly #131/R

SCHMIDT, Gustav (1888-1973) German
£360 $576 €500 Luneburger Heide (80x120cm-31x47in) s. 14-May-3 Dorotheum, Linz #346/R

SCHMIDT, Hans W (1859-1950) German
£304 $474 €450 Heiligenblut in summer (72x106cm-28x42in) i. 31-Mar-3 Dr Fritz Nagel, Stuttgart #6971/R
£7595 $12000 €11393 Happy couple (70x50cm-28x20in) s.d.1909. 23-Apr-3 Christie's, Rockefeller NY #138/R est:15000-20000

SCHMIDT, Heinrich Arad (?) American?
£617 $950 €926 Creation of Earth. 6-Sep-2 Douglas, South Deerfield #4

SCHMIDT, Johann Georg (1694-1767) Austrian
£493 $794 €700 Self portrait at easel (94x75cm-37x30in) 10-May-3 Hans Stahl, Toestorf #100/R

SCHMIDT, Johann Martin (attrib) (1718-1801) German
£1127 $1870 €1600 Mary (43x35cm-17x14in) 11-Jun-3 Dorotheum, Vienna #450/R est:1000-1500
£2899 $4754 €4000 Simon of Kyrene helps Jesus carry the Cross. Crucification with Maria, Johannes and Magdalena (36x24cm-14x9in) paper on board two lit. 27-May-3 Wiener Kunst Auktionen, Vienna #7/R est:3000-20000

SCHMIDT, Karl (1890-1962) American
£3313 $5500 €4804 California landscape with poppies (30x41cm-12x16in) s.d.1917 i.verso board prov. 11-Jun-3 Butterfields, San Francisco #4201/R est:3000-5000
£4042 $6750 €5861 Eucalyptus landscape, California (66x97cm-26x38in) s.d.1934 i.verso. 17-Jun-3 John Moran, Pasadena #101 est:7000-9000

SCHMIDT, Kurt (1901-) German
£396 $633 €550 Friedrich Gulda at the piano (40x50cm-16x20in) s. board. 14-May-3 Dorotheum, Klagenfurt #18

SCHMIDT, Leonhard (1892-1978) German
£3793 $5993 €5500 Winter landscape (55x73cm-22x29in) s.d.1958. 2-Apr-3 Dr Fritz Nagel, Stuttgart #9551/R est:2900
Works on paper
£692 $1079 €1100 Ebnisee (50x74cm-20x29in) s. pastel. 20-Sep-2 Sigalas, Stuttgart #1051/R

SCHMIDT, Paul (1912-) Swiss
£371 $579 €557 In the market (75x86cm-30x34in) s.d.1951. 8-Nov-2 Dobiaschofsky, Bern #168/R (S.FR 850)

SCHMIDT, Richard (1883-?) German
£687 $1085 €1031 Farmer with oxen cart and shepherdess with flock in front of farmhouse (57x84cm-22x33in) s.d.1810. 29-Nov-2 Zofingen, Switzerland #2537 (S.FR 1600)

SCHMIDT, Robert G (1923-) French
£338 $527 €500 Le repos au bouquet (60x73cm-24x29in) s. s.i.verso. 25-Mar-3 Chochon-Barre & Allardi, Paris #195

SCHMIDT, Rosa (1888-?) Italian
£288 $447 €450 Vase of flowers (57x47cm-22x19in) s. cardboard. 5-Dec-2 Stadion, Trieste #669
£426 $689 €600 Il Carso d'inverno (72x100cm-28x39in) board. 22-May-3 Stadion, Trieste #405/R
£1026 $1590 €1600 End of summer fruit (49x63cm-19x25in) s. 5-Dec-2 Stadion, Trieste #684/R

SCHMIDT, Rudolf (19/20th C) Austrian
Works on paper
£440 $682 €700 Karlskirche (12x11cm-5x4in) s. W/C. 1-Oct-2 Dorotheum, Vienna #313/R
£440 $682 €700 Augustinerstrasse from Palais Lobkowitz (12x10cm-5x4in) s. W/C. 1-Oct-2 Dorotheum, Vienna #314/R est:1400-1500
£440 $682 €700 Otscher from Gosing (41x33cm-16x13in) s.i.d.1929 gouache. 1-Oct-2 Dorotheum, Vienna #323/R
£629 $975 €1000 Franziskanerplatz (16x12cm-6x5in) s. W/C. 1-Oct-2 Dorotheum, Vienna #293/R
£629 $975 €1000 Flower market in Vienna (12x16cm-5x6in) s. W/C. 1-Oct-2 Dorotheum, Vienna #304/R est:1800-2000
£755 $1170 €1200 Flower market in Vienna (12x16cm-5x6in) s. W/C. 1-Oct-2 Dorotheum, Vienna #302/R
£755 $1170 €1200 Stephansplatz (10x11cm-4x4in) s. W/C. 1-Oct-2 Dorotheum, Vienna #307/R est:1400-1500
£811 $1265 €1200 Flower market in the square (11x12cm-4x5in) s. W/C. 28-Mar-3 Dorotheum, Vienna #342/R
£1258 $1950 €2000 Market day in Freyung (12x16cm-5x6in) s. W/C. 1-Oct-2 Dorotheum, Vienna #306/R est:1800-2000

SCHMIDT, Wilhelm (1842-1922) German
Sculpture
£20000 $31000 €30000 Bust of Minerva wearing a helmet and armour (34cm-13in) d.1887-1891 gold silver Agathe rec. socle. 1-Oct-2 Christie's, London #124/R est:20000-30000

SCHMIDT, Willem Hendrik (1809-1849) Dutch
£681 $1076 €1022 Kitchen interior with young man proposing to his intended (57x46cm-22x18in) s.d.1831 panel. 2-Dec-2 Rasmussen, Copenhagen #1701/R (D.KR 8000)

SCHMIDT-HAMBURG, R (20th C) German
£519 $774 €800 Sailing ship on choppy sea (72x95cm-28x37in) s. 27-Jun-2 Neumeister, Munich #2820/R

SCHMIDT-HAMBURG, Richard (20th C) German
£544 $865 €800 Thames and Tower Bridge in evening mist (41x31cm-16x12in) s. board. 28-Mar-3 Bolland & Marotz, Bremen #529

SCHMIDT-HAMBURG, Robert (1885-1963) German
£455 $664 €700 Three-mast and other ships on lightly rough sea (32x43cm-13x17in) s. board pencil study verso lit. 15-Jun-2 Hans Stahl, Hamburg #260/R
£600 $1002 €870 Clipper, steamships and sailing vessels near a harbour (49x75cm-19x30in) init. 17-Jun-3 Rosebery Fine Art, London #538
£655 $1035 €950 The Bremen in New York harbour (33x48cm-13x19in) s. tempera gouache lit. 5-Apr-3 Hans Stahl, Hamburg #172/R
£1282 $1987 €2000 Bremen harbour (52x75cm-20x30in) s. 5-Dec-2 Schopman, Hamburg #674 est:1800

SCHMIDT-MICHELSEN, Alexandre (1859-1908) German
£1294 $2122 €1980 Inside the village chapel (95x65cm-37x26in) s. 6-Feb-3 Weidler, Nurnberg #6549 est:2200

SCHMIDT-RASMUSSEN, Christian (1963-) Danish
£286 $478 €415 Insane devils I (60x50cm-24x20in) indis sig.d.97 prov. 17-Jun-3 Rasmussen, Copenhagen #131 (D.KR 3000)

SCHMIDT-ROTTLUFF, Karl (1884-1976) German
£14058 $21789 €21930 Street with sheds and tres (42x33cm-17x13in) s.d.1918 W/C over pencil. 4-Dec-2 Lempertz, Koln #1046/R est:30000-40000

Prints
£1923 $2981 €3000 Out of commission boats (53x43cm-21x17in) s. lithograph. 7-Dec-2 Hauswedell & Nolte, Hamburg #1028/R est:3500
£2152 $3400 €3400 Russian wood (20x26cm-8x10in) s. woodcut prov. 30-Nov-2 Villa Grisebach, Berlin #169/R est:2500-3500
£2201 $3434 €3500 Junge kiefern und sonne (29x23cm-11x9in) s.i.num.2023 drypoint etching. 9-Oct-2 Sotheby's, London #521/R est:2500-3000
£2244 $3545 €3500 Houses and trees in the mountains (60x50cm-24x20in) s.i. woodcut. 14-Nov-2 Neumeister, Munich #685/R est:6500-7000
£2553 $4136 €3600 Petri Fischzug (40x50cm-16x20in) s. woodcut. 24-May-3 Van Ham, Cologne #528/R est:7000
£3169 $5261 €4500 Head (25x18cm-10x7in) s.i. woodcut. 14-Jun-3 Hauswedell & Nolte, Hamburg #1581/R est:6000
£4167 $6458 €6500 Soest (50x40cm-20x16in) s.i. wooduct. 4-Dec-2 Lempertz, Koln #1053/R est:8000
£4430 $7000 €7000 The miraculous draught of fishes (39x50cm-15x20in) s.i. woodcut. 30-Nov-2 Villa Grisebach, Berlin #198/R est:6000-8000
£4800 $7488 €7200 An mombert (50x42cm-20x17in) bears sig woodcut. 10-Oct-2 Sotheby's, London #162/R est:6000-8000
£5063 $8000 €8000 Portrait of O M - Otto Mueller (36x29cm-14x11in) s.i. woodcut prov. 30-Nov-2 Villa Grisebach, Berlin #199/R est:7000-9000
£5435 $8913 €7500 People on beach (40x50cm-16x20in) s.i. woodcut. 29-May-3 Lempertz, Koln #920/R est:10000-12000
£5556 $8833 €8000 Doing the nets (40x49cm-16x19in) s. woodcut. 5-May-3 Ketterer, Munich #953/R est:3000-5000
£5660 $9000 €8490 Madchen mit blumenvase (32x20cm-13x8in) s.d.1911 woodcut. 1-May-3 Swann Galleries, New York #598/R est:7000-10000
£6338 $10521 €9000 Reclining girl (18x24cm-7x9in) s.d. woodcut. 14-Jun-3 Hauswedell & Nolte, Hamburg #1580/R est:12000
£6918 $10792 €11000 Melancholie. s.d.1914 woodcut. 9-Oct-2 Sotheby's, London #517/R est:12500-19000
£7000 $11690 €10150 Madchem mit tamburin (40x33cm-16x13in) s.d. woodcut. 30-Jun-3 Bonhams, New Bond Street #413/R est:7000-10000
£7639 $12146 €11000 Russian landscape (39x50cm-15x20in) s.i. woodcut. 5-May-3 Ketterer, Munich #954/R est:3000-5000
£10256 $15897 €16000 Girl in front of mirror (50x40cm-20x16in) s. woodcut. 7-Dec-2 Hauswedell & Nolte, Hamburg #1029/R est:16000
£13768 $22580 €19000 Girl with tambourine (29x20cm-11x8in) s.d. woodcut prov. 30-May-3 Villa Grisebach, Berlin #24/R est:20000-25000
£76389 $121458 €110000 Model (29x43cm-11x17in) s. col woodcut. 5-May-3 Ketterer, Munich #952/R est:20000-30000

Works on paper
£1392 $2200 €2200 Landscape (33x42cm-13x17in) s.d.19 graphite. 29-Nov-2 Villa Grisebach, Berlin #880/R est:2000-2500
£2400 $3792 €3600 Still life with bottle, vase and glass (30x39cm-12x15in) s. brush ink wax crayon exec.1967 prov.exhib. 3-Apr-3 Christie's, Kensington #204/R
£2437 $3801 €3850 Still life with crooked jug (54x40cm-21x16in) s. i. verso col chk Indian ink prov. 18-Oct-2 Dr Fritz Nagel, Stuttgart #610/R est:4500
£3043 $4991 €4200 Steep coastline (50x70cm-20x28in) s. i. verso Indian ink brush prov. 31-May-3 Villa Grisebach, Berlin #243/R est:5000-6000
£3448 $5448 €5000 Still life with flower vase and bottle (54x40cm-21x16in) s. Indian ink brush col oil chk. 5-Apr-3 Quittenbaum, Hamburg #108/R est:9000
£3500 $5425 €5250 Ostseelandschaft (40x54cm-16x21in) s. brush ink col crayons executed c.1970-72. 5-Dec-2 Christie's, Kensington #132/R est:3000-5000
£4403 $6868 €7000 On the edge of the wood (48x67cm-19x26in) s. s.i.verso W/C brush ink executed c.1932 prov. 9-Oct-2 Sotheby's, London #137/R est:10000-15000
£4808 $7452 €7500 Shoreline (40x54cm-16x21in) s. i.d. verso col chk Indian ink brush. 4-Dec-2 Lempertz, Koln #1050/R est:7500
£6329 $10000 €10000 Still life with pears (26x40cm-10x16in) s. Indian ink brush W/C col chk prov. 30-Nov-2 Villa Grisebach, Berlin #228/R est:6000-8000
£6522 $10696 €9000 Pine trees in front of house (40x26cm-16x10in) s. col chk over Indian ink. 31-May-3 Villa Grisebach, Berlin #246/R est:10000-12000
£6875 $11000 €10313 Composition with bottle and shell (27x19cm-11x7in) W/C. 14-Mar-3 Du Mouchelle, Detroit #2012/R est:5000-8000
£7746 $12472 €11000 Pine tree (53x40cm-21x16in) s. Indian ink brush col chk lit.prov. 9-May-3 Schloss Ahlden, Ahlden #1556/R est:12500
£7746 $12472 €11000 On the cliffs (39x54cm-15x21in) s. Indian ink brush col chk lit.prov. 9-May-3 Schloss Ahlden, Ahlden #1557/R est:12000
£8500 $13940 €12750 Beach with huts (34x43cm-13x17in) s.d.1914 gouache W/C brush ink. 6-Feb-3 Christie's, London #458/R
£8861 $14000 €14000 Chestnuts (51x69cm-20x27in) s. W/C exec.c.1950 prov. 30-Nov-2 Geble, Radolfzell #733 est:13000
£10625 $17000 €15938 Vase with flowers (27x19cm-11x7in) pastel W/C. 14-Mar-3 Du Mouchelle, Detroit #2011/R est:7000-8000
£10870 $17826 €15000 Cool March (50x70cm-20x28in) s.i. i.d.59 verso W/C brush. 31-May-3 Villa Grisebach, Berlin #247/R est:15000-20000
£11076 $17500 €17500 Bottles and jug (66x48cm-26x19in) s.i. brush W/C. 30-Nov-2 Bassenge, Berlin #6601/R est:22000
£11392 $17658 €18000 Blue berries (70x50cm-28x20in) s. i.d.1958 verso wash Indian ink brush prov. 28-Sep-2 Ketterer, Hamburg #249/R est:20000-30000
£12658 $20000 €20000 Stream (48x61cm-19x24in) s. W/C Indian ink brush. 30-Nov-2 Villa Grisebach, Berlin #222/R est:20000-25000
£16000 $26240 €24000 Landscape (51x69cm-20x27in) s.i.d.49 W/C brush ink. 6-Feb-3 Christie's, London #466/R est:15000
£17949 $27821 €28000 Still life with marguerites and iris (70x52cm-28x20in) s. w/C prov. 4-Dec-2 Lempertz, Koln #1047/R est:3000-35000
£19565 $32087 €27000 Still life of flowers - red blooms in glass in window (47x65cm-19x26in) s. W/C. 29-May-3 Lempertz, Koln #919/R est:20000
£21739 $35652 €30000 Tulips in vase (49x69cm-19x27in) s. W/C prov.exhib. 31-May-3 Villa Grisebach, Berlin #249/R est:30000-40000
£30769 $47692 €48000 Red gladiolii (70x50cm-28x20in) s. i. verso W/C prov. 4-Dec-2 Lempertz, Koln #1051/R est:50000-55000

SCHMIECHEN, Hermann (1855-?) German
£833 $1300 €1250 Portrait of a girl (25x20cm-10x8in) s.d.1880. 9-Oct-2 Doyle, New York #104

SCHMIEGELOW, Pedro Ernst Johann (1863-?) German
£728 $1150 €1150 Aqsa Mosque and city wall in Jerusalem (66x100cm-26x39in) s.d.1914. 29-Nov-2 Bolland & Marotz, Bremen #917/R

SCHMINKE, Hans (1908-1990) German
£285 $450 €450 Southern coast (35x41cm-14x16in) mono.d.1958. 30-Nov-2 Arnold, Frankfurt #506/R

SCHMITSON, Teutwart (1830-1863) German
£1731 $2683 €2700 Winter forest with cart filled with wood and two farm hands driving oxen and cows (100x160cm-39x63in) s. 4-Dec-2 Neumeister, Munich #887/R est:2000
£1761 $2835 €2500 Horse dip (46x64cm-18x25in) i. verso lit. 9-May-3 Schloss Ahlden, Ahlden #1451/R est:2800

SCHMITSON, Teutwart (attrib) (1830-1863) German
£260 $387 €400 Rider with horses by farmstead (23x36cm-9x14in) panel prov. 26-Jun-2 Neumeister, Munich #849

SCHMITT, Albert Felix (1873-?) American?
£7547 $12000 €11321 Gloucester marsh and dunes (61x74cm-24x29in) s.indis.d.191. 1-Mar-3 North East Auctions, Portsmouth #734/R est:5000-8000

SCHMITT, Robert (1924-1990) Austrian
£1392 $2172 €2200 Two women in the wind (100x80cm-39x31in) mono.d.58. 15-Oct-2 Dorotheum, Vienna #134/R est:2500-3600

SCHMITZ, Carl Ludwig (19th C) German
£633 $987 €1000 View of Bacharach (67x98cm-26x39in) s. 14-Sep-2 Bergmann, Erlangen #727/R

SCHMITZ, Georg (1851-?) German
£481 $731 €750 Winter landscape (15x27cm-6x11in) s. i. verso panel. 31-Aug-2 Geble, Radolfzell #661
£481 $731 €750 Witner landscape (15x27cm-6x11in) s. panel. 31-Aug-2 Geble, Radolfzell #662/R

SCHMITZ, Jean Paul (19th C) German
£2405 $3800 €3800 Spring at Bodensee with blossoming cherry trees in foreground (65x81cm-26x32in) s. oil tempera. 30-Nov-2 Geble, Radolfzell #693 est:1200

SCHMITZBERGER, J (1851-?) German
£692 $1079 €1100 Deer in winter (105x129cm-41x51in) i. 23-Sep-2 Dr Fritz Nagel, Stuttgart #7042/R

SCHMITZBERGER, Josef (1851-?) German
£4500 $7470 €6525 On the scent (51x76cm-20x30in) s. 12-Jun-3 Christie's, Kensington #300/R est:3000-5000

SCHMOGNER, Walter (1943-) Austrian
Works on paper
£314 $487 €500 Man in mirror (48x64cm-19x25in) s.i.d.82 pencil W/C. 30-Oct-2 Dorotheum, Vienna #202

SCHMOLE-LORETZ, Mathilde (1844-1918) German
Works on paper
£479 $748 €700 Frog prince (71x84cm-28x33in) W/C bodycol htd white. 11-Apr-3 Winterberg, Heidelberg #557

SCHMUTZ, Werner (1910-) ?
£648 $1044 €940 Spring (51x69cm-20x27in) s. masonite. 9-May-3 Dobiaschofsky, Bern #114/R (S.FR 1400)

SCHMUTZER, Ferdinand (1833-1915) Austrian
Works on paper
£439 $685 €650 In the country (32x24cm-13x9in) s. W/C. 28-Mar-3 Dorotheum, Vienna #277/R
£513 $810 €800 Aquaduct with medieval city beyond, possibly Rothenburg o d Tauber (69x90cm-27x35in) s. wash pencil chl. 15-Nov-2 Reiss & Sohn, Konigstein #366/R

SCHMUTZLER, Leopold (1864-1941) German
£1370 $2137 €2000 Young woman in red dress (81x54cm-32x21in) s. board. 10-Apr-3 Van Ham, Cologne #1694/R est:2000
£1410 $2214 €2200 Young woman with rose bouquet (87x65cm-34x26in) s. 23-Nov-2 Arnold, Frankfurt #867/R
£2177 $3461 €3200 Young woman with lyre (97x75cm-38x30in) s. 19-Mar-3 Neumeister, Munich #725/R est:3000
£2405 $3800 €3800 Female musician (94x70cm-37x28in) s. lit. 29-Nov-2 Schloss Ahlden, Ahlden #1368/R est:3800
£4721 $7318 €7082 Amazone with spear (84x72cm-33x28in) s. board. 3-Oct-2 Koller, Zurich #3139/R est:4000-6000 (S.FR 11000)

SCHNABEL, Julian (1951-) American
£8750 $14000 €13125 Self portrait (76x73cm-30x29in) s.d.12.12.70 i.verso prov. 14-May-3 Sotheby's, New York #453/R est:12000-18000
£10127 $16000 €15191 Some Japanes flowers II (254x203cm-100x80in) oil fabric paper collage on canvas painted 1989 prov. 14-Nov-2 Christie's, Rockefeller NY #379/R est:20000-30000
£12500 $19250 €18750 Portrait of my mother (122x102cm-48x40in) s.d.81 verso prov. 23-Oct-2 Christie's, London #151/R est:10000-15000
£14375 $23000 €21563 Bingo I (125x115cm-49x45in) s.i.d.1989 on overlap prov. 16-May-3 Phillips, New York #159/R est:25000-35000
£18987 $30000 €28481 Study of three figures (244x335cm-96x132in) oil rustoleum tarpalin painted 1982 prov.exhib.lit. 13-Nov-2 Sotheby's, New York #554/R est:30000-40000
£25000 $40000 €37500 My first trip to Japan (254x203cm-100x80in) oil printed paper fabric collage paper on canvas painted 1989. 15-May-3 Christie's, Rockefeller NY #373/R est:20000-30000
£43750 $70000 €65625 Untitled (244x305cm-96x120in) oil gesso resin leather velvet drop cloth painted 1991 prov. 15-May-3 Christie's, Rockefeller NY #372/R est:70000-90000
£50000 $80000 €75000 Los patos del buen retiro (206x155cm-81x61in) s.d.91 verso oil wood paper fabric on canvas prov. 14-May-3 Sotheby's, New York #441/R est:50000-60000
£60127 $95000 €90191 Untitled (321x244cm-126x96in) tarpalin painted 1988 prov. 13-Nov-2 Sotheby's, New York #579/R est:100000-150000
£60127 $95000 €90191 Untitled - Mary Heilman (183x152cm-72x60in) oil plates bondo on wood painted 1987 prov. 12-Nov-2 Sotheby's, New York #65/R est:100000-150000
Prints
£2500 $3875 €3900 Loua (277x155cm-109x61in) aquatint exec.1984. 7-Dec-2 Cornette de St.Cyr, Paris #119/R est:6000
Sculpture
£27778 $45833 €40000 Motherhood of Lola Montes (120x102x25cm-47x40x10in) s.i.d.1983 d.1986verso oil plates Bondo wood prov.lit. 3-Jul-3 Christie's, Paris #30/R est:50000-70000
£65625 $105000 €98438 Barbara Bush skipping down the Champs Elysee (427x152x101cm-168x60x40in) painted bronze oil paint executed 1989 prov.exhib. 15-May-3 Christie's, Rockefeller NY #371/R est:50000-70000

SCHNACKENBERG, Walter (1880-1961) German
Prints
£5769 $8942 €9000 German theatre - mainly Munich variety (117x85cm-46x33in) s.i. col lithograph exec.c.1920/25. 6-Dec-2 Ketterer, Munich #12/R est:9000-12000
Works on paper
£468 $725 €730 Reclining female nude (36x49cm-14x19in) s.d.1960 gouache W/C over pencil board. 7-Dec-2 Ketterer, Hamburg #399/R
£513 $795 €800 On the bridge (50x37cm-20x15in) s.d.1956 W/C over Indian ink. 7-Dec-2 Ketterer, Hamburg #401/R

SCHNARS-ALQUIST, Hugo (1855-1939) German
£2089 $3300 €3300 Full-rigged ship at sea near Einbruch in the night (80x120cm-31x47in) s.d.1921. 29-Nov-2 Bolland & Marotz, Bremen #768/R est:3300

SCHNAUDER, Reinhard (1856-1923) German
Sculpture
£1558 $2322 €2400 Steel worker (63cm-25in) s. brown pat.bronze. 26-Jun-2 Neumeister, Munich #39/R est:2500

SCHNEE, Hermann (1840-1926) German
£316 $500 €500 Harz landscape (24x18cm-9x7in) mono. board. 29-Nov-2 Bassenge, Berlin #6056

SCHNEGG, Lucien (1864-1909) French
Sculpture
£2885 $4471 €4500 Torse d'Aphrodite (31x8x8cm-12x3x3in) s. gilt pat bronze exec.1902 lit. 7-Dec-2 Martinot & Savignat, Pontoise #98/R

SCHNEIDAU, Christian von (1893-1976) American
£1129 $1750 €1694 Inspiration (102x71cm-40x28in) s.d.1922 i.verso prov.exhib. 29-Oct-2 John Moran, Pasadena #776 est:2000-3000
£2096 $3500 €3039 Interior scene with young woman playing an organ (56x79cm-22x31in) s. painted c.1925. 22-Jun-3 Jeffery Burchard, Florida #44/R

SCHNEIDER, Alexander (1870-1927) Russian
Works on paper
£2532 $4000 €4000 Standing naked boy holding garland (90x47cm-35x19in) WC over pencil. 30-Nov-2 Bassenge, Berlin #6604/R est:1500

SCHNEIDER, Arthur (1866-1942) American
£1790 $2900 €2685 Ducks in flight (51x61cm-20x24in) s. 24-Jan-3 Freeman, Philadelphia #150/R est:1000-1500

SCHNEIDER, Caspar (1753-1839) German
£4167 $6458 €6500 Farm families bathing at stream edge with timber buildings and castle in middle (48x61cm-19x24in) s.d.1825 copper. 4-Dec-2 Neumeister, Munich #888/R est:4500
£4167 $6458 €6500 Resting farm family on slope of meadow and castle on hilltop (48x61cm-19x24in) s.d.1825 copper. 4-Dec-2 Neumeister, Munich #889/R est:4500

SCHNEIDER, G (?) ?
Works on paper
£2959 $4705 €4350 Composition (47x62cm-19x24in) s.d.48 chl prov. 26-Feb-3 Artcurial Briest, Paris #467/R est:2500-3000

SCHNEIDER, Gerard (1896-1986) Swiss
£943 $1453 €1500 Composition (32x48cm-13x19in) s. paper panel. 22-Oct-2 Campo, Vlaamse Kaai #613
£1603 $2516 €2500 Untitled (37x52cm-15x20in) s.d.70 paper on canvas. 24-Nov-2 Laurence Calmels, Paris #269/R
£1747 $2742 €2621 Opus 48 L (50x61cm-20x24in) s. acrylic. 25-Nov-2 Germann, Zurich #71/R est:5000-6000 (S.FR 4000)

£1772 $2765 €2800 Composition (37x54cm-15x21in) s.d.1973 acrylic paper on canvas. 20-Oct-2 Claude Boisgirard, Paris #53/R est:2500-3000
£1795 $2818 €2800 Composition au vase de fleurs (46x38cm-18x15in) s. 24-Nov-2 Laurence Calmels, Paris #262/R
£1923 $3019 €3000 Untitled (46x55cm-18x22in) s.d.71 acrylic. 24-Nov-2 Laurence Calmels, Paris #261/R
£1987 $3080 €3100 Composition (46x38cm-18x15in) s.d.1971. 7-Dec-2 Cornette de St.Cyr, Paris #81/R
£2027 $3162 €3000 Untitled (39x49cm-15x19in) s.d.78 acrylic card. 26-Mar-3 Finarte Semenzato, Milan #384/R
£2051 $3221 €3200 4K (38x46cm-15x18in) s.d.72 acrylic. 24-Nov-2 Laurence Calmels, Paris #272/R
£2083 $3437 €3000 Composition (37x52cm-15x20in) s.d.70 W/C paper on canvas prov. 1-Jul-3 Artcurial Briest, Paris #786/R est:3000-4000
£2201 $3412 €3500 Composition (33x41cm-13x16in) s.d. acrylic. 30-Oct-2 Artcurial Briest, Paris #440/R est:4000-6000
£2436 $3824 €3800 17K-70 (65x54cm-26x21in) s.d.72 acrylic. 24-Nov-2 Laurence Calmels, Paris #265/R
£2564 $4026 €4000 27K-72 (50x61cm-20x24in) s.d.72 acrylic. 24-Nov-2 Laurence Calmels, Paris #268/R
£2602 $4112 €3903 Composition (37x46cm-15x18in) s.d.52 prov. 1-Apr-3 Rasmussen, Copenhagen #216/R est:20000 (D.KR 28000)
£2885 $4529 €4500 32K (60x73cm-24x29in) s.d.73 acrylic. 24-Nov-2 Laurence Calmels, Paris #271/R
£3061 $4867 €4500 Composition (54x38cm-21x15in) s.d.1971 acrylic paper on canvas. 24-Mar-3 Claude Boisgirard, Paris #149/R
£3125 $4938 €4500 Composition 98L (60x73cm-24x29in) s.d. acrylic prov. 27-Apr-3 Perrin, Versailles #50/R est:5000-5500
£3268 $5229 €5000 Composition (41x33cm-16x13in) s.d.1975. 4-Jan-3 Meeting Art, Vercelli #384
£3269 $5133 €5100 Composition (31x48cm-12x19in) s. panel prov. 15-Dec-2 Perrin, Versailles #56/R
£3800 $6004 €5700 Composition (60x73cm-24x29in) s.d.68. 3-Apr-3 Christie's, Kensington #230/R
£3819 $6035 €5500 Composition 30L (65x81cm-26x32in) s.d. i.verso acrylic prov. 27-Apr-3 Perrin, Versailles #43/R est:5000-6000
£3972 $6434 €5600 Opus 76 h (45x55cm-18x22in) s.d.65 i.verso prov. 26-May-3 Christie's, Milan #155/R est:6000-8000
£4474 $7247 €6800 Composition (46x54cm-18x21in) s.d.1952. 24-Jan-3 Chayette & Cheval, Paris #17/R
£4722 $7461 €6800 Composition 47 i (61x73cm-24x29in) s.d. i.verso acrylic prov. 27-Apr-3 Perrin, Versailles #49/R est:6000-7000
£4808 $7548 €7500 Opus 24 (27x35cm-11x14in) s.d.1964. 23-Nov-2 Meeting Art, Vercelli #65/R
£5128 $8051 €8000 68I-70 (92x73cm-36x29in) s.d.70. 24-Nov-2 Laurence Calmels, Paris #267/R
£5674 $9475 €8000 Composition abstraite (60x73cm-24x29in) s.d.8.53. 20-Jun-3 Piasa, Paris #28/R est:8000-12000
£5882 $9412 €9000 Ink (60x73cm-24x29in) s.d.1976 acrylic. 4-Jan-3 Meeting Art, Vercelli #396
£6090 $9561 €9500 Composition (71x118cm-28x46in) s.d.71. 13-Dec-2 Piasa, Paris #273/R
£6090 $9561 €9500 7H (100x81cm-39x32in) s.d.65 s.i.verso prov.exhib. 24-Nov-2 Laurence Calmels, Paris #270/R
£6944 $11458 €10000 Opus 416 (50x64cm-20x25in) s.d.12-49 prov. 1-Jul-3 Artcurial Briest, Paris #773/R est:6000-8000
£7051 $11071 €11000 Untitled (116x89cm-46x35in) s.d.69. 24-Nov-2 Laurence Calmels, Paris #273/R
£7092 $11489 €10000 Composition 40 G (60x73cm-24x29in) s.d.64 i.d.verso prov.exhib. 26-May-3 Christie's, Milan #339/R est:8000-12000
£8861 $14000 €14000 Untitled (149x108cm-59x43in) s.d.83 tempera paper. 29-Nov-2 Farsetti, Prato #265/R est:15000
£10417 $17188 €15000 Opus 29 (92x73cm-36x29in) s.d.IV-57 prov.exhib. 1-Jul-3 Artcurial Briest, Paris #500/R est:12000-18000
£13072 $20915 €20000 Untitled (114x146cm-45x57in) s.d.1975 acrylic. 4-Jan-3 Meeting Art, Vercelli #625
£14103 $22141 €22000 95J (147x114cm-58x45in) s.d.1971 s.i.verso. 19-Nov-2 Finarte, Milan #194/R est:20000-23000
£14744 $23147 €23000 475 (76x95cm-30x37in) s.d.51 i.verso. 24-Nov-2 Laurence Calmels, Paris #266/R

Works on paper

£419 $624 €629 Abstract composition (21x29cm-8x11in) s. Indian ink pastel chk. 25-Jun-2 Koller, Zurich #6097 (S.FR 950)
£493 $818 €700 Sans titre (10x14cm-4x6in) s.d.64 ink wash pastel dr. 18-Jun-3 Anaf, Lyon #71/R
£690 $1152 €1000 Composition (26x37cm-10x15in) s.d. mixed media. 9-Jul-3 Cornette de St.Cyr, Paris #343
£1135 $1838 €1600 Composition (31x24cm-12x9in) s.d.1940 pastel paper on canvas prov.exhib. 26-May-3 Christie's, Milan #77/R est:2000-3000
£1154 $1812 €1800 Untitled (21x26cm-8x10in) s.d.77 mixed media. 24-Nov-2 Laurence Calmels, Paris #263/R
£1266 $1975 €2000 Untitled (37x52cm-15x20in) s.d.1958 oil tempera gouache board. 18-Oct-2 Dr Fritz Nagel, Stuttgart #619/R est:2200
£1266 $2000 €2000 Composition (24x32cm-9x13in) s.d.1979 gouache prov. 27-Nov-2 Tajan, Paris #18/R
£1266 $1975 €2000 Composition (37x54cm-15x21in) s.d.1965 pastel card. 14-Sep-2 Meeting Art, Vercelli #785/R
£1583 $2532 €2200 Composition (73x54cm-29x21in) s. mixed media paper on canvas. 18-May-3 Neret-Minet, Paris #174 est:2200-2500
£1923 $3019 €3000 Untitled (37x53cm-15x21in) s.d.73 gouache. 24-Nov-2 Laurence Calmels, Paris #260/R
£2885 $4529 €4500 Untitled (36x23cm-14x9in) s. pastel cardboard. 24-Nov-2 Laurence Calmels, Paris #259/R
£3020 $4862 €4500 Composition fond rouge (76x54cm-30x21in) s.d.1984 gouache paper on canvas. 23-Feb-3 Mercier & Cie, Lille #80/R
£3205 $5032 €5000 Untitled (52x74cm-20x29in) s.d.62 gouache. 24-Nov-2 Laurence Calmels, Paris #264/R
£3526 $5535 €5500 Untitled (37x53cm-15x21in) s.d.74 gouache. 24-Nov-2 Laurence Calmels, Paris #274/R
£9810 $15500 €15500 Untitled (147x105cm-58x41in) s.d.1983 mixed media. 29-Nov-2 Farsetti, Prato #462/R est:17000

SCHNEIDER, Herbert (1924-1984) German

Works on paper

£1538 $2431 €2400 Home pleasures (46x56cm-18x22in) s.d.1981 W/C collage. 14-Nov-2 Neumeister, Munich #868/R est:1500-2000

SCHNEIDER, Johan Ludvig (1809-1870) Danish

£605 $962 €908 September day, west side of Tjulstrup Lake (69x97cm-27x38in) 10-Mar-3 Rasmussen, Vejle #246 (D.KR 6500)

SCHNEIDER, Otto Henry (1865-1950) American

£833 $1300 €1250 Seascape. 21-Sep-2 Harvey Clar, Oakland #1524

SCHNEIDER, Otto Ludwig (1858-?) German

£317 $510 €450 Village with church in valley (65x46cm-26x18in) s. 7-May-3 Michael Zeller, Lindau #920

SCHNEIDER, Roland E (1884-1934) American

Photographs

£6329 $10000 €9494 Grotesque shadows (23x18cm-9x7in) i. vintage carbon print prov.exhib. 25-Apr-3 Phillips, New York #214/R est:1500-2500

SCHNEIDT, Max (1858-1937) German

£545 $855 €850 Washerwomen by stream in autumnal landscape (25x33cm-10x13in) s. 21-Nov-2 Van Ham, Cologne #1901

SCHNETZ, Jean Victor (attrib) (1787-1870) French

£2756 $4355 €4300 Mort de la femme du brigand (75x98cm-30x39in) painted 1822. 15-Nov-2 Beaussant & Lefèvre, Paris #76a

SCHNEUER, David (1905-1988) Polish

Works on paper

£544 $865 €800 Cirque. s. ink gouache. 18-Mar-3 Galerie Moderne, Brussels #204
£552 $883 €800 Scene de cafe (25x20cm-10x8in) s. gouache. 12-Mar-3 Rabourdin & Choppin de Janvry, Paris #161/R
£690 $1103 €1000 Figures devant la mer (35x25cm-14x10in) s.d.69 gouache. 12-Mar-3 Rabourdin & Choppin de Janvry, Paris #159/R

SCHNIDER, Adolf (1890-1961) Swiss

£513 $795 €800 Promeneurs en montagne (74x101cm-29x40in) s. 9-Dec-2 Horta, Bruxelles #398

SCHNIDER, Albrecht (1958-) Swiss

£3057 $4769 €4586 Untitled - deposition (237x168cm-93x66in) mono.d.97 verso i. stretcher prov. 6-Nov-2 Dobiaschofsky, Bern #954/R est:5000 (S.FR 7000)

SCHNITZLER, Michael (1782-1861) German

£2200 $3607 €3190 Hunting still life (31x27cm-12x11in) mono. prov. 4-Jun-3 AB Stockholms Auktionsverk #2572/R est:35000-40000 (S.KR 28000)

SCHNOBB, Jean Guy (1946-) Canadian

£382 $599 €573 Cascades (60x90cm-24x35in) s.i.d.2001. 25-Nov-2 Hodgins, Calgary #405/R (C.D 950)

SCHNORR VON CAROLSFELD, Julius (1794-1872) German

Works on paper

£3014 $4701 €4400 David and Bathseba mourning their son (21x26cm-8x10in) pen over pencil. 11-Apr-3 Winterberg, Heidelberg #558/R est:3800
£21605 $35000 €32408 Crucifixion (69x60cm-27x24in) s.i.d.1843 chk wash. 22-Jan-3 Christie's, Rockefeller NY #121/R est:15000
£43590 $67564 €68000 Pavias conquest (46x65cm-18x26in) mono.i.d.1840 pen over pencil ochre sepia wash. 7-Dec-2 Hauswedell & Nolte, Hamburg #1031/R est:40000

SCHNUG, Leo (1878-1933) French

Works on paper

£316 $500 €500 Portrait of soldier (28x22cm-11x9in) mono. pen dr. 1-Dec-2 Livinec, Gaudcheau & Jezequel, Rennes #35/R

SCHNYDER, Albert (1898-1989) German
£1389 $2236 €2014 Promenade dans la foret (81x60cm-32x24in) painted 1971. 9-May-3 Dobiaschofsky, Bern #108/R est:10000 (S.FR 3000)
£1397 $2180 €2096 A la croisee des chemins (50x61cm-20x24in) panel. 8-Nov-2 Dobiaschofsky, Bern #108/R est:6000 (S.FR 3200)
£2620 $4087 €3930 Enfant au chat (81x55cm-32x22in) 8-Nov-2 Dobiaschofsky, Bern #107/R est:8000 (S.FR 6000)
£3148 $5069 €4565 Farmer in the cornfield (72x92cm-28x36in) 9-May-3 Dobiaschofsky, Bern #189/R est:8000 (S.FR 6800)
£5556 $8944 €8056 Promenade dans la ville (116x89cm-46x35in) 9-May-3 Dobiaschofsky, Bern #104/R est:22000 (S.FR 12000)
£6019 $9690 €8728 Les Franches-Montages (50x100cm-20x39in) painted 1978. 9-May-3 Dobiaschofsky, Bern #109/R est:14000 (S.FR 13000)
£6550 $10218 €9825 Rochers a Vicques (73x92cm-29x36in) panel. 8-Nov-2 Dobiaschofsky, Bern #103/R est:20000 (S.FR 15000)
Works on paper
£1233 $1801 €1850 A la croisee des chemins (50x61cm-20x24in) s.i.d.1962 mixed media board. 17-Jun-2 Philippe Schuler, Zurich #4290a est:2500-4000 (S.FR 2800)

SCHOBEL, Georg (1860-1941) German
£903 $1435 €1300 Dejeuner du perroquet (36x44cm-14x17in) s. canvas on cardboard. 30-Apr-3 Tajan, Paris #148

SCHOBINGER, Karl Friedrich (1879-1951) Swiss
£3493 $5450 €5240 Old man in rustic interior - De Saulipuur (102x90cm-40x35in) s.d.1916 prov. 9-Nov-2 Galerie Gloggner, Luzern #120/R est:3800-4500 (S.FR 8000)

SCHOBINGER, Leo (1897-1985) German
£379 $599 €550 Jazz (31x39cm-12x15in) mono. board. 2-Apr-3 Dr Fritz Nagel, Stuttgart #9214/R
£552 $872 €800 White flowers (64x81cm-25x32in) mono.d.1967. 2-Apr-3 Dr Fritz Nagel, Stuttgart #9216/R
Works on paper
£276 $436 €400 La Rochelle (43x61cm-17x24in) s. W/C. 2-Apr-3 Dr Fritz Nagel, Stuttgart #9217/R
£414 $654 €600 Storm clouds over lake (18x29cm-7x11in) s.d.1970 W/C. 2-Apr-3 Dr Fritz Nagel, Stuttgart #9215/R

SCHODDE, Wilhelm (1883-1951) German
£931 $1471 €1350 The three-master, Grossherzogin Elisabeth in Travemunde (61x76cm-24x30in) s. s.i. verso panel. 5-Apr-3 Hans Stahl, Hamburg #106/R

SCHODLBERGER, Johann Nepomuk (1779-1853) Austrian
£4430 $7000 €7000 Extensive landscape at dusk (50x65cm-20x26in) s.d.816. 28-Nov-2 Dorotheum, Vienna #160/R est:7000-9000
Works on paper
£333 $520 €530 Saint Gregorio (15x35cm-6x14in) i. verso pencil. 11-Oct-2 Winterberg, Heidelberg #697

SCHOELLHORN, Hans Karl (1892-1983) Swiss
£349 $552 €524 Rond-point de Rive (48x36cm-19x14in) mono. panel. 17-Nov-2 Koller, Geneva #1208 (S.FR 800)

SCHOENHERR, John (1935-) American
£4114 $6500 €5965 Wyoming monarch (76x102cm-30x40in) s. 26-Jul-3 Coeur d'Alene, Hayden #172/R est:15000-25000

SCHOENMAKERS, Piet (20th C) Dutch
£377 $589 €654 Nude (90x80cm-35x31in) s. prov. 31-Mar-3 Goodman, Sydney #191/R (A.D 1000)

SCHOEVAERDTS, Mathys (c.1665-1723) Flemish
£5500 $8635 €8250 Capriccio of a Mediterranean harbour (42x56cm-17x22in) 10-Dec-2 Bonhams, New Bond Street #254/R est:6000-8000
£7000 $10990 €10500 Landscape with peasants resting beside a stream with buildings beyond (28x40cm-11x16in) bears sig panel. 10-Dec-2 Sotheby's, Olympia #375/R est:4000-6000
£7000 $10920 €10500 Italianate landscape with travelers on a hilly path near a villa (42x60cm-17x24in) 10-Apr-3 Christie's, Kensington #178/R est:6000-8000
£7554 $12086 €10500 Wooded landscape with gypsies, horsemen and travellers (28x40cm-11x16in) panel. 13-May-3 Sotheby's, Amsterdam #6/R est:4000-6000
£16000 $26720 €23200 River landscape with orientals and locals conversing before a set of ruins (54x68cm-21x27in) s. prov. 10-Jul-3 Sotheby's, London #119/R est:15000-20000
£82000 $128740 €123000 Tower of Babel (93x76cm-37x30in) 11-Dec-2 Christie's, London #42/R est:40000-60000

SCHOEVAERDTS, Mathys (attrib) (c.1665-1723) Flemish
£3205 $5032 €5000 Peasants outside city gate (21x32cm-8x13in) panel. 21-Nov-2 Van Ham, Cologne #1418/R est:8000
£5068 $7905 €7500 Villa antique pres du rivage (94x127cm-37x50in) 94. 28-Mar-3 Piasa, Paris #26/R

SCHOEVAERDTS, Mathys (circle) (c.1665-1723) Flemish
£10000 $15500 €15000 Wooded landscape with a caravan of travellers. Wooded landscape with travellers making merry (39x47cm-15x19in) indis init. pair. 30-Oct-2 Christie's, Kensington #26/R est:10000-15000

SCHOFF, Otto (1888-1938) German
£949 $1500 €1500 Portrait of a man with hat and pipe (145x75cm-57x30in) s.d.27. 29-Nov-2 Bolland & Marotz, Bremen #917a/R est:2700

SCHOFFER, Nicolas (1912-) French
Sculpture
£7097 $11000 €10646 Chronos VIII (313x129x129cm-123x51x51in) motorized chrome plated steel executed 1970 prov.exhib. 26-Sep-2 Christie's, Rockefeller NY #802/R est:6000-8000

SCHOFFMANN, Maria (1859-1941) Austrian
£889 $1476 €1289 Marie Louise von Tassio (91x67cm-36x26in) s.i.d.1848. 16-Jun-3 Waddingtons, Toronto #18/R est:2000-3000 (C.D 2000)

SCHOFIELD, John William (?-1944) British
£750 $1163 €1125 Portrait study of a young woman (33x28cm-13x11in) s. 25-Sep-2 Peter Wilson, Nantwich #69
£920 $1444 €1380 Mending the nets (81x60cm-32x24in) s.d.96. 16-Dec-2 Bonhams, Bury St Edmunds #448/R

SCHOFIELD, Kershaw (1872-1941) British
£620 $967 €930 Winter landscape (32x37cm-13x15in) s. board. 25-Mar-3 Bonhams, Leeds #628
£900 $1503 €1305 September, sheep in a water meadow (38x49cm-15x19in) s. board. 19-Jun-3 Lane, Penzance #230/R
£1050 $1649 €1575 Full sail (35x45cm-14x18in) s.i. board prov. 19-Nov-2 Bonhams, Leeds #146 est:600-800

SCHOFIELD, Walter Elmer (1867-1944) American
£11039 $17000 €16559 Summer morning (76x91cm-30x36in) s. 24-Oct-2 Shannon's, Milford #71/R est:20000-30000
£13554 $22500 €19653 The Crossroads (51x61cm-20x24in) s. prov. 11-Jun-3 Butterfields, San Francisco #4075/R est:10000-15000
£17834 $28000 €26751 Early morning winter scene with steam (63x71cm-25x28in) s. prov. 14-Dec-2 Weschler, Washington #680/R est:15000-25000

SCHOJER, K (?) ?
£299 $475 €449 Cattle watering (71x100cm-28x39in) s. 5-May-3 Rasmussen, Vejle #343 (D.KR 3200)

SCHOLANDER, Fredrik (1816-1881) Swedish
Works on paper
£471 $782 €683 Theatre sketch for Den Bergtagna (37x54cm-15x21in) s. W/C. 16-Jun-3 Lilla Bukowskis, Stockholm #931 (S.KR 6100)
£480 $730 €720 Transportation of Scholander's weapon collection (69cm-27in circular) s.d.1869 W/C. 16-Aug-2 Lilla Bukowskis, Stockholm #959 (S.KR 7000)

SCHOLDER, Fritz (1937-) American
£1656 $2600 €2484 Standing Indian (76x60cm-30x24in) s. acrylic exhib. 14-Dec-2 Weschler, Washington #676/R est:2000-3000

SCHOLDERER, Otto (1834-1902) German
£2308 $3623 €3600 Summer landscape with river and cows (44x57cm-17x22in) s.d.1899 board. 23-Nov-2 Arnold, Frankfurt #868/R est:3000

SCHOLLHORN, Hans (1892-1981) Swiss
£258 $407 €387 Mugi, a poodle, sitting in front of swimming pool (50x41cm-20x16in) mono. s.i. verso. 26-Nov-2 Hans Widmer, St Gallen #1351 (S.FR 600)
£386 $610 €579 In front of the circus tent (32x40cm-13x16in) board. 26-Nov-2 Hans Widmer, St Gallen #1349 (S.FR 900)
£386 $610 €579 Riding school (27x40cm-11x16in) paper. 26-Nov-2 Hans Widmer, St Gallen #1350 (S.FR 900)
£391 $610 €587 Clown with artist (45x37cm-18x15in) mono. i.d.1957 verso board. 16-Sep-2 Philippe Schuler, Zurich #3398 (S.FR 900)

£522 $814 €783 Circus (38x32cm-15x13in) mono. i.d.1957 verso masonite. 16-Sep-2 Philippe Schuler, Zurich #3397 (S.FR 1200)

Works on paper

£306 $477 €459 Pipo the clown (50x38cm-20x15in) mono. s.i.d.Sept. 1950 verso. 20-Nov-2 Fischer, Luzern #2695/R (S.FR 700)

SCHOLTEN, Hendrik Jacobus (1824-1907) Dutch

£7500 $11775 €11250 Letter (77x57cm-30x22in) s. 21-Nov-2 Christie's, Kensington #362/R est:6000-8000

SCHOLZ, Georg (1890-1945) German

£100000 $156000 €150000 Das liebespapaar - lovers (49x51cm-19x20in) s.d.1920 verso oil leaf on panel prov.exhib. 9-Oct-2 Sotheby's, London #30/R est:40000-60000

SCHOLZ, Max (1855-?) German

£710 $1100 €1065 Interior scene of a monk seated in a library reading (33x25cm-13x10in) s. panel. 3-Nov-2 Van Blarcom, South Natick #284

SCHOLZ, Richard (1860-?) German

£764 $1192 €1200 Angry wild boar (50x60cm-20x24in) s. lit. 7-Nov-2 Allgauer, Kempten #2954/R

SCHOLZ, Werner (1898-1982) German

£3261 $5348 €4500 Dschott (60x70cm-24x28in) mono. panel lit.exhib. 31-May-3 Villa Grisebach, Berlin #292/R est:4000-6000

Works on paper

£949 $1481 €1500 Fire lilies (43x62cm-17x24in) mono.d.54 pastel. 15-Oct-2 Dorotheum, Vienna #135/R est:1500-2000

£993 $1619 €1500 Young girl (59x40cm-23x16in) mono.d.1934 pastel. 3-Feb-3 Cornette de St.Cyr, Paris #332/R

SCHOMBERG SZYMBERSKA, Sophia de (1884-1945) French/Polish

£283 $439 €450 Vendange (27x35cm-11x14in) mono. s.i.verso painted c.1930-40. 30-Oct-2 Artcurial Briest, Paris #86

£346 $536 €550 Paysage au crepuscule (80x65cm-31x26in) mono. painted c.1926-29. 30-Oct-2 Artcurial Briest, Paris #79

£377 $585 €600 Paysage onirique (80x100cm-31x39in) mono. painted c.1930 exhib. 30-Oct-2 Artcurial Briest, Paris #78/R

£377 $585 €600 Paysage Polonais, Wierzbiorny (46x55cm-18x22in) mono. s.i.verso painted c.1930-40. 30-Oct-2 Artcurial Briest, Paris #80

£377 $585 €600 Composition, paysage (65x80cm-26x31in) mono. painted c.1930 exhib. 30-Oct-2 Artcurial Briest, Paris #82

£692 $1072 €1100 Calvi (80x100cm-31x39in) mono. painted c.1930-40. 30-Oct-2 Artcurial Briest, Paris #83/R

£755 $1170 €1200 Montagnardes (64x80cm-25x31in) mono. painted c.1926-29 exhib. 30-Oct-2 Artcurial Briest, Paris #81

SCHON, Arthur (1887-1940) Belgian

£364 $594 €550 Maternite (80x60cm-31x24in) s.d.1924. 17-Feb-3 Horta, Bruxelles #350

SCHON, Hans (1917-1994) German

£316 $500 €500 Ludwigsburg street (50x60cm-20x24in) s.d.1949 panel. 30-Nov-2 Arnold, Frankfurt #509/R

SCHONAU, Carl (19th C) German

£359 $552 €539 Young middle European man with gun (54x46cm-21x18in) s,. 27-Oct-2 Anders Antik, Landskrona #51/R (S.KR 5200)

SCHONBERGER, Alfred Karl Julius Otto von (1845-?) German

£308 $481 €450 Mountain lake (16x24cm-6x9in) s. panel. 10-Apr-3 Schopman, Hamburg #593

£696 $1078 €1044 Kronberg (17x24cm-7x9in) s. panel. 9-Dec-2 Philippe Schuler, Zurich #3931/R (S.FR 1600)

£2115 $3321 €3300 Landscape with pond (55x75cm-22x30in) 23-Nov-2 Arnold, Frankfurt #870/R est:2000

SCHONBERGER, Armand (1885-1974) Hungarian

£1806 $2817 €2619 Still life of flowers (69x55cm-27x22in) s. tempera. 13-Sep-2 Mu Terem Galeria, Budapest #84/R est:650000 (H.F 700000)

£1816 $2834 €2724 Still life with apple and glass (50x40cm-20x16in) s. tempera. 11-Apr-3 Kieselbach, Budapest #59/R est:380000-400000 (H.F 650000)

£2048 $3276 €3072 Still life of apple with a glass (35x45cm-14x18in) s. 16-May-3 Kieselbach, Budapest #47/R (H.F 700000)

£3912 $6103 €5868 Woman reading in studio (51x37cm-20x15in) s. board. 11-Apr-3 Kieselbach, Budapest #193/R est:1400000 (H.F 1400000)

£12994 $20141 €19491 Cafe interior (80x70cm-31x28in) 1-Oct-2 SOGA, Bratislava #134/R est:120000 (SL.K 825000)

£43028 $66694 €62391 Concert in the coffee house (99x80cm-39x31in) s.d.1928. 9-Dec-2 Mu Terem Galeria, Budapest #218/R est:7500000 (H.F 16000000)

Works on paper

£559 $872 €839 Girl in blue dress (43x28cm-17x11in) s. mixed media. 11-Apr-3 Kieselbach, Budapest #3/R (H.F 200000)

£619 $966 €898 Engrossed in reading (44x30cm-17x12in) s. mixed media. 13-Sep-2 Mu Terem Galeria, Budapest #60/R est:220000 (H.F 240000)

£619 $966 €898 Dream (24x35cm-9x14in) s. pastel tempera. 13-Sep-2 Mu Terem Galeria, Budapest #70/R est:220000 (H.F 240000)

£727 $1133 €1091 Girl reading (46x31cm-18x12in) s. pastel. 11-Apr-3 Kieselbach, Budapest #197/R est:180000-260000 (H.F 260000)

£826 $1288 €1198 Cellist (47x29cm-19x11in) s. chl. 13-Sep-2 Mu Terem Galeria, Budapest #59/R est:220000 (H.F 320000)

£1129 $1751 €1637 Daydreamer (40x34cm-16x13in) Mixed media. 9-Dec-2 Mu Terem Galeria, Budapest #178/R est:320000 (H.F 420000)

£1479 $2293 €2219 Mother and child (31x24cm-12x9in) s. pastel. 6-Dec-2 Kieselbach, Budapest #25/R (H.F 550000)

£1537 $2398 €2229 Railway (49x58cm-19x23in) s. mixed media. 12-Apr-3 Mu Terem Galeria, Budapest #190/R est:280000 (H.F 550000)

£3354 $5232 €4863 In the coffee house (50x35cm-20x14in) s. mixed media. 13-Sep-2 Mu Terem Galeria, Budapest #27/R est:480000 (H.F 1300000)

£3612 $5634 €5418 In a company, 1926 (73x57cm-29x22in) s. mixed media. 11-Sep-2 Kieselbach, Budapest #91/R (H.F 1400000)

SCHONCHEN, Leopold (1855-1935) German

£445 $695 €650 Ship (88x140cm-35x55in) d.1913. 10-Apr-3 Schopman, Hamburg #716

SCHONEBECK, Eugen (1936-) German

Works on paper

£1410 $2186 €2200 Untitled - soldiers (21x25cm-8x10in) s.d.1946 pencil. 3-Dec-2 Lempertz, Koln #413/R est:2000

£3333 $5167 €5200 Untitled (30x21cm-12x8in) mono.d.63 i.d. verso wash Indian ink prov.exhib. 3-Dec-2 Lempertz, Koln #414/R est:3000

SCHONER, Georg Friedrich Adolph (1774-1841) German

£1132 $1755 €1800 Aethra and Theseus (42x37cm-17x15in) s. 2-Oct-2 Dorotheum, Vienna #418/R est:1800-2500

SCHONFELD, Johann Heinrich (1609-1682) German

£3704 $6000 €5556 Saint Sebastian (14x10cm-6x4in) copper. 23-Jan-3 Sotheby's, New York #193/R est:8000

SCHONGAUER, Martin (1445-1491) German

Prints

£2308 $3600 €3462 Crucifixion (16x12cm-6x5in) engraving exec.c.1480. 6-Nov-2 Swann Galleries, New York #8/R est:2500-3500

£2821 $4400 €4232 Christ on the Mount of Olives (16x11cm-6x4in) engraving exec.c.1480. 6-Nov-2 Swann Galleries, New York #4/R est:5000-8000

£2949 $4600 €4424 St Martin dividing his cloak (16x10cm-6x4in) engraving exec.c.1475. 6-Nov-2 Swann Galleries, New York #9/R est:5000-8000

£3077 $4800 €4616 Annunciation (17x12cm-7x5in) engraving exec.c.1480. 6-Nov-2 Swann Galleries, New York #1/R est:3000-5000

£3590 $5600 €5385 Ecce homo (17x12cm-7x5in) engraving exec.c.1480. 6-Nov-2 Swann Galleries, New York #6/R est:6000-9000

£3590 $5600 €5385 Christ carrying the cross (16x12cm-6x5in) engraving. 6-Nov-2 Swann Galleries, New York #7/R est:5000-8000

£7051 $11141 €11000 La prise de Jesus Christ. engraving. 14-Nov-2 Libert, Castor, Paris #46/R est:2000

£12000 $18720 €18000 Christ before Pilate (16x11cm-6x4in) engraving executed c.1475-80. 10-Oct-2 Sotheby's, London #215/R est:10000-12000

£15385 $24000 €23078 Flight into Egypt (25x16cm-10x6in) engraving exec.c.1470-75. 6-Nov-2 Swann Galleries, New York #2/R est:7000-10000

SCHONHAUSER, H F (19/20th C) ?

£1899 $3000 €3000 Children playing in nursery with chicks (53x41cm-21x16in) s.d.1905. 27-Nov-2 James Adam, Dublin #95/R est:3000-5000

SCHONIAN, Alfred (1856-1936) German

£258 $400 €387 Portrait of two women (53x41cm-21x16in) s. panel. 7-Dec-2 Selkirks, St. Louis #736

£261 $429 €400 Hens and turkeys on village street (11x16cm-4x6in) s.i. panel. 5-Feb-3 Neumeister, Munich #812/R

£524 $817 €786 Chicks with butterfly (15x23cm-6x9in) s.i. panel. 6-Nov-2 Dobiaschofsky, Bern #955/R (S.FR 1200)

£747 $1090 €1150 Farm landscape with hens and grey geese (13x26cm-5x10in) s. panel. 15-Jun-2 Hans Stahl, Hamburg #52/R

£1127 $1814 €1600 Poultry by pond (16x24cm-6x9in) s.i. panel lit. 9-May-3 Schloss Ahlden, Ahlden #1429/R est:1600

£2270 $3677 €3200 Poultry yard (40x60cm-16x24in) s. 22-May-3 Dorotheum, Vienna #65/R est:3200-3800

SCHONICKE, E (20th C) German
£962 $1510 €1500 Rider and haywaggon on country track (32x49cm-13x19in) s.d.04 panel. 21-Nov-2 Van Ham, Cologne #1908/R est:1500
£2949 $4629 €4600 Soldiers (45x60cm-18x24in) mono. board. 21-Nov-2 Van Ham, Cologne #1906 est:1200
Works on paper
£2564 $4026 €4000 At the alchemists (118x151cm-46x59in) mono. mixed media board. 21-Nov-2 Van Ham, Cologne #1905/R est:2500

SCHONLEBER, Gustav (1851-1917) German
£4936 $7651 €7700 Summer landscape (31x45cm-12x18in) s.d.91. 5-Dec-2 Dr Fritz Nagel, Stuttgart #703/R est:6800
£5634 $9070 €8000 Besigheim (51x61cm-20x24in) s.d.1902 i. verso lit. 9-May-3 Schloss Ahlden, Ahlden #1448/R est:6500
Works on paper
£949 $1500 €1500 Dune landscape (31x57cm-12x22in) s. wash dr. 29-Nov-2 Sigalas, Stuttgart #1132/R est:1800
£1013 $1600 €1600 Windmill near Vlissingen (43x35cm-17x14in) s.d.1879 wash dr. 29-Nov-2 Sigalas, Stuttgart #1131/R est:1800

SCHONPFLUG, Fritz (1873-1951) Austrian
Works on paper
£353 $554 €550 K and K officer on horse (25x18cm-10x7in) s.d.917 W/C. 21-Nov-2 Dorotheum, Vienna #431/R
£377 $581 €600 The Officer is in a hurry (24x32cm-9x13in) s.d.08 W/C pencil. 22-Oct-2 Wiener Kunst Auktionen, Vienna #1124/R
£1013 $1580 €1600 Dining room with diners and musicians (43x71cm-17x28in) s. Indian ink W/C. 15-Oct-2 Dorotheum, Vienna #5/R est:2000-2600

SCHOOFS, Rudolf (1932-) German
£1449 $2377 €2000 Untitled (95x135cm-37x53in) s.d.1990 s.d. verso. 28-May-3 Lempertz, Koln #393/R est:2000
Works on paper
£1135 $1838 €1600 Utopian architecture (90x100cm-35x39in) s.d.16.9.70 s.d. verso mixed media board. 24-May-3 Van Ham, Cologne #533/R est:1600

SCHOONHOVEN, Jan J (1914-1994) Dutch
£1013 $1600 €1600 Untitled (57x42cm-22x17in) s.d.55 oil gouache on card. 26-Nov-2 Sotheby's, Amsterdam #56/R est:500-700
£3797 $6000 €6000 R60-10 (67x15cm-26x6in) s.i.verso painted paper mache relief. 26-Nov-2 Sotheby's, Amsterdam #270/R est:6000-8000
£24051 $38000 €38000 32 Small schuine vlakjes (42x19cm-17x7in) s. i.d.1966 verso white painted paper-mache relief prov. 26-Nov-2 Sotheby's, Amsterdam #266/R est:30000-40000
Sculpture
£12057 $19532 €17000 Relief (15x10cm-6x4in) s.d.1964 verso papier-mache on board. 26-May-3 Glerum, Amsterdam #305/R est:10000-15000
Works on paper
£696 $1100 €1100 T80-62 (50x32cm-20x13in) s.i.d.1980 ink. 26-Nov-2 Sotheby's, Amsterdam #276a est:1000-1500
£759 $1200 €1200 T82-23 (50x32cm-20x13in) s.i,d.1982 s.i.d. verso ink. 26-Nov-2 Sotheby's, Amsterdam #276/R est:1200-1500
£863 $1416 €1200 T85-176 (50x32cm-20x13in) s.d.1985 brush ink. 3-Jun-3 Christie's, Amsterdam #364/R est:1200-1600
£1007 $1652 €1400 T91-21 (50x32cm-20x13in) s.d.1991 pen brush ink. 3-Jun-3 Christie's, Amsterdam #363/R est:1200-1600
£1154 $1788 €1800 No.607 (48x32cm-19x13in) init.i.d.58 brush ink. 3-Dec-2 Christie's, Amsterdam #147/R est:1800-2200
£1266 $2000 €2000 Untitled (27x33cm-11x13in) s.d.52 W/C ink. 26-Nov-2 Sotheby's, Amsterdam #46/R est:900-1100
£1277 $2068 €1800 T81-24 (40x24cm-16x9in) s.d.1981 i.verso Indian ink. 26-May-3 Glerum, Amsterdam #298/R est:1800-2200
£1582 $2500 €2500 T 62-88 (49x37cm-19x15in) s.i.verso ink prov. 26-Nov-2 Sotheby's, Amsterdam #274/R est:1500-2000
£2564 $3974 €4000 Hatching in two directions (44x26cm-17x10in) s.d.1966 pen ink. 3-Dec-2 Christie's, Amsterdam #144/R est:2000-3000

SCHOOTEN, Floris van (1590-1657) Dutch
£20000 $33400 €29000 Apples, plums and other fruits on a draped ledge (36x50cm-14x20in) panel. 9-Jul-3 Bonhams, New Bond Street #3/R est:7000-10000

SCHOOTEN, Floris van (attrib) (1590-1657) Dutch
£2176 $3481 €3264 Market scene with two women and autumn fruit (51x82cm-20x32in) panel. 17-Mar-3 Blomqvist, Oslo #332/R est:50000-60000 (N.KR 25000)

SCHOPF, Josef (1745-1822) Austrian
£30405 $47432 €45000 Cupid and Pysche (170x125cm-67x49in) s.d.1780 prov. 27-Mar-3 Dorotheum, Vienna #264/R est:30000-40000
Works on paper
£541 $843 €800 Christening of Christ (28x17cm-11x7in) i. verso pencil. 28-Mar-3 Dorotheum, Vienna #10/R

SCHOPFER, Franziska (1763-1836) German
Miniatures
£4200 $6468 €6300 Prince Adalbert and Princess Alexandra of Bavaria (14cm-6in) s.d.1830 card leather wallet frame rec. 24-Oct-2 Sotheby's, Olympia #80/R est:1500-2000
£4200 $6888 €6090 Countess Therese Apponyi in a white dress (12cm-5in) s.d.1807 oval. 3-Jun-3 Christie's, London #186/R est:1500-2500

SCHOPFER, Franziska (attrib) (1763-1836) German
Works on paper
£272 $433 €400 Mountain farm (10x14cm-4x6in) W/C over pencil. 19-Mar-3 Neumeister, Munich #390

SCHOPKE, Philipp (1921-1998) Austrian
Works on paper
£1235 $2000 €1853 Regina frau (40x30cm-16x12in) s.d.verso graphite prov.exhib. 27-Jan-3 Christie's, Rockefeller NY #120/R est:1500-1800

SCHOTEL, Anthonie Pieter (1890-1958) Dutch
£567 $919 €800 Ships in the inner port of Dortrecht (29x38cm-11x15in) s. 26-May-3 Glerum, Amsterdam #37/R
£3819 $6073 €5500 Sardiniers, Douarnenez, Bretagne, France (80x80cm-31x31in) s. i.on stretcher. 29-Apr-3 Christie's, Amsterdam #164/R est:4000-6000

SCHOTEL, Jacoba Petronella Maria (1883-1957) Dutch
£1056 $1701 €1500 View of village in winter (45x74cm-18x29in) s. 7-May-3 Vendue Huis, Gravenhage #68/R est:1500-2000

SCHOTEL, Jan Christianus (1787-1838) Dutch
£11644 $18281 €17000 Shipping in choppy waters, Dordrecht in the distance (31x42cm-12x17in) s. panel. 15-Apr-3 Sotheby's, Amsterdam #169/R est:8000-12000
Works on paper
£2041 $3245 €3000 Boats at shore (26x35cm-10x14in) s. pen Chinese ink wash. 24-Mar-3 Tajan, Paris #24/R

SCHOTEL, Jan Christianus (attrib) (1787-1838) Dutch
£8679 $13540 €13800 Marine (67x92cm-26x36in) 10-Oct-2 Ribeyre & Baron, Paris #28/R est:7000-8000

SCHOTEL, Petrus Jan (1808-1865) Dutch
£1250 $2063 €1800 Sailing vessels on choppy water by a coast (38x47cm-15x19in) s. 1-Jul-3 Christie's, Amsterdam #1/R est:2000-3000
£4934 $7993 €7500 Sailing vessels off the coast on choppy waters (30x41cm-12x16in) s. panel. 21-Jan-3 Christie's, Amsterdam #1/R est:6000-8000
£22866 $37500 €34299 Sailing vessels in rough seas (115x150cm-45x59in) s. prov. 29-May-3 Sotheby's, New York #13/R est:30000-40000
£27397 $42740 €40000 Prince of Orange greeting the English fleet squadron in front of Dutch coast (74x98cm-29x39in) s. panel. 14-Apr-3 Glerum, Amsterdam #23/R est:40000-60000

SCHOTH, Albert (?) ?
£211 $350 €306 Coastal landscape with fisherman (25x46cm-10x18in) s. 11-Jun-3 Boos Gallery, Michigan #573/R

SCHOTH, Anton (1859-1906) Austrian
£250 $390 €375 Continental river scene with figures on the bank (22x45cm-9x18in) s. 23-Sep-2 Bonhams, Chester #968
£320 $522 €480 Continental river scene with figures in the foreground (20x43cm-8x17in) 12-Feb-3 Bonhams, Knightsbridge #58/R
£350 $564 €525 Fishermen loading their baskets with St Michael's Mount in the background (23x43cm-9x17in) s.i.verso. 19-Feb-3 Mallams, Oxford #412/R
£650 $1060 €975 Coastal town, Brittany (25x46cm-10x18in) bears sig. 29-Jan-3 Sotheby's, Olympia #253/R
£1200 $1872 €1800 View of Constantinople (22x46cm-9x18in) indis sig. board. 15-Oct-2 Sotheby's, London #93/R est:1500-2000
£2000 $3140 €3000 Trading vessels before Hagia Sofia, Istanbul (23x46cm-9x18in) s. 16-Apr-3 Christie's, Kensington #587/R est:800-1200

SCHOTTLI, Emanuel (1895-1926) Swiss
£519 $830 €779 Still life (46x38cm-18x15in) s. board. 17-Mar-3 Philippe Schuler, Zurich #8479 (S.FR 1100)

SCHOU, Karl (1870-1938) Danish
£355 $547 €533 From Dyrehaven with Eremitagen in background (34x47cm-13x19in) init. 23-Oct-2 Kunsthallen, Copenhagen #372 (D.KR 4200)

SCHOU, P A (1844-1914) Danish
£310 $475 €465 Self portrait at the easel (39x31cm-15x12in) with sig. verso. 24-Aug-2 Rasmussen, Havnen #2008 (D.KR 3600)
£478 $775 €693 Landscape with green fields (35x50cm-14x20in) mono. 26-May-3 Rasmussen, Copenhagen #1434/R (D.KR 5000)

SCHOU, Sigurd (1875-1944) Danish
£259 $396 €389 Fisherman hanging his nets for drying, Lysnaes (69x95cm-27x37in) mono.d.1914 exhib. 24-Aug-2 Rasmussen, Havnen #2199 (D.KR 3000)

SCHOUBOE, Henrik (1876-1949) Danish
£284 $432 €426 Quiet time in garden behind yellow house (40x45cm-16x18in) mono. 27-Aug-2 Rasmussen, Copenhagen #1940/R (D.KR 3300)

SCHOUBOE, Pablo (1874-1941) Danish
£2885 $4529 €4500 Flowering mimosa (62x72cm-24x28in) s. 10-Dec-2 Dorotheum, Vienna #223/R est:4500-5000

SCHOUMAN, Aert (1710-1792) Dutch
Works on paper
£2000 $3340 €2900 Turkey startling chickens (23x17cm-9x7in) s.verso W/C. 9-Jul-3 Sotheby's, London #113/R est:2500-3500

SCHOUMAN, Izaak (1801-1878) Dutch
£318 $497 €500 Portrait of Joanna van der Star (33x27cm-13x11in) s. d.1839 verso panel. 6-Nov-2 Vendue Huis, Gravenhage #475
£1027 $1603 €1500 Portrait of Adrianus Vos. Portrait of Heilje Joanna von Buul, wife of Adrianus Vos (94x80cm-37x31in) s.d.1829 pair. 14-Apr-3 Glerum, Amsterdam #35/R est:800-1200

SCHOUMAN, Martinus (1770-1848) Dutch
£2000 $3240 €3000 Dutch shipping in a heavy swell (32x43cm-13x17in) s.indis.d.1811 panel. 21-May-3 Christie's, Kensington #535/R est:3000-5000

Works on paper
£493 $794 €700 Sailing and other ships on the river near Dordrecht (40x55cm-16x22in) s.d.1829 W/C. 6-May-3 Vendu Notarishuis, Rotterdam #128

SCHOUTEN, Bartholomeus Francois (1941-2001) Dutch
£305 $500 €458 Still life of yellow roses (41x30cm-16x12in) s. panel. 8-Feb-3 Neal Auction Company, New Orleans #568
£444 $738 €644 Terrace (38x50cm-15x20in) s. panel. 16-Jun-3 Waddingtons, Toronto #237/R est:1000-1500 (C.D 1000)
£577 $900 €866 Paris street scene (38x53cm-15x21in) s. with alias Leroy panel. 12-Oct-2 Neal Auction Company, New Orleans #1192

SCHOUTEN, Cornelia van (1849-1929) Dutch
£4795 $7527 €7000 Flower still life with lilacs (61x86cm-24x34in) s.d.1882. 15-Apr-3 Sotheby's, Amsterdam #34/R est:4000-6000

SCHOUTEN, Henry (1864-1927) Belgian
£426 $689 €600 Vaches dans un paysage fluvial (54x74cm-21x29in) 26-May-3 Amberes, Antwerp #75
£442 $703 €650 Vaches au pre (45x70cm-18x28in) s. 18-Mar-3 Vanderkindere, Brussels #57
£457 $700 €686 Milkmaid with cows (42x57cm-17x22in) s. board. 21-Aug-2 Dunbar Sloane, Auckland #76/R est:1500-2500 (NZ.D 1500)
£476 $757 €700 Les bucherons (33x43cm-13x17in) s. 18-Mar-3 Campo, Vlaamse Kaai #226
£483 $763 €700 Chevres au paturage (60x80cm-24x31in) s. 1-Apr-3 Palais de Beaux Arts, Brussels #580
£506 $790 €800 Coq et poules (30x40cm-12x16in) s. 15-Oct-2 Horta, Bruxelles #69
£513 $805 €800 Trois vaches au pre (50x70cm-20x28in) s. 10-Dec-2 Vanderkindere, Brussels #125
£530 $864 €800 Trois brabancons (61x90cm-24x35in) s. 17-Feb-3 Horta, Bruxelles #54/R
£537 $821 €806 Landscape with horses (70x100cm-28x39in) s. 26-Aug-2 Blomqvist, Lysaker #1348 (N.KR 6200)
£563 $907 €800 Raging bull (67x57cm-26x22in) panel. 12-May-3 Bernaerts, Antwerp #44/R
£577 $906 €900 Vacher et son troupeau a la mare (60x90cm-24x35in) s. 10-Dec-2 Vanderkindere, Brussels #482
£604 $972 €900 Coq et poules (33x39cm-13x15in) s. panel. 18-Feb-3 Vanderkindere, Brussels #29
£612 $978 €850 Shepherd with flock (36x44cm-14x17in) s. panel. 17-May-3 De Vuyst, Lokeren #329
£616 $962 €900 Vache taureau et mouton (70x100cm-28x39in) s. 14-Apr-3 Horta, Bruxelles #32
£647 $1036 €900 Depart de l'etable. s. 19-May-3 Horta, Bruxelles #351
£654 $1052 €1000 Nature morte aux fleurs (50x65cm-20x26in) s. 14-Jan-3 Vanderkindere, Brussels #165
£654 $1052 €1000 Nature morte aux fleurs (50x65cm-20x26in) s. 14-Jan-3 Vanderkindere, Brussels #444
£671 $1081 €1000 Vachere et troupeau (65x114cm-26x45in) s. 18-Feb-3 Vanderkindere, Brussels #67
£683 $1094 €950 La conduite du chariot en hiver (32x24cm-13x9in) s. 19-May-3 Horta, Bruxelles #350
£683 $1094 €950 La traie dans les pres (60x90cm-24x35in) s. 19-May-3 Horta, Bruxelles #352
£685 $1075 €1000 Les chevaux (61x91cm-24x36in) s. 15-Apr-3 Galerie Moderne, Brussels #392
£696 $1079 €1100 Chevaux sur la plage (50x65cm-20x26in) s. 24-Sep-2 Galerie Moderne, Brussels #947
£701 $1093 €1100 Trois vaches dans un paysage (65x56cm-26x22in) s. 11-Nov-2 Horta, Bruxelles #126
£701 $1093 €1100 Vaches s'abreuvant (19x40cm-7x16in) s. pair. 11-Nov-2 Horta, Bruxelles #127
£755 $1162 €1200 Fermiere et son troupeau (80x60cm-31x24in) s. 22-Oct-2 Galerie Moderne, Brussels #1667
£759 $1185 €1200 Les pecheurs de crevettes et leurs chevaux sur la plage (60x90cm-24x35in) s. 15-Oct-2 Vanderkindere, Brussels #52 est:1100-1500
£759 $1200 €1200 Sheep by water (60x45cm-24x18in) s. lit. 29-Nov-2 Schloss Ahlden, Ahlden #1201/R
£782 $1244 €1150 Chevaux de trait et moutons au champ (60x90cm-24x35in) s. 18-Mar-3 Vanderkindere, Brussels #49
£784 $1263 €1200 La sortie du troupeau de moutons (70x100cm-28x39in) s. 20-Jan-3 Horta, Bruxelles #226
£784 $1263 €1200 Troupeau de moutons d'abreuvant (79x58cm-31x23in) s. 20-Jan-3 Horta, Bruxelles #228
£788 $1229 €1150 Farmer with four horses working in a field (61x91cm-24x36in) s. lit. 10-Apr-3 Allgauer, Kempten #2980/R
£818 $1259 €1300 Chevaux (80x60cm-31x24in) s. 22-Oct-2 Galerie Moderne, Brussels #1671
£833 $1308 €1300 Vaches pres de l'abreuvoir (58x88cm-23x35in) 25-Nov-2 Amberes, Antwerp #204
£892 $1391 €1400 Vue du moulin a eau (107x114cm-42x45in) s. 11-Nov-2 Horta, Bruxelles #125/R
£915 $1473 €1400 Deux brabancons dans l'ecurie (78x64cm-31x25in) s. 20-Jan-3 Horta, Bruxelles #227
£946 $1476 €1400 Vaches a la prairie (70x97cm-28x38in) s. 25-Mar-3 Campo & Campo, Antwerp #186/R
£962 $1510 €1500 Bergere et ses moutons (60x90cm-24x35in) s. 19-Nov-2 Vanderkindere, Brussels #56 est:1500-2000
£980 $1578 €1500 La sortie de la bergerie (100x80cm-39x31in) s. 20-Jan-3 Horta, Bruxelles #225 est:1500-2000
£1090 $1711 €1700 Chiens de chasse (40x60cm-16x24in) s. pair. 10-Dec-2 Vanderkindere, Brussels #115 est:1500-2500
£1090 $1711 €1700 Horses at the stable (58x79cm-23x31in) s. 16-Dec-2 Bernaerts, Antwerp #48/R est:1250-1500
£1111 $1789 €1667 Three hunting dogs (75x49cm-30x19in) s. 7-May-3 Dobiaschofsky, Bern #956/R est:2600 (S.FR 2400)
£1149 $1792 €1700 Berger et ses moutons (60x90cm-24x35in) s. 25-Mar-3 Campo & Campo, Antwerp #187 est:1500-2000
£1224 $1947 €1800 Shrimp fishermen with donkeys on beach (60x80cm-24x31in) s. 24-Mar-3 Bernaerts, Antwerp #126/R est:1800-2000
£1295 $2072 €1800 Hunting dogs resting (75x59cm-30x23in) s. 17-May-3 De Vuyst, Lokeren #327/R est:1500-1700
£1361 $2163 €2000 Fighting bulls (60x90cm-24x35in) s. 24-Mar-3 Bernaerts, Antwerp #124/R est:2000-2500
£1392 $2158 €2200 Anes sur la plage (50x65cm-20x26in) s. 24-Sep-2 Galerie Moderne, Brussels #802/R
£1410 $2186 €2200 Troupeau garde par un chien (70x100cm-28x39in) s. 9-Dec-2 Horta, Bruxelles #48 est:1700-2200
£1457 $2375 €2200 Jetee de fleurs (56x66cm-22x26in) s. 17-Feb-3 Horta, Bruxelles #53
£1538 $2385 €2400 Landscape with cows (65x85cm-26x33in) s. 7-Dec-2 De Vuyst, Lokeren #287/R est:1600-2000
£1635 $2535 €2600 Berger et troupeau au repos (100x80cm-39x31in) s. 1-Oct-2 Palais de Beaux Arts, Brussels #522/R est:2500-3750
£1635 $2535 €2600 Watering place (100x80cm-39x31in) s. 5-Oct-2 De Vuyst, Lokeren #320/R est:2800-3600
£1667 $2650 €2400 Canards (50x75cm-20x30in) s. 29-Apr-3 Campo, Vlaamse Kaai #280/R est:2500-3000
£1830 $2946 €2800 Retour a la bergerie avant l'orage (102x180cm-40x71in) s. 20-Jan-3 Horta, Bruxelles #224 est:3500-4500
£1871 $2993 €2600 Dogs walking (75x60cm-30x24in) s. 17-May-3 De Vuyst, Lokeren #326/R est:1900-2000
£2013 $3119 €3200 Chevaux au paturage (80x120cm-31x47in) s. 1-Oct-2 Palais de Beaux Arts, Brussels #520/R est:3250-5000
£2157 $3473 €3300 Chevaux et poules a l'ecurie (70x100cm-28x39in) s. 14-Jan-3 Vanderkindere, Brussels #11 est:2500-3500

£2166 $3378 €3400 Bouc et moutons dans un paysage (89x129cm-35x51in) s. 11-Nov-2 Horta, Bruxelles #123 est:3000-3750
£2200 $3432 €3300 Turkey with chickens in a landscape (64x88cm-25x35in) s. 9-Apr-3 Cheffins Grain & Comins, Cambridge #704/R est:2000-3000
£2293 $3577 €3600 Chevaux et poules dans l'etable (70x100cm-28x39in) s. 11-Nov-2 Horta, Bruxelles #124 est:3500-4000
£2308 $3577 €3600 Cattle market (100x150cm-39x59in) s. 7-Dec-2 De Vuyst, Lokeren #286/R est:2000-3000
£2360 $3800 €3540 Leashed dog near ducks (64x53cm-25x21in) s. 20-Jan-3 Arthur James, Florida #695
£2405 $3752 €3800 Trois anes a la barriere (48x65cm-19x26in) s. panel. 16-Sep-2 Horta, Bruxelles #104/R
£2446 $3914 €3400 Deux amours aux grappes de raisins. Deux amours a la fleche (54x45cm-21x18in) s.verso pair. 13-May-3 Palais de Beaux Arts, Brussels #137/R est:2500-3500
£2532 $3949 €4000 A la bergerie (70x100cm-28x39in) s. s.verso. 15-Oct-2 Horta, Bruxelles #67
£3797 $5924 €6000 Conduite des brabancons (113x176cm-44x69in) s. 15-Oct-2 Horta, Bruxelles #68
£4294 $7000 €6441 Setters putting up duck (51x75cm-20x30in) s. 11-Feb-3 Bonhams & Doyles, New York #155/R est:6000-8000

SCHOUTEN, Hermanus Petrus (attrib) (1747-1822) Dutch
Works on paper
£1361 $2164 €2000 View of La Haye (28x45cm-11x18in) W/C pen ink over crayon. 24-Mar-3 Tajan, Paris #25/R

SCHOUTEN, May (attrib) (19/20th C) ?
£1200 $1944 €1800 Cattle in meadow (79x121cm-31x48in) s. 23-Jan-3 Christie's, Kensington #64/R est:400-600

SCHOUTEN, Paul (1860-1922) Belgian
£282 $454 €400 Stable with sheep and chickens (40x56cm-16x22in) s. 12-May-3 Bernaerts, Antwerp #34/R
£308 $477 €480 Deux ane a la barriere (42x62cm-17x24in) s. 9-Dec-2 Horta, Bruxelles #49
£310 $489 €480 Moutons et poules dans la bergerie (60x90cm-24x35in) s. 17-Dec-2 Palais de Beaux Arts, Brussels #616
£316 $494 €500 Vaches s'abreuvant (54x63cm-21x25in) s. 16-Sep-2 Horta, Bruxelles #484
£426 $711 €600 Marine (50x80cm-20x31in) s. 18-Jun-3 Hotel des Ventes Mosan, Brussels #168
£445 $699 €650 Les vaches (80x100cm-31x39in) s. 15-Apr-3 Galerie Moderne, Brussels #329
£473 $738 €700 Nature morte aux anemones (71x90cm-28x35in) s. 25-Mar-3 Campo & Campo, Antwerp #188
£503 $785 €800 Chickens in the farmyard (70x100cm-28x39in) s. 23-Sep-2 Bernaerts, Antwerp #235
£510 $811 €750 Bergere et ses moutons a l'etable (70x100cm-28x39in) s. 18-Mar-3 Vanderkindere, Brussels #78
£863 $1381 €1200 Combat de coqs (80x100cm-31x39in) s. 13-May-3 Galerie Moderne, Brussels #444

SCHOVELIN, Axel Thorsen (1827-1893) Danish
£255 $403 €383 Landscape from Ordrup Mose (33x48cm-13x19in) s.d.1870. 27-Nov-2 Museumsbygningen, Copenhagen #10 (D.KR 3000)
£265 $426 €398 Road by woodland lake (44x63cm-17x25in) s. 19-Jan-3 Hindemae, Ullerslev #7297/R (D.KR 3000)
£293 $448 €440 Coastal landscape with fishing huts (60x90cm-24x35in) s. 24-Aug-2 Rasmussen, Havnen #2149 (D.KR 3400)
£342 $551 €513 View from Kronborg towards Julebaek (24x38cm-9x15in) s. 22-Feb-3 Rasmussen, Havnen #2298/R (D.KR 3800)
£379 $598 €569 Girl and boy with cattle on country road (42x60cm-17x24in) s. 27-Nov-2 Falkkloos, Malmo #77862/R (S.KR 5400)
£426 $672 €639 Mother and child in spring forest (46x58cm-18x23in) s. 2-Dec-2 Rasmussen, Copenhagen #1257/R (D.KR 5000)
£431 $655 €647 Landscape from Hellebaek (46x66cm-18x26in) s. 27-Aug-2 Rasmussen, Copenhagen #1937/R (D.KR 5000)
£512 $814 €768 Coastal landscape with view towards Copenhagen (42x60cm-17x24in) s. 5-Mar-3 Rasmussen, Copenhagen #1829/R (D.KR 5500)
£676 $1055 €1014 Coastal landscape with farm house (69x95cm-27x37in) s. 11-Aug-2 Hindemae, Ullerslev #7400/R (D.KR 8000)
£700 $1112 €1050 Coastal landscape with beached punts (49x75cm-19x30in) s. 5-May-3 Rasmussen, Vejle #354/R (D.KR 7500)
£1024 $1628 €1536 Summer landscape with woman by cottage (85x126cm-33x50in) s. 10-Mar-3 Rasmussen, Vejle #276/R (D.KR 11000)

SCHOW, May (1913-1993) American
Works on paper
£385 $600 €578 Church social (53x38cm-21x15in) W/C. 19-Oct-2 David Dike, Dallas #140/R
£385 $600 €578 Fish (36x48cm-14x19in) W/C. 19-Oct-2 David Dike, Dallas #143/R

SCHOYEN, Carl (1848-1875) Norwegian
£588 $952 €882 Landscape (26x39cm-10x15in) s. 27-Jan-3 Blomqvist, Lysaker #1227/R (N.KR 6500)

SCHOYERER, Josef (1844-1923) German
£823 $1284 €1300 Paysage montagneux avec torrent (21x25cm-8x10in) s.indis.d. 16-Oct-2 Hotel des Ventes Mosan, Brussels #148
£1026 $1590 €1600 Obersee near Berchtesgaden (79x99cm-31x39in) s.d.1874 i. verso. 5-Dec-2 Neumeister, Munich #2871/R est:1200
£1389 $2236 €2014 View of Jungfrau in sunshine (51x71cm-20x28in) s.i. 9-May-3 Dobiaschofsky, Bern #51/R est:3600 (S.FR 3000)
£1633 $2596 €2400 Niagara Falls (105x80cm-41x31in) s. 25-Feb-3 Dorotheum, Vienna #21/R est:2800-3200
£3901 $6319 €5500 Obersee by Berchtesgaden (79x99cm-31x39in) s.d.1876. 22-May-3 Dorotheum, Vienna #104/R est:3200-3800

SCHRADER, Bertha (1845-1920) German
£5755 $9209 €8000 Waterside town - Krager in the sun (51x59cm-20x23in) s.d.1911. 15-May-3 Neumeister, Munich #349/R est:8000-10000

SCHRAG, F (19th C) German
£303 $479 €455 Quiet hour (38x30cm-15x12in) s.i. board. 27-Nov-2 Deutscher-Menzies, Melbourne #271/R est:900-1200 (A.D 850)

SCHRAM, Alois Hans (1864-1919) Austrian
£1806 $2817 €2709 Woman with guitar, 1905 (40x64cm-16x25in) s.d.1905. 11-Sep-2 Kieselbach, Budapest #190/R (H.F 700000)
£13475 $21830 €19000 The choice (109x125cm-43x49in) s. i.verso. 22-May-3 Dorotheum, Vienna #1/R est:14000-18000

SCHRAMM, Viktor (1865-1929) Rumanian
£9615 $15096 €15000 Scene de guerre entre Turcs et Hongrois (162x244cm-64x96in) s.i.d.96. 16-Dec-2 Gros & Delettrez, Paris #370/R est:20000-30000

SCHRAMM-ZITTAU, Rudolf (1874-1950) German
£535 $834 €850 Turkeys (49x70cm-19x28in) 23-Sep-2 Dr Fritz Nagel, Stuttgart #6938/R
£570 $883 €900 Deer in high mountains (60x80cm-24x31in) 27-Sep-2 Dr Fritz Nagel, Leipzig #3902/R
£769 $1192 €1200 Snow-covered mountain landscape (60x80cm-24x31in) s. lit. 7-Dec-2 Bergmann, Erlangen #807/R
£946 $1476 €1400 English Garden, Munich on sunny winter's day (94x72cm-37x28in) s. prov. 27-Mar-3 Dr Fritz Nagel, Stuttgart #873/R
£1145 $1672 €1718 Ducks in landscape (40x55cm-16x22in) s. 17-Jun-2 Philippe Schuler, Zurich #4390/R est:2000-2500 (S.FR 2600)
£1258 $1962 €2000 Ehrwald on Zugspitze (62x80cm-24x31in) s. 19-Sep-2 Dr Fritz Nagel, Stuttgart #998/R
Works on paper
£1026 $1590 €1600 Chinese tower - Munich (47x58cm-19x23in) s.d.1933 pastel chk. 5-Dec-2 Dorotheum, Graz #196/R est:750

SCHRANZ, Anton (attrib) (19th C) Austrian?
£8000 $12720 €12000 Frigate H.M.S Tagus with Lord Adolphus Fitzclarence aboard running into Marsamaxett Harbour (58x96cm-23x38in) prov. 29-Apr-3 Bonhams, New Bond Street #160/R est:8000-12000

SCHRANZ, Giovanni (1794-1882) Maltese
£27000 $43740 €40500 H.M.S Raleigh entering Grand Harbour, Malta (30x49cm-12x19in) sold with two others by same hand. 23-May-3 Lyon & Turnbull, Edinburgh #24/R est:20000-30000
£98000 $151900 €147000 View of Grand Harbour, Valletta. View of Grand Harbour during a storm (91x132cm-36x52in) prov. pair. 6-Dec-2 Lyon & Turnbull, Edinburgh #79/R est:40000-60000
Works on paper
£1100 $1716 €1650 Fishing boat off Malta (16x23cm-6x9in) s. W/C bodycol. 15-Oct-2 Sotheby's, London #112/R est:800-1200

SCHRANZ, Giovanni (attrib) (1794-1882) Maltese
Works on paper
£4500 $7020 €6750 Figures by the Erectheum, with the Parthenon beyond (15x22cm-6x9in) W/C over pencil. 15-Oct-2 Sotheby's, London #4/R est:2000-3000

SCHRANZ, Giuseppe (1803-?) Maltese
Works on paper
£4400 $6996 €6600 H.M.S Victoria at anchor and drying her sails, Grand Harbour, Valetta (34x49cm-13x19in) W/C. 29-Apr-3 Bonhams, New Bond Street #161/R est:4000-6000

SCHRANZ, Joseph (1803-1847) German
Works on paper
£3000 $4680 €4500 View of Zante (25x41cm-10x16in) pen ink W/C over pencil. 15-Oct-2 Sotheby's, London #14/R est:3000-5000
£3000 $4680 €4500 Golden Horn, Constantinople (37x54cm-15x21in) W/C over pencil bodycol stopping out. 15-Oct-2 Sotheby's, London #73/R est:3000-5000

SCHRANZ, Joseph (attrib) (1803-1847) German
£10000 $15200 €15000 Royal Navy two-decker leading squadron into Grand Harbour, Valletta (83x129cm-33x51in) 15-Aug-2 Bonhams, New Bond Street #411/R est:10000-15000

SCHRAUDOLPH, Robert (1887-1978) German
£272 $433 €400 Fischbachau (60x74cm-24x29in) s. i. verso. 20-Mar-3 Neumeister, Munich #2737/R
£385 $585 €600 Still life with yellow roses in vase (71x61cm-28x24in) s. board. 11-Jul-2 Allgauer, Kempten #2679/R
£442 $703 €650 Reclining female nude (52x70cm-20x28in) s. panel. 21-Mar-3 Auktionhaus Georg Rehm, Augsburg #8081
£481 $745 €750 Spring landscape with view of Allgau mountains (60x80cm-24x31in) s. 6-Dec-2 Michael Zeller, Lindau #912/R
£503 $785 €800 Spring day in the Alps (60x74cm-24x29in) s.d.1930 i. verso. 9-Oct-2 Michael Zeller, Lindau #907/R
£513 $779 €800 Loisachtal with view of Benerberg Abbey (33x48cm-13x19in) s.d.1914 board lit. 11-Jul-2 Allgauer, Kempten #2678/R

SCHRECKENGOST, Victor (1906-) American
Works on paper
£224 $350 €336 Mystery of winter (56x76cm-22x30in) s. W/C board. 21-Sep-2 Rachel Davis, Shaker Heights #670/R
£1013 $1600 €1520 More snow to come (53x74cm-21x29in) s. W/C. 5-Apr-3 DeFina, Austinburg #1356 est:800-1200

SCHREDER, Karl (19/20th C) ?
£1905 $3029 €2800 Detail of mill by river (87x61cm-34x24in) s.i.d.1886 copy after Robert Russ. 25-Feb-3 Dorotheum, Vienna #40/R est:2400-2800

SCHREIBER, Charles Baptiste (1845-1903) French
£380 $600 €600 Jeune musicien (13x8cm-5x3in) s. panel. 1-Dec-2 Peron, Melun #2
£828 $1300 €1242 Artistic pursuits (22x17cm-9x7in) s. panel. 14-Dec-2 Weschler, Washington #604/R est:800-1200
£1027 $1603 €1500 Monk at easel (21x16cm-8x6in) s. panel. 10-Apr-3 Van Ham, Cologne #1698/R est:1500
£1463 $2400 €2121 Breviary (27x21cm-11x8in) s. panel. 4-Jun-3 Christie's, Rockefeller NY #219/R est:3000-5000

SCHREIBER, Charlotte Mount Brook Morrell (1834-1922) Canadian
£2667 $4373 €4001 Portrait of Carol (43x31cm-17x12in) board prov.exhib. 27-May-3 Sotheby's, Toronto #33/R est:6000-8000 (C.D 6000)

SCHREIBER, Conrad Peter (1816-1894) German
£1389 $2292 €2000 Mediterranean landscape with travellers on a patch (76x58cm-30x23in) s.d.1847. 1-Jul-3 Christie's, Amsterdam #152/R est:3000-5000

SCHREIBER, Georges (1904-1977) American
£252 $400 €378 Circus (46x61cm-18x24in) s.d.54. 7-Mar-3 Skinner, Boston #625/R
£1220 $2000 €1769 Woman and cat (71x91cm-28x36in) s.d.1930. 1-Jun-3 Wright, Chicago #182/R est:2500-3500
£2591 $4250 €3757 Japanese woman (89x79cm-35x31in) s.d.1930. 1-Jun-3 Wright, Chicago #188/R est:2500-3500

SCHREIBER, Hugo (19/20th C) ?
£1168 $1811 €1752 Portrait of Nora (26x22cm-10x9in) veneer painted c.1937. 3-Dec-2 SOGA, Bratislava #117/R est:60000 (SL.K 74000)

SCHREIBER, P (?) ?
£2518 $4130 €3500 Jeune femme servant a boire (41x25cm-16x10in) s. panel. 4-Jun-3 Tajan, Paris #313/R est:2300-2500

SCHREINZER, Karl August M (1819-1887) Russian
Works on paper
£2200 $3564 €3300 Portrait of a Bespectacled gentleman (24x20cm-9x8in) s.d.1857 W/C over pencil. 21-May-3 Sotheby's, London #2/R est:1000-1500

SCHREITTER VON SCHWARZENFELD, Adolf (1854-1923) Austrian
£833 $1308 €1300 First study trip (75x100cm-30x39in) mono. after F Defregger. 25-Nov-2 Dorotheum, Vienna #514/R

SCHRETER, Zygmunt (c.1896-1977) French
£440 $682 €700 Paysage aux vignes (50x65cm-20x26in) s. 30-Oct-2 Artcurial Briest, Paris #92
£629 $975 €1000 Bouquet de fleurs (46x38cm-18x15in) s. panel. 30-Oct-2 Artcurial Briest, Paris #88
£629 $975 €1000 Celerina en hiver (50x30cm-20x12in) s.i. panel. 30-Oct-2 Artcurial Briest, Paris #89
£735 $1168 €1080 Bouquet de fleurs roses (73x44cm-29x17in) s. cardboard. 26-Feb-3 Artcurial Briest, Paris #234
£816 $1298 €1200 Nature morte aux bouteilles (46x54cm-18x21in) s. panel. 26-Feb-3 Artcurial Briest, Paris #237
£833 $1308 €1300 Autoportrait (46x27cm-18x11in) 24-Nov-2 Chayette & Cheval, Paris #283
£884 $1406 €1300 Paysanne dans son jardin (30x37cm-12x15in) s. 26-Feb-3 Artcurial Briest, Paris #236
£884 $1406 €1300 Portrait d'homme (92x73cm-36x29in) panel. 26-Feb-3 Artcurial Briest, Paris #238
£955 $1490 €1500 Fleurs dans un vase bleu (33x22cm-13x9in) s. i.verso cardboard. 6-Nov-2 Claude Boisgirard, Paris #50 est:800-1000
£1384 $2145 €2200 Enfant assis (61x38cm-24x15in) s. 30-Oct-2 Artcurial Briest, Paris #91 est:800-1000
£1389 $2209 €2000 Vase de fleurs sur la table (65x46cm-26x18in) s. 29-Apr-3 Artcurial Briest, Paris #250/R est:800-1200
£1389 $2209 €2000 Le champ laboure (50x73cm-20x29in) s. 29-Apr-3 Artcurial Briest, Paris #253/R est:800-1200
£1395 $2217 €2050 Modele assis au fauteuil rouge (73x50cm-29x20in) s. 26-Feb-3 Artcurial Briest, Paris #235
£1528 $2429 €2200 Paysage a Ibiza (50x65cm-20x26in) s. s.d.1958 verso. 29-Apr-3 Artcurial Briest, Paris #251 est:800-1200
£1597 $2540 €2300 Vase de fleurs (73x50cm-29x20in) s. 29-Apr-3 Artcurial Briest, Paris #252 est:800-1200
£1761 $2730 €2800 Paysage, les maisons aux toits rouges (50x61cm-20x24in) s. cardboard. 30-Oct-2 Artcurial Briest, Paris #87/R est:800-1000
£2013 $3119 €3200 Autoportrait (55x33cm-22x13in) s. s.i.d.1946 verso panel. 30-Oct-2 Artcurial Briest, Paris #90/R est:800-1000

SCHREUDER VAN DE COOLWIJK, Jan W H (1868-1962) Dutch
£1974 $3197 €3000 Drinking tea (48x32cm-19x13in) s. 21-Jan-3 Christie's, Amsterdam #162/R est:800-1200
£1974 $3197 €3000 Girl dressing (40x31cm-16x12in) s.d.33. 21-Jan-3 Christie's, Amsterdam #165/R est:1500-2000

SCHREUER, Wilhelm (1866-1933) German
£544 $865 €800 Interior scene (60x80cm-24x31in) init. 1-Mar-3 Stadion, Trieste #482
Works on paper
£822 $1282 €1200 Hussars in extensive river landscape (43x65cm-17x26in) s.d.05 mixed media paper on canvas. 10-Apr-3 Van Ham, Cologne #1701a
£1027 $1603 €1500 Two soldiers on horseback and cattle by river (50x80cm-20x31in) mono. mixed media board. 10-Apr-3 Van Ham, Cologne #1699/R est:1600
£1410 $2214 €2200 Meeting (120x151cm-47x59in) mono. mixed media board. 21-Nov-2 Van Ham, Cologne #1904/R est:2500

SCHREYER, Adolf (1828-1899) German
£600 $978 €900 Autumnal forest landscape with wild boars walking through (39x51cm-15x20in) s. 11-Feb-3 Fellows & Sons, Birmingham #48/R
£2658 $4200 €4200 Hilly landscape with Arab on a horse (30x24cm-12x9in) s. panel. 30-Nov-2 Geble, Radolfzell #695 est:4200
£9000 $15030 €13500 Victor (122x202cm-48x80in) s. 18-Jun-3 Christie's, Kensington #202/R est:10000-15000
£18000 $29520 €27000 Desert canter (71x102cm-28x40in) s. prov. 3-Jun-3 Sotheby's, London #162/R est:15000-20000
£18310 $26000 €27465 Arab rider bearing a tricolor (56x46cm-22x18in) 8-Aug-1 Barridorf, Portland #134/R est:18000-22000
£28846 $45288 €45000 Les guetterus (59x83cm-23x33in) s. prov. 16-Dec-2 Gros & Delettrez, Paris #123/R est:45000-60000

SCHREYER, Adolf (attrib) (1828-1899) German
£2673 $4170 €4250 Arabians on the coast (45x86cm-18x34in) 23-Sep-2 Durán, Madrid #689/R

SCHREYER, Lothar (1886-1966) German
Works on paper
£563 $935 €800 Colour tone 25 (18x19cm-7x7in) mono.i.d. i. verso W/C pencil. 14-Jun-3 Hauswedell & Nolte, Hamburg #1591/R

SCHRIECK, Otto Marseus van (1619-1678) Dutch
£12950 $20719 €18000 Forest floor with still life with mushrooms, snail, moth, adder, nest (52x43cm-20x17in) s.d.1666. 13-May-3 Sotheby's, Amsterdam #82/R est:15000-20000

SCHRIECK, Otto Marseus van (attrib) (1619-1678) Dutch
£9122 $14230 €13500 Still life with frog, butterflies and snail (29x22cm-11x9in) panel. 26-Mar-3 Rieunier, Paris #40/R
£10125 $15693 €15188 Still life with thistle, butterflies and snake (58x45cm-23x18in) s. 3-Oct-2 Koller, Zurich #3049/R est:18000-22000 (S.FR 23590)

SCHRIJNDER, Joseph Alphons (1894-1968) Dutch
£446 $700 €669 Mallards in flight above a marsh (99x80cm-39x31in) s. 14-Dec-2 Weschler, Washington #626/R
£493 $794 €700 Ducks above Loosdrechtse lake (48x38cm-19x15in) s. 7-May-3 Vendue Huis, Gravenhage #39/R
£769 $1208 €1200 Over-flying swans (49x59cm-19x23in) s. 25-Nov-2 Glerum, Amsterdam #67
Works on paper
£556 $917 €800 Ermine in winter (36x26cm-14x10in) s. W/C gouache sold with another by the same hand. 1-Jul-3 Christie's, Amsterdam #574

SCHRIKKEL, Louis (1902-1995) Dutch
£1103 $1754 €1600 Circus scene with a woman on a horse (50x39cm-20x15in) s. panel. 10-Mar-3 Sotheby's, Amsterdam #345/R est:1800-2200
£1118 $1812 €1700 Farmers at work (35x27cm-14x11in) s.d.1936 canvas on board. 21-Jan-3 Christie's, Amsterdam #482/R est:1400-1800

SCHRIVER, L E (19/20th C) Continental
£4006 $6250 €6009 Chess game (46x51cm-18x20in) s. panel. 12-Oct-2 Neal Auction Company, New Orleans #184/R est:1500-2500

SCHRODER, Albert Friedrich (1854-1939) German
£577 $894 €900 Musketeer with pipe by table (18x24cm-7x9in) s. panel. 5-Dec-2 Neumeister, Munich #2872/R
£4192 $7000 €6078 Zechgelage (63x49cm-25x19in) s.i. panel prov. 22-Jun-3 Freeman, Philadelphia #26/R est:6000-10000
£4444 $7378 €6444 Jovial round of men in a tavern (48x60cm-19x24in) s.i. panel. 16-Jun-3 Waddingtons, Toronto #303/R est:8000-10000 (C.D 10000)

SCHRODER, Heinrich (1881-1941) German
£2532 $4000 €4000 Winter in a small town (79x63cm-31x25in) s. 26-Nov-2 Wiener Kunst Auktionen, Vienna #111/R est:4000-6000

SCHRODER, K (19th C) ?
£383 $620 €555 Sketch for a wall decoration in the style of Pompeii (46x20cm-18x8in) s.d.96. 26-May-3 Rasmussen, Copenhagen #1595 (D.KR 4000)

SCHRODER, Max (1879-?) German
£327 $536 €500 Village in valley (54x80cm-21x31in) s.i. i. verso. 29-Mar-3 Dannenberg, Berlin #650/R

SCHRODER, Poul (1894-1957) Danish
£381 $637 €552 Standing model with red hairband (100x74cm-39x29in) s. 17-Jun-3 Rasmussen, Copenhagen #187/R (D.KR 4000)
£572 $955 €829 Still life of objects on table (92x78cm-36x31in) s. 17-Jun-3 Rasmussen, Copenhagen #191/R (D.KR 6000)
£676 $1041 €1014 Summer landscape (65x89cm-26x35in) s. 23-Oct-2 Kunsthallen, Copenhagen #60/R (D.KR 8000)
£836 $1322 €1254 Seated woman (92x60cm-36x24in) prov. 1-Apr-3 Rasmussen, Copenhagen #528/R (D.KR 9000)
£914 $1453 €1371 Still life of flowers on table (50x61cm-20x24in) s. 26-Feb-3 Kunsthallen, Copenhagen #232/R (D.KR 10000)
£1022 $1615 €1533 Girl on sofa (100x86cm-39x34in) s. prov.exhib.lit. 1-Apr-3 Rasmussen, Copenhagen #583/R (D.KR 11000)
£1352 $2083 €2028 Still life of objects on table (82x100cm-32x39in) s/. 23-Oct-2 Kunsthallen, Copenhagen #8/R est:8000 (D.KR 16000)

SCHRODER, Sierk (1903-2002) Dutch
£268 $412 €420 Murese Regius (14x19cm-6x7in) Board painted c.1989. 3-Sep-2 Christie's, Amsterdam #404
£458 $737 €650 Lady sitting (51x39cm-20x15in) s. chl. 7-May-3 Vendue Huis, Gravenhage #200/R
£764 $1192 €1200 Nude bending and other studies (54x44cm-21x17in) s. 6-Nov-2 Vendue Huis, Gravenhage #248
£1146 $1766 €1800 Seated lady reading (18x20cm-7x8in) s.d.71 paper on board. 3-Sep-2 Christie's, Amsterdam #403 est:1000-1500
Works on paper
£382 $596 €600 Nude seated (30x30cm-12x12in) s. crayon. 6-Nov-2 Vendue Huis, Gravenhage #247
£526 $853 €800 Lady reading (27x37cm-11x15in) s.d. brush brown ink. 21-Jan-3 Christie's, Amsterdam #462/R
£599 $964 €850 Portrait of a lady (41x33cm-16x13in) s. chl dr. 7-May-3 Vendue Huis, Gravenhage #208
£764 $1192 €1200 Portrait of a lady (45x30cm-18x12in) s. chl. 6-Nov-2 Vendue Huis, Gravenhage #245/R
£828 $1275 €1300 Reclining nude (30x60cm-12x24in) s. W/C pastel pencil. 3-Sep-2 Christie's, Amsterdam #402
£833 $1375 €1200 Cherry branch. Kneeling nude (47x32cm-19x13in) s.d.85 W/C canvasboard double-sided. 1-Jul-3 Christie's, Amsterdam #259/R
£1019 $1590 €1600 Two studies of a half nude (39x43cm-15x17in) s. W/C prov. 6-Nov-2 Vendue Huis, Gravenhage #246/R est:1500-2000

SCHRODER-GREIFSWALD, Max (1858-?) German
£1039 $1517 €1600 Parade of ships in front of a castle and wooded coast (30x50cm-12x20in) s.indis.i. canvas on canvas. 15-Jun-2 Hans Stahl, Hamburg #261/R

SCHRODER-SONNENSTERN, F (1892-1982) German
Works on paper
£1016 $1626 €1473 Der tote Loewe (50x71cm-20x28in) s.d.59 crayon pencil. 18-May-3 Anders Antik, Landskrona #93 (S.KR 13000)

SCHRODER-SONNENSTERN, Friedrich (1892-1982) German
Works on paper
£633 $1000 €1000 Battle for the moral error (51x73cm-20x29in) s.i.d.1958 s.mono.d. verso col crayon pencil board. 29-Nov-2 Villa Grisebach, Berlin #885/R
£943 $1453 €1500 Devil's ascent (70x48cm-28x19in) s.mono.i.d.1962 s.mono.d. verso col pen board. 26-Oct-2 Dr Lehr, Berlin #478/R
£1367 $2242 €1900 Die flucht vor dem weibe - flight from the wife (50x72cm-20x28in) s.d.1963 col pencil. 3-Jun-3 Christie's, Amsterdam #111/R est:1000-1500
£3846 $5615 €6000 Composition with woman on pig (41x60cm-16x24in) s.i.d.1955 mixed media. 4-Jun-2 Karl & Faber, Munich #413/R est:4000

SCHRODER-TAPIAU, Karl (attrib) (1760-1844) German
£748 $1190 €1100 Old city of Dachau (32x44cm-13x17in) mono. canvas on board. 20-Mar-3 Neumeister, Munich #2738/R

SCHRODL, Anton (1823-1906) Austrian
£604 $972 €900 Farmer's kitchen in Pinzgau, Austria (26x44cm-10x17in) s. board prov. 18-Feb-3 Sotheby's, Amsterdam #316/R est:1200-1800
£705 $1107 €1100 Billy goat (31x37cm-12x15in) s. board. 10-Dec-2 Dorotheum, Vienna #176/R
£738 $1188 €1100 Farmer's haywain (22x32cm-9x13in) board prov.lit. 18-Feb-3 Sotheby's, Amsterdam #315/R est:1500-3000
£805 $1297 €1200 In the cowshed, im Kuhstall (28x45cm-11x18in) s. board prov.lit. 18-Feb-3 Sotheby's, Amsterdam #318/R est:1500-3000
£816 $1298 €1200 In the stable (22x27cm-9x11in) s. 25-Feb-3 Dorotheum, Vienna #187
£940 $1513 €1400 Peasant's hut in Ferleiten, Austria (27x42cm-11x17in) s. board prov. 18-Feb-3 Sotheby's, Amsterdam #288/R est:1200-1800

SCHRODL, Norbert (1842-1912) Austrian
£7746 $12859 €11000 Portrait de petite fille a la brassee de fleurs des champs (127x94cm-50x37in) s.d.1876. 11-Jun-3 Cornette de St.Cyr, Paris #45/R est:10000-15000

SCHRODLER, Gustav (19th C) ?
£1200 $1848 €1800 Sisters (67x56cm-26x22in) s.d.1892. 24-Oct-2 Christie's, Kensington #103/R est:1000-1500

SCHRODTER, Adolf (1805-1875) German
£5899 $9439 €8200 Wood nymph (34x30cm-13x12in) s.d.1854 W/C. 17-May-3 Lempertz, Koln #1340/R est:2600
Works on paper
£264 $420 €380 Long live 21 October (28x21cm-11x8in) s. pencil board. 5-May-3 Ketterer, Munich #312/R

SCHROEDER, Georg Engelhardt (1684-1750) Swedish
£3221 $5282 €4670 Portrait of Admiral Johan von Utfall and his wife Maria Helena (79x63cm-31x25in) one s.verso pair one painted with Fredrik Brander. 4-Jun-3 AB Stockholms Auktionsverk #2139/R est:20000-25000 (S.KR 41000)
£5319 $8245 €7979 Portraits of Fredrik I and Ulrika Eleonora the younger (220x133cm-87x52in) pair prov. 4-Dec-2 AB Stockholms Auktionsverk #1689/R est:200000-250000 (S.KR 75000)

£5532 $8574 €8298 Portrait of Count Nils Bjelke (79x65cm-31x26in) exhib.lit. 3-Dec-2 Bukowskis, Stockholm #399/R est:25000-30000 (S.KR 78000)

SCHROEDER, Georg Engelhardt (attrib) (1684-1750) Swedish
£663 $1041 €995 Portrait of Count Joachim von Duben (78x64cm-31x25in) i.verso. 16-Dec-2 Lilla Bukowskis, Stockholm #588 (S.KR 9400)
£3546 $5496 €5319 Europa and the bull (80x108cm-31x43in) lit. 3-Dec-2 Bukowskis, Stockholm #408/R est:40000-50000 (S.KR 50000)

SCHROTER, Walter (attrib) (1905-1956) German
£535 $834 €850 Farmstead by lake (61x70cm-24x28in) mono. i. stretcher. 21-Sep-2 Bolland & Marotz, Bremen #775/R

SCHROTH, Eugin (1862-1945) Austrian
£719 $1180 €1000 Sunflowers in abbey garden in Durnstein (47x37cm-19x15in) s.d.35 canvas on panel. 5-Jun-3 Dorotheum, Salzburg #519/R

SCHROTTER, Alfred von (1856-1935) Austrian
£473 $738 €700 Soldier on horseback (33x26cm-13x10in) s. panel. 26-Mar-3 Hugo Ruef, Munich #228

SCHRYVER, Louis Marie de (1862-1942) French
£75949 $120000 €113924 Flower seller, Champs Elysees, Rampart Gardens (53x74cm-21x29in) s.d.1897 canvas on board. 24-Apr-3 Sotheby's, New York #5/R est:80000-120000

SCHUBERT, Franz August (1806-1893) German
£288 $447 €450 Holy Family and Infant St John the Baptist with lamb (37x32cm-15x13in) mono.d.1836. 5-Dec-2 Schopman, Hamburg #513

SCHUDER-WOLDAM, Raff (19/20th C) ?
£1139 $1766 €1800 Portrait de femme (95x79cm-37x31in) s.i. 27-Sep-2 Rabourdin & Choppin de Janvry, Paris #57/R est:2300-2500

SCHUFFENECKER, Claude Émile (1851-1934) French
£22378 $37371 €32000 Bord d'etang (54x65cm-21x26in) bears st.sig. prov. 26-Jun-3 Tajan, Paris #258/R est:4000-6000

Works on paper
£625 $1019 €900 Paysage a l'arbre bleu (19x13cm-7x5in) studio st. pastel. 19-Jul-3 Thierry & Lannon, Brest #96
£1014 $1581 €1500 Rue de village (32x44cm-13x17in) studio st. pastel. 28-Mar-3 Charbonneaux, Paris #136/R
£2308 $3577 €3600 Arbres bordant une route (45x36cm-18x14in) studio st. pastel lit. 7-Dec-2 Martinot & Savignat, Pontoise #37/R est:3500
£3846 $6423 €5500 Les porteuses de varech a Yport (48x31cm-19x12in) s.i. chl dr. 26-Jun-3 Tajan, Paris #46/R est:2000-3000

SCHUFRIED, Dominik (1810-?) Austrian
£2837 $4596 €4000 Landscape with figures (36x46cm-14x18in) s.d.1859 panel. 22-May-3 Dorotheum, Vienna #201/R est:4000-5000

SCHUHKNECHT, Adolf (1889-?) German
£655 $1054 €930 Harvest time in the Harz (70x100cm-28x39in) s. i. verso. 7-May-3 Michael Zeller, Lindau #926/R

SCHUHMACHER, Wim (1894-1986) Dutch
£14388 $23597 €20000 Stilleven met crucifix en apeschedel - still life with crucifix and monkey skull (60x32cm-24x13in) s. painted 1937 prov.exhib.lit. 3-Jun-3 Christie's, Amsterdam #214/R est:18000-22000
£35971 $58993 €50000 Stilleven met vissen en vruchten - still life with fruit and fish (65x81cm-26x32in) s. executed 1931 prov.exhib.lit. 3-Jun-3 Christie's, Amsterdam #207/R est:60000-80000

Works on paper
£2405 $3800 €3800 Corsicaase vrouw met hoofddoek (64x50cm-25x20in) s. ink executed 1923 prov.lit. 26-Nov-2 Sotheby's, Amsterdam #29/R est:3200-4500
£2848 $4500 €4500 Zitted Naakt (96x62cm-38x24in) s. ink executed 1924 prov.lit. 26-Nov-2 Sotheby's, Amsterdam #124/R est:4500-6800

SCHUKOFF, Ivan (19th C) Russian
£4430 $7000 €7000 Hunting at dawn (58x82cm-23x32in) s.d.92. 1-Dec-2 Bukowskis, Helsinki #272/R est:5000-7000

SCHULDT, Fritiof (1891-1978) Swedish
£1261 $1968 €1892 Porto d'Ischia (55x65cm-22x26in) s. panel. 6-Nov-2 AB Stockholms Auktionsverk #659/R est:18000-20000 (S.KR 18000)

SCHULE, Gottlieb F (19/20th C) Austrian?

Works on paper
£385 $608 €600 Langobard Oratorium (75x61cm-30x24in) s.i.d.1918 W/C. 18-Nov-2 Dorotheum, Linz #454/R

SCHULER, Hans (1874-?) German

Sculpture
£5068 $7905 €7500 Ariane abandonnee (37x75x30cm-15x30x12in) s.st.f.Siot-Decauville brown pat bronze. 26-Mar-3 Peschetau-Badin Godeau & Leroy, Paris #80/R

SCHULLER, Joseph Carl Paul (19th C) French

Works on paper
£1562 $2500 €2265 Floral still life (121x76cm-48x30in) s. W/C. 16-May-3 Skinner, Boston #22/R est:5000-7000

SCHULMAN, David (1881-1966) Dutch
£255 $392 €400 Farmers at work in a field, a village beyond (28x44cm-11x17in) s.d.09. 3-Sep-2 Christie's, Amsterdam #179
£379 $603 €550 Forest lane in winter (25x27cm-10x11in) s. panel. 10-Mar-3 Sotheby's, Amsterdam #167
£559 $906 €850 Outskirts of a town in summer (41x61cm-16x24in) s. 21-Jan-3 Christie's, Amsterdam #131
£789 $1279 €1200 View of Wijk bij Duurstede (47x75cm-19x30in) s. 21-Jan-3 Christie's, Amsterdam #320/R est:1200-1600
£1447 $2345 €2200 View of the Prins Hendrikkade, Amsterdam (50x70cm-20x28in) s. 21-Jan-3 Christie's, Amsterdam #304/R est:700-900
£1911 $2943 €3000 Winter, Laren - farms covered in snow (48x75cm-19x30in) s. i.stretcher. 3-Sep-2 Christie's, Amsterdam #192/R est:2000-3000
£2025 $3159 €3200 Farm in the snow (54x84cm-21x33in) s. 21-Oct-2 Glerum, Amsterdam #220 est:3000-5000
£2207 $3509 €3200 De betuwe (82x94cm-32x37in) s. exhib. 10-Mar-3 Sotheby's, Amsterdam #246/R est:2000-3000

SCHULT, Hans Jurgen (1939-) German

Sculpture
£1103 $1743 €1600 New Germany (70x70x20cm-28x28x8in) s.i.d. verso sand earth metal plastic col cultures prov. 2-Apr-3 Dr Fritz Nagel, Stuttgart #9554/R est:1000
£1241 $1961 €1800 NY - NY (100x100x16cm-39x39x6in) s.i.d. sand earth metal plastic cultures prov. 2-Apr-3 Dr Fritz Nagel, Stuttgart #9552/R est:1200
£1241 $1961 €1800 Opel land (70x70x16cm-28x28x6in) s.i.d. verso sand earth plastic metal col cultures prov. 2-Apr-3 Dr Fritz Nagel, Stuttgart #9555/R est:1000

SCHULTEN, Arnold (1809-1874) German
£822 $1282 €1200 The Jungfrau from Wnegen (84x125cm-33x49in) s. canvas on board. 10-Apr-3 Van Ham, Cologne #1703/R

SCHULTHEISS, Karl (1852-1944) German
£1410 $2214 €2200 Dancing (88x127cm-35x50in) s. 21-Nov-2 Van Ham, Cologne #1911 est:1500

SCHULTHEISS, Natalie (1865-1952) Austrian
£382 $596 €600 Still life with oysters (36x46cm-14x18in) s. panel. 6-Nov-2 Hugo Ruef, Munich #1301
£1090 $1711 €1700 Still life with grapes and pomegranates (61x82cm-24x32in) s.d.1914. 21-Nov-2 Van Ham, Cologne #1912/R est:1800
£2329 $3633 €3400 Still life of fruit with peaches, melon and grapes on silver plate (59x85cm-23x33in) s. 10-Apr-3 Dorotheum, Vienna #106/R est:3200-3600
£4747 $7500 €7500 Bunch of gladioli (90x60cm-35x24in) i.verso painted 1895. 28-Nov-2 Dorotheum, Vienna #30/R est:4500-5500

SCHULTHESS, Emil (1805-1855) Swiss

Works on paper
£291 $477 €422 Newmarket tower and Niederdorf tower (14x18cm-6x7in) wash Indian ink. 4-Jun-3 Fischer, Luzern #2731/R (S.FR 620)

SCHULTZ, Alexander (1901-1981) Norwegian
£259 $433 €376 Landscape with trees (50x61cm-20x24in) s.d.57. 18-Jun-3 Grev Wedels Plass, Oslo #216 (N.KR 3000)
£302 $505 €438 Mountain brook, Roros (46x56cm-18x22in) s. i.verso. 18-Jun-3 Grev Wedels Plass, Oslo #217 (N.KR 3500)
£368 $588 €552 Landscape with house (50x62cm-20x24in) s.d.71. 13-Jan-3 Rasmussen, Vejle #272 (D.KR 4200)
£647 $984 €971 Landscape with trees (50x61cm-20x24in) s. 31-Aug-2 Grev Wedels Plass, Oslo #99 (N.KR 7500)
£1035 $1574 €1553 From Italy (60x73cm-24x29in) s. i.d.1963 verso. 31-Aug-2 Grev Wedels Plass, Oslo #98 (N.KR 12000)

£1134 $1781 €1701 Landscape with red roof tops (50x61cm-20x24in) s. panel. 25-Nov-2 Blomqvist, Lysaker #1242 est:15000-18000 (N.KR 13000)
£1301 $2029 €1952 Centre-piece of flowers on check table cloth (62x79cm-24x31in) s. 21-Oct-2 Blomqvist, Oslo #373/R est:15000-18000 (N.KR 15000)
£1327 $2097 €1991 Winter landscape with skiers (50x61cm-20x24in) s. 28-Apr-3 Blomqvist, Oslo #379/R est:18000-22000 (N.KR 15000)
£1384 $2187 €2076 Interior scene with woman (74x104cm-29x41in) s. 2-Dec-2 Blomqvist, Oslo #431/R est:25000 (N.KR 16000)

SCHULTZ, Francis (1906-1985) American
£769 $1200 €1154 Summer in West Texas (46x61cm-18x24in) canvasboard. 19-Oct-2 David Dike, Dallas #325/R

SCHULTZ, George F (1869-?) American
£714 $1100 €1071 Figure in an autumn landscape (51x61cm-20x24in) s. canvas on board painted c.1910. 8-Sep-2 Treadway Gallery, Cincinnati #572/R

Works on paper
£701 $1100 €1052 Pastoral landscape (51x36cm-20x14in) s. W/C paper on artist's board. 23-Nov-2 Jackson's, Cedar Falls #56/R

SCHULTZ, Josef (1892-1972) German
£845 $1361 €1200 Sunny lane (76x59cm-30x23in) s.i.d.1923. 7-May-3 Vendue Huis, Gravenhage #141/R

SCHULTZBERG, Anshelm (1862-1945) Swedish
£426 $647 €639 The fountain at Casa Canale, Capri (55x62cm-22x24in) s. d.1891 verso canvas on panel. 16-Aug-2 Lilla Bukowskis, Stockholm #863 (S.KR 6200)
£463 $769 €671 Leckom mountain (45x64cm-18x25in) s.d.1912. 16-Jun-3 Lilla Bukowskis, Stockholm #546 (S.KR 6000)
£560 $885 €840 Winter landscape, evening (72x92cm-28x36in) s.i.d.1902. 16-Nov-2 Crafoord, Lund #92/R (S.KR 8000)
£565 $886 €848 Lake landscape (19x35cm-7x14in) s. 16-Dec-2 Lilla Bukowskis, Stockholm #470 (S.KR 8000)
£567 $879 €851 Autumn landscape with red cottage (61x79cm-24x31in) s. 4-Dec-2 AB Stockholms Auktionsverk #1781/R (S.KR 8000)
£674 $1044 €1011 Southern graveyard in evening (38x56cm-15x22in) s.d.1894 panel. 8-Dec-2 Uppsala Auktionskammare, Uppsala #116/R (S.KR 9500)
£776 $1219 €1164 Landscape from Ugglarp, Halland (51x71cm-20x28in) s. panel. 16-Dec-2 Lilla Bukowskis, Stockholm #872 (S.KR 11000)
£823 $1284 €1235 River landscape - Canche by Etaples (55x65cm-22x26in) s.i.d.1890. 13-Sep-2 Lilla Bukowskis, Stockholm #45 (S.KR 12000)
£922 $1429 €1383 Beech wood in summer sunshine (46x38cm-18x15in) s.d.87. 4-Dec-2 AB Stockholms Auktionsverk #1719/R (S.KR 13000)
£943 $1546 €1367 Winter landscape with red buildings in sunshine (29x45cm-11x18in) s.d.1900. 4-Jun-3 AB Stockholms Auktionsverk #2144/R (S.KR 12000)
£961 $1461 €1442 Winter evening by a chalet in Upper Dalarna (60x80cm-24x31in) s.d.1939. 16-Aug-2 Lilla Bukowskis, Stockholm #434 est:15000 (S.KR 14000)
£1206 $1869 €1809 Outside the cottage (46x96cm-18x38in) s.d.83. 3-Dec-2 Bukowskis, Stockholm #255/R est:25000-30000 (S.KR 17000)
£1206 $1869 €1809 Spring landscape with wanderer (44x29cm-17x11in) s.i.d.1889 prov.exhib. 4-Dec-2 AB Stockholms Auktionsverk #1553/R est:15000-20000 (S.KR 17000)
£1262 $1994 €1893 Winter landscape from Hastaberget, Filipstad (60x80cm-24x31in) s.d.1936. 30-Nov-2 Goteborg Auktionsverk, Sweden #166/R est:20000 (S.KR 18000)
£1335 $2190 €1936 View across Fafangen and Stockholm's inlet (73x93cm-29x37in) s.i.d.1909. 4-Jun-3 AB Stockholms Auktionsverk #2174/R est:15000-18000 (S.KR 17000)
£1560 $2418 €2340 Leksands farm in evening sunshine, winter (94x122cm-37x48in) s.i.d.1910. 4-Dec-2 AB Stockholms Auktionsverk #1555/R est:25000-28000 (S.KR 22000)
£1560 $2418 €2340 By the water, Bellevue (75x100cm-30x39in) s.i.d.1909. 4-Dec-2 AB Stockholms Auktionsverk #1565/R est:22000-25000 (S.KR 22000)
£1571 $2577 €2278 French landscape, Souvenier d'Etaples (27x41cm-11x16in) s.d.1890. 4-Jun-3 AB Stockholms Auktionsverk #2182/R est:15000-18000 (S.KR 20000)
£1629 $2639 €2362 Woodland in winter (81x116cm-32x46in) s.d.1920. 25-May-3 Uppsala Auktionskammare, Uppsala #173/R est:25000-30000 (S.KR 21000)
£1844 $2858 €2766 Karl XII's Square, Stockholm, winter (73x60cm-29x24in) s. 4-Dec-2 AB Stockholms Auktionsverk #1554/R est:15000-18000 (S.KR 26000)
£1844 $2858 €2766 Northern landscape with farm, winter (50x73cm-20x29in) s. 4-Dec-2 AB Stockholms Auktionsverk #1560/R est:25000-30000 (S.KR 26000)
£1939 $3142 €2812 Winter landscape between Klenhyttan and Ludvika (73x100cm-29x39in) s.d.1940. 26-May-3 Bukowskis, Stockholm #104/R est:20000-25000 (S.KR 25000)
£2200 $3607 €3190 Farm in evening sunshine, winter (100x134cm-39x53in) s. 4-Jun-3 AB Stockholms Auktionsverk #2321/R est:25000-30000 (S.KR 28000)
£2270 $3518 €3405 Evening glow (47x76cm-19x30in) s. 3-Dec-2 Bukowskis, Stockholm #357/R est:40000-50000 (S.KR 32000)
£2482 $3848 €3723 Midwinter's day - landscape from Bergslagen (73x110cm-29x43in) s.d.1938. 3-Dec-2 Bukowskis, Stockholm #83/R est:35000-40000 (S.KR 35000)
£2560 $4147 €3712 Winter landscape from Filipstads mining district (69x105cm-27x41in) s. 26-May-3 Bukowskis, Stockholm #105/R est:20000-25000 (S.KR 33000)
£2908 $4507 €4362 Winter landscape from Filipstad Bergslag (73x100cm-29x39in) s. 4-Dec-2 AB Stockholms Auktionsverk #1732/R est:30000-35000 (S.KR 41000)
£2948 $4776 €4275 December in Kol Forest (81x116cm-32x46in) s.d.1924. 26-May-3 Bukowskis, Stockholm #109/R est:25000-30000 (S.KR 38000)

Works on paper
£313 $500 €454 Untitled (13x18cm-5x7in) s. Indian ink wash. 18-May-3 Anders Antik, Landskrona #65 (S.KR 4000)

SCHULTZE, Bernard (1915-) German
£4255 $6894 €6000 Like a collapse umbrella of light (120x90cm-47x35in) s.d.90 s.i.d. verso. 24-May-3 Van Ham, Cologne #538/R est:9500
£7692 $11923 €12000 On the shore (120x100cm-47x39in) s.d.1956 s.i.d.1956 prov.exhib. 6-Dec-2 Ketterer, Munich #167/R est:10000-20000
£8696 $14261 €12000 Debate on different levels (98x98cm-39x39in) s.d.1956 s.i.d. verso oil on canvas with relief. 28-May-3 Lempertz, Koln #394/R est:15000-18000
£10870 $17826 €15000 Mythical woods (140x200cm-55x79in) s.d.86 s.i.d. verso. 28-May-3 Lempertz, Koln #396/R est:18000-20000

Works on paper
£252 $392 €400 Composition (45x66cm-18x26in) s.d.59 ink prov. 11-Oct-2 Binoche, Paris #153
£252 $392 €400 Composition (44x64cm-17x25in) s.d.56 ink prov. 11-Oct-2 Binoche, Paris #154
£660 $1042 €950 Merlins wood (16x25cm-6x10in) s.i.d.1984 W/C Indian ink paper objects. 26-Apr-3 Dr Lehr, Berlin #458/R
£705 $1093 €1100 Untitled (72x50cm-28x20in) s.d.64 ink. 7-Dec-2 Van Ham, Cologne #486/R
£1392 $2158 €2200 Composition (45x62cm-18x24in) s.i. W/C Indian ink pencil oil chk prov. 28-Sep-2 Ketterer, Hamburg #392/R est:1800-2400

SCHULTZE, Carl (1856-1935) German
£566 $883 €900 Landscape with watermill (30x44cm-12x17in) s.i. 19-Sep-2 Dr Fritz Nagel, Stuttgart #1000/R
£4088 $6336 €6500 Konigssee (81x110cm-32x43in) s. 29-Oct-2 Dorotheum, Vienna #17/R est:4500-4800

SCHULTZE, Louis (1820-?) American/German
£329 $550 €477 Distant fire with onlookers (25x51cm-10x20in) s. 21-Jun-3 Selkirks, St. Louis #150/R

SCHULTZE, Max (1845-1926) German
£1000 $1660 €1500 Happy monk (60x47cm-24x19in) s.i. 10-Jun-3 Bonhams, Knightsbridge #272/R est:800-1200

SCHULTZE, Robert (1828-1919) German
£755 $1177 €1200 Pre-alpine landscape (41x49cm-16x19in) mono. 9-Oct-2 Michael Zeller, Lindau #911/R
£1986 $3217 €2800 View of Wallensee, Kanton St Gallen (54x70cm-21x28in) s. 22-May-3 Dorotheum, Vienna #105/R est:3600-4000

SCHULTZE-BERTALLO, Maximilian (1866-?) German
£306 $477 €459 Portrait of elegant woman (64x50cm-25x20in) s.d.1920. 6-Nov-2 Dobiaschofsky, Bern #957/R (S.FR 700)

SCHULZ, Adrien (1851-1931) French
£298 $486 €450 Chasseurs a l'affut (23x20cm-9x8in) s. panel. 16-Feb-3 Mercier & Cie, Lille #288
£345 $524 €518 Moutons a la mare soir d'automme (21x27cm-8x11in) s. panel. 27-Aug-2 Rasmussen, Copenhagen #1885/R (D.KR 4000)
£801 $1242 €1250 Gardienne de moutons (27x35cm-11x14in) s. i.verso panel. 5-Dec-2 Gros & Delettrez, Paris #54

£1004 $1567 €1506 Le chemin de Grez a Montigny-sur-Loing (49x65cm-19x26in) s. i. verso. 6-Nov-2 Dobiaschofsky, Bern #958/R est:4000 (S.FR 2300)

SCHULZ, Charles M (1922-2000) American

Works on paper

£1667 $2750 €2400 Save the world is always in style (30x42cm-12x17in) s. felt pen ink. 3-Jul-3 Christie's, Paris #115/R est:500-700
£2138 $3400 €3207 Linus with the Christmas tree (89x105cm-35x41in) pastel prov. 7-Mar-3 Skinner, Boston #650/R est:2000-4000
£3106 $5000 €4659 Violet's dad has been doing a lot of reading (13x69cm-5x27in) s.i. pen ink. 10-May-3 Illustration House, New York #30/R est:3000-5000
£5128 $8000 €7692 Snoopy thinks his chances are good to win Daisy Hill Puppy Cup (13x69cm-5x27in) s. pen ink. 9-Nov-2 Illustration House, New York #55/R est:5000-7000
£5449 $8500 €8174 Snoopy uses an imaginary round of golf to lull himself to sleep (13x69cm-5x27in) s. pen ink. 9-Nov-2 Illustration House, New York #54/R est:5000-7000
£6211 $10000 €9317 Manager Charlie Brown is humiliated by the other team's reaction (13x69cm-5x27in) s. pen ink prov. 10-May-3 Illustration House, New York #184/R est:5000-7000

SCHULZ, Karl Friedrich (1796-1866) German

£3077 $4831 €4800 Meeting on country track in winter (61x81cm-24x32in) s.d.1845 panel. 21-Nov-2 Van Ham, Cologne #1913/R est:4500
£88608 $140000 €132912 Officers standing before their regiments. Ulans setting out on horseback (77x97cm-30x38in) s.d.1850 pair prov. 23-Apr-3 Christie's, Rockefeller NY #109/R est:25000-35000

SCHULZ-RUMPOLD, Volkmar (1956-) German

Works on paper

£330 $528 €495 Eagle (49x35cm-19x14in) s.d. mixed media. 17-Mar-3 Philippe Schuler, Zurich #4098 (S.FR 700)

SCHULZ-STRADTMANN, Otto (1892-1960) German

£886 $1382 €1400 Valley near Oberfohring (51x70cm-20x28in) s. 14-Sep-2 Weidler, Nurnberg #300/R

SCHULZE, Emil (1863-?) German

£429 $678 €644 Evening at Bachalpsee in Grindelwald (85x100cm-33x39in) s.i.d.1922 verso. 29-Nov-2 Zofingen, Switzerland #3071 (S.FR 1000)
£1603 $2484 €2500 Man on a rock (113x95cm-44x37in) s.d.1909. 5-Dec-2 Gros & Delettrez, Paris #123/R

SCHULZE, Hans Rudolf (20th C) German

£310 $499 €440 Berlin Castle (74x70cm-29x28in) s.d.1913 i. stretcher. 10-May-3 Hans Stahl, Toestorf #60/R

SCHUMACHER, Daniel (fl.1754-1786) American

Works on paper

£828 $1300 €1242 Marriage certificate with central crown flanked by hearts over script (20x30cm-8x12in) d.1784 W/C. 23-Nov-2 Pook & Pook, Downington #420/R

SCHUMACHER, Emil (1912-1999) German

£705 $1093 €1100 Composition in blue and gold (24x20cm-9x8in) s.d.94 fibre-tip wax crayon board. 7-Dec-2 Van Ham, Cologne #490/R
£5500 $8965 €8250 Hirschkuh (90x150cm-35x59in) s.verso acrylic silkscreen ink on card prov. 3-Feb-3 Sotheby's, Olympia #190/R est:5000-7000
£8156 $13213 €11500 Buds on chestnut branch (50x40cm-20x16in) s.d.47 tempera W/C. 24-May-3 Van Ham, Cologne #543/R est:12000
£33333 $51667 €52000 Composition (79x59cm-31x23in) s.d.57 masonite. 3-Dec-2 Lempertz, Koln #422/R est:50000-55000
£45000 $73800 €67500 Monzuba (170x132cm-67x52in) s.d.59 s.i.stretcher oil sand paper on canvas prov.lit. 6-Feb-3 Christie's, London #605/R est:50000-70000
£51282 $79487 €80000 Sur (100x80cm-39x31in) s.d.64 prov.exhib. 4-Dec-2 Lempertz, Koln #31/R est:100000-130000
£78000 $127920 €117000 Campo III (80x100cm-31x39in) s.d.94 i.d.1994 verso exhib. 7-Feb-3 Sotheby's, London #276/R est:40000-60000

Works on paper

£1418 $2298 €2000 Composition (28x35cm-11x14in) s.d.62 Indian ink canvasboard. 24-May-3 Van Ham, Cologne #545/R est:2500
£3546 $5745 €5000 Composition (55x74cm-22x29in) s.d.76 gouache chk. 24-May-3 Van Ham, Cologne #544/R est:5000
£8273 $13568 €11500 Untitled (63x47cm-25x19in) s.d.65 gouache. 3-Jun-3 Christie's, Amsterdam #325/R est:15000-20000
£11594 $19014 €16000 Untitled (82x67cm-32x26in) s.d.73 gouache Indian ink prov. 28-May-3 Lempertz, Koln #402/R est:15000-18000

SCHUMACHER, Ernst (1905-1963) German

£443 $700 €700 Still life with flowers and fruit (50x70cm-20x28in) s.d.1955-61. 30-Nov-2 Arnold, Frankfurt #516/R
£570 $900 €900 Small pineta (50x60cm-20x24in) 30-Nov-2 Bassenge, Berlin #6619

SCHUMACHER, Harald (1836-1912) Danish

£287 $443 €431 From an Italian loggia (55x55cm-22x22in) init. 26-Oct-2 Rasmussen, Havnen #2158/R (D.KR 3400)
£324 $522 €486 From Italy with woman (26x36cm-10x14in) init. panel. 22-Feb-3 Rasmussen, Havnen #2358/R (D.KR 3600)
£382 $596 €573 The Pyramids near Gizeh, the Nile in foreground (27x38cm-11x15in) init. 5-Aug-2 Rasmussen, Vejle #128/R (D.KR 4500)
£698 $1110 €1047 Venetian family at altar in th lagoon (22x33cm-9x13in) mono.d.81. 5-Mar-3 Rasmussen, Copenhagen #1702/R (D.KR 7500)

SCHUMANN, Christian (1970-) American

£11875 $19000 €17813 Summer rust (96x126cm-38x50in) s.i.d.2001 acrylic paper collage graphite col pencil on canvas. 16-May-3 Phillips, New York #108/R est:10000-15000

SCHUMANN, Paul (1876-1946) American

£3526 $5500 €5289 Galveston (23x30cm-9x12in) board. 19-Oct-2 David Dike, Dallas #171/R est:2000-4000

Works on paper

£321 $500 €482 Galveston Coast (20x28cm-8x11in) col pencil. 19-Oct-2 David Dike, Dallas #169/R

SCHUR, A S (20th C) Israeli

£1200 $1944 €1800 Jerusalem (32x48cm-13x19in) s.i. tempera board. 23-Jan-3 Christie's, Kensington #161/R est:300-500

SCHURCH, Johann Robert (1895-1941) Swiss

£926 $1491 €1343 Church in Tessin (47x63cm-19x25in) s. 9-May-3 Dobiaschofsky, Bern #161/R est:2000 (S.FR 2000)
£1223 $1920 €1835 Standing female nude (49x20cm-19x8in) s. panel. 25-Nov-2 Sotheby's, Zurich #43/R est:2000-2500 (S.FR 2800)

Works on paper

£437 $638 €656 Study of woman (51x40cm-20x16in) s. pencil. 4-Jun-2 Germann, Zurich #845 (S.FR 1000)
£472 $755 €708 Standing female nude (46x29cm-18x11in) bears s.i.d. chl over pencil wash. 17-Mar-3 Philippe Schuler, Zurich #4362 est:1400-1800 (S.FR 1000)
£833 $1342 €1208 Myself (26x19cm-10x7in) mono.d.26 ink wash. 9-May-3 Dobiaschofsky, Bern #184/R est:1900 (S.FR 1800)
£1019 $1640 €1478 Tramps by the Seine in Paris (20x26cm-8x10in) s.d.1930 W/C ink wash. 9-May-3 Dobiaschofsky, Bern #185/R est:1600 (S.FR 2200)

SCHURMANN, Maximilian (1890-1960) German?

£599 $928 €899 View of Bratislava (47x68cm-19x27in) board. 1-Oct-2 SOGA, Bratislava #35/R est:48000 (SL.K 38000)

Works on paper

£567 $879 €851 Paris (23x35cm-9x14in) W/C. 1-Oct-2 SOGA, Bratislava #36/R est:32000 (SL.K 36000)

SCHURR, Claude (1920-) French

£443 $691 €700 Marche aux fleurs a Nice (58x71cm-23x28in) s. 20-Oct-2 Chayette & Cheval, Paris #104
£612 $973 €900 Lumieres hivernales (60x73cm-24x29in) s.i. 24-Mar-3 Coutau Begarie, Paris #293
£648 $920 €1050 Port d'Antibes (27x35cm-11x14in) s. 16-Mar-3 Eric Pillon, Calais #243/R
£1027 $1603 €1500 Fetes au Rouret, Alpe Maritimes (54x65cm-21x26in) s. 13-Apr-3 Feletin, Province #87
£1235 $1753 €2000 Voiles a Audierne (100x81cm-39x32in) s. 16-Mar-3 Eric Pillon, Calais #245/R

SCHUSSELE, Christian (1824-1879) American

£2866 $4500 €4299 Catching butterflies (61x51cm-24x20in) s. 19-Nov-2 Butterfields, San Francisco #8002/R est:6000-8000

SCHUSSER, Josef (1864-1941) Czechoslovakian

£827 $1324 €1150 Profil de jeune fille (76x51cm-30x20in) s.d.1894. 13-May-3 Vanderkindere, Brussels #52

SCHUSSLER, Karl (1941-) Austrian
Works on paper
£513 $805 €800 Female nude (59x45cm-23x18in) mono.d.73 mixed media. 20-Nov-2 Dorotheum, Klagenfurt #66

SCHUSTER, C (20th C) ?
£2532 $4000 €4000 Anticoli, back from the fields (100x80cm-39x31in) s. 26-Nov-2 Christie's, Rome #119/R est:4500-5500

SCHUSTER, Donna (1883-1953) American
£3416 $5500 €5124 Canal in Venice (23x18cm-9x7in) s. i.verso board prov. 18-Feb-3 John Moran, Pasadena #11 est:3000-5000

SCHUSTER, Josef (1812-1890) Austrian
£1197 $1927 €1700 Still life with plums in open air (55x75cm-22x30in) s. lit. 10-May-3 Hans Stahl, Toestorf #21/R est:2000

SCHUSTER, Josef (attrib) (1812-1890) Austrian
£833 $1308 €1300 Still life with bird, flowers and other items (57x45cm-22x18in) s. panel. 21-Nov-2 Van Ham, Cologne #1915/R est:1800

SCHUSTER, Karl Maria (1871-1953) Austrian
£347 $552 €500 Corfu square (46x38cm-18x15in) s.i.d.1904 board. 29-Apr-3 Wiener Kunst Auktionen, Vienna #643/R
£347 $552 €500 Bad Gastei Reedsee (39x55cm-15x22in) s.i.d.1914 i. verso. 29-Apr-3 Wiener Kunst Auktionen, Vienna #657/R
£347 $552 €500 Farmsteads in Defreggen valley (35x48cm-14x19in) s.d.1942 i. verso. 29-Apr-3 Wiener Kunst Auktionen, Vienna #670/R
£347 $552 €500 Farmstead in Obertilliach (44x56cm-17x22in) s.i.d.1939. 29-Apr-3 Wiener Kunst Auktionen, Vienna #690/R
£347 $552 €500 Zurich (54x44cm-21x17in) s.i.d.1932. 29-Apr-3 Wiener Kunst Auktionen, Vienna #685/R
£382 $607 €550 Grado (31x47cm-12x19in) canvas on board. 29-Apr-3 Wiener Kunst Auktionen, Vienna #661/R
£385 $596 €600 Ramsau Steiermark (82x53cm-32x21in) s.d.1923. 5-Dec-2 Dorotheum, Graz #57
£476 $757 €700 Peasant woman getting ready to go to church (78x67cm-31x26in) s.i.d.1939. 20-Mar-3 Neumeister, Munich #2740/R
£486 $773 €700 Station XIV on Tonale Pass (40x50cm-16x20in) s.i.d.6./12. 1915. 29-Apr-3 Wiener Kunst Auktionen, Vienna #672/R
£521 $828 €750 Tunisia (45x34cm-18x13in) s.i. 29-Apr-3 Wiener Kunst Auktionen, Vienna #642/R
£625 $994 €900 Riviera (38x53cm-15x21in) canvas on board. 29-Apr-3 Wiener Kunst Auktionen, Vienna #668/R
£694 $1104 €1000 Purgg (68x52cm-27x20in) s.i.d.1943 panel. 29-Apr-3 Wiener Kunst Auktionen, Vienna #699/R
£694 $1104 €1000 Arbe - Insel Rab (39x48cm-15x19in) s.i.d.1920 panel. 29-Apr-3 Wiener Kunst Auktionen, Vienna #669/R
£694 $1104 €1000 Early spring in the mountains (43x64cm-17x25in) s. 29-Apr-3 Wiener Kunst Auktionen, Vienna #696/R
£694 $1104 €1000 Poserhohe Gastein (52x70cm-20x28in) s.i.d.1943. 29-Apr-3 Wiener Kunst Auktionen, Vienna #697/R
£694 $1104 €1000 St Leonhard (50x63cm-20x25in) s.i.d.1941. 29-Apr-3 Wiener Kunst Auktionen, Vienna #705/R
£694 $1104 €1000 Krumpendorf (42x59cm-17x23in) s.i.d.1936. 29-Apr-3 Wiener Kunst Auktionen, Vienna #680/R
£764 $1215 €1100 Arab man, Tunisia 1900 (45x34cm-18x13in) s.i.d.1900. 29-Apr-3 Wiener Kunst Auktionen, Vienna #660/R
£833 $1325 €1200 Terrace with view of lake (45x66cm-18x26in) s. 29-Apr-3 Wiener Kunst Auktionen, Vienna #644/R
£833 $1325 €1200 Krumpendorf (35x46cm-14x18in) s.i.d.1938. 29-Apr-3 Wiener Kunst Auktionen, Vienna #702/R
£903 $1435 €1300 Cairo (45x34cm-18x13in) s.i. 29-Apr-3 Wiener Kunst Auktionen, Vienna #645/R
£903 $1435 €1300 Bad Gastein (57x73cm-22x29in) s.i.d.1946 board. 29-Apr-3 Wiener Kunst Auktionen, Vienna #682/R
£972 $1546 €1400 Bad Gastein (36x55cm-14x22in) s.i.d.1946. 29-Apr-3 Wiener Kunst Auktionen, Vienna #700/R
£1042 $1656 €1500 The prodigal son (138x109cm-54x43in) 29-Apr-3 Wiener Kunst Auktionen, Vienna #648/R est:1500-3000
£1111 $1767 €1600 House in Retz (35x58cm-14x23in) s. 29-Apr-3 Wiener Kunst Auktionen, Vienna #673/R est:1000-2000
£1111 $1767 €1600 St Leonhard in Defreggen valley (55x70cm-22x28in) s.d.1942. 29-Apr-3 Wiener Kunst Auktionen, Vienna #683/R est:1000-2000
£1111 $1767 €1600 Ash trees in Krumbach (69x65cm-27x26in) s.d.1949 panel. 29-Apr-3 Wiener Kunst Auktionen, Vienna #692/R est:1000-2000
£1250 $1987 €1800 Winter (46x62cm-18x24in) s.i.d.28.VIII.1916 board. 29-Apr-3 Wiener Kunst Auktionen, Vienna #675/R est:1400-2000
£1250 $1987 €1800 Bad Gastein (67x56cm-26x22in) s.i.d.1947. 29-Apr-3 Wiener Kunst Auktionen, Vienna #695/R est:1000-2000
£1389 $2208 €2000 Grundlsee (55x41cm-22x16in) s.i.d.1925 panel. 29-Apr-3 Wiener Kunst Auktionen, Vienna #666/R est:1000-2000
£1528 $2429 €2200 Krumpendorf park (62x50cm-24x20in) s.i.d.1924. 29-Apr-3 Wiener Kunst Auktionen, Vienna #656/R est:1200-2500
£1736 $2760 €2500 Bad Gastein (45x56cm-18x22in) s.i.d.1943. 29-Apr-3 Wiener Kunst Auktionen, Vienna #678/R est:1200-2000
£1736 $2760 €2500 Krumpendorf (110x85cm-43x33in) s.i.d.1938. 29-Apr-3 Wiener Kunst Auktionen, Vienna #679/R est:2500-5000
£1944 $3092 €2800 Purgg (70x58cm-28x23in) s.i.d.1943. 29-Apr-3 Wiener Kunst Auktionen, Vienna #694/R est:1500-3000
£1944 $3092 €2800 Forchtenstein (80x60cm-31x24in) s.i.d.1927. 29-Apr-3 Wiener Kunst Auktionen, Vienna #676/R est:1500-3000
£6944 $11042 €10000 On the verandah in Capri (69x53cm-27x21in) s.i.d.1904. 29-Apr-3 Wiener Kunst Auktionen, Vienna #658/R est:2500-5000
£6944 $11042 €10000 Artist's studio (80x102cm-31x40in) s.d.1950 panel. 29-Apr-3 Wiener Kunst Auktionen, Vienna #698/R est:2000-4000
£8333 $13250 €12000 Rome (41x90cm-16x35in) s.i.d.1900. 29-Apr-3 Wiener Kunst Auktionen, Vienna #647/R est:3000-6000

SCHUSTER, Ludwig (1820-1873) Austrian
£1389 $2208 €2000 Fruits and a Chinese Imari bowl on a decorative ledge (50x41cm-20x16in) s. indis d.1856 panel. 29-Apr-3 Christie's, Amsterdam #89/R est:2000-3000

SCHUT, Cornelis (17th C) Flemish
£3322 $4750 €4983 Holy Family (149x109cm-59x43in) 22-Jan-3 Doyle, New York #96/R

SCHUT, Cornelis (attrib) (17th C) Flemish
£1689 $2635 €2500 Fuite en Egypte (65x52cm-26x20in) 28-Mar-3 Piasa, Paris #29/R

SCHUT, Cornelis and SEGHERS, Daniel (17th C) Flemish
£5660 $8774 €9000 Virgin queen of Heaven (65x46cm-26x18in) 7-Oct-2 Ansorena, Madrid #35/R est:8000

SCHUTT, Franz (1908-) German
£1603 $2436 €2500 Young girl wearing underskirt (110x75cm-43x30in) s. 11-Jul-2 Hugo Ruef, Munich #820/R est:2500

SCHUTTE, Thomas (1954-) German
£9295 $14407 €14500 Lemon with blue, yellow and black - and red (141x110cm-56x43in) varnish gouache col chk board. 3-Dec-2 Lempertz, Koln #417/R est:6000
£11000 $16940 €16500 Skizze zu skulptur (130x110cm-51x43in) s.d.1985 verso enamel on paper prov. 23-Oct-2 Christie's, London #234/R est:8000-12000
Works on paper
£6603 $10234 €10300 Lemon with blue, yellow and black (140x110cm-55x43in) varnish gouache col chk board. 3-Dec-2 Lempertz, Koln #416/R est:4000
£35000 $58450 €50750 Study for die fremden, the foreigners (108x197cm-43x78in) s.d.26.4.92 gouache pencil prov. 26-Jun-3 Sotheby's, London #128/R est:15000-20000

SCHUTZ, Christian Georg (18/19th C) German
£2128 $3298 €3192 Landscape from Rhen Valley (42x53cm-17x21in) 4-Dec-2 AB Stockholms Auktionsverk #1977/R est:40000-50000 (S.KR 30000)
£5986 $9937 €8500 River landscapes (26x21cm-10x8in) panel prov. two. 11-Jun-3 Dorotheum, Vienna #155/R est:9000-15000
Works on paper
£379 $603 €550 River landscape with ruins and bridge (10x16cm-4x6in) s.d.1756 gouache. 8-Mar-3 Arnold, Frankfurt #715/R

SCHUTZ, Christian Georg (attrib) (18/19th C) German
£5063 $7848 €8000 River landscapes (41x52cm-16x20in) pair. 25-Sep-2 Neumeister, Munich #514/R est:8000

SCHUTZ, Christian Georg I (1718-1791) German
£360 $601 €522 Moonlit wooded landscape with a peasant on a track (11x17cm-4x7in) s.d.1768 panel. 8-Jul-3 Bonhams, Knightsbridge #110/R

SCHUTZ, Christian Georg I (attrib) (1718-1791) German
£1384 $2158 €2200 River valley (28x38cm-11x15in) 19-Sep-2 Dr Fritz Nagel, Stuttgart #898/R est:1800
£2721 $4327 €4000 River landscape (27x35cm-11x14in) 19-Mar-3 Neumeister, Munich #466/R est:4000

SCHUTZ, Erich (?) Austrian
Works on paper
£422 $650 €633 Harem dancer (30x28cm-12x11in) s. W/C painted c.1915. 8-Sep-2 Treadway Gallery, Cincinnati #728/R

SCHUTZ, Franz (1751-1781) German
£3378 $5270 €5000 Houses on river and figures (19x28cm-7x11in) panel. 27-Mar-3 Dorotheum, Vienna #276/R est:5000-7000

SCHUTZ, Jan Frederik (1817-1888) Dutch
£5769 $9115 €9000 Fishing cutter in calm seas (72x104cm-28x41in) s.d.77. 16-Nov-2 Lempertz, Koln #1580/R est:10000
£7000 $11480 €10500 Coastal trader and fishing barge in calm waters at dawn (71x107cm-28x42in) s.d.78. 5-Jun-3 Christie's, Kensington #748/R est:4000-6000

SCHUTZ, Johann Georg (attrib) (1755-1813) German
£1266 $2000 €2000 Rhein landscape with ships and walkers (22x29cm-9x11in) canvas on canvas. 29-Nov-2 Bolland & Marotz, Bremen #666/R est:2700

SCHUTZ, Johannes (20th C) Swiss
£655 $1022 €983 Lake at St Moritz (36x50cm-14x20in) s. i.d.1936 verso. 6-Nov-2 Dobiaschofsky, Bern #959/R (S.FR 1500)

SCHUTZE, Wilhelm (1840-1898) German
£1474 $2241 €2300 Still life with white and red roses (56x79cm-22x31in) s. lit. 11-Jul-2 Allgauer, Kempten #2688/R
£6463 $10276 €9500 Boy and girl by farmstead (79x63cm-31x25in) s.i. lit. 21-Mar-3 Auktionhaus Georg Rehm, Augsburg #8082/R est:12000
£51643 $84695 €74882 Entry forbidden (73x92cm-29x36in) s.i. lit. 4-Jun-3 Fischer, Luzern #1160/R est:140000-160000 (S.FR 110000)

SCHUTZMANN, Pia (1940-) Italian
£640 $1017 €960 Composition (98x92cm-39x36in) s.d.1990 verso. 26-Feb-3 Kunsthallen, Copenhagen #116/R (D.KR 7000)

SCHUYFF, Peter (1958-) Dutch
£2279 $3623 €3350 Sans titre (160x230cm-63x91in) acrylic paper on cardboard prov. 26-Feb-3 Artcurial Briest, Paris #382/R est:2500-3000
Works on paper
£420 $656 €630 Composition (34x23cm-13x9in) W/C. 6-Nov-2 AB Stockholms Auktionsverk #949/R (S.KR 6000)

SCHUYLENBERGH, Andre von (1953-) Swiss
£786 $1226 €1179 Figure (110x90cm-43x35in) s.i.d.86-88 verso. 6-Nov-2 Dobiaschofsky, Bern #960/R (S.FR 1800)

SCHUZ, Theodor (1830-1900) German
£2817 $4620 €4085 Swabian Alb landscape (19x25cm-7x10in) s.d.1891 board. 4-Jun-3 Fischer, Luzern #1157/R est:6000-9000 (S.FR 6000)

SCHWAB, Eloisa (1894-?) American/Cuban
£260 $400 €390 Christmas season (46x61cm-18x24in) s. board painted c.1940. 8-Sep-2 Treadway Gallery, Cincinnati #704/R

SCHWABE, Alexander Johann Gotlieb Petrovitch (1818-1872) Russian
£32000 $50240 €48000 At the races (73x106cm-29x42in) s.d.1853. 20-Nov-2 Sotheby's, London #10/R est:20000-30000

SCHWABE, Carlos (1866-1926) Swiss
Works on paper
£962 $1490 €1500 D'une baguette s'envolera une tourterelle (31x13cm-12x5in) s.d.1891 W/C ink. 9-Dec-2 Artcurial Briest, Paris #2
£962 $1490 €1500 Offrande (31x21cm-12x8in) W/C ink exhib. 9-Dec-2 Artcurial Briest, Paris #1/R
£962 $1490 €1500 Gift (35x22cm-14x9in) s.d.91 W/C ink. 9-Dec-2 Artcurial Briest, Paris #7
£1026 $1590 €1600 Attente (32x22cm-13x9in) s.d.91 W/C ink gouache. 9-Dec-2 Artcurial Briest, Paris #10
£1218 $1888 €1900 Vision du pere (36x24cm-14x9in) s.d.91 W/C ink htd gouache. 9-Dec-2 Artcurial Briest, Paris #8
£1282 $1987 €2000 Decor (32x22cm-13x9in) s.d.91 W/C ink htd gouache set of 3. 9-Dec-2 Artcurial Briest, Paris #19
£1282 $1987 €2000 Decors (25x17cm-10x7in) s.d.92 W/C ink set of 3. 9-Dec-2 Artcurial Briest, Paris #12
£1667 $2583 €2600 Fuite du mauvais esprit (32x23cm-13x9in) s.d.92 W/C ink gouache. 9-Dec-2 Artcurial Briest, Paris #9
£1795 $2782 €2800 Chant des oiseaux (31x23cm-12x9in) s.d.92 W/C ink. 9-Dec-2 Artcurial Briest, Paris #16
£1795 $2782 €2800 Decor (33x22cm-13x9in) s.d.91 W/C ink set of 3. 9-Dec-2 Artcurial Briest, Paris #11
£2628 $4074 €4100 Madonna and Child (33x23cm-13x9in) i. W/C ink. 9-Dec-2 Artcurial Briest, Paris #3/R
£2949 $4571 €4600 Premonition (29x22cm-11x9in) W/C ink exec.1890. 9-Dec-2 Artcurial Briest, Paris #5/R
£22581 $35000 €33872 Elysian fields (47x30cm-19x12in) s.i.d.1903 pencil W/C gouache prov. 29-Oct-2 Sotheby's, New York #101/R est:30000-50000

SCHWABEDA, Johann Michael (1734-1794) German
£1644 $2564 €2400 Friederike Caroline von Brandenburg-Ansbach (92x75cm-36x30in) mono.d.1766 verso. 10-Apr-3 Van Ham, Cologne #1266/R est:3200

SCHWABEDA, Johann Michael (attrib) (1734-1794) German
£5696 $8829 €9000 Blowing bubbles. House of cards (30x23cm-12x9in) panel two. 25-Sep-2 Neumeister, Munich #515/R est:3000

SCHWABEN, Hans W (19th C) ?
£260 $426 €390 Moonlight over Arran from Little Cumbrae (56x76cm-22x30in) s.d.1887 s.i.d.verso. 5-Jun-3 Christie's, Kensington #732

SCHWACH, Heinrich August (1829-1902) Austrian
£705 $1093 €1100 Madonna and Child (68x51cm-27x20in) s.d.884. 5-Dec-2 Dorotheum, Graz #58

SCHWAGER, Richard (1822-1880) German
Miniatures
£1923 $3019 €3000 Full-length portrait of small blond noble child in white dress (9x7cm-4x3in) s.d.1863 oval. 21-Nov-2 Dorotheum, Vienna #535/R est:1500-2200

SCHWALBE, Ole (1929-1990) Danish
£360 $597 €522 Composition (92x83cm-36x33in) 12-Jun-3 Kunsthallen, Copenhagen #52 (D.KR 3800)
£448 $694 €672 Study (34x27cm-13x11in) s.verso. 4-Dec-2 Kunsthallen, Copenhagen #13 (D.KR 5200)
£660 $1030 €990 Composition in red, black, grey and white (36x32cm-14x13in) s.verso painted c.1960. 11-Nov-2 Rasmussen, Vejle #82/R (D.KR 7700)
£772 $1204 €1158 Neon-blue (92x83cm-36x33in) mono.d.87 verso. 11-Nov-2 Rasmussen, Vejle #91/R (D.KR 9000)
£775 $1202 €1163 Study (58x34cm-23x13in) s.verso. 4-Dec-2 Kunsthallen, Copenhagen #97/R (D.KR 9000)
£775 $1202 €1163 Composition (60x49cm-24x19in) s.d.56-57 verso masonite. 4-Dec-2 Kunsthallen, Copenhagen #164/R (D.KR 9000)
£840 $1335 €1260 Roman picture (55x54cm-22x21in) s.verso. 29-Apr-3 Kunsthallen, Copenhagen #126/R (D.KR 9000)
£931 $1444 €1397 The African carpet (92x83cm-36x33in) mono.d.87 verso. 1-Oct-2 Rasmussen, Copenhagen #29/R (D.KR 11000)
£1270 $1969 €1905 Espace Japonais (92x83cm-36x33in) s.d.88 verso. 1-Oct-2 Rasmussen, Copenhagen #14/R est:16000 (D.KR 15000)
Works on paper
£439 $698 €659 Composition in red, black and white (48x48cm-19x19in) s.d.59 gouache. 26-Feb-3 Kunsthallen, Copenhagen #93 (D.KR 4800)

SCHWAMMBERGER, Hildegard (1950-) German
£753 $1175 €1100 Flowers in vase (60x50cm-24x20in) s. panel. 10-Apr-3 Van Ham, Cologne #1706/R

SCHWANFELDER, Charles Henry (1774-1837) British
£850 $1335 €1275 Conway Castle (30x43cm-12x17in) s. i.verso. 20-Nov-2 Sotheby's, Olympia #21/R

SCHWANTHALER, Johann Franz (1683-1762) Austrian
Sculpture
£4054 $6324 €6000 Resurrected Christ (75cm-30in) lime wood gilt. 25-Mar-3 Dorotheum, Vienna #95/R est:12000-15000
£10063 $15597 €16000 God, the Father with angels and star burst. gilded silvered wood. 3-Oct-2 Dorotheum, Vienna #39/R est:14000-15000
£11321 $17547 €18000 Madonna on cloud with crescent moon (115cm-45in) gilded painted panel. 3-Oct-2 Dorotheum, Vienna #40/R est:30000-37000
£12838 $20027 €19000 Madonna with Child (82x63cm-32x25in) relief. 25-Mar-3 Dorotheum, Vienna #39/R est:32000-34000

SCHWAR, Wilhelm (1860-?) German
£2696 $4205 €4044 Dog lying down with three kittens (33x42cm-13x17in) s.d.1902. 16-Sep-2 Philippe Schuler, Zurich #3497/R est:7000-9000 (S.FR 6200)
£10000 $15600 €15000 Best of friends (33x42cm-13x17in) s.d.1902. 26-Mar-3 Sotheby's, Olympia #248/R est:2000-3000

SCHWARTZ, Andrew T (1867-1942) American
£774 $1200 €1161 Rolling hills (30x41cm-12x16in) s. board two. 25-Sep-2 Doyle, New York #76/R
£1049 $1700 €1521 Brooklyn Bridge (41x30cm-16x12in) s. 21-May-3 Doyle, New York #105/R est:3000-4000
£1389 $2250 €2014 The summit. Country home (41x51cm-16x20in) s. d.1932verso. 21-May-3 Doyle, New York #106/R est:4000-6000
£2357 $3700 €3536 Spring plowing (61x76cm-24x30in) s. 23-Nov-2 Jackson's, Cedar Falls #58/R est:1750-2500
£4167 $6500 €6251 View of the Hudson river valley (81x91cm-32x36in) s. 12-Oct-2 Neal Auction Company, New Orleans #470/R est:7000-10000

SCHWARTZ, Davis F (1879-1969) American
£1218 $1900 €1827 Ships at harbour. 21-Sep-2 Harvey Clar, Oakland #1525

SCHWARTZ, Frans (1850-1917) Danish
£310 $503 €465 Female model (52x53cm-20x21in) s. panel. 25-Jan-3 Rasmussen, Havnen #2004/R (D.KR 3500)
£326 $515 €489 Historical scene. mono. two parts. 13-Nov-2 Kunsthallen, Copenhagen #130 (D.KR 3800)
£438 $701 €657 Portrait of woman with flowers (46x32cm-18x13in) mono. 13-Jan-3 Rasmussen, Vejle #173/R (D.KR 5000)

SCHWARTZ, Herman (20th C) American
£353 $550 €530 Beach scene (20x25cm-8x10in) s. masonite. 18-Sep-2 Alderfer's, Hatfield #316/R
£577 $900 €866 City playground scene with row homes and figures (41x51cm-16x20in) s. masonite. 18-Sep-2 Alderfer's, Hatfield #315

SCHWARTZ, Johann Christian A (attrib) (1756-1814) German
Works on paper
£702 $1137 €1053 Portrait of lady, possibly Mrs Luis Wendtbuch (39x31cm-15x12in) pastel oval. 3-Feb-3 Lilla Bukowskis, Stockholm #420 (S.KR 9800)

SCHWARTZ, Manfred (1909-1970) American
£4938 $8000 €7160 Backstage tableau (76x91cm-30x36in) s. exhib. 21-May-3 Doyle, New York #14/R est:800-1200

SCHWARTZ, Mommie (1876-1942) Dutch
£2128 $3447 €3000 Certosa, Italy (30x38cm-12x15in) s.i. canvas on panel. 26-May-3 Glerum, Amsterdam #24/R est:1500-1800
£5755 $9439 €8000 An alley, possibly Bergen (49x38cm-19x15in) 3-Jun-3 Christie's, Amsterdam #8/R est:5000-7000

SCHWARTZ, William S (1896-1977) American
£833 $1300 €1250 Pansies (28x23cm-11x9in) s. 22-Sep-2 Susanin's, Chicago #5028/R est:800-1200
£1290 $2000 €1935 Italian village (51x61cm-20x24in) init.d. 8-Dec-2 Toomey, Oak Park #770/R est:3000-5000
£3896 $6000 €5844 Red feather and other things (56x66cm-22x26in) s.i.d.1925 board. 8-Sep-2 Treadway Gallery, Cincinnati #708/R est:6000-8000
£8383 $14000 €12155 Village (89x94cm-35x37in) s.i. s.i.d.1927 verso. 18-Jun-3 Christie's, Los Angeles #104/R est:15000-25000
£9146 $15000 €13262 Willy the farmer (102x91cm-40x36in) s. s.i.verso prov. 1-Jun-3 Wright, Chicago #206/R est:20000-30000
£15854 $26000 €22988 Symphonic forms no.4 (76x66cm-30x26in) s. prov. 1-Jun-3 Wright, Chicago #203/R est:25000-30000
Works on paper
£637 $1000 €956 Untitled, shack by the river (20x14cm-8x6in) s. W/C gouache exec.c.1935. 19-Nov-2 Wright, Chicago #119/R
£1274 $2000 €1911 Farmer with Scythe standing in a country lane (53x74cm-21x29in) s. gouache. 14-Dec-2 Weschler, Washington #732/R est:3000-5000
£1401 $2200 €2102 Two women, one standing before a mirror (72x53cm-28x21in) s. gouache. 14-Dec-2 Weschler, Washington #733/R est:2000-3000
£2038 $3200 €3057 Industrail plant (37x53cm-15x21in) s. gouache. 14-Dec-2 Weschler, Washington #734/R est:1500-2500
£2134 $3500 €3094 Female torso (38x46cm-15x18in) s.d.1928 conte crayon prov. 1-Jun-3 Wright, Chicago #201/R est:4000-5000
£3659 $6000 €5306 On the veranda (46x61cm-18x24in) s.i.verso W/C gouache exhib. 1-Jun-3 Wright, Chicago #202/R est:2500-3500

SCHWARTZE, Johann Georg (1814-1874) Dutch
£1529 $2385 €2400 Poet (66x83cm-26x33in) s.d.1855. 6-Nov-2 Vendue Huis, Gravenhage #474/R est:1500-2000
£2675 $4120 €4200 Portrait of Johanna Louise van Eeghen-den Tex (91x75cm-36x30in) s.d.1850 sold with jewelry. 3-Sep-2 Christie's, Amsterdam #128/R est:2000-3000

SCHWARTZENBERG, Simon (1895-?) Rumanian
£319 $497 €500 Place des Vosges (50x61cm-20x24in) s. 5-Nov-2 Tajan, Paris #104/R

SCHWARZ, Alfred (1867-1951) German
£2886 $4589 €4329 Young woman and cupid (96x70cm-38x28in) s. 10-Mar-3 Rasmussen, Vejle #213/R est:50000 (D.KR 31000)
£4500 $7515 €6525 Fresh from the garden (117x100cm-46x39in) s.d.1915. 17-Jun-3 Bonhams, New Bond Street #26/R est:5000-7000

SCHWARZ, Franz Wenzel (1842-1919) German
£6250 $10000 €9375 Farmyard scene with two figures and a bull (65x77cm-26x30in) s. panel. 14-May-3 Butterfields, San Francisco #1082/R est:5000-7000

SCHWARZ, Heinz (1920-) Swiss
Sculpture
£6114 $9537 €9171 Standing female nude with long hair (180cm-71in) s.d.74 Cast.Cera Persa/F. Amici/Mendrisio. 6-Nov-2 Dobiaschofsky, Bern #2194/R est:6500 (S.FR 14000)

SCHWARZER, Bernd (1954-) German
Works on paper
£1854 $3023 €2800 Striped head (70x28cm-28x11in) s.i.d.1987 chk board. 28-Jan-3 Dorotheum, Vienna #279/R est:2800-3500

SCHWARZL, Mizzi von (19/20th C) German
£352 $567 €500 Tegernsee (28x45cm-11x18in) s. i. verso. 7-May-3 Michael Zeller, Lindau #931/R

SCHWATSCHKE, John (1943-) Irish
£483 $772 €700 Celebration (91x61cm-36x24in) 11-Mar-3 Thomas Adams, Dublin #430
£548 $855 €800 Sixty three dollar question (36x55cm-14x22in) s.d.1999. 8-Apr-3 James Adam, Dublin #18/R
£596 $936 €870 Dancing at the Ritz (42x31cm-17x12in) s.i.verso. 15-Apr-3 De Veres Art Auctions, Dublin #100g
£620 $1029 €880 Philomena and George roasting chestnuts (19x24cm-7x9in) s.i.verso prov. 10-Jun-3 James Adam, Dublin #269/R
£890 $1398 €1300 Dawn sweep (89x74cm-35x29in) s.i.verso. 15-Apr-3 De Veres Art Auctions, Dublin #100f est:1500-2000
£900 $1431 €1350 Recital (45x54cm-18x21in) mono.d.1999. 5-Mar-3 John Ross, Belfast #109
£966 $1545 €1400 Late departure (89x61cm-35x24in) 11-Mar-3 Thomas Adams, Dublin #427
£972 $1546 €1400 Educating Archie (61x51cm-24x20in) mono. i.verso. 29-Apr-3 Whyte's, Dublin #231/R est:1500-2000
£1076 $1668 €1700 Altercation in ballyfeale (60x76cm-24x30in) mono. s.i.verso. 24-Sep-2 De Veres Art Auctions, Dublin #100/R est:1500-2000
£1258 $1962 €2000 Red hat (51x76cm-20x30in) mono.d.1999 i.verso. 17-Sep-2 Whyte's, Dublin #178/R est:2000-2500
£2013 $3242 €3000 Waiting room (61x51cm-24x20in) mono. i.verso. 18-Feb-3 Whyte's, Dublin #231/R est:1500-2000
£2222 $3533 €3200 The onconvanience of being single (91x76cm-36x30in) mono. i.verso. 29-Apr-3 Whyte's, Dublin #232/R est:1200-1500
£2564 $4026 €4000 Rendezvous at eight (36x46cm-14x18in) mono. i.verso. 19-Nov-2 Whyte's, Dublin #124/R est:1500-1800

SCHWEGLER, Xaver (1832-1902) Swiss
£694 $1118 €1006 On the path of public worship (38x45cm-15x18in) s. 9-May-3 Dobiaschofsky, Bern #10/R (S.FR 1500)

SCHWEICKHARDT (18th C) German
£962 $1490 €1500 Carpenter's studio (76x63cm-30x25in) s.d.1865. 5-Dec-2 Neumeister, Munich #2874/R est:900

SCHWEICKHARDT, Hendrik Willem (1746-1797) German
£1519 $2400 €2400 Having fun on the ice (28x36cm-11x14in) panel lit. 29-Nov-2 Schloss Ahlden, Ahlden #1142/R est:2400
£1519 $2400 €2400 Enjoying the ice (29x36cm-11x14in) panel lit. 29-Nov-2 Schloss Ahlden, Ahlden #1143/R est:2400

SCHWEINFURTH, Ernst (1818-1877) German
£1104 $1645 €1700 Burg Alt-Eberstein near Baden Baden (31x40cm-12x16in) mono. board. 26-Jun-2 Neumeister, Munich #853/R
£1905 $3029 €2800 Italian villa in pine wood (48x38cm-19x15in) s.d.69 panel. 19-Mar-3 Neumeister, Munich #728/R est:3000

SCHWEIRING, Conrad (1916-1986) American
£1948 $3000 €2922 Blue tetons (30x41cm-12x16in) s. board. 27-Oct-2 Grogan, Boston #83 est:2000-4000

SCHWEITZER, Adolf Gustav (1847-1914) German
£472 $726 €750 Steamer in fjord landscape (35x53cm-14x21in) s. panel. 26-Oct-2 Quittenbaum, Hamburg #50/R
£1056 $1754 €1500 Evening time in winter forest with stream (95x127cm-37x50in) s.i. 14-Jun-3 Arnold, Frankfurt #863/R est:1200
£3165 $5000 €5000 Ice fishermen (77x125cm-30x49in) s.i.d.1875. 28-Nov-2 Dorotheum, Vienna #16/R est:8000-10000

SCHWEIZER, Albert (1886-1948) Swiss
£349 $545 €524 Snowy winter landscape (35x50cm-14x20in) s. panel. 20-Nov-2 Fischer, Luzern #2244 (S.FR 800)
£558 $882 €837 Village scene in Laupersdorf (40x50cm-16x20in) s.i.verso. 29-Nov-2 Zofingen, Switzerland #3074 (S.FR 1300)

£601 $949 €902 Snow-covered Jura landscape near Langenbruck (34x46cm-13x18in) s. board. 29-Nov-2 Zofingen, Switzerland #3072 (S.FR 1400)
£601 $949 €902 Village scene in Egerkingen with view of the Jura (57x72cm-22x28in) s. hessian. 29-Nov-2 Zofingen, Switzerland #3073 (S.FR 1400)

SCHWEIZER, Theo (1929-) German
£435 $678 €653 Pour un zephir (50x50cm-20x20in) s.d.78 s.i.d. verso. 16-Sep-2 Philippe Schuler, Zurich #6489 (S.FR 1000)

SCHWENINGER, Carl (younger) (1854-1903) Austrian
£2064 $3220 €3096 In the castle (63x50cm-25x20in) s. 11-Sep-2 Kieselbach, Budapest #21/R (H.F 800000)
£2134 $3500 €3201 Courtship (94x72cm-37x28in) s. 5-Feb-3 Christie's, Rockefeller NY #176/R est:4000-6000
Works on paper
£380 $600 €570 Untitled (53x41cm-21x16in) s. W/C. 18-Nov-2 Schrager Galleries, Milwaukee #1061

SCHWENINGER, Rosa (1849-1918) Austrian
£276 $422 €414 Portrait of woman (64x48cm-25x19in) s.d.1876 panel. 24-Aug-2 Rasmussen, Havnen #2272 (D.KR 3200)

SCHWERIN, Amelie von (1819-1897) Swedish
£1120 $1859 €1624 Arasof, Farlovs parish, Skaane (46x59cm-18x23in) s.d.1857. 16-Jun-3 Lilla Bukowskis, Stockholm #664 (S.KR 14500)

SCHWERING, Conrad (?) American?
£1667 $2600 €2501 Tetons (30x46cm-12x18in) 9-Nov-2 Altermann Galleries, Santa Fe #192

SCHWETZ, Franz (1910-) Austrian
£625 $994 €900 Roses in vase (44x33cm-17x13in) s.d.1945. 29-Apr-3 Wiener Kunst Auktionen, Vienna #629/R
Works on paper
£321 $503 €500 House fronts in Klausen with Saben mountains behind (37x30cm-15x12in) s.d.1944 W/C. 21-Nov-2 Dorotheum, Vienna #445/R

SCHWETZ, Karl (1888-1965) Austrian
£513 $805 €800 Mountain lake (80x71cm-31x28in) s. 21-Nov-2 Van Ham, Cologne #1917
£513 $805 €800 Inn valley (40x49cm-16x19in) s. canvas on board. 21-Nov-2 Van Ham, Cologne #1918
£651 $1015 €950 Alpine lake (70x85cm-28x33in) s.d.1952 board. 10-Apr-3 Van Ham, Cologne #1709

SCHWICHTENBERG, Martel (1896-1945) German
£577 $842 €900 Flowers in glass vase (45x35cm-18x14in) s. 4-Jun-2 Karl & Faber, Munich #421/R
£641 $936 €1000 Two women (115x55cm-45x22in) 4-Jun-2 Karl & Faber, Munich #419/R
£1154 $1685 €1800 Reclining female nude - Tilla Durieux (79x94cm-31x37in) mono. 4-Jun-2 Karl & Faber, Munich #420/R est:3500
£1603 $2340 €2500 Ponte Decimo (79x93cm-31x37in) lit.exhib. 4-Jun-2 Karl & Faber, Munich #418/R est:5000-6000

SCHWIERING, Conrad (1916-1986) American
£609 $950 €914 Colorado Aspens (30x46cm-12x18in) s. masonite. 12-Apr-3 Weschler, Washington #580/R est:1000-1500

SCHWIMMER, Max (1895-1960) German
Works on paper
£377 $581 €600 Worker and girl (34x24cm-13x9in) s. W/C over pencil. 26-Oct-2 Dr Lehr, Berlin #485/R
£629 $969 €1000 Artist in circus ring (34x24cm-13x9in) s. W/C over pencil. 26-Oct-2 Dr Lehr, Berlin #484/R
£818 $1259 €1300 Harbour scene (31x44cm-12x17in) mono.d.1953 W/C board. 26-Oct-2 Dr Lehr, Berlin #487/R

SCHWIND, Moritz von (1804-1871) Austrian
Works on paper
£591 $939 €850 Sketch for wall decoration with Mozart and Maria Theresa (18x22cm-7x9in) i. pen prov. 5-May-3 Ketterer, Munich #318/R
£1042 $1656 €1500 King on horseback, knight and young woman (29x23cm-11x9in) pencil prov. 5-May-3 Ketterer, Munich #317/R est:1000-1200
£1156 $1839 €1700 Seven silhouette cut-outs (27x36cm-11x14in) i. verso board. 19-Mar-3 Neumeister, Munich #391/R est:1800
£2877 $4488 €4200 Rider (17x73cm-7x29in) W/C pen over pencil prov. 11-Apr-3 Winterberg, Heidelberg #565/R est:2800

SCHWINGE, Friedrich Wilhelm (1852-1913) German
£329 $513 €480 Evening over Nordseeinsel at harvest time (45x64cm-18x25in) s.d.1895 panel. 10-Apr-3 Schopman, Hamburg #689

SCHWINGE, Friedrich Wilhelm (attrib) (1852-1913) German
£2244 $3478 €3500 Mountain lake with buildings in foreground (112x163cm-44x64in) i.d.1878 canvas on board. 4-Dec-2 Neumeister, Munich #899/R est:1200

SCHWITTERS, Kurt (1887-1948) German
£1456 $2300 €2300 Djupvand with rainy skies (60x50cm-24x20in) board exhib.lit. 30-Nov-2 Villa Grisebach, Berlin #301/R est:3000-4000
£5256 $7674 €8200 Landscape with hayricks (60x80cm-24x31in) mono.d.18 verso double-sided. 4-Jun-2 Karl & Faber, Munich #422/R est:8000-9000
£13761 $22982 €19953 Landscape with two trees and cows. Landscape with hayricks (80x60cm-31x24in) mono.d.13 double-sided. 20-Jun-3 Kornfeld, Bern #135/R est:30000 (S.FR 30000)
Sculpture
£6597 $10885 €9500 Little dog (45cm-18in) plaster exec.c.1943-44 prov.lit. 2-Jul-3 Artcurial Briest, Paris #666/R est:10000-15000
Works on paper
£2885 $4471 €4500 I drawing (6x5cm-2x2in) s.i. board lit.prov. 7-Dec-2 Kastern, Hannover #233/R est:2400
£3043 $4991 €4200 Untitled - abstract drawing (13x11cm-5x4in) mono.d.45 pencil prov. 29-May-3 Lempertz, Koln #923/R est:3000
£15385 $23846 €24000 MZ 30, 47 (10x7cm-4x3in) s.i.d.1930 collage board prov.exhib. 4-Dec-2 Lempertz, Koln #1058/R est:30000-35000
£17323 $27024 €27370 Collage (28x20cm-11x8in) collage paper on board exec.1943. 15-Oct-2 Babuino, Rome #271/R est:6000
£17949 $27821 €28000 MZ 30, 34 (12x10cm-5x4in) s.i.d. collage board. 7-Dec-2 Hauswedell & Nolte, Hamburg #1033/R est:28000
£20000 $32800 €30000 MZ442 (18x14cm-7x6in) collage exec.1922 prov.exhib.lit. 5-Feb-3 Sotheby's, London #185/R est:35000
£26087 $40435 €39131 MZ159 rot oben links. MZ183 (18x13cm-7x5in) s.d.20 collage oil W/C pencil prov.exhib.lit. pair. 4-Dec-2 Koller, Zurich #43/R est:50000-60000 (S.FR 60000)
£40000 $62000 €60000 Aufunterbrief (23x17cm-9x7in) s.d.1920 collage oil paper on board prov.exhib.lit. 4-Dec-2 Koller, Zurich #42/R est:90000-140000 (S.FR 92000)
£43578 $72775 €63188 Gaahden - Merz 347 (19x13cm-7x5in) s.i.d.1922 collage paper text exhib. 20-Jun-3 Kornfeld, Bern #136/R est:90000 (S.FR 95000)
£90000 $146700 €135000 Mz "er" (31x23cm-12x9in) s.d.1922 collage prov.exhib.lit. 3-Feb-3 Christie's, London #27/R est:100000-150000

SCHYL, Jules (1893-1977) Swedish
£371 $586 €557 Southern landscape (44x39cm-17x15in) s. 16-Nov-2 Crafoord, Lund #70 (S.KR 5300)
£425 $684 €638 Toledo (51x43cm-20x17in) s.d.1924. 7-May-3 AB Stockholms Auktionsverk #879/R (S.KR 5500)
£506 $804 €759 Nature morte (50x44cm-20x17in) s. 3-Mar-3 Lilla Bukowskis, Stockholm #11 (S.KR 6800)
£561 $875 €842 Girl from S Marco (55x45cm-22x18in) s.verso. 6-Nov-2 AB Stockholms Auktionsverk #767/R (S.KR 8000)
£616 $998 €924 Girl with flowers (81x58cm-32x23in) s.d.1951. 3-Feb-3 Lilla Bukowskis, Stockholm #635 (S.KR 8600)
£863 $1416 €1200 Promeneurs aux abords de la mosquee (66x51cm-26x20in) s. 4-Jun-3 Tajan, Paris #311/R
£1141 $1802 €1712 Model with book (62x61cm-24x24in) s. 28-Apr-3 Bukowskis, Stockholm #213/R est:10000-12000 (S.KR 15000)
£1293 $2043 €1940 Elegance (45x50cm-18x20in) s. d.1928 verso. 28-Apr-3 Bukowskis, Stockholm #212/R est:20000-22000 (S.KR 17000)
£1467 $2362 €2201 Cubist composition (60x42cm-24x17in) s. panel. 7-May-3 AB Stockholms Auktionsverk #728/R est:10000-12000 (S.KR 19000)
£1542 $2405 €2313 At the theatre lodge (51x40cm-20x16in) s. s.d.1930 verso. 5-Nov-2 Bukowskis, Stockholm #48/R est:12000-15000 (S.KR 22000)
£1964 $3102 €2946 Reclining model (64x79cm-25x31in) s. prov. 27-Nov-2 Falkkloos, Malmo #77693/R est:20000 (S.KR 28000)
£2433 $3845 €3650 Southern landscape (56x86cm-22x34in) s. 28-Apr-3 Bukowskis, Stockholm #39/R est:12000-15000 (S.KR 32000)

SCIALOJA, Toti (1914-1998) Italian
£1560 $2528 €2200 Composition (66x42cm-26x17in) s.d.67 oil tempera collage newspaper cardboard on canvas prov. 26-May-3 Christie's, Milan #304/R est:2000-3000
£2384 $3886 €3600 Apollo (85x167cm-33x66in) s.d.1969 s.i.d.verso acrylic collage prov.exhib. 3-Feb-3 Cornette de St.Cyr, Paris #516
£3718 $5837 €5800 Still life (92x65cm-36x26in) s.d.54 prov.exhib.lit. 20-Nov-2 Pandolfini, Florence #104/R est:7000

Works on paper
£1702 $2757 €2400 Untitled (96x77cm-38x30in) s.d.90 mixed media paper on canvas. 26-May-3 Christie's, Milan #51 est:1000-1500
£4514 $7177 €6500 Composition (100x72cm-39x28in) s.d.1989 verso glue on canvas. 1-May-3 Meeting Art, Vercelli #219

SCILTIAN, Gregorio (1900-1985) Russian
Works on paper
£252 $392 €400 Head of woman (17x12cm-7x5in) s. sanguine. 20-Sep-2 Semenzato, Venice #213

SCKELL, Fritz (1885-?) German
£865 $1341 €1350 Mountain lake (109x139cm-43x55in) s. prov. 7-Dec-2 Ketterer, Hamburg #189/R

SCKELL, Ludwig (1833-1912) German
£949 $1472 €1500 Konigsee (77x113cm-30x44in) s.d.1875. 25-Sep-2 Neumeister, Munich #717/R est:2500
£1132 $1743 €1800 Mountain landscape (92x122cm-36x48in) s.i. canvas on panel. 26-Oct-2 Quittenbaum, Hamburg #51/R est:2000
£2089 $3237 €3300 Mountain valley with village, water and animals returning home (28x45cm-11x18in) s. 28-Sep-2 Hans Stahl, Hamburg #35 est:2800
£2405 $3800 €3800 Starnberger See on summer's day (15x25cm-6x10in) s. panel lit. 29-Nov-2 Schloss Ahlden, Ahlden #1207/R est:3800

SCOFFIELD, Hilary (20th C) British
Works on paper
£250 $413 €363 River winding through a wooded valley (29x46cm-11x18in) s. pencil W/C acrylic. 3-Jul-3 Christie's, Kensington #79

SCOGNAMIGLIO, Giovanni (18th C) Italian
£1600 $2496 €2400 Reading lesson (104x74cm-41x29in) s.i. 8-Oct-2 Bonhams, Knightsbridge #95a/R est:1500-2000

SCOGNAMIGLIO, Roberto (1883-1965) Italian
£816 $1298 €1200 Fishing boat on the Capri coast (28x39cm-11x15in) canvas on panel. 25-Feb-3 Dorotheum, Vienna #205/R

SCOLARI, Osman de (?) Italian
£385 $604 €600 Masks. Still life (57x78cm-22x31in) one on canvas one masonite two. 16-Dec-2 Pandolfini, Florence #349

SCOPPA, Gustavo (1857-?) Italian
Works on paper
£769 $1208 €1200 Bergere sur le chemin (51x78cm-20x31in) chl. 16-Dec-2 Millon & Associes, Paris #37/R
£769 $1208 €1200 Bergere gardant ses moutons (47x74cm-19x29in) s. chl. 16-Dec-2 Millon & Associes, Paris #42/R

SCOPPETTA, Pietro (1863-1920) Italian
£300 $489 €450 Shepherd boy and girl. Woman sewing in an Italian landscape (32x46cm-13x18in) s. panel pair. 13-Feb-3 Christie's, Kensington #205/R
£1572 $2421 €2500 Paris at night (14x29cm-6x11in) s. i.verso board. 28-Oct-2 Il Ponte, Milan #210/R
Works on paper
£283 $436 €450 Dance lesson (20x23cm-8x9in) s. W/C. 28-Oct-2 Il Ponte, Milan #216
£503 $775 €800 Boulevard (18x16cm-7x6in) s. i.verso W/C. 28-Oct-2 Il Ponte, Milan #201
£535 $823 €850 Winter on the boulevard (18x18cm-7x7in) s. W/C. 28-Oct-2 Il Ponte, Milan #199
£629 $969 €1000 Parisian scene (32x22cm-13x9in) s. W/C. 28-Oct-2 Il Ponte, Milan #205

SCORDIA, Antonio (1918-) Central American
£513 $805 €800 Girl in red (37x26cm-15x10in) s.d.42 cardboard. 21-Nov-2 Finarte, Rome #196
£2436 $3824 €3800 Interior with relief (162x130cm-64x51in) s.d.81 s.i.d.verso. 21-Nov-2 Finarte, Rome #233/R

SCORIEL, Jean Baptiste (1883-?) Belgian
£823 $1284 €1300 Lever de brume au bord de la Sambre (123x98cm-48x39in) s.d.1928. 16-Sep-2 Horta, Bruxelles #26

SCORZA, Sinibaldo (1589-1631) Italian
£12588 $21022 €18000 Les animaux entrant dans l'arche (175x230cm-69x91in) 25-Jun-3 Tajan, Paris #11/R est:18000-22000
Works on paper
£3041 $4743 €4500 Studies of dogs (13x24cm-5x9in) i. pen ink. 27-Mar-3 Christie's, Paris #14

SCORZELLI, Eugenio (1890-1958) Italian
£1020 $1622 €1500 The Seine in Paris (20x40cm-8x16in) s. cardboard. 18-Mar-3 Finarte, Milan #193/R

SCOTT, Adam Sherriff (1887-1980) Canadian
£488 $766 €732 Near Rawdon, Quebec (41x51cm-16x20in) s. board. 10-Dec-2 Pinneys, Montreal #157 (C.D 1200)
£615 $959 €923 Automne (20x16cm-8x6in) s. cardboard. 10-Sep-2 Iegor de Saint Hippolyte, Montreal #104b (C.D 1500)
£889 $1458 €1334 Sunny sleigh ride (27x35cm-11x14in) s. canvas on board. 3-Jun-3 Joyner, Toronto #266/R est:1000-1500 (C.D 2000)
£1067 $1749 €1601 Fishing amongst reeds (50x60cm-20x24in) s. 3-Jun-3 Joyner, Toronto #421/R est:1200-1500 (C.D 2400)
£1588 $2477 €2382 Shore (51x61cm-20x24in) s. 25-Mar-3 Iegor de Saint Hippolyte, Montreal #130 (C.D 3700)
£2469 $3827 €3704 Inuit encampment (59x60cm-23x24in) s. 3-Dec-2 Joyner, Toronto #6 est:3000-4000 (C.D 6000)
£2489 $3883 €3734 Inuit family (61x91cm-24x36in) s. 25-Mar-3 Iegor de Saint Hippolyte, Montreal #129 (C.D 5800)

SCOTT, Alexander (?-c.1932) British
£1509 $2355 €2400 Daulaghiri, Tibet (150x180cm-59x71in) s. 19-Sep-2 Dr Fritz Nagel, Stuttgart #1001/R est:1500

SCOTT, Brian (20th C) Canadian
£261 $410 €392 1929 Chrysler No.1 (60x75cm-24x30in) s.i. 25-Nov-2 Hodgins, Calgary #202/R (C.D 650)

SCOTT, Charles Hepburn (fl.1907-1924) British
£1906 $3049 €2859 Bridge river country, BC (51x61cm-20x24in) s. s.i.verso prov. 15-May-3 Heffel, Vancouver #125/R est:4000-6000 (C.D 4250)

SCOTT, Clyde Eugene (1884-1959) American
£1299 $2000 €1949 Desert plateau (61x76cm-24x30in) s. painted c.1935. 8-Sep-2 Treadway Gallery, Cincinnati #602/R est:3000-5000

SCOTT, David (1806-1849) British
£3800 $6118 €5700 Study for 'Deposition' (49x41cm-19x16in) s. card on board prov.lit. 20-Feb-3 Christie's, London #302/R

SCOTT, Georgiana Helen (1851-1947) American
£956 $1500 €1434 Musical still life (41x76cm-16x30in) s. 22-Nov-2 Skinner, Boston #95/R est:800-1200

SCOTT, Henry (1911-1966) British
£641 $1000 €962 Homeward bound (23x36cm-9x14in) s. canvasboard. 12-Oct-2 Neal Auction Company, New Orleans #597/R
£1500 $2280 €2250 Thermopylae at anchor (61x91cm-24x36in) s. 15-Aug-2 Bonhams, New Bond Street #373/R est:1000-1500
£2200 $3344 €3300 Encounter between American frigate Chesapeake, British Frigate Shannon (51x76cm-20x30in) s. 15-Aug-2 Bonhams, New Bond Street #375/R est:1000-1500
£2600 $4030 €3900 Flying cloud rounding Cape Horn (51x77cm-20x30in) s. 31-Oct-2 Christie's, Kensington #559/R est:1500-2000
£2778 $4500 €4028 Tranquil morning Foochow (36x51cm-14x20in) s. i.on stretcher. 29-Jul-3 Christie's, Rockefeller NY #183/R est:5000-7000
£4500 $7515 €6525 Night watch - Iron clipper Ivanhoe leading Spindrift (61x100cm-24x39in) s.i.on overlap prov. 18-Jun-3 Sotheby's, Olympia #130/R est:4500-7000

SCOTT, Howard (attrib) (1902-1983) American
Works on paper
£621 $1000 €932 Train conductor reading series of tickets (41x89cm-16x35in) W/C. 19-Feb-3 Illustration House, New York #307/R est:1500-2500

SCOTT, Hugh B (19/20th C) British
£350 $567 €508 At pasture on the marshes (36x47cm-14x19in) s. panel. 20-May-3 Dreweatt Neate, Newbury #267/R

SCOTT, Ian (1945-) New Zealander
£627 $978 €941 Lattice (46x46cm-18x18in) s. d.1982 verso acrylic. 7-Nov-2 International Art Centre, Auckland #5/R est:2800-3800 (NZ.D 2000)
£796 $1250 €1194 Small lattice no.165 (45x45cm-18x18in) s.i.d.1988 PVA on canvas. 10-Dec-2 Peter Webb, Auckland #109/R est:2000-3000 (NZ.D 2500)

£1806 $2817 €2709 Small lattice number 164 (60x60cm-24x24in) s.i.d.1988 verso pva. 8-Apr-3 Peter Webb, Auckland #146/R est:3000-4000 (NZ.D 5200)

Works on paper
£251 $391 €377 Lattice (30x30cm-12x12in) W/C. 6-Aug-2 Peter Webb, Auckland #254 (NZ.D 850)

SCOTT, J (?) British
£340 $530 €510 Off Pendennis Castle, Falmouth (37x53cm-15x21in) s. i.verso. 10-Sep-2 Bonhams, Knightsbridge #233j

SCOTT, James (?) British
£438 $700 €657 Home life in Florida (46x61cm-18x24in) s.i. painted c.1940. 12-Jan-3 William Jenack, New York #295

SCOTT, James Fraser (1877-1932) Australian
£450 $725 €675 In the parlour (41x31cm-16x12in) s. 14-Jan-3 Bonhams, Knightsbridge #152
£760 $1185 €1140 Near Lowestoft (24x34cm-9x13in) s.i. 17-Sep-2 Peter Webb, Auckland #80/R est:2500-3500 (NZ.D 2500)
£912 $1422 €1368 Grand canal, Venice (101x126cm-40x50in) s. 17-Sep-2 Peter Webb, Auckland #155/R est:8000-12000 (NZ.D 3000)

SCOTT, James R (fl.1854-1871) British
£600 $942 €900 Minehead (45x76cm-18x30in) s. 10-Dec-2 Rosebery Fine Art, London #579

SCOTT, Johan (1953-) Scandinavian
Works on paper
£1086 $1694 €1629 Composition (127x97cm-50x38in) s.d.84 mixed media paper on panel exhib.lit. 5-Nov-2 Bukowskis, Stockholm #450/R est:8000-10000 (S.KR 15500)

SCOTT, John (19th C) British
£1100 $1749 €1650 Portrait of Margueurite (65x41cm-26x16in) s.d.1881. 4-Mar-3 Bearnes, Exeter #433/R est:600-900
£4938 $8000 €7160 Chevy Chase in waters off Newcastle-on-Tyne (67x99cm-26x39in) s.d.1849 prov. 29-Jul-3 Christie's, Rockefeller NY #165/R est:10000-15000
£9211 $14000 €13817 Ship Medora, in two positions off Tynemouth (51x74cm-20x29in) s.d.1855. 17-Aug-2 North East Auctions, Portsmouth #669/R est:10000-15000

Works on paper
£1000 $1640 €1500 Arcangel. Collective unconscious. Primary per sonae worship (46x61cm-18x24in) s.d.1982-88 ink dr. set of three prov. 27-May-3 Sotheby's, Toronto #56/R est:2500-3000 (C.D 2250)

SCOTT, John Douglas (fl.1870-1885) British
Works on paper
£550 $869 €825 By a loch (51x83cm-20x33in) s. W/C. 27-Nov-2 Hamptons Fine Art, Godalming #243/R

SCOTT, John Russell (fl.1836-1876) British
£3800 $5928 €5700 Panoramic view of Edinburgh from the south (80x135cm-31x53in) s.d. 28-Mar-3 Bonhams, Edinburgh #178/R est:3000-5000

SCOTT, John W (1907-1987) American
£1863 $3000 €2795 Injured cowboy slugging bandito as gun goes off (76x51cm-30x20in) s. painted c.1935. 10-May-3 Illustration House, New York #170/R est:3000-4500

SCOTT, John W A (1815-1907) American
£641 $1000 €962 Landscape. painted c.1844. 21-Sep-2 Harvey Clar, Oakland #1461

SCOTT, John W A (attrib) (1815-1907) American
£1899 $3000 €2849 Fishing on the river (84x122cm-33x48in) 17-Nov-2 CRN Auctions, Cambridge #14/R

SCOTT, Lorenzo (1934-) American
£316 $500 €474 Baptism (61x76cm-24x30in) s. 5-Apr-3 Neal Auction Company, New Orleans #352/R

SCOTT, Louise (1936-) Canadian
£492 $767 €738 Femme devant un Matisse (61x61cm-24x24in) s. panel. 10-Sep-2 Iegor de Saint Hippolyte, Montreal #104 (C.D 1200)

SCOTT, M (?) ?
£280 $437 €420 View of a cove, thought to be Kynance Cove in Cornwall (40x56cm-16x22in) s.d.1884. 10-Sep-2 Bonhams, Knightsbridge #103

SCOTT, Marguerite (20th C) Canadian
£4667 $7653 €7001 After a storm, Quebec (76x56cm-30x22in) s. board prov.exhib. 27-May-3 Sotheby's, Toronto #168/R est:3000-4000 (C.D 10500)

SCOTT, Marian Dale (1906-1993) Canadian
£711 $1166 €1067 Untitled (80x50cm-31x20in) s.verso acrylic lit. 3-Jun-3 Joyner, Toronto #450/R est:1500-2000 (C.D 1600)
£976 $1532 €1464 Moving figures (61x51cm-24x20in) s.d.47 board. 10-Dec-2 Pinneys, Montreal #197 est:500-700 (C.D 2400)
£1481 $2296 €2222 Variation on a theme no.1 (75x140cm-30x55in) acrylic lit. 3-Dec-2 Joyner, Toronto #335/R est:1500-2000 (C.D 3600)

SCOTT, Patrick (1921-) Irish
£1218 $1912 €1900 Spume, abstract composition (60x50cm-24x20in) i.verso board. 19-Nov-2 Hamilton Osborne King, Dublin #466/R est:2000-3000
£2029 $3328 €2800 Rainbow (124x183cm-49x72in) lit. 28-May-3 Bonhams & James Adam, Dublin #69/R est:1500-2000
£2532 $3924 €4000 Sketch for bog flowers (30x40cm-12x16in) s. 25-Sep-2 James Adam, Dublin #40/R est:2000-3000
£2642 $4121 €4200 Turf stack (41x30cm-16x12in) s. tempera prov.exhib. 17-Sep-2 Whyte's, Dublin #85/R est:4000-5000
£2685 $4322 €4000 Spume (61x51cm-24x20in) i.verso tempera board prov. 18-Feb-3 Whyte's, Dublin #49/R est:2500-3500
£3899 $6083 €6200 Magnetic field (122x152cm-48x60in) s.i.d.1960 verso tempera hardboard exhib. 17-Sep-2 Whyte's, Dublin #84/R est:6000-8000
£7233 $11283 €11500 Romantic landscape (76x84cm-30x33in) tempera prov. 17-Sep-2 Whyte's, Dublin #83/R est:8000-10000
£10417 $16563 €15000 Lakeside (86x112cm-34x44in) s.d.1963 tempera prov.exhib.lit. 29-Apr-3 Whyte's, Dublin #53/R est:10000-12000
£14094 $22691 €21000 Cross (244x244cm-96x96in) s. i.d.1973 verso tempera gold leaf prov. 18-Feb-3 Whyte's, Dublin #48/R est:20000-30000
£15278 $24292 €22000 Gold painting 65 (178x81cm-70x32in) s.i.d.1969 gold leaf tempera prov.exhib.lit. 29-Apr-3 Whyte's, Dublin #51/R est:15000-20000

Works on paper
£1181 $1877 €1700 Gestural drawing (64x48cm-25x19in) s.d.1978 mixed media. 29-Apr-3 Whyte's, Dublin #54/R est:2000-3000
£2319 $3803 €3200 February (106x71cm-42x28in) W/C. 28-May-3 Bonhams & James Adam, Dublin #137/R est:2000-3000

SCOTT, Robert Austin (1941-) Canadian
£201 $315 €302 White Bride (59x156cm-23x61in) s.i.d.1981 acrylic prov. 25-Nov-2 Hodgins, Calgary #191/R (C.D 500)

SCOTT, Robert Bagge (fl.1886-1896) British
£500 $835 €725 Dutch landscape with barges (18x28cm-7x11in) s,. 20-Jun-3 Keys, Aylsham #643
£540 $902 €783 On the dunes, Scheveningen (18x28cm-7x11in) s. 20-Jun-3 Keys, Aylsham #642
£700 $1113 €1050 Truants, Papendrecht (30x55cm-12x22in) s.i.verso. 6-Mar-3 Christie's, Kensington #410/R est:500-700
£1400 $2338 €2030 Afternoon on the marshes (28x33cm-11x13in) s. 20-Jun-3 Keys, Aylsham #633/R est:500-700

SCOTT, Samuel (1703-1772) British
£80000 $124000 €120000 Historic encounter between H.M.S. Lion and two French vessels (103x152cm-41x60in) prov.exhib.lit. 31-Oct-2 Christie's, Kensington #427/R est:40000-60000

Works on paper
£1200 $1896 €1800 Ships at anchor off Margate Pier (22x69cm-9x27in) s.i. i.verso pen ink W/C over pencil. 28-Nov-2 Sotheby's, London #230/R est:1500-2000

SCOTT, Samuel (studio) (1703-1772) British
£20000 $31600 €30000 View of Westminster Bridge and surrounding buildings (70x113cm-28x44in) i. 28-Nov-2 Sotheby's, London #137/R est:8000-12000

SCOTT, Samuel (style) (1703-1772) British
£5500 $8580 €8250 View of Westminster Bridge from the Thames looking west (21x118cm-8x46in) 7-Nov-2 Christie's, Kensington #93/R est:800-1200

SCOTT, Septimus Edwin (1879-c.1952) British

£260 $424 €390 Plough team homeward bound (25x34cm-10x13in) s. board. 28-Jan-3 Bristol Auction Rooms #478
£2900 $4582 €4350 Hunter with dogs in a landscape (43x58cm-17x23in) i.verso board. 18-Dec-2 Mallams, Oxford #673/R est:3000-4000
£4500 $6975 €6750 On the beach (30x39cm-12x15in) s. canvasboard. 4-Dec-2 Christie's, Kensington #454/R est:1000-1500
£5500 $8525 €8250 Sunday morning (30x39cm-12x15in) s. canvasboard. 4-Dec-2 Christie's, Kensington #453/R est:1000-1500

Works on paper

£1950 $3101 €2925 Company of soldiers marching past a ploughman and his boy (48x68cm-19x27in) s. W/C. 27-Feb-3 Bonhams, Chester #404 est:1000-1500

SCOTT, Septimus Edwin (attrib) (1879-c.1952) British

£1400 $2338 €2030 Plough team's luncheon (50x75cm-20x30in) 17-Jun-3 Bristol Auction Rooms #527/R est:200-400

SCOTT, Sir Peter (1909-1989) British

£400 $628 €600 Snow geese (18x28cm-7x11in) indis sig. 13-Dec-2 Keys, Aylsham #736/R
£520 $811 €780 Bewick swans/ mallard 1967 (45x37cm-18x15in) s.d.1967 board exhib. 7-Nov-2 Bonhams, Cornwall #856
£962 $1500 €1443 Five whooperers headed into a stiff southerly wind (24x34cm-9x13in) s.d.1975 board. 20-Sep-2 Sloan, North Bethesda #419/R est:1000-1500
£1000 $1660 €1450 Berwick swans and mallards (44x36cm-17x14in) s.d.1967 canvasboard prov.exhib. 12-Jun-3 Christie's, Kensington #147/R est:1000-1500
£1000 $1580 €1450 Barnacle geese (38x45cm-15x18in) s.d.1939. 22-Jul-3 Bonhams, Knightsbridge #8a/R est:1200-1800
£2215 $3500 €3323 Red breasted geese in flight (51x41cm-20x16in) s.d.1974 prov. 3-Apr-3 Christie's, Rockefeller NY #200/R est:2000-3000
£2800 $4368 €4200 If the nights are moonless, only the last little bunches of pink feet pass across dawn (38x46cm-15x18in) s.d.1936. 6-Nov-2 Sotheby's, Olympia #140/R est:3000-5000
£3000 $5010 €4350 Snow geese in flight over harbour (48x74cm-19x29in) s. sold with copy by Paul Gallico. 20-Jun-3 Keys, Aylsham #683/R est:3000-4000
£3900 $6357 €5850 Whitefronts across Ireland (58x58cm-23x23in) s.d.1935. 14-Feb-3 Keys, Aylsham #685/R est:3000-5000
£4500 $7065 €6750 Mallards rising from pool (48x74cm-19x29in) s.d.1935. 13-Dec-2 Keys, Aylsham #667 est:4500-6000
£9500 $15770 €13775 Snow geese before the squall (76x127cm-30x50in) s.d.1949. 12-Jun-3 Christie's, Kensington #145/R est:7000-10000

Works on paper

£300 $474 €450 Geese in flight (40x31cm-16x12in) s.d.1955 W/C over pencil. 2-Dec-2 Bonhams, Bath #44
£480 $739 €720 Pink footed geese in flight (8x19cm-3x7in) init. pen black ink W/C exhib. 5-Sep-2 Christie's, Kensington #634
£1000 $1660 €1450 Mallard in flight, winter (18x22cm-7x9in) s. pencil W/C htd white. 12-Jun-3 Christie's, Kensington #146/R est:300-500

SCOTT, Thomas McCree (fl.1915-1918) British

Works on paper

£1500 $2505 €2175 Offerton Dene, near Sunderland (24x34cm-9x13in) s.d.1918 W/C. 17-Jun-3 Anderson & Garland, Newcastle #249 est:100-180

SCOTT, Tom (1854-1927) British

Works on paper

£250 $395 €375 St. Mary's Loch (38x55cm-15x22in) s.d.1922 W/C on board. 14-Nov-2 Bonhams, Edinburgh #341
£720 $1116 €1080 Stable door (26x36cm-10x14in) s.d.1911 W/C prov. 5-Dec-2 Bonhams, Edinburgh #118/R
£950 $1511 €1425 Boats in a harbour, thought to be Portknockie, Banff (23x30cm-9x12in) s.i. pencil W/C. 6-Mar-3 Christie's, Kensington #161/R
£1000 $1530 €1500 Memory of English landscape, Norfolk (12x8cm-5x3in) s. W/C pair. 22-Aug-2 Bonhams, Edinburgh #1174 est:600-800
£1200 $1896 €1800 Border landscape with hay gatherers (18x32cm-7x13in) s.indis.d. W/C. 5-Apr-3 Shapes, Edinburgh #356 est:300-500
£1400 $2226 €2100 Ploughman with his team. Plough team (16x23cm-6x9in) s.i.d.1918 W/C chk pair. 6-Mar-3 Christie's, Kensington #163 est:800-1200
£1450 $2262 €2175 Summer, North Berwick, with the Bass Rock behind (24x35cm-9x14in) s.d.1916 W/C. 17-Oct-2 Bonhams, Edinburgh #181 est:1000-2000
£1500 $2370 €2175 Figure, horse and cart in a hay field (25x36cm-10x14in) s.d.1920 W/C. 22-Jul-3 Gorringes, Lewes #1536/R est:1500-2000
£1600 $2544 €2400 Plough team returning home (17x25cm-7x10in) s.d.91 W/C. 6-Mar-3 Christie's, Kensington #162/R est:500-800
£2000 $3160 €3000 Autumn in Selkirk (31x43cm-12x17in) s.d.83 W/C. 28-Nov-2 Bonhams, Knightsbridge #119/R est:2000-3000
£2100 $3213 €3150 Selkirk (22x24cm-9x9in) s. W/C paper on board. 22-Aug-2 Bonhams, Edinburgh #1134/R est:1200-1800
£2200 $3498 €3300 Sir Walter Scott's grave, Dryburgh Abbey (18x26cm-7x10in) s.d.1918 chk W/C. 6-Mar-3 Christie's, Kensington #164/R est:1000-1500
£2200 $3630 €3190 Betchworth Church, Surrey (27x37cm-11x15in) s.i.d.1906 pencil W/C prov. 3-Jul-3 Christie's, Kensington #90/R est:1500-2000
£3500 $5565 €5250 Spring morning, Bowden Burn (48x36cm-19x14in) W/C. 29-Apr-3 Gorringes, Lewes #2360

SCOTT, William (1913-1989) British

£10145 $16638 €14000 Two pears (25x35cm-10x14in) prov. 28-May-3 Bonhams & James Adam, Dublin #71/R est:15000-20000
£12000 $19200 €18000 Poem for a jug, no 7 (25x31cm-10x12in) s.d.80 verso prov. 16-May-3 Sotheby's, London #137/R est:10000-15000
£19000 $31160 €28500 Pale blue and brown still life (30x35cm-12x14in) s.d.63 verso prov. 6-Jun-3 Christie's, London #197/R est:20000-30000
£21500 $35260 €32250 Poem for a jug, no.2 (25x30cm-10x12in) s.d.79-80 verso prov. 6-Jun-3 Christie's, London #65/R est:8000-12000
£42000 $65940 €63000 Still life (41x51cm-16x20in) s. painted 1958 prov. 22-Nov-2 Christie's, London #98/R est:40000-60000
£75000 $123000 €112500 White, brown and black (40x50cm-16x20in) s. i.d.1959 on stretcher prov.exhib.lit. 6-Jun-3 Christie's, London #85/R est:25000-35000
£75000 $123000 €112500 Mug, pans and bowls (40x50cm-16x20in) s. i.d.1958 on stretcher prov.lit. 6-Jun-3 Christie's, London #108/R est:30000-50000

Prints

£1667 $2733 €2300 Two pears (26x36cm-10x14in) s.d.74 num.19/85 lithograph. 28-May-3 Bonhams & James Adam, Dublin #70/R est:1400-1800
£2100 $3297 €3150 Grapes (50x64cm-20x25in) s.d.1979 num.17/150 col lithograph. 17-Apr-3 Christie's, Kensington #150/R est:1200-1600
£2200 $3432 €3300 Frying pan and lemon (59x77cm-23x30in) s. lithograph executed c.1970. 25-Mar-3 Sotheby's, London #151/R est:1500-2000
£2300 $3611 €3450 Still life (67x88cm-26x35in) s.d.1973 num.239/250 col lithograph. 17-Apr-3 Christie's, Kensington #148/R est:2000-2500
£2300 $3611 €3450 Pears (50x65cm-20x26in) s.d.1979 num.17/150 col lithograph. 17-Apr-3 Christie's, Kensington #151/R est:1200-1600
£2600 $4004 €3900 Pears (50x65cm-20x26in) s.d.1979 num.119/150 col lithograph. 24-Oct-2 Christie's, Kensington #155/R est:800-1200
£2600 $4082 €3900 Still life (56x76cm-22x30in) s.d.1976 num.39/40 beige blue black lithograph. 17-Apr-3 Christie's, Kensington #149/R est:2000-2500
£2700 $4158 €4050 Untitled - Marc Rothko memorial (47x52cm-19x20in) s.i.d.1973 col lithograph. 24-Oct-2 Christie's, Kensington #152/R est:1500-2000
£2700 $4158 €4050 Still life (67x88cm-26x35in) s.d.1973 num.239/250 col lithograph. 24-Oct-2 Christie's, Kensington #153/R est:1200-1600

Works on paper

£1007 $1621 €1500 Lyrical - Mariana Hill, film actress (29x41cm-11x16in) s. i.verso pencil. 18-Feb-3 Whyte's, Dublin #182 est:1500-2000
£2200 $3608 €3300 Pines, North Wales (26x37cm-10x15in) s.d.44 brush ink W/C prov.exhib. 6-Jun-3 Christie's, London #64/R est:2500-3500
£2600 $4264 €3900 Uprooted trees, red landscape (27x37cm-11x15in) s.d.44 brush ink W/C prov.exhib. 6-Jun-3 Christie's, London #63/R est:2500-3500
£2800 $4676 €4060 Street scene, Ruabon (23x33cm-9x13in) s.d.44 W/C prov. 24-Jun-3 Bonhams, New Bond Street #53/R est:3000-5000
£4487 $7045 €7000 Pot and pan (21x26cm-8x10in) s.d.1974 gouache. 19-Nov-2 Whyte's, Dublin #19/R est:8000-10000
£4500 $7425 €6525 Composition (50x61cm-20x24in) s. gouache prov. 3-Jul-3 Christie's, Kensington #739 est:2000-3000
£5975 $9321 €9500 Two pears (20x25cm-8x10in) s.d.1974 wax crayon prov. 17-Sep-2 Whyte's, Dublin #81/R est:6000-8000
£8544 $13244 €13500 Orange pan and bowls (47x59cm-19x23in) s. gouache W/C. 24-Sep-2 De Veres Art Auctions, Dublin #149 est:1000-15000
£18000 $29520 €27000 Untitled beige (56x76cm-22x30in) s.d.75 gouache prov.exhib. 6-Jun-3 Christie's, London #198/R est:10000-15000

SCOTT, William Bell (1811-1890) British

£6500 $10465 €9750 Messenger of the New Faith (73x115cm-29x45in) s.i.d.1867 prov.exhib. 20-Feb-3 Christie's, London #88/R

Works on paper

£700 $1134 €1050 Study of a lion's head (20x20cm-8x8in) oil gouache shaped prov. 23-May-3 Lyon & Turnbull, Edinburgh #88

SCOTT, William Edouard (1884-1964) American

£3065 $4750 €4598 Bathers (76x64cm-30x25in) s. board painted c.1920. 8-Dec-2 Toomey, Oak Park #767/R est:5000-7000
£4403 $7000 €6605 Study for mural (9x14cm-4x6in) board painted c.1940. 4-May-3 Treadway Gallery, Cincinnati #603/R est:10000-15000
£5660 $9000 €8490 Pastoral landscape (41x30cm-16x12in) s. board painted c.1920. 2-Mar-3 Toomey, Oak Park #691/R est:7000-9000
£6918 $11000 €10377 Deep sea fishing (46x30cm-18x12in) s. board painted c.1920. 2-Mar-3 Toomey, Oak Park #688/R est:8000-10000

SCOTTI, Domenico (1780-?) Italian
Works on paper
£638 $1066 €900 Scene de l'histoire russe, Pierre le Grand et la revolte des Streltsy (76x133cm-30x52in) s.d.1809 pen wash paper on canvas. 23-Jun-3 Beaussant & Lefèvre, Paris #278/R

SCOTTI, Giosue (1729-1785) Italian
£1014 $1581 €1500 Portrait of the artist (43x33cm-17x13in) panel. 26-Mar-3 Tajan, Paris #29

SCOTTISH SCHOOL (19th C)
Sculpture
£12000 $20040 €17400 Female figurehead - from clipper Star of Tasmania (192cm-76in) painted wood. 18-Jun-3 Sotheby's, Olympia #226/R est:10000-12000

SCOUEZEC, Maurice le (1881-1940) French
£1862 $3110 €2700 Vue de l'arriere Pays de Pont-Aven, aux deux pins (65x81cm-26x32in) s.d.25 paper on canvas. 10-Jul-3 Artcurial Briest, Paris #171/R est:3000-4000
£2038 $3180 €3200 Village cotier (54x95cm-21x37in) s.d.1927. 10-Nov-2 Eric Pillon, Calais #183/R
£2083 $3313 €3000 Paysage a la maison rouge (51x75cm-20x30in) s.d.21 cardboard. 29-Apr-3 Artcurial Briest, Paris #209/R est:3000-4000
£2564 $4026 €4000 Femme africaine (64x84cm-25x33in) paper on canvas lit. 15-Dec-2 Thierry & Lannon, Brest #157
£2692 $4227 €4200 A la terrasse du cafe (26x39cm-10x15in) s. paper. 15-Dec-2 Thierry & Lannon, Brest #156
£2692 $4227 €4200 Jeune garcon lisant (80x64cm-31x25in) s.d.1934. 15-Dec-2 Thierry & Lannon, Brest #155
£3205 $5032 €5000 Nu de face (73x51cm-29x20in) s.d.21 paper on panel. 15-Dec-2 Thierry & Lannon, Brest #159
£3974 $6240 €6200 Auto-portrait au chapeau (64x54cm-25x21in) paper on canvas. 15-Dec-2 Thierry & Lannon, Brest #154
Works on paper
£387 $624 €550 Marins en conversation (18x28cm-7x11in) st. chl. 11-May-3 Thierry & Lannon, Brest #68
£705 $1107 €1100 Visit (48x63cm-19x25in) W/C. 15-Dec-2 Thierry & Lannon, Brest #340
£769 $1208 €1200 Fete a Montmartre (15x17cm-6x7in) init. W/C. 15-Dec-2 Thierry & Lannon, Brest #6
£769 $1208 €1200 Verger (50x67cm-20x26in) d.24 W/C. 15-Dec-2 Thierry & Lannon, Brest #61
£833 $1308 €1300 Portrait de soldat (26x21cm-10x8in) s.i.d.18 W/C lit. 15-Dec-2 Thierry & Lannon, Brest #158
£937 $1528 €1350 Maisons entre Landivisiau et Lampaul Guimiliau (50x65cm-20x26in) studio st.i.d.32 W/C. 19-Jul-3 Thierry & Lannon, Brest #62
£1026 $1610 €1600 Cases en Afrique (49x63cm-19x25in) s.d.31 W/C. 15-Dec-2 Thierry & Lannon, Brest #339
£1154 $1812 €1800 Portrait d'enfant (53x45cm-21x18in) d.34 chl W/C. 15-Dec-2 Thierry & Lannon, Brest #35
£1408 $2268 €2000 Femmes africaines Segou (30x47cm-12x19in) st.i.d.28 W/C. 11-May-3 Thierry & Lannon, Brest #92/R est:2000-2500
£3333 $5433 €4800 Marche a Landivisiau (48x62cm-19x24in) s.i.d.24 W/C. 19-Jul-3 Thierry & Lannon, Brest #64/R est:4000-5000

SCOULER, James (1740-1812) British
Miniatures
£5500 $9020 €7975 Young girl in white silk dress with blue sash (6cm-2in) s.d.1795 gold frame lock of hair seed pears. 3-Jun-3 Christie's, London #126/R est:4000-6000
Works on paper
£800 $1320 €1160 Portrait of a lady (30x23cm-12x9in) s.d.1788 pastel. 2-Jul-3 Sotheby's, Olympia #158/R

SCOUPREMAN, Pierre (1873-1960) Belgian
£278 $434 €440 Vue de la Bourse (51x41cm-20x16in) s. canvas on panel. 16-Sep-2 Horta, Bruxelles #5
£432 $691 €600 Uccle sous la neige (50x60cm-20x24in) s.d.1942 mono.d.verso. 19-May-3 Horta, Bruxelles #487

SCRIVER, Robert Macfie (1914-1999) American
Sculpture
£1258 $2000 €1887 T.R outdoorsman and conservationist (39cm-15in) i. dark brown pat. bronze prov. 4-Mar-3 Christie's, Rockefeller NY #36/R est:4000-6000
£3205 $5000 €4808 Too late for the Hawken (56x74x71cm-22x29x28in) bronze. 9-Nov-2 Altermann Galleries, Santa Fe #88
£8861 $14000 €12848 Return of the Blackfeet riders (41cm-16in) bronze prov.lit. 26-Jul-3 Coeur d'Alene, Hayden #135/R est:10000-15000

SCRIVO (1942-) Belgian?
£3145 $4843 €5000 Life's different roads (60x60cm-24x24in) s. d.1984 verso exhib. 22-Oct-2 Campo & Campo, Antwerp #234/R
£5556 $8833 €8000 Life's different roads (60x50cm-24x20in) s. d.1978 verso cardboard. 29-Apr-3 Campo & Campo, Antwerp #264/R est:5000-6000

SCROPPO, Filippo (1910-1993) Italian
£1486 $2319 €2200 Houses (56x70cm-22x28in) s. painted 1947. 26-Mar-3 Finarte Semenzato, Milan #115/R

SCUDDER, Janet (1873-1940) American
Sculpture
£3774 $5811 €6000 Frog baby fountain (31x20x17cm-12x8x7in) s. bronze. 26-Oct-2 Quittenbaum, Hamburg #119/R est:6000
£16774 $26000 €25161 Cupid and tortoise (47cm-19in) i. verdigris pat. bronze prov. 5-Dec-2 Christie's, Rockefeller NY #53/R est:15000-25000
£24516 $38000 €36774 Young Diana (69cm-27in) i. brown pat. bronze executed 1910. 5-Dec-2 Christie's, Rockefeller NY #66/R est:15000-25000
£35484 $55000 €53226 Flying cupid (133cm-52in) i. verdigris pat. bronze i.f.Alexis Rudier executed c.1912. 5-Dec-2 Christie's, Rockefeller NY #105/R est:30000-50000

SCUFFI, Marcello (1948-) Italian
£609 $956 €950 Circus (50x70cm-20x28in) s. 23-Nov-2 Meeting Art, Vercelli #223/R
£784 $1255 €1200 Remembering the sea, but which one? (60x50cm-24x20in) s. s.i.d.1998 verso. 4-Jan-3 Meeting Art, Vercelli #216
£850 $1359 €1300 Circus outside the village (40x80cm-16x31in) s.i.d.2002 verso. 4-Jan-3 Meeting Art, Vercelli #201
£1266 $1975 €2000 Pour mon amour (40x90cm-16x35in) s. s.i.d.2001 verso. 14-Sep-2 Meeting Art, Vercelli #922/R est:2000
£1282 $2013 €2000 Circus (100x70cm-39x28in) s. painted 1997 lit. 23-Nov-2 Meeting Art, Vercelli #480/R
£1361 $2163 €2000 Landscape and train (80x110cm-31x43in) s. 1-Mar-3 Meeting Art, Vercelli #538
Works on paper
£321 $503 €500 Pour mon amour (35x50cm-14x20in) i.d.1997 W/C card. 23-Nov-2 Meeting Art, Vercelli #434
£417 $654 €650 Target (36x55cm-14x22in) s.i.d.2001 W/C card. 23-Nov-2 Meeting Art, Vercelli #145/R
£962 $1510 €1500 Versilia (60x40cm-24x16in) s. fresco on canvas. 23-Nov-2 Meeting Art, Vercelli #165/R

SCULL, Elsie (?) American?
£288 $450 €432 Fisherman's cottages, Monhegan Island, Maine (41x51cm-16x20in) s.d.56. 18-Sep-2 Alderfer's, Hatfield #274

SCULLY, Sean (1946-) American/Irish
£17000 $27880 €25500 Untitled (122x91cm-48x36in) s.d.1977 verso acrylic prov. 6-Feb-3 Christie's, London #710/R est:10000-15000
£63291 $100000 €94937 Arrest (213x274cm-84x108in) painted 1987 in 2 parts prov. 13-Nov-2 Sotheby's, New York #545/R est:80000-120000
Prints
£1887 $3000 €2831 Without (84x112cm-33x44in) s.i.d.num.2/8 col woodcut. 2-May-3 Sotheby's, New York #592/R est:2500-3500
Works on paper
£3000 $4620 €4500 Change no.34 (21x64cm-8x25in) s.i.d.1975 gouache tape on paper prov. 22-Oct-2 Sotheby's, London #476/R est:3000-4000
£17000 $28390 €24650 Untitled (58x76cm-23x30in) s.d.7.1.88 pastel prov. 27-Jun-3 Christie's, London #245/R est:5000-7000

SDOYA, Carlo (1914-) South African?
£301 $485 €452 Fishing boat in a harbour (75x60cm-30x24in) s. board. 12-May-3 Stephan Welz, Johannesburg #84 est:2500-3500 (SA.R 3500)

SDRUSCIA, Achille (?-1993) Italian
£342 $534 €500 Piazza Navona, Rome (39x50cm-15x20in) s. board. 10-Apr-3 Finarte Semenzato, Rome #147/R

SEABROOKE, Elliott (1886-1950) British
£500 $805 €750 Boats in a harbour (24x30cm-9x12in) s. board. 18-Feb-3 Bonhams, Knightsbridge #73/R

SEABY, Allen William (1867-1953) British
Works on paper
£300 $468 €450 Pippit in flight (37x50cm-15x20in) s. W/C bodycol on linen. 25-Mar-3 Bonhams, Knightsbridge #4/R

SEAFORTH, Charles Henry (attrib) (1801-c.1853) British

£1050 $1638 €1575 Neapolitan harbour (41x61cm-16x24in) canvas on board. 8-Apr-3 Bonhams, Knightsbridge #258/R est:800-1200
£1250 $1950 €1875 Neapolitan harbour (41x61cm-16x24in) canvas on panel prov. 10-Sep-2 Bonhams, Knightsbridge #282/R est:1000-1500

SEAGE, Lucas (1957-) South African?

Works on paper

£602 $969 €903 Love for abstract (100x70cm-39x28in) s. mixed media diptych. 12-May-3 Stephan Welz, Johannesburg #557/R est:7000-10000 (SA.R 7000)

SEAGO, Edward (1910-1974) British

£1400 $2282 €2030 Cottages under an evening sky (33x38cm-13x15in) init.d.36 board. 21-Jul-3 Bonhams, Bath #41/R est:1500-1800
£1500 $2340 €2250 Landscape study, Rutland (14x24cm-6x9in) board prov. 27-Mar-3 Christie's, Kensington #497/R est:1200-1800
£2000 $3280 €3000 Irstead (15x21cm-6x8in) s. board. 3-Jun-3 Sotheby's, Olympia #121/R est:2500-3500
£3000 $4710 €4500 Field Marshal sir Claude Auchinleck (40x30cm-16x12in) s.d.59 canvas on board. 22-Nov-2 Christie's, London #10/R est:3000-5000
£3000 $5010 €4350 Breakers on the shallow (26x42cm-10x17in) s. board prov. 24-Jun-3 Bonhams, New Bond Street #50/R est:2000-3000
£3200 $4960 €4800 Cattle on Threehammer Marsh (27x35cm-11x14in) s. board. 3-Dec-2 Bonhams, New Bond Street #32/R est:3000-5000
£3600 $5724 €5400 Archway Marrakech (30x40cm-12x16in) i.verso board. 26-Feb-3 Sotheby's, Olympia #273/R est:2500-3500
£4000 $6320 €6000 Country track with farm buildings in the middle distance (30x41cm-12x16in) s. board. 18-Dec-2 Mallams, Oxford #655/R est:2000-3000
£4223 $7009 €5770 Olbia (30x41cm-12x16in) s.i.verso masonite prov. 10-Jun-3 Ritchie, Toronto #80/R est:10000-15000 (C.D 9500)
£4400 $6952 €6600 Rainclouds over Ludham Marsh (30x41cm-12x16in) s. board. 18-Dec-2 Mallams, Oxford #656/R est:2000-3000
£5000 $7900 €7500 Winter landscape, Norfolk (39x59cm-15x23in) s. i.verso board. 27-Nov-2 Sotheby's, Olympia #103/R est:5000-7000
£5000 $8350 €7250 Strand on the Green, Chiswick (28x10cm-11x4in) s. i.verso board prov. 24-Jun-3 Bonhams, New Bond Street #47/R est:5000-7000
£5150 $8137 €7725 Lock (41x61cm-16x24in) s. i.verso board prov. 3-Apr-3 Heffel, Vancouver #84/R est:18000-22000 (C.D 12000)
£5500 $8689 €8250 Evening sunlight, Navplion, Greece (49x75cm-19x30in) s. i.verso board. 27-Nov-2 Sotheby's, Olympia #129/R est:6000-8000
£5800 $9338 €8700 Olbia Sardinia (33x48cm-13x19in) s. board prov. 19-Feb-3 Mallams, Oxford #461/R est:6000-8000
£6000 $10020 €8700 Dusk at Honfleur (40x61cm-16x24in) s. board. 24-Jun-3 Bonhams, New Bond Street #45/R est:6000-8000
£6494 $10000 €9741 Spritsail barges racing in the Harwich estuary (51x76cm-20x30in) s. i.verso masonite. 26-Oct-2 Brunk, Ashville #780/R est:15000-25000
£7200 $11376 €10800 Village green, Norfolk (39x59cm-15x23in) s. i.verso board. 27-Nov-2 Sotheby's, Olympia #130/R est:7000-10000
£7500 $12300 €10875 October sky, Ostend (30x40cm-12x16in) s.d.50 i.verso board prov. 4-Jun-3 Sotheby's, London #53/R est:6000-8000
£8000 $12560 €12000 Norflok beach, low tide (53x79cm-21x31in) s. board prov. 22-Nov-2 Christie's, London #78/R est:8000-12000
£8230 $12675 €12345 Evening sunlight, the Acropolis, Athens (49x75cm-19x30in) board. 26-Oct-2 Heffel, Vancouver #48 est:20000-30000 (C.D 20000)
£9000 $14130 €13500 Street in Essaouira, Morocco (66x51cm-26x20in) s. board. 22-Nov-2 Christie's, London #79/R est:10000-15000
£9500 $15009 €14250 Mosques and fishing boats, Istanbul (34x49cm-13x19in) s. i.verso board prov. 27-Nov-2 Sotheby's, Olympia #104/R est:6000-9000
£9500 $15010 €14250 Grey day, Heigham Sounds (46x61cm-18x24in) s. 18-Dec-2 Mallams, Oxford #654/R est:4000-6000
£9500 $15580 €14250 Sailboats (27x35cm-11x14in) s. board exhib. 6-Jun-3 Christie's, London #161/R est:4000-6000
£9800 $16072 €14210 Fishing boats, Dieppe (46x61cm-18x24in) board exhib. 4-Jun-3 Sotheby's, London #61/R est:10000-15000
£10000 $16400 €15000 Afternoon, boats on the Thames (51x76cm-20x30in) s. board prov. 6-Jun-3 Christie's, London #160/R est:8000-12000
£11000 $18040 €16500 Early summer flowers (41x30cm-16x12in) s. board exhib. 6-Jun-3 Christie's, London #7/R est:7000-10000
£11000 $18040 €16500 Quarzazate, Morocco (41x61cm-16x24in) s. board. 6-Jun-3 Christie's, London #29/R est:8000-12000
£11000 $18370 €15950 On the beach, Cascais (30x40cm-12x16in) s. board prov. 24-Jun-3 Bonhams, New Bond Street #49/R est:5000-7000
£12200 $19276 €18300 The round pond, Tuilleries Gardens (43x58cm-17x23in) s. 18-Dec-2 Mallams, Oxford #653/R est:8000-12000
£12444 $20658 €18044 Riverside Kings Lynn (46x61cm-18x24in) s. i.on stretcher. 16-Jun-3 Waddingtons, Toronto #178/R est:15000-20000 (C.D 28000)
£15000 $23550 €22500 Reach on the Upper Seine (51x76cm-20x30in) s. board prov. 22-Nov-2 Christie's, London #76/R est:15000-25000
£16000 $26720 €23200 Brancaster harbour (64x77cm-25x30in) s. prov. 24-Jun-3 Bonhams, New Bond Street #46/R est:15000-20000
£17000 $26350 €25500 Quai at Honfleur (51x76cm-20x30in) s. board prov. 3-Dec-2 Bonhams, New Bond Street #30/R est:15000-20000
£17000 $28050 €24650 Autumn morning, November (66x91cm-26x36in) s. i.verso. 1-Jul-3 Bonhams, Norwich #328/R est:10000-15000
£17834 $28000 €26751 Harbor - Bonifacio (26x36cm-10x14in) s. i.verso masonite prov. 10-Dec-2 Doyle, New York #225/R est:20000-30000
£22222 $36889 €32222 Spinaway, the Centaur and the Memory at Pin Mill Suffolk (91x66cm-36x26in) s.i.verso masonite prov.exhib. 10-Jun-3 Ritchie, Toronto #81/R est:25000-35000 (C.D 50000)

Works on paper

£280 $454 €420 Mn on his bike (17x26cm-7x10in) s.i. pen ink. 20-May-3 Bonhams, Knightsbridge #51
£1100 $1771 €1650 Breydon Water (18x27cm-7x11in) s. W/C prov. 18-Feb-3 Bonhams, Knightsbridge #3/R est:400-600
£1500 $2355 €2250 Cloud study (23x35cm-9x14in) W/C. 21-Nov-2 Clevedon Sale Rooms #245 est:750-1000
£1800 $2826 €2700 Early morning, Ludham (18x26cm-7x10in) s. W/C prov. 14-Dec-2 Lacy Scott, Bury St.Edmunds #477/R
£1900 $3135 €2755 Continental street scene (40x25cm-16x10in) s. W/C. 1-Jul-3 Bonhams, Norwich #193 est:1800-2500
£1900 $3135 €2755 Entrance to a Moroccan village with figures in the foreground (36x46cm-14x18in) s. W/C prov. 3-Jul-3 Ewbank, Send #299/R est:2000-3000
£2500 $4125 €3625 Norfolk landscape (37x55cm-15x22in) s. W/C. 1-Jul-3 Bonhams, Norwich #194/R est:2000-3000
£2700 $4239 €4050 Wet evening, Ostend (27x38cm-11x15in) s. W/C prov. 14-Dec-2 Lacy Scott, Bury St.Edmunds #475/R
£2800 $4340 €4200 Caravans (18x26cm-7x10in) s. W/C prov. 30-Sep-2 Bonhams, Ipswich #353 est:1800-2500
£3600 $5616 €5400 Lock at Liedschendam (34x51cm-13x20in) s. W/C. 23-Apr-3 Rupert Toovey, Partridge Green #20/R est:3500-4500
£3800 $5928 €5700 Tall house, Park Lane (27x36cm-11x14in) s. W/C pencil prov. 25-Mar-3 Bonhams, New Bond Street #51/R est:2000-3000
£4700 $7379 €7050 Street scene in Como (27x38cm-11x15in) s. W/C prov. 14-Dec-2 Lacy Scott, Bury St.Edmunds #476/R
£5800 $9512 €8410 Road in Spain (26x36cm-10x14in) s. pencil W/C prov. 5-Jun-3 Christie's, London #177/R est:3000-5000

SEALY, Allen Culpeper (1850-1927) British

£3205 $4904 €5000 Querido (46x55cm-18x22in) s.d.1907. 23-Aug-2 Deauville, France #157

SEALY, Una (20th C) Irish?

£514 $801 €750 City (61x58cm-24x23in) s.d.95 board. 8-Apr-3 James Adam, Dublin #20/R

SEAMAN, Abraham (fl.1724-1731) British

Miniatures

£1300 $2041 €1950 Young lady, wearing pink dress (4cm-2in) enamel oval prov. 10-Dec-2 Christie's, London #20/R est:600-800

SEAMAN, Noah (fl.1724-1741) British

Miniatures

£3800 $6232 €5510 Young gentleman in a blue coat (5cm-2in) enamel on copper prov. 3-Jun-3 Christie's, London #37/R est:3000-4000

SEARLE, Helen (1830-1884) British

£24516 $38000 €36774 Nature's bounty (45x56cm-18x22in) s.d.1872. 3-Dec-2 Phillips, New York #14/R est:15000-20000

SEARLE, Ronald (1920-) British

Works on paper

£400 $636 €600 News stand near Les Halles. s. pen brown ink prov. 18-Mar-3 Rosebery Fine Art, London #897
£480 $744 €720 Fast food (35x38cm-14x15in) s.i.d.1995 pen black ink. 4-Dec-2 Christie's, Kensington #191
£550 $908 €798 On the road: Herbert Morrison electioneering (34x36cm-13x14in) s.i.d.1951 pencil pen black ink lit. 3-Jul-3 Christie's, Kensington #182
£580 $934 €870 Stars Ball programme (44x34cm-17x13in) s. pen W/C. 18-Feb-3 Bonhams, Knightsbridge #194/R
£650 $1007 €975 Eurosceptic Britannica (38x46cm-15x18in) s.i.d.1997 pencil pen black ink. 4-Dec-2 Christie's, Kensington #189
£700 $1155 €1015 Business of your own: Magical footwear (28x48cm-11x19in) s.i. pen black ink W/C lit. 3-Jul-3 Christie's, Kensington #177
£720 $1145 €1080 Clerical workers enrol here (29x22cm-11x9in) s. pen ink W/C wash with self portrait two. 29-Apr-3 Henry Adams, Chichester #234
£800 $1264 €1200 Mismatch (50x37cm-20x15in) s. pen ink W/C. 27-Nov-2 Sotheby's, Olympia #28/R

£850 $1351 €1275 Artist painting his foot (35x27cm-14x11in) s. pen ink. 26-Feb-3 Sotheby's, Olympia #204/R est:400-600
£900 $1423 €1350 Nelson. Captain Cook. Drake. Galileo (21x17cm-8x7in) s. pen ink prov. four. 27-Nov-2 Sotheby's, Olympia #29/R est:200-400
£900 $1485 €1305 Flight of the ink dart (21x33cm-8x13in) s.i.d.1953 pencil pen black ink lit. 3-Jul-3 Christie's, Kensington #166
£900 $1485 €1305 Pythagorus puzzled (23x25cm-9x10in) s.i.d.1963 pencil pen black ink lit. 3-Jul-3 Christie's, Kensington #167
£950 $1473 €1425 Outwardly cracking (32x25cm-13x10in) s. pencil pen black ink W/C crayon. 4-Dec-2 Christie's, Kensington #190/R
£950 $1473 €1425 Valentine (33x42cm-13x17in) s.i.d.1980 pencil pen black ink W/C crayon. 4-Dec-2 Christie's, Kensington #206
£950 $1568 €1378 Cutting costs (46x32cm-18x13in) s. pen black ink lit. 3-Jul-3 Christie's, Kensington #185/R
£1000 $1560 €1500 Reluctant romeo. Lovelorn lady (46x38cm-18x15in) init.d.1st January 1961 pen ink fabric pair prov. 17-Sep-2 Bonhams, Knightsbridge #112/R est:600-800
£1100 $1705 €1650 Day across the channel (46x38cm-18x15in) s.i.d.1997 pencil pen black ink. 4-Dec-2 Christie's, Kensington #200 est:600-800
£1300 $2015 €1950 Robert Morley as Lord Rawnsley (52x40cm-20x16in) s.i.d.1964 pencil pen black ink W/C. 4-Dec-2 Christie's, Kensington #188/R est:800-1200
£1400 $2170 €2100 Winter time (56x44cm-22x17in) s.i.d.1991 pencil pen black ink lit. 4-Dec-2 Christie's, Kensington #202 est:600-800
£1400 $2170 €2100 Welcome to a film person (36x31cm-14x12in) s.i.d.1984 pencil pen black ink W/C crayon. 4-Dec-2 Christie's, Kensington #203 est:600-800
£1400 $2170 €2100 Should Peason make his knowledge available to everyone (19x27cm-7x11in) s.i.d.1956 pen black ink. 4-Dec-2 Christie's, Kensington #204/R est:700-10000
£1500 $2340 €2250 New years fairy (137x54cm-54x21in) gouache collage prov. 17-Sep-2 Bonhams, Knightsbridge #118/R est:1500-2500
£1500 $2475 €2175 Wicked world of book selling: Added portrait (32x26cm-13x10in) s.i. pencil pen black ink chl W/C lit. 3-Jul-3 Christie's, Kensington #180/R est:700-1000
£1500 $2475 €2175 Molesworth: Our camera club (23x19cm-9x7in) s.i.d.1953 pencil pen black ink lit. 3-Jul-3 Christie's, Kensington #181/R est:600-800
£1600 $2480 €2400 Spirit of autumn (56x38cm-22x15in) s.i.d.1954 pen black ink. 4-Dec-2 Christie's, Kensington #193 est:700-1000
£1600 $2480 €2400 Full sheep of indeterminate age (29x23cm-11x9in) s. pencil pen black ink W/C crayon. 4-Dec-2 Christie's, Kensington #205 est:600-800
£1600 $2640 €2320 Zeus and Co (53x42cm-21x17in) s.i. pencil pen black ink W/C htd white lit. 3-Jul-3 Christie's, Kensington #179/R est:1000-1500
£1700 $2635 €2550 Christmas presents (47x37cm-19x15in) s.d.1993 pen black ink W/C crayon. 4-Dec-2 Christie's, Kensington #197/R est:700-1000
£1700 $2635 €2550 Sitting pretty (21x14cm-8x6in) s.d.1978 pencil pen black ink crayon. 4-Dec-2 Christie's, Kensington #198/R est:600-800
£1700 $2805 €2465 Into the rough (49x40cm-19x16in) s.i. pencil pen black ink W/C lit. 3-Jul-3 Christie's, Kensington #169 est:600-800
£1700 $2805 €2465 Whizz for atoms: The Russian master (30x24cm-12x9in) s.d. pencil pen black ink blue crayon lit. 3-Jul-3 Christie's, Kensington #187 est:700-1000
£1900 $2945 €2850 Meat de-rationed (55x38cm-22x15in) s.i.d.1954 pen black ink. 4-Dec-2 Christie's, Kensington #195 est:800-1200
£1900 $3135 €2755 Molesworth: Provocative action (33x24cm-13x9in) s.i.d.1953 pen black ink lit. 3-Jul-3 Christie's, Kensington #184/R est:700-900
£2000 $3280 €3000 Palm springs, California (43x34cm-17x13in) s.i.d.1963 pen ink W/C pastel. 3-Jun-3 Sotheby's, Olympia #111/R est:2000-3000
£2000 $3300 €2900 St Trinians meets St Custards (39x29cm-15x11in) s.i. pencil pen black ink W/C col chk lit. 3-Jul-3 Christie's, Kensington #176/R est:1000-1500
£2200 $3410 €3300 Moleworth, brave, clear eyed worker, as in documentary films (34x26cm-13x10in) s.i.d.1956 pen black ink. 4-Dec-2 Christie's, Kensington #194/R est:800-1200
£2400 $3720 €3600 Molesworth production line for Latin sentences (35x25cm-14x10in) s.i.d.1956 pen black ink. 4-Dec-2 Christie's, Kensington #199/R est:800-1200
£2400 $3720 €3600 Molesworth, Kane descend whack gosh oo (25x35cm-10x14in) s.i.d.1953 pen black ink. 4-Dec-2 Christie's, Kensington #201/R est:700-1000
£2600 $4030 €3900 Christmas Eve (33x24cm-13x9in) s.d.1982 pencil pen black ink W/C crayon. 4-Dec-2 Christie's, Kensington #196/R est:700-1000
£3200 $5280 €4640 Waiting for walkies (31x46cm-12x18in) s.i. pen black ink W/C lit. 3-Jul-3 Christie's, Kensington #186/R est:800-1200
£3800 $5890 €5700 St Trinians (35x35cm-14x14in) s.i.indis.d.1950 pencil pen black ink W/C crayon. 4-Dec-2 Christie's, Kensington #207/R est:1000-1500
£3800 $6270 €5510 Wicked world of bookselling: Nice set, but one volume missing (32x25cm-13x10in) s.i. pencil pen black ink W/C lit. 3-Jul-3 Christie's, Kensington #183/R est:800-1200
£4500 $6975 €6750 Nigel Molesworth and the Karackter Kup (11x25cm-4x10in) s.i.d.1958 pencil pen black ink. 4-Dec-2 Christie's, Kensington #192/R est:800-1200

SEARLE, W (19th C) British?
£701 $1093 €1100 Cityscape with figures (46x37cm-18x15in) s. 8-Nov-2 Auktionhaus Georg Rehm, Augsburg #8156

SEARS, Francis (1873-1933) British
£388 $637 €540 The boat returning to the ship (29x39cm-11x15in) s.d.18. 4-Jun-3 Bukowskis, Helsinki #502/R

SEARS, Philip Shelton (1867-1953) American
Sculpture
£2500 $4000 €3625 Warrior (40cm-16in) s.d.1929 brown pat bronze. 16-May-3 Skinner, Boston #131/R est:500-700

SEARS, Taber (1870-1950) American
Works on paper
£641 $1000 €962 Boat on the rocks (66x74cm-26x29in) s. W/C. 11-Aug-2 Thomaston Place, Thomaston #54

SEATH, Ethel (20th C) Canadian
Works on paper
£2419 $3823 €3629 Old tree on the Morris property (44x35cm-17x14in) s. W/C prov.exhib. 14-Nov-2 Heffel, Vancouver #223/R est:6000-8000 (C.D 6000)

SEATON, Paul (20th C) British
£1200 $1944 €1800 Peonies in a glass vase (50x66cm-20x26in) init. 21-May-3 Bonhams, Knightsbridge #196/R est:1200-1800
£1500 $2430 €2250 Maidens blush alba roses in a cut glass vase (51x40cm-20x16in) init. 21-May-3 Bonhams, Knightsbridge #194/R est:1200-1800

SEAVEY, George W (1841-1913) American
£414 $650 €621 Still life with red and pink roses (20x40cm-8x16in) s. 22-Nov-2 Skinner, Boston #100/R

SEAWELL, Harry Washington (20th C) American
£1497 $2500 €2171 Figures in nocturnal California mission scene (33x41cm-13x16in) s. prov. 17-Jun-3 John Moran, Pasadena #196 est:1500-2000

SEBEN, Henri van (1825-1913) Belgian
£345 $552 €500 Snowy landscape (16x23cm-6x9in) s. panel. 15-Mar-3 De Vuyst, Lokeren #361
£523 $842 €800 Petit chantier naval (27x39cm-11x15in) s. panel. 20-Jan-3 Horta, Bruxelles #26
£540 $863 €750 Promenade en hiver (16x23cm-6x9in) s. panel. 19-May-3 Horta, Bruxelles #465

SEBES, Pieter Willem (1830-1906) Dutch
£5800 $9686 €8700 Important letter (46x39cm-18x15in) s.d.1858 panel. 18-Jun-3 Christie's, Kensington #47/R est:4000-6000

SEBIDI, Mmakgabo Mapula Helen (1943-) South African
£327 $526 €491 Aunt Queen 1981 (52x36cm-20x14in) s. i.verso board. 12-May-3 Stephan Welz, Johannesburg #533 est:6000-9000 (SA.R 3800)
£413 $664 €620 Little landscape near Bloemfontein (23x28cm-9x11in) s. board prov. 12-May-3 Stephan Welz, Johannesburg #120/R est:3000-5000 (SA.R 4800)
£645 $1038 €968 Woman at the lands near Bloemfontein II (39x28cm-15x11in) s. i.verso board prov. 12-May-3 Stephan Welz, Johannesburg #119 est:5000-7000 (SA.R 7500)
£897 $1399 €1346 Mothers in the fields, near Rustenburg, Transvaal (52x37cm-20x15in) s. s.i.verso board. 11-Nov-2 Stephan Welz, Johannesburg #542/R (SA.R 14000)

SEBILLE, Albert (1874-1953) French
Works on paper
£439 $685 €650 Cale seche (65x59cm-26x23in) s.d.1908 W/C. 27-Mar-3 Maigret, Paris #302

£541 $843 €800 Croiseur (48x62cm-19x24in) s.d.1908 W/C. 27-Mar-3 Maigret, Paris #300
£592 $959 €900 Canoniere (47x67cm-19x26in) s. W/C gouache. 22-Jan-3 Tajan, Paris #26
£676 $1054 €1000 Croiseur (49x62cm-19x24in) s.d.1908 W/C. 27-Mar-3 Maigret, Paris #299/R
£878 $1370 €1300 Escadre francaise (40x66cm-16x26in) s.i.d.1914 pen ink wash gouache. 27-Mar-3 Maigret, Paris #304
£1149 $1792 €1700 Voiliers dans une regate (48x63cm-19x25in) s.d.1908 W/C. 27-Mar-3 Maigret, Paris #303/R

SEBIRE, Gaston (1920-2001) French
£535 $850 €803 La tente rouge (20x48cm-8x19in) s. 7-Mar-3 Skinner, Boston #519/R
£629 $1000 €944 Neige et arbres (82x101cm-32x40in) s. 7-Mar-3 Skinner, Boston #455/R
£696 $1100 €1044 Marine a Villers (33x41cm-13x16in) s. i.stretcher prov. 22-Apr-3 Arthur James, Florida #433
£810 $1304 €1150 La plage de Quiberville (55x65cm-22x26in) s. i.verso. 12-May-3 Lesieur & Le Bars, Le Havre #85/R
£818 $1300 €1227 Trouville au personnage rose (50x65cm-20x26in) s. i.verso paper on canvas prov. 27-Feb-3 Christie's, Rockefeller NY #66/R
£1069 $1700 €1604 Soir au Havre (50x65cm-20x26in) s. s.i.verso prov. 27-Feb-3 Christie's, Rockefeller NY #54/R
£1275 $2053 €1900 Nature morte aux crevettes (65x81cm-26x32in) s. 23-Feb-3 Lesieur & Le Bars, Le Havre #138
£1538 $2400 €2307 Le pecheur et Les Yacht (74x91cm-29x36in) s. s.i.verso prov. 5-Nov-2 Arthur James, Florida #63
£1603 $2516 €2500 Matinee de printemps (65x81cm-26x32in) s.d.45. 24-Nov-2 Lesieur & Le Bars, Le Havre #161

SEBOK, Elizabeth (1908-) South African
£192 $300 €288 Still life of flowers in a black vase (84x77cm-33x30in) s. 11-Nov-2 Stephan Welz, Johannesburg #96 (SA.R 3000)

SEBOROVSKI, Carole (20th C) American?
£833 $1300 €1250 Untitled (61x76cm-24x30in) wood. 5-Nov-2 Doyle, New York #50/R

SEBOY, Ole Johnson (18/19th C) Danish
Works on paper
£745 $1192 €1118 Ship's portrait of Dorothea in high seas (27x37cm-11x15in) s. W/C Indian ink. 16-Mar-3 Hindemae, Ullerslev #365/R (D.KR 8000)
£918 $1506 €1331 Seascape with two yachts and light-house (34x52cm-13x20in) s. gouache W/C. 2-Jun-3 Blomqvist, Oslo #33/R (N.KR 10000)
£4591 $7530 €6657 Seascape with two yachts (38x44cm-15x17in) s.i.d.1820 W/C gouache. 2-Jun-3 Blomqvist, Oslo #32/R est:14000-16000 (N.KR 50000)

SEBREGTS, Lode (20th C) Belgian
£582 $908 €850 Linda (70x110cm-28x43in) s.d.1973 verso. 14-Apr-3 Horta, Bruxelles #242
£1027 $1603 €1500 Sheherazade (85x80cm-33x31in) s.d.1983. 14-Apr-3 Horta, Bruxelles #243 est:750-1000

SEBRON, Hippolyte Victor Valentin (1801-1879) French
£526 $853 €800 Saying prayer (58x48cm-23x19in) s. indis d. 21-Jan-3 Christie's, Amsterdam #16
Works on paper
£1824 $2846 €2700 Corne d'Or (21x44cm-8x17in) s.i.d.1864 W/C. 27-Mar-3 Maigret, Paris #206/R

SECKENDORFF-GUTEND, Hugo von (19th C) German?
£700 $1092 €1050 Figures by an obelisk outside a city wall (48x38cm-19x15in) s.d.87 prov. 15-Oct-2 Sotheby's, London #152/R

SEDDON, Thomas B (1821-1856) British
£55000 $88550 €82500 Arabs at prayer in the desert (63x112cm-25x44in) prov.exhib.lit. 19-Feb-3 Christie's, London #30/R est:80000-120000

SEDELMAYER, Joseph Anton (1797-1863) German
£1623 $2419 €2500 Starnberger See - Ammerland (40x47cm-16x19in) one of pair. 26-Jun-2 Neumeister, Munich #855/R est:2500
£1948 $2903 €3000 Schloss Ammerland on Starnberger See (40x47cm-16x19in) i. verso one of pair. 26-Jun-2 Neumeister, Munich #854/R est:2500

SEDERHOLM, B (19th C) Swedish
£327 $507 €520 Street scene (51x62cm-20x24in) s.d.1895. 6-Oct-2 Bukowskis, Helsinki #345/R

SEDGLEY, Peter (1930-) British
Works on paper
£1800 $2952 €2700 Colour study (76x76cm-30x30in) s.i.d.1966 verso emulsion board exhib. 3-Jun-3 Sotheby's, Olympia #309/R est:1500-2000

SEDLACEK, Franz (1891-1944) German
Prints
£16667 $26167 €26000 Author (50x35cm-20x14in) mono.d.1937 lithograph. 25-Nov-2 Hassfurther, Vienna #75 est:500-900
Works on paper
£2590 $4144 €3600 In flight (16x18cm-6x7in) mono.d.1915 pen. 14-May-3 Dorotheum, Linz #528/R est:440-500
£3472 $5521 €5000 Skeletons (23x43cm-9x17in) s. gouache. 29-Apr-3 Wiener Kunst Auktionen, Vienna #619/R est:3000-5000

SEDLACEK, Stephan (19/20th C) Austrian
£1017 $1607 €1526 Chess party - elegant figures in rococo interior (55x65cm-22x26in) s. 30-Nov-2 Goteborg Auktionsverk, Sweden #195/R (S.KR 14500)
£2400 $3912 €3480 In the harem (50x60cm-20x24in) s. 16-Jul-3 Sotheby's, Olympia #265/R est:1500-2000
£2800 $4368 €4200 Harem dancers (78x59cm-31x23in) s. 26-Mar-3 Sotheby's, Olympia #228/R est:3000-5000

SEDLACEK, Vojtech (1892-1973) Czechoslovakian
Works on paper
£330 $515 €495 Winter (36x54cm-14x21in) s.d.44 W/C. 12-Oct-2 Dorotheum, Prague #192 (C.KR 16000)

SEDOV, Aleksander (1928-) Russian
£903 $1435 €1300 Lenin at the revolution anniversry (51x36cm-20x14in) s. cardboard painted 1947. 1-May-3 Meeting Art, Vercelli #306
£1736 $2760 €2500 At the window (73x107cm-29x42in) s. s.d.1948 verso lit. 1-May-3 Meeting Art, Vercelli #108

SEEBA, Wilfried (1953-) Austrian
£705 $1107 €1100 Allegory to Sisyphus (80x100cm-31x39in) s.d.83 acrylic. 21-Nov-2 Dorotheum, Vienna #322/R

SEEBACH, Lothar von (1853-1930) German
£1923 $3038 €3000 Still life of flowers with chrysanthemums (81x65cm-32x26in) s. 16-Nov-2 Lempertz, Koln #1582/R est:2600

SEEBER, Carl Andreas (1855-?) German
£700 $1099 €1050 Preparing for the ball (70x42cm-28x17in) s. 16-Apr-3 Christie's, Kensington #807/R

SEEBERGER, Gustav (1812-1888) German
£940 $1513 €1400 Baptism (60x71cm-24x28in) s. 18-Feb-3 Sotheby's, Amsterdam #305/R est:1800-2200

SEEFISCH, Hermann Ludwig (1816-1879) German
£3782 $5862 €5900 Isola Bella and Lago Maggiore (69x96cm-27x38in) s. prov.lit. 6-Dec-2 Karlheinz Kaupp, Staufen #2329/R est:5900
£6114 $9659 €9171 Isola Bella (80x105cm-31x41in) s.d.1849. 14-Nov-2 Stuker, Bern #513 est:10000-12000 (S.FR 14000)

SEEGER, Hermann (1857-1920) German
£929 $1515 €1394 Woman on beach looking out to sea (34x44cm-13x17in) s. panel. 17-Feb-3 Blomqvist, Lysaker #1202/R (N.KR 10500)
£6731 $10433 €10500 Two teenager girls playing a lute on the dunes (80x120cm-31x47in) s. 7-Dec-2 Dannenberg, Berlin #732/R est:7000
£6944 $11042 €10000 Looking out to sea (49x69cm-19x27in) s. board. 29-Apr-3 Christie's, Amsterdam #63/R est:5000-7000

SEEHAUS, Paul Adolf (1891-1919) German
Works on paper
£360 $590 €500 Youth drawing sword (42x25cm-17x10in) s.d.1915 Indian ink brush pen. 4-Jun-3 Reiss & Sohn, Konigstein #497/R
£791 $1298 €1100 Expressionist landscape (16x20cm-6x8in) s. chl. 4-Jun-3 Reiss & Sohn, Konigstein #499
£1007 $1652 €1400 View over Thine with figures and ships (35x30cm-14x12in) mono. Indian ink brush. 4-Jun-3 Reiss & Sohn, Konigstein #498/R

SEEKAMP, Hermann (1881-1936) German
£440 $687 €700 Farmstead with river and trees (64x82cm-25x32in) 20-Sep-2 Schloss Ahlden, Ahlden #1242/R

SEEKATZ, Johann Conrad (1719-1768) German
£1935 $2845 €3000 Marauders at night (30x44cm-12x17in) prov. 20-Jun-2 Dr Fritz Nagel, Stuttgart #733/R est:5800
£3000 $4830 €4500 Lady with a parrot at a casement (26x22cm-10x9in) panel. 20-Feb-3 Christie's, Kensington #115/R est:1500-2000

£3822 $5962 €6000 Peasants smoking and drinking. Musician standing nearby smoking peasants (20x22cm-8x9in) panel pair. 6-Nov-2 Christie's, Amsterdam #42/R est:6000-12000
£4000 $6240 €6000 Flight into Egypt (33x29cm-13x11in) prov. 8-Oct-2 Sotheby's, Olympia #376/R est:5000-8000
£6410 $9936 €10000 Covenant of peace of Jakob and Esau (40x51cm-16x20in) 4-Dec-2 Neumeister, Munich #637/R est:3800

SEEKATZ, Johann Conrad (attrib) (1719-1768) German
£1923 $3019 €3000 Old Testament scene (25x20cm-10x8in) panel. 21-Nov-2 Van Ham, Cologne #1421/R est:3000

SEELEY, Eric (1951-) British
£400 $652 €580 Lair, 1996 (50x40cm-20x16in) s.d.1996 board exhib. 15-Jul-3 Bonhams, Knightsbridge #147/R

SEELOS, Gottfried (1829-1900) Austrian
£1006 $1560 €1600 Abbazia, the old harbour (17x21cm-7x8in) s. panel. 29-Oct-2 Dorotheum, Vienna #130 est:1300-1400
£2013 $3119 €3200 Sicilian day (30x25cm-12x10in) s. 29-Oct-2 Dorotheum, Vienna #37/R est:2000-2400
£8228 $13000 €13000 Mountain landscape (59x94cm-23x37in) s.d.877. 28-Nov-2 Dorotheum, Vienna #200/R est:3000-3800
Works on paper
£473 $738 €700 Forest clearing (29x42cm-11x17in) s. pencil. 28-Mar-3 Dorotheum, Vienna #48/R

SEELOS, Gustav (1831-1911) Austrian
£1410 $2214 €2200 Ruins, possibly in southern Tyrol (21x39cm-8x15in) s. 20-Nov-2 Dorotheum, Klagenfurt #17/R est:400
Works on paper
£513 $805 €800 Italian landscape (33x41cm-13x16in) s. pencil W/C paper on canvas. 20-Nov-2 Dorotheum, Klagenfurt #67/R
£897 $1409 €1400 Waterfall in the Gilsenklamm (39x28cm-15x11in) W/C. 20-Nov-2 Dorotheum, Klagenfurt #69/R
£1154 $1812 €1800 Waterfall in Gilsenklamm (38x26cm-15x10in) s.i. bears d. W/C. 20-Nov-2 Dorotheum, Klagenfurt #70/R est:500
£1351 $2108 €2000 Tunnel building in Kunterswege near Bozen (23x34cm-9x13in) s.i. W/C. 28-Mar-3 Dorotheum, Vienna #264/R est:1400-1600
£1410 $2214 €2200 Fortress ruins, possibly southern Tyrol (27x43cm-11x17in) s.i. W/C. 20-Nov-2 Dorotheum, Klagenfurt #68/R est:600

SEEMAN, Enoch (17/18th C) German/Polish
£4400 $6776 €6600 Portrait of young man (46x43cm-18x17in) s.i. 25-Oct-2 Gorringes, Lewes #880
£18000 $28440 €27000 Portrait of gentleman loading his gun, spaniel by his side (237x149cm-93x59in) prov. 26-Nov-2 Christie's, London #18/R est:20000-30000

SEEMAN, Enoch (attrib) (17/18th C) German/Polish
£1800 $2970 €2610 Portrait of William Mackworth Praed of Trevethoe, Cornwall (73x60cm-29x24in) prov. 2-Jul-3 Sotheby's, Olympia #33/R est:2000-3000

SEEREY-LESTER, John (1945-) British
£340 $541 €510 Cross country horse rider riding through woodland (51x76cm-20x30in) s. 18-Mar-3 Capes Dunn, Manchester #567
£340 $541 €510 Cross country horse rider after taking a fence with onlookers (51x76cm-20x30in) s. 18-Mar-3 Capes Dunn, Manchester #568
£1988 $3220 €2883 Bandhavgarth sundown - black panther (30x41cm-12x16in) acrylic on masonite. 23-May-3 Altermann Galleries, Santa Fe #214
£6849 $10000 €10274 Out of the darkness, into the light (61x122cm-24x48in) 18-May-2 Altermann Galleries, Santa Fe #217/R
£9494 $15000 €13766 Winter grazing - bison (91x61cm-36x24in) s. acrylic prov.lit. 26-Jul-3 Coeur d'Alene, Hayden #169/R est:10000-20000
Works on paper
£300 $492 €450 Steam engine on a country line (38x51cm-15x20in) s.d.71 pastel. 4-Jun-3 Bonhams, Chester #327
£410 $652 €615 Mother elephant with its calf, herd beyond (35x51cm-14x20in) s.d.78 pastel. 27-Feb-3 Bonhams, Chester #353

SEERY, John (1941-) American
£253 $400 €380 Summer afternoon (114x145cm-45x57in) acrylic double-sided prov. 3-Apr-3 Boos Gallery, Michigan #263/R

SEERY-LESTER, John (1946-) American
Works on paper
£500 $790 €725 Shoe shiners (37x52cm-15x20in) s.d.80 W/C htd white. 28-Jul-3 David Duggleby, Scarborough #243/R

SEEVAGEN, Lucien (1887-1959) French
£292 $475 €420 Sentier a Brehat (21x27cm-8x11in) s. panel. 19-Jul-3 Thierry & Lannon, Brest #388
£556 $906 €800 Ramendage des filets aux Plomarc'h (38x46cm-15x18in) s. cardboard. 19-Jul-3 Thierry & Lannon, Brest #173
£590 $962 €850 Paysage de l'Ile de Brehat (17x41cm-7x16in) s. cardboard. 19-Jul-3 Thierry & Lannon, Brest #387
£1297 $2050 €2050 Ile de Brehat (50x65cm-20x26in) s. 1-Dec-2 Livinec, Gaudcheau & Jezequel, Rennes #69/R

SEEWALD, Richard Josef (1889-1976) German
Works on paper
£577 $894 €900 Self portrait (29x25cm-11x10in) s.i.d.21 col chk prov. 4-Dec-2 Lempertz, Koln #1060/R
£1258 $1962 €2000 Eberhard Reinacher (64x48cm-25x19in) s.i.d.28 pencil prov. 9-Oct-2 Sotheby's, London #249/R est:3000-4000

SEFARBI, Harry (1917-) American
£839 $1300 €1259 Landscape from a window (46x62cm-18x24in) s.d.64 masonite. 8-Dec-2 Freeman, Philadelphia #125/R
£1090 $1700 €1635 Figures in a room (36x41cm-14x16in) board. 20-Sep-2 Freeman, Philadelphia #105/R est:150-250

SEGAER, Pieter (?-1650) Belgian
£19108 $29809 €30000 River landscape with a fortified tower and windmill (40x56cm-16x22in) panel prov.exhib.lit. 5-Nov-2 Sotheby's, Amsterdam #22/R est:10000-15000

SEGAL, Arthur (1875-1944) Rumanian
£4710 $7725 €6500 Maize (39x50cm-15x20in) s. panel exhib. 31-May-3 Villa Grisebach, Berlin #232/R est:6000-8000
£6329 $10000 €10000 Still life with peppers (39x50cm-15x20in) s.d.1934 panel. 30-Nov-2 Villa Grisebach, Berlin #289/R est:8000-10000
£9565 $14826 €14348 Sailing ship off rocky coast (70x90cm-28x35in) s. prov. 4-Dec-2 Koller, Zurich #105/R est:25000-30000 (S.FR 22000)
£19348 $30183 €29022 In the dream of a monk (69x89cm-27x35in) s. 11-Sep-2 Kieselbach, Budapest #144/R (H.F 7500000)
£20290 $33275 €28000 Street scene (70x90cm-28x35in) s.d.1916 prov. 31-May-3 Villa Grisebach, Berlin #217/R est:20000-30000

SEGAL, George (1924-2000) American
Sculpture
£2817 $4676 €4000 Abbraccio (60x43x22cm-24x17x9in) s.i.d.1970 num.2/15 plaster. 10-Jun-3 Finarte Semenzato, Milan #144/R est:1500-2000
£2866 $4500 €4299 Girl resting (15x15cm-6x6in) s.d. num.15 verso cast plaster. 19-Nov-2 Wright, Chicago #254/R est:5000-7000
£4513 $6995 €6770 Still life (34x53x31cm-13x21x12in) s.num. porcelain edition 43/95 Cast Bernardaud after Cezanne. 3-Dec-2 Shapiro, Sydney #50/R est:14000-18000 (A.D 12500)
£102564 $149744 €160000 Man on a bench (132x120x100cm-52x47x39in) s.num.2/3 white pat bronze metal bench prov. 5-Jun-2 Il Ponte, Milan #143/R est:180000-200000

SEGAL, Simon (1898-1969) French
£774 $1223 €1200 Taureau espagnol (60x73cm-24x29in) s. lit. 17-Dec-2 Rossini, Paris #122/R
Works on paper
£269 $423 €420 Greve de Saint-Marc (21x26cm-8x10in) s.d.1939 crayon. 15-Dec-2 Thierry & Lannon, Brest #314

SEGALA, Giovanni (style) (1663-1720) Italian
£4690 $7410 €6800 Europa's kidnapping (55x81cm-22x32in) 5-Apr-3 Finarte Semenzato, Milan #102/R est:6000

SEGALL, Julius (1860-1925) American/German
£422 $650 €633 Barnyard scene with roosters and chickens (22x32cm-9x13in) s. 9-Sep-2 Schrager Galleries, Milwaukee #458/R

SEGALL, Lasar (1891-1957) Brazilian/Lithuanian
Works on paper
£597 $920 €950 Figure wearing boots (33x25cm-13x10in) i. verso pencil. 26-Oct-2 Dr Lehr, Berlin #489/R

SEGALMAN, Richard (1934-) American
Works on paper
£580 $900 €870 Portrait of a young girl reclining. Portrait of a seated woman (38x28cm-15x11in) s. pencil W/C double-sided. 29-Oct-2 Sotheby's, New York #283/R est:700-900
£838 $1300 €1257 Young man reading in Central Park (32x48cm-13x19in) s. black chk prov.exhib. 29-Oct-2 Sotheby's, New York #282/R est:500-700

£903 $1400 €1355 Portrait of Herb in the front and back yard (47x61cm-19x24in) pencil W/C two prov. 29-Oct-2 Sotheby's, New York #287/R est:800-1200

£967 $1500 €1451 White roses on window ledge. Mountainous landscape. Private conversation (28x35cm-11x14in) s.i. pastel one double-sided. 29-Oct-2 Sotheby's, New York #284/R est:800-1200

£1290 $2000 €1935 Sunday, Raymond and Mario (29x38cm-11x15in) s. pencil W/C one oil on canvas three prov. 29-Oct-2 Sotheby's, New York #288/R est:800-1200

£1451 $2250 €2177 Two portraits of David. Man rowing (52x38cm-20x15in) s. pencil W/C prov. 29-Oct-2 Sotheby's, New York #286/R est:800-1200

SEGANTINI, Giovanni (1858-1899) Italian

£24017 $37707 €36026 Cavallo al guado (44x30cm-17x12in) s. canvas on board exhib.prov.lit. 25-Nov-2 Sotheby's, Zurich #27/R est:60000-80000 (S.FR 55000)

£40773 $64421 €61160 Ritorno all'ovile (63x100cm-25x39in) mono. i. verso panel prov.exhib.lit. 28-Nov-2 Christie's, Zurich #12/R est:80000-120000 (S.FR 95000)

£75472 $122264 €133586 La radice (55x80cm-22x31in) prov.exhib.lit. 26-May-3 Sotheby's, Zurich #39/R est:180000-250000 (S.FR 160000)

SEGANTINI, Gottardo (1882-1974) Italian

£7826 $12130 €11739 Autunno alpestre - view of Majorca (30x40cm-12x16in) s.i.d.1920 i. verso. 4-Dec-2 Koller, Zurich #150/R est:18000-25000 (S.FR 18000)

£14932 $24937 €21651 Still life of fruit, dish and jug (46x32cm-18x13in) s.d.1909. 24-Jun-3 Koller, Zurich #60/R est:20000-30000 (S.FR 33000)

£18696 $28978 €28044 Locarno in the morning (60x80cm-24x31in) s.d.1945 s.i.d. verso pavatex. 4-Dec-2 Koller, Zurich #151/R est:25000-35000 (S.FR 43000)

£18868 $30566 €33396 Rome (65x80cm-26x31in) one s.i.d. s.i.d. verso two. 26-May-3 Sotheby's, Zurich #86/R est:30000-50000 (S.FR 40000)

£21834 $34061 €32751 Larch in autumn landscape near Maloja with Piz Duan (91x75cm-36x30in) s.d.1956 pavatex. 6-Nov-2 Hans Widmer, St Gallen #10/R est:38000-50000 (S.FR 50000)

£27897 $44077 €41846 Alpine hamlet in Engadin (66x85cm-26x33in) s.d.1940. 26-Nov-2 Phillips, Zurich #21/R est:60000-80000 (S.FR 65000)

£28384 $44563 €42576 Alpine roses in copper pan (50x75cm-20x30in) s.d.1948 pavatex. 25-Nov-2 Sotheby's, Zurich #116/R est:30000-40000 (S.FR 65000)

£37118 $58275 €55677 Shepherd with flock in the mountains (66x84cm-26x33in) s.d.1960 pavatex. 25-Nov-2 Sotheby's, Zurich #115/R est:50000-70000 (S.FR 85000)

SEGANTINI, Mario (1885-1916) Italian

£1528 $2415 €2292 Portrait of young blonde man (65x54cm-26x21in) s.i.d.1903 oil gold bronze. 14-Nov-2 Stuker, Bern #515 est:4000-6000 (S.FR 3500)

SEGARINI, Luigi (19th C) Italian

£962 $1490 €1500 Big celebration at the inn (45x79cm-18x31in) s. 5-Dec-2 Stadion, Trieste #681/R

SEGARRA CHIAS, Pablo (1945-) Spanish

£1677 $2650 €2600 What do people say? (58x48cm-23x19in) s.d.91 s.i.d.verso board. 17-Dec-2 Durán, Madrid #202/R

£1774 $2803 €2750 Fisherwoman from Puerta Umbria (56x45cm-22x18in) s.d.91 s.i.d.acrylic board. 17-Dec-2 Durán, Madrid #201/R

SEGE, Alexandre (1818-1885) French

£1200 $1992 €1200 Pecheur au bord du cours d'eau (50x75cm-20x30in) s.d.1857. 16-Jun-3 Horta, Bruxelles #225

SEGER, E (1868-1939) German

Sculpture

£1769 $2812 €2600 Art Deco figure of young woman with hoop (23cm-9in) s. gilt bronze carved ivory marble socle. 24-Mar-3 Bernaerts, Antwerp #159/R est:2500-3000

SEGERS, Adrien (1876-1950) Belgian

£641 $1006 €1000 Rouen (55x46cm-22x18in) s. 16-Dec-2 Rabourdin & Choppin de Janvry, Paris #33

£1277 $1979 €1916 Bras de Seine a Port St Queen (46x65cm-18x26in) s. 3-Dec-2 Bukowskis, Stockholm #185/R est:20000-25000 (S.KR 18000)

SEGERSTRAHLE, Lennart (1892-1975) Finnish

£253 $395 €400 Winter landscape (26x38cm-10x15in) s.d.1913. 12-Sep-2 Hagelstam, Helsinki #983

£272 $433 €400 Landscape (30x40cm-12x16in) s.d.1943. 27-Feb-3 Hagelstam, Helsinki #842/R

£286 $454 €420 Religious scene (44x34cm-17x13in) s. 27-Feb-3 Hagelstam, Helsinki #903/R

£313 $498 €460 Morning (58x42cm-23x17in) s.d.1938. 27-Feb-3 Hagelstam, Helsinki #1025

£443 $691 €700 The old road (27x46cm-11x18in) s.d.40. 15-Sep-2 Bukowskis, Helsinki #280/R

£452 $714 €700 Landscape (28x46cm-11x18in) s. 19-Dec-2 Hagelstam, Helsinki #911

£591 $916 €940 Fisherman's family (42x63cm-17x25in) s.d.38. 6-Oct-2 Bukowskis, Helsinki #274/R

£595 $928 €940 In the country (45x59cm-18x23in) s.d.42. 15-Sep-2 Bukowskis, Helsinki #279/R

£850 $1393 €1300 In flight (50x70cm-20x28in) s.d.13. 9-Feb-3 Bukowskis, Helsinki #353/R

£1367 $2242 €1900 Elks on the marshes (75x105cm-30x41in) s.d.1912. 4-Jun-3 Bukowskis, Helsinki #422/R est:2000

£1392 $2172 €2200 Birds (66x80cm-26x31in) 12-Sep-2 Hagelstam, Helsinki #976/R est:2000

£1503 $2465 €2300 Early spring (26x35cm-10x14in) s.d.1927. 9-Feb-3 Bukowskis, Helsinki #352/R est:1500

£1709 $2700 €2700 View from Borgaa skerries (42x51cm-17x20in) s.d.1929 board. 1-Dec-2 Bukowskis, Helsinki #179/R est:1700-2000

£1962 $3061 €3100 Lapwing (68x97cm-27x38in) s.d.1913. 12-Sep-2 Hagelstam, Helsinki #956/R est:2000

£1962 $3100 €3100 Pair of golden eyes (32x44cm-13x17in) s. 1-Dec-2 Bukowskis, Helsinki #178/R est:2200-2500

£2174 $3435 €3261 Cat creeping along (38x51cm-15x20in) s.d.1914 panel prov. 27-Nov-2 Falkkloos, Malmo #77494/R est:40000 (S.KR 31000)

£2324 $3742 €3300 Birds in flight (37x57cm-15x22in) s.d.1934 board. 10-May-3 Bukowskis, Helsinki #49/R est:2000-2300

£3381 $5410 €4700 Cat. Girl reading (39x52cm-15x20in) s.d.1914 d.1913 verso board double-sided. 17-May-3 Hagelstam, Helsinki #147/R est:5000

£3797 $6000 €6000 Idyll (75x150cm-30x59in) s.d.1931. 1-Dec-2 Bukowskis, Helsinki #175/R est:5000-5500

£3849 $6313 €5581 Goshawk hunting (75x100cm-30x39in) s.d.1915. 4-Jun-3 AB Stockholms Auktionsverk #2315/R est:20000-25000 (S.KR 49000)

£17606 $28345 €25000 Golden-eyes spring play (59x131cm-23x52in) s.d.17. 10-May-3 Bukowskis, Helsinki #86/R est:8000-12000

Works on paper

£272 $433 €400 In the garden (62x49cm-24x19in) s.d.31 W/C. 24-Mar-3 Bukowskis, Helsinki #289/R

£288 $472 €400 View from the window in the artist's studio, Borgaa (49x63cm-19x25in) s.d.1944 W/C. 4-Jun-3 Bukowskis, Helsinki #423/R

£288 $472 €400 Dark haired woman (62x45cm-24x18in) s.d.1939 W/C. 4-Jun-3 Bukowskis, Helsinki #426/R

£321 $494 €510 Landscape (60x46cm-24x18in) s. W/C. 24-Oct-2 Hagelstam, Helsinki #828

£323 $504 €510 Summer verdure (60x45cm-24x18in) s.d.1957 W/C. 15-Sep-2 Bukowskis, Helsinki #278/R

£340 $523 €540 Coastal landscape with flowers on cliffs (34x48cm-13x19in) s.d.1934 W/C. 27-Oct-2 Bukowskis, Helsinki #280/R

£352 $542 €560 The fisherman (59x45cm-23x18in) s.d.45 W/C. 27-Oct-2 Bukowskis, Helsinki #278/R

£446 $732 €620 Coastal landscape (35x54cm-14x21in) s.d.1940 W/C. 4-Jun-3 Bukowskis, Helsinki #425/R

£669 $1077 €950 Mountain landscape with eagle (32x40cm-13x16in) s.d.20 W/C. 10-May-3 Bukowskis, Helsinki #88/R

£1021 $1644 €1450 Crow (29x49cm-11x19in) s.d.19 W/C. 10-May-3 Bukowskis, Helsinki #87/R

SEGHERS, Gerard (1591-1651) Flemish

£70513 $111410 €110000 Christ and Nicodemus (114x158cm-45x62in) 18-Nov-2 Bernaerts, Antwerp #174/R est:20000-30000

SEGHERS, Gerard (attrib) (1591-1651) Flemish

£19000 $31730 €27550 Allegory of music (127x169cm-50x67in) prov. 9-Jul-3 Christie's, London #17/R est:15000-20000

SEGHERS, Gerard (style) (1591-1651) Flemish

£5033 $8104 €7500 Denial of Saint Peter (120x155cm-47x61in) prov.lit. 18-Feb-3 Sotheby's, Amsterdam #201/R est:7000-9000

SEGNA DI BONAVENTURA (attrib) (fl.1298-1326) Italian

£2597 $4026 €3896 Maria with child (50x38cm-20x15in) oil gold panel. 24-Sep-2 Koller, Zurich #6401/R est:7000-9000 (S.FR 6000)

SEGOFFIN, Victor (1867-1925) French

Sculpture

£2152 $3335 €3400 La joueuse de cymbales (59cm-23in) s.d. pat bronze Cast Susse. 27-Sep-2 Rabourdin & Choppin de Janvry, Paris #110/R est:4000-4200

SEGOND-WEBER, Pierre (19/20th C) French?
£2215 $3500 €3500 Femme Ouled-Nail (46x34cm-18x13in) s. panel. 28-Nov-2 Piasa, Paris #66/R est:3500-3800

SEGOURA, Augustin (20th C) Belgian
£345 $545 €500 Portrait de SAR la Princesse Marie-Esmeralda (70x55cm-28x22in) s.d.1966. 2-Apr-3 Vanderkindere, Brussels #269/R

SEGRELLES, Eustaquio (1936-) Spanish
£692 $1065 €1100 Beach by Valencia (27x41cm-11x16in) s. s.i.d.71 verso. 22-Oct-2 Durán, Madrid #77/R
£839 $1325 €1300 Fisherwomen (28x41cm-11x16in) s.d.90 i.d.verso. 18-Dec-2 Ansorena, Madrid #348/R
£968 $1529 €1500 Fishermen (29x41cm-11x16in) s.d.90 i.d.verso. 18-Dec-2 Ansorena, Madrid #347/R
£1225 $1997 €1850 Village in Sagunto (50x78cm-20x31in) s.d.1975 s.i.d.verso. 11-Feb-3 Segre, Madrid #332/R
£1510 $2431 €2250 Albufeira (81x100cm-32x39in) s.d.73 lit. 18-Feb-3 Durán, Madrid #168/R
£1678 $2701 €2500 Valencia beach (38x55cm-15x22in) s. s.i.d.2002 verso. 18-Feb-3 Durán, Madrid #199/R
£2013 $3242 €3000 Valencia beach (38x55cm-15x22in) s. s.i.d.2002 verso. 18-Feb-3 Durán, Madrid #200/R
£2358 $3632 €3750 Valencian fishermen (50x65cm-20x26in) s.d.89 s.i.verso. 22-Oct-2 Durán, Madrid #145/R est:1800
£2590 $4144 €3600 Le retour des pecheurs (61x76cm-24x30in) s. 18-May-3 Eric Pillon, Calais #259/R

SEGRELLES, Jose (1885-1969) Spanish
£1635 $2551 €2600 Caron's boat (51x69cm-20x27in) s. 17-Sep-2 Segre, Madrid #119/R

SEGUI, Antonio (1934-) Argentinian
£3125 $4969 €4500 Arbol flexible (55x38cm-22x15in) s.i.d.84 verso. 29-Apr-3 Artcurial Briest, Paris #399/R est:4000-6000
£4151 $6392 €6600 Trois personnages dans la ville (60x73cm-24x29in) s.d.1990 acrylic. 26-Oct-2 Cornette de St.Cyr, Paris #102/R
£5183 $8500 €7775 Casita secundaria (89x115cm-35x45in) s.d.81 s.i.d.81 verso. 28-May-3 Christie's, Rockefeller NY #132/R est:12000-16000
£5755 $9209 €8000 Composition (100x100cm-39x39in) s.d.65 prov. 17-May-3 De Vuyst, Lokeren #499/R est:6000-8000
£6250 $9938 €9000 Bella vista (100x100cm-39x39in) s. acrylic panel exhib. 29-Apr-3 Artcurial Briest, Paris #386/R est:10000-15000
£10828 $17000 €16242 Parallel tales (130x195cm-51x77in) s.d.81 s.i.d.verso prov.lit. 19-Nov-2 Sotheby's, New York #132/R est:15000
£17201 $26490 €27350 Landscape with crowd (200x200cm-79x79in) s. acrylic prov.exhib. 26-Oct-2 Cornette de St.Cyr, Paris #105/R

Sculpture
£949 $1500 €1500 Compradito (17x9cm-7x4in) s. num.11/24 green pat bronze. 27-Nov-2 Tajan, Paris #105/R
£1181 $1948 €1700 Compradito (17x9x8cm-7x4x3in) s.num.10/24 silver bronze socle. 1-Jul-3 Artcurial Briest, Paris #847/R est:2000-2500
£1389 $2194 €2000 Compradito (16cm-6in) num.5/24 green pat bronze. 27-Apr-3 Perrin, Versailles #127/R est:2000-2500
£1899 $2962 €3000 Compradito (17x9x7cm-7x4x3in) s. num.3/24 green pat.bronze. 31-Jul-2 Tajan, Paris #70/R est:2200-3000
£1899 $2962 €3000 El viajero (16x14x10cm-6x6x4in) s. num.3/24 silvered bronze. 31-Jul-2 Tajan, Paris #71/R est:2500-3000

Works on paper
£449 $704 €700 Figure (40x30cm-16x12in) s. pastel. 15-Dec-2 Lombrail & Teucquam, Paris #14/R
£701 $1093 €1052 La selva de Tarzan (65x50cm-26x20in) s.d.65 pencil Indian ink. 6-Nov-2 AB Stockholms Auktionsverk #930/R (S.KR 10000)
£903 $1426 €1300 Tete (64x50cm-25x20in) s.i.d. pastel gouache. 28-Apr-3 Cornette de St.Cyr, Paris #505
£3741 $5949 €5500 Saltarin (60x73cm-24x29in) s.i.d.1981 mixed media paper on canvas. 24-Mar-3 Claude Boisgirard, Paris #124/R
£4000 $6320 €6000 Apesanteur (100x100cm-39x39in) s.i.d.90 verso chl oil paper on canvas prov.exhib. 3-Apr-3 Christie's, Kensington #233/R
£5000 $7900 €7500 Waking up (129x96cm-51x38in) s.i.d.67 chk gouache paper on canvas. 3-Apr-3 Christie's, Kensington #206/R est:7000
£5500 $8690 €8250 Figures (96x129cm-38x51in) s.d.85 s.i.verso marker pen gouache paper on canvas. 3-Apr-3 Christie's, Kensington #235/R

SEGUIN, Armand (1869-1903) French
£577 $912 €900 Bretonnes au bord de la falaise (65x50cm-26x20in) s.d.1891 exhib. 12-Nov-2 Thierry & Lannon, Brest #96/R

Works on paper
£25000 $41750 €37500 Tete de jeune bretonne (53x43cm-21x17in) s.d.96 pastel chl. 26-Jun-3 Christie's, London #363/R est:20000-30000

SEGUIN-BERTAULT, Paul (1869-1964) French
£4403 $6824 €7000 L'ete (81x56cm-32x22in) s. i.verso. 30-Oct-2 Artcurial Briest, Paris #171/R est:4500-6000

SEGUR LAMOIGNON, Valentine de (1859-1924) ?

Works on paper
£1429 $2271 €2100 Chien couche (25x49cm-10x19in) s.i.d.1872 W/C gouache. 24-Mar-3 Tajan, Paris #174/R

SEGURA IGLESIAS, Agustin (1900-1988) Spanish
£1282 $2013 €2000 Girl with oranges (73x61cm-29x24in) s. 16-Dec-2 Castellana, Madrid #458/R
£1603 $2516 €2500 Girl with jug and flowers (81x65cm-32x26in) s. 16-Dec-2 Castellana, Madrid #53/R

SEGUSO, Armand (20th C) American

Works on paper
£1242 $2000 €1863 Shapely woman adjusting her hair (71x46cm-28x18in) s. W/C pastel. 10-May-3 Illustration House, New York #129/R est:2000-3000

SEGUY, Auguste de (19th C) ?

Works on paper
£385 $596 €600 Jeune femme en sous-bois (92x64cm-36x25in) s.d.1899 W/C. 9-Dec-2 Thierry & Lannon, Brest #250

SEHLSTEDT, Elias (1809-1874) Swedish
£3413 $5530 €4949 Evening view from the Custom-house in Sandhamn (41x58cm-16x23in) init. 26-May-3 Bukowskis, Stockholm #370/R est:35000-40000 (S.KR 44000)
£4500 $7289 €6525 Custom-house in Sandhamn (40x59cm-16x23in) init.d.1860. 26-May-3 Bukowskis, Stockholm #369/R est:45000-50000 (S.KR 58000)

SEIBELS, Carl (1844-1877) German
£648 $1044 €972 Old farmstead in fields (33x46cm-13x18in) s. 7-May-3 Dobiaschofsky, Bern #974/R (S.FR 1400)
£3165 $5000 €5000 Cows in the meadow (63x93cm-25x37in) s. 28-Nov-2 Dorotheum, Vienna #241/R est:6000-6500

SEIBEZZI, Fioravante (1906-1975) Italian
£385 $596 €600 Mazzorbo (25x30cm-10x12in) s. s.verso cardboard. 5-Dec-2 Stadion, Trieste #665/R
£496 $804 €700 Paesaggio (40x50cm-16x20in) s. 22-May-3 Stadion, Trieste #374/R
£851 $1379 €1200 Paesaggio (60x80cm-24x31in) s. 22-May-3 Stadion, Trieste #373/R

SEIBOLD, Christian (attrib) (1697-1768) German
£4225 $6803 €6000 Kaiser Karl VI and wife Elisabeth Christine (90x74cm-35x29in) two. 7-May-3 Dorotheum, Vienna #4/R est:5000-6000

SEIDEL, August (1820-1904) German
£455 $677 €700 Lower alpine landscape (12x24cm-5x9in) mono. board. 26-Jun-2 Neumeister, Munich #858
£566 $883 €900 In the mountains (18x27cm-7x11in) s. canvas on board. 19-Sep-2 Dr Fritz Nagel, Stuttgart #1002/R
£629 $981 €1000 Palace on southern coast (34x23cm-13x9in) mono.d.96 lit. 20-Sep-2 Schloss Ahlden, Ahlden #1222/R
£769 $1192 €1200 Lower alpine landscape (25x32cm-10x13in) mono. i. verso board. 5-Dec-2 Neumeister, Munich #2875/R
£1384 $2158 €2200 Coastal scene (58x88cm-23x35in) s. lit. 20-Sep-2 Schloss Ahlden, Ahlden #1090/R est:2200
£1592 $2484 €2500 Harvesting hay in the high mountains (80x50cm-31x20in) s. 6-Nov-2 Hugo Ruef, Munich #1266/R est:2500

Works on paper
£1268 $2041 €1800 Market (26x35cm-10x14in) s.i.d.68 pencil w/c lit. 9-May-3 Schloss Ahlden, Ahlden #1485/R est:1400

SEIDEL, August (attrib) (1820-1904) German
£779 $1161 €1200 Peasant and dog on river shore (12x19cm-5x7in) bears mono. board. 26-Jun-2 Neumeister, Munich #857/R
£833 $1292 €1300 Extensive landscape with a memorial tablet and figure on path (25x41cm-10x16in) board lit. 4-Dec-2 Neumeister, Munich #902/R

SEIDEL, Brian (1928-) Australian
£287 $428 €431 Interior view (27x75cm-11x30in) i. acrylic pencil paper on board. 27-Aug-2 Christie's, Melbourne #332 (A.D 750)
£321 $501 €482 Burnt tree, Merrijig (41x33cm-16x13in) s. canvas on board lit. 11-Nov-2 Deutscher-Menzies, Melbourne #180/R (A.D 900)
£460 $685 €690 Figure in an interior (53x56cm-21x22in) s.d.67 acrylic paper board. 27-Aug-2 Christie's, Melbourne #343/R est:700-1000 (A.D 1200)
£465 $740 €698 Eltham (71x76cm-28x30in) s.d.75 s.i.d.verso prov. 5-May-3 Sotheby's, Melbourne #242/R (A.D 1200)

£1071 $1671 €1607 Still life interior with orchids (91x91cm-36x36in) s.d.96. 11-Nov-2 Deutscher-Menzies, Melbourne #149/R est:2000-3000 (A.D 3000)
£1643 $2563 €2465 Still life with poppies (61x61cm-24x24in) s.d.95. 11-Nov-2 Deutscher-Menzies, Melbourne #150/R est:1500-2000 (A.D 4600)
£1786 $2785 €2679 Balcony, Kate at Sorrento (106x111cm-42x44in) s.d.82. 11-Nov-2 Deutscher-Menzies, Melbourne #95/R est:5000-7000 (A.D 5000)
£3214 $5046 €4821 Portsea morning (167x183cm-66x72in) s.d.85. 25-Nov-2 Christie's, Melbourne #98/R est:9000-12000 (A.D 9000)

SEIDL, Alois (1897-) German
£331 $523 €480 Sunflowers by window (79x64cm-31x25in) s.d.1924. 5-Apr-3 Quittenbaum, Hamburg #109/R

SEIDL-SEITZ, Josef (1908-1990) German
£287 $447 €450 Pre-alpine landscape (70x100cm-28x39in) s. 6-Nov-2 Hugo Ruef, Munich #1267/R

SEIERL, Wolfgang (1955-) Austrian
£1582 $2453 €2500 Pelting season (248x200cm-98x79in) s.d.91 verso oil mixed media. 24-Sep-2 Wiener Kunst Auktionen, Vienna #326/R est:3000-5000

SEIFERT, Alfred (1850-1901) Czechoslovakian
£400 $652 €600 Study of a girls head (18x14cm-7x6in) 14-Feb-3 Lyon & Turnbull, Edinburgh #138
£652 $1011 €978 Portrait of young woman (24x18cm-9x7in) s. panel. 9-Dec-2 Philippe Schuler, Zurich #3932/R (S.FR 1500)
£3659 $6000 €5489 Procession (63x102cm-25x40in) s. 5-Feb-3 Christie's, Rockefeller NY #186/R est:7000-9000
£6000 $10020 €8700 Innocence (55x32cm-22x13in) s. panel. 17-Jun-3 Bonhams, New Bond Street #32/R est:7000-10000

SEIFERT, David (1896-?) Polish
£486 $773 €700 Paysage du midi (54x81cm-21x32in) s. 29-Apr-3 Artcurial Briest, Paris #254

SEIFERT, Victor Heinrich (1870-1953) German
Sculpture
£1026 $1559 €1600 Children reading (42x30cm-17x12in) s. bronze marble socle. 17-Aug-2 Hans Stahl, Toestorf #499/R est:1600
£1026 $1590 €1600 Fairy-tale (48cm-19in) s.i. gold brown pat bronze. 7-Dec-2 Dannenberg, Berlin #216/R est:1500
£1234 $1900 €1851 Figure of a female nude (71cm-28in) i. brown pat. bronze on marble base. 27-Oct-2 Grogan, Boston #110 est:1500-2000
£1964 $3221 €2848 Thursty - nude girl standing with bowl (141cm-56in) s. pat.bronze incl. red granite base lit. 4-Jun-3 AB Stockholms Auktionsverk #2393/R est:15000-18000 (S.KR 25000)

SEIFFERT, Carl Friedrich (1809-1891) German
£321 $500 €482 Landscape with lake (23x30cm-9x12in) s.d.1849. 18-Sep-2 Boos Gallery, Michigan #173/R
£5479 $8548 €8000 Resting near Mayringen in late summer (56x68cm-22x27in) s.d.1843. 10-Apr-3 Dorotheum, Vienna #242/R est:8000-10000
£6028 $9766 €8500 View of Schachental (111x191cm-44x75in) s. 22-May-3 Dorotheum, Vienna #26/R est:5000-6000

SEIGLE, Henri Julien (1911-) French
£253 $400 €400 Provence (38x61cm-15x24in) s. s.d.57 verso. 27-Nov-2 Blanchet, Paris #115

SEIGLE, Henri Julien and No (20th C) French
£1027 $1613 €1500 Ver luisant (38x61cm-15x24in) mono.d.49 verso. 15-Apr-3 Laurence Calmels, Paris #4411/R
£1233 $1936 €1800 Untitled (55x38cm-22x15in) 15-Apr-3 Laurence Calmels, Paris #4409/R
£2397 $3764 €3500 Untitled (61x50cm-24x20in) d.1929 double-sided. 15-Apr-3 Laurence Calmels, Paris #4408/R
Works on paper
£1370 $2151 €2000 Taupe etoilee (37x23cm-15x9in) gouache ink paper on canvas. 15-Apr-3 Laurence Calmels, Paris #4412/R
£1507 $2366 €2200 Taupe etoilee (37x23cm-15x9in) gouache ink paper on canvas. 15-Apr-3 Laurence Calmels, Paris #4413/R
£2740 $4301 €4000 Projet d'autel (39x35cm-15x14in) i.verso ink. 15-Apr-3 Laurence Calmels, Paris #4414/R
£3425 $5377 €5000 Chouette blanche (30x33cm-12x13in) s. mixed media on canvas. 15-Apr-3 Laurence Calmels, Paris #4410/R

SEIGNAC, Guillaume (1870-1924) French
£9494 $15000 €14241 Venus Marine (55x46cm-22x18in) s. prov. 23-Apr-3 Christie's, Rockefeller NY #108/R est:15000-20000
£10274 $16027 €15000 Femme assise au drape rose (54x37cm-21x15in) s. 14-Apr-3 Horta, Bruxelles #172/R est:12000-15000
£12821 $20000 €19232 Harlequin (61x46cm-24x18in) s. 18-Sep-2 Boos Gallery, Michigan #284/R est:50000-70000
£38749 $62000 €58124 Cupid's arrow (100x74cm-39x29in) s. 14-May-3 Butterfields, San Francisco #1113/R est:30000-50000

SEIGNAC, Paul (1826-1904) French
£5000 $7950 €7500 Helping little sister (27x35cm-11x14in) s. panel. 20-Mar-3 Christie's, Kensington #97/R est:4000-6000
£6500 $10205 €9750 Plate of cherries (41x32cm-16x13in) s. panel. 21-Nov-2 Christie's, Kensington #26/R est:4000-6000
£7500 $11925 €11250 Learning to count (35x27cm-14x11in) s. panel. 20-Mar-3 Christie's, Kensington #99/R est:4000-6000
£12329 $18000 €18494 Morning porridge (38x46cm-15x18in) s. panel. 3-Nov-1 North East Auctions, Portsmouth #1167/R est:8000-10000

SEIJO Y RUBIO, Jose (1881-1970) Spanish
£284 $449 €440 Landscape (11x17cm-4x7in) s. cardboard. 18-Dec-2 Ansorena, Madrid #1/R
£881 $1374 €1400 Landscape with bridge (42x50cm-17x20in) s. 8-Oct-2 Ansorena, Madrid #329/R
£1931 $3070 €2800 Landscape (65x81cm-26x32in) s. 4-Mar-3 Ansorena, Madrid #149/R

SEILER, Carl Wilhelm Anton (1846-1921) German
£1053 $1705 €1600 Listen to this! (17x23cm-7x9in) panel. 21-Jan-3 Christie's, Amsterdam #120/R est:2000-3000
£2302 $3683 €3200 Interrupted worship (29x34cm-11x13in) s.d.1907. 17-May-3 Lempertz, Koln #1487/R est:3000
£4878 $8000 €7317 Game of chess (25x30cm-10x12in) s.indis.d. panel prov. 5-Feb-3 Christie's, Rockefeller NY #178/R est:6000-8000

SEILER, Hans (1907-1986) Swiss
£324 $522 €486 Still life with anenomes in water glass (26x33cm-10x13in) s. d.1934 verso board. 7-May-3 Dobiaschofsky, Bern #975/R (S.FR 700)
£509 $820 €764 Portrait of seated woman (44x32cm-17x13in) i. stretcher. 7-May-3 Dobiaschofsky, Bern #976/R (S.FR 1100)
Works on paper
£306 $480 €459 Untitled (52x58cm-20x23in) s.d.57 gouache. 23-Nov-2 Burkhard, Luzern #200/R (S.FR 700)

SEITER, Daniel (1649-1705) Italian
Works on paper
£2000 $3340 €2900 Judgement of Paris (33x27cm-13x11in) i. pen ink grey wash htd white. 8-Jul-3 Christie's, London #99/R est:3000-5000

SEITER, Daniel (attrib) (1649-1705) Italian
Works on paper
£380 $600 €600 Diana and Endymion (12x12cm-5x5in) pen htd white. 29-Nov-2 Bassenge, Berlin #5506/R

SEITZ, Anton (1829-1900) German
£779 $1161 €1200 Ghost visiting family with lots of children (22x31cm-9x12in) s. panel. 26-Jun-2 Neumeister, Munich #859/R
£1878 $3080 €2723 Tasting the milk (76x58cm-30x23in) s. 4-Jun-3 Fischer, Luzern #1143/R est:4000-4500 (S.FR 4000)

SEITZ, G R (?) ?
£932 $1500 €1398 Sistine Madonna (28x23cm-11x9in) s.i.verso porcelain after Raphael. 19-Jan-3 Jeffery Burchard, Florida #10/R

SEITZ, Gustav (1906-1969) German
Sculpture
£1111 $1756 €1600 Parisian negro woman (29cm-11in) s. dark brown pat.bronze. 26-Apr-3 Dr Lehr, Berlin #466/R est:2000
£1266 $2000 €2000 Small bust of female - Amme (16cm-6in) s. dark brown pat.bronze. 29-Nov-2 Villa Grisebach, Berlin #894/R est:2500-3000
£1392 $2172 €2200 Female torso (20x8x10cm-8x3x4in) s. verso dark brown pat.bronze. 18-Oct-2 Dr Fritz Nagel, Stuttgart #613/R est:1950
£3472 $5486 €5000 Seated nude (16cm-6in) bronze. 26-Apr-3 Dr Lehr, Berlin #465/R est:3000

SEITZ, Johann (?-c.1812) Austrian
£5986 $9937 €8500 Forest floor with thistle, strawberries, birds, butterflies, lizard (45x38cm-18x15in) s.d.1812 prov. 11-Jun-3 Dorotheum, Vienna #149/R est:7000-12000

SEIWERT, Franz Wilhelm (1894-1933) German
£2564 $3974 €4000 Vegetation (24x18cm-9x7in) transparent paper on board. 4-Dec-2 Lempertz, Koln #1065/R est:4500

Works on paper
£962 $1490 €1500 Small landscape (20x25cm-8x10in) mono. W/C over pencil. 4-Dec-2 Lempertz, Koln #1066/R

SEKAER, Peter (1901-1950) American/Danish
Photographs
£2597 $4000 €3896 House with shuttered windows, New Orleans (12x9cm-5x4in) bears another sig.i.verso gelatin silver print exec.c.1939 prov. 25-Oct-2 Phillips, New York #25/R est:4000-6000

SEKOTO, Gerard (1913-1993) South African
£3095 $4984 €4643 White turban (34x26cm-13x10in) s. i.verso board. 12-May-3 Stephan Welz, Johannesburg #531/R est:18000-24000 (SA.R 36000)

Works on paper
£553 $862 €830 Mother with children. Two figures walking (14x9cm-6x4in) s. one d.1972 one d.1973 gouache W/C pair. 15-Oct-2 Stephan Welz, Johannesburg #474 est:3000-4000 (SA.R 9000)
£799 $1246 €1199 Group of figures in the street (31x48cm-12x19in) indis.sig.d.58 gouache. 15-Oct-2 Stephan Welz, Johannesburg #475/R est:14000-18000 (SA.R 13000)
£860 $1342 €1290 Portrait of a woman (48x30cm-19x12in) s.d.60 gouache. 15-Oct-2 Stephan Welz, Johannesburg #476/R est:15000-18000 (SA.R 14000)
£1537 $2398 €2306 Woman with fruit (48x31cm-19x12in) s. gouache lit. 11-Nov-2 Stephan Welz, Johannesburg #586/R est:8000-12000 (SA.R 24000)
£1591 $2561 €2387 Head of a woman wearing a hat (53x34cm-21x13in) s.d.79 gouache. 12-May-3 Stephan Welz, Johannesburg #535 est:8000-12000 (SA.R 18500)
£2412 $3810 €3618 Mother and child (48x31cm-19x12in) s.d.63 gouache. 1-Apr-3 Stephan Welz, Johannesburg #477/R est:12000-18000 (SA.R 30000)

SEKRET, Valery (1950-) Russian
£250 $388 €375 Marine regatta (40x30cm-16x12in) s. canvasboard. 8-Dec-2 John Nicholson, Haslemere #154/R
£275 $426 €413 Beginning of San Michael Boulevard in Paris (38x55cm-15x22in) s. 29-Sep-2 John Nicholson, Haslemere #37
£300 $465 €450 River bank in Trouville (46x38cm-18x15in) s. 8-Dec-2 John Nicholson, Haslemere #159/R
£325 $504 €488 New Bridge, Paris, first light (55x38cm-22x15in) s. 8-Dec-2 John Nicholson, Haslemere #160/R
£450 $698 €675 On the Offing, Normandy (46x65cm-18x26in) s. 8-Dec-2 John Nicholson, Haslemere #31/R
£484 $765 €750 In Normandy (38x61cm-15x24in) s. 17-Dec-2 Durán, Madrid #669/R

SEKULA, Sonja (1918-1963) American/Swiss
£5240 $8227 €7860 New York, Statue de la Liberte (96x66cm-38x26in) s.d.1948 prov. 25-Nov-2 Sotheby's, Zurich #148/R est:8000-12000 (S.FR 12000)

Works on paper
£350 $553 €525 Roots of Rocks, XII (51x66cm-20x26in) s.d.1948 ink W/C. 1-Dec-2 Lots Road, London #341
£415 $606 €623 Transformation (21x12cm-8x5in) s.i.d.1948 gouache over Indian ink pencil. 4-Jun-2 Germann, Zurich #846 (S.FR 950)
£699 $1097 €1049 Untitled (28x25cm-11x10in) s.d.56 mixed media. 23-Nov-2 Burkhard, Luzern #124/R (S.FR 1600)

SELBY, Joe (1893-1960) American
£526 $800 €789 Yacht, Julina, of Boston (25x48cm-10x19in) s.d.1916 paper lit. 17-Aug-2 North East Auctions, Portsmouth #128
£1250 $1900 €1875 Tugboat, John F Lewis of Philadelphia (38x56cm-15x22in) s.d.1922 board lit. 17-Aug-2 North East Auctions, Portsmouth #569/R

Works on paper
£475 $750 €713 Magnet (18x25cm-7x10in) s.i. d.1926 verso gouache paper on board. 17-Nov-2 Jeffery Burchard, Florida #67/R

SELDEN, Henry Bill (1886-1934) American
£250 $400 €375 Harvesting Connecticut wheat (28x38cm-11x15in) s. board. 15-Mar-3 Jeffery Burchard, Florida #28/R

SELDEN, Roger (1945-) American
£2260 $3526 €3300 A thousand hearts (100x80cm-39x31in) s.i.d.1978 verso acrylic. 10-Apr-3 Finarte Semenzato, Rome #308/R

SELF, Colin (1941-) British
Works on paper
£1130 $1752 €1695 Woman rockets lolly (17x43cm-7x17in) s.d.64 col pen pencil prov. 4-Dec-2 Koller, Zurich #199/R est:1200-1800 (S.FR 2600)

SELFRIDGE, Reynolds (1898-?) American
£1032 $1600 €1548 Red barn (51x76cm-20x30in) s. board painted c.1930. 8-Dec-2 Toomey, Oak Park #736/R est:1500-2500

SELIGMAN, Adalbert Franz (1862-1945) Austrian
£2658 $4147 €4200 Nature morte aux raisins (100x76cm-39x30in) s. 10-Sep-2 Vanderkindere, Brussels #359/R est:4000-6000

SELINGER, Jean Paul (1850-1909) American
£319 $500 €479 Head of a Dutch girl (35x25cm-14x10in) s. i.verso. 22-Nov-2 Skinner, Boston #56/R

SELKAINAHO, Reino (1914-1979) Finnish
£261 $429 €400 View from Hango (29x44cm-11x17in) s.d.1958. 9-Feb-3 Bukowskis, Helsinki #357/R

SELL, Christian (elder) (1831-1883) German
£330 $551 €479 Scene from Franco-Prussian war, horseman escorting French prisoners on winter road (18x23cm-7x9in) s. panel. 17-Jun-3 Anderson & Garland, Newcastle #423/R
£352 $585 €500 Ambush on forest path in winter (24x31cm-9x12in) s. 14-Jun-3 Arnold, Frankfurt #864/R
£775 $1247 €1100 Under attack (20x26cm-8x10in) s. panel lit. 9-May-3 Schloss Ahlden, Ahlden #1366/R
£1203 $1900 €1900 Battle, 1870 (31x41cm-12x16in) s. lit. 29-Nov-2 Schloss Ahlden, Ahlden #1270/R est:1900

SELL, Christian (younger) (1854-1925) German
£443 $691 €700 Scene from Franco-German War (26x34cm-10x13in) bears sig. i.d.1870/71 verso board lit. 14-Sep-2 Bergmann, Erlangen #735/R
£577 $894 €900 Prussian soldier on horseback with two French soldiers on foot (11x15cm-4x6in) s. panel lit. 6-Dec-2 Karlheinz Kaupp, Staufen #2332/R
£886 $1400 €1400 Prussian infantry men fighting at night (12x16cm-5x6in) s. panel. 29-Nov-2 Schloss Ahlden, Ahlden #1274/R
£886 $1400 €1400 Prussian infantry men guarding French prisoners (17x22cm-7x9in) s, oabek. 29-Nov-2 Schloss Ahlden, Ahlden #1273/R

SELLAER, Vincent (16th C) Flemish
£11321 $17547 €18000 Virgin and child (78x80cm-31x31in) panel lit. 2-Oct-2 Dorotheum, Vienna #113/R est:17000-24000

SELLAR, Charles A (1856-1926) British
£4294 $7000 €6441 Young navigators (51x76cm-20x30in) s. 16-Feb-3 Butterfields, San Francisco #2046 est:1500-2500

SELLENATI, J (?) Italian
£3618 $5862 €5500 Bustling market scene (32x46cm-13x18in) s. panel. 21-Jan-3 Christie's, Amsterdam #46/R est:2000-3000

SELLENY, Josef (1824-1875) Austrian
Works on paper
£338 $527 €500 Italian woman feeding hens (38x24cm-15x9in) s.i. W/C sketch. 28-Mar-3 Dorotheum, Vienna #182/R
£377 $585 €600 Southern village (21x47cm-8x19in) mono.i.d.2.Juni pencil W/C. 1-Oct-2 Dorotheum, Vienna #202/R
£629 $975 €1000 Piazza San Bocco in Olevano (37x27cm-15x11in) pencil htd white board. 1-Oct-2 Dorotheum, Vienna #133/R

SELLIN, Herbert Otto (1943-) Canadian
£482 $757 €723 Drifted corrals, sunny afternoon (60x90cm-24x35in) s.i.d.1980 board. 25-Nov-2 Hodgins, Calgary #281/R (C.D 1200)

SELLITTO, Carlo (1581-1614) Italian
£2532 $4000 €4000 Saint Bernard's vision (101x76cm-40x30in) 2-Dec-2 Finarte, Milan #147
£19310 $30510 €28000 Portrait of lady as Saint Cecily (103x92cm-41x36in) prov.exhib.lit. 5-Apr-3 Finarte Semenzato, Milan #87/R est:20000

SELMERSHEIM-DESGRANGE, Jeanne (1877-1958) French
Works on paper
£556 $884 €800 Paysage de Provence (25x40cm-10x16in) W/C pencil prov. 29-Apr-3 Artcurial Briest, Paris #34

SELMY, Eugène (1874-?) French
£962 $1510 €1500 Dutch woman in traditional costume knitting (61x50cm-24x20in) s.d.06. 21-Nov-2 Van Ham, Cologne #1921/R est:1800

SELMYHR, Conrad (1877-1944) Norwegian
£433 $662 €650 Mill house and waterfall in winter (79x64cm-31x25in) s. painted 1916. 26-Aug-2 Blomqvist, Lysaker #1350 (N.KR 5000)
£550 $913 €550 Pecheur dans un fjord (53x79cm-21x31in) s. 16-Jun-3 Horta, Bruxelles #444
£594 $915 €891 Fjord in Northern Norway (65x100cm-26x39in) s. painted 1907. 28-Oct-2 Blomqvist, Lysaker #1285/R (N.KR 7000)

SELOUS, Henry Courtney (1811-1890) British
£1913 $2984 €2870 Venice - canal with boats and figures (60x91cm-24x36in) s.d.1885. 16-Sep-2 Philippe Schuler, Zurich #3495/R est:5000-7000 (S.FR 4400)
£4200 $6846 €6300 Banquet (102x142cm-40x56in) s.d.1870. 29-Jan-3 Sotheby's, Olympia #213/R est:3000-5000

SELSKY, Roman (1903-1987) Russian
£407 $680 €590 Crimean landscape (65x92cm-26x36in) i.cyrillic verso. 24-Jun-3 Koller, Zurich #105/R (S.FR 900)

SELTZER, Olaf C (1877-1957) American
£14241 $22500 €20649 C.M Russell on Monte (15x10cm-6x4in) s. board. 26-Jul-3 Coeur d'Alene, Hayden #174/R est:8000-12000
£20570 $32500 €29827 Deer in a mountain landscape (61x61cm-24x24in) s. prov.exhib.lit. 26-Jul-3 Coeur d'Alene, Hayden #72/R est:25000-50000
£23734 $37500 €34414 Heeling a bolter (41x61cm-16x24in) s. board prov. 26-Jul-3 Coeur d'Alene, Hayden #102/R est:40000-60000
£28481 $45000 €41297 Stolen horse (25x25cm-10x10in) s. board. 26-Jul-3 Coeur d'Alene, Hayden #66/R est:20000-30000

Works on paper
£3145 $5000 €4718 Wolf pack at night (18x23cm-7x9in) mono. W/C pen ink. 5-Mar-3 Sotheby's, New York #130/R est:2000-3000
£4747 $7500 €6883 Peace pipe (48x33cm-19x13in) init. mixed media prov. 26-Jul-3 Coeur d'Alene, Hayden #177/R est:15000-25000
£5988 $10000 €8683 Indian chief on a horse (20x17cm-8x7in) s. W/C gouache paper on board prov. 18-Jun-3 Christie's, Los Angeles #29/R est:10000-15000
£10759 $17000 €15601 Scouts on the move (30x23cm-12x9in) s. W/C. 26-Jul-3 Coeur d'Alene, Hayden #199/R est:10000-20000
£11377 $19000 €16497 Indian war party (27x38cm-11x15in) s. W/C gouache on board prov. 18-Jun-3 Christie's, Los Angeles #86/R est:20000-30000
£15823 $25000 €22943 Scouting party (23x30cm-9x12in) s. W/C prov. 26-Jul-3 Coeur d'Alene, Hayden #117/R est:20000-30000
£22152 $35000 €32120 Overlooking the Missouri (23x30cm-9x12in) s. W/C. 26-Jul-3 Coeur d'Alene, Hayden #116/R est:20000-30000

SELTZER, William Steve (1955-) American
£3006 $4750 €4359 Ice on the Yellowstone (76x102cm-30x40in) s. 26-Jul-3 Coeur d'Alene, Hayden #226/R est:6000-9000

SELVATICO, Luigi (1873-1938) Italian
£6452 $10194 €10000 Hospice courtyard (155x188cm-61x74in) s.d.1901 prov.exhib.lit. 18-Dec-2 Finarte, Milan #119/R est:15000-20000

SELWYN, William (1933-) British
Works on paper
£300 $492 €450 Dick Evans (33x27cm-13x11in) s. pencil and wash. 4-Jun-3 Bonhams, Chester #305

SEM (1863-1934) French
Works on paper
£705 $1079 €1100 Hippodrome (53x71cm-21x28in) s. gouache. 23-Aug-2 Deauville, France #153/R

SEMEGHINI, Pio (1878-1964) Italian
£1961 $3137 €3000 Figure (28x19cm-11x7in) s. board. 4-Jan-3 Meeting Art, Vercelli #87
£4487 $7045 €7000 Figure (47x35cm-19x14in) s.d.1930 board. 23-Nov-2 Meeting Art, Vercelli #229/R
£4557 $7200 €7200 White hat (50x38cm-20x15in) s.d.1947 board. 30-Nov-2 Farsetti, Prato #635/R est:8000
£9032 $14271 €14000 Still life with pumpkins (39x55cm-15x22in) s.d.1921 s.i.d.verso board exhib. 18-Dec-2 Christie's, Rome #272/R

SEMENOWSKY, Eisman (19th C) French
£800 $1296 €1200 Young novice with spring flowers (28x23cm-11x9in) s.i. panel. 23-Jan-3 Christie's, Kensington #106/R
£1633 $2596 €2400 Sip of coffee (40x28cm-16x11in) indis.s.i. panel. 25-Feb-3 Dorotheum, Vienna #150/R est:3000-3500
£2000 $3180 €3000 Seated young lady in a shawl (46x18cm-18x7in) s. panel. 20-Mar-3 Christie's, Kensington #192/R est:2000-3000
£2740 $4274 €4000 Girl with bird (67x48cm-26x19in) s.i. panel. 10-Apr-3 Dorotheum, Vienna #108/R est:4000-4500
£3000 $5010 €4500 Eastern beauty (86x27cm-34x11in) s. panel. 18-Jun-3 Christie's, Kensington #199/R est:2000-3000
£4000 $6360 €6000 New necklace (86x28cm-34x11in) s. panel. 20-Mar-3 Christie's, Kensington #191/R est:4000-6000
£6962 $11000 €10443 Classical beauty (86x32cm-34x13in) s. panel. 24-Apr-3 Sotheby's, New York #128/R est:10000-15000
£7097 $11000 €10646 Roman beauty in the baths (87x32cm-34x13in) s. panel. 30-Oct-2 Christie's, Rockefeller NY #193/R est:10000-15000

SEMERTZIDES, Valias (1911-1983) Greek
£3000 $4740 €4500 View of Milos Island (91x122cm-36x48in) 1-Apr-3 Bonhams, New Bond Street #83 est:3000-5000

SEMIAN, Ervin (1921-1965) ?
£473 $690 €710 Meeting a girl (36x25cm-14x10in) painted c.1943. 4-Jun-2 SOGA, Bratislava #98/R est:18000 (SL.K 30000)
£725 $1058 €1088 Self portrait with glass (45x36cm-18x14in) painted c.1944. 4-Jun-2 SOGA, Bratislava #97/R est:22000 (SL.K 46000)

SEMMES, Beverly (1952-) American
Photographs
£2530 $4200 €3669 Starcraft (121x182cm-48x72in) s.d.1998 verso c-print edition of 5 prov. 11-Jun-3 Phillips, New York #541/R est:2000-3000

SEMMONS, Jennifer (20th C) British
Works on paper
£250 $390 €375 Gatehouse I (76x56cm-30x22in) s.d.1988 i.verso mixed media. 16-Oct-2 David Lay, Penzance #222/R

SEMPE (20th C) French
Works on paper
£1319 $2177 €1900 Projet pour le carton d'invitation au defile homme printemps-ete (71x93cm-28x37in) s.i.d.1982 W/C col crayons. 3-Jul-3 Christie's, Paris #33/R est:600-800

SEMPERE ESTEVE, Rafael (1928-) Spanish
Works on paper
£314 $484 €500 Porcelaines (36x54cm-14x21in) s.d.1989 W/C. 22-Oct-2 Durán, Madrid #18/R

SEMPILL, Joseph (19th C) British
£7317 $12000 €10610 Portrait of the Bark, George Kingman of Boston (51x76cm-20x30in) s.d.1874. 8-Jun-3 Skinner, Boston #124/R est:1000-1500

SEN GUPTA, Niren (1940-) Indian
£1000 $1560 €1500 Celebration (51x152cm-20x60in) s.d.1999. 17-Oct-2 Bonhams, Knightsbridge #631/R est:1000-1500

SENATARI, Tom (19th C) ?
£380 $627 €551 Saint and Christ Child (43x33cm-17x13in) s.d.1899. 3-Jul-3 Duke & Son, Dorchester #236

SENAVE, Jacques Albert (1758-1829) Belgian
£782 $1221 €1173 Small family (24x32cm-9x13in) s. panel. 11-Apr-3 Kieselbach, Budapest #44/R est:250000-280000 (H.F 280000)

SENBERGS, Jan (1939-) Australian
£600 $966 €870 Working man (55x85cm-22x33in) s. board painted c.1965. 12-May-3 Joel, Victoria #249 est:1500-2500 (A.D 1500)

Prints
£1720 $2615 €2580 Drive into New Jersey (96x127cm-38x50in) s.d. monotype. 28-Aug-2 Deutscher-Menzies, Melbourne #334/R est:2500-3500 (A.D 4800)

Works on paper
£2857 $4514 €4286 Voyage I 1987 (121x137cm-48x54in) synthetic polymer on linen prov.exhib. 27-Nov-2 Deutscher-Menzies, Melbourne #25/R est:9000-12000 (A.D 8000)

SENE, Louis (1747-c.1804) Swiss
Miniatures
£3000 $5010 €4350 Lady resting against a mossy bank (6cm-2in circular) gold frame exec.c.1790. 25-Jun-3 Sotheby's, Olympia #23/R est:3000-4000

SENECHAL DE KERDREORET, Gustave Edouard le (1840-1920) French
£2564 $4026 €4000 Journee a la plage (32x41cm-13x16in) s.d.1879 panel. 13-Dec-2 Piasa, Paris #170/R

SENEMONT, François (1720-1782) French
Works on paper
£1418 $2369 €2000 Portrait d Mmme de Ladoucette (54x43cm-21x17in) i.d.1776 pastel. 23-Jun-3 Beaussant & Lefèvre, Paris #293/R est:900-1100

SENEQUE, Clement (1896-1930) South African
£804 $1270 €1206 Dunes Durban (39x33cm-15x13in) s. i.verso canvas on board. 1-Apr-3 Stephan Welz, Johannesburg #450/R est:7000-10000 (SA.R 10000)
£1367 $2159 €2051 Formal gardens (45x54cm-18x21in) s.d.23. 1-Apr-3 Stephan Welz, Johannesburg #451/R est:10000-15000 (SA.R 17000)

SENET, Rafael (1856-1926) Spanish
£2303 $3730 €3500 Beach (34x60cm-13x24in) s. 21-Jan-3 Durán, Madrid #686/R
£3045 $4811 €4750 Grand Canal, Venice (31x51cm-12x20in) s. 19-Nov-2 Durán, Madrid #231/R
£3147 $5255 €4500 Vue de Venise (28x39cm-11x15in) s.i. 27-Jun-3 Claude Aguttes, Neuilly #60/R est:6000-8000
£8108 $12649 €12000 Grand Canal (46x61cm-18x24in) s. 25-Mar-3 Durán, Madrid #199/R est:12000
Works on paper
£1069 $1647 €1700 Gra Canal, Venice (31x50cm-12x20in) s. W/C. 22-Oct-2 Durán, Madrid #241/R

SENEZCOURT, V de (19th C) French
£1290 $2039 €2000 Elegante a la rose (25x19cm-10x7in) s. panel. 17-Dec-2 Palais de Beaux Arts, Brussels #486/R est:2000-2800

SENFF, Adolf (1785-1863) German
£1069 $1668 €1700 Child's portrait (63x51cm-25x20in) oval lit. 20-Sep-2 Schloss Ahlden, Ahlden #1148/R est:1800
£8800 $14344 €12760 Flower studies (27x40cm-11x16in) s.i.d.1837 oil paper on cardboard. 16-Jul-3 Sotheby's, Olympia #145/R est:1000-1500
£9500 $15485 €13775 Flower studies (27x40cm-11x16in) s.d.1837 oil paper on cardboard. 16-Jul-3 Sotheby's, Olympia #146/R est:1000-1500

SENGER, Ludwig von (1873-?) German
£962 $1490 €1500 Peasant woman on her way home (80x100cm-31x39in) s. lit. 7-Dec-2 Kastern, Hannover #65/R est:1200

SENGL, Peter (1945-) Austrian
£2278 $3600 €3600 Flecksprung (180x149cm-71x59in) s.i.d.1986 prov. 27-Nov-2 Dorotheum, Vienna #316/R est:3600-5500
Works on paper
£369 $594 €550 Young flamingo (63x51cm-25x20in) s.mono.i.d.86 mixed media. 18-Feb-3 Dorotheum, Vienna #186

SENIOR, Bryan (1935-) British
£320 $496 €480 Reflected corner 1966 (51x51cm-20x20in) s.d.65 prov. 25-Sep-2 Hamptons Fine Art, Godalming #431/R

SENIOR, Mark (1864-1927) British
£3000 $4710 €4500 Ludlow (18x24cm-7x9in) s. i.d.1916 verso panel. 19-Nov-2 Bonhams, Leeds #117/R est:1200-1800
£3400 $5338 €5100 Rough sea (23x28cm-9x11in) s.i.d.1924 panel. 19-Nov-2 Bonhams, Leeds #119 est:1400-1800
£3800 $5852 €5700 Runswick Bay (18x23cm-7x9in) i.verso panel exhib. 5-Sep-2 Christie's, Kensington #231/R est:1000-1500
£5000 $8300 €7500 Ludlow at night (58x49cm-23x19in) s.i. 10-Jun-3 Bonhams, Leeds #207/R est:2000-3000
£5200 $8632 €7800 View of Runswick Bay (19x25cm-7x10in) s. board. 10-Jun-3 Bonhams, Leeds #208/R est:2500-3500
£6800 $10608 €10200 Rural landscape with the sea beyond. Study of the rear of a house (21x26cm-8x10in) s. i.verso panel two. 25-Mar-3 Bonhams, Leeds #614/R est:1500-2000
£41000 $64370 €61500 Nymphs dancing (122x137cm-48x54in) s.d.1912. 19-Nov-2 Bonhams, Leeds #118/R est:15000-20000
Works on paper
£280 $442 €420 Breaking waves (46x28cm-18x11in) s.d.74 mixed media. 24-Apr-3 Richardson & Smith, Whitby #42
£1150 $1806 €1725 Wheelsmith's fire (25x34cm-10x13in) s. i.verso pastel. 19-Nov-2 Bonhams, Leeds #120 est:700-800

SENN, Johannes (1780-1861) Swiss
Works on paper
£372 $592 €558 A life-guard officer (29x19cm-11x7in) s. W/C pen pencil. 5-Mar-3 Rasmussen, Copenhagen #2156/R (D.KR 4000)

SEOANE, Luis (1910-1979) Argentinian
Works on paper
£484 $765 €750 Wall (17x25cm-7x10in) s. ink dr lit. 18-Dec-2 Ansorena, Madrid #956/R
£535 $834 €850 Preparing the fire (36x25cm-14x10in) s.d.45 W/C. 8-Oct-2 Ansorena, Madrid #543/R
£613 $968 €950 Portrait oF Wiliam Shaand (43x26cm-17x10in) s. ink dr. 18-Dec-2 Ansorena, Madrid #972/R
£642 $1001 €950 Starting the fire (34x23cm-13x9in) s. W/C lit. 25-Mar-3 Durán, Madrid #694/R

SEPESHY, Zoltan L (1898-1974) American
£932 $1500 €1398 Northern Michigan landscape (51x61cm-20x24in) s. 15-Jan-3 Boos Gallery, Michigan #466/R est:2000-3000
Works on paper
£602 $1000 €873 Westward (43x64cm-17x25in) gouache. 13-Jun-3 Du Mouchelle, Detroit #2216/R

SERADOUR, Guy (1922-) French
£580 $905 €870 Portrait of a young girl holding a little dog (46x27cm-18x11in) s. 17-Sep-2 Rosebery Fine Art, London #698/R
£719 $1151 €1000 Portrait de jeune garcon, Vincent (27x16cm-11x6in) s. 18-May-3 Charbonneaux, Paris #205/R
£1603 $2516 €2500 Portrait de Delphine (27x22cm-11x9in) s. i.verso. 15-Dec-2 Eric Pillon, Calais #229/R
Works on paper
£962 $1490 €1500 Jeune clown (49x22cm-19x9in) s. pastel. 5-Dec-2 Gros & Delettrez, Paris #44

SERAFINO DA BRESCIA (attrib) (fl.c.1530) Italian
Works on paper
£372 $580 €550 Scene from Roman history (16x32cm-6x13in) i. wash over sanguine. 27-Mar-3 Maigret, Paris #58

SERAILIAN, Mihran Kevork (1867-1957) American
£387 $600 €581 Mt Herman (51x76cm-20x30in) s. painted c.1925. 8-Dec-2 Toomey, Oak Park #642/R

SERDOBBEL, Georges Octave (1834-1907) Belgian
£2484 $3999 €3800 Promeneur et son fils dans un paysage avec riviere (130x180cm-51x71in) s.d.1895. 20-Jan-3 Horta, Bruxelles #197 est:5000-7500

SEREBRIAKOV, Alexander (1907-1994) Russian
Works on paper
£1538 $2569 €2200 Projet de temple au bord du lac du Chateau de Groussay (44x61cm-17x24in) W/C. 25-Jun-3 Artcurial Briest, Paris #545/R est:2000-3000
£1538 $2569 €2200 Projet de tente pour le mirador du parc du Chateau Groussay (39x63cm-15x25in) d.21 juillet 1967 black ink W/C gouache graphite. 25-Jun-3 Artcurial Briest, Paris #546/R est:2000-3000
£1538 $2569 €2200 Projet d'obelisque de face et de profil (50x39cm-20x15in) wax crayon graphite. 25-Jun-3 Artcurial Briest, Paris #547 est:2000-3000
£1958 $3270 €2800 Projet de mirador du part cu Chateau de Groussay (46x30cm-18x12in) W/C brown ink graphite. 25-Jun-3 Artcurial Briest, Paris #549 est:2000-3000
£2448 $4087 €3500 Plan de la tente du mirador du parc du Chateau de Groussay (43x63cm-17x25in) brown ink graphite sold with a dr. 25-Jun-3 Artcurial Briest, Paris #553 est:2000-3000
£2797 $4671 €4000 Projet pour un obelisque pour le Chateau de Groussay (61x43cm-24x17in) crayon W/C gouache graphite. 25-Jun-3 Artcurial Briest, Paris #550/R est:2000-3000
£2797 $4671 €4000 Projet pour un pavillon dans le parc du Chateau de Groussay (33x49cm-13x19in) W/C graphite. 25-Jun-3 Artcurial Briest, Paris #551 est:2000-3000
£2797 $4671 €4000 Avant projet de bateau a Rames (43x63cm-17x25in) mono.d.1 september 1967 red ink W/C gouache graphite. 25-Jun-3 Artcurial Briest, Paris #554/R est:2000-3000
£2867 $4788 €4100 Avant projet de la facade sur le grand lac du parc du Chateau de Groussay (29x43cm-11x17in) brown ink W/C gouache graphite. 25-Jun-3 Artcurial Briest, Paris #552 est:2000-3000

£2937 $4905 €4200 Chateau de Groussay (30x47cm-12x19in) mono.d.1 septembre 1967 black ink W/C gouache graphite. 25-Jun-3 Artcurial Briest, Paris #544/R est:2000-3000
£3205 $5032 €5000 Interior in Paris (61x46cm-24x18in) s.d.1946 W/C. 13-Dec-2 Pierre Berge, Paris #55/R
£3217 $5372 €4600 Projet pour le Chateau de Groussay, facade laterale (30x43cm-12x17in) mono.i.d.1 septembre 1967 brown ink W/C gouache graphite. 25-Jun-3 Artcurial Briest, Paris #555/R est:2000-3000
£8500 $13770 €12750 Grand drawing room interior (62x47cm-24x19in) s. W/C. 21-May-3 Sotheby's, London #53/R est:3500-4500

SEREBRIAKOV, Alexievitch Vasili (1810-1886) Russian
£10638 $16489 €15957 Italian girl with grapes (65x55cm-26x22in) s.d.1853. 4-Dec-2 AB Stockholms Auktionsverk #1843/R est:50000-60000 (S.KR 150000)

SEREBRIAKOVA, Zinaida (1884-1967) Russian
£130000 $204100 €195000 Still life of grapes in basket (54x65cm-21x26in) s.d.1928. 20-Nov-2 Sotheby's, London #106/R est:40000-60000
Works on paper
£15000 $23550 €22500 The orchard in blossom (40x56cm-16x22in) s.d.1908 gouache over pencil. 20-Nov-2 Sotheby's, London #80/R est:15000-20000
£18000 $28260 €27000 Working the soil in the apple orchard (33x54cm-13x21in) s.d.1908 gouache over pencil lit. 20-Nov-2 Sotheby's, London #79/R est:18000-22000
£18000 $28260 €27000 Ploughing, Neskuchnoye (42x56cm-17x22in) gouache lit. 20-Nov-2 Sotheby's, London #81/R est:18000-22000
£35000 $54950 €52500 View over the rooftops, France (48x63cm-19x25in) s.d.1926 gouache over pencil. 20-Nov-2 Sotheby's, London #75/R est:12000-18000
£175000 $274750 €262500 Reclining nude (51x65cm-20x26in) s.i.d.1935 pastel. 20-Nov-2 Sotheby's, London #119/R est:50000-70000

SERGEL, Johan Tobias (1740-1814) Swedish
Sculpture
£3901 $6046 €5852 Gustav III - portrait bust (54cm-21in) painted plaster lit. 4-Dec-2 AB Stockholms Auktionsverk #1830/R est:30000-40000 (S.KR 55000)
£272436 $422276 €425000 Centaure enlacant une bacchante (30x35x16cm-12x14x6in) terracotta exec.c.1770 lit. 9-Dec-2 Rabourdin & Choppin de Janvry, Paris #33/R est:60000
Works on paper
£1396 $2262 €2024 Studies of the Antique (23x35cm-9x14in) red chk exec.c.1772 exhib.lit. 26-May-3 Bukowskis, Stockholm #488/R est:10000-12000 (S.KR 18000)
£1396 $2262 €2024 Danae and the gold rain (18x22cm-7x9in) Indian ink. 26-May-3 Bukowskis, Stockholm #489/R est:12000-15000 (S.KR 18000)

SERGEL, Johan Tobias (attrib) (1740-1814) Swedish
Works on paper
£4648 $7715 €6600 Menelaso with the corpse of Patroklos (17x19cm-7x7in) pen wash. 12-Jun-3 Hauswedell & Nolte, Hamburg #318/R est:1500

SERGENT, René (20th C) Belgian
£450 $693 €675 Figures on the bank of the Seine towards the Trocadero (32x41cm-13x16in) s.d.1930 i.verso panel. 24-Oct-2 Christie's, Kensington #163

SERISAWA, Sueo (1910-) Japanese
£1018 $1700 €1476 Calla lillies and apples (61x51cm-24x20in) s. prov. 17-Jun-3 John Moran, Pasadena #160 est:1000-2000

SERMEI, Cesare (17th C) Italian
Works on paper
£2200 $3674 €3190 Saint Francis dying blessing Assisi (20x27cm-8x11in) i. pencil pen ink double-sided corner made up. 8-Jul-3 Christie's, London #41/R est:1500-2000

SERNA, Ismael de la (1897-1968) Spanish
£385 $608 €600 Portrait de Francoise Mirabeau de Saint-Hernin (24x19cm-9x7in) 13-Nov-2 Mathias Roux, Paris #49
£481 $760 €750 Vase de fleurs (115x80cm-45x31in) paper. 13-Nov-2 Mathias Roux, Paris #53/R
£513 $810 €800 Composition (58x39cm-23x15in) s.d.49 cardboard. 13-Nov-2 Mathias Roux, Paris #43
£513 $810 €800 Composition (74x52cm-29x20in) s. cardboard. 13-Nov-2 Mathias Roux, Paris #76/R
£577 $912 €900 Bateaux (30x46cm-12x18in) s.d.28 cardboard. 13-Nov-2 Mathias Roux, Paris #60
£609 $962 €950 Composition (54x38cm-21x15in) s.d.49. 13-Nov-2 Mathias Roux, Paris #78
£609 $962 €950 Homme au noeud de papillon (60x44cm-24x17in) st.sig. 13-Nov-2 Mathias Roux, Paris #165
£705 $1114 €1100 Composition (61x48cm-24x19in) s. cardboard. 13-Nov-2 Mathias Roux, Paris #77
£833 $1317 €1300 Croissant de lune (98x66cm-39x26in) s.d.50 cardboard lit. 13-Nov-2 Mathias Roux, Paris #70/R
£833 $1317 €1300 Composition metaphysique (36x25cm-14x10in) st.sig. graphite ink. 13-Nov-2 Mathias Roux, Paris #101
£962 $1519 €1500 Cygne (26x35cm-10x14in) s. cardboard. 13-Nov-2 Mathias Roux, Paris #48
£1026 $1621 €1600 Composition aux raisins (33x41cm-13x16in) masonite. 13-Nov-2 Mathias Roux, Paris #75
£1282 $2026 €2000 Composition a la lune (50x60cm-20x24in) s. masonite. 13-Nov-2 Mathias Roux, Paris #69/R
£1410 $2228 €2200 Carafe et verres (55x38cm-22x15in) s.d.23 s.i.d.verso. 13-Nov-2 Mathias Roux, Paris #54/R
£1474 $2329 €2300 Composition a la coupe de fruits (16x17cm-6x7in) s. panel. 13-Nov-2 Mathias Roux, Paris #45
£1603 $2532 €2500 Chevaux galopant (32x41cm-13x16in) 13-Nov-2 Mathias Roux, Paris #46
£1603 $2532 €2500 Nature morte aux fruits (12x30cm-5x12in) cardboard. 13-Nov-2 Mathias Roux, Paris #59
£1603 $2532 €2500 Nuit dans la ville (40x65cm-16x26in) s.d.56 masonite. 13-Nov-2 Mathias Roux, Paris #79/R
£1923 $3038 €3000 Nature morte aux oignons (14x18cm-6x7in) s. 13-Nov-2 Mathias Roux, Paris #51/R
£1987 $3140 €3100 Madame de la Serna et son chien (90x72cm-35x28in) s. paper. 13-Nov-2 Mathias Roux, Paris #42
£2244 $3545 €3500 Autres (97x130cm-38x51in) s.d.33 lit. 13-Nov-2 Mathias Roux, Paris #52/R
£2500 $3975 €3750 Nature morte (15x17cm-6x7in) s. panel prov. 20-Mar-3 Sotheby's, Olympia #66/R est:3000-4000
£2828 $4468 €4100 Fish tank (50x64cm-20x25in) s.d.XXX paper on canvas. 1-Apr-3 Segre, Madrid #172/R
£2885 $4529 €4500 Open window (74x69cm-29x27in) st.sig. masonite painted c.1948. 22-Nov-2 Millon & Associes, Paris #135/R
£2885 $4558 €4500 Palmier (35x27cm-14x11in) s. s.verso cardboard on canvas. 13-Nov-2 Mathias Roux, Paris #44
£2885 $4558 €4500 Bateau fantome (81x58cm-32x23in) s.d.55 cardboard lit. 13-Nov-2 Mathias Roux, Paris #63/R
£2885 $4558 €4500 Composition cubiste au bol et a la pipe (31x39cm-12x15in) painted stucco. 13-Nov-2 Mathias Roux, Paris #73
£3000 $4650 €4500 Los Reyes Magos (56x84cm-22x33in) s.d.31 board. 5-Dec-2 Christie's, Kensington #134/R est:3000-5000
£3077 $4862 €4800 Nature morte devant la fenetre (58x86cm-23x34in) s. oil gouache. 13-Nov-2 Mathias Roux, Paris #80/R
£3077 $4862 €4800 Portrait de Madame de la Serna (66x48cm-26x19in) cardboard. 13-Nov-2 Mathias Roux, Paris #81/R
£3846 $6077 €6000 Composition (120x80cm-47x31in) 13-Nov-2 Mathias Roux, Paris #65/R
£3974 $6279 €6200 Composition au pichet (63x183cm-25x72in) 13-Nov-2 Mathias Roux, Paris #50/R est:3000
£4403 $6824 €7000 Chopin au piano (71x99cm-28x39in) s. panel. 30-Oct-2 Artcurial Briest, Paris #335/R est:3500-5000
£4808 $7452 €7500 Table musicale (49x62cm-19x24in) s. masonite painted 1932 prov.lit. 7-Dec-2 Martinot & Savignat, Pontoise #48/R
£4808 $7596 €7500 Bateau (124x91cm-49x36in) s.d.1950 cardboard. 13-Nov-2 Mathias Roux, Paris #64/R
£5068 $7905 €7500 Nature morte aux fruits (42x58cm-17x23in) s. cardboard. 28-Mar-3 Claude Aguttes, Neuilly #123/R
£5769 $9115 €9000 Composition (100x81cm-39x32in) s.d.1965. 13-Nov-2 Mathias Roux, Paris #66/R
£5789 $9379 €8800 Station (80x99cm-31x39in) s. cardboard on board. 21-Jan-3 Ansorena, Madrid #297/R est:8800
£6376 $10265 €9500 Chopin au piano (71x97cm-28x38in) s. oil collage cardboard. 18-Feb-3 Durán, Madrid #207/R
£8654 $13673 €13500 Fontaine (122x83cm-48x33in) s. masonite. 13-Nov-2 Mathias Roux, Paris #58
£10256 $16205 €16000 Composition (160x117cm-63x46in) s. lit. 13-Nov-2 Mathias Roux, Paris #67/R est:10600
£10577 $16712 €16500 Composition cubiste (72x50cm-28x20in) s.d.1950. 13-Nov-2 Mathias Roux, Paris #56/R est:3800
£10897 $17218 €17000 Nature morte devant la fenetre (175x240cm-69x94in) panel triptych lit. 13-Nov-2 Mathias Roux, Paris #61/R est:12200
£11000 $17490 €16500 Nature morte a l'ananas (75x59cm-30x23in) s. cardboard. 20-Mar-3 Sotheby's, Olympia #67/R est:8000-10000
£12179 $19244 €19000 Composition cubiste (23x18cm-9x7in) s. masonite. 13-Nov-2 Mathias Roux, Paris #55/R est:1200
£15714 $22943 €24200 Still life with figure (92x57cm-36x22in) s.verso board. 17-Jun-2 Ansorena, Madrid #76/R est:14200
£31410 $49628 €49000 Composition au gueridon (82x65cm-32x26in) s.d.XXXI oil gouache crayon masonite lit. 13-Nov-2 Mathias Roux, Paris #71/R est:9100
£32051 $50641 €50000 Composition a la viole (61x72cm-24x28in) s. s.verso painted 1935 lit. 13-Nov-2 Mathias Roux, Paris #57/R
£70513 $111410 €110000 Marche aux puces (200x396cm-79x156in) d.1947 panel windscreen in 4 parts lit. 13-Nov-2 Mathias Roux, Paris #68/R est:40000

Sculpture
£4808 $7596 €7500 Gueridon (75x75cm-30x30in) plaster stucco. 13-Nov-2 Mathias Roux, Paris #188/R est:900

Works on paper
£256 $405 €400 Composition (50x65cm-20x26in) gouache ink. 13-Nov-2 Mathias Roux, Paris #12
£256 $405 €400 Portrait (25x21cm-10x8in) gouache cardboard. 13-Nov-2 Mathias Roux, Paris #21
£256 $405 €400 Cimetiere au clair de lune (50x64cm-20x25in) s. W/C gouache. 13-Nov-2 Mathias Roux, Paris #83
£256 $405 €400 Buste de femme (53x48cm-21x19in) s. gouache cardboard. 13-Nov-2 Mathias Roux, Paris #90
£256 $405 €400 Portrait (40x18cm-16x7in) gouache on foam. 13-Nov-2 Mathias Roux, Paris #93
£256 $405 €400 Ecclesiastique (32x25cm-13x10in) st.sig. graphite. 13-Nov-2 Mathias Roux, Paris #124
£256 $405 €400 Composition (32x32cm-13x13in) ink gouache collage. 13-Nov-2 Mathias Roux, Paris #172
£256 $405 €400 Composition (50x33cm-20x13in) st.sig. gouache. 13-Nov-2 Mathias Roux, Paris #167
£256 $405 €400 Composition (31x24cm-12x9in) st.sig. gouache card. 13-Nov-2 Mathias Roux, Paris #166
£256 $405 €400 Fontaine (51x61cm-20x24in) st.sig. gouache. 13-Nov-2 Mathias Roux, Paris #160
£288 $456 €450 Composition (33x24cm-13x9in) mixed media panel. 13-Nov-2 Mathias Roux, Paris #47
£288 $456 €450 Femme a la lecture (50x32cm-20x13in) st.sig. graphite. 13-Nov-2 Mathias Roux, Paris #106
£288 $456 €450 Moine (31x24cm-12x9in) st.sig. graphite. 13-Nov-2 Mathias Roux, Paris #123
£288 $456 €450 Visages (32x50cm-13x20in) st.sig. ink. 13-Nov-2 Mathias Roux, Paris #114
£288 $456 €450 Fontaine (61x48cm-24x19in) st.sig. gouache W/C. 13-Nov-2 Mathias Roux, Paris #137
£288 $456 €450 Taureau (14x24cm-6x9in) st.sig. ink. 13-Nov-2 Mathias Roux, Paris #175/R
£321 $506 €500 Composition (66x51cm-26x20in) st.sig. gouache ink. 13-Nov-2 Mathias Roux, Paris #13
£321 $506 €500 Scene religieuse (25x17cm-10x7in) gouache cardboard. 13-Nov-2 Mathias Roux, Paris #17
£321 $506 €500 Composition (19x61cm-7x24in) s. gouache masonite. 13-Nov-2 Mathias Roux, Paris #20
£321 $506 €500 Taureau (28x37cm-11x15in) s. ink. 13-Nov-2 Mathias Roux, Paris #148
£321 $506 €500 Chandelier (66x51cm-26x20in) st.sig. gouache. 13-Nov-2 Mathias Roux, Paris #136
£321 $506 €500 Composition (36x24cm-14x9in) s. graphite. 13-Nov-2 Mathias Roux, Paris #169
£321 $506 €500 Derniere onction (50x65cm-20x26in) st.sig. graphite. 13-Nov-2 Mathias Roux, Paris #164
£321 $506 €500 Petit bassin (61x48cm-24x19in) st.sig. gouache. 13-Nov-2 Mathias Roux, Paris #162
£345 $545 €500 Composition with figures (25x19cm-10x7in) s. gouache. 1-Apr-3 Segre, Madrid #316/R
£353 $557 €550 Composition (47x63cm-19x25in) s. gouache card. 13-Nov-2 Mathias Roux, Paris #2
£353 $557 €550 Composition (35x25cm-14x10in) st.sig. ink. 13-Nov-2 Mathias Roux, Paris #95
£353 $557 €550 Composition florale (32x50cm-13x20in) s. gouache graphite. 13-Nov-2 Mathias Roux, Paris #144
£385 $608 €600 Portrait au turban rouge et bleu (66x51cm-26x20in) s. gouache. 13-Nov-2 Mathias Roux, Paris #84
£385 $608 €600 Bocal a poissons (51x66cm-20x26in) s.d.XXX gouache. 13-Nov-2 Mathias Roux, Paris #88
£385 $608 €600 Composition fantastique (16x20cm-6x8in) st.sig. ink. 13-Nov-2 Mathias Roux, Paris #130
£449 $709 €700 Sonnets de Gongora (31x24cm-12x9in) s. i.verso Chinese ink. 13-Nov-2 Mathias Roux, Paris #25/R
£449 $709 €700 Etudiant (44x31cm-17x12in) st.sig. ink graphite double-sided. 13-Nov-2 Mathias Roux, Paris #115
£449 $709 €700 Balustrade (61x48cm-24x19in) s.d.38 gouache col crayon. 13-Nov-2 Mathias Roux, Paris #158
£481 $760 €750 Profil (60x44cm-24x17in) st.sig. ink gouache. 13-Nov-2 Mathias Roux, Paris #15
£513 $810 €800 Nature morte sur table (29x23cm-11x9in) st.sig. graphite. 13-Nov-2 Mathias Roux, Paris #112
£513 $810 €800 Portrait d'homme (28x22cm-11x9in) s. ink graphite. 13-Nov-2 Mathias Roux, Paris #151
£577 $912 €900 Sonnets de Gongora (30x22cm-12x9in) s. i.verso ink. 13-Nov-2 Mathias Roux, Paris #26/R
£577 $912 €900 Composition (51x68cm-20x27in) gouache. 13-Nov-2 Mathias Roux, Paris #29/R
£577 $912 €900 Composition (33x25cm-13x10in) st.sig. ink graphite. 13-Nov-2 Mathias Roux, Paris #121
£609 $962 €950 Composition (50x32cm-20x13in) s. gouache ink. 13-Nov-2 Mathias Roux, Paris #147
£621 $981 €900 Portrait of boy (45x33cm-18x13in) s. gouache. 1-Apr-3 Segre, Madrid #310/R
£641 $1013 €1000 Composition (80x45cm-31x18in) s.d.58 gouache cardboard. 13-Nov-2 Mathias Roux, Paris #28/R
£641 $1013 €1000 Allegorie de la Musique (188x98cm-74x39in) mixed media. 13-Nov-2 Mathias Roux, Paris #74/R
£658 $1066 €1000 Vase of flowers (34x44cm-13x17in) s. ink W/C. 21-Jan-3 Ansorena, Madrid #22/R
£658 $1066 €1000 Still life (34x44cm-13x17in) s. ink W/C. 21-Jan-3 Ansorena, Madrid #21/R
£705 $1114 €1100 Buste de profil (66x51cm-26x20in) s. gouache W/C. 13-Nov-2 Mathias Roux, Paris #1
£705 $1114 €1100 Philosophe (50x65cm-20x26in) s.i. pastel graphite. 13-Nov-2 Mathias Roux, Paris #14
£705 $1114 €1100 Composition (21x15cm-8x6in) W/C ink. 13-Nov-2 Mathias Roux, Paris #18
£705 $1114 €1100 Composition (31x24cm-12x9in) s. s.verso gouache W/C. 13-Nov-2 Mathias Roux, Paris #39/R
£705 $1114 €1100 Visages grotesques (36x25cm-14x10in) st.sig. graphite. 13-Nov-2 Mathias Roux, Paris #119
£705 $1114 €1100 Portrait d'homme (32x24cm-13x9in) s. ink. 13-Nov-2 Mathias Roux, Paris #150
£764 $1207 €1100 Le violoniste (26x20cm-10x8in) st.sig. ink. 28-Apr-3 Cornette de St.Cyr, Paris #271
£769 $1192 €1200 Fontaine d'Aix (81x64cm-32x17in) s.i.d.1938 gouache. 6-Dec-2 Rieunier, Bailly-Pommery, Mathias, Paris #97
£769 $1215 €1200 Compositions surrealistes (27x20cm-11x8in) graphite ink pair. 13-Nov-2 Mathias Roux, Paris #4
£769 $1215 €1200 Composition cubiste (48x31cm-19x12in) wax crayon. 13-Nov-2 Mathias Roux, Paris #27/R
£769 $1215 €1200 Composition (51x65cm-20x26in) s. gouache pigment. 13-Nov-2 Mathias Roux, Paris #30/R
£833 $1317 €1300 Composition (31x21cm-12x8in) s. ink W/C. 13-Nov-2 Mathias Roux, Paris #37/R
£962 $1519 €1500 Composition (31x24cm-12x9in) s. W/C ink. 13-Nov-2 Mathias Roux, Paris #38/R
£1111 $1756 €1600 Femme surrealiste (30x22cm-12x9in) st.sig. ink. 28-Apr-3 Cornette de St.Cyr, Paris #272 est:1200-1500
£1156 $1839 €1700 Composition (38x29cm-15x11in) s.d.41 gouache. 26-Feb-3 Artcurial Briest, Paris #79 est:800-1000
£1184 $1918 €1800 View of town (21x28cm-8x11in) s.d.27 W/C. 21-Jan-3 Ansorena, Madrid #49/R
£1346 $2127 €2100 Composition aux instruments (26x20cm-10x8in) crayon. 13-Nov-2 Mathias Roux, Paris #32/R
£1410 $2228 €2200 Femme aux bras croises (88x61cm-35x24in) s.d.30 gouache. 13-Nov-2 Mathias Roux, Paris #10
£1410 $2228 €2200 Composition (31x24cm-12x9in) s. ink. 13-Nov-2 Mathias Roux, Paris #98
£1474 $2329 €2300 Nature morte. st.sig. graphite. 13-Nov-2 Mathias Roux, Paris #183
£1923 $3038 €3000 Cheval se cabrant (27x37cm-11x15in) s. W/C ink two. 13-Nov-2 Mathias Roux, Paris #11
£1923 $3038 €3000 Gare (80x105cm-31x41in) s. gouache cardboard. 13-Nov-2 Mathias Roux, Paris #31/R
£1987 $3140 €3100 Composition cubiste (34x27cm-13x11in) gouache graphite collage masonite. 13-Nov-2 Mathias Roux, Paris #19
£2179 $3444 €3400 Nature morte cubiste (31x48cm-12x19in) s.d.33 graphite W/C. 13-Nov-2 Mathias Roux, Paris #5
£2244 $3545 €3500 Composition cubiste (26x21cm-10x8in) W/C graphite. 13-Nov-2 Mathias Roux, Paris #16
£3077 $4862 €4800 Nature morte aux oiseaux et fruits (64x65cm-25x26in) s. gouache. 13-Nov-2 Mathias Roux, Paris #22
£5128 $8103 €8000 Composition au violon (50x66cm-20x26in) s.d.1937 W/C gouache graphite. 13-Nov-2 Mathias Roux, Paris #33/R
£6944 $11042 €10000 Composition aux raisins noirs (49x64cm-19x25in) s. gouache lit. 29-Apr-3 Artcurial Briest, Paris #129/R est:2500-3000
£7051 $11141 €11000 Composition aux violons et partitions (37x26cm-15x10in) s.d.XXX graphite ink W/C. 13-Nov-2 Mathias Roux, Paris #35/R
£7586 $11986 €11000 Still life with birds (62x65cm-24x26in) s. mixed media on canvas exec.c.1954. 7-Apr-3 Castellana, Madrid #420/R est:8000
£8013 $12660 €12500 Composition au violon et partition (37x27cm-15x11in) s.d.XXXI W/C ink. 13-Nov-2 Mathias Roux, Paris #36/R est:760
£8333 $13167 €13000 Composition a la guitare et a la bouteille (64x42cm-25x17in) s.i. gouache cardboard. 13-Nov-2 Mathias Roux, Paris #40/R est:5300
£9295 $14686 €14500 Composition a la guitare, verres et bouteille (44x59cm-17x23in) s. W/C graphite ink. 13-Nov-2 Mathias Roux, Paris #34/R
£9615 $15192 €15000 Personnage (121x49cm-48x19in) s. mixed media stucco lit. 13-Nov-2 Mathias Roux, Paris #62/R
£11538 $18231 €18000 Untitled. st.sig. dr album. 13-Nov-2 Mathias Roux, Paris #9/R
£12821 $20256 €20000 Composition (64x49cm-25x19in) s.d.29 W/C graphite ink collage lit. 13-Nov-2 Mathias Roux, Paris #41/R est:6000
£17000 $27880 €25500 Composition (64x50cm-25x20in) s.d.1929 collage ink chl pencil gouache card prov.lit. 5-Feb-3 Sotheby's, London #153/R est:20000

SERNEELS, Clement (1912-1991) Belgian
£961 $1499 €1442 Seated female nude with a cup in the foreground (78x68cm-31x27in) s.d.45. 11-Nov-2 Stephan Welz, Johannesburg #563/R est:8000-12000 (SA.R 15000)
£1154 $1812 €1800 Deux nus (110x90cm-43x35in) s.d.1943. 19-Nov-2 Vanderkindere, Brussels #118 est:700-1000

SERNESI, Raffaello (1838-1866) Italian
£9434 $14528 €15000 Bridge on the Arno (37x70cm-15x28in) s. 28-Oct-2 Il Ponte, Milan #243/R est:30000

SERNESI, Raffaello (attrib) (1838-1866) Italian
£629 $969 €1000 San Marcello Pistoiese (18x34cm-7x13in) board. 28-Oct-2 Il Ponte, Milan #223/R
£1069 $1647 €1700 Beach with figures (34x52cm-13x20in) 28-Oct-2 Il Ponte, Milan #233/R
£1321 $2034 €2100 Rural church (22x35cm-9x14in) exhib. 28-Oct-2 Il Ponte, Milan #257/R
£1887 $2906 €3000 Landscape (14x62cm-6x24in) exhib. 28-Oct-2 Il Ponte, Milan #227/R

SEROPIAN, Roupen (19th C) ?
£950 $1539 €1425 Arabs with a captive tiger (80x100cm-31x39in) s. 23-Jan-3 Christie's, Kensington #139/R

SERPAN, Jaroslav (1922-1976) Czechoslovakian
£321 $500 €482 Riphsan (81x99cm-32x39in) s.i.d.11/21/54. 18-Sep-2 Boos Gallery, Michigan #291
£1973 $3137 €2900 Mufftafogee (114x146cm-45x57in) s. painted 1957. 28-Feb-3 Joron-Derem, Paris #49/R
£1973 $3137 €2900 Checleva (80x73cm-31x29in) s. painted 1961. 28-Feb-3 Joron-Derem, Paris #45/R
£2041 $3245 €3000 Ihun (97x130cm-38x51in) s. painted 1952. 28-Feb-3 Joron-Derem, Paris #50/R

SERR, Janice Jay (?) Canadian?
£215 $335 €323 Mono Lake (122x82cm-48x32in) s. i.d.74 verso canvas on board prov. 25-Mar-3 Ritchie, Toronto #95/R (C.D 500)

SERRA Y AUQUE, Enrico (1859-1918) Spanish
£1301 $2030 €1900 Lagooon in Lazio (39x27cm-15x11in) s. 8-Apr-3 Ansorena, Madrid #68/R
£1678 $2701 €2500 Leon XIII celebrating the Mass (41x66cm-16x26in) s.i.d.1888 board. 18-Feb-3 Durán, Madrid #220/R
£2044 $3189 €3250 Landscape between Rome and Ostia (91x152cm-36x60in) s. 23-Sep-2 Durán, Madrid #119/R
£2553 $4136 €3600 Las Lagunas Pontinas (72x117cm-28x46in) s.d.1893. 20-May-3 Segre, Madrid #94/R est:3000
£4839 $7645 €7500 Lagoons in Italy (60x131cm-24x52in) s. 18-Dec-2 Ansorena, Madrid #72/R est:7500
£10526 $17053 €16000 Travelling musicians (89x127cm-35x50in) s. 21-Jan-3 Ansorena, Madrid #171/R est:12000

SERRA Y FARNES, Pedro (1890-1974) Spanish
£362 $586 €550 Landscape (32x42cm-13x17in) s. canvas on cardboard. 21-Jan-3 Ansorena, Madrid #242/R
£414 $654 €600 Landscape with tree (50x61cm-20x24in) s. 1-Apr-3 Segre, Madrid #38/R

SERRA Y PORSON, Jose (1824-1910) Spanish
£1481 $2104 €2400 Galant reveur (13x9cm-5x4in) s. panel. 16-Mar-3 Eric Pillon, Calais #8/R
£2987 $4660 €4750 Sweet maternity (29x22cm-11x9in) s.d.1883 board. 23-Sep-2 Durán, Madrid #220/R

SERRA, Andreu (20th C) Spanish
£613 $968 €950 Beach on the Costa Brava (50x61cm-20x24in) s. 18-Dec-2 Ansorena, Madrid #43
£625 $1013 €950 Landscape with two figures (47x62cm-19x24in) s. 21-Jan-3 Ansorena, Madrid #277/R

SERRA, Ernesto (1860-?) Italian
£660 $1043 €990 Portrait of girl (71x43cm-28x17in) s. 17-Dec-2 Gorringes, Lewes #1428
£3000 $4770 €4500 Young beauty (72x44cm-28x17in) s. 18-Mar-3 Bonhams, New Bond Street #69/R est:3000-5000

SERRA, Richard (1939-) American
£2866 $4500 €4299 St Louis (42x31cm-17x12in) s. paintstick paper. 19-Nov-2 Wright, Chicago #221/R est:3000-5000
£38000 $63460 €55100 Berlin (189x203cm-74x80in) oilstick on paper painted 1982 prov.exhib.lit. 27-Jun-3 Christie's, London #230/R est:30000-50000

Prints
£1899 $3000 €2849 Allee (77x101cm-30x40in) s.d.1996 num.14/15 etching. 22-Apr-3 Butterfields, San Francisco #2363/R est:3000-4000
£2201 $3500 €3302 Malcolm X (156x133cm-61x52in) s.d.num.AP 5/5 lithograph. 29-Apr-3 Christie's, Rockefeller NY #742/R est:2000-3000
£4430 $7000 €6645 Esna (195x195cm-77x77in) s. num.9/31 silkscreen painstick on coated kozo. 22-Apr-3 Butterfields, San Francisco #2362/R est:4000-6000

Works on paper
£1529 $2400 €2294 Linear composition (27x30cm-11x12in) init.d.verso black crayon. 21-Nov-2 Swann Galleries, New York #195/R est:3000-5000

SERRA, Rosa (1944-) Dutch

Sculpture
£1079 $1770 €1500 Percepcio (23cm-9in) s.num.4/7 marbleized bronze cast 2002 lit. 3-Jun-3 Christie's, Amsterdam #176/R est:1200-1600
£1266 $2000 €2000 Amazone (29cm-11in) i.num.4/7 brown pat. bronze executed 1999 lit. 26-Nov-2 Sotheby's, Amsterdam #74/R est:1400-1800
£1583 $2596 €2200 Mediterrania (25cm-10in) s.num.P/A marbleized bronze cast 1998. 3-Jun-3 Christie's, Amsterdam #198/R est:1500-2000
£1899 $3000 €3000 Woman (58cm-23in) i.num.1/7 brown pat. bronze executed 2000. 26-Nov-2 Sotheby's, Amsterdam #73/R est:3000-4000
£2734 $4483 €3800 Unity (50cm-20in) s.num.1/7 bronze cast 1999. 3-Jun-3 Christie's, Amsterdam #177/R est:3500-4500

SERRALUNGA, Luigi (1880-1940) Italian
£1378 $2164 €2150 Vase with mimosas (80x91cm-31x36in) s. 10-Dec-2 Della Rocca, Turin #353/R

SERRANO RUEDA, Santiago (1942-) Spanish
£503 $775 €800 Untitled (70x50cm-28x20in) s.d.1990 oil collage mixed media paper prov. 28-Oct-2 Segre, Madrid #141/R

SERRANO, Andres (1950-) American

Photographs
£2153 $3401 €3100 De la serie, la morgue (28x36cm-11x14in) s.i.num.42/50 verso col photo. 28-Apr-3 Cornette de St.Cyr, Paris #506/R est:2000-2500
£3000 $5010 €4350 Morgue, death by fire (81x100cm-32x39in) s.i.num.1/7 verso cibachrome print prov.lit. 24-Jun-3 Sotheby's, Olympia #124/R est:3000-5000
£3504 $5466 €5256 Woman with infant (102x83cm-40x33in) s.num.1/7 verso cibachrome silicon plexiglass prov. 5-Nov-2 Bukowskis, Stockholm #485/R est:40000-50000 (S.KR 50000)
£3526 $5535 €5500 Church (100x81cm-39x32in) s.i.d.1991 verso cibachrome prov.exhib.lit. 11-Dec-2 Artcurial Briest, Paris #768/R est:12000
£3750 $6000 €5625 Untitled - ejaculate in trajectory (70x102cm-28x40in) cibachrome on plexiglas executed 1989 prov.exhib.lit. 16-May-3 Phillips, New York #208/R est:6000-8000
£5625 $9000 €8438 Klansman - imperial wizard II (100x81cm-39x32in) s.i.num.1/10 verso cibachrome print mounted on plexiglas prov.lit. 14-May-3 Sotheby's, New York #361/R est:8000-12000
£5625 $9000 €8438 Klansman (100x81cm-39x32in) cibachrome mounted on plexiglas executed 1991 prov.exhib. 16-May-3 Phillips, New York #209/R est:8000-12000
£6013 $9500 €9020 Nomads (165x128cm-65x50in) cibachrome silicone plexiglas executed 1990 prov.exhib. 12-Nov-2 Phillips, New York #174/R est:10000-15000
£6800 $10472 €10200 Klansman - knight hawk of Georgia invisible empire II (151x124cm-59x49in) s.i.num.2/4 verso cibachrome print executed 1990 prov. 22-Oct-2 Sotheby's, London #490/R est:5000-7000
£8861 $14000 €13292 Klansman (152x127cm-60x50in) s.i.num.2/4 cibachrome print mounted on plexiglas prov.exhib. 14-Nov-2 Christie's, Rockefeller NY #454/R est:15000-20000
£10204 $16224 €15000 Nomads (165x128cm-65x50in) s. cibachrome plexiglas exec.1990 one of 4 prov.exhib. 24-Mar-3 Cornette de St.Cyr, Paris #84/R est:20000
£11875 $19000 €17813 Scream (164x114cm-65x45in) cibachrome mounted on plexiglas executed 1986 prov.lit. 16-May-3 Phillips, New York #210/R est:20000-25000
£12000 $20040 €17400 Pieta (70x102cm-28x40in) s.i.d.1985 num.4/10 cibachrome prov.lit. 27-Jun-3 Christie's, London #249/R est:12000-16000
£14063 $22500 €21095 Ecce homo (152x102cm-60x40in) cibachrome print executed 1988 prov. 14-May-3 Sotheby's, New York #327/R est:25000-35000
£15000 $25050 €21750 Piss elegance (150x100cm-59x39in) s.i.num.3/4 verso cibachrome print prov. 26-Jun-3 Sotheby's, London #112/R est:15000-20000
£17089 $27000 €25634 Piss thinker (152x102cm-60x40in) cibachrome silicone plexiglas executed 1988 prov.exhib. 12-Nov-2 Phillips, New York #176/R est:25000-30000
£17089 $27000 €25634 Madonna and Child II (152x101cm-60x40in) s.i.num.3/4 cibachrome print mounted on plexiglas executed 1989. 14-Nov-2 Christie's, Rockefeller NY #453/R est:35000-45000
£18056 $29792 €26000 Church - Sainte Clotilde, II, Paris (152x126cm-60x50in) s.i. num.2/4 cibachrome prov.exhib. 3-Jul-3 Christie's, Paris #123/R est:10000-15000

£23734 $37500 €35601 Gray Moses (152x102cm-60x40in) s. num.1/10 verso c-print prov.exhib. 13-Nov-2 Sotheby's, New York #487/R est:50000-70000
£26000 $43420 €37700 Heaven and hell (102x152cm-40x60in) s.i.num.3/4 verso cibachrome print prov.lit. 26-Jun-3 Sotheby's, London #119/R est:18000-25000

SERRANO, Pablo (1910-1985) Spanish
Sculpture
£1351 $2108 €2000 Bull scene (19x22x31cm-7x9x12in) s. num.18/68 bronze. 25-Mar-3 Durán, Madrid #235/R
£2703 $4216 €4000 Homage to Picasso (30cm-12in) s. num.4/50 brown pat bronze marble base. 25-Mar-3 Durán, Madrid #234/R

SERRASANTA, Jose (1916-2000) Argentinian
£993 $1619 €1500 Two boats (33x41cm-13x16in) s. board. 11-Feb-3 Segre, Madrid #334/R
£2830 $4358 €4500 Beach with fishermen (65x81cm-26x32in) s. 28-Oct-2 Segre, Madrid #284/R est:4000
£2877 $4488 €4200 Cadaques (60x72cm-24x28in) s. 8-Apr-3 Ansorena, Madrid #214/R

SERRE, Jean Adam (1704-1788) Swiss
Miniatures
£2500 $4100 €3625 Young lady, called Madame de Grignon, revealing her right breast (4cm-2in) enamel on copper oval prov.exhib. 3-Jun-3 Christie's, London #32/R est:2500-3500

SERRE, Jean Adam (attrib) (1704-1788) Swiss
Miniatures
£1000 $1540 €1500 Gentleman in a purple coat (6cm-2in) enamel gilt metal mount rec. wood frame oval exec.c.1750. 24-Oct-2 Sotheby's, Olympia #35/R est:1200-1800

SERRE, Pascale (20th C) French
£790 $1248 €1185 Figure composition (100x82cm-39x32in) s.i.d.94 verso. 1-Apr-3 Rasmussen, Copenhagen #386/R (D.KR 8500)

SERRES, Antony (1828-1898) French
£3151 $4979 €4727 Children with bird's nest and dog (114x106cm-45x42in) s. 16-Nov-2 Crafoord, Lund #87/R est:20000 (S.KR 45000)

SERRES, Dominic (1722-1793) British
£2800 $4340 €4200 Squadron of the red arriving at their anchorage (29x42cm-11x17in) s.d.1774 panel. 31-Oct-2 Christie's, Kensington #439/R est:3000-5000
£120000 $194400 €180000 Taking of Belle Isle, 1761 by Commodore Keppel and General Hodgson (37x52cm-15x20in) s.d.1762 set of six. 22-Jan-3 Bonhams, New Bond Street #320/R est:120000-180000
Works on paper
£300 $486 €450 HMS Experiment capturing the French privateer Telemarque (11x14cm-4x6in) pencil W/C sold with a print of the same subject 2 in 1 frame. 21-May-3 Christie's, Kensington #354/R
£320 $534 €464 Lakeland landscape with travellers on a path (14x23cm-6x9in) s. W/C. 25-Jun-3 Cheffins, Cambridge #678
£850 $1377 €1275 Dutch flagship in her anchorage (22x35cm-9x14in) pen grey ink wash prov. 21-May-3 Christie's, Kensington #353/R

SERRES, John Thomas (1759-1825) British
Works on paper
£300 $486 €450 Barges running out to meet the new arrival (13x18cm-5x7in) pen grey ink W/C prov. 21-May-3 Christie's, Kensington #360/R
£550 $891 €825 Admiralty yacht firing a salute to signal her departure (18x24cm-7x9in) s.d.1779 pencil pen black ink W/C. 21-May-3 Christie's, Kensington #361/R
£750 $1140 €1125 Frigate and Naval vessels off a lighthouse (15x18cm-6x7in) s. pen ink wash prov. 15-Aug-2 Bonhams, New Bond Street #383/R
£2963 $4800 €4296 Shipping off Plymouth from the coast at Cawsand (19x80cm-7x31in) s.d.1800 W/C ink on board prov.exhib. 29-Jul-3 Christie's, Rockefeller NY #102/R est:3000-5000

SERRI, Alfredo (1897-1972) Italian
£538 $856 €807 Still life (40x50cm-16x20in) s. 4-Mar-3 Deutscher-Menzies, Melbourne #231/R (A.D 1400)

SERRIER, Jean Pierre (1934-1989) French
£720 $1123 €1080 Solitude en commun (74x91cm-29x36in) s.i.d.66. 26-Mar-3 Woolley & Wallis, Salisbury #182/R

SERRITELLI, Giovanni (1810-1860) Italian
£10000 $16700 €15000 Italian brig and Greek barque anchored off the Neapolitan coast (75x101cm-30x40in) s. 18-Jun-3 Christie's, Kensington #169a/R est:10000-15000

SERRURE, Auguste (1825-1903) Flemish
£750 $1245 €750 Elegante et son chien contemplant un tableau (38x25cm-15x10in) s. panel. 16-Jun-3 Horta, Bruxelles #302
£1135 $1838 €1600 La chasse aux papillons (14x7cm-6x3in) panel. 26-May-3 Amberes, Antwerp #76
£1410 $2214 €2200 Bonne et perroquet dans un interieur (69x55cm-27x22in) 16-Dec-2 Amberes, Antwerp #301
£2658 $4147 €4200 Femme debout devant son piano (71x56cm-28x22in) s. 20-Oct-2 Mercier & Cie, Lille #302/R est:3800-4500
£2770 $4322 €4100 Jeune femme romantique dans une fenetre gothique (102x72cm-40x28in) s.i.d.1848. 30-Mar-3 Anaf, Lyon #249/R
£85443 $133291 €135000 Chess game (49x70cm-19x28in) s.d.1864 panel lit. 21-Oct-2 Bernaerts, Antwerp #95/R est:12500-15000

SERRUYS, Yvonne (attrib) (1873-1953) Belgian
£1538 $2385 €2400 Interior (34x34cm-13x13in) 7-Dec-2 De Vuyst, Lokeren #291/R est:1300-1500

SERT Y BADIA, Jose Maria (1876-1945) Spanish
£3716 $5797 €5500 Good news for the shepherds (63x80cm-25x31in) lit. 25-Mar-3 Durán, Madrid #171/R
£5128 $8103 €8000 Project for decoration (22x12cm-9x5in) panel set of 7 prov. 18-Nov-2 Sotheby's, Paris #101/R est:2000
£75000 $124500 €108750 Offering (244x149cm-96x59in) oil plaster on board. 12-Jun-3 Christie's, London #268/R est:5000-7000
Works on paper
£268 $437 €405 Study for fresco (54x28cm-21x11in) s.d.1925 chl pencil. 11-Feb-3 Segre, Madrid #374/R

SERT, Henri (1938-1964) French
£805 $1336 €1167 Portrait (38x46cm-15x18in) s.d.1959. 12-Jun-3 Kunsthallen, Copenhagen #112/R (D.KR 8500)
£849 $1368 €1274 Composition with figure (65x81cm-26x32in) s.d.59. 7-May-3 AB Stockholms Auktionsverk #890/R (S.KR 11000)
£965 $1495 €1448 Visage (46x38cm-18x15in) s.d.59 i.verso. 4-Dec-2 Kunsthallen, Copenhagen #269/R (D.KR 11200)
£1774 $2767 €2661 Portrait (81x65cm-32x26in) s.d.58. 18-Sep-2 Kunsthallen, Copenhagen #170/R est:20000 (D.KR 21000)
£1866 $2966 €2799 Portrait (81x65cm-32x26in) s.d.1959. 29-Apr-3 Kunsthallen, Copenhagen #72/R est:20000 (D.KR 20000)
£1892 $2952 €2838 Composition (92x72cm-36x28in) s.d.60. 6-Nov-2 AB Stockholms Auktionsverk #945/R est:20000-25000 (S.KR 27000)
Works on paper
£463 $746 €695 Composition with figure (62x48cm-24x19in) s.d.60 pastel. 7-May-3 AB Stockholms Auktionsverk #1116/R (S.KR 6000)

SERULLA, Vidal (1923-) Spanish
£543 $869 €815 Mercado del Lunes (45x54cm-18x21in) s.d.1961. 13-Jan-3 Rasmussen, Vejle #201/R (D.KR 6200)

SERUSIER, Paul (1863-1927) French
£3521 $5669 €5000 Le Bapteme du Christ (32x40cm-13x16in) d.1906 panel. 11-May-3 Thierry & Lannon, Brest #222/R est:8000-10000
£4487 $7045 €7000 Evocation (50x45cm-20x18in) init. lit. 15-Dec-2 Thierry & Lannon, Brest #215
£4516 $7000 €6774 Mary Madeleine et Saint-Jean (55x38cm-22x15in) s. painted 1903 prov.lit. 26-Sep-2 Christie's, Rockefeller NY #526/R est:10000-15000
£4747 $7500 €7500 Vallee (42x39cm-17x15in) s. lit. 2-Dec-2 Tajan, Paris #41/R
£7042 $11338 €10000 Les champignons (38x46cm-15x18in) s. 11-May-3 Thierry & Lannon, Brest #223/R est:12000-15000
£8974 $14090 €14000 Notre-Dame des Portes (140x86cm-55x34in) stump. 15-Dec-2 Thierry & Lannon, Brest #216/R est:15000
£10256 $16103 €16000 Cueillette des pommes (109x70cm-43x28in) init. lit. 15-Dec-2 Thierry & Lannon, Brest #205/R
£10563 $17007 €15000 L'offrande (76x106cm-30x42in) paper on canvas painted 1908. 11-May-3 Thierry & Lannon, Brest #225/R est:18000-20000
£11538 $18115 €18000 Music (65x54cm-26x21in) lit. 15-Dec-2 Thierry & Lannon, Brest #214
£19231 $30192 €30000 Bretonne sous les arbres en fleurs (40x52cm-16x20in) studio st. 15-Dec-2 Thierry & Lannon, Brest #204/R est:22000
£21127 $34014 €30000 Le repos des Chasseresses (90x146cm-35x57in) init. painted 1908. 11-May-3 Thierry & Lannon, Brest #227 est:30000-40000

£26761 $43085 €38000 Composition aux pommes et aux plantes sauvages (73x60cm-29x24in) s.d.10. 11-May-3 Thierry & Lannon, Brest #224/R est:32000-35000
£38462 $60385 €60000 Fees aux balles d'or (40x99cm-16x39in) lit. set of 4. 15-Dec-2 Thierry & Lannon, Brest #211/R est:100000
£39437 $63493 €56000 Laveuse au Pouldu (96x59cm-38x23in) painted 1890. 11-May-3 Thierry & Lannon, Brest #226/R est:45000-60000
£341615 $550000 €512423 Deux lavandieres au bord de la cascade (74x93cm-29x37in) painted c.1890 prov.lit. 6-May-3 Sotheby's, New York #8/R est:700000

Works on paper

£387 $624 €550 Etude de fanneuses (12x17cm-5x7in) st. chl. 11-May-3 Thierry & Lannon, Brest #304
£417 $658 €600 Paysage breton (31x24cm-12x9in) st.sig. crayon. 25-Apr-3 Piasa, Paris #176
£521 $849 €750 Statue d'un Saint Eveque dans sa niche (30x22cm-12x9in) mono. chl col crayon. 19-Jul-3 Thierry & Lannon, Brest #47
£735 $1168 €1080 Ange et rose, etude. Etude de caribou (21x11cm-8x4in) graphite col crayon double-sided prov. 26-Feb-3 Artcurial Briest, Paris #22
£1266 $1962 €2000 L'arbre pres des rochers (26x29cm-10x11in) s. Indian ink dr. 29-Sep-2 Eric Pillon, Calais #184/R
£1392 $2158 €2200 Dans le vallon (23x31cm-9x12in) s. chl dr. 29-Sep-2 Eric Pillon, Calais #183/R
£1531 $2434 €2250 Etude d'arbres (21x17cm-8x7in) s. ink Indian ink wash dr. 26-Feb-3 Artcurial Briest, Paris #19/R est:2000-2500
£1871 $2974 €2750 Etude pour les origines (10x18cm-4x7in) i.verso col crayon exec.c.1909 prov. 26-Feb-3 Artcurial Briest, Paris #18/R est:1500-2000
£3310 $5329 €4700 Nature morte aux coquillages et oursins (16x23cm-6x9in) mono. W/C. 11-May-3 Thierry & Lannon, Brest #100/R est:3500-3800
£8333 $13083 €13000 Etude de bretonnes (39x41cm-15x16in) gouache exec.1901 lit. 15-Dec-2 Thierry & Lannon, Brest #94a/R est:15000
£8803 $14173 €12500 La promenade du bebe (16x63cm-6x25in) W/C executed 1892. 11-May-3 Thierry & Lannon, Brest #101/R est:8000-12000

SERVAES, Albert (1883-1966) Belgian

£586 $938 €850 Evening (40x53cm-16x21in) lit. 15-Mar-3 De Vuyst, Lokeren #287
£692 $1065 €1100 Joueur d'orgue (44x33cm-17x13in) s. paper. 22-Oct-2 Campo, Vlaamse Kaai #615
£943 $1453 €1500 Paysage d'hiver (66x81cm-26x32in) s. exhib. 22-Oct-2 Campo, Vlaamse Kaai #614/R
£1477 $2377 €2200 Crepuscule en Flandres (64cm-25in) s. 18-Feb-3 Galerie Moderne, Brussels #306/R est:2000-3000
£1572 $2421 €2500 Paysage a Laethem-Saint-Martin (60x80cm-24x31in) s.d.1941. 22-Oct-2 Campo & Campo, Antwerp #237/R
£2372 $3724 €3700 Coucher de soleil (65x82cm-26x32in) s.d.1920. 19-Nov-2 Vanderkindere, Brussels #85/R est:3000-4000
£2621 $4141 €3800 Paysage des Flandres (50x60cm-20x24in) s.d.1929. 2-Apr-3 Vanderkindere, Brussels #517/R est:2500-4000
£2695 $4366 €3800 Church (64x79cm-25x31in) s.d.1963 prov. 20-May-3 Dorotheum, Vienna #211/R est:6000-9000
£2837 $4738 €4000 Bord de riviere au clair de lune (51x61cm-20x24in) s.d.19.2. 17-Jun-3 Palais de Beaux Arts, Brussels #623/R est:3500-4500
£3077 $4769 €4800 Work on the field (46x55cm-18x22in) s. painted c.1935-1937 lit. 7-Dec-2 De Vuyst, Lokeren #557/R est:5000-6000
£3172 $5012 €4600 Paysage des Flandres au coucher du soleil (50x65cm-20x26in) s.d.1930. 2-Apr-3 Vanderkindere, Brussels #521/R est:3000-5000
£3448 $5448 €5000 Paysage des Flandres (35x52cm-14x20in) s.d.1931. 2-Apr-3 Vanderkindere, Brussels #512/R est:2500-4000
£3526 $5465 €5500 Snowy landscape (57x65cm-22x26in) s.d.1917 lit. 7-Dec-2 De Vuyst, Lokeren #460/R est:5000-6000

Works on paper

£264 $407 €420 Jeune fille (69x44cm-27x17in) s.d.1927 chl. 22-Oct-2 Campo & Campo, Antwerp #236
£345 $545 €500 Tete d'homme (47x37cm-19x15in) s. chl. 2-Apr-3 Vanderkindere, Brussels #533
£683 $1094 €950 Lake Maggiore at moonlight (51x67cm-20x26in) s.i.d.1946 pastel lit. 17-May-3 De Vuyst, Lokeren #330/R
£692 $1072 €1100 Crucifixion (68x53cm-27x21in) s.d.1961 pastel exhib.lit. 5-Oct-2 De Vuyst, Lokeren #321
£8219 $12822 €12000 La crucifixion (150x150cm-59x59in) s.d.1930 mixed media paper on paper prov. 14-Apr-3 Horta, Bruxelles #108/R est:20000-25000

SERVANDONI, Jean Nicolas (1695-1766) French

£74074 $120000 €111111 Capriccio of a ruined ionic temple and an obelisk with figures (132x98cm-52x39in) s.d.1724 prov. 24-Jan-3 Christie's, Rockefeller NY #58/R est:100000-150000

SERVEAU, Clement (1886-1972) French

£516 $800 €774 Paysage a la riviere (30x41cm-12x16in) s. board painted c.1921. 8-Dec-2 Toomey, Oak Park #754/R
£621 $1037 €900 Roses au vase blanc (38x46cm-15x18in) s.d.45. 10-Jul-3 Artcurial Briest, Paris #166
£791 $1266 €1100 La fanfaire (61x46cm-24x18in) s. 18-May-3 Eric Pillon, Calais #225/R
£1519 $2370 €2400 Buste (51x65cm-20x26in) s. 20-Oct-2 Chayette & Cheval, Paris #74/R
£1772 $2765 €2800 Nature morte au pichet blanc (74x54cm-29x21in) s. 20-Oct-2 Chayette & Cheval, Paris #76

SERVIN, Amedee (1829-1885) French

£1216 $1897 €1800 Veillee dans une chaumiere bretonne (40x55cm-16x22in) s. panel. 26-Mar-3 Rieunier, Paris #19/R

SERVRANCKX, Victor (1897-1965) Belgian

Works on paper

£278 $442 €400 Taureau (50x70cm-20x28in) mono.d.1957 dr. 29-Apr-3 Campo, Vlaamse Kaai #286
£353 $546 €550 Composition (27x21cm-11x8in) init.d.VS-49 col crayon. 3-Dec-2 Christie's, Amsterdam #121/R

SESIA DELLA MERLA, Gianni (1934-) Italian

£253 $395 €400 Gulf war (50x70cm-20x28in) s. s.i.d.2000 verso masonite. 14-Sep-2 Meeting Art, Vercelli #958

SESSA, Nicola (19th C) Italian

£823 $1275 €1235 Landscape with ruins (13x17cm-5x7in) copper. 24-Sep-2 Koller, Zurich #6594 (S.FR 1900)

SESSIONS, James (1882-1962) American

Works on paper

£417 $650 €626 Wharf (41x48cm-16x19in) s. W/C. 10-Nov-2 Selkirks, St. Louis #958
£769 $1200 €1154 Sailboats in harbour (33x43cm-13x17in) s. W/C graphite dr. 10-Nov-2 Selkirks, St. Louis #959/R
£1118 $1800 €1677 Chaotic street scene with people running from burning buildings (58x51cm-23x20in) s. W/C. 22-Feb-3 Pook & Pook, Downington #354/R est:1500-2500
£1258 $2000 €1887 Gloucester harbour (36x46cm-14x18in) s. W/C exec.c.1950. 2-Mar-3 Toomey, Oak Park #690/R est:2000-3000

SET-BYUL LI (1970-) Korean

£915 $1500 €1327 Disguise - face series (43x83cm-17x33in) s.d.2001 acrylic magazine print in 12 parts. 28-May-3 Sotheby's, Amsterdam #148/R est:1500-2000

SETELIK, Jaroslav (1881-1955) Polish

£1239 $1933 €1859 View of the Novotny footbridge and Prague Castle (66x75cm-26x30in) s. 12-Oct-2 Dorotheum, Prague #75 est:60000-90000 (C.KR 60000)
£1652 $2577 €2478 View of Charles Bridge and Prague Castle (80x130cm-31x51in) s. 12-Oct-2 Dorotheum, Prague #58/R est:80000-120000 (C.KR 80000)
£1962 $3061 €2943 View of the Lesser Side (70x110cm-28x43in) s. 12-Oct-2 Dorotheum, Prague #77/R est:80000-120000 (C.KR 95000)

SETHER, Gulbrand (1869-1910) American/Norwegian

Works on paper

£710 $1100 €1065 Tracks through the snow (36x53cm-14x21in) s. W/C gouache exec.c.1910. 8-Dec-2 Toomey, Oak Park #722/R

SETON, John Thomas (fl.1761-1806) British

£3000 $4680 €4500 Portrait of a gentleman, seated in a landscape (75x63cm-30x25in) s. 23-Sep-2 Bonhams, Bayswater #411/R est:4000-6000

SETON, John Thomas (attrib) (fl.1761-1806) British

£9300 $15159 €13950 Portrait of the Right Honourable William Hastings, Governor General of India (126x100cm-50x39in) 29-Jan-3 Hampton & Littlewood, Exeter #421/R est:2000-3000

SETTLE, William F (1821-1897) British

£1600 $2528 €2400 Warship and fishing boats at sunset (10x13cm-4x5in) board. 29-Nov-2 Dee Atkinson & Harrison, Driffield #828 est:2000-3000

Works on paper

£550 $891 €825 Royal Naval First Rate passing an Admiralty cutter in the Channel (18x36cm-7x14in) mono.d.72 pencil W/C. 21-May-3 Christie's, Kensington #434/R

£950 $1501 €1425 Hull citadel and lock houses. Grimsby Royal Docks and water tower (15cm-6in circular) W/C pair. 29-Nov-2 Dee Atkinson & Harrison, Driffield #844
£1600 $2528 €2400 War ships at anchor, steam packet in the distance (23x33cm-9x13in) mono.d.78. 29-Nov-2 Dee Atkinson & Harrison, Driffield #875 est:1000-1500
£1800 $2736 €2700 Ships of war, sail, steam with smaller craft in a flat calm (22x33cm-9x13in) one mono.d.78 W/C pair. 15-Aug-2 Bonhams, New Bond Street #404/R est:800-1200
£2000 $3160 €3000 War ship at anchor with fishing vessels (20x33cm-8x13in) W/C. 29-Nov-2 Dee Atkinson & Harrison, Driffield #874/R est:1000-1500

SEUPHOR, Michel (1901-1999) Belgian
Works on paper
£629 $975 €1000 Silence habite, horizontal (49x60cm-19x24in) s.i.d.10 Dec 72 ink dr. 30-Oct-2 Artcurial Briest, Paris #733
£1410 $2059 €2200 Variations en bleu et rouge (73x50cm-29x20in) s.i.d.58 verso mixed media collage card. 5-Jun-2 Il Ponte, Milan #34
£1944 $3092 €2800 Le cercle et le carre (65x151cm-26x59in) s.d.1967 verso ink dr. 29-Apr-3 Campo & Campo, Antwerp #265/R est:2500-3000

SEURAT, Georges (1859-1891) French
Works on paper
£100000 $164000 €150000 Untitled (14x9cm-6x4in) pencil crayon dr album exec.1881 prov. 6-Feb-3 Christie's, London #416/R est:150000
£224359 $350000 €336539 Les deux charrettes (27x33cm-11x13in) conte crayon executed c.1883 prov.exhib.lit. 5-Nov-2 Sotheby's, New York #6/R est:350000-450000

SEUSS, Dr (1904-1991) American
Works on paper
£9938 $16000 €14907 Man riding in lawnmower-powered chair (25x18cm-10x7in) pen ink W/C. 10-May-3 Illustration House, New York #22/R est:5000-8000
£10559 $17000 €15839 Billiard players on shipboard (23x25cm-9x10in) s. pen ink gouache. 10-May-3 Illustration House, New York #23/R est:5000-8000

SEVEAU, Georges (19/20th C) French
£240 $391 €360 Le chateau de la Reine blanche (54x65cm-21x26in) s.i.verso. 29-Jan-3 Sotheby's, Olympia #292/R

SEVEHON, Francky Boy (1954-) French
£321 $506 €500 La girafe en voiture (100x150cm-39x59in) s.d. acrylic. 14-Nov-2 Credit Municipal, Paris #68
£347 $549 €500 Une bonne petite toile (48x61cm-19x24in) s.i.d. acrylic. 28-Apr-3 Cornette de St.Cyr, Paris #394
£417 $658 €600 No 1 (100x81cm-39x32in) s.i.d. acrylic. 27-Apr-3 Perrin, Versailles #144/R
£417 $658 €600 No 2 (100x81cm-39x32in) s.i.d. acrylic. 27-Apr-3 Perrin, Versailles #145/R

SEVELLEC, Jim (?-c.1971) French
£577 $906 €900 Bretagne, village pres de l'estuaire (46x38cm-18x15in) s. 15-Dec-2 Eric Pillon, Calais #133/R
£660 $1075 €950 La riviere du Faou (46x55cm-18x22in) s. 19-Jul-3 Thierry & Lannon, Brest #174
£724 $1151 €1050 Eglise Lanildut (54x46cm-21x18in) s. 10-Mar-3 Thierry & Lannon, Brest #141/R
£897 $1409 €1400 Vieilles maisons (108x92cm-43x36in) s. panel. 15-Dec-2 Thierry & Lannon, Brest #417
£1026 $1610 €1600 Villa et plage animee (46x55cm-18x22in) s. 15-Dec-2 Thierry & Lannon, Brest #195
£1042 $1698 €1500 Chaumiere pres de la mare en Bretagne (46x54cm-18x21in) s. 19-Jul-3 Thierry & Lannon, Brest #389 est:1500
£1197 $1927 €1700 La pointe du Toulinguet (50x60cm-20x24in) s. 11-May-3 Thierry & Lannon, Brest #393 est:1000-1200
£1410 $2214 €2200 Fontaine de Recouvrance (92x73cm-36x29in) s. 15-Dec-2 Thierry & Lannon, Brest #194
£1603 $2516 €2500 Le Fret (46x55cm-18x22in) s. 15-Dec-2 Thierry & Lannon, Brest #418
Works on paper
£353 $554 €550 Retour au port (16x25cm-6x10in) s. W/C gouache. 15-Dec-2 Thierry & Lannon, Brest #353
£462 $725 €720 Brest (21x30cm-8x12in) s. gouache. 15-Dec-2 Thierry & Lannon, Brest #352

SEVENBOM, Johan (18th C) Swedish
£5499 $9018 €7974 Classical ruin - and harbour view with figures (64x87cm-25x34in) 4-Jun-3 AB Stockholms Auktionsverk #2548/R est:25000-30000 (S.KR 70000)

SEVERDONCK, F van (1809-1889) Belgian
£1170 $1650 €1755 Sheep and ducks by a pond (25x18cm-10x7in) s. board. 12-Feb-2 Lincoln, Orange #487

SEVERDONCK, Franz van (1809-1889) Belgian
£687 $1100 €996 Chickens feeding (15x19cm-6x7in) s.d.1860 panel. 16-May-3 Skinner, Boston #30/R
£1181 $1948 €1700 Poultry by a stream (18x26cm-7x10in) s.d.1885 panel. 1-Jul-3 Christie's, Amsterdam #541/R est:1500-2000
£1282 $1987 €2000 Animaux de basse-cour pres de la ferme (18x26cm-7x10in) s.d.1881 i.verso panel. 9-Dec-2 Horta, Bruxelles #143 est:2000-3000
£1772 $2747 €2800 Three sheep, lamb and ducks in meadow by water (18x26cm-7x10in) s. i. verso panel. 25-Sep-2 Neumeister, Munich #724/R est:1200
£2273 $3386 €3500 Sheep and lambs in meadow (18x26cm-7x10in) s.d.1888 panel. 26-Jun-2 Neumeister, Munich #860/R est:3000
£2483 $3972 €3600 Landscape with cock, chickens, ducks and a pigeon (17x24cm-7x9in) s.d.1871 panel. 15-Mar-3 De Vuyst, Lokeren #414/R est:4000-4800
£3704 $6000 €5371 Sheep in stable (51x69cm-20x27in) s.d.1879 i.verso. 21-May-3 Doyle, New York #184/R est:2500-3500

SEVERDONCK, Joseph van (1819-1905) Belgian
£669 $1077 €950 Falling jockey (44x50cm-17x20in) s. panel. 12-May-3 Bernaerts, Antwerp #46/R
£1392 $2172 €2200 Jeune fille et son chien (76x61cm-30x24in) s.i. 16-Sep-2 Horta, Bruxelles #186

SEVEREN, Dan van (1927-) Belgian
Works on paper
£377 $581 €600 Composition (40x30cm-16x12in) s. dr. 22-Oct-2 Campo & Campo, Antwerp #315

SEVERIN, Jules (1888-1975) Belgian?
£503 $810 €750 Paysan et cheval avec arbres. s. 24-Feb-3 Bernaerts, Antwerp #2/R

SEVERIN, Mark (1906-) British
Works on paper
£430 $671 €645 Vitamins (23x35cm-9x14in) ink wash. 12-Sep-2 Sotheby's, Olympia #219/R

SEVERINI, Gino (1883-1966) Italian
£2152 $3400 €3400 Isabella (47x30cm-19x12in) s. tempera card on board. 30-Nov-2 Farsetti, Prato #616/R
£12025 $19000 €19000 Dancer (70x50cm-28x20in) s. tempera paper on canvas. 30-Nov-2 Farsetti, Prato #687/R est:20000
£25532 $41362 €36000 Femma a la toilette (31x22cm-12x9in) s.i. board prov.exhib.lit. 26-May-3 Christie's, Milan #243/R est:30000-40000
£52258 $82568 €81000 Arlequin and Pulcinella in a room (57x41cm-22x16in) s. s.i.d.1943 verso prov.lit. 18-Dec-2 Christie's, Rome #230/R est:18000
£52903 $83587 €82000 Les objets deviennent peinture (73x60cm-29x24in) s.d.1965 s.i.d.verso prov.exhib.lit. 18-Dec-2 Christie's, Rome #312/R est:70000
£80000 $123200 €120000 Arlequin tournant - mouvement son lumiere (68x40cm-27x16in) s. s.i.d.1957 prov.lit. 22-Oct-2 Christie's, London #1/R est:90000-120000
£95000 $148200 €142500 Nature morte (40x28cm-16x11in) s. s.i.d.1918 verso board prov.exhib.lit. 21-Oct-2 Sotheby's, London #3/R est:80000-120000
Prints
£2179 $3400 €3269 Composition (49x32cm-19x13in) s.num.202/220 col lithograph. 7-Nov-2 Swann Galleries, New York #813/R est:3000-5000
£2179 $3400 €3269 Arlecchino e Pedrolino (65x50cm-26x20in) s.num.3/120 col lithograph. 7-Nov-2 Swann Galleries, New York #814/R est:2000-3000
Works on paper
£1026 $1600 €1539 Abstract. gouache. 19-Oct-2 Harvey Clar, Oakland #1382/R
£1620 $2689 €2300 Natura morta con chitarra (23x29cm-9x11in) s. Indian ink. 10-Jun-3 Finarte Semenzato, Milan #209/R est:2300-2500
£1620 $2689 €2300 Couple de danseurs (27x21cm-11x8in) mono. Indian ink pencil. 10-Jun-3 Finarte Semenzato, Milan #210/R est:2300-2600
£2000 $3160 €3000 Still life (19x25cm-7x10in) s. pen ink W/C. 3-Apr-3 Christie's, Kensington #119/R
£3800 $6042 €5700 Mandoline et ruine (47x29cm-19x11in) s.i. pen ink prov. exec.c.1929-30. 20-Mar-3 Sotheby's, Olympia #83/R est:2500-3000
£20000 $32800 €30000 Sky and sea (65x49cm-26x19in) s. gouache pastel prov. 6-Feb-3 Christie's, London #471/R est:15000

£25180 $41295 €35000 Pierrot napolitian (19x12cm-7x5in) s. gouache executed c.1932 prov.exhib. 3-Jun-3 Christie's, Amsterdam #224/R est:15000-20000
£43000 $71810 €62350 Exercice de composition (57x43cm-22x17in) s. gouache executed c.1919 prov.exhib. 24-Jun-3 Sotheby's, London #233/R est:30000-40000

SEVERINI, Gino (attrib) (1883-1966) Italian
£3165 $4905 €5000 Futuristic composition (80x60cm-31x24in) i.d.1913. 27-Sep-2 Dr Fritz Nagel, Leipzig #3996/R est:9000

SEVERINO, Federico (1953-) Italian
Sculpture
£1293 $2055 €1900 Gradiva (63cm-25in) s.d.2002 verso num.5/6 bronze lit. 1-Mar-3 Meeting Art, Vercelli #746

SEVERN, Joseph Arthur Palliser (1842-1931) British
Works on paper
£420 $655 €630 Stormy harbour (29x42cm-11x17in) s. W/C. 18-Sep-2 Cheffins Grain & Comins, Cambridge #479
£650 $1014 €975 Continental river scene (54x91cm-21x36in) s.d.1887 W/C. 17-Oct-2 Bonhams, Edinburgh #177
£1100 $1694 €1650 Moonlit view of Venice (40x47cm-16x19in) s.d.1882 bodycol. 22-Oct-2 Bonhams, Knightsbridge #76/R est:600-900
£1500 $2340 €2250 Study of breaking waves (61x91cm-24x36in) s.d.1866 W/C. 10-Apr-3 Brightwells, Leominster #886 est:500-700

SEVILL, Louis (fl.1840-1858) Spanish
£1161 $1835 €1800 Portrait of lady with fan (105x89cm-41x35in) s. 18-Dec-2 Ansorena, Madrid #141/R

SEVILLA, Soledad (1944-) Spanish
£3082 $4808 €4900 Lions Patio (130x100cm-51x39in) s.i.d.1986 acrylic prov. 17-Sep-2 Segre, Madrid #168/R est:4900

SEVILLANO, Angel (20th C) Spanish
£4276 $6928 €6500 In a bar (65x81cm-26x32in) s.d.75 s.i.d.verso. 21-Jan-3 Durán, Madrid #136/R

SEVIN, Pierre Paul (1650-1710) French
Works on paper
£629 $900 €944 Civita castellana premiere couchee au sortir de Rome (12x19cm-5x7in) s. pen ink grey wash. 23-Jan-3 Swann Galleries, New York #237/R
£839 $1200 €1259 Vue de castenuovo, la dinee au sortir de Rome, con paste a Rignano (12x18cm-5x7in) s. pen ink wash. 23-Jan-3 Swann Galleries, New York #238/R est:600-900
£2270 $3790 €3200 Le tombeau de Gaston de Foix (43x29cm-17x11in) s.d.1670 gouache htd gold vellum. 19-Jun-3 Piasa, Paris #85/R est:2000-3000

SEWELL, Amos (1901-) American
£994 $1600 €1491 Man carrying trunk away from London taxicab (36x38cm-14x15in) s. board. 20-Feb-3 Illustration House, New York #153/R est:2000-3000

SEWELL, Edward (1800-?) Canadian
£467 $734 €701 Boats at low tide on the lower St Lawrence (30x40cm-12x16in) s. board. 10-Dec-2 Pinneys, Montreal #155 (C.D 1150)

SEWOHL, Waldemar (1887-?) German
£464 $756 €700 Berlin (51x63cm-20x25in) s. 28-Jan-3 Dorotheum, Vienna #28/R
£538 $839 €850 Berlin - Brandenburger Tor (48x68cm-19x27in) s. 14-Sep-2 Weidler, Nurnberg #319/R

SEXTON, Ray (1959-1996) American
£2215 $3500 €3212 Windbreak (43x84cm-17x33in) s. board prov. 26-Jul-3 Coeur d'Alene, Hayden #216/R est:4000-8000
£3006 $4750 €4359 Blackwolf (36x66cm-14x26in) s. board prov. 26-Jul-3 Coeur d'Alene, Hayden #210/R est:3000-5000

SEYDEL, Eduard (1822-1881) Luxembourger
£524 $817 €786 Country scene in village landscape (12x18cm-5x7in) s. panel prov. 9-Nov-2 Galerie Gloggner, Luzern #128/R (S.FR 1200)

SEYLBERGH, Jacques van den (1884-1960) Belgian
Works on paper
£377 $588 €550 Chaumiere en Campine (96x78cm-38x31in) s.d.1945 verso. 14-Apr-3 Horta, Bruxelles #369

SEYLER, Julius (1873-1958) German
£272 $433 €400 Fishing for shrimps on the beach (22x31cm-9x12in) s. board. 20-Mar-3 Neumeister, Munich #2742
£316 $491 €500 Peasant behind ox plough (46x66cm-18x26in) s. board lit. 25-Sep-2 Neumeister, Munich #723
£317 $510 €450 Crab fishermen with horse and cart (35x49cm-14x19in) s. board. 10-May-3 Hans Stahl, Toestorf #23
£331 $540 €500 Shrimp fishing (32x42cm-13x17in) s. board. 14-Feb-3 Paul Kieffer, Pforzhiem #7258
£346 $550 €519 Woman on pier. Road to town (25x36cm-10x14in) s. board double-sided prov. 5-Mar-3 Doyle, New York #54/R
£361 $581 €542 Ploughing the fields (33x43cm-13x17in) s. board. 12-May-3 Stephan Welz, Johannesburg #15 est:2000-3000 (SA.R 4200)
£458 $750 €700 Cattle in field (60x80cm-24x31in) s. board. 6-Feb-3 Weidler, Nurnberg #368/R
£458 $750 €700 Shrimp fishermen with horse on beach (50x70cm-20x28in) s. board. 6-Feb-3 Weidler, Nurnberg #369/R
£476 $757 €700 Peasant with ox cart (35x50cm-14x20in) s. panel. 20-Mar-3 Neumeister, Munich #2741/R
£476 $757 €700 Fishing for shrimps on the beach (22x24cm-9x9in) s. board. 20-Mar-3 Neumeister, Munich #2743
£476 $757 €700 Fishing for shrimps on the beach (35x50cm-14x20in) s. panel. 20-Mar-3 Neumeister, Munich #2744
£506 $800 €800 Horses ploughing (48x65cm-19x26in) s. panel lit. 29-Nov-2 Schloss Ahlden, Ahlden #1399/R
£513 $800 €770 Man with cows in water (38x48cm-15x19in) board. 28-Mar-3 Douglas, South Deerfield #4
£545 $828 €850 Shell fishermen with horse in sandbank (42x60cm-17x24in) s. board. 11-Jul-2 Allgauer, Kempten #2694/R
£545 $850 €818 Abstract men on horseback (69x99cm-27x39in) board. 28-Mar-3 Douglas, South Deerfield #5
£608 $949 €900 Peasant ploughing (60x80cm-24x31in) s. board. 27-Mar-3 Dr Fritz Nagel, Stuttgart #868/R
£633 $981 €1000 Shrimp fishermen with horse and cart on beach (25x42cm-10x17in) s. board. 25-Sep-2 Neumeister, Munich #722/R
£764 $1192 €1200 Nudes represented on lakeside (24x30cm-9x12in) s. paper lit. 7-Nov-2 Allgauer, Kempten #2960/R
£828 $1308 €1200 Shrimp fishermen on beach (61x78cm-24x31in) s. board. 2-Apr-3 Dr Fritz Nagel, Stuttgart #9228/R
£966 $1526 €1400 Landscape with haycart (31x42cm-12x17in) s. paper. 2-Apr-3 Dr Fritz Nagel, Stuttgart #9229/R
£1282 $1949 €2000 Coastal landscape in autumn (30x41cm-12x16in) s. board lit. 11-Jul-2 Allgauer, Kempten #2693/R
£2692 $4092 €4200 Indian buffalo hunt (60x80cm-24x31in) s. mixed media board. 17-Aug-2 Hans Stahl, Toestorf #23/R est:3000
£3718 $5874 €5800 Red Indians (34x43cm-13x17in) s. dark brown pat.bronze. 14-Nov-2 Neumeister, Munich #689/R est:2500-3000
Works on paper
£380 $592 €600 Horseback Indian (46x56cm-18x22in) s. 14-Sep-2 Weidler, Nurnberg #353

SEYMONT, J E (20th C) American
£641 $1000 €962 Interior scene of Catherine the Great and her subjects (74x107cm-29x42in) s. board. 14-Sep-2 Selkirks, St. Louis #204/R est:300-500

SEYMOUR, David (1911-1956) American?
Photographs
£2548 $4000 €3822 Bernard Berenson (41x51cm-16x20in) gelatin silver print. 21-Apr-3 Phillips, New York #10/R est:1000-1500

SEYMOUR, George L (fl.1876-1916) British
£300 $471 €450 Phyllis (29x16cm-11x6in) panel. 16-Apr-3 Christie's, Kensington #753
£900 $1467 €1350 Citrone (45x26cm-18x10in) init. i.verso. 12-Feb-3 Bonhams, Knightsbridge #64/R

SEYMOUR, John (19th C) British
£400 $628 €600 Conway Valley (40x60cm-16x24in) s. 20-Nov-2 Sotheby's, Olympia #22/R

SEYMOUR, Tom (19th C) British
£260 $403 €390 River valley with white washed cottage in the distance (30x50cm-12x20in) s. 24-Sep-2 Anderson & Garland, Newcastle #525
£280 $445 €420 Riverside cottage (25x36cm-10x14in) s. 6-Mar-3 Christie's, Kensington #416/R
£420 $667 €630 Mountain landscape with bridge and watermill, Scotland (40x60cm-16x24in) s,. 29-Apr-3 Kunsthallen, Copenhagen #538/R (D.KR 4500)
£600 $936 €900 Loch landscape, possibly Loch Katrine (41x61cm-16x24in) s. 6-Nov-2 Bonhams, Chester #519
£650 $1014 €975 Cattle in a highland landscape. Cattle watering (41x61cm-16x24in) s. pair. 7-Nov-2 Christie's, Kensington #131/R

£1154	$1812	€1800	Homme ecrivant a son bureau pres d'une fenetre. s.i.d.1892. 13-Dec-2 Piasa, Paris #210
£1400	$2184	€2100	Glen Sannox. Glen Irosa (61x51cm-24x20in) s. pair. 14-Apr-3 Sotheby's, London #43/R est:1000-1500

SEYPPEL, Carl Maria (1847-1913) German

£962	$1510	€1500	Villa Elisabeth in May (53x45cm-21x18in) s. panel. 21-Nov-2 Van Ham, Cologne #1924/R est:800

SEYSSAUD, René (1867-1952) French

£440	$682	€660	Boats in a harbour (40x50cm-16x20in) s. 3-Dec-2 Bonhams, Knightsbridge #266
£1633	$2596	€2400	Nu (18x33cm-7x13in) s. panel painted c.1925-30. 26-Feb-3 Artcurial Briest, Paris #260/R
£1958	$3270	€2800	Paysage de Provence (40x73cm-16x29in) s. 30-Jun-3 Pierre Berge, Paris #59 est:4000-5000
£3481	$5500	€5500	Rivage sur l'etang de Berre (46x38cm-18x15in) s. 2-Dec-2 Tajan, Paris #39
£3704	$5259	€6000	Rivage mediterraneen (46x38cm-18x15in) s. 16-Mar-3 Eric Pillon, Calais #179/R
£4167	$6875	€6000	Paysage aux oliviers, soleil couchant (38x61cm-15x24in) s. 2-Jul-3 Artcurial Briest, Paris #648/R est:6000-8000
£4345	$6952	€6300	Printemps (33x46cm-13x18in) s. 12-Mar-3 E & Eve, Paris #103/R est:2000-3000
£4487	$6955	€7000	Village de Provence (38x61cm-15x24in) s. 4-Dec-2 Pierre Berge, Paris #159/R
£6296	$8941	€10200	Oliviers en PRovence (61x81cm-24x32in) s. 16-Mar-3 Eric Pillon, Calais #114/R
£6369	$9936	€10000	Vue sur la vallee (65x92cm-26x36in) s. 10-Nov-2 Eric Pillon, Calais #35/R
£10345	$16552	€15000	Vaucluse, paysans aux champs (50x65cm-20x26in) s.d. 12-Mar-3 E & Eve, Paris #102/R est:4000-5000

SHAAR, Pinchas (1923-1996) Israeli

£321	$503	€500	Le rabin (33x27cm-13x11in) s.d. panel. 24-Nov-2 Chayette & Cheval, Paris #299
£550	$847	€825	Le repas (50x61cm-20x24in) s.d.1963. 23-Oct-2 Sotheby's, Olympia #804/R
£1181	$1877	€1700	Salomon (100x73cm-39x29in) s. d.1962 verso exhib. 29-Apr-3 Campo & Campo, Antwerp #268/R est:750-1250
Works on paper			
£347	$552	€500	Violoniste (54x36cm-21x14in) s.d.1974 mixed media. 29-Apr-3 Campo & Campo, Antwerp #266
£347	$552	€500	Le coq (54x35cm-21x14in) s.d.1968 mixed media. 29-Apr-3 Campo & Campo, Antwerp #267

SHABUNIN, Nikolai (?) Russian

£1901	$3061	€2700	Woman by pond (41x63cm-16x25in) s. 10-May-3 Bukowskis, Helsinki #399/R est:2000-3000

SHACKLETON, William (1872-1933) British

Works on paper			
£400	$640	€600	Game keeper with his English setter (32x21cm-13x8in) s. gouache. 11-Mar-3 David Duggleby, Scarborough #79
£620	$992	€930	Sea nymphs (40x32cm-16x13in) s.d. W/C gouache. 11-Mar-3 David Duggleby, Scarborough #77/R

SHADBOLT, Jack (1909-1998) Canadian

£1956	$3207	€2836	Composition (76x56cm-30x22in) s.d.1962 acrylic on paper prov. 9-Jun-3 Hodgins, Calgary #99/R est:4000-5000 (C.D 4400)
£2016	$3185	€3024	Autumn calligraphy (63x122cm-25x48in) s.d.1959 s.i.d.verso. 14-Nov-2 Heffel, Vancouver #199/R est:5500-7500 (C.D 5000)
£2621	$4141	€3932	Summer image (81x100cm-32x39in) s.d.1960 s.i.verso prov.lit. 14-Nov-2 Heffel, Vancouver #196/R est:6500-8500 (C.D 6500)
£2823	$4460	€4235	Land ark (76x102cm-30x40in) s.d.87 acrylic board prov. 18-Nov-2 Sotheby's, Toronto #126/R est:7000-9000 (C.D 7000)
£3427	$5415	€5141	Still life with casaba melon (61x81cm-24x32in) s.d.1941 prov.lit. 14-Nov-2 Heffel, Vancouver #121/R est:8000-10000 (C.D 8500)
£3831	$6052	€5747	Signs in a landscape no.11 (124x124cm-49x49in) s.d.1989 i.d.verso acrylic prov. 14-Nov-2 Heffel, Vancouver #200/R est:10000-12000 (C.D 9500)
£4222	$6924	€6333	Greek Island theme (100x76cm-39x30in) s.d.60 s.i.d.verso prov. 27-May-3 Sotheby's, Toronto #87/R est:7000-10000 (C.D 9500)
Works on paper			
£1156	$1895	€1734	Study for the monument (37x26cm-15x10in) s.d.45 W/C. 3-Jun-3 Joyner, Toronto #185/R est:2500-3500 (C.D 2600)
£1325	$2081	€1988	Trees and houses, Victoria, BC (30x41cm-12x16in) s.d.1939 pencil. 25-Nov-2 Hodgins, Calgary #105/R est:1500-2000 (C.D 3300)
£1606	$2522	€2409	Untitled - marina series (76x54cm-30x21in) s.d.1962 col ink. 25-Nov-2 Hodgins, Calgary #120/R est:4500-5000 (C.D 4000)
£1915	$3026	€2873	Still life (76x56cm-30x22in) s.d.60 ink gouache prov. 18-Nov-2 Sotheby's, Toronto #26/R est:4000-6000 (C.D 4750)
£3024	$4778	€4536	Stump clearing (102x198cm-40x78in) s.d.1977 s.i.d.verso chl triptych lit. 14-Nov-2 Heffel, Vancouver #187/R est:8000-10000 (C.D 7500)

SHAEFFER, Henry (20th C) ?

£250	$395	€375	Vessels on a Dutch waterway (22x41cm-9x16in) s. panel. 14-Nov-2 Christie's, Kensington #200

SHAFFER, Gary (20th C) American

£254	$425	€368	Tetralogy (124x124cm-49x49in) s. 28-Jun-3 Harvey Clar, Oakland #1192

SHAHN, Ben (1898-1969) American

Photographs			
£2057	$3250	€3086	Rehabilitation clients, Boone Country, Arkansas (16x24cm-6x9in) ferrotyped warm toned. 23-Apr-3 Sotheby's, New York #199/R est:3000-5000
£2152	$3400	€3228	Linworth, Ohio (22x31cm-9x12in) s.i.verso gelatin silver print prov. 25-Apr-3 Phillips, New York #85/R est:2500-3500
£3571	$5500	€5357	Shop window, man and child (15x22cm-6x9in) s.i.d.1935-36 photograph. 24-Oct-2 Sotheby's, New York #102/R est:4000-6000
£5380	$8500	€8070	Deputy sheriff during strike, Morgantown, West Virginia (20x25cm-8x10in) i.verso gelatin silver print prov.exhib.lit. 25-Apr-3 Phillips, New York #17/R est:4000-6000
Prints			
£2201	$3500	€3302	Phoenix (78x57cm-31x22in) s.num.85-100 hand col screenprint. 29-Apr-3 Christie's, Rockefeller NY #438/R est:2000-3000
£2516	$4000	€3774	Deserted fairground (28x37cm-11x15in) s. col screenprint executed c.1948. 4-Mar-3 Swann Galleries, New York #580/R est:6000-9000
Works on paper			
£3503	$5500	€5255	Ship deck (19x26cm-7x10in) s. ink gouache prov.exhib. 19-Nov-2 Wright, Chicago #163/R est:5000-7000
£6410	$10064	€10000	Couple (35x24cm-14x9in) s.d.32 Chinese ink W/C paper on card. 21-Nov-2 Finarte, Rome #144/R
£10063	$16000	€15095	Credo (77x57cm-30x22in) s. W/C gouache executed 1954 prov.lit. 5-Mar-3 Sotheby's, New York #100/R est:8000-12000
£18493	$28849	€27000	Sacco and Vanzetti (33x44cm-13x17in) s. ink. 10-Apr-3 Finarte Semenzato, Rome #240/R

SHALDERS, George (1826-1873) British

£444	$738	€644	Returning from the hills (18x25cm-7x10in) s. 16-Jun-3 Waddingtons, Toronto #125/R est:1500-2000 (C.D 1000)
£457	$750	€686	River landscape with cows at dusk (20x33cm-8x13in) s. art board. 9-Feb-3 William Jenack, New York #141
£2200	$3432	€3300	Carting seaweed on the Irish coast (24x48cm-9x19in) s.d.60 i.d.verso board. 7-Nov-2 Christie's, Kensington #147 est:1000-1500
£3700	$5920	€5550	View near Guildford Surrey. s.d.1855. 8-Jan-3 Brightwells, Leominster #1057/R est:2000-3000
£4688	$7500	€7032	Extensive landscape at dusk with cows, figures and a dog (62x93cm-24x37in) s.d.1855. 14-May-3 Butterfields, San Francisco #1139/R est:6000-8000
Works on paper			
£1700	$2771	€2465	Evening landscape with sheep at rest (27x48cm-11x19in) s. indis d.72 W/C. 16-Jul-3 Sotheby's, Olympia #51/R est:1000-1500
£1800	$2988	€2700	Summer landscape with sheep (29x44cm-11x17in) s. W/C bodycol htd white prov. 10-Jun-3 Bonhams, Leeds #100/R est:2000-3000
£2500	$3925	€3750	Shepherd and his flock in a meadow. Returning home (29x50cm-11x20in) s.d.1867 pencil W/C bodycol gum arabic two. 21-Nov-2 Christie's, London #57/R est:2500-3500

SHANAHAN, Ray P (1892-1935) American

£416	$650	€624	Sunken ships, Mississippi River, New Orleans (30x46cm-12x18in) s. board. 12-Oct-2 Neal Auction Company, New Orleans #653

SHANKS, Nelson (20th C) American

£903	$1400	€1355	Scot, portrait of the artist's son (41x30cm-16x12in) s.i.d.1970 board. 8-Dec-2 Freeman, Philadelphia #192/R

SHANKS, Tom Hovell (1921-) British

Works on paper			
£320	$499	€480	Rain over Skye cliffs, Bracadale (39x69cm-15x27in) s. W/C. 10-Apr-3 Bonhams, Edinburgh #2

SHANKS, William Somerville (1864-1951) British

£460	$727	€690	An heirloom (19x14cm-7x6in) s. 7-Apr-3 Bonhams, Bath #62/R

£1600 $2576 €2400 Rouge, blanc et bleu (54x44cm-21x17in) s. 15-Jan-3 Cheffins Grain & Comins, Cambridge #452/R
£6000 $9300 €9000 Still life with roses. Still life with oranges (25x35cm-10x14in) s. pair. 31-Oct-2 Christie's, London #123/R est:6000-8000

SHANNON, Charles Haslewood (1863-1937) British
£5500 $8855 €8250 Brown and silver (32x32cm-13x13in) s.i.verso prov. 20-Feb-3 Christie's, London #241/R
£45000 $72450 €67500 Rose and Blanche (107x98cm-42x39in) s. prov.exhib.lit. 20-Feb-3 Christie's, London #240/R est:50000
Works on paper
£1000 $1640 €1450 Study for a bunch of grapes (27x28cm-11x11in) init. col chk. 9-Jun-3 Bonhams, Bath #111/R
£1100 $1705 €1650 Visitation (11x12cm-4x5in) mono. W/C bodycol sold with a lithograph. 24-Sep-2 Bonhams, New Bond Street #5/R est:700-1000

SHANNON, David Michael (1927-1993) Australian
£632 $960 €948 Autumn landscape (50x60cm-20x24in) s.d.78 canvasboard. 19-Aug-2 Joel, Victoria #283/R est:2000-2500 (A.D 1800)
£679 $1052 €1019 Portrait (75x49cm-30x19in) s.d.57 board. 29-Oct-2 Lawson Menzies, Sydney #149 (A.D 1900)
£714 $1121 €1071 House on the beach (39x49cm-15x19in) s.d.65 sold with catalogue prov.exhib. 25-Nov-2 Christie's, Melbourne #405/R (A.D 2000)
£1073 $1598 €1610 Abstract (70x89cm-28x35in) canvas on board prov. 27-Aug-2 Christie's, Melbourne #171/R est:3000-5000 (A.D 2800)
£1149 $1805 €1724 Berry's scrub (50x60cm-20x24in) s.d.85 board. 15-Apr-3 Lawson Menzies, Sydney #230/R est:2500-5000 (A.D 3000)
£1423 $2178 €2135 Heathcote no.2 (91x76cm-36x30in) s.d.98 i.verso prov. 25-Aug-2 Sotheby's, Paddington #144/R est:4000-6000 (A.D 4000)
£5694 $8712 €8541 Composition with saw (107x61cm-42x24in) s.d.58 board prov.exhib. 26-Aug-2 Sotheby's, Paddington #540/R est:18000-25000 (A.D 16000)
Works on paper
£286 $451 €429 Rocks by the sea II (61x76cm-24x30in) s.d.63 s.i.verso synthetic polymer on canvas. 27-Nov-2 Deutscher-Menzies, Melbourne #208/R (A.D 800)

SHANNON, Sir James Jebusa (1862-1923) British/American
£6500 $10335 €9750 Portrait of Lady Grace Dance (100x75cm-39x30in) 30-Apr-3 Hampton & Littlewood, Exeter #469/R est:500-700
£28000 $45080 €42000 Silver ship (117x76cm-46x30in) prov.exhib.lit. 20-Feb-3 Christie's, London #205/R est:30000

SHANNON, Thomas (1947-) American
£646 $1028 €950 Mud ball (100x160cm-39x63in) s.d.1989 s.d.verso acrylic. 3-Mar-3 Marc Kohn, Paris #23/R

SHAPIRO, Boris (1968-) ?
£321 $503 €500 Shana Tova (65x54cm-26x21in) 12-Dec-2 Rabourdin & Choppin de Janvry, Paris #174
£385 $604 €600 Marchand de livres (55x40cm-22x16in) s. 12-Dec-2 Rabourdin & Choppin de Janvry, Paris #190/R

SHAPIRO, Hermon (1933-) British
£1200 $1896 €1800 Two figures (55x38cm-22x15in) init. board. 27-Nov-2 Sotheby's, Olympia #304/R est:300-500

SHAPIRO, Joel (1941-) American
Sculpture
£10127 $16000 €15191 Untitled (15x15x22cm-6x6x9in) st.sig.d.84 golden brown pat bronze prov. 13-Nov-2 Sotheby's, New York #543/R est:20000-25000
£28481 $45000 €42722 Untitled (30x32x10cm-12x13x4in) s.d.1980-81 painted wood prov. 13-Nov-2 Sotheby's, New York #544/R est:30000-40000
£45000 $73800 €67500 Untitled (83x119x117cm-33x47x46in) with sig.num.0/3 gold-brown pat.bronze prov.exhib. 6-Feb-3 Christie's, London #697/R est:40000-60000
£53125 $85000 €79688 Untitled (74x152x90cm-29x60x35in) incised sig.d.86 num.2/3 golden brown pat. bronze prov. 14-May-3 Sotheby's, New York #232/R est:60000-80000

SHAPIRO, Shmuel (1924-1985) American
£586 $926 €850 Under the earth (40x30cm-16x12in) s.d.1977 prov. 2-Apr-3 Dr Fritz Nagel, Stuttgart #9542/R
£1379 $2179 €2000 Composition in red, blue and green (101x100cm-40x39in) s. prov. 2-Apr-3 Dr Fritz Nagel, Stuttgart #9541/R est:3000

SHAPLAND, John (1865-1929) British
Works on paper
£280 $468 €406 Niece, South of France (36x51cm-14x20in) s. W/C. 20-Jun-3 Keys, Aylsham #507
£400 $652 €600 Fluelin, Lake Lucerne, Switzerland (46x28cm-18x11in) s.i. W/C bodycol. 11-Feb-3 Fellows & Sons, Birmingham #65/R
£460 $736 €690 Mediterranean coastal landscape. s. W/C. 13-May-3 Bonhams, Sevenoaks #359
£520 $816 €780 Off the coast of Cornwall. coastal scene near Torquay (28x46cm-11x18in) s. W/C bodycol pair. 21-Nov-2 Tennants, Leyburn #659/R

SHAPLEIGH, Frank Henry (1842-1906) American
£959 $1400 €1439 Old gate, Jackson NH (31x19cm-12x7in) s. i.verso board. 10-May-2 Skinner, Boston #77/R est:1000-1500
£1751 $2750 €2627 Old barn in Brownfield, Maine (25x41cm-10x16in) s.d.1886 i.verso prov. 19-Nov-2 Butterfields, San Francisco #8013/R est:3000-5000
£2673 $4250 €4010 Mt Kearsarge, from Rocky Branch, Bartlett, NH (19x31cm-7x12in) s.d.1886 i.verso board prov. 7-Mar-3 Skinner, Boston #287/R est:800-1200
£2690 $4250 €4035 Old kitchen in Bartlett, NH (25x41cm-10x16in) s.d.1886. 17-Nov-2 CRN Auctions, Cambridge #2/R
£2692 $4200 €4038 Sentinel rock, Yosemite Valley (27x43cm-11x17in) s.d.1872 prov. 12-Apr-3 Weschler, Washington #569/R est:3000-5000
£2975 $4700 €4463 Mt Chacorua from Tamworth (18x30cm-7x12in) s.d.1886 panel. 17-Nov-2 CRN Auctions, Cambridge #1/R
£7186 $12000 €10420 Mt. Washington from Glenn Road Jackson NH (51x76cm-20x30in) s.d.1877 s.i.verso. 22-Jun-3 Freeman, Philadelphia #83/R est:3000-5000

SHARE, Henry Pruett (1853-1905) American
£252 $400 €378 Woman with dog (23x38cm-9x15in) s.d.84 grisaille. 7-Mar-3 Jackson's, Cedar Falls #865/R

SHARP, Dorothea (1874-1955) British
£2419 $3823 €3629 Still life of flowers in a blue vase (61x51cm-24x20in) s. 18-Nov-2 Waddingtons, Toronto #142/R est:4000-6000 (C.D 6000)
£3000 $5010 €4350 On the rocks (30x40cm-12x16in) s. board. 25-Jun-3 Bonhams, Bury St Edmunds #606/R est:3000-5000
£3400 $5576 €5100 Spring flowers (46x38cm-18x15in) s. board prov. 3-Jun-3 Sotheby's, Olympia #42/R est:2000-3000
£3704 $5704 €5556 June flowers (51x41cm-20x16in) board. 26-Oct-2 Heffel, Vancouver #50 est:8000-12000 (C.D 9000)
£4000 $6240 €6000 Mixed bunch (49x39cm-19x15in) s. board. 15-Oct-2 Bearnes, Exeter #425/R est:3000-4000
£4032 $6371 €6048 Still life of flowers in a white pitcher (51x61cm-20x24in) s. canvasboard. 18-Nov-2 Waddingtons, Toronto #141/R est:4000-6000 (C.D 10000)
£5500 $8635 €8250 By the sea (30x41cm-12x16in) s. panel. 22-Nov-2 Christie's, London #3a/R est:6000-8000
£8000 $12400 €12000 Young shepherd, Tossa near Barcelona (102x114cm-40x45in) s. board. 26-Sep-2 Lane, Penzance #130/R est:8000-12000
£9000 $15030 €13050 Sailing yachts on the Round Pond, Tuilleries Gardens, Paris (61x51cm-24x20in) s. 24-Jun-3 Bonhams, New Bond Street #43/R est:10000-15000
£11000 $17270 €16500 Children in the garden (38x46cm-15x18in) s. panel prov. 22-Nov-2 Christie's, London #3/R est:10000-15000
£11500 $17825 €17250 Children on the foreshore (122x147cm-48x58in) init. 26-Sep-2 Lane, Penzance #175/R est:12000-15000
£16935 $26758 €25403 Children on a rocky shore (51x61cm-20x24in) s. prov. 18-Nov-2 Waddingtons, Toronto #153/R est:10000-15000 (C.D 42000)
£17742 $28032 €26613 Young boy playing with doves (76x95cm-30x37in) s. 18-Nov-2 Waddingtons, Toronto #152/R est:15000-18000 (C.D 44000)
£18000 $30060 €26100 Gathering daisies (51x61cm-20x24in) bears sig. 24-Jun-3 Bonhams, New Bond Street #42/R est:15000-20000
£20000 $31000 €30000 On the beach (76x91cm-30x36in) s. 6-Dec-2 Lyon & Turnbull, Edinburgh #105/R est:20000-30000
£22000 $36080 €33000 Children sitting on the rocks. Trees on a shoreline (38x46cm-15x18in) s. panel double-sided. 6-Jun-3 Christie's, London #8/R est:10000-15000
£31847 $50000 €47771 Children playing by the shore (83x85cm-33x33in) s. prov. 14-Dec-2 Weschler, Washington #598/R est:60000-80000
£33000 $51810 €49500 Water babies, Cornish coast (63x76cm-25x30in) s. prov. 22-Nov-2 Christie's, London #2/R est:25000-35000
£41000 $62320 €61500 Garden scene with three children picking flowers (99x81cm-39x32in) s.d.1913. 28-Aug-2 Brightwells, Leominster #1100/R est:3000-5000

SHARP, J H (1859-1934) American
£1000 $1600 €1450 Bird's nest (22x16cm-9x6in) s. board. 16-May-3 Skinner, Boston #83/R est:1500-2500

SHARP, Joseph Henry (1859-1953) American
£1019 $1600 €1529 Zion Valley, South Utah (25x64cm-10x25in) s.i.d.1930 board. 23-Nov-2 Pook & Pook, Downington #399/R est:2000-3000
£4491 $7500 €6512 Blackfeet Water Hole, Glacier Park (25x35cm-10x14in) s. i.d.1901 verso canvas on board. 18-Jun-3 Christie's, Los Angeles #68/R est:6000-8000
£5090 $8500 €7381 Western landscape (15x23cm-6x9in) s. board. 18-Jun-3 Christie's, Los Angeles #66/R est:8000-12000
£5975 $9500 €8963 Just purchased (23x15cm-9x6in) s.i. canvas on board. 2-Mar-3 Toomey, Oak Park #570/R est:10000-20000
£8075 $13000 €12113 Landscape near Banning, CA (9x13cm-4x5in) s. board prov. 18-Feb-3 John Moran, Pasadena #65 est:6000-8000
£11859 $18500 €17789 View from U.S hill near Taos (41x51cm-16x20in) s. i.verso canvas on board prov.lit. 9-Nov-2 Santa Fe Art, Santa Fe #34/R est:20000-25000
£12821 $20000 €19232 Taos Valley from my studio yard (28x38cm-11x15in) 9-Nov-2 Altermann Galleries, Santa Fe #178
£15287 $24000 €22931 Roberto (23x16cm-9x6in) s. i.verso canvasboard prov. 20-Nov-2 Christie's, Los Angeles #20/R est:25000-35000
£15823 $25000 €22943 Montana winter (51x76cm-20x30in).d.1905. 26-Jul-3 Coeur d'Alene, Hayden #50/R est:30000-50000
£16667 $26000 €25001 Moonlight, Taos Pueblo (41x51cm-16x20in) s. prov.lit. 9-Nov-2 Santa Fe Art, Santa Fe #148/R est:50000-75000
£22152 $35000 €32120 Pueblo Indian (25x36cm-10x14in) s. board prov. 26-Jul-3 Coeur d'Alene, Hayden #38/R est:20000-30000
£22436 $35000 €33654 Aspens - Taos canon near the Divide (64x76cm-25x30in) s. prov.lit. 9-Nov-2 Santa Fe Art, Santa Fe #198/R est:40000-60000
£44872 $70000 €67308 Lingering snow (41x61cm-16x24in) s.i. prov.lit. 9-Nov-2 Santa Fe Art, Santa Fe #155/R est:65000-85000
£51389 $83250 €74514 Leaf down - Taos Indian girl (41x51cm-16x20in) 23-May-3 Altermann Galleries, Santa Fe #69
£92466 $135000 €138699 The drummer (51x61cm-20x24in) 18-May-2 Altermann Galleries, Santa Fe #36/R
£96386 $160000 €139760 Indian encampment at sunset (30x41cm-12x16in) s. prov. 11-Jun-3 Butterfields, San Francisco #4110/R est:100000-150000

SHARP, Louis H (1875-1946) American
£3226 $5000 €4839 California sunset (61x76cm-24x30in) s.d.1924 i.verso prov. 29-Oct-2 John Moran, Pasadena #649 est:4000-6000

SHARPE, Alfred (1830-1912) Australian
Works on paper
£12158 $18967 €18237 Harlequin or Sulphur islet, Cpromandel New Zealand (38x62cm-15x24in) s.i.d.1881 W/C. 17-Sep-2 Peter Webb, Auckland #103/R est:45000-60000 (NZ.D 40000)

SHARPE, James (1936-) American
£497 $800 €746 Man with rifle poised on rocky outcrop (71x46cm-28x18in) s. acrylic on board. 20-Feb-3 Illustration House, New York #154/R

SHARPE, Phyllis (fl.1934-1939) British
Works on paper
£300 $468 €450 Way to the Plain (34x25cm-13x10in) s. W/C exhib. 9-Oct-2 Woolley & Wallis, Salisbury #7/R

SHARPE, Wendy (1960-) Australian
£1057 $1670 €1533 German, self portrait (60x50cm-24x20in) s.i. 22-Jul-3 Lawson Menzies, Sydney #191/R est:3000-3500 (A.D 2600)
Works on paper
£335 $522 €503 Dancers (44x34cm-17x13in) s. mixed media. 21-Oct-2 Australian Art Auctions, Sydney #90 (A.D 950)

SHARPE, William (fl.1861-1879) British
Works on paper
£900 $1494 €1350 Billet (31x45cm-12x18in) W/C htd white exhib. 12-Jun-3 Bonhams, New Bond Street #679/R

SHARPLES, James (attrib) (1752-1811) American
£2500 $4075 €3750 Portrait of the Ottley family (26x20cm-10x8in) i. set of five. 29-Jan-3 Sotheby's, Olympia #141/R est:2000-3000
Works on paper
£360 $562 €522 Portrait of Mrs John Corbet (6x6cm-2x2in) pastel. 27-Mar-3 Neales, Nottingham #901/R

SHATTUCK, Aaron Draper (1832-1928) American
£2188 $3500 €3282 Landscape with sheep (30x46cm-12x18in) s. board. 17-May-3 Pook & Pook, Downington #234a/R est:4000-6000
£2969 $4750 €4454 Landscape with cows at a watering hole (33x48cm-13x19in) s. 17-May-3 Pook & Pook, Downington #391/R est:4000-5000
£7547 $12000 €11321 Hay Wain, Granby, Connecticut (46x77cm-18x30in) s. prov. 4-Mar-3 Christie's, Rockefeller NY #6/R est:15000-25000

SHAUL, Ilana (1957-) Israeli
£448 $713 €650 Geisha (100x120cm-39x47in) s.d.97. 10-Mar-3 Sotheby's, Amsterdam #335

SHAVER, Samuel M (attrib) (1816-1878) American
£9032 $14000 €13548 Portrait of a young woman, said to be Anne Elizabeth Stuart Nelson (71x69cm-28x27in) linen sold with a book prov. 20-Jul-2 Brunk, Ashville #698 est:2000-4000

SHAW, A J (19th C) American
£798 $1300 €1197 Still life with fruit (30x41cm-12x16in) s. 2-Feb-3 Grogan, Boston #7

SHAW, Arthur Winter (1869-1948) British
£282 $446 €423 Sunset early spring (36x46cm-14x18in) s. prov. 18-Nov-2 Waddingtons, Toronto #90a/R (C.D 700)
Works on paper
£620 $1004 €930 Lady dancing (26x19cm-10x7in) s.d.1926 W/C two. 21-May-3 Bonhams, Knightsbridge #224/R

SHAW, Charles Green (1892-1974) American
£1299 $2000 €1949 Complex in green (127x102cm-50x40in) s. s.d.1967 verso prov.exhib. 4-Sep-2 Christie's, Rockefeller NY #370/R est:3000-5000
£4403 $7000 €6605 Beyond the now (81x122cm-32x48in) s. s.d.1959 verso prov.exhib. 4-Mar-3 Christie's, Rockefeller NY #76/R est:4000-6000
£5346 $8500 €8019 Moving waters (163x122cm-64x48in) s. s.verso prov.exhib. 4-Mar-3 Christie's, Rockefeller NY #122/R est:5000-7000
£8805 $14000 €13208 Abstraction with red, yellow and black forms (41x30cm-16x12in) s.d.1940 canvasboard prov. 4-Mar-3 Christie's, Rockefeller NY #118/R est:5000-7000
£11321 $18000 €16982 Abstraction with blue, brown and grey forms (41x51cm-16x20in) s.d.1941 canvasboard prov. 4-Mar-3 Christie's, Rockefeller NY #121/R est:4000-6000
Works on paper
£518 $850 €751 Ice bound (13x20cm-5x8in) s. gouache. 1-Jun-3 Wright, Chicago #269/R

SHAW, Charles L (19th C) British
£621 $1000 €932 Autumn landscape with a man in a rowboat (43x28cm-17x11in) s.i.d.1883. 22-Feb-3 Pook & Pook, Downington #92/R
£1090 $1700 €1635 Woodland stream with fisherman (69x51cm-27x20in) s.d.85 s.d.verso. 5-Nov-2 Arthur James, Florida #405
£1090 $1700 €1635 Woman on bridge over woodland stream (69x51cm-27x20in) s.d.85 s.d.verso. 5-Nov-2 Arthur James, Florida #406

SHAW, Dennis Orme (?) Irish?
£320 $496 €480 Tullough River, Co. Tyrone (51x61cm-20x24in) s.d.2002 verso. 2-Oct-2 John Ross, Belfast #262
£380 $555 €570 Kearney, Ards (51x41cm-20x16in) s. 12-Jun-2 John Ross, Belfast #132
£892 $1391 €1400 Cottages near Roundstone, Connemara (49x59cm-19x23in) s. board. 6-Nov-2 James Adam, Dublin #141/R
Works on paper
£280 $434 €420 Farm buildings, Skerry Groom cross roads, Stewartstown, Co. Tyrone (51x76cm-20x30in) s. mixed media. 2-Oct-2 John Ross, Belfast #197

SHAW, Ed (20th C) American
£932 $1500 €1398 Woman buying Alka Seltzer from pharmacist (107x86cm-42x34in) 20-Feb-3 Illustration House, New York #155/R est:1800-2400

SHAW, Jim (1952-) American
Works on paper
£350 $550 €525 Untitled, greyhound middle (43x36cm-17x14in) pencil exhib. 21-Nov-2 Swann Galleries, New York #197/R

SHAW, John Byam (1872-1919) British
£5696 $9000 €8544 Angel before Adam and Eve (46x34cm-18x13in) s. panel prov. 24-Apr-3 Sotheby's, New York #123/R est:15000-20000
£7742 $12000 €11613 Cleopatra (30x25cm-12x10in) s. panel prov.exhib.lit. 30-Oct-2 Christie's, Rockefeller NY #107/R est:15000-20000

SHAW, Joshua (1776-1860) American/British
£1420 $2300 €2130 Pastoral scene with figures (94x135cm-37x53in) 25-Jan-3 Skinner, Boston #839/R est:2000-3000

£2600 $4316 €3900 Italianate lake landscape with figures and boats (32x42cm-13x17in) panel prov. 10-Jun-3 Christie's, London #63/R est:3000-5000

SHAW, Lalu Prasad (1937-) Indian
£2176 $3590 €3155 Man (57x41cm-22x16in) s.d. tempera. 6-Jul-3 Christie's, Hong Kong #95/R est:15000-20000 (HK.D 28000)

SHAW, Mary (1955-) British?
£352 $567 €500 Blackbird on a branch (25x17cm-10x7in) s. panel. 6-May-3 Vendu Notarishuis, Rotterdam #612/R

SHAW, Walter (1851-1933) British
£400 $668 €580 Lion Rock, waves breaking on the Devonshire coast (32x47cm-13x19in) s. i.verso. 19-Jun-3 Lane, Penzance #144
£1950 $3023 €2925 Choppy sea with rocky coastline, possibly Cornwall (102x152cm-40x60in) s.d.1894. 25-Sep-2 Brightwells, Leominster #932/R est:2000-3000

SHAWCROSS, Neal (1940-) British
£1000 $1590 €1500 Yellow pages (38x43cm-15x17in) s.d.1997 acrylic board. 5-Mar-3 John Ross, Belfast #130 est:1200-1400
£4241 $6573 €6700 Still life with lemons (80x93cm-31x37in) s.d.2000 acrylic on paper prov. 24-Sep-2 De Veres Art Auctions, Dublin #23/R est:6000-8000

Works on paper
£1000 $1550 €1500 Still life, teacup and saucer (30x38cm-12x15in) s.d.2001 mixed media. 4-Dec-2 John Ross, Belfast #230 est:1000-1200
£1342 $2161 €2000 Still life of fruit on a plate (20x24cm-8x9in) s. W/C. 18-Feb-3 Whyte's, Dublin #62/R est:1500-2000
£1400 $2170 €2100 Still life of oranges (76x81cm-30x32in) s.d.1990 W/C. 2-Oct-2 John Ross, Belfast #114/R est:1500-1800
£1410 $2214 €2200 Blue nude (46x57cm-18x22in) s.d.1979 W/C pastel. 19-Nov-2 Whyte's, Dublin #16/R est:2500-3000
£1500 $2325 €2250 Table top still life (56x45cm-22x18in) s. W/C. 4-Dec-2 John Ross, Belfast #162 est:800-1000
£1700 $2635 €2550 Table top still life (61x76cm-24x30in) s.d.1989 W/C. 2-Oct-2 John Ross, Belfast #180 est:2000-2500
£1795 $2818 €2800 Chairs (46x56cm-18x22in) s.d.1985 W/C prov. 19-Nov-2 Whyte's, Dublin #15/R est:2000-2500
£1800 $2790 €2700 Still life, ladder back chair (55x35cm-22x14in) s.d.2000 mixed media. 4-Dec-2 John Ross, Belfast #49 est:1250-1500
£2200 $3498 €3300 Still life (45x66cm-18x26in) s.d.2002 W/C. 5-Mar-3 John Ross, Belfast #118 est:2250-2500
£2400 $3720 €3600 Still life (40x56cm-16x22in) s.d.2000 mixed media. 4-Dec-2 John Ross, Belfast #134 est:2000-2500
£3400 $5270 €5100 Still life of vase of flowers (112x91cm-44x36in) s.d.1979 W/C. 2-Oct-2 John Ross, Belfast #107 est:2500-3000

SHAYER, Charles (c.1826-1914) British
Works on paper
£260 $413 €390 Passing the volunteer camp near Richmond (43x77cm-17x30in) s.i.d.1882 W/C. 26-Feb-3 Cheffins Grain & Comins, Cambridge #482/R

SHAYER, Henry and Charles (19th C) British
£1650 $2591 €2475 Village scene with drover, sheep and cattle (30x41cm-12x16in) indis sig. 16-Dec-2 Bonhams, Bury St Edmunds #544/R est:1000-1500
£1778 $2951 €2578 Peasants and cattle by a woodland pool (71x91cm-28x36in) s. prov. 16-Jun-3 Waddingtons, Toronto #152/R est:4000-6000 (C.D 4000)
£3500 $5565 €5250 Milkmaid and cattle by a cottage gate (70x92cm-28x36in) init.d.86 prov. 6-Mar-3 Christie's, Kensington #591/R est:3000-5000
£35000 $55300 €52500 Meet. moving off. On the sent. The kill (66x115cm-26x45in) s. set of four prov. 28-Nov-2 Bonhams, Knightsbridge #131/R est:40000-60000

SHAYER, Henry and Charles (attrib) (19th C) British
£2900 $4582 €4350 Noonday rest - harvest landscape (30x40cm-12x16in) bears sig. 2-Dec-2 Bonhams, Bath #81/R est:1500-2000

SHAYER, W (19th C) British
£709 $1149 €1000 Fisherfolk on a beach (43x37cm-17x15in) panel. 20-May-3 Mealy's, Castlecomer #1037/R est:600-800

SHAYER, William (attrib) (19th C) British
£900 $1404 €1350 Day's catch (46x36cm-18x14in) s.indis d.1877. 7-Nov-2 Christie's, Kensington #220/R
£3500 $5740 €5250 Hampshire farmstead (71x91cm-28x36in) s. 29-May-3 Christie's, Kensington #179a est:3000-5000

SHAYER, William (snr) (1787-1879) British
£380 $592 €600 Shepherd resting with sheep (59x77cm-23x30in) s. lit. 14-Sep-2 Bergmann, Erlangen #750/R
£772 $1204 €1158 Landscape with two cows, South Hampton (27x53cm-11x21in) s. 11-Nov-2 Rasmussen, Vejle #655/R (D.KR 9000)
£900 $1476 €1350 Gamekeepers family (49cm-19in circular) 29-May-3 Christie's, Kensington #250
£949 $1500 €1500 Landscape with resting family of herdsmen (40x41cm-16x16in) s.d.1843. 29-Nov-2 Bolland & Marotz, Bremen #772/R est:1600
£1000 $1670 €1450 Coastal scene with fisherfolk at dawn (22x35cm-9x14in) 26-Jun-3 Mellors & Kirk, Nottingham #918/R est:800-1200
£1300 $2145 €1885 Home with the catch (40x61cm-16x24in) s. 2-Jul-3 Sotheby's, Olympia #342/R est:1500-2000
£1400 $2212 €2100 Sorting the catch (31x46cm-12x18in) 2-Dec-2 Bonhams, Bath #117/R est:1500-2500
£1491 $2400 €2237 Mother and daughter on farmstead (41x58cm-16x23in) s. 20-Jan-3 Arthur James, Florida #136
£1800 $2844 €2700 Long awaited letter (30x25cm-12x10in) s. panel. 13-Nov-2 Halls, Shrewsbury #400/R est:1500-1800
£1823 $2881 €2735 Young girl with boy on donkey by the coast (70x90cm-28x35in) bears sig. 27-Nov-2 Falkkloos, Malmo #78017/R est:25000 (S.KR 26000)
£2201 $3434 €3500 After the catch (64x76cm-25x30in) s.d.1861 masonite lit. 20-Sep-2 Schloss Ahlden, Ahlden #1169/R est:3500
£2500 $3900 €3750 Gypsy encampment (51x66cm-20x26in) prov. 7-Nov-2 Christie's, Kensington #178/R est:3000-5000
£3800 $6194 €5700 Fisherfolk on the foreshore (63x112cm-25x44in) s. 30-Jan-3 Lawrence, Crewkerne #728/R est:4000-6000
£4000 $6520 €6000 Wash day (35x46cm-14x18in) s. panel. 12-Feb-3 Bonhams, Knightsbridge #81/R est:2000-3000
£4600 $7268 €6900 Watering place (56x64cm-22x25in) s. 7-Apr-3 Bonhams, Bath #90/R est:3000-4000
£5800 $9570 €8410 Cattle and sheep by a stream in a landscape (45x60cm-18x24in) s. prov. 2-Jul-3 Sotheby's, Olympia #90/R est:3000-5000
£5800 $9454 €8410 Watering place (56x64cm-22x25in) s. 16-Jul-3 Sotheby's, Olympia #9/R est:6000-8000
£6000 $9480 €9000 Figures and cow by gate in landscape (30x30cm-12x12in) s.d.1846 prov. 26-Nov-2 Christie's, London #68/R est:5000-8000
£6500 $10790 €9750 Gypsies camp (58x49cm-23x19in) panel prov. 12-Jun-3 Sotheby's, London #241/R est:7000-9000
£7000 $11060 €10500 Busy coastline (35x46cm-14x18in) s. panel. 2-Dec-2 Sotheby's, London #42/R est:7000-9000
£16000 $26560 €24000 Gypsy encampment in a wooded landscape (71x91cm-28x36in) s. 10-Jun-3 Christie's, London #65/R est:10000-15000
£24000 $39840 €36000 Summer landscape with harvesters (76x102cm-30x40in) s. 10-Jun-3 Christie's, London #66/R est:20000-30000

SHAYER, William (snr-attrib) (1787-1879) British
£800 $1328 €1160 Cattle by a steam (36x30cm-14x12in) bears sig prov. 16-Jun-3 Waddingtons, Toronto #115/R est:1000-1500 (C.D 1800)
£2400 $3984 €3480 Young fisherfolk Isle of Wight (46x36cm-18x14in) panel prov. 16-Jun-3 Waddingtons, Toronto #141/R est:3000-5000 (C.D 5400)

SHAYER, William (19th C) British
£740 $1214 €1110 Coastal scene with two figures, pony and fish in the foreground (30x24cm-12x9in) s. 10-Feb-3 David Duggleby, Scarborough #603
£940 $1570 €1363 Fisher folk on a beach with sailing boats and cliffs (23x30cm-9x12in) s.d.1839. 24-Jun-3 Neal & Fletcher, Woodbridge #341

SHAYER, William J (1811-1892) British
£800 $1264 €1200 Encampment with figure, horse and dogs in the foreground (49x60cm-19x24in) 12-Nov-2 Bonhams, Knightsbridge #36/R
£1250 $1950 €1875 Two figures with a grey pony on a beach (30x23cm-12x9in) s. 10-Sep-2 David Duggleby, Scarborough #374/R est:1000-1500

SHAYER, William J (attrib) (1811-1892) British
£1150 $1794 €1725 Rest by the wayside (39x29cm-15x11in) indis sig. 6-Nov-2 Bonhams, Chester #463 est:1200-1800

SHAYER, William and WILLIAMS, Edward Charles (19th C) British
£12000 $18960 €18000 Outside the Bell Inn (77x127cm-30x50in) 26-Nov-2 Christie's, London #66/R est:12000-18000

SHEAD, Garry (1942-) Australian
£1219 $1852 €1829 Mermaid (28x20cm-11x8in) s. paper. 28-Aug-2 Deutscher-Menzies, Melbourne #245/R est:4000-6000 (A.D 3400)
£1538 $2446 €2307 Muse resting (19x13cm-7x5in) s. i.verso paper. 4-Mar-3 Deutscher-Menzies, Melbourne #220/R est:2500-3500 (A.D 4000)
£2107 $3140 €3161 Sydney (29x37cm-11x15in) s.d.1980. 27-Aug-2 Christie's, Melbourne #341 est:3000-5000 (A.D 5500)

£2143 $3321 €3215 Chatswood nude (99x79cm-39x31in) s.d.66 oil collage board. 29-Oct-2 Lawson Menzies, Sydney #28/R est:6000-9000 (A.D 6000)
£2500 $3925 €3750 Model in front of window (26x19cm-10x7in) s. paper prov.exhib. 25-Nov-2 Christie's, Melbourne #288/R est:7000-10000 (A.D 7000)
£3571 $5607 €5357 Artist and model with suspenders (27x20cm-11x8in) s. paper prov.exhib. 25-Nov-2 Christie's, Melbourne #208/R est:7000-10000 (A.D 10000)
£3929 $6207 €5894 Portrait of Phillip Cox (185x138cm-73x54in) s.d.1967 board prov. 17-Nov-2 Sotheby's, Paddington #84 est:5000-8000 (A.D 11000)
£9756 $15415 €14146 Metamorphosis II (90x122cm-35x48in) s.d.89 exhib. 22-Jul-3 Lawson Menzies, Sydney #122/R est:14000-20000 (A.D 24000)
£10753 $16344 €16130 D H Lawrence Series (30x52cm-12x20in) s.d.91 board prov. 28-Aug-2 Deutscher-Menzies, Melbourne #63/R est:35000-45000 (A.D 30000)
£16858 $26467 €25287 Before the start 1989 (182x182cm-72x72in) s. prov. 15-Apr-3 Lawson Menzies, Sydney #39/R est:55000-65000 (A.D 44000)
£18846 $29965 €28269 Two Friedas (63x63cm-25x25in) s. composition board. 4-Mar-3 Deutscher-Menzies, Melbourne #28/R est:40000-50000 (A.D 49000)
£20930 $33279 €31395 Fall (60x61cm-24x24in) s. i.verso board prov. 5-May-3 Sotheby's, Melbourne #103/R est:55000-75000 (A.D 54000)
£21505 $32688 €32258 Headland (91x122cm-36x48in) s.d.92 composition board prov.exhib.lit. 28-Aug-2 Deutscher-Menzies, Melbourne #44/R est:60000-80000 (A.D 60000)
£24904 $37107 €37356 Lawrence and kangaroo (51x59cm-20x23in) s. s.i.verso board. 27-Aug-2 Christie's, Melbourne #3/R est:38000-45000 (A.D 65000)
£31873 $52271 €47810 Dancing with the muse (122x152cm-48x60in) s.d.01 prov.exhib. 4-Jun-3 Deutscher-Menzies, Melbourne #25/R est:85000-100000 (A.D 80000)
£44000 $70840 €66000 Secret (91x121cm-36x48in) s. board. 6-May-3 Christie's, Melbourne #26/R est:60000-80000 (A.D 110000)

Works on paper
£345 $541 €518 Chase (41x34cm-16x13in) s. ink. 15-Apr-3 Lawson Menzies, Sydney #191/R (A.D 900)
£536 $842 €804 Lovers (35x26cm-14x10in) s.i.d.8.1.76 ink W/C. 15-Apr-3 Lawson Menzies, Sydney #190/R est:1000-1200 (A.D 1400)
£753 $1144 €1130 Rescue (33x26cm-13x10in) s. ink. 27-Aug-2 Goodman, Sydney #164 (A.D 2100)

SHEARBON, Andrew (fl.1860s) British
£1000 $1540 €1500 Musical interlude (30x41cm-12x16in) s.d.1870. 5-Sep-2 Christie's, Kensington #298/R est:1000-1300

SHEARER, Brody (20th C) Canadian
£269 $422 €404 Landscape (66x86cm-26x34in) s.d.58 board. 24-Jul-2 Walker's, Ottawa #429/R (C.D 650)

SHEARER, Christopher H (1840-1926) American
£597 $950 €896 Early autumn landscape (51x84cm-20x33in) s.d. canvas on board. 4-May-3 Treadway Gallery, Cincinnati #513/R
£2244 $3500 €3366 Spruce cabin run, Monroe Co, PA (51x76cm-20x30in) s.d.1885. 18-Sep-2 Alderfer's, Hatfield #345/R est:2500-3000

Works on paper
£1592 $2500 €2388 Landscapes (25x46cm-10x18in) s. one.i. W/C. 23-Nov-2 Pook & Pook, Downington #230/R est:600-800

SHEARER, Donald M (20th C) British
£400 $652 €600 Gareloch (50x100cm-20x39in) 14-Feb-3 Lyon & Turnbull, Edinburgh #143

SHEARER, Janet (20th C) British?
£820 $1337 €1230 Hopeless dawn (122x168cm-48x66in) after Walter Langle. 13-Feb-3 David Lay, Penzance #460

SHEARER, Larry (1945-2001) American
£355 $550 €533 Lulis (122x91cm-48x36in) s.d.91 i.verso acrylic. 7-Dec-2 Neal Auction Company, New Orleans #930

SHEE, Sir Martin Archer (1769-1850) British
£1650 $2706 €2475 Portrait of Anthony Morris Storer, seated, and wearing a black velvet coat (74x63cm-29x25in) s. indis d. 4-Feb-3 Bonhams, Leeds #391 est:1500-2000
£11500 $19090 €17250 Portrait of John Russell, 6th Duke of Bedford (76x63cm-30x25in) canvas on board prov. 12-Jun-3 Sotheby's, London #73/R est:5000-7000
£12821 $20256 €20000 Portrait of William Fairlie (238x146cm-94x57in) prov.exhib. 12-Nov-2 Mealy's, Castlecomer #1063/R est:25000
£38462 $60769 €60000 Group portrait of Margaret Fairlie with children (239x148cm-94x58in) prov.exhib. 12-Nov-2 Mealy's, Castlecomer #1062/R est:30000

SHEE, Sir Martin Archer (attrib) (1769-1850) British
£12579 $19371 €20000 Portrait du Capitaine Barnaby dans un paysage (234x144cm-92x57in) 22-Oct-2 Palais de Beaux Arts, Brussels #54/R est:5000-7000

SHEELER, Charles (1883-1965) American
£141975 $230000 €212963 Plums on a plate (25x35cm-10x14in) s. i.verso panel painted c.1910 prov.exhib.lit. 21-May-3 Sotheby's, New York #18/R est:60000-80000
£154839 $240000 €232259 Convergence II (15x10cm-6x4in) s.d.1952 tempera on board prov.exhib. 5-Dec-2 Christie's, Rockefeller NY #121/R est:70000-100000

Photographs
£2110 $3250 €3165 Beech tree (19x13cm-7x5in) s.d.1951 photograph prov. 22-Oct-2 Sotheby's, New York #171/R est:5000-8000
£3165 $5000 €4748 Air shaft (24x16cm-9x6in) s.i.d.1949 warm toned photograph. 23-Apr-3 Sotheby's, New York #210/R est:5000-7000
£4870 $7500 €7305 Study of the Brancusi sculpture portrait of Mrs Eugene Meyer (24x14cm-9x6in) i.verso photograph executed 1940 prov. 24-Oct-2 Sotheby's, New York #184/R est:3000-5000
£4878 $8000 €7317 Cactus (22x15cm-9x6in) indis.sig.i. st.verso silver print. 10-Feb-3 Swann Galleries, New York #46/R est:5000-7500
£6169 $9500 €9254 Study of the Brancusi, sculpture La Negresse blanche (24x17cm-9x7in) i. photograph executed c.1940 prov. 24-Oct-2 Sotheby's, New York #183/R est:3000-5000
£31169 $48000 €46754 Coke ovens - River Rouge (22x19cm-9x7in) s.i. photograph prov.exhib.lit. 22-Oct-2 Sotheby's, New York #167/R est:10000-15000
£31169 $48000 €46754 Generator (24x19cm-9x7in) s.i. d.1939 verso photograph prov.exhib.lit. 22-Oct-2 Sotheby's, New York #170/R est:5000-8000
£71429 $110000 €107144 Pulverzer buildings, Ford Plant, Detroit (24x19cm-9x7in) s. photograph prov.exhib.lit. 22-Oct-2 Sotheby's, New York #60/R est:70000-100000

SHEETS, Millard (1907-1989) American
£3614 $6000 €5240 Ships sailing through a channel (76x157cm-30x62in) s. 11-Jun-3 Butterfields, San Francisco #4300/R est:7000-10000
£5096 $8000 €7644 African plains (79x198cm-31x78in) s.d.1964 canvas on board prov. 19-Nov-2 Butterfields, San Francisco #8329/R est:10000-15000
£7097 $11000 €10646 Protea and fruit (102x74cm-40x29in) s.d.1979 acrylic on canvas prov. 29-Oct-2 John Moran, Pasadena #710 est:12000-18000
£8387 $13000 €12581 Poplars in landscape (46x53cm-18x21in) s.d.1927. 29-Oct-2 John Moran, Pasadena #709a est:10000-15000

Works on paper
£449 $700 €674 Burma, two girls washing clothes (23x28cm-9x11in) s.i. W/C. 12-Oct-2 Neal Auction Company, New Orleans #1375
£1553 $2500 €2330 Freighter in moderate seas (30x46cm-12x18in) s. W/C. 18-Feb-3 John Moran, Pasadena #85 est:2000-3000
£2108 $3500 €3057 View of a colourful valley (55x75cm-22x30in) s. pencil W/C prov. 11-Jun-3 Butterfields, San Francisco #4302/R est:4000-6000
£3106 $5000 €4659 Corner of the palace/land of the temples (21x29cm-8x11in) i.d.December 1943 prov. 18-Feb-3 John Moran, Pasadena #81 est:3000-4000
£3822 $6000 €5733 Fisherman's camp (53x74cm-21x29in) s.d.1948 pencil W/C prov. 19-Nov-2 Butterfields, San Francisco #8328/R est:3000-5000
£4037 $6500 €6056 Bay shore (56x76cm-22x30in) s. W/C. 18-Feb-3 John Moran, Pasadena #83c est:5500-7500
£4125 $6600 €5981 India (53x74cm-21x29in) s.i.d. W/C. 17-May-3 Selkirks, St. Louis #430/R est:8000-9000
£4459 $7000 €6689 Central Park (56x76cm-22x30in) s.d.1981 W/C. 20-Nov-2 Christie's, Los Angeles #127/R est:8000-12000
£5128 $8000 €7692 Snow in Monument Valley with seven Indians and a horse (30x61cm-12x24in) s.d.1949 i.verso W/C exhib. 1-Aug-2 Eldred, East Dennis #822/R est:5000-10000
£10323 $16000 €15485 Ladies of Jaliaza (56x71cm-22x28in) s.d.1985 i.verso W/C. 29-Oct-2 John Moran, Pasadena #685 est:7500-10000

SHEFFIELD, George (1839-1892) British

Works on paper
£320 $534 €464 Figures on a bridge in a snowy river landscape (22x29cm-9x11in) init. col chk. 25-Jun-3 Bonhams, Bury St Edmunds #529

£580 $969 €841 Shore scene with ships (52x72cm-20x28in) s.d.1886 black chk. 25-Jun-3 Bonhams, Bury St Edmunds #528

SHEGELMAN, Simon (1933-) Russian
£3797 $6000 €5696 Piano bar (46x61cm-18x24in) s.d.2000 acrylic. 22-Apr-3 Butterfields, San Francisco #6081/R est:3000-5000
£6962 $11000 €10443 Au revoir (86x107cm-34x42in) s.d.2001 acrylic. 22-Apr-3 Butterfields, San Francisco #6082/R est:5000-7000

SHEIL, Edward (1834-1869) British
£14286 $22000 €21429 Home after work (91x71cm-36x28in) s.d.1863 prov.exhib. 24-Oct-2 Shannon's, Milford #128/R est:6000-8000

SHELBOURNE, Anita (20th C) British
£596 $936 €870 Los Baladins (24x46cm-9x18in) s. i.verso. 15-Apr-3 De Veres Art Auctions, Dublin #193/R
£753 $1183 €1100 Untitled (31x46cm-12x18in) board. 15-Apr-3 De Veres Art Auctions, Dublin #28 est:800-1200
£822 $1282 €1200 Landscape (42x46cm-17x18in) s. 8-Apr-3 James Adam, Dublin #110/R
£823 $1275 €1300 Landscape (91x76cm-36x30in) s. s.verso. 24-Sep-2 De Veres Art Auctions, Dublin #88 est:1500-2500
Works on paper
£527 $828 €770 Landscape (22x30cm-9x12in) s.i.verso gouache. 15-Apr-3 De Veres Art Auctions, Dublin #29/R

SHELESNYAK, Henry (20th C) Israeli
£5696 $9000 €8544 Untitled (100x100cm-39x39in) s.d.1971 s.d.verso acrylic airbrush collage pencil on canvas. 27-Apr-3 Sotheby's, Tel Aviv #75/R est:9000-12000

SHELLEY, Samuel (c.1750-1808) British
Miniatures
£4500 $7515 €6525 Major Perryn in red uniform (12cm-5in) s. rec. giltwood gesso frame oval exec.c.1795. 25-Jun-3 Sotheby's, Olympia #36/R est:4000-6000

SHELLHASE, George (20th C) American
Works on paper
£854 $1400 €1238 Norwalk Symphony in rehearsal (41x51cm-16x20in) s. W/C tempera over pencil exec.c.1935. 5-Jun-3 Swann Galleries, New York #214/R

SHELLY, Arthur (1841-1902) British
Works on paper
£950 $1548 €1425 Snowy landscape with house (25x35cm-10x14in) s. indis d. W/C. 29-Jan-3 Sotheby's, Olympia #121/R est:800-1200

SHELOUMOV, A (?) Russian
£2244 $3500 €3366 Russian cavalry (33x58cm-13x23in) 20-Sep-2 Du Mouchelle, Detroit #2021/R est:3000-5000

SHELTON, Alphonse Joseph (1905-1976) American
£549 $900 €824 Rough water (64x91cm-25x36in) s. i.verso. 8-Feb-3 Neal Auction Company, New Orleans #565/R

SHELTON, Margaret D (1915-1984) Canadian
£382 $599 €573 Mt Rundle (45x60cm-18x24in) s.i.d.1982 board. 25-Nov-2 Hodgins, Calgary #330/R (C.D 950)
£391 $610 €653 Artist garden (30x41cm-12x16in) s. i.verso board. 13-Apr-3 Levis, Calgary #106 est:800-1000 (C.D 900)
£489 $802 €709 Bow River, Seebe (40x50cm-16x20in) s.i.d.1977 board. 9-Jun-3 Hodgins, Calgary #54/R est:1000-1500 (C.D 1100)
£489 $802 €709 Mountains landscape (30x41cm-12x16in) paper on board. 1-Jun-3 Levis, Calgary #118/R est:800-1000 (C.D 1100)
£522 $814 €870 Massive range from Campground (41x51cm-16x20in) s.d.1982 board. 13-Apr-3 Levis, Calgary #105/R est:1000-1200 (C.D 1200)
£843 $1333 €1265 Mt Christie (46x61cm-18x24in) canvasboard. 1-Dec-2 Levis, Calgary #96/R est:1500-2000 (C.D 2100)
£1356 $2156 €2034 Thunderstorm, Ghost lake (40x50cm-16x20in) s.i.d.1973 board. 23-Mar-3 Hodgins, Calgary #72/R est:800-1200 (C.D 3200)
Works on paper
£201 $317 €302 Poppies (43x28cm-17x11in) d.1974 W/C. 1-Dec-2 Levis, Calgary #99/R (C.D 500)
£222 $364 €322 Autumn on Vermilion Lakes (33x51cm-13x20in) W/C. 1-Jun-3 Levis, Calgary #119/R (C.D 500)
£251 $394 €377 Mt Rundle in the clouds (33x46cm-13x18in) s.d.1983 W/C. 25-Nov-2 Hodgins, Calgary #93/R (C.D 625)
£261 $412 €392 City scape (33x51cm-13x20in) d.1983 W/C. 1-Dec-2 Levis, Calgary #98/R (C.D 650)
£281 $441 €422 Barn on Indus Road (26x42cm-10x17in) s.d.1982 W/C. 25-Nov-2 Hodgins, Calgary #26/R (C.D 700)
£289 $474 €419 Rundle from Vermillion Lakes (25x35cm-10x14in) W/C. 9-Jun-3 Hodgins, Calgary #362/R (C.D 650)
£333 $547 €483 Wagon on Indus Road (24x34cm-9x13in) W/C. 9-Jun-3 Hodgins, Calgary #147/R (C.D 750)
£341 $536 €512 Farmstead below Mt Nelson (33x49cm-13x19in) s.d.1982 W/C. 25-Nov-2 Hodgins, Calgary #290/R (C.D 850)
£356 $583 €516 Barn at Sylvan lake (25x36cm-10x14in) W/C. 1-Jun-3 Levis, Calgary #120/R (C.D 800)
£391 $610 €653 Untitled - Vermillion Lake (32x50cm-13x20in) s.d.1975 W/C. 13-Apr-3 Levis, Calgary #107/R est:600-800 (C.D 900)
£422 $692 €612 Meeting of the waters (26x33cm-10x13in) s.d.1943 W/C. 9-Jun-3 Hodgins, Calgary #350/R est:700-900 (C.D 950)
£636 $1011 €954 Lake Minnewanka, Mt. Alymer (33x46cm-13x18in) s. W/C prov. 23-Mar-3 Hodgins, Calgary #62/R est:500-700 (C.D 1500)

SHELTON, Peter (1951-) American
Sculpture
£17405 $27500 €26108 Whiteshirt (96x146x8cm-38x57x3in) s. i.d.1984-86 verso fiberglas over wire frame prov.exhib. 13-Nov-2 Sotheby's, New York #117/R est:10000-15000

SHELTON, William Henry (1840-1932) American
£2019 $3250 €3029 Confederate soldiers tracking Union troops at night (33x46cm-13x18in) s. board lit. 10-May-3 Illustration House, New York #47/R est:3000-4000

SHEMI, Yehiel (1922-) Israeli
Sculpture
£8824 $13940 €13236 Wounded bird (52cm-20in) s.num.IV welded metal. 27-Apr-3 Sotheby's, Tel Aviv #73/R est:12000-16000

SHEN DAOHONG (1947-) Chinese
Works on paper
£7770 $12821 €11267 Playing chess (69x179cm-27x70in) s.i. ink scroll. 6-Jul-3 Christie's, Hong Kong #278/R est:120000-150000 (HK.D 100000)

SHEN XINHAI (1909-) Chinese
Works on paper
£435 $713 €600 Scholar with servant and lady in garden (146x39cm-57x15in) i. Indian ink col hanging scroll. 30-May-3 Dr Fritz Nagel, Stuttgart #1279/R

SHEN YINMO and XIE ZHILIU (20th C) Chinese
Works on paper
£3252 $5138 €4878 Green plum blossom, ink bamboo (18x48cm-7x19in) s.i. ink col folding fan. 28-Apr-3 Sotheby's, Hong Kong #544/R est:20000-40000 (HK.D 40000)

SHEN ZHOU (1427-1509) Chinese
Works on paper
£19425 $32051 €28166 Landscape of Jin Shan (28x200cm-11x79in) s.i. ink handscroll. 6-Jul-3 Christie's, Hong Kong #429/R est:300000-400000 (HK.D 250000)
£31080 $51282 €45066 Landscape (51x44cm-20x17in) s.i.d.1502 ink hanging scroll after Li Cheng. 6-Jul-3 Christie's, Hong Kong #408/R est:400000-550000 (HK.D 400000)

SHEPARD, Ernest Howard (1879-1976) British
Works on paper
£250 $405 €375 Sirmione, Lake Garda (25x36cm-10x14in) i.d.1910 W/C pencil. 21-Jan-3 Bonhams, Knightsbridge #154/R
£380 $600 €570 Governess cart and the dragon (28x23cm-11x9in) s. pen ink htd white. 18-Dec-2 Mallams, Oxford #528/R
£700 $1113 €1050 Illustration of the poem Devon by E V Lucas (31x23cm-12x9in) s. ink over pencil. 26-Feb-3 Sotheby's, Olympia #154/R
£700 $1120 €1050 Hay harvest (23x20cm-9x8in) s. pen ink. 11-Mar-3 Gorringes, Lewes #2294/R
£750 $1185 €1125 You are nearer the sun on a tram (31x20cm-12x8in) s. pen ink. 26-Nov-2 Bonhams, Knightsbridge #229/R
£800 $1264 €1200 Illustration for an advertisement of a Punch Almanack (29x38cm-11x15in) s. bodycol. 26-Nov-2 Bonhams, Knightsbridge #232/R

£850 $1377 €1275 Emperor of the road - going to the British Empire exhibition at Wembley (19x31cm-7x12in) s. pen ink htd white. 20-May-3 Sotheby's, Olympia #129/R
£6000 $9960 €9000 You're the very image of her (10x5cm-4x2in) init. pen ink pair prov. 12-Jun-3 Bonhams, New Bond Street #698/R est:4000-6000
£6500 $10790 €9750 Piglet digging a hole (6x7cm-2x3in) i.verso pen ink W/C prov. 12-Jun-3 Bonhams, New Bond Street #697/R est:3000-5000
£7500 $12450 €11250 Look here I find I've left my purse behind (13x9cm-5x4in) init. pen ink prov. 12-Jun-3 Bonhams, New Bond Street #700/R est:3000-5000
£9500 $14725 €14250 Christopher Robin by the fireside (14x11cm-6x4in) init. pencil pen black ink crayon W/C prov. 4-Dec-2 Christie's, Kensington #139/R est:6000-8000
£18000 $29880 €27000 Pooh singing on a stepping stone (20x20cm-8x8in) i. pen ink W/C prov. 12-Jun-3 Bonhams, New Bond Street #696/R est:6000-9000

SHEPHERD, David (1931-) British
£1800 $2862 €2700 Ballerina (56x40cm-22x16in) s. 26-Feb-3 Sotheby's, Olympia #333/R est:1200-1800
£3600 $5724 €5400 Bungle Bungles (61x102cm-24x40in) s.d.1992 i.on overlap prov. 26-Feb-3 Sotheby's, Olympia #334/R est:4000-6000
£6500 $10725 €9425 Snoozing (30x46cm-12x18in) s.d.71 prov. 3-Jul-3 Christie's, Kensington #503/R est:7000-10000
£8500 $13175 €12750 Tiger in the undergrowth (21x30cm-8x12in) s, prov. 4-Dec-2 Christie's, Kensington #476/R est:5000-7000
£14500 $22620 €21750 Bull elephant. Lion head (17x17cm-7x7in) s. two. 27-Mar-3 Christie's, Kensington #543/R est:8000-12000
£18000 $29520 €27000 Elephants, Amboseli (61x91cm-24x36in) s.d.1960 prov. 6-Jun-3 Christie's, London #215/R est:12000-18000
Works on paper
£4000 $6240 €6000 Tiger. Elephant (14x17cm-6x7in) s. pencil pair. 15-Oct-2 Bonhams, Knightsbridge #106/R est:2000-3000

SHEPHERD, F N (19th C) British
£1550 $2418 €2325 Servant girl (59x49cm-23x19in) init. exhib. 15-Oct-2 Bearnes, Exeter #421/R est:800-1200

SHEPHERD, J Clinton (1888-?) American
£871 $1350 €1307 Two dogs in front of a farm, the conflict (64x94cm-25x37in) s. 28-Sep-2 Thomaston Place, Thomaston #37
£2083 $3250 €3125 Young western woman making her way through rocky landscape (97x51cm-38x20in) s. 9-Nov-2 Illustration House, New York #171/R est:3500-5000

SHEPHERD, Michael (1950-) New Zealander
£643 $997 €965 Monopoly board (14x26cm-6x10in) indis.s.d.1969 canvasboard. 4-Dec-2 Dunbar Sloane, Auckland #38/R (NZ.D 2000)

SHEPHERD, Thomas Hosmer (1792-1864) British
Works on paper
£250 $398 €375 Temple Church as restored (9x14cm-4x6in) s. i.verso pencil sepia wash dr. 6-Mar-3 Clevedon Sale Rooms #499
£260 $413 €390 Monument, Fish Street Hill. St Austin, Watling Street (10x6cm-4x2in) s. pencil sepia wash dr. 6-Mar-3 Clevedon Sale Rooms #483
£280 $445 €420 Cordwainers' Hall, Distaff Lane (9x14cm-4x6in) s. pencil sepia wash dr. 6-Mar-3 Clevedon Sale Rooms #474
£300 $477 €450 Shaftesbury House, Alldersgate Street (9x14cm-4x6in) s. i.verso pencil sepia wash dr. 6-Mar-3 Clevedon Sale Rooms #459
£300 $477 €450 Town Hall, Borough High Street (9x14cm-4x6in) s.d.1829 i.verso pencil sepia wash dr. 6-Mar-3 Clevedon Sale Rooms #461
£300 $477 €450 Newgate, Old Bailey (9x14cm-4x6in) s. pencil sepia wash dr. 6-Mar-3 Clevedon Sale Rooms #462
£300 $477 €450 Temple Bar from the Strand (11x12cm-4x5in) s.d.1829 pencil sepia wash dr. 6-Mar-3 Clevedon Sale Rooms #467
£300 $477 €450 Stationers Hall (9x14cm-4x6in) s.d.1829 pencil sepia wash dr. 6-Mar-3 Clevedon Sale Rooms #468
£300 $477 €450 Russell Institution, Great Coram Street (9x14cm-4x6in) s.d.1827 i.verso pencil sepia wash dr. 6-Mar-3 Clevedon Sale Rooms #492
£300 $477 €450 Asylum indigent blind, Westminster Bridge Road (9x14cm-4x6in) s. i.verso pencil sepia wash dr. 6-Mar-3 Clevedon Sale Rooms #494/R
£300 $477 €450 New Church Camden Town (14x9cm-6x4in) s. i.verso pencil sepia wash dr. 6-Mar-3 Clevedon Sale Rooms #497
£300 $468 €450 Mountainous lakeland landscape (19x27cm-7x11in) s. pencil W/C. 27-Mar-3 Christie's, Kensington #80/R
£320 $509 €480 St Paul's, Covent Garden (9x14cm-4x6in) s.d.1829 i.verso pencil sepia wash dr. 6-Mar-3 Clevedon Sale Rooms #471
£380 $604 €570 Lincoln's Inn Hall, Chapel and Chancery Court (10x15cm-4x6in) s.d.1830 pencil sepia wash dr. 6-Mar-3 Clevedon Sale Rooms #475
£400 $636 €600 St Batholomew's Hospital (9x14cm-4x6in) s. i.verso pencil sepia wash dr. 6-Mar-3 Clevedon Sale Rooms #458/R
£400 $636 €600 Theatre Royal, Drury Lane (9x14cm-4x6in) s. i.verso pencil sepia wash dr. 6-Mar-3 Clevedon Sale Rooms #501
£440 $700 €660 United Service, Military Clubhouse, Haymarket Theatre (9x15cm-4x6in) s. i.verso pencil sepia wash dr. 6-Mar-3 Clevedon Sale Rooms #484/R
£450 $716 €675 Clothworkers Hall, Mincing Lane (9x14cm-4x6in) s. pencil sepia wash dr. 6-Mar 3 Clevedon Sale Rooms #460
£450 $716 €675 Mercer's School, Downgate Hill (10x14cm-4x6in) s. i.verso pencil sepia wash dr. 6-Mar-3 Clevedon Sale Rooms #504
£500 $795 €750 Barber Surgeon's Hall, Monkwell Street. Fishmonger's Hall, Thames Street (10cm-4in) s. pencil sepia wash dr. 6-Mar-3 Clevedon Sale Rooms #482
£520 $827 €780 Piccadilly from Coventry Street (9x14cm-4x6in) s.d.1829 pencil sepia wash dr. 6-Mar-3 Clevedon Sale Rooms #466
£580 $922 €870 Trinity House, Tower Hill (9x14cm-4x6in) s.d.1829 pencil sepia wash dr. 6-Mar-3 Clevedon Sale Rooms #470
£580 $922 €870 New Shot Mill near Waterloo Bridge from the Savoy (9x14cm-4x6in) s.d.1823 i.verso pencil sepia wash dr. 6-Mar-3 Clevedon Sale Rooms #503
£600 $954 €900 Draper's Hall, Throgmorton Street (9x14cm-4x6in) s.d.1829 pencil sepia wash dr. 6-Mar-3 Clevedon Sale Rooms #469
£600 $954 €900 St Mary-le-Bone Chapel, St John's Wood Road (9x14cm-4x6in) s. i.verso pencil sepia wash dr. 6-Mar-3 Clevedon Sale Rooms #485
£680 $1081 €1020 London horse and carriage repository (9x14cm-4x6in) s. i.verso pencil sepia wash dr. 6-Mar-3 Clevedon Sale Rooms #493
£700 $1113 €1050 Royal Olympic Theatre, Wynch Street (10x15cm-4x6in) s. pencil sepia wash dr. 6-Mar-3 Clevedon Sale Rooms #456/R
£700 $1113 €1050 Westminster Abbey (11x15cm-4x6in) s. pencil sepia wash dr. 6-Mar-3 Clevedon Sale Rooms #457/R
£700 $1113 €1050 St Paul's Cathedral (10x15cm-4x6in) s. pencil sepia wash dr. 6-Mar-3 Clevedon Sale Rooms #506/R
£750 $1193 €1125 Gray's Inn Hall (10x15cm-4x6in) s. pencil sepia wash dr. 6-Mar-3 Clevedon Sale Rooms #472
£750 $1193 €1125 Park Crescent, East Side (9x14cm-4x6in) s.d.1828 i.verso pencil sepia wash dr. 6-Mar-3 Clevedon Sale Rooms #486
£800 $1272 €1200 Royal College of Surgeons, Lincolns Inn Fields (9x14cm-4x6in) s.d.1827 i.verso pencil sepia wash dr. 6-Mar-3 Clevedon Sale Rooms #500
£900 $1431 €1350 New opening to St Martin's Church from Pall Mall East (9x15cm-4x6in) s. i.verso pencil sepia wash dr. 6-Mar-3 Clevedon Sale Rooms #487/R
£900 $1431 €1350 Bank of England (9x15cm-4x6in) s.d.1827 i.verso pencil sepia wash dr. 6-Mar-3 Clevedon Sale Rooms #502
£1000 $1590 €1500 Marquis of Hertford's Villa, Regent's Park (8x15cm-3x6in) s.d.1826 pencil sepia wash dr. 6-Mar-3 Clevedon Sale Rooms #498 est:500-750

SHEPPARD, Charlotte Lillian (attrib) (?-1925) British
£2000 $3260 €3000 My puppy (64x48cm-25x19in) s.d.1889. 29-Jan-3 Sotheby's, Olympia #206/R est:1000-1500

SHEPPARD, Joseph (1930-) American
£401 $650 €602 Seated nude (51x41cm-20x16in) s. masonite. 24-Jan-3 Freeman, Philadelphia #156/R

SHEPPARD, Maurice (1947-) British
£350 $564 €525 Cut hedge, Kent (59x44cm-23x17in) s.d.1978. 18-Feb-3 Bonhams, Knightsbridge #18/R

SHEPPARD, Peter Clapham (1882-1965) Canadian
£800 $1312 €1200 Picnic under the willows (42x52cm-17x20in) s. 3-Jun-3 Joyner, Toronto #476 est:4000-6000 (C.D 1800)
£1600 $2624 €2400 Circus at Christie Pits, Toronto. Landscape with trees and rolling hills (21x26cm-8x10in) s. panel double-sided. 3-Jun-3 Joyner, Toronto #5/R est:2500-3000 (C.D 3600)
£1600 $2624 €2400 Bathers at Cherry Beach, Toronto (21x26cm-8x10in) s. board. 3-Jun-3 Joyner, Toronto #262/R est:2500-3000 (C.D 3600)
£1956 $3207 €2934 Red sleigh. Sketch of a woman (15x20cm-6x8in) s. board double-sided. 3-Jun-3 Joyner, Toronto #202/R est:3000-4000 (C.D 4400)
£3556 $5831 €5334 Picnic, summer afternoon (32x40cm-13x16in) s. board double-sided. 3-Jun-3 Joyner, Toronto #286/R est:4000-5000 (C.D 8000)

SHEPPARD, Warren W (1858-1937) American
£1104 $1700 €1656 Seascape (51x76cm-20x30in) s. prov. 24-Oct-2 Shannon's, Milford #233/R est:2000-3000

£1178 $1850 €1767 Sunrise over rocky coastline (56x86cm-22x34in) s. 19-Apr-3 James Julia, Fairfield #223/R est:3000-5000
£1244 $2066 €1804 Pink sky at sunset (61x91cm-24x36in) s. 16-Jun-3 Waddingtons, Toronto #9a/R est:3000-4000 (C.D 2800)
£1688 $2600 €2532 Giudecca, Venice (36x56cm-14x22in) s. prov. 24-Oct-2 Shannon's, Milford #179/R est:2500-3500
£2111 $3250 €3167 Hoisting the sails (30x41cm-12x16in) s. 24-Oct-2 Shannon's, Milford #60/R est:3000-5000
£2484 $4000 €3726 Sailboards near the lighthouse (76x61cm-30x24in) s. 20-Jan-3 Arthur James, Florida #26
£2532 $4000 €3798 Coastal sunset (51x76cm-20x30in) s. 24-Apr-3 Shannon's, Milford #64/R est:4000-6000
£2548 $4000 €3822 Grand Canal, Venice (76x51cm-30x20in) s.d.1903. 20-Nov-2 Christie's, Los Angeles #32/R est:4000-6000
£3240 $5184 €4860 View from Venice (56x97cm-22x38in) s. 13-Jan-3 Rasmussen, Vejle #190/R est:10000 (D.KR 37000)
£3395 $5500 €4923 Venice (41x66cm-16x26in) s. 21-May-3 Doyle, New York #90/R est:4000-6000
£4012 $6500 €5817 Boating off Faulkner's Light (41x61cm-16x24in) s. 21-May-3 Doyle, New York #84/R est:5000-7000
£6579 $10000 €9869 Ocean sunset (51x76cm-20x30in) s. 17-Aug-2 North East Auctions, Portsmouth #1099/R est:7000-10000
£9494 $15000 €14241 Afternoon light (51x76cm-20x30in) s. 24-Apr-3 Shannon's, Milford #5/R est:8000-12000

SHERIDAN, Noel (20th C) Irish
£570 $883 €900 Chair (56x65cm-22x26in) s.i.verso board prov. 24-Sep-2 De Veres Art Auctions, Dublin #66c

SHERINGHAM, George (1884-1937) British
£1600 $2464 €2400 Still life of Chinese snuff bottles (36x20cm-14x8in) s. panel. 25-Oct-2 Gorringes, Lewes #912

Works on paper
£350 $546 €525 Pictures on a wall (24x34cm-9x13in) s. gouache. 17-Oct-2 Lawrence, Crewkerne #506/R
£400 $624 €600 Convolvulus (25x34cm-10x13in) s. chl gouache W/C panel. 17-Oct-2 Lawrence, Crewkerne #511/R

SHERLINGH, Michael (19/20th C) American
£1647 $2750 €2388 California foothill landscape (64x76cm-25x30in) s. i.verso prov. 17-Jun-3 John Moran, Pasadena #139 est:2000-3000

SHERLOCK, Marjorie (1897-1973) British
£650 $1014 €975 In the artist studio (50x38cm-20x15in) s.verso. 17-Sep-2 Bonhams, Knightsbridge #44/R

SHERLOCK, William P (1780-?) British
£650 $988 €975 Classical landscape with figures (22x31cm-9x12in) s. panel. 4-Jul-2 Mellors & Kirk, Nottingham #847/R

SHERMAN, Albert (1882-1971) Australian
£429 $664 €644 Reef, Newport (18x25cm-7x10in) s. i.verso board. 29-Oct-2 Lawson Menzies, Sydney #312 (A.D 1200)
£464 $720 €696 Harbour scene (18x36cm-7x14in) s. board. 29-Oct-2 Lawson Menzies, Sydney #111/R (A.D 1300)
£520 $837 €754 Sydney Harbour (23x38cm-9x15in) s. board. 12-May-3 Joel, Victoria #247 est:1200-1500 (A.D 1300)
£643 $1016 €965 Daffodils and figurine (28x31cm-11x12in) s. canvas on board. 18-Nov-2 Joel, Victoria #300 est:2000-3000 (A.D 1800)
£1073 $1684 €1610 White camelias (40x44cm-16x17in) s. board. 15-Apr-3 Lawson Menzies, Sydney #55/R est:3000-5000 (A.D 2800)
£1143 $1806 €1715 Irises (59x48cm-23x19in) s. 18-Nov-2 Goodman, Sydney #50/R est:3000-6000 (A.D 3200)
£1518 $2398 €2277 Still life (54x41cm-21x16in) s. board. 18-Nov-2 Joel, Victoria #250 est:4000-5000 (A.D 4250)

SHERMAN, Cindy (1954-) American

Photographs
£2342 $3700 €3513 Untitled (30x23cm-12x9in) s.i.d.1973-93 num.75/125 verso toned gelatin silver print prov. 24-Apr-3 Phillips, New York #204/R est:2500-3500
£2885 $4500 €4328 Untitled 120 (33x22cm-13x9in) s.i. chromagenic colour. 21-Oct-2 Swann Galleries, New York #324/R est:6000-7000
£4221 $6500 €6332 Untitled (25x20cm-10x8in) s.num.52/100 hand painted gelatin silver print prov. 25-Oct-2 Phillips, New York #157/R est:3000-5000
£4633 $7459 €6950 Untitled (78x55cm-31x22in) s.num.17/90 col photo. 7-May-3 AB Stockholms Auktionsverk #992/R est:18000-22000 (S.KR 60000)
£6250 $10000 €9375 Untitled (64x83cm-25x33in) s.d.1983 num.3/18 verso c-print exhib. 14-May-3 Sotheby's, New York #343/R est:12000-18000
£8500 $13940 €12750 Untitled (127x84cm-50x33in) s.d.1994 verso num.6/6 chromogenic print prov. 6-Feb-3 Christie's, London #750/R est:10000-15000
£9375 $15000 €14063 Untitled (116x76cm-46x30in) color photograph executed 1982 prov.lit. 14-May-3 Sotheby's, New York #308/R est:18000-22000
£11250 $18000 €16875 Untitled no.130 (88x61cm-35x24in) s.d.1983 num.18 verso col photograph prov.exhib.lit. 16-May-3 Phillips, New York #136/R est:20000-30000
£12000 $20040 €17400 Untitled, num 123 (87x60cm-34x24in) cibachrome print edition of 18 prov.exhib.lit. 26-Jun-3 Sotheby's, London #120/R est:12000-15000
£12987 $20000 €19481 Untitled, film still (25x20cm-10x8in) s.d.1979 num.3/10 verso gelatin silver print prov.lit. 25-Oct-2 Phillips, New York #49/R est:22000-28000
£16250 $26000 €24375 Untitled no.109 (105x103cm-41x41in) s.d.1982 num.4/10 verso c-print prov.lit. 14-May-3 Sotheby's, New York #362/R est:20000-30000
£17722 $28000 €26583 Untitled no.119 (44x91cm-17x36in) s.d.1983 num.4/18 verso col coupler print prov.exhib.lit. 14-Nov-2 Christie's, Rockefeller NY #451/R est:30000-40000
£17722 $28000 €26583 Untitled film still no.56 (17x24cm-7x9in) s.d.1980 num.7/10 photograph prov.lit. 23-Apr-3 Sotheby's, New York #286/R est:25000-35000
£23734 $37500 €35601 Untitled film still no.43 (19x24cm-7x9in) s.d.1979 verso photograph prov.lit. 23-Apr-3 Sotheby's, New York #285/R est:25000-35000
£31646 $50000 €47469 Untitled, film still 3 (20x25cm-8x10in) s.d.1977 num.8/10 verso black/white photograph prov.lit. 13-Nov-2 Sotheby's, New York #488/R est:50000-70000
£32500 $52000 €48750 Untitled (44x91cm-17x36in) col coupler print mounted on board prov.exhib.lit. 15-May-3 Christie's, Rockefeller NY #362/R est:20000-30000
£35000 $58450 €52500 Untitled - 95 (61x122cm-24x48in) s.d.1981 num 8/10 verso cibachrome print prov.lit. 25-Jun-3 Sotheby's, London #48/R est:40000-60000
£69620 $110000 €104430 Untitled no.90 (61x122cm-24x48in) s.d.1981 num.5/10 col coupler print prov.exhib.lit. 13-Nov-2 Christie's, Rockefeller NY #72/R est:120000-180000
£70000 $114800 €105000 Untitled no.209 (166x125cm-65x49in) s.d.1989 num6/6 col photograph prov.exhib. 5-Feb-3 Christie's, London #25/R est:80000-120000
£71875 $115000 €107813 Untitled film still no.7 (102x76cm-40x30in) s.d.1978 num.1/3 gelatin silver print prov.exhib.lit. 15-May-3 Christie's, Rockefeller NY #360/R est:100000-150000
£75000 $120000 €112500 Untitled no.183-A (108x72cm-43x28in) col photograph executed 1988 prov. 15-May-3 Phillips, New York #4/R est:80000-120000
£84375 $135000 €126563 Untitled no.85 (61x122cm-24x48in) s.d.1981 num.1/10 col coupler print prov.exhib.lit. 15-May-3 Christie's, Rockefeller NY #361/R est:100000-150000

SHERMAN, John W (1896-?) American
£355 $575 €533 Mountain and rooftop (38x48cm-15x19in) board. 24-Jan-3 Douglas, South Deerfield #7

SHERMUND, Barbara (1910-1978) American

Works on paper
£710 $1100 €1065 Woman hassled by officer at an intersection (38x25cm-15x10in) s.i. black ink W/C card with work by Rube Goldberg two. 25-Sep-2 Doyle, New York #77/R
£955 $1500 €1433 Fishermen's beach and Todd's jetty. The big one, one more snapshot (36x48cm-14x19in) s. i.verso W/C gouache over pencil two. 10-Dec-2 Doyle, New York #161/R est:2000-3000

SHERRIN, D (19/20th C) British
£609 $956 €950 Highland landscape with cattle (59x104cm-23x41in) s. 19-Nov-2 Hamilton Osborne King, Dublin #429/R

SHERRIN, Daniel (1868-1940) British
£260 $408 €390 Sandbanks (25x35cm-10x14in) s.i.d.March 12th 1931. 16-Dec-2 Bonhams, Bury St Edmunds #463
£300 $456 €450 Quiet backwater on the Thames (56x89cm-22x35in) s. 16-Aug-2 Keys, Aylsham #347
£300 $469 €435 Setting sun on a winter stream (51x76cm-20x30in) s. 26-Mar-3 Walker's, Ottawa #74/R (C.D 700)
£360 $565 €540 Highland cattle (61x107cm-24x42in) s. 10-Dec-2 Capes Dunn, Manchester #832/R
£385 $608 €600 Landscape (27x39cm-11x15in) s. cardboard. 19-Nov-2 Durán, Madrid #61/R

£387 $600 €581 Bleak house harbour, Broadstairs (20x28cm-8x11in) s. board. 1-Oct-2 Arthur James, Florida #174
£420 $655 €630 Figures on a path, with sea in background (51x77cm-20x30in) s. 8-Oct-2 Bonhams, Knightsbridge #133/R
£420 $659 €630 Figures by a pond with a cottage and woodland at sunset (51x76cm-20x30in) s. 10-Dec-2 Rosebery Fine Art, London #572/R
£480 $768 €720 Evening in Marden, Kent (51x75cm-20x30in) s. 11-Mar-3 Bonhams, Knightsbridge #52/R
£500 $760 €750 Drover with cattle and further figures in a late summer landscape (46x74cm-18x29in) s. 16-Aug-2 Keys, Aylsham #654
£600 $960 €900 Sunset with trees (51x76cm-20x30in) bears sig. 11-Mar-3 Bonhams, Knightsbridge #57/R
£755 $1200 €1133 Country path (51x76cm-20x30in) s. painted c.1910. 2-Mar-3 Toomey, Oak Park #594/R
£760 $1239 €1140 Quiet retreat (51x67cm-20x26in) s.i. 11-Feb-3 Bonhams, Knowle #91
£774 $1200 €1161 Coastal scene (51x91cm-20x36in) s. painted c.1910. 8-Dec-2 Toomey, Oak Park #634/R
£860 $1410 €1290 The silent evening hour (49x75cm-19x30in) s. bears i.verso. 4-Jun-3 Bonhams, Chester #385
£900 $1413 €1350 Lake Lucerne (61x92cm-24x36in) s. 21-Nov-2 Tennants, Leyburn #812/R
£1076 $1700 €1614 River landscape with two figures (51x76cm-20x30in) s. 16-Nov-2 New Orleans Auction, New Orleans #976/R est:1200-1800
£1100 $1793 €1595 Mountainous landscape (48x74cm-19x29in) s. 17-Jul-3 Thomson, Roddick & Medcalf, Carlisle #22/R
£1300 $2132 €1950 When the sun is set (61x107cm-24x42in) s. 29-May-3 Christie's, Kensington #164/R est:800-1200
£1500 $2340 €2250 Streatley-on-Thames (61x107cm-24x42in) s. 9-Oct-2 Woolley & Wallis, Salisbury #253/R est:400-600
£1500 $2475 €2175 Day on the coast, coastal landscape with dunes and a town in the distance (61x107cm-24x42in) s. 3-Jul-3 Ewbank, Send #337/R est:1500-2000
£1524 $2393 €2286 Sunset, with young couple by the edge of the road (67x94cm-26x37in) s. 10-Dec-2 Pinneys, Montreal #61 est:5000-6000 (C.D 3750)
£1800 $2808 €2700 Landscape at sunset after rain (61x91cm-24x36in) s. pair. 26-Mar-3 Sotheby's, Olympia #51/R est:2000-3000
£2800 $4256 €4200 Invernesshire (61x106cm-24x42in) s. i.on stretcher. 28-Aug-2 Sotheby's, London #811/R est:2000-3000
£6000 $9360 €9000 River landscape with figures on the bank (61x107cm-24x42in) s. 10-Apr-3 Tennants, Leyburn #984/R est:2000-3000

Works on paper
£380 $627 €551 Warwick Castle (28x61cm-11x24in) s. W/C. 1-Jul-3 Bearnes, Exeter #459/R

SHERRIN, Daniel (attrib) (1868-1940) British
£750 $1155 €1125 Shepherd and his flock in a Highland landscape (102x76cm-40x30in) s. 5-Sep-2 Christie's, Kensington #153/R
£950 $1587 €1378 Highland river landscape, with figures fishing (60x90cm-24x35in) bears sig. 8-Jul-3 Bonhams, Knightsbridge #222a/R

SHERRIN, David (19/20th C) British
£380 $600 €570 Windmill coastal scene (49x76cm-19x30in) s. 27-Nov-2 Peter Wilson, Nantwich #10

SHERRIN, John (1819-1896) British
Works on paper
£500 $785 €750 Children playing on a lane before a farm house (19x25cm-7x10in) s. W/C. 10-Dec-2 Lane, Penzance #132
£645 $1000 €968 Primroses with a bird's nest and ivy on a mossy bank (21x26cm-8x10in) s. pencil gouache prov. 29-Oct-2 Sotheby's, New York #135/R est:2000-3000
£645 $1000 €968 Red and yellow primroses with a bird's nest on a mossy bank (30x41cm-12x16in) s. W/C gouache prov. 29-Oct-2 Sotheby's, New York #136/R est:2000-3000
£903 $1400 €1355 Brace of pigeons (33x46cm-13x18in) s. W/C gouache prov. 29-Oct-2 Sotheby's, New York #137/R est:1000-1500
£2000 $3200 €3000 Still life of plums (30x42cm-12x17in) s. W/C bodycol. 11-Mar-3 Bonhams, New Bond Street #118/R est:2000-3000

SHERRIN, Reginald D (1891-1971) British
Works on paper
£280 $445 €420 Moorland landscape (34x74cm-13x29in) s. gouache. 25-Feb-3 Bonhams, Knightsbridge #155/R
£300 $465 €450 Quiet summers day on the North Cornish coast at Watergate Bay (51x76cm-20x30in) s. i.verso W/C bodycol. 31-Oct-2 Duke & Son, Dorchester #148/R
£380 $593 €570 The Lizard, Cornwall (39x100cm-15x39in) s. gouache. 26-Mar-3 Woolley & Wallis, Salisbury #81/R
£450 $698 €675 Extensive Dartmoor landscape (39x101cm-15x40in) s. gouache. 25-Sep-2 Hamptons Fine Art, Godalming #244

SHERWIN, Frank (1896-?) British
Works on paper
£360 $583 €540 Harbour Polperro (29x40cm-11x16in) s. W/C. 23-May-3 Honiton Galleries, Honiton #645

SHERWOOD, Maud Winifred (1880-1956) Australian
£704 $1162 €1021 In the park (34x41cm-13x16in) s. board. 1-Jul-3 Peter Webb, Auckland #46/R est:2000-3000 (NZ.D 2000)
Works on paper
£1212 $1867 €1818 Lady with fan (44x37cm-17x15in) s. W/C. 4-Sep-2 Dunbar Sloane, Wellington #45 est:6000-8000 (NZ.D 4000)

SHERWOOD, William Anderson (1875-1951) American
£466 $750 €699 Brume du soir (61x74cm-24x29in) s. 19-Jan-3 Jeffery Burchard, Florida #42/R

SHEVCHENKO, Alexander (1883-1943) Russian
£5128 $8103 €8000 Seated model (70x35cm-28x14in) s. canvas on board. 13-Nov-2 Ansorena, Madrid #111/R

SHI LU (1919-1982) Chinese
Works on paper
£797 $1307 €1100 Trees (46x35cm-18x14in) seal Indian ink hanging scroll. 30-May-3 Dr Fritz Nagel, Stuttgart #1196/R
£6159 $10101 €8500 Roses in moonlight (135x67cm-53x26in) i. seals Indian ink hanging scroll. 30-May-3 Dr Fritz Nagel, Stuttgart #1176/R est:3000-5000
£7317 $11561 €10976 Mother and daughter (27x27cm-11x11in) sealed i. ink col exhib. 28-Apr-3 Sotheby's, Hong Kong #567/R est:70000-90000 (HK.D 90000)

SHIELDS, Alan (1944-) American
£4054 $6324 €6000 Come on down Billy (211x320cm-83x126in) s.i.verso painted fabric. 26-Mar-3 Millon & Associes, Paris #150/R est:4500-6000

SHIELDS, Henry (fl.1880-1890s) British
£260 $424 €377 Coastal landscape (30x46cm-12x18in) s. 16-Jul-3 Sotheby's, Olympia #11/R

SHIGENAGA, Nishimura (c.1697-1756) Japanese
Prints
£1923 $3000 €2885 Chrysanthemum garden, Oyuki style (32x16cm-13x6in) s. black lacquer col print. 25-Mar-3 Christie's, Rockefeller NY #4/R est:2000-2500

SHIH-FU CHIU YING (?) Chinese
Works on paper
£483 $768 €700 Mountainous landscape with figures. s. ink polychrome silk. 7-Mar-3 Piasa, Paris #313/R

SHIKLER, Aaron (1922-) American
Works on paper
£1290 $2000 €1935 Head study. Seated female nude (28x23cm-11x9in) init.d.70 pencil red brown chk one oil two. 29-Oct-2 Sotheby's, New York #297/R est:4000-6000

SHIKO, Watanabe (1683-1755) Japanese
Works on paper
£1258 $2000 €1887 Hundred turtles (105x36cm-41x14in) s. ink col hanging scroll. 24-Mar-3 Christie's, Rockefeller NY #10/R est:5000-7000

SHIKO, Watanabe (attrib) (1683-1755) Japanese
Works on paper
£5031 $8000 €7547 Birds and flowers of the four seasons, spring and summer (138x334cm-54x131in) ink col silver gold six-panel screen. 24-Mar-3 Christie's, Rockefeller NY #85/R est:20000-30000

SHILLING, Arthur (1941-1986) Canadian
£321 $508 €482 Figures in landscape (38x51cm-15x20in) acrylic hardboard. 1-Dec-2 Levis, Calgary #100/R (C.D 800)
£601 $937 €902 Portrait of woman (51x41cm-20x16in) d.1970 canvasboard prov. 25-Mar-3 Ritchie, Toronto #140/R est:1500-2000 (C.D 1400)
£2133 $3499 €3200 Looking to the future no.2 (65x75cm-26x30in) s. board prov. 3-Jun-3 Joyner, Toronto #432/R est:5000-7000 (C.D 4800)

SHINN, Everett (1876-1953) American

£1242 $2000 €1863 Man peering into outdoor goldfish bowl (56x41cm-22x16in) s.d. oil wash en grisaille board. 10-May-3 Illustration House, New York #91/R est:2000-3000

£2395 $4000 €3473 City scene (9x15cm-4x6in) panel prov.exhib. 18-Jun-3 Christie's, Los Angeles #109/R est:4000-6000

£4630 $7500 €6714 Nightmare (25x284cm-10x112in) s. 21-May-3 Doyle, New York #158/R est:10000-15000

£8176 $13000 €12264 Interior scene with nude (30x40cm-12x16in) prov. 5-Mar-3 Sotheby's, New York #87/R est:12000-18000

£8917 $14000 €13376 Clown with drum (12x11cm-5x4in) s. board painted c.1940 prov. 19-Nov-2 Wright, Chicago #102/R est:15000-20000

£12579 $20000 €18869 Cafe (22x26cm-9x10in) s.d.1934 W/C gouache ink paper on board prov. 4-Mar-3 Christie's, Rockefeller NY #71/R est:12000-18000

£46296 $75000 €69444 Cherry Lane Theater (48x56cm-19x22in) s.d.1948 prov. 22-May-3 Christie's, Rockefeller NY #69/R est:40000-60000

£160494 $260000 €240741 Revue (91x107cm-36x42in) s.d.1929 prov.exhib. 21-May-3 Sotheby's, New York #157/R est:200000-300000

£2129032 $3300000 €3193548 Footlight flirtation (74x92cm-29x36in) s.d.1912. 4-Dec-2 Sotheby's, New York #9/R est:2500000-3500000

Works on paper

£248 $400 €372 Man at door with pistol drawn (30x20cm-12x8in) s.d.1917 pencil wash en grisaille. 20-Feb-3 Illustration House, New York #157/R

£409 $650 €614 Ad for Peggy Roth (48x33cm-19x13in) graphite W/C board. 3-May-3 Rachel Davis, Shaker Heights #158/R

£709 $1100 €1064 Illustrations for the mystery of Edwin Drood by Dickens (18x11cm-7x4in) pencil W/C pair prov. 29-Oct-2 Sotheby's, New York #158/R est:1000-1500

£1341 $2200 €1944 Trinity church (35x24cm-14x9in) s.d. pencil. 5-Jun-3 Swann Galleries, New York #215/R est:1000-1500

£1410 $2200 €2115 Illustration for a fable (39x62cm-15x24in) s.d.1943 chl wash. 9-Nov-2 Sloan, North Bethesda #536/R est:3000-5000

£2389 $3750 €3584 Scene from act one of please help Emily, at the old Lyceum Theatre (28x38cm-11x15in) s. pastel prov. 10-Dec-2 Doyle, New York #134/R est:4000-6000

£10494 $17000 €15741 Olympic theatre (20x25cm-8x10in) s.i.d.1907 verso W/C gouache pencil paper on board prov.exhib. 21-May-3 Sotheby's, New York #63/R est:20000-30000

£11111 $18000 €16667 Nude (56x41cm-22x16in) s. pastel executed c.1910 prov. 21-May-3 Sotheby's, New York #159/R est:25000-35000

£13889 $22500 €20834 Elizabethan dancers (13x22cm-5x9in) s.d.1910 i.verso W/C gouache pencil paper on board prov.exhib.lit. 21-May-3 Sotheby's, New York #61/R est:8000-12000

£16975 $27500 €25463 Bowling the bowler (58x72cm-23x28in) s.d.1916 W/C chl board prov.exhib.lit. 21-May-3 Sotheby's, New York #70/R est:30000-50000

£24193 $37500 €36290 East River Bridge (22x28cm-9x11in) s.d.1940 i.verso W/C on board prov.exhib.lit. 4-Dec-2 Sotheby's, New York #18/R est:25000-35000

£29874 $47500 €44811 Magician (30x40cm-12x16in) s.d.1940 pastel board prov.exhib. 5-Mar-3 Sotheby's, New York #82/R est:50000-75000

£37037 $60000 €55556 Green Park, London (36x46cm-14x18in) s.i.d.1908 pastel prov.exhib.lit. 21-May-3 Sotheby's, New York #69/R est:40000-60000

£38710 $60000 €58065 Old Vanderbilt House (18x25cm-7x10in) s.d.1945 i.verso W/C gouache board prov. 4-Dec-2 Sotheby's, New York #17/R est:30000-50000

£41935 $65000 €62903 Washing Square (22x30cm-9x12in) s.d.1942 W/C gouache prov. 4-Dec-2 Sotheby's, New York #16/R est:40000-60000

£51613 $80000 €77420 Theatre, box in foreground (25x21cm-10x8in) s.i.verso pastel gouache on board executed c.1950 prov. 4-Dec-2 Sotheby's, New York #19/R est:30000-50000

£125806 $195000 €188709 Lunch wagon, Madison Square (22x33cm-9x13in) s.d.1904 pastel gouache prov.exhib.lit. 4-Dec-2 Sotheby's, New York #12/R est:50000-70000

£141935 $220000 €212903 Sixth Avenue elevated after midnight (20x32cm-8x13in) s.d.1899 pastel gouache on board prov.exhib.lit. 4-Dec-2 Sotheby's, New York #10/R est:75000-100000

SHINNORS, John (1950-) Irish

£2516 $3925 €4000 Magpies over Cathedral Square (18x22cm-7x9in) s. i.d.1997 verso canvas on board. 17-Sep-2 Whyte's, Dublin #22/R est:4000-5000

£4110 $6452 €6000 Female scarecrow in snowfield (26x28cm-10x11in) s.i. s.verso. 15-Apr-3 De Veres Art Auctions, Dublin #241/R est:6000-8000

£4247 $6667 €6200 Reclining nude (16x24cm-6x9in) s.d.81 s.i.verso panel. 15-Apr-3 De Veres Art Auctions, Dublin #255/R est:4000-5000

£4679 $7253 €7300 Baby's room (46x64cm-18x25in) s.d.1976 board. 3-Dec-2 Thomas Adams, Dublin #378

£7692 $12077 €12000 Figure in interior (76x66cm-30x26in) s.d.1979 prov. 19-Nov-2 Whyte's, Dublin #26/R est:8000-10000

£9615 $15096 €15000 Figure at the piano (51x76cm-20x30in) s.d.1979 board prov. 19-Nov-2 Whyte's, Dublin #30/R est:5000-7000

£12658 $19620 €20000 Lighthouse, Loop Head (216x241cm-85x95in) s. board in three parts overall size. 24-Sep-2 De Veres Art Auctions, Dublin #80/R est:20000-30000

SHINODA, Toko (1913-) Japanese

Works on paper

£1000 $1630 €1500 Kokord (132x62cm-52x24in) s. ink on platinum ground. 3-Feb-3 Sotheby's, Olympia #174/R est:1000-1500

SHIPSIDES, Frank (1908-) British

Works on paper

£300 $474 €435 Tug moored in Bathurst Basin, Bristol (35x26cm-14x10in) s. pen ink W/C. 22-Jul-3 Bristol Auction Rooms #414/R

£330 $538 €495 Royal Yacht, Victoria and Albert, July 9th 1908, seen at opening of Royal Edward Dock (37x27cm-15x11in) s.d.1981 W/C. 28-Jan-3 Bristol Auction Rooms #523

SHIRAISHI, Yuko (1956-) British/Japanese

Works on paper

£800 $1240 €1200 Sea layers (137x152cm-54x60in) i.verso. 3-Oct-2 Ewbank, Send #531/R

SHIRLEY, Henry (19th C) British

£900 $1440 €1350 View of Llanberis, Wales (60x107cm-24x42in) s.d.1836. 15-May-3 Lawrence, Crewkerne #967/R

SHIRREFF, Charles (c.1750-?) British

Miniatures

£1600 $2592 €2400 Officer wearing blue coat (5cm-2in) init. gold frame seed pearls. 22-May-3 Bonhams, New Bond Street #95/R est:1000-1500

£2600 $4212 €3900 Gentleman wearing blue coat (6cm-2in) gold frame with pearl border. 22-May-3 Bonhams, New Bond Street #94/R est:1500-2500

£4200 $6594 €6300 Young lady wearing a white dress (7cm-3in) silver gilt frame oval. 10-Dec-2 Christie's, London #126/R est:3000-5000

SHISHKIN, Ivan Ivanovich (1832-1898) Russian

£2302 $3683 €3200 Branch. Forest interior (17x24cm-7x9in) s.d.1870 oil sketch pen double-sided paper. 17-May-3 Hagelstam, Helsinki #30/R est:2000

SHOESMITH, Kenneth Denton (1890-1939) British

£2083 $3000 €3125 Last Armada (57x92cm-22x36in) 15-Jan-3 Christie's, Rockefeller NY #133/R

£5000 $7800 €7500 Fight off Portland Hill, Lord Howard on the Ark Royal (102x308cm-40x121in) s. 26-Mar-3 Sotheby's, Olympia #172/R est:5000-7000

Works on paper

£650 $1007 €975 Spanish galleons (38x53cm-15x21in) s. W/C. 2-Oct-2 John Ross, Belfast #171

£750 $1163 €1125 Chinese craft, Hong Kong (61x81cm-24x32in) s.d.19 W/C. 2-Oct-2 John Ross, Belfast #86

SHOKLER, Harry (1896-1978) American

£219 $350 €318 New England valley, September (27x40cm-11x16in) s.d.67 board. 16-May-3 Skinner, Boston #231/R

£452 $700 €678 Rockport Mass in winter (23x30cm-9x12in) s.d.66 canvasboard. 21-Jul-2 Jeffery Burchard, Florida #34/R

£452 $700 €678 Rising fog (30x41cm-12x16in) s.d.67 canvasboard exhib. 21-Jul-2 Jeffery Burchard, Florida #34a/R

SHOR, Zvi (1898-1979) Israeli

£1333 $2213 €1933 Laneway with houses (91x65cm-36x26in) s. 16-Jun-3 Waddingtons, Toronto #321/R est:2000-3000 (C.D 3000)

SHORE, Arnold Joseph Victor (1897-1963) Australian

£321 $508 €482 Landscape (28x39cm-11x15in) s. board prov. 17-Nov-2 Sotheby's, Paddington #76 (A.D 900)

£632 $960 €948 Afternoon, wattle lodge (59x49cm-23x19in) s.d.37 s.i.verso. 19-Aug-2 Joel, Victoria #175 est:1000-2000 (A.D 1800)

£678 $1072 €1017 Bush forms (36x27cm-14x11in) s.d.46 board prov. 18-Nov-2 Joel, Victoria #273 est:2200-2500 (A.D 1900)

SHORE, Henrietta (1880-1963) American
Works on paper
£5389 $9000 €7814 Fantasy landscape (31x43cm-12x17in) s. col pencil paper on board. 18-Jun-3 Christie's, Los Angeles #102/R est:3000-5000

SHORE, Steven (1947-) American
Photographs
£2025 $3200 €3200 2nd Street E and S Main Street, Kalispell, Montana (20x25cm-8x10in) s.i.d.1974 verso col photo lit.exhib. 28-Nov-2 Villa Grisebach, Berlin #1402/R est:1200-1600
£2147 $3500 €3221 El Paso Street, El Paso, Texas (30x38cm-12x15in) s.i.d.1975 verso color coupler print. 12-Feb-3 Christie's, Rockefeller NY #187/R est:2500-3500
£2454 $4000 €3681 2nd Street, Ashland, Wisconsin (30x38cm-12x15in) s.i.d.1973 verso color coupler print. 12-Feb-3 Christie's, Rockefeller NY #188/R est:2500-3500
£2516 $3899 €4000 Untitled (20x25cm-8x10in) s.d.8/13/74 verso col photo kodak lit. 2-Nov-2 Lempertz, Koln #95/R est:3500
£11321 $17547 €18000 Portfolio. s.i. col photos 12. 2-Nov-2 Lempertz, Koln #369/R est:10000-15000

SHORT, Denys (1926-) British
£280 $437 €420 Works, Trehafod (164x121cm-65x48in) i.verso board. 11-Sep-2 Bonhams, Newport #362/R

SHORT, Frederick Golden (1863-1936) British
£320 $512 €480 Scene in autumn (28x38cm-11x15in) s.d.94. 8-Jan-3 George Kidner, Lymington #191
£360 $562 €540 Trees in a forest (29x22cm-11x9in) s.d.1916 board. 26-Mar-3 Woolley & Wallis, Salisbury #245/R
£360 $562 €540 River landscape (16x20cm-6x8in) s.d.1934. 26-Mar-3 Woolley & Wallis, Salisbury #246/R
£380 $608 €570 View in the New forest (23x30cm-9x12in) s. board. 11-Mar-3 Gorringes, Lewes #2339
£380 $597 €570 Beach (22x30cm-9x12in) s.d.1929 board. 15-Apr-3 Bonhams, Knightsbridge #119
£420 $701 €609 Woodland scene (38x54cm-15x21in) s.d.1923. 9-Jul-3 George Kidner, Lymington #155/R
£440 $695 €660 Bluebell wood (28x38cm-11x15in) s. board. 2-Dec-2 Gorringes, Lewes #2777
£450 $747 €675 Fine March morning (36x53cm-14x21in) s.d.95 i.verso. 10-Jun-3 Sworder & Son, Bishops Stortford #457/R
£450 $752 €653 Forest scene with children by a bridge (23x38cm-9x15in) s.d.1902. 9-Jul-3 George Kidner, Lymington #154/R
£540 $875 €810 Heath land, path through the woods (16x21cm-6x8in) s. board sold with another by same hand. 20-May-3 Bonhams, Knightsbridge #142
£550 $880 €825 Scene in the New Forest (28x38cm-11x15in) s.d.1920 board. 11-Mar-3 Gorringes, Lewes #2341
£550 $875 €825 Scene in the New Forest (28x38cm-11x15in) s.d.99. 29-Apr-3 Gorringes, Lewes #2125
£580 $905 €870 View of the New Forest (28x38cm-11x15in) s.d.1909. 9-Oct-2 Woolley & Wallis, Salisbury #272/R
£600 $978 €900 Gorse and oak trees in the New Forest (28x38cm-11x15in) s.d.1902. 28-Jan-3 Gorringes, Lewes #1703
£1000 $1600 €1500 Woodland in summer and autumn (28x38cm-11x15in) s.d.1920 pair. 11-Mar-3 Gorringes, Lewes #2340 est:400-600
£1150 $1794 €1725 Woodland scene in autumn (36x46cm-14x18in) s.d.1929. 10-Apr-3 Brightwells, Leominster #936

SHORT, Obadiah (1803-1886) British
£280 $468 €406 Norfolk country cottage (25x18cm-10x7in) 20-Jun-3 Keys, Aylsham #636
£350 $543 €525 Figure on a country lane (31x23cm-12x9in) panel. 30-Sep-2 Bonhams, Ipswich #448
£380 $593 €570 Old Costessey Bridge, with figure, trees and heavy skies (19x37cm-7x15in) board. 21-Sep-2 Lacy Scott, Bury St.Edmunds #389/R
£460 $759 €667 Woodland path (43x36cm-17x14in) 1-Jul-3 Bonhams, Norwich #212
£800 $1336 €1160 Norfolk wooded landscape with figure in lane by a cottage (23x18cm-9x7in) 20-Jun-3 Keys, Aylsham #637/R

SHORT, Richard (1841-1916) British
£377 $600 €566 Ancient Rome (61x51cm-24x20in) s.d.96. 5-Mar-3 Doyle, New York #55/R
£2000 $3320 €2900 Barry, South Wales - harbour mouth with shipping (74x119cm-29x47in) s.i.verso. 10-Jun-3 Peter Francis, Wales #2/R est:2000-3000

SHORT, Sir Frank (1857-1945) British
£350 $564 €525 Marsh farm (30x40cm-12x16in) board. 18-Feb-3 Bonhams, Knightsbridge #86/R

SHORTHOUSE, Arthur Charles (attrib) (1870-1953) British
Works on paper
£380 $604 €570 Portrait of girl wearing a blue hair band and white dress (25x17cm-10x7in) s. W/C. 19-Mar-3 Rupert Toovey, Partridge Green #205/R

SHOUMATOFF, Elizabeth (1888-1980) American
Works on paper
£531 $850 €797 Girl holding a kitten (21x16cm-8x6in) W/C after Jean Baptiste Perronneau. 14-May-3 Doyle, New York #30

SHOWELL, William (1903-1984) Canadian
£307 $480 €461 House back of pine avenue (20x24cm-8x9in) s. acrylic. 10-Sep-2 Iegor de Saint Hippolyte, Montreal #104d (C.D 750)

SHPILSHER, Keren (1977-) Israeli
Works on paper
£610 $1000 €885 Root canal (100x100cm-39x39in) s. gouache acrylic ink. 28-May-3 Sotheby's, Amsterdam #183/R est:1200-1800
£625 $1000 €906 Beetles (100x100cm-39x39in) s.d. gouache acrylic ink. 13-May-3 Sotheby's, Tel Aviv #75/R est:1200-1800

SHRADY, Henry M (1871-1922) American
Sculpture
£25641 $40000 €38462 An empty saddle (28cm-11in) bronze. 9-Nov-2 Altermann Galleries, Santa Fe #98
£49383 $80000 €74075 Monarch of the plains (34cm-13in) i. reddish brown pat. bronze on wood base prov.lit. 21-May-3 Sotheby's, New York #226/R est:60000-80000

SHRAGER, Ann (1948-) British
£260 $413 €390 Breaker, Climping (24x34cm-9x13in) init. canvasboard. 26-Feb-3 Sotheby's, Olympia #329/R
£380 $604 €570 Beach, Atlantic City (31x43cm-12x17in) init. canvasboard. 26-Feb-3 Sotheby's, Olympia #330/R

SHRAPNEL, Edward Scrope (1847-1920) British/Canadian
£444 $729 €666 Snipe (40x30cm-16x12in) s.d.1889. 3-Jun-3 Joyner, Toronto #372/R est:1000-1500 (C.D 1000)

SHREVE, Racket (20th C) American?
£724 $1100 €1086 Boston pilot schooner, Edwin Forrest (51x76cm-20x30in) artist st.verso. 17-Aug-2 North East Auctions, Portsmouth #510/R

SHU-WU LIN (1970-) Taiwanese
£915 $1500 €1327 Fish (172x71cm-68x28in) s.d.2001 verso. 28-May-3 Sotheby's, Amsterdam #139/R est:1800-2200
£958 $1600 €1389 Prayer (158x86cm-62x34in) s.d.2001 verso. 25-Jun-3 Sotheby's, Moscow #189/R est:1500-2000
£1750 $2800 €2538 Serenade (147x95cm-58x37in) s.d.2002 verso. 13-May-3 Sotheby's, Tel Aviv #2/R est:1500-2000
£2625 $4200 €3806 Fantasia III (196x108cm-77x43in) s.d.2002 verso. 13-May-3 Sotheby's, Tel Aviv #1/R est:1800-2200

SHUFELT, Robert (1935-) American
Works on paper
£288 $450 €432 Untitled - cowboy at campfire (20x28cm-8x11in) chl prov.lit. 9-Nov-2 Santa Fe Art, Santa Fe #24/R
£321 $500 €482 Untitled - cowboy resting (20x23cm-8x9in) init. chl prov.lit. 9-Nov-2 Santa Fe Art, Santa Fe #23/R

SHUKI, Okamoto (c.1807-1862) Japanese
Works on paper
£1887 $3000 €2831 Kingfishers with plum hydrangea (126x44cm-50x17in) s. ink col silk hanging scroll. 24-Mar-3 Christie's, Rockefeller NY #62/R est:2000-3000
£10692 $17000 €16038 Cranes by the sea (124x42cm-49x17in) s. ink col silk hanging scrolls pair. 24-Mar-3 Christie's, Rockefeller NY #66/R est:3000-4000
£20126 $32000 €30189 Peacocks and rose mallows (126x42cm-50x17in) s. ink col gold silk hanging scroll. 24-Mar-3 Christie's, Rockefeller NY #65/R est:3000-4000
£26415 $42000 €39623 Cranes and pine. Turtles beneath a flowering tree (106x43cm-42x17in) s. ink col silk hanging scrolls pair. 24-Mar-3 Christie's, Rockefeller NY #64/R est:5500-6500

SHULMAN, Julius (1910-) German
Photographs

£	$	€	Details
£2754	$4516	€3800	Case study, House No 2 (51x41cm-20x16in) s.i.d. i. verso C-print Kodak paper. 30-May-3 Bassenge, Berlin #4893/R est:2500

SHULZ, Adolph Robert (1869-1963) American

£	$	€	Details
£346	$550	€519	Autumn landscape (15x25cm-6x10in) canvas on board painted c.1910 prov. 2-Mar-3 Toomey, Oak Park #686/R

SHUNKO, Katsukawa (1743-1812) Japanese
Prints

£	$	€	Details
£5449	$8500	€8174	Wrestlers Onogawa Kisaburo and Tanikaze Kajinosuke (39x26cm-15x10in) s. print col. 25-Mar-3 Christie's, Rockefeller NY #31/R est:5000-7000

SHUNSHO, Katsukawa (1726-1792) Japanese
Prints

£	$	€	Details
£1923	$3000	€2885	Wrestlers Uzgafuchi and Onogawa Kisaburo of the Eastern Group (36x25cm-14x10in) s. print col. 25-Mar-3 Christie's, Rockefeller NY #30/R est:3000-4000
£2564	$4000	€3846	Portrait of the actor Nakamura Nazako I as an itinerant pilgrim (32x14cm-13x6in) s. col print prov. 25-Mar-3 Christie's, Rockefeller NY #18/R est:4000-5000

SHURTLEFF, Roswell Morse (1838-1915) American

£	$	€	Details
£1852	$3000	€2778	Race for life (66x97cm-26x38in) s.d.77. 23-Jan-3 Aspire, Cleveland #10 est:3000-6000
£5625	$9000	€8156	Landscape (56x91cm-22x36in) s. 16-May-3 Skinner, Boston #77/R est:800-1200

SHUTE, R W and S A (19th C) American
Works on paper

£	$	€	Details
£15068	$22000	€22602	Portrait of Julia Anne Coolidge Martin (46x30cm-18x12in) i.verso W/C. 3-Nov-1 North East Auctions, Portsmouth #763/R est:20000-40000

SHUTLEWORTH, Allen (19/20th C) British
Works on paper

£	$	€	Details
£360	$572	€540	Clouds lifting off the Passu Glacier, Karakoram Range, Pakistan (30x46cm-12x18in) s.d.1912 W/C. 29-Apr-3 Bonhams, New Bond Street #68

SI CHEN YUAN (1912-1974) ?

£	$	€	Details
£2742	$4250	€4113	Madrid (79x66cm-31x26in) s. prov. 29-Oct-2 John Moran, Pasadena #725 est:4000-6000

SIBBONS, Gudron (?) ?

£	$	€	Details
£800	$1248	€1200	Evening harvest (40x50cm-16x20in) s. 9-Oct-2 Woolley & Wallis, Salisbury #353/R

SIBERECHTS, Jan (1627-1703) Flemish

£	$	€	Details
£100000	$166000	€150000	Extensive river landscape, probably Derbyshire, with drovers and their cattle (82x128cm-32x50in) s. 12-Jun-3 Sotheby's, London #2/R est:50000-70000

SIBIYA, Lucky (1942-1999) South African

£	$	€	Details
£1281	$1999	€1922	Elder and the young girls (56x76cm-22x30in) s.d.95 acrylic paper prov. 11-Nov-2 Stephan Welz, Johannesburg #573 est:4000-6000 (SA.R 20000)

Sculpture

£	$	€	Details
£2580	$4153	€3870	Female figure plus mask (172x62cm-68x24in) s. s.i.verso carved painted wood panel prov. 12-May-3 Stephan Welz, Johannesburg #554/R est:25000-35000 (SA.R 30000)

SIBLEY, Andrew (1933-) Australian

£	$	€	Details
£1147	$1743	€1721	Nudes (70x55cm-28x22in) s.d.May 1986 verso enamel. 27-Aug-2 Goodman, Sydney #221 est:2000-3000 (A.D 3200)
£2299	$3425	€3449	Journey (100x95cm-39x37in) s.d.87 i.stretcher enamel. 27-Aug-2 Christie's, Melbourne #168/R est:7000-10000 (A.D 6000)
£3200	$5152	€4800	Dogs in love (90x100cm-35x39in) s.d.97 i.on stretcher enamel prov. 6-May-3 Christie's, Melbourne #270/R est:8000-12000 (A.D 8000)
£3400	$5474	€5100	Memory window (119x99cm-47x39in) s.d.87 enamel on canvas prov. 6-May-3 Christie's, Melbourne #386/R est:8000-12000 (A.D 8500)
£3831	$5709	€5747	Little king (96x101cm-38x40in) 27-Aug-2 Christie's, Melbourne #94/R est:10000-15000 (A.D 10000)

Works on paper

£	$	€	Details
£1571	$2451	€2357	Cellist (136x121cm-54x48in) s.d.81 synthetic polymer paint canvas prov. 11-Nov-2 Deutscher-Menzies, Melbourne #69/R est:5000-7000 (A.D 4400)

SICARD, Francois Léon (1862-1934) French
Sculpture

£	$	€	Details
£10000	$15700	€15000	Oedipe et le sphinx - Odeipus anf the sphinx (69cm-27in) s. gilt bronze i.f.F Barbedienne. 10-Dec-2 Sotheby's, London #166/R est:10000-12000

SICARD, Pierre (1900-1980) French

£	$	€	Details
£472	$731	€750	Vase de fleurs (81x65cm-32x26in) s. painted c.1920. 30-Oct-2 Artcurial Briest, Paris #328

SICARDI, Louis Marie (1746-1825) French
Miniatures

£	$	€	Details
£1419	$2243	€2200	Portrait d'Antoine Marie (7x5cm-3x2in) s.d.1811 oval. 18-Dec-2 Beaussant & Lefèvre, Paris #6/R

SICHEL, Ernest Leopold (1862-1941) British

£	$	€	Details
£800	$1272	€1200	Portrait of a seated lady (30x23cm-12x9in) s. sold with two sketches by same hand. 26-Feb-3 Sotheby's, Olympia #3/R
£1150	$1829	€1725	Seated female nude (23x30cm-9x12in) s.i.d.1933. 26-Feb-3 Sotheby's, Olympia #5/R est:500-700

SICHEL, Harold (1881-1948) American

£	$	€	Details
£599	$1000	€869	House in landscape - Gilmanton House (20x28cm-8x11in) s.i. canvasboard exhib. 17-Jun-3 John Moran, Pasadena #22b est:1000-1500
£2096	$3500	€3039	Oaks in California landscape, corner of the pasture (20x28cm-8x11in) canvasboard exhib. 17-Jun-3 John Moran, Pasadena #22a est:1000-1500

SICHEL, Nathaniel (1843-1907) German

£	$	€	Details
£1410	$2200	€2115	Orientalist figure (48x41cm-19x16in) s. 9-Oct-2 Doyle, New York #105 est:2000-3000
£2767	$4262	€4400	Belle orientale (50x37cm-20x15in) s. panel. 23-Oct-2 Rabourdin & Choppin de Janvry, Paris #121/R
£4000	$6280	€6000	Lady with red flowers in her hair (63x55cm-25x22in) s. 21-Nov-2 Christie's, Kensington #61/R est:4000-6000

SICHELKOW, Valdemar (19th C) Danish

£	$	€	Details
£6052	$9623	€9078	Still life of lobster, oysters, fruit and vegetables on table (120x89cm-47x35in) s.d.1883. 5-Mar-3 Rasmussen, Copenhagen #1640/R est:60000 (D.KR 65000)

SICILIA, Jose Maria (1954-) Spanish

£	$	€	Details
£4500	$7335	€6750	Untitled - white with black corners (50x50cm-20x20in) s.i.1988 verso acrylic resin prov. 3-Feb-3 Sotheby's, Olympia #106/R est:2500-3500
£6090	$9622	€9500	Untitled (142x92cm-56x36in) s.i.d.1982 verso. 14-Nov-2 Arte, Seville #469/R est:6700
£7292	$11594	€10500	Lessive liquide (112x102cm-44x40in) s.i.d.3.84 verso prov. 29-Apr-3 Artcurial Briest, Paris #525/R est:12000-15000
£8013	$12420	€12500	Industrial vacuum (260x190cm-102x75in) s.i.d.1983 acrylic. 7-Dec-2 Cornette de St.Cyr, Paris #95/R est:15000
£14194	$22000	€21291	Colour flower III (170x85cm-67x33in) s. i.d.86 verso acrylic on two panel. 26-Sep-2 Christie's, Rockefeller NY #834/R est:10000-15000
£14557	$23000	€21836	Tulipa Kobro Huka (145x145cm-57x57in) s.on stretcher i.d.85 verso prov. 13-Nov-2 Sotheby's, New York #585/R est:20000-25000
£16000	$24640	€24000	Tulipa 17 (75x91cm-30x36in) init. s.i.d.1985 verso panel prov. 23-Oct-2 Christie's, London #140/R est:15000-20000
£16290	$27204	€23621	Tulip 5 (260x260cm-102x102in) s.d.85 acrylic prov. 24-Jun-3 Koller, Zurich #187/R est:20000-30000 (S.FR 36000)

Works on paper

£	$	€	Details
£13836	$21308	€22000	Untitled (40x220cm-16x87in) s. on wax. 26-Oct-2 Cornette de St.Cyr, Paris #154/R est:25000

SICKERT, Bernhard (1863-1932) British

£260 $406 €390 Harbour scene with figures and buildings (30x38cm-12x15in) board. 21-Sep-2 Lacy Scott, Bury St.Edmunds #366

SICKERT, Walter Richard (1860-1942) British

£4500 $7020 €6750 Bust portrait of a lady (50x40cm-20x16in) s. prov. 25-Mar-3 Bonhams, New Bond Street #27/R est:5000-7000
£7000 $10990 €10500 Christine Drummond Sickert, nee Angus, buys a gendarmerie (56x43cm-22x17in) s. painted 1920 prov.exhib.lit. 22-Nov-2 Christie's, London #8/R est:8000-12000
£7500 $11775 €11250 Mr Sheepshank's House, Camden Crecent, Bath (35x25cm-14x10in) s. board painted c.1916-18 prov. 22-Nov-2 Christie's, London #13/R est:8000-12000
£8500 $13260 €12750 La giuseppina (54x40cm-21x16in) s. prov. 25-Mar-3 Bonhams, New Bond Street #26/R est:7000-10000
£12000 $18600 €18000 Mamma Mai Poveretta (46x38cm-18x15in) s. prov.exhib.lit. 4-Dec-2 Sotheby's, London #58/R est:12000-18000
£13793 $21793 €20000 Rue de Normandie (19x23cm-7x9in) s.d.1903 panel. 4-Apr-3 Tajan, Paris #151 est:2000
£14000 $21980 €21000 Ghetto, Venice (14x23cm-6x9in) s. panel painted c.1897-98 prov. 22-Nov-2 Christie's, London #12/R est:7000-10000
£14000 $22960 €21000 Street corner, Dieppe (34x27cm-13x11in) s. panel painted c.1907 prov. 6-Jun-3 Christie's, London #47/R est:10000-15000
£16000 $24960 €24000 Haunted house, Dieppe (21x15cm-8x6in) s. panel prov. 25-Mar-3 Bonhams, New Bond Street #24/R est:8000-12000
£17000 $26520 €25500 View of the Place Nationale in Dieppe, with statue of Le Grand Duquesne (65x54cm-26x21in) indis sig. prov. 25-Mar-3 Bonhams, New Bond Street #25/R est:7000-10000
£17000 $27880 €25500 Little shop (23x32cm-9x13in) panel prov.exhib.lit. 6-Jun-3 Christie's, London #45/R est:8000-12000
£20000 $31400 €30000 Little tea shop, Dieppe (23x15cm-9x6in) s. panel prov. 22-Nov-2 Christie's, London #5/R est:20000-30000
£24000 $37680 €36000 View of Milan Catherdral (24x16cm-9x6in) s. panel painted c.1896 prov. 22-Nov-2 Christie's, London #6/R est:20000-30000
£24000 $40080 €34800 Reclining nude (37x45cm-15x18in) s. prov. 24-Jun-3 Bonhams, New Bond Street #28/R est:20000-25000
£28000 $45920 €40600 Reclining nude (38x46cm-15x18in) painted 1906 prov.exhib.lit. 4-Jun-3 Sotheby's, London #13/R est:15000-20000
£30000 $46800 €45000 Camden town interior - The looking glass (51x41cm-20x16in) prov.exhib. 25-Mar-3 Bonhams, New Bond Street #28/R est:20000-25000
£38000 $58900 €57000 La Dogana and santa maria della Salute (32x41cm-13x16in) panel prov.lit. 4-Dec-2 Sotheby's, London #29/R est:25000-35000
£40000 $62000 €60000 La Grand Duquesne, Dieppe (55x46cm-22x18in) s. prov.exhib.lit. 4-Dec-2 Sotheby's, London #25/R est:30000-40000
£48000 $78720 €72000 Conversation (46x38cm-18x15in) s. painted 1903-04 prov.exhib.lit. 6-Jun-3 Christie's, London #125/R est:40000-60000

Works on paper

£700 $1085 €1050 Seated woman (16x14cm-6x6in) chl exec.c.1911-1912. 4-Dec-2 Christie's, Kensington #221/R
£800 $1240 €1200 Study for Old Middlesex (21x14cm-8x6in) pencil pen black ink. 4-Dec-2 Christie's, Kensington #217/R
£820 $1369 €1189 Old Middlesex, figures in a theatre (28x41cm-11x16in) s.i. pencil sketch. 25-Jun-3 Brightwells, Leominster #1019/R
£900 $1386 €1350 Lady wearing a feathered hat (37x24cm-15x9in) s. chl. 5-Sep-2 Christie's, Kensington #507
£950 $1473 €1425 Blind Jimmy (29x16cm-11x6in) pencil. 4-Dec-2 Christie's, Kensington #214/R
£1400 $2310 €2030 Portrait of Maurice Villain (27x19cm-11x7in) s.i. pencil. 3-Jul-3 Christie's, Kensington #243/R est:700-1000
£2000 $3120 €3000 Crouching nude (27x30cm-11x12in) pencil pen ink executed c.1910 exhib. 27-Mar-3 Christie's, Kensington #255/R est:1200-1800
£2400 $3696 €3600 Woman seated on a chaise longue (30x21cm-12x8in) s.indis.i. pencil pen black ink. 5-Sep-2 Christie's, Kensington #529/R est:1000-1500
£2600 $4004 €3900 Old Bedford (27x21cm-11x8in) s.i. black white chk. 5-Sep-2 Christie's, Kensington #526/R est:800-1200
£3000 $4650 €4500 Portrait of Sir Hugh Walpole (28x23cm-11x9in) s.i. pencil col chk pen black ink. 4-Dec-2 Christie's, Kensington #218/R est:700-1000
£3400 $5236 €5100 Cafe des Tribunaux, Dieppe (18x20cm-7x8in) s.i. pen brush brown ink. 5-Sep-2 Christie's, Kensington #567/R est:1000-1500
£3500 $5424 €5250 Fair, Dieppe (23x29cm-9x11in) s. black chk squared for transfer. 4-Dec-2 Sotheby's, London #33/R est:3000-4000
£5000 $8200 €7250 La cafe suisse, sous les arcades, Dieppe (25x15cm-10x6in) i. pen ink bodycol prov. 5-Jun-3 Christie's, London #191/R est:5000-8000
£6500 $10076 €9750 Still life with lobster (25x36cm-10x14in) init. black chk ink executed c.1919. 4-Dec-2 Sotheby's, London #32/R est:4000-6000

SICRE, Gonzalo (1967-) Spanish

£2452 $3874 €3800 Empty museum V (130x97cm-51x38in) s. 18-Dec-2 Ansorena, Madrid #187/R

SIDANER, Henri le (1862-1939) French

£3608 $5700 €5700 Vue de Notre-Dame (13x20cm-5x8in) panel double-sided. 2-Dec-2 Tajan, Paris #56/R
£5714 $9086 €8400 Pecheurs en bord de Seine (14x26cm-6x10in) s. panel painted c.1892-93. 26-Feb-3 Artcurial Briest, Paris #168/R est:4500-5000
£6000 $9240 €9000 Le Trianon a Versailles sous la neige (14x20cm-6x8in) s. panel painted c.1916 lit. 23-Oct-2 Sotheby's, Olympia #645/R est:6000-8000
£7500 $11925 €11250 Notre Dame, Paris (13x17cm-5x7in) s. board. 20-Mar-3 Sotheby's, Olympia #42/R est:6000-8000
£8974 $14090 €14000 Eglise Dolce Acqua (24x19cm-9x7in) s. panel prov.lit. 10-Dec-2 Pierre Berge, Paris #20/R est:18000
£13665 $22000 €20498 L'Eglise Dolceaqua (25x18cm-10x7in) s. panel painted 1911 prov.lit. 7-May-3 Sotheby's, New York #166/R est:20000-25000
£24359 $38000 €36539 Le maison des pecheurs (41x32cm-16x13in) s. panel prov. 7-Nov-2 Christie's, Rockefeller NY #230/R est:30000-40000
£30769 $48000 €46154 Fenetre au crepuscule (41x33cm-16x13in) s. panel painted 1926 prov.lit. 7-Nov-2 Christie's, Rockefeller NY #225/R est:35000-45000
£32051 $50000 €48077 L'estacade, Le Croisic (32x41cm-13x16in) s. panel painted c.1923 prov.exhib. 7-Nov-2 Christie's, Rockefeller NY #251/R est:40000-60000
£59006 $95000 €88509 La maison de jean Jacques Rousseau (65x55cm-26x22in) s. painted 1936 prov.exhib.lit. 8-May-3 Christie's, Rockefeller NY #166/R est:50000-70000
£65000 $108550 €94250 La maison des pecheurs, Villefranche-sur-mer (82x66cm-32x26in) s. painted 1924-25. 25-Jun-3 Christie's, London #137/R est:60000-80000
£72000 $120240 €104400 Le grand canal au clair du lune, Venise (54x65cm-21x26in) s. painted 1931 prov.exhib.lit. 24-Jun-3 Sotheby's, London #133/R est:70000-90000
£75000 $123000 €112500 Arbres fleuris, Gerberoy (55x74cm-22x29in) s. painted 1902 prov.lit. 4-Feb-3 Christie's, London #242/R
£76000 $124640 €114000 Neige a Chartres (65x81cm-26x32in) s. painted 1918 prov.lit. 5-Feb-3 Sotheby's, London #124/R est:100000
£80986 $134436 €115000 Table a Gerberoy (81x65cm-32x26in) s. prov.lit. 12-Jun-3 Tajan, Paris #14/R est:120000-150000
£102564 $160000 €153846 La lanterne (100x81cm-39x32in) painted 1928 prov.exhib.lit. 7-Nov-2 Christie's, Rockefeller NY #253/R est:180000-250000
£147436 $230000 €221154 Les barques (65x81cm-26x32in) s. painted 1923 prov.lit. 6-Nov-2 Sotheby's, New York #167/R est:180000-220000
£170000 $277100 €255000 La table d'apres-midi, Gerberoy (96x79cm-38x31in) s. painted 1933 prov.lit. 3-Feb-3 Bonhams, New Bond Street #31/R est:150000-200000
£170000 $278800 €255000 Table devant la fenetre, Versailles (93x74cm-37x29in) s. painted 1937 prov.exhib.lit. 4-Feb-3 Christie's, London #241/R est:150000
£310000 $517700 €449500 La fenetre, le croisic (100x81cm-39x32in) s. painted 1924 prov.exhib.lit. 24-Jun-3 Sotheby's, London #117/R est:150000-200000
£500000 $835000 €725000 Les baraques, Gerberoy (125x150cm-49x59in) s. painted 1920 prov.exhib.lit. 25-Jun-3 Christie's, London #142/R est:500000-700000

Works on paper

£2532 $4000 €4000 Maison a Gerberoy (32x26cm-13x10in) s. pastel. 27-Nov-2 Marc Kohn, Paris #8/R
£2885 $4471 €4500 Portail a la maison rose (31x27cm-12x11in) s.i. ink chl wax crayon. 4-Dec-2 Pierre Berge, Paris #84/R
£5674 $9475 €8000 Le Pavillon, clair de lune, Gerberoy (32x26cm-13x10in) s. crayon htd pastel prov.lit. 20-Jun-3 Piasa, Paris #8/R est:8000-9000
£6000 $9540 €9000 Le buste, Gerberoy (32x26cm-13x10in) s. col crayon prov.exhib.lit. 20-Mar-3 Sotheby's, Olympia #12/R est:4000-5000
£24845 $40000 €37268 Les barques au clair de lune, Le Treport (54x74cm-21x29in) s. pastel executed 1906 prov.exhib.lit. 7-May-3 Sotheby's, New York #145/R est:40000-60000
£30000 $50100 €45000 Le Chateau de Maintenon (46x38cm-18x15in) s. pastel exec c.1903 prov.exhib.lit. 26-Jun-3 Christie's, London #352/R est:15000-20000

SIDDELL, Peter (1935-) New Zealander

£386 $602 €579 Fig plucker (19x19cm-7x7in) s.d.1982 board. 27-Mar-3 International Art Centre, Auckland #196 (NZ.D 1100)
£955 $1500 €1433 Karekare landscape with cliff face (25x21cm-10x8in) s.d.1974 board. 10-Dec-2 Peter Webb, Auckland #81/R est:3800-4500 (NZ.D 3000)
£955 $1500 €1433 Karekare landscape with cliff face (25x21cm-10x8in) s.d.1974 board. 10-Dec-2 Peter Webb, Auckland #82/R est:3800-4500 (NZ.D 3000)
£955 $1500 €1433 Karekare landscape with cave and rock pool on foreshore (25x21cm-10x8in) s.d.1974 board. 10-Dec-2 Peter Webb, Auckland #83/R est:3800-4500 (NZ.D 3000)

£955 $1500 €1433 Karekare landscape with cave (25x21cm-10x8in) s.d.1974 board. 10-Dec-2 Peter Webb, Auckland #84/R est:3800-4500 (NZ.D 3000)
£4389 $6846 €6584 Hrabour Reach (40x60cm-16x24in) s.d. board prov. 7-Nov-2 International Art Centre, Auckland #37/R est:12000-18000 (NZ.D 14000)
£4912 $7663 €7368 Harbour (30x50cm-12x20in) s.d.1996. 27-Mar-3 International Art Centre, Auckland #31/R est:10000-15000 (NZ.D 14000)
£9155 $15106 €13275 Old and new Auckland (120x78cm-47x31in) s.d.1977. 1-Jul-3 Peter Webb, Auckland #22/R est:25000-35000 (NZ.D 26000)
£11268 $18592 €16339 White cloud (39x59cm-15x23in) s.d.1982 s.i.d.verso board prov. 1-Jul-3 Peter Webb, Auckland #21/R est:20000-35000 (NZ.D 32000)
£31250 $48750 €46875 Suburban inlet (104x139cm-41x55in) s. board prov.exhib. 8-Apr-3 Peter Webb, Auckland #55/R est:80000-120000 (NZ.D 90000)

Works on paper
£737 $1149 €1106 Hill (12x16cm-5x6in) s.d.1997 W/C. 27-Mar-3 International Art Centre, Auckland #157/R (NZ.D 2100)
£1579 $2463 €2369 Puerto (50x33cm-20x13in) s. pastel. 27-Mar-3 International Art Centre, Auckland #32/R est:3500-4500 (NZ.D 4500)

SIDERIS, Alexander (1898-1978) American/Greek
£297 $475 €446 Bathers in a stream (51x41cm-20x16in) s. 8-Jan-3 Doyle, New York #34/R

SIDLER, Alfred (1905-1992) Swiss
£408 $644 €612 Extensive summer landscape (38x51cm-15x20in) s. 29-Nov-2 Zofingen, Switzerland #3075 (S.FR 950)

SIDLEY, S (1829-1896) British
£600 $972 €870 Portrait of a young girl and puppy. s.d.1865 board oval. 23-May-3 Dee Atkinson & Harrison, Driffield #626

SIDLEY, Samuel (1829-1896) British
£4500 $7110 €6750 Please (61x53cm-24x21in) s.d.1865 oval prov. 26-Nov-2 Christie's, London #107/R est:5000-8000

SIDNEY, Thomas (19th C) British
Works on paper
£250 $390 €375 Eel's Foot Inn, Ormesby (25x36cm-10x14in) s.i. W/C on board. 11-Apr-3 Keys, Aylsham #232
£250 $418 €363 Beachy Head (24x38cm-9x15in) s.i. pencil W/C. 26-Jun-3 Mellors & Kirk, Nottingham #816
£350 $560 €525 Lantern Hill, Ilfracombe (25x69cm-10x27in) s.i. W/C. 13-Mar-3 Duke & Son, Dorchester #120
£400 $628 €600 Bamborough Castle (24x52cm-9x20in) s.i. W/C over pencil. 21-Nov-2 Tennants, Leyburn #616
£420 $685 €630 Beachy Head (20x43cm-8x17in) s.d.1924 W/C. 28-Jan-3 Gorringes, Lewes #1658

SIDOROVICZ, Sigmund (1846-1881) Austrian
£2245 $3569 €3300 Woman's portrait (40x31cm-16x12in) s.i.d.1875 board. 19-Mar-3 Neumeister, Munich #731/R est:1200

SIDRONE, John (20th C) American?
Works on paper
£248 $400 €372 Woman in bunny suit with freshly hatched chick (28x23cm-11x9in) s. chl pencil. 20-Feb-3 Illustration House, New York #158/R

SIEBEN, Gottfried (1856-1918) Austrian
Works on paper
£253 $400 €380 Two enticingly clad female grape harvesters (46x30cm-18x12in) s. W/C. 18-Nov-2 Schrager Galleries, Milwaukee #1070

SIEBER, Hans Ruedi (1926-) Swiss
£377 $604 €566 Still life with jug and fruit (61x65cm-24x26in) s. 17-Mar-3 Philippe Schuler, Zurich #8483 (S.FR 800)

SIEBERT, Fritz Anton (1878-?) German
£342 $534 €500 Hamburg harbour (55x65cm-22x26in) s. board. 10-Apr-3 Schopman, Hamburg #717

SIEBERT, Georg (1896-1984) German
Works on paper
£282 $437 €440 Sunflowers (28x27cm-11x11in) s.d.1915 W/C pastel crayon. 7-Dec-2 Van Ham, Cologne #496/R

SIEBNER, Herbert Johannes Joseph (1925-) Canadian
Works on paper
£2261 $3527 €3770 Waiting for the muse (36x39cm-14x15in) s. s.i.d.1982 verso mixed media board prov. 13-Apr-3 Levis, Calgary #108/R est:1200-1500 (C.D 5200)

SIEBURGER, Frida (1862-?) Czechoslovakian
£514 $807 €750 Farmstead with children and ducks by stream (58x79cm-23x31in) s.d.1885. 16-Apr-3 Dorotheum, Salzburg #134/R

SIECK, Rudolf (1877-1957) German
£759 $1200 €1139 Panoramic pastoral landscape with fields of grain (58x69cm-23x27in) s. 26-Apr-3 Jeffery Burchard, Florida #53
£1603 $2436 €2500 Spring meadow with blossoming trees (58x72cm-23x28in) s.d.1906 panel lit. 11-Jul-2 Allgauer, Kempten #2695/R
Works on paper
£1218 $1851 €1900 Figure with pan flute by water (27x29cm-11x11in) mono.d.1927 W/C. 11-Jul-2 Hugo Ruef, Munich #922/R est:300

SIEFFERT, Paul (1874-1957) French
£1700 $2652 €2550 Nude on blue drapery (16x24cm-6x9in) s. board. 26-Mar-3 Sotheby's, Olympia #280/R est:1200-1800
£2500 $4075 €3625 Nude playing patience (50x61cm-20x24in) s. s.verso. 16-Jul-3 Sotheby's, Olympia #263/R est:2500-3500
£2600 $4056 €3900 Reclining nude (17x24cm-7x9in) s. s.i.verso panel. 17-Sep-2 Sotheby's, Olympia #288/R est:1000-1500
£2600 $4342 €3900 Arranging her hair (24x19cm-9x7in) s. panel. 18-Jun-3 Christie's, Kensington #123/R est:2500-3500
£4200 $6594 €6300 Nude with her vanity mirror (55x46cm-22x18in) s. s.verso. 21-Nov-2 Christie's, Kensington #39/R est:4000-6000
£5200 $8164 €7800 Young tennis player (92x73cm-36x29in) s.d.1924. 21-Nov-2 Christie's, Kensington #27/R est:6000-8000

SIEGARD, Par (1877-1961) Swedish
£837 $1322 €1256 Still life of fruit (34x46cm-13x18in) s. 28-Apr-3 Bukowskis, Stockholm #79/R (S.KR 11000)
£4625 $7215 €6938 Landscape from Halland (56x76cm-22x30in) s.d.18. 5-Nov-2 Bukowskis, Stockholm #13/R est:65000-75000 (S.KR 66000)
Works on paper
£981 $1530 €1472 Man, woman and bird (16x11cm-6x4in) init. W/C. 6-Nov-2 AB Stockholms Auktionsverk #743/R est:15000-20000 (S.KR 14000)

SIEGEL, Arthur (1913-1979) American
Photographs
£4747 $7500 €7121 Right of assembly (34x27cm-13x11in) init.d.1939 gelatin silver print prov.lit. 25-Apr-3 Phillips, New York #21/R est:5000-7000
£8228 $13000 €12342 Urban landscapes (17x26cm-7x10in) s.d.1951 three dye transfer prints prov. 25-Apr-3 Phillips, New York #111/R est:4000-6000

SIEGEL, Leo Dink (1910-) American
Works on paper
£264 $425 €396 Tax auditor turns out to be a woman (28x23cm-11x9in) s. ink pencil. 20-Feb-3 Illustration House, New York #159/R
£497 $800 €746 Shedding clothes in a hot air balloon (28x20cm-11x8in) s. ink pencil. 20-Feb-3 Illustration House, New York #160/R

SIEGEN, August (19th C) German
£479 $748 €700 Venice (16x32cm-6x13in) panel on of pair. 10-Apr-3 Dorotheum, Vienna #262/R
£650 $1014 €975 Orientalist town view (58x37cm-23x15in) s. 8-Oct-2 Bonhams, Knightsbridge #245c/R
£685 $1068 €1000 Venice (16x32cm-6x13in). s. panel one of pair. 10-Apr-3 Dorotheum, Vienna #264
£800 $1248 €1200 Figures in a cathedral interior (52x42cm-20x17in) s. panel. 10-Sep-2 Bonhams, Knightsbridge #140/R
£855 $1386 €1300 Oriental village square with a market (54x44cm-21x17in) s. 21-Jan-3 Christie's, Amsterdam #25 est:600-800
£952 $1514 €1400 Venice scene (18x31cm-7x12in) s. panel. 25-Feb-3 Dorotheum, Vienna #139/R
£1088 $1731 €1600 View of Doge's Palace in Venice (18x31cm-7x12in) s. panel. 25-Feb-3 Dorotheum, Vienna #140/R est:1400-1600
£2115 $3321 €3300 Lively harbour in Medieval town on the Ostsee (98x134cm-39x53in) s. bears i. verso. 23-Nov-2 Arnold, Frankfurt #873/R est:4000
£2188 $3500 €3282 View of a bustling town with boats on the canal (53x79cm-21x31in) s. 14-May-3 Butterfields, San Francisco #1078/R est:3000-5000
£2600 $4056 €3900 Nordksov, on the Isle Fyn, Denmark (99x142cm-39x56in) s. 8-Oct-2 Sotheby's, Olympia #425/R est:2000-3000

£2958 $4910 €4200 Oriental city with through-travellers (74x100cm-29x39in) s. 14-Jun-3 Arnold, Frankfurt #868/R est:1800
£3074 $4795 €4457 Bustle in the bazaar (63x79cm-25x31in) s. 12-Apr-3 Mu Terem Galeria, Budapest #122/R est:850000 (H.F 1100000)
£3459 $5500 €5189 Harbour town (31x25cm-12x10in) s. 5-Mar-3 Christie's, Rockefeller NY #68/R est:3000-5000
£5000 $7950 €7500 Rome, seen from the Tiber. Venice seen from the Grand Canal (68x55cm-27x22in) s. pair. 20-Mar-3 Christie's, Kensington #75/R est:6000-8000

SIEGEN, G (?) ?
£4878 $8000 €7073 El cerro de Santa Lucia, Santiago (55x68cm-22x27in) s.d.1873 prov. 27-May-3 Sotheby's, New York #138

SIEGER, Frederik (1902-) Dutch
£851 $1379 €1200 Girl at a table with lamp and clock (104x88cm-41x35in) s. 26-May-3 Glerum, Amsterdam #114/R

SIEGER, Viktor (attrib) (1843-1905) Austrian
£609 $944 €950 Snow-covered winter landscape with trees at the pond (17x39cm-7x15in) panel. 4-Dec-2 Neumeister, Munich #903/R

SIEGERT, August Friedrich (1820-1883) German
£5896 $9552 €8549 The small connoisseur of fine arts (49x42cm-19x17in) s. 26-May-3 Bukowskis, Stockholm #243a/R est:30000-35000 (S.KR 76000)

SIEGLE, Theo (1902-1973) German
Sculpture
£3094 $5073 €4300 Max Slevogt (31cm-12in) terracotta iron. 4-Jun-3 Reiss & Sohn, Konigstein #509/R est:5000

SIEGRIEST, Louis Bassi (1899-1989) American
£1000 $1600 €1500 Church in Mexico (86x63cm-34x25in) s.d.55 s.i.verso masonite. 18-May-3 Butterfields, Los Angeles #7020 est:1000-1500
£1592 $2500 €2388 Cypress trees on the coast (46x51cm-18x20in) s. prov. 19-Nov-2 Butterfields, San Francisco #8338/R est:2500-3500
Works on paper
£1274 $2000 €1911 Colt and mare (33x43cm-13x17in) s. i.verso mixed media paperboard prov. 19-Nov-2 Butterfields, San Francisco #8337/R est:2500-3500

SIEGRIEST, Lundy (1925-1985) American
£1227 $2000 €1841 Pier and hills (38x48cm-15x19in) s. i.verso prov. 16-Feb-3 Butterfields, San Francisco #2114 est:2500-3500

SIEGUMFELDT, Hermann Carl (1833-1912) Danish
£450 $725 €675 Italian coastal landscape with mountains in background (69x95cm-27x37in) s. 22-Feb-3 Rasmussen, Havnen #2087 (D.KR 5000)

SIEGUMFELDT, Hermann Carl (attrib) (1833-1912) Danish
£279 $444 €419 Town street scene with figures (18x27cm-7x11in) s.d.1899 exhib. 10-Mar-3 Rasmussen, Vejle #493 (D.KR 3000)
£328 $501 €492 Woman with rake (40x33cm-16x13in) s.d.1866. 24-Aug-2 Rasmussen, Havnen #2281 (D.KR 3800)

SIEMIRADZKI, Hendrik (1843-1902) Polish
£4800 $7488 €7200 Portrait of a young woman (36x27cm-14x11in) s. 17-Sep-2 Sotheby's, Olympia #272/R est:4000-6000

SIENESE SCHOOL (14th C) Italian
£11500 $19205 €16675 The Crucifixion (30x16cm-12x6in) tempera panel gold ground pointed top. 10-Jul-3 Sotheby's, London #151/R est:7000-9000

SIENESE SCHOOL (17th C) Italian
£9677 $15290 €15000 Sainte Catherine of Alexandria (117x87cm-46x34in) s.d.1604. 18-Dec-2 Piasa, Paris #1/R est:20000

SIEPMAN VAN DEN BERG, Eja (1943-) Dutch
Sculpture
£2188 $3413 €3791 Standing girl (65cm-26in) i.d.1977 bronze prov. 31-Mar-3 Goodman, Sydney #180/R (A.D 5800)

SIEPMANN, Heinrich (1904-) German
£321 $497 €500 Abstract composition (73x50cm-29x20in) s.d.58 paper. 7-Dec-2 Van Ham, Cologne #499
£385 $596 €600 Untitled (60x44cm-24x17in) s.d.59 panel. 7-Dec-2 Van Ham, Cologne #498/R
Works on paper
£609 $944 €950 Abstract composition (49x68cm-19x27in) s.d.59 mixed media collage. 7-Dec-2 Van Ham, Cologne #500/R
£1884 $3090 €2600 Untitled - 38 (49x69cm-19x27in) s.i.d.83 collage board oil pencil. 28-May-3 Lempertz, Koln #408/R est:2500-3000

SIERHUIS, Jan (1928-) Dutch
£553 $923 €802 Lovers (45x55cm-18x22in) s.d.65 prov. 17-Jun-3 Rasmussen, Copenhagen #9/R (D.KR 5800)
£573 $883 €900 De Spaanse (100x80cm-39x31in) s.d.88 s.i.d.verso. 3-Sep-2 Christie's, Amsterdam #445
£620 $1035 €899 Two figures (40x50cm-16x20in) s.d.66 prov. 17-Jun-3 Rasmussen, Copenhagen #122/R (D.KR 6500)
Works on paper
£286 $478 €415 Composition (50x65cm-20x26in) s.d.61 i.verso gouache prov. 17-Jun-3 Rasmussen, Copenhagen #109 (D.KR 3000)
£305 $509 €442 Composition (46x67cm-18x26in) s.d.64 gouache prov. 17-Jun-3 Rasmussen, Copenhagen #143 (D.KR 3200)
£1139 $1800 €1800 Le retable de saint Pierre Martyr (74x55cm-29x22in) s.d.76 col crayon. 26-Nov-2 Sotheby's, Amsterdam #52/R est:1200-1500

SIERIG, Ferdinand Carl (1839-1905) Dutch
£900 $1396 €1350 Playing with the kitten (54x41cm-21x16in) s. 3-Dec-2 Sotheby's, Olympia #277a/R est:1000-1500

SIERRA, Paul (20th C) Cuban
£350 $550 €525 Sisyphus (50x60cm-20x24in) init. 19-Nov-2 Wright, Chicago #305/R

SIETMAN, Ruth Mayer (20th C) American
£689 $1130 €999 Cuyahoga River reflection (48x38cm-19x15in) s.d.44. 30-May-3 Aspire, Cleveland #51/R est:200-400

SIEVAN, Maurice (1898-1981) American
£976 $1600 €1415 Forest hills landscape (56x74cm-22x29in) s. prov. 1-Jun-3 Wright, Chicago #217/R est:900-1200

SIEVERT, Erik (1897-?) Danish
£316 $499 €474 Still life of flowers (65x50cm-26x20in) s. 5-Apr-3 Rasmussen, Havnen #4128 (D.KR 3400)

SIEVERT, Otto (1894-1940) Danish
£366 $581 €549 Self portrait (87x82cm-34x32in) s. lit. 26-Feb-3 Kunsthallen, Copenhagen #363/R (D.KR 4000)

SIEWERT, Feliciano (1942-) Dutch
Works on paper
£526 $853 €800 Koppelpoort, Amersfoort. Culemborg (49x69cm-19x27in) s.d.75 W/C two. 21-Jan-3 Christie's, Amsterdam #324

SIGA, Louis de (19th C) ?
£258 $379 €400 Shepherd and flock (26x37cm-10x15in) s. 24-Jun-2 Dr Fritz Nagel, Stuttgart #5938/R

SIGERIST, Fred G (20th C) American
£484 $750 €726 San Gorgonia Pass (51x71cm-20x28in) s.i.d. 8-Dec-2 Toomey, Oak Park #669/R

SIGG, Hermann-Alfred (1924-) Swiss
£1288 $2034 €1932 Zurich landscape near Regensdorf (71x89cm-28x35in) s.d.48. 29-Nov-2 Falk & Falk, Zurich #506/R est:3000 (S.FR 3000)
£1397 $2180 €2096 Last fruit (92x73cm-36x29in) s.d.56. 6-Nov-2 Hans Widmer, St Gallen #62/R est:1800-3500 (S.FR 3200)

SIGHICELLI, Elisa (1968-) Italian
Photographs
£3500 $5460 €5250 Santiago, red sofa (80x80cm-31x31in) s.i.d.2000 num.1/3 verso c-print on lightbox exhib. 21-Oct-2 Sotheby's, London #71/R est:2600-3200

SIGMUND, Benjamin D (fl.1880-1904) British
Works on paper
£300 $474 €435 Sheep on a coastal path (18x25cm-7x10in) s. W/C. 22-Jul-3 Gorringes, Lewes #1724
£720 $1123 €1080 Casting the line (17x25cm-7x10in) s. W/C. 26-Mar-3 Sotheby's, Olympia #80/R
£800 $1312 €1200 Cottages at Lynmouth (18x25cm-7x10in) s. W/C. 5-Feb-3 John Nicholson, Haslemere #1015

£1600 $2496 €2400 Flowers gathering, Worcestershire. Cottage in Worcestershire lane (25x35cm-10x14in) s. W/C pair. 26-Mar-3 Sotheby's, Olympia #79/R est:1200-1800

SIGMUND, R (19th C) ?

£514 $801 €750 Interior with standing female nude (62x36cm-24x14in) s. canvas on canvas. 10-Apr-3 Allgauer, Kempten #2985/R

SIGNAC, Paul (1863-1935) French

£2800 $4424 €4200 Bateaux a Sieme (10x18cm-4x7in) s.i.d.27 paper on card. 3-Apr-3 Christie's, Kensington #42/R
£4348 $6739 €6522 La Rochelle (21x26cm-8x10in) st.sig. chl. 4-Dec-2 Koller, Zurich #123/R est:8000-12000 (S.FR 10000)
£29114 $45127 €46000 Marseille, le vieux port (27x35cm-11x14in) s. cardboard canvas prov.lit. 28-Sep-2 Christie's, Paris #18/R est:30000-45000
£30968 $48929 €48000 Horizon sur la mer (15x25cm-6x10in) init. panelprov. 18-Dec-2 Tajan, Paris #15/R est:25000
£58974 $92590 €92000 Stands de foire a Asnieres (27x45cm-11x18in) s.i. 10-Dec-2 Renaud, Paris #44/R est:30000
£65217 $105000 €97826 Marseille, le vieux port (27x35cm-11x14in) s. canvasboard painted 1906 prov.lit. 7-May-3 Sotheby's, New York #147/R est:50000-70000
£155279 $250000 €232919 Samois, etude no.10 (27x35cm-11x14in) s. painted 1899 prov.exhib.lit. 7-May-3 Sotheby's, New York #143/R est:150000-200000
£400000 $656000 €600000 Saint-Cloud (46x55cm-18x22in) s.d.03 s.i.d.verso prov.exhib.lit. 4-Feb-3 Sotheby's, London #18/R est:400000
£869565 $1400000 €1304348 Thonier entrant a La Rochelle par soleil couchant (73x92cm-29x36in) s.d.1927 prov.exhib.lit. 6-May-3 Sotheby's, New York #20/R est:1500000-2000000

Prints

£4167 $6500 €6251 En Hollande-La Balise (49x64cm-19x25in) s.num.9/20 col lithograph. 5-Nov-2 Christie's, Rockefeller NY #24/R est:8000-12000
£7971 $13072 €11000 Les Adnelys (30x45cm-12x18in) s. col lithograph. 31-May-3 Villa Grisebach, Berlin #114/R est:11000-13000
£8176 $13000 €12264 Les bateaux a Flessingue (32x40cm-13x16in) s.num.18 col lithograph. 2-May-3 Sotheby's, New York #359/R est:14000-18000
£9434 $15000 €14151 Les Andelys (31x43cm-12x17in) s.num.23 col lithograph edition of 40 prov. 29-Apr-3 Christie's, Rockefeller NY #410/R est:18000-25000
£17949 $28000 €26924 Saint Tropez (43x59cm-17x23in) s. col lithograph edition of 100. 5-Nov-2 Christie's, Rockefeller NY #23/R est:18000-25000

Works on paper

£331 $550 €480 Seascape (41x46cm-16x18in) s.d.96 ink dr. 14-Jun-3 Susanin's, Chicago #5045/R
£1931 $3225 €2800 Saint Tropez, la Place des Lices. Etude de joueur de petanque (17x25cm-7x10in) st.sig.i. chl dr double-sided. 10-Jul-3 Artcurial Briest, Paris #38 est:500-600
£2069 $3455 €3000 Deux voiliers au port (19x25cm-7x10in) st.sig. graphite dr. 10-Jul-3 Artcurial Briest, Paris #35 est:800-1200
£2069 $3455 €3000 Marine (10x16cm-4x6in) st.sig. brown ink dr exec.c.1900. 10-Jul-3 Artcurial Briest, Paris #37 est:400-600
£2215 $3456 €3500 Navire dans un port du Midi (10x14cm-4x6in) s. W/C prov. 31-Jul-2 Tajan, Paris #9/R est:3000-4000
£2621 $4377 €3800 La jetee (11x19cm-4x7in) st.sig. chl dr. 10-Jul-3 Artcurial Briest, Paris #36 est:500-600
£3400 $5406 €5100 Voiliers a port (11x15cm-4x6in) init. W/C over pencil. 20-Mar-3 Sotheby's, Olympia #5/R est:2000-3000
£3793 $6334 €5500 Trieux, bateaux de peche et balise (10x14cm-4x6in) i.d.1 Sept st.sig.verso W/C pencil. 10-Jul-3 Artcurial Briest, Paris #34/R est:1200-1500
£3800 $6194 €5700 Le port d'Honfleur (10x17cm-4x7in) s.i. chl W/C paper on card prov. 3-Feb-3 Bonhams, New Bond Street #27/R est:3000-5000
£3800 $6194 €5700 Pecheurs au port d'Andierne (10x16cm-4x6in) i.d.Sept 30 W/C paper on card prov. 3-Feb-3 Bonhams, New Bond Street #28/R est:4000-6000
£4114 $6418 €6500 Navires au large de Boulogne (12x21cm-5x8in) s.i.d.3-03 W/C prov. 31-Jul-2 Tajan, Paris #10/R est:3000-4000
£4865 $7589 €7200 Vue du port de Marseille (20x30cm-8x12in) i. wash chl prov. 31-Mar-3 Piasa, Paris #112/R
£6474 $10165 €10100 Voilier a Saint-Tropez (21x41cm-8x16in) s. ink wash. 16-Dec-2 Eric Coutrier, Paris #70/R
£6835 $10595 €10800 Rivage mediterraneen (30x45cm-12x18in) s.d.1917 sepia wash. 29-Sep-2 Eric Pillon, Calais #145/R
£6835 $10935 €9500 Voiliers dans le port de Cassis (10x17cm-4x7in) init.d.94 W/C ink. 15-May-3 Christie's, Paris #331/R est:4000-6000
£7801 $12638 €11000 Saint Tropez (22x29cm-9x11in) s. ink wash. 21-May-3 Cornette de St.Cyr, Paris #6/R est:8000-10000
£8099 $13444 €11500 Le vapeur, Sannois (10x17cm-4x7in) init.i.d. gouache prov. 11-Jun-3 Beaussant & Lefèvre, Paris #192/R est:1500
£8500 $13940 €12750 Concarneau (19x25cm-7x10in) s.i. W/C chl prov.exhib. 6-Feb-3 Christie's, London #421/R
£8710 $13761 €13500 Thoniers a l'ancre (29x43cm-11x17in) s.d.34 W/C prov. 18-Dec-2 Digard, Paris #159/R est:15000
£9000 $13860 €13500 Goelettes a quai a Saint Malo (30x45cm-12x18in) init.d.1928 W/C black crayon prov.exhib. 22-Oct-2 Sotheby's, London #101/R est:9000-12000
£9000 $14760 €13500 Treguier (28x43cm-11x17in) s.i.d.27 W/C pencil prov. 5-Feb-3 Sotheby's, London #101/R est:15000
£9459 $14757 €14000 Pont National (19x30cm-7x12in) s.d.1927 W/C prov. 26-Mar-3 Tajan, Paris #3/R
£9615 $15000 €14423 La cale de St. Pierre-Kerity (27x43cm-11x17in) s.i.d.10 Juin 29 W/C pencil paper on card prov. 5-Nov-2 Phillips, New York #102/R est:15000-20000
£9810 $15304 €15500 Voiliers dans le port de Concarneau (28x45cm-11x18in) s.i.d.octobre 32 W/C prov. 31-Jul-2 Tajan, Paris #6/R est:10000-14000
£11000 $18040 €16500 Groix (26x41cm-10x16in) s.i.d.1923 W/C gouache crayon prov. 5-Feb-3 Sotheby's, London #102/R est:15000
£11000 $18040 €16500 Paimpol (27x41cm-11x16in) s.i.d.24 gouache W/C chl. 6-Feb-3 Christie's, London #422/R est:12000
£12048 $20000 €17470 La Rochelle (20x30cm-8x12in) W/C crayon. 13-Jun-3 Du Mouchelle, Detroit #2017/R est:5000-8000
£12821 $20128 €20000 Audierne (27x43cm-11x17in) s.i.d.27 W/C crayon. 10-Dec-2 Artcurial Briest, Paris #471/R est:20000-25000
£12838 $20027 €19000 Quimper (21x28cm-8x11in) s.i.d.1927 W/C prov. 26-Mar-3 Tajan, Paris #2/R
£12903 $20000 €19355 Asnieres (17x25cm-7x10in) st.sig. W/C brush black ink over pencil prov. 26-Sep-2 Christie's, Rockefeller NY #507/R est:10000-15000
£13000 $21710 €19500 Le Havre (28x45cm-11x18in) s.i.d.21 sept 23 gouache W/C pencil prov. 26-Jun-3 Christie's, London #374/R est:8000-12000
£13200 $20328 €19800 Saint Louis (27x43cm-11x17in) st.sig. brush ink crayon executed 1922 prov. 22-Oct-2 Sotheby's, London #245/R est:7000-9000
£13475 $21830 €19000 Saint-Malo (42x27cm-17x11in) s. W/C graphite. 21-May-3 Cornette de St.Cyr, Paris #5/R est:12000-15000
£14103 $22000 €21155 Goelette a quai, Paimpol (30x45cm-12x18in) s.d.25 W/C over black chk prov. 7-Nov-2 Christie's, Rockefeller NY #135/R est:15000-20000
£16000 $24640 €24000 Le Pont de Grenelle a Paris (29x45cm-11x18in) s.d.Aout 27 W/C black crayon prov. 22-Oct-2 Sotheby's, London #102/R est:12000-15000
£16456 $25506 €26000 Thoniers dans un port breton (26x38cm-10x15in) i. W/C chl paper on cardboard prov. 28-Sep-2 Christie's, Paris #9/R est:12000-18000
£17308 $27000 €25962 Loctudy (30x45cm-12x18in) s.i.d.9 Juin 29 W/C pencil paper on card prov. 5-Nov-2 Phillips, New York #103/R est:15000-20000
£18072 $30000 €26204 Au Sierne (25x41cm-10x16in) s. crayon. 13-Jun-3 Du Mouchelle, Detroit #2018/R est:10000-15000
£18634 $30000 €27951 Quai de Louvre (27x42cm-11x17in) s.d.1927 W/C chl prov. 7-May-3 Sotheby's, New York #102/R est:20000-30000
£19149 $29681 €28724 Working on the quays by the Seine (28x45cm-11x18in) s.d.1927 W/C. 8-Dec-2 Uppsala Auktionskammare, Uppsala #201/R est:250000-300000 (S.KR 270000)
£20000 $33400 €29000 Pontrieux (31x45cm-12x18in) s.d.Aout 11.24 W/C gouache over black crayon prov. 24-Jun-3 Sotheby's, London #214/R est:15000-20000
£20423 $33902 €29000 Le port de Saint-Malo (44x63cm-17x25in) s. Indian ink prov.exhib. 12-Jun-3 Tajan, Paris #18/R est:12000-15000
£27823 $44239 €40900 Paris, la Seine, le Pont-Neuf et la Pointe du Vert-Galant (30x45cm-12x18in) s. W/C pencil prov. 26-Feb-3 Artcurial Briest, Paris #32/R est:20000-25000
£28846 $45000 €43269 Barfleur (28x44cm-11x17in) s.d.23 June 1930 W/C pencil paper on card prov. 5-Nov-2 Phillips, New York #101/R est:18000-22000
£39744 $62000 €59616 Riviere de treboule (30x45cm-12x18in) s.i.d.13 Juin 29 W/C pencil paper on card. 5-Nov-2 Phillips, New York #109/R est:20000-25000
£60897 $95000 €91346 Terra nueva a Saint-Malo (28x44cm-11x17in) s.i.d.16 Mars 30 W/C pencil paper on card prov. 5-Nov-2 Phillips, New York #111/R est:25000-30000
£67949 $106000 €101924 Riviere de vannes (29x45cm-11x18in) s.i.d.25 Mai 29 W/C pencil paper on card prov. 5-Nov-2 Phillips, New York #110/R est:25000-30000

SIGNAC, Paul (attrib) (1863-1935) French

Works on paper

£1980 $3128 €2970 View of Pon St. Louis (25x33cm-10x13in) indis sig. W/C. 18-Dec-2 Mallams, Oxford #553/R est:2000-3000

SIGNORE, Littorio del (1938-) Canadian

£581 $906 €872 Pommes et citrouille (61x50cm-24x20in) s. 30-Jul-2 Iegor de Saint Hippolyte, Montreal #40 (C.D 1440)

SIGNORET, Charles Louis (1867-1932) French
£250 $408 €363 Figures in a landscape (23x32cm-9x13in) s. panel. 15-Jul-3 Bonhams, Knightsbridge #206
£641 $1000 €962 Boat on open waters (55x65cm-22x26in) s. 20-Sep-2 Sloan, North Bethesda #400/R est:1000-2000
£648 $920 €1050 Pecheurs a l'entree du port (24x35cm-9x14in) s. 16-Mar-3 Eric Pillon, Calais #94/R

SIGNORI, Carlo Sergio (c.1906-) Italian
Sculpture
£2215 $3456 €3500 Feuille (37cm-15in) white marble. 31-Jul-2 Tajan, Paris #58/R est:3500-3800

SIGNORINI, Telemaco (attrib) (1835-1901) Italian
£1258 $1937 €2000 Cliff at Riomaggiore (10x18cm-4x7in) 28-Oct-2 Il Ponte, Milan #260
Works on paper
£472 $726 €750 Looking at the view (21x14cm-8x6in) s. pencil W/C. 28-Oct-2 Il Ponte, Milan #203

SIGNOVERT, Jean (1919-1981) French
Works on paper
£285 $450 €450 Composition abstraite (62x49cm-24x19in) s. gouache. 27-Nov-2 Blanchet, Paris #132
£709 $1184 €1000 Composition (63x49cm-25x19in) s. Indian ink. 18-Jun-3 Pierre Berge, Paris #92 est:500-1000

SIGRIST, S (19/20th C) ?
£250 $380 €375 Portrait of a young lady seated on a sofa (48x37cm-19x15in) s.d.1919. 3-Jul-2 John Nicholson, Haslemere #645

SIGRISTE, Guido (1864-1915) Swiss
£1296 $2087 €1944 Officers eating outdoors (21x33cm-8x13in) s. panel. 7-May-3 Dobiaschofsky, Bern #982/R est:3400 (S.FR 2800)

SIHLALI, Durant Basi (1935-) South African?
Works on paper
£205 $320 €308 Farmyard with old trucks (35x55cm-14x22in) s.d.82 W/C. 11-Nov-2 Stephan Welz, Johannesburg #582 (SA.R 3200)
£344 $554 €516 Kitchen interior (57x42cm-22x17in) s.d.66 W/C over pencil. 12-May-3 Stephan Welz, Johannesburg #324 est:5000-8000 (SA.R 4000)
£516 $831 €774 Drink with friends (48x67cm-19x26in) s.d.75 i.d.verso W/C over pencil. 12-May-3 Stephan Welz, Johannesburg #548/R est:6000-9000 (SA.R 6000)
£602 $969 €903 Facelessness (130x100cm-51x39in) s.d.90 collage pigment paper pulp. 12-May-3 Stephan Welz, Johannesburg #532/R est:12000-18000 (SA.R 7000)
£602 $969 €903 Roasting mealies (52x72cm-20x28in) s.d.91 W/C. 12-May-3 Stephan Welz, Johannesburg #547 est:6000-9000 (SA.R 7000)
£645 $1038 €968 Wall (138x86cm-54x34in) s.d.91 pigment paper pulp. 12-May-3 Stephan Welz, Johannesburg #506/R est:15000-20000 (SA.R 7500)
£688 $1107 €1032 Alpha centre, Broederstroom (85x150cm-33x59in) s.d.89 pigment on paper pulp. 12-May-3 Stephan Welz, Johannesburg #502/R est:10000-15000 (SA.R 8000)
£946 $1523 €1419 Rhini walls 26, District Six (98x147cm-39x58in) s.d.91 verso pigment paper pulp. 12-May-3 Stephan Welz, Johannesburg #507/R est:18000-24000 (SA.R 11000)

SIIKAMAKI, Arvo (1943-) Finnish
Sculpture
£1439 $2302 €2000 Figure (60cm-24in) s.d.1987 bronze. 17-May-3 Hagelstam, Helsinki #16/R est:2500
£5282 $8504 €7500 Woman resting (83cm-33in) s.d.1999 spectrolite. 10-May-3 Bukowskis, Helsinki #205/R est:30000-35000

SIJTHOFF, Gisbertus Jan (1867-1949) Dutch
£1064 $1649 €1596 Interior scene with woman and child (70x61cm-28x24in) s. 4-Dec-2 AB Stockholms Auktionsverk #1898/R est:18000-20000 (S.KR 15000)
£1736 $2865 €2500 Tending to the goat (60x46cm-24x18in) s. 1-Jul-3 Christie's, Amsterdam #58/R est:1000-1500

SIKORSKI, Eva (20th C) ?
£736 $1200 €1104 Lady with a red hat (122x76cm-48x30in) s. 16-Feb-3 Butterfields, San Francisco #2137

SIKUTA, Gusztav (1919-1985) Hungarian
£568 $885 €824 Still life with pear and cyclamen (60x80cm-24x31in) s. 13-Sep-2 Mu Terem Galeria, Budapest #132/R est:200000 (H.F 220000)

SILBERBAUM, M (?) ?
£647 $1062 €900 La musique. 3-Jun-3 Tajan, Paris #49

SILBERMANN, Jean Claude (1935-) French
£2740 $4301 €4000 Voyante (46x61cm-18x24in) mono. prov.lit. 15-Apr-3 Laurence Calmels, Paris #4415/R
Sculpture
£4795 $7527 €7000 Au grand matou, prince odieux (119x54cm-47x21in) s. oil on wood. 15-Apr-3 Laurence Calmels, Paris #4416/R

SILBERSTEIN, Bernard (20th C) ?
Photographs
£2317 $3800 €3476 Frida Kahlo painting a self portrait while Diego Rivera looks on (43x36cm-17x14in) s.verso silver print exec.c.1940. 10-Feb-3 Swann Galleries, New York #62/R est:2500-3500

SILFVERBERG, Nikolai (1899-1977) Finnish
£388 $637 €540 Imatra waterfall (51x66cm-20x26in) s. 4-Jun-3 Bukowskis, Helsinki #428/R

SILKE, Eris (1907-) South African
Works on paper
£817 $1315 €1226 Young girl and an owl (59cm-23in circular) s. mixed media on panel. 12-May-3 Stephan Welz, Johannesburg #539/R est:10000-15000 (SA.R 9500)

SILLEN, Herman (1857-1908) Swedish
£7801 $12092 €11702 Seascape with sailing vessel and steamboat (48x38cm-19x15in) s.d.1880. 3-Dec-2 Bukowskis, Stockholm #240/R est:50000-60000 (S.KR 110000)

SILLETT, James (1764-1840) British
£3000 $4770 €4500 Narcissi, tulips, carnation and other flowers in a goblet on a ledge (46x38cm-18x15in) s. 6-Mar-3 Christie's, Kensington #633/R est:4000-6000
£3500 $5529 €5250 Still life of flowers in a vase (33x26cm-13x10in) s. 28-Nov-2 Sotheby's, London #198/R est:4000-6000

SILO, Adam (1674-1772) Dutch
£7006 $10930 €11000 Merchantmen, Kaag and other sailing vessels in a stiff breeze (45x55cm-18x22in) 5-Nov-2 Sotheby's, Amsterdam #221/R est:10000-15000
Works on paper
£10000 $16700 €14500 Russian men-o-war ships defeating enemy in sea battle (23x42cm-9x17in) 12-Jul-3 Windibank, Dorking #339/R est:1500-2000

SILVA BRUHNS, Ivan da (1881-1980) French
£780 $1264 €1100 Untitled. s. 26-May-3 Joron-Derem, Paris #99b
Works on paper
£780 $1264 €1100 Projet de tapis rectangulaire (53x26cm-21x10in) gouache paper on paper. 26-May-3 Joron-Derem, Paris #87/R
£1206 $1953 €1700 Projet de tapis rectangulaire (45x35cm-18x14in) s.d.1937 gouache paper on paper. 26-May-3 Joron-Derem, Paris #96/R est:2000-2500
£1277 $2068 €1800 Projet de tapis rectangulaire (23x48cm-9x19in) s.d.1937 gouache paper on paper. 26-May-3 Joron-Derem, Paris #86/R est:2000-2500
£1277 $2068 €1800 Projet de tapis rectangulaire (20x31cm-8x12in) s.d.1933 gouache paper on paper. 26-May-3 Joron-Derem, Paris #93/R est:2000-2500
£1418 $2298 €2000 Projet de tapis rectangulaire (50x30cm-20x12in) s.d.1938 gouache paper on paper. 26-May-3 Joron-Derem, Paris #89/R est:2000-2500
£1418 $2298 €2000 Projet de tapis rectangulaire (14x30cm-6x12in) s.d.1939 gouache paper on paper. 26-May-3 Joron-Derem, Paris #98/R est:2000-2500

£1489 $2413 €2100 Projet de tapis en arc de cercle a decoupe pour empietement (57x77cm-22x30in) s.d.1935 gouache paper on paper. 26-May-3 Joron-Derem, Paris #88/R est:2000-2500

£1489 $2413 €2100 Projet de tapis rectangulaire (17x31cm-7x12in) s.d.1936 gouache paper on paper. 26-May-3 Joron-Derem, Paris #94/R est:2000-2500

£1489 $2413 €2100 Projet de tapis rectangulaire (30x12cm-12x5in) s. gouache paper on paper. 26-May-3 Joron-Derem, Paris #97/R est:2000-2500

£1702 $2757 €2400 Projet de tapis rectangulaire (21x27cm-8x11in) s.d.1939 gouache paper on paper. 26-May-3 Joron-Derem, Paris #99/R est:2000-2500

£1773 $2872 €2500 Projet de tapis rectangulaire (31x50cm-12x20in) s. gouache paper on paper. 26-May-3 Joron-Derem, Paris #92/R est:2000-2500

£1844 $2987 €2600 Projet de tapis rectangulaire (40x55cm-16x22in) s.d.1936 gouache paper on paper. 26-May-3 Joron-Derem, Paris #90/R est:2000-2500

£1844 $2987 €2600 Projet de tapis rectangulaire (35x26cm-14x10in) s.d.1937 gouache paper on paper. 26-May-3 Joron-Derem, Paris #91/R est:2000-2500

£1844 $2987 €2600 Projet de tapis en arc de cercle a decoupe pour empietement (33x46cm-13x18in) s.d.1935 gouache paper on paper. 26-May-3 Joron-Derem, Paris #95/R est:2000-2500

SILVA MAVIGNIER, Almir da (1925-) Brazilian

£7914 $12978 €11000 Deformed circle (100x100cm-39x39in) s.i.d.26-5-64 verso prov.exhib. 6-Jun-3 Ketterer, Munich #145/R est:12000-15000

SILVA, Francis Augustus (1835-1886) American

£11250 $18000 €16875 Dawn over coastline (13x23cm-5x9in) s. board. 11-Jan-3 James Julia, Fairfield #133a est:17500-22500

£38710 $60000 €58065 Off Newport, Rhode Island (36x61cm-14x24in) s.d.75 prov.lit. 4-Dec-2 Sotheby's, New York #106/R est:60000-80000

£61728 $100000 €92592 Clearing off (51x97cm-20x38in) s. exhib. 22-May-3 Christie's, Rockefeller NY #3/R est:100000-150000

£64516 $100000 €96774 Sailing on the Hudson (30x62cm-12x24in) s. prov. 5-Dec-2 Christie's, Rockefeller NY #13/R est:50000-70000

£156250 $250000 €226563 On the coast (51x101cm-20x40in) s.d.1879. 16-May-3 Skinner, Boston #113/R est:30000-50000

Works on paper

£3006 $4750 €4509 Fishing on the Rhode Island shore (10x36cm-4x14in) s.d.1875 W/C. 17-Nov-2 CRN Auctions, Cambridge #9/R

SILVA, William P (1859-1948) American

£1274 $2000 €1911 Carmel shore from the dunes (25x30cm-10x12in) s. board. 10-Dec-2 Doyle, New York #117/R est:2000-3000

£2742 $4250 €4113 Little bridge - garden of dreams (20x25cm-8x10in) s.d.25 canvas on board. 29-Oct-2 John Moran, Pasadena #632 est:1500-2000

£2903 $4500 €4355 Glade - garden of dreams (20x25cm-8x10in) s.d.25 canvas on board. 29-Oct-2 John Moran, Pasadena #631 est:1500-2000

£3313 $5500 €4804 Blue day near Carmel (48x58cm-19x23in) board. 13-Jun-3 Du Mouchelle, Detroit #2113/R est:3000-4000

£22455 $37500 €32560 Springtime, Carolina low country (76x91cm-30x36in) s.d.1931 board exhib. 17-Jun-3 John Moran, Pasadena #65 est:20000-30000

SILVAIN, Christian (1950-) Belgian

£1027 $1603 €1500 Composition (107x75cm-42x30in) s. 14-Apr-3 Horta, Bruxelles #245 est:800-1000

SILVANI, Ferdinando (1823-1899) Italian

£294 $471 €450 Sailing boat in front of lagoon in Venice (18x26cm-7x10in) s. canvas on board lit. 10-Jan-3 Allgauer, Kempten #1752/R

£588 $965 €900 San Georgio Maggiore (41x70cm-16x28in) s. 29-Mar-3 Dannenberg, Berlin #653/R

SILVEN, Jakob (1851-1924) Swedish

£426 $660 €639 Boy on top of hay wagon - early spring (41x70cm-16x28in) mono. 4-Dec-2 AB Stockholms Auktionsverk #1667/R (S.KR 6000)

£709 $1099 €1064 Farmer with oxen by watercourse (50x70cm-20x28in) s.d.1882. 8-Dec-2 Uppsala Auktionskammare, Uppsala #48/R (S.KR 10000)

SILVERMAN, Burton (1928-) American

£401 $650 €602 Black hat (36x25cm-14x10in) s. panel. 24-Jan-3 Freeman, Philadelphia #237/R

Works on paper

£519 $800 €779 Silver medallist (28x25cm-11x10in) W/C. 25-Oct-2 Morris & Whiteside, Hilton Head Island #173

SILVESTRE, Louis (younger) (1675-1760) French

£4839 $7113 €7500 Portrait of Christian Graf vom Loss (84x65cm-33x26in) i. verso. 20-Jun-2 Dr Fritz Nagel, Stuttgart #734/R est:2500

SILVESTRE, Louis (younger-attrib) (1675-1760) French

£4965 $7695 €7448 Portrait of young girl as Diana the Goddess of Hunting (80x64cm-31x25in) 4-Dec-2 AB Stockholms Auktionsverk #1959/R est:80000-100000 (S.KR 70000)

SILVESTRE, Nicolas Charles de (1699-1767) French

Works on paper

£3500 $5845 €5075 Extensive landscape with fishermen and travelers on a bridge, town in the background (26x41cm-10x16in) i. red chk prov. 8-Jul-3 Christie's, London #79/R est:3500-4500

SILVESTRE, Paul (1884-?) French

Sculpture

£1026 $1590 €1600 Marabout (26x11x17cm-10x4x7in) st.f.Susse brown pat bronze. 7-Dec-2 Martinot & Savignat, Pontoise #83/R

SILVESTRI, Tullio (1880-1963) Italian

£1410 $2186 €2200 Thanksgiving procession (107x100cm-42x39in) s. 5-Dec-2 Stadion, Trieste #719

SIMA, Joseph (1891-1971) Czechoslovakian

£12821 $20128 €20000 Soleil froid (61x46cm-24x18in) s.d. prov.exhib.lit. 16-Dec-2 Charbonneaux, Paris #293/R est:10000-12000

£14626 $23255 €21500 Blue landscape, light I (73x92cm-29x36in) s.d.1960 s.i.d.verso prov. 24-Mar-3 Cornette de St.Cyr, Paris #7/R est:25000

£20513 $32205 €32000 Baigneuse (80x100cm-31x39in) s.d.49. 11-Dec-2 Artcurial Briest, Paris #720/R est:20000

Works on paper

£1691 $2705 €2350 Paysage (30x50cm-12x20in) s.d.1960 ink pierre noire. 16-May-3 Lombrail & Teucquam, Paris #182/R

£2269 $3586 €3404 Parisian (84x49cm-33x19in) s.d.1928 col wash ink dr. 30-Nov-2 Dorotheum, Prague #147/R est:100000-150000 (C.KR 110000)

£3616 $5569 €5750 Composition (37x28cm-15x11in) s.d.1960 W/C gouache crayon pastel prov. 26-Oct-2 Cornette de St.Cyr, Paris #9/R

SIMARD, Claude A (1943-) Canadian

£1391 $2170 €2320 Tulips fresh from the garden (61x51cm-24x20in) s.d.1990 s.i.d.verso acrylic. 13-Apr-3 Levis, Calgary #109/R est:2500-3000 (C.D 3200)

£1864 $2964 €2796 Juliana (90x75cm-35x30in) s.i.d.2000. 23-Mar-3 Hodgins, Calgary #24/R est:2000-2500 (C.D 4400)

£1949 $3099 €2924 Fills (75x90cm-30x35in) s.i. 23-Mar-3 Hodgins, Calgary #99/R est:2000-2500 (C.D 4600)

SIMBARI, Nicola (1927-) Italian

£621 $1000 €932 Young lady with floral basket (71x41cm-28x16in) s.d.63. 20-Jan-3 Arthur James, Florida #499

£2500 $4000 €3750 Morning in Mykonos, cafe scene (89x99cm-35x39in) s. i.verso prov. 4-Jan-3 Brunk, Ashville #429/R est:5000-10000

£4088 $6500 €6132 Interior red and green (119x140cm-47x55in) s.d.64 i. on stretcher. 18-Mar-3 Arthur James, Florida #152

SIMBERG, Hugo (1873-1917) Finnish

£949 $1500 €1500 Farmyard (30x41cm-12x16in) cardboard. 30-Nov-2 Hagelstam, Helsinki #91/R est:2500

£3094 $5073 €4300 Washing drying (41x58cm-16x23in) s. 4-Jun-3 Bukowskis, Helsinki #430/R est:2500

£14789 $23810 €21000 Morning at sea (48x67cm-19x26in) s.d.1901. 10-May-3 Bukowskis, Helsinki #46/R est:10000-12000

£20253 $32000 €32000 From Skatudden (48x47cm-19x19in) s.d.1907 lit. 30-Nov-2 Hagelstam, Helsinki #90/R est:14000

£68354 $108000 €108000 Dance on the jetty. s.d.1904 exhib.lit. 1-Dec-2 Bukowskis, Helsinki #180/R est:65000-80000

Prints

£2152 $3400 €3400 Winter road II (13x18cm-5x7in) etching drypoint lit. 30-Nov-2 Hagelstam, Helsinki #70/R est:600

£2405 $3800 €3800 The devil has died (17x26cm-7x10in) init. col etching lit. 30-Nov-2 Hagelstam, Helsinki #66/R est:3000

Works on paper

£289 $446 €460 Der Pilger. sketches for book, sold with book. 24-Oct-2 Hagelstam, Helsinki #969

£504 $806 €700 Hand (12x16cm-5x6in) s.d.1890 pencil exhib. 17-May-3 Hagelstam, Helsinki #47/R

£633 $987 €1000 Landscape view (24x27cm-9x11in) i.verso W/C. 15-Sep-2 Bukowskis, Helsinki #284/R

£2806 $4489 €3900 Landscape with evening glow, Aaland (26x34cm-10x13in) s.d.1905 W/C. 17-May-3 Hagelstam, Helsinki #48/R est:4000

£3165 $5000 €5000 Mountain landscape (23x29cm-9x11in) s. W/C. 1-Dec-2 Bukowskis, Helsinki #181/R est:3000-3500
£5634 $9070 €8000 Model yawning (83x65cm-33x26in) s. lit. 10-May-3 Bukowskis, Helsinki #175/R
£10915 $17574 €15500 For your sake (18x24cm-7x9in) s. W/C gouache prov. 10-May-3 Bukowskis, Helsinki #165/R est:14000-16000
£12176 $19969 €17655 Poor faun carrying twins (13x8cm-5x3in) s.i.verso W/C prov. 4-Jun-3 AB Stockholms Auktionsverk #2494/R est:18000-20000 (S.KR 155000)
£15000 $24600 €22500 Syksy - autumn (23x14cm-9x6in) mono.i.d.7 April 1896 pen black ink prov. 3-Jun-3 Sotheby's, London #210/R est:7000-10000

SIMCOCK, Jack (1929-) British
£480 $773 €696 Rural barn (21x20cm-8x8in) s.d.1965 board. 19-Feb-3 Peter Wilson, Nantwich #58/R

SIMCOX, Albert (fl.1914-1916) British
£250 $390 €375 No 10 Saracus Head, Kings Norton (25x18cm-10x7in) s. 9-Apr-3 Andrew Hartley, Ilkley #962

SIMENSEN, Sigvald (?-1920) Norwegian
£380 $615 €570 Winter landscape with farm (80x129cm-31x51in) s,. 27-Jan-3 Blomqvist, Lysaker #1228 (N.KR 4200)
£419 $658 €629 Winter landscape (38x72cm-15x28in) s. 25-Nov-2 Blomqvist, Lysaker #1245/R (N.KR 4800)
£484 $745 €726 Boat construction by fjord (88x135cm-35x53in) s. 28-Oct-2 Blomqvist, Lysaker #1289 (N.KR 5700)
£526 $811 €789 Fjord landscape with boats (80x120cm-31x47in) s. 28-Oct-2 Blomqvist, Lysaker #1288 (N.KR 6200)

SIMES, Mary Jane (1807-1872) American
Miniatures
£6410 $10000 €9615 Portrait of young woman (2x1cm-1x0in) W/C on ivory gold locket setting prov. 12-Apr-3 Freeman, Philadelphia #1/R est:600-1000

SIMESEN, Viggo Rasmus (1864-1932) Danish
£431 $655 €647 Seascape with sailing vessel in high seas on cloudy day (63x98cm-25x39in) s.d.1907. 27-Aug-2 Rasmussen, Copenhagen #1768/R (D.KR 5000)

SIMETI, Turi (1929-) Italian
£338 $527 €507 Algrevin EF 7 (47cm-19in circular) s.d.66 verso canvas on wood panel. 18-Sep-2 Kunsthallen, Copenhagen #76 (D.KR 4000)
£949 $1481 €1500 Red (70x70cm-28x28in) s.d.1992 acrylic. 14-Sep-2 Meeting Art, Vercelli #737
£1111 $1778 €1700 Pyramid (60x60cm-24x24in) s.i.d.1973 verso acrylic. 4-Jan-3 Meeting Art, Vercelli #618
£1319 $2098 €1900 Untitled (50x50cm-20x20in) s.d.1999 verso. 1-May-3 Meeting Art, Vercelli #405
£1538 $2415 €2400 Black (90x90cm-35x35in) s.d.1988 acrylic. 23-Nov-2 Meeting Art, Vercelli #94/R

SIMI, Filadelfo (1849-1923) Italian
£321 $503 €500 Wood at sunset (29x39cm-11x15in) s. board. 16-Dec-2 Pandolfini, Florence #285
Works on paper
£385 $604 €600 Young peasant woman from Umbria (57x40cm-22x16in) W/C. 16-Dec-2 Pandolfini, Florence #22

SIMIA, Leonardo (?) Italian?
Works on paper
£280 $400 €420 Study of a church interior (49x32cm-19x13in) pen ink wash. 23-Jan-3 Swann Galleries, New York #156/R

SIMKIN, Richard (1840-1926) British
Works on paper
£700 $1106 €1050 Cavalry officer (34x24cm-13x9in) s.d.80 W/C. 26-Nov-2 Bonhams, Knightsbridge #233/R
£720 $1102 €1080 Second Dragoon, Royal Scots grey on his mount (34x24cm-13x9in) s.i.d.81 W/C gouache. 22-Aug-2 Bonhams, Edinburgh #1114/R

SIMKINS, Martha (20th C) American
£1346 $2100 €2019 Magnolia (58x48cm-23x19in) 19-Oct-2 David Dike, Dallas #235/R est:700-1200

SIMMEN, Henri (20th C) ?
Works on paper
£270 $422 €400 Abstraction geometrique (29x47cm-11x19in) s. col crayon. 31-Mar-3 Pierre Berge, Paris #63
£270 $422 €400 L'arbre (29x47cm-11x19in) s. col crayon. 31-Mar-3 Pierre Berge, Paris #64
£270 $422 €400 Personnage fantastique (29x47cm-11x19in) s. col crayon. 31-Mar-3 Pierre Berge, Paris #65
£270 $422 €400 L'orateur (29x47cm-11x19in) s. col crayon. 31-Mar-3 Pierre Berge, Paris #66
£338 $527 €500 La veilleuse (29x47cm-11x19in) s. col crayon. 31-Mar 3 Pierre Berge, Paris #62/R
£439 $685 €650 Personnage fantastique (29x47cm-11x19in) s. col crayons. 31-Mar-3 Pierre Berge, Paris #60

SIMMLER, Friedrich Karl Joseph (1801-1872) German
£1709 $2649 €2700 Boy with cows by mountain lake (30x40cm-12x16in) s. panel. 25-Sep-2 Neumeister, Munich #725/R est:2000

SIMMLER, W (1840-1914) German
£1076 $1668 €1700 Two hunters with dog in winter wood (80x116cm-31x46in) s. 26-Sep-2 Neumeister, Munich #2841/R est:800

SIMMONDS, Julius (1843-1924) German
£964 $1600 €1398 Artists studio (41x33cm-16x13in) s.d.04. 14-Jun-3 Jackson's, Cedar Falls #208/R est:2000-3000

SIMMONS, Charles Eyres (?-1955) British
Works on paper
£880 $1461 €1320 An estuary scene with fishing boats. Devon creek, river Fel (23x43cm-9x17in) s. W/C two. 10-Jun-3 Bonhams, Leeds #103/R

SIMMONS, Edward Emerson (1852-1931) American
£6707 $11000 €9725 Seascape (26x35cm-10x14in) s.d. board. 5-Jun-3 Swann Galleries, New York #221/R est:3000-5000

SIMMONS, Eyres (fl.1902-1914) British
Works on paper
£262 $414 €393 Cornish village scene (26x38cm-10x15in) s. W/C. 18-Nov-2 Waddingtons, Toronto #61a/R (C.D 650)
£383 $605 €575 Fishing boats by a pier (25x35cm-10x14in) s. W/C. 18-Nov-2 Waddingtons, Toronto #61/R (C.D 950)
£400 $652 €600 North Quay, Falmouth (30x18cm-12x7in) s. W/C. 13-Feb-3 David Lay, Penzance #73
£420 $655 €630 View of a coastal town (43x63cm-17x25in) s. W/C. 25-Mar-3 Bonhams, Knightsbridge #80/R

SIMMONS, Gary (1964-) American
Works on paper
£1266 $2000 €1899 Erasure series (70x50cm-28x20in) gesso gouache chk in two parts executed 1992 prov. 12-Nov-2 Phillips, New York #221/R est:3000-4000

SIMMONS, J Deane (fl.1882-1889) British
£600 $984 €900 Henley Reach (61x46cm-24x18in) s.d.1883. 29-May-3 Christie's, Kensington #112/R

SIMMONS, John (1823-1876) British
Works on paper
£1500 $2430 €2250 Chance encounter (55x77cm-22x30in) s.d.1870 W/C htd bodycol. 21-May-3 Bonhams, Knightsbridge #216/R est:1000-1500

SIMON, Andree (1896-1981) French
£288 $456 €450 Untitled (61x50cm-24x20in) s. painted 1950. 18-Nov-2 Rieunier, Paris #69/R
£288 $456 €450 Untitled (61x50cm-24x20in) s. 18-Nov-2 Rieunier, Paris #68/R
£321 $506 €500 Pique-nique (61x46cm-24x18in) s. 18-Nov-2 Rieunier, Paris #33
£321 $506 €500 Composition (50x65cm-20x26in) s. cardboard. 18-Nov-2 Rieunier, Paris #76/R
£321 $506 €500 Untitled (90x90cm-35x35in) painted 1950. 18-Nov-2 Rieunier, Paris #82
£321 $506 €500 Untitled (63x92cm-25x36in) s. 18-Nov-2 Rieunier, Paris #84/R
£333 $527 €520 Untitled (29x29cm-11x11in) cardboard. 18-Nov-2 Rieunier, Paris #41
£353 $557 €550 Demeure faite de cloches d'alarmes (99x132cm-39x52in) d.1954 verso. 18-Nov-2 Rieunier, Paris #57/R
£353 $557 €550 Untitled (69x88cm-27x35in) s. 18-Nov-2 Rieunier, Paris #86
£385 $608 €600 Silence organise (73x84cm-29x33in) 18-Nov-2 Rieunier, Paris #61/R
£385 $608 €600 Paroles legeres (89x131cm-35x52in) s. painted 1952. 18-Nov-2 Rieunier, Paris #81/R
£385 $608 €600 Untitled (69x88cm-27x35in) s. panel. 18-Nov-2 Rieunier, Paris #83/R

£385 $608 €600 Colere (97x130cm-38x51in) s. painted 1956. 18-Nov-2 Rieunier, Paris #90/R
£449 $709 €700 Paysanne (40x32cm-16x13in) 18-Nov-2 Rieunier, Paris #10/R
£481 $760 €750 Nature morte au couteau et a la bouteille (73x92cm-29x36in) s. 18-Nov-2 Rieunier, Paris #13/R
£481 $760 €750 TRicoteuse (92x73cm-36x29in) s. painted 1932. 18-Nov-2 Rieunier, Paris #14/R
£513 $810 €800 Untitled (60x71cm-24x28in) s. cardboard on canvas double-sided. 18-Nov-2 Rieunier, Paris #71/R
£513 $810 €800 Untitled (27x46cm-11x18in) s. panel. 18-Nov-2 Rieunier, Paris #64
£545 $861 €850 Paysage (27x41cm-11x16in) 18-Nov-2 Rieunier, Paris #40
£577 $912 €900 Untitled (114x146cm-45x57in) s. 18-Nov-2 Rieunier, Paris #34
£577 $912 €900 Grand-mere et fillette (33x29cm-13x11in) cardboard. 18-Nov-2 Rieunier, Paris #24/R
£577 $912 €900 Untitled (62x94cm-24x37in) s. 18-Nov-2 Rieunier, Paris #85
£609 $962 €950 Untitled (42x50cm-17x20in) s. double-sided. 18-Nov-2 Rieunier, Paris #12
£705 $1114 €1100 Untitled (54x65cm-21x26in) s. painted 1950. 18-Nov-2 Rieunier, Paris #66/R
£833 $1317 €1300 Nature morte au moulin a cafe (46x27cm-18x11in) mono.d.1945. 18-Nov-2 Rieunier, Paris #26/R
£1090 $1722 €1700 Atelier a Gordes (81x60cm-32x24in) s.d.1945. 18-Nov-2 Rieunier, Paris #15/R
£1987 $3140 €3100 Nature morte (65x81cm-26x32in) s. 18-Nov-2 Rieunier, Paris #35/R
£2885 $4558 €4500 Activite collective (89x131cm-35x52in) 18-Nov-2 Rieunier, Paris #58/R
£3013 $4760 €4700 Jugement integre (54x73cm-21x29in) s. 18-Nov-2 Rieunier, Paris #79/R
£3718 $5874 €5800 Untitled (116x81cm-46x32in) s. painted 1940. 18-Nov-2 Rieunier, Paris #42/R

Works on paper

£256 $405 €400 Paysage (24x32cm-9x13in) s.d.1943 W/C. 18-Nov-2 Rieunier, Paris #6/R
£256 $405 €400 Voulte (22x31cm-9x12in) s.d.42 W/C. 18-Nov-2 Rieunier, Paris #23/R
£256 $405 €400 Composition abstraite (50x65cm-20x26in) s.d.1954 gouache. 18-Nov-2 Rieunier, Paris #106/R
£269 $425 €420 Rocher verdure (36x54cm-14x21in) pen exec.1942. 18-Nov-2 Rieunier, Paris #37/R
£288 $456 €450 Girona, Spain (29x35cm-11x14in) s.d.38 W/C gouache. 18-Nov-2 Rieunier, Paris #4
£288 $456 €450 Composition (32x24cm-13x9in) s.d.49 gouache. 18-Nov-2 Rieunier, Paris #55
£288 $456 €450 Arabesques (31x24cm-12x9in) s.d.49 W/C. 18-Nov-2 Rieunier, Paris #51
£288 $456 €450 Soirs (24x32cm-9x13in) s.d.49 W/C. 18-Nov-2 Rieunier, Paris #49
£288 $456 €450 Tout ce qui sait donner au feu (36x27cm-14x11in) s.d.49 W/C gouache. 18-Nov-2 Rieunier, Paris #45
£321 $506 €500 Troncs (27x38cm-11x15in) s.d.1940 W/C. 18-Nov-2 Rieunier, Paris #38/R
£321 $506 €500 Arabesques (27x35cm-11x14in) s.d.1949 gouache. 18-Nov-2 Rieunier, Paris #43/R
£321 $506 €500 Par le bleu matinal (25x32cm-10x13in) s.d.49 W/C gouache. 18-Nov-2 Rieunier, Paris #47/R
£449 $709 €700 Gordes (24x32cm-9x13in) s. crayon W/C gouache exec.1943. 18-Nov-2 Rieunier, Paris #32/R
£449 $709 €700 Arabesques (27x36cm-11x14in) s.d.49 gouache. 18-Nov-2 Rieunier, Paris #44/R
£513 $810 €800 Ecolieres a la salle de dessin (27x24cm-11x9in) W/C gouache exec.1938. 18-Nov-2 Rieunier, Paris #25/R
£513 $810 €800 Tout ce qui sait donner son coeur au feu (36x27cm-14x11in) s.d.49 W/C gouache. 18-Nov-2 Rieunier, Paris #46/R
£962 $1519 €1500 Nature morte (22x29cm-9x11in) s.d.1935 gouache. 18-Nov-2 Rieunier, Paris #29/R

SIMON, Armand (1906-1981) Belgian

Works on paper

£276 $439 €400 Composition surrealiste (20x16cm-8x6in) s.d.45 Indian ink. 4-Mar-3 Palais de Beaux Arts, Brussels #395
£535 $829 €850 Mon film: les 36000 volontes (21x17cm-8x7in) s.d.27-8-39 Indian ink. 1-Oct-2 Palais de Beaux Arts, Brussels #525
£662 $1079 €1000 Essai sur les chants (23x18cm-9x7in) s.d.39 dr. 17-Feb-3 Horta, Bruxelles #458
£818 $1267 €1300 Composition surrealiste (23x15cm-9x6in) s. Indian ink. 1-Oct-2 Palais de Beaux Arts, Brussels #524
£1027 $1603 €1500 L'ogre (30x24cm-12x9in) s. Indian ink dr exhib. 14-Apr-3 Horta, Bruxelles #298 est:500-700

SIMON, Émile (1890-1976) French

£298 $486 €450 Mer a Camaret (27x41cm-11x16in) s. panel. 3-Feb-3 Chambelland & Giafferi, Paris #341
£862 $1371 €1250 Port de Bretagne (61x46cm-24x18in) s. 9-Mar-3 Feletin, Province #89
£962 $1510 €1500 Bretonne au livre (45x38cm-18x15in) s. i.verso. 15-Dec-2 Thierry & Lannon, Brest #203
£2535 $4082 €3600 Retour de peche (52x63cm-20x25in) s. 11-May-3 Thierry & Lannon, Brest #229/R est:2000-2300

SIMON, Gustav (19th C) Austrian

£342 $534 €500 Portrait of woman wearing Fez (45x35cm-18x14in) bears sig. 10-Apr-3 Schopman, Hamburg #595

SIMON, Herve (1888-?) Belgian

£321 $503 €500 Interieur (50x60cm-20x24in) s. 19-Nov-2 Galerie Moderne, Brussels #210

SIMON, Jacques (1885-1965) French

£1171 $1827 €1850 Paysage anime a Carolles (55x38cm-22x15in) s. 15-Sep-2 Etude Bailleul, Bayeux #61/R
£1905 $3029 €2800 Le port d'Alger (33x40cm-13x16in) s. 24-Mar-3 Rabourdin & Choppin de Janvry, Paris #257/R est:2300-2500

SIMON, Jeanne (19th C) French

Works on paper

£1154 $1812 €1800 Portrait de femme au salon (57x52cm-22x20in) s.d.1895 pastel gouache. 15-Dec-2 Thierry & Lannon, Brest #47

SIMON, Lucien (1861-1945) French

£385 $604 €600 Eveque en procession (37x29cm-15x11in) init. 15-Dec-2 Thierry & Lannon, Brest #201
£641 $1006 €1000 Bigouden et ses enfants (32x25cm-13x10in) s. 15-Dec-2 Thierry & Lannon, Brest #200
£962 $1510 €1500 Procession pres de la chapelle (41x34cm-16x13in) s. panel. 15-Dec-2 Thierry & Lannon, Brest #197
£1154 $1812 €1800 Sainte-Marine (26x40cm-10x16in) s. 15-Dec-2 Thierry & Lannon, Brest #199
£1197 $1927 €1700 Les goemoniers (21x27cm-8x11in) mono. board. 11-May-3 Thierry & Lannon, Brest #230 est:900-1200
£1290 $2000 €1935 Artist's studio (66x81cm-26x32in) s. 29-Oct-2 Sotheby's, New York #86/R est:3000-4000
£1923 $3019 €3000 Bateaux a l'amarre (48x73cm-19x29in) init.verso. 15-Dec-2 Thierry & Lannon, Brest #198
£2113 $3401 €3000 Marche en Bretagne Ploneour Lanvern (27x35cm-11x14in) board. 11-May-3 Thierry & Lannon, Brest #231/R est:1600-1800
£2361 $3849 €3400 Le pardon de la Clarte pres de Douarnenez (40x32cm-16x13in) s. 19-Jul-3 Thierry & Lannon, Brest #179/R est:3500-4000
£2431 $3962 €3500 En Bretagne (35x26cm-14x10in) s. panel painted c.1910-12. 19-Jul-3 Thierry & Lannon, Brest #176/R est:2500-3000
£2482 $4145 €3500 Mere et ses trois enfants (38x46cm-15x18in) s. 23-Jun-3 Beaussant & Lefèvre, Paris #324/R est:3000-4000
£2500 $4075 €3600 Bigoudenes au bain (35x26cm-14x10in) s. panel double-sided. 19-Jul-3 Thierry & Lannon, Brest #177/R est:2500-3000
£15385 $24154 €24000 Brulage de goemon (147x184cm-58x72in) s. 15-Dec-2 Thierry & Lannon, Brest #196/R
£16111 $26261 €23200 Baptemes a la Chapelle de Penhors (100x142cm-39x56in) s. 19-Jul-3 Thierry & Lannon, Brest #178 est:12000-14000

Works on paper

£493 $794 €700 Communiante de profil (12x18cm-5x7in) s. wash. 11-May-3 Thierry & Lannon, Brest #321
£1007 $1641 €1450 Les brodeuses (12x24cm-5x9in) s. wash. 19-Jul-3 Thierry & Lannon, Brest #79
£1149 $1792 €1700 Femme avec missel. Quatre femmes courant. Bretonne et ses enfants. s. wash dr 3 in one frame. 27-Mar-3 Maigret, Paris #282
£1197 $1927 €1700 Animation devant l'eglise (24x32cm-9x13in) s. W/C. 11-May-3 Thierry & Lannon, Brest #102 est:1300-1600
£2014 $3283 €2900 Femmes musulmanes, Marrakech (28x41cm-11x16in) s. gouache. 19-Jul-3 Thierry & Lannon, Brest #97/R est:2000-2500
£2340 $3909 €3300 Bretonne scrutant l'horizon (61x34cm-24x13in) i. W/C. 20-Jun-3 Piasa, Paris #102 est:1500-2000
£9722 $15847 €14000 Le battage au fleau (52x70cm-20x28in) s. gouache. 19-Jul-3 Thierry & Lannon, Brest #98 est:6000-6500

SIMON, Yohanan (1905-1976) Israeli

£2532 $4000 €3798 Landscape (35x41cm-14x16in) s.d.70 prov. 27-Apr-3 Sotheby's, Tel Aviv #48/R est:4000-6000
£3226 $5000 €4839 La rencontre (45x37cm-18x15in) s.d.1958. 26-Sep-2 Christie's, Rockefeller NY #571/R est:5000-7000
£6329 $10000 €9494 Kibbutz scene (41x35cm-16x14in) s.d.50 board. 27-Apr-3 Sotheby's, Tel Aviv #56/R est:10000-15000
£10127 $16000 €15191 Kibbutz scene (51x76cm-20x30in) s. 27-Apr-3 Sotheby's, Tel Aviv #55/R est:12000-15000

Works on paper

£949 $1500 €1424 Abstract landscape (23x15cm-9x6in) s.d.70 gouache. 27-Apr-3 Sotheby's, Tel Aviv #47a/R est:1500-2000

SIMON-AUGUSTE, Simon (1909-1987) French

£563 $900 €816 Woman playing checkers (89x114cm-35x45in) s. 17-May-3 Selkirks, St. Louis #229/R

SIMONAU, Gustave Adolphe (1810-1870) Belgian
Works on paper
£288 $453 €450 Paysage anime (45x31cm-18x12in) s.i.d.1860 W/C. 10-Dec-2 Vanderkindere, Brussels #34

SIMONE, A de (19/20th C) Italian
Works on paper
£550 $891 €825 Steam yacht Vanadis riding out the gale (42x62cm-17x24in) s.i.d.95 bodycol. 21-May-3 Christie's, Kensington #442/R
£600 $930 €900 H.M.S Renown in the Bay of Naples (29x43cm-11x17in) s.i.d.1909 bodycol. 31-Oct-2 Christie's, Kensington #368/R
£600 $972 €900 Royal London Yacht Club's steam yacht Queen Marfisa (30x46cm-12x18in) s.i.d.89 bodycol. 21-May-3 Christie's, Kensington #449/R
£650 $1007 €975 Schooner Vixen in Neapolitan waters (30x46cm-12x18in) s.i.indis d.18 bodycol. 31-Oct-2 Christie's, Kensington #366/R
£800 $1296 €1200 Royal yacht Victoria and Albert III under escort by HMS Cochrane (38x63cm-15x25in) s.i.d.1910 bodycol. 21-May-3 Christie's, Kensington #443/R
£1000 $1550 €1500 Steam yacht Grace Darling at sea (42x61cm-17x24in) s.i. indis d. bodycol. 31-Oct-2 Christie's, Kensington #371/R est:400-600
£1200 $1944 €1800 Schooner Noah in the Bay of Naples (46x63cm-18x25in) i. bodycol. 21-May-3 Christie's, Kensington #448/R est:600-800
£1400 $2268 €2100 British Naval corvette in Bay of Naples and at sea (30x44cm-12x17in) s.d.86 bodycol pair. 21-May-3 Christie's, Kensington #446/R est:1500-2000
£1500 $2325 €2250 Steam yacht Greta in Neapolitan waters. Stream yacht Greta in heavy swell (41x61cm-16x24in) s.i. bodycol two. 31-Oct-2 Christie's, Kensington #369/R est:1500-2500
£1500 $2325 €2250 Steam yacht Onora in the Mediterranean off Naples (16x26cm-6x10in) s.i.d.1901 bodycol. 31-Oct-2 Christie's, Kensington #370/R est:700-900
£1500 $2430 €2250 Steam yacht of Royal Cork Yacht Club in Bay of Naples and at sea (40x56cm-16x22in) bodycol pair. 21-May-3 Christie's, Kensington #445/R est:800-1200
£2200 $3564 €3300 Steam yacht Firefly in Neapolitan waters and at sea (43x63cm-17x25in) s.i.d.95 bodycol pair. 21-May-3 Christie's, Kensington #447/R est:1000-1500
£4000 $6480 €6000 American yawl Xarifa in Bay of Naples and at sea (47x67cm-19x26in) s.i.d.1913 bodycol pair. 21-May-3 Christie's, Kensington #444/R est:1500-2500

SIMONE, A de (attrib) (19/20th C) Italian
Works on paper
£300 $465 €450 Gunboat H.M.S Starling at sea (28x38cm-11x15in) i. bodycol. 31-Oct-2 Christie's, Kensington #367/R
£600 $930 €900 Royal Mail steamer Orotava riding the ocean swell (38x60cm-15x24in) i. bodycol. 31-Oct-2 Christie's, Kensington #372/R
£600 $972 €900 SS Nentmoor in Neapolitan waters (43x63cm-17x25in) i. bodycol. 21-May-3 Christie's, Kensington #440/R

SIMONE, Antonio de (19th C) ?
Works on paper
£300 $477 €450 Royal yacht the Victoria and Albert with an escort, the Cochrane (38x63cm-15x25in) s.i. W/C. 26-Feb-3 Cheffins Grain & Comins, Cambridge #507
£2600 $4160 €3900 Sy Mera in heavy seas. Sy Nerissa in the Bay of Naples (41x61cm-16x24in) s.i. bodycol two. 13-Mar-3 Duke & Son, Dorchester #68/R est:1000-2000

SIMONE, D (?) Italian
Works on paper
£1300 $2080 €1950 Steam yacht, Ravenska with Vesuvius beyond (41x66cm-16x26in) s.d.1911 gouache. 11-Mar-3 Gorringes, Lewes #2361/R est:1000-1500

SIMONE, Michele de (19/20th C) Italian
£816 $1298 €1200 Wood with stream (77x51cm-30x20in) s. 18-Mar-3 Finarte, Milan #198/R

SIMONE, Tommaso de (19th C) Italian
£800 $1296 €1200 British naval paddle sloop off Stromboli (34x51cm-13x20in) s. 21-May-3 Christie's, Kensington #658/R
£2000 $3100 €3000 British racing schooner swinging on her anchor in the Bay of Naples (34x56cm-13x22in) s.d.1863. 31-Oct-2 Christie's, Kensington #480/R est:2000-4000
£3300 $5115 €4950 Bay of Naples, with man-of-war in full sail (38x48cm-15x19in) s.i.d.1863. 5-Oct-2 Finan Watkins & Co, Mere #191/R
£6250 $9500 €9375 The Susan Hinks, off Naples (56x81cm-22x32in) s.d.1869. 17-Aug-2 North East Auctions, Portsmouth #945/R
£8000 $13280 €11600 Squadron of ships of the Royal Navy's Mediterranean fleet lying in Naples Bay (26x66cm-10x26in) one s.d.1886 one s. pair prov. 12-Jun-3 Christie's, London #516/R est:10000-15000
Works on paper
£1708 $2750 €2562 Portrait of the steam yacht Narada (41x61cm-16x24in) i. gouache. 22-Feb-3 Pook & Pook, Downington #356/R est:900-1200
£1800 $2808 €2700 Steam assisted three masted ship at anchor in Bay of Naples (30x43cm-12x17in) s.d.1886 gouache pair. 17-Oct-2 David Lay, Penzance #1204/R est:2000-2500

SIMONE, de (19/20th C) Italian
£2200 $3432 €3300 Marine scene (46x64cm-18x25in) s.d.1861. 15-Oct-2 Canterbury Auctions, UK #152/R
£2400 $3648 €3600 Snow Ocean Belle of Aberystwyth (42x65cm-17x26in) s.i.d.1870. 15-Aug-2 Bonhams, New Bond Street #347/R est:1500-2000
Works on paper
£1455 $2240 €2183 S.Y Firefly (42x62cm-17x24in) s.i.d.1895 gouache pair. 4-Sep-2 Dunbar Sloane, Wellington #81/R est:1000-2000 (NZ.D 4800)

SIMONET Y LOMBARDO, Enrique (1863-1927) Spanish
£974 $1422 €1500 Landscape (19x26cm-7x10in) s. canvas on cardboard. 17-Jun-2 Ansorena, Madrid #121/R

SIMONETTI, Alfonso (1840-1892) Italian
Works on paper
£450 $702 €675 Favourite poem (54x37cm-21x15in) s.i. pencil W/C. 17-Sep-2 Rosebery Fine Art, London #512

SIMONETTI, Attilio (1843-1925) Italian
£769 $1192 €1200 Landscape with lake (15x39cm-6x15in) s.d.1878. 4-Dec-2 Finarte, Rome #798

SIMONETTI, Attilio (attrib) (1843-1925) Italian
£1500 $2445 €2250 Time of change (31x41cm-12x16in) s.i. 13-Feb-3 Christie's, Kensington #188/R est:2000-3000

SIMONETTI, Ettore (19th C) Italian
£15000 $23550 €22500 At the ball (60x96cm-24x38in) s.i. 19-Nov-2 Sotheby's, London #111/R est:8000-12000

SIMONETTI, Gianni Emilio (1940-) Italian
Works on paper
£285 $444 €450 Women prefer, the sipho (100x100cm-39x39in) s.i.d.1967 verso mixed media. 20-Oct-2 Charbonneaux, Paris #155 est:600-800

SIMONI, A de (19th C) Italian
£1293 $2055 €1900 Shepherd with flock and pack donkey (19x43cm-7x17in) s.i. 19-Mar-3 Neumeister, Munich #734/R est:1800

SIMONI, Gustavo (1846-1926) Italian
£1594 $2614 €2200 Paesaggio con pecore e pastori (29x61cm-11x24in) s. 27-May-3 Finarte, Milan #56/R est:2000-2500
Works on paper
£1582 $2468 €2500 Paysanne romaine (100x660cm-39x260in) s. W/C. 20-Oct-2 Mercier & Cie, Lille #306/R est:3000-3500
£3716 $5797 €5500 Concert in the patio (55x38cm-22x15in) s.i.d.1882 W/C. 31-Mar-3 Ribeyre & Baron, Paris #39/R

SIMONI, Mario (19th C) Italian
£1132 $1743 €1800 Pink orchids (60x80cm-24x31in) s. board. 23-Oct-2 Finarte, Milan #4/R

SIMONI, Scipione (19/20th C) Italian
£380 $593 €570 Fishing boats in Bay of Naples (48x69cm-19x27in) s. 15-Oct-2 Gorringes, Lewes #2117 est:300-400
Works on paper
£949 $1500 €1500 Street in Tagliacozzo (59x38cm-23x15in) s.d.1912 W/C card. 26-Nov-2 Christie's, Rome #121/R
£1742 $2700 €2613 Figures resting beside stone steps in an Italian village (74x48cm-29x19in) s.d.1897 W/C. 7-Dec-2 Selkirks, St. Louis #751/R est:1800-2400

SIMONIN, Francine (1942-) Canadian
£309 $478 €464 Les chaises (50x64cm-20x25in) s.d.Oct 86 mixed media lit. 3-Dec-2 Joyner, Toronto #496 (C.D 750)

SIMONIN, Victor (1877-1946) Belgian
£253 $395 €400 Pichet fleuri (73x60cm-29x24in) s. 16-Sep-2 Horta, Bruxelles #234
£302 $486 €450 Vase de fleurs (53x45cm-21x18in) s. 18-Feb-3 Vanderkindere, Brussels #26
£315 $492 €460 Composition au chaudron (75x96cm-30x38in) s. 14-Apr-3 Horta, Bruxelles #247
£316 $494 €500 Paysage d'hiver (50x63cm-20x25in) s.panel. 16-Sep-2 Horta, Bruxelles #235
£321 $503 €500 Nature morte aux fleurs (60x82cm-24x32in) s. cardboard. 19-Nov-2 Galerie Moderne, Brussels #211
£352 $567 €500 Still life with fruit bowl (39x49cm-15x19in) s. board. 7-May-3 Vendue Huis, Gravenhage #162/R
£360 $576 €500 Vase fleuri (51x40cm-20x16in) s. panel. 19-May-3 Horta, Bruxelles #483
£379 $607 €550 Beached boat by moonlight (66x100cm-26x39in) s.d.1903 prov. 15-Mar-3 De Vuyst, Lokeren #290
£414 $646 €650 Nature morte aux condiments (60x71cm-24x28in) s. panel. 11-Nov-2 Horta, Bruxelles #706
£443 $691 €700 Nature morte aux fleurs (60x63cm-24x25in) s. 15-Oct-2 Vanderkindere, Brussels #99
£445 $695 €650 Nature morte aux fleurs (50x70cm-20x28in) s. panel double-sided. 14-Apr-3 Horta, Bruxelles #246
£759 $1185 €1200 Nature morte aux fruits (52x60cm-20x24in) s. 15-Oct-2 Vanderkindere, Brussels #102
£1911 $2981 €3000 Still life with flowers (59x78cm-23x31in) s. panel. 6-Nov-2 Vendue Huis, Gravenhage #534/R est:3000-4000

SIMONINI, Francesco (attrib) (1686-1753) Italian
£1351 $2108 €2000 Choc de cavaalerie (67x88cm-26x35in) 30-Mar-3 Anaf, Lyon #434/R
£3034 $4825 €4400 Choc de cavalerie (53x91cm-21x36in) 5-Mar-3 Oger, Dumont, Paris #52/R est:4000-4500

SIMONINI, Francesco (studio) (1686-1753) Italian
£2857 $4171 €4400 Battle scene (96x135cm-38x53in) 17-Jun-2 Ansorena, Madrid #338/R

SIMONINI, Francesco (style) (1686-1753) Italian
£11000 $17050 €16500 Cavalryman before his troops. Cavalryman leading his troops to battle (68x85cm-27x33in) pair. 30-Oct-2 Christie's, Kensington #159/R est:5000-7000

SIMONKA, Georges (1916-2001) Hungarian
£256 $403 €400 Port de Carole (100x100cm-39x39in) s.d.1068. 24-Nov-2 Chayette & Cheval, Paris #87
£256 $403 €400 Nature morte au chapeau de paille (64x54cm-25x21in) s.d.55 panel. 24-Nov-2 Chayette & Cheval, Paris #93/R
£256 $403 €400 L'arlequin (65x54cm-26x21in) s. 24-Nov-2 Chayette & Cheval, Paris #134
£256 $403 €400 Enfant lisant (46x54cm-18x21in) s. 24-Nov-2 Chayette & Cheval, Paris #149
£256 $403 €400 Chemin de campagne (73x92cm-29x36in) s. 24-Nov-2 Chayette & Cheval, Paris #159
£269 $423 €420 Innocence (100x82cm-39x32in) s. d.94 verso. 24-Nov-2 Chayette & Cheval, Paris #95
£269 $423 €420 Nature morte aux pichets (58x92cm-23x36in) s. 24-Nov-2 Chayette & Cheval, Paris #97/R
£269 $423 €420 Femme nue au foulard blanc (81x60cm-32x24in) s. 24-Nov-2 Chayette & Cheval, Paris #155
£288 $453 €450 Femme au foulard rouge (80x65cm-31x26in) s. 24-Nov-2 Chayette & Cheval, Paris #120
£288 $453 €450 Jeune femme au tee-shirt (130x97cm-51x38in) s.d.73. 24-Nov-2 Chayette & Cheval, Paris #164
£308 $483 €480 Les barques en Mediterranee (54x73cm-21x29in) s. 24-Nov-2 Chayette & Cheval, Paris #133/R
£308 $483 €480 L'atelier (65x81cm-26x32in) s. 24-Nov-2 Chayette & Cheval, Paris #196
£417 $654 €650 Interieur a la palette (130x162cm-51x64in) s. 24-Nov-2 Chayette & Cheval, Paris #208
£417 $654 €650 Femme pres de la lampe a petrole (162x130cm-64x51in) s.d.63. 24-Nov-2 Chayette & Cheval, Paris #210
£449 $704 €700 Femme au repos (82x100cm-32x39in) s. 24-Nov-2 Chayette & Cheval, Paris #91
£449 $704 €700 Peche a la ligne (65x81cm-26x32in) s. 24-Nov-2 Chayette & Cheval, Paris #127
£609 $956 €950 Atelier vert eu jaune (162x130cm-64x51in) s.d.60. 24-Nov-2 Chayette & Cheval, Paris #209
£769 $1208 €1200 L'artiste dans l'atelier (155x201cm-61x79in) s.d.1954 panel. 24-Nov-2 Chayette & Cheval, Paris #211/R
£897 $1409 €1400 Le mariage (214x156cm-84x61in) s.d.1956 panel. 24-Nov-2 Chayette & Cheval, Paris #212/R

SIMONS, Michiel (?-1673) Dutch
£12230 $19568 €17000 Still life with grapes, apples, peaches in bowl, lobster, crayfish (73x94cm-29x37in) 13-May-3 Sotheby's, Amsterdam #45/R est:10000-15000

SIMONSEN, Axel (1884-1962) Danish
£258 $393 €387 From an Italian mountain village (51x66cm-20x26in) s. prov. 27-Aug-2 Rasmussen, Copenhagen #1647 (D.KR 3000)
£258 $393 €387 Piazza del Popolo in sunshine (46x60cm-18x24in) s. prov. 27-Aug-2 Rasmussen, Copenhagen #1712/R (D.KR 3000)
£301 $458 €452 Ruin of an old bridge, the Tiber, Italy (50x64cm-20x25in) s. prov. 27-Aug-2 Rasmussen, Copenhagen #1716/R (D.KR 3500)
£362 $550 €543 Street scene in Terracina (61x77cm-24x30in) s.d.30 prov. 27-Aug-2 Rasmussen, Copenhagen #1651 (D.KR 4200)
£440 $677 €660 Eating melon (130x97cm-51x38in) s.d.27. 26-Oct-2 Rasmussen, Havnen #2180 (D.KR 5200)
£468 $767 €702 Via Appia, Italian landscape with road (50x65cm-20x26in) s. 27-May-3 Museumsbygningen, Copenhagen #455 (D.KR 4800)

SIMONSEN, Niels (1807-1885) Danish
£541 $843 €800 Sad homecoming (800x178cm-315x70in) s.i.d.1849 lit. 28-Mar-3 Karrenbauer, Konstanz #1782
£603 $916 €905 Young lady under palm tree by the sea (31x27cm-12x11in) init. s.stretcher. 27-Aug-2 Rasmussen, Copenhagen #1637 (D.KR 7000)
£1034 $1571 €1551 Monk in monastery in Tyrol (40x33cm-16x13in) s.d.1839. 27-Aug-2 Rasmussen, Copenhagen #1709/R est:8000-10000 (D.KR 12000)
£1435 $2325 €2081 Fisherman's wife by her baby's cradle waiting for husband to return from sea (46x39cm-18x15in) s.i.d.1837. 26-May-3 Rasmussen, Copenhagen #1543/R est:15000 (D.KR 15000)
£1500 $2490 €2175 Faithful hound (84x127cm-33x50in) s.d.1856. 12-Jun-3 Christie's, Kensington #271/R est:1500-2000
£2787 $4348 €4181 Coastal landscape with pirates on way to sailing ship (37x51cm-15x20in) s/d/1847. 23-Sep-2 Rasmussen, Vejle #64/R est:30000-50000 (D.KR 33000)

SIMONSEN, Niels (attrib) (1807-1885) Danish
£1148 $1860 €1665 Italian travellers on donkeys over the mountains (47x63cm-19x25in) 26-May-3 Rasmussen, Copenhagen #1319/R est:10000-15000 (D.KR 12000)

SIMONSEN, Simon (1841-1928) Danish
£383 $605 €575 Dune landscape with house, Jylland (26x35cm-10x14in) s.d.1912. 2-Dec-2 Rasmussen, Copenhagen #1280/R (D.KR 4500)
£651 $1054 €944 Portrait of the inn keeper's poodle Caro (38x29cm-15x11in) s.d.1866. 24-May-3 Rasmussen, Havnen #2156/R (D.KR 6800)
£1248 $1984 €1872 Kitchen interior with kittens and puppy in basket (25x33cm-10x13in) s.d.1866. 10-Mar-3 Rasmussen, Vejle #144/R est:10000 (D.KR 13400)
£1981 $3011 €2972 Not in the mood for playing at the moment - two puppies on steps (38x53cm-15x21in) s.d.1918. 27-Aug-2 Rasmussen, Copenhagen #1781/R est:30000 (D.KR 23000)
£2301 $3750 €3452 Dispute (52x70cm-20x28in) s. 11-Feb-3 Bonhams & Doyles, New York #139/R est:3000-5000
£3404 $5379 €5106 Horses outside a village blacksmith's (45x60cm-18x24in) s.d.1867 exhib. 2-Dec-2 Rasmussen, Copenhagen #1184/R est:60000-80000 (D.KR 40000)
£4085 $6454 €6128 Gundog with bird in his mouth (72x56cm-28x22in) s.d.September 1895. 2-Dec-2 Rasmussen, Copenhagen #1325/R est:50000-75000 (D.KR 48000)

SIMONSSON, Birger (1883-1938) Swedish
£372 $587 €558 Coastal landscape from Lunnevik (50x55cm-20x22in) init.d.1918 panel. 30-Nov-2 Goteborg Auktionsverk, Sweden #631/R (S.KR 5300)

SIMONSSON, Konrad (1843-1916) Swedish
£864 $1417 €1253 Moonlit landscape (65x79cm-26x31in) s. 4-Jun-3 AB Stockholms Auktionsverk #2218/R (S.KR 11000)
£1885 $3092 €2733 Summer landscape with hay stooks and silver birches (65x89cm-26x35in) s.d.1887. 4-Jun-3 AB Stockholms Auktionsverk #2128/R est:18000-20000 (S.KR 24000)

SIMONY, Stefan (1860-1950) Austrian
£2690 $4277 €3900 Harvesting with Salzburg fortress beyond (44x51cm-17x20in) s. panel. 8-Mar-3 Arnold, Frankfurt #720/R est:1200
£2899 $4754 €4000 Tarrenz in Tyrol (54x74cm-21x29in) s.d.1923 panel. 27-May-3 Wiener Kunst Auktionen, Vienna #26/R est:4000-7000

SIMPKINS, Henry J (1906-) Canadian
Works on paper
£222 $350 €333 Long Beach, BC (36x51cm-14x20in) s. W/C. 14-Nov-2 Heffel, Vancouver #242 (C.D 550)

SIMPSON, A (?) ?
£287 $450 €431 Landscape (51x41cm-20x16in) s. 22-Nov-2 Eldred, East Dennis #1105/R

SIMPSON, Charles Walter (1885-1971) British
£279 $435 €419 Derrick (51x64cm-20x25in) s.d.13 exhib. 25-Mar-3 Ritchie, Toronto #71/R (C.D 650)
£3000 $4650 €4500 Portrait of John Garland de pret Roose and his brother on horseback in Rotten Row, Hyde Park (101x127cm-40x50in) s. 3-Dec-2 Bonhams, New Bond Street #18/R est:3000-4000
£4400 $7040 €6600 Loading the hay cart (69x90cm-27x35in) s. 15-May-3 Lawrence, Crewkerne #1010/R est:3000-5000
£6000 $9360 €9000 Grand National, Bechers Brook (71x92cm-28x36in) s. 10-Apr-3 Tennants, Leyburn #1052/R est:4000-6000
Works on paper
£400 $660 €580 Cattle by a hedgerow (50x60cm-20x24in) s.d.13 mixed media. 1-Jul-3 Bearnes, Exeter #436/R
£680 $1122 €986 Ducks feeding by a riverbank (50x60cm-20x24in) s.d.13 mixed media. 1-Jul-3 Bearnes, Exeter #438/R
£850 $1326 €1275 Calves and cats in a barn (29x37cm-11x15in) s.d.1906 W/C htd white. 10-Apr-3 Tennants, Leyburn #878/R

SIMPSON, D J (1966-) British?
£4000 $6160 €6000 Year 1 (305x406cm-120x160in) oil based poster paint on plywood six panel painted 1999 prov. 23-Oct-2 Christie's, London #225/R est:5000-7000

SIMPSON, Jackson (?) ?
Works on paper
£440 $713 €660 Artist's cottage (29x42cm-11x17in) s. W/C. 23-Jan-3 Bonhams, Edinburgh #325

SIMPSON, Joseph (1879-1939) British
£460 $704 €690 Morning haze, Galloway (38x46cm-15x18in) s. s.i.verso panel. 22-Aug-2 Bonhams, Edinburgh #1149

SIMPSON, Lorna (1960-) American
Works on paper
£3548 $5500 €5322 Haze (173x175cm-68x69in) s.i.d.1998 verso serigraph on six panel. 26-Sep-2 Christie's, Rockefeller NY #858/R est:7000-9000

SIMPSON, M E (?) British
Miniatures
£3000 $4740 €4500 Portrait of Mary Isabel Rylands (13cm-5in) ebonised frame rec. 13-Nov-2 Halls, Shrewsbury #136 est:300-500

SIMPSON, W H (19/20th C) British
Works on paper
£2000 $3320 €3000 National Portrait Gallery and St. Martin's in the Fields (29x37cm-11x15in) s.d.1903 W/C. 12-Jun-3 Sotheby's, London #229/R est:2000-3000

SIMPSON, William (1823-1899) British
Works on paper
£420 $664 €630 Shipping off a coast (11x28cm-4x11in) s.i.d.1875 W/C. 27-Nov-2 Hamptons Fine Art, Godalming #226
£2244 $3546 €3366 Landscape from Cheetore, town near Udaipur, North India (26x36cm-10x14in) s.i.d.1866 W/C lit. 27-Nov-2 Falkkloos, Malmo #77563/R est:20000 (S.KR 32000)
£3400 $5270 €5100 Graves of Cathcart's hill of the officers of the Fourth Division (45x70cm-18x28in) s. pencil W/C. 31-Oct-2 Christie's, London #65/R est:3000-5000
£29000 $46110 €43500 Great Wall of China (53x75cm-21x30in) s.i.d.1874 W/C over pencil htd white exhib. 29-Apr-3 Bonhams, New Bond Street #40/R est:12000-18000

SIMS, Charles (1873-1926) British
£900 $1404 €1350 Creation (76x50cm-30x20in) tempera oil. 17-Sep-2 Rosebery Fine Art, London #572/R
£2600 $4290 €3770 Guardian hands (78x58cm-31x23in) canvas on board. 3-Jul-3 Christie's, Kensington #422/R est:1500-2000
£4200 $6930 €6090 Rebel powers that three array (91x71cm-36x28in) s. exhib. 3-Jul-3 Christie's, Kensington #420/R est:2500-3500

SIMSON, William (1800-1847) British
Works on paper
£380 $592 €570 Tivoli (33x46cm-13x18in) s.i.d.1885 pencil W/C htd white. 19-Sep-2 Christie's, Kensington #101

SINCLAIR, Deborah Lougheed (1953-) Canadian
£1441 $2291 €2162 Sunshine - Assiniboine (60x75cm-24x30in) s.i.d.1982 acrylic. 23-Mar-3 Hodgins, Calgary #51/R est:1200-1800 (C.D 3400)

SINCLAIR, Irving (1895-1969) American
£609 $950 €914 Old man hiking. 21-Sep-2 Harvey Clar, Oakland #1536

SINCLAIR, Luckman (20th C) British
Works on paper
£400 $648 €600 M.V Plainsman at Eastham (48x69cm-19x27in) s.i.d.1991 W/C. 21-Jan-3 Bonhams, New Bond Street #164/R

SINCLAIR, Max (fl.1890-1910) British
£755 $1177 €1200 Lake with mountain gorge (50x76cm-20x30in) s. 20-Sep-2 Schloss Ahlden, Ahlden #1266
£800 $1216 €1200 Fair start (30x51cm-12x20in) s. mono.i.verso. 15-Aug-2 Bonhams, New Bond Street #338

SINCLAIR, Robert (1939-) Canadian
Works on paper
£180 $286 €270 Bend (14x19cm-6x7in) s.i.d.1979 W/C. 23-Mar-3 Hodgins, Calgary #123/R (C.D 425)
£254 $404 €381 Front (28x19cm-11x7in) s.i.d.1979 W/C. 23-Mar-3 Hodgins, Calgary #122/R (C.D 600)

SINCLAIR, William Hardie (?) British
£1050 $1701 €1523 Masters feast, three dogs seated before dead game (45x65cm-18x26in) s. 22-May-3 Wintertons, Lichfield #561/R est:300-400

SINDING CHRISTENSEN, Jens (1888-?) Danish
£602 $950 €903 Dutch Harbour (23x36cm-9x14in) mono. 16-Nov-2 New Orleans Auction, New Orleans #318/R

SINDING, Elisabeth (1846-1930) Norwegian
£853 $1331 €1280 Horses at watering place (36x54cm-14x21in) s. painted 1905. 23-Sep-2 Blomqvist, Lysaker #1218/R (N.KR 10000)

SINDING, Knud (1875-1946) Danish
£258 $393 €387 Young couple in the mountains near Civita d'Antonio (70x105cm-28x41in) mono. 27-Aug-2 Rasmussen, Copenhagen #1658/R (D.KR 3000)
£701 $1121 €1052 Bringing home the animals, grandparents and children on road (95x122cm-37x48in) mono. 13-Jan-3 Rasmussen, Vejle #238/R (D.KR 8000)
£1267 $1976 €1901 Young female students on the way to the dunes (120x132cm-47x52in) mono.d.1904. 22-Sep-2 Hindemae, Ullerslev #7211/R est:20000-30000 (D.KR 15000)

SINDING, Otto Ludvig (1842-1909) Norwegian
£366 $575 €549 By the coast (47x60cm-19x24in) s. 25-Nov-2 Blomqvist, Lysaker #1248/R (N.KR 4200)
£475 $721 €713 Rider in oakwood (41x51cm-16x20in) s. 31-Aug-2 Grev Wedels Plass, Oslo #102/R (N.KR 5500)
£1222 $1918 €1833 Landscape from Nordland (25x38cm-10x15in) s. 25-Nov-2 Blomqvist, Lysaker #1247/R est:8000-12000 (N.KR 14000)
£1378 $2095 €2067 Ullensvang in Hardanger, mountains and sheep (38x50cm-15x20in) s. 27-Aug-2 Rasmussen, Copenhagen #1702/R est:10000-15000 (D.KR 16000)
£2281 $3604 €3422 Fishing village in Lofoten (38x50cm-15x20in) s, i.verso. 17-Dec-2 Grev Wedels Plass, Oslo #185/R est:20000-30000 (N.KR 26000)
£3503 $5604 €5255 Frightened fishermen's families on beach after shipwreck (120x225cm-47x89in) painted c.1900. 13-Jan-3 Rasmussen, Vejle #71/R est:35000-40000 (D.KR 40000)

SINDING, Paul (1882-1964) Danish?
£681 $1076 €1022 The corvette Dagmar (82x103cm-32x41in) s,. 2-Dec-2 Rasmussen, Copenhagen #1344/R (D.KR 8000)

£1120 $1702 €1680 The Battle in Koge Bay (121x98cm-48x39in) s.d.1944. 27-Aug-2 Rasmussen, Copenhagen #1764/R est:10000-15000 (D.KR 13000)

SINDING, Sigmund (1875-1936) Norwegian

£575 $938 €863 Girl in boat (89x100cm-35x39in) s. 17-Feb-3 Blomqvist, Lysaker #1205 (N.KR 6500)

SINDING, Stephan (1846-1922) Norwegian

Sculpture

£1396 $2262 €2024 Man and woman (21x31cm-8x12in) s. dark pat.bronze Cast.Gladerbeck. 26-May-3 Bukowskis, Stockholm #300/R est:8000-10000 (S.KR 18000)

£2602 $4059 €3903 Captive mother (40x62x38cm-16x24x15in) s.d.1885 bronze lit. 21-Oct-2 Blomqvist, Oslo #374/R est:40000 (N.KR 30000)

£3064 $4841 €4596 Young girl with folded arms and draped clothing (138cm-54in) s. white marble. 26-Nov-2 Rasmussen, Copenhagen #2404/R est:15000 (D.KR 36000)

£3490 $5480 €5235 The night (20x52cm-8x20in) s. bronze. 21-Nov-2 Grev Wedels Plass, Oslo #42/R est:40000-60000 (N.KR 40000)

£3800 $6080 €5700 Valkyrie riding into battle with a raised sword (84cm-33in) s. bronze st.f.Gladenbeck. 15-May-3 Christie's, Kensington #393/R est:3000-5000

SINEMUS, Willem Frederik (1903-1987) Dutch

Works on paper

£263 $426 €400 Composition (62x47cm-24x19in) s. black chk gouache W/C. 21-Jan-3 Christie's, Amsterdam #494

£962 $1490 €1500 Composition (68x53cm-27x21in) s.d.69 chk gouache. 3-Dec-2 Christie's, Amsterdam #117/R est:1500-2000

SING, Johann Kaspar (1651-1729) German

Works on paper

£625 $994 €900 Ascension and crowning of Mary (28x15cm-11x6in) i. chk prov. framed oval. 5-May-3 Ketterer, Munich #240/R

SINGDAHLSEN, Andreas (1855-1947) Norwegian

£358 $580 €537 Canal in Venice (41x58cm-16x23in) s. 3-Feb-3 Lilla Bukowskis, Stockholm #213 (S.KR 5000)

£1629 $2639 €2444 Winter landscape with farm (55x80cm-22x31in) s. 26-May-3 Grev Wedels Plass, Oslo #34/R est:20000-30000 (N.KR 18000)

SINGER, Arthur B (1917-1990) American

£570 $900 €855 Two bar tailed godwits and four curlews wading (61x43cm-24x17in) s. prov.lit. 3-Apr-3 Christie's, Rockefeller NY #210/R

Works on paper

£253 $400 €380 Agsmi heron (10x16cm-4x6in) s. gouache on board prov.lit. 3-Apr-3 Christie's, Rockefeller NY #228/R

£316 $500 €474 Oyster catchers - five cranes (67x103cm-26x41in) s.d.83 W/C gouache prov. 3-Apr-3 Christie's, Rockefeller NY #204/R

£316 $500 €474 Three black terns in flight (61x42cm-24x17in) s. gouache paperboard prov. 3-Apr-3 Christie's, Rockefeller NY #205/R

£1266 $2000 €1899 Three gray herons and purple heron (61x42cm-24x17in) s. gouache on board prov.lit. 3-Apr-3 Christie's, Rockefeller NY #231/R est:8000-12000

SINGER, Clyde (1908-) American

Works on paper

£488 $800 €708 Islanders walking (37x49cm-15x19in) s.d. W/C. 5-Jun-3 Swann Galleries, New York #222/R

SINGER, Nancy (1912-) American

£325 $500 €488 Abstract forms (43x71cm-17x28in) painted c.1940. 8-Sep-2 Treadway Gallery, Cincinnati #680/R

£487 $750 €731 Abstract forms (48x41cm-19x16in) painted c.1940. 8-Sep-2 Treadway Gallery, Cincinnati #678/R

SINGH OF KOTAH, Maharajah Ram (19th C) Indian

Works on paper

£1600 $2496 €2400 Shooting tiger, seated in a hunting pavilion with European guest (44x66cm-17x26in) gouache exec.c.1850 prov. 17-Oct-2 Bonhams, Knightsbridge #159/R est:2000-3000

SINGH, Arpita (1937-) Indian

£10878 $17949 €15773 Disappearing words and disappearing forms (150x77cm-59x30in) s.d.97. 6-Jul-3 Christie's, Hong Kong #97/R est:90000-120000 (HK.D 140000)

Works on paper

£800 $1248 €1200 Man and woman (38x51cm-15x20in) W/C. 17-Oct-2 Bonhams, Knightsbridge #639/R

SINGH, Paramjit (1935-) Indian

£2486 $4103 €3605 Untitled (91x122cm-36x48in) s.d.2002. 6-Jul-3 Christie's, Hong Kong #90/R est:25000-35000 (HK.D 32000)

SINGIER, Gustave (1909-1985) French

Works on paper

£612 $973 €900 Composition (45x56cm-18x22in) s.d.73 W/C. 26-Feb-3 Artcurial Briest, Paris #569

£759 $1177 €1200 Composition (32x45cm-13x18in) s.d. W/C. 28-Sep-2 Cornette de St.Cyr, Paris #422/R

£759 $1177 €1200 Composition (37x56cm-15x22in) s.d. W/C. 28-Sep-2 Cornette de St.Cyr, Paris #423

£823 $1300 €1300 Composition (56x45cm-22x18in) s.d.65 pastel. 27-Nov-2 Blanchet, Paris #131/R

£935 $1478 €1450 Composition abstraite (8x40cm-3x16in) s.pastel ink. 18-Dec-2 Digard, Paris #61/R

£986 $1568 €1450 Sans titre (45x55cm-18x22in) s.d.60 W/C ink wash prov. 26-Feb-3 Artcurial Briest, Paris #469

£1156 $1839 €1700 Composition (44x55cm-17x22in) s.d.60 W/C gouache prov. 26-Feb-3 Artcurial Briest, Paris #471 est:1200-1500

£1224 $1947 €1800 Baigneuse nuit (44x55cm-17x22in) s.d.60 W/C gouache prov. 26-Feb-3 Artcurial Briest, Paris #470 est:1200-1500

£1702 $2757 €2400 Composition (56x45cm-22x18in) s.d.68 W/C prov.exhib. 26-May-3 Christie's, Milan #368/R est:2000-2500

SINGLETON, Henry (1766-1839) British

£6500 $10855 €9425 Storming of the Bastille (46x61cm-18x24in) 9-Jul-3 Bonhams, New Bond Street #11/R est:3000-5000

SINGLETON, Joseph (c.1751-?) British

Miniatures

£2200 $3432 €3300 Sir Joshua Reynolds wearing two- tone scarlet doctoral robes (8cm-3in) s.i.verso wood frame rec. after Sir Joshua Reynolds. 5-Nov-2 Bonhams, New Bond Street #87/R est:1500-2500

SINGLETON, Joseph (attrib) (c.1751-?) British

Miniatures

£1000 $1640 €1450 Young gentleman in a blue coat (5cm-2in) init. pair of kissing doves in seed pearls. 3-Jun-3 Christie's, London #120/R est:1000-1500

SINGLETON, William (attrib) (?-1793) British

Miniatures

£6000 $9840 €8700 Young girl holding a garland of pink roses (5cm-2in) gold frame plaited hair oval prov. 3-Jun-3 Christie's, London #116/R est:1500-2500

SINIBALDI, Jean Paul (1857-1909) French

£2654 $3769 €4300 Allegorie du Printemps (116x86cm-46x34in) s. 17-Mar-2 Galerie de Chartres, Chartres #126

SINIBALDO, Toroi (1876-1955) Italian

£469 $750 €704 Priest, lady and girl (22x31cm-9x12in) s. panel. 5-Jan-3 Galleria Y Remates, Montevideo #92/R

SINICKI, René (20th C) French?

£219 $350 €329 Fleurs (25x16cm-10x6in) s. 18-May-3 Butterfields, Los Angeles #7015

SINISGALLI, Leonardo (1908-1981) Italian

Works on paper

£303 $486 €440 Life notes. mixed media six in one frame prov. 11-Mar-3 Babuino, Rome #212/R

SINKO, Armand (1934-) French

£573 $894 €900 Bouquet sauvage (50x65cm-20x26in) s. 10-Nov-2 Eric Pillon, Calais #158/R

SINNOTT, Kevin (1947-) British

£2000 $3100 €3000 Adam and Eve (173x144cm-68x57in) init. prov. 3-Dec-2 Bonhams, New Bond Street #130/R est:2000-3000

£2800 $4396 €4200 Wishing (69x130cm-27x51in) init. 20-Nov-2 Sotheby's, Olympia #96/R est:2000-3000

SINSABAUGH, Art (1924-1983) American

Photographs

£7595 $12000 €11393 Chicago landscapes (14x29cm-6x11in) s.d.1964 num.53/8-111 three gelatin silver print. 25-Apr-3 Phillips, New York #274/R est:1500-2500

SINTENIS, Renée (1888-1965) German

Sculpture

£1418 $2298 €2000 Foal with raised back leg (11x8x4cm-4x3x2in) i. bronze marble socle. 24-May-3 Van Ham, Cologne #556/R est:3500
£1899 $3000 €3000 Shetland Pony (10cm-4in) st.mono. dark brown pat.bronze Cast.H.Noack Berlin. 30-Nov-2 Villa Grisebach, Berlin #311/R est:3500-4000
£2051 $3179 €3200 Foal with raised back leg (11cm-4in) mono. dark pat.bronze prov.exhib.lit. 4-Dec-2 Lempertz, Koln #1069/R est:3500-4000
£2436 $3776 €3800 Leaping Shetland pony (9cm-4in) mono. dark brown pat.bronze exhib.lit. 4-Dec-2 Lempertz, Koln #1070/R est:4500
£2899 $4754 €4000 Shetland pony in the wind (7cm-3in) st.mono. brown.pat.bronze. 31-May-3 Villa Grisebach, Berlin #164/R est:3000-4000
£3205 $4968 €5000 Rearing foal (15x14x4cm-6x6x2in) bronze. 7-Dec-2 Hauswedell & Nolte, Hamburg #1037/R est:6000
£3526 $5465 €5500 Foal scratchin muzzle with hoof (7cm-3in) st.mono. dark pat.bronze prov.exhib. 4-Dec-2 Lempertz, Koln #1068/R est:5000-6000
£3986 $6536 €5500 Reclining Shetland pony (5cm-2in) st.mono. dark brown gold pat.bronze. 31-May-3 Villa Grisebach, Berlin #163/R est:6000-8000
£4103 $6359 €6400 Foal (12cm-5in) mono. dark pat.bronze exhib. 4-Dec-2 Lempertz, Koln #1067/R est:5000-6000
£4167 $6458 €6500 Dwarf donkey (13x12x3cm-5x5x1in) bronze. 7-Dec-2 Hauswedell & Nolte, Hamburg #1038/R est:7500
£4173 $6843 €5800 Foal with raised back leg (11x7x2cm-4x3x1in) st.mono. dark brown pat.bronze Cast.H.Noack Berlin. 6-Jun-3 Ketterer, Munich #51/R est:3500-4500
£4430 $7000 €7000 Full blooded foal (21cm-8in) mono. dark brown pat.bronze Cast.H.Noack Berlin. 30-Nov-2 Villa Grisebach, Berlin #309/R est:6000-7000
£5128 $7949 €8000 Pegasus (18cm-7in) mono. bronze exhib.lit. 4-Dec-2 Lempertz, Koln #1071/R est:8000
£5634 $9352 €8000 Pegasus (20x22x10cm-8x9x4in) bronze. 14-Jun-3 Hauswedell & Nolte, Hamburg #1597/R est:9000
£5696 $9000 €9000 Kneeling elephant (7cm-3in) st.mono. dark brown pat.bronze Cast.H.Noack Berlin. 30-Nov-2 Villa Grisebach, Berlin #308/R est:9000-11000
£5823 $9200 €9200 Reclining foal (8cm-3in) st mono. gold brown pat.bronze Cast.H.Noack Berlin. 30-Nov-2 Villa Grisebach, Berlin #310/R est:6000-7000
£7050 $11563 €9800 Crouching dog (6x16x5cm-2x6x2in) st.mono. brown pat.bronze Cast.H.Noack Berlin. 6-Jun-3 Ketterer, Munich #50/R est:3800-4500
£8228 $13000 €13000 Walking elephant - African (11cm-4in) st.mono. dark brown pat.bronze Cast.H.Noack Berlin. 30-Nov-2 Villa Grisebach, Berlin #306/R est:10000-12000
£8228 $13000 €13000 Young elephant (9cm-4in) st.mono. dark brown pat.bronze Cast.H.Noack Berlin. 30-Nov-2 Villa Grisebach, Berlin #307/R est:10000-12000
£10897 $16891 €17000 Elephant running (10cm-4in) st.mono. bronze Cast.H.Noack Berlin. 4-Dec-2 Lempertz, Koln #1072/R est:10000-15000
£12179 $18878 €19000 Young elephant (9x15x6cm-4x6x2in) bronze. 7-Dec-2 Hauswedell & Nolte, Hamburg #1039/R est:15000
£32609 $53478 €45000 Donkey of Seelow (78cm-31in) s. yellow brown pat.bronze prov. 30-May-3 Villa Grisebach, Berlin #55/R est:40000-50000
£108696 $178261 €150000 Great Daphne (144cm-57in) s. brown pat.bronze Cast.H.Noack Berlin prov. 30-May-3 Villa Grisebach, Berlin #39/R est:150000-200000

Works on paper

£316 $500 €500 Foal (22x16cm-9x6in) mono. pencil. 29-Nov-2 Villa Grisebach, Berlin #896/R
£472 $736 €750 Rearing pony (32x25cm-13x10in) s. pencil. 11-Oct-2 Winterberg, Heidelberg #1732

SINTES, Joseph (1829-1913) ?

£1006 $1550 €1600 Marabout dans le sud (24x33cm-9x13in) s. paper on panel. 23-Oct-2 Rabourdin & Choppin de Janvry, Paris #105/R

SION, Peeter (attrib) (1649-1695) Flemish

£2837 $4738 €4000 L'adoration des Mages (22x17cm-9x7in) copper htd gold. 23-Jun-3 Delvaux, Paris #11/R est:4000-5000

SIOPIS, Penelope (1953-) South African

£1720 $2769 €2580 History series 1990 (44x29cm-17x11in) oil collage on board. 12-May-3 Stephan Welz, Johannesburg #537/R est:15000-18000 (SA.R 20000)

SIQUEIROS, David (1896-1974) Mexican

£15854 $26000 €22988 Nino (93x67cm-37x26in) s.d.1923 prov. 27-May-3 Sotheby's, New York #94
£19231 $30000 €28847 Campesino Mexicano (91x76cm-36x30in) s.i.d.60 pyroxlyn panel prov. 14-Oct-2 Butterfields, San Francisco #2145/R est:40000-60000
£24390 $40000 €36585 Arbol florido (65x52cm-26x20in) s. pyroxilin masonite painted c.1965 prov. 28-May-3 Christie's, Rockefeller NY #120/R est:40000-60000
£25478 $40000 €38217 Reverence (79x66cm-31x26in) s. s.i.d.1964 verso panel prov. 19-Nov-2 Sotheby's, New York #119/R est:60000
£50955 $80000 €76433 Head of man (36x30cm-14x12in) s.d.1935 piroxylin copper prov. 19-Nov-2 Sotheby's, New York #8/R
£57325 $90000 €85988 Geographic architecture (123x92cm-48x36in) s.d.59 pyroxylin board prov.exhib. 20-Nov-2 Christie's, Rockefeller NY #27/R est:100000-120000

Works on paper

£39634 $65000 €59451 Autorretrato (47x29cm-19x11in) s.d.1934 black crayon white tempera zinc plate prov.exhib.lit. 28-May-3 Christie's, Rockefeller NY #11/R est:50000-70000

SIRANI, Elisabetta (1638-1665) Italian

£24000 $37680 €36000 Cupid, holding a flaming torch and bow, seated on a shell (91x71cm-36x28in) s.d.1661 prov.lit. 12-Dec-2 Sotheby's, London #188/R est:15000-20000
£25000 $41750 €36250 Pandora (92x76cm-36x30in) 10-Jul-3 Sotheby's, London #169/R est:25000-35000

SIRANI, Elisabetta (attrib) (1638-1665) Italian

£13000 $21710 €18850 Daphne and Apollo (239x161cm-94x63in) 11-Jul-3 Christie's, Kensington #198/R est:5000-8000

Works on paper

£507 $791 €750 Ascalfo transformed in owl (14x21cm-6x8in) i. chk sanguine wash prov. 27-Mar-3 Christie's, Paris #191/R

SIRANI, Giovanni Andrea (1610-1670) Italian

£13000 $20280 €19500 Cimon and Pero (102x84cm-40x33in) 10-Apr-3 Sotheby's, London #79/R est:8000
£16500 $25905 €24750 Esther before Ahasuerus (104x142cm-41x56in) 12-Dec-2 Sotheby's, London #184/R est:12000-18000

SIRANI, Giovanni Andrea (attrib) (1610-1670) Italian

£2703 $4216 €4000 Angel Annunciate (63x50cm-25x20in) prov. 27-Mar-3 Dorotheum, Vienna #74/R est:1800-2500
£3873 $6430 €5500 Cleopatra (119x92cm-47x36in) 11-Jun-3 Dorotheum, Vienna #49/R est:6000-9000

SIRK, Albert (1887-?) Italian

£1277 $2068 €1800 Giovane marinaio (29x24cm-11x9in) s. tempera board. 22-May-3 Stadion, Trieste #239/R est:500-700

SIROMBO, Giovanni (1885-1954) Italian

£306 $487 €450 Grazing (40x50cm-16x20in) s. board. 1-Mar-3 Meeting Art, Vercelli #275

SIRONI, Mario (1885-1961) Italian

£633 $1000 €1000 Composition (10x16cm-4x6in) s. verso W/C Indian ink. 29-Nov-2 Villa Grisebach, Berlin #898/R
£1346 $2113 €2100 Figure (29x12cm-11x5in) s. tempera paper. 23-Nov-2 Meeting Art, Vercelli #467/R
£1795 $2818 €2800 Two figures (27x19cm-11x7in) s. tempera paper. 19-Nov-2 Finarte, Milan #110/R
£2162 $3373 €3200 Landscape (20x30cm-8x12in) s. tempera. 28-Mar-3 Farsetti, Prato #201/R
£2564 $3744 €4000 Composition (30x34cm-12x13in) s.i. mixed media. 4-Jun-2 Karl & Faber, Munich #429/R est:8000
£3846 $6038 €6000 Composition (33x47cm-13x19in) s. tempera paper. 19-Nov-2 Finarte, Milan #236/R
£4000 $6560 €6000 Man meditating (26x39cm-10x15in) s. board prov.exhib. 4-Feb-3 Christie's, London #328/R
£4072 $6801 €5904 The bass player (36x33cm-14x13in) mono. board prov.lit. 24-Jun-3 Koller, Zurich #136/R est:8000-14000 (S.FR 9000)
£4965 $8043 €7000 Mountain landscape (29x44cm-11x17in) s. board prov. 26-May-3 Christie's, Milan #354/R est:8000-12000
£5063 $7899 €8000 Composition (67x49cm-26x19in) s. tempera paper on canvas painted 1939. 14-Sep-2 Meeting Art, Vercelli #983/R

£5128 $7949 €8000 Woman and soldiers (46x45cm-18x18in) s. tempera paper on canvas. 4-Dec-2 Finarte, Milan #333/R est:14000

£5128 $8051 €8000 Mountains (24x40cm-9x16in) s. 23-Nov-2 Meeting Art, Vercelli #492/R est:7000

£5696 $9000 €9000 Composition (34x46cm-13x18in) s. tempera paper on canvas painted 1940. 30-Nov-2 Farsetti, Prato #611/R est:10000

£6383 $10340 €9000 Composition (50x39cm-20x15in) s. paper on canvas prov. 26-May-3 Christie's, Milan #48/R est:10000-15000

£6410 $9936 €10000 Composition (43x47cm-17x19in) s. tempera paper. 4-Dec-2 Finarte, Milan #322/R est:12000

£9177 $14500 €14500 Woman in the suburbs (25x22cm-10x9in) s. tempera ink exhib. 30-Nov-2 Farsetti, Prato #615/R est:15000

£9615 $15096 €15000 Hip hip hurray for the Duce (58x45cm-23x18in) s. cardboard prov.lit. 21-Nov-2 Finarte, Rome #250/R est:15000-16000

£12821 $20128 €20000 Decorative composition (47x51cm-19x20in) s. paper on canvas painted c.1940 exhib. 19-Nov-2 Finarte, Milan #220/R est:22000-26000

£16026 $25160 €25000 Mountains (45x55cm-18x22in) s. painted 1940. 19-Nov-2 Finarte, Milan #169/R est:22000-26000

£21277 $34468 €30000 Mural composition (60x70cm-24x28in) s. prov.exhib. 26-May-3 Christie's, Milan #233/R est:30000-40000

£40000 $62400 €60000 Personaggi (80x100cm-31x39in) s. painted c.1940 prov. 21-Oct-2 Sotheby's, London #18/R est:40000-60000

£44872 $70449 €70000 Composition (80x100cm-31x39in) s. painted 1956 prov.exhib.lit. 19-Nov-2 Finarte, Milan #212/R

Works on paper

£833 $1292 €1300 Cathedral interior (32x23cm-13x9in) s. gouache chl. 4-Dec-2 Finarte, Milan #227/R

£1282 $2013 €2000 Figures (23x15cm-9x6in) s. gouache paper on canvas. 19-Nov-2 Finarte, Milan #10/R

£1620 $2689 €2300 Verso il paradiso, montagne russe (43x22cm-17x9in) s. chl. 10-Jun-3 Finarte Semenzato, Milan #198/R est:2000-2600

£1622 $2530 €2400 Study for illustration (32x31cm-13x12in) s. Chinese ink. 28-Mar-3 Farsetti, Prato #293/R

£1757 $2741 €2600 Train whistling (24x21cm-9x8in) s. gouache paper on board. 26-Mar-3 Finarte Semenzato, Milan #58/R

£1757 $2741 €2600 Three heads (34x25cm-13x10in) gouache. 26-Mar-3 Finarte Semenzato, Milan #122/R

£1899 $3000 €3000 Mountains (25x33cm-10x13in) mixed media paper on canvas. 30-Nov-2 Farsetti, Prato #606/R

£2244 $3522 €3500 Nude (49x38cm-19x15in) s. gouache. 19-Nov-2 Finarte, Milan #39/R

£2877 $4488 €4200 Italy between Art and Science (30x23cm-12x9in) s. pencil chk double-sided exhib.lit. 10-Apr-3 Finarte Semenzato, Rome #280/R

£4759 $7614 €6900 Composition with figures (22x28cm-9x11in) s. pencil dr. 11-Mar-3 Babuino, Rome #191/R

£5128 $8051 €8000 Composition (26x32cm-10x13in) s. mixed media paper on canvas. 19-Nov-2 Finarte, Milan #153/R est:9000

£5229 $8366 €8000 Landscape (37x47cm-15x19in) s. mixed media paper on board exec.1950. 4-Jan-3 Meeting Art, Vercelli #744

£6452 $10194 €10000 Urban landscape with bike (22x28cm-9x11in) s. chk paper on canvas prov. 18-Dec-2 Christie's, Rome #111/R est:15000

£11355 $17941 €17600 Landscape with planes (24x31cm-9x12in) ink tempera paper on canvas exec.c.1930. 18-Dec-2 Christie's, Rome #149 est:20000

£18354 $29000 €29000 Suburbs (24x40cm-9x16in) s. mixed media paper on canvas. 30-Nov-2 Farsetti, Prato #618/R est:15000

SIROT, Sophie (1950-) French

£255 $398 €400 Pour la dame (90x63cm-35x25in) s. 5-Nov-2 Tajan, Paris #8

£255 $398 €400 Fil rouge (80x58cm-31x23in) s. 5-Nov-2 Tajan, Paris #7

SIRTAINE, Albert (1868-1959) French

£256 $403 €400 Cour de ferme (45x55cm-18x22in) s. 11-Dec-2 Hotel des Ventes Mosan, Brussels #242

SISKIND, Aaron (1903-1991) American

Photographs

£1899 $3000 €2849 Gloucester 1H (17x12cm-7x5in) s.d.1944/1956 gelatin silver print lit. 22-Apr-3 Christie's, Rockefeller NY #81/R est:4000-6000

£1899 $3000 €2849 Chicago 42 (39x49cm-15x19in) i. verso gelatin silver print prov.lit. 25-Apr-3 Phillips, New York #109/R est:5000-7000

£2025 $3200 €3038 St. Louis 4 (34x42cm-13x17in) s.i.d.1953 i.verso gelatin silver print prov.lit. 25-Apr-3 Phillips, New York #112/R est:6000-8000

£2025 $3200 €3038 New York (23x33cm-9x13in) i. gelatin silver print prov.lit. 25-Apr-3 Phillips, New York #117/R est:6000-8000

£2658 $4200 €3987 Chicago (27x41cm-11x16in) s.i.d.1948 num.33 verso gelatin silver print prov.lit. 25-Apr-3 Phillips, New York #95/R est:5000-7000

£3101 $4900 €4652 Chicago 30 (37x47cm-15x19in) s.i.d.1949 gelatin silver print prov.lit. 25-Apr-3 Phillips, New York #33/R est:4000-6000

£3481 $5500 €5222 Los Angeles 2 (37x49cm-15x19in) s.i.d.1949 i.verso gelatin silver print prov.lit. 25-Apr-3 Phillips, New York #94/R est:6000-8000

£4747 $7500 €7121 Chicago (14x33cm-6x13in) s.i.d.1949 verso gelatin silver print on board prov.lit. 25-Apr-3 Phillips, New York #93/R est:5000-7000

SISLEY, Alfred (1839-1899) French

£165000 $270600 €247500 Soir d'automne aux environs de Paris (50x65cm-20x26in) s. painted 1879 prov.exhib.lit. 4-Feb-3 Christie's, London #225/R est:240000

£240000 $393600 €360000 Chemin de Butte, retour en foret (37x54cm-15x21in) s.d.89 canvas on board prov.lit. 4-Feb-3 Sotheby's, London #13/R est:350000

£340000 $567800 €510000 Le Pont de Moret et les Moulins - Effet d'hiver (54x65cm-21x26in) s.d.90 prov.exhib.lit. 23-Jun-3 Sotheby's, London #2/R est:200000-300000

£350000 $574000 €525000 Chalands sur le Loing (39x56cm-15x22in) s. painted 1884 prov.lit. 4-Feb-3 Sotheby's, London #9/R est:450000

£576923 $900000 €865385 Bords de Seine a Bougival (39x57cm-15x22in) s.d.76 prov.exhib.lit. 6-Nov-2 Christie's, Rockefeller NY #20/R est:900000-1200000

£833333 $1300000 €1250000 Le loing moret (55x74cm-22x29in) s.d.1886 prov.exhib.lit. 5-Nov-2 Sotheby's, New York #21/R est:1000000-1500000

Prints

£4808 $7500 €7212 Bords de riviere, ou Les Oies (43x57cm-17x22in) s. col lithograph edition of 100. 5-Nov-2 Christie's, Rockefeller NY #25/R est:8000-12000

£6410 $10064 €10000 Bords de riviere ou les oies (215x319cm-85x126in) s. lithograph. 12-Dec-2 Piasa, Paris #148

Works on paper

£75000 $125250 €112500 Bords de Seine a Saint Mammes (28x35cm-11x14in) s. pastel executed c.1885. 26-Jun-3 Christie's, London #350/R est:25000-35000

SISQUELLA, Alfredo (1900-1964) Spanish

£362 $586 €550 Coastal landscape (33x46cm-13x18in) s. 21-Jan-3 Ansorena, Madrid #246/R

SISSON, Laurence P (1928-) American

Works on paper

£350 $550 €525 Harbor sunset (55x74cm-22x29in) s. W/C ink. 22-Nov-2 Skinner, Boston #386/R

£406 $650 €589 Sunset Harbour, Maine (36x72cm-14x28in) s.d.52 W/C. 16-May-3 Skinner, Boston #270/R

£656 $1050 €984 Old boatyard (66x99cm-26x39in) s. W/C. 11-Jan-3 James Julia, Fairfield #391 est:1500-2500

SITHOLE, Lucas (1931-1994) South African

Sculpture

£1206 $1905 €1809 Dancing in the air (103cm-41in) s. wood exhib. 1-Apr-3 Stephan Welz, Johannesburg #521/R est:10000-15000 (SA.R 15000)

£1290 $2077 €1935 Large head (57cm-22in) s. wood copper oxide pat. 12-May-3 Stephan Welz, Johannesburg #529/R est:12000-18000 (SA.R 15000)

£2580 $4153 €3870 Mother of the crocs (38x127cm-15x50in) s. msimbiti wood brown pat. prov.exhib. 12-May-3 Stephan Welz, Johannesburg #542/R est:30000-50000 (SA.R 30000)

£7371 $11499 €11057 Mother and child (142cm-56in) s. ironwood lit. 15-Oct-2 Stephan Welz, Johannesburg #509/R est:25000-35000 (SA.R 120000)

SITJE, Joronn (1897-1982) Norwegian

£259 $393 €389 Grandmother and Bitte (41x33cm-16x13in) s. i.verso panel. 31-Aug-2 Grev Wedels Plass, Oslo #104 (N.KR 3000)

SITTER, Inger (1929-) Norwegian

£5724 $8930 €8586 Coming into existence (180x131cm-71x52in) s. d.21 juli 65 verso exhib. 21-Oct-2 Blomqvist, Oslo #420/R est:70000-90000 (N.KR 66000)

Works on paper

£265 $433 €398 Composition (51x45cm-20x18in) s. mixed media. 17-Feb-3 Blomqvist, Lysaker #1208 (N.KR 3000)

£1990 $3144 €2985 Composition in red, ochre, black and white (50x70cm-20x28in) s. mixed media paper on panel executed 1964-65. 2-Dec-2 Blomqvist, Oslo #490/R est:25000-35000 (N.KR 23000)

£14027 $22724 €21041 White (147x115cm-58x45in) s. s.i.d.august 64 verso plastic collage oil canvas exhib. 26-May-3 Grev Wedels Plass, Oslo #21/R est:100000-150000 (N.KR 155000)

SITU MIAN (1953-) Chinese
£6849 $10000 €10274 Autumn harvest (91x86cm-36x34in) 18-May-2 Altermann Galleries, Santa Fe #242/R
£9583 $15525 €13895 Grandchildren (76x71cm-30x28in) 23-May-3 Altermann Galleries, Santa Fe #43

SITU, W Jason (20th C) American
£870 $1400 €1305 Peaceful morning (36x46cm-14x18in) s. i.verso exhib. 18-Feb-3 John Moran, Pasadena #123a est:1500-2000
£903 $1500 €1309 San Gabriel Canyon (36x46cm-14x18in) s. 11-Jun-3 Butterfields, San Francisco #4347/R est:3000-5000
£1019 $1600 €1529 Palos verdes sky (30x41cm-12x16in) s. 19-Nov-2 Butterfields, San Francisco #8363/R est:3000-5000
£1274 $2000 €1911 Sunny day (41x51cm-16x20in) s.i. 19-Nov-2 Butterfields, San Francisco #8364/R est:3000-5000

SITZMAN, Edward R (1874-1949) American
£1169 $1800 €1754 Autumn landscape (61x81cm-24x32in) s. painted c.1910. 8-Sep-2 Treadway Gallery, Cincinnati #635/R est:1500-2500

SIVELL, Robert (1888-1958) British
£620 $967 €930 Donegal (30x40cm-12x16in) panel. 17-Oct-2 Bonhams, Edinburgh #23/R
£800 $1248 €1200 Portrait of a young man (68x38cm-27x15in) board double-sided. 17-Oct-2 Bonhams, Edinburgh #5/R

SIVERS, Clara von (1854-1924) German
£5063 $8000 €8000 Flower arrangement with white lilac in a Chinese vase (118x88cm-46x35in) s. 28-Nov-2 Dorotheum, Vienna #210/R est:14000-17000

SIVERTSEN, Jan (1951-) Danish
£286 $478 €415 Composition (81x65cm-32x26in) s.i.d.1986 verso prov. 17-Jun-3 Rasmussen, Copenhagen #124 (D.KR 3000)
£635 $984 €953 Whose hou (195x132cm-77x52in) s.d.1990. 1-Oct-2 Rasmussen, Copenhagen #200/R (D.KR 7500)

SIVILLA, E (19/20th C) ?
£2857 $4543 €4200 Street hawker in Tangiers (24x21cm-9x8in) s.i. 19-Mar-3 Neumeister, Munich #735/R est:4000

SJAMAAR, Pieter Geerard (1819-1876) Dutch
£550 $858 €825 Parlour maid by candlelight (31x25cm-12x10in) s. board. 26-Mar-3 Sotheby's, Olympia #188/R
£828 $1292 €1300 Lady sewing by candlelight (28x24cm-11x9in) panel. 6-Nov-2 Vendue Huis, Gravenhage #395
£1210 $1888 €1900 Visitors at the work place (25x35cm-10x14in) s. panel. 6-Nov-2 Vendue Huis, Gravenhage #459 est:2000-3000
£1274 $1987 €2000 Party of musicians by candlelight (27x38cm-11x15in) s. panel. 6-Nov-2 Vendue Huis, Gravenhage #460/R est:2000-3000
£1338 $2087 €2100 Musicians and dance company by candlelight (25x35cm-10x14in) s. 6-Nov-2 Vendue Huis, Gravenhage #396/R est:2000-3000
£1338 $2087 €2100 Visitor (28x37cm-11x15in) s. panel. 6-Nov-2 Vendue Huis, Gravenhage #397 est:2000-3000
£2222 $3667 €3200 Evening at the inn (31x42cm-12x17in) s. panel. 1-Jul-3 Christie's, Amsterdam #62/R est:2500-3500

SJOBERG, Axel (1866-1950) Swedish
£453 $706 €680 Coastal landscape with ducks (31x33cm-12x13in) s. canvas on board. 13-Sep-2 Lilla Bukowskis, Stockholm #377 (S.KR 6600)
£2042 $3350 €2961 Seascape with ducks (70x90cm-28x35in) s. 4-Jun-3 AB Stockholms Auktionsverk #2331/R est:18000-20000 (S.KR 26000)
£2985 $4896 €4328 Swans, Sandhamn (95x127cm-37x50in) s.i.d.1905. 4-Jun-3 AB Stockholms Auktionsverk #2322/R est:30000-35000 (S.KR 38000)

SJOLANDER, Waldemar (1906-1988) Swedish
£252 $399 €378 Mexican fisherwoman (84x40cm-33x16in) s. 30-Nov-2 Goteborg Auktionsverk, Sweden #635/R (S.KR 3600)
£420 $656 €630 Portrait of Inge Schioler and Ragnvald Magnusson (35x25cm-14x10in) init. 6-Nov-2 AB Stockholms Auktionsverk #736/R (S.KR 6000)

Works on paper
£323 $510 €485 Figures by fruit tree (36x43cm-14x17in) s. gouache. 30-Nov-2 Goteborg Auktionsverk, Sweden #634/R (S.KR 4600)

SJOSTRAND, Carl Johan (1789-1857) Swedish
£1647 $2569 €2471 Mythological scene (110x90cm-43x35in) init.verso. 22-Sep-2 Hindemae, Ullerslev #7233/R est:20000 (D.KR 19500)

SJOSTROM, Ina (1883-1969) Finnish
£272 $433 €400 Corn stooks in coastal meadow (33x48cm-13x19in) s. 24-Mar-3 Bukowskis, Helsinki #294/R
£272 $433 €400 Sailing vessel by the coast (29x38cm-11x15in) s. 24-Mar-3 Bukowskis, Helsinki #295/R
£360 $590 €500 Sailing vessel in moonlight (80x40cm-31x16in) s. 5-Jun-3 Hagelstam, Helsinki #802
£449 $714 €660 Landscape (33x48cm-13x19in) s. 27-Feb-3 Hagelstam, Helsinki #919

SJOSTROM, Lars Petter (1820-1896) Swedish
Works on paper
£573 $928 €860 Johan from Fiskebacksil (39x54cm-15x21in) s.d.1868. 3-Feb-3 Lilla Bukowskis, Stockholm #357 (S.KR 8000)
£1332 $2105 €1998 Ship's portrait of the schooner Tre Broder (45x60cm-18x24in) s. W/C gouache. 30-Nov-2 Goteborg Auktionsverk, Sweden #378/R est:20000 (S.KR 19000)

SJOSTROM, Vilho (1873-1944) Finnish
£374 $614 €520 Man reading (61x50cm-24x20in) s.d.40. 4-Jun-3 Bukowskis, Helsinki #432/R
£425 $697 €650 View of farm in winter (28x23cm-11x9in) s. 9-Feb-3 Bukowskis, Helsinki #361/R
£578 $919 €850 St Paul (37x26cm-15x10in) s.d.1920. 27-Feb-3 Hagelstam, Helsinki #865
£588 $965 €900 Coastal landscape (47x63cm-19x25in) s. 9-Feb-3 Bukowskis, Helsinki #362/R
£629 $975 €1000 Trees on mountain peak (53x65cm-21x26in) s.d.1920. 6-Oct-2 Bukowskis, Helsinki #282/R
£633 $1000 €1000 Old pine tree (56x41cm-22x16in) s.d.1918. 1-Dec-2 Bukowskis, Helsinki #184/R
£823 $1300 €1300 In the backwoods (63x43cm-25x17in) s. 1-Dec-2 Bukowskis, Helsinki #183/R
£1187 $1947 €1650 Thinking (83x63cm-33x25in) s.d.1919. 4-Jun-3 Bukowskis, Helsinki #433/R est:800
£1439 $2302 €2000 Coastal landscape (55x47cm-22x19in) s.d.1932. 17-May-3 Hagelstam, Helsinki #136/R est:2500
£2734 $4374 €3800 Day in January (46x55cm-18x22in) s.d.1933 lit. 17-May-3 Hagelstam, Helsinki #135/R est:2500
£3521 $5669 €5000 From Paris (101x66cm-40x26in) s.i.d.1909. 10-May-3 Bukowskis, Helsinki #147/R est:5000-7000
£4430 $7000 €7000 Raumo Market (37x53cm-15x21in) s.d.1907. 1-Dec-2 Bukowskis, Helsinki #182/R est:4000-4500

SKAGERFORS, Olle (1920-1997) Swedish
£455 $719 €683 Landscape (42x50cm-17x20in) mono.d.44. 16-Nov-2 Crafoord, Lund #23/R (S.KR 6500)
£560 $885 €840 Landscape (56x66cm-22x26in) mono.d.45. 16-Nov-2 Crafoord, Lund #36/R (S.KR 8000)
£684 $1081 €1026 Nature morte (41x55cm-16x22in) init. canvas on panel. 28-Apr-3 Bukowskis, Stockholm #281/R (S.KR 9000)
£841 $1312 €1262 Still life (46x54cm-18x21in) init. panel. 5-Nov-2 Bukowskis, Stockholm #251/R (S.KR 12000)
£1699 $2735 €2549 Still life of cup and fruit (37x59cm-15x23in) init. exhib. 7-May-3 AB Stockholms Auktionsverk #850/R est:20000-25000 (S.KR 22000)
£2945 $4654 €4418 Fruit and bottle (66x79cm-26x31in) init. exhib. 30-Nov-2 Goteborg Auktionsverk, Sweden #636/R est:30000 (S.KR 42000)

Works on paper
£561 $886 €842 Self portrait (40x30cm-16x12in) s.d.83 ink. 30-Nov-2 Goteborg Auktionsverk, Sweden #637/R (S.KR 8000)
£608 $961 €912 Self portrait (40x29cm-16x11in) s.d.83 Indian ink. 28-Apr-3 Bukowskis, Stockholm #280/R (S.KR 8000)
£772 $1243 €1158 Mona (41x33cm-16x13in) init. pencil prov. 7-May-3 AB Stockholms Auktionsverk #827/R (S.KR 10000)
£1004 $1616 €1506 Mona sewing (27x35cm-11x14in) init. pencil prov. 7-May-3 AB Stockholms Auktionsverk #828/R (S.KR 13000)
£1197 $1927 €1796 Self-portrait (35x27cm-14x11in) init.d.1990 pencil prov. 7-May-3 AB Stockholms Auktionsverk #826/R est:6000-8000 (S.KR 15500)

SKALA, Karel (1908-2001) Czechoslovakian
£372 $580 €558 Prague in fall (71x87cm-28x34in) s.d.56. 12-Oct-2 Dorotheum, Prague #107 (C.KR 18000)
£1239 $1933 €1859 Finale (100x120cm-39x47in) s.d.1946. 12-Oct-2 Dorotheum, Prague #106/R est:60000-90000 (C.KR 60000)

SKANBERG, Carl (1850-1883) Swedish
£851 $1319 €1277 Beech wood, Fontainebleu (80x98cm-31x39in) s. 4-Dec-2 AB Stockholms Auktionsverk #1767/R (S.KR 12000)
£2172 $3519 €3149 Venice (41x32cm-16x13in) s.d.82 panel. 26-May-3 Bukowskis, Stockholm #70/R est:15000-20000 (S.KR 28000)
£5674 $8794 €8511 Venice (33x54cm-13x21in) s.i.d.82. 4-Dec-2 AB Stockholms Auktionsverk #1605/R est:80000-100000 (S.KR 80000)

SKARBINA, Franz (1849-1910) German
£1582 $2500 €2500 Women and children in field (20x33cm-8x13in) mono. 30-Nov-2 Villa Grisebach, Berlin #119/R est:3000-4000
£2759 $4359 €4000 Friedrich in Rheinsberg (100x69cm-39x27in) 5-Apr-3 Dr Fritz Nagel, Leipzig #3911/R est:7500

Works on paper
£1795 $2782 €2800 Woman with muff seated on chair (39x28cm-15x11in) s.d.1891 W/C gouache. 4-Dec-2 Lempertz, Koln #1073/R est:2500

SKARI, Edvard (1839-1903) Norwegian
£4224 $6927 €6125 Crowd all sails (77x117cm-30x46in) s. 2-Jun-3 Blomqvist, Oslo #98/R est:50000-60000 (N.KR 46000)

SKEAPING, John (1901-1980) British
£2000 $3320 €2900 At the start (38x55cm-15x22in) s.d.64. 12-Jun-3 Christie's, Kensington #114/R est:2000-3000

Sculpture
£4000 $6240 €6000 Over the hedge (37x25cm-15x10in) s.d.70 num.3/3 brown pat. bronze. 6-Nov-2 Sotheby's, Olympia #179/R est:3000-4000
£8000 $13120 €11600 Female figure (62cm-24in) rosewood exec.1934 prov.exhib. 4-Jun-3 Sotheby's, London #22/R est:8000-12000
£21000 $34020 €31500 Group of five race horses (91cm-36in) s.d.77/2/7 brown pat bronze wood base. 22-May-3 Christie's, London #52/R est:12000-18000

Works on paper
£350 $532 €525 Camargue horses (36x64cm-14x25in) s.i.d.60 pen ink drawing. 16-Aug-2 Keys, Aylsham #483/R
£350 $578 €508 Female buck (35x29cm-14x11in) s. pencil prov. 3-Jul-3 Christie's, Kensington #266
£360 $562 €540 Horses (42x56cm-17x22in) s.d.75 pencil chk. 6-Nov-2 Sotheby's, Olympia #97/R
£380 $608 €570 Horse and jockey jumping a fence (41x53cm-16x21in) s.d.59 W/C chl. 11-Mar-3 Gorringes, Lewes #2534
£380 $623 €570 Horse and rider (41x46cm-16x18in) pastel. 7-Feb-3 Biddle & Webb, Birmingham #360
£641 $1006 €1000 Spanish bull fighter on a horse (41x53cm-16x21in) s. gouache. 19-Nov-2 Hamilton Osborne King, Dublin #431/R
£1000 $1560 €1500 Jockey (44x60cm-17x24in) s.d.62 W/C. 6-Nov-2 Sotheby's, Olympia #98/R est:800-1200
£1400 $2282 €2030 Horse and rider (45x53cm-18x21in) s.d.62 W/C. 15-Jul-3 Bonhams, Knightsbridge #21/R est:600-800
£1994 $3250 €2991 Greyhound (48x57cm-19x22in) s.d.73 col chk. 11-Feb-3 Bonhams & Doyles, New York #172/R est:1500-2000

SKEDSMO, Dag (1951-) Norwegian
£277 $424 €416 Composition (110x52cm-43x20in) s. acrylic. 26-Aug-2 Blomqvist, Lysaker #1358/R (N.KR 3200)

SKELTON, John (fl.1735-1759) British

Works on paper
£3000 $4710 €4500 View of Ariccia, Italy (33x37cm-13x15in) pencil pen ink wash prov. 21-Nov-2 Christie's, London #21/R est:3000-5000

SKELTON, John (20th C) Irish
£959 $1505 €1400 Horse and rider in the woods (31x49cm-12x19in) s. canvasboard. 15-Apr-3 De Veres Art Auctions, Dublin #41/R est:1000-1500
£2264 $3532 €3600 Rock fishing, Country Kerry (30x41cm-12x16in) s.i.d.2001 canvasboard. 17-Sep-2 Whyte's, Dublin #153/R est:2000-2500

SKILL, Frederick John (1824-1881) British

Works on paper
£1400 $2184 €2100 Breton children playing at berceau (34x25cm-13x10in) init. W/C. 5-Nov-2 Bonhams, New Bond Street #126/R est:1000-1500

SKIRA, Pierre (1938-) French
£769 $1208 €1200 Nature morte aux livres (80x60cm-31x24in) s. pastel cardboard exec.1990 prov. 15-Dec-2 Perrin, Versailles #179/R

SKLAR, Dorothy (20th C) American
£509 $850 €738 Figure in wooded landscape (46x61cm-18x24in) s. masonite. 17-Jun-3 John Moran, Pasadena #66
£778 $1300 €1128 Figure in McArthur Park, Los Angeles (41x51cm-16x20in) s.d.49. 17-Jun-3 John Moran, Pasadena #123 est:1500-2000
£1398 $2250 €2097 Chinese laundry (36x43cm-14x17in) s.d.45 i.verso. 18-Feb-3 John Moran, Pasadena #57a est:1500-2000

Works on paper
£313 $500 €470 Hurrying along (32x48cm-13x19in) s.d.49 gouache. 18-May-3 Butterfields, Los Angeles #7010
£313 $500 €470 House with a view (34x51cm-13x20in) s.d.44 gouache. 18-May-3 Butterfields, Los Angeles #7011
£466 $750 €699 Street scene (46x64cm-18x25in) s.d. W/C prov. 18-Feb-3 John Moran, Pasadena #84
£548 $850 €822 Amalfi Drive, Palisades (51x66cm-20x26in) s.d.56 W/C. 29-Oct-2 John Moran, Pasadena #688

SKLAVOS (1927-1967) Greek

Sculpture
£3901 $6514 €5500 Les quatre saisons (48x28x26cm-19x11x10in) s.num.3/8 green pat bronze Cast Landowski exhib. 18-Jun-3 Charbonneaux, Paris #128/R est:6000-6500

SKLAVOS, Yerassimos (1927-1967) Greek

Sculpture
£3919 $6114 €5800 Station spatiale 2 (49x22x12cm-19x9x5in) s. num.3/8 black pat bronze Cast Landowsky. 28-Mar-3 Charbonneaux, Paris #168/R

SKODLERRAK, Horst (1920-) German
£308 $477 €480 Blue pump (24x18cm-9x7in) s.d.1971 panel. 7-Dec-2 Ketterer, Hamburg #623/R

SKOGLUND, Sandy (1946-) American

Photographs
£2532 $4000 €3798 Coathangers (65x83cm-26x33in) s.i.d.1980 num.10/20 cibachrome print prov.lit. 24-Apr-3 Phillips, New York #200/R est:2500-3500

SKOLD, Otte (1894-1958) Swedish
£343 $535 €515 Lake landscape, winter (30x94cm-12x37in) s. panel. 13-Sep-2 Lilla Bukowskis, Stockholm #205 (S.KR 5000)
£541 $870 €812 By Gota Canal (14x26cm-6x10in) s. panel. 7-May-3 AB Stockholms Auktionsverk #792/R (S.KR 7000)
£541 $897 €784 Venetian town scene (24x19cm-9x7in) s.i. verso panel. 16-Jun-3 Lilla Bukowskis, Stockholm #69 (S.KR 7000)
£1051 $1640 €1577 From the Tuileri Gardens (40x50cm-16x20in) s. panel exhib. 5-Nov-2 Bukowskis, Stockholm #63/R est:20000-25000 (S.KR 15000)
£1236 $1989 €1854 My window (19x27cm-7x11in) s. lit. 7-May-3 AB Stockholms Auktionsverk #766/R est:15000-18000 (S.KR 16000)
£3861 $6216 €5792 Women with water jugs (166x139cm-65x55in) stamped sig. painted c.1925. 7-May-3 AB Stockholms Auktionsverk #787/R est:60000-80000 (S.KR 50000)
£6657 $10385 €9986 Nature morte (79x86cm-31x34in) s. exhib.lit. 5-Nov-2 Bukowskis, Stockholm #207/R est:100000-125000 (S.KR 95000)
£10646 $16821 €15969 Torget, Stromstad - the market (28x49cm-11x19in) s.i.d.aug.1923 panel prov.exhib.lit. 28-Apr-3 Bukowskis, Stockholm #62/R est:140000-150000 (S.KR 140000)
£28732 $44821 €43098 Men on horsebacks (88x74cm-35x29in) s. exhib.lit. 5-Nov-2 Bukowskis, Stockholm #208/R est:300000-350000 (S.KR 410000)

Works on paper
£284 $440 €426 New York by night (23x21cm-9x8in) s.i. W/C. 8-Dec-2 Uppsala Auktionskammare, Uppsala #217 (S.KR 4000)
£1141 $1802 €1712 Still life (26x25cm-10x10in) s. W/C pencil executed c.1918 prov. 28-Apr-3 Bukowskis, Stockholm #57/R est:20000-25000 (S.KR 15000)

SKOTNES, Cecil (1926-) South African
£1843 $2875 €2765 Trees (101x101cm-40x40in) s. carved painted wood panel. 15-Oct-2 Stephan Welz, Johannesburg #501/R est:12000-16000 (SA.R 30000)
£2050 $3198 €3075 Head of a woman (138x91cm-54x36in) s. carved painted wood panel. 11-Nov-2 Stephan Welz, Johannesburg #502/R est:20000-30000 (SA.R 32000)
£2050 $3198 €3075 Female nude (91x60cm-36x24in) s.d.65 carved painted wood. 11-Nov-2 Stephan Welz, Johannesburg #564 est:18000-24000 (SA.R 32000)
£2562 $3997 €3843 Five figures in a landscape (91x92cm-36x36in) s. carved painted wood panel. 11-Nov-2 Stephan Welz, Johannesburg #541/R est:15000-20000 (SA.R 40000)
£2562 $3997 €3843 Mother and child (68x68cm-27x27in) carved painted wood panel pair prov. 11-Nov-2 Stephan Welz, Johannesburg #565/R est:25000-35000 (SA.R 40000)

Sculpture
£1892 $3046 €2838 Two African warriors (101x100cm-40x39in) s. carved painted wood panel. 12-May-3 Stephan Welz, Johannesburg #520/R est:20000-30000 (SA.R 22000)

Works on paper
£442 $699 €663 Puppets (35x55cm-14x22in) s.i.d.84 pencil W/C. 1-Apr-3 Stephan Welz, Johannesburg #494 est:6000-9000 (SA.R 5500)

SKOU, Sigurd (1878-1929) American
£2099 $3400 €3044 Under the church tower (66x81cm-26x32in) s.d.1927 panel prov. 21-May-3 Doyle, New York #104/R est:2000-3000

SKOVGAARD, Joakim (1856-1933) Danish
£373 $593 €560 Landscape with horses (26x16cm-10x6in) s.d.1877 prov. 5-May-3 Rasmussen, Vejle #458/R (D.KR 4000)
£517 $786 €776 Norwegian landscape with trees, river and mountains. init. painted c.1890. 28-Aug-2 Museumsbygningen, Copenhagen #103/R (D.KR 6000)
£1529 $2386 €2294 Landscape from Halland with two woodcutters and timber (44x62cm-17x24in) s.d.1882-85. 5-Aug-2 Rasmussen, Vejle #205/R est:20000-25000 (D.KR 18000)
£3724 $5922 €5586 Woodland glade with man collecting faggots (93x106cm-37x42in) s.d.1880 exhib. 10-Mar-3 Rasmussen, Vejle #118/R est:40000 (D.KR 40000)

SKOVGAARD, Niels (1858-1938) Danish
£326 $518 €489 Woodland lake with two swans (53x69cm-21x27in) mono. 10-Mar-3 Rasmussen, Vejle #255 (D.KR 3500)
£335 $543 €486 Study of a boy (39x27cm-15x11in) mono.d.april 1903 panel. 24-May-3 Rasmussen, Havnen #2235/R (D.KR 3500)
£340 $530 €510 Road through hilly Norwegian summer landscape (46x73cm-18x29in) mono.i.d.aug.1916 exhib. 5-Aug-2 Rasmussen, Vejle #212 (D.KR 4000)
£560 $851 €840 Landscape study (19x24cm-7x9in) panel prov. 27-Aug-2 Rasmussen, Copenhagen #1785/R (D.KR 6500)
£1676 $2665 €2514 Children playing outside (62x78cm-24x31in) mono.d.1883 and 1902. 10-Mar-3 Rasmussen, Vejle #132/R est:15000-20000 (D.KR 18000)

SKOVGAARD, P C (1817-1875) Danish
£596 $941 €894 Landscape from Furreso (13x19cm-5x7in) mono. 2-Dec-2 Rasmussen, Copenhagen #1241/R (D.KR 7000)
£850 $1325 €1275 Road through summer landscape (26x39cm-10x15in) d.17 aug.1874 with sig.verso exhib. 5-Aug-2 Rasmussen, Vejle #209/R (D.KR 10000)
£1072 $1672 €1608 Landscape with river and trees (30x24cm-12x9in) s.d.Aug 1865. 11-Nov-2 Rasmussen, Vejle #671/R est:5000 (D.KR 12500)

Works on paper
£936 $1479 €1404 Stag (33x26cm-13x10in) i. s.verso pencil W/C. 2-Dec-2 Rasmussen, Copenhagen #1859/R (D.KR 11000)

SKOVGAARD, Peter (1960-) Danish
£600 $937 €900 Composition (100x122cm-39x48in) s. 11-Nov-2 Rasmussen, Vejle #153/R (D.KR 7000)

SKOVGAARD, Peter Christian (1817-1875) Danish
£1021 $1614 €1532 View near Roskile Cathedral (17x22cm-7x9in) s.i.d.1839 verso prov. 27-Nov-2 Museumsbygningen, Copenhagen #23/R est:6000 (D.KR 12000)
£1073 $1706 €1610 Figure by tumbledown thatched house (19x28cm-7x11in) init.d.7 august 1868. 5-May-3 Rasmussen, Vejle #460/R (D.KR 11500)
£1191 $1883 €1787 On the outskirts of Dyrehaven, Knapstrup (26x40cm-10x16in) d.17 aug.1874 exhib.prov. 2-Dec-2 Rasmussen, Copenhagen #1271/R est:15000-20000 (D.KR 14000)
£1292 $1964 €1938 River through wood (35x38cm-14x15in) mono.d.1871. 27-Aug-2 Rasmussen, Copenhagen #1863/R est:12000 (D.KR 15000)
£1957 $3093 €2936 Summer's day in Dyrehaven (31x50cm-12x20in) exhib. 2-Dec-2 Rasmussen, Copenhagen #1270/R est:25000-30000 (D.KR 23000)
£2607 $4145 €3911 Summer landscape, Torvemose (28x41cm-11x16in) mono.d.15 juni 1851 exhib.prov. 5-Mar-3 Rasmussen, Copenhagen #1549/R est:20000-25000 (D.KR 28000)
£3158 $5116 €4579 Landscape from Laeso, thatched farmhouse (30x48cm-12x19in) s. exhib.prov. 26-May-3 Rasmussen, Copenhagen #1103/R est:30000 (D.KR 33000)
£3445 $5237 €5168 The road to the bathing huts at Nyso (35x58cm-14x23in) d.25 August 1850 exhib.prov. 27-Aug-2 Rasmussen, Copenhagen #1423/R est:40000 (D.KR 40000)
£10048 $16278 €14570 Study of clouds near the sea (25x39cm-10x15in) i.verso painted c.1839. 26-May-3 Rasmussen, Copenhagen #1102/R est:30000-40000 (D.KR 105000)

SKOVGAARD, Peter Christian (attrib) (1817-1875) Danish
Works on paper
£613 $986 €920 The ride to Civitella and Olevanum (6x13cm-2x5in) pen W/C. 26-Feb-3 Museumsbygningen, Copenhagen #105 (D.KR 6800)

SKOVGAARD, Suzette Cathrine Holten (1863-1937) Danish
£388 $589 €582 Roses and peonies in front of great grandmother's portrait (34x53cm-13x21in) mono.d.1931 panel exhib. 27-Aug-2 Rasmussen, Copenhagen #1808/R (D.KR 4500)

SKOVGAARD, T (?) Scandinavian
£261 $429 €400 Coastal breakers (97x137cm-38x54in) s. 9-Feb-3 Bukowskis, Helsinki #430/R

SKOYLES, Ian (1964-) British
Works on paper
£778 $1300 €1128 Untitled I (49x72cm-19x28in) s.d. glazed jigsaw puzzles on aluminum. 25-Jun-3 Sotheby's, Moscow #187/R est:900-1200

SKRAMLIK, Jan (1860-?) Czechoslovakian
£1309 $2081 €1964 Knight and innkeeper (81x60cm-32x24in) s.d. 8-Mar-3 Dorotheum, Prague #18/R est:60000-90000 (C.KR 60000)

SKRAMSTAD, Ludwig (1855-1912) Norwegian
£372 $606 €558 Winter at the cheese farm (34x62cm-13x24in) 17-Feb-3 Blomqvist, Lysaker #1213/R (N.KR 4200)
£424 $654 €636 Crows in the field (37x64cm-15x25in) s. panel. 28-Oct-2 Blomqvist, Lysaker #1295 (N.KR 5000)
£427 $666 €641 Crows in the field (37x64cm-15x25in) s. panel. 23-Sep-2 Blomqvist, Lysaker #1221/R (N.KR 5000)
£570 $883 €900 Calm river in autumn (28x34cm-11x13in) s. 25-Sep-2 Neumeister, Munich #726
£654 $1027 €981 Man in rowing boat (30x45cm-12x18in) s. panel. 25-Nov-2 Blomqvist, Lysaker #1253/R (N.KR 7500)
£1214 $1894 €1821 Wooded landscape with tarn in calm (82x127cm-32x50in) s.d.1880. 21-Oct-2 Blomqvist, Oslo #344/R est:18000-22000 (N.KR 14000)
£2618 $4110 €3927 September (83x135cm-33x53in) s. i.verso. 21-Nov-2 Grev Wedels Plass, Oslo #90/R est:30000-40000 (N.KR 30000)

SKREBNESKI, Victor (1929-) American?
Photographs
£4114 $6500 €6171 Vanessa Redgrave, Hollywood (43x43cm-17x17in) s.d.1967/1992 num.20/25 gelatin silver print lit. 22-Apr-3 Christie's, Rockefeller NY #96/R est:7000-9000

SKREDSVIG, Christian (1854-1924) Norwegian
£2715 $4398 €4073 Study for - Farm in Venoix (18x63cm-7x25in) s.i.d.80 canvas on panel. 26-May-3 Grev Wedels Plass, Oslo #5/R est:30000-40000 (N.KR 30000)
£3141 $4932 €4712 Landscape from Veblungsnaes in Romsdalen (43x54cm-17x21in) init.d.1876 i.verso. 21-Nov-2 Grev Wedels Plass, Oslo #84/R est:40000 (N.KR 36000)
£5500 $8580 €8250 Cattle on a country track (63x105cm-25x41in) s.i. 17-Sep-2 Sotheby's, Olympia #278/R est:6000-8000
£10860 $17593 €16290 Study for - Son of the people (85x46cm-33x18in) s.d.90 i.stretcher lit. 26-May-3 Grev Wedels Plass, Oslo #1/R est:80000-100000 (N.KR 120000)

Works on paper
£904 $1465 €1356 Cattle by water, Eggedal (33x53cm-13x21in) s. mixed media. 27-Jan-3 Blomqvist, Lysaker #1235/R (N.KR 10000)

SKREIN, Christian (1945-) Austrian
Photographs
£2516 $3899 €4000 Composition with glass window (40x41cm-16x16in) s.i.d.1968 s. verso gelatin silver. 2-Nov-2 Lempertz, Koln #371/R est:1500

SKULASON, Thorvaldur (1906-1984) Icelandic
£2872 $4480 €4308 Composition (100x80cm-39x31in) init.d.54 verso. 18-Sep-2 Kunsthallen, Copenhagen #72/R est:30000 (D.KR 34000)
£4647 $7342 €6971 Composition in yellow and brown (130x100cm-51x39in) s.verso painted 1958 exhib. 1-Apr-3 Rasmussen, Copenhagen #187/R est:40000-50000 (D.KR 50000)

SKUM, Nils Nilsson (1872-1951) Swedish
£2979 $4617 €4469 Outdoor painting by Kaukirjaure (53x65cm-21x26in) s.d.1940 panel. 3-Dec-2 Bukowskis, Stockholm #92/R est:30000-40000 (S.KR 42000)
Works on paper
£288 $438 €432 Laplander and reindeer (31x49cm-12x19in) s.d.1940 dr. 16-Aug-2 Lilla Bukowskis, Stockholm #115 (S.KR 4200)
£461 $715 €692 Sleigh ride (22x36cm-9x14in) s.d.1938 chk pencil dr. 3-Dec-2 Bukowskis, Stockholm #87/R (S.KR 6500)
£473 $766 €710 Moving the reindeer flock (25x33cm-10x13in) s. chk pencil. 3-Feb-3 Lilla Bukowskis, Stockholm #525 (S.KR 6600)
£520 $842 €754 Flock of reindeer (26x34cm-10x13in) s.i.d.1949 mixed media. 25-May-3 Uppsala Auktionskammare, Uppsala #215/R (S.KR 6700)
£567 $879 €851 Below the mountains (24x34cm-9x13in) s.d.1944 chk pencil dr. 3-Dec-2 Bukowskis, Stockholm #90/R (S.KR 8000)
£709 $1099 €1064 Laplanders village (32x48cm-13x19in) s.d.13/3-1938 chk chl. 3-Dec-2 Bukowskis, Stockholm #93/R (S.KR 10000)
£709 $1099 €1064 Landscape with reindeer and Laplanders (25x34cm-10x13in) s.d.1905 i.verso mixed media. 8-Dec-2 Uppsala Auktionskammare, Uppsala #190/R (S.KR 10000)
£892 $1445 €1293 Driving the flock of reindeer (26x35cm-10x14in) s.d.1942 chk pencil. 26-May-3 Bukowskis, Stockholm #143/R (S.KR 11500)
£922 $1429 €1383 Moving the reindeer on the mountain (26x21cm-10x8in) s.d.1943 pen crayon. 4-Dec-2 AB Stockholms Auktionsverk #1645/R (S.KR 13000)
£1312 $2034 €1968 Moving the reindeer flock (25x35cm-10x14in) s.d.1947 chk pencil dr. 3-Dec-2 Bukowskis, Stockholm #89/R est:10000-12000 (S.KR 18500)

SKURJENI, Matija (1888-1978) Hungarian
£2055 $3226 €3000 Hula-hop (45x37cm-18x15in) s.d.1959 panel exhib.lit. 15-Apr-3 Laurence Calmels, Paris #4223/R

SKUTEZKY, Dominik (1850-1921) Hungarian
£826 $1288 €1239 First step, 1888 (6x12cm-2x5in) s.d.88 board. 11-Sep-2 Kieselbach, Budapest #20/R (H.F 320000)
£1100 $1704 €1650 Crossing the ice (70x45cm-28x18in) s.i. 3-Dec-2 Sotheby's, Olympia #220/R est:600-800
Works on paper
£2205 $3418 €3308 Annual market by pier (22x28cm-9x11in) W/C. 1-Oct-2 SOGA, Bratislava #22/R est:90000 (SL.K 140000)

SKYLLAS, Drossos P (1912-1973) American?
£33951 $55000 €50927 Untitled - roses (71x50cm-28x20in) s. prov. 27-Jan-3 Christie's, Rockefeller NY #121/R est:15000-20000

SKYTTE, L Pedersen (19th C) Danish
£596 $941 €894 Village street scene with man and his dog. St Jorgensbjerg (45x59cm-18x23in) s. 2-Dec-2 Rasmussen, Copenhagen #1213/R (D.KR 7000)

SLABBINCK, Rik (1914-1991) Belgian
£503 $775 €800 Portrait de Stijn Streuvels (73x61cm-29x24in) s. 22-Oct-2 Campo, Vlaamse Kaai #623
£612 $973 €900 Paysage (35x45cm-14x18in) s. panel. 18-Mar-3 Galerie Moderne, Brussels #634/R
£952 $1514 €1400 Paysage en Flandres (60x80cm-24x31in) s. 18-Mar-3 Galerie Moderne, Brussels #551/R
£1250 $1987 €1800 Ballustrade a la mer (74x92cm-29x36in) 29-Apr-3 Campo & Campo, Antwerp #276/R est:2500-3500
£1379 $2207 €2000 Still life with black bottle (38x55cm-15x22in) s. 15-Mar-3 De Vuyst, Lokeren #291/R est:2000-2400
£1389 $2208 €2000 Carina (73x90cm-29x35in) s. 29-Apr-3 Campo, Vlaamse Kaai #289 est:2200-2500
£1517 $2428 €2200 Southern landscape (38x55cm-15x22in) s. panel. 15-Mar-3 De Vuyst, Lokeren #293/R est:1200-1400
£1528 $2429 €2200 Paysage d'ete (27x38cm-11x15in) s. panel. 29-Apr-3 Campo & Campo, Antwerp #273/R est:2250-2750
£1736 $2760 €2500 Nature morte, bleu (37x54cm-15x21in) s. 29-Apr-3 Campo & Campo, Antwerp #272/R est:2750-3250
£1793 $2869 €2600 Southern landscape (38x54cm-15x21in) s. panel. 15-Mar-3 De Vuyst, Lokeren #292/R est:1500-1700
£2083 $3312 €3000 Femme en orange (50x40cm-20x16in) s. 29-Apr-3 Campo & Campo, Antwerp #274/R est:2000-3000
£2089 $3258 €3300 Nu sur un fond rouge et noir (80x60cm-31x24in) s. 15-Oct-2 Vanderkindere, Brussels #96 est:2500-3500
£2264 $3509 €3600 Still life (73x60cm-29x24in) s. 5-Oct-2 De Vuyst, Lokeren #578/R est:3500-4500
£2500 $3975 €3600 Vue d'un champ en Flandre (50x75cm-20x30in) s. 29-Apr-3 Campo & Campo, Antwerp #269/R est:3000-3500
£3526 $5465 €5500 Still life (101x80cm-40x31in) s.d.1946. 7-Dec-2 De Vuyst, Lokeren #475/R est:6000-7000
£4167 $6625 €6000 Arbres, l'atelier (80x130cm-31x51in) s. 29-Apr-3 Campo & Campo, Antwerp #270/R est:7000-8000
£5396 $8633 €7500 Reclining nude (60x100cm-24x39in) s. 17-May-3 De Vuyst, Lokeren #493/R est:6500-7500
Works on paper
£252 $387 €400 Nu (42x29cm-17x11in) s. col dr. 22-Oct-2 Campo, Vlaamse Kaai #622
£443 $700 €700 Nu debout (39x30cm-15x12in) s. ink. 26-Nov-2 Palais de Beaux Arts, Brussels #375
£1006 $1550 €1600 Marine (38x56cm-15x22in) s.verso gouache. 22-Oct-2 Campo, Vlaamse Kaai #626

SLABINCK, Rik (?) ?
£1250 $2025 €1900 Nature morte (32x50cm-13x20in) s. cardboard. 21-Jan-3 Galerie Moderne, Brussels #233/R est:750-1000

SLADE, A H (19th C) American
£7643 $12000 €11465 View of the San Diego coastline from the Hotel del Coronado (62x113cm-24x44in) s.i.d.1890 prov. 19-Nov-2 Butterfields, San Francisco #8189/R est:15000-20000

SLADE, Caleb Arnold (1882-1961) American
£510 $800 €765 South of France (33x41cm-13x16in) s. board. 22-Nov-2 Skinner, Boston #298/R
£1752 $2750 €2628 Notre Dame (23x33cm-9x13in) s. board. 10-Dec-2 Doyle, New York #50/R est:2000-3000
£2949 $4600 €4424 Self portrait of Caleb Arnold Smith with harbour scene (41x33cm-16x13in) s. 28-Mar-3 Eldred, East Dennis #568/R est:800-1200

SLADEK, Jan Vaclav (1909-) Czechoslovakian
£252 $391 €378 Still life (30x47cm-12x19in) cardboard. 1-Oct-2 SOGA, Bratislava #217/R est:15000 (SL.K 16000)

SLAGER, Frederic François (1876-1953) Dutch
£253 $395 €400 Farm boys lying near ships (37x55cm-15x22in) s.indis.d. 21-Oct-2 Glerum, Amsterdam #102
£382 $596 €600 Small farm (21x37cm-8x15in) s. 6-Nov-2 Vendue Huis, Gravenhage #659

SLAGER, Piet (younger) (1871-1938) Dutch
£288 $449 €420 Herder with his sheep herd on a country road with farm in background (35x47cm-14x19in) s. 14-Apr-3 Glerum, Amsterdam #144/R

SLANA, France (1926-) European
Works on paper
£353 $554 €550 Houses in winter (20x61cm-8x24in) s.d.1963 mixed media. 20-Nov-2 Dorotheum, Klagenfurt #71/R

SLANEY, M Noel (1915-) British
£880 $1373 €1320 Mixed flowers (69x44cm-27x17in) s. board. 17-Oct-2 Bonhams, Edinburgh #102/R

SLATER, Charles H (fl.1860-1870) British
Works on paper
£290 $450 €435 Still life branches of purple and yellow plums on a bank (25x20cm-10x8in) s.d.1865. 25-Sep-2 Brightwells, Leominster #915
£400 $636 €600 Still life primroses and a bird's nest (22x15cm-9x6in) s. W/C. 25-Feb-3 Bonhams, Knightsbridge #14/R

SLATER, John Falconar (1857-1937) British
£280 $450 €420 Country landscape with young fisherman by a stream (69x56cm-27x22in) s. 19-Jan-3 Jeffery Burchard, Florida #52/R
£320 $499 €480 View of Whitby (28x44cm-11x17in) s.verso. 18-Sep-2 Cheffins Grain & Comins, Cambridge #532
£330 $515 €495 Mountain scene with sheep and stream (53x71cm-21x28in) s. 10-Sep-2 David Duggleby, Scarborough #326
£360 $562 €540 Hay carts going home (30x49cm-12x19in) s. board. 10-Apr-3 Tennants, Leyburn #1004
£360 $598 €540 Cottage on a river bank at dusk (33x39cm-13x15in) s. canvas on board. 10-Jun-3 Bonhams, Leeds #167
£380 $589 €570 Moonrise on the Durham coast (52x77cm-20x30in) s. 24-Sep-2 Anderson & Garland, Newcastle #478
£400 $668 €580 Cullercoats Bay (27x38cm-11x15in) s.d.1930 board. 17-Jun-3 Anderson & Garland, Newcastle #462
£420 $655 €630 Moorland landscape at sunset, with stream (57x80cm-22x31in) s. 10-Sep-2 David Duggleby, Scarborough #327
£420 $651 €630 Waves breaking on a north eastern shore (70x90cm-28x35in) s. 24-Sep-2 Anderson & Garland, Newcastle #477
£420 $655 €630 Coastal scene at sunset (27x41cm-11x16in) s. board. 10-Apr-3 Tennants, Leyburn #955
£450 $707 €675 Cattle by a stream (46x30cm-18x12in) s. 21-Nov-2 Tennants, Leyburn #814

£450 $752 €653 Shire horse in a stall with a stable hand and poultry (45x56cm-18x22in) s. board. 17-Jun-3 Anderson & Garland, Newcastle #461
£460 $718 €690 Harvest time, country lane scene with horses and carts (29x48cm-11x19in) s. 10-Sep-2 David Duggleby, Scarborough #339
£480 $763 €720 Sweetpeas (56x48cm-22x19in) s. board. 30-Apr-3 Halls, Shrewsbury #268/R
£577 $894 €900 Waves breaking on rocky coast (45x61cm-18x24in) s. 6-Dec-2 Michael Zeller, Lindau #920/R
£600 $936 €900 Hunting scenes (41x55cm-16x22in) s. pair. 10-Apr-3 Tennants, Leyburn #1049
£620 $960 €930 Bridge over a highland stream (77x64cm-30x25in) s. 3-Dec-2 Sotheby's, Olympia #147/R
£700 $1092 €1050 Panoramic river scene (48x89cm-19x35in) s. 20-Sep-2 Richardson & Smith, Whitby #158
£700 $1113 €1050 Ford (51x76cm-20x30in) s.d.1904. 6-Mar-3 Christie's, Kensington #87/R
£705 $1099 €1058 Harvesters (48x73cm-19x29in) s. paper on board. 11-Nov-2 Stephan Welz, Johannesburg #28 (SA.R 11000)
£726 $1147 €1089 Haycart returning from the fields (72x91cm-28x36in) s. prov. 18-Nov-2 Waddingtons, Toronto #125/R (C.D 1800)
£750 $1163 €1125 Sunrise over the sea (89x126cm-35x50in) s. 24-Sep-2 Anderson & Garland, Newcastle #476/R
£750 $1223 €1125 Seascape (76x127cm-30x50in) s. 29-Jan-3 Sotheby's, Olympia #221/R
£750 $1253 €1088 Horse cart approaching a river ford (48x66cm-19x26in) s. 17-Jun-3 Anderson & Garland, Newcastle #463/R
£780 $1201 €1170 Cattle watering on the Derwent (51x76cm-20x30in) s. 24-Oct-2 Thomson, Roddick & Medcalf, Carlisle #322
£800 $1304 €1200 Cattle and poultry in a meadow (33x43cm-13x17in) s. board. 7-Feb-3 Dee Atkinson & Harrison, Driffield #696/R
£900 $1413 €1350 Hen with chicks by a barn (24x29cm-9x11in) s. board. 21-Nov-2 Tennants, Leyburn #775
£1153 $1799 €1730 Winter landscape with horse and cart outside a house (53x78cm-21x31in) s. paper on board. 11-Nov-2 Stephan Welz, Johannesburg #27 est:3000-5000 (SA.R 18000)
£1250 $1938 €1875 Cullercoats cobles at sunrise (53x73cm-21x29in) s. board. 24-Sep-2 Anderson & Garland, Newcastle #479/R est:200-300
£1350 $2133 €2025 Cockbirds and hens (15x20cm-6x8in) s. board pair. 24-Apr-3 Richardson & Smith, Whitby #60/R est:1500-2000
£1380 $2250 €2070 Coastal scene with lighthouse in the background (68x134cm-27x53in) s. 16-Feb-3 Butterfields, San Francisco #2048 est:800-1200
£1452 $2294 €2178 Couple on the beach (76x127cm-30x50in) s. 18-Nov-2 Waddingtons, Toronto #124/R est:3000-4000 (C.D 3600)
£1500 $2280 €2250 Coastal scene (76x136cm-30x54in) s.d.98. 15-Aug-2 Bonhams, New Bond Street #354/R est:1500-2000
£1500 $2370 €2250 Horse and cart by a thatched cottage in wooded river landscape (58x89cm-23x35in) s. 28-Nov-2 Richardson & Smith, Whitby #625
£1600 $2432 €2400 Rocky coast at sunset (92x127cm-36x50in) indis.sig. 15-Aug-2 Bonhams, New Bond Street #355/R est:1000-1500
£1800 $2916 €2700 Farmyard (52x76cm-20x30in) s. 20-May-3 Sotheby's, Olympia #285/R est:800-1200
£2400 $3912 €3480 Winter's evening in the farmyard (102x127cm-40x50in) s. 21-Jul-3 Bonhams, Bath #59/R est:3000-5000

SLATER, John Falconar (attrib) (1857-1937) British
£320 $499 €480 Landscape with bridge over a rocky stream in a heather clad valley (36x53cm-14x21in) s. 17-Sep-2 Goldings, Lincolnshire #648

SLAUGHTER, Stephen (attrib) (?-1765) British
£1600 $2608 €2320 Portrait of a girl, head and shoulders wearing a yellow dress (61x45cm-24x18in) oval. 21-Jul-3 Sotheby's, London #133 est:1000-1500

SLAUGHTER, William A (1923-) American
£962 $1500 €1443 Texas Hill Country (61x91cm-24x36in) s. 14-Sep-2 Selkirks, St. Louis #144 est:1000-1500
£1603 $2500 €2405 Hill Country bluebonnets (51x61cm-20x24in) 19-Oct-2 David Dike, Dallas #335/R est:3000-6000
£3205 $5000 €4808 Texas spring (76x102cm-30x40in) 9-Nov-2 Altermann Galleries, Santa Fe #203

SLAVICEK, Jan (1900-) Czechoslovakian
£567 $902 €851 Suburb (49x59cm-19x23in) s.d.1917. 8-Mar-3 Dorotheum, Prague #97/R est:20000-30000 (C.KR 26000)
£743 $1160 €1115 Still life with pear and goblet (19x24cm-7x9in) s.d.1939 panel. 12-Oct-2 Dorotheum, Prague #114 (C.KR 36000)
£1033 $1611 €1550 Prague (40x50cm-16x20in) s. canvas on cardboard. 12-Oct-2 Dorotheum, Prague #39/R (C.KR 50000)

SLAVONA, Maria (1865-1931) German
£411 $650 €650 Dahlias in blue vase (38x31cm-15x12in) s. oil pastel. 29-Nov-2 Bolland & Marotz, Bremen #922/R

SLEATOR, James Sinton (1889-1950) British
£280 $409 €420 Still life with book (30x36cm-12x14in) board. 12-Jun-2 John Ross, Belfast #125
£943 $1472 €1500 Still life with fan (46x36cm-18x14in) s. prov. 17-Sep-2 Whyte's, Dublin #104/R est:1500-2000

SLEEBE, Ferdinand Joseph (1907-) Dutch
£605 $944 €950 Red table (48x43cm-19x17in) s.d.51. 6-Nov-2 Vendue Huis, Gravenhage #263/R
£955 $1490 €1500 Cathedral (127x64cm-50x25in) s. 6-Nov-2 Vendue Huis, Gravenhage #264/R est:700-1000

SLETTEMARK, Kjartan (1932-) Swedish
£1293 $2043 €1940 Nixon - Muchas gracias. Pair of trousers printed with Nixon's portrait (33x25cm-13x10in) s. enamel mixed media painted 1970s two prov. 28-Apr-3 Bukowskis, Stockholm #930/R est:4000-5000 (S.KR 17000)
£7722 $12432 €11583 Nixon vision (170x140cm-67x55in) s. acrylic. 7-May-3 AB Stockholms Auktionsverk #1080/R est:125000-150000 (S.KR 100000)

Works on paper
£283 $462 €425 Untitled (76x87cm-30x34in) s. collage print on plexiglas. 17-Feb-3 Blomqvist, Lysaker #1215 (N.KR 3200)
£345 $577 €500 Composition (49x63cm-19x25in) s.indis.d.6. 18-Jun-3 Grev Wedels Plass, Oslo #88 (N.KR 4000)

SLEVOGT, Max (1868-1932) German
£6522 $10696 €9000 Black D'Andrade - study (54x39cm-21x15in) s. board. 31-May-3 Villa Grisebach, Berlin #113/R est:7000-9000
£7595 $11772 €12000 Woman in punt (32x42cm-13x17in) s. prov.lit. 28-Sep-2 Ketterer, Hamburg #27/R est:10000-15000

Works on paper
£399 $654 €550 Young man fighting fiends (7x12cm-3x5in) s. pen prov. 31-May-3 Villa Grisebach, Berlin #691/R
£435 $713 €600 Rubezahl showing Emma his castle (12x14cm-5x6in) s. pen gouache prov. 31-May-3 Villa Grisebach, Berlin #690/R
£725 $1188 €1000 Caricature. Arabesque (22x27cm-9x11in) s. pen one W/C two. 29-May-3 Lempertz, Koln #925/R
£972 $1546 €1400 Scene from 'The Magic Flute'. Papageno (11x7cm-4x3in) s. i. verso W/C ink. 5-May-3 Ketterer, Munich #957/R est:500-700

SLINGELANDT, Pieter van (style) (1640-1691) Dutch
£5211 $8390 €7400 Courting couple (40x31cm-16x12in) with sig. 10-May-3 Bukowskis, Helsinki #336/R est:4000-6000

SLINGENEYER, Ernest (1820-1894) Belgian
£18987 $30000 €28481 Proud fisherman (212x125cm-83x49in) s.d.1854. 24-Apr-3 Sotheby's, New York #165/R est:30000-40000

SLINGSBY, Robert (1955-) South African
£723 $1143 €1085 Struck by the light (100x160cm-39x63in) s.d.1993. 1-Apr-3 Stephan Welz, Johannesburg #511/R est:10000-15000 (SA.R 9000)
£1409 $2199 €2114 Sky watch (55x65cm-22x26in) s.d.2000 i.verso. 11-Nov-2 Stephan Welz, Johannesburg #591/R est:8000-12000 (SA.R 22000)

SLIPPER, Gary P (1934-) Canadian
£806 $1274 €1209 Mummer. Untitled. Come away, o human child (15x10cm-6x4in) s. tempera on board oil on plexiglas set of three. 14-Nov-2 Heffel, Vancouver #211 est:2500-3000 (C.D 2000)

SLOAN, John (1871-1951) American
£2597 $4000 €3896 Seated nude (51x61cm-20x24in) prov. 27-Oct-2 Grogan, Boston #112 est:4000-6000
£2922 $4500 €4383 Reclining nude (51x61cm-20x24in) prov. 27-Oct-2 Grogan, Boston #111 est:4000-6000
£13208 $21000 €19812 Nude in an interior (61x51cm-24x20in) s. i.d.verso board painted c.1930. 2-Mar-3 Toomey, Oak Park #647/R est:20000-30000
£16774 $26000 €25161 Nude and Windsor chair (61x76cm-24x30in) s. s.i.verso masonite prov.exhib.lit. 5-Dec-2 Christie's, Rockefeller NY #107/R est:25000-35000
£45161 $70000 €67742 Bench on the palisades (23x28cm-9x11in) s.d.06/XXXI prov.exhib.lit. 5-Dec-2 Christie's, Rockefeller NY #96/R est:60000-80000
£1354839 $2100000 €2032259 Gray and brass (55x67cm-22x26in) s.i. painted 1907. 4-Dec-2 Sotheby's, New York #11/R est:2500000-3500000
£1666667 $2700000 €2500001 Easter Eve (81x66cm-32x26in) s.d.07 prov.exhib.lit. 21-May-3 Sotheby's, New York #141/R est:2000000-3000000

Prints
£1887 $3000 €2831 Connoisseurs of prints (20x18cm-8x7in) s.i. etching. 2-May-3 Sotheby's, New York #43/R est:2000-3000
£1887 $3000 €2831 Seeing New York (6x9cm-2x4in) s.i. etching sold with four other prints prov. 2-May-3 Sotheby's, New York #68 est:1800-2200
£2044 $3250 €3066 Turning out the light (12x17cm-5x7in) s.i. etching prov. 2-May-3 Sotheby's, New York #65/R est:3500-5000

£2083 $3250 €3125 Connoisseurs of prints (12x17cm-5x7in) s.i. etching executed c.1905. 12-Sep-2 Freeman, Philadelphia #210/R est:2000-3500
£2564 $4000 €3846 Night windows (23x28cm-9x11in) s.i. etching. 5-Nov-2 Christie's, Rockefeller NY #94/R est:4000-6000
£2830 $4500 €4245 Snowstorm in the village (17x13cm-7x5in) s.i. etching prov. 2-May-3 Sotheby's, New York #69/R est:6000-8000
£2987 $4750 €4481 Night windows (13x17cm-5x7in) s.i. etching prov. 2-May-3 Sotheby's, New York #67/R est:3000-5000
£3145 $5000 €4718 Robert Henri, painter (35x27cm-14x11in) s.i. etching prov. 2-May-3 Sotheby's, New York #70/R est:3000-5000

SLOAN, John (attrib) (1871-1951) American
£2903 $4587 €4500 Ship during storm (39x49cm-15x19in) s.d.1930. 19-Dec-2 Claude Aguttes, Neuilly #165/R

SLOAN, Junius R (1827-1900) American
Works on paper
£645 $1000 €968 Bridge over a stream (33x64cm-13x25in) s.d. W/C. 8-Dec-2 Toomey, Oak Park #639/R est:800-1200

SLOANE, Eric (1910-1985) American
£2813 $4500 €4220 Boathouse at Lake Hopatcong (56x66cm-22x26in) s. board prov. 11-Jan-3 James Julia, Fairfield #203 est:4000-6000
£3165 $5000 €4748 Star (36x46cm-14x18in) s.i. masonite. 24-Apr-3 Shannon's, Milford #165/R est:4000-6000
£4747 $7500 €7121 Fair weather ahead (41x51cm-16x20in) s.i. masonite. 24-Apr-3 Shannon's, Milford #206/R est:5000-7000
£6962 $11000 €10443 Stone wall (61x76cm-24x30in) s. masonite prov. 24-Apr-3 Shannon's, Milford #47/R est:10000-15000
£7186 $12000 €10420 Skirting the storm (69x119cm-27x47in) s. s.i.verso masonite. 18-Jun-3 Christie's, Los Angeles #61/R est:15000-25000
£8228 $13000 €12342 Birs over the marshes (84x114cm-33x45in) masonite. 24-Apr-3 Shannon's, Milford #46/R est:8000-12000
£9554 $15000 €14331 Covered bridge, New Jersey (71x91cm-28x36in) s.i. masonite. 10-Dec-2 Doyle, New York #93/R est:15000-20000
£10390 $16000 €15585 Covered bridge (61x51cm-24x20in) s. s.i.d.verso masonite prov. 24-Oct-2 Shannon's, Milford #137/R est:9000-12000
£11688 $18000 €17532 Stone barn in winter (51x76cm-20x30in) s. board prov. 24-Oct-2 Shannon's, Milford #45/R est:10000-15000
£13014 $19000 €19521 Old still river bridge 1838 (61x91cm-24x36in) 18-May-2 Altermann Galleries, Santa Fe #237/R
£19718 $28000 €29577 Morning on the farm (58x86cm-23x34in) masonite. 8-Aug-1 Barridorf, Portland #31/R est:15000-25000
£24228 $39250 €35131 Cornwall bridge, Conn (61x107cm-24x42in) board. 23-May-3 Altermann Galleries, Santa Fe #165

SLOANE, James Fullarton (fl.1886-1940) British
£900 $1386 €1350 Portrait of a girl in a pink dress (46x38cm-18x15in) s.d.1905. 5-Sep-2 Christie's, Kensington #70/R

SLOCOMBE, Shirley Charles (fl.1887-1904) British
£282 $468 €400 Portrait of a lady (77x62cm-30x24in) s.d.1898. 14-Jun-3 Arnold, Frankfurt #872/R

SLODKI, Marceli (?) Italian?
£520 $806 €780 Study of a seated clown. s. 9-Dec-2 Lawrences, Bletchingley #1993

SLOOVERE, Georges de (1873-1970) Belgian
£380 $600 €600 Vue de Bruges (60x50cm-24x20in) s. 26-Nov-2 Palais de Beaux Arts, Brussels #303/R
£600 $996 €600 Batisse dans un sous-bois (59x68cm-23x27in) s. 16-Jun-3 Horta, Bruxelles #251
£1218 $1888 €1900 Still life of flowers (60x50cm-24x20in) s. 7-Dec-2 De Vuyst, Lokeren #97/R est:2200-2600

SLOTT-MOLLER, Agnes (1862-1937) Danish
£307 $489 €461 Shepherds in meadow (43x65cm-17x26in) 10-Mar-3 Rasmussen, Vejle #409 (D.KR 3300)
£362 $554 €543 Wooded landscape with cattle (63x27cm-25x11in) s. 24-Aug-2 Rasmussen, Havnen #2314 (D.KR 4200)
£409 $645 €614 Fishing boat off the coast (45x66cm-18x26in) s. 2-Dec-2 Rasmussen, Copenhagen #1355/R (D.KR 4800)
£426 $672 €639 Fjord landscape with Viking ship, large tree in foreground (43x56cm-17x22in) s. panel. 2-Dec-2 Rasmussen, Copenhagen #1246/R (D.KR 5000)
£429 $669 €644 Interior from a Norwegian timber house with table (48x69cm-19x27in) s.d.1915. 11-Nov-2 Rasmussen, Vejle #698/R (D.KR 5000)
£517 $786 €776 An arbour (38x43cm-15x17in) s.d.1889. 27-Aug-2 Rasmussen, Copenhagen #1944/R (D.KR 6000)
£931 $1480 €1397 King Waldemar at supper after the hunt at Lyoe (55x51cm-22x20in) s.d.1927 study. 10-Mar-3 Rasmussen, Vejle #516/R (D.KR 10000)

SLOTT-MOLLER, Harald (1864-1937) Danish
£298 $471 €447 Puppy on stone steps (63x42cm-25x17in) s. 2-Dec-2 Rasmussen, Copenhagen #1341/R (D.KR 3500)
£552 $862 €828 Evening in Ribe (57x38cm-22x15in) s.i.d.21-8-19. 5-Aug-2 Rasmussen, Vejle #275/R (D.KR 6500)
£638 $1009 €957 By Braband Lake, moonlit landscape (46x81cm-18x32in) s. 2-Dec-2 Rasmussen, Copenhagen #1495/R (D.KR 7500)
£838 $1332 €1257 Pan seated on flowering branch playing shawm (142x107cm-56x42in) panel put on folding screen. 5-Mar-3 Rasmussen, Copenhagen #1935/R (D.KR 9000)
£1576 $2522 €2364 Side-wing of Bangsbo Manor, summer's night with moonlight (53x63cm-21x25in) s. 13-Jan-3 Rasmussen, Vejle #11/R est:20000 (D.KR 18000)
£3381 $5207 €5072 Interior scene with woman by window (53x62cm-21x24in) s. 26-Oct-2 Rasmussen, Havnen #2023/R est:7000-10000 (D.KR 40000)
£7656 $12402 €11101 Italian terrace by the sea (72x95cm-28x37in) s.d.1928. 26-May-3 Rasmussen, Copenhagen #1132/R est:100000 (D.KR 80000)

SLOTTE, Arvid (20th C) Finnish?
£253 $395 €400 Firestation, Helsingfors (46x65cm-18x26in) s.d.1946. 12-Sep-2 Hagelstam, Helsinki #869

SLOUN, Frank van (1879-1938) American
£446 $700 €669 Water's edge (24x24cm-9x9in) s. board. 22-Nov-2 Skinner, Boston #245/R
£7006 $11000 €10509 Union Square in winter, New York (74x61cm-29x24in) s. prov.exhib.lit. 19-Nov-2 Butterfields, San Francisco #8174/R est:12000-16000

SLOUS, Gideon (1770-1839) British
Works on paper
£1100 $1815 €1595 Young girl with pink sash (7cm-3in) s.d.1797 gold frame oval. 1-Jul-3 Bonhams, New Bond Street #102/R est:1200-1400

SLUIS, Peter (1929-) Irish/Dutch
£475 $760 €660 Dreamer (33x43cm-13x17in) s. 13-May-3 Thomas Adams, Dublin #366
£822 $1282 €1200 Female nude (46x61cm-18x24in) board. 8-Apr-3 Thomas Adams, Dublin #396
£1026 $1610 €1600 Celtic princess (50x64cm-20x25in) board prov. 19-Nov-2 Whyte's, Dublin #175/R est:1400-1600
£1301 $2043 €1900 Lovers (56x45cm-22x18in) s.d.92 board. 15-Apr-3 De Veres Art Auctions, Dublin #67 est:1500-2000
Works on paper
£446 $696 €700 Female nude with still life and cat (24x16cm-9x6in) s.d.92 W/C. 6-Nov-2 James Adam, Dublin #101/R
£461 $746 €700 Abstract study of a gent (28x43cm-11x17in) W/C. 21-Jan-3 Thomas Adams, Dublin #334
£1258 $1962 €2000 Cobra abstract, white bird with yellow beak (44x58cm-17x23in) s. collage W/C gouache pen ink board. 17-Sep-2 Whyte's, Dublin #92/R est:2000-2500

SLUITER, Willy (1873-1949) Dutch
£274 $427 €400 Ds J J Sluiter, clergyman (47x41cm-19x16in) s. s.i.d.1897 verso canvas on panel. 14-Apr-3 Glerum, Amsterdam #152/R
£1419 $2200 €2129 Beached boat, Katwijk aan Zee (25x18cm-10x7in) s.i.verso board prov. 7-Dec-2 Neal Auction Company, New Orleans #225/R est:3000-5000
£4452 $6990 €6500 View of Katwijk (29x40cm-11x16in) s.d.99 board. 15-Apr-3 Sotheby's, Amsterdam #110/R est:6000-8000
£5128 $8051 €8000 Children playing on the beach (22x28cm-9x11in) s.d.98. 25-Nov-2 Glerum, Amsterdam #125/R est:1000-1500
£7042 $11338 €10000 Three fisherboys from Volendam (64x78cm-25x31in) s. 7-May-3 Vendue Huis, Gravenhage #523/R est:10000-14000
£52083 $82813 €75000 Modern times - promenading on Scheveningen Boulevard (151x100cm-59x39in) s.i.d.1932. 29-Apr-3 Christie's, Amsterdam #160/R est:45000-65000
Works on paper
£313 $516 €450 Football (29x21cm-11x8in) s.i. black chk. 1-Jul-3 Christie's, Amsterdam #238/R
£316 $512 €480 Busy bar in Paris (25x21cm-10x8in) init. black chk. 21-Jan-3 Christie's, Amsterdam #287
£347 $573 €500 Kermis, a kiss at the fair, Volendam (25x31cm-10x12in) s.i.d.1917 black chk. 1-Jul-3 Christie's, Amsterdam #236/R
£382 $630 €550 Fight (76x101cm-30x40in) s.i.d.1920 chl pastel paper on board. 1-Jul-3 Christie's, Amsterdam #475
£417 $688 €600 Joe Beckett versus Tommy Burns (77x101cm-30x40in) s.i.d.1920 chl pastel paper on board. 1-Jul-3 Christie's, Amsterdam #481/R
£724 $1172 €1100 Le guardien. Canal in Venice (22x16cm-9x6in) s.i.d.92 black chk three. 21-Jan-3 Christie's, Amsterdam #288/R est:600-800

£1042 $1719 €1500 Bandy at St Moritz (40x31cm-16x12in) s.i.d.1922 black chk pastel pencil. 1-Jul-3 Christie's, Amsterdam #234/R est:1200-1600
£1842 $2984 €2800 Couple inspecting an artist's work (21x14cm-8x6in) init.i.d.1917 pencil col chks poster design two lit. 21-Jan-3 Christie's, Amsterdam #286/R est:1500-2000
£2817 $4535 €4000 Katwijk beach with wooden boats and shell fisherman (56x76cm-22x30in) s.d.98 W/C. 7-May-3 Vendue Huis, Gravenhage #481/R est:4000-6000

SLUTZKY, Naum (1894-1965) Russian
Sculpture
£11538 $17885 €18000 Form study of a cube (35x6x5cm-14x2x2in) brass copperplate exhib.prov. 7-Dec-2 Quittenbaum, Munich #41/R est:12000

SLUYS, Theo van (19th C) Belgian
£3200 $5024 €4800 Moutons dans la bergerie (41x60cm-16x24in) s. 21-Nov-2 Christie's, Kensington #111/R est:2500-3500

SLUYTERMANN VON LANGEWEYDE, Georg (1903-) German
£260 $387 €400 Sunflowers (26x22cm-10x9in) s. board. 27-Jun-2 Neumeister, Munich #2832

SLUYTERS, Jan (1881-1957) Dutch
£236 $373 €354 Spanish lady (42x33cm-17x13in) s. board painted c.1915. 3-Apr-3 Heffel, Vancouver #85/R (C.D 550)
£903 $1490 €1300 Actress Charlotte Kohler in the role of Electra (101x66cm-40x26in) 1-Jul-3 Christie's, Amsterdam #376/R
£3793 $6031 €5500 Portrait of a woman (44x41cm-17x16in) s. 10-Mar-3 Sotheby's, Amsterdam #381/R est:2100-2400
£5396 $8849 €7500 Unfinished construction of the Tienhoven canal (50x65cm-20x26in) s. painted c.1937. 3-Jun-3 Christie's, Amsterdam #243/R est:8000-12000
£8974 $13910 €14000 Still life with flowers (80x105cm-31x41in) s.d.1917. 3-Dec-2 Christie's, Amsterdam #205/R est:15000-20000
£11392 $18000 €18000 Vrouw van Jan Sluijters en Karin Leyden (30x40cm-12x16in) s. 26-Nov-2 Sotheby's, Amsterdam #116/R est:15000-20000
£17405 $27500 €27500 Blauwe vaas met bloemen (53x48cm-21x19in) s. painted c.1937 prov.exhib. 26-Nov-2 Sotheby's, Amsterdam #87/R est:30000-40000
£19231 $29808 €30000 Anemons (60x50cm-24x20in) s. prov. 3-Dec-2 Christie's, Amsterdam #219/R est:30000-40000
£20144 $33036 €28000 Still life with flowers in a vase (80x60cm-31x24in) s. painted c.1933 prov.exhib. 3-Jun-3 Christie's, Amsterdam #236/R est:12000-16000
£30380 $48000 €48000 Bloemstilleven (81x60cm-32x24in) s. painted c.1937 prov. 26-Nov-2 Sotheby's, Amsterdam #99/R est:30000-40000
£35256 $54647 €55000 View on the Pont Neuf, Paris (27x35cm-11x14in) s.d.06 s.i.verso prov. 3-Dec-2 Christie's, Amsterdam #221/R est:30000-50000
Works on paper
£329 $533 €500 Nu assis. s.d.06. 21-Jan-3 Galerie Moderne, Brussels #127
£521 $859 €750 Ice (20x33cm-8x13in) s.indis.i. pen black ink. 1-Jul-3 Christie's, Amsterdam #368/R
£704 $1134 €1000 Monkey (38x30cm-15x12in) s. W/C gouache. 7-May-3 Vendue Huis, Gravenhage #532/R
£1274 $1962 €2000 Standing nude (30x18cm-12x7in) init. black chk. 3-Sep-2 Christie's, Amsterdam #366/R est:1000-1500
£1274 $1962 €2000 Baby (31x40cm-12x16in) s. pencil W/C. 3-Sep-2 Christie's, Amsterdam #358/R est:2000-3000
£1379 $2193 €2000 Mother with her child (64x42cm-25x17in) s. W/C. 10-Mar-3 Sotheby's, Amsterdam #372/R est:1500-20000
£1418 $2298 €2000 Two ladies (25x16cm-10x6in) mono.d.7 pastel. 26-May-3 Glerum, Amsterdam #28 est:600-700
£3185 $4904 €5000 Portrait of Lesje Sluijters (38x30cm-15x12in) s. col pencil W/C. 3-Sep-2 Christie's, Amsterdam #364/R est:5000-7000
£5036 $8259 €7000 Elegant couple walking (26x20cm-10x8in) mono. black chk col pencil executed c.1906 prov. 3-Jun-3 Christie's, Amsterdam #12/R est:6000-8000
£5449 $8446 €8500 Landscape in the South of France (36x26cm-14x10in) s. W/C chl executed c.1953. 3-Dec-2 Christie's, Amsterdam #200/R est:7000-9000

SMADJA, Alex (1897-1977) ?
£1678 $2701 €2500 Composition (92x65cm-36x26in) s. d.1960 verso. 23-Feb-3 Mercier & Cie, Lille #120/R

SMALL, David (1846-1927) British
Works on paper
£404 $638 €606 Crail (37x52cm-15x20in) s.i. W/C. 18-Nov-2 Waddingtons, Toronto #167/R (C.D 1000)

SMALLFIELD, Frederick (1829-1915) British
Works on paper
£550 $875 €825 Prophet, portrait of a bearded man (23x15cm-9x6in) s. W/C dr. 18-Mar-3 Capes Dunn, Manchester #461/R

SMARGIASSI, Gabriele (1798-1882) Italian
£408 $649 €600 Femme de Tivoli cousant (26x22cm-10x9in) i.verso. 21-Mar-3 Rieunier, Bailly-Pommery, Mathias, Paris #85/R
£1027 $1603 €1500 Le pic-nic (55x37cm-22x15in) s. 13-Apr-3 Feletin, Province #103
£5000 $8200 €7500 Villagers at a monument overlooking the Neapolitan coast (39x67cm-15x26in) s.d.1833. 5-Jun-3 Christie's, Kensington #697/R est:1000-1500

SMART, Jeffrey (1921-) Australian
£6944 $11528 €11832 Mother and Child (30x18cm-12x7in) s. hardboard prov. 10-Jun-3 Shapiro, Sydney #29 est:15000-20000 (A.D 17500)
£10317 $17127 €17578 House and bridge (15x37cm-6x15in) s. prov.lit. 10-Jun-3 Shapiro, Sydney #28/R est:20000-30000 (A.D 26000)
£10769 $17123 €16154 Study for mother and child (25x31cm-10x12in) s. exhib. 4-Mar-3 Deutscher-Menzies, Melbourne #19/R est:35000-45000 (A.D 28000)
£13027 $19410 €19541 Study for the argument, prenestina (64x35cm-25x14in) s. acrylic prov.exhib.lit. 27-Aug-2 Christie's, Melbourne #27/R est:35000-45000 (A.D 34000)
£15385 $24462 €23078 Waiting for the hovercraft, Boulogne (36x48cm-14x19in) s. canvas-paper on canvas prov.exhib.lit. 4-Mar-3 Deutscher-Menzies, Melbourne #76/R est:48000-55000 (A.D 40000)
£28800 $46368 €43200 Study for portrait of Germaine Greer (42x50cm-17x20in) s. acrylic oil fabriano paper on board prov.exhib. 6-May-3 Christie's, Melbourne #3/R est:35000-45000 (A.D 72000)
£46512 $73953 €69768 Ticket boxes at Catania (55x75cm-22x30in) s.d.64 exhib. 5-May-3 Sotheby's, Melbourne #106/R est:120000-180000 (A.D 120000)
£48000 $77280 €72000 Self portrait (47x45cm-19x18in) s. painted 1993 prov.exhib. 6-May-3 Christie's, Melbourne #34/R est:120000-180000 (A.D 120000)
£53846 $85615 €80769 Prohibited area (91x110cm-36x43in) s. canvas on board prov.exhib.lit. 4-Mar-3 Deutscher-Menzies, Melbourne #49/R est:130000-160000 (A.D 140000)
£64516 $98065 €96774 Containers at Pisa Airport (85x115cm-33x45in) s. exhib. 28-Aug-2 Deutscher-Menzies, Melbourne #49/R est:22000-280000 (A.D 180000)
£68966 $108276 €103449 Containers and silos at Livomo (71x95cm-28x37in) s. prov.exhib.lit. 15-Apr-3 Lawson Menzies, Sydney #29a/R est:180000-220000 (A.D 180000)
£76628 $114176 €114942 Stadium I (64x80cm-25x31in) s. painted 1967-68 prov.exhib.lit. 27-Aug-2 Christie's, Melbourne #12/R est:80000-120000 (A.D 200000)
£78846 $125365 €118269 Holiday resort (51x61cm-20x24in) s.d.46 prov.exhib.lit. 4-Mar-3 Deutscher-Menzies, Melbourne #25/R est:150000-180000 (A.D 205000)
Prints
£1786 $2964 €3042 Man with bouquet (24x19cm-9x7in) s. hand col etching prov. 10-Jun-3 Shapiro, Sydney #96/R est:1200-1800 (A.D 4500)
£3203 $4900 €4805 Dome (44x43cm-17x17in) s.i.num.61/100 col aquatint executed c.1980 prov. 26-Aug-2 Sotheby's, Paddington #729/R est:3000-4000 (A.D 9000)
Works on paper
£2682 $3996 €4023 Pietro (44x27cm-17x11in) s.i.d.1958 W/C ink. 27-Aug-2 Christie's, Melbourne #310/R est:7000-10000 (A.D 7000)
£2705 $4138 €4058 Directors (12x75cm-5x30in) s. sepia aquatint executed c.1982 prov. 26-Aug-2 Sotheby's, Paddington #685/R est:3500-4500 (A.D 7600)
£3984 $6534 €5976 Pont carousel (31x38cm-12x15in) s.i.d.49 i.verso W/C. 4-Jun-3 Deutscher-Menzies, Melbourne #115/R est:9000-14000 (A.D 10000)
£6346 $10090 €9519 Morning jogger in parking garage, Adelaide (40x61cm-16x24in) s. pastel prov.exhib.lit. 4-Mar-3 Deutscher-Menzies, Melbourne #10/R est:16000-20000 (A.D 16500)
£10078 $16023 €15117 Study for self portrait (28x39cm-11x15in) s.d.64 gouache prov. 5-May-3 Sotheby's, Melbourne #143/R est:25000-35000 (A.D 26000)

SMART, John (jnr) (1776-1809) British

Miniatures

£5000 $7800 €7500 Sir John Doyle wearing scarlet coat with gold aiguilette black facings (9cm-4in) i.verso gilt mount set in leather case after James Ramsey oval. 5-Nov-2 Bonhams, New Bond Street #94/R est:2500-3500

SMART, John (snr) (1742-1811) British

Miniatures

£4500 $7290 €6750 Gentleman, wearing lavender blue coat (5cm-2in) init.d.1778 gold frame with reeded border. 22-May-3 Bonhams, New Bond Street #52/R est:5000-7000

£4800 $7488 €7200 Mrs Margaret Freeman wearing decollete white dress with lace collar (4cm-2in) init.d.1773 gold bracelet clasp mount oval. 5-Nov-2 Bonhams, New Bond Street #76/R est:6000-8000

£5000 $7850 €7500 Viscountess Gormanston (2cm-1in) init. set in bezel gold ring oval. 10-Dec-2 Christie's, London #283/R est:5000-6000

£5500 $8910 €8250 Lady, wearing dress with frilled white collar (3cm-1in) init. gold frame set with diamonds. 22-May-3 Bonhams, New Bond Street #49/R est:4000-6000

£6500 $10660 €9425 Young gentleman in a red coat (4cm-2in) init.d.1779 gold bracelet clasp oval prov. 3-Jun-3 Christie's, London #77/R est:3500-4500

£8000 $12960 €12000 Gentleman wearing blue coat (4cm-2in) init.d.1771 plaited hair. 22-May-3 Bonhams, New Bond Street #90/R est:10000-15000

£10000 $16400 €14500 Young gentleman in blue velvet coat (4cm-2in) init.d.1770 gold bracelet clasp frame oval. 3-Jun-3 Christie's, London #135/R est:10000-15000

£13000 $20280 €19500 Colonel Charles Reynolds wearing black coat brass buttons white waistcoat (9cm-4in) s.d.1810 i.verso gold frame oval lit. 5-Nov-2 Bonhams, New Bond Street #81/R est:15000-20000

£16000 $25120 €24000 Lieutenant general wearing staff uniform (5cm-2in) init.d.1786 silver gilt oval. 10-Dec-2 Christie's, London #97/R est:10000-15000

£20000 $31400 €30000 James Lucy Dighton (8cm-3in) init.d.1801 silver gilt frame oval. 10-Dec-2 Christie's, London #258/R est:8000-12000

£26000 $40820 €39000 Gentleman of the Dighton family possibly Richard (8cm-3in) init.d.1800 silver gilt frame oval. 10-Dec-2 Christie's, London #257/R est:8000-12000

£28000 $43960 €42000 Portrait of Robert Torin in a red coat (6cm-2in) init.d.1789 gold frame oval. 10-Dec-2 Christie's, London #141/R est:15000-20000

£30000 $47100 €45000 Lieutenant J Sol wearing blue coat (8cm-3in) init.d.1803 oval. 10-Dec-2 Christie's, London #196/R est:15000-20000

£31000 $48670 €46500 Portrait of Benjamin Torin (6cm-2in) s.d.1789 gold frame oval. 10-Dec-2 Christie's, London #142/R est:15000-20000

Works on paper

£2000 $3220 €3000 Boatswain of the Melville Castle (4x4cm-2x2in) W/C prov.exhib. 15-Jan-3 Cheffins Grain & Comins, Cambridge #356/R

SMART, John (1838-1899) British

Works on paper

£262 $414 €393 Figure and dog in a Highland landscape (34x46cm-13x18in) s. W/C. 18-Nov-2 Waddingtons, Toronto #164/R (C.D 650)

£600 $966 €900 Sheep in Highland landscape (64x96cm-25x38in) s.d.1880 W/C. 20-Feb-3 Bonhams, Edinburgh #325

SMART, Sally (1960-) Australian

£2143 $3343 €3215 Pioneer, Mad House History Painting series (179x59cm-70x23in) s.i.d.1990 paper exhib. 11-Nov-2 Deutscher-Menzies, Melbourne #56/R est:3000-5000 (A.D 6000)

SMEDLEY, V J (19/20th C) American?

£1220 $2000 €1769 Real page turner (43x36cm-17x14in) s. 4-Jun-3 Doyle, New York #85 est:1500-2000

SMEERS, Frans (1873-1960) Belgian

£353 $546 €550 Ruelle Ardennaise animee (31x41cm-12x16in) s. canvas on panel. 9-Dec-2 Horta, Bruxelles #328

£1310 $2097 €1900 Jeune femme dans les dunes (34x30cm-13x12in) s.d.37 canvas on panel. 17-Mar-3 Horta, Bruxelles #229 est:1200-1800

£1408 $2268 €2000 Artist in his studio (129x95cm-51x37in) s. 6-May-3 Vendu Notarishuis, Rotterdam #150/R est:2000-2500

£1410 $2214 €2200 Teasing the little kitten (65x48cm-26x19in) s. 16-Dec-2 Bernaerts, Antwerp #47/R est:2000-3000

£1634 $2631 €2500 La dentelliere (35x26cm-14x10in) s. panel. 14-Jan-3 Vanderkindere, Brussels #116 est:2500-3500

£1961 $3157 €3000 Elegante nue se mirant (58x45cm-23x18in) s.d.9121. 20-Jan-3 Horta, Bruxelles #221/R est:3000-5000

£1987 $3238 €3000 Portrait de Madame Brose (90x76cm-35x30in) s.i.d.1923 verso. 17-Feb-3 Horta, Bruxelles #167/R

£9494 $15000 €14241 Flower gatherers (61x50cm-24x20in) s. 24-Apr-3 Sotheby's, New York #156/R est:20000-25000

Works on paper

£364 $594 €550 View of Paris (47x58cm-19x23in) s. Chinese ink dr. 17-Feb-3 Horta, Bruxelles #168

SMEETS, Richard (1955-) Dutch

£415 $648 €719 Windmill (122x92cm-48x36in) s.d.93 acrylic paper on canvas. 31-Mar-3 Goodman, Sydney #181 (A.D 1100)

£452 $706 €785 Three windmills/bird (122x92cm-48x36in) s.d.93 acrylic paper on canvas. 31-Mar-3 Goodman, Sydney #182 (A.D 1200)

£491 $765 €849 Portrait of a lady (89x69cm-35x27in) s.d.89 acrylic paper prov. 31-Mar-3 Goodman, Sydney #179 (A.D 1300)

£585 $912 €1013 Windmill (64x48cm-25x19in) s.i.d.94 acrylic paper prov. 31-Mar-3 Goodman, Sydney #184 (A.D 1550)

£603 $977 €850 Composition with red, yellow and blue (110x90cm-43x35in) s.d.85 acrylic. 26-May-3 Glerum, Amsterdam #290/R

£792 $1236 €1373 Woman (159x130cm-63x51in) s.d.85 verso. 31-Mar-3 Goodman, Sydney #188 (A.D 2100)

£830 $1295 €1437 Long boat (198x46cm-78x18in) prov. 31-Mar-3 Goodman, Sydney #177 (A.D 2200)

£1056 $1648 €1830 Man met hond (200x179cm-79x70in) s.d.1988 verso prov. 31-Mar-3 Goodman, Sydney #197 (A.D 2800)

£1509 $2354 €2615 Malay women (96x68cm-38x27in) s.d.1990 acrylic paper prov. 31-Mar-3 Goodman, Sydney #178/R (A.D 4000)

£2263 $3530 €3921 Roses (170x310cm-67x122in) prov. 31-Mar-3 Goodman, Sydney #195 (A.D 6000)

£2338 $3648 €4052 Femme a la chaire (130x160cm-51x63in) 31-Mar-3 Goodman, Sydney #230/R (A.D 6200)

Works on paper

£603 $941 €1046 Chateau de Menans (90x70cm-35x28in) s.d.1986 collage. 31-Mar-3 Goodman, Sydney #190 (A.D 1600)

SMEETS, Yves (1961-) Belgian

£818 $1259 €1300 Face, tree and ghost (135x115cm-53x45in) s. d.2000 verso. 22-Oct-2 Campo, Vlaamse Kaai #627

SMEKENS, Gerard (1812-?) Belgian

£641 $1006 €1000 Paysage de neige (18x26cm-7x10in) s. panel. 15-Dec-2 Mercier & Cie, Lille #367

SMET, Gustave de (1877-1943) Belgian

£1871 $2993 €2600 Corner of courtyard (36x27cm-14x11in) mono. prov.exhib. painted 1912. 17-May-3 De Vuyst, Lokeren #149/R est:1500-2000

£3957 $6489 €5500 Swans in a castle moat, Bruges (80x133cm-31x52in) s. painted 1890. 3-Jun-3 Christie's, Amsterdam #280/R est:7000-9000

£5319 $8617 €7500 Farm with haystacks (36x45cm-14x18in) s. 26-May-3 Glerum, Amsterdam #12/R est:10000-15000

£6748 $11000 €10122 Le Beguinage a Bruges (61x100cm-24x39in) s. painted 1906 prov.exhib. 12-Feb-3 Sotheby's, New York #18/R est:15000-20000

£7000 $10780 €10500 Jardin a Saint Martens Latem (32x44cm-13x17in) studio st. painted c.1910. 22-Oct-2 Sotheby's, London #204/R est:6000-8000

£7092 $11844 €10000 Lampe a petrole, tasse et sucrier sur une table (34x29cm-13x11in) mono. lit. 17-Jun-3 Palais de Beaux Arts, Brussels #580/R est:4000-5000

£7639 $12146 €11000 Jeune dame assise (82x90cm-32x35in) s.d.1913 lit. 29-Apr-3 Campo & Campo, Antwerp #84/R est:14000-18000

£8966 $14345 €13000 Nude (58x36cm-23x14in) s. oil gouache chl paper painted 1941 exhib.lit. 15-Mar-3 De Vuyst, Lokeren #451/R est:14000-16000

£17266 $27626 €24000 Trees along the path through the field (65x50cm-26x20in) s. painted 1911 lit. 17-May-3 De Vuyst, Lokeren #461/R

£19310 $30897 €28000 La Lys avec a l'arriere-plan un moulin a vent (47x58cm-19x23in) 17-Mar-3 Amberes, Antwerp #200/R

£27778 $44167 €40000 Bouleux (72x45cm-28x18in) s.d.1911 exhib. 29-Apr-3 Campo, Vlaamse Kaai #81/R est:42000-48000

£28777 $46043 €40000 Flowers in a blue jug (77x65cm-30x26in) s. prov.exhib. 17-May-3 De Vuyst, Lokeren #477/R

£220000 $360800 €330000 Femme au rosier (107x131cm-42x52in) s.d.12 prov.exhib.lit. 5-Feb-3 Sotheby's, London #126/R est:350000

SMET, Henri de (1865-1940) Belgian

£304 $499 €420 Maison dans le village (24x35cm-9x14in) s. 27-May-3 Campo & Campo, Antwerp #82

£780 $1303 €1100 Bourgeois interior with seated lady (44x33cm-17x13in) s. 23-Jun-3 Bernaerts, Antwerp #111/R

SMET, Léon de (1881-1966) Belgian

£347 $552 €500 Nu assis (113x84cm-44x33in) s. 29-Apr-3 Campo & Campo, Antwerp #85

£1300 $2067 €1950 Sunlight and trees (38x46cm-15x18in) mono. 5-Mar-3 Bonhams, Bury St Edmunds #396/R est:1000-1500

£2278 $3600 €3600 Paysage a Lathem (50x60cm-20x24in) s. 26-Nov-2 Palais de Beaux Arts, Brussels #67/R est:3700-5000

£5096 $7949 €8000 L'arrivee au chateau en hiver (81x101cm-32x40in) s. 11-Nov-2 Horta, Bruxelles #67 est:2500-3500

£5556 $8833 €8000 Hoeve te Sint Martens-Latem (50x66cm-20x26in) s. 29-Apr-3 Campo, Vlaamse Kaai #82/R est:8000-10000
£7194 $11511 €10000 Still life with flowers (80x62cm-31x24in) s. 17-May-3 De Vuyst, Lokeren #462/R
£7947 $12954 €12000 Vase d'arums (80x65cm-31x26in) s.d.1927. 17-Feb-3 Horta, Bruxelles #147/R
£11724 $18759 €17000 Tulips and lupins in a blue vase (75x65cm-30x26in) s. 15-Mar-3 De Vuyst, Lokeren #528/R est:20000-22500
£17722 $27646 €28000 Composition au vase fleuri, figurine et gravure (70x80cm-28x31in) s.d.1924. 16-Sep-2 Horta, Bruxelles #125/R est:25000-35000
£19231 $29808 €30000 Hyde Park, London (51x69cm-20x27in) s.d.1915 lit. 7-Dec-2 De Vuyst, Lokeren #449/R
£20513 $31795 €32000 Still life with flowers and ships (76x63cm-30x25in) s.d.1923 prov. 7-Dec-2 De Vuyst, Lokeren #456/R
£20690 $33103 €30000 Still life with flowers and shells (76x102cm-30x40in) s.d.1960 exhib. 15-Mar-3 De Vuyst, Lokeren #442/R
£25786 $39969 €41000 View of the Middelland sea (65x80cm-26x31in) s. 5-Oct-2 De Vuyst, Lokeren #465/R
£26000 $43420 €37700 Nature morte devant la fenetre (65x78cm-26x31in) s. painted 1950. 24-Jun-3 Sotheby's, London #131/R est:15000-20000
£50000 $83500 €72500 Vase de fleurs (51x81cm-20x32in) s.d.1916 prov. 24-Jun-3 Sotheby's, London #143/R est:40000-60000
£50360 $82590 €70000 Odalisque au bouquet de roses et compotier (92x200cm-36x79in) s. painted c.1924. 3-Jun-3 Christie's, Amsterdam #278/R est:60000-80000

SMET, Roger de (1923-1992) Belgian?
£440 $678 €700 Paysage (60x70cm-24x28in) s. 22-Oct-2 Campo, Vlaamse Kaai #78

SMETANA, Jan (1918-) Czechoslovakian
£5672 $9018 €8508 Spring rain II (70x90cm-28x35in) s. i. verso. 8-Mar-3 Dorotheum, Prague #124/R est:100000-150000 (C.KR 260000)

SMETHAM, James (1821-1889) British
£400 $616 €600 Labourer and his family (23x18cm-9x7in) s.d.1856 panel. 23-Oct-2 Hamptons Fine Art, Godalming #190/R
£1800 $2808 €2700 Christ preaching to the fishermen (24x41cm-9x16in) s. panel. 8-Oct-2 Bonhams, Knightsbridge #153/R est:1000-2000

SMETS, Louis (19th C) Belgian
£1911 $2943 €3000 Horse-drawn sledge on a frozen waterway (30x38cm-12x15in) s. panel. 3-Sep-2 Christie's, Amsterdam #103/R est:3000-5000

SMIBERT, John (attrib) (1688-1751) American
£5938 $9500 €8907 Portraits of Mr and Mrs Francis Balch (76x64cm-30x25in) painted c. 1740-1750 pair prov. 15-Mar-3 Selkirks, St. Louis #320/R est:3000-4000

SMIDT, Emil Leonhard (1878-1954) German
£514 $801 €750 Holstein landscape with cattle (45x50cm-18x20in) s.d.1915. 10-Apr-3 Schopman, Hamburg #690

SMIDTH, Hans (1839-1917) Danish
£355 $547 €533 Landscape with steep slopes (26x37cm-10x15in) s. 26-Oct-2 Rasmussen, Havnen #2038/R (D.KR 4200)
£366 $581 €549 Landscape (23x37cm-9x15in) s. cardboard. 26-Feb-3 Kunsthallen, Copenhagen #531 (D.KR 4000)
£511 $807 €767 Heath landscape (44x64cm-17x25in) s. 2-Dec-2 Rasmussen, Copenhagen #1800/R (D.KR 6000)
£559 $888 €839 Evening landscape (27x48cm-11x19in) s. 5-Mar-3 Rasmussen, Copenhagen #2040/R (D.KR 6000)
£560 $851 €840 A happy couple (46x32cm-18x13in) init.d.1880. 27-Aug-2 Rasmussen, Copenhagen #1628/R (D.KR 6500)
£560 $890 €840 Landscape with church in background (22x37cm-9x15in) s. 5-May-3 Rasmussen, Vejle #466/R (D.KR 6000)
£652 $1036 €978 Heath landscape with road (30x41cm-12x16in) s. 10-Mar-3 Rasmussen, Vejle #235/R (D.KR 7000)
£698 $1110 €1047 Bull in the turnip field (40x35cm-16x14in) s. 5-Mar-3 Rasmussen, Copenhagen #1900/R (D.KR 7500)
£929 $1449 €1394 Heath landscape with peasant woman (27x39cm-11x15in) s. 23-Sep-2 Rasmussen, Vejle #80/R (D.KR 11000)
£1304 $2073 €1956 Summer landscape with fields and mill (38x56cm-15x22in) s. prov. 5-Mar-3 Rasmussen, Copenhagen #1903/R est:8000 (D.KR 14000)
£1399 $2225 €2099 Heath landscape with thatched houses (46x70cm-18x28in) s. exhib. 5-May-3 Rasmussen, Vejle #445/R est:6000-8000 (D.KR 15000)
£1722 $2790 €2497 View across the heath, Jylland (27x43cm-11x17in) s. 26-May-3 Rasmussen, Copenhagen #1513/R est:10000-12000 (D.KR 18000)
£3191 $4947 €4787 Interior scene with girl reading (30x36cm-12x14in) s. 4-Dec-2 AB Stockholms Auktionsverk #1853/R est:45000-50000 (S.KR 45000)

Works on paper
£472 $736 €708 Oxen and cart on the way to market (30x45cm-12x18in) s. pen W/C. 11-Nov-2 Rasmussen, Vejle #481/R (D.KR 5500)

SMILEY, F. H (19th C) British
£340 $527 €510 Kitchen table (76x61cm-30x24in) s.d.1847. 18-Jul-2 Neales, Nottingham #740

SMILLIE, George H (1840-1921) American
£3896 $6000 €5844 Landscape with foothills (53x41cm-21x16in) s. prov. 24-Oct-2 Shannon's, Milford #194/R est:3000-5000

SMILLIE, Helen Sheldon Jacobs (1854-1926) American
Works on paper
£244 $400 €354 Young girl reading (35x23cm-14x9in) s. W/C card stock. 5-Jun-3 Swann Galleries, New York #225/R

SMILLIE, James David (1833-1909) American
£6918 $11000 €10377 Lake in the mountains (30x56cm-12x22in) mono. 5-Mar-3 Sotheby's, New York #15/R est:10000-15000

SMIRA, Shaoul (1939-) Israeli
Works on paper
£347 $552 €500 Le couple (46x65cm-18x26in) s.d.1985 mixed media. 29-Apr-3 Campo & Campo, Antwerp #278
£347 $552 €500 Pigeon et tete d'homme (45x61cm-18x24in) s. mixed media. 29-Apr-3 Campo & Campo, Antwerp #279
£382 $607 €550 Homme et chevaux (60x48cm-24x19in) s.d.1983 mixed media. 29-Apr-3 Campo & Campo, Antwerp #280
£382 $607 €550 Fall of empire (106x76cm-42x30in) s.d.1970 mixed media. 29-Apr-3 Campo & Campo, Antwerp #281/R

SMIRKE, Robert (attrib) (1752-1845) British
£5500 $8524 €8250 Scenes from Ossian (71x142cm-28x56in) four prov. 3-Dec-2 Sotheby's, Olympia #11/R est:4000-6000

SMIRNOV, Serguei (1954-) Russian
£371 $579 €557 Lakeshore (60x80cm-24x31in) s.d.199 i. verso. 6-Nov-2 Dobiaschofsky, Bern #973/R (S.FR 850)

SMIT, Aernout (attrib) (1641-1710) Dutch
£6115 $9784 €8500 Sailing ships off the coast with a two master making way (77x106cm-30x42in) with sig. 14-May-3 Christie's, Amsterdam #199/R est:8000-12000

SMIT, Arie (1916-) Dutch
£1243 $2051 €1802 Road to the village (30x18cm-12x7in) s.d.96 acrylic. 6-Jul-3 Christie's, Hong Kong #3/R est:16000-20000 (HK.D 16000)
£1491 $2297 €2237 Two herons (27x36cm-11x14in) s.d.97 s.i.d.verso acrylic. 27-Oct-2 Christie's, Hong Kong #12/R est:18000-26000 (HK.D 18000)
£1823 $2807 €2735 Still life (18x24cm-7x9in) s.d.94 s.i.d.verso ca. canvas on board. 27-Oct-2 Christie's, Hong Kong #13/R est:10000-15000 (HK.D 22000)
£2486 $3828 €3729 Flowers (50x36cm-20x14in) s.d.98 s.i.d.verso acrylic. 27-Oct-2 Christie's, Hong Kong #11/R est:30000-40000 (HK.D 30000)
£2486 $4103 €3605 Sanur beach under moonlight (30x22cm-12x9in) s.i.d.1963 i.verso acrylic card. 6-Jul-3 Christie's, Hong Kong #4/R est:15000-20000 (HK.D 32000)
£6628 $10207 €9942 Early morning in the village, Sanur (51x71cm-20x28in) s.d.79 s.i.d.verso. 27-Oct-2 Christie's, Hong Kong #10/R est:55000-65000 (HK.D 80000)
£7457 $11483 €11186 Pura - temple (40x51cm-16x20in) s.d.97 acrylic. 27-Oct-2 Christie's, Hong Kong #35/R est:35000-55000 (HK.D 90000)
£9942 $15311 €14913 Temple on the hill (70x74cm-28x29in) s.d.02 s.i.d.verso acrylic. 27-Oct-2 Christie's, Hong Kong #34/R est:70000-90000 (HK.D 120000)
£16570 $25518 €24855 Joyful life of flowers (116x83cm-46x33in) s.d.89 s.i.d.verso acrylic prov. 27-Oct-2 Christie's, Hong Kong #36/R est:160000-200000 (HK.D 200000)
£19884 $30621 €29826 Pura merah muda - pink temple (91x101cm-36x40in) s.d.98 s.i.d.verso. 27-Oct-2 Christie's, Hong Kong #14/R est:130000-180000 (HK.D 240000)
£21756 $35897 €31546 In a Balinese temple (71x97cm-28x38in) s.d.91 acrylic prov. 6-Jul-3 Christie's, Hong Kong #6/R est:160000-200000 (HK.D 280000)

SMITH OF CHICHESTER, George (1714-1776) British
£2639 $3800 €3959 Wooded landscape with shepherd and flock (55x72cm-22x28in) 15-Jan-3 Christie's, Rockefeller NY #125/R
£9000 $14040 €13500 Wooded landscape with children resting beside a lake in the foreground (66x124cm-26x49in) s. 9-Apr-3 Bonhams, New Bond Street #67/R est:7000-10000

SMITH, A R (?) British
Works on paper
£1300 $2067 €1950 Town scene (29x50cm-11x20in) s. W/C. 25-Feb-3 Bonhams, Knightsbridge #102

SMITH, A W (?) British?
Works on paper
£360 $558 €540 Stroll on the sands, Edwardian family (104x130cm-41x51in) s. W/C. 26-Sep-2 Lane, Penzance #129

SMITH, Alexis (1949-) American
Sculpture
£5625 $9000 €8438 Cinephilia (111x87x9cm-44x34x4in) printed paper candy box feather ribbon bob pins collage prov. 14-May-3 Sotheby's, New York #364/R est:3000-4000

SMITH, Alfred (19/20th C) French
£285 $433 €428 Founder, the late Mr Daniel Smith (117x87cm-46x34in) s. 29-Aug-2 Christie's, Kensington #118/R

SMITH, Archibald Cary (1837-1911) American
£741 $1200 €1074 Sailing on the lake (25x37cm-10x15in) s. board. 29-Jul-3 Christie's, Rockefeller NY #157/R est:2000-3000

SMITH, Arthur (19th C) British
£645 $1000 €968 At the fight (30x25cm-12x10in) s. board painted c.1940. 8-Dec-2 Toomey, Oak Park #775/R

SMITH, Arthur Reginald (1871-1934) British
£540 $886 €810 Between showers. 4-Feb-3 Bonhams, Leeds #348
£1600 $2624 €2400 Early morning above Deepdale. 4-Feb-3 Bonhams, Leeds #347
Works on paper
£280 $437 €420 Old grammar school, Skipton (23x37cm-9x15in) s.d.1898 W/C. 10-Apr-3 Tennants, Leyburn #834
£380 $623 €570 Wetherlam (23x35cm-9x14in) s. pencil W/C. 4-Feb-3 Bonhams, Leeds #325
£400 $656 €600 Summer night, Yorkshire (25x37cm-10x15in) s. pencil W/C. 4-Feb-3 Bonhams, Leeds #359
£420 $689 €630 Attic with figures seated at a table (26x34cm-10x13in) s. pencil W/C. 4-Feb-3 Bonhams, Leeds #333
£420 $689 €630 Haslewood Moor (21x37cm-8x15in) s. pencil W/C. 4-Feb-3 Bonhams, Leeds #336
£420 $689 €630 Descent of Tarn Howes (28x38cm-11x15in) s. pencil W/C. 4-Feb-3 Bonhams, Leeds #345
£420 $689 €630 Outskirts of Richmond, Yorkshire (27x39cm-11x15in) s. pencil W/C. 4-Feb-3 Bonhams, Leeds #367
£450 $738 €675 Fallen tree, Thwaites (30x46cm-12x18in) s. pencil W/C. 4-Feb-3 Bonhams, Leeds #315
£480 $787 €720 Marble quarry in Italy (29x47cm-11x19in) s. pencil W/C. 4-Feb-3 Bonhams, Leeds #332
£500 $820 €750 Children in a street (26x21cm-10x8in) s. pencil W/C. 4-Feb-3 Bonhams, Leeds #334
£540 $886 €810 Pastures near Bolton Abbey (12x28cm-5x11in) s. pencil W/C. 4-Feb-3 Bonhams, Leeds #338
£540 $886 €810 Rome (27x38cm-11x15in) s.d.06 pencil W/C. 4-Feb-3 Bonhams, Leeds #357
£560 $918 €840 Cley, Norfolk (38x25cm-15x10in) s. pencil W/C. 4-Feb-3 Bonhams, Leeds #343
£580 $951 €870 Street scene in the South of France (37x27cm-15x11in) s.i. W/C. 4-Feb-3 Bonhams, Leeds #324
£580 $951 €870 Moor Road. Craven Fells (10x13cm-4x5in) s. pencil W/C pair. 4-Feb-3 Bonhams, Leeds #374
£600 $984 €900 Snow capped Etna, Sicily (37x25cm-15x10in) s. pencil W/C. 4-Feb-3 Bonhams, Leeds #369 est:350-450
£600 $984 €900 Near Capel Curig, North Wales (26x38cm-10x15in) s. pencil W/C. 4-Feb-3 Bonhams, Leeds #375
£620 $1017 €930 Grasswood, near Wharfeale, Yorkshire (27x37cm-11x15in) s. pencil W/C. 4-Feb-3 Bonhams, Leeds #355
£620 $1017 €930 Village with a timber yard (29x21cm-11x8in) s. W/C. 4-Feb-3 Bonhams, Leeds #386
£640 $1050 €960 Yorkshire farm (27x37cm-11x15in) s. pencil W/C. 4-Feb-3 Bonhams, Leeds #331
£660 $1082 €990 Simon's seat, Barden (30x53cm-12x21in) s. pencil W/C. 4-Feb-3 Bonhams, Leeds #317
£680 $1115 €1020 Masdale, evening (27x38cm-11x15in) s. pencil W/C. 4-Feb-3 Bonhams, Leeds #373
£680 $1115 €1020 Rievaulx Abbey (25x37cm-10x15in) s. W/C. 4-Feb-3 Bonhams, Leeds #379
£700 $1148 €1050 Windemere from the Kendal Road (27x38cm-11x15in) s. pencil W/C. 4-Feb-3 Bonhams, Leeds #316
£700 $1148 €1050 Wharfe in winter (16x24cm-6x9in) s. pencil W/C. 4-Feb-3 Bonhams, Leeds #349
£720 $1181 €1080 Autumn, near Burnsall (24x35cm-9x14in) s. pencil W/C. 4-Feb-3 Bonhams, Leeds #377
£740 $1214 €1110 Strid, River Wharfe (33x33cm-13x13in) s. pencil W/C. 4-Feb-3 Bonhams, Leeds #383
£760 $1246 €1140 Early morning, Kettlewell (26x38cm-10x15in) s.d.12 pencil W/C. 4-Feb-3 Bonhams, Leeds #335 est:300-400
£780 $1186 €1170 Rylstone Fell (23x36cm-9x14in) s. W/C. 16-Aug-2 Keys, Aylsham #580/R
£780 $1279 €1170 Wharfe in flood (37x55cm-15x22in) s. pencil W/C. 4-Feb-3 Bonhams, Leeds #351
£780 $1279 €1170 Loup Scar, Burnsall. 4-Feb-3 Bonhams, Leeds #358
£800 $1312 €1200 Honister Pass (25x37cm-10x15in) s. W/C. 4-Feb-3 Bonhams, Leeds #319
£800 $1312 €1200 In the Duddon Valley (26x38cm-10x15in) s. pencil W/C. 4-Feb-3 Bonhams, Leeds #387
£820 $1345 €1230 Canal at Skipton (24x49cm-9x19in) s. pencil W/C. 4-Feb-3 Bonhams, Leeds #337
£820 $1345 €1230 Linton Beck, evening (32x44cm-13x17in) s. pencil W/C. 4-Feb-3 Bonhams, Leeds #344
£820 $1345 €1230 Ravine in Great Whernside (26x38cm-10x15in) s. pencil W/C. 4-Feb-3 Bonhams, Leeds #362
£900 $1476 €1350 Smelt mill, Kettlewell (24x37cm-9x15in) s. pencil W/C. 4-Feb-3 Bonhams, Leeds #370
£900 $1476 €1350 Springtime near Netherside (24x37cm-9x15in) s. pencil W/C. 4-Feb-3 Bonhams, Leeds #376
£900 $1476 €1350 Autumn on the Wharfe (38x43cm-15x17in) s. pencil W/C. 4-Feb-3 Bonhams, Leeds #380
£1000 $1660 €1500 Rylstone Fell (23x37cm-9x15in) s. W/C. 10-Jun-3 Bonhams, Leeds #60/R est:1000-1200
£1050 $1722 €1575 Captain Beck, Yockenthwaite Bridge on the Wharfe (37x55cm-15x22in) s. pencil chl W/C. 4-Feb-3 Bonhams, Leeds #364
£1050 $1722 €1575 Golden hour, Yorkshire (26x37cm-10x15in) s. pencil W/C. 4-Feb-3 Bonhams, Leeds #365
£1100 $1804 €1650 River landscape in winter, possibly a bend on the Wharfe (24x35cm-9x14in) s. W/C. 4-Feb-3 Bonhams, Leeds #320 est:450-550
£1100 $1804 €1650 Quarry near Haworth (35x52cm-14x20in) s. pencil W/C. 4-Feb-3 Bonhams, Leeds #322 est:400-600
£1100 $1804 €1650 Peny-y-ghent (56x79cm-22x31in) s.i.verso pencil W/C. 4-Feb-3 Bonhams, Leeds #323 est:700-900
£1100 $1804 €1650 Yorkshire river, snow (30x44cm-12x17in) s. pencil W/C. 4-Feb-3 Bonhams, Leeds #346
£1100 $1804 €1650 Bend in Skirfare, Wharfedale, Yorkshire (36x53cm-14x21in) s. pencil W/C. 4-Feb-3 Bonhams, Leeds #354
£1100 $1804 €1650 Fishing boats, Dieppe (28x36cm-11x14in) s. pencil W/C. 4-Feb-3 Bonhams, Leeds #360
£1100 $1804 €1650 Street in Chioggia (32x44cm-13x17in) s. pencil W/C. 4-Feb-3 Bonhams, Leeds #382 est:500-700
£1150 $1886 €1725 Wharfe, near Kilnsey Crag (25x35cm-10x14in) s. pencil W/C. 4-Feb-3 Bonhams, Leeds #381
£1200 $1968 €1800 Near Silverdale, figures beside a farmhouse (22x34cm-9x13in) s. pencil W/C. 4-Feb-3 Bonhams, Leeds #328 est:300-400
£1200 $1968 €1800 Gloaming (32x50cm-13x20in) s. pencil W/C. 4-Feb-3 Bonhams, Leeds #342
£1250 $2050 €1875 Bolton Castle (51x29cm-20x11in) s. pencil W/C. 4-Feb-3 Bonhams, Leeds #378
£1350 $2214 €2025 In the Dorset Hills (29x50cm-11x20in) s. pencil W/C. 4-Feb-3 Bonhams, Leeds #329 est:700-900
£1350 $2214 €2025 Early morning, Buckden (37x48cm-15x19in) s. W/C. 4-Feb-3 Bonhams, Leeds #350
£1350 $2214 €2025 Buckden Pike (51x36cm-20x14in) s. pencil W/C. 4-Feb-3 Bonhams, Leeds #371 est:500-700
£1400 $2296 €2100 On the banks of the Wharfe (36x55cm-14x22in) s. pencil W/C. 4-Feb-3 Bonhams, Leeds #340 est:300-400
£1400 $2296 €2100 Italian market place (24x33cm-9x13in) s.d.06 pencil W/C. 4-Feb-3 Bonhams, Leeds #353
£1400 $2296 €2100 On a sunny road (38x27cm-15x11in) s. pencil W/C. 4-Feb-3 Bonhams, Leeds #356
£1450 $2378 €2175 Village in Umbria, early morning (25x37cm-10x15in) s. pencil W/C. 4-Feb-3 Bonhams, Leeds #352
£1550 $2542 €2325 Bolton Priory, Yorkshire (26x36cm-10x14in) s. pencil W/C. 4-Feb-3 Bonhams, Leeds #366
£1600 $2624 €2400 Sunlight and shadow (37x53cm-15x21in) s. pencil W/C. 4-Feb-3 Bonhams, Leeds #385 est:400-600
£1800 $2952 €2700 Spring morning, Skirethorns (27x38cm-11x15in) s. pencil W/C. 4-Feb-3 Bonhams, Leeds #372 est:500-600
£1900 $3116 €2850 Kilnsey Crag, Yorkshire (25x25cm-10x10in) s. pencil W/C. 4-Feb-3 Bonhams, Leeds #327 est:300-500
£2100 $3444 €3150 Meeting of the waters (29x39cm-11x15in) s. pencil W/C. 4-Feb-3 Bonhams, Leeds #368 est:400-600
£2200 $3608 €3300 Village of Kettlewell, Yorkshire (27x43cm-11x17in) s. W/C. 4-Feb-3 Bonhams, Leeds #321 est:800-1000
£2500 $4100 €3750 Crossing the stream, shepherds and sheep in the Dales (27x49cm-11x19in) s. pencil W/C. 4-Feb-3 Bonhams, Leeds #339 est:500-600
£2500 $4100 €3750 Upper Wharfe (35x51cm-14x20in) s. pencil W/C. 4-Feb-3 Bonhams, Leeds #341/R
£2500 $4100 €3750 Snow scene, Wharfdale, above Threshfield (34x54cm-13x21in) s. pencil W/C. 4-Feb-3 Bonhams, Leeds #389 est:500-700

£2600 $4264 €3900 At the washing, Assisi (37x54cm-15x21in) s. W/C. 4-Feb-3 Bonhams, Leeds #326 est:500-700
£2800 $4592 €4200 Early morning, Kettlewell, Wharfedale (37x54cm-15x21in) s. W/C. 4-Feb-3 Bonhams, Leeds #363
£3300 $5412 €4950 Hillside village, Hebden, Yorkshire (35x52cm-14x20in) s. W/C scratching out. 4-Feb-3 Bonhams, Leeds #318 est:1000-1500
£3600 $5904 €5400 Sheep sale (27x49cm-11x19in) s. pencil W/C. 4-Feb-3 Bonhams, Leeds #330 est:600-800
£4500 $7380 €6750 Coniston Bridge on the approach to Coniston village (35x54cm-14x21in) s. pencil W/C. 4-Feb-3 Bonhams, Leeds #361

SMITH, Arthur Reginald (attrib) (1871-1934) British
£500 $815 €725 Dales Farm, with chickens in the foreground. Dales landscape with sheep and lambs (20x30cm-8x12in) s.i.d.1910 board pair. 17-Jul-3 Tennants, Leyburn #857

SMITH, Austin (20th C) British
Works on paper
£280 $437 €420 Extensive view of Tate Hill Sands and Pier (10x33cm-4x13in) s.d.1924 W/C. 10-Sep-2 David Duggleby, Scarborough #124/R
£320 $499 €480 Moored fishing boats in Whitby upper harbour (12x36cm-5x14in) s.d.1922 W/C. 10-Sep-2 David Duggleby, Scarborough #183
£480 $758 €720 Whitby fishing boats returning to harbour (18x36cm-7x14in) s.d.1923 W/C. 24-Apr-3 Richardson & Smith, Whitby #165/R
£520 $822 €780 Steam and sailing vessels off the Scarborough coast in a choppy sea (15x44cm-6x17in) s. W/C htd white. 7-Apr-3 David Duggleby, Scarborough #359
£540 $842 €810 Sailing ship and fishing vessels off Whitby harbour (19x36cm-7x14in) s.d.1923 W/C htd white. 10-Sep-2 David Duggleby, Scarborough #180/R
£600 $984 €900 South bay, Scarborough looking towards the Castle (26x38cm-10x15in) s. W/C. 2-Jun-3 David Duggleby, Scarborough #305/R

SMITH, B (19th C) British
£310 $503 €450 Lake landscape with milkmaid (46x80cm-18x31in) s. 25-May-3 Uppsala Auktionskammare, Uppsala #75/R (S.KR 4000)

SMITH, Blaise (20th C) Irish?
Works on paper
£685 $1075 €1000 Belfast sink study (38x51cm-15x20in) s.i.d.1999 pastel. 15-Apr-3 De Veres Art Auctions, Dublin #96/R est:1000-1500

SMITH, Brett (1958-) American
£9494 $15000 €13766 Falls camp (66x86cm-26x34in) s. 26-Jul-3 Coeur d'Alene, Hayden #27/R est:12000-18000

SMITH, Brett James (20th C) American
Works on paper
£1911 $3000 €2867 River scene with man with long fly rod having fish on which is jumping (53x74cm-21x29in) W/C. 19-Apr-3 James Julia, Fairfield #86/R est:3000-5000

SMITH, C R (19th C) ?
£1014 $1581 €1500 Dargle, Wicklow (53x73cm-21x29in) s.d.1886. 26-Mar-3 James Adam, Dublin #26/R est:1500-2500

SMITH, Carlton A (1853-1946) British
£566 $900 €849 Portrait of a young man (30x25cm-12x10in) s.d.1905. 7-Mar-3 Skinner, Boston #258/R
£3800 $5966 €5700 Young girl holding a doll and an orange (34x20cm-13x8in) s. indis d.92 panel. 21-Nov-2 Tennants, Leyburn #856 est:1200-1800
£9500 $15009 €14250 Hat makers (51x76cm-20x30in) s.d.91. 2-Dec-2 Sotheby's, London #34/R est:7000-9000
Works on paper
£1900 $3002 €2850 Moments rest (26x18cm-10x7in) s.d.1907 W/C bodycol over pencil. 2-Dec-2 Bonhams, Bath #19/R est:800-1200
£3600 $5760 €5400 Cottage kitchen, peeling potatoes (32x49cm-13x19in) s. W/C. 11-Mar-3 Bonhams, New Bond Street #72/R est:4000-6000

SMITH, Carlton A (attrib) (1853-1946) British
Works on paper
£340 $558 €510 A young girl spinning wool (42x45cm-17x18in) bears sig.d.1894 W/C. 3-Jun-3 Bearnes, Exeter #419

SMITH, Charles (fl.1857-1908) British
£1700 $2652 €2550 Valley in North Wales (61x85cm-24x33in) s.d.67 prov. 6-Nov-2 Bonhams, Chester #419/R est:1800-2400
£1900 $3116 €2850 Devon coast (41x102cm-16x40in) s. 29-May-3 Christie's, Kensington #187/R est:1000-1500

SMITH, Charles Hamilton (1776-1859) British
Works on paper
£42000 $67620 €63000 Hoofed animals of the world (42x34cm-17x13in) init.i. W/C drs 64 folio boxes 6. 7-May-3 Sotheby's, London #114/R est:15000-20000

SMITH, Charles L A (1871-1937) American
£590 $950 €885 Chickens in a barnyard (28x36cm-11x14in) s. canvas on masonite. 18-Feb-3 John Moran, Pasadena #103a
£1161 $1800 €1742 California coastal (64x76cm-25x30in) s.d.1934 canvas on board prov. 29-Oct-2 John Moran, Pasadena #639 est:3000-5000
£3871 $6000 €5807 Figures in rolling California landscape (51x76cm-20x30in) s.d.1925. 29-Oct-2 John Moran, Pasadena #635 est:4000-6000

SMITH, Collingwood (20th C) ?
Works on paper
£427 $653 €641 Cross Channel port (23x32cm-9x13in) s. W/C. 21-Aug-2 Dunbar Sloane, Auckland #78/R est:800-1200 (NZ.D 1400)

SMITH, David (1906-1965) American
£9677 $15000 €14516 Untitled (46x58cm-18x23in) s.i.d.Feb 1962 spray enamel gouache prov. 26-Sep-2 Christie's, Rockefeller NY #711/R est:6000-8000
£10968 $17000 €16452 Untitled (44x29cm-17x11in) spray enamel on paper painted 1959 prov.exhib. 26-Sep-2 Christie's, Rockefeller NY #701/R est:15000-20000
Sculpture
£312500 $500000 €468750 Structure (58x24x23cm-23x9x9in) s.i.d.1938 painted steel wire prov.exhib.lit. 13-May-3 Sotheby's, New York #12/R est:600000-800000
£325000 $520000 €487500 Plate of ramparts (63x57x48cm-25x22x19in) s.d.1957 painted steel prov.exhib.lit. 14-May-3 Christie's, Rockefeller NY #37/R est:350000-450000
Works on paper
£5696 $9000 €8544 Untitled (45x29cm-18x11in) spray paint on paper executed 1962-63 prov.exhib. 13-Nov-2 Sotheby's, New York #207/R est:10000-15000
£6329 $10000 €9494 Untitled (44x57cm-17x22in) init.d.12.57 black egg ink prov.exhib. 13-Nov-2 Sotheby's, New York #208/R est:10000-15000
£8387 $13000 €12581 Untitled (46x58cm-18x23in) s.d.1959 egg ink prov.exhib. 26-Sep-2 Christie's, Rockefeller NY #710/R est:10000-15000
£10323 $16000 €15485 Untitled (44x57cm-17x22in) init.d.55 egg ink prov. 26-Sep-2 Christie's, Rockefeller NY #703/R est:15000-20000
£10968 $17000 €16452 Untitled (40x52cm-16x20in) s.d.1963 egg ink prov.exhib. 26-Sep-2 Christie's, Rockefeller NY #704/R est:12000-18000

SMITH, David Murray (1865-1952) British
£300 $492 €435 Edge of the woods (25x30cm-10x12in) s.i.verso board. 3-Jun-3 Capes Dunn, Manchester #116
£1350 $2120 €2025 Misty morning, River Choler (51x76cm-20x30in) s. 19-Nov-2 Riddetts, Bournemouth #836/R
£1450 $2277 €2175 Autumn mist - bridge at Hoe Mills, Essex (61x89cm-24x35in) s. 19-Nov-2 Riddetts, Bournemouth #835/R

SMITH, David Murray (attrib) (1865-1952) British
Works on paper
£250 $398 €375 Hampshire landscape On the Avon (36x51cm-14x20in) W/C. 27-Feb-3 Brightwells, Leominster #822

SMITH, David Seaton (1901-?) Canadian/British
Works on paper
£288 $447 €432 Elora, Ontario (37x42cm-15x17in) s. W/C prov. 3-Dec-2 Joyner, Toronto #401 (C.D 700)

SMITH, Decost (1864-1939) American
£6918 $11000 €10377 Indian warrior (62x46cm-24x18in) s.i.d.1903 prov. 4-Mar-3 Christie's, Rockefeller NY #94/R est:4000-6000

SMITH, Edward (19/20th C) British
£262 $409 €393 Plucking a goose (32x19cm-13x7in) s.d.92 panel. 20-Nov-2 Fischer, Luzern #2263/R (S.FR 600)

SMITH, Edwin (?-1971) British
£280 $440 €420 Agrigento, Sicily (49x60cm-19x24in) 10-Dec-2 Cheffins Grain & Comins, Cambridge #229

Works on paper
£260 $408 €390 Mr Ingram and two geese (46x30cm-18x12in) W/C. 10-Dec-2 Cheffins Grain & Comins, Cambridge #238

SMITH, Edwin Dalton (1800-?) British
Miniatures
£1600 $2592 €2400 General Sir J Dickson, wearing scarlet coat (13cm-5in) s. gilt metal frame. 22-May-3 Bonhams, New Bond Street #130/R est:1000-1500
Works on paper
£44000 $70840 €66000 Flowers (19x19cm-7x7in) W/C drs 199 two volumes album lit. 7-May-3 Sotheby's, London #137/R est:30000-40000

SMITH, Emily Guthrie (1909-1986) American
Works on paper
£1090 $1700 €1635 Bedtime story (41x30cm-16x12in) pastel. 19-Oct-2 David Dike, Dallas #148/R est:1500-3000

SMITH, Ernest Browning (1866-1951) American
£621 $1000 €932 Farm house (71x91cm-28x36in) s.d.1922 i.verso canvas on canvas prov. 18-Feb-3 John Moran, Pasadena #184

SMITH, Francesco (attrib) (?-c.1780) British
£22436 $35224 €35000 La reception de l'Ambassadeur par le Sultan et par le Grand Vizir (47x65cm-19x26in) pair lit. 16-Dec-2 Gros & Delettrez, Paris #270/R est:27000-35000

SMITH, Francis (1881-1961) Portuguese
£8176 $12591 €13000 Le clown (46x38cm-18x15in) s. paper laid down. 22-Oct-2 Palais de Beaux Arts, Brussels #35/R est:600-800
Works on paper
£4777 $7452 €7500 Cavaliers devant une maison (26x19cm-10x7in) s. W/C gouache. 6-Nov-2 Claude Boisgirard, Paris #51 est:1500-2000
£14013 $21860 €22000 La Criee aux poissons (34x47cm-13x19in) s. gouache W/C. 6-Nov-2 Claude Boisgirard, Paris #52/R est:2000-3000

SMITH, Francis Hopkinson (1838-1915) American
Works on paper
£14013 $22000 €21020 Inn of William the conqueror (43x61cm-17x24in) s. W/C gouache black chk. 10-Dec-2 Doyle, New York #47/R est:15000-25000

SMITH, Frank Vining (1879-1967) American
£313 $500 €454 Full sail (41x61cm-16x24in) s. board. 17-May-3 CRN Auctions, Cambridge #54
£685 $1000 €1028 Clipper ship, Marie Luce (43x48cm-17x19in) s. 3-Nov-1 North East Auctions, Portsmouth #99/R
£962 $1500 €1395 Small fry, two cubs and a doe (79x99cm-31x39in) s. board. 13-Oct-2 Cobbs, Peterborough #471
£1480 $2250 €2220 Ship, A J Fuller, of New York (56x81cm-22x32in) s. 17-Aug-2 North East Auctions, Portsmouth #1093/R
£2548 $4000 €3822 Pintails alighting (51x78cm-20x31in) s. i.verso masonite. 22-Nov-2 Skinner, Boston #152/R est:4000-6000
£3289 $5000 €4934 Bark on the Grand Banks (56x76cm-22x30in) s. board. 17-Aug-2 North East Auctions, Portsmouth #1080/R est:5000-8000
£3596 $5250 €5394 Coming in for landing, Canada Geese (51x76cm-20x30in) s. i.verso masonite. 3-Nov-1 North East Auctions, Portsmouth #745/R est:3000-4000
£4747 $7500 €7121 Three masted ship , Bow first portrait (81x61cm-32x24in) s. 30-Nov-2 Thomaston Place, Thomaston #53
£7237 $11000 €10856 Voyage home (86x102cm-34x40in) s. board. 17-Aug-2 North East Auctions, Portsmouth #1082/R est:6000-9000
£8882 $13500 €13323 Sunlit seas (86x104cm-34x41in) s. board. 17-Aug-2 North East Auctions, Portsmouth #1086/R est:6000-9000
£9868 $15000 €14802 Full sail under a cloud of canvas (86x102cm-34x40in) s. 17-Aug-2 North East Auctions, Portsmouth #1078/R est:5000-8000
£10274 $15000 €15411 Passing clippers (76x102cm-30x40in) s. 3-Nov-1 North East Auctions, Portsmouth #58/R est:10000-12000
£10274 $15000 €15411 Square rigger (71x89cm-28x35in) s. 3-Nov-1 North East Auctions, Portsmouth #60/R est:10000-12000
Works on paper
£1800 $2790 €2700 Boats in Malta (46x74cm-18x29in) s. W/C. 24-Sep-2 Rowley Fine Art, Newmarket #354/R
£1800 $2790 €2700 Shipping in Valletta Harbour (46x74cm-18x29in) s. W/C. 24-Sep-2 Rowley Fine Art, Newmarket #355/R
£6000 $9720 €9000 Knight of Malta and P and O Passenger liners in Grand Harbour, Valetta (48x76cm-19x30in) s. pencil W/C pair. 21-May-3 Christie's, Kensington #477/R est:5000-7000

SMITH, Frederick Carl (1868-1955) American
£299 $500 €434 Landscape (64x23cm-25x9in) board prov. 17-Jun-3 John Moran, Pasadena #1
£559 $900 €839 Foothill landscape (13x20cm-5x8in) s. board prov. 18-Feb-3 John Moran, Pasadena #5a
£659 $1100 €956 Landscape - Igelsia del Carmen Cuernavaca, Mexico (30x41cm-12x16in) s. board prov. 17-Jun-3 John Moran, Pasadena #216 est:700-1000
£958 $1600 €1389 Monterey Cypress, Carmel by the sea (30x41cm-12x16in) s. i.verso board prov. 17-Jun-3 John Moran, Pasadena #201 est:800-1200
£1018 $1700 €1476 Foothill landscape (30x41cm-12x16in) indis sig. board prov. 17-Jun-3 John Moran, Pasadena #170 est:800-1200
£1078 $1800 €1563 Caralina Island. Cabin in mountain landscape. Desert in spring (13x23cm-5x9in) s. board set of three prov. 17-Jun-3 John Moran, Pasadena #220 est:600-900
£1198 $2000 €1737 Springtime in the Valley (46x61cm-18x24in) s. prov. 17-Jun-3 John Moran, Pasadena #106b est:1000-2000
£1205 $2000 €1747 Mission of San Luis Rey (25x30cm-10x12in) s.i. board. 11-Jun-3 Butterfields, San Francisco #4272/R est:3000-5000
£1347 $2250 €1953 Red Rock Canyon (64x76cm-25x30in) s. i.on stretcher prov. 17-Jun-3 John Moran, Pasadena #141 est:2000-3000
£1946 $3250 €2822 Landscape, along the Carmen Coast (30x41cm-12x16in) s. board prov. 17-Jun-3 John Moran, Pasadena #217 est:800-1200

SMITH, Geoffrey (20th C) American
£250 $400 €375 Coastal scene (30x46cm-12x18in) s. panel. 15-Mar-3 Eldred, East Dennis #122/R

SMITH, George (attrib) (19/20th C) British
£4000 $6240 €6000 Reading lesson (71x91cm-28x36in) 7-Nov-2 Christie's, Kensington #202/R est:3000-5000

SMITH, George (1829-1901) British
£700 $1092 €1050 Fisherman, wife and child in a river landscape (15x23cm-6x9in) board. 10-Sep-2 Clarke Gammon, Guildford #19
£3000 $4680 €4500 Passing the time (28x23cm-11x9in) s.d.1863 panel. 14-Apr-3 Sotheby's, London #69/R est:3000-5000
£5000 $8300 €7500 Nibble (63x81cm-25x32in) 12-Jun-3 Sotheby's, London #250/R est:5000-7000
£14000 $22540 €21000 Rightful heir. Coming of Age (26x41cm-10x16in) s.i. panel pair prov.exhib. 20-Feb-3 Christie's, London #333/R est:18000

SMITH, George (1870-1934) British
£520 $811 €780 Storm over Ben Nevis (46x76cm-18x30in) s. 15-Oct-2 Canterbury Auctions, UK #162/R
£520 $842 €780 Cattle in pasture (16x24cm-6x9in) s. panel. 23-Jan-3 Bonhams, Edinburgh #319/R
£540 $875 €810 Coal boat at Blackwaterfoot, Arran (39x40cm-15x16in) s. board. 23-Jan-3 Bonhams, Edinburgh #335
£550 $891 €825 Unloading a fishing vessel at low tide (30x51cm-12x20in) s. 23-Jan-3 Christie's, Kensington #225
£700 $1162 €1050 Figure with a white horse in a sunlit wooded glade (30x40cm-12x16in) board. 10-Jun-3 Bonhams, Leeds #189
£1100 $1704 €1650 Wood cart (29x39cm-11x15in) s. board. 3-Dec-2 Sotheby's, Olympia #192/R est:1000-1500
£1200 $1872 €1800 Barra pony, Hebrides (18x25cm-7x10in) indis sig. i.verso panel. 14-Apr-3 Sotheby's, London #153/R est:800-1200
£1300 $2067 €1950 Ponies on the banks of a loch (16x24cm-6x9in) panel. 6-Mar-3 Christie's, Kensington #177/R est:600-800
£1300 $2028 €1950 Stackyard (39x50cm-15x20in) s. board. 26-Mar-3 Woolley & Wallis, Salisbury #166/R est:800-1200
£1500 $2369 €2250 White mare (39x49cm-15x19in) s. board. 27-Nov-2 Sotheby's, Olympia #251/R est:500-700
£1500 $2385 €2250 Duck pond (41x51cm-16x20in) s. board. 6-Mar-3 Christie's, Kensington #176/R est:800-1200
£1600 $2544 €2400 Plough team (30x39cm-12x15in) s. board. 6-Mar-3 Christie's, Kensington #178/R est:800-1200
£1700 $2635 €2550 Cowherd and watering cattle (39x50cm-15x20in) s. board. 5-Dec-2 Bonhams, Edinburgh #124 est:2000-3000
£1900 $2907 €2850 Little cowherd (30x40cm-12x16in) s. canvas on board. 22-Aug-2 Bonhams, Edinburgh #1090 est:1000-1500
£2800 $4368 €4200 Heavy horses ploughing (41x51cm-16x20in) s. 13-Sep-2 Lyon & Turnbull, Edinburgh #111/R est:1000-1500

SMITH, George Washington (1879-1930) American
£833 $1300 €1250 Fisherman (84x102cm-33x40in) s. board. 12-Oct-2 Neal Auction Company, New Orleans #647/R

SMITH, Gerard Arnold Christiaan (1905-1995) Dutch
£318 $497 €500 Still life of flowers (39x34cm-15x13in) s. 6-Nov-2 Vendue Huis, Gravenhage #199/R

SMITH, Gordon Appelby (1919-) Canadian
£685 $1083 €1028 Abstract painting (29x65cm-11x26in) s. board painted c.1955 prov. 14-Nov-2 Heffel, Vancouver #207/R est:1800-2200 (C.D 1700)

£1008 $1593 €1512 Snowy valley in the mountains (29x38cm-11x15in) s. board painted c.1948 prov. 14-Nov-2 Heffel, Vancouver #244/R est:3000-4000 (C.D 2500)
£1457 $2332 €2186 Marshlands (61x76cm-24x30in) s. s.i.d.1979 verso. 15-May-3 Heffel, Vancouver #203 est:2000-3000 (C.D 3250)

SMITH, Grace Cossington (1892-1984) Australian
£3928 $6207 €5892 Bush (53x44cm-21x17in) s. board prov. 27-Nov-2 Deutscher-Menzies, Melbourne #74/R est:12000-18000 (A.D 11000)
£5747 $8563 €8621 Farm in the valley (36x45cm-14x18in) s.d.49 i.verso canvas on board prov. 27-Aug-2 Christie's, Melbourne #63/R est:12000-18000 (A.D 15000)
£7200 $11592 €10800 Rocks in bush (53x40cm-21x16in) s.d.60 i.verso canvas on board. 6-May-3 Christie's, Melbourne #59/R est:22000-28000 (A.D 18000)
£9579 $15038 €14369 Sitting room (24x20cm-9x8in) s.d.1974 board prov. 15-Apr-3 Lawson Menzies, Sydney #20/R est:15000-20000 (A.D 25000)
£12749 $20908 €19124 Everlastings (65x44cm-26x17in) s.d.71 board prov.exhib. 4-Jun-3 Deutscher-Menzies, Melbourne #55/R est:35000-45000 (A.D 32000)
£15658 $23957 €23487 Still life with jug and bottlebush (54x37cm-21x15in) s.d.55 board prov. 25-Aug-2 Sotheby's, Paddington #27/R est:40000-60000 (A.D 44000)
£28470 $43559 €42705 Veranda and garden from the artist's bedroom (60x45cm-24x18in) s.d.56 prov.exhib. 26-Aug-2 Sotheby's, Paddington #506/R est:60000-80000 (A.D 80000)
£28674 $43584 €43011 Wildflowers in a glass (62x51cm-24x20in) s. board painted c.1943 prov.exhib.lit. 28-Aug-2 Deutscher-Menzies, Melbourne #52/R est:65000-85000 (A.D 80000)
£34000 $54740 €51000 Blue glass (46x36cm-18x14in) s. s.d.37 verso board prov.exhib.lit. 6-May-3 Christie's, Melbourne #8/R est:40000-60000 (A.D 85000)
£107143 $169286 €160715 Centre of a city (83x71cm-33x28in) s.d.35 prov.exhib.lit. 17-Nov-2 Sotheby's, Paddington #7/R est:250000-350000 (A.D 300000)

Works on paper
£4615 $7338 €6923 Bedroom doorway (35x25cm-14x10in) s. col pencil prov.exhib. 4-Mar-3 Deutscher-Menzies, Melbourne #120/R est:10000-15000 (A.D 12000)

SMITH, Graham (20th C) British
Works on paper
£280 $448 €420 Devon and Somerset above Dunkery Hill (27x37cm-11x15in) s. W/C bodycol. 15-May-3 Lawrence, Crewkerne #937/R
£310 $496 €465 West Somerset near the Quantock Hills (27x37cm-11x15in) s. W/C bodycol. 15-May-3 Lawrence, Crewkerne #936
£340 $544 €510 Mendip hunt near Cheddar Gorge (27x37cm-11x15in) s. W/C bodycol. 15-May-3 Lawrence, Crewkerne #235
£800 $1264 €1200 Quorn kill below Gailee Hill. Draw at fishponds Spinney, Nevile Holt (27x37cm-11x15in) s. W/C htd white pair. 28-Nov-2 Bonhams, Knightsbridge #118/R
£950 $1482 €1425 Devon and Somerset meet at the Luttrell Arms, Dunster (39x56cm-15x22in) s.i. W/C bodycol. 10-Oct-2 Greenslade Hunt, Taunton #563/R

SMITH, Gwen Matthew (20th C) British
£480 $792 €696 Overy colouring no.1 (33x40cm-13x16in) mono. panel. 1-Jul-3 Bonhams, Norwich #290

SMITH, H Hilliard (1871-1948) American
£250 $400 €363 Fishing village (56x69cm-22x27in) s. prov. 17-May-3 CRN Auctions, Cambridge #2
£469 $750 €680 View of Palermo, Italy (61x66cm-24x26in) s.d.1950 prov. 17-May-3 CRN Auctions, Cambridge #3

SMITH, Hely Augustus Morton (1862-1941) British
£1400 $2226 €2100 Sailing ship at sea (109x168cm-43x66in) 29-Apr-3 Gorringes, Lewes #2201

Works on paper
£256 $400 €384 Soldiers at Sailors Monument, NYC (13x18cm-5x7in) s. W/C prov. 12-Apr-3 Weschler, Washington #515/R

SMITH, Henry Pember (1854-1907) American
£1274 $2000 €1911 Country landscape with a cottage (36x51cm-14x20in) s. 22-Nov-2 Skinner, Boston #69/R est:2000-3000
£1429 $2200 €2144 Autumn (35x51cm-14x20in) s. 4-Sep-2 Christie's, Rockefeller NY #341/R est:3000-5000
£1548 $2400 €2322 Boating on a pond (35x51cm-14x20in) s. 3-Dec-2 Christie's, Rockefeller NY #586/R est:3000-5000
£2932 $4750 €4251 Cottage in the country (51x71cm-20x28in) s. 21-May-3 Doyle, New York #89/R est:4000-6000
£3006 $4750 €4509 Morning at Grassy Hill, CT (51x71cm-20x28in) s. i.verso. 24-Apr-3 Shannon's, Milford #228/R est:3000-5000
£3226 $5000 €4839 Villa on the Canal, Venice (36x51cm-14x20in) s. 3-Dec-2 Christie's, Rockefeller NY #589/R est:3000-5000
£3822 $6000 €5733 New England country home with boy fishing (41x61cm-16x24in) s. prov. 19-Nov-2 Butterfields, San Francisco #8038/R est:6000-8000

SMITH, Hobbe (1862-1942) Dutch
£278 $432 €440 Oriental woman (45x30cm-18x12in) s. i. verso. 26-Sep-2 Neumeister, Munich #2842
£3239 $5215 €4600 Sailing ship (31x48cm-12x19in) s. panel. 7-May-3 Vendue Huis, Gravenhage #585/R est:1500-2000
£27848 $43443 €44000 Floralia (212cm-83in) s.d.1898 triptych exhib. 21-Oct-2 Glerum, Amsterdam #128/R est:15000-20000

SMITH, Holmes (1863-1943) American
£267 $425 €401 Mississippi river scene (20x23cm-8x9in) s. painted c.1900. 2-Mar-3 Toomey, Oak Park #554/R

SMITH, Howard E (1885-1970) American
£4870 $7500 €7305 Two Bailey's ice cream paintings (142x71cm-56x28in) s. canvas on aluminum two. 27-Oct-2 Grogan, Boston #39 est:5000-7000

SMITH, Ian (1950-) Australian
£377 $589 €654 View from the view from the pub with the million dollar view (304x107cm-120x42in) s.d.1994 prov. 31-Mar-3 Goodman, Sydney #42 (A.D 1000)
£830 $1295 €1437 Beast in the architecture (199x201cm-78x79in) s.d.1990 after Molvig and Magritte prov. 31-Mar-3 Goodman, Sydney #163 (A.D 2200)

SMITH, J B (18/19th C) British
£1400 $2282 €2100 Carriage horse, and a black and white spotted dog (60x77cm-24x30in) s.d.1836 prov. 11-Feb-3 Bonhams, Knowle #96/R est:1500-2000

SMITH, J Christopher (1891-1943) American
£2229 $3500 €3344 Still life with calla lilies (102x76cm-40x30in) s. i.d.1927 verso prov. 19-Nov-2 Butterfields, San Francisco #8344/R est:4000-6000

SMITH, Jack Carrington (1908-) Australian
£214 $327 €321 Pear tree (56x73cm-22x29in) s.d.58 prov. 26-Aug-2 Sotheby's, Paddington #648 (A.D 600)
£569 $871 €854 Study window (60x76cm-24x30in) s.d.58 i.verso prov. 26-Aug-2 Sotheby's, Paddington #647 est:1000-2000 (A.D 1600)

SMITH, Jack W (1873-1949) American
£1946 $3250 €2822 Owen's Valley landscape (30x41cm-12x16in) s. canvasboard. 17-Jun-3 John Moran, Pasadena #69 est:4000-6000
£4140 $6500 €6210 Spring runoff (41x51cm-16x20in) s. masonite. 19-Nov-2 Butterfields, San Francisco #8278/R est:7000-10000
£7006 $11000 €10509 Trees by a hillside (41x51cm-16x20in) s. board prov. 19-Nov-2 Butterfields, San Francisco #8279/R est:4000-6000
£12739 $20000 €19109 Hillside sycamore (71x86cm-28x34in) s. i.stretcher. 20-Nov-2 Christie's, Los Angeles #6/R est:25000-35000
£16129 $25000 €24194 Riders in the high sierras (71x86cm-28x34in) s.d.Oct 20 45. 4-Dec-2 Sotheby's, New York #144/R est:40000-60000

SMITH, James Burrell (1824-1897) British
£480 $782 €720 Waterfall (27x21cm-11x8in) s. board. 29-Jan-3 Sotheby's, Olympia #122/R

Works on paper
£300 $465 €450 Continental landscape with watermill and figures by a stream (33x46cm-13x18in) s.d.1865 W/C htd white. 1-Oct-2 Fellows & Sons, Birmingham #188/R
£300 $468 €450 Mount Cenis with a cross in the foreground (12x17cm-5x7in) s.d.1886 pencil W/C gum arabic. 27-Mar-3 Christie's, Kensington #146
£350 $557 €525 Sterling Castle (23x32cm-9x13in) W/C. 29-Apr-3 Bonhams, Knightsbridge #31/R
£400 $624 €600 Hillside village with farmer on path (22x33cm-9x13in) s.d.1867 W/C bodycol. 6-Nov-2 Bonhams, Chester #462
£560 $868 €840 Rural landscape with autumn trees (47x31cm-19x12in) s.d.1842 W/C. 1-Oct-2 Fellows & Sons, Birmingham #187/R
£600 $936 €900 Mount Cenis, Italy (12x17cm-5x7in) s.d.1886 pencil W/C. 17-Oct-2 Christie's, Kensington #93/R

£680 $1061 €1020 Mount Cenis, with a view of an alpine village with elderly figure in the foreground (12x17cm-5x7in) s.d.1886 pencil W/C gum arabic htd white. 17-Oct-2 Christie's, Kensington #94/R

£820 $1279 €1230 Village with figures in the foreground (37x58cm-15x23in) s. one d.1865 W/C pair. 26-Mar-3 Sotheby's, Olympia #46/R

£820 $1304 €1230 Extensive lakeland landscape with cattle on a river bridge (56x107cm-22x42in) s.d.1863 W/C. 19-Mar-3 Brightwells, Leominster #1176/R

£880 $1434 €1320 Highland lakeside views (16x47cm-6x19in) s.d.1866 W/C htd white gun arabic. 29-Jan-3 Dreweatt Neate, Newbury #91/R

£1500 $2325 €2250 Tintern Abbey, Monmouthshire (33x50cm-13x20in) s.d.1884 pencil W/C htd white. 4-Dec-2 Christie's, Kensington #30/R est:1500-2000

£1550 $2527 €2325 View on Mount Cenis, Italy (35x58cm-14x23in) s.i.d.1888 W/C htd white. 29-Jan-3 Dreweatt Neate, Newbury #90/R est:800-1200

£1550 $2542 €2325 Alnwick (28x42cm-11x17in) s.d.1856 W/C htd white. 4-Feb-3 Bonhams, Leeds #279 est:700-900

£1700 $2771 €2550 Village of Grange Borrowdale (47x70cm-19x28in) s.d.1853 W/C. 29-Jan-3 Dreweatt Neate, Newbury #80/R est:800-1200

£2000 $3140 €3000 View of Windsor Castle from across the Thames (34x50cm-13x20in) s.d.1884 pencil W/C gum arabic bodycol scratching out. 21-Nov-2 Christie's, London #60/R est:2500-3500

£2100 $3444 €3150 Cattle on a bridge above Loch Fyne (42x68cm-17x27in) s.d.1879 W/C htd white. 4-Feb-3 Bonhams, Leeds #280 est:1500-2000

£2200 $3652 €3300 Derwentwater with Bassenthwaite beyond, Cumbria (54x105cm-21x41in) s.d.1868 W/C bodycol. 12-Jun-3 Bonhams, New Bond Street #653/R est:2500-3500

SMITH, James William Garrett (fl.1878-1887) British

£4000 $6320 €6000 Thames at Battersea (59x140cm-23x55in) s.i.verso. 2-Dec-2 Sotheby's, London #43/R est:4000-6000

SMITH, Jerome Howard (1861-1941) American

£633 $1000 €950 Hunted hostiles (25x36cm-10x14in) s. i.verso canvasboard. 24-Apr-3 Shannon's, Milford #219/R est:1200-1800

SMITH, Jesse Willcox (1863-1935) American

£16149 $26000 €24224 Little boy climbing dark stairway (61x38cm-24x15in) indis.sig. board lit. 10-May-3 Illustration House, New York #38/R est:25000-35000

Works on paper

£1180 $1900 €1770 Lady seated in an armchair (61x30cm-24x12in) i. chl exec.c.1900. 22-Feb-3 Pook & Pook, Downington #353/R est:1000-1500

£41667 $65000 €62501 Little Red Riding Hood approaching grandmother (64x41cm-25x16in) s. chl oil W/C lit. 9-Nov-2 Illustration House, New York #57/R est:60000-80000

SMITH, John (fl.1854-1876) British

£600 $996 €870 Sunny village street Ceres, Fife (30x41cm-12x16in) s. board. 10-Jun-3 David Lay, Penzance #79/R

SMITH, John Brandon (fl.1859-1884) British

£750 $1245 €1125 Nightfall with a figure on a woodland path (51x68cm-20x27in) s.d.1874. 10-Jun-3 Bonhams, Leeds #185

£850 $1420 €1233 Swallow falls, Vale of Neath (29x24cm-11x9in) i.verso board. 17-Jun-3 Bonhams, New Bond Street #67/R

£900 $1386 €1350 Waterfall in a wooded valley (46x36cm-18x14in) init.verso. 5-Sep-2 Christie's, Kensington #123/R

£2556 $4243 €3706 Highland stream in Spate (51x61cm-20x24in) s. 10-Jun-3 Ritchie, Toronto #71a/R est:4000-6000 (C.D 5750)

£2866 $4500 €4299 Waterfall on the Dulas, South Wales (51x41cm-20x16in) s.d.1874 i.on stretcher prov. 14-Dec-2 Weschler, Washington #594/R est:2000-3000

Prints

£2500 $3900 €3750 Highland torrent (35x46cm-14x18in) s.d.1881. 7-Nov-2 Christie's, Kensington #108/R est:3000-5000

SMITH, John Henry (fl.1852-1893) British

£600 $936 €900 First lady of the line - Portrait of Miss Thermuthis Pharoah (55x46cm-22x18in) s. canvas on board. 6-Nov-2 Bonhams, Chester #397

SMITH, John Raphael (1752-1812) British

Works on paper

£300 $464 €450 Portrait of a lady seated at a table (23x18cm-9x7in) black chk htd white. 30-Sep-2 Sotheby's, Olympia #533/R

£920 $1518 €1334 Portrait of Benjamin Thompson (24x20cm-9x8in) pastel. 2-Jul-3 Sotheby's, Olympia #160/R

£4286 $6771 €6429 Portrait of John Glover (13x12cm-5x5in) i.verso col crayon prov. 26-Nov-2 Sotheby's, Melbourne #150/R est:6000-8000 (A.D 12000)

SMITH, John Raphael (attrib) (1752-1812) British

Works on paper

£1800 $2970 €2610 Portrait of Andrew William Corbett. Portrait of Vincent Corbett (29x21cm-11x8in) pencil col chk pair. 3-Jul-3 Christie's, Kensington #5/R est:700-900

£3500 $5775 €5075 John Corbett of Sundorne. Vincent Corbett. Kynaston (29x21cm-11x8in) pencil col chk three. 3-Jul-3 Christie's, Kensington #3/R est:700-900

SMITH, John Warwick (1749-1831) British

Works on paper

£700 $1162 €1050 Entrance to Chepstow Castle, Wales (15x22cm-6x9in) W/C. 12-Jun-3 Bonhams, New Bond Street #617/R

£900 $1494 €1350 Kings Weston House and Shirehampton Park from the Penpole Gates, Bristol (13x21cm-5x8in) bears i. W/C. 12-Jun-3 Bonhams, New Bond Street #616/R

£1200 $1956 €1800 Villa of Mecenas at Tivoli. Great cascade Tivoli (12x19cm-5x7in) s.i.d.1793 verso W/C pair. 29-Jan-3 Sotheby's, Olympia #38/R est:1000-1500

£1300 $2055 €1950 Figures by a church and some ruins, Italy (30x43cm-12x17in) s. W/C over pencil. 28-Nov-2 Sotheby's, London #249/R est:1500-2000

£1300 $2055 €1950 Convent of La Trinita near la Cava, Italy (25x35cm-10x14in) s. W/C over pencil. 28-Nov-2 Sotheby's, London #250/R est:1500-2000

£1400 $2170 €2100 Loughor Sands, Gower (13x22cm-5x9in) pencil W/C. 4-Dec-2 Christie's, Kensington #70/R est:1200-1800

£2031 $3250 €2945 Pass from the Tyrol into Italy. Near Verona and Cortona (19x31cm-7x12in) one i.verso W/C paper on board two. 16-May-3 Skinner, Boston #33/R est:2500-3500

£2600 $4056 €3900 Coast of Sorrento (26x37cm-10x15in) i. pencil W/C prov. 17-Oct-2 Christie's, Kensington #126/R est:1500-2000

£2600 $4108 €3900 Sailing vessels off the island of Elba (15x22cm-6x9in) i. W/C over pencil scratching out. 28-Nov-2 Sotheby's, London #232/R est:2000-3000

£2800 $4452 €4200 Bissone on the lake of Lugano (30x44cm-12x17in) s. W/C over pencil prov. 19-Mar-3 Sotheby's, London #146/R est:3000-4000

£10000 $14300 €15000 Tintern Abbey by moonlight (13x21cm-5x8in) pencil W/C scratching out prov.exhib.lit. 22-Jan-3 Christie's, London #14/R est:8000

SMITH, John Wells (19th C) British

£450 $734 €675 Country girl reading a letter on a grassy knoll (43x33cm-17x13in) mono. 29-Jan-3 Dreweatt Neate, Newbury #180a

SMITH, Joseph B (1798-1876) American

£658 $1000 €987 Clipper ship, American Eagle (51x61cm-20x24in) s. board. 17-Aug-2 North East Auctions, Portsmouth #944

SMITH, Joseph Clarendon (1778-1810) British

Works on paper

£650 $1066 €975 Thames at Chiswick (23x32cm-9x13in) s. pencil W/C sold with a landscape by circle of Paul Sanby. 6-Jun-3 Christie's, London #92

SMITH, Joseph Lindon (attrib) (1863-1950) American

Works on paper

£545 $845 €850 View of Bergstengarden (34x60cm-13x24in) s.i. W/C gouache over crayon. 4-Dec-2 Piasa, Paris #202/R

SMITH, Joshua (1905-1995) Australian

£731 $1162 €1097 Building in landscape (25x30cm-10x12in) s. canvas on board. 4-Mar-3 Deutscher-Menzies, Melbourne #254/R (A.D 1900)

SMITH, Jules Andre (1880-1959) American

Works on paper

£226 $350 €339 Crapple, Eatonville Florida (41x28cm-16x11in) s.i. W/C. 7-Dec-2 Neal Auction Company, New Orleans #892

£258 $400 €387 In the quarter Eatonville, florida (30x38cm-12x15in) s. W/C. 7-Dec-2 Neal Auction Company, New Orleans #894
£258 $400 €387 Send one home, Eatonville, Florida (28x43cm-11x17in) s. W/C. 7-Dec-2 Neal Auction Company, New Orleans #895
£290 $450 €435 Hardware, Eatonville, Florida (41x28cm-16x11in) s. W/C. 7-Dec-2 Neal Auction Company, New Orleans #893

SMITH, Kathryn Evelyn (20th C) Australian
£1015 $1614 €1523 Under Wylies baths (182x151cm-72x59in) prov. 23-Mar-3 Goodman, Sydney #36/R (A.D 2700)

SMITH, Keith C (1924-) Canadian
£1606 $2522 €2409 Robson Bite area, BC (55x70cm-22x28in) s.i. 25-Nov-2 Hodgins, Calgary #313/R est:5000-7000 (C.D 4000)

SMITH, Ken (?) ?
£712 $1089 €1068 Sea and sky (100x197cm-39x78in) painted c.1979 prov. 26-Aug-2 Sotheby's, Paddington #706 est:300-400 (A.D 2000)

SMITH, Kiki (1954-) American
£5380 $8500 €8070 Hands (59x193cm-23x76in) s. paint on siler leafed Japanese paper painted 1994 prov.exhib. 13-Nov-2 Sotheby's, New York #598/R est:8000-10000
£11250 $18000 €16875 Untitled - hands (59x193cm-23x76in) s. paint on silver leafed vintage Japanese paper painted 1994. 14-May-3 Sotheby's, New York #346/R est:8000-12000

Sculpture
£18987 $30000 €28481 Untitled - head with tongue (21x23x16cm-8x9x6in) i.d.1999 phosphorous bronze in two parts prov. 12-Nov-2 Phillips, New York #146/R est:35000-45000
£20312 $32500 €30468 Virgin Mary (89x43x61cm-35x17x24in) s. prosthetic eyes brush pen ink paper mache assemblage prov. 14-May-3 Sotheby's, New York #369/R est:35000-45000
£43750 $70000 €65625 Flock. white tombasil bronze in 71 parts executed 1998 prov. 14-May-3 Sotheby's, New York #368/R est:35000-45000

Works on paper
£955 $1500 €1433 Bird with wax stamp (22x18cm-9x7in) s.d.1998 mixed media collage. 21-Nov-2 Swann Galleries, New York #198/R est:2000-3000

SMITH, Leon Polk (1906-1996) American
£5063 $8000 €7595 Constellation levelling blue green (107x62cm-42x24in) s. i.d.1967 verso shaped canvas prov. 13-Nov-2 Sotheby's, New York #215/R est:8000-12000

SMITH, Lewis Edward (1871-1926) Canadian?
£333 $546 €500 Home and garden with figure (14x20cm-6x8in) s. panel. 3-Jun-3 Joyner, Toronto #437/R (C.D 750)

SMITH, Lorne Kidd (1880-?) Canadian
£535 $829 €803 Laurentians (51x75cm-20x30in) s. board. 3-Dec-2 Joyner, Toronto #487 est:1200-1500 (C.D 1300)

SMITH, Lowell Ellsworth (1924-) American
Works on paper
£641 $1000 €962 Covered wagon (36x51cm-14x20in) s. W/C prov. 9-Nov-2 Santa Fe Art, Santa Fe #243/R est:1000-2000
£1039 $1600 €1559 Morning at Las Trampas (18x25cm-7x10in) W/C. 25-Oct-2 Morris & Whiteside, Hilton Head Island #123 est:1200-1500

SMITH, Marcella (1887-1963) British
£250 $408 €375 Sheep in a sunlit glade (51x58cm-20x23in) s. 13-Feb-3 David Lay, Penzance #431

SMITH, Marshall D (1874-1973) American
£1772 $2800 €2658 Fountain New Orleans. Ready for the ball, Old New Orleans (41x33cm-16x13in) s. i.d.23 verso board pair prov.exhib. 16-Nov-2 New Orleans Auction, New Orleans #1557/R est:1500-2500
£1948 $3000 €2922 Sunlit courtyard, Old New Orleans (61x91cm-24x36in) s.i. painted c.1935. 8-Sep-2 Treadway Gallery, Cincinnati #571/R est:3000-5000
£2308 $3600 €3462 Afternoon call, Old New Orlands (71x102cm-28x40in) s. i.d.c.1925 exhib.prov. 20-Sep-2 New Orleans Auction, New Orleans #1230/R est:1500-2500

SMITH, Mary (1842-1878) American
£4063 $6500 €5891 Chicks (25x30cm-10x12in) s.d.1863. 17-May-3 CRN Auctions, Cambridge #1
£5247 $8500 €7608 Sharing a meal (30x38cm-12x15in) s. indis.d.18-2. 21-May-3 Doyle, New York #73/R est:4000-6000
£5389 $9000 €7814 Seven chicks (23x30cm-9x12in) i.on stretcher. 22-Jun-3 Freeman, Philadelphia #99/R est:3000-5000
£5389 $9000 €7814 Intruder (23x29cm-9x11in) s.d.1875. 22-Jun-3 Freeman, Philadelphia #100/R est:3000-5000
£5389 $9000 €7814 Object of interest (23x30cm-9x12in) s.d.1875. 22-Jun-3 Freeman, Philadelphia #101/R est:3000-5000
£7784 $13000 €11287 Hen and her chicks (51x61cm-20x24in) s.d.1868 canvas on board. 22-Jun-3 Freeman, Philadelphia #98/R est:8000-12000

SMITH, Mary Tillman (1904-1995) American
£1975 $3200 €2963 Untitled (57x68cm-22x27in) oil on tin prov. 27-Jan-3 Christie's, Rockefeller NY #96/R est:1500-2500

SMITH, Matt Read (1960-) American
£1164 $1700 €1746 Atop Red Mountain pass (41x51cm-16x20in) 18-May-2 Altermann Galleries, Santa Fe #203/R
£1370 $2000 €2055 Distant view of Monument Valley (41x51cm-16x20in) 18-May-2 Altermann Galleries, Santa Fe #202/R

SMITH, Miller (fl.1885-1920) British
£300 $468 €450 Loading the hay cart, farmhand with chickens and barn (24x33cm-9x13in) board. 21-Sep-2 Lacy Scott, Bury St.Edmunds #405

SMITH, Mrs Stewart (fl.1869-1887) British
Works on paper
£500 $780 €750 Edinburgh street scene (53x40cm-21x16in) s. W/C. 26-Mar-3 Woolley & Wallis, Salisbury #69/R

SMITH, Nathaniel Cannon (1866-1943) American
£257 $375 €386 Snowy landscape (41x46cm-16x18in) s.d.23. 10-May-2 Skinner, Boston #207/R

SMITH, Paul K (1893-1978) American
£343 $500 €515 Deserted buildings, Denver Co (46x61cm-18x24in) s. s.i.verso panel. 10-May-2 Skinner, Boston #129/R

SMITH, Peter James (20th C) New Zealander
£1579 $2463 €2369 Elevation of sunlight (36x95cm-14x37in) s.d.1997 acrylic paper on canvas exhib. 27-Mar-3 International Art Centre, Auckland #51/R est:4500-6000 (NZ.D 4500)

SMITH, Ray (1959-) American
£2200 $3586 €3300 Portrait of a boy (40x30cm-16x12in) s.d.1994. 3-Feb-3 Sotheby's, Olympia #150/R est:1500-2000
£2215 $3500 €3323 Fable de la vache (63x75cm-25x30in) s.d.1991 paper prov. 13-Nov-2 Sotheby's, New York #591/R
£2561 $4200 €3842 Odalisque (91x122cm-36x48in) s.d.1988 prov.exhib. 28-May-3 Christie's, Rockefeller NY #146/R est:4000-6000
£5405 $8703 €8108 Euphoria (109x132cm-43x52in) s.d.1997 wood prov. 7-May-3 AB Stockholms Auktionsverk #1048/R est:75000-100000 (S.KR 70000)
£10191 $16000 €15287 Untitled (30x41cm-12x16in) s.d.2000 acrylic prov. 19-Nov-2 Sotheby's, New York #142/R est:25000

Works on paper
£510 $800 €765 Tricolor flags (34x45cm-13x18in) s.d.1991 W/C ink. 21-Nov-2 Swann Galleries, New York #199/R

SMITH, Reginald (1855-1925) British
Works on paper
£320 $499 €480 Coastal scene with waves in a swell (50x106cm-20x42in) s. W/C. 9-Oct-2 Woolley & Wallis, Salisbury #18/R

SMITH, Rhonda (1969-) British
£1300 $2015 €1950 On the beach (89x135cm-35x53in) s. 24-Sep-2 Anderson & Garland, Newcastle #401/R est:500-900

SMITH, Richard (1931-) British
Works on paper
£360 $601 €522 Seven tan shafts (58x73cm-23x29in) s.d.68 col crayon cut card prov. 17-Jun-3 Rosebery Fine Art, London #448
£800 $1240 €1200 Drawing, orange, 2 intersections (100x143cm-39x56in) s.d.70 pastel collage prov. 4-Dec-2 Christie's, Kensington #355

SMITH, Robert Catterson (fl.1880-1890) British
Works on paper
£1076 $1668 €1700 Harvest (45x32cm-18x13in) init. monochrome gouache. 25-Sep-2 James Adam, Dublin #92/R est:1800-2500

SMITH, Robert Edward (20th C) American
£288 $450 €432 Master and the slaves (43x64cm-17x25in) artist name.i.d.73 verso masonite. 12-Oct-2 Neal Auction Company, New Orleans #1419

SMITH, Russell (1812-1896) American
£2968 $4600 €4452 Half mile from sestri, genoese Coast (51x76cm-20x30in) s.i. i.d.1851-71 verso. 7-Dec-2 Neal Auction Company, New Orleans #226/R
£3871 $6000 €5807 Pennypack Park (30x46cm-12x18in) init. i.verso prov. 8-Dec-2 Freeman, Philadelphia #97/R est:4000-6000

SMITH, Russell (attrib) (1812-1896) American
£224 $350 €336 Autumn lake landscape (18x30cm-7x12in) 28-Mar-3 Eldred, East Dennis #567/R

SMITH, Sidney (1912-1982) British
£280 $434 €420 Stroll along the road (25x30cm-10x12in) s.d.46 board. 4-Dec-2 John Ross, Belfast #205

SMITH, Sir Matthew (1879-1959) British
£360 $601 €522 Fish (22x31cm-9x12in) oil on paper. 23-Jun-3 Bonhams, Bath #107
£8800 $13816 €13200 White chrysanthemums and pears (46x61cm-18x24in) init. prov. 22-Nov-2 Christie's, London #42/R est:6000-8000
£9000 $13950 €13500 Still life with bowl and jug (46x56cm-18x22in) 4-Dec-2 Sotheby's, London #11/R est:7000-10000
£10000 $16400 €14500 Pink roses (45x38cm-18x15in) painted c.1934. 4-Jun-3 Sotheby's, London #49/R est:10000-15000
£17000 $27880 €24650 Still life with flowers (91x71cm-36x28in) init. 4-Jun-3 Sotheby's, London #16/R est:18000-25000
£17500 $27475 €26250 Still life with fruit (47x58cm-19x23in) init. card on board painted 1948 prov. 22-Nov-2 Christie's, London #44/R est:15000-25000
£22000 $34320 €33000 Flowers in a jug, red background (80x60cm-31x24in) init. prov.exhib. 25-Mar-3 Bonhams, New Bond Street #88/R est:20000-30000
£24000 $37680 €36000 Tulips and mimosa in a brown jug (65x65cm-26x26in) init. init.verso painted 1933 prov.exhib. 22-Nov-2 Christie's, London #43/R est:15000-25000

Works on paper
£700 $1134 €1015 Still life study with birds (50x35cm-20x14in) s. W/C sold with book. 21-May-3 Rupert Toovey, Partridge Green #170/R

SMITH, Spence (?) ?
£1500 $2490 €2175 By the loch side (50x70cm-20x28in) s. board. 13-Jun-3 Lyon & Turnbull, Edinburgh #129 est:500-700
£1800 $2988 €2610 Morar (63x75cm-25x30in) s. board. 13-Jun-3 Lyon & Turnbull, Edinburgh #132 est:700-900
£3800 $6194 €5700 Children on a country path (70x90cm-28x35in) 14-Feb-3 Lyon & Turnbull, Edinburgh #58

SMITH, Stephen Catterson (19/20th C) British
£1000 $1460 €1500 Buy a box (53x43cm-21x17in) board. 12-Jun-2 John Ross, Belfast #81 est:1000-1200
£1200 $1920 €1800 Portrait of Ian Trant Hamilton, Ist Baron Holmpatrick (76x62cm-30x24in) lit. 16-May-3 Sotheby's, London #6 est:1500-2000
£1500 $2400 €2250 Portrait of Sir Richard John Griffith (128x102cm-50x40in) exhib. 15-May-3 Christie's, London #17/R
£5800 $9628 €8700 Portrait of John Wodehouse, 1st Earl of Kimberley (124x99cm-49x39in) 12-Jun-3 Sotheby's, London #77/R est:3000-4000

SMITH, Stephen Catterson (younger) (1849-1912) British
£347 $573 €500 Cabin by a lake. Upland path with sheep (31x46cm-12x18in) two. 7-Jul-3 Hamilton Osborne King, Dublin #225

SMITH, T (19th C) British
Works on paper
£760 $1155 €1140 View of Margate, with the Bathing Place (28x46cm-11x18in) W/C. 13-Aug-2 Canterbury Auctions, UK #130

SMITH, T B (fl.1918-1937) British
£260 $416 €377 Making home, a freshening breeze (30x35cm-12x14in) s.i.verso board. 17-May-3 Thomson Roddick & Medcalf, Edinburgh #654/R
£800 $1280 €1200 Giants Causeway, Co Antrim. Amidst whistling winds and raging seas (17x22cm-7x9in) s. oil bodycol board. 15-May-3 Christie's, Kensington #204/R

SMITH, Thomas (?) British
Works on paper
£1000 $1640 €1450 Minerva Medica, Rome (25x32cm-10x13in) i. pencil W/C pen ink prov.exhib. 5-Jun-3 Christie's, London #84/R est:1000-1500

SMITH, Tony (1912-1980) American
£14103 $22000 €21155 Untitled (122x152cm-48x60in) painted c.1957 prov.exhib. 5-Nov-2 Doyle, New York #37/R est:15000-20000
Sculpture
£9494 $15000 €14241 Mistake (30x30x20cm-12x12x8in) i.num.1/9 black pat. bronze st.f.T.Smith prov. 12-Nov-2 Phillips, New York #102/R est:20000-30000

SMITH, W Eugene (1918-1978) American
Photographs
£1963 $3200 €2945 Spanish wake (23x33cm-9x13in) s.num.8/25 gelatin silver print. 12-Feb-3 Christie's, Rockefeller NY #256/R est:3000-5000
£2025 $3200 €3038 Easter Sunday, from the essay as from my window I sometimes glance (35x22cm-14x9in) gelatin silver print prov.lit. 22-Apr-3 Christie's, Rockefeller NY #136/R est:4000-6000
£2273 $3500 €3410 Gary Hawkins (31x20cm-12x8in) st.i.verso gelatin silver print prov.exhib.lit. 25-Oct-2 Phillips, New York #118/R est:4000-6000
£2273 $3500 €3410 Mad eyes (32x43cm-13x17in) s. photograph. 24-Oct-2 Sotheby's, New York #214/R est:4000-6000
£2532 $4000 €3798 Untitled - man crossing street (22x34cm-9x13in) gelatin silver print prov.lit. 25-Apr-3 Phillips, New York #138/R est:4000-6000
£3481 $5500 €5222 Untitled - mothers day carnations (24x34cm-9x13in) gelatin silver print prov. 25-Apr-3 Phillips, New York #136/R est:4000-6000
£4294 $7000 €6441 Dancer of the flaming coke, Pittsburg (21x33cm-8x13in) s.num.8/25 gelatin silver print. 12-Feb-3 Christie's, Rockefeller NY #255/R est:3500-5500
£4747 $7500 €7121 Steel worker, Pittsburgh (22x31cm-9x12in) photograph prov. 23-Apr-3 Sotheby's, New York #201/R est:4000-6000
£5380 $8500 €8070 Untitled - street corner (51x40cm-20x16in) i.verso gelatin silver print prov. 25-Apr-3 Phillips, New York #137/R est:4000-6000
£7595 $12000 €11393 Untitled from as from my window (35x25cm-14x10in) i.verso gelatin silver print prov.exhib.lit. 25-Apr-3 Phillips, New York #45/R est:5000-7000
£12025 $19000 €18038 Walk to paradise garden (22x19cm-9x7in) s. gelatin silver print prov.lit. 22-Apr-3 Christie's, Rockefeller NY #129/R est:9000-12000

SMITH, Wallace Herndon (1901-) American
£1603 $2500 €2405 St Mark's, Venice (76x102cm-30x40in) s. board. 14-Sep-2 Selkirks, St. Louis #145/R est:3000-5000

SMITH, Walter Granville (1870-1938) American
£696 $1100 €1044 Inside passage (30x46cm-12x18in) s. i.verso board. 26-Apr-3 Jeffery Burchard, Florida #54

SMITH, William (18/19th C) ?
£750 $1193 €1125 Cattle watering in a wooded landscape (30x41cm-12x16in) s.d.1855 panel. 30-Apr-3 Halls, Shrewsbury #282/R

SMITH, William Collingwood (1815-1887) British
Works on paper
£351 $533 €527 Fairlight Bay, Hastings (34x61cm-13x24in) s. W/C. 19-Aug-2 Joel, Victoria #184/R est:800-1200 (A.D 1000)
£400 $628 €600 Sunset on Lago d'Iseo, Italy (14x38cm-6x15in) s.i.d.1886 pencil W/C htd white. 16-Apr-3 Christie's, Kensington #1079/R
£500 $815 €750 Florence from Piazzale Michelangelo (42x59cm-17x23in) s. pencil W/C htd bodycol. 13-Feb-3 Christie's, Kensington #249/R
£500 $810 €750 Coming out on the tide (23x32cm-9x13in) s. pencil W/C. 21-May-3 Christie's, Kensington #420/R
£520 $822 €754 Haystacks at Broadstairs (22x52cm-9x20in) s. W/C. 22-Jul-3 Bonhams, Knightsbridge #205/R

SMITH, William Harding (1848-1922) British
Works on paper
£1300 $2015 €1950 Medieval interior scene with archbishop and young boy (42x52cm-17x20in) s. W/C. 1-Oct-2 Fellows & Sons, Birmingham #152/R est:350-550

SMITH, William St Thomas (1862-1926) Canadian
Works on paper
£244 $401 €366 Woodland stream (36x26cm-14x10in) s. W/C. 3-Jun-3 Joyner, Toronto #552 (C.D 550)

£267 $437 €401 Autumn stream (39x56cm-15x22in) s. W/C. 3-Jun-3 Joyner, Toronto #500 (C.D 600)

SMITH, Xanthus (1838-1929) American
£1184 $1800 €1776 Steamship, Rusland, on the beach at Long Branch, New Jersey (28x36cm-11x14in) init. i.d.June 1877 verso paper. 17-Aug-2 North East Auctions, Portsmouth #508/R
£1258 $2000 €1887 Dunally Castle, Bay of Oban, Scotland (25x38cm-10x15in) s. painted c.1880. 2-Mar-3 Toomey, Oak Park #601/R est:1800-2200
Works on paper
£597 $950 €896 Strong wind (18x25cm-7x10in) s.d.1892 gouache pencil paper on board. 5-Mar-3 Christie's, Rockefeller NY #88/R
£838 $1400 €1215 Breezing up (16x24cm-6x9in) s.d.1892 W/C. 22-Jun-3 Freeman, Philadelphia #82/R est:1500-2500
£839 $1300 €1259 Atlantic city (19x24cm-7x9in) s.i. W/C sold with another by the same hand. 8-Dec-2 Freeman, Philadelphia #104/R est:500-800

SMITH-HALD, Bjorn (1883-1964) Norwegian
£314 $493 €471 Still life of bottles (52x41cm-20x16in) s. 25-Nov-2 Blomqvist, Lysaker #1254/R (N.KR 3600)
£341 $532 €512 Child with doll (46x55cm-18x22in) s. panel. 23-Sep-2 Blomqvist, Lysaker #1224/R (N.KR 4000)
£386 $610 €579 Landscape from Fjellveien (49x64cm-19x25in) s. i.verso. 17-Dec-2 Grev Wedels Plass, Oslo #273/R (N.KR 4400)
£1735 $2706 €2603 At a street cafe in France (87x114cm-34x45in) s.d.1953. 21-Oct-2 Blomqvist, Oslo #370/R est:30000-35000 (N.KR 20000)
Works on paper
£575 $938 €863 Petit garcon avec bateau (37x56cm-15x22in) s.d.1914 mixed media. 17-Feb-3 Blomqvist, Lysaker #1218 (N.KR 6500)
£575 $938 €863 Jeune fille que dormir (71x53cm-28x21in) s.d.1914 mixed media. 17-Feb-3 Blomqvist, Lysaker #1219 (N.KR 6500)
£1239 $2019 €1859 Two lovely ladies (77x104cm-30x41in) s. W/C. 17-Feb-3 Blomqvist, Lysaker #1217/R est:5000-7000 (N.KR 14000)

SMITH-HALD, Frithjof (1846-1903) Norwegian
£344 $557 €516 Evening in Kabelvaag (27x39cm-11x15in) s. panel. 27-Jan-3 Blomqvist, Lysaker #1238/R (N.KR 3800)
£570 $901 €855 From Smoela (19x24cm-7x9in) s. i.verso panel. 17-Dec-2 Grev Wedels Plass, Oslo #187/R (N.KR 6500)
£746 $1224 €1082 Fjord landscape at sunset (27x40cm-11x16in) s. panel. 4-Jun-3 AB Stockholms Auktionsverk #2445/R (S.KR 9500)
£949 $1538 €1424 From Utne in Hardanger (26x35cm-10x14in) s. panel. 27-Jan-3 Blomqvist, Lysaker #1239/R (N.KR 10500)
£2624 $4252 €3936 Northern landscape with seabirds, Norway (58x79cm-23x31in) s/. 26-May-3 Grev Wedels Plass, Oslo #86/R est:30000-40000 (N.KR 29000)
£3460 $5467 €5190 Woman and children watching fishing boats leaving (47x75cm-19x30in) s.d.88. 2-Dec-2 Blomqvist, Oslo #329/R est:50000-70000 (N.KR 40000)

SMITHEMAN, S Francis (20th C) British
£6000 $9720 €9000 Windjammer Passat near Tower Bridge (51x76cm-20x30in) s. painted c.1930. 21-May-3 Christie's, Kensington #569/R est:2000-3000

SMITHER, Michael (1939-) New Zealander
£442 $690 €663 River and foliage (23x33cm-9x13in) init.d.1985 board. 6-Aug-2 Peter Webb, Auckland #61 est:1800-2500 (NZ.D 1500)
£1212 $1867 €1818 Chaffers Marina, Wellington (38x28cm-15x11in) s.d.1995 board. 4-Sep-2 Dunbar Sloane, Wellington #52/R est:5000-7000 (NZ.D 4000)
£1332 $2078 €1998 From Kati Kara studio (25x64cm-10x25in) s.d.1991 board. 7-Nov-2 International Art Centre, Auckland #15/R est:3000-5000 (NZ.D 4250)
£1724 $2690 €2586 Brooklyn Park, Taranaki (86x65cm-34x26in) s. board exhib. 7-Nov-2 International Art Centre, Auckland #38/R est:6000-10000 (NZ.D 5500)
£1803 $2812 €2705 Back beach, New Plymouth (40x16cm-16x6in) s.d.1974 acrylic board. 7-Nov-2 International Art Centre, Auckland #1/R est:3000-5000 (NZ.D 5750)
£2018 $3147 €3027 Orange mast from the Okahu Bay series (36x36cm-14x14in) s.d.1990 board. 27-Mar-3 International Art Centre, Auckland #34/R est:5500-7500 (NZ.D 5750)
£2431 $3792 €3647 Angel with a dark heart II (92x74cm-36x29in) init.d.1989 board exhib. 8-Apr-3 Peter Webb, Auckland #149/R est:7000-9000 (NZ.D 7000)
£3822 $6000 €5733 Black Rock diptych (75x120cm-30x47in) init.d.1985 board. 10-Dec-2 Peter Webb, Auckland #46/R est:8000-12000 (NZ.D 12000)
£4075 $6357 €6113 Green boat, Okahu Bay (120x120cm-47x47in) s.d.1998 board. 7-Nov-2 International Art Centre, Auckland #41/R est:12000-16000 (NZ.D 13000)
£18025 $28119 €27038 Alfred Road bridge (81x113cm-32x44in) s.d.1971 board prov. 7-Nov-2 International Art Centre, Auckland #33/R est:45000-65000 (NZ.D 57500)
£28472 $44417 €42708 Sarah with cup (88x68cm-35x27in) init.d.1965 board exhib. sold with pencil drawing two. 8-Apr-3 Peter Webb, Auckland #61/R est:65000-75000 (NZ.D 82000)

SMITS, Eugène (1826-1912) Belgian
Works on paper
£342 $534 €500 Elegante a la robe bleue (34x22cm-13x9in) s. W/C. 14-Apr-3 Horta, Bruxelles #303

SMITS, Jakob (1856-1928) Belgian
£576 $921 €800 Paysage des Flandres (17x38cm-7x15in) studio st. i.verso canvas on panel. 13-May-3 Vanderkindere, Brussels #112
£1007 $1621 €1500 Auto-portrait (36x27cm-14x11in) s. canvas on panel. 18-Feb-3 Vanderkindere, Brussels #97
£7547 $11698 €12000 Gardiner (48x32cm-19x13in) s. 5-Oct-2 De Vuyst, Lokeren #446/R est:13000-15000
£12821 $20128 €20000 Coucher de soleil (50x55cm-20x22in) indis.sig. exhib. 10-Dec-2 Renaud, Paris #50/R est:30000
£17931 $28690 €26000 La Sainte Cene (104x128cm-41x50in) 17-Mar-3 Amberes, Antwerp #262/R
£26619 $42590 €37000 Three elephants (92x105cm-36x41in) s. painted 1923 prov.exhib.lit. 17-May-3 De Vuyst, Lokeren #474/R
£38194 $60729 €55000 Scene de famille dans un interieur (100x105cm-39x41in) s. 29-Apr-3 Campo & Campo, Antwerp #282/R est:40000-45000
Works on paper
£252 $392 €400 Le symbole de la campine (21x27cm-8x11in) chl. 14-Oct-2 Amberes, Antwerp #202
£252 $392 €400 Le Christ a table (38x44cm-15x17in) chl. 14-Oct-2 Amberes, Antwerp #204
£252 $392 €400 Dame dans un interieur (20x27cm-8x11in) chl. 14-Oct-2 Amberes, Antwerp #205
£382 $607 €550 Autoportrait (24x25cm-9x10in) st.sig. chl. 29-Apr-3 Campo, Vlaamse Kaai #291
£503 $775 €800 Paysage. Interieur. studio st. chl dr two in one frame. 22-Oct-2 Campo, Vlaamse Kaai #628
£828 $1324 €1200 Vieille dame (41x35cm-16x14in) pencil dr. 17-Mar-3 Amberes, Antwerp #263
£1295 $2072 €1800 Motherhood (21x17cm-8x7in) s. black chk dr. 17-May-3 De Vuyst, Lokeren #334/R est:1400-1800

SMITS, Jan Gerard (1823-1910) Dutch
£987 $1599 €1500 View of Dalfsen (22x28cm-9x11in) s.d.48 panel prov. 21-Jan-3 Christie's, Amsterdam #323/R est:700-900

SMITS, Peter (20th C) American
£617 $950 €926 Harbour scene (61x76cm-24x30in) s. painted c.1940. 8-Sep-2 Treadway Gallery, Cincinnati #575/R

SMITT-HALD, Bjorn (20th C) ?
Works on paper
£287 $447 €450 Girl standing (78x53cm-31x21in) s. gouache htd white. 6-Nov-2 Vendue Huis, Gravenhage #507/R

SMITZ, Gaspar (1635-1707) Dutch
£13000 $20410 €19500 Roemer with peaches, crabs, oysters, pipe and a knife on a stone shelf (24x32cm-9x13in) 13-Dec-2 Christie's, Kensington #98/R est:7000-10000

SMOLDERS, Pol (1921-1997) Belgian
£292 $464 €420 La promenade (38x28cm-15x11in) s. panel. 29-Apr-3 Campo & Campo, Antwerp #807
£694 $1104 €1000 Fille assise (48x37cm-19x15in) s.d.1956. 29-Apr-3 Campo & Campo, Antwerp #285/R
£1250 $1987 €1800 Terrasse ensoleillee dans le parc (56x70cm-22x28in) s. 29-Apr-3 Campo & Campo, Antwerp #283/R est:2000-2500
£1528 $2429 €2200 Dames sur la terrase (63x51cm-25x20in) s.d.1951. 29-Apr-3 Campo & Campo, Antwerp #284/R est:2300-2500
£1793 $2869 €2600 Fillette a la poupee (34x28cm-13x11in) 17-Mar-3 Amberes, Antwerp #265/R
£2069 $3310 €3000 Girl playing (45x50cm-18x20in) s. 15-Mar-3 De Vuyst, Lokeren #302/R est:3000-3600
£2345 $3752 €3400 Terrasse sur la digue (58x68cm-23x27in) 17-Mar-3 Amberes, Antwerp #268/R
Works on paper
£409 $630 €650 Ballerina (62x47cm-24x19in) s. chl. 22-Oct-2 Campo, Vlaamse Kaai #629

£1034 $1655 €1500 Fillette assise avec son chien (72x53cm-28x21in) chk htd pastel dr. 17-Mar-3 Amberes, Antwerp #270
£1310 $2097 €1900 Jeunes dames assises sur une terrasse (74x52cm-29x20in) pencil htd W/C dr. 17-Mar-3 Amberes, Antwerp #272

SMOORENBERG, Dirk (1883-1960) Dutch
£552 $877 €800 Forest lane (45x66cm-18x26in) s. 10-Mar-3 Sotheby's, Amsterdam #315
£987 $1599 €1500 Dutch polder landscape (35x47cm-14x19in) s. two. 21-Jan-3 Christie's, Amsterdam #377 est:1200-1600
£2244 $3478 €3500 Houses along a waterway (49x75cm-19x30in) s.d.11. 3-Dec-2 Christie's, Amsterdam #12/R est:3500-4500
£3448 $5482 €5000 Flower still life (54x40cm-21x16in) s. 10-Mar-3 Sotheby's, Amsterdam #316/R est:5000-7000
£3526 $5465 €5500 Waterlilies (40x50cm-16x20in) s. 3-Dec-2 Christie's, Amsterdam #11/R est:4000-6000
£4861 $8021 €7000 Waterlillies (65x100cm-26x39in) s. 1-Jul-3 Christie's, Amsterdam #381/R est:4000-6000
£6410 $9936 €10000 Willows along a canal (40x50cm-16x20in) s.d.14. 3-Dec-2 Christie's, Amsterdam #17/R est:4000-6000

SMY, Wolfgang (1952-) German
£629 $969 €1000 Dive into water (73x103cm-29x41in) s.d.1988 s.i.d. verso acrylic board. 26-Oct-2 Dr Lehr, Berlin #496/R

SMYTH, Henry (19th C) British
£360 $562 €540 Kidwelly from the canal (40x40cm-16x16in) s. i.verso. 10-Sep-2 Bonhams, Knightsbridge #117

SMYTH, Montague (1863-1965) British
£550 $847 €825 Children on a beach (30x41cm-12x16in) s. wood panel. 3-Sep-2 Gorringes, Lewes #2245

SMYTH, Norman (20th C) Irish
£350 $543 €525 Street figures (46x36cm-18x14in) s. board. 2-Oct-2 John Ross, Belfast #15
£750 $1095 €1125 On Inishlacken, Smyth, Macintyre and Maguire (30x36cm-12x14in) s.d.1998. 12-Jun-2 John Ross, Belfast #104

SMYTHE, Edward Robert (1810-1899) British
£1100 $1716 €1650 Horse watering at a steam by a cottgae with Bramfield church in background (36x28cm-14x11in) s. 11-Apr-3 Keys, Aylsham #617/R est:1200-1500
£1900 $2945 €2850 Hounds study (60x50cm-24x20in) s. prov. 6-Dec-2 Lyon & Turnbull, Edinburgh #26/R est:2000-3000
£2800 $4340 €4200 Figures and animals in a farmyard (51x76cm-20x30in) s. 30-Sep-2 Bonhams, Ipswich #482/R est:2500-3500
£2800 $4396 €4200 Exmoor pony in parkland landscape (69x89cm-27x35in) s. 13-Dec-2 Keys, Aylsham #670/R est:2500-3500
£2800 $4620 €4060 Fisherman and his family (25x35cm-10x14in) s. 1-Jul-3 Bonhams, Norwich #236/R est:1800-2500
£4000 $6200 €6000 Sorting the catch (51x76cm-20x30in) panel. 30-Sep-2 Bonhams, Ipswich #452/R est:4000-6000
£9200 $14260 €13800 Children and ponies on the shire with fleet beyond (61x91cm-24x36in) 30-Sep-2 Bonhams, Ipswich #483/R est:3000-4000
Works on paper
£580 $911 €870 Unloading the catch (34x29cm-13x11in) s. col chk arched top. 16-Dec-2 Bonhams, Bury St Edmunds #410
£720 $1130 €1080 Coach and four crossing a heath (27x33cm-11x13in) s. col chk. 16-Dec-2 Bonhams, Bury St Edmunds #411/R

SMYTHE, Edward Robert (attrib) (1810-1899) British
£290 $447 €435 Noon-day rest (41x57cm-16x22in) 22-Oct-2 Bonhams, Ipswich #300
£700 $1092 €1050 Horse with rider and dog in landscape (38x53cm-15x21in) prov. 11-Apr-3 Keys, Aylsham #616/R

SMYTHE, Lionel Percy (1839-1913) British
Works on paper
£290 $452 €435 Hay field (46x30cm-18x12in) mono. W/C. 11-Apr-3 Keys, Aylsham #850
£1300 $2028 €1950 Shrimping (28x19cm-11x7in) s.d.1882 pencil W/C htd white. 17-Oct-2 Christie's, Kensington #55/R est:600-800
£1900 $2963 €2850 Gleaners (18x30cm-7x12in) s.d.1883 pencil W/C htd bodycol. 19-Sep-2 Christie's, Kensington #170 est:1000-1500
£2500 $3975 €3750 Harvesters (21x32cm-8x13in) s.d.1883 W/C bodycol. 5-Mar-3 Bonhams, Bury St Edmunds #305/R est:500-700

SMYTHE, Minnie (fl.1896-1939) British
Works on paper
£550 $908 €798 Field of daisies (28x19cm-11x7in) mono. pencil W/C. 3-Jul-3 Christie's, Kensington #58/R

SMYTHE, Parks (?) ?
£400 $632 €600 Man sitting fishing at a rocky stream (31x46cm-12x18in) s.d. board. 18-Dec-2 John Nicholson, Haslemere #1305

SMYTHE, Thomas (1825-1906) British
£800 $1240 €1200 Figure before a timbered cottage (25x31cm-10x12in) s. board laid down. 30-Sep-2 Bonhams, Ipswich #473
£1500 $2475 €2175 Cattle drinking at a stream by a cottage. Two peasants talking by a cottage (19x24cm-7x9in) s. pair. 2-Jul-3 Sotheby's, Olympia #133/R est:2000-3000
£1600 $2608 €2400 Pony with game and dog in wooded landscape (33x43cm-13x17in) s. 14-Feb-3 Keys, Aylsham #658/R est:2000-3000
£1650 $2591 €2475 Horse watering at a stream (30x46cm-12x18in) s. 16-Dec-2 Bonhams, Bury St Edmunds #503/R est:1800-2500
£1950 $3023 €2925 Stoke street, Ipswich (32x35cm-13x14in) 30-Sep-2 Bonhams, Ipswich #469 est:1200-1800
£2400 $3720 €3600 Figures at a well with horses and drover and a cottage (28x38cm-11x15in) s. board. 4-Dec-2 Neal & Fletcher, Woodbridge #254/R est:2500-3500
£2800 $4340 €4200 Haywain (40x51cm-16x20in) s. 30-Sep-2 Bonhams, Ipswich #444/R est:3000-5000
£2800 $4620 €4060 Wayside mardle (30x46cm-12x18in) s. 1-Jul-3 Bonhams, Norwich #229/R est:3000-5000
£3000 $4770 €4500 Horses carting timber through the snow (61x45cm-24x18in) s. 5-Mar-3 Bonhams, Bury St Edmunds #408/R est:3000-4000
£3200 $4960 €4800 Figures before thatched cottages and church (39x54cm-15x21in) s. 30-Sep-2 Bonhams, Ipswich #515 est:2000-3000
£4000 $6240 €6000 Washday (28x38cm-11x15in) init. 18-Oct-2 Keys, Aylsham #673/R est:4000-6000
£4200 $7014 €6090 Cart horses on a track in the snow (30x40cm-12x16in) s. 17-Jun-3 Bristol Auction Rooms #552/R est:300-500
£6000 $9720 €8700 Punch and Judy show. The Hurdy Gurdy man (40x40cm-16x16in) s. panel pair round. 29-Jul-3 Henry Adams, Chichester #582/R est:6000-10000
£7000 $10850 €10500 Figures and horse by a cottage with drover and dog in a lane (48x76cm-19x30in) s. 4-Dec-2 Neal & Fletcher, Woodbridge #250/R est:4000-6000
£8600 $13330 €12900 Figures with a horse in a snow covered landscape (29x44cm-11x17in) s. 29-Oct-2 Henry Adams, Chichester #595/R est:1500-2000
£17000 $26350 €25500 Bringing home the holly amidst the snow (30x46cm-12x18in) s. 30-Sep-2 Bonhams, Ipswich #521/R est:4000-6000
Works on paper
£340 $561 €493 Old pier Felixstowe, looking towards Harwich (32x47cm-13x19in) s. W/C. 1-Jul-3 Bonhams, Norwich #78

SNAJDR, Miroslav (1938-) Czechoslovakian
£1136 $1772 €1704 Grand inquisitor (90x69cm-35x27in) s.i.d.73. 12-Oct-2 Dorotheum, Prague #88/R est:40000-60000 (C.KR 55000)

SNAPE, M (fl.1874-1901) British
Works on paper
£520 $827 €780 Norfolk landscape with ducks in the foreground and cattle beyond (18x30cm-7x12in) s. W/C. 6-Mar-3 Bonhams, Cornwall #692
£700 $1113 €1050 River landscape at dusk with cattle grazing. River landscape at dusk with steam tug and barges (25x20cm-10x8in) s. W/C two. 6-Mar-3 Bonhams, Cornwall #693

SNAPE, Sue McCartney (20th C) British
Works on paper
£850 $1403 €1233 Smug couple: Goldman Sachs man and wife so lucky really (37x37cm-15x15in) mono.i.d.00 pencil pen black ink W/C crayon. 3-Jul-3 Christie's, Kensington #164/R
£900 $1485 €1305 Aged symbol: Always wears something in leopard skin print (43x33cm-17x13in) mono.i.d.98 pencil pen black ink W/C. 3-Jul-3 Christie's, Kensington #170/R est:700-900
£1000 $1650 €1450 Bouquet catcher: Grimly determined and wrests it away (53x41cm-21x16in) mono.i.d.00 pencil pen black ink W/C. 3-Jul-3 Christie's, Kensington #165/R est:1000-1500
£1000 $1650 €1450 Dog show judge: Expert on labradors, lurchers and some kind of terrier (51x30cm-20x12in) mono.i.d.02 pencil pen black ink W/C crayon. 3-Jul-3 Christie's, Kensington #168/R est:700-900
£1000 $1650 €1450 Grape expectations (46x44cm-18x17in) mono. pencil W/C red crayon. 3-Jul-3 Christie's, Kensington #171/R est:600-800
£1400 $2310 €2030 A very distinctive nose (52x44cm-20x17in) mono. pencil W/C red crayon. 3-Jul-3 Christie's, Kensington #173/R est:600-800
£1400 $2310 €2030 Bursting with flavour (52x41cm-20x16in) mono. pencil W/C red crayon. 3-Jul-3 Christie's, Kensington #174/R est:600-800
£1700 $2805 €2465 Perhaps in twenty years (48x43cm-19x17in) mono. pencil W/C red crayon. 3-Jul-3 Christie's, Kensington #172/R est:600-800

SNAYERS, Peeter (1592-1666) Flemish
£29605 $47961 €45000 Battle scene (74x104cm-29x41in) s. board. 21-Jan-3 Ansorena, Madrid #99/R est:45000

SNAYERS, Peeter (attrib) (1592-1666) Flemish
£1399 $2336 €2000 La conversion de Saint Paul (28x33cm-11x13in) panel. 25-Jun-3 Artcurial Briest, Paris #475/R est:2000-3000

SNAYERS, Peeter (circle) (1592-1666) Flemish
£7500 $11775 €11250 Equestrian portrait of a nobleman, thought to be Louis XIII (64x49cm-25x19in) panel. 10-Dec-2 Bonhams, New Bond Street #54/R est:7000-10000

SNAYERS, Peeter (studio) (1592-1666) Flemish
£5743 $8959 €8500 Cavalry engagement (53x82cm-21x32in) panel prov. 27-Mar-3 Dorotheum, Vienna #166/R est:4000-6000

SNEBUR (1964-) Italian
£1418 $2298 €2000 Campi spaziali (60x50cm-24x20in) s.i.d.2002 verso acrylic prov. 26-May-3 Christie's, Milan #151/R est:1000-1500

SNEL, Han (1925-) Dutch
£1513 $2451 €2300 Balinese beauty (38x33cm-15x13in) s.i.d.56. 21-Jan-3 Christie's, Amsterdam #445/R est:1200-1600

SNELL, Henry Bayley (1858-1943) American
£370 $600 €555 English castle II (33x28cm-13x11in) board prov. 24-Jan-3 Freeman, Philadelphia #140/R

SNELL, James Herbert (1861-1935) British
£280 $456 €420 Valley of the Derwent looking over Matlock from Crich Carr (50x75cm-20x30in) s. s.i.verso. 12-Feb-3 Bonhams, Knightsbridge #11f
£330 $528 €495 View of an Essex windmill (36x49cm-14x19in) s. 13-May-3 Bonhams, Sevenoaks #350
£350 $539 €525 Peep of St. Pauls from primrose Hill (27x34cm-11x13in) s. i.verso panel. 24-Oct-2 Christie's, Kensington #202
£420 $672 €630 Apple blossom - a corner of the orchard (55x75cm-22x30in) s. s.i.verso. 11-Mar-3 Bonhams, Knightsbridge #35/R
£1900 $3021 €2850 Mirror of the woods (91x122cm-36x48in) s. s.i.verso. 6-Mar-3 Christie's, Kensington #426/R est:1500-2000
£3200 $4928 €4800 Morning in the meadows (91x122cm-36x48in) s. exhib. 5-Sep-2 Christie's, Kensington #217/R est:2000-3000
Works on paper
£260 $405 €390 On the Orwell, Shotley and Dovercourt (29x44cm-11x17in) s. pencil W/C. 19-Sep-2 Christie's, Kensington #167

SNELL, Olive (fl.1910-1940) British
£400 $632 €600 Lady in black dress (92x67cm-36x26in) s. 4-Apr-3 Moore Allen & Innocent, Cirencester #617

SNELL, Peter (?) British?
£851 $1379 €1200 Sunlight through a wooded path with bluebells (49x75cm-19x30in) 20-May-3 Mealy's, Castlecomer #998/R est:400-500

SNELLINCK, Cornelis (?-1669) Dutch
£5660 $8830 €9000 Landscape with figures and windmill (57x91cm-22x36in) s. panel. 23-Sep-2 Wiener Kunst Auktionen, Vienna #19/R est:9000-18000

SNELLINCK, Cornelis (attrib) (?-1669) Dutch
£3521 $5845 €5000 Village view with resting peasants and two monks (72x100cm-28x39in) bears sig. panel prov. 11-Jun-3 Dorotheum, Vienna #104/R est:6000-8000

SNELLINCK, Jan III (1640-1691) Dutch
£2866 $4471 €4500 Wooded landscape with travellers resting (36x49cm-14x19in) mono. panel prov.lit. 5-Nov-2 Sotheby's, Amsterdam #137/R est:5000-7000

SNELLMAN, Anita (1924-) Finnish
£327 $507 €520 Street scene (60x74cm-24x29in) s.d.50. 6-Oct-2 Bukowskis, Helsinki #283/R
£491 $755 €780 Jean-Marc (77x50cm-30x20in) s.d.52. 27-Oct-2 Bukowskis, Helsinki #284/R
£547 $897 €760 Flowers (61x50cm-24x20in) s. 5-Jun-3 Hagelstam, Helsinki #1002/R
£881 $1356 €1400 Landscape (85x85cm-33x33in) s.d.1980. 24-Oct-2 Hagelstam, Helsinki #870

SNELLMAN, Anna (1884-1962) Finnish
£264 $407 €420 Flowers (60x50cm-24x20in) s. 24-Oct-2 Hagelstam, Helsinki #1015/R
£291 $454 €460 Peonies (55x47cm-22x19in) s. 12-Sep-2 Hagelstam, Helsinki #937
£293 $465 €430 Still life of flowers (61x50cm-24x20in) s. 24-Mar-3 Bukowskis, Helsinki #298/R
£304 $474 €480 Flowers (41x33cm-16x13in) s. 12-Sep-2 Hagelstam, Helsinki #1010
£314 $484 €500 Flowers (55x46cm-22x18in) s. 24-Oct-2 Hagelstam, Helsinki #960
£340 $541 €500 Still life of flowers (32x40cm-13x16in) s. 24-Mar-3 Bukowskis, Helsinki #297/R
£986 $1587 €1400 Flowers (56x47cm-22x19in) s.d.1947. 10-May-3 Bukowskis, Helsinki #84/R
Works on paper
£284 $449 €440 Cyclamen (54x45cm-21x18in) s. pastel. 19-Dec-2 Hagelstam, Helsinki #864/R
£327 $507 €520 Crocuses (21x15cm-8x6in) s. pastel. 6-Oct-2 Bukowskis, Helsinki #286/R
£407 $643 €590 Cyclamen (25x19cm-10x7in) s. pastel. 3-Apr-3 Hagelstam, Helsinki #1043

SNELLMAN, Christina (1928-) Finnish
£291 $454 €460 Girl (60x100cm-24x39in) s.d.1962. 12-Sep-2 Hagelstam, Helsinki #890
£302 $468 €480 Street scene in winter (60x81cm-24x32in) s.d.1954. 6-Oct-2 Bukowskis, Helsinki #289/R
£405 $632 €640 Flowers (80x65cm-31x26in) s.d.1972. 12-Sep-2 Hagelstam, Helsinki #839
£642 $988 €1020 The model (101x81cm-40x32in) s.d.1977. 27-Oct-2 Bukowskis, Helsinki #285/R
£692 $1072 €1100 View from Paris (81x65cm-32x26in) s.d.1954. 6-Oct-2 Bukowskis, Helsinki #287/R
£692 $1072 €1100 Quai du Louvre (66x81cm-26x32in) s.d.52. 6-Oct-2 Bukowskis, Helsinki #288/R
£850 $1393 €1300 Grape harvest (80x130cm-31x51in) s.d.1954. 9-Feb-3 Bukowskis, Helsinki #364/R

SNELLMAN, Eero (1890-1951) Finnish
£490 $804 €750 From Vitasaari (42x54cm-17x21in) s.i.d.1928. 9-Feb-3 Bukowskis, Helsinki #365/R
£514 $828 €730 Houses by the sea (47x56cm-19x22in) s.i.d.1928. 10-May-3 Bukowskis, Helsinki #62/R
£566 $872 €900 Paris (38x55cm-15x22in) s.d.1938. 24-Oct-2 Hagelstam, Helsinki #1045
£660 $1017 €1050 Summer (50x61cm-20x24in) s. 24-Oct-2 Hagelstam, Helsinki #913/R
£935 $1496 €1300 Parisian town scene (54x65cm-21x26in) s.i.d.1940. 17-May-3 Hagelstam, Helsinki #142/R

SNELSON, Kenneth (1927-) American
Sculpture
£2404 $3750 €3606 Leda No.7634 (51x72cm-20x28in) st.init.d.69 aluminium wire prov. 5-Nov-2 Doyle, New York #42/R est:4000-6000
£2885 $4500 €4328 Easy k (24x156cm-9x61in) st.init.d.71 aluminium wire lucite base prov. 5-Nov-2 Doyle, New York #41/R est:6000-8000

SNIDOW, Gordon (1936-) British
£3269 $5100 €4904 At first light (41x51cm-16x20in) 9-Nov-2 Altermann Galleries, Santa Fe #173
Works on paper
£2485 $4025 €3603 Benjamin (48x38cm-19x15in) gouache. 23-May-3 Altermann Galleries, Santa Fe #16
£34247 $50000 €51371 Day dreamer (99x84cm-39x33in) gouache. 18-May-2 Altermann Galleries, Santa Fe #162/R

SNIJDERS, Christiaan (1881-1943) Dutch
£500 $785 €750 Barge moored by a windmill on a Dutch waterway. Figure on a punt by Dutch windmill (26x37cm-10x15in) s. pair. 16-Apr-3 Christie's, Kensington #586/R

SNIPER (20th C) British
Works on paper
£250 $393 €375 The Buffs, an officer of the East Kent Regiment (34x22cm-13x9in) s.i. pencil gouache follower of Charles Johnson Payne. 15-Apr-3 Bonhams, Knowle #38
£290 $455 €435 Terriers, study of an officer of the West Kent Yeomanry (34x23cm-13x9in) s.i. pencil gouache follower of Charlie Johnson Payne. 15-Apr-3 Bonhams, Knowle #39

SNOW, Edward Taylor (1844-1913) American
£597 $950 €866 Green Creek, N J (30x51cm-12x20in) s.d. 4-May-3 Treadway Gallery, Cincinnati #509/R

SNOW, John (1911-) Canadian
£1004 $1586 €1506 Interior with figure (74x102cm-29x40in) d.1960. 1-Dec-2 Levis, Calgary #101/R est:3000-3500 (C.D 2500)
£1441 $2291 €2162 Early fall (50x60cm-20x24in) s.i.d.1984. 23-Mar-3 Hodgins, Calgary #92/R est:1200-1800 (C.D 3400)
Works on paper
£391 $610 €653 Yellow bird (43x36cm-17x14in) W/C prov. 13-Apr-3 Levis, Calgary #112/R est:600-800 (C.D 900)

SNOW, John Wray (1801-1854) British
£900 $1404 €1305 Off to market (24x30cm-9x12in) s.d.1835. 27-Mar-3 Neales, Nottingham #1048/R

SNOW, Michael (1929-) Canadian
Sculpture
£42222 $69244 €63333 Sideway (185cm-73in) s.d.62 aluminum painted wood prov.lit. 27-May-3 Sotheby's, Toronto #24/R est:15000-20000 (C.D 95000)

SNOWDON, Lord (20th C) British
£1100 $1704 €1650 Still life of lemons (75x60cm-30x24in) d.1964 board. 30-Sep-2 Sotheby's, Olympia #167 est:150-250

SNOWMAN, Isaac (1874-?) Israeli
£250 $388 €375 Portrait of a lady (65x52cm-26x20in) s. oval. 6-Oct-2 Lots Road, London #360
£5800 $9222 €8700 Reverie (49x66cm-19x26in) s. painted oval. 6-Mar-3 Christie's, Kensington #598/R est:6000-8000

SNYDER, Florence W (20th C) American?
£318 $500 €477 Portrait of a young nude (61x76cm-24x30in) s. 22-Nov-2 Eldred, East Dennis #1015/R

SNYDER, Peter Etril (1944-) Canadian
£333 $547 €483 Homestead, autumn (45x60cm-18x24in) s. board. 9-Jun-3 Hodgins, Calgary #195/R (C.D 750)

SNYDER, Seymour (1897-?) American
£247 $383 €371 Still life (62x51cm-24x20in) s. 3-Dec-2 Ritchie, Toronto #3112/R (C.D 600)

SNYDER, William McKendree (1848-1930) American
£1195 $1900 €1793 Southern Indian beech forest (23x41cm-9x16in) s. painted c.1890. 2-Mar-3 Toomey, Oak Park #672/R est:2000-3000

SNYDERS, Frans (1579-1657) Dutch
Works on paper
£9000 $13950 €13500 Still life with game, fruit, an artichoke and lobster (20x29cm-8x11in) pen ink wash prov. 9-Dec-2 Bonhams, New Bond Street #8/R est:800-1200

SNYDERS, Frans (attrib) (1579-1657) Dutch
£2800 $4396 €4200 Head of a wolf (35x42cm-14x17in) 13-Dec-2 Christie's, Kensington #27/R est:2000-4000

SNYDERS, Frans (circle) (1579-1657) Dutch
£7000 $10850 €10500 Dogs and cats fighting in a kitchen, with an uptured basket (113x173cm-44x68in) 30-Oct-2 Christie's, Kensington #7/R est:7000-10000
£14740 $23879 €21373 Hunting scene with dogs attacking game (187x242cm-74x95in) prov.lit. 26-May-3 Bukowskis, Stockholm #397/R est:150000-175000 (S.KR 190000)

SNYDERS, Frans (studio) (1579-1657) Dutch
£28000 $43960 €42000 Dogs hunting deer in landscape (219x347cm-86x137in) 11-Dec-2 Christie's, London #19/R est:20000-30000

SNYDERS, Frans (style) (1579-1657) Dutch
£6918 $10792 €11000 Small deer, fruit and basket on a draped table (125x186cm-49x73in) 20-Sep-2 Millon & Associes, Paris #742/R est:10000-15000

SOBEL, Jehudith (1924-) American/Polish
£581 $900 €872 Young Israeli girl (76x61cm-30x24in) s.d. 8-Dec-2 Toomey, Oak Park #795/R

SOBRADO, Pedro (1936-) Spanish
£597 $932 €950 Oriental (81x65cm-32x26in) lit. 8-Oct-2 Ansorena, Madrid #622/R
£723 $1114 €1150 Together (73x60cm-29x24in) s. 28-Oct-2 Segre, Madrid #260/R
£818 $1275 €1300 Lunch (54x65cm-21x26in) s. 23-Sep-2 Durán, Madrid #108/R
£869 $1382 €1260 Peasants in the mountains (54x65cm-21x26in) s. 4-Mar-3 Ansorena, Madrid #235/R
£897 $1418 €1400 Couple at moonligght (65x54cm-26x21in) s. 19-Nov-2 Durán, Madrid #146/R
£968 $1529 €1500 Three nudes (73x60cm-29x24in) s. 17-Dec-2 Durán, Madrid #137/R
£968 $1529 €1500 Other time (65x81cm-26x32in) s. 18-Dec-2 Ansorena, Madrid #185/R
£987 $1599 €1500 Arlequin puppet (60x73cm-24x29in) s. 21-Jan-3 Durán, Madrid #110/R
£1058 $1671 €1650 Sardine sellers (92x73cm-36x29in) s. 13-Nov-2 Ansorena, Madrid #32/R
Works on paper
£252 $387 €400 Cart (50x65cm-20x26in) s. W/C. 22-Oct-2 Durán, Madrid #52/R
£258 $408 €400 Winter (50x65cm-20x26in) s. W/C. 17-Dec-2 Durán, Madrid #12/R

SOBRERO, Ettore (1924-) Italian
Sculpture
£962 $1519 €1500 Chemist's tools (34x38x27cm-13x15x11in) assemblage. 15-Nov-2 Farsetti, Prato #4/R

SOBRILE, Giuseppe (1879-1956) Italian
£962 $1510 €1500 Landscape covered in snow (22x26cm-9x10in) s. board. 16-Dec-2 Pandolfini, Florence #290/R
£6918 $10654 €11000 Flowers (69x99cm-27x39in) s.d.1925 egg tempera. 23-Oct-2 Finarte, Milan #43/R est:8000-9000

SOBRINO BUHIGAS, Carlos (1885-1978) Spanish
Works on paper
£3041 $4743 €4500 Farm in Galicia (50x68cm-20x27in) s. pastel. 25-Mar-3 Durán, Madrid #721/R

SOCLET, Arthur Louis (19/20th C) French
Works on paper
£353 $554 €550 Le Havre, quai anime (45x30cm-18x12in) s. W/C. 24-Nov-2 Lesieur & Le Bars, Le Havre #162/R

SODAR, Andre (1829-1903) Belgian
£380 $592 €600 Landscape with ruin (28x37cm-11x15in) s.d.71 panel. 21-Oct-2 Glerum, Amsterdam #120

SODEN, John E (fl.1861-1887) British
£1200 $1860 €1800 Smoking by the fireside (30x35cm-12x14in) s.d.1862 paper on canvas. 3-Dec-2 Sotheby's, Olympia #156/R est:800-1200

SODERBERG, Carl (19th C) ?
£266 $431 €399 Fishermen outside a house (72x100cm-28x39in) 25-Jan-3 Rasmussen, Havnen #2203 (D.KR 3000)
£360 $565 €540 Portrait of two fishermen (44x60cm-17x24in) s. 10-Dec-2 Rosebery Fine Art, London #556

SODING (?) ?
Sculpture
£1800 $2844 €2700 Nude woman blowing bubbles (43cm-17in) s. cold pat. bronze. 14-Nov-2 Christie's, Kensington #208/R est:1500-2000

SODRING, Frederik (1809-1862) Danish
£287 $465 €416 Rocky landscape with foaming river (25x34cm-10x13in) s. 26-May-3 Rasmussen, Copenhagen #1307/R (D.KR 3000)
£3445 $5237 €5168 Romantic landscape with young traveller resting (41x61cm-16x24in) init. 27-Aug-2 Rasmussen, Copenhagen #1437/R est:40000-60000 (D.KR 40000)

SOEBORG, Axel (1872-1939) Danish
£255 $403 €383 Self portrait (50x50cm-20x20in) init.d.17. 2-Dec-2 Rasmussen, Copenhagen #1792/R (D.KR 3000)
£274 $428 €411 Interior scene with man and woman by window (46x49cm-18x19in) mono.indis.d.26. 11-Nov-2 Rasmussen, Vejle #538/R (D.KR 3200)
£331 $517 €497 Dunghill (47x53cm-19x21in) mono. st.verso. 5-Aug-2 Rasmussen, Vejle #75 (D.KR 3900)

SOEDER, Jane (20th C) British
£680 $1061 €1020 Still life of poppies (75x60cm-30x24in) s. 28-Mar-3 Bonhams, Edinburgh #145

SOEKARJA, I Made (1912-1988) Balinese

Works on paper

£8285 $12759 €12428 Story of Jajapala (60x75cm-24x30in) wash pen ink W/C paper on board prov.exhib.lit. 27-Oct-2 Christie's, Hong Kong #19/R est:90000-120000 (HK.D 100000)

SOER, Chris (1882-1961) Dutch

£423 $680 €600 Farm near polder lake (48x78cm-19x31in) s. 7-May-3 Vendue Huis, Gravenhage #38

£2254 $3628 €3200 View of Bruges in the winter (59x87cm-23x34in) s. 7-May-3 Vendue Huis, Gravenhage #37/R est:2500-3000

SOERJOSOEBROTO, Abdullah (1879-1941) Indonesian

£1538 $2415 €2400 Vulcan landscape in Java (50x81cm-20x32in) s. 10-Dec-2 Dorotheum, Vienna #5/R est:2400-2800

SOEST, Gerard van (c.1637-1681) British

£2603 $3800 €3905 Portrait of a girl (76x64cm-30x25in) painted c.1670. 3-Nov-1 North East Auctions, Portsmouth #1152/R est:2200-2800

SOEST, Louis W van (1867-1948) Dutch

£486 $802 €700 Farmland on a sunny day (43x34cm-17x13in) s. cardboard on plywood. 1-Jul-3 Christie's, Amsterdam #135/R

£892 $1373 €1400 Skier (25x29cm-10x11in) plywood prov. 3-Sep-2 Christie's, Amsterdam #268/R

£1146 $1766 €1800 Harbour of Volendam (47x60cm-19x24in) s. 3-Sep-2 Christie's, Amsterdam #341/R est:2000-3000

£1157 $1828 €1736 Winter (130x110cm-51x43in) s. 27-Nov-2 Falkkloos, Malmo #77804/R est:10000 (S.KR 16500)

£1210 $1864 €1900 Volendam Harbour (66x76cm-26x30in) s. 3-Sep-2 Christie's, Amsterdam #326/R est:1500-2000

£1274 $1962 €2000 Sunny day in autumn (63x66cm-25x26in) s. board. 3-Sep-2 Christie's, Amsterdam #238/R est:3000-5000

£1274 $1962 €2000 Early spring, a stream winding through (76x107cm-30x42in) s.indisd.95 prov. 3-Sep-2 Christie's, Amsterdam #269/R est:2500-3500

£1592 $2452 €2500 Sunny day in winter (51x71cm-20x28in) s. prov. 3-Sep-2 Christie's, Amsterdam #278/R est:2500-3500

£3185 $4968 €5000 Winter landscape (75x150cm-30x59in) s. 5-Nov-2 Vendu Notarishuis, Rotterdam #90/R est:2000-2500

Works on paper

£260 $403 €390 Winter landscape (41x58cm-16x23in) s.d.08 W/C. 3-Dec-2 Sworder & Son, Bishops Stortford #960/R

SOEST, Pieter Cornelisz van (17th C) Dutch

£7137 $11562 €10349 Naval battle by Oland's Northern foreland 1566 (51x94cm-20x37in) s. panel. 26-May-3 Bukowskis, Stockholm #443/R est:50000-60000 (S.KR 92000)

£8000 $12400 €12000 Dutch fleet entering the Sound and passing Kronberg Castle, 29 October 1858 (57x68cm-22x27in) 31-Oct-2 Christie's, Kensington #422/R est:10000-15000

SOEST, Pieter Cornelisz van (style) (17th C) Dutch

£18000 $29880 €27000 Battle of Sole Bay, 28th May 1672 (90x120cm-35x47in) 12-Jun-3 Sotheby's, London #48/R est:20000-30000

SOETOPO (1931-) Indonesia

£4557 $7017 €6836 Penjual burung I - bird seller I (128x115cm-50x45in) s.d.1969 lit. 27-Oct-2 Christie's, Hong Kong #81/R est:70000-90000 (HK.D 55000)

SOFFIANTINO, Giacomo (1929-) Italian

£578 $919 €850 Studio (100x80cm-39x31in) s. 1-Mar-3 Meeting Art, Vercelli #455

£784 $1255 €1200 Composition (60x60cm-24x24in) s.d.1967. 4-Jan-3 Meeting Art, Vercelli #585

SOFFICI, Ardengo (1879-1964) Italian

£15385 $24154 €24000 Cabins in Forte (40x50cm-16x20in) s. canvas on cardboard painted 1963 lit. 19-Nov-2 Finarte, Milan #188/R est:22000-26000

£18065 $28542 €28000 Berna's house (40x53cm-16x21in) s. painted 1960. 18-Dec-2 Christie's, Rome #235/R

£22785 $36000 €36000 Road and houses in Poggio a Caiano (50x70cm-20x28in) s.d.61 verso cardboard lit. 30-Nov-2 Farsetti, Prato #702/R est:45000

£32911 $52000 €52000 Farms (74x51cm-29x20in) s.d.49 cardboard lit. 30-Nov-2 Farsetti, Prato #725/R est:65000

£35897 $56359 €56000 Berna's house (51x74cm-20x29in) s.d.50 cardboard exhib. 19-Nov-2 Finarte, Milan #224/R est:52000-62000

Works on paper

£2658 $4200 €4200 Ballerina (30x22cm-12x9in) s.d.1901 pencil col crayon ink card. 30-Nov-2 Farsetti, Prato #602/R

£6081 $9486 €9000 Beach huts at Vittoria Apuana (23x32cm-9x13in) s. W/C paper on canvas lit. 28-Mar-3 Farsetti, Prato #772/R est:7200

SOGLIARI, Giovanni Antonio (1492-1544) Italian

£18919 $29514 €28000 Madonna and Child with St John the Baptist (60x46cm-24x18in) panel. 27-Mar-3 Dorotheum, Vienna #39/R est:25000-35000

SOHL, Will (1906-1969) German

£302 $496 €420 Curled up cat (39x52cm-15x20in) s.i. W/C Indian ink brush. 4-Jun 3 Reiss & Sohn, Konigstein #515/R

£519 $790 €800 Southern coast landscape (45x60cm-18x24in) s. 6-Jul-2 Berlinghof, Heidelberg #246/R

£818 $1275 €1300 Dutch coast with fishing village (40x50cm-16x20in) s.d.31. 21-Sep-2 Bolland & Marotz, Bremen #778/R

Sculpture

£1507 $2351 €2200 Poppies (66x51x220cm-26x20x87in) s.d.8.VI.1945 W/C. 11-Apr-3 Winterberg, Heidelberg #1678/R est:900

Works on paper

£786 $1226 €1250 Larkspur and star flowers (67x51cm-26x20in) s.d.1952 s.i.d. verso W/C. 11-Oct-2 Winterberg, Heidelberg #1745

SOHLBERG, Harald (1869-1935) Norwegian

£50479 $80766 €75719 From Ranviken - Midsummer night (36x54cm-14x21in) s.d.1910 exhib.lit. 17-Mar-3 Blomqvist, Oslo #388/R est:600000-800000 (N.KR 580000)

Prints

£1735 $2706 €2603 From a backyard - girl (55x36cm-22x14in) dr executed 1905 exhib. 21-Oct-2 Blomqvist, Oslo #506/R est:30000-40000 (N.KR 20000)

£8421 $13305 €12632 Winter's night at Rondane (58x62cm-23x24in) s.d.1917 num.25 col lithograph. 17-Dec-2 Grev Wedels Plass, Oslo #44/R est:50000-70000 (N.KR 96000)

£8651 $13668 €12977 Winter night in Rondane (52x60cm-20x24in) s.num.88 col lithograph. 2-Dec-2 Blomqvist, Oslo #389/R est:50000-70000 (N.KR 100000)

£9574 $15318 €14361 Winter night in Rondane (52x60cm-20x24in) s.d.1917 num.242/250 col lithograph. 17-Mar-3 Blomqvist, Oslo #419/R est:70000-90000 (N.KR 110000)

SOHLER, Peter (20th C) German

£884 $1406 €1300 Autumn in English garden (50x60cm-20x24in) s. 21-Mar-3 Auktionhaus Georg Rehm, Augsburg #8091/R

SOHN, Karl Wilhelm (1853-1925) German

£669 $1111 €950 Young flute player (46x26cm-18x10in) s.i.d.1905 panel. 14-Jun-3 Arnold, Frankfurt #871/R

SOHN-RETHEL, Karli (1882-1966) German

Works on paper

£545 $845 €850 South Sea landscape with figures (62x43cm-24x17in) s.d1916 gouache Indian ink graphite. 7-Dec-2 Ketterer, Hamburg #173/R

SOINILA, Liisa (20th C) Finnish

£759 $1200 €1200 Bermut series (95x95cm-37x37in) s.d.2000 verso board. 1-Dec-2 Bukowskis, Helsinki #352/R

£1456 $2300 €2300 Bermut series (95x95cm-37x37in) s.d.1999 verso board. 1-Dec-2 Bukowskis, Helsinki #351/R est:1000-1200

SOKOL, Koloman (1902-) Czechoslovakian

Works on paper

£347 $538 €521 Female nude (57x39cm-22x15in) chk dr exec.c.1924-1925. 3-Dec-2 SOGA, Bratislava #67/R (SL.K 22000)

£992 $1449 €1488 Resting riders (22x33cm-9x13in) ink W/C. 4-Jun-2 SOGA, Bratislava #76/R est:58000 (SL.K 63000)

SOKOLOFF, Anatolio (1891-1971) Russian

£9494 $15000 €14241 Bustling afternoon (70x100cm-28x39in) s. 24-Apr-3 Sotheby's, New York #116/R est:15000-20000

SOKOLOFF, Piotr Fiodorovitch (c.1791-1847) Russian

Works on paper

£1899 $3000 €3000 Young man (26x20cm-10x8in) s.d.1818 W/C. 1-Dec-2 Bukowskis, Helsinki #273/R est:1200-1600

SOKOLOFF, Piotr Petrovitch (1821-1899) Russian

£11585 $19000 €16798 Wolf attack (51x81cm-20x32in) s. 4-Jun-3 Doyle, New York #95/R est:2500-3500

Works on paper
£1200 $1944 €1800 Tales of the war (16x21cm-6x8in) s.d.1859 W/C. 21-May-3 Sotheby's, London #96/R est:1500-2000

SOLANO, Susana (1946-) Spanish
Sculpture
£9375 $15000 €14063 Stanca no.2 (76x138x138cm-30x54x54in) init. steel construction executed 1986 prov. 14-May-3 Sotheby's, New York #379/R est:15000-20000
£10759 $17000 €16139 La caritat, no.5 (183x179x45cm-72x70x18in) init. iron wood executed 1988 prov.exhib. 13-Nov-2 Sotheby's, New York #149/R est:8000-12000
Works on paper
£497 $810 €750 Untitled (29x21cm-11x8in) s.d.1990 pencil. 11-Feb-3 Segre, Madrid #216/R

SOLARI, Luis A (1918-1993) Uruguayan
£293 $460 €440 Pretenders (15x21cm-6x8in) acrylic. 20-Nov-2 Galleria Y Remates, Montevideo #9
Works on paper
£385 $600 €578 Como un general (15x21cm-6x8in) s. collage. 30-Jul-2 Galleria Y Remates, Montevideo #2
£449 $700 €674 Fantasies (25x20cm-10x8in) s.d.72 collage. 10-Oct-2 Galleria Y Remates, Montevideo #14/R

SOLBERG, Morten (1935-) American
£5063 $8000 €7341 On watch (61x122cm-24x48in) s. acrylic on board prov. 26-Jul-3 Coeur d'Alene, Hayden #76/R est:10000-20000

SOLDAN, Uuno (1883-1954) Finnish
£270 $419 €430 The red house (40x48cm-16x19in) s. 6-Oct-2 Bukowskis, Helsinki #292/R
£302 $468 €480 Boat on beach (39x49cm-15x19in) s. 6-Oct-2 Bukowskis, Helsinki #293/R

SOLDAN-BROFELDT, Venny (1863-1945) Finnish
£1079 $1770 €1500 Biblical scene (56x80cm-22x31in) s. 5-Jun-3 Hagelstam, Helsinki #950 est:500
£1772 $2800 €2800 Young girl bathing (29x38cm-11x15in) s. board exhib. 1-Dec-2 Bukowskis, Helsinki #186/R est:2000-2500
£2138 $3378 €3100 Boy dreaming on beach (46x32cm-18x13in) s.d.1941. 3-Apr-3 Hagelstam, Helsinki #1052/R est:2000
£2215 $3456 €3500 Two women on beach (60x84cm-24x33in) s. 12-Sep-2 Hagelstam, Helsinki #800
£2734 $4374 €3800 Forest clearing (31x39cm-12x15in) s. i.verso canvas on board. 17-May-3 Hagelstam, Helsinki #155/R est:4000
£2950 $4837 €4100 Coffee break on the beach (22x28cm-9x11in) s. 4-Jun-3 Bukowskis, Helsinki #438/R est:2000
£3022 $4955 €4200 Composition (60x82cm-24x32in) s.d.1943. 5-Jun-3 Hagelstam, Helsinki #959/R est:3500
£3165 $5000 €5000 Garden with flowers (47x64cm-19x25in) s. 30-Nov-2 Hagelstam, Helsinki #89/R est:3000
£3165 $5000 €5000 On the beach (46x38cm-18x15in) s. 30-Nov-2 Hagelstam, Helsinki #107/R est:4000
£3169 $5102 €4500 Autumn still life (33x46cm-13x18in) s. board. 10-May-3 Bukowskis, Helsinki #64/R est:4500-5000
£3671 $5800 €5800 The artist's friend drawing (34x47cm-13x19in) s.d.30 canvas on board. 1-Dec-2 Bukowskis, Helsinki #185/R est:6000-7000
£3797 $6000 €6000 Children playing in boat (33x47cm-13x19in) s. 1-Dec-2 Bukowskis, Helsinki #187/R est:3000-3500
£4388 $7022 €6100 Summer's day in the skerries (34x50cm-13x20in) s. 17-May-3 Hagelstam, Helsinki #153/R est:4000
£4789 $7710 €6800 In Paradise (134x196cm-53x77in) s.d.1914-18. 10-May-3 Bukowskis, Helsinki #161/R est:6000-8000
£5063 $8000 €8000 Boy on sandy beech (48x34cm-19x13in) s. cardboard. 30-Nov-2 Hagelstam, Helsinki #88/R est:4000
£11511 $18417 €16000 Carelian girl sewing (25x20cm-10x8in) s.d.1890 board. 17-May-3 Hagelstam, Helsinki #154/R est:8000

SOLDATI, Atanasio (1896-1953) Italian
£2564 $4026 €4000 Holy pear (16x11cm-6x4in) s. tempera. 23-Nov-2 Meeting Art, Vercelli #447/R
£14894 $24128 €21000 Composition (33x46cm-13x18in) s. prov.exhib.lit. 26-May-3 Christie's, Milan #328/R est:10000-15000

SOLDATI, Massimo (1959-) Italian
£1702 $2757 €2400 Il volo 4 (100x100cm-39x39in) s.d.1999 verso oil acrylic prov. 26-May-3 Christie's, Milan #165/R est:2000-3000
£2323 $3670 €3600 Rock climber (110x110cm-43x43in) s.d.1998 acrylic oil. 18-Dec-2 Christie's, Rome #89/R

SOLDENHOFF, Alexander Leo (1882-1951) Swiss
£330 $482 €495 Still life with campanulas (63x48cm-25x19in) s. s.i. verso. 17-Jun-2 Philippe Schuler, Zurich #7446 (S.FR 750)
£987 $1560 €1481 Self-portrait (46x38cm-18x15in) s.d.1922. 26-Nov-2 Hans Widmer, St Gallen #1373 est:1800-3400 (S.FR 2300)

SOLDI, Raul (1905-) Argentinian
Works on paper
£750 $1140 €1125 Tres figuras en reposo (35x43cm-14x17in) s.d.77 mixed media. 3-Jul-2 Naón & Cia, Buenos Aires #26

SOLE JORBA, Vicenc (1904-1949) Spanish
£437 $638 €656 Prado Catalan, October (46x61cm-18x24in) s.d.1942. 4-Jun-2 Germann, Zurich #849/R (S.FR 1000)

SOLENGHI, Giuseppe (1879-1944) Italian
£510 $811 €750 Arco della Pace, Milan (25x15cm-10x6in) s. board. 18-Mar-3 Finarte, Milan #216/R
£943 $1453 €1500 Lagoon (35x50cm-14x20in) s.d.1938 board. 23-Oct-2 Finarte, Milan #133/R
£1635 $2518 €2600 Getting down in a rush (66x50cm-26x20in) s.d.1931 board. 23-Oct-2 Finarte, Milan #107/R

SOLER BLASCO, Juan Bautista (1920-1984) Javanese
£921 $1492 €1400 Corpus Domini procession in San Sebastian (46x39cm-18x15in) s. s.i.d.1944 verso board. 21-Jan-3 Ansorena, Madrid #240/R

SOLER FERNANDEZ, Juan (19th C) Cuban
£855 $1386 €1300 Landscape in Cuba (21x33cm-8x13in) s.d.1891 board. 21-Jan-3 Ansorena, Madrid #62/R

SOLER, Domenec (1871-1952) Spanish
£430 $702 €650 Landscape (32x43cm-13x17in) s.d.1916 board. 11-Feb-3 Segre, Madrid #143/R

SOLER, J (20th C) ?
£2142 $3405 €3213 From Bois de Boulogne with ladies walking. Ladies on the beach (33x46cm-13x18in) s. two. 5-Mar-3 Rasmussen, Copenhagen #2041/R est:25000 (D.KR 23000)

SOLER, Juan (20th C) Spanish
£460 $713 €690 On a Paris street (38x46cm-15x18in) s. 25-Sep-2 Hamptons Fine Art, Godalming #333
£480 $749 €720 Parisian street scene (44x37cm-17x15in) s. 26-Mar-3 Woolley & Wallis, Salisbury #189/R
£500 $780 €750 On a Paris street (38x46cm-15x18in) s. 26-Mar-3 Hamptons Fine Art, Godalming #163
£600 $948 €900 Winter outing (38x46cm-15x18in) s. 14-Nov-2 Christie's, Kensington #8/R
£620 $967 €930 Parisian street scene (46x55cm-18x22in) s. 9-Oct-2 Woolley & Wallis, Salisbury #255/R
£650 $1021 €975 Croquet on the beach (38x49cm-15x19in) s. 16-Apr-3 Christie's, Kensington #847/R
£700 $1078 €1050 Elegant figures in the snow before carriages on a Parisian street (33x41cm-13x16in) s. 24-Oct-2 Christie's, Kensington #29/R
£800 $1232 €1200 Elegant figures on a Parisian street (33x41cm-13x16in) s. 24-Oct-2 Christie's, Kensington #162/R
£850 $1377 €1275 Figures before the Arc de Triomphe. Elegant figures on a Parisian boulevard (27x22cm-11x9in) s. pair. 23-Jan-3 Christie's, Kensington #236/R
£1000 $1540 €1500 Carriages on a Parisian street with mother and child. Elegant woman before a horse and carriage (27x22cm-11x9in) s. pair. 24-Oct-2 Christie's, Kensington #45/R est:800-1200
£1000 $1620 €1500 Elegant figures before the Moulin Rouge (60x72cm-24x28in) s. 23-Jan-3 Christie's, Kensington #241/R est:1200-1800
£1300 $2028 €1950 Parisian street scene (55x44cm-22x17in) s. 26-Mar-3 Woolley & Wallis, Salisbury #190/R est:750-1000
£1400 $2212 €2100 Figures in a Parisian square (60x73cm-24x29in) s. 14-Nov-2 Christie's, Kensington #7/R est:1200-1800
£1400 $2198 €2100 Elegant figures and carriages on a Parisian boulevard (65x81cm-26x32in) s. 16-Apr-3 Christie's, Kensington #845/R est:1000-1500
£1400 $2296 €2100 Figures in the snow before the opera house, Paris. Elegant figures after the rain, Paris (27x22cm-11x9in) s. pair. 5-Jun-3 Christie's, Kensington #833/R est:800-1200
£1800 $2952 €2700 Elegant figures before the Hotel Hondew, Paris (60x73cm-24x29in) s. 5-Jun-3 Christie's, Kensington #834/R est:1000-1500

SOLER, Rigoberto (1896-1968) Spanish
£12579 $19371 €20000 Morning light (60x70cm-24x28in) s.i.d.1931 s.i.d.verso. 22-Oct-2 Durán, Madrid #202/R est:15000

SOLERO, Pio (1881-?) Italian
£1795 $2782 €2800 Winter landscape (29x40cm-11x16in) s. board. 5-Dec-2 Stadion, Trieste #835/R
£2179 $3378 €3400 Rhododendrons (48x56cm-19x22in) s. board. 5-Dec-2 Stadion, Trieste #834/R

SOLIMENA, Francesco (1657-1747) Italian
£5000 $7850 €7500 Saint John the Baptist (20cm-8in circular) canvas on panel. 13-Dec-2 Christie's, Kensington #257/R est:5000-7000
£57927 $95000 €86891 Royal hunt of Dido and Aeneas (74x77cm-29x30in) i. prov.exhib.lit. 30-May-3 Christie's, Rockefeller NY #34/R est:100000-150000
£180000 $282600 €270000 Triumph of King Charles of Naples (144x120cm-57x47in) prov.exhib.lit. 11-Dec-2 Christie's, London #104/R est:200000-300000
Works on paper
£1049 $1500 €1574 Faith, Hope and Charity (30x47cm-12x19in) pen brown ink wash. 23-Jan-3 Swann Galleries, New York #108/R est:2000-3000

SOLIMENA, Francesco (attrib) (1657-1747) Italian
£6452 $10000 €9678 Holy Family with St Anne, the infant St John the Baptist and a donor (60x39cm-24x15in) prov. 2-Oct-2 Christie's, Rockefeller NY #128/R est:10000-15000
Works on paper
£490 $700 €735 Mary Magdalene in penitence in a landscape (21x25cm-8x10in) red chk. 23-Jan-3 Swann Galleries, New York #109/R
£709 $1184 €1000 La Sainte famille (20x10cm-8x4in) pen brown ink brown wash black crayon. 19-Jun-3 Piasa, Paris #10/R
£1667 $2650 €2400 Ascension of Mary (28x21cm-11x8in) chk wash prov. 5-May-3 Ketterer, Munich #417/R est:800-1000

SOLIMENA, Francesco (circle) (1657-1747) Italian
£7742 $12232 €12000 Nativity (98x73cm-39x29in) 19-Dec-2 Delvaux, Paris #87/R est:15000

SOLIN, Timo (1947-) Swedish
Sculpture
£3153 $4919 €4730 Girl running with dog (54cm-21in) s.num.4/4 polished green pat.bronze. 6-Nov-2 AB Stockholms Auktionsverk #755/R est:35000-40000 (S.KR 45000)

SOLLIER, Henri Alexandre (1886-?) French
£1092 $1757 €1550 Fillette de Plougastel a l'eglise (75x50cm-30x20in) 11-May-3 Thierry & Lannon, Brest #394 est:1000-1200
£1429 $2257 €2144 Still life (57x77cm-22x30in) s.d.1925. 18-Nov-2 Joel, Victoria #348/R est:4000-5000 (A.D 4000)
Works on paper
£556 $906 €800 Bigoudene en pied (47x31cm-19x12in) s.i.d.34 chl white chk. 19-Jul-3 Thierry & Lannon, Brest #412

SOLOGAUB, Leonida (1884-1956) Russian/Dutch
£955 $1490 €1500 Beach view with figures (14x16cm-6x6in) s. d.1953 verso board. 6-Nov-2 Vendue Huis, Gravenhage #52/R est:1500-1700

SOLOMKO, Sergei (1859-1926) Russian
Works on paper
£600 $948 €900 Portrait of a Roman in green toga (21x13cm-8x5in) s.i.d.1902 pencil W/C. 26-Nov-2 Christie's, Kensington #5/R est:600-900

SOLOMON, Abraham (1824-1862) British
£300 $477 €450 Portrait of a lady head and shoulders (30x26cm-12x10in) i.verso panel oval. 29-Apr-3 Henry Adams, Chichester #273
£4000 $6240 €6000 William Shakespeare, As You Like It, Act III, Scene VII (76x64cm-30x25in) exhib. 17-Sep-2 Sotheby's, Olympia #183/R est:3000-5000
£15000 $24150 €22500 Sketch from memory (30x36cm-12x14in) s.d.1851 painted arch prov.exhib.lit. 20-Feb-3 Christie's, London #105/R est:12000

SOLOMON, Cindstane (?) ?
£300 $456 €450 Scantily dressed lady in an interior (61x41cm-24x16in) s.d.1920. 4-Jul-2 Duke & Son, Dorchester #233/R

SOLOMON, Lance Vaiben (1913-1989) Australian
£325 $514 €471 Farm near Scone (48x59cm-19x23in) s. canvasboard. 22-Jul-3 Lawson Menzies, Sydney #206/R (A.D 800)
£357 $564 €536 Bush mill (49x59cm-19x23in) s. canvas on board. 18-Nov-2 Joel, Victoria #283 est:1000-1250 (A.D 1000)
£430 $654 €645 Cattle feeding north coast (36x38cm-14x15in) s. board. 27-Aug-2 Goodman, Sydney #212 (A.D 1200)
£1145 $1809 €1718 Little farm house near Coffs Harbour (58x49cm-23x19in) s. i.verso canvas on board. 2-Apr-3 Christie's, Melbourne #65 est:1500-2500 (A.D 3000)
£1495 $2287 €2243 Morning on the farm (75x90cm-30x35in) s. i.verso board painted c.1966 prov. 26-Aug-2 Sotheby's, Paddington #635 est:1000-2000 (A.D 4200)

SOLOMON, Rebecca (1832-1886) British
£7500 $12075 €11250 Fashionable couple (48x53cm-19x21in) s.indis.d. prov.exhib.lit. 20-Feb-3 Christie's, London #266/R est:15000
£17000 $27370 €25500 Love letter (53x42cm-21x17in) mono.d.61 prov.exhib. 20-Feb-3 Christie's, London #322/R est:15000

SOLOMON, Simeon (1840-1905) British
£34000 $54740 €51000 Deacon (35x25cm-14x10in) mono.d.63 prov.exhib.lit. 20-Feb-3 Christie's, London #131/R est:20000
Works on paper
£285 $450 €450 Female figure being robbed (9x8cm-4x3in) mono. 29-Nov-2 Bassenge, Berlin #6063/R
£600 $984 €870 Saint Aloysius de Gonzaga (25x18cm-10x7in) i. black chk exhib. 5-Jun-3 Christie's, London #121/R
£900 $1485 €1305 Head of Philomela (35x27cm-14x11in) s.i.indis.d. col chk. 3-Jul-3 Christie's, Kensington #16/R
£1100 $1716 €1650 O pot o pot (20x15cm-8x6in) init.d.1884 pencil col crayon. 17-Oct-2 Christie's, Kensington #37/R est:1000-1500
£1200 $1968 €1740 Sanctus, Sanctus, Sanctus (38x28cm-15x11in) i. pencil blue crayon. 5-Jun-3 Christie's, London #123/R est:1200-1800
£2300 $3772 €3335 Hour before dawn (38x32cm-15x13in) i. pencil. 5-Jun-3 Christie's, London #122/R est:1500-2000
£3500 $5495 €5250 Head of a young man (34x25cm-13x10in) s. W/C bodycol. 21-Nov-2 Christie's, London #82/R est:2500-3500
£6000 $9960 €9000 Angel of children (40x27cm-16x11in) s.i.d.1895 red white chk. 12-Jun-3 Sotheby's, London #203/R est:3000-5000
£22000 $35420 €33000 Heliogabalus, High Priest of the Sun (48x29cm-19x11in) mono.d.1866 pencil W/C htd bodycol gum scratching out prov.lit. 20-Feb-3 Christie's, London #132/R est:15000

SOLOMON, Solomon J (1860-1927) British
£800 $1280 €1200 Portrait of bespectacled and bearded gentleman seated in chair (112x86cm-44x34in) s.d.1887. 11-Mar-3 Gorringes, Lewes #2276
£3600 $5616 €5400 Portrait of Kate Leon seated on a branch reading a book (56x45cm-22x18in) s. 18-Sep-2 Dreweatt Neate, Newbury #168/R est:3000-5000
£8000 $12880 €12000 Study for 'Equipped' (91x62cm-36x24in) prov.exhib. 20-Feb-3 Christie's, London #65/R est:15000

SOLOMONS, Estella Frances (1882-1968) Irish
£342 $530 €540 Stone Christian Cross, Maam (30x39cm-12x15in) board. 25-Sep-2 James Adam, Dublin #46
£725 $1188 €1000 Mountain (26x34cm-10x13in) i.verso canvas on board. 28-May-3 Bonhams & James Adam, Dublin #122/R est:1000-2000
£1042 $1656 €1500 Coastal landscape with clouds over a bluff (41x51cm-16x20in) canvas on board prov. 29-Apr-3 Whyte's, Dublin #110/R est:1500-2000
£1449 $2377 €2000 Dublin Bay (31x38cm-12x15in) i.verso board. 28-May-3 Bonhams & James Adam, Dublin #81/R est:2000-4000
£1554 $2424 €2300 Nude (91x61cm-36x24in) init. i.verso prov. 26-Mar-3 James Adam, Dublin #135/R est:1200-1800
£2162 $3373 €3200 Sandhills, Rush (31x39cm-12x15in) init. board. 26-Mar-3 James Adam, Dublin #69/R est:3000-4000
£7246 $11884 €10000 Moppie Morrow (52x42cm-20x17in) s.d.1918 exhib. 28-May-3 Bonhams & James Adam, Dublin #58/R est:10000-15000

SOLOMOUKHA, Anton (1945-) Russian
Works on paper
£340 $541 €500 Untitled (130x130cm-51x51in) s.d.1992 verso mixed media on canvas. 24-Mar-3 Claude Boisgirard, Paris #198

SOLONEN, Jouko (1920-) Finnish
£845 $1361 €1200 Night and day (90x115cm-35x45in) 10-May-3 Bukowskis, Helsinki #215/R
£850 $1393 €1300 Morning (115x90cm-45x35in) s.d.88 acrylic. 9-Feb-3 Bukowskis, Helsinki #367/R
£915 $1474 €1300 Sleeping model (80x100cm-31x39in) s.d.89 acrylic. 10-May-3 Bukowskis, Helsinki #250/R

SOLOWEY, Ben (1900-1978) American
£272 $425 €408 Portrait of a young woman (51x38cm-20x15in) s.d.1950 chl. 18-Sep-2 Alderfer's, Hatfield #331

SOLVEIG (20th C) ?
Works on paper
£468 $748 €650 Codage temporel (60x60cm-24x24in) s. mixed media canvas. 18-May-3 Neret-Minet, Paris #110

SOMAINI, Francesco (1926-) Italian
Sculpture
£1935 $3058 €3000 Untitled (39x25x35cm-15x10x14in) s.i. bronze prov. 18-Dec-2 Christie's, Rome #45/R

SOMER, Hendrik van (attrib) (1615-1685) Dutch
£2516 $3875 €4000 Saint Jerome (116x135cm-46x53in) 25-Oct-2 Tajan, Paris #77/R est:4000-6000
£4321 $7086 €6265 Harbour scene (74x99cm-29x39in) 4-Jun-3 AB Stockholms Auktionsverk #2546/R est:60000-70000 (S.KR 55000)

SOMERS, Louis (1813-1880) Belgian
£863 $1381 €1200 Le chagrin (50x39cm-20x15in) s. 13-May-3 Vanderkindere, Brussels #39
£3472 $5521 €5000 Entertaining conversation (52x43cm-20x17in) s. panel prov. 29-Apr-3 Christie's, Amsterdam #22/R est:6000-8000

SOMERSCALES, Thomas (1842-1927) British
£1900 $3078 €2850 Barquentine in full sail (12x17cm-5x7in) s.d.1904 oil on card. 22-Jan-3 Bonhams, New Bond Street #368/R est:1000-1500
£2600 $4290 €3770 Shipping off Valparaiso, Chile (39x49cm-15x19in) s. 6-Jul-3 Lots Road, London #345/R est:2000-3000
£3000 $4560 €4500 British battleship under fire (60x107cm-24x42in) s.d.1917. 15-Aug-2 Bonhams, New Bond Street #364/R est:3000-4000
£6400 $10048 €9600 Steamers on the open seas (30x46cm-12x18in) s.d.1902. 16-Dec-2 Sotheby's, Olympia #104/R est:6000-9000
£10000 $15900 €15000 Extensive view of Valparaiso, Chile (28x42cm-11x17in) s.d.79 board. 29-Apr-3 Bonhams, New Bond Street #215/R est:5000-8000
£12000 $20040 €17400 South sea whalers (30x46cm-12x18in) s.d.99. 18-Jun-3 Sotheby's, Olympia #132/R est:12000-18000
£14000 $22120 €21000 Clipper at full sail on open seas (41x56cm-16x22in) s. 15-Nov-2 Sotheby's, London #98/R est:15000-20000

SOMERSET, Richard Gay (1848-1928) British
£500 $780 €750 Bridge over a rocky stream (51x27cm-20x11in) indis sig. 7-Nov-2 Christie's, Kensington #105/R

SOMERVILLE, Edith Oenone (1858-1949) British
Works on paper
£634 $1015 €920 Hunt (20x15cm-8x6in) init. W/C. 11-Mar-3 Thomas Adams, Dublin #445
£897 $1418 €1400 Every dog has his day (44x36cm-17x14in) s.d.1902 W/C pair. 12-Nov-2 Mealy's, Castlecomer #1026/R

SOMERVILLE, Peggy (1918-1975) British
£270 $429 €405 Rural landscape with shepherd and his flock (25x30cm-10x12in) s.d.1939 board. 30-Apr-3 Goldings, Lincolnshire #115
£400 $620 €600 Dutch town scene (30x25cm-12x10in) board prov. 30-Sep-2 Bonhams, Ipswich #438
£420 $651 €630 Cows in a meadow (16x23cm-6x9in) canvasboard. 30-Sep-2 Bonhams, Ipswich #413
£450 $698 €675 Corner of Ruffle's farm, Alpheton (25x30cm-10x12in) s.d.1932 board prov.exhib. 30-Sep-2 Bonhams, Ipswich #424
£1000 $1570 €1500 Still life of flowers in a blue vase (50x40cm-20x16in) s.verso board. 16-Dec-2 Bonhams, Bury St Edmunds #454/R est:800-1200
£6500 $10075 €9750 Harvest landscape, Suffolk (57x84cm-22x33in) 30-Sep-2 Bonhams, Ipswich #369/R est:7000-8000
Works on paper
£360 $594 €522 Flowers on a windowsill (40x29cm-16x11in) studio st. verso W/C. 1-Jul-3 Bonhams, Norwich #164
£450 $743 €653 Autumn evening (25x30cm-10x12in) s.d.1932 gouache on board. 1-Jul-3 Bonhams, Norwich #167/R
£550 $908 €798 Flowers in a vase (29x22cm-11x9in) s.d. pastel. 1-Jul-3 Bonhams, Norwich #163/R

SOMERVILLE, Stuart (1908-1983) British
£280 $437 €420 Hedgerow amongst cornfield (25x31cm-10x12in) board. 17-Sep-2 Bonhams, Knightsbridge #218/R
£300 $465 €450 Summer in Cornwall, figures on a beach (69x104cm-27x41in) s. board. 26-Sep-2 Lane, Penzance #326
£340 $551 €493 Still life study of a vase of summer flowers (34x29cm-13x11in) s. board. 21-May-3 Rupert Toovey, Partridge Green #126
£420 $651 €630 Coastal view, evening, possibly Southwold (29x39cm-11x15in) s. board. 30-Sep-2 Bonhams, Ipswich #430
£420 $668 €630 Still life of a vase of summer flowers (40x35cm-16x14in) i.verso. 27-Feb-3 Greenslade Hunt, Taunton #1316/R
£450 $738 €675 Still life of lily in a vase (56x46cm-22x18in) s. 3-Jun-3 Sotheby's, Olympia #130/R
£550 $908 €798 Spring landscape (25x41cm-10x16in) s. board. 1-Jul-3 Bonhams, Norwich #302
£620 $1023 €899 Suffolk landscape (30x40cm-12x16in) s. board. 1-Jul-3 Bonhams, Norwich #356
£650 $1007 €975 Regatta on the Deven (25x39cm-10x15in) s. paper on board. 30-Sep-2 Bonhams, Ipswich #371/R
£650 $1021 €975 Still life of roses in a vase (21x26cm-8x10in) s. board pair. 16-Dec-2 Bonhams, Bury St Edmunds #471/R
£1750 $2713 €2625 Cattle in the water meadows (46x61cm-18x24in) s. 30-Sep-2 Bonhams, Ipswich #365/R est:1800-2500
£3100 $4805 €4650 Ornamental birds amidst flowering vases with decorative border (183x348cm-72x137in) s.d.1928 four fold screen. 30-Sep-2 Bonhams, Ipswich #368/R est:2000-3000
Works on paper
£270 $446 €392 Study of a seated nude (44x34cm-17x13in) s. pastel. 1-Jul-3 Bonhams, Norwich #176

SOMM, Henry (1844-1907) French
Works on paper
£411 $650 €617 Skater (23x15cm-9x6in) d.1883 W/C. 15-Nov-2 Du Mouchelle, Detroit #1408/R
£828 $1324 €1200 Japonaise a l'eventail (20x15cm-8x6in) s. W/C. 12-Mar-3 Libert, Castor, Paris #179/R
£828 $1324 €1200 Jeune femme au chapeau (32x22cm-13x9in) s. W/C. 12-Mar-3 Libert, Castor, Paris #181/R
£878 $1370 €1300 Communiste par temperament (20x11cm-8x4in) wash W/C over crayon. 26-Mar-3 Piasa, Paris #113/R
£897 $1434 €1300 La Japonaise (19x14cm-7x6in) s. W/C. 12-Mar-3 Libert, Castor, Paris #182
£2903 $4587 €4500 Partie de campagne (30x60cm-12x24in) s. W/C ink. 19-Dec-2 Claude Aguttes, Neuilly #68/R

SOMMAVILLA, E (19th C) Italian
£449 $700 €674 Garden landscape with solitary figure (46x58cm-18x23in) s. 14-Sep-2 Weschler, Washington #576/R

SOMME, Theophile (1871-1952) French
Sculpture
£3041 $4743 €4500 Inspiration (46cm-18in) s. bronze ivory stone socle. 27-Mar-3 Dr Fritz Nagel, Stuttgart #988/R est:1500

SOMMER, Carl Johan Friedrich (1830-1867) German
£1818 $2945 €2636 Houses in Olevano in the Sabine Mountains (41x62cm-16x24in) exhib. 26-May-3 Rasmussen, Copenhagen #1121/R est:15000-25000 (D.KR 19000)

SOMMER, Ferdinand (1822-1901) Swiss
£411 $641 €600 Swiss landscape (32x40cm-13x16in) s. 10-Apr-3 Dorotheum, Vienna #199/R
£786 $1226 €1179 Wetterhorn seen from Grindelwald (16x23cm-6x9in) s. board. 6-Nov-2 Dobiaschofsky, Bern #974/R (S.FR 1800)
£995 $1662 €1443 Unterseen (26x35cm-10x14in) board. 24-Jun-3 Koller, Zurich #14/R est:2000-3000 (S.FR 2200)
£995 $1662 €1443 Lake Thun (26x34cm-10x13in) bears s. board. 24-Jun-3 Koller, Zurich #15/R est:2000-3000 (S.FR 2200)
£1400 $2282 €2030 Cabin in the Alps (89x117cm-35x46in) s. 16-Jul-3 Sotheby's, Olympia #185/R est:1500-2500
£3057 $4769 €4586 Blumlisalp with pleasure boat (24x33cm-9x13in) s. i.verso board. 8-Nov-2 Dobiaschofsky, Bern #1/R est:3900 (S.FR 7000)

SOMMER, Frederick (1905-) American
Photographs
£7143 $11000 €10715 Circumnavigation of the blood (10x14cm-4x6in) s.d.1950 photograph prov.lit. 22-Oct-2 Sotheby's, New York #11/R est:7000-10000

SOMMER, Georg (19th C) German
£1154 $1812 €1800 Forest clearing with stream and deer (82x122cm-32x48in) s.i. 23-Nov-2 Arnold, Frankfurt #874/R est:1000

SOMMER, J (19/20th C) German?
£1046 $1715 €1600 Still life of fruit (48x57cm-19x22in) s.i. 8-Feb-3 Hans Stahl, Hamburg #86/R est:600

SOMMER, William (1867-1949) American
Works on paper
£897 $1400 €1346 Yellow house (18x28cm-7x11in) s.i.d.1948 W/C. 21-Sep-2 Rachel Davis, Shaker Heights #388 est:1000-1500
£988 $1600 €1482 Ohio landscape (30x41cm-12x16in) s.d.1943 W/C. 24-Jan-3 Freeman, Philadelphia #99/R est:1500-2000
£1098 $1800 €1592 Farm with horses (28x38cm-11x15in) s.d. W/C. 5-Jun-3 Swann Galleries, New York #227/R est:800-1200

SOMOGYI, Daniel (1837-1890) Hungarian
£510 $795 €800 Landscape near Munich (17x23cm-7x9in) s.d.1890 board. 6-Nov-2 Hugo Ruef, Munich #1275/R

£566 $877 €900 Mountain lake (49x69cm-19x27in) s. canvas on board. 29-Oct-2 Dorotheum, Vienna #12/R
£14000 $21980 €21000 View of the Konigssee (82x118cm-32x46in) s.d.1877. 19-Nov-2 Sotheby's, London #197/R est:5000-7000

SOMOV, Konstantin (attrib) (1869-1939) Russian
£1266 $1962 €2000 Park landscape with couples (7x16cm-3x6in) i. 27-Sep-2 Dr Fritz Nagel, Leipzig #3991/R est:3000

SOMPEL, Willy van (1948-) Belgian
£2083 $3312 €3000 Dood in Mali (160x200cm-63x79in) s.d.1985. 29-Apr-3 Campo & Campo, Antwerp #329/R est:3500-4000

SOMVILLE, Roger (1923-) Belgian
£3396 $5264 €5400 Couettes (45x44cm-18x17in) s. s.i.d.1964 verso panel. 5-Oct-2 De Vuyst, Lokeren #573/R est:3000-4000
£3797 $6000 €6000 Fumeur (81x100cm-32x39in) s.d.1971. 26-Nov-2 Palais de Beaux Arts, Brussels #371/R est:5500-7000
£10417 $16563 €15000 Untitled (130x180cm-51x71in) s. 5-May-3 Bernaerts, Antwerp #413

Works on paper
£347 $552 €500 Tete d'homme (76x56cm-30x22in) s.d.1969 pastel. 29-Apr-3 Campo & Campo, Antwerp #286/R
£385 $604 €600 Le peintre. s.d.1975 dr. 19-Nov-2 Galerie Moderne, Brussels #197
£396 $633 €550 La sirene (22x27cm-9x11in) s.d.1974 Indian ink wash. 13-May-3 Palais de Beaux Arts, Brussels #310/R
£436 $702 €650 Illustration pour une vie (38x56cm-15x22in) s. dr. 18-Feb-3 Vanderkindere, Brussels #44
£449 $704 €700 Etude pour Notre Temps (45x58cm-18x23in) s.i.d.1974 Indian ink lit. 11-Dec-2 Hotel des Ventes Mosan, Brussels #324
£506 $790 €800 Nu (36x27cm-14x11in) s.d.1979 i.verso Indian ink dr. 16-Oct-2 Hotel des Ventes Mosan, Brussels #275
£544 $865 €800 Portrait. s. ink. 18-Mar-3 Galerie Moderne, Brussels #201
£545 $845 €850 Femme sur l'escalier (53x66cm-21x26in) s. wash Indian ink. 7-Dec-2 De Vuyst, Lokeren #303/R
£719 $1151 €1000 Ouvriers (52x71cm-20x28in) s.d.1965 wash Indian ink. 17-May-3 De Vuyst, Lokeren #335/R
£1032 $1631 €1600 Portrait de femme de profil. s. pastel. 17-Dec-2 Galerie Moderne, Brussels #777/R
£1871 $2993 €2600 La belle Bruxelloise (53x71cm-21x28in) s. pastel. 13-May-3 Palais de Beaux Arts, Brussels #140/R est:1500-2000
£2642 $4094 €4200 Jeune Femme (71x53cm-28x21in) s.d.1968 pastel. 5-Oct-2 De Vuyst, Lokeren #581/R est:4000-5000

SON, Adrian van (attrib) (c.1550-1610) Flemish
£5282 $8768 €7500 Still life with fruit (30x41cm-12x16in) s. panel. 11-Jun-3 Dorotheum, Vienna #81/R est:6000-8000

SON, Adrian van (circle) (c.1550-1610) Flemish
£14000 $23380 €20300 Portrait of King James VI of Scotland, bust length with slashed doublet (53x40cm-21x16in) 9-Jul-3 Bonhams, New Bond Street #44/R est:7000-10000

SON, Johannes (1859-?) French
Works on paper
£385 $604 €600 Bord d'etang (25x39cm-10x15in) s. pastel. 13-Dec-2 Piasa, Paris #209

SON, Joris van (1623-1667) Flemish
£38000 $59660 €57000 Rose, tulip and other flowers with fruit on ledge (56x49cm-22x19in) s. pair. 11-Dec-2 Christie's, London #41/R est:60000

SON, Joris van (attrib) (17th C) Flemish
£3500 $5845 €5075 Madonna and Child in a cartouche decorated with roses, tulips and fruit (76x62cm-30x24in) 11-Jul-3 Christie's, Kensington #71/R est:2000-3000

SONDERBORG, Kurt R H (1923-) Danish
£5797 $9507 €8000 7.IV.59 Paris (55x38cm-22x15in) s. s.i.d.7.IV.59 verso prov. 28-May-3 Lempertz, Koln #411/R est:8000-10000

Works on paper
£252 $390 €400 Composition (21x16cm-8x6in) s. black gouache sold with another by the same artist. 30-Oct-2 Artcurial Briest, Paris #735

SONDERGAARD, Jens (1895-1957) Danish
£296 $459 €444 Fishermen on boat (30x40cm-12x16in) prov. 1-Oct-2 Rasmussen, Copenhagen #354 (D.KR 3500)
£329 $523 €494 Self portrait (46x31cm-18x12in) s. 26-Feb-3 Kunsthallen, Copenhagen #342 (D.KR 3600)
£466 $722 €699 Beached fishing vessels (30x40cm-12x16in) prov. 1-Oct-2 Rasmussen, Copenhagen #287/R (D.KR 5500)
£590 $897 €885 Landscape (90x100cm-35x39in) s.indis.d. 16-Aug-2 Lilla Bukowskis, Stockholm #958 (S.KR 8600)
£1101 $1706 €1652 Landscape with fields and pine trees (39x39cm-15x15in) s. canvas on panel. 1-Oct-2 Rasmussen, Copenhagen #353/R est:10000-12000 (D.KR 13000)
£1119 $1780 €1679 View over hilly landscape (67x79cm-26x31in) s. 5-May-3 Rasmussen, Vejle #30/R est:10000-15000 (D.KR 12000)
£1166 $1854 €1749 Landscape (27x36cm-11x14in) s. 5-May-3 Rasmussen, Vejle #33/R est:5000-7000 (D.KR 12500)
£1301 $2056 €1952 Portrait of Mother, winter - My mother (115x74cm-45x29in) s.d.40 exhib.prov. 1-Apr-3 Rasmussen, Copenhagen #549/R est:15000-18000 (D.KR 14000)
£1396 $2248 €2094 Coastal landscape (81x86cm-32x34in) s.d.1931. 22-Feb-3 Rasmussen, Havnen #2143/R est:10000-15000 (D.KR 15500)
£1430 $2388 €2074 Man and woman sleeping (135x144cm-53x57in) s.d.1944 stretcher exhib.prov. 17-Jun-3 Rasmussen, Copenhagen #224/R est:25000 (D.KR 15000)
£1524 $2362 €2286 Portrait of my mother (121x95cm-48x37in) s.d.1946-1947 verso prov. 1-Oct-2 Rasmussen, Copenhagen #370/R est:20000 (D.KR 18000)
£1673 $2643 €2510 Landscape with houses (80x100cm-31x39in) s. 1-Apr-3 Rasmussen, Copenhagen #85/R est:20000-25000 (D.KR 18000)
£1766 $2790 €2649 Landscape, Thy (44x52cm-17x20in) s. exhib.prov. 1-Apr-3 Rasmussen, Copenhagen #91/R est:15000-20000 (D.KR 19000)
£1766 $2790 €2649 Boat in rough seas with figures on shore (73x73cm-29x29in) s. 1-Apr-3 Rasmussen, Copenhagen #98/R est:12000-18000 (D.KR 19000)
£1766 $2790 €2649 Dune landscape with view of ocean (83x100cm-33x39in) 1-Apr-3 Rasmussen, Copenhagen #501/R est:20000 (D.KR 19000)
£1859 $2937 €2789 Steep slopes and green waves, Vesterhavet (74x83cm-29x33in) s. 1-Apr-3 Rasmussen, Copenhagen #100/R est:20000-25000 (D.KR 20000)
£1866 $2966 €2799 Pine forest (95x100cm-37x39in) s. 29-Apr-3 Kunsthallen, Copenhagen #283/R est:22000 (D.KR 20000)
£1887 $2943 €2831 Sunday (141x152cm-56x60in) s.d.44 s.d.1944 verso exhib.prov. 11-Nov-2 Rasmussen, Vejle #66/R est:20000 (D.KR 22000)
£1944 $2994 €2916 View from Lysnaes Beach towards Hundested (80x87cm-31x34in) s.d.1946 verso. 23-Oct-2 Kunsthallen, Copenhagen #101/R est:25000 (D.KR 23000)
£2498 $3872 €3747 Figures by the sea (138x160cm-54x63in) s.d.1938 verso. 4-Dec-2 Kunsthallen, Copenhagen #331/R est:30000 (D.KR 29000)
£3346 $5286 €5019 Fishing boats on shore (85x100cm-33x39in) s. 1-Apr-3 Rasmussen, Copenhagen #70/R est:35000-40000 (D.KR 36000)
£3346 $5286 €5019 Landscape with figures, animals and church (110x120cm-43x47in) s.d.51 d.1948-51 verso. 1-Apr-3 Rasmussen, Copenhagen #93/R est:40000-50000 (D.KR 36000)
£3839 $6104 €5759 Landscape, Thy, with view of Hurup (81x95cm-32x37in) s. 26-Feb-3 Kunsthallen, Copenhagen #242/R est:30000 (D.KR 42000)
£3973 $6118 €5960 Landscape by Nykobing Mors (117x150cm-46x59in) s.d.1935. 23-Oct-2 Kunsthallen, Copenhagen #67/R est:50000 (D.KR 47000)

Works on paper
£364 $578 €546 Two figures talking (29x45cm-11x18in) s.d.12.7.50 W/C. 29-Apr-3 Kunsthallen, Copenhagen #254 (D.KR 3900)

SONDERGAARD, Palle (1964-) Swedish?
£281 $450 €407 Barbers (46x38cm-18x15in) s. 18-May-3 Anders Antik, Landskrona #57 (S.KR 3600)

SONDERLAND, Fritz (1836-1896) German
£1370 $2137 €2000 Female eavesdropper (67x51cm-26x20in) s.verso canvas on canvas lit. 10-Apr-3 Allgauer, Kempten #2989/R est:4000

SONDERLAND, Johann Baptist (1805-1878) German
£8219 $12822 €12329 Two student beggars (92x77cm-36x30in) 28-Mar-3 Koller, Zurich #3143/R est:8000-12000 (S.FR 18000)

SONDERMANN, Hermann (1832-1901) German
£2885 $4500 €4328 Little girl holding an apple (41x30cm-16x12in) s. 30-Mar-3 Susanin's, Chicago #6062/R est:5000-7000

SONG XU (1525-?) Chinese
Works on paper
£2720 $4487 €3944 Landscape (115x35cm-45x14in) s.i.d.1595 ink col silk hanging scroll. 6-Jul-3 Christie's, Hong Kong #434/R est:40000-50000 (HK.D 35000)

SONNE, Jorgen Valentin (1801-1890) Danish
£718 $1163 €1041 Arab on guard duty (23x18cm-9x7in) s.i.d.1835 i.verso panel. 24-May-3 Rasmussen, Havnen #2212/R (D.KR 7500)

SONNEGA, Auke (1910-1963) Dutch
£1865 $3077 €2704 Balinese beauty (71x49cm-28x19in) s.i.d.57. 6-Jul-3 Christie's, Hong Kong #17/R est:24000-40000 (HK.D 24000)

SONNENFELD, Gotthard (1874-?) German
Sculpture
£7500 $11925 €11250 Lady in a jester's outfit (63cm-25in) i. cold pat. bronze. 27-Feb-3 Sotheby's, Olympia #170/R est:5000-8000

SONNTAG, William L (1822-1900) American
£443 $700 €665 Summer landscape (13x23cm-5x9in) s. board. 1-Dec-2 Susanin's, Chicago #5039/R
£2866 $4500 €4299 Woodland scene with double waterfall of stream lined with boulders and trees (36x48cm-14x19in) s. 19-Apr-3 James Julia, Fairfield #238/R est:1500-2500
£5975 $9500 €8963 In the deep wood (20x30cm-8x12in) s. prov. 4-Mar-3 Christie's, Rockefeller NY #14/R est:7000-10000

SONNTAG, William L (jnr) (1869-?) American
Works on paper
£1290 $2000 €1935 Carriage ride (33x60cm-13x24in) s. W/C gouache pencil paper on board. 3-Dec-2 Christie's, Rockefeller NY #587/R est:3000-5000
£1299 $2000 €1949 Old paddle wheelers (23x51cm-9x20in) s. W/C. 24-Oct-2 Shannon's, Milford #201/R est:2500-3500

SONREL, Elisabeth (1874-1953) French
£3935 $6336 €5903 Portrait of young woman in black (81x59cm-32x23in) s. 7-May-3 Dobiaschofsky, Bern #985/R est:13000 (S.FR 8500)
Works on paper
£986 $1587 €1400 Jeunes Bretonnes de Pont Aven sous le pommiers (25x32cm-10x13in) s.d.1890 W/C. 11-May-3 Thierry & Lannon, Brest #103 est:1500-1600
£1042 $1698 €1500 Deux petites Bretonnes, un jeune Breton et leurs oies (30x40cm-12x16in) s. W/C. 19-Jul-3 Thierry & Lannon, Brest #295/R est:1200-1500
£1250 $2037 €1800 Jeune Bretonne en costume de fete en bord de riviere (29x24cm-11x9in) s. W/C. 19-Jul-3 Thierry & Lannon, Brest #80 est:1400-1600
£2394 $3855 €3400 Jeune bigoudene et sa fille en priere (48x32cm-19x13in) s. W/C. 11-May-3 Thierry & Lannon, Brest #104/R est:3500-4000
£3542 $5773 €5100 Plougastel Daoulas, jour de Bapteme devant le calvaire (47x61cm-19x24in) s. W/C. 19-Jul-3 Thierry & Lannon, Brest #81 est:3200-3800

SOOM, Hippolyte van (19/20th C) Belgian
£253 $395 €400 Bruyere (76x106cm-30x42in) 16-Sep-2 Amberes, Antwerp #274

SOONIUS, Louis (1883-1956) Dutch
£304 $474 €480 View of Ginneken (17x25cm-7x10in) s. panel. 21-Oct-2 Glerum, Amsterdam #134/R
£446 $696 €700 Farm at the ditch (29x42cm-11x17in) s. 6-Nov-2 Vendue Huis, Gravenhage #27/R
£530 $864 €800 Children playing in the garden (32x41cm-13x16in) s. canvas on panel. 28-Jan-3 Dorotheum, Vienna #67/R
£563 $907 €800 Farm with farmer carrying bucket (24x32cm-9x13in) s. panel. 7-May-3 Vendue Huis, Gravenhage #2/R
£1911 $2981 €3000 Beach entertainment (31x45cm-12x18in) s. 5-Nov-2 Vendu Notarishuis, Rotterdam #15 est:3000-4000
£3822 $5962 €6000 Children playing by the Schevening Pier (27x35cm-11x14in) s.d.1939. 6-Nov-2 Vendue Huis, Gravenhage #506/R est:3500-4500

SOPER, Eileen A (1905-1990) British
Works on paper
£400 $652 €600 Michael of Brechqou (18cm-7in circular) s.i.d.1933 W/C. 12-Feb-3 Bonhams, Knightsbridge #149/R

SOPER, George (1870-1942) British
£270 $427 €405 Chicken by barn door (30x37cm-12x15in) 17-Nov-2 Lots Road, London #355
Works on paper
£250 $390 €375 Ploughing the fields (24x36cm-9x14in) s. pencil W/C htd white. 17-Oct-2 Christie's, Kensington #166
£550 $891 €825 Circus ponies (29x46cm-11x18in) W/C prov. 20-May-3 Sotheby's, Olympia #27/R
£620 $1004 €930 Rick yard (24x37cm-9x15in) s.i. W/C gouache. 20-May-3 Sotheby's, Olympia #28/R

SOPHER, Aaron (1905-1972) American
Works on paper
£314 $500 €471 Provincetown (30x48cm-12x19in) s.i. pen ink W/C prov.exhib. 5-Mar-3 Doyle, New York #57/R

SOPHIANOPULO, Cesare C (1889-1968) Italian
£1154 $1788 €1800 Girl (58x48cm-23x19in) s.d.1918. 5-Dec-2 Stadion, Trieste #821/R

SORBI, Giulio (1883-1975) Italian
£949 $1500 €1500 Riders by inn (40x30cm-16x12in) s. 26-Nov-2 Christie's, Rome #79

SORBI, Raffaello (1844-1931) Italian
£759 $1200 €1200 Toast (8x5cm-3x2in) s. board. 26-Nov-2 Christie's, Rome #137/R
£1013 $1600 €1600 Outside the theatre (5x7cm-2x3in) s. board. 26-Nov-2 Christie's, Rome #140/R
£1290 $2039 €2000 Coliseum (3x4cm-1x2in) s. board. 18-Dec-2 Finarte, Milan #2
£1635 $2518 €2600 Playing on the Arno (4x9cm-2x4in) s. board. 23-Oct-2 Finarte, Milan #131
£3425 $5342 €5138 Groups of men (10x8cm-4x3in) s. panel two. 28-Mar-3 Koller, Zurich #3158/R est:3000-5000 (S.FR 7500)
£120000 $186000 €180000 Winning hand (37x57cm-15x22in) s.d.1885. 4-Dec-2 Christie's, London #114/R est:70000-100000

SORDET, Eugène Etienne (1836-1915) Swiss
£413 $640 €620 Vissoie (30x45cm-12x18in) s. panel. 7-Dec-2 Galerie du Rhone, Sion #339 (S.FR 950)
£524 $817 €786 Seelisberg (30x44cm-12x17in) s.d.1863 i. verso board exhib. 6-Nov-2 Dobiaschofsky, Bern #975/R (S.FR 1200)

SOREAU, Isaak (attrib) (1604-?) Dutch
£9615 $15096 €15000 Still life of autumnal fruit (31x36cm-12x14in) copper lit. 21-Nov-2 Van Ham, Cologne #1423/R est:16000

SOREL, Pierre (1928-) ?
£395 $600 €593 Bouquet of flowers (56x46cm-22x18in) s. 15-Aug-2 Doyle, New York #95

SORENSEN, C F (1818-1879) Danish
£287 $465 €416 Malmo Harbour, grey day (21x31cm-8x12in) init.d.1870. 26-May-3 Rasmussen, Copenhagen #1415/R (D.KR 3000)
£331 $533 €497 Seascape with man-o-war in a swell (21x30cm-8x12in) cardboard. 11-May-3 Hindemae, Ullerslev #677/R (D.KR 3500)
£513 $816 €770 Early morning, Arrilsleje 1867 (31x38cm-12x15in) init.i.d.1867. 5-May-3 Rasmussen, Vejle #127 (D.KR 5500)
£569 $911 €854 Fishermen at sea pulling nets (24x34cm-9x13in) 13-Jan-3 Rasmussen, Vejle #93/R (D.KR 6500)
£595 $928 €893 Many sailing vessels off Kronborg (22x29cm-9x11in) indis.init. 5-Aug-2 Rasmussen, Vejle #40/R (D.KR 7000)
£625 $994 €938 Coastal landscape with sailing boats, figures and lighthouse in foreground (45x66cm-18x26in) s.d.23 juli 1860. 5-May-3 Rasmussen, Vejle #280/R (D.KR 6700)
£930 $1432 €1395 Seascape with vessels off coast (21x24cm-8x9in) s. cardboard. 26-Oct-2 Rasmussen, Havnen #3125 (D.KR 11000)
£1034 $1571 €1551 On the Thames - seascape in evening sunshine (21x41cm-8x16in) 27-Aug-2 Rasmussen, Copenhagen #1734/R est:15000-20000 (D.KR 12000)
£1141 $1757 €1712 Sailing boat with figures on the open seas (38x47cm-15x19in) s.d.1848. 26-Oct-2 Rasmussen, Havnen #3006/R est:10000-15000 (D.KR 13500)
£1148 $1860 €1665 Rocks with two boys fishing (30x40cm-12x16in) s.i. exhib.prov. 26-May-3 Rasmussen, Copenhagen #1399/R est:12000 (D.KR 12000)
£1401 $2242 €2102 Boats in the Bay of Naples (32x47cm-13x19in) s.d.10 Aug.1864. 13-Jan-3 Rasmussen, Vejle #63/R est:12000-15000 (D.KR 16000)

SORENSEN, Carl Frederick (1818-1879) Danish
£1098 $1713 €1647 Summer's day by coastal cliffs (38x60cm-15x24in) s. 23-Sep-2 Rasmussen, Vejle #117/R est:12000-15000 (D.KR 13000)
£1377 $2259 €1997 Fjord landscape with vessel (40x58cm-16x23in) s.i.d.29 Juli 1873. 2-Jun-3 Blomqvist, Oslo #5/R est:20000-25000 (N.KR 15000)
£1414 $2319 €2050 Harbour scene (49x66cm-19x26in) s. 4-Jun-3 AB Stockholms Auktionsverk #2426/R est:18000-20000 (S.KR 18000)

£2436 $3824 €3800 Fishermen by boat on beach (19x26cm-7x10in) s.d.1851 panel. 21-Nov-2 Van Ham, Cologne #1926 est:1000
£2883 $4641 €4325 Seascape with boats and sailing vessels (25x35cm-10x14in) s.d.1850. 26-Feb-3 Museumsbygningen, Copenhagen #17/R est:20000-25000 (D.KR 32000)
£2894 $4572 €4341 Evening, possibly off Bergen with boats (42x62cm-17x24in) s.d.1865. 27-Nov-2 Museumsbygningen, Copenhagen #57/R est:30000 (D.KR 34000)
£3574 $5648 €5361 On the beach near Hornbaek with beached fishing boats (25x42cm-10x17in) s.i.d.1852 exhib.prov. 27-Nov-2 Museumsbygningen, Copenhagen #58/R est:25000 (D.KR 42000)
£4200 $6804 €6300 Calm sea (19x26cm-7x10in) s.d.1851 panel. 20-May-3 Sotheby's, Olympia #350/R est:2500-3500
£5263 $8526 €7631 Corvette Valkyrien towed by steamship Horthea leaving Copenhagen for East Indies (37x57cm-15x22in) s.d.1879. 26-May-3 Rasmussen, Copenhagen #1193/R est:30000 (D.KR 55000)
£9500 $14915 €14250 Boats in the Bay of Naples (89x131cm-35x52in) s.d.1877. 21-Nov-2 Christie's, Kensington #135/R est:7000-10000

SORENSEN, Eiler (1869-1953) Danish
£326 $519 €489 Winter landscape with girl (32x22cm-13x9in) s. 5-May-3 Rasmussen, Vejle #728/R (D.KR 3500)
£1034 $1571 €1551 Girl reading by window (33x26cm-13x10in) s.d.1908. 27-Aug-2 Rasmussen, Copenhagen #1905/R est:3000 (D.KR 12000)

SORENSEN, Henrik (1882-1962) Norwegian
£259 $393 €389 Portrait of woman (86x60cm-34x24in) init.d.42 s.d.verso. 31-Aug-2 Grev Wedels Plass, Oslo #109 (N.KR 3000)
£575 $938 €863 Study of a head (45x29cm-18x11in) s.d.1960 panel. 17-Feb-3 Blomqvist, Lysaker #1225/R (N.KR 6500)
£604 $918 €906 Boy and man of the forest (55x74cm-22x29in) init. mixed media. 31-Aug-2 Grev Wedels Plass, Oslo #108/R (N.KR 7000)
£693 $1060 €1040 Summer night (38x47cm-15x19in) s. panel. 26-Aug-2 Blomqvist, Lysaker #1402 (N.KR 8000)
£806 $1242 €1209 Autumn, Vinje (44x54cm-17x21in) s. panel painted 1930. 28-Oct-2 Blomqvist, Lysaker #1315 (N.KR 9500)
£864 $1442 €1253 Landscape from Mostol, Vinje (28x36cm-11x14in) init. s.i.d.1950 verso panel. 18-Jun-3 Grev Wedels Plass, Oslo #229/R (N.KR 10000)
£2176 $3481 €3264 Torrential rain in Vinje (61x71cm-24x28in) init.d.39 i.d.stretcher. 17-Mar-3 Blomqvist, Oslo #383/R est:30000-40000 (N.KR 25000)
£2428 $3788 €3642 Landscape from Eggedal (47x55cm-19x22in) mono.d.44 i.verso panel. 21-Oct-2 Blomqvist, Oslo #385/R est:18000-20000 (N.KR 28000)
£2920 $4614 €4380 Yellow field (46x55cm-18x22in) init.d.50 panel. 28-Apr-3 Blomqvist, Oslo #363/R est:25000-35000 (N.KR 33000)
£5637 $8794 €8456 Woman and horse (95x160cm-37x63in) init.d.56. 21-Oct-2 Blomqvist, Oslo #390/R est:70000-90000 (N.KR 65000)
£8218 $12984 €12327 Mountain landscape, Galderne, Laerdal (80x77cm-31x30in) init.d.26 i.stretcher. 2-Dec-2 Blomqvist, Oslo #379/R est:70000-90000 (N.KR 95000)

Works on paper
£518 $787 €777 Mountain climbing (74x53cm-29x21in) init. mixed media. 31-Aug-2 Grev Wedels Plass, Oslo #107/R (N.KR 6000)

SORENSEN, Jacobus Lorenz (1812-1857) Dutch
£1250 $2025 €1900 Fishermen at work by moonlight (26x36cm-10x14in) s.d.1856 panel. 21-Jan-3 Christie's, Amsterdam #11/R est:1500-2000

SORENSEN, Jens (1887-1953) Danish
£296 $459 €444 Cabaret dancer (83x60cm-33x24in) s. prov. 1-Oct-2 Rasmussen, Copenhagen #292 (D.KR 3500)
£344 $543 €516 View from Bakken with many figures (58x73cm-23x29in) s. 5-Apr-3 Rasmussen, Havnen #4209/R (D.KR 3700)
£418 $661 €627 Horse breaker on horseback (97x100cm-38x39in) s. 1-Apr-3 Rasmussen, Copenhagen #587/R (D.KR 4500)

SORENSEN, Jens Flemming (1933-) Danish
Sculpture
£1478 $2468 €2143 Fragment of head (70x30x30cm-28x12x12in) red brown pat.bronze marble base. 17-Jun-3 Rasmussen, Copenhagen #40/R est:12000 (D.KR 15500)
£2323 $3671 €3485 Face in ball (34cm-13in) bronze incl. pale marble base. 1-Apr-3 Rasmussen, Copenhagen #333/R est:12000-15000 (D.KR 25000)

SORENSEN, Jorgen (1861-1894) Norwegian
£1561 $2435 €2342 Low wooden houses with church spire in background (30x40cm-12x16in) s.d.93 panel. 21-Oct-2 Blomqvist, Oslo #301/R est:15000-18000 (N.KR 18000)
£6632 $10412 €9948 From a country courtyard (24x33cm-9x13in) s.d.90. 21-Nov-2 Grev Wedels Plass, Oslo #25/R est:40000-60000 (N.KR 76000)
£7398 $11836 €11097 Avenue with cart and figures, possibly from Modum (48x72cm-19x28in) s.d.1883. 17-Mar-3 Blomqvist, Oslo #357/R est:100000-120000 (N.KR 85000)

SORENSEN, Jorgine (19th C) Danish
£845 $1318 €1268 Still life of flowers (24x30cm-9x12in) with sig.d.1858 verso panel. 23-Sep-2 Rasmussen, Vejle #146/R (D.KR 10000)

SORENSEN, Laurits (1882-?) Danish
£321 $501 €482 The Aalborg ferry ready to leave (63x93cm-25x37in) s. 23-Sep-2 Rasmussen, Vejle #2104 (D.KR 3800)
£2390 $3704 €3800 Autumn lakeshore (100x119cm-39x47in) s. 29-Oct-2 Dorotheum, Vienna #286/R est:2600-3000

SORENSEN, Soren (1885-1937) Danish
£280 $445 €420 Southern town scene with figures and donkey (80x100cm-31x39in) s.d.1936. 5-May-3 Rasmussen, Vejle #373 (D.KR 3000)
£419 $666 €629 Susanna in the bath (54x38cm-21x15in) init. 5-Mar-3 Rasmussen, Copenhagen #1727/R (D.KR 4500)

SORENSEN-LUND, Hans (20th C) Danish
£673 $1050 €1010 Good vintage (123x89cm-48x35in) s.d.1918. 12-Apr-3 Weschler, Washington #544a/R est:1000-1500

SORGH, Hendrik Martensz (1611-1670) Dutch
£6090 $9622 €9500 Tavern interior with figures (24x34cm-9x13in) panel prov. 16-Nov-2 Lempertz, Koln #1104/R est:10000

SORGH, Hendrik Martensz (circle) (1611-1670) Dutch
£13580 $22000 €20370 Interior with a lady playing the virginals, gentleman in the background coming up the stairway (58x74cm-23x29in) panel prov.exhib.lit. 23-Jan-3 Sotheby's, New York #4/R est:15000-20000

SORI, Hyakurin (18th C) Japanese
Prints
£2532 $4000 €4000 Deux femmes et un enfant sur une terrasse (38x17cm-15x7in) s. 29-Nov-2 Tajan, Paris #277/R est:2000-2500

SORIA AEDO, Francisco (1898-1965) Spanish
£6250 $10125 €9500 Woman from Valencia (95x75cm-37x30in) s. 21-Jan-3 Durán, Madrid #158/R

SORIA, Salvador (1915-) Spanish
£1379 $2179 €2000 Forms (65x55cm-26x22in) s. oil mixed media panel. 1-Apr-3 Segre, Madrid #221/R

SORIANO, Juan (1920-) Mexican
£13415 $22000 €20123 Adan y Eva (65x65cm-26x26in) s.d.53 exhib. 28-May-3 Christie's, Rockefeller NY #86/R est:25000-30000
Sculpture
£3526 $5501 €5289 Luna (31x21x19cm-12x8x7in) s.d.1996 num.32/50 bronze. 17-Oct-2 Louis Morton, Mexico #58/R est:60000-65000 (M.P 56000)

SORIO, Enrico (1838-1909) Italian
£5449 $8446 €8500 After the Mass (100x60cm-39x24in) s. 4-Dec-2 Finarte, Rome #773/R est:3500

SORKAU, Albert (1874-?) French
£629 $981 €1000 Scene d'interieur (35x29cm-14x11in) s. 9-Oct-2 Lombrail & Teucquam, Paris #15/R
£1456 $2300 €2300 Preparation des bouquets (65x80cm-26x31in) s. 1-Dec-2 Anaf, Lyon #157/R

SORLIER, Charles (1887-1985) French?
Prints
£3118 $4926 €4677 L'ange du jugement (51x43cm-20x17in) s.num.196/200 col lithograph after Chagall lit. 28-Apr-3 Bukowskis, Stockholm #385/R est:40000-45000 (S.KR 41000)
£3504 $5466 €5256 Les coquelicots (55x41cm-22x16in) s.num.62/400 col lithograph after Chagall lit. 5-Nov-2 Bukowskis, Stockholm #518/R est:50000-60000 (S.KR 50000)

£4259 $6729 €6389 Maternite (51x67cm-20x26in) s.num.56/300 col lithograph after Chagall lit. 28-Apr-3 Bukowskis, Stockholm #382/R est:50000-60000 (S.KR 56000)

£4715 $7449 €7073 Les cocquelits (55x41cm-22x16in) s. one of 400 col lithograph after Chagall lit. 28-Apr-3 Bukowskis, Stockholm #380/R est:50000-60000 (S.KR 62000)

£5019 $7930 €7529 Les cocquelicots (55x41cm-22x16in) s.num.363/400 col lithograph after Chagall lit. 28-Apr-3 Bukowskis, Stockholm #379/R est:50000-70000 (S.KR 66000)

£5448 $8500 €8172 Sirene with pine (74x53cm-29x21in) s.num.L/LXXV col lithograph after Marc Chagall. 14-Oct-2 Butterfields, San Francisco #1107/R est:5000-7000

£5466 $8527 €8199 Les cocquelicots (55x41cm-22x16in) s.num.179/400 col lithograph after Chagall lit. 5-Nov-2 Bukowskis, Stockholm #519/R est:50000-70000 (S.KR 78000)

£5500 $9075 €7975 Sirene au poete (61x46cm-24x18in) s.num.XXXV/LXXV col lithograph after Marc Chagall. 1-Jul-3 Sotheby's, London #74/R est:5000-7000

£5606 $8746 €8409 La baie des anges au bouquet de roses (61x46cm-24x18in) s.num.110/150 col lithograph after Chagall lit. 5-Nov-2 Bukowskis, Stockholm #521a/R est:60000-80000 (S.KR 80000)

£5660 $9000 €8490 Sirene and fish (61x46cm-24x18in) s.num.XLIX/LXXV col lithograph after Marc Chagall. 2-May-3 Sotheby's, New York #114/R est:5000-7000

£6000 $9900 €8700 Les coquelicots (55x41cm-22x16in) s.num.208/400 col lithograph after Marc Chagall. 2-Jul-3 Christie's, London #63/R est:4000-6000

£6500 $10725 €9425 Sirene au pin (74x52cm-29x20in) s.num.132/150 col lithograph after Marc Chagall. 1-Jul-3 Sotheby's, London #73/R est:6000-8000

£7000 $11550 €10150 La baie des anges au bouquet de roses (61x46cm-24x18in) s.num.XXXV/LXXV col lithograph after Marc Chagall. 1-Jul-3 Sotheby's, London #72/R est:6000-8000

£7708 $12025 €11562 Romeo et Juliette (64x100cm-25x39in) s.i. col lithograph after Chagall lit. 5-Nov-2 Bukowskis, Stockholm #521/R est:100000-150000 (S.KR 110000)

£9000 $14850 €13050 Bataille de fleurs (61x46cm-24x18in) s.num.XLVIII/LXXV col lithograph after Marc Chagall. 1-Jul-3 Sotheby's, London #71/R est:6000-8000

£10692 $17000 €16038 Romeo and Juliet. s.num.176/200 col lithograph after Marc Chagall. 2-May-3 Sotheby's, New York #115/R est:15000-20000

£13308 $21027 €19962 La flute enchantee (99x65cm-39x26in) s.num.188/200 col lithograph after Chagall lit. 28-Apr-3 Bukowskis, Stockholm #384/R est:175000-200000 (S.KR 175000)

£15589 $24631 €23384 Carmen (100x66cm-39x26in) s.num.161/200 col lithograph after Chagall lit. 28-Apr-3 Bukowskis, Stockholm #383/R est:250000-275000 (S.KR 205000)

SORMANI, Marino (1926-1996) Italian

Works on paper

£609 $944 €950 Greek landscape near Poros (45x80cm-18x31in) s. mixed media board. 5-Dec-2 Stadion, Trieste #886/R

SOROLLA Y BASTIDA, Joaquin (1863-1923) Spanish

£3158 $5116 €4800 Architectonical detail (10x18cm-4x7in) board. 21-Jan-3 Ansorena, Madrid #197/R

£4167 $6583 €6500 Royal scene (20x26cm-8x10in) cardboard. 13-Nov-2 Ansorena, Madrid #110/R

£4167 $6583 €6500 Study of face (42x32cm-17x13in) 13-Nov-2 Ansorena, Madrid #181/R

£4717 $7311 €7500 Baroque allegory (20x33cm-8x13in) cardboard. 7-Oct-2 Ansorena, Madrid #61/R est:7500

£4839 $7645 €7500 Bushes in bloom (13x20cm-5x8in) board. 18-Dec-2 Ansorena, Madrid #73/R est:7500

£5263 $8526 €8000 Landscape with shed (10x17cm-4x7in) board. 21-Jan-3 Ansorena, Madrid #181/R est:7000

£5660 $8774 €9000 Flowers (36x41cm-14x16in) 7-Oct-2 Ansorena, Madrid #62/R est:8500

£6034 $9595 €8750 Study of flowers (21x30cm-8x12in) 4-Mar-3 Ansorena, Madrid #169/R

£6507 $10151 €9500 Study of vine (31x41cm-12x16in) 8-Apr-3 Ansorena, Madrid #224/R est:9500

£9379 $14913 €13600 Staircase in bloom, Italy (23x30cm-9x12in) board. 4-Mar-3 Ansorena, Madrid #165/R

£12329 $19233 €18000 Women meeting (20x28cm-8x11in) 8-Apr-3 Ansorena, Madrid #233/R est:18000

£15789 $25579 €24000 Head of nobleman (40x38cm-16x15in) 21-Jan-3 Ansorena, Madrid #188/R est:6500

£19310 $30703 €28000 Study of hands (45x53cm-18x21in) lit. 4-Mar-3 Ansorena, Madrid #174/R

£100000 $157000 €150000 Los guitarristas, costumbres valencianas, Guitar players, Valencia (33x49cm-13x19in) s.d.1889 on joined panel prov.lit. 19-Nov-2 Sotheby's, London #3/R est:120000-180000

£120000 $188400 €180000 La Sierra Nevada desde la Alhambra, Granad - Sierra Nevada from the Alhambra, Granada (50x68cm-20x27in) painted February 1910 prov.exhib.lit. 19-Nov-2 Sotheby's, London #43/R est:120000-180000

£135000 $209250 €202500 Mondando patatas (40x48cm-16x19in) s.d.1891 prov.lit. 4-Dec-2 Christie's, London #23/R est:120000-180000

£150000 $232500 €225000 Desnudos en patio o plaze (50x70cm-20x28in) s. painted 1901 prov.lit. 4-Dec-2 Christie's, London #13/R est:150000-200000

£160000 $251200 €240000 En la playa de valencia - on the beach (62x57cm-24x22in) painted c.1904 prov.lit. 19-Nov-2 Sotheby's, London #13/R est:160000-200000

£230000 $361100 €345000 Ninos en la playa - children on the beach (40x43cm-16x17in) s. prov. 19-Nov-2 Sotheby's, London #19/R est:150000-200000

£480000 $753600 €720000 El rompeolas de San Sebastian - on the breakwater, San Sebastian (52x73cm-20x29in) s. prov.exhib.lit. 19-Nov-2 Sotheby's, London #22/R est:300000-500000

£950000 $1491500 €1425000 Sol de latarde, playa de Valencia - evening sun, Valencia Beach (100x110cm-39x43in) s.d.1910 prov.exhib.lit. 19-Nov-2 Sotheby's, London #16/R est:700000-900000

Works on paper

£974 $1422 €1500 Study of gun (19x29cm-7x11in) W/C. 17-Jun-2 Ansorena, Madrid #7/R

£1226 $1937 €1900 Urban landscape (33x27cm-13x11in) pencil dr. 18-Dec-2 Ansorena, Madrid #964/R

£1290 $2039 €2000 Studies of women (23x34cm-9x13in) ink dr prov. 17-Dec-2 Durán, Madrid #50/R

£2083 $3292 €3250 Studies (22x30cm-9x12in) s. ink dr. 14-Nov-2 Arte, Seville #406/R

SORONGAS, Sotiris (1936-) Greek

£2000 $3100 €3000 Woods (150x200cm-59x79in) prov. 2-Oct-2 Sotheby's, London #121/R

SORRI, Pietro (1556-1621) Italian

£5500 $9185 €7975 Two studies for the assumption of the Virgin and six Apostles, one kneeling (47x30cm-19x12in) oil paper on canvas corner made up. 8-Jul-3 Christie's, London #28/R est:6000-8000

SORVIG, Frederich Martin (1823-1892) Norwegian

Works on paper

£900 $1503 €1305 Marie Sophie at Turhoe (42x61cm-17x24in) s.i.d.1861 gouache. 18-Jun-3 Sotheby's, Olympia #37/R

£7346 $12048 €10652 Ship's portrait - Carl Ronneberg of Tonsberg (52x78cm-20x31in) s.i.d.1869 W/C. 2-Jun-3 Blomqvist, Oslo #59/R est:90000-100000 (N.KR 80000)

SOSA, Hermenegildo (1946-) Mexican

£749 $1183 €1124 Poem 2 (50x60cm-20x24in) s.d.1979. 26-Nov-2 Louis Morton, Mexico #86/R est:16000 (M.P 12000)

SOSEN, Mori (attrib) (1747-1821) Japanese

Works on paper

£700 $1127 €1050 Kakemono (109x42cm-43x17in) s. ink. 19-Feb-3 Sotheby's, Olympia #3/R

SOSNO, Sacha (1937-) French

Sculpture

£949 $1500 €1500 Statues decoupees (26cm-10in) i.d.94 num.1/20 bronze marble base. 26-Nov-2 Sotheby's, Amsterdam #72/R est:1500-2000

SOSPIZIO, Seve (1908-1962) Italian

£289 $453 €450 Along the Sieve (48x39cm-19x15in) s. board. 16-Dec-2 Pandolfini, Florence #282/R

SOTO, Jesus Rafael (1923-) Venezuelan

£6250 $9938 €9000 A la fernanda (38cm-15in circular) s.i.d.verso paint wood metal. 29-Apr-3 Artcurial Briest, Paris #620/R est:7000-9000

£15823 $25000 €23735 Couleur et vibration, bleu et noir (107x107cm-42x42in) s. i.d.1966 verso oil panel metal nylon hanging elements. 13-Nov-2 Sotheby's, New York #297/R est:30000-40000

£15924 $25000 €23886 Colour cross (152x152cm-60x60in) s.i.d.1969 verso panelprov. 19-Nov-2 Sotheby's, New York #110/R est:40000

Sculpture

£7692 $11923 €12000 Carre bleu (107x56x23cm-42x22x9in) s.i.d.1966 verso oil tempera Indian ink panel metal nylon. 6-Dec-2 Hauswedell & Nolte, Hamburg #356/R est:15000

£8537 $14000 €12379 Anello (41x61x31cm-16x24x12in) s.i.d.1971 num.28/33 aluminum nylon thread metal prov.lit. 27-May-3 Sotheby's, New York #119a

£9014 $14332 €13250 Deux baguettes noires et une bleue (30x37cm-12x15in) s.d.1975 verso wood iron. 26-Feb-3 Artcurial Briest, Paris #429/R est:10000-12000

£18000 $30060 €26100 Colory y movimento (106x106x15cm-42x42x6in) s.i.d.1965 verso painted wood metal prov.exhib. 26-Jun-3 Sotheby's, London #156/R est:8000-12000

£19817 $32500 €28735 Tes violets et haus noirs (50x50cm-20x20in) s.i.d.1974 painted wood metal prov. 27-May-3 Sotheby's, New York #114

£30000 $49200 €45000 Tiges bleues et blanches (143x132x25cm-56x52x10in) s.i.d.1974 painted wood metal nylon thread prov. 6-Feb-3 Christie's, London #662/R est:15000-20000

£48000 $80160 €69600 Untitled (89x30x34cm-35x12x13in) s.d.1959/60 verso wood paint metal nails prov.exhib. 26-Jun-3 Sotheby's, London #161/R est:18000-25000

Works on paper

£1087 $1783 €1500 Carre (36x28cm-14x11in) s. collage gouache prov. 27-May-3 Tajan, Paris #35/R est:1500-2000

£2323 $3670 €3600 Composition (35cm-14in circular) s.d.1968 verso mixed media panel. 19-Dec-2 Bondu, Paris #17

SOTO, Rafael Fernandez de (1915-1984) Spanish

£909 $1327 €1400 Santa Maria del Mar (41x31cm-16x12in) s. s.i.d.1965 verso board. 17-Jun-2 Ansorena, Madrid #117/R

SOTO, Raphael de (1904-1987) ?

£2083 $3250 €3125 Crowded bar scene (61x41cm-24x16in) s. board. 9-Nov-2 Illustration House, New York #150/R est:4000-6000

SOTOMAYOR Y ZARAGOZA, Fernando (1875-1960) Spanish

£48000 $74400 €72000 Man and woman in local dress. Two women in similar costume (67x50cm-26x20in) s. canvas on panel. 4-Dec-2 Christie's, London #21/R est:12000-18000

SOTTAS, Solange (20th C) French?

£795 $1295 €1200 Interior (54x65cm-21x26in) s. 31-Jan-3 Rabourdin & Choppin de Janvry, Paris #53

SOTTER, George William (1879-1953) American

£2695 $4500 €3908 Light and shadow (30x23cm-12x9in) s. 22-Jun-3 Freeman, Philadelphia #149/R est:5000-8000

SOTTOCORNOLA, Giovanni (1855-1917) Italian

£4082 $6490 €6000 Granny Ercolina (126x81cm-50x32in) s.d.1916. 18-Mar-3 Finarte, Milan #55/R

Works on paper

£517 $822 €750 Portraits of women (15x13cm-6x5in) init. pencil triptych. 5-Mar-3 Sotheby's, Milan #62

SOUCEK, Karel (1915-1982) Czechoslovakian

£410 $582 €615 Oriental composition (20x23cm-8x9in) board painted c.1918-1922. 26-Mar-2 SOGA, Bratislava #209/R (SL.K 26000)

£454 $709 €681 In the town (48x81cm-19x32in) s.d.70 cardboard. 12-Oct-2 Dorotheum, Prague #144/R (C.KR 22000)

£496 $773 €744 Female nude (58x94cm-23x37in) s.d.45 oil tempera. 12-Oct-2 Dorotheum, Prague #83/R (C.KR 24000)

£619 $978 €929 Rooftops (40x54cm-16x21in) s.i.d.42 plywood. 30-Nov-2 Dorotheum, Prague #95/R (C.KR 30000)

SOUCH, John (attrib) (17th C) British

£27000 $42660 €40500 Portrait of Lady Lawley, wife of Sir Thomas (211x146cm-83x57in) prov. 26-Nov-2 Christie's, London #6/R est:25000-35000

SOUCHON, Marian Sims (1870-1954) American

£3006 $4750 €4509 Parade day (76x71cm-30x28in) board. 5-Apr-3 Neal Auction Company, New Orleans #407/R est:4000-6000

SOUDAN, Octaaf (1872-1948) Belgian

£863 $1381 €1200 After the rain (40x86cm-16x34in) s. panel. 17-May-3 De Vuyst, Lokeren #337

SOUDEIKINE, Sergei (1883-1946) Russian

£3662 $5200 €5493 Children's coop (56x71cm-22x28in) 8-Aug-1 Barridorf, Portland #160/R est:2000-3000

Works on paper

£2800 $4676 €4060 Rainbow in the garden (30x49cm-12x19in) s. bodycol. 25-Jun-3 Cheffins, Cambridge #730/R est:300-400

SOUGEZ, Emmanuel (1889-1972) French?

Photographs

£2564 $4051 €4000 Lingeries (38x29cm-15x11in) i.d.verso gelatin silver print. 16-Nov-2 Christie's, Paris #309/R est:4000-6000

SOUILLET, Georges François (1861-1957) French

£780 $1303 €1100 Port d'Alger (61x46cm-24x18in) s.d. 23-Jun-3 Delvaux, Paris #196 est:800-900

SOUKENS, Hendrik (1680-1711) Dutch

Works on paper

£1608 $2686 €2300 Apollon et les muses (34x47cm-13x19in) s.d.1705 pen ink wash. 27-Jun-3 Claude Aguttes, Neuilly #8/R est:2500-3000

SOUKKA, Tapio (1921-) Finnish

£272 $433 €400 Red (69x97cm-27x38in) s.d.68. 24-Mar-3 Bukowskis, Helsinki #307/R

SOULACROIX, Frederic (1825-1879) French

£9677 $15000 €14516 In the dressing room (60x39cm-24x15in) s. prov. 29-Oct-2 Sotheby's, New York #82/R est:20000-30000

£19355 $30000 €29033 Afternoon tea (41x26cm-16x10in) s.i. 29-Oct-2 Sotheby's, New York #81/R est:40000-60000

£48387 $75000 €72581 Vanitas (76x46cm-30x18in) s. 30-Oct-2 Christie's, Rockefeller NY #78/R est:60000-80000

SOULAGES, Pierre (1919-) French

£16000 $24640 €24000 Peinture (55x46cm-22x18in) s. i.d.13 Juilliet 86 verso prov.exhib.lit. 22-Oct-2 Sotheby's, London #423/R est:15000-20000

£17367 $27614 €26051 Composition (109x75cm-43x30in) s. s.d.1977 verso acrylic paper on canvas exhib. 26-Feb-3 Kunsthallen, Copenhagen #73/R est:200000 (D.KR 190000)

£51266 $81000 €81000 Composition (137x222cm-54x87in) d.90 acrylic exhib.lit. 27-Nov-2 Marc Kohn, Paris #44/R est:80000-100000

£63889 $100944 €92000 Peinture 46x36 cm (46x38cm-18x15in) s. prov.exhib.lit. 27-Apr-3 Perrin, Versailles #40/R est:75000-90000

£72414 $114414 €105000 Peinture (162x130cm-64x51in) s. s.d.71 verso prov.exhib.lit. 2-Apr-3 Christie's, Paris #23/R est:50000-70000

£72414 $114414 €105000 Peinture (97x162cm-38x64in) s.d.71 acrylic vinyl prov.exhib.lit. 2-Apr-3 Christie's, Paris #34/R est:45000-55000

£92000 $153640 €133400 Peinture (130x97cm-51x38in) s. s.d.29.5.56 verso prov.exhib.lit. 26-Jun-3 Sotheby's, London #184/R est:50000-70000

£105556 $174167 €152000 Peinture 81 x 60 cm (81x60cm-32x24in) s.d. exhib.lit. 1-Jul-3 Artcurial Briest, Paris #507/R est:120000-150000

£140000 $233800 €203000 9 Octobre 1955 (162x114cm-64x45in) i.on stretcher painted 1955 prov.exhib.lit. 27-Jun-3 Christie's, London #119/R est:50000-70000

Prints

£2179 $3378 €3400 Eau-forte No 22 (96x95cm-38x37in) s.i. num.79/90 col etching. 3-Dec-2 Lempertz, Koln #431/R est:3300

Works on paper

£6774 $10500 €10161 Composition (75x56cm-30x22in) s.d.77 Indian ink paper on canvas prov. 1-Oct-2 Rasmussen, Copenhagen #12/R est:80000-100000 (D.KR 80000)

£15335 $24229 €23003 Blue and black composition (109x75cm-43x30in) s.d.77 i.stretcher W/C Indian ink paper on canvas. 1-Apr-3 Rasmussen, Copenhagen #182/R est:200000-250000 (D.KR 165000)

£20290 $33275 €28000 Untitled (64x50cm-25x20in) s.i.d.1960 gouache prov. 28-May-3 Lempertz, Koln #415/R est:12000

SOULEN, Henry James (1888-1965) American

£556 $900 €834 Rivals in love (86x91cm-34x36in) s. 24-Jan-3 Freeman, Philadelphia #180/R

£1083 $1700 €1625 Hippopotamus parade (53x66cm-21x26in) s.i. board prov. 23-Nov-2 Pook & Pook, Downington #140/R est:1500-2500

SOULIE, Tony (1955-) French

£886 $1373 €1400 Doks (240x90cm-94x35in) s.d.verso acrylic. 28-Sep-2 Cornette de St.Cyr, Paris #426/R

£952 $1514 €1400 Composition (140x140cm-55x55in) s.d.1990 verso acrylic. 24-Mar-3 Claude Boisgirard, Paris #150

£1042 $1646 €1500 Sans titre (222x236cm-87x93in) s.i.d.verso acrylic. 28-Apr-3 Cornette de St.Cyr, Paris #510/R est:1500-2000

SOULIMENKO, Piotr (1914-) Russian
Works on paper
£350 $550 €525 Storming of the Winter Palace from the Admiralty Arch (55x56cm-22x22in) s. mixed media on card executed 1965. 21-Nov-2 Tennants, Leyburn #858

SOURDILLON, Berthe (1895-1976) French
£268 $432 €400 Collioure (37x55cm-15x22in) s. panel. 23-Feb-3 Lesieur & Le Bars, Le Havre #142
£380 $592 €600 Femme assise (64x100cm-25x39in) s. 18-Oct-2 Rabourdin & Choppin de Janvry, Paris #40
£506 $790 €800 Femme nue allongee (81x115cm-32x45in) s. 18-Oct-2 Rabourdin & Choppin de Janvry, Paris #39/R
£548 $855 €800 Le front de mer (27x72cm-11x28in) s.d.67 isorel. 8-Apr-3 Gioffredo, Nice #79
£856 $1336 €1250 Le port de Nice (46x60cm-18x24in) isorel. 8-Apr-3 Gioffredo, Nice #78/R
£959 $1496 €1400 Tourrettes sur Loup (60x80cm-24x31in) isorel. 8-Apr-3 Gioffredo, Nice #77/R

SOUTER, Camille (1929-) British
£3205 $4968 €5000 Still life, leg of meat (48x36cm-19x14in) s. oil on paper. 3-Dec-2 Thomas Adams, Dublin #398
£3562 $5592 €5200 Spring comes by the harbour (32x29cm-13x11in) s.i.d.1960 i.d.verso oil on paper. 15-Apr-3 De Veres Art Auctions, Dublin #129/R est:4000-6000
£3691 $5943 €5500 Pale shapes (33x43cm-13x17in) s. tissue prov.exhib. 18-Feb-3 Whyte's, Dublin #52/R est:7000-9000
£4317 $6906 €6000 London again (43x58cm-17x23in) s.d.1958 paper. 13-May-3 Thomas Adams, Dublin #388
£4430 $6867 €7000 Gutted fish (26x54cm-10x21in) s.d.1976 oil on paper. 24-Sep-2 De Veres Art Auctions, Dublin #18/R est:6000-9000
£4452 $6990 €6500 Achill Christmas (33x36cm-13x14in) s.d.58 oil on paper. 15-Apr-3 De Veres Art Auctions, Dublin #128/R est:5000-7000
£6962 $10791 €11000 End of summer apples (21x32cm-8x13in) s. board. 25-Sep-2 James Adam, Dublin #14/R est:5000-8000
£10067 $16208 €15000 Hanging meat with cow's hearts (51x38cm-20x15in) s.d.1972 paper prov.exhib.lit. 18-Feb-3 Whyte's, Dublin #41/R est:8000-10000
£15823 $24525 €25000 My still life, Achill Island (64x46cm-25x18in) s.d.1986 oil on paper prov. 25-Sep-2 James Adam, Dublin #83/R est:25000-30000
£19178 $30110 €28000 Front porch in the west (77x56cm-30x22in) s.d.64 i.verso oil on paper. 15-Apr-3 De Veres Art Auctions, Dublin #126 est:20000-30000

SOUTER, David Henry (1862-1935) Australian
Works on paper
£1394 $2286 €2021 By Celias arbour (28x47cm-11x19in) s.i.d.94 W/C. 4-Jun-3 Deutscher-Menzies, Melbourne #146/R est:2400-2800 (A.D 3500)

SOUTER, John Bulloch (1890-1972) British
£400 $624 €600 Still life with apples, glass and jug on a green tablecloth (30x41cm-12x16in) s.d.75 board. 9-Oct-2 Woolley & Wallis, Salisbury #252/R
£900 $1404 €1350 Aurelia (41x35cm-16x14in) s. canvas on board. 27-Mar-3 Christie's, Kensington #411/R
£900 $1485 €1305 Bridge over the river (37x61cm-15x24in) s. board. 3-Jul-3 Christie's, Kensington #458/R

SOUTH AMERICAN SCHOOL, 19th C
£21341 $35000 €30944 Alegoria de America (128x84cm-50x33in) 27-May-3 Sotheby's, New York #131

SOUTH GERMAN SCHOOL, 15th C
£22302 $35683 €31000 Birth of Maria (31x20cm-12x8in) panel prov. 17-May-3 Lempertz, Koln #1129/R est:30000

SOUTH GERMAN SCHOOL, 18th C
£9459 $14757 €14000 Adoration of the shepherds (132x165cm-52x65in) prov. 27-Mar-3 Dorotheum, Vienna #257/R est:8000-15000
Works on paper
£11111 $17667 €16000 Mother of God on clouds with St Sebastian and Jacob below (38x26cm-15x10in) pen over chk wash prov. 5-May-3 Ketterer, Munich #261/R est:1200-1400

SOUTHALL, Andrew (?) ?
£393 $609 €590 Flowers and port decanter II (81x110cm-32x43in) s. s.i.d.84 verso. 29-Oct-2 Lawson Menzies, Sydney #245 (A.D 1100)

SOUTHALL, Joseph Edward (1861-1944) British
Works on paper
£1300 $2028 €1950 On the steps in Venice (23x32cm-9x13in) mono.d.1935 pencil W/C. 27-Mar-3 Christie's, Kensington #306/R est:1200-1800
£2050 $3280 €3075 Fountain at Assisi; ladies conversing in the square (22x15cm-9x6in) mono.d.1926 W/C. 11-Mar-3 Bonhams, Oxford #39/R est:2000-3000

SOUTHERN DUTCH SCHOOL, 17th C
£7500 $11775 €11250 Monk seducing a nun (35x23cm-14x9in) copper. 13-Dec-2 Christie's, Kensington #49/R est:6000-8000

SOUTHGATE, Frank (1872-1916) British
£300 $501 €435 Terrier's head (23cm-9in circular) board. 25-Jun-3 Brightwells, Leominster #1015/R
£600 $960 €900 Ducks taking flight (38x60cm-15x24in) s. 19-May-3 Robin Fenner, Tavistock #326
Works on paper
£350 $532 €525 Spaniel decoying a redshank (20x30cm-8x12in) monotone W/C. 16-Aug-2 Keys, Aylsham #587/R
£420 $655 €630 Mallard on and over mud flats, north Norfolk (33x53cm-13x21in) W/C. 18-Oct-2 Keys, Aylsham #612/R
£440 $726 €638 Crabbing, pier steps, Hunstanton (37x51cm-15x20in) s.d.1897 monochrome wash. 1-Jul-3 Bonhams, Norwich #79/R
£500 $780 €750 Wading birds on and over a beach (30x46cm-12x18in) s.d.1900 monotone W/C. 18-Oct-2 Keys, Aylsham #615/R
£600 $948 €900 Frozen out inland waters (32x51cm-13x20in) s.d.1901 W/C. 28-Nov-2 Bonhams, Knightsbridge #51/R
£900 $1404 €1350 Ducks in bulrushes (48x71cm-19x28in) s. W/C paper on board. 6-Nov-2 Sotheby's, Olympia #135/R est:1500-2000
£1500 $2430 €2250 Waders looking for food (28x49cm-11x19in) s. W/C. 21-Jan-3 Bonhams, Knightsbridge #20/R est:1500-2000
£1800 $2844 €2700 Snipe (28x49cm-11x19in) s. W/C. 28-Nov-2 Bonhams, Knightsbridge #50/R est:2000-3000
£1900 $2964 €2850 Fishing boats at Wells-next-the-Sea (23x33cm-9x13in) s. W/C. 18-Oct-2 Keys, Aylsham #614 est:350-450
£2100 $3423 €3150 Marshland landscape with teal (43x51cm-17x20in) s. W/C. 14-Feb-3 Keys, Aylsham #638/R est:1500-2000
£2200 $3476 €3300 Cock and hen pheasants by lakeside. Geese on a beach (18x43cm-7x17in) s. W/C pair. 28-Nov-2 Bonhams, Knightsbridge #49/R est:2000-3000
£2600 $4108 €3900 Tug boat Marie Lynn at a quayside (40x58cm-16x23in) s. W/C. 2-Apr-3 Edgar Horn, Eastbourne #278/R est:300-400
£3200 $4992 €4800 Heron in flight over marsh land (41x56cm-16x22in) s. W/C. 18-Oct-2 Keys, Aylsham #616/R est:300-400
£5000 $7800 €7500 Black headed gulls feeding their young on a beach (23x30cm-9x12in) s. W/C. 18-Oct-2 Keys, Aylsham #613/R est:500-700

SOUTINE, Chaim (1893-1943) Russian
£46584 $75000 €69876 Glaieuls (61x53cm-24x21in) s. painted 1919 prov.lit. 8-May-3 Christie's, Rockefeller NY #221/R est:80000-100000
£49689 $80000 €74534 La cite Falguiere (46x55cm-18x22in) s. painted c.1914 prov.lit. 8-May-3 Christie's, Rockefeller NY #202/R est:90000-120000
£59006 $95000 €88509 Les pintades (50x65cm-20x26in) s. painted c.1926-27 prov. 8-May-3 Christie's, Rockefeller NY #190/R est:100000-150000
£60897 $95000 €91346 L'atelier de l'artiste a la Cite Falguiere (65x50cm-26x20in) s. s.verso painted c.1915-16 prov.exhib. 7-Nov-2 Christie's, Rockefeller NY #293/R est:120000-160000
£73718 $115000 €110577 La route peu rassurante (65x54cm-26x21in) s. painted 1918-19 prov.exhib.lit. 7-Nov-2 Christie's, Rockefeller NY #314/R est:140000-180000
£100000 $167000 €145000 La femme a l'ombrelle (73x73cm-29x29in) s. painted 1936-37 prov.exhib.lit. 25-Jun-3 Christie's, London #177/R est:100000-150000
£217391 $350000 €326087 Paysage de Cagnes (60x72cm-24x28in) s. painted c.1922 prov. 6-May-3 Sotheby's, New York #26/R est:300000-400000
£224359 $350000 €336539 Fillette a la barriere (115x65cm-45x26in) s. painted 1939 prov.exhib.lit. 5-Nov-2 Sotheby's, New York #45/R est:400000-600000
£266026 $415000 €399039 Les gorges du Loup - la maison hantee IV (72x59cm-28x23in) s. painted c.1923 prov.lit. 7-Nov-2 Christie's, Rockefeller NY #276/R est:300000-400000
£333333 $520000 €500000 La folle (92x61cm-36x24in) s. painted c.1925 prov.exhib. 6-Nov-2 Christie's, Rockefeller NY #50/R est:600000-800000
£416667 $650000 €625001 Le garcon boucher (65x54cm-26x21in) s. executed c.1919-20 prov.exhib.lit. 5-Nov-2 Sotheby's, New York #48/R est:400000-600000

SOUTMAN, Pieter Claesz (attrib) (1580-1657) Dutch
£8784 $13703 €13000 Calling of Matthew (148x193cm-58x76in) prov. 27-Mar-3 Dorotheum, Vienna #185/R est:8000-14000

SOUTO, Alfredo (1862-1940) Spanish
£1763 $2574 €2750 Trees (35x15cm-14x6in) s.d.1902 board. 6-Jun-2 Castellana, Madrid #270/R

SOUTO, Arturo (1901-1964) Spanish
Works on paper
£316 $499 €490 Woman (29x22cm-11x9in) s. pencil dr. 18-Dec-2 Ansorena, Madrid #428/R
£692 $1065 €1100 View of Paris, Montmartre (37x29cm-15x11in) s. W/C. 28-Oct-2 Segre, Madrid #250/R

SOUTTER, Louis (1871-1942) Swiss
Works on paper
£4148 $6472 €6222 Sylphides (22x29cm-9x11in) i. pen ink dr lit. 8-Nov-2 Dobiaschofsky, Bern #280/R est:3400 (S.FR 9500)

SOUVERBIE, Jean (1891-1981) French
£443 $700 €700 Scene d'interieur (64x54cm-25x21in) s. 2-Dec-2 Tajan, Paris #74
£755 $1170 €1200 Roger delivrant Angelique (90x122cm-35x48in) s. panel. 4-Oct-2 Tajan, Paris #219
£886 $1400 €1400 Cigarette (55x46cm-22x18in) s. cardboard. 2-Dec-2 Tajan, Paris #72/R
£1139 $1800 €1800 Portrait de Francoise (34x25cm-13x10in) cardboard. 2-Dec-2 Tajan, Paris #68/R
£1600 $2592 €2400 Peace (36x45cm-14x18in) s. board prov. 20-May-3 Bonhams, Knightsbridge #108/R est:2000-3000
£2069 $3310 €3000 Trois femmes allongees (14x26cm-6x10in) s.d.1927. 12-Mar-3 Libert, Castor, Paris #177/R est:2500-3500
£2532 $4000 €4000 Nu au bord de l'eau (33x41cm-13x16in) s. 2-Dec-2 Tajan, Paris #73
£16667 $26833 €25001 Le modele (73x60cm-29x24in) s. 7-May-3 Dobiaschofsky, Bern #986/R est:12000 (S.FR 36000)
£26235 $42500 €38041 Baigneuses (81x99cm-32x39in) s.d.27 prov. 21-May-3 Doyle, New York #5/R est:3000-5000
£29114 $45417 €46000 Jeunes filles a la fontaine (81x100cm-32x39in) s.d.46 s.d. verso prov. 31-Jul-2 Tajan, Paris #23/R est:15000-18000
Works on paper
£315 $488 €500 Le modele (15x20cm-6x8in) s. W/C. 4-Oct-2 Tajan, Paris #218

SOUZA, Francis Newton (1924-2002) British/Indian
£800 $1248 €1200 Head (32x23cm-13x9in) s.d.62 oil over newsprint board. 17-Oct-2 Bonhams, Knightsbridge #654/R
£1050 $1638 €1575 Still life 1959 (19x24cm-7x9in) s.d.59 exhib. 6-Nov-2 Bonhams, Chester #483 est:400-600
£1400 $2184 €2100 City landscape (28x38cm-11x15in) s.d.1947 paper. 17-Oct-2 Bonhams, Knightsbridge #591/R est:1500-2500
£2000 $3180 €3000 Rock garden (60x75cm-24x30in) s.d.1969 verso. 2-May-3 Christie's, Kensington #572/R est:2000-3000
£2500 $3900 €3750 Bronx at night (41x59cm-16x23in) i.d.1968 verso board. 17-Oct-2 Bonhams, Knightsbridge #555/R est:1200-1400
£3500 $5460 €5250 Polynesian nude (50x127cm-20x50in) s.d.65. 17-Oct-2 Bonhams, Knightsbridge #593/R est:1500-2000
£3800 $5928 €5700 Oklahoma City (61x73cm-24x29in) s.d.71 board. 17-Oct-2 Bonhams, Knightsbridge #655 est:800-1200
£4800 $7488 €7200 Still life with flowers (81x77cm-32x30in) s.d.64. 17-Oct-2 Bonhams, Knightsbridge #590/R est:1500-2000
£5000 $7800 €7500 Green landscape (74x95cm-29x37in) s.d.66. 17-Oct-2 Bonhams, Knightsbridge #589/R est:4000-6000
£6500 $10140 €9750 Nude bust (81x56cm-32x22in) s.d.61 prov. 17-Oct-2 Bonhams, Knightsbridge #551/R est:2000-3000
£7000 $10920 €10500 Christ in the garden (61x91cm-24x36in) s.d.57 board. 17-Oct-2 Bonhams, Knightsbridge #554/R est:2000-3000
£9324 $15385 €13520 Landscape with red houses (62x50cm-24x20in) s.d.53 i.d.1953 verso board. 6-Jul-3 Christie's, Hong Kong #75/R est:55000-75000 (HK.D 120000)
£18000 $28620 €27000 Standing nude (122x61cm-48x24in) s. s.d.1957 verso board lit. 2-May-3 Christie's, Kensington #567/R est:8000-12000
Works on paper
£400 $624 €600 Landscape scene (26x20cm-10x8in) felt pen magazine paper. 17-Oct-2 Bonhams, Knightsbridge #594/R
£600 $936 €900 Woman looking in a mirror. Weeping (25x20cm-10x8in) s.d.1950 pen ink pair. 17-Oct-2 Bonhams, Knightsbridge #653/R
£650 $1034 €975 Susanne and the elders. Nude with still life (24x19cm-9x7in) s.d.59 ink pair. 2-May-3 Christie's, Kensington #578/R

SOUZA, Pascal de (20th C) ?
£280 $442 €420 An Oriental child holding a doll (91x45cm-36x18in) s. board. 14-Nov-2 Christie's, Kensington #105/R

SOUZA-PINTO, Alberto Carlos (19th C) Portuguese
£1139 $1800 €1800 Artist's house in Portugal (20x33cm-8x13in) s. 1-Dec-2 Anaf, Lyon #179
£2025 $3200 €3200 Girl in profile (16x12cm-6x5in) s. 1-Dec-2 Anaf, Lyon #180

SOUZA-PINTO, Jose Giulio (1856-1939) Portuguese
£3165 $5000 €5000 Parc de Sceaux (15x23cm-6x9in) 1-Dec-2 Anaf, Lyon #178/R
£5949 $9400 €9400 Pause du paysan (55x43cm-22x17in) 1-Dec-2 Anaf, Lyon #177/R est:6000

SOUZY, Bernard de (1945-) French?
£690 $1097 €1000 Delon (80x80cm-31x31in) s. d.01 verso. 10-Mar-3 Millon & Associes, Paris #130/R
£1034 $1645 €1500 Marilyn (90x85cm-35x33in) s. d.99 verso. 10-Mar-3 Millon & Associes, Paris #131/R

SOVANKA, Karol (1883-1961) Czechoslovakian
£1231 $1909 €1847 Roe deer with roe-buck (58x77cm-23x30in) painted c.1940. 3-Dec-2 SOGA, Bratislava #21/R est:75000 (SL.K 78000)

SOVIG, Theodor (1840-1892) Norwegian
£13315 $21837 €19307 Bergen seen from the sea (49x76cm-19x30in) s.d.1880 i.stretcher. 2-Jun-3 Blomqvist, Oslo #83/R est:70000-80000 (N.KR 145000)

SOWERBY, James (1756-1822) British
Prints
£12000 $19320 €18000 Flora luxuriens (43x28cm-17x11in) hand col plates folio lit. 7-May-3 Sotheby's, London #115/R est:12000-15000

SOWERBY, John G (fl.1876-1914) British
£1333 $2213 €1933 Blue kirtle (63x114cm-25x45in) s. i.on stretcher. 16-Jun-3 Waddingtons, Toronto #153/R est:4000-6000 (C.D 3000)

SOYA-JENSEN, C M (1860-1912) Danish
£541 $870 €812 Italian landscape with figures (31x52cm-12x20in) s.i. 22-Feb-3 Rasmussen, Havnen #2104/R (D.KR 6000)

SOYEON KIM (20th C) Korean
£479 $800 €695 Spring breeze (65x91cm-26x36in) s.d.2002 verso. 25-Jun-3 Sotheby's, Moscow #220/R
£793 $1300 €1150 Wave in the wind (117x80cm-46x31in) s.d.2002 verso. 28-May-3 Sotheby's, Amsterdam #133/R est:1200-1800
£813 $1300 €1179 Present time (130x99cm-51x39in) s.d.2002 verso. 13-May-3 Sotheby's, Tel Aviv #25/R est:1200-1800

SOYER, Moses (1899-1974) American
£839 $1300 €1259 Head of a girl (36x25cm-14x10in) s. 7-Dec-2 Selkirks, St. Louis #228/R est:1500-2000
£839 $1300 €1259 Lady in red No. 2 (41x30cm-16x12in) s. board. 7-Dec-2 Selkirks, St. Louis #229/R est:1500-2000
£927 $1511 €1400 Girls reading (27x36cm-11x14in) painted 1938 panel prov. 28-Jan-3 Dorotheum, Vienna #71/R
£1069 $1700 €1604 Model in studio (51x25cm-20x10in) s. 7-Mar-3 Skinner, Boston #577/R est:1500-2000
£1796 $3000 €2604 Young woman in white slip (61x46cm-24x18in) s. i.on stretcher. 22-Jun-3 Freeman, Philadelphia #126/R est:3000-5000
£2110 $3250 €3165 Dancers before mirror (41x30cm-16x12in) s. painted c.1940 prov. 8-Sep-2 Treadway Gallery, Cincinnati #681/R est:3000-4000
£3145 $5000 €4718 Seated girl in red skirt (48x38cm-19x15in) s. prov. 4-Mar-3 Christie's, Rockefeller NY #108/R est:7000-10000
£3459 $5500 €5189 Stella painting walkowitz (31x30cm-12x12in) s. prov.exhib.lit. 4-Mar-3 Christie's, Rockefeller NY #106/R est:6000-8000
Works on paper
£488 $800 €708 Young woman (26x23cm-10x9in) s. W/C. 5-Jun-3 Swann Galleries, New York #228/R
£491 $800 €737 Ballerina studies (64x41cm-25x16in) s. pastel. 2-Feb-3 Grogan, Boston #3

SOYER, Raphael (1899-1987) American
£1274 $2000 €1911 Red shawl (30x23cm-12x9in) s. prov. 10-Dec-2 Doyle, New York #147/R est:2500-3500
£1887 $3000 €2831 Blake in blue jeans (61x51cm-24x20in) s. i.d.1971 on stretcher prov. 18-Mar-3 Arthur James, Florida #99
£1911 $3000 €2867 Portrait of a woman in a green shirt (41x30cm-16x12in) s.d.51 prov. 19-Nov-2 Butterfields, San Francisco #8063/R est:3000-5000
£5096 $8000 €7644 Elizabeth and Marcia (25x29cm-10x11in) s. painted c.1960 prov. 19-Nov-2 Wright, Chicago #286/R est:8000-10000
Prints
£8333 $13000 €12500 Bowery nocturne (33x46cm-13x18in) s.i. lithograph. 7-Nov-2 Swann Galleries, New York #818/R est:14000-16000
Works on paper
£457 $750 €663 Anticoli, Italy (20x27cm-8x11in) s. W/C. 5-Jun-3 Swann Galleries, New York #232/R
£516 $800 €774 Reclining nude (44x53cm-17x21in) s. pencil W/C prov. 3-Dec-2 Christie's, Rockefeller NY #612/R
£705 $1100 €1058 Nude with foot on chair (46x33cm-18x13in) s.d.1935 chl. 20-Sep-2 New Orleans Auction, New Orleans #51/R est:1000-1500

£5346 $8500 €8019 Figures study. By the water. Mother and child (43x56cm-17x22in) s. W/C pencil set of four. 4-Mar-3 Christie's, Rockefeller NY #101/R est:4000-6000
£8176 $13000 €12264 Two girls. Dancer. Immigrants (56x42cm-22x17in) s. W/C set of three. 4-Mar-3 Christie's, Rockefeller NY #104/R est:4000-6000

SPACKMAN, Isaac (?-1771) British
Works on paper
£1300 $2119 €1950 Yellow redpole and an American goldfinch (27x21cm-11x8in) s.d.1765 W/C prov. 29-Jan-3 Dreweatt Neate, Newbury #101/R est:1000-1500

SPADARI, Gian Giacomo (1938-) Italian
Works on paper
£256 $403 €400 For a landscape (39x47cm-15x19in) s.i.d.1964 mixed media. 23-Nov-2 Meeting Art, Vercelli #260

SPADINO, Bartolomeo (18th C) Italian
£13000 $21710 €18850 Peaches, apples and grapes on ledge. Peaches, grapes, melon on ledge (22x22cm-9x9in) one bears init.d.1677 copper round. 9-Jul-3 Bonhams, New Bond Street #177/R est:15000-20000

SPADINO, Giovanni Paolo (17th C) Italian
£24476 $40874 €35000 Grappes de raisins et peches sur un entablement (48x39cm-19x15in) pair. 27-Jun-3 Piasa, Paris #25/R est:25000-35000

SPAENDONCK, Cornelis van (1756-1840) French
£2785 $4400 €4400 Flowers (67x50cm-26x20in) lit. 29-Nov-2 Schloss Ahlden, Ahlden #1219/R est:4500
£18000 $28260 €27000 Peaches, grapes, plums, melon and corn on the cob on marble ledge (51x66cm-20x26in) s.d.1806. 11-Dec-2 Christie's, London #40/R est:30000
£30864 $50000 €46296 Still life of flowers in urn with bird's nest (81x65cm-32x26in) s.d.1817 prov. 23-Jan-3 Sotheby's, New York #233/R est:70000

SPAENDONCK, Cornelis van (attrib) (1756-1840) French
£1057 $1544 €1586 Still life with fruit and bird (46x36cm-18x14in) mono. prov. 17-Jun-2 Philippe Schuler, Zurich #7358 (S.FR 2400)

SPAENDONCK, Gerard van (1746-1822) French
£246914 $400000 €370371 Bouquet of tulips roses and an opium poppy, butterfly and sevenspotted ladybird (51x38cm-20x15in) s. oil on marble prov.exhib.lit. 23-Jan-3 Sotheby's, New York #87/R est:400000-600000

SPAENDONCK, Gerard van (attrib) (1746-1822) French
£1582 $2468 €2500 Bouquet de fleurs et nid sur un entablement (34x27cm-13x11in) panel. 15-Oct-2 Vanderkindere, Brussels #24/R est:2500-4000
Miniatures
£1500 $2355 €2250 Still life of flowers in a vase on a table (6cm-2in) indis sig.d.1806 gilt metal rec. 10-Dec-2 Christie's, London #90/R est:1000-1500

SPAGNA, Lo (circle) (c.1450-1528) Italian
£15000 $23250 €22500 Madonna and Child (38x30cm-15x12in) i.d.1730 verso panel. 31-Oct-2 Sotheby's, Olympia #5/R est:4000-6000

SPAGNOLA, G (fl.1900-1940) Italian
£1800 $2826 €2700 Sunny day at the seaside (66x99cm-26x39in) s. canvas on board. 16-Apr-3 Christie's, Kensington #829/R est:2000-3000

SPAGNULO, Giuseppe (1936-) Italian
Sculpture
£2695 $4366 €3800 Untitled (20x50x40cm-8x20x16in) s.d.75 base iron. 26-May-3 Christie's, Milan #143/R est:3000-4000
£3226 $5097 €5000 Untitled (90x49x59cm-35x19x23in) s.d.91 iron. 18-Dec-2 Christie's, Rome #310

SPAHN, Victor (1949-) French
£506 $785 €800 Joueur de polo (73x60cm-29x24in) s. 28-Sep-2 Cornette de St.Cyr, Paris #191

SPALA, Vaclav (1885-1946) Czechoslovakian
Works on paper
£620 $967 €930 Girl (46x25cm-18x10in) mono. W/C. 12-Oct-2 Dorotheum, Prague #205/R (C.KR 30000)

SPALDING, Charles B (attrib) (fl.1832-1875) British
£1700 $2805 €2465 Bay racehorse with jockey up, racecourse beyond (47x60cm-19x24in) 2-Jul-3 Sotheby's, Olympia #152/R est:800-1200

SPALDING, Eliza Hart (attrib) (1807-1851) American
£481 $750 €722 Landscape of old shoemaker ferry, located in Shawnee on the Delaware (43x61cm-17x24in) 21-Sep-2 Pook & Pook, Downington #286/R

SPALLETTI, Ettore (1940-) Italian
£7000 $11480 €10500 Untitled (300x147cm-118x58in) acrylic wood painted 1989-90. 6-Feb-3 Christie's, London #755/R est:7000-10000
Works on paper
£1410 $2186 €2200 Black (30x90cm-12x35in) s.d.1972 verso board metal ball. 4-Dec-2 Finarte, Milan #528/R
£15000 $23400 €22500 Untitled (150x150cm-59x59in) pigment on board executed c.1995 prov. 21-Oct-2 Sotheby's, London #68/R est:12000-15000

SPAMPINATO, Clemente (1912-) American
Sculpture
£382 $600 €573 Bust of Ruth (33cm-13in) s.d.1967 green pat. bronze. 14-Dec-2 Weschler, Washington #727/R
£1529 $2400 €2294 Bucking bronco (68cm-27in) s.d. green pat. bronze. 14-Dec-2 Weschler, Washington #677/R est:1000-1500

SPANG, Michael Henry (fl.1758-1762) British
Works on paper
£360 $594 €522 Design for a frieze, woman being brought to a Greek Commander (8x31cm-3x12in) init.d.1758 pen ink wash over pencil. 2-Jul-3 Sotheby's, Olympia #182/R

SPANGENBURG, Johannes Ernst (fl.1755-1814) American
Works on paper
£513 $800 €770 Stylized floral trees (15x15cm-6x6in) i. W/C ink fraktur prov. 21-Sep-2 Pook & Pook, Downington #225/R
£3148 $5100 €4565 Bible name page (35x42cm-14x17in) W/C pen ink sold with three hand col taufscheins. 22-May-3 Sotheby's, New York #764

SPANISH SCHOOL, 16th C
£6009 $9494 €9014 Christ on the Cross with river landscape in the background (152x108cm-60x43in) panel prov. 29-Nov-2 Zofingen, Switzerland #2290/R est:7000 (S.FR 14000)
£70988 $115000 €106482 Presentation at the Temple. Road to Calvary (112x59cm-44x23in) panel pair. 23-Jan-3 Sotheby's, New York #175/R est:60000

SPANISH SCHOOL, 17th C
£4595 $7168 €6800 Portrait of Infanta (75x54cm-30x21in) 25-Mar-3 Finarte Semenzato, Rome #110/R
£4878 $8000 €7317 Portrait of a boy, in a black coat and white collar (46x55cm-18x22in) 5-Feb-3 Christie's, Rockefeller NY #310/R est:10000-15000
£6000 $9360 €9000 Equestrian portrait of Cardinal Francisco Ximenes de Cisneros (240x194cm-94x76in) 8-Apr-3 Sotheby's, Olympia #135/R est:4000-6000
£6250 $10125 €9500 Visit (130x197cm-51x78in) 21-Jan-3 Durán, Madrid #139/R
£6282 $9926 €9800 Scene from Saint James' life (152x205cm-60x81in) painted c.1640. 15-Nov-2 Beaussant & Lefèvre, Paris #35/R est:4000-6000
£6500 $10205 €9750 Lilies, tulips and other flowers in a porcelain vase on a ledge (69x51cm-27x20in) 13-Dec-2 Christie's, Kensington #162/R est:6000-8000
£6500 $10140 €9750 Saint Jerome (114x97cm-45x38in) prov. 9-Apr-3 Bonhams, New Bond Street #23/R est:4000-6000
£13462 $20865 €21000 Portrait of Philippe IV (210x129cm-83x51in) prov. 6-Dec-2 Millon & Associes, Paris #31/R est:15000
Works on paper
£4630 $7500 €6945 Saint Jerome (24x18cm-9x7in) chk pen ink. 21-Jan-3 Sotheby's, New York #167/R

SPANISH SCHOOL, 18th C
£7006 $10930 €11000 Black Virgin with Child (147x110cm-58x43in) 7-Nov-2 Chochon-Barre & Allardi, Paris #16 est:10000

Works on paper
£47000 $73790 €70500 Views Paestum and Pozzuoli (44x89cm-17x35in) i. W/C over black chk pair. 11-Dec-2 Sotheby's, Olympia #180/R est:12000-18000

SPANISH SCHOOL, 19th C
£1000 $1660 €1450 Running before the wind (27x20cm-11x8in) board sold with W/C by other hands. 12-Jun-3 Christie's, London #575/R est:300-500
£5000 $7850 €7500 Una buena pica - the strike (26x35cm-10x14in) indis sig.i. panel. 19-Nov-2 Sotheby's, London #187/R est:3000-4000
£5000 $8300 €7250 Spanish three masted barque Providencia running into port with the pilot schooner off her stern (74x91cm-29x36in) i. 12-Jun-3 Christie's, London #544/R est:2000-3000
£5500 $8690 €8250 Alhambra palace, Grenada (74x89cm-29x35in) 14-Nov-2 Christie's, Kensington #279/R est:2500-3500
£5769 $9115 €9000 Interior with figures (97x76cm-38x30in) s. 13-Nov-2 Ansorena, Madrid #109/R
£6051 $9439 €9500 Holy woman praying (105x76cm-41x30in) 6-Nov-2 Gioffredo, Nice #43/R
£6918 $10792 €11000 Letter (59x44cm-23x17in) indis.sig. prov. 23-Sep-2 Durán, Madrid #239/R est:10000

SPANJAERT, Jan (17th C) Dutch
£1400 $2184 €2100 Barn interior with a still life of cooking untensil together with mother and child (37x49cm-15x19in) mono. panel. 8-Apr-3 Sotheby's, Olympia #203/R est:1000-1500
£1783 $2782 €2800 Smell, one of the five senses (18x14cm-7x6in) mono. panel exhib.lit. 5-Nov-2 Sotheby's, Amsterdam #62/R est:1500-2000

SPANNEROVA, Edita (1919-) Czechoslovakian
Works on paper
£284 $403 €426 Dreaming girl (42x28cm-17x11in) pastel exec.1984. 26-Mar-2 SOGA, Bratislava #248/R (SL.K 18000)

SPANYI, Bela von (1852-1914) Hungarian
£1129 $1751 €1694 Poppies by the forest (35x44cm-14x17in) s. board. 6-Dec-2 Kieselbach, Budapest #5/R (H.F 420000)
£1300 $2132 €1950 Homeward bound (17x26cm-7x10in) s. board. 3-Jun-3 Sotheby's, London #56/R est:1500-2500
£1956 $3052 €2934 Sheep by brook (75x87cm-30x34in) s. 11-Apr-3 Kieselbach, Budapest #82/R est:650000-700000 (H.F 700000)
£1956 $3052 €2836 Birch-tree forest (60x70cm-24x28in) s. 12-Apr-3 Mu Terem Galeria, Budapest #213/R est:380000 (H.F 700000)
£2555 $3960 €3705 Balaton landscape (70x80cm-28x31in) s. exhib. 9-Dec-2 Mu Terem Galeria, Budapest #155/R est:550000 (H.F 950000)
£3000 $4650 €4500 Flocks of birds at sunset (118x179cm-46x70in) s.d.88. 3-Dec-2 Sotheby's, Olympia #268/R est:3000-5000

SPANYI, Kornel (1858-?) Hungarian
£2555 $3960 €3833 Orient express, honeymoon (105x125cm-41x49in) s. 6-Dec-2 Kieselbach, Budapest #120/R (H.F 950000)
£5379 $8337 €8069 Nude (125x207cm-49x81in) s. 6-Dec-2 Kieselbach, Budapest #59/R (H.F 2000000)

SPARE, Austin Osman (1888-1956) British
£2200 $3674 €3190 Portrait of a girl with red hair (65x31cm-26x12in) init.d.48 pastel pencil board. 17-Jun-3 Bonhams, Knightsbridge #171/R est:800-1200
Works on paper
£250 $403 €375 Portrait of a man in a hat (34x24cm-13x9in) init.d.1953 pastel. 18-Feb-3 Bonhams, Knightsbridge #34
£400 $620 €600 Female heads (33x23cm-13x9in) init. pencil brush green ink collage. 4-Dec-2 Christie's, Kensington #236
£500 $790 €725 Portrait of Mr W B Smith (39x29cm-15x11in) init.i.d.34 pastel. 22-Jul-3 Sworder & Son, Bishops Stortford #325/R
£850 $1343 €1233 Self portrait (22x16cm-9x6in) init.i.d.51 pencil on board. 22-Jul-3 Sworder & Son, Bishops Stortford #326/R
£1100 $1738 €1650 An ascension (41x33cm-16x13in) init. W/C crayon. 2-Dec-2 Bonhams, Bath #39/R est:1000-1500
£3500 $5775 €5075 Mad prophet (38x28cm-15x11in) s.d.1906 pen black ink gold paint prov. 3-Jul-3 Christie's, Kensington #260/R est:1000-1500

SPARKS, Arthur Watson (1870-1919) American
Works on paper
£1946 $3250 €2822 Woman sewing under a tree (51x56cm-20x22in) s.d.1912 pastel. 22-Jun-3 Freeman, Philadelphia #103/R est:1000-1500

SPARKS, Herbert Blande (fl.1892-1893) British
Works on paper
£420 $689 €630 Feeding the swans (56x39cm-22x15in) s. W/C. 4-Jun-3 Bonhams, Chester #406

SPARKS, Will (1862-1937) American
£368 $600 €552 Adobe at night (36x43cm-14x17in) s. prov. 16-Feb-3 Butterfields, San Francisco #2107
£1043 $1700 €1565 Landscape with cattle and mountains in the distance (32x39cm-13x15in) s. prov. 16-Feb-3 Butterfields, San Francisco #2089 est:1500-2000
£2484 $4000 €3726 Autumn evening (25x30cm-10x12in) s. i.verso painted c.1920 prov. 18-Feb-3 John Moran, Pasadena #114 est:3000-4000
£2548 $4000 €3822 Tijuana mission chapel (41x61cm-16x24in) s. prov. 19-Nov-2 Butterfields, San Francisco #8182/R est:5000-7000
£2548 $4000 €3822 Mission San Luis Rey de Francia (41x61cm-16x24in) s. prov. 19-Nov-2 Butterfields, San Francisco #8183/R est:5000-7000
£2548 $4000 €3822 San Antonio de Padua, near King City, California (41x66cm-16x26in) s. prov.exhib. 19-Nov-2 Butterfields, San Francisco #8184/R est:5000-7000
£2581 $4000 €3872 Late sunset, San Joaquin Bayora (23x30cm-9x12in) s. i.verso board prov. 29-Oct-2 John Moran, Pasadena #721 est:3000-5000

SPARRE, Louis (1863-1964) Finnish/Swedish
£1030 $1565 €1545 Coastal landscape with figures at a fishing ground (39x55cm-15x22in) s. panel. 16-Aug-2 Lilla Bukowskis, Stockholm #1043 est:15000 (S.KR 15000)
£2911 $4600 €4600 The young son (97x75cm-38x30in) s.d.1915 board. 1-Dec-2 Bukowskis, Helsinki #188/R est:2500-2700
Works on paper
£354 $562 €520 By the cake oven (15x17cm-6x7in) s.i.d.1892 mixed media. 24-Mar-3 Bukowskis, Helsinki #309/R

SPARRE, Victor (1919-) Norwegian
£1480 $2367 €2220 Still life (65x69cm-26x27in) s.d.43 i.verso panel. 17-Mar-3 Blomqvist, Oslo #432/R est:20000-30000 (N.KR 17000)
£4071 $6432 €6107 The clown (125x125cm-49x49in) s.d.60 exhib. 28-Apr-3 Blomqvist, Oslo #397/R est:30000-40000 (N.KR 46000)

SPARRGREN, Lorens Svensson (attrib) (1763-1828) Swedish
Works on paper
£276 $425 €414 Portrait of gentleman (14x11cm-6x4in) gouache ivory. 27-Oct-2 Anders Antik, Landskrona #115/R (S.KR 4000)

SPARS, Eylert (1903-) German
£1139 $1766 €1800 Two female nudes on beach (59x80cm-23x31in) s.d.49. 28-Sep-2 Hans Stahl, Hamburg #180/R est:2000

SPAT, Gabriel (1890-1967) French
£304 $475 €456 Petit bouquet (10x8cm-4x3in) s. board. 18-Sep-2 Alderfer's, Hatfield #275
£313 $500 €470 Boating on the Marne River (20x30cm-8x12in) indis sig. canvas on board. 8-Jan-3 Doyle, New York #47/R
£513 $800 €770 Floral still life. Fruit filled compote (28x23cm-11x9in) indis.sig. canvas on board pair prov. 9-Oct-2 Doyle, New York #107
£566 $900 €849 Interior scene (10x8cm-4x3in) s. board painted c.1930. 4-May-3 Treadway Gallery, Cincinnati #503/R
£641 $1000 €962 Dans la loge. Au restaurant (13x23cm-5x9in) s. canvas on board. 9-Oct-2 Doyle, New York #106
£649 $1000 €974 Langchamp (10x20cm-4x8in) s. canvas on cardboard prov. 24-Oct-2 Shannon's, Milford #221/R
£962 $1500 €1443 Figures bathing along the shore (18x25cm-7x10in) s. panel prov. 12-Apr-3 Weschler, Washington #572/R est:800-1200

SPAULDING, Henry Plympton (1868-?) American
Works on paper
£344 $550 €499 Pines in Aiken, South Carolina (46x71cm-18x28in) s. W/C gouache board. 16-May-3 Skinner, Boston #228/R

SPAZZALI, Luciano (20th C) Italian
£279 $441 €419 Figures with umbrella (61x39cm-24x15in) s. masonite. 29-Nov-2 Zofingen, Switzerland #2541 (S.FR 650)

SPAZZAPAN, Luigi (1890-1958) Italian
£4808 $7452 €7500 Landscape in Liguria (69x100cm-27x39in) s. tempera paper painted 1938 prov.lit. 4-Dec-2 Finarte, Milan #340/R est:7000
Works on paper
£321 $497 €500 Horses and knights (43x53cm-17x21in) Chinese ink W/C paper on canvas. 4-Dec-2 Finarte, Milan #247
£2115 $3321 €3300 Holy man (60x50cm-24x20in) s. Chinese ink W/C paper on masonite. 23-Nov-2 Meeting Art, Vercelli #192/R

SPEAR, Ruskin (1911-1990) British
£500 $770 €750 Portrait of a gentleman with a bowler hat (91x76cm-36x30in) s. 5-Sep-2 Christie's, Kensington #619

£500 $805 €750 Life study, South Kensington (74x48cm-29x19in) s. panel. 14-Jan-3 Bonhams, Knightsbridge #63/R
£1550 $2589 €2248 Wall by the river (26x50cm-10x20in) board prov. 25-Jun-3 Bonhams, Bury St Edmunds #602 est:1000-1500
£2000 $3340 €2900 Green light for go (32x37cm-13x15in) s.d.81 board prov.exhib. 24-Jun-3 Bonhams, New Bond Street #80/R est:800-1200
£2200 $3432 €3300 Syon Park (70x96cm-28x38in) s. board prov. 25-Mar-3 Bonhams, New Bond Street #73/R est:2500-3500
£2500 $3875 €3750 At the barbers (53x42cm-21x17in) s. board. 3-Dec-2 Bonhams, New Bond Street #56/R est:1000-1500
£4000 $6200 €6000 At the barbers (46x35cm-18x14in) s. 4-Dec-2 Sotheby's, London #54/R est:2000-3000
£5000 $7800 €7500 Margam works, Port Talbot (79x182cm-31x72in) board prov. 25-Mar-3 Bonhams, New Bond Street #63/R est:4000-6000
£5500 $8524 €8250 Red bow (51x40cm-20x16in) s. canvasboard. 4-Dec-2 Sotheby's, London #56/R est:3000-4000
£5500 $9020 €8250 Child in a doorway (74x52cm-29x20in) board exhib. 6-Jun-3 Christie's, London #210/R est:5000-7000
£6000 $9360 €9000 Lights of London (72x99cm-28x39in) 12-Sep-2 Sotheby's, Olympia #232/R est:5000-7000
£14000 $21700 €21000 Waiter (91x71cm-36x28in) s. painted c.1954 prov.exhib. 4-Dec-2 Sotheby's, London #57/R est:5000-7000
£18000 $27900 €27000 Double diamond (96x61cm-38x24in) s. board painted c.1965 prov.exhib. 4-Dec-2 Sotheby's, London #49/R est:8000-12000
£26000 $40300 €39000 In the pub (61x51cm-24x20in) s. 4-Dec-2 Sotheby's, London #51/R est:6000-8000

Works on paper

£600 $942 €900 Cat on a cushion (17x21cm-7x8in) s. pencil crayon. 15-Apr-3 Bonhams, Knightsbridge #177

SPEARS, Ethel (1903-1974) American

£1282 $2000 €1923 Farm yard fantasy (61x56cm-24x22in) 19-Oct-2 David Dike, Dallas #183/R est:2000-4000
£2244 $3500 €3366 St Louis post office competition (79x76cm-31x30in) tempera board. 19-Oct-2 David Dike, Dallas #318/R est:4000-6000

SPEARS, Frank (1906-1991) South African

£221 $345 €332 Roses in a glass (41x54cm-16x21in) s. board. 15-Oct-2 Stephan Welz, Johannesburg #452 est:3500-5000 (SA.R 3600)
£221 $345 €332 St Marks, Venice (48x61cm-19x24in) s. board. 15-Oct-2 Stephan Welz, Johannesburg #453 est:4000-6000 (SA.R 3600)
£257 $406 €386 Holy Family (75x50cm-30x20in) s. board. 1-Apr-3 Stephan Welz, Johannesburg #200 est:3500-5000 (SA.R 3200)
£344 $554 €516 Still life of poppies in a vase (60x44cm-24x17in) s. 12-May-3 Stephan Welz, Johannesburg #73 est:4000-6000 (SA.R 4000)

SPECK, August (1898-1977) Swiss

£303 $470 €455 Landscape with village (37x50cm-15x20in) s. board. 24-Sep-2 Koller, Zurich #6701 (S.FR 700)
£343 $542 €515 Autumn day at landscape in Seebacher reeds (27x38cm-11x15in) s. s.i.verso board. 26-Nov-2 Hans Widmer, St Gallen #1375 (S.FR 800)

SPECK, Loran (1944-) American

£3205 $5000 €4808 Chilli peppers on a ledge (15x28cm-6x11in) 9-Nov-2 Altermann Galleries, Santa Fe #213
£5128 $8000 €7692 Indian pottery with pears (41x51cm-16x20in) 9-Nov-2 Altermann Galleries, Santa Fe #212
£6507 $9500 €9761 Pottery with onions and a pepper (51x41cm-20x16in) 18-May-2 Altermann Galleries, Santa Fe #74/R

SPECKTER, Erwin (1806-1835) German

Works on paper

£486 $773 €700 Portrait of young Italian woman, head study (23x17cm-9x7in) pencil. 5-May-3 Ketterer, Munich #314/R
£764 $1215 €1100 Seated old peasant (12x7cm-5x3in) pencil. 5-May-3 Ketterer, Munich #316/R
£1111 $1767 €1600 The clever and foolish young women (8x24cm-3x9in) pencil sketch verso lit. 5-May-3 Ketterer, Munich #319/R est:800-1000
£4514 $7177 €6500 Portrait of Carl Julius Milde with dog (9x6cm-4x2in) d.27.Febr. lit. 5-May-3 Ketterer, Munich #315/R est:400-500

SPECKTER, Otto (1807-1871) German

Works on paper

£556 $883 €800 Standing boy (29x11cm-11x4in) i. pencil. 5-May-3 Ketterer, Munich #320/R
£764 $1215 €1100 Dresden - Neustadt shore (12x19cm-5x7in) pencil. 5-May-3 Ketterer, Munich #322/R

SPEED, Harold (1872-1957) British

£250 $385 €375 Cliffs near Palermo (29x43cm-11x17in) s. board. 5-Sep-2 Christie's, Kensington #561
£2000 $3220 €3000 Autumn (44x82cm-17x32in) pencil W/C bodycol painted arch prov.lit. 20-Feb-3 Christie's, London #90/R est:5000

Works on paper

£1050 $1670 €1575 Head of a young woman (19x16cm-7x6in) red chk oval. 26-Feb-3 Sotheby's, Olympia #152/R est:600-800

SPEEDY GRAPHITO (1961-) French

£633 $981 €1000 Le roi des animaux est un parc (80x120cm-31x47in) s.i. acrylic collage. 28-Sep-2 Cornette de St.Cyr, Paris #428

SPEICHER, Eugene (1883-1962) American

£968 $1500 €1452 Curved street (41x51cm-16x20in) s. painted c.1940. 8-Dec-2 Toomey, Oak Park #773/R est:2500-4500
£1019 $1600 €1529 Old Buck House (41x51cm-16x20in) s. 23-Nov-2 Pook & Pook, Downington #142/R est:1200-1800
£1911 $3000 €2867 Still life with flowers in a white teapot (56x43cm-22x17in) s. 19-Nov-2 Butterfields, San Francisco #8055/R est:2500-3500
£1911 $3000 €2867 Maureen, the spotted blouse (53x49cm-21x19in) s. i.stretcher exhib. 19-Nov-2 Butterfields, San Francisco #8056/R est:3000-5000
£6369 $10000 €9554 Actress (109x83cm-43x33in) s. prov. 19-Nov-2 Butterfields, San Francisco #8062/R est:6000-8000

Works on paper

£457 $750 €663 Portrait of a young woman (31x26cm-12x10in) s.i.d. pencil. 5-Jun-3 Swann Galleries, New York #234/R
£513 $800 €770 Portrait of a young woman (33x28cm-13x11in) s. chl prov. 20-Sep-2 New Orleans Auction, New Orleans #52/R

SPEICHER, Eugene (attrib) (1883-1962) American

£755 $1200 €1133 Floral still life in an urn (99x74cm-39x29in) 18-Mar-3 Doyle, New York #52/R

SPELMAN, John A (1880-1941) American

£621 $1000 €932 River shore (71x79cm-28x31in) s.d.28. 10-May-3 Susanin's, Chicago #5016
£897 $1400 €1346 Mountains of Tennessee (51x61cm-20x24in) s. prov. 14-Sep-2 Weschler, Washington #616/R est:1000-1500
£1447 $2300 €2171 Landscape (79x71cm-31x28in) s. painted c.1927. 2-Mar-3 Toomey, Oak Park #682/R est:2000-4000

SPELTDOOREN, H (19th C) Belgian

£1379 $2179 €2000 Mere et trois enfants dans un interieur de cuisine (65x52cm-26x20in) s. panel. 1-Apr-3 Palais de Beaux Arts, Brussels #582/R est:1800-2800

SPENCE, Andrew (1947-) American

£1829 $3000 €2652 Untitled - no.110 (274x183cm-108x72in) prov.lit. 1-Jun-3 Wright, Chicago #346/R est:3000-5000

SPENCE, Harry (1860-1928) British

£1100 $1705 €1650 Cabbage garden (61x51cm-24x20in) s.d.1891. 5-Dec-2 Bonhams, Edinburgh #65 est:1200-1800

SPENCE, Percy Frederick Seaton (1868-1933) Australian

£992 $1568 €1488 Farmyard with horses feeding and chickens (15x25cm-6x10in) s.d.1897 cardboard. 2-Apr-3 Christie's, Melbourne #54 est:1500-2000 (A.D 2600)

Works on paper

£345 $541 €518 Distinguished couple (82x48cm-32x19in) s.d.1905 gouache. 15-Apr-3 Lawson Menzies, Sydney #141/R (A.D 900)
£358 $545 €537 Country path (24x18cm-9x7in) s.d.1922 W/C. 27-Aug-2 Goodman, Sydney #101/R (A.D 1000)
£421 $662 €632 Proposal (57x38cm-22x15in) s.i.d.1890 gouache. 15-Apr-3 Lawson Menzies, Sydney #212a/R est:1000-1500 (A.D 1100)

SPENCE, Sir Basil (1907-) British

Works on paper

£1250 $1938 €1875 Bristo church, Edinburgh (56x76cm-22x30in) s.d.1933 pencil gouache. 5-Dec-2 Bonhams, Edinburgh #28 est:1000-1500

SPENCELAYH, Charles (1865-1958) British

£1200 $1908 €1800 Day on the beach (25x16cm-10x6in) init. canvasboard. 18-Mar-3 Bonhams, New Bond Street #109/R est:800-1200
£3800 $5966 €5700 Winning hand (20x25cm-8x10in) s. canvas on board. 21-Nov-2 Tennants, Leyburn #857/R est:2000-3000
£4000 $6360 €6000 In the bluebell wood (38x30cm-15x12in) s. i.verso. 18-Mar-3 Bonhams, New Bond Street #108/R est:4000-6000
£4000 $6360 €6000 Forgotten (51x85cm-20x33in) s. i.verso. 19-Mar-3 Sotheby's, London #251/R est:4000-6000
£4500 $7470 €6750 My favorite (46x30cm-18x12in) s. 12-Jun-3 Sotheby's, London #303/R est:5000-7000
£5000 $7900 €7500 Gathering roses (46x25cm-18x10in) s.d.1910. 26-Nov-2 Christie's, London #159/R est:6000-10000
£5000 $7900 €7500 Snodland ferry, Kent (41x51cm-16x20in) s.d.1893. 2-Dec-2 Sotheby's, London #17/R est:5000-7000
£6800 $10744 €10200 The open door (56x41cm-22x16in) s.d.1957. 26-Nov-2 Christie's, London #154/R est:6000-10000

£9000 $14220 €13500 God's good gifts (64x45cm-25x18in) s.d.1954 panel exhib. 26-Nov-2 Christie's, London #153/R est:7000-10000
£10000 $16300 €15000 Old countryman with a pipe (49x39cm-19x15in) s.d.1897. 30-Jan-3 Lawrence, Crewkerne #705/R est:10000-15000
£13000 $21710 €18850 Dick's new home (15x10cm-6x4in) s. copper. 17-Jun-3 Bonhams, New Bond Street #98/R est:12000-18000
£17000 $28220 €25500 Who dies if England live? (51x76cm-20x30in) s.d.1914 i.verso prov. 12-Jun-3 Sotheby's, London #306/R est:8000-12000
£20000 $33400 €29000 Favourite cravate (40x30cm-16x12in) s. 17-Jun-3 Bonhams, New Bond Street #92/R est:10000-15000
£26000 $43160 €39000 Taking the risk, so near yet so far (56x76cm-22x30in) s. 12-Jun-3 Sotheby's, London #307/R est:8000-12000
£46000 $72680 €69000 Broken string (43x31cm-17x12in) s. 2-Dec-2 Sotheby's, London #31/R est:40000-60000
£50000 $83000 €75000 Zeppelins (52x35cm-20x14in) s. 12-Jun-3 Sotheby's, London #304/R est:50000-70000
£58000 $91060 €87000 Good as new (20x15cm-8x6in) s. panel. 19-Nov-2 Bonhams, New Bond Street #155/R est:40000-60000
£62000 $98580 €93000 Happy memories (25x19cm-10x7in) s. panel. 18-Mar-3 Bonhams, New Bond Street #106/R est:25000-35000
£65000 $103350 €97500 Early Victorian (24x17cm-9x7in) s. panel. 18-Mar-3 Bonhams, New Bond Street #107/R est:25000-35000
£122000 $203740 €176900 Mother's sampler (50x40cm-20x16in) s.i. exhib.lit. 17-Jun-3 Bonhams, New Bond Street #99/R est:70000-100000

Works on paper

£260 $403 €390 His new home (15x13cm-6x5in) s.i.d.31 pencil dr. 4-Dec-2 Andrew Hartley, Ilkley #1087
£280 $437 €420 Gentleman seated at the table (25x18cm-10x7in) s. pencil. 27-Mar-3 Christie's, Kensington #34/R
£950 $1482 €1425 Portrait of an elderly gentleman. Portrait of a seated gentleman (16x18cm-6x7in) s. pencil pair. 19-Sep-2 Christie's, Kensington #19/R est:800-1200
£1200 $1860 €1800 Behind the screen (36x28cm-14x11in) s.i.d.23 pencil dr. 4-Dec-2 Andrew Hartley, Ilkley #1086 est:600-800
£6200 $9734 €9300 Fresh today (8x11cm-3x4in) s. bodycol. 21-Nov-2 Tennants, Leyburn #695a est:1000-1500

SPENCER, Augustus (1860-1924) British

£287 $450 €431 Sussex cottages (76x61cm-30x24in) s. i.stretcher. 23-Nov-2 Jackson's, Cedar Falls #38/R

SPENCER, Fred (fl.1891-1924) British

Works on paper

£350 $546 €525 Still life with grapes, two apples and four hazelnuts (17x25cm-7x10in) s. W/C. 27-Mar-3 Christie's, Kensington #49/R
£600 $984 €870 Still life of apples, and cherries against a mossy bank (13x20cm-5x8in) s. W/C. 3-Jun-3 Capes Dunn, Manchester #50/R
£600 $984 €870 Still life of apples and hazelnuts against a mossy bank (15x23cm-6x9in) s. W/C. 3-Jun-3 Capes Dunn, Manchester #51
£2000 $3280 €2900 Still life of books (24x44cm-9x17in) s. pencil W/C gum arabic. 5-Jun-3 Christie's, London #129/R est:2000-3000

SPENCER, Frederick R (attrib) (1806-1875) American

£625 $1000 €938 Woman. 1-Jan-3 Fallon, Copake #84

SPENCER, Georges (20th C) ?

£789 $1279 €1200 Oriental Seine (49x41cm-19x16in) s. board. 21-Jan-3 Durán, Madrid #116/R

SPENCER, Gervase (1700-1763) British

Miniatures

£1400 $2226 €2100 Young gentleman, wearing a bright blue coat (4cm-2in) enamel oval. 4-Mar-3 Bonhams, New Bond Street #91/R est:1200-1800
£2400 $3816 €3600 Samuel Vandewall, with powdered hair en queue (3cm-1in) init. painted c.1760. 6-Mar-3 Sotheby's, Olympia #1/R est:2500-3500

SPENCER, Gilbert (1892-1979) British

£500 $775 €750 Nativity (33x31cm-13x12in) 24-Sep-2 Bonhams, New Bond Street #52/R
£700 $1092 €1050 Kind father (35x46cm-14x18in) board prov.exhib. 27-Mar-3 Christie's, Kensington #423/R
£780 $1271 €1170 Behind the cottage (34x44cm-13x17in) init. 30-Jan-3 Lawrence, Crewkerne #749/R
£900 $1404 €1350 Portrait of Sydney Carline (43x53cm-17x21in) 27-Mar-3 Christie's, Kensington #420/R
£4500 $7155 €6750 Farm at Great Milton (46x61cm-18x24in) s.d.1924. 26-Feb-3 Sotheby's, Olympia #81/R est:2000-3000
£8000 $13040 €12000 Paris bus (36x53cm-14x21in) s. sold with a pencil study of the same subject prov. 30-Jan-3 Lawrence, Crewkerne #750/R est:1500-2500

Works on paper

£280 $451 €420 Dorset landscape (33x59cm-13x23in) s.d.1947 pen wash W/C. 15-Jan-3 Cheffins Grain & Comins, Cambridge #395/R

SPENCER, John C (19/20th C) American

£519 $800 €779 Still life with grapes (15x33cm-6x13in) s.d.1914 board. 8-Sep-2 DeFina, Austinburg #81
£617 $950 €926 Still life with berries (15x30cm-6x12in) s.d.1912 board. 8-Sep-2 DeFina, Austinburg #80

SPENCER, Lilly Martin (1822-1902) American

Works on paper

£286 $450 €429 Hindu girl (19x26cm-7x10in) i. chl pencil lit. 14-Dec-2 Weschler, Washington #718/R

SPENCER, Richard B (fl.1840-1870) British

£3413 $5530 €4949 The steam ship Svithiod (49x79cm-19x31in) s. 26-May-3 Bukowskis, Stockholm #237/R est:25000-30000 (S.KR 44000)
£4000 $6080 €6000 Three-master Hampden calling for a pilot in the Dover Straits (57x94cm-22x37in) 15-Aug-2 Bonhams, New Bond Street #346/R est:4000-6000
£5592 $8500 €8388 Barque, Cattofield (51x76cm-20x30in) 17-Aug-2 North East Auctions, Portsmouth #929/R est:6000-8000

SPENCER, Richard B (attrib) (fl.1840-1870) British

£950 $1539 €1425 Merchantman under reduced sail in heavy seas (51x76cm-20x30in) 21-May-3 Christie's, Kensington #571/R
£1500 $2430 €2250 Hamburg barque Nurn America under reduced sail (61x91cm-24x36in) 21-May-3 Christie's, Kensington #573/R est:1500-2000

SPENCER, Roy (1918-) British

£280 $442 €406 Lilac nude (74x91cm-29x36in) s.d.92 board. 22-Jul-3 Gorringes, Lewes #1707

SPENCER, Sir Stanley (1891-1959) British

£15500 $24024 €23250 Extensive landscape with a wrought-iron gate (49x70cm-19x28in) prov.lit. 4-Dec-2 Sotheby's, London #26/R est:10000-15000
£39000 $63960 €58500 Portrait of Mrs C P Grant (43x33cm-17x13in) painted c.1920-21 prov.lit. 6-Jun-3 Christie's, London #50/R est:20000-30000
£120000 $196800 €180000 Corner in the garden (76x51cm-30x20in) painted 1936 prov.exhib.lit. 6-Jun-3 Christie's, London #52/R est:120000-180000
£270000 $442800 €391500 Portrait of Lars Larson (76x63cm-30x25in) s.d.1943 verso prov.exhib.lit. 4-Jun-3 Sotheby's, London #51/R est:40000-60000
£295000 $483800 €442500 Wharf, Cookham (71x86cm-28x34in) painted 1936 prov.lit. 6-Jun-3 Christie's, London #158/R est:150000-200000

Works on paper

£380 $593 €570 Study for the Apotheosis of Hilda (76x50cm-30x20in) pencil squared for transfer prov. 27-Mar-3 Christie's, Kensington #257
£1800 $2970 €2610 Study of heaven and hell (24x35cm-9x14in) pencil W/C prov. 3-Jul-3 Christie's, Kensington #271/R est:2000-3000
£2200 $3410 €3300 Portrait of a young man (18x11cm-7x4in) pencil. 3-Dec-2 Bonhams, New Bond Street #39/R est:1000-1500
£2800 $4340 €4200 People picking up and reading love letters (51x75cm-20x30in) i. pencil prov.exhib. 3-Dec-2 Bonhams, New Bond Street #38/R est:3000-5000
£2800 $4340 €4200 Portrait of a woman (50x39cm-20x15in) s.d.1 Jan 47 pencil exhib. 3-Dec-2 Bonhams, New Bond Street #44/R est:2000-3000
£3800 $6232 €5510 Fox gloves with praying disciples. Storing apples (37x23cm-15x9in) i.verso pencil double-sided lit. 4-Jun-3 Sotheby's, London #18/R est:4000-6000
£8000 $13120 €12000 Study for Christ preaching at Cookham Regatta (32x40cm-13x16in) pencil squared for transfer prov. 6-Jun-3 Christie's, London #157/R est:6000-10000

SPENCER, William Barnett (attrib) (19th C) British

£1000 $1580 €1500 Clipper in rough sea off coastline (34x22cm-13x9in) s. board. 27-Nov-2 Bonhams, Brooks & Langlois, Jersey #93/R est:1000-1600

SPENCER-BOWER, Olivia (1905-1884) New Zealander

Works on paper

£242 $373 €363 Avon willows (24x34cm-9x13in) s. W/C. 4-Sep-2 Dunbar Sloane, Wellington #123 (NZ.D 800)
£760 $1185 €1140 Road to mount Sefton (38x54cm-15x21in) s. W/C. 17-Sep-2 Peter Webb, Auckland #78/R est:2500-3500 (NZ.D 2500)
£981 $1442 €1472 Flatford Mill steam, England (39x49cm-15x19in) s. W/C. 19-Jun-2 Watson's, Christchurch #53/R est:3000-6000 (NZ.D 3000)
£1011 $1617 €1466 River scene (35x58cm-14x23in) s. W/C. 13-May-3 Watson's, Christchurch #6/R (NZ.D 2800)
£1061 $1633 €1592 Sicilian Coastal scene (47x65cm-19x26in) s. W/C. 4-Sep-2 Dunbar Sloane, Wellington #66/R est:4000-5000 (NZ.D 3500)
£1767 $2845 €2651 Amalfi, Italy (64x47cm-25x19in) s. W/C. 7-May-3 Dunbar Sloane, Auckland #20/R est:5000-7000 (NZ.D 5000)
£1791 $2615 €2687 Seated woman modelling (53x70cm-21x28in) W/C. 12-Sep-1 Watson's, Christchurch #5 est:7000-12000 (NZ.D 6000)

SPENDER, Humphrey (1910-) British
£350 $546 €525 Stone landscape (29x61cm-11x24in) s.d.58 board exhib. 27-Mar-3 Christie's, Kensington #650

SPENGLER, Alexandre de (1893-1973) Swiss
£324 $522 €470 La barque (46x55cm-18x22in) s.d.30 i. stretcher. 7-May-3 Dobiaschofsky, Bern #990/R (S.FR 700)

SPENLOVE, Frank Spenlove (1868-1933) British
Works on paper
£420 $655 €630 Solitude (29x44cm-11x17in) s. W/C. 26-Mar-3 Sotheby's, Olympia #120/R
£500 $780 €750 Bosham, Sussex (11x25cm-4x10in) s.i. pencil W/C htd white. 17-Oct-2 Christie's, Kensington #105/R
£1000 $1580 €1500 Figures in a stormy landscape (47x59cm-19x23in) s. W/C. 26-Nov-2 Bonhams, Knightsbridge #211/R est:800-1200

SPERL, Johann (1840-1914) German
£649 $968 €1000 Peasant woman sitting outside house (75x100cm-30x39in) canvas on board lit. 26-Jun-2 Neumeister, Munich #867/R
£1688 $2516 €2600 Girl from upper Bavaria (14x9cm-6x4in) s. canvas on board. 26-Jun-2 Neumeister, Munich #866/R est:1000
£2372 $3676 €3700 Yarrow (25x37cm-10x15in) s. paper lit. 4-Dec-2 Neumeister, Munich #905/R est:2500
£5000 $7800 €7500 Little girl feeding the animals (15x21cm-6x8in) s. panel. 17-Sep-2 Sotheby's, Olympia #268/R est:5000-7000

SPERLING, H (?) German
£507 $791 €761 Dog and cat (27x22cm-11x9in) s. panel. 23-Sep-2 Rasmussen, Vejle #208/R (D.KR 6000)
£901 $1450 €1352 Manne and Mini - two dachshund puppies (11x15cm-4x6in) s. 26-Feb-3 Museumsbygningen, Copenhagen #21 (D.KR 10000)

SPERO, Nancy (1926-) American?
Works on paper
£1594 $2614 €2200 Avant de me suicider je demande qu'on m'assure de l'etre artaud (62x49cm-24x19in) s.d.70 gouache gold Indian ink paper collage prov. 28-May-3 Lempertz, Koln #416/R est:2200

SPESCHA, Mathias (1925-) Swiss
Works on paper
£1310 $1913 €1965 Untitled (61x48cm-24x19in) s.d.1968 s. verso gouache collage. 4-Jun-2 Germann, Zurich #851 est:2000-3000 (S.FR 3000)
£1659 $2605 €2489 Untitled (95x69cm-37x27in) s.d.1992 mixed media collage. 25-Nov-2 Germann, Zurich #96/R est:4000-6000 (S.FR 3800)
£1834 $2879 €2751 Vin de Boyes (33x27cm-13x11in) s.d.1925 gouache pencil panel. 25-Nov-2 Germann, Zurich #45/R est:2000-2500 (S.FR 4200)

SPETHMANN, Albert (1894-?) German
£308 $481 €450 African (53x43cm-21x17in) s.d.16. 10-Apr-3 Schopman, Hamburg #647

SPEYER, Christian (1855-1928) German
£719 $1150 €1079 Man on horseback with plow horse on lead watering at stream (89x79cm-35x31in) s.d.1921. 18-May-3 Jeffery Burchard, Florida #72/R

SPICER, Ella (20th C) New Zealander
Works on paper
£533 $831 €800 Auckland waterfront (25x34cm-10x13in) s. W/C. 7-Nov-2 International Art Centre, Auckland #50/R est:1200-1800 (NZ.D 1700)

SPICER, Peggy (c.1900-1982) New Zealander
£245 $348 €368 Spring bunch and fruit (33x36cm-13x14in) s. board prov. 20-Mar-2 Watson's, Christchurch #23/R (NZ.D 800)
£261 $370 €392 Bowl of flowers (33x39cm-13x15in) board prov. 20-Mar-2 Watson's, Christchurch #22/R (NZ.D 850)
Works on paper
£351 $547 €527 St Geroges Bay road, 66, Parnell (25x33cm-10x13in) s. W/C. 27-Mar-3 International Art Centre, Auckland #170/R (NZ.D 1000)
£470 $734 €705 King's College, Remuera (37x55cm-15x22in) s. W/C. 7-Nov-2 International Art Centre, Auckland #112/R est:1500-2500 (NZ.D 1500)

SPICKETT, Ronald (1926-) Canadian
£283 $441 €471 Mexico (114x65cm-45x26in) s.i.d.1956 oil on paper prov. 13-Apr-3 Levis, Calgary #324 (C.D 650)

SPICUZZA, Francesco J (1883-1962) American
£256 $400 €384 Spring apple blossom trees (23x33cm-9x13in) s. i.verso board. 31-Mar-3 Schrager Galleries, Milwaukee #675/R
£256 $400 €384 Washington Park lagoon (23x33cm-9x13in) s. i.verso board. 31-Mar-3 Schrager Galleries, Milwaukee #677/R
£260 $400 €390 Farm buildings in landscape (17x23cm-7x9in) s. board. 9-Sep-2 Schrager Galleries, Milwaukee #977/R
£288 $450 €432 Fishing boats (18x23cm-7x9in) s. i.verso board. 31-Mar-3 Schrager Galleries, Milwaukee #679/R
£321 $500 €482 Indian princess (41x23cm-16x9in) s. i.verso board painted 1908. 31-Mar-3 Schrager Galleries, Milwaukee #680/R
£481 $750 €722 Floral still life (58x48cm-23x19in) s. board. 31-Mar-3 Schrager Galleries, Milwaukee #1069/R
£491 $775 €737 Landscape, summer (23x15cm-9x6in) s. board. 18-Nov-2 Schrager Galleries, Milwaukee #832
£513 $800 €770 Two bathers on beach (18x23cm-7x9in) s. i.verso board. 31-Mar-3 Schrager Galleries, Milwaukee #678/R
£1154 $1800 €1731 Sunlight on bathers (23x23cm-9x9in) s. i.verso board. 31-Mar-3 Schrager Galleries, Milwaukee #676/R

SPIELMANN, Oscar (1901-1974) Austrian
£612 $973 €900 Vue animee de Moulay Idriss, Maroc (38x45cm-15x18in) s. cardboard. 24-Mar-3 Rabourdin & Choppin de Janvry, Paris #206/R

SPIELTER, Carl Johann (1851-1922) German
£3354 $5500 €4863 Letter (99x124cm-39x49in) s.i. 4-Jun-3 Doyle, New York #89/R est:5000-7000
£28000 $45080 €42000 Estate auction (70x100cm-28x39in) s.d.03 prov.lit. 20-Feb-3 Christie's, London #317/R est:18000

SPIERS, Benjamin Walter (fl.1875-1893) British
Works on paper
£3000 $4860 €4500 Property. Poverty (12x19cm-5x7in) s.d.1890 W/C gouache pair prov. 20-May-3 Sotheby's, Olympia #8/R est:1500-2500

SPIERS, Benjamin Walter (attrib) (fl.1875-1893) British
Works on paper
£1900 $3116 €2850 Collector's corner (53x67cm-21x26in) i. pencil W/C bodycol htd gum arabic. 5-Jun-3 Christie's, Kensington #890/R est:2000-3000

SPIERS, Harry (1869-1902) American
Works on paper
£400 $624 €600 Uphill work (36x54cm-14x21in) s.d.95 gouache exhib. 17-Sep-2 Sotheby's, Olympia #141/R

SPIERS, Richard Phene (1838-1916) British
Works on paper
£500 $780 €750 Colossus, Thebes (24x35cm-9x14in) i. pencil W/C. 18-Sep-2 Dreweatt Neate, Newbury #54/R

SPIES, Simon (1921-1984) Danish?
£288 $464 €432 Abstract composition (66x92cm-26x36in) s.d.65. 22-Feb-3 Rasmussen, Havnen #2146 (D.KR 3200)

SPIESS, August (1841-c.1923) German
£1139 $1766 €1800 Lucky chimney sweep (82x62cm-32x24in) s.d.1875 i. verso. 25-Sep-2 Neumeister, Munich #727/R est:1800

SPIESS, Walter (1895-1942) Russian
£435120 $717949 €630924 View across the sawahs to Gunung Agung (62x91cm-24x36in) init. board prov.lit. 6-Jul-3 Christie's, Hong Kong #29/R est:4500000-8000000 (HK.D 5600000)
£662800 $1020713 €994200 Die landschaft und Ihre kinder - landscape and her children (62x91cm-24x36in) board prov.exhib.lit. 27-Oct-2 Christie's, Hong Kong #18/R est:450000-8000000 (HK.D 8000000)
Works on paper
£12432 $20513 €18026 Sitting Balinese man (29x20cm-11x8in) s.d.29 pencil prov. 6-Jul-3 Christie's, Hong Kong #30/R est:200000-240000 (HK.D 160000)

SPILHAUS, Nita (1878-1967) German
£430 $692 €645 Still life of roses in a glass vase (49x39cm-19x15in) mono. s.d.1946 verso board. 12-May-3 Stephan Welz, Johannesburg #370 est:5000-8000 (SA.R 5000)

£577 $899 €866 Cottage beneath the trees (29x30cm-11x12in) mono. canvasboard. 11-Nov-2 Stephan Welz, Johannesburg #561/R (SA.R 9000)
£577 $899 €866 Via Appia, Roma (28x38cm-11x15in) mono. s.i.verso board. 11-Nov-2 Stephan Welz, Johannesburg #562/R (SA.R 9000)
£645 $1006 €968 Newlands, Cape Town (44x59cm-17x23in) mono. board. 15-Oct-2 Stephan Welz, Johannesburg #421/R est:8000-12000 (SA.R 10500)

SPILIMBERGO, Adriano (1908-1975) Italian
£2405 $3800 €3800 Landscape covered in snow (50x60cm-20x24in) s. painted c.1964-65. 30-Nov-2 Farsetti, Prato #752/R est:2000
£3472 $5521 €5000 Dry tree (46x37cm-18x15in) s. 1-May-3 Meeting Art, Vercelli #338
£3716 $5797 €5500 Winter in Bardonecchia (60x79cm-24x31in) s. painted 1955. 26-Mar-3 Finarte Semenzato, Milan #318/R
Works on paper
£608 $949 €900 Vase of flowers (27x19cm-11x7in) s. chk. 26-Mar-3 Finarte Semenzato, Milan #54

SPILLAR, Karel (1871-1939) Czechoslovakian
£6810 $11033 €10215 Micareme (58x75cm-23x30in) s.i. 24-May-3 Dorotheum, Prague #19/R est:240000-380000 (C.KR 300000)

SPILLENBERGER, Johann (1628-1679) Hungarian
£14000 $23380 €20300 Susannah and the elders (69x59cm-27x23in) s. canvas on board prov. 10-Jul-3 Sotheby's, London #181/R est:8000-12000

SPILLIAERT, Léon (1881-1946) Belgian
£1982 $2954 €2973 Morning mist over meadows (25x58cm-10x23in) s. 25-Jun-2 Koller, Zurich #6715 est:2500-3500 (S.FR 4500)
Works on paper
£1509 $2340 €2400 Imaginary city scene, Ostend (49x40cm-19x16in) s.d.1925 Indian ink brush. 5-Oct-2 De Vuyst, Lokeren #336/R est:3000-4000
£1646 $2567 €2600 Dunes (27x37cm-11x15in) s. W/C. 21-Oct-2 Bernaerts, Antwerp #625/R est:4000-5000
£3597 $5755 €5000 Dunes a la mer du Nord (27x37cm-11x15in) s.d.1935 W/C. 19-May-3 Horta, Bruxelles #155/R est:3500-4500
£4114 $6500 €6500 Le village derriere un rideau d'arbres (28x49cm-11x19in) s.d.1924 gouache W/C prov.exhib. 26-Nov-2 Palais de Beaux Arts, Brussels #378/R est:6000-8000
£4762 $7571 €7000 Oostende (45x68cm-18x27in) s.d.1924 gouache. 24-Mar-3 Bernaerts, Antwerp #178/R est:8000-12000
£6835 $11209 €9500 Seascape (33x46cm-13x18in) s.d.1932 W/C. 3-Jun-3 Christie's, Amsterdam #274/R est:6000-8000
£8805 $13648 €14000 Trees (55x38cm-22x15in) s.d.1940 W/C. 5-Oct-2 De Vuyst, Lokeren #468/R est:13000-15000
£8861 $13823 €14000 Heures ternes (52x27cm-20x11in) s. crayon dr Chinese ink wash brush lit. 16-Sep-2 Horta, Bruxelles #165 est:12400-18600
£8861 $13823 €14000 Chanson (37x36cm-15x14in) mixed media lit. 16-Sep-2 Horta, Bruxelles #164 est:20000-30000
£9936 $15401 €15500 Baigneuses - Thetis (49x69cm-19x27in) s.d.1920 W/C pencil. 7-Dec-2 De Vuyst, Lokeren #467/R est:17000-20000
£10345 $16552 €15000 La cuisiniere (43x43cm-17x17in) s.d.1925 gouache. 17-Mar-3 Horta, Bruxelles #122/R est:20000-30000
£11392 $17772 €18000 Personnage nocturne (36x37cm-14x15in) s.d.1917 wash dr lit. 16-Sep-2 Horta, Bruxelles #163 est:20000-30000
£11644 $18164 €17000 La ferme au toit rouge (49x60cm-19x24in) s.d.1929 W/C. 14-Apr-3 Horta, Bruxelles #99/R est:18000-20000
£20645 $32619 €32000 Le bassin de chasse a Ostende (72x75cm-28x30in) s. W/C gouache pastel cardboard prov.exhib. 17-Dec-2 Palais de Beaux Arts, Brussels #632/R est:30000-45000
£21519 $34000 €34000 Paysage au dirigeable (64x49cm-25x19in) s.d.10 pastel paper on Japon exhib. 26-Nov-2 Palais de Beaux Arts, Brussels #156/R est:33000-40000

SPIN, Jacob (1806-1885) Dutch
Works on paper
£1370 $2137 €2000 Portrait of a three mast ship, 'Professor Suringur under captain T W Kuiper' (47x63cm-19x25in) s.d.1861 W/C. 14-Apr-3 Glerum, Amsterdam #9/R est:2000-3000

SPINK, Leon (19/20th C) British
Works on paper
£470 $761 €682 Portrait of a lady, bust length, wearing low cut dress, landscape beyond (75x62cm-30x24in) s.d.1903 pastel. 20-May-3 Dreweatt Neate, Newbury #206/R

SPINKS, Thomas (19th C) British
£355 $522 €550 Romantic river (25x35cm-10x14in) s.d.1885. 20-Jun-2 Dr Fritz Nagel, Stuttgart #826/R
£700 $1092 €1050 Angler in a wooded river landscape (44x60cm-17x24in) s.d.1886 board. 10-Sep-2 David Duggleby, Scarborough #356/R
£720 $1123 €1080 Welsh river landscapes with cattle (43x58cm-17x23in) s. one d.1889 one d.1892 pair. 18-Oct-2 Keys, Aylsham #718/R
£750 $1185 €1125 Angler beside a river (25x36cm-10x14in) s.d.1887 board. 2-Dec-2 Gorringes, Lewes #2896
£1300 $2054 €1950 Pair of river landscapes (31x45cm-12x18in) s.d.1886 pair. 12-Nov-2 Bonhams, Knightsbridge #182/R est:400-600

SPINNER, Louis P (1851-?) American
£3205 $5000 €4808 Still life of peaches (36x46cm-14x18in) s. 21-Sep-2 Pook & Pook, Downington #278/R est:2000-3000

SPINNLER, Rolf (1927-) Swiss
£880 $1416 €1320 Farmstead in the evening (89x109cm-35x43in) mono.d.68. 7-May-3 Dobiaschofsky, Bern #991/R (S.FR 1900)
Works on paper
£787 $1267 €1181 Jura landscape (33x46cm-13x18in) s.d.65 mixed media. 7-May-3 Dobiaschofsky, Bern #1966 (S.FR 1700)

SPIRIDON, Ignace (20th C) Italian
£1400 $2212 €2100 Portrait, bust length, of a beautiful lady (70x59cm-28x23in) s. 12-Nov-2 Bonhams, Knightsbridge #296/R est:800-1200

SPIRO, Eugen (1874-1972) German
£1088 $1731 €1600 Sunny Breton coast (24x45cm-9x18in) s.d.08 board. 28-Mar-3 Bolland & Marotz, Bremen #688/R est:2000
£1090 $1591 €1700 Girl with bow in hair (54x46cm-21x18in) s.i.d.09. 4-Jun-2 Karl & Faber, Munich #432/R
£1154 $1685 €1800 Terrrace overlooking Hiddensee (51x65cm-20x26in) s.d.32. 4-Jun-2 Karl & Faber, Munich #440/R est:4000
£1282 $1872 €2000 French landscape (74x61cm-29x24in) s.d.19. 4-Jun-2 Karl & Faber, Munich #433/R est:4000
£1282 $1872 €2000 Bodensee (65x80cm-26x31in) s.d.31. 4-Jun-2 Karl & Faber, Munich #439/R est:4000
£2244 $3276 €3500 Peter at open window (100x81cm-39x32in) s.d.29. 4-Jun-2 Karl & Faber, Munich #437/R est:7000-8000
£2436 $3556 €3800 Pierre Klossowski (94x76cm-37x30in) s.d.20. 4-Jun-2 Karl & Faber, Munich #434/R est:7000-8000
£2885 $4212 €4500 Cassis, southern France (65x81cm-26x32in) s.d.25. 4-Jun-2 Karl & Faber, Munich #435/R est:8000-9000
£4348 $7130 €6000 Terrace on Hiddensee (52x65cm-20x26in) s.d.32. 31-May-3 Villa Grisebach, Berlin #251/R est:2500-3500
£5036 $8259 €7000 Self portrait in Central Park, NY (82x61cm-32x24in) s.i.d. board prov.exhib. 6-Jun-3 Ketterer, Munich #85/R est:7000-9000
£10145 $16638 €14000 Madeleine smoking (55x46cm-22x18in) s.d.09 canvas on panel. 31-May-3 Villa Grisebach, Berlin #252/R est:6000-8000
£13462 $19654 €21000 Nude washing (100x81cm-39x32in) s.d.30. 4-Jun-2 Karl & Faber, Munich #438/R est:8000-9000
Works on paper
£321 $503 €500 Female nude (27x41cm-11x16in) chl dr exec.c.1910 prov. 21-Nov-2 Dorotheum, Vienna #479/R
£738 $1189 €1100 Bush in bloom (46x35cm-18x14in) W/C. 21-Feb-3 Sigalas, Stuttgart #938/R est:1200

SPIRO, Georges (1909-1994) French
£251 $381 €377 Visage (32x40cm-13x16in) s. 27-Aug-2 Goodman, Sydney #258 (A.D 700)
£491 $780 €737 Surrealistic landscape with flowers (19x23cm-7x9in) s. panel. 3-Mar-3 Lilla Bukowskis, Stockholm #442 (S.KR 6600)
£519 $830 €779 Sureal composition with flowers and head (55x46cm-22x18in) s.d.61. 17-Mar-3 Philippe Schuler, Zurich #4654/R (S.FR 1100)
£576 $921 €800 Fleurs et visage sculpte dans le granit (30x30cm-12x12in) s. 18-May-3 Eric Pillon, Calais #204/R
£683 $1094 €950 Voilier pres des cotes (30x30cm-12x12in) s. 18-May-3 Eric Pillon, Calais #205/R
£717 $1090 €1076 Nude in surrealistic landscape (64x53cm-25x21in) s. 27-Aug-2 Goodman, Sydney #257/R (A.D 2000)
£759 $1185 €1200 Fleurs (55x46cm-22x18in) s. 20-Oct-2 Chayette & Cheval, Paris #109
£873 $1371 €1310 Visage fleurs (62x50cm-24x20in) s.d.1962. 25-Nov-2 Germann, Zurich #8/R est:2500-3500 (S.FR 2000)
£1079 $1727 €1500 Paysage fantastique (81x100cm-32x39in) s. 18-May-3 Eric Pillon, Calais #206/R
£1083 $1689 €1700 Allegorie musicale (100x81cm-39x32in) s. 10-Nov-2 Eric Pillon, Calais #272/R
£1313 $2114 €1970 Paysage aux fleurs (30x35cm-12x14in) s. 7-May-3 AB Stockholms Auktionsverk #1143/R est:12000-15000 (S.KR 17000)
£1467 $2362 €2201 Le joueur de viole (55x46cm-22x18in) s. i.verso. 7-May-3 AB Stockholms Auktionsverk #1144/R est:10000-12000 (S.KR 19000)
£1597 $2523 €2396 L'arbre de vie (63x50cm-25x20in) s. 28-Apr-3 Bukowskis, Stockholm #326/R est:12000-15000 (S.KR 21000)
£2211 $3515 €3250 Paysage surrealiste (25x33cm-10x13in) s. cardboard. 26-Feb-3 Artcurial Briest, Paris #347 est:800-1000
Works on paper
£760 $1202 €1140 La licorne (47x38cm-19x15in) s. mixed media. 28-Apr-3 Bukowskis, Stockholm #325/R (S.KR 10000)

SPITZ, Ernest (1927-1960) Czechoslovakian
Works on paper
£583 $828 €875 Woman with moon (36x26cm-14x10in) mixed media board exec.c.1957. 26-Mar-2 SOGA, Bratislava #256/R (SL.K 37000)

SPITZ, Karl (1853-?) German
£253 $392 €400 Gunterstal near Freiburg (21x31cm-8x12in) s. board. 28-Sep-2 Hans Stahl, Hamburg #38

SPITZER, Franz (1780-?) Austrian
Works on paper
£592 $900 €888 Portrait of a man and a woman (5cm-2in circular) W/C pair. 30-Aug-2 Thomaston Place, Thomaston #122

SPITZER, Walter (1927-) Polish
£641 $1006 €1000 Les amoureux (48x38cm-19x15in) s. painted c.1965. 24-Nov-2 Chayette & Cheval, Paris #292
£962 $1510 €1500 Mishloah Manot (45x55cm-18x22in) s. 12-Dec-2 Rabourdin & Choppin de Janvry, Paris #145/R
£1042 $1656 €1500 Rabbin (116x81cm-46x32in) s.d.1966. 29-Apr-3 Campo & Campo, Antwerp #815
£1698 $2632 €2700 Son village (54x65cm-21x26in) s. i.d.23 mai 1972 verso. 30-Oct-2 Artcurial Briest, Paris #413/R est:2000-2500
£2436 $3824 €3800 Joueur d'orgue (60x81cm-24x32in) s.i.d.1971 verso. 12-Dec-2 Rabourdin & Choppin de Janvry, Paris #143/R
£2564 $4026 €4000 Marchands des chevaux (54x65cm-21x26in) s.i.verso. 12-Dec-2 Rabourdin & Choppin de Janvry, Paris #144/R
£4483 $7172 €6500 Maries en charrette (81x100cm-32x39in) s. s.i.verso. 12-Mar-3 Rabourdin & Choppin de Janvry, Paris #167/R
Sculpture
£1931 $3090 €2800 Porteur d'eau (26cm-10in) s. num.7/8 black pat bronze Cast Valsuani lit. 12-Mar-3 Rabourdin & Choppin de Janvry, Paris #145/R
Works on paper
£641 $1006 €1000 Rabbin (66x47cm-26x19in) s. pastel W/C. 12-Dec-2 Rabourdin & Choppin de Janvry, Paris #146/R
£897 $1409 €1400 Le colporteur (71x55cm-28x22in) s. gouache collage. 24-Nov-2 Chayette & Cheval, Paris #300

SPITZWEG, Carl (1808-1885) German
£802 $1170 €1250 Eight grotesque figures (20x32cm-8x13in) pencil. 4-Jun-2 Karl & Faber, Munich #137/R
£1370 $2137 €2055 Caricature of a writer (29x22cm-11x9in) st.sig. pencil. 28-Mar-3 Koller, Zurich #3111 est:1500-2500 (S.FR 3000)
£1397 $2180 €2096 Overturned coach (9x14cm-4x6in) st.sig. rhombus pencil. 20-Nov-2 Fischer, Luzern #2494/R est:3200-3600 (S.FR 3200)
£11737 $19249 €17019 Landscape with house and figures (6x13cm-2x5in) st.rhombus verso panel. 4-Jun-3 Fischer, Luzern #1134/R est:36000-48000 (S.FR 25000)
£17755 $28231 €26100 On the battlements (27x23cm-11x9in) oil study lit. 19-Mar-3 Neumeister, Munich #738/R est:20000
£25316 $39241 €40000 Girls bathing in woodland pond (38x26cm-15x10in) s. st.sig. verso lit. 25-Sep-2 Neumeister, Munich #730/R est:45000
£31963 $49863 €47945 Cactus lover (34x20cm-13x8in) board prov.exhib.lit. 28-Mar-3 Koller, Zurich #3110/R est:70000-110000 (S.FR 70000)
£38627 $59871 €57941 The philosopher. Hafis (29x24cm-11x9in) mono. lit. 3-Oct-2 Koller, Zurich #3108/R est:80000-120000 (S.FR 90000)
£43668 $68122 €65502 Alpine farm workers in front of Benediktenwand (45x32cm-18x13in) prov.lit. 9-Nov-2 Galerie Gloggner, Luzern #134/R est:60000-80000 (S.FR 100000)
£285714 $425714 €440000 Delivering a love letter (47x26cm-19x10in) lit. 26-Jun-2 Neumeister, Munich #868/R est:450000
Works on paper
£516 $805 €820 Mountains (22x30cm-9x12in) st.sig.mono. pencil. 11-Oct-2 Winterberg, Heidelberg #709
£568 $886 €852 Country clergyman (19x10cm-7x4in) pencil. 6-Nov-2 Dobiaschofsky, Bern #1187/R (S.FR 1300)
£651 $1015 €950 Studies of young woman, man and other figures (21x33cm-8x13in) pencil. 11-Apr-3 Winterberg, Heidelberg #576/R
£680 $1082 €1000 Study of young woman (21x33cm-8x13in) pencil. 19-Mar-3 Neumeister, Munich #392 est:300
£1397 $2180 €2096 Elegant couple (18x18cm-7x7in) st.sig. rhombus pencil. 20-Nov-2 Fischer, Luzern #2493/R est:3200-3600 (S.FR 3200)
£1747 $2725 €2621 Man with bellows (34x21cm-13x8in) st.sig. rhombus pencil. 20-Nov-2 Fischer, Luzern #2496/R est:3600-4800 (S.FR 4000)
£2817 $4535 €4000 Omnibus (15x19cm-6x7in) s. pencil lit. 9-May-3 Schloss Ahlden, Ahlden #1360/R est:3800
£2926 $4564 €4389 Soldier with woman and child (19x16cm-7x6in) st.sig. rhombus pencil. 20-Nov-2 Fischer, Luzern #2495/R est:4500-6000 (S.FR 6700)

SPITZWEG, Carl (circle) (1808-1885) German
£6608 $9846 €9912 River landscape with figures on bank (37x50cm-15x20in) mono. 25-Jun-2 Koller, Zurich #6568/R est:2000-3000 (S.FR 15000)

SPLITGERBER, August (1844-1918) German
£287 $447 €450 Moor landscape (20x27cm-8x11in) bears sig. board. 6-Nov-2 Hugo Ruef, Munich #1279/R
£318 $497 €500 Mountain landscape with trees (20x27cm-8x11in) s. board. 6-Nov-2 Hugo Ruef, Munich #1278/R
£409 $638 €650 Winter landscape (23x36cm-9x14in) s. prov. 19-Sep-2 Dr Fritz Nagel, Stuttgart #1003/R
£541 $845 €850 Old Leopold castle in Munich (66x48cm-26x19in) s. 6-Nov-2 Hugo Ruef, Munich #1277/R
£779 $1161 €1200 Meadow landscape with cows (9x22cm-4x9in) s. panel. 26-Jun-2 Neumeister, Munich #869/R
£1154 $1788 €1800 Mountain chapel in sunny landscape (25x18cm-10x7in) s. panel prov. 7-Dec-2 Ketterer, Hamburg #101/R est:1800-2000
£1266 $2000 €2000 Landscape (15x24cm-6x9in) s.d.8.Juli 09 panel on board. 30-Nov-2 Villa Grisebach, Berlin #132/R est:3000-4000
£7746 $12472 €11000 Food market (33x42cm-13x17in) s. lit. 9-May-3 Schloss Ahlden, Ahlden #1414/R est:8500

SPODE, Samuel (19th C) British
£2800 $4480 €4200 Little Wanderer, a bay racehorse in a landscape (51x61cm-20x24in) s.i. 16-May-3 Sotheby's, London #17/R est:1500-2000
£5128 $7949 €8000 Grey Jack , a hunter (50x60cm-20x24in) s.i. 3-Dec-2 Bonhams & James Adam, Dublin #23/R est:10000-15000

SPOEDE, Jean Jacques (attrib) (c.1680-1757) Dutch
£6452 $10194 €10000 Venus dans la forge de Vulcain (156x98cm-61x39in) 18-Dec-2 Piasa, Paris #11/R

SPOEL, Jacob (1820-1868) Dutch
£637 $994 €1000 Portrait of a man (91x74cm-36x29in) s. 6-Nov-2 Vendue Huis, Gravenhage #479/R

SPOERRI, Daniel (1930-) Swiss
Sculpture
£2628 $4074 €4100 La pharmacie bretonne (104x41x16cm-41x16x6in) i. lit. jars in wooden display case with glass doors. 3-Dec-2 Lempertz, Koln #435/R est:3500
£3165 $4905 €5000 Nouriture piege Nr 1 (40x30x7cm-16x12x3in) s.i.d. food cutlery. 24-Sep-2 Wiener Kunst Auktionen, Vienna #240/R est:5000-8000
£5000 $8350 €7250 Tableau piege (71x71x33cm-28x28x13in) s.i.d.9 Mai 72 i.verso assemblage board plexiglass box prov. 26-Jun-3 Sotheby's, London #162/R est:5000-7000
£5000 $8350 €7250 Tableau piege (71x71x40cm-28x28x16in) s.i.d.1 avril 72 i.verso assemblage board plexiglass box prov. 26-Jun-3 Sotheby's, London #167/R est:5000-7000
£5937 $9500 €8906 Tableau piege (70x70x23cm-28x28x9in) s.i.d.23 Sept 72 dried flowers paper napkin ashtray. 16-May-3 Phillips, New York #154/R est:8000-12000
£6500 $10010 €9750 Tableau piege (71x71x33cm-28x28x13in) s.i.d.72 i.verso assemblage mounted on board in plexiglass prov. 22-Oct-2 Sotheby's, London #355/R est:5000-7000
£6522 $10109 €9783 Tableau piege (197x105cm-78x41in) s.d.20.3.2000 glasses napkins plates wood menu. 4-Dec-2 Koller, Zurich #188/R est:6000-9000 (S.FR 15000)
£20000 $32800 €30000 Hammer-tisch (40x80x201cm-16x31x79in) s.i.d.78 verso ceramic metal silkscreen linen on board prov. 7-Feb-3 Sotheby's, London #205/R est:25000-35000
Works on paper
£325 $514 €488 Composition (50x50cm-20x20in) s.d.77 verso mixed media. 1-Apr-3 Rasmussen, Copenhagen #303/R (D.KR 3500)
£590 $914 €920 You came late, then you came - 1798 - 1959 - 1977 (50x50cm-20x20in) s.d.77 verso mixed media sack on panel. 7-Dec-2 Van Ham, Cologne #518/R
£1111 $1756 €1600 Visa (23x18cm-9x7in) s. collage cardboard prov. 28-Apr-3 Cornette de St.Cyr, Paris #512/R est:1500-1800
£1438 $2301 €2200 Untitled (18x20cm-7x8in) s. mixed media collage card. 4-Jan-3 Meeting Art, Vercelli #616
£1519 $2400 €2400 Rifiutide tegna (20x20cm-8x8in) s. i.d.1969 verso mixed media on panel. 26-Nov-2 Sotheby's, Amsterdam #273/R est:2200-2800
£2000 $3160 €3000 Give us our daily bread ! (94x44cm-37x17in) plastic pearl fl. earth wooden pallet exec.1978. 3-Apr-3 Christie's, Kensington #232/R
£8500 $13940 €12750 Tableau piege (71x71cm-28x28in) s.i.d.72, 30 Nov i.verso assemblage board plexiglass prov. 7-Feb-3 Sotheby's, London #200/R est:5000-7000

SPOHLER, J J (1811-1866) Dutch
£3205 $4968 €5000 Conversation au bord du cours d'eau (40x55cm-16x22in) s.d.1835. 9-Dec-2 Horta, Bruxelles #94 est:6000-8000

SPOHLER, Jan Jacob (1811-1866) Dutch
£4088 $6296 €6500 River landscape in summer (12x21cm-5x8in) s. panel. 23-Oct-2 Christie's, Amsterdam #3/R est:3000-5000
£4100 $6232 €6150 Dutch landscape with figure and dog in a lane by buildings (23x28cm-9x11in) s.indis.d.1832. 16-Aug-2 Keys, Aylsham #634/R
£12179 $18878 €19000 Skaters on a frozen canal (27x35cm-11x14in) s. panel. 7-Dec-2 De Vuyst, Lokeren #415/R est:20000-25000
£12579 $19371 €20000 Summer landscape with boats on the river (41x56cm-16x22in) s. panel. 22-Oct-2 Sotheby's, Amsterdam #143/R est:20000-30000
£17123 $26884 €25000 Figures with a horse drawn sledge on a frozen river (61x83cm-24x33in) s.d.65. 15-Apr-3 Sotheby's, Amsterdam #201/R est:20000-30000
£22642 $34868 €36000 Winter landscape with figures on a frozen waterway (35x47cm-14x19in) s. panel. 23-Oct-2 Christie's, Amsterdam #97/R est:15000-20000
£27000 $44280 €40500 Figures skating on frozen river (63x84cm-25x33in) s. 3-Jun-3 Sotheby's, London #146/R est:30000-50000

SPOHLER, Jan Jacob (attrib) (1811-1866) Dutch
£680 $1082 €1000 Dutch winter landscape (25x33cm-10x13in) s. 19-Mar-3 Neumeister, Munich #739/R est:1200

SPOHLER, Jan Jacob Coenraad (1837-1923) Dutch
£974 $1451 €1500 Dutch landscape in summer (46x30cm-18x12in) s. 26-Jun-2 Neumeister, Munich #870/R
£1783 $2782 €2800 Ferry on the canal with many boats and figures (43x34cm-17x13in) s. 6-Nov-2 Vendue Huis, Gravenhage #380 est:2500-3500
£2400 $3648 €3600 Barges in a calm on a Dutch river estuary (22x35cm-9x14in) s. 29-Aug-2 Christie's, Kensington #257/R est:1500-2000
£2431 $4010 €3500 Shipping on a river by a village (30x46cm-12x18in) s. 1-Jul-3 Christie's, Amsterdam #46/R est:3500-4500
£2830 $4358 €4500 Sunny landscape with washerwomen on a riverbank (16x20cm-6x8in) s. panel. 22-Oct-2 Sotheby's, Amsterdam #5/R est:5000-8000
£3000 $4920 €4500 Dutch river scene with boats and windmills (21x16cm-8x6in) init. panel. 4-Feb-3 Sworder & Son, Bishops Stortford #99/R est:2000-2500
£4000 $6280 €6000 Figures on a frozen river (27x21cm-11x8in) s. panel prov. 19-Nov-2 Bonhams, New Bond Street #9/R est:3000-5000
£4777 $7452 €7500 Wintry view of ice with skaters. Summer view of water with boats (16x11cm-6x4in) mono. panel pair. 6-Nov-2 Vendue Huis, Gravenhage #428/R est:7000-9000
£5600 $9184 €8400 Dutch street scene (20x15cm-8x6in) s. panel. 4-Feb-3 Sworder & Son, Bishops Stortford #98/R est:1500-1800
£6400 $10496 €9600 River landscape with boats and figures (22x16cm-9x6in) s. panel pair. 4-Feb-3 Sworder & Son, Bishops Stortford #101/R est:4500-5000
£6579 $10658 €10000 River landscape with a windmill (67x101cm-26x40in) with sig. 21-Jan-3 Christie's, Amsterdam #111/R est:10000-15000
£8200 $13448 €12300 Winter landscape with figures. Canal scene with windmills (16x19cm-6x7in) s. one indis.d. panel pair. 4-Feb-3 Sworder & Son, Bishops Stortford #100/R est:5000-6000
£10563 $17007 €15000 Winter landscape with skaters (53x81cm-21x32in) 7-May-3 Vendue Huis, Gravenhage #393/R est:20000-22000

SPOHLER, Johannes Franciscus (1853-1894) Dutch
£5200 $8112 €7800 Street scene (15x20cm-6x8in) s. panel. 15-Oct-2 Gorringes, Lewes #2168/R est:5000-7000
£10692 $16465 €17000 Town view with elegant figures (19x15cm-7x6in) s. panel. 23-Oct-2 Christie's, Amsterdam #112/R est:12000-16000
£11111 $17667 €16000 Townsfolk on a sunlit street (24x32cm-9x13in) s. panel. 29-Apr-3 Christie's, Amsterdam #82/R est:12000-16000
£13699 $21507 €20000 View of the Groenburgwal with the Zuiderkerk in the distance, Amsterdam (35x44cm-14x17in) s. 15-Apr-3 Sotheby's, Amsterdam #4/R est:10000-15000

SPOHN, Clay Edgar (1898-1977) American
£710 $1100 €1065 Green and red modulations with illuminations. 7-Dec-2 Harvey Clar, Oakland #1236
£774 $1200 €1161 Fall 1965 (86x107cm-34x42in) s. painted c.1965. 7-Dec-2 Harvey Clar, Oakland #1235
£2258 $3500 €3387 Living moment (272x198cm-107x78in) 7-Dec-2 Harvey Clar, Oakland #1227
£2581 $4000 €3872 Activated painting with blue. s.d.1961. 7-Dec-2 Harvey Clar, Oakland #1248

SPOILUM (school) (18/19th C) ?
£13462 $21000 €20193 View of the foreign factories, Canton (44x58cm-17x23in) 27-Mar-3 Sotheby's, New York #89/R est:18000-25000

SPOILUM (style) (18/19th C) ?
£23026 $35000 €34539 Hongs at Canton (43x58cm-17x23in) 17-Aug-2 North East Auctions, Portsmouth #806/R est:35000-45000

SPOLVERINI, Ilario (1657-1734) Italian
£8108 $12649 €12000 Portrait of gentleman (223x162cm-88x64in) 31-Mar 3 Finarte Semenzato, Milan #503/R

SPONZA, Nicola (1914-1996) Italian
£256 $397 €400 Church in Trieste (19x25cm-7x10in) board. 5-Dec-2 Stadion, Trieste #813/R
£353 $546 €550 Grado (40x80cm-16x31in) s.d.81. 5-Dec-2 Stadion, Trieste #817/R
£449 $696 €700 Borsa Square, Trieste (19x25cm-7x10in) s. board. 5-Dec-2 Stadion, Trieste #814/R
£897 $1391 €1400 Adriatic Yacht Club, Trieste (60x120cm-24x47in) s. 5-Dec-2 Stadion, Trieste #816/R
£1026 $1590 €1600 Canal in Trieste (50x60cm-20x24in) s.d.50 board. 5-Dec-2 Stadion, Trieste #810/R
£1218 $1888 €1900 Trieste seen from above (60x120cm-24x47in) s. 5-Dec-2 Stadion, Trieste #815/R

SPOONER, Arthur (1873-1962) British
£260 $434 €377 St. Malo (30x39cm-12x15in) s. board. 25-Jun-3 Cheffins, Cambridge #812/R
£320 $509 €480 Portrait of a seated lady (91x76cm-36x30in) s.d.1947. 27-Feb-3 Greenslade Hunt, Taunton #1314
£600 $870 €900 Dapple grey mare and foal (36x43cm-14x17in) s. board. 3-May-2 Biddle & Webb, Birmingham #300/R
£1000 $1630 €1500 Clifton near Nottingham (50x59cm-20x23in) s.d.1938. 13-Feb-3 Mellors & Kirk, Nottingham #800/R est:800-1200
£1800 $2790 €2700 Retreat (53x84cm-21x33in) s.d.1890. 25-Sep-2 Peter Wilson, Nantwich #73/R est:2000-3000
£2100 $3276 €3045 Haycart (23x35cm-9x14in) s. 27-Mar-3 Neales, Nottingham #986/R est:2000-3000
£2800 $4424 €4200 Afternoon tea (51x76cm-20x30in) 27-Nov-2 Sotheby's, Olympia #66/R est:2000-3000
£3000 $4560 €4500 Clifton Brook, Nottingham (34x41cm-13x16in) 4-Jul-2 Mellors & Kirk, Nottingham #841 est:2800-3500
£3000 $4980 €4350 The pool, evening (29x34cm-11x13in) s. s.i.verso canvasboard. 10-Jun-3 Mellors & Kirk, Nottingham #853/R est:2500-3000

SPOONER, John Swinton (19th C) British
£500 $780 €750 Waiting at the footbridge (58x48cm-23x19in) panel. 9-Oct-2 Andrew Hartley, Ilkley #732

SPORL, Erich (20th C) German
£385 $596 €600 Schloss Meerseburg on the Bodensee (80x100cm-31x39in) s.i.d.1954 i. verso. 5-Dec-2 Neumeister, Munich #2880/R

SPORRER, Philipp (attrib) (1829-1899) German
£1139 $1766 €1800 Three men at table at mealtime (52x43cm-20x17in) oval. 25-Sep-2 Neumeister, Munich #733 est:2000

SPRANGER, Bartholomaeus (1546-1611) Flemish
Prints
£12000 $20040 €17400 Saint Sebastian bound to a tree (19x9cm-7x4in) etching. 30-Jun-3 Bonhams, New Bond Street #113/R est:10000-15000

SPRANGER, Bartholomaeus (attrib) (1546-1611) Flemish
£2560 $4147 €3712 Hans Droughan 1623 (52x43cm-20x17in) panel prov. 26-May-3 Bukowskis, Stockholm #411/R est:25000-30000 (S.KR 33000)

SPRANGER, Bartholomaeus (circle) (1546-1611) Flemish
£7500 $11775 €11250 Allegory of Alchemy (22x18cm-9x7in) indis i. copper prov.lit. 13-Dec-2 Christie's, Kensington #13/R est:7000-10000
Works on paper
£22222 $35333 €32000 Mars, Venus and Cupid (21x14cm-8x6in) pen htd white. 5-May-3 Ketterer, Munich #214/R est:1000-1500

SPREAT, W (19th C) British
£350 $539 €525 Old bridge (35x51cm-14x20in) s.d.1886. 5-Sep-2 Christie's, Kensington #185/R

SPRECHELSEN, Anna von (19/20th C) German
£373 $593 €560 Mother and child (43x35cm-17x14in) s.d.1935. 5-May-3 Rasmussen, Vejle #440 (D.KR 4000)

SPRINCHORN, Carl (1887-1971) American
£9295 $14500 €13943 Ahoy (81x91cm-32x36in) s. 11-Aug-2 Thomaston Place, Thomaston #25

Works on paper
£944 $1500 €1416 Forest interior (29x44cm-11x17in) s.i.d.39 W/C gouache. 7-Mar-3 Skinner, Boston #417/R est:1000-1500
£2711 $4500 €3931 Bathers on the broadwalk (61x47cm-24x19in) s. mixed media. 11-Jun-3 Butterfields, San Francisco #4099/R est:3000-5000

SPRINGER, Cornelis (1817-1891) Dutch
£1781 $2778 €2600 Self portrait of the artist standing on a frozen canal with a bunch of twigs (45x36cm-18x14in) mono.d.47 prov. 14-Apr-3 Glerum, Amsterdam #16/R est:3000-4000
£19178 $30110 €28000 Skaters on a frozen canal in a Dutch (41x53cm-16x21in) s.d.1838. 15-Apr-3 Sotheby's, Amsterdam #3/R est:5000-7000
£62893 $96855 €100000 Daily activities in a Dutch town (41x34cm-16x13in) mono.d.51 panel prov. 23-Oct-2 Christie's, Amsterdam #126/R est:110000-140000
£120000 $196800 €180000 Street scene in Makkum, Friesland (32x42cm-13x17in) s.d.1873 panel. 4-Feb-3 Sworder & Son, Bishops Stortford #156/R est:40000-60000
£132075 $203396 €210000 Busy street in Weesp (50x40cm-20x16in) s.d.1877 panel prov.lit. 22-Oct-2 Sotheby's, Amsterdam #137/R est:250000-350000
£136986 $215068 €200000 View of the Jodenbreestraat with the Rembrandthuis, Amsterdam (50x40cm-20x16in) mono.d.54 panel. 15-Apr-3 Sotheby's, Amsterdam #187/R est:230000-280000
£251572 $387421 €400000 Figures on a market square in front of the St. Stevens Church (81x101cm-32x40in) mono.d.1849 prov.lit. 22-Oct-2 Sotheby's, Amsterdam #157/R est:425000-525000

Works on paper
£2877 $4516 €4200 View of Monnickendam (45x34cm-18x13in) s.d.79 black chk. 15-Apr-3 Sotheby's, Amsterdam #44/R est:4000-6000
£4403 $6780 €7000 Het huis met de Hoofden on the Keizersgracht, Amsterdam (66x51cm-26x20in) s.d.1853 pencil black ink wash W/C prov. 23-Oct-2 Christie's, Amsterdam #76/R est:7000-9000
£6918 $10654 €11000 Townview with figures on a church square (32x41cm-13x16in) mono. s.verso pencil pen black brown ink W/C prov. 23-Oct-2 Christie's, Amsterdam #73/R est:15000-20000
£9859 $15873 €14000 View of Leeuwarden (42x55cm-17x22in) s.i.d.72 dr. 7-May-3 Vendue Huis, Gravenhage #424/R est:10000-12000
£15000 $23250 €22500 Washerwomen in a village street. Grooms with a horse (25x20cm-10x8in) s. pencil W/C executed 1875 pair. 4-Dec-2 Christie's, London #40/R est:12000-18000
£19444 $30917 €28000 Market te oudewater, farmers market (65x93cm-26x37in) s.i.d.76 pencil chl W/C htd white. 29-Apr-3 Christie's, Amsterdam #76/R est:10000-15000

SPRINGER, Cornelis (attrib) (1817-1891) Dutch
£2482 $3848 €3723 Coastal landscape from Alkmaar (18x24cm-7x9in) panel. 3-Dec-2 Bukowskis, Stockholm #520a/R est:8000-10000 (S.KR 35000)

SPRINGER, Leendert (jnr) (1831-1894) Dutch
£513 $795 €800 Dutch street with figures (32x50cm-13x20in) s. 5-Dec-2 Schopman, Hamburg #546

SPRINGER, Reinhard (1953-) German
Works on paper
£377 $581 €600 House front No 10 (68x42cm-27x17in) s.d.1995 s.i.d. verso mixed media board. 26-Oct-2 Dr Lehr, Berlin #499/R

SPRINGOLO, Nino (1886-1975) Italian
£1761 $2747 €2800 Still life with vase of flowers (44x36cm-17x14in) s. board. 20-Sep-2 Semenzato, Venice #580
£3481 $5500 €5500 Summer evening (38x45cm-15x18in) s. board. 30-Nov-2 Farsetti, Prato #754/R est:3000

SPRONKEN, Arthur (1930-) Dutch
Sculpture
£3453 $5663 €4800 Reclining nude (64x105cm-25x41in) bronze. 3-Jun-3 Christie's, Amsterdam #171/R est:4000-6000
£3846 $5962 €6000 Horse (21cm-8in) bronze prov. 3-Dec-2 Christie's, Amsterdam #370/R est:5000-7000
£3957 $6489 €5500 Paard met vrouw (20cm-8in) mono. bronze. 3-Jun-3 Christie's, Amsterdam #167/R est:3000-5000

SPROSSE, Carl (1819-1874) German
Works on paper
£446 $687 €700 Tomb of the Scala family, Verona (59x45cm-23x18in) s. pencil pen brown ink W/C bodycol. 3-Sep-2 Christie's, Amsterdam #157/R

SPROTTE, Siegward (1913-) German
£705 $1093 €1100 Hallig Hooge (43x41cm-17x16in) s.i. s.i.d. verso board. 7-Dec-2 Ketterer, Hamburg #719/R
Works on paper
£278 $439 €400 Tree (54x39cm-21x15in) s.d1955 Indian ink. 26-Apr-3 Dr Lehr, Berlin #472/R
£577 $894 €900 Dark sea (47x65cm-19x26in) s.d.1965 W/C. 6-Dec-2 Hauswedell & Nolte, Hamburg #360/R
£690 $1090 €1000 Shoreline flowers (76x89cm-30x35in) s.d.1956 W/C. 5-Apr-3 Quittenbaum, Hamburg #166/R est:1100
£755 $1162 €1200 Beach thoughts (50x65cm-20x26in) s.i.d.1986 W/C board. 26-Oct-2 Dr Lehr, Berlin #503/R
£1572 $2421 €2500 Large wave (56x76cm-22x30in) s.d.1986 W/C board. 26-Oct-2 Dr Lehr, Berlin #502/R est:1000

SPRUANCE, Benton (1904-1967) American
Prints
£1783 $2800 €2675 Pass to the flat (41x58cm-16x23in) s.i. lithograph. 14-Dec-2 Weschler, Washington #805/R est:800-1200
£2308 $3600 €3462 Pass to the flat (36x54cm-14x21in) s.i.d. lithograph edition of 45. 7-Nov-2 Swann Galleries, New York #821/R est:3500-5000
£3145 $5000 €4718 People play, summer (35x48cm-14x19in) s.i.d. lithograph. 29-Apr-3 Christie's, Rockefeller NY #442/R est:5000-7000

SPRUCE, Everett (1908-) American
£8974 $14000 €13461 Arroyo and Hawk (36x43cm-14x17in) masonite double-sided. 19-Oct-2 David Dike, Dallas #190/R est:15000-20000
Works on paper
£962 $1500 €1443 West Texas (38x51cm-15x20in) mixed media. 19-Oct-2 David Dike, Dallas #189/R est:2500-3500
£1603 $2500 €2405 Four bare trees (25x36cm-10x14in) gouache executed c.1931. 19-Oct-2 David Dike, Dallas #269/R est:3000-6000
£1603 $2500 €2405 Mulberry River Arkansas (25x36cm-10x14in) W/C executed c.1930. 19-Oct-2 David Dike, Dallas #270/R est:2500-5000
£2564 $4000 €3846 Century plant (61x76cm-24x30in) mixed media board. 19-Oct-2 David Dike, Dallas #186/R est:5000-8000

SPURLING, Jack (1870-1933) British
Works on paper
£2160 $3500 €3132 P and O S.S. Karmala (37x53cm-15x21in) s. gouache paperboard prov. 29-Jul-3 Christie's, Rockefeller NY #116/R est:6000-8000

SPYROPOULOS, Jannis (1912-1990) Greek
£3500 $5425 €5250 Strophi no.3 (54x65cm-21x26in) s. s.i.d.1964 on stretcher oil paper on canvas. 5-Dec-2 Christie's, Kensington #204/R est:3000-5000
£4000 $6320 €6000 View of a harbour (40x50cm-16x20in) 1-Apr-3 Bonhams, New Bond Street #86a est:5000-8000
£6500 $10270 €9750 Page 14 (65x54cm-26x21in) 1-Apr-3 Bonhams, New Bond Street #82 est:4000-6000
£8500 $13430 €12750 Three compositions (40x21cm-16x8in) 1-Apr-3 Bonhams, New Bond Street #89 est:5000-7000
Works on paper
£2800 $4340 €4200 Double-sided composition (50x61cm-20x24in) s. mixed media double-sided. 2-Oct-2 Sotheby's, London #129/R
£3800 $5890 €5700 Night (54x33cm-21x13in) s.d.31 ink oil collage. 2-Oct-2 Sotheby's, London #119/R
£4000 $6200 €6000 Abstract (50x36cm-20x14in) s. mixed media. 2-Oct-2 Sotheby's, London #120/R
£18000 $27900 €27000 Eratini (114x162cm-45x64in) s. s.i.d.1961 verso mixed media on canvas prov. 2-Oct-2 Sotheby's, London #73/R est:18000-25000

SQUIER, Donald Gordon (1895-1987) American
£241 $400 €349 Hills and clouds (28x36cm-11x14in) s. board. 14-Jun-3 Jackson's, Cedar Falls #432

SQUILLACE, Massimiliano (20th C) Italian?
Sculpture
£5000 $7150 €7500 Nude crouching girl with cascading wet hair (43cm-17in) s.d.1997 gilt bronze with scorched timber base. 28-Feb-2 Heathcote Ball, Leicester #276

SQUILLANTINI, Remo (1920-1996) Italian
£1410 $2214 €2200 Figures (50x35cm-20x14in) s. 20-Nov-2 Pandolfini, Florence #77/R

£1538 $2415 €2400 Choice (30x20cm-12x8in) s. paper on masonite painted 1976. 23-Nov-2 Meeting Art, Vercelli #233/R
£2115 $3342 €3300 Figures (30x20cm-12x8in) s. canvas on cardboard painted 1976. 15-Nov-2 Farsetti, Prato #425/R
£2703 $4216 €4000 Derby (50x50cm-20x20in) s. board. 28-Mar-3 Farsetti, Prato #504/R
£2785 $4344 €4400 Figure in red (70x50cm-28x20in) s. board painted 1980. 14-Sep-2 Meeting Art, Vercelli #913/R
£3521 $5845 €5000 Serata di gala (50x50cm-20x20in) s. s.i.verso panel. 10-Jun-3 Finarte Semenzato, Milan #284/R est:3600-4000
£3741 $5949 €5500 Jazz (60x60cm-24x24in) s. board. 1-Mar-3 Meeting Art, Vercelli #498
£3846 $6038 €6000 Derby (70x60cm-28x24in) s. s.i.verso board. 23-Nov-2 Meeting Art, Vercelli #444/R
£4231 $6642 €6600 Jazz (60x60cm-24x24in) s. s.i.verso board. 19-Nov-2 Finarte, Milan #288/R
£5556 $8833 €8000 Politics (80x80cm-31x31in) s. board painted 1985 lit. 1-May-3 Meeting Art, Vercelli #518

Works on paper

£1013 $1580 €1600 Susanna (35x50cm-14x20in) s. mixed media cardboard exec.1986. 14-Sep-2 Meeting Art, Vercelli #885/R
£1021 $1695 €1450 Nudo disteso (48x68cm-19x27in) s. pastel. 10-Jun-3 Finarte Semenzato, Milan #282/R est:1200-1400
£1266 $1975 €2000 Dancers (50x35cm-20x14in) s. s.verso mixed media cardboard exec.1977. 14-Sep-2 Meeting Art, Vercelli #250/R
£1806 $2871 €2600 Painter and model (50x35cm-20x14in) s. mixed media cardboard. 1-May-3 Meeting Art, Vercelli #80

SQUIRE, Geoffrey (1923-) British

£650 $1007 €975 Study of a female nude reading (25x33cm-10x13in) s. board. 31-Oct-2 Ambrose, Loughton #17/R

SQUIRRELL, A M (19th C) British

£349 $566 €506 O'er Crag and Torrent - Scotland (52x92cm-20x36in) mono. 25-May-3 Uppsala Auktionskammare, Uppsala #155 (S.KR 4500)

SQUIRRELL, Leonard (1893-1979) British

Works on paper

£270 $419 €405 Figures outside a mill (23x18cm-9x7in) s.d.1932 mixed media pastel W/C grisaille. 4-Dec-2 Neal & Fletcher, Woodbridge #237
£420 $655 €630 Figures by a Tithe barn, St Osyth's Priory, Essex (24x41cm-9x16in) s.d.1938 i.verso W/C pencil. 19-Sep-2 John Bellman, Billingshurst #1416
£420 $655 €630 Charlotte Square (17x25cm-7x10in) s. gouache. 28-Mar-3 Bonhams, Edinburgh #129
£480 $749 €720 Robins Hoods Bay (23x35cm-9x14in) s.d.1956 W/C. 10-Sep-2 David Duggleby, Scarborough #241/R
£580 $893 €870 Black canopy, Worthing (28x23cm-11x9in) s.d.1955 W/C over pencil. 22-Oct-2 Bonhams, Bath #17
£650 $1014 €975 Odins mine gorge, Castleton, Peak District (23x35cm-9x14in) s.d.1933 W/C. 10-Sep-2 Sworder & Son, Bishops Stortford #769/R
£700 $1092 €1050 Barden Tower (24x36cm-9x14in) s.d.1956 W/C pencil. 25-Mar-3 Bonhams, Leeds #535/R
£1100 $1727 €1650 Cley Marshes, Norfolk (23x33cm-9x13in) s.d.1950 W/C. 13-Dec-2 Keys, Aylsham #588 est:600-800
£1200 $1872 €1800 Barque Killoran at Ipswich (23x30cm-9x12in) s.d.1936 W/C. 18-Oct-2 Keys, Aylsham #631/R est:500-700
£1200 $1956 €1800 Tithe Barn, St Osyth, S Priory (25x41cm-10x16in) s.d.1938 W/C. 14-Feb-3 Keys, Aylsham #566/R est:700-900
£1250 $2088 €1813 Figures on a hill with Canterbury Cathedral beyond (34x45cm-13x18in) s.d.48 W/C bodycol over pencil. 25-Jun-3 Bonhams, Bury St Edmunds #496/R est:1200-1800

SRAMEK, Jano (1886-?) Czechoslovakian

£291 $450 €422 Farm scene with pond (30x38cm-12x15in) board. 7-Dec-2 South Bay, Long Island #58a/R

SRNA, Jozef (1930-1992) Czechoslovakian

£394 $610 €591 Side street (81x90cm-32x35in) 1-Oct-2 SOGA, Bratislava #251/R est:29000 (SL.K 25000)
£457 $649 €686 Behind the barn (105x125cm-41x49in) painted 1982. 26-Mar-2 SOGA, Bratislava #253/R (SL.K 29000)
£457 $667 €686 Shed in Brezovica village (110x105cm-43x41in) painted c.1980. 4-Jun-2 SOGA, Bratislava #250/R est:29000 (SL.K 29000)
£583 $828 €875 In the orchard (125x130cm-49x51in) painted c.1980. 26-Mar-2 SOGA, Bratislava #254/R (SL.K 37000)

ST CLAIR, Linda (1952-) American

£1558 $2400 €2337 Carlolina cool (61x61cm-24x24in) 25-Oct-2 Morris & Whiteside, Hilton Head Island #68 est:3000-3500
£1948 $3000 €2922 American beauty (76x76cm-30x30in) 25-Oct-2 Morris & Whiteside, Hilton Head Island #161 est:3500-4000

STAACKMAN, Heinrich Maria (1852-1940) German

£528 $850 €750 Bedouins resting with horses (41x59cm-16x23in) s.i.d.1966 panel. 7-May-3 Michael Zeller, Lindau #938/R
£1233 $1923 €1800 Arabian rider (64x97cm-25x38in) s.i.d.92 lit. 10-Apr-3 Allgauer, Kempten #2992/R est:1500
£3974 $6240 €6200 Praying in the mosque (27x21cm-11x8in) s. panel. 10-Dec-2 Tajan, Paris #225/R est:5000

STAATEN, Louis van (19th C) Dutch

£1000 $1550 €1500 Hay barges in harbour (71x92cm-28x36in) s. 3-Dec-2 Sotheby's, Olympia #266/R est:1000-2000

Works on paper

£240 $400 €348 Morning in Holland. s. W/C. 28-Jun-3 Harvey Clar, Oakland #1173
£300 $465 €450 Dutch canal scene with windmill (25x36cm-10x14in) s. W/C. 4-Oct-2 Mallams, Oxford #503
£300 $474 €450 Volendam (30x40cm-12x16in) s. W/C. 4-Apr-3 Moore Allen & Innocent, Cirencester #445/R
£360 $554 €540 Dutch river view (40x30cm-16x12in) s. W/C. 22-Oct-2 Bonhams, Knightsbridge #65/R
£400 $648 €600 Dutch canal with a windmill (39x60cm-15x24in) s. W/C. 21-Jan-3 Bonhams, Knightsbridge #3/R
£400 $636 €600 Coastal town (36x55cm-14x22in) s. W/C. 25-Feb-3 Bonhams, Knightsbridge #189/R
£400 $632 €580 Dutch canal scene (30x41cm-12x16in) s. W/C. 22-Jul-3 Gorringes, Lewes #1554/R
£429 $677 €644 Zaanstreek (39x59cm-15x23in) s. W/C. 18-Nov-2 Goodman, Sydney #247 (A.D 1200)
£480 $778 €720 Rowing boat on a Dutch canal (39x59cm-15x23in) s. W/C. 21-Jan-3 Bonhams, Knightsbridge #2/R
£500 $776 €750 Dutch canal scenes (39x28cm-15x11in) s. W/C two. 3-Dec-2 Sotheby's, Olympia #211/R
£500 $780 €750 Haarlem canal, Holland (46x71cm-18x28in) s. W/C. 26-Mar-3 Sotheby's, Olympia #219/R
£550 $864 €825 Boats at a Dutch quayside (38x28cm-15x11in) s. W/C. 13-Dec-2 Keys, Aylsham #569/R
£560 $874 €840 Near Delft. Dordrecht (39x61cm-15x24in) s. W/C pair. 6-Nov-2 Bonhams, Chester #476
£750 $1170 €1125 Mills on Haarlem, Zeere. Near Overschie (58x39cm-23x15in) s. pencil W/C htd white pair. 17-Oct-2 Christie's, Kensington #172
£900 $1404 €1350 Dordrecht (39x60cm-15x24in) s. W/C sold with a companion. 26-Mar-3 Woolley & Wallis, Salisbury #18/R
£1069 $1700 €1550 Busy Dutch canal scene (37x55cm-15x22in) s. W/C sold with another similar. 4-Mar-3 Mealy's, Castlecomer #948/R est:1200-1800
£1200 $1884 €1800 Near Rotterdam. Haarlem River landscape (15x22cm-6x9in) s. W/C pair. 12-Dec-2 Ewbank, Send #505/R est:500-800
£1600 $2608 €2400 Dutch canal scenes with moored vessels, Dordrecht. Near Delft (29x40cm-11x16in) s.i. W/C htd white pair. 11-Feb-3 Fellows & Sons, Birmingham #64/R est:700-1000

STABIAK, Julius (20th C) ?

£426 $660 €639 Hunters with dogs in wooded landscape (50x72cm-20x28in) s.i. 8-Dec-2 Uppsala Auktionskammare, Uppsala #111 (S.KR 6000)

STABLI, Adolf (1842-1901) Swiss

£609 $943 €914 Starnbergersee (25x39cm-10x15in) canvas on board prov. 9-Dec-2 Philippe Schuler, Zurich #3836/R (S.FR 1400)
£1030 $1627 €1545 House between trees at dusk (31x36cm-12x14in) s.d.1869 canvas on canvas. 26-Nov-2 Hans Widmer, St Gallen #1376/R est:1200-2400 (S.FR 2400)
£2575 $4069 €3863 Stormy scene (90x125cm-35x49in) s.d.1896. 28-Nov-2 Christie's, Zurich #3/R est:6000-8000 (S.FR 6000)
£3052 $5005 €4425 Sheep in landscape (56x68cm-22x27in) s. lit. 4-Jun-3 Fischer, Luzern #1232/R est:6500-9500 (S.FR 6500)

STABLI, Adolf (attrib) (1842-1901) Swiss

£705 $1050 €1058 Landscape with rocks (31x47cm-12x19in) bears i. board. 25-Jun-2 Koller, Zurich #6561/R (S.FR 1600)

STACEY, Anna Lee (1871-1943) American

£1958 $3250 €2839 Hotel cafe. Main Street in Banff, twilight (36x41cm-14x16in) one s.d.1919 one canvasboard one board two prov. 11-Jun-3 Butterfields, San Francisco #4057/R est:3000-5000
£5422 $9000 €7862 Harmony in yellow (76x63cm-30x25in) s.d.09 prov.exhib. 11-Jun-3 Butterfields, San Francisco #4056/R est:2000-4000
£15484 $24000 €23226 Garden in autumn (41x51cm-16x20in) s.d.1909 prov. 3-Dec-2 Phillips, New York #60/R est:20000-30000

STACEY, Henry Edward (1838-1915) British

Works on paper

£300 $501 €435 St Mary Redcliffe across Bathurst Basin (25x44cm-10x17in) s.d.1888 W/C. 17-Jun-3 Bristol Auction Rooms #475

STACEY, John F (1859-1941) American
£3145 $5000 €4718 Beech woods (152x178cm-60x70in) s. painted c.1921 exhib. 2-Mar-3 Toomey, Oak Park #660/R est:5000-7000

STACHE, Adolphe (1823-1862) Belgian
£374 $595 €550 Femme au perroquet (64x53cm-25x21in) s.d.1854. 18-Mar-3 Galerie Moderne, Brussels #164

STACHOWSKI, Wladyslaw von (1852-1932) Polish
£393 $613 €590 Summer coastal scene (30x69cm-12x27in) s.i. 6-Nov-2 Dobiaschofsky, Bern #978/R (S.FR 900)

STACK, Josef Magnus (1812-1868) Swedish
£625 $1001 €906 Harbour scene in moonlight (33x45cm-13x18in) s.indis.d.1855. 18-May-3 Anders Antik, Landskrona #84 (S.KR 8000)
£780 $1209 €1170 Landscape with temple ruin from the Roman Campagna (37x52cm-15x20in) s.d.65 prov. 4-Dec-2 AB Stockholms Auktionsverk #1622/R (S.KR 11000)
£1100 $1804 €1595 Stockholm's skerries, winter (55x74cm-22x29in) s. 4-Jun-3 AB Stockholms Auktionsverk #2116/R (S.KR 14000)
£2207 $3399 €3311 Summer landscape with farm and deer in woodland glade (59x95cm-23x37in) mono.d.1836. 27-Oct-2 Anders Antik, Landskrona #82/R est:15000-20000 (S.KR 32000)

STACK, Major Frederick Rice (19th C) New Zealander
£2548 $4000 €3822 Auckland harbour from Bastion Point (31x65cm-12x26in) prov. 10-Dec-2 Peter Webb, Auckland #23/R est:5000-8000 (NZ.D 8000)

STACK, Michael (1947-) American
£6164 $9000 €9246 Evening storm in the mountains (61x76cm-24x30in) 18-May-2 Altermann Galleries, Santa Fe #204/R

STACKMANN, A (20th C) Dutch
£480 $750 €720 Estuary scene with fishing boat and figures in a dory (51x66cm-20x26in) s. 14-Sep-2 Weschler, Washington #571/R

STACQUET, Henri (1838-1907) Belgian
Works on paper
£392 $631 €600 La miettee (23x21cm-9x8in) s. gouache. 20-Jan-3 Horta, Bruxelles #425
£449 $704 €700 Interieur hollandais anime (57x47cm-22x19in) s. gouache. 10-Dec-2 Vanderkindere, Brussels #43
£550 $913 €550 Le tour de l'etang en hiver (24x33cm-9x13in) s. W/C. 16-Jun-3 Horta, Bruxelles #2
£621 $1000 €950 Pecheurs sous les bouleaux (43x29cm-17x11in) s.d.1888 W/C. 20-Jan-3 Horta, Bruxelles #424
£647 $1036 €900 Plage anime. Paysage anime sous la neige (16x26cm-6x10in) s. W/C two. 13-May-3 Vanderkindere, Brussels #220
£750 $1223 €1125 Appartement a Madesmoiselle Gibson (38x31cm-15x12in) s. W/C gouache. 29-Jan-3 Dreweatt Neate, Newbury #60/R

STADELHOFER, Helmut (1914-) German
£301 $500 €436 Lake landscape with figures (69x99cm-27x39in) s. 11-Jun-3 Boos Gallery, Michigan #332
£417 $654 €650 Fishermen on Gnadensee (50x100cm-20x39in) 22-Nov-2 Karrenbauer, Konstanz #1873

STADEMANN, Adolf (1824-1895) German
£616 $962 €900 Dusk in hazy winter landscape with figures (10x15cm-4x6in) mono. panel lit. 10-Apr-3 Allgauer, Kempten #2994/R
£850 $1393 €1300 Winter landscape with skaters, sledges, boats and windmills (16x23cm-6x9in) s. panel. 8-Feb-3 Hans Stahl, Hamburg #45/R est:1200
£850 $1393 €1300 Setting sun on Bavarian lake (16x23cm-6x9in) s. panel. 8-Feb-3 Hans Stahl, Hamburg #46 est:1200
£915 $1501 €1400 Winter landscape with hunters returning home (16x23cm-6x9in) s. panel. 8-Feb-3 Hans Stahl, Hamburg #47/R est:1200
£1282 $1872 €2000 Winter pleasures (20x37cm-8x15in) s. panel. 4-Jun-2 Karl & Faber, Munich #139/R
£1295 $2072 €1800 Winter pleasures (22x36cm-9x14in) s. 14-May-3 Dorotheum, Linz #339/R est:3200-4000
£1310 $2083 €1900 Summer landscape with farmstead and peasants returning home (14x35cm-6x14in) s. panel. 8-Mar-3 Arnold, Frankfurt #722/R est:1600
£1761 $2747 €2800 Winter pleasures (25x33cm-10x13in) s. lit. 20-Sep-2 Karlheinz Kaupp, Staufen #2111 est:800
£2089 $3237 €3300 Winter landscape with adults and children on snowy square (21x27cm-8x11in) s. panel. 25-Sep-2 Neumeister, Munich #736/R est:3000
£2166 $3400 €3249 Skaters on a frozen canal (53x69cm-21x27in) s. 10-Dec-2 Doyle, New York #174/R est:6000-8000
£2381 $3786 €3500 Winter pleasures (57x87cm-22x34in) s. 19-Mar-3 Neumeister, Munich #746/R est:3500
£2785 $4316 €4400 Winter pleasures (19x36cm-7x14in) s. board. 25-Sep-2 Neumeister, Munich #735/R est:4000
£2785 $4400 €4400 Les patineurs pres du village, hiver (31x47cm-12x19in) s. 1-Dec-2 Peron, Melun #145
£3269 $5067 €5100 Dutch winter landscape with ice skaters, sleds and walkers on the frozen water (25x46cm-10x18in) s. 4-Dec-2 Neumeister, Munich #910/R est:3000
£3333 $5167 €5200 Snowy winter village street (14x34cm-6x13in) s. panel lit. 6-Dec-2 Karlheinz Kaupp, Staufen #2327/R est:800
£3846 $5962 €6000 Winter landscape with peasants on the frozen lake (18x47cm-7x19in) s. panel. 4-Dec-2 Neumeister, Munich #909/R est:5500
£3896 $5805 €6000 Winter landscape at sunset (64x105cm-25x41in) s.d.1885. 26-Jun-2 Neumeister, Munich #871/R est:7500
£6090 $9439 €9500 Winter landscape with sledge on the ice and figures collecting twigs (31x46cm-12x18in) s. board. 4-Dec-2 Neumeister, Munich #908/R est:9500
£10256 $15897 €16000 Winter at Starnberger lake with children with ice skates and sledge on the ice (53x108cm-21x43in) s. canvas on canvas. 4-Dec-2 Neumeister, Munich #907/R est:12000

STADING, Evelina (1803-1829) Swedish
£388 $628 €563 View towards Skokloster Palace (43x64cm-17x25in) s. 25-May-3 Uppsala Auktionskammare, Uppsala #148 (S.KR 5000)

STADLER, Toni (1888-1982) German
Sculpture
£4348 $7130 €6000 Female head - Genia (30cm-12in) terracotta. 29-May-3 Lempertz, Koln #927/R est:4000-5000
£4710 $7725 €6500 Girl with jug (39cm-15in) bronze. 29-May-3 Lempertz, Koln #929/R est:5000

STADSKLEIV, Thorleif (1865-1946) Norwegian
£1702 $2671 €2553 Sunny day (45x66cm-18x26in) s. 25-Nov-2 Blomqvist, Lysaker #1259/R est:15000-18000 (N.KR 19500)

STAEHLE, Albert (1899-1974) American/German
£528 $850 €792 Butch watches as miniature breed passes by (53x46cm-21x18in) s. oil gouache board painted c.1955. 10-May-3 Illustration House, New York #28/R

Works on paper
£962 $1500 €1443 Reluctant Butch goes for a walk on a rainy day (30x25cm-12x10in) s.i.d.1955 W/C. 9-Nov-2 Illustration House, New York #11/R est:2000-3000

STAEHR-NIELSEN, Erik (1890-1921) Danish
£507 $781 €761 View across roof tops (87x63cm-34x25in) s.d.1919 cardboard. 23-Oct-2 Kunsthallen, Copenhagen #23 (D.KR 6000)
£1026 $1632 €1539 Jungle picture (81x67cm-32x26in) s.d.1926. 5-May-3 Rasmussen, Vejle #101/R (D.KR 11000)
£2451 $3775 €3677 Jungle picture (85x119cm-33x47in) s.d.1917. 23-Oct-2 Kunsthallen, Copenhagen #22/R est:12000 (D.KR 29000)
£6041 $9545 €9062 Negro and Spahi (61x78cm-24x31in) s.d.1917 veneer exhib. 1-Apr-3 Rasmussen, Copenhagen #23/R est:15000-25000 (D.KR 65000)

Works on paper
£465 $734 €698 Still life of yellow flowers (46x40cm-18x16in) s. gouache cardboard exhib. 1-Apr-3 Rasmussen, Copenhagen #647 (D.KR 5000)

STAEHR-OLSEN, Fritz (1858-1922) Danish
£342 $551 €513 Coastal landscape with view towards Kronborg, North Sjaelland (27x39cm-11x15in) s.d.1918. 22-Feb-3 Rasmussen, Havnen #2267 (D.KR 3800)
£478 $775 €693 Road through Tisvilde Heath (83x130cm-33x51in) s.i.d.1917. 26-May-3 Rasmussen, Copenhagen #1525 (D.KR 5000)

STAEL, Nicolas de (1914-1955) French
£30769 $48308 €48000 Composition (46x33cm-18x13in) s.d.46 verso prov.exhib.lit. 10-Dec-2 Piasa, Paris #219/R est:30000
£32051 $50321 €50000 Construction (41x27cm-16x11in) s.d.46 verso prov.exhib.lit. 10-Dec-2 Piasa, Paris #218/R est:25000
£40385 $63404 €63000 Piege (61x46cm-24x18in) s. s.i.d.47 verso panel prov.exhib.lit. 11-Dec-2 Artcurial Briest, Paris #712/R est:60000-80000
£45000 $75150 €65250 Fantenay (12x22cm-5x9in) oil on card painted 1952 prov.lit. 27-Jun-3 Christie's, London #101/R est:20000-30000
£83333 $129167 €130000 Sang de rouge (91x73cm-36x29in) s. s.i.d.1946 verso exhib.lit. 9-Dec-2 Piasa, Paris #31/R est:45000-60000
£96154 $149038 €150000 Ecart (80x60cm-31x24in) s. s.i.d.47 verso exhib.lit. 9-Dec-2 Piasa, Paris #32/R est:45000-60000

£140000 $233800 €210000 Composition (81x116cm-32x46in) s.d.51 prov.exhib.lit. 26-Jun-3 Christie's, London #16/R est:120000-180000
£260000 $434200 €390000 Syracuse (81x65cm-32x26in) s. s.i.d.1954 verso prov.exhib.lit. 26-Jun-3 Christie's, London #14/R est:200000-300000
£416667 $687500 €600000 Plage, souvenir du midi (65x81cm-26x32in) s. prov.exhib.lit. 1-Jul-3 Artcurial Briest, Paris #506/R est:600000-800000
£1000000 $1670000 €1500000 Ciel (89x116cm-35x46in) s. painted 1955 prov.exhib.lit. 26-Jun-3 Christie's, London #15/R est:600000-800000

Prints

£2692 $4200 €4038 Mediterranee (35x46cm-14x18in) s.i.d.num.28/200 col screenprint. 18-Sep-2 Swann Galleries, New York #78/R est:2500-3500
£5128 $8103 €8000 Composition violette (54x76cm-21x30in) s.i.d.52 col lithograph. 15-Nov-2 Laurence Calmels, Paris #91/R

Works on paper

£3590 $5672 €5600 Composition (41x27cm-16x11in) chl pastel gommage exec.c.1944. 14-Nov-2 Credit Municipal, Paris #48 est:3500-4500
£6250 $10313 €9000 Composition (50x32cm-20x13in) s. Indian ink exec.c.1945. 1-Jul-3 Artcurial Briest, Paris #770/R est:6000-8000
£9211 $14921 €14000 Composition (39x24cm-15x9in) chl dr exec.c.1945/47. 22-Jan-3 Tajan, Paris #119/R est:15000-18000

STAETS, Hendrik (fl.1643-1659) Dutch?

£3400 $5304 €5100 Dutch men-o-war in stormy waters (33x52cm-13x20in) indis mono. panel. 9-Apr-3 Bonhams, New Bond Street #41/R est:2000-3000
£5864 $9500 €8796 Stormy seascape (34x48cm-13x19in) mono. panel prov. 24-Jan-3 Christie's, Rockefeller NY #1/R est:10000-15000

STAGER, Balz (1861-1937) Swiss

£304 $472 €456 Albis with Zugersee (45x59cm-18x23in) s. 9-Dec-2 Philippe Schuler, Zurich #8757 (S.FR 700)
£401 $642 €602 Untitled (54x66cm-21x26in) s.d. 17-Mar-3 Philippe Schuler, Zurich #8485 (S.FR 850)
£522 $814 €783 Walensee in autumn (71x48cm-28x19in) s. 16-Sep-2 Philippe Schuler, Zurich #3401 (S.FR 1200)
£961 $1499 €1442 Group of trees near Unterterzen (65x83cm-26x33in) s.d.1891 canvas on board prov. 9-Nov-2 Galerie Gloggner, Luzern #135/R (S.FR 2200)
£2183 $3406 €3275 Autumn near Quinten (44x59cm-17x23in) s.d.1902 i. stretcher. 6-Nov-2 Hans Widmer, St Gallen #115/R est:1800-3800 (S.FR 5000)
£3930 $6131 €5895 Storm near Quinten (116x140cm-46x55in) s. 6-Nov-2 Hans Widmer, St Gallen #96/R est:6000-14000 (S.FR 9000)

STAGURA, Albert (1866-1947) German

£615 $966 €960 Watzmann with alpine hut (55x65cm-22x26in) s.d.1936 panel. 21-Nov-2 Weidler, Nurnberg #4404/R

Works on paper

£2885 $4385 €4500 Peonies in vase (82x73cm-32x29in) s.i. pastel. 11-Jul-2 Hugo Ruef, Munich #929/R est:4500

STAHL, Benjamin Albert (1910-1987) American

£1667 $2600 €2501 Woman and man dressing simultaneously (25x20cm-10x8in) s.verso panel. 9-Nov-2 Illustration House, New York #140/R est:2000-3000

STAHL, Franz Xaver (1901-) German

£2821 $4372 €4400 Mare and foal standing by a cart (27x38cm-11x15in) s. board. 4-Dec-2 Neumeister, Munich #911/R est:2800

STAHL, Friedrich (1863-1940) German

£377 $588 €550 Study of elegant society (21x19cm-8x7in) s. canvas on board lit. 10-Apr-3 Allgauer, Kempten #2996/R

Works on paper

£405 $628 €640 Ball scene (25x19cm-10x7in) s. gouache grisaille htd white W/C. 27-Sep-2 Venator & Hansten, Koln #1353
£479 $748 €700 Study of an elegant lady in a park landscape (32x24cm-13x9in) s. W/C htd white lit. 10-Apr-3 Allgauer, Kempten #2663/R
£681 $1103 €1022 Lady with black hat (25x18cm-10x7in) s. gouache. 24-May-3 Dorotheum, Prague #219/R est:30000-45000 (C.KR 30000)

STAHLECKER, Adrian (1937-) Dutch

Works on paper

£255 $397 €400 Portrait of a sorrowful pierrot (59x47cm-23x19in) s. dr. 5-Nov-2 Vendu Notarishuis, Rotterdam #565/R

STAHLY-RYCHEN, G (1840-?) Swiss

£873 $1362 €1310 Meyringen before the fire in the year 1891 (73x91cm-29x36in) s.i. 8-Nov-2 Dobiaschofsky, Bern #4/R (S.FR 2000)

STAHLY-RYCHEN, Gottfried (1840-?) Swiss

£353 $557 €550 Alpine landscape with mountain village (29x38cm-11x15in) s. board. 15-Nov-2 Reiss & Sohn, Konigstein #85/R
£479 $748 €700 View over Lake Geneva on the 'Dent du Midi' (20x26cm-8x10in) s. panel prov. 14-Apr-3 Glerum, Amsterdam #96/R

STAIGER, Otto (1894-) Swiss

Works on paper

£300 $475 €450 At the sea (24x31cm-9x12in) s. W/C. 29-Nov 2 Zofingen, Switzerland #3083/R (S.FR 700)

STAINTON, G (fl.1860-1890) British

£2100 $3423 €3150 Seascape with Old Hulks, Portsmouth, at sunset (28x43cm-11x17in) i.verso. 29-Jan-3 Brightwells, Leominster #871/R est:1200-1800

STAINTON, George (fl.1860-1890) British

£1900 $2888 €2850 Coastal barges off Harwich (30x51cm-12x20in) s. s.i.verso. 15-Aug-2 Bonhams, New Bond Street #332/R est:1500-2000
£4000 $6360 €6000 Pulling in the catch, shipping in the mouth of the Thames (61x92cm-24x36in) s. 4-Mar-3 Bonhams, Knightsbridge #331/R est:4000-6000
£6200 $8866 €9300 Fishing boats at dawn (60x90cm-24x35in) s. 11-Apr-2 Mellors & Kirk, Nottingham #565/R est:1000-1500

Works on paper

£1400 $2226 €2100 Evening calm with moored fishing boats (28x43cm-11x17in) s. W/C. 30-Apr-3 Halls, Shrewsbury #261/R est:300-500

STALBEMT, Adriaen van (1580-1662) Flemish

£3741 $5986 €5200 Les baigneuses (53x44cm-21x17in) panel. 13-May-3 Vanderkindere, Brussels #244/R est:3000-5000
£8017 $12426 €12026 Rider and figure by pond (91x136cm-36x54in) 3-Oct-2 Koller, Zurich #3046/R est:22000-32000 (S.FR 18680)
£17808 $27781 €26000 Landscape with Artemis and Acteon (55x76cm-22x30in) board. 8-Apr-3 Ansorena, Madrid #74/R est:24000
£17949 $28359 €28000 Landscape with mills and travellers (13x19cm-5x7in) copper. 13-Nov-2 Marc Kohn, Paris #16/R est:30000-40000

STALBEMT, Adriaen van (attrib) (1580-1662) Flemish

£9259 $15000 €13889 Diana and her nymphs bathing (44x60cm-17x24in) panel prov. 24-Jan-3 Christie's, Rockefeller NY #41/R est:15000-20000

STALBEMT, Adriaen van (circle) (1580-1662) Flemish

£11000 $18370 €15950 Wooded landscape with figures passing through a village (91x136cm-36x54in) 10-Jul-3 Sotheby's, London #111/R est:8000-12000

STALLAERT, Joseph (1825-1903) Belgian

£472 $731 €750 Portrait of a man (81x65cm-32x26in) s.d.1845. 5-Oct-2 De Vuyst, Lokeren #337

STALLER, Gerard Johan (1880-1956) Dutch

£443 $691 €700 Market seller with her vegetables (21x15cm-8x6in) s. 21-Oct-2 Glerum, Amsterdam #200/R
£4795 $7527 €7000 View of the Zeedijk, Amsterdam (22x18cm-9x7in) s. panel exhib. 15-Apr-3 Sotheby's, Amsterdam #97/R est:3000-4000

STALLKNECHT, Alice (1880-1973) American

£976 $1600 €1415 Christ stilling the waves (86x74cm-34x29in) s. prov. 1-Jun-3 Wright, Chicago #226/R est:1500-2000

STALNAKER, Hamilton G (jnr) (20th C) American

£435 $700 €653 Fishing boats, north coast, Calif (66x91cm-26x36in) s. masonite prov. 18-Feb-3 John Moran, Pasadena #172

STALNER, Eric (20th C) French?

Works on paper

£276 $436 €400 Croix de Cazenac (45x32cm-18x13in) s. Chinese ink. 7-Apr-3 Claude Aguttes, Neuilly #92/R
£310 $490 €450 Roman de malemort (45x32cm-18x13in) s. Chinese ink. 7-Apr-3 Claude Aguttes, Neuilly #94
£345 $545 €500 Roman de Malemort (45x32cm-18x13in) s. Chinese ink. 7-Apr-3 Claude Aguttes, Neuilly #93
£469 $741 €680 Croix de Cazenac (45x32cm-18x13in) s. Chinese ink. 7-Apr-3 Claude Aguttes, Neuilly #91/R

STAMOS, Theodoros (1922-1997) American

£611 $960 €917 Infinity field Torino 1 (76x56cm-30x22in) s.i.d.1986 verso acrylic gouache. 25-Nov-2 Germann, Zurich #115/R (S.FR 1400)
£1090 $1700 €1635 Infinity field - lefkada series (77x57cm-30x22in) s.i.d.1980-81 acrylic paper prov. 5-Nov-2 Doyle, New York #28/R est:1400-1800

£4000 $6680 €5800 Infinity field (54x32cm-21x13in) s.i.d.1980 overlap acrylic prov. 24-Jun-3 Sotheby's, Olympia #96/R est:4000-6000
£25000 $40000 €37500 Divide (173x175cm-68x69in) s.i.d.1957-58 verso prov.exhib.lit. 15-May-3 Christie's, Rockefeller NY #114/R est:25000-35000
Works on paper
£1667 $2600 €2501 Unfathomable (28x36cm-11x14in) s.i.d.1946 gouache board. 30-Mar-3 Susanin's, Chicago #6082/R est:3000-4000
£1829 $3000 €2652 Berkshire elegy (33x47cm-13x19in) s. gouache ink card stock. 5-Jun-3 Swann Galleries, New York #235/R est:3000-5000

STAMPART, Frans van (attrib) (1675-1750) Flemish
£1887 $2925 €3000 Portrait of noblewoman (86x71cm-34x28in) 2-Oct-2 Dorotheum, Vienna #272/R est:2500-3000

STAMPFLI, Peter (1937-) Swiss
Works on paper
£2452 $3874 €3800 Rallyems (112x123cm-44x48in) s.d.78 graphite. 18-Dec-2 Digard, Paris #203/R

STAMPFLI, Pierre Victor (1916-1975) Swiss
£480 $749 €720 Artist in studio (75x61cm-30x24in) s.i. 6-Nov-2 Dobiaschofsky, Bern #979/R (S.FR 1100)

STAN, Vladimir (?) ?
£993 $1619 €1500 Le depart (116x89cm-46x35in) s. 1-Feb-3 Claude Aguttes, Neuilly #293 est:1500-1600

STANCHI, Giovanni (attrib) (c.1645-?) Italian
£5172 $8172 €7500 Still life with vase of flowers (64x54cm-25x21in) 5-Apr-3 Finarte Semenzato, Milan #7/R est:8000

STANDING, Henry William (19/20th C) British
Works on paper
£460 $768 €667 Shire horse trotting by a stable (36x51cm-14x20in) s. gouache. 20-Jun-3 Keys, Aylsham #457/R

STANESBY, Alexander (1832-1916) British
Works on paper
£280 $456 €406 Still life of pears, grapes and tomato on a table (21x29cm-8x11in) s.d.1891 W/C bodycol. 17-Jul-3 Tennants, Leyburn #755
£1100 $1793 €1595 Still life of blue and white porcelain, fuschia flower heads. Still life blue and white teapot and f (29cm-11in circular) s.d.1884 W/C gouache pair. 17-Jul-3 Tennants, Leyburn #756 est:300-400

STANFIELD, C (1793-1867) British
Works on paper
£600 $984 €900 Fort Rouge (20x38cm-8x15in) s. W/C. 5-Feb-3 John Nicholson, Haslemere #1008

STANFIELD, Charles (19/20th C) British
£400 $624 €600 Bolton Woods (48x61cm-19x24in) s. i.verso. 9-Apr-3 Andrew Hartley, Ilkley #986
£720 $1123 €1080 Mountain landscape, near Arthog, Merioneth (51x77cm-20x30in) s. one i.verso pair. 17-Sep-2 Bonhams, Sevenoaks #188/R

STANFIELD, Clarkson (1793-1867) British
£1000 $1580 €1450 Moonlight off the coast (75x110cm-30x43in) s.d.1848. 22-Jul-3 Bristol Auction Rooms #426/R est:2000-3000
£2800 $4648 €4060 Cowes Regatta (23x43cm-9x17in) i.verso panel prov. 16-Jun-3 Duke & Son, Dorchester #199/R est:1000-2000
£4000 $6680 €5800 Harbour scene at sunset. Sailing ships in a rough sea (16x30cm-6x12in) s.d.1859 board pair. 9-Jul-3 George Kidner, Lymington #158/R est:4000-6000
£5282 $8504 €7500 Sailing ship on rough sea (39x60cm-15x24in) s.d.1853. 7-May-3 Vendue Huis, Gravenhage #400/R est:3000-5000
£5556 $9000 €8056 View of the English Channel with sailboats in choppy seas off the white cliffs of Dover (51x76cm-20x30in) s. 29-Jul-3 Christie's, Rockefeller NY #129/R est:10000-15000
Works on paper
£280 $437 €420 On the Meuse, Namur (19x27cm-7x11in) s. pencil W/C htd white. 27-Mar-3 Christie's, Kensington #144
£580 $905 €870 Scarborough (20x28cm-8x11in) s.d.1853. 9-Oct-2 Andrew Hartley, Ilkley #691/R
£800 $1312 €1200 Boats off a jetty in a rough sea (21x30cm-8x12in) init. i.verso W/C. 4-Feb-3 Bonhams, Leeds #213

STANFIELD, Clarkson (attrib) (1793-1867) British
£420 $664 €630 Fishing boat and further shipping in a swell (23x38cm-9x15in) s.d.1860. 18-Dec-2 Mallams, Oxford #586
£582 $943 €844 Fishing boat on the way out to sea (48x65cm-19x26in) bears sig. 25-May-3 Uppsala Auktionskammare, Uppsala #78/R (S.KR 7500)
£1053 $1705 €1580 Seascape with beached British three-master by rocky coast (62x75cm-24x30in) s. 21-May-3 Museumsbygningen, Copenhagen #39/R (D.KR 11000)
£5000 $8000 €7500 Fishing vessels and other shipping in heavy seas (64x91cm-25x36in) 13-Mar-3 Duke & Son, Dorchester #230/R est:800-1600

STANFIELD, George Clarkson (1828-1878) British
£1372 $2141 €2058 Saving the catch, boats in high seas near cliffs (40x61cm-16x24in) s.d.1846. 11-Nov-2 Rasmussen, Vejle #629/R est:20000 (D.KR 16000)
£1800 $2898 €2700 Rowing boat with shipping in a stormy sea (23x33cm-9x13in) 15-Jan-3 Cheffins Grain & Comins, Cambridge #426/R
£2400 $3744 €3600 Kirkstall Abbey (43x63cm-17x25in) indis sig.d.1856 exhib. 7-Nov-2 Christie's, Kensington #97/R est:1500-2000
£2658 $4200 €4200 Medieval town in Italy (66x91cm-26x36in) s.d.1852. 30-Nov-2 Hagelstam, Helsinki #50/R est:5000
£3247 $4838 €5000 Mountain lake (61x106cm-24x42in) s. 26-Jun-2 Neumeister, Munich #872/R est:3500
Works on paper
£550 $869 €798 Coblentz. Frankfurt (22x34cm-9x13in) i.d.Sept 24 W/C over pencil pair. 22-Jul-3 Bonhams, Knightsbridge #212/R
£650 $1007 €975 Continental townscape (26x47cm-10x19in) s.d. W/C. 24-Sep-2 Rowley Fine Art, Newmarket #327/R

STANGE, Bernhard (1807-1880) German
£2009 $3134 €3014 Night time landscape in Tyrol (39x49cm-15x19in) s.d.1865. 6-Nov-2 Dobiaschofsky, Bern #980/R est:4500 (S.FR 4600)

STANGERUS, Cornelis (1616-1667) Dutch
£4459 $6955 €7000 Demoritus and Heraclitus (117x97cm-46x38in) bears sig.d.1662 prov.lit. 5-Nov-2 Sotheby's, Amsterdam #49/R est:10000-15000
£48000 $80160 €69600 Gentleman seated at a table with two serving girls (124x142cm-49x56in) prov. 9-Jul-3 Christie's, London #32/R est:15000-20000

STANGL, Heinz (1942-) Austrian
£705 $1114 €1100 Afternoon (100x67cm-39x26in) s.d.1985 mixed media. 12-Nov-2 Dorotheum, Vienna #273/R
£4430 $6867 €7000 Evening group (114x146cm-45x57in) s.d.1988. 24-Sep-2 Wiener Kunst Auktionen, Vienna #304/R est:7000-12000

STANHOPE, John Roddam Spencer (1829-1908) British
Works on paper
£2400 $3936 €3480 Italian landscape (20x53cm-8x21in) pencil W/C bodycol. 5-Jun-3 Christie's, London #141/R est:2500-3500
£2800 $4592 €4060 Women of Sorrento (39x55cm-15x22in) pencil W/C htd bodycol. 5-Jun-3 Christie's, London #140/R est:2000-3000
£2800 $4592 €4060 Tuscan landscape with village and olive grove. Italian valley (30x58cm-12x23in) pencil W/C bodycol two. 5-Jun-3 Christie's, London #142/R est:3000-5000
£4500 $7245 €6750 Washing place (70x123cm-28x48in) pencil W/C bodycol prov.exhib. 20-Feb-3 Christie's, London #295/R est:10000
£12000 $19680 €17400 Pinewoods of Viareggio (135x109cm-53x43in) pencil W/C bodycol gum arabic. 5-Jun-3 Christie's, London #139/R est:6000-10000

STANIALOVSKAJA, V (19/20th C) Russian
£556 $911 €850 Goddess (38x24cm-15x9in) s.d.1901 oil on porcelain. 9-Feb-3 Bukowskis, Helsinki #437/R

STANIER, F (19th C) ?
£650 $1001 €975 Still life of apples, grapes beside a pottery vase (40x66cm-16x26in) s. 5-Sep-2 Morphets, Harrogate #352

STANIER, H (19th C) British
£880 $1364 €1320 Portrait study of three white horses (59cm-23in circular) s. 1-Oct-2 Fellows & Sons, Birmingham #48/R

STANIER, Henry (?-1892) British
Works on paper
£820 $1271 €1230 Middle Eastern scene with woman and child near lake (51x71cm-20x28in) s.d.1876 W/C. 3-Oct-2 Amersham Auction Rooms, UK #296

STANKIEWICZ, Richard (1922-) American
Sculpture
£1020 $1622 €1500 Untitled. metal. 3-Mar-3 Marc Kohn, Paris #48/R

STANKIEWICZ, Zofia (1862-) Polish
£4500 $7066 €6750 Winter's day, Warsaw (62x78cm-24x31in) s.d.94. 19-Nov-2 Sotheby's, London #165/R est:5000-7000

STANLEY OF PENRHOS (18th C) British
Works on paper
£1200 $1884 €1800 Lapwing (39x27cm-15x11in) s.d.1792 pen ink W/C. 20-Nov-2 Sotheby's, Olympia #55/R est:300-500

STANLEY, Caleb Robert (1795-1868) British
Works on paper
£600 $912 €900 Fishing vessels off a quay (25x37cm-10x15in) s. W/C. 15-Aug-2 Bonhams, New Bond Street #209

STANLEY, Cyril (19th C) British
£400 $644 €580 Iffley mill (19x29cm-7x11in) s. 12-May-3 Joel, Victoria #322 est:1000-1500 (A.D 1000)

STANLEY, Henry Morton (1841-1904) British
Photographs
£55000 $85250 €82500 Livingstone search expedition (30x25cm-12x10in) photograph prints two album. 24-Sep-2 Christie's, London #44/R est:20000-30000

STANLEY, John Mix (1814-1872) American
£37975 $60000 €55064 Scene on the Columbia river (43x53cm-17x21in) prov. 26-Jul-3 Coeur d'Alene, Hayden #201/R est:25000-50000

STANLEY, Sidney (1890-1956) British
£400 $616 €600 Old Heatherleys (20x25cm-8x10in) board. 6-Sep-2 Biddle & Webb, Birmingham #30

STANNARD OF BEDFORD, Emily (1875-1907) British
Works on paper
£300 $477 €450 Figure before a rural cottage (37x66cm-15x26in) s. W/C. 29-Apr-3 Bonhams, Knightsbridge #81/R

STANNARD OF NORWICH, Emily (1803-1885) British
£420 $685 €630 Still life study of pheasant and songbird on a marble slab (18x25cm-7x10in) s.indis.d. 14-Feb-3 Keys, Aylsham #655/R

STANNARD, Alexander Molyneux (1878-1975) British
Works on paper
£340 $524 €510 Children before a cottage (23x33cm-9x13in) mono. W/C. 22-Oct-2 Sworder & Son, Bishops Stortford #696/R

STANNARD, Alfred (1806-1889) British
£360 $569 €540 Cottage in a woodland clearing (33cm-13in circular) s. 26-Nov-2 Bonhams, Ipswich #374
£850 $1318 €1275 Whitlingham Lane (51x61cm-20x24in) s.d.1886. 30-Sep-2 Bonhams, Ipswich #500/R
£2000 $3180 €3000 Norfolk landscape with a windmill (17x21cm-7x8in) panel. 19-Mar-3 Sotheby's, London #72/R est:2000-3000

STANNARD, Alfred (attrib) (1806-1889) British
£4200 $6930 €6090 Fishing boats at the entrance to a harbour (28x36cm-11x14in) 1-Jul-3 Bonhams, Norwich #198/R est:4000-6000

STANNARD, Alfred George (1828-1885) British
£1300 $2028 €1950 Old mill (63x76cm-25x30in) s.d.1880. 7-Nov-2 Christie's, Kensington #91/R est:1000-1500
£3600 $5580 €5400 Wherry on the Wensum (46x61cm-18x24in) 30-Sep-2 Bonhams, Ipswich #494/R est:2000-3000

STANNARD, Eloise Harriet (c.1828-1915) British
£1800 $2970 €2610 Marguerites in a basket (23x28cm-9x11in) s.d.1889. 1-Jul-3 Bonhams, Norwich #221/R est:1500-2000
£1900 $3097 €2755 Still life with grapes, plums and a peach. Still life of a basket of fruit (25x33cm-10x13in) s.d.1858 pair. 17-Jul-3 Tennants, Leyburn #901 est:1200-1800
£3800 $6270 €5510 Still life currants and apricots on a blue and white pottery dish (20x30cm-8x12in) s.d.1900 prov. 3-Jul-3 Ewbank, Send #298/R est:2500-4000
£5500 $9185 €7975 Study of birds after strawberries in a basket (18x28cm-7x11in) s.d.1895. 20-Jun-3 Keys, Aylsham #645/R est:5000-7000
£6000 $9360 €9000 Still life of fruit and chillies (27x77cm-11x30in) indis.sig.d. 17-Sep-2 Sotheby's, Olympia #173/R est:6000-8000
£6000 $9540 €9000 Chrysanthemums and apples (43x35cm-17x14in) s.d.1891. 19-Mar-3 Sotheby's, London #255/R est:6000-8000
£6500 $10465 €9750 Study of convolvulus and marigolds (40x30cm-16x12in) card prov. 20-Feb-3 Christie's, London #128/R
£6500 $10725 €9425 Still life of fruit in a silver bowl and tray all on a marble ledge (61x51cm-24x20in) s.d.1883. 1-Jul-3 Bonhams, Norwich #218 est:10000-15000
£6500 $10725 €9425 Russet apples spilling out of a basket (28x36cm-11x14in) s.d.1899. 1-Jul-3 Bonhams, Norwich #223/R est:7000-9000
£10000 $15800 €15000 Roses and strawberries on cabbage leaf. Peach and grapes with other fruit (30cm-12in circular) one indis.sig. one s.d.1864 pair prov. 26-Nov-2 Christie's, London #146/R est:12000-18000
£14000 $22260 €21000 Still life with fruit and convulvulus (47x52cm-19x20in) s.d.1881 prov. 18-Mar-3 Bonhams, New Bond Street #87/R est:15000-20000
£17000 $26860 €25500 Apples and grapes in basket and on wooded ledge with butterfly (61x51cm-24x20in) s.d.1877. 26-Nov-2 Christie's, London #149/R est:18000-25000
£18000 $28440 €27000 Fruit painted from nature (76x71cm-30x28in) s.d.1855. 2-Dec-2 Sotheby's, London #25/R est:20000-30000
£30000 $49500 €43500 Four seasons (44cm-17in circular) 1-Jul-3 Bonhams, Norwich #215/R est:30000-50000

STANNARD, Eloise Harriet (attrib) (c.1828-1915) British
£920 $1463 €1380 Still life of fruit in basket on a marble ledge (23x28cm-9x11in) 5-Mar-3 Bonhams, Bury St Edmunds #407

STANNARD, Henry (1844-1920) British
Works on paper
£300 $468 €450 Stile with cottage beyond within a wooded landscape (24x33cm-9x13in) W/C. 21-Sep-2 Lacy Scott, Bury St.Edmunds #372
£400 $640 €600 Winding rural river scene on a lowland plain, with larger trees over rivers edge (43x58cm-17x23in) s. W/C. 10-Jan-3 Biddle & Webb, Birmingham #192
£550 $891 €825 Shepherd and flock (23x33cm-9x13in) s. W/C. 20-May-3 Sotheby's, Olympia #6/R
£760 $1186 €1140 Spaniel flushing pheasant (24x34cm-9x13in) s. W/C pencil. 17-Oct-2 Lawrence, Crewkerne #1572/R
£1000 $1630 €1500 The cottage garden (24x34cm-9x13in) s. W/C. 29-Jan-3 Sotheby's, Olympia #145/R est:800-1200

STANNARD, Henry Sylvester (1870-1951) British
£280 $442 €420 At a lake side (102x62cm-40x24in) s. 27-Nov-2 Hamptons Fine Art, Godalming #478
£600 $936 €900 Woodland path (26x35cm-10x14in) s. 7-Nov-2 Bonhams, Cornwall #793
£750 $1170 €1125 Toy boat (23x34cm-9x13in) s. scratching out. 7-Nov-2 Bonhams, Cornwall #795/R
£800 $1248 €1200 Harvesters (26x36cm-10x14in) s. 7-Nov-2 Bonhams, Cornwall #794/R
Works on paper
£250 $390 €375 Stream with distant cottage within a landscape (25x34cm-10x13in) W/C. 21-Sep-2 Lacy Scott, Bury St.Edmunds #371
£270 $424 €405 Winter landscape (24x34cm-9x13in) W/C. 14-Dec-2 Lacy Scott, Bury St.Edmunds #459/R
£270 $424 €405 Autumn landscape with blue skies (34x24cm-13x9in) W/C. 14-Dec-2 Lacy Scott, Bury St.Edmunds #460
£300 $468 €450 River landscape with figures by a bridge (26x36cm-10x14in) W/C scratching out. 27-Mar-3 Christie's, Kensington #46
£320 $499 €480 Rustic landscape with trees (24x34cm-9x13in) W/C. 10-Sep-2 Sworder & Son, Bishops Stortford #722/R
£320 $499 €480 Looking to Westminster (17x24cm-7x9in) s.i. W/C htd white. 19-Sep-2 Christie's, Kensington #69
£340 $568 €493 Country house and gardens with delphinium to the fore (25x18cm-10x7in) s. W/C. 25-Jun-3 Goldings, Lincolnshire #350
£380 $593 €570 Landscape in sunset (9x16cm-4x6in) s. W/C. 17-Oct-2 Christie's, Kensington #86/R
£400 $624 €600 Cottage and barn by a country road (32x48cm-13x19in) pencil W/C. 17-Oct-2 Christie's, Kensington #87
£400 $620 €600 View of thatched cottage (25x34cm-10x13in) W/C. 3-Dec-2 Sworder & Son, Bishops Stortford #983/R
£400 $624 €600 Counrty cottage, Bedfordshire (23x34cm-9x13in) s.i. pencil W/C. 27-Mar-3 Christie's, Kensington #126
£420 $655 €630 Rustic moonlight landscape with sheep (24x34cm-9x13in) W/C. 10-Sep-2 Sworder & Son, Bishops Stortford #721/R
£440 $695 €660 Woodland path (25x35cm-10x14in) s. W/C. 26-Nov-2 Bonhams, Knightsbridge #225/R
£470 $733 €705 Barton valley and the clappers, Bedfordshire (33x50cm-13x20in) s. W/C bodycol. 27-Mar-3 Christie's, Kensington #124
£480 $763 €720 Country lane in autumn (27x36cm-11x14in) W/C. 18-Mar-3 Sworder & Son, Bishops Stortford #445/R

£500 $820 €750 Breaking from cover (25x36cm-10x14in) s. W/C. 3-Jun-3 Bonhams, Knightsbridge #24/R
£500 $825 €725 Summer flowering pergola (27x39cm-11x15in) s. W/C. 1-Jul-3 Bonhams, Norwich #94/R
£520 $806 €780 Landscape view with trees and lake (25x34cm-10x13in) W/C. 3-Dec-2 Sworder & Son, Bishops Stortford #982/R
£520 $853 €780 View of a rustic river (36x48cm-14x19in) W/C. 4-Feb-3 Sworder & Son, Bishops Stortford #138/R
£520 $827 €780 Cottages in Devon (27x36cm-11x14in) W/C. 18-Mar-3 Sworder & Son, Bishops Stortford #444/R
£520 $863 €780 Country lane with a cottage (24x34cm-9x13in) W/C. 10-Jun-3 Sworder & Son, Bishops Stortford #513/R
£540 $886 €810 Country house and garden in summer (25x36cm-10x14in) s. W/C. 5-Feb-3 Goldings, Lincolnshire #231
£550 $858 €825 Amberley village, Cotswolds (25x36cm-10x14in) s. pencil W/C. 27-Mar-3 Christie's, Kensington #113
£580 $916 €870 Fisherman in a boat in meandering river (13x23cm-5x9in) s. W/C pair. 18-Dec-2 Mallams, Oxford #558
£580 $951 €870 View of a rustic mill (35x46cm-14x18in) W/C. 4-Feb-3 Sworder & Son, Bishops Stortford #139/R
£650 $1001 €975 Farmstead (24x34cm-9x13in) s. W/C. 23-Oct-2 Hamptons Fine Art, Godalming #102
£650 $1013 €975 Rural cottage in Sourton, Devon (34x48cm-13x19in) i. pencil W/C. 19-Sep-2 Christie's, Kensington #49/R
£650 $1013 €975 Farm landscape with sheep (15x28cm-6x11in) s. W/C. 19-Sep-2 Christie's, Kensington #56/R
£650 $1014 €975 Thatched cottage with a well by a country lane (27x37cm-11x15in) s. pencil W/C. 17-Oct-2 Christie's, Kensington #77/R
£680 $1081 €1020 Bedfordshire cottage (17x30cm-7x12in) s. W/C. 29-Apr-3 Sworder & Son, Bishops Stortford #331/R
£700 $1078 €1050 On a farm track by cottages. Cottage gate (24x34cm-9x13in) s. W/C pair. 23-Oct-2 Hamptons Fine Art, Godalming #104/R
£750 $1178 €1125 Landscape with a thatched cottage (26x36cm-10x14in) W/C prov. 21-Nov-2 Tennants, Leyburn #627
£756 $1254 €1096 Down by the farm at Cuxhaven, Oxfordshire (25x36cm-10x14in) s.i.d.1929 W/C. 16-Jun-3 Waddingtons, Toronto #95/R est:2000-3000 (C.D 1700)
£800 $1248 €1200 Thatched cottage with chickens in a rural landscape (33x48cm-13x19in) s. pencil W/C. 19-Sep-2 Christie's, Kensington #55/R
£800 $1320 €1160 Cottage scene with figures and hens (25x35cm-10x14in) s. W/C. 1-Jul-3 Bonhams, Norwich #91
£850 $1420 €1233 Woodlands at sunset (24x35cm-9x14in) s. W/C. 24-Jun-3 Bonhams, Knightsbridge #19/R
£900 $1467 €1350 Wood gatherers, Steppingly Woods, Bedfordshire (25x36cm-10x14in) s. i.verso W/C. 13-Feb-3 David Lay, Penzance #102
£950 $1463 €1425 Surrey homestead (23x33cm-9x13in) s. W/C. 23-Oct-2 Hamptons Fine Art, Godalming #107
£960 $1526 €1440 Ducks and hens on a lane before a thatched cottage (33x57cm-13x22in) s. W/C. 27-Feb-3 Bonhams, Chester #449/R
£1000 $1540 €1500 Bedfordshire lane (23x33cm-9x13in) s. W/C. 23-Oct-2 Hamptons Fine Art, Godalming #103/R est:700-1000
£1000 $1550 €1500 An idyllic rural cottage (25x35cm-10x14in) s. W/C. 24-Sep-2 Bonhams, Knightsbridge #51/R est:1000-1500
£1000 $1570 €1500 Back of a farm at Tiddington, Oxfordshire (24x34cm-9x13in) s. pencil W/C. 16-Apr-3 Christie's, Kensington #1031/R est:500-700
£1050 $1596 €1575 Quiet summers day at Greenfield, Bedfordshire (25x38cm-10x15in) s. W/C. 16-Aug-2 Keys, Aylsham #594
£1100 $1704 €1650 Old Farm House (33x44cm-13x17in) s. W/C. 3-Dec-2 Sotheby's, Olympia #98/R est:1000-1500
£1100 $1826 €1650 Sheep grazing by moonlight (36x25cm-14x10in) s. W/C. 12-Jun-3 Bonhams, New Bond Street #678/R est:800-1200
£1150 $1794 €1668 Silsoe, Bedfordshire - shepherd and sheep before cottages (25x35cm-10x14in) s. W/C. 27-Mar-3 Lane, Penzance #260 est:1500-2000
£1200 $1956 €1800 Ducks outside a thatched cottage (23x34cm-9x13in) indis sig. W/C. 29-Jan-3 Sotheby's, Olympia #152/R est:1000-2000
£1300 $2171 €1885 Near Sharnbrook, Bedfordshire (25x35cm-10x14in) s. W/C. 24-Jun-3 Bonhams, Knightsbridge #23/R est:500-700
£1300 $2171 €1885 Poultry before a thatched cottage in summer (38x48cm-15x19in) s. W/C. 20-Jun-3 Keys, Aylsham #516 est:1400-1600
£1350 $2093 €2025 Canterbury Cathedral (34x50cm-13x20in) s. W/C. 24-Sep-2 Rowley Fine Art, Newmarket #329/R
£1400 $2170 €2100 Lace seller (34x52cm-13x20in) s. W/C. 3-Dec-2 Sotheby's, Olympia #129/R est:1500-2000
£1500 $2430 €2250 Garden pond (34x50cm-13x20in) s. W/C. 20-May-3 Sotheby's, Olympia #272/R est:1500-2000
£1500 $2505 €2175 Near Stratford on Avon (25x35cm-10x14in) s. W/C. 24-Jun-3 Bonhams, Knightsbridge #22/R est:600-800
£1500 $2505 €2175 Rye Bridge, Ashtead Common (25x35cm-10x14in) s. W/C. 24-Jun-3 Bonhams, Knightsbridge #24/R est:400-600
£1700 $2771 €2550 Going to market (35x50cm-14x20in) s. W/C. 29-Jan-3 Sotheby's, Olympia #151/R est:1500-2000
£1700 $2771 €2550 Crossing the ford (25x35cm-10x14in) s. W/C. 29-Jan-3 Sotheby's, Olympia #153/R est:800-1200
£1700 $2805 €2465 Cottage, Kimbolton, Bedfordshire (25x35cm-10x14in) s. W/C bodycol prov. 3-Jul-3 Christie's, Kensington #67/R est:1000-1500
£1900 $2983 €2850 Bedfordshire cottage (35x50cm-14x20in) s. pencil W/C. 19-Nov-2 Bonhams, Leeds #34/R est:1500-2000
£2000 $3080 €3000 Admiring the ducks (25x36cm-10x14in) s. W/C. 23-Oct-2 Hamptons Fine Art, Godalming #106/R est:800-1200
£2146 $3348 €3112 Tending the chickens (36x51cm-14x20in) s. W/C. 26-Mar-3 Walker's, Ottawa #48/R est:6000-7000 (C.D 5000)
£2200 $3388 €3300 Brookside (25x36cm-10x14in) s. W/C. 23-Oct-2 Hamptons Fine Art, Godalming #99/R est:1000-1500
£2200 $3454 €3300 Near Lidington, Beds (33x48cm-13x19in) s. W/C. 16-Dec-2 Bonhams, Bury St Edmunds #394/R est:1500-2000
£2400 $3720 €3600 Landscape with thatched cottages (33x51cm-13x20in) s. W/C dr. 1-Oct-2 Capes Dunn, Manchester #830/R
£2500 $4150 €3625 Errand for mother (35x25cm-14x10in) s. W/C. 13-Jun-3 Lyon & Turnbull, Edinburgh #65 est:400-600
£2564 $4000 €3846 Children going fishing, farm fields with horse and wagon (23x33cm-9x13in) s. 18-Sep-2 Alderfer's, Hatfield #243/R est:1200-1500
£2600 $4030 €3900 Rural landscape with thatched cottage, sheep and geese (48x35cm-19x14in) s. W/C htd white. 1-Oct-2 Fellows & Sons, Birmingham #179/R est:1500-2500
£2675 $4146 €4013 At Cuxham Oxfordshire (47x73cm-19x29in) s. W/C. 3-Dec-2 Ritchie, Toronto #3007/R est:7000-9000 (C.D 6500)
£2800 $4340 €4200 Watching the ducks from the bridge (25x35cm-10x14in) W/C. 30-Sep-2 Bonhams, Ipswich #343/R est:2000-3000
£2900 $4698 €4350 Home at last (35x25cm-14x10in) s. W/C. 21-May-3 Bonhams, Knightsbridge #133/R est:1500-2000
£3000 $4950 €4350 Collecting summer flowers (34x51cm-13x20in) s. pencil W/C htd white. 3-Jul-3 Christie's, Kensington #68/R est:3000-5000
£3100 $4805 €4650 Feeding the ducks (33x23cm-13x9in) i.verso W/C. 30-Sep-2 Bonhams, Ipswich #345/R est:1500-2000
£3200 $5216 €4800 Shepherd's cottage, near Eastbourne, Berkshire (36x51cm-14x20in) s. i.verso W/C. 29-Jan-3 Sotheby's, Olympia #143/R est:3000-5000
£3200 $5216 €4800 Duck pond (34x52cm-13x20in) s. W/C. 29-Jan-3 Sotheby's, Olympia #144/R est:3000-5000
£3300 $5115 €4950 Children by a stream (24x35cm-9x14in) s. W/C. 30-Sep-2 Bonhams, Ipswich #342/R est:2000-3000
£3300 $5379 €4785 Home farm, Pulloxhill, near Amphill, Bedfordshire (67x99cm-26x39in) s. W/C. 21-Jul-3 Bonhams, Bath #12/R est:1800-2200
£3600 $5616 €5400 Cottage in Devon with a country lass feeding her kitten (36x53cm-14x21in) s. bears i.verso W/C. 5-Nov-2 Bonhams, New Bond Street #167/R est:2000-3000
£4800 $7488 €7200 Country cottage near Bedfordshire with ducks. Bedfordshire cottage with chickens feeding (36x26cm-14x10in) s. pencil W/C htd white pair. 27-Mar-3 Christie's, Kensington #128/R est:3000-5000
£6000 $9240 €9000 Hay making near Wantage (49x75cm-19x30in) s. W/C lit. 23-Oct-2 Hamptons Fine Art, Godalming #109 est:6000-8000

STANNARD, Henry Sylvester (attrib) (1870-1951) British
Works on paper
£2000 $3100 €3000 Rural scene with roadway through village (36x63cm-14x25in) bears sig. W/C. 1-Nov-2 Moore Allen & Innocent, Cirencester #218 est:2000-2500

STANNARD, Joseph (1797-1830) British
£1300 $2132 €1950 Valley of the Yare, Thorpe (16x30cm-6x12in) panel prov.lit. 29-May-3 Christie's, Kensington #78/R est:1000-1200
£1700 $2788 €2550 Valley of the Yare, Thorpe (15x25cm-6x10in) paper on panel prov.lit. 29-May-3 Christie's, Kensington #79/R est:1000-1200

STANNARD, Lilian (1877-1944) British
Works on paper
£380 $604 €570 Cottage garden (10x16cm-4x6in) s. W/C. 18-Mar-3 Sworder & Son, Bishops Stortford #441/R
£420 $672 €630 Garden with colorful flower border (17x24cm-7x9in) s.d.1923 W/C. 11-Mar-3 David Duggleby, Scarborough #146/R
£700 $1148 €1050 Garden at Great Lizagard, Exeter (33x23cm-13x9in) s. W/C. 5-Feb-3 Goldings, Lincolnshire #229
£1200 $1944 €1800 Rose covered trellis in a summer garden (25x34cm-10x13in) s. pencil W/C htd white. 23-Jan-3 Christie's, Kensington #305/R est:1500-2500
£1700 $2652 €2550 Garden path (18x25cm-7x10in) s. W/C. 17-Oct-2 David Lay, Penzance #1149/R est:500-600
£3600 $5832 €5400 An autumnal pathway (17x25cm-7x10in) s. W/C. 21-May-3 Bonhams, Knightsbridge #148/R est:1400-3000
£4200 $6720 €6300 Doves in a cottage garden (36x51cm-14x20in) s. W/C bodycol. 11-Mar-3 Bonhams, New Bond Street #103/R est:3500-5000

STANNARD, T S (1898-1947) British
Works on paper
£560 $868 €840 Stream in woodland glade (25x20cm-10x8in) s. W/C. 6-Dec-2 Chrystals Auctions, Isle of Man #254q

STANNARD, Theresa Sylvester (1898-1947) British
£480 $782 €720 Children before a cottage (8x15cm-3x6in) s. 12-Feb-3 Andrew Hartley, Ilkley #851

Works on paper
£600 $924 €900 Garden of sunshine (34x24cm-13x9in) s. W/C. 23-Oct-2 Hamptons Fine Art, Godalming #95/R
£780 $1217 €1170 Cottage garden scene with well and a bird eating in the garden (36x25cm-14x10in) s. i.verso. 10-Apr-3 Brightwells, Leominster #932/R
£800 $1232 €1200 Country cottage (18x26cm-7x10in) s. W/C. 23-Oct-2 Hamptons Fine Art, Godalming #96/R
£800 $1320 €1160 Cottage (34x24cm-13x9in) s. pencil W/C bodycol. 3-Jul-3 Christie's, Kensington #62/R
£1200 $1848 €1800 Cat on a cottage path (36x25cm-14x10in) s. W/C. 23-Oct-2 Hamptons Fine Art, Godalming #94/R est:1000-1500
£1300 $2145 €1885 Cottage near Newbury, Berkshire (34x24cm-13x9in) s. pencil W/C htd bodycol. 3-Jul-3 Christie's, Kensington #65/R est:800-1200
£1500 $2400 €2250 Near Henley, Oxfordshire (36x25cm-14x10in) s. W/C. 11-Mar-3 Bonhams, New Bond Street #107/R est:1500-2000

STANOWSKY, Mikael (1883-1935) Finnish
£252 $387 €400 Coastal breakers (31x64cm-12x25in) s.d.16. 27-Oct-2 Bukowskis, Helsinki #289/R
£424 $662 €670 Moonlight (101x66cm-40x26in) s.d.1911. 15-Sep-2 Bukowskis, Helsinki #292/R
£582 $908 €920 Ocean (67x94cm-26x37in) s. 12-Sep-2 Hagelstam, Helsinki #968
£949 $1500 €1500 Vessels at the home harbour (54x78cm-21x31in) s. 1-Dec-2 Bukowskis, Helsinki #189/R est:1500-1800

STANSFIELD, John Heber (1878-1953) American
£754 $1100 €1131 Western mountain range (34x46cm-13x18in) s. board. 10-May-2 Skinner, Boston #132/R

STANTON ADKINS, J (19th C) British
Works on paper
£400 $636 €600 Natural arch at Dixcart Bay, Sark (21x27cm-8x11in) s.d.1888 W/C. 20-Mar-3 Martel Maides, Guernsey #66/R

STANTON, A P (?) British
£340 $541 €510 Lake district scene with cattle watering (46x76cm-18x30in) s. 18-Mar-3 Capes Dunn, Manchester #551a

STANTON, Clark (1832-1894) British
£400 $648 €600 Connoisseur (79x51cm-31x20in) s. 23-Jan-3 Christie's, Kensington #115
Works on paper
£1250 $2050 €1875 In the hayfield (34x24cm-13x9in) s.verso W/C. 4-Feb-3 Sworder & Son, Bishops Stortford #133/R est:950-1250

STANTON, Louis Parsons (20th C) American
£613 $950 €920 Ghost hotel (46x30cm-18x12in) s.d. board. 8-Dec-2 Toomey, Oak Park #836/R

STANTON, Samuel Ward (1870-1912) American
Works on paper
£286 $450 €429 Chicago excursion boat Christopher Columbus (23x48cm-9x19in) s. 26-Jul-2 Eldred, East Dennis #244/R
£350 $550 €525 Steamboat Chas MacAlester (13x25cm-5x10in) s. 26-Jul-2 Eldred, East Dennis #243/R

STANZANI, Emilio (1906-1977) Swiss
£287 $448 €431 Three racing cyclists (37x36cm-15x14in) mono. board. 16-Sep-2 Philippe Schuler, Zurich #6653 (S.FR 660)
£352 $515 €528 Relief in gold (41x49cm-16x19in) s. tempera gold spray paper on board. 17-Jun-2 Philippe Schuler, Zurich #4223/R (S.FR 800)
£655 $1028 €983 Composition on red (68x95cm-27x37in) mono. panel. 25-Nov-2 Sotheby's, Zurich #159/R (S.FR 1500)
Sculpture
£1174 $1831 €1761 Untitled (152cm-60in) mono. gold pat.bronze. 16-Sep-2 Philippe Schuler, Zurich #3254/R est:2800-3500 (S.FR 2700)
£1454 $2122 €2181 Horse (37x25x11cm-15x10x4in) mono. grey brown pat.bronze Cast.Erotal lit. 17-Jun-2 Philippe Schuler, Zurich #4249b/R est:2000-3000 (S.FR 3300)

STANZIONE, Massimo (1585-1656) Italian
Works on paper
£443 $700 €700 Bethlehem child murders (10x14cm-4x6in) pen double-sided. 29-Nov-2 Bassenge, Berlin #5518/R

STAPLES, Owen (1866-1949) British
£412 $638 €618 Birch cliff (55x37cm-22x15in) s.i. 3-Dec-2 Joyner, Toronto #326/R est:1000-1500 (C.D 1000)
Works on paper
£348 $540 €522 Toronto harbour (23x31cm-9x12in) s.d.1918 W/C over pencil. 24-Sep-2 Ritchie, Toronto #3094a/R (C.D 850)

STAPLES, Sir Robert Ponsonby (1853-1943) British
Works on paper
£550 $803 €825 Summer (25x36cm-10x14in) s.d.1919 W/C. 12-Jun-2 John Ross, Belfast #279
£2800 $4424 €4200 Earl's Court (25x18cm-10x7in) i. W/C bodycol. 2-Dec-2 Sotheby's, London #11/R est:3000-5000

STAPPERS, Julien (1875-1960) Belgian
£411 $642 €650 Bouquet de fleurs dans un vase (45x57cm-18x22in) s. 10-Sep-2 Vanderkindere, Brussels #378
£500 $790 €750 Still life of roses in a vase and a pot (61x51cm-24x20in) s. 2-Dec-2 Gorringes, Lewes #2574/R
£605 $944 €950 Coupe en porcelaine de Bruxelles fleurie (60x51cm-24x20in) s. 11-Nov-2 Horta, Bruxelles #585
£755 $1177 €1200 Still life with flowers (64x74cm-25x29in) s. 23-Sep-2 Bernaerts, Antwerp #116/R
£769 $1208 €1200 Still life with flowers (60x50cm-24x20in) s. 16-Dec-2 Bernaerts, Antwerp #314/R
£1007 $1612 €1400 Vase de lilas (100x80cm-39x31in) s. 13-May-3 Vanderkindere, Brussels #133
£1295 $2072 €1800 Le jardin fleuri (38x50cm-15x20in) s. panel. 13-May-3 Palais de Beaux Arts, Brussels #312/R est:1800-2400
£1367 $2187 €1900 Vase fleuri d'anemones (50x60cm-20x24in) s. 19-May-3 Horta, Bruxelles #482 est:600-800
£1700 $2652 €2550 Still life of Dahlias (60x80cm-24x31in) s. 17-Sep-2 Sotheby's, Olympia #260/R est:800-1200
£2000 $3120 €3000 Still life of anemones (50x60cm-20x24in) s. 17-Sep-2 Sotheby's, Olympia #261/R est:600-800

STARBUCK, Ellen (19/20th C) American
£1210 $1900 €1815 Yellow hedge and children at Mystic, CT (36x31cm-14x12in) s. board. 22-Nov-2 Skinner, Boston #217/R est:300-500

STARCK, Jules (?) Belgian
£6164 $9678 €9000 Scene orientaliste au les moissons (67x80cm-26x31in) s. 15-Apr-3 Galerie Moderne, Brussels #384/R est:8000-10000

STARCK, Julien Josephus Gaspard (1814-1888) Belgian
£1793 $2869 €2600 Deux jeunes filles se protegeant de la pluie (70x56cm-28x22in) s. 17-Mar-3 Horta, Bruxelles #145/R est:3500-4500
£3000 $4980 €3000 La fuite en Egypte (48x82cm-19x32in) s.d.1876. 16-Jun-3 Horta, Bruxelles #189/R est:3000-4000
£3500 $5460 €5250 News of the capture of Constantinople (19x24cm-7x9in) s. panel. 15-Oct-2 Sotheby's, London #84/R est:4000-6000
£5096 $7949 €8000 Jeune Orientale filant du coton (43x35cm-17x14in) s. panel. 11-Nov-2 Horta, Bruxelles #129/R est:8000-10000
£8654 $13587 €13500 L'ecrivain public au cafe turc (30x48cm-12x19in) s. panel. 16-Dec-2 Gros & Delettrez, Paris #259/R est:10000-12000
£11538 $17885 €18000 Lecture au Harem (86x71cm-34x28in) s. 9-Dec-2 Horta, Bruxelles #114/R est:22000-30000

STARITA, Lorenzo (style) (1842-?) Italian
£5793 $9500 €8400 Play time (79x114cm-31x45in) indis sig.d.1888. 4-Jun-3 Doyle, New York #88/R est:4000-6000

STARITSKY, Anna (1908-1981) French
Works on paper
£641 $1006 €1000 Untitled (105x75cm-41x30in) s. W/C Chinese ink. 24-Nov-2 Laurence Calmels, Paris #276/R
£769 $1208 €1200 Untitled (109x74cm-43x29in) s.d.62 W/C Chinese ink. 24-Nov-2 Laurence Calmels, Paris #275/R

STARK, Arthur James (1831-1902) British
£950 $1473 €1425 Road to the farm (31x49cm-12x19in) prov. 30-Sep-2 Bonhams, Ipswich #447/R
£1200 $1896 €1800 Horse by a stale (18x23cm-7x9in) s. panel. 28-Nov-2 Bonhams, Knightsbridge #102/R est:800-1200
£2100 $3255 €3150 Milking time (43x61cm-17x24in) s. 30-Sep-2 Bonhams, Ipswich #493/R est:1500-2500

STARK, Bruno (1894-1979) German
Works on paper
£577 $894 €900 Holy Family (24x17cm-9x7in) s.d.66 s.i.d. verso pastel. 6-Dec-2 Karlheinz Kaupp, Staufen #2313/R
£690 $1090 €1000 Matmata - desert city, southern Tunisia (20x25cm-8x10in) s.d.1962 s.i.d. verso pastel exhib. 2-Apr-3 Dr Fritz Nagel, Stuttgart #9237/R

STARK, Jack Gage (1882-1950) American
£1667 $2600 €2501 Impressionist landscape (20x25cm-8x10in) s. panel. 29-Mar-3 Charlton Hall, Columbia #645/R est:1000-1500

STARK, James (1794-1859) British
£2500 $4100 €3750 Faggot gatherers by a stream (46x63cm-18x25in) panel prov. 29-May-3 Christie's, Kensington #81/R est:3000-5000
£12000 $19080 €18000 View of Fritton Decoy (40x56cm-16x22in) panel. 19-Mar-3 Sotheby's, London #69/R est:12000-18000
Works on paper
£600 $990 €870 An overgrown farmstead (20x30cm-8x12in) W/C. 1-Jul-3 Bonhams, Norwich #73/R

STARK, James (attrib) (1794-1859) British
£700 $1113 €1050 Edge of the wood (39x49cm-15x19in) prov. 6-Mar-3 Christie's, Kensington #391/R
£1400 $2198 €2100 Norfolk river landscape with figure on wooden bridge by watermill (48x74cm-19x29in) 13-Dec-2 Keys, Aylsham #644 est:750-1000
£1800 $2952 €2700 Travellers on a wooded track (36x46cm-14x18in) 29-May-3 Christie's, Kensington #84/R est:1000-1500

STARK, Karl (1921-) Austrian
£1899 $3000 €3000 Flowers (63x46cm-25x18in) s.d.1976 gouache. 27-Nov-2 Dorotheum, Vienna #212/R est:2000-2800
£2878 $4719 €4000 Still life with flower vase on blue cloth (69x49cm-27x19in) s.d.1994 board. 5-Jun-3 Dorotheum, Salzburg #549/R est:3000-4000
£4114 $6500 €6500 Landscape beneath cloudy skies (35x45cm-14x18in) s.d.81 masonite. 27-Nov-2 Dorotheum, Vienna #213/R est:3200-4500
£4487 $7045 €7000 Windy day in autumn (69x100cm-27x39in) s. board prov. 21-Nov-2 Dorotheum, Vienna #315/R est:7200-10000
£4676 $7669 €6500 Landscape with trees (71x79cm-28x31in) s.d.63 prov. 5-Jun-3 Dorotheum, Salzburg #565/R est:6000-7500

STARK, Melville F (1904-1987) American
£2373 $3750 €3560 Shrimp boat, Cortez (61x76cm-24x30in) s.i.verso masonite. 17-Nov-2 Jeffery Burchard, Florida #51/R
£2564 $4000 €3846 Old springhouse, Helfrick Springs Pond (64x76cm-25x30in) s. i.verso board. 18-Sep-2 Alderfer's, Hatfield #364/R est:1500-2000
£2885 $4500 €4328 Landscape with creek and buildings. Winter landscape (41x51cm-16x20in) s.d.31 board double-sided. 18-Sep-2 Alderfer's, Hatfield #353/R est:1500-2000

STARK, Otto (1859-1926) American
£2581 $4000 €3872 Portrait of H Liebhart (71x56cm-28x22in) s.d.1912. 8-Dec-2 Toomey, Oak Park #737/R est:6000-8000
Works on paper
£671 $1100 €973 River bend (37x49cm-15x19in) s. W/C paper on card stock. 5-Jun-3 Swann Galleries, New York #236/R

STARKER, Erwin (1872-1938) German
£503 $785 €800 Bathers near Unterturkheim (46x60cm-18x24in) s. 19-Sep-2 Dr Fritz Nagel, Stuttgart #1004/R

STARKWEATHER, William Edward (1879-1969) American
£769 $1200 €1154 Ship's carpenter (102x76cm-40x30in) s.i.verso painted c.1939. 28-Mar-3 Eldred, East Dennis #701/R

STARN TWINS (1961-) American
Sculpture
£2278 $3600 €3417 Gut epoch (67x67x13cm-26x26x5in) photo transparencies in a plexiglas lightbox executed 1990-94. 12-Nov-2 Phillips, New York #247/R est:3000-4000

STARNINA, Gherardo (1354-1413) Italian
£854430 $1350000 €1350000 Madonna and Child with angels and saints (95x46cm-37x18in) tempera gold board prov.lit. 29-Nov-2 Semenzato, Venice #408/R

STARR, Sidney (1857-1925) American/British
£760 $1254 €1102 Connoisseur (75x50cm-30x20in) s.d.82. 1-Jul-3 Bearnes, Exeter #520/R
Works on paper
£8000 $12640 €12000 Carriage ride (30x25cm-12x10in) s. chl gouache chk. 3-Apr-3 Christie's, Kensington #51/R

STARRETT, Emma F (20th C) American
£443 $700 €665 Oriental woman next to vase and Buddha idol (89x79cm-35x31in) s.d.1936. 17-Nov-2 Jeffery Burchard, Florida #55/R
£443 $700 €665 Portrait of a Latino woman (69x51cm-27x20in) s.d.1936. 17-Nov-2 Jeffery Burchard, Florida #55a/R

STARREVELD, Pieter (1911-1989) Dutch?
Works on paper
£2414 $3837 €3500 Female nudes. s. gouache set of seven various sizes. 10-Mar-3 Sotheby's, Amsterdam #386/R est:1000-1500

STASESON, Joan Hall (20th C) Canadian
£244 $401 €354 Lilacs (15x15cm-6x6in) s.d. 9-Jun-3 Hodgins, Calgary #70/R (C.D 550)

STASIO, Stefano di (1948-) Italian
£2817 $4676 €4000 Armonie della sera II (85x68cm-33x27in) s.i.d.1986 verso prov. 10-Jun-3 Finarte Semenzato, Milan #364/R est:3800-4500

STASSEN, Franz (1869-?) German
£966 $1535 €1400 Maria with child in paradise garden (50x50cm-20x20in) mono. panel. 8-Mar-3 Arnold, Frankfurt #723/R

STAUB, Josef (1931-) Swiss
Sculpture
£1485 $2168 €2228 Roll (60x68x18cm-24x27x7in) s. painted chrome. 4-Jun-2 Germann, Zurich #90/R est:2000-3000 (S.FR 3400)

STAUDACHER, Hans (1923-) Swiss
£962 $1519 €1500 Untitled (43x61cm-17x24in) s.d.94 mixed media. 12-Nov-2 Dorotheum, Vienna #298/R est:1700-2400
£1090 $1689 €1700 Untitled (50x70cm-20x28in) s.d.1989 oil W/C oil chk Indian ink board. 7-Dec-2 Ketterer, Hamburg #723/R est:1000-1200
£1218 $1924 €1900 Untitled (64x48cm-25x19in) s.d.1980 pen brush Indian ink W/C. 12-Nov-2 Dorotheum, Vienna #248/R est:1800-2600
£2553 $4136 €3600 Head (34x29cm-13x11in) s.d.54 i. stretcher masonite. 20-May-3 Dorotheum, Vienna #200/R est:3200-4500
£2621 $4193 €3800 Untitled (69x50cm-27x20in) s. 11-Mar-3 Dorotheum, Vienna #258/R est:4000-5500
£4747 $7358 €7500 Untitled (100x110cm-39x43in) s.d.1988. 24-Sep-2 Wiener Kunst Auktionen, Vienna #226/R est:7500-12000
£5208 $8229 €7500 Untitled (66x39cm-26x15in) s. d.59 verso masonite. 24-Apr-3 Dorotheum, Vienna #164/R est:6000-8000
£5674 $9191 €8000 Untitled (54x63cm-21x25in) s.d.54 s.d. verso masonite prov. 20-May-3 Dorotheum, Vienna #204/R est:8000-10000
£5960 $9715 €9000 ABC (150x150cm-59x59in) s.i.d.1964 acrylic. 28-Jan-3 Dorotheum, Vienna #184/R est:9000-13000
£7051 $10929 €11000 Untitled (150x150cm-59x59in) s.d.86 s.i.d.1986 verso. 7-Dec-2 Van Ham, Cologne #519/R est:13000
£7801 $12638 €11000 Untitled (62x50cm-24x20in) s.d.55 s.d. verso masonite. 20-May-3 Dorotheum, Vienna #205/R est:6500-9500
£9420 $15449 €13000 Spuren III (100x100cm-39x39in) d.64 s.d.1964 verso. 27-May-3 Wiener Kunst Auktionen, Vienna #185/R est:12000-18000
Works on paper
£545 $845 €850 Untitled (47x67cm-19x26in) s.d.1976 Indian ink brush W/C oil chk bodycol board. 7-Dec-2 Ketterer, Hamburg #729/R
£570 $883 €900 Untitled (48x65cm-19x26in) s.d.1985 Indian ink W/c. 28-Sep-2 Ketterer, Hamburg #620/R
£596 $972 €900 O JA (32x24cm-13x9in) s.d.70 mixed media. 28-Jan-3 Dorotheum, Vienna #250/R
£629 $1025 €950 Untitled (35x25cm-14x10in) s.d.81 mixed media. 28-Jan-3 Dorotheum, Vienna #267/R
£633 $981 €1000 Untitled (48x64cm-19x25in) s.d.1961 Indian ink W/C. 28-Sep-2 Ketterer, Hamburg #619/R
£633 $981 €1000 Untitled (48x64cm-19x25in) s. Indian ink w/C oil chk. 28-Sep-2 Ketterer, Hamburg #621/R
£641 $1013 €1000 Untitled (29x21cm-11x8in) s.d.1978 mixed media. 18-Nov-2 Dorotheum, Linz #455/R
£641 $994 €1000 Untitled (48x64cm-19x25in) s.d.1978 gouache Indian ink oil chk. 7-Dec-2 Ketterer, Hamburg #724/R
£662 $1079 €1000 Good writing (21x20cm-8x8in) s.d.1992 mixed media. 28-Jan-3 Dorotheum, Vienna #302/R
£662 $1079 €1000 Untitled (22x30cm-9x12in) s.d.1992 mixed media. 28-Jan-3 Dorotheum, Vienna #306/R
£705 $1114 €1100 Untitled (30x22cm-12x9in) s. mixed media. 18-Nov-2 Dorotheum, Linz #456/R
£759 $1177 €1200 Untitled (24x32cm-9x13in) s.i.d.1993 Indian ink gouache. 28-Sep-2 Ketterer, Hamburg #622/R
£759 $1214 €1100 Untitled (32x24cm-13x9in) s.d.1963 mixed media. 11-Mar-3 Dorotheum, Vienna #173/R
£903 $1426 €1300 Untitled (64x48cm-25x19in) s.d.94 Indian ink W/C. 24-Apr-3 Dorotheum, Vienna #273/R
£966 $1545 €1400 Untitled (23x32cm-9x13in) s.d.64 mixed media. 11-Mar-3 Dorotheum, Vienna #175/R est:1200-1600
£972 $1536 €1400 Two hearts (64x48cm-25x19in) s.i.d.74 Indian ink w/C. 24-Apr-3 Dorotheum, Vienna #219/R
£1013 $1570 €1600 Landscape (24x32cm-9x13in) s.i.d.1969 mixed media. 24-Sep-2 Wiener Kunst Auktionen, Vienna #215/R est:1000-2500
£1090 $1722 €1700 Untitled (42x54cm-17x21in) s.d.94 mixed media. 18-Nov-2 Dorotheum, Linz #457 est:2400-2600

£1103 $1766 €1600 Untitled (21x29cm-8x11in) s.d.1993 mixed media. 11-Mar-3 Dorotheum, Vienna #280/R est:900-1200
£1250 $1975 €1800 Untitled (48x32cm-19x13in) s.d.1967 mixed media. 24-Apr-3 Dorotheum, Vienna #172/R est:1900-2200
£1392 $2158 €2200 All left (48x64cm-19x25in) s.i.d.64 mixed media. 24-Sep-2 Wiener Kunst Auktionen, Vienna #214/R est:2000-3500
£1392 $2172 €2200 At the lido (28x40cm-11x16in) s.i.d.1950 Indian ink. 15-Oct-2 Dorotheum, Vienna #140/R est:1200-1500
£1418 $2298 €2000 Untitled (52x37cm-20x15in) s. pen Indian ink w/C. 20-May-3 Dorotheum, Vienna #220/R est:2400-3400
£1772 $2800 €2800 So or so (47x63cm-19x25in) s.i.d.1959 mixed media exhib. 27-Nov-2 Dorotheum, Vienna #238/R est:2800-3400
£1923 $2981 €3000 Untitled (56x42cm-22x17in) s. Indian ink W/C. 7-Dec-2 Ketterer, Hamburg #728/R est:1500-1700
£2025 $3200 €3200 Composition (47x64cm-19x25in) s.i.d.63 pen brush Indian ink oil chk w/C. 27-Nov-2 Dorotheum, Vienna #279/R est:2400-3200
£2215 $3434 €3500 Seven stamp poetry II (73x52cm-29x20in) s.d.61 mixed media stamps. 24-Sep-2 Wiener Kunst Auktionen, Vienna #256/R est:2500-4000
£2405 $3800 €3800 Untitled (43x63cm-17x25in) s.d.55 mixed media. 27-Nov-2 Dorotheum, Vienna #229/R est:2600-3400
£2431 $3865 €3500 Parisian colour trial (62x48cm-24x19in) s.i.d.1957 mixed media. 29-Apr-3 Wiener Kunst Auktionen, Vienna #477/R est:3500-5000
£2759 $4414 €4000 Moi de l'agonie (70x50cm-28x20in) s.d.59 mixed media. 11-Mar-3 Dorotheum, Vienna #144/R est:1600-2200
£6383 $10340 €9000 Traces on the road to (113x51cm-44x20in) s.i. panel metal textile oil prov. 20-May-3 Dorotheum, Vienna #199/R est:9000-12000

STAUDACHER, Vitus (1850-1925) German
£603 $940 €880 Figures by cross in town (28x20cm-11x8in) s.d. board. 11-Apr-3 Winterberg, Heidelberg #577
£1497 $2380 €2200 Village street with water trough (27x18cm-11x7in) s.d.1897 panel pair. 19-Mar-3 Neumeister, Munich #749/R est:2200

STAUDER, Jacob Carl (attrib) (1694-1756) Swiss
£437 $690 €656 Anna explaining the Holy Script to her daughter Maria (54x49cm-21x19in) 14-Nov-2 Stuker, Bern #535 (S.FR 1000)

STAUFFER, Bodo (1942-1993) Swiss
£1135 $1771 €1703 Near Heimiswil (80x100cm-31x39in) s.d.89. 8-Nov-2 Dobiaschofsky, Bern #223/R est:2500 (S.FR 2600)

STAUFFER, Fred (1892-1980) Swiss
£437 $681 €656 Autumn bouquet (99x84cm-39x33in) s.d.35 i. stretcher. 6-Nov-2 Dobiaschofsky, Bern #982/R (S.FR 1000)
£742 $1158 €1113 Interior II (89x65cm-35x26in) s.d.38 i. verso. 6-Nov-2 Dobiaschofsky, Bern #985/R (S.FR 1700)
£786 $1226 €1179 Field landscape in summer (39x79cm-15x31in) s.d.72 panel. 8-Nov-2 Dobiaschofsky, Bern #135/R (S.FR 1800)
£1223 $1907 €1835 Bunch of flowers in vase in the garden (70x89cm-28x35in) s.d.42. 8-Nov-2 Dobiaschofsky, Bern #143/R est:3800 (S.FR 2800)
£1354 $2112 €2031 Wood carrier in Lauenen (61x75cm-24x30in) s.d.65 panel. 8-Nov-2 Dobiaschofsky, Bern #142/R est:2800 (S.FR 3100)
£1965 $3066 €2948 Summer landscape near Crissier (69x97cm-27x38in) s.d.1979 panel. 8-Nov-2 Dobiaschofsky, Bern #137/R est:6000 (S.FR 4500)

Works on paper
£278 $447 €417 Figures on jetty (45x33cm-18x13in) s. gouache. 7-May-3 Dobiaschofsky, Bern #3621 (S.FR 600)
£306 $477 €459 Market place with people on summer afternoon (35x39cm-14x15in) s. bodycol. 6-Nov-2 Dobiaschofsky, Bern #983/R (S.FR 700)

STAUFFER-BERN, Karl (1857-1891) Swiss

Works on paper
£3241 $5218 €4699 Self portrait with glasses (37x31cm-15x12in) s.d.84 chl dr. 9-May-3 Dobiaschofsky, Bern #65/R est:5500 (S.FR 7000)

STAVELEY, William (attrib) (fl.1785-1805) British
£500 $780 €750 Portrait of Diana Stuart, Lady Milner (73x61cm-29x24in) oval. 17-Sep-2 Sotheby's, Olympia #91/R

STAVEREN, Jan van (1625-1668) Dutch
£2535 $4082 €3600 Rat on bricks (29x22cm-11x9in) s.d.1650 panel. 7-May-3 Vendue Huis, Gravenhage #321/R est:2000-3000

STAVEREN, Jan van (attrib) (1625-1668) Dutch
£338 $527 €500 St Hieronymous in the hermitage (14x18cm-6x7in) copper. 26-Mar-3 Hugo Ruef, Munich #16

STAVERNUS, Petrus (1634-1654) Dutch
£12000 $18840 €18000 Old woman drinking from a wine glass (76x62cm-30x24in) s. 12-Dec-2 Sotheby's, London #33/R est:12000-18000

STAVRIANOS, Wendy (1941-) Australian
£1600 $2576 €2400 Boat of rose and Thorn (175x350cm-69x138in) s.i.d.86 oil mixed media diptych. 6-May-3 Christie's, Melbourne #319/R est:4000-5000 (A.D 4000)

STAVROWSKY, Oleg (1927-) American
£2130 $3450 €3089 Grim discovery (61x91cm-24x36in) 23-May-3 Altermann Galleries, Santa Fe #139
£2671 $3900 €4007 As I git older this gits heavier (76x61cm-30x24in) 18-May-2 Altermann Galleries, Santa Fe #114/R
£4259 $6900 €6176 Outfit (51x76cm-20x30in) 23-May-3 Altermann Galleries, Santa Fe #136
£5380 $8500 €7801 Lead, follow or get out of the way (86x244cm-34x96in) s. 26-Jul-3 Coeur d'Alene, Hayden #220/R est:25000-45000

STAZEWSKI, Henryk (1894-?) Polish
£8013 $12660 €12500 Abstract composition (46x50cm-18x20in) s. verso prov. 14-Nov-2 Neumeister, Munich #691/R est:12500-15000

STEAD, Fred (1863-1940) British
£1200 $1884 €1800 Landscape with a figure in a horse-drawn cart by a river, possibly at Arnside (31x41cm-12x16in) s. 21-Nov-2 Tennants, Leyburn #813 est:400-600

STEARNS, Junius Brutus (1810-1885) American
£164557 $260000 €238608 Washington and the Indians or Washington in the Indian council (91x127cm-36x50in) s.d.1847 prov.exhib.lit. 26-Jul-3 Coeur d'Alene, Hayden #120/R est:75000-150000

STEBBINGS, J H (?) ?
£352 $550 €528 Rocky coastal scene (25x38cm-10x15in) s. 1-Aug-2 Eldred, East Dennis #937f

STECHOW, Gertrud (1858-?) German
£755 $1177 €1200 Summer landscape with farmstead in Mecklenburg (46x64cm-18x25in) s. board. 21-Sep-2 Bolland & Marotz, Bremen #564/R

STEDING, Konny (20th C) ?
£265 $432 €400 Personnages inverses (100x160cm-39x63in) s.d.2002 verso. 31-Jan-3 Charbonneaux, Paris #162/R

STEEL, George Hammond (1900-1960) British
£380 $635 €551 Still life of flowers in a cream vase (19x14cm-7x6in) s. board. 25-Jun-3 Cheffins, Cambridge #827/R
£380 $635 €551 Still life of cream and red roses in a blue jug (22x17cm-9x7in) s. board. 25-Jun-3 Cheffins, Cambridge #828/R

STEEL, John Sydney (1863-?) British
£520 $837 €780 Winter on the banks of the river (24x32cm-9x13in) s. board. 14-Jan-3 Bonhams, Knightsbridge #5/R
£578 $959 €838 Arabs watering horses in the desert (38x48cm-15x19in) s. 16-Jun-3 Waddingtons, Toronto #204/R est:1500-2000 (C.D 1300)

STEEL, Kenneth (1906-1973) British

Works on paper
£250 $388 €375 London (34x43cm-13x17in) s.i. pencil W/C htd white exhib. 26-Sep-2 Mellors & Kirk, Nottingham #625

STEELE, Christopher (c.1730-1767) British
£3400 $5610 €4930 Portrait of Anne Mawdesley (87x69cm-34x27in) 2-Jul-3 Sotheby's, Olympia #55/R est:2000-3000

STEELE, Christopher (attrib) (c.1730-1767) British
£5000 $7900 €7500 Portrait of Alderman William Oeareth and his wife Anne Jennens (74x61cm-29x24in) painted oval pair prov. 28-Nov-2 Sotheby's, London #155/R est:4000-6000

STEELE, E (19/20th C) British
£822 $1200 €1233 Still life of apples and grapes. s. 3-Nov-1 North East Auctions, Portsmouth #251/R

STEELE, Edwin (19th C) British
£300 $456 €450 Still life of dark red roses on a bank (30x48cm-12x19in) s. 16-Aug-2 Keys, Aylsham #625
£300 $429 €450 Still life with Primroses, dog roses and other flowers (38x27cm-15x11in) s. board. 11-Apr-2 Mellors & Kirk, Nottingham #566
£360 $562 €540 Still life study of assorted fruit. 2-Aug-2 Biddle & Webb, Birmingham #405

£440 $686 €660 Still life, basket of grapes and peaches with further fruit (34x49cm-13x19in) s. 17-Sep-2 Bonhams, Oxford #42

STEELINK, Willem (1826-1913) Dutch
£600 $948 €900 Sheep pool (11x17cm-4x7in) s. board. 7-Apr-3 Bonhams, Bath #112/R
Works on paper
£1200 $1872 €1800 Sheep drinking from a pool (28x52cm-11x20in) s. W/C. 17-Sep-2 Sotheby's, Olympia #222a/R est:800-1200

STEELL, David George (1856-1930) British
£400 $632 €600 Clockwork (44cm-17in circular) s.i.d.1905. 19-Dec-2 Bonhams, Edinburgh #319
£1900 $2888 €2850 Near Callander (36x51cm-14x20in) s.d.1877 s.d.verso board. 28-Aug-2 Sotheby's, London #887/R est:1500-2500
£2761 $4500 €4142 Spot (29x27cm-11x11in) s.d.1882 b,. 11-Feb-3 Bonhams & Doyles, New York #166/R est:1800-2500

STEELL, Gourlay (1819-1894) British
£1282 $2000 €1923 Ratting terrier (58x69cm-23x27in) s. 12-Oct-2 Neal Auction Company, New Orleans #33/R est:3000-5000
£1687 $2750 €2531 Nettle, recumbent Jack Russell terrier (33x36cm-13x14in) s.d.1882 board prov. 11-Feb-3 Bonhams & Doyles, New York #108/R est:2000-3000
£2000 $3120 €3000 Day of rest (70x90cm-28x35in) s. i.verso arched top. 26-Mar-3 Sotheby's, Olympia #166/R est:2000-3000
£6800 $10948 €10200 Moroccan goat herd (38x51cm-15x20in) indis.sig. prov. 20-Feb-3 Christie's, London #289/R est:6000
£11321 $18000 €16982 Bay stallion outside a stable (102x128cm-40x50in) s.d.1845. 30-Apr-3 Sotheby's, New York #562/R est:10000-15000
Works on paper
£1000 $1660 €1450 Mite, a terrier (16x15cm-6x6in) s.i. pencil W/C htd white. 12-Jun-3 Christie's, Kensington #241/R est:1000-1500

STEELL, Sir John Robert (1804-1891) British
Sculpture
£8200 $12710 €12300 Bust of Queen Victoria (56cm-22in) s. white marble exec.c.1840. 29-Oct-2 Bonhams, New Bond Street #183/R est:2500-3000

STEEN, Erling (1945-) Danish
£394 $630 €591 Si Parva Licet Componere Magnis (60x50cm-24x20in) s.d.1979. 13-Jan-3 Rasmussen, Vejle #277/R (D.KR 4500)

STEEN, Jan (c.1626-1679) Dutch
£7051 $10929 €11000 Peasants playing backgammon in tavern (42x52cm-17x20in) 5-Dec-2 Dr Fritz Nagel, Stuttgart #630/R est:4500
£10692 $16679 €17000 Peasant wedding (56x72cm-22x28in) s. lit. 20-Sep-2 Schloss Ahlden, Ahlden #1060/R est:16500
£35000 $54950 €52500 Old woman singing and holding a beer jug (22x17cm-9x7in) panel oval prov. 12-Dec-2 Sotheby's, London #34/R est:10000-15000
£36000 $56520 €54000 Saint John the Baptist preaching in the wilderness (79x77cm-31x30in) panel prov.lit. 11-Dec-2 Christie's, London #65/R est:40000-60000
£42000 $70140 €60900 May Dance (55x44cm-22x17in) s. indis.d.1647 prov.lit. 10-Jul-3 Sotheby's, London #127/R est:20000-30000
£95000 $158650 €137750 De duiventil, an allegory of love (65x81cm-26x32in) mono. prov.exhib.lit. 10-Jul-3 Sotheby's, London #25/R est:40000-60000

STEEN, Jan (circle) (c.1626-1679) Dutch
£5822 $9140 €8500 Dancing in the park (110x150cm-43x59in) 16-Apr-3 Dorotheum, Salzburg #25/R est:10000-12000
£17000 $26690 €25500 Lean kitchen, with starving family. Fat kitchen, with gluttonous family (36x31cm-14x12in) bears sig. panel pair prov.exhib.lit. 12-Dec-2 Sotheby's, London #148/R est:10000-15000

STEEN, Knut (1924-) Norwegian
Sculpture
£2076 $3280 €3114 Woman and man (19x32x40cm-7x13x16in) marble metal on marble socle. 2-Dec-2 Blomqvist, Oslo #467/R est:18000-22000 (N.KR 24000)

STEEN-JOHNSEN, Soren (1903-1979) Norwegian
£737 $1150 €1106 Man by tree (73x123cm-29x48in) s.d.53 canvas on panel. 21-Oct-2 Blomqvist, Oslo #387/R (N.KR 8500)

STEENE, William (1888-1965) American
£1006 $1600 €1509 Rural autumn landscape (41x51cm-16x20in) s. painted c.1924. 22-Mar-3 New Orleans Auction, New Orleans #1261/R est:1800-2500
£1125 $1800 €1631 Still life with flowers (51x61cm-20x24in) s. 17-May-3 CRN Auctions, Cambridge #46

STEENWYCK, Hendrik van (younger) (1580-1649) Flemish
£4268 $7000 €6402 Interior of a gothic cathedral with a mass being celebrated in a side chapel (16x22cm-6x9in) mono. panel prov.exhib. 29-May-3 Sotheby's, New York #1/R est:10000-15000
£8025 $13000 €12038 Entrance to a church (26x20cm-10x8in) with sig.d.1621 panel prov.lit. 24-Jan-3 Christie's, Rockefeller NY #6/R est:10000-15000
£22000 $36740 €31900 Saint Jerome in his study (26x37cm-10x15in) s.d.1604 panel on canvas. 9-Jul-3 Christie's, London #13/R est:10000-15000

STEENWYCK, Hendrik van (younger-attrib) (1580-1649) Flemish
£5500 $9185 €7975 Liberation of Saint Peter (39x50cm-15x20in) panel. 8-Jul-3 Sotheby's, Olympia #400/R est:4000-6000

STEEPLE, John (1816-1887) British
£900 $1404 €1350 Spring, children in a wooded landscape (31x41cm-12x16in) s.i.verso. 8-Oct-2 Bonhams, Knightsbridge #131/R
Works on paper
£250 $410 €375 Moorland scene with solitary figure (25x36cm-10x14in) s. W/C. 7-Feb-3 Biddle & Webb, Birmingham #58
£360 $522 €540 Figure on horseback with cattle and a dog on heathland (18x38cm-7x15in) mono.d.1871. 3-May-2 Biddle & Webb, Birmingham #273
£380 $623 €570 Figures on a track by a river (33x48cm-13x19in) s.d. W/C exhib. 4-Feb-3 Bonhams, Leeds #291
£500 $795 €750 Walk in North Wales (57x82cm-22x32in) s.d.1861 W/C. 27-Feb-3 Bonhams, Chester #411
£920 $1435 €1380 Upland river landscape with cattle in a meadow (57x82cm-22x32in) s.d.1861 W/C. 6-Nov-2 Bonhams, Chester #420

STEER, Henry Reynolds (1858-1928) British
Works on paper
£700 $1134 €1050 Gay lights and shadows twinkling on the ground (51x36cm-20x14in) s. W/C scratching out. 23-Jan-3 Christie's, Kensington #304/R

STEER, Philip Wilson (1860-1942) British
£5000 $7950 €7500 Portrait of Alice Rothenstein (56x46cm-22x18in) painted c.1904-07 prov.lit. 26-Feb-3 Sotheby's, Olympia #37/R est:3000-5000
£5500 $8580 €8250 Musidor (61x51cm-24x20in) s.d.1900 prov.exhib.lit. 27-Mar-3 Christie's, Kensington #409/R est:6000-8000
£5800 $9048 €8700 Figures in a wood (102x128cm-40x50in) 12-Sep-2 Sotheby's, Olympia #95/R est:5000-7000
£7000 $10990 €10500 Girl and cat (57x46cm-22x18in) painted 1901 prov.exhib.lit. 22-Nov-2 Christie's, London #29/R est:10000-15000
Works on paper
£260 $426 €377 Portrait of a lady (33x23cm-13x9in) W/C prov. 1-Jun-3 Lots Road, London #341
£300 $495 €435 River bank near Sandwich (19x27cm-7x11in) s.d.1931 W/C prov. 3-Jul-3 Christie's, Kensington #289
£340 $547 €510 Evening, Isle of Wight (20x32cm-8x13in) s.d.1919 W/C prov. 15-Jan-3 Cheffins Grain & Comins, Cambridge #405/R
£350 $574 €525 Long Crendon (18x28cm-7x11in) W/C exhib. 3-Jun-3 Sotheby's, Olympia #11/R
£380 $597 €570 Grove (22x33cm-9x13in) s.d.1925 W/C. 15-Apr-3 Bonhams, Knightsbridge #87/R
£400 $616 €600 Painswick Hill (24x34cm-9x13in) s.d.1915 pencil W/C. 5-Sep-2 Christie's, Kensington #509
£400 $620 €600 Landscape, Richmond, York (20x28cm-8x11in) s.d.1903 pencil W/C. 4-Dec-2 Christie's, Kensington #219
£440 $735 €638 Autumn sunshine Framlingham (34x23cm-13x9in) s.d.1928 W/C prov. 19-Jun-3 Lane, Penzance #222
£500 $780 €750 Coastal landscape (23x31cm-9x12in) s.d.1931 W/C. 12-Sep-2 Sotheby's, Olympia #51/R
£500 $780 €750 Windmill on the hill (23x30cm-9x12in) s.d.1923 pencil W/C. 15-Oct-2 Bonhams, Knightsbridge #15/R
£500 $825 €725 View at Richmond, Yorkshire (25x37cm-10x15in) i.verso pencil W/C prov.exhib. 3-Jul-3 Christie's, Kensington #77
£700 $1127 €1050 View of a house, through the trees (22x30cm-9x12in) s.d.1933 W/C. 14-Jan-3 Bonhams, Knightsbridge #68/R

STEFAN, Ross (1934-1999) American
£1667 $2600 €2501 Man from Kayenta. Smudged glasses (61x41cm-24x16in) s. i.verso two prov.lit. 9-Nov-2 Santa Fe Art, Santa Fe #27/R est:1000-2000
£2404 $3750 €3606 Nambe (30x41cm-12x16in) s. i.verso linen prov.lit. 9-Nov-2 Santa Fe Art, Santa Fe #16/R est:2500-3500
£3082 $4500 €4623 Finally caught (61x91cm-24x36in) 18-May-2 Altermann Galleries, Santa Fe #153/R

£5380 $8500 €7801 Magic circles (71x102cm-28x40in) s. prov. 26-Jul-3 Coeur d'Alene, Hayden #187/R est:8000-12000

STEFANELLI, Romano (1931-) Italian
Works on paper
£347 $552 €500 Monteccasino (78x57cm-31x22in) s. s.i.verso sanguine cardboard on board. 1-May-3 Meeting Art, Vercelli #156

STEFANI, Pierre (1938-) French?
£288 $460 €400 Le village de pecheurs (22x33cm-9x13in) s. panel. 18-May-3 Eric Pillon, Calais #41/R
£306 $477 €480 Beach scene near Schevening (12x17cm-5x7in) panel. 5-Nov-2 Vendu Notarishuis, Rotterdam #678/R
£318 $497 €500 Beach scene near Schevening (12x17cm-5x7in) panel. 5-Nov-2 Vendu Notarishuis, Rotterdam #679
£352 $567 €500 Stevening beach with pier (12x17cm-5x7in) s. panel. 6-May-3 Vendu Notarishuis, Rotterdam #585
£352 $567 €500 Beach scene near Westkapelle (12x17cm-5x7in) s. panel. 6-May-3 Vendu Notarishuis, Rotterdam #626
£423 $680 €600 Beach view near Ostend (17x24cm-7x9in) s. panel. 6-May-3 Vendu Notarishuis, Rotterdam #600
£423 $680 €600 Beach view near Berckplage (17x23cm-7x9in) s. panel. 6-May-3 Vendu Notarishuis, Rotterdam #601
£458 $737 €650 Beach scene near Domburg (12x17cm-5x7in) s. panel. 6-May-3 Vendu Notarishuis, Rotterdam #625/R
£586 $932 €850 View ofZandvoort (12x18cm-5x7in) s. s.i.verso panel. 10-Mar-3 Sotheby's, Amsterdam #211/R est:500-700
£655 $1042 €950 View of Zandvoort (12x18cm-5x7in) s.i. panel. 10-Mar-3 Sotheby's, Amsterdam #210 est:500-700

STEFANO, Arturo di (1955-) British
£330 $541 €479 Portrait of Francis Bacon (98x98cm-39x39in) prov. 1-Jun-3 Lots Road, London #370

STEFANONI, Tino (1937-) Italian
£641 $1006 €1000 Souvenir for Cristoforo Colombo (25x30cm-10x12in) s.i.d.1992 board. 23-Nov-2 Meeting Art, Vercelli #63/R
£769 $1215 €1200 Untitled (32x38cm-13x15in) s.d.1995 verso. 15-Nov-2 Farsetti, Prato #30
£811 $1265 €1200 Tables (95x80cm-37x31in) s.i. acrylic. 26-Mar-3 Finarte Semenzato, Milan #135/R
£811 $1305 €1217 Senza titulo (30x40cm-12x16in) s.d.1990 verso acrylic. 7-May-3 AB Stockholms Auktionsverk #1131/R (S.KR 10500)
£1111 $1767 €1600 Composition (36x36cm-14x14in) s.d.2002 verso. 1-May-3 Meeting Art, Vercelli #407
£1282 $2013 €2000 Untitled M17 (32x46cm-13x18in) s.d.2000 verso. 23-Nov-2 Meeting Art, Vercelli #347/R
£1307 $2092 €2000 Landscape in pink (32x42cm-13x17in) s.verso painted 2002. 4-Jan-3 Meeting Art, Vercelli #206
£1307 $2092 €2000 Still life (36x36cm-14x14in) s.verso painted 2002. 4-Jan-3 Meeting Art, Vercelli #727
£1361 $2163 €2000 Night scene (31x41cm-12x16in) s.d.2001. 1-Mar-3 Meeting Art, Vercelli #477
£1389 $2208 €2000 Landscape (32x46cm-13x18in) s.d.199. 1-May-3 Meeting Art, Vercelli #233
£1392 $2172 €2200 Landscape (36x36cm-14x14in) s.d.2002 verso. 14-Sep-2 Meeting Art, Vercelli #825/R
£1497 $2380 €2200 Interior with lamp (32x45cm-13x18in) s.d.2001 verso. 1-Mar-3 Meeting Art, Vercelli #481
£1961 $3137 €3000 Beach (32x110cm-13x43in) s.d.2002. 4-Jan-3 Meeting Art, Vercelli #521
Works on paper
£321 $503 €500 Cube (100x80cm-39x31in) s.i.verso mixed media linen. 23-Nov-2 Meeting Art, Vercelli #8
£801 $1258 €1250 Funnel (60x50cm-24x20in) s.d.1976 verso mixed media on canvas. 23-Nov-2 Meeting Art, Vercelli #29/R

STEFANOU, Nikos (1933-) Greek
£3000 $4740 €4500 Visitor in landscape (80x90cm-31x35in) 1-Apr-3 Bonhams, New Bond Street #103 est:2500-4500

STEFFAN, Johann Gottfried (1815-1905) Swiss
£350 $571 €508 Alpine landscape (36x32cm-14x13in) s. panel. 16-Jul-3 Sotheby's, Olympia #143/R
£487 $726 €750 Forest clearing (30x43cm-12x17in) s.d.Octbr 1853 paper on panel. 26-Jun-2 Neumeister, Munich #875/R
£793 $1158 €1190 Bavarian landscape (35x45cm-14x18in) s.d.1875. 17-Jun-2 Philippe Schuler, Zurich #4292/R (S.FR 1800)
£974 $1451 €1500 Mountain landscape (33x47cm-13x19in) s.i.d.1846 paper on board. 26-Jun-2 Neumeister, Munich #874/R
£1083 $1689 €1700 Rocky part of a mountain torrent (38x46cm-15x18in) s. lit. 7-Nov-2 Allgauer, Kempten #2966/R est:1300
£2260 $3526 €3300 Fishermen hauling in nets on the Chiemsee (37x55cm-15x22in) s.d.1877 panel. 10-Apr-3 Van Ham, Cologne #1719/R est:4000
£2358 $3774 €3537 Klontalersee (72x109cm-28x43in) s.d. 17-Mar-3 Philippe Schuler, Zurich #4561 est:7000-9000 (S.FR 5000)
£3659 $6000 €5489 View of waterfalls (36x44cm-14x17in) s.d.63 oil paper on canvas prov. 29-May-3 Sotheby's, New York #39/R est:6000-8000
£10730 $16631 €16095 Handeggfall (146x101cm-57x40in) s.d.1854 prov. 3-Oct-2 Koller, Zurich #3117/R est:25000-35000 (S.FR 25000)
£12963 $21000 €19445 Waterfall (46x60cm-18x24in) s.d.1849. 23-Jan-3 Sotheby's, New York #186/R est:12000

STEFFEK, Carl (1818-1890) German
£545 $845 €850 Bad mannered dog (31x26cm-12x10in) s. 7-Dec-2 Ketterer, Hamburg #112/R

STEFFEN, Walter Arnold (1924-1982) Swiss
£437 $638 €656 Magical richness. Building site III (50x92cm-20x36in) s.i.d.1967 verso board. 4-Jun-2 Germann, Zurich #853 (S.FR 1000)
£437 $681 €656 Colourful light abstract composition with face (45x57cm-18x22in) s. masonite. 8-Nov-2 Dobiaschofsky, Bern #274/R (S.FR 1000)
£437 $681 €656 Portrait of a lady (50x44cm-20x17in) s. masonite. 8-Nov-2 Dobiaschofsky, Bern #275/R (S.FR 1000)
£437 $686 €656 Flowers (51x45cm-20x18in) mono.d.1963 s.d. verso board. 25-Nov-2 Germann, Zurich #822 (S.FR 1000)
£873 $1371 €1310 Still life of flowers. Composition. s. one d.1967 pavatex two. 25-Nov-2 Germann, Zurich #824 est:400-600 (S.FR 2000)
£1528 $2384 €2292 House in the woods (51x54cm-20x21in) mono.d.63 panel. 8-Nov-2 Dobiaschofsky, Bern #276/R est:1800 (S.FR 3500)

STEFFENS, Hans Hermann (20th C) ?
Works on paper
£544 $865 €800 Composition (24x31cm-9x12in) s.d.1989 mixed media paper on cardboard. 24-Mar-3 Claude Boisgirard, Paris #116/R

STEFFENSEN, E (1884-1964) Danish
£638 $1009 €957 Winter landscape (90x130cm-35x51in) s. 2-Dec-2 Rasmussen, Copenhagen #1556/R (D.KR 7500)

STEFFENSEN, Hans Voigt (1941-) Danish
£253 $395 €380 House gables (65x75cm-26x30in) s.d.67. 18-Sep-2 Kunsthallen, Copenhagen #155 (D.KR 3000)
£743 $1175 €1115 Autumn landscape (100x100cm-39x39in) s. d.73 verso. 1-Apr-3 Rasmussen, Copenhagen #379/R (D.KR 8000)
£1101 $1706 €1652 Nude girl (120x100cm-47x39in) s. s.d.85 verso. 1-Oct-2 Rasmussen, Copenhagen #146/R est:15000-20000 (D.KR 13000)
£1270 $1969 €1905 Girls dancing (120x100cm-47x39in) s. s.d.89 verso. 1-Oct-2 Rasmussen, Copenhagen #245/R est:15000-20000 (D.KR 15000)
£2111 $3294 €3167 Spring in Paris (120x100cm-47x39in) s. painted 1990. 18-Sep-2 Kunsthallen, Copenhagen #173/R est:30000 (D.KR 25000)
£2202 $3412 €3303 Ballerina (180x140cm-71x55in) s. s.d.88 verso. 1-Oct-2 Rasmussen, Copenhagen #248/R est:25000 (D.KR 26000)
£3378 $5270 €5067 Regatta in Venice (140x180cm-55x71in) s. painted 1989 exhib. 18-Sep-2 Kunsthallen, Copenhagen #252/R est:40000 (D.KR 40000)

STEFFENSEN, Poul (1866-1923) Danish
£313 $488 €470 Landscape from Lynnerupgaard near Limfjord (31x46cm-12x18in) init.d.1905. 23-Sep-2 Rasmussen, Vejle #2126 (D.KR 3700)
£326 $508 €489 Woman on woodland path (30x44cm-12x17in) init.d.08. 11-Nov-2 Rasmussen, Vejle #664/R (D.KR 3800)
£597 $950 €896 Landscape with cows (43x71cm-17x28in) s. painted c.1920. 4-May-3 Treadway Gallery, Cincinnati #467/R
£680 $1060 €1020 Field landscape with waterway and cattle (75x111cm-30x44in) s.d.1910. 5-Aug-2 Rasmussen, Vejle #200/R (D.KR 8000)
£788 $1261 €1182 Summer landscape with three cows by water's edge (66x100cm-26x39in) s.d.1917. 13-Jan-3 Rasmussen, Vejle #38/R (D.KR 9000)
£887 $1383 €1331 Farmer ploughing field (36x51cm-14x20in) s. 22-Sep-2 Hindemae, Ullerslev #7246/R (D.KR 10500)
£931 $1480 €1397 Watering the cattle at waterpump in farmyard (68x102cm-27x40in) init.d.1906. 10-Mar-3 Rasmussen, Vejle #108/R (D.KR 10000)
£1007 $1611 €1511 Summer landscape with horses by gate (68x90cm-27x35in) s. 13-Jan-3 Rasmussen, Vejle #42/R (D.KR 11500)
£1117 $1777 €1676 Harvesting scene with peasants bringing home the hay on cart (69x109cm-27x43in) mono.d.1905. 10-Mar-3 Rasmussen, Vejle #98/R est:12000 (D.KR 12000)
£1627 $2635 €2359 Cattle watering, Rye (59x90cm-23x35in) s. 26-May-3 Rasmussen, Copenhagen #1468/R est:12000-15000 (D.KR 17000)

STEFKO, M (20th C) Czechoslovakian
£551 $783 €827 Harvest (94x160cm-37x63in) painted c.1930. 26-Mar-2 SOGA, Bratislava #23/R (SL.K 35000)

STEFULA, Dorothea (1914-) Swiss?
£613 $981 €920 Still life with bottle and sewing pins (24x29cm-9x11in) s.d.65. 17-Mar-3 Philippe Schuler, Zurich #4655/R (S.FR 1300)

STEGER, Milly (1881-1948) German
Sculpture
£2174 $3565 €3000 Woman carrying jug (55cm-22in) mono. plaster exhib.lit. 29-May-3 Lempertz, Koln #930/R est:1200

STEGMANN, Franz (1831-1892) German
£1006 $1600 €1509 Skating party (20x26cm-8x10in) s. 7-Mar-3 Skinner, Boston #220/R est:2000-4000

STEGMEIER, Heinrich (fl.1797-1819) Austrian
£692 $1079 €1100 Portrait of gentleman (85x65cm-33x26in) s.d.1834. 23-Sep-2 Wiener Kunst Auktionen, Vienna #67/R

STEHLE, Alois (1854-1932) German
Sculpture
£4500 $7020 €6750 Roman gladiator (69cm-27in) s. brown pat bronze st.Guss C Leyrer lit. 9-Apr-3 Sotheby's, London #139/R est:3000-5000

STEIB, Josef (1898-1957) German
£335 $543 €486 Arabian street scene (61x51cm-24x20in) s. 26-May-3 Rasmussen, Copenhagen #1334/R (D.KR 3500)
£417 $654 €650 Oriental street (64x48cm-25x19in) s. 23-Nov-2 Arnold, Frankfurt #876/R

STEICHEN, Edward J (1879-1973) American
Photographs
£1899 $3000 €2849 Marion Morehouse in a Chanel gown (24x20cm-9x8in) i.verso photograph. 23-Apr-3 Sotheby's, New York #140/R est:3000-5000
£2110 $3250 €3165 Time-space continuum (34x43cm-13x17in) photograph prov.exhib.lit. 22-Oct-2 Sotheby's, New York #150/R est:5000-8000
£2848 $4500 €4272 Gary Cooper (24x19cm-9x7in) i. photograph prov.exhib.lit. 23-Apr-3 Sotheby's, New York #147/R est:5000-8000
£3038 $4800 €4557 Blois (27x40cm-11x16in) i.num.9 verso toned gelatin silver print. 24-Apr-3 Phillips, New York #93/R est:6000-8000
£3247 $5000 €4871 Rockefeller Center (43x34cm-17x13in) i.verso oversized photograph prov.lit. 22-Oct-2 Sotheby's, New York #79/R est:5000-8000
£3247 $5000 €4871 Portrait of Rodin (29x22cm-11x9in) gum print prov. 22-Oct-2 Sotheby's, New York #152/R est:7000-10000
£3481 $5500 €5222 Beach (17x16cm-7x6in) s. gelatin silver print prov. 25-Apr-3 Phillips, New York #18/R est:4000-6000
£3896 $6000 €5844 Portrait of the Nast children (25x19cm-10x7in) s.d.1917 photographs two. 22-Oct-2 Sotheby's, New York #148/R est:3000-5000
£4304 $6800 €6456 Sunday night on 40th Street (42x35cm-17x14in) i.d.1925 gelatin silver print prov. 25-Apr-3 Phillips, New York #76/R est:4000-6000
£5195 $8000 €7793 Portrait of Beatrice Baxter (20x16cm-8x6in) i. platinum print prov. 22-Oct-2 Sotheby's, New York #138/R est:10000-15000
£5696 $9000 €8544 Empire State Building, New York (25x20cm-10x8in) num. photograph prov.lit. 23-Apr-3 Sotheby's, New York #146/R est:10000-15000
£6329 $10000 €9494 Breadline on 42nd Street (25x20cm-10x8in) i.verso gelatin silver print prov.lit. 25-Apr-3 Phillips, New York #5/R est:12000-18000
£8442 $13000 €12663 Backbone and ribs of a sunflower (19x24cm-7x9in) i.num.78 verso warm toned photograph prov.lit. 22-Oct-2 Sotheby's, New York #28/R est:15000-25000
£9091 $14000 €13637 Eternity, as M Brancusi, the sculptor, conceives it (24x20cm-9x8in) i.d.1926 verso gelatin silver print prov.exhib.lit. 25-Oct-2 Phillips, New York #10/R est:18000-22000
£9091 $14000 €13637 Lady and the lamp (19x13cm-7x5in) warm toned photograph prov.exhib. 22-Oct-2 Sotheby's, New York #34/R est:10000-15000
£9740 $15000 €14610 Stars on Sixth Avenue (34x27cm-13x11in) i.verso photograph prov. 22-Oct-2 Sotheby's, New York #57/R est:20000-30000
£14286 $22000 €21429 Diagram of Doom-3 (20x24cm-8x9in) photograph prov.lit. 22-Oct-2 Sotheby's, New York #149/R est:10000-15000
£18987 $30000 €28481 Untitled (25x20cm-10x8in) i. negative gelatin silver print executed c.1932 prov. 24-Apr-3 Phillips, New York #28/R est:30000-50000
£19481 $30000 €29222 Gertrude Lawrence (42x33cm-17x13in) oversized warm toned photograph prov.exhib.lit. 22-Oct-2 Sotheby's, New York #56/R est:15000-25000
£40260 $62000 €60390 Dolor (20x13cm-8x5in) platinum print prov. 22-Oct-2 Sotheby's, New York #38/R est:70000-100000
£41139 $65000 €61709 George Washington Bridge (119x89cm-47x35in) s. i.verso gelatin silver print on masonite prov. 24-Apr-3 Phillips, New York #117/R est:15000-20000

STEIGER, Dominik (1940-) Austrian
Works on paper
£506 $785 €800 Untitled (29x21cm-11x8in) s.d.83 mixed media. 24-Sep-2 Wiener Kunst Auktionen, Vienna #246/R

STEIN, Anna (1936-) ?
Sculpture
£1245 $1930 €1980 Portrait de deesse (40cm-16in) s. bronze Cast Poseidon Sylva. 7-Oct-2 Claude Aguttes, Neuilly #111

STEIN, Georges (1870-?) French
£1221 $2002 €1770 La Corniche de Moulleau a Arcachon (37x52cm-15x20in) s.i.d.1915. 4-Jun-3 Fischer, Luzern #1081/R est:2500-3000 (S.FR 2600)
£1643 $2695 €2382 Elegant couple on quayside (38x61cm-15x24in) s.i. 4-Jun-3 Fischer, Luzern #1079/R est:3500-4000 (S.FR 3500)
£2113 $3465 €3064 Avenue de l'Opera (46x65cm-18x26in) s.i. 4-Jun-3 Fischer, Luzern #1102/R est:4500-5000 (S.FR 4500)
£4676 $7482 €6500 L'opera (44x58cm-17x23in) s. 14-May-3 Rabourdin & Choppin de Janvry, Paris #54/R est:9000-10000
Works on paper
£1582 $2500 €2500 Paris, la nuit (36x53cm-14x21in) gouache chl wax crayon. 29-Nov-2 Coutau Begarie, Paris #16
£2207 $3531 €3200 Le Carrefour de l'Opera (32x24cm-13x9in) s.i. gouache W/C. 12-Mar-3 Libert, Castor, Paris #184/R est:1200-1500
£2414 $3862 €3500 Sur les quais (31x22cm-12x9in) s.i. W/C gouache. 12-Mar-3 Libert, Castor, Paris #183/R est:1000-1200
£2436 $3824 €3800 Caleche sur l'Avenue Foch (27x39cm-11x15in) s.i. W/C. 21-Nov-2 Neret-Minet, Paris #17/R
£2590 $4144 €3600 Paris, le quai aux fleurs et la conciergerie (24x33cm-9x13in) s. W/C. 18-May-3 Eric Pillon, Calais #3/R
£2734 $4374 €3800 Paris, les grands boulevards (23x35cm-9x14in) s. W/C gouache. 18-May-3 Eric Pillon, Calais #1/R

STEIN, J G (19th C) ?
£1974 $3197 €3000 Spring idyl (54x145cm-21x57in) s. 21-Jan-3 Christie's, Amsterdam #61/R est:3000-5000

STEIN, Janos (?) ?
£861 $1334 €1292 Before bath (46x34cm-18x13in) s. canvas on canvasboard. 6-Dec-2 Kieselbach, Budapest #58/R (H.F 320000)

STEIN, Peter (1922-) Swiss
£741 $1193 €1112 Composition (71x25cm-28x10in) s.d.87. 7-May-3 Dobiaschofsky, Bern #997/R (S.FR 1600)
£833 $1342 €1208 Winter II (33x55cm-13x22in) s.d.52. 9-May-3 Dobiaschofsky, Bern #239/R (S.FR 1800)

STEINACH, Anton Victor Alexander (1819-1891) German
£641 $994 €1000 Guard room with sleeping farm hands (58x48cm-23x19in) s.d.1845 lit. 7-Dec-2 Bergmann, Erlangen #753/R

STEINACKER, Alfred (1838-1914) Austrian
£294 $482 €450 At the races (16x43cm-6x17in) s. panel. 5-Feb-3 Neumeister, Munich #822/R
£385 $585 €600 Horse market near Comsen, Hungary (18x30cm-7x12in) s. panel. 11-Jul-2 Hugo Ruef, Munich #829
£570 $900 €900 Hunter's lunch (32x39cm-13x15in) s.i. 1-Dec-2 Bukowskis, Helsinki #275/R
£775 $1247 €1100 Hunting party (16x30cm-6x12in) s.pseudonym R Stone panel lit. 9-May-3 Schloss Ahlden, Ahlden #1464/R
£775 $1247 €1100 Hunting (16x30cm-6x12in) s.pseudonym R Stone panel lit. 9-May-3 Schloss Ahlden, Ahlden #1465/R
£1111 $1789 €1667 Hunting scene (15x31cm-6x12in) s. panel. 7-May-3 Dobiaschofsky, Bern #998/R est:2500 (S.FR 2400)

STEINBERG, Saul (1914-1999) American
£6803 $10816 €10000 Architectural space (44x61cm-17x24in) s. mixed media prov. 24-Mar-3 Cornette de St.Cyr, Paris #92/R
£9000 $15030 €13050 Girls table (45x61cm-18x24in) s.d.1980 oil on card wood collage on panel prov. 27-Jun-3 Christie's, London #196/R est:10000-15000
Works on paper
£7500 $12000 €11250 Buenos Aires table (58x73cm-23x29in) s.d.1969 pen ink col pencil collage prov. 16-May-3 Phillips, New York #157/R est:12000-18000
£14241 $22500 €21362 Sag Harbour (76x102cm-30x40in) s.d.1970 W/C ink prov.exhib. 13-Nov-2 Sotheby's, New York #205/R est:15000-20000

STEINER, Albert (1877-1965) Swiss?
Photographs
£6438 $10172 €9657 Winter landscape in Rosegtal (17x22cm-7x9in) s.i. gelatin silver print lit. 26-Nov-2 Phillips, Zurich #52/R est:1500-2000 (S.FR 15000)
£8155 $12884 €12233 Skier at Piz Palu (16x22cm-6x9in) s.i. gelatin silver print. 26-Nov-2 Phillips, Zurich #51/R est:2000-2500 (S.FR 19000)

STEINER, Clement Leopold (1853-1899) French
Sculpture
£3077 $4800 €4616 Mythological figure with an urn (56cm-22in) s. bronze. 22-Sep-2 Susanin's, Chicago #5055/R est:3000-5000

STEINER, Josef (1877-?) Austrian
£472 $731 €750 Still life of flowers (50x43cm-20x17in) s. panel. 29-Oct-2 Dorotheum, Vienna #285/R

STEINER, Leonhard (1836-1920) Swiss
£306 $477 €459 Meadow above Vierwaldstadtersee (37x58cm-15x23in) s. i. verso panel. 6-Nov-2 Dobiaschofsky, Bern #3712 (S.FR 700)

STEINER, Lilly (1884-1962) Austrian
£962 $1519 €1500 Paysage Breton (46x38cm-18x15in) s. s.i.d.1945 verso. 12-Nov-2 Dorotheum, Vienna #144/R est:1600-2200

STEINER, Minou (1940-) British?
Works on paper
£250 $418 €363 Red mullet (38x53cm-15x21in) s. mixed media. 19-Jun-3 Lane, Penzance #69

STEINER, Ralph (1899-1986) American
Photographs
£3896 $6000 €5844 Bridge (25x20cm-10x8in) photograph prov.exhib.lit. 22-Oct-2 Sotheby's, New York #68/R est:7000-10000

STEINERT, Otto (1915-1978) German
Photographs
£3896 $6000 €5844 Punkte und linien (30x39cm-12x15in) st.i.verso gelatin silver print prov.lit. 25-Oct-2 Phillips, New York #101/R est:6000-8000
£3896 $6000 €5844 Sonnenuntergang in hirtshals (36x30cm-14x12in) st.i.verso gelatin silver print prov.lit. 25-Oct-2 Phillips, New York #102/R est:6000-8000
£12579 $19497 €20000 Lamps of the Place de la Concorde 3 (42x60cm-17x24in) s.d.1952 gelatin silver lit. 2-Nov-2 Lempertz, Koln #96/R est:12000

STEINFELD, Franz (1787-1868) Austrian
£2848 $4500 €4500 Street near Bad-Ischl (20x27cm-8x11in) s.i. 28-Nov-2 Dorotheum, Vienna #165/R
£4747 $7500 €7500 Coastal landscape with Marterl am Ufer in background and alpine panorama (31x28cm-12x11in) s.d.834 board. 28-Nov-2 Dorotheum, Vienna #221/R est:2800-3400
Works on paper
£1014 $1581 €1500 Traunsee (16x22cm-6x9in) s.i. W/C. 28-Mar-3 Dorotheum, Vienna #273/R est:1500-1600

STEINFELDT, Cecilia Neuheisel (20th C) American
Works on paper
£385 $600 €578 Nude (41x30cm-16x12in) W/C. 19-Oct-2 David Dike, Dallas #8/R

STEINHARDT, J (19th C) German
£1759 $2832 €2551 Chess game (39x28cm-15x11in) s. panel. 7-May-3 Dobiaschofsky, Bern #999/R est:4000 (S.FR 3800)

STEINHARDT, Jakob (1887-1968) Israeli
£2532 $4000 €3798 House in landscape (26x36cm-10x14in) s.d.41. 27-Apr-3 Sotheby's, Tel Aviv #9/R est:3000-4000
Works on paper
£550 $853 €825 Blindman (45x34cm-18x13in) s.d.1952 pencil wash dr. 3-Dec-2 Bonhams, Knightsbridge #274/R
£641 $1000 €962 Jews at the Apocalypse (34x34cm-13x13in) init.d.1944 black crayon wash. 19-Sep-2 Swann Galleries, New York #776/R
£1603 $2500 €2405 Village scene with Jewish men (33x40cm-13x16in) s.d. W/C black chk. 18-Sep-2 Swann Galleries, New York #39/R est:1500-2500
£2278 $3600 €3417 Desert (28x35cm-11x14in) s.d.1954 W/C chl. 27-Apr-3 Sotheby's, Tel Aviv #10/R est:3500-4500

STEINHART, Anton (1889-1964) Austrian
Works on paper
£468 $748 €650 Linz with Postlingberg (30x40cm-12x16in) s.d.1955 Indian ink. 14-May-3 Dorotheum, Linz #506/R

STEINHEIL, Adolphe Charles Edouard (1850-1908) French
£250 $395 €375 Portrait d'homme (16x13cm-6x5in) s. panel. 14-Nov-2 Christie's, Kensington #12

STEINHEIL, Carl Friedrich (1860-1917) German
£514 $801 €750 Sheep in stable (32x27cm-13x11in) s. panel. 10-Apr-3 Dorotheum, Vienna #169/R

STEININGER, Ludwig (1890-1979) German
£353 $554 €550 Winter landscape in the Upper Pfalz (45x60cm-18x24in) s.d.7.2.34. 21-Nov-2 Van Ham, Cologne #1929

STEINKE, Bettina (1913-1999) American
Works on paper
£4808 $7500 €7212 Navajo (51x41cm-20x16in) pastel. 9-Nov-2 Altermann Galleries, Santa Fe #58

STEINLEN, Marguerite (20th C) French?
Works on paper
£1773 $2872 €2500 Femme metamorphose d'Eve (21x10cm-8x4in) mono. W/C gouache collage. 23-May-3 Camard, Paris #104/R est:2700-3000

STEINLEN, Theophile Alexandre (1859-1923) Swiss
£2158 $3453 €3000 Chat noir, chat roux (59x46cm-23x18in) s. pochoir. 16-May-3 Lombrail & Teucquam, Paris #113/R
£3892 $6500 €5643 Luxembourg Gardens (25x35cm-10x14in) indis sig. panel prov. 22-Jun-3 Freeman, Philadelphia #42/R est:7000-10000
Prints
£1923 $3000 €2885 Ete, chat sur une balustrade (21x63cm-8x25in) col lithograph. 5-Nov-2 Christie's, Rockefeller NY #26/R est:4000-6000
£2055 $3205 €3000 Seated cat (34x29cm-13x11in) s. col monotype. 11-Apr-3 Winterberg, Heidelberg #584/R est:3800
£2179 $3400 €3269 Le vieux chat (19x30cm-7x12in) s.num.2/25 col soft ground etching drypoint aquatint. 7-Nov-2 Swann Galleries, New York #495/R est:2500-3500
£2564 $4000 €3846 La traite des blanches (80x59cm-31x23in) col lithograph. 14-Oct-2 Butterfields, San Francisco #1196/R est:2000-3000
Sculpture
£7801 $12638 €11000 Chat allonge (23cm-9in) i. num.570 brown pat bronze. 23-May-3 Camard, Paris #45/R est:10000-12000
Works on paper
£217 $337 €326 C'est epatant (24x19cm-9x7in) s. chl. 7-Dec-2 Galerie du Rhone, Sion #341 (S.FR 500)
£253 $392 €400 Homme debout (26x19cm-10x7in) s. ink. 28-Sep-2 Cornette de St.Cyr, Paris #193
£255 $397 €400 Bodies in water beneath bridge (31x51cm-12x20in) s. chk. 5-Nov-2 Hartung & Hartung, Munich #5134/R
£261 $404 €392 Ah mes petits canassons (24x19cm-9x7in) s. chl. 7-Dec-2 Galerie du Rhone, Sion #340/R (S.FR 600)
£268 $432 €400 Femme marchant sous la pluie (28x24cm-11x9in) s. chl htd W/C. 18-Feb-3 Vanderkindere, Brussels #2
£296 $495 €430 A propos de bottes (34x26cm-13x10in) s. chl dr. 10-Jul-3 Artcurial Briest, Paris #6
£338 $527 €500 Figure studies (38x29cm-15x11in) col pen sketch verso. 28-Mar-3 Ketterer, Hamburg #124/R
£395 $640 €600 Les poulbots (35x24cm-14x9in) s. chl dr. 22-Jan-3 Tajan, Paris #217
£432 $691 €600 Trois femmes discutant (14x10cm-6x4in) s.d.mai 1902 W/C graphite cardboard prov. 15-May-3 Christie's, Paris #44/R
£432 $708 €600 La fouille (25x32cm-10x13in) s.i. pencil col chk. 4-Jun-3 Reiss & Sohn, Konigstein #297/R
£473 $738 €700 Chat assis (13x20cm-5x8in) s. chl. 26-Mar-3 Rieunier, Paris #4/R
£490 $779 €720 Mere et son enfant (34x25cm-13x10in) s. sepia ink W/C dr. 26-Feb-3 Artcurial Briest, Paris #1
£516 $815 €800 Fillette au noeud blanc, Paris (34x27cm-13x11in) s.i.d. pastel dr. 17-Dec-2 Rossini, Paris #48
£517 $828 €750 Elegante (35x22cm-14x9in) init. chl wash. 12-Mar-3 Libert, Castor, Paris #185
£735 $1168 €1080 Etudes de tetes. col crayon chl Indian ink double-sided. 26-Feb-3 Artcurial Briest, Paris #2
£839 $1401 €1200 Chat (16x22cm-6x9in) mono. col crayon chl dr. 26-Jun-3 Tajan, Paris #3/R
£962 $1500 €1443 Cat walking. Cat sitting (11x14cm-4x6in) one s. one init. pen ink drs pair. 19-Sep-2 Swann Galleries, New York #779/R est:700-1000

£962 $1490 €1500 Street scene (42x35cm-17x14in) s. chk sketch verso. 4-Dec-2 Lempertz, Koln #1080/R est:1500
£1200 $1908 €1800 Nu debout (36x10cm-14x4in) st.mono. chl prov. 20-Mar-3 Sotheby's, Olympia #77/R est:800-1200
£1218 $1900 €1827 Le matin (43x55cm-17x22in) s.i. black crayon exec.c.1900. 18-Sep-2 Swann Galleries, New York #17/R est:2000-3000
£1282 $2000 €1923 Nu de dos (40x45cm-16x18in) s. chl. 19-Sep-2 Swann Galleries, New York #778/R est:2500-3500
£1300 $2041 €1950 Quand les poetes s'en vont par trois (53x37cm-21x15in) s. col crayon. 16-Dec-2 Sotheby's, London #80/R est:1500-2000
£1351 $2108 €2000 Silhouettesde femmes sur les quais de l'Hotel de Ville (48x62cm-19x24in) s. chl. 26-Mar-3 Piasa, Paris #135/R
£1528 $2460 €2216 Peasant woman smoking (54x41cm-21x16in) s. mixed media panel. 7-May-3 Dobiaschofsky, Bern #1000/R est:2600 (S.FR 3300)
£2452 $3800 €3678 Bon appetit (34x27cm-13x11in) s. col wax over pen India ink paper on board. 26-Sep-2 Christie's, Rockefeller NY #531/R est:3000-5000
£2893 $4600 €4340 Deux chats (24x27cm-9x11in) s. pencil executed c.1900. 3-Mar-3 Swann Galleries, New York #32/R est:3000-5000
£3205 $5032 €5000 Deux passantes (59x44cm-23x17in) s. chl dr. 15-Dec-2 Eric Pillon, Calais #89/R
£3302 $5349 €5844 Le depart des poilus (112x117cm-44x46in) s.d.1916 chl col pen white prov. 26-May-3 Sotheby's, Zurich #109/R est:5000-7000 (S.FR 7000)
£7742 $12000 €11613 Cats sleeping in the studio (48x63cm-19x25in) s.d.3 Avril 22 black chk prov. 29-Oct-2 Sotheby's, New York #110/R est:2500-3500

STEINLEN, Theophile Alexandre (attrib) (1859-1923) Swiss
£1515 $2348 €2273 Woman's portrait (73x51cm-29x20in) 24-Sep-2 Koller, Zurich #6659 est:2500-3500 (S.FR 3500)

STEINMETZ-NORIS, Fritz (1860-?) German
£274 $427 €400 Village by river (31x34cm-12x13in) s. board. 10-Apr-3 Van Ham, Cologne #1721
£655 $1022 €983 Bozen in summer (31x41cm-12x16in) s.i. panel. 6-Nov-2 Dobiaschofsky, Bern #995/R (S.FR 1500)
£897 $1400 €1346 In the library (18x15cm-7x6in) s.d.1888 panel. 30-Mar-3 Susanin's, Chicago #6066/R

STEINMULLER, G (?) German
£2013 $3242 €3000 Battle scene in Northern Africa (67x55cm-26x22in) s. 18-Feb-3 Sotheby's, Amsterdam #987/R est:1200-1800

STEIR, Pat (1940-) American
£7097 $11000 €10646 Studio waterfall (183x122cm-72x48in) painted 1989 prov. 26-Sep-2 Christie's, Rockefeller NY #833/R est:12000-18000

STELLA, Frank (1936-) American
£13889 $22917 €20000 Polar coordinate (96x96cm-38x38in) s.d.87 acrylic mixed media screenprint prov. 1-Jul-3 Artcurial Briest, Paris #524b/R est:20000-25000
£100000 $160000 €150000 Lapa I (193x305cm-76x120in) acrylic on aluminum painted 1975 prov. 14-May-3 Sotheby's, New York #242/R est:125000-175000
£104430 $165000 €156645 Gray scramble XV single (176x176cm-69x69in) s.d.69 i.on stretcher acrylic prov. 13-Nov-2 Sotheby's, New York #110/R est:200000-300000
£192308 $300000 €288462 Sacramento mall proposal no.2 (267x267cm-105x105in) acrylic painted 1978 prov. 11-Nov-2 Phillips, New York #17/R est:300000-400000
£253165 $400000 €379748 Les Indes galantes (182x182cm-72x72in) alkyd on canvas painted 1962 prov.exhib.lit. 14-Nov-2 Christie's, Rockefeller NY #170/R est:150000-200000
£343750 $550000 €515625 Pratfall (329x329cm-130x130in) acrylic painted 1974 prov.exhib. 13-May-3 Sotheby's, New York #34/R est:300000-400000
£2437500 $3900000 €3656250 Bethlehem's hospital (213x335cm-84x132in) enamel painted 1959 prov.exhib.lit. 14-May-3 Christie's, Rockefeller NY #30/R est:5000000-7000000

Prints
£1923 $3000 €2885 Shards II (101x115cm-40x45in) s.d.num.83/100 col offset lithograph silkscreen. 14-Oct-2 Butterfields, San Francisco #1364/R est:4000-5000
£1935 $3000 €2903 Libertinia, from Imaginary places (55x125cm-22x49in) s.d.1995 num. col relief screenprint etching aquatint. 25-Sep-2 Christie's, Rockefeller NY #413/R est:3000-4000
£1935 $3000 €2903 Calvinia, from Imaginary places (52x133cm-20x52in) s.d.1995 col screenprint lithograph etching relief. 25-Sep-2 Christie's, Rockefeller NY #414/R est:3000-4000
£1963 $3200 €2945 Swan engraving framed II (147x109cm-58x43in) s.d.84 etching. 13-Feb-3 Christie's, Rockefeller NY #358/R
£2013 $3200 €3020 Sinjerli variation (64x64cm-25x25in) s.d.num.26/100 col offset lithograph screenprint. 29-Apr-3 Christie's, Rockefeller NY #750/R est:4000-6000
£2044 $3250 €3066 Shards II (101x115cm-40x45in) s.d.num.55/100 col screenprint offset lithograph. 2-May-3 Sotheby's, New York #602/R est:3000-4000
£2044 $3250 €3066 Calnogor (67cm-26in circular) s.d.num.12/34 col etching aquatint relief stamping. 2-May-3 Sotheby's, New York #622/R est:2500-3500
£2201 $3500 €3302 Riallaro (117x81cm-46x32in) s.d.num.4/24 col screenprint etching aquatint collagraph. 2-May-3 Sotheby's, New York #611/R est:3500-4500
£2201 $3500 €3302 Libertinia (55x125cm-22x49in) s.i.d. col relief screenprint etching aquatint lithograph. 2-May-3 Sotheby's, New York #614/R est:3500-4500
£2400 $3720 €3600 Sinjerli variation la (81x107cm-32x42in) s.d.1977 num.13/100 col lithograph. 3-Dec-2 Christie's, London #235/R est:1500-2500
£2500 $4125 €3625 Fanattia (139x104cm-55x41in) s.d.num.13/24 col etching engraving lithograph woodcut mezzotint. 2-Jul-3 Christie's, London #357/R est:2500-3000
£2516 $4000 €3774 Referedum (81x81cm-32x32in) s.d.num.121/200 col screenprint. 29-Apr-3 Christie's, Rockefeller NY #745/R est:4000-5000
£2516 $4000 €3774 Feneralia (117x105cm-46x41in) s.i.d. col lithograph etching aquatint collagraph relief print. 2-May-3 Sotheby's, New York #613/R est:3500-4500
£2642 $4200 €3963 Inaccessible island rail (86x117cm-34x46in) s.d.num.AP.XVI col offset lithograph screenprint. 29-Apr-3 Christie's, Rockefeller NY #749/R est:5000-7000
£2830 $4500 €4245 Shards I (115x101cm-45x40in) s.i.d. col screenprint offset lithograph. 2-May-3 Sotheby's, New York #601/R est:3000-4000
£2885 $4500 €4328 Shards III (115x101cm-45x40in) s.d.num.66/100 col offset lithograph screenprint. 5-Nov-2 Christie's, Rockefeller NY #486/R est:4000-6000
£2903 $4500 €4355 Shards variant (101x115cm-40x45in) s.d.1982 num.CTP.IV col offset lithograph. 25-Sep-2 Christie's, Rockefeller NY #411/R est:3500-4500
£2903 $4500 €4355 Spectralia, from Imaginary Place (67x81cm-26x32in) s.d.94num. lithograph etching relife engraving screenprint. 25-Sep-2 Christie's, Rockefeller NY #412/R est:3000-4000
£2987 $4750 €4481 Shards IV (101x115cm-40x45in) s.i.d. col screenprint offset lithograph. 2-May-3 Sotheby's, New York #603/R est:3000-4000
£2987 $4750 €4481 Spectralia (68x83cm-27x33in) s.i.d. col screenprint etching lithograph aquatint engraving. 2-May-3 Sotheby's, New York #612/R est:3500-4500
£3019 $4800 €4529 Polar co-ordinates VIII (98x97cm-39x38in) s.d.num.PP.IV col offset lithograph screenprint. 29-Apr-3 Christie's, Rockefeller NY #751/R est:5000-7000
£3019 $4800 €4529 Desparia (44x123cm-17x48in) s.d.num.10/50 col aquatint etching relief lithograph engraving. 29-Apr-3 Christie's, Rockefeller NY #753/R est:6000-8000
£3077 $4800 €4616 Then came water and quenched the fire (137x132cm-54x52in) s.d.84 num.39/60 col lithograph linocut screenprint collage. 5-Nov-2 Christie's, Rockefeller NY #488/R est:5000-7000
£3077 $4800 €4616 Candles (147x99cm-58x39in) s.num.35/65 col lithograph screenprint collage. 5-Nov-2 Christie's, Rockefeller NY #489/R est:4500-5000
£3097 $4800 €4646 East Euralia (61x77cm-24x30in) s.d.1995 num. lithograph screenprint etching aquatint relief. 25-Sep-2 Christie's, Rockefeller NY #415/R est:3000-4000
£3145 $5000 €4718 Affidavit (154x113cm-61x44in) s.d.num.20/38 col screenprint lithograph etching aquatint relief. 2-May-3 Sotheby's, New York #609/R est:5000-7000
£3313 $5400 €4970 Los alamitos (51x203cm-20x80in) s.d.1972 col screenprint. 13-Feb-3 Christie's, Rockefeller NY #357/R
£3459 $5500 €5189 Then came an ox and drank the water (137x133cm-54x52in) s.d.84 num.52/60 col screenprint lithograph linoleum cut. 2-May-3 Sotheby's, New York #605/R est:5000-7000
£3500 $5775 €5075 Juan (198x150cm-78x59in) s.d.num.6/16 col relief woodcut etching lithograph 2 sheets. 2-Jul-3 Christie's, London #358/R est:6000-8000

£3623	$5942	€5000	From 'Imaginary Places' (72x68cm-28x27in) s.d. num.17/35 col graphic etching lithograph serigraph drypoint. 28-May-3 Lempertz, Koln #417/R est:5000
£3774	$6000	€5661	La penna di hu, black and white (195x148cm-77x58in) s.i.d. etching aquatint. 2-May-3 Sotheby's, New York #607/R est:7000-8000
£3871	$6000	€5807	Juam, state I (198x152cm-78x60in) s.d.1997 etching aquatint woodcut relief. 25-Sep-2 Christie's, Rockefeller NY #417/R est:5000-7000
£4403	$7000	€6605	Polar co-ordinates III (97x96cm-38x38in) s.i.d. col offset lithograph screenprint. 2-May-3 Sotheby's, New York #596/R est:5000-7000
£4403	$7000	€6605	Imola three I (168x130cm-66x51in) s.i.d. col relief print etching engraving. 2-May-3 Sotheby's, New York #600/R est:9000-10000
£4430	$7000	€7000	Then came a dog and bit the cat (137x131cm-54x52in) s.d. col lithograph linocut serigraph. 30-Nov-2 Villa Grisebach, Berlin #429/R est:6000-7000
£4747	$7500	€7121	Port au basques (81x162cm-32x64in) s.d.1971 col lithograph silkscreen. 22-Apr-3 Butterfields, San Francisco #2365/R est:8000-10000
£5031	$8000	€7547	Inaccessible island rail (84x114cm-33x45in) s.i.d. col offset lithograph screenprint. 29-Apr-3 Christie's, Rockefeller NY #748/R est:10000-15000
£5128	$8000	€7692	York factory (47x37cm-19x15in) s.d.num.10/100 col screenprint. 5-Nov-2 Christie's, Rockefeller NY #485/R est:8000-10000
£7547	$12000	€11321	Estoril five I (168x131cm-66x52in) s.i.d. col relief print etching woodcut. 2-May-3 Sotheby's, New York #599/R est:16000-20000
£7547	$12000	€11321	Imola three II (168x132cm-66x52in) s.d.num.10/30 col relief print woodcut. 2-May-3 Sotheby's, New York #606/R est:12000-15000
£7692	$12000	€11538	Bonne Bay (97x178cm-38x70in) s.i.d. col lithograph silkscreen edition of 58. 14-Oct-2 Butterfields, San Francisco #1362/R est:12000-15000
£15823	$25000	€23735	From circuits - estoril five (173x130cm-68x51in) s.d.1982 num.13/30 woodcut relief. 22-Apr-3 Butterfields, San Francisco #2366/R est:18000-24000
£25157	$40000	€37736	Talladega three II (168x130cm-66x51in) s.d.num.AP IX col etching. 29-Apr-3 Christie's, Rockefeller NY #752/R est:50000-70000

Sculpture

£18750	$30000	€28125	Lass of glenshee (61x39x15cm-24x15x6in) sig.d.85 num.2/3 painted metal prov. 14-May-3 Sotheby's, New York #247/R est:10000-15000
£27500	$44000	€41250	Noguchi's Okinawa woodpecker (46x58x10cm-18x23x4in) relief oil glitter lacquer exec.1976 prov.exhib.lit. 15-May-3 Christie's, Rockefeller NY #184/R est:30000-40000
£31646	$50000	€47469	Jarmolince I (241x208x8cm-95x82x3in) s.d.73 verso wall relief oil fabric felt corrugated cardboard. 14-Nov-2 Christie's, Rockefeller NY #172/R est:50000-70000
£37975	$60000	€56963	Cassock (141x236x80cm-56x93x31in) wall relief acrylic enamel on aluminum executed 1988 prov. 14-Nov-2 Christie's, Rockefeller NY #212/R est:80000-120000
£40000	$65600	€60000	The battle with the ladle (122x158x40cm-48x62x16in) oil paint anodised aluminium prov. 6-Feb-3 Christie's, London #691/R est:30000-40000
£43038	$68000	€64557	Playskool gym (237x236x102cm-93x93x40in) mixed media cast aluminum executed 1982-1984 prov.exhib. 12-Nov-2 Phillips, New York #126/R est:70000-90000
£44872	$65513	€70000	Western holdings (304x284x248cm-120x112x98in) painted aluminium prov.lit. 5-Jun-2 Il Ponte, Milan #146/R est:80000-100000
£112500	$180000	€168750	The forge - S-10 3D version (248x273x164cm-98x107x65in) cast metal mixed media cast 1988 prov.exhib.lit. 15-May-3 Phillips, New York #35/R est:150000-200000
£151899	$240000	€227849	Thruxton XVIII, 4.75X (295x320x58cm-116x126x23in) wall relief oil col oilstick glitter lacquer etched magnesium. 14-Nov-2 Christie's, Rockefeller NY #182/R est:150000-200000

Works on paper

£4461	$7048	€6692	Ahab's leg - from the series - The waves (190x140cm-75x55in) s.d.89 graphic mixed media prov. 1-Apr-3 Rasmussen, Copenhagen #206/R est:50000-75000 (D.KR 48000)
£28125	$45000	€42188	Noguchi's okinawa woodpecker (156x216cm-61x85in) s.d.80 mixed media on tycore board prov. 14-May-3 Sotheby's, New York #245/R est:35000-45000
£34375	$55000	€51563	Green solitaire (156x217cm-61x85in) s.d.80 mixed media on tycore board prov. 14-May-3 Sotheby's, New York #246/R est:35000-45000
£71875	$115000	€107813	Karpathenburg I (297x343cm-117x135in) mixed media on canvas prov.exhib. 15-May-3 Christie's, Rockefeller NY #192/R est:150000-200000
£250000	$400000	€375000	Jacques le fataliste (343x343cm-135x135in) synthetic polymer paint on canvas executed 1974 prov.exhib. 15-May-3 Phillips, New York #28/R est:400000-600000
£297468	$470000	€446202	Bijoux indiscrets (343x343cm-135x135in) synthetic polymer on canvas executed 1974 prov.exhib. 13-Nov-2 Christie's, Rockefeller NY #23/R est:400000-600000

STELLA, Jacques de (1596-1657) French

£26761	$44423	€38000	Enee au festin de didon (118x164cm-46x65in) 16-Jun-3 Claude Aguttes, Neuilly #4/R est:40000-60000

Works on paper

£3919	$6114	€5800	Masked figures (23x31cm-9x12in) chk pen ink wash htd white prov. 27-Mar-3 Christie's, Paris #86/R

STELLA, Jacques de (attrib) (1596-1657) French

Works on paper

£705	$1093	€1100	Putto vu de dos (12x21cm-5x8in) pen ink wash htd gouache. 4-Dec-2 Piasa, Paris #62

STELLA, Joseph (1877-1946) American

£2927	$4800	€4244	Shepherd and shepherdess (27x33cm-11x13in) s. linen canvas. 5-Jun-3 Swann Galleries, New York #239/R est:4000-6000
£24691	$40000	€37037	Song of birds (48x18cm-19x7in) s. painted c.1919 prov. 21-May-3 Sotheby's, New York #79/R est:30000-50000
£37037	$60000	€55556	Tree of Nice (81x65cm-32x26in) s. painted c.1928-30 prov.exhib. 21-May-3 Sotheby's, New York #77/R est:60000-80000

Works on paper

£240	$375	€360	Portrait of a man in a fedora (17x11cm-7x4in) s. pencil prov. 12-Apr-3 Weschler, Washington #585/R
£290	$475	€421	Seated man with a hat (17x10cm-7x4in) s. pencil. 5-Jun-3 Swann Galleries, New York #242/R
£335	$550	€486	Study - woman in profile (18x13cm-7x5in) s. pencil ink wash prov. 1-Jun-3 Wright, Chicago #117/R
£350	$550	€525	Bust of a young woman (28x46cm-11x18in) s.d.1900 pencil prov.exhib. 14-Dec-2 Weschler, Washington #719/R
£396	$650	€574	Portrait of David Burliuk (33x24cm-13x9in) s.i.d. pencil col pencil. 5-Jun-3 Swann Galleries, New York #244/R
£457	$750	€663	Untitled, abstraction (23x11cm-9x4in) brush ink. 5-Jun-3 Swann Galleries, New York #241/R
£671	$1100	€973	Cafe scene. Peasant women (10x9cm-4x4in) s. pencil drs pair. 5-Jun-3 Swann Galleries, New York #245/R
£732	$1200	€1061	Desegni Origina del Celebre Barto Pinelli de Patria (17x15cm-7x6in) s. pencil paper on drawing paper. 5-Jun-3 Swann Galleries, New York #237/R
£1410	$2200	€2115	Pears in a dish (23x28cm-9x11in) s. pastel pencil prov. 20-Sep-2 New Orleans Auction, New Orleans #50/R est:2500-4000
£1613	$2500	€2420	Study for three heads (19x14cm-7x6in) s. pencil col chk prov.exhib. 29-Oct-2 Sotheby's, New York #298/R est:2000-3000
£2927	$4800	€4244	Italianate landscape with hill town (57x41cm-22x16in) s. W/C pastel crayon exec.c.1912. 5-Jun-3 Swann Galleries, New York #238/R est:3000-5000
£5660	$9000	€8490	Cityscape (24x16cm-9x6in) s. W/C gouache prov. 5-Mar-3 Sotheby's, New York #81/R est:7000-10000
£9740	$15000	€14610	Lilies and sparrow (73x54cm-29x21in) s.i.d.1931 crayon silverpoint paperboard prov. 4-Sep-2 Christie's, Rockefeller NY #368/R est:5000-7000
£216049	$350000	€324074	Telegraph pole (63x50cm-25x20in) s.d.1917 gouache ink. 21-May-3 Sotheby's, New York #4/R est:150000-200000

STELLINGWERFF, Jacobus (?-1736) Dutch

Works on paper

£344	$537	€540	View of Castle Westerbeek (12x16cm-5x6in) s.i. pen grey ink. 5-Nov-2 Sotheby's, Amsterdam #230/R

STELZMANN, Volker (1940-) German

£3774	$5811	€6000	Self portrait with identity tag (43x37cm-17x15in) mono.d.1975 panel. 26-Oct-2 Dr Lehr, Berlin #504/R est:2500

STELZNER, Heinrich (1833-1910) German
£2041 $3245 €3000 Artist painting portrait in studio (58x97cm-23x38in) s. 19-Mar-3 Neumeister, Munich #750/R est:1000

STEN, John (1879-1922) Swedish
£3504 $5466 €5256 Rusty red sails, fishing village in Brittany (60x75cm-24x30in) prov.lit. 5-Nov-2 Bukowskis, Stockholm #14/R est:40000-50000 (S.KR 50000)

STEN-KNUDSEN, Nina (20th C) Scandinavian
£1144 $1910 €1659 Uma-na (105x170cm-41x67in) s.d.85 verso acrylic pastel chk canvas lit.exhib. 17-Jun-3 Rasmussen, Copenhagen #61/R est:8000 (D.KR 12000)

STENBERG, Carl (19/20th C) Swedish
£476 $757 €714 In front of the mirror (126x92cm-50x36in) s.d.12. 3-Mar-3 Lilla Bukowskis, Stockholm #306 (S.KR 6400)

STENBERG, Ron (1919-) New Zealander?
£313 $489 €470 Self at 35 (55x41cm-22x16in) s. 7-Nov-2 International Art Centre, Auckland #130/R est:1000-2000 (NZ.D 1000)
£351 $547 €527 Still life with green bottles on table (75x90cm-30x35in) s. board. 27-Mar-3 International Art Centre, Auckland #59/R (NZ.D 1000)
£862 $1345 €1293 Crail, Scotland (58x116cm-23x46in) s. board. 7-Nov-2 International Art Centre, Auckland #48/R est:4000-7000 (NZ.D 2750)
£940 $1467 €1410 Winter in Omapere (60x97cm-24x38in) s. board. 7-Nov-2 International Art Centre, Auckland #47/R est:4000-6000 (NZ.D 3000)

STENBERG, Vladimir (1899-1982) Russian
Works on paper
£7000 $11340 €10500 Film poster designs for construction (27x19cm-11x7in) s.d.1918 gouache set of four. 21-May-3 Sotheby's, London #214/R est:5000-7000

STENERSEN, Gudmund (1863-1934) Norwegian
£436 $685 €654 Windy evening (79x96cm-31x38in) s. 25-Nov-2 Blomqvist, Lysaker #1261/R (N.KR 5000)
£853 $1331 €1280 Breaking peak, Jaeren (59x94cm-23x37in) s. painted 1902. 23-Sep-2 Blomqvist, Lysaker #1231/R (N.KR 10000)

STENGEL, George J (1872-1937) American
£1911 $3000 €2867 New England fishing village (51x41cm-20x16in) 19-Nov-2 Butterfields, San Francisco #8053/R est:3000-5000

STENGEL, Hans (19/20th C) American
Works on paper
£4348 $7000 €6522 Three people in a theatre balcony (28x20cm-11x8in) s. ink W/C sold with magazine cover. 10-May-3 Illustration House, New York #6/R est:4500-6000

STENGELIN, Alphonse (1852-1938) French
£1122 $1761 €1750 Landscape (23x35cm-9x14in) s. board. 19-Nov-2 Castellana, Madrid #453/R

STENIUS, Per (1922-) Finnish
£392 $612 €620 Composition - landscape (50x60cm-20x24in) s.d.1975. 12-Sep-2 Hagelstam, Helsinki #872
£696 $1100 €1100 Mountain lake (50x61cm-20x24in) s. board. 1-Dec-2 Bukowskis, Helsinki #354/R

STENN, Henri (20th C) ?
£327 $526 €500 Bord de riviere a Le Thillay, Seine et Oise (22x27cm-9x11in) s. panel. 19-Jan-3 Feletin, Province #131
£545 $855 €850 Bords de Marne (38x55cm-15x22in) s. 13-Dec-2 Piasa, Paris #231/R

STENNEBERG, Piet (1902-1972) Dutch
£313 $516 €450 Composition (25x35cm-10x14in) oil gouache wallpaper prov. 1-Jul-3 Christie's, Amsterdam #436

STENNER, Hermann (1891-1914) German
£1899 $3000 €3000 Landscape with trees (49x40cm-19x16in) s. canvas on board. 27-Nov-2 Dr Fritz Nagel, Stuttgart #3215/R est:4000

STENNETT, Ralph (18/19th C) British
Works on paper
£360 $558 €540 Sparrows with young (15x23cm-6x9in) s.d.1845 W/C dr. 5-Oct-2 Finan Watkins & Co, Mere #196

STENVALL, Kaj (1951-) Finnish
£3544 $5600 €5600 Der einen Monument - animals of stone (100x130cm-39x51in) s.d.1989. 1-Dec-2 Bukowskis, Helsinki #356/R est:5000-6000
£5380 $8500 €8500 Creating his own image (100x130cm-39x51in) s.d.1991. 1-Dec-2 Bukowskis, Helsinki #355/R est:5000-6000
£6962 $11000 €11000 Eternal spectator (150x120cm-59x47in) s.d.1991. 30-Nov-2 Hagelstam, Helsinki #173/R est:4000

STENVERT, Curt (1920-1994) Austrian
Works on paper
£313 $494 €450 Bulls (31x46cm-12x18in) mono.d.1946 Indian ink. 24-Apr-3 Dorotheum, Vienna #143/R

STENVINKEL, Jan (1933-1989) Swedish
£877 $1385 €1316 The well (200x180cm-79x71in) s. 30-Nov-2 Goteborg Auktionsverk, Sweden #639/R (S.KR 12500)

STEPHAN, Gary (1942-) American
£466 $750 €699 Guest ice (274x213cm-108x84in) s.i.d.1986 i.verso acrylic. 23-Feb-3 Butterfields, Los Angeles #7059

STEPHAN, Joseph (1709-1786) German
£33784 $52703 €50000 The four seasons (48x68cm-19x27in) mono. copper four. 27-Mar-3 Dr Fritz Nagel, Stuttgart #784/R

STEPHAN, Joseph (attrib) (1709-1786) German
£3226 $5097 €5000 Hallali du sanglier (29x38cm-11x15in) copper. 20-Dec-2 Tajan, Paris #75/R est:6000

STEPHANOFF, Francis Philip (1788-1860) British
£427 $700 €619 Parlor merriment (25x20cm-10x8in) panel prov. 4-Jun-3 Doyle, New York #90
£681 $1076 €1022 Romantic scene with young girl refusing a proposal (51x55cm-20x22in) s. panel. 2-Dec-2 Rasmussen, Copenhagen #1715/R (D.KR 8000)

STEPHENS, Alice Barber (1858-1932) American
£4088 $6500 €6132 Apple picking (47x28cm-19x11in) s.d.98 canvasboard. 7-Mar-3 Skinner, Boston #308/R est:2000-4000

STEPHENSON, Benjamin Turner (1886-1973) American
£219 $350 €318 Quiet Cove, possibly Monhegan (38x53cm-15x21in) s. 16-May-3 Skinner, Boston #280/R

STEPHENSON, Lionel Macdonald (1854-1907) Canadian
£1200 $1968 €1800 Canoeing past fort Garry (25x46cm-10x18in) init.i.d.69 board. 3-Jun-3 Joyner, Toronto #232/R est:1500-2000 (C.D 2700)
£1235 $1914 €1853 Rapids below the bridge, Red River (31x46cm-12x18in) s. board. 3-Dec-2 Joyner, Toronto #376 est:1400-1800 (C.D 3000)
£2366 $3668 €3549 Dog sled team, Fort Garry (30x46cm-12x18in) init.i. board. 3-Dec-2 Joyner, Toronto #179/R est:2500-3500 (C.D 5750)

STEPHENSON, Peter (1823-1860) American
£1992 $3267 €2988 White leader third rescue (152x167cm-60x66in) s.d.01 s.i.d.2001 verso. 4-Jun-3 Deutscher-Menzies, Melbourne #113/R est:6000-9000 (A.D 5000)
£3400 $5474 €5100 White leader, 2nd rescue (179x179cm-70x70in) s.d.2001 s.i.d.verso. 6-May-3 Christie's, Melbourne #328/R est:5000-6000 (A.D 8500)

Works on paper
£478 $784 €717 Hot sea, white leader (73x98cm-29x39in) s.i.d.2000 pencil pastel. 4-Jun-3 Deutscher-Menzies, Melbourne #277/R (A.D 1200)
£577 $917 €866 Blue leader IV (56x68cm-22x27in) s.i.d.2000 pastel. 4-Mar-3 Deutscher-Menzies, Melbourne #173/R (A.D 1500)

STEPHENSON, Philippa Anna Frederica (fl.1896-1899) British
Works on paper
£340 $547 €510 Damascus Gate, Jerusalem (26x18cm-10x7in) s.i.verso W/C. 15-Jan-3 Cheffins Grain & Comins, Cambridge #371/R

STEPHENSON, Willie (fl.1893-1938) British
Works on paper
£650 $1027 €975 Beached fishing boat on the coast of North Wales (30x48cm-12x19in) s. W/C. 13-Nov-2 Halls, Shrewsbury #325/R

STEPPE, Jacques (20th C) ?

£650 $1001 €975 Portrait of a lady, seated (150x117cm-59x46in) s.d.1936. 24-Oct-2 Christie's, Kensington #193/R

STEPPE, Romain (1859-1927) Belgian

£283 $442 €450 Landscape with high trees near the water (32x24cm-13x9in) s. panel. 23-Sep-2 Bernaerts, Antwerp #27/R
£288 $460 €400 Sur l'escaut soir de septembre (25x15cm-10x6in) s. panel. 13-May-3 Palais de Beaux Arts, Brussels #313
£288 $460 €400 Cote anglaise (19x24cm-7x9in) s. panel. 13-May-3 Palais de Beaux Arts, Brussels #314
£302 $486 €450 View of the Scheldt (48x70cm-19x28in) s. 24-Feb-3 Bernaerts, Antwerp #110/R
£317 $506 €440 En mer (18x24cm-7x9in) s. panel. 13-May-3 Palais de Beaux Arts, Brussels #315
£326 $535 €450 Nocturne d'octobre (16x24cm-6x9in) s. panel. 27-May-3 Campo & Campo, Antwerp #211
£342 $538 €500 Marine (30x45cm-12x18in) s. 15-Apr-3 Galerie Moderne, Brussels #374
£346 $536 €550 Before the Dover coast (21x32cm-8x13in) s. 5-Oct-2 De Vuyst, Lokeren #338
£353 $554 €550 Marine (28x41cm-11x16in) panel. 25-Nov-2 Amberes, Antwerp #212
£377 $585 €600 Snow-covered city (30x45cm-12x18in) s.i.d.1887. 5-Oct-2 De Vuyst, Lokeren #339
£385 $604 €600 Moulin a vent a Anvers (43x54cm-17x21in) 25-Nov-2 Amberes, Antwerp #211
£387 $612 €600 Bord de ;'Escaut (17x29cm-7x11in) s. panel. 17-Dec-2 Palais de Beaux Arts, Brussels #625
£390 $632 €550 Barques de peche en pleine mer (48x40cm-19x16in) 26-May-3 Amberes, Antwerp #78
£399 $654 €550 Ferme au bord de l'Escaut (16x24cm-6x9in) s.d.1915 panel. 27-May-3 Campo & Campo, Antwerp #213
£399 $654 €550 Bord de l'Escaut (16x24cm-6x9in) s. panel. 27-May-3 Campo & Campo, Antwerp #214
£411 $642 €650 Plage flamande (24x32cm-9x13in) s. panel. 21-Oct-2 Bernaerts, Antwerp #9/R
£417 $646 €650 Bord d'un etang en pays Flammand (24x32cm-9x13in) s. panel. 7-Dec-2 De Vuyst, Lokeren #310/R
£426 $711 €600 Marina with two yachts (30x42cm-12x17in) s. panel. 23-Jun-3 Bernaerts, Antwerp #93
£461 $747 €650 Paysage fluvial au coucher du soleil (48x40cm-19x16in) 26-May-3 Amberes, Antwerp #77
£563 $907 €800 La malle d'Ostende a Douvres au matin (49x70cm-19x28in) s. 12-May-3 Bernaerts, Antwerp #193/R
£563 $907 €800 Three master at sunset (49x70cm-19x28in) s. 12-May-3 Bernaerts, Antwerp #194/R
£580 $951 €800 Bateau en pleine mer (28x40cm-11x16in) s. 27-May-3 Campo & Campo, Antwerp #216
£603 $1007 €850 Marina with sailing boat and steamer (23x36cm-9x14in) s. panel. 23-Jun-3 Bernaerts, Antwerp #94
£616 $1010 €850 Jour d'ete a Boom (45x55cm-18x22in) s. 27-May-3 Campo & Campo, Antwerp #215
£625 $987 €900 Barques de peche sur l'Escaut (23x31cm-9x12in) panel. 28-Apr-3 Amberes, Antwerp #317
£625 $987 €900 Voiliers en pleine mer au claire de lune (36x46cm-14x18in) 28-Apr-3 Amberes, Antwerp #318
£694 $1097 €1000 Barques de peche sur l'Escaut (23x31cm-9x12in) panel. 28-Apr-3 Amberes, Antwerp #316
£704 $1134 €1000 Fishing boat at sunset (70x48cm-28x19in) s. 12-May-3 Bernaerts, Antwerp #192/R
£845 $1361 €1200 Soir d'automne (100x70cm-39x28in) s. 12-May-3 Bernaerts, Antwerp #191/R
£886 $1382 €1400 Fishing boats (24x16cm-9x6in) s. panel pair. 21-Oct-2 Bernaerts, Antwerp #8/R
£1079 $1727 €1500 North Sea, Ostend, after midday in October (49x59cm-19x23in) s. i.verso. 17-May-3 De Vuyst, Lokeren #338/R est:1600-1800
£1392 $2172 €2200 Cargo au crepuscule (70x101cm-28x40in) s. 15-Oct-2 Horta, Bruxelles #155

STERCHI, Eda Elizabeth (1885-?) American

£252 $400 €378 Portrait of an Indian girl (25x18cm-10x7in) s. board painted c.1911 prov. 2-Mar-3 Toomey, Oak Park #614/R
£419 $650 €629 Tunis man with flag (71x53cm-28x21in) s. painted c.1915. 8-Dec-2 Toomey, Oak Park #671/R
£440 $700 €660 Taos figure (25x18cm-10x7in) s.i. board painted c.1911 prov. 2-Mar-3 Toomey, Oak Park #612/R
£710 $1100 €1065 Tunis man (71x53cm-28x21in) s. painted c.1915. 8-Dec-2 Toomey, Oak Park #641/R
£1258 $2000 €1887 Portrait of an officer (61x51cm-24x20in) s. painted c.1911 prov. 2-Mar-3 Toomey, Oak Park #644/R est:3000-5000

STERIO, Charles (1821-1862) Hungarian

£1748 $2709 €2622 Children with a puppy (37x29cm-15x11in) s. 6-Dec-2 Kieselbach, Budapest #93/R (H.F 650000)

STERIS, Gerasimos (1895-1985) Greek

£5200 $8216 €7800 Kiss (46x38cm-18x15in) 1-Apr-3 Bonhams, New Bond Street #72 est:5000-7000

STERK DE JONG, J H (19th C) Dutch

£1418 $2199 €2127 Interior scene with woman seated and baby in cradle (65x50cm-26x20in) s. 4-Dec-2 AB Stockholms Auktionsverk #1852/R est:25000-30000 (S.KR 20000)

STERL, Robert Hermann (1867-1932) German

£472 $736 €750 Bavarian landscape (25x33cm-10x13in) i. 23-Sep-2 Dr Fritz Nagel, Stuttgart #7023/R
£6164 $9616 €9000 Portrait of peasant boy before landscape (60x49cm-24x19in) s. lit. 10-Apr-3 Van Ham, Cologne #1722/R est:13000

Works on paper

£293 $457 €460 Old man finds young girl on snowy steps (15x11cm-6x4in) W/C. 5-Nov-2 Hartung & Hartung, Munich #5135/R
£513 $810 €800 Horse market in Russia (26x31cm-10x12in) mono.d.1914 gouache over W/C chk board prov. 15-Nov-2 Reiss & Sohn, Konigstein #86/R

STERLING, Marc (1898-1976) Russian

£1702 $2843 €2400 Nature morte aux poissons (65x92cm-26x36in) s. 17-Jun-3 Claude Boisgirard, Paris #121/R est:2500-3000

Works on paper

£1042 $1656 €1500 Metamorphose (63x48cm-25x19in) s. wax pastel. 29-Apr-3 Artcurial Briest, Paris #258 est:1500-1800

STERN, Bernhard (1920-) American

Works on paper

£577 $906 €900 Lovers' wall (114x145cm-45x57in) s.i.d.1983 verso mixed media on canvas. 15-Dec-2 Perrin, Versailles #172/R
£641 $1006 €1000 Mur de l'inquietude (114x145cm-45x57in) s. i.d.1983 verso mixed media on canvas. 15-Dec-2 Perrin, Versailles #170/R

STERN, Bert (1930-) American

Photographs

£1948 $3000 €2922 Marilyn Monroe with pearls and glitter (24x34cm-9x13in) num. photograph prov.lit. 24-Oct-2 Sotheby's, New York #225/R est:3000-5000
£2000 $3240 €3000 Marilyn Monroe lying on bed (50x60cm-20x24in) s.d.1982 verso toned silver print lit. 22-May-3 Sotheby's, London #184/R est:800-1200
£2200 $3564 €3300 Marilyn Monroe with orange and yellow striped scarf (42x33cm-17x13in) s.d.1982 verso col print lit. 22-May-3 Sotheby's, London #186/R est:800-1200
£4500 $7290 €6750 Marilyn Monroe with pearl necklace (50x61cm-20x24in) s.versod.1982 verso silver print lit. 22-May-3 Sotheby's, London #181/R est:4000-6000

STERN, Grete (1904-1999) German

Photographs

£2075 $3217 €3300 Paper in glass (38x29cm-15x11in) s.d.1927 silver gelatine masonite. 31-Oct-2 Van Ham, Cologne #329/R est:3600

STERN, Ignaz (1680-1748) German

£3378 $5270 €5000 Madonna and Child with angels (90x66cm-35x26in) prov. 27-Mar-3 Dorotheum, Vienna #253/R est:4000-7000

STERN, Irma (1894-1966) South African

£13758 $22150 €20637 Harbour (43x54cm-17x21in) s.d.1955 oil paper on board. 12-May-3 Stephan Welz, Johannesburg #469/R est:180000-240000 (SA.R 160000)
£17685 $27942 €26528 Blue jug with fruit (55x42cm-22x17in) s.d.1934 lit. 1-Apr-3 Stephan Welz, Johannesburg #448/R est:180000-240000 (SA.R 220000)
£18917 $30456 €28376 Extensive landscape with banana trees (67x67cm-26x26in) s.d.1946. 12-May-3 Stephan Welz, Johannesburg #452/R est:150000-200000 (SA.R 220000)
£21496 $34609 €32244 Still life with buli stool (68x62cm-27x24in) s.d.1940 lit. 12-May-3 Stephan Welz, Johannesburg #466/R est:200000-300000 (SA.R 250000)
£32674 $52605 €49011 Two nudes (97x82cm-38x32in) s.d.1941. 12-May-3 Stephan Welz, Johannesburg #527/R est:400000-600000 (SA.R 380000)
£36114 $58143 €54171 Seated Zanzibar woman (83x66cm-33x26in) s.d.1948. 12-May-3 Stephan Welz, Johannesburg #526/R est:300000-500000 (SA.R 420000)

Works on paper

£688 $1107 €1032 Seated ballerina (19x24cm-7x9in) s.d.1943 pencil crayon. 12-May-3 Stephan Welz, Johannesburg #305 est:5000-7000 (SA.R 8000)
£1537 $2398 €2306 Crouching fruit picker (27x21cm-11x8in) s.d.1956 chl ball point pen pastel gouache. 11-Nov-2 Stephan Welz, Johannesburg #590/R est:5000-7000 (SA.R 24000)
£2150 $3354 €3225 Flower seller (32x24cm-13x9in) s.d.1946 gouache pencil crayon. 15-Oct-2 Stephan Welz, Johannesburg #435/R est:25000-30000 (SA.R 35000)
£2150 $3461 €3225 Three Zanzibar women (17x21cm-7x8in) s.d.1941 col pencil gouache. 12-May-3 Stephan Welz, Johannesburg #447/R est:9000-12000 (SA.R 25000)
£2178 $3398 €3267 Dar-es-Salaam (36x54cm-14x21in) s.d.1942 gouache. 11-Nov-2 Stephan Welz, Johannesburg #492/R est:15000-20000 (SA.R 34000)
£2894 $4572 €4341 Mother and child (37x27cm-15x11in) s.d.1959 gouache. 1-Apr-3 Stephan Welz, Johannesburg #446/R est:30000-50000 (SA.R 36000)
£2923 $4707 €4385 Seated nude with a basket of fruit (43x28cm-17x11in) s.d.1934 gouache. 12-May-3 Stephan Welz, Johannesburg #465/R est:20000-30000 (SA.R 34000)
£3698 $5842 €5547 Canoes on the Congo River (26x36cm-10x14in) s.d.1942 gouache. 1-Apr-3 Stephan Welz, Johannesburg #447/R est:35000-50000 (SA.R 46000)

STERN, Max (1872-?) German
£685 $1068 €1000 Monastery garden (32x27cm-13x11in) s. canvas on board. 10-Apr-3 Van Ham, Cologne #1723
£705 $1093 €1100 Village procession (19x21cm-7x8in) s. canvas on board lit. 7-Dec-2 Bergmann, Erlangen #841/R
£1449 $2377 €2000 Fisherwoman (38x27cm-15x11in) s. canvas on board. 29-May-3 Lempertz, Koln #932/R est:2500
£1972 $3175 €2800 Portrait of woman wearing white bonnet (34x29cm-13x11in) s. canvas on board lit. 9-May-3 Schloss Ahlden, Ahlden #1477/R est:2200

STERNBERG, Harry (1904-) American
£380 $600 €570 Royalty (53x41cm-21x16in) s.d.1956 i.verso oil gold paint masonite. 2-Apr-3 Doyle, New York #64/R

STERNBERG, Nicolas (1901-) Hungarian
£285 $444 €450 Musical clowns (81x60cm-32x24in) 18-Oct-2 Dr Fritz Nagel, Stuttgart #326/R

STERNE, Maurice (1878-1957) American
£545 $850 €818 Native woman of the island of Bali (51x28cm-20x11in) s. i.verso oil on paper prov.exhib. 12-Apr-3 Weschler, Washington #3589/R
£793 $1300 €1150 Pears and grapes (33x43cm-13x17in) s. board. 1-Jun-3 Wright, Chicago #223/R est:1000-1500
£1043 $1700 €1565 Musicians at rest (43x56cm-17x22in) s. board. 2-Feb-3 Grogan, Boston #42 est:400-600
£1166 $1900 €1749 Mending the nets (61x89cm-24x35in) s. board. 2-Feb-3 Grogan, Boston #44 est:600-900
£1350 $2200 €2025 Beach scene (41x51cm-16x20in) s. board. 2-Feb-3 Grogan, Boston #43 est:300-500

STERRE DE JONG, Jacobus (1866-1920) Dutch
£1076 $1678 €1700 Reader (50x40cm-20x16in) s. 21-Oct-2 Glerum, Amsterdam #76/R est:1200-1500

STERREN, Ge Karel van der (1969-) Dutch
£2405 $3800 €3800 Leeuw (47x47cm-19x19in) s.d.1994 verso prov. 26-Nov-2 Sotheby's, Amsterdam #302/R est:4000-5000

STERREN, John van der (1938-) Dutch/Indonesian
£3108 $5128 €4507 Landscape near Mageland, Gunung Sumbing (60x70cm-24x28in) s.d.90 s.d.verso lit. 6-Jul-3 Christie's, Hong Kong #14/R est:10000-12000 (HK.D 40000)

STERRER, Josef (elder) (1807-1888) Austrian
£288 $460 €400 Donau ships with Pfenningberg (36x51cm-14x20in) s.d.1865 tempera. 14-May-3 Dorotheum, Linz #478

STERRER, Karl (1885-1960) Austrian
£1931 $3090 €2800 Deer (94x66cm-37x26in) s.d.1943 W/C gouache board exhib.prov. 11-Mar-3 Dorotheum, Vienna #96/R est:3000-3800

Works on paper

£345 $552 €500 Female nude (39x18cm-15x7in) s.d.47 chk. 11-Mar-3 Dorotheum, Vienna #97/R

STERUP-HANSEN, Dan (1918-1995) Danish
£802 $1252 €1203 Talking around table (102x135cm-40x53in) init. exhib. 18-Sep-2 Kunsthallen, Copenhagen #250/R (D.KR 9500)

STETKA, Gyula (1855-1925) Hungarian
£1496 $2319 €2244 In the pub (38x56cm-15x22in) painted c.1910. 1-Oct-2 SOGA, Bratislava #20/R est:95000 (SL.K 95000)

STETSON, William D (19th C) American
£994 $1600 €1491 Sailboats at sea (76x102cm-30x40in) s.d.02. 20-Jan-3 Arthur James, Florida #27

STETTEN, Carl von (1857-?) German
£448 $713 €650 Still life with ceramic jug (49x45cm-19x18in) s. board. 8-Mar-3 Arnold, Frankfurt #725/R
£510 $795 €800 Girl with wild flowers in front of a Holy figure (79x45cm-31x18in) mono. lit. 7-Nov-2 Allgauer, Kempten #2970/R
£1076 $1678 €1700 Girl at ruins entrance (21x14cm-8x6in) mono. panel lit. 14-Sep-2 Bergmann, Erlangen #729/R est:1500

STETTEN, Carl von (attrib) (1857-?) German
£1249 $2023 €1874 Contemplation (78x45cm-31x18in) s. 24-May-3 Dorotheum, Prague #20/R est:40000-60000 (C.KR 55000)

STETTNER, Louis (1922-) American

Photographs

£3038 $4800 €4557 Times Square (46x31cm-18x12in) s.d.1954 gelatin silver print prov. 25-Apr-3 Phillips, New York #269/R est:3000-5000

STEUART, Ronald Hewison (1898-1988) Australian
£320 $490 €480 Garden composition (71x100cm-28x39in) s. prov. 26-Aug-2 Sotheby's, Paddington #671 est:400-600 (A.D 900)

STEUERWALDT, Wilhelm (attrib) (1815-1871) German
£3205 $5032 €5000 Snow on Heisterbach ruins (71x81cm-28x32in) 21-Nov-2 Van Ham, Cologne #1930/R est:4500

STEVAN, Jean (1896-1962) Belgian
£396 $633 €550 Fermette au printemps (40x38cm-16x15in) s. 19-May-3 Horta, Bruxelles #285

STEVEN, Fernand (1895-1955) Belgian
£1000 $1600 €1450 Jouets (69x59cm-27x23in) 15-Mar-3 De Vuyst, Lokeren #310/R

STEVENS, A (?) ?
£2878 $4604 €4000 Jeune femme lisant un livre (75x55cm-30x22in) s. 13-May-3 Palais de Beaux Arts, Brussels #142/R est:4000-5000

STEVENS, Agapit (1849-1917) Belgian
£828 $1292 €1300 Elegante au bouquet de lilas (70x55cm-28x22in) s. 11-Nov-2 Horta, Bruxelles #85
£1258 $2051 €1900 Joueuse de mandoline (75x55cm-30x22in) s. s.verso. 17-Feb-3 Horta, Bruxelles #164
£1401 $2186 €2200 Jeune fille a la rose (76x55cm-30x22in) s. 11-Nov-2 Horta, Bruxelles #84 est:2500-3500
£2722 $4218 €4300 Femme et son perroquet dans un interieur (61x47cm-24x19in) s. panel. 27-Sep-2 Rabourdin & Choppin de Janvry, Paris #51/R est:4800-5000

STEVENS, Aime (1879-?) Belgian
£705 $1107 €1100 Portrait du pere et de la mere de Aime Stevens (90x131cm-35x52in) s.d.1900 pair. 10-Dec-2 Vanderkindere, Brussels #216

STEVENS, Albert (fl.1872-1902) British

Works on paper

£500 $815 €725 Misty day, Lugano (39x68cm-15x27in) pencil W/C. 17-Jul-3 Tennants, Leyburn #734

STEVENS, Albert George (1863-1925) British

Works on paper

£600 $960 €900 Golden grove, near Whitby (23x30cm-9x12in) s. W/C. 11-Mar-3 David Duggleby, Scarborough #25/R
£1250 $1950 €1875 Orchard in blossom with a girl in a bonnet (26x37cm-10x15in) s. W/C. 10-Sep-2 David Duggleby, Scarborough #161/R est:1200-1600

£2050 $3198 €3075 Dock end, Whitby with Abbey in the background (25x36cm-10x14in) s. W/C. 10-Sep-2 David Duggleby, Scarborough #43/R est:1000-1500

STEVENS, Alfred (1823-1906) Belgian
£1176 $1929 €1800 Musicians in big room (50x39cm-20x15in) s.d.1875 panel. 7-Feb-3 Oger, Dumont, Paris #137/R
£2254 $3741 €3200 Marine (18x11cm-7x4in) init. panel. 11-Jun-3 Beaussant & Lefèvre, Paris #200/R est:1500
£3600 $5832 €5400 Seascape (46x37cm-18x15in) s. board exhib. 20-May-3 Sotheby's, Olympia #384/R est:2000-3000
£4088 $6336 €6500 Seascape with sailing ships (41x32cm-16x13in) s. panel prov.lit. 5-Oct-2 De Vuyst, Lokeren #431/R est:6500-8500
£4329 $6710 €6494 Woman with fan (35x25cm-14x10in) s. panel. 24-Sep-2 Koller, Zurich #6512/R est:10000-15000 (S.FR 10000)
£5769 $8942 €9000 Elegante a la poupee (87x60cm-34x24in) s. 9-Dec-2 Horta, Bruxelles #166 est:3500-5500
£6552 $10483 €9500 Temps de brise au large du Havre (41x32cm-16x13in) s.d.83 panel prov. 11-Mar-3 Christie's, Paris #423/R

STEVENS, Dorothy (1888-1966) Canadian
£9778 $16036 €14667 Lady with parasol (85x75cm-33x30in) s. 3-Jun-3 Joyner, Toronto #97/R est:12000-15000 (C.D 22000)

STEVENS, Edward John (jnr) (1923-1988) American
Works on paper
£976 $1600 €1415 Mexican cat (46x53cm-18x21in) s.d.1945 mixed media prov. 1-Jun-3 Wright, Chicago #247/R est:1000-1500

STEVENS, Eion (1952-) New Zealander
£316 $493 €474 Taking the suburbs (84x115cm-33x45in) s.d.1987 board. 27-Mar-3 International Art Centre, Auckland #162/R (NZ.D 900)

STEVENS, Gustav Max (1871-1946) German
£2609 $4278 €3600 La Sultane (80x90cm-31x35in) s. 27-May-3 Campo, Vlaamse Kaai #221/R est:1500-1800
Works on paper
£580 $951 €800 Fillette au bandeau (42x32cm-17x13in) s.d.1918. 27-May-3 Campo, Vlaamse Kaai #222
£1076 $1678 €1700 Nude in front of a landscape (70x50cm-28x20in) s. pastel oval. 21-Oct-2 Bernaerts, Antwerp #573/R est:1500-1800

STEVENS, John (1793-1868) British
£400 $628 €600 Tranquil woodland river landscape (50x76cm-20x30in) s. 10-Dec-2 Rosebery Fine Art, London #564/R
£400 $624 €600 In the gardens at Versailles (45x34cm-18x13in) s. 26-Mar-3 Woolley & Wallis, Salisbury #262/R

STEVENS, Mary (fl.1886-1924) British
Works on paper
£700 $1106 €1015 Wild flowers in wood and by lake (28x23cm-11x9in) s. W/C pair. 24-Jul-3 John Nicholson, Haslemere #1060

STEVENS, Quinn (20th C) American
£1341 $2200 €2012 Still life with vase of flowers (76x63cm-30x25in) s. 5-Feb-3 Christie's, Rockefeller NY #12/R est:300-500

STEVENS, Will Henry (1881-1949) American
Works on paper
£1282 $2000 €1923 North Carolina landscape (43x38cm-17x15in) s. pastel. 12-Oct-2 Neal Auction Company, New Orleans #605/R est:2500-3500
£2174 $3500 €3261 House and barn in atmospheric landscape (13x15cm-5x6in) s.d.29 pastel. 18-Feb-3 John Moran, Pasadena #68 est:2000-3000

STEVENS, William Lester (1888-1969) American
£974 $1500 €1461 Still life of flowers in a copper pitcher (74x61cm-29x24in) 6-Sep-2 Douglas, South Deerfield #2
£1299 $2000 €1949 Winter landscape (51x61cm-20x24in) s. 27-Oct-2 Grogan, Boston #98 est:3000-5000
£1708 $2750 €2562 Houses in autumn landscape (51x61cm-20x24in) s. prov. 18-Feb-3 John Moran, Pasadena #35 est:3000-4000
£1863 $3000 €2795 Late winter farm scene with snow melting off barns and outbuildings (48x58cm-19x23in) s. board. 22-Feb-3 Pook & Pook, Downington #343/R est:2000-2500
£1911 $3000 €2867 Rocky sea scene (51x61cm-20x24in) s. 22-Nov-2 Eldred, East Dennis #851/R est:2000-3000
£2083 $3250 €3125 Nantucket coastal. 21-Sep-2 Harvey Clar, Oakland #1472
£2987 $4750 €4481 Fisherman (77x63cm-30x25in) s. 7-Mar-3 Skinner, Boston #495/R est:3000-5000
£5120 $8500 €7424 New England village covered in snow (91x103cm-36x41in) s. prov. 11-Jun-3 Butterfields, San Francisco #4085/R est:6000-8000
Works on paper
£701 $1100 €1052 Churchyard with church building with stained glass window and bell tower steeple (56x48cm-22x19in) s. W/C. 19-Apr-3 James Julia, Fairfield #242/R

STEVENSON, Harold (1929-) American
Works on paper
£347 $549 €500 Sans titre (73x53cm-29x21in) s. mixed media prov. 27-Apr-3 Perrin, Versailles #78/R

STEVENSON, J Walter (fl.1882) British
£800 $1304 €1200 Botanical Gardens, Jamaica (34x23cm-13x9in) bears i.d.1882 verso panel. 30-Jan-3 Lawrence, Crewkerne #709/R

STEVENSON, James (?-1844) British
Works on paper
£1304 $2100 €1956 Young skateboarder leaves the Guggenheim Museum (38x33cm-15x13in) s. chl wash. 10-May-3 Illustration House, New York #20/R est:1200-1800

STEVENSON, James (attrib) (?-1844) British
Works on paper
£3200 $4896 €4800 Prospect of Linlithgow Palace and town (69x109cm-27x43in) W/C. 22-Aug-2 Bonhams, Edinburgh #1112/R est:2000-3000

STEVENSON, Leo W (20th C) British
£400 $648 €600 Golden Lion in a stiff breeze (71x91cm-28x36in) s. 21-May-3 Christie's, Kensington #678/R

STEVENSON, Patric (1909-1983) Irish
Works on paper
£570 $918 €850 Coast at Shrove, Co Donegal (27x34cm-11x13in) s.d.1959 gouache board. 18-Feb-3 Whyte's, Dublin #30/R

STEVENSON, Robert Macaulay (1860-1952) British
£1550 $2418 €2325 Loch Lomond and Ben Lomond from Luss Straits (55x90cm-22x35in) s.d.1883. 10-Apr-3 Bonhams, Edinburgh #142 est:1000-1500

STEVENSON, William Grant (1849-1919) British
£400 $656 €600 Ducks beside a loch gate (24x36cm-9x14in) s.i. 7-Feb-3 Honiton Galleries, Honiton #253
£800 $1240 €1200 Sent for assistance, retriever on a snow covered doorstep (38x48cm-15x19in) mono. 5-Dec-2 Scarborough Perry Fine Arts, Hove #613

STEVENSON, William Leroy (1905-1966) Canadian
£333 $547 €483 Woman reading (40x33cm-16x13in) s. board. 9-Jun-3 Hodgins, Calgary #412/R (C.D 750)
£341 $539 €512 Autumn glade (25x30cm-10x12in) hardboard. 1-Dec-2 Levis, Calgary #103/R (C.D 850)

STEVER, George (20th C) Danish
£1162 $1836 €1743 Pale blue composition (100x80cm-39x31in) s.d.73 verso canvas on veneer exhib.prov. 1-Apr-3 Rasmussen, Copenhagen #385/R est:6000 (D.KR 12500)

STEVNS, Niels Larsen (1864-1941) Danish
£487 $799 €731 Return of the Prodigal Son (34x30cm-13x12in) study lit. 27-May-3 Museumsbygningen, Copenhagen #533 (D.KR 5000)
£5338 $8915 €7740 Wooden fencing at Kimmerslev lake (70x98cm-28x39in) s.d.1935 exhib.prov. 17-Jun-3 Rasmussen, Copenhagen #68/R est:30000-40000 (D.KR 56000)
Works on paper
£254 $394 €381 Panorama landscape (31x52cm-12x20in) mono. W/C pencil. 1-Oct-2 Rasmussen, Copenhagen #341 (D.KR 3000)
£327 $507 €491 Heath landscape near Viborg (35x52cm-14x20in) W/C. 4-Dec-2 Kunsthallen, Copenhagen #324/R (D.KR 3800)
£560 $868 €840 Summer landscape (51x73cm-20x29in) W/C. 4-Dec-2 Kunsthallen, Copenhagen #366/R (D.KR 6500)
£732 $1135 €1098 Village at foot of mountains, Southern Germany (49x60cm-19x24in) W/C sold with etching. 4-Dec-2 Kunsthallen, Copenhagen #325/R (D.KR 8500)

STEWARD, Joseph (1753-1822) American
£6849 $10000 €10274 Portrait of Michael Bull of Hartford, Connecticut (76x66cm-30x26in) lit. 3-Nov-1 North East Auctions, Portsmouth #857/R est:2000-3000

STEWART, Alan (20th C) British
£480 $782 €720 Portrait of the violinist H J Furber (114x91cm-45x36in) s.d.1923. 13-Feb-3 David Lay, Penzance #254
£600 $912 €900 Engagement between HMS Penguin and USS Hornet 23rd March 1815 (61x86cm-24x34in) s. 15-Aug-2 Bonhams, New Bond Street #378/R

STEWART, Cecil Thornley (1881-1967) South African
£205 $320 €308 Summer skies (49x75cm-19x30in) s. board. 11-Nov-2 Stephan Welz, Johannesburg #236 (SA.R 3200)

STEWART, Frank Algernon (1877-1945) British
Works on paper
£950 $1520 €1425 Hunt in a village street, with hounds in the foreground (38x53cm-15x21in) s.d.24 W/C bodycol. 13-Mar-3 Duke & Son, Dorchester #148/R
£1050 $1754 €1523 Fox hunting scenes (33x46cm-13x18in) s. sepia set of three. 24-Jun-3 Holloways, Banbury #487
£1100 $1716 €1650 The 1928 Grand National. the canal turn second time around (38x30cm-15x12in) s. monochrome pen ink wash. 6-Nov-2 Sotheby's, Olympia #79/R est:600-800
£1200 $1872 €1800 Boxing Day field (34x27cm-13x11in) s. monochrome wash pen ink htd bodycol. 6-Nov-2 Sotheby's, Olympia #78/R est:500-700
£1500 $2505 €2175 Opening the gate for a lady, foxhunting scene (37x29cm-15x11in) s. W/C. 24-Jun-3 Holloways, Banbury #486/R est:400-600

STEWART, J E (19th C) British
£700 $1085 €1050 Before Alnwick Castle (18x24cm-7x9in) s.d.1841 i.verso board. 30-Sep-2 Bonhams, Ipswich #504/R

STEWART, James Lawson (fl.1883-1889) British
Works on paper
£350 $553 €525 Bower Bruage, Exe Island, Exeter (49x35cm-19x14in) s. W/C. 18-Dec-2 John Nicholson, Haslemere #1088
£480 $782 €720 Durham cathedral from the river (62x97cm-24x38in) mono. W/C over pencil htd white. 11-Feb-3 Bonhams, Knowle #32
£500 $791 €750 Westminster Hall and Westminster Abbey (34x49cm-13x19in) mono. W/C over pencil htd bodycol. 28-Nov-2 Sotheby's, London #279/R

STEWART, Jeanne M (1868-?) American
£357 $550 €536 Circus scene (71x61cm-28x24in) s. painted c.1930. 8-Sep-2 Treadway Gallery, Cincinnati #730/R

STEWART, John (19/20th C) British
£320 $496 €480 American Clipper, Red Jacket, in Southern Ocean (71x91cm-28x36in) s.d.73. 25-Sep-2 Hamptons Fine Art, Godalming #410/R
£850 $1377 €1275 American clipper Red Jacket in the southern ocean (71x91cm-28x36in) s.d.73. 21-May-3 Christie's, Kensington #693/R
Works on paper
£360 $547 €540 Sterling Castle in Zanzibar Passage (38x53cm-15x21in) s. gouache W/C. 15-Aug-2 Bonhams, New Bond Street #291
£450 $684 €675 Mauritania off Bishops Rock (38x53cm-15x21in) s. W/C gouache. 15-Aug-2 Bonhams, New Bond Street #289
£600 $912 €900 Queen Mary off Bembridge Ledge (38x53cm-15x21in) s. gouache W/C. 15-Aug-2 Bonhams, New Bond Street #290
£820 $1246 €1230 Titanic off Cowes, Isle of Wight (38x53cm-15x21in) s. W/C gouache. 15-Aug-2 Bonhams, New Bond Street #288/R

STEWART, Julius L (1855-1919) American
£7547 $12000 €11321 In the boudior (91x49cm-36x19in) s.d.97. 4-Mar-3 Christie's, Rockefeller NY #41/R est:12000-18000
£17284 $28000 €25926 Portrait of a woman (135x107cm-53x42in) s.d.1908 prov. 22-May-3 Christie's, Rockefeller NY #55/R est:30000-50000

STEWART, Kerry (1965-) British
Sculpture
£2000 $3280 €3000 Untitled - pregnant schoolgirl (150cm-59in) enamel paint plaster prov.exhib.lit. 6-Feb-3 Christie's, London #763/R est:3000-5000

STEWART, Mark (1951-) American
Works on paper
£2922 $4500 €4383 Crazy quilt (48x71cm-19x28in) W/C. 25-Oct-2 Morris & Whiteside, Hilton Head Island #101 est:5500-6500

STEWART, Merle (fl.1978) Canadian
Works on paper
£201 $315 €302 Purple and white flowers (78x99cm-31x39in) s.d.1991 W/C. 25-Nov-2 Hodgins, Calgary #409/R (C.D 500)

STEWART, Ron (1941-) Canadian
Works on paper
£833 $1300 €1250 Fired on (38x56cm-15x22in) s.i. gouache prov. 9-Nov-2 Santa Fe Art, Santa Fe #58/R est:1000-2000

STEWART, W (?) ?
Works on paper
£520 $816 €780 Getting ready for the day's work. Off Boulogne (18x29cm-7x11in) s. W/C pair. 14-Dec-2 Lacy Scott, Bury St.Edmunds #469

STEWART, William (?) British
£800 $1256 €1200 Figures in a sunlit alley, possibly a scene at Runswick Bay (46x36cm-18x14in) s.d.1900. 19-Nov-2 Bonhams, Leeds #168
Works on paper
£300 $477 €450 Arran from Bute (17x25cm-7x10in) init. W/C bodycol. 6-Mar-3 Christie's, Kensington #136/R
£340 $537 €510 Boats moored on shore (19x41cm-7x16in) s. W/C. 27-Nov-2 Peter Wilson, Nantwich #118/R

STEYAERT, B (20th C) Belgian?
£283 $436 €450 Estacade (86x110cm-34x43in) s. 22-Oct-2 Campo, Vlaamse Kaai #280

STEYER, Peter (1927-) German
Sculpture
£759 $1200 €1200 Arab mother (52cm-20in) mono. brown pat.bronze Cast.W.Geisler Berlin. 29-Nov-2 Villa Grisebach, Berlin #909/R
£1013 $1600 €1600 Amir standing (71cm-28in) mono. yellow brown pat.bronze Cast.H.Noack Berlin. 29-Nov-2 Villa Grisebach, Berlin #908/R est:1500-2000
£1310 $2070 €1900 Leapfrog (70cm-28in) mono. brown pat.bronze lit. 2-Apr-3 Dr Fritz Nagel, Stuttgart #9548/R est:1900

STEYN, Stella (1907-1987) British/Irish
£818 $1275 €1300 Rooftops (51x76cm-20x30in) studio st.verso. 17-Sep-2 Whyte's, Dublin #66/R
£823 $1275 €1300 Still life (54x66cm-21x26in) board prov. 24-Sep-2 De Veres Art Auctions, Dublin #107 est:3000-5000
£1203 $1864 €1900 Still life (51x61cm-20x24in) board prov. 24-Sep-2 De Veres Art Auctions, Dublin #181/R est:2000-4000
£1410 $2214 €2200 Still life with peaches and mixed flowers (51x61cm-20x24in) board. 19-Nov-2 Whyte's, Dublin #151/R est:2000-3000
£1646 $2551 €2600 Jug and pot (49x71cm-19x28in) prov. 24-Sep-2 De Veres Art Auctions, Dublin #108 est:3000-5000
£1849 $2903 €2700 Self portrait (34x20cm-13x8in) s.verso board. 15-Apr-3 De Veres Art Auctions, Dublin #117/R est:1800-2200
Works on paper
£701 $1093 €1100 Gentleman and lady. Knight and maiden (24x15cm-9x6in) s. W/C pair. 6-Nov-2 James Adam, Dublin #158/R

STICKS, George Blackie (1843-1938) British
£840 $1327 €1218 Coastal scene at sunset (39x46cm-15x18in) s.d.1894. 22-Jul-3 Sworder & Son, Bishops Stortford #323/R
£1100 $1749 €1650 Sunset at Invergarry, Pethshire (46x38cm-18x15in) s.d.1893 i.d.verso. 6-Mar-3 Christie's, Kensington #84/R est:800-1200
£1923 $2808 €3000 River landscape (105x152cm-41x60in) s.d.1883. 5-Jun-2 Il Ponte, Milan #241
£2584 $3928 €3876 Romantic mountain landscape with castle and lake (90x70cm-35x28in) s.d.1878. 27-Aug-2 Rasmussen, Copenhagen #1929/R est:35000-40000 (D.KR 30000)

STICKS, Harry (1867-1938) British
Works on paper
£380 $589 €570 Cumbrian cottage (24x19cm-9x7in) s. W/C. 24-Sep-2 Anderson & Garland, Newcastle #317

STIEGLITZ, Alfred (1864-1946) American
Photographs
£1899 $3000 €2849 Icy night (13x16cm-5x6in) i. photogravure executed c.1903. 25-Apr-3 Phillips, New York #202/R est:2000-3000
£2194 $3400 €3291 Georgia O'Keeffe and Frank Prosser, Lake George (23x28cm-9x11in) warm toned silver print. 5-Dec-2 Swann Galleries, New York #575/R est:3500-4500
£2848 $4500 €4272 Steerage (19x15cm-7x6in) format photogravure lit. 22-Apr-3 Christie's, Rockefeller NY #194/R est:5000-7000
£4870 $7500 €7305 Dying chestnut tree, life and death. Study of Margaret Prosser at lake George (23x16cm-9x6in) photograph two prov.lit. 22-Oct-2 Sotheby's, New York #164/R est:10000-15000
£6494 $10000 €9741 Dorothy Norman (12x9cm-5x4in) i. photograph prov.exhib.lit. 22-Oct-2 Sotheby's, New York #162/R est:4000-6000
£7595 $12000 €11393 Steerage (33x26cm-13x10in) large format photogravure on vellum. 23-Apr-3 Sotheby's, New York #58/R est:10000-15000
£7792 $12000 €11688 Steerage (33x26cm-13x10in) photogravure on vellum. 24-Oct-2 Sotheby's, New York #71/R est:4000-6000
£9091 $14000 €13637 Picturesque bits (29x22cm-11x9in) photograph portfolio prov.lit. 24-Oct-2 Sotheby's, New York #83/R est:10000-15000
£10390 $16000 €15585 November days - Munich (20x15cm-8x6in) s.i.d.1934 photograph prov.lit. 22-Oct-2 Sotheby's, New York #43/R est:10000-15000
£12338 $19000 €18507 Equivalent, set c2 no.5. This is G (11x9cm-4x4in) s.i.d.1935 one 1929 photograph two. 22-Oct-2 Sotheby's, New York #45/R est:20000-30000
£16883 $26000 €25325 Venetian gamin (19x16cm-7x6in) s.i.d.1894 photograph prov.lit. 22-Oct-2 Sotheby's, New York #44/R est:10000-15000
£18182 $28000 €27273 Songs of the sky (9x11cm-4x4in) i.verso photograph prov.lit. 22-Oct-2 Sotheby's, New York #46/R est:30000-50000
£37975 $60000 €56963 Katharine Rhoades (22x19cm-9x7in) platinum print lit. 24-Apr-3 Phillips, New York #23/R est:30000-40000

STIELER, Joseph Karl (1781-1858) German
£1761 $2747 €2800 Portrait of Max Joseph I, King of Bavaria (70x57cm-28x22in) lit. 20-Sep-2 Schloss Ahlden, Ahlden #1088/R est:2400

STIENON DU PRE, Caroline (1883-1979) Belgian
£449 $704 €700 Dans la cour de l'hotel Continental (17x24cm-7x9in) s. d.aout 1917 verso cardboard. 10-Dec-2 Vanderkindere, Brussels #39

STIENTJES, Staf (1883-1974) Belgian
£417 $663 €600 Paysage d'hiver (42x57cm-17x22in) s.d.1931. 29-Apr-3 Campo, Vlaamse Kaai #297

STIEPEVICH, Vincent G (1841-1910) Russian
£2966 $4716 €4449 Reclining beauty (51x76cm-20x30in) s. 18-Mar-3 Maynards, Vancouver #28/R est:10000-15000 (C.D 7000)

STIERHOUT, Joop (1911-1997) Dutch
£298 $483 €420 Gladioli (100x79cm-39x31in) s. 26-May-3 Glerum, Amsterdam #164

STIFTER, Moritz (1857-1905) Austrian
£463 $745 €695 Portrait of young woman in historical costume (28x21cm-11x8in) s.d.1883 panel. 7-May-3 Dobiaschofsky, Bern #1003/R (S.FR 1000)
£463 $745 €695 Portrait of young boy in historical costume (28x22cm-11x9in) s.d.1883 panel. 7-May-3 Dobiaschofsky, Bern #1004/R (S.FR 1000)
£1438 $2358 €2200 Fairy dance (24x47cm-9x19in) s. panel. 5-Feb-3 Neumeister, Munich #824/R est:800
£5000 $7800 €7500 At the bazaar (40x32cm-16x13in) s.d.1892 panel. 15-Oct-2 Sotheby's, London #221/R est:5000-6000

STIKVOORT, Koos (1891-?) Dutch
£449 $704 €700 Three elegant ladies on the beach (53x44cm-21x17in) 25-Nov-2 Glerum, Amsterdam #69
£780 $1264 €1100 Still life with apples (21x26cm-8x10in) s. panel. 26-May-3 Glerum, Amsterdam #105

STILL, Clyfford (1904-1980) American
£32051 $50000 €48077 Portrait of a gentleman, at the piano, Harald Logan. Untitled, abstraction (96x107cm-38x42in) bears sig. stretcher double-sided painted c.1937-41 prov.lit. 14-Oct-2 Butterfields, San Francisco #2041a/R est:60000-80

STILLER, Ludwig (1872-?) German
£253 $392 €400 Man on horse with beggars (19x24cm-7x9in) s.i.d.06 panel. 26-Sep-2 Neumeister, Munich #2849/R

STILLING, H C (?) ?
Works on paper
£372 $592 €558 From the little Temple in Karnak (37x26cm-15x10in) s.i.d.1854 pencil W/C. 5-Mar-3 Rasmussen, Copenhagen #2080/R (D.KR 4000)

STILLING, Harald (1815-1891) Danish
Works on paper
£500 $780 €750 Blue mosque, Constantinople (24x33cm-9x13in) init.i. pencil. 15-Oct-2 Sotheby's, London #99/R
£3309 $5427 €4600 Staircase in Albrechtsburg, Meissen (37x29cm-15x11in) s.d. wash Indian ink brush pen sepia board. 4-Jun-3 Reiss & Sohn, Konigstein #299/R est:5000

STILLING, Kenn Andre (1945-) Danish
£340 $538 €510 Face to face (130x97cm-51x38in) s.d.87 s.d.1987 verso. 30-Nov-2 Rasmussen, Havnen #2120 (D.KR 4000)

STINGEL, Rudolf (1956-) Austrian
£421 $700 €632 Untitled (41x35cm-16x14in) s.d.94 verso paper prov. 11-Jun-3 Phillips, New York #352
£3291 $5200 €4937 Untitled (81x81cm-32x32in) s.d.98 oil enamel on canvas prov. 12-Nov-2 Phillips, New York #234/R est:4000-6000

STINTON, Harry I (1882-1968) British
Works on paper
£615 $960 €923 Highland cattle (13x22cm-5x9in) s. W/C. 8-Apr-3 Christie's, Melbourne #86 est:1500-2500 (A.D 1600)

STINTON, James (1870-1961) British
Works on paper
£250 $398 €375 Pair of pheasants amongst shrub (13x18cm-5x7in) s. W/C bodycol exec.c.1930. 30-Apr-3 Brightwells, Leominster #921
£270 $427 €405 Mallard in flight below a lake edge and reeds (29x23cm-11x9in) s. W/C. 27-Nov-2 Wintertons, Lichfield #765/R
£320 $506 €480 Cock and hen pheasant (18x11cm-7x4in) s. W/C. 27-Nov-2 Wintertons, Lichfield #751/R
£520 $806 €780 Cock and hen pheasants in an autumnal landscape (16x16cm-6x6in) s. W/C. 25-Sep-2 Wintertons, Lichfield #553/R
£550 $858 €825 Highland cattle watering in a misty landscape (18x14cm-7x6in) s. pencil W/C htd white. 19-Sep-2 Christie's, Kensington #43
£550 $891 €798 Pheasants in a open landscape (15x20cm-6x8in) s. W/C. 22-May-3 Wintertons, Lichfield #534/R
£580 $922 €870 Pheasants in woodland (18x27cm-7x11in) s. W/C. 4-Mar-3 Bearnes, Exeter #401/R
£600 $954 €900 Pheasants (18x18cm-7x7in) s. W/C pair. 27-Feb-3 Brightwells, Leominster #861/R
£731 $1140 €1097 Grouse in a moorland hollow (24x37cm-9x15in) s. W/C. 8-Apr-3 Christie's, Melbourne #85 est:1500-2500 (A.D 1900)
£750 $1193 €1125 Pheasants in a woodland clearing (25x36cm-10x14in) s. W/C. 29-Apr-3 Gorringes, Lewes #2005
£1538 $2400 €2307 Pheasants in a glade (30x24cm-12x9in) s. W/C. 8-Apr-3 Christie's, Melbourne #84/R est:2000-3000 (A.D 4000)

STINTON, John (20th C) British
Works on paper
£846 $1320 €1269 Cattle by a cottage (25x32cm-10x13in) s. W/C. 8-Apr-3 Christie's, Melbourne #87/R est:1000-2000 (A.D 2200)

STIRLING, David (1889-1971) American
£220 $350 €330 Mountain stream in fall (61x51cm-24x20in) s. board. 7-Mar-3 Jackson's, Cedar Falls #1001/R
£255 $400 €383 Western landscape (46x51cm-18x20in) s. board. 20-Nov-2 Boos Gallery, Michigan #414/R
£270 $420 €405 Landscape (46x53cm-18x21in) s. board. 23-Sep-2 Aspire, Cleveland #10
£366 $600 €549 Alpenglow Colorado. s. board. 31-May-3 Harvey Clar, Oakland #1204
£516 $800 €774 Twin Sister's Mountain, Rocky Mountain National Park (61x71cm-24x28in) s. board. 7-Dec-2 Harvey Clar, Oakland #1192

STIRNBRAND, Franz Seraph (1788-1882) Austrian
£613 $1000 €920 Wedding portrait (66x55cm-26x22in) s.i.d.1833 verso. 16-Feb-3 Butterfields, San Francisco #2031

STIXRUD, Chr (1900-1968) Norwegian
£277 $424 €416 Factory buildings (54x46cm-21x18in) s. panel. 26-Aug-2 Blomqvist, Lysaker #1377 (N.KR 3200)

STOBART, John (1929-) British
£1700 $2754 €2550 M.V Craftaman and Linguist (59x90cm-23x35in) s. 21-Jan-3 Bonhams, New Bond Street #192/R est:400-600

£2200 $3564 €3300 M.V Benefactor at Greenwich (60x90cm-24x35in) s. 21-Jan-3 Bonhams, New Bond Street #193/R est:500-700
£2200 $3564 €3300 M.V Adventurer at Vera Cruz (60x90cm-24x35in) s. 21-Jan-3 Bonhams, New Bond Street #200/R est:400-600
£2200 $3564 €3300 M.V Wayfarer (59x90cm-23x35in) s. 21-Jan-3 Bonhams, New Bond Street #204/R est:300-500
£2600 $4212 €3900 M.V Adventurer at Trinidad (60x90cm-24x35in) s. 21-Jan-3 Bonhams, New Bond Street #199/R est:500-700
£2800 $4536 €4200 M.V Inventor (61x90cm-24x35in) s. 21-Jan-3 Bonhams, New Bond Street #195/R est:500-700
£3000 $4860 €4500 M.V Trader in the English Channel (60x90cm-24x35in) s. 21-Jan-3 Bonhams, New Bond Street #194/R est:300-500
£3000 $4860 €4500 M.V Statesman at Grenada (60x90cm-24x35in) s. 21-Jan-3 Bonhams, New Bond Street #197/R est:500-700
£4400 $7128 €6600 M.V Merchant off Liverpool (60x90cm-24x35in) s. 21-Jan-3 Bonhams, New Bond Street #196/R est:500-700
£4500 $7290 €6750 M.V Explorer in West India Dock, London (50x75cm-20x30in) s. 21-Jan-3 Bonhams, New Bond Street #198/R est:500-700
£4600 $7452 €6900 M.V Plainsman at Jamaica (60x90cm-24x35in) s. 21-Jan-3 Bonhams, New Bond Street #201/R est:400-600
£6500 $10530 €9750 M.V Administrator at Dar-Es-Salaam (60x90cm-24x35in) s. 21-Jan-3 Bonhams, New Bond Street #202/R est:300-500
£7500 $12150 €11250 M.V Governor at Barbados (59x90cm-23x35in) s. 21-Jan-3 Bonhams, New Bond Street #203/R est:500-700

STOBBAERTS, Jan (1838-1914) Belgian
£443 $691 €700 Nature morte: le petit dejeuner (14x20cm-6x8in) panel. 16-Sep-2 Amberes, Antwerp #254
£3205 $4968 €5000 Chiens jouant dans 'atelier (37x48cm-15x19in) s. panel. 3-Dec-2 Campo & Campo, Antwerp #279/R est:1500-2000

STOBBAERTS, Marcel (c.1899-1979) Belgian
£301 $470 €440 Jeune femme nue allongee (38x46cm-15x18in) s. 14-Apr-3 Horta, Bruxelles #51
£408 $649 €600 Nature morte aux fleurs et coquillages (45x37cm-18x15in) s. 18-Mar-3 Galerie Moderne, Brussels #158
£3022 $4835 €4200 Les poissons rouges (65x53cm-26x21in) s.d.1927 verso. 13-May-3 Palais de Beaux Arts, Brussels #146/R est:2000-3000
Works on paper
£616 $962 €900 Construction. Paysage (34x40cm-13x16in) s. mixed media pair. 14-Apr-3 Horta, Bruxelles #50
£1282 $1987 €2000 Vieux port le soir, Marseille (34x50cm-13x20in) s.i. gouache W/C. 7-Dec-2 De Vuyst, Lokeren #312/R est:1500-1700

STOBBAERTS, Pieter (1865-1948) Belgian
£314 $484 €500 Casbah a Tanger (40x30cm-16x12in) s.d.1914 panel. 22-Oct-2 Campo, Vlaamse Kaai #632
£580 $951 €800 Paysage d'automne (27x40cm-11x16in) s. 27-May-3 Campo & Campo, Antwerp #220
£11321 $17434 €18000 Paysage a Uccle (26x37cm-10x15in) s. 22-Oct-2 Campo, Vlaamse Kaai #633

STOCK, Ignatius van der (17th C) Dutch
£7194 $11511 €10000 Wooded landscape with travelers on a path (66x98cm-26x39in) 14-May-3 Christie's, Amsterdam #127/R est:10000-15000

STOCKFLETH, J (19th C) German?
£523 $858 €800 Cattle (30x43cm-12x17in) s.d.1919. 8-Feb-3 Hans Stahl, Hamburg #116/R

STOCKHOLDER, Jessica (1959-) American
Sculpture
£2258 $3500 €3387 No.204 (96x157x152cm-38x62x60in) garbage pail metal wood paper pastel wires prov.exhib.lit. 26-Sep-2 Christie's, Rockefeller NY #892/R est:7000-9000

STOCKLEIN, Christian (1741-1795) Swiss
£4000 $6240 €6000 Interior of a Gothic church with elegant company conversing in the aisle (33x39cm-13x15in) s. panel. 10-Apr-3 Christie's, Kensington #150/R est:4000-6000
£5479 $8548 €8219 View of city from an interior (26x30cm-10x12in) s. bears d. panel. 28-Mar-3 Koller, Zurich #3145a/R est:10000-15000 (S.FR 12000)
£6173 $10000 €9260 Interior of a cathedral (32x39cm-13x15in) panel prov. 24-Jan-3 Christie's, Rockefeller NY #7/R est:15000-20000

STOCKLER, Emanuel (1819-1893) German
Works on paper
£5986 $9937 €8500 Portrait of lady in elegant boudoir (119x80cm-47x31in) W/C paper on canvas prov. 11-Jun-3 Dorotheum, Vienna #175/R est:8500-10000

STOCKLIN, Friedrich (1770-1828) Swiss
£2800 $4368 €4200 Church interior with a lady and gentleman. Church interior with a cavaliers in foreground (30x27cm-12x11in) s. panel pair. 8-Apr-3 Sotheby's, Olympia #266/R est:3000-5000

STOCKMAN, Billy (1925-) Australian
Works on paper
£325 $504 €488 Untitled (46x61cm-18x24in) s.verso synthetic polymer paint plywood exec.c.1975. 3-Dec-2 Shapiro, Sydney #186 (A.D 900)
£325 $504 €488 Untitled (46x61cm-18x24in) s.verso synthetic polymer paint plywood exec.c.1975. 3-Dec-2 Shapiro, Sydney #187 (A.D 900)

STOCKS, Arthur (1846-1889) British
£2357 $3865 €3418 The flute player (58x41cm-23x16in) s.d.1872 panel. 4-Jun-3 AB Stockholms Auktionsverk #2452/R est:15000-20000 (S.KR 30000)

STOCKS, Minna (1846-1928) German
£475 $750 €750 Horse and foal in the field (20x28cm-8x11in) s. board. 29-Nov-2 Bolland & Marotz, Bremen #774/R

STOCKUM, Hilda van (1908-) Dutch
£1400 $2170 €2100 Still life, copper pan (35x50cm-14x20in) mono. board. 4-Dec-2 John Ross, Belfast #16 est:1250-1500
£1918 $3011 €2800 Nasturtiums (36x31cm-14x12in) init. s.i.d.1985 board prov. 15-Apr-3 De Veres Art Auctions, Dublin #187/R est:3000-4000
£2300 $3565 €3450 Still life (50x61cm-20x24in) mono. board. 4-Dec-2 John Ross, Belfast #62 est:2500-3000
£2397 $3764 €3500 Five eggs on pewter platter (29x38cm-11x15in) init. i.d.1989 verso board. 15-Apr-3 De Veres Art Auctions, Dublin #108/R est:3500-4500
£3623 $5942 €5000 Autumn glow (55x39cm-22x15in) init. s.i.d.1986 verso board. 28-May-3 Bonhams & James Adam, Dublin #153/R est:5000-7000
£3624 $5835 €5400 Jug, tankard and flowers (51x60cm-20x24in) init. i.d.1988 verso board. 18-Feb-3 Whyte's, Dublin #140/R est:4000-5000

STOCQUART, Ildephonse (1819-1889) Belgian
£4430 $6911 €7000 Chasseur et son chien avant l'orage (60x83cm-24x33in) s. panel. 15-Oct-2 Horta, Bruxelles #154/R

STODDARD, Alice Kent (1893-1976) American
£774 $1200 €1161 Portrait of David Krumbhaar (63x53cm-25x21in) s. s.i.d.1935 verso. 8-Dec-2 Freeman, Philadelphia #135/R
£938 $1500 €1407 Girl in Boston rocker (81x61cm-32x24in) s. 11-Jan-3 James Julia, Fairfield #287 est:5000-7000
£1026 $1600 €1539 Seascape (46x66cm-18x26in) s. 18-Sep-2 Alderfer's, Hatfield #296 est:1500-1700
£2500 $3800 €3750 Six people and dachshund stroll down a path to Main Street Monhegan Island (56x66cm-22x26in) 30-Aug-2 Thomaston Place, Thomaston #52

STODDART, M O (1865-1934) New Zealander
Works on paper
£1601 $2449 €2402 Market day Pacific Island La Tele (24x34cm-9x13in) s. W/C prov. 21-Aug-2 Dunbar Sloane, Auckland #131/R est:6000-9000 (NZ.D 5250)

STODDART, Margaret Olrog (1865-1934) New Zealander
Works on paper
£760 $1185 €1140 River landscape (26x38cm-10x15in) s. W/C. 17-Sep-2 Peter Webb, Auckland #173/R est:4000-6000 (NZ.D 2500)
£1100 $1804 €1650 Street scene (34x24cm-13x9in) s.d.1905 pencil chl W/C. 5-Jun-3 Christie's, Kensington #863/R est:800-1200
£1307 $1922 €1961 Camellias on brick step (17x24cm-7x9in) W/C prov. 19-Jun-2 Watson's, Christchurch #50/R est:4000-10000 (NZ.D 4000)
£1929 $2990 €2894 Country cottage scene (25x34cm-10x13in) s. W/C. 4-Dec-2 Dunbar Sloane, Auckland #30/R est:6000-10000 (NZ.D 6000)
£2465 $4067 €3574 West coast beach scene (38x50cm-15x20in) s. W/C. 1-Jul-3 Peter Webb, Auckland #96/R est:7000-9000 (NZ.D 7000)
£2762 $3922 €4143 From the Port Hills to the Southern Alps (42x46cm-17x18in) s. W/C prov. 21-Nov-1 Watson's, Christchurch #58/R est:6500-12000 (NZ.D 9500)
£3052 $4334 €4578 Picnic amongst the bluebells, Hagley Park (24x34cm-9x13in) s. W/C prov. 21-Nov-1 Watson's, Christchurch #10/R est:10000-20000 (NZ.D 10500)
£3158 $4926 €4737 Sunlight and shadow, North Canterbury (24x34cm-9x13in) s. W/C. 27-Mar-3 International Art Centre, Auckland #120/R est:7000-10000 (NZ.D 9000)

£3268 $4804 €4902 Primroses on brick step (17x24cm-7x9in) init. W/C prov. 19-Jun-2 Watson's, Christchurch #40/R est:12000-20000 (NZ.D 10000)
£3860 $6021 €5790 Almond blossoms, Diamond Harbour (26x36cm-10x14in) s. W/C. 27-Mar-3 International Art Centre, Auckland #106/R est:10000-15000 (NZ.D 11000)
£4211 $6568 €6317 Amalfi courtyard with wisteria (38x28cm-15x11in) s.d.1905 W/C. 27-Mar-3 International Art Centre, Auckland #79/R est:12000-16000 (NZ.D 12000)
£4561 $7116 €6842 Canterbury stream (35x24cm-14x9in) s. W/C. 27-Mar-3 International Art Centre, Auckland #64/R est:7000-10000 (NZ.D 13000)
£5016 $7824 €7524 Poppies (34x25cm-13x10in) s. W/C. 7-Nov-2 International Art Centre, Auckland #54/R est:10000-15000 (NZ.D 16000)
£5054 $8087 €7328 Banks Peninsula, Port Hills Series (37x49cm-15x19in) s. W/C. 13-May-3 Watson's, Christchurch #15/R est:10000-15000 (NZ.D 14000)
£6119 $8934 €9179 Bowl of roses (46x58cm-18x23in) s. W/C. 12-Sep-1 Watson's, Christchurch #15/R est:22000-33000 (NZ.D 20500)

STOECKLI, Paul (1906-1992) Swiss
£349 $548 €524 House in landscape (32x40cm-13x16in) s. 23-Nov-2 Burkhard, Luzern #210/R (S.FR 800)
£880 $1416 €1276 Untitled (58x45cm-23x18in) s.d.63. 9-May-3 Dobiaschofsky, Bern #240/R (S.FR 1900)
£1397 $2194 €2096 Untitled (35x33cm-14x13in) s. pavatex. 23-Nov-2 Burkhard, Luzern #213/R est:2000-3000 (S.FR 3200)
£2052 $3222 €3078 Untitled (49x84cm-19x33in) s. pavatex. 23-Nov-2 Burkhard, Luzern #212/R est:4500-5000 (S.FR 4700)
Works on paper
£371 $583 €557 Untitled (18x22cm-7x9in) s. Indian ink W/C. 23-Nov-2 Burkhard, Luzern #237/R (S.FR 850)
£480 $754 €720 Collage (30x25cm-12x10in) s. paper collage. 23-Nov-2 Burkhard, Luzern #238/R (S.FR 1100)
£611 $960 €917 Collage (34x32cm-13x13in) s. paper collage. 23-Nov-2 Burkhard, Luzern #239/R (S.FR 1400)
£1092 $1714 €1638 Diary page (100x70cm-39x28in) s. Indian ink newspaper prov. 25-Nov-2 Sotheby's, Zurich #164/R est:2500-4500 (S.FR 2500)

STOECKLIN, Niklaus (1896-1982) Swiss
£329 $539 €477 Toad (12x17cm-5x7in) s.d.44 W/C pencil. 4-Jun-3 Fischer, Luzern #2681/R (S.FR 700)
£1204 $1938 €1746 Ruins in Vairano (60x80cm-24x31in) s.i. 9-May-3 Dobiaschofsky, Bern #142/R est:5000 (S.FR 2600)
£1310 $2044 €1965 Carrousel du Louvre (23x32cm-9x13in) s.d.52 board. 8-Nov-2 Dobiaschofsky, Bern #192/R est:2500 (S.FR 3000)
£1651 $2675 €2922 Beetle (16x21cm-6x8in) s.d.1953 pavatex. 26-May-3 Sotheby's, Zurich #130/R est:3000-5000 (S.FR 3500)
£1747 $2725 €2621 Caserne des gardes de la republique (33x41cm-13x16in) s.d.31. 8-Nov-2 Dobiaschofsky, Bern #194/R est:5000 (S.FR 4000)
£2098 $3504 €3042 Sils-Baselgia (16x22cm-6x9in) s.d.46 board. 24-Jun-3 Koller, Zurich #57/R est:5000-7000 (S.FR 4635)
£2778 $4472 €4028 San Abbondio (55x46cm-22x18in) s.d.48. 9-May-3 Dobiaschofsky, Bern #202/R est:5000 (S.FR 6000)
£3275 $5109 €4913 Still life with fish and parsley (44x61cm-17x24in) s.d.66. 8-Nov-2 Dobiaschofsky, Bern #185/R est:8000 (S.FR 7500)
£5579 $8815 €8369 Beduin camp (33x41cm-13x16in) s.d.27 i.d. stretcher. 28-Nov-2 Christie's, Zurich #68/R est:5000-7000 (S.FR 13000)
£15094 $24453 €26717 Autumn fair in Basle (80x51cm-31x20in) 26-May-3 Sotheby's, Zurich #123/R est:25000-45000 (S.FR 32000)
Works on paper
£399 $654 €579 Aesche, Silersee (19x31cm-7x12in) s.d.1972 W/C. 4-Jun-3 Fischer, Luzern #2680/R (S.FR 850)
£463 $745 €695 Chickens (23x21cm-9x8in) s.d.70 mixed media. 7-May-3 Dobiaschofsky, Bern #1006/R (S.FR 1000)
£556 $894 €834 Three fried eggs in pan (21x21cm-8x8in) s.d.50 mixed media paper. 7-May-3 Dobiaschofsky, Bern #1005/R (S.FR 1200)
£699 $1090 €1049 Ananas (15x16cm-6x6in) mono.i. pencil W/C. 6-Nov-2 Dobiaschofsky, Bern #997/R (S.FR 1600)
£1073 $1695 €1610 Italian village (35x51cm-14x20in) s.d.1954 wash pen ink dr. 29-Nov-2 Zofingen, Switzerland #3089/R est:3000 (S.FR 2500)
£1092 $1703 €1638 Rue Mazarin (36x27cm-14x11in) s.i.d.56 W/C over pencil. 8-Nov-2 Dobiaschofsky, Bern #193/R est:3000 (S.FR 2500)

STOFFE, Jan van der (1611-1682) Dutch
£3185 $4968 €5000 Cavalry battle scene (34x55cm-13x22in) s. panel prov. 5-Nov-2 Sotheby's, Amsterdam #288/R est:5000-7000
£15172 $24124 €22000 Figures by gate (47x77cm-19x30in) s. board. 4-Mar-3 Ansorena, Madrid #61/R

STOHR, Alvin (1874-1941) Scandinavian
£381 $606 €560 Laplanders (75x92cm-30x36in) s.d.17. 24-Mar-3 Bukowskis, Helsinki #399/R

STOHR, Philipp Gerhard (1795-?) Austrian
Works on paper
£570 $900 €900 Reclining female nude (21x24cm-8x9in) pencil. 29-Nov-2 Bassenge, Berlin #6070

STÖHRER, Walter (1937-2000) German
£3077 $4769 €4800 Untitled (70x100cm-28x39in) s.d.81 acrylic gouache col chk carpenter's pencil. 3-Dec-2 Lempertz, Koln #443/R est:5000
£9220 $14936 €13000 Nr 5 (130x100cm-51x39in) s.d.62 i. verso. 24-May-3 Van Ham, Cologne #563/R est:7000
Works on paper
£461 $747 €650 Figure alphabet (42x30cm-17x12in) s. i. verso Indian ink brush millimetre paper. 24-May-3 Van Ham, Cologne #565/R
£475 $750 €750 Composition (56x39cm-22x15in) s.i.d.77 W/C col pen wax chk felt pen over etching. 29-Nov-2 Villa Grisebach, Berlin #914/R
£570 $900 €900 Composition (36x25cm-14x10in) s.d.1983 mixed media. 30-Nov-2 Arnold, Frankfurt #538/R
£1282 $1987 €2000 Black Toscana (48x32cm-19x13in) s.d.78 s.i.d. verso graphite Indian ink gouache. 3-Dec-2 Lempertz, Koln #439/R est:2000
£1899 $3000 €3000 Untitled (55x38cm-22x15in) i. gouache col chks graph paper. 30-Nov-2 Villa Grisebach, Berlin #438/R est:3000-4000
£2089 $3300 €3300 Cut up (51x73cm-20x29in) s.d.71 gouache chks. 30-Nov-2 Villa Grisebach, Berlin #437/R est:4000-5000
£3237 $5309 €4500 Each natural preference takes the shortest route (23x31cm-9x12in) s.i. s.i.d.78 verso mixed media board. 5-Jun-3 Dorotheum, Salzburg #869/R est:7000-9000
£7278 $11500 €11500 Untitled (89x118cm-35x46in) s.d.1984 mixed media. 30-Nov-2 Villa Grisebach, Berlin #439/R est:12000-14000
£10870 $17826 €15000 Picture No 1 (180x160cm-71x63in) s.d.75 i. verso mixed media prov. 31-May-3 Villa Grisebach, Berlin #365/R est:15000-20000
£10897 $16891 €17000 Picture 2.5 (150x100cm-59x39in) s.d.1963 i. verso. 6-Dec-2 Hauswedell & Nolte, Hamburg #361/R est:20000

STOILOFF, C (1850-1924) Austrian/Russian
£1769 $2812 €2600 Transport of guards (70x105cm-28x41in) s. 25-Feb-3 Dorotheum, Vienna #79/R est:2800-3200
£1769 $2812 €2600 Wild travel (70x105cm-28x41in) s. 25-Feb-3 Dorotheum, Vienna #76 est:2800-3200
£2013 $3119 €3200 Cossacks (66x53cm-26x21in) s. 29-Oct-2 Dorotheum, Vienna #40/R est:1800-2000

STOILOFF, Constantin (1850-1924) Austrian/Russian
£949 $1500 €1500 Fishermen on the beach (69x106cm-27x42in) s. 1-Dec-2 Bukowskis, Helsinki #231/R est:2500-3000
£962 $1462 €1500 Transporting gold (31x47cm-12x19in) s. panel. 17-Aug-2 Hans Stahl, Toestorf #28/R
£1156 $1918 €1676 Troika pursued by troops (51x81cm-20x32in) s. i.on stretcher prov. 16-Jun-3 Waddingtons, Toronto #345/R est:2500-3500 (C.D 2600)
£1210 $1888 €1900 Roman wagon race in Circus Maximus (82x129cm-32x51in) s. lit. 7-Nov-2 Allgauer, Kempten #2745/R est:1800
£1310 $2044 €1965 Le gouverneur en voyage (68x105cm-27x41in) s. 6-Nov-2 Hans Widmer, St Gallen #100/R est:3000-5500 (S.FR 3000)
£1579 $2447 €2369 Scene from Hypodrom (82x130cm-32x51in) painted c.1880. 3-Dec-2 SOGA, Bratislava #157/R est:68000 (SL.K 100000)
£1748 $2709 €2622 Wedding in Galicia (89x124cm-35x49in) s. 6-Dec-2 Kieselbach, Budapest #99/R (H.F 650000)
£1914 $3100 €2775 Horse and sleigh in a snow storm (69x118cm-27x46in) s. 26-May-3 Rasmussen, Copenhagen #1481/R est:20000-25000 (D.KR 20000)
£1944 $3131 €2916 L'escorte (68x105cm-27x41in) s. i. stretcher. 7-May-3 Dobiaschofsky, Bern #1007/R est:5000 (S.FR 4200)
£1964 $3221 €2848 Winter landscape with sleigh and horses (70x104cm-28x41in) s. 4-Jun-3 AB Stockholms Auktionsverk #2460/R est:20000-30000 (S.KR 25000)
£2199 $3408 €3299 Transporting gold (69x105cm-27x41in) s. 3-Dec-2 Bukowskis, Stockholm #176/R est:20000-25000 (S.KR 31000)
£2278 $3600 €3600 The wedding procession (58x79cm-23x31in) s. 1-Dec-2 Bukowskis, Helsinki #230/R est:3000-4000
£3205 $5000 €4808 Escort (51x41cm-20x16in) panel. 20-Sep-2 Du Mouchelle, Detroit #2020/R est:3000-6000
£3521 $5669 €5000 The fish market (82x128cm-32x50in) s. 10-May-3 Bukowskis, Helsinki #379/R est:5000-6000
£4366 $7030 €6200 Fishermen in harbour (81x130cm-32x51in) s. 10-May-3 Bukowskis, Helsinki #396/R est:4000-5000
£4487 $7000 €6731 Russian Cossacks (64x91cm-25x36in) 20-Sep-2 Du Mouchelle, Detroit #2018/R est:6000-8000
£6500 $10206 €9750 Charging the Caucasian convoy (68x100cm-27x39in) s. 20-Nov-2 Sotheby's, London #55/R est:4000-6000
£6500 $10530 €9750 Siberian gold convoy (68x106cm-27x42in) s. 21-May-3 Sotheby's, London #30/R est:4500-6500

STOILOV, Vasil (1904-) Russian
Works on paper
£897 $1418 €1400 Mother with children (43x55cm-17x22in) s.cyrillic mixed media. 12-Nov-2 Dorotheum, Vienna #153/R

STOITZNER, Carl (1866-1943) Austrian
Works on paper
£507 $791 €750 Hay harvest before storm (16x21cm-6x8in) s. W/C board. 28-Mar-3 Dorotheum, Vienna #325/R

STOITZNER, Constantin (1863-1934) Austrian
£250 $408 €375 Old man clutching a glass of ale (20x15cm-8x6in) s. 17-Feb-3 Bonhams, Bath #69
£260 $424 €390 Call out - seaman going to the rescue (57x78cm-22x31in) s. 17-Feb-3 Bonhams, Bath #56
£380 $608 €570 Study of two fishermen on the quayside (57x35cm-22x14in) s. 11-Mar-3 David Duggleby, Scarborough #245/R
£500 $770 €750 Interesting news, figures on a quayside reading a newspaper (57x79cm-22x31in) s. 22-Oct-2 Bonhams, Bath #218
£897 $1400 €1346 Fishermen conversing by the sea. Fishermen with telescope (58x37cm-23x15in) s. pair. 12-Apr-3 Weschler, Washington #547/R est:2000-3000
£950 $1549 €1425 Reading the news. Good vintage (21x15cm-8x6in) one s.i. one s. panel pair. 13-Feb-3 Christie's, Kensington #56/R
£1007 $1652 €1400 Still life with asters in a vase (100x101cm-39x40in) s.d.1914. 5-Jun-3 Dorotheum, Salzburg #537/R
£1013 $1600 €1600 The latest news (41x53cm-16x21in) s.i.d.891 panel lit. 29-Nov-2 Schloss Ahlden, Ahlden #1169/R est:1600
£1603 $2484 €2500 Peasant interior with corner shrine (75x90cm-30x35in) s. 6-Dec-2 Michael Zeller, Lindau #929/R est:2500
£1923 $3038 €3000 Still life of fruit (31x42cm-12x17in) s. board. 18-Nov-2 Dorotheum, Linz #342/R est:2800-3200
£2313 $3678 €3400 Card party in workhouse (75x100cm-30x39in) s. 25-Feb-3 Dorotheum, Vienna #38/R est:2800-3200

STOITZNER, Constantin (attrib) (1863-1934) Austrian
£1103 $1766 €1600 Peasant room (74x90cm-29x35in) i. 11-Mar-3 Dorotheum, Vienna #35/R est:1800-2600

STOITZNER, Egon (20th C) Austrian
£278 $447 €417 Hilly landscape (47x52cm-19x20in) s.d.65. 7-May-3 Dobiaschofsky, Bern #1008/R (S.FR 600)

STOITZNER, Josef (1884-1951) Austrian
£3165 $5000 €5000 Still life with teddy bear (45x55cm-18x22in) s. masonite. 27-Nov-2 Dorotheum, Vienna #164/R est:5000-7000
£3433 $5356 €4978 Farm in winter (56x74cm-22x29in) s. prov. 26-Mar-3 Walker's, Ottawa #38/R est:7000-8000 (C.D 8000)
£3797 $6000 €6000 Peonies (80x70cm-31x28in) s. 27-Nov-2 Dorotheum, Vienna #165/R est:7000-10000
£3863 $6026 €5601 Lake at dawn (56x77cm-22x30in) s. prov. 26-Mar-3 Walker's, Ottawa #37/R est:7000-8000 (C.D 9000)
£6000 $9840 €9000 Blaues interieur - interior in blue (86x105cm-34x41in) s. prov. 3-Jun-3 Sotheby's, London #60/R est:7000-10000
£6757 $10541 €10000 Sailing ship (60x80cm-24x31in) s. 25-Mar-3 Wiener Kunst Auktionen, Vienna #126/R est:9000-12000
£8696 $14261 €12000 Hohe Tauern in winter, viewed from Bramberg (42x47cm-17x19in) s. board. 27-May-3 Hassfurther, Vienna #62/R est:5000-7000
£15823 $25000 €25000 Hay barn in St Gilgen (100x89cm-39x35in) s.d.1920. 26-Nov-2 Wiener Kunst Auktionen, Vienna #94/R est:7000-9000

STOITZNER, Siegfried (1892-1976) Austrian
£1034 $1655 €1500 Windmill near Retz (40x50cm-16x20in) s. panel. 11-Mar-3 Dorotheum, Vienna #84/R est:900-1400
£4483 $7172 €6500 Durnstein with ruins (74x62cm-29x24in) s.d.1923 prov. 11-Mar-3 Dorotheum, Vienna #33/R est:2600-3600
Works on paper
£946 $1476 €1400 Castle ruins in pre-alpine area (49x64cm-19x25in) s. W/C board. 28-Mar-3 Dorotheum, Vienna #322/R

STOJANOW, C (19th C) Russian
£280 $437 €420 Pursued by wolves in the snow (31x53cm-12x21in) 18-Sep-2 Dreweatt Neate, Newbury #127
£1761 $2730 €2800 Capturing the Turkish flag at Semlin (90x123cm-35x48in) s. 29-Oct-2 Dorotheum, Vienna #33/R est:1500-1800

STOJANOW, Pjotr (fl.1887-1894) Russian
£974 $1481 €1500 Wedding party in horse drawn cart (56x69cm-22x27in) s. 6-Jul-2 Berlinghof, Heidelberg #250/R est:1300
£2014 $3223 €2800 Winter landscape with horse drawn carts (79x58cm-31x23in) s. 17-May-3 Lempertz, Koln #1492/R est:2000
£3500 $5565 €5250 Wolves attaking a troika, Returning home with a kill (51x82cm-20x32in) s. pair. 18-Mar-3 Bonhams, New Bond Street #26/R est:3000-5000

STOK, Jacobus van der (1795-1864) Dutch
£1887 $2906 €3000 Winter landscape with skaters on a frozen river (20x30cm-8x12in) s. panel. 22-Oct-2 Sotheby's, Amsterdam #17/R est:5000-7000

STOKELD, James (1827-1877) British
£800 $1240 €1200 Seaham harbour with figures on the beach (40x55cm-16x22in) s.d.1866. 24-Sep-2 Anderson & Garland, Newcastle #474/R

STOKES, Adrian (1854-1935) British
£850 $1326 €1275 On Hampstead Heath (63x76cm-25x30in) 12-Sep-2 Sotheby's, Olympia #107/R
£2381 $3786 €3500 Angler on river shore (41x61cm-16x24in) s.d.18 bears i. 19-Mar-3 Neumeister, Munich #752/R est:3000
Works on paper
£420 $655 €630 Highland landscape with children (36x44cm-14x17in) s. W/C. 28-Mar-3 Bonhams, Edinburgh #151
£1100 $1716 €1650 Portrait of a young boy and girl (56x47cm-22x19in) s.d.1886 pencil W/C. 17-Oct-2 Christie's, Kensington #1/R est:1000-1500

STOKES, Adrian (1902-1972) British
£500 $825 €725 Le pont de Charistan dauphine, France. Afterglow on Rosengarten (21x27cm-8x11in) s. board two. 3-Jul-3 Christie's, Kensington #675

STOKES, Constance (1906-1991) Australian
£358 $545 €537 Rickett's Point (29x40cm-11x16in) i.verso. 28-Aug-2 Deutscher-Menzies, Melbourne #381/R (A.D 1000)
£1394 $2286 €2091 Portrait of the artist's daughter (59x47cm-23x19in) s.d.61 board. 4-Jun-3 Deutscher-Menzies, Melbourne #306/R est:4000-6000 (A.D 3500)
£4286 $6771 €6429 Two children (107x71cm-42x28in) d.1954 verso prov. 26-Nov-2 Sotheby's, Melbourne #37/R est:20000-30000 (A.D 12000)
£10078 $16023 €15117 Rehearsal (55x70cm-22x28in) s. i.verso board prov.exhib. 5-May-3 Sotheby's, Melbourne #125/R est:26000-34000 (A.D 26000)
£22000 $35420 €33000 Three Graces (70x56cm-28x22in) s. board painted c.1951 exhib. 6-May-3 Christie's, Melbourne #47/R est:40000-60000 (A.D 55000)
Works on paper
£450 $711 €675 Seated nude (32x25cm-13x10in) s. pen black ink oil. 15-Nov-2 Sotheby's, London #11

STOKES, Emiline (20th C) British
Works on paper
£460 $745 €690 Fading light (32x29cm-13x11in) s. W/C. 21-May-3 Bonhams, Knightsbridge #35/R

STOKES, George Vernon (1873-1954) British
£550 $858 €825 Portrait of an alsation (49x59cm-19x23in) s.d.1931. 8-Apr-3 Bonhams, Knightsbridge #119
£650 $1027 €975 One that got away - fox escaping from hounds up a fellside crag (60x50cm-24x20in) s. 7-Apr-3 Bonhams, Bath #65/R
£1200 $1872 €1800 Portrait of a black Labrador with mallard (59x48cm-23x19in) s. 14-Sep-2 Cumbria Auction Rooms, UK #58/R est:800-1200

STOKES, Margaret (1916-1996) British
£1034 $1655 €1500 Provencal rooftops (36x46cm-14x18in) init. 11-Mar-3 Thomas Adams, Dublin #444
£1208 $1945 €1800 Phases of the moon (30x41cm-12x16in) init. i.verso canvasboard exhib. 18-Feb-3 Whyte's, Dublin #12/R est:1000-1500
£1507 $2366 €2200 Sunbathing by parasol (40x54cm-16x21in) canvasboard prov. 15-Apr-3 De Veres Art Auctions, Dublin #92/R est:1500-2000

STOLKER, Jan (1724-1785) Dutch
£597 $920 €950 Portrait de l'amiral tromp (11x8cm-4x3in) i. verso grisaille copper oval. 25-Oct-2 Tajan, Paris #82
£828 $1292 €1300 Portrait of the painter Frans Floris (10x9cm-4x4in) i. copper oval prov.lit. 5-Nov-2 Sotheby's, Amsterdam #126/R est:1000-1500

STOLKER, Jan (attrib) (1724-1785) Dutch
£780 $1303 €1100 Portrait d'un gentilhomme et de son epouse (12x9cm-5x4in) panel pair. 23-Jun-3 Delvaux, Paris #21

STOLL, Leopold (1792-1850) German
£256 $403 €400 Bunch of flowers (36x27cm-14x11in) s.d.1884 canvas on canvas. 21-Nov-2 Dorotheum, Vienna #133/R
£274 $430 €400 Flowers (36x27cm-14x11in) s.d.1884. 16-Apr-3 Dorotheum, Salzburg #65/R
£6918 $10723 €11000 Large ornamental still life wit fruit and parrot (95x72cm-37x28in) s.d.1850. 2-Oct-2 Dorotheum, Vienna #249/R est:14000-18000

STOLLER, Ezra (1915-) American
Photographs
£16456 $26000 €24684 Seagram building. Views of Seagram building (20x25cm-8x10in) 38 gelatin silver print prov. 25-Apr-3 Phillips, New York #48/R est:9000-12000

STOLLREITHER, Paul (1886-1973) German
£504 $826 €700 River landscape in autumn (50x60cm-20x24in) s.d.28. 5-Jun-3 Dorotheum, Salzburg #589/R

STOLTENBERG, Fritz (1855-1921) German
£1923 $3019 €3000 Village street in autumn (109x138cm-43x54in) s. 23-Nov-2 Arnold, Frankfurt #877/R est:1600

STOLTENBERG, Hans John (1880-1963) American
£274 $450 €397 Sunset (16x23cm-6x9in) s.d. board. 5-Jun-3 Swann Galleries, New York #248/R

STOLTENBERG, Mattias (1799-1871) Norwegian
£2715 $4398 €4073 Portrait of Consul Mack (33x28cm-13x11in) s.d.1836 exhib.lit. 26-May-3 Grev Wedels Plass, Oslo #88/R est:50000-70000 (N.KR 30000)

STOLTZ, Jette Birgitta (1923-) Swedish
£268 $421 €389 Untitled. prov. 15-Dec-2 Anders Antik, Landskrona #1223 (S.KR 3800)
£282 $443 €409 Untitled. prov. 15-Dec-2 Anders Antik, Landskrona #1224 (S.KR 4000)

STOLZ SEGUI, Ramon (1872-1924) Spanish
£409 $638 €650 Landscape (17x25cm-7x10in) s. board. 23-Sep-2 Durán, Madrid #157

STOLZ, Albert (1875-?) Austrian
£4054 $6324 €6000 Bozen with the Rosengarten behind (50x80cm-20x31in) s. 26-Mar-3 Hugo Ruef, Munich #237/R est:800

STOLZ, Rudolf (1874-1960) Austrian
£31646 $50000 €50000 The three kings (100x128cm-39x50in) s.d. tempera. 27-Nov-2 Dorotheum, Vienna #144/R est:3600-5000

STOLZER, Berthold (attrib) (1881-?) German
Sculpture
£2052 $3263 €3078 Nude woman fixing her hair (50cm-20in) s. marble torso. 5-May-3 Rasmussen, Vejle #127/R est:15000 (D.KR 22000)

STOMER, Matthias I (circle) (c.1600-c.1650) Flemish
£20000 $31600 €29000 The good Samaritan (118x78cm-46x31in) 5-Apr-3 Finarte Semenzato, Milan #91/R est:12000-15000

STONE, C W (19th C) British
£1800 $2880 €2700 Landscape overlooking Leominster, Herefordshire. s.i.verso. 8-Jan-3 Brightwells, Leominster #995 est:300-400

STONE, Charles W (?) British?
£310 $484 €465 Near Leominster, Herefordshire (59x90cm-23x35in) s. s.i.d.1881 verso. 17-Oct-2 Lawrence, Crewkerne #493
£1150 $1783 €1725 Winter landscape with horse-cart of holly in the foreground (60x90cm-24x35in) i.verso. 24-Sep-2 Anderson & Garland, Newcastle #524/R est:800-1200

STONE, Don (1929-) American
Works on paper
£313 $500 €470 Lobster trap (36x53cm-14x21in) s. W/C. 11-Jan-3 James Julia, Fairfield #288
£563 $900 €845 Second field (36x53cm-14x21in) s. W/C. 11-Jan-3 James Julia, Fairfield #289 est:1500-2500

STONE, Louis K (1902-1984) American
£3049 $5000 €4421 Untitled (38x33cm-15x13in) masonite painted c.1939. 1-Jun-3 Wright, Chicago #133/R est:6000-8000
£6369 $10000 €9554 Untitled (32x26cm-13x10in) s. painted c.1930 prov. 19-Nov-2 Wright, Chicago #159/R est:3000-5000

STONE, Marcus (1840-1921) British
£360 $583 €540 Bush warbler with grapes (45x30cm-18x12in) s. 20-May-3 Sotheby's, Olympia #66/R
£720 $1166 €1080 Robin (22x17cm-9x7in) s. panel. 20-May-3 Sotheby's, Olympia #67/R
£30189 $46491 €48000 Reverie (56x31cm-22x12in) s.d.96 canvas board. 23-Oct-2 Christie's, Amsterdam #20/R est:5000-7000
£55000 $88550 €82500 Study for 'My lady is a widow and childless' (57x37cm-22x15in) s. prov.exhib. 20-Feb-3 Christie's, London #259/R est:30000
£100000 $161000 €150000 My lady is a widow and childless (186x124cm-73x49in) s. prov.exhib.lit. 19-Feb-3 Christie's, London #14/R est:150000-200000
Works on paper
£600 $948 €900 Royal nursery. Edward II and Piers Gaveston (26x41cm-10x16in) W/C gouache pair prov. 27-Nov-2 Hamptons Fine Art, Godalming #155/R
£900 $1305 €1350 Merchants in a Venetian square (25x23cm-10x9in) s.d.1877 W/C. 3-May-2 Biddle & Webb, Birmingham #280/R

STONE, Mrs Coward (19th C) British
£2000 $3180 €3000 View near Bedgellert, Wales, at dusk (59x92cm-23x36in) i.verso exhib. 19-Mar-3 Sotheby's, London #80/R est:2500-4000

STONE, R (fl.1900) British
£1000 $1630 €1500 Hunting scene (16x30cm-6x12in) bears s. panel. 13-Feb-3 Mellors & Kirk, Nottingham #807 est:600-700
£6000 $9780 €9000 Hunting scenes (13x29cm-5x11in) s. panel four. 13-Feb-3 Mellors & Kirk, Nottingham #806/R est:5000-6000

STONE, Reynolds (1909-) British
Works on paper
£320 $506 €480 Lower orchard with mulberry (39x53cm-15x21in) s.d.74 W/C over pencil. 2-Dec-2 Bonhams, Bath #35

STONE, Rudolf (19/20th C) British
£1000 $1580 €1500 Hunting scenes (18x33cm-7x13in) s. board pair. 2-Dec-2 Gorringes, Lewes #2630 est:150-200
£1000 $1660 €1450 Meet (16x32cm-6x13in) panel. 12-Jun-3 Christie's, Kensington #17/R est:600-800
£1400 $2268 €2100 Hunting scene (16x31cm-6x12in) s. panel pair. 20-May-3 Sotheby's, Olympia #204/R est:1000-1500
£1548 $2400 €2322 Landscapes with horse-drawn coaches, and huntsmen on horseback (13x27cm-5x11in) s. panel set of four. 2-Oct-2 Christie's, Rockefeller NY #180/R est:3000-5000
£3450 $5727 €5003 Meet. Setting off. In full gallop. The kill (16x33cm-6x13in) s. panel set of four. 12-Jun-3 Christie's, Kensington #14/R est:4000-6000
£3800 $6308 €5510 Setting off. On the scent. Over the hedge. The kill (15x32cm-6x13in) s. panel set of four prov. 12-Jun-3 Christie's, Kensington #18/R est:4000-6000

STONE, Sarah (18th C) ?
Works on paper
£5000 $7900 €7500 Eagle. Owl and fledgling. snowy owl (35x24cm-14x9in) one s. W/C over pencil set of three. 28-Nov-2 Sotheby's, London #309/R est:3000-4000

STONE, Thomas Albert (1897-1978) Canadian
£200 $328 €300 Caledon beech woods (30x40cm-12x16in) s. board. 3-Jun-3 Joyner, Toronto #560 (C.D 450)
£222 $364 €333 Muskoka Lake (30x40cm-12x16in) s. canvas on board prov. 3-Jun-3 Joyner, Toronto #353/R (C.D 500)
£222 $364 €333 Gatineau Road, evening (30x40cm-12x16in) s. board prov. 3-Jun-3 Joyner, Toronto #497 (C.D 500)
£356 $583 €534 Old pine tree, Drag River (30x40cm-12x16in) s. 3-Jun-3 Joyner, Toronto #332/R (C.D 800)
£356 $583 €534 Open water, Credit River (30x40cm-12x16in) s. board. 3-Jun-3 Joyner, Toronto #594 (C.D 800)
£535 $829 €803 Pine, Muskoka Lake (30x40cm-12x16in) s. 3-Dec-2 Joyner, Toronto #383 est:700-900 (C.D 1300)
£601 $937 €902 Lake Opeongo (56x76cm-22x30in) s. 25-Mar-3 Ritchie, Toronto #104 est:600-800 (C.D 1400)
£658 $1021 €987 After the snowfall (51x61cm-20x24in) s. 3-Dec-2 Joyner, Toronto #365 est:800-1200 (C.D 1600)
£658 $1021 €987 Winter sunset, lake of Bays (45x60cm-18x24in) s. board. 3-Dec-2 Joyner, Toronto #414 est:800-1200 (C.D 1600)

STONE, W (19/20th C) British
£560 $862 €840 Winter landscape with church and figures (38x61cm-15x24in) 6-Sep-2 Biddle & Webb, Birmingham #148

STONE, W R (19/20th C) British
£1050 $1743 €1575 Rural cottage scene with figure on a bridge (43x79cm-17x31in) 10-Jun-3 Lawrences, Bletchingley #1522/R

STONE, Walter King (1875-1949) American
Works on paper
£299 $475 €449 Forest landscape reflected in pond (36x48cm-14x19in) s. pastel gouache on board. 22-Mar-3 New Orleans Auction, New Orleans #1147/R

STONE, William (19/20th C) British
£260 $411 €390 Wintry landscape (61x41cm-24x16in) s. 18-Dec-2 Bonhams, Knowle #385
£360 $558 €540 Figure beside cottage in snowy wooded landscape (38x28cm-15x11in) s. 25-Sep-2 Brightwells, Leominster #946/R
£480 $787 €720 Mountain landscape with a girl driving cattle a stone bridge (48x73cm-19x29in) s. 3-Jun-3 Bonhams, Oxford #68
£520 $811 €780 Cottage in winter, near Warwick (25x41cm-10x16in) s. 26-Mar-3 Sotheby's, Olympia #63/R
£550 $875 €825 Winter scene near Shirley with Sarehole Mill (41x61cm-16x24in) s. i.verso. 7-Mar-3 Biddle & Webb, Birmingham #421
£600 $948 €900 View of figures and timbered house. River landscape (23x33cm-9x13in) s. pair. 12-Nov-2 Bonhams, Knightsbridge #95c/R
£600 $1002 €870 Elan Valley Radnorshire (46x61cm-18x24in) s. s.i.verso. 26-Jun-3 Mellors & Kirk, Nottingham #919/R

STONE-HENDERICK, Jose (?) ?
£690 $1090 €1000 Portrait d'Henri Baels en tenue de Gouverneur de Flandre Orientale (160x94cm-63x37in) s. 2-Apr-3 Vanderkindere, Brussels #557

STONEHOUSE, Fred (20th C) American
£255 $400 €383 Untitled, devil and berries (7x5cm-3x2in) acrylic prov.exhib. 19-Nov-2 Wright, Chicago #327/R

STONELAKE, Frank P (1879-1929) British
£620 $955 €930 Jet, black stallion in woodland (45x59cm-18x23in) s. 22-Oct-2 Bonhams, Bath #133

STOOP, Dirk (1618-1681) Dutch
£2581 $4078 €4000 Halte chez le marechal-ferrand (48x46cm-19x18in) panel. 20-Dec-2 Tajan, Paris #70/R
£5128 $7949 €8000 River battle on a pendulum bridge (26x37cm-10x15in) s. panel lit. 4-Dec-2 Neumeister, Munich #639/R est:9000
£5319 $8617 €7500 Charge de Cavalerie (66x89cm-26x35in) panel. 26-May-3 Joron-Derem, Paris #85/R est:10000-15000
Works on paper
£576 $921 €800 Rocky landscape with riders, figures, horses and dogs (13x18cm-5x7in) pen wash double-sided. 17-May-3 Lempertz, Koln #1256/R

STOOPENDAAL, Mosse (1901-1948) Swedish
£573 $928 €860 Signal funnel (55x75cm-22x30in) s.d.1938. 3-Feb-3 Lilla Bukowskis, Stockholm #18 (S.KR 8000)
£770 $1217 €1155 Mallards in flight, evening (34x50cm-13x20in) s. 16-Nov-2 Crafoord, Lund #81/R (S.KR 11000)
£776 $1219 €1164 Eiderducks over stormy water (56x78cm-22x31in) s. 16-Dec-2 Lilla Bukowskis, Stockholm #72 (S.KR 11000)
£829 $1326 €1202 Winter hare (25x35cm-10x14in) s. 18-May-3 Anders Antik, Landskrona #98 (S.KR 10600)
£922 $1429 €1383 Woodcock in Mai (50x65cm-20x26in) s.d.39. 4-Dec-2 AB Stockholms Auktionsverk #1655/R (S.KR 13000)
£931 $1508 €1350 The pass - winter landscape with hare (45x60cm-18x24in) s.d.43. 25-May-3 Uppsala Auktionskammare, Uppsala #190/R (S.KR 12000)
£953 $1496 €1430 Winter landscape with deer (63x50cm-25x20in) s. 16-Dec-2 Lilla Bukowskis, Stockholm #766 (S.KR 13500)
£1099 $1704 €1649 Edge of wood with birds in flight (55x81cm-22x32in) s. 4-Dec-2 AB Stockholms Auktionsverk #1571/R est:20000-25000 (S.KR 15500)
£1100 $1804 €1595 Ducks in flight (35x50cm-14x20in) s/. 4-Jun-3 AB Stockholms Auktionsverk #2083/R est:15000-18000 (S.KR 14000)
£1170 $1814 €1755 Crows in spring (55x75cm-22x30in) s.d.1940. 3-Dec-2 Bukowskis, Stockholm #41/R est:20000-22000 (S.KR 16500)
£1175 $1904 €1763 Crows (65x92cm-26x36in) s. 27-Jan-3 Blomqvist, Lysaker #1245/R est:15000-17000 (N.KR 13000)
£1277 $1979 €1916 Squirrel on branch in winter (53x64cm-21x25in) s. 3-Dec-2 Bukowskis, Stockholm #112/R est:20000-25000 (S.KR 18000)
£1401 $2213 €2102 Blue-tits in snow (45x32cm-18x13in) s.d.30. 16-Nov-2 Crafoord, Lund #82/R est:12000 (S.KR 20000)
£1414 $2319 €2050 Winter landscape with fox (27x35cm-11x14in) s.d.39. 4-Jun-3 AB Stockholms Auktionsverk #2085/R est:12000-15000 (S.KR 18000)
£1418 $2199 €2127 Ducks in flight (55x81cm-22x32in) s. 4-Dec-2 AB Stockholms Auktionsverk #1569/R est:20000-25000 (S.KR 20000)
£1482 $2327 €2223 Bullfinches (20x40cm-8x16in) s.d.43. 16-Dec-2 Lilla Bukowskis, Stockholm #428/R est:10000-15000 (S.KR 21000)
£1510 $2295 €2265 Sparrow (84x92cm-33x36in) s.d.1943 s.verso. 16-Aug-2 Lilla Bukowskis, Stockholm #805 est:22000-25000 (S.KR 22000)
£1773 $2748 €2660 Great titmouse (30x40cm-12x16in) s.d.45 s.d.verso. 3-Dec-2 Bukowskis, Stockholm #40/R est:15000-18000 (S.KR 25000)
£1964 $3221 €2848 Winter landscape with bullfinches (46x54cm-18x21in) s.d.1947 panel. 4-Jun-3 AB Stockholms Auktionsverk #2104/R est:30000-40000 (S.KR 25000)
£2592 $4251 €3758 Winter landscape with great-tits (45x33cm-18x13in) s.d.30. 4-Jun-3 AB Stockholms Auktionsverk #2320/R est:40000-45000 (S.KR 33000)
£2695 $4177 €4043 Greater blackbacked gulls (83x144cm-33x57in) s.d.1933. 3-Dec-2 Bukowskis, Stockholm #112a/R est:50000-60000 (S.KR 38000)
£3086 $4875 €4629 Winter landscape with eagle attacking hare (60x92cm-24x36in) s. 27-Nov-2 Falkkloos, Malmo #77801/R est:50000 (S.KR 44000)
£3181 $5153 €4612 Blackgrouse (55x75cm-22x30in) s.d.1940. 26-May-3 Bukowskis, Stockholm #53b/R est:30000-40000 (S.KR 41000)
£3191 $4947 €4787 Coot in last year's reeds (66x90cm-26x35in) s.d.1936. 4-Dec-2 AB Stockholms Auktionsverk #1733/R est:20000-25000 (S.KR 45000)
£3258 $5279 €4724 Young owls and lemon butterfly (46x61cm-18x24in) s.d.34. 26-May-3 Bukowskis, Stockholm #56/R est:15000-20000 (S.KR 42000)
£3972 $6156 €5958 Bullfinches (37x54cm-15x21in) s. 3-Dec-2 Bukowskis, Stockholm #39/R est:30000-35000 (S.KR 56000)
£4242 $6957 €6151 Seascape with goosanders in flight (84x150cm-33x59in) s.d.1924. 4-Jun-3 AB Stockholms Auktionsverk #2105/R est:30000-40000 (S.KR 54000)
£4539 $7035 €6809 Swans by reeds (60x62cm-24x24in) s. 3-Dec-2 Bukowskis, Stockholm #44/R est:35000-40000 (S.KR 64000)
£4610 $7145 €6915 Wooded landscape with blackgrouse (70x98cm-28x39in) s.d.1930. 4-Dec-2 AB Stockholms Auktionsverk #1716/R est:50000-60000 (S.KR 65000)
Works on paper
£479 $795 €695 Hare by snow-covered pine tree (34x46cm-13x18in) s.d.1944 mixed media. 16-Jun-3 Lilla Bukowskis, Stockholm #726 (S.KR 6200)

STOOPS, Herbert Morton (1887-1948) American
£435 $700 €653 Figures relaxing with cigarette, while laborers move boulders (43x97cm-17x38in) 20-Feb-3 Illustration House, New York #166/R
£602 $1000 €873 Retreat of the British after the battle at Bennington, August 1777 (61x91cm-24x36in) s. 14-Jun-3 Jackson's, Cedar Falls #18/R
£745 $1200 €1118 Two white mwn seated at gathering of headhunters (81x112cm-32x44in) 20-Feb-3 Illustration House, New York #167/R est:1500-2000
£1226 $1950 €1839 Dough boy with shoemaker (69x64cm-27x25in) s. painted c.1942. 7-Mar-3 Jackson's, Cedar Falls #627/R est:1750-2500
Works on paper
£385 $600 €578 One brave shaking a blanket. W/C. 21-Sep-2 Harvey Clar, Oakland #1488
£385 $600 €578 One chief raising arms. W/C. 21-Sep-2 Harvey Clar, Oakland #1489

STOOTER, Cornelis Leonardsz (1602-1655) Dutch
£7914 $12662 €11000 Shipping off the coast in a stiff breeze, figure on the shoreline (43x63cm-17x25in) mono. panel prov. 14-May-3 Christie's, Amsterdam #198/R est:9000-12000
£21583 $34532 €30000 Shipping in choppy seas with fishermen on the shore (40x62cm-16x24in) s. panel. 14-May-3 Christie's, Amsterdam #175/R est:12000-18000

STORCH, Anton (1892-1979) Austrian
Works on paper
£316 $494 €500 Venice, St Marks Square (27x40cm-11x16in) s.d.28.VI.48 chk W/C. 15-Oct-2 Dorotheum, Vienna #113/R

STORCH, Frederik (1805-1883) Danish
£1490 $2369 €2235 Italian women playing with a child at water's edge (54x42cm-21x17in) s.d.1866. 5-Mar-3 Rasmussen, Copenhagen #1566/R est:15000-20000 (D.KR 16000)
£3445 $5478 €5168 Neapolitan genre scene with family happiness (77x84cm-30x33in) s.d.72 exhib.prov. 5-Mar-3 Rasmussen, Copenhagen #1568/R est:60000 (D.KR 37000)

STORCH, Frederik (attrib) (1805-1883) Danish
£861 $1395 €1292 Coastal landscape with seated woman and two children, man playing mandolin (75x62cm-30x24in) 21-May-3 Museumsbygningen, Copenhagen #78 (D.KR 9000)

STORCH, Karl (elder) (1864-1954) German
£1139 $1800 €1800 Still life with quinces (37x46cm-15x18in) s.d.1936. 29-Nov-2 Bolland & Marotz, Bremen #777/R est:1900
£1139 $1800 €1800 Winter in Ostpreussen (50x69cm-20x27in) s. 29-Nov-2 Bolland & Marotz, Bremen #778/R
£1709 $2700 €2700 East Prussian guest house (48x62cm-19x24in) s.d.1945 board. 29-Nov-2 Bolland & Marotz, Bremen #775/R est:1900

STORCK, Abraham (c.1635-c.1710) Dutch
£7258 $11468 €10887 Arrival of merchant ships. Shipping in Mediterranean harbour (30x45cm-12x18in) pair. 18-Nov-2 Waddingtons, Toronto #204/R est:20000-30000 (C.D 18000)
£12230 $19568 €17000 Dutch harbour on Zuiderzee with boats (46x55cm-18x22in) s. 13-May-3 Sotheby's, Amsterdam #51/R est:8000-12000
£38000 $59660 €57000 Mediterranean harbour scene (83x69cm-33x27in) prov. 12-Dec-2 Sotheby's, London #29/R est:30000-40000
£72000 $113040 €108000 Capriccio of a Mediteranean harbour with a man-o-war (49x66cm-19x26in) s. prov. 10-Dec-2 Bonhams, New Bond Street #326/R est:30000-50000
£85000 $132600 €127500 Mediterranean port scenes with figures (20x27cm-8x11in) s. panel pair prov. 10-Apr-3 Sotheby's, London #66/R est:50000-70000

STORCK, Abraham (attrib) (c.1635-c.1710) Dutch
£1986 $3217 €2800 Caravelle devant la cote dans une mer agitee (57x83cm-22x33in) 26-May-3 Amberes, Antwerp #79

STORCK, Abraham (studio) (c.1635-c.1710) Dutch
£7000 $10850 €10500 Dutch pinks and man o'war sailing on the Ij with fishermen on the bank (56x68cm-22x27in) 30-Oct-2 Bonhams, New Bond Street #155/R est:7000-9000
£9554 $14904 €15000 Mediterranean harbour scene with a San Giorgio Maggiore and the Biblioteca Marziana of Venice (66x81cm-26x32in) prov. 5-Nov-2 Sotheby's, Amsterdam #222/R est:15000-20000

STORCK, Jacob (1641-1687) Dutch
£2129 $3130 €3300 Southern harbour (32x40cm-13x16in) s. 20-Jun-2 Dr Fritz Nagel, Stuttgart #735/R est:4800
£3000 $4710 €4500 Town on the Vecht with yacht, ferry and other boats (34x48cm-13x19in) with sig. panel prov. 13-Dec-2 Christie's, Kensington #75/R est:3000-5000
£12414 $19738 €18000 Vue d'une ville fluviale hollandaise (76x105cm-30x41in) 7-Mar-3 Rabourdin & Choppin de Janvry, Paris #56/R est:25000-28000
£18919 $29514 €28000 View of Kaub Castle in the Rhine (60x84cm-24x33in) s. panel. 27-Mar-3 Dorotheum, Vienna #131/R est:30000-50000
£21475 $34574 €32000 Amsterdam, view on the Overtoom (61x84cm-24x33in) bears sig.d.1674 prov.lit. 18-Feb-3 Sotheby's, Amsterdam #241/R est:12000-15000

STORCK, Jacob (attrib) (1641-1687) Dutch
£5892 $9662 €8543 Mediterranean harbour scene (63x78cm-25x31in) bears sig.d.1683. 4-Jun-3 AB Stockholms Auktionsverk #2551/R est:50000-60000 (S.KR 75000)
£11000 $17050 €16500 Mediterranean harbour with a capriccio of classical ruins and a palace with a Dutch man-o-war (60x83cm-24x33in) s. panel. 30-Oct-2 Christie's, Kensington #40/R est:8000-12000

STORELLI, Felix Marie Ferdinand (1778-1854) Italian
£4321 $7000 €6482 View of Roman countryside (51x73cm-20x29in) s.i.d.1835 exhib. 23-Jan-3 Sotheby's, New York #187/R

STORELLI, Ferdinand Michel (1805-?) French
£1502 $2464 €2178 Coastal landscape (73x100cm-29x39in) s.d.1851. 4-Jun-3 Fischer, Luzern #1069/R est:2500-3500 (S.FR 3200)
£22378 $37371 €32000 La maison du Tasse. Danseurs Napolitains devant le Vesuve (102x160cm-40x63in) s.d.1877 pair. 25-Jun-3 Artcurial Briest, Paris #511/R est:30000-40000

STORER, Charles (1817-1907) American
£312 $500 €452 Still life with peaches and pears (13x30cm-5x12in) s.d.1903 panel. 16-May-3 Skinner, Boston #92/R

STOREY, George Adolphus (1834-1919) British
£1200 $1788 €1800 Two girls reading by a river (33x53cm-13x21in) mono.d.1910 oval exhib. 28-Jun-2 Chrystals Auctions, Isle of Man #159a est:1200-1600
£60000 $96600 €90000 Orphans (103x128cm-41x50in) s.d.1879 prov.exhib.lit. 20-Feb-3 Christie's, London #271/R est:50000

STOREY, Harold (1888-1965) British
£750 $1208 €1125 Newton Mearns, snow in the village (55x75cm-22x30in) s. board exhib. 15-Jan 3 Cheffins Grain & Comins, Cambridge #451/R
£1000 $1590 €1500 Snow in the village, Newton Mearns (56x76cm-22x30in) s.i. board. 6-Mar-3 Christie's, Kensington #167/R est:1000-1500

STOREY, Terence Lionel (1923-) British
£300 $486 €450 M.V Astronomer at Kingston, Jamaica (59x90cm-23x35in) s. 21-Jan-3 Bonhams, New Bond Street #185/R
£400 $648 €600 M.V Specialist (59x90cm-23x35in) s. 21-Jan-3 Bonhams, New Bond Street #186/R
£550 $858 €825 Schooner in calm seas (41x51cm-16x20in) s. board one by same hand two. 26-Mar-3 Hamptons Fine Art, Godalming #160

STORK, Mary (1938-) British
Works on paper
£250 $390 €375 On wings of love (25x36cm-10x14in) s.d.1989 i.verso gouache. 16-Oct-2 David Lay, Penzance #230/R
£290 $484 €421 Sita, seated nude (44x32cm-17x13in) s.d.1995 mixed media. 19-Jun-3 Lane, Penzance #348
£370 $574 €555 Illuminate, seated nude (152x91cm-60x36in) s.d.12.03.01 mixed media. 26-Sep-2 Lane, Penzance #1
£500 $775 €750 Open, kneeling nude (175x117cm-69x46in) s.d.01 mixed media. 26-Sep-2 Lane, Penzance #309/R

STORM VAN S'GRAVENSANDE, Carel Nicolaas (1841-1924) Dutch
£1062 $1656 €1550 Still life of French breakfast with newspaper and flowers (45x54cm-18x21in) mono. board. 14-Apr-3 Glerum, Amsterdam #165/R est:500-700

STORM, Juan (1927-1995) Uruguayan
£929 $1450 €1394 Still life (90x95cm-35x37in) s.d.72. 10-Oct-2 Galleria Y Remates, Montevideo #76/R
£1156 $1850 €1734 Still life with mirror (73x73cm-29x29in) s.d.92. 5-Jan-3 Galleria Y Remates, Montevideo #103/R
£1258 $2000 €1887 Horse, rider and moon (51x61cm-20x24in) s.d.87. 2-Mar-3 Galleria Y Remates, Montevideo #111/R
£1274 $2000 €1911 Knight (80x100cm-31x39in) s.d.86. 20-Nov-2 Galleria Y Remates, Montevideo #59/R
£1274 $2000 €1911 Building (50x61cm-20x24in) s.d.75. 20-Nov-2 Galleria Y Remates, Montevideo #60/R
£1384 $2200 €2076 Molles station (65x81cm-26x32in) s.d.76 cardboard. 2-Mar-3 Galleria Y Remates, Montevideo #110/R
£1538 $2400 €2307 Naturaleza muerta, ventana y vapor (60x73cm-24x29in) s.d.77. 30-Jul-2 Galleria Y Remates, Montevideo #93/R est:1600-1800
£2893 $4600 €4340 Getting to church (81x100cm-32x39in) s.d.85. 2-Mar-3 Galleria Y Remates, Montevideo #86/R
£2949 $4600 €4424 Mates (99x199cm-39x78in) s.d.90 i.verso. 10-Oct-2 Galleria Y Remates, Montevideo #62/R

STORM, Paul (1880-1951) German
£418 $647 €660 Meadow in bloom (70x50cm-28x20in) s. 28-Sep-2 Hans Stahl, Hamburg #183/R

STORM, Per Palle (1910-1994) Norwegian
Sculpture
£3122 $4871 €4683 Dog playing with ball (32x57x35cm-13x22x14in) bronze. 21-Oct-2 Blomqvist, Oslo #375/R est:15000-18000 (N.KR 36000)

STORMONT, Howard Gull (fl.1884-1923) British
Works on paper
£270 $451 €392 Figures and cattle in a river landscape (41x66cm-16x26in) s.d.1892 W/C over pencil. 24-Jun-3 Bonhams, Knowle #12

STORN, Willibald (1936-) Norwegian/Austrian
Works on paper
£303 $464 €455 Scaly (57x83cm-22x33in) s. mixed media. 26-Aug-2 Blomqvist, Lysaker #1379 (N.KR 3500)
£1301 $2029 €1952 Goodbye to Billi (158x124cm-62x49in) s.i.d.96 mixed media. 21-Oct-2 Blomqvist, Oslo #427/R est:25000-35000 (N.KR 15000)

STORRIER, Tim (1949-) Australian
£794 $1231 €1191 Untitled, Tim Storrier (102x76cm-40x30in) i. oil synthetic polymer paint prov. 3-Dec-2 Shapiro, Sydney #67/R (A.D 2200)
£1128 $1793 €1692 Untitled (165x165cm-65x65in) s. painted c.1971 prov. 3-Mar-3 Lawson Menzies, Sydney #462 est:3500-5000 (A.D 3000)

£1626 $2569 €2358 Mangoes (60x60cm-24x24in) s.d.1978. 22-Jul-3 Lawson Menzies, Sydney #144/R est:4500-7000 (A.D 4000)
£1714 $2657 €2571 Untitled (165x165cm-65x65in) s. painted c.1971 prov. 29-Oct-2 Lawson Menzies, Sydney #136 est:3500-5000 (A.D 4800)
£4800 $7728 €7200 House of sticks I (102x152cm-40x60in) s.i.d.1987 acrylic prov.lit. 6-May-3 Christie's, Melbourne #1/R est:12000-18000 (A.D 12000)
£7317 $11561 €10610 Lord Skye (39x49cm-15x19in) s.i. acrylic on board. 22-Jul-3 Lawson Menzies, Sydney #1/R est:12000-16000 (A.D 18000)
£9286 $14579 €13929 Dusk, the night runner (103x152cm-41x60in) s.i. acrylic prov. 25-Nov-2 Christie's, Melbourne #91/R est:25000-30000 (A.D 26000)
£11071 $17493 €16607 Sunset, evening line (39x49cm-15x19in) s.i. oil rope on board. 26-Nov-2 Sotheby's, Melbourne #32/R est:14000-18000 (A.D 31000)
£14286 $22286 €21429 Arm, Will (139x200cm-55x79in) s.i.d.1986. 11-Nov-2 Deutscher-Menzies, Melbourne #24/R est:40000-60000 (A.D 40000)
£15412 $23427 €23118 Noon fire (102x150cm-40x59in) s.i.d.1990 acrylic prov. 27-Aug-2 Goodman, Sydney #141/R est:28000-38000 (A.D 43000)
£17921 $27240 €26882 Light line, evening (61x183cm-24x72in) s.i. oil rope prov. 28-Aug-2 Deutscher-Menzies, Melbourne #7/R est:50000-60000 (A.D 50000)
£21138 $33398 €30650 Arm - Will (139x200cm-55x79in) s.i.d.1986 oil rope on canvas. 22-Jul-3 Lawson Menzies, Sydney #34/R est:55000-70000 (A.D 52000)
£23904 $39203 €35856 Kennel memory, Colonial state (154x245cm-61x96in) s.i.d.1989 prov. 4-Jun-3 Deutscher-Menzies, Melbourne #46/R est:36000-55000 (A.D 60000)
£28674 $43584 €43011 Capricorn waterline (106x244cm-42x96in) s. s.i.d.2001 stretcher prov. 28-Aug-2 Deutscher-Menzies, Melbourne #30/R est:68000-85000 (A.D 80000)
£30651 $45671 €45977 Burning logs (61x243cm-24x96in) s. acrylic. 27-Aug-2 Christie's, Melbourne #10/R est:50000-70000 (A.D 80000)
£36585 $57805 €53048 Detritus of noon (122x244cm-48x96in) s. i.d.2002 verso. 22-Jul-3 Lawson Menzies, Sydney #29/R est:80000-120000 (A.D 90000)

Works on paper
£2191 $3593 €3287 Small Balinese composition (25x37cm-10x15in) s.i.d.1980 W/C bodycol col pencil. 4-Jun-3 Deutscher-Menzies, Melbourne #154/R est:4800-5500 (A.D 5500)
£3065 $4812 €4598 Saddle and equipment (60x53cm-24x21in) s.d.1982 W/C pencil. 15-Apr-3 Lawson Menzies, Sydney #201/R est:8000-12000 (A.D 8000)
£3571 $5643 €5357 Australia 1980 (100x150cm-39x59in) s.d.80 W/C. 27-Nov-2 Deutscher-Menzies, Melbourne #13/R est:15000-20000 (A.D 10000)
£3846 $6115 €5769 Palm tree (121x91cm-48x36in) s.d.74 synthetic polymer paint canvas prov. 4-Mar-3 Deutscher-Menzies, Melbourne #150/R est:10000-15000 (A.D 10000)
£4643 $7335 €6965 Bottle saddle for primary surveyor I (126x126cm-50x50in) s.i.d.1982 pencil. 27-Nov-2 Deutscher-Menzies, Melbourne #65/R est:15000-20000 (A.D 13000)
£5179 $8494 €7769 Centurion, night runner (40x50cm-16x20in) s.i. synthetic polymer paint board exec.c.1990. 4-Jun-3 Deutscher-Menzies, Melbourne #122/R est:10000-15000 (A.D 13000)
£5578 $9147 €8367 Red belly and distance (40x50cm-16x20in) s.i.d.2000 synthetic polymer paint board. 4-Jun-3 Deutscher-Menzies, Melbourne #89/R est:15000-20000 (A.D 14000)
£6071 $9471 €9107 Evening fire on the plain (30x45cm-12x18in) s. synthetic polymer paint canvas. 11-Nov-2 Deutscher-Menzies, Melbourne #14/R est:10000-15000 (A.D 17000)
£6154 $9785 €9231 Lord sky (40x50cm-16x20in) s. synthetic polymer paint board. 4-Mar-3 Deutscher-Menzies, Melbourne #54/R est:18000-24000 (A.D 16000)
£6538 $10396 €9807 Evening log (40x50cm-16x20in) s. synthetic polymer paint board. 4-Mar-3 Deutscher-Menzies, Melbourne #14/R est:18000-24000 (A.D 17000)
£8602 $13075 €12903 Canslakom (122x182cm-48x72in) s. i.verso synthetic polymer paint painted c.1975. 28-Aug-2 Deutscher-Menzies, Melbourne #108/R est:14000-18000 (A.D 24000)
£8765 $14375 €13148 Equipment II (100x150cm-39x59in) s.i.d.82 W/C. 4-Jun-3 Deutscher-Menzies, Melbourne #90/R est:28000-35000 (A.D 22000)
£9231 $14677 €13847 Burning rope (41x151cm-16x59in) s. synthetic polymer paint rope card. 4-Mar-3 Deutscher-Menzies, Melbourne #1/R est:20000-30000 (A.D 24000)
£11628 $18488 €17442 Night train (98x149cm-39x59in) s.i.d.1986 polymer prov. 5-May-3 Sotheby's, Melbourne #1/R est:30000-50000 (A.D 30000)
£12749 $20908 €19124 Colonial garden (152x152cm-60x60in) mono. synthetic polymer paint canvas. 4-Jun-3 Deutscher-Menzies, Melbourne #73/R est:35000-45000 (A.D 32000)
£12857 $20186 €19286 Saddle (127x96cm-50x38in) s.i.d.1996 W/C acrylic timber rope leather metal. 25-Nov-2 Christie's, Melbourne #58/R est:32000-38000 (A.D 36000)
£16429 $25629 €24644 Still life and fire (101x152cm-40x60in) s.i.d.1990 synthetic polymer paint. 11-Nov-2 Deutscher-Menzies, Melbourne #77/R est:25000-35000 (A.D 46000)
£17530 $28749 €26295 Evening, fire line (91x198cm-36x78in) s.i.d.1991 synthetic polymer paint rope canvas. 4-Jun-3 Deutscher-Menzies, Melbourne #28/R est:40000-60000 (A.D 44000)
£21154 $33634 €31731 Evening line (61x183cm-24x72in) s. i.verso synthetic polymer paint rope canvas prov. 4-Mar-3 Deutscher-Menzies, Melbourne #49b/R est:50000-60000 (A.D 55000)
£21429 $33857 €32144 Evening reflection 1999 (91x183cm-36x72in) s. synthetic polymer on canvas exhib. 27-Nov-2 Deutscher-Menzies, Melbourne #23/R est:65000-80000 (A.D 60000)
£27132 $43140 €40698 Point to point; line blaze (151x243cm-59x96in) s.i.d.1988 synthetic polymer mixed media. 5-May-3 Sotheby's, Melbourne #114/R est:70000-100000 (A.D 70000)
£67857 $107214 €101786 Wave (183x304cm-72x120in) s.d.1998 synthetic polymer prov. 26-Nov-2 Sotheby's, Melbourne #12/R est:150000-200000 (A.D 190000)

STORRS, John (1885-1956) American
Sculpture
£49383 $80000 €74075 Architectural form no.3 (50cm-20in) mono.i. limestone black painted base prov.exhib. 21-May-3 Sotheby's, New York #34/R est:80000-120000
£117284 $190000 €175926 Study in pure from (31cm-12in) mono.i. steel copper brass on black marble base prov.lit. 21-May-3 Sotheby's, New York #33/R est:60000-80000

Works on paper
£3185 $5000 €4778 Study for Rostrum, Century of Progress (10x13cm-4x5in) pencil prov.exhib. 19-Nov-2 Wright, Chicago #150/R est:5000-6000

STORSTEIN, Aage (1900-1983) Norwegian
£597 $932 €896 Rocks and trees, Ronna, Justoy (37x46cm-15x18in) s. panel painted 1965. 23-Sep-2 Blomqvist, Lysaker #1234/R (N.KR 7000)
£896 $1398 €1344 From the bay, Ronna, Justoy (46x61cm-18x24in) s. panel painted 1965. 23-Sep-2 Blomqvist, Lysaker #1235/R (N.KR 10500)
£1286 $2108 €1865 Coastal landscape, Ronna, Justo (50x61cm-20x24in) s.d.53 s.i.d.1953 verso panel. 2-Jun-3 Blomqvist, Oslo #101/R est:18000-20000 (N.KR 14000)
£1448 $2346 €2172 Country garden at Nedgaren in Smorklepp, Vinje (38x46cm-15x18in) s. i.d.1949 verso panel. 26-May-3 Grev Wedels Plass, Oslo #74/R est:18000-20000 (N.KR 16000)
£6574 $10388 €9861 Still life of bottle and jug (65x75cm-26x30in) s.d.27. 2-Dec-2 Blomqvist, Oslo #422/R est:35000-45000 (N.KR 76000)

STORTENBEKER, Johannes (1821-1899) Dutch
£414 $646 €650 Two nudes with putto and pigeons (29x23cm-11x9in) s.indis.d. panel. 6-Nov-2 Vendue Huis, Gravenhage #482/R

STOSSEL, Oskar (1879-?) Austrian
£310 $497 €450 Portrait of army officer (100x79cm-39x31in) s. 11-Mar-3 Dorotheum, Vienna #14/R

STOTHARD, Thomas (1755-1834) British
£560 $874 €840 Sir Walter Raleigh at the court of Queen Elizabeth (48x71cm-19x28in) 6-Nov-2 Bonhams, Chester #459/R
£750 $1170 €1125 Children receiving the blessings from paradise (36x45cm-14x18in) 17-Sep-2 Sotheby's, Olympia #98/R
£1000 $1550 €1500 Ulysses and the sirens (39x50cm-15x20in) panel. 3-Dec-2 Sotheby's, Olympia #17/R est:1000-2000
£9000 $14490 €13500 Sylvia and the outlaws (70x52cm-28x20in) indis.sig. prov. 20-Feb-3 Christie's, London #68/R

STOTHARD, Thomas (attrib) (1755-1834) British
£1500 $2475 €2175 An innocent strategem. The power of innocence (34x44cm-13x17in) board oval pair. 2-Jul-3 Sotheby's, Olympia #125/R est:400-600

STOTT, Edward (1859-1918) British
£950 $1511 €1425 Moonrise over a stack (24x35cm-9x14in) s. 4-Mar-3 Bearnes, Exeter #449/R
£1883 $2900 €2825 Winters night, Sussex village. Winchelsea churchyard (15x23cm-6x9in) s. panel pair. 27-Oct-2 Grogan, Boston #51 est:500-700
£9000 $14760 €13500 Maternity (62x66cm-24x26in) s. exhib. 6-Jun-3 Christie's, London #3/R est:10000-15000
£11000 $18040 €16500 Milking time, early morn (46x51cm-18x20in) s. s.i.verso exhib.lit. 6-Jun-3 Christie's, London #2/R est:12000-18000
£18000 $29520 €27000 Shepherd (61x76cm-24x30in) s. s.i.verso prov.exhib.lit. 6-Jun-3 Christie's, London #1/R est:20000-30000
£30000 $48300 €45000 On a summer afternoon (56x72cm-22x28in) painted 1892 prov.exhib.lit. 20-Feb-3 Christie's, London #57/R est:60000
£35000 $57400 €52500 Harvester's return (57x55cm-22x22in) init. prov.exhib.lit. 6-Jun-3 Christie's, London #4/R est:15000-25000
£56000 $91840 €84000 Portrait of a young girl (31x27cm-12x11in) s.d.1885 prov. 6-Jun-3 Christie's, London #5/R est:12000-18000
Works on paper
£720 $1188 €1044 Sheep in a Suffolk landscape (24x34cm-9x13in) init. pastel. 1-Jul-3 Bonhams, Norwich #93/R
£900 $1404 €1350 Study of a woman and two children (32x23cm-13x9in) s. pastel. 17-Oct-2 Christie's, Kensington #26/R

STOTT, William R S (fl.1905-1934) British
£4400 $6908 €6600 Walk by the sea (52x37cm-20x15in) s. board. 10-Dec-2 Lane, Penzance #60/R est:4000-4500

STOTZER, Werner (1931-) German
Works on paper
£314 $484 €500 Kneeling female nude (70x50cm-28x20in) s.d.1992 gouache transparent paper. 26-Oct-2 Dr Lehr, Berlin #506/R

STOWELL, Flaxney (19/20th C) ?
Works on paper
£700 $1169 €1015 Near St. John's Isle of Man (15x24cm-6x9in) s. pencil W/C htd white. 26-Jun-3 Mellors & Kirk, Nottingham #810
£700 $1169 €1015 Silver Burn near Castletown Isle of man (16x23cm-6x9in) s. pencil W/C htd white. 26-Jun-3 Mellors & Kirk, Nottingham #811
£1300 $2171 €1885 Castletown, Isle of Man. Coastal scene (24x34cm-9x13in) s. W/C two. 9-Jul-3 George Kidner, Lymington #132/R est:150-250
£4500 $7515 €6525 Castletown from Qualtrough's Yard Isle of Man (41x56cm-16x22in) s.d.1904 W/C htd white. 26-Jun-3 Mellors & Kirk, Nottingham #808/R est:1500-2000

STOWER, Willy (1864-1931) German
£1923 $2981 €3000 Boats at sea (70x101cm-28x40in) s.d.1920. 7-Dec-2 Hans Stahl, Hamburg #155/R est:4000
Works on paper
£258 $407 €387 Sailing ship in full flight before the coast (20x31cm-8x12in) s. W/C paper on board. 26-Nov-2 Hans Widmer, St Gallen #1389 (S.FR 600)
£258 $407 €387 Attacking warship in front of the coast (20x33cm-8x13in) s. W/C paper on board. 26-Nov-2 Hans Widmer, St Gallen #1392 (S.FR 600)
£279 $441 €419 Sailing ships in harbour at Horn of Africa (19x32cm-7x13in) s.indis.i. W/C paper on board. 26-Nov-2 Hans Widmer, St Gallen #1388/R (S.FR 650)
£279 $441 €419 War ship in front of the fleet (20x32cm-8x13in) s. W/C paper on board. 26-Nov-2 Hans Widmer, St Gallen #1390 (S.FR 650)
£429 $678 €644 Warships at full speed (28x39cm-11x15in) s. W/C paper on board. 26-Nov-2 Hans Widmer, St Gallen #1387 (S.FR 1000)

STRAATEN, Bruno van (snr) (1786-1870) Dutch
£962 $1510 €1500 Kitchen interior with figures (40x33cm-16x13in) panel. 19-Nov-2 Servarts Themis, Bruxelles #268/R
£962 $1510 €1500 Halte (39x50cm-15x20in) s.d.1821. 19-Nov-2 Servarts Themis, Bruxelles #267/R

STRACHAN, Claude (1865-1929) British
£875 $1400 €1269 Beached dories on the coast (60x45cm-24x18in) s.d.1894 board. 16-May-3 Skinner, Boston #111/R est:1800-2200
£2200 $3586 €3300 Boats moored on the beach (30x43cm-12x17in) s.d.1894 board. 29-Jan-3 Sotheby's, Olympia #198/R est:800-1200
Works on paper
£260 $403 €390 Mural scene with figures and a cat (30x23cm-12x9in) s. W/C. 6-Dec-2 Biddle & Webb, Birmingham #453/R
£800 $1248 €1200 Old Darwen Street, Blackburn (36x26cm-14x10in) s. W/C. 6-Nov-2 Bonhams, Chester #327/R
£1355 $2100 €2033 Whitbourne Cottage, Hertfordshire (38x28cm-15x11in) s. W/C. 6-Dec-2 Eldred, East Dennis #758/R est:4000-6000
£1800 $2808 €2700 In a cottage garden (29x22cm-11x9in) s. W/C bodycol pair. 6-Nov-2 Bonhams, Chester #513 est:2000-3000
£2300 $3841 €3335 Cottage garden (37x27cm-15x11in) s. W/C. 17-Jun-3 Anderson & Garland, Newcastle #301/R est:600-1000
£2700 $4158 €4050 Village inn (25x17cm-10x7in) s. W/C sold with another similar. 22-Oct-2 Sworder & Son, Bishops Stortford #679/R est:1500-2500
£3000 $4860 €4500 Cottage garden in summer (27x45cm-11x18in) s. W/C. 20-May-3 Sotheby's, Olympia #271/R est:2000-3000
£4208 $6648 €6312 Scene in Worcestershire (35x47cm-14x19in) s. W/C. 30-Nov-2 Goteborg Auktionsverk, Sweden #222 est:8000 (S.KR 60000)

STRACHAN, David Edgar (1919-1970) British
£1786 $2821 €2679 Fisher girl (34x46cm-13x18in) s.d.45 i.verso board exhib.lit. 17-Nov-2 Sotheby's, Paddington #19/R est:8000-12000 (A.D 5000)
£2692 $4281 €4038 Head of a girl (40x40cm-16x16in) s.d.44 board. 4-Mar-3 Deutscher-Menzies, Melbourne #108/R est:6000-9000 (A.D 7000)
£2713 $4314 €4070 Still life of flowers and fish (39x30cm-15x12in) s.d.44 board prov.exhib. 5-May-3 Sotheby's, Melbourne #322/R est:7000-10000 (A.D 7000)
£7143 $11286 €10715 Old wall (97x151cm-38x59in) s.d.60 exhib. 17-Nov-2 Sotheby's, Paddington #51/R est:15000-20000 (A.D 20000)

STRACKE, Franz (1820-1898) Dutch
Sculpture
£5172 $8276 €7500 Diana (50cm-20in) s.d.1881 Cast.Nelli, Rome. 17-Mar-3 Horta, Bruxelles #155/R est:8000-10000

STRADONE, Giovanni (1911-1981) Italian
£839 $1325 €1300 Carnations and rose (40x30cm-16x12in) s.i.d.64 verso. 18-Dec-2 Christie's, Rome #161
£968 $1529 €1500 Horse amongst ruins (50x35cm-20x14in) s.i.d.64 prov. 18-Dec-2 Christie's, Rome #154
£1161 $1835 €1800 Church in Argentina (50x40cm-20x16in) s.i.d.57 prov. 18-Dec-2 Christie's, Rome #223/R
£1526 $2411 €2380 Vatican gardens (50x34cm-20x13in) board painted 1968. 12-Nov-2 Babuino, Rome #323/R
£2877 $4488 €4200 Roses at sea (60x50cm-24x20in) s.verso cardboard on canvas. 10-Apr-3 Finarte Semenzato, Rome #187/R
£2903 $4587 €4500 Coliseum at night (100x70cm-39x28in) s.i.d.1957 verso prov. 18-Dec-2 Christie's, Rome #224/R
£3014 $4701 €4400 Coliseum (50x60cm-20x24in) s. board. 10-Apr-3 Finarte Semenzato, Rome #175/R

STRAET, Jan van der (1523-1605) Flemish
Prints
£17000 $27370 €25500 Fowling, fishing and hunting scenes (27x33cm-11x13in) engraved plates 104 sold with 12 others by Straet lit. 7-May-3 Sotheby's, London #119/R est:15000-20000
Works on paper
£6173 $10000 €9260 Prophet Zechariah (16x13cm-6x5in) s. chk pen ink htd white oval prov. 22-Jan-3 Christie's, Rockefeller NY #1/R

STRAET, Jan van der (attrib) (1523-1605) Flemish
Works on paper
£24516 $38000 €36774 Prancing horse (28x33cm-11x13in) graphite. 2-Nov-2 North East Auctions, Portsmouth #101/R est:2000-4000

STRAETEN, George van der (1856-1928) Belgian
Sculpture
£1000 $1520 €1500 Gentleman rider - happy jockey (39cm-15in) s. brown pat. bronze. 28-Aug-2 Sotheby's, London #824/R est:1000-1500

STRAGER, A (?) ?
£280 $426 €420 Jolly tavern scene (40x50cm-16x20in) s. board. 13-Aug-2 Gildings, Market Harborough #251

STRAHALM, Franz (1879-1935) American/Austrian
£344 $550 €516 Cloud burst (60x80cm-24x31in) s. 18-May-3 Butterfields, Los Angeles #7035

STRAIN, John Paul (1955-) American
Works on paper
£4747 $7500 €6883 Grizzly bears in camp (53x69cm-21x27in) s. gouache. 26-Jul-3 Coeur d'Alene, Hayden #33/R est:4000-6000

STRAND, Paul (1890-1976) American
Photographs
£2273 $3500 €3410 Portrait of a farmer, Luzzara, Italy (12x15cm-5x6in) photograph prov. 24-Oct-2 Sotheby's, New York #126a/R est:4000-6000

£6329 $10000 €9494 New York (13x16cm-5x6in) photogravure prov.exhib.lit. 25-Apr-3 Phillips, New York #205/R est:2000-3000
£8442 $13000 €12663 White horse, Rancho de Taos, New Mexico (23x29cm-9x11in) s.i.d.1932 verso photograph. 22-Oct-2 Sotheby's, New York #48/R est:20000-30000
£17722 $28000 €28000 Gaspe (12x15cm-5x6in) silver gelatin lit.exhib. 28-Nov-2 Villa Grisebach, Berlin #1415/R est:28000-32000
£34810 $55000 €52215 Mullen in rain, Maine (24x19cm-9x7in) i.verso gelatin silver print prov.lit. 22-Apr-3 Christie's, Rockefeller NY #20/R est:60000-80000
£41139 $65000 €61709 Corea, house on hill, New England (24x19cm-9x7in) s.i.d.1945 gelatin silver print prov.lit. 22-Apr-3 Christie's, Rockefeller NY #199/R est:70000-90000
£44156 $68000 €66234 Church doors, New England (24x19cm-9x7in) s.i.verso gelatin silver print board prov.lit. 25-Oct-2 Phillips, New York #24/R est:70000-90000

STRAND, Rebecca Salsbury (20th C) American
£43210 $70000 €64815 White and pink vase (38x30cm-15x12in) s.i.d.1936 double-sided prov. 21-May-3 Sotheby's, New York #124/R est:20000-30000

STRAND, Svein (1934-) Norwegian
£2035 $3216 €3053 Still life of white bowl and other objects on table (78x55cm-31x22in) s. i.stretcher exhib. 28-Apr-3 Blomqvist, Oslo #386/R est:30000-40000 (N.KR 23000)
£3469 $5412 €5204 Window towards romantic place (61x47cm-24x19in) s. i.stretcher exhib. 21-Oct-2 Blomqvist, Oslo #440/R est:50000-70000 (N.KR 40000)

STRANDQVIST, Kjell (1944-) Swedish
£1051 $1640 €1577 Untitled (151x151cm-59x59in) init.d.88 acrylic prov. 6-Nov-2 AB Stockholms Auktionsverk #915/R est:10000-15000 (S.KR 15000)

STRANG, William (1859-1921) British
£4500 $7155 €6750 Portrait of a lady (76x63cm-30x25in) s. 6-Mar-3 Christie's, Kensington #201/R est:3000-5000

Works on paper
£600 $942 €900 Study of William Duthie (38x30cm-15x12in) s.d.89 pencil dr. 16-Dec-2 Bonhams, Bury St Edmunds #428/R
£1742 $2700 €2613 Portraits of Archie, Marion Service, Edward Service. Young man (41x27cm-16x11in) s.i.d.chl col chk set of four. 29-Oct-2 Sotheby's, New York #155/R est:3000-4000

STRANGE, Albert (1855-1917) British
£300 $468 €450 Fishermen on a river with mountain beyond (48x72cm-19x28in) s.d.94. 26-Mar-3 Woolley & Wallis, Salisbury #113/R

STRANGE, Christopher William (19th C) ?
£385 $600 €558 Moonlight East Garston (36x46cm-14x18in) s. 30-Mar-3 Simpson's, Houston #177

STRANSKY, Ferdinand (1904-) Austrian
£3986 $6536 €5500 Portrait (53x60cm-21x24in) s.d.34 panel. 27-May-3 Wiener Kunst Auktionen, Vienna #48/R est:3000-5000
£4114 $6418 €6500 Still life (48x60cm-19x24in) s.d.67 masonite. 15-Oct-2 Dorotheum, Vienna #165/R est:3000-3600

Works on paper
£506 $785 €800 Untitled (30x42cm-12x17in) s.d.62 pencil. 24-Sep-2 Wiener Kunst Auktionen, Vienna #206/R
£556 $883 €800 Untitled (36x30cm-14x12in) s.d.64 W/C bodycol. 29-Apr-3 Wiener Kunst Auktionen, Vienna #439/R
£570 $883 €900 Landscape (40x56cm-16x22in) s.d.81 chl. 24-Sep-2 Wiener Kunst Auktionen, Vienna #202/R
£633 $981 €1000 Untitled (44x53cm-17x21in) s.d.56 W/C bodycol wrapping paper. 24-Sep-2 Wiener Kunst Auktionen, Vienna #205/R
£696 $1079 €1100 Untitled (36x48cm-14x19in) s.d.66 mixed media. 24-Sep-2 Wiener Kunst Auktionen, Vienna #203/R
£833 $1325 €1200 Village landscape (32x42cm-13x17in) s. pastel. 29-Apr-3 Wiener Kunst Auktionen, Vienna #423/R

STRASSBERGER, Richard (1868-?) German
£705 $1107 €1100 Head of a woman (36x31cm-14x12in) s.d.1903 board. 10-Dec-2 Dorotheum, Vienna #69/R

STRASSER, Arthur (1854-1927) Austrian

Sculpture
£2692 $4227 €4200 Girl carrying water jug (87cm-34in) i. brown pat.bronze. 21-Nov-2 Van Ham, Cologne #1237/R est:1500

STRASSER, Roland (1892-1974) Austrian
£383 $605 €575 Japanese temple (89x63cm-35x25in) s. 18-Nov-2 Waddingtons, Toronto #25/R (C.D 950)

STRASSNER, Ernst (1905-1991) Austrian

Works on paper
£269 $425 €420 Weir in orchard (43x60cm-17x24in) s.d.1967 s.i. verso gouache. 15-Nov-2 Reiss & Sohn, Konigstein #699

STRASZEWSKY, Leo von (19/20th C) ?

Works on paper
£311 $500 €467 Toil in the fields (38x53cm-15x21in) s.d.1913 gouache. 19-Feb-3 Doyle, New York #74

STRATEMEYER, George (19th C) American
£3300 $5215 €4950 Volcanic eruptions at Honolulu, Hawaii (36x61cm-14x24in) s.d.85. 15-Nov-2 Sotheby's, London #74/R est:3000-4000

STRATEN, Georges van der (19/20th C) ?

Sculpture
£1013 $1580 €1600 Printemps (51cm-20in) brown pat bronze. 20-Oct-2 Mercier & Cie, Lille #116/R est:1300-1500

STRATER, Henry (1896-?) American
£395 $600 €593 Yellow house (41x51cm-16x20in) s. i.on stretcher. 15-Aug-2 Doyle, New York #97

STRATHDEE, Barbara (20th C) New Zealander
£351 $547 €527 Love and the pink whale (120x100cm-47x39in) s.d.2000. 27-Mar-3 International Art Centre, Auckland #15/R (NZ.D 1000)

STRATHERN, Allan (20th C) New Zealander

Sculpture
£2951 $4604 €4427 Acrobatic figurative composition (92x55cm-36x22in) st.sig. bronze. 8-Apr-3 Peter Webb, Auckland #135/R est:3000-5000 (NZ.D 8500)

STRATMANN, Robert (1877-?) German
£475 $750 €750 Niedersachsisches farmhouse in May (80x110cm-31x43in) s. 29-Nov-2 Bolland & Marotz, Bremen #825/R

STRATTON, Lily (fl.1901-1940) Canadian
£258 $402 €374 Portrait of May Stratton (46x33cm-18x13in) s. 26-Mar-3 Walker's, Ottawa #278/R (C.D 600)
£429 $670 €622 Portrait of a young boy (48x38cm-19x15in) 26-Mar-3 Walker's, Ottawa #277/R est:400-500 (C.D 1000)

STRATTON, May (fl.1901-1940) Canadian

Works on paper
£236 $368 €342 Portrait of Lily Stratton painting (31x30cm-12x12in) s.d.1899 W/C. 26-Mar-3 Walker's, Ottawa #272/R (C.D 550)

STRAUBE, William (1871-1954) German
£285 $441 €450 Carnival mask (44x51cm-17x20in) s.i.d.1912 verso panel. 27-Sep-2 Karrenbauer, Konstanz #1680
£380 $600 €600 Red wine drinker (35x27cm-14x11in) s.d.1924 board. 30-Nov-2 Bassenge, Berlin #6637a/R
£641 $994 €1000 Man's portrait (92x73cm-36x29in) s. 4-Dec-2 Lempertz, Koln #1083/R
£696 $1079 €1100 Portrait of Frl Klaist (43x33cm-17x13in) s. i.d.1931 verso canvas on panel. 27-Sep-2 Karrenbauer, Konstanz #1682
£759 $1200 €1200 Portrait of girl (45x37cm-18x15in) s.i.d.1914 verso board. 27-Nov-2 Dr Fritz Nagel, Stuttgart #3218/R

Works on paper
£253 $392 €400 Winter sun (34x45cm-13x18in) s.i.d.1924 col chk. 27-Sep-2 Karrenbauer, Konstanz #1681
£288 $472 €400 Figures before landscape (24x32cm-9x13in) s. pastel chk. 4-Jun-3 Reiss & Sohn, Konigstein #517/R
£319 $517 €450 Tree lined path (29x33cm-11x13in) mono. pastel chk. 24-May-3 Van Ham, Cologne #566/R
£405 $632 €600 Bodensee landscape (34x46cm-13x18in) s. col chk. 28-Mar-3 Karrenbauer, Konstanz #1788/R

STRAUBINGER, Klaus (1839-?) German

Works on paper
£377 $589 €600 Beach holiday (60x76cm-24x30in) mono.d.82 i. verso gouache. 21-Sep-2 Bolland & Marotz, Bremen #779/R

STRAUCH, Lorenz (1554-1630) German
£3767 $5877 €5500 Man's portrait. Portrait of Margreta Lengin (50x37cm-20x15in) mono.i. panel pair. 11-Apr-3 Winterberg, Heidelberg #187/R est:850
£4747 $7358 €7500 Child's portrait - Margareta Fetzerin (82x55cm-32x22in) mono.d.93 canvas on panel and canvas. 25-Sep-2 Neumeister, Munich #516/R est:2000

STRAUCH, Ludwig Karl (1875-1959) Austrian
£685 $1068 €1000 Jeitendorf near Pottenbrunn (36x55cm-14x22in) s.i. board. 10-Apr-3 Dorotheum, Vienna #140/R

STRAUS, Meyer (1831-1905) American/German
£417 $650 €626 Merced River (20x33cm-8x13in) panel painted c.1900. 21-Sep-2 Harvey Clar, Oakland #1544

STRAWINSKY, Theodore (1907-1989) Russian
£926 $1491 €1343 Town view with trees (21x27cm-8x11in) s. board prov. 9-May-3 Dobiaschofsky, Bern #154/R (S.FR 2000)
£2400 $3768 €3600 Still life of pitcher and fruit (24x41cm-9x16in) s. 20-Nov-2 Sotheby's, London #186/R est:2000-3000
Works on paper
£328 $517 €492 Still life (18x24cm-7x9in) s. gouache. 17-Nov-2 Koller, Geneva #1276 (S.FR 750)

STRAWINSKY, Theodore (attrib) (1907-1989) Russian
Works on paper
£328 $517 €492 Still life (26x30cm-10x12in) pastel. 17-Nov-2 Koller, Geneva #1277/R (S.FR 750)

STREATOR, Harold A (1861-1926) American
£479 $800 €695 Cabins in mountain landscape (51x61cm-20x24in) s. 17-Jun-3 John Moran, Pasadena #36a
£2000 $3200 €3000 Summer valley landscape with mountains (64x74cm-25x29in) s. 17-May-3 Pook & Pook, Downington #327/R est:2500-3500

STREBELLE, Jean Marie (1916-) Belgian
Works on paper
£329 $533 €500 Les pecheurs. s. W/C. 21-Jan-3 Galerie Moderne, Brussels #294/R

STREBELLE, Olivier (1927-) Belgian
Sculpture
£4167 $6458 €6500 Menavogel II (213cm-84in) bronze cast c.1955-59 lit. 3-Dec-2 Christie's, Amsterdam #59/R est:2000-3000

STREBELLE, Rodolphe (1880-1959) Belgian
Works on paper
£300 $468 €450 Le Faubourg de Collioure (43x55cm-17x22in) s.i.d.1926 gouache. 17-Sep-2 Sotheby's, Olympia #253/R
£385 $604 €600 Femme au collier (107x61cm-42x24in) s. chl. 19-Nov-2 Vanderkindere, Brussels #114
£411 $642 €650 Bord de mer (37x56cm-15x22in) s. i.d.juin 1926 verso W/C. 15-Oct-2 Vanderkindere, Brussels #101
£417 $654 €650 Vue de Nieuport (39x53cm-15x21in) s.d.1955 W/C. 19-Nov-2 Vanderkindere, Brussels #95/R
£601 $950 €950 Jeune femme accoudee dans un fauteuil (35x25cm-14x10in) s. mixed media. 26-Nov-2 Palais de Beaux Arts, Brussels #381

STREBELLE, Vincent (1946-) Belgian
£1519 $2400 €2400 Guitare de Jara (240x150cm-94x59in) s. oil varnish sold with chair and plaster sculpture. 26-Nov-2 Palais de Beaux Arts, Brussels #159/R est:6000-8000

STRECKENBACH, Max T (1865-1936) German
£385 $608 €600 Still life of flowers (57x47cm-22x19in) s. 18-Nov-2 Dorotheum, Linz #343/R
£449 $709 €700 Still life of flowers (69x47cm-27x19in) s.d.07. 18-Nov-2 Dorotheum, Linz #344/R
£1509 $2340 €2400 Still life with Christmas stars (55x64cm-22x25in) s. 2-Nov-2 Hans Stahl, Toestorf #88/R est:2600
£1701 $2704 €2500 Sunflowers (66x57cm-26x22in) s. i. verso. 28-Mar-3 Bolland & Marotz, Bremen #531/R est:2700
£1731 $2631 €2700 Still life of fruit (53x41cm-21x16in) s. 17-Aug-2 Hans Stahl, Toestorf #108/R est:2500
£1761 $2730 €2800 Summer flowers in dark yellow vase (53x54cm-21x21in) s. canvas on panel. 2-Nov-2 Hans Stahl, Toestorf #89/R est:3200
£1781 $2778 €2600 Still life of fruit (50x72cm-20x28in) s.d.00 board. 10-Apr-3 Schopman, Hamburg #694 est:3000
£2115 $3279 €3300 Autumn bouquet in Delft vase (66x55cm-26x22in) s. 5-Dec-2 Schopman, Hamburg #645 est:2500
£2500 $3800 €3900 Pansies in bowl (32x43cm-13x17in) s. 17-Aug-2 Hans Stahl, Toestorf #109/R est:2500

STRECKER, Emil (1841-1925) German
£1309 $2081 €1964 Rest (22x17cm-9x7in) s.i. panel. 8-Mar-3 Dorotheum, Prague #8/R est:30000-45000 (C.KR 60000)

STREECK, Hendrik van (1659-1719) Dutch
£14388 $23022 €20000 Interior of Protestant Gothic church with figures during sermon (62x53cm-24x21in) 13-May-3 Sotheby's, Amsterdam #92/R est:10000-15000

STREECK, Jurriaen van (1632-1687) Dutch
£71942 $115108 €100000 Blue and white wan-li Klapmuts bowl with peaches, lemon and an orange (49x41cm-19x16in) s. prov. 14-May-3 Christie's, Amsterdam #177/R est:20000-30000

STREET, Frank (20th C) American
£288 $450 €432 Cowboy. 12-Oct-2 Fallon, Copake #366
£477 $750 €716 Boston tea party (85x63cm-33x25in) s. indis d. 14-Dec-2 Weschler, Washington #689/R

STREET, Robert (1796-1865) American
£313 $500 €470 Portrait of a gentleman with landscape in background (74x61cm-29x24in) s. prov. 17-May-3 Pook & Pook, Downington #229/R
£417 $650 €626 Portrait of a gentleman, holding spectacles (76x64cm-30x25in) s.d.1838 canvas on board. 18-Sep-2 Alderfer's, Hatfield #229/R
£1198 $2000 €1737 Portrait of a gentleman, said to be John Pizant (100x75cm-39x30in) 22-Jun-3 Freeman, Philadelphia #70/R est:2500-4000
£1763 $2750 €2645 Portraits of a husband and wife (74x61cm-29x24in) s.d.1842 pair. 21-Sep-2 Pook & Pook, Downington #104/R est:2500-3500

STREETON, Sir Arthur Ernest (1867-1943) Australian
£4808 $7548 €7500 Figures in a park, with a lake and rowing boat (53x38cm-21x15in) i.d.1904 verso. 19-Nov-2 Hamilton Osborne King, Dublin #556/R est:3000-5000
£6429 $10157 €9644 Sun shadows after rain, Apsley House (30x45cm-12x18in) init. prov.exhib. 17-Nov-2 Sotheby's, Paddington #25/R est:18000-22000 (A.D 18000)
£7200 $11592 €10800 Eventide - Glenville (31x36cm-12x14in) s. canvas on board prov. 6-May-3 Christie's, Melbourne #127/R est:10000-15000 (A.D 18000)
£11039 $16780 €16559 In a Yorkshire farmyard (46x55cm-18x22in) s.d.1910 lit. 28-Aug-2 Deutscher-Menzies, Melbourne #118/R est:35000-45000 (A.D 30800)
£13523 $20690 €20285 Mr Streeton potato crop (60x49cm-24x19in) s. painted 1927 prov.exhib. 25-Aug-2 Sotheby's, Paddington #74/R est:25000-35000 (A.D 38000)
£19573 $29947 €29360 Blue Bay and Olympic Mountains (51x76cm-20x30in) s. painted 1923 prov.exhib. 26-Aug-2 Sotheby's, Paddington #520/R est:55000-65000 (A.D 55000)
£21073 $31398 €31610 Cherry blossom (75x62cm-30x24in) s.d.1938 prov.exhib. 27-Aug-2 Christie's, Melbourne #23/R est:40000-60000 (A.D 55000)
£21352 $32669 €32028 Blue and gold, Olinda (52x78cm-20x31in) s. canvas on board painted 1926 prov.exhib. 26-Aug-2 Sotheby's, Paddington #512/R est:80000-120000 (A.D 60000)
£22115 $35163 €33173 Sunflowers (91x71cm-36x28in) s.d.28 prov.exhib.lit. 4-Mar-3 Deutscher-Menzies, Melbourne #136/R est:60000-80000 (A.D 57500)
£25896 $42470 €38844 Glade (76x51cm-30x20in) s.d.1907 exhib. 4-Jun-3 Deutscher-Menzies, Melbourne #70/R est:55000-65000 (A.D 65000)
£30769 $48923 €46154 Gold honeysuckles and blue sea (17x65cm-7x26in) s.d.1907 panel prov.exhib.lit. 4-Mar-3 Deutscher-Menzies, Melbourne #45/R est:90000-120000 (A.D 80000)
£34615 $55038 €51923 Red roofs crown the Gums of Cremorne (17x66cm-7x26in) s.i. i.verso panel prov.exhib.lit. 4-Mar-3 Deutscher-Menzies, Melbourne #44/R est:100000-140000 (A.D 90000)
£44484 $68060 €66726 Shipping in the Giudecca, Venice (53x65cm-21x26in) init. i.verso painted c.1908. 25-Aug-2 Sotheby's, Paddington #19/R est:70000-90000 (A.D 125000)
£58140 $92442 €87210 Sydney Harbour (19x61cm-7x24in) s.d.95 exhib. 5-May-3 Sotheby's, Melbourne #146/R est:150000-180000 (A.D 150000)

£70000 $112700 €105000 Shall we gather at the river (77x64cm-30x25in) s. painted c.1938 prov.exhib. 6-May-3 Christie's, Melbourne #57/R est:90000-120000 (A.D 175000)
£72519 $114580 €108779 Sirius Cove, New South Wales (11x30cm-4x12in) s.d.95 panel prov. 2-Apr-3 Christie's, Melbourne #12/R est:120000-180000 (A.D 190000)
£84000 $135240 €126000 Santa Maria della Salute - sunny (49x75cm-19x30in) painted 1908 prov.exhib.lit. 6-May-3 Christie's, Melbourne #25/R est:220000-280000 (A.D 210000)

Works on paper
£1231 $1957 €1847 Window (24x34cm-9x13in) s. pencil. 4-Mar-3 Deutscher-Menzies, Melbourne #238/R est:1000-1500 (A.D 3200)
£2789 $4573 €4184 Winter scene (39x29cm-15x11in) s.d.1903 W/C. 4-Jun-3 Deutscher-Menzies, Melbourne #160/R est:5000-7000 (A.D 7000)

STREICHMAN, Yehezkel (1906-1993) Israeli
£9494 $15000 €14241 View from window (89x69cm-35x27in) init.d.81 verso. 27-Apr-3 Sotheby's, Tel Aviv #63/R est:15000-20000

Works on paper
£1772 $2800 €2658 Landscape (27x20cm-11x8in) W/C over pencil two. 27-Apr-3 Sotheby's, Tel Aviv #8/R est:2000-3000

STREITT, Franciszek (1839-1890) Polish
£3165 $5000 €5000 Babysitter (35x26cm-14x10in) panel. 28-Nov-2 Dorotheum, Vienna #159/R est:5500-6000

STRELZOVA, Nadeshda (1970-) Russian
£628 $980 €930 Still life with roses and lilies (80x60cm-31x24in) s. 26-Mar-3 Hugo Ruef, Munich #317

STREMPEL, Horst (1904-1975) German

Works on paper
£314 $491 €500 Still life with landscape (76x55cm-30x22in) s.d.37 i.d. verso W/C pastel. 21-Sep-2 Dannenberg, Berlin #599/R

STRENG, W (19/20th C) ?
£552 $872 €800 Winter landscape (68x51cm-27x20in) s.d.1911. 3-Apr-3 Hagelstam, Helsinki #871

STRETTON, Philip Eustace (fl.1884-1919) British
£3550 $5645 €5325 Best friends (44x60cm-17x24in) s.d.1907 oval. 30-Apr-3 Hampton & Littlewood, Exeter #490/R est:3000-5000
£15337 $25000 €23006 Harvester's companions (40x51cm-16x20in) s.d.1892. 11-Feb-3 Bonhams & Doyles, New York #202/R est:25000-35000

Works on paper
£420 $651 €630 Bloodhounds resting (25x38cm-10x15in) s.d.1894 ink wash. 4-Dec-2 Andrew Hartley, Ilkley #1030

STREVENS, John (1902-1990) British
£258 $408 €400 Young woman in Paris (35x46cm-14x18in) s. 17-Dec-2 Durán, Madrid #190/R
£260 $406 €390 Red glove (51x41cm-20x16in) s. 17-Sep-2 Bonhams, Knightsbridge #10/R
£280 $451 €420 Jose (45x35cm-18x14in) s. s.i.verso. 14-Jan-3 Bonhams, Knightsbridge #141/R
£420 $664 €630 Hold tight; winter scene depicting children with a dog skating on a frozen river (48x58cm-19x23in) s.i.verso. 3-Apr-3 Amersham Auction Rooms, UK #255
£480 $758 €720 Jingle bells; woman and two children in a horsedrawn sleigh (48x61cm-19x24in) s.i.verso. 3-Apr-3 Amersham Auction Rooms, UK #257
£560 $890 €840 Sophie (46x36cm-18x14in) s. s.i.verso. 27-Feb-3 Bonhams, Chester #440
£570 $901 €855 Children in snow; head and shoulders study of three children (61x48cm-24x19in) s.i.verso. 3-Apr-3 Amersham Auction Rooms, UK #256
£600 $978 €900 Notre fidele amie (46x36cm-18x14in) sold with a companion. 14-Feb-3 Lyon & Turnbull, Edinburgh #154
£600 $990 €870 In the Bois de Bologne. Notre fidele (46x35cm-18x14in) s.d.54 s.i.verso two. 3-Jul-3 Christie's, Kensington #413/R
£650 $1014 €975 Moment musicale (41x51cm-16x20in) s. s.i.verso. 27-Mar-3 Christie's, Kensington #445/R
£850 $1309 €1275 By the kiosk (46x36cm-18x14in) s.i.verso prov. 5-Sep-2 Christie's, Kensington #554/R
£1300 $2028 €1950 Au jardin d'hiver (50x61cm-20x24in) s. s.i.verso. 27-Mar-3 Christie's, Kensington #448/R est:800-1200

STRICH-CHAPELL, Walter (1877-1960) German
£1384 $2158 €2200 Snow scene (67x77cm-26x30in) s. i. stretcher. 11-Oct-2 Winterberg, Heidelberg #797/R est:2250

Works on paper
£608 $948 €960 Winter landscape (35x44cm-14x17in) s.d.1931 gouache board. 18-Oct-2 Dr Fritz Nagel, Stuttgart #337/R

STRICKLAND, Anthony (1920-) South African?
£258 $415 €387 Bird and the boy (35x50cm-14x20in) s. i.verso canvas on board. 12-May-3 Stephan Welz, Johannesburg #241 est:1800-2400 (SA.R 3000)
£344 $554 €516 School girls (50x35cm-20x14in) s. indis i. verso board. 12-May-3 Stephan Welz, Johannesburg #253 est:1500-2000 (SA.R 4000)

STRIEFFLER, Heinrich (1872-1949) German
£1948 $2903 €3000 Vineyard in autumn (39x50cm-15x20in) s. canvas on masonite. 26-Jun-2 Neumeister, Munich #877/R est:3000

STRINGER, Terry (1946-) New Zealander

Sculpture
£1250 $1950 €1875 Figure in Cruciform (35x26cm-14x10in) st.sig. bronze exec.1978. 8-Apr-3 Peter Webb, Auckland #132/R est:1500-2500 (NZ.D 3600)
£1286 $1994 €1929 Woman (27cm-11in) s.num.2/3 d.1981 bronze black marble base. 4-Dec-2 Dunbar Sloane, Auckland #48/R est:3000-4000 (NZ.D 4000)
£2113 $3486 €3064 Beatrice (34x15cm-13x6in) s.d.1979 painted bronze on wood plinth prov. 1-Jul-3 Peter Webb, Auckland #50/R est:4000-6000 (NZ.D 6000)
£2113 $3486 €3064 Mask (24x15cm-9x6in) s.d.1979 bronze. 1-Jul-3 Peter Webb, Auckland #51/R est:5500-7000 (NZ.D 6000)
£2917 $4550 €4376 Female foe. init.d.86 num.173 bronze. 8-Apr-3 Peter Webb, Auckland #131/R est:3000-4000 (NZ.D 8400)

STRINGER, Thomas (1722-1790) British
£7500 $12150 €11250 Two spaniels in a wooded river landscape (46x62cm-18x24in) init.d.1772. 22-May-3 Christie's, London #64/R est:5000-8000

STRISIK, Paul (1918-1998) American
£449 $700 €674 Untitled (30x41cm-12x16in) canvasboard. 19-Oct-2 David Dike, Dallas #94/R
£1697 $2715 €2546 Silvery light, Arroyo Hondo (20x30cm-8x12in) s. masonite. 11-Jan-3 James Julia, Fairfield #273 est:1500-2500
£2188 $3500 €3282 Angel Cove. Maine coastal scene (41x61cm-16x24in) s. masonite. 11-Jan-3 James Julia, Fairfield #272 est:2750-3250
£3247 $5000 €4871 Boats on the beach (56x81cm-22x32in) s. masonite prov. 24-Oct-2 Shannon's, Milford #229/R est:2500-3500
£3313 $5500 €4804 Morning light at Pigeon Cove, Massachusetts (41x61cm-16x24in) s. prov. 11-Jun-3 Butterfields, San Francisco #4088/R est:2000-3000
£3571 $5500 €5357 Docks and gulls (51x76cm-20x30in) s. prov. 24-Oct-2 Shannon's, Milford #227/R est:2500-3500

Works on paper
£1146 $1800 €1719 Beals inlet (35x53cm-14x21in) s. W/C. 22-Nov-2 Skinner, Boston #378/R est:700-900

STROBECH, Niels (1944-) Danish
£8467 $13124 €12701 Rosenborg (56x35cm-22x14in) s.d.1985 panel. 1-Oct-2 Rasmussen, Copenhagen #52/R est:50000-75000 (D.KR 100000)

STROBEL, Daniele de (1873-1942) Italian
£9184 $14602 €13500 Jeanne d'Arc (165x144cm-65x57in) s. lit. 18-Mar-3 Finarte, Milan #57/R est:13000

STROBL, Franzl (1915-) Austrian
£449 $696 €700 Alpine flowers (41x45cm-16x18in) s. board. 6-Dec-2 Michael Zeller, Lindau #930/R

STRODTMANN, Christian (1793-1839) German
£775 $1178 €1163 Farmers from Skjoldemose (42x56cm-17x22in) s.d.1825. 27-Aug-2 Rasmussen, Copenhagen #1490/R (D.KR 9000)

STROEBEL, Johann Anthonie Balthasar (1821-1905) Dutch
£1572 $2421 €2500 De regentenkamer, discussing the accounts (19x25cm-7x10in) s. panel. 23-Oct-2 Christie's, Amsterdam #38/R est:2500-3500
£4225 $7014 €6000 Huntsmen and artist in extensive landscape (69x101cm-27x40in) s. 11-Jun-3 Dorotheum, Vienna #183/R est:6000-10000
£5031 $7748 €8000 At the Notary (70x90cm-28x35in) s. indis d. 22-Oct-2 Sotheby's, Amsterdam #163/R est:10000-15000

STROHLING, Peter Eduard (1768-1826) Russian

Miniatures

£1600 $2464 €2400 Young gentleman holding a walking stick (8cm-3in) s. metal plush rec. mount oval exec.c.1795 exhib. 24-Oct-2 Sotheby's, Olympia #34/R est:800-1200

£3000 $4710 €4500 Russian nobleman (6cm-2in) gilt wood frame oval lit. 10-Dec-2 Christie's, London #106/R est:2500-3500

£3100 $4774 €4650 Gentleman in a white coat with mauve facings (9cm-4in) s. gilt metal bezel oval exec.c.1795 prov.exhib. 24-Oct-2 Sotheby's, Olympia #33/R est:800-1200

STROHLING, Peter Eduard (attrib) (1768-1826) Russian

Miniatures

£1300 $2106 €1950 General Baron Etienne Brouard, wearing uniform (6cm-2in) gilt mounted square wiid frame. 22-May-3 Bonhams, New Bond Street #69/R est:600-800

STROHMAYER, Antal Jozsef (19th C) Hungarian

£6993 $11678 €10000 Nature morte aux raisins, grenade et perroquet (28x34cm-11x13in) s. 25-Jun-3 Tajan, Paris #42/R est:7000-9000

STROMBERG, Julia (1851-1920) Swedish

£4823 $7475 €7235 View across the Royal Gardens from Hamngatan (75x120cm-30x47in) s.d.1886. 3-Dec-2 Bukowskis, Stockholm #11/R est:50000-60000 (S.KR 68000)

STROMME, Olav (1909-1978) Norwegian

£305 $479 €458 Black and brown composition (38x46cm-15x18in) exhib. 25-Nov-2 Blomqvist, Lysaker #1265 (N.KR 3500)

£346 $530 €519 Composition with blue (33x41cm-13x16in) s. panel. 26-Aug-2 Blomqvist, Lysaker #1388 (N.KR 4000)

£398 $609 €597 Ochre composition (35x50cm-14x20in) s. panel painted 1961. 26-Aug-2 Blomqvist, Lysaker #1384 (N.KR 4600)

£433 $662 €650 Christ (64x59cm-25x23in) s. panel. 26-Aug-2 Blomqvist, Lysaker #1386 (N.KR 5000)

£442 $676 €663 Composition (40x33cm-16x13in) s. panel. 26-Aug-2 Blomqvist, Lysaker #1385 (N.KR 5100)

£614 $970 €921 Composition (66x75cm-26x30in) s.d.68 panel. 17-Dec-2 Grev Wedels Plass, Oslo #275 (N.KR 7000)

£865 $1367 €1298 Oriental town (70x70cm-28x28in) s.indis.d. i.verso panel. 2-Dec-2 Blomqvist, Oslo #445/R (N.KR 10000)

£1062 $1731 €1593 Man wearing theatre costume (41x33cm-16x13in) s.d.1958 panel. 17-Feb-3 Blomqvist, Lysaker #1223 (N.KR 12000)

£1480 $2367 €2220 Composition (49x70cm-19x28in) s.d.68 panel. 17-Mar-3 Blomqvist, Oslo #451/R est:20000-30000 (N.KR 17000)

£1915 $3064 €2873 Thoughts of the Roman Quartet (70x50cm-28x20in) s. exhib.lit. 17-Mar-3 Blomqvist, Oslo #435/R est:35000-45000 (N.KR 22000)

£3620 $5864 €5430 Roman ruins (75x171cm-30x67in) s.d.68 i.verso exhib. 26-May-3 Grev Wedels Plass, Oslo #105/R est:50000-70000 (N.KR 40000)

Works on paper

£2082 $3247 €3123 Flowers (100x70cm-39x28in) mixed media panel painted c.1935. 21-Oct-2 Blomqvist, Oslo #411/R est:40000-50000 (N.KR 24000)

STRONG, Ray Stanford (1905-) American

£2724 $4250 €4086 Morning shadows, Lucas Valley. 21-Sep-2 Harvey Clar, Oakland #1528

STROOBANT, François (1819-1916) Belgian

£7586 $12138 €11000 View near the old Saint Jans hospital in Bruges (95x120cm-37x47in) s.d.1884. 15-Mar-3 De Vuyst, Lokeren #510/R est:11000-13000

STROPPA, Leonardo (1900-1991) Italian

£327 $523 €500 Flamingoes (50x70cm-20x28in) s. 4-Jan-3 Meeting Art, Vercelli #140

STROUD, Clara (1890-?) American

Works on paper

£514 $750 €771 Sailing ships, southern landscape (28x38cm-11x15in) s. W/C. 10-May-2 Skinner, Boston #237/R

STROUD, Ken (1937-) British

£250 $388 €375 Lion charging (54x44cm-21x17in) s. canvasboard. 3-Dec-2 Sotheby's, Olympia #209/R

STROUDLEY, James (1906-1985) British

£700 $1078 €1050 Portrait of a seated lady (91x76cm-36x30in) 5-Sep-2 Christie's, Kensington #505

STROUVE, Sophie (20th C) ?

£319 $497 €500 Soiree (46x38cm-18x15in) s. s.i.d.1973 verso. 5-Nov-2 Tajan, Paris #100

£573 $894 €900 Chateau et parc (48x64cm-19x25in) s.d.1964 i.verso. 5-Nov-2 Tajan, Paris #99

£1083 $1689 €1700 Place de l'Archeveche (55x46cm-22x18in) s.d.1965 s.i.verso. 5-Nov-2 Tajan, Paris #97

STROZZI, Bernardo (1581-1644) Italian

£24691 $40000 €37037 Actaeon (77x39cm-30x15in) prov.lit. 24-Jan-3 Christie's, Rockefeller NY #149/R est:30000-50000

£60000 $94200 €90000 Crucifixion, with Saints Mary Magdalene, Nicholas and Peter (37x30cm-15x12in) prov.exhib.lit. 12-Dec-2 Sotheby's, London #49/R est:12000-16000

£64103 $99359 €100000 Saint John the Baptist (170x124cm-67x49in) d.1619. 4-Dec-2 Christie's, Rome #429/R est:100000-150000

STRUCK, Hermann (1876-1944) German

£1261 $1990 €1892 Haifa area in spring (31x29cm-12x11in) s. panel. 27-Apr-3 Sotheby's, Tel Aviv #12/R est:2500-3500

£1639 $2590 €2459 Lake Kinneret, Galilee (33x50cm-13x20in) s.d.1936. 27-Apr-3 Sotheby's, Tel Aviv #11/R est:3000-5000

Works on paper

£962 $1500 €1443 Judisch Mann, Jerusalem (31x25cm-12x10in) s.d.1925 W/C. 19-Sep-2 Swann Galleries, New York #783/R est:2000-3000

STRUDEL, Paul (1648-1708) Austrian

Works on paper

£962 $1519 €1500 Triumph of hope over the plague (27x18cm-11x7in) pen sepia wash prov. 16-Nov-2 Lempertz, Koln #1278/R est:1400

STRUPLER, Hans Rudolf (1935-) Swiss

£961 $1508 €1442 Composition in blue (33x35cm-13x14in) mono. 25-Nov-2 Sotheby's, Zurich #147/R est:1000-1500 (S.FR 2200)

Works on paper

£377 $604 €566 Gondolier (32x37cm-13x15in) mono. gouache. 17-Mar-3 Philippe Schuler, Zurich #4368/R (S.FR 800)

£529 $772 €794 Untitled fantasy landscape (48x67cm-19x26in) mono. gouache. 17-Jun-2 Philippe Schuler, Zurich #4225 (S.FR 1200)

STRUSS, Karl (1886-1981) American

Photographs

£5696 $9000 €8544 Henrietta Crossman, New York (9x11cm-4x4in) s.i.d.1910 verso platinum print prov. 25-Apr-3 Phillips, New York #74/R est:6000-9000

£6013 $9500 €9020 Untitled (11x9cm-4x4in) s.d.1911 platinum print prov. 25-Apr-3 Phillips, New York #75/R est:5000-7000

£8861 $14000 €13292 Roof tops - 291 Fifth Avenue (12x10cm-5x4in) s.i.d. platinum print prov. 25-Apr-3 Phillips, New York #2/R est:8000-12000

£32911 $52000 €49367 City of dreams (34x27cm-13x11in) s. s.d.1926 on mount photograph exhib.prov. 25-Apr-3 Phillips, New York #1/R est:6000-8000

STRUTH, Thomas (1954-) German

Photographs

£2222 $3534 €3200 Zhejiang Zhoug for Shangai (43x55cm-17x22in) s.i.num.16/20 verso col photo. 29-Apr-3 Artcurial Briest, Paris #524/R est:3500-4000

£2400 $4008 €3480 Hillside road, Kiwado (44x55cm-17x22in) gelatin silver print 3 in edition of 10. 24-Jun-3 Sotheby's, Olympia #49/R est:2000-3000

£2532 $4000 €3798 Zhejiang zhong fu, Shanghai (44x56cm-17x22in) s.i.d.1997 verso chromogenic col print prov. 24-Apr-3 Phillips, New York #65/R est:4000-6000

£2642 $4094 €4200 Zhe Jiang Zhong Lu, Shanghai (44x56cm-17x22in) s.i.d.1997 verso col photo. 2-Nov-2 Lempertz, Koln #450/R est:3500-4000

£2812 $4500 €4218 Sashi ER LU s, Shanghai (47x58cm-19x23in) s.i.d.1997 verso col photograph prov.exhib. 16-May-3 Phillips, New York #211/R est:4000-6000

£3000 $4620 €4500 North Garland Court, Chicago Illinois (44x55cm-17x22in) s.i.d.1991 num.5/10 silver gelatin print lit. 22-Oct-2 Sotheby's, London #306/R est:4000-6000

£3165 $5000 €5000 Zhejiang Zhong Fu, Shanghai (44x56cm-17x22in) s.i.d.1997 verso col photo. 28-Nov-2 Villa Grisebach, Berlin #1422/R est:5000-7000
£3797 $6000 €5696 Daily news building (31x41cm-12x16in) ferrotyped. 23-Apr-3 Sotheby's, New York #264/R est:5000-7000
£3797 $6000 €5696 116th St. and Park Ave, E (31x43cm-12x17in) ferrotyped. 23-Apr-3 Sotheby's, New York #265/R est:5000-7000
£4114 $6500 €6171 Greenwich St, Franklin St. South, New York City (31x40cm-12x16in) s.i.d.1978 ferroyped. 23-Apr-3 Sotheby's, New York #263/R est:5000-7000
£4430 $7000 €6645 Pflanze nr. 7 Mehrjahringer blauer Rittersporn winterthur (58x40cm-23x16in) s.i.d.1992 num.3/10 col coupler print exhib. 14-Nov-2 Christie's, Rockefeller NY #410/R est:10000-15000
£5000 $8000 €7500 Panorama - beau gremelle, Paris (60x84cm-24x33in) black white photograph executed 1979 prov. 14-May-3 Sotheby's, New York #384/R est:6000-8000
£6200 $10354 €8990 Shinju-ku, with Ben Johnson (41x58cm-16x23in) s.i.d.1987 num.4/10 verso cibachrome print prov. 26-Jun-3 Sotheby's, London #284/R est:4000-6000
£7000 $10780 €10500 Crosby Street, New York (35x50cm-14x20in) s.i.d.1978 verso silver gelatin print prov.lit. 22-Oct-2 Sotheby's, London #305/R est:4000-6000
£9494 $15000 €14241 Park Avenue. West 25th Street New York. Layfayette Street at Grand New York (46x61cm-18x24in) s.i.d. set of three gelatin silver print executed 1978 prov. 14-Nov-2 Christie's, Rockefeller NY #407/R est:12000-18000
£11500 $18860 €17250 Street views (48x61cm-19x24in) s.i.d.1990 num.4/10, 5/10, 6/10, 7/10 verso black white photos 4. 7-Feb-3 Sotheby's, London #106/R est:8000-12000
£15000 $24000 €22500 Landscape no.14, winterthur (93x116cm-37x46in) s.i.d.1992-94 num.5/10 verso c-print prov. 14-May-3 Sotheby's, New York #394/R est:20000-30000
£16000 $26240 €24000 Landschaft nr 10 baume hinter dem gartenhaus em lindberg winterthur (126x100cm-50x39in) s.i.d.1992 num.3/10 verso cibachrome print prov. 7-Feb-3 Sotheby's, London #119/R est:10000-15000
£16250 $26000 €24375 Piazza San Ignazio I-III Rome (46x59cm-18x23in) s.i.d.1991 num.4/10 three gelatin silver print prov.exhib. 15-May-3 Christie's, Rockefeller NY #350/R est:15000-20000
£18750 $30000 €28125 Chong Wen Meng Dong Beijing, 1996 (138x160cm-54x63in) s. col coupler print prov. 15-May-3 Christie's, Rockefeller NY #351/R est:15000-20000
£20000 $32800 €30000 Boats at Wushan, Yangtse Gorge, China (160x200cm-63x79in) s.verso num.2/10 C-print mounted behind plexiglas. 6-Feb-3 Christie's, London #721/R est:25000-35000
£20253 $32000 €30380 Paradise 7, Daintree, Australia (190x237cm-75x93in) col coupler print mounted on plexiglas executed 1998 prov. 14-Nov-2 Christie's, Rockefeller NY #412/R est:40000-60000
£24000 $39360 €36000 Drammen II (173x229cm-68x90in) s.num.1/10 verso C-print/diasec prov. 6-Feb-3 Christie's, London #720/R est:18000-22000
£25316 $40000 €37974 Tien an men, Beijing (183x225cm-72x89in) s. col coupler print prov.exhib.lit. 14-Nov-2 Christie's, Rockefeller NY #406/R est:40000-60000
£31646 $50000 €47469 Paradise 16, Yakushima, Japan (181x220cm-71x87in) s. col coupler print mounted on plexiglas executed 1999. 14-Nov-2 Christie's, Rockefeller NY #405/R est:80000-120000
£38000 $58520 €57000 Gerhard Richter, Madrid (190x240cm-75x94in) s. col coupler print executed 1994 prov.lit. 23-Oct-2 Christie's, London #246/R est:35000-45000
£50000 $80000 €75000 Paradise 3, Daintree, Australia (190x236cm-75x93in) cibachrome print exec.1998 prov.lit. 13-May-3 Sotheby's, New York #36b/R est:40000-60000
£57692 $90000 €86538 Galleria dell'accademia II, Venice (227x187cm-89x74in) s.i.d.1995 col coupler print prov.exhib. 11-Nov-2 Phillips, New York #44/R est:120000-160000
£65625 $105000 €98438 Kunsthistorisches museum I Vienna (179x234cm-70x92in) col coupler print executed 1989 prov.exhib. 15-May-3 Phillips, New York #39/R est:100000-150000
£81250 $130000 €121875 Musee d'Orsay 2, Paris (224x183cm-88x72in) s.i.d.1989 num.8 col coupler print prov.exhib.lit. 15-May-3 Christie's, Rockefeller NY #348/R est:70000-90000
£100000 $167000 €145000 Musee du Louvre I (139x189cm-55x74in) cibachrome print 1 from edition of 10 prov.lit. 26-Jun-3 Sotheby's, London #113/R est:50000-80000

STRUTT, Alfred William (1856-1924) British
Works on paper
£350 $578 €508 Study of four horses in a landscape (13x22cm-5x9in) s. W/C. 3-Jul-3 Locke & England, Leamington Spa #157

STRUTT, Alfred William (attrib) (1856-1924) British
£15000 $23250 €22500 Love in a barrow - two children kissing in wheelbarrow with terrier (32x42cm-13x17in) i.verso painted c.1880. 26-Sep-2 Locke & England, Leamington Spa #326/R est:800-1200

STRUTT, Arthur John (1819-1888) British
Works on paper
£700 $1091 €1050 Italian peasants travelling on an oxcart (31x41cm-12x16in) s.d.1862 pencil W/C. 19-Sep-2 Christie's, Kensington #106

STRUTT, William (1826-1915) British
£1000 $1560 €1500 Boy at prayer (22x17cm-9x7in) s.d.1877 board. 17-Sep-2 Sotheby's, Olympia #197/R est:400-600
Works on paper
£286 $449 €429 Horse (17x24cm-7x9in) pencil. 25-Nov-2 Christie's, Melbourne #302/R (A.D 800)
£620 $967 €930 Lion studies (9x17cm-4x7in) d.May 25th/98 pencil wash sold with two landscapes and books. 17-Sep-2 Sotheby's, Olympia #131/R

STRUTZEL, Otto (1855-1930) German
£408 $649 €600 Isar valley from Schaftlarn (26x37cm-10x15in) s.d.1898 i. verso board. 20-Mar-3 Neumeister, Munich #2749
£411 $641 €600 Landscape study with rocks and grasses (20x30cm-8x12in) mono.i.d.86 paper lit. 10-Apr-3 Allgauer, Kempten #3005/R
£449 $682 €700 Moorland meadow in pre-alps (20x30cm-8x12in) s. board. 11-Jul-2 Hugo Ruef, Munich #834
£490 $784 €750 Tree study in landscape (21x32cm-8x13in) mono.i.d.90 canvas on board lit. 10-Jan-3 Allgauer, Kempten #1759/R
£1076 $1668 €1700 Isar valley near Tolz (19x25cm-7x10in) s. i. verso board. 25-Sep-2 Neumeister, Munich #741/R est:1200
£1338 $2154 €1900 Shepherd with flock in morning mist (30x40cm-12x16in) s.d.15.X.84 i. verso board. 10-May-3 Berlinghof, Heidelberg #319 est:1900
£1410 $2186 €2200 Early spring at forest edge with a small pond in foreground (34x48cm-13x19in) s.d.1901. 4-Dec-2 Neumeister, Munich #916/R est:2400
£1582 $2453 €2500 Peasant ploughing field (76x99cm-30x39in) s.i. 25-Sep-2 Neumeister, Munich #740/R est:3000
£1633 $2596 €2400 Three girls in boats on Bodensee (30x39cm-12x15in) mono. i.d.1906, 3. Sept verso board lit. 19-Mar-3 Neumeister, Munich #755/R est:1500
£2585 $4110 €3800 Farmstead beneath trees in spring landscape (52x57cm-20x22in) s.d.5.1904 i. stretcher. 19-Mar-3 Neumeister, Munich #754/R est:2500
£12579 $19623 €20000 In the wood (113x85cm-44x33in) s.i. i. verso lit. 20-Sep-2 Schloss Ahlden, Ahlden #1134/R est:18500
Works on paper
£779 $1161 €1200 Two figures in evening light (33x51cm-13x20in) s.d.1898 i. verso gouache. 26-Jun-2 Neumeister, Munich #603/R

STRUYKEN, Peter (1939-) Dutch
£2817 $4535 €4000 Reclining nude (48x98cm-19x39in) s.d.62. 7-May-3 Vendue Huis, Gravenhage #207/R est:4000-6000
Works on paper
£321 $497 €500 Shft 25 (26x25cm-10x10in) i.d.28 Sep 83 ink. 3-Dec-2 Christie's, Amsterdam #180a

STRY, Abraham van (18/19th C) Dutch
Works on paper
£446 $687 €700 Couple reading by candlelight (16x14cm-6x6in) s. black chk pen brown ink brown wash prov. 3-Sep-2 Christie's, Amsterdam #92/R
£7006 $10930 €11000 Winter landscape with skaters and sledges on the ice, bridge a mill beyond (37x47cm-15x19in) s. black chk grey wash prov.lit. 5-Nov-2 Sotheby's, Amsterdam #129/R est:12000-15000

STRY, Abraham van (elder) (1753-1826) Dutch
Works on paper
£4514 $7177 €6500 Field workers resting (17x24cm-7x9in) s. brush ink over chl wash. 5-May-3 Ketterer, Munich #457/R est:1000-1500

£24051 $38000 €38000 Portraits, des vues de villes et d'architecture, et des animaux (34x23cm-13x9in) black chk brown wash W/C drs 80 album prov.exhib. 27-Nov-2 Christie's, Paris #19/R est:20000-30000

STRY, Jacob van (1756-1815) Dutch

£8261 $12887 €12392 Winter landscape with a figures (60x83cm-24x33in) s. wood. 12-Oct-2 Dorotheum, Prague #4/R est:100000-150000 (C.KR 400000)

Works on paper

£686 $1105 €1050 Scene de patinage en Hollande (14x21cm-6x8in) s.verso wash. 14-Jan-3 Vanderkindere, Brussels #103

£966 $1535 €1400 Peasant with cattle resting by a river (32x41cm-13x16in) bears sig W/C prov. 10-Mar-3 Sotheby's, Amsterdam #12 est:1500-2000

£1795 $2836 €2800 Country scene (35x48cm-14x19in) s. brush. 16-Nov-2 Lempertz, Koln #1277/R est:2000

STRY, Jacob van (attrib) (1756-1815) Dutch

£1020 $1622 €1500 Dutch canal landscape (20x29cm-8x11in) mono. bears d. panel. 19-Mar-3 Neumeister, Munich #469/R est:1800

£13376 $20866 €21000 Head of a bull with a view over an extensive landscape (105x85cm-41x33in) prov. 5-Nov-2 Sotheby's, Amsterdam #40/R est:8000-12000

STRYDONCK, Guillaume van (1861-1937) Belgian

£4483 $7172 €6500 L'artiste dans son alelier (64x80cm-25x31in) s. 15-Mar-3 De Vuyst, Lokeren #363/R est:5000-6000

STRYI-LEITGEB, Gerda (1905-) German?

£333 $517 €520 Village on bay lit by setting sun (59x79cm-23x31in) s. i. verso lit. 7-Dec-2 Hans Stahl, Hamburg #34/R

STRYOWSKI, Wilhelm August (1834-1917) German

£5150 $7983 €7725 The ambush (100x79cm-39x31in) s.d.1888. 3-Oct-2 Koller, Zurich #3099/R est:12000-15000 (S.FR 12000)

STUART, Alexander Charles (1831-1898) American

£3205 $5000 €4808 Seascape, with three masted frigate and passenger steamer (48x74cm-19x29in) s.d.88. 21-Sep-2 Pook & Pook, Downington #35/R est:8000-10000

STUART, Alexander Charles (attrib) (1831-1898) American

£1154 $1800 €1731 Ship run aground. Shipping at dusk (30x58cm-12x23in) s. board pair. 20-Sep-2 Freeman, Philadelphia #98/R est:400-600

STUART, C (19th C) British

£1600 $2480 €2400 Peacock and poultry in landscape (47x58cm-19x23in) s.d.1792. 3-Dec-2 Sotheby's, Olympia #73/R est:1000-1500

STUART, Charles (19th C) British

£300 $480 €450 On a highland path (60x50cm-24x20in) s.d.1881. 13-May-3 Bonhams, Sevenoaks #348

£481 $750 €722 Rainy weather going to clear up (46x67cm-18x26in) s.d. s.i.stretcher. 9-Nov-2 Sloan, North Bethesda #566/R

£1400 $2282 €2030 Scottish mountain viewed from across a river (60x45cm-24x18in) s. 21-Jul-3 Bonhams, Bath #62/R est:800-1200

£1442 $2250 €2163 Forest scene. s. 19-Oct-2 Harvey Clar, Oakland #1592

£2350 $3619 €3525 Highland glen (61x46cm-24x18in) s. 5-Sep-2 Christie's, Kensington #152/R est:1500-2000

£3250 $5135 €4875 Two young girls on a pathway talking (87x122cm-34x48in) s. 18-Dec-2 John Nicholson, Haslemere #1221/R est:3000-4000

£3900 $6201 €5850 Highland landscape with deer (61x46cm-24x18in) s. pair. 18-Mar-3 Sworder & Son, Bishops Stortford #413b/R est:1000-1500

£6500 $10335 €9750 Stag with hinds by a loch (61x91cm-24x36in) s. pair. 6-Mar-3 Christie's, Kensington #58/R est:5000-7000

Works on paper

£300 $474 €435 Alone in the highlands (49x34cm-19x13in) s. bodycol. 22-Jul-3 Bonhams, Knightsbridge #174/R

STUART, Ernest (fl.1889-1903) British

Works on paper

£350 $546 €525 River landscape with fisherman in a boat by a jetty (49x74cm-19x29in) s. W/C. 10-Apr-3 Tennants, Leyburn #850

£500 $835 €725 Blowing fresh, Torbay (26x75cm-10x30in) s. W/C. 24-Jun-3 Bonhams, Knightsbridge #26/R

£700 $1113 €1050 Fresh breeze, Yorkshire coast (32x97cm-13x38in) s. W/C. 5-Mar-3 Bonhams, Bury St Edmunds #251

STUART, Gilbert (1755-1828) American

£18000 $28440 €27000 Portraits of Sir John Lees and Mary, Lady Lees (76x63cm-30x25in) painted ovals pair prov. 26-Nov-2 Christie's, London #39/R est:20000-30000

£103226 $160000 €154839 Portrait of George Washington (74x60cm-29x24in) prov.exhib. 4-Dec-2 Sotheby's, New York #131/R est:80000-120000

£255000 $400000 €369750 George Washington (74x61cm-29x24in) prov. 15-Apr-3 Lincoln, Orange #460

STUART, Gilbert (after) (1755-1828) American

Miniatures

£3125 $5000 €4531 Portrait of George Washington (15x13cm-6x5in) black lacquered frame. 17-May-3 New Orleans Auction, New Orleans #20/R est:1200-1800

STUART, Gilbert (attrib) (1755-1828) American

£4037 $6500 €6056 Portrait of Mr James Milligan (74x61cm-29x24in) canvas on canvas prov. 18-Feb-3 John Moran, Pasadena #27 est:6000-9000

STUART, James Everett (1852-1941) American

£240 $375 €360 Sunset (56x36cm-22x14in) s.d.1881 pressboard. 23-Sep-2 Aspire, Cleveland #7

£641 $1000 €962 Autumn tints near Milo, Maine, 1909. 21-Sep-2 Harvey Clar, Oakland #1527

£745 $1200 €1118 Bay and live oaks near Menlo Park, California (51x61cm-20x24in) s.d.Aug 3 1917 i.verso prov. 18-Feb-3 John Moran, Pasadena #91a

£955 $1500 €1433 Adobe shacks, Monterey, CA (38x51cm-15x20in) s.d.1925 i.d.Feb 25 1925 verso artists board. 23-Nov-2 Jackson's, Cedar Falls #64/R est:800-1200

£1062 $1700 €1593 Dick's Peak in the distance from Eagle Lake. s.i.d.Aug 22 1912. 16-Mar-3 Butterfields, San Francisco #1029 est:1000-1500

£1730 $2750 €2595 Indian camp near the Dalles on Columbia River (25x36cm-10x14in) s.d.1893 s.i.d.verso prov. 5-Mar-3 Sotheby's, New York #128/R est:2000-3000

£3503 $5500 €5255 Near Stinson's Beach, Marin County, California (36x51cm-14x20in) s.i.d.1877 i.verso prov. 19-Nov-2 Butterfields, San Francisco #8144/R est:3000-5000

£4819 $8000 €6988 Great Treadwell mill and mine (46x76cm-18x30in) s.d.1901. 11-Jun-3 Butterfields, San Francisco #4192/R est:6000-8000

£5031 $8000 €7547 Indian camp on the Columbia, near Celilo, Oregon (51x76cm-20x30in) s.d.86 i.verso prov.exhib. 5-Mar-3 Sotheby's, New York #119/R est:5000-7000

£5137 $7500 €7706 June strawberries (20x25cm-8x10in) s.i.d.June 17 1904 s.i.verso. 3-Nov-1 North East Auctions, Portsmouth #248/R est:2000-3000

£17296 $27500 €25944 Sunset looking down the Columbia River (61x121cm-24x48in) s.d.1884 s.i.d.verso prov. 5-Mar-3 Sotheby's, New York #120/R est:10000-20000

STUART, James Lawson (?) British

Works on paper

£340 $530 €510 Norman doorway, Oakhampton Castle (34x51cm-13x20in) mono. W/C. 10-Sep-2 Sworder & Son, Bishops Stortford #797/R

STUART, W E D (19th C) British

£2400 $3960 €3480 Still life of fruit (60x60cm-24x24in) s.d.1830 oval. 2-Jul-3 Sotheby's, Olympia #359/R est:2000-3000

STUART, William (19th C) British

£1300 $2106 €1950 Amsterdam State Yacht in the company of the Dutch fleet (4x61cm-2x24in) s.indis.d.1879. 21-May-3 Christie's, Kensington #542/R est:1500-2500

STUART, William E D (attrib) (fl.1846-1858) British

£820 $1304 €1230 Grapes, pears, plums, chillies, lemon and poppies on a ledge (57x43cm-22x17in) 6-Mar-3 Christie's, Kensington #620/R

STUBBS, George (1724-1806) British

£360000 $583200 €540000 Bay hunter galloping in a mountainous landscape (60x71cm-24x28in) s.d.1775 panel prov.lit. 22-May-3 Christie's, London #38/R est:200000-300000

£1750000 $2922500 €2537500 Dark bay thoroughbred in a landscape (102x127cm-40x50in) prov.lit. 9-Jul-3 Bonhams, New Bond Street #57/R est:400000-600000

STUBBS, R (19th C) British
£3000 $4560 €4500 Dorset coastal scene (25x48cm-10x19in) s.d.1866/69 pair. 14-Aug-2 Andrew Hartley, Ilkley #702/R est:1200-1800

STUBBS, Ralph (1774-1845) British
£760 $1216 €1140 Artist painting on the moors, near Whitby (34x46cm-13x18in) s. board. 11-Mar-3 David Duggleby, Scarborough #218/R

STUBBS, Ralph Reuben (1820-1879) British
£2500 $3950 €3750 Extensive landscape near Pickering with figures fishing and cattle grazing (58x112cm-23x44in) s.d.1861. 7-Apr-3 David Duggleby, Scarborough #369 est:2500-3000
£4000 $6320 €6000 Danes Dyke. Flamborough (25x51cm-10x20in) one s.d.1869 one s.d.1868 exhib. pair. 29-Nov-2 Dee Atkinson & Harrison, Driffield #829/R est:2500-3500
Works on paper
£260 $426 €390 Gypsy Race, Bridlington (27x45cm-11x18in) s.d.1865 W/C. 2-Jun-3 David Duggleby, Scarborough #288

STUBBS, William P (1842-1909) American
£1274 $2000 €1911 Two masted schooner Mary Camden (56x81cm-22x32in) s. 26-Jul-2 Eldred, East Dennis #611/R est:3000-4000
£2632 $4000 €3948 Schooner, Elsie Faye (56x91cm-22x36in) s.d.84. 17-Aug-2 North East Auctions, Portsmouth #980/R
£7643 $12000 €11465 Two masted schooner Skylark (61x91cm-24x36in) s. 26-Jul-2 Eldred, East Dennis #524/R est:12000-15000
£8904 $13000 €13356 Three masted, Martha P Tucker, leaving harbour (64x91cm-25x36in) s. canvas on masonite prov. 3-Nov-1 North East Auctions, Portsmouth #51/R est:10000-15000
£12500 $19000 €18750 The EO Clark, off Thatcher's Light (58x91cm-23x36in) s. 17-Aug-2 North East Auctions, Portsmouth #1046/R est:10000-12000

STUBBS, William P (attrib) (1842-1909) American
£1741 $2750 €2612 Schooner Charles Buckeye (56x91cm-22x36in) 17-Nov-2 CRN Auctions, Cambridge #12/R

STUBENRAUCH, Philipp von (1784-1848) Austrian
Works on paper
£2394 $3855 €3400 Kaiser Franz I (38x30cm-15x12in) s.d.1825 W/C. 7-May-3 Dorotheum, Vienna #37/R est:2500-4000

STUBER, Dedrick B (1878-1954) American
£838 $1400 €1215 River landscape at sunset (51x76cm-20x30in) s. 29-Jun-3 Butterfields, Los Angeles #7001/R est:2500-3500
£898 $1500 €1302 Rural landscape (46x38cm-18x15in) s. board pair. 29-Jun-3 Butterfields, Los Angeles #7000/R est:3000-5000
£1592 $2500 €2388 Still life with mums (51x41cm-20x16in) s. board. 20-Nov-2 Christie's, Los Angeles #86/R est:2500-3500
£2395 $4000 €3473 Afternoon at sea (51x61cm-20x24in) s. masonite prov. 17-Jun-3 John Moran, Pasadena #134 est:4500-6500
£3012 $5000 €4367 Big Tujunga Wash (28x36cm-11x14in) s. i.verso board. 11-Jun-3 Butterfields, San Francisco #4269/R est:4000-6000
£4192 $7000 €6078 Monterey coastal (76x102cm-30x40in) s. prov. 17-Jun-3 John Moran, Pasadena #54 est:5000-7000

STUCHLIK, Camill (1863-1940) Czechoslovakian
£620 $967 €930 Profile of a young lady (44x34cm-17x13in) s.d.1902 canvas on cardboard. 12-Oct-2 Dorotheum, Prague #38/R (C.KR 30000)

STUCK, Franz von (1863-1928) German
£26923 $41731 €42000 Duel (60x69cm-24x27in) s.d.1914 panel prov.lit. 6-Dec-2 Ketterer, Munich #8/R est:50000-70000
£160000 $248000 €240000 Liebesfruhling (106x116cm-42x46in) s.d.1917 prov.lit. 4-Dec-2 Christie's, London #53/R est:80000-120000
Sculpture
£4487 $6955 €7000 Athlete (66x32x28cm-26x13x11in) i. blackish-brown pat bronze exec.c.1906 prov.exhib.lit. 6-Dec-2 Ketterer, Munich #9/R est:8000-12000
£6500 $10855 €9425 Athlete (65cm-26in) s.i. dk brown pat bronze. 8-Jul-3 Sotheby's, London #211/R est:4000-6000
£7000 $10850 €10500 Amazon on horseback (64cm-25in) s.i. brown pat bronze rec. plinth and base. 29-Oct-2 Bonhams, New Bond Street #180/R est:7000-10000
£7692 $12077 €12000 Temptation (70x74cm-28x29in) plaster lit. 21-Nov-2 Van Ham, Cologne #1249/R est:5000
£10063 $15497 €16000 Spear throwing amazon (64cm-25in) i. pat.bronze lit. 26-Oct-2 Auktionhaus Herr, Cologne #150/R est:11800
£11000 $17050 €16500 Verwundeter Zentaur (64x34cm-25x13in) s. brown pat. bronze st.f.Priessmann Bauer conceived 1892. 4-Dec-2 Christie's, London #55/R est:7000-10000
£16000 $24800 €24000 Amazone (65x38cm-26x15in) s. brown pat. bronze st.f.Munchen Guss C.Leyrer prov. 4-Dec-2 Christie's, London #54/R est:12000-18000
£40000 $62000 €60000 Helena (71cm-28in) s.i. gilt bronze prov.lit. 4-Dec-2 Christie's, London #49/R est:40000-60000
Works on paper
£1689 $2635 €2500 Allegories and emblems (28x21cm-11x8in) mono. Indian ink two. 26-Mar-3 Hugo Ruef, Munich #365/R est:2500
£7000 $10850 €10500 Tochter Mary mit hut (55x48cm-22x19in) s. pencil pastel on board prov. 4-Dec-2 Christie's, London #51/R est:7000-10000
£9353 $14964 €13000 Mary Stuck (42x31cm-17x12in) s. pastel chk bodycol pencil board. 15-May-3 Neumeister, Munich #355/R est:8000-8500
£28000 $43400 €42000 Tochter Mary als Griechin (55x48cm-22x19in) s. pencil col chks executed 1910 prov. 4-Dec-2 Christie's, London #48/R est:15000-20000

STUCKELBERG, Ernst (1831-1903) Swiss
£649 $1006 €974 Cupid hiding behind rose bush (73x97cm-29x38in) s.d.1884. 24-Sep-2 Koller, Zurich #6627/R (S.FR 1500)
£972 $1565 €1409 Portrait of a young Oriental (55x46cm-22x18in) s.d.1871. 9-May-3 Dobiaschofsky, Bern #71/R (S.FR 2100)
£3433 $5425 €5150 Child with rose (58x44cm-23x17in) s.d.1872. 26-Nov-2 Phillips, Zurich #1/R est:8000-10000 (S.FR 8000)

STUCKENBERG, Fritz (1881-1944) German
£7595 $12000 €12000 Mechanic (46x37cm-18x15in) s.d.1926 oil cardboard. 29-Nov-2 Villa Grisebach, Berlin #53/R est:12000-15000
Works on paper
£316 $500 €500 Alpine violets (36x27cm-14x11in) s.d.1923 W/C gouache. 29-Nov-2 Bolland & Marotz, Bremen #926/R
£641 $994 €1000 Still life (25x19cm-10x7in) s.i.d. Indian ink brush pen. 7-Dec-2 Hauswedell & Nolte, Hamburg #1045/R
£769 $1192 €1200 Embrace (36x27cm-14x11in) s.i.d. Indian ink brush. 7-Dec-2 Hauswedell & Nolte, Hamburg #1044/R

STUCKGOLD, Stanislaw (1868-1933) Polish
£2405 $3800 €3800 Scene with apes - Zodiac (40x40cm-16x16in) s. board on canvas. 30-Nov-2 Villa Grisebach, Berlin #304/R est:5500-6500

STUDD, Mabel A (?) British
Works on paper
£1900 $2964 €2850 Asleep on a chair (47x61cm-19x24in) mono. pastel with sketch by same hand two. 26-Mar-3 Hamptons Fine Art, Godalming #34/R est:400-600

STUDDY, George Ernest (1878-1948) British
Works on paper
£1200 $1872 €1800 Hell for leather ! (27x28cm-11x11in) s.d.22 i.verso W/C. 5-Nov-2 Bonhams, New Bond Street #170/R est:1200-1800
£1400 $2184 €2100 Dormy six (37x28cm-15x11in) s.d.22 i.verso W/C. 5-Nov-2 Bonhams, New Bond Street #171/R est:1200-1800

STUDENY, Frantisek (1911-1980) Czechoslovakian
£284 $403 €426 Fish on plate II (22x37cm-9x15in) painted 1968. 26-Mar-2 SOGA, Bratislava #244/R (SL.K 18000)
£315 $447 €473 Fish on plate I (35x47cm-14x19in) canvas on plywood painted 1944. 26-Mar-2 SOGA, Bratislava #243/R (SL.K 20000)

STUDENY, Michal (1939-) Czechoslovakian
Works on paper
£583 $851 €875 Picture (266x167cm-105x66in) mixed media. 4-Jun-2 SOGA, Bratislava #277/R est:35000 (SL.K 37000)

STUDER, Bernhard (1832-1868) Swiss
£330 $492 €495 Farmstead on country track (29x41cm-11x16in) s.d.1865. 25-Jun-2 Koller, Zurich #6452 (S.FR 750)
£2051 $3179 €3200 Evening landscape with Hintersee and Hohen Goll (65x100cm-26x39in) s.d.1856. 6-Dec-2 Michael Zeller, Lindau #931/R est:3200

STUDER, Carl (17/18th C) German
£371 $579 €557 Allegory in autumn (58x73cm-23x29in) s.indis.i. prov. 9-Nov-2 Galerie Gloggner, Luzern #138/R (S.FR 850)

STUDER, Harold (1942-) Swiss
Works on paper
£463 $745 €671 Male nude in wood (50x50cm-20x20in) s.d.15.2.92 verso mixed media canvas. 7-May-3 Dobiaschofsky, Bern #1011/R (S.FR 1000)

STUEMPFIG, Walter (1914-1970) American/German
£2581 $4000 €3872 Art student (87x82cm-34x32in) s. exhib. 29-Oct-2 Sotheby's, New York #265/R est:4000-6000
£3548 $5500 €5322 Sea shells (64x76cm-25x30in) prov.exhib. 8-Dec-2 Freeman, Philadelphia #149/R est:3000-5000

STUHLMULLER, Karl (1858-1930) German
£2092 $3346 €3200 Shepherd boy and cattle in ruin landscape (45x34cm-18x13in) s. panel lit. 10-Jan-3 Allgauer, Kempten #1761/R est:6000
£2372 $3676 €3700 Avenue in winter in Munich suburbs with horses and carriages (25x39cm-10x15in) i. 6-Dec-2 Michael Zeller, Lindau #932/R est:2500
£5128 $7949 €8000 Cattle market in winter in front of a village in Dachau country (16x32cm-6x13in) 4-Dec-2 Neumeister, Munich #920/R est:6000
£5769 $8942 €9000 Cattle market in Dachau country in winter (34x56cm-13x22in) s.i. board. 4-Dec-2 Neumeister, Munich #919/R est:8000

STULL, Henry (attrib) (1851-1913) American
£641 $1000 €962 By a nose (20x25cm-8x10in) academy board. 12-Oct-2 Neal Auction Company, New Orleans #399/R

STULTUS, Dyalma (1902-1977) Italian
£297 $472 €446 Candeli (99x109cm-39x43in) s. i.verso board. 23-Mar-3 Goodman, Sydney #113 (A.D 790)
£769 $1215 €1200 Venice (55x45cm-22x18in) s. canvas on cardboard painted 1966. 15-Nov-2 Farsetti, Prato #600/R
Works on paper
£272 $433 €400 Portrait of girl (40x33cm-16x13in) s.d. pastel. 1-Mar-3 Stadion, Trieste #476

STUMMEL, Friedrich Franz Maria (1850-1919) German
£7639 $12146 €11000 In the castle park (61x48cm-24x19in) s.d.1874. 30-Apr-3 Tajan, Paris #140/R est:12000-15000

STUNTZ, Electrina (1797-1847) German
Works on paper
£405 $632 €600 Madonna with carnation. s.i.d.1821 Indian ink brush. 26-Mar-3 Hugo Ruef, Munich #369/R

STUPAR, Marko (1936-) ?
£387 $600 €581 Paris (46x56cm-18x22in) s.d. 8-Dec-2 Toomey, Oak Park #796/R

STURDEE, Percy (fl.1885-1902) British
£940 $1485 €1410 Lady at her writing desk (51x76cm-20x30in) s.d.1909. 27-Nov-2 Bonhams, Knowle #228
£2000 $3120 €3000 Young lady writing at her desk in an interior (51x76cm-20x30in) s.d.1909. 10-Apr-3 Tennants, Leyburn #1132a/R est:600-800

STURE, David (1950-) Norwegian
£870 $1393 €1305 16 homemade stories (122x187cm-48x74in) init.d.88 i.stretcher. 17-Mar-3 Blomqvist, Oslo #460/R (N.KR 10000)

STURGEON, E R (?) ?
Works on paper
£2600 $3874 €3900 View of Windsor Castle (49x66cm-19x26in) s. W/C. 27-Jun-2 Greenslade Hunt, Taunton #740/R est:1200-1600
£2800 $4172 €4200 Market square and cathedral, Wells (49x74cm-19x29in) s. W/C. 27-Jun-2 Greenslade Hunt, Taunton #741/R est:1500-2500

STURGESS, Reginald Ward (1890-1932) Australian
Works on paper
£324 $512 €486 Sturgess room - studio (17x25cm-7x10in) s. W/C. 2-Apr-3 Christie's, Melbourne #57 (A.D 850)
£325 $513 €488 Sun gleams through the heat (23x29cm-9x11in) s. W/C prov. 7-Apr-3 Shapiro, Sydney #412 (A.D 850)
£550 $858 €825 Australian landscape (23x36cm-9x14in) s. W/C. 26-Mar-3 Hamptons Fine Art, Godalming #104
£601 $955 €902 Harvest (25x30cm-10x12in) s. W/C. 5-May-3 Sotheby's, Melbourne #365 (A.D 1550)
£1069 $1689 €1604 Fishermen sorting their nets (27x42cm-11x17in) s. W/C. 2-Apr-3 Christie's, Melbourne #59/R est:2000-3000 (A.D 2800)

STURLA, Luisa (1930-) Italian
£633 $987 €1000 Still life (80x80cm-31x31in) s.d.1959. 19-Oct-2 Semenzato, Venice #144/R

STURM, Friedrich (1822-1898) Austrian
£2516 $3925 €4000 Diana in battle cart (134x320cm-53x126in) gouache board. 23-Sep-2 Wiener Kunst Auktionen, Vienna #52/R est:1200-2500

STURM, Fritz Ludwig Christian (1834-1906) German
£1288 $2034 €1932 Capri marina (39x52cm-15x20in) s. canvas on canvas. 29-Nov-2 Zofingen, Switzerland #2543 est:4500 (S.FR 3000)

STURM, Fritz Ludwig Christian (attrib) (1834-1906) German
£714 $1064 €1100 Seascape (30x52cm-12x20in) i.d.1872. 26-Jun-2 Neumeister, Munich #878/R

STURM, George (1855-1923) Dutch
£3472 $5521 €5000 Colourful roses (73x47cm-29x19in) s. 29-Apr-3 Christie's, Amsterdam #111/R est:6000-8000

STURM, Helmut (1932-) German
£513 $795 €800 Untitled (29x21cm-11x8in) s.d.89 acrylic W/C. 3-Dec-2 Lempertz, Koln #447
£570 $900 €900 Composition (36x46cm-14x18in) s. acrylic. 29-Nov-2 Villa Grisebach, Berlin #91/R
£725 $1188 €1000 Untitled (30x21cm-12x8in) s.d.84 acrylic on paper collage board. 28-May-3 Lempertz, Koln #419/R
£1139 $1766 €1800 Abstract composition (55x73cm-22x29in) s.d.1978 acrylic board. 28-Sep-2 Ketterer, Hamburg #627/R est:1800-2400
£1811 $3025 €2626 Figure composition (53x33cm-21x13in) s. masonite painted 1960s. 17-Jun-3 Rasmussen, Copenhagen #10/R est:15000 (D.KR 19000)
£2756 $4272 €4134 Composition (53x33cm-21x13in) s. masonite painted c.1961. 4-Dec-2 Kunsthallen, Copenhagen #118/R est:30000 (D.KR 32000)
£3526 $5465 €5500 Untitled (130x110cm-51x43in) s.d.89 acrylic on paper collage masonite. 3-Dec-2 Lempertz, Koln #445/R est:8000
Works on paper
£962 $1519 €1500 Composition (29x34cm-11x13in) s.d.1985 mixed media tempera col chks. 14-Nov-2 Neumeister, Munich #877/R est:1200-1300

STURM-SKRLA, Eugen (1894-1943) Austrian
£633 $987 €1000 Landscape (54x66cm-21x26in) s.d.1930. 15-Oct-2 Dorotheum, Vienna #92/R

STURROCK, Alick Riddell (1885-1953) British
£450 $711 €675 Coastal landscape (76x91cm-30x36in) s. 27-Nov-2 Sotheby's, Olympia #89/R
£500 $780 €750 Orton farm (48x64cm-19x25in) 11-Apr-3 Keys, Aylsham #623

STURSA, Jan (1880-1925) Czechoslovakian
Sculpture
£1260 $1789 €1890 Melancholy (21cm-8in) bronze. 26-Mar-2 SOGA, Bratislava #220/R est:20000 (SL.K 80000)

STURTEVANT, Elaine (1926-) American
£1250 $1975 €1800 Warhol, etude pour Marilyn (60x45cm-24x18in) s. acrylic ink serigraphique. 28-Apr-3 Cornette de St.Cyr, Paris #518 est:2000-2500
£1319 $2085 €1900 Warhol, etude pour Marilyn (60x45cm-24x18in) s. acrylic ink serigraphique. 28-Apr-3 Cornette de St.Cyr, Paris #517/R est:2000-2500
£3797 $6000 €5696 Study for Warhol flowers (28x28cm-11x11in) s.i.d.70-71 i.verso acrylic prov. 13-Nov-2 Sotheby's, New York #345/R est:4000-5000
Works on paper
£12925 $20551 €19000 Warhol four Marylins (96x72cm-38x28in) s.i.d.1972 verso ink acrylic on canvas. 24-Mar-3 Cornette de St.Cyr, Paris #81/R est:15000

STURTEVANT, Helena (1872-1946) American
£443 $700 €665 Second beach, Newport (25x30cm-10x12in) s. 17-Nov-2 CRN Auctions, Cambridge #57/R

STURZENEGGER, Hans (1875-1943) Swiss
£308 $450 €462 Bodensee bay (37x47cm-15x19in) mono. 17-Jun-2 Philippe Schuler, Zurich #4293 (S.FR 700)

£519 $830 €779 Terrace near Schmerikon (45x51cm-18x20in) mono. exhib. 17-Mar-3 Philippe Schuler, Zurich #4562/R (S.FR 1100)
£1572 $2452 €2358 Track to Busingen (45x55cm-18x22in) mono. 6-Nov-2 Hans Widmer, St Gallen #87/R est:1400-3800 (S.FR 3600)

STUTTERHEIM, Lodewyk Philippus (1873-1943) Dutch
£658 $1066 €1000 Leading the cows along a path (40x30cm-16x12in) s. 21-Jan-3 Christie's, Amsterdam #228 est:1000-1500
£894 $1404 €1341 Ecluse d'un canal en Hollande (40x61cm-16x24in) s. 12-Dec-2 Iegor de Saint Hippolyte, Montreal #97 (C.D 2200)

STUVEN, Ernst (1660-1712) German
£3503 $5465 €5500 Still life of an orange, prunes, grapes on a table draped with a green cloth (48x39cm-19x15in) mono. canvas on panel. 5-Nov-2 Sotheby's, Amsterdam #320/R est:4000-6000

STY, van (?) ?
£851 $1379 €1200 Cattle, sheep and horses in a wooded landscape (50x45cm-20x18in) 21-May-3 James Adam, Dublin #34 est:600-800

STYKA, Adam (1890-c.1970) French
£4276 $6799 €6200 Marchand de cuivres dans les souks (100x71cm-39x28in) s. 4-Mar-3 Palais de Beaux Arts, Brussels #409/R est:5000-7000
£4810 $7600 €7215 Couple smoking (90x70cm-35x28in) s. 15-Nov-2 Naón & Cia, Buenos Aires #121/R
£4938 $8000 €7160 Three friends (61x74cm-24x29in) s. init.i.verso. 21-May-3 Doyle, New York #187/R est:8000-10000
£5500 $8635 €8250 Happy couple (51x61cm-20x24in) s.d.1923 board. 21-Nov-2 Christie's, Kensington #206/R est:6000-8000
£6500 $10855 €9750 Desert flirtation (89x70cm-35x28in) s. 18-Jun-3 Christie's, Kensington #191/R est:7000-9000
£7143 $11357 €10500 Homme et femme aux bijoux (90x80cm-35x31in) s. 24-Mar-3 Rabourdin & Choppin de Janvry, Paris #84/R est:13000-15000
£7500 $11700 €11250 Lovers (81x65cm-32x26in) s. 15-Oct-2 Sotheby's, London #250/R est:7000-9000
£20408 $32449 €30000 Les amoureux (91x80cm-36x31in) s. 24-Mar-3 Rabourdin & Choppin de Janvry, Paris #215/R est:30000-35000
£44605 $73152 €62000 Les amoureux (81x65cm-32x26in) s. 4-Jun-3 Tajan, Paris #317/R est:30000-35000

STYKA, Jan (1858-1925) French
£5532 $9238 €7800 Femme sur un cheval (66x81cm-26x32in) s.d. 17-Jun-3 Claude Boisgirard, Paris #122/R est:9000-11000

STYKA, Tade (1889-1954) French
£2000 $3280 €3000 At the watering hole (60x79cm-24x31in) s. canvas on board. 5-Jun-3 Christie's, Kensington #771/R est:1200-1800
£3097 $4800 €4646 Portrait of a woman with a dog (81x66cm-32x26in) 7-Dec-2 South Bay, Long Island #60/R

STYRING, Elizabeth (fl.1911-1938) British
Works on paper
£700 $1169 €1015 Moored vessel and fisherfolk on the quayside, Whitby, towards the Abbey. s. W/C. 26-Jun-3 Richardson & Smith, Whitby #565

STYRSKY, Jindrich (1899-1942) Czechoslovakian
£75342 $117534 €110000 Roots (46x82cm-18x32in) s.d.34 exhib.lit. 14-Apr-3 Laurence Calmels, Paris #4078/R est:20000
Works on paper
£578 $902 €867 Figure (19x11cm-7x4in) s.d.24 Indian ink dr. 12-Oct-2 Dorotheum, Prague #250/R (C.KR 28000)
£764 $1215 €1100 Composition (15x12cm-6x5in) graphite dr. prov.exhib. 29-Apr-3 Artcurial Briest, Paris #107
£1944 $3091 €2800 Feuille d'etudes de tetes cubistes (24x33cm-9x13in) wax crayon dr prov. exec.c.1922. 29-Apr-3 Artcurial Briest, Paris #106 est:3000-4000
£8219 $12904 €12000 Untitled (20x26cm-8x10in) s. mixed media cardboard. 15-Apr-3 Laurence Calmels, Paris #4417/R

SU LIU PENG (19th C) Chinese
Works on paper
£1709 $2821 €2478 Third visit (25x38cm-10x15in) s.i. ink scroll. 6-Jul-3 Christie's, Hong Kong #378/R est:15000-20000 (HK.D 22000)
£8943 $14130 €13415 Gathering of the eighteen scholars (121x57cm-48x22in) s.i.d.1850 ink col hanging scroll. 28-Apr-3 Sotheby's, Hong Kong #650/R est:30000-50000 (HK.D 110000)

SUAREZ, Antonio (1923-) Spanish
£252 $387 €400 Flower (25x35cm-10x14in) s. paper. 28-Oct-2 Segre, Madrid #181/R
£252 $392 €400 Untitled (25x34cm-10x13in) s. paper. 8-Oct-2 Ansorena, Madrid #646/R
£265 $432 €400 Untitled (21x31cm-8x12in) s. paper. 11-Feb-3 Segre, Madrid #278/R
£629 $969 €1000 Composition (20x24cm-8x9in) s. s.verso painted 1964. 22-Oct-2 Durán, Madrid #143/R
Works on paper
£269 $425 €420 Composition (29x36cm-11x14in) s.d.90 mixed media. 19-Nov-2 Durán, Madrid #743/R

SUAREZ, Aurelio (1911-) Spanish
£6289 $9686 €10000 Continuously garding (38x46cm-15x18in) s. s.i.d.1944 verso. 22-Oct-2 Durán, Madrid #201/R est:10000

SUCASAS, Alfonso (1940-) Spanish
Works on paper
£629 $981 €1000 Woman by curtain (55x37cm-22x15in) s.d.1982 chl. 17-Sep-2 Segre, Madrid #198/R

SUCH, W T (fl.1847-1857) British
£2899 $4754 €4000 Palude con volo di beccaccini (70x90cm-28x35in) s.d.1857. 27-May-3 Finarte, Milan #136/R est:1000-1500

SUCHET, Joseph François (1824-1896) French
£516 $815 €800 Bateaux en mer (38x46cm-15x18in) s. 19-Dec-2 Claude Aguttes, Neuilly #206/R

SUCHY, Adalbert (1783-1849) Austrian
£1892 $2951 €2800 Portrait de Francois I, empereur d'Autriche (74x60cm-29x24in) s.d.1820. 26-Mar-3 Rieunier, Paris #42
£2897 $4837 €4200 Portrait d'homme (74x59cm-29x23in) s.i.d. 9-Jul-3 Millon & Associes, Paris #114 est:2500-3000
Miniatures
£1000 $1540 €1500 Officer in uniform with decorations (9cm-4in) s.d.1831 gilt metal mount rec. leather frame oval. 24-Oct-2 Sotheby's, Olympia #48/R est:1200-1500

SUDARSONO, Shrihadi (1931-) Indonesian
£7382 $12179 €10704 Horizon (80x100cm-31x39in) s.d.1973. 6-Jul-3 Christie's, Hong Kong #52/R est:45000-65000 (HK.D 95000)
£14913 $22966 €22370 Horizon (100x110cm-39x43in) s. s.i.d.70 verso. 27-Oct-2 Christie's, Hong Kong #79/R est:70000-100000 (HK.D 180000)
£27195 $44872 €39433 Temple at Sanur beach (137x110cm-54x43in) s.d.1966 prov. 6-Jul-3 Christie's, Hong Kong #54/R est:100000-400000 (HK.D 350000)
£28998 $44656 €43497 Dancers (130x101cm-51x40in) s.d.89. 27-Oct-2 Christie's, Hong Kong #85/R est:140000-180000 (HK.D 350000)

SUDDABY, Rowland (1912-1973) British
£290 $450 €435 Stormy day, East Anglia (48x58cm-19x23in) s.d.49. 4-Oct-2 Mallams, Oxford #546
£300 $495 €435 Figure on a country lane (31x57cm-12x22in) s. oil on paper. 1-Jul-3 Bonhams, Norwich #304
£480 $749 €720 Sculpture on a coastline (39x56cm-15x22in) s. board. 27-Mar-3 Christie's, Kensington #613/R
£550 $908 €798 Village shop (32x44cm-13x17in) 1-Jul-3 Bonhams, Norwich #292/R
£750 $1163 €1125 Fishing boats leaving harbour, possibly Lowestoft (18x25cm-7x10in) s. board. 30-Sep-2 Bonhams, Ipswich #405
£800 $1288 €1200 Cottage by the pond (65x75cm-26x30in) s. 18-Feb-3 Bonhams, Knightsbridge #70/R
£800 $1320 €1160 Regent's Park (50x61cm-20x24in) s. panel prov. 3-Jul-3 Christie's, Kensington #436/R
£1000 $1540 €1500 Stream with fence and trees (25x35cm-10x14in) s.indis.d. prov. 5-Sep-2 Christie's, Kensington #669/R est:800-1200
£1000 $1670 €1450 Still life of flowers on a table top (52x56cm-20x22in) s.d.49 board. 24-Jun-3 Bonhams, New Bond Street #37/R est:1000-1500
£1050 $1628 €1575 Spring still life (30x34cm-12x13in) s. 30-Sep-2 Bonhams, Ipswich #396 est:1200-1800
£1500 $2325 €2250 Delphiniums and lilies, in a jug (61x45cm-24x18in) s.d.65. 30-Sep-2 Bonhams, Ipswich #443/R est:1500-2000
£2000 $3100 €3000 Flowers in a yellow jug (34x34cm-13x13in) board. 30-Sep-2 Bonhams, Ipswich #363/R est:2000-3000
£2200 $3498 €3300 Daffodils and japonica in window (59x75cm-23x30in) s. s.i.verso board. 26-Feb-3 Sotheby's, Olympia #212/R est:1500-2500
Works on paper
£260 $429 €377 Stormy winter day, Thetford Chase (34x56cm-13x22in) s. mixed media. 1-Jul-3 Bonhams, Norwich #125/R
£320 $496 €480 Hyde Park (50x50cm-20x20in) s.d.37 W/C. 30-Sep-2 Bonhams, Ipswich #288
£320 $528 €464 Cafe Royal, April (40x51cm-16x20in) s.d.6/37 pen ink W/C. 1-Jul-3 Bonhams, Norwich #140
£360 $558 €540 Low tide on the Blackwater, Essex (38x54cm-15x21in) s. ink W/C prov. 30-Sep-2 Bonhams, Ipswich #321
£360 $572 €540 Moor's edge (33x53cm-13x21in) s.d.46 W/C gouache. 26-Feb-3 Sotheby's, Olympia #206/R
£420 $655 €630 Pond, Yorkshire (42x54cm-17x21in) s.d.52 W/C ink prov. 15-Oct-2 Bonhams, Knightsbridge #247/R

£450 $715 €675 Looking down on Sudbury (35x55cm-14x22in) s. gouache W/C. 26-Feb-3 Sotheby's, Olympia #207/R
£900 $1404 €1350 Back of the farmhouse (44x56cm-17x22in) s. pen ink W/C. 27-Mar-3 Christie's, Kensington #332/R
£900 $1404 €1350 Still life with anemones and basket (48x61cm-19x24in) s.d.47 brush ink W/C. 27-Mar-3 Christie's, Kensington #346/R

SUDEIKIN, Sergei Yurievich (1882-1946) Russian
£6500 $10206 €9750 Stage design for the ballet - La fille mal guarde (23x41cm-9x16in) s. i.d.1941 stretcher. 20-Nov-2 Sotheby's, London #133/R est:6000-8000

Works on paper
£3800 $5966 €5700 Costume design for a mask (51x41cm-20x16in) s.i. gouache. 20-Nov-2 Sotheby's, London #159/R est:2800-3500

SUDEK, Josef (1896-1976) Czechoslovakian
Photographs
£1899 $3000 €3000 Untitled (23x17cm-9x7in) s.d.1969 i. verso silver gelatin lit.exhib. 28-Nov-2 Villa Grisebach, Berlin #1428/R est:2000-3000
£1899 $3000 €2849 Branch (17x12cm-7x5in) warm toned photograph. 23-Apr-3 Sotheby's, New York #184/R est:3000-5000
£2025 $3200 €3038 Still life - egg on plate (12x16cm-5x6in) s. gelatin silver print lit. 22-Apr-3 Christie's, Rockefeller NY #86/R est:3500-4500
£2927 $4800 €4391 Kalemdror, mistletoe (25x15cm-10x6in) st.i.verso silver print. 10-Feb-3 Swann Galleries, New York #49/R est:3000-4000
£3718 $5874 €5800 Urn and wheelbarrow (13x17cm-5x7in) s.i.d.1965 i.d.verso gelatin silver print exec.c.1935. 16-Nov-2 Christie's, Paris #322/R est:5000-7000
£7595 $12000 €11393 Window of my studio (22x17cm-9x7in) warm toned pigment print executed c.1944. 23-Apr-3 Sotheby's, New York #169/R est:10000-15000
£9494 $15000 €14241 Nude (23x17cm-9x7in) warm toned prov.lit. 23-Apr-3 Sotheby's, New York #183/R est:15000-25000

SUDRE, Raymond (1870-?) French
Sculpture
£2900 $4495 €4350 Mercury, holding aloft his caduceus (97cm-38in) s. brown pat bronze metal base circular marble plinth. 29-Oct-2 Bonhams, New Bond Street #165/R est:1000-1500

SUE, Louis (1875-1968) French
£1006 $1600 €1509 Sur la plage (20x18cm-8x7in) s. canvasboard. 7-Mar-3 Skinner, Boston #528/R est:1000-1500
£1135 $1895 €1600 La conversation (26x35cm-10x14in) s. panel exhib. 20-Jun-3 Piasa, Paris #116/R est:1200-1500
£1631 $2724 €2300 La lecture (26x35cm-10x14in) s. panel. 20-Jun-3 Piasa, Paris #115/R est:1200-1500

SUERMONDT, Robert (1961-) Dutch
£1295 $2124 €1800 Untitled (75x115cm-30x45in) s.d.91 on stretcher prov. 3-Jun-3 Christie's, Amsterdam #377/R est:1200-1600

SUEUR, Eustache le (1617-1655) French
£197531 $320000 €296297 Marcus Curtius leaping into the void (112x91cm-44x36in) prov.lit. 24-Jan-3 Christie's, Rockefeller NY #90/R est:400000-600000

Works on paper
£4459 $6957 €6600 Etude de femme agenouillee, main droite posee sur la poitrine (29x22cm-11x9in) i. pierre noire stump htd white. 26-Mar-3 Rossini, Paris #95/R est:6000
£19231 $29808 €30000 Etude d'homme a terre (26x36cm-10x14in) crayon chk prov.lit. 4-Dec-2 Piasa, Paris #53/R est:40000
£21154 $32788 €33000 Etudde de femme drapee (40x22cm-16x9in) crayon chk. 4-Dec-2 Piasa, Paris #52/R est:30000
£47840 $77500 €71760 Study of two women (37x26cm-15x10in) i. chk prov. 21-Jan-3 Sotheby's, New York #45/R est:80000

SUEUR, Eustache le (circle) (1617-1655) French
£37179 $57628 €58000 Christ dispels the money-changer from the temple (120cm-47in circular) canvas on canvas. 4-Dec-2 Neumeister, Munich #642/R est:15000

SUGAI, Kumi (1919-1996) Japanese
£4800 $7584 €7200 Untitled (88x78cm-35x31in) s. s.d.1971 verso. 3-Apr-3 Christie's, Kensington #202/R
£6159 $10101 €8500 La marche de l'auto route No 3 (99x81cm-39x32in) s.d.65 s.i.d. verso prov. 28-May-3 Lempertz, Koln #420/R est:8000-10000
£11000 $17380 €16500 Nami (81x64cm-32x25in) s. s.i.d.1958 verso prov. 3-Apr-3 Christie's, Kensington #188/R est:8000
£11426 $18167 €17139 The brook (92x126cm-36x50in) s.i.d.58 verso exhib.prov. 26-Feb-3 Kunsthallen, Copenhagen #82/R est:150000 (D.KR 125000)
Sculpture
£1899 $3000 €3000 Untitled (32x18cm-13x7in) s. num.1/6 stainless steel marble socle. 27-Nov-2 Tajan, Paris #44/R est:3000
Works on paper
£946 $1476 €1419 Triangular composition (28x24cm-11x9in) s.d.57 W/C paper on cardboard. 5-Nov-2 Bukowskis, Stockholm #306/R est:10000-12000 (S.KR 13500)
£2051 $3241 €3200 Untitled (50x28cm-20x11in) s. mixed media. 14-Nov-2 Neumeister, Munich #878/R est:1800-2000
£2279 $3600 €3600 Composition verte et orange 2 (48x62cm-19x24in) s.d.1966 gouache prov. 27-Nov-2 Tajan, Paris #40/R est:2800-3500
£2436 $3824 €3800 Untitled (87x23cm-34x9in) s.d.1956 gouache tempera exhib. 15-Dec-2 Perrin, Versailles #42/R

SUGARS, Fanny (fl.1882-1926) British
£420 $651 €630 Still life study of apples, pears and other fruit in a basket (41x60cm-16x24in) s.d.1885. 24-Sep-2 Anderson & Garland, Newcastle #411/R

SUGHI, Alberto (1928-) Italian
£922 $1494 €1300 Pittore e modella (35x50cm-14x20in) s. tempera board on canvas. 22-May-3 Stadion, Trieste #273/R est:1200-1600
£1266 $1975 €2000 Yellow house (80x60cm-31x24in) s. tempera paper painted 1990. 14-Sep-2 Meeting Art, Vercelli #858/R
£2065 $3262 €3200 Portrait of woman (80x70cm-31x28in) s. 18-Dec-2 Christie's, Rome #159
£2885 $4529 €4500 Interior scene (60x80cm-24x31in) s. 20-Nov-2 Pandolfini, Florence #62/R
£3268 $5229 €5000 Untitled (90x90cm-35x35in) s. painted 1991. 4-Jan-3 Meeting Art, Vercelli #713
£3784 $5903 €5600 Seated figure (60x80cm-24x31in) s. oil tempera. 28-Mar-3 Farsetti, Prato #344/R
Works on paper
£353 $554 €550 Marine (34x48cm-13x19in) s. pencil. 21-Nov-2 Finarte, Rome #116
£1026 $1610 €1600 Thoughtful girl (70x50cm-28x20in) s. mixed media. 21-Nov-2 Finarte, Rome #39
£1233 $1923 €1800 Mysterious interior (80x98cm-31x39in) s. mixed media card exec.1970. 10-Apr-3 Finarte Semenzato, Rome #87
£1312 $2126 €1850 Camera da letto (32x46cm-13x18in) s. mixed media. 22-May-3 Stadion, Trieste #365/R est:600-800
£2838 $4427 €4200 Girl with record-player (40x60cm-16x24in) s.d.69 mixed media on canvas. 28-Mar-3 Farsetti, Prato #215/R

SUGIMOTO, Hiroshi (1948-) Japanese
£3145 $4874 €5000 Cabot Street Cineman, MA (41x54cm-16x21in) s.i.d.1977 verso gelatin silver lit. 2-Nov-2 Lempertz, Koln #451/R est:6000-7000

Photographs
£3681 $6000 €5522 Hall of thirty-three bays (42x54cm-17x21in) s. num.2/25035 gelatin silver print. 12-Feb-3 Christie's, Rockefeller NY #151/R est:4000-6000
£4000 $6160 €6000 Hunting dog (51x61cm-20x24in) s.i.d.1980 num.4/25 gelatin silver print. 23-Oct-2 Christie's, London #205/R est:6000-8000
£4200 $6888 €6300 Permian land (41x51cm-16x20in) blindstamped i.num.2/25 gelatin silver print. 6-Feb-3 Christie's, London #744/R est:5000-7000
£4500 $7380 €6750 The Royal Family (51x61cm-20x24in) blindstamped i.num.6/25 d.1994 gelatin silver print. 6-Feb-3 Christie's, London #743/R est:5000-7000
£4747 $7500 €7121 Hall of thirty three bays (42x52cm-17x20in) s. num.2/25 gelatin silver print. 22-Apr-3 Christie's, Rockefeller NY #116/R est:4000-6000
£5312 $8500 €7968 Electric chair (51x61cm-20x24in) gelatin silver print executed 1994 prov.exhib. 16-May-3 Phillips, New York #225/R est:6000-8000
£5484 $8500 €8226 UA Rivoli Theater New York (47x60cm-19x24in) s.i.num.20/25 gelatin silver print. 26-Sep-2 Christie's, Rockefeller NY #776/R est:7000-9000
£5500 $9020 €8250 Sanjusangendo, the Hall of the Thirty-Three Bays (47x60cm-19x24in) s.num.4/25 gelatin silver print prov.lit. 7-Feb-3 Sotheby's, London #127/R est:3000-5000
£5806 $9000 €8709 Sea of Japan, Hokkaido II, summer 86 (50x61cm-20x24in) s.i.d.86 num.2/25 gelatin silver print. 26-Sep-2 Christie's, Rockefeller NY #777/R est:7000-9000

£6329	$10000	€9494	Cinema rise (47x57cm-19x22in) s.d.1996 num.4/25 gelatin silver print lit. 13-Nov-2 Sotheby's, New York #452/R est:10000-15000
£6500	$10010	€9750	Ligurian Sea (42x54cm-17x21in) i.num.6/25 s.i.d.num.on mount gelatin silver print prov. 22-Oct-2 Sotheby's, London #302/R est:6000-8000
£6500	$10010	€9750	Pacific Ocean Iwate (50x61cm-20x24in) s.i.d.1986 num.8/24 verso gelatin silver print. 23-Oct-2 Christie's, London #204/R est:6000-8000
£6500	$10660	€9750	Ionian Sea, Santa Cesera III (51x61cm-20x24in) s. blindstamped i.d.1990 num.15/25 gelatin silver print prov. 6-Feb-3 Christie's, London #741/R est:6000-8000
£6500	$10660	€9750	Tyrrhenian Sea, Scilla (42x54cm-17x21in) s. blindstamp i.num.18/25 gelatin silver print prov. 6-Feb-3 Christie's, London #766/R est:6000-8000
£7000	$10780	€10500	Palms, Michigan (42x54cm-17x21in) i.d.1980 num.12/25 216 gelatin silver print prov. 23-Oct-2 Christie's, London #191/R est:4000-6000
£7500	$11550	€11250	Eiffel tower (58x47cm-23x19in) num.3/25 gelatin silver print executed 1998 prov. 23-Oct-2 Christie's, London #180/R est:7000-10000
£8000	$12320	€12000	Tasman sea, Ngarupupu (43x54cm-17x21in) i.d.1986 num.20/25 gelatin print prov. 22-Oct-2 Sotheby's, London #301/R est:6000-8000
£8125	$13000	€12188	Stadium drive in orange (47x60cm-19x24in) s.i.d.1993 gelatin silver print prov.exhib. 15-May-3 Christie's, Rockefeller NY #398/R est:10000-15000
£8125	$13000	€12188	South Bay drive in South Bay (47x60cm-19x24in) s.i.num.3/25 726 gelatin silver print prov.exhib.lit. 15-May-3 Christie's, Rockefeller NY #399/R est:10000-15000
£8861	$14000	€13292	Still life, polar bear (41x55cm-16x22in) s.d.1976 num.2/25 gelatin silver print prov. 25-Apr-3 Phillips, New York #63/R est:8000-12000
£9000	$14760	€13500	EUR Palazzo della Civilta Romana (58x47cm-23x19in) blindstamped num.3/25 gelatin silver print prov. 6-Feb-3 Christie's, London #742/R est:6000-8000
£9091	$14000	€13637	Civic, New Zealand (42x54cm-17x21in) i.d.1991 num.9/25 photograph. 24-Oct-2 Sotheby's, New York #234/R est:15000-20000
£9494	$15000	€14241	Sea of Japan, Hokkaido (47x60cm-19x24in) s.i.d.1986 gelatin silver print one of 25 prov.exhib.lit. 13-Nov-2 Sotheby's, New York #425/R est:12000-15000
£9494	$15000	€14241	Chapel of Notre Dame du Haut - Le Corbusier (51x61cm-20x24in) s.num.4/25 gelatin silver print executed 1998 prov. 14-Nov-2 Christie's, Rockefeller NY #427/R est:12000-18000
£10000	$16400	€15000	Carpenter Center Richmond (42x54cm-17x21in) blindstamp i.num.8/25 d.1993 prov. 6-Feb-3 Christie's, London #765/R est:4000-6000
£10000	$16000	€15000	Hyena jackal vulture (51x61cm-20x24in) s.i.d.1996 num.8/25 gelatin silver print prov.lit. 15-May-3 Christie's, Rockefeller NY #400/R est:10000-15000
£10390	$16000	€15585	Beacon, New York (51x61cm-20x24in) s.i.d.1979 num.11/25 gelatin silver print prov. 25-Oct-2 Phillips, New York #156/R est:9000-12000
£11392	$18000	€17088	Winnetika Drive-In, Paramount (47x60cm-19x24in) s.d.1998 gelatin silver print prov.exhib.lit. 14-Nov-2 Christie's, Rockefeller NY #429/R est:12000-18000
£11392	$18000	€17088	La Paloma, Encinitas (51x61cm-20x24in) st. num 15/25. 14-Nov-2 Christie's, Rockefeller NY #485/R est:8000-12000
£11688	$18000	€17532	Carpenter center, Richmond (42x54cm-17x21in) s.num.5/25 photograph. 24-Oct-2 Sotheby's, New York #233/R est:15000-20000
£11875	$19000	€17813	Scottsdale drive-in, Scottsdale (47x60cm-19x24in) i.d.1993 num.1/25 gelatin silver print prov.lit. 14-May-3 Sotheby's, New York #356/R est:8000-12000
£12000	$19680	€18000	Los Altos drive-in, Lake Wood (48x58cm-19x23in) s.i.d.1993 num.15/25 gelatin silver print prov.lit. 7-Feb-3 Sotheby's, London #105/R est:6000-8000
£12025	$19000	€18038	Metropolitan Orpheum, Los Angeles (51x61cm-20x24in) st. num 11/25. 14-Nov-2 Christie's, Rockefeller NY #484/R est:8000-12000
£12500	$20000	€18750	Lake Michigan, Gills Lock (51x61cm-20x24in) s.i.d.1995 num.8/25 gelatin silver print prov. 14-May-3 Sotheby's, New York #392/R est:15000-20000
£12500	$20000	€18750	Lake Superior, cascade river (51x61cm-20x24in) s.i.d.1995 num.15/25 gelatin silver print prov.exhib. 14-May-3 Sotheby's, New York #393/R est:15000-20000
£12658	$20000	€18987	Tyrrhenian sea, Positano (42x54cm-17x21in) s.i.d.1990 num.5/25 gelatin silver print prov.lit. 22-Apr-3 Christie's, Rockefeller NY #118/R est:15000-20000
£13750	$22000	€20625	Bay of Sagami, Atami (51x61cm-20x24in) embossed sig.i.d.1997 num. gelatin silver print prov.exhib. 14-May-3 Sotheby's, New York #328/R est:15000-20000
£13924	$22000	€20886	Cabot street cinema, Beverly, Massachusetts (42x54cm-17x21in) s.d.1979 verso gelatin silver print prov.exhib.lit. 25-Apr-3 Phillips, New York #64/R est:10000-15000
£15190	$24000	€22785	Chrysler building - William Van Alen (51x61cm-20x24in) s.num.17/25 gelatin silver print executed 1997. 14-Nov-2 Christie's, Rockefeller NY #426/R est:12000-18000
£15584	$24000	€23376	Tri-city-drive-in- San Bernardino, California (50x66cm-20x26in) s.i.num.5/25 gelatin silver print prov.lit. 25-Oct-2 Phillips, New York #63/R est:12000-18000
£17000	$28390	€24650	English Channel Weston Cliff (42x54cm-17x21in) s.mount i.d.1994 num.13/25 gelatin silver print prov.exhib.lit. 26-Jun-3 Sotheby's, London #108/R est:6000-8000
£17722	$28000	€26583	Union City drive in, Union City (47x60cm-19x24in) s.d.1998 num.16/25 gelatin silver print prov.exhib.lit. 14-Nov-2 Christie's, Rockefeller NY #428/R est:12000-18000
£32000	$53440	€48000	Henry V (149x119cm-59x47in) s.d.1999 gelatin silver print prov.lit. 25-Jun-3 Sotheby's, London #49/R est:25000-35000

SUHRLANDT, Kunit (?) Belgian?

£313	$494	€450	Nature morte au vase fleuri (104x82cm-41x32in) 28-Apr-3 Amberes, Antwerp #319

SUIRE, Herman von le (1861-1926) German

£338	$527	€500	Sachrang with Geigelstein (23x28cm-9x11in) s. board. 26-Mar-3 Hugo Ruef, Munich #161

SUIRE, Louis (1899-1987) French

£486	$792	€700	Cour de maison a l'Ilse de Re (33x41cm-13x16in) s.i. panel. 19-Jul-3 Thierry & Lannon, Brest #391

SUISSE, Gaston (1896-1988) French

Works on paper

£321	$503	€500	Aigle (25x28cm-10x11in) s. crayon dr chl pastel. 20-Nov-2 Claude Boisgirard, Paris #29
£486	$802	€700	Buffle (24x28cm-9x11in) s. chl. 1-Jul-3 Claude Aguttes, Neuilly #139/R
£541	$843	€800	Aigle evorant (25x25cm-10x10in) s. crayon pastel lit. 25-Mar-3 Claude Aguttes, Neuilly #104/R
£548	$866	€850	Merle (40x19cm-16x7in) s. chl chk pastel. 17-Dec-2 Claude Aguttes, Neuilly #30/R
£748	$1190	€1100	Ecureuil de Malaisie (27x20cm-11x8in) s. chl pastel crayon exhib. 19-Mar-3 Claude Boisgirard, Paris #27/R
£1014	$1581	€1500	Toucan (31x24cm-12x9in) s.d.1927 crayon. 25-Mar-3 Claude Aguttes, Neuilly #103/R
£1020	$1622	€1500	Maki (27x20cm-11x8in) s. chl pastel crayon. 19-Mar-3 Claude Boisgirard, Paris #26/R
£1081	$1686	€1600	Taureau (31x24cm-12x9in) s. crayon. 25-Mar-3 Claude Aguttes, Neuilly #102/R
£1250	$2063	€1800	Panthere (14x32cm-6x13in) s. crayon. 1-Jul-3 Claude Aguttes, Neuilly #137/R est:300-500
£1293	$2055	€1900	Diamants mandarins (62x45cm-24x18in) s. pastel oil exhib. 19-Mar-3 Claude Boisgirard, Paris #25/R
£1310	$2083	€1900	L'aigle (25x30cm-10x12in) s. chl crayon. 10-Mar-3 Coutau Begarie, Paris #140/R
£1319	$2177	€1900	Paysage chinois (74x33cm-29x13in) mono. crayon estompe wax pastel. 1-Jul-3 Claude Aguttes, Neuilly #138/R est:500-600
£1484	$2345	€2300	Colibris (70x21cm-28x8in) s. pastel gold. 17-Dec-2 Claude Aguttes, Neuilly #28/R est:2000-2200
£1613	$2548	€2500	Garulax (67x39cm-26x15in) s.d.1930 pastel gold. 17-Dec-2 Claude Aguttes, Neuilly #29/R est:2000-2500
£1959	$3057	€2900	Rouge-gorges dans les greckos (14x26cm-6x10in) s. pastel crayon. 28-Mar-3 Camard, Paris #129/R
£4677	$7483	€6500	Poissons exotiques (34x75cm-13x30in) s. lacquer ivory panel exhib. 19-May-3 Tajan, Paris #37/R est:4000-5000

SUKER, Arthur (1857-?) British

£320	$512	€480	By the lakeside (33x51cm-13x20in) s. 14-Mar-3 Gardiner & Houlgate, Bath #82/R
£420	$668	€630	Stormy coastal scene at south coast, Guernsey (59x40cm-23x16in) init. 20-Mar-3 Martel Maides, Guernsey #64

Works on paper

£280 $434 €420 View in Devonshire (28x48cm-11x19in) W/C. 4-Oct-2 Mallams, Oxford #504

£380 $604 €570 On the north Cornish coast (46x68cm-18x27in) s. 19-Mar-3 James Thompson, Kirby Lonsdale #20

£400 $620 €600 Paignton from Marldon Hill (30x46cm-12x18in) s.d.1928 W/C. 25-Sep-2 Hamptons Fine Art, Godalming #125/R

£480 $763 €720 Les Antelets, Isle of Sark (40x60cm-16x24in) s. i.verso W/C. 4-Mar-3 Bearnes, Exeter #343/R

SUKHODOLSKY, Pyotr Alexandrovich (1835-1903) Russian

£2466 $3847 €3600 Wooded landscape with stream (39x30cm-15x12in) s.d.1891. 10-Apr-3 Van Ham, Cologne #1727/R est:3000

£3200 $5056 €4800 Village river (26x39cm-10x15in) s. 26-Nov-2 Christie's, Kensington #15/R est:3000-5000

SULLIVAN, Louis Henry (1856-1924) American

Works on paper

£27097 $42000 €40646 Ornamental stencil from Chicago Stock Exhange (32x83cm-13x33in) stencilled paint on canvas prov.lit. 8-Dec-2 Wright, Chicago #271/R est:25000-35000

SULLIVAN, William Holmes (?-1908) British

£300 $465 €450 Portrait of Henry Dawson (51x40cm-20x16in) s. 2-Oct-2 George Kidner, Lymington #144/R

£440 $695 €638 Henry V at Honfleur (46x36cm-18x14in) s. 22-Jul-3 Gorringes, Lewes #1654

£1316 $2132 €2000 Gambler's wife (51x40cm-20x16in) s.d.1882 s.i.d.verso. 21-Jan-3 Christie's, Amsterdam #59/R est:1500-2000

£1900 $3173 €2755 Portrait of the artist Henry Dawson (50x40cm-20x16in) 26-Jun-3 Mellors & Kirk, Nottingham #846/R

SULLIVANT, Thomas S (1854-1926) American

Works on paper

£932 $1500 €1398 Caveman walking away from two cavewomen (33x53cm-13x21in) s. pen ink. 10-May-3 Illustration House, New York #25/R est:1800-2400

£1863 $3000 €2795 King Solomon's homecoming (33x56cm-13x22in) s. pen ink exec.c.1920. 10-May-3 Illustration House, New York #183/R est:3000-4000

SULLY, Thomas (1783-1872) American/British

£1667 $2600 €2501 Portrait of a young girl (51cm-20in) s. oval. 21-Sep-2 Pook & Pook, Downington #29/R est:4000-5000

£9434 $15000 €14151 Portrait of Sarah Jane Hall (66x74cm-26x29in) mono.d.1849 prov. 5-Mar-3 Sotheby's, New York #32/R est:8000-12000

£10180 $17000 €14761 Portrait of Sir Walter Scott (51x42cm-20x17in) s. indis d. 22-Jun-3 Freeman, Philadelphia #69/R est:2000-3000

£13836 $21585 €22000 Portrait of elegant lady by table (115x104cm-45x41in) painted c.1860. 17-Sep-2 Segre, Madrid #60b/R est:16850

£23148 $37500 €34722 General Jackson after the battle of New Orleans (65x42cm-26x17in) mono.i. prov.lit. 21-May-3 Sotheby's, New York #204/R est:20000-30000

Miniatures

£3618 $5500 €5427 Portrait of a young man. init. W/C on ivory. 30-Aug-2 Thomaston Place, Thomaston #35/R

Works on paper

£111111 $180000 €166667 Portrait of Thomas Jefferson (24x16cm-9x6in) s.i. i.verso W/C gouache pencil prov.lit. 22-May-3 Christie's, Rockefeller NY #53/R est:100000-150000

SULLY, Thomas (attrib) (1783-1872) American/British

£1795 $2800 €2693 Portrait of a young girl with red ribbons (46x38cm-18x15in) mono.d.1861 verso. 12-Apr-3 Weschler, Washington #551/R est:1500-2500

£3145 $5000 €4718 Portrait of a man (76x64cm-30x25in) prov.exhib. 5-Mar-3 Sotheby's, New York #33/R est:3000-5000

£4140 $6500 €6210 Portrait of a seated gentleman wearing double breasted jacket (86x71cm-34x28in) 23-Nov-2 Pook & Pook, Downington #255/R est:4000-5000

SULTAN, Donald (1951-) American

£3503 $5500 €5255 July 23, 1977 (26x23cm-10x9in) init.i. s.d.verso oil linoleum tile wood prov. 19-Nov-2 Wright, Chicago #264/R est:6000-8000

Prints

£2673 $4250 €4010 Black lemons (156x119cm-61x47in) init.d.Dec.14 1984 aquatint. 2-May-3 Sotheby's, New York #625/R est:3000-4000

£2830 $4500 €4245 Six red flowers (70x89cm-28x35in) init.i. red woodcut. 2-May-3 Sotheby's, New York #629/R est:2500-3500

Works on paper

£3525 $5500 €5288 Black lemon (127x96cm-50x38in) init.i.d.June 16 1984 chl prov. 14-Oct-2 Butterfields, San Francisco #2093/R est:6000-8000

SULZER, David (1784-1864) Swiss

£969 $1415 €1454 Portraits of J Jak Sulzer, his wife and daughter (32x26cm-13x10in) mono. one on board three. 17-Jun-2 Philippe Schuler, Zurich #4294 (S.FR 2200)

SULZER, David (attrib) (1784-1864) Swiss

£301 $484 €452 Frau Gritli Obner in Interlaken (16x13cm-6x5in) i. verso paper. 7-May-3 Dobiaschofsky, Bern #3631 (S.FR 650)

SULZER, Julius von (attrib) (1818-1889) Swiss

£1972 $3234 €2859 Portrait of girl with cat and dog (49x39cm-19x15in) 4-Jun-3 Fischer, Luzern #2321/R est:1500-1800 (S.FR 4200)

SUMIDA, Gregory (20th C) American?

Works on paper

£481 $750 €722 Night Omen (18x25cm-7x10in) s. i.verso gouache on board prov. 9-Nov-2 Santa Fe Art, Santa Fe #253/R

SUMMA, Emily B (1875-?) American

£256 $400 €384 Autumn in the Ozarks (30x41cm-12x16in) s. 10-Nov-2 Selkirks, St. Louis #970

£481 $750 €722 Landscape with haystacks (25x30cm-10x12in) s. board prov. 10-Nov-2 Selkirks, St. Louis #969/R

SUMMERS, Charles (after) (1827-1878) British

Sculpture

£9877 $15309 €14816 Story of Ruth - book of Ruth Chapters 1-2-3 (127cm-50in) i. white marble with pedestal. 3-Dec-2 Ritchie, Toronto #3133/R est:7000-9000 (C.D 24000)

SUMMERS, John (1896-1969) British

£520 $806 €780 Bright birds (16x34cm-6x13in) s. canvasboard. 25-Sep-2 Hamptons Fine Art, Godalming #364

SUMMERS, Robert (1940-) American

Sculpture

£1731 $2700 €2597 Spirit of the mountains (28x15cm-11x6in) bronze. 9-Nov-2 Altermann Galleries, Santa Fe #130

SUMNER, Maud (1902-1985) South African

£1226 $1900 €1839 Three pears (20x25cm-8x10in) s. canvasboard prov. 25-Sep-2 Doyle, New York #80/R est:800-1200

£4421 $6986 €6632 Still life with anthiriums and tiger lilies in a vase (90x71cm-35x28in) s. 1-Apr-3 Stephan Welz, Johannesburg #457/R est:30000-50000 (SA.R 55000)

£5221 $8145 €7832 Still life with flowers and fruit (77x67cm-30x26in) s. canvas on board. 15-Oct-2 Stephan Welz, Johannesburg #444/R est:60000-90000 (SA.R 85000)

£6086 $9494 €9129 Interior with fruit and flowers (63x53cm-25x21in) s. canvas on board. 11-Nov-2 Stephan Welz, Johannesburg #472/R est:70000-100000 (SA.R 95000)

£6450 $10061 €9675 Red interior (45x53cm-18x21in) s. i.stretcher. 15-Oct-2 Stephan Welz, Johannesburg #445/R est:80000-120000 (SA.R 105000)

Works on paper

£205 $320 €308 Boat, with bridge in the background (23x53cm-9x21in) s. W/C. 11-Nov-2 Stephan Welz, Johannesburg #252 (SA.R 3200)

£256 $400 €384 Trees near a dam (47x62cm-19x24in) s. pen ink koki-pen prov. 11-Nov-2 Stephan Welz, Johannesburg #558 (SA.R 4000)

£257 $406 €386 View of the Thames (29x42cm-11x17in) s. pen ink W/C. 1-Apr-3 Stephan Welz, Johannesburg #196 est:3500-5000 (SA.R 3200)

£269 $420 €404 Albert bridge (29x42cm-11x17in) s. i.verso ball point pen W/C. 11-Nov-2 Stephan Welz, Johannesburg #253 (SA.R 4200)

£288 $450 €432 Gathering (25x33cm-10x13in) s. pen ink. 11-Nov-2 Stephan Welz, Johannesburg #588 (SA.R 4500)

£448 $700 €672 Winter street scene (30x41cm-12x16in) s.d.40 W/C. 11-Nov-2 Stephan Welz, Johannesburg #456 (SA.R 7000)

£603 $953 €905 Alpine village (59x44cm-23x17in) s. W/C pen ink. 1-Apr-3 Stephan Welz, Johannesburg #456/R est:5000-8000 (SA.R 7500)

£769 $1199 €1154 Still life of Proteas (59x44cm-23x17in) s.d.44 chl W/C. 11-Nov-2 Stephan Welz, Johannesburg #527/R (SA.R 12000)

SUN BIN (1953-) Chinese
Works on paper
£2331 $3846 €3380 Mount Hua (104x54cm-41x21in) s.d.2002 ink scroll. 6-Jul-3 Christie's, Hong Kong #270/R est:30000-40000 (HK.D 30000)

SUNBEAM, Dede (20th C) French?
Works on paper
£4110 $6452 €6000 Breton chez la voyante (17x23cm-7x9in) i.d.1925 ink. 15-Apr-3 Laurence Calmels, Paris #4418/R est:4000-5000

SUNDBERG, Fanny Klingbom (1861-1926) Swedish
£393 $644 €570 Summer landscape with man on road (23x32cm-9x13in) s.d.1885. 4-Jun-3 AB Stockholms Auktionsverk #2142/R (S.KR 5000)

SUNDBLAD, Fanny (1858-1918) Finnish
£327 $504 €520 Flowers (28x31cm-11x12in) s.i.d.1891. 27-Oct-2 Bukowskis, Helsinki #291/R
£1013 $1600 €1600 Spring flowers in basket (50x39cm-20x15in) s.d.maj 1907. 1-Dec-2 Bukowskis, Helsinki #191/R est:1300-1500
£7746 $12472 €11000 Beautiful flowers (53x45cm-21x18in) s.i.d.1873 porcelain. 10-May-3 Bukowskis, Helsinki #38/R est:1200-1500

SUNDBLOM, Haddon Hubbard (1899-1976) American
£10345 $15000 €15518 Lady with hat in garden (84x71cm-33x28in) painted c.1932. 1-Jun-2 Russ Antiques, Waterford #80
£10897 $17000 €16346 Woman skier relaxes (74x53cm-29x21in) 9-Nov-2 Illustration House, New York #110/R est:18000-24000
Works on paper
£460 $750 €690 Roman ruins (0x25cm-0x10in) s.i. gouache board. 2-Feb-3 Simpson's, Houston #148a

SUNDELL, Thure (1864-1924) Finnish
£1127 $1814 €1600 Landscape (38x46cm-15x18in) s. 10-May-3 Bukowskis, Helsinki #68/R est:2000-2300

SUNDERLAND, Thomas (1744-1828) British
Works on paper
£550 $858 €825 Goldsbro grounds, Yorkshire (19x28cm-7x11in) pencil pen ink col wash exhib. 19-Sep-2 Christie's, Kensington #36/R
£550 $858 €825 Views near Hollow Oak, near Burnthwaite (18x25cm-7x10in) pen ink wash two. 5-Nov-2 Bonhams, New Bond Street #26
£550 $858 €825 West view of Peel Castle, Lancashire. Abbey, Furness, Lancashire (22x32cm-9x13in) pen ink wash two. 5-Nov-2 Bonhams, New Bond Street #27
£1100 $1716 €1650 Views of Glenridding on Ullswater (20x30cm-8x12in) pen ink set of three. 5-Nov-2 Bonhams, New Bond Street #25/R est:1200-1800

SUNDSTROM, Alf (1888-1961) Swedish
£319 $500 €479 Hotel du tertre (31x65cm-12x26in) s. board. 22-Nov-2 Skinner, Boston #319/R
£553 $874 €830 View towards town in the Swedish skerries (49x62cm-19x24in) s. 2-Dec-2 Rasmussen, Copenhagen #1234/R (D.KR 6500)

SUNDT-OHLSEN, Thoralv (1884-1948) Norwegian
£362 $586 €543 Fjord landscape (47x68cm-19x27in) s. panel. 27-Jan-3 Blomqvist, Lysaker #1251 (N.KR 4000)
£1130 $1831 €1695 Snow is thawing, Staavi, Baerum (66x84cm-26x33in) s,. 27-Jan-3 Blomqvist, Lysaker #1252/R (N.KR 12500)

SUNE SIMORRA, Mariano (19/20th C) Spanish
£818 $1259 €1300 Landscape (140x70cm-55x28in) s. 22-Oct-2 Durán, Madrid #140/R

SUNER CARRIO, Francisco (1922-1994) Spanish
£629 $981 €1000 San Fermin (33x46cm-13x18in) s.i.d.1977 verso board. 8-Oct-2 Ansorena, Madrid #621/R

SUNESSON, Stina (1925-1998) Swedish
Works on paper
£459 $720 €689 Wood anemones and common hepatica (20x18cm-8x7in) s.d.1967 W/C. 16-Dec-2 Lilla Bukowskis, Stockholm #113 (S.KR 6500)
£621 $975 €932 Sunflowers against brown background (60x49cm-24x19in) s.d.1971 W/C. 16-Dec-2 Lilla Bukowskis, Stockholm #112 (S.KR 8800)
£957 $1484 €1436 Early spring (20x24cm-8x9in) s.d.1972 gouache. 3-Dec-2 Bukowskis, Stockholm #14/R est:10000-12000 (S.KR 13500)
£1335 $2190 €1936 Girl under apple tree (18x22cm-7x9in) s. gouache. 4-Jun-3 AB Stockholms Auktionsverk #2264/R est:12000-15000 (S.KR 17000)

SUNQUA (attrib) (19th C) Chinese
£6579 $10000 €9869 Portrait of an East Indiaman off the China coast (51x61cm-20x24in) lit. 17-Aug-2 North East Auctions, Portsmouth #964/R est:7000-10000

SUNYER VIVES, Raimon (20th C) Spanish
£514 $801 €750 View of Barcelona harbour (54x65cm-21x26in) s. s.i.verso. 8-Apr-3 Ansorena, Madrid #34/R

SUNYER, Joachim (1875-1956) Spanish
£11000 $17270 €16500 Nina tejiendo - girl knitting (46x36cm-18x14in) s. canvasboard. 19-Nov-2 Sotheby's, London #73/R est:10000-15000
£12000 $18480 €18000 Nu assis dans la verdure (46x38cm-18x15in) s. 23-Oct-2 Sotheby's, Olympia #654/R est:6000-8000
£14000 $21980 €21000 Paisaje de grasse, Francia - view of Grasse, France (48x63cm-19x25in) s.d.1937 lit. 19-Nov-2 Sotheby's, London #11/R est:12000-18000
£17857 $26071 €27500 Landscape (65x85cm-26x33in) s. 12-Jun-2 Castellana, Madrid #103/R
£38000 $59660 €57000 Desnudo durmiendo con mar al fondo - sleeping nude (62x84cm-24x33in) s.d.1926 prov.exhib.lit. 19-Nov-2 Sotheby's, London #12/R est:30000-50000
Works on paper
£577 $842 €900 Untitled (14x24cm-6x9in) s. gouache. 6-Jun-2 Castellana, Madrid #28/R
£577 $842 €900 Untitled (14x24cm-6x9in) s. gouache. 6-Jun-2 Castellana, Madrid #27/R
£16000 $25120 €24000 Rue lepic, Paris (63x48cm-25x19in) s. pastel painted 1900 lit. 19-Nov-2 Sotheby's, London #39/R est:6000-8000

SUOMALAINEN, Kari (1920-1999) Finnish
Works on paper
£345 $545 €500 Talouselama (32x20cm-13x8in) s. Indian ink W/C. 3-Apr-3 Hagelstam, Helsinki #921
£360 $590 €500 I'm utilitarian traffic (22x30cm-9x12in) s. Indian ink W/C. 4-Jun-3 Bukowskis, Helsinki #442/R
£377 $581 €600 Untitled (18x40cm-7x16in) s. mixed media. 24-Oct-2 Hagelstam, Helsinki #932

SUP, Karel (1897-?) Czechoslovakian
Works on paper
£284 $440 €426 Musicians (60x80cm-24x31in) W/C exec.c.1939. 3-Dec-2 SOGA, Bratislava #221/R (SL.K 18000)

SUPPANTSCHITSCH, Max (1865-1953) Austrian
£3191 $5170 €4500 View from the Belvedere in Vienna (30x44cm-12x17in) s.d.95 oil mixed media panel. 22-May-3 Dorotheum, Vienna #167/R est:4500-6000
£8861 $14000 €14000 Garden in Weissenkirchen a/d Donau (30x39cm-12x15in) s. bears d. panel. 27-Nov-2 Dorotheum, Vienna #134/R est:9000-13000
£14764 $23770 €22000 In the garden of a church ruin near Durnstein, Austria (81x111cm-32x44in) s. 18-Feb-3 Sotheby's, Amsterdam #331/R est:6000-8000

SUPPARO, Ange Jacques (1870-?) French
£621 $1000 €932 Constantinople (51x61cm-20x24in) s. board. 19-Feb-3 Doyle, New York #14

SUPPIN, Lucas (1911-1998) Austrian
Works on paper
£576 $944 €800 Composition (65x50cm-26x20in) s.d.1982 mixed media. 5-Jun-3 Dorotheum, Salzburg #654/R

SURAND, Gustave (1860-1937) French
£417 $654 €650 French coast (4x27cm-2x11in) s.i.indis.d. paper on board. 21-Nov-2 Dorotheum, Vienna #188/R
£3333 $5233 €5200 Voiles jaunes (81x65cm-32x26in) s.d.1887 i.verso. 22-Nov-2 Millon & Associes, Paris #75
£4747 $7500 €7500 Male lion in the savannah (71x100cm-28x39in) s. 29-Nov-2 Sigalas, Stuttgart #1136/R est:7000

SURAUD, Roger (1938-) French
£566 $877 €900 Violoniste (79x63cm-31x25in) s. 30-Oct-2 Coutau Begarie, Paris #156/R

£612 $973 €900 Guitariste (81x65cm-32x26in) s.d.1966 i.verso. 24-Mar-3 Coutau Begarie, Paris #302

SURBEK, Victor (1885-1975) Swiss
£370 $596 €555 House and garden (21x34cm-8x13in) mono. i. verso canvas on panel. 7-May-3 Dobiaschofsky, Bern #3632 (S.FR 800)
£437 $681 €656 Still life (29x39cm-11x15in) s. board. 8-Nov-2 Dobiaschofsky, Bern #154/R (S.FR 1000)
£833 $1342 €1208 Isalt forest (88x129cm-35x51in) s. i.verso canvas on masonite. 9-May-3 Dobiaschofsky, Bern #89/R (S.FR 1800)
£2358 $3821 €4175 Lake landscape (87x148cm-34x58in) s. 26-May-3 Sotheby's, Zurich #83/R est:5000-8000 (S.FR 5000)

SURBER, Paul (20th C) American
£310 $500 €465 Cheyenne scalp dance (114x198cm-45x78in) s.d.1984 acrylic board. 23-Feb-3 Butterfields, Los Angeles #7040
Works on paper
£933 $1531 €1353 Indian encampment (43x69cm-17x27in) s.d.1979 W/C. 9-Jun-3 Hodgins, Calgary #340/R est:2000-2500 (C.D 2100)

SURBONE, Mario (1932-) Italian
£256 $403 €400 Projection GB (45x45cm-18x18in) s.d.1969 cardboard. 23-Nov-2 Meeting Art, Vercelli #299

SURDI, Luigi (1897-1959) Italian
£449 $704 €700 View of the Coliseum (24x32cm-9x13in) s.d.39 board. 21-Nov-2 Finarte, Rome #202

SUREDA, Andre (1872-1930) French
£1583 $2595 €2200 Les etudiants du Kottab (92x73cm-36x29in) s. 4-Jun-3 Tajan, Paris #315/R est:2200-3000
£2014 $3303 €2800 Danseuse en blanc (65x54cm-26x21in) s. panel. 4-Jun-3 Tajan, Paris #314/R est:2800-3000
Works on paper
£577 $905 €900 Jeune fille en bleu (31x23cm-12x9in) s. chl crayon gouache. 10-Dec-2 Tajan, Paris #229/R
£705 $1107 €1100 Jeune femme au tambourin. Jeune femme a la cruche (30x19cm-12x7in) s. W/C pair. 10-Dec-2 Tajan, Paris #229a/R
£2759 $4414 €4000 Mauresque tenant son voile (65x49cm-26x19in) s. i.verso chl gouache exhib. 12-Mar-3 E & Eve, Paris #85/R est:2500-3000

SURIE, Jacoba (1879-1970) Dutch
£288 $449 €420 Young cobbler (70x40cm-28x16in) s. 14-Apr-3 Glerum, Amsterdam #141
£448 $713 €650 Flower still life with a fan (20x31cm-8x12in) s. panel. 10-Mar-3 Sotheby's, Amsterdam #137
£890 $1389 €1300 Still life with dish and a glass pot (39x49cm-15x19in) s. prov. 14-Apr-3 Glerum, Amsterdam #119/R
£1690 $2721 €2400 Still life of various artist's items (29x39cm-11x15in) s. 6-May-3 Vendu Notarishuis, Rotterdam #55/R est:1500-2000

SURREY, Philip Henry (1910-1990) Canadian
£329 $507 €494 Pigeon Point Beach, Tobago (15x20cm-6x8in) panel. 22-Oct-2 Iegor de Saint Hippolyte, Montreal #103 (C.D 800)
£400 $656 €600 Summer landscape (30x40cm-12x16in) s.d.44 board. 3-Jun-3 Joyner, Toronto #541 est:800-1000 (C.D 900)
£494 $760 €741 Petty Baie St Paul, IL-aux-Coudres in background (20x28cm-8x11in) s. 22-Oct-2 Iegor de Saint Hippolyte, Montreal #106 (C.D 1200)
£578 $948 €867 Stroll on a country road (30x40cm-12x16in) s.d.44 board. 3-Jun-3 Joyner, Toronto #326/R est:1000-1500 (C.D 1300)
£823 $1276 €1235 Frisbee (30x40cm-12x16in) board prov. 3-Dec-2 Joyner, Toronto #359 est:1500-2000 (C.D 2000)
£988 $1531 €1482 Vedette, Martinique. Evening at L'Anse Mitan, Martinique (20x15cm-8x6in) s.i.d.1964 board two prov. 3-Dec-2 Joyner, Toronto #430 est:1500-2000 (C.D 2400)
£988 $1531 €1482 Icebergs and moon. Devon Island with floes (15x20cm-6x8in) s.i.d.1958 verso board two. 3-Dec-2 Joyner, Toronto #432 est:1500-2000 (C.D 2400)
£1152 $1786 €1728 Sunday morning, Mt. Royal.Brome lake (15x20cm-6x8in) s.i.d.1938 verso board two. 3-Dec-2 Joyner, Toronto #431 est:1500-2000 (C.D 2800)
£2444 $4009 €3666 Nox nocti indicat scientiam (61x76cm-24x30in) s. 27-May-3 Sotheby's, Toronto #9/R est:6000-8000 (C.D 5500)
£13333 $21867 €20000 Place Ville Marie II (80x120cm-31x47in) s. board painted c.1965 prov.exhib. 3-Jun-3 Joyner, Toronto #27/R est:35000-45000 (C.D 30000)
£16000 $26240 €24000 La plage, Ile bizard (80x120cm-31x47in) s. board painted c.1966 prov.exhib.lit. 3-Jun-3 Joyner, Toronto #62/R est:35000-40000 (C.D 36000)
Works on paper
£181 $296 €272 At the restaurant (16x23cm-6x9in) s. pencil W/C. 12-Feb-3 Iegor de Saint Hippolyte, Montreal #174 (C.D 450)
£203 $319 €305 Promeneurs (15x30cm-6x12in) s. crayon W/C prov. 12-Dec-2 Iegor de Saint Hippolyte, Montreal #116 (C.D 500)
£262 $427 €393 A road in the evening (25x35cm-10x14in) s. col pencil W/C panel. 12-Feb-3 Iegor de Saint Hippolyte, Montreal #173 (C.D 650)
£285 $447 €428 Promeneurs (19x30cm-7x12in) s. crayon W/C. 12-Dec-2 Iegor de Saint Hippolyte, Montreal #98 (C.D 700)
£741 $1141 €1112 Rue Roy and St Denis (20x25cm-8x10in) s. mixed media. 22-Oct-2 Iegor de Saint Hippolyte, Montreal #104 (C.D 1800)
£864 $1331 €1296 In the train (30x40cm-12x16in) s. chl W/C. 22-Oct-2 Iegor de Saint Hippolyte, Montreal #101/R (C.D 2100)
£2889 $4738 €4334 La Rafale, place d'armes (27x42cm-11x17in) s.d.1954 gouache prov. 3-Jun-3 Joyner, Toronto #144/R est:7000-9000 (C.D 6500)

SURTEES, John (1819-1915) British
£2700 $4509 €3915 Morning at Llanelltyd, North Wales (42x75cm-17x30in) s. 17-Jun-3 Anderson & Garland, Newcastle #443/R est:1000-1600

SURTEL, Paul (1893-1985) French
£242 $384 €350 View of a village (46x55cm-18x22in) s. board. 10-Mar-3 Sotheby's, Amsterdam #231
£310 $493 €450 L'Eglise de caromb (33x41cm-13x16in) s. board. 10-Mar-3 Sotheby's, Amsterdam #233
£317 $510 €450 Village enneige (55x46cm-22x18in) * 2030512LL.LH 21P. 12-May-3 Lesieur & Le Bars, Le Havre #89
£493 $794 €700 Rue du village (46x55cm-18x22in) s. isorel. 12-May-3 Lesieur & Le Bars, Le Havre #88
£517 $823 €750 Soir en Quercy (33x41cm-13x16in) s. board sold with another by same hand. 10-Mar-3 Sotheby's, Amsterdam #232
£899 $1439 €1250 L'eglise de Caromb (33x41cm-13x16in) s. panel. 18-May-3 Eric Pillon, Calais #130/R

SURVAGE, Leopold (1879-1968) French
£1835 $2900 €2900 Nu et feuillage (41x3cm-16x1in) s.d.55. 26-Nov-2 Camard, Paris #79/R
£2128 $3553 €3000 Homme a l'oiseau (12x8cm-5x3in) s.d.40 panel. 20-Jun-3 Piasa, Paris #187/R est:2000-3000
£2829 $4583 €4300 Personnages (65x46cm-26x18in) s.d.48 cardboard exhib. 22-Jan-3 Tajan, Paris #216/R est:4500-6000
£5128 $8051 €8000 Homme, arbre, femme (46x55cm-18x22in) s.d.1939. 20-Nov-2 Binoche, Paris #18/R est:10500-11000
£5256 $8253 €8200 Bateau a quai (60x73cm-24x29in) painted 1925. 20-Nov-2 Binoche, Paris #25/R
£5595 $9343 €8000 Le village (46x55cm-18x22in) s.d.1913. 26-Jun-3 Tajan, Paris #123/R est:8000-10000
£8333 $13083 €13000 Maison Saint-Jean pres de Collioure (46x55cm-18x22in) s.d.1924. 20-Nov-2 Binoche, Paris #26/R
£10256 $16103 €16000 Fuite (57x150cm-22x59in) s.d.37. 20-Nov-2 Binoche, Paris #22/R est:21500-22000
£10897 $17109 €17000 Vagabond (54x66cm-21x26in) s.d.1929. 20-Nov-2 Binoche, Paris #23/R est:11500-12000
£12579 $19497 €20000 Plage, cheval et voilier (81x129cm-32x51in) s.d.1945 caseine paint panel. 30-Oct-2 Artcurial Briest, Paris #93/R est:15000-20000
£13000 $21710 €18850 Femme et oiseau (92x73cm-36x29in) s.d.27 prov. 25-Jun-3 Christie's, London #223/R est:10000-15000
£14103 $22141 €22000 Femmes aux oiseaux (108x184cm-43x72in) s.d.1959. 20-Nov-2 Binoche, Paris #19/R est:33000-35000
£28846 $45288 €45000 Dynamisme (98x128cm-39x50in) s.d.1938. 10-Dec-2 Artcurial Briest, Paris #496/R est:40000-45000
£29371 $49049 €42000 L'arbre (41x33cm-16x13in) s. cardboard lit. 30-Jun-3 Artcurial Briest, Paris #55/R est:20000-30000
£30769 $48308 €48000 Homme dans la ville verte (73x60cm-29x24in) exhib.lit. 20-Nov-2 Binoche, Paris #17/R est:60000-65000
£32051 $50321 €50000 Homme dans la ville (80x64cm-31x25in) s. painted c.1920 prov.lit. 10-Dec-2 Artcurial Briest, Paris #491/R est:45000-55000
£33333 $52333 €52000 Homme dans la ville (70x73cm-28x29in) exhib.lit. 20-Nov-2 Binoche, Paris #16/R est:75000-80000
£33566 $56056 €48000 Paysage de Bretagne (73x92cm-29x36in) s. exhib.lit. 30-Jun-3 Artcurial Briest, Paris #54/R est:45000-65000
£65000 $106600 €97500 Vase au camelia et a l'oiseau (159x89cm-63x35in) sd.19 prov. 4-Feb-3 Christie's, London #349/R est:45000
Works on paper
£255 $397 €400 Spa (55x44cm-22x17in) s.i.d.1961 ink dr. 10-Nov-2 Eric Pillon, Calais #254/R
£255 $397 €400 Spa (55x44cm-22x17in) s.i.d.1961 ink dr. 10-Nov-2 Eric Pillon, Calais #253/R
£290 $450 €435 Figures (18x44cm-7x17in) init.d.36 pencil. 3-Dec-2 Bonhams, Knightsbridge #332
£304 $474 €450 Portrait d'homme (31x23cm-12x9in) s. graphite. 26-Mar-3 Millon & Associes, Paris #56
£312 $496 €450 Ete de visage (27x21cm-11x8in) s.d.44 ink dr. 29-Apr-3 Artcurial Briest, Paris #94
£314 $487 €500 Personnage a l'arbre (25x20cm-10x8in) mono.d.46 ink graphite dr. 30-Oct-2 Artcurial Briest, Paris #96
£314 $487 €500 Trois personnages et tete de taureau (27x21cm-11x8in) mono.d.33 graphite dr. 30-Oct-2 Artcurial Briest, Paris #98
£338 $527 €500 Landscape (10x16cm-4x6in) s.d.39 W/C. 26-Mar-3 Millon & Associes, Paris #54

£345 $576 €500 La village (21x31cm-8x12in) s. W/C graphite. 9-Jul-3 Millon & Associes, Paris #216
£353 $554 €550 Cave (10x16cm-4x6in) studio st. graphite. 20-Nov-2 Binoche, Paris #1/R
£379 $633 €550 Baigneuses. Portrait de femme (18x24cm-7x9in) mono. W/C graphite double-sided. 9-Jul-3 Millon & Associes, Paris #214/R
£379 $633 €550 Composition (19x17cm-7x7in) s. W/C gouache graphite. 9-Jul-3 Millon & Associes, Paris #234
£382 $596 €600 Ruines a Taormine (37x45cm-15x18in) s.i.d.1956 W/C. 10-Nov-2 Eric Pillon, Calais #169/R
£382 $607 €550 Le couple (21x14cm-8x6in) s. graphite dr. 29-Apr-3 Artcurial Briest, Paris #92
£472 $731 €750 Deux femmes (27x21cm-11x8in) s.d.29 graphite dr. 30-Oct-2 Artcurial Briest, Paris #99
£481 $755 €750 Composition (55x38cm-22x15in) s.dd.1968 W/C. 15-Dec-2 Eric Pillon, Calais #259/R
£483 $806 €700 Composition, lune et soleil (17x19cm-7x7in) s. W/C graphite. 9-Jul-3 Millon & Associes, Paris #235/R
£483 $806 €700 Composition aux visages (17x7cm-7x3in) s.d.46 W/C graphite. 9-Jul-3 Millon & Associes, Paris #238/R
£503 $780 €800 Femme de collioure et deux personnages (28x22cm-11x9in) mono. graphite dr. 30-Oct-2 Artcurial Briest, Paris #97a
£552 $921 €800 Agriculteurs aux champs (13x19cm-5x7in) mono.d.50 W/C graphite. 9-Jul-3 Millon & Associes, Paris #225
£566 $877 €900 Personnages et arabesque (22x28cm-9x11in) s.d.35 graphite dr. 30-Oct-2 Artcurial Briest, Paris #97
£586 $979 €850 Ville et visages (10x16cm-4x6in) mono.d.38 W/C graphite. 9-Jul-3 Millon & Associes, Paris #232/R
£593 $990 €860 Portrait d'homme (16x10cm-6x4in) mono.d.39 W/C graphite. 9-Jul-3 Millon & Associes, Paris #227/R
£621 $1037 €900 Femme a la coupe. La cueillette (28x22cm-11x9in) mono. one d.26 graphite pair. 9-Jul-3 Millon & Associes, Paris #259/R
£621 $1037 €900 Etude de personnages. Trois femmes (22x28cm-9x11in) s.d.32 graphite pair. 9-Jul-3 Millon & Associes, Paris #266
£637 $994 €1000 Paysage. Scene d'interieur (7x10cm-3x4in) studio st. graphite dr pair. 10-Nov-2 Eric Pillon, Calais #269/R
£642 $1001 €950 Contes d'Hoffmann (30x24cm-12x9in) s. wash W/C ink. 26-Mar-3 Millon & Associes, Paris #49
£655 $1094 €950 Vue de village (15x24cm-6x9in) mono. gouache W/C graphite. 9-Jul-3 Millon & Associes, Paris #242
£694 $1104 €1000 Nature morte au gueridon (27x21cm-11x8in) studio st. graphite dr. 29-Apr-3 Artcurial Briest, Paris #93
£759 $1267 €1100 Ville en bord de mer (11x14cm-4x6in) mono. i.verso W/C graphite. 9-Jul-3 Millon & Associes, Paris #236
£764 $1215 €1100 Projet de decoration (17x62cm-7x24in) s. gouache. 29-Apr-3 Artcurial Briest, Paris #96
£816 $1298 €1200 Nu feminin dans l'atelier (44x27cm-17x11in) s.d.25 graphite dr. 26-Feb-3 Artcurial Briest, Paris #88
£828 $1382 €1200 L'arbre du vie (14x10cm-6x4in) s.d.38 W/C graphite. 9-Jul-3 Millon & Associes, Paris #228/R
£897 $1497 €1300 Scene d'interieur (15x20cm-6x8in) mono. W/C graphite. 9-Jul-3 Millon & Associes, Paris #237
£900 $1440 €1350 Dancing figures (18x38cm-7x15in) s. gouache. 11-Mar-3 Gorringes, Lewes #2443
£931 $1555 €1350 Ville cubiste (24x18cm-9x7in) s.d.15 W/C. 9-Jul-3 Millon & Associes, Paris #230
£966 $1612 €1400 Composition (11x14cm-4x6in) s. graphite gouache W/C. 9-Jul-3 Millon & Associes, Paris #256
£1060 $1727 €1600 Femme et taureau (27x22cm-11x9in) s. gouache. 3-Feb-3 Cornette de St.Cyr, Paris #335
£1282 $2013 €2000 Composition cubiste (29x52cm-11x20in) s. gouache. 15-Dec-2 Eric Pillon, Calais #261/R
£1346 $2087 €2100 Arbre vert (12x13cm-5x5in) s. W/C. 6-Dec-2 Rieunier, Bailly-Pommery, Mathias, Paris #81
£1410 $2214 €2200 Femme a la feuille (10x8cm-4x3in) s.d.1942 caseine cardboard. 20-Nov-2 Binoche, Paris #10/R
£1410 $2214 €2200 Composition aux figures (32x24cm-13x9in) s.d.58 W/C felt-tip pen. 22-Nov-2 Millon & Associes, Paris #31
£1483 $2476 €2150 Ville cubiste. Bas de visage d'homme (23x15cm-9x6in) mono. col crayon graphite double-sided. 9-Jul-3 Millon & Associes, Paris #224 est:500-600
£1517 $2534 €2200 La ville. Visage masculin (15x23cm-6x9in) s.d.22 i.verso W/C graphite double-sided. 9-Jul-3 Millon & Associes, Paris #231/R est:600-800
£1519 $2400 €2400 Nature morte aux pommes (18x14cm-7x6in) s.d.30 gouache prov. 27-Nov-2 Dorotheum, Vienna #27/R est:2500-3000
£1586 $2649 €2300 La ville (13x21cm-5x8in) mono. W/C graphite. 9-Jul-3 Millon & Associes, Paris #233
£1731 $2717 €2700 Albi, cathedrale (36x48cm-14x19in) s.i. casein panel. 16-Dec-2 Rabourdin & Choppin de Janvry, Paris #98/R
£1759 $2937 €2550 La ville (24x16cm-9x6in) mono. W/C graphite. 9-Jul-3 Millon & Associes, Paris #215/R est:500-600
£1806 $2871 €2600 Etude pour les baigneuses (27x21cm-11x8in) studio st. ink wash dr exec.c.1912. 29-Apr-3 Artcurial Briest, Paris #90/R est:500-700
£1806 $2979 €2600 Couple dans la ville (32x24cm-13x9in) s.d.58 W/C ink. 2-Jul-3 Artcurial Briest, Paris #659/R est:2000-3000
£1879 $3045 €2650 Deux visages (32x41cm-13x16in) s.d. gouache. 21-May-3 Cornette de St.Cyr, Paris #63/R est:2000-3000
£1923 $3019 €3000 Naples (35x50cm-14x20in) s.i.d.1952 chl W/C pastel felt-tip pen. 20-Nov-2 Binoche, Paris #3/R
£1923 $3019 €3000 Composition au coq (39x32cm-15x13in) s.d.1949 W/C lit. 20-Nov-2 Binoche, Paris #5/R
£2279 $3623 €3350 Femme et vache dans un paysage (34x39cm-13x15in) s.d. W/C. 26-Feb-3 Artcurial Briest, Paris #87/R est:2700-3300
£2308 $3623 €3600 Mage (40x50cm-16x20in) s.d.1950 pastel. 20-Nov-2 Binoche, Paris #9/R
£2628 $4126 €4100 Declaration (18x13cm-7x5in) s.d.1948 casein panel. 20-Nov-2 Binoche, Paris #12/R est:3500-4000
£3205 $5032 €5000 Fruit (49x39cm-19x15in) s.d.1960 gouache W/C. 20-Nov-2 Binoche, Paris #6/R
£4167 $6875 €6000 Sans titre (62x59cm-24x23in) collage mirror paint wood panel exec.c.1930. 1-Jul-3 Rossini, Paris #58/R
£5449 $8554 €8500 Homme dans la ville (21x17cm-8x7in) s.d.1921 W/C crayon. 20-Nov-2 Binoche, Paris #13/R
£5556 $9167 €8000 Personnages (64x46cm-25x18in) s.d.48 caseine panel prov.exhib. 2-Jul-3 Artcurial Briest, Paris #658/R est:8000-12000
£9091 $15182 €13000 La ville (23x30cm-9x12in) s. gouache. 26-Jun-3 Tajan, Paris #122/R est:4000-6000

SURY, Jacob van (attrib) (19th C) Dutch
£696 $1100 €1044 Landscape with cattle (61x84cm-24x33in) painted c.1810. 1-Dec-2 Susanin's, Chicago #5004/R

SUS, Gustav Konrad (1823-1881) German
£291 $460 €460 Two young girls sleeping (14x17cm-6x7in) s. wood. 29-Nov-2 Bolland & Marotz, Bremen #781
£669 $1111 €950 Young blood in the hen house (52x41cm-20x16in) s. 14-Jun-3 Arnold, Frankfurt #877/R
£1203 $1876 €1900 Chick with beetle (14x14cm-6x6in) s. panel lit. 14-Sep-2 Bergmann, Erlangen #758/R
Works on paper
£806 $1274 €1209 Den Flinschska Papierfabriken im Freiburg, Baden (44x56cm-17x22in) s. i.verso W/C executed c.1845 prov. 27-Nov-2 Falkkloos, Malmo #77776/R (S.KR 11500)

SUSENIER, Abraham (1620-1664) Dutch
£11354 $17712 €17031 Still life (65x59cm-26x23in) panel. 6-Nov-2 Dobiaschofsky, Bern #1005/R est:27000 (S.FR 26000)

SUSI, Nanna (?) Finnish
£748 $1190 €1100 Ansa (85x124cm-33x49in) s. 27-Feb-3 Hagelstam, Helsinki #1017

SUSILUOTO, Ahti (1940-) Finnish
Works on paper
£272 $433 €400 Kukkomiehiaja machonaisia (58x74cm-23x29in) s.d.93 mixed media. 24-Mar-3 Bukowskis, Helsinki #315/R

SUSINI, Antonio (circle) (?-1624) Italian
Sculpture
£62500 $98750 €90000 Cheval attaque par un lion (21x30x24cm-8x12x9in) pat bronze prov. 25-Apr-3 Beaussant & Lefèvre, Paris #80/R est:45000-60000

SUSINI, Gian Francesco (c.1575-1646) Italian
Sculpture
£3226 $5097 €5000 Crucifixion (62x45cm-24x18in) dark pat bronze. 19-Dec-2 Semenzato, Venice #43/R

SUSINI, Gian Francesco (studio) (c.1575-1646) Italian
Sculpture
£18000 $30060 €26100 Sleeping Hermaphrodite (13x40x16cm-5x16x6in) bronze. 8-Jul-3 Sotheby's, London #89/R est:20000-30000

SUSS, Johann J (1857-1937) Austrian
£413 $644 €620 Courting (42x51cm-17x20in) s. cardboard. 11-Sep-2 Kieselbach, Budapest #179/R (H.F 160000)

SUSS, Margarethe (19th C) German?
£458 $750 €700 Walserthal, Vorarlberg (24x37cm-9x15in) mono.d.68 i. verso i. verso. 29-Mar-3 Dannenberg, Berlin #659/R

SUSSMEIER, Josef (1896-1971) German
£1538 $2338 €2400 Nude girl (47x30cm-19x12in) s. board. 11-Jul-2 Hugo Ruef, Munich #809/R est:2000

SUSTERMANS, Justus (1597-1681) Flemish
£3097 $4893 €4800 Portrait presume de Claudia di Ferdinando de Medici (66x50cm-26x20in) 20-Dec-2 Tajan, Paris #56/R
£26000 $40820 €39000 Portrait of gentleman in crimson robes of office (116x88cm-46x35in) prov.lit. 11-Dec-2 Christie's, London #116/R est:20000-30000

SUSTRIS, Friedrich (1540-1599) Dutch
£526 $767 €820 Sketch for fresco with putti (9x23cm-4x9in) pen wash. 4-Jun-2 Karl & Faber, Munich #42/R
Works on paper
£170000 $283900 €246500 Siege and destruction of Firsple by the Goths in 405, tapestry design (26x38cm-10x15in) black chk ink wash squared in black prov. 8-Jul-3 Christie's, London #25/R est:100000-150000

SUSTRIS, Friedrich (attrib) (1540-1599) Dutch
Works on paper
£566 $877 €900 Archangel Michael (22x16cm-9x6in) wash pen. 1-Oct-2 Dorotheum, Vienna #31/R

SUSTRIS, Lambert (c.1515-1568) Dutch
Prints
£3038 $4800 €4800 Raising of Lazurus (21x32cm-8x13in) burin diamond needle. 29-Nov-2 Bassenge, Berlin #5233/R est:3500

SUSTRIS, Lambert (attrib) (c.1515-1568) Dutch
£6757 $10541 €10000 Enlevement de Proserpine (94x126cm-37x50in) 26-Mar-3 Tajan, Paris #141/R est:12000
Works on paper
£2051 $3241 €3200 Hercules on pyre (19x25cm-7x10in) pen wash htd white. 16-Nov-2 Lempertz, Koln #1281/R est:3000

SUSTRIS, Lambert (style) (c.1515-1568) Dutch
£22436 $34776 €35000 Venus and Love (51x108cm-20x43in) 4-Dec-2 Christie's, Rome #440/R est:7000-10000

SUTCLIFFE, Elizabeth Trevor (fl.1886-1928) British
£310 $487 €465 Still life of yellow primroses in a blue and white bowl (11x34cm-4x13in) s. board. 19-Nov-2 Bonhams, Leeds #154
£480 $754 €720 Still life of violets in a glass bowl (19x23cm-7x9in) s. board. 19-Nov-2 Bonhams, Leeds #153

SUTCLIFFE, Frank Meadow (1853-1941) British
Photographs
£2405 $3800 €3608 Excitement (22x30cm-9x12in) i. carbon print prov. 24-Apr-3 Phillips, New York #80/R est:1500-2000
Works on paper
£400 $624 €600 Fishing vessels, upper harbour, Whitby (56x71cm-22x28in) init. sepia photo. 20-Sep-2 Richardson & Smith, Whitby #40

SUTCLIFFE, Harriette F A (fl.1881-1922) British
£4750 $7458 €7125 Presenting the posy (152x100cm-60x39in) mono. 21-Nov-2 Tennants, Leyburn #855/R est:6000-8000

SUTCLIFFE, Irene (1883-1959) British
Works on paper
£400 $624 €600 Rose in autumn (8x5cm-3x2in) oil ivory panel. 20-Sep-2 Richardson & Smith, Whitby #143

SUTCLIFFE, John E (1876-1922) British
Works on paper
£280 $434 €420 Cottage scene (31x49cm-12x19in) s. W/C. 3-Nov-2 Lots Road, London #346

SUTCLIFFE, Lester (1848-1933) British
£700 $1092 €1050 Picnic by the river (38x55cm-15x22in) s. 13-Sep-2 Lyon & Turnbull, Edinburgh #126/R
£720 $1130 €1080 Woodland scene with a girl standing beside silver birch trees (35x25cm-14x10in) s. board. 19-Nov-2 Bonhams, Leeds #145
Works on paper
£250 $390 €375 Robin Hood's Bay (20x28cm-8x11in) s. W/C. 20-Sep-2 Richardson & Smith, Whitby #54

SUTER, Ernst (1904-1987) Swiss
£423 $693 €613 Tinzen (56x44cm-22x17in) s.d.1920. 4-Jun-3 Fischer, Luzern #2322/R (S.FR 900)
Sculpture
£1717 $2712 €2576 Female nude standing with sun hat (43cm-17in) bronze st.f.Amici. 29-Nov-2 Zofingen, Switzerland #2234/R est:2500 (S.FR 4000)
£2103 $3323 €3155 Female nude standing (67cm-26in) bronze. 29-Nov-2 Zofingen, Switzerland #2233/R est:4000 (S.FR 4900)
£2146 $3391 €3219 Female nude sitting (42cm-17in) pat bronze st.f.Brotal. 29-Nov-2 Zofingen, Switzerland #2235/R est:6000 (S.FR 5000)

SUTER, Jakob (1805-1874) Swiss
Works on paper
£845 $1386 €1225 Two monks on path with St Peter beyond (34x43cm-13x17in) s.i.d.1833 W/C. 4-Jun-3 Fischer, Luzern #2682/R est:1500-1800 (S.FR 1800)

SUTHERLAND, David (1883-1973) British
£580 $905 €870 Ploughing at Ryie (33x50cm-13x20in) s. conte. 17-Oct-2 Bonhams, Edinburgh #28
£950 $1473 €1425 Day's catch on rocks (31x38cm-12x15in) init. canvasboard. 5-Dec-2 Bonhams, Edinburgh #97/R
£1210 $1900 €1815 Marketplace (26x38cm-10x15in) s. canvasboard. 22-Nov-2 Skinner, Boston #320/R est:1200-1800
£1800 $2808 €2700 Distant hills of Skye (41x52cm-16x20in) s.indis.d. panel double-sided exhib. 10-Apr-3 Bonhams, Edinburgh #36/R est:2000-3000

SUTHERLAND, Fanny (fl.1876-1886) British
Works on paper
£1000 $1560 €1500 Queen sits alone at Linlithgow (72x49cm-28x19in) s.d.1879 bodycol exhib. 10-Apr-3 Bonhams, Edinburgh #121 est:200-300

SUTHERLAND, Graham (1903-1980) British
£2800 $4368 €4200 Potted plant (31x22cm-12x9in) s.d.50 board prov. 12-Sep-2 Sotheby's, Olympia #128/R est:3000-5000
£8200 $13038 €12300 Honeysuckle (79x64cm-31x25in) s. 26-Feb-3 Sotheby's, Olympia #263/R est:2000-3000
£8800 $13992 €13200 Birdcage (35x30cm-14x12in) init.d.1959. 26-Feb-3 Sotheby's, Olympia #266/R est:6000-8000
£85000 $133450 €127500 Standing form over water II (99x81cm-39x32in) s.d.46 s.i.d.verso prov.exhib. 22-Nov-2 Christie's, London #90/R est:50000-70000
Works on paper
£400 $624 €600 Fabric design (19x17cm-7x7in) pencil brush ink gouache prov. 27-Mar-3 Christie's, Kensington #651/R
£500 $780 €750 Rock plants (5x10cm-2x4in) W/C. 16-Oct-2 David Lay, Penzance #288/R
£800 $1312 €1200 Study for thorn tree (6x8cm-2x3in) init.d.1946 pen ink prov. 3-Jun-3 Sotheby's, Olympia #244/R
£850 $1403 €1233 Study for palm (16x17cm-6x7in) init. pencil gouache prov. 3-Jul-3 Christie's, Kensington #657/R
£900 $1386 €1350 Study for palm (17x18cm-7x7in) init. brush ink W/C bodycol prov. 5-Sep-2 Christie's, Kensington #713/R est:1000-1500
£900 $1404 €1350 Study for staring tree form (27x19cm-11x7in) init. pencil pastel prov. 27-Mar-3 Christie's, Kensington #629/R
£950 $1568 €1378 Study for painting (9x9cm-4x4in) pencil pastel W/C bodycol prov. 3-Jul-3 Christie's, Kensington #658/R
£1000 $1640 €1500 Study for thorn head (12x10cm-5x4in) s. pen ink prov. 3-Jun-3 Sotheby's, Olympia #243/R est:1000-1500
£1200 $1872 €1800 The Crucifixion (21x16cm-8x6in) i. pastel sold with other works. 12-Sep-2 Sotheby's, Olympia #132/R est:800-1200
£1400 $2184 €2100 Study for chimere (21x14cm-8x6in) pencil pastel executed 1946 prov. 27-Mar-3 Christie's, Kensington #628/R est:1500-2000
£1400 $2310 €2030 Study for pergola (27x19cm-11x7in) init. pencil col crayons prov. 3-Jul-3 Christie's, Kensington #655/R est:1500-2000
£1800 $2808 €2700 Peacock (24x18cm-9x7in) pencil pen brush htd white executed 1979 prov. 27-Mar-3 Christie's, Kensington #630/R est:1200-1800
£2000 $3120 €3000 Study for pergola (27x19cm-11x7in) init. pencil pastel prov. 27-Mar-3 Christie's, Kensington #632/R est:1500-2000
£2200 $3410 €3300 Objects against a cliff (26x20cm-10x8in) s.d.1939 pencil brush black ink W/C bodycol prov. 4-Dec-2 Christie's, Kensington #344/R est:2000-3000
£2500 $3951 €3750 Machine form (44x29cm-17x11in) init.d.1961 ink col crayon W/C exhib. 27-Nov-2 Sotheby's, Olympia #180/R est:2500-3500
£2600 $4004 €3900 L'Abeille (37x31cm-15x12in) init.d.78 pen brush ink htd white prov. 5-Sep-2 Christie's, Kensington #706/R est:1500-2000
£3200 $4960 €4800 Neo romantic landscape study (5x20cm-2x8in) pen ink gouache pair. 3-Dec-2 Bonhams, New Bond Street #69/R est:2000-3000
£3500 $5845 €5075 Barren landscape with rocks (33x24cm-13x9in) s.d.1951 W/C gouache chl prov. 24-Jun-3 Bonhams, New Bond Street #69/R est:3000-3500
£3800 $5928 €5700 Armadillo (64x49cm-25x19in) s.d.2.1.67 pencil chl brush ink W/C bodycol. 27-Mar-3 Christie's, Kensington #631/R est:3000-5000
£4500 $7515 €6525 Viaduct (24x50cm-9x20in) s.d.52 gouache chl wax crayon. 24-Jun-3 Bonhams, New Bond Street #66/R est:4000-6000

£4600 $7268 €6900 Black and yellow landscape (28x21cm-11x8in) s.d.1940 W/C pen black ink gouache crayon prov. 27-Nov-2 Sotheby's, Olympia #58/R est:3000-4000
£4800 $7488 €7200 Welsh landscape (29x43cm-11x17in) s.d.1978 ink W/C gouache prov. 12-Sep-2 Sotheby's, Olympia #130/R est:5000-7000
£5000 $8200 €7500 Figure in landscape (23x18cm-9x7in) s.d.44 pen brush ink W/C bodycol prov. 6-Jun-3 Christie's, London #169/R est:2000-3000
£5500 $8580 €8250 Roses (45x48cm-18x19in) s.d.1973 ink gouache col chk W/C prov. 12-Sep-2 Sotheby's, Olympia #133/R est:6000-8000
£5500 $9020 €8250 Landscape with uprushing wind (67x46cm-26x18in) s.d.1940 gouache ink W/C wash exhib. 3-Jun-3 Sotheby's, Olympia #245/R est:4000-6000
£5500 $9020 €8250 Study (67x47cm-26x19in) s.d.40 gouache ink W/C wash. 3-Jun-3 Sotheby's, Olympia #246/R est:4000-6000
£5500 $9075 €7975 Swimmer (66x49cm-26x19in) s.d.1973 pastel W/C bodycol. 3-Jul-3 Christie's, Kensington #659/R est:3000-5000
£7000 $10990 €10500 Landscape with low cliffs and woods (47x80cm-19x31in) s. i.verso W/C brush ink wash pencil paper on panel executed 1938. 21-Nov-2 Christie's, London #135/R est:8000-12000
£7000 $11480 €10150 Folded hills (20x25cm-8x10in) s.d.1943 W/C gouache ink chk pencil prov. 4-Jun-3 Sotheby's, London #68/R est:5000-7000
£7372 $10763 €11500 Insect simulating seed-study (66x50cm-26x20in) s.d.1967 mixed media prov. 5-Jun-2 Il Ponte, Milan #140/R est:7000-8000
£8000 $13120 €12000 Roses (44x35cm-17x14in) s.d.51 crayon W/C bodycol prov. 6-Jun-3 Christie's, London #118/R est:7000-10000
£8000 $13120 €12000 Palm tree (72x54cm-28x21in) s.i.d.10.3.65 bodycol prov. 6-Jun-3 Christie's, London #168/R est:4000-6000
£8000 $13120 €11600 Trees on a foreshore (26x31cm-10x12in) s. W/C gouache ink chk wax crayon pencil prov. 4-Jun-3 Sotheby's, London #70/R est:6000-8000
£8500 $13940 €12750 Rock and hills (29x37cm-11x15in) s.d.1944 gouache pen ink W/C chk prov. 6-Jun-3 Christie's, London #170/R est:6000-8000
£9500 $14724 €14250 Fruit trees in the garden at Trottiscliffe (36x27cm-14x11in) s.d.1944 i.verso W/C gouache pen. 4-Dec-2 Sotheby's, London #67/R est:10000-15000
£11000 $17160 €16500 Blast furnace sketch book (30x25cm-12x10in) i. ink gouache W/C 17 sketches prov. 12-Sep-2 Sotheby's, Olympia #131/R est:2000-3000
£15000 $25050 €21750 Stone, study II (51x49cm-20x19in) s.d.1973 W/C gouache Indian ink pen prov. 24-Jun-3 Bonhams, New Bond Street #65/R est:7000-10000

SUTHERLAND, Jane (1855-1928) Australian
Works on paper
£394 $599 €591 Landscape with cart (22x34cm-9x13in) s. pastel exhib. 28-Aug-2 Deutscher-Menzies, Melbourne #342/R (A.D 1100)

SUTTER, Hans (1887-1916) German
£1887 $2943 €3000 Seated man with cigar and dog (89x77cm-35x30in) s.d.III 1914. 11-Oct-2 Winterberg, Heidelberg #1764/R est:220

SUTTER, Jules de (1895-1970) Belgian
£540 $863 €750 Nature morte aux pommes (60x64cm-24x25in) prov. 13-May-3 Vanderkindere, Brussels #117
£1195 $1852 €1900 Fieldwork (50x60cm-20x24in) s. prov. 5-Oct-2 De Vuyst, Lokeren #475/R est:2000-3000
£6918 $10654 €11000 Travail aux champs (90x100cm-35x39in) s. 22-Oct-2 Campo & Campo, Antwerp #79 est:8000
Works on paper
£252 $387 €400 Jeune femme (30x22cm-12x9in) mono. pastel. 22-Oct-2 Campo, Vlaamse Kaai #476
£283 $436 €450 Nu (35x27cm-14x11in) mono. pastel. 22-Oct-2 Campo, Vlaamse Kaai #477
£321 $497 €500 Nude sitting (34x26cm-13x10in) mono. pastel. 7-Dec-2 De Vuyst, Lokeren #100
£443 $700 €700 Nu assis (34x25cm-13x10in) mono. pastel. 26-Nov-2 Palais de Beaux Arts, Brussels #74
£449 $696 €700 Horse and cart (25x35cm-10x14in) s. pastel. 7-Dec-2 De Vuyst, Lokeren #99

SUTTERBY, Rod (1944-) British
£1800 $2844 €2700 Otter and grilse (61x50cm-24x20in) s. s.d.2000 verso. 28-Nov-2 Christie's, Kensington #11/R est:2000-3000

SUTTON, Ernest E (20th C) British
Works on paper
£520 $806 €780 Cromer from the beach, Norfolk (24x34cm-9x13in) s.i.d.1926 W/C. 30-Sep-2 Bonhams, Ipswich #309/R

SUTTON, Ivan (1944-) Irish?
£573 $894 €900 Galway hooker, low tide, passage east, Co Waterford (40x50cm-16x20in) s. board. 6-Nov-2 James Adam, Dublin #129/R
£634 $1052 €900 Reading of the will (51x41cm-20x16in) s. board. 10-Jun-3 James Adam, Dublin #94/R
£685 $1068 €1000 Falmouth, oyster dredgers (16x20cm-6x8in) s. board. 8-Apr-3 James Adam, Dublin #70/R
£705 $1107 €1100 View of Roundstone harbour, with Twelve Pins in the background (34x43cm-13x17in) s. i.verso board. 19-Nov-2 Hamilton Osborne King, Dublin #460/R est:800-1200
£822 $1290 €1200 Jorgensen's stand at the Irish antique dealers fair (51x76cm-20x30in) s.i.verso. 15-Apr-3 De Veres Art Auctions, Dublin #45/R est:1400-1800
£890 $1389 €1300 Musicians at the art gallery (16x20cm-6x8in) s. board. 8-Apr-3 James Adam, Dublin #64/R
£1076 $1668 €1700 Galway hookers berthed at Roundstone (51x64cm-20x25in) s. i.verso board. 24-Sep-2 De Veres Art Auctions, Dublin #77/R est:1400-1800
£1154 $1812 €1800 Musicians on view (40x50cm-16x20in) s. i.verso. 19-Nov-2 Hamilton Osborne King, Dublin #461/R est:1200-1600
£1538 $2415 €2400 Kilmore Quay Harbour and Marina, County Wexford (51x76cm-20x30in) s. board. 19-Nov-2 Whyte's, Dublin #135/R est:2500-3500
£1635 $2551 €2600 Coliemore harbour, Dalkey, County Dublin (41x51cm-16x20in) s. canvasboard. 17-Sep-2 Whyte's, Dublin #190/R est:1500-2000
£1667 $2650 €2400 Ready to launch, Aran Mor, County Galway (51x76cm-20x30in) s. s.i.verso canvasboard. 29-Apr-3 Whyte's, Dublin #208/R est:1800-2200
£1736 $2865 €2500 Coliemore Harbour, Dalkey, Co Dublin (40x50cm-16x20in) s. board. 7-Jul-3 Hamilton Osborne King, Dublin #213/R est:1500-2000
£1745 $2809 €2600 Galway hooker berthed at Kinvarra, Co Galway (66x76cm-26x30in) s. s.i.verso board. 18-Feb-3 Whyte's, Dublin #164/R est:3000-4000
£1806 $2979 €2600 Roundstone harbour, Co Galway (40x50cm-16x20in) s. board. 7-Jul-3 Hamilton Osborne King, Dublin #214/R est:1500-2000
£2083 $3312 €3000 Galway hookers racing off Kinvara, County Galway (51x61cm-20x24in) s. i.verso canvasboard. 29-Apr-3 Whyte's, Dublin #206/R est:1500-2000
£2685 $4322 €4000 Launching the currach, Aran Mor, Co Galway (58x76cm-23x30in) s. s.i.verso board. 18-Feb-3 Whyte's, Dublin #162/R est:2500-3500

SUTTON, Linda (1947-) British
Works on paper
£650 $1040 €975 Wedding (76x69cm-30x27in) s. mixed media. 14-Mar-3 Gardiner & Houlgate, Bath #28/R

SUTTON, Philip (1928-) British
£520 $848 €780 Clatford Bottom - landscape (90x90cm-35x35in) s.i.d.1960 verso. 17-Feb-3 Bonhams, Bath #31
£550 $891 €825 Battersea (45x40cm-18x16in) s.i.verso. 20-May-3 Bonhams, Knightsbridge #183/R
£2200 $3674 €3190 Zadadier nude, number two (127x127cm-50x50in) i.d.June 1967 verso. 24-Jun-3 Bonhams, New Bond Street #127/R est:1000-1500
£2800 $4676 €4060 Flowers (111x11cm-44x4in) s.i.d.1972 verso. 25-Jun-3 Bonhams, Bury St Edmunds #603/R est:3000-5000
£3500 $5845 €5075 Rebekah's flowers (101x111cm-40x44in) s.d.1983 verso. 24-Jun-3 Bonhams, New Bond Street #128/R est:3500-4500

SUTTON, Thomas (1819-1875) British
Photographs
£3200 $5184 €4800 Ruined tower, Jersey (28x20cm-11x8in) i.num.478 mount Blanquart-Evrard process print prov.lit. 21-May-3 Christie's, London #25/R est:1000-1500

SUTTON, William A (1917-2000) New Zealander
Works on paper
£848 $1357 €1230 Boulder Bay, Taylors Mistake, Christchurch (24x34cm-9x13in) s.d.45 W/C. 13-May-3 Watson's, Christchurch #85/R (NZ.D 2350)
£1569 $2306 €2354 Lyttelton harbour (32x55cm-13x22in) s.d.86 W/C prov. 19-Jun-2 Watson's, Christchurch #8/R est:5500-7500 (NZ.D 4800)

SUVEE, Joseph Benoit (1743-1807) Flemish
£1266 $2000 €2000 Tetes de vieillards (41x33cm-16x13in) s.indis.d. oval pair. 27-Nov-2 Christie's, Paris #52/R
£3972 $6434 €5600 Portrait d'hommes de profil (40x32cm-16x13in) s. oval pair. 26-May-3 Joron-Derem, Paris #74/R est:3000-4000
£4196 $7007 €6000 L'Ange Raphael disparaissant au milieu de la Famille de Tobie (40x47cm-16x19in) 25-Jun-3 Sotheby's, Paris #47/R est:6000-8000

SUVEE, Joseph Benoit (attrib) (1743-1807) Flemish
£1097 $1733 €1700 Portrait de jeune homme en buste (13x11cm-5x4in) paper on cardboard. 20-Dec-2 Tajan, Paris #172

SUVERO, Mark di (1933-) American
Sculpture
£968 $1500 €1452 Longing (69x56x16cm-27x22x6in) incised sig. four piece saw cut nickel plated aluminum. 25-Sep-2 Christie's, Rockefeller NY #419 est:700-900
£9375 $15000 €14063 Untitled (26x53x25cm-10x21x10in) welded painted steel in two parts executed c.1964 prov. 14-May-3 Sotheby's, New York #187/R est:20000-30000

SUYDAM, Henry (19th C) American
£3797 $6000 €5696 Lakeside activities (36x61cm-14x24in) s. prov. 24-Apr-3 Shannon's, Milford #126/R est:4000-6000

SUYDAM, James Augustus (1819-1865) American
£77419 $120000 €116129 At river's bend (15x25cm-6x10in) init. canvas on board painted c.1855 prov. 3-Dec-2 Phillips, New York #4/R est:35000-55000

SUZOR-COTE, Marc-Aurele de Foy (1869-1937) Canadian
£1000 $1640 €1500 Paysage d'automne (6x8cm-2x3in) s. i.d.1916 verso board prov. 27-May-3 Sotheby's, Toronto #99/R est:1800-2000 (C.D 2250)
£2218 $3504 €3327 Vieille maison (20x23cm-8x9in) s. board painted c.1910 prov. 14-Nov-2 Heffel, Vancouver #249/R est:5500-6500 (C.D 5500)
£2469 $3827 €3704 Woman in red (26x21cm-10x8in) s.d.1906 panel prov. 3-Dec-2 Joyner, Toronto #102/R est:4000-5000 (C.D 6000)
£3433 $5356 €5150 Effet de soleil au village de Fourcherolles (26x34cm-10x13in) s. cardboard. 25-Mar-3 Iegor de Saint Hippolyte, Montreal #134 (C.D 8000)
£3704 $5741 €5556 Coucher de soleil (11x17cm-4x7in) s. panel prov. 3-Dec-2 Joyner, Toronto #151/R est:12000-15000 (C.D 9000)
£4098 $6393 €6147 Sous-bois en automne (16x23cm-6x9in) s. 10-Sep-2 Iegor de Saint Hippolyte, Montreal #107/R (C.D 10000)
£7407 $11481 €11111 Coucher de soleil, Arthabaska (25x35cm-10x14in) s.d.1908 panel. 3-Dec-2 Joyner, Toronto #73/R est:15000-20000 (C.D 18000)
£8266 $13474 €12399 House in the summer (22x46cm-9x18in) s.d.1911. 12-Feb-3 Iegor de Saint Hippolyte, Montreal #177/R (C.D 20500)
£9053 $14033 €13580 La ferme (45x65cm-18x26in) s.d.1899. 3-Dec-2 Joyner, Toronto #117 est:40000-50000 (C.D 22000)
£24664 $39462 €36996 Suger Bush, winter (66x84cm-26x33in) s. prov. 15-May-3 Heffel, Vancouver #45/R est:100000-125000 (C.D 55000)
£24664 $39462 €36996 Portrait d'un Vieux Paralyse (61x51cm-24x20in) s.d.1898 s.d.verso prov.exhib.lit. 15-May-3 Heffel, Vancouver #51/R est:40000-60000 (C.D 55000)
£29234 $46190 €43851 Pastoral landscape (51x65cm-20x26in) s. prov.lit. 18-Nov-2 Sotheby's, Toronto #16/R est:60000-80000 (C.D 72500)
Sculpture
£6379 $9887 €9569 Les epoux chapdelaine (36cm-14in) s.i.d.1922 bronze. 3-Dec-2 Joyner, Toronto #162/R est:9000-12000 (C.D 15500)
£8000 $13120 €12000 Itch - Le modele (38cm-15in) s.d.1925 bronze st.f. Roman prov.lit. 27-May-3 Sotheby's, Toronto #199/R est:5000-7000 (C.D 18000)
£8065 $12742 €12098 L'indienne (39cm-15in) s.i. bronze prov. 18-Nov-2 Sotheby's, Toronto #18/R est:9000-12000 (C.D 20000)
£13169 $20412 €19754 Femmes de caughnawaga (43x55cm-17x22in) s.i. bronze wood base i.f.Roman prov.lit. 3-Dec-2 Joyner, Toronto #100a/R est:15000-20000 (C.D 32000)
£14444 $23689 €21666 Hydrographer (52cm-20in) s.num.688 bronze st.f.Roman prov. 27-May-3 Sotheby's, Toronto #105/R est:15000-20000 (C.D 32500)
Works on paper
£383 $624 €575 Amerindian (45x30cm-18x12in) s.d.1923 chl. 12-Feb-3 Iegor de Saint Hippolyte, Montreal #176 (C.D 950)
£524 $854 €786 L'homme a la houe (60x40cm-24x16in) s. chl. 12-Feb-3 Iegor de Saint Hippolyte, Montreal #175 (C.D 1300)
£629 $981 €944 Femme assise (35x22cm-14x9in) s.d.1923 chl. 30-Jul-2 Iegor de Saint Hippolyte, Montreal #162 (C.D 1560)
£978 $1604 €1467 Portrait of a woman (30x22cm-12x9in) s.d.99 chl htd white. 3-Jun-3 Joyner, Toronto #308/R est:1500-2000 (C.D 2200)
£1067 $1749 €1601 Grandmother (47x36cm-19x14in) s. chl. 3-Jun-3 Joyner, Toronto #391/R est:2000-2500 (C.D 2400)
£1317 $2028 €1976 Coucher de soleil Arthabaska (28x32cm-11x13in) chl col crayon. 22-Oct-2 Iegor de Saint Hippolyte, Montreal #107 (C.D 3200)
£1333 $2187 €2000 Portrait of a young man (42x34cm-17x13in) s.d.96 W/C. 3-Jun-3 Joyner, Toronto #215/R est:3000-4000 (C.D 3000)
£2469 $3827 €3704 Salmon (60x38cm-24x15in) s.d.1919 pastel. 3-Dec-2 Joyner, Toronto #149/R est:8000-10000 (C.D 6000)
£3111 $5102 €4667 Dam near Arthabaska, Que (46x60cm-18x24in) s. pastel. 3-Jun-3 Joyner, Toronto #249/R est:8000-10000 (C.D 7000)
£4527 $7016 €6791 Portrait of a lady (71x52cm-28x20in) s.i.d.05 pastel prov. 3-Dec-2 Joyner, Toronto #98/R est:20000-25000 (C.D 11000)

SUZUKI, James (1933-) Japanese
£252 $400 €378 Tako (46x36cm-18x14in) s.i. painted c.1960. 2-Mar-3 Toomey, Oak Park #800/R
£256 $400 €384 Tako (46x36cm-18x14in) s. exhib. 10-Nov-2 Selkirks, St. Louis #613

SUZUKI, Shintaro (1895-1989) Japanese
Works on paper
£256 $400 €384 Figures by the shore (19x25cm-7x10in) s.d.1937 mixed media board. 9-Nov-2 Sloan, North Bethesda #553/R
£353 $550 €530 House with fire hydrant (30x39cm-12x15in) s.d.1934 W/C white black conti. 9-Nov-2 Sloan, North Bethesda #552/R

SUZUKI, Toshiyuki (1935-) Japanese
£1282 $2013 €2000 Composition (53x83cm-21x33in) s.d.1971 oil mixed media paper. 23-Nov-2 Meeting Art, Vercelli #85/R
Works on paper
£694 $1104 €1000 Butterflies (59x44cm-23x17in) s.d.1971 mixed media card. 1-May-3 Meeting Art, Vercelli #386

SVABINSKY, Max (1873-1962) Czechoslovakian
Works on paper
£537 $838 €806 Portrait of a young lady (43x36cm-17x14in) s.d.904 chl white chk double-sided. 12-Oct-2 Dorotheum, Prague #217/R (C.KR 26000)

SVANBERG, Max Walter (1912-1995) Swedish
Works on paper
£446 $709 €669 Composition with women (44x35cm-17x14in) s.indis.d. mixed media. 3-Mar-3 Lilla Bukowskis, Stockholm #581 (S.KR 6000)
£510 $786 €765 Imaginary female figure (45x37cm-18x15in) s. gouache. 27-Oct-2 Anders Antik, Landskrona #519/R (S.KR 7400)
£857 $1337 €1286 Le corps en fleur de la journee rouge (43x34cm-17x13in) s.i.d.62 mixed media collage on lithograph. 13-Sep-2 Lilla Bukowskis, Stockholm #292 (S.KR 12500)
£8904 $13890 €13000 La grossesse etrange de la rencontre etrange (46x38cm-18x15in) s.d.53 ink exhib.lit. 14-Apr-3 Laurence Calmels, Paris #4004/R est:2000

SVANLUND, Olle (1909-1996) Swedish
£266 $421 €399 Fishermen in harbour (70x80cm-28x31in) s.d.47. 30-Nov-2 Goteborg Auktionsverk, Sweden #643/R (S.KR 3800)

SVEINSDOTTIR, Juliana (1889-1966) Icelandic
£957 $1550 €1388 Landscape with thatched house (59x68cm-23x27in) s. 24-May-3 Rasmussen, Havnen #4070 (D.KR 10000)
£1185 $1837 €1778 Waterfall among mountains (49x55cm-19x22in) s. 1-Oct-2 Rasmussen, Copenhagen #364 est:8000 (D.KR 14000)

SVENDSEN, Frederik (1885-1975) Danish
£239 $375 €359 Cottages with chickens (30x41cm-12x16in) s. 23-Nov-2 Jackson's, Cedar Falls #31/R

SVENDSEN, Georg Anton (1846-1882) Danish
£670 $1085 €1005 A visitor - bluetit visiting the nest of a wren (26x26cm-10x10in) init.d.81 lit. 21-May-3 Museumsbygningen, Copenhagen #17/R (D.KR 7000)

SVENDSEN, Svend (1864-1934) Norwegian/American
£272 $425 €408 Winter (64x43cm-25x17in) 30-Mar-3 Susanin's, Chicago #6015/R
£353 $550 €530 Winter (23x43cm-9x17in) canvas on board. 30-Mar-3 Susanin's, Chicago #6012/R
£355 $550 €533 Path through the snow (61x46cm-24x18in) s. painted c.1900. 8-Dec-2 Toomey, Oak Park #735/R
£387 $600 €581 Fire's glow (61x46cm-24x18in) s. painted c.1900. 8-Dec-2 Toomey, Oak Park #750/R
£535 $850 €803 Dusk (28x36cm-11x14in) s. board painted c.1900. 2-Mar-3 Toomey, Oak Park #606/R

£692 $1100 €1038 Tall ship off the coast (53x76cm-21x30in) s. painted c.1915. 4-May-3 Treadway Gallery, Cincinnati #508/R
£750 $1200 €1088 Winter light (81x61cm-32x24in) s. 16-May-3 Skinner, Boston #259/R
£974 $1500 €1461 Winter landscape (46x61cm-18x24in) s. painted c.1900. 8-Sep-2 Treadway Gallery, Cincinnati #639/R est:2000-3000

SVENSSON, Christian Fredrik (1834-1909) Swedish
£316 $492 €474 Seascape with vessel and man in rowing boat (66x47cm-26x19in) s. 13-Sep-2 Lilla Bukowskis, Stockholm #61 (S.KR 4600)
£469 $751 €680 Sailing boat and breakers (30x45cm-12x18in) s. 18-May-3 Anders Antik, Landskrona #86 (S.KR 6000)
£590 $897 €885 From the skerries, Stockholm (75x125cm-30x49in) s.d.1883. 16-Aug-2 Lilla Bukowskis, Stockholm #19 (S.KR 8600)
£1489 $2309 €2234 Fishing vessels (69x130cm-27x51in) s. 8-Dec-2 Uppsala Auktionskammare, Uppsala #110/R est:20000-25000 (S.KR 21000)
£1862 $3016 €2700 Seascape with sailing vessel Af Chapman (48x68cm-19x27in) s. 26-May-3 Bukowskis, Stockholm #96/R est:15000-20000 (S.KR 24000)
£2183 $3515 €3100 Summer cottage (75x124cm-30x49in) s.d.1883. 10-May-3 Bukowskis, Helsinki #356/R est:3000-4000
£2560 $4147 €3712 Seascape with Vanadis returning from West Indies (60x89cm-24x35in) s.d.79. 26-May-3 Bukowskis, Stockholm #14/R est:30000-35000 (S.KR 33000)
£3121 $4837 €4682 The steam boat Vanadis (48x87cm-19x34in) s. 3-Dec-2 Bukowskis, Stockholm #239/R est:30000-35000 (S.KR 44000)

SVENSSON, Gunnar (1892-1977) Swedish
£615 $959 €923 Le Sacre-Coeur a Montmartre (51x61cm-20x24in) s. 10-Sep-2 Iegor de Saint Hippolyte, Montreal #109 (C.D 1500)
£771 $1203 €1157 Summer landscape from near Stockholm (48x61cm-19x24in) s. panel exhib. 6-Nov-2 AB Stockholms Auktionsverk #690/R (S.KR 11000)
£927 $1492 €1391 Still life of jugs and flowers (65x81cm-26x32in) s. 7-May-3 AB Stockholms Auktionsverk #661/R (S.KR 12000)
£1086 $1694 €1629 Still life of flowers (73x92cm-29x36in) s. 6-Nov-2 AB Stockholms Auktionsverk #646/R est:10000-12000 (S.KR 15500)
£2548 $4103 €3822 Still life of wild flowers (55x45cm-22x18in) s. panel exhib.prov. 7-May-3 AB Stockholms Auktionsverk #816/R est:25000-30000 (S.KR 33000)

SVENSSON, Roland (1910-) Swedish
£386 $641 €560 The studio at Mejan (46x55cm-18x22in) s.d.1937. 16-Jun-3 Lilla Bukowskis, Stockholm #614 (S.KR 5000)
Works on paper
£301 $500 €436 Nimba Range (27x44cm-11x17in) s.d.1969 W/C. 16-Jun-3 Lilla Bukowskis, Stockholm #613 (S.KR 3900)
£888 $1474 €1288 Archipelago (16x31cm-6x12in) s. pastel. 16-Jun-3 Lilla Bukowskis, Stockholm #463 (S.KR 11500)
£943 $1546 €1367 On the Waxholm boat (12x21cm-5x8in) s. mixed media. 4-Jun-3 AB Stockholms Auktionsverk #2343/R (S.KR 12000)
£1433 $2321 €2150 Stora Nassa (28x42cm-11x17in) s. W/C. 3-Feb-3 Lilla Bukowskis, Stockholm #198 est:15000 (S.KR 20000)
£1844 $2858 €2766 Kaninholm - winter in the skerries (26x42cm-10x17in) s.d.45.2 pastel panel. 4-Dec-2 AB Stockholms Auktionsverk #1640/R est:15000-20000 (S.KR 26000)
£1915 $2968 €2873 Morning in Kejsarhamn, Bomarsund at Aaland (24x44cm-9x17in) s.d.1967 W/C. 4-Dec-2 AB Stockholms Auktionsverk #1796/R est:30000-35000 (S.KR 27000)

SVENUNGSSON, Jan (1961-) Swedish
Works on paper
£385 $601 €578 Study for Phycho-Mapping Europe No.12 (76x57cm-30x22in) s.d.1989 W/C Indian ink. 6-Nov-2 AB Stockholms Auktionsverk #859/R (S.KR 5500)

SVERTSCHKOFF, Nicolas Gregorovitch (1817-1898) Russian
£12579 $19371 €20000 Rushing home (46x78cm-18x31in) s. 23-Oct-2 Christie's, Amsterdam #94/R est:7000-9000
£19000 $29830 €28500 Drawing water from the well (50x73cm-20x29in) s. 20-Nov-2 Sotheby's, London #21/R est:15000-20000
£24000 $37680 €36000 Monkeys (36x54cm-14x21in) s.d.1896. 20-Nov-2 Sotheby's, London #16/R est:8000-12000
£30000 $47100 €45000 Transporting the horses (77x120cm-30x47in) s.d.1858. 20-Nov-2 Sotheby's, London #13/R est:40000-60000
£52564 $81474 €82000 Wolf pack seizing a Russian horse sledge in snow-covered landscape (81x130cm-32x51in) s.d.1864. 4-Dec-2 Neumeister, Munich #922/R est:10000
£79137 $126619 €110000 Hunters on the steppe (102x160cm-40x63in) s.d.1873. 17-May-3 Hagelstam, Helsinki #31/R est:65000
Works on paper
£7000 $11340 €10500 Carriage with four horses (17x30cm-7x12in) s.i.d.1863 W/C over pencil. 21-May-3 Sotheby's, London #28/R est:1500-2000

SVETOSLAVSKY, Sergei Ivanovich (1857-1931) Russian
£1150 $1817 €1725 Street scene in Samarkand (41x61cm-16x24in) s. board. 27-Nov-2 Bonhams, Knowle #217
£7801 $12638 €11000 Interesting novelty (45x62cm-18x24in) s.verso. 22-May-3 Dorotheum, Vienna #200/R est:4000-5000

SVIRIDOV, Sergei (1964-) Russian
£387 $612 €600 Table in the garden (33x41cm-13x16in) s. 17-Dec-2 Durán, Madrid #671/R
£550 $853 €825 Terrace in Nice (50x61cm-20x24in) s. 29-Sep-2 John Nicholson, Haslemere #75/R
£597 $920 €950 Terrace (52x65cm-20x26in) s. 22-Oct-2 Durán, Madrid #703/R
£650 $1007 €975 Sunny terrace in Crimea (50x61cm-20x24in) s. 29-Sep-2 John Nicholson, Haslemere #79
£700 $1085 €1050 Terrace with wild rose (50x61cm-20x24in) s. 8-Dec-2 John Nicholson, Haslemere #188/R

SVOBODA, Jaroslav (1879-?) Czechoslovakian
£394 $559 €591 In the autumn woods (89x89cm-35x35in) painted c.1920. 26-Mar-2 SOGA, Bratislava #208/R (SL.K 25000)
£441 $626 €662 Tatra mountains (89x89cm-35x35in) painted c.1920. 26-Mar-2 SOGA, Bratislava #207/R (SL.K 28000)

SVOLINSKY, Karel (1896-1986) Czechoslovakian?
Works on paper
£341 $552 €512 Fire bird (24x29cm-9x11in) s.d.1942 ink W/C. 24-May-3 Dorotheum, Prague #169/R est:6000-9000 (C.KR 15000)

SWABIAN SCHOOL (15th C) German
Works on paper
£80247 $130000 €120371 Christ as the gardener (24x11cm-9x4in) i. pen ink. 22-Jan-3 Christie's, Rockefeller NY #84/R est:120000

SWABIAN SCHOOL (16th C) German
Sculpture
£11538 $18231 €18000 Proclamation (80x9cm-31x4in) wood. 16-Nov-2 Lempertz, Koln #1156/R est:8500

SWAEN, Hugo (1825-1910) Dutch
£282 $437 €440 Couple in romantic forest landscape (26x19cm-10x7in) s.d.1862 board lit. 7-Dec-2 Bergmann, Erlangen #819/R

SWAGEMAKERS, Theo (1898-1994) Dutch
£278 $458 €400 Still life with pears (24x32cm-9x13in) s.d.71 board prov. 1-Jul-3 Christie's, Amsterdam #416
£590 $974 €850 Flowers in a white jug (32x25cm-13x10in) s.d.73 board prov. 1-Jul-3 Christie's, Amsterdam #419
£694 $1146 €1000 Pink roses in a glass vase (35x30cm-14x12in) s. board prov. 1-Jul-3 Christie's, Amsterdam #412
£972 $1604 €1400 Still life with teapot and roses in a white vase (50x60cm-20x24in) s. board. 1-Jul-3 Christie's, Amsterdam #485/R

SWAGERS, Frans (1756-1836) Dutch
£1026 $1621 €1600 Landscape with cattle resting (20x29cm-8x11in) bears i. panel. 16-Nov-2 Lempertz, Koln #1110/R est:2000
£1026 $1621 €1600 Landscape with cattle and young herdress (20x29cm-8x11in) panel. 16-Nov-2 Lempertz, Koln #1111/R est:2000
£1474 $2315 €2300 Couple de vachers et son troupeau au bord de la riviere (47x56cm-19x22in) s. 19-Nov-2 Vanderkindere, Brussels #438/R est:2000-3000
£2000 $3120 €3000 Hunter and his dogs in a wooded river landscape, windmill and boats beyond (32x24cm-13x9in) s. 10-Apr-3 Christie's, Kensington #138/R est:2000-3000
£3448 $5483 €5000 Bateaux sur l'estuaire (22x39cm-9x15in) s.d.1787 panel. 5-Mar-3 Doutrebente, Paris #23/R est:4000-4500
£4516 $7135 €7000 Marine aux abords d'une ville hollandaise (50x69cm-20x27in) s. 18-Dec-2 Piasa, Paris #60/R
£4828 $7676 €7000 Vue d'un estuaire en Hollande (31x40cm-12x16in) s.d.1787 panel. 5-Mar-3 Doutrebente, Paris #22/R est:5000-6000
£9859 $15873 €14000 Village view with figures, cows, horses and sheep (46x58cm-18x23in) s. panel. 12-May-3 Bernaerts, Antwerp #620/R est:15000-18000

SWAGERS, Frans (attrib) (1756-1836) Dutch
£3459 $5327 €5500 Paysage pastoral pres d'un rivage hollandais (38x45cm-15x18in) s. panel pair. 25-Oct-2 Tajan, Paris #46/R est:3000-4000

SWAINE, Francis (1740-1782) British

£750 $1215 €1125 Announcing the arrival off a fortified town (29x46cm-11x18in) s. 21-May-3 Christie's, Kensington #531/R
£1921 $2997 €2882 Man-o'-war off the coast (15x20cm-6x8in) s. copper prov. 9-Nov-2 Galerie Gloggner, Luzern #139/R est:2000-2500 (S.FR 4400)
£2183 $3406 €3275 Morning gun (15x20cm-6x8in) s. copper prov. 9-Nov-2 Galerie Gloggner, Luzern #140/R est:2000-2500 (S.FR 5000)
£2800 $4536 €4200 Men-o'war in the Channel (16x20cm-6x8in) s. copper. 21-May-3 Christie's, Kensington #526/R est:2500-3000
£3000 $4680 €4500 Morning gun (15x20cm-6x8in) copper. 26-Mar-3 Hamptons Fine Art, Godalming #150/R est:3000-4000
£3600 $5832 €5400 Men-o'war in coastal waters. Shipping riding out a gale (16x20cm-6x8in) s. copper pair. 21-May-3 Christie's, Kensington #532/R est:4000-6000
£7500 $11400 €11250 British squadron reefed down in a gale (15x20cm-6x8in) s. copper. 15-Aug-2 Bonhams, New Bond Street #387/R est:5000-7000

Works on paper

£400 $648 €600 Study of warships (16x21cm-6x8in) pen grey ink wash. 21-May-3 Christie's, Kensington #356/R

SWAINE, Francis (attrib) (1740-1782) British

£700 $1127 €1015 Tilbury Fort, figures unloading a boat (13x17cm-5x7in) 7-May-3 Gorringes, Bexhill #906

SWAINSON, William (fl.1884-1888) British

Works on paper

£273 $420 €410 My cottage from the valley, Dandinory ? police station (19x13cm-7x5in) i.d.25 July 1853 pencil dr. 4-Sep-2 Dunbar Sloane, Wellington #61 (NZ.D 900)
£614 $958 €921 Great black fern, Lower Hutt Valley. Akiaki Tree of the New Zealanders (18x11cm-7x4in) s. one d.1848 one d.1849 dr pair. 27-Mar-3 International Art Centre, Auckland #93/R (NZ.D 1750)

SWAMINATHAN, Jagdish (1928-1993) Indian

£10101 $16667 €14646 Mountain, tree and bird series (82x65cm-32x26in) 6-Jul-3 Christie's, Hong Kong #89/R est:85000-100000 (HK.D 130000)

SWAN, Douglas (1930-) American

£278 $442 €400 Composition (100x70cm-39x28in) s.d.1961. 1-May-3 Meeting Art, Vercelli #369

SWAN, John (20th C) American

£12025 $19000 €17436 River guide (61x91cm-24x36in) s. 26-Jul-3 Coeur d'Alene, Hayden #114/R est:15000-25000

SWAN, John Macallan (1847-1910) British

£14000 $22540 €21000 Piping fisher boy (31x42cm-12x17in) s. panel prov.exhib.lit. 20-Feb-3 Christie's, London #203/R est:15000

Sculpture

£2000 $3240 €3000 Lioness (12cm-5in) s.i.num.2 bronze. 20-May-3 Sotheby's, Olympia #117/R est:600-800

Works on paper

£500 $825 €725 Study of a leopard feeding (15x21cm-6x8in) s. col chk prov. 3-Jul-3 Christie's, Kensington #163
£550 $858 €825 Lioness. Lions wrestling (20x33cm-8x13in) s. chl col chk two. 15-Oct-2 Gorringes, Lewes #2173/R
£4000 $6560 €5800 Study of a sleeping tiger (24x35cm-9x14in) s. col chk prov. 5-Jun-3 Christie's, London #114/R est:1500-2000

SWAN, John Macallan and WARDLE, Arthur (19/20th C) British

£300 $471 €450 Old adversaries, leopard and a snake (29x46cm-11x18in) s. 24-Jul-2 Hamptons Fine Art, Godalming #244

SWAN, Robert John (1888-1980) British

£1456 $2300 €2300 Lioness with cubs (62x106cm-24x42in) s. lit. 29-Nov-2 Schloss Ahlden, Ahlden #1338/R est:2200

SWANE, Christine (1876-1960) Danish

£311 $494 €467 Street scene (35x46cm-14x18in) i.stretcher painted c.1921. 26-Feb-3 Kunsthallen, Copenhagen #336 (D.KR 3400)
£384 $610 €576 Summer landscape with view of the sea (40x50cm-16x20in) init.d.1957. 26-Feb-3 Kunsthallen, Copenhagen #271/R (D.KR 4200)
£389 $599 €584 Summer landscape (58x66cm-23x26in) init. 23-Oct-2 Kunsthallen, Copenhagen #61 (D.KR 4600)
£575 $885 €863 View from Holtbjerge, Vendsussel (60x75cm-24x30in) init.d.1954 exhib. 23-Oct-2 Kunsthallen, Copenhagen #108/R (D.KR 6800)
£700 $1112 €1050 Still life of bottles on window ledge (45x55cm-18x22in) init. s.d.1955 verso. 5-May-3 Rasmussen, Vejle #1/R (D.KR 7500)
£2323 $3671 €3485 Green plants (130x85cm-51x33in) mono. exhib. 1-Apr-3 Rasmussen, Copenhagen #72/R est:30000 (D.KR 25000)

Works on paper

£326 $518 €489 Still life of potted plant, mug and carafe (60x47cm-24x19in) init.d.1945 pen W/C. 10-Mar-3 Rasmussen, Vejle #567/R (D.KR 3500)

SWANE, Lars (1913-2002) Danish

£255 $398 €383 The light house at Fynshoved (65x75cm-26x30in) s. 5-Aug-2 Rasmussen, Vejle #2331 (D.KR 3000)
£272 $424 €408 View through pine trees towards small house (51x41cm-20x16in) s. 5-Aug-2 Rasmussen, Vejle #2034 (D.KR 3200)
£274 $428 €411 Coastal landscape, Lundsgaard Klint from Kerteminde (65x75cm-26x30in) s.d.58. 11-Nov-2 Rasmussen, Vejle #63/R (D.KR 3200)
£279 $441 €419 Landscape with houses in background (90x100cm-35x39in) init.d.45 s.d.1944 verso. 1-Apr-3 Rasmussen, Copenhagen #499 (D.KR 3000)
£309 $482 €464 Landscape (46x55cm-18x22in) s.d.59. 11-Nov-2 Rasmussen, Vejle #56/R (D.KR 3600)
£350 $560 €525 View of fields from a hilltop (75x90cm-30x35in) s.d.65. 13-Jan-3 Rasmussen, Vejle #283 (D.KR 4000)
£372 $587 €558 Landscape (67x99cm-26x39in) s.d.1985. 5-Apr-3 Rasmussen, Havnen #4162 (D.KR 4000)
£525 $841 €788 Landscape with fields and farm, storm approaching (101x121cm-40x48in) s.d.57. 13-Jan-3 Rasmussen, Vejle #2265 (D.KR 6000)

SWANE, Sigurd (1879-1973) Danish

£254 $394 €381 Landscape, Portugal (32x38cm-13x15in) init. masonite. 1-Oct-2 Rasmussen, Copenhagen #284 (D.KR 3000)
£254 $394 €381 Landscape, Southern Europe (53x56cm-21x22in) init. 1-Oct-2 Rasmussen, Copenhagen #367 (D.KR 3000)
£270 $417 €405 House, Plejerup (46x55cm-18x22in) init. 23-Oct-2 Kunsthallen, Copenhagen #78 (D.KR 3200)
£290 $449 €435 Village street (68x68cm-27x27in) init.d.33. 28-Sep-2 Rasmussen, Havnen #2168 (D.KR 3400)
£322 $534 €467 Fyrregrene in bojan (54x61cm-21x24in) 12-Jun-3 Kunsthallen, Copenhagen #275 (D.KR 3400)
£335 $529 €503 Landscape with trees and house in background (60x47cm-24x19in) init. 1-Apr-3 Rasmussen, Copenhagen #649 (D.KR 3600)
£339 $525 €509 Water carrier in Spanish landscape (65x68cm-26x27in) init. 1-Oct-2 Rasmussen, Copenhagen #371 (D.KR 4000)
£353 $558 €530 Still life of flowers in jug (46x31cm-18x12in) init. painted april 1968. 1-Apr-3 Rasmussen, Copenhagen #533 (D.KR 3800)
£355 $547 €533 Tulips in glass vase (40x30cm-16x12in) init. 23-Oct-2 Kunsthallen, Copenhagen #54 (D.KR 4200)
£372 $587 €558 Still life of narcissus (54x33cm-21x13in) init. 1-Apr-3 Rasmussen, Copenhagen #625 (D.KR 4000)
£395 $615 €593 Canal view with figures (33x41cm-13x16in) init.d.37. 11-Nov-2 Rasmussen, Vejle #38 (D.KR 4600)
£406 $625 €609 Flower picture (53x51cm-21x20in) init.d.1915. 23-Oct-2 Kunsthallen, Copenhagen #122 (D.KR 4800)
£432 $696 €648 Wooded landscape with house in background (71x71cm-28x28in) init. 22-Feb-3 Rasmussen, Havnen #2241 (D.KR 4800)
£446 $705 €669 South European landscape (51x61cm-20x24in) init. 1-Apr-3 Rasmussen, Copenhagen #618 (D.KR 4800)
£465 $716 €698 Spring landscape (52x75cm-20x30in) init.d.35. 23-Oct-2 Kunsthallen, Copenhagen #137 (D.KR 5500)
£591 $922 €887 Village street in Spain (73x70cm-29x28in) init. exhib. 18-Sep-2 Kunsthallen, Copenhagen #33 (D.KR 7000)
£600 $937 €900 Town scene with figures, Portugal (57x65cm-22x26in) init. exhib. 11-Nov-2 Rasmussen, Vejle #19/R (D.KR 7000)
£617 $963 €926 Field landscape with trees (60x73cm-24x29in) init.d.35. 11-Nov-2 Rasmussen, Vejle #47/R (D.KR 7200)
£652 $1036 €978 Ro - half-timbered farm (96x119cm-38x47in) init.d.33 i.d.1933 verso. 4-Mar-3 Museumsbygningen, Copenhagen #558 (D.KR 7000)
£725 $1145 €1088 Still life of flowers (56x44cm-22x17in) init.d.37. 1-Apr-3 Rasmussen, Copenhagen #584/R (D.KR 7800)
£763 $1274 €1106 Green landscape (34x31cm-13x12in) init. 17-Jun-3 Rasmussen, Copenhagen #194/R (D.KR 8000)
£933 $1483 €1400 Fjord landscape (70x80cm-28x31in) init. 5-May-3 Rasmussen, Vejle #54/R (D.KR 10000)
£1673 $2643 €2510 Still life of yellow and red flowers (67x51cm-26x20in) s.d.36 exhib. 1-Apr-3 Rasmussen, Copenhagen #87/R est:18000 (D.KR 18000)
£1860 $2864 €2790 Sunshine through trees (119x128cm-47x50in) init. 23-Oct-2 Kunsthallen, Copenhagen #68/R est:15000 (D.KR 22000)
£1860 $2864 €2790 Still life of flowers in vase (69x74cm-27x29in) init.d.29. 23-Oct-2 Kunsthallen, Copenhagen #95/R est:10000 (D.KR 22000)

SWANE, Sigurd (attrib) (1879-1973) Danish

£699 $1132 €1014 Portrait of the vicar Bechman's wife in Vaerslev (60x56cm-24x22in) prov. 24-May-3 Rasmussen, Havnen #4161 (D.KR 7300)

SWANENBURGH, Isaac Claesz van (attrib) (1538-1614) Flemish

£26415 $40679 €42000 Peasant celebrations (108x218cm-43x86in) s.d.1608. 28-Oct-2 Il Ponte, Milan #82/R est:25000

SWANENBURGH, Jacob Isaacsz (1571-1638) Flemish

£37037 $60000 €55556 Hell (49x71cm-19x28in) copper prov. 24-Jan-3 Christie's, Rockefeller NY #17/R est:20000-30000

SWANENBURGH, Jacob Isaacsz (circle) (1571-1638) Flemish

£5096 $7949 €8000 Underworld (19x25cm-7x10in) indis mono. copper. 6-Nov-2 Christie's, Amsterdam #51/R est:8000-12000

SWANEVELT, Herman van (1600-1655) Dutch

£1000 $1610 €1500 Peasant before a barn (33x38cm-13x15in) mono.d.1650. 20-Feb-3 Christie's, Kensington #268/R est:2000-3000
£9487 $14895 €14800 Figures in landscape (67x93cm-26x37in) s.i.d.1656. 13-Dec-2 Rossini, Paris #150 est:12000
£9615 $14904 €15000 Stormy landscape (47x64cm-19x25in) s.i.indis.d. panel lit. 4-Dec-2 Neumeister, Munich #643/R est:9000
£22000 $34320 €33000 Italianate river landscape with travellers conversing on a path and peasants fishing from a boat (77x102cm-30x40in) s.i.d.1654. 9-Apr-3 Christie's, London #42/R est:10000-15000
£35000 $58450 €50750 Southern landscape with fisherman and figures conversing on a road (127x174cm-50x69in) s.i.indis.d. prov. 10-Jul-3 Sotheby's, London #54/R est:30000-50000

Works on paper

£3704 $6000 €5556 Wooded river landscape with angel (22x20cm-9x8in) pen ink wash prov. 21-Jan-3 Sotheby's, New York #64/R

SWANEVELT, Herman van (circle) (1600-1655) Dutch

£14764 $23770 €22000 Classical landscape with the rest on the Flight into Egypt (47x66cm-19x26in) prov.lit. 18-Feb-3 Sotheby's, Amsterdam #220/R est:6000-8000

SWANSON, Garry R (1914-) American

£6289 $10000 €9434 Big horn sheep (76x61cm-30x24in) s.i. masonite on panel prov. 4-Mar-3 Christie's, Rockefeller NY #92/R est:5000-7000

SWANSON, Ray (1937-) American

£8220 $12000 €12330 Navajo babies (66x102cm-26x40in) 18-May-2 Altermann Galleries, Santa Fe #102/R
£9615 $15000 €14423 Her first baby girl (102x76cm-40x30in) 9-Nov-2 Altermann Galleries, Santa Fe #82
£9938 $16100 €14410 Drum chant (66x76cm-26x30in) 26. 23-May-3 Altermann Galleries, Santa Fe #45
£23973 $35000 €35960 Shearing the Churro sheep (132x157cm-52x62in) 18-May-2 Altermann Galleries, Santa Fe #101/R

SWANWICK, Betty (1915-1989) British

Works on paper

£3600 $5904 €5400 Net (39x63cm-15x25in) s. s.i.backboard pencil W/C. 3-Jun-3 Sotheby's, Olympia #110/R est:800-1200

SWANWICK, Harold (1866-1929) British

£1778 $2951 €2578 Children with their dog near forest fence (39x57cm-15x22in) s. 10-Jun-3 Ritchie, Toronto #42/R est:2000-2500 (C.D 4000)

Works on paper

£1600 $2512 €2400 Last gleam, Silver Strand, North of Peel, Isle of Man (75x125cm-30x49in) s.d.1894 W/C. 16-Dec-2 Sotheby's, Olympia #113/R est:800-1200
£1650 $2558 €2475 The end of the day (18x25cm-7x10in) s.d.1893 W/C htd gum arabic exhib. 2-Oct-2 Bonhams, Knowle #49 est:500-800
£5800 $9280 €8700 Farmyard, early morning (65x110cm-26x43in) s.d.1901 W/C prov. 11-Mar-3 Bonhams, New Bond Street #69/R est:4000-6000

SWANZY, Mary (1882-1978) Irish

£3767 $5914 €5500 Irish landscape (31x42cm-12x17in) s. i.verso canvas on board. 15-Apr-3 De Veres Art Auctions, Dublin #153/R est:6000-9000
£5137 $8065 €7500 Path by a large tree (50x42cm-20x17in) prov. 15-Apr-3 De Veres Art Auctions, Dublin #142/R est:8000-10000
£14493 $23768 €20000 Allegory (63x71cm-25x28in) prov.exhib.lit. 28-May-3 Bonhams & James Adam, Dublin #88/R est:20000-30000

Works on paper

£950 $1520 €1425 At the market (18x24cm-7x9in) s.d.6 col pencil. 15-May-3 Christie's, Kensington #161/R
£1233 $1936 €1800 Street scene, South of France (25x19cm-10x7in) crayon prov. 15-Apr-3 De Veres Art Auctions, Dublin #190/R est:1200-1800
£1370 $2151 €2000 Giant palm tree, Samoa (25x19cm-10x7in) crayon. 15-Apr-3 De Veres Art Auctions, Dublin #197/R est:1200-1800

SWANZY, Mary (attrib) (1882-1978) Irish

£2900 $4727 €4350 Cubist coastal houses (11x17cm-4x7in) s. board. 12-Feb-3 Andrew Hartley, Ilkley #945 est:800-1200

SWART, Cristianus Hendricus de (1818-1897) Dutch

£1477 $2377 €2200 Summer landscape. Winter landscape (73x95cm-29x37in) s.d.1849 pair. 18-Feb-3 Sotheby's, Amsterdam #427a est:1500-2500

SWEATMAN, Jo (1872-1956) Australian

£640 $1030 €928 Country town (35x48cm-14x19in) s. 12-May-3 Joel, Victoria #311 est:1500-2000 (A.D 1600)

SWEBACH, Bernard Edouard (1800-1870) French

Works on paper

£449 $704 €700 Cavalier (18x30cm-7x12in) s. W/C. 11-Dec-2 Maigret, Paris #101/R
£655 $1042 €950 Cheval au trot (18x30cm-7x12in) W/C. 10-Mar-3 Coutau Begarie, Paris #124

SWEBACH-DESFONTAINES, Jacques François (1769-1823) French

£2484 $3875 €3900 Choc de cavalerie. Convoi (12x25cm-5x10in) s.d.1790 panel pair. 8-Nov-2 Pierre Berge, Paris #25/R
£2581 $4078 €4000 Halte de cavaliers (31x34cm-12x13in) panel. 18-Dec-2 Tajan, Paris #48/R est:6000

Works on paper

£1090 $1689 €1700 Assassinat de Le Pelletier (19x24cm-7x9in) pen W/C dr. 4-Dec-2 Libert, Castor, Paris #23/R
£1351 $2108 €2000 Foire (25x33cm-10x13in) s.d.1792 pen ink wash W/C gouache. 26-Mar-3 Piasa, Paris #78/R
£2532 $3949 €4000 Charge de cavalerie (26x35cm-10x14in) s.d.1792 pen Chinese ink htd white gouache. 18-Oct-2 Rabourdin & Choppin de Janvry, Paris #99/R

SWEBACH-DESFONTAINES, Jacques François (attrib) (1769-1823) French

Works on paper

£1560 $2528 €2200 La charrette du tonnelier dans un paysage (25x35cm-10x14in) pen W/C. 23-May-3 Beaussant & Lefèvre, Paris #48/R est:800-1200
£1773 $2872 €2500 Personnages dans la campagne pres d'une villa (24x35cm-9x14in) bears mono. pen W/C. 23-May-3 Beaussant & Lefèvre, Paris #47/R est:800-1200

SWEDLUND, Pelle (1865-1947) Swedish

£1135 $1759 €1703 Harbour scene (72x90cm-28x35in) init.d.03. 4-Dec-2 AB Stockholms Auktionsverk #1737/R est:20000-25000 (S.KR 16000)

SWEDMAN, Carl Wilhelm (1762-1840) Swedish

£1418 $2199 €2127 The Golden Calf - Book of Moses Chap.32 (131x103cm-52x41in) exhib. 3-Dec-2 Bukowskis, Stockholm #415/R est:25000-30000 (S.KR 20000)

SWEELINK, Gerrit Pietersz (1566-1645) Dutch

£797 $1307 €1100 La fuite en Egypte (41x55cm-16x22in) panel. 27-May-3 Campo & Campo, Antwerp #221

SWEERTS, Michiel (1618-1664) Flemish

£20144 $32230 €28000 Elegant hunting company resting (62x77cm-24x30in) 13-May-3 Sotheby's, Amsterdam #40/R est:20000-30000
£40000 $66800 €58000 Artist sketching by a fountain (64x88cm-25x35in) prov.lit. 9-Jul-3 Christie's, London #38/R est:40000-60000

SWEET, W H (20th C) British

Works on paper

£300 $465 €450 Scene of the Valley of Rocks, Lynmouth (52x17cm-20x7in) W/C. 30-Oct-2 Bonhams, Knowle #257

SWEET, Walter H (1889-1943) British

Works on paper

£300 $477 €450 Figures on a lane passing a thatched cottage (18x25cm-7x10in) s. W/C. 29-Apr-3 Gorringes, Lewes #2038
£300 $501 €435 Dunster (27x37cm-11x15in) s. W/C. 19-Jun-3 Lane, Penzance #254
£360 $569 €522 Seaton (18x25cm-7x10in) s. W/C. 23-Jul-3 Mallams, Oxford #198/R

£430 $671 €645 Beer (25x35cm-10x14in) s. W/C. 17-Sep-2 Bearnes, Exeter #483
£500 $810 €750 Clovelly, Devon (35x25cm-14x10in) s. W/C. 21-Jan-3 Bonhams, Knightsbridge #297/R
£620 $1017 €930 Corner of Frog Street, Exeter (36x26cm-14x10in) s. W/C. 7-Feb-3 Honiton Galleries, Honiton #352/R
£667 $1107 €967 Penzance from Newlyn (25x36cm-10x14in) s. W/C. 16-Jun-3 Waddingtons, Toronto #66/R est:700-900 (C.D 1500)
£711 $1180 €1031 Woman and child outside cottage. Old courtyard in Cathedral Close, Exeter (35x25cm-14x10in) s. W/C two. 16-Jun-3 Waddingtons, Toronto #52/R est:1000-1500 (C.D 1600)
£1018 $1608 €1527 Fisherman's cottage, Mousehole near Penzance (34x25cm-13x10in) s. W/C. 18-Nov-2 Joel, Victoria #384 est:4000-5000 (A.D 2850)
£1156 $1918 €1676 Newlyn, near the harbour. Mousehole. St.Ives (28x18cm-11x7in) s.i.verso W/C set of three. 16-Jun-3 Waddingtons, Toronto #48/R est:1200-1500 (C.D 2600)

SWERINGEN, Ron van (1936-) American
£1282 $2000 €1923 Girl with poodle (76x46cm-30x18in) 1-Aug-2 Eldred, East Dennis #150/R est:1800-2000

SWERINGEN, Ron van (attrib) (1936-) American
£304 $475 €456 Trotter and sulky (30x41cm-12x16in) board. 1-Aug-2 Eldred, East Dennis #151
£416 $650 €624 Still life (41x51cm-16x20in) board. 1-Aug-2 Eldred, East Dennis #158/R
£769 $1200 €1154 Allegorical portrait of Diana, Goddess of the hunt (69x56cm-27x22in) 1-Aug-2 Eldred, East Dennis #157/R
£1026 $1600 €1539 Lady with parrot (71x56cm-28x22in) 1-Aug-2 Eldred, East Dennis #149/R est:1200-1800

SWERTOHKAW, Nicolas de (19th C) French?
Works on paper
£385 $608 €600 Voyage en fiacre (17x30cm-7x12in) s.i.d. W/C. 14-Nov-2 Credit Municipal, Paris #31

SWERTS, Jan (1820-1879) Belgian
£688 $1129 €950 Scene de famille (100x90cm-39x35in) s. 27-May-3 Campo & Campo, Antwerp #222

SWERTSCHKOFF, George (20th C) German
Works on paper
£650 $1079 €943 Head of a bridled racehorse (20x24cm-8x9in) s.i.d.1909 W/C htd white. 12-Jun-3 Christie's, Kensington #76a

SWETSCHNIKOV, A (19th C) ?
£1282 $2013 €2000 Portrait of young woman wearing headscarf (80x90cm-31x35in) s.d.1865. 21-Nov-2 Van Ham, Cologne #1938/R est:6000

SWIESZEWSKI, Alexander (1839-1895) Polish
£1019 $1590 €1600 Southern lake landscape (34x54cm-13x21in) mono. 6-Nov-2 Hugo Ruef, Munich #1283/R est:800
£1831 $3039 €2600 On Bodensee (16x32cm-6x13in) panel. 14-Jun-3 Arnold, Frankfurt #878/R est:1600
£4430 $7000 €7000 Travelling in wild Kaiser with Totenkirchl in background (80x125cm-31x49in) s. 28-Nov-2 Dorotheum, Vienna #10/R est:6500-9000

SWIEYKOWSKI, Alfred (1869-1953) Russian
£513 $811 €800 Vase d'anemones (46x38cm-18x15in) s. 18-Nov-2 Tajan, Paris #127
£774 $1223 €1200 Bouquet sur une sellette (83x63cm-33x25in) s. 17-Dec-2 Rossini, Paris #123

SWIFT, Clement (1846-1918) American
£633 $1000 €950 Seaweed gatherers, Brittany (38x76cm-15x30in) s. 17-Nov-2 CRN Auctions, Cambridge #47/R

SWIFT, John Warkup (1815-1869) British
£270 $429 €405 River landscape with figures, a boat and windmill (25x35cm-10x14in) s.d.1852. 10-Mar-3 Bonhams, Bath #147
£520 $848 €754 Windmill (26x37cm-10x15in) s.d.1882 exhib. 16-Jul-3 Sotheby's, Olympia #64/R
£560 $874 €840 Marine scene (53x76cm-21x30in) s. 15-Oct-2 Canterbury Auctions, UK #151/R

SWIFT, Patrick (1927-1983) Irish
£3500 $5600 €5250 Cupid in garden (35x46cm-14x18in) s. canvasboard painted c.1952 prov.exhib. 15-May-3 Christie's, London #97/R est:6000
£19231 $29808 €30000 Portuguese harvester, Luis Cego (78x38cm-31x15in) prov.exhib.lit. 3-Dec-2 Bonhams & James Adam, Dublin #96/R est:30000-40000

SWIMBERGHE, Gilbert (1927-) Belgian
Works on paper
£278 $442 €400 Variatie van potlood nr 4-5 (96x96cm-38x38in) s.d.1979 dr. 29-Apr-3 Campo & Campo, Antwerp #820

SWINNERTON, James G (1875-1974) American
£481 $750 €722 Smoke tree and soap weed (36x46cm-14x18in) s.i. panel prov.lit. 9-Nov-2 Santa Fe Art, Santa Fe #234/R
£1018 $1700 €1476 Landscape (46x71cm-18x28in) s. 17-Jun-3 John Moran, Pasadena #121a est:1000-2000
£1122 $1750 €1683 Joshua trees at sunset (30x41cm-12x16in) s.i.verso canvas on board prov.lit. 9-Nov-2 Santa Fe Art, Santa Fe #70/R est:2000-4000
£1763 $2750 €2645 Near Colton (38x33cm-15x13in) s.d.10 canvas on board prov.lit. 9-Nov-2 Santa Fe Art, Santa Fe #108/R est:3000-4000
£4217 $7000 €6115 Monument called Agatha (46x60cm-18x24in) s. canvasboard prov. 11-Jun-3 Butterfields, San Francisco #4332/R est:5000-7000
£4487 $7000 €6731 Hogan near upper End Grand Canyon (56x71cm-22x28in) s. prov.lit. 9-Nov-2 Santa Fe Art, Santa Fe #201/R est:12000-17000
£4518 $7500 €6551 Hogans near the Little Colorado (71x86cm-28x34in) s. 11-Jun-3 Butterfields, San Francisco #4333/R est:5000-7000
£5389 $9000 €7814 Agathian Needle, in shadow (102x76cm-40x30in) s. i.on stretcher. 17-Jun-3 John Moran, Pasadena #115b est:10000-15000
£5689 $9500 €8249 Monument Valleu - Mittens (76x102cm-30x40in) s. i.on stretcher. 17-Jun-3 John Moran, Pasadena #115a est:10000-15000
£8333 $13000 €12500 Desert smoke trees (66x76cm-26x30in) s. linen prov.lit. 9-Nov-2 Santa Fe Art, Santa Fe #39/R est:18000-25000
Works on paper
£597 $950 €896 Smoking cowboy (26x30cm-10x12in) s.i.d.May 21 09 pen ink W/C. 7-Mar-3 Skinner, Boston #374/R

SWINSTEAD, George Hillyard (1860-1926) British
Works on paper
£400 $616 €600 French town with figures on the banks of a river (33x25cm-13x10in) s. pastel. 3-Sep-2 Gorringes, Lewes #2222

SWISS SCHOOL, 17th C
£10000 $15700 €15000 Village kermesse, near Lucerne (73x111cm-29x44in) prov.lit. 13-Dec-2 Christie's, Kensington #166/R est:10000-15000

SWISS SCHOOL, 19th C
£5161 $8155 €8000 Paysage a la cascade (68x45cm-27x18in) bears sig. 18-Dec-2 Beaussant & Lefèvre, Paris #35/R

SWITZER, William (20th C) American
£687 $1100 €1031 Angela pitcher (76x61cm-30x24in) s.i. d.94 verso board. 16-Mar-3 Butterfields, San Francisco #1102 est:600-800

SWOBODA, Rudolf (elder) (1819-1859) Austrian
£1139 $1800 €1800 Cattle on alpine pasture (40x50cm-16x20in) s.d.1893 canvas on panel lit. 29-Nov-2 Schloss Ahlden, Ahlden #1197/R est:2400

SWORD, James Brade (1839-1915) American
Works on paper
£1039 $1600 €1559 Chicken house. Coming squall at Mattapoisett, Mass (36x53cm-14x21in) s. i.verso W/C board two. 4-Sep-2 Christie's, Rockefeller NY #356/R est:1200-1800

SWYNCOP, Charles (1895-1970) Belgian
£641 $994 €1000 Dimanche a la mer du Nord (22x34cm-9x13in) s. panel. 9-Dec-2 Horta, Bruxelles #423
£962 $1510 €1500 Bunches of flowers (55x75cm-22x30in) s. 10-Dec-2 Dorotheum, Vienna #201/R est:1800-2200

SWYNCOP, Philippe (1878-1949) Belgian
£692 $1065 €1100 Musicienne espagnole (100x80cm-39x31in) s. 22-Oct-2 Galerie Moderne, Brussels #1700
£1392 $2172 €2200 Portrait de jeune enfant (125x78cm-49x31in) 15-Oct-2 Horta, Bruxelles #149
£1519 $2370 €2400 Portrait de fillette au chapeau noir (46x38cm-18x15in) s. d.1932 panel. 15-Oct-2 Vanderkindere, Brussels #65/R est:1250-1750
£1772 $2800 €2800 Danseuse gitane (125x80cm-49x31in) s. 26-Nov-2 Palais de Beaux Arts, Brussels #382 est:3000-3500
£5172 $8276 €7500 Girl with pink dress (100x100cm-39x39in) s. 15-Mar-3 De Vuyst, Lokeren #527/R est:7500-8500

SWYNNERTON, Annie (1844-1933) British
£700 $1106 €1050 Portrait of George Lewis, seated in a garden (103x79cm-41x31in) init.d.1917 prov. 14-Nov-2 Christie's, Kensington #171

£6000 $9480 €9000 Oleander (20x27cm-8x11in) s.d.1883 panel. 2-Dec-2 Sotheby's, London #103/R est:6000-8000

SYBERG, Ernst (1906-1981) Danish

£274 $428 €411 Landscape with cows (47x67cm-19x26in) s. 11-Nov-2 Rasmussen, Vejle #50/R (D.KR 3200)
£276 $419 €414 Landscape with road - Linieveien, Bakkebolle Fredsgaard (68x105cm-27x41in) s.d.1955 exhib. 3-Sep-2 Museumsbygningen, Copenhagen #473/R (D.KR 3200)
£279 $441 €419 Landscape with view across water (47x67cm-19x26in) s. 1-Apr-3 Rasmussen, Copenhagen #571/R (D.KR 3000)

SYBERG, Fritz (1862-1939) Danish

£254 $391 €381 Landscape with farm (47x65cm-19x26in) mono. 23-Oct-2 Kunsthallen, Copenhagen #457 (D.KR 3000)
£380 $586 €570 Praestedammen in Svanninge - village pond (62x70cm-24x28in) mono.d.1931. 23-Oct-2 Kunsthallen, Copenhagen #45 (D.KR 4500)
£465 $734 €698 Landscape with view of water (67x97cm-26x38in) s. 1-Apr-3 Rasmussen, Copenhagen #624 (D.KR 5000)
£495 $798 €743 From Pilegarden near Munkebo (56x66cm-22x26in) mono. 22-Feb-3 Rasmussen, Havnen #2337 (D.KR 5500)
£614 $989 €921 Landscape with farm (47x66cm-19x26in) init. 11-May-3 Hindemae, Ullerslev #363/R (D.KR 6500)
£698 $1110 €1047 View through window across roof tops, hyacinths in foreground (53x43cm-21x17in) mono.d.1905. 10-Mar-3 Rasmussen, Vejle #569/R (D.KR 7500)
£719 $1107 €1079 Landscape with poplars (67x95cm-26x37in) mono. 23-Oct-2 Kunsthallen, Copenhagen #410/R (D.KR 8500)
£719 $1107 €1079 Winter's day with showers (94x134cm-37x53in) mono.d.1927. 26-Oct-2 Rasmussen, Havnen #2030/R (D.KR 8500)
£1418 $2283 €2127 Landscape with fields and rainbow (135x193cm-53x76in) init.d.32. 11-May-3 Hindemae, Ullerslev #351/R est:25000-30000 (D.KR 15000)
£1490 $2384 €2235 Seascape with figures in rowing boat, southern Fyn (27x53cm-11x21in) mono.d.1907. 16-Mar-3 Hindemae, Ullerslev #543/R est:12000-15000 (D.KR 16000)
£1679 $2670 €2519 Landscape view, winter (67x85cm-26x33in) mono.d.1936. 5-May-3 Rasmussen, Vejle #29/R est:15000-20000 (D.KR 18000)
£1862 $2961 €2793 Boys bathing by stony beach (76x105cm-30x41in) mono.d.1905. 4-Mar-3 Museumsbygningen, Copenhagen #511/R est:15000 (D.KR 20000)
£1862 $2961 €2793 Landscape with farmer and horses ploughing field (132x190cm-52x75in) mono.d.1922-24. 10-Mar-3 Rasmussen, Vejle #616/R est:30000 (D.KR 20000)
£2193 $3662 €3180 Autumn landscape (132x188cm-52x74in) mono.d.1924-32 prov.lit. 17-Jun-3 Rasmussen, Copenhagen #66/R est:25000-30000 (D.KR 23000)

Works on paper

£283 $451 €425 Street scene with figures along the river Arno, Pisa (35x48cm-14x19in) mono. W/C. 26-Feb-3 Kunsthallen, Copenhagen #338 (D.KR 3100)
£309 $482 €464 Adam and Eve seated (79x100cm-31x39in) mono.d.1918 pencil W/C Indian ink lit. 11-Nov-2 Rasmussen, Vejle #9/R (D.KR 3600)
£309 $482 €464 Adam and Eve walking (79x107cm-31x42in) mono.d.1914 pencil W/C Indian ink. 11-Nov-2 Rasmussen, Vejle #15/R (D.KR 3600)
£359 $578 €539 Landscape (31x43cm-12x17in) init.i.d.1926 pencil Indian ink. 11-May-3 Hindemae, Ullerslev #364/R (D.KR 3800)
£379 $629 €550 Heather hill (45x62cm-18x24in) mono. W/C. 12-Jun-3 Kunsthallen, Copenhagen #279/R (D.KR 4000)
£392 $623 €588 Ploughed field, spring (46x62cm-18x24in) mono.d.1917 W/C. 29-Apr-3 Kunsthallen, Copenhagen #222 (D.KR 4200)
£474 $720 €711 Autumn landscape with fields and small lakes (46x58cm-18x23in) mono.d.1917 W/C. 27-Aug-2 Rasmussen, Copenhagen #1978/R (D.KR 5500)
£603 $916 €905 Spring landscape with tree by water (47x64cm-19x25in) mono. W/C. 27-Aug-2 Rasmussen, Copenhagen #1976/R (D.KR 7000)

SYBRANDS, Wilfried (1912-) Belgian

£764 $1215 €1100 Les baigneuses (39x49cm-15x19in) s. 29-Apr-3 Campo & Campo, Antwerp #290/R

SYCHKOV, Feodor Vasilievich (1870-1958) Russian

£28000 $45360 €42000 Happy mushroom gatherers (81x99cm-32x39in) s. 21-May-3 Sotheby's, London #122/R est:20000-30000

SYDNEY, Berenice (1944-1983) British?

Works on paper

£450 $693 €675 Fireworks (51x77cm-20x30in) s.d.67 pastel. 5-Sep-2 Christie's, Kensington #749/R
£600 $924 €900 Brush drawing on tiptoes (58x40cm-23x16in) s.i.d.3'77 pen ink W/C sold with another by the same hand. 5-Sep-2 Christie's, Kensington #750/R

SYER, John (1815-1885) British

£400 $628 €600 River landscape at dusk, possibly Ely Cathedral beyond (77x128cm-30x50in) s. 16-Dec-2 Bonhams, Bury St Edmunds #447
£400 $656 €600 Scarborough harbour with steam and sailing vessels (29x48cm-11x19in) s. 10-Feb-3 David Duggleby, Scarborough #573/R
£950 $1463 €1425 Rustic scene of a man and woman working in a field (22x35cm-9x14in) s.d.1859 board. 3-Sep-2 Bristol Auction Rooms #519
£1039 $1600 €1559 Bracelet Baym The Mumbles (18x51cm-7x20in) s. 27-Oct-2 Grogan, Boston #58 est:800-1200
£1206 $2013 €1700 Paysage cotier anime (26x39cm-10x15in) mono.d.53. 18-Jun-3 Hotel des Ventes Mosan, Brussels #167 est:1200-1500

Works on paper

£260 $426 €390 Fishing boats entering harbour in stormy seas (48x80cm-19x31in) s.d.1886 W/C. 10-Feb-3 Robin Fenner, Tavistock #646/R
£280 $437 €420 Rural landscape (30x48cm-12x19in) s. W/C. 20-Sep-2 Richardson & Smith, Whitby #187
£350 $571 €525 Figures in a punt on the river (48x74cm-19x29in) s. W/C. 14-Feb-3 Keys, Aylsham #501/R
£380 $600 €570 River Esk, Near Whitby (33x48cm-13x19in) s. W/C. 24-Apr-3 Richardson & Smith, Whitby #234
£750 $1193 €1125 Coastal scene with castle, figure in the foreground (31x49cm-12x19in) s.d.1870 W/C. 27-Feb-3 Locke & England, Leamington Spa #142/R

SYER, John C (1846-1913) British

£274 $425 €411 Autumn landscape with river (25x48cm-10x19in) s. panel. 7-Dec-2 Selkirks, St. Louis #107
£962 $1500 €1443 English landscape (30x46cm-12x18in) s.d.1881. 9-Nov-2 Sloan, North Bethesda #585/R est:2000-3000

SYKES, Dorcie (1908-) British

£550 $864 €825 Newlyn Harbour by moonlight (38x49cm-15x19in) s. canvasboard. 10-Dec-2 Lane, Penzance #112

SYKES, Henry (1855-1921) British

Works on paper

£1400 $2184 €2100 Autumn melody (28x51cm-11x20in) s. i.verso pencil W/C. 17-Oct-2 Christie's, Kensington #63/R est:1000-1500

SYKES, John Gutteridge (1866-1941) British

Works on paper

£250 $390 €375 Cattle in a meadow (28x38cm-11x15in) s. W/C. 17-Oct-2 David Lay, Penzance #1316
£480 $778 €720 Mending the nets at low tide (29x45cm-11x18in) s. W/C. 21-Jan-3 Bonhams, Knightsbridge #4/R
£500 $775 €750 Cornish lane (25x36cm-10x14in) s. pair. 4-Dec-2 Andrew Hartley, Ilkley #1114

SYLVAIN, Christiaen (1950-) ?

Works on paper

£692 $1065 €1100 Monsieur Taboulle (74x104cm-29x41in) s. mixed media. 22-Oct-2 Campo & Campo, Antwerp #250

SYLVESTER, Frederick Oakes (1869-1915) American

£641 $1000 €962 Lake Como (20x30cm-8x12in) s. canvasboard. 14-Sep-2 Selkirks, St. Louis #146/R
£6250 $9750 €9375 Purple Grafton Heights (41x51cm-16x20in) s.d.1911-12. 10-Nov-2 Selkirks, St. Louis #971/R est:3000-5000

SYLVESTER, Ida Pond (?-1935) American

£267 $425 €401 Red barn (41x51cm-16x20in) painted c.1920. 2-Mar-3 Toomey, Oak Park #666/R
£346 $550 €519 Coastal scene (41x51cm-16x20in) s. painted c.1920. 2-Mar-3 Toomey, Oak Park #560/R

SYLVESTER, Leif (1940-) Danish

£641 $1039 €929 Warrior (75x60cm-30x24in) s.d.1990. 24-May-3 Rasmussen, Havnen #4216 (D.KR 6700)

SYLVESTRE, Joseph Noel (1847-1926) French

£1800 $2844 €2700 Collector (73x59cm-29x23in) s. panel. 14-Nov-2 Christie's, Kensington #306/R est:2000-3000

SYLVESTRE, Louis (younger-attrib) (1675-1760) French
£405 $632 €600 Crucifixion (108x66cm-43x26in) 26-Mar-3 Tajan, Paris #67/R

SYLVIUS, Richard (?-1677) Swedish
£6525 $10113 €9788 Portrait of Peter Makeleer (107x89cm-42x35in) s.d.1675 prov.lit. 3-Dec-2 Bukowskis, Stockholm #398/R est:50000-60000 (S.KR 92000)

SYME, Eveline W (1888-1961) Australian
£411 $649 €617 Standing nude (56x37cm-22x15in) 27-Nov-2 Deutscher-Menzies, Melbourne #227/R est:1000-1500 (A.D 1150)
Prints
£1912 $3136 €2868 San Domenico, Siena (21x13cm-8x5in) s.i.d.num.13/25 col linocut lit. 4-Jun-3 Deutscher-Menzies, Melbourne #207/R est:1500-2000 (A.D 4800)
£2191 $3593 €3287 Lily tower, Siena (18x12cm-7x5in) s.i.num.1/50 col linocut lit. 4-Jun-3 Deutscher-Menzies, Melbourne #208/R est:1000-1500 (A.D 5500)

SYME, John (1795-1861) British
£3000 $4650 €4500 Portrait of Hugh Stewart in uniform (144x108cm-57x43in) 5-Dec-2 Bonhams, Edinburgh #81/R est:3000-5000

SYMONS, George Gardner (1863-1930) American
£1198 $2000 €1737 First snow (18x23cm-7x9in) s. prov. 18-Jun-3 Christie's, Los Angeles #15/R est:2500-3500
£1500 $2400 €2250 Log cabin and cows in a wooded landscape (33x41cm-13x16in) init. board. 17-May-3 Pook & Pook, Downington #158a/R est:2500-3000
£3293 $5500 €4775 Autumn landscape (20x25cm-8x10in) s. prov. 18-Jun-3 Christie's, Los Angeles #12/R est:3000-5000
£3915 $6500 €5677 The Threshers (20x25cm-8x10in) init. i.verso canvasboard prov. 11-Jun-3 Butterfields, San Francisco #4066/R est:3000-5000
£8280 $13000 €12420 Harbour scene (32x41cm-13x16in) s. panel exhib. 19-Nov-2 Butterfields, San Francisco #8026/R est:10000-15000
£10191 $16000 €15287 River scene, winter (46x62cm-18x24in) s. 20-Nov-2 Christie's, Los Angeles #81/R est:20000-30000
£17516 $27500 €26274 Early snow fall (76x91cm-30x36in) s. i.verso. 10-Dec-2 Doyle, New York #56/R est:25000-35000
£17516 $27500 €26274 Meandering winter stream (76x91cm-30x36in) s. 19-Nov-2 Butterfields, San Francisco #8021/R est:40000-60000
£22581 $35000 €33872 Berkshire Hills, winter (51x64cm-20x25in) s. prov. 4-Dec-2 Sotheby's, New York #42/R est:20000-30000
£55556 $90000 €83334 Snow clad fields in morning light (128x153cm-50x60in) s. painted c.1910 prov.exhib.lit. 21-May-3 Sotheby's, New York #166/R est:40000-60000
Works on paper
£357 $550 €536 Forest landscape in winter (46x56cm-18x22in) s. W/C gouache. 27-Oct-2 Grogan, Boston #90

SYMONS, George Gardner (attrib) (1863-1930) American
£2400 $3768 €3600 River snow scene (15x21cm-6x8in) bears sig board. 16-Dec-2 Bonhams, Bury St Edmunds #525/R est:700-1000

SYMONS, William Christian (1845-1911) British
Works on paper
£600 $924 €900 Pride of the family (36x25cm-14x10in) W/C. 5-Sep-2 Clevedon Sale Rooms #136/R

SYNAVE, Tancrede (1860-?) French
£1277 $2132 €1800 Nu au sofa (73x122cm-29x48in) s. 23-Jun-3 Delvaux, Paris #137/R est:2000-2200
£2044 $3250 €3066 Sharing a cocktail (38x46cm-15x18in) s. prov. 7-Mar-3 Skinner, Boston #584/R est:500-700
£3191 $5170 €4500 Scene de plage (89x89cm-35x35in) s. prov. 26-May-3 Joron-Derem, Paris #41/R est:3000-4000

SYNDON, Jean (19/20th C) French
£372 $592 €558 A prophet (23x19cm-9x7in) s.d.1900. 5-Mar-3 Rasmussen, Copenhagen #1657 (D.KR 4000)

SYS, Maurice (1880-1972) Belgian
£2308 $3577 €3600 Volendam pier (31x36cm-12x14in) s. tempera board prov.lit. 7-Dec-2 De Vuyst, Lokeren #445/R est:3500-4500
£5396 $8633 €7500 Canetons et poule aux bords d'un etang (29x37cm-11x15in) s. panel. 13-May-3 Palais de Beaux Arts, Brussels #148/R est:5000-7500
£9434 $14528 €15000 Windmill in a summer landscape (60x71cm-24x28in) s. 22-Oct-2 Sotheby's, Amsterdam #91/R est:4000-6000
£13103 $20966 €19000 Winter view of Saint Michael's Bridge (91x106cm-36x42in) s. exhib.lit. 15-Mar-3 De Vuyst, Lokeren #439/R est:19000-22000
Works on paper
£2014 $3223 €2800 Nu allonge vu de dos (27x41cm-11x16in) s. pastel. 13-May-3 Palais de Beaux Arts, Brussels #147/R est:1250-1750

SZABO AKOS (20th C) ?
Works on paper
£833 $1275 €1300 Depart de chasse (35x34cm-14x13in) s. col crayon dr. 23-Aug-2 Deauville, France #213

SZABO, Alexander (1921-) Czechoslovakian
Works on paper
£347 $492 €521 Abstract composition (90x70cm-35x28in) mixed media painted 1968. 26-Mar-2 SOGA, Bratislava #255/R (SL.K 22000)
£347 $506 €521 Non-figurative composition II (75x90cm-30x35in) mixed media. 4-Jun-2 SOGA, Bratislava #292/R est:22000 (SL.K 22000)

SZABO, Joseph (1932-) Hungarian?
£217 $336 €326 Untitled (89x120cm-35x47in) s.i.verso. 3-Dec-2 Shapiro, Sydney #42/R (A.D 600)

SZABO, Vladimir (1905-1991) Hungarian
£1341 $2092 €1944 Macskapatrona (60x40cm-24x16in) s. panel. 12-Apr-3 Mu Terem Galeria, Budapest #211/R est:240000 (H.F 480000)
£1345 $2084 €1950 Animal tales (60x50cm-24x20in) s.d.82 panel. 9-Dec-2 Mu Terem Galeria, Budapest #204/R est:460000 (H.F 500000)

SZAFRAN, Sam (1930-) French
Works on paper
£1736 $2743 €2500 Cavalier (48x63cm-19x25in) s.i. chl ink wash exec.c.1960 prov. 27-Apr-3 Perrin, Versailles #59/R est:2500-3000
£3459 $5362 €5500 Sans titre, plants (72x47cm-28x19in) s. W/C. 30-Oct-2 Artcurial Briest, Paris #736/R est:3500-4000
£4167 $6875 €6000 Philodendron (72x47cm-28x19in) s. chl pastel prov. 1-Jul-3 Artcurial Briest, Paris #804/R est:5000-6000
£17949 $28179 €28000 Escalier et interieur (40x24cm-16x9in) s. crayon wax crayon. 11-Dec-2 Artcurial Briest, Paris #725/R est:20000
£19231 $30192 €30000 Escalier et interieur (31x18cm-12x7in) s. crayon pastel. 11-Dec-2 Artcurial Briest, Paris #724/R est:20000
£24359 $38244 €38000 Escalier et interieur (42x29cm-17x11in) s. crayon wax crayon. 11-Dec-2 Artcurial Briest, Paris #722/R est:20000
£28846 $45288 €45000 Escalier et interieur (35x22cm-14x9in) s. crayon wax crayon. 11-Dec-2 Artcurial Briest, Paris #723/R est:20000
£39744 $62397 €62000 Escalier (140x91cm-55x36in) s. gouache wash. 11-Dec-2 Artcurial Briest, Paris #726/R est:45000
£43590 $68436 €68000 Escalier anamorphique (80x131cm-31x52in) s. W/C wash. 11-Dec-2 Artcurial Briest, Paris #727/R est:35000

SZAKMARY, Laszlo (20th C) Hungarian
£13457 $21531 €20186 Fun fair (42x50cm-17x20in) s.d.924. 16-May-3 Kieselbach, Budapest #48/R (H.F 4600000)

SZALAY, Gejza (1902-1963) Czechoslovakian
£362 $514 €543 Girls on meadow (70x100cm-28x39in) painted 1937. 26-Mar-2 SOGA, Bratislava #15/R (SL.K 23000)
£457 $708 €686 Girl of Zdiar village (80x58cm-31x23in) painted c.1935. 1-Oct-2 SOGA, Bratislava #17/R est:29000 (SL.K 29000)

SZAMOSSY, Elek (1826-1888) Hungarian
£1238 $1932 €1857 Flora, 1866 (90x71cm-35x28in) s. 11-Sep-2 Kieselbach, Budapest #53/R (H.F 480000)

SZANKOWSKI, Boleslaw von (1873-1953) Polish
£409 $638 €650 Young female nude with cloth and hat in forest clearing (45x35cm-18x14in) s. 21-Sep-2 Dannenberg, Berlin #601/R
£2500 $4000 €3750 Portrait of Adrienne, daughter of the artist (55x49cm-22x19in) s. 17-Mar-3 Philippe Schuler, Zurich #4656/R est:3000-5000 (S.FR 5300)

SZANTHO, Maria (1898-1984) Hungarian
£320 $499 €480 Reclining female nude with red flowers in her hair (49x68cm-19x27in) s. 8-Apr-3 Bonhams, Knightsbridge #283
£400 $624 €600 Portrait of a female nude (79x58cm-31x23in) s. 8-Apr-3 Bonhams, Knightsbridge #298/R
£700 $1092 €1050 Reclining sleeping female nude (68x98cm-27x39in) 8-Apr-3 Bonhams, Knightsbridge #230/R
£723 $1200 €1048 Demure model (66x53cm-26x21in) s. 14-Jun-3 Jackson's, Cedar Falls #209/R
£769 $1208 €1200 Modele au tambourin (85x70cm-33x28in) s. 13-Dec-2 Piasa, Paris #218
£1200 $1956 €1800 Reclining female nude (65x110cm-26x43in) s. 13-Feb-3 Christie's, Kensington #55/R est:700-1000

£1500 $2340 €2250 Nude with a violin (70x85cm-28x33in) painted oval. 8-Oct-2 Bonhams, Knightsbridge #71/R est:1500-2500
£1800 $2880 €2700 Reclining female nude (78x130cm-31x51in) s. 11-Mar-3 Bonhams, Knightsbridge #122/R est:2000-3000
£2200 $3476 €3300 Reclining female nude (51x71cm-20x28in) 14-Nov-2 Christie's, Kensington #246/R est:600-800

SZARKOWSKI, John (1925-) American
Photographs
£2848 $4500 €4272 House, Monticello, Minnesota (25x32cm-10x13in) s.i.d. gelatin silver print prov.exhib.lit. 25-Apr-3 Phillips, New York #44/R est:4000-6000

SZASZ, Istvan (1878-1965) Hungarian
£290 $475 €400 La toilette (100x74cm-39x29in) s. 27-May-3 Campo & Campo, Antwerp #223

SZCZUKA, Mieczyslaw (1898-1927) Polish
Works on paper
£1193 $1838 €1790 Blok (55x39cm-22x15in) s. collage ink gouache. 22-Oct-2 Iegor de Saint Hippolyte, Montreal #108/R (C.D 2900)
£1317 $2028 €1976 Block (39x29cm-15x11in) s. collage ink gouache. 22-Oct-2 Iegor de Saint Hippolyte, Montreal #110 (C.D 3200)
£1399 $2155 €2099 Aktiva (44x32cm-17x13in) s. collage ink gouache. 22-Oct-2 Iegor de Saint Hippolyte, Montreal #109 (C.D 3400)
£1399 $2155 €2099 Pegasy (69x52cm-27x20in) s.d.24 gouache collage. 22-Oct-2 Iegor de Saint Hippolyte, Montreal #112 (C.D 3400)
£1440 $2218 €2160 Reklana (65x44cm-26x17in) s. gouache collage. 22-Oct-2 Iegor de Saint Hippolyte, Montreal #111 (C.D 3500)
£1481 $2281 €2222 Zenit grafika (65x47cm-26x19in) s. gouache collage. 22-Oct-2 Iegor de Saint Hippolyte, Montreal #113 (C.D 3600)
£1646 $2535 €2469 Modernistow (61x47cm-24x19in) s. gouache collage. 22-Oct-2 Iegor de Saint Hippolyte, Montreal #114/R (C.D 4000)
£2642 $4148 €3963 Composition (30x20cm-12x8in) mono.d.18 collage ink gouache. 12-Dec-2 Iegor de Saint Hippolyte, Montreal #119 (C.D 6500)
£4472 $7020 €6708 Composition au vase (39x29cm-15x11in) mono.d.18 collage ink gouache. 12-Dec-2 Iegor de Saint Hippolyte, Montreal #120 (C.D 11000)
£6911 $10850 €10367 Composition a la scie (44x34cm-17x13in) mono.d.18 collage ink gouache. 12-Dec-2 Iegor de Saint Hippolyte, Montreal #121 (C.D 17000)

SZEKELY, Bertalan (1835-1910) Hungarian
£1174 $1831 €1761 Landscape with forest (33x43cm-13x17in) s. board. 11-Apr-3 Kieselbach, Budapest #83/R est:420000 (H.F 420000)
£4902 $7646 €7353 Girl with chaplet-Rachael (53x42cm-21x17in) s. 11-Sep-2 Kieselbach, Budapest #99/R (H.F 1900000)
£36117 $56342 €54176 Court of King Laszlo 5th (126x226cm-50x89in) 11-Sep-2 Kieselbach, Budapest #168/R (H.F 14000000)

SZEMERE-SZMRTNIK, Mikulas (1894-1961) Czechoslovakian
£284 $440 €426 Road in forest (71x100cm-28x39in) painted c.1920. 3-Dec-2 SOGA, Bratislava #35/R (SL.K 18000)

SZENDY, A (1902-?) Hungarian
£301 $500 €436 Goose girl (51x61cm-20x24in) s. 14-Jun-3 Jackson's, Cedar Falls #214/R

SZENES, Arpad (1897-1985) French
£4723 $7509 €6800 Composition (18x36cm-7x14in) paper on canvas painted c.1975 prov.lit. 29-Apr-3 Artcurial Briest, Paris #591/R est:6000-8000
£5755 $9209 €8000 Paysage mineral (20x30cm-8x12in) s.d.1971 masonite. 13-May-3 Galerie Moderne, Brussels #425/R est:1000-1500
Works on paper
£742 $1166 €1113 Untitled (28x13cm-11x5in) s. gouache prov. 23-Nov-2 Burkhard, Luzern #176/R (S.FR 1700)

SZENTGYORGYI, Janos (1794-1860) Hungarian
£8383 $13078 €12575 Still life (73x100cm-29x39in) s. 11-Apr-3 Kieselbach, Budapest #175/R est:2800000-3000000 (H.F 3000000)

SZEPESI-KUSZKA, Eugen (1885-?) Czechoslovakian
£284 $414 €426 River (22x26cm-9x10in) board painted c.1914. 4-Jun-2 SOGA, Bratislava #27/R est:22000 (SL.K 18000)
£347 $538 €521 Cottages near a river (21x26cm-8x10in) cardboard painted c.1910. 3-Dec-2 SOGA, Bratislava #27/R (SL.K 22000)
£378 $552 €567 Tarn in high Tatras (25x39cm-10x15in) painted c.1914. 4-Jun-2 SOGA, Bratislava #26/R est:24000 (SL.K 24000)
£599 $850 €899 Houses along river (19x32cm-7x13in) board painted c.1914. 26-Mar-2 SOGA, Bratislava #42/R (SL.K 38000)
£630 $977 €945 In winter (21x26cm-8x10in) wood painted c.1920. 1-Oct-2 SOGA, Bratislava #28/R est:16000 (SL.K 40000)
£995 $1591 €1493 Snowy pine forest (49x70cm-19x28in) s. board. 16-May-3 Kieselbach, Budapest #49/R (H.F 340000)

SZERBAKOW, Fedor (1911-) German?
£442 $703 €650 Sailing boat on lakeshore (60x80cm-24x31in) s.d.52 panel. 28-Mar-3 Bolland & Marotz, Bremen #369/R
£538 $850 €850 Beautiful autumn evening in Teufel fen (47x67cm-19x26in) s.d.77 board. 29-Nov-2 Bolland & Marotz, Bremen #576

SZERNER, Vladyslav (1836-1915) Polish
£4029 $6446 €5600 Fileuse (48x28cm-19x11in) s. 17-May-3 De Vuyst, Lokeren #341/R est:2500-3000
£10000 $16400 €15000 Resting Cossacks (40x80cm-16x31in) s. prov. 3-Jun-3 Sotheby's, London #26/R est:12000-18000

SZIGETI, Jeno (1881-?) Hungarian
Works on paper
£1006 $1569 €1509 Farm courtyard (50x63cm-20x25in) pastel. 11-Apr-3 Kieselbach, Budapest #94/R est:300000-360000 (H.F 360000)
£1285 $2005 €1928 Sunlit house (50x70cm-20x28in) s. pastel. 11-Apr-3 Kieselbach, Budapest #95/R est:300000-460000 (H.F 460000)

SZILAGYI, Jolan (1895-1971) Hungarian
£300 $462 €450 Still life (39x28cm-15x11in) s. board. 22-Oct-2 Sworder & Son, Bishops Stortford #648/R

SZINYEI MERSE, Pal von (1845-1920) Hungarian
£8663 $13427 €12995 Brook (32x41cm-13x16in) board. 1-Oct-2 SOGA, Bratislava #115/R est:480000 (SL.K 550000)
£32271 $50020 €48407 Edge of Lake Balaton (60x70cm-24x28in) s. 6-Dec-2 Kieselbach, Budapest #169/R (H.F 12000000)

SZIRMAY, S (19/20th C) Hungarian?
£310 $483 €465 Race Horsing, 1902 (41x46cm-16x18in) s.d.1902. 11-Sep-2 Kieselbach, Budapest #27/R (H.F 120000)

SZLANYI, Lajos (1869-?) Hungarian
£326 $505 €489 Market scene (20x29cm-8x11in) s. panel. 9-Dec-2 Philippe Schuler, Zurich #8682 (S.FR 750)
£447 $697 €671 Spring garden (50x75cm-20x30in) s. 11-Apr-3 Kieselbach, Budapest #29/R est:90000-160000 (H.F 160000)

SZOBEL, Geza (1905-) Czechoslovakian
£604 $972 €900 Abstraction (113x87cm-44x34in) s. panel. 23-Feb-3 Mercier & Cie, Lille #161/R
£638 $1066 €900 Les amoureux (76x51cm-30x20in) s. panel. 17-Jun-3 Claude Boisgirard, Paris #124
£1203 $1876 €1900 Composition (74x55cm-29x22in) s. 15-Sep-2 Feletin, Province #70

SZOBOTKA, Imbre (1890-1961) Hungarian
£2286 $3543 €3315 Detail of a street at Szentendre (79x57cm-31x22in) s. 9-Dec-2 Mu Terem Galeria, Budapest #188/R est:800000 (H.F 850000)
£6148 $9591 €8915 Day-labourers (54x65cm-21x26in) s. 12-Apr-3 Mu Terem Galeria, Budapest #205/R est:1500000 (H.F 2200000)
£20638 $32196 €30957 Doubled self portrait (67x54cm-26x21in) s. canvas on cardboard. 11-Sep-2 Kieselbach, Budapest #131/R (H.F 8000000)
£38697 $60367 €58046 Cubistic still life (90x64cm-35x25in) 11-Sep-2 Kieselbach, Budapest #66/R (H.F 15000000)

SZONTAGH, Geza (1841-1891) Czechoslovakian
£568 $881 €852 Near the well (49x58cm-19x23in) painted c.1900. 3-Dec-2 SOGA, Bratislava #116/R (SL.K 36000)
£726 $1126 €1089 Edge of the village (49x58cm-19x23in) painted c.1900. 3-Dec-2 SOGA, Bratislava #115/R (SL.K 46000)

SZONYI, Istvan (1894-1960) Hungarian
£1677 $2616 €2516 House in Zebegeny (34x42cm-13x17in) s. 11-Apr-3 Kieselbach, Budapest #57/R est:600000 (H.F 600000)
£4386 $6842 €6579 Landscape of Nagybanya, 1917 (56x65cm-22x26in) s. 11-Sep-2 Kieselbach, Budapest #64/R (H.F 1700000)
£4644 $7244 €6966 By the Danube, 1935 (71x100cm-28x39in) s. tempera. 11-Sep-2 Kieselbach, Budapest #111/R (H.F 1800000)
£6191 $9659 €9287 Rest at noon (80x120cm-31x47in) s. temera. 11-Sep-2 Kieselbach, Budapest #71/R (H.F 2400000)
£6454 $10004 €9358 Woman chatting at Zebegeny (60x80cm-24x31in) s. egg tempera. 9-Dec-2 Mu Terem Galeria, Budapest #143/R est:2000000 (H.F 2400000)
£9143 $14172 €13715 Evening bathing (100x70cm-39x28in) s. tempera. 6-Dec-2 Kieselbach, Budapest #69/R (H.F 3400000)
£9946 $15914 €14919 On a hill at Zebegeny (48x72cm-19x28in) 16-May-3 Kieselbach, Budapest #4/R (H.F 3400000)
£10060 $15694 €14587 In the yard (70x100cm-28x39in) s. 12-Apr-3 Mu Terem Galeria, Budapest #82/R est:2500000 (H.F 3600000)
£14791 $22926 €22187 In the room, me and mother (122x85cm-48x33in) s. 6-Dec-2 Kieselbach, Budapest #111/R (H.F 5500000)

£25798 $40245 €37407 My wife and Zsuzsa (110x100cm-43x39in) s.d.1930 prov.exhib.lit. 13-Sep-2 Mu Terem Galeria, Budapest #93/R est:4500000 (H.F 10000000)

£146272 $234034 €219408 Danube, bend by Zebegeny with a viaduct (90x100cm-35x39in) s. 16-May-3 Kieselbach, Budapest #84/R (H.F 50000000)

Works on paper

£861 $1334 €1292 At the bank of the River Danube by Zebegeny (18x33cm-7x13in) s. mixed media. 6-Dec-2 Kieselbach, Budapest #158/R (H.F 320000)

£929 $1449 €1347 Spring landscape (25x35cm-10x14in) s.d.1936 W/C. 13-Sep-2 Mu Terem Galeria, Budapest #146/R est:190000 (H.F 360000)

£968 $1501 €1404 Hillside at Zebegeny (36x55cm-14x22in) s.d.1939 W/C. 9-Dec-2 Mu Terem Galeria, Budapest #187/R est:240000 (H.F 360000)

£1397 $2180 €2026 On the riverside (27x40cm-11x16in) s. W/C. 12-Apr-3 Mu Terem Galeria, Budapest #18/R est:220000 (H.F 500000)

£1677 $2616 €2432 Zebegeny (30x32cm-12x13in) s.d.1931 W/C gouache. 12-Apr-3 Mu Terem Galeria, Budapest #12/R est:190000 (H.F 600000)

£1748 $2709 €2535 Woman on the riverbank (39x55cm-15x22in) s. W/C. 9-Dec-2 Mu Terem Galeria, Budapest #18/R est:360000 (H.F 650000)

SZULE, Peter (1886-1944) Hungarian

£1006 $1569 €1459 Writing a letter (25x19cm-10x7in) s.d.923 panel. 12-Apr-3 Mu Terem Galeria, Budapest #125/R est:200000 (H.F 360000)

SZUMINSKI, Szymon (1936-1988) Polish

£340 $541 €500 Still life with two jugs (50x60cm-20x24in) s. 28-Mar-3 Bolland & Marotz, Bremen #691

£476 $757 €700 Harbour at night (67x97cm-26x38in) s.d.1959. 28-Mar-3 Bolland & Marotz, Bremen #689/R

£476 $757 €700 Autumn landscape with houses (65x80cm-26x31in) s.d.1959. 28-Mar-3 Bolland & Marotz, Bremen #690/R

SZYDLOWSKI, Henryk (1950-) New Zealander

£1404 $2189 €2106 Blue door from the lovely dream (64x83cm-25x33in) s.d.1992. 27-Mar-3 International Art Centre, Auckland #147/R est:4500-6500 (NZ.D 4000)

SZYK, Arthur (1894-1951) Polish

Works on paper

£1026 $1600 €1539 Signum temporis (18x15cm-7x6in) s.i.d.1943 pen ink. 19-Sep-2 Swann Galleries, New York #788/R est:1500-2500

£1410 $2200 €2115 Procession of Nazis lead by Royal Canadian Mountie (15x23cm-6x9in) s.d.1940 pen ink W/C. 9-Nov-2 Illustration House, New York #76/R est:3000-4500

SZYMANSKI, Rolf (1928-) German

Sculpture

£3768 $6180 €5200 Calypso in the wood (35cm-14in) s.i. brown pat.bronze prov. 28-May-3 Lempertz, Koln #422/R est:4000

SZYSZLO, Fernando de (1925-) Peruvian

£2595 $4048 €4100 Composition (120x80cm-47x31in) s.d.1954 verso. 19-Oct-2 Semenzato, Venice #67/R

£7006 $11000 €10509 Lurin sea (150x150cm-59x59in) s. i.d.89 verso prov. 20-Nov-2 Christie's, Rockefeller NY #106/R est:15000-20000

£7927 $13000 €11891 Mar de Lurin (99x99cm-39x39in) s. i.d.91 verso prov. 28-May-3 Christie's, Rockefeller NY #137/R est:16000-18000

£10976 $18000 €15915 Mar de Lurin (152x152cm-60x60in) s. s.i.d.88 verso acrylic prov.lit. 27-May-3 Sotheby's, New York #147

T A D M (19th C) British

£5800 $9164 €8700 Portrait of black and white Angora rabbit (42x62cm-17x24in) indis sig.d. 26-Nov-2 Bonhams, Oxford #74/R

T W (?) ?

£800 $1328 €1160 Scottish hunter and his dog resting in a highland landscape (51x61cm-20x24in) init.d.1847. 16-Jun-3 Waddingtons, Toronto #199/R est:700-900 (C.D 1800)

TAAFFE, Philip (1955-) American

£51282 $80000 €76923 Reliquary (28x142cm-11x56in) oil mixed media on canvas painted 1996 prov. 11-Nov-2 Phillips, New York #41/R est:60000-80000

£66456 $105000 €99684 Black volta (262x356cm-103x140in) s. i.d.1994-95 mixed media on canvas prov.exhib. 12-Nov-2 Sotheby's, New York #62/R est:60000-80000

Prints

£11250 $18000 €16875 Untitled - scroll (185x10cm-73x4in) s.i.d.1986 verso silkscreen acrylic collage on awning fabric prov. 14-May-3 Sotheby's, New York #436/R est:15000-20000

Works on paper

£93750 $150000 €140625 Adam, Eve (223x447cm-88x176in) s.d.1984 verso collage linoprint acrylic paper diptych prov.exhib. 14-May-3 Christie's, Rockefeller NY #58/R est:150000-200000

TABACCHI, Odoardo (1831-1905) Italian

Sculpture

£15000 $24900 €15000 Tuffolina (115cm-45in) s.i.d.1879 Carrare marble painted wooden base. 16-Jun-3 Horta, Bruxelles #106/R est:12500-15000

TABAR, François Germain Leopold (1818-1869) French

£3526 $5535 €5500 Fontaine aux environs d'Alger. Sidi Rassa, environs d'Alger (33x46cm-13x18in) s.i. pair. 16-Dec-2 Gros & Delettrez, Paris #186/R est:3000-4000

TABARD, Maurice (1897-1984) French

Photographs

£2760 $4250 €4140 Study of a hand (22x30cm-9x12in) solarized photograph prov. 22-Oct-2 Sotheby's, New York #84/R est:5000-8000

£2922 $4500 €4383 Multiple exposure of dancer Georges Pomies (23x17cm-9x7in) s.d.1931 photograph prov.lit. 22-Oct-2 Sotheby's, New York #86/R est:5000-8000

£6494 $10000 €9741 Jardin des modes (28x22cm-11x9in) i.d.1930 gelatin silver print negative on paper prov. 25-Oct-2 Phillips, New York #21/R est:10000-15000

TABARY, Celine Marie (1908-) French

£513 $800 €770 Pink carnation (73x60cm-29x24in) s. 20-Sep-2 Sloan, North Bethesda #376/R

£529 $825 €794 Parisian park (46x61cm-18x24in) s. board. 20-Sep-2 Sloan, North Bethesda #377/R

TABERNER, Luis (19th C) Spanish

£897 $1418 €1400 Woman from Madrid (29x22cm-11x9in) s.i.d.1885. 14-Nov-2 Arte, Seville #335/R

TABNER, Len (1936-) British

Works on paper

£1500 $2355 €2250 Wave midnight, Barra (77x132cm-30x52in) s.i.d.1986 gouache. 15-Apr-3 Bonhams, Knightsbridge #230/R est:1200-1800

£2800 $4452 €4200 Mapfra (72x105cm-28x41in) gouache. 18-Mar-3 Bonhams, Knightsbridge #212 est:800-1200

£5800 $9222 €8700 Snow blowing over the road (73x105cm-29x41in) s.i.d.November 21 1988 pencil gouache. 18-Mar-3 Bonhams, Knightsbridge #211 est:1000-1500

TABUCHI, Yasse (1921-) Japanese

£620 $961 €930 En ete, un apres midi (81x65cm-32x26in) s.d.61 prov. 4-Dec-2 Kunsthallen, Copenhagen #16 (D.KR 7200)

£724 $1188 €1000 L'ombre isolee (80x100cm-31x39in) s.d.1960. 27-May-3 Tajan, Paris #12/R est:1000-1500

£771 $1203 €1157 La mauresque (101x99cm-40x39in) s.d.66. 5-Nov-2 Bukowskis, Stockholm #365/R (S.KR 11000)

£1325 $2159 €2000 Southern door (146x97cm-57x38in) s.d.1972 acrylic prov. 3-Feb-3 Cornette de St.Cyr, Paris #524

£1509 $2340 €2400 Le volcan en Mai (113x89cm-44x35in) s. s.i.d.1983 verso oil gold prov. 30-Oct-2 Artcurial Briest, Paris #737 est:3000-3800

Works on paper

£1295 $2072 €1800 Composition (40x30cm-16x12in) s.d.89 W/C. 17-May-3 De Vuyst, Lokeren #342/R est:1700-2000

TABUENA, Romeo (1921-) Mexican

£637 $1000 €956 Barrio (69x109cm-27x43in) s. masonite. 28-Jul-2 William Jenack, New York #159

£962 $1500 €1443 Boat scene (39x69cm-15x27in) s.d.1963 masonite. 20-Sep-2 Sloan, North Bethesda #421/R est:3000-5000

£1560 $2464 €2340 Musicians (110x92cm-43x36in) s.d.1995. 26-Nov-2 Louis Morton, Mexico #66/R (M.P 25000)

£1747 $2760 €2621 Family (110x92cm-43x36in) s.d.1995. 26-Nov-2 Louis Morton, Mexico #76/R est:29000 (M.P 28000)

TABUSSO, Francesco (1930-) Italian

£2838 $4427 €4200 Study of boat (100x70cm-39x28in) init.d.1959 prov. 26-Mar-3 Finarte Semenzato, Milan #113/R

£2848 $4500 €4500 Montecomposto Hill, Turin (99x60cm-39x24in) s.d.56 board double-sided. 30-Nov-2 Farsetti, Prato #753/R

£5556 $8833 €8000 Winter landscape (70x100cm-28x39in) s. 1-May-3 Meeting Art, Vercelli #557

TACCA (studio) (17th C) Italian
Sculpture
£22727 $32500 €34091 Pacing horse (18cm-7in) brown pat bronze. 22-Jan-3 Doyle, New York #167/R est:25000

TACK, Augustus Vincent (1870-1949) American
Works on paper
£491 $800 €737 Sketch of death (51x41cm-20x16in) pencil prov. 16-Feb-3 Butterfields, San Francisco #2099

TACLA, Jorge (1958-) Chilean
£7927 $13000 €11494 Projective correspondence (178x183cm-70x72in) s.i.d.1993 verso jute prov.lit. 27-May-3 Sotheby's, New York #149

TADASKY, Kuwayama (20th C) Japanese
£1829 $3000 €2652 C-106 (84x84cm-33x33in) s.i. prov. 1-Jun-3 Wright, Chicago #289/R est:1000-1500

TADEMA-GROENEVELD, Thamine Henriette Bartholde Jacoba (1871-1938) Dutch
£535 $850 €776 Along the shoreline (56x81cm-22x32in) s. canvas on board painted c.1910. 4-May-3 Treadway Gallery, Cincinnati #465/R
£1806 $2979 €2600 Bomschuiten on the beach with shellfishers in the distance (64x100cm-25x39in) s. canvas on board. 1-Jul-3 Christie's, Amsterdam #126/R est:1800-2500
Works on paper
£1042 $1719 €1500 Working on the beach (36x47cm-14x19in) s. black chk W/C. 1-Jul-3 Christie's, Amsterdam #150/R est:1500-1800

TADEUSZ, Norbert (1940-) German
£390 $632 €550 Seated nude (46x39cm-18x15in) board. 24-May-3 Van Ham, Cologne #570
Works on paper
£284 $460 €400 Female nude (20x15cm-8x6in) s. W/C gouache pencil prov. 24-May-3 Van Ham, Cologne #571/R
£426 $689 €600 Untitled (20x15cm-8x6in) s.d.67 gouache oil W/C. 24-May-3 Van Ham, Cologne #572/R
£993 $1609 €1400 Reclining nude (70x100cm-28x39in) s.d.90 W/C chl oil chk prov. 24-May-3 Van Ham, Cologne #569/R

TADINI, Emilio (1927-2002) Italian
£599 $994 €850 Personaggi (50x35cm-20x14in) s. tempera pencil paper. 10-Jun-3 Finarte Semenzato, Milan #266/R
£806 $1257 €1209 Archeologia (55x46cm-22x18in) s.d.1973 verso. 5-Nov-2 Bukowskis, Stockholm #327/R (S.KR 11500)
£962 $1510 €1500 Endless house (30x25cm-12x10in) s.i.verso. 21-Nov-2 Finarte, Rome #213
£962 $1510 €1500 Fairy tale (25x30cm-10x12in) s. paper on masonite. 23-Nov-2 Meeting Art, Vercelli #272/R
£962 $1490 €1500 Archeology (46x38cm-18x15in) s.d.73 verso acrylic. 5-Dec-2 Stadion, Trieste #725/R
£1111 $1767 €1600 Fairy tale (30x30cm-12x12in) s.i.verso. 1-May-3 Meeting Art, Vercelli #175
£1132 $1755 €1800 Paesaggio (73x92cm-29x36in) s.i.verso. 5-Oct-2 De Vuyst, Lokeren #344 est:1000-1200
£1373 $2196 €2100 Fairy tale (40x50cm-16x20in) s. card. 4-Jan-3 Meeting Art, Vercelli #225
£1597 $2524 €2300 Testo (73x92cm-29x36in) s.i.d.verso acrylic lit. 28-Apr-3 Cornette de St.Cyr, Paris #519 est:2000-3000
£1667 $2617 €2600 Still life (45x55cm-18x22in) s.i.verso painted 1994. 19-Nov-2 Finarte, Milan #49/R
£2025 $3159 €3200 Archeology (46x38cm-18x15in) s.i.d.1973 acrylic. 14-Sep-2 Meeting Art, Vercelli #766/R
£2308 $3623 €3600 Oversea (50x60cm-20x24in) s.verso acrylic painted 1992. 21-Nov-2 Finarte, Rome #313/R
£2466 $3847 €3600 Archeology (55x46cm-22x18in) s. painted 1973. 10-Apr-3 Finarte Semenzato, Rome #176/R
£2516 $3899 €4000 Paesaggio Nello studio - Color and Co (130x162cm-51x64in) s.i.d.1970 verso. 5-Oct-2 De Vuyst, Lokeren #343/R est:2800-3300
£10274 $16027 €15000 Nothing (80x100cm-31x39in) s.verso painted 1970. 10-Apr-3 Finarte Semenzato, Rome #247 est:9000
Works on paper
£327 $523 €500 Fairy tale (50x35cm-20x14in) s. mixed media. 4-Jan-3 Meeting Art, Vercelli #468
£359 $575 €550 Image magie (50x35cm-20x14in) s. mixed media. 4-Jan-3 Meeting Art, Vercelli #553
£417 $654 €650 Fairy tale (50x35cm-20x14in) s. mixed media card. 23-Nov-2 Meeting Art, Vercelli #19/R
£451 $718 €650 Film (35x50cm-14x20in) s.i. pencil acrylic. 1-May-3 Meeting Art, Vercelli #27
£1370 $2137 €2000 Untitled (50x62cm-20x24in) s. mixed media. 10-Apr-3 Finarte Semenzato, Rome #227

TADOLINI, Giulio (1849-1918) Italian
Sculpture
£2000 $3120 €3000 Judith (20x19cm-8x7in) terracotta. 9-Apr-3 Sotheby's, London #76/R est:1000-1500
£2400 $3768 €3600 Allegorical female figures (32cm-13in) painted stucco two prov. 10-Dec-2 Sotheby's, London #133/R est:2000-3000
£12162 $18973 €18000 Hannibal (178x76x50cm-70x30x20in) s.d.1897 white marble. 25-Mar-3 Finarte Semenzato, Rome #215/R est:18000

TADOLINI, Giulio (attrib) (1849-1918) Italian
Sculpture
£23226 $36000 €34839 La toilette (231cm-91in) marble with marble pedestal incl. base. 29-Oct-2 Sotheby's, New York #45/R est:30000-50000

TAE JEONG KIM (1963-) Korean
Works on paper
£539 $900 €782 Bardo - equivalent III (31x47cm-12x19in) s.d.4334 pencil dr. lithographic monoprint. 25-Jun-3 Sotheby's, Moscow #202/R

TAE KYOUNG LEE (1973-) Korean
£838 $1400 €1215 Chriqui II (100x73cm-39x29in) s.d.2002 s.d.verso. 25-Jun-3 Sotheby's, Moscow #191/R est:1500-2000
£838 $1400 €1215 Chriqui III (100x73cm-39x29in) s.d.2002 s.d.verso. 25-Jun-3 Sotheby's, Moscow #192/R est:1500-2000
£1375 $2200 €1994 Farah (130x81cm-51x32in) s.d.2002. 13-May-3 Sotheby's, Tel Aviv #29/R est:1800-2200
£1916 $3200 €2778 Chriqui I (100x73cm-39x29in) s.d.2002 s.d.verso. 25-Jun-3 Sotheby's, Moscow #190/R est:1500-2000

TAELEMANS, Jean François (1851-1931) Belgian
£2014 $3223 €2800 Village sous la neige (50x75cm-20x30in) s. 13-May-3 Palais de Beaux Arts, Brussels #319/R est:2000-3500

TAEUBER-ARP, Sophie (1889-1943) Swiss
£239437 $397465 €340000 Dada composition, flat head (27x34cm-11x13in) init.i.d.1920 canvas on cardboard exhib.lit. 12-Jun-3 Laurence Calmels, Paris #7/R est:300000-400000
Sculpture
£211268 $350704 €300000 Dada bowl (20cm-8in) black lacquered wood. 12-Jun-3 Laurence Calmels, Paris #36/R est:80000-120000
£704225 $1169014 €1000000 Dada head (30cm-12in) init.i.d.1920 painted wood exhib.lit. 12-Jun-3 Laurence Calmels, Paris #6/R est:400000-500000
£845070 $1402817 €1200000 Dada head (23cm-9in) indis.sig.i.d.1920 painted wood glass pearls wire exhib.lit. 12-Jun-3 Laurence Calmels, Paris #34/R est:300000-400000
Works on paper
£35714 $57500 €53571 White and yellow slotted figure (27x25cm-11x10in) s.d.1936 gouache prov. 7-May-3 Sotheby's, New York #310/R est:35000-45000

TAEYE, Camille de (1938-) Belgian
£288 $460 €400 Personnage fantastique (30x21cm-12x8in) s.d.1988 tempera. 13-May-3 Vanderkindere, Brussels #173
£503 $775 €800 Geranium et arbre (36x36cm-14x14in) s.d.1992. 22-Oct-2 Campo & Campo, Antwerp #80

TAFFYN, Jan (17th C) Flemish
£7500 $11700 €11250 Finding Moses (86x137cm-34x54in) s.d.1634 prov.lit. 9-Apr-3 Bonhams, New Bond Street #26/R est:3000-4000

TAFURI, Clemente (1903-1971) Italian
£680 $1082 €1000 Boy (25x30cm-10x12in) s. 18-Mar-3 Finarte, Milan #160/R
£4200 $6678 €6300 My people (160x94cm-63x37in) s.d.1944. 18-Mar-3 Bonhams, New Bond Street #86/R est:3000-5000

TAGGART, Elizabeth (20th C) British
£460 $713 €690 Another bide (91x91cm-36x36in) s. i.d.1979 verso. 1-Oct-2 Bonhams, Leeds #327
Works on paper
£600 $960 €900 Magical landscape (56x80cm-22x31in) s.d.1969 pen black ink W/C gold paint. 15-May-3 Christie's, Kensington #223/R

TAGLIABUE, Carlo Costantino (1880-1960) Italian
£1677 $2650 €2600 Farm in Valsassina (72x50cm-28x20in) s. board. 18-Dec-2 Finarte, Milan #133/R
£3165 $5000 €5000 Mount Pelmo (57x70cm-22x28in) s.d.1906. 26-Nov-2 Christie's, Rome #148/R

TAGUE, Robert Bruce (1912-1985) American
£1220 $2000 €1769 1950 revisited , H7 (81x61cm-32x24in) s.d.1970 i.d.verso. 1-Jun-3 Wright, Chicago #277/R est:700-900
£1585 $2600 €2298 Untitled (81x61cm-32x24in) s.d.1970. 1-Jun-3 Wright, Chicago #278/R est:700-900

TAHSIN, Diyarbakirli (1875-1937) Turkish
£16774 $26503 €26000 View of the Bosphorus (70x94cm-28x37in) s.d.11931. 19-Dec-2 Claude Aguttes, Neuilly #125/R est:30000

TAIB, Salomon (1877-?) French
£1798 $2949 €2500 Fete mauresque a Alger. Glycines a Alger (27x22cm-11x9in) s. cardboard pair. 4-Jun-3 Tajan, Paris #319/R est:2500-3000

TAIBO GONZALEZ, German (1889-1919) Spanish
£1415 $2179 €2250 Marine (24x35cm-9x14in) s. 22-Oct-2 Durán, Madrid #178/R

TAILFEATHERS, Gerald (1925-1975) Canadian
£1822 $2897 €2733 Sentinel, mounted warrior (45x35cm-18x14in) s.d.1961 canvasboard prov. 23-Mar-3 Hodgins, Calgary #65/R est:2500-3500 (C.D 4300)

TAILLANDIER, Yvon (1926-) French
£355 $592 €500 Machine volante a longe nez (50x65cm-20x26in) s. acrylic. 18-Jun-3 Charbonneaux, Paris #117
£355 $592 €500 Deux capitipedes (61x50cm-24x20in) s. acrylic. 18-Jun-3 Charbonneaux, Paris #118
£927 $1511 €1400 Taillandier land (180x120cm-71x47in) s. acrylic panel triptych double-sided. 3-Feb-3 Cornette de St.Cyr, Paris #526

Works on paper
£340 $541 €500 Untitled (48x63cm-19x25in) s.d.1978-82 mixed media. 24-Mar-3 Claude Boisgirard, Paris #189

TAIT, Arthur Fitzwilliam (1819-1905) American
£5484 $8500 €8226 Five chicks (25x30cm-10x12in) s.i. board. 2-Nov-2 North East Auctions, Portsmouth #24/R est:7000-9000
£7831 $13000 €11355 At home; a happy family in the Adirondacks (42x31cm-17x12in) s.i.d.84 i.verso prov. 11-Jun-3 Butterfields, San Francisco #4001/R est:15000-20000
£8805 $14000 €13208 Quail and young (20x25cm-8x10in) s.d.67 s.i.d.verso board lit. 4-Mar-3 Christie's, Rockefeller NY #13/R est:8000-12000
£451613 $700000 €677420 Trappers following the trail, at fault (92x127cm-36x50in) s.i.d.1851 prov.lit. 5-Dec-2 Christie's, Rockefeller NY #164/R est:800000-1200000

TAIT, John Robinson (1834-1909) American
£1689 $2804 €2449 Cattle drovers in an extensive mountain landscape (66x110cm-26x43in) s.d.61. 16-Jun-3 Waddingtons, Toronto #10/R est:4000-6000 (C.D 3800)

TAJIRI, Shinkichi (1923-) Dutch

Sculpture
£10256 $15897 €16000 Column for meditation (73cm-29in) s.d.57 bronze pumice stone. 3-Dec-2 Christie's, Amsterdam #58/R est:9000-12000

Works on paper
£353 $558 €530 Figure composition (63x48cm-25x19in) s.d.1960 col Indian ink. 1-Apr-3 Rasmussen, Copenhagen #287/R (D.KR 3800)

TAJONAR, S Ortiz (20th C) Mexican
£1039 $1600 €1559 Harvesting corn (69x58cm-27x23in) indis.sig. painted c.1930. 8-Sep-2 Treadway Gallery, Cincinnati #709/R est:1500-2500

TAKAHASHI, K (19th C) Japanese
£5723 $9500 €8298 Still life with grapes (46x91cm-18x36in) s.d.91 prov. 11-Jun-3 Butterfields, San Francisco #4144/R est:3000-5000

TAKALA, Veikko (1923-) Finnish
£272 $433 €400 Trees with hoar-frost (54x83cm-21x33in) s.d.77. 24-Mar-3 Bukowskis, Helsinki #319/R
£348 $543 €550 Jakobstads market (45x73cm-18x29in) s. 12-Sep-2 Hagelstam, Helsinki #882/R

TAKIS (1925-) Greek

Sculpture
£5769 $9058 €9000 Signal (205cm-81in) electric system. 24-Nov-2 Laurence Calmels, Paris #307/R

TAL COAT, Pierre (1905-1985) French
£759 $1200 €1200 Composition (24x15cm-9x6in) s. 29-Nov-2 Drouot Estimations, Paris #112
£1111 $1766 €1600 Maisons bretonnes dans un paysage (46x55cm-18x22in) s. painted c.1926. 29-Apr-3 Artcurial Briest, Paris #216 est:1000-1200
£1119 $1868 €1600 Nature morte (37x55cm-15x22in) s. 26-Jun-3 Tajan, Paris #325 est:1500-2000
£1736 $2760 €2500 Le lapin ecorche (26x41cm-10x16in) s. panel painted c.1941 prov. 29-Apr-3 Artcurial Briest, Paris #215 est:2500-3000
£1899 $2943 €3000 Composition (40x80cm-16x31in) painted c.1970. 28 Sep-2 Cornette de St.Cyr, Paris #434/R est:3000-4000
£3194 $5079 €4600 Nature morte (29x77cm-11x30in) s. paper on panel. 29-Apr-3 Artcurial Briest, Paris #213/R est:3500-4500
£3750 $5925 €5400 Composition (60x74cm-24x29in) mono. 27-Apr-3 Perrin, Versailles #25/R est:6000-8000
£5714 $9086 €8400 Nature morte aux raisins (46x61cm-18x24in) s. painted c.1943-44 prov.lit. 26-Feb-3 Artcurial Briest, Paris #306/R est:6000-7000
£7051 $10929 €11000 Composition (73x116cm-29x46in) s.d.1960 prov. 4-Dec-2 Pierre Berge, Paris #121/R est:12000
£13889 $22917 €20000 Composition (100x10cm-39x4in) mono. painted c.1951 prov. 1-Jul-3 Artcurial Briest, Paris #497/R est:8000-12000

Works on paper
£230 $373 €350 Nu opulent (40x28cm-16x11in) s. Indian ink pen dr. 22-Jan-3 Tajan, Paris #275
£268 $432 €400 Composition (30x21cm-12x8in) s. ink. 23-Feb-3 Mercier & Cie, Lille #48
£527 $853 €800 Sans titre (35x47cm-14x19in) mono. W/C. 22-Jan-3 Tajan, Paris #266
£637 $980 €956 Paysage (49x23cm-19x9in) s. chl executed 1974. 28-Oct-2 Blomqvist, Lysaker #1318 (N.KR 7500)
£764 $1260 €1100 Sans titre (66x51cm-26x20in) mono. Indian ink wash. 1-Jul-3 Artcurial Briest, Paris #776
£966 $1612 €1400 Composition (52x74cm-20x29in) s. ink. 9-Jul-3 Millon & Associes, Paris #167
£1042 $1656 €1500 Sans titre (60x40cm-24x16in) s.i. wash. 29-Apr-3 Artcurial Briest, Paris #592/R est:1000-1400
£5137 $8065 €7500 Nature morte au pot de terre, au verre, au pichet et a la pipe (26x32cm-10x13in) s. i.verso pastel. 15-Apr-3 Laurence Calmels, Paris #4419/R

TAL R (1967-) Israeli
£4647 $7342 €6971 Okay-Okay (180x180cm-71x71in) init. s.d.1997 verso exhib. 1-Apr-3 Rasmussen, Copenhagen #205/R est:40000-50000 (D.KR 50000)

TALBOT, William Henry Fox (1800-1877) British

Photographs
£1875 $3000 €2813 Loch Katrine, Scotland (8x11cm-3x4in) salted paper print from calotype negative. 15-May-3 Swann Galleries, New York #258/R est:4000-5000
£2000 $3200 €3000 Stonehouse (8x11cm-3x4in) salted paper print from a calotype negative. 15-May-3 Swann Galleries, New York #259/R est:4000-5000
£3125 $5000 €4688 Patroclus (15x15cm-6x6in) salted paper print from calotype negative. 15-May-3 Swann Galleries, New York #261/R est:5000-7000
£3659 $6000 €5489 View of the boulevards of Paris (15x20cm-6x8in) i.verso salted paper print. 10-Feb-3 Swann Galleries, New York #4/R est:8000-12000
£4375 $7000 €6563 Windsor Chapel, East End of St. George's (16x20cm-6x8in) salted paper print from a calotype negative. 15-May-3 Swann Galleries, New York #260/R est:7000-10000
£6098 $10000 €9147 Articles of glassware (13x15cm-5x6in) i. salted paper print. 10-Feb-3 Swann Galleries, New York #5/R est:15000-20000
£6329 $10000 €9494 Nelson's column under construction, Trafalgar square (17x21cm-7x8in) salted paper print lit. 22-Apr-3 Christie's, Rockefeller NY #188/R est:10000-15000
£18987 $30000 €28481 Bust of Patroclus (16x14cm-6x6in) d.22 Sept 1841 negative prov.lit. 24-Apr-3 Phillips, New York #5/R est:30000-50000

TALBOYS, Agnes Augusta (fl.1920) British
£425 $667 €638 How happy I would be with either (25x30cm-10x12in) s. board. 21-Nov-2 Clevedon Sale Rooms #221
£900 $1396 €1350 Cosy corner (51x76cm-20x30in) s. 3-Dec-2 Sotheby's, Olympia #90/R est:1000-1500

TALLENTIRE, Anne (1949-) British
£320 $509 €480 Giants causeway, County Antrim (35x45cm-14x18in) mono. board. 5-Mar-3 John Ross, Belfast #192
£500 $775 €750 Carting turf, Connemara (40x61cm-16x24in) mono. 4-Dec-2 John Ross, Belfast #271
£518 $736 €850 Bothreen ban (50x74cm-20x29in) s. prov. 5-Mar-2 Thomas Adams, Dublin #322

£729 $1159 €1050 Giants causeway (36x46cm-14x18in) mono. board. 29-Apr-3 Whyte's, Dublin #119/R est:1200-1500
£833 $1308 €1300 Fisherman's cottage, Atlantic Drive, Donegal (38x76cm-15x30in) s. i.verso. 19-Nov-2 Whyte's, Dublin #201/R

TALLONE, Cesare (1853-1919) Italian
£818 $1259 €1300 Mountainous landscape with woman (32x45cm-13x18in) s. 28-Oct-2 Il Ponte, Milan #323

TALLONE, Guido (1894-1967) Italian
£1069 $1668 €1700 Portrait of elegant bearded man (81x63cm-32x25in) s.d.1911 lit. 20-Sep-2 Karlheinz Kaupp, Staufen #2057/R
£1290 $2039 €2000 Young woman (38x33cm-15x13in) s. cardboard. 18-Dec-2 Finarte, Milan #108/R
£2027 $3162 €3000 Gladiola (70x60cm-28x24in) s. exhib. 26-Mar-3 Finarte Semenzato, Milan #366/R

TALMAGE, Algernon (1871-1939) British
£1241 $1986 €1800 Figures strolling in parkland (15x21cm-6x8in) one s.d.08 board pair. 12-Mar-3 James Adam, Dublin #129/R est:1200-1600
£1341 $2200 €1944 Flowers in glass bowl (76x64cm-30x25in) s.d.30 exhib. 4-Jun-3 Doyle, New York #92 est:3000-4000
£1900 $2964 €2850 In Dedham Valley (41x51cm-16x20in) s. prov. 27-Mar-3 Christie's, Kensington #468/R est:2000-3000
£2000 $3100 €3000 Moonrise, St. Ives (36x46cm-14x18in) s. 3-Dec-2 Bonhams, Knightsbridge #1/R est:2000-3000
£3500 $5460 €5250 Day at the seaside (65x82cm-26x32in) s. 27-Mar-3 Christie's, Kensington #469/R est:3000-5000
£3800 $5928 €5700 French harvest (63x81cm-25x32in) s.d.26 exhib. 27-Mar-3 Christie's, Kensington #467/R est:3000-5000
£3800 $5928 €5700 November morning (76x91cm-30x36in) s.d.33 exhib. 27-Mar-3 Christie's, Kensington #472/R est:3000-5000
£4000 $6240 €6000 Suffolk haying (71x102cm-28x40in) s.d.29 exhib. 27-Mar-3 Christie's, Kensington #470/R est:4000-6000

TALMAN, John (1677-1726) British
Works on paper
£645 $1000 €968 Alter decoration in St. Marks, Venice (15x13cm-6x5in) ink dr. 2-Nov-2 North East Auctions, Portsmouth #403

TALPINO, Enea (attrib) (c.1558-1626) Italian
Works on paper
£700 $1169 €1015 King seated at the top of a flight of steps, flanked by courtiers (24x21cm-9x8in) i. ink. 9-Jul-3 Bonhams, Knightsbridge #55/R

TALWINSKI, Igor (1907-) Polish
£380 $604 €570 Sweet seventeen (56x46cm-22x18in) s. 18-Mar-3 Rosebery Fine Art, London #795/R
£500 $810 €750 Nude with white cloth (56x46cm-22x18in) s. 20-May-3 Bonhams, Knightsbridge #117/R
£650 $1014 €975 Nude with red ribbon (61x50cm-24x20in) s. 15-Oct-2 Bonhams, Knightsbridge #20/R
£800 $1248 €1200 Nude holding a book (56x46cm-22x18in) s. 15-Oct-2 Bonhams, Knightsbridge #23/R

TAMARIZ, Eduardo (1945-) Mexican
£742 $1187 €1076 Donde la ilusion termina (75x90cm-30x35in) s.d.1982 prov. 15-May-3 Louis Morton, Mexico #15 (M.P 12000)

TAMAYO, Jorge (20th C) Venezuelan?
Prints
£8537 $14000 €12379 Dos personajes atacados por perros (151x241cm-59x95in) s.num.61/75 col mixografia prov.lit. 27-May-3 Sotheby's, New York #120

TAMAYO, Rufino (1899-1991) Mexican
£35032 $55000 €52548 Figure (29x80cm-11x31in) s.d.62 oil sand masonite exhib. 20-Nov-2 Christie's, Rockefeller NY #92/R est:80000-100000
£79268 $130000 €118902 Man and woman (101x81cm-40x32in) s.d.72 i.verso oil sand prov.exhib. 28-May-3 Christie's, Rockefeller NY #13/R est:120000-160000
£85366 $140000 €123781 Cry in the night (50x40cm-20x16in) s.d.0-53 oil sand masonite prov.exhib.lit. 27-May-3 Sotheby's, New York #20
£127389 $200000 €191084 Nude in red (80x60cm-31x24in) s.d.30 prov.lit. 19-Nov-2 Sotheby's, New York #18/R est:250000
£140127 $220000 €210191 Two figures (97x130cm-38x51in) s.d.68 oil sand prov.exhib.lit. 20-Nov-2 Christie's, Rockefeller NY #28/R est:150000-200000
£152866 $240000 €229299 Double portrait (80x101cm-31x40in) s.d.69 prov. 19-Nov-2 Sotheby's, New York #12/R
£203822 $320000 €305733 Still life (58x48cm-23x19in) s.d.28 prov.lit. 19-Nov-2 Sotheby's, New York #4/R est:300000
£509554 $800000 €764331 Dancers (117x91cm-46x36in) s.d.42 prov.exhib.lit. 20-Nov-2 Christie's, Rockefeller NY #25/R est:800000-1000000
£533537 $875000 €773629 Sandias (100x81cm-39x32in) s.d.0-53 prov. 27-May-3 Sotheby's, New York #13
Prints
£1763 $2750 €2645 Dos personages (64x92cm-25x36in) s.num.85/100 col lithograph. 14-Oct-2 Butterfields, San Francisco #1057 est:1800-2500
£1887 $3000 €2831 Pumpkin on a table (75x55cm-30x22in) s.i. col etching exec.c.1980. 2-May-3 Sotheby's, New York #47/R est:1500-2000
£1887 $3000 €2831 Hombre negro en fondo rojo (75x58cm-30x23in) s.i. col mixograph. 1-May-3 Swann Galleries, New York #610/R est:2000-3000
£3774 $6000 €5661 Personage con dos arboles (75x57cm-30x22in) s.i. col etching. 2-May-3 Sotheby's, New York #46/R est:4000-6000
£5346 $8500 €8019 Dos personajes (102x173cm-40x68in) s.num.12/30 col mixograph. 29-Apr-3 Christie's, Rockefeller NY #443/R est:15000-20000
£6410 $10000 €9615 Dos personajes atacados por perros (151x241cm-59x95in) s.num.60/75 col mixograph. 5-Nov-2 Christie's, Rockefeller NY #96/R est:15000-20000
Works on paper
£2051 $3200 €3077 No 14 (32x25cm-13x10in) s.d.72 W/C pencil prov. 14-Sep-2 Weschler, Washington #653/R est:3000-5000
£4487 $7000 €6731 Sandias (23x32cm-9x13in) s.d.68 crayon pencil prov. 14-Sep-2 Weschler, Washington #654/R est:10000-15000
£5096 $8000 €7644 Woman (233x25cm-92x10in) s.d.67 graphite crayon. 19-Nov-2 Sotheby's, New York #102/R
£10976 $18000 €16464 Campesino con sombrero verde (30x23cm-12x9in) s.d.1939 i.verso W/C pencil prov. 28-May-3 Christie's, Rockefeller NY #81/R est:20000-30000
£13376 $21000 €20064 Figures (56x75cm-22x30in) s.d.69 graphite col pencil. 19-Nov-2 Sotheby's, New York #103/R est:25000
£17197 $27000 €25796 Man and woman (23x30cm-9x12in) s.d.26 gouache prov. 19-Nov-2 Sotheby's, New York #80/R
£20382 $32000 €30573 Two men with fruit (35x42cm-14x17in) s.d.40 gouache prov. 19-Nov-2 Sotheby's, New York #5/R
£34247 $53425 €50000 Deux femmes (72x58cm-28x23in) s.d.1945 graphite pastel. 14-Apr-3 Laurence Calmels, Paris #4034/R est:15000
£39634 $65000 €59451 Mujer y vaca (32x47cm-13x19in) s.d.32 gouache prov.exhib.lit. 28-May-3 Christie's, Rockefeller NY #14/R est:70000-90000

TAMBURI, Orfeo (1910-1994) Italian
£272 $433 €400 Composition (38x29cm-15x11in) s. tempera W/C paper. 1-Mar-3 Meeting Art, Vercelli #593
£490 $784 €750 Study for theatre scenery (21x21cm-8x8in) s.d.1939 tempera paper. 4-Jan-3 Meeting Art, Vercelli #471
£680 $1082 €1000 Roman hills (46x37cm-18x15in) s. tempera paper. 1-Mar-3 Meeting Art, Vercelli #693
£705 $1107 €1100 Landscape (20x25cm-8x10in) s. cardboard on canvas. 21-Nov-2 Finarte, Rome #330
£753 $1175 €1100 Paris roofs (17x22cm-7x9in) s. tempera card. 10-Apr-3 Finarte Semenzato, Rome #72/R
£1062 $1699 €1540 Houses in Paris (22x28cm-9x11in) s. tempera W/C paper on canvas. 11-Mar-3 Babuino, Rome #130/R
£1076 $1678 €1700 Paris windows (25x35cm-10x14in) s. tempera paper on canvas. 14-Sep-2 Meeting Art, Vercelli #924/R
£1154 $1812 €1800 Portrait of woman (35x30cm-14x12in) s.d.49. 19-Nov-2 Finarte, Milan #183/R
£1266 $1975 €2000 Paris street (30x24cm-12x9in) s. tempera paper. 14-Sep-2 Meeting Art, Vercelli #938/R
£1410 $2214 €2200 Landscape (18x26cm-7x10in) s. tempera paper. 19-Nov-2 Finarte, Milan #43/R
£1410 $2214 €2200 Moulin Rouge (30x36cm-12x14in) s. tempera W/C paper on canvas. 23-Nov-2 Meeting Art, Vercelli #424/R
£1560 $2528 €2200 Urban landscape (17x21cm-7x8in) s. tempera W/C paper on canvas. 26-May-3 Christie's, Milan #41/R est:1000-1500
£1765 $2824 €2700 Kiosk (22x23cm-9x9in) s. 4-Jan-3 Meeting Art, Vercelli #729
£2564 $4026 €4000 Ruins (40x50cm-16x20in) s. s.i.d.1945 verso lit. 21-Nov-2 Finarte, Rome #322/R
£2778 $4417 €4000 Morgat, beach (33x16cm-13x6in) s. canvas on masonite. 1-May-3 Meeting Art, Vercelli #307
£2778 $4417 €4000 Paris (22x16cm-9x6in) s. canvas on board. 1-May-3 Meeting Art, Vercelli #585
£3226 $5097 €5000 Farm in Tuscany (62x49cm-24x19in) s. s.i.d.1959 verso prov.exhib. 18-Dec-2 Christie's, Rome #74/R
£3716 $5797 €5500 Yard (46x36cm-18x14in) s. painted 1963. 26-Mar-3 Finarte Semenzato, Milan #360/R
£4114 $6500 €6500 Houses in Paris (30x40cm-12x16in) s. 30-Nov-2 Farsetti, Prato #741/R est:6000
£4808 $7548 €7500 Big windows (70x50cm-28x20in) s. painted 1962. 19-Nov-2 Finarte, Milan #105/R
£5449 $8554 €8500 Paris at night (63x53cm-25x21in) s. i.d.1958 verso prov. 20-Nov-2 Pandolfini, Florence #21/R est:8000
£9615 $15192 €15000 Paris street (45x70cm-18x28in) s. painted 1986. 15-Nov-2 Farsetti, Prato #358/R est:17000
Works on paper
£294 $471 €450 Portrait (41x31cm-16x12in) s. Chinese ink card. 4-Jan-3 Meeting Art, Vercelli #485
£340 $541 €500 Woman in armchair (32x24cm-13x9in) s.d.1958 pen. 1-Mar-3 Meeting Art, Vercelli #446

£340	$541	€500	Woman at sink (35x27cm-14x11in) s. Chinese ink exec.1952. 1-Mar-3 Meeting Art, Vercelli #675
£449	$704	€700	Flying tube (23x31cm-9x12in) s. gouache. 20-Nov-2 Pandolfini, Florence #5
£521	$828	€750	Gardens in Paris (37x29cm-15x11in) s.d.1972 mixed media card on canvas. 1-May-3 Meeting Art, Vercelli #86
£641	$1006	€1000	Bridge on the Seine. Boats on the Seine (8x15cm-3x6in) s. ink pair. 21-Nov-2 Finarte, Rome #188
£822	$1282	€1200	Pireo-Abano statue (35x27cm-14x11in) s. W/C exec.1972. 10-Apr-3 Finarte Semenzato, Rome #88
£1135	$1838	€1600	Lotto di quattro opere (35x47cm-14x19in) s.i.d.1959 pen Indian ink W/C pastel five prov. 26-May-3 Christie's, Milan #64 est:1500-3000

TAMBURINI, Arnaldo (1843-?) Italian

£355	$500	€533	Monk counting money (30x23cm-12x9in) s. board. 12-Feb-2 Lincoln, Orange #491
£426	$600	€639	Seated monk with mortar and pestle (23x18cm-9x7in) s. board. 12-Feb-2 Lincoln, Orange #488
£613	$1000	€920	Cavalier (36x23cm-14x9in) d.1879. 14-Feb-3 Du Mouchelle, Detroit #51/R
£1049	$1500	€1574	Monks seated pouring glass of wine (41x30cm-16x12in) s. board. 11-Dec-1 Lincoln, Orange #465
£1220	$2000	€1769	Anticipation (24x19cm-9x7in) s.i. panel. 4-Jun-3 Christie's, Rockefeller NY #221/R est:2000-3000

TAMBURINI, Jose Maria (1856-1932) Spanish

£671	$1081	€1000	Landscape with peasant woman (29x38cm-11x15in) 18-Feb-3 Durán, Madrid #126/R
£7432	$11595	€11000	Young lady with flowers (70x100cm-28x39in) s. 25-Mar-3 Durán, Madrid #139/R est:8500

Works on paper

£1724	$2741	€2500	Portrait of young woman with shawl (86x64cm-34x25in) s.pastel. 4-Mar-3 Ansorena, Madrid #376/R

TAMM, Franz Werner (1658-1724) German

£10692	$16572	€17000	Large bouquet in metal vase (128x96cm-50x38in) 2-Oct-2 Dorotheum, Vienna #220/R est:13000-15000
£18000	$28080	€27000	Mixed flowers in glass vase on a stone ledge. Mixed flowers in a glass vase on a stone ledge (32x25cm-13x10in) s.d.1699 copper pair. 9-Apr-3 Christie's, London #62/R est:20000-30000

TAMM, Franz Werner (attrib) (1658-1724) German

£6410	$9936	€10000	Still life of flowers in a basket (83x107cm-33x42in) indis.mono. canvas on canvas. 4-Dec-2 Neumeister, Munich #643a/R est:12000
£6918	$10792	€11000	Still life with dead birds and flowers (66x80cm-26x31in) 23-Sep-2 Wiener Kunst Auktionen, Vienna #17/R est:11000-22000
£9607	$14987	€14411	Flora holding flower basket (129x95cm-51x37in) 20-Nov-2 Fischer, Luzern #1056/R est:12000-18000 (S.FR 22000)

TAMM, Franz Werner (circle) (1658-1724) German

£5200	$8164	€7800	Lilies, sunflowers and other flowers in an urn, in a wooded landscape (127x104cm-50x41in) 13-Dec-2 Christie's, Kensington #141/R est:5000-8000

TAMMARO, F (?) Italian

£1200	$1944	€1800	Elegant figures and carriages on a Parisian Boulevard (30x60cm-12x24in) s. board. 23-Jan-3 Christie's, Kensington #244/R est:1200-1800

TAMMARO, Francesco (?) Italian

£531	$850	€797	Untitled (30x41cm-12x16in) board. 10-Jan-3 Du Mouchelle, Detroit #2071/R
£539	$900	€782	Paris along the River Seine (30x61cm-12x24in) s. board. 21-Jun-3 Charlton Hall, Columbia #188/R
£688	$1100	€1032	Untitled (30x41cm-12x16in) board. 10-Jan-3 Du Mouchelle, Detroit #2070/R
£1200	$1968	€1800	Bustling Paris boulevard (30x60cm-12x24in) s. board. 5-Jun-3 Christie's, Kensington #832/R est:1000-1500
£1400	$2296	€2100	Anglers on the Seine, Paris (28x51cm-11x20in) s. board. 5-Jun-3 Christie's, Kensington #831/R est:800-1200

TAMURA, Maki (1973-) American?

Works on paper

£625	$1000	€938	Fit cake cheese blintz (56x76cm-22x30in) s.d.10.26/99 W/C linoeum paint two prov. 16-May-3 Phillips, New York #200/R est:2500-3500

TANABE, Takao (1926-) Canadian

£933	$1531	€1353	Faraday passage (65x120cm-26x47in) s.i.d.1985 acrylic. 9-Jun-3 Hodgins, Calgary #176/R est:2500-3500 (C.D 2100)
£2667	$4373	€4001	In the channel (87x150cm-34x59in) s.i.verso acrylic. 3-Jun-3 Joyner, Toronto #422/R est:3000-4000 (C.D 6000)
£6048	$9556	€9072	Off Awaya Point (105x243cm-41x96in) s. s.i.verso acrylic prov.lit. 18-Nov-2 Sotheby's, Toronto #120/R est:6000-9000 (C.D 15000)

TANAKA, Akira (1918-1982) Japanese

£1410	$2214	€2200	Street musician (65x91cm-26x36in) s. 16-Dec-2 Rabourdin & Choppin de Janvry, Paris #133/R
£1724	$2741	€2500	Les philatelistes (65x81cm-26x32in) s. 10-Mar-3 Thierry & Lannon, Brest #201/R

TANAKA, Shu (1908-) Japanese

£280	$448	€420	Abstract (81x53cm-32x21in) s. 14-Mar-3 Gardiner & Houlgate, Bath #19/R
£545	$861	€850	Old house (45x54cm-18x21in) s. s.i.d.1958 verso. 14-Nov-2 Neumeister, Munich #887/R

TANAKA, Yasushi (1886-1941) Japanese

£646	$1028	€950	Paysage de bord de mer (27x35cm-11x14in) studio st.verso cardboard. 26-Feb-3 Artcurial Briest, Paris #273
£884	$1406	€1300	Branches, fleurs et fruits (21x32cm-8x13in) s. cardboard. 26-Feb-3 Artcurial Briest, Paris #274
£884	$1406	€1300	Voilier a Sainte-Maxime (22x27cm-9x11in) i.d.1926 verso cardboard. 26-Feb-3 Artcurial Briest, Paris #275
£884	$1406	€1300	Avignon, le Palais-des-Papes (27x22cm-11x9in) s.i.d.1927 verso cardboard. 26-Feb-3 Artcurial Briest, Paris #276
£2000	$3320	€3000	La Seine au Soir, Paris (55x66cm-22x26in) s.d.20. 12-Jun-3 Bonhams, New Bond Street #842/R est:1500-2000
£2041	$3245	€3000	Baigneuse au voile (50x25cm-20x10in) s. cardboard. 26-Feb-3 Artcurial Briest, Paris #271 est:1500-1800
£2687	$4272	€3950	Femme assise (65x54cm-26x21in) s. 26-Feb-3 Artcurial Briest, Paris #272 est:2000-2500
£3265	$5192	€4800	Nu au divan. Paysage de neige (49x56cm-19x22in) s. cardboard double-sided. 26-Feb-3 Artcurial Briest, Paris #269/R est:2200-3000
£3435	$5462	€5050	Baigneuse au bord de l'eau (48x52cm-19x20in) s. cardboard. 26-Feb-3 Artcurial Briest, Paris #270/R est:2200-3000
£6923	$10869	€10800	Nu devant la fenetre (151x77cm-59x30in) s. 11-Dec-2 Artcurial Briest, Paris #527/R est:12000
£7692	$12077	€12000	Nu dans sa chambre (144x60cm-57x24in) s. panel. 11-Dec-2 Artcurial Briest, Paris #528/R

TANCREDI (1927-1964) Italian

£4387	$6932	€6800	Fantasy (48x67cm-19x26in) s. tempera pastel wax crayon paper prov.exhib. 18-Dec-2 Christie's, Rome #262/R
£7742	$12232	€12000	Untitled (70x100cm-28x39in) s. tempera pastel. 18-Dec-2 Christie's, Rome #186/R est:10000
£14103	$21859	€22000	Untitled (73x116cm-29x46in) painted 1958 exhib.lit. 4-Dec-2 Finarte, Milan #310/R est:28000
£30000	$46200	€45000	Polvere d'erba (89x115cm-35x45in) s. s.i.d.1957 on stretcher prov.exhib.lit. 22-Oct-2 Christie's, London #21/R est:30000-50000
£82000	$127920	€123000	Proposito di venezia (177x195cm-70x77in) d.1958 tempera paper on canvas prov.exhib.lit. 21-Oct-2 Sotheby's, London #55/R est:50000-70000

Works on paper

£513	$810	€800	Untitled (23x14cm-9x6in) s. chl exec.1950. 15-Nov-2 Farsetti, Prato #273/R
£545	$861	€850	Untitled (23x14cm-9x6in) s. chl exec.1950 lit. 15-Nov-2 Farsetti, Prato #277/R
£705	$1114	€1100	Untitled (22x14cm-9x6in) s. chl exec.1950 lit. 15-Nov-2 Farsetti, Prato #256/R
£833	$1317	€1300	Untitled (23x14cm-9x6in) s. chl exec.1950. 15-Nov-2 Farsetti, Prato #278/R
£1026	$1621	€1600	Untitled (24x34cm-9x13in) s. ink col crayon collage. 15-Nov-2 Farsetti, Prato #255/R
£1026	$1621	€1600	Untitled (24x34cm-9x13in) s. col crayon. 15-Nov-2 Farsetti, Prato #274/R
£1218	$1924	€1900	Untitled (24x34cm-9x13in) s. col crayon. 15-Nov-2 Farsetti, Prato #268/R
£1474	$2329	€2300	Untitled (33x45cm-13x18in) s. mixed media. 15-Nov-2 Farsetti, Prato #267/R
£1667	$2633	€2600	Untitled (34x45cm-13x18in) s. mixed media exec.1950-51 lit. 15-Nov-2 Farsetti, Prato #280
£6383	$10340	€9000	Untitled (70x100cm-28x39in) s. s.i.verso pastel lit. 26-May-3 Christie's, Milan #112/R est:9000-13000
£7051	$11141	€11000	Untitled (35x50cm-14x20in) s. mixed media cardboard exec.1951 lit. 15-Nov-2 Farsetti, Prato #284/R est:10500-11500
£8511	$13787	€12000	Untitled (69x73cm-27x29in) mixed media paper on canvas lit. 26-May-3 Christie's, Milan #111/R est:8000-12000
£12057	$19532	€17000	Untitled (99x70cm-39x28in) mixed media prov.exhib.lit. 26-May-3 Christie's, Milan #98/R est:8000-12000
£41772	$66000	€66000	Composition (92x124cm-36x49in) s. mixed media board painted 1954-55 exhib.lit. 29-Nov-2 Farsetti, Prato #307/R est:75000

TANDBERG, Odd (1924-) Norwegian

£384	$599	€576	Composition (86x44cm-34x17in) s. painted 1959. 23-Sep-2 Blomqvist, Lysaker #1243/R (N.KR 4500)

TANG DAI and SHEN YUAN (17/18th C) Chinese
Works on paper
£13986 $23077 €20280 Island palace (58x58cm-23x23in) s. ink col silk hanging scroll. 7-Jul-3 Christie's, Hong Kong #514/R est:150000-200000 (HK.D 180000)

TANG HAIWEN (1929-1991) Chinese
Works on paper
£2486 $4103 €3605 Islands (70x100cm-28x39in) s. ink diptych prov.exhib.lit. 6-Jul-3 Christie's, Hong Kong #172/R est:30000-50000 (HK.D 32000)
£4274 $7051 €6197 Mountains (70x50cm-28x20in) s. W/C prov.exhib. 6-Jul-3 Christie's, Hong Kong #171/R est:40000-60000 (HK.D 55000)

TANG KUI HONG (attrib) (20th C) Chinese
£650 $1053 €975 Ambassador's children (40cm-16in circular) s. board. 23-Jan-3 Christie's, Kensington #41/R

TANG YUN (1910-1993) Chinese
Works on paper
£870 $1426 €1200 Three birds at a river (96x59cm-38x23in) i. seals Indian ink hanging scroll. 30-May-3 Dr Fritz Nagel, Stuttgart #1145/R
£1707 $2698 €2561 Lotus pond (19x50cm-7x20in) s.i.d.1944 i.verso ink col folding fan. 28-Apr-3 Sotheby's, Hong Kong #559/R est:15000-20000 (HK.D 21000)

TANG YUN and ZHOU LIAN XIA (20th C) Chinese
Works on paper
£362 $594 €500 Cicada on branch (109x27cm-43x11in) i. seals Indian ink col. 30-May-3 Dr Fritz Nagel, Stuttgart #1221/R

TANGEN, Olof (1903-1997) Norwegian
£345 $525 €518 From Kragero (38x46cm-15x18in) s.d.49 s.i.d.verso sketch panel. 31-Aug-2 Grev Wedels Plass, Oslo #110 (N.KR 4000)
£432 $721 €626 Red (81x100cm-32x39in) s.d.92 i.verso exhib. 18-Jun-3 Grev Wedels Plass, Oslo #230 (N.KR 5000)
£1538 $2492 €2307 Farm at the mouth of the fjord, Portor (66x81cm-26x32in) s.d.44. 26-May-3 Grev Wedels Plass, Oslo #66/R est:8000-10000 (N.KR 17000)
£1842 $2911 €2763 From Blindtarmen in Kragero (73x92cm-29x36in) s.d.1944 panel. 17-Dec-2 Grev Wedels Plass, Oslo #279/R est:15000-20000 (N.KR 21000)

TANGRY, Morel de (1857-1930) French
£414 $691 €600 Nocturne au Cap Ferrat (60x81cm-24x32in) s.d.1923. 8-Jul-3 Gioffredo, Nice #28/R
£1401 $2186 €2200 Menton perle de la Cote d'Azur (180x110cm-71x43in) s.d.1906. 6-Nov-2 Gioffredo, Nice #26/R
£1783 $2782 €2800 Baou et Saint-Jeannet (220x100cm-87x39in) s. 6-Nov-2 Gioffredo, Nice #27/R
£1975 $3080 €3100 Cote d'Azur (100x70cm-39x28in) panel. 6-Nov-2 Gioffredo, Nice #28/R

TANGUY, Yves (1900-1955) American/French
£67308 $105000 €100962 Titre inconnu (37x68cm-15x27in) s.d.27 panel prov.exhib.lit. 7-Nov-2 Christie's, Rockefeller NY #331/R est:100000-150000
£155279 $250000 €232919 L'extinction des especes (35x27cm-14x11in) s.d.36 canvasboard prov.exhib.lit. 7-May-3 Sotheby's, New York #312/R est:150000-200000
£230000 $377200 €345000 Rue aux levres (44x36cm-17x14in) s.d.39 prov.exhib.lit. 4-Feb-3 Sotheby's, London #44/R est:300000
£330000 $537900 €495000 Second message III (64x73cm-25x29in) s.d.30 prov.exhib.lit. 3-Feb-3 Christie's, London #164/R est:600000
£372671 $600000 €559007 Filles des consequences (73x60cm-29x24in) s.d.37 prov.exhib.lit. 6-May-3 Sotheby's, New York #37/R est:500000-700000
£684932 $1075343 €1000000 Armoire de Protee (61x50cm-24x20in) s.d.31 exhib.lit. 15-Apr-3 Laurence Calmels, Paris #4420/R est:1000000
Works on paper
£5975 $9500 €8963 Untitled (41x30cm-16x12in) s.d.47 pen ink prov. 27-Feb-3 Christie's, Rockefeller NY #38/R
£11180 $18000 €16770 Sans titre (5x54cm-2x21in) s.d.45 W/C pen India ink prov. 8-May-3 Christie's, Rockefeller NY #126/R est:14000-18000
£18000 $29520 €27000 Untitled (43x34cm-17x13in) s.d.28 pen brush ink pastel pencil prov.exhib. 5-Feb-3 Sotheby's, London #189/R est:25000
£20000 $32800 €30000 Untitled (43x34cm-17x13in) s.d.28 pen brush ink pastel pencil prov.exhib. 5-Feb-3 Sotheby's, London #190/R est:30000
£24000 $39360 €36000 Untitled (43x34cm-17x13in) s.d.28 pen brush ink pastel pencil prov.exhib. 5-Feb-3 Sotheby's, London #188/R est:30000
£24000 $39360 €36000 Untitled (43x34cm-17x13in) s.d.28 pen brush ink pastel pencil prov.exhib. 5-Feb-3 Sotheby's, London #187/R est:35000
£38000 $61940 €57000 Untitled (8x31cm-3x12in) s.d.36 gouache pencil prov.exhib.lit. 3-Feb-3 Christie's, London #171/R est:60000
£40373 $65000 €60560 Sans titre (12x27cm-5x11in) s.d.44 gouache pencil prov.lit. 8-May-3 Christie's, Rockefeller NY #128/R est:70000-90000

TANNAES, Marie (1854-1939) Norwegian
£708 $1154 €1062 Autumn, Hof Jarlsberg (35x57cm-14x22in) s. 17-Feb-3 Blomqvist, Lysaker #1230/R (N.KR 8000)
£950 $1586 €1378 Woodland path (58x86cm-23x34in) s.d.90. 18-Jun-3 Grev Wedels Plass, Oslo #231/R (N.KR 11000)
£1469 $2410 €2130 Sailing boats in Oslofjorden (60x80cm-24x31in) s. 2-Jun-3 Blomqvist, Oslo #104/R est:15000-20000 (N.KR 16000)

TANNER, E L (19/20th C) British?
£850 $1343 €1275 Kitty, bay horse in a stable (51x61cm-20x24in) s.i.d.1915. 28-Nov-2 Christie's, Kensington #157/R

TANNER, Edwin (1920-1980) Australian
£12903 $19613 €19355 Untitled (116x76cm-46x30in) s.d.56 verso canvasboard exhib. 28-Aug-2 Deutscher-Menzies, Melbourne #58/R est:25000-35000 (A.D 36000)
Works on paper
£8915 $14174 €13373 Toe the line better blue one than red (167x182cm-66x72in) s.d.1976 synthetic polymer canvas prov. 5-May-3 Sotheby's, Melbourne #140/R est:20000-30000 (A.D 23000)

TANNER, Henry Ossawa (1859-1937) American
Prints
£2138 $3400 €3207 Disciples see Christ walking on water (18x24cm-7x9in) s.num.102/120 etching. 1-May-3 Swann Galleries, New York #24/R est:1500-2500

TANNER, Liisa (?) Finnish
£293 $465 €430 Still life of flowers (70x60cm-28x24in) s. 24-Mar-3 Bukowskis, Helsinki #320/R

TANNER, Robert (1940-) Swiss
Works on paper
£652 $1011 €978 Composition cinetique (90x90cm-35x35in) s.d.1969 i.verso gouache paper on verre cannele. 7-Dec-2 Galerie du Rhone, Sion #498/R (S.FR 1500)

TANNERT, Volker (1955-) German
£3043 $4991 €4200 Untitled (200x150cm-79x59in) s.i.d.82 verso on two canvases. 28-May-3 Lempertz, Koln #425/R est:5000

TANNING, Dorothea (1910-) American
£1528 $2400 €2292 L'amour c'est la foret (46x38cm-18x15in) s.d.1965 s.i.d. verso exhib.lit. 25-Nov-2 Germann, Zurich #72/R est:6000-8000 (S.FR 3500)
£2800 $4312 €4200 Un pont brule (33x41cm-13x16in) s. s.i.d.1965 verso prov. 23-Oct-2 Sotheby's, Olympia #782/R est:2500-3500
Sculpture
£2436 $3824 €3800 Le Nil (11cm-4in) st.sig. gold pair lit. 11-Dec-2 Artcurial Briest, Paris #561/R
£2692 $4227 €4200 Groutcho (6x6x6cm-2x2x2in) st.sig. gold lit. 11-Dec-2 Artcurial Briest, Paris #556/R

TANNOCK OF KILMARNOCK, William (19th C) British
£750 $1208 €1125 Tam o'shanter (25x26cm-10x10in) init.d.1855 panel. 20-Feb-3 Christie's, London #343/R

TANOBE, Miyuki (20th C) Canadian
£2016 $3185 €3024 Le coin aux fleurs (61x76cm-24x30in) s.i.d.1973 s.verso board prov. 14-Nov-2 Heffel, Vancouver #14/R est:6000-8000 (C.D 5000)

TANOUX, Adrien Henri (1865-1923) French
£833 $1300 €1250 Sewing by an open window (56x38cm-22x15in) s.d.1907. 9-Oct-2 Doyle, New York #110/R
£1852 $2981 €2778 Mother's joy (73x60cm-29x24in) s.d.1906. 7-May-3 Dobiaschofsky, Bern #1014/R est:6000 (S.FR 4000)
£8013 $12580 €12500 L'entree du Harem (55x38cm-22x15in) s.d.1905. 16-Dec-2 Gros & Delettrez, Paris #73/R est:9000-12000
£18000 $28260 €27000 Harem beauties (73x50cm-29x20in) s. 21-Nov-2 Christie's, Kensington #203/R est:12000-18000

TANSEY, Francis (1959-) Irish
£2500 $3975 €3600 Complementaries in red (71x71cm-28x28in) s.i.d.May 1989 verso acrylic. 29-Apr-3 Whyte's, Dublin #131/R est:2000-3000
£3056 $4858 €4400 Receding red (213x61cm-84x24in) s. i.d.1985 verso acrylic. 29-Apr-3 Whyte's, Dublin #129/R est:5000-7000
£3819 $6073 €5500 Spatial dialogue no.2 (112x112cm-44x44in) s.i.d.May 1989 verso acrylic. 29-Apr-3 Whyte's, Dublin #130/R est:4000-6000

TANSEY, Mark (1949-) American
£569620 $900000 €854430 Achilles and the tortoise (282x193cm-111x76in) s. i.d.1986 verso prov.exhib.lit. 12-Nov-2 Sotheby's, New York #23/R est:500000-700000

TANTTU, Erkki (1907-1985) Finnish
Works on paper
£294 $482 €450 Hakkapeliitan Joulu (44x34cm-17x13in) s. gouache. 9-Feb-3 Bukowskis, Helsinki #370/R
£579 $891 €920 At the railway station (34x29cm-13x11in) s.d.39 gouache. 27-Oct-2 Bukowskis, Helsinki #292/R

TANZI, Léon Louis Antoine (1846-1913) French
£5190 $8200 €8200 Nenuphars (123x198cm-48x78in) s.d.1899. 1-Dec-2 Livinec, Gaudcheau & Jezequel, Rennes #86/R

TAO LENGYUE (1895-1985) Chinese
Works on paper
£507 $832 €700 River landscape (79x37cm-31x15in) i.d.1986 seals Indian ink col hanging scroll. 30-May-3 Dr Fritz Nagel, Stuttgart #1283/R
£543 $891 €750 Scholar looking at moon (60x24cm-24x9in) i. seals Indian ink. 30-May-3 Dr Fritz Nagel, Stuttgart #1260/R

TAPIA, Ramiro (1931-) Spanish
£290 $459 €450 Landscape (50x65cm-20x26in) s. 17-Dec-2 Durán, Madrid #7/R
£484 $765 €750 Boar (81x100cm-32x39in) s.d.1969. 17-Dec-2 Durán, Madrid #117/R

TAPIES, Antonio (1923-) Spanish
£962 $1490 €1500 Untitled (29x37cm-11x15in) s.i. stamp oil pencil scratching. 3-Dec-2 Lempertz, Koln #461/R est:1800
£5000 $7700 €7500 Escrituras y manchas sobre papel de embalaje - writing and smudges on wrapping paper (45x65cm-18x26in) s. oil pencil brown wrapping paper executed 1970 prov.exhib.lit. 22-Oct-2 Sotheby's, London #376/R est:6000-8000
£9000 $13860 €13500 Serie la clau del no.27 - key of fire series no.27 (32x49cm-13x19in) s. oil pencil on paper painted 1973 prov. 22-Oct-2 Sotheby's, London #375/R est:7000-10000
£11921 $19430 €18000 Untitled (32x50cm-13x20in) s.d.1961 acrylic pencil decoupage paper prov.exhib.lit. 11-Feb-3 Segre, Madrid #236/R est:18000
£12000 $20040 €17400 Espuma con escuadra (41x62cm-16x24in) s. household paint on foam painted 1986 prov.exhib.lit. 27-Jun-3 Christie's, London #244/R est:6000-8000
£12821 $19872 €20000 A Corazon - rouge et noir agite (64x50cm-25x20in) s. acrylic prov. 3-Dec-2 Lempertz, Koln #451/R est:18000-20000
£15278 $25208 €22000 Arc noir sur vernis (127x65cm-50x26in) s. acrylic varnish prov.exhib.lit. 1-Jul-3 Artcurial Briest, Paris #512/R est:10000-15000
£16000 $26240 €24000 Botella (91x63cm-36x25in) s. paper on canvas prov.exhib.lit. 6-Feb-3 Christie's, London #634/R est:15000-20000
£22000 $36740 €31900 Cloth and collage on canvas (90x65cm-35x26in) s.verso oil cloth collage prov.exhib.lit. 26-Jun-3 Sotheby's, London #220/R est:15000-20000
£27848 $44000 €44000 Papier ocre et noir plie (124x91cm-49x36in) s. acrylic paper painted 1963 prov.exhib.lit. 27-Nov-2 Tajan, Paris #66/R est:48000-60000
£30000 $49200 €45000 Caligrafias (78x61cm-31x24in) s. acrylic marble dust paper on canvas prov.exhib.lit. 6-Feb-3 Christie's, London #629/R est:20000-30000
£30000 $50100 €43500 Papel secante con relieve azul (62x50cm-24x20in) s.d.1961 paint relief blotting paper on canvas prov.exhib.lit. 27-Jun-3 Christie's, London #125/R est:30000-40000
£40000 $65600 €60000 Efecto de baston en relieve (139x112cm-55x44in) s.verso acrylic chl linen on canvas prov.exhib.lit. 7-Feb-3 Sotheby's, London #202/R est:30000-40000
£42000 $70140 €60900 Nariz (91x92cm-36x36in) oil on felt painted 1985 prov.exhib.lit. 27-Jun-3 Christie's, London #129/R est:18000-22000
£60000 $98400 €90000 Gris con dos agujeros (130x97cm-51x38in) s.verso oil sand prov.exhib.lit. 6-Feb-3 Christie's, London #633/R est:70000-90000
£100000 $163000 €150000 Landscape (81x100cm-32x39in) s.i.d.1950 verso prov.exhib.lit. 3-Feb-3 Christie's, London #177/R est:150000
Prints
£2200 $3630 €3190 Les vostres mans (57x76cm-22x30in) s.num.21/45 col aquatint screenprint. 2-Jul-3 Christie's, London #362/R est:1000-1500
£2400 $3960 €3480 Portail (121x80cm-48x31in) s.num.23/50 col etching screenprint carborundum. 2-Jul-3 Christie's, London #364/R est:1000-1500
Sculpture
£13500 $22005 €20250 Paisage (29x50x31cm-11x20x12in) s. terracotta executed 1987 prov. 3-Feb-3 Sotheby's, Olympia #99/R est:5000-7000
Works on paper
£455 $664 €700 Untitled (32x24cm-13x9in) s. engraving. 17-Jun-2 Ansorena, Madrid #268/R
£2405 $3800 €3800 Untitled (19x13cm-7x5in) s.d.1961 wax crayon dr prov. 27-Nov-2 Tajan, Paris #67/R
£6027 $9402 €9041 Untitled (43x30cm-17x12in) s. mixed media collage. 5-Nov-2 Bukowskis, Stockholm #308/R est:60000-80000 (S.KR 86000)
£7051 $10929 €11000 Aile (36x50cm-14x20in) s. varnish graphite Indian ink prov. 3-Dec-2 Lempertz, Koln #450/R est:10000
£7092 $10993 €10638 Composition with red lines and black splashes (29x38cm-11x15in) s. mixed media. 8-Dec-2 Uppsala Auktionskammare, Uppsala #271/R est:60000-80000 (S.KR 100000)
£10127 $16000 €16000 To Peter Roth (45x63cm-18x25in) s.i. mixed media material lit. 27-Nov-2 Dorotheum, Vienna #61/R est:18000-22000
£11000 $18040 €16500 Gato. Serie Historia Natural (50x33cm-20x13in) s.i.d.51 ink prov.exhib.lit. 6-Feb-3 Christie's, London #626/R est:7000-9000
£14000 $23380 €20300 Untitled (51x37cm-20x15in) s. gouache chk pencil paper on jute exec.c.1980 prov. 26-Jun-3 Sotheby's, London #219/R est:12000-18000
£15385 $22462 €24000 Composition (75x105cm-30x41in) s. mixed media exec.1976. 5-Jun-2 Il Ponte, Milan #131/R est:20000-25000
£32051 $50321 €50000 Abstraction (68x87cm-27x34in) mixed media cardboard on canvas. 16-Dec-2 Castellana, Madrid #806/R est:18000
£38000 $63460 €55100 Traces of ochre material on brown (65x50cm-26x20in) s.d.1962 verso mixed media canvas prov.exhib.lit. 26-Jun-3 Sotheby's, London #216/R est:25000-35000
£44000 $73480 €63800 Collage de la fuente (75x54cm-30x21in) s.verso mixed media prov.exhib.lit. 26-Jun-3 Sotheby's, London #212/R est:35000-45000
£360000 $601200 €540000 Relieve Rojo - Red relief (195x150cm-77x59in) s.verso mixed media canvas on panel exc.1958 prov.exhib.lit. 25-Jun-3 Sotheby's, London #23/R est:300000-400000

TAPIOLA, Marjatta (1951-) Finnish
£1646 $2600 €2600 Bloody beach (100x180cm-39x71in) s.d.1982 exhib. 1-Dec-2 Bukowskis, Helsinki #361/R est:3000-4000
£2014 $3304 €2800 Composition (130x130cm-51x51in) s.d.1997. 5-Jun-3 Hagelstam, Helsinki #963 est:1000
Works on paper
£282 $454 €400 Reclining model (70x110cm-28x43in) s.d.81 W/C. 10-May-3 Bukowskis, Helsinki #214/R

TAPIRO Y BARO, Jose (1830-1913) Spanish
Works on paper
£2600 $4056 €3900 Sunlit terrace (22x28cm-9x11in) gouache pair. 5-Nov-2 Bonhams, New Bond Street #22/R est:800-1200
£8219 $12904 €12000 Siesta in the sistine chapel (36x24cm-14x9in) s. W/C htd white. 15-Apr-3 Sotheby's, Amsterdam #47/R est:4000-6000

TAPISSIER, Edmond Anne Antoine (1861-1943) French
£256 $397 €400 Bord de mer provencale (27x35cm-11x14in) s. 9-Dec-2 Thierry & Lannon, Brest #252

TAPLIN, Guy (1939-) British
Sculpture
£1100 $1694 €1650 Mallard (47cm-19in) s.i. painted wood. 5-Sep-2 Christie's, Kensington #718/R est:700-900
£1200 $1848 €1800 Red headed duck (46cm-18in) s. painted wood. 5-Sep-2 Christie's, Kensington #722/R est:700-900
£1400 $2170 €2100 Grebe (62cm-24in) s.i. painted wood. 4-Dec-2 Christie's, Kensington #516/R est:800-1200
£1600 $2480 €2400 Snow goose (51cm-20in) carved painted wooded body metal stand with base. 31-Oct-2 Duke & Son, Dorchester #529/R est:1000-2000
£1800 $2844 €2700 Six shore birds (31cm-12in) painted wood metal construction. 28-Nov-2 Bonhams, Knightsbridge #44/R est:2000-3000
£1800 $2790 €2700 Egret (109cm-43in) carved painted body on twisted metal stand with base. 31-Oct-2 Duke & Son, Dorchester #528/R est:1500-3000
£3000 $4770 €4500 Three curlews (91cm-36in) s.i. wood painted steel rods. 26-Feb-3 Sotheby's, Olympia #336/R est:3000-5000

TAPPER, Garth (1927-1999) New Zealander
£625 $975 €938 Gayle (21x29cm-8x11in) s.d.1973 s.i.d.1973 verso board. 8-Apr-3 Peter Webb, Auckland #178/R (NZ.D 1800)
£1404 $2189 €2106 Jackie (67x56cm-26x22in) s. board. 27-Mar-3 International Art Centre, Auckland #57/R est:5000-8000 (NZ.D 4000)
£1439 $2244 €2159 Reclining nude (47x60cm-19x24in) s. board. 27-Mar-3 International Art Centre, Auckland #108/R est:4500-6500 (NZ.D 4100)
£1524 $2332 €2286 Landscape and trees with red roof cottages (111x188cm-44x74in) s.d.88 board. 21-Aug-2 Dunbar Sloane, Auckland #24/R est:5000-8000 (NZ.D 5000)
£1562 $2437 €2343 Prosecution (39x33cm-15x13in) s. s.i.d.1982 verso board. 8-Apr-3 Peter Webb, Auckland #177/R est:4000-6000 (NZ.D 4500)
£2351 $3668 €3527 Bob Charles shirt (40x50cm-16x20in) s. board. 7-Nov-2 International Art Centre, Auckland #31/R est:5000-7000 (NZ.D 7500)
£4407 $6875 €6611 Puhoi timber milling (73x99cm-29x39in) s.i.d.1986 s.i.d.verso. 17-Sep-2 Peter Webb, Auckland #135/R est:9000-12000 (NZ.D 14500)
£4474 $6979 €6711 Bishops tea party (36x44cm-14x17in) s.d.1994 canvasboard. 27-Mar-3 International Art Centre, Auckland #39/R est:8000-12000 (NZ.D 12750)
£6369 $10000 €9554 Merchant bankers (90x135cm-35x53in) s. s.i.verso board. 10-Dec-2 Peter Webb, Auckland #52/R est:15000-20000 (NZ.D 20000)

TAPPER, Kain (1930-) Finnish
Sculpture
£2183 $3515 €3100 Centipede (90cm-35in) s.d.70 stone. 10-May-3 Bukowskis, Helsinki #203/R est:2500-3000
Works on paper
£2324 $3742 €3300 Triangle (42x64cm-17x25in) s.d.91 mixed media. 10-May-3 Bukowskis, Helsinki #253/R est:1800-2000

TAPPERT, Georg (1880-1957) German
£23188 $38029 €32000 Trees in hilly landscape (80x80cm-31x31in) s. 29-May-3 Lempertz, Koln #935/R est:35000-40000
Works on paper
£314 $484 €500 Woman seated at table (32x22cm-13x9in) Indian ink brush. 26-Oct-2 Dr Lehr, Berlin #520/R
£471 $772 €650 Head (43x34cm-17x13in) s. chl sold with linocut. 31-May-3 Villa Grisebach, Berlin #695/R
£655 $956 €983 Snake charmer (25x20cm-10x8in) s. W/C Indian ink. 4-Jun-2 Germann, Zurich #110/R (S.FR 1500)
£759 $1177 €1200 Reclining female nude (11x28cm-4x11in) s. wash Indian ink. 28-Sep-2 Ketterer, Hamburg #97/R
£833 $1325 €1200 Nu debout (37x19cm-15x7in) s. W/C pencil gouache exec.c.1910. 29-Apr-3 Artcurial Briest, Paris #138
£1944 $3091 €2800 Femme assise au fauteuil (46x29cm-18x11in) s. W/C Indian ink wash prov. 29-Apr-3 Artcurial Briest, Paris #137/R est:3000-4000

TAQUOY, Maurice (1878-1952) French
Prints
£1923 $2942 €3000 Retour de chasse (30x49cm-12x19in) s.d.1925 pochoir. 23-Aug-2 Deauville, France #156/R
Works on paper
£1384 $2145 €2200 Courses a auteuil (29x42cm-11x17in) s.d.1926 gouache. 30-Oct-2 Artcurial Briest, Paris #267 est:2000-2500

TARAVAL, Hugues (1729-1785) French
£1935 $3058 €3000 Petit Saint-Jean Baptiste (32x41cm-13x16in) 20-Dec-2 Tajan, Paris #117/R est:4000

TARBELL, Edmund C (1862-1938) American
£419355 $650000 €629033 Portrait of Mrs C - Mrs H.M. Channing (102x109cm-40x43in) s.d.1911 prov.exhib.lit. 5-Dec-2 Christie's, Rockefeller NY #72/R est:600000-800000

TARBET, J A Henderson (?-1927) British
Works on paper
£404 $638 €606 Village on the Fife coast (36x25cm-14x10in) s. i.verso W/C. 18-Nov-2 Waddingtons, Toronto #166/R (C.D 1000)

TARCHIANI, Giacomo (fl.1620-1633) Italian
£25000 $41750 €36250 Allegory of the Arts (199x298cm-78x117in) s. indis.d.1620 prov. 10-Jul-3 Sotheby's, London #172/R est:25000-35000

TARDIA, Enzo (1960-) Italian
£321 $503 €500 Untitled (80x80cm-31x31in) s. painted 1993. 23-Nov-2 Meeting Art, Vercelli #263/R

TARDOS-KRENNER, Viktor (1866-1927) Hungarian
£800 $1304 €1200 Bacchante reclining on a tiger (80x132cm-31x52in) s. 13-Feb-3 Christie's, Kensington #2

TARENGHI, Enrico (1848-?) Italian
Works on paper
£3019 $4709 €4800 Oriental man holding gun (54x38cm-21x15in) s.d.1896 W/C. 8-Oct-2 Christie's, Paris #46/R
£3800 $5928 €5700 At prayer (75x53cm-30x21in) s. W/C pencil prov. 15-Oct-2 Sotheby's, London #134/R est:4000-5000

TARKHOFF, Nicolas (1871-1930) Russian
£2041 $3245 €3000 Branche de digitales en fleurs (45x35cm-18x14in) s. paper. 26-Feb-3 Artcurial Briest, Paris #251 est:1000-1500
£2917 $4754 €4200 Paysages, sous-bois, riviere et bord de mer (19x13cm-7x5in) panel five in one frame. 19-Jul-3 Thierry & Lannon, Brest #180 est:2500-3000
£7870 $12671 €11805 Fleurs dans vase (32x423cm-13x167in) st.sig. board. 7-May-3 Dobiaschofsky, Bern #1015/R est:7000 (S.FR 17000)
£10000 $15700 €15000 Paris under snow (49x31cm-19x12in) s. paper on canvas. 20-Nov-2 Sotheby's, London #84/R est:8000-12000
£10646 $16928 €15650 Bouquet de fleurs jaunes (46x60cm-18x24in) s. cardboard. 26-Feb-3 Artcurial Briest, Paris #250/R est:3500-4500
£80000 $125600 €120000 Beach scene (53x65cm-21x26in) s. s.i.verso board painted c.1905. 20-Nov-2 Sotheby's, London #76/R est:18000-25000
£100000 $157000 €150000 The sunny boulevard (100x81cm-39x32in) s. s.i.verso painted c.1905. 20-Nov-2 Sotheby's, London #78/R est:30000-40000
Works on paper
£355 $574 €500 Chat au fauteuil (25x42cm-10x17in) d.24 VII 1916 studio st. crayon. 23-May-3 Camard, Paris #27
£426 $689 €600 Fic-Fic en couche (25x42cm-10x17in) d.1916 studio st. crayon. 23-May-3 Camard, Paris #28

TARNOCZY, Bertha von (1846-1936) Austrian
£1258 $1950 €2000 Summer's day on Lake Garda (45x68cm-18x27in) s. 29-Oct-2 Dorotheum, Vienna #242/R est:1600-1800

TARNOGROCKI, Otto (1875-?) German
£288 $447 €450 Snowy river landscape (46x63cm-18x25in) s. double-sided lit. 7-Dec-2 Hans Stahl, Hamburg #88/R

TARRAGO, Leticia (1940-) Mexican
£312 $493 €468 Dusk (45x60cm-18x24in) s. 26-Nov-2 Louis Morton, Mexico #29/R est:7000 (M.P 5000)

TARRANT, Margaret W (1888-1959) British
Works on paper
£2000 $3160 €2900 White Christmas (15x12cm-6x5in) s. W/C. 22-Jul-3 Bonhams, Knightsbridge #175/R est:800-1000

TARRANT, Percy (fl.1881-1930) British
Works on paper
£2300 $3657 €3450 Returning from market (38x25cm-15x10in) mono. W/C. 4-Mar-3 Bearnes, Exeter #384/R est:500-700

TARRES, Maty (20th C) Italian?
£506 $790 €800 Painting H-1-M (70x50cm-28x20in) s. s.i.verso. 19-Oct-2 Semenzato, Venice #27/R

TASKER, W (1808-1852) British
£714 $1064 €1100 Race horse Alrick (30x46cm-12x18in) init. 28-Jun-2 Woodwards, Cork #206

TASKER, William (1808-1852) British
£1500 $2370 €2250 Dogs in an extensive landscape (48x61cm-19x24in) s.d.1839. 28-Nov-2 Christie's, Kensington #331/R est:1500-2000

TASKINEN, Matti (1895-1972) Finnish
£380 $592 €600 Uspenski Cathedral, Helsingfors (65x53cm-26x21in) s.d.1934. 12-Sep-2 Hagelstam, Helsinki #826

TASLITZKY, Boris (1911-) French
£423 $701 €600 Nature morte en escalier (55x38cm-22x15in) s.d.32. 11-Jun-3 Beaussant & Lefèvre, Paris #199

TASSAERT, Octave (1800-1874) French
£5128 $8103 €8000 Jeune mere (41x32cm-16x13in) s.d.1856. 18-Nov-2 Sotheby's, Paris #43/R est:5000

TASSEL, Edmond Louis Charles (fl.c.1870-1900) French
Sculpture
£1007 $1621 €1500 Le passage du ruisseau (55cm-22in) s. brown pat.bronze. 18-Feb-3 Galerie Moderne, Brussels #1010/R est:1700-2200

TASSEL, Etienne (1870-1900) French
Sculpture
£2564 $3974 €4000 Le passage du ruisseau (59cm-23in) s. brown pat bronze red marble socle. 9-Dec-2 Horta, Bruxelles #131/R est:5000-6000

TASSEL, Jean (attrib) (1608-1667) French
£2400 $4008 €3480 Study of a seated youth (37x33cm-15x13in) canvas on panel. 9-Jul-3 Bonhams, New Bond Street #102/R est:1000-1500

TASSI, Agostino (1565-1644) Italian
£16779 $27013 €25000 Attack. drying the nets (21x27cm-8x11in) copper octagonal two. 19-Feb-3 Semenzato, Venice #32/R est:32000
Works on paper
£4938 $8000 €7407 Miracle of the loaves and fishes (15x21cm-6x8in) pen ink over chk prov.lit. 21-Jan-3 Sotheby's, New York #48/R

TASSI, Agostino (studio) (1565-1644) Italian
£5313 $8500 €7970 Capriccio landscape with galleons in a bay and figures on the shore (93x128cm-37x50in) 14-May-3 Butterfields, San Francisco #1013/R est:6000-8000

TATAFIORE, Ernesto (1943-) Italian
£385 $596 €600 Untitled. s. acrylic oval stretcher. 3-Dec-2 Lempertz, Koln #462/R
£2821 $4456 €4400 Mozart (114x151cm-45x59in) s.i. tempera board on canvas. 14-Nov-2 Neumeister, Munich #888/R est:2000-2500
Works on paper
£349 $548 €524 Untitled - from Robespierre series (48x65cm-19x26in) s. pencil tempera prov. 25-Nov-2 Germann, Zurich #831 (S.FR 800)
£349 $548 €524 Untitled - from Robespierre series (48x65cm-19x26in) s. pencil tempera prov. 25-Nov-2 Germann, Zurich #832 (S.FR 800)
£349 $548 €524 Untitled - from Robespierre series (48x65cm-19x26in) s. pencil tempera prov. 25-Nov-2 Germann, Zurich #833 (S.FR 800)
£699 $1097 €1049 Il pittore pinge se stesso (25x33cm-10x13in) s. pencil W/C collage prov. 23-Nov-2 Burkhard, Luzern #183/R (S.FR 1600)
£736 $1148 €1104 Senza titolo (30x23cm-12x9in) s. W/C pencil collage prov. 5-Nov-2 Bukowskis, Stockholm #433/R (S.KR 10500)
£1135 $1783 €1703 Untitled (56x38cm-22x15in) s. pencil collage prov. 23-Nov-2 Burkhard, Luzern #184/R est:2200-2600 (S.FR 2600)

TATHAM, Frederick (1805-1878) British
Works on paper
£400 $648 €600 Portrait of a lady (47x35cm-19x14in) s. W/C. 21-Jan-3 Bonhams, Knightsbridge #239/R
£550 $847 €825 Portrait of a gentleman. Portrait of a lady (58x41cm-23x16in) s.d.1846 W/C htd white pair. 22-Oct-2 Bonhams, Knightsbridge #221/R

TATO (1896-1974) Italian
£2692 $4227 €4200 Dynamism (60x80cm-24x31in) s.d.1922 s.i.d.verso exhib. 21-Nov-2 Finarte, Rome #256/R est:4000-5000

TATOSSIAN, Armand (1948-) Canadian
£225 $349 €338 Foret l'automne (61x76cm-24x30in) s. 24-Sep-2 Iegor de Saint Hippolyte, Montreal #119 (C.D 550)
£322 $502 €467 Spring breakup (51x61cm-20x24in) s. 26-Mar-3 Walker's, Ottawa #210/R (C.D 750)
£387 $604 €581 House near Mont Fort (46x61cm-18x24in) s. 30-Jul-2 Iegor de Saint Hippolyte, Montreal #166 (C.D 960)
£472 $736 €684 Spring, St. Hilaire (61x76cm-24x30in) s.i.d.1976. 26-Mar-3 Walker's, Ottawa #406/R est:1200-1600 (C.D 1100)
£484 $755 €726 Automne, Rawdon (61x76cm-24x30in) s. 30-Jul-2 Iegor de Saint Hippolyte, Montreal #167 (C.D 1200)
£658 $1021 €987 Shimmering stream, winter (75x60cm-30x24in) s. 3-Dec-2 Joyner, Toronto #242/R est:2500-3000 (C.D 1600)
£667 $1093 €1001 Main - rue St. Laurent, Montreal (40x50cm-16x20in) s. 3-Jun-3 Joyner, Toronto #267/R est:1500-2000 (C.D 1500)
£889 $1458 €1334 Old Montreal (40x50cm-16x20in) s. 3-Jun-3 Joyner, Toronto #360/R est:1200-1500 (C.D 2000)
£947 $1467 €1421 Promenade (75x100cm-30x39in) s. 3-Dec-2 Joyner, Toronto #294/R est:3000-4000 (C.D 2300)
£988 $1531 €1482 La vitrine (50x60cm-20x24in) s. 3-Dec-2 Joyner, Toronto #317/R est:2000-2500 (C.D 2400)
£1244 $2041 €1866 Bonsecours Market (60x75cm-24x30in) s. 3-Jun-3 Joyner, Toronto #334/R est:2500-3000 (C.D 2800)
£1317 $2041 €1976 Le patineur (50x60cm-20x24in) s. 3-Dec-2 Joyner, Toronto #283/R est:2000-2500 (C.D 3200)
£1317 $2041 €1976 Lac megantic (75x100cm-30x39in) s. 3-Dec-2 Joyner, Toronto #309/R est:3000-4000 (C.D 3200)
£1502 $2343 €2178 House near Hudson, Quebec (91x122cm-36x48in) s.i. lit. 26-Mar-3 Walker's, Ottawa #407/R est:2500-3500 (C.D 3500)
£1511 $2478 €2267 Birch trees along the riverbank (75x100cm-30x39in) s. 3-Jun-3 Joyner, Toronto #275/R est:3000-4000 (C.D 3400)
£1893 $2934 €2840 Les eboulement (75x100cm-30x39in) with sig. 3-Dec-2 Joyner, Toronto #324/R est:3000-4000 (C.D 4600)
£2756 $4519 €4134 Glorious fall (120x10cm-47x4in) s. 3-Jun-3 Joyner, Toronto #260/R est:5000-7000 (C.D 6200)
£3333 $5467 €5000 Forest interior, summer (148x147cm-58x58in) s. 3-Jun-3 Joyner, Toronto #322/R est:5000-7000 (C.D 7500)
£4938 $7654 €7407 Chemin en automne (150x150cm-59x59in) s. 3-Dec-2 Joyner, Toronto #333/R est:5000-6000 (C.D 12000)

TATSCHL, Werner (1940-1993) German
£396 $633 €550 House front in Venice (40x51cm-16x20in) s.i. mixed media board. 14-May-3 Dorotheum, Klagenfurt #53

TATTEGRAIN, Francis (1852-1915) French
£517 $822 €750 Nantes (19x24cm-7x9in) s.i. panel. 4-Mar-3 Livinec, Gaudcheau & Jezequel, Rennes #24
£705 $1114 €1100 Le rivage (46x56cm-18x22in) s.d.1908. 18-Nov-2 Tajan, Paris #149
£3846 $6038 €6000 En bateaux c'est comme ca (65x44cm-26x17in) s.i.d.20 mars 81. 16-Dec-2 Millon & Associes, Paris #121 est:5000-6000
£7692 $12077 €12000 Pecheurs ramenant leurs filets (159x206cm-63x81in) s. 15-Dec-2 Eric Pillon, Calais #21/R

TAUBA, C (?) ?
Sculpture
£2600 $4264 €3770 North American Indian with feathered head dress and rifle (23cm-9in) s. painted bronze. 28-May-3 Riddetts, Bournemouth #47

TAUBE, Eugen (1860-1913) Finnish
£633 $987 €1000 Moonlight (13x22cm-5x9in) s.d.88. 15-Sep-2 Bukowskis, Helsinki #296/R
£1266 $2000 €2000 Lights from the windows (29x46cm-11x18in) s. board. 1-Dec-2 Bukowskis, Helsinki #194/R est:1200-1500
£1456 $2271 €2300 Moonlight (28x55cm-11x22in) s. 12-Sep-2 Hagelstam, Helsinki #945/R est:2500
£1582 $2500 €2500 Summer clouds (29x49cm-11x19in) s. 1-Dec-2 Bukowskis, Helsinki #192/R est:2000-2500
£1724 $2724 €2500 Autumn landscape (41x31cm-16x12in) s.d.1887. 3-Apr-3 Hagelstam, Helsinki #1041 est:1200
£1772 $2800 €2800 Coastal landscape (28x47cm-11x19in) s. 30-Nov-2 Hagelstam, Helsinki #119/R est:2000
£2089 $3300 €3300 Moonlight (27x20cm-11x8in) s. board. 1-Dec-2 Bukowskis, Helsinki #193/R est:2000-2500
£2590 $4144 €3600 Sunset (84x34cm-33x13in) s. 17-May-3 Hagelstam, Helsinki #81/R est:3500
£3022 $4835 €4200 Coastal landscape with beach (26x38cm-10x15in) s. board. 17-May-3 Hagelstam, Helsinki #82/R est:3000
£4317 $6906 €6000 Moonlight (60x105cm-24x41in) s.d.1893. 17-May-3 Hagelstam, Helsinki #80/R est:5000
£7911 $12500 €12500 Moonlight (138x85cm-54x33in) s,. 30-Nov-2 Hagelstam, Helsinki #118/R est:4000

TAUBERT, Bertoldo (1915-1974) French
£314 $500 €471 La toilette (56x46cm-22x18in) s.i. painted c.1955. 2-Mar-3 Toomey, Oak Park #724/R

TAUNAY, Adrien Aime (1803-1828) French
Works on paper
£2200 $3410 €3300 Waigiou, 1818 Phalanger de Waigiou (36x26cm-14x10in) s.d.1818 pen ink W/C four. 26-Sep-2 Christie's, London #70/R est:1500-2500
£3200 $4960 €4800 Scenes of Timor (36x28cm-14x11in) s.i. pen ink W/C set of seven. 26-Sep-2 Christie's, London #59/R est:3000-5000
£6000 $9300 €9000 Guham, 1818 Tamors des carolines (35x25cm-14x10in) s.i.d.1819 W/C. 26-Sep-2 Christie's, London #72/R est:3000-5000
£8000 $12400 €12000 Timor 1818, scene Malaise, diner chinois (29x35cm-11x14in) two s. i. pen ink W/C set of six. 26-Sep-2 Christie's, London #48/R est:8000-12000
£9500 $14725 €14250 Voyage de 'uranie, poissons (34x25cm-13x10in) s.d.1819 pencil pen ink W/C exhib. 26-Sep-2 Christie's, London #74/R est:4000-6000
£17500 $27125 €26250 Timor, Ombsy, baye des chiens marins (35x27cm-14x11in) s.i. W/C. 26-Sep-2 Christie's, London #44/R est:2000-3000

TAUNAY, Nicolas Antoine (1755-1830) French
£645 $1019 €1000 Etude de figures (11x17cm-4x7in) 20-Dec-2 Tajan, Paris #140/R
£6962 $10861 €11000 L'enface de Paul et Virginie. Virginie apprend qu'elle va devoir partir (17x20cm-7x8in) panel pair. 20-Oct-2 Mercier & Cie, Lille #282/R est:12000-18000

£8000 $13360 €11600 Saint Francis preaching in an extensive landscape (129x180cm-51x71in) exhib. 11-Jul-3 Christie's, Kensington #184/R est:8000-12000

TAUSS, Herbert (1929-2001) American
£870 $1400 €1305 Waiting room at airport (71x76cm-28x30in) s. 10-May-3 Illustration House, New York #139/R

TAVAGNACCO, Guido (20th C) Italian
£353 $546 €550 Oil and sunflower (50x40cm-20x16in) s. 5-Dec-2 Stadion, Trieste #667

TAVARONE, Lazzaro (1556-1641) Italian
Works on paper
£475 $750 €750 Joseph en prison (18x14cm-7x6in) i. pen brown ink grey wash. 27-Nov-2 Christie's, Paris #45/R
£8784 $13703 €13000 Cheval cabre (34x23cm-13x9in) i. chk. 27-Mar-3 Christie's, Paris #10/R

TAVE, Georgette (1925-) French
£3000 $4650 €4500 Still life, au pot d'apothicarie (122x124cm-48x49in) s. 26-Sep-2 Lane, Penzance #120/R est:4000-6000

TAVEL, Auguste (1859-?) Swiss
£873 $1362 €1310 Bastide Mallet (73x92cm-29x36in) exhib. 6-Nov-2 Dobiaschofsky, Bern #1008/R (S.FR 2000)

TAVELLA, Carlo Antonio (1668-1738) Italian
£7692 $11923 €12000 Baptist in the desert (70x58cm-28x23in) 4-Dec-2 Christie's, Rome #426/R est:12000-18000
£26282 $40737 €41000 River landscape with figures (156x123cm-61x48in) 4-Dec-2 Christie's, Rome #462/R est:20000-30000
£26282 $40737 €41000 River landscape with cattle (156x123cm-61x48in) 4-Dec-2 Christie's, Rome #461/R est:20000-30000

TAVELLA, Carlo Antonio (attrib) (1668-1738) Italian
£2482 $4145 €3500 Paysan et son troupeau dans la campagne Italienne (59x73cm-23x29in) 18-Jun-3 Tajan, Paris #19 est:2000-3000
£2800 $4368 €4200 Italianate landscape with figures on a track and classical ruins beyond (51x72cm-20x28in) 10-Apr-3 Christie's, Kensington #287/R est:2000-3000
£14000 $21840 €21000 Classical landscape with Elijah and the Angel (100x136cm-39x54in) prov. 8-Apr-3 Sotheby's, Olympia #183/R est:6000-8000

TAVENRAAT, Johannes (1809-1881) Dutch
£528 $850 €750 Panoramic landscape with walkers in the foreground (14x21cm-6x8in) s.d.1849 panel. 7-May-3 Vendue Huis, Gravenhage #464/R

TAVERNIER, Andrea (1858-1932) Italian
£4167 $6542 €6500 Wood (40x30cm-16x12in) s. board. 10-Dec-2 Della Rocca, Turin #313/R est:6500
Works on paper
£962 $1510 €1500 Woman in the garden (22x37cm-9x15in) s. pastel. 10-Dec-2 Della Rocca, Turin #386/R

TAVERNIER, Armand (1899-1991) Belgian
£1509 $2340 €2400 Snowy landscape (24x30cm-9x12in) s.d.1959 verso. 5-Oct-2 De Vuyst, Lokeren #346/R est:2400-2800
£3846 $5962 €6000 Winter landscape (70x70cm-28x28in) s. 7-Dec-2 De Vuyst, Lokeren #561/R est:6000-7000

TAVERNIER, Jules (1844-1899) French
£10843 $18000 €15722 Yosemite Valley scene with cathedral spires in the distance (49x30cm-19x12in) s.i.d.1882 canvas on board prov. 11-Jun-3 Butterfields, San Francisco #4163/R est:20000-30000
Works on paper
£13174 $22000 €19102 Hilo (81x51cm-32x20in) s.i.d.1887 pastel prov. 18-Jun-3 Christie's, Los Angeles #20/R est:15000-25000

TAVERNIER, Jules (attrib) (1844-1899) French
£2707 $4250 €4061 Punt near autumn shores (25x46cm-10x18in) 19-Nov-2 Butterfields, San Francisco #8162/R est:5000-7000

TAVERNIER, Julien Louis (1879-?) French
Works on paper
£372 $592 €540 Les baigneuses farniente (18x23cm-7x9in) s. W/C gouache. 10-Mar-3 Thierry & Lannon, Brest #81

TAXELL, Sophie (1911-) Finnish
£253 $395 €400 Nude (66x79cm-26x31in) s.d.1963. 15-Sep-2 Bukowskis, Helsinki #297/R

TAXIS, Baroness Iris (20th C) ?
Works on paper
£260 $403 €390 Madonna della Gace (33x44cm-13x17in) s. pastel gouache. 1-Oct-2 Fellows & Sons, Birmingham #197/R

TAYLER, Albert Chevallier (1862-1925) British
£4500 $7065 €6750 Fishergirl, Boulogne (35x25cm-14x10in) s.d.99 prov. 22-Nov-2 Christie's, London #28/R est:5000-8000

TAYLER, D (?) ?
£1509 $2400 €2264 Steamer at sea (61x91cm-24x36in) s. 18-Mar-3 Arthur James, Florida #101

TAYLER, Edward (1828-1906) British
Works on paper
£350 $546 €525 Portrait of a young lady (31x26cm-12x10in) s. W/C. 25-Mar-3 Bonhams, Knightsbridge #199/R
£500 $795 €750 Portrait of a firl with a peacock feather (29x23cm-11x9in) s. W/C. 25-Feb-3 Bonhams, Knightsbridge #16/R

TAYLER, John Frederick (1802-1889) British
Works on paper
£300 $477 €450 Study of dead game, deer and gun in a landscape (33x43cm-13x17in) init.d.1862 W/C. 6-Mar-3 Bonhams, Cornwall #709
£360 $562 €540 In the Highlands (12x19cm-5x7in) pencil W/C sold with another by the same hand. 17-Sep-2 Sotheby's, Olympia #2/R
£480 $763 €720 In the Scottish Highlands with four boys fishing by a bridge (31x48cm-12x19in) s. W/C. 19-Mar-3 Rupert Toovey, Partridge Green #126/R
£1300 $2106 €1950 Sophia and Squire Weston (37x49cm-15x19in) init. W/C. 20-May-3 Sotheby's, Olympia #183/R est:600-900
£2300 $3749 €3450 Hawking (40x57cm-16x22in) init.d.67. 29-Jan-3 Dreweatt Neate, Newbury #24/R est:2500-3000

TAYLER, Norman E (1843-1915) British
Works on paper
£1300 $2119 €1885 Persuasion (57x43cm-22x17in) s.d.1884 W/C htd white. 17-Jul-3 Tennants, Leyburn #761/R est:1000-1500

TAYLOR, Charles (19th C) British
Works on paper
£280 $442 €420 Ships in a swell (22x48cm-9x19in) W/C. 26-Nov-2 Bonhams, Knightsbridge #159/R

TAYLOR, Charles (jnr) (fl.1841-1883) British
Works on paper
£400 $648 €600 Sailing trader and paddle tug running down Channel (40x58cm-16x23in) s. pencil W/C htd bodycol. 21-May-3 Christie's, Kensington #436/R
£420 $701 €609 Sea sketch (12x28cm-5x11in) s.i. W/C scratching out. 18-Jun-3 Sotheby's, Olympia #70/R
£600 $972 €900 Paddle steamer in a squall (38x56cm-15x22in) s. W/C scratching out. 21-May-3 Christie's, Kensington #438/R
£680 $1095 €986 In full sail (24x54cm-9x21in) s. W/C. 12-May-3 Joel, Victoria #283 est:1500-2500 (A.D 1700)
£900 $1458 €1350 Ship of the line off a lightship (25x44cm-10x17in) W/C htd white. 22-Jan-3 Bonhams, New Bond Street #339/R
£1000 $1520 €1500 Topsail schooner-rigged steam yacht of the Royal Thames yacht club (42x70cm-17x28in) W/C htd white. 15-Aug-2 Bonhams, New Bond Street #402/R est:1000-1500
£2300 $3726 €3450 Off the Sovereign light - Beachy Head in the distance (29x60cm-11x24in) s. W/C htd white. 22-Jan-3 Bonhams, New Bond Street #337/R est:1000-2000

TAYLOR, Dennis (?) New Zealander?
Works on paper
£705 $1100 €1058 J class yachts, Challenger series, America's cup (53x72cm-21x28in) s. W/C. 7-Nov-2 International Art Centre, Auckland #79/R est:2500-3500 (NZ.D 2250)

TAYLOR, E A (?) British
£2300 $3565 €3450 Road to Brodick (47x62cm-19x24in) s. 31-Oct-2 Ambrose, Loughton #25/R est:500-700

TAYLOR, Edward R (1838-1912) British
£450 $716 €675 Old mill pond (30x46cm-12x18in) s.d.1884. 6-Mar-3 Christie's, Kensington #441/R

TAYLOR, Ernest Archibald (1874-1952) British
Works on paper
£450 $747 €653 Farmyard scene (23x17cm-9x7in) chl wash. 13-Jun-3 Lyon & Turnbull, Edinburgh #57

TAYLOR, Frank (fl.1980s) British
Works on paper
£280 $468 €406 Walk in the dark (34x45cm-13x18in) s. W/C. 17-Jun-3 Bonhams, Knightsbridge #65/R

TAYLOR, Frederick Bourchier (1906-1987) Canadian
£667 $1093 €1001 Near St. Francois, Ile D'Orleans, Que (21x26cm-8x10in) s.d.47 panel. 3-Jun-3 Joyner, Toronto #425/R est:400-600 (C.D 1500)
£1222 $2005 €1833 Barra de Navidad, Jalisco, Mexico (68x120cm-27x47in) s.d.66 s.d.verso prov. 27-May-3 Sotheby's, Toronto #4/R est:3000-5000 (C.D 2750)

TAYLOR, George Thomas (1838-1913) Canadian?
Works on paper
£1156 $1895 €1734 Paddling upstream (47x37cm-19x15in) s.d.1890 W/C. 3-Jun-3 Joyner, Toronto #428/R est:4000-5000 (C.D 2600)

TAYLOR, Henry King (fl.1857-1869) British
£1645 $2500 €2468 Fishing boats off Dungeness Spit in a squall (76x127cm-30x50in) s. 17-Aug-2 North East Auctions, Portsmouth #1074/R
£2000 $3100 €3000 Fishing boats pulling out against the tide off the Dungeness lighthouse (67x107cm-26x42in) s. 31-Oct-2 Christie's, Kensington #487/R est:2000-3000
£2300 $3588 €3450 Fishermen hauling in their nets off Tennison Down (42x54cm-17x21in) s. canvas on board prov. 9-Oct-2 Woolley & Wallis, Salisbury #212/R est:2000-3000

TAYLOR, John (1739-1838) British
£1000 $1650 €1450 Portraits of the Rev. Mr Carter and Mrs Carter, nee Nelthorpe (16x13cm-6x5in) plumbago pair prov. 2-Jul-3 Sotheby's, Olympia #45/R est:1000-1500

TAYLOR, John D (fl.1880-1900) British
£1400 $2296 €2100 Mussel gathering at Auchmith, Fifeshire (43x76cm-17x30in) s. i.verso. 29-May-3 Christie's, Kensington #199/R est:1500-2000
£2800 $4452 €4200 Low tide (51x76cm-20x30in) s. 6-Mar-3 Christie's, Kensington #115/R est:3000-5000

TAYLOR, John W (?) American?
£248 $400 €372 Mallard in flight about to land on lake (58x38cm-23x15in) board. 21-Feb-3 York Town, York #702

TAYLOR, Leonard Campbell (1874-1963) British
£250 $380 €375 Cypress trees before a farm (35x26cm-14x10in) s. panel. 29-Aug-2 Christie's, Kensington #227
£2900 $4611 €4350 Portrait of Guy Kortright in a mountainous landscape (76x91cm-30x36in) s. 18-Mar-3 Sworder & Son, Bishops Stortford #421a/R est:3000-4000
£9300 $14508 €13950 Needlework (46x36cm-18x14in) s. 17-Sep-2 Sotheby's, Olympia #206/R est:6000-8000
£38000 $63080 €57000 Persuasion (37x29cm-15x11in) s. s.i.verso painted 1914 prov.exhib.lit. 12-Jun-3 Sotheby's, London #39/R est:30000-40000

TAYLOR, Neil (1953-) Australian
£536 $830 €804 Dobroyd Head II (183x122cm-72x48in) s. acrylic. 29-Oct-2 Lawson Menzies, Sydney #424 (A.D 1500)

TAYLOR, Newton (19th C) British
£300 $498 €450 Vicar of Wakefield (91x72cm-36x28in) init.d.1878. 10-Jun-3 Bonhams, Knightsbridge #182/R

TAYLOR, Richard (fl.1743-1796) British
Works on paper
£870 $1400 €1305 Man in nightclothes followed by flying woman (18x25cm-7x10in) s. W/C. 20-Feb-3 Illustration House, New York #168/R est:1600-2200

TAYLOR, Robert (19th C) British
£500 $810 €750 Four masted barque Crown of Germany under full sail (65x89cm-26x35in) s.i.d.1903. 21-May-3 Christie's, Kensington #576/R
£1000 $1590 €1500 Clipper Ariel (51x76cm-20x30in) s.i.d.1881. 4-Mar-3 Bonhams, Knightsbridge #328/R est:1500-2000

TAYLOR, Robert (attrib) (19th C) British
£400 $648 €600 Ariel of Liverpool in coastal waters (41x96cm-16x38in) i. board. 21-May-3 Christie's, Kensington #575/R

TAYLOR, Rolla S (1874-?) American
£1538 $2400 €2307 San Antonio River at the Commerce Street Bridge (51x61cm-20x24in) board. 19-Oct-2 David Dike, Dallas #95/R est:1500-3000
£1763 $2750 €2645 Mountain huts, Mexico (30x41cm-12x16in) canvasboard painted c.1935. 19-Oct-2 David Dike, Dallas #276/R est:2500-5000
£7692 $12000 €11538 Hill Country sunset (76x102cm-30x40in) board. 19-Oct-2 David Dike, Dallas #255/R est:10000-20000
£10256 $16000 €15384 San Antonio (56x41cm-22x16in) linen painted c.1919. 19-Oct-2 David Dike, Dallas #175/R est:8000-12000

TAYLOR, Stephen (attrib) (19th C) British
£1600 $2480 €2400 Cat in an interior with a red drape beyond (51x61cm-20x24in) 31-Oct-2 Duke & Son, Dorchester #200/R est:600-1200

TAYLOR, Vic E (19th C) Irish
£709 $1149 €1000 Adare manor, Co. Limerick (30x40cm-12x16in) s.i.d.1890. 20-May-3 Mealy's, Castlecomer #1023/R est:400-600

TAYLOR, William Hughes (1891-?) Canadian
£1016 $1596 €1524 St Fereol, Quebec (26x40cm-10x16in) s. i.verso board prov. 10-Dec-2 Pinneys, Montreal #136 est:1200-1500 (C.D 2500)

TAYLOR-GHEE, Robert Eagar (1869-1951) Australian
£400 $644 €580 Moonrise (40x30cm-16x12in) init. board. 12-May-3 Joel, Victoria #361 est:1000-2000 (A.D 1000)
£2682 $3996 €4023 Droving cattle on a summers day (35x52cm-14x20in) s. prov. 27-Aug-2 Christie's, Melbourne #247/R est:7000-10000 (A.D 7000)

TAYLOR-WOOD, Sam (1967-) British
Photographs
£3800 $6346 €5510 Basil, Ray, Steve and Kline (74x74cm-29x29in) silver gelatin print prov.exhib.lit. 24-Jun-3 Sotheby's, Olympia #36/R est:3000-4000
£6000 $9840 €9000 Five Revolutionary Seconds XIV (28x203cm-11x80in) C-print num.three of three prov. 6-Feb-3 Christie's, London #732/R est:8000-12000
£13000 $20020 €19500 Five revolutionary seconds VI (21x200cm-8x79in) c-print executed 1996 prov.lit. 23-Oct-2 Christie's, London #188/R est:10000-12000
£18000 $27720 €27000 Five revolutionary second II (72x757cm-28x298in) col photograph on vinyle cassette prov.lit. 22-Oct-2 Sotheby's, London #310/R est:20000-30000
£40000 $61600 €60000 Soliloquy VII (225x257cm-89x101in) two c-prints executed 2000. 23-Oct-2 Christie's, London #247/R est:40000-60000

TAYMANS, Louis (1826-1877) Belgian
£845 $1361 €1200 Mother with child (52x42cm-20x17in) s. panel. 7-May-3 Vendue Huis, Gravenhage #362
£897 $1391 €1400 Landscape with two woman (64x49cm-25x19in) s.d.1871 panel. 7-Dec-2 De Vuyst, Lokeren #314

TCHEKHONINE, Sergei (1878-1936) Russian
Works on paper
£586 $979 €850 Le clown (29x20cm-11x8in) s.d. W/C. 9-Jul-3 Cornette de St.Cyr, Paris #199
£2390 $3704 €3800 Etude de costume pour un ballet (31x21cm-12x8in) s. W/C. 30-Oct-2 Artcurial Briest, Paris #102/R est:4000-5000
£9000 $14580 €13500 Costume design for the snow maiden (36x4cm-14x2in) s. gouache. 21-May-3 Sotheby's, London #150/R est:5000-7000
£9422 $14981 €13850 La peri (62x46cm-24x18in) s. gouache exec.c.1925 exhib. 26-Feb-3 Artcurial Briest, Paris #85/R est:12000-15000

TCHELITCHEV, Pavel (1898-1957) American/Russian
£31056 $50000 €46584 Portrait of Chaeles Henri Ford with the river Seine (105x79cm-41x31in) oil sand nails on board painted 1934 prov.exhib. 7-May-3 Sotheby's, New York #326/R est:60000-80000

Works on paper

£950	$1473	€1425	Figures studies (26x20cm-10x8in) s.d.1932 pen brush sepia. 3-Dec-2 Bonhams, Knightsbridge #112/R
£976	$1600	€1415	Figure studies (33x23cm-13x9in) s.d.37 sepia ink. 1-Jun-3 Wright, Chicago #197/R est:1200-1500
£1200	$1884	€1800	The mask (33x21cm-13x8in) s.d.1926 ink pair prov.lit. 20-Nov-2 Sotheby's, London #137/R est:1500-2000
£1635	$2600	€2453	Deux enfants dans le vent (28x21cm-11x8in) s.d.1939 pen ink brush wash. 27-Feb-3 Christie's, Rockefeller NY #113/R est:4000
£3086	$5000	€4475	Two heads in profile (53x38cm-21x15in) s.d.1938 India ink wash prov. 21-May-3 Doyle, New York #30/R est:2000-3000
£3957	$6331	€5500	Pierrot (65x35cm-26x14in) s.d.27 ink gouache. 15-May-3 Christie's, Paris #135/R est:2000-3000
£4000	$6480	€6000	Cubo-futurist figure (22x17cm-9x7in) s. gouache. 21-May-3 Sotheby's, London #162/R est:2000-3000
£5000	$8150	€7500	Three male nudes (55x26cm-22x10in) s.d.1929 W/C. 3-Feb-3 Bonhams, New Bond Street #19/R est:1000-2000
£38462	$60000	€57693	Green straw hat - Giovanni (65x50cm-26x20in) s.d.35 gouache paper on board prov. 6-Nov-2 Sotheby's, New York #291/R est:40000-60000

TCHERKESSOFF, Georges (1900-1943) Russian

£256	$403	€400	Nature morte au jeu des petits chevaux (46x55cm-18x22in) 11-Dec-2 Maigret, Paris #72/R
£256	$403	€400	Jeune garcon lisant accoude a son bureau (46x55cm-18x22in) 11-Dec-2 Maigret, Paris #73/R
£256	$403	€400	Peniches et barques au bord de l'eau (46x61cm-18x24in) 11-Dec-2 Maigret, Paris #92
£288	$453	€450	Paysage Provencal (54x65cm-21x26in) 11-Dec-2 Maigret, Paris #56
£288	$453	€450	Paysage Provencal (54x65cm-21x26in) 11-Dec-2 Maigret, Paris #58
£321	$503	€500	Canal et ecluse (46x55cm-18x22in) 11-Dec-2 Maigret, Paris #48
£353	$554	€550	Paysage Provencal (54x65cm-21x26in) 11-Dec-2 Maigret, Paris #55
£353	$554	€550	Paysage de la cote d'Azur, montagne et vignes en escalier (50x65cm-20x26in) s.d.27. 11-Dec-2 Maigret, Paris #60
£353	$554	€550	Paysage, chemin menant vers une ferme (38x61cm-15x24in) 11-Dec-2 Maigret, Paris #67/R
£353	$554	€550	Paysage Provencal. Nature morte de poissons (38x46cm-15x18in) s.d.33. 11-Dec-2 Maigret, Paris #75
£385	$604	€600	Paysage de la cote d'Azur, rue, palmiers (61x50cm-24x20in) s.d.31. 11-Dec-2 Maigret, Paris #52
£385	$604	€600	Paysage Provencal, vue sur le parc d'une propriete (54x65cm-21x26in) 11-Dec-2 Maigret, Paris #81
£417	$654	€650	Paysage Provencal (60x73cm-24x29in) 11-Dec-2 Maigret, Paris #71
£449	$704	€700	Nature morte au col vert (61x50cm-24x20in) s.d.28. 11-Dec-2 Maigret, Paris #50
£481	$755	€750	Paysage et pecheurs au bord d'une riviere (50x61cm-20x24in) 11-Dec-2 Maigret, Paris #53
£481	$755	€750	Quai de la Seine, vue sur la gare d'Orsay. Etude de nu feminin (50x65cm-20x26in) s.d.33 double-sided. 11-Dec-2 Maigret, Paris #62
£481	$755	€750	Paysage Provencal, oliviers, champs et habitations (54x73cm-21x29in) 11-Dec-2 Maigret, Paris #64
£513	$805	€800	Paysage de la Cote d'Azur, village sur la gauche (50x65cm-20x26in) s.d.27. 11-Dec-2 Maigret, Paris #61
£513	$805	€800	Quai de la Seine, vue sur le pont neuf (46x55cm-18x22in) s.d.37. 11-Dec-2 Maigret, Paris #88
£545	$855	€850	Paysage Provencal, et montagneux, Alpilles (54x73cm-21x29in) s.d.1931. 11-Dec-2 Maigret, Paris #63
£545	$855	€850	Vue de la montagne Sainte Victoire (73x60cm-29x24in) 11-Dec-2 Maigret, Paris #84
£577	$906	€900	Vue de la montagne St Victoire. Nature morte au pichet (55x46cm-22x18in) s.d.32 double-sided. 11-Dec-2 Maigret, Paris #49
£638	$1066	€900	Les toits rouges (38x46cm-15x18in) s.d. 17-Jun-3 Claude Boisgirard, Paris #126
£641	$1006	€1000	Paysage de la Cote d'Azur, vue sur la mer. Paysage (50x65cm-20x26in) s.d.32 double-sided. 11-Dec-2 Maigret, Paris #70
£673	$1057	€1050	Paysage montagneux. Fenetre ouverte sur la campagne (65x81cm-26x32in) double-sided. 11-Dec-2 Maigret, Paris #65
£705	$1107	€1100	Paysage Provencal. Route dans un paysage Provencal (54x65cm-21x26in) double-sided. 11-Dec-2 Maigret, Paris #59
£769	$1208	€1200	Vue de jardin des Tuileries (54x73cm-21x29in) s.d.33. 11-Dec-2 Maigret, Paris #54/R
£769	$1208	€1200	Paysage Provencal (50x60cm-20x24in) s.d.33. 11-Dec-2 Maigret, Paris #68/R
£1154	$1812	€1800	Paysage Provencal (73x60cm-29x24in) s.d.31. 11-Dec-2 Maigret, Paris #85 est:450-500
£1154	$1812	€1800	Peniches au bord de l'eau, ouvriers chargeant (46x61cm-18x24in) 11-Dec-2 Maigret, Paris #91 est:400-500
£1346	$2113	€2100	Paysage de la Cote d'Azur (65x80cm-26x31in) s.d.28. 11-Dec-2 Maigret, Paris #66/R est:500-800
£1795	$2818	€2800	Paysage de neige, maisons et jardins (45x55cm-18x22in) s.d.23. 11-Dec-2 Maigret, Paris #82 est:300-500
£2244	$3522	€3500	Port et quai sur la Cote d'Azur (50x65cm-20x26in) s.d.29. 11-Dec-2 Maigret, Paris #87/R est:500-600
£2244	$3522	€3500	Quais de la Seine, vue sur le Grand Palais (38x55cm-15x22in) 11-Dec-2 Maigret, Paris #90/R est:500-700

Works on paper

£6803	$10816	€10000	Le port de Toulon (40x50cm-16x20in) s. W/C. 3-Mar-3 Claude Boisgirard, Paris #98/R est:350-400

TCHERNIAWSKY, Charles (1900-) Russian

Works on paper

£288	$452	€420	Collioure, bateaux dans le port (71x51cm-28x20in) s.i.d.55 gouache W/C. 21-Apr-3 Rabourdin & Choppin de Janvry, Paris #18
£329	$516	€480	Arbres pres de la mer (54x68cm-21x27in) s. gouache W/C. 21-Apr-3 Rabourdin & Choppin de Janvry, Paris #15

TCHOUMAKOFF, Theodore (1823-1911) Russian

£635	$965	€990	Sledge in snowy landscape (53x41cm-21x16in) s. prov. 17-Aug-2 Hans Stahl, Toestorf #62/R
£1284	$2003	€1900	Jeune femme rousse au voile bleu (27x21cm-11x8in) s. panel. 31-Mar-3 Rossini, Paris #26/R
£1321	$2100	€1982	Portrait of a young woman (35x26cm-14x10in) s. board. 7-Mar-3 Skinner, Boston #249/R est:1200-1800
£1554	$2424	€2300	Femme a la mantille noire (27x21cm-11x8in) s. panel. 31-Mar-3 Rossini, Paris #27/R
£7500	$11774	€11250	Praying to the Virgin (92x72cm-36x28in) s. 20-Nov-2 Sotheby's, London #53/R est:10000-15000

TEAGUE, Donald (1897-1991) American

£4658	$7500	€6987	Poker game in western bunk house interior (71x107cm-28x42in) s.indis.d.1927 s.d.1928 verso prov. 18-Feb-3 John Moran, Pasadena #110 est:9000-12000

Works on paper

£2097	$3250	€3146	Street in Vejer de la Frontera (15x23cm-6x9in) s. s.i.verso W/C prov. 29-Oct-2 John Moran, Pasadena #616 est:1000-2000
£3106	$5000	€4659	Embracing couple in front of covered wagons in desert (46x69cm-18x27in) s.pseudonym gouache exhib. 10-May-3 Illustration House, New York #180/R est:5000-7500
£9581	$16000	€13892	Old mill, Toledo, Spain (51x76cm-20x30in) s. W/C prov. 18-Jun-3 Christie's, Los Angeles #62/R est:20000-30000

TEAGUE, Violet Helen (1872-1951) Australian

£561	$853	€842	Lovers lane, Lockmaben, Tasmania (27x35cm-11x14in) s. panel. 19-Aug-2 Joel, Victoria #229 est:1500-2000 (A.D 1600)
£571	$903	€857	Portrait of Mr Buggy (35x26cm-14x10in) s. board painted c.1916. 18-Nov-2 Joel, Victoria #355 est:1500-2500 (A.D 1600)
£800	$1288	€1200	Onboard ship (44x35cm-17x14in) s. canvas on board. 6-May-3 Christie's, Melbourne #374 est:2000-4000 (A.D 2000)

TEASDALE, Percy Morton (1870-?) British

£1300	$2041	€1950	Seated figure with a pram in a park (24x35cm-9x14in) s. canvasboard. 19-Nov-2 Bonhams, Leeds #123 est:600-800
£2200	$3586	€3190	Harbour scene with lady seated on a quay and a horse nearby (36x35cm-14x14in) s. panel. 17-Jul-3 Tennants, Leyburn #823/R est:600-800

TEBBITT, Henri (1852-1926) Australian

Works on paper

£357	$564	€536	Castle (63x47cm-25x19in) s. W/C. 18-Nov-2 Goodman, Sydney #48 (A.D 1000)
£360	$580	€522	Yachting, Sydney Harbour (40x70cm-16x28in) s. W/C. 12-May-3 Joel, Victoria #334 est:1500-2000 (A.D 900)
£480	$773	€696	Calm waters (57x89cm-22x35in) s. W/C. 12-May-3 Joel, Victoria #357 est:2000-3000 (A.D 1200)
£561	$853	€842	Meandering morning stream (59x115cm-23x45in) s. W/C. 19-Aug-2 Joel, Victoria #192 est:1000-1500 (A.D 1600)
£880	$1417	€1276	Waves crashing on the shore (40x70cm-16x28in) s. W/C. 12-May-3 Joel, Victoria #401 est:1500-2000 (A.D 2200)
£1200	$1932	€1740	Rocky shore (75x129cm-30x51in) s. W/C. 12-May-3 Joel, Victoria #374 est:3000-4000 (A.D 3000)
£1951	$3083	€2829	Coastal scene (74x129cm-29x51in) s. W/C. 22-Jul-3 Lawson Menzies, Sydney #80/R est:3000-4000 (A.D 4800)

TECZELY, A (?) ?

£497	$775	€746	Judaic scene (51x61cm-20x24in) i.verso. 14-Sep-2 Selkirks, St. Louis #739

TEED, Douglas Arthur (1864-1929) American

£513	$800	€770	Landscape with waterfall (25x43cm-10x17in) 20-Sep-2 Du Mouchelle, Detroit #2049/R
£1125	$1800	€1688	Mosque interior (48x67cm-19x26in) s.d.1908. 16-Mar-3 Butterfields, San Francisco #1032 est:2000-3000
£1863	$3000	€2795	Marshes in atmospheric landscape (20x25cm-8x10in) s.d.1917 prov. 18-Feb-3 John Moran, Pasadena #70 est:2000-3000
£2083	$3250	€3125	Peacocks in a garden (61x74cm-24x29in) 18-Oct-2 Du Mouchelle, Detroit #2069/R est:2000-2500

TEELING, Norman (1944-) Irish

£1611	$2593	€2400	Molly Malone's sculpture, Grafton Street (64x76cm-25x30in) s. board. 18-Feb-3 Whyte's, Dublin #225/R est:1500-2000

TEERLINK, Abraham (1776-1857) Dutch
£2500 $3975 €3750 In the Roman campagna (43x57cm-17x22in) s.d.1840. 20-Mar-3 Christie's, Kensington #77/R est:2500-3500

TEERLINK, Abraham (attrib) (1776-1857) Dutch
£2000 $3040 €3000 Scene in the campagna de Roma (41x56cm-16x22in) s. 4-Jul-2 Duke & Son, Dorchester #256/R

TEGTMEIER, Wilhelm (1895-1968) German
£316 $500 €500 Evening on the North Sea dunes (36x45cm-14x18in) s.d.1935 canvas on panel. 29-Nov-2 Bolland & Marotz, Bremen #578/R
£886 $1400 €1400 Evening in Norden harbour. mono. board painted c.1925/30. 29-Nov-2 Bolland & Marotz, Bremen #577/R

TEICHEL, Franz (1816-?) German
Works on paper
£900 $1422 €1350 Military review and encampment (29x47cm-11x19in) s. pencil W/C. 26-Nov-2 Christie's, Kensington #10/R

TEICHMAN, Sabina (1905-) American
£305 $500 €442 It is spring again (71x91cm-28x36in) s. prov. 1-Jun-3 Wright, Chicago #235/R

TEIXEIRA DE MATTOS, Joseph (1892-1971) Dutch
£2482 $4021 €3500 Perfumerie de Buffalo (63x52cm-25x20in) mono.d.1945 panel. 26-May-3 Glerum, Amsterdam #65/R est:1500-2000
Works on paper
£270 $422 €400 Colonne Morris, Paris (48x30cm-19x12in) mono.i. pastel W/C chl. 31-Mar-3 Piasa, Paris #138

TEIXIDOR, Jordi (1941-) Spanish
£2830 $4358 €4500 Untitled (150x95cm-59x37in) s.i.d.2000 verso prov. 28-Oct-2 Segre, Madrid #138/R est:5500

TEJEDOR, Jose Alcazar (1850-?) Spanish
£2200 $3498 €3300 Grey day in Capri - Marina Grande (29x40cm-11x16in) mono.i. panel prov. 20-Mar-3 Christie's, Kensington #65/R est:2000-3000

TEKEL, Teodor (1902-1975) Czechoslovakian
Works on paper
£362 $562 €543 Resurrection (21x30cm-8x12in) pastel. 1-Oct-2 SOGA, Bratislava #82/R est:13000 (SL.K 23000)
£441 $684 €662 Pieta (20x15cm-8x6in) pastel. 1-Oct-2 SOGA, Bratislava #83/R est:12000 (SL.K 28000)

TELARIK, Alois (1884-1961) ?
£851 $1345 €1277 Dutch interior with three girls at table (74x100cm-29x39in) s. 2-Dec-2 Rasmussen, Copenhagen #1702/R (D.KR 10000)
£1286 $2007 €1929 The housemaids enjoying themselves at a table (74x100cm-29x39in) s. 11-Nov-2 Rasmussen, Vejle #699/R est:15000-20000 (D.KR 15000)

TELARIK, Alois (attrib) (1884-1961) ?
£3243 $5384 €4702 Diana, Goddess of Hunting (70x140cm-28x55in) s. 16-Jun-3 Lilla Bukowskis, Stockholm #853/R est:20000-25000 (S.KR 42000)

TELEMAQUE, Herve (1937-) Haitian
£3129 $4976 €4600 L'accident (120x120cm-47x47in) i.d.1970 s.verso acrylic. 26-Feb-3 Artcurial Briest, Paris #401/R est:4500-6000
£4194 $6626 €6500 En selle (65x80cm-26x31in) s. acrylic painted 1977. 19-Dec-2 Ruellan, Paris #144/R

TELEPY, Karoly (1828-1906) Hungarian
£380 $589 €600 Rocky coast (49x88cm-19x35in) s.d.899. 26-Sep-2 Neumeister, Munich #2850
£838 $1308 €1257 In the grange (12x24cm-5x9in) s. 11-Apr-3 Kieselbach, Budapest #5/R (H.F 300000)
£838 $1308 €1257 Italian landscape (12x24cm-5x9in) s. 11-Apr-3 Kieselbach, Budapest #41/R est:280000-300000 (H.F 300000)
£926 $1491 €1389 Summer in the mountains (17x28cm-7x11in) s. board. 7-May-3 Dobiaschofsky, Bern #1016/R (S.FR 2000)
£929 $1449 €1394 Evening landscape (12x22cm-5x9in) s.verso board. 11-Sep-2 Kieselbach, Budapest #33/R (H.F 360000)
£1129 $1751 €1637 Carpathians (25x20cm-10x8in) s. 9-Dec-2 Mu Terem Galeria, Budapest #40/R est:320000 (H.F 420000)
£1174 $1831 €1761 Landscape with avenue (9x17cm-4x7in) s. panel. 11-Apr-3 Kieselbach, Budapest #103/R est:280000-420000 (H.F 420000)
£1537 $2398 €2306 Waterside landscape with pine forest (31x42cm-12x17in) s.d.1902 canvas on board. 11-Apr-3 Kieselbach, Budapest #150/R est:550000 (H.F 550000)
£2515 $3923 €3647 Alpine landscape (40x68cm-16x27in) s. 12-Apr-3 Mu Terem Galeria, Budapest #53/R est:750000 (H.F 900000)
£2580 $4024 €3870 Backyard (27x39cm-11x15in) s. cardboard. 11-Sep-2 Kieselbach, Budapest #102/R (H.F 1000000)
£2580 $4024 €3741 Mountain lake (24x40cm-9x16in) s.d.880 prov.exhib. 13-Sep-2 Mu Terem Galeria, Budapest #48/R est:420000 (H.F 1000000)
£2620 $4087 €3930 Mountain lakeshore in the summer (72x98cm-28x39in) s. 6-Nov-2 Dobiaschofsky, Bern #1010/R est:2400 (S.FR 6000)
£4034 $6253 €6051 Landscape by the Danube (37x55cm-15x22in) 6-Dec-2 Kieselbach, Budapest #62/R (H.F 1500000)
£4751 $7411 €6889 Lake between the mountains (42x67cm-17x26in) s. 12-Apr-3 Mu Terem Galeria, Budapest #134/R est:1100000 (H.F 1700000)
£7530 $11671 €11295 Landscape with hunters (59x100cm-23x39in) s. 6-Dec-2 Kieselbach, Budapest #182/R (H.F 2800000)
£8383 $13078 €12575 Riverside landscape with castle (47x70cm-19x28in) s. 11-Apr-3 Kieselbach, Budapest #184/R est:1700000-3000000 (H.F 3000000)
£10060 $15694 €15090 Landscape with brook and walking people (63x100cm-25x39in) s.d.1904. 11-Apr-3 Kieselbach, Budapest #30/R est:2500000-3600000 (H.F 3600000)

TELFER, Henry Monteath (fl.1880s) British
Works on paper
£600 $936 €900 End of October (54x38cm-21x15in) s.d.1885 W/C prov. 17-Sep-2 Sotheby's, Olympia #16/R

TELFNER, Josef (1874-1948) Austrian
£1154 $1788 €1800 Two tree trunks in the mountains (40x29cm-16x11in) s. board. 5-Dec-2 Neumeister, Munich #2885/R est:600

TELIGA, Stanley Frederick de (1924-1998) Australian
£249 $381 €374 Surf board rider (89x120cm-35x47in) s.d.61 i.verso board prov. 26-Aug-2 Sotheby's, Paddington #609 (A.D 700)
£268 $415 €402 Calm (94x134cm-37x53in) s.d.86. 29-Oct-2 Lawson Menzies, Sydney #214 (A.D 750)

TELKESSY, Valeria (1870-?) Hungarian
£1100 $1804 €1650 Primulas, anenomes and other flowers on a table. Springs blossoms (59x79cm-23x31in) s. pair. 5-Jun-3 Christie's, Kensington #804/R est:1000-1500

TELLA, Garcia (1906-1938) ?
£795 $1295 €1200 Barricada (60x73cm-24x29in) s. s.i.verso isorel. 31-Jan-3 Charbonneaux, Paris #168/R

TELLAECHE, Julian de (1884-1960) Spanish
£839 $1325 €1300 Fisherman (41x33cm-16x13in) i.verso. 17-Dec-2 Durán, Madrid #35/R
Works on paper
£903 $1427 €1400 Basque sailor (57x48cm-22x19in) s. chl dr. 18-Dec-2 Ansorena, Madrid #959/R

TELLANDER, Frederic A (1878-?) American
£3892 $6500 €5643 Arc de Triomphe (76x91cm-30x36in) 22-Jun-3 Freeman, Philadelphia #125/R est:1000-1500

TELLES, Sergio (1936-) French?
£769 $1208 €1200 Aux deux magots, Paris (19x29cm-7x11in) s. i.d.2001 verso panel. 16-Dec-2 Charbonneaux, Paris #296/R

TELLIER, Ed (19th C) French
£728 $1135 €1150 Bateaux a maree basse (115x120cm-45x47in) s. 20-Oct-2 Galerie de Chartres, Chartres #120 est:1200-1800

TELLIER, Jean Baptiste Joseph le (fl.1759-1812) French
Miniatures
£1600 $2624 €2320 Young lady in a loose gold bordered mauve dress (6cm-2in circular) s. silver gilt frame prov. 3-Jun-3 Christie's, London #166/R est:1500-2500
£1700 $2669 €2550 Young lady in a landscape holding her pug (7cm-3in) gilt metal. 10-Dec-2 Christie's, London #134/R est:1000-1500

TEMPEL, Abraham van den (attrib) (1622-1672) Dutch
£9000 $14040 €13500 Portrait of young lady holding sprig of orange blossom (118x89cm-46x35in) 10-Apr-3 Sotheby's, London #36/R est:8000

TEMPEST, Victor (1913-) British
£550 $919 €798 North Woolwich (40x50cm-16x20in) s. board. 17-Jun-3 Bonhams, Knightsbridge #220/R

TEMPESTA, Antonio (1555-1630) Italian
Works on paper
£3704 $6000 €5556 Christ on the road to Calvary (16x22cm-6x9in) i. prov. 21-Jan-3 Sotheby's, New York #46/R est:6000

TEMPESTA, Antonio (attrib) (1555-1630) Italian
£10638 $16489 €15957 Battle between Greeks and Turks (100x148cm-39x58in) prov. 3-Dec-2 Bukowskis, Stockholm #472/R est:150000-175000 (S.KR 150000)
Works on paper
£1409 $2269 €2100 Cavaliers chassant l'ours et le lion (14x41cm-6x16in) pen ink wash. 18-Feb-3 Vanderkindere, Brussels #100

TEMPESTA, Antonio (circle) (1555-1630) Italian
£8000 $12560 €12000 Conversion of the Emperor Constantine (42x32cm-17x13in) on glass. 11-Dec-2 Christie's, London #117/R est:7000-10000

TEMPLE, Hans (1857-1931) Austrian
£1027 $1603 €1500 Portrait of young woman in traditional costume (59x46cm-23x18in) s.i.d.89. 10-Apr-3 Dorotheum, Vienna #191/R est:1800-2500

TEMPLE, Robert Scott (fl.1874-1900) British
£280 $437 €420 Landscape with a mill by a waterfall (92x72cm-36x28in) s. 17-Sep-2 Bonhams, Ipswich #431
£480 $758 €720 Watermill beside a waterfall near Dundee (82x71cm-32x28in) s. i.verso. 15-Nov-2 Rowley Fine Art, Newmarket #404/R
£750 $1193 €1125 Abernyte, near Dundee (91x71cm-36x28in) s. i.verso. 6-Mar-3 Christie's, Kensington #85/R

TEMPLE, Vere (1898-?) British
Works on paper
£300 $473 €450 Study of rabbits (37x44cm-15x17in) s.d.1931 chl. 27-Nov-2 Sotheby's, Olympia #16/R

TEN BERGE, Bernardus Gerardus (1825-1875) Dutch
£1096 $1710 €1600 Shepherd and sheep in wooded landscape (51x69cm-20x27in) s. 9-Apr-3 Neumeister, Munich #646/R est:800

TEN CATE, Johannes Marinus (1859-1896) Dutch
£1500 $2400 €2250 Children playing in snow by houses (42x52cm-17x20in) s. 29-Jan-3 Wingetts, Wrexham #237 est:2500-3500
£3699 $5807 €5400 Donkey ride (29x44cm-11x17in) s. 15-Apr-3 Sotheby's, Amsterdam #36/R est:6000-8000
Works on paper
£5000 $8000 €7500 Polynesian village scene with figures hosting a European gentleman (16x23cm-6x9in) s. pencil W/C. 14-May-3 Butterfields, San Francisco #1063/R est:2000-3000

TEN CATE, Siebe Johannes (1858-1908) Dutch
£1887 $2925 €3000 Le moulin, effet de soleil (39x55cm-15x22in) s.d.1905. 30-Oct-2 Artcurial Briest, Paris #172/R est:3000-4000
£2639 $4196 €3800 Sur le quai, Le Havre (75x100cm-30x39in) s.i.d.1904. 29-Apr-3 Christie's, Amsterdam #150/R est:4000-6000
£2885 $4529 €4500 Paysage a Moret (35x27cm-14x11in) s.i.d.1903. 15-Dec-2 Mercier & Cie, Lille #394/R
Works on paper
£346 $550 €519 Les courses a Vicennes (26x34cm-10x13in) s.i.d.25 avril 1908 pastel paper on canvas. 7-Mar-3 Skinner, Boston #541/R
£690 $1103 €1000 Rue du village de Mouy (26x33cm-10x13in) s.d.93 pastel. 12-Mar-3 Libert, Castor, Paris #189
£828 $1324 €1200 Le pont (31x39cm-12x15in) s.d.89 pastel. 12-Mar-3 Libert, Castor, Paris #190
£1517 $2428 €2200 Vue de Paris (26x33cm-10x13in) s.d.1909 pastel. 12-Mar-3 Libert, Castor, Paris #188 est:800-1000
£2128 $3553 €3000 Vue du port de Rotterdam (25x39cm-10x15in) s.i. pastel. 19-Jun-3 Piasa, Paris #211/R est:3000-4000

TEN COMPE, Jan (1713-1761) Dutch
£19424 $31079 €27000 Haarlem: view of the town hall with elegant figures promenading (28x37cm-11x15in) s. panel. 13-May-3 Sotheby's, Amsterdam #91/R est:10000-15000

TEN HOLT, Friso (1921-1997) Dutch
£701 $1079 €1100 Beach (60x79cm-24x31in) s.d.74 prov. 3-Sep-2 Christie's, Amsterdam #423

TEN HOMPEL, Ludwig (1887-?) German
£468 $767 €650 Portrait en face (44x41cm-17x16in) s. 4-Jun-3 Reiss & Sohn, Konigstein #409/R

TEN HOVEN, H (19/20th C) Dutch
£440 $682 €660 Canal scene, Amsterdam (56x86cm-22x34in) s. 3-Dec-2 Bonhams, Knightsbridge #338

TEN KATE, Herman (1822-1891) Dutch
£2069 $3290 €3000 Elegant figures in a park (19x24cm-7x9in) s.d.1855 panel. 10-Mar-3 Sotheby's, Amsterdam #71/R est:2000-3000
£2174 $3370 €3261 Tavern with soldiers, women and children (21x26cm-8x10in) s.d.1850 panel prov. 9-Dec-2 Philippe Schuler, Zurich #3938/R est:6000-8000 (S.FR 5000)
£2516 $3874 €4000 Drawing lesson (13x17cm-5x7in) s. panel. 22-Oct-2 Sotheby's, Amsterdam #44/R est:5000-7000
£3425 $5377 €5000 Elegant figures in an interior (41x56cm-16x22in) s.d.1852 panel. 15-Apr-3 Sotheby's, Amsterdam #1/R est:6000-8000
£3425 $5377 €5000 Street fight outside a tavern (14x25cm-6x10in) s. panel. 15-Apr-3 Sotheby's, Amsterdam #83/R est:5000-7000
£3800 $6042 €5700 Cavaliers drinking in the tavern (32x43cm-13x17in) s. panel. 20-Mar-3 Christie's, Kensington #155/R est:4000-6000
£5208 $8594 €7500 Latest news (50x65cm-20x26in) s. panel. 1-Jul-3 Christie's, Amsterdam #59/R est:6000-8000
£5660 $8717 €9000 Fisher family from marken conversing by a hut in winter (71x100cm-28x39in) s.i.d.1853 prov. 23-Oct-2 Christie's, Amsterdam #11/R est:10000-15000
£12000 $19080 €18000 Council of War (61x93cm-24x37in) s. panel. 18-Mar-3 Bonhams, New Bond Street #2/R est:10000-15000
£18868 $29057 €30000 Interior with soldiers conversing (61x94cm-24x37in) s. panel. 22-Oct-2 Sotheby's, Amsterdam #177/R est:27000-32000
Works on paper
£320 $500 €480 Family resting near a doorway, a beggar seated alongside (25x22cm-10x9in) s.d.1845 pen ink W/C. 11-Nov-2 Stephan Welz, Johannesburg #59 (SA.R 5000)
£400 $644 €580 Fish seller (20x16cm-8x6in) s. W/C. 12-May-3 Joel, Victoria #340 est:1000-2000 (A.D 1000)
£552 $877 €800 Bible lesson (28x46cm-11x18in) s.d.1864 W/C. 10-Mar-3 Sotheby's, Amsterdam #111
£900 $1476 €1350 Brawl in a tavern (16x28cm-6x11in) s.d.57 pencil W/C htd white. 4-Feb-3 Bonhams, Leeds #312
£2390 $3681 €3800 Intimate at the inn (15x23cm-6x9in) s.d.48 pencil pen ink wash W/C htd white. 23-Oct-2 Christie's, Amsterdam #69/R est:1500-2000

TEN KATE, Jan Jacob Lodewijk (1850-1929) Dutch
£1701 $2704 €2500 Duck hunting (58x84cm-23x33in) s.i. 19-Mar-3 Neumeister, Munich #601/R est:3000

TEN KATE, Johan Mari (1831-1910) Dutch
£2207 $3509 €3200 At the spring (18x19cm-7x7in) s.d.1850 panel prov. 10-Mar-3 Sotheby's, Amsterdam #74/R est:3000-5000
£2821 $4428 €4400 On the beach (29x44cm-11x17in) s. 21-Nov-2 Van Ham, Cologne #1713/R est:2500
£5500 $8745 €8250 Market day (42x71cm-17x28in) s. 20-Mar-3 Christie's, Kensington #154/R est:4000-6000
£6289 $9686 €10000 Moment of rest (40x56cm-16x22in) s. panel. 22-Oct-2 Sotheby's, Amsterdam #178/R est:15000-20000
£8219 $12904 €12000 Vegetable stall (54x79cm-21x31in) s. 15-Apr-3 Sotheby's, Amsterdam #158/R est:10000-15000
£12903 $20000 €19355 Afternoon nap (60x91cm-24x36in) s. 30-Oct-2 Christie's, Rockefeller NY #113/R est:20000-30000
Works on paper
£2398 $3500 €3597 In the artist's studio (23x22cm-9x9in) s. W/C gouache paperboard. 10-May-2 Skinner, Boston #46/R est:4000-6000
£2900 $4524 €4350 Children playing in a frozen landscape (23x35cm-9x14in) s. W/C. 9-Oct-2 Woolley & Wallis, Salisbury #142/R est:750-1000

TEN KATE, Johan Mari (attrib) (1831-1910) Dutch
£2000 $3140 €3000 On the seashore (62x107cm-24x42in) indis sig. 21-Nov-2 Christie's, Kensington #109/R est:2000-3000
£2436 $3824 €3800 Children playing (15x22cm-6x9in) s. panel. 21-Nov-2 Van Ham, Cologne #1713a/R est:2500

TENIERS, Abraham (1629-1670) Flemish
£7000 $11690 €10150 Village scene with peasants playing skittles (24x34cm-9x13in) bears mono. oak panel unidentified panel verso prov. 10-Jul-3 Sotheby's, London #120/R est:8000-10000
£7600 $12692 €11020 Landscape with a boor playing the bagpipes with a dog on a path (37x28cm-15x11in) s. panel. 8-Jul-3 Sotheby's, Olympia #372/R est:3000-4000

TENIERS, D (younger) (1610-1690) Flemish
£25201 $39061 €37802 Hermitage (55x66cm-22x26in) painted c.1640. 1-Oct-2 SOGA, Bratislava #137/R est:800000 (SL.K 1600000)

TENIERS, David (17th C) Flemish

£	$	€	Description
£18310	$30394	€26000	Portrait of young theriac vendor (24x16cm-9x6in) s. panel. 11-Jun-3 Dorotheum, Vienna #99/R est:25000-35000

TENIERS, David (elder) (1582-1649) Flemish

£	$	€	Description
£833	$1308	€1300	Peasants making merry (30x38cm-12x15in) 23-Nov-2 Arnold, Frankfurt #878/R est:3000
£11565	$18388	€17000	Repos pendant la fuite en Egypte (95x74cm-37x29in) s. 18-Mar-3 Campo, Vlaamse Kaai #240/R est:18000-25000

TENIERS, David (elder-attrib) (1582-1649) Flemish

£	$	€	Description
£980	$1549	€1470	Outside the inn, figures smoking and drinking (30x36cm-12x14in) 16-Nov-2 Crafoord, Lund #101/R est:15000 (S.KR 14000)
£17089	$27000	€27000	Singes a l'auberge (26x35cm-10x14in) copper on panel. 2-Dec-2 Rieunier, Paris #70/R est:18000

TENIERS, David (younger) (1610-1690) Flemish

£	$	€	Description
£6222	$10329	€9022	Peasants and puppeteer in a tavern interior (42x46cm-17x18in) mono. 16-Jun-3 Waddingtons, Toronto #257/R est:20000-30000 (C.D 14000)
£12195	$20000	€18293	Christ before Pilate (16x23cm-6x9in) panel after Andrea Schiavone prov.lit. 29-May-3 Sotheby's, New York #7/R est:10000-15000
£14194	$22000	€21291	Drunken husband (65x82cm-26x32in) init. prov. 2-Oct-2 Christie's, Rockefeller NY #163/R est:20000-30000
£16000	$26720	€23200	Shepherd with sheep conversing with a traveller at the edge of a village (62x73cm-24x29in) prov. 10-Jul-3 Sotheby's, London #121/R est:12000-18000
£16561	$25834	€26000	Peasants drinking at a table near an inn in a landscape (23x30cm-9x12in) s. panel. 5-Nov-2 Sotheby's, Amsterdam #284/R est:25000-35000
£23022	$36835	€32000	Interior of inn with dog and kitchen utensils (28x36cm-11x14in) s. panel. 13-May-3 Sotheby's, Amsterdam #9/R est:25000-35000
£35000	$54950	€52500	Pastoral landscape with shepherd (85x59cm-33x23in) s. prov. 11-Dec-2 Christie's, London #36/R est:25000-35000
£42000	$65940	€63000	Peasant holding a stoneware jug and pipe, another filling his pipe (22x16cm-9x6in) mono. panel prov.exhib.lit. 12-Dec-2 Sotheby's, London #16/R est:40000-60000
£55000	$86350	€82500	Peasant holding a large flagon, another smoking a pipe (22x16cm-9x6in) s. panel. 12-Dec-2 Sotheby's, London #17/R est:40000-60000
£60000	$94200	€90000	Temptation of St Anthony (81x110cm-32x43in) s. prov. 12-Dec-2 Sotheby's, London #18/R est:60000-80000
£65409	$101384	€104000	Alchemist in his workshop (23x18cm-9x7in) s. panel prov.lit. 4-Nov-2 Glerum, Amsterdam #43/R est:12000-16000
£444444	$720000	€666666	Interior of a picture gallery (39x49cm-15x19in) copper prov.lit. 23-Jan-3 Sotheby's, New York #70/R est:250000-350000
£460000	$768200	€667000	Interior of an inn with peasants smoking by a table and conversing before a fire (35x44cm-14x17in) s.d.1650 panel prov.lit. 9-Jul-3 Christie's, London #18/R est:150000-250000

TENIERS, David (younger) and HELMONT, Matheus van (17th C) Dutch/Flemish

£	$	€	Description
£41379	$65793	€60000	Figures in inn interior (40x59cm-16x23in) s. 4-Mar-3 Ansorena, Madrid #64/R

TENIERS, David (younger-after) (1610-1690) Flemish

£	$	€	Description
£6000	$9360	€9000	Interior of a palace kitchen (118x162cm-46x64in) prov. 10-Apr-3 Christie's, Kensington #66/R est:6000-8000

TENIERS, David (younger-attrib) (1610-1690) Flemish

£	$	€	Description
£823	$1300	€1235	Untitled (23x33cm-9x13in) s.d.1641 panel. 18-Nov-2 Schrager Galleries, Milwaukee #1292
£3205	$4968	€5000	Temptation of St Anthony (34x50cm-13x20in) panel prov. 5-Dec-2 Dr Fritz Nagel, Stuttgart #633/R est:5000
£5031	$7799	€8000	Peasants drinking by fireside (13x10cm-5x4in) panel. 2-Oct-2 Dorotheum, Vienna #100/R est:8000-10000
£15094	$23396	€24000	Peasants playing skittles with farmhouse and village pond (121x197cm-48x78in) prov. 2-Oct-2 Dorotheum, Vienna #101/R est:23000-26000

TENIERS, David (younger-circle) (1610-1690) Flemish

£	$	€	Description
£4286	$6600	€6429	Village inn (83x121cm-33x48in) i.verso prov. 3-Sep-2 Shapiro, Sydney #436/R est:15000-20000 (A.D 12000)

TENIERS, David (younger-style) (1610-1690) Flemish

£	$	€	Description
£5000	$7850	€7500	Peasants smoking and drinking in an interior (37x55cm-15x22in) init. panel. 10-Dec-2 Bonhams, New Bond Street #87/R est:5000-7000
£5500	$8580	€8250	River landscape with a drovers and cattle (75x110cm-30x43in) 8-Apr-3 Sotheby's, Olympia #152/R est:2000-3000
£6884	$11290	€9500	Interieur de cuisine avec couple epie par une commere (41x59cm-16x23in) 27-May-3 Palais de Beaux Arts, Brussels #303/R est:10000-15000
£8800	$13816	€13200	Landscape with herdsman resting with his flock (40x61cm-16x24in) bears sig. 10-Dec-2 Sotheby's, Olympia #367/R est:6000-8000
£24000	$37200	€36000	Kitchen maid cleaning a bucket with an old man courting her (42x60cm-17x24in) bears sig. panel. 30-Oct-2 Bonhams, New Bond Street #180/R est:5000-7000

TENIERS, David III (1638-1685) Flemish

£	$	€	Description
£10063	$15597	€16000	St Valentien receiving rosary from Madonna (75x61cm-30x24in) s.d.1677 copper. 2-Oct-2 Dorotheum, Vienna #106/R est:15000-20000

TENNANT, Alice (1890-?) South African/French

Works on paper

£	$	€	Description
£258	$415	€387	Field of flowers (18x27cm-7x11in) s. chl pastel W/C. 12-May-3 Stephan Welz, Johannesburg #168 est:3000-5000 (SA.R 3000)

TENNANT, Dorothy (1855-1926) British

£	$	€	Description
£550	$902	€825	Cupid with two cherubs (25x35cm-10x14in) paper on panel. 29-May-3 Christie's, Kensington #296/R
£550	$902	€825	Afrika (10x7cm-4x3in) mono.d.1890 copper. 29-May-3 Christie's, Kensington #303/R
£550	$902	€825	At the waters edge (18x14cm-7x6in) s.d.1887 panel. 29-May-3 Christie's, Kensington #304/R
£650	$1066	€975	Nymph with two cherubs (20x15cm-8x6in) mono. i.verso panel. 29-May-3 Christie's, Kensington #298/R
£650	$1066	€975	Fauns piping a nymph (17x17cm-7x7in) panel sold with an oil by the same hand. 29-May-3 Christie's, Kensington #300/R
£700	$1148	€1050	Blinded by love (27x23cm-11x9in) s.d.1925. 29-May-3 Christie's, Kensington #289/R
£800	$1312	€1200	Portrait of Leon Gambetta, at a writing desk (44x34cm-17x13in) s.d.1883 sold with two others. 29-May-3 Christie's, Kensington #302/R
£1000	$1640	€1500	La source (19x30cm-7x12in) 29-May-3 Christie's, Kensington #297/R est:300-500
£1200	$1968	€1800	Blinded by love (28x24cm-11x9in) sold with four female nudes by the same hand. 29-May-3 Christie's, Kensington #297a est:500-700
£1500	$2460	€2250	L'amour blesse (30x53cm-12x21in) s.d.1895. 29-May-3 Christie's, Kensington #295/R est:1200-1800
£1800	$2952	€2700	Rival supplicants (66x50cm-26x20in) s.d.89 exhib. 29-May-3 Christie's, Kensington #291/R est:1200-1800
£2000	$3280	€3000	Female nude on a rocky coastline (14x10cm-6x4in) panel sold with five female nudes. 29-May-3 Christie's, Kensington #301/R est:600-800
£2200	$3608	€3300	Suspiria (74x44cm-29x17in) s.d.1899 exhib. 29-May-3 Christie's, Kensington #292/R est:1200-1800
£2600	$4264	€3900	Cherub on a tortoise (22x18cm-9x7in) panel sold with 3 oils 2 W/C and 1 mezzotint by S Cousins. 29-May-3 Christie's, Kensington #305/R est:300-500
£3200	$5248	€4800	Waterlily (25x19cm-10x7in) s.d.1921 i.verso canvasboard sold with an oil by the same hand. 29-May-3 Christie's, Kensington #299/R est:500-800
£3400	$5576	€5100	Guardians (66x91cm-26x36in) s.d.1900. 29-May-3 Christie's, Kensington #293/R est:2000-3000
£3800	$6232	€5700	Bathers (114x81cm-45x32in) s.d.1901 exhib. 29-May-3 Christie's, Kensington #290/R est:3000-5000

Works on paper

£	$	€	Description
£420	$697	€630	The Lovers (14x21cm-6x8in) mono. pencil. 10-Jun-3 Sworder & Son, Bishops Stortford #462/R

TENNANT, John F (1796-1872) British

£	$	€	Description
£4800	$7968	€7200	Romantic highland scene with two figures meeting on a footpath (83x152cm-33x60in) s.d.1843. 10-Jun-3 Sworder & Son, Bishops Stortford #523/R est:5000-7000

TENNANT, Stephen (1906-1987) British

Works on paper

£	$	€	Description
£620	$961	€930	Lascar - story of the maritime boulevard (54x36cm-21x14in) s.d.1942 pen ink W/C wash. 24-Sep-2 Bonhams, New Bond Street #58

TENNIEL, J (19th C) British
Works on paper
£280 $454 €406 Interior scene with King Charles I and family. s.d.1838 pen ink W/C. 23-May-3 Moore Allen & Innocent, Cirencester #1006

TENRE, Henry (1864-1924) French
£1250 $2000 €1875 Soldier courting a young woman sewing in a genre French interior (30x36cm-12x14in) s. cardboard on panel. 18-May-3 Jeffery Burchard, Florida #67/R est:3000-5000
£2345 $3728 €3400 Le salon de Jacques Doucet rue Spontini (33x41cm-13x16in) s. cardboard. 5-Mar-3 Oger, Dumont, Paris #53/R est:600-700
£3846 $6000 €5769 Flower girl (66x46cm-26x18in) s. 22-Sep-2 Susanin's, Chicago #5039/R est:2400-3400

TEPLER, Samuel (1918-1998) Israeli
£422 $701 €612 Seated boy (47x38cm-19x15in) s.d.1950. 16-Jun-3 Waddingtons, Toronto #317/R est:700-900 (C.D 950)

TEPPER, Saul (1899-1987) American
£1282 $2000 €1923 Couple in modern office, yelling boss, office boy looking on (74x104cm-29x41in) mono.d.1931 blue black. 9-Nov-2 Illustration House, New York #182/R est:2500-4000
£4167 $6500 €6251 Children playing with toy boats by refrigerator, General Electric 1931 (84x84cm-33x33in) s.d.1931. 9-Nov-2 Illustration House, New York #8/R est:6000-9000

TER HIMPEL, Aarnout (1634-1686) Dutch
Works on paper
£2200 $3674 €3190 Wooded landscape with two figures resting by a stream (20x33cm-8x13in) bears i.verso blk chk pen brown ink grey wash. 9-Jul-3 Sotheby's, London #101/R est:1400-1800

TER MEULEN, Frans Pieter (1843-1927) Dutch
£828 $1292 €1300 Flock of sheep (45x62cm-18x24in) s. panel. 6-Nov-2 Vendue Huis, Gravenhage #548/R
Works on paper
£517 $823 €750 Malle jan (26x47cm-10x19in) s. gouache. 10-Mar-3 Sotheby's, Amsterdam #149/R

TERA, Teppo (1935-) Finnish
£4430 $7000 €7000 Partridges (39x49cm-15x19in) s.d.79 board. 1-Dec-2 Bukowskis, Helsinki #195/R est:5000-5500

TERAMARU, B A (19/20th C) ?
£950 $1587 €1378 Oriental seated lady holding a child (63x48cm-25x19in) s.d.1909. 12-Jul-3 Windibank, Dorking #332

TERAOKA, Masami (1936-) American
Prints
£1887 $3000 €2831 Longing samurai (65x97cm-26x38in) s.d.num.5/30 col woodcut etching aquatint. 2-May-3 Sotheby's, New York #633/R est:2500-3500
£1887 $3000 €2831 Catfish envy (68x98cm-27x39in) s.d.num.5/30 col woodcut etching aquatint exhib. 2-May-3 Sotheby's, New York #634/R est:2500-3500

TERBOIS, Pierre (1932-) Swiss
£300 $475 €450 Abstract composition (50x70cm-20x28in) s.d.1957 verso panel exhib. 29-Nov-2 Zofingen, Switzerland #3100 (S.FR 700)

TERBORCH, Moses (1645-1667) Dutch
Works on paper
£4392 $6851 €6500 Young man seated (21x14cm-8x6in) chk prov. 27-Mar-3 Christie's, Paris #140/R est:8000
£11976 $20000 €17365 Portrait of a man seated with head tilting (15x13cm-6x5in) red chk. 21-Jun-3 Selkirks, St. Louis #1045/R est:4000-5000

TERBRUGGHEN, Hendrick (1588-1629) Dutch
£200000 $334000 €290000 Youth playing the violin (104x82cm-41x32in) s.d.1626 prov.lit. 10-Jul-3 Sotheby's, London #17/R est:200000-300000

TERECHKOVITCH, Costia (1902-1978) French
£300 $474 €450 Still life of fruit (16x34cm-6x13in) s. card. 3-Apr-3 Christie's, Kensington #135/R
£705 $1107 €1100 Grande Serre (38x46cm-15x18in) s. cardboard. 13-Dec-2 Piasa, Paris #212
£1090 $1689 €1700 Falaises (50x65cm-20x26in) s. 4-Dec-2 Pierre Berge, Paris #161
£1800 $2844 €2700 Canal a Haarlem (60x73cm-24x29in) s.i.d.928. 3-Apr-3 Christie's, Kensington #102/R
£1982 $2894 €2973 Paysage de Finlande (51x80cm-20x31in) s. s.i. stretcher prov. 17-Jun-2 Philippe Schuler, Zurich #4391/R est:5000-7000 (S.FR 4500)
£1987 $3238 €3000 Bouquet (54x73cm-21x29in) s.d.1926 prov. 3-Feb-3 Cornette de St.Cyr, Paris #336/R
£2390 $3704 €3800 Coin de rue anime (60x81cm-24x32in) s. 30-Oct-2 Artcurial Briest, Paris #112/R est:4000-6000
£2465 $4092 €3500 Fillette au chapeau (34x27cm-13x11in) s. cardboard. 13-Jun-3 Rabourdin & Choppin de Janvry, Paris #151/R est:4000-5000
£2532 $4000 €4000 Portrait de fillette assise (63x46cm-25x18in) s. canvas on paper. 2-Dec-2 Tajan, Paris #167
£3544 $5600 €5600 Modele au chapeau jaune (54x39cm-21x15in) s. cardboard. 2-Dec-2 Tajan, Paris #167a/R
£5556 $8778 €8000 Nathalie au gueridon (65x50cm-26x20in) s. 23-Apr-3 Rabourdin & Choppin de Janvry, Paris #47/R
£13665 $22000 €20498 Coucher de soleil au palmier (81x65cm-32x26in) s. prov.exhib. 7-May-3 Sotheby's, New York #401/R est:8000-12000
Works on paper
£759 $1199 €1100 Nouvel an russe (58x1cm-23x0in) s. gouache. 4-Apr-3 Tajan, Paris #180
£1172 $1864 €1700 Elegant lady (64x84cm-25x33in) s. W/C pencil. 10-Mar-3 Sotheby's, Amsterdam #380/R est:800-1200

TERESZCZUK, P (20th C) Austrian
Sculpture
£1103 $1699 €1655 Dreaming couple. bronze. 27-Oct-2 Anders Antik, Landskrona #594/R est:20000-30000 (S.KR 16000)
£1986 $3078 €2979 Girl with flowers (56cm-22in) s. pat.bronze ivory. 4-Dec-2 AB Stockholms Auktionsverk #1831/R est:15000-20000 (S.KR 28000)

TERHELL, Adriaan Christiaan Willem (1863-1949) Dutch
£283 $436 €450 Schwabische Alb (50x60cm-20x24in) s. cardboard. 22-Oct-2 Campo, Vlaamse Kaai #636
Works on paper
£234 $383 €339 Man in a sailing barge (26x36cm-10x14in) s. W/C. 9-Jun-3 Hodgins, Calgary #375/R (C.D 525)

TERLIKOWSKI, Vladimir de (1873-1951) Polish
£385 $604 €600 Paysage (40x70cm-16x28in) s. 16-Dec-2 Charbonneaux, Paris #297
£709 $1184 €1000 Pont a Venise (41x27cm-16x11in) s.indis.d.1925. 17-Jun-3 Claude Boisgirard, Paris #127
£723 $1121 €1150 Militaire de la Grande Guerre (55x46cm-22x18in) s.d. 4-Oct-2 Tajan, Paris #220
£755 $1170 €1200 Anemones dans un vase (46x33cm-18x13in) s.d.1948. 30-Oct-2 Coutau Begarie, Paris #119/R
£1783 $2782 €2800 Sta Maria della Salute (55x38cm-22x15in) s.d.1932. 6-Nov-2 Claude Boisgirard, Paris #55 est:3000-3500
£1986 $3316 €2800 Fruits et bouquet d'anemones (61x46cm-24x18in) s.indis.d.1917. 17-Jun-3 Claude Boisgirard, Paris #129/R est:2800-3000
£2128 $3553 €3000 Rue du village (73x54cm-29x21in) s. 17-Jun-3 Claude Boisgirard, Paris #130/R est:3000-3200
£2270 $3790 €3200 Bateau dans une crique (54x73cm-21x29in) s.d. 17-Jun-3 Claude Boisgirard, Paris #128/R est:2000-2500
£3395 $4821 €5500 Canal in Venise (92x65cm-36x26in) s.d.1935. 16-Mar-3 Eric Pillon, Calais #209/R
£4113 $6870 €5800 Canal a Venise (61x46cm-24x18in) s.d. 17-Jun-3 Claude Boisgirard, Paris #131/R est:3200-3500
Works on paper
£1986 $3316 €2800 Femmes voilees (92x60cm-36x24in) s.d.1931. 20-Jun-3 Piasa, Paris #41/R est:2500-3000

TERLOUW, Kees (1890-1948) Dutch
£285 $444 €450 Interieur de ferme anime (33x41cm-13x16in) s. 15-Oct-2 Vanderkindere, Brussels #86
£538 $850 €850 Maison au bord de l'etang (50x100cm-20x39in) s. 2-Dec-2 Tajan, Paris #16
£552 $877 €800 Cows grazing in front of a farm (52x72cm-20x28in) s. 10-Mar-3 Sotheby's, Amsterdam #355
£833 $1292 €1300 Retour de peche (55x65cm-22x26in) s. 5-Dec-2 Gros & Delettrez, Paris #94
£833 $1317 €1300 Barques de peche sur la greve (65x54cm-26x21in) s. 14-Nov-2 Credit Municipal, Paris #53

TERMOHLEN, Karl E (1863-?) American
£245 $400 €368 Still life with violin (51x76cm-20x30in) s.d.1910 verso. 2-Feb-3 Grogan, Boston #19
£387 $600 €581 Forest and lake at sunrise (76x102cm-30x40in) s. 7-Dec-2 Harvey Clar, Oakland #1156

TERNEU, Albert (19/20th C) Belgian?
£420 $685 €630 Portrait of a lady, standing by a pillar (39x27cm-15x11in) s.d.1908. 13-Feb-3 Christie's, Kensington #43/R

TERNI, A L (?) Italian
£430 $688 €624 Italian coastal scene (68x105cm-27x41in) s. 18-May-3 Anders Antik, Landskrona #131 (S.KR 5500)
£452 $732 €678 Italian landscape (56x69cm-22x27in) s. 27-Jan-3 Blomqvist, Lysaker #1263/R (N.KR 5000)

TERNITE, Wilhelm (1786-1871) German
£2814 $4361 €4221 Prince William of Prussia (72x60cm-28x24in) s.d.1843. 24-Sep-2 Koller, Zurich #6554/R est:1800-2400 (S.FR 6500)

TERNO, Nina (1935-) Finnish
Sculpture
£3671 $5800 €5800 Man on horseback (32cm-13in) s. pat.bronze. 30-Nov-2 Hagelstam, Helsinki #7/R est:2500

TERPENING, Sonya (1954-) American
£2564 $4000 €3846 By the blue door (61x76cm-24x30in) 9-Nov-2 Altermann Galleries, Santa Fe #229
£2840 $4600 €4118 Calle de flores (51x76cm-20x30in) oil on linen. 23-May-3 Altermann Galleries, Santa Fe #178
£3082 $4500 €4623 Sunset at Santa Cruz (61x76cm-24x30in) 18-May-2 Altermann Galleries, Santa Fe #188/R

TERPNING, Howard A (1927-) American
£8861 $14000 €12848 Pause in the hunt (41x51cm-16x20in) s. board. 26-Jul-3 Coeur d'Alene, Hayden #145/R est:10000-15000
£37671 $55000 €56507 Chiracahua Apache (41x25cm-16x10in) 18-May-2 Altermann Galleries, Santa Fe #25/R
£54795 $80000 €82193 Crossing Wind river (76x51cm-30x20in) 18-May-2 Altermann Galleries, Santa Fe #24/R
£97945 $143000 €146918 Time stood still (46x66cm-18x26in) 18-May-2 Altermann Galleries, Santa Fe #23/R
£183544 $290000 €266139 Woman of the Sioux (102x81cm-40x32in) s.d.1982 exhib.lit. 26-Jul-3 Coeur d'Alene, Hayden #99/R est:150000-250000

TERPNING, Susan (1953-) American
£3493 $5100 €5240 Lame pony (46x61cm-18x24in) 18-May-2 Altermann Galleries, Santa Fe #92/R

TERRELL, Allen Townsend (1897-?) American
£469 $750 €680 Young sailor at sea (76x63cm-30x25in) s. 16-May-3 Skinner, Boston #149/R
£1883 $2900 €2825 Flowering garden (64x76cm-25x30in) s.d.1927. 8-Sep-2 Treadway Gallery, Cincinnati #560/R est:3000-5000

TERRINI, Alberto (?) Italian?
£499 $803 €749 Panaroma, Venezia (57x88cm-22x35in) s. i.verso. 12-May-3 Stephan Welz, Johannesburg #419/R est:7000-10000 (SA.R 5800)

TERRIS, John (1865-1914) British
Works on paper
£520 $811 €780 In harbour (18x24cm-7x9in) s. W/C. 17-Oct-2 Bonhams, Edinburgh #168
£660 $1069 €957 Afterglow, Tarbert, Loch Tyne, a harbour scene (75x50cm-30x20in) s. W/C. 24-May-3 Windibank, Dorking #300

TERRUELLA, Joaquim (1891-1957) Spanish
£503 $775 €800 Veronica (333x41cm-131x16in) s.d.56. 22-Oct-2 Durán, Madrid #222/R
£1039 $1704 €1590 Swansd (22x26cm-9x10in) cardboard. 5-Feb-3 Arte, Seville #769/R
£1135 $1838 €1600 Pase de muleta (20x23cm-8x9in) s. board prov. 20-May-3 Segre, Madrid #112/R est:1500
£1418 $2298 €2000 Corrida de toros (26x32cm-10x13in) s. board. 20-May-3 Segre, Madrid #98/R est:1900
£3548 $5606 €5500 Landscape with trees and sea beyond (44x37cm-17x15in) s. board. 17-Dec-2 Segre, Madrid #86/R
£4255 $6894 €6000 En el tentadero (56x47cm-22x19in) s. exhib. 20-May-3 Segre, Madrid #111/R est:6000
£4636 $7556 €7000 View of Palam (33x46cm-13x18in) s. 11-Feb-3 Segre, Madrid #135/R
£10345 $16448 €15000 Fishing harbour (46x55cm-18x22in) s. 4-Mar-3 Ansorena, Madrid #157/R

TERRUS, E (?) ?
£1830 $3001 €2800 Plage et bord de mer (44x60cm-17x24in) s. 7-Feb-3 Oger, Dumont, Paris #136

TERRUSO, Saverio (1939-) Italian
£340 $541 €500 Seated lady (24x18cm-9x7in) s. board. 1-Mar-3 Meeting Art, Vercelli #351
£359 $575 €550 Procession seen from a terrace (21x26cm-8x10in) s. s.i.d.1975 verso oil gold leaf board. 4-Jan-3 Meeting Art, Vercelli #419
£517 $822 €760 Untitled (20x30cm-8x12in) s. 1-Mar-3 Meeting Art, Vercelli #739
£521 $828 €750 Musical instruments (24x18cm-9x7in) s. s.i.verso. 1-May-3 Meeting Art, Vercelli #302
£521 $828 €750 At the table (20x20cm-8x8in) s. s.i.verso. 1-May-3 Meeting Art, Vercelli #513
£521 $828 €750 Harvest (35x50cm-14x20in) s. s.i.d.2001 verso acrylic. 1-May-3 Meeting Art, Vercelli #523
£578 $919 €850 Praying (70x50cm-28x20in) s. s.i.d.1999 verso acrylic paper on canvas. 1-Mar-3 Meeting Art, Vercelli #375
£641 $1006 €1000 Procession (40x50cm-16x20in) s.d.1971. 23-Nov-2 Meeting Art, Vercelli #171/R
£660 $1049 €950 Blue window (50x35cm-20x14in) s. acrylic painted 2001. 1-May-3 Meeting Art, Vercelli #305
£694 $1104 €1000 At the window (50x70cm-20x28in) s. acrylic. 1-May-3 Meeting Art, Vercelli #59
£705 $1107 €1100 Still life (70x50cm-28x20in) s. s.i.d.1990 verso acrylic. 23-Nov-2 Meeting Art, Vercelli #152/R
£729 $1159 €1050 In Sicily (50x70cm-20x28in) s. s.i.d.1999 verso acrylic paper on canvas. 1-May-3 Meeting Art, Vercelli #368
£748 $1190 €1100 Still life (55x66cm-22x26in) s. acrylic paper on canvas. 1-Mar-3 Meeting Art, Vercelli #527
£850 $1352 €1250 Musical instruments (50x70cm-20x28in) s. tempera acrylic. 1-Mar-3 Meeting Art, Vercelli #584
£884 $1406 €1300 Tree (20x30cm-8x12in) s. 1-Mar-3 Meeting Art, Vercelli #449
£903 $1435 €1300 Harvest (20x30cm-8x12in) s. s.verso. 1-May-3 Meeting Art, Vercelli #65
£915 $1464 €1400 At the window (50x70cm-20x28in) s. 4-Jan-3 Meeting Art, Vercelli #469
£915 $1520 €1300 Alberi (45x65cm-18x26in) s. s.i.verso acrylic. 10-Jun-3 Finarte Semenzato, Milan #287/R est:1300-1500
£962 $1510 €1500 Still life (40x50cm-16x20in) s. 19-Nov-2 Finarte, Milan #278/R
£1176 $1882 €1800 Figure at table (70x50cm-28x20in) s. painted 1986. 4-Jan-3 Meeting Art, Vercelli #220
£1282 $1987 €2000 Figures and fruit (70x50cm-28x20in) s. s.i.verso. 5-Dec-2 Stadion, Trieste #715
£1528 $2429 €2200 Figure at table (50x70cm-20x28in) s. s.i.verso. 1-May-3 Meeting Art, Vercelli #570
£1667 $2617 €2600 Procession (80x80cm-31x31in) s. s.i.verso. 19-Nov-2 Finarte, Milan #146/R
£1923 $3019 €3000 Player (68x49cm-27x19in) s. s.i.verso. 19-Nov-2 Finarte, Milan #51/R
£1973 $3137 €2900 Bullfight (50x70cm-20x28in) s. 1-Mar-3 Meeting Art, Vercelli #767

TERRY, David (20th C) American
£641 $1000 €962 Marathon old house II (51x61cm-20x24in) painted c.2002. 19-Oct-2 David Dike, Dallas #164/R

TERRY, Henry (fl.1879-1920) British
Works on paper
£300 $477 €450 Memories (31x25cm-12x10in) s. W/C exhib. 27-Feb-3 Bonhams, Chester #462
£2000 $3120 €2900 An old salt - fisherman seated reading his newspaper (41x30cm-16x12in) s. W/C. 27-Mar-3 Lane, Penzance #280/R est:2000-2500

TERRY, Joseph Alfred (1872-1939) British
£350 $543 €525 Landscape Slate Heights (30x35cm-12x14in) s.d.1906 exhib. 4-Dec-2 Christie's, Kensington #434
£400 $616 €600 Vale of York (33x41cm-13x16in) s. board. 3-Sep-2 Gorringes, Lewes #2126
£720 $1123 €1080 Figures walking in a formal garden with a lake beyond (15x25cm-6x10in) s. board. 10-Sep-2 David Duggleby, Scarborough #298/R
£2000 $3080 €3000 Garden party (65x80cm-26x31in) s. prov. 5-Sep-2 Christie's, Kensington #530/R est:2000-3000
Works on paper
£650 $1007 €975 Watching the boats (20x26cm-8x10in) W/C bodycol prov. 4-Dec-2 Christie's, Kensington #224/R

TERSTEGEN, Hermann (1886-?) German
£284 $443 €426 River landscape with trees at dusk (88x91cm-35x36in) s. study verso. 6-Nov-2 Dobiaschofsky, Bern #1012/R (S.FR 650)

TERWESTEN, Matheus (1670-1757) Dutch
£3716 $5797 €5500 Bacchanal (64x79cm-25x31in) 26-Mar-3 Tajan, Paris #140/R est:4000

TERZIAN, Georges (1935-) French
£304 $480 €480 Composition a la guitare (46x38cm-18x15in) s. 27-Nov-2 Blanchet, Paris #170
£483 $768 €700 Nature morte a l'as de trefle (73x60cm-29x24in) s. 10-Mar-3 Millon & Associes, Paris #110/R

TESCHNER, Richard (1879-1948) Austrian
£576 $944 €800 Still life with tea cosy and toy figure (60x59cm-24x23in) s. 5-Jun-3 Dorotheum, Salzburg #595/R
Works on paper
£278 $442 €400 Scientist (6cm-2in circular) mono.d.34 i. verso W/C paper glass leather. 29-Apr-3 Wiener Kunst Auktionen, Vienna #242/R

TESDORPF-EDENS, Ilse (1892-1966) German
£1234 $1801 €1900 Still life with sunflowers and apples (62x50cm-24x20in) s. 15-Jun-2 Hans Stahl, Hamburg #225/R
£1429 $2086 €2200 Still life with peonies in a vase (48x38cm-19x15in) board. 15-Jun-2 Hans Stahl, Hamburg #227/R

TESHIGAHARA, Sofu (1900-) Japanese
Works on paper
£345 $566 €480 Untitled (182x91cm-72x36in) s. ink goldpaper on plywood executed 1968. 3-Jun-3 Christie's, Amsterdam #106/R
£417 $646 €650 Untitled (83x170cm-33x67in) brush ink. 3-Dec-2 Christie's, Amsterdam #107/R
£481 $745 €750 Composition (182x90cm-72x35in) gouache. 3-Dec-2 Christie's, Amsterdam #101/R
£577 $894 €900 Man da Ra (90x185cm-35x73in) s. brush ink paper on plywood. 3-Dec-2 Christie's, Amsterdam #102/R
£719 $1180 €1000 Untitled (181x91cm-71x36in) ink silverpaper on plywood executed c.1968. 3-Jun-3 Christie's, Amsterdam #95/R est:600-800
£791 $1298 €1100 Tableau graphisme (142x69cm-56x27in) s. ink W/C. 3-Jun-3 Christie's, Amsterdam #101/R est:500-700
£897 $1391 €1400 Untitled (172x372cm-68x146in) s. brush ink six leaf screen. 3-Dec-2 Christie's, Amsterdam #104/R est:1500-2000
£1007 $1652 €1400 Untitled - six leaf folding screen (172x376cm-68x148in) s. in paper on plywood. 3-Jun-3 Christie's, Amsterdam #93/R est:1600-2000
£1090 $1689 €1700 Dragon (170x366cm-67x144in) brush ink gouache six leaf folding screen sold with a plate. 3-Dec-2 Christie's, Amsterdam #106/R est:1000-1500
£1151 $1888 €1600 Nichirin - six leaf folding screen (175x390cm-69x154in) s.i.d.1968 ink goldpaper on plywood. 3-Jun-3 Christie's, Amsterdam #98/R est:1800-2200
£1151 $1888 €1600 Otoko on na - six leaf folding screen (173x382cm-68x150in) s. i.d.verso ink gold paper on plywood. 3-Jun-3 Christie's, Amsterdam #100/R est:1800-2200
£1154 $1788 €1800 I Ro Ha Ni (177x390cm-70x154in) mono. brush ink six leaf screen. 3-Dec-2 Christie's, Amsterdam #103/R est:1800-2000

TESKEY, Donald (20th C) Irish?
£1781 $2796 €2600 Droichead beag (31x41cm-12x16in) s.d.1992 oil paper on board exhib. 15-Apr-3 De Veres Art Auctions, Dublin #272 est:1000-1500
£3145 $4906 €5000 Wild woodlands (58x79cm-23x31in) s. board. 17-Sep-2 Whyte's, Dublin #18/R est:6000-8000
£8562 $13442 €12500 Broad shadows, Bridgefoot Street (80x100cm-31x39in) s.i.d.2001 verso. 15-Apr-3 De Veres Art Auctions, Dublin #160/R est:10000-15000
£10067 $16208 €15000 Women on Synge Street (75x104cm-30x41in) s.d.1995 paper exhib. 18-Feb-3 Whyte's, Dublin #61/R est:7000-8000

TESSIER, O L (?) French
£1238 $1956 €1857 Street in Paris (47x69cm-19x27in) s. 30-Nov-2 Dorotheum, Prague #83/R est:26000-35000 (C.KR 60000)

TESSON, Louis (19th C) French
Works on paper
£300 $477 €450 Townsfolk awaiting the return of the frigate (18x26cm-7x10in) W/C. 4-Mar-3 Bonhams, Knightsbridge #238/R
£400 $636 €600 Break in the sun (13x22cm-5x9in) s. W/C. 4-Mar-3 Bonhams, Knightsbridge #243/R
£440 $678 €700 Port en Orient (32x22cm-13x9in) s. W/C. 23-Oct-2 Rabourdin & Choppin de Janvry, Paris #120/R
£440 $678 €700 Village en Orient (24x33cm-9x13in) s. W/C. 23-Oct-2 Rabourdin & Choppin de Janvry, Paris #119/R
£709 $1107 €1050 Rue. Eglise. s. W/C pair. 27-Mar-3 Maigret, Paris #205

TESTA, Pietro (1611-1650) Italian
£20000 $33400 €29000 Rest on the Flight into Egypt (70x100cm-28x39in) i. 9-Jul-3 Christie's, London #90/R est:30000-40000

TESTAS, Willem de Famars (1834-1896) Dutch
£6250 $9938 €9000 Oasis in Egypt (36x54cm-14x21in) s. 29-Apr-3 Christie's, Amsterdam #73/R est:4000-6000
Works on paper
£1111 $1833 €1600 Bustling square in the Orient (22x29cm-9x11in) s. pencil W/C. 1-Jul-3 Christie's, Amsterdam #157/R est:800-1200

TESTELIN, Henri (1616-1695) French
£35256 $55353 €55000 Louis XIV enfant (59x54cm-23x21in) oval prov.lit. 20-Nov-2 Binoche, Paris #56/R est:30000-40000

TESTORI, Giovanni (1923-) Italian
Works on paper
£962 $1510 €1500 Orchid (70x90cm-28x35in) pencil exec.1975 exhib. 21-Nov-2 Finarte, Rome #114/R

TESTU, P (19/20th C) French
£968 $1529 €1500 L'au-revoir au pecheur (54x65cm-21x26in) s. 17-Dec-2 Rossini, Paris #126/R
£1410 $2200 €2115 Gleaners (64x91cm-25x36in) 20-Sep-2 Du Mouchelle, Detroit #2005/R est:2000-2500

TESTU, Pierre (19/20th C) French
£769 $1208 €1200 Retour de peche (46x61cm-18x24in) s. 15-Dec-2 Thierry & Lannon, Brest #420

TETAR VAN ELVEN, Jan Baptist (1805-1889) Dutch
£1635 $2518 €2600 PO. d'orientale (78x59cm-31x23in) s. 23-Oct-2 Rabourdin & Choppin de Janvry, Paris #95/R

TETAR VAN ELVEN, Pierre Henri Theodore (1828-1908) Dutch
£2639 $4196 €3800 Winter, gothic fountain in a German town (51x62cm-20x24in) s. 29-Apr-3 Christie's, Amsterdam #36/R est:4000-6000
£2740 $4301 €4000 View of Antwerp (140x62cm-55x24in) s. 15-Apr-3 Sotheby's, Amsterdam #59/R est:5000-7000
£3774 $5811 €6000 Elegant ladies in a cour carre (81x51cm-32x20in) s.d.1874 exhib. 23-Oct-2 Christie's, Amsterdam #19/R est:6000-8000
£16000 $24960 €24000 Street scene, Beirut (37x55cm-15x22in) s. 15-Oct-2 Sotheby's, London #119/R est:8000-12000
Works on paper
£550 $891 €825 Mother and child (29x24cm-11x9in) s. pencil W/C gum arabic. 23-Jan-3 Christie's, Kensington #301/R

TETSIS, Panayiotis (1925-) Greek
£10000 $15500 €15000 Olive trees (66x133cm-26x52in) s. prov. 2-Oct-2 Sotheby's, London #63/R est:8000-12000

TETSU (1913-) French
Works on paper
£319 $517 €450 Sur l'ile (28x23cm-11x9in) s. gouache W/C Indian ink. 23-May-3 Camard, Paris #162
£461 $747 €650 Le pistolet (32x25cm-13x10in) s. gouache W/C Indian ink. 23-May-3 Camard, Paris #163

TETZNER, Heinz (1920-) German?
£833 $1317 €1200 Flowers (36x29cm-14x11in) s. s.i.d.1973 verso board. 26-Apr-3 Dr Lehr, Berlin #489/R
£975 $1501 €1550 Still life - roses (40x33cm-16x13in) s.i.d.1977 verso. 26-Oct-2 Dr Lehr, Berlin #523/R est:1200
Works on paper
£625 $987 €900 Landscape with sunset (51x72cm-20x28in) s. W/C board. 26-Apr-3 Dr Lehr, Berlin #490/R

TEUBER, Hermann (1894-1985) German
£1139 $1800 €1800 Still life with bottle and vase (34x48cm-13x19in) s.d.1963 board. 30-Nov-2 Bassenge, Berlin #6647/R
£2516 $3874 €4000 Garden wall (82x101cm-32x40in) s.d.1969 s.i.d. verso panel. 26-Oct-2 Dr Lehr, Berlin #524/R est:5000

TEUBNER, Kurt (1903-1990) German
Works on paper
£903 $1426 €1300 Occupant (66x50cm-26x20in) i. verso collage oil panel. 26-Apr-3 Dr Lehr, Berlin #494/R

TEUNN (20th C) Dutch?
£346 $550 €519 Portrait of a man (48x30cm-19x12in) s.d.69. 7-Mar-3 Skinner, Boston #645/R

TEUPKEN, Dirk Antoon (19th C) Dutch
Works on paper
£1200 $1944 €1800 Dutch brig, Herta in two positions (46x68cm-18x27in) s.i.d.1851 W/C bodycol. 21-May-3 Christie's, Kensington #429/R est:1500-2000

£1400 $2268 €2100 British brig Rosella in two positions off the Low Countries (48x70cm-19x28in) s.i.d.1835 pencil pen grey ink W/C. 21-May-3 Christie's, Kensington #646/R est:2000-3000

TEURE, Fanny (19th C) French
£1006 $1570 €1600 Portrait de jeune homme (61x50cm-24x20in) s.d.1827. 8-Oct-2 Christie's, Paris #28/R

TEVET, Nachum (1946-) Israeli
Sculpture
£6962 $11000 €10443 Still life with pistol and boat (89x93x76cm-35x37x30in) s.d.85 verso acrylic wood stainless steel. 27-Apr-3 Sotheby's, Tel Aviv #81/R est:12000-16000

TEXIER, Charles Felix Marie (attrib) (1802-1871) French
Works on paper
£2979 $4974 €4200 Nicomedie, vue de la citerne d'Imbaher (24x39cm-9x15in) s. W/C prov. 23-Jun-3 Beaussant & Lefèvre, Paris #94/R est:400-500

TEXIER, Richard (1955-) French
£284 $443 €420 Horizon Stellae (33x24cm-13x9in) s.i.d.1990 paint collage cardboard. 28-Mar-3 Charbonneaux, Paris #143
£497 $829 €720 Sans titre (40x40cm-16x16in) mono.d. canvas on canvas. 9-Jul-3 Cornette de St.Cyr, Paris #348/R
£1111 $1833 €1600 Galilee la nuit (80x80cm-31x31in) s.i.d. i.verso. 1-Jul-3 Artcurial Briest, Paris #806/R est:1400-1600
£1139 $1766 €1800 Epsiode (88x107cm-35x42in) s.d.90 verso acrylic. 28-Sep-2 Cornette de St.Cyr, Paris #435/R est:2000-3000
Works on paper
£414 $691 €600 Luna (126x34cm-50x13in) s.d.verso mixed media panel. 9-Jul-3 Cornette de St.Cyr, Paris #349
£795 $1295 €1200 Sans titre (54x45cm-21x18in) s.d. collage mixed media. 31-Jan-3 Charbonneaux, Paris #169/R
£886 $1373 €1400 Grille de lecture (50x61cm-20x24in) s.i.d.verso mixed media. 28-Sep-2 Cornette de St.Cyr, Paris #436/R
£993 $1619 €1500 Composition (195x130cm-77x51in) s.d.1984 verso mixed media canvas. 1-Feb-3 Claude Aguttes, Neuilly #178 est:3050-4573

TEXTOR, Franz Josef (1741-?) Austrian
£4403 $6824 €7000 Market scene (27x38cm-11x15in) mono. copper one of pair. 2-Oct-2 Dorotheum, Vienna #215/R est:8000-12000
£5031 $7799 €8000 Market scene (27x38cm-11x15in) mono. copper one of pair. 2-Oct-2 Dorotheum, Vienna #216/R est:8000-12000
£8805 $13648 €14000 Village views (27x38cm-11x15in) mmono. panel two. 2-Oct-2 Dorotheum, Vienna #214/R est:16000-20000

THAL, Sam (1903-1964) American
£1250 $2000 €1813 Indigenous Americana (66x81cm-26x32in) s. i.verso masonite. 16-May-3 Skinner, Boston #373/R est:300-500

THALINGER, E Oscar (1885-?) American
£452 $700 €678 House in St Louis (51x61cm-20x24in) init.i. board painted c.1950. 8-Dec-2 Toomey, Oak Park #776/R
£641 $1000 €962 Carnival (56x97cm-22x38in) s.d.43 masonite. 14-Sep-2 Selkirks, St. Louis #147

THAMER, Otto (1892-1975) German
£321 $487 €500 Flensburg (52x80cm-20x31in) s. 17-Aug-2 Hans Stahl, Toestorf #111/R

THAMES, Emmett (20th C) American
Works on paper
£886 $1400 €1329 Mississippi landscape (53x74cm-21x29in) s.d.75 W/C. 5-Apr-3 Neal Auction Company, New Orleans #360/R est:1200-1800

THAMM, Adolf (1859-1925) German
£930 $1497 €1320 Campagna near Rome in autumn (32x48cm-13x19in) s.i.d.93 board lit. 9-May-3 Schloss Ahlden, Ahlden #1492/R
£1923 $2923 €3000 Idyllic backyard with figures and poultry (55x46cm-22x18in) s. board lit. 11-Jul-2 Allgauer, Kempten #2717/R

THAMM, Walter (1885-?) German
£288 $453 €450 Ramsau with view of Dachstein (18x25cm-7x10in) s. plywood. 21-Nov-2 Dorotheum, Vienna #258/R

THAN, Mor (1828-1899) Hungarian
£5379 $8337 €8069 Renunciation of Queen Izabella (160x126cm-63x50in) s. 6-Dec-2 Kieselbach, Budapest #179/R (H.F 2000000)

THANCOUPIE (1937-) Australian
Sculpture
£9125 $14144 €13688 Pot (37x39cm-15x15in) slip oxide earthenware exec.c.1989 prov. 3-Dec-2 Shapiro, Sydney #140/R est:20000-25000 (A.D 25280)

THAREL, Léon (?-1902) French
Sculpture
£2200 $3432 €3300 Young sleeping street musician (31cm-12in) s.st.f.Susse brown pat bronze green marble base. 5-Nov-2 Sotheby's, London #179/R est:2500-3000

THARRATS, Juan Jose (1918-2001) Spanish
£314 $484 €500 Untitled (35x48cm-14x19in) s. acrylic collage monotype card. 28-Oct-2 Segre, Madrid #191a/R
£658 $1066 €1000 Untitled (38x54cm-15x21in) s. acrylic cardboard. 21-Jan-3 Ansorena, Madrid #321/R
£1032 $1600 €1548 Feu coleur D'or Ciel (97x130cm-38x51in) s. s.i.d.1960 verso prov. 16-Jul-2 Arthur James, Florida #91
£3355 $5301 €5200 Abstract landscape (65x81cm-26x32in) s. 18-Dec-2 Ansorena, Madrid #182/R
Works on paper
£759 $1206 €1100 Shapes (24x34cm-9x13in) mixed media collage. 4-Mar-3 Ansorena, Madrid #237/R
£769 $1215 €1200 Forms (24x34cm-9x13in) s. mixed media collage cardboard. 13-Nov-2 Ansorena, Madrid #51/R

THAULOW, Fritz (1847-1906) Norwegian
£1579 $2495 €2369 Harbour scene in Holland (19x25cm-7x10in) init. panel. 17-Dec-2 Grev Wedels Plass, Oslo #193/R est:20000-30000 (N.KR 18000)
£4516 $7135 €7000 Bord de lac (32x41cm-13x16in) mono.i.d.1905 cardboard. 19-Dec-2 Delvaux, Paris #41/R est:10000
£5249 $8503 €7874 Street scene in Cordoba (35x40cm-14x16in) init. i.verso. 26-May-3 Grev Wedels Plass, Oslo #97/R est:50000 (N.KR 58000)
£5912 $9223 €8868 Street scene with figures (61x50cm-24x20in) s. 23-Sep-2 Rasmussen, Vejle #300/R est:75000 (D.KR 70000)
£8000 $13120 €12000 Vinter i Paris, winter in Paris (41x27cm-16x11in) s. painted c.1898-1902 prov. 3-Jun-3 Sotheby's, London #228/R est:8000-12000
£9740 $15000 €14610 Spring thaw (36x41cm-14x16in) s.d.97 prov. 24-Oct-2 Shannon's, Milford #131/R est:12000-18000
£10408 $16236 €15612 French canal landscape (45x55cm-18x22in) s. 21-Oct-2 Blomqvist, Oslo #315/R est:150000-200000 (N.KR 120000)
£10638 $16489 €15957 French river landscape with water running calmly (24x33cm-9x13in) s. panel prov. 4-Dec-2 AB Stockholms Auktionsverk #1910/R est:125000-150000 (S.KR 150000)
£13548 $21000 €20322 Cottage by a stream (65x82cm-26x32in) s. 29-Oct-2 Sotheby's, New York #119/R est:30000-50000
£15044 $23770 €22566 From the Fort at Montetreuil (60x77cm-24x30in) s.i.d.mars 94. 28-Apr-3 Blomqvist, Oslo #317/R est:200000-250000 (N.KR 170000)
£17406 $27850 €26109 From Quimperle in Brittany (46x55cm-18x22in) s. 17-Mar-3 Blomqvist, Oslo #348/R est:250000-350000 (N.KR 200000)
£17419 $27000 €26129 On the canal (46x56cm-18x22in) s. prov.exhib. 2-Nov-2 North East Auctions, Portsmouth #80/R est:15000-25000
£24433 $38360 €36650 Garden steps in snow (47x55cm-19x22in) s. 21-Nov-2 Grev Wedels Plass, Oslo #29/R est:200000-300000 (N.KR 280000)
£25952 $41003 €38928 French autumn landscape with river (46x55cm-18x22in) s. 2-Dec-2 Blomqvist, Oslo #328/R est:200000-250000 (N.KR 300000)
£45000 $73800 €67500 Sommerlandskap - summer landscape (48x56cm-19x22in) s. painted c.1896-97. 3-Jun-3 Sotheby's, London #233/R est:50000-70000
£53901 $83546 €80852 Winter's day with man, horse and sledge (60x88cm-24x35in) s.d.Febr 91. 3-Dec-2 Bukowskis, Stockholm #243/R est:350000-400000 (S.KR 760000)
Prints
£2243 $3410 €3365 Spring (61x47cm-24x19in) s.num.52 col etching. 31-Aug-2 Grev Wedels Plass, Oslo #27/R est:20000-30000 (N.KR 26000)
£2534 $4105 €3801 Winter in Norway (50x60cm-20x24in) s.num.5 col etching. 26-May-3 Grev Wedels Plass, Oslo #58/R est:20000-30000 (N.KR 28000)
£2632 $4158 €3948 Impression of snow (42x60cm-17x24in) with sig. col etching hand coloured. 17-Dec-2 Grev Wedels Plass, Oslo #48/R est:40000-50000 (N.KR 30000)
£3633 $5740 €5450 Washerwomen at Quimperle (45x56cm-18x22in) s.num.192 col etching. 2-Dec-2 Blomqvist, Oslo #392/R est:25000-28000 (N.KR 42000)

Works on paper

£6878 $11142 €10317 From Bergen Harbour (44x66cm-17x26in) s.i.d.30 nov.85 pastel. 26-May-3 Grev Wedels Plass, Oslo #16/R est:100000-150000 (N.KR 76000)

£14516 $22500 €21774 Winter at Simoa River (62x99cm-24x39in) s.d.92 pastel. 29-Oct-2 Sotheby's, New York #115/R est:30000-40000

£20645 $32000 €30968 Winter on the Isle of Stord (48x65cm-19x26in) s.d.89 pastel prov.exhib. 30-Oct-2 Christie's, Rockefeller NY #7/R est:40000-60000

£20645 $32000 €30968 Winter at Simoa River (62x94cm-24x37in) s.i. pastel prov.exhib. 30-Oct-2 Christie's, Rockefeller NY #8/R est:40000-60000

£22152 $35000 €33228 River landscape (72x98cm-28x39in) s.d.94 pastel on canvas. 24-Apr-3 Sotheby's, New York #86/R est:40000-60000

£47120 $73979 €70680 Winter near Aker river (81x65cm-32x26in) s. pastel canvas. 21-Nov-2 Grev Wedels Plass, Oslo #30/R est:400000 (N.KR 540000)

THAYER, Abbott H (1849-1921) American

£500 $800 €750 Head of a girl (20x15cm-8x6in) oil on paper. 8-Jan-3 Doyle, New York #24/R

£1282 $2000 €1923 Angel with trumpet (56x41cm-22x16in) bears sig. 15-Oct-2 Winter Associates, Plainville #28 est:450-550

THECLA (20th C) American

Photographs

£2435 $3750 €3653 Jacqueline Kennedy in Paris (34x49cm-13x19in) num. photograph prov.lit. 24-Oct-2 Sotheby's, New York #189/R est:3000-5000

THEDY, Marc (1858-1924) German

£440 $700 €660 Little Dutch girl. s. board. 8-Mar-3 Harvey Clar, Oakland #1150

£2452 $3923 €3678 Interior scene with woman reading letter (46x36cm-18x14in) s.i. 13-Jan-3 Rasmussen, Vejle #204/R est:30000 (D.KR 28000)

Works on paper

£913 $1425 €1370 Portrait of young woman (18x13cm-7x5in) pencil. 28-Mar-3 Koller, Zurich #3169/R est:1500-2000 (S.FR 2000)

THEDY, Marc (attrib) (1858-1924) German

£617 $1000 €926 Sweet note (28x23cm-11x9in) bears sig panel. 24-Jan-3 Freeman, Philadelphia #157/R est:1000-1500

THEER, Robert (1808-1863) Austrian

Miniatures

£2400 $3936 €3480 Young lady in deep blue velvet dress (17cm-7in) s.d.1851 gilt metal frame. 3-Jun-3 Christie's, London #238/R est:2500-3500

Works on paper

£811 $1265 €1200 Portrait of young woman in white dress (8x6cm-3x2in) s.d.1836 W/C ivory oval. 28-Mar-3 Dorotheum, Vienna #366/R

THEGERSTROM, Robert (1857-1919) Swedish

£458 $743 €687 Still life of blue and white jug (54x65cm-21x26in) s.d.1876. 3-Feb-3 Lilla Bukowskis, Stockholm #569 (S.KR 6400)

£887 $1374 €1331 Fruit sellers, Cairo (66x54cm-26x21in) s.i.d.1888. 3-Dec-2 Bukowskis, Stockholm #195/R (S.KR 12500)

£1241 $1924 €1862 View of the sea in summer (80x100cm-31x39in) s. 4-Dec-2 AB Stockholms Auktionsverk #1559/R est:18000-20000 (S.KR 17500)

£2595 $4100 €3893 Interior scene with woman sewing, artist's reflection in mirror in background (56x44cm-22x17in) s.i. 27-Nov-2 Falkkloos, Malmo #77829/R est:20000 (S.KR 37000)

THELANDER, Par Gunnar (1936-) Swedish

£452 $709 €678 On the proposal path, winter's night (80x88cm-31x35in) s. 16-Dec-2 Lilla Bukowskis, Stockholm #862 (S.KR 6400)

£7008 $10932 €10512 Un Banquier (105x80cm-41x31in) s. s.d.2000 verso. 5-Nov-2 Bukowskis, Stockholm #384/R est:100000-125000 (S.KR 100000)

£7708 $12025 €11562 Ostrich with construction (180x146cm-71x57in) s. 5-Nov-2 Bukowskis, Stockholm #385/R est:100000-125000 (S.KR 110000)

Works on paper

£842 $1330 €1263 Fungus in pot (55x66cm-22x26in) s. mixed media. 30-Nov-2 Goteborg Auktionsverk, Sweden #647/R (S.KR 12000)

£877 $1385 €1316 Potato game (56x67cm-22x26in) s. mixed media. 30-Nov-2 Goteborg Auktionsverk, Sweden #646/R (S.KR 12500)

THELEN, J (?) ?

£600 $930 €900 Bust portrait of a young woman wearing a red striped dress (30x25cm-12x10in) oval panel. 24-Sep-2 Anderson & Garland, Newcastle #503

THELWELL, Norman (1923-) British

Works on paper

£800 $1248 €1200 Punch and Judy show (20x30cm-8x12in) s.i. pen wash. 17-Sep-2 Bonhams, Knightsbridge #32/R

THEMER, Wilhelm (1815-1849) German

£1223 $1907 €1835 Coastal landscape with figures and animals (48x60cm-19x24in) s.d.1845 panel prov. 9-Nov-2 Galerie Gloggner, Luzern #141/R est:1200-1500 (S.FR 2800)

THENOT, Francois (?) French

Sculpture

£2548 $3975 €4000 Antilopes. Felins (18x31cm-7x12in) s. bronze relief pair. 6-Nov-2 Tajan, Paris #26/R est:3500-4000

THEODORIDIS, Antonis (1915-) Greek

£12000 $18600 €18000 Mending the nets (57x70cm-22x28in) s. s.i.verso. 2-Oct-2 Sotheby's, London #102/R est:4000-6000

THERKILDSEN, Michael (1850-1925) Danish

£284 $457 €426 Landscape from Fyn (32x46cm-13x18in) mono.d.1892. 11-May-3 Hindemae, Ullerslev #674/R (D.KR 3000)

£409 $646 €614 Landscape with cattle and horse (52x72cm-20x28in) init.d.04. 5-Apr-3 Rasmussen, Havnen #2075 (D.KR 4400)

£419 $666 €629 Three goats in landscape (40x60cm-16x24in) init.d.97. 5-Mar-3 Rasmussen, Copenhagen #1854/R (D.KR 4500)

THERME, Henri (20th C) French?

£1103 $1766 €1600 Mon village de Bourgogne (65x54cm-26x21in) s.i. 11-Mar-3 Christie's, Paris #259/R

THERMIGNON, Carlo (1857-1938) Italian

Works on paper

£1156 $1839 €1700 Oriental scene (34x24cm-13x9in) s. W/C. 18-Mar-3 Finarte, Milan #217/R

THERO, Manjushri (20th C) Indian?

Works on paper

£550 $875 €825 Untitled (50x65cm-20x26in) s. gouache. 2-May-3 Christie's, Kensington #579/R

THERRIEN, Robert (1947-) American

£8228 $13000 €12342 No title (43x39cm-17x15in) init. acrylic paper collage in two parts painted 1991 prov. 13-Nov-2 Sotheby's, New York #114/R est:8000-12000

£8750 $14000 €13125 No title (61x49cm-24x19in) tempera paper on aluminum executed 1988 prov. 14-May-3 Sotheby's, New York #302/R est:6000-8000

Sculpture

£18987 $30000 €28481 Untitled (81x28x9cm-32x11x4in) s.d.1980 verso wood enamel. 13-Nov-2 Sotheby's, New York #542/R est:20000-30000

£23418 $37000 €35127 Untitled - snowman (102x43x10cm-40x17x4in) init.d.85 verso oil wood prov. 13-Nov-2 Sotheby's, New York #115/R est:30000-40000

£26563 $42500 €39845 Black bird relief (48x363x9cm-19x143x4in) init. wood executed c.1985 prov. 14-May-3 Sotheby's, New York #303/R est:40000-60000

£43750 $70000 €65625 Untitled - bent cone (291x96cm-115x38in) brown pat. bronze prov. 14-May-3 Sotheby's, New York #348/R est:80000-120000

THESLEFF, Ellen (1869-1954) Finnish

£1699 $2787 €2600 On the park bench (40x40cm-16x16in) i. 9-Feb-3 Bukowskis, Helsinki #372/R est:2000

£1899 $3000 €3000 Composition (47x39cm-19x15in) 1-Dec-2 Bukowskis, Helsinki #196/R est:4000-4500

£3813 $6101 €5300 Landscape (31x31cm-12x12in) s.indis.d.19.8 exhib. 17-May-3 Hagelstam, Helsinki #111/R est:8000

£8993 $14388 €12500 Still life of orange, apple, pear and grapes (26x28cm-10x11in) s.d.1919 exhib.lit. 17-May-3 Hagelstam, Helsinki #110/R est:12000

£41139 $65000 €65000 Landscape (39x56cm-15x22in) s. exhib.lit. 30-Nov-2 Hagelstam, Helsinki #105/R est:65000

£359712 $575540 €500000 Echo (61x43cm-24x17in) s.d.1891 prov.exhib.lit. 17-May-3 Hagelstam, Helsinki #109/R est:500000

Works on paper
£3380 $5442 €4800 Still life of flowers in vase (47x27cm-19x11in) s. pastel. 10-May-3 Bukowskis, Helsinki #172/R est:4000-4500

THEUERKAUFF, Carl Rudolph (1875-1926) German
£659 $1100 €956 Landscape with lake (46x61cm-18x24in) s. 21-Jun-3 Charlton Hall, Columbia #223/R est:500-700

THEVENET, Jacques (1891-?) French
£1262 $1917 €1893 La Seine a l'Institut (31x48cm-12x19in) s.d. oil gouache board. 28-Aug-2 Deutscher-Menzies, Melbourne #448/R est:1800-2500 (A.D 3520)

THEVENET, Louis (1874-1930) Belgian
£451 $718 €650 Paysage a Halle (47x60cm-19x24in) s.d.1908. 29-Apr-3 Campo, Vlaamse Kaai #299
£629 $969 €1000 Soldat en repos (29x37cm-11x15in) s.d.1913. 22-Oct-2 Campo & Campo, Antwerp #254
£654 $1052 €1000 Interieur (30x40cm-12x16in) s.d.1928. 14-Jan-3 Vanderkindere, Brussels #464
£993 $1658 €1400 Jour de fete (23x31cm-9x12in) s.d.1919. 17-Jun-3 Palais de Beaux Arts, Brussels #626/R
£1132 $1743 €1800 Mon jardin a Alsembergh (80x60cm-31x24in) s.d.1920. 22-Oct-2 Campo, Vlaamse Kaai #637
£1277 $2132 €1800 La kermesse (24x33cm-9x13in) s. cardboard. 17-Jun-3 Palais de Beaux Arts, Brussels #625/R est:1000-1500
£1282 $2013 €2000 Vase de fleurs (39x30cm-15x12in) s.d.1920. 10-Dec-2 Vanderkindere, Brussels #475/R est:2000-3000
£1307 $2105 €2000 L'eglise de Halle sous la neige (71x60cm-28x24in) s.d.1918 mono.verso. 14-Jan-3 Vanderkindere, Brussels #442/R est:2000-3000
£1667 $2583 €2600 Yellow chair (54x45cm-21x18in) s. paper on plywood. 3-Dec-2 Christie's, Amsterdam #34/R est:3000-5000
£1724 $2759 €2500 Nature morte au rouget, moules et cafetiere (40x50cm-16x20in) s.d.1939. 17-Mar-3 Horta, Bruxelles #163 est:3500-4500
£2055 $3226 €3000 Moules frites (32x46cm-13x18in) s.d.26. 15-Apr-3 Galerie Moderne, Brussels #388/R est:3000-4000
£2308 $3623 €3600 La table (50x40cm-20x16in) s. 10-Dec-2 Campo, Vlaamse Kaai #494 est:3500-4000
£3448 $5517 €5000 Les eglefins (62x72cm-24x28in) s.d.1919. 17-Mar-3 Horta, Bruxelles #159/R est:8000-12000
£3724 $5959 €5400 Les travaux de couture (40x50cm-16x20in) s.d.1929. 17-Mar-3 Horta, Bruxelles #160/R est:8000-12000
£8054 $12966 €12000 Les vierges (80x70cm-31x28in) s. 18-Feb-3 Galerie Moderne, Brussels #390/R est:10000-15000
£11511 $18417 €16000 Interieur de la maison Spitaels a hal (70x60cm-28x24in) s.d.1929. 17-May-3 De Vuyst, Lokeren #470/R est:14000-16000

THEVENET, Pierre (1870-1937) Belgian
£321 $497 €500 Quai Saint Nicolas (22x26cm-9x10in) s. cardboard. 9-Dec-2 Horta, Bruxelles #278
£506 $790 €800 Train a vapeur au bord de la Seine (50x66cm-20x26in) s. 15-Oct-2 Horta, Bruxelles #50
£769 $1192 €1200 Paris, au bord de la Seine (31x39cm-12x15in) s. board. 7-Dec-2 De Vuyst, Lokeren #316
£1139 $1777 €1800 Vue de la Seine (70x80cm-28x31in) s. paper on panel. 16-Sep-2 Horta, Bruxelles #126

THEVENOT, Adrien (20th C) French
£340 $530 €510 Nude in a landscape (11x8cm-4x3in) s. s.i.verso panel. 17-Oct-2 Lawrence, Crewkerne #482

THEYNET, Max (1875-1949) Swiss
£396 $579 €594 Neuenbergersee in winter (59x82cm-23x32in) s. board. 17-Jun-2 Philippe Schuler, Zurich #7447 (S.FR 900)

THEYRE, M (?) ?
£380 $578 €570 Grand National, horses and riders clearing Beecher's Brook (23x30cm-9x12in) indis.sig. 16-Aug-2 Keys, Aylsham #496

THEYS, Ivan (1936-) Belgian
£503 $775 €800 Composition (90x130cm-35x51in) s. 22-Oct-2 Campo, Vlaamse Kaai #638
£1529 $2385 €2400 Swing (160x128cm-63x50in) s. prov. 5-Nov-2 Vendu Notarishuis, Rotterdam #131/R est:500-700
£2244 $3478 €3500 Zwarte bloemen (100x81cm-39x32in) s.d.1969 i.on stretcher prov. 3-Dec-2 Christie's, Amsterdam #335/R est:3000-5000
£2446 $4012 €3400 Untitled (92x130cm-36x51in) s. 3-Jun-3 Christie's, Amsterdam #134/R est:2000-3000
Works on paper
£719 $1180 €1000 Couple (48x63cm-19x25in) s.d.84 pastel. 3-Jun-3 Christie's, Amsterdam #136/R est:1000-1500
£2013 $3099 €3200 Adam et Eve (34x25cm-13x10in) s. pastel. 22-Oct-2 Campo, Vlaamse Kaai #640

THIBAULT, Jean Thomas (1757-1826) French
Works on paper
£2179 $3422 €3400 Paysage avec projet de Piranese (27x39cm-11x15in) s.d.1784 pen sepia ink wash. 13-Dec-2 Pierre Berge, Paris #23/R

THIBAULT, Marcel (20th C) French
£692 $1065 €1100 Marchand d'oranges (22x16cm-9x6in) s.i.verso panel. 23-Oct-2 Rabourdin & Choppin de Janvry, Paris #195/R

THIBESART, Raymond (1874-?) French
£1447 $2345 €2200 La tetee (75x45cm-30x18in) s.i.d.1920. 21-Jan-3 Christie's, Amsterdam #408/R est:1500-2000

THICKE, Charlotte (fl.1802-1846) British
Miniatures
£2100 $3255 €3150 Officer of the Rifle brigade (9cm-4in) s.i.verso gilt mount paper mache frame rec. 1-Oct-2 Bonhams, New Bond Street #303/R est:600-800
£2400 $3720 €3600 Naval captain, seascape background (9cm-4in) gilt mount papier mache frame rec. 1-Oct-2 Bonhams, New Bond Street #297/R est:800-1200

THIEBAUD, Wayne (1920-) American
£88608 $140000 €132912 Childs's black (28x33cm-11x13in) s.d.1963 prov.exhib. 13-Nov-2 Sotheby's, New York #245/R est:80000-120000
£268750 $430000 €403125 Cup cakes (51x66cm-20x26in) s.d.61 s.i.on stretcher prov. 14-May-3 Sotheby's, New York #196/R est:250000-350000
£293750 $470000 €440625 Sugar, salt and pepper (33x43cm-13x17in) s. s.verso painted 1970 prov. 15-May-3 Christie's, Rockefeller NY #124/R est:300000-400000
£506329 $800000 €759494 Day city - bright city (122x91cm-48x36in) s.d.1982 s.d.verso oil chl prov.exhib. 12-Nov-2 Sotheby's, New York #21/R est:800000-1200000
£569620 $900000 €854430 Moring down street (152x122cm-60x48in) s.d.1987 s.d.verso prov. 13-Nov-2 Christie's, Rockefeller NY #50/R est:900000-1200000
£1772152 $2800000 €2658228 Freeways (122x152cm-48x60in) s. s.i.d.1975-79 oil chl on linen prov.exhib. 12-Nov-2 Sotheby's, New York #10/R est:1500000-2000000
Prints
£2358 $3750 €3537 Freeway curve (47x55cm-19x22in) s.d.num.14/50 col etching aquatint. 2-May-3 Sotheby's, New York #636a/R est:2000-3000
£2516 $4000 €3774 Nickel machine (20x13cm-8x5in) s.d.num.6/15 etching. 29-Apr-3 Christie's, Rockefeller NY #754/R est:1500-2500
£2530 $4200 €3795 Untitled, cherry cakes (58x75cm-23x30in) s.d.1979 col etching aquatint edition of 50. 11-Jun-3 Phillips, New York #538/R est:2500-3500
£2581 $4000 €3872 Freeway curve, from recent etchings I (58x76cm-23x30in) s.d.1979 num.32/50 etching aquatint drypoint. 25-Sep-2 Christie's, Rockefeller NY #425/R est:2000-3000
£2987 $4750 €4481 Steep street (75x55cm-30x22in) s.d.num.11/50 col aquatint drypoint spitbite. 2-May-3 Sotheby's, New York #638/R est:4000-6000
£3846 $6000 €5769 Daffodil (76x59cm-30x23in) s.i.d. col etching aquatint. 14-Oct-2 Butterfields, San Francisco #1366/R est:4000-6000
£3846 $6000 €5769 Park place (100x76cm-39x30in) s.d.num.34/50 etching drypoint spitbite col aquatint. 14-Oct-2 Butterfields, San Francisco #1367/R est:3000-5000
£5128 $8000 €7692 Dark cake (52x57cm-20x22in) s.d.num.114/200 col woodcut. 5-Nov-2 Christie's, Rockefeller NY #492/R est:6000-8000
£16352 $26000 €24528 Candy apples (39x41cm-15x16in) s.d.num.95/200 col woodcut. 29-Apr-3 Christie's, Rockefeller NY #755/R est:10000-15000
Works on paper
£20253 $32000 €30380 Pie (20x23cm-8x9in) s.d.1958 gouache W/C wax crayon graphite. 14-Nov-2 Christie's, Rockefeller NY #132/R est:30000-40000
£66456 $105000 €99684 Down 18TH (56x38cm-22x15in) s.d.1975 pencil chl prov. 13-Nov-2 Sotheby's, New York #253/R est:80000-120000
£196203 $310000 €294305 Pastel rows (41x51cm-16x20in) s.d.1972 pastel pencil prov.exhib. 13-Nov-2 Sotheby's, New York #248/R est:150000-200000

THIEL, Frank (20th C) German
Photographs
£2500 $3850 €3750 Cottbus (182x192cm-72x76in) s. c-print/diasec in frame prov.exhib. 23-Oct-2 Christie's, London #195/R est:3000-5000

THIELE, Alexander (1924-) German
£256 $397 €400 Garden cafe by the Wannsee, Berlin (50x60cm-20x24in) s. s.i. verso lit. 6-Dec-2 Karlheinz Kaupp, Staufen #2280
£288 $447 €450 Munich beer garden (60x50cm-24x20in) s. s.i. verso lit. 6-Dec-2 Karlheinz Kaupp, Staufen #2436/R

£409 $638 €650 Beer garden in English Garden, Munich (50x61cm-20x24in) s. s.i. verso. 21-Sep-2 Dannenberg, Berlin #603/R
£425 $697 €650 Hofgarten, Munich (50x60cm-20x24in) s. s.i. verso. 29-Mar-3 Dannenberg, Berlin #661/R
£425 $697 €650 Cafe garden (60x50cm-24x20in) s. s.i. verso. 29-Mar-3 Dannenberg, Berlin #662/R
£439 $685 €650 Hofgartencafe in Munich (50x60cm-20x24in) s. i. verso. 26-Mar-3 Hugo Ruef, Munich #241
£458 $750 €700 Toscana in the evening (80x100cm-31x39in) s. s.i. verso. 29-Mar-3 Dannenberg, Berlin #663/R
£545 $845 €850 Cafe garden at Starnberger lake (50x60cm-20x24in) s. i.verso. 7-Dec-2 Dannenberg, Berlin #737/R
£723 $1128 €1150 Garden cafe in Wannsee, Berlin (50x60cm-20x24in) s. s.i. verso. 21-Sep-2 Dannenberg, Berlin #602/R

THIELE, Anton (1838-1902) Danish
£574 $930 €832 View of Salene Bay towards Gudhjem, Bornholm (57x82cm-22x32in) 26-May-3 Rasmussen, Copenhagen #1395/R (D.KR 6000)
£723 $1143 €1085 View from Herculanum with ruins (35x47cm-14x19in) paper on canvas prov. 27-Nov-2 Museumsbygningen, Copenhagen #66/R (D.KR 8500)

THIELE, Arthur (1841-1919) German
£1074 $1729 €1600 Valley of Klein Arl, Austria (65x90cm-26x35in) s.d.92 prov. 18-Feb-3 Sotheby's, Amsterdam #290/R est:1500-2000
£7382 $11885 €11000 Chamois grazing in the snow (65x106cm-26x42in) s.d. 18-Feb-3 Sotheby's, Amsterdam #292/R est:2000-3000

THIELE, Franz (1868-1945) Austrian
£1135 $1839 €1646 Girl with water lilies (61x54cm-24x21in) s. board. 24-May-3 Dorotheum, Prague #31/R est:15000-23000 (C.KR 50000)

THIELE, Johann Alexander (1685-1752) German
£4110 $6411 €6000 Extensive river landscape with travellers (76x100cm-30x39in) 10-Apr-3 Van Ham, Cologne #1275/R est:9000

THIELE, Johann Alexander (attrib) (1685-1752) German
£371 $590 €557 Mother and child (18x23cm-7x9in) s. panel. 18-Mar-3 Maynards, Vancouver #59/R (C.D 875)
£1392 $2158 €2200 Mountain landscape (30x35cm-12x14in) 25-Sep-2 Neumeister, Munich #521/R est:2500
£1500 $2325 €2250 Italianate landscape with cowherd, shepherdess, cattle and sheep (73x98cm-29x39in) 30-Oct-2 Bonhams, New Bond Street #121/R est:1500-2000
£2581 $4078 €4000 Diane et Acteon (37x64cm-15x25in) 20-Dec-2 Tajan, Paris #84/R

THIELE, Johann Alexander (style) (1685-1752) German
£7500 $11700 €11250 River landscape with untsmen and shepherds (43x54cm-17x21in) panel oval prov.exhib. 10-Apr-3 Sotheby's, London #93/R

THIELE, Johann Friedrich Alexander (1747-1803) German
£6081 $9487 €9000 Landscape in German countryside (52x42cm-20x17in) copper. 26-Mar-3 Tajan, Paris #148/R est:12000

THIELEMANN, Alfred (1883-?) German
£610 $1000 €915 Extensive landscape (68x114cm-27x45in) s. canvas on board. 5-Feb-3 Christie's, Rockefeller NY #203/R est:1000-1500

THIELEN, Jan Philips van (1618-1667) Flemish
£9130 $14243 €13695 Still life of flowers (63x53cm-25x21in) pair prov. 16-Sep-2 Philippe Schuler, Zurich #3498/R est:30000-40000 (S.FR 21000)
£19000 $31730 €27550 Still life with tulips and roses in a stoneware vase (53x41cm-21x16in) s. oak panel. 10-Jul-3 Sotheby's, London #122/R est:10000-15000
£187050 $299281 €260000 Tulips, yellow roses and dog roses in a glass vase on stone ledge (89x68cm-35x27in) s.i. prov.exhib.lit. 14-May-3 Christie's, Amsterdam #180/R est:60000-80000

THIELER, Fred (1916-1999) German
£1377 $2258 €1900 IV. S. 57 (65x99cm-26x39in) s.d.1957 s.i.d. verso board. 31-May-3 Villa Grisebach, Berlin #347/R est:3000-4000
£1456 $2300 €2300 XIII.D.57 (68x96cm-27x38in) s.d.57 s.i.d. verso board. 30-Nov-2 Villa Grisebach, Berlin #404/R est:3000-4000
£1772 $2800 €2800 I.K.57 (100x65cm-39x26in) s.d.1957 s.i.d. verso board. 30-Nov-2 Villa Grisebach, Berlin #405/R est:3500-4500

Works on paper
£1282 $1987 €2000 Untitled (50x64cm-20x25in) s.d.55 mixed media board. 3-Dec-2 Lempertz, Koln #466/R est:2500
£1736 $2743 €2500 M.I.57 (68x96cm-27x38in) s.d.1957 s.i.d. verso oil tempera gouache board. 26-Apr-3 Dr Lehr, Berlin #496/R est:4000

THIEM, Paul (1858-1922) German
£286 $426 €440 Pre-alpine landscape in spring (37x47cm-15x19in) s. 27-Jun-2 Neumeister, Munich #2838

THIEME, Anthony (1888-1954) American/Dutch
£2031 $3250 €3047 Stucco courtyard with blue doors (20x25cm-8x10in) etched sig. board. 11-Jan-3 James Julia, Fairfield #80 est:4000-6000
£2308 $3600 €3462 Punta Jorge Laguna de Atitlan, Guatemala (63x76cm-25x30in) s. i.d.verso. 9-Nov-2 Sloan, North Bethesda #594/R est:4000-6000
£2467 $3750 €3701 Breton villagers looking out to sea (114x33cm-45x13in) s. board. 17-Aug-2 North East Auctions, Portsmouth #562/R
£2690 $4250 €4035 Laundry day (23x30cm-9x12in) s. canvasboard. 5-Apr-3 Neal Auction Company, New Orleans #316/R est:4000-6000
£3145 $5000 €4718 Summer street, Rockport (30x41cm-12x16in) s. i.verso board. 7-Mar-3 Skinner, Boston #487/R est:4000-6000
£3614 $6000 €5240 Sunny street (51x61cm-20x24in) s. i.verso prov. 11-Jun-3 Butterfields, San Francisco #4082/R est:8000-10000
£3822 $6000 €5733 Farmhouse in an extensive landscape (63x76cm-25x30in) s. 19-Nov-2 Butterfields, San Francisco #8034/R est:12000-16000
£3915 $6500 €5677 Villefranche, French Riviera (63x76cm-25x30in) s. i. on stretcher prov. 11-Jun-3 Butterfields, San Francisco #4081/R est:8000-12000
£4299 $6750 €6449 Punta Jorge, Laguna de Atitlan Guatemala (64x76cm-25x30in) s. i.d.1948 verso. 19-Apr-3 James Julia, Fairfield #153/R est:8000-10000
£7831 $13000 €11355 Los Aicos a Santa Clara (63x76cm-25x30in) s. i.verso prov. 11-Jun-3 Butterfields, San Francisco #4091b/R est:10000-15000
£9639 $16000 €13977 Leaving port (63x76cm-25x30in) s. i.verso prov. 11-Jun-3 Butterfields, San Francisco #4978/R est:10000-15000
£10127 $16000 €15191 At the dock, Rockport (76x91cm-30x36in) s. exhib. 24-Apr-3 Shannon's, Milford #168/R est:15000-25000

Works on paper
£1090 $1700 €1635 Tuillerie Gardens (28x42cm-11x17in) s.i. W/C. 9-Nov-2 Sloan, North Bethesda #550/R est:1500-2500

THIEME, Friedrich (fl.1870-1880) German
£548 $860 €800 Landscape with Ortler (52x39cm-20x15in) s. 16-Apr-3 Dorotheum, Salzburg #156/R

THIEME, Theodor (1823-1901) German
£641 $994 €1000 Young man (83x64cm-33x25in) s.d.1866 canvas on board. 5-Dec-2 Dr Fritz Nagel, Stuttgart #705/R

THIENON, Claude (1772-1846) French

Works on paper
£641 $1006 €1000 Vue d'Italie (18x23cm-7x9in) s. W/C. 13-Dec-2 Pierre Berge, Paris #16/R
£2469 $4000 €3704 View of the falls at Tivoli (72x65cm-28x26in) s.i. 21-Jan-3 Sotheby's, New York #194/R est:7000
£2932 $4750 €4398 View of the park at Roosendael (37x46cm-15x18in) s.i. chk. 21-Jan-3 Sotheby's, New York #198/R

THIENON, Louis (1812-?) French

Works on paper
£676 $1054 €1000 View of Loches (13x20cm-5x8in) s.d.40 graphite chk pen ink W/C. 27-Mar-3 Christie's, Paris #154/R

THIER, Barend Hendrik (1751-1814) Dutch
£955 $1471 €1500 Landscape with a shepherd overlooking a river, cow, sheep and horses (29x39cm-11x15in) s.d.1779 panel. 3-Sep-2 Christie's, Amsterdam #64/R est:1500-2500
£1429 $2129 €2200 Cow and sheep by water in meadow landscape (24x35cm-9x14in) s. panel. 26-Jun-2 Neumeister, Munich #881/R est:2000

THIERRIAT, Augustin Alexandre (1789-1870) French

Works on paper
£545 $845 €850 Bouquet de fleurs (39x30cm-15x12in) W/C. 4-Dec-2 Piasa, Paris #162
£1486 $2319 €2200 Salle du XIII siecle (36x26cm-14x10in) s.i.d.1817 pe ink W/C htd white. 27-Mar-3 Christie's, Paris #159/R

THIERRY, Hilaire (19th C) French

Works on paper
£8865 $14362 €12500 Interieur (17x25cm-7x10in) i. verso W/C htd white gouache. 21-May-3 Piasa, Paris #363/R est:2500-3000

THIERRY, Wilhelm Adam (1761-1823) German
Works on paper
£506 $800 €800 Lovers by water pump (15x20cm-6x8in) s.d.21.8bris 1796 silver pen pencil board. 29-Nov-2 Bassenge, Berlin #5762/R

THIERY, Gaston (1922-) French
£272 $433 €400 Sedelle au Trou du Chauma (46x55cm-18x22in) s. s.i.verso. 24-Mar-3 Coutau Begarie, Paris #305

THIEVAERT, Daniel (1613-1657) Dutch
£4140 $6459 €6500 Silvio and Dorinde (32x29cm-13x11in) panel en grisaille. 5-Nov-2 Sotheby's, Amsterdam #324/R est:7000-9000

THIM, Cornelis (1755-1813) Dutch
Works on paper
£1500 $2325 €2250 Man o war and fishing vessels in calm seas (25x37cm-10x15in) s.d.1810 verso pen ink grey wash. 6-Dec-2 Lyon & Turnbull, Edinburgh #49/R est:1500-2000

THIMGAN, David D (1955-) American
£3636 $5600 €5454 Schooner towing up Hoquiam River (36x66cm-14x26in) 25-Oct-2 Morris & Whiteside, Hilton Head Island #102 est:5000-6000

THIOLAT, Dominique (1946-) French
£1218 $1912 €1900 Pomme (206x194cm-81x76in) s.d.79 verso. 15-Dec-2 Perrin, Versailles #178/R
Works on paper
£347 $552 €500 Abstraction I (49x49cm-19x19in) s.d.1989 mixed media. 29-Apr-3 Campo & Campo, Antwerp #292
£347 $552 €500 Abstraction III (49x49cm-19x19in) s.d.1989 mixed media. 29-Apr-3 Campo & Campo, Antwerp #294
£382 $607 €550 Abstraction II (49x49cm-19x19in) s.d.1989 mixed media. 29-Apr-3 Campo & Campo, Antwerp #293
£417 $663 €600 Abstraction IV (49x49cm-19x19in) s.d.1989 mixed media. 29-Apr-3 Campo & Campo, Antwerp #295

THIOLLIER, Felix (1842-1914) French
Photographs
£1900 $3078 €2850 Tipping a coal bin (30x40cm-12x16in) silver print exec.c.1900 exhib. 22-May-3 Sotheby's, London #52/R est:1500-2500
£2800 $4536 €4200 Industrial landscape with children in the foreground (27x37cm-11x15in) silver print exec.c.1900. 22-May-3 Sotheby's, London #53/R est:1000-1500

THIRKETTLE, Sharon (20th C) Canadian
£311 $510 €451 Marmot lake I (40x50cm-16x20in) s.i. acrylic. 9-Jun-3 Hodgins, Calgary #182/R (C.D 700)
£402 $631 €603 Merging waters (38x75cm-15x30in) s.i. board. 25-Nov-2 Hodgins, Calgary #152/R (C.D 1000)

THIRTLE, John (1777-1839) British
Works on paper
£2000 $3100 €3000 Overstrand beach with boats (39x67cm-15x26in) W/C prov. 30-Sep-2 Bonhams, Ipswich #301/R

THISSEN, Lou (20th C) ?
£1474 $2256 €2300 Polo (100x100cm-39x39in) acrylic painted 1996. 23-Aug-2 Deauville, France #219/R est:2500
£2628 $4021 €4100 San Marco (100x100cm-39x39in) acrylic painted 2000. 23-Aug-2 Deauville, France #216/R est:2500

THIVET, Antoine Auguste (attrib) (1856-1927) French
£316 $494 €500 Soldat (41x28cm-16x11in) s.d.1881 panel. 10-Sep-2 Vanderkindere, Brussels #281

THOGER, Palle (1912-) Danish?
Sculpture
£2371 $3675 €3557 Girl drying herself (173cm-68in) s. green pat.bronze executed c.1937 lit. 1-Oct-2 Rasmussen, Copenhagen #141/R est:25000-30000 (D.KR 28000)

THOL, Hendrick Otto von (1859-1902) Dutch
£352 $567 €500 Shepherd in hilly landscape (30x51cm-12x20in) s. 7-May-3 Vendue Huis, Gravenhage #74

THOLEN, W B (1860-1931) Dutch
£694 $1104 €1000 Sablonniere (47x63cm-19x25in) s. 29-Apr-3 Campo, Vlaamse Kaai #300

THOLEN, Willem Bastiaan (1860-1931) Dutch
£377 $588 €550 Birch forest of Barbizon (28x17cm-11x7in) init.d.87 panel prov. 14-Apr-3 Glerum, Amsterdam #52/R
£637 $994 €1000 Summer afternoon in Holland (28x38cm-11x15in) s. panel. 6-Nov-2 Hugo Ruef, Munich #1314/R
£701 $1093 €1100 Winter landscape (54x81cm-21x32in) s. 5-Nov-2 Vendu Notarishuis, Rotterdam #284 est:2000-2500
£1042 $1719 €1500 Sunlit winter landscape (56x82cm-22x32in) s. 1-Jul-3 Christie's, Amsterdam #222/R est:2000-3000
£1401 $2186 €2200 Beach scene with figures and boats (19x22cm-7x9in) s. 5-Nov-2 Vendu Notarishuis, Rotterdam #295/R est:3000-4000
£1656 $2583 €2600 Boat on the sea (22x35cm-9x14in) s. 6-Nov-2 Vendue Huis, Gravenhage #540/R est:2000-3000
£2740 $4301 €4000 Polder landscape (30x43cm-12x17in) s. canvas on panel prov. 15-Apr-3 Sotheby's, Amsterdam #117/R est:3000-5000
£2803 $4372 €4400 Seascape with fishing boat (27x39cm-11x15in) s.d.13. 5-Nov-2 Vendu Notarishuis, Rotterdam #283/R est:3000-4000
£3694 $5763 €5800 Small bridge at Giethoorn (49x39cm-19x15in) s. 5-Nov-2 Vendu Notarishuis, Rotterdam #285/R est:4000-5000
£3774 $5811 €6000 Farmer working in his garden (32x46cm-13x18in) s. prov. 23-Oct-2 Christie's, Amsterdam #148/R est:8000-12000
£4795 $7527 €7000 Enkhuizen Harbour (29x41cm-11x16in) s.d.18 canvas on panel prov. 15-Apr-3 Sotheby's, Amsterdam #121/R est:7000-10000
£5137 $8065 €7500 River landscape at sunset (30x45cm-12x18in) s. panel. 15-Apr-3 Sotheby's, Amsterdam #112/R est:6000-8000
£5479 $8603 €8000 View of the draw bridge Connecting the Drommedaris with the Zuiderspui, Enkhuizen (45x70cm-18x28in) s. 15-Apr-3 Sotheby's, Amsterdam #148/R est:6000-8000
£8451 $14028 €12000 Summer landscape with farmhouse, pond and cattle (76x100cm-30x39in) s. 14-Jun-3 Arnold, Frankfurt #882/R est:4000
Works on paper
£263 $426 €400 Botters in open water (23x34cm-9x13in) s. black chk sold with three studies by same hand. 21-Jan-3 Christie's, Amsterdam #244/R
£263 $426 €400 Afsluitdijk (21x30cm-8x12in) black chk col crayon. 21-Jan-3 Christie's, Amsterdam #317
£316 $512 €480 Drawing lesson at the Pulchri Studio (35x44cm-14x17in) s. black chk. 21-Jan-3 Christie's, Amsterdam #246
£601 $938 €950 Pair of city views. one s. chl chk pair. 21-Oct-2 Glerum, Amsterdam #23/R
£955 $1471 €1500 Jeugdportet (40x32cm-16x13in) s. chl lit. 3-Sep-2 Christie's, Amsterdam #258
£1053 $1705 €1600 Enkhuizen (37x26cm-15x10in) s. black chk W/C bodycol. 21-Jan-3 Christie's, Amsterdam #311/R est:300-500
£1266 $1975 €2000 Interior of ship-building yard (50x65cm-20x26in) s. dr. 21-Oct-2 Glerum, Amsterdam #27/R est:1000-1500
£2516 $3874 €4000 Bridge in Giethoorn (51x41cm-20x16in) s. W/C prov. 23-Oct-2 Christie's, Amsterdam #158/R est:4000-6000
£3333 $5300 €4800 Playing in the woods (36x50cm-14x20in) s. pencil W/C htd white exhib. 29-Apr-3 Christie's, Amsterdam #175/R est:3000-5000

THOLSTRUP, Anne (1952-) Danish
£550 $853 €825 Figure composition (100x81cm-39x32in) init. s.d.1989 verso. 1-Oct-2 Rasmussen, Copenhagen #186/R (D.KR 6500)
£1335 $2229 €1936 Figure composition (200x150cm-79x59in) init. s.d.1988 verso. 17-Jun-3 Rasmussen, Copenhagen #56/R est:12000-15000 (D.KR 14000)

THOM, James Crawford (1835-1898) American
£926 $1500 €1343 Walk along the river (25x56cm-10x22in) s. 21-May-3 Doyle, New York #67/R est:2000-3000
£943 $1500 €1415 Crossing paths (25x48cm-10x19in) s. 5-Mar-3 Doyle, New York #59/R est:2000-3000
£1852 $3000 €2685 Children at a well (56x91cm-22x36in) s. indis.d.1890. 21-May-3 Doyle, New York #66/R est:3000-5000
£1852 $3000 €2685 Sunset on the River Oise, France (30x48cm-12x19in) s.i. s.d.88 verso panel prov. 21-May-3 Doyle, New York #79/R est:2000-3000
£1946 $3250 €2822 Mischievous kitten (34x30cm-13x12in) s. 22-Jun-3 Freeman, Philadelphia #85/R est:1000-1500
£3500 $5565 €5250 Returning from the wood in winter (35x46cm-14x18in) s.d.1861 panel prov. 6-Mar-3 Christie's, Kensington #570/R est:1000-1500
£3704 $6000 €5371 Window shopping. Feeding bunnies (56x43cm-22x17in) s.d.77 two prov. 21-May-3 Doyle, New York #78/R est:8000-12000

THOMA, Emil (attrib) (1869-?) Swiss
£390 $581 €600 Portrait of Oberammergau passion actor (36x24cm-14x9in) paper on panel. 27-Jun-2 Neumeister, Munich #2839

THOMA, Hans (1839-1924) German
£818 $1300 €1227 Luncheon (27x34cm-11x13in) s.i.d.91 board. 7-Mar-3 Skinner, Boston #246/R est:1000-1500
£7000 $11480 €10500 Der Verlorene Sohn - Prodigal Son (88x113cm-35x44in) mono.d.85 prov.lit. 3-Jun-3 Sotheby's, London #62/R est:4000-6000

£15649 $24412 €23474 Lovers on beach at sunset (68x86cm-27x34in) s.d.92. 11-Apr-3 Kieselbach, Budapest #147/R est:5600000 (H.F 5600000)

Works on paper

£366 $601 €531 Moorland with tree (8x7cm-3x3in) mono.d.1919 W/C. 4-Jun-3 Fischer, Luzern #2558/R (S.FR 780)
£393 $613 €590 Woodland with bridge over narrow stream (20x15cm-8x6in) mono.d.15. Okt. 68 Indian ink. 6-Nov-2 Dobiaschofsky, Bern #1190/R (S.FR 900)
£1370 $2137 €2000 Mountain landscape (48x58cm-19x23in) mono.d.93 mixed media paper on panel. 10-Apr-3 Van Ham, Cologne #1728/R est:2500

THOMA, Josef (1828-1899) Austrian

£1021 $1614 €1532 Hallstadter See mit Hallstadt (102x150cm-40x59in) s. 2-Dec-2 Rasmussen, Copenhagen #1576/R est:10000-15000 (D.KR 12000)
£1027 $1603 €1500 Zell am See and Kitzsteinhorn (74x101cm-29x40in) s.d.1864. 10-Apr-3 Dorotheum, Vienna #24/R est:2000-2500
£1096 $1721 €1600 Mountain stream (58x36cm-23x14in) s. panel. 16-Apr-3 Dorotheum, Salzburg #62/R est:1800-2400
£1139 $1800 €1800 Alpine village in front of a mountain lake with family praying in foreground (74x100cm-29x39in) s.d.1868. 29-Nov-2 Sigalas, Stuttgart #1137/R est:1800
£1186 $1838 €1850 At the main bridge in Sachsenhausen (80x63cm-31x25in) s. 7-Dec-2 Dannenberg, Berlin #739/R est:1800
£1266 $2000 €2000 Moored fishing boats (47x92cm-19x36in) s.d.1876. 26-Nov-2 Wiener Kunst Auktionen, Vienna #34/R est:2000-3000
£1439 $2302 €2000 Sunset over mountain lake (39x59cm-15x23in) s. 17-May-3 Lempertz, Koln #1494/R est:2000
£1497 $2380 €2200 Vast mountain landscape with hunter (85x126cm-33x50in) s.d.1864. 25-Feb-3 Dorotheum, Vienna #165/R est:2400-2800
£1795 $2818 €2800 Zell am See (69x98cm-27x39in) s. canvas on canvas. 21-Nov-2 Dorotheum, Vienna #134/R est:3000-4500
£2347 $3850 €3403 Hammer mill near Lermos - Tyrol (69x105cm-27x41in) s. 4-Jun-3 Fischer, Luzern #1151/R est:4000-6000 (S.FR 5000)
£2532 $4000 €4000 Rapid mountain stream (68x105cm-27x41in) s. 28-Nov-2 Dorotheum, Vienna #244/R est:3800-4200

THOMA-HOEFELE, Carl (1866-1923) Swiss

£628 $980 €930 Still life with peaches (14x18cm-6x7in) s. panel. 26-Mar-3 Hugo Ruef, Munich #245

THOMAE, Benjamin (1682-1751) German

Sculpture

£60000 $100200 €87000 Allegorical of Charity (157cm-62in) sandstone lit. 8-Jul-3 Sotheby's, London #134/R est:60000-80000

THOMANN, Adolf (1874-1961) Swiss

£264 $394 €396 Horses drinking (49x70cm-19x28in) s.d.93. 25-Jun-2 Koller, Zurich #6569 (S.FR 600)
£346 $537 €519 Southern landscape (40x55cm-16x22in) s.d.1922. 24-Sep-2 Koller, Zurich #6669/R (S.FR 800)
£390 $604 €585 Herdsman with animals (50x61cm-20x24in) s.d.1920. 24-Sep-2 Koller, Zurich #6670 (S.FR 900)
£413 $640 €620 Bettmer Alp in summer (49x65cm-19x26in) s.d.1931. 9-Dec-2 Philippe Schuler, Zurich #3838 (S.FR 950)
£696 $1085 €1044 Peasant woman with child riding on donkey (67x49cm-26x19in) s.d.1907 board on masonite. 16-Sep-2 Philippe Schuler, Zurich #3406/R (S.FR 1600)

THOMAS, A (19/20th C) American

£260 $395 €390 Figures harvesting (18x28cm-7x11in) s. board. 14-Aug-2 Andrew Hartley, Ilkley #658

THOMAS, Adolph (1834-1887) German

£1266 $1962 €2000 Southern coastal landscape (76x64cm-30x25in) s.d.75 board. 25-Sep-2 Neumeister, Munich #744/R est:1500

THOMAS, Alain (20th C) French

£435 $700 €653 Paysage printanier aux trois chemins (41x33cm-16x13in) s. s.i.verso board prov. 18-Feb-3 Arthur James, Florida #165

THOMAS, Alice Blair (1857-1945) American/Canadian

£590 $950 €885 Sheep in tonal landscape (25x18cm-10x7in) s.d.1933. 18-Feb-3 John Moran, Pasadena #177
£968 $1500 €1452 Red roses, Chinese vase and Wedgwood cup and saucer (46x36cm-18x14in) s. board. 29-Oct-2 John Moran, Pasadena #606 est:500-800
£1032 $1600 €1548 Tall trees and sheep, sunset landscape (165x102cm-65x40in) s.d.1926 prov. 29-Oct-2 John Moran, Pasadena #795 est:1000-1500
£1161 $1800 €1742 Lake Agnes in the clouds, Canadian Rockies (109x183cm-43x72in) s.d.1916 prov. 29-Oct-2 John Moran, Pasadena #794 est:1500-2000

THOMAS, Alma Woolsey (1896-1978) American

£59375 $95000 €89063 Garden of blue flowers rhapsody (152x127cm-60x50in) s.on stretcher acrylic painted 1976 prov. 16-May-3 Phillips, New York #174/R est:20000-30000

Works on paper

£5096 $8000 €7644 Untitled (56x76cm-22x30in) s.d.74 W/C prov. 14-Dec-2 Weschler, Washington #736/R est:1000-1500

THOMAS, Barry (1961-) American

£2055 $3000 €3083 My first puppy (61x76cm-24x30in) 18-May-2 Altermann Galleries, Santa Fe #232/R
£3425 $5000 €5138 Cooling off - lemonade (91x61cm-36x24in) 18-May-2 Altermann Galleries, Santa Fe #231/R

THOMAS, David (?) British

£345 $541 €518 Yellow and orange (60x76cm-24x30in) s.i.d.2002 verso acrylic on linen. 15-Apr-3 Lawson Menzies, Sydney #82/R (A.D 900)
£345 $541 €518 Black and white (50x65cm-20x26in) s.d.2000 verso acrylic on linen. 15-Apr-3 Lawson Menzies, Sydney #83/R (A.D 900)
£800 $1248 €1200 Palace Theatre, Cambridge Circus, London (91x183cm-36x72in) s.d.87. 27-Mar-3 Christie's, Kensington #571/R
£800 $1248 €1200 Temple, London (64x107cm-25x42in) s.d.1965. 27-Mar-3 Christie's, Kensington #618/R

THOMAS, Dean F (?) American

£288 $450 €432 Cuttalossa Creek, Solebury, winter landscape at dusk (43x36cm-17x14in) s. board. 18-Sep-2 Alderfer's, Hatfield #336/R

THOMAS, E L Osman (19th C) British

Works on paper

£550 $864 €825 Pre Raphaelite figures by a arched doorway (53x36cm-21x14in) s. W/C. 13-Dec-2 Keys, Aylsham #515
£850 $1335 €1275 Cartoon for mural at the Mary Datchelor School for girls (36x74cm-14x29in) s.d.1885 W/C. 13-Dec-2 Keys, Aylsham #514

THOMAS, Felix (1815-1875) French

Works on paper

£355 $592 €500 Vue de l'Acropole, Athenes (12x26cm-5x10in) s.i. was brown ink gouache. 20-Jun-3 Piasa, Paris #98

THOMAS, Francis Wynne (1907-) British

£280 $468 €406 Zugspitze from Lermoss, Austria (39x49cm-15x19in) s. 23-Jun-3 Bonhams, Bath #240
£320 $534 €464 Trout farm at Bibury (49x59cm-19x23in) s. 23-Jun-3 Bonhams, Bath #241

THOMAS, George Housman (1824-1868) British

Works on paper

£300 $477 €450 Camp before Sebastopol (41x60cm-16x24in) i.d.1854 W/C bodycol. 25-Feb-3 Bonhams, Knightsbridge #190/R

THOMAS, Gerard (1663-1720) Flemish

£7643 $11924 €12000 Doctor's visit (67x87cm-26x34in) prov.exhib.lit. 5-Nov-2 Sotheby's, Amsterdam #9/R est:7000-10000

THOMAS, Grosvenor (1856-1923) British

£480 $758 €720 Still life of flowers in a bowl (24x34cm-9x13in) s. 7-Apr-3 Bonhams, Bath #61/R
£600 $948 €900 Still life of flowers in a blue bowl (24x29cm-9x11in) s. 7-Apr-3 Bonhams, Bath #60/R

THOMAS, Henri Joseph (1878-1972) Belgian

£705 $1107 €1100 Nu alonge (70x100cm-28x39in) s.indis.d.1934. 10-Dec-2 Vanderkindere, Brussels #22
£719 $1151 €1000 Vase d'oeillets (29x40cm-11x16in) s. panel. 13-May-3 Vanderkindere, Brussels #176
£759 $1185 €1200 Vase de roses (45x55cm-18x22in) s. panel. 10-Sep-2 Vanderkindere, Brussels #363
£1043 $1669 €1450 Nu au drape noir (35x23cm-14x9in) s. canvas on panel. 13-May-3 Vanderkindere, Brussels #130
£1634 $2631 €2500 Femme allongee (38x28cm-15x11in) s. panel. 14-Jan-3 Vanderkindere, Brussels #113 est:1500-2000
£2313 $3678 €3400 Nu allonge (70x90cm-28x35in) s. 18-Mar-3 Galerie Moderne, Brussels #578/R est:5000-7000
£2893 $4484 €4600 Elegante a la fleur sous la pergola (70x50cm-28x20in) s. 1-Oct-2 Palais de Beaux Arts, Brussels #531/R est:4500-6000
£3526 $5535 €5500 Portrait of a young lady in blue dress (102x73cm-40x29in) s. 10-Dec-2 Dorotheum, Vienna #56/R est:3500-3800
£10127 $16000 €16000 Jeune fille au bouquet de fleurs (67x46cm-26x18in) s. 26-Nov-2 Palais de Beaux Arts, Brussels #164/R est:4500-6000

Works on paper
£288 $453 €450 Nu aux cheveux roux. s.i. pastel. 19-Nov-2 Servarts Themis, Bruxelles #123
£548 $855 €800 Jeunes femmes nues (28x23cm-11x9in) s. mixed media sold with another by C J Watelet. 14-Apr-3 Horta, Bruxelles #244

THOMAS, J (1617-1678) Flemish
£440 $686 €660 Mountain river landscape with sheep grazing, angler and figures. s.d.99 canvas on board. 23-Sep-2 Bonhams, Chester #986

THOMAS, Karl (1948-) American
£3896 $6000 €5844 North rim sunset (91x122cm-36x48in) 25-Oct-2 Morris & Whiteside, Hilton Head Island #144 est:7000-9000
£5324 $8625 €7720 Winter landscape (102x152cm-40x60in) 23-May-3 Altermann Galleries, Santa Fe #187

THOMAS, Les (1962-) Canadian
£241 $378 €362 Lemon slices and cup (26x25cm-10x10in) s.i.d.1991 board. 25-Nov-2 Hodgins, Calgary #299/R (C.D 600)
£341 $536 €512 Tap and plug (26x24cm-10x9in) s.i.d.1991 board. 25-Nov-2 Hodgins, Calgary #262/R (C.D 850)
£3111 $5102 €4511 Black bear (120x120cm-47x47in) s.i.d.1998 oil wax on panel. 9-Jun-3 Hodgins, Calgary #381/R est:3500-4500 (C.D 7000)
Works on paper
£2133 $3499 €3093 Crane (171x110cm-67x43in) s.i.d.1998. 9-Jun-3 Hodgins, Calgary #104/R est:3000-4000 (C.D 4800)

THOMAS, Margaret (1916-) British
£400 $624 €600 Medway (51x61cm-20x24in) mono.d.51. 17-Sep-2 Bonhams, Knightsbridge #270/R

THOMAS, Marjorie H (1885-?) American
£692 $1100 €1038 Noon hour (61x82cm-24x32in) s. 7-Mar-3 Skinner, Boston #619/R

THOMAS, Mrs Vernon (1894-?) American
Works on paper
£1538 $2400 €2307 Little girl on roller skates with dog (58x48cm-23x19in) s. pastel chl gouache ink exhib. 9-Nov-2 Illustration House, New York #3/R est:2000-3000

THOMAS, Paul (1859-1910) French
£755 $1200 €1133 Early spring (23x33cm-9x13in) s.i. i.verso board. 22-Mar-3 New Orleans Auction, New Orleans #104/R est:1500-2500

THOMAS, Percy (1846-1922) British
Works on paper
£201 $317 €302 Swannage Pier, 1888 (28x43cm-11x17in) d.1888 W/C. 1-Dec-2 Levis, Calgary #237/R (C.D 500)

THOMAS, Philippe (1951-1995) French
£5128 $8051 €8000 Luciano Inga-Pin (97x130cm-38x51in) acrylic prov.exhib. 11-Dec-2 Artcurial Briest, Paris #764/R est:12000

THOMAS, Pieter Hendrik (1814-1866) Dutch
£1389 $2292 €2000 Sailing vessels on choppy water by a coast (50x65cm-20x26in) s. canvas on plywood. 1-Jul-3 Christie's, Amsterdam #72/R est:2000-3000

THOMAS, Richard D (1935-) American
£4795 $7000 €7193 Passage through winter's bite (51x81cm-20x32in) 18-May-2 Altermann Galleries, Santa Fe #4/R

THOMAS, Robert Strickland (1787-1853) British
£3000 $4650 €4500 At the height of the storm (81x124cm-32x49in) s.d.1845 prov. 6-Dec-2 Lyon & Turnbull, Edinburgh #78/R est:4000-6000
£13500 $20925 €20250 HMS Queen flagship of the Mediterranean fleet leaving Malta (70x105cm-28x41in) s.d.1842 prov. 6-Dec-2 Lyon & Turnbull, Edinburgh #77/R est:7000-10000

THOMAS, Rover (c.1926-1998) Australian
Works on paper
£2708 $4197 €4062 Milky way (52x72cm-20x28in) s.i.verso natural pigments binder prov. 3-Dec-2 Shapiro, Sydney #154 est:7000-9000 (A.D 7500)
£3249 $5036 €4874 Untitled, landscape with waterhole (45x52cm-18x20in) natural pigments wood panel prov. 3-Dec-2 Shapiro, Sydney #206/R est:10000-15000 (A.D 9000)
£3249 $5036 €4874 Untitled (40x50cm-16x20in) i.verso natural pigments canvas exec.c.1993. 3-Dec-2 Shapiro, Sydney #209/R est:10000-15000 (A.D 9000)
£4874 $7554 €7311 Nargoroon Hills, Texas Downs country (110x90cm-43x35in) s.i.verso natural pigments binder prov. 3-Dec-2 Shapiro, Sydney #153/R est:15000-25000 (A.D 13500)

THOMAS, T (19th C) British
£410 $652 €615 On the Lugg, Pont-y-Pair, North Wales (51x76cm-20x30in) s.d. 27-Feb-3 Brightwells, Leominster #835

THOMAS, Thomas (19th C) British
£480 $768 €720 Cottage in wooded landscape, woman and child at a fence (30x50cm-12x20in) s.d.76. 13-May-3 Bonhams, Sevenoaks #336
£1500 $2385 €2250 Maid and cattle in a wooded river landscape (51x76cm-20x30in) s.d.1875. 30-Apr-3 Halls, Shrewsbury #274/R est:1500-2000

THOMAS, Thomas (attrib) (19th C) British
£300 $474 €450 Farmyard with outbuildings, children in foreground (44x77cm-17x30in) 12-Nov-2 Bonhams, Knightsbridge #95b/R

THOMAS-SOYER, Mathilde (1860-1940) French
Sculpture
£2384 $3886 €3600 Cuirassier a cheval (58cm-23in) s. brown pat bronze. 17-Feb-3 Horta, Bruxelles #44

THOMASSIN, Desire (1858-1933) Austrian
£443 $687 €700 Scene from Holland (17x23cm-7x9in) s.i. i. verso board. 25-Sep-2 Neumeister, Munich #748/R
£493 $799 €750 Peasant women resting on the heath (23x30cm-9x12in) s. cardboard. 21-Jan-3 Christie's, Amsterdam #30
£987 $1599 €1500 Fishing village in winter at dusk (16x27cm-6x11in) s.i. panel. 21-Jan-3 Christie's, Amsterdam #36/R est:1500-2000
£993 $1549 €1450 Haymaking in lower alpine landscape (40x50cm-16x20in) s. lit. 10-Apr-3 Allgauer, Kempten #3012/R
£1210 $1888 €1900 Hay-making in the Lower Alps landscape (40x50cm-16x20in) s.verso lit. 7-Nov-2 Allgauer, Kempten #2977/R est:1900
£1266 $1962 €2000 Six hunters in snowy wood (60x48cm-24x19in) s.i. 25-Sep-2 Neumeister, Munich #747/R est:2500
£1410 $2186 €2200 Shepherd with his flock and dog on the meadow plus farmhouse (25x36cm-10x14in) s. canvas on canvas. 4-Dec-2 Neumeister, Munich #925/R est:2200
£1899 $2943 €3000 Hay harvest in pre-alpine landscape (20x27cm-8x11in) s.i.d.1911 panel. 25-Sep-2 Neumeister, Munich #746/R est:3000
£2585 $4110 €3800 Hay harvest (20x35cm-8x14in) s.d.1903 panel. 19-Mar-3 Neumeister, Munich #764/R est:3000
Works on paper
£6000 $9420 €9000 Brining in the catch (70x100cm-28x39in) s.d.1929. 19-Nov-2 Sotheby's, London #135/R est:6000-8000

THOMASSIN, Louise (20th C) French
£327 $523 €500 Roses in vase with insects (70x60cm-28x24in) s. lit. 10-Jan-3 Allgauer, Kempten #1765/R
£784 $1255 €1200 Wild flowers in vase with insects (71x61cm-28x24in) s. 10-Jan-3 Allgauer, Kempten #1766/R

THOMASTON, Stone (18/19th C) American
£1154 $1800 €1731 Younger pliny reproved; JOs. s. 12-Oct-2 Fallon, Copake #33

THOME, Verner (1878-1953) Finnish
£915 $1501 €1400 Wing of Urajarvi Manor (39x46cm-15x18in) s.d.1941. 9-Feb-3 Bukowskis, Helsinki #373/R
£1151 $1888 €1600 Horse (61x49cm-24x19in) s.d.1901. 4-Jun-3 Bukowskis, Helsinki #445/R est:1900
Works on paper
£730 $1168 €1015 In the skerries (32x51cm-13x20in) s. mixed media. 17-May-3 Hagelstam, Helsinki #140/R

THOMING, Frederik Christian (1802-1873) Danish
£5957 $9413 €8936 Marina Piccola, Capri (49x67cm-19x26in) s.i. 2-Dec-2 Rasmussen, Copenhagen #1141/R est:60000-80000 (D.KR 70000)
£12920 $19638 €19380 Fishermen in boats off Naples (55x72cm-22x28in) s.d.1848. 27-Aug-2 Rasmussen, Copenhagen #1427/R est:175000-200000 (D.KR 150000)

THOMKINS, Andre (1930-1985) Swiss
Works on paper
£524 $823 €786 Skyscrapers (21x20cm-8x8in) s.i.d.1958 W/C. 25-Nov-2 Germann, Zurich #84/R (S.FR 1200)
£655 $956 €983 Blau du alb (29x21cm-11x8in) s.i.d.1958 mixed media. 4-Jun-2 Germann, Zurich #7/R (S.FR 1500)

£655 $1028 €983 Appenzell landscape (21x15cm-8x6in) mono.i.d.1977 Indian ink over W/C. 25-Nov-2 Germann, Zurich #36/R est:1500-2000 (S.FR 1500)
£1616 $2537 €2424 Watteau a voile (11x17cm-4x7in) s.i.d.1974 pencil. 23-Nov-2 Burkhard, Luzern #232/R est:4000-5000 (S.FR 3700)
£2029 $3328 €2800 Speech bubble - self talk (15x17cm-6x7in) s.i.d.1975 collage petals seeds exhib. 28-May-3 Lempertz, Koln #432/R est:2800

THOMMESEN, Erik (1916-) Danish
Sculpture
£7900 $12481 €11850 Self portrait (110cm-43in) carved ash prov.lit. 1-Apr-3 Rasmussen, Copenhagen #110/R est:60000-80000 (D.KR 85000)

THOMON, Thomas de (attrib) (1754-1813) French
Works on paper
£1282 $1987 €2000 Vue des thermes de Titus (34x51cm-13x20in) i. W/C. 4-Dec-2 Piasa, Paris #110/R

THOMOPOULOS, Epaminondas (1878-1974) Greek
£1200 $1896 €1800 Bouquet in a glass (34x35cm-13x14in) 1-Apr-3 Bonhams, New Bond Street #37 est:1200-1800
£1842 $2745 €2763 Canal a Venise (29x29cm-11x11in) s. cardboard. 26-Jun-2 Iegor de Saint Hippolyte, Montreal #85/R (C.D 4200)
£2200 $3476 €3300 Train (19x52cm-7x20in) 1-Apr-3 Bonhams, New Bond Street #38 est:2200-2800
£7000 $10850 €10500 Harvesters (60x129cm-24x51in) s. 2-Oct-2 Sotheby's, London #104/R est:12000
£11000 $17380 €16500 Harvesters (89x89cm-35x35in) 1-Apr-3 Bonhams, New Bond Street #39 est:6000-8000

THOMPSON, Adrian (20th C) British
£700 $1099 €1050 Feeling the breeze, Princess Dock (91x122cm-36x48in) s. 16-Dec-2 Sotheby's, Olympia #184/R
Works on paper
£450 $729 €653 Gothic in King George Dock, Hull (30x41cm-12x16in) s. W/C. 1-Aug-3 Dee Atkinson & Harrison, Driffield #667/R

THOMPSON, Albert (1853-?) American
£262 $414 €393 Cows and ducks in a sunlit pool (23x30cm-9x12in) s. 18-Nov-2 Waddingtons, Toronto #17/R (C.D 650)

THOMPSON, Alfred Wordsworth (1840-1896) American
£2244 $3500 €3366 Figures on the shore (55x83cm-22x33in) s. 9-Nov-2 Sloan, North Bethesda #593/R est:4500-5500
£29032 $45000 €43548 Garden at Monte Carlo (49x82cm-19x32in) s.i. prov.exhib.lit. 3-Dec-2 Phillips, New York #49/R est:25000-35000

THOMPSON, Arthur (19th C) American
Works on paper
£457 $713 €686 Reynold Street, Freemans Bay (35x46cm-14x18in) s.d.1974 ink W/C. 6-Aug-2 Peter Webb, Auckland #203/R est:1200-2000 (NZ.D 1550)
£457 $713 €686 Freeman Bay Villas (34x50cm-13x20in) s.d.1974 ink W/C. 6-Aug-2 Peter Webb, Auckland #204/R est:1200-2000 (NZ.D 1550)

THOMPSON, Bob (1937-1966) American
£24516 $38000 €36774 St. George et le dragon (96x76cm-38x30in) s.d.61 s.i.d.verso prov. 26-Sep-2 Christie's, Rockefeller NY #758/R est:25000-35000
Works on paper
£9677 $15000 €14516 Diana and her bathers (28x26cm-11x10in) s.d.65 s.i.d.verso gouache prov. 26-Sep-2 Christie's, Rockefeller NY #759/R est:10000-15000

THOMPSON, Charles H (fl.1894-1923) British
£300 $471 €450 Waves breaking on the Cornish coast (46x62cm-18x24in) s. 10-Dec-2 Lane, Penzance #345

THOMPSON, Edward H (1866-1949) British
£1450 $2320 €2175 Scawfell from the Gt. Gable (30x43cm-12x17in) s.i. on mount. 14-Mar-3 Gardiner & Houlgate, Bath #81/R est:700-1000
Works on paper
£400 $628 €600 Derwent water (24x39cm-9x15in) s.d.1920 W/C. 19-Nov-2 James Thompson, Kirby Lonsdale #9
£400 $628 €600 In the Trossachs above Arduli, near Loch Lomond (35x25cm-14x10in) s. pencil W/C prov. 16-Apr-3 Christie's, Kensington #1015/R
£500 $795 €750 Eventide, the jaws of Borrowdale and Derwentwater from near Friars Crag (28x41cm-11x16in) s.d.1922 W/C. 6-Mar-3 Mitchells, Cockermouth #880
£500 $785 €750 From above the beacon (25x35cm-10x14in) s. pencil W/C. 16-Apr-3 Christie's, Kensington #1025/R
£580 $916 €870 Lakeland landscape, in the Lake District (25x41cm-10x16in) s. W/C. 24-Apr-3 Richardson & Smith, Whitby #76
£650 $1021 €975 Eventide, Rydal Water (18x25cm-7x10in) s.d.1904 W/C. 21-Nov-2 Tennants, Leyburn #628
£700 $1113 €1050 In the blue light of summer, Bassenthwaite Lake with the Keswick Fells (28x43cm-11x17in) s.d.1922 W/C. 6-Mar-3 Mitchells, Cockermouth #859
£700 $1113 €1050 On the Solway Firth (33x73cm-13x29in) s.d.1917 W/C htd white. 29-Apr-3 Bonhams, Knightsbridge #61/R
£720 $1130 €1080 On the heathery moors of Troutbeck, near Keswick (17x25cm-7x10in) s. W/C bodycol prov. 19-Nov-2 Bonhams, Leeds #27/R
£750 $1193 €1125 View on the Solway coast (15x28cm-6x11in) s.d.1923 W/C. 6-Mar-3 Mitchells, Cockermouth #807/R
£750 $1193 €1125 View on the Solway coast with small vessel, bay and building (13x28cm-5x11in) s.d.1923 W/C. 6-Mar-3 Mitchells, Cockermouth #808/R
£780 $1271 €1170 Coniston Water from Waterhead (24x36cm-9x14in) s. W/C. 29-Jan-3 Dreweatt Neate, Newbury #13
£800 $1272 €1200 Friars Crag, Derwentwater (30x43cm-12x17in) s.d.1931 W/C. 6-Mar-3 Mitchells, Cockermouth #879/R
£800 $1248 €1200 Walla Crag, Derwentwater (29x44cm-11x17in) s. W/C bodycol. 10-Apr-3 Tennants, Leyburn #852
£800 $1288 €1160 Loch scene (25x37cm-10x15in) s. W/C. 12-May-3 Joel, Victoria #345 est:1000-1200 (A.D 2000)
£850 $1352 €1275 Windermere and the Langdale Pikes from the Ambleside Road (25x36cm-10x14in) s. W/C. 6-Mar-3 Mitchells, Cockermouth #805/R
£880 $1399 €1320 Eventide, Ennerdale Lake with Bowness Knott, Pillar Rock and Iron Crags (25x36cm-10x14in) s. W/C. 6-Mar-3 Mitchells, Cockermouth #828/R
£889 $1476 €1289 Highland stream with bluebells (29cm-11in circular) s. W/C. 16-Jun-3 Waddingtons, Toronto #51/R est:500-700 (C.D 2000)
£900 $1494 €1305 Summer spate in Borrowdale (30x43cm-12x17in) s. W/C. 10-Jun-3 David Lay, Penzance #242/R
£980 $1597 €1421 Lake District scene (25x38cm-10x15in) s. W/C. 17-Jul-3 Thomson, Roddick & Medcalf, Carlisle #43/R
£1000 $1560 €1500 Loch Etive (23x45cm-9x18in) s. W/C. 18-Sep-2 James Thompson, Kirby Lonsdale #50
£1100 $1793 €1650 Snow at dusk (26x36cm-10x14in) s. W/C. 29-Jan-3 Sotheby's, Olympia #168/R est:500-700
£1100 $1793 €1595 Coniston (24x34cm-9x13in) s. W/C. 16-Jul-3 James Thompson, Kirby Lonsdale #265
£1115 $1750 €1673 Derwentwater (24x34cm-9x13in) s. W/C. 10-Dec-2 Peter Webb, Auckland #158/R est:1000-2000 (NZ.D 3500)
£1115 $1750 €1673 Ullswater (24x34cm-9x13in) s. W/C. 10-Dec-2 Peter Webb, Auckland #159/R est:1000-2000 (NZ.D 3500)
£1200 $1872 €1800 Early spring, Loch Lush. Morning clouds, Loch Maree (26x36cm-10x14in) s. W/C pair. 6-Nov-2 Bonhams, Chester #352 est:700-1000
£1250 $1950 €1875 Heathertime on the Argyllshire moors (23x45cm-9x18in) s. W/C. 18-Sep-2 James Thompson, Kirby Lonsdale #51
£1250 $2050 €1813 Nearing the end of the day, Winter near Bassenthwaite (18x25cm-7x10in) s. W/C. 3-Jun-3 Capes Dunn, Manchester #85/R
£1300 $2054 €1950 Lake District view with trees and distant hills (28x43cm-11x17in) s.d.1921 W/C. 24-Apr-3 Scarborough Perry Fine Arts, Hove #594
£1450 $2291 €2175 Misty Lake District view with distant hills (28x43cm-11x17in) s.d.1924 W/C. 24-Apr-3 Scarborough Perry Fine Arts, Hove #593
£1600 $2592 €2400 Lake landscape (44cm-17in circular) s.d.1924 W/C. 21-Jan-3 Bonhams, Knightsbridge #162/R est:1000-1500
£1700 $2754 €2550 Figure on a village street (44cm-17in circular) s.d.1924 W/C. 21-Jan-3 Bonhams, Knightsbridge #160/R est:800-1200
£1850 $3016 €2683 Bassenthwaite and Skiddaw (30x45cm-12x18in) s. W/C. 16-Jul-3 James Thompson, Kirby Lonsdale #100/R
£1850 $3016 €2683 Loweswater and Melbreak (30x45cm-12x18in) s. W/C. 16-Jul-3 James Thompson, Kirby Lonsdale #101/R
£2000 $3280 €3000 Lakeland landscapes (33x48cm-13x19in) s.d.1923 W/C pair. 4-Jun-3 Bonhams, Chester #273 est:2000-3000
£2200 $3498 €3300 Tinted with the glow of evening, Loweswater and Melbreak (23x33cm-9x13in) s.d.1928 W/C. 6-Mar-3 Mitchells, Cockermouth #804/R est:700-1000

THOMPSON, J Christian (19th C) British
£1100 $1738 €1650 Sandy, a border terrier (46x38cm-18x15in) mono.d.1865 i.verso painted oval. 28-Nov-2 Christie's, Kensington #279/R est:800-1200

THOMPSON, Michael (20th C) British
£380 $593 €570 Head of a man (92x74cm-36x29in) s.d.46. 17-Sep-2 Bonhams, Knightsbridge #4/R

THOMPSON, Michel (1921-) French
Works on paper
£355 $561 €550 Nature morte aux utensils de cuisine (49x32cm-19x13in) s.d.99 pastel. 19-Dec-2 Ruellan, Paris #129/R

THOMPSON, Nelson (1918-1989) New Zealander
Works on paper
£236 $368 €354 Maori where church (23x32cm-9x13in) init. ink W/C. 6-Aug-2 Peter Webb, Auckland #166/R (NZ.D 800)

THOMPSON, Pauline (1942-) New Zealander
£382 $600 €573 Waterfront drive (45x60cm-18x24in) init.d.1984. 10-Dec-2 Peter Webb, Auckland #97/R est:1200-1800 (NZ.D 1200)

THOMPSON, Philip (20th C) British
£500 $775 €750 Du novo (57x39cm-22x15in) s.d.1938 board. 25-Sep-2 Peter Wilson, Nantwich #99

THOMPSON, Richard (?) American?
£484 $750 €726 Showin off (104x274cm-41x108in) s.i.d.1978 verso. 29-Sep-2 Butterfields, Los Angeles #4441/R

THOMPSON, Sydney Lough (1877-1973) New Zealander
£1060 $1707 €1590 Village Square (37x45cm-15x18in) s. 7-May-3 Dunbar Sloane, Auckland #99 (NZ.D 3000)
£2128 $3319 €3192 Waiau bluff (45x53cm-18x21in) s.i.d.1959 i.on verso. 17-Sep-2 Peter Webb, Auckland #132/R est:8000-12000 (NZ.D 7000)
£2744 $4198 €4116 Lake Herron (49x60cm-19x24in) s. 21-Aug-2 Dunbar Sloane, Auckland #64/R est:10000-15000 (NZ.D 9000)
£2797 $4336 €4196 Blossom tree, Concarneau (59x48cm-23x19in) s. 4-Dec-2 Dunbar Sloane, Auckland #2/R est:4000-7000 (NZ.D 8700)
£3430 $5487 €4974 Morning light on the seaward Kaikouras (50x59cm-20x23in) s. i.verso. 13-May-3 Watson's, Christchurch #30/R est:9000-14000 (NZ.D 9500)
£3860 $6021 €5790 Pardon of St Anne de Fouesnat, Brittany (32x40cm-13x16in) s. board. 27-Mar-3 International Art Centre, Auckland #113/R est:10000-15000 (NZ.D 11000)
£4659 $7082 €6989 Boat harbour Brittany (30x39cm-12x15in) s. prov. 27-Aug-2 Goodman, Sydney #134/R est:10000-15000 (A.D 13000)
£5329 $8313 €7994 Tunney boat, Concarneau (32x40cm-13x16in) s. board. 7-Nov-2 International Art Centre, Auckland #82/R est:20000-28000 (NZ.D 17000)
£5338 $8167 €8007 Concarneau (46x55cm-18x22in) i. d.1920 verso prov. 25-Aug-2 Sotheby's, Paddington #168/R est:6000-10000 (A.D 15000)
£5522 $7841 €8283 Le Vieux Mas, Tourette sur loup (49x60cm-19x24in) s. board prov. 20-Mar-2 Watson's, Christchurch #20/R est:24000-30000 (NZ.D 18000)
£5893 $9311 €8840 Boat Harbour (37x45cm-15x18in) s. 18-Nov-2 Goodman, Sydney #241/R est:5500-8000 (A.D 16500)
£6667 $10267 €10001 Wellington Harbour, late afternoon (45x54cm-18x21in) s. painted c.1936. 4-Sep-2 Dunbar Sloane, Wellington #34/R est:25000-35000 (NZ.D 22000)
£8070 $12589 €12105 Old man (69x47cm-27x19in) s. board painted c.1900. 27-Mar-3 International Art Centre, Auckland #114/R est:20000-30000 (NZ.D 23000)
£8303 $13285 €12039 Paysage Provencal (49x60cm-19x24in) s. painted c.1950. 13-May-3 Watson's, Christchurch #16/R est:17500-30000 (NZ.D 23000)
£8303 $13285 €12039 Balcon, St Jeannet, Ara (60x50cm-24x20in) s.d.1948. 13-May-3 Watson's, Christchurch #87/R est:17500-25000 (NZ.D 23000)
£9649 $15053 €14474 Return of the fishing fleet, Concarneau (38x45cm-15x18in) s. 27-Mar-3 International Art Centre, Auckland #63/R est:30000-40000 (NZ.D 27500)
£15152 $23333 €22728 Sunlit sails (51x62cm-20x24in) s. prov. 4-Sep-2 Dunbar Sloane, Wellington #30/R est:50000-70000 (NZ.D 50000)
£17361 $27083 €26042 Sunlit sails, Concarneau (53x63cm-21x25in) s. 8-Apr-3 Peter Webb, Auckland #85/R est:70000-90000 (NZ.D 50000)
Works on paper
£2779 $4085 €4169 Le Lavoir en bretagne (35x49cm-14x19in) s. prov. 19-Jun-2 Watson's, Christchurch #58/R est:9000-14000 (NZ.D 8500)
£6866 $10024 €10299 Brittany fisherfolk (36x50cm-14x20in) s. gouache. 12-Sep-1 Watson's, Christchurch #20 est:30000-40000 (NZ.D 23000)

THOMPSON, Thomas Clement (attrib) (1778-1857) British
£4600 $7268 €6900 Portrait of Captain James Gage (140x103cm-55x41in) prov. 28-Nov-2 Sotheby's, London #176/R est:2500-4000

THOMPSON, Tim (1951-) British
£889 $1476 €1289 British 50 gun ship under shortened sail (23x28cm-9x11in) s. panel prov. 16-Jun-3 Waddingtons, Toronto #137/R est:2500-3500 (C.D 2000)
£889 $1476 €1289 East Indiaman off north foreland (20x29cm-8x11in) s. panel prov. 16-Jun-3 Waddingtons, Toronto #138/R est:2500-3500 (C.D 2000)
£889 $1476 €1289 Yacht running astern of Dutch East Indiaman (23x28cm-9x11in) s. panel prov. 16-Jun-3 Waddingtons, Toronto #139/R est:2500-3500 (C.D 2000)
£3185 $5000 €4778 Yacht race off Brenton (30x41cm-12x16in) s. 26-Jul-2 Eldred, East Dennis #528/R est:5500-6000
£4200 $6510 €6300 Crossing the line off the Royal Yacht Squadron at Cowes (42x51cm-17x20in) s. 31-Oct-2 Christie's, Kensington #406/R est:2000-4000
£5200 $8060 €7800 Yachts of the Royal Yacht Squadron racing in Fernian Bay Guernsey (46x61cm-18x24in) s. 31-Oct-2 Christie's, Kensington #407/R est:2000-3000

THOMPSON, Walter W (1881-1948) American
£329 $550 €477 Sangre de Chrinto (30x41cm-12x16in) i.d.1922 verso canvasboard. 17-Jun-3 John Moran, Pasadena #157

THOMPSON, William John (attrib) (1771-1845) British
£900 $1440 €1350 Half length study of a male nude (66x38cm-26x15in) s.i. 11-Mar-3 Bonhams, Knightsbridge #179/R

THOMSEN, August Carl Wilhelm (1813-1886) Danish
£885 $1406 €1328 Spring day in the forest with wood anemones (47x37cm-19x15in) s. 5-Mar-3 Rasmussen, Copenhagen #1884/R (D.KR 9500)
£4655 $7402 €6983 The exiled King Christian II seeking comfort in Luther's new teaching (95x98cm-37x39in) s. exhib. 5-Mar-3 Rasmussen, Copenhagen #1588/R est:50000 (D.KR 50000)

THOMSEN, Emma Augusta (1822-1897) Danish
£1818 $2945 €2636 Woodland scene with many flowers (57x47cm-22x19in) s. 24-May-3 Rasmussen, Havnen #2118/R est:10000-15000 (D.KR 19000)

THOMSEN, Jens Lauritzen (1874-1971) Danish?
£272 $424 €408 Winter landscape with children playing on the ice (23x32cm-9x13in) init. 5-Aug-2 Rasmussen, Vejle #217/R (D.KR 3200)

THOMSEN, Svend (1909-1956) Danish
£515 $803 €773 Women bathing (115x74cm-45x29in) init.d.49 panel exhib.lit. 11-Nov-2 Rasmussen, Vejle #39/R (D.KR 6000)

THOMSEN, V (?) ?
£313 $488 €470 Cottage interior with seated woman and cat playing (60x50cm-24x20in) s.d.27. 23-Sep-2 Rasmussen, Vejle #31/R (D.KR 3700)

THOMSON OF DUDDINGTON, Rev John (1778-1840) British
£750 $1170 €1125 Distant view of Edinburgh from Donibristle (50x76cm-20x30in) 13-Sep-2 Lyon & Turnbull, Edinburgh #138/R
£1300 $2028 €1950 Ravenscraig - with boys bathing (50x76cm-20x30in) s. i.verso panel. 6-Nov-2 Bonhams, Chester #525/R est:800-1200
£1400 $2268 €2100 Iverlochy Castle (57x90cm-22x35in) lit. 23-May-3 Lyon & Turnbull, Edinburgh #29a est:1500-2000

THOMSON, Adam Bruce (1885-1976) British
Works on paper
£600 $918 €900 Rising mist Lochcarron (31x42cm-12x17in) s. black ink wash. 22-Aug-2 Bonhams, Edinburgh #962
£3400 $5202 €5100 Northwards from Iona (37x53cm-15x21in) s. W/C. 22-Aug-2 Bonhams, Edinburgh #967/R est:1500-2000

THOMSON, Alexander P (?-1962) British
Works on paper
£1500 $2385 €2250 Perthshire village (51x46cm-20x18in) s. pencil W/C exhib. 6-Mar-3 Christie's, Kensington #170/R est:1000-1500

THOMSON, Alfred Reginald (1895-1979) British
£1100 $1782 €1650 Protest (39x49cm-15x19in) s. s.i.verso canvasboard. 20-May-3 Sotheby's, Olympia #139/R est:400-600
Works on paper
£350 $543 €525 Interior scene, sitting in the House of Lords (43x59cm-17x23in) pencil W/C htd white. 24-Sep-2 Rowley Fine Art, Newmarket #340/R

THOMSON, Ann (1933-) Australian
£786 $1241 €1179 Harbour (115x168cm-45x66in) s.verso prov. 17-Nov-2 Sotheby's, Paddington #87/R est:3000-5000 (A.D 2200)
£1301 $2055 €1886 Untitled (123x123cm-48x48in) s.d.1994 verso board. 22-Jul-3 Lawson Menzies, Sydney #194/R est:3000-5000 (A.D 3200)
£2500 $3900 €3750 Turnpike (168x231cm-66x91in) s.i.d.85 verso prov. 11-Nov-2 Deutscher-Menzies, Melbourne #38/R est:8000-12000 (A.D 7000)
£3065 $4567 €4598 Ripcord (172x240cm-68x94in) s.i.d.79 acrylic prov. 27-Aug-2 Christie's, Melbourne #317/R est:10000-15000 (A.D 8000)
£6429 $10029 €9644 Newcastle (140x215cm-55x85in) s.verso prov. 11-Nov-2 Deutscher-Menzies, Melbourne #91/R est:10000-15000 (A.D 18000)
Works on paper
£283 $442 €491 Untitled (49x32cm-19x13in) s.d.94 mixed media prov. 31-Mar-3 Goodman, Sydney #18 (A.D 750)

THOMSON, Carl Christian Frederik Jakob (1847-1912) Danish
£560 $890 €840 Gathering at table in lamp-light (21x27cm-8x11in) panel. 29-Apr-3 Kunsthallen, Copenhagen #539/R (D.KR 6000)
£638 $1009 €957 Young girl by antique ruin, Italy (84x40cm-33x16in) init. 2-Dec-2 Rasmussen, Copenhagen #1509/R (D.KR 7500)
£697 $1101 €1046 Church interior with figures. From Snoldelev Church (53x63cm-21x25in) init. double-sided. 5-Apr-3 Rasmussen, Havnen #2041/R (D.KR 7500)
£1340 $2170 €1943 Interior scene with lady playing the piano (40x53cm-16x21in) mono. 26-May-3 Rasmussen, Copenhagen #1138/R est:15000-20000 (D.KR 14000)
£2392 $3876 €3468 Evald's first meeting with Arendse (75x89cm-30x35in) mono.d.1875 exhib. 26-May-3 Rasmussen, Copenhagen #1104/R est:30000-40000 (D.KR 25000)
£6052 $9623 €9078 Mother and children in park, summer's day (60x47cm-24x19in) mono.d.86. 5-Mar-3 Rasmussen, Copenhagen #1593/R est:50000-75000 (D.KR 65000)

THOMSON, Douglas (1955-) British
£2000 $3260 €3000 Three figures (122x122cm-48x48in) s. s.i.d.90 verso prov.exhib.lit. 3-Feb-3 Sotheby's, Olympia #181/R est:2000-4000

THOMSON, George (1868-1965) Canadian
£222 $364 €333 Elevated viewpoint (25x30cm-10x12in) board. 3-Jun-3 Joyner, Toronto #559 (C.D 500)
£309 $478 €464 Hills of Muskoka (30x40cm-12x16in) s. board. 3-Dec-2 Joyner, Toronto #451 (C.D 750)

THOMSON, Henry (1773-1843) British
£260 $426 €390 Love sheltered (46x66cm-18x26in) 29-May-3 Mallams, Cheltenham #343

THOMSON, John Murray (1885-1974) British
£520 $822 €780 Feeding time (46x61cm-18x24in) s. canvasboard. 28-Nov-2 Christie's, Kensington #316/R
£629 $1000 €944 Arctic scene with polar bears (44x94cm-17x37in) s. panel. 7-Mar-3 Skinner, Boston #378/R
Works on paper
£310 $484 €465 Study of mare and her foal in a summer pasture (26x34cm-10x13in) s. gouache. 17-Sep-2 Holloways, Banbury #321/R
£350 $574 €525 Birds amongst thistle (33x24cm-13x9in) s. W/C. 10-Feb-3 Robin Fenner, Tavistock #672
£450 $702 €675 Hawker's pony (21x29cm-8x11in) s. gouache prov. 17-Sep-2 Sotheby's, Olympia #61/R

THOMSON, Keith (1934-) American?
Works on paper
£600 $984 €870 Nature walk (68x47cm-27x19in) s. W/C. 9-Jun-3 Hodgins, Calgary #184/R est:800-1000 (C.D 1350)

THOMSON, Mackenzie (19/20th C) British?
Works on paper
£540 $842 €810 Portrait of a steamer (30x49cm-12x19in) s. W/C. 10-Sep-2 David Duggleby, Scarborough #259/R
£1100 $1782 €1650 HMS Reynard at sea. HMS Royal Sovereign at sea (29x45cm-11x18in) s. pencil W/C pair. 21-May-3 Christie's, Kensington #475/R est:500-700

THOMSON, Tom (1877-1917) Canadian
£17284 $26790 €25926 Huntsvill (20x17cm-8x7in) s. board painted c.1912 lit. 3-Dec-2 Joyner, Toronto #81/R est:40000-50000 (C.D 42000)
£22222 $36444 €33333 Landscape with storm clouds (25x17cm-10x7in) s. canvas on board prov.lit. 3-Jun-3 Joyner, Toronto #86/R est:30000-40000 (C.D 50000)
£60484 $95565 €90726 Canoe Lake, Algonquin Park (22x27cm-9x11in) i.verso canvas on board prov. 14-Nov-2 Heffel, Vancouver #85/R est:150000-180000 (C.D 150000)
£76233 $121973 €114350 Boathouse, Go Home Bay (18x23cm-7x9in) panel prov. 15-May-3 Heffel, Vancouver #107/R est:70000-90000 (C.D 170000)
£102881 $159465 €154322 In Oetawawa Gorges, spring (21x26cm-8x10in) i.d.1916 verso panel prov.exhib.lit. 3-Dec-2 Joyner, Toronto #33/R est:150000-200000 (C.D 250000)
£106667 $174933 €160001 Last snow, Algonquin Park (21x26cm-8x10in) s. panel prov.exhib. 3-Jun-3 Joyner, Toronto #50/R est:125000-175000 (C.D 240000)

THOMSON, William (1927-1990) British
£300 $471 €450 Standing nude (120x61cm-47x24in) init.d.1957. 15-Apr-3 Bonhams, Knightsbridge #48
£850 $1343 €1275 Still life with fruit and a figure (99x71cm-39x28in) s. 27-Nov-2 Sotheby's, Olympia #239/R

THON, William (1916-2000) American
£1481 $2400 €2222 Moonrise (56x91cm-22x36in) s. board prov. 24-Jan-3 Freeman, Philadelphia #211/R est:700-1000
Works on paper
£926 $1500 €1343 The Villa (58x97cm-23x38in) s. W/C gouache ink silver paint prov. 21-May-3 Doyle, New York #13/R est:800-1000

THONY, Eduard (1866-1950) German
Works on paper
£1154 $1685 €1800 Officer shaking hands with another officer on horse (35x23cm-14x9in) mono.d.99 Indian ink chk pencil col pen bodycol. 4-Jun-2 Karl & Faber, Munich #453/R est:1800

THONY, Wilhelm (1888-1949) Austrian
£47297 $73784 €70000 Mr and Mrs Thony with officer (35x45cm-14x18in) canvas on panel lit. 25-Mar-3 Wiener Kunst Auktionen, Vienna #137/R est:50000-100000
£60127 $95000 €95000 Fete au bois 1890 (41x53cm-16x21in) s. board lit. 26-Nov-2 Wiener Kunst Auktionen, Vienna #114/R est:70000-120000
Works on paper
£2516 $3874 €4000 Woman smoking cigarette (27x21cm-11x8in) s. W/C pencil. 22-Oct-2 Wiener Kunst Auktionen, Vienna #1126/R est:2000-10000

THORBURN, Archibald (1860-1935) British
£2200 $3432 €3300 Caspian plover (17x24cm-7x9in) s. lit. 25-Mar-3 Gildings, Market Harborough #391/R est:800-1200
Works on paper
£260 $421 €390 Snipe and redwing (20x15cm-8x6in) pencil prov. 20-May-3 Sotheby's, Olympia #40/R
£280 $434 €420 Study of Lousewort (17x18cm-7x7in) s.d.June 10 1924 W/C. 24-Sep-2 Bonhams, Knightsbridge #194/R
£280 $465 €406 Studies of the red-necked nightjar (15x23cm-6x9in) init. pencil W/C. 12-Jun-3 Christie's, Kensington #137/R
£300 $468 €450 Roaring stag (22x17cm-9x7in) indis i. pencil prov. 17-Oct-2 Christie's, Kensington #38
£350 $578 €508 Rocky outcrop (33x46cm-13x18in) W/C htd bodycol. 2-Jul-3 Sotheby's, Olympia #290/R
£550 $869 €825 On the edge of the moor (27x43cm-11x17in) pencil W/C. 28-Nov-2 Christie's, Kensington #39/R
£650 $1079 €943 Owl on a branch (23x15cm-9x6in) s.d.1933 W/C bodycol. 10-Jun-3 David Lay, Penzance #42
£800 $1328 €1160 Mandarin duck (18x13cm-7x5in) s.d.1928 W/C bodycol. 10-Jun-3 David Lay, Penzance #41
£820 $1337 €1230 Study of a cat (23x33cm-9x13in) init.d.July 16 1890 W/C. 29-Jan-3 Sotheby's, Olympia #234/R
£880 $1426 €1320 Blackbird (8x12cm-3x5in) s.d.1914 W/C gouache two prov. 20-May-3 Sotheby's, Olympia #41/R
£880 $1461 €1276 Head study of Merlin (13x10cm-5x4in) init. W/C sold with a companion. 10-Jun-3 Louis Taylor, Stoke on Trent #945
£900 $1485 €1305 Ptamigan in a snow driven landscape (13x17cm-5x7in) s. W/C. 1-Jul-3 Bearnes, Exeter #440/R
£1013 $1600 €1520 Two pintails in a natural setting (47x69cm-19x27in) s.d.1896 W/C gouache prov. 3-Apr-3 Christie's, Rockefeller NY #216/R est:6000-8000
£1050 $1670 €1575 Lapwing on a shore (16x13cm-6x5in) s.d.1928 W/C bodycol. 5-Mar-3 Bonhams, Bury St Edmunds #297/R est:700-900
£1100 $1716 €1650 Robin in a winter branch (18x13cm-7x5in) s.d.1923 W/C bodycol. 17-Oct-2 David Lay, Penzance #1042/R est:1000-1500
£1100 $1749 €1650 Great Shearwater (15x23cm-6x9in) init. W/C. 29-Apr-3 Gorringes, Lewes #2006

£1150 $1806 €1725 Bullfinches aidst apple blossom. Cuckoo (14x11cm-6x4in) init. W/C bodycol pair. 16-Dec-2 Bonhams, Bury St Edmunds #436/R est:1000-1500

£1200 $1908 €1800 Long tailed tit perched on a gorse bush (13x19cm-5x7in) s.d.1934 pencil W/C. 6-Mar-3 Christie's, Kensington #125 est:1500-2000

£1200 $1908 €1800 Black tern (15x23cm-6x9in) s. W/C. 29-Apr-3 Gorringes, Lewes #2007

£1200 $1908 €1800 Common gull (15x23cm-6x9in) s. W/C. 29-Apr-3 Gorringes, Lewes #2008

£1400 $2226 €2100 Ivory gull (15x23cm-6x9in) s. W/C. 29-Apr-3 Gorringes, Lewes #2009

£1500 $2445 €2250 Chinese ring necked pheasant (17x21cm-7x8in) s. W/C. 29-Jan-3 Sotheby's, Olympia #232/R est:1000-1500

£1900 $3021 €2850 Little gull (15x23cm-6x9in) s. W/C. 29-Apr-3 Gorringes, Lewes #2010

£1900 $3173 €2755 Study of a red grouse (29x34cm-11x13in) s. W/C. 17-Jun-3 Anderson & Garland, Newcastle #235/R est:2000-3000

£2100 $3339 €3150 Magpies on a fence. Ptarmigan and an Arctic hare (7x15cm-3x6in) init. W/C pair. 4-Mar-3 Bearnes, Exeter #416/R est:1500-2500

£2400 $3816 €3600 Field mouse (15x14cm-6x6in) s. W/C bodycol. 5-Mar-3 Bonhams, Bury St Edmunds #300/R est:1500-2000

£2500 $4050 €3750 Kingfisher (18x13cm-7x5in) s.d.1927 gouache W/C prov. 20-May-3 Sotheby's, Olympia #39/R est:1000-2000

£2500 $4050 €3750 Goldfinch on thistle (17x12cm-7x5in) s.d.1921 gouache W/C prov. 20-May-3 Sotheby's, Olympia #43/R est:1000-2000

£2800 $4340 €4200 Wood pigeon (27x19cm-11x7in) s.d.1905 i.verso pencil W/C bodycol. 31-Oct-2 Christie's, London #45/R est:3000-5000

£2800 $4424 €4200 Blue tits (35x25cm-14x10in) s.d.1930 W/C bodycol. 2-Dec-2 Sotheby's, London #77/R est:3000-4000

£3000 $4680 €4500 Studies of highland cattle (19x34cm-7x13in) W/C prov. 5-Nov-2 Bonhams, New Bond Street #143/R est:3000-5000

£3000 $4740 €4500 Chaffinch (27x18cm-11x7in) s.d.1933 W/C bodycol. 2-Dec-2 Sotheby's, London #78/R est:2000-3000

£3200 $5216 €4800 Snowy owls (17x23cm-7x9in) s. W/C. 29-Jan-3 Sotheby's, Olympia #233/R est:3000-5000

£3200 $5088 €4800 Studies of grouse (26x17cm-10x7in) s. W/C pencil. 4-Mar-3 Bearnes, Exeter #418/R est:3000-5000

£3400 $5304 €5100 Willow grouse in flight (21x15cm-8x6in) s. W/C gouache. 18-Sep-2 Dreweatt Neate, Newbury #94/R est:400-600

£4000 $6240 €6000 Egrets on a river bank (20x28cm-8x11in) s.d.1925 W/C bodycol. 17-Oct-2 David Lay, Penzance #1038/R est:4000-6000

£4000 $6200 €6000 Longtailed ducks (18x27cm-7x11in) s.d.1916 i.verso pencil W/C bodycol. 31-Oct-2 Christie's, London #36/R est:4000-6000

£4200 $6510 €6300 Golden plover (28x19cm-11x7in) s.d.1905 i.verso pencil W/C bodycol vignette. 31-Oct-2 Christie's, London #44/R est:4000-6000

£4800 $7776 €7200 Hobbies (18x27cm-7x11in) s.d.1925 W/C gouache prov. 20-May-3 Sotheby's, Olympia #44/R est:3000-5000

£5000 $7750 €7500 Smew (18x27cm-7x11in) s.d.1916 i.verso pencil W/C bodycol. 31-Oct-2 Christie's, London #35/R est:5000-8000

£5000 $7900 €7500 Red grouse in flight (21x15cm-8x6in) s. W/C. 28-Nov-2 Bonhams, Knightsbridge #40/R est:5000-7000

£5000 $7950 €7500 Cock and hen pheasant (27x37cm-11x15in) s.d.1926 W/C. 4-Mar-3 Bearnes, Exeter #412/R est:5000-7000

£5400 $8424 €8100 Bullfinch and apple blossom (27x18cm-11x7in) s.d.1906 W/C. 10-Sep-2 Sworder & Son, Bishops Stortford #760/R est:3000-4000

£5500 $8910 €8250 Tree sparrow and bullfinches (18x26cm-7x10in) s.d.1924 gouache W/C prov. 20-May-3 Sotheby's, Olympia #42/R est:5000-7000

£5700 $8835 €8550 Lapwing or peewit (19x28cm-7x11in) s.d.1915 pencil W/C bodycol prov. 31-Oct-2 Christie's, London #37/R est:4000-6000

£5800 $9222 €8700 Teal in a winter landscape (16x24cm-6x9in) s. W/C. 4-Mar-3 Bearnes, Exeter #410/R est:3000-5000

£5800 $9396 €8700 Brambling and two chaffinches (27x18cm-11x7in) s.d.1924 W/C gouache. 20-May-3 Sotheby's, Olympia #45/R est:5000-7000

£6000 $9300 €9000 Snipe (27x19cm-11x7in) s.d.1905 i.verso pencil W/C bodycol vignette. 31-Oct-2 Christie's, London #42/R est:6000-8000

£6500 $10530 €9750 Pheasant on a woodland path, late autumn (24x40cm-9x16in) s.d.1897 i.verso grisaille. 22-May-3 Christie's, London #23/R est:2500-3500

£6800 $11016 €10200 Lapwing and golden plover on the shore (27x37cm-11x15in) s.d.1922 W/C gouache prov. 20-May-3 Sotheby's, Olympia #46/R est:6000-8000

£7200 $11448 €10800 Partridges and chicks (18x27cm-7x11in) s.d.1933 W/C. 4-Mar-3 Bearnes, Exeter #408/R est:5000-7000

£7400 $11766 €11100 Snipe in a winter landscape (20x28cm-8x11in) s.d.1926 W/C. 4-Mar-3 Bearnes, Exeter #413/R est:3000-5000

£7600 $12084 €11400 Mallard in the snow (41x56cm-16x22in) s.d.1904 W/C. 4-Mar-3 Bearnes, Exeter #411/R est:5000-7000

£7800 $13026 €11310 Redstarts. Bullfinches (27x18cm-11x7in) s.d.1922 W/C pair. 17-Jun-3 Anderson & Garland, Newcastle #237/R est:3000-5000

£8000 $12720 €12000 Partridges at dusk (35x51cm-14x20in) s.d.1897 W/C. 4-Mar-3 Bearnes, Exeter #415/R est:8000-12000

£8200 $12710 €12300 Golden plover (18x27cm-7x11in) s.d.1915 pencil W/C bodycol prov. 31-Oct-2 Christie's, London #38/R est:3000-5000

£8500 $13770 €12750 Lapwing or peewit (27x19cm-11x7in) s.d.1905 i.verso pencil W/C bodycol vignette. 22-May-3 Christie's, London #26/R est:3000-5000

£8600 $13674 €12900 Woodcock sheltering (18x27cm-7x11in) s.d.1919 W/C. 4-Mar-3 Bearnes, Exeter #414/R est:3000-5000

£9000 $14580 €13500 Wigeon (27x19cm-11x7in) s.d.1905 i.verso pencil W/C htd bodycol vignette. 22-May-3 Christie's, London #25/R est:4000-6000

£9500 $14725 €14250 Oyster catchers, redshank and dunlin (22x37cm-9x15in) s.d.1913 pencil W/C htd bodycol. 31-Oct-2 Christie's, London #48/R est:5000-8000

£9500 $15105 €14250 Blackcock on a hillside (18x27cm-7x11in) s.d.1919 W/C. 4-Mar-3 Bearnes, Exeter #417/R est:6000-9000

£11000 $17050 €16500 Woodcock (27x19cm-11x7in) s.d.1905 i.verso pencil W/C bodycol vignette. 31-Oct-2 Christie's, London #43/R est:7000-10000

£11000 $17380 €16500 Partridge in flight (33x54cm-13x21in) s.d.1922 pencil W/C htd bodycol. 27-Nov-2 Christie's, London #28/R est:12000-18000

£14000 $21700 €21000 Mallard in the snow (38x56cm-15x22in) s.d.1928 pencil W/C bodycol prov. 31-Oct-2 Christie's, London #41/R est:15000-20000

£15000 $22800 €22500 Approach of winter (55x38cm-22x15in) s.d.1905 i.verso W/C bodycol. 28-Aug-2 Sotheby's, London #842/R est:15000-20000

£15000 $23250 €22500 Ptarmigan, adult male, female and young, autumn plumage (51x41cm-20x16in) s.d.1908 pencil W/C bodycol lit. 31-Oct-2 Christie's, London #31/R est:15000-20000

£17000 $26350 €25500 Mallard, tufted duck and kingfisher at the water's edge (38x56cm-15x22in) s.d.1928 pencil W/C bodycol prov. 31-Oct-2 Christie's, London #40/R est:18000-25000

£17000 $27710 €25500 Grouse in flight (42x54cm-17x21in) s.d.1892 W/C. 29-Jan-3 Sotheby's, Olympia #231/R est:10000-15000

£18000 $29160 €27000 Teal and widgeon (59x89cm-23x35in) s.d.1912 pencil W/C htd bodycol prov. 22-May-3 Christie's, London #22/R est:18000-25000

£20000 $31800 €30000 Grouse on a moor (38x54cm-15x21in) s.d.1919 W/C. 4-Mar-3 Bearnes, Exeter #407/R est:8000-12000

£22000 $34980 €33000 Ptarmigan in the highlands (26x37cm-10x15in) s.d.1922 W/C. 4-Mar-3 Bearnes, Exeter #409/R est:8000-12000

£26000 $40300 €39000 Gyr falcon (75x56cm-30x22in) s.d.1911 pencil W/C bodycol. 31-Oct-2 Christie's, London #30/R est:25000-35000

£30000 $46800 €45000 On the high tops (37x51cm-15x20in) s.d.1903 W/C bodycol. 5-Nov-2 Bonhams, New Bond Street #142/R est:25000-35000

£30000 $46500 €45000 On the edge of the moor, blackcock displaying (56x39cm-22x15in) s.d.1911 i.verso pencil W/C bodycol. 31-Oct-2 Christie's, London #39/R est:30000-50000

£30000 $46500 €45000 Tawny owls (75x53cm-30x21in) s.d.1925 pencil W/C bodycol prov. 31-Oct-2 Christie's, London #49/R est:15000-20000

£42000 $65100 €63000 Black cock and grey hen, on a Rowan tree (74x53cm-29x21in) s.d.1910 pencil W/C bodycol. 31-Oct-2 Christie's, London #29/R est:30000-50000

THORBURN, Robert (1818-1885) British

Works on paper

£4100 $6847 €5945 Study of a partridge (24x35cm-9x14in) W/C. 17-Jun-3 Anderson & Garland, Newcastle #236/R est:1800-2600

THOREL, S H (20th C) ?

£1037 $1700 €1504 Dice players (56x69cm-22x27in) s. 4-Jun-3 Doyle, New York #93 est:1000-1500

THOREN, Bjarne (20th C) Norwegian

£561 $937 €813 Children on bare rock face (44x58cm-17x23in) s.d.1933. 18-Jun-3 Grev Wedels Plass, Oslo #237/R (N.KR 6500)

THOREN, Esaias (1901-1981) Swedish

£430 $696 €645 Fish (19x38cm-7x15in) s. panel. 3-Feb-3 Lilla Bukowskis, Stockholm #930 (S.KR 6000)

£504 $817 €731 Fish (22x51cm-9x20in) s.d.47 panel. 25-May-3 Uppsala Auktionskammare, Uppsala #306/R (S.KR 6500)

£579 $932 €869 Composition (47x55cm-19x22in) s. panel. 7-May-3 AB Stockholms Auktionsverk #667/R (S.KR 7500)

£595 $987 €863 Surrealistic scene with transparent female figure (27x35cm-11x14in) s. panel. 16-Jun-3 Lilla Bukowskis, Stockholm #621 (S.KR 7700)

£610 $969 €915 The red fish (37x45cm-15x18in) s. canvas on panel. 3-Mar-3 Lilla Bukowskis, Stockholm #780 (S.KR 8200)

£618 $995 €927 The shell (49x60cm-19x24in) s.d.80 panel. 7-May-3 AB Stockholms Auktionsverk #668/R (S.KR 8000)

£674 $1044 €1011 Dove of peace (32x40cm-13x16in) s. panel. 8-Dec-2 Uppsala Auktionskammare, Uppsala #246 (S.KR 9500)

£695 $1119 €1043 Composition (44x53cm-17x21in) s.d.81 panel. 7-May-3 AB Stockholms Auktionsverk #653/R (S.KR 9000)

£695 $1154 €1008 The dream (38x46cm-15x18in) s.d.1948 panel. 16-Jun-3 Lilla Bukowskis, Stockholm #238 (S.KR 9000)

£701 $1093 €1052 Two heads (23x33cm-9x13in) s.d.1948 panel. 6-Nov-2 AB Stockholms Auktionsverk #526/R (S.KR 10000)

£842 $1330 €1263 When heaven and sea becomes one (34x50cm-13x20in) s. d.11/8 1973 verso. 27-Nov-2 Falkkloos, Malmo #77587/R (S.KR 12000)
£1016 $1626 €1473 Pigeon with eggs (33x41cm-13x16in) s. panel. 18-May-3 Anders Antik, Landskrona #55 est:12000 (S.KR 13000)
£1039 $1683 €1559 Woman resting (38x46cm-15x18in) s. panel. 3-Feb-3 Lilla Bukowskis, Stockholm #890 (S.KR 14500)
£1122 $1773 €1683 Two profiles (24x35cm-9x14in) s. panel. 30-Nov-2 Goteborg Auktionsverk, Sweden #649/R est:12000 (S.KR 16000)
£1612 $2514 €2418 Fantasy landscape with shells (45x55cm-18x22in) s. panel. 5-Nov-2 Bukowskis, Stockholm #194/R est:15000-20000 (S.KR 23000)
£1822 $2842 €2733 Cliff formation and female torso (46x55cm-18x22in) s. panel. 5-Nov-2 Bukowskis, Stockholm #195/R est:16000-18000 (S.KR 26000)
£1977 $3124 €2966 Still life of guitar (96x77cm-38x30in) s.d.1977 panel. 28-Apr-3 Bukowskis, Stockholm #186/R est:25000-30000 (S.KR 26000)
£2586 $4085 €3879 Cliff formation (45x55cm-18x22in) s. panel. 28-Apr-3 Bukowskis, Stockholm #187/R est:25000-30000 (S.KR 34000)
£3194 $5046 €4791 Still life (53x65cm-21x26in) s.d.48 panel exhib. 28-Apr-3 Bukowskis, Stockholm #185/R est:40000-45000 (S.KR 42000)
£3422 $5407 €5133 Still life by window (54x65cm-21x26in) s.d.47 panel. 28-Apr-3 Bukowskis, Stockholm #184/R est:50000-60000 (S.KR 45000)
£8365 $13217 €12548 Construction IX (34x24cm-13x9in) init.i.d.27 panel exhib. 28-Apr-3 Bukowskis, Stockholm #40/R est:100000-125000 (S.KR 110000)
£9886 $15620 €14829 The two trees (43x33cm-17x13in) s.d.1926 panel. 28-Apr-3 Bukowskis, Stockholm #134/R est:80000-100000 (S.KR 130000)

Works on paper
£529 $831 €794 Fragment (42x39cm-17x15in) s. gouache exhib. 16-Dec-2 Lilla Bukowskis, Stockholm #601 (S.KR 7500)
£677 $1064 €1016 Evening is near (32x41cm-13x16in) s.d.43 gouache. 16-Dec-2 Lilla Bukowskis, Stockholm #602 (S.KR 9600)

THOREN, Otto von (1828-1889) Austrian
£961 $1499 €1442 Two riders with hunting dogs (33x42cm-13x17in) s. panel. 6-Nov-2 Hans Widmer, St Gallen #99/R (S.FR 2200)
£1620 $2609 €2430 Two riders with dogs (33x42cm-13x17in) s. 7-May-3 Dobiaschofsky, Bern #1019/R est:4500 (S.FR 3500)
£6803 $10816 €10000 Landscape with haycart and cattle (115x199cm-45x78in) s. lit. 21-Mar-3 Auktionhaus Georg Rehm, Augsburg #8099/R est:14000

THORENFELD, Anton Erik (1839-1907) Danish
£270 $435 €405 Fjord landscape with sailing vessels (31x43cm-12x17in) mono.d.73. 22-Feb-3 Rasmussen, Havnen #2099/R (D.KR 3000)
£340 $538 €510 From Svendborg Sund (29x45cm-11x18in) s.d.11/9 73. 30-Nov-2 Rasmussen, Havnen #2241 (D.KR 4000)
£448 $712 €672 From Hulerod towards Kullen (32x47cm-13x19in) mono.d.05 i.verso exhib. 5-May-3 Rasmussen, Vejle #456 (D.KR 4800)
£450 $725 €675 Half-timbered house with boy on stone wall (39x61cm-15x24in) s.d.71. 22-Feb-3 Rasmussen, Havnen #2094/R (D.KR 5000)
£515 $803 €773 Sunset over town (28x43cm-11x17in) mono.d.97 exhib. 11-Nov-2 Rasmussen, Vejle #632/R (D.KR 6000)
£652 $1036 €978 Coastal landscape (41x59cm-16x23in) mono.d.98 i.verso. 10-Mar-3 Rasmussen, Vejle #262/R (D.KR 7000)
£1244 $2015 €1804 Sunset from Amager near Kallebodstrand towards Copenhagen (33x50cm-13x20in) mono.d.96 exhib. 26-May-3 Rasmussen, Copenhagen #1394/R est:8000-10000 (D.KR 13000)

THORMA, Janos (1870-1937) Hungarian
£1882 $2918 €2823 In the field (55x69cm-22x27in) s. 6-Dec-2 Kieselbach, Budapest #175/R (H.F 700000)
£1935 $3018 €2903 Girl in red dress with autumn landscape of Nagybanya (49x79cm-19x31in) s. 11-Sep-2 Kieselbach, Budapest #77/R (H.F 750000)
£3511 $5617 €5267 Autumn in Nagybanya (60x78cm-24x31in) s. 16-May-3 Kieselbach, Budapest #25/R (H.F 1200000)

THORNAM, Emmy (1852-1935) Danish
£270 $422 €405 Still life of flowers in basket (39x49cm-15x19in) s. 23-Sep-2 Rasmussen, Vejle #147/R (D.KR 3200)
£317 $503 €476 Flowers (41x38cm-16x15in) s. 10-Mar-3 Rasmussen, Vejle #501 (D.KR 3400)
£400 $631 €600 Still life of flowers (36x47cm-14x19in) s. 5-Apr-3 Rasmussen, Havnen #2088/R (D.KR 4300)
£446 $696 €669 Rhododendron in flower (66x60cm-26x24in) s. 11-Nov-2 Rasmussen, Vejle #531 (D.KR 5200)
£507 $791 €761 Still life of flowers (28x37cm-11x15in) s. 23-Sep-2 Rasmussen, Vejle #148/R (D.KR 6000)
£698 $1110 €1047 Purple and white flowers (53x61cm-21x24in) s. 10-Mar-3 Rasmussen, Vejle #554/R (D.KR 7500)
£719 $1107 €1079 Wooded landscape with wild flowers (57x75cm-22x30in) s.d.1907. 26-Oct-2 Rasmussen, Havnen #2064/R (D.KR 8500)
£1200 $1992 €1740 Jay, sparrow and ducklings (37x28cm-15x11in) s. 12-Jun-3 Christie's, Kensington #136/R est:800-1200
£1702 $2689 €2553 Still life of wild grasses and white flowers (71x50cm-28x20in) s. 2-Dec-2 Rasmussen, Copenhagen #1471/R est:20000 (D.KR 20000)

THORNBORG, Andreas (1730-1780) Danish/Norwegian
Miniatures
£1000 $1640 €1450 King Christian VII of Denmark (4cm-2in) gilt metal frame oval. 3-Jun-3 Christie's, London #93/R est:400-600

THORNE, Alfred (1850-1916) Swedish
£603 $953 €905 Cottage by watercourse (62x38cm-24x15in) s. 27-Nov-2 Falkkloos, Malmo #77546/R (S.KR 8600)
£1135 $1759 €1703 Coastal landscape, Namndofjarden (36x57cm-14x22in) s.d.1888. 4-Dec-2 AB Stockholms Auktionsverk #1557/R est:12000-15000 (S.KR 16000)
£1631 $2528 €2447 Landscape from Kolmarden (74x55cm-29x22in) s.d.1891. 3-Dec-2 Bukowskis, Stockholm #37/R est:15000-20000 (S.KR 23000)
£2270 $3518 €3405 Waterway in woodland glade (126x75cm-50x30in) s. 4-Dec-2 AB Stockholms Auktionsverk #1730/R est:20000-25000 (S.KR 32000)

THORNELEY, Charles (attrib) (fl.1858-1898) British
£4015 $6666 €5822 Seascapes with vessels (25x41cm-10x16in) bears indis.sig. pair. 16-Jun-3 Lilla Bukowskis, Stockholm #656/R est:20000 (S.KR 52000)

THORNHILL, Sir James (1675-1734) British
£6400 $10624 €9600 Triumph of Napture and Amphitrite (32x44cm-13x17in) 12-Jun-3 Sotheby's, London #95/R est:3000-5000

Works on paper
£1600 $2624 €2320 Portrait of Charles Brideman (20x19cm-8x7in) s.i. pencil prov.exhib.lit. 5-Jun-3 Christie's, London #1/R est:1500-2000

THORNHILL, Sir James (attrib) (1675-1734) British
£4823 $7475 €7235 Neptunus and Amphitrite's wedding (33x45cm-13x18in) sketch. 3-Dec-2 Bukowskis, Stockholm #502/R est:8000-10000 (S.KR 68000)

THORNILD, Christian (19/20th C) Danish?
£429 $669 €644 Interior scene with woman seen from behind, sewing (49x38cm-19x15in) s.d.22. 11-Nov-2 Rasmussen, Vejle #507/R (D.KR 5000)

THORNLEY (?) ?
£1377 $2300 €1997 Ships at harbour (25x38cm-10x15in) s. 21-Jun-3 Selkirks, St. Louis #480 est:1000-1500

THORNLEY, Geoff (1942-) New Zealander
£2431 $3792 €3647 Ogee Park (150x150cm-59x59in) s.i.d.94 verso. 8-Apr-3 Peter Webb, Auckland #97/R est:12000-18000 (NZ.D 7000)

THORNLEY, Georges W (1857-1935) French
£2244 $3522 €3500 Rue Vauban a Antibes (63x52cm-25x20in) s. i.verso. 22-Nov-2 Millon & Associes, Paris #70/R

Works on paper
£556 $917 €800 Barques de peche aux environs de Saint Tropez (34x52cm-13x20in) s. W/C. 1-Jul-3 Rossini, Paris #43/R

THORNLEY, Hubert (19th C) British
£1529 $2400 €2294 Whitby (36x30cm-14x12in) s. 10-Dec-2 Doyle, New York #172/R est:3000-4000
£1800 $2934 €2610 Warships, tug and other vessels in an estuary (25x40cm-10x16in) s. 21-Jul-3 Bonhams, Bath #70/R est:1000-1500
£1800 $2934 €2610 Shipping off a coastal town with figures on a jetty (25x40cm-10x16in) s. 21-Jul-3 Bonhams, Bath #71/R est:1000-1500
£2800 $4564 €4060 Coastal scene with fishing boats and figures at low tide (41x31cm-16x12in) s. 17-Jul-3 Tennants, Leyburn #819/R est:1500-2000
£3500 $5495 €5250 Harbour scene with steamboat (26x41cm-10x16in) s. s.verso. 16-Dec-2 Sotheby's, Olympia #101/R est:3000-5000
£3500 $5705 €5075 View of St. Michael's Mount with figures on a beach (36x31cm-14x12in) s. 17-Jul-3 Tennants, Leyburn #818/R est:2500-3000
£4200 $6594 €6300 Shipping at dawn. Shipping at dusk (35x62cm-14x24in) s. pair. 16-Dec-2 Sotheby's, Olympia #99/R est:4000-6000
£4800 $7824 €6960 St. Michael's Mount, figures and fishing boats at low tide (25x41cm-10x16in) s.i.verso. 17-Jul-3 Tennants, Leyburn #820/R est:2500-3500
£5200 $8164 €7800 Beach scene at sunset. Beach scene (33x28cm-13x11in) s. pair. 16-Dec-2 Sotheby's, Olympia #128/R est:3000-4000

£6000 $9720 €9000 Sunset on the Medway. Busy shipping lanes (25x41cm-10x16in) s. pair. 22-Jan-3 Bonhams, New Bond Street #372/R est:5000-8000

THORNLEY, L H (19/20th C) British
£1389 $2000 €2084 Heavy seas off the Sussex coast (39x60cm-15x24in) s. i.on stretcher. 15-Jan-3 Christie's, Rockefeller NY #136/R est:6000

THORNLEY, William (19/20th C) British
£377 $585 €600 Mountainous landscape (46x61cm-18x24in) s. 6-Oct-2 Livinec, Gaudcheau & Jezequel, Rennes #47
£380 $578 €570 Fishing vessels and a rowing boat entering harbour (25x41cm-10x16in) s. 15-Aug-2 Bonhams, New Bond Street #331
£650 $1047 €975 Fishermen off a jetty at dusk (18x38cm-7x15in) s. 19-Feb-3 Mallams, Oxford #413/R
£880 $1382 €1320 Shipping off the coast (20x40cm-8x16in) s. 16-Dec-2 Sotheby's, Olympia #102/R
£950 $1473 €1425 Hay barges and a paddle tug on the Medway. Fisherfolk on the shore of the estuary (15x20cm-6x8in) panel pair. 31-Oct-2 Christie's, Kensington #528/R
£1000 $1620 €1500 Fisherman ashore awaiting dawn (20x41cm-8x16in) s. 21-May-3 Christie's, Kensington #636/R est:1000-1500
£1026 $1610 €1600 Fishing boat in front of the coast (20x40cm-8x16in) s. 10-Dec-2 Dorotheum, Vienna #51/R est:1500-2000
£1100 $1782 €1650 Fishing boats running into a Channel port on the tide (23x34cm-9x13in) s. canvas on board. 21-May-3 Christie's, Kensington #637/R est:800-1200
£1100 $1782 €1650 Unloading the catch at dusk (20x30cm-8x12in) s. 21-May-3 Christie's, Kensington #702/R est:500-700
£1300 $2015 €1950 Fishing smacks at the entrance to the harbour (25x41cm-10x16in) indis sig. 31-Oct-2 Christie's, Kensington #514/R est:1500-2000
£1400 $2268 €2100 Fishing boats passing the Wolf Rock Lighthouse by moonlight (20x41cm-8x16in) s. 22-Jan-3 Bonhams, New Bond Street #385/R est:800-1200
£1500 $2430 €2250 Haybarge and other shipping off a coastal town (25x41cm-10x16in) s. 22-Jan-3 Bonhams, New Bond Street #380/R est:1500-2000
£1500 $2400 €2250 Fishing boats off the coast (25x41cm-10x16in) s. 11-Mar-3 Gorringes, Lewes #2397/R est:1500-2000
£1550 $2449 €2325 Evening on the Thames (20x29cm-8x11in) s. 2-Dec-2 Bonhams, Bath #130/R est:700-900
£1600 $2480 €2400 Fishermen dragging in their nets before St. Michael's Mount (25x41cm-10x16in) s. 31-Oct-2 Christie's, Kensington #534 est:1200-1800
£1800 $2790 €2700 Rough weather near Whitby (24x39cm-9x15in) s. 26-Sep-2 Mellors & Kirk, Nottingham #722/R
£1800 $2844 €2700 Coastal shipping at anchor off a town (34x28cm-13x11in) s. 7-Apr-3 Bonhams, Bath #104/R est:600-900
£1800 $2880 €2700 Shipping in choppy seas off the coast (19x40cm-7x16in) s. 11-Mar-3 David Duggleby, Scarborough #226/R est:2000-3000
£2000 $3260 €2900 Scarborough (19x29cm-7x11in) s.i. panel. 21-Jul-3 Bonhams, Bath #68/R est:1200-1800
£2200 $3410 €3300 Sunset, Essex coast (30x20cm-12x8in) s. i.verso panel. 31-Oct-2 Christie's, Kensington #527/R est:800-1200
£2700 $4374 €3915 Coastal scene with fishing boats landing (24x39cm-9x15in) s. 21-May-3 Edgar Horn, Eastbourne #262/R est:1500-1700
£2800 $4452 €4200 Thames at Millwall (25x20cm-10x8in) i.verso panel. 6-Mar-3 Christie's, Kensington #498/R est:1000-1500
£2948 $4600 €4422 Shipping on a moonlit bay. Shipping at sunset (34x60cm-13x24in) s. pair. 15-Oct-2 Stephan Welz, Johannesburg #402 est:7000-10000 (SA.R 48000)
£3000 $4770 €4500 Scarborough (36x30cm-14x12in) s. 6-Mar-3 Christie's, Kensington #497/R est:2000-3000
£3100 $5053 €4495 Gravesend (19x29cm-7x11in) s.i. panel. 21-Jul-3 Bonhams, Bath #69/R est:1000-1500
£3200 $5024 €4800 Shipping in harbour (15x23cm-6x9in) s. board pair. 16-Dec-2 Sotheby's, Olympia #100/R est:1000-1500
£3200 $5312 €4640 Low tide Ramsgate. Shipping off Margate (34x27cm-13x11in) one s. pair. 10-Jun-3 Mellors & Kirk, Nottingham #861/R est:3000-4000
£3400 $5338 €5100 Dock scene with ships provisioning (25x20cm-10x8in) s. panel pair. 16-Dec-2 Bonhams, Bury St Edmunds #537/R est:2500-3500
£3400 $5678 €4930 Harbour scene with steamboat (25x40cm-10x16in) s. 18-Jun-3 Sotheby's, Olympia #77/R est:1500-2500
£3600 $5472 €5400 Rough weather on the Yorkshire coast. Moonlight fishing luggers ashore (19x30cm-7x12in) s. pair. 15-Aug-2 Bonhams, New Bond Street #323 est:1500-2000
£3800 $6156 €5700 Crowded waters off Whitby (41x91cm-16x36in) s. 21-May-3 Christie's, Kensington #639/R est:2500-3000
£4000 $6080 €6000 Figures besides a moonlight shore, boats beyond (20x40cm-8x16in) s. 15-Aug-2 Bonhams, New Bond Street #324/R est:1200-1800
£4200 $6804 €6300 Unloading the catch from the fishing fleet. Hay barges on the Medway (31x51cm-12x20in) s. pair. 21-May-3 Christie's, Kensington #638/R est:3000-5000
£5500 $8525 €8250 Hay barges at the mouth of the Medway. Shipping in a calm off the south coast (25x46cm-10x18in) s. pair. 31-Oct-2 Christie's, Kensington #515/R est:1500-2500

THORNTON, Cerindon (20th C) New Zealander
£251 $391 €377 Fendalton Street scene (24x27cm-9x11in) s. canvasboard. 7-Nov-2 International Art Centre, Auckland #91/R (NZ.D 800)

THORNTON, Mildred Valley (1890-1967) Canadian
£1233 $1973 €1850 Mrs Mary Dick, Lytton, BC (61x46cm-24x18in) s. i. prov. 15-May-3 Heffel, Vancouver #140 est:1500-2000 (C.D 2750)

THORNTON, Robert John (1768-1837) British
Prints
£25000 $40250 €37500 Various flowers (56x44cm-22x17in) col engraving aquatint mezzotint 2 sheets 29 folio lit. 7-May-3 Sotheby's, London #5/R est:25000-35000

THORNTON, Wallace Keogh (1915-1991) Australian
£1143 $1806 €1715 Music in the afternoon (92x122cm-36x48in) s.d.54. 17-Nov-2 Sotheby's, Paddington #20/R est:3000-5000 (A.D 3200)

THORNYCROFT, Hamo (1850-1925) British
Sculpture
£3200 $4960 €4800 Athlete putting a stone (68cm-27in) s.num.6/60 black brown pat bronze rec. base. 29-Oct-2 Bonhams, New Bond Street #181/R est:3500-5000
£4222 $7009 €6122 Joy (37cm-15in) s.d.1897 brown pat. bronze. 16-Jun-3 Waddingtons, Toronto #99a/R est:6000-8000 (C.D 9500)
£15000 $23400 €22500 Mower (59cm-23in) s.d.1884 and 1890 brown pat bronze lit. 9-Apr-3 Sotheby's, London #98/R est:10000-15000

THORNYCROFT, Hamo (after) (1850-1925) British
Sculpture
£4800 $7728 €7200 Warrior bearing wounded youth from the field of battle (71cm-28in) bronze prov.lit. 20-Feb-3 Christie's, London #141/R

THORNYCROFT, Helen (1848-1912) British
Works on paper
£1200 $1872 €1800 Honeysuckle, young woman with flowers in her hair (25x20cm-10x8in) s.d.1876 W/C bodycol. 18-Sep-2 Dreweatt Neate, Newbury #57/R est:800-1200

THORNYCROFT, Mary (1814-1895) British
Sculpture
£3600 $5508 €5400 Boy in highland dress (136cm-54in) i. marble. 22-Aug-2 Bonhams, Edinburgh #639/R est:4000-6000

THORPE, Augusta (19th C) British
£560 $935 €812 Portrait of Charles I (73x59cm-29x23in) 24-Jun-3 Bonhams, Knowle #70

THORPE, J E (?) British
£1100 $1716 €1650 Portrait of Joseph Grimaldi the celebrated clown (40x30cm-16x12in) 21-Sep-2 Lacy Scott, Bury St.Edmunds #367

THORPE, Mackenzie (20th C) British
Works on paper
£750 $1178 €1125 Sheep in a landscape (21x15cm-8x6in) s.d.92 pastel. 21-Nov-2 Tennants, Leyburn #708
£1100 $1727 €1650 Sheep in a landscape (24x18cm-9x7in) mono.d.92 pastel. 21-Nov-2 Tennants, Leyburn #709 est:400-600
£1800 $2934 €2610 Landscape (47x70cm-19x28in) init.d.91 pastel. 17-Jul-3 Tennants, Leyburn #784/R est:1800-2500
£4800 $7488 €7200 Sheep in a stormy landscape (39x55cm-15x22in) init.d.90 pastel. 10-Apr-3 Tennants, Leyburn #1145/R est:2000-3000

THORRESTRUP, Christian (1823-1892) Danish
£337 $546 €506 Cottage interior with man seated at table (31x33cm-12x13in) s.i.d.1862 cardboard. 25-Jan-3 Rasmussen, Havnen #2009 (D.KR 3800)

£478 $775 €693 Cottage interior with man seated at table (33x33cm-13x13in) s.i.d.1862. 26-May-3 Rasmussen, Copenhagen #1462/R (D.KR 5000)

THORS, Joseph (fl.1863-1900) British
£360 $601 €522 Burnham Beeches (24x29cm-9x11in) s.d.1871. 26-Jun-3 Mellors & Kirk, Nottingham #903
£380 $608 €570 Figure by a fallen tree (21x30cm-8x12in) s. 7-Jan-3 Bonhams, Knightsbridge #285n/R
£600 $936 €900 Shepherd and sheep in a country lane, gypsy encampment in distance (25x41cm-10x16in) s. 18-Oct-2 Keys, Aylsham #745
£641 $1000 €962 Children fishing in a stream (28x23cm-11x9in) s. 12-Oct-2 Neal Auction Company, New Orleans #153
£650 $1014 €975 Cottage in landscape (15x20cm-6x8in) s. board. 15-Oct-2 Gorringes, Lewes #2268/R
£760 $1269 €1102 Figures in a wooded clearing (30x46cm-12x18in) s. 24-Jun-3 Bonhams, Knowle #80
£800 $1248 €1200 An angler by a river (23x30cm-9x12in) s. 10-Sep-2 Bonhams, Knightsbridge #227/R
£800 $1240 €1200 Figures gathering wood by pool (32x45cm-13x18in) s. panel prov. 2-Oct-2 Bonhams, Knowle #85/R
£980 $1558 €1470 Arrow Pool, Cofton Hackett, Worcestershire (23x30cm-9x12in) s. i.on stretcher. 4-Mar-3 Bearnes, Exeter #465/R
£1218 $1900 €1827 Figures by a streambank, Surrey (49x65cm-19x26in) i.verso. 20-Sep-2 Sloan, North Bethesda #432/R est:3000-4000
£1282 $2000 €1923 Figures by a riverbank, Surrey (50x65cm-20x26in) i.verso. 20-Sep-2 Sloan, North Bethesda #433/R est:3000-4000
£1300 $2015 €1950 Rural cottage (15x23cm-6x9in) s. panel. 4-Oct-2 Mallams, Oxford #516 est:400-600
£1300 $2171 €1885 Woodland near Malvern (20x30cm-8x12in) s. 24-Jun-3 Bonhams, Knowle #98 est:1000-1500
£1450 $2378 €2175 Country lanes with thatched cottages (22x30cm-9x12in) one s. pair. 10-Feb-3 David Duggleby, Scarborough #592/R est:500-700
£1550 $2558 €2248 The road home (17x23cm-7x9in) s. panel. 2-Jul-3 Sotheby's, Olympia #339/R est:1000-1500
£1800 $2808 €2700 Figures by a pond (25x35cm-10x14in) s. board. 8-Apr-3 Bonhams, Knightsbridge #123/R est:2000-3000
£1850 $3090 €2683 Rural scene with figures approaching a yard (20x28cm-8x11in) s. 18-Jun-3 Andrew Hartley, Ilkley #1143/R est:1000-1500
£1900 $3116 €2850 Figure on a wooded track (22x32cm-9x13in) s. 29-May-3 Christie's, Kensington #145/R est:1200-1800
£1900 $3154 €2850 Country river landscape, with figure collecting water (62x49cm-24x19in) s. 10-Jun-3 Bonhams, Knightsbridge #228/R est:1500-2000
£1935 $3058 €2903 Rustic cottage by a marsh (30x47cm-12x19in) s. 18-Nov-2 Waddingtons, Toronto #108/R est:2500-3000 (C.D 4800)
£2000 $3200 €3000 Extensive country landscape, with figures on track (49x75cm-19x30in) s. 11-Mar-3 Bonhams, Knightsbridge #81/R est:1000-1500
£2400 $3912 €3480 View near Colles Hill, Warwickshire (25x35cm-10x14in) s.i.on stretcher. 16-Jul-3 Sotheby's, Olympia #89/R est:1000-1500
£2535 $4208 €3600 Evening landscape (40x49cm-16x19in) s.d.1857. 12-Jun-3 Hauswedell & Nolte, Hamburg #405/R est:2000
£2600 $4160 €3900 Woman standing outside a cottage by a pond with ducks (48x81cm-19x32in) s. 14-Mar-3 Gardiner & Houlgate, Bath #209/R est:2000-3000
£3000 $4770 €4500 Figure walking on a country lane (41x60cm-16x24in) s. 18-Mar-3 Bonhams, New Bond Street #61/R est:3000-5000
£3900 $6357 €5655 View near Guildford, Surrey (75x62cm-30x24in) s. 21-Jul-3 Bonhams, Bath #53/R est:1000-1500
£4100 $6355 €6150 Rural landscape with figures by a duck pond and cottages to the rear (46x32cm-18x13in) s. pair. 1-Oct-2 Fellows & Sons, Birmingham #103/R est:1500-2500
£4700 $7473 €7050 Woman gathering firewood on a heathland track (71x89cm-28x35in) s. 30-Apr-3 Halls, Shrewsbury #287/R est:4000-6000
£5000 $7850 €7500 Children fishing beside a stream. River landscape with a figure on a path (25x35cm-10x14in) s. panel pair. 19-Nov-2 Bonhams, Leeds #225/R est:5000-7000

THORS, Joseph (attrib) (fl.1863-1900) British
£250 $408 €375 Wooded landscape with distant windmills by moonlight (24x34cm-9x13in) 14-Feb-3 Lyon & Turnbull, Edinburgh #30
£380 $619 €551 Estuary scene (25x40cm-10x16in) bears sig. 16-Jul-3 Sotheby's, Olympia #15/R
£700 $1141 €1015 Wooded landscape with a shepherd and sheep (20x30cm-8x12in) with sig. panel. 17-Jul-3 Tennants, Leyburn #837
£980 $1597 €1470 Stormy river landscape with figures in rowing boat in foreground (48x79cm-19x31in) 14-Feb-3 Keys, Aylsham #687/R
£1500 $2505 €2175 Figures on a lane by a wooded river with fields and cottages beyond (36x52cm-14x20in) s. prov. 17-Jun-3 Rosebery Fine Art, London #542/R est:600-800

THORSEN, Hakon (1866-1925) Danish
£652 $1036 €978 An old captain (98x80cm-39x31in) mono. 5-Mar-3 Rasmussen, Copenhagen #1745/R (D.KR 7000)

THORSEN, Jens Jorgen (1932-) Scandinavian
Works on paper
£339 $525 €509 Composition (85x75cm-33x30in) s.i.d.1966 collage. 1-Oct-2 Rasmussen, Copenhagen #160/R (D.KR 4000)

THORSEN, Lars (1876-1952) American?
£542 $850 €813 At sea (51x66cm-20x26in) s. 22-Nov-2 Skinner, Boston #341/R

THORVALDSEN, Bertel (1770-1844) Danish
Sculpture
£22595 $35248 €35700 Bible scenes (65x47cm-26x19in) terracotta relief set of four. 15-Oct-2 Babuino, Rome #160/R est:8000-12000
£208333 $331250 €300000 Mythological figures (100x125cm-39x49in) stone relief. 4-May-3 Finarte, Venice #621/R est:240000-280000
Works on paper
£468 $754 €702 Portrait of young lady (13x13cm-5x5in) i. pencil. 26-Feb-3 Museumsbygningen, Copenhagen #74 (D.KR 5200)
£1676 $2665 €2514 Dante and Virgil on Geryon's back (33x27cm-13x11in) pencil chk exhib. 5-Mar-3 Rasmussen, Copenhagen #2077/R est:10000-15000 (D.KR 18000)
£2400 $4008 €3480 Study for a funerary relief (19x26cm-7x10in) i. pen brown ink lit. 9-Jul-3 Sotheby's, London #60/R est:1500-2000

THORVALDSEN, Bertel (after) (1770-1844) Danish
Sculpture
£5489 $8563 €8234 Hebe (254cm-100in) white marble incl.marble socle prov. 11-Nov-2 Rasmussen, Vejle #713/R est:75000-100000 (D.KR 64000)

THRASHER, Leslie (1889-1936) American
£1282 $2000 €1923 Children putting glue inside father's hat (41x36cm-16x14in) s. 9-Nov-2 Illustration House, New York #5/R est:3000-4000
£1299 $2000 €1949 Patriot, Liberty magazine cover (46x41cm-18x16in) s.d.1931 prov. 24-Oct-2 Shannon's, Milford #126/R est:2000-3000
£1667 $2600 €2501 Package from home (53x43cm-21x17in) s. 28-Mar-3 Eldred, East Dennis #702/R est:1500-2000

THRASHER, W R (1908-1997) American
£1026 $1600 €1539 Texas bluebonnets (46x61cm-18x24in) board. 19-Oct-2 David Dike, Dallas #259/R est:600-1200

THRUSH, Michael (1974-) American
£1341 $2200 €1944 Land o'margarine (122x122cm-48x48in) s.i.d.2002 panel. 28-May-3 Sotheby's, Amsterdam #113/R est:2200-2800
£1341 $2200 €1944 Breast milk (122x122cm-48x48in) s.i.d.2001 s.i.d.verso panel. 28-May-3 Sotheby's, Amsterdam #114/R est:2200-2800
£1375 $2200 €1994 Deconstructed duck (122x122cm-48x48in) s.i.d.2001 s.i.d.verso panel. 13-May-3 Sotheby's, Tel Aviv #21/R est:2200-2800
£2563 $4100 €3716 Blow pop (122x122cm-48x48in) s.i.d.2002 s.i.d.verso panel. 13-May-3 Sotheby's, Tel Aviv #22/R est:2200-2800

THUE, Henry (1890-1921) Norwegian?
£786 $1288 €1140 In deep thought (100x80cm-39x31in) s.i.d.1920. 4-Jun-3 AB Stockholms Auktionsverk #2499/R (S.KR 10000)

THULDEN, Theodor van (1606-1669) Dutch
£11765 $19294 €18000 Madonna and Child sourrended by flowers (56x44cm-22x17in) copper. 9-Feb-3 Anaf, Lyon #249/R

THULDEN, Theodor van (attrib) (1606-1669) Dutch
£1538 $2431 €2400 L'annonciation (33x44cm-13x17in) copper. 12-Nov-2 Palais de Beaux Arts, Brussels #78/R est:2000-3000
£2014 $3223 €2800 Daniel in the lion's den (46x64cm-18x25in) panel after Rubens. 17-May-3 Hagelstam, Helsinki #20/R est:2000

THULSTRUP, Thure de (1848-1930) American
Works on paper
£671 $1100 €973 Mexican street scene (55x34cm-22x13in) s. brush ink gouache. 5-Jun-3 Swann Galleries, New York #251/R

THUM, Christian (attrib) (1625-1696) Swedish
£4255 $6596 €6383 Money changers (76x104cm-30x41in) bears sig.-Rembrandt. 8-Dec-2 Uppsala Auktionskammare, Uppsala #21/R est:40000-50000 (S.KR 60000)

THUM, Patty Prather (1853-1926) American
£1290 $2000 €1935 Wild rose (13x25cm-5x10in) s. board painted c.1900. 8-Dec-2 Toomey, Oak Park #621/R est:1000-2000

THUMANN, Paul (1834-1908) German
£2300 $3726 €3450 Portrait of lady (45x38cm-18x15in) bears sig cradled panel. 20-May-3 Sotheby's, Olympia #383/R est:800-1200

THUMSER, G (19th C) Swiss?
£1135 $1771 €1703 Moonlit lake landscape (42x58cm-17x23in) s. 20-Nov-2 Fischer, Luzern #2279/R est:1800-2500 (S.FR 2600)

THUNMAN, Olof (1879-1944) Swedish
£305 $473 €458 Winter beach coastal landscape in moonlight (44x73cm-17x29in) s.d.05. 8-Dec-2 Uppsala Auktionskammare, Uppsala #160 (S.KR 4300)
£851 $1319 €1277 Husgards Lake in evening sunshine (36x54cm-14x21in) s. d.1918 verso. 4-Dec-2 AB Stockholms Auktionsverk #1782/R (S.KR 12000)
£851 $1319 €1277 The fields at Uppsala (29x59cm-11x23in) s.d.16. 4-Dec-2 AB Stockholms Auktionsverk #1797/R (S.KR 12000)
£993 $1539 €1490 Spring work - man and horse ploughing field (70x110cm-28x43in) s.d.16. 8-Dec-2 Uppsala Auktionskammare, Uppsala #138/R (S.KR 14000)
£1552 $2514 €2250 Song swans in flight, evening sunshine (72x128cm-28x50in) s.i.d.1919. 25-May-3 Uppsala Auktionskammare, Uppsala #193/R est:15000-18000 (S.KR 20000)

THURAU, Friedrich (?-1888) German
£3544 $5494 €5600 Sailing ships and figures on shore (62x84cm-24x33in) s.d.1851 lit. 28-Sep-2 Hans Stahl, Hamburg #41/R est:4500
£3653 $5699 €5480 Swiss shore of Bodensee (50x73cm-20x29in) s.d.1852. 28-Mar-3 Koller, Zurich #3149/R est:5000-8000 (S.FR 8000)

THURBER, James Grover (1894-1961) American
Works on paper
£1026 $1600 €1539 Embracing couple (13x8cm-5x3in) s.d.1940 pencil prov. 9-Nov-2 Illustration House, New York #87/R est:3000-4000

THURIN, Rene (1874-1951) French
£266 $415 €420 La roulotte sur le chimin (36x45cm-14x18in) s. canvas on cardboard. 15-Sep-2 Etude Bailleul, Bayeux #186

THURLBY, Fred (20th C) British
£7000 $11620 €10150 Stout winner of 12 first and 8 second prizes at various shows. Madam (46x61cm-18x24in) s.d.1909 pair. 12-Jun-3 Christie's, Kensington #81/R est:2000-3000

THURM, Willy (1880-1964) German
£420 $701 €609 Haymaking (58x78cm-23x31in) s. 25-Jun-3 Cheffins, Cambridge #777/R

THURMAN, Peder (1839-1919) Norwegian
£1561 $2560 €2263 Afternoon coffee (31x48cm-12x19in) s. s.i.stretcher. 2-Jun-3 Blomqvist, Oslo #163/R est:15000-18000 (N.KR 17000)

THURMANN, Oystein (1925-1988) Norwegian
£918 $1506 €1331 The white horse (130x75cm-51x30in) s.d.78. 2-Jun-3 Blomqvist, Oslo #202/R (N.KR 10000)
Works on paper
£262 $411 €393 Mermaids (54x74cm-21x29in) s. w/. 25-Nov-2 Blomqvist, Lysaker #1273 (N.KR 3000)

THURSTON, Eugene (1896-1993) American
£1667 $2600 €2501 Mt Franklin from Logan Heights (41x51cm-16x20in) 19-Oct-2 David Dike, Dallas #13/R est:2000-3000

THYGESEN, Rudolf (1880-1953) Norwegian
£299 $466 €449 Farmyard (66x82cm-26x32in) s. painted 1936. 23-Sep-2 Blomqvist, Lysaker #1248 (N.KR 3500)
£849 $1307 €1274 Autumn landscape with house (65x81cm-26x32in) s. painted 1936. 28-Oct-2 Blomqvist, Lysaker #1323 (N.KR 10000)
£877 $1386 €1316 Summer landscape (60x73cm-24x29in) init.d.42. 17-Dec-2 Grev Wedels Plass, Oslo #284/R (N.KR 10000)
£1010 $1657 €1465 Autumn landscape (60x73cm-24x29in) init.d.41. 2-Jun-3 Blomqvist, Oslo #184/R est:10000 (N.KR 11000)
£1010 $1657 €1465 Spring landscape II (65x81cm-26x32in) init.d.38 exhib. 2-Jun-3 Blomqvist, Oslo #185/R (N.KR 11000)
£1357 $2199 €2036 House and trees (60x73cm-24x29in) init.d.32. 26-May-3 Grev Wedels Plass, Oslo #25/R est:15000-20000 (N.KR 15000)

THYIEBAUT, Emile (?) French
£550 $897 €825 Drying the nests (64x112cm-25x44in) i.verso. 14-Feb-3 Keys, Aylsham #458

THYS, Pieter (attrib) (1624-1677) Flemish
£943 $1453 €1500 La crucifixion (137x88cm-54x35in) 25-Oct-2 Tajan, Paris #64 est:1599-2999

THYS, Susy Kathy (1936-) Swiss
£261 $404 €392 Still life of flowers (27x22cm-11x9in) s. 9-Dec-2 Philippe Schuler, Zurich #8761 (S.FR 600)

THYSEBAERT, Émile (1873-1962) Belgian
£321 $503 €500 Ferme (16x22cm-6x9in) s. panel. 10-Dec-2 Campo, Vlaamse Kaai #498
£377 $585 €600 Woman with bag (120x90cm-47x35in) s. panel. 5-Oct-2 De Vuyst, Lokeren #347
£458 $737 €700 Promeneur dans un paysage hivernal (60x37cm-24x15in) s. 20-Jan-3 Horta, Bruxelles #27
£475 $741 €750 Vase de fleurs (108x59cm-43x23in) s. 16-Sep-2 Horta, Bruxelles #352
£769 $1192 €1200 Festivites populaires (36x53cm-14x21in) s. panel. 9-Dec-2 Horta, Bruxelles #375

TIAN LIMING (20th C) Chinese
Works on paper
£290 $475 €400 Calligrapher at desk with banana leaf (104x68cm-41x27in) s.i.d.1988 Indian ink col hanging scroll. 30-May-3 Dr Fritz Nagel, Stuttgart #1301

TIARINI, Alessandro (circle) (1577-1668) Italian
£14000 $21700 €21000 Resurrection (36x29cm-14x11in) copper. 30-Oct-2 Christie's, Kensington #116/R est:5000-7000
£15172 $23972 €22000 Saint Sebastian looked after by charitable women (94x76cm-37x30in) 5-Apr-3 Finarte Semenzato, Milan #126/R est:15000

TIARINI, Alessandro (style) (1577-1668) Italian
£10897 $17109 €17000 Vierge a l'enfant (118x140cm-46x55in) 19-Nov-2 Vanderkindere, Brussels #5/R est:5000-7000

TIBALDI, Pellegrino (attrib) (1527-1596) Italian
Works on paper
£6944 $11042 €10000 Sketch for memorial (20x19cm-8x7in) i. pen sepia wash paper on board. 5-May-3 Ketterer, Munich #357/R est:800-1000

TIBBITS, William (1837-1906) Australian
Works on paper
£1004 $1525 €1506 Dhurringile (22x39cm-9x15in) s.i. W/C. 28-Aug-2 Deutscher-Menzies, Melbourne #330/R est:3500-4500 (A.D 2800)

TIBERTELLI DE PISIS, Bona (1926-2000) Italian
Works on paper
£1507 $2366 €2200 Untitled (38x55cm-15x22in) s. i.verso mixed media on canvas. 15-Apr-3 Laurence Calmels, Paris #4124/R

TIBOR, Erno (1885-1945) Hungarian
£559 $872 €811 Sailing boats (36x45cm-14x18in) s. board. 12-Apr-3 Mu Terem Galeria, Budapest #84/R est:150000 (H.F 200000)
£568 $885 €824 Harbour scene (25x34cm-10x13in) s. 13-Sep-2 Mu Terem Galeria, Budapest #16/R est:150000 (H.F 220000)
£903 $1409 €1355 Still life (70x99cm-28x39in) s. cardboard. 11-Sep-2 Kieselbach, Budapest #200/R (H.F 350000)
£1129 $1751 €1637 Venetian gondolier (74x98cm-29x39in) s. card. 9-Dec-2 Mu Terem Galeria, Budapest #21/R est:360000 (H.F 420000)
£1291 $2001 €1872 Tourists by the lake shore (71x100cm-28x39in) s. card. 9-Dec-2 Mu Terem Galeria, Budapest #58/R est:340000 (H.F 480000)
£1479 $2293 €2145 Sailing boats in Bretagne (51x68cm-20x27in) s. card. 9-Dec-2 Mu Terem Galeria, Budapest #24/R est:140000 (H.F 550000)

TICHO, Anna (1894-1980) Israeli
Works on paper
£6329 $10000 €9494 View of hills (55x55cm-22x22in) s. chl brown chk prov. 27-Apr-3 Sotheby's, Tel Aviv #33/R est:12000-15000

TICULIN, Mario (19/20th C) Italian
£381 $606 €560 Venice (70x50cm-28x20in) s. board. 1-Mar-3 Stadion, Trieste #44

TIDEMAND, Adolph (1814-1876) Norwegian
£9183 $15060 €13315 Announcing for confirmation (20x23cm-8x9in) s.d.1847 lit. 2-Jun-3 Blomqvist, Oslo #161/R est:200000 (N.KR 100000)

£30461 $48738 €45692 Small girl wearing national costume (46x32cm-18x13in) s.d.1868 lit. 17-Mar-3 Blomqvist, Oslo #317/R est:250000-300000 (N.KR 350000)
£112688 $164524 €169032 Farewell to the old parents (45x41cm-18x16in) s.d.1855 prov.exhib.lit. 27-May-2 Blomqvist, Oslo #319/R est:1800000-2200000 (N.KR 1350000)
£113122 $183258 €169683 Advice from the neighbour - interior with mother, baby and woman (39x47cm-15x19in) s.d.1861 i.verso panel lit. 26-May-3 Grev Wedels Plass, Oslo #30/R est:1000000-1500000 (N.KR 1250000)
£270000 $442800 €405000 Bestemors brudekrone - grandmother's bridal crown (71x63cm-28x25in) s.d.1867 prov.lit. 3-Jun-3 Sotheby's, London #224/R est:270000-350000
£537728 $838855 €806592 Grandmother's wedding crown (118x102cm-46x40in) s.d.1865 prov.exhib.lit. 21-Oct-2 Blomqvist, Oslo #320/R est:3000000-4000000 (N.KR 6200000)

TIDMAN, Bruer (20th C) British
Works on paper
£250 $413 €363 Clown, black and white (73x58cm-29x23in) s.d.84 mixed media. 1-Jul-3 Bonhams, Norwich #359
£300 $465 €450 Portrait of a seated woman (137x101cm-54x40in) s.d.96 s.i.verso mixed media canvas. 30-Sep-2 Bonhams, Ipswich #391
£360 $558 €540 Dancer (67x67cm-26x26in) s.d.95 bodycol. 30-Sep-2 Bonhams, Ipswich #390
£400 $620 €600 Portrait (46x44cm-18x17in) s.d.94 mixed media. 30-Sep-2 Bonhams, Ipswich #442
£900 $1485 €1305 Burlesque figure in the spotlight (147x120cm-58x47in) s.d.86 mixed media. 1-Jul-3 Bonhams, Norwich #362/R

TIDY, Marsha (20th C) ?
Works on paper
£283 $442 €491 Red haired woman on a chair (50x35cm-20x14in) s.d.Aug 1979 W/C ink. 31-Mar-3 Goodman, Sydney #218/R (A.D 750)

TIEBERT, Hermann (1895-) German
£1258 $1962 €2000 Swabian peasant smoking pipe (50x40cm-20x16in) s.d.1935 i. verso panel. 9-Oct-2 Michael Zeller, Lindau #936/R est:2000

TIECHE, Adolf (1877-1957) Swiss
£377 $604 €566 French barock castle (63x79cm-25x31in) s. 17-Mar-3 Philippe Schuler, Zurich #8490 (S.FR 800)
Works on paper
£231 $373 €347 Bellinzona in sunshine (48x61cm-19x24in) s. W/C over pencil. 7-May-3 Dobiaschofsky, Bern #1022/R (S.FR 500)

TIEDJEN, W (1881-1950) German
£692 $1079 €1100 Ducks in water (52x71cm-20x28in) i. 23-Sep-2 Dr Fritz Nagel, Stuttgart #7075/R

TIEDJEN, Willy (1881-1950) German
£301 $470 €440 Ships in harbour (47x72cm-19x28in) s.d.15. 9-Apr-3 Neumeister, Munich #755/R
£377 $589 €600 Ducks (36x51cm-14x20in) s. board. 21-Sep-2 Dannenberg, Berlin #605/R
£506 $800 €800 Troublemaker in the poultry yard (44x68cm-17x27in) s.d.33 panel. 29-Nov-2 Schloss Ahlden, Ahlden #1388/R
£573 $894 €900 Spring meadow with goats (66x88cm-26x35in) s. lit. 7-Nov-2 Allgauer, Kempten #2978/R
£637 $994 €1000 Old snow in front of the Karwendel mountains (68x90cm-27x35in) s. 7-Nov-2 Allgauer, Kempten #2979/R
£651 $1015 €950 Cows in the meadow (46x63cm-18x25in) s.d.13 board on panel lit. 10-Apr-3 Allgauer, Kempten #3014/R
£845 $1403 €1200 After the rain (49x76cm-19x30in) s. 14-Jun-3 Arnold, Frankfurt #885
£1154 $1800 €1731 Duck pond (53x74cm-21x29in) s. 18-Sep-2 Jackson's, Cedar Falls #926/R

TIEFENTHALER-HORNSTEINER, Paula (1881-1942) Austrian
£892 $1391 €1400 Two girls from Tyrol (47x62cm-19x24in) s. 6-Nov-2 Hugo Ruef, Munich #1147/R

TIEL, Quiryn Martinus Adrianus van (1900-1967) Dutch
£6329 $10000 €10000 Kat en vogel (90x100cm-35x39in) s.d.66 prov.exhib. 26-Nov-2 Sotheby's, Amsterdam #244/R est:7000-9000

TIELE, Jan C (1884-1956) Dutch
£380 $593 €570 Carnations (14x17cm-6x7in) s.d.21 board. 17-Oct-2 Bonhams, Edinburgh #202

TIELENS, Alexandre (1868-1959) Belgian
£1000 $1660 €1000 Retour du potager (57x77cm-22x30in) s.d.1933. 16-Jun-3 Horta, Bruxelles #348

TIEPOLO, Giovanni Battista (1696-1770) Italian
£27972 $40000 €41958 Madonna and Child with goldfinch (50x40cm-20x16in) oval prov.lit. 22-Jan-3 Doyle, New York #76/R est:60000
£154321 $250000 €231482 Erato, the muse of love and poetry. Terpsichore, the muse of dance (71x71cm-28x28in) oil gold ground on canvas pair prov.lit. 24-Jan-3 Christie's, Rockefeller NY #67/R est:300000-500000
Prints
£2200 $3630 €3190 Half dressed nymph with two children, surrounded by four men (22x17cm-9x7in) etching exec.c.1735-40. 2-Jul-3 Christie's, London #45 est:1000-1500
£3077 $4862 €4800 La decouverte du tombeau de Polichinelle. etching. 14-Nov-2 Libert, Castor, Paris #49/R est:1500
Works on paper
£1235 $2000 €1853 Portrait of Sperone Speroni (22x17cm-9x7in) s.i. chk prov. 22-Jan-3 Christie's, Rockefeller NY #51/R
£3797 $6000 €6000 Caricature of a Venetian nobleman (16x9cm-6x4in) pen wash. 29-Nov-2 Bassenge, Berlin #5763/R est:4000
£6500 $10855 €9425 Caricature of a standing cavalier leaning on a staff. Figure studies (21x14cm-8x6in) pen ink wash double-sided. 8-Jul-3 Christie's, London #50/R est:7000-10000
£9259 $15000 €13889 Caricature of a cavalier (21x12cm-8x5in) chk ink wash prov. 22-Jan-3 Christie's, Rockefeller NY #50/R est:7000
£12346 $20000 €18519 Marsyas standing in profile (30x20cm-12x8in) i. chk pen ink wash prov. 22-Jan-3 Christie's, Rockefeller NY #49/R est:30000
£14000 $23380 €20300 Caricature of a man, seen from behind, wearing white robes and cap (17x10cm-7x4in) pen blk ink grey wash pen brown ink. 9-Jul-3 Sotheby's, London #50/R est:8000-12000
£14085 $23380 €20000 Oriental head (16x13cm-6x5in) pen brush wash. 12-Jun-3 Hauswedell & Nolte, Hamburg #323/R est:16000
£26000 $43420 €37700 Annunciation (24x20cm-9x8in) pen ink wash prov.exhib.lit. 8-Jul-3 Christie's, London #48/R est:25000-35000
£37037 $60000 €55556 Saint Anthony of Padua with the Child (28x19cm-11x7in) chk htd white prov.exhib.lit. 21-Jan-3 Sotheby's, New York #80/R est:80000
£50000 $83500 €72500 Madonna and Child with Saint Anthony of Padua kneeling and two other Saints (32x22cm-13x9in) black chk pen ink corner made up prov.exhib.lit. 8-Jul-3 Christie's, London #47/R est:50000-80000
£96154 $149038 €150000 Head of man in profile (25x18cm-10x7in) sanguine chk. 4-Dec-2 Piasa, Paris #8/R est:60000

TIEPOLO, Giovanni Battista (attrib) (1696-1770) Italian
£33951 $55000 €50927 Samson and the lion (89x63cm-35x25in) octagonal. 23-Jan-3 Sotheby's, New York #47/R est:40000-60000
Works on paper
£6993 $10000 €10490 Christ on the Cross (44x31cm-17x12in) black chk. 23-Jan-3 Swann Galleries, New York #125/R est:2500-3500

TIEPOLO, Giovanni Domenico (1727-1804) Italian
Works on paper
£759 $1200 €1200 Etude d'une draperie (17x13cm-7x5in) i. col chk prov. 27-Nov-2 Christie's, Paris #98/R
£878 $1370 €1300 Man seated by tree (21x17cm-8x7in) chk pen ink wash. 27-Mar-3 Christie's, Paris #41/R
£1100 $1727 €1650 Hercules seated under a tree (20x14cm-8x6in) chk ink wash. 13-Dec-2 Christie's, Kensington #292/R est:700-1000
£1543 $2500 €2315 Head of man wearing fur hat (20x16cm-8x6in) chk prov. 21-Jan-3 Sotheby's, New York #81/R
£2600 $4342 €3770 Two studies of Ganymade and one of Hercules. Two studies of Hercules (26x16cm-10x6in) s. black chk ink wash double-sided prov. 8-Jul-3 Christie's, London #53/R est:3000-5000
£5068 $7905 €7500 Two angels with putti (20x28cm-8x11in) s. pen ink wash prov. 27-Mar-3 Christie's, Paris #40/R
£7500 $12525 €10875 Baptism of Christ (29x20cm-11x8in) s. black chk pen ink wash prov. 8-Jul-3 Christie's, London #52/R est:5000-8000
£11111 $18000 €16667 Saint Anthony of Padua with the Child in glory (23x17cm-9x7in) s. pen ink wash. 21-Jan-3 Sotheby's, New York #82/R est:22000
£12000 $20040 €17400 Centaur carrying off nymph, accompanied by putti (27x30cm-11x12in) s. pen ink wash prov.lit. 8-Jul-3 Christie's, London #51/R est:6000-8000
£13606 $21634 €20000 Centaure enlevant une faunesse (19x27cm-7x11in) i. pen ink wash over crayon. 24-Mar-3 Tajan, Paris #44/R est:20000
£19000 $31730 €27550 Stag by a riverbank (18x25cm-7x10in) s. pen brown ink wash. 9-Jul-3 Sotheby's, London #57/R est:10000-15000
£40123 $65000 €60185 Good Samaritan (45x36cm-18x14in) chk pen ink wash. 22-Jan-3 Christie's, Rockefeller NY #54/R est:50000

£46296 $75000 €69444 Orientals riding camels near pyramid (19x28cm-7x11in) s. pe ink wash over chk prov. 21-Jan-3 Sotheby's, New York #77/R est:70000

TIEPOLO, Giovanni Domenico (studio) (1727-1804) Italian
£19000 $31730 €27550 Head of a young boy (39x30cm-15x12in) 9-Jul-3 Bonhams, New Bond Street #13/R est:5000-7000

TIEPOLO, Lorenzo (1736-1776) Italian
Prints
£8800 $14520 €12760 Graces and mars (56x40cm-22x16in) etching after Giovanni Battista Tiepolo. 1-Jul-3 Sotheby's, London #57/R est:5000-7000
Works on paper
£6419 $10014 €9500 Study of heads of two old men and two young men (24x29cm-9x11in) wash pen brush. 28-Mar-3 Dorotheum, Vienna #38/R est:3000-4000

TIEPOLO, Lorenzo (attrib) (1736-1776) Italian
Works on paper
£6419 $10014 €9500 Young woman with her boy (47x37cm-19x15in) pastel. 26-Mar-3 Tajan, Paris #31/R est:4000

TIER, Adeline (?-1916) ?
£588 $965 €900 Still life of flowers (49x30cm-19x12in) s. 9-Feb-3 Bukowskis, Helsinki #432/R

TIERCE, Jean-Baptiste Antoine (attrib) (1737-1790) French
Works on paper
£1266 $1975 €2000 Paysage a la cascade (54x44cm-21x17in) pen ink wash. 18-Oct-2 Rabourdin & Choppin de Janvry, Paris #73

TIETJENS, M H (20th C) American
Works on paper
£417 $650 €626 Pumpkin harvest (20x18cm-8x7in) s. W/C graphite dr prov. 10-Nov-2 Selkirks, St. Louis #975

TIETZE, Hugo (20th C) German
Works on paper
£466 $740 €699 Portrait of Thyra Schmiegelow (99x68cm-39x27in) s.d.1938 gouache. 10-Mar-3 Rasmussen, Vejle #415/R (D.KR 5000)

TIFFANY, Louis Comfort (1848-1933) American
£12676 $18000 €19014 River sunset (20x25cm-8x10in) board. 8-Aug-1 Barridorf, Portland #192/R est:4000-6000

TIFFIN, Sheila (?) British
£310 $487 €465 Summertime, children on the beach (27x34cm-11x13in) s. 10-Dec-2 Lane, Penzance #11
£400 $620 €600 Self portrait of the artist dressing (193x155cm-76x61in) s.d.1990. 26-Sep-2 Lane, Penzance #231

TIFFINGER, R (?) ?
£480 $730 €720 Waterfall near Bern (99x74cm-39x29in) s. 4-Jul-2 Duke & Son, Dorchester #225

TIGHE, Francis Browne (fl.1885-1926) British
Works on paper
£370 $603 €555 Meadow scene with blossom trees (25x33cm-10x13in) s.d.1901 W/C. 7-Feb-3 Dee Atkinson & Harrison, Driffield #739/R

TIGLIO, Marcos (1903-1976) Argentinian
£3399 $5370 €5099 Still life with vase and fruit (37x59cm-15x23in) s.d.52 cardboard. 15-Nov-2 Naón & Cia, Buenos Aires #5/R
£6728 $10630 €10092 Still life with blue bowl (43x53cm-17x21in) s.d.52 cardboard. 15-Nov-2 Naón & Cia, Buenos Aires #6/R

TIHANYI, Lajos (1885-1939) Hungarian
£49016 $76465 €73524 Composition (90x68cm-35x27in) s. 11-Sep-2 Kieselbach, Budapest #142/R (H.F 19000000)
£53095 $82828 €76988 Portrait of a young lady (102x75cm-40x30in) s.d.1916. 12-Apr-3 Mu Terem Galeria, Budapest #184/R est:10000000 (H.F 19000000)
£79710 $130725 €110000 Riverbank, bridge (75x55cm-30x22in) s. s.i.d. stretcher prov.exhib.lit. 30-May-3 Villa Grisebach, Berlin #50/R est:5000-7000
£108351 $169027 €157109 Portrait of Gyorgy Boloni (86x70cm-34x28in) s.d.912 prov.exhib.lit. 13-Sep-2 Mu Terem Galeria, Budapest #201/R est:12000000 (H.F 42000000)
Works on paper
£516 $805 €774 Nude outdoors (39x30cm-15x12in) blue indian ink. 11-Sep-2 Kieselbach, Budapest #42/R (H.F 200000)
£1956 $3052 €2836 Nude woman (39x28cm-15x11in) s.i.d.912 ink prov.exhib. 12-Apr-3 Mu Terem Galeria, Budapest #146/R est:400000 (H.F 700000)
£1956 $3052 €2934 Man and woman (38x30cm-15x12in) s.d.913 Indian ink. 11-Apr-3 Kieselbach, Budapest #39/R est:350000-700000 (H.F 700000)
£2580 $4024 €3870 Love (32x22cm-13x9in) s. indian ink. 11-Sep-2 Kieselbach, Budapest #126/R (H.F 1000000)
£32271 $50020 €46793 Self-portrait (57x47cm-22x19in) s. pastel. 9-Dec-2 Mu Terem Galeria, Budapest #109/R est:7500000 (H.F 12000000)

TIKKANEN, Ulf (1920-1969) Finnish
Sculpture
£1408 $2268 €2000 Solitary crane (99cm-39in) s. bronze. 10-May-3 Bukowskis, Helsinki #11/R est:2000-2500
£1901 $3061 €2700 Cranes (35cm-14in) bronze. 10-May-3 Bukowskis, Helsinki #21/R est:1300-1500
£4225 $6803 €6000 Lynx (83cm-33in) s. granite. 10-May-3 Bukowskis, Helsinki #10/R est:6000-8000

TILBORCH, Gillis van (c.1625-1678) Flemish
£7692 $11923 €12000 Drinkers at table in inn (33x27cm-13x11in) s. panel octagonal prov. 6-Dec-2 Millon & Associes, Paris #3/R
£10828 $16892 €17000 Couple sitting having a meal (24x35cm-9x14in) init. panel prov. 6-Nov-2 Christie's, Amsterdam #58/R est:10000-15000
£14000 $21980 €21000 Elegant company at table (61x49cm-24x19in) panel. 11-Dec-2 Christie's, London #33/R est:20000
£19000 $29830 €28500 Domestic interior with family eating and drinking (57x80cm-22x31in) bears sig. prov. 12-Dec-2 Sotheby's, London #139/R est:12000-18000

TILBORCH, Gillis van (attrib) (c.1625-1678) Flemish
£962 $1510 €1500 Reading (20x17cm-8x7in) panel. 14-Dec-2 Artcurial Briest, Paris #32/R

TILBURNE, Albert Roanoke (1887-1965) American
£932 $1500 €1398 Stalking tiger (76x53cm-30x21in) s. 20-Feb-3 Illustration House, New York #169/R est:2000-3000

TILEMAN-PETERSEN, Christian (1874-1926) Danish
£1282 $2026 €2000 Danemark, interieur de musee (55x55cm-22x22in) s.d. 18-Nov-2 Tajan, Paris #154/R est:2500-2800

TILGNER, Victor Oskar (1844-1896) Austrian
Sculpture
£2993 $4759 €4400 Portrait of the painter Alois Schonn (95cm-37in) s.i. bronze marble socle. 19-Mar-3 Neumeister, Munich #211/R est:2500

TILIPAU-KISTLER, Maria (1884-1963) Austrian
£324 $531 €450 Still life with alpine flowers and willow basket (19x21cm-7x8in) s. board. 5-Jun-3 Dorotheum, Salzburg #556/R
£385 $608 €600 Still life with alpine flowers (27x23cm-11x9in) s. board. 18-Nov-2 Dorotheum, Linz #304/R

TILLER, Lars (1924-1994) Norwegian
£645 $1044 €968 Composition (75x50cm-30x20in) s.d.62 panel. 3-Feb-3 Lilla Bukowskis, Stockholm #366 (S.KR 9000)

TILLERS, Imants (1950-) Australian
£2692 $4281 €4038 New litany (75x70cm-30x28in) canvasboard six prov. 4-Mar-3 Deutscher-Menzies, Melbourne #149/R est:6500-8500 (A.D 7000)
Works on paper
£13571 $20900 €20357 Pearls of wisdom (202x512cm-80x202in) synthetic polymer gouache oilstick on 126 canvas board. 8-Sep-2 Sotheby's, Melbourne #22/R est:30000-50000 (A.D 38000)
£15714 $24514 €23571 Words not yet spoken (227x212cm-89x83in) st.verso synthetic polymer paint gouache oilstick canvasboards 54. 11-Nov-2 Deutscher-Menzies, Melbourne #41/R est:20000-30000 (A.D 44000)

TILLMANS, Wolfgang (1968-) German
Photographs
£2000 $3340 €2900 Leaf (41x61cm-16x24in) s.i.d.05-95 num.1/3 verso col photo prov.lit. 24-Jun-3 Sotheby's, Olympia #41/R est:2000-3000

£2000 $3340 €2900 Rachel Auburn and son (40x30cm-16x12in) s.i.d.95 num.2/10 col photo prov.lit. 24-Jun-3 Sotheby's, Olympia #120/R est:2000-3000
£2000 $3340 €2900 Cerith, Michael Stefan, Gregorio (40x30cm-16x12in) s.i.d.98 num.3/10 verso col photo lit. 24-Jun-3 Sotheby's, Olympia #121/R est:2000-3000
£2244 $3522 €3500 Domenico Planet (41x30cm-16x12in) s.i.d.1992 verso cibachrome prov. 11-Dec-2 Artcurial Briest, Paris #793/R
£2400 $4008 €3480 Rats on trash bags (40x30cm-16x12in) s.i.d.11.95 num.3/10 verso col photo lit. 24-Jun-3 Sotheby's, Olympia #42/R est:2000-3000
£3600 $5544 €5400 Paula, typewriter, looking (61x51cm-24x20in) s.i.d.verso col photograph prov.lit. 22-Oct-2 Sotheby's, London #498/R est:2500-3500
£4000 $6160 €6000 Paul, New York (50x60cm-20x24in) s.i.d.1994 verso col coupler print prov.lit. 23-Oct-2 Christie's, London #245/R est:3500-4500
£4114 $6500 €6171 O.M (51x61cm-20x24in) c-print executed 1996 prov. 13-Nov-2 Sotheby's, New York #135/R est:5000-7000
£8000 $12320 €12000 Luts and Alex sitting in the trees (61x51cm-24x20in) s.i.d.Aug 92 num.2/3 col photograph prov.lit. 22-Oct-2 Sotheby's, London #312/R est:8000-12000
£12821 $20000 €19232 Still life, New York (203x137cm-80x54in) c-print on board executed 2001 prov.exhib. 11-Nov-2 Phillips, New York #46/R est:20000-30000
£15190 $24000 €22785 Suzanne and Lutz white dress, army skirt (61x81cm-24x32in) s.d.7.3.93 col coupler print prov.exhib.lit. 14-Nov-2 Christie's, Rockefeller NY #480/R est:15000-20000
£26582 $42000 €39873 After midnight (132x157cm-52x62in) s. chromogenic development print executed 1999 prov. 12-Nov-2 Phillips, New York #166/R est:20000-30000

TILLNER, Michal (1895-1975) ?
£299 $425 €449 Cottages (35x50cm-14x20in) painted c.1960. 26-Mar-2 SOGA, Bratislava #230/R (SL.K 19000)

TILLY, Vilhelm Eyvind (1860-1935) Danish
£2788 $4406 €4350 Dogs. Cats (50x61cm-20x24in) s. pair. 17-Nov-2 Herbette, Doullens #54/R

TILLYER, William (1938-) British
£5000 $7800 €7500 Untitled English landscape (76x91cm-30x36in) s.verso acrylic prov. 25-Mar-3 Bonhams, New Bond Street #147/R est:3000-5000

TILMAN, Mary (20th C) Belgian
£506 $790 €800 Vase de roses et corbeille de fruits (80x113cm-31x44in) s. 16-Sep-2 Horta, Bruxelles #391

TILMANS, Émile Henri (1888-1960) Belgian
£403 $648 €600 Foret en automne (50x60cm-20x24in) s. d.45 verso isorel. 23-Feb-3 Lesieur & Le Bars, Le Havre #144

TILSON, Joe (1928-) British
£305 $483 €458 Dionysos Ampelikos 3 (75x56cm-30x22in) s.d.1985 i.d.verso g/. 1-Apr-3 Stephan Welz, Johannesburg #420/R est:4000-6000 (SA.R 3800)
£1090 $1689 €1700 Sappho, fragment (30x40cm-12x16in) s.i.d.1979 verso panel. 4-Dec-2 Finarte, Milan #550/R
£1500 $2385 €2250 Dionysus prassinos, B (95x99cm-37x39in) 18-Mar-3 Bonhams, Knightsbridge #221 est:1000-1500
£4000 $6240 €6000 Labyrinth lyttos (117x96cm-46x38in) s.i.d.1981 i.verso oil wood relief. 17-Sep-2 Bonhams, Knightsbridge #146/R est:4000-6000

Works on paper
£500 $805 €750 Abstract composition (14x34cm-6x13in) mixed media. 14-Jan-3 Bonhams, Knightsbridge #59/R
£513 $805 €800 Composition (89x54cm-35x21in) s.i. collage stained wood. 16-Dec-2 Charbonneaux, Paris #298
£550 $858 €825 Persephone (28x27cm-11x11in) s.d.1986 chl acrylic collage. 27-Mar-3 Christie's, Kensington #663/R
£1000 $1580 €1500 Writing from the river Lu (55x74cm-22x29in) s.i.d.1972 pen ink gouache. 27-Nov-2 Sotheby's, Olympia #211/R est:600-800

TILTON, John Rollin (1833-1888) American
£1465 $2300 €2198 Lake Como (23x37cm-9x15in) s. i.verso board. 22-Nov-2 Skinner, Boston #133/R est:2000-3000

TIMENES, Frank (20th C) Norwegian
£393 $616 €590 Next time I meet a beautiful woman I'm going to sit down and think (92x73cm-36x29in) s. acrylic. 25-Nov-2 Blomqvist, Lysaker #1279 (N.KR 4500)

TIMLIN, William M (1893-1943) South African

Works on paper
£224 $350 €336 Muizenberg beach, looking towards Fishhoek (17x36cm-7x14in) s.d.20 pastel. 11-Nov-2 Stephan Welz, Johannesburg #280 (SA.R 3500)
£384 $600 €576 Leper ship (35x50cm-14x20in) s.i.d.1920 mixed media board. 11-Nov-2 Stephan Welz, Johannesburg #479 (SA.R 6000)
£416 $650 €624 Equestrian portrait (32x50cm-13x20in) s.i.d.1933 W/C over pencil. 11-Nov-2 Stephan Welz, Johannesburg #452/R (SA.R 6500)
£512 $799 €768 Harbour fairies (35x44cm-14x17in) s.i. W/C over red chk. 11-Nov-2 Stephan Welz, Johannesburg #451/R (SA.R 8000)

TIMMEL, Vito (1886-1949) Austrian
£1410 $2186 €2200 Fireworks (40x20cm-16x8in) s.d.39 tempera paper. 5-Dec-2 Stadion, Trieste #875
£18440 $29872 €26000 Vacanza veneziana (98x98cm-39x39in) s. exhib. 22-May-3 Stadion, Trieste #194/R est:25000-30000

Works on paper
£1773 $2872 €2500 Palazzo Ducale (38x38cm-15x15in) s.d.1944 mixed media. 22-May-3 Stadion, Trieste #408/R est:3000-4000
£3333 $5400 €4700 Gli alberi (59x59cm-23x23in) mm board. 22-May-3 Stadion, Trieste #407/R est:4000-6000

TIMMER, Hans (1912-) Dutch
£417 $688 €600 Flower still life with a painter's palette (100x80cm-39x31in) s.d.1950 s.stretcher. 1-Jul-3 Christie's, Amsterdam #290/R

TIMMERMAN, Eleanor C (20th C) American
£377 $600 €566 Portrait of a black man with a blue hat (61x46cm-24x18in) canvasboard. 22-Mar-3 New Orleans Auction, New Orleans #1080/R

TIMMERMANS, H (1858-1942) Belgian
£2128 $3447 €3000 Dame au repos dans un hamac (39x69cm-15x27in) 26-May-3 Amberes, Antwerp #83/R

TIMMERMANS, Henri (1858-1942) Belgian
£411 $642 €650 Pecheur fumant la pipe (30x22cm-12x9in) 16-Sep-2 Amberes, Antwerp #256
£892 $1391 €1400 L'amateur d'oiseaux (32x42cm-13x17in) s. panel. 11-Nov-2 Horta, Bruxelles #36
£1154 $1788 €1800 Quatre joueurs aux cartes dans un interieur (30x39cm-12x15in) s. panel. 3-Dec-2 Campo & Campo, Antwerp #285/R est:2000-3000

TIMMERMANS, Jean (1899-1986) Belgian
£425 $684 €650 Champ de ble (80x100cm-31x39in) s. 20-Jan-3 Horta, Bruxelles #419
£4403 $6824 €7000 Sitting woman (100x80cm-39x31in) s.d.21. 5-Oct-2 De Vuyst, Lokeren #464/R est:7500-8500

Works on paper
£316 $494 €500 Jeune fille redigeant (46x58cm-18x23in) s. W/C. 16-Sep-2 Horta, Bruxelles #4
£327 $526 €500 Barque de pecheur a Ibiza (52x72cm-20x28in) s. W/C. 20-Jan-3 Horta, Bruxelles #420

TIMMERMANS, Louis (1846-1910) French
£714 $1086 €1100 At sea (72x126cm-28x50in) s. 5-Jul-2 Weidler, Nurnberg #8743/R
£886 $1400 €1400 Rochers sur la cote (27x41cm-11x16in) s. 1-Dec-2 Peron, Melun #97
£1419 $2200 €2129 Sailing ships docked at a port (38x46cm-15x18in) s. panel. 2-Oct-2 Christie's, Rockefeller NY #802/R est:2500-3500
£2817 $4535 €4000 La Chapelle, la Tour Vauban et barques sous voiles au mouillage a Camaret (38x55cm-15x22in) s. 11-May-3 Thierry & Lannon, Brest #232/R est:4000-4500

Works on paper
£521 $849 €750 Voilier rentrant au port (21x32cm-8x13in) s. W/C. 19-Jul-3 Thierry & Lannon, Brest #82
£878 $1370 €1300 Ports en Bretagne. Port en Normandie. s. W/C set of 3. 27-Mar-3 Maigret, Paris #305

TIMMERS, Adriaan (1886-1952) Dutch
£360 $598 €540 Still life of books, a pipe and candlestick (45x55cm-18x22in) s.d.1940. 10-Jun-3 Bonhams, Knightsbridge #36/R

TIMMINS, William (20th C) American
Works on paper
£419 $650 €629 Cutting edge (20x30cm-8x12in) s. W/C. 7-Dec-2 Harvey Clar, Oakland #1194

TIMOFEEV, Vasilii Timofeevich (1835-1914) Russian
Works on paper
£327 $536 €500 Girl (43x37cm-17x15in) chl. 9-Feb-3 Bukowskis, Helsinki #433/R

TINDLE, David (1932-) British
£320 $522 €464 Small girl standing (20x15cm-8x6in) board. 15-Jul-3 Bonhams, Knightsbridge #156
£480 $773 €720 Egg and cake (16x23cm-6x9in) s.d.66 verso board prov. 14-Jan-3 Bonhams, Knightsbridge #156
£900 $1395 €1350 Sea at Abroath (41x56cm-16x22in) s.d.57 s.i.d.verso board. 4-Dec-2 Christie's, Kensington #452/R
£950 $1473 €1425 Two eggs (20x25cm-8x10in) s.d.1955 s.d.verso board. 4-Dec-2 Christie's, Kensington #595/R
£1800 $2970 €2610 Arbroath harbour (65x91cm-26x36in) s.d.1957 board. 3-Jul-3 Christie's, Kensington #707/R est:1500-2000
£2400 $3696 €3600 Heavy frost (25x31cm-10x12in) init. s.i.d.1980 verso acrylic board. 5-Sep-2 Christie's, Kensington #698/R est:2000-3000
Works on paper
£250 $418 €363 Girl with cat (16x15cm-6x6in) init. W/C board. 17-Jun-3 Bonhams, Knightsbridge #133/R
£600 $1002 €870 East Anglian harbour scene (33x48cm-13x19in) s.d.1957 W/C. 17-Jun-3 Gildings, Market Harborough #445

TING, Walasse (1929-1998) Chinese
£449 $696 €700 Two parrots (21x28cm-8x11in) st.sig. acrylic paper. 7-Dec-2 De Vuyst, Lokeren #321
£500 $774 €750 Composition (33x41cm-13x16in) s.verso. 4-Dec-2 Kunsthallen, Copenhagen #31/R (D.KR 5800)
£1144 $1910 €1659 Japanese women with parrots and flowers (37x49cm-15x19in) paper on canvas. 17-Jun-3 Rasmussen, Copenhagen #134/R est:10000-12000 (D.KR 12000)
£1493 $2373 €2240 Composition (50x70cm-20x28in) mono. acrylic paper on canvas. 29-Apr-3 Kunsthallen, Copenhagen #16/R est:18000 (D.KR 16000)
£1554 $2564 €2253 Black abstraction (77x74cm-30x29in) s.d.1961 verso mixed media canvas. 6-Jul-3 Christie's, Hong Kong #170/R est:30000-60000 (HK.D 20000)
£4570 $7267 €6855 Catch me a grasshopper (102x127cm-40x50in) s.d.79 verso. 26-Feb-3 Kunsthallen, Copenhagen #98/R est:30000 (D.KR 50000)
£5815 $9711 €8432 Hot love - woman with flowers (75x100cm-30x39in) s.d.77 verso. 17-Jun-3 Rasmussen, Copenhagen #37/R est:25000-30000 (D.KR 61000)
Works on paper
£316 $500 €500 Nu couche a la coupe de fruits (12x17cm-5x7in) s.d.99 verso mixed media. 26-Nov-2 Palais de Beaux Arts, Brussels #410
£316 $500 €500 Nu allonge (12x17cm-5x7in) s.d.99 verso mixed media. 26-Nov-2 Palais de Beaux Arts, Brussels #411
£962 $1500 €1443 Two faces and two parrots (33x48cm-13x19in) W/C. 20-Sep-2 Du Mouchelle, Detroit #87/R est:1500-2000
£2885 $4471 €4500 Lady with flowers in her hair (44x56cm-17x22in) brush ink W/C. 3-Dec-2 Christie's, Amsterdam #179/R est:2000-3000
£2903 $4500 €4355 Untitled (69x108cm-27x43in) s. gouache W/C. 26-Sep-2 Christie's, Rockefeller NY #828/R est:3000-5000
£4808 $7452 €7500 Bulb field (123x243cm-48x96in) gouache. 3-Dec-2 Christie's, Amsterdam #293/R est:8000-12000
£7595 $12000 €12000 Nude with cat (95x176cm-37x69in) artist st. gouache. 26-Nov-2 Sotheby's, Amsterdam #237/R est:4500-5500

TINGQUA (fl.1840-1870) Chinese
Miniatures
£7895 $12000 €11843 Portrait of William S S Russell (10x8cm-4x3in) i.verso prov. 17-Aug-2 North East Auctions, Portsmouth #607/R est:5000-8000
Works on paper
£2632 $4000 €3948 Boca Tigris on the Pearl River (18x28cm-7x11in) gouache exec.c.1850 painted with studio. 17-Aug-2 North East Auctions, Portsmouth #880/R est:4000-6000
£4605 $7000 €6908 View of Hong Kong island (18x28cm-7x11in) gouache painted with studio exec.c.1845. 17-Aug-2 North East Auctions, Portsmouth #778/R est:8000-12000

TINGUELY, Jean (1925-1991) Swiss
£700 $1085 €1050 Sans titre (30x30cm-12x12in) acrylic gold silver paint on card prov. 5-Dec-2 Christie's, Kensington #226/R
£4151 $6392 €6600 O.T. (30x42cm-12x17in) s. acrylic collage ink paper prov. 26-Oct-2 Cornette de St.Cyr, Paris #48/R
Sculpture
£14103 $21859 €22000 Ecrevisse (40x65x17cm-16x26x7in) s.i.d.1962 verso relief sculpture aluminium board motor masonite. 3-Dec-2 Lempertz, Koln #470/R est:22000-25000
£25000 $41000 €37500 Untitled (207x189x100cm-81x74x39in) floor lamp iron stand electric bulbs motor prov.exhib.lit. 6-Feb-3 Christie's, London #669/R est:15000-20000
Works on paper
£316 $500 €500 Composition with balls (25x18cm-10x7in) s. mixed media. 30-Nov-2 Arnold, Frankfurt #558/R
£1088 $1731 €1600 Composition (32x21cm-13x8in) s. gouache W/C pastel chk. 28-Feb-3 Joron-Derem, Paris #44/R
£1154 $1788 €1800 Lieber jan (21x27cm-8x11in) ball point pen felt pen executed c.1968-69 prov. 3-Dec-2 Christie's, Amsterdam #156/R est:1500-2000
£1603 $2484 €2500 Dear Jan (27x21cm-11x8in) s.d.2 Dec 1968 mixed media prov. 3-Dec-2 Christie's, Amsterdam #152/R est:1500-2000
£1603 $2484 €2500 Cher M Jan (24x38cm-9x15in) i. ball point pen col pencil executed 1969 prov. 3-Dec-2 Christie's, Amsterdam #155/R est:2000-3000
£1719 $2871 €2493 Chaos I - Columbus Indiana (22x28cm-9x11in) s. collage gouache offset print lit. 24-Jun-3 Koller, Zurich #68/R est:4000-6000 (S.FR 3800)
£2153 $3401 €3100 Sans titre (30x22cm-12x9in) s.i.d.16 VI 72 pastel felt ballpoint pen collage. 28-Apr-3 Cornette de St.Cyr, Paris #523/R est:1500-2000
£2318 $3778 €3500 Composition (18x32cm-7x13in) s.d.1982 W/C wax crayon collage. 3-Feb-3 Cornette de St.Cyr, Paris #530/R
£2449 $3894 €3600 Correspondance (28x38cm-11x15in) s.i.d.1966 ink W/C pastel dr. 26-Feb-3 Artcurial Briest, Paris #417/R est:2500-3000
£3019 $4649 €4800 Cher Claude Parent: oublie pas tout a fait le labyrinthe dynamique, alias Latour Lunatour (33x49cm-13x19in) s.d.64 ink felt-tip pen collage. 26-Oct-2 Cornette de St.Cyr, Paris #52/R
£3930 $6170 €5895 Dear Hans (29x42cm-11x17in) s.d.1987 mixed media collage. 25-Nov-2 Sotheby's, Zurich #160/R est:9000-12000 (S.FR 9000)
£3930 $6170 €5895 Etude pour une machine (22x38cm-9x15in) s.d.1977 mixed media board prov. 23-Nov-2 Burkhard, Luzern #218/R est:10000-14000 (S.FR 9000)
£5046 $7871 €7569 Pour Joakim (44x43cm-17x17in) s.i.d.nov.71 mixed media. 5-Nov-2 Bukowskis, Stockholm #309/R est:40000-50000 (S.KR 72000)
£6481 $10435 €9397 La transparence (37x41cm-15x16in) s.d.88 W/C inc col pencil. 9-May-3 Dobiaschofsky, Bern #260/R est:12000 (S.FR 14000)

TINMAN, Dorothy (20th C) British
£250 $398 €375 Teelin, Donegal (35x45cm-14x18in) s.d.2003 verso. 5-Mar-3 John Ross, Belfast #129
£350 $557 €525 Bog pool, Bluestacks (50x40cm-20x16in) s.d.2002 verso. 5-Mar-3 John Ross, Belfast #33

TINSLEY, Barry (20th C) American
£748 $1100 €1122 Silver blade. 23-Jun-2 Susanin's, Chicago #5133/R

TINTORE, Simone del (1630-1708) Italian
£54225 $87303 €77000 Portrait of Domenico Bartoli (72x122cm-28x48in) i. prov. 11-May-3 Finarte, Venice #61/R est:110000-140000

TINTORE, Simone del (attrib) (1630-1708) Italian
£6289 $9686 €10000 Still life with birds and basket with vegetables (74x61cm-29x24in) 23-Oct-2 Finarte, Rome #506/R
£8108 $12649 €12000 Still life with grapes and fruit (46x76cm-18x30in) one of pair. 27-Mar-3 Dorotheum, Vienna #79/R est:12000-15000

TINTORETTO, Domenico (1560-1635) Italian
£21605 $35000 €32408 Portrait of a gentleman, said to be Vincenzo Morosini (120x87cm-47x34in) prov. 24-Jan-3 Christie's, Rockefeller NY #81/R est:25000-35000
£22000 $36740 €31900 Portrait of a Venetian Senator in office robes, by a green curtain, landscape beyond (147x129cm-58x51in) 9-Jul-3 Christie's, London #108/R est:20000-30000
£24138 $38138 €35000 Portrait of gentleman (93x76cm-37x30in) lit. 5-Apr-3 Finarte Semenzato, Milan #45/R est:45000
£27027 $42162 €40000 Coronation of the Virgin (141x115cm-56x45in) prov. 27-Mar-3 Dorotheum, Vienna #43/R est:20000-30000
£28963 $47500 €43445 Portrait of a Venetian Senator (128x108cm-50x43in) prov.exhib.lit. 29-May-3 Sotheby's, New York #53/R est:30000-40000

TINTORETTO, Domenico (style) (1560-1635) Italian
£15000 $25050 €21750 Portrait of a gentleman in a red shirt and black waistcoat (68x57cm-27x22in) 11-Jul-3 Christie's, Kensington #191/R est:3000-5000

TINTORETTO, Jacopo (1518-1594) Italian
£10563 $17007 €15000 Portrait of Carlo cappello (115x86cm-45x34in) i. 11-May-3 Finarte, Venice #62/R est:20000
£20638 $32196 €30957 Venus and Amor (118x96cm-46x38in) 11-Sep-2 Kieselbach, Budapest #195/R (H.F 8000000)
£75472 $116981 €120000 Portrait of Doge Girolamo Priuli (100x81cm-39x32in) prov.lit. 7-Oct-2 Ansorena, Madrid #2/R est:120000
£100000 $167000 €145000 The last supper (121x216cm-48x85in) prov.lit. 10-Jul-3 Sotheby's, London #34/R est:100000-150000

TINTORETTO, Jacopo (attrib) (1518-1594) Italian
£3774 $5849 €6000 Scourging of Christ (89x63cm-35x25in) 2-Oct-2 Dorotheum, Vienna #257/R est:5800-7000

TINTORETTO, Jacopo (studio) (1518-1594) Italian
£23000 $38410 €33350 Portrait of a nobleman in coat trimmed with ermine, seated at his desk with his secretary (132x120cm-52x47in) prov. 9-Jul-3 Christie's, London #109/R est:15000-20000

TINTORETTO, Jacopo (style) (1518-1594) Italian
£12025 $19480 €17436 Portrait of man (52x42cm-20x17in) prov. 26-May-3 Bukowskis, Stockholm #383/R est:40000-50000 (S.KR 155000)

TIPARY, Dezso (1887-?) Hungarian
£1006 $1569 €1509 By the road (95x98cm-37x39in) s.d.1920. 11-Apr-3 Kieselbach, Budapest #168/R est:240000-360000 (H.F 360000)
Works on paper
£774 $1207 €1161 Estergom (43x29cm-17x11in) s. pastel. 11-Sep-2 Kieselbach, Budapest #60/R (H.F 300000)
£914 $1417 €1325 Woman seated (60x43cm-24x17in) s.d.1926 pastel. 9-Dec-2 Mu Terem Galeria, Budapest #179/R est:320000 (H.F 340000)
£1022 $1584 €1482 View of the cathedral in Esztergom from the Danube (29x43cm-11x17in) s.d.1923 Indian ink W/C. 9-Dec-2 Mu Terem Galeria, Budapest #14/R est:140000 (H.F 380000)

TIPOFF, P (19/20th C) Russian
Works on paper
£1026 $1600 €1539 Polish soldier on horseback (48x38cm-19x15in) W/C. 20-Sep-2 Du Mouchelle, Detroit #2023/R est:1000-1500

TIPPETT, William Vivian (1833-1910) British
£480 $754 €720 Cattle grazing with farmyard beyond (32x38cm-13x15in) s. 16-Dec-2 Bonhams, Bury St Edmunds #530
£600 $924 €900 Haymaking (34x52cm-13x20in) s.d.90. 22-Oct-2 Bonhams, Bath #274
£620 $955 €930 Cattle watering by a stone bridge (51x75cm-20x30in) s.d.88. 22-Oct-2 Bonhams, Bath #275
£720 $1109 €1080 River landscape with cattle watering (43x70cm-17x28in) s.d.83. 22-Oct-2 Bonhams, Bath #273

TIRATELLI, Aurelio (1842-1900) Italian
£15000 $25050 €22500 Country market (67x136cm-26x54in) s. 18-Jun-3 Christie's, Kensington #151/R est:15000-20000

TIRELLI, Marco (1956-) Italian
£915 $1520 €1300 Untitled (52x37cm-20x15in) s.i.studio st.verso panel. 10-Jun-3 Finarte Semenzato, Milan #352/R est:1200-1400
£1575 $2458 €2300 Untitled (100x72cm-39x28in) s.i.d.1990 verso paper on canvas. 10-Apr-3 Finarte Semenzato, Rome #298/R

TIREN, Johan (1853-1911) Swedish
£1414 $2319 €2050 Summer landscape with Laplanders (43x62cm-17x24in) mono. panel. 4-Jun-3 AB Stockholms Auktionsverk #2234/R est:25000-30000 (S.KR 18000)
£2221 $3597 €3332 Wolves (73x60cm-29x24in) s. panel. 3-Feb-3 Lilla Bukowskis, Stockholm #237 est:20000-25000 (S.KR 31000)
Works on paper
£1629 $2639 €2362 Carl Larsson and family (66x56cm-26x22in) init. W/C. 26-May-3 Bukowskis, Stockholm #164/R est:25000-30000 (S.KR 21000)
£5532 $8574 €8298 Laplander family outside their tent (77x131cm-30x52in) s. pastel. 3-Dec-2 Bukowskis, Stockholm #91/R est:60000-70000 (S.KR 78000)
£16312 $25284 €24468 Mountain landscape with Laplander woman and man with dog (91x78cm-36x31in) s.d.88 W/C paper on canvas. 4-Dec-2 AB Stockholms Auktionsverk #1558/R est:75000-100000 (S.KR 230000)

TIREN, Karl (1869-1955) Swedish
£315 $498 €473 Mountain landscape from Lapporten, autumn (53x126cm-21x50in) indis.sig.d.1925 panel. 16-Nov-2 Crafoord, Lund #63 (S.KR 4500)

TIREN, Nils (1885-1935) Swedish
£851 $1345 €1277 Winter landscape with hare in hiding (70x100cm-28x39in) s.d.1915. 2-Dec-2 Rasmussen, Copenhagen #1555/R (D.KR 10000)
£892 $1356 €1338 Late winter landscape with hare (63x80cm-25x31in) s.d.1908 prov. 16-Aug-2 Lilla Bukowskis, Stockholm #178 (S.KR 13000)

TIRINNANZI, Nino (1923-) Italian
£1149 $1792 €1700 Tuscan farm (30x40cm-12x16in) s. cardboard on canvas. 28-Mar-3 Farsetti, Prato #639/R
£1923 $3038 €3000 Seascape (50x70cm-20x28in) s.d.964. 15-Nov-2 Farsetti, Prato #505/R
£1987 $3120 €3100 Road with houses (40x60cm-16x24in) s. masonite. 16-Dec-2 Pandolfini, Florence #334/R
Works on paper
£833 $1317 €1300 Poggio Square in Caiano (50x74cm-20x29in) s.d.1966 mixed media paper on board. 15-Nov-2 Farsetti, Prato #420

TIRVERT, Eugène (1881-1948) French
£1154 $1812 €1800 Neige a Blainville (55x46cm-22x18in) s. 15-Dec-2 Lombrail & Teucquam, Paris #19/R

TISCHBEIN, Anton (1730-1804) German
Works on paper
£348 $550 €550 The sacrifice of Iphigenia (17x20cm-7x8in) s.i. pen wash. 29-Nov-2 Bassenge, Berlin #5772/R

TISCHBEIN, Anton (attrib) (1730-1804) German
£2201 $3390 €3500 Une prisonniere presentee au sultan (37x47cm-15x19in) 25-Oct-2 Tajan, Paris #96/R est:3000-4000

TISCHBEIN, Christian Wilhelm (1751-1824) German
Works on paper
£1489 $2487 €2100 Fantaisie architecturale (26x39cm-10x15in) bears sig.i. pen black ink W/C gouache. 20-Jun-3 Rieunier, Paris #9/R est:2000-3000

TISCHBEIN, Jakob Heinrich (attrib) (1760-1804) German
£1419 $2086 €2200 Portrait of young mother with son holding book (88x68cm-35x27in) 20-Jun-2 Dr Fritz Nagel, Stuttgart #740/R est:3000

TISCHBEIN, Johann Friedrich August (1750-1812) German
£1233 $1923 €1800 Elegant woman (69x48cm-27x19in) s.d. oval. 11-Apr-3 Winterberg, Heidelberg #323/R est:2800

TISCHBEIN, Johann Friedrich August (attrib) (1750-1812) German
£897 $1391 €1400 Portrait of youthful lady (83x64cm-33x25in) lit. 7-Dec-2 Bergmann, Erlangen #760/R
£2027 $3162 €3000 Portrait of lady in red fur trimmed dress (58x45cm-23x18in) prov. one of pair. 27-Mar-3 Dorotheum, Vienna #424/R est:3000-5000
£2027 $3162 €3000 Portrait of lady in green dress (58x45cm-23x18in) prov. one of pair. 27-Mar-3 Dorotheum, Vienna #425/R est:3000-5000
Works on paper
£755 $1170 €1200 Probably Herzogin Anna Amalie von Sachsen-Weimar Eisenach (42x29cm-17x11in) wash chk brush htd white. 1-Oct-2 Dorotheum, Vienna #17/R

TISCHBEIN, Johann Heinrich (elder) (1722-1789) German
£28000 $43400 €42000 The muse of music, probably Terpsichore (56x46cm-22x18in) s.i.1759. 31-Oct-2 Sotheby's, Olympia #168/R est:6000-8000
Works on paper
£285 $450 €450 Warrior saying farewell to his family (16x20cm-6x8in) pen wash. 29-Nov-2 Bassenge, Berlin #5773/R
£538 $850 €850 Thusnelda receiving Hermann after the victory (19x28cm-7x11in) i. pen wash pen. 29-Nov-2 Bassenge, Berlin #5774

TISCHBEIN, Johann Heinrich Wilhelm (1751-1829) German
Works on paper
£617 $1000 €926 Cows in a flooded meadow at sunset, with an army on a hill beyond (21x34cm-8x13in) black chk pen grey ink grey wash W/C. 22-Jan-3 Christie's, Rockefeller NY #147/R

£949 $1500 €1500 Figure studies (21x34cm-8x13in) pen. 29-Nov-2 Bassenge, Berlin #5776 est:1800
£1050 $1700 €1575 Hunting scenes (21x33cm-8x13in) black chk pen brown ink W/C four. 22-Jan-3 Christie's, Rockefeller NY #161/R est:3000-5000
£1111 $1800 €1667 Deerhound following a scent, with stag escaping into a wood (21x35cm-8x14in) black chk pen brown ink bodycol. 22-Jan-3 Christie's, Rockefeller NY #158/R est:1000-1500
£1111 $1800 €1667 Polyphemus hurling a rock at Acis and Galatea (80x54cm-31x21in) black chk pen brown ink wash and four drs after Annibale Carracci. 22-Jan-3 Christie's, Rockefeller NY #189/R est:2000-3000
£1173 $1900 €1760 Traveller on a white horse, a mountain landscape beyond (33x21cm-13x8in) black chk brown ink col wash W/C. 22-Jan-3 Christie's, Rockefeller NY #207/R est:3000-5000
£1358 $2200 €2037 Goose and gander watching their goslings hatch in a barn (19x32cm-7x13in) black chk pen brown ink brown wash W/C. 22-Jan-3 Christie's, Rockefeller NY #143/R est:3000-5000
£1358 $2200 €2037 Pack of dogs cornering a wild boar in dense woodland (50x66cm-20x26in) black chk pen brown ink W/C. 22-Jan-3 Christie's, Rockefeller NY #162/R est:4000-6000
£1605 $2600 €2408 Lion and fox at the mouth of a cave approached by geese (55x43cm-22x17in) black chk pen brown ink W/C. 22-Jan-3 Christie's, Rockefeller NY #180/R est:5000-7000
£1852 $3000 €2778 Cats and kittens playing at the foot of a tree (23x38cm-9x15in) black chk pen brown ink W/C. 22-Jan-3 Christie's, Rockefeller NY #167/R est:1500-2000
£1975 $3200 €2963 River landscape with stork and mallard. Mallards among rushes (20x33cm-8x13in) black chk pen brown ink grey wash W/C pair. 22-Jan-3 Christie's, Rockefeller NY #146/R est:3000-5000
£1975 $3200 €2963 Wild boar and sow beneath an oak tree (40x33cm-16x13in) black chk pen brown ink brown wash W/C. 22-Jan-3 Christie's, Rockefeller NY #154/R est:2000-3000
£1975 $3200 €2963 Wild boar chasing fireflies, with a fairy seated on a rock beyond. black chk pen col ink album sold with drs in a further album. 22-Jan-3 Christie's, Rockefeller NY #155/R est:5000-7000
£1975 $3200 €2963 Family of monkeys drinking from a dish in a jungle landscape (20x33cm-8x13in) black chk pen grey ink grey wash W/C. 22-Jan-3 Christie's, Rockefeller NY #168/R est:3000-5000
£1975 $3200 €2963 Scenes of peasant life (21x33cm-8x13in) two d.1807 seven d.1809 black chk pen brown ink wash eight. 22-Jan-3 Christie's, Rockefeller NY #209/R est:5000-7000
£2161 $3500 €3242 Swans chasing a fox. Goose, gander and goslings surprised by foxes (20x33cm-8x13in) black chk pen brown ink brown wash W/C pair. 22-Jan-3 Christie's, Rockefeller NY #178/R est:4000-6000
£2346 $3800 €3519 Geese fighting in a landscape (20x33cm-8x13in) black chk pen brown ink grey wash W/C. 22-Jan-3 Christie's, Rockefeller NY #142/R est:2000-3000
£2469 $4000 €3704 Mastiff, lurcher and dachshund in an extensive landscape (21x32cm-8x13in) black chk pen brown ink W/C sold with two drs. 22-Jan-3 Christie's, Rockefeller NY #159/R est:1500-2000
£2469 $4000 €3704 Hunted animals taking revenge (41x81cm-16x32in) black chk pen brown ink W/C two joined sheets after Paulus Potter. 22-Jan-3 Christie's, Rockefeller NY #163/R est:8000-12000
£2469 $4000 €3704 Reynard the fox and Braun the bear searching for honey (16x25cm-6x10in) black chk pen brown ink W/C. 22-Jan-3 Christie's, Rockefeller NY #182/R est:1500-2000
£2469 $4000 €3704 Four humours. one oil on paper two pen grey ink three. 22-Jan-3 Christie's, Rockefeller NY #216/R est:5000-7000
£2593 $4200 €3890 Peacock and peahen on a garden wall (32x20cm-13x8in) black chk pen brown ink brown wash W/C. 22-Jan-3 Christie's, Rockefeller NY #140/R est:2000-3000
£2778 $4500 €4167 Sparrowhawks in an oak tree. Tawny owls in an oak tree (20x32cm-8x13in) black chk pen brown ink brown wash W/C pair. 22-Jan-3 Christie's, Rockefeller NY #139/R est:3000-5000
£2778 $4500 €4167 Mastiff, lurcher and other dogs. Dog head studies (21x34cm-8x13in) i.d.1806 black chk pen brown ink W/C bodycol pair. 22-Jan-3 Christie's, Rockefeller NY #157/R est:1500-2000
£2778 $4500 €4167 Head of a wolf (45x34cm-18x13in) black chk pen brown ink W/C. 22-Jan-3 Christie's, Rockefeller NY #173/R est:2500-3500
£2778 $4500 €4167 Head of a lynx, and fox and other animal studies. black chk pen brown ink W/C thirteen. 22-Jan-3 Christie's, Rockefeller NY #174/R est:3000-5000
£2778 $4500 €4167 Figures in landscapes and farmyard scenes. one i.d.1810 four d.1816 black chk pen brown ink col wash seven. 22-Jan-3 Christie's, Rockefeller NY #208/R est:4000-6000
£2963 $4800 €4445 Geese and swans. Ostriches. Cat chasing birds. Sea fish. Butterflies (20x32cm-8x13in) two d.1807 black chk pen brown ink col wash W/C five. 22-Jan-3 Christie's, Rockefeller NY #145/R est:3000-5000
£2963 $4800 €4445 Wild boar hidden in dense woodland (20x32cm-8x13in) black chk pen brown ink W/C. 22-Jan-3 Christie's, Rockefeller NY #153/R est:2000-4000
£3086 $5000 €4629 Four zebras in a rocky landscape (32x40cm-13x16in) black chk pen brown ink col wash W/C. 22-Jan-3 Christie's, Rockefeller NY #136/R est:5000-7000
£3086 $5000 €4629 Solitary oak tree, with doe and stag grazing (26x20cm-10x8in) black chk pen grey ink W/C. 22-Jan-3 Christie's, Rockefeller NY #204/R est:2000-3000
£3395 $5500 €5093 Four lynxes in a mossy cave (32x40cm-13x16in) black chk pen brown ink W/C. 22-Jan-3 Christie's, Rockefeller NY #132/R est:6000-8000
£3395 $5500 €5093 Fox lying in wait, with sow and her farrow beyond (33x42cm-13x17in) black chk pen brown ink brown wash W/C. 22-Jan-3 Christie's, Rockefeller NY #152/R est:4000-6000
£3395 $5500 €5093 Scenes from Michelangelo's frescos for the Sistine Chapel. black chk grey ink W/C nine. 22-Jan-3 Christie's, Rockefeller NY #191/R est:6000-8000
£3704 $6000 €5556 Geese with sheep, on a shore, ducks with ducklings and ducks by a lake (20x35cm-8x14in) d.1807 black chk pen brown ink col wash W/C four. 22-Jan-3 Christie's, Rockefeller NY #141/R est:4000-6000
£3704 $6000 €5556 Scenes with sheep and goats. black chk pen brown ink col wash W/C six. 22-Jan-3 Christie's, Rockefeller NY #148/R est:3000-5000
£4013 $6500 €6020 Sow with farrow and a hen with chicks. Fox in wait, a sow and farrow beyond (21x33cm-8x13in) black chk pen brown ink brown wash W/C pair. 22-Jan-3 Christie's, Rockefeller NY #151/R est:4000-6000
£4013 $6500 €6020 Lion and fox at the mouth of a cave approached by geese (43x34cm-17x13in) black chk pen brown ink W/C. 22-Jan-3 Christie's, Rockefeller NY #179/R est:5000-7000
£4321 $7000 €6482 Great cats, tigers, lion, leopard, cheetah, lynx, ocelot and civet cat (34x60cm-13x24in) i.d.11 Martz 1805 black chk pen brown ink grey wash. 22-Jan-3 Christie's, Rockefeller NY #130/R est:8000-12000
£4321 $7000 €6482 Head of an ostrich, an eagle and scenes with various other birds. three d.1807 one d.1806 black chk pen brown ink wash nine. 22-Jan-3 Christie's, Rockefeller NY #144/R est:4000-6000
£4321 $7000 €6482 Wild boat with piglets under an oak tree (32x40cm-13x16in) black chk pen brown ink brown wash W/C. 22-Jan-3 Christie's, Rockefeller NY #150/R est:4000-6000
£4321 $7000 €6482 Various scenes with figures and animals and head studies of Christ. one i.d.1812 five d.1808 black chk pen brown ink wash fifteen. 22-Jan-3 Christie's, Rockefeller NY #210/R est:6000-8000
£4630 $7500 €6945 View of a lions head and other animals (28x39cm-11x15in) col chk sixteen. 22-Jan-3 Christie's, Rockefeller NY #172/R est:3000-5000
£4630 $7500 €6945 Animal studies. black chk pen brown ink col wash W/C twelve. 22-Jan-3 Christie's, Rockefeller NY #175/R est:4000-6000
£4630 $7500 €6945 Trees in various landscapes. black chk pen brown ink brown wash W/C nine. 22-Jan-3 Christie's, Rockefeller NY #206/R est:4000-6000
£4938 $8000 €7407 Various dog breeds in landscapes and head of a bulldog and mastiff (20x31cm-8x12in) black chk pen brown ink brown wash six. 22-Jan-3 Christie's, Rockefeller NY #160/R est:3000-5000
£4938 $8000 €7407 Blasted pear tree bound with ropes, one branch laden with fruit (20x32cm-8x13in) black chk pen brown ink grey wash W/C. 22-Jan-3 Christie's, Rockefeller NY #202/R est:2000-3000
£5864 $9500 €8796 Scene from Wilhem Tischbeins Idyllen. black chk pen brown ink grey wash four sold with an etching. 22-Jan-3 Christie's, Rockefeller NY #212/R est:4000-6000
£6173 $10000 €9260 Girl leading a pig on a leash, in a classical landscape (21x33cm-8x13in) black chk pen brown ink W/C. 22-Jan-3 Christie's, Rockefeller NY #156/R est:2000-3000
£6173 $10000 €9260 Various landscapes. i.d.1818 black chk pen col ink W/C nine. 22-Jan-3 Christie's, Rockefeller NY #205/R est:7000-10000
£6790 $11000 €10185 Marmots in an alpine landscape (32x40cm-13x16in) black chk pen brown ink col wash W/C. 22-Jan-3 Christie's, Rockefeller NY #138/R est:5000-8000
£6790 $11000 €10185 Head studies (38x32cm-15x13in) col chk brown wash W/C fifteen. 22-Jan-3 Christie's, Rockefeller NY #194/R est:4000-6000

£6790 $11000 €10185 Scenes from Goethe's Wilhelm Tischbeins Idyllen. black chk pen brown ink grey wash W/C three. 22-Jan-3 Christie's, Rockefeller NY #213/R est:5000-7000

£7407 $12000 €11111 Reynard the fox led to the gibbet by Braun the bear and other animals (24x38cm-9x15in) black chk pen brown ink W/C. 22-Jan-3 Christie's, Rockefeller NY #183/R est:3000-5000

£8025 $13000 €12038 Animal portraits. black chk pen brown ink twenty-four. 22-Jan-3 Christie's, Rockefeller NY #176/R est:5000-7000

£8025 $13000 €12038 Scenes from Wilhelm Tischbeins Idyllen. black chk pen grey ink W/C twelve. 22-Jan-3 Christie's, Rockefeller NY #214/R est:10000-15000

£8642 $14000 €12963 Beavers building a dam, a waterfall beyond (33x40cm-13x16in) black chk pen brown ink wash W/C. 22-Jan-3 Christie's, Rockefeller NY #137/R est:5000-7000

£10494 $17000 €15741 Sun shining through clouds onto a meadow with a river landscape (28x44cm-11x17in) i.d.1809 black chk pen brown ink col wash W/C. 22-Jan-3 Christie's, Rockefeller NY #201/R est:5000-7000

£10494 $17000 €15741 Oak tree, cypress and Roman pine growing together (59x56cm-23x22in) black chk pen brown ink brown wash W/C sold with manuscripts. 22-Jan-3 Christie's, Rockefeller NY #211/R est:2000-4000

£11111 $18000 €16667 Prehistoric stone circle on a mound, extensive landscape beyond (20x32cm-8x13in) black chk pen brown ink brown wash sold with a dr. 22-Jan-3 Christie's, Rockefeller NY #197/R est:7000-10000

£11111 $18000 €16667 Scenes from Goethe's Wilhelm Tischbeins Idyllen. black chk pen brown ink col wash W/C. 22-Jan-3 Christie's, Rockefeller NY #215/R est:6000-8000

£11111 $18000 €16667 Strength of man. i. black chk brown ink brown wash eleven album. 22-Jan-3 Christie's, Rockefeller NY #217/R est:6000-8000

£11111 $18000 €16667 Images and prose on an Anacreontic theme (25x21cm-10x8in) i. black chk pen grey ink W/C seven album. 22-Jan-3 Christie's, Rockefeller NY #224/R est:7000-10000

£11728 $19000 €17592 Heads of Homer and others in the Trojan War (49x38cm-19x15in) i. black chk pen brown ink W/C eight album. 22-Jan-3 Christie's, Rockefeller NY #226/R est:25000-35000

£14815 $24000 €22223 Prehistoric dolmen on a rocky mound, horses beyond (32x41cm-13x16in) black chk pen brown ink col wash W/C. 22-Jan-3 Christie's, Rockefeller NY #200/R est:6000-8000

£14815 $24000 €22223 Dolmen by edge of a wood, a rocky spring and trees in landscapes. black chk pen brown ink brown wash W/C six. 22-Jan-3 Christie's, Rockefeller NY #203/R est:7000-10000

£16049 $26000 €24074 Head of a lion (57x68cm-22x27in) black chk pen col ink brown wash pair. 22-Jan-3 Christie's, Rockefeller NY #169/R est:25000-35000

£16049 $26000 €24074 Anacreontic prose. i. black chk pen brown ink W/C htd gold leaf eleven album. 22-Jan-3 Christie's, Rockefeller NY #223/R est:15000-20000

£17284 $28000 €25926 Head of a lioness (57x69cm-22x27in) col chk. 22-Jan-3 Christie's, Rockefeller NY #171/R est:7000-10000

£17284 $28000 €25926 Prehistoric dolmen on a desolate heath (22x33cm-9x13in) i. black chk pen brown ink col wash W/C. 22-Jan-3 Christie's, Rockefeller NY #198/R est:7000-10000

£19753 $32000 €29630 Head of a tiger (46x34cm-18x13in) black chk pen brown ink W/C pair. 22-Jan-3 Christie's, Rockefeller NY #170/R est:8000-12000

£21605 $35000 €32408 Prehistoric standing stones by a lake and on a knoll (21x33cm-8x13in) d.1808 black chk pen col ink col wash W/C pair. 22-Jan-3 Christie's, Rockefeller NY #199/R est:7000-10000

£23457 $38000 €35186 Fantasies and glimpses of nature and art (52x36cm-20x14in) i. black chk pen brown ink W/C twenty-one album. 22-Jan-3 Christie's, Rockefeller NY #225/R est:20000-30000

£58642 $95000 €87963 Court of the animals (48x89cm-19x35in) black chk pen brown ink W/C six joined sheets. 22-Jan-3 Christie's, Rockefeller NY #181/R est:30000-50000

TISCHBEIN, Johann Heinrich Wilhelm (attrib) (1751-1829) German

£10563 $17007 €15000 Prince Friedrich von Gotha and tutor, Baron von Thun (110x142cm-43x56in) lit. 9-May-3 Schloss Ahlden, Ahlden #1340/R est:16500

£11000 $17050 €16500 Portrait of a as Flora (65x54cm-26x21in) oval. 30-Oct-2 Christie's, Kensington #85/R est:4000-6000

TISCHLER, Victor (1890-1951) Austrian

£2848 $4500 €4500 Seated child (64x55cm-25x22in) s. prov. 27-Nov-2 Dorotheum, Vienna #1155/R est:6000-8000

TISDALL, Hans (1910-) British

£600 $930 €900 Still life with a basket of fruit (91x71cm-36x28in) s. 4-Dec-2 Christie's, Kensington #593

Works on paper

£350 $546 €525 Abstract composition (59x77cm-23x30in) s. W/C bodycol. 27-Mar-3 Christie's, Kensington #578

TISIO, Benvenuto da Garofalo (1481-1559) Italian

£2514 $4123 €3645 The last Holy Communion (15x21cm-6x8in) panel. 4-Jun-3 AB Stockholms Auktionsverk #2514/R est:12000-15000 (S.KR 32000)

TISIO, Benvenuto da Garofalo (studio) (1481-1559) Italian

£16768 $27500 €25152 Holy Family (60x47cm-24x19in) panel prov. 29-May-3 Sotheby's, New York #113/R est:8000-12000

£24359 $38487 €38000 Nativite (30x38cm-12x15in) panel. 15-Nov-2 Drouot Estimations, Paris #78/R est:12000-15000

TISIO, Benvenuto da Garofalo (style) (1481-1559) Italian

£5128 $7949 €8000 Annunciation (193x135cm-76x53in) board. 4-Dec-2 Christie's, Rome #325/R est:5000-8000

£7137 $11562 €10349 Madonna and Child and Saint Catherine (122x70cm-48x28in) panel. 26-May-3 Bukowskis, Stockholm #371/R est:80000-100000 (S.KR 92000)

TISSANDIER, Albert (1839-1906) French

Works on paper

£5245 $8759 €7500 Paris, vue prise du Haut des Tours de Notre-Dame (97x66cm-38x26in) s.d.1872 chl black crayon gouache exhib. 25-Jun-3 Sotheby's, Paris #95/R est:4000-6000

TISSOT, James Jacques Joseph (1836-1902) French

£28000 $46480 €42000 Portrait of Vicomtesse de Senonnes, seated on a sofa (102x81cm-40x32in) en grisaille lit. 10-Jun-3 Christie's, London #128/R est:6000-10000

£750000 $1207500 €1125000 Good bye - on the Mersey (84x54cm-33x21in) s. indis i.on stretcher prov.exhib.lit. 19-Feb-3 Christie's, London #21/R est:600000-1000000

£1400000 $2212000 €2100000 Seaside - also known as July, La Reverie, or Ramsgate Harbour (86x60cm-34x24in) s.i. prov.exhib.lit. 27-Nov-2 Christie's, London #19/R est:2000000-3000000

£1400000 $2324000 €2100000 La cheminee (51x34cm-20x13in) s. prov.exhib.lit. 11-Jun-3 Christie's, London #13/R est:800000-1200000

Prints

£1899 $3000 €2849 Le hamac (28x19cm-11x7in) etching drypoint. 22-Apr-3 Butterfields, San Francisco #2218/R est:2000-3000

£1923 $3000 €2885 Sur l'Herbe (20x27cm-8x11in) etching drypoint edition of 100. 7-Nov-2 Swann Galleries, New York #498/R est:2500-3500

£2027 $3162 €3000 Journal (38x29cm-15x11in) eau forte drypoint. 31-Mar-3 Piasa, Paris #234/R

£2930 $4600 €4395 Young woman with umbrella (41x23cm-16x9in) s.d.1878 etching drypoint. 20-Nov-2 Boos Gallery, Michigan #453/R est:1000-1200

£3077 $4769 €4800 From the terrace (34x25cm-13x10in) s.d.1878 etching prov. 7-Dec-2 Ketterer, Hamburg #126/R est:500-550

£3205 $5000 €4808 Trafalgar tavern, Greenwich (35x24cm-14x9in) etching drypoint. 7-Nov-2 Swann Galleries, New York #497/R est:3000-5000

£3590 $5600 €5385 L'ete (38x21cm-15x8in) etching drypoint edition of 100. 7-Nov-2 Swann Galleries, New York #499a/R est:5000-8000

£3681 $6000 €5522 Sunay morning (40x19cm-16x7in) etching drypoint exec.1883. 13-Feb-3 Christie's, Rockefeller NY #195/R

£3774 $6000 €5661 Entre les deux cocur balance (25x35cm-10x14in) s.i. etching drypoint. 3-Mar-3 Swann Galleries, New York #8/R est:6000-9000

£3774 $6000 €5661 Promenade dans la neige (57x27cm-22x11in) etching drypoint. 1-May-3 Swann Galleries, New York #366/R est:7000-10000

£3988 $6500 €5982 Summer (37x21cm-15x8in) etching drypoint one of 100 exec.1878. 13-Feb-3 Christie's, Rockefeller NY #193/R

£5215 $8500 €7823 Hammock (28x18cm-11x7in) etching drypoint one of 100 exec.1880. 13-Feb-3 Christie's, Rockefeller NY #194/R

£6500 $10075 €9750 October (59x33cm-23x13in) s. etching drypoint. 3-Dec-2 Christie's, London #234/R est:7000-10000

Works on paper

£3871 $6000 €5807 Sketch for le depart du Finace (15x29cm-6x11in) s. indis i. verso W/C gouache prov. 29-Oct-2 Sotheby's, New York #74/R est:12000-18000

TITCOMB, Mary Bradish (1858-1927) American

£1948 $3000 €2922 Morning coffee (41x51cm-16x20in) s. prov. 24-Oct-2 Shannon's, Milford #177/R est:3000-5000

£7784 $13000 €11287 View of Rockport (36x51cm-14x20in) exhib. 17-Jun-3 John Moran, Pasadena #104 est:15000-20000
£9938 $16000 €14907 Newburyport Marshes, plum Island in distance (12x16cm-5x6in) s. i.verso prov.exhib. 18-Feb-3 John Moran, Pasadena #59 est:10000-15000

TITI, Tiberio di (1573-1627) Italian
£9494 $15000 €15000 Portrait of gentleman (200x115cm-79x45in) i. 27-Nov-2 Finarte, Milan #74

TITIAN (after) (c.1488-1576) Italian
£5172 $8224 €7500 Cupid and Psyche or Danae and the Golden Rain (115x167cm-45x66in) 4-Mar-3 Mealy's, Castlecomer #1008/R est:2000-3000
£6000 $10020 €8700 The Venus of Urbino (57x46cm-22x18in) 8-Jul-3 Sotheby's, Olympia #320/R est:6000-8000
£15942 $26145 €22000 Diane et Acteon (154x186cm-61x73in) 27-May-3 Palais de Beaux Arts, Brussels #726/R est:17500-25000
£19000 $29640 €28500 Venus of Urbino (120x170cm-47x67in) prov.lit. 10-Apr-3 Christie's, Kensington #216/R est:4000-7000

TITIAN (studio) (c.1488-1576) Italian
£50000 $83500 €72500 Venus and Adonis (150x200cm-59x79in) prov.lit. 10-Jul-3 Sotheby's, London #4/R est:20000-30000
£175000 $292250 €253750 Portrait of Gabriel Tandino, wearing robes of the Order of the Kights of Malta (116x105cm-46x41in) i. prov.exhib.lit. 10-Jul-3 Sotheby's, London #155/R est:25000-35000

TITIAN (style) (c.1488-1576) Italian
£6500 $10140 €9750 Portrait of a gentleman in a black doublet, a pair of gloves in his right hand (116x95cm-46x37in) 10-Apr-3 Christie's, Kensington #208/R est:4000-6000
£7500 $12525 €10875 Lady as Venus, reclining on a bed (90x131cm-35x52in) 11-Jul-3 Christie's, Kensington #199/R est:5000-7000
£7800 $12246 €11700 Ecce Homo (32x24cm-13x9in) copper prov. 10-Dec-2 Sotheby's, Olympia #309/R est:3000-4000
£10500 $16485 €15750 Portrait of Pope Paul III (10x79cm-4x31in) prov. 13-Dec-2 Christie's, Kensington #215/R est:5000-8000
£19000 $29830 €28500 Study of Christ (62x51cm-24x20in) painted c.1600. 12-Dec-2 Sotheby's, London #115/R est:6000-8000
£22866 $37500 €34299 Portraits of Roman Emperors (95x76cm-37x30in) i. set of ten. 29-May-3 Sotheby's, New York #106/R est:10000-15000
£44000 $73480 €63800 Rape of Europa (185x237cm-73x93in) prov.lit. 10-Jul-3 Sotheby's, London #5/R est:20000-30000

TITMARSH, Maric (20th C) Australian?
£358 $559 €621 Sensation no 2 (18x29cm-7x11in) s.i.verso acrylic ink three panels prov. 31-Mar-3 Goodman, Sydney #235 (A.D 950)

TITO, Ettore (1859-1941) Italian
£9119 $14044 €14500 Portrait of girl (63x46cm-25x18in) s.d.913 board. 23-Oct-2 Finarte, Milan #102/R est:14000-16000

TITO, Santi di (1536-1603) Italian
£20000 $31400 €30000 Portrait of a lady, in a white and gold embroidered dress with her dog (89x65cm-35x26in) prov. 12-Dec-2 Sotheby's, London #46/R est:20000-30000

TITO, Santi di (attrib) (1536-1603) Italian
Works on paper
£3500 $5845 €5075 Nude youth with his arm extended over his head (40x25cm-16x10in) i. blk chk brown wash htd white prov. 9-Jul-3 Sotheby's, London #20/R est:2000-3000

TITO, Santi di (style) (1536-1603) Italian
£10000 $15500 €15000 Portrait of lady wearing embroidered dress (105x87cm-41x34in) prov. 31-Oct-2 Sotheby's, Olympia #18/R est:6000-8000

TITONEL, Angelo (1938-) Italian
£1026 $1610 €1600 Night thoughts (83x88cm-33x35in) s.d.82 s.i.d.verso. 21-Nov-2 Finarte, Rome #68/R
£1064 $1681 €1660 Subway passengers (70x50cm-28x20in) painted 1982. 12-Nov-2 Babuino, Rome #13/R

TITOV, Eugene (1969-) Russian
£345 $548 €500 Belle epoque (60x30cm-24x12in) s. 10-Mar-3 Millon & Associes, Paris #100
£345 $548 €500 Tendres souvenirs (60x30cm-24x12in) s. 10-Mar-3 Millon & Associes, Paris #101
£655 $1042 €950 Sonate d'ete (61x50cm-24x20in) s. 10-Mar-3 Millon & Associes, Paris #104/R
£690 $1097 €1000 Jardins d'Eden (65x46cm-26x18in) s. 10-Mar-3 Millon & Associes, Paris #102
£690 $1097 €1000 Reveries (61x50cm-24x20in) s. 10-Mar-3 Millon & Associes, Paris #103/R

TITOV, Konstantin (1913-1998) Russian
£513 $800 €770 Eternal glory for those who died for their motherland (29x48cm-11x19in) i.verso board. 20-Sep-2 Sloan, North Bethesda #424/R

TITTELBACH, Voitech (1900-1971) Czechoslovakian
£2063 $3260 €3095 January from calendar cycle (37x50cm-15x20in) s. plywood exhib. 30-Nov-2 Dorotheum, Prague #112/R est:100000-150000 (C.KR 100000)

TITTENSOR, Harry (1887-1942) British
Works on paper
£320 $499 €480 Market place, Honfleur (33x40cm-13x16in) s. i.verso W/C. 6-Nov-2 Bonhams, Chester #469

TITUS-CARMEL, Gerard (1942-) French
Works on paper
£742 $1084 €1113 Grande deambulatoire (150x250cm-59x98in) s.d.1973 graphite prov. 4-Jun-2 Germann, Zurich #31/R (S.FR 1700)
£743 $1175 €1115 Summer sticks lie, zigzaguant (56x76cm-22x30in) s.d.74 graphite pins parchment paper exhib.prov. 1-Apr-3 Rasmussen, Copenhagen #243/R (D.KR 8000)
£759 $1177 €1200 Extrait sur craie carree no 4 (116x116cm-46x46in) s.i.d. pierre noir chk prov. 28-Sep-2 Cornette de St.Cyr, Paris #437/R
£1250 $1975 €1800 Suite Italienne, Guido Cavalcanti (95x65cm-37x26in) s.i.d. collage dr exhib.lit. 28-Apr-3 Cornette de St.Cyr, Paris #526 est:2000-2500
£1859 $2881 €2900 Dedicace XI (114x145cm-45x57in) s.d.1992 s.i.d.verso sanguine acrylic paper on canvas. 7-Dec-2 Cornette de St.Cyr, Paris #134/R

TITZ, Louis (1859-1932) Belgian
Works on paper
£396 $633 €550 Vue de Bruges (45x31cm-18x12in) s. W/C. 19-May-3 Horta, Bruxelles #1
£3526 $5465 €5500 North station in Brussels (34x55cm-13x22in) s. W/C. 7-Dec-2 De Vuyst, Lokeren #535/R est:6000-7000

TJAKAMARA, Michael Nelson (1928-) Australian
£813 $1285 €1179 Untitled (107x99cm-42x39in) acrylic. 22-Jul-3 Lawson Menzies, Sydney #66/R est:2500-3500 (A.D 2000)

TJAKAMARRA, Frank Nelson (c.1948-) Australian
£360 $580 €522 Walpa jukurrpa - wind dreaming (120x180cm-47x71in) acrylic. 12-May-3 Joel, Victoria #378 est:1000-1500 (A.D 900)
£400 $644 €580 Bush potato and Willy willy dreaming (173x92cm-68x36in) ac, on linen. 12-May-3 Joel, Victoria #302 est:1500-1800 (A.D 1000)

TJAKAMARRA, Jack Ross (c.1925-) Australian
£1463 $2312 €2121 Untitled - snake and firestick dreaming (97x139cm-38x55in) ac prov. 22-Jul-3 Lawson Menzies, Sydney #67/R est:3000-5000 (A.D 3600)

TJAKAMARRA, Long Jack Phillipus (1932-1993) Australian
£732 $1156 €1061 Untitled (119x77cm-47x30in) acrylic. 22-Jul-3 Lawson Menzies, Sydney #52/R est:2500-3000 (A.D 1800)

TJAMPITJINPA, Kaapa Mbitjana (c.1920-1989) Australian
Works on paper
£650 $1007 €975 Untitled (41x51cm-16x20in) i.verso synthetic polymer paint canvasboard exec.c.1975. 3-Dec-2 Shapiro, Sydney #191 (A.D 1800)

TJAMPITJINPA, Ronnie (c.1943-) Australian
£2107 $3308 €3161 Tingari (142x130cm-56x51in) s.verso acrylic. 15-Apr-3 Lawson Menzies, Sydney #103/R est:6000-8000 (A.D 5500)
Works on paper
£1707 $2698 €2475 Tingari 1995 (183x91cm-72x36in) polyvinylacetate on canvas. 22-Jul-3 Lawson Menzies, Sydney #57/R est:4000-6000 (A.D 4200)

TJANGALA, George Yapa (c.1950-) Australian
Works on paper
£1372 $2126 €2058 Ceremonial designs associated with site of Narwulkul (183x76cm-72x30in) i.verso synthetic polymer paint canvas prov. 3-Dec-2 Shapiro, Sydney #179/R est:4000-6000 (A.D 3800)

TJANGALA, Michael Mutji (c.1940-) Australian
Works on paper
£794 $1231 €1191 Tjindarr, near the Canning Stock Route, WA (118x79cm-46x31in) i.verso synthetic polymer paint linen prov. 3-Dec-2 Shapiro, Sydney #228/R (A.D 2200)

TJANGALA, Uta Uta (1920-1990) Australian
Works on paper
£6000 $9660 €9000 Yinyilingi waterholes (121x90cm-48x35in) synthetic polymer on canvas executed 1979 prov. 6-May-3 Christie's, Melbourne #97/R est:14000-18000 (A.D 15000)

TJAPALTJARI, Clifford Possum (1934-) Australian
Works on paper
£598 $980 €867 Spear dreaming (135x59cm-53x23in) i.d.1996 verso synthetic polymer paint canvas. 3-Jun-3 Lawson Menzies, Sydney #812 (A.D 1500)

TJAPALTJARRI, Mick Namerari (1926-1998) Australian
Works on paper
£2708 $4197 €4062 Tjunginpa, mouse dreaming (61x91cm-24x36in) synthetic polymer paint linen prov. 3-Dec-2 Shapiro, Sydney #195/R est:4000-6000 (A.D 7500)

TJAPALTJARRI, Paddy Sims (c.1916-) Australian
£1073 $1684 €1610 Warlukurlangu artists (122x76cm-48x30in) s.verso acrylic. 15-Apr-3 Lawson Menzies, Sydney #111/R est:2000-3000 (A.D 2800)

TJAPANGATI, Charlie (20th C) Australian
Works on paper
£1040 $1674 €1560 Untitled (140x100cm-55x39in) synthetic polymer on canvas prov. 6-May-3 Christie's, Melbourne #327/R est:2500-3500 (A.D 2600)
£2200 $3542 €3300 Tingari story - Yurru Turru (182x152cm-72x60in) synthetic polymer paint on canvas. 6-May-3 Christie's, Melbourne #252/R est:5000-8000 (A.D 5500)

TJAPANGATI, Nolan (20th C) Australian
Works on paper
£498 $817 €722 Dreamtime goanna, Ngintaka at Yuwalki waterhole (122x182cm-48x72in) synthetic polymer linen. 3-Jun-3 Lawson Menzies, Sydney #816 (A.D 1250)

TJUNGARRAYI, Charlie Tarawa (c.1921-) Australian
Works on paper
£975 $1511 €1463 Untitled (54x44cm-21x17in) synthetic polymer paint artist's board exec.c.1970 prov. 3-Dec-2 Shapiro, Sydney #184/R est:4000-6000 (A.D 2700)

TJUNGURRAYI, Don (c.1938-) Australian
£320 $515 €464 Malliera ceremony, Yunda, Mount Wedge 1986 (152x182cm-60x72in) acrylic on linen. 12-May-3 Joel, Victoria #301 (A.D 800)

TJUNGURRAYI, George (c.1947-) Australian
Works on paper
£1155 $1791 €1733 Tingari story (107x28cm-42x11in) i.verso synthetic polymer paint canvas prov. 3-Dec-2 Shapiro, Sydney #159/R est:2800-3500 (A.D 3200)

TJUPURRULA, Frank Ward (c.1955-) Australian
Works on paper
£903 $1399 €1355 Untitled (106x50cm-42x20in) i.verso synthetic polymer paint linen prov. 3-Dec-2 Shapiro, Sydney #177/R est:2000-4000 (A.D 2500)

TJUPURRULA, Turkey Tolson (c.1938-) Australian
£2682 $4211 €4023 Straightening spears 1997 (90x90cm-35x35in) acrylic on linen. 15-Apr-3 Lawson Menzies, Sydney #99/R est:2500-3500 (A.D 7000)

TOBEEN, Felix-Elie (1880-1938) French
£3597 $5899 €5000 Still life with dahlias in a vase (46x38cm-18x15in) s. prov. 3-Jun-3 Christie's, Amsterdam #28/R est:5000-7000

TOBEY, Mark (1890-1976) American
£4687 $7500 €7031 Still life with white head (54x79cm-21x31in) s.d.33 board prov.exhib.lit. 14-May-3 Sotheby's, New York #103/R est:8000-12000
£4803 $7493 €7205 Untitled (56x31cm-22x12in) s.d.61 tempera monotype. 6-Nov-2 Hans Widmer, St Gallen #38/R est:9000-16000 (S.FR 11000)
£4808 $7452 €7500 Red trails (51x71cm-20x28in) s.d.1984 gouache Indian ink wash paper on cardboard prov. 6-Dec-2 Ketterer, Munich #174/R est:7500-8500
£10000 $16000 €15000 New York (45x30cm-18x12in) s.d.54 tempera on paper prov. 14-May-3 Sotheby's, New York #124/R est:6000-8000
£11250 $18000 €16875 Meditative series (45x30cm-18x12in) s.d.54 tempera on paper prov. 14-May-3 Sotheby's, New York #125/R est:8000-12000
£11790 $18511 €17685 Blue interval (65x50cm-26x20in) s.d.69/70 tempera. 23-Nov-2 Burkhard, Luzern #149/R est:28000-34000 (S.FR 27000)
£13000 $21710 €18850 Anges (60x87cm-24x34in) s.d.56 tempera paper on board prov.exhib. 26-Jun-3 Sotheby's, London #176/R est:8000-12000
£37500 $60000 €56250 Red, white and blue town (93x63cm-37x25in) s. tempera on masonite painted 1961 prov.exhib. 14-May-3 Sotheby's, New York #105/R est:25000-35000

Works on paper
£903 $1400 €1355 Portrait of Paul McCool (57x40cm-22x16in) s.d.1923 chl. 3-Dec-2 Christie's, Rockefeller NY #614/R
£926 $1491 €1389 Untitled (31x20cm-12x8in) s. Indian ink wash. 7-May-3 Dobiaschofsky, Bern #2019/R (S.FR 2000)
£1000 $1580 €1500 Untitled (21x13cm-8x5in) s. W/C bodycol card exec.c.1965. 3-Apr-3 Christie's, Kensington #209/R
£1667 $2633 €2600 Composition (12x12cm-5x5in) W/C exec.1957. 12-Nov-2 Babuino, Rome #220/R

TOBIAS, Ben (c.1901-1985) Canadian
£1250 $2038 €1875 Penzance (51x61cm-20x24in) s.i.d.1957 board. 13-Feb-3 David Lay, Penzance #268/R est:800-1200

TOBIASSE, Theo (1927-) Israeli
£1402 $2186 €2103 Venise de Tobiasse (22x27cm-9x11in) s.d.71. 5-Nov-2 Bukowskis, Stockholm #315/R est:10000-12000 (S.KR 20000)
£1853 $2984 €2780 Pastrale en bleu (39x46cm-15x18in) s. 7-May-3 AB Stockholms Auktionsverk #1098/R est:20000-25000 (S.KR 24000)
£2115 $3321 €3300 Les trois pichets (22x27cm-9x11in) s.i.d. 24-Nov-2 Chayette & Cheval, Paris #294/R est:3000-4000
£2642 $4200 €3963 Petite maternite (33x24cm-13x9in) s.i. 27-Feb-3 Christie's, Rockefeller NY #119/R est:6000
£2710 $4200 €4065 La Torah bleue (33x23cm-13x9in) s.i. 26-Sep-2 Christie's, Rockefeller NY #569/R est:3000-5000
£2756 $4328 €4300 Le vieil homme et la mariee (24x33cm-9x13in) s.i.d. 24-Nov-2 Chayette & Cheval, Paris #278/R est:3500-4500
£2885 $4529 €4500 Les delices de la Thora (35x27cm-14x11in) s.i.d. 24-Nov-2 Chayette & Cheval, Paris #285/R est:3500-4500
£3007 $4931 €4600 Rues de Paris (24x33cm-9x13in) s.i.d. 9-Feb-3 Anaf, Lyon #250/R
£4000 $6160 €6000 Afin que tu te souviennes tous les jours (89x116cm-35x46in) s.i. oil paper collage. 23-Oct-2 Sotheby's, Olympia #805/R est:4000-6000
£4700 $7473 €7050 La pomme sur le phono (73x60cm-29x24in) s.i.d.60 oil mixed media prov. 20-Mar-3 Sotheby's, Olympia #210/R est:5000-7000
£5161 $8000 €7742 Le cheval fou des quai de la Seine (72x91cm-28x36in) s.i.d.66. 26-Sep-2 Christie's, Rockefeller NY #570/R est:7000-9000
£5200 $8008 €7800 Deux hommes sur un chat (65x81cm-26x32in) s.i.d.64 s.stretcher. 23-Oct-2 Sotheby's, Olympia #802/R est:6000-8000
£5245 $8759 €7500 La Dame de Venise (50x50cm-20x20in) s. 25-Jun-3 Claude Aguttes, Neuilly #208/R est:7500-8500
£5500 $8470 €8250 Un printemps d'Israel (81x100cm-32x39in) s.i.d.70 oil wax crayon. 23-Oct-2 Sotheby's, Olympia #803/R est:6000-8000
£5864 $8327 €9500 Vache et garde-barriere (54x65cm-21x26in) s.i. 16-Mar-3 Eric Pillon, Calais #266/R
£5975 $9500 €8963 Burgers d'Israel (81x100cm-32x39in) s.i. painted 1966. 27-Feb-3 Christie's, Rockefeller NY #110/R est:12000
£7372 $11574 €11500 Venise et les fleurs rouges (81x65cm-32x26in) s.i.d. 24-Nov-2 Chayette & Cheval, Paris #275a/R est:12000-15000
£7547 $12000 €11321 Des fruits dans le rire de Jerusalem (81x100cm-32x39in) s.i.d.74. 27-Feb-3 Christie's, Rockefeller NY #82/R est:9000
£7547 $12000 €11321 Famille du Roi David (100x80cm-39x31in) s.i. oil collage prov. 27-Feb-3 Christie's, Rockefeller NY #121/R est:18000

Sculpture

£818 $1267 €1300 Composition au personnage (16x12cm-6x5in) s. oil metal marble socle. 30-Oct-2 Artcurial Briest, Paris #607

Works on paper

£896 $1497 €1300 Les fleurs geantes poussent derriere les paroles des hommes (58x74cm-23x29in) s.i.d.19.V.87 graphite wax crayon dr. 10-Jul-3 Artcurial Briest, Paris #110 est:1000-1200
£1000 $1550 €1500 Deux femmes a saute-mouton. Femme assise aux leves (49x34cm-19x13in) s.i. pencil W/C wax crayon two. 5-Dec-2 Christie's, Kensington #108/R est:1000-1500
£1457 $2375 €2200 L'enfant et les violons (89x59cm-35x23in) s. gouache. 1-Feb-3 Claude Aguttes, Neuilly #329/R est:3800-4600
£2581 $4000 €3872 Nortre Dame, le fleurs et la roulotte (49x66cm-19x26in) s.i.d.66 gouache paper on board. 26-Sep-2 Christie's, Rockefeller NY #627/R est:5000-7000
£2857 $4543 €4200 Le rossignol et l'Empereur de Chine (50x65cm-20x26in) s.i.d.74 gouache. 26-Feb-3 Artcurial Briest, Paris #329/R est:2800-3500
£3265 $5192 €4800 Sous le saule, Hans-Christian Andersen (50x65cm-20x26in) s.i.d.74 gouache. 26-Feb-3 Artcurial Briest, Paris #328/R est:2800-3500
£3567 $5564 €5600 Homme a la recherche d'une poupeegeante (58x73cm-23x29in) s.i. mixed media. 10-Nov-2 Eric Pillon, Calais #232/R
£3586 $5989 €5200 Carrosse pour enfant delire emprisonne dans des habits de silence (57x77cm-22x30in) s.i.d.4/84 W/C pastel graphite collage. 10-Jul-3 Artcurial Briest, Paris #109/R est:3000-4000
£3774 $5849 €6000 Entre deux recontres (100x69cm-39x27in) s.i. mixed media prov. 30-Oct-2 Artcurial Briest, Paris #606/R est:5000-6000
£4013 $6260 €6300 Noces sublimes (69x51cm-27x20in) s.i. mixed media. 10-Nov-2 Eric Pillon, Calais #208/R
£4088 $6336 €6500 Couleur voyage (100x69cm-39x27in) s.i. mixed media prov. 30-Oct-2 Artcurial Briest, Paris #604/R est:5000-6000
£4088 $6336 €6500 Femme portrait (100x69cm-39x27in) s.i.d.81 mixed media prov. 30-Oct-2 Artcurial Briest, Paris #605/R est:5000-6000
£5161 $8000 €7742 Les fleurs du cirque (50x67cm-20x26in) s.d.73 gouache brush black ink. 26-Sep-2 Christie's, Rockefeller NY #619/R est:4000-6000
£6051 $9439 €9500 Cantique des cantiques (63x49cm-25x19in) s.i. mixed media. 10-Nov-2 Eric Pillon, Calais #211/R
£8387 $13000 €12581 Le chevre et le joueur de flute (52x68cm-20x27in) s.d.60 gouache pen India ink. 26-Sep-2 Christie's, Rockefeller NY #604/R est:5000-7000

TOCHILKIN, Mark (1958-) Ukranian

£1602 $2500 €2403 Untitled, pianist (32x75cm-13x30in) s. 14-Oct-2 Butterfields, San Francisco #2036/R est:3000-5000
£2756 $4328 €4300 Violoniste (44x30cm-17x12in) s. 12-Dec-2 Rabourdin & Choppin de Janvry, Paris #154/R

TOCQUE, Louis (attrib) (1696-1772) French

£10256 $16103 €16000 Portrait de Joachim de Pierre (80x64cm-31x25in) 14-Dec-2 Artcurial Briest, Paris #57/R est:15000

TOCQUE, Louis (circle) (1696-1772) French

£6329 $9873 €10000 Portrait presume de Marc-Pierre de Voyer (39x31cm-15x12in) i.verso prov.lit. 20-Oct-2 Mercier & Cie, Lille #273/R est:7500-10000

TOD, Joanne (20th C) Canadian

£4435 $7008 €6653 145 West 55th, 11th floor (61x90cm-24x35in) s.d.2002 prov. 18-Nov-2 Sotheby's, Toronto #140/R est:5000-7000 (C.D 11000)

TODD, Arthur Ralph Middleton (1891-c.1967) British

Works on paper

£720 $1188 €1044 Music hath charms (24x16cm-9x6in) s.d.11 W/C. 1-Jul-3 Bearnes, Exeter #413/R

TODD, F G (19th C) British?

£860 $1342 €1290 Still life with fruit (29x24cm-11x9in) 12-Sep-2 Hobbs Parker, Ashford #659/R

TODD, Henry George (1846-1898) British

£400 $620 €600 Still life of fruit (18x23cm-7x9in) s.d.1887. 30-Sep-2 Bonhams, Ipswich #492
£550 $858 €825 Still life study of grapes, strawberries, and plums on a mossy bank (23x28cm-9x11in) s.d.1881 card. 18-Oct-2 Keys, Aylsham #685/R
£550 $864 €825 Still life of grapes and other fruit on a mossy bank (23x28cm-9x11in) s.d.1894. 13-Dec-2 Keys, Aylsham #655/R
£550 $897 €825 Still life of fruit (31x26cm-12x10in) s.d.1897. 29-Jan-3 Sotheby's, Olympia #180/R
£750 $1223 €1125 Still life study of grapes and plums on a marble slab (23x18cm-9x7in) s. 14-Feb-3 Keys, Aylsham #651/R
£1000 $1520 €1500 Plums, apple and bunch of grapes. Pear, plum and bunch of grapes (18x23cm-7x9in) one s.d.1879 one indis.s. pair. 29-Aug-2 Christie's, Kensington #21/R est:1000-1500
£1210 $1864 €1900 Still life with violets in a Venetian vase (46x37cm-18x15in) s.d.69 panel. 3-Sep-2 Christie's, Amsterdam #152/R est:1000-1500
£5500 $8745 €8250 Still life of fruit and leaves in a bowl on a marble ledge (61x50cm 24x20in) s.d.1896. 5-Mar-3 Bonhams, Bury St Edmunds #418/R est:5000-7000
£14500 $23055 €21750 Still life of fruit on a ledge (61x50cm-24x20in) s.d.1897. 5-Mar-3 Bonhams, Bury St Edmunds #382 est:2000-4000

TODD, Henry Stanley (1872-1941) American

£736 $1200 €1104 Seated woman (102x84cm-40x33in) s.d.1903. 2-Feb-3 Grogan, Boston #15

TODD, Milan (1922-) Yugoslavian

£491 $747 €737 Chattering II (58x88cm-23x35in) s. 19-Aug-2 Joel, Victoria #232 est:2500-3000 (A.D 1400)
£760 $1223 €1102 Summer in the wetlands (150x210cm-59x83in) s.d.85 acrylic. 12-May-3 Joel, Victoria #364 est:2000-3000 (A.D 1900)

TODD, Ralph (1856-1932) British

£1700 $2822 €2465 Evening reverie (36x23cm-14x9in) s. 10-Jun-3 David Lay, Penzance #419/R est:1200-1800

Works on paper

£580 $899 €870 Sweet thoughts, lady in a cottage interior (94x64cm-37x25in) s. W/C. 26-Sep-2 Lane, Penzance #66
£580 $899 €870 Girl with hoe before a cottage (99x124cm-39x49in) W/C prov. 26-Sep-2 Lane, Penzance #67
£680 $1061 €1020 Trawlers in a calm (24x34cm-9x13in) s. W/C. 15-Oct-2 Bearnes, Exeter #374/R
£750 $1185 €1125 Newlyn portrait (25x18cm-10x7in) s. W/C. 24-Apr-3 Richardson & Smith, Whitby #176
£2200 $3586 €3190 Fisherman's daughter (27x37cm-11x15in) s. W/C. 16-Jul-3 Sotheby's, Olympia #53/R est:500-700
£2600 $4342 €3770 Waiting for the fleet (42x28cm-17x11in) s. W/C. 19-Jun-3 Lane, Penzance #135/R est:2500-3500

TODD, Wilson (20th C) American

Photographs

£3205 $5000 €4808 Genesko and accent (25x20cm-10x8in) gelatin silver print exhib. 10-Nov-2 Selkirks, St. Louis #712/R est:6000-7000

TODD-BROWN, William (1875-1952) British

£500 $785 €750 Still life a pewter tankard of mallow and gypsophila (60x49cm-24x19in) s. 10-Dec-2 Lane, Penzance #294

TODERI, Grazia (1963-) Italian?

Photographs

£5500 $8580 €8250 Random (120x150cm-47x59in) s.d.2001 num.5/5 cibachrome on plexiglass lit. 21-Oct-2 Sotheby's, London #70/R est:5000-6000

TODESCHINI, Giambattista (1857-1938) Italian

£1090 $1689 €1700 Lombard landscape (29x50cm-11x20in) s. board. 5-Dec-2 Stadion, Trieste #735/R

TODESCHINI, Lucio (1892-1969) Italian

£355 $561 €550 Still life with corn (40x50cm-16x20in) s. board. 18-Dec-2 Finarte, Milan #213
£387 $612 €600 Still life (40x50cm-16x20in) s. board. 18-Dec-2 Finarte, Milan #215
£387 $612 €600 Still life with mushrooms (40x50cm-16x20in) s. board. 18-Dec-2 Finarte, Milan #214

TODESCHINI, Piero (19/20th C) Italian?

£725 $1188 €1000 Velleita (70x60cm-28x24in) s.i. panel. 27-May-3 Finarte, Milan #142/R
£725 $1188 €1000 Ave Maria (70x60cm-28x24in) s.i. panel. 27-May-3 Finarte, Milan #141/R

TODHUNTER, Francis Augustus (1884-1963) American

£1019 $1600 €1529 Homestead (40x51cm-16x20in) s. i.verso canvasboard. 19-Nov-2 Butterfields, San Francisco #8305/R est:2000-3000

TOEFAERT, Albert (1856-1909) Flemish

£306 $471 €480 Circus dogs (45x60cm-18x24in) s.d.93. 3-Sep-2 Christie's, Amsterdam #177
£1019 $1569 €1600 Kittens in a basket (45x60cm-18x24in) s.d.1891. 3-Sep-2 Christie's, Amsterdam #188/R est:600-800

TOEPUT, Lodewyk (1550-1603) Flemish
£26000 $40820 €39000 Parable of the rich and poor man (89x129cm-35x51in) 12-Dec-2 Sotheby's, London #121/R est:20000-30000
£33951 $55000 €50927 Nine muses (99x201cm-39x79in) 23-Jan-3 Sotheby's, New York #56/R est:60000-80000

TOEPUT, Lodewyk (attrib) (1550-1603) Flemish
£5128 $7949 €8000 Wooded landscape with hunters (74x93cm-29x37in) 6-Dec-2 Maigret, Paris #67/R est:7000
£10063 $15597 €16000 Stag hunt (110x146cm-43x57in) prov. 2-Oct-2 Dorotheum, Vienna #14/R est:12000-16000

TOFANARI, Sabrino (20th C) Italian
£284 $460 €400 Coucher de soleil sur le lac de Come (65x52cm-26x20in) s. 26-May-3 Joron-Derem, Paris #58

TOFANARI, Sirio (1886-1969) Italian
Sculpture
£3396 $5264 €5400 Hug (24x64x53cm-9x25x21in) s. bronze exec.1909. 29-Oct-2 Finarte, Milan #302
£9000 $14040 €13500 Caress (23cm-9in) s. brown pat bronze oval base lit. 9-Apr-3 Sotheby's, London #225/R est:10000-12000

TOFANO, Edouardo (1838-1920) Italian
Works on paper
£3712 $5790 €5568 Young woman in interior (17x22cm-7x9in) s.i.d.75 W/C prov. 9-Nov-2 Galerie Gloggner, Luzern #142/R est:1200-1400 (S.FR 8500)

TOFFOLI, Louis (1907-1999) French
£484 $765 €750 Port de Vendee (20x25cm-8x10in) s. canvas on cardboard. 17-Dec-2 Rossini, Paris #130
£548 $866 €850 Bateaux echoues (20x25cm-8x10in) s. cardboard. 17-Dec-2 Rossini, Paris #128
£548 $866 €850 Bateau a la riviere (33x24cm-13x9in) s. cardboard double-sided. 17-Dec-2 Rossini, Paris #129
£1139 $1800 €1800 Saint-Gilles, le port (27x22cm-11x9in) s. panel. 29-Nov-2 Drouot Estimations, Paris #88
£1795 $2818 €2800 Church (46x38cm-18x15in) s.d.53. 13-Dec-2 Piasa, Paris #270
£2128 $3447 €3000 Voile bleue (27x22cm-11x9in) s. i.verso. 21-May-3 Cornette de St.Cyr, Paris #93/R est:1500-2000
£2656 $4250 €3851 Le travail. Moment for reflection (74x53cm-29x21in) s. i.verso. 16-May-3 Skinner, Boston #363/R est:3500-4500
£6835 $10935 €9500 Maternite (60x50cm-24x20in) s. panel. 16-May-3 Lombrail & Teucquam, Paris #133/R
£10494 $14901 €17000 Buveurs de biere (162x97cm-64x38in) s. 16-Mar-3 Eric Pillon, Calais #267/R
Works on paper
£432 $691 €600 Paris, La Place de la Concorde (37x29cm-15x11in) s.i. chl. 18-May-3 Charbonneaux, Paris #206

TOFT, Albert (1862-1949) British
Sculpture
£2000 $3120 €3000 Metal pourer (30cm-12in) s.d.1913 bronze. 5-Nov-2 Woolley & Wallis, Salisbury #116/R est:1000-1500

TOFT, Peter (1825-1901) Danish
Works on paper
£320 $502 €480 Loo Rock Madeira - breakwater and fort on the coast (24x33cm-9x13in) s.i. W/C. 10-Dec-2 Lane, Penzance #114
£340 $527 €510 High Level Bridge, Newcastle upon Tyne (53x36cm-21x14in) s.d.1879 W/C. 24-Sep-2 Anderson & Garland, Newcastle #312
£4459 $7000 €6689 Great crossing (34x51cm-13x20in) mono.i. W/C paper on board prov.exhib. 20-Nov-2 Christie's, Los Angeles #22/R est:3000-5000

TOGNI, Ponziano (1906-) Italian
£349 $548 €524 Three women by tree (26x24cm-10x9in) s. pavatex. 25-Nov-2 Germann, Zurich #834 (S.FR 800)
£568 $829 €852 Still life of fruit (29x39cm-11x15in) s. 4-Jun-2 Germann, Zurich #858 (S.FR 1300)

TOGORES, Jose de (1893-1970) Spanish
£1007 $1621 €1500 Elegant lady (100x73cm-39x29in) s. 18-Feb-3 Durán, Madrid #139/R
£8079 $12603 €12119 Oliviers pres de Bandol (50x65cm-20x26in) s. 6-Nov-2 Dobiaschofsky, Bern #1015/R est:7000 (S.FR 18500)

TOHER, Thomas M (19/20th C) ?
£452 $700 €678 Desert death (51x61cm-20x24in) s.d. 8-Dec-2 Toomey, Oak Park #668/R

TOIT, Paul du (1922-1986) South African
£1206 $1905 €1809 Cedarberg landscape (59x39cm-23x15in) s. canvas on board. 1-Apr-3 Stephan Welz, Johannesburg #490/R est:16000-20000 (SA.R 15000)
£1351 $2108 €2027 Abstracted landscape (79x80cm-31x31in) s.d.78. 15-Oct-2 Stephan Welz, Johannesburg #498/R est:12000-16000 (SA.R 22000)

TOJETTI, Virgilio (1851-1901) American
Works on paper
£417 $650 €626 Starting the fire (41x56cm-16x22in) s. W/C. 22-Sep-2 Susanin's, Chicago #5024/R

TOL, Dominicus van (1635-1676) Dutch
£16106 $25931 €24000 Two children blowing bubbles at a window (26x20cm-10x8in) panel prov.exhib.lit. 18-Feb-3 Sotheby's, Amsterdam #257/R est:6000-8000

TOLA, Jose (1943-) Peruvian
£14650 $23000 €21975 Self-portrait (190x170cm-75x67in) s.d.98 prov.exhib.lit. 20-Nov-2 Christie's, Rockefeller NY #158/R est:18000-22000

TOLE, Charles (1903-1989) New Zealander
£1567 $2445 €2351 Waihi landscape (23x28cm-9x11in) s.d.1943. 7-Nov-2 International Art Centre, Auckland #61/R est:5000-7000 (NZ.D 5000)
£2821 $4401 €4232 From Pukekohe Hill (40x50cm-16x20in) s. board. 7-Nov-2 International Art Centre, Auckland #46/R est:8000-12000 (NZ.D 9000)

TOLE, John (1890-1967) New Zealander
£2744 $4198 €4116 Still life with red decanter (39x34cm-15x13in) s. board. 21-Aug-2 Dunbar Sloane, Auckland #37/R est:9000-15000 (NZ.D 9000)

TOLEDO SCHOOL (17th C) Spanish
£7547 $11774 €12000 Calvary (134x104cm-53x41in) 23-Sep-2 Durán, Madrid #262/R

TOLEDO, Francisco (1940-) Mexican
£10828 $17000 €16242 Two bulls (48x73cm-19x29in) s.verso oil sand canvas on masonite prov. 20-Nov-2 Christie's, Rockefeller NY #126/R est:20000-30000
£24390 $40000 €35366 Hombres dentro du una vaca (60x73cm-24x29in) s.verso jute painted c.1963 prov. 27-May-3 Sotheby's, New York #124
£31847 $50000 €47771 Untitled (92x73cm-36x29in) oil sand painted 1963 prov.lit. 19-Nov-2 Sotheby's, New York #39/R est:80000
Works on paper
£566 $872 €900 Visage bleu (48x63cm-19x25in) pastel. 22-Oct-2 Campo & Campo, Antwerp #266
£928 $1484 €1346 Gallina (64x48cm-25x19in) s.d.1959 crayon. 15-May-3 Louis Morton, Mexico #137/R est:10000-28000 (M.P 15000)
£1384 $2131 €2200 Figure in blue and orange (47x38cm-19x15in) s. gouache. 22-Oct-2 Campo & Campo, Antwerp #264
£2134 $3500 €3201 Sin titulo (24x32cm-9x13in) s.d.63 gouache prov. 28-May-3 Christie's, Rockefeller NY #133/R est:4000-6000
£2548 $4000 €3822 Horse (47x59cm-19x23in) s.d.1980 pen ink prov. 20-Nov-2 Christie's, Rockefeller NY #134/R
£4878 $8000 €7073 Sin titulo (50x69cm-20x27in) s.d.Juchitan 69 gouache ink. 27-May-3 Sotheby's, New York #123
£5414 $8500 €8121 Man (42x28cm-17x11in) s. W/C ink painted c.1960 prov. 20-Nov-2 Christie's, Rockefeller NY #144/R
£6707 $11000 €10061 Hombre y toro (41x35cm-16x14in) s. gouache W/C ink prov. 28-May-3 Christie's, Rockefeller NY #106/R est:8000-10000
£7317 $12000 €10976 Sin titulo. Sin titulo. Sin titulo (23x28cm-9x11in) two s. W/C exec.c.1965 one s.d.63 W/C three prov. 28-May-3 Christie's, Rockefeller NY #129/R est:12000-15000
£7643 $12000 €11465 Untitled (55x75cm-22x30in) s. ink wash prov. 19-Nov-2 Sotheby's, New York #111/R est:15000
£10976 $18000 €15915 Escorpion (28x21cm-11x8in) s. gouache sand W/C exec.c.1969 prov. 27-May-3 Sotheby's, New York #78
£12739 $20000 €19109 Untitled (47x65cm-19x26in) s. gouache W/C ink exec.c.1965 prov. 19-Nov-2 Sotheby's, New York #112/R est:18000
£15244 $25000 €22104 Alumbrando. Toro (25x34cm-10x13in) s. gouache W/C ink double-sided prov.lit. 27-May-3 Sotheby's, New York #122
£31847 $50000 €47771 Fish (70x100cm-28x39in) s. i.verso gouache pen exec.1978 prov.exhib. 20-Nov-2 Christie's, Rockefeller NY #32/R est:60000-80000

TOLEDO, Irma Rafaela (1910-2002) Swiss
Works on paper
£288 $472 €400 Summer comes once more (46x59cm-18x23in) s.i.d. ink W/C. 5-Jun-3 Dorotheum, Salzburg #804/R

TOLGYESSY, Arthur (1853-1920) Hungarian
£654 $1041 €981 On the pasture (27x19cm-11x7in) s. board. 8-Mar-3 Dorotheum, Prague #27/R est:30000-45000 (C.KR 30000)
£3803 $6085 €5705 Mill on the riverside (76x117cm-30x46in) s. 16-May-3 Kieselbach, Budapest #64/R (H.F 1300000)

TOLLET, Tony (1857-?) French
£541 $843 €800 Dame de qualite en robe decolletee (72x59cm-28x23in) s. panel oval. 30-Mar-3 Anaf, Lyon #437

TOLLI (1953-) Icelandic
£929 $1468 €1394 Morning - landscape composition (50x88cm-20x35in) s.verso exhib. 1-Apr-3 Rasmussen, Copenhagen #356/R (D.KR 10000)

TOLLIVER, Mose (1919-) American
£1000 $1600 €1500 Portrait of Philip M Golomb, Mose E Tolliver and his wife Willie Mae (114x69cm-45x27in) s.i.d.December 26 1987 verso house paint plywood. 4-Jan-3 Brunk, Ashville #187/R est:800-1500
£1125 $1800 €1688 Adam and Eve standing beside a tree with cats and other animals (99x64cm-39x25in) s. s.i.verso house paint plywood. 4-Jan-3 Brunk, Ashville #423/R est:400-800
£1188 $1900 €1782 Portrait of Nall (74x61cm-29x24in) s. s.i.verso oil house paint plywood pop-top hanger. 4-Jan-3 Brunk, Ashville #421/R est:800-1500

TOLLIVER, William (1951-2000) American
£1795 $2800 €2693 Impressionist landscape (51x76cm-20x30in) s. 12-Oct-2 Neal Auction Company, New Orleans #691/R est:2500-3500
£1923 $3000 €2885 Mother and child (102x76cm-40x30in) s. 12-Oct-2 Neal Auction Company, New Orleans #690/R est:3000-5000
£1923 $3000 €2885 Portrait of a woman (91x56cm-36x22in) s. oil crayon. 12-Oct-2 Neal Auction Company, New Orleans #692/R est:2000-3000

TOLMAN, Stacy (1860-1935) American
£287 $450 €431 Dunes (20x25cm-8x10in) s. board. 22-Nov-2 Skinner, Boston #349/R

TOLNAY, Akos (1861-?) Hungarian
£480 $749 €720 Young woman on park bench (20x14cm-8x6in) s. panel. 20-Nov-2 Fischer, Luzern #2283/R (S.FR 1100)

TOLOMEO, Carla (1944-) Italian
£321 $503 €500 The statue again (100x100cm-39x39in) s.i.d.1988 verso. 23-Nov-2 Meeting Art, Vercelli #296

TOLZNER, E (19th C) German
£5535 $8634 €8800 Woman reading (72x60cm-28x24in) s.i.d.1872. 20-Sep-2 Schloss Ahlden, Ahlden #1180/R est:8500

TOM, Jan Bedys (1813-1894) Dutch
£5031 $7748 €8000 Shepherd and his flock at rest (40x56cm-16x22in) s.d.1855 panel. 22-Oct-2 Sotheby's, Amsterdam #39/R est:8000-12000

TOM-PETERSEN, Peter (1861-1926) Danish
£256 $396 €384 Small boy by gate at Gavno Palace (32x34cm-13x13in) s.d.88. 28-Sep-2 Rasmussen, Havnen #2058 (D.KR 3000)
£345 $524 €518 Street scene with woman and wheel barrow (52x47cm-20x19in) s. 27-Aug-2 Rasmussen, Copenhagen #1831/R (D.KR 4000)
£439 $685 €659 Summer's day in Vestergade, Faaborg (39x46cm-15x18in) s. 23-Sep-2 Rasmussen, Vejle #251/R (D.KR 5200)
£450 $725 €675 Landscape from Ribe with man walking (32x36cm-13x14in) s. 22-Feb-3 Rasmussen, Havnen #2023/R (D.KR 5000)
£495 $798 €743 From Aeroskobing (42x37cm-17x15in) s.d.1922. 22-Feb-3 Rasmussen, Havnen #2032 (D.KR 5500)
£511 $807 €767 Street scene, Fiolstraede (43x35cm-17x14in) s. 2-Dec-2 Rasmussen, Copenhagen #1212/R (D.KR 6000)
£957 $1550 €1388 From Humlebaek Harbour (38x35cm-15x14in) s.d.89. 26-May-3 Rasmussen, Copenhagen #1387/R (D.KR 10000)
£1014 $1562 €1521 Many figures at Amager Square, Copenhagen (30x39cm-12x15in) s.d.1881. 26-Oct-2 Rasmussen, Havnen #2056/R est:6000-8000 (D.KR 12000)
£1072 $1672 €1608 Axel Square in Faaborg with two figures (97x86cm-38x34in) s.d.1896 exhib. 11-Nov-2 Rasmussen, Vejle #686/R est:15000 (D.KR 12500)
£1435 $2325 €2081 Rosina - Italian woman in doorway with wine and fruit (95x65cm-37x26in) s.d.1890. 26-May-3 Rasmussen, Copenhagen #1331/R est:15000 (D.KR 15000)
£1583 $2517 €2375 Market day at the Gammel Square (30x39cm-12x15in) s.d.1884. 5-Mar-3 Rasmussen, Copenhagen #1941/R est:20000 (D.KR 17000)
£2200 $3607 €3190 Market in Copenhagen (43x40cm-17x16in) s.d.1887. 4-Jun-3 AB Stockholms Auktionsverk #2418/R est:35000-40000 (S.KR 28000)
£3165 $5000 €5000 Canal view in Copenhagen (47x65cm-19x26in) s. 28-Nov-2 Dorotheum, Vienna #231/R est:3400-4000

TOMA, Giovacchino (1836-1891) Italian
Works on paper
£1195 $1840 €1900 Donkey (42x52cm-17x20in) s.i.d.1857 pen dr. 28-Oct-2 Il Ponte, Milan #226/R

TOMA, Giovacchino (attrib) (1836-1891) Italian
£440 $678 €700 Caricature of man eating fruit (31x22cm-12x9in) s.d.1857 i.verso. 28-Oct-2 Il Ponte, Milan #262

TOMA, Matthias Rudolf (1792-1869) Austrian
£568 $886 €852 Old farmstead (30x39cm-12x15in) s.d.1829. 6-Nov-2 Dobiaschofsky, Bern #1016/R (S.FR 1300)
£616 $962 €900 Resting by ruins (28x21cm-11x8in) mono. i.d.1828 verso. 10-Apr-3 Dorotheum, Vienna #253

TOMALTY, Terry (1935-) Canadian?
£222 $364 €333 Hockey player (20x25cm-8x10in) s.d.85 board prov. 3-Jun-3 Joyner, Toronto #566 (C.D 500)
£685 $1083 €1028 Ben's (20x25cm-8x10in) s.i. s.verso board prov. 14-Nov-2 Heffel, Vancouver #140/R est:900-1100 (C.D 1700)
£711 $1166 €1067 Hockey game - evening (40x50cm-16x20in) s. prov. 3-Jun-3 Joyner, Toronto #195/R est:1800-2200 (C.D 1600)
£717 $1148 €1076 Ice hockey (30x41cm-12x16in) s. board prov. 15-May-3 Heffel, Vancouver #100/R est:1000-1500 (C.D 1600)
£741 $1148 €1112 Pommes gelee (40x50cm-16x20in) s. indis d. board. 3-Dec-2 Joyner, Toronto #311/R est:1200-1500 (C.D 1800)
£1244 $2041 €1866 Winter, McGill (40x50cm-16x20in) s. 3-Jun-3 Joyner, Toronto #229/R est:1800-2200 (C.D 2800)
£1310 $2071 €1965 Adam Street ring (30x41cm-12x16in) s. i.verso prov. 14-Nov-2 Heffel, Vancouver #206/R est:1200-1500 (C.D 3250)
£1333 $2187 €2000 McGill evening (30x40cm-12x16in) s. 3-Jun-3 Joyner, Toronto #464 est:1200-1500 (C.D 3000)

TOMANECK, Joseph (1889-?) American
£1274 $2000 €1911 Nude (36x30cm-14x12in) s. board prov. 20-Nov-2 Christie's, Los Angeles #85/R est:2500-3500

TOMAS, G (19th C) American?
£1958 $3250 €2839 Hunt scene (61x74cm-24x29in) board. 13-Jun-3 Du Mouchelle, Detroit #2028/R est:4000-6000

TOMASELLI, Fred (1956-) American?
£9494 $15000 €14241 Number three (51x51cm-20x20in) s.i.d.1994 verso acrylic hemp leaves pills. 12-Nov-2 Phillips, New York #190/R est:20000-30000
£24051 $38000 €36077 Double negative (91x330cm-36x130in) acrylic hemp roots acrylic resin on panel executed 1994 prov. 14-Nov-2 Christie's, Rockefeller NY #337/R est:35000-45000

Works on paper
£21875 $35000 €32813 Very nervous system (61x61cm-24x24in) s.i.d.1998 verso pill leafs photocollage acrylic rein on wood. 14-May-3 Sotheby's, New York #325/R est:20000-30000

TOMASELLO, Luis (1915-) Argentinian
Sculpture
£1822 $2842 €2733 Athmospere cromoplastique No.77 (90x90cm-35x35in) s.verso painted wood relief executed 1961 prov. 6-Nov-2 AB Stockholms Auktionsverk #819/R est:12000-15000 (S.KR 26000)

Works on paper
£9028 $14896 €13000 Atmosphere chromoplastique no 192 (187x187cm-74x74in) s.i.d.1968 painted wood relief prov.exhib. 1-Jul-3 Artcurial Briest, Paris #523/R est:12000-15000

TOMASI, Eugenio (attrib) (1873-1969) Italian
£1361 $2163 €2000 St Marks, Venice (17x22cm-7x9in) s. copper. 19-Mar-3 Neumeister, Munich #766 est:1000

TOMASO, Rico (1898-1985) American
£559 $900 €839 Landscape, European town on a river (61x152cm-24x60in) s. 20-Feb-3 Illustration House, New York #170/R

TOMASOVSKY, Karl (1918-1995) Austrian
£285 $444 €450 Village (67x50cm-26x20in) s. tempera. 15-Oct-2 Dorotheum, Vienna #230/R

TOMBA, Casimiro (1857-1929) Italian
Works on paper
£480 $730 €720 Target practice (53x37cm-21x15in) s. pencil W/C htd white. 4-Jul-2 Mellors & Kirk, Nottingham #800/R
£1274 $1987 €2000 Orientale accoudee (53x33cm-21x13in) s. W/C. 11-Nov-2 Horta, Bruxelles #541 est:2000-3000

TOMBELOS, I Ketut (1912-) Balinese
Works on paper
£1657 $2552 €2486 Men fighting with Kris and spears with a demon like woman in a tree (48x41cm-19x16in) wash pen ink W/C executed c.1935 prov. 27-Oct-2 Christie's, Hong Kong #21/R est:28000-38000 (HK.D 20000)

TOMBEUR, L H (?) French?
£909 $1427 €1364 Roses and chrysanthemum on a marble ledge (74x122cm-29x48in) s. 24-Jul-2 Walker's, Ottawa #43/R est:1500-2000 (C.D 2200)

TOMEA, Fiorenzo (1910-1960) Italian
£1987 $3080 €3100 Rural house (30x40cm-12x16in) s. board. 5-Dec-2 Stadion, Trieste #865/R
£2581 $4077 €4000 Landscape (47x34cm-19x13in) s. board prov. 18-Dec-2 Christie's, Rome #227/R
£5161 $8155 €8000 Flowers (50x40cm-20x16in) s. s.i.d.1955 verso. 18-Dec-2 Christie's, Rome #164/R
£5380 $8500 €8500 Winter landscape (53x49cm-21x19in) s. 30-Nov-2 Farsetti, Prato #743/R
£5449 $8554 €8500 Lamps (45x60cm-18x24in) s. s.i.verso painted 1955 exhib. 19-Nov-2 Finarte, Milan #198/R
Works on paper
£284 $443 €420 Landscape in Cadore (33x24cm-13x9in) s.d.1941 Chinese ink. 28-Mar-3 Farsetti, Prato #236

TOMEC, Heinrich (1863-1928) Austrian
£454 $736 €658 Old town square, Prague (26x18cm-10x7in) s.d.1923 panel. 24-May-3 Dorotheum, Prague #55/R est:12000-18000 (C.KR 20000)
£3481 $5500 €5500 Evening on the Wachau (60x80cm-24x31in) s. 26-Nov-2 Wiener Kunst Auktionen, Vienna #47/R est:3000-7000

TOMESCU, Aida (1955-) Australian
£1429 $2257 €2144 Shadeland (182x212cm-72x83in) i.d.90 prov. 27-Nov-2 Deutscher-Menzies, Melbourne #120/R est:4500-6500 (A.D 4000)
Works on paper
£1290 $1961 €1935 VII (121x80cm-48x31in) s.d.91 mixed media prov. 28-Aug-2 Deutscher-Menzies, Melbourne #362/R est:3000-5000 (A.D 3600)

TOMINETTI, Achille (1848-1917) Italian
£6410 $9359 €10000 Silence (70x93cm-28x37in) s.d.82. 5-Jun-2 Il Ponte, Milan #263/R est:4000-6000
£13605 $21633 €20000 Landscape with herds and farmers (50x64cm-20x25in) s.d.81. 18-Mar-3 Finarte, Milan #104/R
£14103 $21859 €22000 Shepherdess with sheep on alpine meadow in high mountain-chain (90x149cm-35x59in) s. 4-Dec-2 Neumeister, Munich #927/R est:7000
£18065 $28542 €28000 Landscape with sheeps (94x152cm-37x60in) s.d.1891. 18-Dec-2 Finarte, Milan #91/R est:22000

TOMINZ, Alfredo (1854-1936) Italian
£638 $1034 €900 Ritratto d'uomo con la rosa all'occhiello (60x50cm-24x20in) s. 22-May-3 Stadion, Trieste #238/R
£816 $1298 €1200 Landscape with farms (21x19cm-8x7in) s. cardboard. 18-Mar-3 Finarte, Milan #43/R
£5128 $8051 €8000 Outing on the beach (58x37cm-23x15in) s.d.07. 21-Nov-2 Van Ham, Cologne #1948/R est:4000
£6099 $9881 €8600 Passeggiata in carrozza (63x45cm-25x18in) s.d.05. 22-May-3 Stadion, Trieste #392/R est:4500-5500

TOMKINS, William (attrib) (1730-1792) British
£5000 $7750 €7500 Landscape with church, possibly Bere Regis, Dorset (59x87cm-23x34in) 3-Dec-2 Sotheby's, Olympia #10/R est:3000-5000

TOMLIN, Bradley Walker (1899-1953) American
£13750 $22000 €20625 Number 3 (57x86cm-22x34in) s.d.50 prov. 15-May-3 Christie's, Rockefeller NY #113/R est:15000-20000
£500000 $800000 €750000 Number 15 (117x193cm-46x76in) s. painted 1953 prov.exhib.lit. 13-May-3 Sotheby's, New York #11/R est:350000-450000
Works on paper
£1602 $2500 €2403 Self portrait (28x21cm-11x8in) s. pencil prov. 14-Oct-2 Butterfields, San Francisco #2040/R est:3000-5000

TOMMASI FERRONI, Riccardo (1934-2000) Italian
£1474 $2315 €2300 Portrait of Dafne expecting (70x50cm-28x20in) s. s.i.d.1991 verso. 21-Nov-2 Finarte, Rome #212/R
£2692 $4227 €4200 Self-portrait with Venus and Love (35x50cm-14x20in) s. s.i.verso. 23-Nov-2 Meeting Art, Vercelli #225/R
£2885 $4558 €4500 Moses saved from the river (70x100cm-28x39in) s. painted 1980. 15-Nov-2 Farsetti, Prato #582/R
Works on paper
£609 $956 €950 Icarus and satyrs (38x48cm-15x19in) s. mixed media paper on board exec.1996. 21-Nov-2 Finarte, Rome #115

TOMMASI, Adolfo (1851-1933) Italian
£1266 $2000 €2000 Tuscan landscape (17x25cm-7x10in) i.verso cavas on cardboard prov. 26-Nov-2 Christie's, Rome #145/R
£4839 $7645 €7500 Landscape (33x45cm-13x18in) s. cardboard. 18-Dec-2 Finarte, Milan #80/R est:9000

TOMMASI, Ludovico (1866-1941) Italian
£2041 $3245 €3000 Boats (27x37cm-11x15in) s. board. 18-Mar-3 Finarte, Milan #31/R
£2245 $3569 €3300 Washerwomen (37x27cm-15x11in) s.d.1911 i.verso board. 18-Mar-3 Finarte, Milan #109/R
£2449 $3894 €3600 Geese girl (12x17cm-5x7in) s. card. 18-Mar-3 Finarte, Milan #33/R
£2692 $4254 €4200 Peasant in landscape (37x44cm-15x17in) s. cardboard. 15-Nov-2 Farsetti, Prato #540/R
£3774 $5811 €6000 Rotonda dell'Ardenza (37x52cm-15x20in) s. cardboard. 23-Oct-2 Finarte, Milan #65/R
£7547 $11623 €12000 Pine grove at Campo Lecciano (63x83cm-25x33in) s. board. 23-Oct-2 Finarte, Milan #38/R est:12000-14000

TOMMASI, Publio de (1849-1914) Italian
£8800 $13816 €13200 Temptation beyond pearls (61x112cm-24x44in) s.i. 16-Dec-2 Bonhams, Bury St Edmunds #513/R est:5000-7000

TOMMASO (?) Italian
£9000 $15030 €13050 Announciation to Zaccharias (20x44cm-8x17in) panel prov.exhib.lit. 9-Jul-3 Bonhams, New Bond Street #1/R est:10000-15000

TOMPKINS, Riduan (1941-) New Zealander
£351 $558 €527 Two figures in colour plane (135x135cm-53x53in) s.d.1986-87 verso. 25-Feb-3 Peter Webb, Auckland #244 est:2000-3000 (NZ.D 1000)
£1115 $1750 €1673 Standing female figures - horizon red, gold, yellow (106x106cm-42x42in) s.d.1986-88 verso. 10-Dec-2 Peter Webb, Auckland #105/R est:4000-6000 (NZ.D 3500)

TONDEUR, Alexander (1829-1905) German
Sculpture
£3000 $4620 €4500 Bust of Frederick William Crown Prince of Prussia (59cm-23in) s.i. bronze. 5-Sep-2 Sotheby's, Olympia #99/R est:1500-2000

TONDL, Karel (1893-1980) Czechoslovakian
£268 $424 €402 Landscape with lake (28x44cm-11x17in) s. 30-Nov-2 Dorotheum, Prague #82/R (C.KR 13000)

TONER, Thomas N (1941-) American
£297 $475 €431 Sculptor (30x81cm-12x32in) s. board painted c.1970. 17-May-3 Selkirks, St. Louis #444

TONGE, Lammert van der (1871-1937) Dutch
£385 $600 €578 Young woman by a window (61x48cm-24x19in) s. 9-Oct-2 Doyle, New York #113

TONGEREN, Jan van (1897-1991) Dutch
£1389 $2292 €2000 Ribeauville (50x65cm-20x26in) s.d.1970. 1-Jul-3 Christie's, Amsterdam #369/R est:1500-2000
£3237 $5309 €4500 Stilleven in grijzen (62x80cm-24x31in) s.d.1954. 3-Jun-3 Christie's, Amsterdam #204/R est:5000-7000
£4676 $7669 €6500 Stilleven met tinnen kan - still life with pewter jar (55x60cm-22x24in) s.d.48 s.i.stretcher. 3-Jun-3 Christie's, Amsterdam #200/R est:6000-8000

£7692 $11923 €12000 Stilleven met rode bus (55x75cm-22x30in) s.d.1966 prov.exhib. 3-Dec-2 Christie's, Amsterdam #189/R est:12000-16000

TONK, Ernest (1889-1968) American
£2108 $3500 €3057 Today's Old West (61x76cm-24x30in) s. i.verso masonite prov. 11-Jun-3 Butterfields, San Francisco #4137/R est:3000-5000

TONKISS, Sam (20th C) British
Sculpture
£1900 $2983 €2850 Head of L S Lowry (33cm-13in) s.num.24/36 bronze i.f.Morris Singer. 21-Nov-2 Tennants, Leyburn #883/R est:500-800
£4000 $6360 €6000 Head of L S Lowry. Sold with photograph of Lowry (33cm-13in) edition 16 of 36 bronze marble plinth Cast Morris Moore. 18-Mar-3 Capes Dunn, Manchester #449/R

TONKS, Henry (1862-1937) British
Works on paper
£7500 $11925 €11250 Standing figure (42x22cm-17x9in) pencil pastel. 26-Feb-3 Sotheby's, Olympia #36/R est:800-1200

TONNA, Jean Baptiste (18th C) French
Works on paper
£473 $738 €700 Etude de pieds et de mains (22x31cm-9x12in) pierre noir chk. 31-Mar-3 Piasa, Paris #17

TONNANCOUR, Jacques de (1917-) Canadian
£762 $1220 €1143 Plaines de Novembre - Ciel Lourd (27x41cm-11x16in) s.d.1961 i.verso board prov. 15-May-3 Heffel, Vancouver #82 est:1500-2000 (C.D 1700)
£1156 $1895 €1734 Snowscape (40x60cm-16x24in) s.d.62 board. 3-Jun-3 Joyner, Toronto #228/R est:1500-2000 (C.D 2600)
£1345 $2152 €2018 l'essence de citron (61x61cm-24x24in) board prov. 15-May-3 Heffel, Vancouver #66/R est:4000-5000 (C.D 3000)
£1778 $2916 €2667 Baie Saint Paul (46x61cm-18x24in) s. panel prov. 27-May-3 Sotheby's, Toronto #65/R est:3000-5000 (C.D 4000)
£2419 $3823 €3629 Tree tops (40x61cm-16x24in) s.d.63 masonite prov.lit. 18-Nov-2 Sotheby's, Toronto #107/R est:7000-9000 (C.D 6000)
£5778 $9476 €8667 Femme au chandail gris - woman in grey (75x60cm-30x24in) s.d.59 board prov. 3-Jun-3 Joyner, Toronto #88/R est:8000-12000 (C.D 13000)
£9778 $16036 €14667 Still life (90x120cm-35x47in) s.d.59 board prov. 3-Jun-3 Joyner, Toronto #104/R est:25000-30000 (C.D 22000)
Works on paper
£2140 $3317 €3210 La fleche - the arrow (57x57cm-22x22in) s.d.71 mixed media prov. 3-Dec-2 Joyner, Toronto #150/R est:2000-3000 (C.D 5200)

TOOKER, George (1920-) American
£245161 $380000 €367742 Coney Island (49x67cm-19x26in) s. egg tempera panel prov.exhib.lit. 5-Dec-2 Christie's, Rockefeller NY #127/R est:250000-350000

TOORENVLIET, Jacob (1635-1719) Dutch
£1500 $2355 €2250 Washerwoman holding a roemer in her right hand (29x23cm-11x9in) canvas on panel. 10-Dec-2 Bonhams, New Bond Street #136/R est:1500-2000
£1509 $2355 €2400 Drunk (24x20cm-9x8in) mono. panel lit. 20-Sep-2 Schloss Ahlden, Ahlden #1064/R est:2400

TOOROP, Jan Th (1858-1928) Dutch
£282 $454 €400 Portrait of Aegidius Timmermans. s. lit. 7-May-3 Vendue Huis, Gravenhage #242
£282 $454 €400 Woman peeling potatoes. s. lit. 7-May-3 Vendue Huis, Gravenhage #243
£1348 $2183 €1900 Portrait of RP Chr de Greeve SJ (52x36cm-20x14in) s.i.d.1909 prov. 26-May-3 Glerum, Amsterdam #72/R est:2000-3000
£3503 $5465 €5500 Quay of Veere with figures and boats (10x14cm-4x6in) s.i.d.1903. 6-Nov-2 Vendue Huis, Gravenhage #574/R est:5000-7000
£35971 $58993 €50000 Zomer in Engels landschap - summer in English landscape (36x41cm-14x16in) s. oil pencil canvas on cardboard painted c.1897 prov.exhib.lit. 3-Jun-3 Christie's, Amsterdam #233/R est:60000-80000
Works on paper
£411 $642 €650 Portrait of Hugo Verriest (18x13cm-7x5in) s.i.d.1913. 21-Oct-2 Bernaerts, Antwerp #767
£764 $1192 €1200 Study of Abraham and Hagar in the desert (26x17cm-10x7in) s.d.1918 pencil dr. 6-Nov-2 Vendue Huis, Gravenhage #573/R
£1013 $1600 €1600 Vrouwen portret (42x35cm-17x14in) i. black chk. 26-Nov-2 Sotheby's, Amsterdam #27/R est:1500-2000
£1519 $2370 €2400 Figures at the quay (29x42cm-11x17in) s. pencil. 21-Oct-2 Bernaerts, Antwerp #620 est:2500-3000
£1600 $2608 €2400 Figure in armour (22x13cm-9x5in) s.d.1922 pencil prov. 3-Feb-3 Bonhams, New Bond Street #3/R est:800-1200
£4577 $7370 €6500 Flower (7x8cm-3x3in) s. dr W/C. 7-May-3 Vendue Huis, Gravenhage #533/R est:600-800
£10063 $16000 €15095 Portrait of Emma Bellwidt on Domburg beach (29x30cm-11x12in) s.d.1905 pastel chl pencil. 27-Feb-3 Christie's, Rockefeller NY #23/R est:30000
£14388 $23597 €20000 Jeanne d'Arc (16x11cm-6x4in) s.i.d.1898 pencil col pencil prov. 3-Jun-3 Christie's, Amsterdam #239/R est:4000-6000

TOPELIUS-ACKE, Eva (1855-1929) Finnish
Works on paper
£884 $1406 €1300 Landscape (47x40cm-19x16in) s.d.1894 W/C. 27-Feb-3 Hagelstam, Helsinki #965/R

TOPFFER, Wolfgang Adam (1766-1847) Swiss
£18868 $30566 €27359 River landscape (87x69cm-34x27in) s.i.d. 26-May-3 Sotheby's, Zurich #13/R est:28000-35000 (S.FR 40000)
£103226 $163097 €160000 Conscrits (55x76cm-22x30in) 18-Dec-2 Tajan, Paris #56/R est:120000-180000

TOPFFER, Wolfgang Adam (attrib) (1766-1847) Swiss
£5068 $7906 €7500 Study of tree (31x28cm-12x11in) paper on panel. 26-Mar-3 Tajan, Paris #109/R

TOPHAM, Francis William (1808-1877) British
£7609 $12478 €10500 Seaweed gatherers (59x83cm-23x33in) s.d.1873. 28-May-3 Bonhams & James Adam, Dublin #25/R est:10000-15000
Works on paper
£350 $567 €508 Girl with pitcher (30x22cm-12x9in) s.i.verso pencil W/C. 20-May-3 Dreweatt Neate, Newbury #161/R
£728 $1187 €1100 Family (36x44cm-14x17in) s.d.183 W/C. 11-Feb-3 Segre, Madrid #96/R
£1218 $1912 €1900 Girl listening to a seashell (25x22cm-10x9in) s. W/C htd white bodycol prov. 19-Nov-2 Whyte's, Dublin #95/R est:2000-3000
£1923 $2981 €3000 Irish cabin (23x33cm-9x13in) s.d.1849 W/C. 3-Dec-2 Bonhams & James Adam, Dublin #13/R est:2500-3000
£5128 $8051 €8000 Girl with basket of hens and a dog (64x52cm-25x20in) s.d.1872 W/C htd white bodycol. 19-Nov-2 Whyte's, Dublin #93/R est:8000-10000
£8176 $12755 €13000 Women and children listening to an Uillean piper, outside a cottage (44x62cm-17x24in) s.d.1862 W/C htd white. 17-Sep-2 Whyte's, Dublin #122/R est:10000-12000

TOPHAM, Frank William Warwick (1838-1929) British
£700 $1120 €1050 Portrait of a woman at a well (50x35cm-20x14in) s. 13-May-3 Bonhams, Knightsbridge #46/R
£1100 $1738 €1595 Figures on a Spanish terrace (51x36cm-20x14in) s.d.1873. 22-Jul-3 Gorringes, Lewes #1685 est:300-400
£3000 $4620 €4500 Prize in the lottery (56x79cm-22x31in) s.d.1880 exhib. 5-Sep-2 Christie's, Kensington #309/R est:3000-5000

TOPLIS, William A (fl.1875-1922) British
Works on paper
£1600 $2496 €2400 Sark rocks (34x25cm-13x10in) s.i.d.1890 W/C. 26-Mar-3 Bonhams & Langlois, Jersey #187/R est:300-400
£2100 $3255 €3150 Coast of Sark from Eperquerie (37x52cm-15x20in) s.d.99 W/C over pencil sold with miniature. 2-Oct-2 Bonhams, Knowle #42 est:1000-1500

TOPLIS, William A (attrib) (fl.1875-1922) British
Works on paper
£300 $474 €450 Le souffleur (23x33cm-9x13in) W/C. 27-Nov-2 Bonhams, Brooks & Langlois, Jersey #79/R

TOPOLSKI, Feliks (1907-1989) Polish
£680 $1054 €1020 Triumphant procession (71x92cm-28x36in) s.d.43. 3-Dec-2 Sotheby's, Olympia #312/R
£2500 $3900 €3750 Studio with Jan Stevenson, Yuki, Desmond Morris, Lady Diana Cooper (244x151cm-96x59in) 6-Nov-2 Dreweatt Neate, Newbury #318/R est:3000-4000
Works on paper
£280 $434 €420 Two Chinamen (29x34cm-11x13in) init. pen ink. 3-Dec-2 Bonhams, Knightsbridge #31/R
£280 $454 €420 Self portrait (25x21cm-10x8in) s.d.44 pen ink. 20-May-3 Bonhams, Knightsbridge #102
£500 $795 €750 Portrait of a gentleman (50x34cm-20x13in) s. chl. 20-Mar-3 Martel Maides, Guernsey #157
£540 $902 €783 Equestrian study (32x24cm-13x9in) s. pen W/C. 17-Jun-3 Bonhams, Knightsbridge #130/R

£780 $1217 €1170 Yuki fashion show (30x23cm-12x9in) one i. one d.85 pastel pair. 6-Nov-2 Dreweatt Neate, Newbury #94/R
£800 $1248 €1200 Yuki at Aspley House (22x30cm-9x12in) i. pastel. 6-Nov-2 Dreweatt Neate, Newbury #93/R
£820 $1279 €1230 Yuki fashion show (30x23cm-12x9in) i. pastel. 6-Nov-2 Dreweatt Neate, Newbury #95/R
£1500 $2340 €2250 Rome, Cappella Sistina - allied soldiers in Italy (76x54cm-30x21in) s.i.d.1944 pen ink wash. 25-Mar-3 Bonhams, New Bond Street #142/R est:1500-2000

TOPOR, Roland (1938-1997) French
£11644 $18281 €17000 Femme a la boule orange (54x65cm-21x26in) 15-Apr-3 Laurence Calmels, Paris #4226/R est:2000
Works on paper
£364 $594 €550 Homme pique-fleur (22x22cm-9x9in) s. Chinese ink. 3-Feb-3 Cornette de St.Cyr, Paris #536
£397 $648 €600 Ours (23x29cm-9x11in) s.i.d.1992 ink felt-tip pen col crayon. 3-Feb-3 Cornette de St.Cyr, Paris #537
£475 $741 €750 Languish (23x31cm-9x12in) s.d.1979 dr Indian ink W/C. 21-Oct-2 Bernaerts, Antwerp #651/R
£737 $1165 €1150 Peau d'ane (32x24cm-13x9in) s. W/C ink prov. 14-Nov-2 Credit Municipal, Paris #61
£764 $1260 €1100 Paysage (37x55cm-15x22in) ink col crayons spray. 3-Jul-3 Christie's, Paris #35/R
£1126 $1835 €1700 Grosse rousse (23x31cm-9x12in) s.d.1977 col crayon pastel Chinese ink. 3-Feb-3 Cornette de St.Cyr, Paris #535
£4167 $6875 €6000 Portrait de Jean-Charles de Castelbajac (32x25cm-13x10in) s. s.i.d.8-9-77 ink col crayons. 3-Jul-3 Christie's, Paris #44/R est:2000-3000

TOPP, Arnold (1887-1945) German
£19231 $29808 €30000 The town (85x60cm-33x24in) s.d. oil collage panel. 7-Dec-2 Hauswedell & Nolte, Hamburg #1050/R est:35000
Works on paper
£12821 $19872 €20000 Composition (36x27cm-14x11in) s.i.d. gouache. 7-Dec-2 Hauswedell & Nolte, Hamburg #1051/R est:20000

TOPPELIUS, Woldemar (1858-1933) Russian
£884 $1406 €1300 Coastal landscape (36x50cm-14x20in) s.d.1912. 24-Mar-3 Bukowskis, Helsinki #328/R
£915 $1474 €1300 Foam on the beach (22x31cm-9x12in) s.d.01 board. 10-May-3 Bukowskis, Helsinki #181/R
£949 $1500 €1500 West coast (36x50cm-14x20in) s.d.07 board. 1-Dec-2 Bukowskis, Helsinki #198/R est:2000-2500
£1384 $2145 €2200 Home bay (30x45cm-12x18in) s. 6-Oct-2 Bukowskis, Helsinki #303/R est:2000
£1392 $2200 €2200 Red cliffs (33x46cm-13x18in) s.d.1916. 30-Nov-2 Hagelstam, Helsinki #125/R est:2500
£2109 $3353 €3100 Coastal landscape (19x33cm-7x13in) s.d.04. 24-Mar-3 Bukowskis, Helsinki #329/R est:1500
£2405 $3800 €3800 Summer's day (32x49cm-13x19in) s. 1-Dec-2 Bukowskis, Helsinki #197/R est:2500-3000
£2785 $4400 €4400 Sailing in the skerries (33x28cm-13x11in) S.D.98. 1-Dec-2 Bukowskis, Helsinki #199/R est:2500-2800

TOPPING, James (1879-1949) American
£506 $800 €759 Among the Hilla O'Brown county (23x25cm-9x10in) s. board. 5-Apr-3 Susanin's, Chicago #5015/R
£1656 $2600 €2484 Autumn landscape (36x33cm-14x13in) s. board. 14-Dec-2 Charlton Hall, Columbia #454/R est:1000-1500
£1761 $2800 €2642 Old willows (24x28cm-9x11in) s. painted c.1920. 4-May-3 Treadway Gallery, Cincinnati #551/R est:2000-3000
£2044 $3250 €2964 Clouds of Illinois (24x28cm-9x11in) s. painted c.1920. 4-May-3 Treadway Gallery, Cincinnati #553/R est:2000-3000

TORAL, Cristobal (1938-) Spanish
£14189 $22135 €21000 Luggage with blue bag (38x46cm-15x18in) s. exhib. 25-Mar-3 Durán, Madrid #203/R est:21000

TORCHET, Julie (?) ?
£253 $395 €400 Pecheurs dans un paysage fluvial (50x58cm-20x23in) 16-Sep-2 Amberes, Antwerp #257

TORCIA, Francesco Saverio (1840-?) Italian
£270 $418 €405 Village street with figures in sunshine (23x39cm-9x15in) s. panel. 8-Dec-2 Uppsala Auktionskammare, Uppsala #57/R (S.KR 3800)

TORDI, Sinibaldo (1876-1955) Italian
£400 $632 €600 Serenade (20x30cm-8x12in) s. 14-Nov-2 Christie's, Kensington #130

TORDOFF, Fred (20th C) American?
£223 $350 €335 West Point Lighthouse, River Hudson, New York (28x36cm-11x14in) s. panel. 22-Nov-2 Eldred, East Dennis #665/R
£255 $400 €383 American whaleship in the ice (20x28cm-8x11in) s. panel. 26-Jul-2 Eldred, East Dennis #374/R
£255 $400 €383 South seas whaling (20x43cm-8x17in) s. panel. 22-Nov-2 Eldred, East Dennis #669/R
£256 $400 €384 Whalers in the north (33x36cm-13x14in) s. 28-Mar-3 Eldred, East Dennis #623/R
£256 $400 €384 Ship passing the Diamond Shoal Lightship (41x51cm-16x20in) s. 28-Mar-3 Eldred, East Dennis #625/R
£271 $425 €407 French blockade of Yorktown (71x81cm-28x32in) 28-Jul-2 William Jenack, New York #352
£288 $450 €432 Whaling ship departing Nantucket (25x46cm-10x18in) s. 28-Mar-3 Eldred, East Dennis #624/R
£382 $600 €573 Town of Hudson from four mile point, Hudson River (28x36cm-11x14in) s. panel. 22-Nov-2 Eldred, East Dennis #668/R
£385 $600 €578 American whale ship with whale sounding (30x41cm-12x16in) s. 1-Aug-2 Eldred, East Dennis #1097
£637 $1000 €956 The Boston packet ship Chariot of fame (51x61cm-20x24in) s. 26-Jul-2 Eldred, East Dennis #372/R est:700-900
£673 $1050 €1010 Shipping off Cape Town (64x76cm-25x30in) s. 1-Aug-2 Eldred, East Dennis #1094/R
£1210 $1900 €1815 Ship Belle of the West (74x97cm-29x38in) s. 26-Jul-2 Eldred, East Dennis #373/R est:800-1200

TORELLI, Felice (1667-1748) Italian
£32000 $53440 €46400 Rebekah at the well (125x186cm-49x73in) 9-Jul-3 Christie's, London #100/R est:30000-40000

TORELLI, Stefano (attrib) (1712-1784) Italian
£1809 $2749 €2714 Portrait of Count Heinrich Carl Schimmelmann (52x40cm-20x16in) 28-Aug-2 Museumsbygningen, Copenhagen #25/R est:25000-30000 (D.KR 21000)

TORETTI, P (19/20th C) Italian
£1117 $1777 €1676 River landscape with young couple flirting, Italy (69x105cm-27x41in) s. 10-Mar-3 Rasmussen, Vejle #524/R est:12000-15000 (D.KR 12000)

TORGERSEN, Thorvald (1862-1943) Norwegian
£1301 $2029 €1952 View of Nykoping (58x47cm-23x19in) s.i.d.1913. 21-Oct-2 Blomqvist, Oslo #341/R est:20000 (N.KR 15000)
£2755 $4518 €3995 Quiet time in evening (98x53cm-39x21in) s.d.1901. 2-Jun-3 Blomqvist, Oslo #177/R est:18000-22000 (N.KR 30000)
£3489 $5723 €5059 Sun, summer and children (61x66cm-24x26in) s. 2-Jun-3 Blomqvist, Oslo #86/R est:40000-50000 (N.KR 38000)
£3633 $5740 €5450 Children on bare rock-face (66x86cm-26x34in) s. 2-Dec-2 Blomqvist, Oslo #367/R est:40000-50000 (N.KR 42000)

TORGGLER, Hermann (1878-1939) Austrian
£432 $708 €600 Lady with hat seated (106x95cm-42x37in) s.d.1906. 5-Jun-3 Dorotheum, Salzburg #515/R

TORHAMN, Gunnar (1894-1955) Swedish
£241 $372 €362 Four Arabian men (60x90cm-24x35in) s. 27-Oct-2 Anders Antik, Landskrona #568/R (S.KR 3500)
£302 $471 €453 Meeting by the gate (18x27cm-7x11in) s. panel. 13-Sep-2 Lilla Bukowskis, Stockholm #757 (S.KR 4400)
£1004 $1666 €1456 Walking on the west coast in spring (38x46cm-15x18in) s. panel. 16-Jun-3 Lilla Bukowskis, Stockholm #910 (S.KR 13000)
£1552 $2514 €2250 Fishing village with women working (50x60cm-20x24in) s. panel. 25-May-3 Uppsala Auktionskammare, Uppsala #262/R est:10000-12000 (S.KR 20000)
£1648 $2669 €2472 Fishermen from the West coast (53x65cm-21x26in) S. PA. 3-Feb-3 Lilla Bukowskis, Stockholm #622 est:10000-12000 (S.KR 23000)
£1773 $2748 €2660 Figures by the sea, Blekinge (55x65cm-22x26in) s. panel. 8-Dec-2 Uppsala Auktionskammare, Uppsala #208/R est:10000-15000 (S.KR 25000)
£2242 $3498 €3363 Woman with violin (53x40cm-21x16in) 5-Nov-2 Bukowskis, Stockholm #221/R est:25000-30000 (S.KR 32000)

TORHAMN, Ingegerd (1898-1994) Swedish
£343 $522 €515 Displaced heath (46x55cm-18x22in) mono. panel. 16-Aug-2 Lilla Bukowskis, Stockholm #17 (S.KR 5000)

TORIMARU, Gnyuki (20th C) British?
Works on paper
£350 $546 €525 Original design for white evening dress for Princess Diana (31x25cm-12x10in) s.d.1986 pencil W/C. 6-Nov-2 Dreweatt Neate, Newbury #519/R
£400 $624 €600 Original design for red evening gown for Princess Diana (31x25cm-12x10in) s.d.1986 pencil pen W/C. 6-Nov-2 Dreweatt Neate, Newbury #513/R

£420 $655 €630 Original design for green evening dress for Princess Diana (31x25cm-12x10in) s.d.1986 pencil W/C. 6-Nov-2 Dreweatt Neate, Newbury #517/R
£500 $780 €750 Original design for a blue evening dress for Princess Diana (31x25cm-12x10in) s. pencil pen W/C. 6-Nov-2 Dreweatt Neate, Newbury #515/R
£520 $811 €780 Original design for red strapless evening dress for Princess Diana (31x25cm-12x10in) s.d.1986 pencil pen W/C. 6-Nov-2 Dreweatt Neate, Newbury #514/R
£520 $811 €780 Original sketch for an evening dress worn by Princess Diana (30x20cm-12x8in) d.86 pencil. 6-Nov-2 Dreweatt Neate, Newbury #549/R
£580 $905 €870 Original design for white evening dress for Princess Diana (31x25cm-12x10in) s.d.1986 pencil pen W/C. 6-Nov-2 Dreweatt Neate, Newbury #520/R
£600 $936 €900 Original design for black and white ensemble for Princess Diana (31x25cm-12x10in) s.d.1986 pencil pen W/C. 6-Nov-2 Dreweatt Neate, Newbury #522/R
£650 $1014 €975 Original design for black and white evening ensemble for Princess Diana (31x25cm-12x10in) s.d.1986 pencil pen W/C. 6-Nov-2 Dreweatt Neate, Newbury #521/R
£720 $1123 €1080 Original design for an esemble with green, purple, white for Princess Diana (31x25cm-12x10in) s.d.1986 pencil pen W/C. 6-Nov-2 Dreweatt Neate, Newbury #523/R
£800 $1248 €1200 Original design for evening dress for Princess Diana (31x25cm-12x10in) s.d.1986 pencil W/C. 6-Nov-2 Dreweatt Neate, Newbury #518/R
£900 $1404 €1350 Original design for blue evening dress for Princess Diana (31x25cm-12x10in) s.d.1986 pencil pen W/C. 6-Nov-2 Dreweatt Neate, Newbury #516/R

TORNA, Oscar (1842-1894) Swedish
£350 $553 €525 Gypsy family in prison (44x36cm-17x14in) s. canvas on panel. 16-Nov-2 Crafoord, Lund #95/R (S.KR 5000)
£772 $1282 €1119 Winter landscape at sunset (35x64cm-14x25in) s.i.d.1876. 16-Jun-3 Lilla Bukowskis, Stockholm #484 (S.KR 10000)
£775 $1247 €1100 Summer evening (61x92cm-24x36in) 10-May-3 Bukowskis, Helsinki #369/R
£965 $1602 €1399 Moonlit landscape from Drottningholm (80x64cm-31x25in) s.d.1885 sold with letter. 16-Jun-3 Lilla Bukowskis, Stockholm #669 (S.KR 12500)
£1571 $2577 €2278 Moonlight over Vattern (93x74cm-37x29in) s.d.1892. 4-Jun-3 AB Stockholms Auktionsverk #2222/R est:30000-40000 (S.KR 20000)
£1773 $2748 €2660 Lake landscape with jetty (60x84cm-24x33in) s. 4-Dec-2 AB Stockholms Auktionsverk #1592/R est:20000-25000 (S.KR 25000)
£1844 $2858 €2766 Children on a road, Medevi (53x46cm-21x18in) s.i. 4-Dec-2 AB Stockholms Auktionsverk #1589/R est:15000-20000 (S.KR 26000)
£2482 $3848 €3723 Chemin des vaches (148x114cm-58x45in) s.d.Decembre 1877 prov. 3-Dec-2 Bukowskis, Stockholm #30/R est:50000-55000 (S.KR 35000)
£3404 $5277 €5106 Lake landscape with cattle grazing (79x119cm-31x47in) s.d.1869. 3-Dec-2 Bukowskis, Stockholm #30a/R est:40000-50000 (S.KR 48000)

TORNABUONI, Lorenzo (1934-) Italian
£1154 $1812 €1800 Seated man (90x40cm-35x16in) s.d.1973 oil mixed media board. 21-Nov-2 Finarte, Rome #284/R
Works on paper
£342 $534 €500 Figures (36x59cm-14x23in) s. Chinese ink W/C. 10-Apr-3 Finarte Semenzato, Rome #111

TORNAI, Gyula (1861-1928) Hungarian
£1419 $2213 €2058 Entrance of a church in Kioto (50x34cm-20x13in) s. panel exhib. 13-Sep-2 Mu Terem Galeria, Budapest #144/R est:280000 (H.F 550000)
£3800 $6346 €5700 Oriental lute player (98x69cm-39x27in) s. board. 18-Jun-3 Christie's, Kensington #186/R est:4000-6000
£5806 $9174 €9000 Antiquaire (105x60cm-41x24in) s. cardboard. 19-Dec-2 Claude Aguttes, Neuilly #141/R est:10000
£5916 $9170 €8578 Ladies of the harem (89x81cm-35x32in) papercard. 9-Dec-2 Mu Terem Galeria, Budapest #153/R est:1300000 (H.F 2200000)
£12371 $19174 €18557 Oriental scene (168x134cm-66x53in) s. 6-Dec-2 Kieselbach, Budapest #124/R (H.F 4600000)

TORNEMAN, Axel (1880-1925) Swedish
£14352 $23251 €20810 The violin player - the lunatic (170x93cm-67x37in) exhib.prov. 26-May-3 Bukowskis, Stockholm #128/R est:250000-300000 (S.KR 185000)

TORNER, Carl Erik (1862-1911) Scandinavian
£496 $770 €744 Gnome playing with ants (95x68cm-37x27in) s.d.1 jan 03 8-Dec-2 Uppsala Auktionskammare, Uppsala #87/R (S.KR 7000)

TORNIOLI, Niccolo (1598-1651) Italian
£12903 $20000 €19355 Madonna and Child with the Infant St John the Baptist (74x61cm-29x24in) 2-Oct-2 Christie's, Rockefeller NY #129/R est:20000-30000

TORNIOLI, Niccolo (attrib) (1598-1651) Italian
£3586 $5738 €5200 David and Saul's guards (79x125cm-31x49in) lit. 17-Mar-3 Pandolfini, Florence #585/R est:6000-8000

TORNOE, Wenzel (1844-1907) Danish
£258 $393 €387 Two musicians (34x30cm-13x12in) s.d.1866. 27-Aug-2 Rasmussen, Copenhagen #1602/R (D.KR 3000)
£650 $1086 €943 Wistful thought (54x35cm-21x14in) 8-Jul-3 Bonhams, Knightsbridge #142/R
£766 $1240 €1111 Cottage interior with woman carding wool (57x42cm-22x17in) indis sig. 26-May-3 Rasmussen, Copenhagen #1329/R (D.KR 8000)
£957 $1550 €1388 Italian man wearing red (37x31cm-15x12in) init.d.1890. 26-May-3 Rasmussen, Copenhagen #1551/R (D.KR 10000)
£2326 $3535 €3489 Girl reading wearing pink party-dress (38x28cm-15x11in) init. 27-Aug-2 Rasmussen, Copenhagen #1456/R est:15000-25000 (D.KR 27000)
£3349 $5426 €4856 From an inn with young man flirting with Italian woman while another looks jealous (80x104cm-31x41in) s. prov. 26-May-3 Rasmussen, Copenhagen #1129/R est:60000-80000 (D.KR 35000)
£4307 $6546 €6461 Homely pursuits - Grandmother and small girl sewing (80x64cm-31x25in) s. 27-Aug-2 Rasmussen, Copenhagen #1457/R est:50000 (D.KR 50000)

TORNQUIST, Jorrit (1938-) Austrian
£811 $1265 €1200 Untitled (55x110cm-22x43in) s.i.d.1969 verso acrylic. 26-Mar-3 Finarte Semenzato, Milan #386/R

TORNYAI, Janos (1869-1936) Hungarian
£370 $573 €555 Mother and child (19x25cm-7x10in) panel. 9-Dec-2 Philippe Schuler, Zurich #8684 (S.FR 850)
£722 $1127 €1047 Landscape by sunset (36x49cm-14x19in) s. 13-Sep-2 Mu Terem Galeria, Budapest #88/R est:180000 (H.F 280000)
£838 $1308 €1215 Autumn trees (36x48cm-14x19in) s. board. 12-Apr-3 Mu Terem Galeria, Budapest #214/R est:220000 (H.F 300000)
£968 $1501 €1404 Landscape of the plain (41x35cm-16x14in) s. card. 9-Dec-2 Mu Terem Galeria, Budapest #137/R est:280000 (H.F 360000)

TORO, Attilio (1892-?) Italian
£1203 $1900 €1900 Girl, half length (31x25cm-12x10in) s. cardboard. 26-Nov-2 Christie's, Rome #260/R
£1266 $2000 €2000 Girl at mirror (40x31cm-16x12in) s. panel. 26-Nov-2 Christie's, Rome #257/R
£1392 $2200 €2200 Young woman (28x20cm-11x8in) s. panel. 26-Nov-2 Christie's, Rome #258/R
£1899 $3000 €3000 Nude (50x40cm-20x16in) s. panel. 26-Nov-2 Christie's, Rome #259/R
£2721 $4327 €4000 Interior with young woman smiling (65x54cm-26x21in) s. 18-Mar-3 Finarte, Milan #128/R

TORO, Luigi (1836-1900) Italian
£620 $967 €930 Portrait of a girl (38x28cm-15x11in) s. board. 26-Mar-3 Woolley & Wallis, Salisbury #183/R

TORO, Raffaello (?) Italian
£10000 $16700 €14500 Venice, view of the Riva Degli Schiavoni. View of the Church Santa Maria Della Salute (39x61cm-15x24in) one s.verso pair after M Marieschi and Canaletto. 8-Jul-3 Sotheby's, Olympia #493/R est:6000-8000

TOROK, Eduard (1836-1892) Hungarian
£419 $654 €629 In the school (27x36cm-11x14in) s.d.1869. 11-Apr-3 Kieselbach, Budapest #183/R est:140000-150000 (H.F 150000)

TORRE, Flaminio (1621-1661) Italian
Works on paper
£750 $1253 €1088 Virgin and Child accompanied by cherubim appearing to a monk (29x19cm-11x7in) black chk within cartouche. 9-Jul-3 Bonhams, Knightsbridge #46/R

TORRE, Flaminio (attrib) (1621-1661) Italian
£3500 $5459 €5250 Sibyl (48x39cm-19x15in) 19-Sep-2 Christie's, Kensington #216/R est:4000-6000

TORRE, Giulio del (1856-1932) Italian
£4717 $7264 €7500 Little smokers (24x18cm-9x7in) s.d.1893 panel. 22-Oct-2 Wiener Kunst Auktionen, Vienna #1081/R est:600-1400
£6000 $9540 €9000 Boys peeling oranges. Boys playing cards (2x23cm-1x9in) s.d.1907 panel pair. 20-Mar-3 Christie's, Kensington #49/R est:6000-8000

TORREGIANI, Bartolomeo (1590-c.1675) Italian
£3049 $5000 €4574 Finding of Moses (77x96cm-30x38in) 5-Feb-3 Christie's, Rockefeller NY #268/R est:6000-8000
£6918 $10723 €11000 View of the Castello di Populonia (40x90cm-16x35in) 2-Oct-2 Dorotheum, Vienna #66/R est:10000-16000

TORRES FUSTER, Alberto (19th C) Spanish
£820 $1337 €1230 Spanish beauty (28x21cm-11x8in) s.d.95 panel. 29-Jan-3 Sotheby's, Olympia #282/R

TORRES FUSTER, Antonio (1874-1945) Spanish
£494 $820 €716 Woman (61x45cm-24x18in) s. 16-Jun-3 Lilla Bukowskis, Stockholm #64 (S.KR 6400)

TORRES, Augusto (1913-1992) Uruguayan
£2250 $3600 €3375 Still life with flask (70x82cm-28x32in) s. 5-Jan-3 Galleria Y Remates, Montevideo #97/R
£2875 $4600 €4313 Montparnasse (45x59cm-18x23in) s. 5-Jan-3 Galleria Y Remates, Montevideo #96/R
£3019 $4800 €4529 Urban landscape with bar (41x51cm-16x20in) s. cardboard. 2-Mar-3 Galleria Y Remates, Montevideo #78/R

TORRES, Horacio (1924-1976) Uruguayan
£314 $500 €471 Arlequin (50x36cm-20x14in) s.d.1960. 2-Mar-3 Galleria Y Remates, Montevideo #33/R
£1987 $3100 €2981 Iglesia Romanica (80x70cm-31x28in) 30-Jul-2 Galleria Y Remates, Montevideo #87/R est:3500-4500

TORRES-GARCIA, Joaquin (1874-1949) Uruguayan
£19745 $31000 €29618 Plate with cheese (33x41cm-13x16in) s.d.28 prov.lit. 19-Nov-2 Sotheby's, New York #92/R est:35000
£24375 $39000 €36563 Objects on table (42x51cm-17x20in) s.d.43 cardboard exhib. 5-Jan-3 Galleria Y Remates, Montevideo #93/R est:45000
£25610 $42000 €38415 Rostro de mujer (38x28cm-15x11in) s.d.40 prov. 28-May-3 Christie's, Rockefeller NY #115/R est:20000-25000
£27244 $42772 €42500 Boats (60x72cm-24x28in) s. 16-Dec-2 Castellana, Madrid #932/R est:18000
£33333 $53000 €50000 Still life (36x59cm-14x23in) s.d.28 canvas on cardboard. 2-Mar-3 Galleria Y Remates, Montevideo #71/R est:70000
£146341 $240000 €219512 Composicion (51x40cm-20x16in) s.d.31 tempera prov. 28-May-3 Christie's, Rockefeller NY #24/R est:250000-350000
£203822 $320000 €305733 Constructif avec ritmes denteles (85x54cm-33x21in) s.d.31 tempera prov.exhib. 20-Nov-2 Christie's, Rockefeller NY #18/R est:200000-250000
Sculpture
£2483 $3923 €3600 Constructive (26x16cm-10x6in) s.st.f.Taba s.verso num.1/2 bronze. 1-Apr-3 Segre, Madrid #179/R
Works on paper
£1122 $1638 €1750 Untitled (23x15cm-9x6in) s.d.1945 ink pencil. 6-Jun-2 Castellana, Madrid #26/R
£10976 $18000 €15915 Compositions (22x17cm-9x7in) one s. two d. graphite five. 27-May-3 Sotheby's, New York #115
£14650 $23000 €21975 Untitled (14x19cm-6x7in) one s.d. graphite exec.1942 set of 5 lit. 19-Nov-2 Sotheby's, New York #91/R est:18000

TORRESPRAT, Enric (1938-) Spanish
£822 $1282 €1200 Pond (64x91cm-25x36in) s. 8-Apr-3 Ansorena, Madrid #19/R
£1507 $2351 €2200 Girl on the beach (92x65cm-36x26in) s. 8-Apr-3 Ansorena, Madrid #18/R est:1200

TORRICO PARDO, Gonzalo (20th C) Mexican
£187 $302 €281 Six pears (60x50cm-24x20in) s. 21-Jan-3 Louis Morton, Mexico #82 (M.P 3200)
£292 $473 €438 Women from Tehuantepec (88x69cm-35x27in) s. 21-Jan-3 Louis Morton, Mexico #72 (M.P 5000)

TORRIGLIA, Giovanni Battista (1858-1937) Italian
£26000 $40820 €39000 Bath time (73x111cm-29x44in) s. 19-Nov-2 Bonhams, New Bond Street #86/R est:20000-30000
£75000 $123000 €112500 Web of life (73x111cm-29x44in) s. 3-Jun-3 Sotheby's, London #170/R est:60000-80000

TORRINI, E (19th C) Italian
£1195 $1900 €1793 Mending (35x45cm-14x18in) s. 7-Mar-3 Skinner, Boston #241/R est:800-1200

TORRISET, Kjell (1950-) Norwegian
£398 $649 €597 Figure walking (60x114cm-24x45in) s.verso tempera. 17-Feb-3 Blomqvist, Lysaker #1241 (N.KR 4500)
£692 $1093 €1038 Deep stream (50x109cm-20x43in) init. s.i.d.1987 verso. 2-Dec-2 Blomqvist, Oslo #488/R (N.KR 8000)
Works on paper
£708 $1154 €1062 Man in boat with ladder (77x104cm-30x41in) s. gouache. 17-Feb-3 Blomqvist, Lysaker #1243/R (N.KR 8000)

TORSCHENKO, Igor (1965-) Russian
£1667 $2633 €2600 Fire in the heart (140x120cm-55x47in) mono.i.cyrillic.d.98 mollino. 12-Nov-2 Dorotheum, Vienna #288/R est:4000-5000

TORSLEFF, August (1884-1968) Danish
£345 $524 €518 Portrait of young girl wearing white dress (100x74cm-39x29in) s.d.1919. 27-Aug-2 Rasmussen, Copenhagen #1872/R (D.KR 4000)

TORSO, Alessandro del (1883-?) Italian
£461 $747 €650 Case in alta montagna (53x40cm-21x16in) board prov. 22-May-3 Stadion, Trieste #388/R

TORSSLOW, Harald (1838-1909) Swedish
£1853 $2817 €2780 Summer landscape with water and small holding (110x150cm-43x59in) s.d.1884. 16-Aug-2 Lilla Bukowskis, Stockholm #773 est:25000-30000 (S.KR 27000)
£3671 $5800 €5800 Summer morning (60x98cm-24x39in) s.d.1879. 1-Dec-2 Bukowskis, Helsinki #277/R est:2500-3000

TORTEZ, Victor (1890-?) French
£2655 $4141 €3983 Parisian model in painter's studio (81x54cm-32x21in) s. 11-Apr-3 Kieselbach, Budapest #79/R est:800000-950000 (H.F 950000)

TOSANI, Patrick (20th C) ?
Photographs
£3401 $5408 €5000 Niveau plus 1 (119x152cm-47x60in) s.i.d.1990 num.2/3 cibachrome print prov.exhib. 24-Mar-3 Cornette de St.Cyr, Paris #179/R est:6000

TOSCANI, Giovanni di Francesco (c.1370-1430) Italian
£118056 $187708 €170000 Madonna of Humility (110x50cm-43x20in) board lit. 4-May-3 Finarte, Venice #575/R est:180000-210000

TOSI, Arturo (1871-1956) Italian
£5449 $8554 €8500 Portofino seen from Rapallo (40x32cm-16x13in) s. 19-Nov-2 Finarte, Milan #270/R
£6383 $10340 €9000 Venezia, Punta della Dogana (40x32cm-16x13in) s. prov. 26-May-3 Christie's, Milan #316/R est:10000-12000
£6410 $10064 €10000 Landscape by Rovetta (31x40cm-12x16in) s. painted 1950 lit. 23-Nov-2 Meeting Art, Vercelli #495/R est:10000
£6738 $10915 €9500 Autumn (50x60cm-20x24in) s. c.1937-38 prov. 26-May-3 Christie's, Milan #119/R est:9000-13000
£7097 $11213 €11000 Still life (49x60cm-19x24in) s. board prov.exhib. 18-Dec-2 Christie's, Rome #271/R
£8497 $13595 €13000 Landscape (50x60cm-20x24in) s. painted 1940 lit. 4-Jan-3 Meeting Art, Vercelli #748 est:13000
£10323 $16310 €16000 Zoagli (70x90cm-28x35in) s. painted c.1938 prov.exhib. 18-Dec-2 Christie's, Rome #226/R est:20000
Works on paper
£1361 $2163 €2000 Landscape (28x34cm-11x13in) s. pastel. 1-Mar-3 Meeting Art, Vercelli #493
£1389 $2208 €2000 Landscape (24x35cm-9x14in) s. W/C. 1-May-3 Meeting Art, Vercelli #295

TOSINI, Michele (1503-1577) Italian
£11702 $18957 €16500 Young man portrait with allegorical arts medallion (58x47cm-23x19in) wood circle of Michele di Ridolfo del Ghirlandaio. 20-May-3 Babuino, Rome #5/R est:5000-7000

TOSINI, Michele (studio) (1503-1577) Italian
£24000 $40080 €34800 Madonna and Child with the infant Saint John the Baptist (102x81cm-40x32in) panel. 10-Jul-3 Sotheby's, London #164/R est:8000-12000

TOSSEY, Verne (19/20th C) American
Works on paper
£373 $600 €560 Head of woman applying lipstick (38x25cm-15x10in) s.d.1950 gouache. 20-Feb-3 Illustration House, New York #171/R
£897 $1400 €1346 Boy reading magazine next to newstand (33x25cm-13x10in) gouache. 9-Nov-2 Illustration House, New York #129/R

TOSSYN, J (19th C) ?
£641 $1000 €962 Portrait of a lady (65x51cm-26x20in) s.d.1880 panel. 20-Sep-2 Sloan, North Bethesda #429/R est:600-800

TOT, Amerigo (1919-) Italian
Sculpture
£3911 $6102 €6180 Maternity (42x24x26cm-17x9x10in) bronze exec.1947. 15-Oct-2 Babuino, Rome #334/R

TOTH, Pavol (1928-1988) Czechoslovakian
Sculpture
£1575 $2441 €2363 Sitting (49cm-19in) bronze marble base. 1-Oct-2 SOGA, Bratislava #285/R est:40000 (SL.K 100000)

TOTH, Sandor (1904-1980) Hungarian
£16136 $25010 €24204 Escaping nymph (89x66cm-35x26in) s. 6-Dec-2 Kieselbach, Budapest #106/R (H.F 6000000)

TOTH, Tibor (1962-2001) Hungarian
£256 $403 €400 Bali I (80x100cm-31x39in) s.d.1994 tempera board prov. 21-Nov-2 Dorotheum, Vienna #518/R
£256 $403 €400 Oriental night (80x100cm-31x39in) s.d.1994 tempera board prov. 21-Nov-2 Dorotheum, Vienna #519/R

TOTT, Alois (1870-1939) Austrian
£476 $757 €700 Tyrolean mountain village (30x42cm-12x17in) s. i. verso board. 20-Mar-3 Neumeister, Munich #2755/R
Works on paper
£314 $487 €500 Summers day in Ruhrsdorf, Wachau (28x39cm-11x15in) i. gouache board. 1-Oct-2 Dorotheum, Vienna #337/R

TOTTIE, Sophie (1964-) Swedish
£2357 $3725 €3536 Untitled (200x100cm-79x39in) oil on stainless steel painted 1992-93 prov. 28-Apr-3 Bukowskis, Stockholm #961/R est:15000-20000 (S.KR 31000)

TOUDOUZE, Simon Alexandre (1850-1909) French
£349 $545 €524 La mare aux fees (36x49cm-14x19in) s.i.d.1887 panel. 6-Nov-2 Dobiaschofsky, Bern #1018/R (S.FR 800)

TOULMOUCHE, Auguste (1829-1890) French
£556 $884 €800 La jeune servante (16x8cm-6x3in) s. paper on panel. 29-Apr-3 Artcurial Briest, Paris #154
£2000 $3100 €3000 Tranquil afternoon (43x61cm-17x24in) s. 5-Dec-2 Christie's, Kensington #12/R est:1800-2200

TOULOUSE-LAUTREC, Henri de (1864-1901) French
£3974 $6240 €6200 Malrome (17x10cm-7x4in) panel painted c.1883 lit. 13-Dec-2 Piasa, Paris #221/R
£6731 $10567 €10500 Deux boeufs sur le joug (20x16cm-8x6in) panel lit. 13-Dec-2 Piasa, Paris #222/R est:9000
£40000 $66800 €58000 Chien de chasse (33x42cm-13x17in) mono.d.1881 prov.exhib.lit. 25-Jun-3 Christie's, London #113/R est:40000-50000
£68323 $110000 €102485 Yvette Guilbert (51x28cm-20x11in) mono.i.verso partially painted glazed ceramic executed 1895 lit. 8-May-3 Christie's, Rockefeller NY #139/R est:50000-70000
£68323 $110000 €102485 L'image - Marthe Mellot debout de profil (48x33cm-19x13in) mono.i. thinned oil pen India ink pencil collage on board prov. 8-May-3 Christie's, Rockefeller NY #152/R est:120000-160000
£99379 $160000 €149069 Academie d'homme nu buste (81x65cm-32x26in) s. painted c.1883 prov.exhib.lit. 8-May-3 Christie's, Rockefeller NY #147/R est:100000-150000
£237180 $370000 €355770 L loge (38x28cm-15x11in) painted c.1889 prov.exhib.lit. 6-Nov-2 Sotheby's, New York #124/R est:300000-400000
Prints
£1824 $2846 €2700 Aube (61x80cm-24x31in) col lithograph exec.1896. 31-Mar-3 Tajan, Paris #397/R
£1840 $3000 €2760 Au pied de l'Echafaud (83x61cm-33x24in) col lithograph exec.1893. 13-Feb-3 Christie's, Rockefeller NY #197/R
£1887 $3000 €2831 Madameoiselle Marcelle Lender, en buste (84x64cm-33x25in) d.1895 col lithograph. 30-Apr-3 Doyle, New York #311/R
£1923 $3000 €2885 Le petit trottin (35x27cm-14x11in) stencil col lithograph. 5-Nov-2 Christie's, Rockefeller NY #31/R est:2500-3500
£1944 $3092 €2800 Yvette Guilbert, A Menilmontant de Bruant (29x24cm 11x9in) mono. lithograph. 5-May-3 Ketterer, Munich #88/R est:800-1200
£2044 $3250 €3066 May Milton (196x150cm-77x59in) d.1895 col lithograph one of 100. 30-Apr-3 Doyle, New York #313/R est:1500-2000
£2051 $3200 €3077 Truffier et Moreno, dans les femmes savantes (38x28cm-15x11in) st.mono.num.20 lithograph edition of 50. 5-Nov-2 Christie's, Rockefeller NY #32/R est:4000-6000
£2051 $3200 €3077 La tige, Moulin Rouge (38x28cm-15x11in) st.mono.num.22 lithograph edition of 100. 5-Nov-2 Christie's, Rockefeller NY #44/R est:4000-6000
£2069 $3290 €3000 Les vielles hisoires (44x63cm-17x25in) s. col lithograph vellum. 5-Mar-3 Doutrebente, Paris #13 est:2000-2500
£2083 $3312 €3000 La modiste, Renee Vert (46x29cm-18x11in) mono. col lithograph. 5-May-3 Ketterer, Munich #63/R est:1500-2500
£2200 $3630 €3190 Mademoiselle Marcelle Lender en buste (43x34cm-17x13in) st.mono.num.98/100 col lithograph. 1-Jul-3 Sotheby's, London #148/R est:1500-2000
£2331 $3800 €3497 Jeanne Granier (39x32cm-15x13in) lithograph exec.1898. 13-Feb-3 Christie's, Rockefeller NY #202/R
£2373 $3750 €3560 Mademoiselle Mercelle Lender, debout (36x24cm-14x9in) lithograph olive green one of 15 executed c.1895. 12-Nov-2 Doyle, New York #381/R est:4000-6000
£2400 $3960 €3480 Souper a Londres (35x46cm-14x18in) s. grey lithograph from edition of 100. 2-Jul-3 Christie's, London #208/R est:1500-2000
£2431 $3865 €3500 La coiffure. Programme du Theatre Libre (32x24cm-13x9in) col lithograph. 5-May-3 Ketterer, Munich #60/R est:5000-7000
£2564 $4000 €3846 Bartet et Mounet-Sully, dans Antigone (38x28cm-15x11in) st.mono.num.29 col lithograph edition of 65 prov. 5-Nov-2 Christie's, Rockefeller NY #34/R est:4000-6000
£2564 $4000 €3846 Le Tocsin (58x49cm-23x19in) blue lithograph. 5-Nov-2 Christie's, Rockefeller NY #59/R est:5000-8000
£2778 $4417 €4000 A l'Opera. Madame Caron dans Faust (36x26cm-14x10in) st.mono. lithograph. 5-May-3 Ketterer, Munich #68/R est:2000-3000
£2897 $4606 €4200 Programme pour l'Argent (32x24cm-13x9in) s. col lithograph vellum. 5-Mar-3 Doutrebente, Paris #16/R est:3000-3800
£2917 $4638 €4200 Yvette Guilbert, linger, longer, loo (30x24cm-12x9in) mono. lithograph. 5-May-3 Ketterer, Munich #92/R est:1200-1500
£3125 $4969 €4500 Di Ti Fellow, anglaise au cafe concert (32x26cm-13x10in) mono. lithograph. 5-May-3 Ketterer, Munich #94/R est:5500-6500
£3200 $5280 €4640 Anna held, dans Toutes ces Dames au Theatre (33x21cm-13x8in) s.i. lithograph prov. 2-Jul-3 Christie's, London #213/R est:3000-5000
£3205 $5000 €4808 Souper a Londres (31x36cm-12x14in) lithograph edition of 100. 7-Nov-2 Swann Galleries, New York #507/R est:5000-8000
£3226 $5000 €4839 Lender assise (51x40cm-20x16in) lithograph. 25-Sep-2 Christie's, Rockefeller NY #222/R est:6000-8000
£3333 $5300 €4800 La Tige, Moulin Rouge (30x25cm-12x10in) mono. lithograph. 5-May-3 Ketterer, Munich #78/R est:2800-3500
£3459 $5500 €5189 Souper a Londres (31x36cm-12x14in) s. grey lithograph edition of 100. 2-May-3 Sotheby's, New York #364 est:3000-4000
£3526 $5500 €5289 La valse des lapins (38x28cm-15x11in) st.mono.num.10 lithograph. 5-Nov-2 Christie's, Rockefeller NY #56/R est:6000-8000
£3526 $5500 €5289 L'Aube (59x79cm-23x31in) blue lithograph on linen. 5-Nov-2 Christie's, Rockefeller NY #65/R est:8000-12000
£3526 $5500 €5289 Le marchand de marrons (30x23cm-12x9in) s. lithograph edition of 25. 5-Nov-2 Christie's, Rockefeller NY #71/R est:800-1200
£3532 $5580 €5298 Babylone d'Allemagne (122x86cm-48x34in) s.d.94 col lithograph lit. 1-Apr-3 Rasmussen, Copenhagen #58/R est:25000 (D.KR 38000)
£3800 $6270 €5510 Au hanneton (26x25cm-10x10in) s.num.79 brown lithograph prov. 2-Jul-3 Christie's, London #206/R est:3000-5000
£3819 $6073 €5500 Guy et Mealy, dans Paris qui Marche (28x23cm-11x9in) st.sig.mono.i. lithograph. 5-May-3 Ketterer, Munich #95/R est:3500-4500
£3846 $6000 €5769 La loge au mascaron dore (48x32cm-19x13in) s.num.7 col lithograph edition of 100. 5-Nov-2 Christie's, Rockefeller NY #80/R est:6000-8000
£4000 $6200 €6000 Mademoiselle Marcelle Lender (56x37cm-22x15in) mono.num.13/100 col lithograph. 5-Dec-2 Sotheby's, London #184/R est:4000-6000
£4088 $6500 €6132 Aristide Bruant (78x57cm-31x22in) col lithograph on linen. 29-Apr-3 Christie's, Rockefeller NY #414/R est:5000-7000
£4167 $6500 €6251 Judic (46x31cm-18x12in) st.mono. lithograph edition of 110. 5-Nov-2 Christie's, Rockefeller NY #41/R est:4000-6000
£4167 $6500 €6251 La Goulue (35x27cm-14x11in) olive green lithograph prov. 5-Nov-2 Christie's, Rockefeller NY #43/R est:2000-3000

£4167	$6583	€6500	Mademoiselle Pois Vert. lithograph. 14-Nov-2 Libert, Castor, Paris #136 est:6000
£4225	$7014	€6000	Mlle Marcelle Lender (35x24cm-14x9in) mono. lithograph. 14-Jun-3 Hauswedell & Nolte, Hamburg #1611/R est:8000
£4375	$6956	€6300	Lender de face, dans Chilperic (37x26cm-15x10in) mono. lithograph. 5-May-3 Ketterer, Munich #77/R est:3000-5000
£4487	$7000	€6731	May Belfort (79x60cm-31x24in) col lithograph. 14-Oct-2 Butterfields, San Francisco #1201/R est:8000-12000
£4487	$7000	€6731	Aristide Bruant (82x61cm-32x24in) col lithograph. 14-Oct-2 Butterfields, San Francisco #1200/R est:6000-8000
£4487	$7000	€6731	Programme pour L'Argent (32x24cm-13x9in) col lithograph. 5-Nov-2 Christie's, Rockefeller NY #48/R est:6000-10000
£4487	$7000	€6731	Mademoiselle Marcelle Lender (48x30cm-19x12in) s.num.44 sanguine lithograph edition of 45. 5-Nov-2 Christie's, Rockefeller NY #73/R est:8000-12000
£4800	$7920	€6960	Pourquoi pas, une fois n'est pas costume (31x25cm-12x10in) s.i. col lithograph edition of 100. 2-Jul-3 Christie's, London #205/R est:5000-7000
£4861	$7729	€7000	Au Moulin rouge, un Rude! - un vrai Rude! (36x25cm-14x10in) st.mono. lithograph. 5-May-3 Ketterer, Munich #71/R est:3000-5000
£4936	$7651	€7700	Mademoiselle Marcelle Lender, en buste (33x24cm-13x9in) col lithograph. 7-Dec-2 Ketterer, Hamburg #138/R est:7000-9000
£5128	$8000	€7692	Le coiffeur, programme du theatre libre (48x33cm-19x13in) num.16 col lithograph edition of 100 prov. 5-Nov-2 Christie's, Rockefeller NY #33/R est:10000-12000
£5128	$8000	€7692	Cecy Loftus (44x29cm-17x11in) olive green lithograph edition of 25. 5-Nov-2 Christie's, Rockefeller NY #45/R est:10000-15000
£5128	$8000	€7692	Mademoiselle Marcelle Lender (37x28cm-15x11in) col lithograph edition of 1211. 5-Nov-2 Christie's, Rockefeller NY #46/R est:8000-12000
£5128	$8000	€7692	Mademoiselle Pois Vert (51x39cm-20x15in) olive green lithograph edition of 25. 5-Nov-2 Christie's, Rockefeller NY #49/R est:10000-12000
£5128	$8000	€7692	La Troupe de Mademoiselle Eglantine (60x80cm-24x31in) col lithograph. 5-Nov-2 Christie's, Rockefeller NY #83/R est:12000-15000
£5208	$8281	€7500	Lugne Poe et Berthe Bady dans Image (32x23cm-13x9in) mono. lithograph. 5-May-3 Ketterer, Munich #72/R est:5500-6500
£5208	$8281	€7500	Lender saluant (32x26cm-13x10in) mono. lithograph. 5-May-3 Ketterer, Munich #75/R est:2800-3500
£5449	$8500	€8174	Le pendu (128x93cm-50x37in) col lithograph on linen. 5-Nov-2 Christie's, Rockefeller NY #28/R est:5000-8000
£5449	$8500	€8174	Petite fille Anglaise, Miss Dolly (45x31cm-18x12in) s.i. lithograph. 5-Nov-2 Christie's, Rockefeller NY #75/R est:10000-12000
£5606	$8746	€8409	Au Hanneton (36x25cm-14x10in) s.st.num.66 of 100 lithograph lit. 5-Nov-2 Bukowskis, Stockholm #651/R est:100000-120000 (S.KR 80000)
£5769	$9000	€8654	May Belfort (79x60cm-31x24in) olive green lithograph on linen. 5-Nov-2 Christie's, Rockefeller NY #57/R est:10000-12000
£6000	$9900	€8700	La loge au mascaron dore (31x24cm-12x9in) col lithograph. 2-Jul-3 Christie's, London #204/R est:8000-12000
£6250	$9938	€9000	Femme a glace, la glace a main (52x40cm-20x16in) s.mono. col lithograph. 5-May-3 Ketterer, Munich #85/R est:9000-12000
£6410	$10064	€10000	A merry Christmas and a happy new year (190x160cm-75x63in) lithograph. 12-Dec-2 Piasa, Paris #154/R
£6438	$10172	€9657	Proces Arton (37x48cm-15x19in) mono.d.1896 crayon lithograph lit. 26-Nov-2 Hans Widmer, St Gallen #1678/R est:9000-15000 (S.FR 15000)
£6488	$10251	€9732	Au Hanneton (36x25cm-14x10in) s.num.64 lithograph printed in black. 2-Dec-2 Blomqvist, Oslo #397/R est:80000-100000 (N.KR 75000)
£7042	$11690	€10000	La revue blanche - poster (126x91cm-50x36in) mono.d. col lithograph. 14-Jun-3 Hauswedell & Nolte, Hamburg #1613/R est:6000
£7051	$11000	€10577	Femme au lit, profil, au petit lever, from Elles (40x51cm-16x20in) col lithograph edition of 100. 5-Nov-2 Christie's, Rockefeller NY #62/R est:10000-15000
£7051	$11141	€11000	Cecy Loftus. lithograph. 14-Nov-2 Libert, Castor, Paris #135/R est:11000
£7433	$11595	€11000	Mademoiselle Marcelle Lender en buste (52x37cm-20x15in) col lithograph exec.1895. 31-Mar-3 Tajan, Paris #399/R
£7547	$12000	€11321	Mademoiselle Marcelle Lender en buste (32x24cm-13x9in) i. col lithograph edition of 100. 2-May-3 Sotheby's, New York #362/R est:6000-8000
£7547	$12000	€11321	Miss May Belfort saluant (37x27cm-15x11in) st.mono. col lithograph edition of 65. 2-May-3 Sotheby's, New York #363/R est:14000-18000
£7692	$12000	€11538	Jane Avril (127x92cm-50x36in) col lithograph. 5-Nov-2 Christie's, Rockefeller NY #37/R est:15000-20000
£7986	$12698	€11500	Lender de dos, dansant le Bolero, dans Chilperic (37x26cm-15x10in) mono. 5-May-3 Ketterer, Munich #82/R est:6500-8500
£8108	$12649	€12000	Revue blanche (125x91cm-49x36in) col lithograph exec.1895. 31-Mar-3 Tajan, Paris #398/R
£8500	$13515	€12750	Jane Avril (124x91cm-49x36in) col lithograph. 29-Apr-3 Gorringes, Lewes #2158
£9294	$14684	€13941	Divan Japonais (79x60cm-31x24in) s. col lithograph executed 1893 lit. 1-Apr-3 Rasmussen, Copenhagen #59/R est:80000-100000 (D.KR 100000)
£9434	$15000	€14151	Frontispiece for Elles (52x40cm-20x16in) num.74 col lithograph. 2-May-3 Sotheby's, New York #366/R est:10000-15000
£9615	$15000	€14423	La revue blanche (129x94cm-51x37in) col lithograph on linen. 5-Nov-2 Christie's, Rockefeller NY #82/R est:18000-25000
£9615	$15096	€15000	Le cafe concert (440x330cm-173x130in) lithograph 11 and 11 by Ibel. 12-Dec-2 Piasa, Paris #153/R
£9722	$15458	€14000	Madame le Margoin, modiste (32x24cm-13x9in) mono. lithograph. 5-May-3 Ketterer, Munich #96/R est:8000-10000
£10063	$16000	€15095	La revue blanche (130x94cm-51x37in) col lithograph. 29-Apr-3 Christie's, Rockefeller NY #416/R est:15000-20000
£10063	$16000	€15095	Divan Japonais (79x60cm-31x24in) col lithograph. 2-May-3 Sotheby's, New York #369/R est:20000-40000
£10692	$17000	€16038	Debauche (23x32cm-9x13in) s.num.19/50 col lithograph. 2-May-3 Sotheby's, New York #365/R est:20000-30000
£10692	$17000	€16038	La revue blanche (129x93cm-51x37in) col lithograph. 2-May-3 Sotheby's, New York #370/R est:15000-20000
£12000	$18600	€18000	Mademoiselle Marcelle Lender (37x30cm-15x12in) col lithograph. 5-Dec-2 Sotheby's, London #188/R est:12000-14000
£12179	$19000	€18269	Irish American Bar, Rue Royal, The Chap Book (42x60cm-17x24in) col lithograph. 14-Oct-2 Butterfields, San Francisco #1202/R est:15000-20000
£12500	$19875	€18000	Femme au lit, profil, au petit lever (40x52cm-16x20in) mono.i. col lithograph. 5-May-3 Ketterer, Munich #86/R est:15000-20000
£12500	$19875	€18000	Debauche (24x32cm-9x13in) mono. col lithograph. 5-May-3 Ketterer, Munich #87/R est:7000-9000
£13208	$20472	€21000	La goulue (38x28cm-15x11in) st.num.57 lithograph brush pencil crachis. 30-Oct-2 Artcurial Briest, Paris #559/R est:11000-12000
£13208	$21000	€19812	May Belfort (79x61cm-31x24in) col lithograph. 1-May-3 Swann Galleries, New York #375/R est:20000-30000
£13836	$22000	€20754	La passagere du 54 - Promenade en yacht (60x40cm-24x16in) col lithograph. 29-Apr-3 Christie's, Rockefeller NY #417/R est:20000-25000
£14103	$22000	€21155	Divan Japonais (81x60cm-32x24in) col lithograph. 5-Nov-2 Christie's, Rockefeller NY #81/R est:18000-22000
£14151	$22500	€21227	Couverture de l'estampe originale (58x83cm-23x33in) s.i. col lithograph edition of 100. 2-May-3 Sotheby's, New York #361/R est:20000-30000
£15278	$24292	€22000	La passagere du 54 ou Promenade en yacht (60x41cm-24x16in) mono. col lithograph. 5-May-3 Ketterer, Munich #97/R est:3000-5000
£15385	$24000	€23078	Femme au tub, le tub, from Elles (40x52cm-16x20in) num.14 col lithograph edition of 100. 5-Nov-2 Christie's, Rockefeller NY #61/R est:30000-50000
£16000	$26400	€23200	Le jockey (51x36cm-20x14in) lithograph. 1-Jul-3 Sotheby's, London #150/R est:10000-15000
£17606	$29225	€25000	Eldorado, aristide bruant (14x97cm-6x38in) col lithograph. 12-Jun-3 Piasa, Paris #165/R
£19231	$30000	€28847	Aristide Bruant, dans con cabaret (134x96cm-53x38in) col lithograph on linen. 5-Nov-2 Christie's, Rockefeller NY #40/R est:30000-50000
£20513	$32000	€30770	Couverture de l'estampe originale (58x79cm-23x31in) s.num.82 col lithograph edition of 100. 5-Nov-2 Christie's, Rockefeller NY #29/R est:40000-60000
£21000	$32550	€31500	Eldorado Aristide (141x99cm-56x39in) lithograph. 5-Dec-2 Sotheby's, London #187/R est:10000-15000
£25641	$40000	€38462	Aux Ambassadeurs, chanteuse au cafe concert (61x42cm-24x17in) s. col lithograph edition of 100. 5-Nov-2 Christie's, Rockefeller NY #42/R est:45000-55000
£26923	$42000	€40385	Caudieux (128x91cm-50x36in) col lithograph. 5-Nov-2 Christie's, Rockefeller NY #38/R est:10000-60000
£29577	$49099	€42000	Le jockey (52x36cm-20x14in) col lithograph edition of 100. 12-Jun-3 Piasa, Paris #163/R
£31690	$52606	€45000	Ambassadeurs, aristide bruant (135x92cm-53x36in) col lithograph. 12-Jun-3 Piasa, Paris #164/R
£38462	$60000	€57693	La grande loge (52x40cm-20x16in) i. col lithograph. 5-Nov-2 Christie's, Rockefeller NY #68/R est:350000-450000
£41667	$65000	€62501	Partie de campagne (40x51cm-16x20in) st.mono.num.12 col lithograph. 5-Nov-2 Christie's, Rockefeller NY #70/R est:80000-120000
£41667	$65833	€65000	Partie de campagne. lithograph. 14-Nov-2 Libert, Castor, Paris #138/R est:45000

£64103 $100000 €96155 La chanson du Matelot, au Star, Le Havre (40x29cm-16x11in) col lithograph. 5-Nov-2 Christie's, Rockefeller NY #67/R est:120000-150000
£230769 $364615 €360000 La grande loge. lithograph. 14-Nov-2 Libert, Castor, Paris #137/R est:225000

Sculpture

£57692 $90000 €86538 Yvette Guilbert (51x28cm-20x11in) mono.i. partially painted ceramic plaque executed 1895 prov.lit. 7-Nov-2 Christie's, Rockefeller NY #210/R est:50000-70000

Works on paper

£1258 $2000 €1887 Tete de face (11x19cm-4x7in) st.mono. pencil prov.lit. 27-Feb-3 Christie's, Rockefeller NY #18/R
£1282 $2013 €2000 En barque (9x13cm-4x5in) crayon dr. lit. 13-Dec-2 Piasa, Paris #220/R
£1646 $2567 €2600 Jockey (16x26cm-6x10in) st.mono.i. pencil prov.lit. 18-Oct-2 Dr Fritz Nagel, Stuttgart #641/R est:2200
£1710 $2771 €2600 Pelleas et Melisande (12x20cm-5x8in) s.i.d.mai 93 Indian ink pen dr. 22-Jan-3 Tajan, Paris #41/R est:2000-3000
£1961 $3216 €3000 Charge de Princeteau (16x27cm-6x11in) crayon double-sided lit. 9-Feb-3 Anaf, Lyon #253
£2482 $4145 €3500 Femme (20x14cm-8x6in) col.crayons prov.lit. 20-Jun-3 Piasa, Paris #89 est:1000-1200
£2532 $4000 €3798 Manches a gigot. Tete d'homme (10x16cm-4x6in) mono. pencil double-sided lit. 22-Apr-3 Butterfields, San Francisco #6015/R est:4000-6000
£3041 $4743 €4500 Femme dansant (15x9cm-6x4in) s.i. graphite prov. 27-Mar-3 Christie's, Paris #176/R
£3716 $5797 €5500 Femme assise de profil (15x10cm-6x4in) s. graphite prov. 27-Mar-3 Christie's, Paris #177/R
£3797 $6000 €6000 Henri de Toulouse Lautrec par lui-meme et masque de Maurice Guibert (31x21cm-12x8in) st.mono. pen exhib.lit. 30-Nov-2 Villa Grisebach, Berlin #100/R est:4000-5000
£4000 $6200 €6000 Un dandy. Croquis de mains (27x16cm-11x6in) pencil double-sided prov.lit. 5-Dec-2 Christie's, Kensington #6/R est:3000-4000
£4247 $6838 €6371 Tetes et visages d'hommes, uniforme, casques, tete de cheval (23x16cm-9x6in) stamped sig. ink pencil exhib. 7-May-3 AB Stockholms Auktionsverk #1101/R est:60000-70000 (S.KR 55000)
£5696 $9000 €9000 Etudes d'hommes et de jardinier (22x31cm-9x12in) st.sig. crayon. 28-Nov-2 Tajan, Paris #195/R est:9000-10000
£7500 $11550 €11250 Etudes (15x10cm-6x4in) one pen ink two pencil three prov.exhib.lit. 23-Oct-2 Sotheby's, Olympia #605/R est:5000-7000

TOULZA OF MARSEILLES, J Étienne (fl.1802-1822) French

Works on paper

£9868 $15000 €14802 Three Sisters of Charleston (43x56cm-17x22in) s.i. W/C prov. 17-Aug-2 North East Auctions, Portsmouth #935/R est:5000-7000

TOUPIN, Fernand (1930-) Canadian

£287 $448 €431 Juillet (30x23cm-12x9in) s.d.78 acrylic. 10-Sep-2 Iegor de Saint Hippolyte, Montreal #110 (C.D 700)
£902 $1407 €1353 Jour d'Octobre (111x148cm-44x58in) s.i.d.1972 verso. 10-Sep-2 Iegor de Saint Hippolyte, Montreal #112 (C.D 2200)
£3219 $5021 €4829 Pervenche (128x91cm-50x36in) s.d.61 s.i.d.verso exhib. 25-Mar-3 Iegor de Saint Hippolyte, Montreal #143 (C.D 7500)

Works on paper

£205 $320 €308 Bijou broye (20x14cm-8x6in) mixed media panel. 10-Sep-2 Iegor de Saint Hippolyte, Montreal #111 (C.D 500)

TOURNACHON, Gaspard Felix (1820-1910) French

£1092 $1703 €1638 Les chicards (28x21cm-11x8in) s. i. verso gouache over pencil. 6-Nov-2 Dobiaschofsky, Bern #857/R est:3000 (S.FR 2500)

Photographs

£8974 $14179 €14000 Madame Labiche (20x15cm-8x6in) s.i. i.verso salt print exec.c.1855 prov. 16-Nov-2 Christie's, Paris #233/R est:15000-20000

Works on paper

£1092 $1703 €1638 Les chicards (28x21cm-11x8in) s. i. verso gouache over pencil. 6-Nov-2 Dobiaschofsky, Bern #856/R est:3000 (S.FR 2500)

TOURNE, Didier (1882-?) French

£943 $1462 €1500 Port de Douarnenez (46x55cm-18x22in) s.i. 6-Oct-2 Livinec, Gaudcheau & Jezequel, Rennes #62/R

TOURNES, Étienne (1857-1931) French

£372 $592 €558 Interior scene with woman reading a girl's school report (94x64cm-37x25in) s. 5-Mar-3 Rasmussen, Copenhagen #1717/R (D.KR 4000)

TOURNIOL, Renée (19/20th C) French

£680 $1082 €1000 Le palais de Safi (59x49cm-23x19in) s.i. 24-Mar-3 Raboudin & Choppin de Janvry, Paris #195/R

TOURNY, Joseph Gabriel (1817-1880) French

£1655 $2648 €2400 Jeune fille a l'eventail et au billet doux (63x89cm-25x35in) mono. 17-Mar-3 Horta, Bruxelles #212 est:1800-2200

TOURRIER, Alfred Holst (1836-1892) British

£2143 $3386 €3215 Orator (30x25cm-12x10in) s. 18-Nov-2 Joel, Victoria #296 est:1000-1500 (A.D 6000)

Works on paper

£1361 $2163 €2000 Vathek and Carathis consult the planets (16x12cm-6x5in) s. W/C four in one frame. 24-Mar-3 Bernaerts, Antwerp #182/R est:800-1000

TOURTE, Suzanne (1904-1979) French

£329 $510 €520 La maison rose (64x49cm-25x19in) s. 28-Sep-2 Cornette de St.Cyr, Paris #199
£380 $589 €600 La cage aux colombes (82x100cm-32x39in) s.d. 28-Sep-2 Cornette de St.Cyr, Paris #197
£633 $981 €1000 Flutiste dans la foret (92x75cm-36x30in) s.d. 28-Sep-2 Cornette de St.Cyr, Paris #198

Works on paper

£414 $691 €600 Les roches noires (32x24cm-13x9in) s.i. gouache. 9-Jul-3 Millon & Associes, Paris #209g/R
£469 $783 €680 Couple buvant (38x28cm-15x11in) s. gouache. 9-Jul-3 Millon & Associes, Paris #209h
£517 $828 €750 Les vignes (50x65cm-20x26in) s. gouache. 12-Mar-3 Libert, Castor, Paris #191
£572 $956 €830 Semailles (48x32cm-19x13in) s. gouache. 9-Jul-3 Millon & Associes, Paris #209e

TOUSIGNANT, Claude (1932-) Canadian

£242 $394 €363 Round green on red background (30x46cm-12x18in) s. acrylic paper collage. 12-Feb-3 Iegor de Saint Hippolyte, Montreal #185 (C.D 600)
£282 $460 €423 Untitled (45x30cm-18x12in) s. acrylic paper collage. 12-Feb-3 Iegor de Saint Hippolyte, Montreal #183 (C.D 700)
£1290 $2103 €1935 Untitled (51x51cm-20x20in) 12-Feb-3 Iegor de Saint Hippolyte, Montreal #181/R (C.D 3200)
£2179 $3400 €3269 Petit Oeil (58x71cm-23x28in) s.i.d.verso exhib. 20-Sep-2 New Orleans Auction, New Orleans #1406/R est:700-1000
£3629 $5915 €5444 Accelerateur chromatique (91cm-36in circular) s.i.d.10/76 acrylic. 12-Feb-3 Iegor de Saint Hippolyte, Montreal #179/R (C.D 9000)
£5242 $8282 €7863 Mon chapeau de paille d'italie. s.d.10.64 acrylic prov. 18-Nov-2 Sotheby's, Toronto #75/R est:8000-10000 (C.D 13000)
£6855 $11173 €10283 Le premier baiser (117x129cm-46x51in) s.d.57. 12-Feb-3 Iegor de Saint Hippolyte, Montreal #180 (C.D 17000)

Sculpture

£1815 $2958 €2723 Construction polychromique 1959 (47x33x5cm-19x13x2in) s.d. s.i.d. verso painted wood. 12-Feb-3 Iegor de Saint Hippolyte, Montreal #182 (C.D 4500)

TOUSSAINT, F (1873-1956) Belgian

£980 $1608 €1500 Portrait of a girl (27x31cm-11x12in) s.i. panel double-sided. 5-Feb-3 Neumeister, Munich #827 est:250

TOUSSAINT, Fernand (1873-1956) Belgian

£1013 $1580 €1600 Elegante de profil (54x41cm-21x16in) s. 16-Sep-2 Horta, Bruxelles #80
£1401 $2186 €2200 Vase fleuri sur fond japonisant (40x30cm-16x12in) s.d. i.verso. 11-Nov-2 Horta, Bruxelles #545 est:2000-3000
£1727 $2763 €2400 Le retour du garde et de son chien (45x55cm-18x22in) s. 19-May-3 Horta, Bruxelles #157 est:2500-3500
£2405 $3752 €3800 Elegante assise (32x24cm-13x9in) s. panel. 15-Oct-2 Horta, Bruxelles #130
£2897 $4634 €4200 Elegante au collier de malachite (117x106cm-46x42in) s.d.31. 17-Mar-3 Horta, Bruxelles #165/R est:4000-6000
£3401 $5408 €5000 La robe verte (27x22cm-11x9in) panel. 24-Mar-3 Bernaerts, Antwerp #171/R est:2800-3000
£3544 $5529 €5600 Still life with yellow roses in Brussels litre jug with Chinese pot and cover (42x32cm-17x13in) s. 21-Oct-2 Bernaerts, Antwerp #110/R est:2000-2500
£3597 $5755 €5000 Jeune femme pensive (100x80cm-39x31in) 13-May-3 Palais de Beaux Arts, Brussels #150/R est:1250-1750
£3797 $6000 €6000 Elegante au chien (73x55cm-29x22in) s. 26-Nov-2 Palais de Beaux Arts, Brussels #379/R est:6000-8000
£4452 $6945 €6500 Elegante au canape vert (116x106cm-46x42in) s. 14-Apr-3 Horta, Bruxelles #103 est:8000-12000
£5248 $8765 €7400 Jeune femme pensive, assise dans un fauteuil (41x33cm-16x13in) s. canvas on cardboard. 17-Jun-3 Palais de Beaux Arts, Brussels #643/R est:6000-8000

£5769 $9058 €9000 Portrait d'une elegante (46x38cm-18x15in) s. panel. 19-Nov-2 Vanderkindere, Brussels #90/R est:8000-12000
£8497 $13680 €13000 Table dressee au bouquet de roses (44x54cm-17x21in) s. canvas on panel. 20-Jan-3 Horta, Bruxelles #174/R est:5000-7000
£11644 $18164 €17000 Jeune elegante a la robe rose (97x80cm-38x31in) s. 14-Apr-3 Horta, Bruxelles #102 est:12000-18000
£17123 $26712 €25000 Composition au gueridon, ombrelle, gants et vase fleuri (80x100cm-31x39in) s. 14-Apr-3 Horta, Bruxelles #101/R est:15000-20000

Works on paper
£822 $1282 €1200 Elegante de profil (49x0cm-19x0in) s. W/C. 14-Apr-3 Horta, Bruxelles #104
£949 $1481 €1500 Elegante de profil (50x39cm-20x15in) s.i.d.1910 mixed media oval. 16-Sep-2 Horta, Bruxelles #81
£1342 $2161 €2000 Portrait d'elegante (75x55cm-30x22in) s.d.1916 W/C oval. 18-Feb-3 Vanderkindere, Brussels #3/R
£1646 $2567 €2600 Elegante au manchon (27x20cm-11x8in) mono. mixed media. 16-Sep-2 Horta, Bruxelles #82
£2800 $4648 €2800 Coquetterie (45x37cm-18x15in) s. mixed media. 16-Jun-3 Horta, Bruxelles #87 est:3500-4000

TOUSSAINT, Maurice (19th C) French
Works on paper
£256 $403 €400 La charge (38x28cm-15x11in) s. 16-Dec-2 Millon & Associes, Paris #55/R
£1987 $3140 €3100 General Bonaparte au passage des Alpes (40x29cm-16x11in) s. W/C gouache. 17-Nov-2 Osenat, Fontainebleau #219

TOUSSAINT, Pierre Joseph (1822-1888) Belgian
£690 $1097 €1000 Devoot meisje (35x25cm-14x10in) s.d.1864 panel. 10-Mar-3 Sotheby's, Amsterdam #92 est:1000-2000

TOUSSAINT, Raphael (1937-) French
£1293 $2055 €1900 Retour du Bourg un Dimanche soir (27x19cm-11x7in) s. s.i.d.janvier 75 verso panel. 26-Feb-3 Artcurial Briest, Paris #348 est:1000-1500
£2166 $3378 €3400 Dimanche a Rochard sur la Sevre nantaise (24x35cm-9x14in) s. s.i.d.1987 verso panel. 5-Nov-2 Tajan, Paris #131
£2229 $3478 €3500 Berges de la Seine (24x35cm-9x14in) s. s.i.verso paper. 5-Nov-2 Tajan, Paris #130/R

TOUTAIN, Charles Victorien (1899-1945) French
£418 $652 €660 Les meules (15x21cm-6x8in) s.d.1924 cardboard. 15-Sep-2 Etude Bailleul, Bayeux #105/R
£506 $790 €800 Vue de Conde, Ifs (33x41cm-13x16in) s.d.1941 cardboard. 15-Sep-2 Etude Bailleul, Bayeux #106/R

TOWERS, Samuel (1862-1943) British
Works on paper
£360 $572 €540 Evening in Anglesey (29x44cm-11x17in) s. W/C. 4-Mar-3 Bearnes, Exeter #365/R
£460 $727 €690 Kings Arms, Ombersley (38x58cm-15x23in) s.d.1896 W/C. 27-Nov-2 Hamptons Fine Art, Godalming #169

TOWN, Harold Barling (1924-1990) Canadian
£889 $1458 €1334 Toy horse (24x30cm-9x12in) s.d.79 oil pastel prov. 3-Jun-3 Joyner, Toronto #300/R est:800-1200 (C.D 2000)
£2016 $3185 €3024 Untitled (61x71cm-24x28in) s.d.60 oil on masonite prov. 18-Nov-2 Sotheby's, Toronto #128/R est:5000-7000 (C.D 5000)
£2088 $3300 €3132 Time slice, in profile (30x46cm-12x18in) d.1959 oil lucite. 1-Dec-2 Levis, Calgary #331/R (C.D 5200)
£2222 $3644 €3333 Tumbled shore (30x30cm-12x12in) s.d.58 s.i.d.verso oil lucite 44 on masonite prov. 27-May-3 Sotheby's, Toronto #29/R est:4000-6000 (C.D 5000)
£2667 $4373 €4001 Wanted permission to land (60x75cm-24x30in) s.d.59 board. 3-Jun-3 Joyner, Toronto #238/R est:2500-3000 (C.D 6000)
£4000 $6560 €6000 Dead boat echo (92x63cm-36x25in) s.d.59 s.i.d.verso prov. 27-May-3 Sotheby's, Toronto #25/R est:10000-15000 (C.D 9000)
£6222 $10204 €9333 Green plan (122x152cm-48x60in) s.d.59-60 i.d.verso masonite prov. 27-May-3 Sotheby's, Toronto #143/R est:15000-20000 (C.D 14000)
£8468 $13379 €12702 At noon in Bay Ice (102x168cm-40x66in) s.d.56 s.i.d.verso oil lucite on canvas. 18-Nov-2 Sotheby's, Toronto #127/R est:15000-20000 (C.D 21000)

Works on paper
£429 $670 €644 Vale variation no.38 (51x66cm-20x26in) s.d.9.10.72 mixed media prov.exhib. 25-Mar-3 Ritchie, Toronto #187/R est:1200-1500 (C.D 1000)
£617 $957 €926 Untitled (49x74cm-19x29in) s.d.1975 mixed media. 3-Dec-2 Joyner, Toronto #199/R est:1500-2000 (C.D 1500)
£1070 $1658 €1605 Shore and sun (75x55cm-30x22in) s.d.1962 brush pen ink prov.lit. 3-Dec-2 Joyner, Toronto #350 est:800-1200 (C.D 2600)
£1378 $2260 €2067 Warm within (27x27cm-11x11in) s.d.60 mixed media collage prov. 3-Jun-3 Joyner, Toronto #206/R est:1500-2000 (C.D 3100)
£2444 $4009 €3666 Vale variation no.221 (57x73cm-22x29in) s.d.78 i.verso gouache on card prov. 27-May-3 Sotheby's, Toronto #141/R est:3000-5000 (C.D 5500)

TOWNE, Charles (1763-1840) British
£560 $913 €840 Cattle, sheep and a donkey in a landscape (24x29cm-9x11in) s.d.1834 board. 17-Feb-3 Bonhams, Bath #157
£7000 $11340 €10500 Marlborough spaniel in a wooded landscape, an urn beyond (18x23cm-7x9in) s.d.1820 board. 22-May-3 Christie's, London #31/R est:6000-8000
£7500 $12150 €11250 Stallions in a wooded paddock (30x41cm-12x16in) s. panel exhib. 22-May-3 Christie's, London #32/R est:7000-10000

TOWNE, Charles (attrib) (1763-1840) British
£520 $816 €780 Study of sheep (16x16cm-6x6in) panel. 21-Nov-2 Clevedon Sale Rooms #218
£1135 $1759 €1703 Landscape with sheep and cattle (29x37cm-11x15in) panel. 4-Dec-2 AB Stockholms Auktionsverk #1917/R est:18000-20000 (S.KR 16000)

TOWNE, Francis (1740-1816) British
£4500 $7110 €6750 Via Nomentana with churches Sant'Agnese and Santa Constanza (38x57cm-15x22in) with sig.d.1801. 26-Nov-2 Christie's, London #56/R est:5000-8000

Works on paper
£360 $572 €540 Castle on the edge of a village (16x24cm-6x9in) pen ink wash. 4-Mar-3 Bearnes, Exeter #352
£400 $636 €600 Cattle in a village landscape (21x27cm-8x11in) W/C. 4-Mar-3 Bearnes, Exeter #345
£2400 $3936 €3480 From west India docks (11x18cm-4x7in) s.i.d.1813 pencil pen ink W/C prov.exhib.lit. 5-Jun-3 Christie's, London #51/R est:2000-3000
£3800 $6232 €5510 Windsor Castle and St. George's Chapel (11x18cm-4x7in) i. pen ink W/C prov.exhib.lit. 5-Jun-3 Christie's, London #49/R est:4000-6000
£5500 $9020 €7975 Lake of Wallenstadt, between the cantons of St. Gall and Glarus, East Switzerland (16x21cm-6x8in) s.i.d.1781 pen ink wash prov.exhib.lit. 5-Jun-3 Christie's, London #46/R est:5000-7000
£5500 $9020 €7975 Warwick Castle (18x52cm-7x20in) i. pencil ink W/C two joined sheets. 5-Jun-3 Christie's, London #53/R est:6000-8000
£6000 $9840 €8700 Lake Windermere, Lake District (27x38cm-11x15in) i. pen ink W/C prov.exhib. 5-Jun-3 Christie's, London #81/R est:5000-8000
£6500 $10660 €9425 Devon landscape (11x18cm-4x7in) i. s.i.verso pen ink W/C prov.exhib.lit. 5-Jun-3 Christie's, London #50/R est:3000-5000
£7200 $11376 €10800 Bickleigh Vale and Shaugh Church, Devon (14x23cm-6x9in) s.verso pen ink W/C prov.lit. 28-Nov-2 Sotheby's, London #261/R est:4000-6000
£12000 $17160 €18000 Civita Castellana near Rome (16x22cm-6x9in) s.i.d.1781 pencil ink W/C prov.exhib.lit. 22-Jan-3 Christie's, London #8/R est:20000
£14000 $22960 €20300 Castello Madamo, above the Anio, near Tivoli (23x32cm-9x13in) s.d.1781 pen ink W/C prov.exhib.lit. 5-Jun-3 Christie's, London #38/R est:15000-25000
£15000 $21450 €22500 Looking towards Castello Madama, Italy (23x32cm-9x13in) s.i.d.1781 pencil ink wash prov.exhib. 22-Jan-3 Christie's, London #7/R est:20000
£22000 $36080 €31900 Lake of Lugano, Switzerland (29x46cm-11x18in) s.i.d.1781 pen ink wash prov.exhib.lit. 5-Jun-3 Christie's, London #40/R est:30000-50000
£22000 $36080 €31900 Grove, Werrington Park, Devon (34x48cm-13x19in) i. i.verso pen ink wash prov.exhib.lit. 5-Jun-3 Christie's, London #48/R est:15000-25000
£35000 $57400 €50750 Head of Lake Windermere, Lake District (15x23cm-6x9in) s.d.1791 pen ink W/C prov.exhib.lit. 5-Jun-3 Christie's, London #47/R est:10000-15000
£60000 $98400 €87000 Town of Lugano, Switzerland seen from Paradiso with the church of Santa Maria degli Angeli (29x47cm-11x19in) s.i.d.1781 pen ink wash prov.exhib.lit. 5-Jun-3 Christie's, London #39/R est:40000-60000
£60000 $98400 €87000 Waterfall between Chiavenna and Mount Splugen, Switzerland (47x57cm-19x22in) i.d.1781 pen ink wash two joined sheets prov.exhib.lit. 5-Jun-3 Christie's, London #41/R est:70000-100000

TOWNLEY, Charles (1746-1800) British
£1400 $2184 €2100 Cattle resting near ruins (32x41cm-13x16in) s. panel. 8-Apr-3 Bonhams, Knightsbridge #117/R est:1500-2000

TOWNSEND, Ernest Nathaniel (1893-1945) American
£3500 $5495 €5250 Seated woman in Austrian jacket (25x20cm-10x8in) board. 16-Dec-2 Bonhams, Bury St Edmunds #519/R est:300-500

TOWNSEND, Graeme (1954-) Australian
£5233 $8320 €7850 Botanical gardens (151x210cm-59x83in) s. s.i.verso prov.exhib. 5-May-3 Sotheby's, Melbourne #34/R est:8000 (A.D 13500)

TOWNSEND, H William (1940-) Canadian
£333 $547 €483 Century Sam Lake, BC (50x40cm-20x16in) s.i. board. 9-Jun-3 Hodgins, Calgary #38/R (C.D 750)
£622 $1020 €902 Boat dock near Lunenburgm NS (40x50cm-16x20in) s.i. 9-Jun-3 Hodgins, Calgary #429/R est:1000-1500 (C.D 1400)
£978 $1604 €1418 Clouds over Lake McArthur (60x75cm-24x30in) s.i. 9-Jun-3 Hodgins, Calgary #43/R est:2000-2500 (C.D 2200)

TOWNSEND, John R (19th C) British
£250 $408 €375 Blacksmith (23x18cm-9x7in) mono. millboard. 13-Feb-3 Heathcote Ball, Leicester #567
£270 $440 €405 Donkeys on a beach (20x25cm-8x10in) mono. millboard. 13-Feb-3 Heathcote Ball, Leicester #566
£420 $655 €609 Sophistication (29x19cm-11x7in) s. board. 27-Mar-3 Neales, Nottingham #1061/R

TOWNSEND, William H (19th C) American
£317 $521 €476 On the river near Terrace, BC (41x51cm-16x20in) s. s.i.verso. 6-Feb-3 Heffel, Vancouver #046/R (C.D 800)
£511 $838 €741 Rain has washed waiting eyes (40x50cm-16x20in) s.i. 9-Jun-3 Hodgins, Calgary #78/R est:1000-1500 (C.D 1150)

TOWNSHEND, Arthur Louis (fl.1880-1912) British
£400 $668 €580 Cadet, a chestnut hunter (20x25cm-8x10in) mono.i.verso panel. 25-Jun-3 Cheffins, Cambridge #799/R

TOWNSHEND, Geoffrey K (1888-1969) Australian
Works on paper
£268 $421 €402 Shoreline (33x43cm-13x17in) s. W/C. 15-Apr-3 Lawson Menzies, Sydney #214/R (A.D 700)

TOWNSHEND, James A (?-1949) British
£3000 $4920 €4500 Bend of the river (51x76cm-20x30in) s. 29-May-3 Christie's, Kensington #121/R est:800-1200

TOWNSHEND, James A (attrib) (?-1949) British
£1338 $2034 €2007 Children in punt (51x76cm-20x30in) bears sig. 16-Aug-2 Lilla Bukowskis, Stockholm #259/R est:8000-10000 (S.KR 19500)

TOWNSHEND, Pamela (1920-) British
£420 $655 €630 Rainy day in Paris (49x60cm-19x24in) s.d.71 board. 9-Apr-3 Cheffins Grain & Comins, Cambridge #734/R

TOYEN (1902-1980) Russian
£116438 $181644 €170000 Je vous souhaite bonne sante (87x66cm-34x26in) s.d.43 exhib.lit. 14-Apr-3 Laurence Calmels, Paris #4032/R est:30000

TOYEN, Marie Germinova (1902-1980) Czechoslovakian
£37671 $59144 €55000 A l'arbre d'or (42x53cm-17x21in) s.d.51 exhib.lit. 15-Apr-3 Laurence Calmels, Paris #4423/R
£39726 $62370 €58000 Si loin, si ancien (38x55cm-15x22in) s.d.54 exhib. 15-Apr-3 Laurence Calmels, Paris #4424/R est:18000
£47945 $75274 €70000 Development (46x52cm-18x20in) s.d.45 i.verso exhib.lit. 15-Apr-3 Laurence Calmels, Paris #4421/R est:30000
£54795 $86027 €80000 Ficelee-deficelee (24x30cm-9x12in) s.i.d.1948 cardboard prov.exhib.lit. 15-Apr-3 Laurence Calmels, Paris #4422/R est:18000
Works on paper
£496 $804 €700 Composition (28x20cm-11x8in) s.d. ink W/C paper on cardboard. 23-May-3 Binoche, Paris #17
£24306 $38646 €35000 Empreintes si fragiles dans l'oubli (73x92cm-29x36in) s.d.55 i.verso. 29-Apr-3 Artcurial Briest, Paris #593/R est:8000-10000

TOYOHIKO, Okamoto (1773-1840) Japanese
Works on paper
£1087 $1783 €1500 Appearance of a tragically dead beauty (87x27cm-34x11in) s. Indian ink silk scroll. 31-May-3 Dr Fritz Nagel, Stuttgart #1663/R est:1500

TOYOKUNI, Utagawa (1769-1825) Japanese
Works on paper
£8805 $14000 €13208 Beauty and attendant with cherry blossoms (78x35cm-31x14in) s. ink col silk hanging scroll prov. 24-Mar-3 Christie's, Rockefeller NY #27/R est:7000-9000

TOYOMASA (1773-1856) Japanese
Sculpture
£9204 $14451 €13806 Dragon in a gourd (5cm-2in) s. bronze. 25-Nov-2 Stephan Welz, Johannesburg #172/R est:40000-60000 (SA.R 140000)

TOZER, H S (1864-c.1938) British
£2000 $3340 €2900 Preparing fuel. Preparing dinner (25x38cm-10x15in) s.d.1926 pair. 18-Jun-3 Andrew Hartley, Ilkley #1127/R est:600-900

TOZER, H Spernon (1864-c.1938) British
£650 $1014 €975 By the fire (25x36cm-10x14in) s.d.1934. 7-Nov-2 Christie's, Kensington #203/R
£750 $1245 €1125 Woolpack Inn, Fareham Surrey (25x30cm-10x12in) 10-Jun-3 Bonhams, Knightsbridge #66/R
Works on paper
£600 $930 €900 Feeding the chickens (21x331cm-8x130in) s. bears d.1911 W/C over pencil htd white. 2-Oct-2 Bonhams, Knowle #45
£600 $1002 €870 Morning paper (31x22cm-12x9in) s.d.06 W/C. 24-Jun-3 Bonhams, Knightsbridge #43/R
£1900 $3173 €2755 Violinist. Thoughtful game of cards (35x49cm-14x19in) s.d.1908 W/C pair. 24-Jun-3 Bonhams, Knightsbridge #42/R est:2000-3000

TOZER, Henry E (fl.1889-1892) British
£480 $730 €720 Sailing boat at sea, distant steam ship (25x36cm-10x14in) s. 16-Aug-2 Keys, Aylsham #618/R

TOZZI, Mario (1895-1979) Italian
£8163 $12980 €12000 Geometric composition (33x46cm-13x18in) s. painted 1961 lit. 1-Mar-3 Meeting Art, Vercelli #760
£8228 $13000 €13000 Little head (22x23cm-9x9in) s.d.65. 30-Nov-2 Farsetti, Prato #746/R est:16000
£9804 $15686 €15000 Girl (35x27cm-14x11in) s. painted 1977 lit. 4-Jan-3 Meeting Art, Vercelli #530 est:15000
£13548 $21406 €21000 Vase of flowers (68x53cm-27x21in) s. 18-Dec-2 Christie's, Rome #168/R est:12000
£16026 $25160 €25000 Ponytail (55x46cm-22x18in) s. s.verso painted 1974 lit. 23-Nov-2 Meeting Art, Vercelli #241/R est:25000
£16774 $26503 €26000 Composition with figure (55x46cm-22x18in) s. painted 1975 lit. 18-Dec-2 Christie's, Rome #260/R
£18440 $29872 €26000 L'enfant (65x46cm-26x18in) s. prov. 26-May-3 Christie's, Milan #315/R est:20000-25000
£24051 $38000 €38000 Figure (55x46cm-22x18in) s.d.1970 lit. 30-Nov-2 Farsetti, Prato #698/R est:42000
£28846 $45288 €45000 Staircase (83x60cm-33x24in) s. painted 1973 lit. 19-Nov-2 Finarte, Milan #242/R est:42000-48000
£67308 $105673 €105000 Spring, figures at balcony (116x81cm-46x32in) s.d.930 exhib.lit. 19-Nov-2 Finarte, Milan #202/R est:100000-120000
Works on paper
£1795 $2782 €2800 Figures (51x33cm-20x13in) s. pencil paper on canvas exec.1930. 4-Dec-2 Finarte, Milan #204/R
£2821 $4372 €4400 Head (46x31cm-18x12in) s.d. pastel. 4-Dec-2 Finarte, Milan #195/R est:3000
£6013 $9500 €9500 Nude (71x50cm-28x20in) s. chl stump exec.1921 lit. 30-Nov-2 Farsetti, Prato #610/R est:13000

TRACHE, Rudolph (1866-?) German
£3166 $5034 €4749 Circus in town, young artists warming themselves by fire (82x112cm-32x44in) s.i. after L Knaus. 5-Mar-3 Rasmussen, Copenhagen #1723/R est:15000-20000 (D.KR 34000)

TRACHEL, Antoine (19th C) French
Works on paper
£355 $561 €550 Pecheurs sur les bords de la Baie des Anges (13x21cm-5x8in) W/C. 17-Dec-2 Claude Boisgirard, Paris #48

TRACHEL, Domenico (1830-1897) French
£355 $561 €550 Fete pour l'arrivee des enfants de V E a Villefranche, Nice (27x37cm-11x15in) s. wood. 17-Dec-2 Claude Boisgirard, Paris #54/R
£419 $663 €650 Masque de fer St Marguerite pres de Cannes (16x27cm-6x11in) mono. cardboard. 17-Dec-2 Claude Boisgirard, Paris #56
£1465 $2285 €2300 Barque de pecheurs (46x27cm-18x11in) s. 6-Nov-2 Gioffredo, Nice #7/R

TRACHEL, Ercole (1820-1872) French
Works on paper
£323 $510 €500 La charite de Marguerite de Provence (22x17cm-9x7in) grey pencil wash exec.c.1843. 17-Dec-2 Claude Boisgirard, Paris #34/R

TRACHSEL, Albert (1863-1929) Swiss
Works on paper
£283 $438 €425 Le jeune arbre (27x42cm-11x17in) s. W/C. 7-Dec-2 Galerie du Rhone, Sion #434/R (S.FR 650)
£437 $681 €656 Hilly landscape with some houses (24x35cm-9x14in) s. mixed media. 6-Nov-2 Dobiaschofsky, Bern #1019/R (S.FR 1000)

TRAFFELET, Fritz (1897-1954) Swiss
£463 $745 €695 Portrait of young woman (73x50cm-29x20in) s.d.43. 7-May-3 Dobiaschofsky, Bern #1024/R (S.FR 1000)
£516 $847 €748 Seated female nude (83x72cm-33x28in) s.d.25. 4-Jun-3 Fischer, Luzern #2333/R (S.FR 1100)
£1019 $1640 €1478 Swiss infantry in snowy landscape (59x80cm-23x31in) s. 9-May-3 Dobiaschofsky, Bern #86/R (S.FR 2200)
£1310 $2070 €1965 Woman's portrait (73x60cm-29x24in) s.d.46. 14-Nov-2 Stuker, Bern #549 est:4500-5000 (S.FR 3000)
Works on paper
£262 $409 €393 Swiss soldier walking (53x34cm-21x13in) s.d.49 chl. 6-Nov-2 Dobiaschofsky, Bern #1971/R (S.FR 600)
£1111 $1789 €1611 Soldiers in the field (51x33cm-20x13in) s. W/C over pencil painted 1971. 9-May-3 Dobiaschofsky, Bern #85/R (S.FR 2400)

TRAGARDH, Carl (1861-1899) Swedish
£2128 $3298 €3192 Watering the sheep (60x81cm-24x32in) s.d.97. 3-Dec-2 Bukowskis, Stockholm #202/R est:35000-40000 (S.KR 30000)
£2870 $4650 €4162 French spring landscape with geese (36x27cm-14x11in) s.d.1886 panel. 26-May-3 Bukowskis, Stockholm #3/R est:30000-35000 (S.KR 37000)

TRAIES, William (1789-1872) British
£1600 $2640 €2320 River landscape with fishermen at a pool (74x62cm-29x24in) 1-Jul-3 Bearnes, Exeter #490/R est:1500-2500
£2100 $3276 €3150 Capriccio river landscape (70x90cm-28x35in) 15-Oct-2 Bearnes, Exeter #416/R est:2000-3000
£9800 $16170 €14210 View of Exeter from Trews War with cattle and figures (69x90cm-27x35in) 1-Jul-3 Bearnes, Exeter #489/R est:3000-5000

TRAIES, William (attrib) (1789-1872) British
£400 $652 €600 Figure on stepping stones in a wooded river landscape (30x40cm-12x16in) 30-Jan-3 Lawrence, Crewkerne #718/R
£500 $790 €750 Extensive upland landscape with travellers on a path (40x54cm-16x21in) 7-Apr-3 Bonhams, Bath #78

TRAIN, Edward (1801-1866) British
£400 $620 €600 Rocky gorge in the highlands with figures and dog (19x29cm-7x11in) s. 24-Sep-2 Anderson & Garland, Newcastle #430/R
£540 $837 €810 Highland loch scene (24x21cm-9x8in) s. 24-Sep-2 Anderson & Garland, Newcastle #429/R
£650 $1014 €975 Scottish mountainous river landscape with figures (36x56cm-14x22in) s.d.1833. 18-Oct-2 Keys, Aylsham #674/R
£900 $1431 €1350 Figures on the banks of a loch (23x21cm-9x8in) s. board. 6-Mar-3 Christie's, Kensington #40/R
£900 $1431 €1350 Figures in a highland landscape (19x29cm-7x11in) s. 6-Mar-3 Christie's, Kensington #41/R

TRAKAL, S Z (20th C) Russian
£28000 $43960 €42000 Nicholas II reviewing the troops in Kharkov (54x121cm-21x48in) s.i.d.1904. 20-Nov-2 Sotheby's, London #34/R est:15000-20000

TRAMASURE, Pierre de (1790-?) Belgian
£949 $1481 €1500 Chariot dans un chemin creux (51x71cm-20x28in) s.d.1831. 16-Sep-2 Horta, Bruxelles #43

TRAMPEDACH, Kurt (1943-) Danish
£2534 $3953 €3801 Portrait of Annette (66x42cm-26x17in) init.d.88 oil crayon paper on canvas. 18-Sep-2 Kunsthallen, Copenhagen #169/R est:20000 (D.KR 30000)
£2834 $4505 €4251 Portrait (47x37cm-19x15in) s.d.1990 oil acrylic. 26-Feb-3 Kunsthallen, Copenhagen #193/R est:35000 (D.KR 31000)
£4290 $7164 €6221 Portrait (60x50cm-24x20in) s.i.d.86 exhib. paper on canvas. 17-Jun-3 Rasmussen, Copenhagen #34/R est:50000 (D.KR 45000)
£5338 $8915 €7740 Demon portrait 2002 (150x150cm-59x59in) s.i. oil on verso of carpet. 17-Jun-3 Rasmussen, Copenhagen #26/R est:80000-120000 (D.KR 56000)
£6101 $10189 €8846 Annette (70x100cm-28x39in) s.d.84 paper on canvas. 17-Jun-3 Rasmussen, Copenhagen #42/R est:50000 (D.KR 64000)
Sculpture
£5112 $8076 €7668 Boy sleeping (30x137x47cm-12x54x19in) mixed media executed 1974 lit. 1-Apr-3 Rasmussen, Copenhagen #163/R est:75000 (D.KR 55000)
Works on paper
£286 $478 €415 Double portrait (32x43cm-13x17in) s.d.marts 1976 pencil wash page from Diary. 17-Jun-3 Rasmussen, Copenhagen #103/R (D.KR 3000)
£286 $478 €415 Double portrait (33x44cm-13x17in) s.d.April-Mai 1976 pencil wash page from Diary. 17-Jun-3 Rasmussen, Copenhagen #106/R (D.KR 3000)
£508 $787 €762 Self portrait (21x30cm-8x12in) s. col crayons. 1-Oct-2 Rasmussen, Copenhagen #212/R (D.KR 6000)
£3160 $4993 €4740 Ava (123x113cm-48x44in) s.d.82 W/C graphite crayon exhib.prov. 1-Apr-3 Rasmussen, Copenhagen #223/R est:40000 (D.KR 34000)
£3273 $5073 €4910 Blue man with couple on his forehead (33x28cm-13x11in) oil W/C pencil paper on canvas. 4-Dec-2 Kunsthallen, Copenhagen #90/R est:40000 (D.KR 38000)

TRAN BIHN LOC (20th C) ?
Works on paper
£1206 $1953 €1700 Danseuses (63x47cm-25x19in) s.d.1939 gouache silk. 26-May-3 Joron-Derem, Paris #40 est:150-220

TRAN LONG, Mara (1935-) ?
Works on paper
£316 $500 €500 Mere et enfant (53x36cm-21x14in) s.d.72 gouache. 27-Nov-2 Blanchet, Paris #80

TRAN VAN HA (20th C) Vietnamese
Works on paper
£3728 $5742 €5592 Quietude (55x97cm-22x38in) s.d.1934 s.verso gouache ink on silk. 27-Oct-2 Christie's, Hong Kong #57/R est:40000-60000 (HK.D 45000)

TRAPOLIN, Tim (20th C) American
£320 $525 €464 Portrait of a young black girl (38x48cm-15x19in) s.d.71. 7-Jun-3 Neal Auction Company, New Orleans #427

TRAQUANDI, Gerard (1952-) French?
Works on paper
£319 $533 €450 Personnages (33x32cm-13x13in) s.d.1983 gouache chl collage. 18-Jun-3 Pierre Berge, Paris #82/R

TRAUB, Gustav (1885-1955) German
Works on paper
£616 $962 €900 Skier at a wayside shrine (29x42cm-11x17in) s. s.i.d.1917 verso mixed media board. 10-Apr-3 Allgauer, Kempten #3015/R

TRAUTMANN, Johann Georg (1713-1769) German
£1500 $2340 €2250 Village at night with figures fleeing from a burning house (24x27cm-9x11in) 8-Apr-3 Bonhams, Knightsbridge #97/R est:1200-1800
£3000 $5010 €4350 Poultry sellers by a shack. Vegetable sellers by a cottage (27x30cm-11x12in) init. panel pair. 11-Jul-3 Christie's, Kensington #150/R est:3000-5000

TRAUTMANN, Johann Georg (attrib) (1713-1769) German
£576 $921 €800 Heads of four bearded old men (18x13cm-7x5in) paper on board. 17-May-3 Lempertz, Koln #1136
£1703 $2844 €2400 Scene de Rixe (23x30cm-9x12in) metal. 18-Jun-3 Tajan, Paris #95 est:2000-3000
£3463 $5368 €5195 Figures partying in a wood (65x103cm-26x41in) 24-Sep-2 Koller, Zurich #6466/R est:8000-12000 (S.FR 8000)

TRAUTSCHOLD, Carl Friedrich Wilhelm (1815-1877) German
Works on paper
£1400 $2282 €2100 Stag and hind in a woodland glade with an obelisk (72x49cm-28x19in) s.d.1871 pastel. 17-Feb-3 Bonhams, Bath #149 est:500-700

TRAUTTWEILLER, Stefanie von (1888-?) German
£377 $600 €566 Pink peonies (76x61cm-30x24in) s. 7-Mar-3 Skinner, Boston #550/R
£481 $755 €750 Still life with meadow flowers and cherries (70x99cm-28x39in) s. 21-Nov-2 Dorotheum, Vienna #252/R
£500 $795 €750 Still life, flowers in a vase (55x44cm-22x17in) s. 18-Mar-3 Sworder & Son, Bishops Stortford #448/R

TRAVER, Charles Warde (1880-?) American
£512 $850 €742 Twilight lake scene (71x76cm-28x30in) s. 14-Jun-3 Jackson's, Cedar Falls #38

TRAVERSARI (19th C) French?
£10000 $16100 €14200 La galerie d'Apollon au Louvre (70x106cm-28x42in) s.d.1883. 11-May-3 Lombrail & Teucquam, Paris #165/R

TRAVERSI, Gaspare (attrib) (?-1769) Italian
£1200 $1872 €1800 Judith with the head of Holdfernes and her maidservant (59x53cm-23x21in) 8-Apr-3 Sotheby's, Olympia #225/R est:1500-2000
£2201 $3390 €3500 Portrait d'un ecclesiastique (39x29cm-15x11in) oval. 25-Oct-2 Tajan, Paris #39/R est:2500-3000
£8000 $12560 €12000 Cardplayers (26x34cm-10x13in) 10-Dec-2 Bonhams, New Bond Street #191/R est:6000-8000

TRAVERSI, Gaspare (circle) (?-1769) Italian
£3896 $6000 €5844 Portrait of a gentleman, holding a snuff box (92x72cm-36x28in) prov.exhib. 4-Sep-2 Christie's, Rockefeller NY #223/R est:2000-3000

TRAVERSO, Mattia (1885-1956) Italian
£1538 $2415 €2400 Gilrs with theatre masks (100x31cm-39x12in) pair. 10-Dec-2 Della Rocca, Turin #341/R est:2000

TRAVI, Antonio (attrib) (1608-1665) Italian
£7500 $11775 €11250 Coastal landscape with fishermen with their boats (35x52cm-14x20in) mono. 10-Dec-2 Sotheby's, Olympia #383/R est:2500-3500

TRAVIS, Kathryn Hail (1888-1972) American
£288 $447 €432 Blue hills (25x35cm-10x14in) s. s.i.verso board. 3-Dec-2 Ritchie, Toronto #3144/R (C.D 700)

TRAVIS, Olin Herman (1888-1975) American
£1282 $2000 €1923 River scene (30x41cm-12x16in) board. 19-Oct-2 David Dike, Dallas #102/R est:1500-3000
£1987 $3100 €2981 Sycamore and brook, White Rock Lake (30x41cm-12x16in) encaustic. 19-Oct-2 David Dike, Dallas #97/R est:3000-5000
£3205 $5000 €4808 In the Ozarks (51x66cm-20x26in) 19-Oct-2 David Dike, Dallas #305/R est:5000-10000
Works on paper
£449 $700 €674 Ute McCullough (46x36cm-18x14in) chl. 19-Oct-2 David Dike, Dallas #168/R
£5769 $9000 €8654 Cotton picking in the Ozarks (76x132cm-30x52in) encaustic board. 19-Oct-2 David Dike, Dallas #174a

TRAVIS, Paul Bough (1891-1975) American
£6962 $11000 €10443 Masai lion hunt (102x147cm-40x58in) exhib. 3-Apr-3 Christie's, Rockefeller NY #179/R est:3000-5000
Works on paper
£311 $510 €451 Pygmy hunters (25x38cm-10x15in) s.d.1956 graphite exhib. 30-May-3 Aspire, Cleveland #120/R

TRAYER, Jules (1824-1908) French
£6000 $9840 €9000 Lace maker (54x46cm-21x18in) s. panel prov. 3-Jun-3 Sotheby's, London #151/R est:4000-6000
Works on paper
£884 $1406 €1300 Jeune Bretonne assise (34x25cm-13x10in) s.i.d.1875 W/C. 26-Feb-3 Artcurial Briest, Paris #138

TRAYLOR, Bill (1854-1947) American
Works on paper
£6173 $10000 €9260 Untitled (23x20cm-9x8in) col pencil executed c.1939-1942 prov. 27-Jan-3 Christie's, Rockefeller NY #64/R est:8000-12000
£9259 $15000 €13889 Red bird (18x25cm-7x10in) gouache on cardboard executed c.1939-42 prov.exhib. 27-Jan-3 Christie's, Rockefeller NY #10/R est:12000-18000
£27778 $45000 €41667 Untitled - couple fighting (55x35cm-22x14in) graphite col pencil cardboard executed c.1939-42 prov.exhib. 27-Jan-3 Christie's, Rockefeller NY #11/R est:45000-65000

TREACY, Liam (1934-) Irish
£732 $1032 €1200 Barges on the canal (41x48cm-16x19in) s. 7-Feb-2 Woodwards, Cork #263
£822 $1290 €1200 Roses in studio window (24x19cm-9x7in) s. i.verso canvasboard. 15-Apr-3 De Veres Art Auctions, Dublin #100t est:900-1200
£1021 $1695 €1450 Interior (24x29cm-9x11in) s. 10-Jun-3 James Adam, Dublin #109/R est:1000-1500
£1039 $1579 €1600 Pub interior (38x48cm-15x19in) s. 2-Jul-2 Thomas Adams, Dublin #356
£1154 $1812 €1800 Arklow Harbour, County Wicklow (25x30cm-10x12in) s. board. 19-Nov-2 Whyte's, Dublin #137 est:800-1000
£1164 $1816 €1700 Bridgewood Street (34x43cm-13x17in) s. board. 8-Apr-3 James Adam, Dublin #29/R est:1000-1500
£1233 $1936 €1800 Studio table (34x24cm-13x9in) s. i.verso. 15-Apr-3 De Veres Art Auctions, Dublin #68/R est:1400-1800
£1384 $2158 €2200 Corner of Grafton Street, Dublin (30x41cm-12x16in) s. 17-Sep-2 Whyte's, Dublin #219 est:1500-2000
£2390 $3728 €3800 Mill at Castlebridge, County Wexford (36x46cm-14x18in) s. exhib. 17-Sep-2 Whyte's, Dublin #186/R est:2000-2500

TRECCANI, Ernesto (1920-1994) Italian
£244 $382 €380 Study for the man from the hill (25x24cm-10x9in) s.i.d.1964-65. 19-Nov-2 Finarte, Milan #18
£256 $403 €400 Untitled. s. s.i.d.1974 verso. 20-Nov-2 Pandolfini, Florence #74
£261 $418 €400 Figure (40x20cm-16x8in) s. s.verso. 4-Jan-3 Meeting Art, Vercelli #466
£272 $433 €400 Figure (40x20cm-16x8in) s. 1-Mar-3 Meeting Art, Vercelli #570
£285 $444 €450 Figure (40x20cm-16x8in) s. s.verso. 14-Sep-2 Meeting Art, Vercelli #953
£294 $471 €450 Figure (50x35cm-20x14in) s. 4-Jan-3 Meeting Art, Vercelli #113
£294 $471 €450 Figure (40x20cm-16x8in) s. 4-Jan-3 Meeting Art, Vercelli #445
£294 $471 €450 Figure (40x20cm-16x8in) s. 4-Jan-3 Meeting Art, Vercelli #690
£313 $497 €450 Figure (50x35cm-20x14in) s. s.verso. 1-May-3 Meeting Art, Vercelli #78
£316 $494 €500 Face (40x30cm-16x12in) s. s.verso. 14-Sep-2 Meeting Art, Vercelli #55
£321 $503 €500 Landscape (20x40cm-8x16in) s. s.verso. 23-Nov-2 Meeting Art, Vercelli #57
£327 $523 €500 Flag by the sea (35x25cm-14x10in) s. 4-Jan-3 Meeting Art, Vercelli #230
£327 $523 €500 Figure (70x30cm-28x12in) s. 4-Jan-3 Meeting Art, Vercelli #486
£347 $552 €500 Castles (35x50cm-14x20in) s. painted 1998. 1-May-3 Meeting Art, Vercelli #165
£353 $546 €550 Face (50x35cm-20x14in) s. 4-Dec-2 Finarte, Milan #338
£353 $554 €550 Figure (50x35cm-20x14in) s. 23-Nov-2 Meeting Art, Vercelli #239
£353 $554 €550 Maternity (50x35cm-20x14in) s. s.verso. 23-Nov-2 Meeting Art, Vercelli #396/R
£353 $554 €550 Figure (60x30cm-24x12in) s. s.verso. 23-Nov-2 Meeting Art, Vercelli #404/R
£359 $575 €550 Face (35x25cm-14x10in) s. 4-Jan-3 Meeting Art, Vercelli #187
£374 $595 €550 Figure amongst flowers (60x30cm-24x12in) s. 1-Mar-3 Meeting Art, Vercelli #451
£476 $757 €700 Face of woman (60x40cm-24x16in) s. 1-Mar-3 Meeting Art, Vercelli #702
£513 $795 €800 Flowers (50x50cm-20x20in) s. 4-Dec-2 Finarte, Milan #350
£577 $912 €900 Figures (35x50cm-14x20in) s. acrylic. 15-Nov-2 Farsetti, Prato #202/R
£590 $939 €850 Flight (70x50cm-28x20in) s. 1-May-3 Meeting Art, Vercelli #46
£625 $994 €900 Figure amongst flowers (50x50cm-20x20in) s. s.verso. 1-May-3 Meeting Art, Vercelli #37
£633 $987 €1000 Family (35x50cm-14x20in) s. s.verso. 14-Sep-2 Meeting Art, Vercelli #883/R
£641 $1006 €1000 Napoleon and flowers (70x50cm-28x20in) s. s.verso. 23-Nov-2 Meeting Art, Vercelli #412/R
£645 $1019 €1000 Figures (24x18cm-9x7in) s. pair. 18-Dec-2 Christie's, Rome #8
£680 $1082 €1000 Figure (70x50cm-28x20in) s. 1-Mar-3 Meeting Art, Vercelli #735
£705 $1107 €1100 Woman (110x35cm-43x14in) s.verso. 19-Nov-2 Finarte, Milan #69
£737 $1157 €1150 Seagulls (40x60cm-16x24in) s. s.verso. 23-Nov-2 Meeting Art, Vercelli #144/R
£868 $1380 €1250 Sunset on the sea (70x50cm-28x20in) s. 1-May-3 Meeting Art, Vercelli #275
£1111 $1767 €1600 Outdoor concert (70x100cm-28x39in) s. 1-May-3 Meeting Art, Vercelli #543
£1149 $1792 €1700 Milan: gold concrete (45x60cm-18x24in) s. painted 1960. 28-Mar-3 Farsetti, Prato #242
£1346 $2113 €2100 Tropics (90x45cm-35x18in) s. s.verso. 23-Nov-2 Meeting Art, Vercelli #200/R
£1731 $2717 €2700 Family (80x120cm-31x47in) s. 23-Nov-2 Meeting Art, Vercelli #472/R

TRECCHI, Walter (1964-) Italian
Works on paper
£993 $1609 €1400 Ex VIII (164x149cm-65x59in) s.i.d.2002 verso mixed media canvas. 20-May-3 Porro, Milan #54/R est:1800-2000

TRECHSLIN, Anne Marie (1927-) Swiss
£480 $749 €720 Two birds between yellow blossom (35x25cm-14x10in) s. W/C over pencil. 6-Nov-2 Dobiaschofsky, Bern #3744/R (S.FR 1100)
Works on paper
£278 $447 €403 Rose in bloom (35x26cm-14x10in) s. W/C over pencil. 7-May-3 Dobiaschofsky, Bern #3653 (S.FR 600)
£1092 $1703 €1638 Rose - Compression (32x23cm-13x9in) s. W/C. 6-Nov-2 Hans Widmer, St Gallen #146/R est:2000-2800 (S.FR 2500)

TREFFTZ, Gundula von (19/20th C) ?
Works on paper
£256 $390 €400 Bad Tolz (23x32cm-9x13in) pastel. 11-Jul-2 Hugo Ruef, Munich #934

TREGO, William Brooke Thomas (1859-1909) American
£1801 $2900 €2702 Winter scene of Washington reviewing the troops at Valley Forge (61x119cm-24x47in) s.d.1883. 22-Feb-3 Pook & Pook, Downington #208/R est:1500-2000

TREIDLER, Adolph (1846-1905) German
£962 $1500 €1443 Farmer driving oxcart up eastern Canadian hill (61x48cm-24x19in) s. tempera exhib. 9-Nov-2 Illustration House, New York #36/R est:3000-4000

TREMBATH, Ernest (1943-) Australian
£316 $480 €474 Misty morning in the valley (62x86cm-24x34in) s. board. 19-Aug-2 Joel, Victoria #211/R (A.D 900)
Works on paper
£300 $501 €435 Through the tall timber King Lake (17x31cm-7x12in) s. W/C. 24-Jun-3 Rowley Fine Art, Newmarket #355

TREMBLAY, Claude (20th C) Canadian
£422 $692 €633 Un silence que va (90x120cm-35x47in) s. acrylic. 3-Jun-3 Joyner, Toronto #413/R est:800-1000 (C.D 950)

TREMBLAY, Louis (1949-) Canadian
£341 $536 €512 Fin d'apres-midi, ile verte (30x35cm-12x14in) s.i. board. 25-Nov-2 Hodgins, Calgary #271/R (C.D 850)

TREMBLE, Leopold Paul (1924-) Canadian
Works on paper
£515 $803 €773 Alma (51x66cm-20x26in) s. pastel. 25-Mar-3 Iegor de Saint Hippolyte, Montreal #144 (C.D 1200)

TREMISOT, Leon (19th C) French
£385 $596 €600 Marine, barques de pecheurs (21x32cm-8x13in) s. 9-Dec-2 Thierry & Lannon, Brest #231
£2308 $3577 €3600 Saint-Malo (41x65cm-16x26in) s. 9-Dec-2 Thierry & Lannon, Brest #230/R est:3000

TREML, Johann Friedrich (1816-1852) Austrian
£6081 $9486 €9000 Memories of the battle at Wagram 1809 (32x26cm-13x10in) s.d.1809 panel. 25-Mar-3 Wiener Kunst Auktionen, Vienna #105/R est:7000-15000
Works on paper
£833 $1292 €1300 Farewell outside tavern (19x26cm-7x10in) i. verso W/C. 5-Dec-2 Dorotheum, Graz #129/R

TREMLETT, David (1945-) British
Works on paper
£625 $994 €900 1,9,8,7, (48x64cm-19x25in) pastel gouache pencil prov. 29-Apr-3 Artcurial Briest, Paris #529/R

TREMOHARS (?) French?
£1056 $1701 €1500 Le port de Doelan depart pour la peche (74x90cm-29x35in) s.i. 11-May-3 Thierry & Lannon, Brest #283 est:1200-1500
Works on paper
£458 $737 €650 Douarnenez (77x28cm-30x11in) s. gouache. 11-May-3 Thierry & Lannon, Brest #281
£481 $755 €750 Port de Douarnenez (68x47cm-27x19in) s. gouache. 15-Dec-2 Thierry & Lannon, Brest #261
£483 $768 €700 Animation dans le Port de Concarneau (50x65cm-20x26in) s. gouache. 10-Mar-3 Thierry & Lannon, Brest #205/R

TREMOIS, Pierre Yves (1921-) French
Works on paper
£340 $541 €500 Chasseurs et chiens (29x34cm-11x13in) s. crayon. 21-Mar-3 Rieunier, Bailly-Pommery, Mathias, Paris #106
£476 $757 €700 Deux cerfs (36x28cm-14x11in) s.d.44 pen Chinese ink gouache. 21-Mar-3 Rieunier, Bailly-Pommery, Mathias, Paris #105

TREMOLIERE, Pierre Charles (attrib) (1703-1739) French
£2482 $3848 €3723 Venus and Cupid (45x35cm-18x14in) 4-Dec-2 AB Stockholms Auktionsverk #2046/R est:40000-50000 (S.KR 35000)

TRENCH, Marianne L (1888-?) British
£360 $569 €540 Figure at a Mediterranean village pump (32x39cm-13x15in) s. 7-Apr-3 Bonhams, Bath #63

TRENK, Franz (1899-1960) Austrian
£350 $564 €525 Farmhouse with snow capped moutains beyond (97x106cm-38x42in) s.d.1945 i.d.verso. 14-Jan-3 Bonhams, Knightsbridge #109

TRENNERY, Horace Hurtle (1899-1958) Australian
£2071 $3190 €3107 Still life - sweet peas (30x40cm-12x16in) s.d.1917. 3-Sep-2 Shapiro, Sydney #365/R est:3500-4500 (A.D 5800)
£17794 $27224 €26691 Road to Maslins (48x57cm-19x22in) s. cardboard painted 1940 prov.exhib. 26-Aug-2 Sotheby's, Paddington #549/R est:25000-35000 (A.D 50000)

TRENTIN, Angelo (1850-1912) Austrian
£890 $1389 €1300 Woman with bunch of violets (52x39cm-20x15in) s.d.1889 panel. 10-Apr-3 Dorotheum, Vienna #216/R

TRETCHIKOFF, Vladimir (1913-) Russian
£550 $919 €798 Sunflower vendor (66x76cm-26x30in) s. 17-Jun-3 Bonhams, Knightsbridge #202
£1290 $2077 €1935 Still life of proteas in a brass vase (121x60cm-48x24in) s. 12-May-3 Stephan Welz, Johannesburg #562/R est:15000-20000 (SA.R 15000)
£2236 $3599 €3354 Pin-cushion proteas and a blue vase (70x90cm-28x35in) s.d.58. 12-May-3 Stephan Welz, Johannesburg #565/R est:15000-20000 (SA.R 26000)
£3859 $6096 €5789 Xhosa warrior (72x78cm-28x31in) s.d.59. 1-Apr-3 Stephan Welz, Johannesburg #475/R est:25000-30000 (SA.R 48000)

TREVEDY, Yves (1916-) French
£304 $480 €480 Jardin boise (37x28cm-15x11in) s. panel. 1-Dec-2 Livinec, Gaudcheau & Jezequel, Rennes #61

TREVELYAN, Julian (1910-1989) British
£1600 $2672 €2320 Santa Maria del Fiore (50x61cm-20x24in) s.d.65. 24-Jun-3 Bonhams, New Bond Street #84/R est:1000-1500
£2200 $3608 €3300 Two dockers (40x51cm-16x20in) s.d.87 board. 3-Jun-3 Sotheby's, Olympia #206/R est:2000-3000
£3200 $5248 €4800 Windmills (51x61cm-20x24in) s.d.88. 3-Jun-3 Sotheby's, Olympia #208/R est:3000-5000
£4800 $7488 €7200 Leaving Dunkirk (41x51cm-16x20in) s.d.87. 27-Mar-3 Christie's, Kensington #610/R est:3000-5000
£5000 $7750 €7500 Weir (51x61cm-20x24in) s.d.63 exhib. 4-Dec-2 Christie's, Kensington #566/R est:2000-3000
£5200 $8684 €7540 Swans at Chiswick Reach (76x91cm-30x36in) s.d.62. 24-Jun-3 Bonhams, New Bond Street #88/R est:2000-3000
£5500 $9020 €8250 Easter festival (76x91cm-30x36in) s.d.65. 3-Jun-3 Sotheby's, Olympia #163/R est:3000-5000
£6500 $10205 €9750 Durham wharf (76x61cm-30x24in) s.d.56 prov.exhib. 16-Dec-2 Sotheby's, London #94/R est:5000-7000
£7500 $11849 €11250 Le Havre (121x182cm-48x72in) s.d.87 board exhib. 27-Nov-2 Sotheby's, Olympia #291/R est:6000-8000
£10000 $16400 €15000 St. Tropez (33x41cm-13x16in) s.d.29 s.d.verso panel. 6-Jun-3 Christie's, London #30/R est:3000-5000
£13500 $21465 €20250 Paddle steamer (61x77cm-24x30in) s.d.85. 26-Feb-3 Sotheby's, Olympia #343/R est:4000-6000
£14500 $23780 €21750 Durham Wharf (61x76cm-24x30in) s.d.57 prov. 6-Jun-3 Christie's, London #113/R est:5000-8000
Works on paper
£1800 $2844 €2700 County Clare landscape (34x52cm-13x20in) s.d.35 gouache over pencil. 27-Nov-2 Sotheby's, Olympia #289/R est:1500-2000
£4200 $6888 €6090 Mediterranean townscape (54x74cm-21x29in) s.d.58 W/C. 4-Jun-3 Sotheby's, London #77/R est:3000-4000

TREVILLE, Richard de (1864-1929) American
£342 $550 €513 Study of a quail in a landscape (25x20cm-10x8in) s. prov. 18-Feb-3 John Moran, Pasadena #116a
£932 $1500 €1398 Mt Shasta mountain landscape (33x61cm-13x24in) s. prov. 18-Feb-3 John Moran, Pasadena #40a est:1500-2000

TREVISANI, Francesco (1656-1746) Italian
£2516 $3874 €4000 Allegory of Moderation (47x37cm-19x15in) oval. 23-Oct-2 Finarte, Rome #470/R
£6000 $10020 €8700 Agony in the garden (36cm-14in circular) copper. 11-Jul-3 Christie's, Kensington #249/R est:5000-8000
£10000 $15600 €15000 Portrait of Cardinal Pietro Ottoboni (74x61cm-29x24in) painted oval. 9-Apr-3 Christie's, London #99/R est:10000-15000
Works on paper
£811 $1265 €1200 Flagellation (18x21cm-7x8in) sanguine. 27-Mar-3 Maigret, Paris #3

TREVISANI, Francesco (attrib) (1656-1746) Italian
£2564 $3974 €4000 Ecce Homo (70x52cm-28x20in) 4-Dec-2 Christie's, Rome #372
Works on paper
£308 $484 €450 Christ being nailed to the Cross, watched by Mary and Magdalena (28x18cm-11x7in) i. sepia paper on board. 16-Apr-3 Dorotheum, Salzburg #172/R
£2590 $4144 €3600 Reclining Bacchus (56x41cm-22x16in) i. verso chk. 17-May-3 Lempertz, Koln #1258/R est:2600

TREVISANI, Francesco (circle) (1656-1746) Italian
£5500 $9185 €7975 Holy Family with the Infant Saint John the Baptist (99x80cm-39x31in) 11-Jul-3 Christie's, Kensington #208/R est:2000-3000

TREVOR, George (?) British
Works on paper
£720 $1102 €1080 View of the old course clubhouse, and 18th fairway (17x26cm-7x10in) s. W/C. 22-Aug-2 Bonhams, Edinburgh #549/R est:800-1200

TREW, E Florence (fl.1887-1890) British
£300 $501 €435 Still life, study of daffodils and a green jug (28x43cm-11x17in) i.verso. 25-Jun-3 Brightwells, Leominster #965/R

TREZISE, Percy (20th C) Australian
£239 $392 €359 Water birds, Kennedy lakes (61x91cm-24x36in) s. composition board. 4-Jun-3 Deutscher-Menzies, Melbourne #405/R (A.D 600)

TRIBE, Barbara (1913-2000) Australian
Sculpture
£1400 $2310 €2030 Female torso (48cm-19in) s.num.3/12 green pat. bronze. 3-Jul-3 Christie's, Kensington #816/R est:600-800

TRICKER, Florence (20th C) American
£688 $1100 €1032 Sunny morning near Woodstock, Katskills (64x76cm-25x30in) s.i. 17-May-3 Pook & Pook, Downington #200e est:800-1000

TRICKETT, John (1952-) British
£300 $468 €435 Shooting in a snow covered river landscape (23x35cm-9x14in) s. 27-Mar-3 Neales, Nottingham #1042
£450 $689 €675 Black labrador seated in a landscape (76x61cm-30x24in) s.i. 20-Aug-2 Bonhams, Leeds #307
£450 $702 €675 On frozen pond (46x61cm-18x24in) s. 10-Apr-3 Tennants, Leyburn #1022
£600 $924 €900 Stag in landscape with rising mountains and forest to background. s. 6-Sep-2 Moore Allen & Innocent, Cirencester #820
£650 $1079 €943 Stags in a highland landscape (51x76cm-20x30in) s. 12-Jun-3 Christie's, Kensington #124/R
£900 $1422 €1350 Black labrador (50x39cm-20x15in) s. board. 28-Nov-2 Christie's, Kensington #364/R

TRIER, Hann (1915-1999) German
£638 $1034 €900 Untitled (51x72cm-20x28in) mono.d.59 W/C. 24-May-3 Van Ham, Cologne #597/R
£2553 $4136 €3600 Attack I (41x33cm-16x13in) mono.d.62 i. stretcher lit. 24-May-3 Van Ham, Cologne #596/R est:5000
£3404 $5515 €4800 Contraddanza (115x88cm-45x35in) s.d.69 s.i.d. verso exhib.lit. 24-May-3 Van Ham, Cologne #595/R est:6000
£4058 $6655 €5600 Revolution (130x89cm-51x35in) s.d.61 s.i. verso prov.exhib. 28-May-3 Lempertz, Koln #435/R est:8000-10000
£9295 $14407 €14500 Mariposa II (88x130cm-35x51in) s.d.61 oil egg tempera prov. 3-Dec-2 Lempertz, Koln #471/R est:10000-12000
Works on paper
£353 $546 €550 Untitled (49x62cm-19x24in) mono.d.69 ink gouache. 7-Dec-2 Van Ham, Cologne #552/R
£513 $810 €800 Untitled (78x103cm-31x41in) mono.d.1963 Indian ink brush was. 14-Nov-2 Neumeister, Munich #891/R
£513 $795 €800 Bullfight study (29x44cm-11x17in) mono.d.55 W/C Indian ink. 3-Dec-2 Lempertz, Koln #474/R

TRIGLER, Martin (1867-?) Austrian
£577 $894 €900 Rest on the Flight (100x90cm-39x35in) s. 5-Dec-2 Dorotheum, Graz #60

TRIGO, Modesto (1960-) Spanish
£377 $589 €600 Still life with salmon (65x80cm-26x31in) s.d.89. 8-Oct-2 Ansorena, Madrid #306/R
£425 $684 €650 Still life with lobster (73x92cm-29x36in) s.d.89. 14-Jan-3 Castellana, Madrid #37/R

TRINCOT, Georges (1921-) French
£466 $750 €699 Course (46x61cm-18x24in) s.d.66. 20-Jan-3 Arthur James, Florida #503

TRINDALL, Gordon Lyall (1886-1965) Australian
£319 $523 €463 Still life, magnolias (48x90cm-19x35in) s. canvasboard. 3-Jun-3 Lawson Menzies, Sydney #883 (A.D 800)

TRINKEWITZ, Karl (1891-?) German
£669 $1111 €950 View over Seelenberg to the Feldberg (67x80cm-26x31in) s. 14-Jun-3 Arnold, Frankfurt #887/R

TRINQUESSE, Louis Rolland (1746-1800) French
Works on paper
£1090 $1689 €1700 Jeune femme lisant (39x23cm-15x9in) sanguine. 4-Dec-2 Piasa, Paris #96/R
£2568 $4005 €3800 Portrait de femme en buste vue de profil, a droite (20cm-8in circular) s.i.d.1772 chk. 27-Mar-3 Christie's, Paris #47/R

TRIOS, Enrico Giulio (?) Italian
£452 $700 €678 St. Maria della salute Venice (28x38cm-11x15in) 4-Oct-2 Douglas, South Deerfield #2

TRIPE, Linnaeus (1822-1902) British
Photographs
£4807 $7500 €7211 Inscription around the basement of the Bimanum of Great Pagoda (22x611cm-9x241in) albumen print. 14-Oct-2 Butterfields, San Francisco #1402a/R est:4000-6000
£9500 $15390 €14250 Temple study, Madura (34x27cm-13x11in) albumen print exec.c.1858 prov. 21-May-3 Christie's, London #95/R est:12000-15000
£11000 $17820 €16500 Views in Madura, part II (25x36cm-10x14in) st.mono.i. albumenised salt prints 9 folio. 22-May-3 Sotheby's, London #12/R est:12000-18000
£16000 $25920 €24000 Views in Madura, part 1 (26x35cm-10x14in) st.mono.i. albumenised salt prints 10 folio lit. 22-May-3 Sotheby's, London #11/R est:12000-18000
£115000 $186300 €172500 Tanjore (25x36cm-10x14in) st.mono. albumenised salt prints 23 folio. 22-May-3 Sotheby's, London #13/R est:30000-50000

TRIPE, Mary Elizabeth (1867-1939) New Zealander
£3333 $5200 €5000 Brass cleaner (67x57cm-26x22in) 27-Mar-3 International Art Centre, Auckland #97/R est:7000-10000 (NZ.D 9500)
Works on paper
£708 $1104 €1062 Wellington (23x17cm-9x7in) s.d.1918 W/C. 6-Aug-2 Peter Webb, Auckland #228/R est:800-1600 (NZ.D 2400)

TRISCOTT, Samuel Peter Rolt (1846-1925) American
Works on paper
£976 $1600 €1415 Rocky coastal scene with figures and dories on shore (28x64cm-11x25in) W/C. 31-May-3 Van Blarcom, South Natick #103/R est:300-500
£1646 $2600 €2469 Wetlands with distant mountains (53x64cm-21x25in) s.d.1886 W/C. 30-Nov-2 Thomaston Place, Thomaston #8
£1711 $2600 €2567 Brook in Cutler, Maine (43x53cm-17x21in) W/C. 30-Aug-2 Thomaston Place, Thomaston #53
£1741 $2750 €2612 Coastal Maine inlet, tide out (30x48cm-12x19in) s. W/C. 26-Apr-3 Thomaston Place, Thomaston #220
£3947 $6000 €5921 End of the salt Creek, Ogunqit, Maine (66x56cm-26x22in) W/C. 30-Aug-2 Thomaston Place, Thomaston #56

TRISTAN MILAN, Jacques (19/20th C) French?
Works on paper
£1712 $2688 €2500 Portrait de femme (9x8cm-4x3in) s.d.16 gouache. 15-Apr-3 Laurence Calmels, Paris #4227/R

TRISTAN, Luis (1586-1624) Spanish
£6452 $10194 €10000 Guerison (140x73cm-55x29in) panel prov. 18-Dec-2 Piasa, Paris #17/R est:18000

TRISTRAM, J W (1872-1938) Australian
Works on paper
£323 $490 €485 Early morning (31x37cm-12x15in) s.d.1918 W/C. 28-Aug-2 Deutscher-Menzies, Melbourne #407/R (A.D 900)

TRITT, Wolfgang (1913-1983) German?
£1200 $1884 €1800 Odeonsplatz. view of Munich (40x59cm-16x23in) s. two. 21-Nov-2 Christie's, Kensington #115/R est:1200-1800

TRITTEN, Gottfried (1923-) Swiss
Works on paper
£349 $545 €524 T Ishtar (96x64cm-38x25in) s.i. W/C Indian ink collage. 6-Nov-2 Dobiaschofsky, Bern #1975/R (S.FR 800)
£524 $817 €786 Bacchus (120x80cm-47x31in) s.i. i. verso Indian ink bodycol exhib. 6-Nov-2 Dobiaschofsky, Bern #1974/R (S.FR 1200)

TRIVIGNO, Helen (1920-1985) American
Works on paper
£854 $1400 €1281 Field of flowers (38x30cm-15x12in) s. enamel. 8-Feb-3 Neal Auction Company, New Orleans #403 est:1200-1800

TROCKEL, Rosemarie (1952-) German
£2692 $4173 €4200 Untitled (20x13cm-8x5in) paper. 6-Dec-2 Hauswedell & Nolte, Hamburg #376/R est:2000
Sculpture
£8228 $13000 €12342 Untitled - Juliette/ Justine (200x49x30cm-79x19x12in) wood pedestal shirt hanger vitrine and spider executed 1988. 12-Nov-2 Phillips, New York #197/R est:15000-20000
Works on paper
£1424 $2250 €2136 Untitled (27x20cm-11x8in) s.d.88 ink marker prov. 13-Nov-2 Sotheby's, New York #595/R
£3200 $5248 €4800 Untitled, mermaids (15x21cm-6x8in) s.d.87 verso gouache prov.exhib. 7-Feb-3 Sotheby's, London #187/R est:2000-3000

TROGER, Paul (1698-1762) Austrian
£10135 $15811 €15000 Vision of St Elizabeth (78cm-31in) prov.lit. 27-Mar-3 Dorotheum, Vienna #154/R est:16000-22000
£16352 $25346 €26000 Pieta (64x39cm-25x15in) prov.lit. 2-Oct-2 Dorotheum, Vienna #248/R est:12000-18000
Works on paper
£2027 $3162 €3000 God the Father above the clouds (30x22cm-12x9in) pen. 28-Mar-3 Dorotheum, Vienna #75/R est:3000-3500

TROGER, Simon (studio) (1694-1768) Austrian
Sculpture
£7500 $11850 €11250 Cain and abel (35cm-14in) mono. ivory walnut lit. 14-Nov-2 Christie's, London #68/R est:5000-8000

TROIANI, Don (1949-) American
£9938 $16100 €14410 Forlorn Hope (97x122cm-38x48in) 23-May-3 Altermann Galleries, Santa Fe #133

TROILI, Uno (attrib) (1815-1875) Swedish
£372 $603 €558 Italian model (43x31cm-17x12in) oval. 3-Feb-3 Lilla Bukowskis, Stockholm #502 (S.KR 5200)

TROKES, Heinz (1913-1997) German
£2532 $3924 €4000 Remains of coloured monument (101x57cm-40x22in) s.d.1956 s.i.d.15.1.56 verso. 28-Sep-2 Ketterer, Hamburg #320/R est:4000-5000
£5063 $8000 €8000 Disturbed peace (92x71cm-36x28in) s.d.65 i. verso. 30-Nov-2 Villa Grisebach, Berlin #418/R est:6000-8000
Works on paper
£603 $977 €850 Goldberg (51x73cm-20x29in) s.63 gouache pencil board. 24-May-3 Van Ham, Cologne #598/R
£638 $1034 €900 Untitled (47x61cm-19x24in) s.d. Indian ink. 24-May-3 Van Ham, Cologne #599
£1101 $1695 €1750 Figures (47x61cm-19x24in) s.d.1946 i. verso gouache board. 26-Oct-2 Dr Lehr, Berlin #529/R est:2000

TROMBADORI, Francesco (1886-1961) Italian
£2244 $3522 €3500 Via dell'Impero (13x18cm-5x7in) s. board painted 1958. 21-Nov-2 Finarte, Rome #55/R
Works on paper
£890 $1389 €1300 Dancer (24x18cm-9x7in) mixed media paper on card. 10-Apr-3 Finarte Semenzato, Rome #96/R

TROMBINI, Giuliano (1953-) Italian
£316 $494 €500 Girls at the bar (70x50cm-28x20in) s. s.verso. 14-Sep-2 Meeting Art, Vercelli #893
£327 $523 €500 Cafe (50x60cm-20x24in) s. s.verso. 4-Jan-3 Meeting Art, Vercelli #675
£475 $741 €750 Loneliness (100x70cm-39x28in) s. s.verso. 14-Sep-2 Meeting Art, Vercelli #899/R

TROMETTA, Nicolo (16/17th C) Italian
Works on paper
£922 $1540 €1300 Etude pour la naissance de la Vierge (25x18cm-10x7in) pen brown ink brown wash. 19-Jun-3 Piasa, Paris #7/R
£1700 $2839 €2465 St. Anthony of Padua. Studies of arms (22x14cm-9x6in) pen ink wash over black chk double-sided. 9-Jul-3 Bonhams, Knightsbridge #26/R est:2000-3000

TROMP, Jan Zoetelief (1872-1947) Dutch
£6289 $9686 €10000 Awaiting the return at the Meelzak, Katwijk Aan Zee (31x41cm-12x16in) s. lit. 22-Oct-2 Sotheby's, Amsterdam #103/R est:10000-15000
£15278 $24292 €22000 Pet goat, children taking a walk in summer (24x34cm-9x13in) s. panel prov. 29-Apr-3 Christie's, Amsterdam #135/R est:18000-22000
£82222 $136489 €118242 Children carrying a lamb on a country lane (63x98cm-25x39in) s. 16-Jun-3 Waddingtons, Toronto #254/R est:40000-60000 (C.D 185000)
£119497 $184025 €190000 Beach fun (68x95cm-27x37in) s. s.verso exhib. 22-Oct-2 Sotheby's, Amsterdam #186/R est:45000-55000
Works on paper
£2740 $4301 €4000 Returning from the fields (17x24cm-7x9in) s. W/C. 15-Apr-3 Sotheby's, Amsterdam #132/R est:4000-5000

TROMP, Jan Zoetelief (circle) (1872-1947) Dutch
£5200 $8424 €7800 Children in a meadow (47x63cm-19x25in) bears sig. 20-May-3 Sotheby's, Olympia #386/R est:1000-1500

TRONCET, Antony (1879-1939) French
Works on paper
£1800 $2826 €2700 Une femme s'essuyant (81x60cm-32x24in) s. pastel on linen. 21-Nov-2 Christie's, Kensington #41/R est:1500-2000

TROOD, William Henry Hamilton (1848-1899) British
£2301 $3750 €3452 Zoe (28x25cm-11x10in) s.i.d.1882. 11-Feb-3 Bonhams & Doyles, New York #210/R est:3000-5000
£3681 $6000 €5522 Come and get it ! (30x41cm-12x16in) s. 11-Feb-3 Bonhams & Doyles, New York #182/R est:7000-9000
£8750 $13300 €13125 Two puppies and a frog (28x38cm-11x15in) s.d.1884. 14-Aug-2 Andrew Hartley, Ilkley #646/R est:5000-7000

TROOST, Cornelis (1697-1750) Dutch
£450 $698 €675 Study of a procession (12x25cm-5x10in) monochrome sketch on canvas. 26-Sep-2 Mellors & Kirk, Nottingham #696

TROOST, Willem (18/19th C) Dutch
£53853 $82933 €80780 Garden facade of the Old Palce of the Governor General at Buitenzorg (62x82cm-24x32in) prov.exhib.lit. 27-Oct-2 Christie's, Hong Kong #38/R est:650000-850000 (HK.D 650000)
Works on paper
£7006 $10930 €11000 Market scene with figures by a quayside, mountains and river beyond (25x24cm-10x9in) s. gouache prov. 5-Nov-2 Sotheby's, Amsterdam #125/R est:10000-12000

TROOST, Willem I (1684-1759) Dutch
Works on paper
£1119 $1600 €1679 Imaginary Rhine landscape with boats, fishermen and a castle on a hill (34x48cm-13x19in) gouache. 23-Jan-3 Swann Galleries, New York #210/R est:2000-3000

TROSHIN, Nikolai (1897-1990) Russian
£1918 $2992 €2800 Still life of flowers with yellow background (75x64cm-30x25in) s.cyrillic d.1965. 10-Apr-3 Schopman, Hamburg #649 est:2800

TROSO, Ferdinando (20th C) Italian
£269 $425 €420 Bridge on the Tiber (60x80cm-24x31in) painted 1971. 12-Nov-2 Babuino, Rome #178/R
£308 $486 €480 Harbour (60x80cm-24x31in) painted 1971. 12-Nov-2 Babuino, Rome #363/R

TROST, Dolfi (1916-1966) Rumanian
£2055 $3226 €3000 Angoisse cosmique (41x33cm-16x13in) s.i.d.1952 cardboard. 15-Apr-3 Laurence Calmels, Paris #4122/R

TROTIN, Hector (1894-1966) French
£1000 $1590 €1500 Ascension d'un ballon militaire Anglaise en 1785 (24x19cm-9x7in) indis.i. board prov. 20-Mar-3 Sotheby's, Olympia #174/R est:1000-1500
£2600 $4004 €3900 Diligence-voiture a vapeur avec lanterne a l'avant (25x32cm-10x13in) i. i.verso board prov. 22-Oct-2 Sotheby's, London #150/R est:2500-3500
£3500 $5390 €5250 Premiere experience aerostatique effectuee en autriche au prater de vienne le 7 Juillet 1784 (35x24cm-14x9in) s. i.verso board prov. 22-Oct-2 Sotheby's, London #147/R est:2000-3000
£3500 $5390 €5250 Ascension au Luxembourg de MM. Labbe morolan, bredin et janiriet 1784 (25x17cm-10x7in) s. i.verso board prov. 22-Oct-2 Sotheby's, London #148/R est:1000-1500
£5000 $7700 €7500 Chemin de fer francais sur la ligne du nord, 1850 (23x56cm-9x22in) s. i.verso board prov. 22-Oct-2 Sotheby's, London #149/R est:6000-8000

TROTTER, Newbold Hough (1827-1898) American
£1097 $1700 €1646 Mountain lion (39x49cm-15x19in) s. s.i.verso board. 8-Dec-2 Freeman, Philadelphia #110/R est:400-600

TROTTI, Giovanni Battista (1555-1619) Italian
Works on paper
£4000 $6680 €5800 Study of an evangelist, standing with an open book (33x22cm-13x9in) pen brown ink grey wash squared pricked for transfer prov. 9-Jul-3 Sotheby's, London #17/R est:4000-6000
£4000 $6680 €5800 Adoration of the shepherds (57x63cm-22x25in) bears mono. i. pen brown ink blk chk joined sheets prov. 9-Jul-3 Sotheby's, London #21/R est:4000-6000
£9810 $15500 €15500 Un eveque tourne vers la gauche (28x16cm-11x6in) black chk pen brown ink grey wash. 27-Nov-2 Christie's, Paris #41/R est:15000-20000
£13000 $21710 €18850 Holy Trinity with angels, putti and a congregation of Saints (42x92cm-17x36in) black chk ink squares in black prov.lit. 8-Jul-3 Christie's, London #26/R est:3000-5000

TROTTI, Sandro (20th C) Italian
£321 $503 €500 Cranes and boats (50x70cm-20x28in) s. s.i.verso. 21-Nov-2 Finarte, Rome #270

TROTZIER, Jean Bernard (1950-) French
£352 $567 €500 Discussion sur le chemin de campagne (38x55cm-15x22in) s. 11-May-3 Thierry & Lannon, Brest #284

TROTZIG, Ulf (1925-) Norwegian
£255 $403 €383 Ash landscape (97x196cm-38x77in) s. s.d.62 verso. 30-Nov-2 Rasmussen, Havnen #2185 (D.KR 3000)
£1583 $2517 €2375 Composition (130x195cm-51x77in) s.d.62. 10-Mar-3 Rasmussen, Vejle #671/R est:25000 (D.KR 17000)

TROUBETZKOY, Prince Paolo (1866-1938) Russian
£19000 $30780 €28500 Female portrait (108x82cm-43x32in) s.d.1910. 21-May-3 Sotheby's, London #55/R est:12000-18000
Sculpture
£2449 $3894 €3600 Chienne de chasse gestante (24cm-9in) s.d.1897 gold pat bronze. 26-Feb-3 Artcurial Briest, Paris #149/R est:3500-4500
£2532 $4000 €4000 Dog sitting (24cm-9in) s.d.1891 bronze. 1-Dec-2 Bukowskis, Helsinki #223/R est:2500-3000
£3000 $4680 €4500 Sir William Garthwaite, 1st BT (44cm-17in) s.d.1924 brown pat bronze st.f.Valsuani prov. 9-Apr-3 Sotheby's, London #222/R est:5000-7000
£6115 $9784 €8500 La troika epuisee (29x57cm-11x22in) s.d.1898 pat bronze. 18-May-3 Rabourdin & Choppin de Janvry, Paris #84/R est:11000-13000
£7092 $11844 €10000 Portrait de Lev Tolstoy (50cm-20in) s.d. plaster prov. 17-Jun-3 Claude Boisgirard, Paris #133 est:12000-15000

TROUBETZKOY, Prince Pierre (1864-1936) American
£480 $750 €720 Portrait of Pietro Menctti (24x16cm-9x6in) s.d.1906 canvasboard. 14-Sep-2 Weschler, Washington #626/R

TROUILLE, Clovis (1889-1975) French
£164384 $256438 €240000 Religieuse italienne fumant la cigarette (61x46cm-24x18in) s. exhib.lit. 14-Apr-3 Laurence Calmels, Paris #4021/R est:80000

TROUILLEBERT, Paul Desire (1829-1900) French
£2200 $3498 €3300 Launching the punt (19x24cm-7x9in) s. 18-Mar-3 Bonhams, New Bond Street #121/R est:2000-3000
£2658 $4200 €4200 Le nettoyage de la bergerie (48x17cm-19x7in) s. 1-Dec-2 Peron, Melun #37
£2800 $4368 €4200 Harvest time (42x33cm-17x13in) s. panel. 26-Mar-3 Hamptons Fine Art, Godalming #162/R est:2500-3500
£3302 $5283 €4953 Forest clearing with pond and washerwoman (49x39cm-19x15in) s. i.d.juillet 1890 verso prov. 17-Mar-3 Philippe Schuler, Zurich #4639/R est:8000-12000 (S.FR 7000)
£4200 $7014 €6300 Reclining nude (23x39cm-9x15in) s. panel. 18-Jun-3 Christie's, Kensington #9a/R est:3000-5000
£4695 $7700 €6808 Sous bois (65x49cm-26x19in) s. prov. 4-Jun-3 Fischer, Luzern #1054/R est:12000-14000 (S.FR 10000)
£5931 $9905 €8600 Les saules a Tillezes (65x81cm-26x32in) s. 9-Jul-3 Millon & Associes, Paris #96/R est:10000-12000
£6173 $8765 €10000 Barque en bord de riviere (33x41cm-13x16in) s. 16-Mar-3 Eric Pillon, Calais #38/R
£7099 $10080 €11500 Pecheur ramenant ses filets (33x41cm-13x16in) s. 16-Mar-3 Eric Pillon, Calais #39/R
£7692 $12154 €12000 Still life with glasses, oysters and lemon (37x56cm-15x22in) s. prov. 15-Nov-2 Reiss & Sohn, Konigstein #89/R est:12000
£8310 $13379 €11800 Bord de mer anime (25x41cm-10x16in) s. 12-May-3 Lesieur & Le Bars, Le Havre #92/R
£8500 $13855 €12325 Le moulin, a French village beside a river, house nearby (41x48cm-16x19in) s. mono.i.verso prov. 17-Jul-3 Tennants, Leyburn #870/R est:7000-10000
£8741 $14598 €12500 Bord de riviere (28x46cm-11x18in) s. 27-Jun-3 Claude Aguttes, Neuilly #29/R est:12000-15000
£11392 $18000 €17088 Au bord de la Riviere (51x61cm-20x24in) s.i. prov. 5-Apr-3 Neal Auction Company, New Orleans #174/R est:20000-25000
£19718 $32732 €28000 Untitled (66x80cm-26x31in) s. exhib. 11-Jun-3 Beaussant & Lefèvre, Paris #202/R est:15000-20000

TROUILLEBERT, Paul Desire (attrib) (1829-1900) French
£1013 $1479 €1520 Girl in blue dress (36x22cm-14x9in) s. canvas on board. 17-Jun-2 Philippe Schuler, Zurich #4360a/R (S.FR 2300)
£1454 $2122 €2181 Peasant in straw hat (33x19cm-13x7in) s. 17-Jun-2 Philippe Schuler, Zurich #4360b/R est:1000-1500 (S.FR 3300)
£1793 $2761 €2690 River landscape (37x61cm-15x24in) s. panel. 27-Oct-2 Anders Antik, Landskrona #180/R est:8000-10000 (S.KR 26000)

TROVA, Ernest (1927-) American
Sculpture
£1154 $1800 €1731 Gox no 2 (28x20x8cm-11x8x3in) d.1987 num.44/99 steel epoxy bronze sold with catalogue lit. 14-Oct-2 Butterfields, San Francisco #2098/R est:2500-3500
£3548 $5500 €5322 Standing man (70x13x13cm-28x5x5in) mono.num.4/6 chrome plated bronze prov.exhib.lit. 26-Sep-2 Christie's, Rockefeller NY #768/R est:6000-8000

TROY, François de (1645-1730) French
£9028 $14264 €13000 Portrait presume de M Michel de Sainte-Marie. Portrait presume de M.me de Sainte-Marie (81x65cm-32x26in) pair. 25-Apr-3 Beaussant & Lefèvre, Paris #14/R
£22222 $36000 €33333 Portrait of H Bernard de Roqueleyne, the Baron de Longepierre (131x97cm-52x38in) prov.exhib.lit. 24-Jan-3 Christie's, Rockefeller NY #92/R est:20000-30000
Works on paper
£4167 $6458 €6500 Prevots des Marchands et les Echevins de Paris (34x27cm-13x11in) crayon wash gouache prov. 4-Dec-2 Piasa, Paris #57/R

TROY, François de (attrib) (1645-1730) French
£3846 $6423 €5500 Portrait d'un architecte (100x80cm-39x31in) oval. 27-Jun-3 Piasa, Paris #92/R est:5000-6000
Works on paper
£633 $1000 €1000 Un homme de trois quart, la main droite levee (12x14cm-5x6in) red chk. 27-Nov-2 Christie's, Paris #140/R

TROY, Jean François de (1679-1752) French
£18293 $30000 €27440 Guitar player (86x74cm-34x29in) oval prov.lit. 29-May-3 Sotheby's, New York #141/R est:20000-30000
£26000 $43420 €37700 Pan and Syrinx. The rape of Europa (101x103cm-40x41in) pair round painted with studio prov.lit. 10-Jul-3 Sotheby's, London #209/R est:15000-20000
£40506 $64000 €64000 Evanouissement d'Esther (80x101cm-31x40in) s.d.1714 prov.lit. 27-Nov-2 Christie's, Paris #35/R est:40000-60000
£61728 $100000 €92592 Zephyr and Flora (85x153cm-33x60in) prov.exhib.lit. 23-Jan-3 Sotheby's, New York #86/R est:100000-150000
Works on paper
£2279 $3600 €3600 Jeune femme allongee (40x52cm-16x20in) sanguine chk. 28-Nov-2 Tajan, Paris #27/R est:5000

TROY, Jean François de (attrib) (1679-1752) French
£7097 $11213 €11000 Portrait d'Antoine Lemiere (80x64cm-31x25in) i.verso. 18-Dec-2 Piasa, Paris #75/R est:15000

TROY, Mary (20th C) Australian
£1154 $1834 €1731 Home after shopping (109x68cm-43x27in) s. s.i.verso composition board. 4-Mar-3 Deutscher-Menzies, Melbourne #257/R est:2800-3500 (A.D 3000)

TROYA, Rafael (19th C) Ecuadorian
£750 $1170 €1125 View near Riobamba, Ecuador (46x74cm-18x29in) i. 17-Oct-2 Lawrence, Crewkerne #473/R

TROYEN, Rombout van (1605-c.1650) Dutch
£3041 $4743 €4500 Joseph vendu par ses freres dans un paysage de grottes (48x71cm-19x28in) panel. 26-Mar-3 Tajan, Paris #147/R
£4459 $6955 €7000 Banishment of king Nebuchadnezzar (33x61cm-13x24in) s.d.64 panel prov. 5-Nov-2 Sotheby's, Amsterdam #120/R est:8000-12000
Works on paper
£573 $894 €900 Christ in the house of Mary and Martha (20x29cm-8x11in) col chk prov. 5-Nov-2 Sotheby's, Amsterdam #31/R

TROYER, Prosper de (1880-1961) Belgian
£283 $436 €450 Nature morte (72x50cm-28x20in) s.d.1913. 22-Oct-2 Campo & Campo, Antwerp #81
£694 $1104 €1000 Nature morte aux fleurs (72x59cm-28x23in) s. panel. 29-Apr-3 Campo & Campo, Antwerp #89/R

TROYON, Constant (1810-1865) French
£1452 $2366 €2178 White bull (41x52cm-16x20in) panel. 12-Feb-3 Iegor de Saint Hippolyte, Montreal #187 (C.D 3600)
£2083 $3354 €3125 Cows in field (35x49cm-14x19in) s. panel. 7-May-3 Dobiaschofsky, Bern #1025/R est:8000 (S.FR 4500)
£2466 $3847 €3600 Stream at edge of wood (60x73cm-24x29in) s.d.1853. 10-Apr-3 Van Ham, Cologne #1731/R est:2000
£2828 $4524 €4100 Jeune vache se frottant l'encolure a un hetre (72x94cm-28x37in) s. 14-Mar-3 Libert, Castor, Paris #44
£3094 $5073 €4300 Two cows lying down in field (32x45cm-13x18in) 4-Jun-3 Reiss & Sohn, Konigstein #172/R est:4000
£3291 $5200 €5200 Jeune paysanne tenant une branche (45x32cm-18x13in) prov. 1-Dec-2 Peron, Melun #62
£6329 $10000 €9494 Shepherd and flock (28x23cm-11x9in) s. panel prov. 24-Apr-3 Sotheby's, New York #101/R est:8000-12000
£34810 $55000 €52215 Crossing the ford (76x98cm-30x39in) s. prov.exhib.lit. 24-Apr-3 Sotheby's, New York #27/R est:20000-30000
Works on paper
£288 $453 €450 Moulin a vent (32x24cm-13x9in) s. chl dr. 13-Dec-2 Piasa, Paris #216
£3924 $6122 €6200 L'abattage d'un arbre (65x51cm-26x20in) s. pencil col chk. 15-Oct-2 Regis & Thiollet, Argentuil #165

TROYON, Constant (attrib) (1810-1865) French
£1442 $2250 €2163 Farmhouse (28x48cm-11x19in) s. canvas on masonite. 12-Oct-2 Neal Auction Company, New Orleans #294/R est:3000-5000

TRUBNER, Wilhelm (1851-1917) German
£629 $981 €1000 Young woman with horse (62x46cm-24x18in) s. 19-Sep-2 Dr Fritz Nagel, Stuttgart #1006/R
£2138 $3336 €3400 Death of Alexander VI (28x51cm-11x20in) mono.d.1883. 11-Oct-2 Winterberg, Heidelberg #735/R est:2800
£3205 $4968 €5000 Castle grounds in Bad Homburg (44x59cm-17x23in) s. 4-Dec-2 Lempertz, Koln #1086/R est:6000-8000
£5797 $9507 €8000 Starnberger See (59x44cm-23x17in) s.d.1912. 31-May-3 Villa Grisebach, Berlin #134/R est:10000-12000
£6000 $9840 €9000 Madchen mit springseil - girl with skipping rope (62x76cm-24x30in) s.d.1907 lit. 3-Jun-3 Sotheby's, London #64/R est:6000-8000
£16981 $26491 €27000 Schloss Hemsbach with fountain (60x76cm-24x30in) s. 11-Oct-2 Winterberg, Heidelberg #736/R est:23500

TRUDEAU, Angus (1908-1984) Canadian?
£4032 $6371 €6048 Norgoma. Maintoulin (60x119cm-24x47in) plywood on panel pair prov. 18-Nov-2 Sotheby's, Toronto #24/R est:5000-7000 (C.D 10000)
£4032 $6371 €6048 Chi-cheemaun. Manitou (60x119cm-24x47in) i. plywood on panel pair prov. 18-Nov-2 Sotheby's, Toronto #25/R est:5000-7000 (C.D 10000)

TRUE, Allen Tupper (1881-1955) American
£1282 $2000 €1923 Woman brought before pirate captain (74x48cm-29x19in) s.d.1908 en grisaille. 9-Nov-2 Illustration House, New York #179/R est:2500-4000

TRUE, David (1942-) American
Works on paper
£549 $900 €796 Study for wind and geometry (76x102cm-30x40in) graphite exhib. 1-Jun-3 Wright, Chicago #332/R

TRUEDSSON, Folke (1913-) Scandinavian
Sculpture
£1682 $2624 €2523 Sunbird (34cm-13in) s.num.2/5 gold pat.bronze on marble socle lit. 5-Nov-2 Bukowskis, Stockholm #151/R est:20000-25000 (S.KR 24000)

TRUEFITT, George (fl.1873-1886) British
Works on paper
£1100 $1727 €1650 China collection (65x78cm-26x31in) s.d.1873 W/C. 10-Dec-2 Bristol Auction Rooms #895/R est:250-350
£1500 $2460 €2250 Collection of china (65x77cm-26x30in) indis sig. pencil W/C bodycol. 5-Jun-3 Christie's, Kensington #893/R est:1500-2000

TRUESDELL, Gaylord Sangston (1850-1899) American
£8974 $14000 €13461 Landscape with girl, goats, farm house and cows in the distance (127x91cm-50x36in) s.d.1893. 22-Sep-2 Jeffery Burchard, Florida #56

TRUFFAUT, Fernand (1866-1955) French
Works on paper
£506 $800 €800 Port de Cannes (37x55cm-15x22in) s. W/C. 27-Nov-2 Blanchet, Paris #69/R
£617 $877 €1000 Paris, Place de la Madeleine (36x50cm-14x20in) s. W/C. 16-Mar-3 Eric Pillon, Calais #79/R
£648 $920 €1050 Paris, Porte Saint-Denis (45x63cm-18x25in) s. W/C. 16-Mar-3 Eric Pillon, Calais #80/R
£987 $1540 €1550 Casino de Deauville (37x54cm-15x21in) s.d.1923 W/C. 10-Nov-2 Deauville, France #28/R

TRULSSON, Anders (1874-1911) Swedish
£1823 $2881 €2735 View of Kulturen in Lund (65x80cm-26x31in) mono.d.1902 lit. 27-Nov-2 Falkkloos, Malmo #77661/R est:15000 (S.KR 26000)

TRUMAN, Herbert (fl.1912-1933) British
£300 $465 €450 Low tide, St Ives harbour (32x39cm-13x15in) s.i.verso board. 2-Oct-2 George Kidner, Lymington #155/R
£300 $468 €450 St Ives (41x51cm-16x20in) i.verso. 17-Oct-2 David Lay, Penzance #1171
£380 $635 €551 Harbour scene with fishing boats (35x50cm-14x20in) s. board. 19-Jun-3 Clevedon Sale Rooms #154
£850 $1360 €1275 Low tide, St. Ives Harbour (33x41cm-13x16in) s.verso board. 13-Mar-3 Duke & Son, Dorchester #270/R

TRUMBULL, John (style) (1756-1843) American
£10274 $15000 €15411 Battle of Monmouth (99x150cm-39x59in) 3-Nov-1 North East Auctions, Portsmouth #101/R est:5000-8000

TRUMPER, G (?) ?
£488 $693 €800 Shipping scene (51x62cm-20x24in) s. prov. 5-Mar-2 Thomas Adams, Dublin #347

TRUPHEMUS, Jacques (1922-) French
£2215 $3434 €3500 Quai de la Saone (41x33cm-16x13in) s.d.59 prov. 28-Sep-2 Christie's, Paris #27/R est:1800-2700
£4902 $8039 €7500 Quais a Lyon (52x72cm-20x28in) s.d.1960 prov. 9-Feb-3 Anaf, Lyon #254/R
£5253 $8142 €8300 Venise, les deux campaniles roses (46x55cm-18x22in) s.d.60 s.verso prov. 28-Sep-2 Christie's, Paris #26/R est:4500-6000

TRUPPE, Karl (1887-1959) Austrian

£1154 $1812 €1800 Sattnitz near Viktring (19x17cm-7x7in) board. 20-Nov-2 Dorotheum, Klagenfurt #20/R est:1800
£3205 $5032 €5000 Chess game with death (28x40cm-11x16in) mono. panel. 20-Nov-2 Dorotheum, Klagenfurt #21/R est:5000
£3793 $5993 €5500 Reclining female nude (35x48cm-14x19in) s.d. masonite. 2-Apr-3 Dr Fritz Nagel, Stuttgart #9547/R est:5000

Works on paper

£572 $955 €829 Reclining models (22x30cm-9x12in) gouache artist's board. 17-Jun-3 Rasmussen, Copenhagen #209/R (D.KR 6000)

TRUSSARDI, Giacinto (1881-1947) Italian

£415 $647 €623 Lake on Bernina Pass at night (72x97cm-28x38in) s. 6-Nov-2 Dobiaschofsky, Bern #3746/R (S.FR 950)

TRUSTTUM, Philip (1940-) New Zealander

£349 $495 €524 Mediterranean series (32x54cm-13x21in) s. prov. 21-Nov-1 Watson's, Christchurch #60/R (NZ.D 1200)
£608 $948 €912 Abstract composition (44x79cm-17x31in) i. acrylic. 17-Sep-2 Peter Webb, Auckland #179/R est:2000-3000 (NZ.D 2000)
£940 $1467 €1410 Garden at St. Albans (90x77cm-35x30in) jute on board. 7-Nov-2 International Art Centre, Auckland #23/R est:4000-6000 (NZ.D 3000)
£1929 $2990 €2894 Garden series (84x63cm-33x25in) s.d.1973 board. 4-Dec-2 Dunbar Sloane, Auckland #5/R est:5000-7000 (NZ.D 6000)
£2195 $3359 €3293 Pacific feet. oil on five loose canvas. 21-Aug-2 Dunbar Sloane, Auckland #36/R est:4500-7500 (NZ.D 7200)
£3521 $5810 €5105 Abstract composition (117x73cm-46x29in) s.d.1964 board. 1-Jul-3 Peter Webb, Auckland #82/R est:10000-15000 (NZ.D 10000)

Works on paper

£307 $435 €461 Horse, man on ground (15x20cm-6x8in) s. W/C prov. 20-Mar-2 Watson's, Christchurch #24/R est:1800-4000 (NZ.D 1000)
£583 $828 €875 Looking up (24x20cm-9x8in) s. W/C acrylic prov. 20-Mar-2 Watson's, Christchurch #30/R est:1200-2000 (NZ.D 1900)
£705 $1100 €1058 Jokerman (38x30cm-15x12in) s.d.1975 W/C. 7-Nov-2 International Art Centre, Auckland #4/R est:2500-3500 (NZ.D 2250)
£843 $1198 €1265 Horse and rider (30x21cm-12x8in) s.d.88 W/C prov. 20-Mar-2 Watson's, Christchurch #27/R est:2800-4000 (NZ.D 2750)
£982 $1394 €1473 Horse and rider (41x33cm-16x13in) s. W/C prov. 20-Mar-2 Watson's, Christchurch #26/R est:3200-4500 (NZ.D 3200)
£1994 $2831 €2991 Horse and masked rider (177x101cm-70x40in) s.d.88 collage prov. 20-Mar-2 Watson's, Christchurch #25/R est:9000-12000 (NZ.D 6500)

TRUTKOVSKY, Konstantin Alexandrovich (1827-1893) Russian

£11000 $17820 €16500 Flirting at the well (48x66cm-19x26in) s.d.1888. 21-May-3 Sotheby's, London #21/R est:12000-15000
£19000 $29830 €28500 City travellers being offered fruit at Ukrainian roadside dwelling (36x60cm-14x24in) s.d.1873. 20-Nov-2 Sotheby's, London #15/R est:20000-30000

TRYGGELIN, Erik (1878-1962) Swedish

£1489 $2309 €2234 Bridge across river, evening in Stockholm (14x21cm-6x8in) s.d.1950-51 panel. 4-Dec-2 AB Stockholms Auktionsverk #1549/R est:6000-8000 (S.KR 21000)
£9310 $15081 €13500 End of the school year (69x89cm-27x35in) s.d.2-8/8 1908. 25-May-3 Uppsala Auktionskammare, Uppsala #119/R est:100000-125000 (S.KR 120000)

TRYON, Dwight W (1849-1925) American

£6507 $9500 €9761 Brittany street scene (51x76cm-20x30in) s.d.1881. 3-Nov-1 North East Auctions, Portsmouth #234/R
£10241 $17000 €14849 After showers (29x41cm-11x16in) s.d.1921 i.verso board prov. 11-Jun-3 Butterfields, San Francisco #4015/R est:5000-7000
£19355 $30000 €29033 End of the day (56x83cm-22x33in) s. indis d.1883 prov. 4-Dec-2 Sotheby's, New York #124/R est:20000-30000
£19481 $30000 €29222 End of day (28x41cm-11x16in) s.d.1919 panel prov. 27-Oct-2 Grogan, Boston #38 est:8000-12000
£20968 $32500 €31452 Dawn-May (27x41cm-11x16in) s.i.d.1910 panel prov. 4-Dec-2 Sotheby's, New York #123/R est:30000-50000

Works on paper

£1899 $3000 €2849 Old anchor (20x33cm-8x13in) s. W/C prov. 24-Apr-3 Shannon's, Milford #73/R est:3000-5000
£2597 $4000 €3896 Farmhouse, night (20x30cm-8x12in) s.d.1906 pastel prov. 24-Oct-2 Shannon's, Milford #155/R est:4000-6000

TSAROUKHIS, Yannis (1910-1989) Greek

£15000 $23250 €22500 Player (17x25cm-7x10in) s.d.48 prov. 2-Oct-2 Sotheby's, London #48/R est:10000-15000

Works on paper

£1500 $2325 €2250 Evzon changing (9x12cm-4x5in) s. W/C over pencil. 2-Oct-2 Sotheby's, London #51/R
£1500 $2325 €2250 Portrait of sailor (46x31cm-18x12in) s.d.85 pastel chk. 2-Oct-2 Sotheby's, London #109/R
£2500 $3950 €3625 Set design for the Persians. Set design for the Birds (26x40cm-10x16in) s.i.d.64 s.d.62 W/C gouache 2 with 5 designs by other artists. 22-Jul-3 Sotheby's, Olympia #265/R est:400-600

TSARYK, Tetyana (20th C) Irish?

£324 $538 €460 Portrait of a girl in a hat (80x58cm-31x23in) s. 10-Jun-3 James Adam, Dublin #283/R
£329 $513 €480 Still life with oranges (37x25cm-15x10in) s,. 8-Apr-3 James Adam, Dublin #46/R
£352 $585 €500 O'Connell Bridge (53x73cm-21x29in) s. 10-Jun-3 James Adam, Dublin #152/R
£387 $643 €550 Flower seller, Grafton Street (49x60cm-19x24in) s. 10-Jun-3 James Adam, Dublin #153/R
£685 $1068 €1000 Grafton Street, premonition of holiday (63x50cm-25x20in) s. 8-Apr-3 James Adam, Dublin #48/R

TSCHACBASOV, Nahum (1899-1984) Russian

£318 $500 €477 Young girl (102x76cm-40x30in) s.d.51 encaustic panel. 23-Nov-2 Jackson's, Cedar Falls #39/R
£545 $850 €818 Portrait of a young girl with flowers (122x76cm-48x30in) s.d.1953. 10-Nov-2 Selkirks, St. Louis #980/R
£881 $1400 €1322 Woman with birds (76x91cm-30x36in) s. board painted c.1950. 2-Mar-3 Toomey, Oak Park #823/R
£1707 $2800 €2475 Flower pot (137x114cm-54x45in) s.d.1946 prov. 1-Jun-3 Wright, Chicago #224/R est:2000-3000

TSCHAGGENY, Charles Philogene (1815-1894) Belgian

£382 $596 €600 Horse near the stables (40x36cm-16x14in) s. 6-Nov-2 Vendue Huis, Gravenhage #405
£6000 $9960 €6000 Le retour des fagoteurs (67x94cm-26x37in) s.d.1868. 16-Jun-3 Horta, Bruxelles #181/R est:7500-9500
£6051 $9439 €9500 La moisson (48x72cm-19x28in) s. panel. 11-Nov-2 Horta, Bruxelles #111/R est:7500-9000
£6981 $11099 €10472 Grazing horses (41x51cm-16x20in) s.d.1850 panel. 8-Mar-3 Dorotheum, Prague #10/R est:320000-480000 (C.KR 320000)

TSCHAGGENY, Edmond (1818-1873) Belgian

Works on paper

£380 $592 €600 Bergere et ses moutons (17x27cm-7x11in) s. W/C. 10-Sep-2 Vanderkindere, Brussels #340
£538 $850 €850 Vache (20x31cm-8x12in) pencil dr. 2-Dec-2 Amberes, Antwerp #1363

TSCHARNER, Johann Wilhelm von (1886-1946) Swiss

£328 $511 €492 Still life with lemons and apple (50x61cm-20x24in) s. prov. 9-Nov-2 Galerie Gloggner, Luzern #150/R (S.FR 750)
£370 $577 €555 Landscape (50x65cm-20x26in) s. 16-Sep-2 Philippe Schuler, Zurich #3408 (S.FR 850)

TSCHARNER, Theodore (1826-1906) Belgian

£1795 $2782 €2800 Famille de pecheurs et leurs anes (34x54cm-13x21in) s. 9-Dec-2 Horta, Bruxelles #377 est:1200-1800

TSCHIRTNER, Oswald (1920-) ?

Works on paper

£1081 $1686 €1600 Kneeling figures (20x14cm-8x6in) s.i.d.14.9.1972 Indian ink. 25-Mar-3 Wiener Kunst Auktionen, Vienna #44/R est:1500-2500
£1351 $2108 €2000 Jesus carrying cross over shoulder (20x14cm-8x6in) s.d.10.Dez.1971 mixed media. 25-Mar-3 Wiener Kunst Auktionen, Vienna #45/R est:1500-2500

TSCHUDI, Lill (1911-) German

Prints

£2800 $4620 €4060 Jazz orchestra (27x52cm-11x20in) s.i.num.26/50 linocut. 1-Jul-3 Sotheby's, London #157/R est:1500-2000
£3000 $4950 €4350 Helmsman (30x20cm-12x8in) s.i.d.num.26/50 col linocut. 1-Jul-3 Sotheby's, London #153/R est:1800-2000
£3000 $4950 €4350 Skier (30x20cm-12x8in) s.i.num.14/50 col linocut. 1-Jul-3 Sotheby's, London #154/R est:1500-2000
£4200 $6930 €6090 French porters (28x26cm-11x10in) s.i.num.27/50 col linocut. 1-Jul-3 Sotheby's, London #160/R est:1800-2000
£4598 $6851 €6897 French porters (27x26cm-11x10in) s.num.34/50 linoblock executed 1935. 27-Aug-2 Christie's, Melbourne #201/R est:2000-3000 (A.D 12000)
£5000 $8250 €7250 Ice hockey (26x28cm-10x11in) s.i.num.46/50 col linocut. 1-Jul-3 Sotheby's, London #159/R est:4000-5000
£5800 $9570 €8410 Cleaning sail (25x30cm-10x12in) s.i.num.14/50 col linocut. 1-Jul-3 Sotheby's, London #161/R est:1800-2000

TSCHUMI, Otto (1904-1985) Swiss
Works on paper
£3241 $5218 €4699 Three figures (56x41cm-22x16in) s.d.57 i.verso W/C pastel wax board. 9-May-3 Dobiaschofsky, Bern #271/R est:8500 (S.FR 7000)

TSE-YE-MU (?) ?
Works on paper
£500 $800 €750 Deer dancer (28x35cm-11x14in) s. W/C. 13-Jan-3 Christie's, Rockefeller NY #61/R
£875 $1400 €1313 Eagle dance (46x61cm-18x24in) s. W/C. 13-Jan-3 Christie's, Rockefeller NY #62/R

TSENG KWONG CHI (1950-1990) Chinese
Photographs
£2727 $4200 €4091 New York, New York (25x20cm-10x8in) i.d.1979 num.31C verso gelatin silver print prov. 25-Oct-2 Phillips, New York #52/R est:6000-8000

TSINGOS, Thanos (1914-1965) Greek
£1000 $1550 €1500 Flowers on blue background (20x30cm-8x12in) s.d.60 canvasboard. 2-Oct-2 Sotheby's, London #125/R
£1300 $2015 €1950 White flowers (20x30cm-8x12in) s. canvasboard. 2-Oct-2 Sotheby's, London #124/R
£1500 $2325 €2250 Abstract composition (41x33cm-16x13in) s.d.55 canvasboard. 2-Oct-2 Sotheby's, London #126/R
£1528 $2521 €2200 Coquelicots (61x50cm-24x20in) s. 1-Jul-3 Artcurial Briest, Paris #777/R est:2500-3000
£1800 $2808 €2700 Abstract in red (73x92cm-29x36in) s.d.55. 15-Oct-2 Sotheby's, London #61/R est:2000-3000
£2000 $3100 €3000 Abstract (60x73cm-24x29in) s. canvas on board. 5-Dec-2 Christie's, Kensington #227/R est:2000-3000
£2200 $3410 €3300 Garden (54x65cm-21x26in) s. 2-Oct-2 Sotheby's, London #131/R
£3400 $5372 €5100 Abstract composition (55x46cm-22x18in) 1-Apr-3 Bonhams, New Bond Street #102 est:1500-2000
£3636 $6073 €5200 Fleurs des champs (54x65cm-21x26in) s.d. 26-Jun-3 Tajan, Paris #305 est:6000-8000
£3700 $5846 €5550 Untitled (35x27cm-14x11in) pair. 1-Apr-3 Bonhams, New Bond Street #79 est:4000-6000
£4200 $6510 €6300 Flowers (55x46cm-22x18in) s.d.55 canvasboard. 2-Oct-2 Sotheby's, London #132/R est:3000
£4800 $7584 €7200 Fleurs (40x32cm-16x13in) 1-Apr-3 Bonhams, New Bond Street #99 est:3200-4200
£5500 $8580 €8250 White flowers on green background (101x76cm-40x30in) s.d.60. 15-Oct-2 Sotheby's, London #62/R est:1500-2000
£7200 $11376 €10800 Fleurs sur fond noir (65x54cm-26x21in) 1-Apr-3 Bonhams, New Bond Street #91 est:4000-6000
Works on paper
£1700 $2635 €2550 House in the woods (24x68cm-9x27in) mixed media canvas on paper. 2-Oct-2 Sotheby's, London #130/R

TSIRIGOTI, I (19th C) Russian
£14063 $22500 €21095 Evening landscape with Mt. Kazbek in the Caucasus (81x132cm-32x52in) s. 17-May-3 Pook & Pook, Downington #373/R est:10000-15000

TSUNETOSHI (19th C) Japanese
Sculpture
£2600 $4342 €3770 Woodcutter binding a bundle of faggots (17cm-7in) s. ivory group. 18-Jun-3 Christie's, London #146/R est:3000-4000

TSVETKOV, Andrei (1975-) Russian
£450 $698 €675 Odalisque (50x30cm-20x12in) s. 8-Dec-2 John Nicholson, Haslemere #209/R
£805 $1297 €1200 Oriental dancer (50x80cm-20x31in) 18-Feb-3 Durán, Madrid #681/R

TUAILLON, Louis (1862-1919) German
Sculpture
£2055 $3205 €3000 Amazone (37cm-15in) i. bronze Cast.Gladenbeck Berlin. 10-Apr-3 Van Ham, Cologne #1117/R est:2200

TUBBECKE, Paul (1848-1924) German
£353 $554 €550 Lake landscape with angler (20x31cm-8x12in) s. i.verso plywood. 21-Nov-2 Dorotheum, Vienna #169/R
£417 $654 €650 Lake landscape (25x37cm-10x15in) s. i.verso board. 21-Nov-2 Dorotheum, Vienna #171/R
£513 $805 €800 Ducks on the lake (20x30cm-8x12in) s. board. 21-Nov-2 Dorotheum, Vienna #170/R

TUBKE, Werner (1929-) ?
Works on paper
£629 $969 €1000 Anne is ill again (29x21cm-11x8in) s.i.d.1954 pencil. 26-Oct-2 Dr Lehr, Berlin #532/R
£633 $1000 €1000 Mourning nobleman (27x41cm-11x16in) s.d.78 i. verso pencil. 30-Nov-2 Bassenge, Berlin #6657
£696 $1100 €1100 Portrait of young woman wearing hat (29x18cm-11x7in) s.i.d.81 i. verso pencil. 30-Nov-2 Bassenge, Berlin #6658/R
£755 $1162 €1200 Anne (29x22cm-11x9in) s.d.1954 pencil. 26-Oct-2 Dr Lehr, Berlin #533/R
£943 $1453 €1500 Male nude (63x45cm-25x18in) s.d.1971 ochre chk. 26-Oct-2 Dr Lehr, Berlin #534/R
£1635 $2518 €2600 Reconstruction of National Gallery, Berlin (29x17cm-11x7in) s.d.1954 pencil. 26-Oct-2 Dr Lehr, Berlin #531/R est:1500
£2431 $3840 €3500 Portrait of Monika S (30x19cm-12x7in) s.d.1979 W/C over pencil. 26-Apr-3 Dr Lehr, Berlin #501/R est:4500
£3819 $6035 €5500 Soldiers waiting (68x44cm-27x17in) s.d.1970 chl wash htd white ochre board. 26-Apr-3 Dr Lehr, Berlin #502/R est:5500

TUCH, Prof (1882-?) Austrian?
Sculpture
£1000 $1580 €1500 Woman looking in the mirror (39cm-15in) s. bronze. 14-Nov-2 Christie's, Kensington #207/R est:1000-1500

TUCHOLSKI, Herbert (1896-1984) German
Works on paper
£521 $823 €750 Untitled harbour (32x42cm-13x17in) s.d.1924 col oil chk over W/C board. 26-Apr-3 Dr Lehr, Berlin #512/R

TUCK, Harry (19/20th C) British
Works on paper
£375 $600 €563 Helping hand (60x91cm-24x36in) s. pencil W/C paper on board. 14-May-3 Butterfields, San Francisco #1167/R

TUCK, Marie (1872-1947) Australian
£2289 $3617 €3966 Village gathering (37x44cm-15x17in) s. 1-Apr-3 Goodman, Sydney #47/R est:6000-10000 (A.D 6000)

TUCKER, Albert (1914-1999) Australian
£3125 $4875 €4688 Desert and trees (45x61cm-18x24in) s.d.1961 pva cement board prov. 8-Apr-3 Peter Webb, Auckland #108/R est:10000-15000 (NZ.D 9000)
£4231 $6727 €6347 Resting ibis (45x60cm-18x24in) s.d.66 oil mixed media composition board. 4-Mar-3 Deutscher-Menzies, Melbourne #163/R est:8000-12000 (A.D 11000)
£4286 $6729 €6429 Blue wren (44x60cm-17x24in) s.d.1963 board prov. 25-Nov-2 Christie's, Melbourne #73a/R est:10000-15000 (A.D 12000)
£4598 $6851 €6897 Ibis in flight (37x49cm-15x19in) s. board. 27-Aug-2 Christie's, Melbourne #67/R est:15000-20000 (A.D 12000)
£4982 $7623 €7473 Native companion (60x81cm-24x32in) s.d.63 exhib. 25-Aug-2 Sotheby's, Paddington #116/R est:12000-18000 (A.D 14000)
£9286 $14579 €13929 Bush and parrot (60x75cm-24x30in) s.d.65 board prov. 25-Nov-2 Christie's, Melbourne #88/R est:25000-35000 (A.D 26000)
£11628 $18488 €17442 Parrots in a Queensland landscape (76x61cm-30x24in) s. 5-May-3 Sotheby's, Melbourne #132/R est:20000-30000 (A.D 30000)
£13571 $21307 €20357 Faun (120x90cm-47x35in) s.d.66 i.verso board prov. 25-Nov-2 Christie's, Melbourne #26a/R est:20000-30000 (A.D 38000)
£30651 $45671 €45977 Faun and parrots (121x151cm-48x59in) s.d.65 oil sand on board prov. 27-Aug-2 Christie's, Melbourne #21/R est:120000-160000 (A.D 80000)
£38618 $61016 €55996 Faun attacked by parrots (121x91cm-48x36in) s.d.67 i.verso prov. 22-Jul-3 Lawson Menzies, Sydney #30/R est:100000-120000 (A.D 95000)
£39146 $59893 €58719 Portrait (76x61cm-30x24in) s.d.68 board prov. 26-Aug-2 Sotheby's, Paddington #509/R est:100000-150000 (A.D 110000)
Works on paper
£5385 $8562 €8078 Tram, image of modern evil (20x31cm-8x12in) s.d.1945 W/C gouache chl exhib. 4-Mar-3 Deutscher-Menzies, Melbourne #124/R est:15000-20000 (A.D 14000)

TUCKER, Alfred Robert (1849-1914) British
Works on paper
£320 $509 €480 Ugandan village (36x50cm-14x20in) s. W/C. 29-Apr-3 Bonhams, New Bond Street #173

TUCKER, Allen (1866-1939) American
£1890 $3025 €2835 Fall landscape (36x48cm-14x19in) s. 11-Jan-3 James Julia, Fairfield #514 est:1750-2500

£3145	$5000	€4718	Snowy landscape (51x61cm-20x24in) s.d.1925. 7-Mar-3 Skinner, Boston #460/R est:3000-5000
£7742	$12000	€11613	Storm (76x86cm-30x34in) s. painted c.1920. 8-Dec-2 Toomey, Oak Park #756/R est:9000-12000

TUCKER, Arthur (1864-1929) British

Works on paper

£270	$451	€392	Country cottages with woman and child (25x33cm-10x13in) s. 18-Jun-3 Andrew Hartley, Ilkley #1047
£280	$437	€420	View of a village street with a church tower in the distance (27x17cm-11x7in) s. pencil W/C. 19-Sep-2 Christie's, Kensington #53
£280	$456	€420	Lady with poultry in village street (18x28cm-7x11in) s. W/C. 14-Feb-3 Keys, Aylsham #268
£300	$477	€450	Ben Ledi, Perthshire (24x34cm-9x13in) s. W/C. 4-Mar-3 Bearnes, Exeter #331/R
£310	$499	€465	Westmorland farmstead (17x27cm-7x11in) W/C. 15-Jan-3 James Thompson, Kirby Lonsdale #102
£310	$493	€465	Study of spring flowers (36x20cm-14x8in) s. W/C. 7-Mar-3 Biddle & Webb, Birmingham #307
£355	$550	€533	Tintagel, Cornwall (30x46cm-12x18in) s. pencil W/C. 29-Oct-2 Sotheby's, New York #147/R
£360	$565	€540	Hilltop farm (47x73cm-19x29in) s. W/C over pencil. 15-Apr-3 Bonhams, Knowle #87
£580	$905	€870	Windermere (23x36cm-9x14in) s. 9-Oct-2 Andrew Hartley, Ilkley #661
£1700	$2652	€2550	Buttermere, Cumberland (30x44cm-12x17in) s. W/C. 27-Mar-3 Christie's, Kensington #123/R est:300-500
£2550	$3978	€3825	Runswick Bay (49x73cm-19x29in) s. W/C. 10-Sep-2 David Duggleby, Scarborough #270/R est:2000-3000

TUCKER, Edward (c.1830-1909) British

Works on paper

£185	$285	€278	Country cottage (32x43cm-13x17in) W/C. 26-Oct-2 Heffel, Vancouver #2 (C.D 450)
£360	$558	€540	Off Scarborough (23x39cm-9x15in) s. W/C. 24-Sep-2 Anderson & Garland, Newcastle #334/R
£500	$790	€750	Crofters cottages (28x46cm-11x18in) s. W/C. 13-Nov-2 Halls, Shrewsbury #353/R
£850	$1325	€1275	View of a harbour (27x48cm-11x19in) s. pencil W/C htd white. 19-Sep-2 Christie's, Kensington #177
£850	$1386	€1275	On the Rhine (22x31cm-9x12in) s.i. W/C. 29-Jan-3 Dreweatt Neate, Newbury #41/R
£2700	$4509	€3915	Abandon ship (66x100cm-26x39in) s. W/C. 18-Jun-3 Sotheby's, Olympia #32/R est:3000-5000

TUCKER, Frederick (fl.1880-1915) British

Works on paper

£330	$518	€495	Grassmoor, near Crummock Water (33x45cm-13x18in) s. W/C. 19-Nov-2 James Thompson, Kirby Lonsdale #14
£360	$558	€540	Lake District view (58x91cm-23x36in) s. W/C. 3-Dec-2 Sotheby's, Olympia #62/R
£480	$763	€720	Silverdale, on the Lune Estuary (34x69cm-13x27in) s. W/C. 27-Feb-3 Bonhams, Chester #337
£480	$763	€720	Lake District cottage (23x38cm-9x15in) s. W/C. 6-Mar-3 Mitchells, Cockermouth #874/R
£550	$852	€825	Lake District view (63x98cm-25x39in) W/C. 3-Dec-2 Sotheby's, Olympia #61/R

TUCKER, John Wallace (18/19th C) British

£3200	$5088	€4800	Exmouth beach scenes with shipping (9x14cm-4x6in) s.i.d.1866/67 panel set of five. 4-Mar-3 Bearnes, Exeter #421/R est:1200-1800

TUCKERMAN, Ernest (attrib) (20th C) American

£2025	$3159	€3200	Tombeau de Sidi Abder Rhaman (62x91cm-24x36in) 20-Oct-2 Anaf, Lyon #243/R est:3500-4000

TUCKERMAN, Stephen Salisbury (attrib) (1830-1904) American

£4878	$8000	€7073	Representation of the Bark, Cadet (46x76cm-18x30in) indis sig. 8-Jun-3 Skinner, Boston #119/R est:4000-6000

TUCKSON, John Anthony (1921-1973) Australian

£12186	$18523	€18279	Cocktails for two II (85x100cm-33x39in) painted c.1950 exhib.lit. 28-Aug-2 Deutscher-Menzies, Melbourne #32/R est:32000-40000 (A.D 34000)

Works on paper

£932	$1416	€1398	TD 1853 (56x76cm-22x30in) pencil ink exec.c.1952-56 prov.exhib. 28-Aug-2 Deutscher-Menzies, Melbourne #195/R est:3200-3800 (A.D 2600)
£2500	$3900	€3750	Three women. Two women (54x75cm-21x30in) ink double-sided. 11-Nov-2 Deutscher-Menzies, Melbourne #79/R est:3000-5000 (A.D 7000)
£2867	$4358	€4301	Family group I (76x101cm-30x40in) gouache chl exec.c.1952-56 prov. 28-Aug-2 Deutscher-Menzies, Melbourne #243/R est:5500-7500 (A.D 8000)

TUDELA Y PERALES, Joaquin (1892-?) Spanish

£844	$1258	€1300	Spring landscape possibly Mollorca (60x73cm-24x29in) s. 26-Jun-2 Neumeister, Munich #885/R

TUDELA, Ana de (?) Spanish

£269	$425	€420	Vase of flowers (62x47cm-24x19in) s. 13-Nov-2 Ansorena, Madrid #4/R

TUDGAY (19th C) British

£6406	$9994	€9609	East Indian in two positions off Table Bay (67x105cm-26x41in) 11-Nov-2 Stephan Welz, Johannesburg #459/R est:50000-70000 (SA.R 100000)

TUDGAY, Frederick J (fl.1863-1876) British

£9868	$15000	€14802	Star of Russia, in full sail (64x89cm-25x35in) prov. 17-Aug-2 North East Auctions, Portsmouth #668/R est:15000-20000
£13158	$20000	€19737	Miltiades off the White Cliffs of Dover (61x91cm-24x36in) s.d.1872. 17-Aug-2 North East Auctions, Portsmouth #788/R est:15000-25000

TUDGAY, I (19th C) British

£2800	$4536	€4200	Danish full-rigged ship heaving to off an island (61x91cm-24x36in) s.d.1855. 21-May-3 Christie's, Kensington #640/R est:3000-5000

TUERENHOUT, Jef van (1926-) Belgian

Works on paper

£612	$978	€850	Composition (48x33cm-19x13in) s.d.71 gouache. 17-May-3 De Vuyst, Lokeren #383/R
£1871	$2993	€2600	Brittany (83x103cm-33x41in) s. wax sold with documents. 17-May-3 De Vuyst, Lokeren #381/R est:3000-3600
£2014	$3223	€2800	Birds (70x97cm-28x38in) s.i. gouache chl exec.1985 lit. 17-May-3 De Vuyst, Lokeren #518/R est:4000-5000
£4861	$7729	€7000	Armure en or (66x49cm-26x19in) s. mixed media. 29-Apr-3 Campo & Campo, Antwerp #330/R est:7000-8000

TUFF, Richard (?) British?

£820	$1337	€1230	Untitled. two. 13-Feb-3 David Lay, Penzance #145

TUFFERY, Michael (20th C) New Zealander

Works on paper

£702	$1095	€1053	Changing currents (49x260cm-19x102in) mixed media tapa cloth. 27-Mar-3 International Art Centre, Auckland #11/R (NZ.D 2000)

TUFNELL, E (20th C) ?

Works on paper

£987	$1500	€1481	British Sir Lancelot, at Whampoa Island (36x51cm-14x20in) s.i. W/C. 17-Aug-2 North East Auctions, Portsmouth #881/R est:2000-3000

TUGEL, Otto (1892-1973) German

Works on paper

£816	$1298	€1200	Young couple (45x62cm-18x24in) s. mixed media panel. 28-Mar-3 Bolland & Marotz, Bremen #372/R est:2700

TUGGENER, Jakob (1904-1988) Swiss

Works on paper

£343	$542	€515	Three ladies in front of the fireplace with kettle (32x50cm-13x20in) s.d.44 W/C over pencil. 26-Nov-2 Hans Widmer, St Gallen #1401/R (S.FR 800)

TUGWELL, Christopher (1938-) South African

£338	$527	€507	Poplars along a tranquil river (45x80cm-18x31in) s. board. 15-Oct-2 Stephan Welz, Johannesburg #222 est:2000-3000 (SA.R 5500)

£344 $554 €516 Extensive Bushveld landscape with a tree (39x70cm-15x28in) s. board. 12-May-3 Stephan Welz, Johannesburg #150 est:2000-3000 (SA.R 4000)
£442 $699 €663 Goatherd and his flock (34x49cm-13x19in) s. board. 1-Apr-3 Stephan Welz, Johannesburg #243 est:2500-4000 (SA.R 5500)

TUKE, Alfred (attrib) (?) British?
£1000 $1670 €1450 Dogs squabbling over a bone (33x41cm-13x16in) bears sig. 24-Jun-3 Rowley Fine Art, Newmarket #369 est:1000-1500

TUKE, Henry Scott (1858-1929) British
£7600 $11780 €11400 Shipping at anchor in a squall, Falmouth (74x152cm-29x60in) s.d.1888 prov. 26-Sep-2 Lane, Penzance #270/R est:8000-9000
£8000 $13280 €11600 Three masters at anchor in Falmouth Roads (25x48cm-10x19in) s. 10-Jun-3 David Lay, Penzance #457/R est:6500-8500
£11000 $17270 €16500 Portrait of Ida Hamilton (60x42cm-24x17in) s.i.d.1909 prov.exhib.lit. 22-Nov-2 Christie's, London #9/R est:12000-18000
£17000 $26520 €25500 Boys on a beach (66x41cm-26x16in) s.d.1909 prov. 26-Mar-3 Hamptons Fine Art, Godalming #250/R est:18000-25000
£65000 $107900 €97500 Return from fishing (120x87cm-47x34in) s.d.1907 prov.exhib.lit. 11-Jun-3 Christie's, London #21/R est:80000-120000
£240000 $386400 €360000 Midsummer morning (186x137cm-73x54in) s.d.1908 prov.exhib.lit. 19-Feb-3 Christie's, London #23/R est:250000-350000
Sculpture
£12258 $19000 €18387 Watcher (32cm-13in) s.d.1916 green brown bronze wooden base. 29-Oct-2 Sotheby's, New York #104/R est:20000-30000
£19000 $31160 €28500 Watcher (32cm-13in) s.d.1916 dark green brown pat. bronze lit. 6-Jun-3 Christie's, London #43/R est:15000-20000
Works on paper
£296 $480 €450 Italian landscape at dusk (17x25cm-7x10in) s.d.1914 W/C prov. 21-Jan-3 Christie's, Amsterdam #87
£540 $842 €783 Genoa harbour view (13x20cm-5x8in) s.i. W/C. 27-Mar-3 Lane, Penzance #168
£850 $1318 €1275 St. Michael's mount (17x25cm-7x10in) s.i.d.Aug 30 1920 W/C. 31-Oct-2 Christie's, Kensington #337/R
£900 $1413 €1350 Sailing boat alongside a quay (20x12cm-8x5in) s. W/C. 16-Apr-3 George Kidner, Lymington #83/R
£1700 $2652 €2550 Country track (13x21cm-5x8in) s.d.1909 W/C. 25-Mar-3 Bonhams, New Bond Street #2/R est:1000-1500
£2000 $3240 €3000 Quiet anchorage (13x21cm-5x8in) s.d.1926 W/C. 22-Jan-3 Bonhams, New Bond Street #355/R est:1200-1800
£2200 $3674 €3190 Study of a blonde boy wearing a cap lying on a beach (9x15cm-4x6in) init.d.96 W/C. 24-Jun-3 Rowley Fine Art, Newmarket #378/R est:800-1200
£2600 $4056 €3900 Clippers at Falmouth (25x30cm-10x12in) s. W/C. 17-Oct-2 David Lay, Penzance #1057 est:2500-3500
£2800 $4620 €4060 Study of a young man, probably Donald Rolph (33x24cm-13x9in) init.d.1893 pastel. 1-Jul-3 Bearnes, Exeter #414/R est:800-1200
£3800 $6346 €5510 Norwegian ship at anchor (30x44cm-12x17in) s.d.1821 W/C. 19-Jun-3 Lane, Penzance #140/R est:4000-4500
£4800 $7296 €7200 Sunset in the harbour (30x45cm-12x18in) s.d.1906 W/C. 15-Aug-2 Bonhams, New Bond Street #444/R est:4000-6000
£5000 $7750 €7500 Schooners at anchor, Falmouth (86x127cm-34x50in) s. W/C. 26-Sep-2 Lane, Penzance #320 est:5000-7000
£5000 $7750 €7500 Marechal de Castrus, French barque at anchor, Falmouth (76x112cm-30x44in) s.d.1916 i.verso W/C prov. 26-Sep-2 Lane, Penzance #325/R est:5000-7000

TUKE, Henry Scott (attrib) (1858-1929) British
Works on paper
£540 $853 €810 Shipping in harbour (15x20cm-6x8in) init. W/C. 2-Dec-2 Gorringes, Lewes #2786

TUKIAINEN, Aimo (1917-1996) Finnish
Sculpture
£1329 $2100 €2100 Men floating logs (55cm-22in) s, bronze. 1-Dec-2 Bukowskis, Helsinki #12/R est:1500-1800

TULLI, Wladimiro (1922-2003) Italian
£696 $1086 €1100 If there's a cock, it sings (70x80cm-28x31in) s. painted 1963. 19-Oct-2 Semenzato, Venice #147/R
£823 $1284 €1300 River tale (70x100cm-28x39in) painted 1957. 19-Oct-2 Semenzato, Venice #3/R
£1712 $2671 €2500 Small peach (20x30cm-8x12in) s. board exhib. 10-Apr-3 Finarte Semenzato, Rome #279
Works on paper
£411 $641 €600 Untitled (38x54cm-15x21in) s. mixed media. 10-Apr-3 Finarte Semenzato, Rome #285

TULLOCH, Maurice (1894-1974) British
£380 $593 €570 Whistler, a chestnut colt in a landscape (51x66cm-20x26in) s.d.1960. 6-Nov-2 Sotheby's, Olympia #99/R
£600 $936 €900 Duke's delight and Nobleness at the Hadrian stud, Newmarket (51x66cm-20x26in) s.i. 6-Nov-2 Sotheby's, Olympia #96/R

TULLY, Sidney Strickland (1860-1911) British
£444 $729 €666 Houses on the hill (12x17cm-5x7in) mono. canvas on panel. 3-Jun-3 Joyner, Toronto #236/R est:800-1000 (C.D 1000)
£978 $1604 €1467 Gateway (35x44cm-14x17in) mono. canvas on panel exhib. 3-Jun-3 Joyner, Toronto #427/R est:2500-3000 (C.D 2200)
Works on paper
£489 $802 €709 Evening return (135x77cm-53x30in) s. indis d. pastel. 9-Jun-3 Hodgins, Calgary #413/R est:1500-2500 (C.D 1100)

TUMAKOV, Sergei Pavlovich (1919-) Russian
£2489 $4156 €3609 Female nude (113x83cm-44x33in) s. lit. 24-Jun-3 Koller, Zurich #106/R est:2000-3000 (S.FR 5500)

TUMARKIN, Igael (1933-) Israeli
£2244 $3522 €3500 Composition (65x81cm-26x32in) s.d.1959 s.v oil collage metal prov. 15-Dec-2 Perrin, Versailles #37/R
Works on paper
£1900 $2926 €2850 Visit Sinai now (81x61cm-32x24in) s.d.69 s.i.d.verso mixed media board prov. 23-Oct-2 Sotheby's, Olympia #806/R est:2500-3500

TUNICA, Hermann August Theodor (1826-1907) German
£2390 $3704 €3800 Herders with cattle by roadside shrine (72x105cm-28x41in) s.d.1868. 29-Oct-2 Dorotheum, Vienna #46/R est:3200-3600

TUNICK, Spencer (1967-) American
Photographs
£8228 $13000 €12342 Momentum (121x147cm-48x58in) s.d.1996 num.2/6 verso gelatin silver print prov. 13-Nov-2 Sotheby's, New York #486/R est:8000-12000

TUNINETTO, Adriano (1930-) Italian
£340 $541 €500 Connection (80x100cm-31x39in) s. painted 1991. 1-Mar-3 Meeting Art, Vercelli #598
£347 $552 €500 Connection (80x100cm-31x39in) s. s.i.d.1991 verso. 1-May-3 Meeting Art, Vercelli #185
£476 $757 €700 Topology (80x100cm-31x39in) s. s.i.d.1994 verso. 1-Mar-3 Meeting Art, Vercelli #419

TUNNARD, John (1900-1971) British
£420 $659 €630 Untitled (13x18cm-5x7in) s.d.63-64 oil pastel. 15-Apr-3 Bonhams, Knightsbridge #195/R
£1800 $2790 €2700 Abstract (56x61cm-22x24in) s. board. 4-Dec-2 Christie's, Kensington #615/R est:2000-3000
£4500 $7065 €6750 Abstract composition with fish (56x38cm-22x15in) oil on gesso board. 22-Nov-2 Christie's, London #88/R est:5000-7000
£26000 $40300 €39000 Promise (56x35cm-22x14in) s.d.45 board prov.exhib.lit. 4-Dec-2 Sotheby's, London #68/R est:15000-20000
Works on paper
£320 $502 €480 Abstract in blue and red (17x16cm-7x6in) studio st.verso W/C gouache. 15-Apr-3 Bonhams, Knightsbridge #198/R
£500 $785 €750 Untitled (13x18cm-5x7in) s.d.63-64 mixed media. 15-Apr-3 Bonhams, Knightsbridge #192/R
£600 $936 €900 Untitled (13x18cm-5x7in) gouache. 15-Oct-2 Bonhams, Knightsbridge #33/R
£650 $1014 €975 Untitled (18x26cm-7x10in) gouache. 15-Oct-2 Bonhams, Knightsbridge #34/R
£700 $1092 €1050 Untitled (21x27cm-8x11in) gouache. 15-Oct-2 Bonhams, Knightsbridge #37/R
£750 $1193 €1125 Abstract with butterflies (36x53cm-14x21in) W/C panel. 19-Mar-3 John Nicholson, Haslemere #1149
£900 $1404 €1350 Christmas card (13x18cm-5x7in) s.d.1965 wash pencil ink. 15-Oct-2 Bonhams, Knightsbridge #36/R
£1200 $1872 €1800 Marsh (52x38cm-20x15in) gouache exhib. 15-Oct-2 Bonhams, Knightsbridge #32/R est:1200-1800
£1200 $1872 €1800 Aftermath (36x54cm-14x21in) gouache prov. 15-Oct-2 Bonhams, Knightsbridge #35/R est:1200-1800
£1400 $2338 €2030 West country farmhouse (34x55cm-13x22in) W/C gouache. 19-Jun-3 Lane, Penzance #114/R est:1200-1400
£1500 $2340 €2250 Penwith sunset (41x56cm-16x22in) studio st.i.verso mixed media. 17-Oct-2 David Lay, Penzance #1399/R est:1200-1800
£1700 $2652 €2550 Mooncradle (36x54cm-14x21in) s.d.1962 W/C crayon wax resist prov.exhib. 25-Mar-3 Bonhams, New Bond Street #101/R est:1000-1500
£1900 $2964 €2850 Jewels (36x36cm-14x14in) s. ink W/C gouache. 12-Sep-2 Sotheby's, Olympia #225/R est:1500-2000
£2623 $4250 €3803 Untitled (36x43cm-14x17in) s. gouache col chk crayon pencil. 21-May-3 Doyle, New York #37/R est:6000-8000
£72000 $118080 €104400 Painting (54x77cm-21x30in) s.d.44 i.verso casein board prov.exhib.lit. 4-Jun-3 Sotheby's, London #28/R est:12000-18000

TUNNICLIFFE, Charles Frederick (1901-1979) British

£	$	€	Details
£3000	$4680	€4500	Diver (61x32cm-24x13in) s. prov. 27-Mar-3 Christie's, Kensington #433/R est:1000-1500
£3400	$5304	€5100	Snow in March (32x66cm-13x26in) exhib. 25-Mar-3 Gildings, Market Harborough #387/R

Works on paper

£	$	€	Details
£400	$624	€600	Shepherd and sheep crossing a stone bridge, artist at work in one corner (50x36cm-20x14in) sketch htd bodycol. 25-Mar-3 Gildings, Market Harborough #389
£650	$1053	€975	Study of a white tumbler (23x28cm-9x11in) i. pencil gouache crayon. 20-May-3 Sotheby's, Olympia #51/R
£750	$1170	€1088	Lochinver, pair of R B Magansers feeding below the village, immature drake (24x32cm-9x13in) s.i. W/C. 13-May-3 Holloways, Banbury #639/R
£760	$1186	€1102	Teal feeding on soft mud of pool side, Siddington Hall (23x27cm-9x11in) s.i. W/C. 13-May-3 Holloways, Banbury #637/R
£920	$1490	€1380	Study of a yellow saxon spot (22x27cm-9x11in) i. pencil gouache crayon. 20-May-3 Sotheby's, Olympia #52/R
£1000	$1560	€1450	Flock of widgeon grazing on the pasture near the lake side (23x27cm-9x11in) s.i. W/C. 13-May-3 Holloways, Banbury #638/R
£1100	$1705	€1650	Mustang (43x61cm-17x24in) s. W/C. 4-Dec-2 Christie's, Kensington #331/R est:1200-1800
£1100	$1782	€1650	Shire stallion (26x18cm-10x7in) s. gouache W/C prov.lit. 20-May-3 Sotheby's, Olympia #56/R est:700-1000
£1300	$2028	€1950	Flannelled fools and muddy oafs (29x24cm-11x9in) init. W/C gouache. 12-Sep-2 Sotheby's, Olympia #211/R est:800-1200
£1300	$2106	€1950	Hampshire down Ewes in a lambing fold (26x18cm-10x7in) W/C gouache prov.lit. 20-May-3 Sotheby's, Olympia #55/R est:700-1000
£2000	$3160	€3000	Swans flying in the from the sea, Malltraeth, Anglesey (36x56cm-14x22in) s. W/C. 13-Nov-2 Halls, Shrewsbury #370/R est:1500-2000
£2000	$3240	€3000	Hen harrier (47x58cm-19x23in) s. W/C prov. 20-May-3 Sotheby's, Olympia #48/R est:2000-3000
£2600	$4212	€3900	Clydsdale mare and foal (26x18cm-10x7in) W/C gouache prov.lit. 20-May-3 Sotheby's, Olympia #57/R est:600-800
£3400	$5508	€5100	Welsh ponies amongst the gorse (39x70cm-15x28in) s. W/C prov. 20-May-3 Sotheby's, Olympia #47/R est:3000-5000
£3700	$5846	€5550	Falcon with Llandeilo Castle in the background (37x57cm-15x22in) s. W/C. 7-Apr-3 Bonhams, Bath #50/R est:1000-1500

TUOHY (1894-1930) British

£	$	€	Details
£500	$710	€820	Dublin roofs, possibly broadstone roofs (51x61cm-20x24in) s. 5-Mar-2 Thomas Adams, Dublin #201

TUOHY, Patrick (1894-1930) British

£	$	€	Details
£4189	$6535	€6200	City roof tops (49x59cm-19x23in) s. 26-Mar-3 James Adam, Dublin #82/R est:2000-3000

TUOHY, Patrick (attrib) (1894-1930) British

Works on paper

£	$	€	Details
£256	$403	€400	Choir boy (51x35cm-20x14in) W/C. 19-Nov-2 Hamilton Osborne King, Dublin #452

TUPKE-GRANDE, Helene (1876-?) German

£	$	€	Details
£346	$540	€550	River harbour with boats in evening (54x46cm-21x18in) s. bears i. verso canvas on panel. 21-Sep-2 Bolland & Marotz, Bremen #664/R

TUPPER, Margaret (1887-1979) American

Works on paper

£	$	€	Details
£288	$450	€432	Sam Miguel de Allende (41x30cm-16x12in) W/C. 19-Oct-2 David Dike, Dallas #320/R

TURBEVILLE, Deborah (1937-) American

Works on paper

£	$	€	Details
£417	$688	€600	Projet pour le carton d'invitation au defile femme automne-hiver (31x17cm-12x7in) s.d. collage blk white pin. 3-Jul-3 Christie's, Paris #37/R

TURCATO, Giulio (1912-1995) Italian

£	$	€	Details
£1111	$1767	€1600	Archipelagus (36x51cm-14x20in) s. card. 1-May-3 Meeting Art, Vercelli #28
£1538	$2415	€2400	Collage (50x70cm-20x28in) s. s.verso oil collage. 20-Nov-2 Pandolfini, Florence #105/R
£1736	$2760	€2500	Itineraries (36x51cm-14x20in) s. s.verso oil acrylic card. 1-May-3 Meeting Art, Vercelli #209
£1830	$2928	€2800	Archipelagus (40x50cm-16x20in) s. 4-Jan-3 Meeting Art, Vercelli #393
£1973	$3137	€2900	Shapes (60x80cm-24x31in) s. oil mixed media. 1-Mar-3 Meeting Art, Vercelli #644
£2027	$3162	€3000	Venetian stream (50x70cm-20x28in) s. 28-Mar-3 Farsetti, Prato #270/R
£2065	$3262	€3200	Mine (70x50cm-28x20in) s. tempera paper on cardboard. 18-Dec-2 Christie's, Rome #54
£2179	$3422	€3400	Untitled (50x70cm-20x28in) s. acrylic sand. 19-Nov-2 Finarte, Milan #267/R
£2452	$3874	€3800	Changing yellow (39x54cm-15x21in) s. oil mixed media. 18-Dec-2 Christie's, Rome #87/R
£2452	$3874	€3800	Fluid (80x100cm-31x39in) oil sand prov. 18-Dec-2 Christie's, Rome #107/R
£2564	$4026	€4000	Untitled (60x45cm-24x18in) s. 21-Nov-2 Finarte, Rome #272
£2671	$4167	€3900	Canal in Venice (50x40cm-20x16in) s. 10-Apr-3 Finarte Semenzato, Rome #171/R
£2692	$4227	€4200	Changing orange (65x80cm-26x31in) s. oil mixed media. 23-Nov-2 Meeting Art, Vercelli #102/R
£2703	$4216	€4000	Archipelagus (50x70cm-20x28in) s. s.i.verso oil mixed media lit. 28-Mar-3 Farsetti, Prato #109/R
£2745	$4392	€4200	Changing (40x50cm-16x20in) s. oil mixed media. 4-Jan-3 Meeting Art, Vercelli #224
£2885	$4471	€4500	Composition (50x70cm-20x28in) s. acrylic sand painted 1969. 4-Dec-2 Finarte, Milan #312/R
£3125	$4969	€4500	Changing (50x70cm-20x28in) s. oil mixed media. 1-May-3 Meeting Art, Vercelli #226
£3265	$5192	€4800	Composition (70x100cm-28x39in) s. oil mixed media. 1-Mar-3 Meeting Art, Vercelli #353
£3378	$5270	€5000	Archipelagus (50x60cm-20x24in) s. oil mixed media. 26-Mar-3 Finarte Semenzato, Milan #383/R
£3462	$5435	€5400	Shape with itinerary (70x100cm-28x39in) s.verso oil mixed media. 20-Nov-2 Pandolfini, Florence #116/R est:6500
£3526	$5535	€5500	Moon surface (55x44cm-22x17in) s. s.verso oil mixed media foam on board. 23-Nov-2 Meeting Art, Vercelli #317/R
£3526	$5535	€5500	Changing red (120x60cm-47x24in) s. oil mixed media. 23-Nov-2 Meeting Art, Vercelli #359/R
£3725	$5961	€5700	Changing orange (80x100cm-31x39in) s. oil mixed media. 4-Jan-3 Meeting Art, Vercelli #612
£3922	$6275	€6000	Itineraries (70x100cm-28x39in) s. painted 1973. 4-Jan-3 Meeting Art, Vercelli #385 est:5000
£4167	$6625	€6000	Changing white and red (80x100cm-31x39in) s. oil mixed media. 1-May-3 Meeting Art, Vercelli #435 est:5000
£4747	$7405	€7500	Moon surface (70x100cm-28x39in) s. oil mixed media foam. 14-Sep-2 Meeting Art, Vercelli #829/R
£6234	$9975	€9040	Composition (50x70cm-20x28in) s. tempera oil cardboard. 11-Mar-3 Babuino, Rome #330/R
£6452	$10194	€10000	Monn landscape (61x82cm-24x32in) s.verso acrylic foam prov. 18-Dec-2 Christie's, Rome #209/R est:15000

Works on paper

£	$	€	Details
£385	$562	€600	Untitled (50x70cm-20x28in) s. mixed media. 5-Jun-2 Il Ponte, Milan #56
£481	$702	€750	Untitled (50x70cm-20x28in) s. mixed media. 5-Jun-2 Il Ponte, Milan #24
£481	$702	€750	Untitled (50x70cm-20x28in) s. mixed media. 5-Jun-2 Il Ponte, Milan #21
£481	$702	€750	Untitled (50x70cm-20x28in) s. mixed media. 5-Jun-2 Il Ponte, Milan #46
£481	$702	€750	Untitled (50x70cm-20x28in) s. mixed media. 5-Jun-2 Il Ponte, Milan #52
£513	$749	€800	Untitled (50x70cm-20x28in) s. mixed media. 5-Jun-2 Il Ponte, Milan #62
£609	$956	€950	Untitled (56x75cm-22x30in) s. mixed media card. 21-Nov-2 Finarte, Rome #47
£833	$1217	€1300	Untitled (50x70cm-20x28in) s. s.verso mixed media on canvas. 5-Jun-2 Il Ponte, Milan #58
£2692	$4227	€4200	Untitled (50x70cm-20x28in) s. s.verso collage acrylic prov. 19-Nov-2 Finarte, Milan #121/R
£3097	$4893	€4800	Moon surface (52x59cm-20x23in) s. s.verso mixed media foam on board prov.exhib. 18-Dec-2 Christie's, Rome #97/R
£17687	$28122	€26000	Big composition (96x10cm-38x4in) s. mixed media collage on canvas. 1-Mar-3 Meeting Art, Vercelli #648

TURCHI, Alessandro (1578-1649) Italian

Works on paper

£	$	€	Details
£700	$1099	€1050	Adoration of the Magi (28x37cm-11x15in) black chk prov. 11-Dec-2 Sotheby's, Olympia #8

TURENNE, O L (19th C) French

£	$	€	Details
£433	$671	€650	Figures in music room (55x69cm-22x27in) s. 24-Sep-2 Koller, Zurich #6516 (S.FR 1000)
£693	$1074	€1040	Figures playing chess (56x68cm-22x27in) s. 24-Sep-2 Koller, Zurich #6517 (S.FR 1600)

TURFORD, Jane (attrib) (20th C) British

£	$	€	Details
£350	$546	€525	Lady before a watermill (36x46cm-14x18in) indis sig. 7-Nov-2 Christie's, Kensington #165/R

TURIN, Andre (20th C) French

£	$	€	Details
£952	$1514	€1400	Maison de pecheurs a Loctudy (38x46cm-15x18in) s. i.verso panel. 24-Mar-3 Coutau Begarie, Paris #224/R
£1079	$1727	€1500	Le port et le beffroi (73x92cm-29x36in) s. 18-May-3 Eric Pillon, Calais #133/R

TURINA Y AREAL, Joaquin (1847-1903) Spanish
£3045 $4780 €4750 Celebrating in Seville (25x20cm-10x8in) s. board. 19-Nov-2 Castellana, Madrid #24/R
£5031 $7849 €8000 Alfalfa Square, Seville (27x17cm-11x7in) s. board. 23-Sep-2 Durán, Madrid #235/R
Works on paper
£621 $987 €900 Woman with shawl and fan (28x21cm-11x8in) s. W/C. 4-Mar-3 Ansorena, Madrid #667/R

TURK, Gavin (1967-) British?
£1500 $2505 €2175 Roisicross (21x28cm-8x11in) s.i.d.1997 printed sheet prov.exhib.lit. 24-Jun-3 Sotheby's, Olympia #2/R est:1500-2000
Photographs
£4000 $6680 €5800 Camouflage, self portrait (90x90cm-35x35in) s.i.d.1998 num.1/10 verso r-type col print foamex prov.lit. 26-Jun-3 Sotheby's, London #296/R est:3000-4000

TURKINGTON, James (20th C) New Zealander?
£4930 $8134 €7149 Horses in a landscape (74x151cm-29x59in) s.d.1945 prov. 1-Jul-3 Peter Webb, Auckland #73/R est:12000-18000 (NZ.D 14000)

TURNBULL, William (1922-) British
£2800 $4620 €4060 19-1963 (254x188cm-100x74in) s. prov. 3-Jul-3 Christie's, Kensington #732/R est:1500-2000
Sculpture
£2000 $3120 €3000 Untitled (17cm-7in) i. bronze. 12-Sep-2 Sotheby's, Olympia #134/R est:2000-3000
£18000 $27900 €27000 Large siren (183cm-72in) mono.num.3/4 mottled green pat on stone base prov. 4-Dec-2 Sotheby's, London #86/R est:20000-30000

TURNER OF OXFORD, William (1789-1862) British
£980 $1529 €1470 View of the south coast, figure on a horse with cattle and cliffs beyond (21x31cm-8x12in) 17-Sep-2 Bonhams, Oxford #33
Works on paper
£420 $697 €609 Study from nature in Cumner Field (18x28cm-7x11in) s.d.1837 i.on mount W/C. 16-Jun-3 Duke & Son, Dorchester #118
£2200 $3432 €3300 Sunset at Pereril Castle, Castleton, Derbyshire (27x40cm-11x16in) s. W/C. 5-Nov-2 Bonhams, New Bond Street #76/R est:1500-2000
£2600 $3718 €3900 Wychwood forest (12x9cm-5x4in) i. pencil W/C scratching out prov.lit. 22-Jan-3 Christie's, London #17/R
£2600 $4264 €3900 View from Birdlip Hill, Gloucestershire (40x70cm-16x28in) s.i. W/C. 4-Feb-3 Bonhams, Leeds #267 est:2000-3000
£3500 $5529 €5250 Arthur's castle, Tintagel, Cornwall - evening after a stormy day (27x40cm-11x16in) s.verso W/C over pencil stopping out gum arabic. 28-Nov-2 Sotheby's, London #295/R est:4000-6000
£3800 $6308 €5700 View of Derwent water from Castle Hill, Cumberland (24x35cm-9x14in) W/C over pencil. 12-Jun-3 Sotheby's, London #137/R est:3000-4000
£4200 $6636 €6300 Approaching to Glencoe from Ballachulish, Argyllshire (27x37cm-11x15in) s.verso W/C over pencil htd bodycol. 28-Nov-2 Sotheby's, London #296/R est:4000-6000
£5500 $7865 €8250 Salisbury plain with Old Sarum (12x18cm-5x7in) pencil W/C gum scratching out prov. 22-Jan-3 Christie's, London #18/R est:6000
£5500 $9020 €7975 View of Snowdon, Wales (50x72cm-20x28in) s. pencil W/C htd white gum arabic prov.exhib. 5-Jun-3 Christie's, London #71/R est:6000-8000
£7500 $12000 €11250 Portsmouth Harbour and the Isle of Wight from Portsdown Hill (61x102cm-24x40in) W/C. 11-Mar-3 Bonhams, New Bond Street #41/R est:8000-12000
£16000 $22880 €24000 Stratus clouds, evening (18x26cm-7x10in) d.1848 W/C bodycol prov.exhib.lit. 22-Jan-3 Christie's, London #19/R est:8000

TURNER, Benjamin Brecknell (1815-1894) British
Photographs
£7500 $12150 €11250 Bredicot Court, Worcestershire (21x26cm-8x10in) i.verso albumen print prov.lit. 21-May-3 Christie's, London #31/R est:800-1200
£17000 $27540 €25500 Causeway, head of the lake, Losely Park (29x39cm-11x15in) i.verso albumen print prov. 21-May-3 Christie's, London #30/R est:6000-8000
£32000 $51840 €48000 Walter Chamberlain hiding behind Bredicot pump (26x30cm-10x12in) i.verso salt print exec.c.1850. 21-May-3 Christie's, London #28/R est:10000-15000

TURNER, Charles E (1883-1965) British
Works on paper
£320 $518 €464 Morning mist - Calshot sea bi-plane over water (25x45cm-10x18in) W/C. 23-May-3 Bracketts, Tunbridge Wells #951/R
£460 $727 €690 Casquets, Channel Islands (41x60cm-16x24in) s. W/C. 27-Nov-2 Bonhams, Brooks & Langlois, Jersey #88/R

TURNER, Daniel (fl.1782-1817) British
£192 $300 €288 Blackfriars bridge (15x22cm-6x9in) s.i. oval. 11-Nov-2 Stephan Welz, Johannesburg #24 (SA.R 3000)
£720 $1188 €1044 View of London Bridge from the south looking across the Thames (13x20cm-5x8in) init. panel prov. 2-Jul-3 Sotheby's, Olympia #108/R
£2000 $3340 €2900 View of the Thames looking east with St Paul's Cathedral in the distance (78x106cm-31x42in) 9-Jul-3 Bonhams, New Bond Street #74/R est:2000-3000

TURNER, Dennis Knight (1924-) New Zealander
Works on paper
£526 $821 €789 Caledonian Hotel (34x54cm-13x21in) s.d.1963 W/C. 27-Mar-3 International Art Centre, Auckland #43/R (NZ.D 1500)
£526 $821 €789 Greyhound Hotel (38x54cm-15x21in) s. W/C. 27-Mar-3 International Art Centre, Auckland #44/R (NZ.D 1500)

TURNER, Desmond (20th C) Irish
£288 $449 €420 Killary Harbour, Leenane (50x60cm-20x24in) 8-Apr-3 James Adam, Dublin #141/R

TURNER, Edward (19th C) British
£600 $954 €870 Delivering the blacksmith lunch (44x60cm-17x24in) 26-Feb-3 John Bellman, Billingshurst #1810

TURNER, F J (19th C) British
£300 $468 €450 Young woman seated by a tree with a basket of fruit. s. 20-Sep-2 Moore Allen & Innocent, Cirencester #988/R

TURNER, Frances Calcott (1795-1865) British
£460 $727 €690 Fisherman's catch (26x22cm-10x9in) s. panel. 2-Dec-2 Bonhams, Bath #161/R

TURNER, Francis Calcraft (c.1782-1846) British
£2000 $3240 €2900 Leamington steeplechase (34x42cm-13x17in) s.d.1834. 29-Jul-3 Henry Adams, Chichester #607/R est:2000-3000
£4400 $7216 €6600 Horses in landscape with stallion chasing dog. Horses with foals in landscape (38x53cm-15x21in) s.d.1836 pair. 4-Feb-3 Sworder & Son, Bishops Stortford #86/R est:4000-6000
£6500 $10530 €9750 Shooting party (25x30cm-10x12in) prov. 22-May-3 Christie's, London #34/R est:3000-5000
£12000 $18960 €18000 Gentleman driving in landscape. Lady riding with companion (41x23cm-16x9in) s. one d.1833 pair. 27-Nov-2 Christie's, London #65/R est:10000-15000

TURNER, Frank (fl.1866-1874) British
£840 $1335 €1260 Children playing on country road gate (45x61cm-18x24in) s.d.71. 5-May-3 Rasmussen, Vejle #673/R (D.KR 9000)

TURNER, George (1843-1910) British
£600 $960 €900 Lane near Ashley, Derbyshire with figures on a path (23x34cm-9x13in) s.i.verso board. 11-Mar-3 Bonhams, Oxford #56
£600 $1002 €870 Winston's Brook, Kirk Ireton, Derbyshire (39x60cm-15x24in) s.i.d.1906 verso. 9-Jul-3 George Kidner, Lymington #156
£730 $1219 €1059 Wooded river scene (41x66cm-16x26in) s.d.1872. 24-Jun-3 Bonhams, Knowle #78
£1100 $1716 €1595 Sweetwater Lane (11x17cm-4x7in) s. i.verso panel. 27-Mar-3 Neales, Nottingham #1014 est:1000-1400
£1150 $1817 €1725 Moel siabod from the Llugwy, Capel Curig, North Wales (18x38cm-7x15in) s.i.verso board. 2-Dec-2 Bonhams, Bath #112/R est:600-800
£1800 $2808 €2700 Rain cloud over the river (31x45cm-12x18in) s.d.80 s.i.on stretcher. 26-Mar-3 Sotheby's, Olympia #53/R est:2000-3000
£1818 $2800 €2727 Figures resting in a summer landscape (40x66cm-16x26in) s. prov. 4-Sep-2 Christie's, Rockefeller NY #328/R est:2500-3500
£2000 $3160 €3000 Trent near Gills Hill, Ingleby, Derbyshire (26x38cm-10x15in) s. i.verso board. 27-Nov-2 Hamptons Fine Art, Godalming #327/R est:2000-3000
£2255 $3518 €3383 Beddgelert Mill North Wales (49x75cm-19x30in) s. 14-Sep-2 Windibank, Dorking #285/R
£2300 $3588 €3335 Derbyshire lane (11x15cm-4x6in) s. board. 27-Mar-3 Neales, Nottingham #1013/R est:1200-2000

£2600 $4030 €3900 Flock of sheep in lee of bank, beside oak trees (48x74cm-19x29in) s.d.1913. 25-Sep-2 Brightwells, Leominster #912/R est:500-800
£3000 $4920 €4500 Shepherd with his flock resting in a sunlit wood (53x79cm-21x31in) s. 29-May-3 Christie's, Kensington #181 est:3000-5000
£3700 $6142 €5365 Scene at Milton, Derbyshire (51x76cm-20x30in) s.d.91 s.i.d.verso. 10-Jun-3 Mellors & Kirk, Nottingham #847/R est:1000-1500
£4200 $6552 €6300 River landscape (41x66cm-16x26in) s. 17-Sep-2 Sotheby's, Olympia #168/R est:1000-2000
£5800 $9164 €8700 Scene Knowle Hills, Derbyshire (50x75cm-20x30in) s. s.i.d.1887 verso. 27-Nov-2 Wintertons, Lichfield #789/R est:4000-6000

TURNER, George (attrib) (1843-1910) British
£410 $640 €615 Country lane with sheep resting beside a tree, possibly Froggat Edge, Derbyshire (71x102cm-28x40in) 25-Mar-3 Bonhams, Leeds #623
£7500 $12000 €11250 Crossing the ford (94x132cm-37x52in) 13-Mar-3 Duke & Son, Dorchester #240

TURNER, Helen M (1858-1958) American
£52314 $80000 €78471 The sisters (28x20cm-11x8in) s. prov.exhib. 7-Dec-2 Neal Auction Company, New Orleans #465/R est:100000-150000

TURNER, J A (19th C) British
£3571 $5536 €5357 Mare and foal (98x68cm-39x27in) s.d.1905. 29-Oct-2 Lawson Menzies, Sydney #21/R est:6000-7000 (A.D 10000)
£4660 $7082 €6990 Cobb and Co coach (30x61cm-12x24in) s.d.1891. 28-Aug-2 Deutscher-Menzies, Melbourne #120/R est:16500-18500 (A.D 13000)
£10036 $15254 €15054 Exciting times (40x71cm-16x28in) s. prov. 28-Aug-2 Deutscher-Menzies, Melbourne #122/R est:30000-40000 (A.D 28000)

TURNER, James Alfred (?-1908) Australian
£932 $1416 €1398 By the track (19x40cm-7x16in) s.d.1891. 27-Aug-2 Goodman, Sydney #39 (A.D 2600)
£1491 $2267 €2237 In charge (21x28cm-8x11in) s. board. 19-Aug-2 Joel, Victoria #320 est:3500-4500 (A.D 4250)
£1800 $2898 €2610 When the wattle blooms (22x31cm-9x12in) s. board. 12-May-3 Joel, Victoria #286 est:2000-2500 (A.D 4500)
£2000 $3220 €2900 Bullock team (20x39cm-8x15in) s.d.1901 canvasboard. 12-May-3 Joel, Victoria #243 est:3500-4500 (A.D 5000)
£2481 $3920 €3722 Closing (31x23cm-12x9in) s. board. 2-Apr-3 Christie's, Melbourne #27/R est:4000-6000 (A.D 6500)
£2847 $4356 €4271 Sheep in the mist (14x45cm-6x18in) s.d.1900 board. 25-Aug-2 Sotheby's, Paddington #241/R est:8000-12000 (A.D 8000)
£3400 $5474 €4930 Sawmill (29x55cm-11x22in) s.d.1901. 12-May-3 Joel, Victoria #275 est:8000-10000 (A.D 8500)
£6810 $10351 €10215 Logger (69x100cm-27x39in) s. 27-Aug-2 Goodman, Sydney #145/R est:20000-30000 (A.D 19000)
Works on paper
£632 $960 €948 Coming home (23x16cm-9x6in) s. W/C. 19-Aug-2 Joel, Victoria #265/R est:1200-1500 (A.D 1800)
£1550 $2465 €2325 Fetching water (22x38cm-9x15in) s.d.1899 W/C card. 5-May-3 Sotheby's, Melbourne #307/R est:3000-5000 (A.D 4000)

TURNER, Johann Christoph (c.1690-1744) Bohemian
£3846 $5962 €6000 Enjoyment on the ice (23x35cm-9x14in) s. panel lit. 7-Dec-2 Bergmann, Erlangen #762/R est:4500

TURNER, John Davenall (1900-1980) Canadian
£191 $299 €287 Spring sketch, Parr's Field (26x34cm-10x13in) s. board. 25-Nov-2 Hodgins, Calgary #125/R (C.D 475)
£222 $364 €322 Prairie water hole, early spring in Alberta (35x45cm-14x18in) s.i. board prov. 9-Jun-3 Hodgins, Calgary #122/R (C.D 500)
£333 $547 €483 West from Bearspaw (45x60cm-18x24in) s.i.d.1955 board exhib. 9-Jun-3 Hodgins, Calgary #27/R (C.D 750)
£884 $1387 €1326 Elbow River (90x120cm-35x47in) s.i.d.1979. 25-Nov-2 Hodgins, Calgary #371/R est:1500-2000 (C.D 2200)
Works on paper
£211 $331 €317 West of Calgary (34x50cm-13x20in) s.i. W/C prov. 25-Nov-2 Hodgins, Calgary #144/R (C.D 525)

TURNER, Joseph Mallord William (1775-1851) British
£14465 $22277 €23000 Bay by Pozzuoli (83x157cm-33x62in) s. prov.lit. 28-Oct-2 Il Ponte, Milan #251/R est:15000
Works on paper
£11000 $17490 €16500 No. 8 view near Reichenbach (36x24cm-14x9in) i. pencil grey wash after J R Cozens. 29-Apr-3 Sworder & Son, Bishops Stortford #384/R est:1000-2000
£16000 $25280 €24000 Dog asleep by its kennel outside a cottage (25x20cm-10x8in) W/C over pencil prov.lit. 28-Nov-2 Sotheby's, London #253/R est:15000-20000
£22000 $36080 €31900 View of Naples with Vesuvius in the distance, morning (29x41cm-11x16in) s.i.d.1820 pencil W/C prov.exhib.lit. 5-Jun-3 Christie's, London #162/R est:25000-35000
£26000 $40820 €39000 Beech trees at Cassiobury Park, Hertfordshire (23x37cm-9x15in) pencil wash prov. 21-Nov-2 Christie's, London #41/R est:15000-20000
£40000 $63600 €60000 Bolton Abbey, Yorkshire on the Wharfe (27x39cm-11x15in) W/C over pencil bodycol prov. 19-Mar-3 Sotheby's, London #148/R est:20000-30000
£55000 $78650 €82500 Hasborough sands (21x17cm-8x7in) i. pencil W/C bodycol prov.exhib.lit. 22-Jan-3 Christie's, London #20/R est:80000
£69444 $108333 €104166 Fishmarket, Rotterdam (13x19cm-5x7in) W/C pencil prov. 8-Apr-3 Peter Webb, Auckland #103/R est:200000-300000 (NZ.D 200000)
£70000 $116200 €105000 Study of a castle by a lake. Castle on a river (14x21cm-6x8in) W/C pencil double-sided exhib. 12-Jun-3 Sotheby's, London #19/R est:40000-60000
£77000 $127820 €115500 Genoa (13x18cm-5x7in) pen col ink W/C over pencil bodycol scratching out prov. 12-Jun-3 Sotheby's, London #26/R est:80000-120000
£100000 $166000 €150000 Lake Albano (29x42cm-11x17in) pencil W/C gum arabic scratching out prov.exhib.lit. 11-Jun-3 Christie's, London #2/R est:100000-150000
£105000 $172200 €152250 Fishing boats off Hastings (18x30cm-7x12in) pencil W/C scratching out prov. 5-Jun-3 Christie's, London #90/R est:50000-80000
£720000 $1137600 €1080000 Mont blanc from Fort Roch, Val d'aosta (69x104cm-27x41in) s. pencil W/C bodycol gum arabic scratching out prov.exhib. 27-Nov-2 Christie's, London #6/R est:600000-800000

TURNER, Matilda Hutchinson (1869-?) American
£343 $500 €515 Warehouses at the wharf (25x20cm-10x8in) init. board. 10-May-2 Skinner, Boston #262/R

TURNER, Maud M (fl.1891-1908) British
Works on paper
£360 $554 €540 Two children imprisoned in a cell (52x73cm-20x29in) s. W/C. 22-Oct-2 Sworder & Son, Bishops Stortford #647/R

TURNER, Michael (20th C) American
£340 $554 €510 Tiffy break; World War II RAF pilots enjoying a tea break (74x59cm-29x23in) s.d.80 i.verso. 11-Feb-3 Fellows & Sons, Birmingham #54/R

TURNER, Prudence (?) British
£450 $711 €675 Mountainous lake scene (59x90cm-23x35in) s. 27-Nov-2 Peter Wilson, Nantwich #16
£450 $698 €675 Highland scene with cattle in the foreground (60x91cm-24x36in) s. 6-Dec-2 ELR Auctions, Sheffield #221

TURNER, Ross Sterling (1847-1915) American
Works on paper
£250 $400 €363 Courtyard (22x32cm-9x13in) s.d.1900 W/C. 16-May-3 Skinner, Boston #120/R
£897 $1400 €1346 Along the Seine (22x28cm-9x11in) s.i.d.1915 gouache crayon pair. 14-Sep-2 Weschler, Washington #622/R est:1500-2500

TURNER, S (?) ?
£2200 $3410 €3300 Hunter with cockerels outside a brick built stable (84x135cm-33x53in) s.d.1878. 31-Oct-2 Duke & Son, Dorchester #218/R est:400-700

TURNER, W E (19th C) British
£8500 $13430 €12750 Gem of gems, foal by Blair Athol. Cremorne, North Kilmorne and Rochdale (64x102cm-25x40in) s.d.1880 pair. 28-Nov-2 Bonhams, Knightsbridge #96/R est:6000-8000

TURNER, William Eddowes (c.1820-1885) British
£600 $978 €900 Cattle on a hillside (40x55cm-16x22in) s. 12-Feb-3 Bonhams, Knightsbridge #287/R
£800 $1240 €1200 Chestnut hunter and Jack (51x61cm-20x24in) s. 6-Dec-2 Chrystals Auctions, Isle of Man #158
£1100 $1694 €1650 Bay mare. Grey gelding (34x44cm-13x17in) init. pair. 22-Oct-2 Bonhams, Bath #23 est:800-1200
£2100 $3486 €3045 Chestnut racehorse and Jack Russell in a stable (51x61cm-20x24in) s. 12-Jun-3 Christie's, Kensington #48/R est:1000-1500

TURNER, William Lakin (1867-1936) British
£390 $605 €585 Misty lakeland view (21x30cm-8x12in) s. 24-Sep-2 Anderson & Garland, Newcastle #523
£460 $718 €690 Derwentwater and Skiddaw from Ashness (25x35cm-10x14in) s. s.i.d.1910 verso. 6-Nov-2 Bonhams, Chester #313
£650 $1014 €975 Kings Howe, Grange Bridge, near Keswick (25x35cm-10x14in) s. panel. 7-Nov-2 Christie's, Kensington #144/R
£1000 $1650 €1450 Figures punting on a lake in Scotland or the Lake District (61x91cm-24x36in) s. 3-Jul-3 Ewbank, Send #338/R est:1000-1500
£1200 $1848 €1800 Children on a bridge, near Barrow on Trent (30x46cm-12x18in) s. i.stretcher. 5-Sep-2 Christie's, Kensington #130/R est:1500-2000
£1250 $1938 €1875 Grange Bridge with angler in the foreground (34x52cm-13x20in) s.d.1920. 24-Sep-2 Anderson & Garland, Newcastle #529/R est:450-650
£1500 $2310 €2250 Mist and loch (23x36cm-9x14in) s.d.1922 panel. 5-Sep-2 Christie's, Kensington #150/R est:700-1000
£1900 $3173 €2755 Wast water (30x46cm-12x18in) s. board. 26-Jun-3 Mellors & Kirk, Nottingham #922/R est:800-1200

TURNERELLI, Peter (1774-1839) British
Sculpture
£7500 $11775 €11250 Bust of Arthur Wellesley 1st. Duke of Wellington (75cm-30in) white marble. 10-Dec-2 Sotheby's, London #143/R est:3000-5000

TURNHERR, Ferdinand (1875-?) Swiss
£329 $513 €480 Lower alpine landscape with castle (54x70cm-21x28in) s. lit. 10-Apr-3 Allgauer, Kempten #3017/R

TURPIN DE CRISSE, Lancelot Theodore (1782-1859) French
£3704 $6000 €5556 Mountainous landscape with a view of the temple of Segesta, Sicily (34x48cm-13x19in) prov. 24-Jan-3 Christie's, Rockefeller NY #130/R est:10000-15000
Works on paper
£506 $800 €800 Southern city street (10x7cm-4x3in) st.mono. brush. 29-Nov-2 Bassenge, Berlin #6087
£601 $950 €950 Hillside (12x4cm-5x2in) st.mono. W/C. 29-Nov-2 Bassenge, Berlin #6086
£1139 $1800 €1800 Extensive mountain landscape with lake (8x13cm-3x5in) st.mono. W/C. 29-Nov-2 Bassenge, Berlin #6085/R est:800

TURPIN, Louis (20th C) British?
£800 $1336 €1160 At the water's edge (76x60cm-30x24in) s.d.99. 17-Jun-3 Bonhams, Knightsbridge #166/R

TURRELL, James (1943-) American
Works on paper
£6500 $10010 €9750 Early sight place and section with survey nets (103x149cm-41x59in) s.d.92 beeswax photographic emulsion oil pastel acrylic. 23-Oct-2 Christie's, London #218/R est:4000-6000

TURRI, Michele (20th C) Italian
£405 $632 €600 Piazza in Florence (70x100cm-28x39in) s. 28-Mar-3 Karrenbauer, Konstanz #1793/R

TURTIAINEN, Jorma (1936-) Finnish
£253 $395 €400 Making road signs (46x55cm-18x22in) s.d.90. 15-Sep-2 Bukowskis, Helsinki #301/R
£345 $545 €500 Old woman (60x47cm-24x19in) s. 3-Apr-3 Hagelstam, Helsinki #1063
£523 $858 €800 Woman gathering twigs II (59x46cm-23x18in) s.d.1978. 9-Feb-3 Bukowskis, Helsinki #375/R

TURTLE, Arnold E (1892-1954) American/British
£535 $850 €776 Cabin in the woods (24x30cm-9x12in) s. painted c.1920. 4-May-3 Treadway Gallery, Cincinnati #540/R

TURVILLE, Serge de (1924-) French
£411 $642 €650 Murs a cagnes (120x60cm-47x24in) s. s.i.d.1967 verso panel. 20-Oct-2 Charbonneaux, Paris #157 est:600-800

TURY, Gyula (1866-1932) Hungarian
£755 $1177 €1200 Summers day in the country (19x42cm-7x17in) s.d.1928. 9-Oct-2 Michael Zeller, Lindau #937/R

TUSCAN SCHOOL (15th C) Italian
£10811 $16865 €16000 Annunciation to the Virgin and Saints. gilded panel two prov. 27-Mar-3 Dorotheum, Vienna #36/R est:9000-14000

TUSCAN SCHOOL (16th C) Italian
£76730 $118164 €122000 Deposition (134x86cm-53x34in) board. 28-Oct-2 Il Ponte, Milan #115/R est:20000
Sculpture
£6757 $10541 €10000 Madonna and Child (61x43cm-24x17in) polychrome terracotta. 31-Mar-3 Finarte Semenzato, Milan #248/R
£7383 $11886 €11000 Holy woman (96cm-38in) painted wood. 19-Feb-3 Semenzato, Venice #71/R est:12000
Works on paper
£8642 $14000 €12963 Studies (28x22cm-11x9in) pen ink wash double-sided. 21-Jan-3 Sotheby's, New York #36/R est:12000

TUSCAN SCHOOL (17th C) Italian
£4528 $6974 €7200 Flowers in a jug (41x31cm-16x12in) board. 28-Oct-2 Il Ponte, Milan #105/R
£20690 $32690 €30000 Still life with tulips, daffodils and other flowers in landscape (95x76cm-37x30in) prov. 5-Apr-3 Finarte Semenzato, Milan #151/R est:12000
Sculpture
£13608 $21228 €21500 Salomon's judgement (55x84cm-22x33in) terracotta relief. 19-Oct-2 Semenzato, Venice #234/R est:18000-22000

TUSCAN SCHOOL (19th C) Italian
£8654 $13673 €13500 Man (70x53cm-28x21in) 15-Nov-2 Farsetti, Prato #541/R est:16000

TUSSENBROEK, Otto van (1882-1956) Dutch
£428 $693 €650 Pont Alexandre, Paris (20x41cm-8x16in) indis sig.d.1912 prov. 21-Jan-3 Christie's, Amsterdam #188/R

TUTTLE, Richard (1941-) American
£68750 $110000 €103125 Untitled (100x184cm-39x72in) dyed shaped unstretched canvas painted 1967 prov. 15-May-3 Phillips, New York #12/R est:80000-120000
£75000 $120000 €112500 Cloth piece (98x155cm-39x61in) dyed canvas painted 1969 prov.exhib.lit. 13-May-3 Sotheby's, New York #3/R est:80000-120000
Sculpture
£26899 $42500 €40349 Forms in classicism (15x145x39cm-6x57x15in) wood acrylic model airplane paper in five parts prov.exhib. 13-Nov-2 Sotheby's, New York #105/R est:25000-35000
Works on paper
£700 $1141 €1050 Loophole (50x35cm-20x14in) s.i. mixed media collage aluminium set in a box. 3-Feb-3 Sotheby's, Olympia #50/R
£833 $1292 €1300 Loophole (50x36cm-20x14in) i. verso collage gold bronze canvas board. 3-Dec-2 Lempertz, Koln #478/R
£2500 $4000 €3750 PT. drawing no.24 (36x28cm-14x11in) s.i.d.1974 pencil gouache prov. 14-May-3 Sotheby's, New York #226/R est:3000-4000
£2600 $4108 €3900 Untitled (24x35cm-9x14in) i.d.1982 gouache prov. 3-Apr-3 Christie's, Kensington #248/R
£3057 $4463 €4586 Centre point drawing No 197: Florida works 17 (43x35cm-17x14in) pencil W/C s.i.d.1975 verso prov.lit. 4-Jun-2 Germann, Zurich #32/R est:4500-5500 (S.FR 7000)
£8125 $13000 €12188 Untitled (35x45cm-14x18in) s.d.1990 verso gouache pencil in four parts prov. 14-May-3 Sotheby's, New York #311/R est:10000-15000
£18750 $30000 €28125 Nica life-off (17x12cm-7x5in) W/C pencil homosote oil glass tape in 15 parts prov. 14-May-3 Sotheby's, New York #312/R est:15000-20000
£37975 $60000 €56963 Portland works group I (23x15cm-9x6in) i.verso W/C airmail paper in 39 parts executed 1976 prov. 13-Nov-2 Sotheby's, New York #112/R est:70000-90000

TUTUNDJIAN, Léon (1905-1968) French/Armenian
Works on paper
£347 $573 €500 Arc et deux disques (24x32cm-9x13in) s.d. black crayon chl estompe. 1-Jul-3 Rossini, Paris #44
£372 $580 €550 Sans titre, brun (23x30cm-9x12in) s.d. crayon dr. 31-Mar-3 Rossini, Paris #102
£497 $810 €750 Composition (33x25cm-13x10in) s.d.1960 chl dr. 3-Feb-3 Cornette de St.Cyr, Paris #539/R
£704 $1169 €1000 Sans titre (26x19cm-10x7in) init. Indian ink dr. pair. 18-Jun-3 Anaf, Lyon #72/R
£2342 $3653 €3700 Nature morte aux fruits (40x46cm-16x18in) s.d.1926 W/C pastel ink. 20-Oct-2 Claude Boisgirard, Paris #31/R est:2500-3000

TUXEN, Laurits (1853-1927) Danish

£328 $501 €492 Author Sophus Bauditz (33x25cm-13x10in) mono.d.8/2 06 study exhib. 24-Aug-2 Rasmussen, Havnen #2056 (D.KR 3800)
£526 $853 €763 In the outskirts of Skagen Plantage (33x37cm-13x15in) init.d.7-9-13 i.verso. 26-May-3 Rasmussen, Copenhagen #1510/R (D.KR 5500)
£552 $862 €828 Gudhjem Harbour (29x20cm-11x8in) init. panel. 5-Aug-2 Rasmussen, Vejle #96/R (D.KR 6500)
£553 $874 €830 Cloud study (22x31cm-9x12in) s.d.1890. 27-Nov-2 Museumsbygningen, Copenhagen #81/R (D.KR 6500)
£574 $930 €832 War minister J J Bahnson (52x36cm-20x14in) init. sketch prov. 26-May-3 Rasmussen, Copenhagen #1344/R (D.KR 6000)
£596 $941 €894 Landscape study from St Barbara, California (21x50cm-8x20in) init.d.18. 2-Dec-2 Rasmussen, Copenhagen #1261/R (D.KR 7000)
£681 $1076 €1022 The Rising of Lazarus (90x76cm-35x30in) 2-Dec-2 Rasmussen, Copenhagen #1746/R (D.KR 8000)
£836 $1322 €1254 Summer's day in the garden (33x42cm-13x17in) init.d.2/5 13. 5-Apr-3 Rasmussen, Havnen #2009/R (D.KR 9000)
£1191 $1883 €1787 Beached boats (36x42cm-14x17in) init.i. 2-Dec-2 Rasmussen, Copenhagen #1414/R est:10000 (D.KR 14000)
£2488 $4031 €3608 Landscape from Nymindegab with two women and sheep, evening (47x74cm-19x29in) init.d.78. 24-May-3 Rasmussen, Havnen #2276/R est:15000-20000 (D.KR 26000)
£2514 $3997 €3771 Two small girls in the dunes at Skagen Strand (38x59cm-15x23in) init. 5-Mar-3 Rasmussen, Copenhagen #1506/R est:25000 (D.KR 27000)
£3243 $5222 €4865 Coastal landscape from Skagen with beached boats (37x58cm-15x23in) mono. 26-Feb-3 Museumsbygningen, Copenhagen #121/R est:12000-15000 (D.KR 36000)
£4758 $7422 €7137 Frederikke Tuxen with Yvonne and Nina (91x106cm-36x42in) init.d.1905 exhib.lit. 5-Aug-2 Rasmussen, Vejle #24/R est:60000-80000 (D.KR 56000)
£5321 $8301 €7982 Storm approaching, Skagen - with girl and two dogs in the dunes (90x115cm-35x45in) init. exhib. 23-Sep-2 Rasmussen, Vejle #105/R est:50000 (D.KR 63000)
£5438 $8483 €8157 Skagen Sonderstrand with three men in rowing boat (50x61cm-20x24in) init.d.5/8 16 lit. 5-Aug-2 Rasmussen, Vejle #35/R est:40000 (D.KR 64000)
£5599 $8510 €8399 Model study from Bonnat's studio (62x50cm-24x20in) init.d.77. 27-Aug-2 Rasmussen, Copenhagen #1497/R est:20000-25000 (D.KR 65000)
£8209 $13052 €12314 Bathing nymph (102x68cm-40x27in) init.d.12/6 10 lit. 5-May-3 Rasmussen, Vejle #254/R est:50000-75000 (D.KR 88000)
£39277 $64415 €56952 Susanna in the bath (90x180cm-35x71in) s.i.d.1892. 4-Jun-3 AB Stockholms Auktionsverk #2472/R est:500000-600000 (S.KR 500000)
£40191 $65110 €58277 At low tide on the coast of France with mussel gatherers (53x74cm-21x29in) init.d.88 exhib. 26-May-3 Rasmussen, Copenhagen #1126/R est:400000 (D.KR 420000)

Works on paper

£450 $725 €675 Mythological scene (84x105cm-33x41in) s.d.04 chk pencil sketch. 22-Feb-3 Rasmussen, Havnen #2343 (D.KR 5000)
£718 $1163 €1077 Fishermen on beach with basket (67x49cm-26x19in) mono. W/C. 21-May-3 Museumsbygningen, Copenhagen #57 (D.KR 7500)

TUXEN, Nicoline (1847-1931) Danish

£723 $1143 €1085 Peony in vase on window ledge (41x33cm-16x13in) mono. 2-Dec-2 Rasmussen, Copenhagen #1763 (D.KR 8500)

TUYMANS, Luc (1958-) Belgian

£34375 $55000 €51563 Grune wolken (43x34cm-17x13in) s.d.89 verso. 15-May-3 Christie's, Rockefeller NY #330/R est:40000-60000

Works on paper

£8750 $14000 €13125 Untitled (37x27cm-15x11in) s.d.90 W/C paper cut on board prov. 15-May-3 Christie's, Rockefeller NY #331/R est:8000-12000

TVETER, Kare (1922-) Norwegian

£259 $393 €389 Figures around table (33x41cm-13x16in) s. i.verso panel. 31-Aug-2 Grev Wedels Plass, Oslo #111 (N.KR 3000)
£297 $458 €446 Porkalla - fela (33x24cm-13x9in) s. panel painted 1952. 28-Oct-2 Blomqvist, Lysaker #1326 (N.KR 3500)
£382 $588 €573 Snowfall (27x34cm-11x13in) s. panel painted 1952. 28-Oct-2 Blomqvist, Lysaker #1327 (N.KR 4500)
£1316 $2026 €1974 Towards winter evening (65x82cm-26x32in) s. painted 1970. 28-Oct-2 Blomqvist, Lysaker #1328 est:12000-15000 (N.KR 15500)
£1474 $2300 €2211 Snow-covered landscape (70x85cm-28x33in) s. 21-Oct-2 Blomqvist, Oslo #430/R est:20000-25000 (N.KR 17000)
£2082 $3247 €3123 Winter landscape with house and pine trees (65x80cm-26x31in) s. 21-Oct-2 Blomqvist, Oslo #419/R est:20000-25000 (N.KR 24000)

Works on paper

£255 $392 €383 Green landscape (21x27cm-8x11in) s. W/C. 28-Oct-2 Blomqvist, Lysaker #1331 (N.KR 3000)
£272 $418 €408 Landscape (20x24cm-8x9in) s. W/C. 28-Oct-2 Blomqvist, Lysaker #1329/R (N.KR 3200)
£289 $444 €434 Winter landscape with trees (19x24cm-7x9in) s. W/C. 28-Oct-2 Blomqvist, Lysaker #1330 (N.KR 3400)

TVRDON, Martin (1914-) Czechoslovakian

£347 $492 €521 Inside the forest (51x73cm-20x29in) painted 1957. 26-Mar-2 SOGA, Bratislava #246/R (SL.K 22000)

TWACHTMAN, John Henry (1853-1902) American

£74074 $120000 €111111 Landing, Newport (20x30cm-8x12in) s. panel painted c.1889 prov.exhib. 21-May-3 Sotheby's, New York #52/R est:75000-100000
£103226 $160000 €154839 Waterfall, Yellowstone (77x63cm-30x25in) s. painted c.1895 prov.exhib.lit. 4-Dec-2 Sotheby's, New York #25/R est:200000-300000
£129032 $200000 €193548 Waterfall (56x77cm-22x30in) painted c.1890-1899 prov. 4-Dec-2 Sotheby's, New York #4/R est:60000-80000
£234568 $380000 €351852 Tiger lilies (76x56cm-30x22in) s. painted c.1890-95 prov.exhib.lit. 21-May-3 Sotheby's, New York #26/R est:250000-350000
£253247 $390000 €379871 Pier, Gloucester (64x64cm-25x25in) est.st. prov. 24-Oct-2 Shannon's, Milford #65/R est:80000-120000

Works on paper

£3963 $6500 €5746 Cottage (20x25cm-8x10in) s. pastel. 31-May-3 Susanin's, Chicago #5015/R est:1500-2000

TWEDDLE, Isabel Hunter (1877-1945) Australian

£400 $644 €580 Mixed bunch, roses and lilies (49x40cm-19x16in) mono. canvasboard. 12-May-3 Joel, Victoria #336 est:1000-1500 (A.D 1000)
£423 $672 €635 Manly, Sydney (34x20cm-13x8in) board. 4-Mar-3 Deutscher-Menzies, Melbourne #252/R (A.D 1100)

TWELLS, Arthur H (1921-) British

£260 $403 €390 Quiet evening, Lough Levally (25x30cm-10x12in) s. 2-Oct-2 John Ross, Belfast #175
£350 $557 €525 Near Whiterocks, County Antrim (50x71cm-20x28in) s. board. 5-Mar-3 John Ross, Belfast #175
£400 $636 €600 St. Johns Point, Donegal (50x71cm-20x28in) s. 5-Mar-3 John Ross, Belfast #126
£460 $672 €690 Oil boat near Rathmullan, Kinnegar Strand (25x41cm-10x16in) s. 12-Jun-2 John Ross, Belfast #240
£550 $875 €825 Cottages on the Antrim coast (50x71cm-20x28in) s. board. 5-Mar-3 John Ross, Belfast #212
£660 $1049 €950 Broken silence - dusk, Gortin Glen, County Tyrone (25x30cm-10x12in) s. i.verso. 29-Apr-3 Whyte's, Dublin #171/R
£1500 $2325 €2250 Hearing the news (61x79cm-24x31in) s. board. 2-Oct-2 John Ross, Belfast #232 est:600-800

TWELVETREES, Charles (20th C) American

Works on paper

£621 $1000 €932 Little girl bride and dog (48x33cm-19x13in) s. W/C gouache. 19-Feb-3 Illustration House, New York #215/R est:1500-2000
£745 $1200 €1118 Little boy and dog in speeding roadster (51x33cm-20x13in) s. gouache W/C. 19-Feb-3 Illustration House, New York #214/R est:1500-2000
£994 $1600 €1491 Little boy painting fall foliage as dog looks on (51x33cm-20x13in) s. gouache W/C. 19-Feb-3 Illustration House, New York #212/R est:1500-2000
£994 $1600 €1491 Little boy chef riding determined turkey (46x36cm-18x14in) s. W/C gouache. 19-Feb-3 Illustration House, New York #213/R est:1500-2000

TWISS, Greer (1937-) New Zealander

Sculpture

£1056 $1743 €1531 Instead of an introduction (121x60cm-48x24in) init.d.1987 lead. 1-Jul-3 Peter Webb, Auckland #52/R est:4000-6000 (NZ.D 3000)
£1562 $2437 €2343 Foot plate (19x146x21cm-7x57x8in) s.i.d.1974 bronze. 8-Apr-3 Peter Webb, Auckland #128/R est:3000-5000 (NZ.D 4500)
£1910 $2979 €2865 Hands holding rope (100x125cm-39x49in) s.d.1972 bronze rope. 8-Apr-3 Peter Webb, Auckland #127/R est:3500-5500 (NZ.D 5500)

£1910 $2979 €2865 Seated female form sitting (190x300x310cm-75x118x122in) painted bronze wooden plinth. 8-Apr-3 Peter Webb, Auckland #130/R est:2500-3500 (NZ.D 5500)

TWOMBLY, Cy (1929-) American

£93750 $150000 €140625 Untitled (87x70cm-34x28in) s.d.1970 oi oilstick paper prov. 15-May-3 Christie's, Rockefeller NY #172/R est:100000-150000
£93750 $150000 €140625 Untitled (49x60cm-19x24in) s.d.62 verso oil wax crayon pencil prov. 14-May-3 Sotheby's, New York #225/R est:140000-180000
£120000 $200400 €180000 Untitled (69x100cm-27x39in) s.d.1959 oil pencil col.pencil paper prov.exhib. 25-Jun-3 Sotheby's, London #14/R est:50000-70000
£160000 $246400 €240000 Untitled (70x101cm-28x40in) acrylic wax crayon on paper painted 1971 prov. 23-Oct-2 Christie's, London #132/R est:120000-160000
£206250 $330000 €309375 Untitled (102x76cm-40x30in) s.d.1970 verso oil crayon prov.exhib. 14-May-3 Sotheby's, New York #217/R est:100000-150000
£237500 $380000 €356250 First part of the return from Paranssus (70x100cm-28x39in) s.i.d.1961 verso oil crayon pencil paper on canvas prov. 13-May-3 Sotheby's, New York #26/R est:400000-500000
£350000 $574000 €525000 Roman notes (140x86cm-55x34in) s.i.d.1970 acrylic wax crayon prov. 5-Feb-3 Christie's, London #15/R est:300000-500000
£1093750 $1750000 €1640625 Bolsena (200x250cm-79x98in) s.d.1969 house paint crayon graphite on canvas prov.exhib.lit. 15-May-3 Phillips, New York #13/R est:2500000-3500000
£1400000 $2338000 €2100000 Bolsena (195x222cm-77x87in) oil based housepaints wax crayon exc.1974 prov.exhib.lit. 26-Jun-3 Christie's, London #33/R est:1400000-1800000
£1666667 $2600000 €2500001 Bolsena (201x240cm-79x94in) oil based house paint wax on canvas painted 1969 prov.exhib.lit. 11-Nov-2 Phillips, New York #22/R est:2500000-3500000
£3227848 $5100000 €4841772 Untitled (155x190cm-61x75in) s.d.1970 oil based house paint wax crayon prov. 12-Nov-2 Sotheby's, New York #32/R est:4000000-6000000

Prints

£2229 $3500 €3344 Untitled, from homage a Picasso (30x22cm-12x9in) s.num. lithograph collage edition of 120. 19-Nov-2 Wright, Chicago #222/R est:3500-4500
£2821 $4428 €4400 Untitled (24x26cm-9x10in) s. num.30/60 lithograph. 21-Nov-2 Finarte, Rome #108/R
£3312 $5200 €4968 Untitled (57x77cm-22x30in) s.d.1971 num.16/24 ochre lithograph. 21-Nov-2 Swann Galleries, New York #215/R est:3000-5000
£5449 $8500 €8174 Roman notes (88x70cm-35x28in) s.d.num.12/100 verso col lithograph. 5-Nov-2 Christie's, Rockefeller NY #494/R est:7000-9000
£6090 $9500 €9135 Untitled, from On the Bowery (65x65cm-26x26in) s.num.24/100 verso col screenprint. 5-Nov-2 Christie's, Rockefeller NY #495/R est:9000-12000
£7692 $12000 €11538 Roman notes (88x70cm-35x28in) s.d.num.12/100 verso col lithograph. 5-Nov-2 Christie's, Rockefeller NY #493/R est:7000-9000
£8176 $13000 €12264 Roman notes (87x70cm-34x28in) s.d.num.12/100 verso col lithograph. 2-May-3 Sotheby's, New York #639/R est:7000-9000

Works on paper

£3972 $6434 €5600 Colosseo (29x31cm-11x12in) s.i.d.58 ink paper on cardboard prov. 26-May-3 Christie's, Milan #80/R est:5000-6000
£5800 $9686 €8410 Reflection (86x67cm-34x26in) s.i. pencil col crayon prov. 27-Jun-3 Christie's, London #203/R est:8000-12000
£15000 $25050 €21750 Untitled, study for triumph of love (28x35cm-11x14in) s.i.d.Nov 23 1960 pencil black ball point pen pastel prov. 26-Jun-3 Sotheby's, London #173/R est:15000-20000
£25000 $41750 €36250 Untitled, study for triumph of love (27x35cm-11x14in) s.i.d.Nov 22 1960 pencil black ball point pen pastel prov. 26-Jun-3 Sotheby's, London #174/R est:25000-35000
£26000 $43420 €37700 Untitled, study for triumph of love (21x29cm-8x11in) s.d.April 1961 pencil pastel prov. 26-Jun-3 Sotheby's, London #172/R est:25000-35000
£28000 $46760 €40600 Untitled, study for triumph of live (27x35cm-11x14in) s.d.Nov 25 1960 pencil black ball point pen pastel prov. 26-Jun-3 Sotheby's, London #171/R est:20000-30000
£28125 $45000 €42188 Untitled (50x70cm-20x28in) s.d.1963 pencil col crayon ink prov. 14-May-3 Sotheby's, New York #228/R est:35000-45000
£30000 $50100 €45000 Study for 'Triumph of Love' (22x30cm-9x12in) s.i.d.April 1961 pencil pastel prov. 25-Jun-3 Sotheby's, London #13/R est:35000-45000
£60000 $100200 €87000 Roman notes (70x87cm-28x34in) s.d.Mar 1970 verso oil on paper prov. 27-Jun-3 Christie's, London #207/R est:70000-90000
£66000 $110220 €95700 Untitled (61x91cm-24x36in) s.i.d.59 pencil prov. 27-Jun-3 Christie's, London #202/R est:10000-15000
£75000 $125250 €108750 Untitled (70x100cm-28x39in) s.d.1964 col crayon pencil ballpoint pen prov. 27-Jun-3 Christie's, London #206/R est:40000-60000
£85000 $141950 €123250 Untitled (112x96cm-44x38in) gouache wax crayon pencil card exec.c.1970-71 prov.exhib. 26-Jun-3 Sotheby's, London #151/R est:80000-120000
£125000 $200000 €187500 Untitled (22x30cm-9x12in) s.d.1957 pencil oilstick in 7 parts prov. 13-May-3 Sotheby's, New York #36a/R est:200000-300000

TWORKOV, Jack (1900-1982) American

Works on paper

£11875 $19000 €17813 Flowering white (66x63cm-26x25in) s. s.d.49 verso ink oil on canvas prov.lit. 14-May-3 Sotheby's, New York #126/R est:15000-20000

TYCK-GEENS, Jo (20th C) Belgian?

£408 $649 €600 Le petit demon (42x27cm-17x11in) s. 24-Mar-3 Bernaerts, Antwerp #167/R

TYDEN, Nils (1889-1976) Swedish

£1121 $1749 €1682 View from Smedsudden, Stockholm (37x34cm-15x13in) s.d.1923 panel. 6-Nov-2 AB Stockholms Auktionsverk #758/R est:8000-10000 (S.KR 16000)

TYLER, Bayard Henry (1855-1931) American

£500 $800 €750 Hudson River landscape with steamboat (41x30cm-16x12in) s. board. 12-Jan-3 William Jenack, New York #399
£637 $1000 €956 Palisades (41x51cm-16x20in) s.d.1922. 22-Nov-2 Skinner, Boston #252/R est:2000-3000

TYLER, James Gale (1855-1931) American

£478 $750 €717 Sailing ship, moonlight (51x76cm-20x30in) s. 28-Jul-2 William Jenack, New York #223
£637 $1000 €956 Rocky coastal landscape (61x76cm-24x30in) s. 20-Nov-2 Boos Gallery, Michigan #522/R
£813 $1300 €1179 Full sail (36x30cm-14x12in) s.d.1904. 17-May-3 CRN Auctions, Cambridge #7
£1125 $1800 €1631 Tugboat in the rough sea (30x46cm-12x18in) s.d.1904 panel. 17-May-3 CRN Auctions, Cambridge #8
£1132 $1800 €1698 Moonlight sail (51x41cm-20x16in) s. panel. 5-Mar-3 Doyle, New York #60/R est:2000-3000
£1465 $2300 €2198 Moonlit scene with sailboat in full sail and lighthouse (51x41cm-20x16in) s. 19-Apr-3 James Julia, Fairfield #63/R est:3000-5000
£2070 $3250 €3105 At full sail (69x43cm-27x17in) s. 10-Dec-2 Doyle, New York #52/R est:4000-6000
£2548 $4000 €3822 Seascape with large crashing wave hitting rock ledge causing white foam (71x102cm-28x40in) s. 19-Apr-3 James Julia, Fairfield #62/R est:4000-6000
£3185 $5000 €4778 Shipwreck flying an American flag with men in the rigging (51x76cm-20x30in) s. 26-Jul-2 Eldred, East Dennis #529/R est:4000-6000
£8642 $14000 €12531 Standing out to sea (76x102cm-30x40in) s.d.1883. 29-Jul-3 Christie's, Rockefeller NY #158/R est:12000-18000

Works on paper

£382 $600 €573 Barbara off the coast (41x54cm-16x21in) s.d.1873 W/C. 14-Dec-2 Weschler, Washington #646/R
£1111 $1800 €1611 Hudson River sloops off the Palisades (28x47cm-11x19in) s.d.1889 W/C. 29-Jul-3 Christie's, Rockefeller NY #109/R est:2000-3000

TYLER, James Gale (attrib) (1855-1931) American

£855 $1300 €1283 America's Cup (13x20cm-5x8in) board roundel. 17-Aug-2 North East Auctions, Portsmouth #419/R

TYLER, William R (1825-1896) American

£1625 $2600 €2356 Shoreline with hulk (30x51cm-12x20in) s. 16-May-3 Skinner, Boston #103/R est:1000-1500
£10000 $16000 €14500 Pastoral landscape (40x66cm-16x26in) s. 16-May-3 Skinner, Boston #70/R est:5000-7000

TYNDALE, Thomas Nicholson (1858-1936) British

£1000 $1580 €1500 English country houses (18x25cm-7x10in) s. W/C pair. 17-Dec-2 Gorringes, Lewes #1432

Works on paper

£360 $554 €540 Herding sheep down a rural lane (23x34cm-9x13in) s. W/C. 22-Oct-2 Bonhams, Knightsbridge #197

£500 $835 €725 Figures on the bridge at Baddelsey Clinton Hall (26x20cm-10x8in) s. W/C. 24-Jun-3 Bonhams, Knightsbridge #14/R
£2400 $3720 €3600 Ripe, Sussex (21x31cm-8x12in) s. W/C. 3-Dec-2 Sotheby's, Olympia #97/R est:2000-3000

TYNDALE, Walter (1855-1943) British
Works on paper
£360 $562 €540 Venice from lagoon (23x34cm-9x13in) s. W/C. 6-Nov-2 Bonhams, Chester #405
£400 $636 €600 Court in Venice (25x34cm-10x13in) s. W/C. 27-Feb-3 Bonhams, Chester #414
£480 $744 €720 Middle Eastern market scene (17x24cm-7x9in) s. W/C. 3-Dec-2 Sworder & Son, Bishops Stortford #907/R
£1300 $2132 €1950 High street, Haslemere (21x31cm-8x12in) s.i.d.1896 pencil W/C sold with Attrib A Goodwin W B Gardner. 5-Jun-3 Christie's, Kensington #870 est:300-500
£1300 $2119 €1885 Cavaliers resting in a courtyard (35x25cm-14x10in) s. pencil W/C. 17-Jul-3 Tennants, Leyburn #768/R est:500-700
£3600 $5616 €5400 Vegetable stall under the Colonnade, the Rialto, Venice. Venetian vegetable stall (25x35cm-10x14in) s. W/C pair. 5-Nov-2 Bonhams, New Bond Street #103/R est:3000-5000
£4286 $6771 €6429 Farewell Japanese village scene (34x25cm-13x10in) s. W/C. 18-Nov-2 Joel, Victoria #249/R est:12000-15000 (A.D 12000)

TYNDALE, Walter (attrib) (1855-1943) British
Works on paper
£300 $465 €450 Middle Eastern man seated on a ledge (34x23cm-13x9in) W/C. 3-Dec-2 Sworder & Son, Bishops Stortford #908/R

TYNG, Margaret Fuller (1878-1965) American
Works on paper
£427 $700 €619 Cape Cod dunes (30x36cm-12x14in) s. col pastel card stock sold with another by F H Mason. 5-Jun-3 Swann Galleries, New York #252/R

TYRELL, Charles (20th C) ?
Works on paper
£274 $430 €400 Untitled (21x21cm-8x8in) s.d.1980 mixed media. 15-Apr-3 De Veres Art Auctions, Dublin #57

TYROLEAN SCHOOL (16th C) Austrian
£6289 $9748 €10000 Christ's Circumcision (47x43cm-19x17in) panel prov. 2-Oct-2 Dorotheum, Vienna #243/R est:10000-14000

TYSHLER, Aleksander (1898-1980) Russian
£20000 $31400 €30000 Girl with still-life (85x70cm-33x28in) s.d.73. 20-Nov-2 Sotheby's, London #184/R est:20000-30000
£50000 $78500 €75000 The colour of the moon (100x100cm-39x39in) s.d.1976. 20-Nov-2 Sotheby's, London #182/R est:40000-60000
Works on paper
£326 $535 €450 Figure in Russian courtyard (21x16cm-8x6in) s.d.29 cyrillic W/C Indian ink. 29-May-3 Lempertz, Koln #937/R

TYSON, Carroll (1878-1956) American
£581 $900 €872 Night sea (26x21cm-10x8in) s.i.d.1913 verso board. 8-Dec-2 Freeman, Philadelphia #111/R

TYSON, Keith (1969-) British
£13000 $21710 €18850 Artificial gravitation painting no.1 (105x100cm-41x39in) s.i.d.1998 on stretcher prov.exhib. 27-Jun-3 Christie's, London #271/R est:8000-12000

TYSON, Nicola (1960-) British
Works on paper
£1032 $1600 €1548 Dark haired girl (86x67cm-34x26in) s. i.d.1998 verso gouache prov. 26-Sep-2 Christie's, Rockefeller NY #880/R est:2000-4000

TYSSENS, Jacobus (18th C) Flemish
£4000 $6200 €6000 Pastoral scene. Itinerant company before tavern (114x89cm-45x35in) s. pair. 31-Oct-2 Sotheby's, Olympia #75/R est:4000-6000

TYSZBLAT, Michel (1936-) French
£1603 $2516 €2500 Avran (100x81cm-39x32in) s.d.1975 prov.exhib.lit. 15-Dec-2 Perrin, Versailles #175/R
Works on paper
£253 $392 €400 Fragments A (113x152cm-44x60in) s.d. mixed media. 28-Sep-2 Cornette de St.Cyr, Paris #439

TYTGAT, Edgard (1879-1957) Belgian
£1519 $2400 €2400 Une vue de Woluwe, la briqueterie en demolition (60x73cm-24x29in) s.d.1924 prov.exhib. 26-Nov-2 Palais de Beaux Arts, Brussels #394/R est:2000-3000
£2025 $3200 €3200 Interieur de la chambre de mon pere (35x19cm-14x7in) s.d.1905 prov. 26-Nov-2 Palais de Beaux Arts, Brussels #393 est:350-500
£6962 $11000 €11000 La fenetre ouverte (115x89cm-45x35in) s.d.1936 prov.exhib. 26-Nov-2 Palais de Beaux Arts, Brussels #383/R est:10000-15000
£12414 $19862 €18000 Spring in the studio (81x65cm-32x26in) s.d.1954 i.verso prov.exhib.lit. 15-Mar-3 De Vuyst, Lokeren #475/R est:15000-20000
Works on paper
£380 $600 €600 Nu assis vu de dos (22x19cm-9x7in) s.d.1940 wash prov.exhib. 26-Nov-2 Palais de Beaux Arts, Brussels #386
£443 $700 €700 Marche aux puces (21x14cm-8x6in) s.d.1940 wash prov. 26-Nov-2 Palais de Beaux Arts, Brussels #389
£481 $745 €750 Madame Hortense (30x22cm-12x9in) s.i. wash dr. 9-Dec-2 Horta, Bruxelles #303
£601 $950 €950 La ligue des peintres wallons - Doe still voort (23x23cm-9x9in) i. Indian ink prov. 26-Nov-2 Palais de Beaux Arts, Brussels #390
£690 $1103 €1000 Toilette de Suzanne (12x16cm-5x6in) s. col pencil pen ink dr exec.c.1910-1912 exhib.lit. 15-Mar-3 De Vuyst, Lokeren #316
£696 $1100 €1100 Theatre populaire (10x8cm-4x3in) studio st. i.verso pen dr prov. 26-Nov-2 Palais de Beaux Arts, Brussels #391
£696 $1100 €1100 Coin d'atelier (26x20cm-10x8in) s.d.1952 wash exhib. 26-Nov-2 Palais de Beaux Arts, Brussels #395
£719 $1151 €1000 Vue de Liege (35x51cm-14x20in) s.d.1932 W/C exhib.lit. 13-May-3 Palais de Beaux Arts, Brussels #152/R
£823 $1300 €1300 Temple de l'inspiration (22x21cm-9x8in) d.1929 studio st.verso. 26-Nov-2 Palais de Beaux Arts, Brussels #392
£1154 $1788 €1800 Baigneurs a Saint-Raphael (36x44cm-14x17in) s.i.d.1956 W/C prov.exhib.lit. 7-Dec-2 De Vuyst, Lokeren #324/R est:2000-2400
£1295 $2072 €1800 L'artiste et son modele (27x21cm-11x8in) s.d.1932 mixed media. 13-May-3 Palais de Beaux Arts, Brussels #151/R est:1400-1800
£2025 $3200 €3200 Mes beaux-parents a Watermael (46x50cm-18x20in) s.d.juillet 1914 W/C prov.exhib. 26-Nov-2 Palais de Beaux Arts, Brussels #384/R est:1500-2000

TYTGAT, Medard (1871-1948) Belgian
£586 $926 €850 Fillette au ballon (80x48cm-31x19in) s. 1-Apr-3 Palais de Beaux Arts, Brussels #585
£784 $1263 €1200 Le pierrot fatigue (60x50cm-24x20in) s.d.1913. 14-Jan-3 Vanderkindere, Brussels #69

TYTGAT, Medard Siegfried (1916-) Belgian
£1250 $1987 €1800 Nature morte aux colombes (170x339cm-67x133in) s.d.71 panel. 5-May-3 Bernaerts, Antwerp #227/R
£1389 $2208 €2000 Paysage avec le canal de Damme. s.d.71 panel. 5-May-3 Bernaerts, Antwerp #403/R
£1806 $2871 €2600 Nature morte au chat (110x320cm-43x126in) s.d.71 panel. 5-May-3 Bernaerts, Antwerp #226/R

UBAC, Raoul (1910-1985) Belgian
£4200 $6846 €6300 Portrait of a woman (61x51cm-24x20in) s.d.1940 verso. 3-Feb-3 Sotheby's, Olympia #163/R est:1200-1800
Sculpture
£4167 $6458 €6500 Ardoise (16x29cm-6x11in) slate stone relief exhib. 3-Dec-2 Christie's, Amsterdam #61/R est:2000-3000
Works on paper
£1369 $2163 €2054 Objets devant la femme (65x50cm-26x20in) init.d.48 W/C sketch verso. 28-Apr-3 Bukowskis, Stockholm #304/R est:20000-30000 (S.KR 18000)
£2222 $3667 €3200 Propositions (49x65cm-19x26in) mono.d.50 W/C cardboard exhib. 1-Jul-3 Artcurial Briest, Paris #774/R est:2000-3000
£2436 $3824 €3800 Objets familiers (73x44cm-29x17in) init.d.1946 s.i.d.verso W/C chl prov. 10-Dec-2 Piasa, Paris #399/R
£2564 $4026 €4000 Nature morte (50x65cm-20x26in) init.i.d.1948 s.verso W/C prov. 10-Dec-2 Piasa, Paris #404 est:3500
£2885 $4529 €4500 Marelle (76x48cm-30x19in) init. W/C gouache chl double-sided prov. 10-Dec-2 Piasa, Paris #402/R
£3077 $4769 €4800 La lampe (65x48cm-26x19in) s.d.51 gouache W/C exhib. 3-Dec-2 Christie's, Amsterdam #261/R est:4000-6000
£3205 $5032 €5000 Grande marelle (84x49cm-33x19in) init.i.d.1947 s.verso W/C chl prov. 10-Dec-2 Piasa, Paris #401 est:3500
£3718 $5837 €5800 Forestier (84x50cm-33x20in) init.d.1946 W/C prov. 10-Dec-2 Piasa, Paris #400
£4082 $6490 €6000 Chemin de croix (63x49cm-25x19in) s.d.1955 gouache lit. 26-Feb-3 Artcurial Briest, Paris #472/R est:2500-3000
£4359 $6844 €6800 Soleil (64x50cm-25x20in) init. s.i.d.1948 verso W/C. 10-Dec-2 Piasa, Paris #129/R
£4808 $7548 €7500 Sous-bois (50x65cm-20x26in) init.i.d.1948 s.verso W/C prov. 10-Dec-2 Piasa, Paris #403/R

UBAGHS, Jean (1852-?) Belgian
£823 $1300 €1300 Vue de plage a Knokke (41x62cm-16x24in) s. 26-Nov-2 Palais de Beaux Arts, Brussels #161/R

UBEDA, Augustin (1925-) Spanish
£719 $1200 €1043 Cerca de Madrid (25x33cm-10x13in) s. i.verso. 21-Jun-3 Charlton Hall, Columbia #219/R est:1500-2500
£903 $1427 €1400 Mirror (45x54cm-18x21in) s. s.i.verso. 17-Dec-2 Durán, Madrid #56/R
£1132 $1755 €1800 La poule (33x41cm-13x16in) s. 4-Oct-2 Tajan, Paris #223 est:1000-1200
£1321 $2034 €2100 Figure in landscape (27x35cm-11x14in) s. d.1966 verso. 22-Oct-2 Durán, Madrid #181/R
£1415 $2179 €2250 By the pony (27x35cm-11x14in) s. s.i.d.1966 verso. 22-Oct-2 Durán, Madrid #182/R
£1441 $2248 €2162 Town in evening (54x73cm-21x29in) s. 6-Nov-2 Dobiaschofsky, Bern #1021/R est:4500 (S.FR 3300)
£2201 $3434 €3500 Imaginary town (60x73cm-24x29in) s. 23-Sep-2 Durán, Madrid #198/R
£2887 $4649 €4100 Venise (60x72cm-24x28in) s. 11-May-3 Thierry & Lannon, Brest #286/R est:2500-3000
Works on paper
£258 $408 €400 Girls (50x65cm-20x26in) s. ink dr lit. 17-Dec-2 Segre, Madrid #143/R
£755 $1162 €1200 Angel dressing a bride (48x68cm-19x27in) s. s.i.verso W/C wash. 28-Oct-2 Segre, Madrid #120/R

UBELESSKI, Alexandre (attrib) (1649-1718) French
Works on paper
£1182 $1845 €1750 Mort d'Eurydice (37x52cm-15x20in) sanguine wash crayon. 31-Mar-3 Piasa, Paris #131

UBERTALLI, Romolo (1871-1928) Italian
£340 $541 €500 Sunset at the seaside (27x76cm-11x30in) s. board. 1-Mar-3 Meeting Art, Vercelli #189

UBERTINI, Francesco (style) (1494-1557) Italian
£17834 $27822 €28000 Saint Mary Magdalene (34x25cm-13x10in) panel prov. 6-Nov-2 Christie's, Amsterdam #26/R est:4500-5500

UCHERMANN, Karl (1855-1940) Norwegian
£4152 $6561 €6228 Everybody wants food (76x109cm-30x43in) s. 2-Dec-2 Blomqvist, Oslo #340/R est:20000-25000 (N.KR 48000)
£5204 $8118 €7806 English setter hunting (89x125cm-35x49in) s.d.1889. 21-Oct-2 Blomqvist, Oslo #322/R est:70000-90000 (N.KR 60000)
£8239 $12853 €12359 Woodland birds with their young (39x51cm-15x20in) s.d.85. 21-Oct-2 Blomqvist, Oslo #323/R est:60000-70000 (N.KR 95000)
Works on paper
£789 $1247 €1184 The fox has caught the goose (19x30cm-7x12in) s. pencil W/C. 17-Dec-2 Grev Wedels Plass, Oslo #194/R (N.KR 9000)
£929 $1515 €1394 Chickens (21x15cm-8x6in) s. W/C. 17-Feb-3 Blomqvist, Lysaker #1245/R (N.KR 10500)

UCLES, Josep (1952-) Spanish
Works on paper
£397 $648 €600 Dreams (87x63cm-34x25in) s. W/C gouache cardboard. 11-Feb-3 Segre, Madrid #264/R

UDELLO, Maurice (?) ?
£260 $411 €390 Latin supper (30x41cm-12x16in) s. panel. 2-Dec-2 Gorringes, Lewes #2631
£285 $447 €428 Spanish figures settled for lunch (30x41cm-12x16in) s. panel. 16-Apr-3 Christie's, Kensington #809/R

UDEN, Lucas van (1595-1672) Flemish
£5000 $8350 €7250 Extensive river landscape with figures on a road (55x79cm-22x31in) 8-Jul-3 Sotheby's, Olympia #364/R est:5000-7000
£7595 $12000 €12000 Wooded landscape with Saint Hubert (46x63cm-18x25in) panel prov. 27-Nov-2 Christie's, Paris #8/R est:12000-18000
£8108 $12649 €12000 River landscape with five figures (25x39cm-10x15in) s. copper. 26-Mar-3 Tajan, Paris #123/R est:7000
£14650 $22854 €23000 Extensive river landscape with figures stacking hay in a field and shepherds with their herd (71x113cm-28x44in) s.d.1669 prov. 5-Nov-2 Sotheby's, Amsterdam #278/R est:25000-35000
Works on paper
£21154 $32788 €33000 Bosquet de bouleaux (34x22cm-13x9in) pen ink wash over crayon prov. 4-Dec-2 Piasa, Paris #36/R est:20000

UDEN, Lucas van (studio) (1595-1672) Flemish
£5449 $8609 €8500 Wooded landscape with figures and cattle (29x35cm-11x14in) panel. 15-Nov-2 Beaussant & Lefèvre, Paris #76/R est:3000-3500

UDEN, Lucas van and TENIERS, David (younger) (17th C) Flemish
£35000 $58450 €50750 Extensive river landscape with peasant couple in the foreground (82x127cm-32x50in) mono. 9-Jul-3 Christie's, London #9/R est:15000-20000

UDVARDY, Gyula (1839-?) Hungarian
£446 $696 €700 Young girl excited about the first snowfall (32x22cm-13x9in) s. board lit. 7-Nov-2 Allgauer, Kempten #2983/R

UDVARY, Pal (1900-) Hungarian
£4303 $6669 €6239 Summer afternoon (70x85cm-28x33in) s. 9-Dec-2 Mu Terem Galeria, Budapest #198/R est:550000 (H.F 1600000)

UECKER, Gunther (1930-) German
£18841 $30899 €26000 Untitled (87x87cm-34x34in) s.i.d.64 verso painted nails panel canvas prov. 28-May-3 Lempertz, Koln #445/R est:18000-20000
Sculpture
£10759 $17000 €17000 Untitled (24x24x6cm-9x9x2in) s. i.d.65 verso nails white paint canvas on board. 26-Nov-2 Sotheby's, Amsterdam #267/R est:6000-9000
Works on paper
£432 $691 €600 Carrara (25x35cm-10x14in) s.d. pencil marble glue prov. 15-May-3 Neumeister, Munich #556/R
£1223 $1920 €1835 Ash picture (38x28cm-15x11in) s. verso ash mixed media. 23-Nov-2 Burkhard, Luzern #221/R est:3000-4000 (S.FR 2800)
£1223 $1920 €1835 Ash picture (38x28cm-15x11in) s. verso ash mixed media. 23-Nov-2 Burkhard, Luzern #220/R est:3000-4000 (S.FR 2800)
£1223 $1920 €1835 Ash picture (38x28cm-15x11in) s. verso ash mixed media. 23-Nov-2 Burkhard, Luzern #222/R est:3000-4000 (S.FR 2800)
£6028 $9766 €8500 Untitled (74x74cm-29x29in) s.d.69 verso nails board. 24-May-3 Van Ham, Cologne #602/R est:10000
£8681 $13802 €12500 Composition aux clous (39x39cm-15x15in) s. d.1976 verso assemblage lit. 29-Apr-3 Campo & Campo, Antwerp #297/R est:5000-7000

UEMURA, Shoen (1875-1949) Japanese
Works on paper
£10063 $16000 €15095 Beauty refreshing herself in summer (116x41cm-46x16in) s. ink col gold silk hanging scroll. 24-Mar-3 Christie's, Rockefeller NY #205/R est:15000-20000
£220126 $350000 €330189 Beauties of the twelve months (103x35cm-41x14in) s.d.1897 ink col gold silk six-panel pair. 24-Mar-3 Christie's, Rockefeller NY #204/R est:400000-500000

UFER, Walter (attrib) (1876-1936) American
Works on paper
£321 $500 €482 Trough in the mountains. gouache. 19-Oct-2 Harvey Clar, Oakland #1412

UHDE, Fritz von (1848-1911) German
£886 $1400 €1400 Bust portrait of a man (74x60cm-29x24in) mono. painted 1878. 29-Nov-2 Bolland & Marotz, Bremen #783/R
£3636 $5418 €5600 Girls playing in summer garden (31x40cm-12x16in) s. canvas on board lit. 26-Jun-2 Neumeister, Munich #887/R est:1800
Works on paper
£282 $468 €400 Beach carts in Zandvoort (13x22cm-5x9in) mono.i. Indian ink pencil chk. 14-Jun-3 Hauswedell & Nolte, Hamburg #1616/R
£399 $618 €630 Difficult journey - journey to Bethlehem (19x15cm-7x6in) s. chl htd white. 26-Sep-2 Neumeister, Munich #2626/R

UHDE, Fritz von (attrib) (1848-1911) German
£1111 $1778 €1700 Jesus saying grace to our guests (61x71cm-24x28in) i.verso lit. 10-Jan-3 Allgauer, Kempten #1770/R est:1700

UHER, Rudolf (1913-1987) German?
Sculpture
£1008 $1562 €1512 Untitled (30cm-12in) bronze. 1-Oct-2 SOGA, Bratislava #110/R est:80000 (SL.K 64000)

UHL, Ernst (1887-1971) German?
£570 $883 €900 Gril feeding birds in courtyard (41x23cm-16x9in) s. panel. 26-Sep-2 Neumeister, Munich #2854/R

UHL, S Jerome (1842-1916) American
£1266 $2000 €1836 Floral still life of rose in a gilt mounted porcelain vase (76x64cm-30x25in) s. 26-Apr-3 Jeffery Burchard, Florida #71a

UHLIG, Max (1937-) German

£1538 $2385 €2400 Untitled (43x89cm-17x35in) s.d.73. 3-Dec-2 Lempertz, Koln #484/R est:3000
£3043 $4991 €4200 Mountain landscape (80x180cm-31x71in) s.d.82 s.i.d. verso. 28-May-3 Lempertz, Koln #447/R est:4000-5000
£5072 $8319 €7000 Franziska I study (180x130cm-71x51in) s.d.88 s.i.d.Febr 88 verso lit.exhib. 31-May-3 Villa Grisebach, Berlin #367/R est:3000-4000

Works on paper

£252 $387 €400 Untitled landscape formation (36x62cm-14x24in) s.d.26.VII.78 W/C. 26-Oct-2 Dr Lehr, Berlin #545/R
£290 $475 €400 People on the street (52x72cm-20x28in) s.d.April 85 chl. 31-May-3 Villa Grisebach, Berlin #928/R
£314 $484 €500 Untitled portrait (63x49cm-25x19in) s.d.Marz 1981 Indian ink brush. 26-Oct-2 Dr Lehr, Berlin #552/R
£347 $549 €500 Clouds over water and coast (42x83cm-17x33in) s.d.1989 W/C. 26-Apr-3 Dr Lehr, Berlin #517/R
£348 $570 €480 Mountain wood (56x98cm-22x39in) s.d.88 W/C. 31-May-3 Villa Grisebach, Berlin #927/R
£362 $594 €500 Two people under an umbrella (63x30cm-25x12in) s.d.85 chl. 31-May-3 Villa Grisebach, Berlin #929/R
£377 $581 €600 Landscape formation (30x80cm-12x31in) s.d.Oktober 1980 W/C. 26-Oct-2 Dr Lehr, Berlin #547/R
£506 $800 €800 Landscape formation (27x68cm-11x27in) s.d.26.VII.88 W/C. 30-Nov-2 Bassenge, Berlin #6660
£507 $832 €700 Untitled (36x29cm-14x11in) s.d.Jan 86 i. verso Indian ink brush transparent paper. 28-May-3 Lempertz, Koln #450/R
£580 $951 €800 Untitled (53x97cm-21x38in) s.d.83 W/C. 28-May-3 Lempertz, Koln #449/R
£688 $1129 €950 Untitled - female portrait (41x28cm-16x11in) s.d.72 Indian ink. 28-May-3 Lempertz, Koln #448/R

UHLIR, Frantisek (1900-) Czechoslovakian

£454 $736 €658 Still life with apples and carafe (39x46cm-15x18in) s.d.46. 24-May-3 Dorotheum, Prague #117/R est:6000-9000 (C.KR 20000)

UHLMAN, Fred (1901-1985) British

£580 $905 €870 Winter (24x29cm-9x11in) s. board. 9-Apr-3 Cheffins Grain & Comins, Cambridge #739/R
£700 $1162 €1050 Church by moonlight (30x24cm-12x9in) s. canvasboard. 10-Jun-3 Sworder & Son, Bishops Stortford #473/R
£1000 $1670 €1450 Landscape near Auribeau (26x38cm-10x15in) s. s.i.verso board. 24-Jun-3 Bonhams, New Bond Street #99/R est:1000-1500
£1300 $2028 €1950 Coast (29x33cm-11x13in) s. board. 12-Sep-2 Sotheby's, Olympia #97/R est:1200-1800
£1300 $2015 €1950 Sunset over the Valley, Wales (61x91cm-24x36in) s. 4-Dec-2 Christie's, Kensington #549/R est:1500-2000
£1300 $2067 €1950 Cardigan Bay (41x51cm-16x20in) s. board prov. 26-Feb-3 Sotheby's, Olympia #215/R est:1500-2000
£1400 $2170 €2100 Winter evening (28x40cm-11x16in) s. board prov. 3-Dec-2 Bonhams, Knightsbridge #401/R est:1000-1500
£1400 $2212 €2100 Moonlit landscape (24x29cm-9x11in) board. 27-Nov-2 Sotheby's, Olympia #140/R est:400-600
£2000 $3300 €2900 Scilly Island (28x41cm-11x16in) board prov. 3-Jul-3 Christie's, Kensington #698/R est:1000-1500
£2400 $3936 €3600 Shells and bottles (29x39cm-11x15in) s. board prov. 3-Jun-3 Sotheby's, Olympia #133/R est:1000-1500
£2600 $4342 €3770 New York (61x91cm-24x36in) s.d.59. 24-Jun-3 Bonhams, New Bond Street #98/R est:2500-3500
£2800 $4452 €4200 Italian harbour (24x33cm-9x13in) s.i. board prov. 26-Feb-3 Sotheby's, Olympia #309/R est:2000-3000
£8000 $12480 €12000 Central Park, New York (38x56cm-15x22in) s. 12-Sep-2 Sotheby's, Olympia #103/R est:5000-7000

UHLMANN, Hans (1900-1975) German

Works on paper

£580 $951 €800 Untitled - metal game (31x43cm-12x17in) s.d.1954 Indian ink lit. 31-May-3 Villa Grisebach, Berlin #932/R
£688 $1129 €950 Untitled (45x12cm-18x5in) s.d.48 Indian ink W/C. 31-May-3 Villa Grisebach, Berlin #931/R
£696 $1100 €1100 Untitled (48x40cm-19x16in) s.d.47 Indian ink brush W/C. 29-Nov-2 Villa Grisebach, Berlin #935/R
£797 $1307 €1100 Composition (45x58cm-18x23in) s.d.1956 Indian ink. 31-May-3 Villa Grisebach, Berlin #934/R
£1266 $2000 €2000 Figures (44x59cm-17x23in) s.i.d.51 Indian ink brush W/C. 30-Nov-2 Villa Grisebach, Berlin #409/R est:2500-3500

UHRDIN, Sam (1886-1964) Swedish

£463 $731 €695 Portrait of woman wearing yellow dress (92x73cm-36x29in) s/d/1928. 27-Nov-2 Falkkloos, Malmo #77768/R (S.KR 6600)
£504 $817 €731 Interior scene with woman and baby (64x53cm-25x21in) s. panel. 25-May-3 Uppsala Auktionskammare, Uppsala #124/R (S.KR 6500)
£602 $975 €903 Eva by the fire (72x91cm-28x36in) s.d.1948. 3-Feb-3 Lilla Bukowskis, Stockholm #827 (S.KR 8400)
£621 $1005 €900 The old frock - interior scene with woman sewing (90x74cm-35x29in) s.d.47. 25-May-3 Uppsala Auktionskammare, Uppsala #121/R (S.KR 8000)
£709 $1099 €1064 Kerstin doing the washing (73x60cm-29x24in) s. 3-Dec-2 Bukowskis, Stockholm #305/R (S.KR 10000)
£781 $1241 €1172 In the glow of the fire-place (83x92cm-33x36in) s.d.1938. 3-Mar-3 Lilla Bukowskis, Stockholm #164 (S.KR 10500)
£938 $1501 €1360 Handmangel, Leksand (73x92cm-29x36in) s.d.39. 18-May-3 Anders Antik, Landskrona #72 (S.KR 12000)
£1348 $2089 €2022 At the spinning wheel (66x84cm-26x33in) s.d.38. 3-Dec-2 Bukowskis, Stockholm #307/R est:20000-25000 (S.KR 19000)
£1773 $2748 €2660 Idyll - cottage interior with mother and baby in crib (100x81cm-39x32in) s. 4-Dec-2 AB Stockholms Auktionsverk #1750/R est:25000-30000 (S.KR 25000)

UITZ, Bela (1887-1972) Hungarian

Works on paper

£1345 $2084 €2018 In the steam bath (40x28cm-16x11in) s. Indian ink. 6-Dec-2 Kieselbach, Budapest #49/R (H.F 500000)
£5379 $8337 €8069 Woman with a cup of coffee (53x36cm-21x14in) mixed media. 6-Dec-2 Kieselbach, Budapest #45/R (H.F 2000000)
£19348 $30183 €29022 Sitting woman (73x54cm-29x21in) s. walnut stain indian ink. 11-Sep-2 Kieselbach, Budapest #16/R (H.F 7500000)

UJHAZY, Ferenc (1827-1921) Hungarian

£1614 $2501 €2421 Traveller in front of the inn (36x47cm-14x19in) s. 6-Dec-2 Kieselbach, Budapest #91/R (H.F 600000)
£4386 $6842 €6579 Before the judge (71x106cm-28x42in) s. 11-Sep-2 Kieselbach, Budapest #150/R (H.F 1700000)

UJVARY, Ference (1898-?) Hungarian

£1769 $2812 €2600 Idyllic rural scene (59x80cm-23x31in) s. 25-Feb-3 Dorotheum, Vienna #175/R est:1800-2000

UJVARY, Ignac (1880-1927) Hungarian

£5000 $8200 €7500 Spatsommer - late summer (69x90cm-27x35in) s. prov.lit. 3-Jun-3 Sotheby's, London #91/R est:6000-8000
£12000 $19680 €18000 Poppy field (101x130cm-40x51in) s. 3-Jun-3 Sotheby's, London #93/R est:12000-16000

ULFSTEN, Nicolai Martin (1854-1895) Norwegian

£1384 $2187 €2076 Monk in Maulbrun Monastery in Worstenberg (40x31cm-16x12in) s.indis.d.75 panel. 2-Dec-2 Blomqvist, Oslo #358/R est:20000-30000 (N.KR 16000)
£2437 $3899 €3656 Landscape from Jaeren (29x60cm-11x24in) s.i.d.78. 17-Mar-3 Blomqvist, Oslo #303/R est:35000-45000 (N.KR 28000)
£3307 $5292 €4961 Sailing boats and bare rock-face (49x42cm-19x17in) s.d.84. 17-Mar-3 Blomqvist, Oslo #324/R est:50000-70000 (N.KR 38000)

ULFT, Jacob van der (1627-1689) Dutch

Works on paper

£1911 $2981 €3000 Italianate architectural capriccio (17x22cm-7x9in) s.d.1666 pen brown ink wash. 5-Nov-2 Sotheby's, Amsterdam #95/R est:3000-4000
£22152 $35000 €35000 Un caprice architectural avec un cortege au premier plan (18x26cm-7x10in) s. gouache vellum. 27-Nov-2 Christie's, Paris #18/R est:40000-60000

ULINGER, Johann Caspar (1703-1768) Swiss

Works on paper

£696 $1100 €1100 Paysage montagneux avec le chateau de Hiljibon (19x30cm-7x12in) i. pen brown ink grey wash. 27-Nov-2 Christie's, Paris #307/R

ULISSE (1957-) Italian

£316 $494 €500 Two staircases (30x70cm-12x28in) s. board painted 2000. 14-Sep-2 Meeting Art, Vercelli #955
£340 $541 €500 Amaretto di Saronno (50x40cm-20x16in) s. board. 1-Mar-3 Meeting Art, Vercelli #678

ULLIK, Hugo (1838-1881) Czechoslovakian

£295 $465 €443 Fort on cliff by sea (33x42cm-13x17in) s. 27-Nov-2 Falkkloos, Malmo #77726/R (S.KR 4200)
£3924 $6121 €5886 Mountainous landscape with lake (57x78cm-22x31in) s. 12-Oct-2 Dorotheum, Prague #16/R est:190000-300000 (C.KR 190000)

ULLMAN, Alfred (19/20th C) Swedish

£362 $586 €543 Landscape (63x73cm-25x29in) s. 27-Jan-3 Blomqvist, Lysaker #1278/R (N.KR 4000)

ULLMAN, Eugene P (1877-1953) American

£968 $1500 €1452 Recumbent nude (66x81cm-26x32in) 8-Dec-2 Freeman, Philadelphia #130/R est:1500-2500

£968 $1500 €1452 Lady in interior (46x55cm-18x22in) s. 8-Dec-2 Freeman, Philadelphia #164/R est:1500-2500
£968 $1500 €1452 Spring landscape with cows feeding (46x55cm-18x22in) s. 8-Dec-2 Freeman, Philadelphia #170/R est:1500-2500
£1097 $1700 €1646 Lady playing piano (38x46cm-15x18in) s. 8-Dec-2 Freeman, Philadelphia #118/R est:1000-1500

ULLMAN, Josef (1870-1922) Czechoslovakian
£636 $1030 €922 On a filed (48x58cm-19x23in) s. board. 24-May-3 Dorotheum, Prague #60/R est:20000-30000 (C.KR 28000)
£929 $1450 €1394 SUNSET (48x57cm-19x22in) s. cardboard. 12-Oct-2 Dorotheum, Prague #57/R (C.KR 45000)

ULLMANN, Robert (1903-1966) Austrian
Sculpture
£1126 $1835 €1700 Freedom for Africa (82cm-32in) s.num.4/5 green dark-gold pat bronze. 28-Jan-3 Dorotheum, Vienna #157/R est:3400-4500

ULMANN, Raoul Andre (1867-?) French
£687 $1100 €996 On the river (50x64cm-20x25in) s. board. 16-May-3 Skinner, Boston #49/R

ULMER, Hans (1886-) German
£679 $1100 €1019 Young woman sweeping (46x51cm-18x20in) s. s.verso panel painted c.1928. 23-Jan-3 Aspire, Cleveland #15 est:3000-5000

ULNITZ, E C (1856-1933) Danish
£300 $468 €450 Yellow roses (27x18cm-11x7in) s.d.1932. 11-Nov-2 Rasmussen, Vejle #555/R (D.KR 3500)
£558 $881 €837 Still life of fruit in basket (35x48cm-14x19in) s. 5-Apr-3 Rasmussen, Havnen #2118/R (D.KR 6000)
£630 $1009 €945 Still life of grapes, peaches and vine leaves (31x45cm-12x18in) s. 13-Jan-3 Rasmussen, Vejle #44/R (D.KR 7200)
£745 $1184 €1118 Baskets of flowers (10x12cm-4x5in) s.d.1892 pair. 10-Mar-3 Rasmussen, Vejle #490 (D.KR 8000)
£1117 $1777 €1676 Still life of yellow roses and forget-me-nots on stone ledge (15x18cm-6x7in) s.d.1890. 10-Mar-3 Rasmussen, Vejle #488 est:12000 (D.KR 12000)

ULNITZ, Emil C (1856-1933) Danish
£274 $427 €400 Public gardens with running stream and view of a town (23x35cm-9x14in) s. i.verso board lit. 10-Apr-3 Allgauer, Kempten #3019/R
£3258 $5279 €4724 Still life of raspberries and peaches (23x30cm-9x12in) s.d.1889. 26-May-3 Bukowskis, Stockholm #275/R est:12000-15000 (S.KR 42000)

ULREICH, Fritzi (20th C) Austrian
£540 $885 €750 View of Roman countryside from castle-terrace of Villa d'Este (67x100cm-26x39in) s.i. lit. 5-Jun-3 Dorotheum, Salzburg #694/R

ULRICH, Geza (1881-?) Hungarian
£1032 $1610 €1548 Budapest in winter with the chain bridge (100x120cm-39x47in) s. 11-Sep-2 Kieselbach, Budapest #1/R (H.F 400000)

ULRICH, Johann (1798-1877) Swiss
£485 $722 €728 Foggy harbour (19x27cm-7x11in) board. 25-Jun-2 Koller, Zurich #6553 (S.FR 1100)
£837 $1247 €1256 Bassin de la Villeta, Paris (22x30cm-9x12in) paper on pavatex. 25-Jun-2 Koller, Zurich #6548 (S.FR 1900)
£1057 $1575 €1586 Gulf of Naples (23x30cm-9x12in) board. 25-Jun-2 Koller, Zurich #6549/R est:2500-4000 (S.FR 2400)
£1145 $1707 €1718 Sea coast (19x30cm-7x12in) paper on board. 25-Jun-2 Koller, Zurich #6552 est:1800-2500 (S.FR 2600)
£6410 $10064 €10000 Cows at pasture (64x84cm-25x33in) s. 13-Dec-2 Piasa, Paris #13/R est:15000

ULRICH, Johann (attrib) (1798-1877) Swiss
£700 $1106 €1050 Figures beside a river with cattle watering and mill beyond (69x86cm-27x34in) 2-Dec-2 Gorringes, Lewes #2846
£742 $1158 €1113 Boats on mountain lake in summer (48x59cm-19x23in) 6-Nov-2 Dobiaschofsky, Bern #1022/R (S.FR 1700)

ULVING, Even (1863-1952) Norwegian
£368 $582 €552 From Beaulieu, French Riviera (32x46cm-13x18in) s. i.verso. 17-Dec-2 Grev Wedels Plass, Oslo #286/R (N.KR 4200)
£524 $822 €786 Valley (44x59cm-17x23in) s. panel. 25-Nov-2 Blomqvist, Lysaker #1283 (N.KR 6000)
£594 $915 €891 Landscape from Nottero (34x46cm-13x18in) s. 28-Oct-2 Blomqvist, Lysaker #1337/R (N.KR 7000)
£678 $1099 €1017 Valley (444x59cm-175x23in) s. panel. 27-Jan-3 Blomqvist, Lysaker #1279 (N.KR 7500)
£1061 $1634 €1592 Fjord landscape with buildings (50x70cm-20x28in) s. panel. 28-Oct-2 Blomqvist, Lysaker #1336/R (N.KR 12500)
£1218 $1950 €1827 Stacking logs at water's edge (73x60cm-29x24in) s. panel. 17-Mar-3 Blomqvist, Oslo #378/R est:18000-22000 (N.KR 14000)
£1741 $2785 €2612 Mill by waterfall (55x81cm-22x32in) s. 17-Mar-3 Blomqvist, Oslo #390/R est:25000-30000 (N.KR 20000)
£1817 $2870 €2726 Landscape from Tromoen, Arendal in morning (50x71cm-20x28in) s. i.stretcher. 2-Dec-2 Blomqvist, Oslo #365/R est:20000-25000 (N.KR 21000)
£1920 $3014 €2880 Landscape from Hjorundfjord, Saebo (32x50cm-13x20in) s. i.verso. 21-Nov-2 Grev Wedels Plass, Oslo #77/R est:5000 (N.KR 22000)
£2193 $3465 €3290 Woman reading, possibly the artist's mother (57x46cm-22x18in) s.d.86. 17-Dec-2 Grev Wedels Plass, Oslo #198/R est:30000 (N.KR 25000)
£3490 $5480 €5235 Woman with coffee grinder by open fire (75x91cm-30x36in) s/. 21-Nov-2 Grev Wedels Plass, Oslo #78/R est:40000-60000 (N.KR 40000)
£5051 $8283 €7324 Coastal landscape - morning at Ula (49x72cm-19x28in) s. 2-Jun-3 Blomqvist, Oslo #87/R est:25000-35000 (N.KR 55000)

UMBEHR, Otto (1902-1980) German
Photographs
£1899 $3000 €3000 Untitled - New York (22x17cm-9x7in) bromide silver gelatin. 28-Nov-2 Villa Grisebach, Berlin #1443/R est:3000-4000
£2215 $3500 €3500 San Joaquin Valley pipeline (19x24cm-7x9in) i. verso silver gelatin. 28-Nov-2 Villa Grisebach, Berlin #1445/R est:3000-4000

UMBRIAN SCHOOL (15th C) Italian
£8000 $12480 €12000 Saint James the Greater (85x42cm-33x17in) gold ground panel pointed top. 9-Apr-3 Christie's, London #85/R est:8000-12000
£58642 $95000 €87963 Portrait of a man. Still life of flowers in a vase (49x31cm-19x12in) tempera panel double-sided. 23-Jan-3 Sotheby's, New York #57/R est:40000-60000

UMBRIAN SCHOOL (16th C) Italian
£25676 $40054 €38000 Holy Family with angel (88cm-35in circular) board prov. 25-Mar-3 Finarte Semenzato, Rome #105/R est:14000

UMBRICHT, Honore Louis (1860-?) French
£427 $691 €619 Portrait of boy (42x32cm-17x13in) s. panel. 26-May-3 Bukowskis, Stockholm #250/R (S.KR 5500)

UMGELTER, Hermann Ludwig (1891-1962) German
£274 $427 €400 Flowers in vase (50x40cm-20x16in) s. board. 11-Apr-3 Sigalas, Stuttgart #465
£436 $702 €650 Allgau mountain landscape (45x56cm-18x22in) s. board. 21-Feb-3 Sigalas, Stuttgart #939

UNBEREIT, Paul (1884-1937) German/Austrian
£692 $1072 €1100 Inner courtyard (29x21cm-11x8in) s. board. 29-Oct-2 Dorotheum, Vienna #272/R
£816 $1298 €1200 View of courtyard (40x30cm-16x12in) s. board. 25-Feb-3 Dorotheum, Vienna #99

UNCETA Y LOPEZ, Marcelino de (1835-1905) Spanish
£4800 $8016 €7200 Carga arabe (73x50cm-29x20in) s. oil paper on canvas prov. 18-Jun-3 Christie's, Kensington #201/R est:6000-8000
£12000 $18600 €18000 Carga arabe (73x50cm-29x20in) s. prov. 4-Dec-2 Christie's, London #14/R est:12000-18000
Works on paper
£372 $580 €550 Soldier on horseback (24x17cm-9x7in) s. W/C. 25-Mar-3 Durán, Madrid #91/R
£559 $906 €850 Soldier (43x29cm-17x11in) s. W/C. 21-Jan-3 Durán, Madrid #64/R

UNCINI, Giuseppe (1929-) Italian
Sculpture
£2089 $3258 €3300 Space and concrete (67x46cm-26x18in) s.i.d.1995 verso concrete iron. 14-Sep-2 Meeting Art, Vercelli #720/R
£2532 $3949 €4000 Iron spaces (50x32cm-20x13in) s.i.d.1991 concrete iron. 14-Sep-2 Meeting Art, Vercelli #800/R
£4965 $8043 €7000 Rilievo no. 115 (80x54cm-31x21in) s.i.d.2001 verso cement iron. 26-May-3 Christie's, Milan #166/R est:7000-8000
£20000 $31200 €30000 Cementarmato (55x70x4cm-22x28x2in) s.i.d.1960 verso iron concrete exhib. 21-Oct-2 Sotheby's, London #27/R est:20000-40000
£31915 $51702 €45000 Cementarmato (123x78cm-48x31in) s.i.d.1959 verso cemento armato prov.lit. 26-May-3 Christie's, Milan #265/R est:45000-60000

Works on paper
£385 $604 €600 Untitled (40x60cm-16x24in) s. mixed media exec.1970. 21-Nov-2 Finarte, Rome #119/R
£993 $1609 €1400 Untitled (70x100cm-28x39in) s.d.1975 collage. 26-May-3 Christie's, Milan #71/R

UNDERHILL, Frederick Charles (fl.1851-1896) British
£355 $574 €500 Young anglers (52x42cm-20x17in) 20-May-3 Mealy's, Castlecomer #980/R
£550 $836 €825 Overtaken by the tide (28x46cm-11x18in) board. 14-Aug-2 Andrew Hartley, Ilkley #674

UNDERHILL, Frederick Thomas (fl.1868-1896) British
Works on paper
£550 $858 €825 Young man gathering wood in the snow (28x22cm-11x9in) s.d.1880 pencil W/C htd white. 17-Oct-2 Christie's, Kensington #66

UNDERWOOD, Léon (1890-1975) British
Sculpture
£1100 $1705 €1650 Lot's wife (26cm-10in) init.num.II/VII dark brown pat. bronze. 4-Dec-2 Christie's, Kensington #495/R est:1200-1800
£1500 $2325 €2250 40, 000 Years (70cm-28in) s.i.num.40.000 dark brown pat. bronze. 4-Dec-2 Christie's, Kensington #491/R est:1000-1500
£5500 $8689 €8250 Herald of new day (45cm-18in) s.d.1951 bronze with base. 27-Nov-2 Sotheby's, Olympia #176/R est:2500-3500
£8000 $12400 €12000 Chosen (53cm-21in) s.num.U/III/VII dark brown pat. bronze. 4-Dec-2 Christie's, Kensington #509/R est:3000-5000

UNG, Per (1933-) Norwegian
Sculpture
£2035 $3113 €3053 Lovers (20cm-8in) s. bronze. 26-Aug-2 Blomqvist, Lysaker #1432/R est:20000-25000 (N.KR 23500)
£2035 $3216 €3053 Woman and man (19x25x18cm-7x10x7in) s. bronze. 28-Apr-3 Blomqvist, Oslo #371/R est:20000-25000 (N.KR 23000)
£6071 $9471 €9107 The kiss (56x27x22cm-22x11x9in) s. bronze. 21-Oct-2 Blomqvist, Oslo #376/R est:60000-70000 (N.KR 70000)

UNGER, Hans (1872-1936) German
£325 $474 €500 Young lady out of doors (60x48cm-24x19in) s. 15-Jun-2 Hans Stahl, Hamburg #140
£2315 $3727 €3473 Female nude with parrot (97x61cm-38x24in) s. panel. 7-May-3 Dobiaschofsky, Bern #1027/R est:7500 (S.FR 5000)

UNGERER, Tomi (1931-) ?
Works on paper
£278 $447 €417 Abstract house (21x31cm-8x12in) W/C bodycol htd. 7-May-3 Dobiaschofsky, Bern #1028/R (S.FR 600)
£1242 $2000 €1863 Men tying giant sausages (53x56cm-21x22in) ink wash crayon. 10-May-3 Illustration House, New York #19/R est:1200-1800

UNGERN, Ragnar (1885-1955) Finnish
£626 $995 €920 Signe (25x21cm-10x8in) s.d.18.IX.1918. 24-Mar-3 Bukowskis, Helsinki #332/R
£696 $1086 €1100 Coastal view (68x53cm-27x21in) s.d.1913. 12-Sep-2 Hagelstam, Helsinki #821/R
£1690 $2721 €2400 Home harbour (32x27cm-13x11in) s.d.22. 10-May-3 Bukowskis, Helsinki #36/R est:1200-1500
£1701 $2704 €2500 Evening clouds (17x16cm-7x6in) s.d.1930. 27-Feb-3 Hagelstam, Helsinki #936/R est:850

UNGERS, Sybille (20th C) Irish?
£1781 $2778 €2600 Salley gap (220x151cm-87x59in) s.i.d.89 verso. 8-Apr-3 James Adam, Dublin #135/R est:500-800

UNGETA, Marcelino de (?) ?
£680 $1082 €1000 Entree de Murat et son Etat Major (25x21cm-10x8in) s. cardboard e grisaille. 26-Feb-3 Coutau Begarie, Paris #172

UNGEWITTER, Hugo (1869-c.1944) German
£6164 $9616 €9000 Leopard hunt (81x109cm-32x43in) s.d.1921. 10-Apr-3 Van Ham, Cologne #1734/R est:1000

UNOLD, Max (1885-1964) German
£1859 $2826 €2900 Village scene II - Tyrol village (51x61cm-20x24in) s. lit. 11-Jul-2 Allgauer, Kempten #2743/R
£1923 $2808 €3000 Still life with bottles (50x60cm-20x24in) s. 4-Jun-2 Karl & Faber, Munich #458/R est:6000-7000
£2055 $3205 €3000 Portrait of a young lady with handbag (71x48cm-28x19in) s. lit. 10-Apr-3 Allgauer, Kempten #3036/R est:3000
£2372 $3463 €3700 Grape harvest (90x70cm-35x28in) s. 4-Jun-2 Karl & Faber, Munich #459/R est:7000-8000

UNSELD, Albert (1879-?) German
£286 $454 €420 Forest interior (60x64cm-24x25in) s. i.d.1929 verso. 20-Mar-3 Neumeister, Munich #2760/R

UNTERBERGER, Franz Richard (1838-1902) Belgian
£4000 $6560 €6000 Hardangerjorden - hardanger fjord (52x77cm-20x30in) s.i. 3-Jun-3 Sotheby's, London #267/R est:5000-7000
£7000 $11130 €10500 Via Appia, Rome (30x60cm-12x24in) s. s.i.d.1875 verso panel. 20-Mar-3 Christie's, Kensington #76/R est:6000-8000
£7595 $12000 €11393 Lady leaving the city. 16-Nov-2 Harvey Clar, Oakland #1386
£7911 $12500 €12500 Ortler mountain range with Konigsspitze (79x100cm-31x39in) s.d.1877. 26-Nov-2 Wiener Kunst Auktionen, Vienna #45/R est:7000-10000
£9000 $14760 €13500 Rocca d'Amalfi (82x70cm-32x28in) s. s.i.verso. 3-Jun-3 Sotheby's, London #169/R est:10000-15000
£10714 $16821 €16071 Gulf of Salerno (115x101cm-45x40in) s. prov. 25-Nov-2 Christie's, Melbourne #128/R est:30000-40000 (A.D 30000)
£10870 $17826 €15000 In the Otztal (84x76cm-33x30in) 27-May-3 Wiener Kunst Auktionen, Vienna #25/R est:11000-16000
£29000 $47560 €43500 Die Amalfi kuste - Amalfi coast (82x70cm-32x28in) s. 3-Jun-3 Sotheby's, London #165/R est:30000-50000
£38710 $60000 €58065 Amalfi, the Gulf of Salerno (82x70cm-32x28in) s. s.i.verso. 29-Oct-2 Sotheby's, New York #66/R est:30000-50000
£85000 $141950 €127500 Piazerra St. Maggiore, Venice (81x131cm-32x52in) s. s.i.verso. 19-Jun-3 Christie's, London #48/R est:70000-90000

UNTERBERGER, Hartwig (1934-) Austrian
£353 $554 €550 Oh Feuergeist Lob sei Dir (70x70cm-28x28in) mono. 21-Nov-2 Dorotheum, Vienna #319/R

UNTERBERGER, Ignaz (1748-1797) Austrian
£280000 $467600 €406000 Rome, the Grotta dei Vini, or Tinello, in the gardens of the Villa Pinciana (104x137cm-41x54in) s.i.d.1773 panel lit. 10-Jul-3 Sotheby's, London #51/R est:40000-60000
Prints
£6962 $11000 €11000 Venus in her chariot surrounded by torch bearing putti (20x20cm-8x8in) mezzotint. 29-Nov-2 Bassenge, Berlin #5239/R est:2000

UNTERBERGER, Michelangelo (1695-1758) Austrian
Works on paper
£2639 $4196 €3800 Apotheosis of a Saint (16x14cm-6x6in) s. pen wash paper on board. 5-May-3 Ketterer, Munich #262/R est:400-600

UNTERBERGER, Michelangelo (attrib) (1695-1758) Austrian
£2000 $3340 €2900 Judgement of Solomon (48x64cm-19x25in) 8-Jul-3 Sotheby's, Olympia #448/R est:3000-5000
£2115 $3279 €3300 Worshipping the King (58x42cm-23x17in) canvas on canvas. 4-Dec-2 Neumeister, Munich #654/R est:1500

UNTERLUGGAUER, Michael (1953-) Austrian
£414 $662 €600 Golden rule (40x30cm-16x12in) s.d.01 s. verso acrylic. 11-Mar-3 Dorotheum, Vienna #288/R

UNTERSEHER, Franz Xaver (1888-1954) German
Works on paper
£359 $575 €550 Capri landscape (62x80cm-24x31in) s.d.1929 mixed media canvas on board. 10-Jan-3 Allgauer, Kempten #1812/R

UNVERDROSS, Raphael Oskar (1873-?) German
£377 $589 €600 Landscape at dusk (22x29cm-9x11in) s.d.04. 21-Sep-2 Bolland & Marotz, Bremen #570

UOTILA, Aukusti (1858-1886) Finnish
£4304 $6800 €6800 Hostess from Tavastland (41x32cm-16x13in) exhib.lit. 30-Nov-2 Hagelstam, Helsinki #130/R est:2500

UPHOFF, Carl Emil (1885-1971) German
£506 $800 €800 Three bunches of flowers (55x65cm-22x26in) s. 29-Nov-2 Bolland & Marotz, Bremen #582/R

UPHOFF, Fritz (1890-1966) German
£690 $1090 €1000 After the rain: Worpsweder landscape (38x49cm-15x19in) s. i. verso board. 5-Apr-3 Hans Stahl, Hamburg #110/R
£2041 $3245 €3000 Wumme landscape in the autumn sun (110x140cm-43x55in) s. panel. 28-Mar-3 Bolland & Marotz, Bremen #373 est:2700

UPHUES, Josef (1850-1911) German
Sculpture
£3800 $6118 €5700 Hercules and the Stymphalian bird (60cm-24in) s. bronze prov. 20-Feb-3 Christie's, London #279/R

UPPER ITALIAN SCHOOL, 15th C
£6475 $10360 €9000 St John the Baptist and St Peter (154x54cm-61x21in) tempera gold panel altar screen. 17-May-3 Lempertz, Koln #1095/R est:10000

UPRKA, Joza (1861-?) Czechoslovakian
£1239 $1933 €1859 Girls from Maratice (30x60cm-12x24in) mono. panel. 12-Oct-2 Dorotheum, Prague #40/R est:50000-75000 (C.KR 60000)

UPSON, Tony (20th C) ?
£400 $616 €600 Alfa Romeo 8C 2900B (60x40cm-24x16in) s. acrylic. 6-Sep-2 Bonhams, Knightsbridge #43
£600 $924 €900 Lagonda V12 team car no 5 at Le Mans 1939 (60x40cm-24x16in) s. acrylic. 6-Sep-2 Bonhams, Knightsbridge #44

URACH, Albrecht Furst von (1903-1969) German
£417 $633 €650 View from Besigheim (39x50cm-15x20in) s.d.1921 lit. 11-Jul-2 Allgauer, Kempten #2745

URBAIN, Alexandre (1875-1953) French
£344 $561 €520 Jeunes femmes au puits dans un paysage luxuriant (60x73cm-24x29in) s. prov. 2-Feb-3 Muizon & Le Coent, Paris #44
£676 $1054 €1000 Chalutiers a quai (38x46cm-15x18in) s.d.34 cardboard. 30-Mar-3 Anaf, Lyon #250

URBAN, Bohumil (1903-) Czechoslovakian
£413 $652 €620 Still life with bottles (54x67cm-21x26in) s.d.1932. 30-Nov-2 Dorotheum, Prague #99/R (C.KR 20000)

URBAN, Hermann (1866-1946) German
£338 $527 €500 Tree by track (53x42cm-21x17in) s. 26-Mar-3 Hugo Ruef, Munich #247
£1401 $2186 €2200 Mermaid at the bottom of cliffs (95x125cm-37x49in) s. 6-Nov-2 Hugo Ruef, Munich #1319/R est:1800

URBASEK, Milos (1932-1988) Czechoslovakian
Works on paper
£916 $1419 €1374 Collage 2 X 1964 (68x49cm-27x19in) mixed media exec.1964. 3-Dec-2 SOGA, Bratislava #293/R (SL.K 58000)

URDAL, Atle (1913-1988) Norwegian
£276 $461 €400 Figures (36x74cm-14x29in) s.d.1963. 18-Jun-3 Grev Wedels Plass, Oslo #245 (N.KR 3200)

UREN, J C (1845-1932) British
Works on paper
£1050 $1712 €1575 St Michael's Mount (18x38cm-7x15in) s. W/C. 13-Feb-3 David Lay, Penzance #283 est:550-650

UREN, John C (1845-1932) British
Works on paper
£222 $369 €322 Arthur's Seat, Tintagel (28x46cm-11x18in) s. W/C prov. 10-Jun-3 Ritchie, Toronto #27/R (C.D 500)
£250 $408 €363 St Michael's Mount (23x41cm-9x16in) s. gouache. 17-Jul-3 Thomson, Roddick & Medcalf, Carlisle #11
£300 $497 €435 Rocky coast Cornwall (46x70cm-18x28in) s. W/C. 16-Jun-3 Waddingtons, Toronto #65/R (C.D 675)
£404 $638 €606 Sailing vessels off the coast of Cornwall (28x43cm-11x17in) s. W/C. 18-Nov-2 Waddingtons, Toronto #66/R (C.D 1000)
£460 $768 €667 Kynance Cove, The Lizard (32x52cm-13x20in) s. W/C bodycol. 19-Jun-3 Lane, Penzance #289
£524 $828 €786 Fisherman's cottage, Mullion, Cornwall (29x46cm-11x18in) s. W/C. 18-Nov-2 Waddingtons, Toronto #71/R (C.D 1300)
£560 $918 €840 Coastal scene with men salvaging a mast (35x56cm-14x22in) s.d.1876 W/C. 4-Jun-3 Bonhams, Chester #336
£580 $893 €870 Mounts Bay, Cornwall (27x43cm-11x17in) s. W/C. 3-Sep-2 Bristol Auction Rooms #484
£720 $1130 €1080 Lion Rock, Perranporth - Cornish coastline with shipping (24x49cm-9x19in) s. W/C. 10-Dec-2 Lane, Penzance #18

URGELL Y INGLADA, Modesto (1839-1919) Spanish
£2987 $4660 €4750 Landscape with church (85x50cm-33x20in) s. 23-Sep-2 Durán, Madrid #140/R
£3014 $4701 €4400 Night landscape (85x50cm-33x20in) s. 8-Apr-3 Ansorena, Madrid #239/R

URIA-MONZON, Antonio (1929-1997) Spanish
£690 $1090 €1000 Landscape with church (47x62cm-19x24in) s. oil gouache wax crayon. 1-Apr-3 Segre, Madrid #309/R

URIBURU, Nicolas Garcia (1937-) Argentinian
£1063 $1680 €1595 Red crab (45x59cm-18x23in) s. board. 15-Nov-2 Naón & Cia, Buenos Aires #13/R
£2551 $4030 €3827 Ombu (50x60cm-20x24in) s. acrylic. 15-Nov-2 Naón & Cia, Buenos Aires #46/R

URLASS, Louis (1809-?) German
£1781 $2778 €2600 Chocolate girl. s.verso. 8-Apr-3 Thomas Adams, Dublin #398
£4459 $6866 €7000 Reclining Venus with cupids (54x64cm-21x25in) after Francesco Albani. 3-Sep-2 Christie's, Amsterdam #1/R est:2000-3000

URLAUB, Georg Anton Abraham (1744-1788) German
£692 $1079 €1100 Self portrait (51x48cm-20x19in) canvas on panel oval prov. 19-Sep-2 Dr Fritz Nagel, Stuttgart #903/R
£818 $1275 €1300 Portrait of Anna Dorothea Schmittin von Frankenwinheim (51x48cm-20x19in) i.d.1776 prov. 19-Sep-2 Dr Fritz Nagel, Stuttgart #904/R
Works on paper
£28302 $43868 €45000 Portraits (64x48cm-25x19in) s.d.1784 pastel four prov.lit. 2-Oct-2 Dorotheum, Vienna #197/R est:40000-60000

URLAUB, Georg Johann Christian (1844-1914) German
£478 $745 €750 Hunter in autumn landscape (14x27cm-6x11in) s. canvas on panel. 6-Nov-2 Hugo Ruef, Munich #1320

URSULA (1921-) German
£4487 $6955 €7000 He is untouchable (100x111cm-39x44in) s.d.1965 s.i.d. verso. 3-Dec-2 Lempertz, Koln #485/R est:5000-6000

URTEIL, Andreas (1933-1963) Austrian
Sculpture
£1139 $1777 €1800 Twisted figure (44cm-17in) s. dark pat.bronze Cast.Venturi Arte, Bologna. 15-Oct-2 Dorotheum, Vienna #158/R est:2000-2600
£11392 $18000 €18000 Fencer (50cm-20in) s.i.d.1960 light pat.bronze prov. 27-Nov-2 Dorotheum, Vienna #234/R est:18000-26000
Works on paper
£2848 $4500 €4500 Figure walking left (59x44cm-23x17in) s. pen Indian ink exhib. 27-Nov-2 Dorotheum, Vienna #235/R est:2400-3200

URTIN, Paul François Marie (1874-1962) French
£952 $1514 €1400 Salon des Huet (91x73cm-36x29in) s. 24-Mar-3 Coutau Begarie, Paris #187b/R
£1258 $1950 €2000 Promenade en Dauphine (80x60cm-31x24in) s.d.1918. 30-Oct-2 Coutau Begarie, Paris #120/R

URY, Lesser (1861-1931) German
£3750 $6000 €5625 Landscape with a pond at sunset (36x45cm-14x18in) s. 14-May-3 Butterfields, San Francisco #1088/R est:8000-10000
£12658 $20000 €20000 On the way to the windmill (36x52cm-14x20in) prov. 30-Nov-2 Villa Grisebach, Berlin #124/R est:20000-30000
£16987 $25821 €26500 Lively street scene in large city (9x16cm-4x6in) s. canvas on board prov. 31-Aug-2 Geble, Radolfzell #667 est:7000
£18841 $30899 €26000 Champs Elysees, Paris (9x16cm-4x6in) s.i.d.1928 canvas on board on panel prov. 31-May-3 Villa Grisebach, Berlin #145/R est:18000-24000
£26087 $42783 €36000 Man and woman in coffee house (27x36cm-11x14in) s. 29-May-3 Lempertz, Koln #939/R est:25000
Works on paper
£2532 $4000 €4000 Woman peeling potatoes with child (22x14cm-9x6in) s.d.84 brush pen. 30-Nov-2 Villa Grisebach, Berlin #122/R est:4000-5000
£6522 $10696 €9000 Tiergartenstrasse in the rain (51x36cm-20x14in) s.i. chl. 31-May-3 Villa Grisebach, Berlin #146/R est:9000-12000
£9353 $15338 €13000 Sailing boats on a lake (35x50cm-14x20in) s. pastel prov. 3-Jun-3 Christie's, Amsterdam #245/R est:12000-16000
£11511 $18878 €16000 View on the river Seine, Paris (33x46cm-13x18in) s.i.d.1928 pastel cardboard. 3-Jun-3 Christie's, Amsterdam #246/R est:12000-16000
£32911 $52000 €52000 Grunewald in the evening (36x50cm-14x20in) s.d.95 pastel cardboard prov. 29-Nov-2 Villa Grisebach, Berlin #8/R est:25000-35000
£34783 $57043 €48000 Autumnal avenue in Tiergarten, Berlin (35x50cm-14x20in) s. pastel prov. 30-May-3 Villa Grisebach, Berlin #9/R est:40000-60000
£37681 $61797 €52000 Quai Voltaire in the rain (35x50cm-14x20in) s.i.d.1928 pastel board prov.exhib. 31-May-3 Villa Grisebach, Berlin #143/R est:25000-35000
£39130 $64174 €54000 Hardenbergstrasse with Bahnhof Zoo (35x49cm-14x19in) s. pastel prov. 29-May-3 Lempertz, Koln #940/R est:45000-50000

URZAY, Dario (1958-) Spanish
£4906 $7653 €7800 Untitled (162x162cm-64x64in) s. oil mixed media canvas on board prov. 17-Sep-2 Segre, Madrid #164/R est:7200

USADEL, Max (?) German?
£786 $1242 €1179 View of Lake Lugano (51x66cm-20x26in) s.d.1922. 14-Nov-2 Stuker, Bern #561 est:1800-2200 (S.FR 1800)

USELLINI, Gian Filippo (1903-1971) Italian
£1154 $1788 €1800 Diana hunting (45x16cm-18x6in) s.d.1939 tempera card. 4-Dec-2 Finarte, Milan #241/R
Works on paper
£616 $962 €900 Well wishing (66x22cm-26x9in) s. mixed media card. 10-Apr-3 Finarte Semenzato, Rome #75/R

USLE, Juan (1953-) Spanish
£2065 $3262 €3200 Untitled (79x109cm-31x43in) oil collage mixed media paper on cardboard painted 1985 prov. 17-Dec-2 Segre, Madrid #182/R est:2900
£4221 $6162 €6500 Composition (100x81cm-39x32in) s.d.78 board. 17-Jun-2 Ansorena, Madrid #55/R
£4545 $6636 €7000 Untitled (100x81cm-39x32in) 17-Jun-2 Ansorena, Madrid #56/R

USSING, J L (1813-1899) Danish
£298 $462 €447 Nature morte (43x35cm-17x14in) s.d.1887. 28-Sep-2 Rasmussen, Havnen #2182/R (D.KR 3500)

USSING, Stephan (1868-1958) Danish
£255 $398 €383 Spring in Frederiksberg Garden with the Japanese Bridge. s. 5-Aug-2 Rasmussen, Vejle #2279 (D.KR 3000)
£3404 $5379 €5106 Girl sewing - study by candle light (51x66cm-20x26in) s.d.1905. 2-Dec-2 Rasmussen, Copenhagen #1127/R est:40000 (D.KR 40000)

UTAMARO, Kitagawa (1753-1806) Japanese
Prints
£2564 $4000 €3846 Beauty threading a needle (38x26cm-15x10in) s. print prov. 25-Mar-3 Christie's, Rockefeller NY #55/R est:4000-6000
£9615 $15000 €14423 Pleasure boat, Sumida river (38x25cm-15x10in) s. col print triptych. 25-Mar-3 Christie's, Rockefeller NY #57/R est:15000-20000
£10897 $17000 €16346 About to breastfeed (38x26cm-15x10in) s. col print. 25-Mar-3 Christie's, Rockefeller NY #54/R est:9000-12000
£13000 $20540 €19500 Yoshiwara courtesan with cartouche of plovers flying over a river (38x25cm-15x10in) s. col print. 13-Nov-2 Christie's, London #6/R est:15000-20000

UTANOSUKE, Kano (attrib) (?-c.1575) Japanese
Works on paper
£7547 $12000 €11321 Hawk on a pine branch (84x42cm-33x17in) sealed ink hanging scroll. 24-Mar-3 Christie's, Rockefeller NY #2/R est:6000-8000

UTHAUG, Jorleif (1911-1990) Norwegian
Sculpture
£1388 $2165 €2082 Woman with sheaf of corn (127x66x7cm-50x26x3in) metal col glass on panel relief. 21-Oct-2 Blomqvist, Oslo #405/R est:35000-45000 (N.KR 16000)
£1837 $3012 €2664 Woman with sheaf of corn (127x66x7cm-50x26x3in) metal col glass on panel. 2-Jun-3 Blomqvist, Oslo #205/R est:30000-40000 (N.KR 20000)
£2263 $3621 €3395 Reclining woman (70x200cm-28x79in) s.d.1959 metal col glass relief. 17-Mar-3 Blomqvist, Oslo #421/R est:20000-25000 (N.KR 26000)

UTRECHT, Adriaen van (1599-1653) Flemish
£27439 $45000 €41159 Vanitas still life with a bouquet and a skull (67x86cm-26x34in) i.d.1643 prov.exhib.lit. 29-May-3 Sotheby's, New York #33/R est:25000-35000

UTRECHT, Adriaen van (attrib) (1599-1653) Flemish
£1818 $2709 €2800 Hunting still life (91x71cm-36x28in) prov. 26-Jun-2 Neumeister, Munich #666/R est:1000

UTRECHT, Adriaen van (style) (1599-1653) Flemish
£10638 $16489 €15957 Still life of grapes, strawberries, oysters and pomegranates (106x169cm-42x67in) prov. 4-Dec-2 AB Stockholms Auktionsverk #1934/R est:150000-200000 (S.KR 150000)

UTRILLO, Maurice (1883-1955) French
£7500 $11625 €11250 Bouquet de fleurs (13x9cm-5x4in) s. prov. 5-Dec-2 Christie's, Kensington #65/R est:5000-7000
£9310 $14897 €13500 Les chapeaux de Lucie Valore (22x27cm-9x11in) s.d.mars 1942. 12-Mar-3 Libert, Castor, Paris #194/R est:5000-6000
£11000 $18370 €15950 Les chapeaux de lucie valore (24x33cm-9x13in) s. painted c.1942 prov. 24-Jun-3 Sotheby's, London #197/R est:12000-15000
£11034 $17655 €16000 Les chapeaux (23x30cm-9x12in) s. 12-Mar-3 Libert, Castor, Paris #193 est:6000-7000
£16312 $27241 €23000 La maison de Mimi Pinson sous la neige (33x41cm-13x16in) s. c.1948-50 prov. 20-Jun-3 Piasa, Paris #21/R est:25000-30000
£17081 $27500 €25622 Le palais du Bardo (41x27cm-16x11in) s. painted c.1940. 7-May-3 Sotheby's, New York #407/R est:30000-40000
£18065 $28000 €27098 Chatillon d'Azergues - Rhone (54x72cm-21x28in) s.d.1931 s.i.d.verso prov.lit. 26-Sep-2 Christie's, Rockefeller NY #598/R est:30000-35000
£18244 $28460 €27000 Pommier en fleurs (35x27cm-14x11in) s.d.1922 prov.lit. 26-Mar-3 Tajan, Paris #34/R
£20000 $33400 €29000 La rue Saint Vincent et la maison au toit de chaume a Montmatre (49x38cm-19x15in) s. oil paper on canvas painted c.1911 prov.exhib.lit. 25-Jun-3 Christie's, London #154/R est:15000-20000
£20161 $31855 €30242 Rue a Montmartre (38x46cm-15x18in) s. prov. 18-Nov-2 Waddingtons, Toronto #251/R est:80000-120000 (C.D 50000)
£22436 $35000 €33654 Auberge de lapin blance (23x33cm-9x13in) s. 7-Nov-2 Christie's, Rockefeller NY #361/R est:35000-45000
£23602 $38000 €35403 Eglise de Rampillonm Seine et Marne (46x55cm-18x22in) s.d.1931 s.i.d.verso prov. 8-May-3 Christie's, Rockefeller NY #205/R est:40000-60000
£26950 $45007 €38000 Rue Carnot a Stains sous la neige (33x38cm-13x15in) s. painted c.1938 prov.lit. 23-Jun-3 Claude Boisgirard, Paris #110/R est:60000-80000
£27000 $41580 €40500 Le moulin de la galette et le sacre coeur (24x33cm-9x13in) s.i. panel painted c.1940 prov. 22-Oct-2 Sotheby's, London #171/R est:28000-35000
£27027 $43514 €40541 Soissons, l'Arquebuse, la porte (54x65cm-21x26in) s. i.verso cardboard prov.exhib.lit. 7-May-3 AB Stockholms Auktionsverk #1102/R est:300000-350000 (S.KR 350000)
£32000 $53440 €46400 Le moulin de la Galette a Montmartre (46x55cm-18x22in) s. panel painted c.1950 prov.lit. 25-Jun-3 Christie's, London #164/R est:30000-40000
£32692 $51654 €51000 Lapin Agile (50x60cm-20x24in) s.i. cardboard prov.lit. 15-Nov-2 Laurence Calmels, Paris #17a/R est:80000
£35000 $57400 €52500 Chateau de Chasseneuil, Charente (61x50cm-24x20in) s.i.d.1935 lit. 4-Feb-3 Christie's, London #299/R est:45000
£35000 $57400 €52500 Rue Saint-Vincent (46x38cm-18x15in) s.i.d.1936 prov. 5-Feb-3 Sotheby's, London #267/R est:45000
£35256 $55000 €52884 Rue a Stains (38x46cm-15x18in) s. painted 1937 prov. 7-Nov-2 Christie's, Rockefeller NY #299/R est:70000-90000
£36000 $59040 €54000 Rue Saint-Vincent (46x38cm-18x15in) s. painted c.1918 prov.lit. 5-Feb-3 Sotheby's, London #268/R est:60000
£37179 $58000 €55769 Eglise d'Auvers-sur-Oise (45x55cm-18x22in) s. painted c.1937-38 prov.lit. 7-Nov-2 Christie's, Rockefeller NY #286/R est:40000-60000
£37267 $60000 €55901 Rue Saint Rustique a Montmartre (27x22cm-11x9in) s. board. 8-May-3 Christie's, Rockefeller NY #195/R est:35000-45000
£38000 $63460 €55100 Eglise de Boursonne, Oise (50x62cm-20x24in) s. painted 1935 prov.lit. 25-Jun-3 Christie's, London #185/R est:25000-35000
£39241 $60823 €62000 Rue de Banileue (54x65cm-21x26in) s. painted c.1945 prov. 28-Sep-2 Christie's, Paris #35/R est:50000-65000
£39744 $62397 €62000 Chateau de la Clayette (54x65cm-21x26in) s.d.1934 prov.lit. 13-Dec-2 Piasa, Paris #15/R est:60000
£40000 $64000 €58000 L'eglise de Chatillon-sur-Seine (55x46cm-22x18in) s.d.1942. 12-Mar-3 Libert, Castor, Paris #192/R est:30000-40000
£46584 $75000 €69876 Le lapin agile (33x41cm-13x16in) s. prov. 8-May-3 Christie's, Rockefeller NY #200/R est:60000-80000
£50000 $83500 €72500 Le restaurant a la Tourelle, Montmartre (38x55cm-15x22in) s.i. painted c.1935 prov.lit. 25-Jun-3 Christie's, London #148/R est:30000-40000
£50000 $83500 €72500 Le petit chateau sous la neige (50x60cm-20x24in) s. painted c.1920 prov.lit. 25-Jun-3 Christie's, London #157/R est:50000-70000
£55000 $90200 €82500 Place du Tertre a Montmartre (54x65cm-21x26in) s. painted c.1915 prov.lit. 4-Feb-3 Christie's, London #258/R est:100000
£55000 $90200 €82500 Escalier du passage Cottin (55x46cm-22x18in) s.i.d.1922 s.i.d.on stretcher prov.exhib.lit. 4-Feb-3 Christie's, London #300/R est:65000
£56962 $90000 €90000 Eglise de Pontoise (56x76cm-22x30in) s. cardboard on canvas painted c.1935 lit. 30-Nov-2 Farsetti, Prato #721/R est:110000
£57241 $91586 €83000 Rue du Mont-Cenis et la maison de Berlioz a Montmartre (46x55cm-18x22in) s. 12-Mar-3 Libert, Castor, Paris #195/R est:45000-60000
£57433 $89596 €85000 Place publique (46x55cm-18x22in) s.d.1935 prov.lit. 26-Mar-3 Tajan, Paris #5/R

£62112 $100000 €93168 Rue a Asnieres (53x63cm-21x25in) s. cardboard on canvas painted c.1936 prov.lit. 7-May-3 Sotheby's, New York #178/R est:80000-120000
£64103 $100000 €96155 Ancien reservoir de Montmartre, Place Jean Baptiste Clement (60x94cm-24x37in) s. board painted c.1921 prov.lit. 6-Nov-2 Sotheby's, New York #188/R est:120000-150000
£70513 $110000 €105770 Rue d'Orsel (57x78cm-22x31in) s.i. board painted c.1912-14 exhib. 7-Nov-2 Christie's, Rockefeller NY #167/R est:80000-100000

Sculpture

£7692 $12000 €11538 La maison de berlioz (37cm-15in) s. painted ceramic prov.lit. 6-Nov-2 Sotheby's, New York #352/R est:15000-20000

Works on paper

£4789 $7949 €6800 Montmartre, le moulin de la Galette (28x44cm-11x17in) s. col crayon dr exec.c.1924-25 lit. 11-Jun-3 Beaussant & Lefèvre, Paris #205/R est:8000-10000
£5000 $8350 €7500 L'eglise de Saint-Bernard (24x32cm-9x13in) s. chl. exec c.1938-39 lit. 26-Jun-3 Christie's, London #387/R est:1500-2000
£7042 $11690 €10000 Montmartre, le moulin de la Galette (19x20cm-7x8in) s. chl col crayon dr prov. 11-Jun-3 Beaussant & Lefèvre, Paris #204/R est:2500-3000
£10559 $17000 €15839 Le moulin de la galette a Montmartre (38x48cm-15x19in) s. gouache W/C on board executed 1926-27 prov.lit. 8-May-3 Christie's, Rockefeller NY #121/R est:15000-20000
£11216 $17497 €16600 Belle Gabrielle (28x38cm-11x15in) s. gouache prov. 26-Mar-3 Millon & Associes, Paris #43/R
£12949 $20329 €20200 Paris, Maquis de Montmartre (18x14cm-7x6in) s.i. col crayon dr. 15-Dec-2 Eric Pillon, Calais #110/R
£12963 $21000 €18796 Rue de Poteau a Montmartre (23x30cm-9x12in) s.i. i.verso gouache prov. 21-May-3 Doyle, New York #45/R est:25000-35000
£14189 $22135 €21000 Eglise de Saint-Bernard sous la neige (17x26cm-7x10in) s.i.d.1929 gouache. 30-Mar-3 Anaf, Lyon #251/R est:25000
£16879 $26331 €26500 Moulin de Sannois (28x36cm-11x14in) s.i. gouache. 10-Nov-2 Eric Pillon, Calais #73/R
£17791 $29000 €26687 Anciene eglise de Doremy-La Pucelle (48x63cm-19x25in) s.i.d.14 Avril 1935 gouache oil paper on card prov.lit. 12-Feb-3 Sotheby's, New York #106/R est:20000-30000
£19000 $31730 €28500 Rue animee a Ivry (23x29cm-9x11in) s.d.April 1924 pencil gouache card. 26-Jun-3 Christie's, London #382a/R est:10000-15000
£22000 $36080 €33000 Eglise de Simandre-les-Ormes (49x64cm-19x25in) s.i.d.1928 gouache W/C pencil. 6-Feb-3 Christie's, London #423/R est:18000
£22000 $36740 €31900 Le moulin de la galette, Montmartre (50x32cm-20x13in) s.d.Juillet 14.1940 gouache prov. 24-Jun-3 Sotheby's, London #283/R est:25000-35000
£28000 $45920 €42000 Presbytere Jean Bienheureux (48x62cm-19x24in) s.i.d.1935 gouache prov. 5-Feb-3 Sotheby's, London #256/R est:40000
£28170 $46762 €40000 La ferme Debray a Montmartre (30x40cm-12x16in) s.i. gouache prov.exhib.lit. exec.c.1939. 12-Jun-3 Tajan, Paris #37/R est:40000-45000
£28846 $45000 €43269 Eglise se Saint-Bernard - Ain (56x65cm-22x26in) s.d.Octobre 1925 W/C gouache paper on canvas prov.lit. 7-Nov-2 Christie's, Rockefeller NY #152/R est:50000-70000
£35000 $58450 €52500 Montmartre (32x24cm-13x9in) s.i. gouache pencil card exec c.1936. 26-Jun-3 Christie's, London #391/R est:35000-45000
£36859 $57500 €55289 Sacre coeur de Montmartre et rue Sainte-Rustique (36x48cm-14x19in) s.i. gouache executed c.1938. 6-Nov-2 Sotheby's, New York #195/R est:50000-70000
£41176 $67529 €63000 Montmartre et le Sacre-Coeur (41x50cm-16x20in) s.i.d. gouache prov.lit. 9-Feb-3 Anaf, Lyon #114/R
£42000 $70140 €63000 Montmartre (31x43cm-12x17in) s.i. gouache. 26-Jun-3 Christie's, London #390/R est:25000-35000
£55000 $91850 €79750 Le lapin agile (48x63cm-19x25in) s.i. gouache on card executed c.1937 prov.lit. 24-Jun-3 Sotheby's, London #284/R est:40000-60000

UTRILLO, Maurice (attrib) (1883-1955) French

£22581 $35000 €33872 Le vieux Montmartre (34x47cm-13x19in) s. board on cradled panel lit. 26-Sep-2 Christie's, Rockefeller NY #592/R est:35000-45000

UTTECH, Tom (1942-) American

£479 $800 €695 Midnight aurora on Mittagami river (117x130cm-46x51in) 29-Jun-3 Butterfields, Los Angeles #7086/R
£1078 $1800 €1563 From Akkahauk Mountain (86x91cm-34x36in) s.d.1989. 29-Jun-3 Butterfields, Los Angeles #7089/R est:400-600
£1347 $2250 €1953 Tanaltavik lake (152x168cm-60x66in) s. i.d.1988 verso. 29-Jun-3 Butterfields, Los Angeles #7065/R est:400-600
£2096 $3500 €3039 Tossakid, sunrise (157x173cm-62x68in) s. 29-Jun-3 Butterfields, Los Angeles #7088/R est:400-600

UTTER, Andre (1886-1948) French

£903 $1426 €1300 Village de Provence (60x80cm-24x31in) s. 28-Apr-3 Cornette de St.Cyr, Paris #305
£1135 $1771 €1703 Summer river landscape with bridge (81x100cm-32x39in) s.d.28. 6-Nov-2 Dobiaschofsky, Bern #1024/R est:2900 (S.FR 2600)

UTTER, Bror (1913-1933) American

Works on paper

£641 $1000 €962 Venice (33x43cm-13x17in) W/C. 19-Oct-2 David Dike, Dallas #155/R

UTZON-FRANK, Ejnar (1888-1955) Danish

Sculpture

£1787 $2824 €2681 Girl doing her hair (41cm-16in) init.d.1917 pat.bronze Cast Rasmussen lit. 27-Nov-2 Museumsbygningen, Copenhagen #688/R est:30000 (D.KR 21000)
£2029 $3124 €3044 Bathing girl (42cm-17in) init. bronze st.f.Rasmussen lit. 23-Oct-2 Kunsthallen, Copenhagen #210/R est:25000 (D.KR 24000)
£2669 $4458 €3870 Beatrice, genius of poetry (174cm-69in) s. brown pat.bronze incl.wood and marble base exec.c.1924 lit. 17-Jun-3 Rasmussen, Copenhagen #84/R est:30000 (D.KR 28000)

UUSIKYLA, Pentii (1923-) Finnish

£277 $426 €440 Red peep (41x59cm-16x23in) s.d.89 acrylic. 27-Oct-2 Bukowskis, Helsinki #302/R

UUTINEN, Marianna (1961-) Finnish

£1236 $1989 €1854 Untitled (120x150cm-47x59in) s.d.1996 acrylic. 7-May-3 AB Stockholms Auktionsverk #1047/R est:20000-25000 (S.KR 16000)
£1892 $2952 €2838 Idol in the room (148x122cm-58x48in) s.d.1993 verso acrylic plexiglas exhib.lit. 6-Nov-2 AB Stockholms Auktionsverk #827/R est:30000-35000 (S.KR 27000)

UVA, Cesare (1824-1886) Italian

£570 $900 €900 Outside the cathedral (74x57cm-29x22in) s. cardboard. 26-Nov-2 Christie's, Rome #108
£1772 $2800 €2800 Cart in Roman countryside (40x30cm-16x12in) tempera card oval pair. 26-Nov-2 Christie's, Rome #47

Works on paper

£1314 $2050 €1971 Street scene with horsecart (33x57cm-13x22in) s. gouache. 20-Sep-2 Sloan, North Bethesda #323/R est:500-700
£1800 $2808 €2700 Fishing boats off coast (51x86cm-20x34in) gouache. 15-Oct-2 Gorringes, Lewes #2278 est:800-1000
£2051 $3179 €3200 Sorrento coast (37x54cm-15x21in) s. mixed media. 4-Dec-2 Finarte, Rome #788
£2300 $3634 €3450 Views of Naples (38x56cm-15x22in) s. gouache pair. 2-Dec-2 Gorringes, Lewes #2694 est:600-800

UWINS, Thomas (1782-1857) British

Works on paper

£6500 $10465 €9750 Back from school (29x21cm-11x8in) pencil W/C htd white gum arabic prov.exhib.lit. 20-Feb-3 Christie's, London #40/R est:3000

UYTTENBROECK, Moses van (1590-1648) Dutch

£7692 $11923 €12000 Alphee et Arethuse (33x40cm-13x16in) mono. panel. 6-Dec-2 Rieunier, Bailly-Pommery, Mathias, Paris #21/R est:18000
£8917 $13911 €14000 Italianate landscape with shepherds resting their cattle near a ruin (38x61cm-15x24in) init.d.1626 panel exhib. 6-Nov-2 Christie's, Amsterdam #81/R est:14000-18000

UYTTERSCHAUT, Victor (1847-1917) Belgian

Works on paper

£360 $569 €540 Windmills (32x47cm-13x19in) s. W/C graphite. 7-Apr-3 Bonhams, Bath #36/R

UZZELL EDWARDS, John (1937-) British

£400 $620 €600 Interior of a boatyard (86x64cm-34x25in) s. board. 4-Dec-2 Brightwells, Leominster #1422/R

VAAMONDE, Joaquin (1872-1900) Spanish

£1923 $3038 €3000 Study of figure (33x26cm-13x10in) s.i. cardboard. 13-Nov-2 Ansorena, Madrid #102/R

Works on paper
£484 $765 €750 Elderly woman (39x29cm-15x11in) s. chl dr. 18-Dec-2 Ansorena, Madrid #973/R

VAARBERG, Johannes Christoffel (1825-1871) Dutch
£1757 $2741 €2600 Vegetable and poultry stall lit by candles (44x36cm-17x14in) s. panel. 27-Mar-3 Dr Fritz Nagel, Stuttgart #878/R est:1500
£7000 $10920 €10500 Fruit seller (58x71cm-23x28in) s.d.58 panel. 26-Mar-3 Sotheby's, Olympia #263/R est:2500-3500

VAARDT, Jan van der (1647-1721) Dutch
£13000 $21580 €19500 Portrait of lady seated in a brown dress with a blue cloak, red curtain with a white cockatoo (122x101cm-48x40in) 10-Jun-3 Christie's, London #21/R est:8000-12000

VAARULA, Olavi (1927-1989) Finnish
£314 $487 €500 The merciful (15x13cm-6x5in) s.d.1974. 6-Oct-2 Bukowskis, Helsinki #308/R
£352 $567 €500 Saint (24x20cm-9x8in) s.d.1980 board. 10-May-3 Bukowskis, Helsinki #260/R

VACCARI, Alfredo (1877-1933) Italian
£1644 $2564 €2400 Chiens de chasse (46x36cm-18x14in) s. 8-Apr-3 Gioffredo, Nice #76/R

VACCARO, Andrea (c.1598-1670) Italian
£25000 $39250 €37500 Adoration of the Shepherds (132x184cm-52x72in) 10-Dec-2 Bonhams, New Bond Street #289/R est:25000-35000
£44828 $70828 €65000 Judith with Olopherne's head (127x101cm-50x40in) prov.exhib.lit. 3-Apr-3 Porro, Milan #20/R est:80000

VACCHI, Sergio (1925-) Italian
£1282 $2013 €2000 Woman in bloom and man in tailcoat (70x50cm-28x20in) s.d.1989. 23-Nov-2 Meeting Art, Vercelli #207/R
£1410 $2214 €2200 Head (70x60cm-28x24in) s.d.1956. 19-Nov-2 Finarte, Milan #37
£1538 $2385 €2400 Small souvenirs for Laura (40x50cm-16x20in) s.d.1959. 4-Dec-2 Finarte, Milan #343
£1667 $2617 €2600 Planet flower (90x100cm-35x39in) s. s.i.d.1971 verso exhib. 19-Nov-2 Finarte, Milan #34/R
£1667 $2617 €2600 Green universe (67x47cm-26x19in) s.d.1989. 21-Nov-2 Finarte, Rome #63/R
£1667 $2617 €2600 Grotti night (70x50cm-28x20in) s.d.2000 s.i.d.verso. 21-Nov-2 Finarte, Rome #340
£2436 $3824 €3800 Ritual landscape (70x90cm-28x35in) s.d.1959. 19-Nov-2 Finarte, Milan #89/R
£3526 $5535 €5500 Night water-lilies (110x145cm-43x57in) s. painted 1971. 21-Nov-2 Finarte, Rome #244/R
Works on paper
£475 $741 €750 Lysa from Ethiopia (50x70cm-20x28in) s.d.1971 mixed media. 14-Sep-2 Meeting Art, Vercelli #891/R

VACHA, Fernand (1903-) French
Works on paper
£473 $690 €710 Carmen (43x31cm-17x12in) pastel exec.c.1935. 4-Jun-2 SOGA, Bratislava #206/R est:22000 (SL.K 30000)

VACHA, Rudolf (1860-?) Czechoslovakian
£654 $1041 €981 Lady wearing blue dress (100x73cm-39x29in) s.d.1906. 8-Mar-3 Dorotheum, Prague #160/R est:30000-45000 (C.KR 30000)

VACHAL, Josef (1884-1969) Czechoslovakian
£2497 $4045 €3746 Landscape with hanged man (95x70cm-37x28in) s. board. 24-May-3 Dorotheum, Prague #105/R est:100000-150000 (C.KR 110000)

VACHE, Jacques (1895-1919) French
Works on paper
£19178 $29918 €28000 Ces messieurs (31x20cm-12x8in) i. ink graphite col crayon exhib. 14-Apr-3 Laurence Calmels, Paris #4029/R est:8000

VACHER, Charles (1818-1883) British
£580 $928 €870 Suez canal (48x99cm-19x39in) mono.d.1865. 14-Mar-3 Gardiner & Houlgate, Bath #65/R
Works on paper
£900 $1503 €1305 Market boat, Lago, Maggiori early morning (46x69cm-18x27in) mono.d.1870 W/C. 20-Jun-3 Keys, Aylsham #517
£1100 $1716 €1650 Coast at Taormina, Sicily (28x91cm-11x36in) s.d.1849 W/C. 5-Nov-2 Bonhams, New Bond Street #6/R est:1000-1500
£4838 $7500 €7257 Karnak, upper Egypt (55x132cm-22x52in) s.i. pencil W/C prov. 29-Oct-2 Sotheby's, New York #150/R est:3000-5000

VADASZ, Endre (1901-1944) Hungarian
£1032 $1610 €1548 Italian harbour, 1938-39 (58x83cm-23x33in) s. tempera paper. 11-Sep-2 Kieselbach, Budapest #162/R (H.F 400000)
Works on paper
£3803 $6085 €5705 In the port (59x49cm-23x19in) s. mixed media. 16-May-3 Kieselbach, Budapest #18/R (H.F 1300000)

VADDER, Frans de (1862-1935) Belgian
£507 $832 €700 Chasseur dans la bruyere (70x50cm-28x20in) s. 27-May-3 Campo, Vlaamse Kaai #70

VADDER, Lodewyk de (1605-1655) Flemish
£6115 $9784 €8500 Wooded dune landscape with peasants on path (45x63cm-18x25in) s. panel. 13-May-3 Sotheby's, Amsterdam #24/R est:7000-9000
Works on paper
£4459 $6955 €7000 Abbey of Rouge-Cloitre. Trees (19x31cm-7x12in) pen brown ink col wash double-sided prov.exhib. 5-Nov-2 Sotheby's, Amsterdam #22/R est:8000-10000

VADDER, Lodewyk de (attrib) (1605-1655) Flemish
£1560 $2418 €2340 Landscape with figures (17x22cm-7x9in) panel. 3-Dec-2 Bukowskis, Stockholm #446a/R est:15000-20000 (S.KR 22000)

VAERENBERGH, G van (19/20th C) Belgian
Sculpture
£1064 $1777 €1500 Young woman with garland (40cm-16in) s. alabaster col pat bronze. 23-Jun-3 Bernaerts, Antwerp #204/R est:1000-1200
£1418 $2369 €2000 Bust of a young girl with hood (56cm-22in) s. alabaster col pat bronze marble stand. 23-Jun-3 Bernaerts, Antwerp #207/R est:2000-2500

VAERNEWIJCK, Lode van (20th C) Belgian
£283 $442 €450 Ferme dans un paysage (89x99cm-35x39in) 14-Oct-2 Amberes, Antwerp #220

VAERTEN, Jan (1909-1980) Belgian
Works on paper
£252 $387 €400 Untitled (68x53cm-27x21in) s.d.1959 verso gouache. 22-Oct-2 Campo & Campo, Antwerp #267

VAES, Walter (1882-1958) Belgian
£377 $589 €600 Nature morte d'un coq (49x57cm-19x22in) 14-Oct-2 Amberes, Antwerp #210
£1781 $2778 €2600 Vase fleuri d'oeillets (33x40cm-13x16in) s. 14-Apr-3 Horta, Bruxelles #323 est:1000-1500
£1887 $2906 €3000 Still life with carnation (50x60cm-20x24in) s. canvas on panel prov. 22-Oct-2 Sotheby's, Amsterdam #90/R est:3000-5000
£2177 $3461 €3200 Portrait of an officer (101x90cm-40x35in) s.d.1912. 24-Mar-3 Bernaerts, Antwerp #254 est:3750-4000
£3472 $5521 €5000 Nature morte aux moules (25x35cm-10x14in) s. panel. 29-Apr-3 Campo & Campo, Antwerp #301/R est:2000-3000

VAGH WEINMANN, Elemer (1906-) Hungarian
£285 $444 €450 Flowers (57x48cm-22x19in) s. 20-Oct-2 Chayette & Cheval, Paris #94

VAGH WEINMANN, Emeric (1919-) Hungarian
£288 $447 €450 Pivoine II (92x73cm-36x29in) s.d.1969. 6-Dec-2 Rieunier, Bailly-Pommery, Mathias, Paris #103

VAGH WEINMANN, Nandor (1897-?) Hungarian
£284 $474 €400 A la ferme (50x61cm-20x24in) s.verso panel. 17-Jun-3 Claude Boisgirard, Paris #136

VAGLIERI, Tino (1929-2000) Italian
£272 $433 €400 Composition (70x50cm-28x20in) s.d.1983 tempera pastel cardboard. 1-Mar-3 Meeting Art, Vercelli #309
£1026 $1610 €1600 Still life (60x50cm-24x20in) s. 19-Nov-2 Finarte, Milan #120/R
£1218 $1778 €1900 Situation (87x69cm-34x27in) s.d.1960 s.d.verso. 5-Jun-2 Il Ponte, Milan #42/R
Works on paper
£481 $755 €750 Composition (49x69cm-19x27in) s.d.1963 mixed media exhib. 19-Nov-2 Finarte, Milan #130/R

VAGNER, Ivan (?) ?
£272 $424 €408 Bathing the horse (60x69cm-24x27in) s. 5-Aug-2 Rasmussen, Vejle #92 (D.KR 3200)

VAGNETTI, Gianni (1898-1956) Italian
£481 $755 €750 Study for 'Aroldo' (50x70cm-20x28in) init. tempera pastel collage cardboard. 20-Nov-2 Pandolfini, Florence #3/R
£641 $1006 €1000 Cathedral (40x50cm-16x20in) s. board. 19-Nov-2 Finarte, Milan #117/R
£1667 $2617 €2600 Portrait of Maganzini (86x72cm-34x28in) s.d.1931 board. 20-Nov-2 Pandolfini, Florence #15/R
£2692 $4254 €4200 Seated figure (89x80cm-35x31in) s. 15-Nov-2 Farsetti, Prato #469/R
£2703 $4216 €4000 Girl with white collar (73x57cm-29x22in) s.d.1932 lit. 28-Mar-3 Farsetti, Prato #533/R

VAGO, Valentino (1931-) Italian
£719 $1150 €1100 E254 (92x73cm-36x29in) s.i.d.1973. 4-Jan-3 Meeting Art, Vercelli #375
£728 $1135 €1150 C60 (92x73cm-36x29in) s.i.verso. 14-Sep-2 Meeting Art, Vercelli #729/R
£833 $1325 €1200 Composition E 298 (92x73cm-36x29in) s.d.1973. 1-May-3 Meeting Art, Vercelli #230
£1699 $2719 €2600 Untitled (200x150cm-79x59in) s.d.1971 verso. 4-Jan-3 Meeting Art, Vercelli #598

VAHEY, Brian (20th C) Irish
£411 $645 €600 Achill (25x36cm-10x14in) s. board diptych. 15-Apr-3 De Veres Art Auctions, Dublin #100i
£616 $968 €900 View from the kitchen (51x76cm-20x30in) s. canvasboard. 15-Apr-3 De Veres Art Auctions, Dublin #100h

VAIKUNTAM, Thotha (1942-) Indian
£800 $1272 €1200 Telegana women (55x76cm-22x30in) s. acrylic. 2-May-3 Christie's, Kensington #575/R

VAILLANT, Wallerant (1623-1677) Dutch
Works on paper
£705 $1029 €1100 Portrait of Kaiser Leopold I (52x38cm-20x15in) chk. 4-Jun-2 Karl & Faber, Munich #45/R
£2166 $3378 €3400 Pair of portraits of a lady and gentleman. Sketch of a boy (39x34cm-15x13in) one s.i.d.1650 one s.i.indis.d. double-sided black chk pair. 5-Nov-2 Sotheby's, Amsterdam #36/R est:2000-3000

VAILLANT, Wallerant (attrib) (1623-1677) Dutch
£3041 $4743 €4500 Portrait of the Duke Armand de Caumont La Force (122x105cm-48x41in) i.verso. 26-Mar-3 Tajan, Paris #48/R
£3871 $6116 €6000 Portrait de gentilhomme en armure (84x66cm-33x26in) 20-Dec-2 Tajan, Paris #60/R est:5500

VAINIO, Armas (1923-) Finnish
£277 $426 €440 Still life (68x80cm-27x31in) s.d.1961. 24-Oct-2 Hagelstam, Helsinki #1037
£478 $741 €760 View of farmhouses and yard (46x65cm-18x26in) s.d.76. 6-Oct-2 Bukowskis, Helsinki #309/R

VAISMAN, Meyer (1960-) American
Sculpture
£3797 $6000 €5696 Untitled - turkey XVI, Peg (84x55x75cm-33x22x30in) taxidermied turkey synthetic hair steel wire ribbon prov. 13-Nov-2 Sotheby's, New York #140/R est:7000-9000

VAJDA, Julia (1913-1982) Hungarian
£1062 $1657 €1540 Circle and landscape (54x46cm-21x18in) s.d.1977 s.i.verso oil pencil canvas on fibreboard. 12-Apr-3 Mu Terem Galeria, Budapest #111/R est:360000 (H.F 380000)
Works on paper
£753 $1167 €1092 Figure in armchair (29x21cm-11x8in) s.d.945 W/C exhib. 9-Dec-2 Mu Terem Galeria, Budapest #90/R est:200000 (H.F 280000)

VAJDA, Lajos (1908-1941) Hungarian
Works on paper
£1230 $1918 €1784 Houses with weeping willows (31x44cm-12x17in) pencil exhib.lit. 12-Apr-3 Mu Terem Galeria, Budapest #106/R est:400000 (H.F 440000)
£1479 $2293 €2145 Houses, fence, plate (28x41cm-11x16in) pencil prov.exhib.lit. 9-Dec-2 Mu Terem Galeria, Budapest #89/R est:400000 (H.F 550000)
£1677 $2616 €2432 Stefan Makszimovics. Houses of a village (21x31cm-8x12in) s.d.1937 pencil double-sided. 13-Sep-2 Mu Terem Galeria, Budapest #102/R est:400000 (H.F 650000)

VALADIE, Jean Baptiste (1933-) French
£818 $1267 €1300 Le lecon de poney (73x92cm-29x36in) s.d.72. 30-Oct-2 Artcurial Briest, Paris #413a
£1282 $2013 €2000 Femme de plumes (56x46cm-22x18in) s. i.verso painted 1974. 15-Dec-2 Eric Pillon, Calais #234/R
£1591 $2418 €2450 Modele au chapeau en dentelle (55x46cm-22x18in) s. 7-Jul-2 Lombrail & Teucquam, Paris #75/R

VALADON, Suzanne (1865-1938) French
£3448 $5483 €5000 Deux nus a leur toilette (28x22cm-11x9in) chl estompe dr. 5-Mar-3 Doutrebente, Paris #33/R est:4000-5000
£3500 $5425 €5250 Une route a la campagne (39x52cm-15x20in) s.d.1918 oil paper on canvas prov. 5-Dec-2 Christie's, Kensington #13/R est:2000-3000
£4106 $6693 €6200 Esquisse pour le portrait de Franck Wooster (40x40cm-16x16in) exec.c.1930 prov.lit. 31-Jan-3 Charbonneaux, Paris #173 est:3000-3500
£10345 $16552 €15000 Le sentier dans le bois (73x54cm-29x21in) s. 12-Mar-3 Libert, Castor, Paris #201/R est:6000-7500
£14198 $20160 €23000 Petit vase de muguet (46x38cm-18x15in) s.d.1931 lit. 16-Mar-3 Eric Pillon, Calais #110/R
£16000 $26720 €23200 Sous-bois (73x54cm-29x21in) s. painted 1915 prov.exhib. 24-Jun-3 Sotheby's, London #209/R est:10000-12000
£23000 $35420 €34500 Vase de fleurs (40x30cm-16x12in) s.d.1933 panel prov.exhib. 22-Oct-2 Sotheby's, London #168/R est:20000-30000
£23292 $37500 €34938 Nu allonge sur un canape (50x65cm-20x26in) s.d.1919 prov.lit. 7-May-3 Sotheby's, New York #182/R est:40000-60000
£25532 $42638 €36000 Vase de fleurs sur une table (61x50cm-24x20in) s.d. lit. 23-Jun-3 Claude Boisgirard, Paris #84/R est:10000-15000
£32751 $51419 €49127 Nu dans un paysage (81x60cm-32x24in) s.d.1923 s.i. verso prov. 25-Nov-2 Germann, Zurich #28/R est:50000-70000 (S.FR 75000)
Works on paper
£769 $1285 €1100 Profil de femme (17x16cm-7x6in) s.d. sanguine prov.lit. 27-Jun-3 Claude Aguttes, Neuilly #87/R
£1026 $1600 €1539 Le bidet (18x16cm-7x6in) s. brush ink exec.c.1900. 18-Sep-2 Swann Galleries, New York #16/R est:1500-2500
£1195 $1900 €1793 Female nude seated (30x23cm-12x9in) s. conte crayon. 3-May-3 Rachel Davis, Shaker Heights #88/R est:1000-1500
£2482 $4145 €3500 Maurice Utrillo nu debout de profil (23x10cm-9x4in) s. crayon c.1894 prov.exhib.lit. 20-Jun-3 Piasa, Paris #61/R est:2000-3000
£2781 $4534 €4200 Toilette (21x16cm-8x6in) s. graphite prov.exhib. 3-Feb-3 Cornette de St.Cyr, Paris #338
£4167 $6542 €6500 Fleurs sur un entablement (27x25cm-11x10in) s.d.1909 W/C gouache. 11-Dec-2 Maigret, Paris #150/R est:7000-9000
£4895 $8175 €7000 Apres le bain (26x20cm-10x8in) s. sanguine prov.lit. 27-Jun-3 Claude Aguttes, Neuilly #88/R est:3500-4500
£6028 $10067 €8500 Le depart pour l'ecole Maurice et Catherine (28x15cm-11x6in) s.d.94 drawing lit. 20-Jun-3 Piasa, Paris #58/R est:3000-5000
£7092 $11844 €10000 Etude de nus (40x60cm-16x24in) s.d.1902 drawing sanguine blk crayon. 20-Jun-3 Piasa, Paris #62/R est:3000-4000
£10993 $18358 €15500 La toilette (31x27cm-12x11in) s.d.94 drawing lit. 20-Jun-3 Piasa, Paris #60/R est:5000-7000

VALCKX, Petrus (1920-) Belgian
£333 $530 €480 Nature morte avec nappe bleue (67x86cm-26x34in) s. 29-Apr-3 Campo & Campo, Antwerp #831

VALDIVIESO, Antonio (1918-2000) Spanish
Works on paper
£552 $872 €800 Dance in the woods (34x24cm-13x9in) s. W/C. 1-Apr-3 Segre, Madrid #308/R

VALE, Florence Gertrude (1909-) Canadian
Works on paper
£206 $319 €309 Hitchhiker (29x21cm-11x8in) s.d.72 mixed media collage prov.exhib. 3-Dec-2 Joyner, Toronto #485 (C.D 500)

VALENCIA, Manuel (1856-1935) American
£719 $1200 €1043 Stream in sunset landscape (33x41cm-13x16in) s. canvasboard prov. 17-Jun-3 John Moran, Pasadena #41 est:800-1200
£1647 $2750 €2388 Mission Delrose San Francisco (61x41cm-24x16in) s. i.verso prov. 17-Jun-3 John Moran, Pasadena #108 est:1200-1800
£2096 $3500 €3039 Flower field in rolling California landscape (23x30cm-9x12in) s. board prov. 17-Jun-3 John Moran, Pasadena #107 est:1200-1800

VALENCIAN SCHOOL (16th C) Spanish
£9615 $15096 €15000 Man of Sorrows (53x43cm-21x17in) panel. 13-Dec-2 Pierre Berge, Paris #67/R

VALENCIENNES, Pierre Henri de (1750-1819) French
£5449 $8446 €8500 Vue de la pyramide de Cestius, Rome (28x41cm-11x16in) paper. 5-Dec-2 Oger, Dumont, Paris #28/R

VALENCIENNES, Pierre Henri de (circle) (1750-1819) French
£6875 $11000 €10313 Landscape, possibly South American with cascade and teater in foreground (100x154cm-39x61in) 14-May-3 Doyle, New York #65/R est:20000-30000

VALENKAMPH, Theodor Victor Carl (1868-1924) American
£764 $1200 €1146 Stormy seas (50x92cm-20x36in) s. 22-Nov-2 Skinner, Boston #123/R est:1200-1800
£818 $1300 €1227 Schooner (61x91cm-24x36in) s. 29-Apr-3 Doyle, New York #39
£1645 $2500 €2468 Ship riding the waves (51x61cm-20x24in) s. 17-Aug-2 North East Auctions, Portsmouth #1076/R est:2500-3500
£1875 $3000 €2813 Rocky coast Rockport view (30x51cm-12x20in) s. 11-Jan-3 James Julia, Fairfield #410 est:1800-2400

VALENSI, Henry (1883-1960) French
Works on paper
£689 $1151 €1000 Tennis, le jeu (29x58cm-11x23in) s.i.d.1930 gouache graphite. 10-Jul-3 Artcurial Briest, Paris #250

VALENTI, Italo (1912-1995) Italian
£349 $548 €524 Composition (24x18cm-9x7in) s. paper. 25-Nov-2 Germann, Zurich #76 (S.FR 800)
£1652 $2577 €2478 Still life with chair (28x24cm-11x9in) s. panel. 16-Sep-2 Philippe Schuler, Zurich #3524/R est:5000-6000 (S.FR 3800)
£1923 $3019 €3000 Untitled (50x70cm-20x28in) s. cardboard. 19-Nov-2 Finarte, Milan #14
£2065 $3262 €3200 Armchair in interior (47x49cm-19x19in) s.d.1948. 18-Dec-2 Christie's, Rome #268/R
£2183 $3188 €3275 Oleggio IV (31x39cm-12x15in) canvas on panel pavatex s.i.d.1967 verso prov.lit. 4-Jun-2 Germann, Zurich #36/R est:4000-5000 (S.FR 5000)
£2183 $3428 €3275 Bise (44x62cm-17x24in) s. s.i.d.1964 verso oil gouache collage panel. 23-Nov-2 Burkhard, Luzern #148/R est:5000-7000 (S.FR 5000)
£3057 $4463 €4586 Mesure (40x27cm-16x11in) s. lit. 4-Jun-2 Germann, Zurich #57/R est:5500-7500 (S.FR 7000)
£3712 $5419 €5568 Studio (31x33cm-12x13in) s.i.d.1968 verso lit. 4-Jun-2 Germann, Zurich #35/R est:6000-8000 (S.FR 8500)
£5677 $8913 €8516 Tambours negres (90x120cm-35x47in) s.i.d.1962 verso collage paper on pavatex prov.exhib.lit. 25-Nov-2 Germann, Zurich #77/R est:15000-18000 (S.FR 13000)
Works on paper
£1174 $1820 €1761 Conte de pluie et de lune (24x18cm-9x7in) s. collage prov. 9-Dec-2 Philippe Schuler, Zurich #3475/R est:3000-5000 (S.FR 2700)
£2402 $3771 €3603 Cerf volant (28x28cm-11x11in) s. i.d.X 84 verso collage on panel pavatex prov.exhib.lit. 25-Nov-2 Germann, Zurich #75/R est:6000-8000 (S.FR 5500)
£2446 $3865 €3669 La scala di giacobbe (49x49cm-19x19in) s. s.i.d.1972 verso collage exhib.lit. 26-Nov-2 Phillips, Zurich #94/R est:6000-8000 (S.FR 5700)
£3913 $6065 €5870 Mistral (42x43cm-17x17in) s. i.d. verso collage gouache paper on panel. 4-Dec-2 Koller, Zurich #167/R est:10000-18000 (S.FR 9000)
£4367 $6376 €6551 La chasse (51x52cm-20x20in) collage paper on pavatex s.i.d.1964 verso exhib.lit. 4-Jun-2 Germann, Zurich #37/R est:5000-7000 (S.FR 10000)

VALENTIN, Paul (19th C) Danish?
£557 $870 €836 Coastal landscape with figures (32x55cm-13x22in) s.d.1893. 11-Nov-2 Rasmussen, Vejle #636/R (D.KR 6500)

VALENTINE, A C (20th C) Canadian
£341 $536 €512 Moraine Lake (20x25cm-8x10in) s.i. board. 25-Nov-2 Hodgins, Calgary #380/R (C.D 850)

VALENTINE-DAINES, Sherree (1956-) British
£280 $434 €420 Lady in red (16x12cm-6x5in) init. 3-Dec-2 Bonhams, Knightsbridge #399a/R

VALENTINI, Walter (1912-1995) Italian
Works on paper
£705 $1107 €1100 Sky (35x35cm-14x14in) s.i. mixed media board. 23-Nov-2 Meeting Art, Vercelli #31/R
£1519 $2370 €2400 Time wall (45x90cm-18x35in) mixed media canvas on board. 14-Sep-2 Meeting Art, Vercelli #807/R

VALENTINO, Gian Domenico (17th C) Italian
£18987 $30000 €30000 Kitchen interieur with kitchen (77x116cm-30x46in) prov.lit. 27-Nov-2 Finarte, Milan #58/R est:30000-40000

VALENTINO, Gian Domenico (attrib) (17th C) Italian
£5500 $8635 €8250 Copper pots, earthenware jugs, a mortar and pestle. Copper pots, glass bottles and a barrel (63x75cm-25x30in) pair. 13-Dec-2 Christie's, Kensington #222/R est:5000-7000

VALENY, T (18th C) Italian
£6410 $10000 €9615 Parlor scene (84x66cm-33x26in) with sig. 11-Apr-3 Du Mouchelle, Detroit #2004/R est:4000-6000

VALERI, Andre Pravot (?) French?
£390 $612 €585 Seaweed gatherers (30x23cm-12x9in) board. 19-Nov-2 Riddetts, Bournemouth #858

VALERO, Carlos (1888-?) Spanish
£321 $506 €500 Still life with squids (52x63cm-20x25in) s. paper. 13-Nov-2 Ansorena, Madrid #7/R

VALES, Edmond (1918-2001) ?
£1923 $3019 €3000 Jeune femme de Meknes (45x38cm-18x15in) s. s.i.verso. 16-Dec-2 Gros & Delettrez, Paris #149/R est:1100-1500
£2568 $4005 €3800 Fantasia au Maroc (51x66cm-20x26in) s.verso panel. 28-Mar-3 Claude Aguttes, Neuilly #219/R est:3500

VALETTE, Adolphe (1861-1942) French
£700 $1113 €1050 Valldemosa (20x31cm-8x12in) s. board. 18-Mar-3 Bearnes, Exeter #527
£2400 $3912 €3600 Beaujolais landscape with cottages and blue hills (48x59cm-19x23in) s. s.i.stretcher. 30-Jan-3 Lawrence, Crewkerne #746/R est:800-1200
£3000 $4680 €4500 Vineyard owner (40x32cm-16x13in) prov. 6-Nov-2 Bonhams, Chester #347/R est:1500-2000
Works on paper
£280 $451 €420 Julian (33x28cm-13x11in) s.d.1910 pencil exhib. 14-Jan-3 Bonhams, Knightsbridge #173
£750 $1193 €1125 Naked female (25x20cm-10x8in) init. pencil dr. 18-Mar-3 Capes Dunn, Manchester #410

VALETTI, Vittorio Garnier (19th C) Italian
£305 $482 €458 Isola, Lago D'Orta (26x32cm-10x13in) 7-Apr-3 Shapiro, Sydney #509/R (A.D 800)

VALEUR, Cecil (1910-1985) ?
£466 $742 €699 Field workers (68x97cm-27x38in) s. 5-May-3 Rasmussen, Vejle #7/R (D.KR 5000)

VALIGURSKY, Ed (1926-) American
£1180 $1900 €1770 Space station with astronauts replacing fuel tanks (66x51cm-26x20in) board. 10-May-3 Illustration House, New York #168/R est:1500-2500

VALINOTTI, Domenico (1889-1962) Italian
£577 $906 €900 Mountainous landscape (48x60cm-19x24in) s.d.1929. 10-Dec-2 Della Rocca, Turin #360/R
£1282 $2013 €2000 Village (48x60cm-19x24in) s.d.1930. 10-Dec-2 Della Rocca, Turin #357/R

VALK, Hendrik Jacobus (1897-1986) Dutch
£1295 $2124 €1800 Brienzer meer (19x27cm-7x11in) init.d.58 s.i.verso oil on cardboard. 3-Jun-3 Christie's, Amsterdam #137/R est:2000-3000
£2014 $3304 €2800 De Verloren zoon - Prodigal son (39x28cm-15x11in) init.d.58 s.i.verso cardboard. 3-Jun-3 Christie's, Amsterdam #74/R est:3000-5000

VALK, Hendrik de (fl.1693-1717) Dutch
£6081 $9486 €9000 Merry making party (59x82cm-23x32in) s. 27-Mar-3 Dorotheum, Vienna #195/R est:9000-12000
£8000 $12400 €12000 Interior with a family eating around a table, an artist's studio beyond (44x38cm-17x15in) s. 30-Oct-2 Christie's, Kensington #49/R est:5000-7000

VALK, Maurits van der (1857-1935) Dutch
£1034 $1644 €1500 Still life with fruit and a jug (31x47cm-12x19in) s. 10-Mar-3 Sotheby's, Amsterdam #122/R est:1500-2000
Works on paper
£1241 $1974 €1800 Moored boats in a canal (31x46cm-12x18in) s. W/C. 10-Mar-3 Sotheby's, Amsterdam #132
£5137 $8065 €7500 View of the Slatuintjes, Amsterdam (59x73cm-23x29in) s. W/C col pencil prov. 15-Apr-3 Sotheby's, Amsterdam #141/R est:2000-3000

VALKENBORCH, Frederick van (1570-1623) Flemish
£6329 $10000 €10000 Prise de Troie (40x58cm-16x23in) mono.d.95 prov. 27-Nov-2 Christie's, Paris #26/R est:10000-15000

VALKENBORCH, Lucas van (1535-1597) Flemish
£79137 $126619 €110000 Extensive river landscape with millers on a road approaching a watermill (25x37cm-10x15in) panel prov.exhib.lit. 14-May-3 Christie's, Amsterdam #165/R est:70000-100000

VALKENBURG, Bertha (1862-1929) Dutch
£1180 $1865 €1770 Woman washing (48x31cm-19x12in) s. prov. 3-Apr-3 Heffel, Vancouver #92/R est:2000-2500 (C.D 2750)

VALKENBURG, Dirk (1675-1727) Dutch
£28846 $45000 €43269 Cat and dog fighting over rooster, grapes and fruit. s. 21-Sep-2 Nadeau, Windsor #125/R est:10000-15000

VALKENBURG, Dirk (circle) (1675-1727) Dutch
£7500 $11775 €11250 Italianate villa and garden with figures, still life of fruit and vegetables in the foreground (83x60cm-33x24in) 13-Dec-2 Christie's, Kensington #113/R est:7000-10000

VALKENBURG, Hendrik (1826-1896) Dutch
£3014 $4701 €4400 Young girl sitting by cradle (52x67cm-20x26in) s.d.1871. 10-Apr-3 Van Ham, Cologne #1735/R est:5000
Works on paper
£1529 $2400 €2294 Return home (19x27cm-7x11in) s. W/C htd white. 10-Dec-2 Doyle, New York #188/R est:2500-3500

VALKI, Jean (19th C) French
Works on paper
£1139 $1777 €1800 Femme a la robe verte (190x87cm-75x34in) s. pastel. 20-Oct-2 Chayette & Cheval, Paris #16/R

VALLANCE, William Fleming (1827-1904) British
Works on paper
£550 $858 €825 Edinburgh from Craigmillar (35x61cm-14x24in) s.d.1873 W/C gouache. 10-Apr-3 Bonhams, Edinburgh #141

VALLARINO, Vincent (1929-) ?
Photographs
£2273 $3500 €3410 Luxembourg woods (54x76cm-21x30in) s.i.d.1974 num.5/25 photograph. 24-Oct-2 Sotheby's, New York #246/R est:4000-6000

VALLAYER-COSTER, Anne (1744-1818) French
Works on paper
£8392 $12000 €12588 White roses (36x27cm-14x11in) i. W/C exhib. 22-Jan-3 Doyle, New York #72/R est:7000

VALLE, A Ramiro del (20th C) Spanish
£516 $815 €800 Beach scene (75x116cm-30x46in) s. 17-Dec-2 Durán, Madrid #573/R

VALLEDOR, Leo (1936-1989) American
£355 $550 €533 Aurora (61x305cm-24x120in) s. acrylic painted c.1965. 7-Dec-2 Harvey Clar, Oakland #1250
£625 $1000 €938 Reg wind (163x302cm-64x119in) s. acrylic. 11-Jan-3 Harvey Clar, Oakland #1293

VALLEE, Armand Frederick (1921-) Canadian
£402 $631 €603 Oil sketch on location (30x40cm-12x16in) s.d.1984 i.verso. 25-Nov-2 Hodgins, Calgary #123/R (C.D 1000)
Works on paper
£1610 $2560 €2415 Kananaskis country (55x75cm-22x30in) s.i.d.1991 W/C. 23-Mar-3 Hodgins, Calgary #101/R est:2000-2500 (C.D 3800)

VALLEE, Étienne Maxime (19th C) French
£620 $1011 €930 Figures by a woodland pool (32x40cm-13x16in) 14-Feb-3 Lyon & Turnbull, Edinburgh #131
£786 $1226 €1179 Peasant woman in garden (59x73cm-23x29in) s. 6-Nov-2 Dobiaschofsky, Bern #1026/R (S.FR 1800)
£1299 $2013 €1949 Landscape with ducks on pond (65x92cm-26x36in) s. 24-Sep-2 Koller, Zurich #6513/R est:3000-5000 (S.FR 3000)
£1761 $2747 €2800 Washerwomen by wooded lake (100x165cm-39x65in) s.d.1876. 19-Sep-2 Dr Fritz Nagel, Stuttgart #1007/R est:2000
£3148 $4470 €5100 Lavandieres au bord de la riviere (100x165cm-39x65in) s.d.1876. 16-Mar-3 Eric Pillon, Calais #52/R

VALLELY, Henry E (20th C) American
£2640 $4250 €3960 Couple in roadster stopped by police officer (58x86cm-23x34in) s. painted c.1920. 10-May-3 Illustration House, New York #71/R est:2500-3500

VALLELY, John B (1941-) British
£2000 $2920 €3000 Fiddle and pipes (51x61cm-20x24in) mono. 12-Jun-2 John Ross, Belfast #107 est:2500-3000
£2113 $3507 €3000 Musicians (25x30cm-10x12in) init. 10-Jun-3 James Adam, Dublin #51/R est:2000-3000
£3250 $4745 €4875 Breeze from No.3 (36x30cm-14x12in) mono. 12-Jun-2 John Ross, Belfast #72 est:3500-3800
£3800 $6080 €5700 Blue accordian (20x28cm-8x11in) init. board. 15-May-3 Christie's, Kensington #169/R est:4000-6000
£4718 $7832 €6700 Four musicians (46x56cm-18x22in) s. 10-Jun-3 James Adam, Dublin #82/R est:4000-6000
£5000 $8000 €7500 Milltown Malbay Street session (35x46cm-14x18in) init. 15-May-3 Christie's, Kensington #168/R est:5000-8000
£5342 $8334 €7800 Three musicians (45x61cm-18x24in) init. 8-Apr-3 James Adam, Dublin #69/R
£8000 $11680 €12000 Eight fiddlers (61x76cm-24x30in) mono. 12-Jun-2 John Ross, Belfast #202 est:8000-10000
£14000 $20440 €21000 Band of fiddlers (76x102cm-30x40in) mono. 12-Jun-2 John Ross, Belfast #20 est:14000-16000
Works on paper
£1250 $1987 €1800 Musicians (25x33cm-10x13in) mixed media on card prov. 29-Apr-3 Whyte's, Dublin #43/R est:2000-3000

VALLES, Lorenzo (1830-1910) Spanish
£638 $1034 €900 Pajaros (13x35cm-5x14in) s. 20-May-3 Segre, Madrid #301/R
£1935 $3058 €3000 Easter week in Perugia (28x17cm-11x7in) s.i.d.75 board. 17-Dec-2 Durán, Madrid #206/R
£8725 $14047 €13000 Admiring art (28x42cm-11x17in) s. board. 18-Feb-3 Durán, Madrid #219/R est:12000

VALLET, Edouard (1876-1929) Swiss
£437 $681 €656 Old houses in La Capite (24x18cm-9x7in) mono.i. board. 8-Nov-2 Dobiaschofsky, Bern #106/R (S.FR 1000)
Works on paper
£330 $482 €495 Girl's portrait (23x20cm-9x8in) s. pencil chl wah. 17-Jun-2 Philippe Schuler, Zurich #4230 (S.FR 750)
£8696 $13478 €13044 Derriere le rideau (57x30cm-22x12in) s.d.1913 init.verso chl white chk wash. 7-Dec-2 Galerie du Rhone, Sion #491/R est:20000-25000 (S.FR 20000)

VALLET, Jean (?) ?
£274 $430 €400 Le clown (80x60cm-31x24in) s. 15-Apr-3 Galerie Moderne, Brussels #387
£329 $533 €500 Le clown (80x60cm-31x24in) d.87. 21-Jan-3 Galerie Moderne, Brussels #262

VALLET, Pierre (1884-1971) French
Works on paper
£338 $527 €500 Pavillon a Saint-Cloud (42x47cm-17x19in) s.d.1917 W/C. 27-Mar-3 Maigret, Paris #220/R

VALLET-BISSON, Frederic (1865-?) French
£797 $1307 €1100 Jeune femme (67x89cm-26x35in) s. 27-May-3 Campo & Campo, Antwerp #226

VALLETTE, Henri (1877-1962) French
Sculpture
£25000 $39250 €37500 Seated greyhound (103x87x45cm-41x34x18in) s. pink marble prov. 10-Dec-2 Sotheby's, London #172/R est:25000-30000

VALLGREN, Ville (1855-1940) French
Sculpture
£1127 $1814 €1600 Tear bottle (18cm-7in) s. bronze. 10-May-3 Bukowskis, Helsinki #20/R est:1700-2000

£1408	$2268	€2000	Girl (29cm-11in) bronze. 10-May-3 Bukowskis, Helsinki #14/R est:1500-2000
£4460	$7137	€6200	Taarflaska - bottle shape (33cm-13in) s.i.d.1896 pat.bronze. 17-May-3 Hagelstam, Helsinki #14/R est:6000

VALLIER, Etienne (?) French?

£400	$624	€600	Le fiacre sur le quai. s.d.15-7-96 panel. 17-Sep-2 Rosebery Fine Art, London #667/R

VALLIN, Golli Hugo (?) ?

£1900	$3097	€2755	Venetian Canal (37x45cm-15x18in) s. 16-Jul-3 Sotheby's, Olympia #255/R est:1000-2000
£4200	$6552	€6090	Venice (20x25cm-8x10in) s. prov. 27-Mar-3 Neales, Nottingham #980/R est:2000-4000
£4400	$6864	€6380	Venetian evening (20x25cm-8x10in) s. prov. 27-Mar-3 Neales, Nottingham #981/R est:2000-4000

VALLIN, Hugo Golli (19/20th C) French

£4054	$6324	€6000	Venise (54x65cm-21x26in) s. 25-Mar-3 Chochon-Barre & Allardi, Paris #206/R est:6000-6200

VALLIN, Jacques Antoine (1760-1831) French

£1923	$3019	€3000	Jeunes bacchantes (20x15cm-8x6in) panel pair. 14-Dec-2 Artcurial Briest, Paris #55/R
£3846	$6423	€5500	Portrait d'une elegante dans un jardin (40x22cm-16x9in) i.verso panel. 25-Jun-3 Tajan, Paris #77/R est:6000-8000
£5369	$8644	€8000	Erotic scene (19x24cm-7x9in) s. cardboard oval. 19-Feb-3 Semenzato, Venice #37/R est:10000
£8392	$14014	€12000	Portraits de jeunes femmes (30x23cm-12x9in) s.d.1821 three panel four. 25-Jun-3 Tajan, Paris #78/R est:12000-15000

VALLIN, Robert (?-1915) French

£1800	$2862	€2700	St. Mark's Square, Venice (53x66cm-21x26in) s. 20-Mar-3 Christie's, Kensington #42/R est:2000-3000

VALLMAN, Uno (1913-) Swedish

£252	$399	€378	Changing (46x62cm-18x24in) s.d.48 panel. 30-Nov-2 Goteborg Auktionsverk, Sweden #655/R (S.KR 3600)
£284	$440	€426	Composition with flowers (68x33cm-27x13in) s.d.1961. 8-Dec-2 Uppsala Auktionskammare, Uppsala #260 (S.KR 4000)
£302	$471	€453	Flowers (35x28cm-14x11in) s.d.1951. 13-Sep-2 Lilla Bukowskis, Stockholm #254 (S.KR 4400)
£355	$550	€533	View of the old part of town (47x55cm-19x22in) s.d.1964. 8-Dec-2 Uppsala Auktionskammare, Uppsala #259/R (S.KR 5000)
£357	$567	€536	Still life of flowers (35x27cm-14x11in) s.d.48 panel. 2-Mar-3 Uppsala Auktionskammare, Uppsala #45/R (S.KR 4800)
£446	$709	€669	Boats in harbour, Honfleur (51x43cm-20x17in) s.d.46 exhib. 2-Mar-3 Uppsala Auktionskammare, Uppsala #44/R (S.KR 6000)
£469	$751	€680	Fruit pickers (32x22cm-13x9in) s. panel. 18-May-3 Anders Antik, Landskrona #64 (S.KR 6000)
£582	$943	€844	Southern landscape (55x47cm-22x19in) s.d.48 panel. 25-May-3 Uppsala Auktionskammare, Uppsala #322 (S.KR 7500)
£674	$1044	€1011	Landscape (39x47cm-15x19in) s. 8-Dec-2 Uppsala Auktionskammare, Uppsala #263/R (S.KR 9500)
£892	$1419	€1338	Bathers (38x47cm-15x19in) s.d.1961. 3-Mar-3 Lilla Bukowskis, Stockholm #417 (S.KR 12000)

Works on paper

£463	$769	€671	Figure composition (29x40cm-11x16in) s.d.1955 mixed media paper on panel. 16-Jun-3 Lilla Bukowskis, Stockholm #457 (S.KR 6000)

VALLOIS, Paul Felix (19th C) French

£1226	$1937	€1900	Monte Carlo (33x45cm-13x18in) s.d.1894. 19-Dec-2 Claude Aguttes, Neuilly #220/R

VALLOTTON, Felix (1865-1925) Swiss

£10092	$16853	€14633	Le faisan - nature morte, un faisan pendu (97x64cm-38x25in) s.d.12 prov. 20-Jun-3 Kornfeld, Bern #142/R est:25000 (S.FR 22000)
£19907	$32051	€28865	Femme retenant sa chemise (92x73cm-36x29in) s.d.14 prov.lit. 9-May-3 Dobiaschofsky, Bern #159/R est:50000 (S.FR 43000)
£25751	$40687	€38627	Leda (88x114cm-35x45in) s.d.13 prov.lit. 26-Nov-2 Phillips, Zurich #57/R est:60000-80000 (S.FR 60000)
£28302	$45849	€50094	Femme au chale rouge (116x89cm-46x35in) s.d.1915 prov.exhib.lit. 26-May-3 Sotheby's, Zurich #64/R est:65000-75000 (S.FR 60000)
£37037	$59630	€53704	Torse de femme nue sur fond paravent bleu (81x65cm-32x26in) s.d.07 prov.lit. 9-May-3 Dobiaschofsky, Bern #141/R est:85000 (S.FR 80000)
£52174	$80870	€78261	La plaine vaudoise (26x50cm-10x20in) s.d.1900 board prov. 4-Dec-2 Koller, Zurich #125/R est:130000-200000 (S.FR 120000)
£85837	$135622	€128756	Oranges et myosotis (81x65cm-32x26in) s.d.14 prov.lit. 26-Nov-2 Phillips, Zurich #35/R est:100000-150000 (S.FR 200000)
£99291	$160851	€140000	Coquetterie (89x116cm-35x46in) s.d.11 prov.exhib.lit. 20-May-3 Dorotheum, Vienna #6/R est:160000-180000
£174672	$274236	€262008	Suzanne et les vieillards (59x81cm-23x32in) st.sig.d.93 prov.exhib. 25-Nov-2 Sotheby's, Zurich #50/R est:400000-600000 (S.FR 400000)
£235849	$382075	€417453	Les parasols a Trouville (54x73cm-21x29in) s.d.1925 prov.exhib.lit. 26-May-3 Sotheby's, Zurich #85/R est:280000-350000 (S.FR 500000)

Prints

£1923	$3019	€3000	La foule a Paris (139x195cm-55x77in) woodcut. 12-Dec-2 Piasa, Paris #169/R
£1991	$3325	€2887	La nuit (18x22cm-7x9in) s.mono.i. woodcut. 24-Jun-3 Koller, Zurich #506/R est:6000-8000 (S.FR 4400)
£2402	$3771	€3603	Les cygnes (132x175cm-52x69in) s. woodcut prov. 25-Nov-2 Sotheby's, Zurich #47/R est:6000-8000 (S.FR 5500)
£6410	$10000	€9615	Le bain (18x23cm-7x9in) s.num.50 woodcut edition of 100. 7-Nov-2 Swann Galleries, New York #509/R est:12000-18000
£13761	$22982	€19953	La paresse (18x22cm-7x9in) s.i. woodcut. 20-Jun-3 Kornfeld, Bern #140/R est:30000 (S.FR 30000)
£61927	$103417	€89794	Intimites (54x44cm-21x17in) s.i. etching ten. 20-Jun-3 Kornfeld, Bern #139/R est:125000 (S.FR 135000)

Works on paper

£435	$674	€653	Standing female nude (21x12cm-8x5in) mono. pencil. 4-Dec-2 Koller, Zurich #125a (S.FR 1000)
£435	$674	€653	Standing female nude (22x14cm-9x6in) mono. chl. 4-Dec-2 Koller, Zurich #125b (S.FR 1000)
£541	$843	€800	Etude de nu (18x23cm-7x9in) mono.i. crayon. 28-Mar-3 Delvaux, Paris #17
£625	$994	€900	Nu assis de dos (26x17cm-10x7in) init. graphite dr prov. 29-Apr-3 Artcurial Briest, Paris #58
£661	$965	€992	Standing female nude (34x18cm-13x7in) mono. 17-Jun-2 Philippe Schuler, Zurich #4231/R (S.FR 1500)
£694	$1104	€1000	Deux nus assis (18x27cm-7x11in) init. graphite dr prov. 29-Apr-3 Artcurial Briest, Paris #56
£870	$1348	€1305	Standing female nude (22x13cm-9x5in) mono. pencil. 4-Dec-2 Koller, Zurich #125c est:600-800 (S.FR 2000)
£870	$1235	€1400	Portrait masculin (16x23cm-6x9in) pen Indian ink. 20-Mar-2 Chayette & Cheval, Paris #83/R
£903	$1435	€1300	Modele assis, tete tournee vers la gauche (22x14cm-9x6in) init. graphite dr prov. 29-Apr-3 Artcurial Briest, Paris #55/R est:1000-1200
£1266	$1975	€2000	Nu de femme (28x18cm-11x7in) s. pencil. 20-Oct-2 Claude Boisgirard, Paris #1/R est:1500-2000

VALLS SANMARTI, Ernesto (19/20th C) Spanish

£2632	$4263	€4000	Women (100x81cm-39x32in) s. 21-Jan-3 Durán, Madrid #128/R

VALLS, Dino (1959-) Spanish

£7051	$11141	€11000	Third bank of the river (92x73cm-36x29in) s.i.verso. 13-Nov-2 Ansorena, Madrid #39/R est:6000

VALLS, Xavier (1923-) Spanish

£5449	$8609	€8500	Acacia a la maison rose (65x54cm-26x21in) s. s.i.d.1965 verso pencil. 15-Nov-2 Laurence Calmels, Paris #33a/R est:8000
£5769	$9115	€9000	Nature morte au pavot (55x46cm-22x18in) mono. s.i.d.71 verso prov. 15-Nov-2 Laurence Calmels, Paris #34a/R

Works on paper

£545	$861	€850	Bosquet a Mosnes (18x26cm-7x10in) mono.d.70 W/C prov. 15-Nov-2 Laurence Calmels, Paris #35a
£705	$1114	€1100	Nu de dos (49x34cm-19x13in) mono. s.i.d.1977 verso crayon prov. 15-Nov-2 Laurence Calmels, Paris #37a
£1090	$1722	€1700	Vase de primeveres (29x24cm-11x9in) mono. s.i.d.1971 verso W/C prov. 15-Nov-2 Laurence Calmels, Paris #32a/R
£3526	$5571	€5500	Porte s'ouvrant sur deux arbres (41x33cm-16x13in) mono. s.i.d.1967 verso prov. 15-Nov-2 Laurence Calmels, Paris #36a/R

VALLUY, P (20th C) French?

£2397	$3764	€3500	Femme nue accroupie (65x54cm-26x21in) s.d.65. 15-Apr-3 Laurence Calmels, Paris #4228/R

VALMIER, Georges (1885-1937) French

£2639	$4196	€3800	Motif decoratif (10x13cm-4x5in) s. paper on canvas prov.lit. 29-Apr-3 Artcurial Briest, Paris #115/R est:4000-5000

Works on paper

£14744	$23147	€23000	Piano (11x12cm-4x5in) s. gouache exec.1920 lit. 10-Dec-2 Piasa, Paris #57/R est:10000-12000
£28000	$44240	€42000	Composition (63x48cm-25x19in) s.d.1922 pencil oil on canvas lit. 3-Apr-3 Christie's, Kensington #125/R est:20000-30000

VALOIS, Jean Chretien (younger) (1809-?) Dutch

Works on paper

£419	$666	€629	Portrait of young man (19x16cm-7x6in) s.d.1839 W/C. 5-Mar-3 Rasmussen, Copenhagen #2140 (D.KR 4500)

VALTAT, Louis (1869-1952) French

£2000 $3180 €3000 Deux pommes (13x14cm-5x6in) st.init. board on panel lit. 20-Mar-3 Sotheby's, Olympia #156/R est:2500-3000
£2468 $3826 €3900 Paysage d'automne (24x32cm-9x13in) st.init. 29-Sep-2 Eric Pillon, Calais #170/R
£2568 $4005 €3800 Cabanon (24x19cm-9x7in) init. panel. 28-Mar-3 Claude Aguttes, Neuilly #132
£2581 $4000 €3872 La conversation au bois (18x13cm-7x5in) init. board painted 1911 prov. 26-Sep-2 Christie's, Rockefeller NY #567/R est:4000-6000
£2642 $4200 €3963 Deux figures (18x11cm-7x4in) st.init. board on panel prov. 27-Feb-3 Christie's, Rockefeller NY #99/R est:5000
£2885 $4471 €4500 Vache dans la campagne (27x41cm-11x16in) s. 6-Dec-2 Rieunier, Bailly-Pommery, Mathias, Paris #84/R
£3000 $4650 €4500 La chienne briard et son chiot (35x40cm-14x16in) init. oil paper on card. 5-Dec-2 Christie's, Kensington #66/R est:3000-4000
£3526 $5500 €5289 Panier (32x37cm-13x15in) s. panel prov. 12-Apr-3 Weschler, Washington #533/R est:8000-12000
£3871 $6000 €5807 Vase en fleurs (32x16cm-13x6in) init. 26-Sep-2 Christie's, Rockefeller NY #576/R est:5000-7000
£4000 $6360 €6000 La fete (27x21cm-11x8in) init. 20-Mar-3 Sotheby's, Olympia #58/R est:3000-5000
£4088 $6500 €6132 Femme a la robe violette (26x20cm-10x8in) st.init. painted 1926 prov.lit. 27-Feb-3 Christie's, Rockefeller NY #51/R est:9000
£4088 $6500 €6132 Bouquet de fleurs (21x21cm-8x8in) st.init. painted c.1920 prov. 27-Feb-3 Christie's, Rockefeller NY #93/R
£4140 $6459 €6500 Couturieres (20x14cm-8x6in) studio st. painted c.1925. 7-Nov-2 Chochon-Barre & Allardi, Paris #235/R
£4500 $6930 €6750 Le porte-montre (46x38cm-18x15in) s. prov.lit. 23-Oct-2 Sotheby's, Olympia #678/R est:5000-7000
£4839 $7500 €7259 Jean Valtat, enfant (41x27cm-16x11in) init. painted c.1911 prov. 26-Sep-2 Christie's, Rockefeller NY #561/R est:4000-6000
£5578 $8869 €8200 Bouquet (17x16cm-7x6in) mono. canvas on panel. 28-Feb-3 Joron-Derem, Paris #30/R
£6207 $10366 €9000 Jeune femme et son modele (55x46cm-22x18in) mono. prov.lit. 10-Jul-3 Artcurial Briest, Paris #178/R est:10000-12000
£6475 $10360 €9000 Maison dans les arbres (24x19cm-9x7in) init. panel. 18-May-3 Eric Pillon, Calais #58/R
£7051 $11071 €11000 Vase de ioletes (27x35cm-11x14in) s. prov. 10-Dec-2 Pierre Berge, Paris #15/R est:15000
£7693 $12847 €11000 Fleurs dans un vase (28x26cm-11x10in) mono. panel prov.exhib. 26-Jun-3 Tajan, Paris #252/R est:9000-12000
£9000 $15030 €13050 La corbeille de fruits, le pain et l'huilier (38x46cm-15x18in) init. painted c.1910 prov. 24-Jun-3 Sotheby's, London #203/R est:10000-15000
£9422 $14981 €13850 Bouquet de fleurs (27x21cm-11x8in) s. panel lit. 26-Feb-3 Artcurial Briest, Paris #254/R est:9000-12000
£10000 $16300 €15000 Paysage en Normandie (40x65cm-16x26in) init. lit. 3-Feb-3 Bonhams, New Bond Street #24/R est:10000-15000
£10000 $16000 €14500 Paysage au bord de la mer (27x41cm-11x16in) init. 12-Mar-3 Libert, Castor, Paris #200/R est:5000-6000
£10063 $16000 €15095 Nature morte aux fruits (37x53cm-15x21in) init. board. 27-Feb-3 Christie's, Rockefeller NY #101/R est:18000
£10256 $16103 €16000 Le lac du bois de Boulogne (27x35cm-11x14in) s. cardboard prov. 11-Dec-2 Maigret, Paris #105/R est:10000-12000
£10500 $17535 €15225 Vase de fleurs sur fond rouge (24x19cm-9x7in) s. board painted c.1940. 24-Jun-3 Sotheby's, London #194/R est:7000-9000
£10791 $17266 €15000 Le fils de l'artiste dans sa voiturette (50x50cm-20x20in) mono. lit. 18-May-3 Eric Pillon, Calais #61/R
£10993 $17809 €15500 Au theatre (30x21cm-12x8in) st.mono. cardboard on panel lit. 23-May-3 Binoche, Paris #48/R est:7500-8500
£11354 $17712 €17031 Bouquet d'anemones (27x21cm-11x8in) s. panel. 6-Nov-2 Dobiaschofsky, Bern #1027/R est:25000 (S.FR 26000)
£11392 $17658 €18000 Anemones et tulipes jaunes (55x46cm-22x18in) s. painted c.1920 prov.lit. 28-Sep-2 Christie's, Paris #37/R est:20000-28000
£11392 $18000 €18000 Bouquet de tulipes et d'iris (55x38cm-22x15in) s. painted c.1930. 1-Dec-2 Anaf, Lyon #185/R est:25000
£12422 $20000 €18633 Bouquet de violettes au vase Lenoble (27x35cm-11x14in) s. painted c.1930. 7-May-3 Sotheby's, New York #181/R est:18000-25000
£13986 $23357 €20000 Champs de ble et de coquelicots (47x55cm-19x22in) s. lit. 30-Jun-3 Artcurial Briest, Paris #71/R est:20000-30000
£14286 $23000 €21429 Anemones (41x33cm-16x13in) s. painted c.1930 prov. 8-May-3 Christie's, Rockefeller NY #198/R est:22000-28000
£14828 $23724 €21500 Femme dans une galerie (28x18cm-11x7in) s. cardboard. 12-Mar-3 Libert, Castor, Paris #199 est:3000-4000
£15385 $24000 €23078 Voiliers a Ouistreham (27x41cm-11x16in) st.mono. painted 1930 lit. 6-Nov-2 Sotheby's, New York #160/R est:20000-30000
£15723 $24371 €25000 Debut de printemps dans l'esterel (60x73cm-24x29in) st.sig. painted c.1900 prov. 30-Oct-2 Artcurial Briest, Paris #327/R est:18000-22000
£15823 $24684 €25000 Nature morte aux apricots (33x46cm-13x18in) s.d.1945 prov. 20-Oct-2 Claude Boisgirard, Paris #24/R est:23000-25000
£16552 $26483 €24000 Bouquet de muguet sur un table (39x46cm-15x18in) init. 12-Mar-3 Libert, Castor, Paris #198/R est:12000-15000
£17391 $28000 €26087 Portrait de femme (81x65cm-32x26in) init. 8-May-3 Christie's, Rockefeller NY #145/R est:35000-45000
£17722 $27468 €28000 Vase d'anemones a la draperie bleue (46x38cm-18x15in) s. prov.lit. 28-Sep-2 Christie's, Paris #38/R est:24000-30000
£18000 $29520 €27000 Deux enfants sur la place (81x100cm-32x39in) st.sig. 4-Feb-3 Christie's, London #296/R est:24000
£20000 $32800 €30000 Roses blanches au vase de Sevres (81x66cm-32x26in) s. painted c.1920 prov. 4-Feb-3 Christie's, London #259/R est:18000
£20979 $35035 €30000 Anemones et fleurs de printemps (55x46cm-22x18in) s. lit. 30-Jun-3 Artcurial Briest, Paris #70/R est:30000-40000
£24359 $38000 €36539 Le port (54x65cm-21x26in) init. 20-Sep-2 Sloan, North Bethesda #372/R est:40000-50000
£25676 $40055 €38000 Embouchure de l'Orne (45x55cm-18x22in) s. prov.lit. 26-Mar-3 Tajan, Paris #27/R
£26000 $40040 €39000 Les chaumieres (54x65cm-21x26in) s. painted c.1903 prov.exhib. 22-Oct-2 Sotheby's, London #208/R est:20000-30000
£29114 $45127 €46000 Apres-midi dans le jardin de Choisel (54x73cm-21x29in) s. painted c.1935 prov. 28-Sep-2 Christie's, Paris #41/R est:25000-35000
£30000 $50100 €43500 Le Rastel d'Agay (46x61cm-18x24in) s. painted c.1898 prov. 25-Jun-3 Christie's, London #147/R est:18000-24000
£30406 $47433 €45000 Massif de fleurs et roches rouges (60x73cm-24x29in) s. prov. 26-Mar-3 Tajan, Paris #26/R
£31056 $50000 €46584 Bouquet de roses a la cruche verte (55x38cm-22x15in) s. painted 1907 lit. 8-May-3 Christie's, Rockefeller NY #155/R est:40000-60000
£32258 $50968 €50000 Vase de chardons (65x54cm-26x21in) s. painted 1934 lit. 18-Dec-2 Ferri, Paris #111/R est:60000
£38820 $62500 €58230 Le port (54x65cm-21x26in) init. painted c.1900. 7-May-3 Sotheby's, New York #148/R est:50000-70000
£40000 $62000 €60000 Bouquet de lilac a la poitiche chinoise (81x65cm-32x26in) s. painted c.1925. 5-Dec-2 Christie's, Kensington #67/R est:20000-30000
£45000 $75150 €65250 Pins en bord de mer, Antheor (82x100cm-32x39in) painted c.1899 prov.exhib. 25-Jun-3 Christie's, London #139/R est:18000-24000
£53103 $84966 €77000 Personnages dans un rue (46x61cm-18x24in) init. panel prov. 12-Mar-3 Libert, Castor, Paris #197/R est:30000-40000
£55128 $86000 €82692 Vase de fleurs (74x60cm-29x24in) s.d.1930 prov. 7-Nov-2 Christie's, Rockefeller NY #302/R est:60000-80000
£66456 $103006 €105000 Catalogne, le Mas Reig a Banyuls (54x65cm-21x26in) s. prov.exhib.lit. 28-Sep-2 Christie's, Paris #10/R est:30000-40000
£76552 $122483 €111000 La marchande de parapluies (40x51cm-16x20in) init. panel. 12-Mar-3 Libert, Castor, Paris #196/R est:30000-40000

Works on paper

£426 $689 €600 Dans un jardin (16x23cm-6x9in) mono. ink. 21-May-3 Cornette de St.Cyr, Paris #10/R
£489 $817 €700 Enfants a la poupee (31x23cm-12x9in) mono. chl dr. 26-Jun-3 Tajan, Paris #74/R
£496 $829 €700 Femme assise de dos (26x23cm-10x9in) studio st. crayon W/C. 23-Jun-3 Claude Boisgirard, Paris #59
£570 $889 €900 Portraits de femmes (8x9cm-3x4in) st.sig. W/C conte pencil pair. 20-Oct-2 Mercier & Cie, Lille #344
£641 $1006 €1000 Jeune femme assise devant le feu (18x25cm-7x10in) st.init. W/C. 13-Dec-2 Piasa, Paris #265/R
£1035 $1728 €1500 Les elegantes (27x20cm-11x8in) st.mono. W/C pencil. 10-Jul-3 Artcurial Briest, Paris #31/R est:1500-2000
£1799 $2950 €2500 Scene de faubourg (30x23cm-12x9in) st.sig. W/C. 4-Jun-3 Marc Kohn, Paris #34/R est:2000-2500
£2000 $3080 €3000 Portrait de femme au chapeau bleu (38x28cm-15x11in) st.init. pastel chl exec.c.1918-20 prov. 23-Oct-2 Sotheby's, Olympia #667/R est:800-1200
£2200 $3586 €3300 Sous-bois fleuri (21x26cm-8x10in) init. W/C over pencil executed c.1909 prov. 3-Feb-3 Bonhams, New Bond Street #8/R est:1000-1500
£8228 $12753 €13000 Paysage de Normandie (32x51cm-13x20in) init. W/C chl exec.c.1910 prov.exhib. 28-Sep-2 Christie's, Paris #11/R est:6000-9000

VALTER, Florence E (19/20th C) British

Works on paper

£244 $400 €366 Working the land (36x51cm-14x20in) s. W/C. 31-May-3 Harvey Clar, Oakland #1140

VALTER, Frederick E (1850-1930) British

£260 $406 €390 Cattle in a landscape (22x33cm-9x13in) s. 25-Mar-3 Gildings, Market Harborough #366
£652 $1017 €1088 Sheep in a snowstorm, the rescue (48x84cm-19x33in) s. s.i.verso prov. 13-Apr-3 Levis, Calgary #217/R est:2000-2500 (C.D 1500)

Works on paper

£280 $456 €420 Sheep and cattle resting in a pasture, farmhouse to the distance (41x17cm-16x7in) s.d.1894 W/C. 11-Feb-3 Fellows & Sons, Birmingham #130/R
£340 $524 €510 Sheep and cattle in a rural landscape (34x58cm-13x23in) s. W/C. 22-Oct-2 Bonhams, Knightsbridge #41/R
£340 $527 €510 Cattle at rest in landscape (23x33cm-9x13in) s.d.1910 W/C. 17-Jul-2 Goldings, Lincolnshire #344
£450 $734 €675 Cattle watering at sunset (24x18cm-9x7in) s.d.1905 pencil W/C bodycol gum arabic. 29-Jan-3 Dreweatt Neate, Newbury #15

VALTER, Henry (fl.1854-1864) British
£650 $1066 €975 Dutch schuyt entering harbour (51x68cm-20x27in) s. s.i.verso. 5-Jun-3 Christie's, Kensington #761/R

VALTON, Charles (1851-1918) French
Sculpture
£1500 $2280 €2250 Marco - standing setter (33x42cm-13x17in) s.i. dark brown pat. bronze. 28-Aug-2 Sotheby's, London #836/R est:1500-2000
£6800 $10608 €10200 Guard dog (89x69cm-35x27in) s.st.Prenez Garde brown pat bronze green marble base gilt metal. 9-Apr-3 Sotheby's, London #176/R est:3000-5000

VALTON, Edmond Eugène (1836-1910) French
£1200 $1824 €1800 Young puppeteer (37x45cm-15x18in) s. panel. 29-Aug-2 Christie's, Kensington #79/R est:800-1200

VAN GOOL STUDIOS (20th C) French
Works on paper
£265 $432 €400 Cendrillon (32x50cm-13x20in) ink gouache col crayon. 3-Feb-3 Cornette de St.Cyr, Paris #267
£397 $648 €600 Trois petits cochons (35x43cm-14x17in) ink gouache col crayon. 3-Feb-3 Cornette de St.Cyr, Paris #264
£397 $648 €600 Pinocchio (65x50cm-26x20in) ink gouache col crayon. 3-Feb-3 Cornette de St.Cyr, Paris #262/R
£530 $864 €800 Livre de la Jungle (41x53cm-16x21in) ink gouache col crayon. 3-Feb-3 Cornette de St.Cyr, Paris #260/R

VANAISE, Gustaaf (1854-1902) Belgian
£481 $755 €750 Le coin d'atelier (35x20cm-14x8in) studio st. 16-Dec-2 Millon & Associes, Paris #169

VANCE, William (20th C) French?
Works on paper
£421 $665 €610 Bob Morane (48x36cm-19x14in) s. Chinese ink. 7-Apr-3 Claude Aguttes, Neuilly #100

VANDENBERG, Philippe (1952-) Belgian?
£2115 $3279 €3300 Composition (100x120cm-39x47in) s.d.1988 verso prov. 7-Dec-2 De Vuyst, Lokeren #500/R est:2800-3300

VANDENBRANDEN, Guy (1926-) Belgian
£486 $773 €700 Trois carres noir (90x90cm-35x35in) s. d.1975 verso panel. 29-Apr-3 Campo & Campo, Antwerp #307
Works on paper
£346 $533 €550 Abstraction in black and orange (48x17cm-19x7in) s. ink tempera. 22-Oct-2 Campo & Campo, Antwerp #277
£382 $607 €550 Composition (33x56cm-13x22in) s.d.1965 mixed media verso. 29-Apr-3 Campo, Vlaamse Kaai #364

VANDERBANK, John (1694-1739) British
£2400 $3960 €3480 Portrait of a gentleman (125x100cm-49x39in) s.d.1728. 2-Jul-3 Sotheby's, Olympia #22/R est:2500-3500
Works on paper
£560 $902 €840 Two figures on horseback approached by huntsman with dogs (23x36cm-9x14in) s.d.1724 W/C bodycol. 9-May-3 Mallams, Oxford #64/R

VANDERCAM, Serge (1924-) Danish
£1439 $2302 €2000 Composition (107x71cm-42x28in) s.d.67 acrylic paper. 17-May-3 De Vuyst, Lokeren #361/R est:2000-2600
Sculpture
£1069 $1657 €1700 Vogel (85x37cm-33x15in) s.d.75 wood. 5-Oct-2 De Vuyst, Lokeren #358/R
Works on paper
£629 $969 €1000 Composition (33x50cm-13x20in) s.d.1984 mixed media. 22-Oct-2 Campo, Vlaamse Kaai #673

VANDERCAMMEN, Edmond (1901-1980) Belgian
£2878 $4604 €4000 Paysage cubiste (47x66cm-19x26in) s.d.29. 13-May-3 Palais de Beaux Arts, Brussels #168/R est:4000-5000

VANDEREYKEN (?) Belgian?
Works on paper
£1266 $2000 €2000 La paix, dame avec une colombe dans les bras (76x57cm-30x22in) mixed media. 2-Dec-2 Amberes, Antwerp #1370

VANDERLICK, Armand (1897-1985) Belgian
£655 $1048 €950 Trois jeunes femmes conversant (22x42cm-9x17in) s. panel. 17-Mar-3 Horta, Bruxelles #68
£962 $1490 €1500 Ostend harbour (48x51cm-19x20in) s.d.1938. 7-Dec-2 De Vuyst, Lokeren #341/R est:1600-2000
£2158 $3453 €3000 Beach huts (46x65cm-18x26in) s. s.i. 17-May-3 De Vuyst, Lokeren #481/R est:2500-3000
£2483 $3972 €3600 Beach (50x58cm-20x23in) s.d.38 panel. 15-Mar-3 De Vuyst, Lokeren #556/R est:3300-4000
£5556 $8833 €8000 Cabines de plage (65x80cm-26x31in) s.d.1961. 29-Apr-3 Campo & Campo, Antwerp #311/R est:3500-4500
£5660 $8774 €9000 Beach huts (45x76cm-18x30in) s.d.60. 5-Oct-2 De Vuyst, Lokeren #565/R est:4000-5000
£6289 $9748 €10000 Still life (110x125cm-43x49in) s.d.52 exhib.lit. 5-Oct-2 De Vuyst, Lokeren #480/R est:10000-12000
Works on paper
£324 $518 €450 Woman seated (24x26cm-9x10in) s. W/C. 17-May-3 De Vuyst, Lokeren #363
£597 $926 €950 Still life (35x47cm-14x19in) s. gouache exec.c.1970-1975. 5-Oct-2 De Vuyst, Lokeren #360
£629 $975 €1000 Femme au chapeau (26x35cm-10x14in) s. gouache. 5-Oct-2 De Vuyst, Lokeren #361

VANDERMEER, Arthur (?) ?
£272 $425 €408 Ship ablaze (18x23cm-7x9in) board. 30-Mar-3 Susanin's, Chicago #6040/R

VANDERMOERE, Henri (1939-) Belgian
£828 $1324 €1200 Fallen into decay (100x140cm-39x55in) s. 15-Mar-3 De Vuyst, Lokeren #329/R
£1195 $1852 €1900 Show-case cupboard (100x90cm-39x35in) s. 5-Oct-2 De Vuyst, Lokeren #363/R
£1195 $1852 €1900 Frituur Moderne (100x120cm-39x47in) s. 5-Oct-2 De Vuyst, Lokeren #364/R est:1700-2000

VANDERPANT, John (1884-1939) Canadian
Photographs
£1210 $1911 €1815 Generosity (20x25cm-8x10in) s.i.num.81-D-081 verso vintage silver bromide print prov.exhib. 14-Nov-2 Heffel, Vancouver #70/R est:2500-3500 (C.D 3000)
£2218 $3504 €3327 Tower in white (35x27cm-14x11in) s.i.num.2 vintage silver bromide print prov.lit. 14-Nov-2 Heffel, Vancouver #74/R est:2500-3500 (C.D 5500)

VANDERSANDEN, Raymond (1917-) Belgian
£588 $947 €900 Vue du port d'Anvers (22x28cm-9x11in) s. panel. 14-Jan-3 Vanderkindere, Brussels #170

VANDERSTEEN, Germain (1925-) French
£255 $398 €400 Bol rouge et bleu (66x52cm-26x20in) s. 5-Nov-2 Tajan, Paris #88/R
£319 $497 €500 Arretes (65x53cm-26x21in) s. s.i.verso. 5-Nov-2 Tajan, Paris #83/R
£319 $497 €500 Arriere petit gringalet (60x72cm-24x28in) s. 5-Nov-2 Tajan, Paris #85/R
£328 $511 €492 Nativite au pot a lait (46x37cm-18x15in) s. i. verso board. 6-Nov-2 Dobiaschofsky, Bern #3756 (S.FR 750)
£382 $596 €600 Chat hippy (60x72cm-24x28in) s. s.verso. 5-Nov-2 Tajan, Paris #84/R
£414 $654 €600 Apres-midi d'un faune (50x61cm-20x24in) s.d.1945 s.i.verso panel. 4-Apr-3 Tajan, Paris #13
£414 $654 €600 Jungle (45x60cm-18x24in) s. panel. 4-Apr-3 Tajan, Paris #12/R
£446 $696 €700 Inspire de la musique du genial Beethoven (55x73cm-22x29in) s.i.d.1946 s.verso exhib. 5-Nov-2 Tajan, Paris #81/R
£510 $795 €800 Et moi, et moi? Oiseau glouton (66x54cm-26x21in) s.i. s.verso. 5-Nov-2 Tajan, Paris #86/R
£510 $795 €800 Chat aux grosses moustaches noires (65x54cm-26x21in) s. s.i.verso. 5-Nov-2 Tajan, Paris #82/R
£966 $1526 €1400 World creation (69x80cm-27x31in) s. s.i.on stretcher after Darius Milhaud exhib. 4-Apr-3 Tajan, Paris #36/R
£1035 $1635 €1500 Big blue cat ad red spider (65x54cm-26x21in) s.d.1967 panel exhib. 4-Apr-3 Tajan, Paris #14/R
£1724 $2724 €2500 Oiseaux (65x54cm-26x21in) s. masonite prov. 4-Apr-3 Tajan, Paris #16/R est:1200
Works on paper
£223 $348 €350 Flowers (64x50cm-25x20in) s. goo. 5-Nov-2 Tajan, Paris #89/R
£241 $381 €350 Bouquet (31x23cm-12x9in) s. s.i.verso col crayon dr. 4-Apr-3 Tajan, Paris #35
£252 $390 €400 Oiseau fantastique (64x48cm-25x19in) s.i. W/C ink. 30-Oct-2 Artcurial Briest, Paris #380
£255 $398 €400 Fleurs dans un vase jaune (64x49cm-25x19in) s. gouache. 5-Nov-2 Tajan, Paris #92
£276 $436 €400 Bouquet, vase vert (65x50cm-26x20in) s. col ink paper on cardboard. 4-Apr-3 Tajan, Paris #31
£759 $1199 €1100 Green and red cat (63x48cm-25x19in) s. W/C. 4-Apr-3 Tajan, Paris #15

VANDEVERDONCK, Franz (19th C) Belgian

£460 $718 €690 Dog in harness pulling a cart with farmers wares (22x38cm-9x15in) s.d.1862 indis.i.verso panel. 23-Sep-2 Bonhams, Chester #956

£1200 $1896 €1800 Poultry in a landscape at springtime (18x24cm-7x9in) s.d.1867 panel. 14-Nov-2 Christie's, Kensington #178/R est:700-1000

£2000 $3080 €3000 Sheep and ducks at a pond. Donkey, sheep at a pond (18x26cm-7x10in) s.indis d. panel two. 24-Oct-2 Christie's, Kensington #88/R est:1000-1500

VANE, Richard (19th C) British?

£450 $702 €675 Small boys and a toy yacht in a rock pool (51x76cm-20x30in) s.d.1880. 8-Oct-2 Bonhams, Knightsbridge #167/R

VANEST, Alfred (?) Belgian

£1007 $1621 €1500 Beguine dans les urelles (65x80cm-26x31in) s. 18-Feb-3 Galerie Moderne, Brussels #404/R est:1500-2000

VANGELLI, Antonio (1917-) Italian

£2436 $3824 €3800 View of Civitella (80x100cm-31x39in) painted 1959 lit. 21-Nov-2 Finarte, Rome #216/R

VANGELLI, Sandro (1902-) Italian

£559 $894 €810 Portrait of seated woman (31x24cm-12x9in) s. board. 11-Mar-3 Babuino, Rome #152/R

VANGI, Giuliano (1931-) Italian

Works on paper

£833 $1308 €1300 Man (68x46cm-27x18in) s.d.93 pencil. 19-Nov-2 Finarte, Milan #5/R

£2365 $3689 €3500 Meeting (50x70cm-20x28in) s.i. pastel. 28-Mar-3 Farsetti, Prato #377/R

VANGO, David (20th C) British?

Works on paper

£330 $551 €479 Sounds like green (42x42cm-17x17in) s. pastel exhib. 17-Jun-3 Anderson & Garland, Newcastle #157

VANHOOF, Jan (1911-) Belgian

£1304 $2139 €1800 La fandouch et la fontaine mefjarine (100x80cm-39x31in) s.d.1942. 27-May-3 Campo & Campo, Antwerp #248 est:2200-2500

VANMOUR, Jan Baptiste (1671-1737) Flemish

£54839 $86645 €85000 Portrait de femme (76x63cm-30x25in) 19-Dec-2 Claude Aguttes, Neuilly #110/R est:60000

£54839 $86645 €85000 PO. d'homme (76x63cm-30x25in) 19-Dec-2 Claude Aguttes, Neuilly #109/R est:60000

£464516 $733936 €720000 Sultan et suite (76x150cm-30x59in) prov.lit. 19-Dec-2 Claude Aguttes, Neuilly #112/R est:300000

£464516 $733936 €720000 Grand vizir et suite (76x150cm-30x59in) prov.lit. 19-Dec-2 Claude Aguttes, Neuilly #111/R est:300000

VANMOUR, Jan Baptiste (style) (1671-1737) Flemish

£6000 $9360 €9000 Portrait of a Sultan (31x19cm-12x7in) i. panel. 15-Oct-2 Sotheby's, London #65/R est:2000-3000

£10000 $15600 €15000 Portrait of a Sultan (31x20cm-12x8in) i. panel. 15-Oct-2 Sotheby's, London #64/R est:3000-5000

VANNI, Francesco (c.1563-1610) Italian

£74074 $120000 €111111 Rest on the Flight into Egypt - Madonna della Pappa (119x88cm-47x35in) prov.lit. 24-Jan-3 Christie's, Rockefeller NY #84/R est:40000-60000

Works on paper

£437 $681 €656 Biblical scene (20x41cm-8x16in) s.mono.d.1553 WC sold with another. 6-Nov-2 Dobiaschofsky, Bern #1191/R (S.FR 1000)

£1013 $1600 €1600 Le couronnement de la Vierge (19x25cm-7x10in) i. black chk pen brown ink brown wash. 27-Nov-2 Christie's, Paris #56/R est:1200-1600

£5000 $8350 €7250 Madonna interceding with Christ on behalf of Saint Francis, attended by a female Saint (24x16cm-9x6in) black white chk. 8-Jul-3 Christie's, London #11/R est:4000-6000

£23000 $38410 €33350 Portrait of Pasitea Crogi, her eyes closed (18x14cm-7x6in) black red white chk pastel prov.lit. 8-Jul-3 Christie's, London #30/R est:20000-30000

VANNI, Francesco (attrib) (c.1563-1610) Italian

Works on paper

£2568 $4005 €3800 Head of women (12x17cm-5x7in) chk. 27-Mar-3 Christie's, Paris #64/R

VANNI, Sam (1908-1992) Finnish

£379 $599 €550 Girl seated (64x54cm-25x21in) s.i.d.1931. 3-Apr-3 Hagelstam, Helsinki #973/R

£510 $811 €750 Coastal landscape (54x65cm-21x26in) s.d.1941. 27-Feb-3 Hagelstam, Helsinki #989

£791 $1266 €1100 Park (38x47cm-15x19in) s.d.1943. 17-May-3 Hagelstam, Helsinki #201/R

£1076 $1700 €1700 Evening light (50x65cm-20x26in) s.d.40. 1-Dec-2 Bukowskis, Helsinki #363/R est:1300-1500

£1361 $2163 €2000 Composition (56x36cm-22x14in) s.d.1954. 27-Feb-3 Hagelstam, Helsinki #975 est:2500

£9155 $14739 €13000 Composition (72x175cm-28x69in) s.d.60. 10-May-3 Bukowskis, Helsinki #220/R est:8000-10000

Works on paper

£633 $1000 €1000 Construction (65x40cm-26x16in) s.d.75 gouache. 1-Dec-2 Bukowskis, Helsinki #364/R

£762 $1211 €1120 Composition (45x60cm-18x24in) s.d.1970 gouache. 27-Feb-3 Hagelstam, Helsinki #990/R

£1079 $1727 €1500 Composition (59x76cm-23x30in) s.d.1965 gouache. 17-May-3 Hagelstam, Helsinki #200/R est:1500

£3165 $5000 €5000 Red tension (15x87cm-6x34in) s. gouache. 30-Nov-2 Hagelstam, Helsinki #168/R est:1700

VANNINI, Ottavio (1585-1643) Italian

£6289 $9748 €10000 Badonna with child (35x30cm-14x12in) prov. 2-Oct-2 Dorotheum, Vienna #60/R est:12000-16000

VANNINI, Ottavio (attrib) (1585-1643) Italian

£11408 $18367 €17000 Ceres, personifaction of summer (99x73cm-39x29in) 18-Feb-3 Sotheby's, Amsterdam #402/R est:16000-18000

VANNUTELLI, Scipione (attrib) (1834-1894) Italian

£1500 $2385 €2250 L'Arco di Constantino, Roma (61x50cm-24x20in) i.verso. 20-Mar-3 Christie's, Kensington #79/R est:1500-2000

VANSTON, Dairine (1903-1988) Irish

Works on paper

£890 $1398 €1300 From the window (43x28cm-17x11in) gouache. 15-Apr-3 De Veres Art Auctions, Dublin #233/R est:800-1200

VANTINI, Domenico (attrib) (1764-1821) Italian

Miniatures

£1000 $1650 €1450 Young lady with pearls in her hair (6cm-2in circular) gold back frame gilt metal border. 1-Jul-3 Bonhams, New Bond Street #110/R est:1000-1500

VANTORE, Mogens (1895-1977) Danish

£299 $475 €449 Summer's day in Paris (55x68cm-22x27in) s.i. 5-May-3 Rasmussen, Vejle #423 (D.KR 3200)

£300 $483 €450 Street scene in Paris (70x54cm-28x21in) s.i. 19-Jan-3 Hindemae, Ullerslev #7516/R (D.KR 3400)

£309 $482 €464 Street scene from Paris with figures (96x121cm-38x48in) s.i. 11-Nov-2 Rasmussen, Vejle #709/R (D.KR 3600)

£321 $495 €482 Parisian street scene (58x45cm-23x18in) s. 26-Oct-2 Rasmussen, Havnen #2018 (D.KR 3800)

£339 $525 €509 Autumn scene in Paris (75x99cm-30x39in) s.i. 1-Oct-2 Rasmussen, Copenhagen #294/R (D.KR 4000)

£343 $535 €515 Painter in morning sunshine (90x70cm-35x28in) s.d.1966 lit. 11-Nov-2 Rasmussen, Vejle #41/R (D.KR 4000)

£389 $606 €584 Flowers in jug (70x57cm-28x22in) s.d.75. 23-Sep-2 Rasmussen, Vejle #2298 (D.KR 4600)

£391 $622 €587 Still life of fruit and potted plant on table (80x66cm-31x26in) s. 10-Mar-3 Rasmussen, Vejle #534 (D.KR 4200)

£431 $655 €647 View from Christianshavn (86x100cm-34x39in) s. 27-Aug-2 Rasmussen, Copenhagen #1703/R (D.KR 5000)

£705 $1093 €1100 Nanna in cornfield (62x50cm-24x20in) s.d.1935 panel. 5-Dec-2 Schopman, Hamburg #601

£1200 $1968 €1800 Street scene in Montmartre, Sacre Coeur beyond (150x182cm-59x72in) s.i.d.37. 5-Jun-3 Christie's, Kensington #723/R est:800-1200

VAQUER, Miguel (?) Spanish

£617 $901 €950 Rotas, Denia (73x60cm-29x24in) s. s.i.d.1949 verso. 17-Jun-2 Ansorena, Madrid #136/R

VAQUERO TURCIOS, Joaquin (1933-) Spanish

£1655 $2615 €2400 Boat (50x61cm-20x24in) s. board painted 1995 prov. 1-Apr-3 Segre, Madrid #243/R

£2069 $3290 €3000 Venice (66x81cm-26x32in) s. 4-Mar-3 Ansorena, Madrid #232/R

Works on paper
£779 $1138 €1200 Sailing boats (49x71cm-19x28in) s. pastel. 17-Jun-2 Ansorena, Madrid #22/R

VARBERG, H (19th C) Swedish
£1490 $2369 €2235 Wooded landscape at sunset (104x155cm-41x61in) s.d.1888. 5-Mar-3 Rasmussen, Copenhagen #1910/R est:5000-7000 (D.KR 16000)

VARENNE, O (?) ?
£444 $738 €644 At the inn (54x47cm-21x19in) with sig. panel. 10-Jun-3 Ritchie, Toronto #138/R est:1000-1500 (C.D 1000)

VARGA, Istvan (1895-1978) Hungarian
£1548 $2415 €2322 Still life, 1927 (57x44cm-22x17in) s. 11-Sep-2 Kieselbach, Budapest #80/R (H.F 600000)
£2048 $3276 €3072 Boys on the sunlit street in Szentendre (48x54cm-19x21in) s. board. 16-May-3 Kieselbach, Budapest #67/R (H.F 700000)

VARGAS RUIZ, Guillermo (1910-1990) Spanish
£1290 $2039 €2000 Seated woman (33x35cm-13x14in) s. 18-Dec-2 Ansorena, Madrid #151/R

VARGAS, Alberto (20th C) American
Works on paper
£5449 $8500 €8174 Beautiful woman in Mexican town square (46x74cm-18x29in) s. W/C chl pen ink. 9-Nov-2 Illustration House, New York #104/R est:5000-7000
£22436 $35000 €33654 Woman in striped one piece bathing suit and broad-brimmed sunhat (97x41cm-38x16in) s. W/C executed c.1955. 9-Nov-2 Illustration House, New York #133/R est:40000-60000

VARI, Sophie (1940-) Greek
Works on paper
£2313 $3678 €3400 Ombres nostalgiques (100x80cm-39x31in) s.d.95 mixed media collage prov. 26-Feb-3 Artcurial Briest, Paris #573 est:1000-1500
£2381 $3786 €3500 Eternite secrete (100x80cm-39x31in) s.d.95 i.verso mixed media collage. 26-Feb-3 Artcurial Briest, Paris #572 est:1000-1500
£2449 $3894 €3600 Crime passionnel (100x80cm-39x31in) s.d.96 i.verso mixed media collage. 26-Feb-3 Artcurial Briest, Paris #570/R est:1000-1500
£2449 $3894 €3600 Ailes du charbon (100x80cm-39x31in) s.d.96 i.verso mixed media collage. 26-Feb-3 Artcurial Briest, Paris #571/R est:1000-1500

VARLEY, Cornelius (1781-1873) British
Works on paper
£350 $578 €508 Young boy resting near a village (48x38cm-19x15in) s. pen ink wash over pencil htd stopping out. 2-Jul-3 Sotheby's, Olympia #293/R
£700 $1148 €1015 View of Exeter cathedral (25x36cm-10x14in) i.verso pencil W/C prov. 5-Jun-3 Christie's, London #102/R est:800-1200
£900 $1485 €1305 Loading a sailing barge grounded at low tide (37x32cm-15x13in) s.i.d.1823 pencil W/C prov.exhib. 3-Jul-3 Christie's, Kensington #135
£1800 $2844 €2700 View of Kidbrook, Sussex (37x53cm-15x21in) s. brown wash over pencil. 28-Nov-2 Sotheby's, London #312/R est:2000-3000
£1800 $2790 €2700 Brampton, Cambridgeshire (25x37cm-10x15in) init.i.d.1807 pencil W/C. 4-Dec-2 Christie's, Kensington #111/R est:2000-3000
£3000 $4920 €4350 Welsh mine (22x30cm-9x12in) pencil W/C prov. 5-Jun-3 Christie's, London #96/R est:800-1200

VARLEY, Cornelius (attrib) (1781-1873) British
Works on paper
£310 $499 €465 Welsh landscape, Snowdon from Capel Curig (20x30cm-8x12in) W/C. 9-May-3 Mallams, Oxford #51/R

VARLEY, Edgar J (1839-1888) British
Works on paper
£350 $557 €525 Fishing by the riverbank (21x14cm-8x6in) s.d.1876 i.verso. 20-Mar-3 Martel Maides, Guernsey #160a

VARLEY, Frederick Horsman (1881-1969) Canadian/British
£5381 $8610 €8072 Manya, Portrait of Miriam Kennedy (30x38cm-12x15in) d.1942 verso panel prov.lit. 15-May-3 Heffel, Vancouver #60/R est:12000-15000 (C.D 12000)
£5823 $9201 €8735 Western Pass, BC (30x38cm-12x15in) d.1935 panel. 1-Dec-2 Levis, Calgary #105/R est:14000-18000 (C.D 14500)
£6667 $10933 €10001 Veterans (38x32cm-15x13in) i.d.1943 verso panel prov. 27-May-3 Sotheby's, Toronto #22/R est:12000-15000 (C.D 15000)
£8000 $13120 €12000 Grey day (30x38cm-12x15in) with sig.i.d.1948 board prov.lit. 27-May-3 Sotheby's, Toronto #210/R est:12000-15000 (C.D 18000)
£11111 $18222 €16667 Natasha (38x30cm-15x12in) s. panel prov.exhib. 27-May-3 Sotheby's, Toronto #148/R est:15000-18000 (C.D 25000)
£14574 $23318 €21861 Sand bar (30x36cm-12x14in) s.i.verso panel prov. 15-May-3 Heffel, Vancouver #91/R est:30000-35000 (C.D 32500)
£29148 $46637 €43722 Bridge over Lynn Creek (31x38cm-12x15in) s. painted c.1933 panel prov. 15-May-3 Heffel, Vancouver #58/R est:40000-50000 (C.D 65000)
£31111 $51022 €46667 Gypsy blood (60x50cm-24x20in) s. painted 1919 prov.exhib.lit. 3-Jun-3 Joyner, Toronto #71/R est:125000-175000 (C.D 70000)
£40323 $63710 €60485 Arctic seas composition no.1 (86x102cm-34x40in) s. prov.lit. 18-Nov-2 Sotheby's, Toronto #49/R est:100000-150000 (C.D 100000)
£82305 $127572 €123458 Portrait of Alice Massey (60x40cm-24x16in) painted c.1924-25 prov.lit. 3-Dec-2 Joyner, Toronto #63/R est:200000-300000 (C.D 200000)
Works on paper
£363 $573 €545 Workman resting. Smiling girl (18x13cm-7x5in) pencil executed c.1930 two prov. 14-Nov-2 Heffel, Vancouver #39 est:900-1200 (C.D 900)
£444 $701 €666 Maude and Fred Varley sitting by the fire. Black faced sheep, Lynn (20x26cm-8x10in) pencil double-sided prov. 14-Nov-2 Heffel, Vancouver #37 est:900-1200 (C.D 1100)
£524 $828 €786 Pumpkins, Thornhill (28x37cm-11x15in) i.d.1915 pencil prov. 14-Nov-2 Heffel, Vancouver #32 est:1500-2000 (C.D 1300)
£800 $1312 €1200 Doon Hill (21x26cm-8x10in) s. chl pastel double-sided. 3-Jun-3 Joyner, Toronto #252/R est:2000-2500 (C.D 1800)
£823 $1276 €1235 Vancouver houses, elevator and mountains (20x22cm-8x9in) sepia ink dr. executed c.1929 prov. 3-Dec-2 Joyner, Toronto #31/R est:2000-3000 (C.D 2000)
£978 $1604 €1467 Indian children, bras D'Or Lake (16x19cm-6x7in) s. pencil prov. 3-Jun-3 Joyner, Toronto #217/R est:1500-2000 (C.D 2200)
£978 $1604 €1418 Rocky mountains (22x28cm-9x11in) s. chl prov. 9-Jun-3 Hodgins, Calgary #58/R est:2250-2750 (C.D 2200)
£1333 $2187 €2000 Sumac (34x61cm-13x24in) s. chl prov. 27-May-3 Sotheby's, Toronto #195/R est:4000-5000 (C.D 3000)
£6278 $10045 €9417 Evening hike, Lynn Valley, BC (21x25cm-8x10in) s. W/C executed c.1934 prov.lit. 15-May-3 Heffel, Vancouver #128/R est:15000-18000 (C.D 14000)
£6855 $10831 €10283 Moonlight, the trail from Rice Lake (19x25cm-7x10in) s.i.d.1935 W/C prov.exhib.lit. 14-Nov-2 Heffel, Vancouver #77/R est:12000-15000 (C.D 17000)
£8889 $14578 €13334 Trees (24x33cm-9x13in) s. W/C pencil prov. 27-May-3 Sotheby's, Toronto #193/R est:5000-7000 (C.D 20000)

VARLEY, John (1778-1842) British
Works on paper
£250 $395 €363 River landscape with distant view of Viaduct (20x36cm-8x14in) s.d.1840 W/C. 23-Jul-3 Mallams, Oxford #208
£280 $437 €420 Highland landscape with cattle on a hilltop (16x26cm-6x10in) s. W/C. 6-Nov-2 Bonhams, Chester #537
£340 $530 €510 Castle in a wooded landscape (14x22cm-6x9in) W/C prov. 9-Apr-3 Cheffins Grain & Comins, Cambridge #561/R
£500 $815 €750 Hilly landscape, with figure and animals (15x27cm-6x11in) s.d.1841 W/C exhib. 30-Jan-3 Lawrence, Crewkerne #611/R
£540 $859 €810 Tranquil river landscape with cattle before a bridge (19x27cm-7x11in) s. W/C. 27-Feb-3 Bonhams, Chester #450
£550 $908 €798 Martello tower on the South Coast (13x20cm-5x8in) pencil W/C prov. 3-Jul-3 Christie's, Kensington #98/R
£580 $945 €870 Cows drinking at dusk (9x13cm-4x5in) W/C. 29-Jan-3 Sotheby's, Olympia #46/R
£800 $1248 €1200 Cattle watering at twilight (14x28cm-6x11in) s.d.1838 W/C. 5-Nov-2 Bonhams, New Bond Street #47/R est:800-1200
£800 $1312 €1200 Coastal scene with fisherfolk and beached vessels beyond (16x23cm-6x9in) s. pencil W/C sold with W/C by Circle of John Varley. 6-Jun-3 Christie's, London #101/R
£820 $1287 €1230 Fishing vessel off the coast with church on a cliff (19x30cm-7x12in) s. wash over pencil sold with two other dr. by same hand. 16-Dec-2 Bonhams, Bury St Edmunds #429
£900 $1395 €1350 Landscape with figures (15x28cm-6x11in) s.d.1841 W/C dr. 1-Oct-2 Capes Dunn, Manchester #823/R
£920 $1435 €1380 Figures outside a churchyard (16x23cm-6x9in) s. W/C. 15-Oct-2 Bearnes, Exeter #352/R
£1000 $1590 €1500 Bolton Abbey, Yorkshire (7x11cm-3x4in) W/C over pencil htd bodycol. 19-Mar-3 Sotheby's, London #202/R est:1000-1500

£1000 $1590 €1500 Berry Pomeroy Castle, above the River Dart (8x12cm-3x5in) s. W/C over pencil htd bodycol. 19-Mar-3 Sotheby's, London #203/R est:1000-1500
£1000 $1590 €1500 Scaletta, Sicily (8x11cm-3x4in) W/C over pencil htd stopping out. 19-Mar-3 Sotheby's, London #204/R est:1000-1500
£1200 $1872 €1800 Thames from Richmond Hill (18x27cm-7x11in) s.d.1834 W/C prov. 5-Nov-2 Bonhams, New Bond Street #40/R est:1200-1800
£1200 $1920 €1800 Figures near a lake, sunset (15x27cm-6x11in) s.d.1841 W/C htd gum arabic. 11-Mar-3 Bonhams, New Bond Street #39/R est:700-1000
£1600 $2544 €2400 River Thames at Chiswick (8x12cm-3x5in) W/C over pencil htd bodycol. 19-Mar-3 Sotheby's, London #200/R est:1000-1500
£1700 $2805 €2465 Tegwin ferry, Snowdon from near Harlech (37x49cm-15x19in) s.d.1819 pencil W/C scratching out. 3-Jul-3 Christie's, Kensington #80/R est:1000-1500
£2100 $3319 €3150 Cader Idris, North Wales (16x24cm-6x9in) s. W/C over pencil htd scratching out. 28-Nov-2 Sotheby's, London #299/R est:1500-2000
£2200 $3432 €3300 Figuerira (41x67cm-16x26in) s.d.1813 pencil W/C scratching out. 17-Oct-2 Christie's, Kensington #151/R est:1200-1800
£2400 $3744 €3600 Dolgellau bridge, North Wales (11x16cm-4x6in) W/C prov. 5-Nov-2 Bonhams, New Bond Street #70/R est:1500-2000
£2600 $4056 €3900 View in Battersea field near Nine Elms (32x43cm-13x17in) s.d.1830 W/C. 5-Nov-2 Bonhams, New Bond Street #36/R est:2000-3000
£2600 $4264 €3770 On the terrace (18x28cm-7x11in) s.i. pencil W/C gum arabic. 5-Jun-3 Christie's, London #66/R est:2500-3500
£2800 $4452 €4200 Harlech Castle, Merionethshire (8x13cm-3x5in) s. W/C over pencil htd stopping out. 19-Mar-3 Sotheby's, London #201/R est:1000-1500
£3000 $4920 €4350 Caernavon Castle, North Wales (11x17cm-4x7in) s. pencil W/C scratching out. 5-Jun-3 Christie's, London #63/R est:2500-3500
£3200 $5248 €4640 Thames near Windsor (13x19cm-5x7in) s.d.1827 pencil W/C prov.exhib. 5-Jun-3 Christie's, London #64/R est:2500-3500
£3600 $5760 €5400 Conway Castle, North Wales (47x53cm-19x21in) s.d.1812 W/C exhib. 11-Mar-3 Bonhams, New Bond Street #13/R est:3000-5000
£3800 $6004 €5700 Harlech Castle (18x25cm-7x10in) s. W/C prov.exhib. 27-Nov-2 Hamptons Fine Art, Godalming #171/R est:3000-4000
£5200 $7436 €7800 Harlech Castle (10x16cm-4x6in) pencil W/C gum scratching out prov.exhib.lit. 22-Jan-3 Christie's, London #24/R
£7500 $10725 €11250 On the Thames (20x28cm-8x11in) pencil W/C prov.lit. 22-Jan-3 Christie's, London #22/R est:12000
£8000 $13120 €11600 Conway Castle, Wales (43x74cm-17x29in) pencil W/C prov.exhib. 5-Jun-3 Christie's, London #65/R est:5000-8000
£16000 $22880 €24000 Plains of Marathon (17x26cm-7x10in) s.i.d.1834 verso pencil W/C scratching out prov.exhib.lit. 22-Jan-3 Christie's, London #21/R est:12000
£16000 $22880 €24000 Bamborough Castle (19x26cm-7x10in) s.i.d.1827 pencil W/C scratching out prov.exhib.lit. 22-Jan-3 Christie's, London #23/R est:12000

VARLEY, John (attrib) (1778-1842) British
Works on paper
£400 $616 €600 Dolgelly Bridge (11x16cm-4x6in) W/C. 5-Sep-2 Morphets, Harrogate #367/R
£400 $628 €600 Two anglers beside a loch (22x30cm-9x12in) pencil W/C prov. 19-Nov-2 Bonhams, Leeds #55
£500 $800 €750 Figure beside a lake with a castle and mountains beyond (20x33cm-8x13in) W/C. 13-Mar-3 Duke & Son, Dorchester #181/R

VARLEY, John (jnr) (?-1899) British
£550 $858 €825 Southwold Common, Suffolk (20x27cm-8x11in) s. board. 10-Apr-3 Tennants, Leyburn #981
£1493 $2448 €2165 School of Sheikh El Roulam in the Hassaneyn quarter, Cairo (61x46cm-24x18in) s.d.82 i.verso. 4-Jun-3 AB Stockholms Auktionsverk #2405/R est:25000-30000 (S.KR 19000)
£2800 $4368 €4200 On the Mahmoudieh Canal, Alexandria (45x61cm-18x24in) s. i.verso. 15-Oct-2 Sotheby's, London #202/R est:2000-3000
£4610 $7468 €6500 View of Oriental street (45x60cm-18x24in) s.d.1882. 22-May-3 Dorotheum, Vienna #126/R est:3400-4000
Works on paper
£400 $632 €600 Sunset at the Pyramids, Giza (25x36cm-10x14in) s. W/C. 26-Nov-2 Bonhams, Knightsbridge #7/R
£600 $972 €900 On the outside of Cairo (17x37cm-7x15in) s. pencil W/C. 23-Jan-3 Christie's, Kensington #338/R
£1200 $1992 €1800 Torii gate at Miyajima, Japan (52x69cm-20x27in) s.d.90 W/C. 12-Jun-3 Bonhams, New Bond Street #847/R est:1000-1500
£2400 $3984 €3600 Senjokaku pavilion and the pagoda, Miyajima, Japan (36x52cm-14x20in) s.d.90 W/C. 12-Jun-3 Bonhams, New Bond Street #849/R est:1200-1800
£2600 $4238 €3770 Sketch from nature on the Thames (28x40cm-11x16in) s.i. W/C. 21-Jul-3 Bonhams, Bath #8/R est:300-500

VARLIN, Willy Guggenheim (1900-1977) Swiss
£11354 $17825 €17031 London (56x88cm-22x35in) s. i.d.1955 verso prov.exhib.lit. 25-Nov-2 Sotheby's, Zurich #90/R est:20000-30000 (S.FR 26000)
£20087 $29328 €30131 Friedrich Kuhn (212x79cm-83x31in) pavatex two prov.exhib.lit. 4-Jun-2 Germann, Zurich #39/R est:45000-55000 (S.FR 46000)
£20283 $32453 €30425 Cafe de la Solitude, Lausanne (54x65cm-21x26in) s. exhib.lit.prov. 17-Mar-3 Philippe Schuler, Zurich #4564/R est:50000-70000 (S.FR 43000)
Works on paper
£905 $1511 €1312 New York police (30x22cm-12x9in) s. W/C Indian ink prov. 24-Jun-3 Koller, Zurich #74/R (S.FR 2000)
£15451 $24412 €23177 Cab in Malaga (53x80cm-21x31in) s. s.i.d.1959 gouache oil canvas exhib.lit. 26-Nov-2 Phillips, Zurich #79/R est:25000-35000 (S.FR 36000)

VARMETTI, Prof A (?) ?
Sculpture
£3038 $4800 €4557 The letter, Napoleon standing with his horse (44x51x20cm-17x20x8in) s. bronze marble base. 26-Nov-2 Christie's, Rockefeller NY #195/R est:3000-5000

VARMING, Agnete (20th C) Danish
£395 $615 €593 Marble Bridge (53x63cm-21x25in) s. exhib. 11-Nov-2 Rasmussen, Vejle #20/R (D.KR 4600)
£613 $981 €920 Interior scene with mother and children looking at starry sky (40x28cm-16x11in) s.d.36. 13-Jan-3 Rasmussen, Vejle #166/R (D.KR 7000)

VARO, Remedios (1900-1963) Spanish
£35616 $55918 €52000 Struggle for life (58x69cm-23x27in) i.verso. 15-Apr-3 Laurence Calmels, Paris #4425/R est:30000
£85366 $140000 €123781 Vampiro (46x27cm-18x11in) s. masonite prov.exhib.lit. 27-May-3 Sotheby's, New York #10
Works on paper
£13699 $21507 €20000 Hunger (32x46cm-13x18in) s. i.verso gouache chl exhib.lit. 15-Apr-3 Laurence Calmels, Paris #4426/R est:15000

VAROTARI, Alessandro (1588-1648) Italian
£20423 $32880 €29000 Allegory of the Dolfin family (7x123cm-3x48in) lit. 11-May-3 Finarte, Venice #25/R est:34000-40000
£44207 $72500 €66311 Ariadne on Naxos with Bacchus in the distance (116x149cm-46x59in) 29-May-3 Sotheby's, New York #9/R est:15000-20000

VAROTARI, Alessandro (circle) (1588-1648) Italian
£34000 $56780 €49300 Bathsheba (81x104cm-32x41in) 11-Jul-3 Christie's, Kensington #237/R est:3000-5000

VARRONE, Johann (1832-1910) Austrian
£478 $741 €717 Bellinzona, le Chateau d'Unterwald (17x21cm-7x8in) s.d.1868 paper oval. 7-Dec-2 Galerie du Rhone, Sion #118/R (S.FR 1100)
£674 $1045 €1011 Vue de Bellinzona (17x21cm-7x8in) s.d.1868 paper oval. 7-Dec-2 Galerie du Rhone, Sion #119/R (S.FR 1550)
£818 $1267 €1300 Island of Capri near Naples (20x23cm-8x9in) s.d.1907 i. verso board framed oval. 29-Oct-2 Dorotheum, Vienna #235/R

VARTAYAN, Gervasya (1927-) ?
£2207 $3509 €3200 Spring, young woman amongst blossoms (176x100cm-69x39in) s.d.1973. 4-Mar-3 Mealy's, Castlecomer #1120/R est:1200-1800

VARUTTI-KLEFENHAUSEN, Marco (1917-1989) German
£329 $514 €494 Sunset over Venice (30x42cm-12x17in) s. panel. 23-Sep-2 Rasmussen, Vejle #210/R (D.KR 3900)

VARVIN, Kjell (1939-) Norwegian
£640 $998 €960 In thin air (134x134cm-53x53in) s. exhib. 23-Sep-2 Blomqvist, Lysaker #1261 (N.KR 7500)

VASARELY, Victor (1908-1997) Hungarian
£694 $1104 €1000 Composition (50x50cm-20x20in) s. under glass. 29-Apr-3 Campo, Vlaamse Kaai #366
£1486 $2319 €2200 Orom-Ki (15x12cm-6x5in) s. s.i.d.verso paint panel. 31-Mar-3 Rossini, Paris #103/R
£1519 $2400 €2279 Zoeld blue, red and orange. 1-Dec-2 Susanin's, Chicago #5062/R
£2315 $3750 €3357 Proton III (20x20cm-8x8in) s. s.i.d.1966 verso tempera board on panel prov. 21-May-3 Doyle, New York #40/R est:2000-4000

£2471 $3978 €3707 Kodd V (29x29cm-11x11in) s. tempera cardboard. 7-May-3 AB Stockholms Auktionsverk #1154/R est:40000-50000 (S.KR 32000)
£2564 $4000 €3846 Vega-argent (51x51cm-20x20in) s.i.d.1969 verso tempera panel prov. 5-Nov-2 Doyle, New York #34/R est:6000-8000
£3205 $4968 €5000 Horna (90x62cm-35x24in) s. s.i.d.1987 verso. 7-Dec-2 Van Ham, Cologne #574/R est:8000
£3790 $5874 €5685 Saluces (53x47cm-21x19in) s.d.47 i.verso masonite exhib. 4-Dec-2 Kunsthallen, Copenhagen #95/R est:50000 (D.KR 44000)
£4487 $7000 €6731 Vega-arny (100x100cm-39x39in) s.i.d.1971 verso tempera masonite prov. 5-Nov-2 Doyle, New York #35/R est:6000-8000
£4788 $7708 €7182 Multisence (54x54cm-21x21in) s. panel prov. 7-May-3 AB Stockholms Auktionsverk #1112/R est:55000-65000 (S.KR 62000)
£4905 $7652 €7358 Saara (66x66cm-26x26in) s.d.1988 verso acrylic. 6-Nov-2 AB Stockholms Auktionsverk #948/R est:75000-85000 (S.KR 70000)
£4906 $7555 €7800 Cleo (54x46cm-21x18in) s. cardboard painted 1973 lit. 26-Oct-2 Cornette de St.Cyr, Paris #179/R
£5000 $7700 €7500 Gordos (66x66cm-26x26in) s. s.i.d.1976 verso oil paper on board prov. 22-Oct-2 Sotheby's, London #352/R est:4000-6000
£5256 $8253 €8200 Cain (84x84cm-33x33in) s. s.i.d.1978-90 verso. 15-Dec-2 Perrin, Versailles #52/R
£5380 $8500 €8500 Kettoe (85x45cm-33x18in) s.i.d.1979-1990. 27-Nov-2 Dorotheum, Vienna #95/R est:9000-12000
£5625 $9000 €8438 Izzo (81x81cm-32x32in) s. s.i.d.1965 verso tempera board on panel prov. 14-May-3 Sotheby's, New York #140/R est:6000-8000
£5769 $8423 €9000 Stri Arct II (60x60cm-24x24in) s. board painted 1973 prov. 5-Jun-2 Il Ponte, Milan #153/R est:8000-10000
£5946 $9573 €8919 Pali (63x56cm-25x22in) s. s.i.d.1955-62 verso acrylic panel. 7-May-3 AB Stockholms Auktionsverk #1111/R est:70000-80000 (S.KR 77000)
£6000 $9480 €9000 Actium (65x60cm-26x24in) s.i.verso. 3-Apr-3 Christie's, Kensington #183/R
£6000 $9480 €9000 Oslop-3 (93x82cm-37x32in) s. s.i.d.1983 verso prov. 3-Apr-3 Christie's, Kensington #268a/R
£6452 $10000 €9678 Lango-4 (74x66cm-29x26in) s. i.d.1971-1987 verso acrylic prov.exhib. 26-Sep-2 Christie's, Rockefeller NY #798/R est:10000-15000
£7000 $11480 €10500 Untitled (41x34cm-16x13in) s. cardboard prov. 7-Feb-3 Sotheby's, London #217/R est:2300-4000
£7336 $11811 €11004 Sreeh (120x120cm-47x47in) s. s.i.d.1983 verso acrylic. 7-May-3 AB Stockholms Auktionsverk #1152/R est:100000-125000 (S.KR 95000)
£7722 $12432 €11583 Deuton -VB (73x73cm-29x29in) s. acrylic panel. 7-May-3 AB Stockholms Auktionsverk #1149/R est:100000-125000 (S.KR 100000)
£7801 $12638 €11000 Salvin (73x88cm-29x35in) s. s.i.d.1949-1987 verso. 26-May-3 Christie's, Milan #188/R est:10000-15000
£8000 $12320 €12000 Sipontum K (65x50cm-26x20in) s. s.i.d.1952 verso prov. 22-Oct-2 Sotheby's, London #353/R est:6000-8000
£8000 $13120 €12000 Orgovan (46x40cm-18x16in) s. s.i.d.1950-55 verso card on board on panel prov. 7-Feb-3 Sotheby's, London #218/R est:6000-8000
£8000 $13360 €11600 Abydos (65x60cm-26x24in) s. s.i.d.1951-55 verso prov. 27-Jun-3 Christie's, London #141/R est:8000-12000
£8500 $13940 €12750 Oeta II (72x60cm-28x24in) s. s.i.d.1956 verso prov. 6-Feb-3 Christie's, London #663/R
£8654 $13587 €13500 Sinkkaso (40x37cm-16x15in) s. s.i.d.1957 verso panel. 11-Dec-2 Artcurial Briest, Paris #719/R est:15000
£8750 $14000 €13125 Zur-2 (90x90cm-35x35in) s. i.d.1976 verso prov. 14-May-3 Sotheby's, New York #144/R est:8000-12000
£9615 $15096 €15000 Kallo (74x74cm-29x29in) s. s.i.d.1964 verso acrylic cardboard on board. 23-Nov-2 Meeting Art, Vercelli #109/R est:15000
£10000 $16000 €15000 Gestalt-2 (79x49cm-31x19in) s. s.i.d.1969 verso board prov. 14-May-3 Sotheby's, New York #145/R est:5000-7000
£10000 $16700 €14500 Helion-neg (41x50cm-16x20in) s. s.i.d.1957 verso panel prov. 26-Jun-3 Sotheby's, London #160/R est:5000-7000
£10500 $16590 €15750 Form-M (60x60cm-24x24in) s. s.i.d.1972 verso prov. 3-Apr-3 Christie's, Kensington #270/R est:8000
£11111 $18333 €16000 VAD (88x80cm-35x31in) s. s.i.d.verso prov. 1-Jul-3 Artcurial Briest, Paris #522/R est:8000-10000
£12500 $20875 €18125 Quito (65x60cm-26x24in) s.i.d.1954-56 verso prov. 27-Jun-3 Christie's, London #142/R est:8000-12000
£14000 $22120 €21000 Cheyt-stri-piros (144x102cm-57x40in) s. s.i.d.1976 verso prov. 3-Apr-3 Christie's, Kensington #269/R
£15000 $23700 €22500 Obor (72x70cm-28x28in) s. s.i.d.1988 verso prov. 3-Apr-3 Christie's, Kensington #271/R est:8000
£15278 $24292 €22000 Makk (95x95cm-37x37in) s. painted 1972 lit. 1-May-3 Meeting Art, Vercelli #238 est:15000
£16000 $26240 €24000 Gordos (120x72cm-47x28in) s. i.d.verso prov. 7-Feb-3 Sotheby's, London #207/R est:7000-9000
£16000 $26720 €23200 Naini (72x60cm-28x24in) s. s.i.d.1957 verso prov. 26-Jun-3 Sotheby's, London #158/R est:12000-15000
£18056 $28528 €26000 Avall (192x164cm-76x65in) s. i.verso. 28-Apr-3 Cornette de St.Cyr, Paris #537/R est:28000-30000
£20000 $32800 €30000 Garam (89x130cm-35x51in) s. s.i.d.1949 verso prov. 7-Feb-3 Sotheby's, London #208/R est:8000-12000
£20886 $32582 €33000 Sin-Tuz (121x121cm-48x48in) s. painted 1973. 14-Sep-2 Meeting Art, Vercelli #838/R est:30000

Sculpture

£1207 $1883 €2091 Two cubes (42x24x5cm-17x9x2in) s. painted wood edition 15/50 prov. 31-Mar-3 Goodman, Sydney #210/R (A.D 3200)
£1389 $2194 €2000 Orion multicolor (100x105cm-39x41in) s.num.32/100 verso plastic aluminium paint. 28-Apr-3 Cornette de St.Cyr, Paris #541 est:2200-2500
£1389 $2194 €2000 Zoeld grey/gold 0-4 (101x101cm-40x40in) plastic aluminium. 28-Apr-3 Cornette de St.Cyr, Paris #543 est:2200-2500
£1899 $3000 €2849 Kezdi (71x57cm-28x22in) s.num.158/175 handpainted wood. 22-Apr-3 Butterfields, San Francisco #2375/R est:3000-5000
£3205 $5032 €5000 Topaze blanche, positif (45x45cm-18x18in) s.i. painted wood relief. 24-Nov-2 Laurence Calmels, Paris #277/R
£14626 $23255 €21500 Multicolore (75x78x4cm-30x31x2in) s. painted wood relief. 24-Mar-3 Cornette de St.Cyr, Paris #172/R est:18000

Works on paper

£314 $487 €500 Gordes, la plaine (33x50cm-13x20in) s.i.d.49 pencil dr. 30-Oct-2 Artcurial Briest, Paris #745
£372 $580 €550 Untitled (55x100cm-22x39in) s.d.46 crayon dr prov. 28-Mar-3 Charbonneaux, Paris #149
£476 $757 €700 Troya (17x16cm-7x6in) s. gouache collage. 24-Mar-3 Coutau Begarie, Paris #260
£621 $882 €1000 Le plastocoat (21x26cm-8x10in) s.d. mixed media cardboard. 20-Mar-2 Chayette & Cheval, Paris #118
£1000 $1670 €1450 Recherche optique et vibratoire a partir d'un construction (30x24cm-12x9in) i. ink gouache graphite. 9-Jul-3 Cornette de St.Cyr, Paris #358
£1181 $1865 €1700 Composition rouge, verte, jaune et bleue (25x20cm-10x8in) s. collage. 28-Apr-3 Cornette de St.Cyr, Paris #538 est:1800-2000
£1266 $2000 €2000 Orion blanc (107x107cm-42x42in) s.i. collage relief exec.1970 prov. 27-Nov-2 Tajan, Paris #43/R
£1325 $2159 €2000 Composition orange et rouge sur fond bleu (63x49cm-25x19in) s. collage. 3-Feb-3 Cornette de St.Cyr, Paris #544
£1325 $2159 €2000 Composition octogonale (35x23cm-14x9in) s. collage. 3-Feb-3 Cornette de St.Cyr, Paris #542/R
£1325 $2159 €2000 Carres et ronds (33x30cm-13x12in) s. collage. 3-Feb-3 Cornette de St.Cyr, Paris #541
£1325 $2159 €2000 Composition multcolore (48x18cm-19x7in) s. collage. 3-Feb-3 Cornette de St.Cyr, Paris #540/R
£1429 $2271 €2100 Etres et fantomes (31x25cm-12x10in) s.d.1949 collage ink. 24-Mar-3 Cornette de St.Cyr, Paris #173/R
£1448 $2419 €2100 Etude de LUM (64x50cm-25x20in) i. felt tip crayon. 9-Jul-3 Cornette de St.Cyr, Paris #353/R est:1800-2000
£1497 $2380 €2200 Etres et fantomes (30x24cm-12x9in) s.d.1950 collage ink. 24-Mar-3 Cornette de St.Cyr, Paris #169/R
£1497 $2380 €2200 Etres et fantomes (30x24cm-12x9in) s.d.1948 collage ink. 24-Mar-3 Cornette de St.Cyr, Paris #168/R
£1517 $2534 €2200 Composition cinetique (34x29cm-13x11in) s. ink collage. 9-Jul-3 Cornette de St.Cyr, Paris #354/R est:2200-2500
£1528 $2429 €2200 Untitled (28x24cm-11x9in) s. gouache Indian ink two. 29-Apr-3 Wiener Kunst Auktionen, Vienna #488/R
£1583 $2500 €2500 Para vista (48x29cm-19x11in) crayon exec.1965 prov.exhib. 27-Nov-2 Tajan, Paris #41/R est:2500-3000
£1597 $2524 €2300 Ronds et carres noirs et blancs (31x31cm-12x12in) s. collage. 28-Apr-3 Cornette de St.Cyr, Paris #533/R est:2500-3000
£1600 $2528 €2400 Untitled (13x12cm-5x5in) pencil gouache paper on paper exec.1964. 3-Apr-3 Christie's, Kensington #211/R
£1667 $2633 €2400 Carres noirs et blancs (31x31cm-12x12in) s.d. gouache collage. 28-Apr-3 Cornette de St.Cyr, Paris #534/R est:2500-3000
£1854 $3023 €2800 Oslop (38x25cm-15x10in) s.i.d.1978 verso decoupage cardboard. 3-Feb-3 Cornette de St.Cyr, Paris #543
£1950 $3003 €3100 Composition (31x25cm-12x10in) s.d.1950 collage. 26-Oct-2 Cornette de St.Cyr, Paris #180/R
£2014 $3182 €2900 Composition cinetique (41x41cm-16x16in) s. collage. 28-Apr-3 Cornette de St.Cyr, Paris #535/R est:2500-3000
£2107 $3245 €3350 Composition (31x25cm-12x10in) s.d.1952 collage. 26-Oct-2 Cornette de St.Cyr, Paris #181/R
£2564 $4000 €3846 Para vista (49x33cm-19x13in) i. gouache. 19-Sep-2 Swann Galleries, New York #809/R est:4000-6000
£2564 $4000 €3846 Untitled (47x62cm-19x24in) s.d.1947 mixed media paper collage sandpaper prov. 5-Nov-2 Doyle, New York #36/R est:4000-6000
£2600 $4238 €3900 Sans titre (56x32cm-22x13in) s. gouache. 3-Feb-3 Bonhams, New Bond Street #86/R est:3000-5000
£3125 $4938 €4500 De la serie Oslop (39x31cm-15x12in) s. collage. 28-Apr-3 Cornette de St.Cyr, Paris #536/R est:2200-2500

VASARI, Andrea (?) Italian

Works on paper

£352 $550 €528 Italian bay (27x37cm-11x15in) s. W/C. 13-Apr-3 Butterfields, Los Angeles #7074

VASARI, Giorgio (1511-1574) Italian

Works on paper

£2041 $3245 €3000 Crowning of the Virgin (7x23cm-3x9in) i.verso pen ink. 24-Mar-3 Tajan, Paris #4/R
£4430 $7000 €7000 St Blaise, St Luc et St Dominique assis dans un paysage (34x27cm-13x11in) i. black chk pen brown ink. 27-Nov-2 Christie's, Paris #29/R est:3000-5000

VASARRI, Emilio (19/20th C) Italian
£833 $1317 €1300 Resting in the fields (24x33cm-9x13in) s. i.verso panel. 18-Nov-2 Sotheby's, Paris #71/R

VASI, Giuseppe (1710-1782) Italian
Prints
£3000 $4650 €4500 Prospetto del alma citta di Rome vista del Monte Giancolo (260x96cm-102x38in) engraving on twelve sheets. 3-Dec-2 Christie's, London #83 est:3000-5000
£4500 $6975 €6750 Prospetto del Alma Citta di Rome visto del Monte Gianicolo (260x96cm-102x38in) engraving. 3-Dec-2 Christie's, London #85 est:5000-7000
£5380 $8500 €8500 Plan of Rome (262x103cm-103x41in) eau forte. 28-Nov-2 Semenzato, Venice #20/R est:11000

VASILIEV, G (20th C) Russian
£2200 $3476 €3300 Meeting of minds, Popov and Edison (155x199cm-61x78in) s. 14-Nov-2 Christie's, Kensington #267/R est:700-900

VASILOVSKY, Sergei Ivanovich (1854-1917) Russian
£7042 $11338 €10000 Svetogorsk Monastery (24x36cm-9x14in) s. board. 10-May-3 Bukowskis, Helsinki #377/R est:5500-6000

VASKINEN, Yrjo (1892-1963) Finnish
Works on paper
£359 $590 €550 Architect's drawing (67x47cm-26x19in) s.d.1915 mixed media. 9-Feb-3 Bukowskis, Helsinki #378/R

VASLET, Lewis (1742-1808) British
Miniatures
£1063 $1700 €1541 Young Georgian officer of a Royal Regiment (5x5cm-2x2in) seed pearl. 17-May-3 New Orleans Auction, New Orleans #2/R est:1400-1800

VASLET, Lewis (attrib) (1742-1808) British
£1500 $2445 €2175 Portrait of a mother and child holding her doll (51x43cm-20x17in) oval. 21-Jul-3 Sotheby's, London #1/R est:2000-3000

VASNETZOV, Apollinar M (1856-1933) Russian
£22000 $34540 €33000 Celebration near the Kremlin (58x50cm-23x20in) s.d.1901 board. 20-Nov-2 Sotheby's, London #43/R est:20000-30000

VASQUEZ, Carlos (1869-1944) Spanish
Works on paper
£355 $574 €500 Florista (33x26cm-13x10in) s. gouache pastel. 20-May-3 Segre, Madrid #76/R

VASS, Elemer (1887-1957) Hungarian
£564 $874 €880 Sunlit sailing boats (52x63cm-20x25in) s.d.1930 panel. 6-Dec-2 Michael Zeller, Lindau #944/R
£671 $1046 €973 Spring in the fruit garden (49x69cm-19x27in) s. 13-Sep-2 Mu Terem Galeria, Budapest #187/R est:180000 (H.F 260000)
£1006 $1569 €1509 Flowers i vase (60x49cm-24x19in) s.d.1932 board. 11-Apr-3 Kieselbach, Budapest #47/R est:300000-360000 (H.F 360000)
£1397 $2180 €2026 Bank of the Mediterranean Sea (50x65cm-20x26in) s. panel. 12-Apr-3 Mu Terem Galeria, Budapest #66/R est:200000 (H.F 500000)
£1902 $3042 €2853 Tulips (64x53cm-25x21in) s.d.1932 board. 16-May-3 Kieselbach, Budapest #44/R (H.F 650000)

VASSALLO, Antonio Maria (attrib) (17th C) Italian
£11000 $18370 €15950 Annunciation of the shepherds (138x99cm-54x39in) 10-Jul-3 Sotheby's, London #189/R est:12000-15000

VASSELON, Alice (?) ?
£36000 $60120 €54000 Bouquet if field flowers in a pail (126x159cm-50x63in) s.d.1880. 19-Jun-3 Christie's, London #45/R est:25000-35000

VASSELON, Marius (19th C) French
£6000 $9420 €9000 Nature morte a la citrouille, Fleurs a la fontaine (168x89cm-66x35in) s. pair. 21-Nov-2 Christie's, Kensington #93/R est:7000-9000

VASSILIEFF, Danila (1897-1958) Australian/Russian
£893 $1411 €1340 Coconut grove, West Indies (35x46cm-14x18in) init.d.1933. 18-Nov-2 Goodman, Sydney #98/R (A.D 2500)
£1800 $2898 €2700 Bristol street scene (37x57cm-15x22in) s. canvasboard. 6-May-3 Christie's, Melbourne #399 est:3000-4000 (A.D 4500)
£5814 $9244 €8721 Dog walkers, Fitzroy (34x42cm-13x17in) s. board prov. 5-May-3 Sotheby's, Melbourne #155/R est:15000-20000 (A.D 15000)
£8571 $13543 €12857 Joe Deuter and his cart 1942 (40x51cm-16x20in) s. plywood prov.exhib. 27-Nov-2 Deutscher-Menzies, Melbourne #16/R est:25000-35000 (A.D 24000)
£8571 $13543 €12857 Collingwood lane (36x42cm-14x17in) s. i.verso board. 18-Nov-2 Goodman, Sydney #96/R est:18000-28000 (A.D 24000)
Sculpture
£1571 $2483 €2357 Whistler's mother 1948 (17x11x16cm-7x4x6in) warrandyte stone lit. 27-Nov-2 Deutscher-Menzies, Melbourne #96/R est:4000-6000 (A.D 4400)
Works on paper
£268 $423 €402 Study of a girl with brown hair and blue eyes (32x24cm-13x9in) s. W/C. 18-Nov-2 Goodman, Sydney #108/R (A.D 750)
£464 $734 €696 Portrait study (33x24cm-13x9in) W/C. 18-Nov-2 Goodman, Sydney #109/R (A.D 1300)
£497 $785 €746 Portrait study with red lips (31x23cm-12x9in) init. W/C. 18-Nov-2 Goodman, Sydney #107/R est:3000-4000 (A.D 1390)
£518 $849 €777 Portrait of Helen (33x23cm-13x9in) s. gouache. 4-Jun-3 Deutscher-Menzies, Melbourne #360/R (A.D 1300)
£679 $1072 €1019 Girl wearing a red hat (34x26cm-13x10in) init. W/C. 18-Nov-2 Goodman, Sydney #105/R (A.D 1900)
£714 $1129 €1071 Study of three figures (24x33cm-9x13in) init. W/C. 18-Nov-2 Goodman, Sydney #103/R (A.D 2000)
£1357 $2131 €2036 Two men (48x69cm-19x27in) s. gouache. 25-Nov-2 Christie's, Melbourne #399/R est:3000-5000 (A.D 3800)
£1498 $2278 €2247 Fashionable lady (37x24cm-15x9in) W/C bodycol exec.c.1952 prov. 28-Aug-2 Deutscher-Menzies, Melbourne #232/R est:4200-5000 (A.D 4180)
£2200 $3542 €3300 Racing people (27x40cm-11x16in) i.verso gouache executed c.1950 prov. 6-May-3 Christie's, Melbourne #306/R est:3000-5000 (A.D 5500)
£2330 $3541 €3495 Peter and the wolf (28x39cm-11x15in) s.d.58 W/C gouache. 28-Aug-2 Deutscher-Menzies, Melbourne #231/R est:4500-6000 (A.D 6500)
£2600 $4186 €3900 Looking at TV (28x38cm-11x15in) s. i.verso gouache paper on board. 6-May-3 Christie's, Melbourne #237/R est:4000-6000 (A.D 6500)
£7857 $12414 €11786 Melbourne factory (46x40cm-18x16in) s. gouache W/C. 18-Nov-2 Goodman, Sydney #95/R est:20000-30000 (A.D 22000)

VASSILIEFF, Marie (1894-1955) Russian
Works on paper
£1410 $2214 €2200 Tete de femme (29x23cm-11x9in) s.i.d.1937 mixed media collage. 16-Dec-2 Raboudrin & Choppin de Janvry, Paris #145/R

VASSILIOU, Spyros (1902-1984) Greek
£2400 $3792 €3600 Landscape (20x22cm-8x9in) 1-Apr-3 Bonhams, New Bond Street #50 est:1500-2000
£3000 $4740 €4500 Chairs on a beach (25x36cm-10x14in) 1-Apr-3 Bonhams, New Bond Street #84 est:3000-5000
£5200 $8112 €7800 Harbour view (80x118cm-31x46in) s.d.70. 26-Mar-3 Sotheby's, Olympia #287/R est:5000-7000
£8000 $12480 €12000 Mid day (102x187cm-40x74in) s.d.63 canvas on board exhib. 17-Sep-2 Sotheby's, Olympia #296/R est:10000-15000
£11500 $18170 €17250 End of season (89x130cm-35x51in) 1-Apr-3 Bonhams, New Bond Street #98 est:10000-15000
£12000 $18600 €18000 Carousel (92x65cm-36x26in) s.d.81. 2-Oct-2 Sotheby's, London #70/R est:20000
£15000 $23700 €22500 Festival, Athens (24x35cm-9x14in) 1-Apr-3 Bonhams, New Bond Street #78 est:15000-25000
£18000 $28440 €27000 Aegina (54x73cm-21x29in) 1-Apr-3 Bonhams, New Bond Street #86 est:10000-15000
£22000 $34100 €33000 Caiques and people (66x91cm-26x36in) s.d. canvas on board. 2-Oct-2 Sotheby's, London #108/R est:10000-15000
Works on paper
£2500 $3875 €3750 Over the hills (24x34cm-9x13in) s. W/C. 2-Oct-2 Sotheby's, London #90/R

VASSTROM, Eric (1887-1958) Finnish
£442 $703 €650 The esplanade (38x46cm-15x18in) s.d.1930. 27-Feb-3 Hagelstam, Helsinki #898/R
£516 $794 €820 Hay harvest (100x118cm-39x46in) s.d.1940. 27-Oct-2 Bukowskis, Helsinki #305/R

VASTAGH, Geza (1866-1919) Hungarian
£654 $1041 €981 Poultry on the yard (24x33cm-9x13in) s. 8-Mar-3 Dorotheum, Prague #28/R est:30000-45000 (C.KR 30000)

VASZARY, Janos (1867-1939) Hungarian
£1174 $1831 €1702 Landscape (10x26cm-4x10in) s. canvas on board. 12-Apr-3 Mu Terem Galeria, Budapest #133/R est:400000 (H.F 420000)

£1935 $3018 €2806 Spanish courtyard (13x24cm-5x9in) s. panel. 13-Sep-2 Mu Terem Galeria, Budapest #30/R est:650000 (H.F 750000)
£2794 $4359 €4051 Bride (38x24cm-15x9in) panel. 12-Apr-3 Mu Terem Galeria, Budapest #187/R est:950000 (H.F 1000000)
£3765 $5836 €5648 Joy of life, riders (26x40cm-10x16in) s. board. 6-Dec-2 Kieselbach, Budapest #147/R (H.F 1400000)
£4192 $6540 €6288 Still life of flowers (60x80cm-24x31in) s. 6-Nov-2 Dobiaschofsky, Bern #1028/R est:8000 (S.FR 9600)
£5676 $8854 €8230 Sewing lady (28x42cm-11x17in) s.d.906 panel. 13-Sep-2 Mu Terem Galeria, Budapest #137/R est:1500000 (H.F 2200000)
£6707 $10462 €10061 In the park (35x43cm-14x17in) s. mixed media. 11-Apr-3 Kieselbach, Budapest #132/R est:2400000 (H.F 2400000)
£6707 $10462 €10061 Girl in pink dress with cat (48x59cm-19x23in) s. board. 11-Apr-3 Kieselbach, Budapest #171/R est:2400000 (H.F 2400000)
£7266 $11334 €10536 Steps of Versailles (35x49cm-14x19in) s.d.1925 board. 12-Apr-3 Mu Terem Galeria, Budapest #68/R est:2500000 (H.F 2600000)
£8771 $13683 €13157 Still life of roses (35x42cm-14x17in) s. 11-Sep-2 Kieselbach, Budapest #18/R (H.F 3400000)
£9501 $14822 €14252 Girls in Sunday best (79x66cm-31x26in) s. 11-Apr-3 Kieselbach, Budapest #179/R est:3400000 (H.F 3400000)
£10757 $16673 €16136 Still life with apples (53x63cm-21x25in) s. 6-Dec-2 Kieselbach, Budapest #148/R (H.F 4000000)
£17480 $27094 €26220 Roses in a vase (50x34cm-20x13in) cardboard. 6-Dec-2 Kieselbach, Budapest #184/R (H.F 6500000)
£19561 $30516 €29342 Cat among pillows (45x64cm-18x25in) s. 11-Apr-3 Kieselbach, Budapest #208/R est:4500000-7000000 (H.F 7000000)
£24508 $38232 €35537 Vase with flower (49x69cm-19x27in) s. 13-Sep-2 Mu Terem Galeria, Budapest #135/R est:6000000 (H.F 9500000)
£25798 $40245 €37407 Miramar (48x59cm-19x23in) s.d.1927. 13-Sep-2 Mu Terem Galeria, Budapest #149/R est:7500000 (H.F 10000000)
£26893 $41683 €40340 Still life of flowers with lilies and roses (64x54cm-25x21in) s. 6-Dec-2 Kieselbach, Budapest #131/R (H.F 10000000)
£33537 $52318 €50306 Restaurant on the promonade (45x66cm-18x26in) cardboard. 11-Sep-2 Kieselbach, Budapest #44/R (H.F 13000000)
£40956 $65530 €61434 Circus (90x87cm-35x34in) s. 16-May-3 Kieselbach, Budapest #71/R (H.F 14000000)
£41917 $65391 €60780 Breakfast table (63x79cm-25x31in) s.d.918 prov.exhib.lit. 12-Apr-3 Mu Terem Galeria, Budapest #31/R est:6500000 (H.F 15000000)
£49732 $79572 €74598 French Riviera (45x70cm-18x28in) s. 16-May-3 Kieselbach, Budapest #20/R (H.F 17000000)
£50000 $82000 €75000 On the beach (65x80cm-26x31in) s. tempera prov. 3-Jun-3 Sotheby's, London #103/R est:30000-50000
£50300 $78469 €72935 Roses (51x72cm-20x28in) s. board. 12-Apr-3 Mu Terem Galeria, Budapest #167/R est:8500000 (H.F 18000000)
£55000 $90200 €82500 Overlooking Rapallo Beach (42x66cm-17x26in) s.i.d.1914 prov. 3-Jun-3 Sotheby's, London #100/R est:15000-20000
£70210 $112337 €105315 Still life of flowers, gladioluses (86x66cm-34x26in) s. 16-May-3 Kieselbach, Budapest #52/R (H.F 24000000)
£70210 $112337 €105315 Danube promenade, with the Royal Castle in the background (53x84cm-21x33in) s. 16-May-3 Kieselbach, Budapest #63/R (H.F 24000000)
£76061 $121698 €114092 Before riding out in the park in Tata (80x101cm-31x40in) s.d.918. 16-May-3 Kieselbach, Budapest #16/R (H.F 26000000)
£76061 $121698 €114092 Still life with green pitcher, chrysanthemums (67x82cm-26x32in) s. 16-May-3 Kieselbach, Budapest #33/R (H.F 26000000)
£86056 $133387 €124781 Before mass in Assissi (68x80cm-27x31in) s. prov.exhib.lit. 9-Dec-2 Mu Terem Galeria, Budapest #84/R est:12000000 (H.F 32000000)
£89423 $139500 €134135 Women sitting in garden in the park (77x104cm-30x41in) s. 11-Apr-3 Kieselbach, Budapest #136/R est:18000000-32000000 (H.F 32000000)
£89423 $139500 €134135 Nude with blue lamp (68x87cm-27x34in) s. 11-Apr-3 Kieselbach, Budapest #32/R est:18000000-32000000 (H.F 32000000)
£107570 $166734 €161355 In the park (62x80cm-24x31in) s. 6-Dec-2 Kieselbach, Budapest #48/R (H.F 40000000)

Works on paper

£457 $709 €663 Tourists at Rapallo (21x29cm-8x11in) s.d.1934 pencil. 9-Dec-2 Mu Terem Galeria, Budapest #184/R est:120000 (H.F 170000)
£538 $834 €780 On the beach at Alassio (21x29cm-8x11in) s.d.922 pencil. 9-Dec-2 Mu Terem Galeria, Budapest #16/R est:160000 (H.F 200000)
£774 $1207 €1161 Assisi, 1926 (16x25cm-6x10in) s. mixed media. 11-Sep-2 Kieselbach, Budapest #173/R (H.F 300000)
£807 $1251 €1211 Rapallo (20x27cm-8x11in) s. pencil. 6-Dec-2 Kieselbach, Budapest #36/R (H.F 300000)
£826 $1288 €1239 Self portrait, 1886 (35x27cm-14x11in) s.d.86 pencil white bodycol. 11-Sep-2 Kieselbach, Budapest #175/R (H.F 320000)
£1022 $1584 €1533 Resting (24x33cm-9x13in) s. pastel. 6-Dec-2 Kieselbach, Budapest #44/R (H.F 380000)
£1237 $1917 €1856 Cafe at the main square in Triest (24x31cm-9x12in) s. mixed media. 6-Dec-2 Kieselbach, Budapest #21/R (H.F 460000)
£1397 $2180 €2096 Red scarved girl (40x49cm-16x19in) s.d.1930 gouache. 11-Apr-3 Kieselbach, Budapest #101/R est:440000-500000 (H.F 500000)
£2322 $3622 €3483 Lady with black boa, 1911 (57x38cm-22x15in) s. W/C. 11-Sep-2 Kieselbach, Budapest #143/R (H.F 900000)
£7266 $11334 €10536 Lady in black (34x44cm-13x17in) s. pastel. 12-Apr-3 Mu Terem Galeria, Budapest #153/R est:850000 (H.F 2600000)
£8606 $13339 €12909 Vamp (44x59cm-17x23in) s. mixed media. 6-Dec-2 Kieselbach, Budapest #2/R (H.F 3200000)
£9501 $14822 €13776 Lady in hat with pearls (60x45cm-24x18in) s. mixed media. 12-Apr-3 Mu Terem Galeria, Budapest #16/R est:850000 (H.F 3400000)
£34960 $54189 €52440 Chanteuse on a blue sofa (31x47cm 12x19in) s. W/C. 6-Dec-2 Kieselbach, Budapest #74/R (H.F 13000000)

VASZKO, Erzsebet (1902-1986) Hungarian

Works on paper

£1174 $1831 €1702 Composition (67x72cm-26x28in) s.d.1970 pastel. 12-Apr-3 Mu Terem Galeria, Budapest #118/R est:300000 (H.F 420000)

VASZKO, Odon (1896-1945) Hungarian

£4128 $6439 €6192 Still life in Atelier, 1929 (55x68cm-22x27in) s. 11-Sep-2 Kieselbach, Budapest #43/R (H.F 1600000)

VATNEODEGARD, Magne (1950-) Norwegian

£393 $616 €590 The animal (155x102cm-61x40in) s. painted 1980-83. 25-Nov-2 Blomqvist, Lysaker #1286 (N.KR 4500)

VAUDECHAMP, Joseph (1790-1866) French

£7500 $12000 €10875 Portrait of a young girl, possibly a member of the Duplantier of Forstall families (81x64cm-32x25in) s.d.1839. 17-May-3 New Orleans Auction, New Orleans #924/R est:10000-15000

VAUDOU, Gaston (1891-1957) French

£326 $505 €489 Route de Port Manech (54x81cm-21x32in) s. i.verso. 7-Dec-2 Galerie du Rhone, Sion #436/R (S.FR 750)

Works on paper

£301 $484 €452 Quai de Javel in Paris (28x40cm-11x16in) s. gouache. 7-May-3 Dobiaschofsky, Bern #3663 (S.FR 650)

VAUGHAN, Keith (1912-1974) British

£1400 $2226 €2100 Untitled (52x38cm-20x15in) s.i.d.18 nov. 26-Feb-3 Sotheby's, Olympia #202/R est:600-800
£3200 $4960 €4800 Portrait of his brother Dick (46x35cm-18x14in) s.d.1935 verso canvasboard. 3-Dec-2 Bonhams, New Bond Street #79/R est:3000-5000
£4500 $7380 €6750 Heath, cinnamon and blue (43x39cm-17x15in) s. board. 3-Jun-3 Sotheby's, Olympia #247/R est:5000-7000
£9000 $14220 €13500 Farm landscape (25x36cm-10x14in) s.d.53 board. 27-Nov-2 Sotheby's, Olympia #60/R est:3000-4000
£10000 $15400 €15000 Cottage in Kerry (35x42cm-14x17in) s.d.55 board prov. 5-Sep-2 Christie's, Kensington #659/R est:5000-7000

Works on paper

£280 $445 €420 Portrait study (21x16cm-8x6in) 26-Feb-3 Sotheby's, Olympia #201/R
£320 $506 €480 Seated nude (27x19cm-11x7in) pencil. 27-Nov-2 Sotheby's, Olympia #261/R
£360 $562 €540 Standing figure (21x13cm-8x5in) bears studio st. pencil. 17-Sep-2 Bonhams, Knightsbridge #229/R
£360 $572 €540 Reclining male nude (10x16cm-4x6in) s.d.58 pencil prov. 18-Mar-3 Rosebery Fine Art, London #935
£380 $600 €570 Man with spade (24x17cm-9x7in) d.58 pencil. 27-Nov-2 Sotheby's, Olympia #262/R
£380 $635 €551 Wooded landscape (38x48cm-15x19in) s.d.71 pen ink W/C over pencil. 25-Jun-3 Goldings, Lincolnshire #344
£420 $668 €630 Figure studies (28x20cm-11x8in) pencil. 26-Feb-3 Sotheby's, Olympia #203/R
£450 $738 €675 Divers (13x18cm-5x7in) studio st.verso pencil. 3-Jun-3 Sotheby's, Olympia #242/R
£500 $815 €750 Compositional study (27x20cm-11x8in) mono. pencil dr prov. 1-Feb-3 Shapes, Edinburgh #311/R
£550 $858 €825 Boy with bird (12x15cm-5x6in) bears studio st.verso gouache ink. 17-Sep-2 Bonhams, Knightsbridge #221/R
£550 $853 €825 Study for harvest (28x22cm-11x9in) init.i.d.1960 pencil prov. 4-Dec-2 Christie's, Kensington #293/R
£550 $875 €825 Landscape study, against the sun (25x20cm-10x8in) i. pencil. 26-Feb-3 Sotheby's, Olympia #200/R
£600 $984 €900 Industrial town (14x19cm-6x7in) studio st.verso pen ink wash. 3-Jun-3 Sotheby's, Olympia #241/R
£650 $1007 €975 Skin divers (28x20cm-11x8in) studio st.i.d.1962 pencil prov. 4-Dec-2 Christie's, Kensington #290/R
£680 $1081 €1020 Standing male nude studies (28x37cm-11x15in) pen ink wash sheet of two. 26-Feb-3 Sotheby's, Olympia #196/R
£750 $1193 €1125 Figures studies (38x28cm-15x11in) pencil sheet of five prov. 26-Feb-3 Sotheby's, Olympia #190/R
£750 $1230 €1125 Standing male nude studies (28x37cm-11x15in) pen ink wash two sheets prov. 3-Jun-3 Sotheby's, Olympia #240/R
£850 $1351 €1275 Male figure studies (28x37cm-11x15in) pen ink wash sheet of three. 26-Feb-3 Sotheby's, Olympia #195/R est:700-900
£880 $1399 €1320 Untitled (50x40cm-20x16in) s. pastel. 26-Feb-3 Sotheby's, Olympia #199/R est:500-700
£950 $1463 €1425 Set design (15x18cm-6x7in) W/C gouache exhib. 5-Sep-2 Christie's, Kensington #662/R

£1000 $1580 €1500 Tree Felling, Ashton Gifford (19x27cm-7x11in) ink wash. 27-Nov-2 Sotheby's, Olympia #260/R est:600-800
£1000 $1590 €1500 Male torso studies (28x38cm-11x15in) pen ink wash sheet of eight prov. 26-Feb-3 Sotheby's, Olympia #189/R est:1000-1500
£1300 $2002 €1950 Recruit reading a letter (13x20cm-5x8in) s. pen black ink W/C bodycol. 5-Sep-2 Christie's, Kensington #603/R est:1200-1800
£1600 $2640 €2320 Men with animals II (13x18cm-5x7in) s.d.65 W/C bodycol ink prov. 3-Jul-3 Christie's, Kensington #647/R est:800-1200
£1700 $2652 €2550 Study for the garden (16x11cm-6x4in) gouache. 25-Mar-3 Bonhams, New Bond Street #103/R est:1500-2000
£2800 $4592 €4200 Three figures (26x30cm-10x12in) red ball point pen W/C bodycol executed 1967 exhib. 6-Jun-3 Christie's, London #60/R est:1500-2000
£3200 $4928 €4800 Coal fatigue (37x51cm-15x20in) s.d.42 brush pen black ink prov. 5-Sep-2 Christie's, Kensington #600/R est:3000-5000
£3200 $4960 €4800 Execution (16x13cm-6x5in) s.i.d.1954 gouache pencil exhib. 3-Dec-2 Bonhams, New Bond Street #78/R est:2000-3000
£6400 $10112 €9600 Village and figures (21x31cm-8x12in) s.d.1943 mixed media W/C bodycol. 7-Apr-3 Bonhams, Bath #67/R est:800-1200
£6500 $10660 €9750 Metamorphoses (42x39cm-17x15in) s.d.71 gouache collage. 3-Jun-3 Sotheby's, Olympia #248/R est:3000-5000

VAUMANOIR (1928-) French
£573 $894 €900 Sortie d'ecole dans la neige (38x46cm-15x18in) s. s.i.verso painted 1978. 5-Nov-2 Tajan, Paris #76/R
£573 $894 €900 Petite neige a Meounes (33x24cm-13x9in) s.d.1982. 5-Nov-2 Tajan, Paris #75/R

VAUTHIER, Pierre (1845-1916) French
£2202 $3500 €3303 Along the Seine (38x55cm-15x22in) s.i.d.1885. 7-Mar-3 Skinner, Boston #344/R est:800-1200
£3000 $4680 €4500 Shipping on the Tyne (146x213cm-57x84in) s.i.d.Dec 91. 26-Mar-3 Sotheby's, Olympia #175/R est:3000-5000
£3503 $5465 €5500 Apres-midi a Triel (38x55cm-15x22in) s.d. 7-Nov-2 Claude Aguttes, Neuilly #76/R est:6000-8000
Works on paper
£1773 $2961 €2500 A l'Exposition Universelle (31x24cm-12x9in) s.d.89 pastel. 20-Jun-3 Piasa, Paris #9/R est:2000-3000

VAUTHRIN, Ernest Germain (1878-1949) French
£1795 $2818 €2800 Retour de goelette (50x100cm-20x39in) s.d.1947. 15-Dec-2 Thierry & Lannon, Brest #219

VAUTIER, Benjamin (elder) (1829-1898) German
£391 $610 €587 Tete de pretre (17x12cm-7x5in) canvas on board. 16-Sep-2 Philippe Schuler, Zurich #3409 (S.FR 900)
£2911 $4542 €4600 Interior with children playing music (77x61cm-30x24in) s. 21-Oct-2 Bernaerts, Antwerp #732/R est:4500-6000
£4525 $7557 €6561 Portrait of a girl (17x14cm-7x6in) s.d.68 panel. 24-Jun-3 Koller, Zurich #6/R est:14000-22000 (S.FR 10000)
£6987 $10900 €10481 In the studio (27x31cm-11x12in) s. 20-Nov-2 Fischer, Luzern #1268/R est:16000-18000 (S.FR 16000)
£14151 $22925 €20519 Sourire matinal (28x34cm-11x13in) s. 26-May-3 Sotheby's, Zurich #19/R est:15000-20000 (S.FR 30000)
£54795 $85479 €82193 In the cloister (77x99cm-30x39in) s.d.74 prov.lit. 28-Mar-3 Koller, Zurich #3115/R est:130000-220000 (S.FR 120000)
Works on paper
£253 $392 €400 Petitioner (11x15cm-4x6in) s. W/C over pencil. 25-Sep-2 Neumeister, Munich #444/R
£304 $474 €450 Scene from the 'Bare foot girl' (19x23cm-7x9in) s.d.Juni 1871 pencil. 27-Mar-3 Dr Fritz Nagel, Stuttgart #720/R
£304 $474 €450 From Auerbach's 'Bare foot girl' (19x23cm-7x9in) s.i. pencil. 27-Mar-3 Dr Fritz Nagel, Stuttgart #721/R

VAUTIER, Benjamin (younger) (1895-1974) Swiss
£961 $1518 €1442 Rade de geneve (64x80cm-25x31in) s.d.1962. 17-Nov-2 Koller, Geneva #1339 (S.FR 2200)

VAUTIER, Otto (1863-1919) Swiss
£655 $1022 €983 Still life of carnations and vase (30x60cm-12x24in) s. panel prov. 20-Nov-2 Fischer, Luzern #2294/R est:1600-1800 (S.FR 1500)
£708 $1146 €1253 Church doorway (46x37cm-18x15in) s. panel. 26-May-3 Sotheby's, Zurich #74/R (S.FR 1500)
£1310 $2070 €1965 Paysage avec forteresse (79x54cm-31x21in) s. 17-Nov-2 Koller, Geneva #1275/R (S.FR 3000)
£2123 $3439 €3758 Jeune femme a la rose (73x60cm-29x24in) s. 26-May-3 Sotheby's, Zurich #99/R est:4500-5500 (S.FR 4500)
£3219 $5086 €4829 Femme lisant (92x73cm-36x29in) s. 28-Nov-2 Christie's, Zurich #58/R est:5000-7000 (S.FR 7500)
Works on paper
£319 $524 €463 Seated young woman (74x46cm-29x18in) s. pastel. 4-Jun-3 Fischer, Luzern #2688 (S.FR 680)
£352 $515 €528 Une reunion (24x35cm-9x14in) s.d.1889 i. verso W/C double-sided. 17-Jun-2 Philippe Schuler, Zurich #4233 (S.FR 800)
£1288 $2034 €1932 Standing female nude (63x37cm-25x15in) s. chk. 28-Nov-2 Christie's, Zurich #57/R est:3000-4000 (S.FR 3000)
£3066 $4967 €5427 Jeunes filles valaisannes (75x55cm-30x22in) s.i.d.1905 pastel. 26-May-3 Sotheby's, Zurich #75/R est:6000-8000 (S.FR 6500)

VAVASSEUR, Cyprien Louis Pierre le (19th C) French
£6000 $9720 €9000 Matelots hoisting a flag signal from the deck of a French torpedo boat (93x61cm-37x24in) s.d.94. 21-May-3 Christie's, Kensington #699/R est:4000-6000

VAVPOTIC, Ivan (1877-1943) Czechoslovakian
£2842 $4405 €4263 Young lady on a horse (86x100cm-34x39in) painted c.1910-20. 3-Dec-2 SOGA, Bratislava #192/R est:130000 (SL.K 180000)

VAVRINA, Charles (1928-) American
£1840 $3000 €2760 Village entrance (28x61cm-11x24in) s. 2-Feb-3 Simpson's, Houston #248

VAWSER, George Robert (jnr) (fl.1836-1875) British
Works on paper
£480 $749 €720 Melbourne great pool (18x46cm-7x18in) W/C prov. 8-Oct-2 Sotheby's, Olympia #418/R

VAZ, Oscar (1909-1987) Argentinian
£2266 $3580 €3399 Harbour (60x80cm-24x31in) 15-Nov-2 Naón & Cia, Buenos Aires #31/R
£2835 $4480 €4253 Quay (70x90cm-28x35in) 15-Nov-2 Naón & Cia, Buenos Aires #30/R

VAZQUEZ DIAS, Daniel (1881-1969) Spanish
£1623 $2370 €2500 At night (24x18cm-9x7in) s. cardboard lit. 12-Jun-2 Castellana, Madrid #267/R
£4392 $6851 €6500 Landscape (18x24cm-7x9in) s. s.i.verso cardboard. 25-Mar-3 Durán, Madrid #195/R
Works on paper
£385 $608 €600 Landscape with boats (15x18cm-6x7in) dr. 19-Nov-2 Durán, Madrid #130/R
£393 $613 €625 Bank (24x22cm-9x9in) dr. 23-Sep-2 Durán, Madrid #81/R
£449 $709 €700 Landscape with church (26x22cm-10x9in) pencil dr. 13-Nov-2 Ansorena, Madrid #433/R
£500 $790 €775 Path amongst trees (24x22cm-9x9in) pencil dr. 17-Dec-2 Segre, Madrid #125/R
£537 $864 €800 House (22x24cm-9x9in) dr. 18-Feb-3 Durán, Madrid #93/R
£548 $855 €800 Arches (33x29cm-13x11in) s. chl dr. 8-Apr-3 Ansorena, Madrid #643/R
£566 $872 €900 Landscape (22x24cm-9x9in) pencil. 28-Oct-2 Segre, Madrid #258/R
£604 $972 €900 Landscape with house (29x34cm-11x13in) s. dr. 18-Feb-3 Durán, Madrid #631/R
£690 $1097 €1000 Garden (22x24cm-9x9in) chl dr. 4-Mar-3 Ansorena, Madrid #378/R
£966 $1526 €1400 Blind man (31x23cm-12x9in) s.i. 1-Apr-3 Segre, Madrid #161/R
£1282 $1872 €2000 Coimbra in the morning (23x33cm-9x13in) s.i. col crayon dr. 6-Jun-2 Castellana, Madrid #25/R

VAZQUEZ, Sergio (?) Spanish
£472 $736 €750 Night landscape (72x81cm-28x32in) s. 17-Sep-2 Segre, Madrid #219/R

VAZQUEZ, Xesus (1946-) Spanish
£7742 $12232 €12000 Gettysburg (235x250cm-93x98in) s. s.d.1991 verso silk prov. 17-Dec-2 Segre, Madrid #172/R est:6000

VBROVA, Miloslava (1909-) ?
£306 $477 €459 Young ballet dancer trying on shoes (43x33cm-17x13in) s. panel. 6-Nov-2 Dobiaschofsky, Bern #1035/R (S.FR 700)

VEAL, Hayward (1913-1968) Australian
£280 $468 €406 Moored boats (51x61cm-20x24in) s. 17-Jun-3 Bonhams, Knightsbridge #12/R
£420 $685 €630 Boulle market, Prenasse (61x51cm-24x20in) s. 13-Feb-3 Christie's, Kensington #142/R
£900 $1404 €1350 Dieppe (40x50cm-16x20in) s. sold with two others by the same hand. 17-Sep-2 Bonhams, Knightsbridge #20/R
£1120 $1803 €1680 Streetscape in rain (60x39cm-24x15in) s. 6-May-3 Christie's, Melbourne #351 est:2000-3000 (A.D 2800)

VECCHIA, Pietro della (1605-1678) Italian
£19014 $30613 €27000 Education to reading (83x102cm-33x40in) 11-May-3 Finarte, Venice #66/R est:35000
£19014 $30613 €27000 Man's ages (47x90cm-19x35in) 11-May-3 Finarte, Venice #76/R est:34000

VECCHIA, Pietro della (attrib) (1605-1678) Italian
£3546 $5922 €5000 Saint Pierre (74x59cm-29x23in) 18-Jun-3 Tajan, Paris #5/R est:5000-7000

VECCHIO, Phyllis del (20th C) Irish?
Works on paper
£599 $994 €850 Depth of winter (37x55cm-15x22in) s. W/C. 10-Jun-3 James Adam, Dublin #223/R

VECCIA, Franz (1909-1980) French
£253 $395 €400 Les Champs Elysees (116x89cm-46x35in) s. exhib. 20-Oct-2 Charbonneaux, Paris #162 est:600-800

VECENAJ, Yvan (1920-) Yugoslavian
£3449 $5449 €5000 Eclipse (70x90cm-28x35in) s. painted 1968 prov. 4-Apr-3 Tajan, Paris #73

VECSEY, Koloman (19/20th C) Hungarian
£252 $368 €378 Watering horses (30x45cm-12x18in) board painted c.1950. 4-Jun-2 SOGA, Bratislava #111/R est:10000 (SL.K 16000)
£284 $414 €426 Conveying hay (48x68cm-19x27in) board painted c.1950. 4-Jun-2 SOGA, Bratislava #110/R est:18000 (SL.K 18000)

VEDDER, Elihu (1836-1923) American
£4245 $6750 €6368 Old bastion and pergola (20x28cm-8x11in) i.d.Sep 11 66 verso panel prov. 1-Mar-3 North East Auctions, Portsmouth #694/R est:2000-3000
Works on paper
£903 $1400 €1355 Classical female figure holding book (36x25cm-14x10in) pastel. 7-Dec-2 South Bay, Long Island #139/R
£1039 $1600 €1559 Century magazine illustration (23x16cm-9x6in) ink pencil prov.exhib. 4-Sep-2 Christie's, Rockefeller NY #365/R est:1200-1800

VEDEL, Herman (1875-1948) Danish
£426 $672 €639 Interior scene with to women seated (70x61cm-28x24in) init. 27-Nov-2 Museumsbygningen, Copenhagen #35 (D.KR 5000)
£652 $1036 €978 Interior scene with woman seen from behind (66x80cm-26x31in) mono. 10-Mar-3 Rasmussen, Vejle #30/R (D.KR 7000)
£653 $1038 €980 Still life of jugs and bottles on table (55x61cm-22x24in) mono. 5-May-3 Rasmussen, Vejle #592/R (D.KR 7000)

VEDOVA, Emilio (1919-) Italian
£10638 $17234 €15000 Untitled (58x78cm-23x31in) s.d.90 board prov. 26-May-3 Christie's, Milan #225/R est:10000-15000
£15385 $24154 €24000 Composition with orange and yellow (98x70cm-39x28in) s.d.83 oil paper on canvas prov. 20-Nov-2 Pandolfini, Florence #113/R est:26000
£20567 $33319 €29000 Oggetti sul tavolo (72x77cm-28x30in) s. prov.exhib. 26-May-3 Christie's, Milan #350/R est:15000-20000
£89744 $140897 €140000 Contemporary vision (130x170cm-51x67in) prov.exhib.lit. 20-Nov-2 Pandolfini, Florence #112/R est:130000
Prints
£2658 $4120 €4200 Untitled (57x77cm-22x30in) monotype. 28-Sep-2 Ketterer, Hamburg #854/R est:2200-2600
£10633 $16481 €16800 Untitled (127x103cm-50x41in) monotype. 28-Sep-2 Ketterer, Hamburg #853/R est:3000-4000
Works on paper
£2614 $4183 €4000 Untitled (21x28cm-8x11in) s.d.1955 chl. 4-Jan-3 Meeting Art, Vercelli #605
£3205 $4679 €5000 Composition (34x48cm-13x19in) s. mixed media exec. with A R Penck. 5-Jun-2 Il Ponte, Milan #104/R est:6000-8000
£5396 $8849 €7500 Composition (38x51cm-15x20in) s.d. chl whisked. 6-Jun-3 Ketterer, Munich #134/R est:3500-4000
£6028 $9766 €8500 Untitled (47x34cm-19x13in) s.d.82 mixed media paper on canvas prov. 26-May-3 Christie's, Milan #54 est:2000-3000

VEDRES, Mark Weinberger (1870-1961) Hungarian
Sculpture
£1677 $2616 €2516 Boy playing flute (26cm-10in) s. bronze. 11-Apr-3 Kieselbach, Budapest #96/R est:480000-600000 (H.F 600000)

VEEN, Gerardus van (17th C) Dutch
Works on paper
£1689 $2635 €2500 Trois faisans (19x9cm-7x4in) mono.i.d.1670 pen ink wash htd W/C. 31-Mar-3 Piasa, Paris #25/R

VEEN, Karel van (1898-1988) Dutch
£903 $1490 €1300 Seated ballerina (45x34cm-18x13in) mono.d.1954 board. 1-Jul-3 Christie's, Amsterdam #310

VEEN, Otto van (1556-1629) Flemish
£1631 $2528 €2447 Landscape with figures (50x60cm-20x24in) 4-Dec-2 AB Stockholms Auktionsverk #1970/R est:15000-20000 (S.KR 23000)

VEEN, Otto van (attrib) (1556-1629) Flemish
£1065 $1778 €1500 Marie Madeleine abandonnant ses bijoux (51x38cm-20x15in) panel. 18-Jun-3 Tajan, Paris #54/R est:2000-3000
£2374 $3799 €3300 Apollo with figures (116x161cm-46x63in) 17-May-3 De Vuyst, Lokeren #520/R est:4000-6000
£50000 $77500 €75000 Portrait of Duke Alessandro Farnese (20x13cm-8x5in) gold copper. 6-Dec-2 Lyon & Turnbull, Edinburgh #19/R est:10000-15000
Works on paper
£1100 $1837 €1595 Meeting of Abraham and Melchizedek (21x35cm-8x14in) pen blk ink blk grey wash htd white lunette shaped prov. 9-Jul-3 Sotheby's, London #106/R est:1200-1500

VEEN, van der (?) Belgian?
Works on paper
£800 $1264 €1200 Moonlit Napoleonic harbour (36x43cm-14x17in) 2-Dec-2 Gorringes, Lewes #2580/R

VEENENDAAL, Hendrik (1889-1931) Belgian
£318 $497 €500 Sunny courtyard (39x59cm-15x23in) s. 5-Nov-2 Vendu Notarishuis, Rotterdam #2/R

VEERKAMP, Peter (1872-1947) Flemish
£321 $503 €500 Dutch harbour by moonlight (15x30cm-6x12in) s. panel. 21-Nov-2 Dorotheum, Vienna #210/R

VEGA DE SEOANE, Eduardo (1955-) Spanish
Works on paper
£769 $1215 €1200 Patriots (98x147cm-39x58in) s. mixed media on canvas exhib. 19-Nov-2 Durán, Madrid #172/R

VEGA OSORIO, Jose (1945-) Spanish
£962 $1519 €1500 Still life on table (39x47cm-15x19in) s. board. 13-Nov-2 Ansorena, Madrid #27/R

VEGA, Enrique (1953-) Spanish
£1448 $2288 €2100 Big jug (200x150cm-79x59in) s.i.d.1988 prov.exhib. 1-Apr-3 Segre, Madrid #197/R

VEGA, J de la (19/20th C) ?
£800 $1296 €1200 Spanish ladies (34x23cm-13x9in) s. pair. 21-May-3 James Thompson, Kirby Lonsdale #48

VEGA, Jose Ignacio de la (?) South American?
Works on paper
£1497 $2366 €2246 Bright (40x30cm-16x12in) s. mixed media on canvas. 26-Nov-2 Louis Morton, Mexico #23/R est:6000-9000 (M.P 24000)

VEHRINGS, Ursula (1893-1972) German
£253 $395 €400 Two boys in spring landscape (50x40cm-20x16in) s. 18-Oct-2 Dr Fritz Nagel, Stuttgart #364/R

VEILHAN, Xavier (1963-) French
Sculpture
£2848 $4500 €4500 Tete de mort (50x40x62cm-20x16x24in) painted resin prov. 27-Nov-2 Tajan, Paris #112/R est:8000-10000
£3611 $5958 €5200 Esturgeon (27x95cm-11x37in) s. num.2/6 painted plywood prov.lit. 3-Jul-3 Christie's, Paris #109/R est:2000-3000

VEILLON, Auguste-Louis (1834-1890) Swiss
£478 $741 €717 Venise, S Giorgio Maggiore et la Salute (30x45cm-12x18in) 7-Dec-2 Galerie du Rhone, Sion #526/R (S.FR 1100)
£957 $1483 €1436 Canal d'Ismai'lia (33x46cm-13x18in) mono. i.d.1874 verso paper on board. 9-Dec-2 Philippe Schuler, Zurich #3840/R (S.FR 2200)
£1957 $3052 €2936 Coastal landscape at sunset (47x80cm-19x31in) s. 16-Sep-2 Philippe Schuler, Zurich #3410/R est:4000-6000 (S.FR 4500)
£2968 $4630 €4452 Mountain landscape (114x173cm-45x68in) s. prov. 28-Mar-3 Koller, Zurich #3140a/R est:6000-10000 (S.FR 6500)
£5931 $9134 €8897 Seascape with figures, camel, sheep and ruins (114x192cm-45x76in) 27-Oct-2 Anders Antik, Landskrona #128a est:30000-40000 (S.KR 86000)
£6009 $9313 €9014 Prayer in the desert (41x63cm-16x25in) s. 3-Oct-2 Koller, Zurich #3085/R est:10000-15000 (S.FR 14000)
£7725 $11974 €11588 Nomads with camel by Red Sea (115x194cm-45x76in) s. 3-Oct-2 Koller, Zurich #3084/R est:18000-25000 (S.FR 18000)
£15284 $23843 €22926 Vision de l'orient (117x194cm-46x76in) s. 6-Nov-2 Dobiaschofsky, Bern #1037/R est:35000 (S.FR 35000)

VEILLON, Margot (1907-) Swiss
£261 $407 €392 Seated Bedouin girl in red dress (41x29cm-16x11in) s. masonite. 16-Sep-2 Philippe Schuler, Zurich #3413/R (S.FR 600)
£348 $543 €522 Fisherman casting net (98x68cm-39x27in) s.d.1961 masonite. 16-Sep-2 Philippe Schuler, Zurich #6658 (S.FR 800)
£391 $607 €587 Busy oasis (43x66cm-17x26in) s. 9-Dec-2 Philippe Schuler, Zurich #8763 (S.FR 900)

VEIT, Philipp (1793-1877) German
Works on paper
£633 $1000 €1000 Young girl with fawn in landscape (35x29cm-14x11in) mono. chk. 29-Nov-2 Bassenge, Berlin #6088/R

VEITH, Eduard (1856-1925) Austrian
£4552 $7010 €6828 Portrait of two women (98x69cm-39x27in) s. 27-Oct-2 Anders Antik, Landskrona #128/R est:60000-80000 (S.KR 66000)

VEKEMANS, Bruno (20th C) Belgian?
£972 $1546 €1400 Portrait d'homme aux lunettes (76x73cm-30x29in) s.d.1990 oil gouache paper. 29-Apr-3 Campo & Campo, Antwerp #332/R
£1006 $1550 €1600 Boxeur (123x68cm-48x27in) s.d.1989 paper. 22-Oct-2 Campo & Campo, Antwerp #317/R
Works on paper
£1667 $2650 €2400 Biljart Palace (112x74cm-44x29in) s.d.1991 mixed media. 29-Apr-3 Campo & Campo, Antwerp #334/R est:2250-2750

VEL, Gaston de (20th C) New Zealander
£368 $586 €552 Reclining nude (38x47cm-15x19in) s.d.1987. 25-Feb-3 Peter Webb, Auckland #28/R est:1000-2000 (NZ.D 1050)
£388 $566 €582 Taramakau, Arthurs Pass (29x39cm-11x15in) s. 12-Sep-1 Watson's, Christchurch #43 est:1200-2200 (NZ.D 1300)
£470 $734 €705 Fishing boats, Tauranga (40x52cm-16x20in) s.d.1970. 7-Nov-2 International Art Centre, Auckland #88/R est:1500-2500 (NZ.D 1500)

VELA ZANETTI, Jose (1913-1999) Spanish
£3310 $5230 €4800 Natives (54x40cm-21x16in) s.d.1959 board. 1-Apr-3 Segre, Madrid #136/R est:3000
£5161 $8155 €8000 Landscape (46x55cm-18x22in) s.d.85 s.i.d.verso. 17-Dec-2 Durán, Madrid #213/R
£5263 $8526 €8000 Squatting figure (95x61cm-37x24in) s. board. 21-Jan-3 Durán, Madrid #141/R
£9032 $14271 €14000 Afternoon nap (65x81cm-26x32in) s.d.1988 board. 17-Dec-2 Segre, Madrid #94/R est:7000
£11321 $17434 €18000 Peasants (80x100cm-31x39in) s.d.74 lit. 22-Oct-2 Durán, Madrid #268/R est:10200
£16774 $26503 €26000 Woman combing her hair (80x65cm-31x26in) s. 17-Dec-2 Segre, Madrid #99/R
Works on paper
£728 $1187 €1100 Gothic Christ (66x48cm-26x19in) s.d.53 W/C cardboard. 11-Feb-3 Segre, Madrid #377/R

VELASCO (1960-) Italian
£1282 $2013 €2000 Segesta (48x54cm-19x21in) s. painted 2001. 19-Nov-2 Finarte, Milan #126/R
£3129 $4976 €4600 Lights (40x50cm-16x20in) s. s.i.d.1997 verso. 1-Mar-3 Meeting Art, Vercelli #602 est:2000
Works on paper
£753 $1175 €1100 The Grona (35x50cm-14x20in) s. pencil exec.1990 exhib. 10-Apr-3 Finarte Semenzato, Rome #60/R

VELASCO, Javier (1963-) Spanish
Works on paper
£288 $456 €450 Underneath (46x38cm-18x15in) s.d.1994 mixed media on canvas. 14-Nov-2 Arte, Seville #447/R

VELASCO, Jose Maria (1840-1912) Mexican
£7557 $11788 €11336 Paisaje (8x13cm-3x5in) s.d.1910 paper. 17-Oct-2 Louis Morton, Mexico #99/R est:90000-120000 (M.P 120000)
£21769 $34612 €32000 Mexican coast line (53x87cm-21x34in) s. 19-Mar-3 Neumeister, Munich #780/R est:5000
Works on paper
£1732 $2771 €2511 Castillo de Chapultepec (21x31cm-8x12in) s. crayon. 15-May-3 Louis Morton, Mexico #140/R est:28000-32000 (M.P 28000)

VELASCO, Marco (1965-) Italian
Works on paper
£327 $523 €500 Artist's end (100x70cm-39x28in) s.i.d.2002 verso mixed media paper on canvas. 4-Jan-3 Meeting Art, Vercelli #458

VELASQUEZ, Diego Rodriguez de Silva y (style) (1599-1660) Spanish
£6289 $9748 €10000 Infanta Margarita Teresa, aged 5 (58x49cm-23x19in) lit. 2-Oct-2 Dorotheum, Vienna #322/R est:7000-9000

VELASQUEZ, Jose Antonio (1906-1983) Honduran
£968 $1500 €1452 Mission (69x48cm-27x19in) s. canvas laid down painted c.1950. 8-Dec-2 Toomey, Oak Park #819/R est:2000-3000

VELAZQUEZ, Eugenio Lucas (1817-1870) Spanish
£2013 $3242 €3000 Singing (22x29cm-9x11in) s. board. 18-Feb-3 Durán, Madrid #225/R
£5769 $9115 €9000 Study of party (31x49cm-12x19in) board. 14-Nov-2 Arte, Seville #240/R
£7000 $10990 €10500 Velazquez pintando a las meninas - Velazuez painting the mininas (32x41cm-13x16in) panel. 19-Nov-2 Sotheby's, London #26/R est:7000-10000
£9615 $15192 €15000 Sphynx and pyramids (25x32cm-10x13in) 14-Nov-2 Arte, Seville #298/R
£9934 $16192 €15000 Bull scene (50x35cm-20x14in) 11-Feb-3 Castellana, Madrid #363/R est:20000
£35000 $54950 €52500 Los miserables - poverty (106x76cm-42x30in) painted c.1860-65. 19-Nov-2 Sotheby's, London #28/R est:38000-45000
£38710 $61161 €60000 Day out (77x114cm-30x45in) 18-Dec-2 Castellana, Madrid #24/R est:90000

VELAZQUEZ, Eugenio Lucas (attrib) (1817-1870) Spanish
£1769 $2813 €2654 Bull fighting (31x43cm-12x17in) with sig. verso panel. 5-Mar-3 Rasmussen, Copenhagen #1818/R est:6000-8000 (D.KR 19000)

VELDE, Adriaen van de (1636-1672) Dutch
£1486 $2319 €2200 Musiciens a l'entree d'une taverne (43x31cm-17x12in) pair. 30-Mar-3 Anaf, Lyon #252/R
£3188 $4973 €4782 Study for wooded landscape (38x31cm-15x12in) s. panel. 6-Nov-2 Dobiaschofsky, Bern #1038/R est:8000 (S.FR 7300)
£8000 $13360 €11600 Horseman asking directions of a shepherd, with cattle and sheep (21x27cm-8x11in) s.d.1670 panel prov.lit. 9-Jul-3 Bonhams, New Bond Street #4/R est:8000-12000

VELDE, Adriaen van de (attrib) (1636-1672) Dutch
£1258 $1937 €2000 Scene de paturage (36x39cm-14x15in) 25-Oct-2 Tajan, Paris #62/R est:2000-3000
£1282 $2013 €2000 Berger et troupeau dans un paysage (30x24cm-12x9in) mono. panel. 10-Dec-2 Vanderkindere, Brussels #414 est:2000-3000
Works on paper
£979 $1400 €1469 Studies of sheep (17x26cm-7x10in) red chk. 23-Jan-3 Swann Galleries, New York #203/R est:1000-1500

VELDE, Bram van (1895-1981) Dutch
Works on paper
£40000 $65600 €60000 Composition (100x70cm-39x28in) gouache paper on canvas prov.exhib.lit. 6-Feb-3 Christie's, London #611/R est:40000-60000

VELDE, Charles William Meredith van de (1818-1898) Dutch
Works on paper
£350 $567 €525 Western entrance to the Bay of Ajaccio, Corsica (20x28cm-8x11in) s. W/C. 21-May-3 Bonhams, Knightsbridge #202/R

VELDE, Esaias van de (1587-1630) Dutch
£27673 $43170 €44000 Rider by ruins (14cm-6in circular) s.d.1624 i. verso panel prov. 19-Sep-2 Dr Fritz Nagel, Stuttgart #905/R est:8000
£31210 $48688 €49000 River landscape with travellers on a path near a waterfall (13cm-5in circular) s.d.1623 panel circular prov.exhib.lit. 6-Nov-2 Christie's, Amsterdam #69/R est:35000-45000

VELDE, Geer van (1898-c.1977) Dutch
£5696 $9000 €9000 Figure a la table (80x100cm-31x39in) s. painted 1932 prov. 26-Nov-2 Sotheby's, Amsterdam #209/R est:12000-15000
£7692 $11923 €12000 Jerusalem (51x42cm-20x17in) init. executed 1973. 3-Dec-2 Christie's, Amsterdam #251/R est:10000-15000
£9615 $14904 €15000 Composition - solution pour un rose (80x60cm-31x24in) init. painted c.1940. 3-Dec-2 Christie's, Amsterdam #252/R est:16000-20000
£16026 $24840 €25000 Composition (64x62cm-25x24in) st.init. painted 1968-69 lit. 9-Dec-2 Piasa, Paris #39/R est:10000-12000
£27338 $44835 €38000 Interieur (84x100cm-33x39in) init. 3-Jun-3 Christie's, Amsterdam #301/R est:30000-50000
Works on paper
£1656 $2583 €2600 Landscape (31x48cm-12x19in) init. gouache. 6-Nov-2 Vendue Huis, Gravenhage #138/R est:1500-2000
£1731 $2717 €2700 Personnage dans un interieur (21x27cm-8x11in) s. gouache. 16-Dec-2 Charbonneaux, Paris #200/R est:3000-3500

£1923 $3019 €3000 Composition (21x21cm-8x8in) mono. W/C. 11-Dec-2 Artcurial Briest, Paris #700/R
£1923 $3019 €3000 Composition (20x26cm-8x10in) s. gouache. 16-Dec-2 Charbonneaux, Paris #199/R est:3000-3500
£2215 $3500 €3500 Untitled (19x25cm-7x10in) s. gouache. 26-Nov-2 Sotheby's, Amsterdam #206/R est:3500-5000
£2302 $3776 €3200 Untitled (20x25cm-8x10in) init. black chk W/C prov. 3-Jun-3 Christie's, Amsterdam #53/R est:4000-6000
£4167 $6542 €6500 Femme debout (23x11cm-9x4in) mono. gouache exec.c.1925-30 lit. 10-Dec-2 Piasa, Paris #64/R est:1500

VELDE, Jan Jansz van de (1620-1662) Dutch
£17834 $27822 €28000 Still life with pasglas, smoker's utensils. playing cards (15x12cm-6x5in) s. panel prov.exhib. 5-Nov-2 Sotheby's, Amsterdam #298/R est:18000-25000

VELDE, Jan van de II (c.1593-1641) Dutch
Prints
£2215 $3500 €3500 Temple of the Sibyl at Tivoli in wooded landscape (20x22cm-8x9in) etching. 29-Nov-2 Bassenge, Berlin #5234/R est:2000

VELDE, Pieter van de (1634-1687) Flemish
£2000 $3340 €2900 Mediteranean landscape with Dutch men o'war, a pink and rowing boat (38x52cm-15x20in) 9-Jul-3 Bonhams, New Bond Street #79/R est:2000-3000
£5660 $8830 €9000 Southern harbour (80x114cm-31x45in) i. 23-Sep-2 Wiener Kunst Auktionen, Vienna #15/R est:9000-18000
£9500 $15865 €13775 Dutch vessels on the Scheldt river off Antwerp. Shipping off the port of Flushing (58x83cm-23x33in) pair prov. 8-Jul-3 Sotheby's, Olympia #403/R est:8000-12000

VELDE, Pieter van de (attrib) (1634-1687) Flemish
£2797 $4671 €4000 Le dechargement de navires sur la cote Hollandaise (41x60cm-16x24in) 27-Jun-3 Piasa, Paris #58/R est:4000-6000

VELDE, Serge van de (1950-) Belgian
Works on paper
£252 $387 €400 Deux oiseaux (75x106cm-30x42in) s.d.1975 ink dr. 22-Oct-2 Campo & Campo, Antwerp #286

VELDE, Willem van de (attrib) (17/18th C) Dutch
Works on paper
£600 $960 €900 Shipping off the shore (15x23cm-6x9in) pen ink. 11-Mar-3 Gorringes, Lewes #2528/R

VELDE, Willem van de (elder) (1611-1693) Dutch
Works on paper
£5096 $7949 €8000 Warships and other boats at anchor (17x40cm-7x16in) bears i.verso black chk grey wash prov. 5-Nov-2 Sotheby's, Amsterdam #107/R est:2500-3500
£7500 $12150 €11250 Dutch warship seen from the stern (33x47cm-13x19in) grey wash. 21-May-3 Christie's, Kensington #389/R est:1500-2500

VELDE, Willem van de (elder-attrib) (1611-1693) Dutch
Works on paper
£1700 $2669 €2550 Brig and other small boats in a flat calm (31x38cm-12x15in) black chk pen ink prov. 13-Dec-2 Christie's, Kensington #310 est:800-1200
£4676 $7482 €6500 Becalmed boats (31x38cm-12x15in) chk pen sepia prov. 17-May-3 Lempertz, Koln #1259/R est:6200

VELDE, Willem van de (style) (17/18th C) Dutch
£5245 $7500 €7868 Ships off shore (76x102cm-30x40in) 22-Jan-3 Doyle, New York #126/R est:15000

VELDE, Willem van de (younger) (1633-1707) Dutch
£16000 $25120 €24000 English yacht in a gale force wind (107x184cm-42x72in) s. painted with studio prov.lit. 12-Dec-2 Sotheby's, London #165/R est:15000-20000

Works on paper
£400 $648 €600 Flagship at anchor offshore (11x18cm-4x7in) pencil prov. 21-May-3 Christie's, Kensington #350/R
£3243 $5059 €4800 Two sailing boats and other ships (10x17cm-4x7in) i. pen ink. 27-Mar-3 Christie's, Paris #50/R
£4459 $6955 €7000 Views of ships at sea. black chk grey wash painted with studio seven. 5-Nov-2 Sotheby's, Amsterdam #108/R est:1500-2000
£9877 $16000 €14816 Portrait of Dutch ship (26x40cm-10x16in) chk wash. 21-Jan-3 Sotheby's, New York #142/R est:15000

VELDE, Willem van de (younger-after) (1633-1707) Dutch
£5000 $7750 €7500 King Charles II's visit to the fleet at the Nore, 6 June 1672 (88x127cm-35x50in) 31-Oct-2 Christie's, Kensington #421/R est:6000-8000

VELDE, Willem van de (younger-studio) (1633-1707) Dutch
£11511 $18417 €16000 Fishing boats near shore (34x41cm-13x16in) prov. 17-May-3 Lempertz, Koln #1141/R est:15000

VELDEN, Adrianus Dirk Blok van der (1913-1980) Dutch
£481 $755 €750 Texel (50x70cm-20x28in) s.i.d.75. 25-Nov-2 Glerum, Amsterdam #106
£577 $906 €900 Coastal landscape of Texel (40x50cm-16x20in) s.i.d.1948. 25-Nov-2 Glerum, Amsterdam #151/R

VELDEN, Petrus van der (1837-1915) New Zealander/Dutch
£1075 $1569 €1613 Dutch scene, with woman and windmill (30x50cm-12x20in) 12-Sep-1 Watson's, Christchurch #80 est:3500-5000 (NZ.D 3600)
£1800 $2862 €2700 Otira gorge, New Zealand (143x81cm-56x32in) s. 29-Apr-3 Bonhams, New Bond Street #3/R est:800-1200
£5263 $8211 €7895 Peasant girl with suitor (110x69cm-43x27in) s. 27-Mar-3 International Art Centre, Auckland #119/R est:14000-18000 (NZ.D 15000)
£5329 $8313 €7994 Fishing boats at low tide (59x91cm-23x36in) s. 7-Nov-2 International Art Centre, Auckland #76/R est:15000-25000 (NZ.D 17000)
£10972 $17116 €16458 Disillusioned (86x111cm-34x44in) s.d.1872 board. 7-Nov-2 International Art Centre, Auckland #73/R est:40000-70000 (NZ.D 35000)

Works on paper
£236 $368 €354 French farmyard (22x32cm-9x13in) W/C. 6-Aug-2 Peter Webb, Auckland #22/R (NZ.D 800)
£1228 $1916 €1842 Beached sailing ship (55x73cm-22x29in) s. pencil W/C lit. 27-Mar-3 International Art Centre, Auckland #165/R est:3500-6500 (NZ.D 3500)

VELDHUIZEN, Willem van (1954-) Dutch
£4317 $7079 €6000 Narrow view (200x31cm-79x12in) s.d. lit. 3-Jun-3 Christie's, Amsterdam #357/R est:6000-8000

VELICKOVIC, Vladimir (1935-) Yugoslavian
£1448 $2419 €2100 Homme de marche (32x29cm-13x11in) s. oil collage cardboard prov. 9-Jul-3 Cornette de St.Cyr, Paris #360/R est:1200-1500
£3459 $5362 €5500 Obstacle (81x100cm-32x39in) s.i.d.1972 verso. 30-Oct-2 Artcurial Briest, Paris #484/R est:6800-7600
Works on paper
£443 $687 €700 Le triangle (57x46cm-22x18in) s.i.d. mixed media collage dr. 28-Sep-2 Cornette de St.Cyr, Paris #441/R
£694 $1146 €1000 Feu no 17 (56x37cm-22x15in) s.d.1997 mixed media cardboard on panel. 1-Jul-3 Artcurial Briest, Paris #839/R
£705 $1107 €1100 Sans titre (75x55cm-30x22in) s.d.10-06-1981 Indian ink red ink collage. 16-Dec-2 Charbonneaux, Paris #201
£903 $1435 €1300 Mouvement figure III (102x66cm-40x26in) s.i.d.1.4.1989 Indian ink red ink dr. 29-Apr-3 Artcurial Briest, Paris #623/R est:1500-1800
£962 $1510 €1500 Movements LXXVI (102x66cm-40x26in) s.i.d.84 ink dr. 15-Dec-2 Perrin, Versailles #108/R
£1195 $1864 €1900 Untitled (107x74cm-42x29in) s.d.1976 Chinese ink gouache collage. 8-Oct-2 Christie's, Paris #162/R

VELIM, Anton (1892-1954) Austrian
£590 $933 €850 Man with pram (25x20cm-10x8in) board. 24-Apr-3 Dorotheum, Vienna #22/R

VELLAN, Felice (1889-1976) Italian
£340 $541 €500 Busson (23x28cm-9x11in) s.d.1954 cardboard. 1-Mar-3 Meeting Art, Vercelli #175
£349 $545 €524 Rocky coastal landscape on Ligurian Riviera (28x34cm-11x13in) s.d.1929 i. verso panel. 6-Nov-2 Dobiaschofsky, Bern #1039 (S.FR 800)
£786 $1226 €1179 Sunny woodland path (30x36cm-12x14in) s.d.1929 i. verso panel. 6-Nov-2 Dobiaschofsky, Bern #1040/R (S.FR 1800)
£1156 $1839 €1700 Winter in Salice d'Ulzio (45x38cm-18x15in) s.d.1945 board. 1-Mar-3 Meeting Art, Vercelli #79

VELMEN, G van (20th C) Dutch?
£1146 $1800 €1719 Froup of fishing boats at sea (119x99cm-47x39in) s. panel. 14-Dec-2 Weschler, Washington #625/R est:2000-3000

VELSEN, Con van (1948-) Dutch
£828 $1316 €1200 In Veilige Haven (8x15cm-3x6in) s.d.1999 panel. 10-Mar-3 Sotheby's, Amsterdam #337 est:300-500
£896 $1425 €1300 Lenteuitje (10x12cm-4x5in) s. panel. 10-Mar-3 Sotheby's, Amsterdam #338 est:300-500
£1034 $1644 €1500 Aan de Voet van de Heuvel (13x14cm-5x6in) s.d.1999 panel. 10-Mar-3 Sotheby's, Amsterdam #336 est:300-500
£1793 $2851 €2600 Zomerleed, winterpret (30x24cm-12x9in) s.d.1998 panel. 10-Mar-3 Sotheby's, Amsterdam #339 est:300-500

VELTEN, W (1847-1929) Russian
£1419 $2086 €2200 Riders in conversation (16x23cm-6x9in) s. 24-Jun-2 Dr Fritz Nagel, Stuttgart #5902/R
£1935 $2845 €3000 Horse market (16x23cm-6x9in) s. 24-Jun-2 Dr Fritz Nagel, Stuttgart #5903/R

VELTEN, Wilhelm (1847-1929) Russian
£1056 $1701 €1500 Ox and horse harnessed to cart (18x29cm-7x11in) s. board. 7-May-3 Michael Zeller, Lindau #956/R est:1200
£1081 $1686 €1600 Resting outside tavern (10x14cm-4x6in) s. panel. 26-Mar-3 Hugo Ruef, Munich #248 est:800
£1818 $2709 €2800 Hunting society in front of Blutenburg Castle near Obermenzing (15x22cm-6x9in) s. panel. 28-Jun-2 Sigalas, Stuttgart #874/R
£1921 $2997 €2882 Royal outing (20x30cm-8x12in) s. panel. 6-Nov-2 Dobiaschofsky, Bern #1041/R est:8000 (S.FR 4400)
£2019 $3250 €3029 Departing from the hunt (20x30cm-8x12in) s. 20-Jan-3 Arthur James, Florida #692
£2721 $4327 €4000 Horse trading before old town (15x23cm-6x9in) s. panel. 19-Mar-3 Neumeister, Munich #781/R est:3200
£2800 $4368 €4200 Hussar's camp (41x32cm-16x13in) s. panel prov. 17-Sep-2 Sotheby's, Olympia #235/R est:2000-3000

VELTENS, Johan Diderik Cornelis (1814-1894) Dutch
£329 $533 €500 Figures near a farm in a hilly landscape (22x31cm-9x12in) s.d.49 panel. 21-Jan-3 Christie's, Amsterdam #63/R

VELTHUYSEN, Henry van (1881-1954) Dutch
£590 $974 €850 Activity on an Indonesian river (58x78cm-23x31in) s.d.1929. 1-Jul-3 Christie's, Amsterdam #298

VELTZ, Ivan (1866-1926) Russian
£11709 $18500 €18500 Night in a southern city (76x53cm-30x21in) s.d.1910. 1-Dec-2 Bukowskis, Helsinki #279/R est:5000-7000
£19014 $30613 €27000 Village street in Italy (53x76cm-21x30in) s.d.1911 exhib. 10-May-3 Bukowskis, Helsinki #385/R est:5000-7000

VEN, E E G van der (1866-1944) Dutch
£586 $938 €850 Pastoral scene (90x69cm-35x27in) s. 18-May-3 Anders Antik, Landskrona #100 (S.KR 7500)

VEN, Emil (1902-1984) Hungarian?
£1291 $2001 €1872 Harbour on the Adriatic (80x60cm-31x24in) s. 9-Dec-2 Mu Terem Galeria, Budapest #196/R est:280000 (H.F 480000)
£3074 $4795 €4457 Market in Toulon (70x80cm-28x31in) s. 12-Apr-3 Mu Terem Galeria, Budapest #191/R est:360000 (H.F 1100000)
£4192 $6539 €6078 Harbour in Toulon (70x81cm-28x32in) s. s.i.d.1983 verso. 12-Apr-3 Mu Terem Galeria, Budapest #71/R est:400000 (H.F 1500000)

VEN, Jan Cornelis van der (19th C) Belgian?
£382 $600 €573 Still life with purple lilacs with green leaves and striped blue and white vase (51x41cm-20x16in) s. 19-Apr-3 James Julia, Fairfield #357/R

VEN, Willem van den (1898-1958) Dutch
£288 $447 €432 Late summer afternoon on the farm (56x46cm-22x18in) s. 3-Dec-2 Ritchie, Toronto #3098/R (C.D 700)

VENARD, Claude (1913-1999) French
£192 $300 €288 Abstract flowers and birds (46x55cm-18x22in) s. 11-Nov-2 Stephan Welz, Johannesburg #39 (SA.R 3000)
£278 $441 €400 La grille (27x35cm-11x14in) s. painted c.1950 prov. 29-Apr-3 Artcurial Briest, Paris #273
£280 $426 €420 Nature morte et modeles (19x48cm-7x19in) s. 29-Aug-2 Christie's, Kensington #170
£513 $805 €800 Paysage (32x41cm-13x16in) s. 16-Dec-2 Charbonneaux, Paris #302
£704 $1169 €1000 Nature morte (31x39cm-12x15in) s. 13-Jun-3 Rabourdin & Choppin de Janvry, Paris #145
£759 $1267 €1100 Montmartre (38x46cm-15x18in) s. 10-Jul-3 Artcurial Briest, Paris #239
£769 $1200 €1154 Still life with flowers (58x58cm-23x23in) s. 12-Oct-2 Neal Auction Company, New Orleans #292/R
£769 $1200 €1154 Port (54x65cm-21x26in) s. 5-Nov-2 Doyle, New York #5/R
£823 $1284 €1300 Nature morte a l'echiquier (102x75cm-40x30in) s. 16-Sep-2 Horta, Bruxelles #209
£845 $1403 €1200 Les poires (38x46cm-15x18in) s. i.verso. 15-Jun-3 Anaf, Lyon #206/R
£850 $1335 €1275 Nature morte a la bouteille (22x27cm-9x11in) prov.exhib. 10-Dec-2 Rosebery Fine Art, London #645/R
£886 $1400 €1400 Nature morte aux pipes, bouteilles et pommes (42x34cm-17x13in) s. 29-Nov-2 Drouot Estimations, Paris #111
£962 $1510 €1500 Montmartre (54x65cm-21x26in) s. 13-Dec-2 Piasa, Paris #268
£980 $1608 €1500 Compotier aux fruits (27x19cm-11x7in) s. painted c.1960. 9-Feb-3 Anaf, Lyon #255
£1456 $2256 €2300 Nature morte (50x62cm-20x24in) s. 28-Sep-2 Cornette de St.Cyr, Paris #202 est:800-1000
£1523 $2483 €2300 Bateaux a quai (60x73cm-24x29in) s. 3-Feb-3 Cornette de St.Cyr, Paris #340
£1854 $3023 €2800 Eiffel tower, Paris (117x89cm-46x35in) s. 28-Jan-3 Dorotheum, Vienna #142/R est:2600-3800
£1892 $2951 €2800 Composition (74x74cm-29x29in) s.d.1957. 28-Mar-3 Claude Aguttes, Neuilly #137/R
£2025 $3200 €3200 Bateaux dans le port (75x75cm-30x30in) s. 26-Nov-2 Camard, Paris #103
£2098 $3504 €3000 L'arlequin (116x89cm-46x35in) s. 26-Jun-3 Tajan, Paris #307 est:2200-2500
£2112 $3400 €3168 Sailboats in harbor (102x102cm-40x40in) s. prov. 18-Feb-3 Arthur James, Florida #412
£2465 $4092 €3500 La boite a sel (24x34cm-9x13in) s. 15-Jun-3 Anaf, Lyon #207/R est:4000-5000
£2465 $4092 €3500 Paysage (100x100cm-39x39in) s. 15-Jun-3 Anaf, Lyon #209/R est:2500-3000
£2484 $4073 €3800 Interieur de l'atelier (46x55cm-18x22in) s. painted c.1955. 9-Feb-3 Anaf, Lyon #256/R
£2617 $4214 €3900 Nature morte (31x76cm-12x30in) s.d.1952 panel. 23-Feb-3 Lesieur & Le Bars, Le Havre #147/R
£2676 $4442 €3800 Nu a sa toilette (135x194cm-53x76in) s. 15-Jun-3 Anaf, Lyon #208/R est:4000-4500
£2715 $4426 €4100 Nature morte (74x75cm-29x30in) s. 3-Feb-3 Cornette de St.Cyr, Paris #342/R
£2905 $4532 €4300 Composition (100x100cm-39x39in) s.d.55. 28-Mar-3 Claude Aguttes, Neuilly #136/R
£3061 $4867 €4500 Tour d'argent (114x146cm-45x57in) s.d.1960 prov. 24-Mar-3 Claude Boisgirard, Paris #187/R
£3185 $4968 €5000 Nature morte (75x75cm-30x30in) s. 10-Nov-2 Eric Pillon, Calais #244/R
£6500 $10010 €9750 Le jeu de jacquet (146x89cm-57x35in) s. oil sand on canvas prov. 22-Oct-2 Sotheby's, London #181/R est:7000-9000

Works on paper
£696 $1100 €1044 Figure and vase of flowers (99x99cm-39x39in) s. 2-Apr-3 Doyle, New York #74/R
£2115 $3321 €3300 Montmartre et le Moulin de la Galette (100x100cm-39x39in) mixed media on canvas. 16-Dec-2 Eric Coutrier, Paris #99/R

VENDWIG, G (18th C) German?
£1859 $2881 €2900 Cavalry battle (109x160cm-43x63in) s.i.d.1702. 5-Dec-2 Dr Fritz Nagel, Stuttgart #634/R est:2900

VENET, Bernar (1941-) French
£1935 $3000 €2903 Position of two arcs (625cm-246in circular) s.i.d.1978 verso acrylic. 29-Sep-2 Butterfields, Los Angeles #4445/R est:2000-3000
£2516 $3899 €4000 Two undetermined lines (74x74cm-29x29in) s.i.d.89 paper prov. 30-Oct-2 Artcurial Briest, Paris #602 est:3000-4000
£5755 $9209 €8000 Undetermined line (76x75cm-30x30in) s.i.d.1990 oil-crayon paper prov. 17-May-3 De Vuyst, Lokeren #511/R est:8500-9500

Sculpture
£1900 $3002 €2850 185 4 Arc (41x40x40cm-16x16x16in) i. painted steel toy cars. 3-Apr-3 Christie's, Kensington #273/R

Works on paper
£1500 $2310 €2250 Undetermined line (33x46cm-13x18in) s.i.d.96 chl acrylic oilstick paper collage prov. 23-Oct-2 Christie's, London #216/R est:1400-1800
£1597 $2540 €2300 Undetermined line (37x34cm-15x13in) s.i.d.84 chl collage. 29-Apr-3 Artcurial Briest, Paris #549/R est:1500-2000
£4710 $7725 €6500 Ligne indeterminee (76x76cm-30x30in) s.i.d.1969 gouache prov. 27-May-3 Tajan, Paris #33/R est:6500-8000
£4800 $7392 €7200 Undertermined line (90x152cm-35x60in) s.i.d.1988 chl prov. 23-Oct-2 Christie's, London #215/R est:3000-5000

VENETIAN SCHOOL, Italian
£36000 $60120 €52200 Doge's Palace and the Riva degli Schiavoni, Venice. Grand Canal, Venice (87x116cm-34x46in) pair. 11-Jul-3 Christie's, Kensington #265/R est:15000-20000

VENETIAN SCHOOL (14th C) Italian
£23581 $36786 €35372 Madonna with child (55x41cm-22x16in) tempera gold panel prov. 20-Nov-2 Fischer, Luzern #1002/R est:18000-25000 (S.FR 54000)

VENETIAN SCHOOL (16th C) Italian
£40000 $66800 €58000 David with the head of Goliath (79x65cm-31x26in) panel prov.exhib. 9-Jul-3 Christie's, London #106/R est:15000-25000
£122000 $189100 €183000 Portrait of young bearded man (58x52cm-23x20in) 31-Oct-2 Sotheby's, Olympia #14/R est:6000-8000

VENETIAN SCHOOL (17th C) Italian
£4697 $7563 €7000 Lamentation (172x129cm-68x51in) 18-Feb-3 Sotheby's, Amsterdam #195/R est:4000-6000
£5975 $9321 €9500 Portrait de doge (141x106cm-56x42in) i. 8-Oct-2 Christie's, Paris #21/R est:6000
£7927 $13000 €11891 Adoration of the Magi (126x156cm-50x61in) prov. 5-Feb-3 Christie's, Rockefeller NY #274/R est:10000-15000
£9615 $14904 €15000 Mocking of Christ (133x220cm-52x87in) 5-Dec-2 Dr Fritz Nagel, Stuttgart #635/R est:9000
£12751 $20528 €19000 Scenes from the life of Saint Jerome (83x110cm-33x43in) panel. 18-Feb-3 Sotheby's, Amsterdam #188/R est:6000-8000
£19000 $31730 €27550 Saint John the Baptist (73x63cm-29x25in) within painted oval. 10-Jul-3 Sotheby's, London #180/R est:8000-12000
Sculpture
£35664 $59559 €51000 Bustes d'enfants (43x41cm-17x16in) black marble alabaster white marble piedouche pair. 25-Jun-3 Sotheby's, Paris #12/R est:20000-30000

VENETIAN SCHOOL, 17th/18th C Italian
Sculpture
£5500 $9185 €7975 Una and the lion (68x146cm-27x57in) marble relief prov. 8-Jul-3 Sotheby's, London #146/R est:6000-8000

VENETIAN SCHOOL (18th C) Italian
£5488 $9000 €8232 Portrait of Luisa Bergalli (74x57cm-29x22in) i. 29-May-3 Sotheby's, New York #10/R est:10000-15000
£5677 $8856 €8516 La negra allegory on the continent of Africa (50x39cm-20x15in) 20-Nov-2 Fischer, Luzern #1066/R est:5500-6500 (S.FR 13000)
£10000 $15600 €15000 Philosopher at a table (115x90cm-45x35in) with sig.i. 9-Apr-3 Christie's, London #114/R est:7000-10000
£12000 $18720 €18000 View of the Basilica from the Doge's Palace (73x113cm-29x44in) i. 10-Apr-3 Sotheby's, London #96/R est:18000
£15000 $23550 €22500 Head of a bearded man (65x49cm-26x19in) 10-Dec-2 Bonhams, New Bond Street #232/R est:2000-3000
£25000 $39250 €37500 A view of the Piazzetta, Venice. View of the Molo and Doge's palace (63x102cm-25x40in) pair prov. 10-Dec-2 Bonhams, New Bond Street #283/R est:25000-35000
£26000 $43420 €37700 Rio dei Mendicanti, Venice, with the Scuolo di S Marco. SS. Giovannie e Paolo, Venice (61x98cm-24x39in) pair. 11-Jul-3 Christie's, Kensington #268/R est:10000-15000
£72770 $119343 €105517 Flowers in metal vases (96x77cm-38x30in) voal six. 4-Jun-3 Fischer, Luzern #1035/R est:24000-30000 (S.FR 155000)
Works on paper
£570 $900 €900 Procession with the Ark of the Covenant (41x65cm-16x26in) pen. 29-Nov-2 Bassenge, Berlin #5788

VENETIAN SCHOOL (19th C) Italian
£36000 $60120 €52200 Venice, view of the entrance to Grand Canal. View of the Molo with Doge's Palace (44x64cm-17x25in) one bears sig. i. pair. 8-Jul-3 Sotheby's, Olympia #501/R est:6000-8000
Works on paper
£15957 $26649 €22500 Deux vues de Venise (24x41cm-9x16in) gouache. 19-Jun-3 Piasa, Paris #35/R est:6000-7500

VENETO SCHOOL (16th C) Italian
£5517 $8717 €8000 Adoration of the Magi (51x42cm-20x17in) copper. 5-Apr-3 Finarte Semenzato, Milan #1/R est:12000
£5743 $8959 €8500 Madonna enthroned amongst saints (20x85cm-8x33in) i. board. 25-Mar-3 Finarte Semenzato, Rome #104/R est:7500
£6419 $10014 €9500 Madonna and Child with Saint John (37x30cm-15x12in) board. 31-Mar-3 Finarte Semenzato, Milan #438/R
£6757 $10541 €10000 Madonna and Child with Saint Catherine (48x40cm-19x16in) board. 31-Mar-3 Finarte Semenzato, Milan #508/R
£13793 $21793 €20000 Madonna and Child (91x130cm-36x51in) i. 5-Apr-3 Finarte Semenzato, Milan #149/R est:25000

VENETO SCHOOL (17th C) Italian
£5743 $8959 €8500 Mythological scene (97x125cm-38x49in) 31-Mar-3 Finarte Semenzato, Milan #468 est:4500
£6289 $9686 €10000 Mythological scene (44x104cm-17x41in) 28-Oct-2 Il Ponte, Milan #118/R est:15000

VENETO SCHOOL (17th/18th C) Italian
Sculpture
£9655 $15448 €14000 Venus and Cupid. Mars (41cm-16in) bronze pair. 17-Mar-3 Pandolfini, Florence #751/R est:16000

VENETO SCHOOL (18th C) Italian
£10566 $16483 €16800 Figures (188x148cm-74x58in) oval pair. 22-Sep-2 Semenzato, Venice #116/R est:15000-25000
£10690 $17103 €15500 Landscapes with figures (119x87cm-47x34in) pair oval. 17-Mar-3 Pandolfini, Florence #637/R est:16500
£11950 $18403 €19000 Pastoral scene (29x37cm-11x15in) on glass set of 4. 23-Oct-2 Finarte, Rome #137/R
£12324 $19842 €17500 Landscape with villa (127x166cm-50x65in) 11-May-3 Finarte, Venice #32/R est:19000
£22069 $34869 €32000 Saint Mark's square (57x81cm-22x32in) 5-Apr-3 Finarte Semenzato, Milan #61/R est:15000

VENETO-CRETAN SCHOOL (17th C) Italian
£6038 $9419 €9600 Composition with St Catherine (59x70cm-23x28in) 21-Sep-2 Semenzato, Venice #152/R est:8000-10000

VENETO-GREEK SCHOOL (17th C-) Italian/Greek
£7170 $11185 €11400 Adoration of the Magi (64x50cm-25x20in) 21-Sep-2 Semenzato, Venice #131/R est:10000-13000

VENEZIANO, Paolo (style) (fl.1320-1362) Italian
£18293 $30000 €27440 Virgin and Child, with Saints Nicolas and Peter in the upper corners (55x41cm-22x16in) gold ground panel. 29-May-3 Sotheby's, New York #81/R est:15000-20000

VENITIEN, Jean (1911-) French
£800 $1264 €1200 Entree de l'Arcachon (22x27cm-9x11in) s. 3-Apr-3 Christie's, Kensington #64/R

VENNE, A P van de (1589-1662) Dutch
£2564 $4051 €4000 Scene de carnaval (64x105cm-25x41in) panel. 15-Nov-2 Drouot Estimations, Paris #64 est:8500-9000

VENNE, Adolf van der (1828-1911) Austrian
£753 $1175 €1100 Postcoach outside inn (62x80cm-24x31in) s. 10-Apr-3 Van Ham, Cologne #1736
£988 $1531 €1482 Sleigh party (27x44cm-11x17in) s.d.88 panel. 3-Dec-2 Ritchie, Toronto #3085/R est:1200-1600 (C.D 2400)
£1321 $2100 €1982 Make haste (58x78cm-23x31in) s.i.d.86. 7-Mar-3 Skinner, Boston #236/R est:3000-5000
£1410 $2186 €2200 Peasant with horses on a tow path at river edge (102x125cm-40x49in) s.indis.d. 4-Dec-2 Neumeister, Munich #948/R est:1500
£1497 $2380 €2200 Hay laden ox cart on narrow track (108x87cm-43x34in) s.d.874. 19-Mar-3 Neumeister, Munich #784/R est:2500
£2143 $3193 €3300 Hungarian peasant with horses under stormy skies (53x72cm-21x28in) s.d.869. 26-Jun-2 Neumeister, Munich #897/R est:3000

VENNE, Adriaen Pietersz van de (1589-1662) Dutch
£5500 $8635 €8250 Lady dancing and playing the lute in a landscape (28x21cm-11x8in) panel. 13-Dec-2 Christie's, Kensington #34/R est:5000-7000
£16561 $25834 €26000 Male wijsheyt (37x29cm-15x11in) i. panel prov. 6-Nov-2 Christie's, Amsterdam #5/R est:5000-7000
£179856 $287770 €250000 Cavalier at dressing table with servant holding mirror (40x33cm-16x13in) s.i.d.16 panel grisaille. 13-May-3 Sotheby's, Amsterdam #20/R est:40000-60000
Works on paper
£19108 $29809 €30000 Adam and Eve with their children (10x14cm-4x6in) i.verso pen brown ink grey wash prov.exhib.lit. 5-Nov-2 Sotheby's, Amsterdam #37/R est:30000-40000
£85987 $134140 €135000 Bridal couple with musicians and dancers (11x15cm-4x6in) s. i.verso pen brown ink grey wash prov.lit. 5-Nov-2 Sotheby's, Amsterdam #34/R est:30000-40000

VENNE, Fritz van der (19/20th C) German
£360 $601 €522 Wolves attacking a troika (18x27cm-7x11in) s.i. panel. 25-Jun-3 Bonhams, Bury St Edmunds #566
£443 $687 €700 Horses in meadow (35x57cm-14x22in) s.i. i. stretcher. 25-Sep-2 Neumeister, Munich #766
£503 $785 €800 Peasant watering horse (11x16cm-4x6in) s. panel. 21-Sep-2 Bolland & Marotz, Bremen #571/R
£641 $994 €1000 Post coach in snowy landscape (23x36cm-9x14in) s.i. panel. 5-Dec-2 Dr Fritz Nagel, Stuttgart #706/R
£786 $1242 €1179 Post coach in snowy landscape (16x21cm-6x8in) s. panel. 14-Nov-2 Stuker, Bern #566 est:2400-3000 (S.FR 1800)
£828 $1316 €1200 De hooiwagen (16x21cm-6x8in) s. panel. 10-Mar-3 Sotheby's, Amsterdam #130/R est:1000-1500
£1486 $2319 €2200 Horse drawn cart in winter (68x106cm-27x42in) s. 26-Mar-3 Hugo Ruef, Munich #249/R est:1500

£2244 $3410 €3500 Le retour a la ferme (40x60cm-16x24in) s.i. 10-Jul-2 Rabourdin & Choppin de Janvry, Paris #47/R est:3800-4000

VENNE, Jan van de (circle) (1636-?) Dutch
£5500 $9185 €7975 Nativity (127x163cm-50x64in) 11-Jul-3 Christie's, Kensington #98/R est:6000-8000

VENNE, Jan van de (?-c.1650) Flemish
£2158 $3453 €3000 Bagpipe player (48x43cm-19x17in) panel. 13-May-3 Sotheby's, Amsterdam #27/R est:3000-4000
£5000 $7850 €7500 Rabbi reading the Torah (47x40cm-19x16in) panel. 10-Dec-2 Sotheby's, Olympia #352/R est:4000-6000
£12500 $19625 €18750 Portraits of young boys wearing turbans (29x22cm-11x9in) panel oval pair. 10-Dec-2 Sotheby's, Olympia #351/R est:4000-6000

VENNE, P van de (?) ?
£346 $540 €550 Derniers rayons. s.i.verso. 23-Sep-2 Bernaerts, Antwerp #659

VENNE, Pieter van der (?-1657) Dutch
£30488 $50000 €45732 Still life of flowers in a glass vase with butters, seashells and pocket watch (97x76cm-38x30in) prov. 29-May-3 Sotheby's, New York #32/R est:60000-80000

VENNE, Pseudo van de (17th C) Belgian
£2535 $4208 €3600 Male head (24x20cm-9x8in) panel prov. 11-Jun-3 Dorotheum, Vienna #92/R est:3500-4500

VENNE, van de (17th C) Dutch
£2179 $3378 €3400 Bagpiper (48x43cm-19x17in) panel lit. 4-Dec-2 Neumeister, Munich #632/R est:2000

VENNEMAN, Camille (1827-1868) Belgian
£1500 $2385 €2250 Bit of mischief (55x68cm-22x27in) s. 20-Mar-3 Christie's, Kensington #95/R est:2000-3000
£10256 $16103 €16000 Lecture amusante (44x35cm-17x14in) panel. 16-Dec-2 Amberes, Antwerp #315/R

VENNEMAN, Camille and Rosa (19th C) Belgian
£1019 $1569 €1600 Cowherd and cattle in a summer landscape (62x75cm-24x30in) s.i.d.1860. 3-Sep-2 Christie's, Amsterdam #110/R est:1500-2000

VENNEMAN, Charles (1802-1875) Flemish
£342 $534 €500 In the hayloft (31x27cm-12x11in) s. panel. 14-Apr-3 Glerum, Amsterdam #106/R
£1961 $3157 €3000 Les benedicites (49x40cm-19x16in) s. 20-Jan-3 Horta, Bruxelles #222 est:3000-4000
£2100 $3256 €3150 Tickling the dreamer (53x67cm-21x26in) s.d.1840 panel. 3-Dec-2 Sotheby's, Olympia #249/R est:1200-1800
£3034 $4855 €4400 Le repas bien arrose (52x67cm-20x26in) s.d.1846. 17-Mar-3 Horta, Bruxelles #143/R est:5000-7000
£17610 $27119 €28000 Singing exercise (61x74cm-24x29in) s.d.1839 panel. 22-Oct-2 Sotheby's, Amsterdam #92/R est:10000-15000

VENNEMAN, Charles (attrib) (1802-1875) Flemish
£2051 $3179 €3200 Flea (22x17cm-9x7in) panel. 7-Dec-2 De Vuyst, Lokeren #507/R est:2000-2500

VENNEMAN, J (?) Dutch
£992 $1568 €1488 Untitled, gambling with cards (34x43cm-13x17in) s. board. 7-Apr-3 Shapiro, Sydney #520/R est:1200-1800 (A.D 2600)

VENNEMAN, Rosa (19th C) Belgian
£380 $592 €600 Deux vaches au pre (33x42cm-13x17in) 16-Sep-2 Amberes, Antwerp #275

VENOT, Cyprien François (1808-1886) French
Sculpture
£1401 $2186 €2200 Amur aux colombes (51cm-20in) s.d.1853 col pat bronze. 11-Nov-2 Horta, Bruxelles #55/R est:3000-3700

VENTNOR, Arthur (fl.1896-1926) British
£1300 $2119 €1950 Norwich river landscape with figures and wherries by Cow Tower at sunset (91x122cm-36x48in) 14-Feb-3 Keys, Aylsham #708/R est:600-800

VENTRONE, Luciano (1942-) Italian
£3526 $5535 €5500 After the bath (80x60cm-31x24in) s. 21-Nov-2 Finarte, Rome #228/R

VENUSTI, Marcello (circle) (c.1515-1579) Italian
£36000 $56520 €54000 Annunciation (197x128cm-78x50in) panel. 10-Dec-2 Bonhams, New Bond Street #297/R est:20000-30000

VERA, Cristino de (1931-) Spanish
£4605 $7461 €7000 Abstraction (74x101cm-29x40in) s.d.61. 21-Jan-3 Ansorena, Madrid #294/R est:7000
£8276 $13076 €12000 Garlands and window (100x75cm-39x30in) s.d.1965 prov.lit. 1-Apr-3 Segre, Madrid #205/R est:12000
Works on paper
£724 $1172 €1100 Landscape (31x34cm-12x13in) s.d1957 chl dr. 21-Jan-3 Ansorena, Madrid #834/R
£789 $1279 €1200 Castillian landscape (30x20cm-12x8in) s.d.1957 chl dr. 21-Jan-3 Ansorena, Madrid #835/R

VERA, Enrique (1886-1956) Spanish
£705 $1114 €1100 House in Toledo (48x36cm-19x14in) s.d.1930. 14-Nov-2 Arte, Seville #416/R

VERAG, Lucienne (1914-1994) Belgian
£828 $1324 €1200 Mefiance (50x40cm-20x16in) s. 15-Mar-3 De Vuyst, Lokeren #368/R

VERAGUTH, Gerold (1914-1997) Swiss
£278 $447 €417 Abstract flowers on blue background (81x100cm-32x39in) s.d.93 i. verso. 7-May-3 Dobiaschofsky, Bern #1033 (S.FR 600)
£324 $522 €486 Nature morte fond rouge (116x89cm-46x35in) s.d.65 i. stretcher. 7-May-3 Dobiaschofsky, Bern #1034/R (S.FR 700)

VERBEECK, François Xavier Henri (1686-1755) Flemish
£2229 $3478 €3500 Sense of taste, elegant company eating and drinking by a draped table (27x34cm-11x13in) s. panel. 6-Nov-2 Christie's, Amsterdam #34/R est:4000-6000
£2548 $3975 €4000 Sense of hearing, elegant company making music in an interior (27x34cm-11x13in) panel. 6-Nov-2 Christie's, Amsterdam #35/R est:3000-5000

VERBEECK, François Xavier Henri (attrib) (1686-1755) Flemish
£1006 $1560 €1600 Scene from play (32x25cm-13x10in) panel prov. 2-Oct-2 Dorotheum, Vienna #367/R est:100-2000

VERBEECK, Pieter Cornelisz (1610-1654) Dutch
£4459 $6955 €7000 Dune landscape with a horsedrawn wagon on a path (25x20cm-10x8in) s. panel prov.exhib.lit. 5-Nov-2 Sotheby's, Amsterdam #16/R est:8000-12000
£5063 $7899 €8000 Horse resting (22x21cm-9x8in) s.d.1642 panel prov. 18-Oct-2 Rabourdin & Choppin de Janvry, Paris #131/R

VERBEKE, Pierre (1895-1962) Belgian
£252 $387 €400 Vue du port d'Ostende (60x65cm-24x26in) s. 22-Oct-2 Campo, Vlaamse Kaai #343

VERBOECKHOVEN, Eugène (1798-1881) Belgian
£858 $1356 €1287 Scene in the highlands (17x24cm-7x9in) s. panel prov. 3-Apr-3 Heffel, Vancouver #94/R est:2000-2500 (C.D 2000)
£949 $1472 €1500 Sheep and lambs in meadow (33x45cm-13x18in) i. 25-Sep-2 Neumeister, Munich #767/R est:3000
£1139 $1766 €1800 Two sheep in landscape (32x42cm-13x17in) s.d.1863 prov. 28-Sep-2 Ketterer, Hamburg #2/R est:2000-2500
£1180 $1865 €1770 Summer pastures (19x24cm-7x9in) s. panel prov. 3-Apr-3 Heffel, Vancouver #95/R est:2000-2500 (C.D 2750)
£2405 $3800 €3800 Summer meadow (14x18cm-6x7in) s.d.1837 panel lit. 29-Nov-2 Schloss Ahlden, Ahlden #1333/R est:3800
£3660 $5893 €5600 Tete de mouton (41x39cm-16x15in) 20-Jan-3 Horta, Bruxelles #206/R est:4000-6000
£3800 $6080 €5700 Sheep and poultry in an extensive landscape (58x78cm-23x31in) s.d.1853 panel. 13-May-3 Bonhams, Knightsbridge #104/R est:2000-3000
£4403 $6780 €7000 Moutons dans une etable (21x30cm-8x12in) s.d.1857 panel. 23-Oct-2 Christie's, Amsterdam #35/R est:8000-12000
£4800 $8016 €7200 Sheep, ducks and chickens in a landscape (15x20cm-6x8in) i.verso panel. 18-Jun-3 Christie's, Kensington #42/R est:3000-5000
£6419 $10014 €9500 Sheep and ram in mountains with gathering storm (75x97cm-30x38in) s.d.1854. 26-Mar-3 Hugo Ruef, Munich #250/R est:9500
£6855 $10831 €10283 Sheep and poultry in a stable (27x36cm-11x14in) s.d.1870 panel prov. 18-Nov-2 Waddingtons, Toronto #33/R est:8000-12000 (C.D 17000)
£7547 $11623 €12000 Brebie avec agneaux (15x21cm-6x8in) one s.d.1858 one s.d.1862 panel pair. 23-Oct-2 Christie's, Amsterdam #118/R est:15000-20000
£12230 $19568 €17000 Sheep, cockerel, hens and chickens in a stall (27x35cm-11x14in) s.d.1863 panel. 17-May-3 De Vuyst, Lokeren #421/R est:10000-15000

£13014 $20432 €19000 Bull and sheep in a meadow (29x24cm-11x9in) s.d.1845 panel. 15-Apr-3 Sotheby's, Amsterdam #206/R est:16000-20000
£24823 $41454 €35000 Dans la prairie (87x103cm-34x41in) s.d.1840. 20-Jun-3 Piasa, Paris #3/R est:20000-30000
£27778 $44167 €40000 Farmyard friends (27x36cm-11x14in) s.i.d.1849 panel octagonal prov. 29-Apr-3 Christie's, Amsterdam #35/R est:12000-16000
£45000 $70650 €67500 Guardian of the flook (97x79cm-38x31in) s.d.1862 prov. 19-Nov-2 Sotheby's, London #147/R est:30000-50000
Works on paper
£414 $646 €650 View on a canal near Liege (10x16cm-4x6in) init. black lead. 5-Nov-2 Sotheby's, Amsterdam #234/R
£480 $778 €720 Shepherd grazing his flock (19x27cm-7x11in) s. W/C. 21-May-3 Bonhams, Knightsbridge #207/R
£616 $1010 €850 Quatre animaux (13x35cm-5x14in) mono.d.1868 dr. 27-May-3 Campo & Campo, Antwerp #260/R
£646 $1028 €950 La halte des voyageurs (9x14cm-4x6in) s.d.1836 ink dr. 18-Mar-3 Vanderkindere, Brussels #30
£696 $1079 €1100 Two sheep (47x67cm-19x26in) s.d.1840 col chks. 25-Sep-2 Neumeister, Munich #445/R
£1000 $1570 €1500 Farm labourer. Fisherman (26x19cm-10x7in) one s.i.d.1828 one init.d.28 pencil pair. 19-Nov-2 Bonhams, New Bond Street #7/R est:1000-1500
£1379 $2207 €2000 Hilly landscape with sheep and nanny goat (66x51cm-26x20in) mono.d.1864 black white chk dr. 15-Mar-3 De Vuyst, Lokeren #369/R est:2200-2400

VERBOECKHOVEN, Eugène and VERWEE, Louis (19th C) Belgian
£7500 $11775 €11250 Riverside watering place (64x92cm-25x36in) s. 19-Nov-2 Bonhams, New Bond Street #4/R est:6000-8000
£22000 $34540 €33000 Winter landscape (42x54cm-17x21in) s.i.d.45 board prov. 19-Nov-2 Sotheby's, London #148/R est:25000-35000

VERBOECKHOVEN, Louis (1802-1889) Belgian
£1223 $1957 €1700 Fishing boats in the sea (12x17cm-5x7in) indis.s. paper on panel. 17-May-3 De Vuyst, Lokeren #389/R est:1500-1800
£1400 $2324 €1400 Pecheur par gros temps (11x14cm-4x6in) s. 16-Jun-3 Horta, Bruxelles #26
£1772 $2800 €2800 Surprised by the storm (27x39cm-11x15in) s. lit. 29-Nov-2 Schloss Ahlden, Ahlden #1242/R est:2800
£1900 $3078 €2850 Boulogne lugger offshore in a swell (18x27cm-7x11in) s. canvasboard. 21-May-3 Christie's, Kensington #660/R est:1000-1500
£2158 $3453 €3000 Voiliers sur une mer agitee (16x21cm-6x8in) s. 13-May-3 Palais de Beaux Arts, Brussels #169/R est:3000-4500
£2179 $3378 €3400 Bateaux de peche dans la tempete (49x73cm-19x29in) s. 9-Dec-2 Horta, Bruxelles #211 est:4000-6000
£2446 $3914 €3400 Seascape (15x18cm-6x7in) s. panel. 17-May-3 De Vuyst, Lokeren #388/R est:2500-3000
£2449 $3894 €3600 Fishing boats on beach (25x32cm-10x13in) s. 24-Mar-3 Bernaerts, Antwerp #119/R est:4000-4500
£2953 $4754 €4400 Bateaux a l'approche d'un port (33x46cm-13x18in) s. panel. 18-Feb-3 Galerie Moderne, Brussels #402/R est:5000-7000
£3145 $4843 €5000 Sailing vessels at sea (23x35cm-9x14in) s. panel. 22-Oct-2 Sotheby's, Amsterdam #10/R est:6000-8000
£5172 $8276 €7500 Moored fishing boats (20x30cm-8x12in) s. panel. 15-Mar-3 De Vuyst, Lokeren #413/R est:7500-8500
£5755 $9209 €8000 Fishing boats on calm sea (38x46cm-15x18in) s. 17-May-3 De Vuyst, Lokeren #424/R est:7000-8000

VERBOECKHOVEN, Louis II (1827-1884) Belgian
£1384 $2145 €2200 Seascape with sailing boats (8x12cm-3x5in) s. panel. 5-Oct-2 De Vuyst, Lokeren #397/R est:2200-2600

VERBOLS, Jean (?) Belgian?
£387 $612 €600 Elegante sur la plage (24x32cm-9x13in) s. panel. 17-Dec-2 Galerie Moderne, Brussels #681

VERBOOM, Adriaen (attrib) (1628-1670) Dutch
£5063 $7899 €8000 La halte des cavaliers (76x117cm-30x46in) 10-Sep-2 Vanderkindere, Brussels #372/R est:5000-7500

VERBRUGGE, Émile (1856-?) Belgian
£506 $790 €800 Marchand et ane (33x22cm-13x9in) s. panel. 16-Sep-2 Horta, Bruxelles #413
£609 $944 €950 Couple dans un interieur (100x136cm-39x54in) s. 3-Dec-2 Campo & Campo, Antwerp #330

VERBRUGGEN, Gaspar Pieter (attrib) (17/18th C) Flemish
£3041 $4743 €4500 Bouquet of flowers with roses, carnations and other flowers in metal vase (100x67cm-39x26in) 27-Mar-3 Dorotheum, Vienna #376/R est:4500-7000

VERBRUGGEN, Gaspar Pieter I (1635-1687) Flemish
£12000 $18720 €18000 Garland of rose, tulips, cornflowers and other flowers (75x100cm-30x39in) 9-Apr-3 Christie's, London #3/R est:12000-18000
£15000 $23400 €22500 Peonies, roses, chrysanthemums, flowers in an urn on a stone ledge (57x47cm-22x19in) s. 9-Apr-3 Christie's, London #19/R est:15000-20000
£32000 $53440 €46400 Lilies, passiflora, jasmine and other flowers in an urn on stone ledge. Roses and other flowers (90x81cm-35x32in) pair. 9-Jul-3 Christie's, London #20/R est:15000-20000

VERBRUGGEN, Gaspar Pieter I (attrib) (1635-1687) Flemish
£7000 $10990 €10500 Parrot tulip, rose and other flowers in a bouquet (41x32cm-16x13in) 13-Dec-2 Christie's, Kensington #105/R est:6000-8000
£8000 $13360 €11600 Garland of roses, tulips and other flowers surrounding a stone cartouche (159x123cm-63x48in) with sig i. 11-Jul-3 Christie's, Kensington #67/R est:8000-12000

VERBRUGGEN, Gaspar Pieter I (circle) (1635-1687) Flemish
£7500 $11625 €11250 Roses, tulips and other flowers before a stone plinth (233x86cm-92x34in) with sig. exhib. 30-Oct-2 Christie's, Kensington #29/R est:8000-12000
£11000 $17160 €16500 Garland of tulips, roses and other flowers surrounding a stone cartouche (165x121cm-65x48in) indis sig.d.1666. 9-Apr-3 Christie's, London #26/R est:10000-15000

VERBRUGGEN, Gaspar Pieter II (1664-1730) Flemish
£8696 $14261 €12000 Vase de fleurs sur un entablement (81x61cm-32x24in) 27-May-3 Palais de Beaux Arts, Brussels #732/R est:12500-17500
£9615 $15096 €15000 Vases of fruit and bouquets on ledge (48x38cm-19x15in) pair. 21-Nov-2 Neret-Minet, Paris #66/R est:12000-15000
£16049 $26000 €24074 Tulips, roses, narcissi, peonies in a circular garland (127x95cm-50x37in) 24-Jan-3 Christie's, Rockefeller NY #143/R est:25000-35000

VERBRUGGEN, Gaspar Pieter II (attrib) (1664-1730) Flemish
£38298 $59362 €57447 Allegory of summer (96x134cm-38x53in) prov. 8-Dec-2 Uppsala Auktionskammare, Uppsala #11/R est:100000-150000 (S.KR 540000)

VERBRUGGHE, Charles (1877-1974) Belgian
£278 $434 €440 Vallee avant l'orage (50x100cm-20x39in) s. 16-Sep-2 Horta, Bruxelles #281
£510 $795 €800 Vue de Boulogne-sur-Mer (50x66cm-20x26in) s.d.1927 panel. 10-Nov-2 Eric Pillon, Calais #18/R
£545 $845 €850 Pont du beguinage a Bruges (38x45cm-15x18in) s. i.verso panel. 7-Dec-2 De Vuyst, Lokeren #381

VERBURGH, Cornelis Gerrit (1802-1879) Dutch
£2260 $3526 €3300 Deer in wooded summer landscape (57x46cm-22x18in) s.d.1835 panel. 10-Apr-3 Van Ham, Cologne #1737/R est:3000
£10959 $17205 €16000 Winter landscape with many figures on the ice (65x77cm-26x30in) s. 15-Apr-3 Sotheby's, Amsterdam #183/R est:8000-12000

VERBURGH, Dionys (1655-1722) Dutch
£4054 $6324 €6000 Extensive river landscape with ruin and figures (57x82cm-22x32in) mono. panel. 27-Mar-3 Dorotheum, Vienna #108/R est:6000-9000

VERBURGH, Medard (1886-1957) Belgian
£1096 $1710 €1600 Pichet fleuri (60x50cm-24x20in) s. 14-Apr-3 Horta, Bruxelles #87 est:1800-2200
£1655 $2648 €2400 Vieux bateaux de peche, Ostende (50x60cm-20x24in) s. painted 1922 exhib.lit. 15-Mar-3 De Vuyst, Lokeren #539/R est:2500-3500
£1899 $3000 €3000 Ruelle a Ibiza (62x78cm-24x31in) s. 26-Nov-2 Palais de Beaux Arts, Brussels #399/R est:3000-5000
£3503 $5465 €5500 Nature morte aux plies et vives (80x100cm-31x39in) s.d.1927. 11-Nov-2 Horta, Bruxelles #88/R est:7000-9000
£8633 $13813 €12000 Femme a sa toilette (118x80cm-46x31in) s.d.1918 exhib.lit. 13-May-3 Palais de Beaux Arts, Brussels #171/R est:12500-17500
Works on paper
£1871 $2993 €2600 Nu devant le miroir (70x54cm-28x21in) s.d.1919 chl pastel. 13-May-3 Palais de Beaux Arts, Brussels #170/R est:2500-3000

VERDEGEM, Jos (1897-1957) Belgian
£962 $1490 €1500 Flower vase (54x51cm-21x20in) board. 7-Dec-2 De Vuyst, Lokeren #384/R est:1400-1600
Works on paper
£292 $464 €420 Dame reposante (24x32cm-9x13in) s.d.1944. 29-Apr-3 Campo & Campo, Antwerp #335
£481 $745 €750 Soldier (48x38cm-19x15in) pastel exhib. 7-Dec-2 De Vuyst, Lokeren #386
£641 $994 €1000 In the law courts (43x37cm-17x15in) s.i.d.1928 W/C pen dr exhib. 7-Dec-2 De Vuyst, Lokeren #385

£1006 $1560 €1600 Reclining woman (44x58cm-17x23in) s.d.1944 W/C Indian ink exhib. 5-Oct-2 De Vuyst, Lokeren #400/R est:1700-2000

VERDET, Andre (20th C) French
£385 $608 €600 Composition (45x53cm-18x21in) painted 1960. 12-Nov-2 Babuino, Rome #260/R

VERDICKT, Gisleen (1883-1926) Belgian
£312 $521 €440 Champs en ete (29x59cm-11x23in) s. cardboard. 17-Jun-3 Palais de Beaux Arts, Brussels #640
£532 $888 €750 Ferme ensoleille (61x81cm-24x32in) s. 17-Jun-3 Palais de Beaux Arts, Brussels #638
£532 $888 €750 Paysage ensoleille avec chard e foin (95x84cm-37x33in) s.d.1924. 17-Jun-3 Palais de Beaux Arts, Brussels #639

VERDIER, François (1651-1730) French
Works on paper
£270 $422 €400 Scene de la vie d'Alexandre (16x28cm-6x11in) crayon wash htd chk prov. 31-Mar-3 Piasa, Paris #37
£629 $900 €944 Christ healing the sick (27x18cm-11x7in) black chk brush ink wash htd white. 23-Jan-3 Swann Galleries, New York #242/R

VERDIER, François (attrib) (1651-1730) French
Works on paper
£253 $392 €400 Family of Darius with Alexander (18x26cm-7x10in) pen Indian ink brush htd white. 27-Sep-2 Venator & Hansten, Koln #1152/R

VERDIER, Jean (20th C) French
£641 $1000 €962 Florals (36x3cm-14x1in) board pair. 18-Oct-2 Du Mouchelle, Detroit #2077/R

VERDIER, Maurice (1919-) French
£276 $441 €400 Maisons et arbres (41x33cm-16x13in) s. 12-Mar-3 Libert, Castor, Paris #203

VERDILHAN, Andre (20th C) French
£828 $1382 €1200 Environs de Marseille (46x55cm-18x22in) s. 10-Jul-3 Artcurial Briest, Paris #146
£1013 $1600 €1520 Untitled (58x46cm-23x18in) s. 1-Dec-2 Susanin's, Chicago #5001/R

VERDILHAN, Mathieu (1875-1928) French
£20915 $34301 €32000 Port de Marseille (64x79cm-25x31in) s. 9-Feb-3 Anaf, Lyon #257/R est:20000
£21583 $34532 €30000 Caboteurs au port (59x72cm-23x28in) s. 15-May-3 Christie's, Paris #328/R est:8000-12000
Works on paper
£2222 $3511 €3200 Sur un banc (24x29cm-9x11in) s. pastel. 25-Apr-3 Piasa, Paris #180/R

VERDONCK, Cornelis (18th C) Dutch
£2420 $3776 €3800 Landscape during the vendage, a castle in foreground (32x39cm-13x15in) s. panel. 6-Nov-2 Christie's, Amsterdam #38/R est:4000-6000

VERDONCK, Cornelis (attrib) (18th C) Dutch
£800 $1240 €1200 Mountainous river landscape with travellers on horseback (20x28cm-8x11in) panel. 30-Oct-2 Bonhams, New Bond Street #139/R

VERDOODT, Jan (1908-1980) Belgian
£523 $842 €800 Composition a la pierre et aux prunes (43x56cm-17x22in) s. panel. 20-Jan-3 Horta, Bruxelles #421

VERDU, Pons (20th C) ?
£272 $430 €425 Landscape (50x61cm-20x24in) s. s.verso. 19-Nov-2 Durán, Madrid #660/R

VERDUN, Raymond (1873-1954) French
£521 $849 €750 Paysage symboliste (45x60cm-18x24in) s. 19-Jul-3 Thierry & Lannon, Brest #394

VERDUSSEN, Jan Peeter (1700-1763) Flemish
£1277 $2132 €1800 Prise d'une ville du nord, probablement Douai (40x52cm-16x20in) bears sig. 18-Jun-3 Tajan, Paris #85 est:1200-1500
£5661 $8717 €9000 Six mois de l'annee: octobre, aout, juillet, septembre, octobre, novembre, decembre (13x18cm-5x7in) s. six. 25-Oct-2 Tajan, Paris #94/R est:6000-9000

VERDUSSEN, Paul (1868-1945) Belgian
£411 $641 €600 Les falaises (74x125cm-29x49in) s.d.1898. 14-Apr-3 Horta, Bruxelles #390

VERDYEN, Eugène (1836-1903) Belgian
£12000 $19920 €12000 Les jeux de cache-cache du jardin (117x85cm-46x33in) s. indis.d.188. 16-Jun-3 Horta, Bruxelles #165/R est:7500-8500

VERDYK, Gerard (1934-) Dutch
Works on paper
£417 $654 €650 Untitled (70x100cm-28x39in) s.d.82 mixed media. 25-Nov-2 Glerum, Amsterdam #223

VERELST, Herman (c.1641-1690) Dutch
£15000 $24900 €22500 Double portrait of a boy and a girl of the Lister family (128x102cm-50x40in) s.d.1694. 10-Jun-3 Christie's, London #8/R est:8000-12000

VERELST, John (fl.1698-1734) Flemish
£5605 $8632 €8800 Portrait of two young girls with pigeon and dog (123x99cm-48x39in) s.d.1728. 4-Sep-2 James Adam, Dublin #71/R est:6000-8000

VERELST, Maria (circle) (1680-1744) Austrian
£6500 $10010 €9750 Portrait of a lady, with a lamb, in a river landscape (127x103cm-50x41in) 5-Sep-2 Christie's, Kensington #39/R est:3000-5000

VERELST, Pieter (c.1618-1668) Dutch
£4777 $7452 €7500 Peasant smoking and drinking in an inn (51x39cm-20x15in) exhib.lit. 5-Nov-2 Sotheby's, Amsterdam #2/R est:7000-10000
£22293 $34777 €35000 Elegant company drinking wine in an interior (44x56cm-17x22in) s. indis d.1664 panel prov. 5-Nov-2 Sotheby's, Amsterdam #257/R est:45000-55000

VERELST, Simon (attrib) (1644-1721) Dutch
£8000 $12560 €12000 Still life of flowers in a glass vase, and butterfly on a stone ledge (55x44cm-22x17in) 12-Dec-2 Sotheby's, London #161/R est:8000-12000

VERELST, Simon (style) (1644-1721) Dutch
£5500 $8635 €8250 Still life with roses, tulips and other flowers in a glass vase on a stone ledge (54x42cm-21x17in) mono. 10-Dec-2 Sotheby's, Olympia #376/R est:6000-8000

VERENDAEL, Nicolas van (1640-1691) Flemish
£1667 $2583 €2600 Still life with meat and wine glass (32x41cm-13x16in) s.d.1679. 5-Dec-2 Dr Fritz Nagel, Stuttgart #636/R est:2500
£25610 $42000 €38415 Swag of tulips, peonies and other flowers with butterfly in stone niche (56x41cm-22x16in) prov. 30-May-3 Christie's, Rockefeller NY #4/R est:15000-20000

VERESS, Zoltan (1868-1935) Hungarian
£450 $720 €675 Spring (170x61cm-67x24in) s. 11-Mar-3 Bonhams, Knightsbridge #120d/R

VERET, A (19th C) Italian?
£1389 $2209 €2000 Conversation galante en Italie (73x58cm-29x23in) s.d.1840. 30-Apr-3 Tajan, Paris #1/R

VERETSHCHAGIN, Vassily Petrovich (attrib) (1835-1909) Russian
£23885 $37500 €35828 Palace Moscow (16x11cm-6x4in) init. oil oner black ink. 10-Dec-2 Doyle, New York #216/R est:8000-10000

VERETSHCHAGIN, Vassily Vasilievich (1842-1904) Russian
£4969 $8000 €7454 Bethany (41x61cm-16x24in) s.i.d.1885. 19-Feb-3 Doyle, New York #72/R est:5000-7000
£6000 $10020 €9000 Panorama of Cairo (60x100cm-24x39in) indis sig.d.1892 verso. 18-Jun-3 Christie's, Kensington #180/R est:3000-5000
£6200 $10044 €9300 Military road to Tiflis (22x17cm-9x7in) init. 21-May-3 Sotheby's, London #31/R est:3000-4000

VEREYCKEN, Edouard (1893-1967) Belgian
£641 $1006 €1000 Vase crecque et fruits (31x43cm-12x17in) s. 16-Dec-2 Bernaerts, Antwerp #321/R
Sculpture
£1795 $2836 €2800 Femme a la guirlande de roses (47cm-19in) st.f.Bataroy brown pat bronze. 18-Nov-2 Tajan, Paris #187/R est:3000-3800

VERGESGRAU, Jose (1925-1989) Spanish
£411 $641 €600 Llagrimar Lluner (60x73cm-24x29in) s. s.i.verso board. 8-Apr-3 Ansorena, Madrid #285/R

VERHAAF (20th C) ?
£754 $1177 €1307 Abstract (120x150cm-47x59in) s. 31-Mar-3 Goodman, Sydney #174 (A.D 2000)

VERHAECHT, Tobias (1561-1631) Flemish
£30000 $47100 €45000 Mountainous river landscape with goatherder (72x86cm-28x34in) panel. 11-Dec-2 Christie's, London #28/R est:30000-50000

VERHAECHT, Tobias (attrib) (1561-1631) Flemish
£5732 $8943 €9000 Peasants on a path in a rocky landscape near a farmhouse with watermill (40x65cm-16x26in) panel prov.lit. 6-Nov-2 Christie's, Amsterdam #55/R est:10000-15000

Works on paper
£741 $1200 €1112 Ruined bath with figures (17x23cm-7x9in) i. chk pen ink wash prov. 22-Jan-3 Christie's, Rockefeller NY #89/R

VERHAECHT, Tobias (circle) (1561-1631) Flemish
£5000 $7800 €7500 Rocky landscape with waterfall and two figures by a river (82x121cm-32x48in) 10-Apr-3 Christie's, Kensington #18/R est:6000-8000

VERHAEGEN, Fernand (1884-1976) Belgian
£2405 $3800 €3800 Paysage cotier en Mediterranee (45x50cm-18x20in) s. 26-Nov-2 Palais de Beaux Arts, Brussels #173/R est:2000-3000
£2649 $4318 €4000 Marche (40x60cm-16x24in) s. 17-Feb-3 Horta, Bruxelles #182/R
£3481 $5430 €5500 Procession devant Walcourt (60x70cm-24x28in) s. 16-Sep-2 Horta, Bruxelles #144/R
£8333 $12917 €13000 Two steps, Harry Pilser at Gaby Dorsey au Casino de Paris (130x100cm-51x39in) s.d.1924 exhib. 9-Dec-2 Horta, Bruxelles #206/R est:12000-15000
£10759 $16785 €17000 Port de monaco (102x112cm-40x44in) s. painted c.1923-24. 16-Sep-2 Horta, Bruxelles #143/R est:20000-30000

VERHAEREN, Alfred (1849-1924) Belgian
£550 $880 €825 Still life with Chinese cabinet (66x57cm-26x22in) init. 11-Mar-3 Bonhams, Knightsbridge #274/R

VERHAEREN, Carolus (1908-1956) ?
£1557 $2600 €2258 Native American potter (56x71cm-22x28in) s. after R W Amick prov. 18-Jun-3 Christie's, Los Angeles #33/R est:6000-8000
£1796 $3000 €2604 Stony indian (51x41cm-20x16in) s. i.on stretcher prov. 18-Jun-3 Christie's, Los Angeles #32/R est:3000-5000

VERHAERT, Dirck (attrib) (17th C) Dutch
£5000 $7850 €7500 Classical landscape with figures before ruins (79x120cm-31x47in) mono. panel. 10-Dec-2 Sotheby's, Olympia #369/R est:5000-7000

VERHAERT, Piet (1852-1908) Flemish
£597 $932 €950 The good bottle (23x17cm-9x7in) panel. 14-Oct-2 Amberes, Antwerp #223
£641 $1006 €1000 Farmer near the fireplace (34x49cm-13x19in) s. 16-Dec-2 Bernaerts, Antwerp #49/R
£1103 $1766 €1600 Dame devant une petite maison (43x70cm-17x28in) 17-Mar-3 Amberes, Antwerp #281
£6954 $11334 €10500 Couple assis a l'entree du village (50x88cm-20x35in) s. painted c.1900. 16-Feb-3 Mercier & Cie, Lille #225/R est:12000-15000

VERHAGEN, Pierre Jean Joseph (1728-1811) Flemish
£21000 $32970 €31500 Adoration of the shepherds (139x167cm-55x66in) 12-Dec-2 Sotheby's, London #191/R est:10000-15000

VERHAS, Frans (c.1827-1897) Belgian
£850 $1368 €1300 Composition aux roses (21x25cm-8x10in) s. panel. 20-Jan-3 Horta, Bruxelles #50
£11034 $17655 €16000 Kimono (48x30cm-19x12in) panel. 15-Mar-3 De Vuyst, Lokeren #509/R est:16000-18000

VERHAS, Jan Frans (1834-1896) Belgian
£769 $1192 €1200 View of dunes (34x24cm-13x9in) mono.d.85 prov. 7-Dec-2 De Vuyst, Lokeren #390/R
£1392 $2200 €2200 Fillettes jouant a la poupee (35x25cm-14x10in) s. 26-Nov-2 Palais de Beaux Arts, Brussels #174/R est:2000-3000
£30968 $48000 €46452 Hide and seek (86x60cm-34x24in) s.d.1873 panel. 30-Oct-2 Christie's, Rockefeller NY #51/R est:40000-60000

VERHAS, Theodor (1811-1872) German
Works on paper
£274 $427 €400 Mountain landscape with stream (10x15cm-4x6in) s. pencil board. 11-Apr-3 Winterberg, Heidelberg #610

VERHAS, Theodor (attrib) (1811-1872) German
Works on paper
£280 $400 €420 Rocky landscape (40x33cm-16x13in) black chk. 23-Jan-3 Swann Galleries, New York #381/R

VERHEGGEN, Hendrik Frederik (1809-1883) Dutch
£3418 $5400 €5400 Berger et troupeau traversant la foret (58x46cm-23x18in) s. 26-Nov-2 Palais de Beaux Arts, Brussels #400/R est:5300-7000

VERHEVICK, Firmin (1874-1962) Belgian
Works on paper
£340 $569 €480 Vases de fleurs (70x99cm-28x39in) s. W/C. 17-Jun-3 Palais de Beaux Arts, Brussels #644
£396 $633 €550 Baesrode sur Escaut (61x81cm-24x32in) s. W/C. 13-May-3 Vanderkindere, Brussels #252
£432 $691 €600 Le miroir aux oiseaux a Martigues (75x55cm-30x22in) s. W/C. 13-May-3 Vanderkindere, Brussels #254
£1046 $1684 €1600 Le marche Ste Catherine (50x69cm-20x27in) s. W/C. 14-Jan-3 Vanderkindere, Brussels #406 est:1500-2500

VERHEYDEN, François (1806-1889) Belgian
£1795 $2782 €2800 Mangeur de moules (36x34cm-14x13in) s. panel. 3-Dec-2 Campo & Campo, Antwerp #336/R est:3000-4000
£7111 $11804 €10311 Secrets (104x83cm-41x33in) s.d.1861 prov. 16-Jun-3 Waddingtons, Toronto #25/R est:5000-7000 (C.D 16000)

VERHEYDEN, Isidore (1848-1905) Belgian
£475 $741 €750 Pecheur a la tombee du jour (32x46cm-13x18in) s. 15-Oct-2 Horta, Bruxelles #395
£791 $1266 €1100 Le cueillette des choux (58x81cm-23x32in) s. exhib. 19-May-3 Horta, Bruxelles #133
£943 $1462 €1500 Village in winter (19x26cm-7x10in) s. panel. 5-Oct-2 De Vuyst, Lokeren #402/R est:1400-1600
£1258 $1950 €2000 Lane in autumn (32x25cm-13x10in) s. panel. 5-Oct-2 De Vuyst, Lokeren #403/R est:1400-1600
£1367 $2187 €1900 Chemin anime en Campine (72x59cm-28x23in) s. 13-May-3 Vanderkindere, Brussels #242 est:1500-2500
£1517 $2428 €2200 Landscape (38x58cm-15x23in) s. exhib.lit. sold with exhibition catalogues. 15-Mar-3 De Vuyst, Lokeren #421/R est:2500-3000
£2038 $3180 €3200 Verge en ete (38x57cm-15x22in) s. 11-Nov-2 Horta, Bruxelles #186 est:3000-4000
£2532 $4000 €4000 Fermette dans les champs (32x45cm-13x18in) s. 26-Nov-2 Palais de Beaux Arts, Brussels #175/R est:4000-5500
£2581 $4077 €4000 Village sous la neige (35x59cm-14x23in) s. panel. 17-Dec-2 Palais de Beaux Arts, Brussels #646/R est:3500-5000
£8633 $13813 €12000 Composition aux roses (32x23cm-13x9in) s. panel painted c.1900. 19-May-3 Horta, Bruxelles #134 est:800-900

VERHEYEN, Bart (1963-) Belgian
£314 $484 €500 Untitled (50x70cm-20x28in) mono.d.1998. 22-Oct-2 Campo & Campo, Antwerp #319/R

VERHEYEN, Jan Hendrik (1778-1846) Dutch
£4452 $6990 €6500 View of a Dutch town (38x45cm-15x18in) s.d.1817 panel. 15-Apr-3 Sotheby's, Amsterdam #13/R est:6500-7500
£7547 $11623 €12000 Figures by a canal in a town square (56x46cm-22x18in) indis i. panel prov. 23-Oct-2 Christie's, Amsterdam #41/R est:8000-12000
£13836 $21308 €22000 View of the walled city of Utrecht with the Dom-Tower (37x47cm-15x19in) s. panel. 22-Oct-2 Sotheby's, Amsterdam #184/R est:15000-20000

VERHEYEN, Jan Hendrik (style) (1778-1846) Dutch
£7000 $10920 €10500 View of Utrecht with barge and rowing boat on canal by bridge (48x64cm-19x25in) panel. 10-Apr-3 Sotheby's, London #92/R est:4000-6000

VERHEYEN, Jef (1932-) Belgian
£2174 $3565 €3000 Untitled (49x50cm-19x20in) s.d.1964 verso tempera prov. 28-May-3 Lempertz, Koln #456/R est:3000
£3056 $4858 €4400 La fleche (130x130cm-51x51in) s. 29-Apr-3 Campo & Campo, Antwerp #337/R est:4000-5000
£4557 $7200 €7200 A la velocita del Suono (180x180cm-71x71in) d.21 maart 73 verso exhib. 26-Nov-2 Palais de Beaux Arts, Brussels #263/R est:5000-7500

VERHEYEN, Joseph Petrus (1899-1976) Dutch
Works on paper
£461 $746 €700 Prinseneiland van de Noordzijde, Amsterdam (50x66cm-20x26in) s. i.verso. 21-Jan-3 Christie's, Amsterdam #296/R

VERHOEF, Pieter (1896-1965) Dutch
£1592 $2452 €2500 Proud mother (22x29cm-9x11in) s.d.1918. 3-Sep-2 Christie's, Amsterdam #243/R est:300-500

VERHOESEN, Albertus (1806-1881) Dutch
£655 $1022 €983 Poultry yard with country landscape beyond (14x18cm-6x7in) s.d.1873 panel. 6-Nov-2 Dobiaschofsky, Bern #1044/R (S.FR 1500)
£724 $1172 €1100 Milking time (21x24cm-8x9in) s.d.1856 panel. 21-Jan-3 Christie's, Amsterdam #21 est:400-600
£816 $1298 €1200 Travellers near wood (29x30cm-11x12in) s. panel. 24-Mar-3 Bernaerts, Antwerp #49/R est:500-700
£903 $1490 €1300 Barn interior with poultry by baskets and pots (27x34cm-11x13in) indis.sig.d. panel. 1-Jul-3 Christie's, Amsterdam #5/R
£1176 $1894 €1800 Traie de vache pres du bouc (17x23cm-7x9in) s.d.1846 panel. 20-Jan-3 Horta, Bruxelles #73 est:2000-3000
£1258 $1937 €2000 Poultry near a ruin (13x18cm-5x7in) s. indis d.1870 panel. 23-Oct-2 Christie's, Amsterdam #6/R est:2000-3000
£1338 $2087 €2100 Dutch landscape with cows (28x35cm-11x14in) s. panel lit. 7-Nov-2 Allgauer, Kempten #2998/R est:3400
£1389 $2292 €2000 Cattle in a sunlit landscape (62x80cm-24x31in) s.d.1851. 1-Jul-3 Christie's, Amsterdam #546/R est:2500-3500
£1438 $2300 €2157 Rooster, hens and chicks (15x18cm-6x7in) s.indis.d. panel. 15-Mar-3 Eldred, East Dennis #211/R est:3500-4500
£1840 $3000 €2760 Greyhounds in a landscape (13x16cm-5x6in) s.d.1869 panel. 11-Feb-3 Bonhams & Doyles, New York #147/R est:3000-4000
£1923 $2981 €3000 Poultry yard with classical ruins (40x51cm-16x20in) s. panel prov. 7-Dec-2 Ketterer, Hamburg #89/R est:4000-4500
£1944 $3092 €2800 Going into the henhouse, a goodnights rest (13x17cm-5x7in) s.d.1871 panel. 29-Apr-3 Christie's, Amsterdam #45/R est:2000-3000
£1944 $3208 €2800 Cows by a fence (21x27cm-8x11in) s.d.1846 panel. 1-Jul-3 Christie's, Amsterdam #543/R est:1800-2200
£2201 $3390 €3500 Poultry and ducks by a ruin (25x34cm-10x13in) s.d.1869 panel. 23-Oct-2 Christie's, Amsterdam #37/R est:4000-6000
£2500 $4050 €3800 Groom and horses (34x45cm-13x18in) s.d.1864. 21-Jan-3 Christie's, Amsterdam #41 est:2000-3000
£2866 $4414 €4500 Pedling the pots (62x80cm-24x31in) s.d.1848. 3-Sep-2 Christie's, Amsterdam #112/R est:1500-2000
£3022 $4835 €4200 Peacock in poultry yard (34x46cm-13x18in) s.d.1866 prov. 17-May-3 Lempertz, Koln #1497/R est:4200
£3082 $4839 €4500 Bulls and goats in an extensive summer landscape (62x81cm-24x32in) s.d.1850. 15-Apr-3 Sotheby's, Amsterdam #17/R est:5000-7000
£3459 $5327 €5500 Poultry by a ruin, country house in the distance (34x47cm-13x19in) s.d.1869. 23-Oct-2 Christie's, Amsterdam #14/R est:4000-6000
£3459 $5327 €5500 Poultry and peacocks in a meadow (34x46cm-13x18in) s.d.1862. 23-Oct-2 Christie's, Amsterdam #62/R est:5000-7000
£5556 $8833 €8000 Poultry by a ruin, an extensive landscape beyond (40x51cm-16x20in) s. panel. 29-Apr-3 Christie's, Amsterdam #6/R est:5000-7000
£5822 $9140 €8500 Grazing cows (10x13cm-4x5in) s.d.1858 panel set of four. 15-Apr-3 Sotheby's, Amsterdam #20/R est:6000-8000
£5975 $9201 €9500 Poultry and a peacock by a ruin (30x39cm-12x15in) s.d.1869 panel. 23-Oct-2 Christie's, Amsterdam #66/R est:6000-8000

VERHOESEN, J M (1832-1898) Dutch
£1538 $2415 €2400 Poules (35x74cm-14x29in) s. panel. 10-Dec-2 Campo, Vlaamse Kaai #566 est:2500-3000

VERHOEVEN-BALL, Adrien Joseph (1824-1882) Belgian
Works on paper
£481 $745 €750 Vendeuses de gibier (45x33cm-18x13in) s. W/C. 3-Dec-2 Campo & Campo, Antwerp #339/R

VERHOOG, Adrianus (1933-) Dutch
£461 $746 €700 Zoekend in het gras (70x70cm-28x28in) s.d.1969 tempera exhib. 21-Jan-3 Christie's, Amsterdam #497/R
£603 $977 €850 Golfer (110x120cm-43x47in) s.d.88 acrylic. 26-May-3 Glerum, Amsterdam #237/R

VERHUELSDONK, Alexander (1943-) German
Works on paper
£3846 $5962 €6000 Red cross (100x100cm-39x39in) mono.d.2001 s.i.d. verso mixed media acrylic wire mesh plasters. 7-Dec-2 Ketterer, Hamburg #766/R est:7000-9000

VERHULST, Antoine Pierre (1751-1809) Flemish
£1911 $3000 €2867 To town (58x69cm-23x27in) s. panel. 22-Nov-2 Skinner, Boston #10/R est:3000-5000

VERIN, Noel (1947-) French
£567 $948 €800 Iracq (50x40cm-20x16in) s.d. oil mixed media cardboard. 18-Jun-3 Charbonneaux, Paris #119/R
£851 $1421 €1200 Femme sur fond rose (35x24cm-14x9in) s.d.02 acrylic mixed media cardboard. 18-Jun-3 Charbonneaux, Paris #120

VERITE, Lucien Henri Alphonse (1866-1926) French
£993 $1619 €1500 Travaux de outure (61x51cm-24x20in) s.d.1895. 17-Feb-3 Horta, Bruxelles #205

VERITY, Colin (?) ?
£380 $616 €570 M.V Pisces Pioneer under Vancouver Bridge (49x74cm-19x29in) s. 21-Jan-3 Bonhams, New Bond Street #179/R
£950 $1539 €1425 M.V Author at Cartagena (50x75cm-20x30in) s. 21-Jan-3 Bonhams, New Bond Street #180/R
£1200 $1944 €1800 M.V Ben Nevis at the Seaforth terminal, December, 1979 (59x89cm-23x35in) s. 21-Jan-3 Bonhams, New Bond Street #181/R est:300-500
£1450 $2349 €2175 M.V Successor in Channel (49x74cm-19x29in) s. 21-Jan-3 Bonhams, New Bond Street #180a/R est:200-300
£2400 $3888 €3600 M.V Inanda at Trinidad (49x89cm-19x35in) s. 21-Jan-3 Bonhams, New Bond Street #182/R est:300-500
Works on paper
£260 $421 €390 The Inanda loading at Trinidad (20x30cm-8x12in) s. pencil W/C. 21-Jan-3 Bonhams, New Bond Street #170/R
£600 $996 €870 SS Athenic in harbour (41x61cm-16x24in) s. W/C. 12-Jun-3 Gorringes, Lewes #1734

VERKADE, Kees (1941-) Dutch
Sculpture
£5346 $8286 €8500 Ludmilla (133x48cm-52x19in) st.sig d.1979 num.3/6 brown pat bronze. 5-Oct-2 De Vuyst, Lokeren #502/R est:9000-12000

VERKOLJE, Jan (1650-1693) Dutch
£12230 $19568 €17000 Portrait of Mathijs van Son. Portrait of Elisabeth van Son (53x45cm-21x18in) s.d.1692 copper pair prov.lit. 14-May-3 Christie's, Amsterdam #195/R est:16000-26000

VERKOLJE, Nicolaes (1673-1746) Dutch
£1157 $1863 €1736 Interior with two men drinking and smoking (42x32cm-17x13in) 7-May-3 Dobiaschofsky, Bern #1036/R est:5000 (S.FR 2500)

VERLAT, Charles Michel Maria (1824-1890) Belgian
£588 $947 €900 Combat entre le taureau, le lion et le chevalier (58x51cm-23x20in) s. 14-Jan-3 Vanderkindere, Brussels #465
£863 $1381 €1200 Cows by the bank (32x40cm-13x16in) s.d.1856 panel. 17-May-3 De Vuyst, Lokeren #398/R
£1088 $1731 €1600 Singe musician (53x43cm-21x17in) s. 19-Mar-3 Hotel des Ventes Mosan, Brussels #208 est:1000-1200

VERLET, Raoul (1857-1923) French
Sculpture
£2500 $3875 €3750 Orpheus and Cerberus (82cm-32in) s.num.925 gold brown pat bronze circular base st.f.F.Barbedienne. 29-Oct-2 Bonhams, New Bond Street #162/R est:2500-3000
£3165 $5000 €4748 Figure of Orpheus and Cerberus (97cm-38in) i. verso bronze. 24-Apr-3 Christie's, Rockefeller NY #216/R est:5000-8000
£7500 $11700 €11250 La jeunesse et l'amour (84cm-33in) s.st.f.Valsuani brown pat bronze red green marble plinth lit. 5-Nov-2 Sotheby's, London #150/R est:5000-8000

VERLINDE, Claude (1927-) ?
Works on paper
£2270 $3677 €3200 La revolte des sous (41x29cm-16x11in) s.i.d. black crayon gouache W/C. 23-May-3 Binoche, Paris #57/R est:1000-1200

VERMA, Prabhulal (?) Indian
£764 $1108 €1200 Portrait of Prince Rajpoute (58x43cm-23x17in) s.d.1953. 31-May-2 Blanchet, Paris #35

VERMAAS, Jacob (fl.1846-1882) Dutch
£2400 $3720 €3600 Portrait of a ship of the Swedish Navy in a storm (63x89cm-25x35in) s.d.1863. 26-Sep-2 Mellors & Kirk, Nottingham #705/R est:2500-3500

VERMEER OF HAARLEM, Jan (younger) (1656-1705) Dutch
£3433 $5322 €5150 Herding couple with animals (60x72cm-24x28in) s.d.1677 prov. 3-Oct-2 Koller, Zurich #3039/R est:8000-12000 (S.FR 8000)
Works on paper
£432 $691 €600 River landscape with shepherds (7x9cm-3x4in) indian ink brush over pencil. 17-May-3 Lempertz, Koln #1261/R

VERMEER OF HAARLEM, Jan (younger-attrib) (1656-1705) Dutch
£2564 $3974 €4000 Soldiers stopping by camp (17x24cm-7x9in) 4-Dec-2 Christie's, Rome #359/R

VERMEHREN, Gustav (1863-1931) Danish
£465 $716 €698 Interior scene with man writing (39x45cm-15x18in) s.d.1926. 26-Oct-2 Rasmussen, Havnen #2154/R (D.KR 5500)
£642 $989 €963 Interior scene with woman peeling potatoes (48x58cm-19x23in) s.d.1925. 26-Oct-2 Rasmussen, Havnen #2159/R (D.KR 7600)
£773 $1221 €1160 Interior scene with woman reading (44x57cm-17x22in) s.d.1900. 17-Nov-2 Hindemae, Ullerslev #7671/R (D.KR 9000)
£930 $1432 €1395 Interior scene with man reading (39x45cm-15x18in) s.d.1926. 26-Oct-2 Rasmussen, Havnen #2152/R (D.KR 11000)

VERMEHREN, Sophus (1866-1950) Danish
£316 $499 €474 Interior (46x51cm-18x20in) s. 5-Apr-3 Rasmussen, Havnen #2010/R (D.KR 3400)
£650 $1014 €975 Interior with an old man filling his pipe (65x59cm-26x23in) s. 10-Apr-3 Tennants, Leyburn #1124
£1286 $2007 €1929 From St Jorgensberg in Roskilde with two children (35x52cm-14x20in) init.d.1904. 11-Nov-2 Rasmussen, Vejle #666/R est:18000 (D.KR 15000)
£1723 $2618 €2585 Summer's day with two girls chatting and one girl knitting by farmhouse (42x57cm-17x22in) s. 27-Aug-2 Rasmussen, Copenhagen #1496/R est:15000-20000 (D.KR 20000)

VERMEHREN, Yelva (1880-1978) Danish
£280 $445 €420 Woodland ground with flowers (38x32cm-15x13in) s. 5-May-3 Rasmussen, Vejle #476 (D.KR 3000)
£383 $620 €555 Woodland with fungi (44x65cm-17x26in) s. 24-May-3 Rasmussen, Havnen #2265 (D.KR 4000)
£755 $1170 €1200 Tulips and daffodils (50x54cm-20x21in) s. 29-Oct-2 Dorotheum, Vienna #263/R
£1323 $2130 €1985 Still life of lobster, fruit and vegetables (62x98cm-24x39in) s. 19-Jan-3 Hindemae, Ullerslev #7300/R est:15000 (D.KR 15000)

VERMEIR, Alfons (1905-1994) Belgian
£290 $461 €420 Street scene with people standing in front of a house (60x64cm-24x25in) s. board. 10-Mar-3 Sotheby's, Amsterdam #256
£377 $581 €600 Paysage crepusculaire (50x65cm-20x26in) s. 22-Oct-2 Campo, Vlaamse Kaai #354
£409 $630 €650 Assis devant la fenetre (60x50cm-24x20in) s. cardboard. 22-Oct-2 Campo, Vlaamse Kaai #353
£409 $634 €650 At the farmyard (50x60cm-20x24in) s. panel. 5-Oct-2 De Vuyst, Lokeren #405/R
£409 $630 €650 Ferme a Burcht (41x51cm-16x20in) s.d.1972 lit. 22-Oct-2 Campo & Campo, Antwerp #321
£481 $755 €750 Vue de village (60x70cm-24x28in) s. panel. 10-Dec-2 Campo, Vlaamse Kaai #568
£482 $767 €700 Harbour of Antwerpen (71x80cm-28x31in) s.d.39. 10-Mar-3 Sotheby's, Amsterdam #206/R
£513 $795 €800 Flax harvest (60x70cm-24x28in) s. lit. 7-Dec-2 De Vuyst, Lokeren #394/R
£566 $872 €900 Ferme (81x100cm-32x39in) s.d.1972 lit. 22-Oct-2 Campo & Campo, Antwerp #320/R

VERMEULE, Koen (1965-) Dutch?
£2436 $3776 €3800 Zanbak (50x80cm-20x31in) s.d.95 verso acrylic prov. 3-Dec-2 Christie's, Amsterdam #382/R est:1500-2000

VERMEULEN, Andries (1763-1814) Dutch
£2800 $4340 €4200 Wooded landscape with rider, horse and cart and hunter with dogs (55x73cm-22x29in) s. 30-Oct-2 Bonhams, New Bond Street #17/R est:3000-4000
£4468 $7462 €6300 Patineurs sur un lac gele (44x60cm-17x24in) 23-Jun-3 Beaussant & Lefèvre, Paris #264/R est:6000-7000
£8633 $13813 €12000 Winter landscape with horse drawn cart on bridge (46x62cm-18x24in) s. panel. 13-May-3 Sotheby's, Amsterdam #88/R est:12000-18000

VERMEULEN, Andries (attrib) (1763-1814) Dutch
£7000 $10850 €10500 Winter landscape with skaters and a cart on a frozen river near a village (67x84cm-26x33in) s. 30-Oct-2 Christie's, Kensington #70/R est:5000-8000

VERMEULEN, Andries (style) (1763-1814) Dutch
£6207 $9869 €9000 Scene de patinage (51x69cm-20x27in) panel. 7-Mar-3 Rabourdin & Choppin de Janvry, Paris #57/R est:6200-6500

VERMEULEN, Eugene (?) ?
£4800 $8016 €7200 On the river by a Dutch town (47x57cm-19x22in) s.d.1832 panel. 18-Jun-3 Christie's, Kensington #54/R est:4000-6000

VERMEYLEN, Alphonse (1882-1939) Belgian
£521 $828 €750 Ferme dans un paysage (85x100cm-33x39in) s. 29-Apr-3 Campo & Campo, Antwerp #338

VERMI, Arturo (1929-1988) Italian
£393 $574 €590 Traiettoria (92x116cm-36x46in) acrylic canvas on panel prov. 4-Jun-2 Germann, Zurich #859 (S.FR 900)
Works on paper
£449 $704 €700 Untitled (70x50cm-28x20in) s.d.1963 mixed media paper on canvas. 23-Nov-2 Meeting Art, Vercelli #295

VERMIGLIO, Giuseppe (attrib) (16/17th C) Italian
£6000 $10020 €8700 Baptism of Christ (95x72cm-37x28in) 9-Jul-3 Bonhams, New Bond Street #186/R est:4000-6000
£7642 $11921 €11463 Ascension of Maria (208x114cm-82x45in) 20-Nov-2 Fischer, Luzern #1027/R est:22000-25000 (S.FR 17500)

VERMUNT, Adrianus Petrus Nicolaas (1907-) Dutch
£822 $1282 €1200 Winter landscape with frozen river (15x22cm-6x9in) s. panel. 10-Apr-3 Dorotheum, Vienna #204/R

VERNA, Claudio (1937-) Italian
£418 $661 €627 Otto bande gialle (100x140cm-39x55in) s.d.74 verso prov. 1-Apr-3 Rasmussen, Copenhagen #300/R (D.KR 4500)
£1056 $1754 €1500 Enigma della notte (60x90cm-24x35in) s.i.d.1999 verso. 10-Jun-3 Finarte Semenzato, Milan #231/R est:1500-1700

VERNARD, Claude (20th C) French
£833 $1300 €1250 Abstract fish (99x99cm-39x39in) s. 30-Mar-3 Susanin's, Chicago #6054/R

VERNAY, François (1821-1896) French
£2564 $4026 €4000 Carafe, pomme poires et raisins dans un plat (34x45cm-13x18in) s. panel. 16-Dec-2 Millon & Associes, Paris #79/R est:4000-5000
£3101 $4900 €4900 Lavoirs au bord de la riviere (36x55cm-14x22in) s. 2-Dec-2 Cornette de St.Cyr, Paris #42/R
£4557 $7109 €7200 Nature morte aux peches et raisins (33x41cm-13x16in) s. exhib. 20-Oct-2 Anaf, Lyon #245/R

VERNAZZA, Eduardo (1910-1991) ?
£491 $780 €737 Dance (50x60cm-20x24in) s. cardboard. 2-Mar-3 Galleria Y Remates, Montevideo #96/R

VERNER, Elizabeth O'Neill (1884-1979) American
Works on paper
£5806 $9000 €8709 Old George himself and his watchfob (20x20cm-8x8in) s. s.i.verso pastel silk. 20-Jul-2 Brunk, Ashville #140 est:8000-15000
£7742 $12000 €11613 Cabin in southern landscape with black children dancing in front yard (33x46cm-13x18in) s.i.verso pastel silk prov. 20-Jul-2 Brunk, Ashville #141 est:15000-25000
£8280 $13000 €12420 Farm workers cabins (46x36cm-18x14in) s. pastel on masonite. 10-Dec-2 Doyle, New York #112/R est:15000-20000
£8387 $13000 €12581 Susie, flower seller holding quince and narcissus (20x20cm-8x8in) s. i.verso pastel silk prov. 20-Jul-2 Brunk, Ashville #139 est:8000-15000
£24516 $38000 €36774 Rebecca's house, Rifle Range Road (41x51cm-16x20in) s. i.verso pastel wood panel prov. 20-Jul-2 Brunk, Ashville #138 est:20000-40000

VERNER, Frederick Arthur (1836-1928) Canadian
£1205 $1892 €1808 Sitting Bull (33x25cm-13x10in) s.i.d.1900 canvas on board prov. 25-Nov-2 Hodgins, Calgary #55/R est:4000-5000 (C.D 3000)
£1333 $2187 €2000 Afterglow, Burnham (51x77cm-20x30in) s.d.1911 prov. 27-May-3 Sotheby's, Toronto #72/R est:3000-4000 (C.D 3000)
£1333 $2187 €2000 Foraging in the forest (61x91cm-24x36in) s.d.1892 prov. 27-May-3 Sotheby's, Toronto #73/R est:3000-4000 (C.D 3000)
£4000 $6560 €6000 Moose hunter (42x69cm-17x27in) s.d.1874 prov. 27-May-3 Sotheby's, Toronto #94/R est:10000-15000 (C.D 9000)
£12179 $18878 €19000 Sitting Bull, chef indien (63x52cm-25x20in) s.d.1888 canvas on panel. 9-Dec-2 Horta, Bruxelles #123/R est:5500-6500
£12444 $20409 €18666 Indians tending birchbark canoes (40x75cm-16x30in) s.d.1876 prov. 27-May-3 Sotheby's, Toronto #159a/R est:15000-20000 (C.D 28000)

Works on paper

£184 $286 €276 Floral still life (32x23cm-13x9in) s.d.1896 W/C prov. 24-Sep-2 Ritchie, Toronto #3067 (C.D 450)
£307 $476 €461 Forest waterfall at sunset (10x14cm-4x6in) s.d.1886 W/C prov. 24-Sep-2 Ritchie, Toronto #3076/R (C.D 750)
£321 $504 €482 Floral still life, the Queen's Jubilee (32x22cm-13x9in) s.d.1897 W/C. 25-Nov-2 Hodgins, Calgary #91/R (C.D 800)
£361 $571 €542 Foreland, North Devon (23x38cm-9x15in) indis.d.188 W/C. 1-Dec-2 Levis, Calgary #106/R (C.D 900)
£370 $574 €555 Riverside cottage (26x42cm-10x17in) s.d.1880 W/C. 3-Dec-2 Joyner, Toronto #389 (C.D 900)
£378 $619 €567 Sunset over a marsh (17x30cm-7x12in) s. W/C prov. 3-Jun-3 Joyner, Toronto #543 (C.D 850)
£652 $1017 €1088 Autumn near Sandwich (25x51cm-10x20in) s.d.1904 W/C prov. 13-Apr-3 Levis, Calgary #117/R est:2000-3000 (C.D 1500)
£823 $1276 €1235 Affectionate stroll (39x59cm-15x23in) s.d.1878 W/C. 3-Dec-2 Joyner, Toronto #273/R est:2500-3500 (C.D 2000)
£933 $1531 €1353 Grazing sheep (50x33cm-20x13in) s.d.1899 W/C. 9-Jun-3 Hodgins, Calgary #369/R est:2500-3000 (C.D 2100)
£1066 $1652 €1599 Castle Scarborough (45x32cm-18x13in) s.i.d.1879 W/C prov. 24-Sep-2 Ritchie, Toronto #3083/R est:900-1200 (C.D 2600)
£1121 $1794 €1682 Trappers on snowshoes (32x63cm-13x25in) W/C prov. 15-May-3 Heffel, Vancouver #95/R est:2000-3000 (C.D 2500)
£1156 $1895 €1734 Wild ducks (29x62cm-11x24in) s.d.1883 W/C. 3-Jun-3 Joyner, Toronto #297/R est:3000-4000 (C.D 2600)
£1311 $2071 €1967 Near Clear Creek, Ontario (38x56cm-15x22in) s.d.1919 i.verso W/C sold with painting by Frederick Brigden. 18-Nov-2 Sotheby's, Toronto #105/R est:3000-5000 (C.D 3250)
£1399 $2169 €2099 In a village lane (50x70cm-20x28in) s.d.1907 W/C prov. 3-Dec-2 Joyner, Toronto #131 est:3000-4000 (C.D 3400)
£2667 $4373 €4001 Indians loading canoes (33x58cm-13x23in) s.d.1878 W/C prov. 27-May-3 Sotheby's, Toronto #94a/R est:7000-10000 (C.D 6000)
£2915 $4664 €4373 Detroit River, winter (36x67cm-14x26in) s.d.1885 i.verso W/C prov. 15-May-3 Heffel, Vancouver #105/R est:6000-8000 (C.D 6500)
£3778 $6196 €5667 Ojibway Indians, among the islands of the lake on a misty morning (39x76cm-15x30in) s.d.1885 W/C prov. 27-May-3 Sotheby's, Toronto #159/R est:5000-7000 (C.D 8500)
£4444 $7289 €6666 Buffalo grazing on the prairie, winter (50x72cm-20x28in) s. indis d. W/C. 3-Jun-3 Joyner, Toronto #140/R est:12000-15000 (C.D 10000)

VERNET, Alice (1865-?) French

£481 $790 €697 Parisian street scenes (30x36cm-12x14in) s. canvas on board pair. 30-May-3 Aspire, Cleveland #37/R

VERNET, Carle (1758-1836) French

£82278 $130000 €123417 Skirmish with the Cossacks during Napoleon's Russian campaign of 1812 (89x115cm-35x45in) s.d.1814 prov. 23-Apr-3 Christie's, Rockefeller NY #26/R est:150000-200000
£141935 $224258 €220000 Jockey sur monture (58x72cm-23x28in) s.i.d.1832 prov.exhib. 18-Dec-2 Tajan, Paris #54/R est:150000-210000
£264516 $417936 €410000 Traversee de Senlis (111x145cm-44x57in) s.d.1828 prov. 18-Dec-2 Tajan, Paris #53/R est:200000-300000

Works on paper

£1090 $1689 €1700 Deux chevaux luttant (26x34cm-10x13in) s. wash htd gouache over crayon. 4-Dec-2 Piasa, Paris #186
£3141 $4963 €4900 Cheval dans un campement arabe (17x21cm-7x8in) s. wash over crayon. 17-Nov-2 Osenat, Fontainebleau #217 est:3000
£4200 $6552 €6300 Study of a horse (20x27cm-8x11in) s.i.d.1820 W/C prov. 17-Sep-2 Sotheby's, Olympia #225/R est:700-900
£26923 $42538 €42000 Empereur Napoleon a cheval (80x60cm-31x24in) W/C gouache dr. 17-Nov-2 Osenat, Fontainebleau #220

VERNET, Carle (attrib) (1758-1836) French

£4321 $7000 €6482 Head of horse (62x48cm-24x19in) 23-Jan-3 Sotheby's, New York #151/R est:15000

VERNET, Horace (1789-1863) French

£5161 $8000 €7742 Village musicians (52x44cm-20x17in) s.i.d.1832. 29-Oct-2 Sotheby's, New York #7/R est:8000-12000
£61290 $96839 €95000 Cheval selle attache a une barriere (80x120cm-31x47in) s.d.1821 prov. 18-Dec-2 Tajan, Paris #55/R est:90000-120000
£67901 $110000 €101852 Napoleon rising from out of his tomb (64x54cm-25x21in) s.d.1840. 23-Jan-3 Sotheby's, New York #99/R est:140000-180000

Works on paper

£280 $440 €420 Caricature of Eugene Isabey as an owl (21x18cm-8x7in) s.i. black chk brush wash. 13-Dec-2 Christie's, Kensington #323
£288 $447 €450 Scene de l'Iliade (27x38cm-11x15in) pen ink wash. 4-Dec-2 Piasa, Paris #185
£641 $994 €1000 Scene de combat (20x27cm-8x11in) wash over crayon. 4-Dec-2 Piasa, Paris #181
£1958 $3270 €2800 Episode de la Bataille d'Isly (10x15cm-4x6in) mono. pen brown ink prov. 25-Jun-3 Sotheby's, Paris #58/R est:3000-4000
£2885 $4471 €4500 Chasse a courre (23x31cm-9x12in) s. W/C gouache. 4-Dec-2 Piasa, Paris #190/R

VERNET, Horace (attrib) (1789-1863) French

£516 $816 €800 Saint franciscain (41x33cm-16x13in) 20-Dec-2 Tajan, Paris #168

VERNET, Horace (circle) (1789-1863) French

£10490 $17518 €15000 Portrait de Louis Philippe (91x74cm-36x29in) oval. 25-Jun-3 Tajan, Paris #85/R est:9000-12000

VERNET, Joseph (1714-1789) French

£17606 $28345 €25000 Shipwreck (31x41cm-12x16in) s.d.1753 lit. 9-May-3 Schloss Ahlden, Ahlden #1326/R est:28000
£25000 $39000 €37500 Cove on rocky Mediterranean coast (32x49cm-13x19in) s.d.1747 prov. 10-Apr-3 Sotheby's, London #100/R est:40000
£25786 $39710 €41000 Pecheur et paysanne sur le rivage mediterraneen (32x40cm-13x16in) s. 25-Oct-2 Tajan, Paris #142/R est:8000-10000
£37931 $59931 €55000 Seascape with travellers (51x77cm-20x30in) s. 3-Apr-3 Porro, Milan #33/R est:75000
£2100000 $3507000 €3045000 Landscape at sunset with fisherman returning. Shipwreck in stormy seas (114x163cm-45x64in) s.d.1773 pair. 10-Jul-3 Sotheby's, London #65/R est:1200000-1600000

VERNET, Joseph (after) (1714-1789) French

£755 $1170 €1200 Shipwreck off rocky coast (18x23cm-7x9in) panel. 29-Oct-2 Dorotheum, Vienna #259

VERNET, Joseph (attrib) (1714-1789) French

£10811 $16865 €16000 Harbour scene (84x145cm-33x57in) bears sig. 31-Mar-3 Finarte Semenzato, Milan #474/R

Works on paper

£1090 $1711 €1700 Vue de port anime (92x116cm-36x46in) mono.d.1774 gouache. 10-Dec-2 Vanderkindere, Brussels #9/R est:1800-2500
£1135 $1838 €1600 Marine par gros temps (21x34cm-8x13in) s. brush grey blk wash on sheet. 26-May-3 Joron-Derem, Paris #76 est:1000-1500
£1429 $2271 €2100 Marine par gros temps (21x34cm-8x13in) brush wash. 28-Feb-3 Joron-Derem, Paris #28

VERNET, Joseph (circle) (1714-1789) French

£6129 $9684 €9500 Pecheurs ramassant leur filet (63x55cm-25x22in) 20-Dec-2 Tajan, Paris #166/R est:4000

VERNET, Joseph (style) (1714-1789) French

£5290 $8359 €8200 Scene de port mediterraneen (78x141cm-31x56in) 18-Dec-2 Piasa, Paris #89/R
£5500 $8580 €8250 Fishermen arriving on shore before a storm (55x80cm-22x31in) bears sig. 8-Apr-3 Sotheby's, Olympia #248/R est:6000-8000
£7500 $11625 €11250 View of Posillipo near Naples, morning fog (99x136cm-39x54in) 31-Oct-2 Sotheby's, Olympia #165/R est:5000-7000
£8200 $12792 €12300 Mediterranean coastal landscape fishing tending their nets (21x34cm-8x13in) panel. 8-Apr-3 Sotheby's, Olympia #246/R est:2000-3000
£15000 $23550 €22500 Southern harbour by moonlight (71x97cm-28x38in) bears sig.indis.d. prov. 12-Dec-2 Sotheby's, London #204/R est:8000-12000

VERNIER, Émile Louis (1829-1887) French

£1007 $1621 €1500 Bateaux a quai dans le port du Havre (38x46cm-15x18in) s.i.d.92. 23-Feb-3 Lesieur & Le Bars, Le Havre #149/R
£1700 $2788 €2550 Fisherfolk at Isigny (42x63cm-17x25in) s.d.81. 5-Jun-3 Christie's, Kensington #624/R est:1000-1500

VERNIER, Jules (1862-?) French

£1000 $1570 €1500 Seascape and steamer (62x78cm-24x31in) s. 16-Dec-2 Sotheby's, Olympia #127/R est:1000-1500

VERNIZZI, Renato (1904-1972) Italian

£1667 $2583 €2600 Garden in autumn (70x90cm-28x35in) s.d.63. 5-Dec-2 Stadion, Trieste #863/R

VERNON, Arthur Langley (fl.1871-1922) British

£10968 $17000 €16452 Love letter (67x110cm-26x43in) s.d.1880 prov. 30-Oct-2 Christie's, Rockefeller NY #175/R est:15000-20000

VERNON, Ellen (fl.1882-1910) British

Works on paper

£250 $388 €375 Peat maker (27x37cm-11x15in) s. W/C bodycol. 3-Dec-2 Sotheby's, Olympia #70/R

VERNON, Emile (19/20th C) British

£7000 $11130 €10500 Wistful gaze (76x51cm-30x20in) s.d.09. 20-Mar-3 Christie's, Kensington #115/R est:7000-10000

£7006 $11000 €10509 Waiting for her match (91x66cm-36x26in) s. 23-Nov-2 Jackson's, Cedar Falls #5/R est:12000-14000
£11000 $17270 €16500 Sweet as roses (91x71cm-36x28in) s.d.05. 21-Nov-2 Christie's, Kensington #46/R est:8000-12000
£17000 $26690 €25500 Young girl with a kitten (65x54cm-26x21in) s.d.1919. 19-Nov-2 Bonhams, New Bond Street #172/R est:15000-20000
£21000 $32970 €31500 Beauty on a balcony (65x54cm-26x21in) s.d.1919. 19-Nov-2 Bonhams, New Bond Street #171/R est:15000-20000
£22152 $35000 €33228 Young girl holding a nest (46x38cm-18x15in) painted 1919 prov. 23-Apr-3 Christie's, Rockefeller NY #142/R est:20000-30000
£39873 $63000 €59810 Pet rabbit (54x65cm-21x26in) s.d.1915 prov. 23-Apr-3 Christie's, Rockefeller NY #15/R est:30000-40000
£48387 $75000 €72581 Best of friends (54x65cm-21x26in) s.d.1917. 30-Oct-2 Christie's, Rockefeller NY #50/R est:30000-40000

VERNON, Paul (1796-1875) French
£400 $640 €600 Landscape with trees (23x33cm-9x13in) s. indis i.d.76 panel. 13-May-3 Bonhams, Knightsbridge #113/R
£719 $1200 €1043 Gypsy family (41x32cm-16x13in) s. panel. 22-Jun-3 Freeman, Philadelphia #40/R est:1500-2000
£795 $1295 €1200 Paysage a la riviere (50x65cm-20x26in) s. 16-Feb-3 Mercier & Cie, Lille #286 est:1200-1400

VERNON, R Warren (fl.1882-1908) British
£500 $820 €750 Scarborough South Bay, towing in the Norwegian (17x52cm-7x20in) s.i.indis d. 10-Feb-3 David Duggleby, Scarborough #569

VERNON, Walter (?) ?
£500 $800 €750 Jockeys and horses in a landscape (61x91cm-24x36in) s. 15-Mar-3 Selkirks, St. Louis #86

VERNON, William H (1820-1909) British
£520 $827 €780 At Conway - fishermen and boats before a cottage (32x46cm-13x18in) s. s.i.verso. 27-Feb-3 Bonhams, Chester #397

VERON, Alexandre Paul Joseph (1773-?) French
£3459 $5327 €5500 Scene de kermesse (19x23cm-7x9in) panel. 25-Oct-2 Tajan, Paris #153/R est:2500-3000
£5743 $8959 €8500 Repos des cavaliers (25x31cm-10x12in) panel. 26-Mar-3 Tajan, Paris #89/R
£6452 $10194 €10000 Scene de bal sous les arcades. Partie de colin-maillard (25x35cm-10x14in) panel pair. 18-Dec-2 Tajan, Paris #47/R est:15000

VERON, Alexandre René (1826-1897) French
£1346 $2113 €2100 Paysanne dans la foret de Fontainebleau (46x65cm-18x26in) s.d.1854. 21-Nov-2 Neret-Minet, Paris #29
£1875 $2981 €2700 Pecheurs et paysannes au bord de la riviere (43x60cm-17x24in) s.d.1875. 30-Apr-3 Tajan, Paris #105/R
£2448 $4087 €3500 Les lavandieres (44x75cm-17x30in) s. 27-Jun-3 Claude Aguttes, Neuilly #34/R est:3000-4000
£4630 $7500 €6714 On the banks of a river (79x117cm-31x46in) s.d.1874. 21-May-3 Doyle, New York #202/R est:8000-12000

VERONESE SCHOOL (16th C) Italian
£8276 $13076 €12000 Madonna and Child (51x40cm-20x16in) board. 5-Apr-3 Finarte Semenzato, Milan #148/R est:20000

VERONESE SCHOOL (17th C) Italian
£6122 $9735 €9000 Venus and Adonis (40x88cm-16x35in) slate. 19-Mar-3 Neumeister, Munich #490/R est:8000

VERONESE, Paolo (1528-1588) Italian
£49383 $80000 €74075 Judith with the head of Holofernes (41x37cm-16x15in) paper on panel exhib.lit. 23-Jan-3 Sotheby's, New York #157a/R est:120000

VERONESE, Paolo (attrib) (1528-1588) Italian
Works on paper
£5405 $8432 €8000 Head of young man (22x17cm-9x7in) pierre noire. 27-Mar-3 Maigret, Paris #52/R

VERONESE, Paolo (studio) (1528-1588) Italian
£7725 $11974 €11588 Judith and Holofernes (186x115cm-73x45in) 3-Oct-2 Koller, Zurich #3030/R est:15000-25000 (S.FR 18000)
£22222 $36000 €33333 Poet choosing Virtue over Vice (216x268cm-85x106in) i. lit. 23-Jan-3 Sotheby's, New York #164/R est:40000

VERONESE, Paolo (style) (1528-1588) Italian
£5778 $9591 €8378 Warrior before the king and his assembly (75x105cm-30x41in) 16-Jun-3 Waddingtons, Toronto #335/R est:2500-3500 (C.D 13000)
£32000 $53440 €46400 Portrait of a Moorish woman (37x26cm-15x10in) canvas on panel. 11-Jul-3 Christie's, Kensington #251/R est:2000-3000

VERONESI, Luigi (1908-1998) Italian
£845 $1403 €1200 Composition (25x19cm-10x7in) s.d.96 acrylic. 10-Jun-3 Finarte Semenzato, Milan #230/R
£2292 $3644 €3300 Composition KSZ7 (40x40cm-16x16in) s.d.1990 s.i.d.verso. 1-May-3 Meeting Art, Vercelli #406
£2885 $4529 €4500 Untitled (40x30cm-16x12in) s.d.1943-82 board. 21-Nov-2 Finarte, Rome #229/R
£3472 $5521 €5000 Untitled (70x50cm-28x20in) s.d.1957 oil collage card. 1-May-3 Meeting Art, Vercelli #1812
£4422 $7031 €6500 Composition (80x60cm-31x24in) s.i.d.1986 verso. 1-Mar-3 Meeting Art, Vercelli #376
£4861 $7729 €7000 Construction Kan (80x60cm-31x24in) s.d.1990. 1-May-3 Meeting Art, Vercelli #425 est:6000
Works on paper
£349 $548 €524 Composition (39x28cm-15x11in) s.d.89 W/C Indian ink pencil prov. 23-Nov-2 Burkhard, Luzern #42/R (S.FR 800)
£516 $815 €800 Composition (57x38cm-22x15in) s.d.86 pencil Chinese ink W/C prov. 18-Dec-2 Christie's, Rome #60
£696 $1086 €1100 Composition (22x22cm-9x9in) s.d.1963 Chinese ink paper on board. 14-Sep-2 Meeting Art, Vercelli #712/R
£704 $1169 €1000 Composition (33x33cm-13x13in) s.d.1961 collage. 10-Jun-3 Finarte Semenzato, Milan #251/R
£2721 $4327 €4000 Composition (60x44cm-24x17in) s.d.1960. 1-Mar-3 Meeting Art, Vercelli #359

VERPOORTEN, Oscar (1895-1948) Belgian
£347 $552 €500 Ferme dans un paysage (35x35cm-14x14in) s. paper. 29-Apr-3 Campo & Campo, Antwerp #340
£451 $718 €650 Bateaux sur l'Escaut (48x58cm-19x23in) s. paper. 29-Apr-3 Campo & Campo, Antwerp #342
£472 $736 €750 Fishing boats at the shore (50x50cm-20x20in) s. 23-Sep-2 Bernaerts, Antwerp #36/R
£544 $865 €800 Chevaux de trait au port (90x100cm-35x39in) s. 18-Mar-3 Campo, Vlaamse Kaai #292
£612 $973 €900 Sur l'Escaut (90x100cm-35x39in) s. 18-Mar-3 Campo, Vlaamse Kaai #293
£655 $1048 €950 Hilly landscape (77x120cm-30x47in) s. 15-Mar-3 De Vuyst, Lokeren #383
£1020 $1622 €1500 Harbour view, lock with docker and horses (80x90cm-31x35in) s. 24-Mar-3 Bernaerts, Antwerp #179/R est:1500-2000
£1667 $2650 €2400 Cabaret (60x70cm-24x28in) s. 29-Apr-3 Campo & Campo, Antwerp #341 est:300-400

VERREYT, Jacob Johan (1807-1872) Flemish
£1020 $1622 €1500 Cossacks taking horses from peasant (41x53cm-16x21in) bears sig. i. stretcher. 28-Mar-3 Bolland & Marotz, Bremen #534/R est:1600

VERRON, Laurent (20th C) French
Works on paper
£276 $436 €400 Odilon Verjus (48x36cm-19x14in) s. Chinese ink. 7-Apr-3 Claude Aguttes, Neuilly #101/R

VERRYCK, Theodor (1734-1786) Dutch
Works on paper
£1656 $2583 €2600 Shipping in an estuary by a village, a city beyond (24x36cm-9x14in) s. W/C prov.exhib. 5-Nov-2 Sotheby's, Amsterdam #167/R est:3500-4500

VERRYCK, Theodor (attrib) (1734-1786) Dutch
£680 $1088 €1020 Dutch canal scene with figures in boats near buildings (39x53cm-15x21in) bears sig. canvas on panel. 15-May-3 Lawrence, Crewkerne #904

VERSAILLE, H (19th C) ?
£1500 $2325 €2250 Queen Elizabeth coming into Dunkerque (61x91cm-24x36in) s.i.d.1889. 31-Oct-2 Christie's, Kensington #498/R est:800-1200

VERSCHAEREN, Bart (1888-1946) Belgian
£1410 $2186 €2200 Fair (80x100cm-31x39in) s. 7-Dec-2 De Vuyst, Lokeren #397/R est:1500-2000

VERSCHAEREN, Theodoor (1874-1937) Belgian
£345 $552 €500 Girl with fruit bowl (67x54cm-26x21in) s.d.1913. 15-Mar-3 De Vuyst, Lokeren #384

VERSCHAFFELT, Edouard (1874-1955) Belgian
£2759 $4386 €4000 Scene de rue orientaliste (80x60cm-31x24in) s. 4-Mar-3 Palais de Beaux Arts, Brussels #410/R est:4000-6000
£3145 $4874 €5000 L'heure du the (84x60cm-33x24in) s. 1-Oct-2 Palais de Beaux Arts, Brussels #543/R est:2500-3750

VERSCHAFFELT, Peter Anton von (1710-1793) Flemish
Works on paper
£597 $932 €950 Najade and Triton resting on rock (19x27cm-7x11in) ochre wash Indian ink. 11-Oct-2 Winterberg, Heidelberg #471

VERSCHNEIDER, Jean (1872-1943) French
Sculpture
£1042 $1719 €1500 La frontiere (51cm-20in) s.i. brown pat bronze. 1-Jul-3 Claude Aguttes, Neuilly #185/R est:1500-1800

VERSCHUER, Julia van (1926-) Dutch
Sculpture
£1042 $1719 €1500 Potbellied pig (22x38cm-9x15in) bronze. 1-Jul-3 Christie's, Amsterdam #523/R est:500-700

VERSCHUREN, Charles (jnr) (1891-1955) Dutch
£2848 $4500 €4500 Feest in volendam (41x51cm-16x20in) s. 26-Nov-2 Sotheby's, Amsterdam #131/R est:3500-4500

VERSCHURING, Hendrik (1627-1690) Dutch
£4268 $7000 €6189 Cavalry skirmish outside the gates of a city (60x73cm-24x29in) indis.sig. prov.exhib. 4-Jun-3 Christie's, Rockefeller NY #184/R est:6000-8000
£6550 $10349 €9825 Battle scene (59x79cm-23x31in) s.d.1673. 14-Nov-2 Stuker, Bern #572 est:6000-8000 (S.FR 15000)

VERSCHUUR, Cornelius (19th C) Dutch
£844 $1402 €1224 Woodcutter (51x71cm-20x28in) s. 16-Jun-3 Waddingtons, Toronto #240/R est:1500-2500 (C.D 1900)

VERSCHUUR, Wouter (jnr) (1841-1936) Dutch
£248 $400 €372 Horses in a stable (20x30cm-8x12in) bears s. panel. 19-Feb-3 Doyle, New York #46
£4100 $6560 €6150 Carthorses in a stable (24x33cm-9x13in) s. panel sold with a companion. 7-Jan-3 Bonhams, Knightsbridge #250/R est:3000-5000

VERSCHUUR, Wouter (snr) (1812-1874) Dutch
£576 $921 €800 Le cavalier (12x12cm-5x5in) copper. 13-May-3 Galerie Moderne, Brussels #352/R
£4459 $7000 €6689 Setters at the pond (8x10cm-3x4in) a. panel. 10-Dec-2 Doyle, New York #184/R est:12000-18000
£5500 $8580 €8250 Foundry cart (134x167cm-53x66in) 17-Sep-2 Sotheby's, Olympia #223/R est:6000-8000
£22013 $33899 €35000 Horses at rest near the beach (27x22cm-11x9in) s. panel. 22-Oct-2 Sotheby's, Amsterdam #159/R est:20000-25000
£35000 $54950 €52500 Four horses in a stable (26x39cm-10x15in) s. panel prov. 19-Nov-2 Sotheby's, London #145/R est:20000-30000
£37736 $58113 €60000 Tending the horses (36x50cm-14x20in) s. panel. 23-Oct-2 Christie's, Amsterdam #105/R est:70000-90000
£50314 $77484 €80000 Loading a malle Jan in a village street (37x53cm-15x21in) s. panel. 23-Oct-2 Christie's, Amsterdam #136/R est:60000-80000
Works on paper
£900 $1413 €1350 Beat of friends (16x23cm-6x9in) s.d.13.Jany 1868 pencil W/C. 21-Nov-2 Christie's, Kensington #112/R
£3125 $5156 €4500 Taking a break, horses watering after a hunt (56x75cm-22x30in) pen col ink W/C. 1-Jul-3 Christie's, Amsterdam #562/R est:5000-7000

VERSTAPPEN, Martin (attrib) (1773-1853) Belgian
£1900 $2945 €2850 Italian woodland landscape with figures on a path (99x73cm-39x29in) s. 31-Oct-2 Ambrose, Loughton #31/R est:2000-4000

VERSTER, Floris (1861-1927) Dutch
£26027 $40863 €38000 Doode Kraaien (21x54cm-8x21in) s.d.07 lit. 15-Apr-3 Sotheby's, Amsterdam #245/R est:10000-15000

VERSTRAETE, T (1850-1907) Belgian
£1026 $1610 €1600 Paysages (23x30cm-9x12in) panel pair. 16-Dec-2 Amberes, Antwerp #316

VERSTRAETE, Theodore (1850-1907) Belgian
Works on paper
£2089 $3258 €3300 Wife with dog - Two woman - Tree boys near the water (85x28cm-33x11in) s. W/C gouache painted with Charles Nys and Emile Claus on fan. 21-Oct-2 Bernaerts, Antwerp #629/R est:4000-5000

VERSTRAETEN, Edmond (1870-1956) Belgian
£590 $939 €850 Les moissonneurs (28x35cm-11x14in) mono.d.1912. 29-Apr-3 Campo & Campo, Antwerp #344
£629 $975 €1000 Landscape (27x35cm-11x14in) mono.d.1927. 5-Oct-2 De Vuyst, Lokeren #409
£692 $1065 €1100 Maison dans le bois (100x100cm-39x39in) s. 22-Oct-2 Campo & Campo, Antwerp #322/R
£1132 $1766 €1800 Children with cows in late summer landscape (60x80cm-24x31in) s. 9-Oct-2 Michael Zeller, Lindau #949/R
£1304 $2139 €1800 Crepuscule dans la foret (118x125cm-46x49in) mono. 27-May-3 Campo & Campo, Antwerp #264 est:800-1200
£1887 $2925 €3000 Summer landscape with corn sheaves (85x100cm-33x39in) mono.d.40. 5-Oct-2 De Vuyst, Lokeren #407/R est:3300-3800
£2564 $3974 €4000 Snowy landscape of Waasmunster (65x126cm-26x50in) mono. 7-Dec-2 De Vuyst, Lokeren #544/R est:3800-4400

VERSTRALEN, Anthonie (attrib) (1594-1641) Dutch
£20126 $31195 €32000 Dutch winter landscape (21x32cm-8x13in) d.1620 panel prov.lit. 2-Oct-2 Dorotheum, Vienna #175/R est:15000-20000

VERTANGEN, Daniel (1598-1684) Dutch
£5031 $7799 €8000 Diana and companions in landscape (19x23cm-7x9in) s. copper. 2-Oct-2 Dorotheum, Vienna #151/R est:8000-10000
£9500 $14725 €14250 Italianate landscape with Diana and her nymphs bathing and resting (34x43cm-13x17in) s. panel. 31-Oct-2 Sotheby's, Olympia #69/R est:5000-7000
£13836 $21447 €22000 Diana and nymphs bathing in southern landscape (29x39cm-11x15in) s. 2-Oct-2 Dorotheum, Vienna #152/R est:16000-20000

VERTES, Marcel (1895-1961) French
£476 $757 €700 Loulou (33x41cm-13x16in) s. 28-Feb-3 Joron-Derem, Paris #40
£1122 $1785 €1650 L'Amazone (46x61cm-18x24in) s. 26-Feb-3 Artcurial Briest, Paris #292 est:1500-1800
£5500 $8525 €8250 Le peintre et ses modeles (150x282cm-59x111in) s.d.1953. 5-Dec-2 Christie's, Kensington #104/R est:4000-6000
Works on paper
£1528 $2414 €2200 Moulin Rouge (59x48cm-23x19in) s.i. gouache. 25-Apr-3 Piasa, Paris #187

VERTEVILLE, Christian de la (1949-) French
Works on paper
£513 $785 €800 Hallali (14x17cm-6x7in) s. gouache. 23-Aug-2 Deauville, France #215
£705 $1079 €1100 Scene de chasse (23x30cm-9x12in) s. gouache. 23-Aug-2 Deauville, France #214/R

VERTIN, Petrus Gerardus (1819-1893) Dutch
£816 $1298 €1200 Dutch street scene with figures (21x18cm-8x7in) i. panel lit. 21-Mar-3 Auktionhaus Georg Rehm, Augsburg #8113/R
£1972 $3175 €2800 Old Dutch street with many figures in winter (26x20cm-10x8in) s. panel. 6-May-3 Vendu Notarishuis, Rotterdam #48/R est:2000-2500
£2166 $3378 €3400 City canal with houses and lifting bridge (29x24cm-11x9in) s.d.88 panel. 6-Nov-2 Vendue Huis, Gravenhage #412/R est:7000-9000
£2201 $3390 €3500 Infantrists on a bridge entering a castle (34x25cm-13x10in) s.d.45 panel. 23-Oct-2 Christie's, Amsterdam #40/R est:4500-5500
£3103 $4934 €4500 Vue de ville Hollandaise (17x13cm-7x5in) s. panel. 4-Mar-3 Livinec, Gaudcheau & Jezequel, Rennes #34/R
£3125 $4969 €4500 Canal scene in Haarlem (22x18cm-9x7in) s.d.89 panel. 29-Apr-3 Christie's, Amsterdam #52/R est:3000-5000
£3521 $5669 €5000 Old Dutch street view with canal (23x19cm-9x7in) s. panel. 6-May-3 Vendu Notarishuis, Rotterdam #100/R est:3000-4000
£3800 $5966 €5700 Flower market in a Dutch town (36x40cm-14x16in) s. 21-Nov-2 Christie's, Kensington #102/R est:2000-3000
£4277 $6586 €6800 Villagers in the streets of a Dutch town (21x16cm-8x6in) s.d.58 panel. 22-Oct-2 Sotheby's, Amsterdam #63/R est:6000-8000
£4403 $6780 €7000 Village scene with a church in the background (23x16cm-9x6in) s.d.59 panel. 22-Oct-2 Sotheby's, Amsterdam #58/R est:6000-8000
£4795 $7527 €7000 Villagers in the streets of a Dutch town (18x14cm-7x6in) s. panel. 15-Apr-3 Sotheby's, Amsterdam #31/R est:6000-8000
£4795 $7527 €7000 View of Alkmaar (22x19cm-9x7in) s.i.d.1881 verso panel. 15-Apr-3 Sotheby's, Amsterdam #42/R est:7000-9000
£5031 $7748 €8000 View of Leiden in winter (30x24cm-12x9in) s.d.79 panel. 22-Oct-2 Sotheby's, Amsterdam #51/R est:8000-12000
£5660 $8717 €9000 Villagers in streets of a Dutch town (24x19cm-9x7in) s.d.85 panel. 22-Oct-2 Sotheby's, Amsterdam #20/R est:6000-8000
£7547 $11623 €12000 Town scene in summer, Alkmaar (23x19cm-9x7in) s.d.88 panel. 22-Oct-2 Sotheby's, Amsterdam #49/R est:5500-7000
£9028 $14354 €13000 Busy market street (36x28cm-14x11in) s.d.68 panel. 29-Apr-3 Christie's, Amsterdam #7/R est:4000-6000

Works on paper
£2083 $3437 €3000 City scene with figures conversing (43x35cm-17x14in) s.d.63 pencil pen ink W/C. 1-Jul-3 Christie's, Amsterdam #16/R est:3000-5000

VERVEER, Elchanon Leonardus (1826-1900) Dutch
£1389 $2292 €2000 Helping hand (36x50cm-14x20in) s. 1-Jul-3 Christie's, Amsterdam #70/R est:2000-3000
£1796 $3000 €2604 Tall tale (69x82cm-27x32in) s.d.1877. 22-Jun-3 Freeman, Philadelphia #12/R est:4000-6000
Works on paper
£650 $1014 €975 Two elderly fishermen walking in the dunes (24x34cm-9x13in) s. W/C. 9-Oct-2 Woolley & Wallis, Salisbury #144/R

VERVEER, Mauritz (1817-1903) Dutch
£1164 $1816 €1700 Beach scene with fishermen fastening the boat (15x20cm-6x8in) s.d.51 panel lit. 10-Apr-3 Allgauer, Kempten #3039/R est:1500

VERVEER, Salomon Leonardus (1813-1876) Dutch
£2394 $3855 €3400 River scene with ferry (17x22cm-7x9in) s. 7-May-3 Vendue Huis, Gravenhage #372/R est:2500-3000
£7547 $11623 €12000 Fishing village in the dunes (40x58cm-16x23in) s. panel prov. 22-Oct-2 Sotheby's, Amsterdam #131/R est:12000-15000
£8917 $13911 €14000 Fishing village (39x33cm-15x13in) s.d.75. 6-Nov-2 Vendue Huis, Gravenhage #415/R est:12000-16000
£20755 $31962 €33000 Op de Duinen te Scheveningen - in the dunes of Scheveningen (77x112cm-30x44in) s.d.76 i.on stretcher. 22-Oct-2 Sotheby's, Amsterdam #134/R est:40000-60000
Works on paper
£987 $1599 €1500 View of a snow covered town (38x28cm-15x11in) s.d.1839 pencil pen ink W/C. 21-Jan-3 Christie's, Amsterdam #19/R est:2000-3000

VERVISCH, Godfried (1930-) Belgian
£1509 $2340 €2400 Girl in front of window (130x100cm-51x39in) s.d.64. 5-Oct-2 De Vuyst, Lokeren #410/R est:2000-2500
£1538 $2385 €2400 Reclining nude (150x180cm-59x71in) s.d.90. 7-Dec-2 De Vuyst, Lokeren #399/R est:2500-3000
Works on paper
£566 $877 €900 Standing nude. Figure (61x41cm-24x16in) one s. gouache pastel black chk one s.d.71 ink dr two. 5-Oct-2 De Vuyst, Lokeren #411

VERVISCH, Jean (1896-1977) Belgian
£301 $484 €460 Composition au voilier et aux fruits (60x40cm-24x16in) s.d.41. 20-Jan-3 Horta, Bruxelles #384
£680 $1082 €1000 Nature morte aux conques (61x50cm-24x20in) s. panel. 18-Mar-3 Galerie Moderne, Brussels #529/R

VERVLOET, Frans (1795-1872) Dutch
£37736 $58868 €60000 Promenade on Bay of Naples with view of Vesuvius (46x65cm-18x26in) s.d.1831. 21-Sep-2 Bolland & Marotz, Bremen #572/R est:29000
£45517 $71917 €66000 Naples from Castelnuovo (36x49cm-14x19in) exhib.lit. 3-Apr-3 Porro, Milan #54/R est:90000
£47771 $74522 €75000 Historical view of Naples Bay with activity at the quay (37x50cm-15x20in) s.d.1827. 5-Nov-2 Vendu Notarishuis, Rotterdam #279/R est:5000-8000
£55172 $87172 €80000 Naples from Santa Lucia (35x48cm-14x19in) s.indis.d. prov.exhib.lit. 3-Apr-3 Porro, Milan #53/R est:100000
Works on paper
£270 $422 €400 Gondole a Venice (18x35cm-7x14in) s. W/C. 25-Mar-3 Campo & Campo, Antwerp #245

VERVOORT, Frank (1930-1983) Canadian
£932 $1482 €1398 Bragg Creek sun shadow (65x75cm-26x30in) s.d.1979. 23-Mar-3 Hodgins, Calgary #75/R est:1200-1800 (C.D 2200)

VERVOU, P (1822-1913) Belgian
£1006 $1570 €1600 Voiliers dans un port (60x91cm-24x36in) panel. 14-Oct-2 Amberes, Antwerp #224
£3000 $4860 €4350 Offloading trade, Dutch river scene (90x71cm-35x28in) mono. board. 22-May-3 Wintertons, Lichfield #565/R est:2500-3500

VERWEE, Alfred Jacques (1838-1895) Belgian
£955 $1490 €1500 L'etalon blanc (50x42cm-20x17in) s. 11-Nov-2 Horta, Bruxelles #152 est:1500-2000
£1783 $2782 €2800 Brabancon a la barriere (85x65cm-33x26in) s. 11-Nov-2 Horta, Bruxelles #151 est:2000-3000
£1911 $2981 €3000 Trois vaches dans un paysage (65x81cm-26x32in) s. 11-Nov-2 Horta, Bruxelles #149 est:3500-4000
£2102 $3279 €3300 Troupeau de vaches dans un paysage (65x80cm-26x31in) s. 11-Nov-2 Horta, Bruxelles #150 est:2500-3700
£2278 $3554 €3600 Landscape with travellers (39x55cm-15x22in) s. panel. 21-Oct-2 Bernaerts, Antwerp #179/R est:2000-2500
£2420 $3776 €3800 Deux chevaux dans un paysage (64x75cm-25x30in) s. 11-Nov-2 Horta, Bruxelles #148 est:3500-4000
£3165 $5065 €4400 Cows in the polders surrounding Knokke (63x82cm-25x32in) s. painted c.1880. 17-May-3 De Vuyst, Lokeren #442/R est:4500-5500

VERWEE, Louis Pierre (1807-1877) Belgian
£881 $1313 €1322 Landscape with cows, sheep and goats (44x49cm-17x19in) s. 25-Jun-2 Koller, Zurich #6481 (S.FR 2000)
£1582 $2453 €2500 Meadow landscape with sheep resting (53x75cm-21x30in) s. prov. 28-Sep-2 Ketterer, Hamburg #3/R est:3000-3500
£18868 $29057 €30000 Herdman with cattle fording a stream in a valley. Shepherd with a flock of sheep resting in a valley (99x131cm-39x52in) s.d.1833 pair. 23-Oct-2 Christie's, Amsterdam #117/R est:30000-50000
£48611 $77292 €70000 Extensive winter landscape with figures on a frozen river (81x115cm-32x45in) s.d.40 panel. 29-Apr-3 Christie's, Amsterdam #38/R est:35000-50000

VERWEE, Louis Pierre and VERBOECKHOVEN, Eugène (19th C) Belgian
£3200 $5088 €4800 Cattle and drover on a country road (49x84cm-19x33in) s. panel. 18-Mar-3 Bonhams, New Bond Street #12/R est:4000-6000

VERWEY, Hans (1928-) Dutch
Works on paper
£935 $1534 €1300 Landscape (160x110cm-63x43in) s. s.d.on stretcher felt pen on canvas. 3-Jun-3 Christie's, Amsterdam #145/R est:1000-1500

VERWEY, Kees (1900-1995) Dutch
£7194 $11799 €10000 Still life with flowers (65x80cm-26x31in) s. prov. 3-Jun-3 Christie's, Amsterdam #252/R est:10000-15000
Works on paper
£1645 $2664 €2500 Still life with flowers (49x39cm-19x15in) s.d.73 gouache prov. 21-Jan-3 Christie's, Amsterdam #450/R est:2500-3500
£1923 $3019 €3000 Still life with narcissus (52x38cm-20x15in) s. W/C. 25-Nov-2 Glerum, Amsterdam #187/R est:3000-5000

VERWILT, François (1620-1691) Dutch
£3459 $5362 €5500 Adoration of the shepherds (39x49cm-15x19in) s. panel. 2-Oct-2 Dorotheum, Vienna #359/R est:5000-9000
£6200 $9672 €9300 Adoration of the shepherds, with the Annunciation (100x95cm-39x37in) s. 8-Apr-3 Sotheby's, Olympia #146/R est:3000-5000

VERWORNER, Ludolf (1867-1927) German
£449 $704 €700 Women in the wind (39x54cm-15x21in) init. exhib. 16-Dec-2 Pandolfini, Florence #217

VESCO, Lino (1879-?) Austrian
£2302 $3776 €3200 Animation dans la galerie des Abencerage (26x20cm-10x8in) s. panel. 4-Jun-3 Tajan, Paris #318/R est:3000-4000

VESCO, Lino (attrib) (1879-?) Austrian
£372 $603 €558 Interior from Alhambra (26x20cm-10x8in) bears sig. panel. 3-Feb-3 Lilla Bukowskis, Stockholm #972 (S.KR 5200)

VESELY, Boris Theo (20th C) French
£1223 $1907 €1835 Busy street (55x45cm-22x18in) s.d.905. 20-Nov-2 Fischer, Luzern #1182/R est:2800-3500 (S.FR 2800)

VESIN, Jaroslav Fr Julius (1859-1915) Bulgarian
£619 $978 €929 Portrait of a girl (43x45cm-17x18in) mono. board. 30-Nov-2 Dorotheum, Prague #9/R (C.KR 30000)
£705 $1093 €1100 Winter landscape with horse drawn sledge (19x30cm-7x12in) s. lit. 6-Dec-2 Karlheinz Kaupp, Staufen #2288
£3000 $5010 €4350 Sleigh ride (60x73cm-24x29in) s. 17-Jun-3 Bonhams, New Bond Street #25/R est:3000-5000
£4648 $7483 €6600 Happy couple in sleigh (69x56cm-27x22in) 10-May-3 Bukowskis, Helsinki #405/R est:6000-8000
£11000 $18040 €16500 Sledge ride (55x95cm-22x37in) s.i.d.1890. 3-Jun-3 Sotheby's, London #27/R est:10000-15000

VESIN, Jaroslav Fr Julius (attrib) (1859-1915) Bulgarian
£1258 $1950 €2000 Meeting in winter landscape (31x20cm-12x8in) mono.d.1890 panel. 29-Oct-2 Dorotheum, Vienna #65/R est:2200-2400

VESPIGNANI, Renzo (1924-2001) Italian
£962 $1510 €1500 Male nude (104x68cm-41x27in) s.d.1963 oil mixed media paper. 20-Nov-2 Pandolfini, Florence #67/R

£2048 $3277 €2970 Suburbs (60x80cm-24x31in) s. 11-Mar-3 Babuino, Rome #363/R
£3333 $5233 €5200 Piles on the beach (30x51cm-12x20in) s.d.1947 verso board. 21-Nov-2 Finarte, Rome #286/R
£4965 $8043 €7000 Mia madre (170x150cm-67x59in) s.d.70 prov. 26-May-3 Christie's, Milan #126/R est:8000-12000
Works on paper
£823 $1300 €1235 Portrait of a convalescing friend. Grazielle. s.d.1948 one s.d.1950 ink two different sizes. 24-Apr-3 Sotheby's, New York #173/R est:1000-1500
£1410 $2214 €2200 In high grass (102x72cm-40x28in) s.i.d.1965 pencil. 19-Nov-2 Finarte, Milan #35/R
£2692 $4173 €4200 Suburbs (66x103cm-26x41in) s. mixed media paper on canvas exec.1963. 4-Dec-2 Finarte, Milan #292/R
£2740 $4274 €4000 Suburbs (50x50cm-20x20in) s. mixed media card. 10-Apr-3 Finarte Semenzato, Rome #80/R
£2770 $4322 €4100 Suburbs (69x100cm-27x39in) s. mixed media paper on canvas. 28-Mar-3 Farsetti, Prato #353/R

VEST, Jim (20th C) Canadian
£241 $378 €362 Winter street scene (50x60cm-20x24in) s.i. acrylic board. 25-Nov-2 Hodgins, Calgary #416/R (C.D 600)

VESTENICKY, Vladimir (1919-1979) Czechoslovakian
£347 $538 €521 ZUPNE Square in Bratislava (40x76cm-16x30in) veneer painted 1967. 3-Dec-2 SOGA, Bratislava #257/R (SL.K 22000)
£410 $636 €615 Autumn vineyards (70x122cm-28x48in) painted 1973. 3-Dec-2 SOGA, Bratislava #258/R (SL.K 26000)

VESTER, Willem (1824-1871) Dutch
£1300 $2028 €1950 Cows in a summer landscape (30x46cm-12x18in) s. 26-Mar-3 Sotheby's, Olympia #210/R est:1000-2000
£3472 $5521 €5000 Panoramic dune landscape with sportsman in the foreground (42x53cm-17x21in) s.d.51 panel prov. 29-Apr-3 Christie's, Amsterdam #80/R est:4000-6000

VESTIER, Antoine (1740-1824) French
£3497 $5839 €5000 Portrait d'homme a la veste decoree d'une rose (65x54cm-26x21in) s.d.1762. 27-Jun-3 Piasa, Paris #105/R est:5000-6000
Miniatures
£1100 $1716 €1650 Gentleman wearing red coat with gold buttons and frogging (3cm-1in) s.d.1767 gold mount red leather reverse oval prov.lit. 5-Nov-2 Bonhams, New Bond Street #37/R est:800-1200
£2452 $3874 €3800 Portrait de femme et de sa fille (7cm-3in circular) s.i.d.1780. 18-Dec-2 Beaussant & Lefèvre, Paris #1/R
Works on paper
£1081 $1686 €1600 Portrait of young woman in pink dress (5x4cm-2x2in) s.d.1783 W/C ivory. 28-Mar-3 Dorotheum, Vienna #363/R est:1400-1600

VESTINGER (?) ?
£1043 $1700 €1512 Still life the flowers (58x43cm-23x17in) 18-Jul-3 Du Mouchelle, Detroit #1095/R est:1200-1800

VETCOUR, Fernand (1908-) Belgian
£340 $569 €480 Paysage en Provence (46x38cm-18x15in) s. panel. 18-Jun-3 Hotel des Ventes Mosan, Brussels #289
£353 $554 €550 Vue de village, en bordure d'un champs (54x68cm-21x27in) s. panel. 11-Dec-2 Hotel des Ventes Mosan, Brussels #267
£355 $592 €500 Sous-boix aux fougeres, foret de Saint-Hubert (50x65cm-20x26in) s. panel. 18-Jun-3 Hotel des Ventes Mosan, Brussels #304

VETERE, Giovanni (1940-) Italian
Works on paper
£476 $757 €700 Family in the park (80x52cm-31x20in) mono. mixed media fresco. 28-Mar-3 Bolland & Marotz, Bremen #703/R
£680 $1082 €1000 Summer's day (99x50cm-39x20in) s. mixed media fresco panel. 28-Mar-3 Bolland & Marotz, Bremen #702/R

VETSCH, Christian (20th C) Swiss
£330 $492 €495 Winter landscape with cows (34x59cm-13x23in) s.d.1974 pavatex. 25-Jun-2 Koller, Zurich #6628 (S.FR 750)
£374 $558 €561 Figures and cows in meadow (33x58cm-13x23in) s. 25-Jun-2 Koller, Zurich #6627 (S.FR 850)

VETTER, Charles (1858-1936) German
£1961 $3137 €3000 Rainy day in Halle/Saale with view of market church (61x51cm-24x20in) s. 10-Jan-3 Allgauer, Kempten #1816/R est:7000
£5449 $8554 €8500 Odeon Square with Feldherrn Hall and Theatiner Church in Munich (54x45cm-21x18in) s.d.1920. 21-Nov-2 Van Ham, Cologne #1952/R est:2200

VETTER, Charles (attrib) (1858-1936) German
£3600 $5832 €5400 Karlplatz Munich (61x49cm-24x19in) indis sig. 20-May-3 Sotheby's, Olympia #425/R est:4000-6000

VETTRIANO, Jack (1954-) British
£520 $848 €780 Headphones (51x40cm-20x16in) 14-Feb-3 Lyon & Turnbull, Edinburgh #25
£520 $848 €780 Optical instrument (37x27cm-15x11in) 14-Feb-3 Lyon & Turnbull, Edinburgh #26
£3000 $4680 €4500 Edinburgh Castle (50x40cm-20x16in) s. prov. 14-Apr-3 Sotheby's, London #195/R est:3000-5000
£3500 $5425 €5250 Artist's studio (46x35cm-18x14in) s. 6-Dec-2 Lyon & Turnbull, Edinburgh #93/R est:2000-3000
£5000 $7800 €7500 Links Fair, Kirkcaldy (20x24cm-8x9in) s. 14-Apr-3 Sotheby's, London #194/R est:5000-7000
£6000 $9540 €9000 Cheating hearts (61x51cm-24x20in) s. 6-Mar-3 Christie's, Kensington #272/R est:6000-10000
£7000 $10710 €10500 Girls on the beach (29x24cm-11x9in) s.i.d.Nov 91 verso canvasboard. 22-Aug-2 Bonhams, Edinburgh #1047/R est:5000-7000
£7800 $12168 €11700 On the beach (19x29cm-7x11in) s. canvasboard. 10-Apr-3 Bonhams, Edinburgh #56/R est:3000-5000
£11000 $16830 €16500 Adjusting the veil (49x39cm-19x15in) s. 22-Aug-2 Bonhams, Edinburgh #996/R est:7000-10000
£14000 $21420 €21000 Going nowhere (38x30cm-15x12in) s. exhib. 22-Aug-2 Bonhams, Edinburgh #1049/R est:10000-15000
£18000 $28080 €27000 Mark of Cain (51x40cm-20x16in) s. prov.exhib. 14-Apr-3 Sotheby's, London #196/R est:12000-18000
£34000 $52020 €51000 Red room (60x50cm-24x20in) s. exhib. 22-Aug-2 Bonhams, Edinburgh #995/R est:18000-25000
£37000 $56240 €55500 City cafe (81x71cm-32x28in) s. exhib. 28-Aug-2 Sotheby's, London #1104/R est:25000-35000
£55000 $85800 €82500 Railway station blues (81x71cm-32x28in) s. prov.exhib. 14-Apr-3 Sotheby's, London #197/R est:30000-40000

VEYRASSAT, Jules Jacques (1828-1893) French
£3546 $5922 €5000 Relais de chevaux (32x40cm-13x16in) s. panel prov. 20-Jun-3 Piasa, Paris #6/R est:9000-11000
£4114 $6500 €6171 Ploughing in the Nivernais (65x124cm-26x49in) s. 24-Apr-3 Sotheby's, New York #104/R est:8000-12000
£5380 $8500 €8500 Chevaux de hallage sur le chemin (24x35cm-9x14in) s. panel. 1-Dec-2 Peron, Melun #68
£5696 $9000 €9000 Chevaux sous un pommier (27x41cm-11x16in) s. exhib. 1-Dec-2 Peron, Melun #43

VEZELAY, Paule (20th C) ?
£950 $1473 €1425 Paysage - three pushing shoots (27x22cm-11x9in) painted 1931 exhib. 4-Dec-2 Christie's, Kensington #605/R
Works on paper
£350 $543 €525 Three lines (21x30cm-8x12in) s.d.1950 chl exhib. 4-Dec-2 Christie's, Kensington #304

VEZZANI, F (19th C) Italian?
£6289 $9811 €10000 Painter having a dring (38x24cm-15x9in) s. board. 23-Sep-2 Durán, Madrid #242/R est:10000

VEZZOLI, Francesco (1971-) Italian
Prints
£19000 $29640 €28500 Bitter tears of Vera von Lehndorff (56x46cm-22x18in) colour laser print on canvas metallic embroidery prov. 21-Oct-2 Sotheby's, London #69/R est:6000-8000

VIALA, Eugene (1859-1913) French
Works on paper
£642 $1001 €950 Sous-bois (48x70cm-19x28in) s. W/C exec.c.1910. 28-Mar-3 Delvaux, Paris #23

VIALI, Carlo (20th C) Italian
£1310 $2083 €1900 Kitten (80x100cm-31x39in) s. 7-Mar-3 Semenzato, Venice #154/R

VIALLAT, Claude (1936-) French
£414 $691 €600 Empreintes (100x70cm-39x28in) acrylic. 9-Jul-3 Cornette de St.Cyr, Paris #361/R
£719 $1158 €1100 Empreintes (60x70cm-24x28in) acrylic. 20-Jan-3 Cornette de St.Cyr, Paris #622
£1250 $2063 €1800 Sans titre (53x54cm-21x21in) paint pillowslip flax. 1-Jul-3 Artcurial Briest, Paris #863/R est:2000-2500
£2051 $3241 €3200 Composition (292x309cm-115x122in) 18-Nov-2 Rieunier, Paris #141/R
£2436 $3849 €3800 Composition (290x228cm-114x90in) 18-Nov-2 Rieunier, Paris #142/R
£3077 $4862 €4800 Composition (328x240cm-129x94in) 18-Nov-2 Rieunier, Paris #136/R
£3205 $5064 €5000 Composition (320x260cm-126x102in) 18-Nov-2 Rieunier, Paris #138/R

£3526 $5571 €5500 Composition (290x222cm-114x87in) 18-Nov-2 Rieunier, Paris #140/R
£3846 $6077 €6000 Composition (330x185cm-130x73in) 18-Nov-2 Rieunier, Paris #139/R
£4167 $6583 €6500 Composition in blue and red (330x180cm-130x71in) 18-Nov-2 Rieunier, Paris #137
£5068 $7905 €7500 Composition (177x214cm-70x84in) 26-Mar-3 Rieunier, Paris #24/R est:4000
£6597 $10885 €9500 Sans titre (230x170cm-91x67in) i.verso paint prov. 1-Jul-3 Artcurial Briest, Paris #552/R est:10000-15000
£7547 $11698 €12000 Sans titre (456x196cm-180x77in) board prov. 30-Oct-2 Artcurial Briest, Paris #466/R est:12000-15000
Works on paper
£1042 $1656 €1500 Empreintes de filets (31x64cm-12x25in) paint prov. 29-Apr-3 Artcurial Briest, Paris #468/R est:900-1200

VIANDIER, Richard (1858-1949) Belgian
£1793 $2851 €2600 Musiciennes et danseuses dans le desert (55x75cm-22x30in) s. 4-Mar-3 Palais de Beaux Arts, Brussels #413/R est:2800-4000

VIANE, Etienne (18th C) ?
Works on paper
£2200 $3476 €3300 French slave ship on open seas (38x50cm-15x20in) s.d.1786 pen grey ink W/C. 15-Nov-2 Sotheby's, London #77/R est:1500-2000

VIANELLI, Achille (1803-1894) Italian
£4483 $7083 €6500 Agro Campano (25x32cm-10x13in) s.d.1839. 3-Apr-3 Porro, Milan #58/R est:9000
Works on paper
£339 $540 €500 Ancient aqueduc (27x43cm-11x17in) s.i.d.1824 crayon. 24-Mar-3 Tajan, Paris #104
£339 $540 €500 Vue du Castel Gandolfo (25x38cm-10x15in) s. crayon. 24-Mar-3 Tajan, Paris #103
£545 $866 €800 Habitation de paysan (26x36cm-10x14in) s.i. crayon. 24-Mar-3 Tajan, Paris #106
£816 $1298 €1200 Vue du Chateau d'Ischia (21x32cm-8x13in) s.i. crayon. 24-Mar-3 Tajan, Paris #127a
£1020 $1621 €1500 Vallee pres d'Amaalfi (26x33cm-10x13in) s.i. crayon. 24-Mar-3 Tajan, Paris #109
£1100 $1738 €1650 San Genarro di Poveri (25x19cm-10x7in) s.i.d.1834 pen wash with another wash dr two. 26-Nov-2 Bonhams, Knightsbridge #49c/R est:600-900
£1500 $2445 €2175 Arco di Constantino (16x23cm-6x9in) s.i.d.1837 W/C. 16-Jul-3 Sotheby's, Olympia #151/R est:1000-1500
£1646 $2600 €2600 Madonna del Carmine. s.d.1869 W/C card. 26-Nov-2 Christie's, Rome #96/R
£2000 $3260 €2900 L'arco di Pantano, Roma (29x20cm-11x8in) s.i.d.1836 W/C. 16-Jul-3 Sotheby's, Olympia #155/R est:1000-1500
£4000 $6520 €5800 Campo Vaccino (20x31cm-8x12in) s.i.d.1836 W/C. 16-Jul-3 Sotheby's, Olympia #153/R est:1000-1500
£5000 $8150 €7250 Tempio di vesta, Roma (20x28cm-8x11in) s.i.d.1836 W/C. 16-Jul-3 Sotheby's, Olympia #152/R est:1000-1500
£9000 $14670 €13050 Piazza Colonna, Roma (29x21cm-11x8in) s.i.d.1836 W/C. 16-Jul-3 Sotheby's, Olympia #154/R est:1000-1500

VIANELLI, Alberto (1841-1927) Italian
Works on paper
£262 $409 €393 Le Forum a Pompei (21x30cm-8x12in) s.i.d.1906 W/C over pencil. 6-Nov-2 Dobiaschofsky, Bern #3760/R (S.FR 600)

VIANELLO, Cesare (19th C) Italian
£1258 $1962 €2000 Flower seller outside shop (22x27cm-9x11in) s. 20-Sep-2 Schloss Ahlden, Ahlden #1224/R est:1900
£1500 $2340 €2250 Flower seller (27x35cm-11x14in) s. 26-Mar-3 Sotheby's, Olympia #243/R est:1500-2000

VIANI, Antonio Maria (attrib) (c.1555-1620) Italian
Works on paper
£881 $1374 €1400 David and Goliath (14x19cm-6x7in) wash pen. 11-Oct-2 Winterberg, Heidelberg #344/R

VIANI, Giovanni Maria (1636-1700) Italian
Works on paper
£839 $1200 €1259 Study of a resting male figure (19x21cm-7x8in) black white chk. 23-Jan-3 Swann Galleries, New York #91/R est:1200-1800

VIANI, Giovanni Maria (attrib) (1636-1700) Italian
Works on paper
£2160 $3542 €3132 Madonna with child (23x20cm-9x8in) ochre chl pastel oval. 4-Jun-3 Fischer, Luzern #2447/R est:1500-1800 (S.FR 4600)

VIANI, Lorenzo (1882-1936) Italian
£7051 $11071 €11000 Nudes in the pinewood (47x69cm-19x27in) s. cardboard painted c.1909 prov.exhib.lit. 19-Nov-2 Finarte, Milan #279/R
£13924 $22000 €22000 Boats at fire (60x84cm-24x33in) s. board painted 1932 exhib.lit. 30-Nov-2 Farsetti, Prato #691/R est:25000
£18987 $30000 €30000 Miserable (97x68cm-38x27in) s. cardboard painted 1929 exhib.lit. 30-Nov-2 Farsetti, Prato #722/R est:40000
Works on paper
£225 $353 €350 Man with hat (17x13cm-7x5in) s. Chinese ink. 16-Dec-2 Pandolfini, Florence #226
£439 $685 €650 Old man with pipe (30x20cm-12x8in) s.d.1931 ink dr. 28-Mar-3 Farsetti, Prato #240
£1014 $1581 €1500 Allegory (21x23cm-8x9in) s. Chinese ink. 26-Mar-3 Finarte Semenzato, Milan #47
£1014 $1581 €1500 Figure (28x21cm-11x8in) s. Chinese ink. 26-Mar-3 Finarte Semenzato, Milan #48
£1014 $1581 €1500 Figures on bech. Animals at pasture (31x21cm-12x8in) s. ink two. 26-Mar-3 Finarte Semenzato, Milan #67
£1026 $1621 €1600 Prisoner (50x33cm-20x13in) s. chl dr exec.1917-18. 15-Nov-2 Farsetti, Prato #206/R
£1392 $2200 €2200 Soldier (41x32cm-16x13in) s. chl dr. 30-Nov-2 Farsetti, Prato #620/R
£1892 $2951 €2800 Figures at bar. Maternity (31x22cm-12x9in) ink two. 26-Mar-3 Finarte Semenzato, Milan #66/R
£5380 $8500 €8500 Traveller (39x29cm-15x11in) s. Chinese ink tempera. 30-Nov-2 Farsetti, Prato #612/R est:12000

VIANI, Lorenzo (attrib) (1882-1936) Italian
£3724 $5922 €5586 Figures in Mediterranean town (40x63cm-16x25in) indis.sig. 5-Mar-3 Rasmussen, Copenhagen #1804/R est:40000 (D.KR 40000)

VIARDOT, Léon (1805-1900) French
£5929 $9250 €8894 Portrait of a woman against a red velvet curtain (218x147cm-86x58in) 14-Sep-2 Selkirks, St. Louis #725/R est:8000-9000

VIAVANT, George L (1872-1925) American
£5289 $8250 €7934 After the kill, American bald eagle with duck prey (76x64cm-30x25in) s.verso. 12-Oct-2 Neal Auction Company, New Orleans #477/R est:8000-12000
Works on paper
£949 $1500 €1424 Nature morte; morning dove or possibly a passenger pigeon (41x20cm-16x8in) s.d.1912 W/C. 5-Apr-3 Neal Auction Company, New Orleans #433/R est:1500-2500
£1582 $2500 €2373 Nature morte; cedarwax wing and eastern blue bird (48x30cm-19x12in) s.d.1913 W/C. 5-Apr-3 Neal Auction Company, New Orleans #434/R est:3000-5000

VIBERT, C L (19th C) French
Sculpture
£1259 $2102 €1800 Vase a decor de femme pechant (40cm-16in) s. gilt bronze Cast Siot. 25-Jun-3 Artcurial Briest, Paris #45/R est:800-900

VIBERT, Jean Georges (1840-1902) French
£962 $1510 €1500 Personnages dans la casbah (42x28cm-17x11in) s.i. 16-Dec-2 Gros & Delettrez, Paris #369 est:1500-2000
£18000 $29520 €27000 Un secret d'etat (46x38cm-18x15in) s.d.1875 panel prov.lit. 3-Jun-3 Sotheby's, London #171/R est:10000-15000
£18987 $30000 €28481 Rest by the fountain (65x43cm-26x17in) s. panel prov. 24-Apr-3 Sotheby's, New York #127/R est:30000-40000
Works on paper
£346 $550 €519 Cardinal (84x61cm-33x24in) s. gouache. 7-Mar-3 Jackson's, Cedar Falls #524/R
£645 $1000 €968 Guitar player (36x26cm-14x10in) s. pencil W/C gouache on board prov.exhib. 29-Oct-2 Sotheby's, New York #71/R est:2000-3000
£1560 $2606 €2200 L'intransigeant (28x18cm-11x7in) s. gouache. 20-Jun-3 Piasa, Paris #157 est:2000-3000
£1935 $3000 €2903 Figaro and a priest (27x19cm-11x7in) s. pencil W/C exhib.lit. 29-Oct-2 Sotheby's, New York #72/R est:4000-6000
£6329 $10000 €9494 Connoisseur (71x53cm-28x21in) s. pencil W/C gouache on card prov. 23-Apr-3 Christie's, Rockefeller NY #111/R est:10000-15000
£20886 $33000 €31329 Le vue (37x28cm-15x11in) s. gouache. 24-Apr-3 Sotheby's, New York #67/R est:20000-30000

VICARY, Charles Lane (19/20th C) British
Works on paper
£320 $506 €480 Steaming bowl, blazing fire, what greater good can heart desire (51x31cm-20x12in) s.i.d.1907 pencil pen ink W/C. 28-Nov-2 Christie's, Kensington #107/R

VICCHIO, Giulio da (1925-1997) Italian
£473 $738 €700 Old friends (40x30cm-16x12in) s. 28-Mar-3 Farsetti, Prato #516
£582 $943 €844 Fishermen preparing their nets (60x70cm-24x28in) s. 25-May-3 Uppsala Auktionskammare, Uppsala #214/R (S.KR 7500)

VICENTE, Eduardo (1909-1968) Spanish
£271 $428 €420 Procession (20x16cm-8x6in) s. board. 18-Dec-2 Ansorena, Madrid #21/R
Works on paper
£552 $872 €800 Landscape with two figures (34x75cm-13x30in) s. W/C. 1-Apr-3 Segre, Madrid #304/R
£633 $981 €1000 Untitled (31x21cm-12x8in) s. pencil dr pair. 26-Sep-2 Castellana, Madrid #353/R

VICENTE, Esteban (1906-2001) American/Spanish
£14241 $22500 €21362 Untitled (173x142cm-68x56in) s.d.1983 prov. 22-Apr-3 Butterfields, San Francisco #6083/R est:15000-20000
Works on paper
£641 $1013 €1000 Woman in the street (90x63cm-35x25in) W/C. 13-Nov-2 Ansorena, Madrid #192/R
£641 $1013 €1000 Winter landscape with figure (90x64cm-35x25in) s. W/C. 13-Nov-2 Ansorena, Madrid #191/R
£1602 $2500 €2403 Untitled (18x13cm-7x5in) s. mixed media collage prov. 14-Oct-2 Butterfields, San Francisco #2059/R est:3000-5000

VICENZINO, Giuseppe (17/18th C) Italian
£10127 $16000 €16000 Still life of flowers (75x57cm-30x22in) 2-Dec-2 Finarte, Milan #81/R est:15000
£17586 $27786 €25500 Still life with roses, daffodils and grapes (36x46cm-14x18in) 5-Apr-3 Finarte Semenzato, Milan #101/R est:8000

VICHI, Ferdinando (19th C) Italian
Sculpture
£2949 $4629 €4600 Bust of woman (54cm-21in) s.i. marble. 16-Dec-2 Pandolfini, Florence #196/R
£28481 $45000 €42722 Young maiden with roses (153cm-60in) s.i. marble. 24-Apr-3 Sotheby's, New York #57/R est:50000-70000

VICK, Horace Valentine (1902-) Canadian
£782 $1212 €1173 Lake Superior spruces (50x65cm-20x26in) s. board. 3-Dec-2 Joyner, Toronto #329/R est:4000-6000 (C.D 1900)

VICKERS, A H (fl.1853-1907) British
£550 $847 €825 Village on the bank of a tranquil river (23x41cm-9x16in) s. 5-Sep-2 Christie's, Kensington #169/R
£700 $1120 €1050 Extensive view of a river scene with figures, boats and figures (18x38cm-7x15in) 10-Jan-3 Biddle & Webb, Birmingham #278

VICKERS, Alfred (19th C) British
£250 $388 €375 Rural landscape with figures in the foreground (19x24cm-7x9in) s. 4-Oct-2 ELR Auctions, Sheffield #303
£1000 $1670 €1450 Cattle grazing by a river (28x38cm-11x15in) s. 8-Jul-3 Bonhams, Knightsbridge #70/R est:800-1200
£1050 $1659 €1575 River landscape with figures in a boat, cattle beyond (27x37cm-11x15in) s.d.1861. 2-Dec-2 Bonhams, Bath #127 est:700-900
£1100 $1694 €1650 East Anglian landscape (22x45cm-9x18in) s. panel. 8-Sep-2 Lots Road, London #340 est:500-800
£1800 $2952 €2700 River landscape (20x43cm-8x17in) s. panel prov. 5-Feb-3 John Nicholson, Haslemere #1088 est:1000-1500
£3000 $4860 €4500 Running into harbour with the tide (58x100cm-23x39in) s. 21-May-3 Christie's, Kensington #608/R est:3000-5000

VICKERS, Alfred (attrib) (19th C) British
£863 $1416 €1200 Summer landscape with hay harvest (19x27cm-7x11in) panel prov. 4-Jun-3 Reiss & Sohn, Konigstein #173/R
£1800 $2826 €2700 Wooden landscape with figures and cattle (43x61cm-17x24in) with sig.d.51. 21-Nov-2 Tennants, Leyburn #795/R est:600-800
Works on paper
£250 $415 €363 Shipwreck off the Isle of Wight (13x18cm-5x7in) W/C. 16-Jun-3 Duke & Son, Dorchester #143

VICKERS, Alfred (snr) (1786-1868) British
£438 $700 €657 View of Lake Windermere, Lake District (46x76cm-18x30in) s. 12-Jan-3 William Jenack, New York #299
£462 $729 €693 Pastoral harbour (10x20cm-4x8in) panel painted c.1862. 1-Dec-2 Levis, Calgary #238/R (C.D 1150)
£680 $1068 €1020 Harvest time banks of the Menai Straits (19x26cm-7x10in) s. board. 10-Dec-2 Lane, Penzance #332
£1350 $2201 €1958 Cattle watering near a waterfall (69x100cm-27x39in) s.d.1859. 21-Jul-3 Bonhams, Bath #55/R est:1000-1500

VICKERS, Alfred (snr-attrib) (1786-1868) British
£472 $750 €708 British panorama (30x45cm-12x18in) 7-Mar-3 Skinner, Boston #222/R
Works on paper
£500 $790 €750 Anglers in a wooded river landscape with distant village (36x53cm-14x21in) 13-Nov-2 Halls, Shrewsbury #392/R

VICKERS, Alfred Gomersal (1810-1837) British
£300 $501 €435 Figures in a punt on a quiet stretch of the river (18x23cm-7x9in) s. board. 25-Jun-3 Bonhams, Bury St Edmunds #572/R
£2500 $3875 €3750 Waterloo Bridge (45x63cm-18x25in) s.d.1828. 31-Oct-2 Christie's, Kensington #458/R est:3000-5000

VICKERS, Alfred H (fl.1853-1907) British
£350 $546 €525 Figures on riverside road (20x31cm-8x12in) s. 7-Nov-2 Christie's, Kensington #113
£384 $600 €576 Extensive landscape with river (24x39cm-9x15in) s. 11-Nov-2 Stephan Welz, Johannesburg #66 (SA.R 6000)
£400 $640 €600 An extensive river landscape (17x37cm-7x15in) 13-May-3 Bonhams, Knightsbridge #244/R
£450 $693 €675 Lakeside town (30x61cm-12x24in) 5-Sep-2 Christie's, Kensington #132/R
£450 $702 €675 Going to church (20x29cm-8x11in) indis sig. 7-Nov-2 Christie's, Kensington #164/R
£500 $770 €750 Country lane (41x61cm-16x24in) s.d.1898. 5-Sep-2 Christie's, Kensington #133/R
£500 $820 €750 River valley (25x41cm-10x16in) s. 29-May-3 Christie's, Kensington #120/R
£580 $945 €841 Village on the Rhine. Mill on the Rhine (30x25cm-12x10in) s.d.1894 pair. 16-Jul-3 Sotheby's, Olympia #108/R
£650 $1060 €943 Fishermen on the river. Riverside farm (21x40cm-8x16in) one s. pair. 16-Jul-3 Sotheby's, Olympia #101/R
£950 $1473 €1425 Continental river and townscape (56x81cm-22x32in) s. 26-Sep-2 Lane, Penzance #241
£1100 $1793 €1595 Devonshire landscape. River landscape (19x29cm-7x11in) s. two. 21-Jul-3 Sotheby's, London #131 est:400-600
£2000 $3280 €3000 Figures on the bank of the Rhine (46x76cm-18x30in) s. 29-May-3 Christie's, Kensington #205/R est:800-1200
£4200 $6888 €6300 Ferry (46x76cm-18x30in) s. 29-May-3 Christie's, Kensington #140/R est:800-1200

VICKERS, Alfred H (attrib) (fl.1853-1907) British
£1000 $1560 €1500 Coastal scene. River scene (20x41cm-8x16in) pair. 17-Sep-2 Bonhams, Oxford #48/R est:600-800

VICKERS, Charles (19th C) British
£260 $406 €390 Flowers pickers (30x41cm-12x16in) s. 8-Oct-2 Bonhams, Knightsbridge #18f
£750 $1163 €1125 Country inn scene with figures and hay cart (23x28cm-9x11in) s. 4-Dec-2 Neal & Fletcher, Woodbridge #246
£800 $1240 €1200 Farmyard scene with figures, cattle and church spire (23x30cm-9x12in) s. 4-Dec-2 Neal & Fletcher, Woodbridge #247

VICKERS, Henry Harold (1851-1919) British
£524 $828 €786 Meadows at Grafton, Worcestershire. Backwater on the Avon (15x22cm-6x9in) s. s.i.d.1909 verso board pair. 18-Nov-2 Waddingtons, Toronto #97a/R (C.D 1300)
£1778 $2916 €2667 Road cross the Woodcote Common, Worcestershire. Warwickshire England (15x22cm-6x9in) s.d.1906 board two. 27-May-3 Sotheby's, Toronto #70/R est:3000-5000 (C.D 4000)

VICKERS, Russ (1923-1997) American
£3082 $4500 €4623 The fortune seekers (30x91cm-12x36in) 18-May-2 Altermann Galleries, Santa Fe #176

VICKERY, Charles (1913-1998) American
£269 $425 €404 Away at sea (28x41cm-11x16in) s. canvas on board. 5-Apr-3 Susanin's, Chicago #5087/R
£380 $600 €570 Approaching the dock (18x25cm-7x10in) s. board. 5-Apr-3 Susanin's, Chicago #5086/R
£943 $1500 €1415 Summer night (61x91cm-24x36in) s. painted c.1960. 2-Mar-3 Toomey, Oak Park #628/R est:2000-4000

VICKREY, Robert (1926-) American
£596 $929 €894 The big S 1989 (17x22cm-7x9in) s. tempera panel prov. 5-Nov-2 Bukowskis, Stockholm #322/R (S.KR 8500)
£1274 $2000 €1911 Clown with ruff (25x18cm-10x7in) s. tempera on masonite prov. 10-Dec-2 Doyle, New York #154/R est:1500-2500
£2389 $3750 €3584 Puppet, 1952 (58x89cm-23x35in) s.d. tempera on masonite prov. 10-Dec-2 Doyle, New York #153/R est:2000-3000

£4717 $7500 €7076 Wooden boat (30x41cm-12x16in) s. masonite. 4-Mar-3 Christie's, Rockefeller NY #111/R est:5000-7000
£12903 $20000 €19355 Edge of the shadow (91x122cm-36x48in) s.d.51 masonite prov.exhib. 5-Dec-2 Christie's, Rockefeller NY #123/R est:25000-35000

VICTOR IV (1929-1986) Dutch
Works on paper
£2270 $3677 €3200 Amsterdam 48 XI (65x60cm-26x24in) i.verso polychrome wood. 26-May-3 Glerum, Amsterdam #291/R est:1400-1600

VICTORIA, Salvador (1929-1994) Spanish
Works on paper
£1348 $2183 €1900 Collage no. 9 (66x44cm-26x17in) s.d.1969 collage W/C board exhib. 20-May-3 Segre, Madrid #158/R est:1900

VICTORS, Jacobus (1640-1705) Dutch
£15094 $23396 €24000 Landscape with ducks by pond (127x56cm-50x22in) 7-Oct-2 Ansorena, Madrid #3/R est:24000

VICTORS, Jan (1620-1676) Dutch
£3901 $6046 €5852 David and Goliath (114x116cm-45x46in) 4-Dec-2 AB Stockholms Auktionsverk #2022/R est:50000-60000 (S.KR 55000)
£12000 $18720 €18000 Portrait of lady, wearing black and holding book (71x60cm-28x24in) indis.sig. prov. 10-Apr-3 Sotheby's, London #37/R est:18000
£18000 $28080 €27000 Group portrait of a family, pastoral dress, in landscape (114x144cm-45x57in) prov.lit. 9-Apr-3 Christie's, London #31/R est:12000-18000

VICTORYNS, Anthonie (attrib) (1612-1655) Flemish
£2000 $3140 €3000 Peasants in a cottage interior (24x35cm-9x14in) panel. 13-Dec-2 Christie's, Kensington #25/R est:3000-5000
£2657 $4438 €3800 Le concert des paysans. Le chirurgien de village (17x26cm-7x10in) panel pair. 27-Jun-3 Piasa, Paris #54/R est:2000-3000

VIDAL SOUTO, Jose (1948-) Spanish
£481 $760 €750 Girl (82x66cm-32x26in) s. acrylic. 19-Nov-2 Durán, Madrid #114/R
£613 $968 €950 Souvenir of Lugo (74x60cm-29x24in) s. 17-Dec-2 Durán, Madrid #92/R

VIDAL, Eugène (19/20th C) French
£3165 $4937 €5000 Dans l'atelier du peintre (19x24cm-7x9in) s. panel painted c.1880. 20-Oct-2 Mercier & Cie, Lille #311/R est:4000-5000

VIDAL, Francisco (fl.1867-1879) Spanish?
£550 $913 €798 British Naval cutter at sea with a dreadnought off her stern (14x21cm-6x8in) s. panel. 12-Jun-3 Christie's, London #528/R
£800 $1328 €1160 Mediterranean small craft at anchor (16x25cm-6x10in) s. panel. 12-Jun-3 Christie's, London #574/R
£1000 $1660 €1450 Spanish barque making sail out of port Mahon, Minorca (22x30cm-9x12in) s. panel. 12-Jun-3 Christie's, London #527/R est:600-800
£1300 $2158 €1885 Steam yacht Dobhran lying in a Mediterranean harbour (26x45cm-10x18in) s.i. panel. 12-Jun-3 Christie's, London #540/R est:800-1200
£2000 $3320 €2900 Shipping off Gibraltar with fleet in harbour, morning and evening sceens (17x25cm-7x10in) s. panel pair. 12-Jun-3 Christie's, London #505/R est:1200-1800
£2400 $3984 €3480 Spanish brigantine under full sail (48x67cm-19x26in) s. 12-Jun-3 Christie's, London #543/R est:1200-1800
£3500 $5810 €5075 Three master lying at anchor in Port Mahon, Minorca (25x42cm-10x17in) init.d.1878 oil on white metal. 12-Jun-3 Christie's, London #539/R est:1500-2000
£5000 $8300 €7250 Spanish three masted barque Ignacio Fuster under full sail (48x67cm-19x26in) s.d.1879. 12-Jun-3 Christie's, London #519/R est:2000-3000
£6500 $10790 €9425 Spanish paddle frigate Herman Cortes towing Amistad into port, 3 December 1872 (46x68cm-18x27in) s.i. 12-Jun-3 Christie's, London #532/R est:3000-5000

VIDAL, Gustave (?) ?
£242 $382 €363 Berger (61x107cm-24x42in) s. prov. 18-Nov-2 Waddingtons, Toronto #230/R (C.D 600)
£469 $750 €704 Coastal scene with boats and figures (53x64cm-21x25in) s. 18-May-3 Jeffery Burchard, Florida #100/R

VIDAL, Louis (attrib) (1754-1807) French
Works on paper
£3077 $4769 €4800 Plante a racines decouvertes (58x46cm-23x18in) gouache. 4-Dec-2 Libert, Castor, Paris #22

VIDAL, Louis (1831-1892) French
Sculpture
£1250 $1988 €1800 Cerf (54x38x17cm-21x15x7in) s. brown green pat bronze. 30-Apr-3 Tajan, Paris #43

VIDAL, Louis (1935-1991) French
£324 $518 €450 Le laboureur (46x55cm-18x22in) s. 18-May-3 Eric Pillon, Calais #136/R

VIDAL, Margarita Hahn (1919-) American
£609 $950 €914 Floral study (28x23cm-11x9in) s. masonite. 12-Apr-3 Weschler, Washington #581/R est:800-1200
£3630 $5300 €5445 Splendour (99x64cm-39x25in) 18-May-2 Altermann Galleries, Santa Fe #253/R

VIEGENER, Eberhard (1890-1969) German
£343 $535 €515 View of Mols with vessels and houses (70x102cm-28x40in) mono.d.1953. 11-Nov-2 Rasmussen, Vejle #60/R (D.KR 4000)
£962 $1490 €1500 Soester Boerde in late summer (69x104cm-27x41in) mono.d.43 i.verso plywood. 7-Dec-2 Van Ham, Cologne #577/R est:2500
£1307 $2144 €2000 Cornfields with distant villages (51x74cm-20x29in) mono.d.1941 s.i. verso panel. 8-Feb-3 Hans Stahl, Hamburg #61/R est:2900
£7051 $10929 €11000 Sleeping peasant (29x22cm-11x9in) s.d.1924 s.i.d.verso panel. 4-Dec-2 Lempertz, Koln #1092/R est:14000-15000

VIEGERS, Bernardus Petrus (1886-1947) Dutch
£384 $600 €576 Evening street scene with figures (54x44cm-21x17in) s. 11-Nov-2 Stephan Welz, Johannesburg #19 (SA.R 6000)
£397 $620 €596 Farmhouse in winter (40x60cm-16x24in) 11-Nov-2 Stephan Welz, Johannesburg #429 (SA.R 6200)
£532 $862 €750 Fenced in meadow (39x50cm-15x20in) s. canvas on board. 26-May-3 Glerum, Amsterdam #44/R
£625 $1031 €900 Het Witte Huis, Rotterdam (30x24cm-12x9in) s. 1-Jul-3 Christie's, Amsterdam #179
£704 $1134 €1000 Lutheran church in Amsterdam (45x40cm-18x16in) s. prov. 7-May-3 Vendue Huis, Gravenhage #49/R
£705 $1099 €1058 Canal scene, winter (40x50cm-16x20in) s. 11-Nov-2 Stephan Welz, Johannesburg #430 (SA.R 11000)
£732 $1143 €1150 Peasant in yard (31x43cm-12x17in) s. 6-Nov-2 Vendue Huis, Gravenhage #19
£764 $1260 €1100 Swans by a bridge (50x75cm-20x30in) s. 1-Jul-3 Christie's, Amsterdam #180
£972 $1604 €1400 Bridge in autumn (40x50cm-16x20in) s. 1-Jul-3 Christie's, Amsterdam #138
£1019 $1590 €1600 Caravan scene with figures (38x48cm-15x19in) s. 6-Nov-2 Vendue Huis, Gravenhage #1/R est:1000-1200
£1111 $1833 €1600 Riverside cottage (39x50cm-15x20in) s. 1-Jul-3 Christie's, Amsterdam #98 est:300-500
£1127 $1814 €1600 Farmer feeding hens in the country near Nunspeet (37x60cm-15x24in) s. lit. 7-May-3 Vendue Huis, Gravenhage #50/R est:1800-2000
£1135 $1838 €1600 Corn stacks (49x59cm-19x23in) s. 26-May-3 Glerum, Amsterdam #166 est:500-700
£1185 $1849 €1778 View of a Dutch town (63x100cm-25x39in) 11-Nov-2 Stephan Welz, Johannesburg #431/R est:7000-10000 (SA.R 18500)
£1206 $1953 €1700 View of a town on a river (23x44cm-9x17in) s. panel. 26-May-3 Glerum, Amsterdam #143 est:800-1200
£1389 $2292 €2000 Mill at dusk (59x51cm-23x20in) s. 1-Jul-3 Christie's, Amsterdam #159/R est:1800-2200
£1549 $2494 €2200 Town view in winter (45x57cm-18x22in) s. 7-May-3 Vendue Huis, Gravenhage #65/R est:2000-3000
£1698 $2717 €2547 Dutch canal landscape in winter (38x54cm-15x21in) s. 17-Mar-3 Philippe Schuler, Zurich #4657/R est:2500-3000 (S.FR 3600)
£1972 $3175 €2800 Flower market, probably Delft (38x48cm-15x19in) s. 7-May-3 Vendue Huis, Gravenhage #51/R est:2000-2200
£2763 $4476 €4200 Hollands Spoor Station. The Hague (14x18cm-6x7in) s. cardboard pair. 21-Jan-3 Christie's, Amsterdam #331/R est:2500-3500
£3521 $5669 €5000 Farm in winter (49x59cm-19x23in) s. lit. 7-May-3 Vendue Huis, Gravenhage #520/R est:3600-4000
Prints
£5894 $9194 €8841 Mick Jagger (110x73cm-43x29in) s.num.30/50 col silkscreen also signed by Mick Jagger. 11-Nov-2 Stephan Welz, Johannesburg #444/R est:60000-90000 (SA.R 92000)

VIEGERS, Emile H P (1921-) Dutch?
£2420 $3776 €3800 Le Marais, Paris (70x60cm-28x24in) s. 6-Nov-2 Vendue Huis, Gravenhage #585/R est:2500-3000

VIEILLARD, Lucien (1923-) French
£637 $993 €1000 Neige a Saint-Victor (32x40cm-13x16in) s. 5-Nov-2 Tajan, Paris #80/R

£955 $1490 €1500 Avenue de la Gare a Feletin (46x55cm-18x22in) s. 5-Nov-2 Tajan, Paris #132/R

VIEIRA DA SILVA, Maria Elena (1908-1992) French/Portuguese
£13291 $21000 €21000 Following (21x62cm-8x24in) s. tempera paper prov. 27-Nov-2 Tajan, Paris #9/R est:15000-22000
£58710 $92761 €91000 Effet de nuit (55x46cm-22x18in) s.d.1956 prov.lit. 19-Dec-2 Claude Aguttes, Neuilly #151/R est:60000
£60000 $92400 €90000 Le bout du monde (97x130cm-38x51in) s.d.86 prov.exhib.lit. 22-Oct-2 Sotheby's, London #438/R est:90000-120000
£115000 $188600 €172500 Composition (73x92cm-29x36in) s. s.i.on stretcher prov.exhib.lit. 6-Feb-3 Sotheby's, London #23/R est:120000
£158621 $250621 €230000 Untitled (65x81cm-26x32in) s.d.49 prov.exhib.lit. 2-Apr-3 Christie's, Paris #13/R est:120000-180000
Works on paper
£10000 $16700 €14500 Echafaudage (29x13cm-11x5in) s.d.54 d.54 verso gouache prov.exhib.lit. 26-Jun-3 Sotheby's, London #202/R est:8000-12000
£11282 $17713 €17600 Composition (23x15cm-9x6in) s. gouache W/C crayon ink prov.exhib. 15-Dec-2 Perrin, Versailles #75/R est:20000
£14493 $23768 €20000 Et puis voila (24x15cm-9x6in) s. gouache Indian ink. 29-May-3 Lempertz, Koln #946/R est:18000-20000
£25000 $41000 €37500 La rue (63x50cm-25x20in) s.d.56 gouache paper on canvas prov.exhib.lit. 7-Feb-3 Sotheby's, London #228/R est:25000-35000
£29167 $48125 €42000 Sans titre (35x69cm-14x27in) s.d.56 W/C prov.lit. 1-Jul-3 Artcurial Briest, Paris #491/R est:25000-35000
£55000 $90200 €82500 Composition aux damiers bleus (48x62cm-19x24in) s.d.49 gouache prov.exhib.lit. 7-Feb-3 Sotheby's, London #229/R est:30000-40000

VIERIN, Emmanuel (1869-1954) Belgian
£6090 $9561 €9500 Vue de beguinage (110x158cm-43x62in) s. 11-Dec-2 Hotel des Ventes Mosan, Brussels #289/R est:1800-2000

VIERTEL, Carl (1772-1834) Danish
£567 $913 €851 Cupid and a half nude woman (36x45cm-14x18in) s. 11-May-3 Hindemae, Ullerslev #171/R (D.KR 6000)

VIET, Hugo (?) Swiss
£629 $1051 €900 Chalet dans la montagne (60x40cm-24x16in) 26-Jun-3 Tajan, Paris #209

VIETH, Friedrich Ludwig von (1768-1848) German
Works on paper
£769 $1208 €1200 Portrait of a man in a blue coat (10x8cm-4x3in) s. ivory oval prov. 19-Nov-2 Hamilton Osborne King, Dublin #402/R

VIETINGHOFF, Egon Alexis von (1903-1994) German
£515 $814 €773 Carline thistle (35cm-14in) s. canvas on masonite. 29-Nov-2 Zofingen, Switzerland #3109 (S.FR 1200)
£611 $954 €917 Still life with cherries in dish (50x61cm-20x24in) s. 6-Nov-2 Dobiaschofsky, Bern #1047/R (S.FR 1400)

VIETTI, Nicola (1945-) French
£261 $418 €400 Priests (40x50cm-16x20in) s. 4-Jan-3 Meeting Art, Vercelli #740
£294 $471 €450 Girl with cat (30x40cm-12x16in) s. cardboard on canvas oval. 4-Jan-3 Meeting Art, Vercelli #718
£306 $487 €450 Red rose (60x40cm-24x16in) s. 1-Mar-3 Meeting Art, Vercelli #661
£347 $552 €500 Dancing night (70x90cm-28x35in) s. s.verso. 1-May-3 Meeting Art, Vercelli #351
£359 $575 €550 Lovers (60x120cm-24x47in) s. 4-Jan-3 Meeting Art, Vercelli #732
£417 $663 €600 Three graces (50x70cm-20x28in) s. s.verso. 1-May-3 Meeting Art, Vercelli #544

VIETZE, Josef (1902-) Austrian
£476 $757 €700 Red roses (55x45cm-22x18in) s.d.58. 28-Mar-3 Bolland & Marotz, Bremen #579/R

VIGE, Jens (1864-1912) Danish
£775 $1178 €1163 Avenue in shadow (59x54cm-23x21in) init.d.89. 27-Aug-2 Rasmussen, Copenhagen #1787/R (D.KR 9000)

VIGEE, Louis (attrib) (1715-1767) French
Works on paper
£1216 $1897 €1800 Portrait de femme au manchon (64x53cm-25x21in) s.d. pastel. 26-Mar-3 Piasa, Paris #79/R

VIGEE-LEBRUN, Marie Louise Elisabeth (1755-1842) French
£432099 $700000 €648149 Portrait of Countess Kagenek as Flora (75x63cm-30x25in) s.d.1792 i.verso painted oval prov.exhib.lit. 23-Jan-3 Sotheby's, New York #78/R est:500000-700000

VIGEE-LEBRUN, Marie Louise Elisabeth (style) (1755-1842) French
£5674 $9191 €8000 Portrait du dauphin Louis Charles avec son chien (60x49cm-24x19in) 21-May-3 Piasa, Paris #373/R est:6000-8000

VIGELAND, Gustav (1869-1943) Norwegian
Sculpture
£2941 $4647 €4412 Man and woman - the embrace (23x11x16cm-9x4x6in) plaster prov.lit. 2-Dec-2 Blomqvist, Oslo #357/R est:35000-40000 (N.KR 34000)

VIGER DU VIGNEAU, Jean Louis Victor (1819-1879) French
£1154 $1800 €1731 Andoche junot, duc d'abrantes (64x53cm-25x21in) s.i. 9-Oct-2 Doyle, New York #117 est:1400-1800

VIGH, Bertolan (1890-1946) Hungarian
£1702 $2689 €2553 Harlequin and Columbine (100x73cm-39x29in) 2-Dec-2 Rasmussen, Copenhagen #1727/R est:25000 (D.KR 20000)

VIGIER DU VIGNEAU, Jean Louis (1819-1875) French
£2552 $4083 €3700 Bouquet de fleurs variees sur entablement (87x68cm-34x27in) s.d.1855. 14-Mar-3 Libert, Castor, Paris #42/R

VIGNAL, Pierre (1855-1925) French
Works on paper
£571 $884 €890 Place de la Republique, Paris (18x25cm-7x10in) s. W/C. 7-Dec-2 Martinot & Savignat, Pontoise #6
£1115 $1784 €1550 Paris, la Place de la Republique (17x24cm-7x9in) s. W/C. 18-May-3 Eric Pillon, Calais #14/R

VIGNALI, Jacopo (1592-1664) Italian
Works on paper
£3497 $5000 €5246 Moses defending the daughters of Jericho (23x40cm-9x16in) black chk htd white. 23-Jan-3 Swann Galleries, New York #66/R est:1200-1800

VIGNALI, Jacopo (attrib) (1592-1664) Italian
£2264 $3668 €3283 Portrait of young man with open shirt (72x58cm-28x23in) prov. 24-May-3 Galerie Gloggner, Luzern #116/R est:3800-4500 (S.FR 4800)
£13924 $22000 €22000 Isabelle, Zerlino and the hermit (115x148cm-45x58in) 2-Dec-2 Finarte, Milan #185/R est:22000
Works on paper
£1818 $2600 €2727 Seated male academy (22x16cm-9x6in) red chk. 23-Jan-3 Swann Galleries, New York #67/R est:700-1000

VIGNANDO, Clea (20th C) French
£324 $518 €450 Paysage elephant (130x130cm-51x51in) s.verso. 18-May-3 Neret-Minet, Paris #104

VIGNANI, Giuseppe (1932-) Italian
£458 $732 €700 Chasing (40x60cm-16x24in) s. 4-Jan-3 Meeting Art, Vercelli #431

VIGNATO, Elisabetta (1964-) Italian
£2411 $3906 €3400 Stanche di sentire (130x160cm-51x63in) 20-May-3 Porro, Milan #55/R est:3300-3500

VIGNE, Edouard de (1808-1866) Belgian
£5068 $7905 €7500 Femme dans un paysage montagneux (115x160cm-45x63in) s. 25-Mar-3 Campo & Campo, Antwerp #58/R est:6000-8000

VIGNOLES, Andre (1920-) French
£1100 $1793 €1650 Nature morte avec fraises et bouteille de vin (73x93cm-29x37in) s.d.61 prov. 3-Feb-3 Bonhams, New Bond Street #93/R est:1200-1800

VIGNON, Claude (1593-1670) French
£1613 $2548 €2500 Larmes de Saint-Pierre (23x17cm-9x7in) copper. 18-Dec-2 Beaussant & Lefèvre, Paris #22/R
£2581 $4077 €4000 Joseph et Jesus (25x18cm-10x7in) copper. 18-Dec-2 Piasa, Paris #70/R
£7742 $12232 €12000 Saint-Paul (111x84cm-44x33in) 20-Dec-2 Tajan, Paris #112/R est:15000

VIGNON, Jules de (1815-1885) French
£1115 $1762 €1673 Still life of fruit (55x65cm-22x26in) s. 5-Apr-3 Rasmussen, Havnen #2102/R est:15000 (D.KR 12000)

£17000 $26350 €25500 Vivanti, Italian dance (154x202cm-61x80in) s. 4-Dec-2 Christie's, London #106/R est:18000-24000

VIGNON, Victor Alfred Paul (1847-1909) French
£850 $1326 €1275 Late summer landscape with corn stooks (22x34cm-9x13in) s. panel. 13-Sep-2 Jacobs & Hunt, Petersfield #183/R
£4200 $6468 €6300 Verre et peches (31x42cm-12x17in) s. prov. 23-Oct-2 Sotheby's, Olympia #634/R est:3500-5000

VIGNY, Sylvain (1902-1970) French
£253 $395 €400 Village (50x65cm-20x26in) s. oil gouache paper. 20-Oct-2 Chayette & Cheval, Paris #83
£253 $395 €400 Fleurs (68x53cm-27x21in) s. panel. 20-Oct-2 Chayette & Cheval, Paris #81
£265 $432 €400 Young man with hat (59x46cm-23x18in) s. masonite. 28-Jan-3 Dorotheum, Vienna #116/R
£278 $441 €400 La place du village (46x55cm-18x22in) s. panel. 29-Apr-3 Artcurial Briest, Paris #288
£286 $427 €429 Bouquet de fleurs au vase transparent (56x42cm-22x17in) s. board. 25-Jun-2 Koller, Zurich #6658 (S.FR 650)
£336 $540 €500 Village (61x73cm-24x29in) s. 23-Feb-3 Lesieur & Le Bars, Le Havre #151
£348 $543 €550 Rue animee (50x61cm-20x24in) s. 20-Oct-2 Chayette & Cheval, Paris #82
£350 $546 €550 Scene de plage. 6-Nov-2 Gioffredo, Nice #118
£369 $594 €550 Crepuscule sur la mer (65x81cm-26x32in) s.d.1959. 23-Feb-3 Lesieur & Le Bars, Le Havre #150
£380 $592 €600 Fleurs (62x46cm-24x18in) s. panel. 20-Oct-2 Chayette & Cheval, Paris #78
£409 $650 €614 Promenade dans un parc (36x53cm-14x21in) s.d.38 paper. 7-Mar-3 Skinner, Boston #527/R
£601 $938 €950 Bouquets (92x60cm-36x24in) s. 20-Oct-2 Chayette & Cheval, Paris #79
£1054 $1677 €1550 Vase de fleurs (50x38cm-20x15in) s. cardboard. 3-Mar-3 Claude Boisgirard, Paris #100 est:1000-1200
Works on paper
£331 $530 €480 Portrait de jeune fille (44x28cm-17x11in) s. W/C. 12-Mar-3 E & Eve, Paris #120

VIGON, Louis Jacques (1897-1985) French
£261 $421 €400 Riviere traversant le lac, Var (38x55cm-15x22in) s. 19-Jan-3 Feletin, Province #136
£516 $815 €800 Petit port d'Agay (38x46cm-15x18in) s. 18-Dec-2 Ferri, Paris #108

VIHOS, George (1937-) American
£962 $1500 €1443 Untitled (198x259cm-78x102in) 11-Apr-3 Du Mouchelle, Detroit #2059/R est:2000-3000
£1380 $2250 €2001 Untitled (198x259cm-78x102in) 18-Jul-3 Du Mouchelle, Detroit #2069/R est:1500-2000

VIKE, Harald (1906-1987) Australian/Norwegian
£287 $436 €431 Gorge, Bachus March (43x55cm-17x22in) s. board. 27-Aug-2 Goodman, Sydney #239 (A.D 800)

VIKHAGEN, Havard (1952-) Norwegian
£1681 $2657 €2522 Landscape (50x61cm-20x24in) init. panel. 28-Apr-3 Blomqvist, Oslo #401/R est:20000-25000 (N.KR 19000)
£2163 $3417 €3245 Composition (63x58cm-25x23in) init. 2-Dec-2 Blomqvist, Oslo #470/R est:35000-40000 (N.KR 25000)

VIKSTEN, Hans (1926-1987) Swedish
£240 $365 €360 Chemist's shop (82x66cm-32x26in) s.i.d.19/6-61. 16-Aug-2 Lilla Bukowskis, Stockholm #741 (S.KR 3500)

VILA PUIG, Juan (1890-1963) Spanish
£329 $533 €500 Landscape with river (25x43cm-10x17in) s. board. 21-Jan-3 Ansorena, Madrid #218
£346 $540 €550 Landscape (33x42cm-13x17in) s. 23-Sep-2 Durán, Madrid #597/R
£362 $586 €550 Landscape (41x51cm-16x20in) s. 21-Jan-3 Ansorena, Madrid #227
£566 $883 €900 Landscape (47x57cm-19x22in) s. s.verso. 17-Sep-2 Segre, Madrid #81/R
£617 $901 €950 Landscape (12x19cm-5x7in) s. board. 17-Jun-2 Ansorena, Madrid #118/R
£2258 $3568 €3500 Landscape with bridge (73x100cm-29x39in) s. s.verso. 17-Dec-2 Durán, Madrid #211/R

VILA Y PRADES, Julio (1873-1930) Spanish
£2453 $3777 €3900 Military parade for Alfonso XIII (25x62cm-10x24in) s.i.d.1905. 28-Oct-2 Segre, Madrid #34/R

VILADECANS, Joan Pere (1948-) Spanish
£927 $1511 €1400 Barba Juana (72x52cm-28x20in) s.d.1980 paint collage paper exhib.lit. 11-Feb-3 Segre, Madrid #225/R

VILAIN, Walter (1938-) Belgian
£253 $400 €400 Composition geometrique. 2-Dec-2 Amberes, Antwerp #1372
Works on paper
£348 $550 €550 Ce ne sont que festons. Ce ne sont qu'astragales (62x46cm-24x18in) s.i.d.27/12/1990 wash pair. 2-Dec-2 Amberes, Antwerp #1371

VILALLONGA, Jesus Carlos de (1927-) Canadian
£208 $325 €312 Amor y austronaute (41x51cm-16x20in) s.i.d.63 acrylic on masonite. 25-Mar-3 Ritchie, Toronto #190 (C.D 485)
£214 $332 €321 Toro (51x40cm-20x16in) s.d.58 masonite prov. 24-Sep-2 Ritchie, Toronto #3216 (C.D 520)
£215 $335 €312 Before the combat (81x41cm-32x16in) s.i.d.59 prov. 26-Mar-3 Walker's, Ottawa #430/R (C.D 500)
£222 $350 €333 Baigneuse (41x30cm-16x12in) s. board prov. 14-Nov-2 Heffel, Vancouver #210 (C.D 550)
£226 $351 €339 Head of a woman (30x40cm-12x16in) s.d.66 acrylic on board. 3-Dec-2 Joyner, Toronto #476 (C.D 550)
£269 $430 €404 Leda (51x41cm-20x16in) s.d.1977 s.verso board prov. 15-May-3 Heffel, Vancouver #231 (C.D 600)
£279 $435 €419 La fille au yoyo (51x41cm-20x16in) s.d.74 acrylic on masonite. 25-Mar-3 Ritchie, Toronto #192/R (C.D 650)
£288 $447 €432 Niki (75x50cm-30x20in) s.d.64 prov. 3-Dec-2 Joyner, Toronto #502 (C.D 700)
£309 $478 €464 Apparition - La Dona de Cadaques (50x75cm-20x30in) s. indis d. board prov. 3-Dec-2 Joyner, Toronto #501 (C.D 750)
£346 $542 €519 Profile of a young woman (41x30cm-16x12in) s.d.72 board prov. 10-Dec-2 Pinneys, Montreal #198 (C.D 850)
£369 $572 €554 Pregnant woman (61x30cm-24x12in) s. masonite prov. 24-Sep-2 Ritchie, Toronto #3217 (C.D 900)
£403 $637 €605 Testa fina (41x30cm-16x12in) s.d.1968 board. 14-Nov-2 Heffel, Vancouver #214 est:700-900 (C.D 1000)
£412 $638 €618 Myself and I. Truth of love (75x50cm-30x20in) s.d. board two. 3-Dec-2 Joyner, Toronto #500 est:300-500 (C.D 1000)
£429 $670 €644 Maternite no.2 (30x25cm-12x10in) s. acrylic on masonite. 25-Mar-3 Ritchie, Toronto #191/R est:900-1000 (C.D 1000)
£429 $670 €622 Self portrait with woman in red (61x91cm-24x36in) s.d.59 board prov. 26-Mar-3 Walker's, Ottawa #429/R est:1200-1600 (C.D 1000)
£493 $789 €740 Head of a woman (41x30cm-16x12in) s. board prov. 15-May-3 Heffel, Vancouver #151 est:700-900 (C.D 1100)
£605 $956 €908 Tour male, Tour femelle (61x51cm-24x20in) i.d.1979 i.verso board prov. 14-Nov-2 Heffel, Vancouver #212 est:800-1200 (C.D 1500)
£726 $1147 €1089 Cavalier (51x41cm-20x16in) s.i. masonite prov. 18-Nov-2 Sotheby's, Toronto #65/R est:2000-2500 (C.D 1800)
£806 $1274 €1209 Wave (61x51cm-24x20in) s. s.i.verso masonite prov. 18-Nov-2 Sotheby's, Toronto #63/R est:2500-3000 (C.D 2000)
£1008 $1593 €1512 Mere univers (101x75cm-40x30in) s.d.1982 s.d.verso board prov. 14-Nov-2 Heffel, Vancouver #213 est:1500-2000 (C.D 2500)
£1073 $1674 €1610 Le genie de Sawama (51x61cm-20x24in) s. tempera isorel. 25-Mar-3 Igor de Saint Hippolyte, Montreal #146 (C.D 2500)
£1109 $1752 €1664 Palais de cristal, Serenade (122x122cm-48x48in) s.d.1987 s.verso board prov. 14-Nov-2 Heffel, Vancouver #215/R est:2500-3500 (C.D 2750)
£1111 $1722 €1667 Wheel of life (80x62cm-31x24in) s.d.76 board prov. 3-Dec-2 Joyner, Toronto #234/R est:1500-2000 (C.D 2700)
£1202 $1875 €1803 Adeau Vallmitjana (63x91cm-25x36in) s. i.verso panel. 25-Mar-3 Igor de Saint Hippolyte, Montreal #145 (C.D 2800)
£1317 $2041 €1976 L'espoir (75x100cm-30x39in) s.d.76 board prov. 3-Dec-2 Joyner, Toronto #194/R est:2000-2500 (C.D 3200)
£1333 $2187 €2000 Houses (51x40cm-20x16in) s.d.75 masonite prov. 27-May-3 Sotheby's, Toronto #26/R est:2500-3000 (C.D 3000)
Works on paper
£143 $222 €215 Skating party (30x60cm-12x24in) s. mixed media masonite prov. 24-Sep-2 Ritchie, Toronto #3214/R (C.D 350)

VILANUS, E (?) ?
Sculpture
£1401 $2186 €2200 Sapho (56cm-22in) bronze. 5-Nov-2 Vendu Notarishuis, Rotterdam #5041/R est:2200-2600

VILARO, Jorge Paez (1922-) Uruguayan
Works on paper
£253 $395 €400 La mina es un lugo (51x40cm-20x16in) s. wax chk. 15-Oct-2 Dorotheum, Vienna #151/R

VILATO, Javier (1921-2000) French
£800 $1240 €1200 Abstract, la fem (81x58cm-32x23in) s. d.1960 verso. 26-Sep-2 Lane, Penzance #60/R

VILLA BASOLS, Guillermo (1917-) Colombian
£621 $987 €900 Cadaques (50x65cm-20x26in) s. s.i.d.1990 verso. 4-Mar-3 Ansorena, Madrid #133/R

VILLA, Miguel (1901-1988) Spanish
£613 $968 €950 San Diego beach (19x24cm-7x9in) s.i.d.1983 verso oil collage prov. 17-Dec-2 Segre, Madrid #106/R
£645 $1019 €1000 Tide (22x27cm-9x11in) s.i.d.1976 verso prov. 17-Dec-2 Segre, Madrid #104/R
£1538 $2431 €2400 Landscape with houses (22x28cm-9x11in) s.d.1962 verso. 13-Nov-2 Ansorena, Madrid #46/R
£1824 $2845 €2900 Tafi Viejo (22x26cm-9x10in) s.i.d.1942 verso. 17-Sep-2 Segre, Madrid #154/R
£2270 $3677 €3200 Autorretrato (27x22cm-11x9in) s.i.d.1947 verso. 20-May-3 Segre, Madrid #120/R est:3600
£5172 $8172 €7500 Boat (46x55cm-18x22in) i.d.1951 verso. 7-Apr-3 Castellana, Madrid #465/R est:6000

VILLA, Rino (1904-) Italian
£252 $392 €400 By Conegliano (51x45cm-20x18in) s.d.1939. 20-Sep-2 Semenzato, Venice #564

VILLACRES, Cesar A (1880-?) Ecuadorian
£541 $850 €812 Rainy street scene, Paris (51x61cm-20x24in) s. 14-Dec-2 Weschler, Washington #610/R

VILLALBA, Dario (1939-) Spanish
£1069 $1668 €1700 Double dog (102x70cm-40x28in) s.d.1979 oil emulsion canvas on cardboard exhib.lit. 17-Sep-2 Segre, Madrid #277/R
£3205 $4968 €5000 Integration (200x160cm-79x63in) s.i.d.1982 verso oil mixed media. 7-Dec-2 De Vuyst, Lokeren #400/R est:3500-4000
£5705 $9185 €8500 Integration 82 (200x160cm-79x63in) s.d.82. 18-Feb-3 Durán, Madrid #205/R
£5806 $9174 €9000 Two coats (116x89cm-46x35in) s.d.1985 s.i.d.verso oil collage photograph prov. 17-Dec-2 Segre, Madrid #168/R est:9000

VILLALTA YBARRA, B (?) Spanish
£570 $883 €900 Northern landscape (73x91cm-29x36in) s.d.47. 26-Sep-2 Castellana, Madrid #8/R

VILLAMENA, Francesco (attrib) (1566-1624) Italian
Works on paper
£1905 $3029 €2800 Saint Hilarion de Chypre (27x19cm-11x7in) pen ink. 24-Mar-3 Tajan, Paris #13/R

VILLANI, Gennaro (1885-1948) Italian
£531 $844 €780 Donkey resting (12x16cm-5x6in) s. cardboard. 1-Mar-3 Meeting Art, Vercelli #221
£680 $1082 €1000 Female nude at the piano (60x43cm-24x17in) s. board. 18-Mar-3 Finarte, Milan #148/R

VILLANIS, E (19th C) French
Sculpture
£993 $1619 €1500 Mignon. green pat bronze. 17-Feb-3 Amberes, Antwerp #450
£1500 $2400 €2250 Lucrece (54cm-21in) s. bronze. 15-May-3 Christie's, Kensington #379/R est:1800-2500
£1656 $2699 €2500 Saida. brown pat bronze Cast Societe des bronzes de Paris. 17-Feb-3 Amberes, Antwerp #451

VILLANIS, Emmanuele (19th C) Italian
Sculpture
£1076 $1678 €1700 Laila (50cm-20in) s.i. gilt brown pat bronze. 16-Oct-2 Hotel des Ventes Mosan, Brussels #258 est:500-600
£1076 $1678 €1700 Mignon (57cm-22in) s. gilt pat bronze. 16-Sep-2 Horta, Bruxelles #100
£1083 $1689 €1700 Diane (65cm-26in) s. alabaster. 11-Nov-2 Horta, Bruxelles #30 est:1500-2000
£1122 $1739 €1750 La Sibylle (52cm-20in) i. brown pat.bronze Cast.Societe des Bronzes de Paris. 5-Dec-2 Schopman, Hamburg #389 est:1500
£1154 $1788 €1800 Lalla Roukh (42cm-17in) s. dark pat bronze. 9-Dec-2 Horta, Bruxelles #134 est:1800-2200
£1282 $1987 €2000 Lola (49cm-19in) s. brown pat bronze. 9-Dec-2 Horta, Bruxelles #133/R est:2000-3000
£1361 $2163 €2000 Seule (50x33x16cm-20x13x6in) s.i. green brown pat.bronze. 19-Mar-3 Hotel des Ventes Mosan, Brussels #321 est:800-1200
£1772 $2765 €2800 Esmeralda (40cm-16in) s. green pat bronze. 15-Oct-2 Horta, Bruxelles #232
£1899 $2962 €3000 Peinture (66cm-26in) s. Carrara marble. 15-Oct-2 Horta, Bruxelles #233
£2532 $3949 €4000 Sapho (90cm-35in) s.st.f.Societe des Bronzes brown pat bronze. 16-Sep-2 Horta, Bruxelles #55
£2600 $4134 €3900 Lucrece (38cm-15in) s. bronze. 27-Feb-3 Sotheby's, Olympia #69/R est:1500-1800
£2848 $4500 €4272 Esmeralda (58cm-23in) bronze. 15-Nov-2 Du Mouchelle, Detroit #2039/R est:4000-6000

VILLANUEVA, Tobias (20th C) Mexican
£828 $1300 €1242 El caballero (130x89cm-51x35in) s.d.1940. 14-Dec-2 Charlton Hall, Columbia #207/R est:800-1200

VILLAR, Isabel (1934-) Spanish
Prints
£4194 $6626 €6500 Shepherdess (40x30cm-16x12in) s. num.140/180 engraving. 18-Dec-2 Ansorena, Madrid #1015
Works on paper
£270 $422 €400 Eve in the Paradise (23x33cm-9x13in) s.d.74 felt-tip pen dr. 25-Mar-3 Durán, Madrid #64/R

VILLASENOR, Manuel Lopez (1924-1996) Spanish
£1299 $1974 €2000 Sarita (53x40cm-21x16in) s.d.1953. 3-Jul-2 Castellana, Madrid #150/R

VILLE, Vickers de (1856-1925) British
£1000 $1540 €1500 Kite flyers (23x23cm-9x9in) s. canvasboard prov. 5-Sep-2 Christie's, Kensington #216/R est:400-600
£1400 $2226 €2100 On the common, kite flying (41x51cm-16x20in) s.d.07 i.d.verso. 6-Mar-3 Christie's, Kensington #596/R est:1000-1500

VILLEGAS Y CORDERO, Jose (1848-1922) Spanish
£743 $1159 €1100 Arabian scene (9x6cm-4x2in) s. cardboard. 25-Mar-3 Durán, Madrid #82/R
£1887 $2943 €3000 Dinner (28x48cm-11x19in) s. 8-Oct-2 Ansorena, Madrid #472/R
£3962 $6142 €6300 Still life of fruit and flowers (49x60cm-19x24in) s. 7-Oct-2 Ansorena, Madrid #57/R
£13158 $21316 €20000 Woman with fan (70x52cm-28x20in) s. 21-Jan-3 Ansorena, Madrid #162/R est:15000
£15101 $24312 €22500 Woman and dogs (73x37cm-29x15in) s.d.1898. 18-Feb-3 Durán, Madrid #239/R est:4500
£18456 $29715 €27500 View of Venice (48x73cm-19x29in) s.d.89 exhib.lit. 18-Feb-3 Durán, Madrid #221/R
Works on paper
£1800 $2808 €2700 Collecting water from the well (75x36cm-30x14in) s. W/C gouache. 17-Sep-2 Sotheby's, Olympia #246/R est:2000-3000

VILLEGLE, Jacques de la (1926-) French
Works on paper
£313 $494 €450 Arrachage (17x11cm-7x4in) s. torn poster cardboard. 28-Apr-3 Cornette de St.Cyr, Paris #457
£2774 $4383 €4300 Affiches (30x35cm-12x14in) d.1970 verso torn posters. 19-Dec-2 Ruellan, Paris #133/R
£3671 $5800 €5800 Place de la Bourse (65x54cm-26x21in) s. s.i.d.1982 verso torn posters. 27-Nov-2 Tajan, Paris #38/R est:8000
£4965 $8291 €7000 Carrefour Vavin-Raspail (97x75cm-38x30in) s.d.verso poster collage. 18-Jun-3 Pierre Berge, Paris #99/R est:6000-7000
£6383 $10660 €9000 Square Emile-Chautemps, Paris (76x86cm-30x34in) s.d. i.verso poster collage. 18-Jun-3 Pierre Berge, Paris #94/R est:6000-7000
£7547 $11698 €12000 Turbigo-reaumur (177x249cm-70x98in) s. i.d.1986 verso torn poster canvas lit. 30-Oct-2 Artcurial Briest, Paris #457/R est:10000-15000
£9028 $14264 €13000 Gaite-Montparnasse (250x217cm-98x85in) s.i.d.mai 1987 verso torn poster on canvas prov.exhib.lit. 27-Apr-3 Perrin, Versailles #94/R est:15000-18000
£9434 $14623 €15000 55 rue Vercingetorix (81x64cm-32x25in) s. s.i.d.verso torn poster canvas. 30-Oct-2 Artcurial Briest, Paris #456/R est:10000-15000
£9780 $15061 €15550 Rue Saint-Louis (69x96cm-27x38in) torn posters exec.1964 prov.exhib.lit. 26-Oct-2 Cornette de St.Cyr, Paris #41/R est:10000

VILLELIA, Moises (1928-) Spanish
Sculpture
£1793 $2833 €2600 Composition (44x7x6cm-17x3x2in) painted wood. 1-Apr-3 Segre, Madrid #189/R
£1931 $3051 €2800 Composition (34x18x7cm-13x7x3in) painted wood. 1-Apr-3 Segre, Madrid #190/R
£2194 $3466 €3400 Untitled (44x12x13cm-17x5x5in) bamboo stone prov. 17-Dec-2 Segre, Madrid #136/R est:1300

VILLENEUVE (?) French
Works on paper
£535 $829 €850 Allegory of music (55x36cm-22x14in) s.i.d.1767 ochre. 1-Oct-2 Dorotheum, Vienna #140/R

VILLENEUVE, Arthur (1910-1990) Canadian
£287 $445 €431 Village (23x30cm-9x12in) s.d.1974. 24-Sep-2 Iegor de Saint Hippolyte, Montreal #124 (C.D 700)

£685 $1117 €1028 Val Jalbert 1924 (51x61cm-20x24in) s.i.d.3/12/64. 12-Feb-3 Iegor de Saint Hippolyte, Montreal #192 (C.D 1700)

VILLENEUVE, Cecile (1824-1901) French
Miniatures
£1200 $1968 €1740 Claire Roussel in a black velvet dress (10cm-4in) s.i.d.1859 ormolu easel frame. 3-Jun-3 Christie's, London #221/R est:1200-1800

VILLEON, Emmanuel de la (1858-1944) French
£478 $745 €750 Printemps, paysage de legende (23x35cm-9x14in) s. panel lit. 7-Nov-2 Claude Aguttes, Neuilly #58
£566 $877 €900 Paysage hivernal (33x50cm-13x20in) s.d.1901. 4-Oct-2 Tajan, Paris #135
£833 $1308 €1300 Sous-bois (38x46cm-15x18in) s. panel exhib. 21-Nov-2 Neret-Minet, Paris #35
£862 $1440 €1250 Neige a Yonville, Somme (27x46cm-11x18in) s. cardboard on canvas lit. 10-Jul-3 Artcurial Briest, Paris #134 est:1500-2000
£2041 $3245 €3000 Printemps. s. panel. 26-Feb-3 Fraysse & Associes, Paris #27/R est:3000-4000
£2158 $3453 €3000 La vallon au printemps (32x40cm-13x16in) s. 18-May-3 Eric Pillon, Calais #50/R
£2377 $3970 €3400 Automne, le bois de Salvar, Nievres (55x46cm-22x18in) s. exhib.lit. 26-Jun-3 Tajan, Paris #225/R est:4000-6000
£2390 $3704 €3800 Neige a Salvar, Nievre (59x48cm-23x19in) s.d.1929 lit. 30-Oct-2 Artcurial Briest, Paris #179/R est:4000-5000
£2642 $4094 €4200 Conte Breton (141x170cm-56x67in) s.d.1912. 30-Oct-2 Artcurial Briest, Paris #181/R est:4500-6000
£3357 $5606 €4800 Arbres au printemps (65x49cm-26x19in) s.d. 26-Jun-3 Tajan, Paris #224/R est:5000-7000
£3846 $6038 €6000 Repos dans le verger de Bel Air, Suisse (55x65cm-22x26in) s. painted 1896 prov.exhib.lit. 21-Nov-2 Neret-Minet, Paris #34/R est:3500-4500
£4304 $6714 €6800 Etang sous les arbres (60x73cm-24x29in) s. lit. 20-Oct-2 Anaf, Lyon #186/R
Works on paper
£552 $922 €800 Ile de la rande jatte (60x43cm-24x17in) s.i.d.1890 graphite col crayon lit. 10-Jul-3 Artcurial Briest, Paris #2/R
£1218 $1888 €1900 Landscape wit htrees (20x29cm-8x11in) s. W/C pencil. 4-Dec-2 Lempertz, Koln #851/R est:1500

VILLERET, François Etienne (1800-1866) French
Works on paper
£280 $468 €406 Antwerp Cathedral (23x15cm-9x6in) s. W/C. 24-Jun-3 Bonhams, Knightsbridge #165/R
£1410 $2186 €2200 Vue de l'hotel Saint-Paul. Vue du couvent des Celestins, Paris (13x18cm-5x7in) s. W/Cgouache over crayon pair. 4-Dec-2 Piasa, Paris #171/R

VILLERI, Jean (1896-1982) French
£647 $1036 €900 L'infini a notre mesure (147x114cm-58x45in) s.d.verso. 18-May-3 Charbonneaux, Paris #212/R

VILLERS, Andre (1930-) French
Works on paper
£256 $403 €400 Ex-foto (15x10cm-6x4in) s.d.69 collage prov.exhib. 24-Nov-2 Laurence Calmels, Paris #278/R
£353 $554 €550 Ex-foto (30x22cm-12x9in) s.d.70 prov.exhib. 24-Nov-2 Laurence Calmels, Paris #280/R
£503 $780 €800 Atelier d'artiste (49x58cm-19x23in) s.d.86 collage black white photo. 30-Oct-2 Artcurial Briest, Paris #748/R

VILLERS, Jacob de (1616-1667) Dutch
£2258 $3319 €3500 Landscape with waterfall (20x26cm-8x10in) panel. 20-Jun-2 Dr Fritz Nagel, Stuttgart #743/R

VILLODAS DE LA TORRE, Ricardo de (1846-1904) Spanish
£7692 $12154 €12000 Portrait of lady. Portrait of gentleman (103x76cm-41x30in) s.d.1897 pair. 13-Nov-2 Ansorena, Madrid #114/R est:12000
Works on paper
£409 $638 €650 Study of lady (31x22cm-12x9in) chl dr. 8-Oct-2 Ansorena, Madrid #531

VILLON, Eugène (1879-?) French
Works on paper
£513 $805 €800 Bord de Seine (21x30cm-8x12in) s. W/C. 13-Dec-2 Piasa, Paris #234

VILLON, Jacques (1875-1963) French
£1542 $2405 €2313 Marcel (22x16cm-9x6in) s.d.61 prov. 5-Nov-2 Bukowskis, Stockholm #297/R est:15000-20000 (S.KR 22000)
£2564 $4026 €4000 Village (80x63cm-31x25in) s.d.1926. 21-Nov-2 Weidler, Nurnberg #4506 est:400
£5000 $7700 €7500 Portrait de Michel Mare, architecte (35x27cm-14x11in) s.d.40 canvasboard prov. 22-Oct-2 Sotheby's, London #145/R est:8000-12000
£5864 $8327 €9500 Buste de Maggy (41x33cm-16x13in) s. s.i.d.1945 verso. 17-Mar-2 Galerie de Chartres, Chartres #159
£6000 $9240 €9000 Le quartier de veau (86x31cm-34x12in) s.d.1943 i.verso prov. 22-Oct-2 Sotheby's, London #144/R est:10000-15000
£9091 $15182 €13000 Petite maison close (13x19cm-5x7in) s. s.i.d.49 verso prov.lit. 30-Jun-3 Artcurial Briest, Paris #84/R est:10000-15000
£9615 $15096 €15000 Entree du jardin (65x981cm-26x386in) s. s.i.d.48 verso exhib.lit. 10-Dec-2 Piasa, Paris #79/R est:12000-15000
£10764 $17760 €15500 Le depart (55x65cm-22x26in) s.d.54 s.i.d.verso prov. 2-Jul-3 Artcurial Briest, Paris #672/R est:18000-25000
£11888 $19853 €17000 L'atre (46x33cm-18x13in) s.d.54 s.i.d.verso prov.lit. 30-Jun-3 Artcurial Briest, Paris #83/R est:18000-20000
£15385 $25692 €22000 Ascension, comme il vous Plaira (34x27cm-13x11in) s.d.57 s.i.d.verso prov.lit. 30-Jun-3 Artcurial Briest, Paris #65/R est:25000-35000
£19231 $30192 €30000 Styx (73x92cm-29x36in) s.d.40 i.verso lit. 10-Dec-2 Piasa, Paris #80/R est:20000-30000
£19231 $30192 €30000 Taureau noir (30x40cm-12x16in) s. s.i.d.44 verso exhib.lit. 10-Dec-2 Piasa, Paris #83/R est:10000-12000
£33333 $52333 €52000 Aile (61x50cm-24x20in) s.d.22 s.d.verso lit. 10-Dec-2 Piasa, Paris #81/R est:10000-15000
£35256 $54647 €55000 Acrobate au saut perilleux (73x92cm-29x36in) s. s.i.d.45 verso exhib.lit. 9-Dec-2 Piasa, Paris #28/R est:40000-60000
£35256 $55353 €55000 Homme a la blouse (41x27cm-16x11in) s. s.i.d.49 verso exhib.lit. 10-Dec-2 Piasa, Paris #82/R est:8000-10000
£41667 $64583 €65000 Comedie (46x38cm-18x15in) s.d.32 s.i.d.verso exhib.lit. 9-Dec-2 Piasa, Paris #27/R est:10000-15000
£51282 $80513 €80000 Haleurs nus (73x92cm-29x36in) s.d.29 lit. 10-Dec-2 Piasa, Paris #78/R est:5000-7000
£54487 $84455 €85000 Portrait de R D Raymond Duchamp (93x65cm-37x26in) s.d.1900 s.i.d.verso exhib.lit. 9-Dec-2 Piasa, Paris #25/R est:20000-30000
£115385 $178846 €180000 Homme dessinant (116x81cm-46x32in) s. painted 1935 exhib.lit. 9-Dec-2 Piasa, Paris #26/R est:20000-30000
Prints
£1899 $2943 €3000 Les roses (38x49cm-15x19in) s.i. col aquatint etching. 28-Sep-2 Ketterer, Hamburg #175/R est:3000-3500
£2051 $3200 €3077 La banc de Pierre (54x42cm-21x17in) s.num.18/20 drypoint. 7-Nov-2 Swann Galleries, New York #824/R est:4000-6000
£2051 $3221 €3200 Musiciens chez le bistrot (268x233cm-106x92in) s.i. etching. 12-Dec-2 Piasa, Paris #181
£2357 $3725 €3536 Femme a la cruche (47x30cm-19x12in) s. col aquatint after Fernand Leger. 28-Apr-3 Bukowskis, Stockholm #450/R est:25000-30000 (S.KR 31000)
£2357 $3725 €3536 Sous la tente, sur la plage - Blonville (47x58cm-19x23in) s.num.43 of 50 col aquatint lit. 28-Apr-3 Bukowskis, Stockholm #532/R est:35000-40000 (S.KR 31000)
£3194 $5046 €4791 Odalisque sur la Terrasse (48x60cm-19x24in) s.num.117/200 col aquatint after Henri Matisse lit. 28-Apr-3 Bukowskis, Stockholm #459/R est:12000-15000 (S.KR 42000)
£3400 $5338 €5100 L'Espagnole a la mantille (44x33cm-17x13in) s.num.12/200 col aquatint after Henri Matisse. 17-Apr-3 Christie's, Kensington #361/R est:1500-2000
£7051 $11071 €11000 Minne au tub (237x167cm-93x66in) etching aquatint. 12-Dec-2 Piasa, Paris #179/R
£7692 $12000 €11538 L'Espagnole (40x28cm-16x11in) s. col aquatint after and signed by Matisse. 18-Sep-2 Swann Galleries, New York #70/R est:5000-8000
£8654 $13673 €13500 Yvonne D de face. drypoint exec.1913. 13-Nov-2 Piasa, Paris #298/R est:10000-12000
£8917 $13911 €14000 Composition (65x50cm-26x20in) s.d.27 lithograph. 7-Nov-2 Chochon-Barre & Allardi, Paris #64
£9859 $16366 €14000 Cabaret de Nuit ou Le Restaurant La Nuit (48x39cm-19x15in) s.d. col aquatint etching. 14-Jun-3 Hauswedell & Nolte, Hamburg #1624/R est:10000
£29874 $47500 €44811 Yvonne D de profil (54x1cm-21x0in) s.num.21/23 drypoint. 2-May-3 Sotheby's, New York #372/R est:30000-50000
Works on paper
£252 $392 €400 Paysage montagneux (18x27cm-7x11in) s.i.d. crayon dr. 11-Oct-2 Pierre Berge, Paris #32
£288 $460 €400 Personnage (16x11cm-6x4in) s. Indian ink col crayon W/C. 14-May-3 Blanchet, Paris #60
£314 $515 €480 Femme a une table de cafe (35x34cm-14x13in) s. crayon. 7-Feb-3 Piasa, Paris #180
£346 $550 €519 For a portrait (15x10cm-6x4in) pen ink exec.1940. 3-May-3 Rachel Davis, Shaker Heights #141/R
£349 $545 €524 Landscape (20x25cm-8x10in) s. Indian ink pencil W/C. 6-Nov-2 Dobiaschofsky, Bern #1996/R (S.FR 800)
£362 $605 €525 Figural composition (22x14cm-9x6in) s. pen Indian ink. 24-Jun-3 Koller, Zurich #133/R (S.FR 800)

£366 $574 €549 Un homme dans sa chambre (21x13cm-8x5in) s. W/C. 10-Dec-2 Pinneys, Montreal #97 (C.D 900)
£377 $585 €600 La Colombe (27x13cm-11x5in) s.d.24 graphite dr. 30-Oct-2 Artcurial Briest, Paris #262
£417 $663 €600 Danseuses du moulin rouge, Jeanne Avril (28x35cm-11x14in) s.i. pencil ink W/C exhib. 29-Apr-3 Artcurial Briest, Paris #32
£610 $957 €915 Un Zouave dans le cafe (20x11cm-8x4in) s. W/C. 10-Dec-2 Pinneys, Montreal #52 (C.D 1500)
£633 $1000 €1000 Nu debout (40x26cm-16x10in) s. W/C. 27-Nov-2 Blanchet, Paris #16
£696 $1100 €1100 Jeune enfant (44x29cm-17x11in) s.d.1903 Chinese ink wash. 27-Nov-2 Blanchet, Paris #15
£900 $1422 €1350 Paysage (20x25cm-8x10in) s. pencil pen ink W/C. 3-Apr-3 Christie's, Kensington #120/R
£1154 $1812 €1800 Noce (55x44cm-22x17in) s.i. chl dr lit. 10-Dec-2 Piasa, Paris #91/R
£1391 $2157 €2087 Composition architectonique (46x63cm-18x25in) s. ink W/C prov. 7-Dec-2 Galerie du Rhone, Sion #513/R est:2000-3000 (S.FR 3200)
£1410 $2214 €2200 Jeanne Bloch (21x13cm-8x5in) s.i. W/C lit. 10-Dec-2 Piasa, Paris #87/R
£1583 $2532 €2200 Scene d'interieur (15x12cm-6x5in) s.d. W/C gouache. 18-May-3 Eric Pillon, Calais #177/R
£1689 $2635 €2500 Etude de crane (21x18cm-8x7in) s. pen ink htd gouache. 31-Mar-3 Piasa, Paris #136/R
£1774 $2767 €2661 Composition (17x22cm-7x9in) s. gouache Indian ink cardboard. 18-Sep-2 Kunsthallen, Copenhagen #10/R est:10000 (D.KR 21000)
£1795 $2818 €2800 Poissons (20x31cm-8x12in) s. chi dr exec.c.1930 lit. 10-Dec-2 Piasa, Paris #94/R
£2051 $3221 €3200 Manege des petits chevaux (48x31cm-19x12in) s. crayon dr exec.c.1900 lit. 10-Dec-2 Piasa, Paris #88/R
£2244 $3522 €3500 Portrait de Robert Azaria (48x27cm-19x11in) s. Chinese ink dr exec.c.1945 lit. 10-Dec-2 Piasa, Paris #96/R
£2436 $3824 €3800 Portrait de Robert Azaria (22x19cm-9x7in) s.d.47 Chinese ink dr lit. 10-Dec-2 Piasa, Paris #93/R
£2564 $4026 €4000 Tete de femme (16x9cm-6x4in) ink wash lit. 10-Dec-2 Piasa, Paris #89
£2885 $4529 €4500 Concert sur la plage (40x26cm-16x10in) s. Chinese ink exec.1907 lit. 10-Dec-2 Piasa, Paris #92/R est:4000
£3077 $4831 €4800 Universe (21x16cm-8x6in) s. W/C exec.c.1951 lit. 10-Dec-2 Piasa, Paris #90/R
£3205 $5032 €5000 Buste (18x13cm-7x5in) s. W/C exec.1949 lit. 10-Dec-2 Piasa, Paris #85
£5128 $8051 €8000 Masque (21x16cm-8x6in) s. Chinese ink wax crayon lit. 10-Dec-2 Piasa, Paris #95/R est:2000
£8974 $14090 €14000 Manet, Olympia (20x27cm-8x11in) s.i. W/C exec.c.1926-27 lit. 10-Dec-2 Piasa, Paris #86/R est:3000-4000

VILLORESI, Franco (1920-1975) Italian
£753 $1175 €1100 Old smoking car (30x40cm-12x16in) s. painted 1957. 10-Apr-3 Finarte Semenzato, Rome #152
£1027 $1603 €1500 Men reading (45x55cm-18x22in) s. 10-Apr-3 Finarte Semenzato, Rome #160/R

VINAY, Jean (1907-1978) French
£280 $440 €420 Pont de L'ile St Louis, Paris (55x81cm-22x32in) s. prov. 10-Dec-2 Rosebery Fine Art, London #618
£301 $475 €452 Bouquet a la table blanche (53x36cm-21x14in) s. prov. 5-Apr-3 DeFina, Austinburg #1332
£878 $1370 €1300 La rue du Mont Cenis a Montmartre (45x54cm-18x21in) s. 25-Mar-3 Chochon-Barre & Allardi, Paris #207

VINCENT, Antoine Paul (18/19th C) French
Miniatures
£1800 $2952 €2610 Young gentleman in blue coat (6cm-2in circular) s.d. gilt metal frame. 3-Jun-3 Christie's, London #165/R est:800-1200

VINCENT, E (19th C) ?
£4051 $6319 €6400 Quai Saint-Antoine en hiver, Lyon (82x117cm-32x46in) s. 20-Oct-2 Anaf, Lyon #262
£4052 $6646 €6200 Quai Saint-Antoine en hiver, Lyon (82x117cm-32x46in) s. 9-Feb-3 Anaf, Lyon #177/R

VINCENT, François Andre (1746-1816) French
£74074 $120000 €111111 Belisarius, reduced to begging, recognised by a soldier from the army of Emperor Justinian (59x74cm-23x29in) s.d.1776. 23-Jan-3 Sotheby's, New York #100/R est:80000-120000

VINCENT, François Andre (attrib) (1746-1816) French
Works on paper
£755 $1177 €1200 Eight heads of mythical and historical heroes (21x43cm-8x17in) pen. 11-Oct-2 Winterberg, Heidelberg #472
£5696 $8886 €9000 A la niche (23x37cm-9x15in) sanguine. 18-Oct-2 Raboudin & Choppin de Janvry, Paris #81/R

VINCENT, George (1796-c.1831) British
£500 $780 €750 Cattle and figures before a cottage (18x28cm-7x11in) indis sig. panel. 7-Nov-2 Christie's, Kensington #92/R
£1848 $2883 €3081 Untitled - Windmill with figures on road (32x51cm-13x20in) s. indis d. prov. 13-Apr-3 Levis, Calgary #218/R est:6000-8000 (C.D 4250)
£2500 $4125 €3625 Cattle grazing before a windmill in an extensive landscape (32x43cm-13x17in) panel. 1-Jul-3 Bonhams, Norwich #207/R est:2500-3500

VINCENT, George (attrib) (1796-c.1831) British
£3000 $4770 €4500 Postwick Grove (38x51cm-15x20in) 19-Mar-3 Sotheby's, London #71/R est:3000-4000

VINCENT, Harry A (1864-1931) American
£9554 $15000 €14331 Lifting fog, Rockport (71x91cm-28x36in) s. i.verso. 22-Nov-2 Skinner, Boston #346/R est:6000-8000

VINCENZINA, Giuseppe (18th C) Italian
£8333 $13083 €13000 Still life of flowers, fruit and dead game (103x86cm-41x34in) 15-Dec-2 Mercier & Cie, Lille #320/R est:18000-23000

VINCHE, Lionel (1936-) Belgian
£833 $1325 €1200 La gamine torne le neud papillon (107x72cm-42x28in) s. d.1988 verso. 29-Apr-3 Campo & Campo, Antwerp #346

VINCIDOR, Tommaso di Andrea (16th C) Italian
Works on paper
£24691 $40000 €37037 Head of a man (39x41cm-15x16in) gouache over black chk fragment painted with unknow artist exhib. 23-Jan-3 Sotheby's, New York #55/R est:40000-60000

VINCK, Franz (1827-1903) Belgian
£1200 $1956 €1740 Medieval street scene (61x82cm-24x32in) s. prov. 16-Jul-3 Sotheby's, Olympia #202/R est:1500-2000

VINCK, Joseph (1900-1979) Belgian
£283 $436 €450 Vue de ville (37x38cm-15x15in) s.d.1962 panel. 22-Oct-2 Campo, Vlaamse Kaai #681
£566 $872 €900 Travail au champ (15x20cm-6x8in) s. cardboard. 22-Oct-2 Campo, Vlaamse Kaai #683
£3041 $4743 €4500 Landscape with figures bathing in pond (36x63cm-14x25in) panel. 27-Mar-3 Dorotheum, Vienna #192/R est:4000-6000
Works on paper
£503 $775 €800 Paysage (20x17cm-8x7in) s. chl. 22-Oct-2 Campo, Vlaamse Kaai #682

VINCKEBOONS, David (1576-1629) Flemish
£32051 $50641 €50000 Summer. Automn (74x104cm-29x41in) pair. 13-Nov-2 Marc Kohn, Paris #15/R est:50000-60000
£32051 $50641 €50000 Winter. Spring (74x104cm-29x41in) pair. 13-Nov-2 Marc Kohn, Paris #14/R est:50000-60000
£75540 $120863 €105000 Blind hurdy-gurdy player with children and peasants (27x38cm-11x15in) mono. panel. 13-May-3 Sotheby's, Amsterdam #8/R est:30000-40000
Prints
£2642 $4121 €4200 Men and animals fighting against death and time (28x38cm-11x15in) copperplate. 11-Oct-2 Winterberg, Heidelberg #345/R est:2200
Works on paper
£8917 $13911 €14000 Danae (7x12cm-3x5in) pen black ink grey wash prov.exhib. 5-Nov-2 Sotheby's, Amsterdam #7/R est:4500-6000

VINCKEBOONS, David (after) (1576-1629) Flemish
£6500 $10335 €9750 Figures and horsemen on a bridge before a village, distant town beyond (36x64cm-14x25in) panel prov. 30-Apr-3 Halls, Shrewsbury #304/R est:6000-8000

VINCKEBOONS, David (circle) (1576-1629) Flemish
£15924 $24841 €25000 Wooded landscape with peasants returning from market (97x118cm-38x46in) prov.exhib. 6-Nov-2 Christie's, Amsterdam #56/R est:25000-35000

VINCKEBOONS, David (studio) (1576-1629) Flemish
£6918 $10723 €11000 Hold up in forested river landscape (33x54cm-13x21in) panel prov.lit. 2-Oct-2 Dorotheum, Vienna #180/R est:6000-10000

VINDFELDT, Ejnar (1905-1953) Danish
£578 $920 €867 Landscape with cattle (30x42cm-12x17in) s.d.44. 5-May-3 Rasmussen, Vejle #601/R (D.KR 6200)
£3681 $6000 €5522 Out of reach (43x37cm-17x15in) s. 11-Feb-3 Bonhams & Doyles, New York #140/R est:6000-8000

VINEA, Francesco (1845-1902) Italian
£4088 $6296 €6500 Portrait of girl with hat and red ribbon (54x41cm-21x16in) s.d.78. 28-Oct-2 Il Ponte, Milan #286/R est:7000

VINELLA, Ray (?) ?
£2083 $3250 €3125 Rabbit hunt (41x51cm-16x20in) s.i. oil masonite on panel prov. 9-Nov-2 Santa Fe Art, Santa Fe #45/R est:3500-4500

VINELLA, W (?) ?
£700 $1084 €1050 Ducks at the edge of the pond (61x91cm-24x36in) s. 3-Dec-2 Ritchie, Toronto #3113/R est:1800-2200 (C.D 1700)

VINES, Hernando (1904-1993) Spanish
£1763 $2785 €2750 Landscape (19x24cm-7x9in) s. cardboard. 19-Nov-2 Durán, Madrid #155/R
£1888 $3153 €2700 Nu (27x22cm-11x9in) cardboard. 26-Jun-3 Tajan, Paris #286 est:1500-2000
£2724 $4304 €4250 Jug (33x24cm-13x9in) s. 14-Nov-2 Arte, Seville #429/R
£3526 $5571 €5500 Still life (24x31cm-9x12in) s. canvas on board. 13-Nov-2 Ansorena, Madrid #22/R est:5500
£13000 $20410 €19500 Joven sentada - seated girl (81x65cm-32x26in) s. 19-Nov-2 Sotheby's, London #72/R est:6000-8000
£15079 $24580 €22770 Young woman seated (81x65cm-32x26in) s.d.1930 lit. 11-Feb-3 Segre, Madrid #152/R est:20000
£18705 $29928 €26000 Le dessinateur (73x92cm-29x36in) s.d.28. 15-May-3 Christie's, Paris #125/R est:12000-18000
Works on paper
£1226 $1937 €1900 Sea from the window (48x64cm-19x25in) s. W/C. 17-Dec-2 Durán, Madrid #145/R
£1310 $2083 €1900 Seascape in France (55x43cm-22x17in) s. gouache. 4-Mar-3 Ansorena, Madrid #274/R

VINKELES, Reinier (1741-1816) Dutch
Works on paper
£552 $900 €828 Untitled (25x36cm-10x14in) W/C. 14-Feb-3 Du Mouchelle, Detroit #2044/R
£602 $1000 €873 Untitled (25x36cm-10x14in) W/C. 13-Jun-3 Du Mouchelle, Detroit #2281/R
£5096 $7949 €8000 Horse and his Creole jockey (12x18cm-5x7in) s. pen black ink grey wash htd white. 5-Nov-2 Sotheby's, Amsterdam #172/R est:4000-6000

VINKLER, Laszlo (1912-1980) Hungarian
Works on paper
£645 $1000 €935 Storm (61x87cm-24x34in) s.d.1977 Indian ink lit. 9-Dec-2 Mu Terem Galeria, Budapest #98/R est:220000 (H.F 240000)

VINNE, Jan Vincents van der (1663-1721) Dutch
£1500 $2355 €2250 Wooded landscape with a stag hunt (39x51cm-15x20in) s. 13-Dec-2 Christie's, Kensington #119/R est:2000-3000

VINNE, Jan van der (elder) (1663-1721) Dutch
£1300 $2028 €1950 Head of an old man in profile (26x20cm-10x8in) panel octagonal. 10-Apr-3 Christie's, Kensington #102/R est:1500-2000

VINNE, Vincent Laurensz van der (17/18th C) Dutch
Works on paper
£1266 $2000 €2000 Haarlem city wall (19x30cm-7x12in) i. verso chk. 29-Nov-2 Bassenge, Berlin #5555/R est:2000

VINNEN, Carl (1863-1922) German
£1020 $1622 €1500 Cuxhaven harbour in the evening (36x46cm-14x18in) s.i. verso board. 28-Mar-3 Bolland & Marotz, Bremen #377/R est:2000

VINTER, John Alfred (1828-1905) British
£1773 $2748 €2660 The cats recital (71x107cm-28x42in) s.indis.d.188. 4-Dec-2 AB Stockholms Auktionsverk #1878/R est:35000-40000 (S.KR 25000)

VINTON, Frederick Porter (1846-1911) American
£687 $1100 €996 Sketch of a doorway (41x31cm-16x12in) prov. 16-May-3 Skinner, Boston #346/R

VINZIO, Giulio Cesare (1881-1940) Italian
£417 $654 €650 Village street (22x28cm-9x11in) s. board. 10-Dec-2 Della Rocca, Turin #317/R
£516 $815 €800 Sunset on the coast in Liguria (30x40cm-12x16in) s. board prov. 18-Dec-2 Finarte, Milan #153

VIO, Giovanni (19th C) Italian
£1103 $1754 €1600 Vineyard (34x41cm-13x16in) s. cardboard sold with oil by Francesco Speranza exhib. 5-Mar-3 Sotheby's, Milan #55

VIOLA, Ferdinand (19th C) French
£3125 $5000 €4688 Baby's first pet (84x140cm-33x55in) s. 14-May-3 Butterfields, San Francisco #1123/R est:4000-6000

VIOLA, Giuseppe (1933-) Italian
£523 $837 €800 Santa Margherita Ligure (50x35cm-20x14in) s.i. painted 1987. 4-Jan-3 Meeting Art, Vercelli #179
£654 $1046 €1000 Romagnoli at harbour (45x54cm-18x21in) s. cardboard. 4-Jan-3 Meeting Art, Vercelli #34
£694 $1104 €1000 Fishermen (50x35cm-20x14in) s. painted 1989. 1-May-3 Meeting Art, Vercelli #77
£694 $1104 €1000 Pomegranates with pumpkin (40x50cm-16x20in) s. 1-May-3 Meeting Art, Vercelli #297
£719 $1150 €1100 Old angler with lamp (28x20cm-11x8in) s. painted 1998. 4-Jan-3 Meeting Art, Vercelli #652
£962 $1510 €1500 House in Rapallo (30x40cm-12x16in) s. painted 1987. 23-Nov-2 Meeting Art, Vercelli #178/R
£962 $1510 €1500 Vase of flowers (80x45cm-31x18in) s. s.d.1958. 23-Nov-2 Meeting Art, Vercelli #414/R
£1020 $1622 €1500 Fishermen (50x60cm-20x24in) s. board. 1-Mar-3 Meeting Art, Vercelli #479
£1042 $1656 €1500 Boy with grapes (60x40cm-24x16in) s. painted 1989. 1-May-3 Meeting Art, Vercelli #334
£1361 $2163 €2000 Via Cosseria (55x65cm-22x26in) s.i. 1-Mar-3 Meeting Art, Vercelli #526
£1389 $2208 €2000 Grapes harvest (70x50cm-28x20in) s. s.i.d.1990 verso. 1-May-3 Meeting Art, Vercelli #315
£1389 $2208 €2000 Gondole in Venice (50x70cm-20x28in) s. s.i.verso. 1-May-3 Meeting Art, Vercelli #571
£1899 $2962 €3000 Man with basket of fruit (80x60cm-31x24in) s. painted 2001. 14-Sep-2 Meeting Art, Vercelli #951/R
£1961 $3137 €3000 Peasant with cock (80x60cm-31x24in) s. painted 1995 lit. 4-Jan-3 Meeting Art, Vercelli #505
Works on paper
£475 $741 €750 Fishermen (32x22cm-13x9in) s. gouache paper on canvas. 14-Sep-2 Meeting Art, Vercelli #868/R
£490 $784 €750 Fisherman on a boat (32x22cm-13x9in) s. i.verso Chinese ink paper on canvas. 4-Jan-3 Meeting Art, Vercelli #464
£510 $811 €750 Ice-cream parlour (35x25cm-14x10in) s. gouache exec.1984. 1-Mar-3 Meeting Art, Vercelli #668

VIOLA, Manuel (1919-1987) Spanish
£377 $589 €600 Painting (38x28cm-15x11in) s. board. 17-Sep-2 Segre, Madrid #192/R
£464 $756 €700 Grey abstraction (28x21cm-11x8in) s. board. 11-Feb-3 Segre, Madrid #280/R
£497 $810 €750 Orange abstraction (24x16cm-9x6in) s. board. 11-Feb-3 Segre, Madrid #276/R
£625 $1013 €950 Composition (14x24cm-6x9in) 21-Jan-3 Ansorena, Madrid #328
£676 $1054 €1000 Composition abstraite (28x17cm-11x7in) s. paper on canvas prov. 28-Mar-3 Charbonneaux, Paris #154
£1014 $1581 €1500 Composition abstraite (33x46cm-13x18in) s. prov. 28-Mar-3 Charbonneaux, Paris #152
£1399 $2336 €2000 Composition (99x65cm-39x26in) s. 26-Jun-3 Tajan, Paris #324/R est:2000-2500
£1538 $2569 €2200 The watching (92x60cm-36x24in) s. 26-Jun-3 Tajan, Paris #323/R est:2000-2500
£2128 $3447 €3000 Abstraccion azul (41x60cm-16x24in) s. acrylic panel. 20-May-3 Segre, Madrid #159/R est:3000
£2649 $4318 €4000 Cocks fighting (50x66cm-20x26in) s. board. 11-Feb-3 Segre, Madrid #281/R
£2685 $4322 €4000 Dynamic tension. Butterfly (46x39cm-18x15in) acrylic double-sided. 18-Feb-3 Durán, Madrid #192/R
£10526 $17053 €16000 Untitled (200x200cm-79x79in) s. exhib. 21-Jan-3 Durán, Madrid #165/R est:16000
Works on paper
£743 $1159 €1100 Composition abstraite (21x34cm-8x13in) s. mixed media prov. 28-Mar-3 Charbonneaux, Paris #153

VIOLANTE, Italo (20th C) Italian
£270 $422 €400 Port de Bari (40x50cm-16x20in) s. canvas on masonite exhib. 30-Mar-3 Anaf, Lyon #439
£270 $422 €400 Nazaree (40x50cm-16x20in) s. canvas on masonite exhib. 30-Mar-3 Anaf, Lyon #440

VIOLET, Pierre Noel (1749-1819) French
Miniatures
£2100 $3255 €3150 Officer of the 14th Light dragoons (9cm-4in) s.indis.d.18 rec. veneered wood frame oval. 1-Oct-2 Bonhams, New Bond Street #296/R est:600-800
£6500 $10205 €9750 Countess de Genlis se St. Aubin (7cm-3in) s. silver mount oval. 10-Dec-2 Christie's, London #138/R est:1000-1500

VIONOJA, Veikko (1909-2001) Finnish
£931 $1471 €1350 Kerttu - portrait of girl (38x32cm-15x13in) s.d.1947 exhib. 3-Apr-3 Hagelstam, Helsinki #959/R
£1156 $1839 €1700 Field of hay (59x58cm-23x23in) s.d.1947. 27-Feb-3 Hagelstam, Helsinki #1008 est:2000
£1203 $1876 €1900 Boat on beach (57x66cm-22x26in) s.i.d.1942. 12-Sep-2 Hagelstam, Helsinki #883
£1310 $2070 €1900 Landscape (47x51cm-19x20in) s.d.1947. 3-Apr-3 Hagelstam, Helsinki #970/R est:1600
£1635 $2518 €2600 Interior (29x36cm-11x14in) s. 24-Oct-2 Hagelstam, Helsinki #1030 est:1200
£1724 $2724 €2500 Rooves (74x64cm-29x25in) s. 3-Apr-3 Hagelstam, Helsinki #975/R est:2000
£1899 $2962 €3000 Table (51x40cm-20x16in) s.d.1984. 12-Sep-2 Hagelstam, Helsinki #936/R
£1899 $3000 €3000 Composition (55x70cm-22x28in) s.d.1975 board. 30-Nov-2 Hagelstam, Helsinki #145/R est:3000
£2535 $4082 €3600 Coastal landscape (47x53cm-19x21in) s.d.74 board. 10-May-3 Bukowskis, Helsinki #160/R est:2200-2500
£3072 $5038 €4700 Approaching thunder storm (66x100cm-26x39in) s.d.83. 9-Feb-3 Bukowskis, Helsinki #381/R est:5000
£3165 $5000 €5000 The home village, Kylanpaa, Ylistaro (97x116cm-38x46in) s.d.68. 1-Dec-2 Bukowskis, Helsinki #200/R est:4500-5000
£3453 $5525 €4800 Half moon (108x65cm-43x26in) s. 17-May-3 Hagelstam, Helsinki #204/R est:5000
£3544 $5600 €5600 Still life with window (60x73cm-24x29in) s.d.66. 1-Dec-2 Bukowskis, Helsinki #201/R est:4000-4500
Works on paper
£252 $387 €400 Light by window (26x36cm-10x14in) s.d.1965. 24-Oct-2 Hagelstam, Helsinki #831

VIRCHAUX, Paul (1862-1930) Swiss
£1048 $1635 €1572 Country landscape in the evening with peasant woman (64x89cm-25x35in) s. d.1912 stretcher. 6-Nov-2 Dobiaschofsky, Bern #1048/R est:1400 (S.FR 2400)
£2913 $4515 €4370 Jeune, Saviesanne, a la pomme rouge (43x32cm-17x13in) s. init.verso. 7-Dec-2 Galerie du Rhone, Sion #494/R est:9000-12000 (S.FR 6700)
£5217 $8087 €7826 Le noyer, Saviese (64x47cm-25x19in) s.d.1904 init.verso prov. 7-Dec-2 Galerie du Rhone, Sion #493/R est:12000-15000 (S.FR 12000)

VIRNICH, Thomas (1957-) German
Sculpture
£3043 $4991 €4200 Milanese cathedral (54x81x19cm-21x32x7in) s.d.1991/94 lead ceramic. 28-May-3 Lempertz, Koln #458/R est:4200

VIRTUE, John (1947-) British
Works on paper
£360 $558 €540 Spittens farm (53x74cm-21x29in) pen ink. 3-Dec-2 Bonhams, Knightsbridge #19/R
£3000 $4650 €4500 Landscape 87 (299x169cm-118x67in) s.i.d.1988-89 pen ink acrylic three panel with ten works of art. 3-Dec-2 Bonhams, New Bond Street #132/R est:2000-3000

VIRY, Paul Alphonse (19th C) French
£690 $1097 €1000 Still life with musical instruments (70x112cm-28x44in) s.d.1893. 4-Mar-3 Ansorena, Madrid #15/R
£1974 $3197 €3000 FFeeding the doves (24x19cm-9x7in) s. board. 21-Jan-3 Ansorena, Madrid #201/R est:3000
£11392 $18000 €17088 Declaration (30x35cm-12x14in) s. panel prov. 24-Apr-3 Sotheby's, New York #69/R est:20000-30000

VISANTI, Lyyli (1893-1971) Finnish
£360 $590 €500 Runeberg Street (50x45cm-20x18in) s. 4-Jun-3 Bukowskis, Helsinki #456/R
Works on paper
£288 $472 €400 Flowers (37x45cm-15x18in) s.d.1936 pastel. 5-Jun-3 Hagelstam, Helsinki #1001

VISBY, Frederick Mayer (1839-1926) Danish?
£2618 $4084 €3927 View from Saint Thomas towards Christiansfort (46x63cm-18x25in) s. 22-Sep-2 Hindemae, Ullerslev #7195/R est:30000-40000 (D.KR 31000)

VISCA, Rodolfo (1939-) Uruguayan
£276 $441 €400 Composition (27x21cm-11x8in) init. cardboard. 11-Mar-3 Castellana, Madrid #347/R
£321 $503 €500 Untitled (33x14cm-13x6in) s. board. 16-Dec-2 Castellana, Madrid #933/R
£577 $906 €900 Untitled (36x25cm-14x10in) s. acrylic cardboard. 16-Dec-2 Castellana, Madrid #919/R

VISCARDI, G (19th C) Italian
£1659 $2589 €2489 Evening river landscape with herders and cattle (62x88cm-24x35in) s.d.1861. 20-Nov-2 Fischer, Luzern #1072/R est:4000-5000 (S.FR 3800)

VISCONTI, Adolfo Ferraguti (1850-1924) Italian
£1762 $2626 €2643 Portrait of gypsy woman (56x48cm-22x19in) s. 25-Jun-2 Koller, Zurich #6547/R est:6000-9000 (S.FR 4000)

VISEUX, Claude (1927-) French
£256 $403 €400 Planche (65x49cm-26x19in) s.d.69 cardboard. 24-Nov-2 Laurence Calmels, Paris #282/R
£321 $503 €500 Planche (65x50cm-26x20in) s.d.69 cardboard. 24-Nov-2 Laurence Calmels, Paris #283/R
£385 $604 €600 Algues (50x61cm-20x24in) s.d.58 paper on canvas. 24-Nov-2 Laurence Calmels, Paris #290/R
£385 $604 €600 Algues (50x65cm-20x26in) s.d.58 paper on canvas. 24-Nov-2 Laurence Calmels, Paris #289/R
£513 $805 €800 Sputateur (89x130cm-35x51in) s.d.54 s.i.d.verso. 24-Nov-2 Laurence Calmels, Paris #286/R
£577 $906 €900 Untitled (50x65cm-20x26in) s.d.58 paper on canvas. 24-Nov-2 Laurence Calmels, Paris #284/R
£577 $906 €900 Sur la plage (65x46cm-26x18in) s.d.54 s.d.verso. 24-Nov-2 Laurence Calmels, Paris #288/R
£641 $1006 €1000 Fouisseurs (130x97cm-51x38in) s.d.60 prov.exhib. 24-Nov-2 Laurence Calmels, Paris #287/R
£769 $1208 €1200 Halterie-halterophile (130x97cm-51x38in) s.d.1957 s.i.d.verso. 24-Nov-2 Laurence Calmels, Paris #285/R
Sculpture
£962 $1510 €1500 Informateur (58x36cm-23x14in) s.d.LXXI stainless steel assemblage prov.exhib. 24-Nov-2 Laurence Calmels, Paris #312/R
£1154 $1812 €1800 Corps flotteurs suspendus (200cm-79in) plastic fabric exec.1968 exhib. 24-Nov-2 Laurence Calmels, Paris #313/R
£3169 $5261 €4500 Tabouret (66cm-26in) polished metal. 18-Jun-3 Anaf, Lyon #30/R est:3000-3200

VISHNIAC, Roman (1897-1990) Polish
Photographs
£1923 $3000 €2885 Street peddlers, Warsaw (20x25cm-8x10in) silver. 21-Oct-2 Swann Galleries, New York #275/R est:4000-5000
£11688 $18000 €17532 Vanished world (27x34cm-11x13in) s.num.5 photographs portfolio. 24-Oct-2 Sotheby's, New York #171/R est:20000-30000

VISKI, Janos (1891-1965) Hungarian
£256 $400 €384 Galloping horses (58x79cm-23x31in) 14-Sep-2 Selkirks, St. Louis #740
£295 $463 €460 Argentine gaucho with wild horses (60x78cm-24x31in) s. 21-Nov-2 Van Ham, Cologne #1954
£327 $536 €500 Horse drawn cart (59x79cm-23x31in) s. 6-Feb-3 Weidler, Nurnberg #6614

VISO, Nicola (18th C) Italian
£6761 $10885 €9600 River landscape with ruins (59x86cm-23x34in) 11-May-3 Finarte, Venice #41/R est:9000-12000

VISO, Nicola (attrib) (18th C) Italian
£1500 $2355 €2250 Vertumnus and Pomona (29x37cm-11x15in) 10-Dec-2 Bonhams, New Bond Street #100/R est:1500-2000

VISSCHER, Cornelis de (attrib) (1619-1662) Dutch
Works on paper
£2500 $3875 €3900 Portrait of young man (19x17cm-7x7in) crayon vellum. 4-Dec-2 Piasa, Paris #41/R

VISSCHER, Reinder (1904-1973) Dutch
£321 $503 €500 Morning in "t Gooi" (81x61cm-32x24in) s. 25-Nov-2 Glerum, Amsterdam #81

VISSER, Adri (1887-1933) Dutch
£346 $550 €502 Interior of a church (61x51cm-24x20in) s. painted c.1920. 4-May-3 Treadway Gallery, Cincinnati #470/R

VISSER, Carel (1928-) Dutch
Sculpture
£1923 $2981 €3000 Schroefdak - terraeders (76cm-30in) bronze executed 1993 prov. 3-Dec-2 Christie's, Amsterdam #75/R est:3500-4500
£3526 $5465 €5500 Gat - opening (24x24cm-9x9in) s.i.d. welded steel executed 1968 exhib.lit. 3-Dec-2 Christie's, Amsterdam #66/R est:6000-8000
£4317 $7079 €6000 Construction (28cm-11in) welded iron executed c.1954. 3-Jun-3 Christie's, Amsterdam #403/R est:7000-9000
£4487 $6955 €7000 Half-cylindrisch II (25x50x100cm-10x20x39in) steel object in four parts executed 1975 prov.exhib. 3-Dec-2 Christie's, Amsterdam #372/R est:7000-9000
£6115 $10029 €8500 Mating bird (35cm-14in) welded iron executed c.1954. 3-Jun-3 Christie's, Amsterdam #402/R est:7000-9000
£11511 $18878 €16000 Familie - family (65cm-26in) welded iron executed c.1954-55 prov.lit. 3-Jun-3 Christie's, Amsterdam #196/R est:7000-9000
Works on paper
£1603 $2484 €2500 Vliegende peruviaan - flying Peruvian (128x183cm-50x72in) s.d.90 pencil collage prov. 3-Dec-2 Christie's, Amsterdam #306/R est:2500-3500
£2885 $4471 €4500 Running (81x91cm-32x36in) s.d.2001 pencil collage. 3-Dec-2 Christie's, Amsterdam #304/R est:4500-5500

VISSON, Philippe (1942-) French
£231 $373 €347 Face (69x49cm-27x19in) s.d.1991 acrylic paper. 7-May-3 Dobiaschofsky, Bern #1040 (S.FR 500)
£472 $746 €708 Head (100x81cm-39x32in) mono.i.d.1971 verso masonite exhib. 29-Nov-2 Zofingen, Switzerland #3111/R (S.FR 1100)

VISSOTSKY, K S (1867-?) Russian?
£425 $663 €638 Snow covered branch with king-fisher (50x67cm-20x26in) 5-Aug-2 Rasmussen, Vejle #106/R (D.KR 5000)
£1872 $2958 €2808 Snow covered branch with jay (50x67cm-20x26in) 2-Dec-2 Rasmussen, Copenhagen #1552/R est:5000 (D.KR 22000)

VITA, Miguel de (1923-2001) South American
£1000 $1600 €1500 Medecine Faculty (81x64cm-32x25in) s. 5-Jan-3 Galleria Y Remates, Montevideo #130

VITAL, Edgar (1883-?) Swiss
£306 $477 €459 Flower bouquet in blue vase (45x60cm-18x24in) s.d.1945 panel. 6-Nov-2 Dobiaschofsky, Bern #1049/R (S.FR 700)
£306 $477 €459 Still life of flowers (54x58cm-21x23in) s.d.1946 panel. 6-Nov-2 Dobiaschofsky, Bern #1050/R (S.FR 700)
£1717 $2712 €2576 Sils lake (57x62cm-22x24in) s.d.1951 pavatex. 26-Nov-2 Phillips, Zurich #73/R est:4000-6000 (S.FR 4000)

VITALE, Carlo (1902-1996) Italian
£680 $1082 €1000 Paris (38x54cm-15x21in) s.d.1947 cardboard. 1-Mar-3 Meeting Art, Vercelli #36

VITALE, Massimo (1944-) ?
Photographs
£10127 $16000 €15191 Rosignano sea No.2 (152x183cm-60x72in) cibachrome prints mounted on plexiglas executed 1997 prov. 14-Nov-2 Christie's, Rockefeller NY #476/R est:10000-15000

VITALI, Alberto (1898-1974) Italian
£3607 $5771 €5230 Landscape (40x50cm-16x20in) s.d.1936 board prov. 11-Mar-3 Babuino, Rome #277/R

VITALIS, Macario (1898-1990) Philippino
£2320 $3572 €3480 In a restaurant (48x66cm-19x26in) s. 27-Oct-2 Christie's, Hong Kong #64/R est:14000-16000 (HK.D 28000)

VITEZ, Matyas (1891-?) Hungarian
£1000 $1640 €1500 Returning home (46x46cm-18x18in) s. 3-Jun-3 Sotheby's, London #109/R est:3000-5000
£1183 $1834 €1775 Market (120x95cm-47x37in) s. 6-Dec-2 Kieselbach, Budapest #90/R (H.F 440000)

VITI, Eugenio (1881-1952) Italian
£1218 $1912 €1900 Farm with vegetable garden (50x66cm-20x26in) s. cardboard. 21-Nov-2 Finarte, Rome #328
£2215 $3500 €3500 Sorreto coast (40x48cm-16x19in) s. cardboard. 26-Nov-2 Christie's, Rome #252/R
£2848 $4500 €4500 Female nude (48x37cm-19x15in) s. cardboard prov.lit. 26-Nov-2 Christie's, Rome #253/R

VITIELLO, Raffaele (1875-?) Italian
£2179 $3378 €3400 Fishermen leaving (85x100cm-33x39in) s. 5-Dec-2 Stadion, Trieste #674/R

VITRINGA, Wigerus (attrib) (1657-1721) Dutch
£10256 $16205 €16000 Dutch ships in stormy seas (89x73cm-35x29in) 16-Nov-2 Lempertz, Koln #1125/R est:12000
£20144 $32230 €28000 Dutch threemaster and other shipping in choppy waters (89x112cm-35x44in) 14-May-3 Christie's, Amsterdam #197/R est:20000-25000

VITTINI, Giulio (1888-1968) Italian
£4808 $7549 €7500 Femme voilee devant portail (81x60cm-32x24in) s. 10-Dec-2 Tajan, Paris #234/R

VITTORIA, Alessandro (circle) (1525-1608) Italian
Sculpture
£16000 $25120 €24000 Venetian nobleman (81cm-32in) marble on socle. 10-Dec-2 Sotheby's, London #109/R est:12000-18000

VITY, Antonio de (1901-) Italian
£301 $475 €452 Parisian street scene (61x119cm-24x47in) s. 1-Dec-2 Susanin's, Chicago #5086/R

VIUDES, Vincente (1916-) Spanish?
£1987 $3238 €3000 Butterfly II (75x100cm-30x39in) s.d.1963 i.verso. 11-Feb-3 Segre, Madrid #250/R

VIVANCOS, Miguel Garcia (1895-1972) Spanish
£3082 $4839 €4500 Tour de l'horloge, Avallon (41x27cm-16x11in) s. s.i.d.1948 verso. 15-Apr-3 Laurence Calmels, Paris #4230/R
£3767 $5914 €5500 Eglise Saint-Ouen, Rouen (55x46cm-22x18in) s.d.53 s.i.d.verso. 15-Apr-3 Laurence Calmels, Paris #4229/R

VIVARINI, Bartolommeo (attrib) (c.1432-c.1499) Italian
£9871 $15300 €14807 Madonna with child (33x26cm-13x10in) panel. 3-Oct-2 Koller, Zurich #3009/R est:6000-8000 (S.FR 23000)

VIVES AYNE, Ramon (1815-1894) Spanish
£1026 $1621 €1600 Portrait of boy (69x58cm-27x23in) 14-Nov-2 Arte, Seville #224/R

VIVES-ATSARA, Jose (1919-1988) Mexican
£577 $900 €866 Flores (51x41cm-20x16in) canvasboard. 19-Oct-2 David Dike, Dallas #237/R
£962 $1500 €1443 Bodegon (41x51cm-16x20in) 19-Oct-2 David Dike, Dallas #232/R est:2000-4000

VIVIAN, J (19th C) British
£2612 $4153 €3918 Coastal landscape, southern scene with fishermen and boats (44x79cm-17x31in) s. 5-May-3 Rasmussen, Vejle #296/R est:30000 (D.KR 28000)
£3500 $5565 €5250 Customs House and the entrance to the Grand canal Venice. Gondolas on the Venetian backwater (30x25cm-12x10in) indis sig. pair. 6-Mar-3 Christie's, Kensington #506/R est:4000-6000
£6222 $10329 €9022 Doges Palace from the Dogana (46x81cm-18x32in) s. canvas on board. 16-Jun-3 Waddingtons, Toronto #176/R est:10000-15000 (C.D 14000)
£6351 $9972 €9527 Canal Grande, Venice (46x81cm-18x32in) s. 16-Dec-2 Lilla Bukowskis, Stockholm #538 est:5000-7000 (S.KR 90000)
£7200 $11664 €10800 Vessels before Santa Maria della Salute, Venice. Vessels on the lagoon (41x61cm-16x24in) s. pair. 23-Jan-3 Christie's, Kensington #143/R est:3000-5000

VIVIAN, Miss Jane (fl.1869-1877) British
£7500 $11925 €11250 Venetian canal scene (80x45cm-31x18in) s. 19-Mar-3 Anthemion, Cardiff #427/R est:2500-3000

VIVIANI, Giuseppe (1898-1965) Italian
£1378 $2178 €2150 Mushrooms (29x39cm-11x15in) board painted 1929. 12-Nov-2 Babuino, Rome #285/R
£2564 $4026 €4000 Woman reading (41x59cm-16x23in) s.d.936 cardboard. 19-Nov-2 Finarte, Milan #274/R
Prints
£2027 $3162 €3000 Kite (32x38cm-13x15in) s.d.952 eau forte on copper lit. 28-Mar-3 Farsetti, Prato #276/R
£2027 $3162 €3000 Lampreys (26x33cm-10x13in) s.d.941 eau forte on copper lit. 28-Mar-3 Farsetti, Prato #364/R
£2095 $3268 €3100 Dog and arum lilies (18x23cm-7x9in) s.d.942 eau forte on copper lit. 28-Mar-3 Farsetti, Prato #96/R
£2162 $3373 €3200 Watermelon and chair (37x28cm-15x11in) s.d.938 eau forte on copper lit. 28-Mar-3 Farsetti, Prato #135/R
£2432 $3795 €3600 Still life in Bocca d'Arno (35x28cm-14x11in) s. drypoint exec.1936 lit. 28-Mar-3 Farsetti, Prato #137/R

VIVIANI, Prof G (20th C) Italian
Sculpture
£1600 $2528 €2400 Female figure (82cm-32in) i. alabaster. 14-Nov-2 Christie's, Kensington #121/R est:1500-2000

VIVIANI, Raoul (1883-1965) Italian
£516 $815 €800 White roses (48x33cm-19x13in) s. cardboard. 18-Dec-2 Finarte, Milan #250
£1154 $1685 €1800 Landscape (80x115cm-31x45in) s. 5-Jun-2 Il Ponte, Milan #3
£2581 $4077 €4000 Venice, Palazzo Ducale (122x112cm-48x44in) s. 18-Dec-2 Finarte, Milan #148/R est:5000

VIVIN, Louis (1861-1936) French
£552 $872 €800 Vaches (25x33cm-10x13in) s. canvas on panel prov.exhib. 4-Apr-3 Tajan, Paris #11/R
£1293 $2055 €1900 Montmartre (46x38cm-18x15in) s. 28-Feb-3 Joron-Derem, Paris #36/R
£2013 $3200 €3020 Scene de village (38x55cm-15x22in) s. painted c.1930 prov. 27-Feb-3 Christie's, Rockefeller NY #126/R est:5000
£3949 $6160 €6200 Tigres (49x60cm-19x24in) s. exhib. 5-Nov-2 Tajan, Paris #60/R est:7000-8000
£6500 $10010 €9750 Le dejeuner sur l'herbe (38x55cm-15x22in) s. painted c.1925 prov. 22-Oct-2 Sotheby's, London #151/R est:6000-8000

VIVO, Tommaso de (1790-1884) Italian
£101266 $160000 €151899 Allegory of America (208x316cm-82x124in) s. 24-Apr-3 Sotheby's, New York #41/R est:180000-220000

VIVOT, Lea (1952-) Canadian/Czech
Sculpture
£2263 $3508 €3395 New generation (36cm-14in) s.d.99 num.7/12 bronze. 3-Dec-2 Joyner, Toronto #229/R est:5000-6000 (C.D 5500)
£2469 $3827 €3704 Hammock (50cm-20in) s.d.96 num.3/12 bronze. 3-Dec-2 Joyner, Toronto #144/R est:8000-10000 (C.D 6000)
£2675 $4146 €4013 On the swing (50cm-20in) s.d.95 num.A/P bronze. 3-Dec-2 Joyner, Toronto #192/R est:7000-8000 (C.D 6500)

VIVREL, Andre (1886-?) French
Works on paper
£305 $500 €458 Portrait of a woman in black (56x46cm-22x18in) s.d.1929 pastel paper on canvas. 5-Feb-3 Doyle, New York #73/R

VIZKELETY, Emerich (1819-1895) Hungarian
£280 $428 €420 Dutch flower market on the quayside (76x60cm-30x24in) s. 20-Aug-2 Rosebery Fine Art, London #535
£321 $506 €500 Man playing violin with woman tending baby in crib (61x79cm-24x31in) s. 15-Nov-2 Reiss & Sohn, Konigstein #91/R
£952 $1514 €1400 Flower market (50x70cm-20x28in) s. 25-Feb-3 Dorotheum, Vienna #174/R

VIZZARDI, Laura (1965-) Italian
£2278 $3554 €3600 Monica (150x100cm-59x39in) init.i. s.d.2001 verso. 14-Sep-2 Meeting Art, Vercelli #778/R

VLAANDEREN, Karel van (1903-1983) Belgian
£314 $484 €500 Nu dans un paysage (40x50cm-16x20in) canvas on cardboard exhib. 22-Oct-2 Campo, Vlaamse Kaai #332

VLADIMIROFF, Ivan Alexeievitch (1869-1947) Russian
£1127 $1814 €1600 Stormy sea (32x42cm-13x17in) s. board. 10-May-3 Bukowskis, Helsinki #381/R est:2000-2500
£1899 $3000 €3000 The siege of Petrograd (53x70cm-21x28in) s.d.1917. 1-Dec-2 Bukowskis, Helsinki #284/R est:3000-4000
Works on paper
£2817 $4535 €4000 Guarding the factory (48x71cm-19x28in) s. W/C. 10-May-3 Bukowskis, Helsinki #412/R est:2000-2500

VLAMINCK, Janny (20th C) Belgian
£577 $906 €900 Still life with Arlequin, feather and letter (53x44cm-21x17in) s.d.1986 panel. 16-Dec-2 Bernaerts, Antwerp #812

VLAMINCK, Maurice de (1876-1958) French
£3526 $5535 €5500 Composition florale (41x55cm-16x22in) lit. 15-Dec-2 Eric Pillon, Calais #171/R
£8784 $13703 €13000 Vase de fleurs (46x33cm-18x13in) s. 26-Mar-3 Millon & Associes, Paris #85/R
£10000 $15600 €15000 Street scene (46x55cm-18x22in) s. prov. 10-Apr-3 Tennants, Leyburn #1130 est:10000-15000
£11000 $16940 €16500 Jetee de fleurs (27x34cm-11x13in) board. 22-Oct-2 Sotheby's, London #167/R est:12000-15000
£12903 $20387 €20000 Nature morte aux oignons (50x61cm-20x24in) s. prov. 18-Dec-2 Ferri, Paris #112/R est:35000
£15000 $24600 €22500 Nature morte aux poissons (54x74cm-21x29in) s. prov. 5-Feb-3 Sotheby's, London #271/R est:25000
£16000 $26720 €23200 Bouquet de fleurs (46x38cm-18x15in) s. 24-Jun-3 Sotheby's, London #183/R est:16000-18000
£16564 $27000 €24846 Vase de fleurs (66x51cm-26x20in) s. painted 1917 prov. 12-Feb-3 Sotheby's, New York #123/R est:25000-35000
£16892 $26351 €25000 Route de campagnea et maison (50x61cm-20x24in) s. prov. 26-Mar-3 Millon & Associes, Paris #84/R est:45000
£18065 $28000 €27098 Moulin a vent, paysage orageux (54x65cm-21x26in) s. painted 1938 prov. 26-Sep-2 Christie's, Rockefeller NY #597/R est:30000-35000
£18354 $28449 €29000 Bouquet de fleurs (55x38cm-22x15in) s. paper on canvas prov. 28-Sep-2 Christie's, Paris #33/R est:2800-34000
£19000 $31160 €28500 Rue de village en hiver (33x41cm-13x16in) s. painted c.1930 prov. 5-Feb-3 Sotheby's, London #262/R est:30000
£20000 $30800 €30000 Paysage de mer (63x81cm-25x32in) s. 22-Oct-2 Sotheby's, London #211/R est:20000-30000
£20000 $32800 €30000 Bouquet de fleurs (46x38cm-18x15in) s. 4-Feb-3 Christie's, London #287/R est:30000
£20000 $32800 €30000 Paysage de tempete (60x73cm-24x29in) s. 4-Feb-3 Christie's, London #337/R est:30000
£22000 $36080 €33000 Meule (54x65cm-21x26in) s. prov. 5-Feb-3 Sotheby's, London #225/R est:35000
£22436 $35000 €33654 Paysage (46x55cm-18x22in) s. prov. 7-Nov-2 Christie's, Rockefeller NY #358/R est:35000-45000
£22436 $35224 €35000 Rue de village (46x61cm-18x24in) s. prov. 10-Dec-2 Pierre Berge, Paris #44/R est:35000
£24038 $37500 €36057 Rue de village (46x55cm-18x22in) s. prov. 6-Nov-2 Sotheby's, New York #353/R est:40000-60000
£24845 $40000 €37268 Bouquet de capucines (46x33cm-18x13in) s. prov. 8-May-3 Christie's, Rockefeller NY #186/R est:35000-45000
£25641 $40256 €40000 Vase de fleurs (65x50cm-26x20in) s. lit. 10-Dec-2 Artcurial Briest, Paris #483/R est:40000-50000
£25806 $40774 €40000 Chateau (54x73cm-21x29in) s. painted 1926 lit. 18-Dec-2 Tajan, Paris #67/R est:50000
£25806 $40774 €40000 Vase de fleurs (38x46cm-15x18in) s. prov.lit. 18-Dec-2 Tajan, Paris #69/R est:45000
£26000 $42640 €39000 Bouquet de fleurs (55x46cm-22x18in) s. 4-Feb-3 Christie's, London #285/R est:35000
£26000 $42640 €39000 Vase de fleurs (53x45cm-21x18in) s. prov. 4-Feb-3 Christie's, London #333/R est:30000
£27950 $45000 €41925 Vase de fleurs (73x55cm-29x22in) s. prov. 8-May-3 Christie's, Rockefeller NY #224/R est:40000-60000
£28846 $45000 €43269 Village en hiver (65x81cm-26x32in) s. prov. 6-Nov-2 Sotheby's, New York #351/R est:50000-70000
£28846 $45000 €43269 Vase de fleurs (55x38cm-22x15in) s. 7-Nov-2 Christie's, Rockefeller NY #280/R est:35000-45000
£30000 $50100 €43500 Roses de noel (55x38cm-22x15in) s. painted 1933-35 prov. 25-Jun-3 Christie's, London #171/R est:22000-28000
£32000 $53440 €46400 Route de village en hiver (54x65cm-21x26in) s. prov.exhib. 25-Jun-3 Christie's, London #146/R est:35000-45000
£35000 $58450 €50750 Paysage a bougival (38x55cm-15x22in) s. painted 1914-15. 24-Jun-3 Sotheby's, London #201/R est:40000-60000
£35256 $55353 €55000 Bord de riviere (60x73cm-24x29in) s. 20-Nov-2 Binoche, Paris #47/R est:55000-60000
£35256 $55705 €55000 Paysage de neige (54x65cm-21x26in) s. 15-Nov-2 Laurence Calmels, Paris #16a/R est:60000
£37267 $60000 €55901 Paysage (50x65cm-20x26in) s. 8-May-3 Christie's, Rockefeller NY #219/R est:35000-45000
£38462 $60000 €57693 Paysage en ete (65x81cm-26x32in) s. prov. 6-Nov-2 Sotheby's, New York #191/R est:70000-90000
£41667 $65000 €62501 Une cour de ferme (73x91cm-29x36in) s. 6-Nov-2 Sotheby's, New York #196/R est:70000-90000
£43165 $70791 €60000 Paysage (46x55cm-18x22in) s. 4-Jun-3 Marc Kohn, Paris #39/R est:60000-65000
£45513 $71910 €71000 Paysage au champ de ble (60x73cm-24x29in) s. 15-Nov-2 Laurence Calmels, Paris #19a/R
£49689 $80000 €74534 Le village (65x81cm-26x32in) s. painted c.1918 prov. 8-May-3 Christie's, Rockefeller NY #196/R est:100000-150000
£50633 $78987 €80000 Silhouette pres d'un village aux abords d'un canal (67x81cm-26x32in) s. prov.lit. 31-Jul-2 Tajan, Paris #21/R est:90000-120000
£57692 $90000 €86538 Village au bord de la riviere (65x82cm-26x32in) s. prov. 7-Nov-2 Christie's, Rockefeller NY #275/R est:80000-100000
£58000 $96860 €84100 Village sous la neige (65x78cm-26x31in) s. 25-Jun-3 Christie's, London #165/R est:40000-60000
£68000 $113560 €98600 Nature morte au pichet bleu (60x73cm-24x29in) s. painted 1910-12 prov. 24-Jun-3 Sotheby's, London #146/R est:70000-90000
£68323 $110000 €102485 Village en hiver (81x100cm-32x39in) s. prov. 8-May-3 Christie's, Rockefeller NY #180/R est:70000-90000
£74534 $120000 €111801 Voilier (60x76cm-24x30in) s. painted c.1915 prov. 7-May-3 Sotheby's, New York #179/R est:100000-150000
£75000 $125250 €108750 Bord de la riviere (65x81cm-26x32in) s. painted c.1912 prov. 25-Jun-3 Christie's, London #187/R est:60000-80000
£275641 $432756 €430000 Paysage au bord de l'eau, Chatou (81x65cm-32x26in) s. painted c.1907. 22-Nov-2 Millon & Associes, Paris #66/R
£372671 $600000 €559007 Paysage a Chatou (74x55cm-29x22in) s. prov. 6-May-3 Sotheby's, New York #22/R est:700000
Prints
£2051 $3221 €3200 Le Sausseron (465x630cm-183x248in) s.i. lithograph. 12-Dec-2 Piasa, Paris #194/R
Works on paper
£1517 $2534 €2200 La ferme (22x28cm-9x11in) s. Indian ink dr. 9-Jul-3 Cornette de St.Cyr, Paris #201/R est:2500-3000

£2207 $3686 €3200 Le port (19x26cm-7x10in) s. Indian ink dr. 9-Jul-3 Cornette de St.Cyr, Paris #200/R est:3500-4000
£4295 $6657 €6700 Rue de village (23x31cm-9x12in) s. gouache. 6-Dec-2 Rieunier, Bailly-Pommery, Mathias, Paris #73/R
£4930 $8183 €7000 Route un soir d'orage (24x31cm-9x12in) s. W/C ink prov.lit. 11-Jun-3 Beaussant & Lefèvre, Paris #203/R est:6000-8000
£4965 $8043 €7000 Maison (31x42cm-12x17in) s. W/C gouache. 21-May-3 Cornette de St.Cyr, Paris #55/R est:8000-10000
£5484 $8500 €8226 L'arbe au bord de l'eau (45x55cm-18x22in) s. W/C gouache prov.exhib. 26-Sep-2 Christie's, Rockefeller NY #566/R est:8000-12000
£5860 $8497 €9200 Village (45x54cm-18x21in) s. ink W/C gouache. 31-May-2 Blanchet, Paris #40/R
£6000 $9360 €9000 French town (44x53cm-17x21in) s. W/C brush ink bodycol prov. 10-Apr-3 Tennants, Leyburn #909/R est:6000-8000
£6410 $9744 €10000 Bouquet de fleurs (36x28cm-14x11in) s. W/C prov.lit. 16-Aug-2 Deauville, France #45/R
£6962 $10791 €11000 Paysage (49x60cm-19x24in) s. W/C ink prov.lit. 28-Sep-2 Cornette de St.Cyr, Paris #208/R est:12000-15000
£7742 $12000 €11613 Scene de rue (45x54cm-18x21in) s. gouache brush India ink wash paper on board prov. 26-Sep-2 Christie's, Rockefeller NY #605/R est:12000-16000
£8000 $13120 €12000 Paysage avec arbre (45x55cm-18x22in) s. W/C gouache pen ink prov. 5-Feb-3 Sotheby's, London #241/R est:12000
£8500 $13090 €12750 Village (45x53cm-18x21in) s. pen brush ink gouache W/C. 22-Oct-2 Sotheby's, London #210/R est:8000-10000
£10000 $15400 €15000 Chaponval (46x61cm-18x24in) s. gouache W/C brush ink prov. 22-Oct-2 Sotheby's, London #244/R est:9000-12000
£11656 $19000 €17484 Rue de village (49x61cm-19x24in) s. gouache executed c.1935 prov. 12-Feb-3 Sotheby's, New York #56/R est:20000-30000
£12000 $20040 €17400 Le village (25x33cm-10x13in) s. gouache pen ink paper on canvas prov. 24-Jun-3 Sotheby's, London #273/R est:10000-15000
£13665 $22000 €20498 Les meules (39x47cm-15x19in) s. gouache W/C brush ink paper on board executed c.1920-25 prov. 8-May-3 Christie's, Rockefeller NY #134/R est:18000-25000
£17628 $27500 €26442 Vue de village sous la neige (50x65cm-20x26in) s. W/C gouache prov. 6-Nov-2 Sotheby's, New York #343/R est:25000-35000

VLASSELAER, Julien (1907-1982) Belgian
£361 $574 €520 Centaur (36x32cm-14x13in) s.d.1936 paper. 29-Apr-3 Campo & Campo, Antwerp #331/R

VLEUGHELS, Nicolas (attrib) (1668-1737) French
£2027 $3162 €3000 Apollo in the Chariot of the Sun with allegories of the four seasons (30x44cm-12x17in) paper on canvas. 27-Mar-3 Dorotheum, Vienna #383/R est:2800-3500

VLIEGER, Simon de (1600-1653) Dutch
£8537 $14000 €12806 Fishing boats and other vessels offshore in a choppy sea (46x74cm-18x29in) panel prov.exhib. 29-May-3 Sotheby's, New York #19/R est:15000-20000
£780000 $1302600 €1131000 Squadron of Admiral Maerten Harpertsz Tromp preparing to make sail, the flagship (45x71cm-18x28in) panel prov. 9-Jul-3 Christie's, London #41/R est:100000-150000

VLIEGER, Simon de (attrib) (1600-1653) Dutch
£968 $1423 €1500 Calm sea (36x48cm-14x19in) panel oval. 20-Jun-2 Dr Fritz Nagel, Stuttgart #744/R

VLIET, Hendrik Cornelisz van der (1611-1675) Dutch
£2548 $3975 €4000 Portrait of Cleric, aged 65 (77x61cm-30x24in) s.i.d.1669 prov.exhib.lit. 5-Nov-2 Sotheby's, Amsterdam #108/R est:5000-7000

VLIET, Hendrik Cornelisz van der (attrib) (1611-1675) Dutch
£1348 $2089 €2022 Church interior with figures (32x29cm-13x11in) indis.sig. panel. 3-Dec-2 Bukowskis, Stockholm #492/R est:25000-30000 (S.KR 19000)

VLIST, Leendert van der (1894-1962) Dutch
£350 $546 €550 Still life with pottery and pipe from Gouda (33x70cm-13x28in) s. 6-Nov-2 Vendue Huis, Gravenhage #617/R

VLIST, Leendert van der (attrib) (1894-1962) Dutch
£280 $468 €406 Feeding chickens in a yard by a church with a village (60x45cm-24x18in) s.d.20 canvas on board. 17-Jun-3 Rosebery Fine Art, London #520

VOCHOC, Jan (19/20th C) ?
£1403 $2245 €1950 Le jardin du Luxembourg (33x46cm-13x18in) s. painted c.1900. 14-May-3 Blanchet, Paris #75

VODICKA, Rudolf (1879-1924) Austrian
Works on paper
£338 $527 €500 Evening (33x49cm-13x19in) s.d.1916 W/C. 28-Mar-3 Dorotheum, Vienna #271/R

VOELCKER, Rudolph A (1873-?) American
£645 $1000 €968 Ships graveyard with figure digging on the shore (76x91cm-30x36in) s. 21-Jul-2 Jeffery Burchard, Florida #36a/R

VOELLMY, Fritz (1863-?) Swiss
£545 $855 €850 Dutch dune landscape with windmill (60x92cm-24x36in) s. 21-Nov-2 Van Ham, Cologne #1955/R

VOERMAN, Jan (jnr) (1890-1976) Dutch
£690 $1097 €1000 Forest lane (30x20cm-12x8in) s.d.43 plywood. 10-Mar-3 Sotheby's, Amsterdam #205 est:1000-1500
£1645 $2664 €2500 Vlaamse Kaai in winter (27x21cm-11x8in) s. canvas on board. 21-Jan-3 Christie's, Amsterdam #270/R est:3000-5000
£1645 $2664 €2500 Still life with hyacinth and tulips (24x18cm-9x7in) s. canvas on panel. 21-Jan-3 Christie's, Amsterdam #277/R est:1800-2200
£1806 $2979 €2600 Precious flowers (22x16cm-9x6in) s. canvas on board. 1-Jul-3 Christie's, Amsterdam #174/R est:1200-1600

VOERMAN, Jan (snr) (1857-1941) Dutch
£3019 $4649 €4800 Het kleine veer (27x35cm-11x14in) init. canvas on panel prov. 23-Oct-2 Christie's, Amsterdam #161/R est:5000-7000
£3822 $5885 €6000 Rivel Ussel on a cloudy day (31x53cm-12x21in) s. panel. 3-Sep-2 Christie's, Amsterdam #275/R est:4000-6000
Works on paper
£4717 $7264 €7500 Cows along the river Ijssel (59x80cm-23x31in) init. W/C. 22-Oct-2 Sotheby's, Amsterdam #119/R est:3500-4500

VOET, Jacob Ferdinand (1639-c.1700) Flemish
£13000 $20280 €19500 Portrait of Emmanuel Theodore de la Tour d'Auvergne (73x60cm-29x24in) 10-Apr-3 Sotheby's, London #76/R est:12000

VOET, Jacob Ferdinand (attrib) (1639-c.1700) Flemish
£3012 $5000 €4367 Portrait of Roman woman in Renaissance dress (74x61cm-29x24in) 11-Jun-3 Boos Gallery, Michigan #402/R est:6000-8000
£5500 $9185 €7975 Portrait of a lady in pearl drop earrings, pearl necklace (72x58cm-28x23in) oval. 11-Jul-3 Christie's, Kensington #182/R est:5000-8000
£15000 $23400 €22500 Portrait of a gentleman in a red bow tie (49x38cm-19x15in) prov. 9-Apr-3 Christie's, London #71/R est:15000-20000

VOGEL, Bernard (1683-1737) German
£811 $1265 €1200 New York (39x29cm-15x11in) s.d.1997 acrylic collage cardboard cloth newspaper board. 28-Mar-3 Ketterer, Hamburg #679/R
Works on paper
£949 $1481 €1500 Still life of roses (54x74cm-21x29in) s. W/C. 15-Oct-2 Dorotheum, Vienna #268/R est:1400-2000

VOGEL, H (19/20th C) ?
£348 $540 €550 Ruin landscape by moonlight with figures (86x98cm-34x39in) s.d.1900 panel. 27-Sep-2 Weidler, Nurnberg #8972/R
£2987 $4451 €4600 Dream of love (72x131cm-28x52in) s.d.1917. 26-Jun-2 Neumeister, Munich #898/R est:3000

VOGEL, Louis (fl.1850-1860) German
£2300 $3657 €3335 Half length portrait of a lady in a black dress (43x36cm-17x14in) s.i.verso. 19-Mar-3 John Nicholson, Haslemere #1169 est:2500-3000

VOGEL, Ludwig (1788-1879) Swiss
£349 $552 €524 Blooming stems of rhubarb (27x19cm-11x7in) 14-Nov-2 Stuker, Bern #578 (S.FR 800)
Works on paper
£641 $1013 €1000 Expulsion of Hagar (16x20cm-6x8in) s.d.1819 pen wash prov. 16-Nov-2 Lempertz, Koln #1412

VOGEL, Ludwig (attrib) (1788-1879) Swiss
£325 $503 €488 Male nude (59x44cm-23x17in) canvasboard. 24-Sep-2 Koller, Zurich #6611/R (S.FR 750)

VOGEL, Valentine (1906-) American
£276 $425 €414 Still life (76x64cm-30x25in) s. painted c.1945. 8-Sep-2 Treadway Gallery, Cincinnati #647/R

VOGEL, Werner (1889-?) German
£314 $491 €500 Summer idyll on the Eifel (60x80cm-24x31in) s. panel. 21-Sep-2 Bolland & Marotz, Bremen #668/R

VOGEL, Willy (1910-1987) German
£253 $400 €400 Clear winter evening on the fens (60x80cm-24x31in) s. board. 29-Nov-2 Bolland & Marotz, Bremen #586

VOGEL-JORGENSEN, Age (1888-1964) Danish
£422 $659 €633 Composition (56x48cm-22x19in) init. masonite. 18-Sep-2 Kunsthallen, Copenhagen #269/R (D.KR 5000)

VOGELAER, Karel van (1653-1695) Dutch
£11585 $19000 €17378 Still life of flowers in a vase (63x50cm-25x20in) bears false i. 29-May-3 Sotheby's, New York #50/R est:15000-20000
£12000 $20040 €17400 Peonies, roses, tulips and other flowers in a glass vase (99x74cm-39x29in) 9-Jul-3 Bonhams, New Bond Street #22/R est:10000-15000

VOGELER, Heinrich (1872-1942) German
£629 $981 €1000 Theatre scene (15x20cm-6x8in) s. col chk over pencil. 21-Sep-2 Bolland & Marotz, Bremen #414/R

VOGELS, Guillaume (1836-1896) Belgian
£1026 $1621 €1600 Landscape in the fall with figure. 18-Nov-2 Bernaerts, Antwerp #321/R est:1000-1500
£2138 $3293 €3400 Still life with vase (24x20cm-9x8in) s. panel. 22-Oct-2 Campo & Campo, Antwerp #325/R
£2288 $3683 €3500 Paysage boise (21x28cm-8x11in) s. canvas on panel. 14-Jan-3 Vanderkindere, Brussels #73 est:600-800
£3034 $4855 €4400 Path in the snow (50x30cm-20x12in) s. painted c.1877 exhib.lit. 15-Mar-3 De Vuyst, Lokeren #392/R est:4000-5000
£4808 $7452 €7500 Winter - snow (34x49cm-13x19in) s. painted c.1875 prov.lit. 7-Dec-2 De Vuyst, Lokeren #435a/R est:7500-8500
Works on paper
£517 $828 €750 Chemin a la campagne (23x34cm-9x13in) s. W/C gouache prov.exhib.lit. 15-Mar-3 De Vuyst, Lokeren #393

VOGELSANG, Christian Rudolf (1824-1911) Danish
£299 $475 €449 Portrait of girl (25x20cm-10x8in) init. 5-May-3 Rasmussen, Vejle #413/R (D.KR 3200)

VOGLAR, Karl (1888-1972) Austrian
£288 $438 €450 Still life of flowers in two pots (80x70cm-31x28in) s.d.38. 31-Aug-2 Geble, Radolfzell #668
£769 $1169 €1200 Cat on table (80x70cm-31x28in) s.d.54. 31-Aug-2 Geble, Radolfzell #669/R
£1346 $2046 €2100 View through forest clearing of city, possibly Graz (85x73cm-33x29in) s. 31-Aug-2 Geble, Radolfzell #670/R est:400

VOGLER, Paul (1852-1904) French
£705 $1107 €1100 Paysage de bords de riviere (27x46cm-11x18in) s. 16-Dec-2 Millon & Associes, Paris #153/R

VOGT, Adolf (1843-1871) American
£305 $479 €458 Sunlight's beam inside the stable (18x23cm-7x9in) s. board. 10-Dec-2 Pinneys, Montreal #139 (C.D 750)

VOGT, Helene (1902-1994) French
£2518 $4130 €3500 Fillette Marocaine (65x50cm-26x20in) s. panel. 4-Jun-3 Tajan, Paris #316/R est:2700-3000

VOHRABAL, Josef (1908-) Czechoslovakian
£280 $443 €420 Composition with volumes (48x68cm-19x27in) s. i.d.1968 verso canvas on panel prov. 16-Nov-2 Crafoord, Lund #85/R (S.KR 4000)

VOIGT, Bruno (1912-1989) German
Works on paper
£463 $745 €695 Morning in the bar (47x35cm-19x14in) mono.d.3.III.1933 Indian ink W/C. 7-May-3 Dobiaschofsky, Bern #1042/R (S.FR 1000)
£521 $823 €750 Self portrait (27x20cm-11x8in) mono. W/C col pen over pencil board. 26-Apr-3 Dr Lehr, Berlin #527/R
£1014 $1664 €1400 Class against class (30x25cm-12x10in) mono. Indian ink paper on board two. 31-May-3 Villa Grisebach, Berlin #714/R est:1400-1800
£1304 $2139 €1800 In the pub (47x30cm-19x12in) mono. Indian ink. 31-May-3 Villa Grisebach, Berlin #713/R est:1800-2400
£1594 $2614 €2200 Outside the pub (51x36cm-20x14in) mono.d.5.6.39 W/C Indian ink. 31-May-3 Villa Grisebach, Berlin #711/R est:2200-2500
£2609 $4278 €3600 Worker (50x33cm-20x13in) mono.d.5.7.39 W/C Indian ink. 31-May-3 Villa Grisebach, Berlin #710/R est:2000-2400

VOIGT, David (1944-) Australian
£438 $719 €635 Abstract landscape (120x150cm-47x59in) s. 3-Jun-3 Lawson Menzies, Sydney #903 (A.D 1100)

VOIGT, Julie (19th C) German
£307 $500 €461 Wedding dress (61x46cm-24x18in) i.verso painted c.1840. 2-Feb-3 Grogan, Boston #4

VOIRIN, Leon-Joseph (1833-1887) French
£6800 $11016 €10200 Sur les quais de la Seine (38x47cm-15x19in) s. 20-May-3 Sotheby's, Olympia #422/R est:2000-3000

VOIRIOT, Guillaume (attrib) (1713-1799) French
Works on paper
£962 $1510 €1500 Portrait d'homme (60x50cm-24x20in) pastel. 21-Nov-2 Neret-Minet, Paris #59/R

VOIS, Arie de (circle) (1631-1680) Flemish
£12000 $18720 €18000 Portrait of a gentleman, said to be Adrian van der Werff, as Bacchus (20x17cm-8x7in) i. copper prov. 9-Apr-3 Christie's, London #52/R est:6000-8000

VOISARD-MARGERIE, A G (1867-1954) French
£2158 $3453 €3000 Portrait de deux jeunes filles en pied (164x131cm-65x52in) 16-May-3 Lombrail & Teucquam, Paris #103

VOITELLIER, Marie Theophile (fl.1845-1859) French
£3901 $6319 €5500 Large bunch of flowers with butterflies and pineapple (100x61cm-39x24in) s.d.1852. 22-May-3 Dorotheum, Vienna #114/R est:3600-4200

VOKOS, Nicolaos (1861-1902) Greek
£4800 $7584 €7200 Still life with fish (33x46cm-13x18in) 1-Apr-3 Bonhams, New Bond Street #11 est:3500-5000

VOLAIRE, Pierre Jacques (1729-1802) French
£20000 $31400 €30000 Vesuvius erupting at night (98x128cm-39x50in) 11-Dec-2 Christie's, London #84/R
Works on paper
£13836 $21585 €22000 Nocturnal fishing (53x63cm-21x25in) s. gouache prov. 20-Sep-2 Millon & Associes, Paris #332/R est:25000-40000

VOLANEK, Raimund (20th C) Austrian
£685 $1075 €1000 Kals in Isar valley (26x21cm-10x8in) s. panel. 16-Apr-3 Dorotheum, Salzburg #124/R
£685 $1075 €1000 Maria Zell in the Steiermark (26x21cm-10x8in) s. panel. 16-Apr-3 Dorotheum, Salzburg #125/R

VOLANG, Jean (1921-) Vietnamese
£1338 $2154 €1900 Le mat penche (54x65cm-21x26in) s. 11-May-3 Thierry & Lannon, Brest #285/R est:1500-2000

VOLBRECHT, Ernst (1877-1964) German
£380 $593 €570 Sunset over landscape (39x52cm-15x20in) s. board. 17-Sep-2 Bonhams, Knightsbridge #89

VOLCKAERT, Piet (1902-1973) Belgian
£253 $395 €400 Ruelle de Bruxelles animee sous la pluie (60x50cm-24x20in) s. 10-Sep-2 Vanderkindere, Brussels #396
£266 $415 €420 Ruelle animee (60x50cm-24x20in) s. 16-Sep-2 Horta, Bruxelles #276
£446 $696 €700 Peniches au quai de chargement (40x50cm-16x20in) s. 11-Nov-2 Horta, Bruxelles #565
£470 $756 €700 Ruelle ensoleillee (50x40cm-20x16in) s. 18-Feb-3 Galerie Moderne, Brussels #374
£481 $755 €750 Entree de la ferme blanche (100x100cm-39x39in) s. 19-Nov-2 Vanderkindere, Brussels #153
£545 $855 €850 Ruelle animee au pied du Palais de Justice de Bruxelles (80x60cm-31x24in) s. 19-Nov-2 Vanderkindere, Brussels #159
£680 $1082 €1000 Vue de ville (50x60cm-20x24in) s. 18-Mar-3 Galerie Moderne, Brussels #506
£1154 $1812 €1800 Le marche aux puces (70x90cm-28x35in) s. 19-Nov-2 Vanderkindere, Brussels #198 est:1250-1500

VOLCKANISECK, A (19th C) ?
£1335 $2190 €1936 Still life of flowers with red drapery background (112x75cm-44x30in) s. 4-Jun-3 AB Stockholms Auktionsverk #2496/R est:20000-30000 (S.KR 17000)

VOLCKER, Robert (1854-1924) German
£775 $1247 €1100 Young girl in traditional costume (32x23cm-13x9in) s.i. panel. 7-May-3 Michael Zeller, Lindau #957/R

VOLCKERT, Hugo (attrib) (19th C) German
£255 $397 €400 Deer in forest clearing (29x36cm-11x14in) paper. 7-Nov-2 Allgauer, Kempten #2999/R

VOLKER, Karl (1889-1962) German
Works on paper
£1069 $1647 €1700 Mother with child (38x53cm-15x21in) s.d.1920 W/C over pencil board. 26-Oct-2 Dr Lehr, Berlin #563/R est:1500

VOLKERS, Emil (1831-1905) German
£1020 $1622 €1500 Invitation to play (24x32cm-9x13in) s.d.1890. 28-Mar-3 Bolland & Marotz, Bremen #535/R est:2700
£1026 $1610 €1600 White horse in stable (24x32cm-9x13in) s.d.98 panel. 21-Nov-2 Van Ham, Cologne #1958/R est:1800
£1282 $2013 €2000 Horse portrait (24x32cm-9x13in) s.d.97 panel. 21-Nov-2 Van Ham, Cologne #1957/R est:1800
£1479 $2381 €2100 Horse portrait (23x32cm-9x13in) s. panel. 10-May-3 Hans Stahl, Toestorf #46/R est:2200
£1942 $3108 €2700 Saddled horse and dog in stable (48x60cm-19x24in) s.d.1892. 17-May-3 Lempertz, Koln #1499/R est:3000
£2092 $3346 €3200 Brown horse with saddle in stable (32x44cm-13x17in) s.d.1901 panel lit. 10-Jan-3 Allgauer, Kempten #1818/R est:2000
£3019 $4679 €4800 Horse portrait (48x60cm-19x24in) s.d.1892. 2-Nov-2 Hans Stahl, Toestorf #32/R est:2800
£3221 $5187 €4800 Portrait of a saddled horse (48x60cm-19x24in) s. 18-Feb-3 Sotheby's, Amsterdam #969/R est:800-1200
£5128 $7949 €8000 Horse (33x44cm-13x17in) s.d.1899. 7-Dec-2 Hans Stahl, Hamburg #51/R est:2200
£6552 $10352 €9500 Horse (27x36cm-11x14in) s.d.1894. 5-Apr-3 Hans Stahl, Hamburg #49/R est:4500

VOLKERS, Karl (1868-1944) German
£506 $800 €800 Portrait of a horse and rider (70x100cm-28x39in) s.d.1944. 29-Nov-2 Bolland & Marotz, Bremen #784/R
£1494 $2225 €2300 Dream - brown horse (54x67cm-21x26in) s.i. 26-Jun-2 Neumeister, Munich #901/R est:1100
Works on paper
£563 $907 €800 Before setting off (33x47cm-13x19in) s.i.d.1893 gouache lit. 9-May-3 Schloss Ahlden, Ahlden #1479/R

VOLKERT, Edward Charles (1871-1935) American
£4459 $7000 €6689 Cattle resting in a lush landscape (20x28cm-8x11in) s. canvasboard prov. 19-Nov-2 Butterfields, San Francisco #8031/R est:3000-5000
Works on paper
£818 $1300 €1227 Cattle (35x50cm-14x20in) s. W/C pair. 7-Mar-3 Skinner, Boston #280/R est:700-900

VOLKMANN, Hans Richard von (1860-1927) German
£605 $944 €950 Bruyeres en automne (55x76cm-22x30in) s.d.1896. 11-Nov-2 Horta, Bruxelles #525
£886 $1382 €1400 Meadows (52x64cm-20x25in) s.d.1907. 18-Oct-2 Dr Fritz Nagel, Stuttgart #367/R
£962 $1510 €1500 Eifel landscape (52x64cm-20x25in) s. 21-Nov-2 Van Ham, Cologne #1960/R est:2000
£1565 $2488 €2300 Italian mountain landscape with farmstead (34x25cm-13x10in) s.d.1893. 28-Mar-3 Bolland & Marotz, Bremen #537/R est:1500
£1633 $2596 €2400 Evening in the Eifel (63x93cm-25x37in) s.d.Oct 1903/4. 28-Mar-3 Bolland & Marotz, Bremen #536/R est:2100
£1731 $2717 €2700 Kasselburg near Gerolstein (62x90cm-24x35in) s.d.1896. 21-Nov-2 Van Ham, Cologne #1959/R est:2800
£1849 $2885 €2700 Summer landscape with birch trees in the evening (50x65cm-20x26in) s.d.VIII 1911. 10-Apr-3 Van Ham, Cologne #1746 est:1800
Works on paper
£1132 $1766 €1800 Woman by temple. Woman with dog (29x42cm-11x17in) s. board lit. two. 20-Sep-2 Schloss Ahlden, Ahlden #1196/R est:1400

VOLKMAR, Charles (1841-1914) American
£1013 $1600 €1520 On the Irish coast (28x53cm-11x21in) s. 17-Nov-2 CRN Auctions, Cambridge #49/R

VOLL, Christoph (1897-1939) German
Works on paper
£260 $400 €390 Landscape (56x43cm-22x17in) s. gouache exec.c.1930. 8-Sep-2 Treadway Gallery, Cincinnati #688/R
£260 $400 €390 Artist painting at easel (56x43cm-22x17in) s. gouache exec.c.1930. 8-Sep-2 Treadway Gallery, Cincinnati #689/R
£267 $425 €401 Artist painting at easel (56x43cm-22x17in) s. gouache exec.c.1930. 2-Mar-3 Toomey, Oak Park #714/R
£377 $600 €566 Landscape (56x43cm-22x17in) s. gouache exec.c.1930. 2-Mar-3 Toomey, Oak Park #712/R
£513 $795 €800 Small child (65x50cm-26x20in) s. Indian ink. 4-Dec-2 Lempertz, Koln #1098/R
£641 $994 €1000 Man with boat (38x52cm-15x20in) s.d.22 W/C. 4-Dec-2 Lempertz, Koln #1100/R

VOLLBEHR, Ernst (1876-?) German
Works on paper
£440 $678 €700 Plon (38x54cm-15x21in) s.i. gouache. 26-Oct-2 Quittenbaum, Hamburg #129/R

VOLLERDT, Johann Christian (1708-1769) German
£692 $1079 €1100 Medieval town on fire (16x22cm-6x9in) panel. 9-Oct-2 Michael Zeller, Lindau #605/R
£755 $1177 €1200 Moonlit classical river landscape (16x22cm-6x9in) panel. 9-Oct-2 Michael Zeller, Lindau #606/R

VOLLEVENS, Johannes (elder) (1649-1728) Dutch
£8633 $13813 €12000 Market scene with two boys by a vegetable seller making lace (119x170cm-47x67in) s.d.1668. 14-May-3 Christie's, Amsterdam #193/R est:15000-25000

VOLLEVENS, Johannes (younger) (1685-1758) Dutch
£3500 $5845 €5075 Portrait of a gentleman, full length wearing armour and red velvet cloak (23x140cm-9x55in) s.d.1719 prov. 8-Jul-3 Sotheby's, Olympia #461/R est:4000-6000

VOLLIER, Nicolas Victor (19th C) French
£641 $1006 €1000 Sketch book (33x23cm-13x9in) s.d.1869 panel. 10-Dec-2 Dorotheum, Vienna #173/R

VOLLON, Alexis (1865-1945) French
£1923 $3019 €3000 Portrait d'Helene Vollon (130x97cm-51x38in) s.d.1934 exhib. 15-Dec-2 Eric Pillon, Calais #73/R

VOLLON, Antoine (1833-1900) French
£1100 $1826 €1595 Grey in a landscape (39x55cm-15x22in) s. canvas on board. 12-Jun-3 Christie's, Kensington #52/R est:1200-1800
£1410 $2200 €2115 Pitcher of beer and mussels (46x56cm-18x22in) s. 28-Mar-3 Aspire, Cleveland #2/R est:2500-3500
£1783 $2782 €2800 Singe fumeur dans un atelier d'artiste (45x38cm-18x15in) s. 11-Nov-2 Horta, Bruxelles #242 est:3500-4000
£2500 $4000 €3750 Still life of a violin (36x75cm-14x30in) s. 13-May-3 Bonhams, Knightsbridge #51/R est:400-600
£5500 $8635 €8250 Vase de fleurs (28x22cm-11x9in) s. panel. 21-Nov-2 Christie's, Kensington #83/R est:2000-3000
Works on paper
£762 $1241 €1150 Vue d'une ville du Nord (13x16cm-5x6in) studio st. graphite W/C htd white gouache. 2-Feb-3 Muizon & Le Coent, Paris #41

VOLLON, L (19th C) French?
£355 $574 €533 Still life of pewter dish, melons and grapes (90x116cm-35x46in) s. 25-Jan-3 Rasmussen, Havnen #2172 (D.KR 4000)

VOLOCHINE, Maximilien (1877-1932) ?
Works on paper
£2000 $3160 €3000 Landscape (26x34cm-10x13in) mono.d.1928 pen W/C paper on cardboard. 26-Nov-2 Christie's, Kensington #16/R est:2000-3000

VOLOVICK, Lazare (1902-1977) Russian
£1154 $1812 €1800 Vue de Notre-Dame (50x65cm-20x26in) s. 24-Nov-2 Chayette & Cheval, Paris #294a est:2000-2500
£1795 $2818 €2800 Vase de fleurs (65x54cm-26x21in) s. exhib. 12-Dec-2 Rabourdin & Choppin de Janvry, Paris #43/R

VOLPATO, Giovanni (1733-1803) Italian
Prints
£3205 $5032 €5000 View of the Pantheon in Rome (52x74cm-20x29in) i. engraving htd W/C. 21-Nov-2 Neret-Minet, Paris #9/R
£3946 $6116 €5919 Rome (74x51cm-29x20in) i. etching. 3-Oct-2 Koller, Zurich #3351/R est:4000-7000 (S.FR 9195)
Works on paper
£1244 $2015 €1804 Vue de la Villa Negrone a Rome (51x74cm-20x29in) s.i. W/C pen pencil. 26-May-3 Rasmussen, Copenhagen #1575/R est:8000-12000 (D.KR 13000)

VOLPE, Alessandro la (1820-1887) Italian

£2115 $3087 €3173 Southern landscape with ships and figures (18x26cm-7x10in) s. board. 17-Jun-2 Philippe Schuler, Zurich #4351/R est:2000-2500 (S.FR 4800)
£4600 $7130 €6900 Tornati dalla pesca (52x104cm-20x41in) s.d.68. 3-Dec-2 Sotheby's, Olympia #282/R est:4500-6000
£4630 $7454 €6714 Sorrento coast (43x71cm-17x28in) s. 7-May-3 Dobiaschofsky, Bern #760/R est:7500 (S.FR 10000)
£7025 $11029 €10538 Children and boats in the Bay of Naples (69x130cm-27x51in) s.d.85. 24-Jul-2 Walker's, Ottawa #36/R est:3000-5000 (C.D 17000)
£9119 $14044 €14500 View of Pompei with the Vesuvius (131x87cm-52x34in) s. 28-Oct-2 Il Ponte, Milan #282/R est:16000
£11500 $19205 €17250 Fishing vessels drying their sails off the coast of Capri (66x108cm-26x43in) s.d.79. 18-Jun-3 Christie's, Kensington #161/R est:7000-10000

Works on paper

£558 $882 €837 Facing Mt Vesuvius, Bay of Naples (29x53cm-11x21in) s. i.verso W/C. 3-Apr-3 Heffel, Vancouver #53/R (C.D 1300)

VOLPE, Vincenzo (1855-1929) Italian

£1000 $1560 €1500 Portrait of a young girl with flowers (88x57cm-35x22in) s. 8-Apr-3 Bonhams, Knightsbridge #128/R est:800-1200

VOLPINI, Renato (1934-) Italian

£1986 $3217 €2800 Il primo cosmonauta nell'universo stratificato dei mistificatori del sesso (100x80cm-39x31in) s.d.65 s.i.d.verso oil pencil. 26-May-3 Christie's, Milan #187/R est:2000-2500

VOLSCHENK, Jan E A (1853-1936) South African

£372 $580 €558 On the Highveld (18x24cm-7x9in) s.d.1909 s.i.d.1909 verso. 11-Nov-2 Stephan Welz, Johannesburg #545 (SA.R 5800)
£436 $680 €654 Extensive landscape (16x29cm-6x11in) bears sig. 11-Nov-2 Stephan Welz, Johannesburg #546 (SA.R 6800)
£500 $825 €725 Bywoners dwelling (18x33cm-7x13in) s. i.d.1911 verso. 3-Jul-3 Duke & Son, Dorchester #294/R
£1548 $2492 €2322 Vette River glen, riverside (37x49cm-15x19in) s.d.1926 s.i.d.verso. 12-May-3 Stephan Welz, Johannesburg #477/R est:15000-20000 (SA.R 18000)
£2236 $3599 €3354 Riversdale landscape, rock, bush and aloes (37x55cm-15x22in) s.d.1933 s.i.d.verso. 12-May-3 Stephan Welz, Johannesburg #476/R est:18000-24000 (SA.R 26000)

VOLTI, Antoniucci (1915-1990) French

Sculpture

£964 $1513 €1446 Crouching nude (15cm-6in) s. num.4/6 bronze. 25-Nov-2 Hodgins, Calgary #304/R est:1000-1250 (C.D 2400)
£1333 $2187 €2000 Resting girl (15cm-6in) s.num.5/6 bronze. 3-Jun-3 Joyner, Toronto #388/R est:1500-2000 (C.D 3000)
£1554 $2424 €2300 Femme nue en boule (8x14cm-3x6in) s. num.1/8 green pat bronze. 26-Mar-3 Millon & Associes, Paris #175/R
£2482 $4145 €3500 Modele les genoux replies le bras croises (18cm-7in) s. terracotta. 20-Jun-3 Piasa, Paris #126/R est:3000-5000
£2752 $4430 €4100 Les trois graces (40x27cm-16x11in) num.2/6 bronze bas relief. 23-Feb-3 Lesieur & Le Bars, Le Havre #153
£3077 $4831 €4800 Modele assis (19cm-7in) s. terracotta. 13-Dec-2 Piasa, Paris #260
£3165 $4937 €5000 Les deux amies (31x17x15cm-12x7x6in) s. num.1/8 green pat.bronze. 31-Jul-2 Tajan, Paris #50/R est:5500-6000
£3742 $5912 €5800 Pomone (28cm-11in) s. terracotta prov. 18-Dec-2 Digard, Paris #173/R
£4025 $6279 €6400 Nu assis jambes croisees (22cm-9in) s. num.1/8 green pat.bronze. 9-Oct-2 Lombrail & Teucquam, Paris #13/R
£4082 $6490 €6000 Le modele allonge, un bras replie (15x25x22cm-6x10x9in) s. terracotta. 2-Mar-3 Lombrail & Teucquam, Paris #167/R
£4088 $6336 €6500 Jeune femme accroupie (21x12x15cm-8x5x6in) s.num.4/6 blue green pat bronze Cast Susse. 30-Oct-2 Artcurial Briest, Paris #272/R est:6000-7000
£4113 $6870 €5800 Le repos du modele (14x33cm-6x13in) s. terracotta. 20-Jun-3 Piasa, Paris #127/R est:5000-8000
£4317 $6906 €6000 Nu en boule, bras et jambes replies (8x14cm-3x6in) s.num.1/8 green brown pat bronze Cast Godard. 18-May-3 Eric Pillon, Calais #186/R
£4747 $7405 €7500 Maternite debout (40cm-16in) s. num.2/8 black pat.bronze. 31-Jul-2 Tajan, Paris #51/R est:8000-10000
£4747 $7500 €7500 Nu allonge (15x31cm-6x12in) s. num.4/6 pat bronze Cast Godard. 27-Nov-2 Blanchet, Paris #75/R
£5063 $7899 €8000 La femme assise (22x18x18cm-9x7x7in) s. num.3/8 green pat.bronze. 31-Jul-2 Tajan, Paris #52/R est:7000-7500
£5935 $9378 €9200 Maternity (36cm-14in) s. num.4/6 grey pat bronze. 18-Dec-2 Digard, Paris #172/R
£6122 $9735 €9000 Fleur (22x47x48cm-9x19x19in) s.num.2/6 glue pat bronze st.f.Toronto prov.exhib. 26-Feb-3 Artcurial Briest, Paris #334/R est:8000-10000
£8861 $14000 €14000 Mama (30x25x20cm-12x10x8in) s. num.EA4/4 blue pat bronze Cast Delval. 27-Nov-2 Marc Kohn, Paris #53/R est:15000-18000
£11888 $19853 €17000 Carleen (47x40x23cm-19x16x9in) s.num.I/IV bronze st.f.Susse. 27-Jun-3 Claude Aguttes, Neuilly #69/R est:20000-25000
£15190 $24000 €24000 Endormie (22x53x32cm-9x21x13in) s. num.1/8 blue pat bronze Cast Susse. 27-Nov-2 Marc Kohn, Paris #54/R est:23000-25000
£18987 $30000 €30000 Carleen (47x23x40cm-19x9x16in) s. num.8/8 blue pat bronze Cast Susse. 27-Nov-2 Marc Kohn, Paris #52/R est:23000-25000
£19048 $30286 €28000 Femme assise de face (40x31x34cm-16x12x13in) s.num.6/6 green pat bronze st.f.Valsuani. 2-Mar-3 Lombrail & Teucquam, Paris #166/R

Works on paper

£566 $877 €900 Portrait de jeune femme (54x43cm-21x17in) s. sanguine. 30-Oct-2 Artcurial Briest, Paris #273
£576 $921 €800 Nu a genoux (33x26cm-13x10in) s. chl dr. 18-May-3 Eric Pillon, Calais #198/R
£647 $1036 €900 Nu allongee (50x63cm-20x25in) s. sanguine. 18-May-3 Eric Pillon, Calais #192/R
£755 $1209 €1050 Nu assis, jambes repliees (63x50cm-25x20in) s. chl. 18-May-3 Eric Pillon, Calais #194/R
£926 $1315 €1500 Portrait de jeune femme (55x44cm-22x17in) s. sanguine. 16-Mar-3 Eric Pillon, Calais #230/R
£935 $1496 €1300 Nu en buste au collier (60x47cm-24x19in) s. sanguine chl. 18-May-3 Eric Pillon, Calais #190/R
£1007 $1612 €1400 Nu allonge (31x47cm-12x19in) s. chl dr. 18-May-3 Eric Pillon, Calais #193/R
£1190 $1893 €1750 Le model (47x60cm-19x24in) s. sanguine. 2-Mar-3 Lombrail & Teucquam, Paris #168/R
£1210 $1888 €1900 Nu allonge (48x59cm-19x23in) s. sanguine. 10-Nov-2 Eric Pillon, Calais #170/R
£1223 $1957 €1700 Nu en buste (63x49cm-25x19in) s. sanguine. 18-May-3 Eric Pillon, Calais #185/R
£1439 $2360 €2000 Nu feminin (50x65cm-20x26in) s. sanguine. 4-Jun-3 Marc Kohn, Paris #50 est:1800-2200
£2734 $4374 €3800 Nu allonge, jambes repliees (49x64cm-19x25in) s. sanguine. 18-May-3 Eric Pillon, Calais #188/R
£3448 $5483 €5000 Nu allangui (92x73cm-36x29in) s. chl wax crayon panel. 7-Mar-3 Rabourdin & Choppin de Janvry, Paris #39/R est:3000-3500
£3453 $5525 €4800 Nu assis penche en avant (46x70cm-18x28in) s. sanguine. 18-May-3 Eric Pillon, Calais #187/R
£3453 $5525 €4800 Nu assis de dos (61x47cm-24x19in) s. sanguine. 18-May-3 Eric Pillon, Calais #189/R
£4747 $7500 €7500 Femme nue endormie (92x73cm-36x29in) s. chl crayon. 27-Nov-2 Marc Kohn, Paris #55
£5298 $8636 €8000 Nus assis (55x44cm-22x17in) s.d.1957 gouache dr. 1-Feb-3 Claude Aguttes, Neuilly #144/R est:915-1220

VOLTZ, F (1817-1886) German

£968 $1423 €1500 Cows on the ford (21x47cm-8x19in) s. 24-Jun-2 Dr Fritz Nagel, Stuttgart #6109/R

VOLTZ, Friedrich (1817-1886) German

£641 $994 €1000 Ox (30x40cm-12x16in) s. canvas on board. 5-Dec-2 Dr Fritz Nagel, Stuttgart #708/R
£980 $1569 €1500 Study of pair of shepherds and flock in Italian landscape (34x43cm-13x17in) paper on canvas. 10-Jan-3 Allgauer, Kempten #1820/R est:1800
£987 $1599 €1500 Cow's head (15x21cm-6x8in) oil paper on board prov. 21-Jan-3 Christie's, Amsterdam #28 est:700-900
£1132 $1766 €1800 Horse study (20x21cm-8x8in) s.i. board lit. 20-Sep-2 Schloss Ahlden, Ahlden #1233/R est:1800
£1223 $2006 €1700 Alpine lake (16x32cm-6x13in) mono. paper on board. 4-Jun-3 Reiss & Sohn, Konigstein #174/R est:2000
£1233 $1923 €1800 Herdress with three cows in moutain landscape (13x18cm-5x7in) mono. panel. 11-Apr-3 Winterberg, Heidelberg #612/R est:2800
£1300 $2119 €1950 Travellers on the way home from market in an Italianate landscape (28x34cm-11x13in) s. panel oval. 13-Feb-3 Christie's, Kensington #212/R est:700-1000
£1410 $2186 €2200 Bushes and flower plants in front of rocky stone (41x53cm-16x21in) board. 4-Dec-2 Neumeister, Munich #952/R est:1600
£1477 $2377 €2200 Cow in sunlit meadow (29x36cm-11x14in) mono. canvas on board. 21-Feb-3 Sigalas, Stuttgart #971/R est:1480
£1899 $3000 €3000 Interior of a stall (36x49cm-14x19in) mono. board. 28-Nov-2 Dorotheum, Vienna #188/R est:3000-4000
£2027 $3162 €3000 Landscape with cattle (16x31cm-6x12in) mono. panel. 27-Mar-3 Dr Fritz Nagel, Stuttgart #874/R est:800
£2115 $3279 €3300 Ox (26x36cm-10x14in) mono. panel. 4-Dec-2 Neumeister, Munich #954/R est:1000
£2158 $3540 €3000 Cattle (36x40cm-14x16in) s. 6-Jun-3 Ketterer, Munich #3/R est:5000-7000
£2324 $3858 €3300 Bull, cow and goat on a hill (18x24cm-7x9in) s.d.1878 panel. 14-Jun-3 Arnold, Frankfurt #930/R est:3000

£2344 $3750 €3516 Study of sheep (29x36cm-11x14in) s. paper on board. 14-May-3 Butterfields, San Francisco #1096/R est:3000-50000

£4601 $7500 €6902 Cows in a stream (86x102cm-34x40in) s. 2-Feb-3 Simpson's, Houston #340

£5229 $8366 €8000 Shepherd with cattle at watering spot (93x90cm-37x35in) s. lit. 10-Jan-3 Allgauer, Kempten #1819/R est:10000

£12579 $19623 €20000 Cows on shore of Starnberger See (40x92cm-16x36in) s.d.1881 bears i. panel. 19-Sep-2 Dr Fritz Nagel, Stuttgart #1009/R est:28000

£15385 $24308 €24000 Cattle on lakeshore with gathering storm (32x80cm-13x31in) s.d.82 panel prov.lit. 16-Nov-2 Lempertz, Koln #1594/R est:22000

VOLTZ, Friedrich (attrib) (1817-1886) German

£405 $632 €600 Cows in water (31x51cm-12x20in) 26-Mar-3 Hugo Ruef, Munich #252

£507 $791 €750 Cows in water (31x51cm-12x20in) 26-Mar-3 Hugo Ruef, Munich #253

£633 $981 €1000 Rocky outcrop (35x43cm-14x17in) i. verso canvas on board. 26-Sep-2 Neumeister, Munich #2859/R

Prints

£788 $1229 €1150 Shepherd with flock and peasant woman milking cow (47x48cm-19x19in) 11-Apr-3 Sigalas, Stuttgart #408

VOLTZ, Johann Michael (1784-1858) German

£8497 $13595 €13000 View of Nordlingen with wealthy figures (33x39cm-13x15in) mono. paper on board lit. 10-Jan-3 Allgauer, Kempten #1821/R est:13000

VOLTZ, Ludwig (1825-1911) German

£329 $513 €480 Dog with letter (27x21cm-11x8in) mono. board. 9-Apr-3 Neumeister, Munich #76

£538 $834 €850 Deer in landscape (21x35cm-8x14in) moo. panel. 26-Sep-2 Neumeister, Munich #2860/R

£1497 $2380 €2200 Boy with horse and foal (30x28cm-12x11in) s. panel lit. 21-Mar-3 Auktionhaus Georg Rehm, Augsburg #8116/R est:1500

VOLTZ, Richard (1859-1933) German

£321 $498 €482 Cow in dappled sunlight (41x56cm-16x22in) s. canvasboard. 29-Oct-2 Lawson Menzies, Sydney #465 (A.D 900)

£442 $703 €650 Landscape with trees (53x72cm-21x28in) mono. 20-Mar-3 Neumeister, Munich #2768/R

£476 $757 €700 Cows by pond (36x53cm-14x21in) s. panel. 20-Mar-3 Neumeister, Munich #2769/R

VOLZ, Wilhelm (1855-1901) German

£255 $397 €400 Yard entrance (38x48cm-15x19in) s. board lit. 7-Nov-2 Allgauer, Kempten #3001/R

VONASEK, Soter (1891-?) Yugoslavian

£590 $956 €885 Girl nude (90x67cm-35x26in) s. 24-May-3 Dorotheum, Prague #86/R est:26000-37000 (C.KR 26000)

VONCK, Elias (1605-1652) Dutch

£32903 $51987 €51000 Jeune chasseur devant trophee de chasse (161x145cm-63x57in) s. prov.lit. 18-Dec-2 Tajan, Paris #31/R est:45000

VONCK, Elias (attrib) (1605-1652) Dutch

£3379 $5271 €5000 Still life with dead game (92x71cm-36x28in) 26-Mar-3 Tajan, Paris #159/R

VONCK, Jan (attrib) (1630-?) Dutch

£603 $934 €905 Dog and ducks (22x29cm-9x11in) bears sig. panel. 8-Dec-2 Uppsala Auktionskammare, Uppsala #14 (S.KR 8500)

VONGPOOTHORN, Savanhdary (1971-) Australian

£571 $903 €857 Sprit figure (60x60cm-24x24in) s. i.d.1995 verso string acrylic. 27-Nov-2 Deutscher-Menzies, Melbourne #123/R est:900-1400 (A.D 1600)

VONLANTHEN, Louis (1889-1937) Swiss

£1747 $2725 €2621 Castle and cathedral in Neuchatel in the sunshine (72x89cm-28x35in) s. 8-Nov-2 Dobiaschofsky, Bern #126/R est:3800 (S.FR 4000)

VONNOH, Bessie Potter (1872-1955) American

Sculpture

£5031 $8000 €7547 Good night (23cm-9in) i. brown pat. bronze prov. 5-Mar-3 Sotheby's, New York #28/R est:8000-12000

£5660 $9000 €8490 Julia Marlowe as Juliet (50cm-20in) i.num.9/9 brown pat. bronze lit. 4-Mar-3 Christie's, Rockefeller NY #39/R est:7000-9000

£8735 $14500 €12666 Seated young woman, possibly Daphne (20cm-8in) s.num.18/250 brown pat bronze st.f.Roman Bronze Works. 14-Jun-3 Jackson's, Cedar Falls #9/R est:7000-10000

£11446 $19000 €16597 Motherhood (43cm-17in) s.st.f.Roman Bronze Works green brown pat bronze. 14-Jun-3 Jackson's, Cedar Falls #7/R est:8000-12000

£11613 $18000 €17420 Good night (23cm-9in) i. brown pat. bronze prov.exhib.lit. 5-Dec-2 Christie's, Rockefeller NY #76/R est:15000-25000

£15484 $24000 €23226 Waterlillies (73cm-29in) green pat. bronze executed 1913 prov. 5-Dec-2 Christie's, Rockefeller NY #81/R est:30000-50000

£15663 $26000 €22711 Scarf (33cm-13in) s.st.f.Roman B9ronze Works green brown pat bronze exec.c.1908. 14-Jun-3 Jackson's, Cedar Falls #8/R est:8000-12000

£16774 $26000 €25161 Motherhood (42cm-17in) i. brown pat. bronze prov. 5-Dec-2 Christie's, Rockefeller NY #39/R est:20000-30000

£17742 $27500 €26613 Dancing girl (157cm-62in) i.num.IV green pat. bronze prov. 4-Dec-2 Sotheby's, New York #94/R est:35000-45000

£20645 $32000 €30968 Young mother and children (30cm-12in) i. brown pat. bronze prov. 5-Dec-2 Christie's, Rockefeller NY #38/R est:40000-60000

£22581 $35000 €33872 Butterflies (33cm-13in) i. greenish brown pat. bronze i.f.Roman prov. 5-Dec-2 Christie's, Rockefeller NY #75/R est:15000-25000

£37037 $60000 €55556 Bird fountain (166cm-65in) i. weathered green pat. bronze executed c.1920 prov.exhib.lit. 21-May-3 Sotheby's, New York #185/R est:60000-80000

£80645 $125000 €120968 Water nymph (129cm-51in) i. verdigris pat. bronze. 5-Dec-2 Christie's, Rockefeller NY #86/R est:60000-80000

VONNOH, Robert (1858-1933) American

£1517 $2534 €2200 Hiver (24x19cm-9x7in) mono.i. cardboard. 10-Jul-3 Artcurial Briest, Paris #216/R est:2500-3000

VONTILLIUS, Jeppe (1915-1994) Danish

£279 $444 €419 Interior scene with seated woman (37x22cm-15x9in) init. 4-Mar-3 Museumsbygningen, Copenhagen #492 (D.KR 3000)

£287 $465 €416 Landscape (25x30cm-10x12in) init. cardboard. 24-May-3 Rasmussen, Havnen #4390 (D.KR 3000)

£379 $587 €569 Landscape (50x65cm-20x26in) init. masonite. 4-Dec-2 Kunsthallen, Copenhagen #322 (D.KR 4400)

£379 $580 €569 Snowy landscape (30x35cm-12x14in) init. 24-Aug-2 Rasmussen, Havnen #2105 (D.KR 4400)

£442 $689 €663 Green fields (50x71cm-20x28in) init.d.54. 5-Aug-2 Rasmussen, Vejle #339/R (D.KR 5200)

£1691 $2604 €2537 Model resting (70x150cm-28x59in) init. 23-Oct-2 Kunsthallen, Copenhagen #370/R est:12000 (D.KR 20000)

VONZUN, Anny (1910-) Swiss

£284 $446 €426 Still life (38x72cm-15x28in) s.d.1960 exhib. 25-Nov-2 Germann, Zurich #841 (S.FR 650)

£509 $820 €764 Sashas Pierrot (81x54cm-32x21in) s.d.61. 7-May-3 Dobiaschofsky, Bern #1043/R (S.FR 1100)

VOOGD, Hendrik (1766-1839) Dutch

Works on paper

£701 $1093 €1100 Two cows, one lying, one standing (20x27cm-8x11in) s.d.1831 black chk. 5-Nov-2 Sotheby's, Amsterdam #228/R

VOORDEN, August Willem van (1881-1921) Dutch

£694 $1146 €1000 Visch karen (37x32cm-15x13in) s. s.i.verso plywood. 1-Jul-3 Christie's, Amsterdam #161/R

£1447 $2345 €2200 Inner harbour scene (31x40cm-12x16in) s. 21-Jan-3 Christie's, Amsterdam #343/R est:1200-1600

£11321 $17434 €18000 In de sneeuw - horse and carriage on a busy quay in winter (133x181cm-52x71in) s. prov.exhib. 23-Oct-2 Christie's, Amsterdam #193/R est:12000-16000

VOORHEES, Clark Greenwood (1871-1933) American

£2344 $3750 €3399 Lifting fog (38x51cm-15x20in) s. 16-May-3 Skinner, Boston #277/R est:4000-6000

VOORHIES, Stephen J (20th C) American

Works on paper

£4348 $7000 €6522 Making the connection from train to bus en route to New York (41x36cm-16x14in) s. gouache W/C exec.c.1931. 10-May-3 Illustration House, New York #68/R est:3000-4000

VOORHOUT, Johannes (attrib) (1647-1723) Dutch

£943 $1453 €1500 Portrait de femme assise tenant une rose (100x81cm-39x32in) 25-Oct-2 Tajan, Paris #81/R est:1000-1200

VORAUER, Anton (1905-) Swiss
£360 $576 €500 Flowers in vase (70x60cm-28x24in) s.d.52 board. 14-May-3 Dorotheum, Linz #359

VORDEMBERGE, Friedrich (1897-1980) German
Works on paper
£1026 $1590 €1600 Villa Massimo (75x56cm-30x22in) s. s.i.d.71 verso W/C. 4-Dec-2 Lempertz, Koln #1104/R est:1300

VORDEMBERGE-GILDEWART, Friedrich (1899-1963) German
Works on paper
£1923 $2981 €3000 Untitled (31x24cm-12x9in) s.d.1959 collage folded sheet prov. 3-Dec-2 Christie's, Amsterdam #153/R est:1500-2000

VORLOVA-VLCKOVA, Zdenka (1872-?) Czechoslovakian
£371 $590 €557 Peonies (54x65cm-21x26in) s.d.1912. 8-Mar-3 Dorotheum, Prague #66 est:10000-15000 (C.KR 17000)

VOROS, Bela (1899-1983) Hungarian
Sculpture
£3125 $5156 €4500 L'accordeoniste (41x39cm-16x15in) s. stone. 2-Jul-3 Artcurial Briest, Paris #37/R est:4000-5000

VOROS, Erno (1883-1922) Hungarian
£1677 $2616 €2516 Sunny street (90x115cm-35x45in) s. 11-Sep-2 Kieselbach, Budapest #47/R (H.F 650000)

VOROS, Geza (1897-?) Hungarian
£615 $959 €892 Dose (25x33cm-10x13in) s.d.47. 12-Apr-3 Mu Terem Galeria, Budapest #176/R est:160000 (H.F 220000)
£980 $1529 €1470 Sunflowers (40x51cm-16x20in) s. 11-Sep-2 Kieselbach, Budapest #8/R (H.F 380000)
£1537 $2398 €2306 Boy in striped shirt with dog (49x45cm-19x18in) s. 11-Apr-3 Kieselbach, Budapest #23/R est:420000-550000 (H.F 550000)
£1816 $2834 €2724 Szentendre (50x72cm-20x28in) s. board. 11-Apr-3 Kieselbach, Budapest #65/R est:40000-650000 (H.F 650000)
£3870 $6037 €5612 Interior with a bouquet of flowers (60x80cm-24x31in) s.d.956. 13-Sep-2 Mu Terem Galeria, Budapest #177/R est:350000 (H.F 1500000)
£4000 $6560 €6000 View of Szentendre (53x65cm-21x26in) s. prov. 3-Jun-3 Sotheby's, London #85/R est:4000-6000
£5266 $8425 €7899 Bunch of bluebells (98x71cm-39x28in) s.d.36. 16-May-3 Kieselbach, Budapest #70/R (H.F 1800000)
£5266 $8425 €7899 Still life with a Picasso book (100x73cm-39x29in) s. 16-May-3 Kieselbach, Budapest #85/R (H.F 1800000)
£8255 $12878 €12383 Szentendre (66x85cm-26x33in) s. tempera. 11-Sep-2 Kieselbach, Budapest #37/R (H.F 3200000)
£10532 $16850 €15798 Woman in striped blouse in a room (100x73cm-39x29in) s. 16-May-3 Kieselbach, Budapest #28/R (H.F 3600000)
£11117 $17787 €16676 Still life with violin (68x96cm-27x38in) s.d.XXXII tempera. 16-May-3 Kieselbach, Budapest #36/R (H.F 3800000)
Works on paper
£722 $1127 €1047 Parisian detail (22x22cm-9x9in) s.d.931 Indian ink W/C. 13-Sep-2 Mu Terem Galeria, Budapest #9/R est:200000 (H.F 280000)

VORST, Joseph Paul (1897-1947) American/German
£962 $1500 €1443 Apple pickers (41x30cm-16x12in) s. board prov. 10-Nov-2 Selkirks, St. Louis #981 est:800-1200

VORSTER, Andreas (1727-1785) Swiss
£550 $858 €825 Pewter jug, tobacco, pipe and wine glass on a draped table (29x37cm-11x15in) s. 10-Apr-3 Christie's, Kensington #135/R

VORSTER, Gordon (1924-1988) South African
£384 $600 €576 Zimbabwe ruins (120x113cm-47x44in) board. 11-Nov-2 Stephan Welz, Johannesburg #605 (SA.R 6000)
Works on paper
£320 $500 €480 Impala in a landscape (47x68cm-19x27in) s. mixed media. 11-Nov-2 Stephan Welz, Johannesburg #235 (SA.R 5000)

VOS, Cornelis de (1585-1651) Flemish
£7914 $12662 €11000 Portrait of lady wearing black dress with white lace cuffs and collar (122x91cm-48x36in) 13-May-3 Sotheby's, Amsterdam #63/R est:4000-6000

VOS, Maria (1824-1906) Dutch
£2778 $4417 €4000 Fish for dinner, kitchen still life (41x34cm-16x13in) s. prov. 29-Apr-3 Christie's, Amsterdam #49/R est:3000-5000
£6507 $10216 €9500 Kitchen still life with asparagus (31x25cm-12x10in) s. panel. 15-Apr-3 Sotheby's, Amsterdam #32a est:7000-9000

VOS, Martin de (attrib) (1532-1603) Flemish
£800 $1280 €1200 Portrait of a lady (25x23cm-10x9in) d.1584 panel. 11-Mar-3 Gorringes, Lewes #2529/R

VOS, Martin de (circle) (1532-1603) Flemish
£9868 $15987 €15000 Samaritan (112x156cm-44x61in) 21-Jan-3 Durán, Madrid #163/R est:15000

VOS, Paul de (1596-1678) Flemish
£4630 $7454 €6945 Fighting over the spoils (101x122cm-40x48in) 7-May-3 Dobiaschofsky, Bern #1045/R est:14000 (S.FR 10000)

VOS, Paul de (attrib) (1596-1678) Flemish
£3767 $5914 €5500 Dog pack attacking wild boar in wood (156x184cm-61x72in) 16-Apr-3 Dorotheum, Salzburg #14/R est:11000-18000
£5137 $8065 €7500 Dog pack attacking deer in wood (156x283cm-61x111in) one of pair. 16-Apr-3 Dorotheum, Salzburg #15/R est:15000-24000
£13699 $21507 €20000 Dog pack attacking bear (156x283cm-61x111in) one of pair. 16-Apr-3 Dorotheum, Salzburg #16/R est:20000-30000

VOS, Paul de (style) (1596-1678) Flemish
£19858 $30780 €29787 The animals in The Garden of Eden (109x152cm-43x60in) 3-Dec-2 Bukowskis, Stockholm #431/R est:150000-200000 (S.KR 280000)

VOS, Rik de (20th C) ?
£443 $691 €700 Landscapsvreter (100x119cm-39x47in) s. 21-Oct-2 Bernaerts, Antwerp #666

VOS, Simon de (1603-1676) Flemish
£6000 $9420 €9000 Continence of Scipio (55x71cm-22x28in) init.indis d.164. 13-Dec-2 Christie's, Kensington #52/R est:7000-10000
£13836 $21447 €22000 Triumph of Bacchus in India (120x254cm-47x100in) prov. 2-Oct-2 Dorotheum, Vienna #161/R est:20000-30000

VOS, Simon de (attrib) (1603-1676) Flemish
£755 $1162 €1200 Concert dans un interieur (31x31cm-12x12in) panel. 25-Oct-2 Tajan, Paris #67
£2624 $4067 €3936 Figures merrymaking (50x62cm-20x24in) panel. 4-Dec-2 AB Stockholms Auktionsverk #2031/R est:40000-50000 (S.KR 37000)

VOS, Vincent de (1829-1875) Belgian
£980 $1578 €1500 Interieur d'etable anime (37x47cm-15x19in) s.d.1870. 14-Jan-3 Vanderkindere, Brussels #10/R est:1500-2000
£1000 $1590 €1500 Terrier surprised by mice (14x18cm-6x7in) s. panel. 20-Mar-3 Christie's, Kensington #158/R est:1200-1800
£1410 $2186 €2200 La mere et son petit (18x24cm-7x9in) s. i.verso panel. 9-Dec-2 Horta, Bruxelles #145 est:2500-3500
£1519 $2370 €2400 Chien apportant le panier de pique-nique (25x41cm-10x16in) s. 16-Sep-2 Horta, Bruxelles #47
£1727 $2763 €2400 Chienne et deux chiots (18x25cm-7x10in) s. panel. 13-May-3 Palais de Beaux Arts, Brussels #59/R est:2000-3000
£1795 $2782 €2800 Deux chiots dans un panier sous surveillance (18x25cm-7x10in) s. i.verso panel. 9-Dec-2 Horta, Bruxelles #144/R est:2500-3500

VOSBERG, Heinrich (1833-1891) German
£1538 $2431 €2400 Alpine landscape with lakeside city, possibly Lucern (86x132cm-34x52in) s.d.1865. 16-Nov-2 Lempertz, Koln #1595/R est:3000

VOSCHER, Leopold Heinrich (1830-1877) Austrian
£1048 $1635 €1572 Landscape at Urner lake with view of Urirotstock and Gitschen (82x101cm-32x40in) s. prov. 9-Nov-2 Galerie Gloggner, Luzern #144/R (S.FR 2400)
£2778 $4417 €4000 Shepherds in mountain landscape (63x85cm-25x33in) s. 29-Apr-3 Wiener Kunst Auktionen, Vienna #538/R est:3000-5000

VOSMAER, Abraham (1618-?) Dutch
£10959 $17096 €16000 Varia still life with grapes, large turnip, pears and songbird (64x94cm-25x37in) s.d.16 panel. 10-Apr-3 Van Ham, Cologne #1282/R est:6000

VOSS, Jan (1936-) German
£443 $687 €700 Untitled (54x41cm-21x16in) s.d.1958 tempera board. 28-Sep-2 Ketterer, Hamburg #389/R
£1105 $1723 €1658 Composition (38x61cm-15x24in) s.d.87 acrylic. 5-Aug-2 Rasmussen, Vejle #354/R est:12000-15000 (D.KR 13000)
£1351 $2108 €2027 Oasis (47x62cm-19x24in) s.d.81 acrylic. 18-Sep-2 Kunsthallen, Copenhagen #203/R est:20000 (D.KR 16000)
£3846 $6077 €6000 When you fly into my arms (73x60cm-29x24in) s.d.64 i.verso. 15-Nov-2 Laurence Calmels, Paris #38/R est:9000

Works on paper
£1554 $2471 €2331 Die Grunen. s.d.84 gouache W/C crayon collage paper on canvas. 26-Feb-3 Kunsthallen, Copenhagen #137/R est:15000 (D.KR 17000)
£2365 $3689 €3548 Composition (70x100cm-28x39in) s.d.82 W/C crayon. 18-Sep-2 Kunsthallen, Copenhagen #100/R est:30000 (D.KR 28000)
£2412 $3738 €3618 Shukuko (66x100cm-26x39in) s.d.82 gouache W/C crayon paper on canvas. 4-Dec-2 Kunsthallen, Copenhagen #144/R est:30000 (D.KR 28000)
£2949 $4571 €4600 Untitled (65x100cm-26x39in) s.d.84 W/C Indian ink paper collage prov. 3-Dec-2 Lempertz, Koln #495/R est:5000
£4000 $6520 €6000 Untitled (160x128cm-63x50in) s.d.64 crayon pastel gouache paper on canvas. 3-Feb-3 Sotheby's, Olympia #186/R est:4000-6000

VOSSEN, Andre van der (1893-1963) Dutch
£478 $736 €750 Composition (50x70cm-20x28in) mono board exhib. 3-Sep-2 Christie's, Amsterdam #417
£637 $981 €1000 Action (80x60cm-31x24in) mono. s.i.stretcher. 3-Sep-2 Christie's, Amsterdam #416/R
Works on paper
£329 $533 €500 Untitled (33x47cm-13x19in) init. gouache. 21-Jan-3 Christie's, Amsterdam #464

VOSTELL, Wolf (1932-1998) German
Sculpture
£1042 $1719 €1500 Zyklus calatayud nr 23 (41x29cm-16x11in) s.d.73 mixed media metal panel wood box exhib. 1-Jul-3 Artcurial Briest, Paris #821/R est:1500-2000
£1582 $2500 €2500 Concrete cadillacs - model (35cm-14in) s.d.86 brown pat.bronze Cast.Bildgiesserei Kraas I Berlin. 29-Nov-2 Villa Grisebach, Berlin #951/R est:2500-3000
Works on paper
£475 $750 €750 Lovers (40x30cm-16x12in) s.d.81 chk sold with another. 29-Nov-2 Villa Grisebach, Berlin #948/R

VOTH, Hannsjorg (1940-) German
£609 $890 €950 Stone boat (29x42cm-11x17in) s.i. mixed media. 4-Jun-2 Karl & Faber, Munich #464/R

VOUET, Simon (1590-1649) French
£41772 $66000 €66000 Vierge et l'Enfant a la colonne (118x90cm-46x35in) painted with studio. 2-Dec-2 Rieunier, Paris #72/R est:60000
Works on paper
£801 $1258 €1250 Crucifixion (28x20cm-11x8in) i. pierre noire. 13-Dec-2 Rossini, Paris #127

VOUET, Simon (attrib) (1590-1649) French
£12838 $20027 €19000 Madonna and Child (97x44cm-38x17in) 28-Mar-3 Piasa, Paris #44/R

VOULKOS, Peter (1924-2002) American
Sculpture
£4807 $7500 €7211 Untitled, charger (46x46cm-18x18in) s.d.73 glazed porcelain ceramic plate. 14-Oct-2 Butterfields, San Francisco #2082/R est:7000-9000

VOULLEMIER, Anne Nicole (1796-1886) French
Miniatures
£1500 $2475 €2175 Lady wearing a low cut dress (7cm-3in) s. gilt metal frame oval. 1-Jul-3 Bonhams, New Bond Street #114/R est:800-1200

VOYER, Marie (1942-) Canadian
£378 $620 €548 Morning paper (15x60cm-6x24in) s.i. board. 9-Jun-3 Hodgins, Calgary #418/R (C.D 850)

VRANCX, Sebastian (1573-1647) Flemish
£15095 $23246 €24000 La chasse au cerf dans un foret (118x169cm-46x67in) 25-Oct-2 Tajan, Paris #1/R est:2000-3000
£15827 $25324 €22000 Attack (62x77cm-24x30in) panel. 17-May-3 Lempertz, Koln #1158/R est:25000
£17949 $28359 €28000 Cavalry battle (45x65cm-18x26in) panel prov. 16-Nov-2 Lempertz, Koln #1130/R est:25000
£35000 $58450 €50750 Allegory of Spring (52x65cm-20x26in) oak panel painted with studio. 10-Jul-3 Sotheby's, London #110/R est:30000-40000

VRANCX, Sebastian (circle) (1573-1647) Flemish
£11392 $18000 €18000 Paysans revenant du marche sur chemin au bord de riviere (43x64cm-17x25in) panel. 27-Nov-2 Christie's, Paris #12/R est:18000-22000

VRBOVA, Miloslava (20th C) Czechoslovakian
£588 $965 €900 Three ballerinas tying their shoes (50x80cm-20x31in) s. masonite. 5-Feb-3 Neumeister, Munich #832/R
£748 $1190 €1100 Ballet dancers (100x80cm-39x31in) s. panel. 20-Mar-3 Neumeister, Munich #2770/R
£952 $1476 €1428 Ballerina (58x48cm-23x19in) s. pavatex. 24-Sep-2 Koller, Zurich #6758/R (S.FR 2200)

VREDENBURGH, C L van (fl.1880s) ?
£745 $1200 €1118 Cats standing in Victorian dress, one poor, one rich (25x20cm-10x8in) s. painted c.1880 pair. 10-May-3 Illustration House, New York #27/R est:3500-5000

VREEDENBURGH, Cornelis (1880-1946) Dutch
£1831 $2948 €2600 Dutch coastal landscape (20x35cm-8x14in) s.d.06 panel lit. 9-May-3 Schloss Ahlden, Ahlden #1490/R est:2800
£2803 $4372 €4400 Polder landscape with cow at ditch (20x35cm-8x14in) s. 6-Nov-2 Vendue Huis, Gravenhage #657/R est:5000-7000
£2917 $4638 €4200 Cornsheaves on a summer's day (39x76cm-15x30in) s.d.1917. 29-Apr-3 Christie's, Amsterdam #158/R est:4000-6000
£7639 $12146 €11000 View of the Spaarne, Haarlem (71x101cm-28x40in) s.d.1937. 29-Apr-3 Christie's, Amsterdam #151/R est:12000-16000
£12102 $18879 €19000 Summer day in Bloemendaal (29x39cm-11x15in) s.d.1933. 6-Nov-2 Vendue Huis, Gravenhage #642/R est:10000-15000
£18056 $28708 €26000 View of the open haven front with the St. Nicolaas church in the distance (62x109cm-24x43in) s.d.1924 canvas on board. 29-Apr-3 Christie's, Amsterdam #165/R est:14000-18000
Works on paper
£486 $802 €700 Construction work on a canal, Amsterdam (31x40cm-12x16in) s.d.1922 pencil W/C bodycol. 1-Jul-3 Christie's, Amsterdam #213
£510 $795 €800 On the skaters track (18x45cm-7x18in) W/C. 6-Nov-2 Vendue Huis, Gravenhage #640
£915 $1474 €1300 View of Frankrijk church (23x30cm-9x12in) s. W/C. 6-May-3 Vendu Notarishuis, Rotterdam #142/R

VREELAND, Francis William van (1879-1954) American
Works on paper
£413 $649 €620 Mother and child in an interior (28x33cm-11x13in) s. W/C. 24-Jul-2 Walker's, Ottawa #11/R est:800-1000 (C.D 1000)
£414 $650 €621 Dutch scene with young girl feeding chicken and chicks (33x46cm-13x18in) s. 19-Apr-3 James Julia, Fairfield #349/R

VREESE, Godefroid (1861-1941) Belgian
Sculpture
£1192 $1943 €1800 Fier paysan (72cm-28in) s. brown pat bronze. 17-Feb-3 Horta, Bruxelles #367
£2785 $4400 €4400 Pursang (50x38x15cm-20x15x6in) s.d.92 pat bronze. 26-Nov-2 Palais de Beaux Arts, Brussels #87/R est:4500-6250

VRIENDT, Juliaan de (1842-1935) Belgian
£609 $944 €950 Femme lisante (48x35cm-19x14in) s. 3-Dec-2 Campo & Campo, Antwerp #78
Works on paper
£449 $696 €700 Jeunes mendiants (22x29cm-9x11in) W/C prov. 3-Dec-2 Campo & Campo, Antwerp #77/R

VRIES, Abraham de (1590-c.1662) Dutch
£7006 $10930 €11000 Portrait of Simon Elsevier. Portrait of Jenneke de Bosch (68x55cm-27x22in) i. panel oval pair exhib.lit. 5-Nov-2 Sotheby's, Amsterdam #93/R est:8000-12000

VRIES, E de (1816-1875) Dutch
£1887 $2943 €3000 Pecheurs et barques de peche au port (60x82cm-24x32in) 14-Oct-2 Amberes, Antwerp #146/R

VRIES, Emanuel de (1816-1875) Dutch
£3288 $5129 €4800 Seascape with a three-mast ship and other ships. Seascape with boats (31x43cm-12x17in) one s. one indis.s. d.1848 panel two. 14-Apr-3 Glerum, Amsterdam #25/R est:5000-8000

VRIES, Hubert de (1899-1979) Belgian
£252 $392 €400 Voiliers (38x43cm-15x17in) 14-Oct-2 Amberes, Antwerp #147

£282 $437 €440 Sint-Franciscus (110x60cm-43x24in) s. 7-Dec-2 De Vuyst, Lokeren #103

£283 $436 €450 Bateaux de peche (70x80cm-28x31in) s. 22-Oct-2 Campo, Vlaamse Kaai #81

£283 $442 €450 Yachts and steamers in the harbour (84x100cm-33x39in) s.d.62. 23-Sep-2 Bernaerts, Antwerp #54/R

£346 $533 €550 Le manege (56x38cm-22x15in) s. 22-Oct-2 Campo, Vlaamse Kaai #80

£347 $552 €500 Kermesse (60x35cm-24x14in) s.d.1969. 29-Apr-3 Campo & Campo, Antwerp #535

£590 $939 €850 Chevaux vertes dans le cirque (79x55cm-31x22in) s. 29-Apr-3 Campo & Campo, Antwerp #536

VRIES, Jan Feytsz de (17th C) Dutch

£5000 $7800 €7500 Naval action, probably the Battle of the Downs (49x93cm-19x37in) init. panel. 10-Apr-3 Sotheby's, London #61/R est:6000-8000

VRIES, Michiel de (?-c.1702) Dutch

£1878 $3080 €2723 River landscape with stone building and fishing boat (53x40cm-21x16in) panel. 4-Jun-3 Fischer, Luzern #1021/R est:4000-6000 (S.FR 4000)

VRIES, Michiel de (attrib) (?-c.1702) Dutch

£2838 $4428 €4257 House on the river (39x34cm-15x13in) panel. 20-Nov-2 Fischer, Luzern #1023/R est:7000-8000 (S.FR 6500)

VRIES, Roelof van (1631-1681) Dutch

£3459 $5396 €5500 Landscape with church spire (45x63cm-18x25in) panel. 23-Sep-2 Wiener Kunst Auktionen, Vienna #18/R est:2300-6500

£4459 $6866 €7000 River landscape with peasants and travellers on a path (55x46cm-22x18in) s. 3-Sep-2 Christie's, Amsterdam #49/R est:5000-7000

£4577 $7599 €6500 Le depart pour la chasse au faucon (90x83cm-35x33in) 16-Jun-3 Claude Aguttes, Neuilly #9/R est:6000-8000

£5000 $7750 €7500 River landscape with houses above ramparts on edge of water (38x50cm-15x20in) mono. panel. 31-Oct-2 Sotheby's, Olympia #63/R est:5000-7000

£8784 $13703 €13000 Peasants resting in wooded landscape (36x27cm-14x11in) s. panel. 27-Mar-3 Dorotheum, Vienna #143/R est:12000-16000

£10811 $16865 €16000 Two rider resting before tavern (90x69cm-35x27in) panel. 27-Mar-3 Dorotheum, Vienna #130/R est:12000-16000

VROLYK, Adrianus Jacobus (1834-1862) Dutch

£2800 $4452 €4200 Dutch quay side (24x36cm-9x14in) s. panel prov. 18-Mar-3 Bonhams, New Bond Street #5/R est:1500-2000

VROLYK, Jan (1845-1894) Dutch

Works on paper

£446 $696 €700 Peasant with cow by a fence (42x27cm-17x11in) s. W/C. 5-Nov-2 Vendu Notarishuis, Rotterdam #261

VU CAO DAM (1908-2000) Vietnamese

£1243 $1914 €1865 Venice (40x32cm-16x13in) s.i.d.1953. 27-Oct-2 Christie's, Hong Kong #39/R est:10000-20000 (HK.D 15000)

£1258 $2000 €1887 In the garden (34x41cm-13x16in) s.d.73. 7-Mar-3 Skinner, Boston #610/R est:500-700

£1517 $2200 €2276 Combat de coques (46x61cm-18x24in) painted c.1972. 1-Jun-2 Russ Antiques, Waterford #202

£2548 $4000 €3822 Divinite (22x18cm-9x7in) i. s.d.1984 verso prov. 10-Dec-2 Doyle, New York #249/R est:2000-3000

£2667 $4427 €3867 Le cavalier (50x61cm-20x24in) s.d.1971 prov. 16-Jun-3 Waddingtons, Toronto #354/R est:800-1200 (C.D 6000)

£2690 $3900 €4035 Cheval noir (43x36cm-17x14in) painted c.1965. 1-Jun-2 Russ Antiques, Waterford #44

£2778 $4472 €4167 Happy family (64x54cm-25x21in) s.d.1961. 7-May-3 Dobiaschofsky, Bern #1046/R est:2400 (S.FR 6000)

£34965 $57692 €50699 Lovers in the garden (157x57cm-62x22in) s.d.72 canvas on board three. 6-Jul-3 Christie's, Hong Kong #37/R est:220000-300000 (HK.D 450000)

Works on paper

£10101 $16667 €14646 Two women (60x88cm-24x35in) s. ink col silk. 6-Jul-3 Christie's, Hong Kong #35/R est:90000-120000 (HK.D 130000)

VUAGNAT, François (1910-) French

£440 $708 €660 Chevres (39x29cm-15x11in) s. i. stretcher. 7-May-3 Dobiaschofsky, Bern #1047/R (S.FR 950)

VUCHT, Gerrit van (1610-1699) Dutch

£3800 $5890 €5700 Roemer of wine, violin, candlestick, and other items, on a table (22x19cm-9x7in) panel. 30-Oct-2 Bonhams, New Bond Street #2/R est:2000-3000

£5036 $8058 €7000 Still life with small child and upturned jug (16x13cm-6x5in) panel. 17-May-3 Lempertz, Koln #1159/R est:4000

£9310 $15081 €13500 Still life of pewter jugs, glass and grapes (59x80cm-23x31in) init. panel lit. 26-May-3 Bukowskis, Stockholm #400/R est:150000-200000 (S.KR 120000)

VUCHT, Jan van der (1603-1637) Dutch

£2134 $3500 €3201 Figures in a domed interior (19x23cm-7x9in) bears false sig.d.1646 prov. 29-May-3 Sotheby's, New York #26/R est:4000-6000

VUEZ, Arnold de (1644-1720) French

Works on paper

£608 $949 €900 Allegory of Peace (40x26cm-16x10in) pen ink wash over crayon. 27-Mar-3 Maigret, Paris #23

VUGHT, Reinoud van (1960-) Dutch

£709 $1149 €1000 Untitled (150x210cm-59x83in) s.d.1995 verso acrylic. 26-May-3 Glerum, Amsterdam #244

VUILLARD, Edouard (1868-1940) French

£4938 $8000 €7160 Boy playing in sand dunes (25x33cm-10x13in) st. pastel paper on board prov. 21-May-3 Doyle, New York #226/R est:10000-15000

£6500 $10010 €9750 Etude de sculpture (64x35cm-25x14in) st.sig. oil peinture a l'essence on board. 22-Oct-2 Sotheby's, London #129/R est:7000-9000

£31056 $50000 €46584 Table dressee (17x24cm-7x9in) st.sig. painted c.1902 prov.exhib. 8-May-3 Christie's, Rockefeller NY #144/R est:40000-60000

£33566 $56056 €48000 Deux silhouettes de femmes (27x37cm-11x15in) st.sig. prov.exhib.lit. 30-Jun-3 Artcurial Briest, Paris #81g/R est:50000-60000

£45455 $75909 €65000 Madame Hessel en Normandie (58x67cm-23x26in) s.d.05 cardboard exhib.lit. 30-Jun-3 Artcurial Briest, Paris #81b/R est:70000-100000

£55046 $91927 €79817 Femmes dans le salon de 'La Terrasse' a Vasouy (28x42cm-11x17in) st.sig. board. 20-Jun-3 Kornfeld, Bern #146/R est:100000 (S.FR 120000)

£76923 $120769 €120000 Maison de Mallarme a Valvins (14x42cm-6x17in) s. panel prov.exhib. 10-Dec-2 Pierre Berge, Paris #28/R est:180000

£80128 $125000 €120192 Carton d'etudesI, pont-l'Eveque (81x125cm-32x49in) board on panel painted 1932 prov.exhib.lit. 7-Nov-2 Christie's, Rockefeller NY #269/R est:140000-180000

£288462 $450000 €432693 Femme brossant un vetement - Femme a la fenetre (27x22cm-11x9in) init. board on panel painted c.1891 prov.exhib.lit. 6-Nov-2 Christie's, Rockefeller NY #25/R est:300000-400000

Prints

£6597 $10490 €9500 La partie de dames (34x26cm-13x10in) col lithograph. 5-May-3 Ketterer, Munich #102/R est:3000-5000

£9028 $14354 €13000 L'avenue (31x41cm-12x16in) s. col lithograph. 5-May-3 Ketterer, Munich #98/R est:12000-15000

Works on paper

£600 $924 €900 Visage de jeune fille, de profil (17x10cm-7x4in) st.init.indis.i. pencil pen ink exec.c.1920 prov. 23-Oct-2 Sotheby's, Olympia #614/R

£705 $1107 €1100 Deux amies (19x11cm-7x4in) st.init. crayon dr. 13-Dec-2 Piasa, Paris #250/R

£900 $1386 €1350 Branchage d'arbre (16x10cm-6x4in) st.init. pencil prov. 23-Oct-2 Sotheby's, Olympia #608/R

£1300 $2002 €1950 La petite Annette Roussel (13x8cm-5x3in) st.init. pencil exec.c.1904 prov. 23-Oct-2 Sotheby's, Olympia #611/R est:400-600

£1500 $2385 €2250 Buste de femme de profil (13x10cm-5x4in) st.init. pencil. 20-Mar-3 Sotheby's, Olympia #14/R est:400-600

£1500 $2385 €2250 Femme lisant (20x11cm-8x4in) st.init. pen ink pencil. 20-Mar-3 Sotheby's, Olympia #16/R est:1200-1500

£1600 $2464 €2400 La liseuse (17x12cm-7x5in) st.init. pencil exec.c.1920 prov. 23-Oct-2 Sotheby's, Olympia #613/R est:800-1200

£1700 $2618 €2550 Yvonne Printemps allongee sur son lit (19x11cm-7x4in) st.init. pencil pen ink exec.c.1920 prov. 23-Oct-2 Sotheby's, Olympia #610/R est:1200-1500

£1700 $2703 €2550 Femme sur un divan (19x12cm-7x5in) init. pencil. 20-Mar-3 Sotheby's, Olympia #13/R est:1200-1500

£2100 $3234 €3150 L'allee aux grands arbres, au Chateau des Clayes (16x10cm-6x4in) init. pencil exec.c.1930 prov. 23-Oct-2 Sotheby's, Olympia #607/R est:1500-2000

£2350 $3737 €3525 Femme au lit (12x21cm-5x8in) st.init. pencil. 20-Mar-3 Sotheby's, Olympia #17/R est:2000-3000

£2600 $4030 €3900 Le repas au chateau claes (13x29cm-5x11in) init. pencil pastel. 5-Dec-2 Christie's, Kensington #49/R est:2500-3500

£5500 $8745 €8250 Le bonnet rouge (22x13cm-9x5in) st.init. pastel exec.c.1890. 20-Mar-3 Sotheby's, Olympia #18/R est:4000-6000

£10993 $18358 €15500 Lucy Hessel dans le salon du Cos Cezanne (23x30cm-9x12in) mono. pastel exec.c.1921-1925 prov.lit. 23-Jun-3 Claude Boisgirard, Paris #83/R est:12000-15000
£11801 $19000 €17702 Meules and buste d'homme en costume (23x22cm-9x9in) init, pastel double-sided executed c.1890. 7-May-3 Sotheby's, New York #144/R est:18000-25000
£12000 $20040 €18000 Devant la fenetre a Vaucresson (25x33cm-10x13in) studio st. pastel chl. exec c.1920 prov. 26-Jun-3 Christie's, London #371/R est:12000-15000
£14474 $23448 €22000 Les mats de Pouliguen (62x48cm-24x19in) st.sig. peinture a la colle cardboard on canvas prov. 22-Jan-3 Tajan, Paris #111/R est:10000-15000
£16000 $26240 €24000 Partie de cartes (26x37cm-10x15in) s. pastel exec.1923 prov. 6-Feb-3 Christie's, London #419/R est:12000
£16129 $25484 €25000 Sommeil (29x23cm-11x9in) s. pastel chl prov. 18-Dec-2 Tajan, Paris #17/R est:25000-40000
£18000 $29520 €27000 Portrait de madame Marie des Jardins-Fontaine (62x50cm-24x20in) st.sig. peinture a la colle board exec.c.1901 prov. 4-Feb-3 Christie's, London #253/R est:30000
£18182 $30364 €26000 Homme a barbiche de profil (26x18cm-10x7in) studio st. pastel. 30-Jun-3 Artcurial Briest, Paris #45/R est:20000-30000
£18750 $30937 €27000 Lucie Hessel dans le pre a Amfreville (15x21cm-6x8in) st.mono. pastel dr. 2-Jul-3 Artcurial Briest, Paris #620/R est:10000-12000
£20000 $33400 €29000 La Muette, l'arroseur (78x92cm-31x36in) indis sig. peinture a la colle paper on canvas prov.exhib. 25-Jun-3 Christie's, London #156/R est:25000-35000
£24000 $39360 €36000 Scene de cafe (47x52cm-19x20in) st.init. pastel peinture a la cole prov.exhib. 5-Feb-3 Sotheby's, London #113/R est:30000
£25641 $40000 €38462 Madame Rosengart avec sa fille (77x89cm-30x35in) s. pastel chl paper on canvas executed c.1928 prov. 6-Nov-2 Sotheby's, New York #128/R est:50000-70000
£28000 $46760 €40600 Le square apres la pluie (44x55cm-17x22in) st.sig pastel chl executed c.1910 prov. 24-Jun-3 Sotheby's, London #222/R est:30000-40000
£37179 $58000 €55769 Portrait de Jacques Laroche enfant (42x37cm-17x15in) s. pastel paper on board executed 1917 prov.lit. 7-Nov-2 Christie's, Rockefeller NY #121/R est:40000-60000
£236025 $380000 €354038 Le banc, square Vintimille (65x54cm-26x21in) s. peinture a la colle paper on canvas painted 1917-18 prov.exhib. 8-May-3 Christie's, Rockefeller NY #179/R est:250000-350000
£320513 $500000 €480770 Madame Josse Hessels dans l'atelier de Vuillard (70x63cm-28x25in) s. pastel executed 1915 prov.exhib. 6-Nov-2 Christie's, Rockefeller NY #18/R est:500000-700000

VUILLIER, Gaston Charles (1847-1915) French
Works on paper
£288 $456 €450 Platrerie a Murcie (36x44cm-14x17in) s. W/C. 14-Nov-2 Credit Municipal, Paris #46/R

VUKOVIC, Svetislav (1901-) ?
£506 $800 €800 Street scene (60x80cm-24x31in) s. 29-Nov-2 Schloss Ahlden, Ahlden #1398/R
£873 $1387 €1310 View of mosque (57x41cm-22x16in) s. 8-Mar-3 Dorotheum, Prague #154/R est:30000-45000 (C.KR 40000)

VULLIAMY, Gerard (1909-) French
Works on paper
£1139 $1777 €1800 Composition (46x55cm-18x22in) s.d.1948 s.d. verso mixed media. 20-Oct-2 Claude Boisgirard, Paris #38/R est:1300-1400

VUORI, Antti (1935-) Finnish
£425 $697 €650 Strange birds (75x72cm-30x28in) s. oil pastel exhib. 9-Feb-3 Bukowskis, Helsinki #384/R
Works on paper
£510 $836 €780 Dog training (44x61cm-17x24in) s. gouache. 9-Feb-3 Bukowskis, Helsinki #383/R

VUORI, Ilmari (1898-1975) Finnish
£261 $429 €400 Gladiolus (93x66cm-37x26in) s.d.64. 9-Feb-3 Bukowskis, Helsinki #385/R
£261 $429 €400 Flowers in vase (80x64cm-31x25in) s.d.45. 9-Feb-3 Bukowskis, Helsinki #387/R
£294 $482 €450 Flowers (60x73cm-24x29in) s.d.49. 9-Feb-3 Bukowskis, Helsinki #388/R

VUORI, Kaarlo (1863-1914) Finnish
£3597 $5755 €5000 By the coast (47x80cm-19x31in) s. 17-May-3 Hagelstam, Helsinki #104/R est:5000

VUORISALO, Pauli (20th C) Finnish
£253 $400 €400 The joy of the sea (115x115cm-45x45in) s.d.68. 1-Dec-2 Bukowskis, Helsinki #366/R

VUUREN, Jan van (1871-1941) Dutch
£704 $1134 €1000 Farmer with wheelbarrow near barn (31x59cm-12x23in) s. panel. 7-May-3 Vendue Huis, Gravenhage #66

VYLBRIEF, Ernst (1934-) Dutch
£690 $1097 €1000 Untitled (70x100cm-28x39in) s.d.1962 verso. 4-Mar-3 Ansorena, Madrid #213/R
£1290 $2039 €2000 Untitled (70x100cm-28x39in) s.d.1962. 18-Dec-2 Ansorena, Madrid #190/R

VYTLACIL, Vaclav (1892-1984) American
£503 $800 €755 Figure (66x45cm-26x18in) s.d.1961 board. 7-Mar-3 Skinner, Boston #624/R
£562 $900 €815 Still life with fish (30x47cm-12x19in) s.d.48 canvasboard. 16-May-3 Skinner, Boston #361/R
£625 $1000 €906 Fish-pier (62x47cm-24x19in) s.d.1951. 16-May-3 Skinner, Boston #269/R
£944 $1500 €1416 Modern harbour view (53x71cm-21x28in) s. board. 7-Mar-3 Skinner, Boston #627/R est:500-700
£1069 $1700 €1604 Entrance (33x38cm-13x15in) s.d.1915 canvasboard. 7-Mar-3 Skinner, Boston #386/R est:500-700
£4012 $6500 €5817 Still life with fruit (51x64cm-20x25in) s. s.i.verso board prov. 21-May-3 Doyle, New York #9/R est:2500-3500

WAAGEN, Adalbert (1833-1898) German
£573 $894 €900 In Frascati (13x21cm-5x8in) s.i. 6-Nov-2 Hugo Ruef, Munich #1323/R
£685 $1075 €1000 Mountain valley (17x22cm-7x9in) i. verso panel. 16-Apr-3 Dorotheum, Salzburg #66/R

WAAGEN, Arthur (19th C) French
Sculpture
£949 $1500 €1500 Chien Rabatjoie (29x28cm-11x11in) s.i. brown pat bronze. 29-Nov-2 Drouot Estimations, Paris #129
£5063 $8000 €7595 La gloire de fer (96cm-38in) s.i. brown pat. bronze. 24-Apr-3 Sotheby's, New York #164/R est:8000-12000
£55000 $85800 €82500 Return from the hunt (122x105cm-48x41in) s.st.f.E.Martin polychrome col brown pat bronze lit. 5-Nov-2 Sotheby's, London #153/R est:35000-45000

WAAGREZ, Vincent (19th C) ?
£300 $462 €450 Autumn river landscape (90x71cm-35x28in) s.i.verso. 23-Oct-2 Hampton & Littlewood, Exeter #446

WAAGSTEIN, Joen (1879-1949) Scandinavian
£1022 $1615 €1533 Coastal landscape from Faroe Islands (39x78cm-15x31in) s. 1-Apr-3 Rasmussen, Copenhagen #561/R (D.KR 11000)

WAARDEN, Jan van der (19/20th C) Dutch
£3822 $6000 €5733 Floral and fruit still life (71x56cm-28x22in) 13-Dec-2 Du Mouchelle, Detroit #2084/R est:5000-6000

WAAY, Nicolaas van der (1855-1936) Dutch
£700 $1141 €1050 Chickens before a woodland cottage (53x40cm-21x16in) s. 13-Feb-3 Christie's, Kensington #214/R
£1572 $2421 €2500 Amsterdam orphan (26x19cm-10x7in) s. panel. 22-Oct-2 Sotheby's, Amsterdam #116/R est:2500-3500
£4110 $6452 €6000 Amsterdam orphan girl by a window (33x15cm-13x6in) s. panel prov. 15-Apr-3 Sotheby's, Amsterdam #115/R est:2500-3500
Works on paper
£886 $1382 €1400 Two Amsterdam orphans in front of show-case cupboard (80x60cm-31x24in) s. chl. 21-Oct-2 Glerum, Amsterdam #22/R
£1507 $2351 €2200 Two ladies in costume at the Monte Pincio in Rome (49x34cm-19x13in) s. W/C. 14-Apr-3 Glerum, Amsterdam #44/R est:1000-1500
£1519 $2370 €2400 Amsterdam orphan in front of a mirror (81x50cm-32x20in) s. chl. 21-Oct-2 Glerum, Amsterdam #21/R est:1000-2000
£1944 $3208 €2800 Fascinated feline (48x32cm-19x13in) s. W/C. 1-Jul-3 Christie's, Amsterdam #577/R est:1200-1600
£2603 $4086 €3800 Portrait of an Amsterdam orphan girl (50x40cm-20x16in) s. pastel. 15-Apr-3 Sotheby's, Amsterdam #101/R est:4000-6000
£4088 $6296 €6500 Zuidelijke Wandelweg Amsterdam - girl returning home from school (39x29cm-15x11in) s. chl W/C htd white. 23-Oct-2 Christie's, Amsterdam #157/R est:5000-7000

WABEL, Henry (1889-1981) Swiss
£368 $570 €552 Still life with pear, banana and grapes (60x46cm-24x18in) s.d.50 panel. 24-Sep-2 Koller, Zurich #6699/R (S.FR 850)
£1130 $1752 €1695 Coastal landscape (38x46cm-15x18in) s.d.1968. 9-Dec-2 Philippe Schuler, Zurich #3843/R est:1800-2400 (S.FR 2600)

WACH, Aloys (1892-1940) German
Works on paper
£269 $425 €420 St Sebastian by tree pierced by arrows (23x19cm-9x7in) s. W/C Indian ink brush. 15-Nov-2 Reiss & Sohn, Konigstein #723/R
£769 $1215 €1200 Drawings. one s.d.913 one mono.d.913 chl Indian pencil three. 12-Nov-2 Dorotheum, Vienna #13/R
£1392 $2172 €2200 Absinthe (20x26cm-8x10in) s.d.1913 Indian ink brush. 15-Oct-2 Dorotheum, Vienna #34/R est:800-1200

WACHENHUSEN, Fritz (1859-1925) German
Works on paper
£417 $646 €650 Two fishing boats in Priel (34x50cm-13x20in) s. W/C. 5-Dec-2 Schopman, Hamburg #647

WACHSMUTH, Maximilian (1859-1912) German
£409 $634 €650 Stag at wood's edge (52x77cm-20x30in) s. 4-Oct-2 Paul Kieffer, Pforzhiem #9945/R

WACHTEL, Elmer (1864-1929) American
£3012 $5000 €4367 Coachella Valley with Mt San Jacinto in the distance (30x41cm-12x16in) s. prov. 11-Jun-3 Butterfields, San Francisco #4335/R est:5000-7000
£5988 $10000 €8683 Stream in Arroyo landscape (36x43cm-14x17in) mono. prov. 17-Jun-3 John Moran, Pasadena #47 est:10000-16000
£9032 $14000 €13548 Stream in Arroyo landscape (36x43cm-14x17in) s. 29-Oct-2 John Moran, Pasadena #621 est:1000-16000

WACHTEL, Elmer and Marion K (19/20th C) American
£3548 $5500 €5322 Landscape (33x43cm-13x17in) s. board. 29-Oct-2 John Moran, Pasadena #641 est:5000-7000

WACHTEL, Marion K (1876-1954) American
£4192 $7000 €6078 Verbena in foothill landscape (46x53cm-18x21in) s. canvasboard prov. 17-Jun-3 John Moran, Pasadena #60a est:9000-14000
£4194 $6500 €6291 Arroyo landscape (33x41cm-13x16in) s. canvasboard. 29-Oct-2 John Moran, Pasadena #708a est:3000-5000
£4969 $8000 €7454 Landscape (28x33cm-11x13in) s. canvasboard prov. 18-Feb-3 John Moran, Pasadena #55 est:4000-6000
£6129 $9500 €9194 Foothill landscape (33x43cm-13x17in) s. canvasboard. 29-Oct-2 John Moran, Pasadena #666 est:10000-15000
£12739 $20000 €19109 Desert rainbow (56x70cm-22x28in) s. canvas on board. 20-Nov-2 Christie's, Los Angeles #62/R est:20000-30000
£25449 $42500 €36901 Foothill eucalyptus landscape (71x61cm-28x24in) s. prov. 17-Jun-3 John Moran, Pasadena #30 est:25000-35000
Works on paper
£5689 $9500 €8249 High Sierras river landscape (48x38cm-19x15in) s. W/C. 17-Jun-3 John Moran, Pasadena #42a est:9000-12000
£8280 $13000 €12420 Streambed surrounded by eucalyptus trees at sunset (30x23cm-12x9in) s. W/C prov. 19-Nov-2 Butterfields, San Francisco #8311/R est:10000-15000

WACKER, Rudolf (1893-1939) Austrian
£1474 $2315 €2300 Reclining female nude (24x33cm-9x13in) mono.d.24 chl. 25-Nov-2 Hassfurther, Vienna #81/R est:2200-3000
£17949 $28179 €28000 Interior with window view (40x31cm-16x12in) board on paper on canvas. 25-Nov-2 Hassfurther, Vienna #77/R est:30000-35000
£101449 $166377 €140000 Portrait of Rosalie Haller (72x50cm-28x20in) s.d.26 i.verso lit. 27-May-3 Hassfurther, Vienna #63/R est:100000-150000
Prints
£2244 $3522 €3500 Self portrait drawing (39x30cm-15x12in) lithograph. 25-Nov-2 Hassfurther, Vienna #83 est:1300-1700
£2899 $4754 €4000 Doll with raised arm (52x38cm-20x15in) mono.d.37 num.11/12 lithograph. 27-May-3 Hassfurther, Vienna #69/R est:3000-4000
£3846 $6038 €6000 Self portrait (43x32cm-17x13in) mono.d.21 lithograph. 25-Nov-2 Hassfurther, Vienna #82/R est:1300-1700
Works on paper
£2029 $3328 €2800 Head (29x22cm-11x9in) mono.d. pencil. 27-May-3 Wiener Kunst Auktionen, Vienna #86/R est:1800-4000
£2174 $3565 €3000 Reclining nude (42x29cm-17x11in) mono.d.32 black chk lit. 27-May-3 Hassfurther, Vienna #67/R est:2200-3000
£2536 $4159 €3500 Sanding nude viewed from the back (48x29cm-19x11in) mono.d.37 red ochre lit. 27-May-3 Hassfurther, Vienna #66/R est:2000-3000
£2536 $4159 €3500 Portrait Rosalie Haller (43x31cm-17x12in) mono.d.24 black chk lit. 27-May-3 Hassfurther, Vienna #68/R est:3500-4500
£2885 $4529 €4500 Frau Klimesch wearing stockings (58x43cm-23x17in) mono.d.23 chk lit. 25-Nov-2 Hassfurther, Vienna #80/R est:2200-3000
£3859 $6058 €6020 Night shadows in Romania (38x27cm-15x11in) mono.d.1924 i. verso chk. 25-Nov-2 Hassfurther, Vienna #79/R est:2200-3000
£3986 $6536 €5500 Mrs Klimesch (61x48cm-24x19in) mono.d.24 brush ink. 27-May-3 Hassfurther, Vienna #65/R est:2200-3200
£4710 $7725 €6500 Woman seated (37x27cm-15x11in) mono. blue chk exec.1924 lit. 27-May-3 Hassfurther, Vienna #64/R est:5000-7000
£6410 $10064 €10000 Portrait of my mother in her 70th year (68x48cm-27x19in) mono.d. chk transparent paper lit. 25-Nov-2 Hassfurther, Vienna #78/R est:4400-5000

WACKERLE, Joseph (1880-1959) German
Sculpture
£1026 $1621 €1600 Woman on dolphin (82cm-32in) i. gilded bronze exhib. 14-Nov-2 Neumeister, Munich #463/R est:3500-4000

WADALL, G G (19th C) Swedish
£467 $719 €701 Oscar II (127x80cm-50x31in) s. painted 1895. 28-Oct-2 Blomqvist, Lysaker #1340 (N.KR 5500)

WADDINGTON, Phillip J (20th C) New Zealander
Works on paper
£242 $373 €363 Thoughts of a Tohunga whare Kauri Tahuna (58x46cm-23x18in) s.d.1978 mixed media. 4-Sep-2 Dunbar Sloane, Wellington #132 (NZ.D 800)

WADE, David (20th C) American
£8228 $13000 €11931 Threat on the horizon (76x102cm-30x40in) s. board. 26-Jul-3 Coeur d'Alene, Hayden #152/R est:10000-15000

WADE, George Edward (1853-1933) British
Sculpture
£1800 $2808 €2700 Grenadier guard (57cm-22in) s.i.d.1889 brown pat bronze wood plinth st.f.Luppens lit. 9-Apr-3 Sotheby's, London #137/R est:2000-3000

WADE, Jonathan (1960-) British
£260 $400 €390 Warm south (19x26cm-7x10in) s. s.i.verso board. 5-Sep-2 Christie's, Kensington #635/R
£400 $616 €600 Indurness (20x35cm-8x14in) s. board. 5-Sep-2 Christie's, Kensington #640/R
£450 $715 €675 En famille (61x91cm-24x36in) s. s.i.verso board. 26-Feb-3 Sotheby's, Olympia #365/R
£450 $738 €675 Fevrier (51x76cm-20x30in) s. canvasboard. 3-Jun-3 Sotheby's, Olympia #198/R
£550 $847 €825 St Pancras Day (61x78cm-24x31in) s. s.i.verso board. 5-Sep-2 Christie's, Kensington #624/R
£550 $853 €825 Drinks (32x52cm-13x20in) s. s.i.verso board. 4-Dec-2 Christie's, Kensington #520/R
£550 $858 €825 Teabullies (51x61cm-20x24in) s. s.i.verso board. 27-Mar-3 Christie's, Kensington #561/R
£550 $908 €798 Proposal (30x66cm-12x26in) s. board. 3-Jul-3 Christie's, Kensington #552/R
£600 $924 €900 Flit (46x66cm-18x26in) s. s.i.verso canvasboard. 5-Sep-2 Christie's, Kensington #636/R
£750 $1170 €1125 System and aspiration (32x73cm-13x29in) s. board. 12-Sep-2 Sotheby's, Olympia #122/R
£750 $1185 €1125 David and Bathsheba (61x76cm-24x30in) s. s.i.verso board. 27-Nov-2 Sotheby's, Olympia #213/R
£750 $1193 €1125 Love boat (49x74cm-19x29in) s. board. 26-Feb-3 Sotheby's, Olympia #366/R
£850 $1394 €1275 Pub in the sticks (30x46cm-12x18in) s. board. 3-Jun-3 Sotheby's, Olympia #197/R
£1100 $1793 €1595 Walk (29x83cm-11x33in) s. board. 17-Jul-3 Tennants, Leyburn #936/R est:500-700
£1200 $1872 €1800 Tempus fugit (30x81cm-12x32in) s. s.i.verso board. 10-Apr-3 Tennants, Leyburn #1144/R est:500-600
£1700 $2669 €2550 Wednesday afternoon (29x83cm-11x33in) s. s.i.verso board. 21-Nov-2 Tennants, Leyburn #863/R est:500-700
Works on paper
£650 $1073 €943 Sunday afternoon (35x25cm-14x10in) s. W/C bodycol pen ink. 3-Jul-3 Christie's, Kensington #554/R

WADE, Thomas (1828-1891) British
Works on paper
£320 $522 €480 North Hill, Clovelly Devon (68x50cm-27x20in) s.d.1883 W/C over pencil. 11-Feb-3 Bonhams, Knowle #26

WADE, Thomas (attrib) (1828-1891) British
Works on paper
£350 $553 €508 Grange (31x45cm-12x18in) mono.d.74 W/C. 22-Jul-3 Sotheby's, Olympia #111

WADHAM, R S (19th C) American
£938 $1500 €1360 Full length portrait of Priscilla Lodge, Sheffield, Mass (81x69cm-32x27in) s. 17-May-3 CRN Auctions, Cambridge #51

WADHAM, William Joseph (1863-1950) Australian
Works on paper
£400 $664 €580 Rapids (47x72cm-19x28in) s. W/C gouache. 16-Jun-3 Waddingtons, Toronto #13/R est:1000-1500 (C.D 900)

WADSWORTH, Edward (1889-1949) British
£3800 $5928 €5700 Framework of the future (35x35cm-14x14in) gouache. 12-Sep-2 Sotheby's, Olympia #169/R est:4000-6000
£10000 $15500 €15000 Les plats du jour (53x38cm-21x15in) s.d.1938 i.verso tempera on board prov.exhib.lit. 3-Dec-2 Bonhams, New Bond Street #71/R est:12000-18000
£23000 $35880 €34500 Ship in dry dock (50x60cm-20x24in) s.d.1941 tempera prov.exhib. 12-Sep-2 Sotheby's, Olympia #164/R est:10000-15000
£36000 $60120 €52200 Offing (41x35cm-16x14in) s.d.1936 tempera panel prov.exhib. 24-Jun-3 Bonhams, New Bond Street #63/R est:15000-20000
Works on paper
£1400 $2184 €2100 Acid test (29x38cm-11x15in) init. ink gouache. 12-Sep-2 Sotheby's, Olympia #167/R est:1500-2000
£6000 $9360 €9000 Omega and alpha (40x39cm-16x15in) W/C gouache. 12-Sep-2 Sotheby's, Olympia #163/R est:5000-7000

WAEL, Cornelis de (1592-1667) Flemish
£12000 $20040 €17400 Wooded landscape with bandits ambushing travellers (75x101cm-30x40in) 10-Jul-3 Sotheby's, London #112/R est:12000-18000
£26843 $43218 €40000 Coastal landscape with warships and galleys unloading trade (40x60cm-16x24in) copper. 18-Feb-3 Sotheby's, Amsterdam #225/R est:15000-20000

WAEL, Cornelis de (attrib) (1592-1667) Flemish
£16106 $25931 €24000 Camp scene with soldiers resting and playing dice (78x115cm-31x45in) prov.lit. 18-Feb-3 Sotheby's, Amsterdam #214/R est:10000-15000
Works on paper
£380 $597 €570 Market scene with a man, mule and a monkey (19x29cm-7x11in) pen ink wash. 11-Dec-2 Sotheby's, Olympia #72/R

WAEL, Cornelis de (style) (1592-1667) Flemish
£6500 $10205 €9750 Soldiers with mixed company at a banquet (49x72cm-19x28in) 10-Dec-2 Bonhams, New Bond Street #205/R est:2500-3500
£10000 $15700 €15000 Dentist. Soldiers returning home (34x45cm-13x18in) pair. 10-Dec-2 Sotheby's, Olympia #373/R est:3000-4000

WAENERBERG, Thorsten (1846-1917) Finnish
£1379 $2179 €2000 Hogland - coastal landscape (21x33cm-8x13in) s. 3-Apr-3 Hagelstam, Helsinki #870/R est:2000
£1517 $2397 €2200 Coastal landscape (38x20cm-15x8in) s.d.1890. 3-Apr-3 Hagelstam, Helsinki #867/R est:1000
£1709 $2700 €2700 The home beach (28x40cm-11x16in) s.d.II/V 1890 board. 1-Dec-2 Bukowskis, Helsinki #203/R est:2200-2500
£1972 $3175 €2800 The cliffs near Alicante (33x55cm-13x22in) s.d.1899. 10-May-3 Bukowskis, Helsinki #153/R est:3000-4000
£2158 $3453 €3000 Seascape with fishing boats (17x24cm-7x9in) s.d.1870 canvas on board. 17-May-3 Hagelstam, Helsinki #103/R est:2500

WAENTIG, Walter (1881-1962) German
£845 $1361 €1200 Bodensee landscape with cherry tree in bloom (60x70cm-24x28in) s.d.28. 7-May-3 Michael Zeller, Lindau #960/R

WAERHERT, Arthur de (1881-1944) Belgian?
£633 $987 €1000 Cinq moutons dans un paysage (50x65cm-20x26in) s. 15-Oct-2 Horta, Bruxelles #72

WAERYEL, Petronella van (?) Swedish
£430 $696 €645 Still life of flowers (49x39cm-19x15in) s. 3-Feb-3 Lilla Bukowskis, Stockholm #469 (S.KR 6000)

WAGEMAEKERS, Victor (1876-1953) Belgian
£478 $745 €750 La mare aux canards (40x50cm-16x20in) s. 11-Nov-2 Horta, Bruxelles #501
£530 $864 €800 Interieur de cafe (48x38cm-19x15in) s. panel. 17-Feb-3 Horta, Bruxelles #78
£548 $855 €800 Mare aux canards et moulin a eau (54x64cm-21x25in) s. 14-Apr-3 Horta, Bruxelles #55
£588 $947 €900 Paysage au ruisseau (45x55cm-18x22in) s. 14-Jan-3 Vanderkindere, Brussels #449
£949 $1481 €1500 Etang aux canards (67x65cm-26x26in) s. 16-Sep-2 Horta, Bruxelles #383
£1233 $1923 €1800 Vase fleuri d'anemones (50x60cm-20x24in) s. 14-Apr-3 Horta, Bruxelles #54 est:1800-2200
£2014 $3223 €2800 Le Chateau de Grimbergen sous le soleil d'automne (90x120cm-35x47in) s. 13-May-3 Palais de Beaux Arts, Brussels #174/R est:3000-5000
Works on paper
£284 $474 €400 Paysage de dunes (53x104cm-21x41in) gouache paper on canvas. 18-Jun-3 Hotel des Ventes Mosan, Brussels #219

WAGEMAKER, Jaap (1906-1972) Dutch
Works on paper
£2590 $4247 €3600 Marecage (130x105cm-51x41in) s.d.58 s.i.d.verso mixed media on canvas prov.lit. 3-Jun-3 Christie's, Amsterdam #59/R est:3000-5000
£5769 $8942 €9000 Opeenstapeling (100x65cm-39x26in) s. s.i.on stretcher mixed media prov.lit. 3-Dec-2 Christie's, Amsterdam #285/R est:10000-15000

WAGEMAN, Michael Angelo (fl.1837-1879) British
Works on paper
£420 $647 €630 Rabbits in a hutch (27x37cm-11x15in) s.d.72 W/C. 22-Oct-2 Bonhams, Knightsbridge #2/R

WAGEMAN, Thomas Charles (1787-1863) British
Works on paper
£300 $462 €450 Portrait of a seated lady, half length (20x15cm-8x6in) s.d.1825 pencil with two other by same hand three. 9-Sep-2 Bonhams, Ipswich #120
£500 $820 €725 Portraits of ladies (26x21cm-10x8in) s.d.1837 W/C pair. 9-Jun-3 Bonhams, Bath #112/R

WAGEMANS, Maurice (1877-1927) Belgian
£315 $492 €460 Deux elegantes a la lecture (39x59cm-15x23in) s. 14-Apr-3 Horta, Bruxelles #396
£348 $543 €550 Fermette ensoleillee (71x50cm-28x20in) s. canvas on panel. 15-Oct-2 Horta, Bruxelles #450
£1392 $2172 €2200 Pont sur la Seine (29x44cm-11x17in) s.i.d.1909 panel. 16-Sep-2 Horta, Bruxelles #189
£1655 $2632 €2400 Le peintre dans son atelier (69x44cm-27x17in) s. 4-Mar-3 Palais de Beaux Arts, Brussels #408 est:1200-1600

WAGEMANS, Pieter Johannes Alexander (1879-1955) Dutch
£1274 $1962 €2000 Shipping activities, Rotterdam Harbour (60x100cm-24x39in) s. 3-Sep-2 Christie's, Amsterdam #332/R est:2000-3000

WAGENBAUER, Max Josef (1774-1829) German
Works on paper
£1603 $2340 €2500 Kurn Castle near Regenstauf in Upper Pfalz (35x43cm-14x17in) s. W/C pen. 4-Jun-2 Karl & Faber, Munich #145/R est:5000
£11111 $17667 €16000 Altenhausen near Freising (21x26cm-8x10in) s.d.1821 i. verso chk W/C htd white. 5-May-3 Ketterer, Munich #328/R est:1200-1500

WAGENSCHOEN, Franz Xaver (1726-1790) Austrian
Works on paper
£350 $500 €525 Triumph of Venus (20x30cm-8x12in) s.i. pencil. 23-Jan-3 Swann Galleries, New York #342/R

WAGNER, Alexander von (1838-1919) Hungarian
£256 $397 €400 Graz, Steiermark (26x21cm-10x8in) s. i. verso panel. 6-Dec-2 Michael Zeller, Lindau #947/R

WAGNER, Carl (1796-1857) German
Works on paper
£468 $767 €650 Wood near Meiningen with walker (38x25cm-15x10in) i. 4-Jun-3 Reiss & Sohn, Konigstein #306
£540 $885 €750 Schonbach, near Meiningen (25x38cm-10x15in) i. W/C chk. 4-Jun-3 Reiss & Sohn, Konigstein #305/R
£541 $845 €850 Building over stream (50x37cm-20x15in) mono.i.d.31 Aug 44 W/C chk. 5-Nov-2 Hartung & Hartung, Munich #5147/R

WAGNER, Cornelis (1870-1956) German
£569 $899 €825 Hamburg harbour (46x66cm-18x26in) s. 5-Apr-3 Hans Stahl, Hamburg #143/R
£1295 $2072 €1800 Dutch harbour (63x90cm-25x35in) s. 17-May-3 Lempertz, Koln #1503/R est:2000

WAGNER, Ferdinand (19/20th C) German
£25478 $40000 €38217 Allegory of the Arts (246x508cm-97x200in) s.d.93 oval. 21-Nov-2 Sotheby's, New York #182/R est:30000-40000

WAGNER, Ferdinand (jnr) (1847-1927) German
£1875 $3000 €2813 Allegorical scene with figures, study for Lunette (23x87cm-9x34in) s.i.d.1912 board. 14-May-3 Butterfields, San Francisco #1074/R est:3500-5500
£3425 $5342 €5000 Roses in Delft vase (75x42cm-30x17in) s.i.d.1819. 10-Apr-3 Dorotheum, Vienna #64/R est:5500-6000

WAGNER, Fred (1864-1940) American
Works on paper
£290 $450 €435 Houses in winter (19x20cm-7x8in) s. pastel. 8-Dec-2 Freeman, Philadelphia #122/R
£516 $800 €774 Philadelphia, the Schuylkill River (20x25cm-8x10in) s. s.i.verso pastel. 8-Dec-2 Freeman, Philadelphia #121/R
£548 $800 €822 Hillside in winter (58x53cm-23x21in) s. gouache W/C. 3-Nov-1 North East Auctions, Portsmouth #267/R
£645 $1000 €968 Landscape with trees and house (23x26cm-9x10in) s. pastel cardboard. 8-Dec-2 Freeman, Philadelphia #112/R

WAGNER, Fritz (20th C) German
£338 $527 €500 The Sass Songher in the Dolomites (75x100cm-30x39in) s. 26-Mar-3 Hugo Ruef, Munich #256
£377 $581 €600 Monk and clergyman tasting wine (26x35cm-10x14in) s.i. panel. 23-Oct-2 Neumeister, Munich #769/R
£692 $1079 €1100 Reflective monk writing letter (30x25cm-12x10in) s. 20-Sep-2 Sigalas, Stuttgart #1055/R
£2083 $3437 €3000 Cardinal sampling the wine (30x25cm-12x10in) s. 1-Jul-3 Christie's, Amsterdam #144/R est:2000-3000
£4717 $7264 €7500 Good vintage (40x35cm-16x14in) s.i. 22-Oct-2 Sotheby's, Amsterdam #71/R est:3000-5000
£6410 $9936 €10000 Dutch interior with drinkers sitting at a table (70x60cm-28x24in) s.i. 4-Dec-2 Neumeister, Munich #957/R est:2500
£6463 $10276 €9500 Dutch noblemen breakfasting (80x100cm-31x39in) s.i. 19-Mar-3 Neumeister, Munich #797/R est:2000
£6707 $11000 €10061 Dice game (51x61cm-20x24in) s.i. prov. 5-Feb-3 Christie's, Rockefeller NY #181/R est:5000-7000
£9434 $14528 €15000 An interesting story (60x50cm-24x20in) s. prov. 22-Oct-2 Sotheby's, Amsterdam #74/R est:8000-12000
£11950 $18403 €19000 Interesting letter (66x81cm-26x32in) s. 22-Oct-2 Sotheby's, Amsterdam #78/R est:6000-8000

WAGNER, Fritz (1896-1939) German
£1042 $1656 €1500 Reading cardinal (24x18cm-9x7in) s. 29-Apr-3 Christie's, Amsterdam #56/R est:1500-2000
£3421 $5542 €5200 Tasting the wine (26x20cm-10x8in) s. 21-Jan-3 Christie's, Amsterdam #103/R est:2000-3000
£4110 $6452 €6000 Important visitor (60x75cm-24x30in) s.i. 15-Apr-3 Sotheby's, Amsterdam #87/R est:5000-8000
£4403 $6780 €7000 Merry company (70x86cm-28x34in) s.i. 22-Oct-2 Sotheby's, Amsterdam #66/R est:8000-12000

WAGNER, Hans (1885-?) Swiss
£414 $650 €621 Italian Riviera (36x51cm-14x20in) board. 13-Dec-2 Du Mouchelle, Detroit #2037/R
£581 $900 €872 Woman kneeling at a woodland shrine (36x28cm-14x11in) init. 7-Dec-2 Selkirks, St. Louis #735

WAGNER, Hans Joachim (20th C) German
£329 $539 €477 Grotto entrance (71x35cm-28x14in) s.i. 4-Jun-3 Fischer, Luzern #2346/R (S.FR 700)

WAGNER, Jacob (1852-1896) American
£2044 $3250 €3066 Spring landscape (51x61cm-20x24in) s. 7-Mar-3 Skinner, Boston #409/R est:3000-5000

WAGNER, Johan Georg (1744-1767) German
Works on paper
£274 $427 €400 River with bridge and tower (14x15cm-6x6in) s.d. pen over pencil. 11-Apr-3 Winterberg, Heidelberg #326

WAGNER, Johann Friedrich (1801-?) German
£522 $814 €783 Coast with sailing ships (50x100cm-20x39in) s. 16-Sep-2 Philippe Schuler, Zurich #6491 (S.FR 1200)

WAGNER, Johann Martin (attrib) (1777-1858) German
£1600 $2528 €2400 Assembling for the fight for Troy (58x85cm-23x33in) 14-Nov-2 Christie's, Kensington #281/R est:1500-2200

WAGNER, K (?) ?
£503 $785 €800 Dutch fishing village (69x56cm-27x22in) i. 23-Sep-2 Dr Fritz Nagel, Stuttgart #7060/R
£1507 $2351 €2200 Southern Italian harbour town (73x99cm-29x39in) s. 10-Apr-3 Van Ham, Cologne #1748/R est:2300

WAGNER, Karl (19/20th C) Austrian/German
£321 $503 €500 Liensohn - horse portrait (24x34cm-9x13in) mono.d.3.VII.1906 canvas on board. 21-Nov-2 Van Ham, Cologne #1961
£377 $581 €600 Dutch harbour (69x55cm-27x22in) s. 26-Oct-2 Quittenbaum, Hamburg #66/R
£429 $678 €644 View from Sacking with storm (68x88cm-27x35in) s.i.verso. 29-Nov-2 Zofingen, Switzerland #2555 (S.FR 1000)
£755 $1177 €1200 Hunting dog with deer (88x120cm-35x47in) s.d.26. 21-Sep-2 Bolland & Marotz, Bremen #573/R
£1656 $2583 €2600 City view with inner harbour, moored barge carriers and figures (70x98cm-28x39in) s. 5-Nov-2 Vendu Notarishuis, Rotterdam #21/R est:1200-1600
£1781 $2778 €2600 Gulf of Naples (75x100cm-30x39in) s. 10-Apr-3 Schopman, Hamburg #600/R est:1000

WAGNER, Ludwig Christian (1799-1839) German
£2550 $4106 €3800 Wooded landscape with a couple resting near a stream (39x48cm-15x19in) s.d.1830 pair after Jacob van Ruisdael Wetzlar. 18-Feb-3 Sotheby's, Amsterdam #661/R est:1500-2000
£5033 $8104 €7500 Wooded landscape with a couple on a horse-cart (72x97cm-28x38in) s.d.1833. 18-Feb-3 Sotheby's, Amsterdam #427/R est:1500-2000

WAGNER, Melanie von (1866-?) German
£766 $1210 €1149 Watering the horse (59x70cm-23x28in) s. 2-Dec-2 Rasmussen, Copenhagen #1342/R (D.KR 9000)

WAGNER, Nanette (19th C) Swiss?
Works on paper
£873 $1380 €1310 Still life of flowers. s.d.1824 W/C two. 14-Nov-2 Stuker, Bern #9631 est:800-1200 (S.FR 2000)

WAGNER, Ottmar (?) Austrian?
£385 $608 €600 Landscape (55x63cm-22x25in) s.d.58 panel. 18-Nov-2 Dorotheum, Linz #347/R
£504 $806 €700 Ottensheim (70x75cm-28x30in) s. panel. 14-May-3 Dorotheum, Linz #393/R

WAGNER, Paul Hermann (1852-?) German
£4000 $6280 €6000 Chasing dragon flies (103x64cm-41x25in) s.i.d.1885. 19-Nov-2 Bonhams, New Bond Street #32/R est:4000-6000

WAGNER, Peter (studio) (18/19th C) Austrian
Sculpture
£7962 $12420 €12500 Portrait of Karl Theodors von Dahlberg (45cm-18in) i. verso alabaster relief. 6-Nov-2 Hugo Ruef, Munich #2116/R est:900

WAGNER, Pierre (1897-?) French
£690 $1097 €1000 Dundees au mouillage, Douarnenez (38x46cm-15x18in) s. panel. 7-Mar-3 Rabourdin & Choppin de Janvry, Paris #38
£1013 $1570 €1600 Le retour des pecheurs (50x61cm-20x24in) s. 29-Sep-2 Eric Pillon, Calais #182/R

WAGNER, Richard (19th C) ?
Photographs
£2600 $4290 €3770 Untitled. s.i.d.1901 photograph. 3-Jul-3 Duke & Son, Dorchester #404/R
£3200 $5280 €4640 Richard and Cosiman Wagner. three photographs in one frame. 3-Jul-3 Duke & Son, Dorchester #403/R

WAGNER, Wilhelm (?-1887) German
£417 $658 €650 Paris, Pont St Michel (60x73cm-24x29in) s. i. stretcher. 15-Nov-2 Reiss & Sohn, Konigstein #93/R

WAGNER, Willem George (1814-1855) Dutch
£2949 $4629 €4600 Watch tower in small Dutch town (59x77cm-23x30in) s.d.1839 panel. 21-Nov-2 Van Ham, Cologne #1963/R est:4800

WAGNER-DEINES, Johann (1803-1880) German
£316 $491 €500 Winter pleasures (16x20cm-6x8in) s. panel. 25-Sep-2 Neumeister, Munich #770/R

WAGNER-HOHENBERG, Josef (1870-1939) German
£1315 $2156 €1907 Settlement day (55x70cm-22x28in) s. prov. 4-Jun-3 Fischer, Luzern #1141/R est:2500-3000 (S.FR 2800)
£3275 $5109 €4913 The loan (70x101cm-28x40in) s. 20-Nov-2 Fischer, Luzern #1178/R est:6000-8000 (S.FR 7500)

WAGONER, Harry B (1889-1950) American
£778 $1300 €1128 Capistrano mission (56x46cm-22x18in) s. 17-Jun-3 John Moran, Pasadena #26 est:1000-2000

WAGONER, Robert B (1928-) American
£2564 $4000 €3846 Mooring reflections (76x61cm-30x24in) 9-Nov-2 Altermann Galleries, Santa Fe #27

WAHL, Irene (20th C) Canadian
Works on paper
£200 $328 €290 Pink petals (51x34cm-20x13in) s. W/C. 9-Jun-3 Hodgins, Calgary #23/R (C.D 450)
£234 $383 €339 Autumn (25x35cm-10x14in) s. W/C. 9-Jun-3 Hodgins, Calgary #123/R (C.D 525)

WAHLBERG, Alfred (1834-1906) Swedish
£398 $621 €597 River landscape with buildings (22x31cm-9x12in) mono. 13-Sep-2 Lilla Bukowskis, Stockholm #892 (S.KR 5800)
£511 $837 €741 Harvesting landscape with figures, evening light (23x33cm-9x13in) s. panel. 4-Jun-3 AB Stockholms Auktionsverk #2205/R (S.KR 6500)
£565 $886 €848 Sailing boat at sunset (52x70cm-20x28in) s.d.1891. 16-Dec-2 Lilla Bukowskis, Stockholm #336 (S.KR 8000)
£567 $879 €851 Windy coast (17x26cm-7x10in) s. panel. 4-Dec-2 AB Stockholms Auktionsverk #1722/R (S.KR 8000)
£652 $991 €978 View of Venice (25x37cm-10x15in) s. canvas on panel exhib. 16-Aug-2 Lilla Bukowskis, Stockholm #490 (S.KR 9500)
£776 $1257 €1125 Northern landscape, summer (36x48cm-14x19in) s.d.aug.1903 panel. 26-May-3 Bukowskis, Stockholm #171/R (S.KR 10000)
£780 $1209 €1170 Tree in summer verdure (52x34cm-20x13in) s.i.d.23 juli 95. 4-Dec-2 AB Stockholms Auktionsverk #1710/R (S.KR 11000)
£943 $1546 €1367 Breakers and rocky coast, Kullen (43x72cm-17x28in) s. 4-Jun-3 AB Stockholms Auktionsverk #2184/R (S.KR 12000)
£1170 $1814 €1755 Landscape view from Lago Maggiore, Italy (33x45cm-13x18in) s. 3-Dec-2 Bukowskis, Stockholm #194/R est:22000-25000 (S.KR 16500)
£1414 $2319 €2050 Landscape from Normandy (33x43cm-13x17in) s.d.10 juli 93. 4-Jun-3 AB Stockholms Auktionsverk #2130/R est:30000-35000 (S.KR 18000)
£1544 $2564 €2239 Lake landscape at dusk (65x91cm-26x36in) s.d.71. 16-Jun-3 Lilla Bukowskis, Stockholm #1100 est:20000-25000 (S.KR 20000)
£1728 $2834 €2506 Coastal town in moonlight (60x92cm-24x36in) s. 4-Jun-3 AB Stockholms Auktionsverk #2097/R est:15000-20000 (S.KR 22000)
£4085 $6699 €5923 Coastal landscape with punts (36x47cm-14x19in) s. 4-Jun-3 AB Stockholms Auktionsverk #2145/R est:40000-50000 (S.KR 52000)
£9000 $14760 €13500 Ruiner vid Bohus - ruins at Bohus (99x151cm-39x59in) s. prov.exhib.lit. 3-Jun-3 Sotheby's, London #271/R est:10000-15000

WAHLBERG, Ruth (20th C) American
£1419 $2200 €2129 Composition (76x51cm-30x20in) s. painted c.1947 exhib. 8-Dec-2 Toomey, Oak Park #789/R est:700-900

WAHLBERG, Ulf (1938-) Swedish
£734 $1181 €1101 Studio interior (100x81cm-39x32in) s.d.87 tempera. 7-May-3 AB Stockholms Auktionsverk #864/R (S.KR 9500)
Works on paper
£1135 $1759 €1703 Dumping place for cars (24x31cm-9x12in) s.d.1977 mixed media. 8-Dec-2 Uppsala Auktionskammare, Uppsala #280/R est:10000-12000 (S.KR 16000)

WAHLBERGSON, Erik (1808-1865) Swedish
£328 $525 €476 Portrait of Mr Frederik Hook (32x25cm-13x10in) i.d.1845 verso. 18-May-3 Anders Antik, Landskrona #29 (S.KR 4200)
£3546 $5745 €5000 Reclining beauty (57x69cm-22x27in) s.d.1847. 22-May-3 Dorotheum, Vienna #74/R est:6000-7000

WAHLBERGSON, Erik (attrib) (1808-1865) Swedish
£325 $510 €471 Portrait of Louise Hook. d.1845. 15-Dec-2 Anders Antik, Landskrona #202 (S.KR 4600)

WAHLBOM, Carl (1810-1858) Swedish
£931 $1434 €1397 Falstaff exciting shy young woman (44x39cm-17x15in) s. 27-Oct-2 Anders Antik, Landskrona #131/R (S.KR 13500)

WAHLQVIST, Ehrnfried (1814-1895) Swedish
£426 $647 €639 By the carpenter's bench (31x39cm-12x15in) s.indis.d.186. 16-Aug-2 Lilla Bukowskis, Stockholm #957 (S.KR 6200)
£943 $1546 €1367 Chatarinahissen, Stockholm (21x29cm-8x11in) init.d.1886 panel. 4-Jun-3 AB Stockholms Auktionsverk #2114/R (S.KR 12000)
£1241 $2011 €1799 Vessels in moonlight by Kronborg Palace (52x92cm-20x36in) s.d.1865. 25-May-3 Uppsala Auktionskammare, Uppsala #81/R est:8000-10000 (S.KR 16000)
£1257 $2061 €1823 Karlberg Canal (21x30cm-8x12in) init.d.1886 panel. 4-Jun-3 AB Stockholms Auktionsverk #2115/R est:8000-10000 (S.KR 16000)
£1493 $2448 €2165 View of Riddarfjarden and Kungsholmen from Sodermalm (21x30cm-8x12in) init.d.1886 panel. 4-Jun-3 AB Stockholms Auktionsverk #2113/R est:8000-10000 (S.KR 19000)
£1629 $2639 €2362 View across Stockholm towards the Old Town (52x77cm-20x30in) mono.d.1883. 25-May-3 Uppsala Auktionskammare, Uppsala #83/R est:12000-15000 (S.KR 21000)

WAHLROOS, Dora (1870-1947) Finnish
£1799 $2878 €2500 Gypsy woman (55x46cm-22x18in) s. exhib. 17-May-3 Hagelstam, Helsinki #146/R est:2500

WAHLROOS, Walter (1901-1968) Finnish
£294 $482 €450 Sandy beaches, Hango (46x55cm-18x22in) s.d.45. 9-Feb-3 Bukowskis, Helsinki #390/R

WAHLSTEDT, Walter (1898-1962) German
Works on paper
£673 $1043 €1050 Geometric composition (16x13cm-6x5in) s.i.d.1946 gouache paper on board. 7-Dec-2 Ketterer, Hamburg #300/R

WAHLSTROM, Charlotte (1849-1924) Swedish
£377 $581 €600 Sunset (55x47cm-22x19in) s. 27-Oct-2 Bukowskis, Helsinki #348/R
£781 $1241 €1172 Summer landscape (68x98cm-27x39in) s. 3-Mar-3 Lilla Bukowskis, Stockholm #404 (S.KR 10500)
£1030 $1565 €1545 Lake landscape with stags (85x112cm-33x44in) s.d.84. 16-Aug-2 Lilla Bukowskis, Stockholm #873 est:15000-20000 (S.KR 15000)
£1338 $2154 €1900 Deer watering (84x113cm-33x44in) s.d.87. 10-May-3 Bukowskis, Helsinki #361/R est:1500-2000

WAHORN, Andras (1953-) Hungarian
£980 $1529 €1470 Mother playing ball with her son (50x70cm-20x28in) s. board. 11-Sep-2 Kieselbach, Budapest #122/R (H.F 380000)

WAIDMANN, Pierre (1860-1937) French
£2658 $4147 €4200 La find de journee (60x130cm-24x51in) s. i.verso. 20-Oct-2 Mercier & Cie, Lille #333/R est:4500-5000

WAILAND, Friedrich (1821-1904) Austrian
Works on paper
£1892 $2951 €2800 Portrait of young woman wearing fur stole (8x6cm-3x2in) s. W/C ivory oval. 28-Mar-3 Dorotheum, Vienna #362/R est:1200-1500

WAILLY, Léon de (19th C) French
Miniatures
£1418 $2298 €2000 Le Duc de Berry (6x5cm-2x2in) s.d.1828 gilded brass surround prov. 21-May-3 Piasa, Paris #328/R est:1500-2000

WAIN, L (19th C) British
Works on paper
£310 $484 €465 Golfing cats (47x34cm-19x13in) s.d. W/C. 18-Sep-2 James Thompson, Kirby Lonsdale #38

WAIN, Louis (1860-1939) British
Works on paper
£270 $440 €405 Head study of a cat (6cm-2in circular) s. grey wash dr. 30-Jan-3 Lawrence, Crewkerne #661
£380 $593 €570 Bear hunting traps, Thibet (44x35cm-17x14in) s.i. pen ink. 5-Nov-2 Bonhams, New Bond Street #182/R
£400 $624 €600 Animal's institute, 9 Kinnerton Street, Belgravia (28x41cm-11x16in) s.i. pen ink. 5-Nov-2 Bonhams, New Bond Street #174/R
£420 $697 €630 Caricature portrait of a cat (11x9cm-4x4in) s.i.d.23.11.21 pen ink dr. in a note book. 10-Jun-3 Bonhams, Leeds #74
£500 $775 €750 Gentleman cat (18x9cm-7x4in) s. pen ink. 4-Dec-2 Christie's, Kensington #187/R

£550 $908 €798 Sideways glance (22x17cm-9x7in) s. pencil bodycol. 3-Jul-3 Christie's, Kensington #237
£650 $1079 €975 Oooh - what a shock I (16x15cm-6x6in) s. col chk. 12-Jun-3 Bonhams, New Bond Street #703/R
£700 $1092 €1050 None may enter here (27x40cm-11x16in) s.i. W/C. 5-Nov-2 Bonhams, New Bond Street #181/R
£700 $1085 €1050 Surprise (20x15cm-8x6in) pen black ink. 4-Dec-2 Christie's, Kensington #181/R
£700 $1120 €1050 Rough-haired basset hound (33x25cm-13x10in) s.i. W/C htd white prov. 11-Mar-3 Bonhams, New Bond Street #151/R
£700 $1092 €1050 Evening, study of a ginger cat (19x17cm-7x7in) s. bodycol. 10-Apr-3 Tennants, Leyburn #918/R
£700 $1113 €1050 Study of cats. s. ink pen wash. 30-Apr-3 Halls, Shrewsbury #251/R
£750 $1170 €1125 Other peoples's pets (44x32cm-17x13in) s.i. pen ink. 5-Nov-2 Bonhams, New Bond Street #177
£900 $1494 €1350 Tis said that a cat may look at a king (22x14cm-9x6in) s.i. brush ink. 12-Jun-3 Bonhams, New Bond Street #706/R
£900 $1494 €1350 Starry eyed cat (23x18cm-9x7in) s. pencil. 12-Jun-3 Bonhams, New Bond Street #707/R
£1000 $1600 €1500 Dog's tea party (16x24cm-6x9in) s. W/C bodycol exhib. 11-Mar-3 Bonhams, New Bond Street #144/R est:1200-1800
£1000 $1600 €1500 I'm off to the dentist (36x23cm-14x9in) s. W/C. 11-Mar-3 Bonhams, New Bond Street #148/R est:1000-1500
£1200 $1860 €1800 Those with feelings wondrous kind can love with kitties ever blind (18x15cm-7x6in) s.i.d.Dec 17 1920 pen black ink. 4-Dec-2 Christie's, Kensington #185/R est:1200-1800
£1200 $1956 €1800 She kept on kissing me, cat,. Shovelling coal (40x29cm-16x11in) s. one i. pen ink wash pair. 29-Jan-3 Sotheby's, Olympia #181/R est:600-800
£1200 $1920 €1800 Jack's little Mary is upset, throw physic to the dogs (39x25cm-15x10in) s. W/C bodycol. 11-Mar-3 Bonhams, New Bond Street #149/R est:800-1200
£1300 $2028 €1950 Musical madness (29x23cm-11x9in) s. W/C bodycol. 5-Nov-2 Bonhams, New Bond Street #184/R est:1000-1500
£1300 $2145 €1885 Doggy music hall (42x33cm-17x13in) s. pencil W/C pen brush black ink W/C htd white. 3-Jul-3 Christie's, Kensington #238/R est:1500-2500
£1400 $2184 €2100 Is it love or lobster salad (35x21cm-14x8in) s.i. W/C bodycol. 5-Nov-2 Bonhams, New Bond Street #183/R est:1000-1500
£1900 $2964 €2850 Home sweet home. Laughing cat (22x17cm-9x7in) s. gouache pair. 17-Sep-2 Sotheby's, Olympia #201/R est:1200-1800
£1900 $2964 €2850 Sitting a Persian cat (11x17cm-4x7in) s. W/C. 5-Nov-2 Bonhams, New Bond Street #180/R est:1800-2200
£2300 $3565 €3450 Recital (18x28cm-7x11in) s. pen grey wash. 25-Sep-2 Hamptons Fine Art, Godalming #235/R est:500-800
£2300 $3657 €3450 Siple Simon (28x20cm-11x8in) s. W/C bodycol. 30-Apr-3 Goldings, Lincolnshire #114/R
£2600 $4134 €3900 Portrait of a winking cat (15x15cm-6x6in) s. red chk. 19-Mar-3 Brightwells, Leominster #1175/R est:1500-2000
£3000 $4680 €4500 Portrait of a cat (22x17cm-9x7in) s. W/C prov. 10-Sep-2 Sworder & Son, Bishops Stortford #759/R est:300-500
£3000 $4680 €4500 Tabby cat within a decorative border (18x23cm-7x9in) s. col crayon exhib. 5-Nov-2 Bonhams, New Bond Street #179/R est:2000-3000
£3200 $4992 €4800 Where are you going my pretty maid ? (28x22cm-11x9in) s.i. W/C bodycol. 5-Nov-2 Bonhams, New Bond Street #176/R est:2000-3000
£3500 $5425 €5250 Sweets (25x18cm-10x7in) s. pencil W/C htd white. 4-Dec-2 Christie's, Kensington #184/R est:3500-4500
£3700 $5883 €5550 Four singing cats (18x25cm-7x10in) s. i.verso W/C. 19-Mar-3 Brightwells, Leominster #1173/R est:3000-5000
£4000 $6240 €6000 Barrister cat (30x23cm-12x9in) s. W/C bodycol exhib. 5-Nov-2 Bonhams, New Bond Street #175/R est:2000-3000
£4000 $6400 €6000 Tabby cat holding a rose (18x23cm-7x9in) s. W/C bodycol prov. 11-Mar-3 Bonhams, New Bond Street #145/R est:3000-4000
£4400 $6864 €6600 And then justice (41x28cm-16x11in) s.i. W/C. 5-Nov-2 Bonhams, New Bond Street #173/R est:2500-3500
£4400 $6864 €6600 Consultant (23x18cm-9x7in) s. bodycol prov. 5-Nov-2 Bonhams, New Bond Street #178/R est:2000-3000
£4600 $7268 €6900 Teatime story (18x15cm-7x6in) s. W/C. 18-Dec-2 Mallams, Oxford #579 est:1000-1500
£4600 $7636 €6900 Three's a crowd! (15x26cm-6x10in) s. W/C bodycol prov. 12-Jun-3 Bonhams, New Bond Street #705/R est:3000-5000
£5200 $8320 €7800 Perfect cat (36x25cm-14x10in) i.verso bodycol red chk prov.exhib. 11-Mar-3 Bonhams, New Bond Street #147/R est:2000-3000

WAINEWRIGHT, Thomas Francis (19th C) British
Works on paper
£600 $930 €900 Two ewes with lambs in moorland landscape (20x36cm-8x14in) s.d.1861. 25-Sep-2 Brightwells, Leominster #909/R
£660 $1089 €957 Cattle on a riverbank, a shower approaching (27x50cm-11x20in) s.d.1879 W/C. 1-Jul-3 Bearnes, Exeter #433/R
£1100 $1793 €1595 Cattle beside a river with a meadow beyond. Cattle on a coastal peninsula, possibly Cornwall (12x19cm-5x7in) s.d.1881 W/C pair. 17-Jul-3 Tennants, Leyburn #721/R est:700-900

WAINEWRIGHT, Thomas Francis (attrib) (19th C) British
£650 $1053 €975 Cattle and sheep by a pond in an extensive landscape (42x61cm-17x24in) 23-Jan-3 Christie's, Kensington #60

WAINIO, Urpo (1910-1975) Finnish
£1013 $1600 €1600 At the restaurant (33x44cm-13x17in) s. 1-Dec-2 Bukowskis, Helsinki #367/R est:1000-1200

WAINWRIGHT, John (19th C) British
£900 $1485 €1305 Still life of flowers and a nest (29x39cm-11x15in) s. panel. 1-Jul-3 Bearnes, Exeter #514/R
£2222 $3689 €3222 Finches and beetle in a thistle patch with wild roses (61x51cm-24x20in) bears sig prov. 16-Jun-3 Waddingtons, Toronto #160/R est:5000-7000 (C.D 5000)
£3000 $4560 €4500 Still life of dead game. Still life of vegetables and dead game (28x33cm-11x13in) s. one d.1861 pair. 28-Aug-2 Sotheby's, London #903/R est:2000-3000

WAINWRIGHT, John (attrib) (19th C) British
£1429 $2257 €2144 Still life of grapes and peaches, birds nest on a ledge (30x43cm-12x17in) init. 26-Nov-2 Sotheby's, Melbourne #231/R est:2500-3500 (A.D 4000)

WAINWRIGHT, Thomas (attrib) (19th C) British
£1234 $1900 €1851 Still life of flowers in a ceramic pot (61x51cm-24x20in) i. verso. 27-Oct-2 Grogan, Boston #23/R est:1000-1500

WAINWRIGHT, W J (1855-1931) British
£372 $574 €558 Pastoral landscape with cattle and ducks (51x76cm-20x30in) s. 27-Oct-2 Anders Antik, Landskrona #287/R (S.KR 5400)
Works on paper
£2000 $2900 €3000 Strange sail (28x18cm-11x7in) s.d.1902 W/C. 3-May-2 Biddle & Webb, Birmingham #330 est:2000-3000

WAINWRIGHT, William John (1855-1931) British
£450 $707 €675 Portrait of an 83 year old woman (25x23cm-10x9in) mono.i.verso after Rembrandt. 15-Apr-3 Bonhams, Knowle #108

WAIS, Alfred (1905-) German
£1646 $2567 €2600 Blue pot (64x77cm-25x30in) masonite. 18-Oct-2 Dr Fritz Nagel, Stuttgart #639/R est:1200

WAITE, Edward Wilkins (fl.1878-1927) British
£540 $837 €810 Silver birchwood with girl gathering faggots (36x28cm-14x11in) 29-Oct-2 Gorringes, Lewes #1299
£3000 $4680 €4500 Rustic scene with lady carrying water beside cottages (45x29cm-18x11in) s. 10-Sep-2 Sworder & Son, Bishops Stortford #753/R est:2000-3000
£3600 $5724 €5400 Sunlit cottages (46x30cm-18x12in) s. 6-Mar-3 Christie's, Kensington #471/R est:4000-6000
£4000 $6240 €6000 Rustic scene with geese and a cottage (46x31cm-18x12in) s.d.1891. 10-Sep-2 Sworder & Son, Bishops Stortford #752/R est:1200-1500
£4000 $6280 €6000 Sea blue bird of March (101x76cm-40x30in) s. exhib. 19-Nov-2 Bonhams, New Bond Street #151/R est:4000-6000
£8500 $13430 €12750 Catching sticklebacks (50x41cm-20x16in) s.d.1896 prov. 26-Nov-2 Christie's, London #94/R est:7000-10000
£10500 $16590 €15750 Now autumn's fire burns (102x153cm-40x60in) s. prov. 26-Nov-2 Christie's, London #120/R est:7000-10000

WAITE, James Clarke (1832-1921) British
£720 $1159 €1044 Portrait of a lady (106x73cm-42x29in) s. 12-May-3 Joel, Victoria #344 est:2000-3000 (A.D 1800)
£7634 $12061 €11451 Tit bit for Dobbin (77x96cm-30x38in) s. s.i.verso. 2-Apr-3 Christie's, Melbourne #61/R est:8000-12000 (A.D 20000)

WAITE, Robert Thorne (1842-1935) British
£1950 $3101 €2925 Fishermen drawing in their catch, before a hilltop castle (85x120cm-33x47in) s. 27-Feb-3 Bonhams, Chester #389/R est:2000-3000
£2100 $3360 €3150 Building the rick (28x38cm-11x15in) s. 14-Mar-3 Gardiner & Houlgate, Bath #61/R est:900-1200
Works on paper
£270 $427 €405 Haymaking in hilly landscape (13x21cm-5x8in) s.d.1909 pencil W/C. 26-Nov-2 Bonhams, Oxford #30/R
£400 $624 €600 On the beach (29x44cm-11x17in) s. pencil W/C bodycol. 27-Mar-3 Christie's, Kensington #158/R
£440 $700 €660 Extensive country landscape with farmer and sheep (34x52cm-13x20in) W/C. 27-Feb-3 Bonhams, Chester #390
£460 $731 €690 River scene (35x51cm-14x20in) s. W/C. 27-Feb-3 Bonhams, Chester #392

£620 $967 €930 Heavy horses by a stream (27x40cm-11x16in) s. W/C. 26-Mar-3 Sotheby's, Olympia #78/R
£650 $1034 €975 Haymaking (13x21cm-5x8in) s.d.1909 W/C. 25-Feb-3 Bonhams, Knightsbridge #8/R
£680 $1074 €986 Harvesting on the South Downs (25x43cm-10x17in) s. W/C. 24-Apr-3 Scarborough Perry Fine Arts, Hove #654
£1050 $1659 €1575 South Downs near Kingly Vale, Chichester (38x54cm-15x21in) s. W/C. 7-Apr-3 Bonhams, Bath #19/R est:800-1200
£1250 $1988 €1875 Seaweed gathering at Parkgate, Cheshire (42x72cm-17x28in) s. W/C. 27-Feb-3 Bonhams, Chester #394/R est:1400-1800
£1250 $1988 €1875 Sussex Downs from the Surrey border (35x52cm-14x20in) s. W/C. 29-Apr-3 Henry Adams, Chichester #243/R est:1500-2000
£1550 $2449 €2325 Water mill, Danbury, farm workers and plough horses in a mill stream (36x53cm-14x21in) s. W/C. 26-Nov-2 Bonhams, Oxford #16 est:500-800
£1600 $2480 €2400 Cornfield near Norwich (35x51cm-14x20in) s. s.i.verso pencil W/C htd bodycol. 4-Dec-2 Christie's, Kensington #40/R est:600-800
£2300 $3772 €3450 Haymakers (12x37cm-5x15in) s. pencil W/C. 4-Feb-3 Bonhams, Leeds #223 est:400-600
£3100 $5084 €4650 Harvesters on the downs near Lewes (35x51cm-14x20in) s. pencil W/C. 4-Feb-3 Bonhams, Leeds #224 est:1200-1800
£3400 $5304 €5100 Harvest time (32x49cm-13x19in) s. pencil W/C bodycol scratching out prov. 27-Mar-3 Christie's, Kensington #103/R est:1500-2000

WAITE, Robert Thorne (attrib) (1842-1935) British
Works on paper
£600 $954 €900 Harvest (26x44cm-10x17in) W/C. 4-Mar-3 Bearnes, Exeter #405/R
£600 $936 €900 Children playing by a footbridge over a brook (33x44cm-13x17in) s. W/C. 26-Mar-3 Hamptons Fine Art, Godalming #38

WAITT, Richard (18th C) British
£1500 $2385 €2250 Portrait of Anne Seton, seated in a blue dress (129x113cm-51x44in) s.d.1724 i.verso. 6-Mar-3 Christie's, Kensington #6/R est:1500-2000

WAKE, John Cheltenham (fl.1858-1875) British
£1050 $1659 €1575 Off the coast (49x74cm-19x29in) s.d.69. 12-Nov-2 Bonhams, Knightsbridge #240/R est:1000-1500
£1400 $2226 €2100 Shipping in the Channel of Dover (36x53cm-14x21in) s.d.1878. 4-Mar-3 Bonhams, Knightsbridge #292/R est:1000-1500
£1800 $2952 €2700 St Mallon Church, Rouen (76x63cm-30x25in) s.d.72. 29-May-3 Christie's, Kensington #203/R est:2000-3000

WAKELIN, Roland Shakespeare (1887-1971) Australian
£498 $782 €747 Pastoral scene (19x25cm-7x10in) s.d.1940 board. 15-Apr-3 Lawson Menzies, Sydney #177/R est:800-1200 (A.D 1300)
£500 $785 €750 Landscape (22x30cm-9x12in) s.d.56 card on board. 25-Nov-2 Christie's, Melbourne #370 (A.D 1400)
£632 $960 €948 Still life with apples (52x44cm-20x17in) s.d.44 board. 19-Aug-2 Joel, Victoria #275 est:3000-5000 (A.D 1800)
£996 $1564 €1494 Artist daughter (49x35cm-19x14in) s.d.1935 board. 15-Apr-3 Lawson Menzies, Sydney #178/R est:1500-2000 (A.D 2600)
£1374 $2171 €2061 Thames London (23x30cm-9x12in) s.d.56. 7-Apr-3 Shapiro, Sydney #417/R est:2000-4000 (A.D 3600)
£1429 $2257 €2144 Landscape with cottage (42x55cm-17x22in) s.d.51 prov. 26-Nov-2 Sotheby's, Melbourne #72/R est:3000-5000 (A.D 4000)
£1450 $2292 €2175 Labourers at work (34x46cm-13x18in) prov. 7-Apr-3 Shapiro, Sydney #410/R est:4000-6000 (A.D 3800)
£1533 $2284 €2300 Country road (41x54cm-16x21in) canvas on board prov. 27-Aug-2 Christie's, Melbourne #249/R est:4000-6000 (A.D 4000)
£2137 $3377 €3206 Red hat, portrait of Beth Mayne (58x43cm-23x17in) i.verso board painted c.1960 prov.lit. 7-Apr-3 Shapiro, Sydney #461/R est:5000-7000 (A.D 5600)
£2357 $3724 €3536 Pastoral landscape (47x63cm-19x25in) s.d.58 canvas on board prov. 17-Nov-2 Sotheby's, Paddington #45/R est:5000-8000 (A.D 6600)
£4878 $7707 €7073 Interior with two figures (68x59cm-27x23in) s. board. 22-Jul-3 Lawson Menzies, Sydney #14/R est:13000-15000 (A.D 12000)
£4982 $7623 €7473 View of Sydney Harbour (61x74cm-24x29in) s.d.62 board prov. 25-Aug-2 Sotheby's, Paddington #176/R est:6000-8000 (A.D 14000)
£5578 $9147 €8367 Boathouse, Sydney (43x54cm-17x21in) s.d.1926 card prov. 4-Jun-3 Deutscher-Menzies, Melbourne #56/R est:15000-20000 (A.D 14000)
£11039 $16780 €16559 Barrack St., Sydney (75x38cm-30x15in) s.d.42 canvas on board. 28-Aug-2 Deutscher-Menzies, Melbourne #136/R est:35000-45000 (A.D 30800)

Works on paper
£462 $734 €693 From a window in Fetta Lane, London (26x16cm-10x6in) init.i.d.1924 pencil. 4-Mar-3 Deutscher-Menzies, Melbourne #248/R (A.D 1200)

WAKSVIK, Skule (1927-) Norwegian
Sculpture
£1150 $1818 €1725 Female bear with cubs (29x25x30cm-11x10x12in) s.d.1980 bronze. 28-Apr-3 Blomqvist, Oslo #374/R est:12000-15000 (N.KR 13000)
£1858 $2936 €2787 Elk lying down (29x25x47cm-11x10x19in) s.d.1981 bronze. 28-Apr-3 Blomqvist, Oslo #376/R est:18000-22000 (N.KR 21000)
£3077 $4985 €4616 Stag and hind (53x63x24cm-21x25x9in) s. bronze. 26-May-3 Grev Wedels Plass, Oslo #52/R est:30000-40000 (N.KR 34000)

WALBOURN, Ernest (1872-1927) British
£400 $624 €600 Wixford, Warwickshire (30x41cm-12x16in) s.d.98. 26-Mar-3 Hamptons Fine Art, Godalming #135
£567 $879 €851 Woman with geese (46x30cm-18x12in) s.d.1902. 4-Dec-2 AB Stockholms Auktionsverk #1860/R (S.KR 8000)
£582 $943 €844 Returning home with flock of sheep (31x41cm-12x16in) s. 25-May-3 Uppsala Auktionskammare, Uppsala #108 (S.KR 7500)
£900 $1404 €1350 Picking lavender (50x77cm-20x30in) s. 17-Sep-2 Sotheby's, Olympia #179/R
£962 $1500 €1443 English country landscape (25x30cm-10x12in) s. panel. 30-Mar-3 Simpson's, Houston #494
£1410 $2200 €2115 Young woman standing beside a duck pond (61x46cm-24x18in) s. 12-Apr-3 Weschler, Washington #510/R est:2000-3000
£1600 $2544 €2400 Pretty girl feeding ducks (46x30cm-18x12in) s.d.1902. 19-Mar-3 John Nicholson, Haslemere #1177/R est:1500-2000
£1950 $3081 €2925 Hard times, snowy landscape with gypsy caravan outside a village (60x90cm-24x35in) s. 26-Nov-2 Bonhams, Oxford #45 est:2000-3000
£2315 $3727 €3357 Woman knitting beside river (51x76cm-20x30in) s. 7-May-3 Dobiaschofsky, Bern #1049/R est:5500 (S.FR 5000)
£2817 $4648 €4085 Farmyard in England (50x74cm-20x29in) s.d.1900 prov. 1-Jul-3 Peter Webb, Auckland #115/R est:10000-15000 (NZ.D 8000)
£3127 $5004 €4534 Young woman by gate (60x45cm-24x18in) 18-May-3 Anders Antik, Landskrona #12 est:20000 (S.KR 40000)
£3200 $5216 €4640 Idle moments (76x51cm-30x20in) s. exhib. 17-Jul-3 Tennants, Leyburn #910/R est:2000-2500
£3438 $5500 €5157 Farmgirl and geese by a brook (61x46cm-24x18in) s. 14-May-3 Butterfields, San Francisco #1160/R est:3000-5000
£3600 $6012 €5220 Highland cattle by a loch (49x74cm-19x29in) s. 26-Jun-3 Mellors & Kirk, Nottingham #904/R est:1500-2000
£3659 $6000 €5489 Outside the cottage (61x91cm-24x36in) s. 5-Feb-3 Christie's, Rockefeller NY #187/R est:7000-9000
£3700 $5291 €5550 View at Woolhampton (34x44cm-13x17in) panel. 11-Apr-2 Mellors & Kirk, Nottingham #578/R est:2000-4000
£3900 $6357 €5655 Summer landscape with a young girl standing beside a vegetable patch (92x130cm-36x51in) s. 17-Jul-3 Tennants, Leyburn #847/R est:3000-4000
£4500 $7065 €6750 Gathering wild flowers (62x45cm-24x18in) s. s.i.verso. 19-Nov-2 Bonhams, New Bond Street #139/R est:2500-3500
£4500 $7111 €6750 Young lady at the mill pond (61x46cm-24x18in) s. 2-Dec-2 Sotheby's, London #18/R est:5000-7000
£5000 $8000 €7500 At the well (61x46cm-24x18in) s. 14-May-3 Butterfields, San Francisco #1158/R est:3000-5000
£5500 $9020 €8250 Feeding the geese (51x76cm-20x30in) s.d.1900. 29-May-3 Christie's, Kensington #263/R est:5000-8000

WALCH, Charles (1896-1948) French
£1419 $2243 €2200 Petit bouquet (41x33cm-16x13in) s. exec.c.1943-1945 exhib. 17-Dec-2 Rossini, Paris #133/R
£2483 $4146 €3600 Canal dans la ville (54x45cm-21x18in) s. painted c.1926-1927. 10-Jul-3 Artcurial Briest, Paris #213/R est:3000-4000
£2579 $3971 €4100 Pont dans la ville (54x45cm-21x18in) s. 22-Oct-2 Campo & Campo, Antwerp #326/R

WALCH, Paul Johann (1881-1958) German
£268 $417 €420 Mountain goats (100x70cm-39x28in) s.i. lit. 8-Nov-2 Auktionhaus Georg Rehm, Augsburg #8181/R
£374 $595 €550 Path through autumnal park (70x80cm-28x31in) s.i. 20-Mar-3 Neumeister, Munich #2772/R
£728 $1187 €1100 Sunflowers (77x68cm-30x27in) s.i. canvas on chipboard. 28-Jan-3 Dorotheum, Vienna #69/R

WALCH, Thomas (1867-1843) Austrian
£1250 $1975 €1800 In the mountains (44x61cm-17x24in) paper on panel. 24-Apr-3 Dorotheum, Vienna #81/R est:1800-2600
£1250 $1975 €1800 Child of the mountains (41x32cm-16x13in) s. panel. 24-Apr-3 Dorotheum, Vienna #92/R est:1200-1600
£1948 $2903 €3000 Young peasant couple on high mountain pasture (45x64cm-18x25in) s.i. 26-Jun-2 Neumeister, Munich #906/R est:4000
£2553 $4136 €3600 Shepherd boy with flock gazing into the distance (65x90cm-26x35in) s. 20-May-3 Dorotheum, Vienna #162/R est:4500-6000
£3125 $4938 €4500 Two children with flowers and butterfly (30x40cm-12x16in) s. panel. 24-Apr-3 Dorotheum, Vienna #94/R est:2600-3400

WALCOT, William (1874-1943) British

£800 $1304 €1200 Street scene (21x27cm-8x11in) board. 12-Feb-3 Bonhams, Knightsbridge #220/R

Works on paper

£350 $564 €525 Memorial in a church building (37x29cm-15x11in) W/C. 18-Feb-3 Bonhams, Knightsbridge #60/R

£440 $682 €660 London view (17x27cm-7x11in) s. etching. 3-Dec-2 Sworder & Son, Bishops Stortford #984/R

£450 $693 €675 Street scene (23x31cm-9x12in) s. W/C brush ink. 5-Sep-2 Christie's, Kensington #568

£450 $729 €675 Interior of a church (35x46cm-14x18in) pencil chl wash. 20-May-3 Bonhams, Knightsbridge #82

£1700 $2703 €2550 Street scene (18x22cm-7x9in) s.d.08 mixed media. 29-Apr-3 Henry Adams, Chichester #221 est:600-800

WALD, Ingrid Theodora (1943-) Austrian

£769 $1215 €1200 Woodland meadow (80x90cm-31x35in) s.i.d.1999. 12-Nov-2 Dorotheum, Vienna #301/R

WALDAU, Grete (1868-?) German

£423 $680 €600 Room in the Berlin castle, possible Throne Room (80x60cm-31x24in) s. 7-May-3 Michael Zeller, Lindau #976/R

WALDBERG, Isabelle (1917-) French?

Sculpture

£2778 $4416 €4000 Palais I (48x29x39cm-19x11x15in) s.num.1/3 bronze prov.lit. 29-Apr-3 Artcurial Briest, Paris #624/R est:4000-5000

£3741 $5949 €5500 Montagne II (47x32x26cm-19x13x10in) s. num.1/2 bronze lit. 24-Mar-3 Claude Boisgirard, Paris #87/R

WALDE, Alfons (1891-1958) Austrian

£7971 $13072 €11000 Stylish lady (26x26cm-10x10in) tempera board. 27-May-3 Hassfurther, Vienna #11/R est:6000-8000

£8511 $13787 €12000 Reclining and standing nude (29x21cm-11x8in) board. 20-May-3 Dorotheum, Vienna #153/R est:12000-16000

£12821 $20128 €20000 Interior with nude (20x25cm-8x10in) oil tempera board. 25-Nov-2 Hassfurther, Vienna #10/R est:16000-19000

£13514 $21081 €20000 Reflection in lake near Kitzbuhl (19x26cm-7x10in) board. 25-Mar-3 Wiener Kunst Auktionen, Vienna #148/R est:15000-25000

£16892 $26351 €25000 The meeting (16x18cm-6x7in) mono. board. 25-Mar-3 Wiener Kunst Auktionen, Vienna #149/R est:35000-50000

£21739 $35652 €30000 Farmers in front of the house (27x30cm-11x12in) board. 27-May-3 Hassfurther, Vienna #9/R est:26000-30000

£27000 $45090 €39150 Vorfruhling - early spring (42x66cm-17x26in) s. board painted 1930 prov. 24-Jun-3 Sotheby's, London #188/R est:30000-40000

£28846 $45288 €45000 Alpine pasture (32x51cm-13x20in) s. board. 25-Nov-2 Hassfurther, Vienna #7/R est:40000-50000

£28846 $45288 €45000 Kitzbuhl in spring (32x27cm-13x11in) s. board. 25-Nov-2 Hassfurther, Vienna #9/R est:29000-37000

£30769 $48308 €48000 Farmstead and barn (56x43cm-22x17in) s. board. 25-Nov-2 Hassfurther, Vienna #8/R est:60000-70000

£38462 $59615 €60000 Woman on the church path (28x24cm-11x9in) s. cardboard painted 1933 prov. 6-Dec-2 Ketterer, Munich #90/R est:45000-55000

£43478 $71304 €60000 Woman on church path (35x29cm-14x11in) s. board. 27-May-3 Hassfurther, Vienna #5/R est:50000-70000

£44304 $70000 €70000 Tyrolean peasant (40x37cm-16x15in) s. board. 27-Nov-2 Dorotheum, Vienna #163/R est:22000-30000

£48077 $75481 €75000 Mountains in spring (50x70cm-20x28in) s. board. 25-Nov-2 Hassfurther, Vienna #5/R est:80000-90000

£50725 $83188 €70000 Alms in the snow in front of Wilde Kaiser (45x56cm-18x22in) s. board. 27-May-3 Hassfurther, Vienna #6/R est:50000-60000

£50725 $83188 €70000 The short day (30x40cm-12x16in) s. plywood. 27-May-3 Hassfurther, Vienna #7/R est:60000-70000

£54348 $89130 €75000 In the tavern (27x29cm-11x11in) board lit. 27-May-3 Hassfurther, Vienna #8/R est:50000-60000

£57971 $95072 €80000 Mountain village in Tyrol with Auracher Church (39x29cm-15x11in) s. board. 27-May-3 Hassfurther, Vienna #3/R est:50000-90000

£57971 $95072 €80000 Solitary mountain hut (42x67cm-17x26in) s. board exhib. 27-May-3 Hassfurther, Vienna #4/R est:60000-80000

£60811 $94865 €90000 Winter idyll (40x52cm-16x20in) s. board lit.prov. 25-Mar-3 Wiener Kunst Auktionen, Vienna #147/R est:50000-100000

£67376 $109149 €95000 Trattalmen, Kitzbuhl (59x54cm-23x21in) s. board. 20-May-3 Dorotheum, Vienna #152/R est:90000-120000

£69620 $110000 €110000 Sunday in the Tyrol (39x29cm-15x11in) s. board. 27-Nov-2 Dorotheum, Vienna #162/R est:50000-70000

£70513 $110705 €110000 Houses in the mountains (81x121cm-32x48in) s. lit. 25-Nov-2 Hassfurther, Vienna #3/R est:80000-120000

£70513 $110705 €110000 Snow covered alpine pasture (35x27cm-14x11in) s. board. 25-Nov-2 Hassfurther, Vienna #4/R est:50000-60000

£83333 $130833 €130000 Late winter (42x67cm-17x26in) s. board. 25-Nov-2 Hassfurther, Vienna #2/R est:80000-100000

£123188 $202029 €170000 Town in Tauschnee (54x60cm-21x24in) s. 27-May-3 Hassfurther, Vienna #2/R est:100000-130000

£237179 $372371 €370000 Uphill climb (42x59cm-17x23in) s. lit. board. 25-Nov-2 Hassfurther, Vienna #1/R est:70000-120000

£304348 $499130 €420000 Ascent of the skiers (49x77cm-19x30in) s. board. 27-May-3 Hassfurther, Vienna #1/R est:120000-150000

Works on paper

£2027 $3162 €3000 Erotic nudes (16x6cm-6x2in) chl. 25-Mar-3 Wiener Kunst Auktionen, Vienna #150/R est:3000-5000

£2027 $3162 €3000 Erotic nudes (16x6cm-6x2in) mono. chl. 25-Mar-3 Wiener Kunst Auktionen, Vienna #151/R est:3000-5000

£2027 $3162 €3000 Erotic nudes (16x6cm-6x2in) chl. 25-Mar-3 Wiener Kunst Auktionen, Vienna #155/R est:3000-5000

£2703 $4216 €4000 Erotic nudes (16x6cm-6x2in) mono. chl. 25-Mar-3 Wiener Kunst Auktionen, Vienna #154/R est:3000-5000

£4730 $7378 €7000 Woman in anticipation (36x16cm-14x6in) gouache board. 25-Mar-3 Wiener Kunst Auktionen, Vienna #156/R est:7000-15000

£6000 $9240 €9000 Die Brixentalerin - girl from the Brixental (43x30cm-17x12in) init. gouache over chl on card. 22-Oct-2 Sotheby's, London #223/R est:8000-12000

£7051 $11071 €11000 Woman's head (31x24cm-12x9in) i. verso mixed media. 25-Nov-2 Hassfurther, Vienna #11/R est:7000-9000

£11392 $18000 €18000 Primula (42x28cm-17x11in) s.d.20 pencil oil tempera. 27-Nov-2 Dorotheum, Vienna #135/R est:18000-24000

WALDE, Franz (1863-1951) Austrian

£517 $828 €750 Kitchen interior (21x27cm-8x11in) s. board. 11-Mar-3 Dorotheum, Vienna #69/R

WALDE, Volker (1906-) Austrian

£288 $472 €400 In St Angelo harbour (45x36cm-18x14in) s.i. board. 5-Jun-3 Dorotheum, Salzburg #533/R

WALDEGG (?) Austrian

£945 $1380 €1418 Winter forest (71x100cm-28x39in) painted c.1920. 4-Jun-2 SOGA, Bratislava #169/R est:39000 (SL.K 60000)

WALDEK, H (?) ?

£1006 $1560 €1600 Two beauties (68x47cm-27x19in) s. 29-Oct-2 Dorotheum, Vienna #55/R est:2000-2200

WALDEMAR, P F (19th C) ?

£1006 $1560 €1600 Landscape with waterfall and figures (117x143cm-46x56in) s. 29-Oct-2 Dorotheum, Vienna #7/R est:2000-2200

WALDEN, Nell (1887-1975) ?

£938 $1501 €1360 Autorno (50x44cm-20x17in) mono. 18-May-3 Anders Antik, Landskrona #73 (S.KR 12000)

Works on paper

£360 $575 €522 Rote blute (21x15cm-8x6in) mono.d.70 W/C. 18-May-3 Anders Antik, Landskrona #43 (S.KR 4600)

WALDMANN, Karl (20th C) Dutch

Works on paper

£277 $429 €440 Explosion 10 (40x30cm-16x12in) mono. dr collage. 5-Oct-2 De Vuyst, Lokeren #415

£353 $546 €550 Angel (36x26cm-14x10in) mono. dr collage. 7-Dec-2 De Vuyst, Lokeren #404

WALDMULLER, Ferdinand (1816-1885) Austrian

£3205 $5064 €5000 Portrait of young man (86x71cm-34x28in) s.d.1850. 16-Nov-2 Lempertz, Koln #1596/R est:4000

WALDMULLER, Ferdinand Georg (1793-1865) Austrian

£9220 $14936 €13000 Triumph of Emperor Titus (62x77cm-24x30in) s.d.819 after Gian Antonio Pellegrinis lit. 22-May-3 Dorotheum, Vienna #23/R est:15000-17000

£15942 $26145 €22000 Portrait of a lady (36x30cm-14x12in) s.d.1839 panel. 27-May-3 Wiener Kunst Auktionen, Vienna #17/R est:18000-50000

£75949 $120000 €120000 Idyllic landscape with travellers with view of the Schneeberg (26x32cm-10x13in) s. i.verso panel. 28-Nov-2 Dorotheum, Vienna #149/R est:32000-40000

Works on paper

£741 $1193 €1112 Portrait of woman with lace cap (15x11cm-6x4in) s. pencil. 7-May-3 Dobiaschofsky, Bern #1199/R (S.FR 1600)

WALDORF, Gunter (1924-) Austrian

Works on paper

£705 $1093 €1100 Southern landscape (15x19cm-6x7in) s. mixed media. 5-Dec-2 Dorotheum, Graz #204/R

WALDORP, Antonie (1803-1866) Dutch

£2516 $3874 €4000 Villagers on a town square in winter (35x46cm-14x18in) s. panel. 22-Oct-2 Sotheby's, Amsterdam #40/R est:4000-5000

£3744 $5579 €5616 Dutch sailing boats (35x46cm-14x18in) s.d.64 panel. 25-Jun-2 Koller, Zurich #6485/R est:3000-4000 (S.FR 8500)

£3836 $6022 €5600 Shipping off the Dutch coast (35x46cm-14x18in) s.d.64 panel. 15-Apr-3 Sotheby's, Amsterdam #79/R est:6000-8000
£6289 $9686 €10000 Daily activities in a fisher village (101x120cm-40x47in) s. 23-Oct-2 Christie's, Amsterdam #60/R est:14000-18000

Works on paper
£461 $746 €700 Ferry in a calm (55x80cm-22x31in) s. pencil W/C. 21-Jan-3 Christie's, Amsterdam #86
£556 $894 €850 L'acostage (29x37cm-11x15in) s. wash. 14-Jan-3 Vanderkindere, Brussels #102

WALE, John Porter (1860-1920) British
Works on paper
£420 $655 €630 Still life of vase of anemones (25x15cm-10x6in) s. W/C. 10-Apr-3 Tennants, Leyburn #897
£650 $1014 €975 Still life of flowers (46x30cm-18x12in) s. W/C. 26-Mar-3 Sotheby's, Olympia #110/R
£650 $1073 €943 Bowl of flowers (24x44cm-9x17in) s. pencil W/C htd white. 3-Jul-3 Christie's, Kensington #43/R
£920 $1426 €1380 Spring delight, still life with flowers (26x24cm-10x9in) s. bears i.verso W/C. 1-Oct-2 Fellows & Sons, Birmingham #168/R
£1100 $1793 €1650 Still life of field flowers in a vase (33x23cm-13x9in) s. W/C. 28-Jan-3 Gorringes, Lewes #1764 est:200-300

WALE, Samuel (?-1786) British
Works on paper
£850 $1352 €1275 Group of dissenters in Norfolk during Robert Ketts rebellion of 1549 (17x11cm-7x4in) pen ink wash over pencil. 19-Mar-3 Sotheby's, London #125/R

WALIE, Salah (20th C) Irish?
£461 $747 €650 Egyptian beauties by the sea (59x79cm-23x31in) s. 20-May-3 Mealy's, Castlecomer #1022

WALKENSTEINER, Wolfgang (1949-) Austrian
£353 $554 €550 Head (65x49cm-26x19in) s.d.74 pencil. 20-Nov-2 Dorotheum, Klagenfurt #104

WALKER, Ada Hill (?-1956) British
£400 $664 €580 On Burnside Moor (38x25cm-15x10in) s.d.1904 canvasboard. 10-Jun-3 Ritchie, Toronto #65/R est:1000-1500 (C.D 900)

WALKER, Bernard Eyre (1886-?) British
Works on paper
£300 $471 €450 Autumn morning, Windermere (23x35cm-9x14in) indis sig. W/C. 19-Nov-2 James Thompson, Kirby Lonsdale #63
£550 $858 €825 Lakeland views (30x46cm-12x18in) s.d.1941 W/C pair. 10-Apr-3 Tennants, Leyburn #584

WALKER, Dame Ethel (1861-1951) British
£250 $388 €375 Seated female nude (61x51cm-24x20in) 4-Dec-2 Christie's, Kensington #428/R
£300 $477 €450 Nude study (32x19cm-13x7in) paper on board. 18-Mar-3 Sworder & Son, Bishops Stortford #438/R
£520 $822 €780 Ursula (38x29cm-15x11in) s. i.verso panel on card. 28-Nov-2 Morphets, Harrogate #554/R
£580 $905 €870 Figure with sheep in a sunlit wooded lane (43x33cm-17x13in) s. 11-Apr-3 Keys, Aylsham #524/R
£700 $1085 €1050 Horses at the ford (65x81cm-26x32in) 4-Dec-2 Christie's, Kensington #451/R
£800 $1272 €1200 Portrait of a lady (73x57cm-29x22in) s.indis d. 26-Feb-3 Sotheby's, Olympia #84/R
£1100 $1749 €1650 Seascape (28x35cm-11x14in) board. 26-Feb-3 Sotheby's, Olympia #231/R est:300-500
£1500 $2325 €2250 Allegorical scene (152x101cm-60x40in) 3-Dec-2 Bonhams, New Bond Street #25/R est:3000-5000
£1800 $2772 €2700 Summer landscape (51x61cm-20x24in) prov. 5-Sep-2 Christie's, Kensington #556/R est:2000-3000
£2400 $3816 €3600 Still life of flowers in a vase (74x62cm-29x24in) 26-Feb-3 Sotheby's, Olympia #213/R est:2500-3500
£3200 $4928 €4800 Contre jour (51x61cm-20x24in) prov. 5-Sep-2 Christie's, Kensington #585/R est:1500-2000
Works on paper
£3500 $5460 €5250 Paris and the goddesses (48x58cm-19x23in) s.d.1930 pencil W/C. 27-Mar-3 Christie's, Kensington #278/R est:500-800

WALKER, David Bond (1891-1977) Irish
£900 $1440 €1350 Farm cottages (21x30cm-8x12in) s. panel prov. 15-May-3 Christie's, Kensington #202/R

WALKER, Dorothy (20th C) American
£382 $600 €573 Brighton Beach (30x46cm-12x18in) s. 14-Dec-2 Weschler, Washington #645/R

WALKER, Edward (1879-1951) British
Works on paper
£400 $624 €600 Spanish peasants by an arch (36x25cm-14x10in) s. W/C prov. 11-Apr-3 Keys, Aylsham #451/R

WALKER, Frederick (1840-1875) British
£429 $700 €644 Landscape (33x48cm-13x19in) 14-Feb-3 Du Mouchelle, Detroit #2016/R
Works on paper
£2900 $4582 €4350 Mussel gatherer (17x12cm-7x5in) init. W/C bodycol executed c.1862. 2-Dec-2 Bonhams, Bath #15/R est:1000-1500
£8000 $12880 €12000 At the sick man's door (9x13cm-4x5in) init. pencil W/C bodycol gum arabic prov.exhib.lit. 20-Feb-3 Christie's, London #120/R est:15000

WALKER, Henry (fl.1852) British
Works on paper
£840 $1310 €1260 Interior portraits of a mother, father and son (34x28cm-13x11in) one i.d.23rd March 1852 W/C three. 17-Oct-2 Lawrence, Crewkerne #403/R

WALKER, Hirst (1868-1957) British
Works on paper
£250 $395 €375 Mountainous lakeland landscape (28x46cm-11x18in) s. i.verso W/C. 28-Nov-2 Richardson & Smith, Whitby #635

WALKER, Horatio (1858-1938) Canadian
£391 $606 €587 Floral study (31x23cm-12x9in) init. panel. 3-Dec-2 Joyner, Toronto #422 (C.D 950)
£412 $638 €618 Petronille young girl with kitten (42x34cm-17x13in) init. canvas on board prov. 3-Dec-2 Joyner, Toronto #109/R est:2000-3000 (C.D 1000)
£947 $1467 €1421 Nude study of a girl (17x14cm-7x6in) init.d.78 oil paper on canvas. 3-Dec-2 Joyner, Toronto #440 est:1000-1500 (C.D 2300)
£1333 $2187 €2000 Cow under a tree (33x38cm-13x15in) bears sig canvas on board prov.lit. 27-May-3 Sotheby's, Toronto #106/R est:3000-5000 (C.D 3000)
£1337 $2073 €2006 Cow grazing under a tree (32x39cm-13x15in) s. canvas on board prov.lit. 3-Dec-2 Joyner, Toronto #153/R est:4000-5000 (C.D 3250)
£1481 $2296 €2222 Ile aux grues (22x29cm-9x11in) init. panel prov. 3-Dec-2 Joyner, Toronto #281/R est:2000-3000 (C.D 3600)
£1811 $2807 €2717 Gray horse (35x33cm-14x13in) init. canvas on board. 3-Dec-2 Joyner, Toronto #421 est:1000-1500 (C.D 4400)
£3556 $5831 €5334 Evening (58x76cm-23x30in) s.d.1925 prov.exhib. 27-May-3 Sotheby's, Toronto #108/R est:10000-12000 (C.D 8000)
£9778 $16036 €14667 Early morning (71x59cm-28x23in) s.d.1914 prov.exhib.lit. 27-May-3 Sotheby's, Toronto #12/R est:12000-18000 (C.D 22000)
£21399 $33169 €32099 Evening milking (84x114cm-33x45in) s.d.1912 prov.exhib.lit. 3-Dec-2 Joyner, Toronto #17/R est:30000-40000 (C.D 52000)
Works on paper
£266 $413 €399 Study of plowing (14x17cm-6x7in) graphite dr prov. 24-Sep-2 Ritchie, Toronto #3061/R (C.D 650)
£370 $574 €555 Bowl of sweet peas (32x39cm-13x15in) s.d.1927 W/C. 3-Dec-2 Joyner, Toronto #467 (C.D 900)
£453 $702 €680 Ox cart, Ile d'Orleans (11x22cm-4x9in) W/C. 3-Dec-2 Joyner, Toronto #364 est:700-900 (C.D 1100)
£894 $1404 €1341 Dans l'Ecurie (38x32cm-15x13in) s. W/C prov. 10-Dec-2 Pinneys, Montreal #27 est:2500-3500 (C.D 2200)
£3498 $5422 €5247 Woman and cow, Ile D'Orleans (44x31cm-17x12in) s. W/C prov. 3-Dec-2 Joyner, Toronto #42/R est:12000-15000 (C.D 8500)

WALKER, Inez Nathaniel (1911-1990) American
Works on paper
£1605 $2600 €2408 Untitled (55x76cm-22x30in) s.d.1976 graphite col pencil prov. 27-Jan-3 Christie's, Rockefeller NY #81/R est:1000-2000

WALKER, J D (?) British
Works on paper
£420 $664 €630 Boston Stump, view from Wormgate (36x25cm-14x10in) s. W/C over pencil. 12-Nov-2 Goldings, Lincolnshire #148

WALKER, J Hanson (jnr) (fl.1900-1925) British
£859 $1400 €1289 Mr Goodsall's dog (34x25cm-13x10in) s.d.1931 i.verso panel. 11-Feb-3 Bonhams & Doyles, New York #209/R est:1500-2000
£6135 $10000 €9203 Four bulls (44x61cm-17x24in) s.d.1906. 11-Feb-3 Bonhams & Doyles, New York #183/R est:10000-15000

WALKER, James (19th C) British
£16774 $26000 €25161 General Winfield Scott's Artillery troops (77x128cm-30x50in) s.d.1881 prov. 5-Dec-2 Christie's, Rockefeller NY #169/R est:30000-50000

WALKER, James Alexander (1841-1898) British
£1300 $2002 €1950 Reconnaissance (44x62cm-17x24in) s. 5-Sep-2 Christie's, Kensington #313/R est:1000-1500
£1447 $2257 €2300 Soldiers (62x48cm-24x19in) s. 8-Oct-2 Christie's, Paris #47/R
£1698 $2700 €2547 Reconnoitering (50x65cm-20x26in) s.d.1881 st.verso. 7-Mar-3 Skinner, Boston #238/R est:4000-6000

WALKER, John (1939-) British
£561 $875 €842 Untitled (40x31cm-16x12in) s.d.82 verso. 5-Nov-2 Bukowskis, Stockholm #441/R (S.KR 8000)
£2000 $3100 €3000 Form and image (216x154cm-85x61in) s.d.83 verso prov. 3-Dec-2 Bonhams, New Bond Street #122/R est:2000-3000
£4643 $7243 €6965 Memory and myrrh (213x168cm-84x66in) s.i.d.1990 verso prov. 11-Nov-2 Deutscher-Menzies, Melbourne #45/R est:15000-20000 (A.D 13000)

Works on paper
£600 $936 €900 Untitled (87x115cm-34x45in) s.d.70 pastel. 27-Mar-3 Christie's, Kensington #658/R

WALKER, John Crampton (1890-1942) Irish
£943 $1472 €1500 Cottage in Kerry (51x76cm-20x30in) s.d.1925 i.verso. 17-Sep-2 Whyte's, Dublin #196 est:1500-2000
£1100 $1737 €1650 Strand, Dugort (45x61cm-18x24in) s. exhib. 27-Nov-2 Sotheby's, Olympia #142/R est:700-900
£1154 $1788 €1800 Connemara twilight (38x49cm-15x19in) init. 3-Dec-2 Bonhams & James Adam, Dublin #88/R est:1500-2000
£1218 $1912 €1900 Thatched cottage (33x48cm-13x19in) s. 19-Nov-2 Whyte's, Dublin #60/R est:1200-1500
£2192 $3441 €3200 West of Ireland landscape with cottage and geese (51x61cm-20x24in) s. 15-Apr-3 De Veres Art Auctions, Dublin #206/R est:2500-3500
£2215 $3434 €3500 Cottage in Achill landscape (44x59cm-17x23in) s. board. 25-Sep-2 James Adam, Dublin #120/R est:3000-5000

WALKER, John Hanson (1844-1933) British
£1550 $2403 €2325 Portrait of a young woman (58x48cm-23x19in) s. 4-Dec-2 Andrew Hartley, Ilkley #1197/R est:500-700
£4500 $7470 €6750 Portrait of a girl, possibly the artist's daughter Dorothy (62x53cm-24x21in) s.d.1894 panel. 10-Jun-3 Christie's, London #100/R est:5000-8000

WALKER, John Robert (1957-) Australian
£800 $1288 €1200 Snjeza (122x152cm-48x60in) s.i.d.88 acrylic prov. 6-May-3 Christie's, Melbourne #321/R est:2000-3000 (A.D 2000)

WALKER, Joseph Francis (19th C) British
£3800 $6042 €5700 Purity, a prize cow (36x46cm-14x18in) s.i. 6-Mar-3 Christie's, Kensington #522/R est:4000-6000

WALKER, Kara (1969-) American
Prints
£1887 $3000 €2831 I'll be a monkey's uncle (101x89cm-40x35in) s.d.num.9/25 lithograph. 29-Apr-3 Christie's, Rockefeller NY #757/R est:2500-3500
£8176 $13000 €12264 The means to an end, a shadow drama in five acts (84x325cm-33x128in) s.i.d.num.7/20 hard ground etching aquatint 5 sheets in 1 frame. 29-Apr-3 Christie's, Rockefeller NY #756/R est:7000-9000
Sculpture
£1582 $2500 €2373 Cannisters (28x10x10cm-11x4x4in) sand etching on glass in 6 parts one of 100 prov. 13-Nov-2 Sotheby's, New York #474/R
Works on paper
£9494 $15000 €14241 Untitled (211x133cm-83x52in) ink cut paper collage executed 1997 prov. 14-Nov-2 Christie's, Rockefeller NY #354/R est:10000-15000

WALKER, Leonard (1877-1964) British
Works on paper
£750 $1170 €1125 Zena (43x43cm-17x17in) W/C pencil exhib. 17-Oct-2 Lawrence, Crewkerne #416/R

WALKER, R (1607-1658) British
£1589 $2591 €2400 Souvenir (162x113cm-64x44in) s.d. 17-Feb-3 Horta, Bruxelles #189

WALKER, Robert Hollands (fl.1892-1920) British
Works on paper
£350 $546 €525 Warwickshire village (15x25cm-6x10in) s.i. pencil W/C htd white. 27-Mar-3 Christie's, Kensington #108
£550 $858 €825 Haddon Hall and the River Wye (25x39cm-10x15in) s.i.d.1902 pencil W/C htd white. 17-Oct-2 Christie's, Kensington #59/R
£705 $1099 €1058 Upper Reach, Ullswater. Near Arnside (33x53cm-13x21in) s.i. W/C pair. 11-Nov-2 Stephan Welz, Johannesburg #32 (SA.R 11000)

WALKER, Samuel (attrib) (19th C) ?
£6400 $10048 €9600 Group portrait of Mrs Margaret Stapylton, Martin Bryan Stapylton and Henry Miles Stapylton (143x112cm-56x44in) s.d.d.1844 verso. 19-Nov-2 Bonhams, Leeds #171/R est:3000-5000

WALKER, Thornton (?) ?
£2151 $3269 €3227 Number VII (101x96cm-40x38in) s.i.d.90 verso. 28-Aug-2 Deutscher-Menzies, Melbourne #53/R est:5000-7000 (A.D 6000)
£2321 $3621 €3482 Composition with bowls (107x91cm-42x36in) init.d.98 s.i.d.96-98 verso. 11-Nov-2 Deutscher-Menzies, Melbourne #103/R est:4000-6000 (A.D 6500)

WALKER, William Aiken (1838-1921) American
£4487 $7000 €6731 Male cotton picker (30x15cm-12x6in) s. i.verso academy board. 12-Oct-2 Neal Auction Company, New Orleans #474/R est:5000-7000
£4688 $7500 €7032 Portrait of a female cotton picker balancing a basket on her head, smoking a pipe (33x15cm-13x6in) s. board. 17-May-3 Pook & Pook, Downington #368/R est:8000-10000
£5031 $8000 €7547 Laundry day (15x30cm-6x12in) init. board. 4-Mar-3 Christie's, Rockefeller NY #5a/R est:10000-15000
£5479 $8000 €8219 Man and woman in cotton field (20x10cm-8x4in) one mono. one s. artist board pair. 3-Nov-1 North East Auctions, Portsmouth #728/R est:6000-8000
£5625 $9000 €8156 Field hands (20x10cm-8x4in) s. board two. 16-May-3 Skinner, Boston #96/R est:4000-6000
£5689 $9500 €8249 Male cotton picker. Female cotton picker (21x10cm-8x4in) s. board pair. 22-Jun-3 Freeman, Philadelphia #107/R est:7000-10000
£5750 $9200 €8625 Coastal scene with sand dunes, palm trees and breaking surf (10x23cm-4x9in) s. fiberboard. 4-Jan-3 Brunk, Ashville #702/R est:4000-8000
£7012 $11500 €10167 Cabin scene (25x28cm-10x11in) s. board on masonite. 7-Jun-3 Neal Auction Company, New Orleans #331/R est:6000-8000
£7097 $11000 €10646 Cabin scene (15x30cm-6x12in) s. board. 7-Dec-2 Neal Auction Company, New Orleans #426/R est:12000-18000
£7143 $11000 €10715 Cabin scene (15x30cm-6x12in) s. board. 24-Oct-2 Shannon's, Milford #98/R est:9000-12000

WALKER, William Eyre (1847-1930) British
Works on paper
£820 $1361 €1230 Russett woodlands (38x77cm-15x30in) s.d.1885 W/C. 10-Jun-3 Bonhams, Leeds #104/R

WALKLEY, David B (1849-1934) American
£1375 $2200 €2063 Mystic Conn, scene shows wharf with docked two masted rowboat (25x20cm-10x8in) s. board. 11-Jan-3 James Julia, Fairfield #481 est:1800-2200
£1687 $2700 €2446 Preparing the sails, a harbour view, Connecticut (46x53cm-18x21in) s. 16-May-3 Skinner, Boston #289/R est:700-900

WALKOWITZ, Abraham (1878-1965) American/Russian
Works on paper
£335 $550 €486 Bathing figures on a rocky coast (44x58cm-17x23in) s. W/C over pencil. 5-Jun-3 Swann Galleries, New York #254/R
£352 $550 €528 Two dancers (25x18cm-10x7in) s. ink pencil. 12-Apr-3 Weschler, Washington #586/R
£457 $750 €663 Coastal landscape (39x58cm-15x23in) s. W/C. 5-Jun-3 Swann Galleries, New York #255/R
£457 $750 €663 Isadora Duncan with raised leg (33x21cm-13x8in) s. W/C pen ink exec.c.1910. 5-Jun-3 Swann Galleries, New York #256/R
£479 $800 €695 Isidora Duncan (25x20cm-10x8in) s.i.d.1909 ink W/C. 22-Jun-3 Freeman, Philadelphia #129/R
£516 $800 €774 Isadora Duncan (36x21cm-14x8in) s.indis.i. W/C ink pencil prov. 3-Dec-2 Christie's, Rockefeller NY #615/R

£549 $900 €796 Isadora Duncan (36x23cm-14x9in) s. ink wash prov. 1-Jun-3 Wright, Chicago #120/R
£579 $950 €840 Isadora Duncan (48x30cm-19x12in) s.d.1917 chl pencil prov. 1-Jun-3 Wright, Chicago #121/R
£671 $1100 €973 Rabbi (29x17cm-11x7in) W/C. 5-Jun-3 Swann Galleries, New York #257/R
£701 $1100 €1052 Abstraction (12x9cm-5x4in) s.d.1913 W/C exhib. 19-Nov-2 Wright, Chicago #105/R
£988 $1600 €1433 Bathers (13x18cm-5x7in) s. pencil W/C. 21-May-3 Doyle, New York #152/R est:700-900
£1159 $1900 €1681 Improvisations of New York (18x13cm-7x5in) s.d.1910 pencil W/C prov. 1-Jun-3 Wright, Chicago #122/R est:2000-3000
£1384 $2200 €2076 Isadora Duncan figural sketch (34x21cm-13x8in) s. pen ink W/C prov. 7-Mar-3 Skinner, Boston #604/R est:2000-4000
£1429 $2200 €2144 Isadora dancing in grey (36x20cm-14x8in) s. ink W/C exec.c.1910. 8-Sep-2 Treadway Gallery, Cincinnati #676/R est:1500-2000
£1442 $2250 €2163 Isodora Duncan dancing (36x23cm-14x9in) s.i. W/C pen ink board prov. pair. 5-Nov-2 Doyle, New York #2/R est:2000-3000
£1623 $2500 €2435 Improvisations of New York (28x20cm-11x8in) s. pencil dr exec.c.1913. 8-Sep-2 Treadway Gallery, Cincinnati #674/R est:1500-2500
£1852 $3000 €2685 Isadora Duncan dancing (36x20cm-14x8in) s.i. W/C pen ink pencil wash four prov. 21-May-3 Doyle, New York #23/R est:2500-35000

WALL, Jeff (1946-) Canadian
Photographs
£28481 $45000 €42722 Diagonal composition (50x56cm-20x22in) cibachrome transparency fluorescent light display executed 1993. 14-Nov-2 Christie's, Rockefeller NY #423/R est:50000-70000
£57500 $92000 €86250 Little children (135cm-53in circular) col photographic transparency illuminated lightbox prov.exhib.lit. 15-May-3 Phillips, New York #40/R est:80000-120000

WALL, William Archibald (1828-1875) British/American
£680 $1061 €1020 On Hampstead Heath (21x41cm-8x16in) s. 26-Mar-3 Sotheby's, Olympia #112/R
£900 $1404 €1350 On the Thames near Twickenham (34cm-13in circular) mono. i.stretcher circle. 26-Mar-3 Hamptons Fine Art, Godalming #248

WALL, William Coventry (1810-1886) American
£550 $886 €825 Fishing boats on the shore (19x39cm-7x15in) s. board. 15-Jan-3 Cheffins Grain & Comins, Cambridge #419/R

WALL, Wing (20th C) American
£1509 $2400 €2264 Indian brave reconnoitring (61x61cm-24x24in) 4-Mar-3 Christie's, Rockefeller NY #96/R est:3000-5000

WALLA, August (1936-2001) Austrian
£993 $1609 €1400 Untitled, Walla for sister Hedi! (30x40cm-12x16in) pencil col pen board prov. 20-May-3 Dorotheum, Vienna #247/R
£1702 $2757 €2400 I am called Nero's horse! Wallla Voorusso! (30x40cm-12x16in) i. verso pencil col pen gouache board prov. 20-May-3 Dorotheum, Vienna #249/R est:2000-2600

Works on paper
£690 $1103 €1000 Herrgott Sabaoth Zebaoth Cion! (30x21cm-12x8in) i. i. verso col pen board two. 11-Mar-3 Dorotheum, Vienna #199/R
£690 $1103 €1000 Joseph (30x21cm-12x8in) col pen board two. 11-Mar-3 Dorotheum, Vienna #201/R
£993 $1609 €1400 In fairytales pigs have a king! Wallla? (30x40cm-12x16in) i. verso pencil col pen gouache prov. 20-May-3 Dorotheum, Vienna #250/R
£1986 $3217 €2800 Walla swims in all the water of the world! (30x40cm-12x16in) i. verso pencil col pen biro board. 20-May-3 Dorotheum, Vienna #252/R est:2000-2600

WALLA, Erich (1947-) Austrian
Works on paper
£609 $962 €950 What is the world worth or dancing clowns (44x57cm-17x22in) s.d.1995 wax chk board. 12-Nov-2 Dorotheum, Vienna #304/R
£625 $987 €900 Harlequins' party (60x88cm-24x35in) s.d.1975 pencil w/C. 24-Apr-3 Dorotheum, Vienna #294/R

WALLACE, Ethel A (1885-1968) American
£9677 $15000 €14516 Still life of mixed flowers in a vase (76x63cm-30x25in) canvas laid down. 8-Dec-2 Freeman, Philadelphia #144/R est:8000-12000

WALLACE, H Frank (1881-1962) British
Works on paper
£340 $544 €510 Spanish Ibex (23x33cm-9x13in) s. W/C htd white. 14-Mar-3 Gardiner & Houlgate, Bath #64/R
£400 $624 €600 Deer in a highland landscape (24cm-9in circular) gouache. 18-Sep-2 Dreweatt Neate, Newbury #95
£2600 $4108 €3900 Driven off, Kyles of Lochalsh. Rising mists, Glen Affric (34x53cm-13x21in) s. W/C pair. 28-Nov-2 Bonhams, Knightsbridge #83 est:2000-3000

WALLACE, John (1841-1905) British
£450 $693 €675 Farmyard scene (44x60cm-17x24in) s.d.1892. 8-Sep-2 Lots Road, London #336

WALLACE, Marjorie (1925-) British
£643 $1016 €965 Interior of a house (53x79cm-21x31in) s. 1-Apr-3 Stephan Welz, Johannesburg #230 est:2000-3000 (SA.R 8000)

WALLACE, R Craig (19/20th C) British
£450 $747 €653 Regatta on Loch Long (50x76cm-20x30in) s. 13-Jun-3 Lyon & Turnbull, Edinburgh #42

WALLACE, William (?) British
£260 $416 €390 Cattle in a Highland landscape (27x47cm-11x19in) bears sig. after Langley. 11-Mar-3 Bonhams, Knightsbridge #220

WALLAERT, Pierre Joseph (1753-1812) French
£3500 $5845 €5075 Classical river landscape with figures on a path (66x85cm-26x33in) s.d.1809. 11-Jul-3 Christie's, Kensington #172/R est:3000-5000
£6918 $10792 €11000 Shipwrecked woman (149x208cm-59x82in) s. 20-Sep-2 Millon & Associes, Paris #788/R est:12000-20000

WALLANDER, Alf (1862-1914) Swedish
£589 $966 €854 Appleblossom in village street scene (92x70cm-36x28in) s,. 4-Jun-3 AB Stockholms Auktionsverk #2158/R (S.KR 7500)
Works on paper
£1418 $2199 €2127 Gentleman reading newspaper (88x61cm-35x24in) s.d.85 i.d.1885 verso pastel. 8-Dec-2 Uppsala Auktionskammare, Uppsala #106/R est:10000-12000 (S.KR 20000)

WALLANDER, Josef Wilhelm (1821-1888) Swedish
£2805 $4432 €4208 A spinning-wheel party, Delsbo, Halssingland (71x92cm-28x36in) s.d.1873 lit. 27-Nov-2 Falkkloos, Malmo #77817/R est:30000 (S.KR 40000)
£36170 $56064 €54255 Hops harvest in Askarboda, Osteraker I (120x167cm-47x66in) s.d. lit. 4-Dec-2 AB Stockholms Auktionsverk #1680/R est:500000-600000 (S.KR 510000)

WALLAT, Paul (1879-?) German
£253 $400 €400 Strong breakers at harbour entrance (68x96cm-27x38in) s. 29-Nov-2 Bolland & Marotz, Bremen #830

WALLEN, Gustaf Teodor (1860-1948) Swedish
£12025 $19480 €17436 From the harbour pier, Torekov (103x145cm-41x57in) s.d.1886 exhib.lit. 26-May-3 Bukowskis, Stockholm #9/R est:80000-100000 (S.KR 155000)

WALLENBERG, Axel Gereon (1898-1996) Swedish
Sculpture
£1064 $1649 €1596 The girl and the bird (65cm-26in) s.d.1950 gold pat.bronze incl. stone socle Cast Bergman. 4-Dec-2 AB Stockholms Auktionsverk #1812/R est:8000-10000 (S.KR 15000)

WALLENSTRAND, C U (18/19th C) Swedish?
£2411 $3738 €3617 Officer with horse (62x55cm-24x22in) s.d.1807. 8-Dec-2 Uppsala Auktionskammare, Uppsala #42/R est:10000-12000 (S.KR 34000)

WALLER, Arthur Bassett (fl.1911-1928) British
Works on paper
£250 $418 €363 Harbour scene with fishing boats (33x48cm-13x19in) s. 18-Jun-3 Andrew Hartley, Ilkley #995

WALLER, Frank (1842-1923) American

£2800 $4368 €4200 Part of the ruins at Philae at sunset (50x76cm-20x30in) s. 15-Oct-2 Sotheby's, London #193/R est:3000-5000

WALLER, Lucy (fl.1890-1900) British

£1700 $2822 €2465 Puppies (55x75cm-22x30in) s. 12-Jun-3 Christie's, Kensington #317/R est:800-1200

WALLER, Margaret Mary (1916-1997) British

Works on paper

£320 $506 €480 La Fregondee Sark (24x34cm-9x13in) s. W/C exec.c.1956. 28-Nov-2 Martel Maides, Guernsey #16

£480 $758 €720 Sark farmhouse (24x34cm-9x13in) s. W/C. 28-Nov-2 Martel Maides, Guernsey #11/R

WALLER, Mervyn Napier (1894-1972) Australian

Works on paper

£3226 $4903 €4839 Hunt (34x62cm-13x24in) s. W/C exec.c.1925 prov.exhib. 28-Aug-2 Deutscher-Menzies, Melbourne #65/R est:9000-12000 (A.D 9000)

WALLET, Taf (1902-2000) Belgian

£523 $842 €800 Bouquet a la rose jaune (100x80cm-39x31in) s. i.verso. 20-Jan-3 Horta, Bruxelles #445

£601 $938 €950 Pichet de Bruxelles fleuri sur fond de chinoiseries (55x45cm-22x18in) s.d.42. 16-Sep-2 Horta, Bruxelles #412

£655 $1048 €950 Landscape near Nieuwpoort (50x65cm-20x26in) s. s.i. panel. 15-Mar-3 De Vuyst, Lokeren #397

£971 $1554 €1350 Trois cabines sur la plage (14x26cm-6x10in) s. canvas on panel. 13-May-3 Vanderkindere, Brussels #79

£1250 $1987 €1800 Nature morte au homard (80x105cm-31x41in) s. 29-Apr-3 Campo & Campo, Antwerp #349/R est:2000-3000

£1266 $1975 €2000 Pichet de Bruxelles fleuri sur une chaise (86x64cm-34x25in) s. 15-Oct-2 Horta, Bruxelles #108

£1310 $2097 €1900 Bouquet de fleurs (69x59cm-27x23in) s.d.27 s.i.verso. 15-Mar-3 De Vuyst, Lokeren #396/R est:2200-2600

£2778 $4417 €4000 Un jour d'ete a la c'te avec chaises longues et parasols (81x131cm-32x52in) s. 29-Apr-3 Campo & Campo, Antwerp #348/R est:3250-3750

Works on paper

£545 $845 €850 Fruits de mon jardin (25x35cm-10x14in) s. i.verso mixed media panel. 9-Dec-2 Horta, Bruxelles #376

WALLIN, Carl E (1879-?) American

£943 $1500 €1415 Siren (22x16cm-9x6in) s.d. board painted c.1934. 4-May-3 Treadway Gallery, Cincinnati #549/R est:2000-3000

WALLIN, David (1876-1957) Swedish

£425 $663 €638 Midsummer (80x67cm-31x26in) s. exhib. 13-Sep-2 Lilla Bukowskis, Stockholm #301 (S.KR 6200)

£4000 $6560 €6000 Intet ar som vantanstider - path of spring brings with it expectation (159x102cm-63x40in) s.i.d.1906 verso. 3-Jun-3 Sotheby's, London #237/R est:4000-6000

WALLIN, Ellis (1888-1972) Swedish

£372 $591 €558 View from Flusterpramarna (53x60cm-21x24in) s.d.1923. 2-Mar-3 Uppsala Auktionskammare, Uppsala #140 (S.KR 5000)

£390 $605 €585 Still life of flowers and apples (116x82cm-46x32in) s.indis.d.33. 8-Dec-2 Uppsala Auktionskammare, Uppsala #179 (S.KR 5500)

£426 $660 €639 Town view (72x143cm-28x56in) s. 8-Dec-2 Uppsala Auktionskammare, Uppsala #192/R (S.KR 6000)

WALLINGER, Mark (1959-) British

£14000 $22960 €21000 Brown's, Mrs L S Brown (110x110cm-43x43in) s.d.1993 overlap linen prov. 7-Feb-3 Sotheby's, London #112/R est:8000-12000

£19000 $31160 €28500 Brown's, Mr W S Brown (110x110cm-43x43in) s.d.1993 overlap linen prov. 7-Feb-3 Sotheby's, London #111/R est:8000-12000

WALLIS, Alfred (1855-1942) British

£8500 $13940 €12750 White cottages (20x28cm-8x11in) oil card on panel prov. 6-Jun-3 Christie's, London #127/R est:7000-10000

£10000 $16700 €14500 Box flap (10x21cm-4x8in) house paint on cardboard prov. 19-Jun-3 Lane, Penzance #250/R est:10000-12000

£72000 $118080 €108000 Schooner passing a lighthouse (37x99cm-15x39in) s. board. 6-Jun-3 Christie's, London #129/R est:25000-35000

Works on paper

£900 $1485 €1305 Sailing ships (25x39cm-10x15in) pencil prov.exhib. 3-Jul-3 Christie's, Kensington #651/R

£3800 $5928 €5700 House on the shore (7x13cm-3x5in) pencil oil on card. 27-Mar-3 Christie's, Kensington #599/R est:1000-1500

£4000 $6560 €6000 Sailing boat with figures and lighthouse (18x28cm-7x11in) s. pencil W/C bodycol prov. 6-Jun-3 Christie's, London #128/R est:3000-5000

£6400 $10176 €9600 Trees (29x41cm-11x16in) chl oil board. 26-Feb-3 Sotheby's, Olympia #217/R est:5000-7000

WALLIS, Joshua (1789-1862) British

Works on paper

£2500 $3975 €3750 Figures on a path near a ruined castle. Boy fishing. Figures fishing. Cattle watering (23x33cm-9x13in) W/C over pencil gum arabic set of four. 19-Mar-3 Sotheby's, London #178/R est:2000-3000

WALLIS, Rosa (1857-?) British

Works on paper

£300 $489 €450 Looking across the Guidecca Venice (20x13cm-8x5in) s. W/C. 29-Jan-3 Sotheby's, Olympia #179/R

WALLNER, Katharina (1891-1969) Austrian

£321 $503 €500 Winter landscape (38x39cm-15x15in) s. board. 21-Nov-2 Dorotheum, Vienna #254/R

WALLNER, Thure (1888-1965) Swedish

£248 $385 €372 White tailed eagle (24x22cm-9x9in) s. panel. 8-Dec-2 Uppsala Auktionskammare, Uppsala #176 (S.KR 3500)

£274 $428 €411 Hunters (23x29cm-9x11in) s. canvas on panel. 13-Sep-2 Lilla Bukowskis, Stockholm #707 (S.KR 4000)

£421 $665 €632 Eiderducks swimming in moonlight (45x90cm-18x35in) 30-Nov-2 Goteborg Auktionsverk, Sweden #173/R (S.KR 6000)

£423 $685 €635 Fish on the surface (29x41cm-11x16in) s. panel. 3-Feb-3 Lilla Bukowskis, Stockholm #34 (S.KR 5900)

£508 $798 €762 Red-backed shrike on wild rose (24x18cm-9x7in) s. panel. 16-Dec-2 Lilla Bukowskis, Stockholm #68 (S.KR 7200)

£510 $846 €740 In the nest (35x27cm-14x11in) s. panel. 16-Jun-3 Lilla Bukowskis, Stockholm #1155 (S.KR 6600)

£530 $859 €795 Hare in autumn leaves (46x55cm-18x22in) s. panel. 3-Feb-3 Lilla Bukowskis, Stockholm #90 (S.KR 7400)

£565 $886 €848 Goldfinch on thistle (33x24cm-13x9in) s. panel. 16-Dec-2 Lilla Bukowskis, Stockholm #67 (S.KR 8000)

£565 $886 €848 Starlings on apple blossom (27x16cm-11x6in) s. panel. 16-Dec-2 Lilla Bukowskis, Stockholm #70 (S.KR 8000)

£618 $939 €927 Red-backed shrike (32x35cm-13x14in) s. panel. 16-Aug-2 Lilla Bukowskis, Stockholm #412 (S.KR 9000)

£650 $1066 €975 Traveller crossing a river on a woodland track (30x15cm-12x6in) s. panel. 5-Jun-3 Christie's, Kensington #678/R

£680 $1128 €986 Ducks by water's edge (30x34cm-12x13in) s. cardboard. 16-Jun-3 Lilla Bukowskis, Stockholm #994 (S.KR 8800)

£716 $1160 €1074 Cat hunting (38x42cm-15x17in) s. panel. 3-Feb-3 Lilla Bukowskis, Stockholm #35 (S.KR 10000)

£786 $1288 €1140 Fox on large stone (33x41cm-13x16in) s. 4-Jun-3 AB Stockholms Auktionsverk #2101/R (S.KR 10000)

£851 $1319 €1277 Apollo butterfly (33x24cm-13x9in) s. panel. 4-Dec-2 AB Stockholms Auktionsverk #1582/R (S.KR 12000)

£922 $1429 €1383 Small birds by nest in green bush (36x27cm-14x11in) s.d.1912. 8-Dec-2 Uppsala Auktionskammare, Uppsala #182/R (S.KR 13000)

£943 $1546 €1367 Greyhen in wooded landscape (33x23cm-13x9in) s.d.44 panel. 4-Jun-3 AB Stockholms Auktionsverk #2084/R (S.KR 12000)

£1059 $1662 €1589 Winter landscape with fox (38x46cm-15x18in) s. panel. 16-Dec-2 Lilla Bukowskis, Stockholm #69 est:15000-18000 (S.KR 15000)

£1100 $1804 €1595 Mallards on sandy beach (73x92cm-29x36in) s. 4-Jun-3 AB Stockholms Auktionsverk #2092/R (S.KR 14000)

£1100 $1804 €1595 Red-backed shrike by dog-roses (24x18cm-9x7in) s. panel. 4-Jun-3 AB Stockholms Auktionsverk #2312/R est:12000-15000 (S.KR 14000)

£1277 $1979 €1916 Goshawk and squirrel (78x61cm-31x24in) s. 3-Dec-2 Bukowskis, Stockholm #42/R est:25000-30000 (S.KR 18000)

£1414 $2319 €2050 Garden warbler (35x27cm-14x11in) s.d.1912. 4-Jun-3 AB Stockholms Auktionsverk #2238/R est:18000-20000 (S.KR 18000)

£1631 $2528 €2447 Capercaillie among heather (24x33cm-9x13in) s. panel. 4-Dec-2 AB Stockholms Auktionsverk #1570/R est:10000-15000 (S.KR 23000)

£1702 $2638 €2553 Coastal landscape with pair of swans in reeds (74x101cm-29x40in) s. 4-Dec-2 AB Stockholms Auktionsverk #1562/R est:30000-35000 (S.KR 24000)

£1702 $2638 €2553 Wooded landscape with elks in evening light (72x100cm-28x39in) s. 4-Dec-2 AB Stockholms Auktionsverk #1649/R est:20000-25000 (S.KR 24000)

£2057 $3188 €3086 Swedish birds (60x93cm-24x37in) s. 3-Dec-2 Bukowskis, Stockholm #110/R est:35000-40000 (S.KR 29000)

WALLS, William (1860-1942) British

£400 $616 €600 Dead stork (55x85cm-22x33in) s. 7-Sep-2 Shapes, Edinburgh #432

£2000 $3260 €3000 Two lion cubs at play (58x41cm-23x16in) s. canvasboard. 12-Feb-3 Bonhams, Knightsbridge #301/R est:2000-3000

WALLWORK, Richard (1882-1955) British
£414 $588 €621 Along the Kaikoura Coast (39x50cm-15x20in) s. prov. 20-Mar-2 Watson's, Christchurch #60/R est:400-1000 (NZ.D 1350)

WALMSLEY, James Ulric (1860-1954) British
Works on paper
£1100 $1716 €1650 Ramsdale Mille, Robin Hoods Bay (26x19cm-10x7in) s. W/C. 10-Sep-2 David Duggleby, Scarborough #159/R est:700-900

WALMSLEY, Thomas (1763-1806) British
Works on paper
£250 $388 €375 The Nunnery, Isle of Man (24x34cm-9x13in) i. verso W/C over pencil prov. 2-Oct-2 Bonhams, Knowle #8
£420 $693 €609 Church ruin in a river landscape (24x35cm-9x14in) W/C bodycol. 2-Jul-3 Sotheby's, Olympia #209/R
£900 $1396 €1350 Conway Castle (28x43cm-11x17in) s.i.d.1799 verso W/C gouache. 3-Dec-2 Sotheby's, Olympia #32/R est:1000-1500

WALMSLEY, Thomas (attrib) (1763-1806) British
£900 $1440 €1350 Shipping off an estuary. Herdsmen and cattle on the bank of an estuary (14x17cm-6x7in) panel pair. 13-May-3 Bonhams, Knightsbridge #74/R

WALRAVEN, Jan (1827-?) Dutch
£1629 $2639 €2362 Interior from a school (60x50cm-24x20in) s. 26-May-3 Bukowskis, Stockholm #257/R est:20000-22000 (S.KR 21000)

WALRAVENS, Emile (1879-1914) Belgian
£1164 $1816 €1700 Travaux devant la fenetre (100x80cm-39x31in) s.d.1911. 14-Apr-3 Horta, Bruxelles #346 est:700-900

WALSCHARTZ, Francois (attrib) (c.1597-1678) Belgian
£4167 $6542 €6500 La Sainte famille (203x139cm-80x55in) 19-Nov-2 Vanderkindere, Brussels #10/R est:6500-8500

WALSER, Karl (1877-1943) Swiss
Works on paper
£253 $400 €400 Alpine King, messenger (9x8cm-4x3in) mono. gouache over pencil board. 29-Nov-2 Villa Grisebach, Berlin #952/R

WALSETH, Niels (1914-2001) Danish
£203 $319 €305 Fisherman mending his nets (50x41cm-20x16in) s. 10-Dec-2 Pinneys, Montreal #73 (C.D 500)
£274 $428 €411 Farmyard with peasant boy (70x100cm-28x39in) s. 11-Nov-2 Rasmussen, Vejle #2045 (D.KR 3200)
£278 $450 €417 Boats and wheelbarrow (69x99cm-27x39in) 24-Jan-3 Douglas, South Deerfield #4

WALSH, Alfred Wilson (1859-1916) New Zealander
Works on paper
£278 $433 €417 Rowboat on lake, Hagley Park (15x12cm-6x5in) s. W/C exec.c.1900 prov. 8-Apr-3 Peter Webb, Auckland #166/R (NZ.D 800)

WALSH, John (?) New Zealander?
£640 $980 €960 Carrying culture (10x36cm-4x14in) s.d.98 canvas on wood. 21-Aug-2 Dunbar Sloane, Auckland #12/R est:2000-4000 (NZ.D 2100)
£1212 $1867 €1818 Untitled (22x48cm-9x19in) board. 4-Sep-2 Dunbar Sloane, Wellington #62a/R est:2000-3000 (NZ.D 4000)
£2105 $3284 €3158 Ko Wai to Tekoteko Kei Runga (35x65cm-14x26in) s.d.2001 board. 27-Mar-3 International Art Centre, Auckland #1/R est:3000-6000 (NZ.D 6000)

WALSH, Owen (1933-) Irish
£295 $459 €430 Self portrait (43x36cm-17x14in) s. board. 8-Apr-3 James Adam, Dublin #145/R
£886 $1373 €1400 Dublin street scene (51x61cm-20x24in) 24-Sep-2 De Veres Art Auctions, Dublin #180/R est:1000-2000
Works on paper
£308 $481 €450 Coastal landscape (39x56cm-15x22in) s.d. pastel. 8-Apr-3 James Adam, Dublin #147/R

WALSH, Peter (?) Australian?
£528 $824 €915 Two seated figures (153x137cm-60x54in) prov. 31-Mar-3 Goodman, Sydney #136 (A.D 1400)

WALSH, Tom (20th C) Irish
Works on paper
£411 $645 €600 Kerry images (44x66cm-17x26in) s. gouache prov. 15-Apr-3 De Veres Art Auctions, Dublin #63

WALSHAW, James William (19th C) British
Works on paper
£380 $589 €570 Chester street scene (30x20cm-12x8in) s. 4-Dec-2 Andrew Hartley, Ilkley #1051

WALSHAW, Thomas W (19th C) British
£270 $443 €405 Lower Bridge Street, Chester, with the Old Edgar Inn (15x31cm-6x12in) 4-Feb-3 Bonhams, Chester #685
Works on paper
£280 $445 €420 Bidston village (35x53cm-14x21in) s. W/C. 27-Feb-3 Bonhams, Chester #316

WALT DISNEY PRODUCTIONS (20th C) American
Works on paper
£1231 $2044 €1785 Dumbo (24x30cm-9x12in) s.i. gouache celluloid. 12-Jun-3 Kunsthallen, Copenhagen #116/R est:15000 (D.KR 13000)

WALT DISNEY STUDIOS (20th C) American
Works on paper
£508 $833 €700 King Lionheart (21x22cm-8x9in) mixed media transparent foil. 31-May-3 Villa Grisebach, Berlin #941/R
£1100 $1826 €1650 Dopey with the animals (19x23cm-7x9in) bodycol col chk prov. 12-Jun-3 Bonhams, New Bond Street #702/R est:1000-1500
£3200 $5344 €4640 Snow white and quilt (18x16cm-7x6in) gouache on celluloid prov. 26-Jun-3 Mellors & Kirk, Nottingham #831/R est:1500-2000

WALTENSPERGER, Charles (1870-1931) American
£968 $1500 €1452 Spring maidens (56x66cm-22x26in) s. painted c.1910. 8-Dec-2 Toomey, Oak Park #644/R est:2000-3000

WALTER, Christian J (1872-1938) American
£1200 $1860 €1800 Artist in the countryside (27x35cm-11x14in) s. board. 3-Dec-2 Sotheby's, Olympia #299/R est:1000-2000

WALTER, Johannes (17th C) German?
£5000 $7850 €7500 Tulips, laurustines and other flowers in a blue and white delf vase, with insects (35x29cm-14x11in) s.indis d. bodycol on vellum. 13-Dec-2 Christie's, Kensington #305/R est:1500-2000

WALTER, Joseph (1783-1856) British
£10000 $15200 €15000 Frigate under reduced sail in the Channel (40x53cm-16x21in) s.d.1852. 15-Aug-2 Bonhams, New Bond Street #394/R est:6000-8000

WALTER, Louis (fl.1853-1869) British
£280 $431 €420 Valley farm (62x52cm-24x20in) init. 22-Oct-2 Bonhams, Bath #267
£300 $462 €450 Weir (39x49cm-15x19in) s.d.1869. 22-Oct-2 Bonhams, Bath #268
£300 $462 €450 Cornfield (62x52cm-24x20in) s.d.1868 canvas laid down after Constable. 22-Oct-2 Bonhams, Bath #269

WALTER, Martha (1875-1976) American
£2390 $3800 €3585 Still life with tulips (61x51cm-24x20in) s. canvasboard prov. 4-Mar-3 Christie's, Rockefeller NY #86/R est:4000-6000
£4140 $6500 €6210 Mother and child (46x38cm-18x15in) s. canvasboard prov. 10-Dec-2 Doyle, New York #111/R est:6000-8000
£5346 $8500 €8019 Showery day at Biarritz (37x46cm-15x18in) s. i.verso canvasboard prov. 5-Mar-3 Sotheby's, New York #45/R est:12000-18000
£6129 $9500 €9194 Spring landscape with figure (61x51cm-24x20in) estate st. prov. 8-Dec-2 Freeman, Philadelphia #154/R est:6000-8000
£12579 $20000 €18869 At the babie's health station, New York City (36x44cm-14x17in) s.i.d.1922 s.verso board. 5-Mar-3 Sotheby's, New York #47/R est:8000-12000
£13889 $22500 €20834 Anne (66x53cm-26x21in) s. prov.lit. 21-May-3 Sotheby's, New York #144/R est:8000-12000
Works on paper
£3571 $5500 €5357 Gloucester Harbour (38x46cm-15x18in) s. W/C prov. 24-Oct-2 Shannon's, Milford #52/R est:5000-7000
£6962 $11000 €10443 Green umbrella (36x41cm-14x16in) W/C prov. 24-Apr-3 Shannon's, Milford #9/R est:8000-12000

WALTER, Martha (attrib) (1875-1976) American
Works on paper
£1266 $2000 €1899 Parisian cafe scene (36x46cm-14x18in) W/C. 16-Nov-2 New Orleans Auction, New Orleans #328/R est:2000-4000

WALTERS, Curt (1958-) American
£2130 $3450 €3089 Placidity (71x71cm-28x28in) 23-May-3 Altermann Galleries, Santa Fe #206
£6164 $9000 €9246 Stateliness (91x91cm-36x36in) 18-May-2 Altermann Galleries, Santa Fe #185/R

WALTERS, Emile (1893-?) American
£807 $1300 €1211 Impressionistic painting of houses nestled at foothills (58x48cm-23x19in) s. canvas on board. 21-Feb-3 York Town, York #1067

WALTERS, George Stanfield (1838-1924) British
£350 $557 €525 Fishing smack off a coast on a choppy sea (46x38cm-18x15in) s.d.1883. 29-Apr-3 Peter Francis, Wales #5/R
£1200 $1896 €1800 Great Tor - Gower, South Wales (44x75cm-17x30in) s.d.1873. 7-Apr-3 Bonhams, Bath #96/R est:1000-1500
Works on paper
£241 $378 €362 Boats in the harbour (28x44cm-11x17in) s. W/C. 25-Nov-2 Hodgins, Calgary #398/R (C.D 600)
£260 $416 €390 Vessel in choppy waters leaving harbour (19x34cm-7x13in) init.d.84 W/C. 13-May-3 Bonhams, Sevenoaks #362
£300 $467 €450 Coastal view with boats on the horizon (26x36cm-10x14in) s. pencil W/C htd bodycol. 19-Sep-2 Christie's, Kensington #153/R
£300 $477 €450 Lowestoft trawlers (30x48cm-12x19in) s. W/C. 29-Apr-3 Gorringes, Lewes #2034
£350 $581 €508 Trinity Wharfs, Yarmouth (33x51cm-13x20in) s.i.verso W/C. 10-Jun-3 David Lay, Penzance #274
£360 $583 €540 Setting sail in the early morning light (25x34cm-10x13in) s. W/C. 21-Jan-3 Bonhams, Knightsbridge #227/R
£380 $604 €570 Man of war in harbour (23x33cm-9x13in) s. W/C. 29-Apr-3 Gorringes, Lewes #2324
£397 $648 €600 Seascape (32x50cm-13x20in) s. W/C. 11-Feb-3 Segre, Madrid #13/R
£400 $636 €600 Caught in a swell off port (24x34cm-9x13in) s. W/C bodycol. 29-Apr-3 Bonhams, Knightsbridge #59/R
£400 $636 €600 Fishing boat and vessels at sea (23x33cm-9x13in) s. W/C. 29-Apr-3 Gorringes, Lewes #2323
£400 $636 €600 Sunset on the Dort, Holland (24x34cm-9x13in) s. W/C. 29-Apr-3 Henry Adams, Chichester #215/R
£450 $747 €653 Barges on a Dutch waterway (30x48cm-12x19in) s. W/C. 10-Jun-3 David Lay, Penzance #214/R
£450 $747 €653 Towing down the Thames, off the Nore (33x51cm-13x20in) s.i.verso W/C. 10-Jun-3 David Lay, Penzance #272
£450 $747 €653 Fresh weather on the Maas, Holland (33x51cm-13x20in) s.i.verso W/C. 10-Jun-3 David Lay, Penzance #273
£500 $775 €750 Sailing, fishing vessels and steamer off coast at Dover (32x49cm-13x19in) s. W/C over pencil htd scratching out. 2-Oct-2 Bonhams, Knowle #40
£600 $930 €900 Hauling in the pots at daybreak (32x49cm-13x19in) s. pencil W/C htd white. 31-Oct-2 Christie's, Kensington #380/R
£720 $1116 €1080 Sunset on the Stour at Harwich (25x35cm-10x14in) s. W/C. 30-Sep-2 Bonhams, Ipswich #344/R

WALTERS, Gordon (1919-1995) New Zealander
£2508 $3912 €3762 Untitled (16x12cm-6x5in) s.d.1976 acrylic. 7-Nov-2 International Art Centre, Auckland #45/R est:8000-12000 (NZ.D 8000)
£5035 $7854 €7553 Untitled (50x41cm-20x16in) s.d.1990 verso acrylic. 8-Apr-3 Peter Webb, Auckland #74/R est:13000-18000 (NZ.D 14500)
£5329 $8313 €7994 Koru 3 (20x22cm-8x9in) s. d.1968 verso acrylic on paper. 7-Nov-2 International Art Centre, Auckland #43/R est:20000-30000 (NZ.D 17000)
£9091 $14000 €13637 Koru I (30x22cm-12x9in) i.d.1970 verso acrylic prov. 4-Sep-2 Dunbar Sloane, Wellington #24/R est:25000-35000 (NZ.D 30000)

WALTERS, Miles (1774-1849) British
£4938 $8000 €7160 Homeward bound brig Commerce, under full sail (43x69cm-17x27in) s.d.1822 i.on stretcher lit. 29-Jul-3 Christie's, Rockefeller NY #168/R est:8000-10000

WALTERS, Samuel (1811-1882) British
£6500 $10855 €9425 Brazil packet in two position off the coast (70x105cm-28x41in) 18-Jun-3 Sotheby's, Olympia #24/R est:4000-6000
£12800 $21376 €18560 Sandy Cove, near Dublin (67x107cm-26x42in) s.d.1861 exhib.lit. 18-Jun-3 Sotheby's, Olympia #25/R est:3000-5000

WALTERS, Wes (1928-) Australian
Works on paper
£857 $1354 €1286 Abstract (84x106cm-33x42in) s.d.01 mixed media on cardboard. 27-Nov-2 Deutscher-Menzies, Melbourne #157/R est:3000-4000 (A.D 2400)

WALTHER, Christoph Abraham (1625-1680) German
Works on paper
£2292 $3644 €3300 Sleeping Venus surprised by Satyr and Chronos (13x18cm-5x7in) i. pen over chl chk. 5-May-3 Ketterer, Munich #241/R est:200-300

WALTHER, Franz-Erhard (1939-) German
Works on paper
£385 $596 €600 Untitled (29x21cm-11x8in) i. s.i.d.64 verso col pen pencil over W/C. 3-Dec-2 Lempertz, Koln #499/R
£414 $654 €600 Untitled (70x50cm-28x20in) s.d.1991 W/C pencil. 2-Apr-3 Dr Fritz Nagel, Stuttgart #9250/R
£552 $872 €800 Untitled (44x31cm-17x12in) s.d.1979 gouache W/C pencil board. 2-Apr-3 Dr Fritz Nagel, Stuttgart #9251/R
£690 $1090 €1000 Untitled (30x21cm-12x8in) s.d.69/71 W/C pencil two. 2-Apr-3 Dr Fritz Nagel, Stuttgart #9249/R

WALTHER, Karl (1905-1981) German
£890 $1389 €1300 Shepherd with his flock near water with foothills in the distance (52x78cm-20x31in) s. canvas on canvas lit. 10-Apr-3 Allgauer, Kempten #3042/R

WALTNER, Alexander (1967-) Austrian
£3546 $5745 €5000 Untitled (87x274cm-34x108in) s.d.97 verso acrylic panel. 20-May-3 Dorotheum, Vienna #288/R est:4000-5000

WALTON, Constance (1865-1960) British
Works on paper
£1500 $2295 €2250 Pink roses (62x52cm-24x20in) s. W/C. 22-Aug-2 Bonhams, Edinburgh #1053/R est:1500-2000
£1700 $2652 €2550 Still life of pansies (33x47cm-13x19in) s. W/C. 17-Sep-2 Sotheby's, Olympia #71/R est:1500-2000

WALTON, Edward Arthur (1860-1922) British
£5000 $7800 €7500 Head of a girl (35x29cm-14x11in) s.d.86 prov. 10-Apr-3 Bonhams, Edinburgh #174/R est:5000-8000
£12000 $18360 €18000 Woodyard (70x95cm-28x37in) s. prov. 22-Aug-2 Bonhams, Edinburgh #1026/R est:12000-15000
£13000 $19760 €19500 Children playing near a cottage (71x91cm-28x36in) s. 28-Aug-2 Sotheby's, London #1069/R est:10000-15000

WALTON, Elijah (1832-1880) British
Works on paper
£380 $623 €570 Cimade Rozeg and Forano Glacier (9x16cm-4x6in) d.4.9.76 W/C. 7-Jun-3 Shapes, Edinburgh #350
£460 $727 €667 Sunset on the Nile (32x43cm-13x17in) s.i.d.1874 verso W/C bodycol. 22-Jul-3 Bristol Auction Rooms #416a
£1300 $2119 €1950 Ravine near Cortina d'amberra, Tyrol. Piz Cambri and Ober Barinna Glacier (17x12cm-7x5in) one s. W/C gouache pair. 29-Jan-3 Sotheby's, Olympia #174/R est:400-600

WALTON, Frank (1840-1928) British
£3200 $4928 €4800 Autumnal landscape (51x76cm-20x30in) s. 5-Sep-2 Christie's, Kensington #180/R est:2000-3000
Works on paper
£380 $619 €570 Dundrum Bay (33x23cm-13x9in) s.d.1878. 13-Feb-3 David Lay, Penzance #464
£1500 $2339 €2250 Severn Sea. Rabbits by a hayrick (32x23cm-13x9in) s. pencil W/C htd bodycol pair exhib. 19-Sep-2 Christie's, Kensington #164/R est:1800-2500

WALTON, Frank (attrib) (1840-1928) British
£529 $831 €767 Untitled. 15-Dec-2 Anders Antik, Landskrona #57 (S.KR 7500)

WALTON, Henry (19th C) British
£533 $885 €773 Morning, Capel Curig, North Wales (51x76cm-20x30in) s. i.on stretcher. 16-Jun-3 Waddingtons, Toronto #119/R est:1200-1800 (C.D 1200)

WALTON, Henry (1746-1813) British
£1000 $1590 €1500 Portrait of a lady wearing white dress and headress (45x40cm-18x16in) panel. 19-Mar-3 Sotheby's, London #51/R est:1500-2000

WALTON, James Trout (1818-1867) British
£1500 $2324 €2250 River Dee, Lochnagar in the distance (79x108cm-31x43in) s.indisd. 3-Dec-2 Sotheby's, Olympia #138/R est:1200-1800

WALTON, John Whitehead (attrib) (19th C) British
£547 $876 €793 Contemplation (91x71cm-36x28in) 18-May-3 Anders Antik, Landskrona #107 (S.KR 7000)

WANDESFORDE, Juan B (1817-1902) American
£7643 $12000 €11465 Mount Shasta (51x86cm-20x34in) s.d.1868. 20-Nov-2 Christie's, Los Angeles #76/R est:15000-25000

WANDSCHEER, Marie (1856-1936) Dutch
£625 $1031 €900 Lelies en zinnias (65x55cm-26x22in) s. s.i.verso. 1-Jul-3 Christie's, Amsterdam #212/R

WANE, Richard (1852-1904) British
£280 $445 €420 Near Tenby, fishermen tending their high and dry boats (27x59cm-11x23in) s. 4-Mar-3 Bristol Auction Rooms #373
Works on paper
£270 $448 €405 Cornfield at Mart Wood, Deganwy, North Wales (21x36cm-8x14in) s. W/C. 10-Jun-3 Bonhams, Leeds #105
£320 $477 €480 Sugar Loaf (25x36cm-10x14in) s. W/C. 28-Jun-2 Chrystals Auctions, Isle of Man #143a

WANG GUXIANG (1501-1568) Chinese
Works on paper
£10101 $16667 €14646 Birthday gathering of immortals (125x52cm-49x20in) s.i.d.1556 ink hanging scroll. 6-Jul-3 Christie's, Hong Kong #413/R est:50000-70000 (HK.D 130000)

WANG HUAIQING (1944-) Chinese
£17094 $28205 €24786 Concave and convex (112x145cm-44x57in) s. 6-Jul-3 Christie's, Hong Kong #119/R est:250000-350000 (HK.D 220000)

WANG HUI (1632-1717) Chinese
Works on paper
£73815 $121795 €107032 Travellers in a snowy forest (153x122cm-60x48in) s.i.d.1706 ink col hanging scroll in the style of WANG WEI. 6-Jul-3 Christie's, Hong Kong #463/R est:850000-1000000 (HK.D 950000)

WANG JIPING (1961-) Chinese
Works on paper
£272 $433 €400 Canards (77x63cm-30x25in) s. ink wash. 24-Mar-3 Coutau Begarie, Paris #318

WANG JUN YING (20th C) Chinese
£3774 $5849 €6000 Young woman from Xiao-Lau (80x60cm-31x24in) s.d.98. 7-Oct-2 Claude Aguttes, Neuilly #294/R

WANG KUI (20th C) Canadian
£301 $473 €452 Red willows (35x45cm-14x18in) s.i. 25-Nov-2 Hodgins, Calgary #127/R (C.D 750)
£348 $543 €580 Weeping willows (48x49cm-19x19in) s i.verso. 13-Apr-3 Levis, Calgary #70/R (C.D 800)

WANG SU (1794-1877) Chinese
Works on paper
£543 $891 €750 Two scholars under tree watching moon (178x41cm-70x16in) i. seal Indian ink col hanging scroll. 30-May-3 Dr Fritz Nagel, Stuttgart #1274/R

WANG YOUZHENG (1941-) Chinese
Works on paper
£290 $475 €400 Portrait of girl (84x49cm-33x19in) i.d.1988 Indian ink col hanging scroll. 30-May-3 Dr Fritz Nagel, Stuttgart #1294/R

WANG YUANSHUI (1870-1948) Chinese
Works on paper
£3415 $5395 €5123 Living leisurely in the mountains (136x67cm-54x26in) s.i.d.1925 ink col hanging scroll. 28-Apr-3 Sotheby's, Hong Kong #641/R est:60000-80000 (HK.D 42000)

WANG YUNHE (1939-) Chinese
£6993 $11538 €10140 Glamour of Shanghai city (91x73cm-36x29in) s.d.2000. 6-Jul-3 Christie's, Hong Kong #169/R est:90000-110000 (HK.D 90000)

WANG ZHEN (1866-1938) Chinese
Works on paper
£4065 $6423 €6098 Zhong Kui (118x59cm-46x23in) s.i.d.1927 ink col hanging scroll. 28-Apr-3 Sotheby's, Hong Kong #660/R est:50000-70000 (HK.D 50000)

WANG ZIWU (20th C) Chinese
Works on paper
£942 $1545 €1300 Portrait of Qi Baishi (138x68cm-54x27in) i.d.1987 seals Indian ink hanging scroll sold with another prov. 30-May-3 Dr Fritz Nagel, Stuttgart #1150/R
£1159 $1901 €1600 The poet Li Bai says cheers to the moon (68x138cm-27x54in) s. seal Indian ink col prov. 30-May-3 Dr Fritz Nagel, Stuttgart #1241/R est:600-800
£1739 $2852 €2400 Lotus (96x171cm-38x67in) s.d.1977 seal Indian ink col scroll. 30-May-3 Dr Fritz Nagel, Stuttgart #1193/R est:1000-1500

WANG, Aage (1879-1959) Danish
£689 $1047 €1034 Two young girls on the way to Grenen, Skagen (57x82cm-22x32in) s. 27-Aug-2 Rasmussen, Copenhagen #1739/R (D.KR 8000)

WANG, Albert Edward (1864-1930) Danish
£270 $417 €405 Coastal landscape (30x50cm-12x20in) 26-Oct-2 Rasmussen, Havnen #2051 (D.KR 3200)
£335 $543 €486 Seascape off the coast at sunset (63x104cm-25x41in) mono.d.1909. 24-May-3 Rasmussen, Havnen #2117 (D.KR 3500)
£421 $682 €610 Seascape off the coast at sunset (30x94cm-12x37in) s.d.07 panel. 24-May-3 Rasmussen, Havnen #2116 (D.KR 4400)
£729 $1137 €1094 Sunset over the ocean (95x158cm-37x62in) s.d.1915. 11-Nov-2 Rasmussen, Vejle #635/R (D.KR 8500)

WANG, Jens Waldemar (1859-1926) Norwegian
£542 $879 €813 Still life of objects on table (114x190cm-45x75in) s. 27-Jan-3 Blomqvist, Lysaker #1284/R (N.KR 6000)

WANING, Cornelis Anthony van (1861-1929) Dutch
£519 $810 €820 Ships in a city canal (44x34cm-17x13in) s. 21-Oct-2 Glerum, Amsterdam #9/R
£625 $1031 €900 View of a canal in a town (46x64cm-18x25in) s. 1-Jul-3 Christie's, Amsterdam #181

WANING, Martin van (1889-1972) Dutch
£310 $493 €450 Shipping on a river with a town in the background (46x38cm-18x15in) s. board. 10-Mar-3 Sotheby's, Amsterdam #186/R
£655 $1042 €950 View of Dordrecht (90x120cm-35x47in) s.i. 10-Mar-3 Sotheby's, Amsterdam #217/R est:900-1200

WANKE, Johannes (1923-) Austrian
Works on paper
£385 $596 €600 Hunting still life (44x62cm-17x24in) s. pencil w/C. 5-Dec-2 Dorotheum, Graz #130/R

WANKIE, Wladyslaw (c.1860-1925) Polish
£956 $1500 €1434 Chance meeting (35x24cm-14x9in) s. panel. 22-Nov-2 Skinner, Boston #35 est:3000-5000

WANNENMACHER, Joseph (1722-1780) German
£3741 $5949 €5500 Annunciation (43x61cm-17x24in) s.d.1744 one of pair. 19-Mar-3 Neumeister, Munich #492/R est:2500
£3741 $5949 €5500 Adoration of the Kings (43x61cm-17x24in) s.d.7. Jan 1745 one of pair. 19-Mar-3 Neumeister, Munich #493/R est:2500
Works on paper
£833 $1325 €1200 Saint appearing on cloud to Mary and Christ (24x13cm-9x5in) i. pen wash. 5-May-3 Ketterer, Munich #263/R

WANSLEBEN, Arthur (attrib) (1861-1917) German
£285 $444 €450 Lower Rhine landscape with figures and cows (27x45cm-11x18in) s. board. 14-Sep-2 Weidler, Nurnberg #302/R

WAPLINGTON, Paul (1938-) British
£1100 $1793 €1650 Urban landscape, Nottinghamshire (90x121cm-35x48in) s. board. 13-Feb-3 Mellors & Kirk, Nottingham #797 est:500-600
£1600 $2608 €2400 Nottingham panorama (91x121cm-36x48in) s. 13-Feb-3 Mellors & Kirk, Nottingham #798/R est:1000-1400

WARBURTON, Greg (20th C) ?
£607 $953 €911 Summer visit (181x167cm-71x66in) init.d.87 s.i.d.87 verso acrylic. 25-Nov-2 Christie's, Melbourne #402/R (A.D 1700)

WARBURTON, Samuel (1874-1938) British
Works on paper
£300 $462 €450 Punt on the Thames, near Windsor (38x51cm-15x20in) s.d.1923 W/C. 3-Sep-2 Gorringes, Lewes #2138

WARD OF HULL, John (1798-1849) British
£4000 $6160 €6000 Boats (25x33cm-10x13in) s. panel. 25-Oct-2 Gorringes, Lewes #895
£5000 $8100 €7500 Shipping off Northfleet, Thames (12x17cm-5x7in) i.verso panel. 22-Jan-3 Bonhams, New Bond Street #374/R est:2000-3000

WARD, Arthur E (1863-1928) American
£491 $800 €737 Evening, Rockport harbour, MA (51x41cm-20x16in) s. i.verso. 2-Feb-3 Grogan, Boston #49

WARD, Charles Caleb (c.1831-1896) American
Works on paper
£1563 $2500 €2345 Indian father carrying child across a stream (46x36cm-18x14in) s.d.1887 W/C. 18-May-3 Jeffery Burchard, Florida #34a/R est:2000-3000
£2813 $4500 €4220 Asleep in a sunny corner (46x64cm-18x25in) s.d.1856 W/C. 18-May-3 Jeffery Burchard, Florida #34/R est:4000-6000

WARD, Charles D (1872-?) British
£300 $477 €450 Pagoda (61x51cm-24x20in) s.d.1930. 6-Mar-3 Christie's, Kensington #638/R
£2300 $3588 €3450 Four seasons (30x47cm-12x19in) s.i. panel vignettes four. 17-Oct-2 Bonhams, Edinburgh #207/R est:1200-1800

WARD, Cyril (1863-1935) British
Works on paper
£300 $477 €450 View of a coastal town (29x46cm-11x18in) s. W/C. 25-Feb-3 Bonhams, Knightsbridge #180/R
£380 $593 €570 Hill top farm, N Wales (43x77cm-17x30in) s. s.i.verso W/C. 10-Oct-2 Bonhams, Edinburgh #313
£1100 $1705 €1650 Cottage garden on a bright summer's day (29x45cm-11x18in) s. W/C. 24-Sep-2 Bonhams, Knightsbridge #170/R est:800-1200

WARD, Edgar Melville (1839-1915) American
£3226 $5000 €4839 Wood carver (46x38cm-18x15in) s. i.verso panel prov. 29-Oct-2 Sotheby's, New York #162/R est:1500-2000

WARD, Edmund F (1892-1991) American
£497 $800 €746 Young couple with books at gate (33x66cm-13x26in) s.d.1917 board. 20-Feb-3 Illustration House, New York #191/R
Works on paper
£559 $900 €839 Standing woman pointing from waters edge as businessman and laborers look on (46x28cm-18x11in) s. W/C. 20-Feb-3 Illustration House, New York #190/R

WARD, Edward Matthew (1816-1879) British
£2700 $4185 €4050 Charlotte Corday - her last toilette before her execution (75x63cm-30x25in) s.d.1862 arched top. 6-Dec-2 Lyon & Turnbull, Edinburgh #30/R est:2000-3000
£3500 $5810 €5250 Hogarths studio, 1739 Holiday visit of Foundlings to view the Portrait of Captain Coram (46x62cm-18x24in) s. 10-Jun-3 Christie's, London #119/R est:4000-6000
£10500 $16905 €15750 A year after the battle (91x71cm-36x28in) s.d.1876 arched top prov.exhib.lit. 20-Feb-3 Christie's, London #258/R est:12000

WARD, Edward Norton (1928-) American
£2259 $3750 €3276 Morning light. Drying the nets (51x41cm-20x16in) s. pair. 11-Jun-3 Butterfields, San Francisco #4072/R est:3000-5000

WARD, Edwin Arthur (fl.1883-1927) British
£450 $707 €675 Portrait of a gentleman, in a dark coat (61x51cm-24x20in) s.d.1906. 24-Jul-2 Hamptons Fine Art, Godalming #424
£1800 $2808 €2700 Portrait of Edward Taylor, in evening dress (61x51cm-24x20in) s.i.d.1905. 7-Nov-2 Christie's, Kensington #66/R est:600-800

WARD, Irene M (19/20th C) British
£580 $945 €870 Summer flowers (58x48cm-23x19in) 14-Feb-3 Lyon & Turnbull, Edinburgh #94

WARD, J (19/20th C) ?
£1500 $2430 €2250 Meeting (101x152cm-40x60in) s.d.1872. 20-May-3 Sotheby's, Olympia #267/R est:1000-2000

WARD, J H (19th C) British
£8641 $14171 €12529 Dogs, studies (53x37cm-21x15in) indis sig. 4-Jun-3 AB Stockholms Auktionsverk #2458/R est:15000-20000 (S.KR 110000)

WARD, J Stephen (1876-?) American
£481 $750 €722 Noyo Bay (51x61cm-20x24in) s.i.verso. 20-Sep-2 Freeman, Philadelphia #49/R

WARD, James (1769-1859) British
£550 $864 €825 Portrait of William Lister Fenton Scott (60x51cm-24x20in) mono. canvas on board oval. 21-Nov-2 Tennants, Leyburn #733
£1450 $2262 €2175 Study of a hare (27x44cm-11x17in) s. panel. 15-Oct-2 Bearnes, Exeter #396/R est:1500-2500
£8500 $13431 €12750 What is it (85x111cm-33x44in) indis sig. exhib. 28-Nov-2 Sotheby's, London #200/R est:10000-15000
£40000 $63200 €60000 Group portrait of Jan, Theophilius and Frances Levett, two seated on donkey (91x71cm-36x28in) s.d.1811 exhib.lit. 26-Nov-2 Christie's, London #48/R est:40000-60000
Works on paper
£2600 $4082 €3900 Studies of female figures and a child (10x14cm-4x6in) mono. pencil W/C. 21-Nov-2 Christie's, London #18/R est:1000-1500

WARD, James (attrib) (19th C) British
£320 $525 €480 Windmill in an extensive landscape (43x57cm-17x22in) 5-Jun-3 Christie's, Kensington #664

WARD, James Charles (fl.1830-1859) British
£750 $1230 €1125 Grapes, strawberries, peach, red and whitecurrants with bird's nest on a ledge (30x43cm-12x17in) init. 5-Jun-3 Christie's, Kensington #807/R
£17000 $26860 €25500 Still life of fruit, a gourd and parrot on stone ledge (71x91cm-28x36in) s.d.1855. 26-Nov-2 Christie's, London #81/R est:18000-25000

WARD, John (attrib) (fl.1808-1847) British
£400 $636 €580 Travellers in an open landscape (30x41cm-12x16in) 29-Apr-3 Gorringes, Lewes #2166

WARD, John (1917-) British
Works on paper
£260 $413 €390 Horse and trap in a London square (30x23cm-12x9in) s.d.1967 ink wash. 30-Apr-3 Halls, Shrewsbury #252
£280 $454 €420 Santiago (23x31cm-9x12in) s.i.d.21 June 89 W/C gouache. 20-May-3 Sotheby's, Olympia #130/R
£450 $693 €675 Trevi Fountain, Rome (45x59cm-18x23in) pen brush black ink W/C. 5-Sep-2 Christie's, Kensington #571/R
£800 $1248 €1200 Portrait of Isabel (69x60cm-27x24in) s.i.d.1991 pastel. 27-Mar-3 Christie's, Kensington #299

WARD, Martin Theodore (1799-1874) British
£949 $1472 €1500 Dog guarding mouse hole (44x53cm-17x21in) s. 25-Sep-2 Neumeister, Munich #771/R est:1500
£3600 $5904 €5400 Portrait of a Suffolk punch with a terrier (61x74cm-24x29in) s. 3-Jun-3 Bonhams, Knightsbridge #46/R est:2000-3000

WARD, Martin Theodore (attrib) (1799-1874) British
£700 $1162 €1015 Head of a terrier. Head of a lurcher (15x18cm-6x7in) board pair. 12-Jun-3 Christie's, Kensington #227/R

WARD, Reginald P (20th C) American
£306 $475 €459 East coast scene (30x41cm-12x16in) s. i.verso canvasboard painted c.1920. 8-Dec-2 Toomey, Oak Park #673/R

WARD, Sir Leslie (1851-1922) British
Works on paper
£4500 $7245 €6750 Caricature of William Powell Frith (30x18cm-12x7in) s.i. pencil W/C htd bodycol gum arabic prov.lit. 20-Feb-3 Christie's, London #334/R

WARD, Stephen (20th C) British
Works on paper
£700 $1099 €1050 Portrait of Christine Keeler (35x29cm-14x11in) s. black chk htd white. 10-Dec-2 Rosebery Fine Art, London #577

WARD, Velox (1901-1994) American
£1218 $1900 €1827 Texas cabin (25x36cm-10x14in) panel. 19-Oct-2 David Dike, Dallas #317/R est:1000-2000

WARD, Vernon (1905-1985) British
£450 $698 €675 Red roses (36x25cm-14x10in) s. board. 3-Dec-2 Bonhams, Knightsbridge #113/R
£450 $752 €653 Armoury (15x20cm-6x8in) s.d.34 board. 18-Jun-3 Andrew Hartley, Ilkley #1146
£500 $780 €750 Morning walk (31x39cm-12x15in) canvasboard. 6-Nov-2 Bonhams, Chester #503
£550 $913 €798 Canada geese arriving at high tide (25x34cm-10x13in) s. canvasboard. 12-Jun-3 Christie's, Kensington #141/R
£650 $1034 €975 Study of a pink rose (35x25cm-14x10in) s.d.1978 oil on paper. 26-Feb-3 Sotheby's, Olympia #257/R
£900 $1422 €1350 Light in the dale, Widgeons rising from a pool (51x61cm-20x24in) s.d.47 prov. 28-Nov-2 Christie's, Kensington #15/R
£1200 $1860 €1800 Bouquet of summer flowers in a vase (73x60cm-29x24in) s.d.1950. 3-Nov-2 Lots Road, London #343 est:600-900
£1600 $2656 €2320 October flight, Blakeney, Norfolk (56x84cm-22x33in) s.d.51 i.on stretcher. 12-Jun-3 Christie's, Kensington #142/R est:1000-1500

Works on paper
£300 $465 €450 Wisteria (23x16cm-9x6in) s. pencil W/C. 3-Dec-2 Bonhams, Knightsbridge #316
£450 $702 €675 Still life with butterflies and a spray of flowers (53x37cm-21x15in) s. mixed media. 9-Oct-2 Woolley & Wallis, Salisbury #147/R

WARD, William (jnr) (?-1935) American
£440 $700 €660 Harbour scene with fishing boats (51x91cm-20x36in) s. 22-Mar-3 New Orleans Auction, New Orleans #111

WARD-THOMPSON, Ramon (1941-) New Zealander
£932 $1416 €1398 Spit, Middle harbour, Sydney (70x90cm-28x35in) s. board. 27-Aug-2 Goodman, Sydney #34/R (A.D 2600)

WARDEN, Bill (1927-1991) American
£513 $800 €770 Portrait of Frank Reaugh (76x53cm-30x21in) paper. 19-Oct-2 David Dike, Dallas #327/R

WARDI, Rafael (1928-) Finnish
£1156 $1839 €1700 Fruit (28x32cm-11x13in) 27-Feb-3 Hagelstam, Helsinki #995 est:1700
£1345 $2125 €1950 Wanderers (29x46cm-11x18in) s.d.1964. 3-Apr-3 Hagelstam, Helsinki #919/R est:2000
£1511 $2417 €2100 Still life (36x48cm-14x19in) s. 17-May-3 Hagelstam, Helsinki #194/R est:2500
£1646 $2600 €2600 After the bath (55x46cm-22x18in) s. board. 1-Dec-2 Bukowskis, Helsinki #368/R est:2000-2200
£2230 $3568 €3100 View from Drumso (61x48cm-24x19in) s.verso. 17-May-3 Hagelstam, Helsinki #193/R est:1500
£2532 $4000 €4000 Women in the street (81x65cm-32x26in) s.d.69 verso. 1-Dec-2 Bukowskis, Helsinki #369/R est:2000-2500
£6338 $10204 €9000 Friends (116x81cm-46x32in) s. 10-May-3 Bukowskis, Helsinki #210/R est:6000-8000
£7042 $11338 €10000 Flowers (77x94cm-30x37in) exhib. 10-May-3 Bukowskis, Helsinki #239/R est:3000-4000

Works on paper
£289 $448 €460 Flowers (37x27cm-15x11in) s. W/C. 6-Oct-2 Bukowskis, Helsinki #314/R

WARDLE, Arthur (1864-1947) British
£1300 $2067 €1950 Whiting, a lobster and oysters on a ledge (60x51cm-24x20in) s.i.d.1878. 6-Mar-3 Christie's, Kensington #624/R est:1500-2000
£1840 $3000 €2760 Greyhound in a landscape (41x54cm-16x21in) s. prov. 11-Feb-3 Bonhams & Doyles, New York #167/R est:6000-8000
£2761 $4500 €4142 Exploring the forest (61x42cm-24x17in) s. 11-Feb-3 Bonhams & Doyles, New York #253/R est:5000-7000
£3000 $4890 €4500 Retrieved (61x48cm-24x19in) s. 29-Jan-3 Sotheby's, Olympia #205/R est:3000-5000
£4601 $7500 €6902 Guarding the day's bag (51x40cm-20x16in) s. 11-Feb-3 Bonhams & Doyles, New York #224/R est:3000-5000
£6500 $10271 €9750 Setters on the moors (41x50cm-16x20in) s. 2-Dec-2 Sotheby's, London #76/R est:7000-10000
£7000 $11060 €10500 Friendly welcome (77x56cm-30x22in) s. 2-Dec-2 Sotheby's, London #80/R est:7000-10000
£7200 $12024 €10440 Jack Russell terriers (26x36cm-10x14in) s. i.on stretcher. 25-Jun-3 Cheffins, Cambridge #794/R est:3500-4000
£9500 $14725 €14250 Shooting with English setters (37x52cm-15x20in) s. prov. 6-Dec-2 Lyon & Turnbull, Edinburgh #54/R est:3000-5000
£10500 $16380 €15750 Mr Dunford's champion wire haired fox terrier Barrington (46x60cm-18x24in) s. 6-Nov-2 Sotheby's, Olympia #156/R est:5000-7000
£12000 $18960 €18000 Hounds of the Leicestershire pack (36x46cm-14x18in) s. pair prov. 28-Nov-2 Christie's, Kensington #304/R est:7000-10000
£13000 $20410 €19500 Walk in the forest (76x51cm-30x20in) s. 19-Nov-2 Bonhams, New Bond Street #152/R est:7000-10000
£16000 $25760 €24000 Comforting friend in moment of grief (51x63cm-20x25in) s. prov.exhib. 20-Feb-3 Christie's, London #264/R est:12000
£16312 $25284 €24468 Silent watchers - pair of lions among rocks (87x127cm-34x50in) s. exhib. 3-Dec-2 Bukowskis, Stockholm #323/R est:80000-100000 (S.KR 230000)
£26074 $42500 €39111 Good day in the field (46x61cm-18x24in) s. 11-Feb-3 Bonhams & Doyles, New York #258/R est:20000-30000

Works on paper
£700 $1141 €1050 Springer spaniel (23x17cm-9x7in) pastel. 12-Feb-3 Bonhams, Knightsbridge #150/R
£720 $1166 €1080 Red Indian hunting buffalo (25x35cm-10x14in) s. W/C prov. 20-May-3 Sotheby's, Olympia #62/R
£900 $1404 €1350 Mermaid and polar bears (33x58cm-13x23in) s. pencil col chks. 27-Mar-3 Christie's, Kensington #43/R
£1000 $1630 €1500 Scotties (23x16cm-9x6in) pastel. 12-Feb-3 Bonhams, Knightsbridge #147/R est:600-800
£1227 $2000 €1841 English cocker spaniel (39x51cm-15x20in) s. pastel paper on board. 11-Feb-3 Bonhams & Doyles, New York #254/R est:2000-3000
£2000 $3100 €3000 Startled (39x60cm-15x24in) s. pastel. 3-Dec-2 Sotheby's, Olympia #89/R est:2000-3000
£7500 $12150 €11250 Pair of black cocker spaniels. Pair of English setters (46x30cm-18x12in) s. pastel pair. 22-May-3 Christie's, London #13/R est:6000-8000

WARDLE, Arthur (attrib) (1864-1947) British
£380 $604 €570 Head portrait of a terrier (35x25cm-14x10in) init. 27-Feb-3 Greenslade Hunt, Taunton #1301/R

WARDLE, Peter (20th C) British
Works on paper
£736 $1200 €1104 Long haired basset hound (23x39cm-9x15in) s. pastel prov. 11-Feb-3 Bonhams & Doyles, New York #228 est:800-1200

WARDLEWORTH, J L (19th C) British
£1000 $1550 €1500 Highland cattle watering (29x35cm-11x14in) s.d.1908. 2-Oct-2 George Kidner, Lymington #151/R
£1447 $2300 €2171 Scene from Othello (193x323cm-76x127in) s. 7-Mar-3 Jackson's, Cedar Falls #537/R est:500-750

WARGH, Carl (elder) (1895-1937) Finnish
£316 $494 €500 Harbour (24x35cm-9x14in) s. exhib. 12-Sep-2 Hagelstam, Helsinki #881/R
£570 $889 €900 Bridge (46x55cm-18x22in) s. exhib. 12-Sep-2 Hagelstam, Helsinki #889

WARHOL, Andy (1928-1987) American
£2302 $3776 €3200 Queen Margareth of Denmark (99x79cm-39x31in) s,num.36/40 col screenprint. 3-Jun-3 Christie's, Amsterdam #591/R est:3000-4000
£5000 $8000 €7500 Untitled (20x27cm-8x11in) acrylic pencil printed paper collage on paper in two parts. 14-May-3 Sotheby's, New York #177/R est:6000-8000
£12579 $19497 €20000 Portrait de Roy Lichtenstein (14x10cm-6x4in) s.d.1967 verso acrylic serigraph prov. 30-Oct-2 Artcurial Briest, Paris #447/R est:20000-25000
£14103 $21859 €22000 Marilyn Monroe (91x91cm-36x36in) s. verso col serigraph. 7-Dec-2 Ketterer, Hamburg #549/R est:28000-35000
£15000 $23100 €22500 Querelle (102x102cm-40x40in) acrylic silkscreen ink on board executed 1982 prov. 22-Oct-2 Sotheby's, London #467/R est:10000-15000
£17187 $27500 €25781 Clockwork panda drummer (36x28cm-14x11in) s.d.83 acrylic silkscreen on canvas. 14-May-3 Sotheby's, New York #249/R est:15000-20000
£17187 $27500 €25781 Space ship (28x36cm-11x14in) s.d.83 acrylic silkscreen on canvas prov. 14-May-3 Sotheby's, New York #250/R est:12000-18000
£18000 $29700 €26100 Ingrid Bergman, herself, the nun and with hat (96x96cm-38x38in) s.num.207/250 col silkscreen three. 1-Jul-3 Sotheby's, London #226/R est:12000-15000
£19000 $31160 €28500 Ladies and gentlemen (36x28cm-14x11in) s.overlap acrylic silkscreen. 7-Feb-3 Sotheby's, London #259/R est:18000-25000
£20312 $32500 €30468 Portrait of Jacob Weintraub (102x102cm-40x40in) s.d.86 overlap acrylic silkscreen on canvas prov. 14-May-3 Sotheby's, New York #259/R est:35000-45000
£21250 $34000 €31875 Untitled - flowers (12x12cm-5x5in) s. on overlap acrylic silkscreen on canvas painted 1965 prov. 16-May-3 Phillips, New York #160/R est:25000-35000

£21875 $35000 €32813 Portrait of Bronka Weintraub (102x102cm-40x40in) s.d.86 overlap acrylic silkscreen on canvas prov. 14-May-3 Sotheby's, New York #260/R est:35000-45000

£23438 $37500 €35157 Dollar (25x20cm-10x8in) acrylic silkscreen on canvas painted 1982 prov. 14-May-3 Sotheby's, New York #255/R est:15000-20000

£25316 $40000 €37974 Flowers (13x13cm-5x5in) s.d.1964 verso acrylic silkscreen ink on canvas prov. 13-Nov-2 Sotheby's, New York #238/R est:30000-40000

£30000 $49200 €45000 Hammer and sickle (27x43cm-11x17in) estate st.num.PA25.014 overlap acrylic silkscreen ink prov.exhib. 7-Feb-3 Sotheby's, London #260/R est:35000-45000

£31646 $50000 €47469 Hammer and sickle (25x36cm-10x14in) acrylic prov. 13-Nov-2 Sotheby's, New York #341/R est:70000-90000

£32000 $52480 €48000 Flower (51x40cm-20x16in) estate st.num.PA69.018 overlap acrylic silkscreen ink execc.1983. 7-Feb-3 Sotheby's, London #268/R est:10000-15000

£34375 $55000 €51563 Flowers (20x20cm-8x8in) s.d.64 on overlap acrylic silkscreen on canvas prov. 14-May-3 Sotheby's, New York #198/R est:30000-40000

£36250 $58000 €54375 Untitled - flowers (20x20cm-8x8in) s.d.64 verso acrylic silkscreen on canvas prov. 16-May-3 Phillips, New York #161/R est:50000-70000

£37975 $60000 €56963 Flowers (20x20cm-8x8in) init.d.64 overlap acrylic silkscreen ink prov. 13-Nov-2 Sotheby's, New York #234/R est:45000-65000

£40625 $65000 €60938 Untitled (40x30cm-16x12in) s. gold leaf ink col paper executed 1957 prov. 14-May-3 Sotheby's, New York #180/R est:70000-90000

£52000 $85280 €78000 Portrait of Pia Isadora (102x102cm-40x40in) estate st.overlap acrylic silkscreen ink exec.c.1983 prov. 7-Feb-3 Sotheby's, London #179/R est:45000-60000

£53125 $85000 €79688 Campbell's chicken noodle soup box (51x51cm-20x20in) ac silkscreen on canvas painted 1986 prov. 14-May-3 Sotheby's, New York #251/R est:50000-70000

£60000 $98400 €90000 Untitled, society portrait (102x102cm-40x40in) s.d.1980 overlap acrylic silkscreen ink prov.exhib. 7-Feb-3 Sotheby's, London #178/R est:45000-60000

£62000 $101680 €93000 Portrait of Florinda Bolkan (102x102cm-40x40in) s.d.1981 overlap acrylic silkscreen ink prov. 7-Feb-3 Sotheby's, London #177/R est:50000-70000

£62000 $101680 €93000 Portrait of Willy Brandt (102x102cm-40x40in) s.d.76 overlap acrylic silkscreen prov.exhib. 7-Feb-3 Sotheby's, London #180/R est:50000-70000

£63291 $100000 €94937 Liza (36x36cm-14x14in) s.i.d.78 on overlap acrylic silkscreen ink on canvas prov. 13-Nov-2 Sotheby's, New York #235/R est:50000-70000

£64000 $104960 €96000 Portrait of Baroness Thyssen (102x102cm-40x40in) estate st.overlap acrylic silkscreen ink prov. 7-Feb-3 Sotheby's, London #181/R est:70000-90000

£68000 $104720 €102000 Portrait of Princess Caroline of Monaco (103x102cm-41x40in) acrylic silkscreen ink on board executed 1983 prov. 22-Oct-2 Sotheby's, London #468/R est:15000-20000

£72000 $118080 €108000 Portrait of Mrs Zoppas-Sachs (102x102cm-40x40in) s.overlap acrylic silkscreen ink prov. 7-Feb-3 Sotheby's, London #176/R est:70000-90000

£75000 $123000 €112500 Michael Jackson (76x66cm-30x26in) s.d.84 overlap acrylic silkscreen ink prov. 7-Feb-3 Sotheby's, London #169/R est:40000-60000

£85000 $139400 €127500 Torso (81x66cm-32x26in) acrylic silkscreen ink painted 1977 prov.exhib. 6-Feb-3 Sotheby's, London #39/R est:120000

£98101 $155000 €147152 Three flower painting (20x61cm-8x24in) init.d.64 overlap acrylic silkscreen ink canvas prov. 13-Nov-2 Sotheby's, New York #267/R est:120000-180000

£98101 $155000 €147152 Diamond dust shoes (127x107cm-50x42in) acrylic diamond dust on canvas painted 1983 prov.lit. 13-Nov-2 Sotheby's, New York #331/R est:150000-200000

£100000 $160000 €150000 Jackie (51x41cm-20x16in) s.d.64 on overlap acrylic silkscreen on canvas prov. 14-May-3 Sotheby's, New York #191/R est:100000-150000

£105000 $175350 €152250 Ladies and gentlemen (35x28cm-14x11in) s.d.75 overlap acrylic silkscreen ink four parts prov.exhib. 26-Jun-3 Sotheby's, London #148/R est:60000-80000

£118750 $190000 €178125 Marilyn - reversal (46x36cm-18x14in) i. acrylic silkscreen on canvas painted 1979-86 prov.exhib. 15-May-3 Phillips, New York #30/R est:180000-250000

£125000 $200000 €187500 Self portrait (41x33cm-16x13in) s.d.1978 s.d.verso acrylic silkscreen on canvas prov. 14-May-3 Sotheby's, New York #199/R est:250000-350000

£125000 $208750 €187500 Cambells's Soup (183x152cm-72x60in) s.d.85 overlap acrylic silkscreen ink prov.exhib.lit. 25-Jun-3 Sotheby's, London #36/R est:100000-150000

£145000 $242150 €217500 Ladies and Gentlemen (126x101cm-50x40in) s.d.75 overlap acrylic silkscreen ink prov.exhib. 25-Jun-3 Sotheby's, London #35/R est:120000-150000

£151899 $240000 €227849 Lana (102x102cm-40x40in) s. i.d.85 overlap acrylic silkscreen ink on canvas prov.exhib. 12-Nov-2 Sotheby's, New York #22/R est:150000-200000

£177215 $280000 €265823 Penis (102x102cm-40x40in) s.d.1977 on overlap acrylic silkscreen ink pencil set of three. 13-Nov-2 Sotheby's, New York #335/R est:100000-150000

£180000 $300600 €270000 Flowers (22x22cm-9x9in) s.d.64 overlap acrylic silkscreen ink prov.exhib.lit. 25-Jun-3 Sotheby's, London #9/R est:200000-300000

£180000 $300600 €270000 Diamond dust shoes (229x179cm-90x70in) st. i.overlap acrylic silkscreen ink diamond dust prov.exhib. 25-Jun-3 Sotheby's, London #42/R est:180000-250000

£202532 $320000 €303798 Gold Jackie (51x41cm-20x16in) acrylic silkscreen ink on canvas painted 1964 prov.exhib. 12-Nov-2 Sotheby's, New York #31/R est:400000-600000

£221519 $350000 €332279 Flowers (56x56cm-22x22in) s.d.1954 on overlap acrylic silkscreen ink on canvas prov.exhib. 12-Nov-2 Sotheby's, New York #50/R est:350000-450000

£230000 $377200 €345000 Campbell's soup (183x152cm-72x60in) acrylic silkscreen ink painted 1965 prov.exhib.lit. 6-Feb-3 Sotheby's, London #37/R est:180000

£231250 $370000 €346875 Knives (229x178cm-90x70in) acrylic silkscreen ink painted 1981-82 prov.exhib. 13-May-3 Sotheby's, New York #43/R est:380000-480000

£237500 $380000 €356250 Four reversal Marilyns (91x71cm-36x28in) acrylic silkscreen ink painted 1979-86 prov. 13-May-3 Sotheby's, New York #39/R est:400000-600000

£256410 $400000 €384615 Two multicolored Marilyns (46x71cm-18x28in) s.i. acrylic silkscreen on canvas painted 1979 prov.exhib. 11-Nov-2 Phillips, New York #31/R est:300000-400000

£260000 $426400 €390000 Marilyn (46x35cm-18x14in) s.d.79-86 acrylic silkscreen ink prov. 6-Feb-3 Sotheby's, London #41/R est:120000

£291139 $460000 €436709 Flowers (61x61cm-24x24in) s.d.64 on overlap acrylic silkscreen ink pencil on canvas prov. 13-Nov-2 Sotheby's, New York #240/R est:350000-450000

£337862 $520307 €537200 Dollar sign (229x178cm-90x70in) acrylic ink painted 1981 prov. 26-Oct-2 Cornette de St.Cyr, Paris #76/R est:500000

£379747 $600000 €569621 Happy (181x150cm-71x59in) acrylic silkscreen ink on canvas executed 1968 prov.lit. 12-Nov-2 Sotheby's, New York #54/R est:500000-700000

£632911 $1000000 €949367 Self portrait (57x57cm-22x22in) s.i. on overlap acrylic silkscreen ink on canvas painted 1967 prov. 12-Nov-2 Sotheby's, New York #40/R est:1000000-1500000

£1187500 $1900000 €1781250 Four foot flowers (122x122cm-48x48in) acrylic silkscreen ink painted 1964 prov.lit. 13-May-3 Sotheby's, New York #29/R est:2000000-3000000

£1518987 $2400000 €2278481 Self portrait (203x203cm-80x80in) s.d.1986 acrylic silkscreen ink on canvas prov.exhib. 12-Nov-2 Sotheby's, New York #25/R est:220000-280000

£2658228 $4200000 €3987342 Lavender Marilyn 1 (51x41cm-20x16in) s.d.62 verso acrylic silkscreen ink on canvas prov.exhib.lit. 12-Nov-2 Sotheby's, New York #34/R est:4000000-6000000

Photographs

£1800 $2934 €2700 Santa Claus (11x8cm-4x3in) estate st.num. verso polaroid. 3-Feb-3 Sotheby's, Olympia #61/R est:2000-3000

£1899 $3000 €2849 Joseph Beuys (112x76cm-44x30in) s.num.14/15 silkscreen on cardboard executed 1980-83 prov. 12-Nov-2 Phillips, New York #265/R est:7000-9000

£3247 $5000 €4871 Arnie Schwartzenegger (11x9cm-4x4in) st. polaroid print prov.lit. 25-Oct-2 Phillips, New York #141/R est:5000-7000

£4000 $6680 €5800 Jean Michel Basquiat (11x9cm-4x4in) st.sig. num.FA05.01706 verso col Polaroid photo prov. 26-Jun-3 Sotheby's, London #262/R est:3000-4000

£5000	$8000	€7500	Self portrait - fright wig (10x10cm-4x4in) polaroid executed 1986 prov.exhib. 14-May-3 Sotheby's, New York #188/R est:8000-12000
£5696	$9000	€8544	Self portrait - fright wig (10x10cm-4x4in) polaroid executed 1986 prov.exhib. 13-Nov-2 Sotheby's, New York #264/R est:10000-15000
£6329	$10000	€9494	Untitled (55x70cm-22x28in) four stitched gelatin silver print prov. 24-Apr-3 Phillips, New York #182/R est:10000-15000
£6494	$10000	€9741	Jane Fonda (11x9cm-4x4in) st. polaroid print prov. 25-Oct-2 Phillips, New York #142/R est:5000-7000
£9494	$15000	€14241	Untitled - self portrait (20x4cm-8x2in) black white photograph prov.exhib. 13-Nov-2 Sotheby's, New York #266/R est:15000-20000
£10127	$16000	€15191	Untitled (55x70cm-22x28in) four stitched gelatin silver print prov.exhib. 24-Apr-3 Phillips, New York #181/R est:10000-15000
£11039	$17000	€16559	Untitled (54x70cm-21x28in) s.d.1986 verso gelatin silver print stitched board four prov. 25-Oct-2 Phillips, New York #158/R est:10000-15000
£12338	$19000	€18507	Untitled (55x70cm-22x28in) st.verso gelatin silver print stitched board four prov.exhib. 25-Oct-2 Phillips, New York #47/R est:12000-18000
£12658	$20000	€18987	Brooke Shields (69x55cm-27x22in) s. stitched together photographs four exhib. 23-Apr-3 Sotheby's, New York #255/R est:20000-30000
£23438	$37500	€35157	Nine daisies (91x84cm-36x33in) lenticular col photograph executed 1967-71 prov. 14-May-3 Sotheby's, New York #190/R est:20000-30000

Prints

£1740	$2750	€2610	Space fruit, apple (76x102cm-30x40in) s.num.XXI/XXX col silkscreen. 22-Apr-3 Butterfields, San Francisco #2386/R est:1000-1500
£1800	$2934	€2700	Gee, merrie shoes (23x20cm-9x8in) estate st. offset lithograph. 3-Feb-3 Sotheby's, Olympia #51/R est:3000-4000
£1887	$3000	€2831	After the party (55x77cm-22x30in) s.num.631/1000 col screenprint. 4-Mar-3 Swann Galleries, New York #619/R est:2000-3000
£1899	$3000	€2849	Muhammad Ali (102x76cm-40x30in) s.num.52/150 col silkscreen. 22-Apr-3 Butterfields, San Francisco #2384/R est:3000-4000
£2000	$3120	€3000	Camouflage (96x96cm-38x38in) s.num.64/80 col silkscreen. 25-Mar-3 Sotheby's, London #230/R est:1500-2000
£2000	$3300	€2900	Hammer and sickle (76x102cm-30x40in) s.num.50/50 col silkscreen. 1-Jul-3 Sotheby's, London #214/R est:2500-3000
£2044	$3250	€3066	Paolo Uccello, St George and the dragon (67x95cm-26x37in) s.num.37/50 col screenprint. 2-May-3 Sotheby's, New York #661/R est:2000-3000
£2083	$3313	€3000	Reigning queens, Queen Ntombi Twala, reine du Swaziland (100x80cm-39x31in) s.num.R 3/30 col serigraph museum board Royal edition. 29-Apr-3 Artcurial Briest, Paris #415/R est:3000-3500
£2144	$3345	€3216	Queen Margrethe II (100x80cm-39x31in) s.num.PP5/5 serigraph in col. 11-Nov-2 Rasmussen, Vejle #139/R est:25000-30000 (D.KR 25000)
£2152	$3400	€3228	Jimmy carter II (97x74cm-38x29in) s.num.6/100 silkscreen. 1-Dec-2 Susanin's, Chicago #5143/R est:3000-5000
£2158	$3540	€3000	Neuschwanstein (85x60cm-33x24in) s.i. col silkscreen. 6-Jun-3 Ketterer, Munich #176/R est:4000-4500
£2183	$3428	€3275	From 'Ladies and Gentlemen' (110x72cm-43x28in) s.d.75 verso col serigraph. 23-Nov-2 Burkhard, Luzern #215/R est:5000-6000 (S.FR 5000)
£2215	$3500	€3323	Sam (35x25cm-14x10in) i.verso lithograph executed c.1955. 12-Nov-2 Phillips, New York #258/R est:4000-6000
£2222	$3667	€3200	Perrier (77x53cm-30x21in) bears st.verso col screenprint. 2-Jul-3 Artcurial Briest, Paris #95/R est:3500-4000
£2302	$3776	€3200	Cow (71x115cm-28x45in) s. col screenprint. 3-Jun-3 Christie's, Amsterdam #590/R est:1500-1800
£2372	$3676	€3700	Sunset (86x96cm-34x38in) s.d.1972 verso num.27/40 col silk screen board. 7-Dec-2 Van Ham, Cologne #587/R est:4500
£2374	$3894	€3300	Electric chair (90x121cm-35x48in) s.i.d. verso col silkscreen. 6-Jun-3 Ketterer, Munich #169/R est:2500-3000
£2400	$3720	€3600	Mao (102x75cm-40x30in) s. col silkscreen. 5-Dec-2 Sotheby's, London #243/R est:1200-1500
£2400	$3744	€3600	Camouflage (96x96cm-38x38in) s.i.num.25/80 col silkscreen. 25-Mar-3 Sotheby's, London #232/R est:2000-2500
£2405	$3800	€3800	Electric chair (90x122cm-35x48in) s.num.198/250 col serigraph prov.lit. 27-Nov-2 Tajan, Paris #138/R
£2420	$3800	€3630	In her sweet little Alice blue shoes (25x35cm-10x14in) s. hand col W/C offset lithograph. 21-Nov-2 Swann Galleries, New York #218/R est:4000-6000
£2436	$3776	€3800	Queen Margareth of Denmark, from reigning queens (99x79cm-39x31in) s.num.12/40 col screenprint. 3-Dec-2 Christie's, Amsterdam #518/R est:3000-4000
£2500	$4050	€3800	Queen Beatrix, from reigning queens (100x80cm-39x31in) col screenprint lit. 21-Jan-3 Christie's, Amsterdam #518 est:3000-5000
£2500	$4125	€3625	Campbell's Soup II, old fashioned vegetable (89x58cm-35x23in) s.num.75/250 verso col silkscreen. 1-Jul-3 Sotheby's, London #224/R est:2500-3500
£2516	$4000	€3774	When I'm calling shoe (24x34cm-9x13in) s. photolithograph hand col W/C. 3-Mar-3 Swann Galleries, New York #93/R est:4000-6000
£2532	$4000	€4000	Electric chair (90x122cm-35x48in) s.num.APXIV/L col serigraph prov.lit. 27-Nov-2 Tajan, Paris #137/R
£2532	$4000	€4000	Electric chair (90x121cm-35x48in) s.d.1971 screenprint. 26-Nov-2 Sotheby's, Amsterdam #407/R est:2500-3500
£2532	$4000	€3798	Hammer and sickle (77x102cm-30x40in) s.num.25/50 col silkscreen. 22-Apr-3 Butterfields, San Francisco #2383/R est:4000-5000
£2564	$4000	€3846	New England Clam Chowder (89x58cm-35x23in) s.num.177/250 col silkscreen. 14-Oct-2 Butterfields, San Francisco #1377/R est:3000-5000
£2564	$4000	€3846	Santa Claus (97x97cm-38x38in) s.num.132/200 col screenprint diamond dust board. 5-Nov-2 Christie's, Rockefeller NY #516/R est:3000-5000
£2600	$4186	€3770	Marilyn (82x82cm-32x32in) screenprint. 12-May-3 Joel, Victoria #225/R est:1000-2000 (A.D 6500)
£2600	$4030	€3900	Tomato beef noodle O's (89x59cm-35x23in) s.num.246/250 col screenprint. 3-Dec-2 Christie's, London #238/R est:3000-5000
£2600	$4030	€3900	Sunset (86x86cm-34x34in) s.d.1972 verso num.334/470 col screenprint. 3-Dec-2 Christie's, London #239/R est:2000-3000
£2600	$4030	€3900	Dollar (27x18cm-11x7in) col screenprint executed c.1982. 3-Dec-2 Christie's, London #241a/R est:2800-3200
£2621	$4036	€3932	Brooklyn Bridge (100x100cm-39x39in) s.num.58/200 serigraph. 27-Oct-2 Anders Antik, Landskrona #549/R est:35000-40000 (S.KR 38000)
£2662	$4205	€3993	The nun - From Ingrid Bergman (96x96cm-38x38in) s.num.107/250 col silkscreen lit. 28-Apr-3 Bukowskis, Stockholm #527/R est:40000-45000 (S.KR 35000)
£2675	$4200	€4013	Self portrait (58x58cm-23x23in) s.num.251/300 verso silver coated offset lithograph. 21-Nov-2 Swann Galleries, New York #220/R est:4000-6000
£2688	$4085	€4032	Queen Margrethe II of Denmark (100x80cm-39x31in) s.num.40/40 col screenprint. 28-Aug-2 Deutscher-Menzies, Melbourne #291/R est:8000-12000 (A.D 7500)
£2715	$4534	€3937	Campbell's soup II. New England clam chowder (89x58cm-35x23in) s. verso col serigraph. 24-Jun-3 Koller, Zurich #514/R est:6000-9000 (S.FR 6000)
£2799	$4450	€4199	Queen Margrethe - from the series Reigning Queens. s.num.38/40 col serigraph. 29-Apr-3 Kunsthallen, Copenhagen #385/R est:35000 (D.KR 30000)
£2800	$4620	€4060	Mao (101x75cm-40x30in) s. col silkscreen. 1-Jul-3 Sotheby's, London #217/R est:1500-2000
£2830	$4500	€4245	Black bean (81x78cm-32x31in) s.num.182/250 col screenprint. 29-Apr-3 Christie's, Rockefeller NY #763/R est:5000-7000
£2838	$4456	€4257	Vote McGovern (107x107cm-42x42in) s.i. verso num.165/250 col serigraph. 23-Nov-2 Burkhard, Luzern #113/R est:7000-10000 (S.FR 6500)
£2884	$4500	€4326	Cow (116x76cm-46x30in) s. col silkscreen. 14-Oct-2 Butterfields, San Francisco #1378 est:1000-2000
£2893	$4600	€4340	Sarah Bernhardt (102x81cm-40x32in) s.num.187/200 col screenprint. 1-May-3 Swann Galleries, New York #619/R est:3000-5000
£2987	$4750	€4481	Vesuvius. s.num.132/250 col screenprint. 2-May-3 Sotheby's, New York #664/R est:3500-4500
£3000	$4680	€4500	Camouflage (96x96cm-38x38in) s.i. col silkscreen. 25-Mar-3 Sotheby's, London #231/R est:1500-2000
£3041	$4743	€4562	Queen Margrethe. s.num.8/40 col serigraph. 18-Sep-2 Kunsthallen, Copenhagen #358/R est:40000 (D.KR 36000)
£3200	$4928	€4800	Vesuvius (80x100cm-31x39in) s.num.16/250 col screenprint. 24-Oct-2 Christie's, Kensington #399/R est:2000-3000
£3200	$4960	€4800	Jackie I (53x42cm-21x17in) s.num.200 silkscreen printed in silver. 5-Dec-2 Sotheby's, London #233/R est:2500-3000
£3200	$4992	€4800	Jackie I (61x50cm-24x20in) s.num.62/200 silkscreen. 25-Mar-3 Sotheby's, London #215/R est:1500-2000
£3200	$4992	€4800	Kiku (50x66cm-20x26in) s.num.187/300 col silkscreen. 25-Mar-3 Sotheby's, London #233/R est:2000-2500
£3200	$4992	€4800	Kiku (50x66cm-20x26in) s.num.187/300 col silkscreen. 25-Mar-3 Sotheby's, London #234/R est:2000-2500
£3205	$5032	€5000	Electric chair (90x122cm-35x48in) s.d.1971 verso num.7/250 serigraph. 21-Nov-2 Finarte, Rome #94/R
£3205	$4968	€5000	Campbell's soup II (89x58cm-35x23in) s.i.verso col serigraph exec.1969 lit. 4-Dec-2 Finarte, Milan #175/R
£3243	$5222	€4865	Beef soup, from Campbell's Soup I (81x47cm-32x19in) s.num.151/250 verso col silkscreen lit. 7-May-3 AB Stockholms Auktionsverk #1279/R est:25000-30000 (S.KR 42000)

£3275 $4782 €4913 The Nun, from 'Ingrid Bergman' (96x96cm-38x38in) col serigraph lit. 4-Jun-2 Germann, Zurich #522/R est:6500-8500 (S.FR 7500)
£3459 $5500 €5189 Hot dog bean (89x58cm-35x23in) s.num.41/250 col screenprint. 2-May-3 Sotheby's, New York #647/R est:5000-7000
£3459 $5500 €5189 Ingrid Bergman, the nun (96x96cm-38x38in) s.num.243/250 col screenprint. 2-May-3 Sotheby's, New York #60/R est:6000-8000
£3493 $5100 €5240 Scotch Broth, from 'Campbell's Soup II' (88x59cm-35x23in) s. col serigraph lit. 4-Jun-2 Germann, Zurich #527/R est:6500-8000 (S.FR 8000)
£3500 $5460 €5250 Ingrid Bergman, the nun (96x96cm-38x38in) s.i. col silkscreen. 10-Oct-2 Sotheby's, London #283/R est:3000-4000
£3500 $5425 €5250 Cowboys and Indians, Indian head nickel (91x91cm-36x36in) s.num.210/250 col silkscreen. 5-Dec-2 Sotheby's, London #239/R est:1500-2000
£3500 $5425 €5250 Ingrid Bergman, the nun (96x96cm-38x38in) s.num.118/250 col silkscreen. 5-Dec-2 Sotheby's, London #247/R est:2000-3000
£3500 $5460 €5250 Cow (115x71cm-45x28in) s.d.1966 num.146 verso col silkscreen. 25-Mar-3 Sotheby's, London #221/R est:3000-4000
£3504 $5466 €5256 The nun - from Ingrid Bergman (96x96cm-38x38in) s.num.143/250 col silkscreen lit. 5-Nov-2 Bukowskis, Stockholm #662/R est:50000-60000 (S.KR 50000)
£3526 $5465 €5500 Campbell's soup I (89x58cm-35x23in) s.num.95/250 col screenprint. 3-Dec-2 Christie's, Amsterdam #516/R est:2500-3500
£3718 $5800 €5577 Uncle Sam (97x97cm-38x38in) s.num.132/200 col screenprint diamond dust board. 5-Nov-2 Christie's, Rockefeller NY #513/R est:3000-5000
£3768 $6180 €5200 Vesuvius (80x100cm-31x39in) s.i. col serigraph board. 28-May-3 Lempertz, Koln #466/R est:4000
£3774 $6000 €5661 Vegetarian vegetable (89x58cm-35x23in) s.num.42/250 col screenprint. 2-May-3 Sotheby's, New York #645/R est:5000-7000
£3774 $6000 €5661 Sunset (89x117cm-35x46in) s.i.indis.d.verso col screenprint exec.c.1972. 2-May-3 Sotheby's, New York #651/R est:2000-3000
£3784 $5903 €5676 Goethe (96x96cm-38x38in) s.num.64/100 col silkscreen. 5-Nov-2 Bukowskis, Stockholm #660/R est:50000-70000 (S.KR 54000)
£3797 $6000 €5696 Gee, Merrie shoes (23x20cm-9x8in) s.i. hand col offset lithograph executed c.1957 prov. 13-Nov-2 Sotheby's, New York #233/R est:10000-15000
£3800 $5928 €5700 Ingrid Bergman, the nun (96x96cm-38x38in) s.i. col silkscreen. 10-Oct-2 Sotheby's, London #285/R est:2500-3500
£3800 $6232 €5700 Untitled, red shoe (25x35cm-10x14in) estate st.num.PM29.0031 verso offset lithograph W/C exec.c.1957. 7-Feb-3 Sotheby's, London #251/R est:4000-6000
£3800 $5928 €5700 Myths mammy (96x96cm-38x38in) s.num.13/30 silkscreen diamond dust. 25-Mar-3 Sotheby's, London #210/R est:2500-3500
£3822 $6000 €5733 Flowers (91x91cm-36x36in) s.num.203/250 verso col lithograph. 20-Nov-2 Boos Gallery, Michigan #467/R est:4000-5000
£3871 $6000 €5807 Jacqueline Kennedy I (61x51cm-24x20in) signed with rubber stamp silver screenprint. 25-Sep-2 Christie's, Rockefeller NY #430/R est:4000-6000
£4000 $6160 €6000 Sam (35x24cm-14x9in) s.i. num.pm06.0052 verso offset lithograph W/C executed c.1956 pro. 22-Oct-2 Sotheby's, London #456/R est:4000-6000
£4000 $6200 €6000 Cow (117x75cm-46x30in) s. col silkscreen. 5-Dec-2 Sotheby's, London #241/R est:2000-2500
£4000 $6240 €6000 Jackie II (61x76cm-24x30in) st.sig.num.122/200 col silkscreen. 25-Mar-3 Sotheby's, London #214/R est:2000-2500
£4000 $6680 €5800 Love (76x56cm-30x22in) estate st.num.121C UT.002 verso silkscreen print prov. 26-Jun-3 Sotheby's, London #269/R est:4000-6000
£4088 $6500 €6132 Onion (89x59cm-35x23in) s.num.151/250 verso col screenprint. 2-May-3 Sotheby's, New York #643/R est:5000-7000
£4088 $6500 €6132 Chicken 'n dumplings (89x58cm-35x23in) s.num.42/250 col screenprint. 2-May-3 Sotheby's, New York #646/R est:5000-7000
£4166 $6500 €6249 Liz (59x59cm-23x23in) s.d. col offset lithograph. 14-Oct-2 Butterfields, San Francisco #1374/R est:3000-5000
£4167 $6500 €6251 Ingrid Bergman as the nun (97x97cm-38x38in) s.num.3/30 col screenprint board. 5-Nov-2 Christie's, Rockefeller NY #524/R est:4500-6500
£4167 $6500 €6251 Ingrid Bergman as the nun (97x97cm-38x38in) s.num.1/30 col screenprint board. 5-Nov-2 Christie's, Rockefeller NY #525/R est:4500-6500
£4167 $6500 €6251 Ingrid Bergman as the nun (97x97cm-38x38in) s.num.14/30 col screenprint board. 5-Nov-2 Christie's, Rockefeller NY #526/R est:4500-6500
£4200 $6510 €6300 Ingrid Bergman (96x96cm-38x38in) s.num.42/250 col screenprint. 3-Dec-2 Christie's, London #241/R est:3500-4500
£4200 $6552 €6300 Flowers (58x58cm-23x23in) s.d.1964 col offset lithograph. 10-Oct-2 Sotheby's, London #281/R est:3000-4000
£4200 $6552 €6300 Red Lenin (100x74cm-39x29in) s.num.84.120 col silkscreen. 25-Mar-3 Sotheby's, London #216/R est:3000-4000
£4236 $6693 €6100 Liz (59x59cm-23x23in) s.d. col offset lithograph edition of 300. 26-Apr-3 Cornette de St.Cyr, Paris #102/R est:4000-6000
£4300 $6708 €6450 Reigning Queens, Queen Elizabeth II of the United Kingdom (100x80cm-39x31in) s.i. col silkscreen. 10-Oct-2 Sotheby's, London #287/R est:3000-4000
£4317 $7079 €6000 Queen Beatrix (99x79cm-39x31in) s.i.num.11/30 col screenprint. 3-Jun-3 Christie's, Amsterdam #589/R est:8000-12000
£4345 $6778 €6518 Mao (91x91cm-36x36in) s.st.num.86/250 verso col silkscreen lit. 5-Nov-2 Bukowskis, Stockholm #657/R est:50000-70000 (S.KR 62000)
£4403 $7000 €6605 Scotch broth (89x58cm-35x23in) s.num.42/250 col screenprint. 2-May-3 Sotheby's, New York #644/R est:5000-7000
£4403 $7000 €6605 Tomato-beef noodle (89x58cm-35x23in) s.num.42/250 col screenprint. 2-May-3 Sotheby's, New York #648/R est:5000-7000
£4430 $7000 €7000 Ingrid Bergman. The nun (96x96cm-38x38in) s.num.117/250 two col silkscreen. 26-Nov-2 Sotheby's, Amsterdam #406a est:6400-7400
£4500 $7425 €6525 Flowers (91x91cm-36x36in) s.num.45/250 verso col silkscreen. 1-Jul-3 Sotheby's, London #227/R est:3000-4000
£4500 $7515 €6525 Polo player (80x59cm-31x23in) estate st.num.40.06 verso silkscreen prov. 26-Jun-3 Sotheby's, London #268/R est:4000-6000
£4516 $7000 €6774 Portraits of the artists, from Ten from Leo Castelli (51x51cm-20x20in) init.num.176/200 col screenprint. 25-Sep-2 Christie's, Rockefeller NY #432/R est:5000-7000
£4552 $7010 €6828 Indian head Nickel - from Cowboys and Indians (91x91cm-36x36in) s.num.TP 34/36 serigraph. 27-Oct-2 Anders Antik, Landskrona #555/R est:40000-50000 (S.KR 66000)
£4615 $7200 €6923 Witch (97x97cm-38x38in) s.num.132/200 verso col screenprint diamond dust board. 5-Nov-2 Christie's, Rockefeller NY #514/R est:4500-6500
£4625 $7215 €6938 Herself - from Ingrid Bergman (96x96cm-38x38in) s.num.143/250 col silkscreen lit. 5-Nov-2 Bukowskis, Stockholm #661/R est:50000-70000 (S.KR 66000)
£4800 $7488 €7200 Ingrid Bergman, herself (96x96cm-38x38in) s.i. col silkscreen. 10-Oct-2 Sotheby's, London #284/R est:3500-4500
£4800 $7488 €7200 Ingrid Bergman, herself (96x96cm-38x38in) s.i. col silkscreen. 10-Oct-2 Sotheby's, London #286/R est:3000-4000
£4800 $7488 €7200 Campbells soup II (90x58cm-35x23in) s.num.100/250 col silkscreen. 25-Mar-3 Sotheby's, London #226/R est:2500-3500
£4808 $7500 €7212 African elephant (97x97cm-38x38in) s.num.120/150 col screenprint board. 5-Nov-2 Christie's, Rockefeller NY #518/R est:3000-5000
£4905 $7652 €7358 Details of Renaissance Paintings - Sandro Botticelli, Birth of Venus (63x94cm-25x37in) s.num.36/70 col serigraph 1984 lit. 6-Nov-2 AB Stockholms Auktionsverk #1071/R est:50000-60000 (S.KR 70000)
£4965 $8043 €7000 Truck (100x100cm-39x39in) s. col silkscreen board. 24-May-3 Van Ham, Cologne #627/R est:7500
£5000 $7700 €7500 Frolunda hockey player (101x81cm-40x32in) estate st. s.verso silkscreen print on paper executed 1986 prov. 22-Oct-2 Sotheby's, London #328/R est:5000-7000
£5000 $7700 €7500 Shoe (66x50cm-26x20in) estate st. num.pm16.0321 verso offset lithograph W/C exec.c 1957. 22-Oct-2 Sotheby's, London #457/R est:5000-7000
£5000 $7750 €7500 Mao (91x91cm-36x36in) s.num.13/50 col silkscreen. 5-Dec-2 Sotheby's, London #232/R est:5000-7000
£5000 $7800 €7500 Flowers (91x91cm-36x36in) s.num.77/250 silkscreen. 25-Mar-3 Sotheby's, London #207/R est:4000-6000
£5000 $8250 €7250 Myths, mammy (96x96cm-38x38in) s.num.21/30 col silkscreen diamond dust. 1-Jul-3 Sotheby's, London #228/R est:4000-5000
£5000 $8350 €7250 Sam (35x25cm-14x10in) s.i.num.PM06.0080 verso col lt. 24-Jun-3 Sotheby's, Olympia #59/R est:2000-3000
£5031 $8000 €7547 Witch (97x97cm-38x38in) s.num.142/200 verso col screenprint diamond dust Museum board. 29-Apr-3 Christie's, Rockefeller NY #769/R est:5000-7000
£5128 $8000 €7692 Tomato soup (89x58cm-35x23in) s.num.71/250 verso col screenprint. 5-Nov-2 Christie's, Rockefeller NY #505/R est:6000-8000
£5128 $8000 €7692 Howdy doody (97x97cm-38x38in) s.num.132/200 col screenprint diamond dust board. 5-Nov-2 Christie's, Rockefeller NY #515/R est:6000-8000
£5171 $8170 €7757 From - Details of Renaissance paintings - Sandro Botticelli, Birth of Venus (63x94cm-25x37in) s.num.48/70 col silkscreen lit. 28-Apr-3 Bukowskis, Stockholm #529/R est:60000-70000 (S.KR 68000)
£5200 $8008 €7800 After the party (54x77cm-21x30in) estate st. num.0785 silkscreen print executed 1979 prov. 22-Oct-2 Sotheby's, London #464/R est:4000-6000
£5200 $8060 €7800 Ingrid Bergman, with hat (96x96cm-38x38in) s.num.118/250 col silkscreen. 5-Dec-2 Sotheby's, London #248/R est:2500-3000

£5200 $8112 €7800 Mao (91x91cm-36x36in) s.num.15/50 col silkscreen. 25-Mar-3 Sotheby's, London #208/R est:5000-7000
£5253 $8195 €7880 Mick Jagger (111x73cm-44x29in) s.num.30/50 col silkscreen also signed by Mick Jagger. 11-Nov-2 Stephan Welz, Johannesburg #443/R est:60000-90000 (SA.R 82000)
£5346 $8500 €8019 Shoe of the evening, beautiful shoe (25x35cm-10x14in) photolithograph hand col W/C. 3-Mar-3 Swann Galleries, New York #94/R est:8000-12000
£5346 $8500 €8019 Electric chair (90x121cm-35x48in) s.d.num.43/250 verso col screenprint. 2-May-3 Sotheby's, New York #649/R est:5000-7000
£5346 $8500 €8019 Black Rhinoceros (244x244cm-96x96in) s.d.1983 num.25/150 col screenprint. 30-Apr-3 Doyle, New York #317/R est:4000-6000
£5380 $8392 €8500 Red Lenin (100x75cm-39x30in) col serigraph. 18-Oct-2 Dr Fritz Nagel, Stuttgart #644/R est:9000
£5380 $8500 €8500 Cow 1976 (116x75cm-46x30in) s. col serigraph. 30-Nov-2 Villa Grisebach, Berlin #431/R est:4000-4500
£5449 $8500 €8174 Campbell's soup (229x142cm-90x56in) num.12/20 felt. 30-Mar-3 Susanin's, Chicago #6057/R est:6000-8000
£5449 $8500 €8174 Liz (59x59cm-23x23in) s.d.67 col offset lithograph. 5-Nov-2 Christie's, Rockefeller NY #498/R est:7000-9000
£5449 $8500 €8174 Ingrid Bergman as herself (97x97cm-38x38in) s.num.16/30 col screenprint board. 5-Nov-2 Christie's, Rockefeller NY #520/R est:4500-6500
£5449 $8500 €8174 Ingrid Bergman as herself (97x97cm-38x38in) s.num.8/30 col screenprint board. 5-Nov-2 Christie's, Rockefeller NY #521/R est:4500-6500
£5449 $8500 €8174 Ingrid Bergman as herself (97x97cm-38x38in) s.num.1/30 col screenprint board. 5-Nov-2 Christie's, Rockefeller NY #522/R est:5000-7000
£5449 $8500 €8174 Ingrid Bergman as herself (97x97cm-38x38in) s.num.5/30 col screenprint board. 5-Nov-2 Christie's, Rockefeller NY #523/R est:6000-8000
£5500 $8525 €8250 Jean Cocteau (80x58cm-31x23in) estate st.num.up.41.30 verso screenprint. 5-Dec-2 Christie's, Kensington #220/R est:6000-8000
£5500 $8580 €8250 Flowers (91x91cm-36x36in) s.num.75/250 col silkscreen. 25-Mar-3 Sotheby's, London #206/R est:4000-6000
£5500 $8580 €8250 Reigning queen Elizabeth II of United Kingdom (100x80cm-39x31in) s.num.3/40 col silkscreen. 25-Mar-3 Sotheby's, London #217/R est:3000-4000
£5500 $8580 €8250 Mumammad (102x76cm-40x30in) s.num.39/150 col silkscreen. 25-Mar-3 Sotheby's, London #220/R est:2500-3500
£5500 $9075 €7975 Mao (91x91cm-36x36in) s.num.185/250 col silkscreen. 1-Jul-3 Sotheby's, London #213/R est:5000-7000
£5500 $9075 €7975 Red Lenin (100x74cm-39x29in) num.33/120 col silkscreen. 1-Jul-3 Sotheby's, London #216/R est:5000-7000
£5627 $8891 €8441 From - Details of Renaissance paintings - Sandro Botticelli, Birth of Venus (63x94cm-25x37in) s.num.48/70 col silkscreen lit. 28-Apr-3 Bukowskis, Stockholm #528/R est:60000-70000 (S.KR 74000)
£5660 $9000 €8490 John Wayne (91x91cm-36x36in) s.i. col screenprint Lennox Museum board. 29-Apr-3 Christie's, Rockefeller NY #771/R est:8000-10000
£5660 $9000 €8490 Witch (97x96cm-38x38in) s.num.127/200 verso col screenprint diamond dust. 2-May-3 Sotheby's, New York #656/R est:6000-8000
£5696 $9000 €8544 Flowers (92x92cm-36x36in) s.d.1970 num.75/250 col silkscreen. 22-Apr-3 Butterfields, San Francisco #2377/R est:6000-8000
£5755 $9439 €8000 Queen Beatrix (100x40cm-39x16in) s.num.32/40 screenprint. 3-Jun-3 Christie's, Amsterdam #588/R est:8000-12000
£5769 $9000 €8654 Ingrid Berman as herself (97x97cm-38x38in) Sun. 6/30 col screenprint board. 5-Nov-2 Christie's, Rockefeller NY #519/R est:4500-6500
£5932 $9372 €8898 9 US dollars (102x81cm-40x32in) s.num.24/35 col silkscreen lit. 28-Apr-3 Bukowskis, Stockholm #525/R est:60000-70000 (S.KR 78000)
£6000 $9840 €9000 Torso, double (77x109cm-30x43in) estate st.num.UP56.03 verso silkscreen print diamond dust prov. 7-Feb-3 Sotheby's, London #269/R est:5000-7000
£6000 $9360 €9000 Ingrid Bergman (96x96cm-38x38in) s.num.9/30 col silkscreen. 25-Mar-3 Sotheby's, London #229/R est:2500-3000
£6000 $9900 €8700 Mao (91x91cm-36x36in) s.i.num.39/50 verso col screenprint. 2-Jul-3 Christie's, London #216/R est:5000-7000
£6013 $9500 €9020 Mao (92x92cm-36x36in) s.num.225/250 col silkscreen. 22-Apr-3 Butterfields, San Francisco #2378/R est:7000-9000
£6028 $9766 €8500 Cologne Cathedral (100x80cm-39x31in) s. silkscreen board. 24-May-3 Van Ham, Cologne #626/R est:9500
£6090 $9500 €9135 Mao (91x91cm-36x36in) s.num.172/250 verso col screenprint. 5-Nov-2 Christie's, Rockefeller NY #507/R est:9000-12000
£6282 $9800 €9423 Ingrid Bergman with hat (97x97cm-38x38in) s.num.7/30 col screenprint board. 5-Nov-2 Christie's, Rockefeller NY #528/R est:6000-8000
£6289 $10000 €9434 Flowers (56x56cm-22x22in) s.d. col offset lithograph. 29-Apr-3 Christie's, Rockefeller NY #758/R est:3000-5000
£6289 $10000 €9434 Mao (91x91cm-36x36in) s.num.160/250 verso col screenprint. 29-Apr-3 Christie's, Rockefeller NY #766/R est:5000-7000
£6289 $10000 €9434 Mao (91x91cm-36x36in) s.num.75/250 col screenprint. 2-May-3 Sotheby's, New York #652/R est:7000-9000
£6410 $10000 €9615 Ingrid Bergman with hat (97x97cm-38x38in) s.num.10/30 col screenprint board. 5-Nov-2 Christie's, Rockefeller NY #527/R est:5000-7000
£6410 $10000 €9615 Sandro Botticelli, birth of Venus (82x116cm-32x46in) s.num.31/70 col screenprint. 5-Nov-2 Christie's, Rockefeller NY #529/R est:4500-6500
£6500 $10075 €9750 Mao (91x91cm-36x36in) s.num.13/50 col silkscreen. 5-Dec-2 Sotheby's, London #231/R est:5000-7000
£6500 $10140 €9750 Cowboys and Indians, mother and child (91x91cm-36x36in) s.i. col silkscreen. 25-Mar-3 Sotheby's, London #228/R est:2000-3000
£6604 $10500 €9906 Liz (59x59cm-23x23in) s.d.1965 offset col lithograph. 1-May-3 Swann Galleries, New York #618/R est:5000-8000
£6800 $10608 €10200 Mao (91x91cm-36x36in) s.num.112/250 col silkscreen. 10-Oct-2 Sotheby's, London #282/R est:4000-5000
£6800 $11152 €10200 Untitled, shoe (66x51cm-26x20in) estate st.num.PM16.0315 verso offset lithograph W/C exec.c.1957. 7-Feb-3 Sotheby's, London #255/R est:4000-6000
£6918 $11000 €10377 Oyster stew (81x48cm-32x19in) s.num.104/250 col screenprint. 29-Apr-3 Christie's, Rockefeller NY #764/R est:5000-7000
£6970 $11013 €10455 Indian head Nickel (90x90cm-35x35in) s.num.TP 34/36 col serigraph lit. 1-Apr-3 Rasmussen, Copenhagen #421/R est:75000 (D.KR 75000)
£7000 $11690 €10150 Untitled, fish (108x77cm-43x30in) estate.st.num.23.55 verso silkscreen prov. 26-Jun-3 Sotheby's, London #256/R est:4000-6000
£7143 $11357 €10500 Jean Cocteau (80x59cm-31x23in) serigraph exec.1983 lit. 24-Mar-3 Cornette de St.Cyr, Paris #97/R est:12000
£7400 $11470 €11100 Mick Jagger (110x74cm-43x29in) s.num.21/250 silkscreen. 5-Dec-2 Sotheby's, London #234/R est:4000-6000
£7500 $11625 €11250 Flash November 22 (54x54cm-21x21in) s.num.9 screenprints set of 11. 3-Dec-2 Christie's, London #237/R est:5000-7000
£7595 $12000 €11393 Sam (36x25cm-14x10in) s.i. handcol offset lithograph executed c.1955 prov. 13-Nov-2 Sotheby's, New York #230/R est:10000-15000
£7595 $12000 €12000 Lenin (100x75cm-39x30in) s. col serigraph. 30-Nov-2 Villa Grisebach, Berlin #430/R est:11000-13000
£7692 $12000 €11538 Marilyn (91x91cm-36x36in) init.d.num.74/250 verso col screenprint. 5-Nov-2 Christie's, Rockefeller NY #501/R est:15000-20000
£7800 $12168 €11700 Marilyn (90x90cm-35x35in) s.num.153/250 col silkscreen. 25-Mar-3 Sotheby's, London #209/R est:8000-10000
£8500 $13260 €12750 Mick Jagger (110x74cm-43x29in) s.num.184/250 col silkscreen. 25-Mar-3 Sotheby's, London #219/R est:5000-7000
£8654 $13500 €12981 Flash-November 22 1963, Briarcliff Manor, New York (53x53cm-21x21in) s.num. col screenprints set of 11. 5-Nov-2 Christie's, Rockefeller NY #504/R est:12000-18000
£8800 $14432 €13200 Love (80x60cm-31x24in) estate st.num.UT.014 verso silkscreen prov. 7-Feb-3 Sotheby's, London #166/R est:4000-6000
£8805 $14000 €13208 Anniversary Donald Duck (78x109cm-31x43in) s.num.6/30 col screenprint. 29-Apr-3 Christie's, Rockefeller NY #770/R est:14000-18000
£8917 $14000 €13376 Marilyn Monroe (91x91cm-36x36in) s.num.140/250 verso col screenprint. 21-Nov-2 Swann Galleries, New York #221/R est:10000-15000
£9000 $13950 €13500 Dollar (50x40cm-20x16in) num.7/15 col silkscreen. 5-Dec-2 Sotheby's, London #240/R est:4000-6000
£9110 $14212 €13665 Marilyn Monroe (91x91cm-36x36in) s.st.num.231/250 verso col silkscreen. 5-Nov-2 Bukowskis, Stockholm #655/R est:150000-200000 (S.KR 130000)
£9434 $15000 €14151 Jackie III (102x76cm-40x30in) artist st.num.SLIV col screenprint. 29-Apr-3 Christie's, Rockefeller NY #759/R est:4000-5000
£9615 $14904 €15000 Marilyn Monroe - Marilyn (91x91cm-36x36in) mono.d.1967 verso col serigraph. 6-Dec-2 Hauswedell & Nolte, Hamburg #389/R est:12000
£9800 $16072 €14700 Polo player (76x62cm-30x24in) estate st.num.UP 40.04 verso silkscreen prov. 7-Feb-3 Sotheby's, London #167/R est:4000-6000
£10000 $15500 €15000 Marilyn Monroe (91x91cm-36x36in) init.d.1967 col screenprint. 3-Dec-2 Christie's, London #236/R est:12000-18000
£10000 $15600 €15000 Moonwalk (96x96cm-38x38in) st.sig.num.52/160 col silkscreen. 25-Mar-3 Sotheby's, London #211/R est:7000-9000
£10000 $15600 €15000 Moonwalk (96x96cm-38x38in) st.sig.num.52/160 col silkscreen. 25-Mar-3 Sotheby's, London #212/R est:7000-9000
£10127 $16000 €15191 Torso double (77x109cm-30x43in) estate st. num.UP56.12 verso screenprint executed c.1982. 14-Nov-2 Christie's, Rockefeller NY #221/R est:20000-30000

£10646 $16821 €15969 Three portraits of Ingrid Bergman by Andy Warhol (96x96cm-38x38in) s.num.108/250 portfolio of three col silkscreens lit. 28-Apr-3 Bukowskis, Stockholm #526/R est:140000-150000 (S.KR 140000)

£10897 $17000 €16346 Flowers (104x69cm-41x27in) init. s.d.num.243/250 verso hand col screenprint set of 10. 5-Nov-2 Christie's, Rockefeller NY #509/R est:10000-15000

£11000 $18150 €15950 Moonwalk (96x96cm-38x38in) st.sig.num.31/160 col silkscreen. 1-Jul-3 Sotheby's, London #220/R est:7000-9000

£11000 $18150 €15950 Moonwalk (96x96cm-38x38in) st.sig.num.31/160 col silkscreen. 1-Jul-3 Sotheby's, London #221/R est:7000-9000

£11321 $18000 €16982 Grace Kelly (101x81cm-40x32in) s.i. col screenprint. 2-May-3 Sotheby's, New York #659/R est:8000-10000

£11538 $18000 €17307 Marilyn (91x91cm-36x36in) init.d.num.125/250 col screenprint. 5-Nov-2 Christie's, Rockefeller NY #503/R est:14000-18000

£11765 $19647 €17059 Ingrid Bergman. Herself. The nun. With hat (96x96cm-38x38in) s.i. col serigraph three. 24-Jun-3 Koller, Zurich #515/R est:22000-28000 (S.FR 26000)

£11950 $19000 €17925 Grace Kelly (101x81cm-40x32in) s.i. col screenprint. 2-May-3 Sotheby's, New York #658/R est:8000-10000

£12179 $19000 €18269 Marilyn (91x91cm-36x36in) s.num.124/250 verso col screenprint. 5-Nov-2 Christie's, Rockefeller NY #502/R est:12000-16000

£12500 $19250 €18750 Perrier (86x63cm-34x25in) estate st.num.up38.02 silkscreen print on paper prov. 22-Oct-2 Sotheby's, London #327/R est:5000-7000

£12500 $20000 €18750 Querelle (102x102cm-40x40in) screenprint on Lenox Museum board prov. 14-May-3 Sotheby's, New York #261/R est:15000-20000

£12761 $19652 €20290 Joseph Beuys (51x40cm-20x16in) s. serigraph exec.1980. 26-Oct-2 Cornette de St.Cyr, Paris #86/R est:12000

£13000 $20020 €19500 Madonna and self portrait with skeleton's arm (81x101cm-32x40in) estate st. num.up35.30 verso silkscreen print on paper. 22-Oct-2 Sotheby's, London #465/R est:4000-6000

£13836 $22000 €20754 Marilyn (91x91cm-36x36in) s.num.180/20 verso col screenprint. 2-May-3 Sotheby's, New York #641/R est:12000-15000

£13836 $22000 €20754 Grace Kelly (102x81cm-40x32in) s.num.225/225 col screenprint. 2-May-3 Sotheby's, New York #657/R est:10000-12000

£13924 $22000 €20886 Shadow (35x28cm-14x11in) estate st.verso synthetic polymer paint silkscreen on canvas prov. 12-Nov-2 Phillips, New York #120/R est:25000-30000

£14000 $21840 €21000 Myths, Superman (96x96cm-38x38in) s.num.79/200 col silkscreen diamond dust. 25-Mar-3 Sotheby's, London #235/R est:10000-12000

£14063 $22500 €21095 Flower for Tacoma Dome (95x95cm-37x37in) screenprint on paper executed 1982. 14-May-3 Sotheby's, New York #264/R est:25000-35000

£14194 $22000 €21291 Marilyn Monroe (91x91cm-36x36in) s.num.159/200 col screenprint. 25-Sep-2 Christie's, Rockefeller NY #433/R est:10000-15000

£15000 $25050 €21750 Mick Jagger (110x72cm-43x28in) s.i.numA177.032 verso silkscreen ink executed 1975 prov. 27-Jun-3 Christie's, London #222/R est:18000-22000

£15094 $24000 €22641 Marilyn Monroe (91x91cm-36x36in) s.num.F verso black grey screenprint. 29-Apr-3 Christie's, Rockefeller NY #761/R est:20000-30000

£15646 $24878 €23000 Marylin (79x59cm-31x23in) st.sig.verso serigraph exec.c.1979 prov. 24-Mar-3 Cornette de St.Cyr, Paris #79/R est:30000

£15723 $25000 €23585 Electric chair (90x122cm-35x48in) s.d.num.60/250 verso col screenprint ten portfolio. 2-May-3 Sotheby's, New York #650/R est:40000-60000

£16352 $26000 €24528 Marilyn (91x91cm-36x36in) s.num.180/250 verso grey black screenprint. 2-May-3 Sotheby's, New York #642/R est:15000-20000

£16667 $26000 €25001 Marilyn Monroe (91x91cm-36x36in) s.num.163/250 verso col screenprint. 5-Nov-2 Christie's, Rockefeller NY #499/R est:15000-20000

£17187 $27500 €25781 Electric chair (90x122cm-35x48in) screenprint on paper executed c.1971 prov. 14-May-3 Sotheby's, New York #262/R est:25000-35000

£17949 $28000 €26924 Marilyn (61x61cm-24x24in) s.num.90/250 verso black grey screenprint. 5-Nov-2 Christie's, Rockefeller NY #500/R est:25000-35000

£18000 $27900 €27000 Ingrid Bergman, Herself, the nun and with hat (96x96cm-38x38in) s.num.119/250 col silkscreen set of three. 5-Dec-2 Sotheby's, London #246/R est:8000-12000

£20000 $32800 €30000 Wild raspberries (44x28cm-17x11in) s.i.num.A191.3 18 off-set lithographs bound lit. 6-Feb-3 Christie's, London #674/R est:10000-15000

£20253 $32000 €32000 Queen Beatrix (100x80cm-39x31in) s.num.PP1/2 silkscreen diamond dust set of four. 26-Nov-2 Sotheby's, Amsterdam #408/R est:27000-36000

£20513 $31795 €32000 Queen Beatrix of the Netherlands, from Reigning Queens (100x80cm-39x31in) s.num.7/10 col screenprints set of four prov. 3-Dec-2 Christie's, Amsterdam #517/R est:32000-36000

£21795 $34000 €32693 Cowboys and Indians (92x92cm-36x36in) s.num.129/250 col screenprints set of 10. 5-Nov-2 Christie's, Rockefeller NY #530/R est:30000-40000

£22000 $36080 €33000 Vesuvius (81x101cm-32x40in) st.sig.i.verso silkscreen inks board prov. 6-Feb-3 Christie's, London #680/R est:15000-20000

£22152 $35000 €33228 Marilyn (79x59cm-31x23in) estate st.verso silkscreen executed 1978 prov.lit. 12-Nov-2 Phillips, New York #119/R est:40000-60000

£22152 $35000 €33228 Untitled - panda drummer (35x28cm-14x11in) estate st.on overlap synthetic polymer silkscreen executed 1983. 12-Nov-2 Phillips, New York #121/R est:35000-45000

£22152 $35000 €33228 American flag (55x70cm-22x28in) s.verso four stitched gelatin silver prints executed 1976-86. 14-Nov-2 Christie's, Rockefeller NY #213/R est:25000-35000

£22152 $35000 €35000 Campbell Soup Box (34x34cm-13x13in) s.d.1986 verso serigraph prov.lit. 27-Nov-2 Tajan, Paris #73/R est:40000-50000

£23000 $37950 €33350 Marilyn (91x92cm-36x36in) s.num.103/250 verso col screenprint. 2-Jul-3 Christie's, London #220/R est:18000-22000

£24000 $37200 €36000 Marilyn (91x91cm-36x36in) s.num.72/250 col silkscreen. 5-Dec-2 Sotheby's, London #230/R est:18000-22000

£24051 $38000 €36077 Georgia O'keefe (113x76cm-44x30in) estate st. screenprint diamond dust executed c.1979 prov.lit. 14-Nov-2 Christie's, Rockefeller NY #222/R est:40000-60000

£24359 $38000 €36539 A la recherche du shoe perdu (63x48cm-25x19in) s.i. letterpress illustrations 14 and cover exec.c.1955. 5-Nov-2 Christie's, Rockefeller NY #497/R est:40000-60000

£25316 $40000 €37974 Flowers (61x46cm-24x18in) s.num.A112.0210 screenprint executed 1964 prov. 14-Nov-2 Christie's, Rockefeller NY #204/R est:20000-30000

£26000 $40560 €39000 Myths Micky mouse (96x96cm-38x38in) s.num.13/30 col silkscreen diamond dust. 25-Mar-3 Sotheby's, London #218/R est:15000-20000

£28000 $43120 €42000 Oberkassel (127x107cm-50x42in) s.d.1981 synthetic polymer silkscreen ink diamond dust on canvas. 23-Oct-2 Christie's, London #145/R est:30000-40000

£28481 $45000 €42722 Daisy (102x152cm-40x60in) silkscreen on Lenox Museum board executed c.1982 lit. 13-Nov-2 Sotheby's, New York #346/R est:30000-40000

£30000 $46200 €45000 Double dollar sing no.3 (50x40cm-20x16in) s.verso synthetic polymer silkscreen ink on canvas. 23-Oct-2 Christie's, London #135/R est:30000-40000

£31000 $51770 €44950 Shoes (102x151cm-40x59in) estate st.num.A.184.032 verso silkscreen diamond dust prov. 26-Jun-3 Sotheby's, London #270/R est:15000-20000

£31447 $50000 €47171 Mao (91x91cm-36x36in) s.verso two num.22/250 two num.104/250 col screenprint set of 10. 29-Apr-3 Christie's, Rockefeller NY #765/R est:60000-80000

£32051 $49679 €50000 Duty Free (102x102cm-40x40in) synthetic resin silkcut canvas. 6-Dec-2 Hauswedell & Nolte, Hamburg #386/R est:75000

£32911 $52000 €49367 Daisy (102x152cm-40x60in) estate st.i. screenprint executed c.1982 prov.lit. 14-Nov-2 Christie's, Rockefeller NY #205/R est:30000-40000

£38000 $62700 €55100 Electric chair (90x122cm-35x48in) s.d.num.104/250 verso col silkscreen 10 portfolio. 1-Jul-3 Sotheby's, London #230/R est:15000-20000

£54487 $85000 €81731 Mao (91x91cm-36x36in) s.num.188/250 verso col screenprints set of 10. 5-Nov-2 Christie's, Rockefeller NY #506/R est:80000-100000

£59748 $95000 €89622 Ads (96x96cm-38x38in) s.num.82/190 col screenprint ten portfolio box. 2-May-3 Sotheby's, New York #663/R est:60000-80000

£94937 $150000 €142406 Men in her life (42x69cm-17x27in) s.d.1962 on overlap silkscreen on canvas prov.lit. 13-Nov-2 Sotheby's, New York #247/R est:150000-200000

£113924 $180000 €170886 Ambulance disaster (102x76cm-40x30in) screenprint on paper executed 1963 prov. 13-Nov-2 Sotheby's, New York #246/R est:150000-200000

£240000	$400800	€348000	Flowers (36x36cm-14x14in) s.d.64 silkscreen ink synthetic polymer set of four prov. 27-Jun-3 Christie's, London #208/R est:220000-280000
£384615	$600000	€576923	Crosses (229x179cm-90x70in) num.pa14.028 synthetic polymer silkscreen on canvas. 11-Nov-2 Phillips, New York #28/R est:500000-700000
£1100000	$1804000	€1650000	Six skulls (129x102cm-51x40in) s.d.1976 synthetic polymer silkscreen ink on canvas six. 5-Feb-3 Christie's, London #8/R est:1200000-1600000
£2564103	$4000000	€3846155	Silver Liz (102x230cm-40x91in) s.postdated 1965 silkscreen ink acrylic spray paint two parts. 11-Nov-2 Phillips, New York #14/R est:4000000-6000000

Sculpture

£2107	$3245	€3350	Brillo soap pads (20x17x6cm-8x7x2in) s. washing powder box. 26-Oct-2 Cornette de St.Cyr, Paris #73/R
£35000	$57400	€52500	Brillo Box (44x44x36cm-17x17x14in) synthetic polymer silkscreen inks wood prov.exhib. 6-Feb-3 Christie's, London #690/R est:35000-45000
£35000	$58450	€50750	Brillo box (43x43x36cm-17x17x14in) acrylic silkscreen ink wood exec.c.1968 prov.exhib. 26-Jun-3 Sotheby's, London #153/R est:35000-45000
£41139	$65000	€61709	Brillo box (44x44x36cm-17x17x14in) st.num.A100.0110 synthetic polymer silkscreen ink on wood. 14-Nov-2 Christie's, Rockefeller NY #139/R est:50000-70000
£59375	$95000	€89063	Campbell's tomato juice box (25x48x24cm-10x19x9in) s. polymer ink wood plexiglas bocxc exec.1964 prov. 15-May-3 Christie's, Rockefeller NY #127/R est:50000-70000
£290000	$475600	€435000	Four Heinz boxes (22x39x27cm-9x15x11in) silkscreen ink plywood in 4 parts exec.1964 prov.exhib.lit. 6-Feb-3 Sotheby's, London #14/R est:300000
£367089	$580000	€550634	Del monte boxes - peach halves (24x39x30cm-9x15x12in) silkscreen ink on plywood in six parts executed 1964. 12-Nov-2 Sotheby's, New York #33/R est:400000-600000
£468750	$750000	€703125	Campbell's boxes - tomato juice (25x48x24cm-10x19x9in) s. silkscreen ink wood exec.1964 set of 3 prov.exhib.lit. 13-May-3 Sotheby's, New York #15/R est:600000-800000

Works on paper

£913	$1442	€1370	Study for can (29x22cm-11x9in) s. Indian ink. 28-Apr-3 Bukowskis, Stockholm #909/R (S.KR 12000)
£952	$1514	€1400	Campbell soup (21x13cm-8x5in) s. felt-tip pen dr. 24-Mar-3 Cornette de St.Cyr, Paris #93/R
£1095	$1751	€1588	Campbell's Sketch (32x25cm-13x10in) s.i. original dr on paper bag. 18-May-3 Anders Antik, Landskrona #121 (S.KR 14000)
£1154	$1788	€1800	Campbell soup (13x7cm-5x3in) s.i. felt-tip pen board. 7-Dec-2 Van Ham, Cologne #585/R est:3000
£1500	$2445	€2250	Campbell's tomato soup, the philosophy of Andy Warhol (21x14cm-8x6in) s.i. felt tip pen. 3-Feb-3 Sotheby's, Olympia #45/R est:2000-3000
£1774	$2750	€2661	Campbell soup dress. paper exec.c.1968. 29-Sep-2 Butterfields, Los Angeles #4447/R est:1200-1500
£1899	$3000	€3000	Campbell's tomato soup - the philosophy of Andy Warhol (20x13cm-8x5in) s. felt pen. 27-Nov-2 Dorotheum, Vienna #82/R est:3000-3500
£1900	$3173	€2755	Campbells chicken soup (19x13cm-7x5in) s.i. felt tip. 24-Jun-3 Sotheby's, Olympia #58/R est:1000-1500
£1923	$2981	€3000	Untitled (16x10cm-6x4in) s.i. feltpen. 6-Dec-2 Hauswedell & Nolte, Hamburg #387/R est:2500
£2083	$3250	€3125	Untitled, man's head, eyes and lips (42x36cm-17x14in) st.verso pencil prov. 14-Oct-2 Butterfields, San Francisco #2050/R est:3000-5000
£2724	$4250	€4086	Untitled, young man (42x36cm-17x14in) st.verso pen ink prov. 14-Oct-2 Butterfields, San Francisco #2047/R est:4000-6000
£2724	$4250	€4086	Untitled, young man (42x35cm-17x14in) st.verso pen ink prov. 14-Oct-2 Butterfields, San Francisco #2048/R est:4000-6000
£4000	$6560	€6000	Untitled, fruit and berries (18x33cm-7x13in) estate st.num.313.043 verso ink-blot W/C exec.c.1957 prov. 7-Feb-3 Sotheby's, London #254/R est:4000-6000
£4000	$6680	€5800	Shoe (22x27cm-9x11in) estate st. ink gouache pencil exec.c.1957 prov. 26-Jun-3 Sotheby's, London #179/R est:4000-6000
£4166	$6500	€6249	Untitled, man's torso (42x36cm-17x14in) st.verso pen ink prov. 14-Oct-2 Butterfields, San Francisco #2051/R est:6000-8000
£4375	$7000	€6563	Portrait of Kenny Lane (43x35cm-17x14in) ballpoint pen ink executed c.1958 prov. 14-May-3 Sotheby's, New York #178/R est:5000-7000
£5000	$8200	€7500	Untitled, angel (21x27cm-8x11in) estate st. num.272.071 verso ink exec.c.1953 prov. 7-Feb-3 Sotheby's, London #253/R est:5000-7000
£6452	$10000	€9678	Perrier bottles (102x69cm-40x27in) synthetic polymer silkscreen ink collage executed c.1984 prov. 26-Sep-2 Christie's, Rockefeller NY #749/R est:15000-20000
£8750	$14000	€13125	Cosmetic surgery (81x60cm-32x24in) graphite col pencil exec.1985-86 prov.exhib. 15-May-3 Christie's, Rockefeller NY #179/R est:12000-18000
£10000	$15400	€15000	Vesuvius (80x100cm-31x39in) s. st.verso synthetic polymer paint silkscreen ink cardboard prov. 22-Oct-2 Sotheby's, London #326/R est:10000-15000
£11000	$18040	€16500	Space fruit, watermelon (77x103cm-30x41in) estate st.num.191.016 verso silkscreen ink board prov. 7-Feb-3 Sotheby's, London #271/R est:10000-15000
£12025	$19000	€18038	Untitled (104x71cm-41x28in) s. graphite executed 1976 prov. 14-Nov-2 Christie's, Rockefeller NY #207/R est:25000-35000
£12258	$19000	€18387	Scream (102x81cm-40x32in) st. synthetic polymer silkscreen inks executed 1983 prov. 26-Sep-2 Christie's, Rockefeller NY #757/R est:25000-35000
£13605	$21633	€20000	Hamburger (25x30cm-10x12in) ink acrylic on canvas exec.1985. 24-Mar-3 Cornette de St.Cyr, Paris #80/R est:28000
£14063	$22500	€21095	Skull (51x70cm-20x28in) pencil executed c.1978 prov. 14-May-3 Sotheby's, New York #258/R est:20000-25000
£15000	$24000	€22500	Flowers (46x31cm-18x12in) s.d.64 synthetic polymer silkscreen ink prov. 15-May-3 Christie's, Rockefeller NY #151/R est:40000
£15190	$24000	€22785	Gerald Ford (36x28cm-14x11in) estate st. synthetic polymer silkscreen ink executed 1975 prov. 14-Nov-2 Christie's, Rockefeller NY #203/R est:25000-35000
£15625	$25000	€23438	Hamburger (25x30cm-10x12in) s.i.d.86 overlap silkscreen acrylic on canvas prov. 14-May-3 Sotheby's, New York #257/R est:20000-30000
£15625	$25000	€23438	Modern Madonna (102x79cm-40x31in) pencil executed 1981 prov.exhib. 14-May-3 Sotheby's, New York #263/R est:30000-40000
£16000	$26240	€24000	Querelle (103x103cm-41x41in) estate st.num.UPH6.30 A.135.0210 verso silkscreen ink board prov. 7-Feb-3 Sotheby's, London #270/R est:10000-15000
£17500	$28000	€26250	Shadow (36x28cm-14x11in) s.i.d.1978 verso synthetic polymer silkscreen ink on canvas prov. 15-May-3 Christie's, Rockefeller NY #180/R est:20000-30000
£17500	$28000	€26250	Monkey (36x28cm-14x11in) s.d.83 synthetic polymer silkscreen ink on canvas prov. 15-May-3 Christie's, Rockefeller NY #206/R est:20000-30000
£17500	$28000	€26250	Monkey (36x28cm-14x11in) s.d.83 synthetic polymer silkscreen ink on canvas prov. 15-May-3 Christie's, Rockefeller NY #205/R est:20000-30000
£20000	$32000	€30000	Self-portrait (46x61cm-18x24in) s.d.67 synthetic polymer silkscreen ink prov.lit. 15-May-3 Christie's, Rockefeller NY #152/R est:35000-45000
£21875	$35000	€32813	Flowers (12x12cm-5x5in) init.d.64 synthetic polymer silkscreen ink on canvas prov. 15-May-3 Christie's, Rockefeller NY #121/R est:25000-35000
£22000	$36080	€33000	Lenin (80x60cm-31x24in) s.d.87 graphite executed 1986-87 prov.exhib. 6-Feb-3 Christie's, London #678/R est:25000-35000
£22000	$36080	€33000	Campbell's noodle soup box (51x51cm-20x20in) st.sig. synthetic polymer silkscreen inks. 6-Feb-3 Christie's, London #686/R est:25000-35000
£22000	$36740	€31900	Clockwork panda drummer (35x28cm-14x11in) s.d.83 on overlap synthetic polymer silkscreen prov. 27-Jun-3 Christie's, London #211/R est:12000-16000
£23810	$37857	€35000	Self-portrait (56x45cm-22x18in) s. ink prov.exhib. 24-Mar-3 Cornette de St.Cyr, Paris #78/R est:50000
£24051	$38000	€36077	Northwest coast mask (102x76cm-40x30in) estate st. num.73.022 brush synthetic polymer prov. 14-Nov-2 Christie's, Rockefeller NY #210/R est:30000-40000
£25000	$41750	€36250	Knives (54x40cm-21x16in) estate st. synthetic polymer silkscreen executed 1981-82 prov.exh. 27-Jun-3 Christie's, London #220/R est:30000-50000
£30000	$49200	€45000	Alex Guiness (25x48cm-10x19in) s.i. ink gold leaf applique exec.c.1956-57 prov. 7-Feb-3 Sotheby's, London #252/R est:35000-45000
£30380	$48000	€45570	Van Heusen - Ronald Reagan (56x56cm-22x22in) s.d.85 on overlap synthetic polymer silkscreen ink on canvas prov. 14-Nov-2 Christie's, Rockefeller NY #102/R est:40000-60000
£31646	$50000	€47469	Flowers (21x21cm-8x8in) s.d.64 synthetic polymer silkscreen ink on canvas prov. 14-Nov-2 Christie's, Rockefeller NY #131/R est:50000-70000

£31646 $50000 €50000 Portrait of Mrs Zoppas-Sachs (101x101cm-40x40in) synthetic polymer silkscreen on canvas. 29-Nov-2 Farsetti, Prato #544/R est:50000

£37500 $60000 €56250 With love (46x33cm-18x13in) s.i. ink gold leaf collage exec.c.1957 prov. 15-May-3 Christie's, Rockefeller NY #122/R est:70000-90000

£37975 $60000 €56963 Joseph Beuys (51x41cm-20x16in) estate st.num.PA62 005 synthetic polymer silkscreen ink prov. 14-Nov-2 Christie's, Rockefeller NY #198/R est:80000-120000

£39000 $63960 €58500 Flower for Tacoma dome (101x101cm-40x40in) estate st.num.A.149.025 verso silkscreen ink board prov. 7-Feb-3 Sotheby's, London #272/R est:15000-20000

£40625 $65000 €60938 Dollar sign (28x51cm-11x20in) s.d.82 verso synthetic polymer silkscreen ink on canvas. 15-May-3 Christie's, Rockefeller NY #207/R est:40000-60000

£43038 $68000 €64557 Campbell's soup box - chicken rice (51x51cm-20x20in) s.d.86 on overlap synthetic polymer silkscreen ink on canvas prov. 14-Nov-2 Christie's, Rockefeller NY #101/R est:40000-60000

£46875 $75000 €70313 VW Beetle (41x51cm-16x20in) i. synthetic polymer silkscreen ink exec.1969 prov. 14-May-3 Christie's, Rockefeller NY #1/R est:60000-80000

£47468 $75000 €71202 Adrian (38x27cm-15x11in) s.i. ink gold leaf applique on collage paper executed c.1956 prov. 13-Nov-2 Sotheby's, New York #229/R est:70000-90000

£47610 $73319 €75700 Two dollar bill (15x26cm-6x10in) s.d.1962 verso ink acrylic on canvas prov.exhib.lit. 26-Oct-2 Cornette de St.Cyr, Paris #75/R est:50000

£60000 $100200 €87000 Princess Ashraf Pahlevi of Iran (102x102cm-40x40in) estate st.num.synthetic polymer silkscreen executed 1977 prov. 27-Jun-3 Christie's, London #217/R est:60000-80000

£63291 $100000 €94937 Mao (30x25cm-12x10in) st.num.A 102.0110 overlap synthetic polymer silkscreen ink. 14-Nov-2 Christie's, Rockefeller NY #199/R est:120000-180000

£70000 $116900 €105000 Untitled - Legs and high heels (62x49cm-24x19in) st. i.verso gold leaf ink st.gold collage exc.1955 prov.exhib. 25-Jun-3 Sotheby's, London #41/R est:40000-60000

£80000 $131200 €120000 Camouflage (102x102cm-40x40in) st.sig.i. synthetic polymer silkscreen inks canvas prov.exhib. 6-Feb-3 Christie's, London #679/R est:80000-120000

£94937 $150000 €142406 Diamond dust shoes (127x107cm-50x42in) estate.st. num.PA70.046 synthetic polymer silkscreen ink diamond. 14-Nov-2 Christie's, Rockefeller NY #189/R est:150000-200000

£95000 $155800 €142500 Ladies and gentlemen (81x66cm-32x26in) s.d.75 synthetic polymer silkscreen inks canvas prov.lit. 6-Feb-3 Christie's, London #688/R est:100000-150000

£95000 $158650 €142500 Self-Portrait (30x25cm-12x10in) st.overlap synthetic polymer silkscreen inks canvas prov. 26-Jun-3 Christie's, London #23/R est:120000-180000

£112500 $180000 €168750 Ambulance disaster (102x76cm-40x30in) synthetic polymer silkscreen ink prov.lit. 15-May-3 Christie's, Rockefeller NY #155/R est:180000-220000

£125000 $200000 €187500 Jackie (51x41cm-20x16in) s.d.1964 synthetic polymer silkscreen ink on canvas prov. 15-May-3 Christie's, Rockefeller NY #154/R est:200000-300000

£131250 $210000 €196875 Diamond dust shoes (127x107cm-50x42in) s.d.82 synthetic polymer silkscreen ink diamond dust on canvas. 15-May-3 Christie's, Rockefeller NY #195/R est:150000-200000

£143750 $230000 €215625 Self-portrait (48x32cm-19x13in) s. graphite exec.1942 prov.exhib.lit. 15-May-3 Christie's, Rockefeller NY #119/R est:100000-150000

£150000 $240000 €225000 Ladies and gentlemen (127x102cm-50x40in) s.d.75 synthetic polymer silkscreen ink on canvas prov.exhib. 15-May-3 Christie's, Rockefeller NY #169/R est:250000-350000

£158228 $250000 €237342 Mao (30x25cm-12x10in) i.on overlap synthetic polymer silkscreen ink painted 1972 prov. 14-Nov-2 Christie's, Rockefeller NY #154/R est:150000-200000

£164557 $260000 €246836 Mona Lisa (63x51cm-25x20in) estate st.num.PA63.066 on overlap synthetic polymer silkscreen. 14-Nov-2 Christie's, Rockefeller NY #191/R est:250000-300000

£187500 $300000 €281250 Be somebody with a body (127x152cm-50x60in) synthetic polymer paint on canvas prov.exhib. 15-May-3 Christie's, Rockefeller NY #159/R est:350000-450000

£189873 $300000 €284810 Twenty fuchsia Maos (100x96cm-39x38in) s.i.d.79 on overlap synthetic polymer silkscreen ink on canvas. 14-Nov-2 Christie's, Rockefeller NY #111/R est:200000-300000

£200000 $320000 €300000 Diamond dust shoes (229x178cm-90x70in) estate st. synthetic polymer diamond dust silkscreen prov. 15-May-3 Phillips, New York #15/R est:300000-400000

£212500 $340000 €318750 Jackie - two works (50x41cm-20x16in) synthetic polymer silkscreen on canvas pair prov. 15-May-3 Phillips, New York #19/R est:400000-600000

£230000 $384100 €345000 Two Maos (30x25cm-12x10in) s.d.73 synthetic polymer silkscreen inks canvas two prov.exhib. 26-Jun-3 Christie's, London #3/R est:250000-350000

£275000 $440000 €412500 Flowers (61x61cm-24x24in) s.d.64 synthetic polymer silkscreen ink on canvas prov. 15-May-3 Christie's, Rockefeller NY #123/R est:300000-400000

£284810 $450000 €427215 Flower (61x61cm-24x24in) s.num.A111.956 synthetic polymer silkscreen ink graphite canvas. 14-Nov-2 Christie's, Rockefeller NY #148/R est:350000-450000

£300000 $501000 €450000 Dollar sign (229x178cm-90x70in) st. overlap synthetic polymer silkscreen inks canvas prov. 26-Jun-3 Christie's, London #44/R est:220000-300000

£406250 $650000 €609375 Self portrait - two (56x56cm-22x22in) synthetic polymer silkscreen on canvas pair executed 1986 prov. 15-May-3 Phillips, New York #17/R est:800000-1200000

£474684 $750000 €712026 Untitled - Rorschach series (411x292cm-162x115in) liquitex on canvas executed 1984 prov.exhib. 13-Nov-2 Christie's, Rockefeller NY #45/R est:900000-1200000

£687500 $1100000 €1031250 Hammer and sickle (183x218cm-72x86in) s.d.1977 verso synthetic polymer silkscreen ink on canvas prov.ex. 14-May-3 Christie's, Rockefeller NY #26/R est:850000-950000

£696203 $1100000 €1044305 Campbell's soup can - pepper pot (51x41cm-20x16in) casein pencil on linen executed 1961 prov.exhib.lit. 13-Nov-2 Christie's, Rockefeller NY #62/R est:1000000-1500000

£1139241 $1800000 €1708862 Two Marilyns (74x36cm-29x14in) s.on overlap silkscreen ink pencil on linen prov.exhib.lit. 12-Nov-2 Sotheby's, New York #36/R est:2500000-3500000

£1250000 $2000000 €1875000 Dance diagram (177x137cm-70x54in) casein graphite on canvas exec.1962 prov.exhib.lit. 14-May-3 Christie's, Rockefeller NY #23/R est:2000000-3000000

£1343750 $2150000 €2015625 Campbell's soup can - pepper pot (51x41cm-20x16in) s.d.62 verso casein graphite on canvas prov.exhib.lit. 14-May-3 Christie's, Rockefeller NY #5/R est:1500000-2000000

£1518987 $2400000 €2278481 Self portrait (51x81cm-20x32in) s.i.d.64 on overlap synthetic polymer silkscreen two panel. 13-Nov-2 Christie's, Rockefeller NY #8/R est:2500000-3500000

£2812500 $4500000 €4218750 Marlon (104x117cm-41x46in) s.i. silkscreen ink linen exec.1966 prov.exhib. 14-May-3 Christie's, Rockefeller NY #16/R est:4000000-5000000

£2848101 $4500000 €4272152 Big electric chair (137x188cm-54x74in) synthetic polymer silkscreen ink on canvas painted 1967 prov.lit. 13-Nov-2 Christie's, Rockefeller NY #28/R est:3000000-4000000

WARING, R (19/20th C) British

£4605 $7000 €6908 Ship portrait of the Ellerman Line's SS Albanian of Liverpool (43x84cm-17x33in) s.d.1907. 17-Aug-2 North East Auctions, Portsmouth #1038/R est:7000-10000

WARISN, G E (?) American?

£1316 $2000 €1974 Watching sailboats from a grassy bank (33x41cm-13x16in) s. 17-Aug-2 North East Auctions, Portsmouth #147

WARLAND, C (19th C) Belgian

£619 $1010 €929 Cattle at watering place (90x135cm-35x53in) s. 17-Feb-3 Blomqvist, Lysaker #1109 (N.KR 7000)

WARLAND, Charles (19th C) Belgian

£530 $864 €800 Vue du Bocq (69x83cm-27x33in) s. 17-Feb-3 Horta, Bruxelles #353

£1620 $2608 €2300 View of forest with cows watering (69x95cm-27x37in) s.d.88. 7-May-3 Vendue Huis, Gravenhage #459 est:1500-2000

WARLINCOURT, Joseph (1784-1841) British?
£11728 $19000 €17592 Figures in the salon d'apollon in the Louvre with a view of Notre Dame (45x60cm-18x24in) bears i. exhib. 23-Jan-3 Sotheby's, New York #106/R est:18000-25000

WARLING, Elisabeth (1858-1915) Swedish
£289 $446 €460 Woman wearing black dress (90x150cm-35x59in) s. 27-Oct-2 Bukowskis, Helsinki #349/R
£1400 $2282 €2100 Moat (71x59cm-28x23in) s. 29-Jan-3 Sotheby's, Olympia #350/R est:800-1400
£1807 $2963 €2620 French backyard with sunflowers, Montigny (52x43cm-20x17in) s.i. 4-Jun-3 AB Stockholms Auktionsverk #2159/R est:18000-20000 (S.KR 23000)

WARMINGTON, E A (19th C) British
Works on paper
£480 $730 €720 Rydal Water from the bank (23x51cm-9x20in) s. W/C executed c.1898. 16-Aug-2 Keys, Aylsham #450/R

WARNBERGER, Simon (1769-1847) German
Works on paper
£313 $497 €450 Trees along woodland path (36x29cm-14x11in) s.d.1828 chk. 5-May-3 Ketterer, Munich #324/R
£700 $1169 €1015 Goatherd with goats beneath a tree. pencil sepia wash. 9-Jul-3 Bonhams, Knightsbridge #33/R
£3611 $5742 €5200 Mountainous landscape near Rome (20x25cm-8x10in) s. pen W/C. 5-May-3 Ketterer, Munich #325/R est:1800-2200

WARNE-BROWN, Alfred J (fl.1890-1900) British
Works on paper
£547 $876 €793 Landscape with sheep (49x68cm-19x27in) s. W/C. 18-May-3 Anders Antik, Landskrona #11 (S.KR 7000)

WARNEKE, Heinz (1895-?) American/German
Sculpture
£1000 $1600 €1450 Three horses (16x33cm-6x13in) s. green pat bronze. 16-May-3 Skinner, Boston #153/R est:1000-1500

WARNER, Everett L (1877-1963) American
£881 $1400 €1322 Connecticut river (32x41cm-13x16in) s. b/. 7-Mar-3 Skinner, Boston #410/R est:800-1200
£3293 $5500 €4775 Covered bridge (30x41cm-12x16in) s. board. 18-Jun-3 Christie's, Los Angeles #17/R est:3000-5000

WARNER, Nell Walker (1891-1970) American
£1452 $2250 €2178 Floral still life (20x25cm-8x10in) s. board prov. 29-Oct-2 John Moran, Pasadena #608 est:1500-2000
£1946 $3250 €2822 Floral still life, gold bouquet (51x41cm-20x16in) s. i.verso canvasboard. 17-Jun-3 John Moran, Pasadena #93 est:2000-3000
£2096 $3500 €3039 Wooded stream in landscape (64x76cm-25x30in) s. 17-Jun-3 John Moran, Pasadena #148/R est:2500-3500
£2259 $3750 €3276 Early spring. View of docks in a harbour (20x25cm-8x10in) one s. i.verso masonite one s. canvasboard two prov. 11-Jun-3 Butterfields, San Francisco #4311/R est:4000-6000
£2545 $4250 €3690 Chrysanthemums (66x76cm-26x30in) s. i.on stretcher prov. 17-Jun-3 John Moran, Pasadena #29 est:3000-5000
£2548 $4000 €3822 Still life with morning glories and a figurine in a bowl (67x77cm-26x30in) s. prov. 19-Nov-2 Butterfields, San Francisco #8257/R est:3000-5000
£2795 $4500 €4193 Blue and gold, floral still life (66x76cm-26x30in) s. i.stretcher. 18-Feb-3 John Moran, Pasadena #109 est:2500-4000
£3106 $5000 €4659 Blue and gold, floral still life (51x41cm-20x16in) s. canvasboard prov. 18-Feb-3 John Moran, Pasadena #25 est:2000-3000
£3185 $5000 €4778 Matiliya poppies and iris (92x77cm-36x30in) s. i.stretcher prov. 19-Nov-2 Butterfields, San Francisco #8256/R est:3000-5000
£3822 $6000 €5733 Ranunculas and brass (66x76cm-26x30in) s. 10-Dec-2 Doyle, New York #149/R est:8000-10000
£4192 $7000 €6078 River landscape (51x61cm-20x24in) s. prov. 17-Jun-3 John Moran, Pasadena #193 est:2000-3000

WAROQUIER, Henry de (1881-1970) French
Works on paper
£272 $433 €400 Un homme (31x23cm-12x9in) s.d.1916 and 1920 mixed media. 18-Mar-3 Galerie Moderne, Brussels #543/R
£329 $533 €500 Visage rond (27x21cm-11x8in) s.d.1937 ink wash. 22-Jan-3 Tajan, Paris #117
£828 $1324 €1200 Le Grand Canal de l'Academie a Venise (35x49cm-14x19in) s.i. W/C. 12-Mar-3 Libert, Castor, Paris #208/R

WARREN, Barbara (1925-) Irish?
£959 $1505 €1400 Self portrait - into the 1990's (55x50cm-22x20in) s.i.verso. 15-Apr-3 De Veres Art Auctions, Dublin #170/R est:1500-2000
£1370 $2151 €2000 Evening Lettermore (23x43cm-9x17in) s. prov. 15-Apr-3 De Veres Art Auctions, Dublin #194/R est:1400-1800

WARREN, C L (19th C) British?
£800 $1264 €1200 Good smoke after tea (62x47cm-24x19in) s.d.98. 14-Nov-2 Christie's, Kensington #73/R

WARREN, Charles Wyatt (1908-) British
£260 $424 €390 Moel Hebog (23x53cm-9x21in) s. board. 28-Jan-3 Gorringes, Lewes #1784
£280 $437 €420 Farm at Gran (19x34cm-7x13in) s. board. 11-Sep-2 Bonhams, Newport #420
£320 $499 €480 Yr Aran from Haford Lwyfog (19x34cm-7x13in) s. board. 11-Sep-2 Bonhams, Newport #421
£400 $624 €600 Snowdon from Llyn Mymber (24x54cm-9x21in) s. board. 11-Sep-2 Bonhams, Newport #367
£420 $655 €630 Bridge near Bettws (24x54cm-9x21in) s. board. 11-Sep-2 Bonhams, Newport #368
£420 $651 €630 River in autumn (23x54cm-9x21in) s. board. 4-Dec-2 Wingetts, Wrexham #231/R
£480 $744 €720 Cwm Pennant (23x54cm-9x21in) s. board. 4-Dec-2 Wingetts, Wrexham #230/R
£580 $899 €870 Snowdon from Llyn Padrn in winter (37x89cm-15x35in) s. board. 4-Dec-2 Wingetts, Wrexham #229/R

WARREN, Edmund George (1834-1909) British
Works on paper
£1800 $2916 €2700 Harvesting corn (42x62cm-17x24in) s. W/C. 20-May-3 Sotheby's, Olympia #195/R est:2000-3000
£2600 $4160 €3900 Going to the hayfield (51x36cm-20x14in) s.d.1861 W/C bodycol. 11-Mar-3 Bonhams, New Bond Street #99/R est:2000-3000
£6000 $9960 €9000 Resting by the lock gate (60x96cm-24x38in) s. W/C. 12-Jun-3 Sotheby's, London #265/R est:6000-8000

WARREN, Edward P (?) British?
Works on paper
£2401 $3745 €3602 Landscape with figures by river (55x99cm-22x39in) s. W/C. 13-Sep-2 Lilla Bukowskis, Stockholm #262 est:5000-7000 (S.KR 35000)

WARREN, Elizabeth Boardman (1886-?) American
Works on paper
£346 $550 €519 Hillside landscape (17x24cm-7x9in) s.d.1903 W/C gouache. 7-Mar-3 Skinner, Boston #415/R

WARREN, Emily (1869-1956) Canadian
Works on paper
£217 $339 €363 Lake Louise (25x37cm-10x15in) s. W/C. 13-Apr-3 Levis, Calgary #630/R (C.D 500)

WARREN, Joseph (20th C) British
£764 $1200 €1146 Woman in red with collie dog and horse (81x61cm-32x24in) s. 22-Nov-2 Eldred, East Dennis #1132/R

WARREN, Melvin C (1920-1995) American
£7534 $11000 €11301 The old farm (61x76cm-24x30in) 18-May-2 Altermann Galleries, Santa Fe #110/R
£9589 $14000 €14384 Run for the pass (61x91cm-24x36in) 18-May-2 Altermann Galleries, Santa Fe #111/R
£42208 $65000 €63312 Texas ranger border patrol (91x152cm-36x60in) 25-Oct-2 Morris & Whiteside, Hilton Head Island #33 est:65000-75000
Sculpture
£1282 $2000 €1923 Commander (25x8cm-10x3in) bronze. 9-Nov-2 Altermann Galleries, Santa Fe #135
£1667 $2600 €2501 Words of wisdom (25x36x20cm-10x14x8in) bronze. 9-Nov-2 Altermann Galleries, Santa Fe #133
£1923 $3000 €2885 Drifter (23x8cm-9x3in) bronze. 9-Nov-2 Altermann Galleries, Santa Fe #134

WARRENER, Lowrie Lyle (1900-) Canadian
£1205 $1892 €1808 Desolation, Northern Ontario (35x44cm-14x17in) s.i.d.1927 board prov. 25-Nov-2 Hodgins, Calgary #62/R est:2000-2500 (C.D 3000)

WARRENS, Marc (1956-) Belgian
£1410 $2186 €2200 Rouge et noir (40x50cm-16x20in) s. panel. 3-Dec-2 Campo & Campo, Antwerp #351/R est:1500-2000

WARRENS, Tony (1960-) ?
£3145 $4843 €5000 Seeing the light (142x160cm-56x63in) s.d.2000 verso. 22-Oct-2 Campo & Campo, Antwerp #328

WARSHAWSKY, Abel George (1883-1962) American
£597 $950 €896 Portrait of a woman (81x64cm-32x25in) s. painted c.1920. 2-Mar-3 Toomey, Oak Park #567/R
£1497 $2500 €2171 Landscape - Carmel Valley from Hator Field, springtime (51x61cm-20x24in) i.verso board. 17-Jun-3 John Moran, Pasadena #22 est:4000-6000
£1688 $2600 €2532 Floral still life (53x46cm-21x18in) s. painted c.1930. 8-Sep-2 Treadway Gallery, Cincinnati #651/R est:1000-2000
£1887 $3000 €2831 Paris unconquered (61x51cm-24x20in) s. painted c.1920 sold with a book. 2-Mar-3 Toomey, Oak Park #645/R est:5000-7000
£1946 $3250 €2822 Parisian street scene (51x61cm-20x24in) s. board. 17-Jun-3 John Moran, Pasadena #21 est:4000-6000
£1986 $3316 €2800 Le Goyen a Pont Croix (33x40cm-13x16in) s. s.i.d.verso cardboard. 17-Jun-3 Claude Boisgirard, Paris #142/R est:1500-2000
£2813 $4500 €4220 Rocky hills. s. 11-Jan-3 Harvey Clar, Oakland #1442
£3205 $5000 €4808 Apple blossoms (64x81cm-25x32in) s. 22-Sep-2 Susanin's, Chicago #5120/R est:6000-8000

WARSHAWSKY, Alexander (1887-1945) American
£491 $800 €737 Hillside village (66x81cm-26x32in) s. 2-Feb-3 Grogan, Boston #53
£1347 $2250 €1953 Figures on a garden path (38x46cm-15x18in) s.d.1918. 17-Jun-3 John Moran, Pasadena #113 est:2000-3000
£2419 $3750 €3629 California ranch by the sea (46x56cm-18x22in) s. masonite prov. 29-Oct-2 John Moran, Pasadena #745a est:4000-5500

WARSINSKI, Richard (1937-1996) Norwegian/Polish
£10009 $16014 €15014 Figure I - 1966-1968 (98x98cm-39x39in) vinyl canvas on panel exhib.lit. 17-Mar-3 Blomqvist, Oslo #433/R est:40000-60000 (N.KR 115000)

Works on paper
£543 $880 €815 Composition with figures (74x61cm-29x24in) init. W/C crayon. 26-May-3 Grev Wedels Plass, Oslo #41/R (N.KR 6000)

WARUN-SEKRET, Eugen von (1896-1963) German
£449 $704 €700 Girl in traditional costume in summer meadow (76x101cm-30x40in) s. 23-Nov-2 Arnold, Frankfurt #950/R

WASER, Joseph H (1901-) Swiss
£324 $522 €486 Walk by the sea (33x41cm-13x16in) s. 7-May-3 Dobiaschofsky, Bern #3675 (S.FR 700)

WASHBOURN, Enga (20th C) New Zealander
Works on paper
£325 $520 €471 Arthurs Pass (32x22cm-13x9in) s. W/C. 13-May-3 Watson's, Christchurch #116/R (NZ.D 900)

WASHBURN, Kenneth Leland (1904-) American
£475 $750 €713 Minot's Ledge (41x51cm-16x20in) s. i.verso masonite exhib. 17-Nov-2 Jeffery Burchard, Florida #38a/R

WASHBURN, Lawrence (1940-) Canadian
£234 $383 €339 Lacombe (30x40cm-12x16in) s.i.d.1985 board. 9-Jun-3 Hodgins, Calgary #183/R (C.D 525)
£267 $437 €387 Crossfield farm (30x40cm-12x16in) s.i.d.1982 board. 9-Jun-3 Hodgins, Calgary #294/R (C.D 600)

WASHINGTON, Elizabeth Fisher (19/20th C) American
£38710 $60000 €58065 Winter in Bucks County (91x97cm-36x38in) s. exhib. 4-Dec-2 Sotheby's, New York #44/R est:30000-50000

WASHINGTON, Georges (1827-1910) French
£3493 $5450 €5240 Procession resting (43x80cm-17x31in) s. 6-Nov-2 Dobiaschofsky, Bern #1061/R est:10000 (S.FR 8000)
£5000 $7950 €7500 Arab horseman (39x57cm-15x22in) s. 29-Apr-3 Bonhams, New Bond Street #109/R est:5000-8000
£13462 $21135 €21000 Cavaliers arabes (60x80cm-24x31in) s. 13-Dec-2 Piasa, Paris #30/R est:15000

WASKE, Erich (1889-?) German
£319 $505 €460 Untitled - island t sunset (26x56cm-10x22in) s. panel. 26-Apr-3 Dr Lehr, Berlin #535/R

WASLEY, F (1848-1934) British
Works on paper
£500 $835 €725 Venice with St. Marks (25x44cm-10x17in) indis sig. W/C. 9-Jul-3 Edgar Horn, Eastbourne #289

WASLEY, Frank (1848-1934) British
£700 $1120 €1050 Roman capriccio (56x96cm-22x38in) s. 11-Mar-3 Bonhams, Knightsbridge #209/R
£1200 $1920 €1800 Estuary view (53x94cm-21x37in) s. 7-Jan-3 Bonhams, Knightsbridge #149/R est:1200-1800
£3000 $4560 €4500 Lagoon, Venice (58x104cm-23x41in) 14-Aug-2 Andrew Hartley, Ilkley #697 est:2000-3000

Works on paper
£320 $499 €480 Venice (28x38cm-11x15in) s. gouache. 17-Oct-2 David Lay, Penzance #1507
£330 $511 €495 Figures on a beach (18x26cm-7x10in) W/C bodycol. 24-Sep-2 Bonhams, Knightsbridge #229/R
£400 $620 €600 Grand Canal, Venice (23x53cm-9x21in) s. exhib. 3-Dec-2 Louis Taylor, Stoke on Trent #951
£600 $924 €900 Bosphorus, Seraglio Point. Moonlight on the Thames at Marlow (27x38cm-11x15in) s. W/C bodycol pair. 22-Oct-2 Bonhams, Bath #34
£1000 $1560 €1500 Fishing boats (33x47cm-13x19in) s. W/C. 10-Sep-2 David Duggleby, Scarborough #73/R est:600-800
£1000 $1650 €1450 River Thames at Westminster (27x35cm-11x14in) s. W/C htd bodycol. 3-Jul-3 Christie's, Kensington #46/R est:600-800
£1100 $1716 €1650 Venice, water carnival (36x53cm-14x21in) s. i.verso W/C. 20-Sep-2 Richardson & Smith, Whitby #139 est:550-600
£1100 $1815 €1595 Venice canal by night (44x25cm-17x10in) s. s.i.verso W/C bodycol. 2-Jul-3 Sotheby's, Olympia #232/R est:700-900
£1250 $2063 €1813 Venice (18x49cm-7x19in) s. W/C. 1-Jul-3 Bearnes, Exeter #453/R est:300-500
£3200 $5088 €4800 St. Paul's from the South Bank (55x44cm-22x17in) s. bodycol. 6-Mar-3 Christie's, Kensington #530/R est:800-1200

WASMANN, Friedrich (1805-1886) German
Works on paper
£382 $608 €550 Shepherd boy (20x7cm-8x3in) pencil double-sided. 5-May-3 Ketterer, Munich #326/R

WASMER, Erich (1915-1972) Swiss
£415 $647 €623 Annunciation (22x12cm-9x5in) board. 6-Nov-2 Dobiaschofsky, Bern #1062/R (S.FR 950)
£1441 $2248 €2162 View of Cuno Amiets studio in Oschwand (58x81cm-23x32in) s.d.43. 8-Nov-2 Dobiaschofsky, Bern #204/R est:4000 (S.FR 3300)
£1965 $3066 €2948 Landscape with young couple and easel (73x54cm-29x21in) lit. 8-Nov-2 Dobiaschofsky, Bern #203/R est:5500 (S.FR 4500)
£2096 $3270 €3144 Girl with branch (55x46cm-22x18in) s.d.42. 8-Nov-2 Dobiaschofsky, Bern #202/R est:4000 (S.FR 4800)
£2402 $3747 €3603 Leda with swan (27x37cm-11x15in) i. panel exhib. 8-Nov-2 Dobiaschofsky, Bern #206/R est:3000 (S.FR 5500)
£2620 $4087 €3930 Bremgarten at night (60x73cm-24x29in) s.d.38. 8-Nov-2 Dobiaschofsky, Bern #201/R est:5000 (S.FR 6000)
£2838 $4428 €4257 Self portrait with cigarette (58x48cm-23x19in) s.d.42 canvas on board. 8-Nov-2 Dobiaschofsky, Bern #200/R est:7500 (S.FR 6500)
£3057 $4769 €4586 Oberramsern hermitage (50x61cm-20x24in) s.d.43 lit. 8-Nov-2 Dobiaschofsky, Bern #208/R est:4500 (S.FR 7000)
£3275 $5109 €4913 Young pair with deer (74x57cm-29x22in) lit. 8-Nov-2 Dobiaschofsky, Bern #205/R est:5000 (S.FR 7500)
£20087 $31336 €30131 Palais des Merveilles (89x116cm-35x46in) s.i.d.54. 8-Nov-2 Dobiaschofsky, Bern #199/R est:18000 (S.FR 46000)

Works on paper
£393 $613 €590 Young dancer (22x11cm-9x4in) W/C over pencil. 6-Nov-2 Dobiaschofsky, Bern #1999/R (S.FR 900)

WASSENAAR, W A (1873-1956) Dutch
£1644 $2564 €2400 Tulip fields in full bloom in Dutch landscape (25x40cm-10x16in) s. panel. 10-Apr-3 Van Ham, Cologne #1750/R est:2000

WASSENBERGH, Elisabeth Geertruida (circle) (1726-1782) Dutch
£10828 $16892 €17000 Elegant company making music in an interior (60x48cm-24x19in) 6-Nov-2 Christie's, Amsterdam #43/R est:5000-7000

WASSENBERGH, Jan Abel (1689-1750) Dutch
£2000 $3140 €3000 Suffer the little children (54x66cm-21x26in) s. 10-Dec-2 Bonhams, New Bond Street #74/R est:2000-3000

WATANABE, Kazan (1793-1841) Japanese
Works on paper
£1006 $1600 €1509 Fisherman returning home (126x42cm-50x17in) s.i.d.1835 ink col hanging scroll. 24-Mar-3 Christie's, Rockefeller NY #52/R est:2000-3000

£1384 $2200 €2076 Bamboo and rock (129x28cm-51x11in) s.d.1832 ink hanging scroll prov.exhib. 24-Mar-3 Christie's, Rockefeller NY #50/R est:2000-3000
£10063 $16000 €15095 Autumn grasses (164x159cm-65x63in) s.d.1846 ink col gold gold leaf two-panel screens pair. 24-Mar-3 Christie's, Rockefeller NY #90/R est:20000-30000

WATELET, Charles Joseph (1867-1954) Belgian
£359 $579 €550 Fillette et sa poupee (60x47cm-24x19in) s.i.d.1930. 20-Jan-3 Horta, Bruxelles #20
£545 $845 €850 Elegante au chapeau vert (40x35cm-16x14in) s.d.1938. 9-Dec-2 Horta, Bruxelles #23
£654 $1052 €1000 Elegante a la robe verte (92x72cm-36x28in) s.d.1908. 20-Jan-3 Horta, Bruxelles #21
£680 $1082 €1000 Nu au miroir (64x45cm-25x18in) s.d.1937. 18-Mar-3 Vanderkindere, Brussels #130
£701 $1093 €1100 Elegante a la robe verte (92x72cm-36x28in) s.d.1908. 11-Nov-2 Horta, Bruxelles #110
£705 $1093 €1100 Timidite, jeune femme nue allongee (42x64cm-17x25in) s. 9-Dec-2 Horta, Bruxelles #24
£1923 $3000 €2885 Lady on a purple sofa (74x114cm-29x45in) s. 12-Oct-2 Neal Auction Company, New Orleans #159/R est:3500-4500
£2293 $3577 €3600 Portrait de jeune femme au collier de perles (117x87cm-46x34in) s.i. 11-Nov-2 Horta, Bruxelles #109 est:3000-5000
Works on paper
£517 $828 €750 Elegante au jardin (66x37cm-26x15in) s. chl. 17-Mar-3 Horta, Bruxelles #101

WATELIN, Louis (1838-1907) French
£550 $869 €825 Figure in a wooded river landscape (32x24cm-13x9in) s. 12-Nov-2 Bonhams, Knightsbridge #210/R

WATERFORD, Louisa Marchioness of (1818-1891) British
Works on paper
£480 $744 €720 Flower girl (24x16cm-9x6in) W/C. 24-Sep-2 Bonhams, Knightsbridge #69/R
£750 $1170 €1125 Portrait of young girl with an apple (29x23cm-11x9in) W/C sold with head study by same hand. 25-Mar-3 Bonhams, Knightsbridge #246/R
£1100 $1793 €1650 Story time (11x22cm-4x9in) W/C over pencil sold with four ink sketches. 29-Jan-3 Sotheby's, Olympia #57/R est:600-800
£1700 $2687 €2550 Four muses (10x19cm-4x7in) i. W/C over pencil set of four. 28-Nov-2 Sotheby's, London #248/R est:800-1200

WATERHOUSE, Alfred (1830-1905) British
Works on paper
£360 $565 €540 From San Miniato (26x36cm-10x14in) init.d.22 April 1870 pencil W/C. 19-Nov-2 Bonhams, Leeds #56
£950 $1520 €1425 From San Miniato, Italy (26x37cm-10x15in) init.i.d.70 W/C. 11-Mar-3 Bonhams, New Bond Street #54/R

WATERHOUSE, John William (1849-1917) British
£82000 $136120 €123000 Study for the Lady of shallot (91x52cm-36x20in) prov. 12-Jun-3 Sotheby's, London #42/R est:40000-60000
£220000 $365200 €330000 Listening to my sweet pipings (60x104cm-24x41in) s. prov.exhib.lit. 12-Jun-3 Sotheby's, London #36/R est:150000-200000
£500000 $790000 €750000 Spring spreads one green lap of flowers (106x77cm-42x30in) s.d.1910. 28-Nov-2 Sotheby's, London #29/R est:500000-700000
£600000 $966000 €900000 Mariamne (267x183cm-105x72in) s.d.1887. 19-Feb-3 Christie's, London #32/R est:1000000-1500000

WATERLOO, Anthonie (1609-1690) Flemish
Works on paper
£881 $1365 €1400 View of a valley (27x40cm-11x16in) pencil grey black chk. 4-Nov-2 Glerum, Amsterdam #101/R
£1032 $1600 €1548 Man and two donkeys in a wooded landscape (23x27cm-9x11in) pen black ink white chk grey wash. 3-Dec-2 Christie's, Rockefeller NY #55/R est:1000-1500
£1656 $2583 €2600 Hilly landscape (36x47cm-14x19in) black chk grey wash. 5-Nov-2 Sotheby's, Amsterdam #79/R est:2500-3500
£2264 $3509 €3600 Landscape with road (27x40cm-11x16in) pencil grey black chk. 4-Nov-2 Glerum, Amsterdam #98/R est:800-1200
£5500 $9185 €7975 Extensive landscape with a tavern among trees (15x18cm-6x7in) black chk W/C htd white pen ink prov.exhib. 8-Jul-3 Christie's, London #103/R est:6000-10000
£12000 $20040 €17400 View of Bloemendaal, with Haarlem in the distance (32x64cm-13x25in) black chk wash prov. 8-Jul-3 Christie's, London #104/R est:6000-8000

WATERLOO, Joannes Petrus (1790-1870) Dutch
£881 $1374 €1400 House and cart in wood (72x83cm-28x33in) s.d.1836 canvas on panel. 21-Sep-2 Bolland & Marotz, Bremen #575/R

WATERLOW, Sir Ernest Albert (1850-1919) British
Works on paper
£420 $655 €630 Down pasture Sussex (24x44cm-9x17in) s.i. pencil W/C scratching out. 27-Mar-3 Christie's, Kensington #136/R
£640 $998 €960 Down pastures, Sussex (23x43cm-9x17in) s. 9-Oct-2 Andrew Hartley, Ilkley #630
£700 $1105 €1050 Woman with ducks outside a cottage (32x43cm-13x17in) s. W/C over pencil htd bodycol stopping out. 28-Nov-2 Sotheby's, London #334/R

WATERMAN, Marcus (1834-1914) American
£3648 $5618 €5800 Reunion de dignitaires (51x40cm-20x16in) s. 23-Oct-2 Rabourdin & Choppin de Janvry, Paris #114/R
£3774 $5811 €6000 Hommes en bleu a l'entree de la casbah (51x40cm-20x16in) s.d.1887. 23-Oct-2 Rabourdin & Choppin de Janvry, Paris #115/R

WATERS, Billie (1896-1979) British
£600 $936 €900 Happy place (30x34cm-12x13in) s. board. 15-Oct-2 Bonhams, Knightsbridge #147/R
£700 $1092 €1050 Donkeys watering (72x91cm-28x36in) s. board. 27-Mar-3 Christie's, Kensington #619/R
£2000 $3140 €3000 Seal pup (35x51cm-14x20in) s. board. 15-Apr-3 Bonhams, Knightsbridge #30/R est:2000-3000
Works on paper
£360 $565 €540 Still life with flowers and shells (38x41cm-15x16in) s. gouache pastel. 15-Apr-3 Bonhams, Knightsbridge #83/R
£1200 $1860 €1800 Young fawn resting on a river bank (36x38cm-14x15in) s.i. verso mixed media. 4-Oct-2 Mallams, Oxford #556/R est:1200-1500

WATERS, George W (1832-1912) American
£566 $900 €849 Alpine landscape with figures (46x61cm-18x24in) s. 7-Mar-3 Jackson's, Cedar Falls #619/R est:800-1200
£5844 $9000 €8766 Bringing the herd back from pasture (66x112cm-26x44in) s.d.1876 prov. 24-Oct-2 Shannon's, Milford #83/R est:9000-12000

WATERS, J S (?) ?
Works on paper
£460 $718 €690 Venetian scene (24x44cm-9x17in) 31-Jul-2 James Thompson, Kirby Lonsdale #105

WATERS, Susan (1823-1900) American
£3503 $5500 €5255 Winter landscape with three sheep (51x64cm-20x25in) s. 23-Nov-2 Pook & Pook, Downington #171/R est:3000-5000
£8889 $14400 €12889 Lambs and sheep in a landscape (60x74cm-24x29in) s.d.1885. 22-May-3 Sotheby's, New York #767

WATERSTON, Dorothea (fl.1912-1935) British
Works on paper
£300 $465 €450 Up, up and away (39x35cm-15x14in) s.d.3-1912 pencil W/C. 4-Dec-2 Christie's, Kensington #166/R

WATHAN, Ernest (19th C) ?
£1379 $2193 €2000 Women in courtyard (58x40cm-23x16in) s. 5-Mar-3 Sotheby's, Milan #61 est:4000

WATKINS, B Colles (1833-1891) Irish
£946 $1476 €1400 Lakes of Killarney (19x39cm-7x15in) s. 26-Mar-3 James Adam, Dublin #7/R est:1200-1800

WATKINS, Carleton E (1829-1916) American
Photographs
£2532 $4000 €3798 Piwyac, the Vernal falls (30x19cm-12x7in) albumen print prov. 24-Apr-3 Phillips, New York #73/R est:5000-7000
£8861 $14000 €13292 Grizzly giant (51x36cm-20x14in) s. albumen print. 23-Apr-3 Sotheby's, New York #47/R est:10000-15000
£16234 $25000 €24351 Mirror view of the North Dome, Yosemite Valley (52x63cm-20x25in) albumen print exec.c.1865-1866 prov.lit. 25-Oct-2 Phillips, New York #3/R est:20000-25000

WATKINS, Dick (1937-) Australian
Works on paper
£1514 $2483 €2271 Number 15 (198x78cm-78x31in) s.i.d.1972 stretcher synthetic polymer paint canvas prov. 4-Jun-3 Deutscher-Menzies, Melbourne #350/R est:4500-6500 (A.D 3800)
£2500 $3975 €3750 Sketch for a half hearted homage to Henri Matisse (108x80cm-43x31in) s.i.d.1979-82 verso synthetic polymer paint canvas. 4-Mar-3 Deutscher-Menzies, Melbourne #166/R est:4500-6500 (A.D 6500)

WATKINS, Franklin Chenault (1894-1972) American
£1317 $2200 €1910 Surf fishermen (38x66cm-15x26in) init. i.verso. 22-Jun-3 Freeman, Philadelphia #133/R est:1000-1500
£4192 $7000 €6078 Man laughing at a woman (76x102cm-30x40in) s. prov. 22-Jun-3 Freeman, Philadelphia #119/R est:6000-10000

WATKINS, John Samuel (1886-1942) Australian
£9542 $15076 €14313 Portrait of the artist's wife. Seated nude (64x43cm-25x17in) s. double-sided. 2-Apr-3 Christie's, Melbourne #51/R est:7000-10000 (A.D 25000)
Works on paper
£421 $640 €632 Boy and dog (22x29cm-9x11in) s. W/C. 19-Aug-2 Joel, Victoria #331 est:1200-1500 (A.D 1200)

WATKINS, Kenneth (attrib) (1847-1933) New Zealander
£3135 $4890 €4703 Mitre Peak, Milford Sound (60x120cm-24x47in) 7-Nov-2 International Art Centre, Auckland #85/R est:10000-15000 (NZ.D 10000)

WATKINS, Richard John (1937-) Australian
Works on paper
£232 $358 €348 Untitled (56x75cm-22x30in) init.d.93 synthetic polymer on paper. 8-Sep-2 Sotheby's, Melbourne #60 (A.D 650)
£339 $522 €509 Untitled (56x76cm-22x30in) init.d.93 synthetic polymer on paper. 8-Sep-2 Sotheby's, Melbourne #96 est:500-800 (A.D 950)
£339 $522 €509 Untitled (57x76cm-22x30in) init.d.93 synthetic polymer on canvas. 8-Sep-2 Sotheby's, Melbourne #111 est:500-800 (A.D 950)
£357 $550 €536 Untitled (56x76cm-22x30in) init.d.93 synthetic polymer on paper. 8-Sep-2 Sotheby's, Melbourne #108 est:500-800 (A.D 1000)
£3500 $5390 €5250 Leaving the scene (152x122cm-60x48in) s.d.1988 i.verso synthetic polymer on canvas. 8-Sep-2 Sotheby's, Melbourne #30/R est:8000-12000 (A.D 9800)
£10000 $15400 €15000 Midnight ramble (152x244cm-60x96in) init.d.1991 i.verso synthetic polymer prov.exhib. 8-Sep-2 Sotheby's, Melbourne #4/R est:10000-12000 (A.D 28000)

WATKINS-PITCHFORD, Denys James (attrib) (1905-1990) British
Works on paper
£290 $470 €435 Grouse in flight (29x46cm-11x18in) s.d.1963 W/C. 20-May-3 Bonhams, Knowle #266

WATKISS, Gill (1938-) British
£310 $518 €450 Figures in a landscape St. Austell (27x29cm-11x11in) s.d.1999 board. 19-Jun-3 Lane, Penzance #345
£460 $750 €690 Wedding day, St Just (60x52cm-24x20in) s. board. 17-Feb-3 Bonhams, Bath #166
£520 $863 €754 Wedding day, St Just (61x53cm-24x21in) s. board. 10-Jun-3 David Lay, Penzance #148
£550 $858 €825 Cape Cornwall (61x76cm-24x30in) d.2002. 17-Oct-2 David Lay, Penzance #1147/R
£600 $936 €900 On the road to Pendeen (61x76cm-24x30in) s.d.2000 board. 17-Oct-2 David Lay, Penzance #1146
£650 $1014 €975 Last day of summer (58x74cm-23x29in) s.d.1989 board. 17-Oct-2 David Lay, Penzance #1148

WATRIN, Étienne (19/20th C) ?
Sculpture
£1146 $1800 €1719 He loves me (38cm-15in) s. ivory bronze. 23-Nov-2 Jackson's, Cedar Falls #254/R est:500-800

WATRIN, G (19/20th C) French?
£446 $700 €669 Cour de L'abbaye (70x51cm-28x20in) s.i.d.Avril 1912. 14-Dec-2 Weschler, Washington #614/R

WATSON, Adele (1873-1947) American?
£435 $700 €653 Anthropomorphic series, figures, landscape (53x66cm-21x26in) s.d.1928 oil mixed media board prov. 18-Feb-3 John Moran, Pasadena #145
£481 $750 €722 Point Lobos (77x102cm-30x40in) s. 13-Apr-3 Butterfields, Los Angeles #7013
£559 $900 €839 Anthropomorphic series, figures, landscape (53x69cm-21x27in) s.d.1928 oil mixed media board prov. 18-Feb-3 John Moran, Pasadena #146
£621 $1000 €932 Anthropomorphic series, figures, landscape (53x66cm-21x26in) s.d.1928 oil mixed media board prov. 18-Feb-3 John Moran, Pasadena #144
£870 $1400 €1305 Anthropomorphic series, figures, landscape (53x66cm-21x26in) s.d.1928 oil mixed media board prov.exhib. 18-Feb-3 John Moran, Pasadena #143 est:2000-3000

WATSON, Albert (1942-) American
Photographs
£2435 $3750 €3653 Elvis on South 3rd Street, Las Vegas, Nevada (61x50cm-24x20in) s.i.d.2000 photograph. 24-Oct-2 Sotheby's, New York #269/R est:4000-6000
£3571 $5500 €5357 Heel on stove top, Las Vegas, Nevada (45x61cm-18x24in) s.i.d.2001 photograph. 24-Oct-2 Sotheby's, New York #268/R est:4000-6000

WATSON, C (19th C) British
£1350 $2147 €2025 Highland cattle grazing (33x51cm-13x20in) s.d.1901. 3-Mar-3 Louis Taylor, Stoke on Trent #843

WATSON, Charles John (1846-1927) British
Works on paper
£560 $890 €840 Rimini (18x25cm-7x10in) s.i.d.1893 W/C. 4-Mar-3 Bearnes, Exeter #325
£580 $899 €870 Walberswick (14x30cm-6x12in) i.d.Aug 24th 1887 W/C over pencil. 30-Sep-2 Bonhams, Ipswich #287/R
£840 $1336 €1260 Bosham, Sussex (19x34cm-7x13in) s.i.d.1888 W/C. 4-Mar-3 Bearnes, Exeter #392

WATSON, Charles John (attrib) (1846-1927) British
Works on paper
£330 $521 €479 Figures on the coast (25x38cm-10x15in) mono.d.73 W/C. 23-Jul-3 Mallams, Oxford #103/R

WATSON, Donald (20th C) British
£260 $429 €377 Migrating geese (19x34cm-7x13in) s. board. 1-Jul-3 Bearnes, Exeter #540/R
Works on paper
£280 $431 €420 Peregrine falcon in diving flight (36x25cm-14x10in) s.d.1965 W/C. 24-Oct-2 Thomson, Roddick & Medcalf, Carlisle #341
£500 $770 €750 Geese over the border hills, ducks in the estuary below (28x46cm-11x18in) s.d.1975 W/C. 24-Oct-2 Thomson, Roddick & Medcalf, Carlisle #340

WATSON, Elizabeth Villa Taylor (1863-1949) American
£2987 $4600 €4481 Portrait of a young girl holding a brass basket (89x61cm-35x24in) s. 26-Oct-2 Brunk, Ashville #433/R est:2000-4000

WATSON, George (1767-1837) British
£7200 $11160 €10800 Full length portrait of Major General Dudgeon (233x151cm-92x59in) prov. 6-Dec-2 Lyon & Turnbull, Edinburgh #23/R est:6000-8000

WATSON, George (attrib) (1767-1837) British
£420 $693 €609 Portrait of a gentleman (75x62cm-30x24in) 2-Jul-3 Sotheby's, Olympia #56/R

WATSON, George Spencer (1869-1934) British
£900 $1449 €1350 Dunshay, the goats yard (63x76cm-25x30in) double-sided. 14-Jan-3 Bonhams, Knightsbridge #120/R
£4900 $7644 €7350 Marishka (112x86cm-44x34in) s. prov.exhib. 27-Mar-3 Christie's, Kensington #417/R est:6000-8000

WATSON, Harry (1871-1936) British
£420 $693 €609 Pool of London (25x36cm-10x14in) s. 6-Jul-3 Lots Road, London #351
Works on paper
£215 $339 €323 Songbirds on branches (44x32cm-17x13in) s.d.Marz 96 W/C over pencil htd white. 29-Nov-2 Falk & Falk, Zurich #486/R (S.FR 500)
£440 $704 €660 Castle at the end of Loch Awe (31x41cm-12x16in) s. W/C. 15-May-3 Lawrence, Crewkerne #855/R

WATSON, Henry S (1868-1933) American
£1195 $1900 €1793 Fly fishing (76x51cm-30x20in) s. canvasboard. 7-Mar-3 Skinner, Boston #431/R est:1200-1800

WATSON, Homer Ransford (1855-1936) Canadian
£535 $829 €803 Rock formation edge of the forest (16x23cm-6x9in) init, board double-sided. 3-Dec-2 Joyner, Toronto #307/R est:800-1200 (C.D 1300)

£667 $1093 €1001 Bend in the river, winter (25x34cm-10x13in) s. board. 3-Jun-3 Joyner, Toronto #245/R est:2000-3000 (C.D 1500)
£738 $1143 €1107 Banks of the Credit (32x42cm-13x17in) s. i.verso board prov. 24-Sep-2 Ritchie, Toronto #3141/R est:1800-2400 (C.D 1800)
£907 $1433 €1361 James Watson's old mill at Doon (30x41cm-12x16in) s.i. verso board prov. 14-Nov-2 Heffel, Vancouver #127 est:2000-2500 (C.D 2250)
£978 $1604 €1467 Farmhouse and stream (35x25cm-14x10in) s. board. 27-May-3 Sotheby's, Toronto #161/R est:1500-2000 (C.D 2200)
£988 $1531 €1482 Train by a farmstead (19x28cm-7x11in) s. board. 3-Dec-2 Joyner, Toronto #154/R est:1000-1500 (C.D 2400)
£1070 $1658 €1605 Landscape with fence (31x41cm-12x16in) s. board prov. 3-Dec-2 Joyner, Toronto #398 est:2000-2500 (C.D 2600)
£1481 $2296 €2222 Durham cathedral (25x34cm-10x13in) s. board. 3-Dec-2 Joyner, Toronto #325/R est:2000-3000 (C.D 3600)
£1646 $2551 €2469 Grand river banks below Galt (31x41cm-12x16in) s. board. 3-Dec-2 Joyner, Toronto #260/R est:2000-2500 (C.D 4000)
£2044 $3353 €3066 Village by the water (44x59cm-17x23in) s. 3-Jun-3 Joyner, Toronto #114/R est:3000-4000 (C.D 4600)
£6996 $10844 €10494 November among the oaks (56x77cm-22x30in) s. exhib. 3-Dec-2 Joyner, Toronto #112/R est:15000-20000 (C.D 17000)

WATSON, J (?) ?
£350 $539 €525 Barges at a Continental quay (51x41cm-20x16in) s. 24-Oct-2 Christie's, Kensington #96

WATSON, J D (1832-1892) British
£2000 $3080 €3000 Going to market (63x109cm-25x43in) 5-Sep-2 Christie's, Kensington #280/R est:1500-2000

WATSON, James (19/20th C) British
£400 $624 €600 Lady Palmer's cottage (18x23cm-7x9in) s. board. 20-Sep-2 Richardson & Smith, Whitby #199
£480 $773 €720 River landscape with figure in a rowing boat (84x127cm-33x50in) 19-Feb-3 Mallams, Oxford #454/R
£620 $980 €930 Moored Cobles with Henrietta Street and the abbey beyond (20x30cm-8x12in) s. board. 24-Apr-3 Richardson & Smith, Whitby #70/R
£820 $1279 €1230 Cliff top cottage at Runswick Bay (21x29cm-8x11in) i. panel. 10-Sep-2 David Duggleby, Scarborough #300/R
Works on paper
£350 $546 €525 Windswept heathland landscape (38x58cm-15x23in) s.d.1906 W/C. 18-Oct-2 Keys, Aylsham #597

WATSON, Jenny (1951-) Australian
£4563 $7575 €7768 Crimean wars pm (274x183cm-108x72in) s.d.1985 verso oil acrylic gouache cotton duck prov.exhib.lit. 10-Jun-3 Shapiro, Sydney #48/R est:12000-18000 (A.D 11500)
£6429 $10029 €9644 My father's music (152x183cm-60x72in) s.d.1987 oil synthetic polymer paint collage damask. 11-Nov-2 Deutscher-Menzies, Melbourne #55/R est:8000-12000 (A.D 18000)
£8214 $12650 €12321 Horse series painting no.6, single green ribbon (182x246cm-72x97in) s.d.1974 s.i.d.verso oil synthetic polymer on canvas. 8-Sep-2 Sotheby's, Melbourne #52/R est:8000-12000 (A.D 23000)
Works on paper
£1964 $3025 €2946 Cobwebs (203x294cm-80x116in) mixed media on linen executed c.1993. 8-Sep-2 Sotheby's, Melbourne #73/R est:2000-3000 (A.D 5500)

WATSON, John (early 20th C) British?
£580 $893 €870 Rural snow scene at dusk with figures (30x39cm-12x15in) s. 22-Oct-2 Sworder & Son, Bishops Stortford #606/R
£850 $1420 €1233 Still life with lobster, bread and wine (98x84cm-39x33in) s.d.91 s.i.d.verso. 17-Jun-3 Bonhams, Knightsbridge #54/R

WATSON, John Dawson (1832-1892) British
£323 $510 €485 Fine wine (36x25cm-14x10in) init.d.1891 panel. 18-Nov-2 Waddingtons, Toronto #110/R (C.D 800)
£700 $1120 €1050 Young girl leaning against a wall with red shawl (30x26cm-12x10in) mono. 11-Mar-3 Bonhams, Knightsbridge #227/R
£3797 $6000 €5696 On the way to the battle front (112x86cm-44x34in) init.d.1878. 1-Apr-3 Christie's, Rockefeller NY #187/R est:6000-8000
Works on paper
£350 $546 €525 Terrace at Haddon Hall, Derbyshire (23x34cm-9x13in) mono.d.1857 pencil W/C. 19-Sep-2 Christie's, Kensington #86

WATSON, Judy (1959-) Australian
Works on paper
£3585 $5880 €5378 Haze (193x88cm-76x35in) s.i.d.99 verso pigment ink prov.exhib. 4-Jun-3 Deutscher-Menzies, Melbourne #104/R est:7000-10000 (A.D 9000)

WATSON, P Fletcher (1842-1907) British
Works on paper
£480 $782 €720 Launching the fishing boat in St Ives (18x30cm-7x12in) s.i.d.1898 W/C. 13-Feb-3 David Lay, Penzance #133/R
£1400 $2184 €2100 Beautiful gate of Pardon, Sevilla (62x36cm-24x14in) s.i.d.1906 pencil W/C. 26-Mar-3 Sotheby's, Olympia #76/R est:300-400

WATSON, Percy Edward (1919-) Australian
£279 $457 €405 Houses, Warnambool, Victoria, facing Flagstaff Hill (29x35cm-11x14in) s. canvas on board. 4-Jun-3 Deutscher-Menzies, Melbourne #363/R (A.D 700)

WATSON, Raymond (1935-) British
Works on paper
£280 $440 €420 Magpie (46x58cm-18x23in) s. W/C. 13-Dec-2 Keys, Aylsham #577

WATSON, Robert (fl.1877-1920) British
£289 $457 €419 Highland cattle (51x76cm-20x30in) s. 18-Nov-2 Goodman, Sydney #39 (A.D 810)
£400 $640 €600 On guard, the legend of Beddgelert (51x75cm-20x30in) s.d.1896. 13-May-3 Bonhams, Sevenoaks #340/R
£720 $1145 €1080 Sheep and lambs on a hillside (20x30cm-8x12in) s.d.1899. 27-Feb-3 Bonhams, Chester #368
£1333 $2213 €1933 Shepherd and flock in a highland landscape (91x71cm-36x28in) s.d.1903. 10-Jun-3 Ritchie, Toronto #64/R est:3000-5000 (C.D 3000)
£2800 $4256 €4200 Highland cattle (51x76cm-20x30in) s.d.1913. 28-Aug-2 Sotheby's, London #832/R est:2000-3000
£3000 $4560 €4500 Sheep in a highland landscape (51x76cm-20x30in) s.d.1893. 28-Aug-2 Sotheby's, London #930/R est:2000-3000
£3000 $4680 €4500 Highland cattle (79x58cm-31x23in) s. indis d. 14-Apr-3 Sotheby's, London #44/R est:3000-5000
£3200 $4864 €4800 Shepherd with his flock in a highland valley. Highland cattle crossing a stream (30x25cm-12x10in) s. pair. 28-Aug-2 Sotheby's, London #906/R est:2500-3000
£4000 $6080 €6000 Sheep resting in a highland landscape (51x76cm-20x30in) s.d.1891. 28-Aug-2 Sotheby's, London #856/R est:2000-3000
£5200 $8164 €7800 Highland with their flock in a mountainous landscape (61x91cm-24x36in) s.d.1896. 16-Dec-2 Bonhams, Bury St Edmunds #482/R est:2500-4000
£5500 $8580 €8250 Near Loch Katrine (40x60cm-16x24in) s.d.1912 sold with another similar. 10-Apr-3 Bonhams, Edinburgh #109/R est:6000-8000

WATSON, Robert (1865-1916) British
£2200 $3608 €3300 Highland cattle watering (35x53cm-14x21in) s.d.1901. 29-May-3 Christie's, Kensington #89/R est:1500-2000
£4200 $6510 €6300 Highland cattle at a stream (91x71cm-36x28in) s.d.1909. 31-Oct-2 Christie's, London #81/R est:4000-6000

WATSON, Rosalie (fl.1877-1887) British
Works on paper
£2400 $3960 €3480 Portrait of a girl (46x43cm-18x17in) mono.d.1880 W/C gum arabic. 2-Jul-3 Sotheby's, Olympia #308/R est:1000-1500

WATSON, Sydney A (19th C) British
£4000 $6160 €6000 Near Loch Long, Argyllshire, Scotland (33x48cm-13x19in) s. i.verso. 5-Sep-2 Christie's, Kensington #149/R est:2500-3500

WATSON, Walter J (1879-?) British
£4167 $6708 €6251 Valley of the Machno (40x66cm-16x26in) s.d.1908 i. verso. 7-May-3 Dobiaschofsky, Bern #1051/R est:9000 (S.FR 9000)
£5500 $8910 €8250 Glen Nevis, Inverness shire (51x76cm-20x30in) s.d.1933 s.i.verso. 20-May-3 Sotheby's, Olympia #264/R est:1000-2000
£5645 $8919 €8468 On the Machno, north Wales. On the Conway (33x48cm-13x19in) s.d.1927 s.i.verso pair prov. 18-Nov-2 Waddingtons, Toronto #134/R est:8000-10000 (C.D 14000)
£11000 $18370 €15950 Cattle watering in a river landscape. On Conway, North Wales (40x65cm-16x26in) s.d.1923 pair. 17-Jun-3 Bonhams, New Bond Street #59/R est:6000-8000

WATSON, William (19/20th C) British
£2823 $4460 €4235 Highland sheep in mountain landscape (86x67cm-34x26in) s.d.1898 prov. 18-Nov-2 Waddingtons, Toronto #143/R est:5000-7000 (C.D 7000)

£3200 $5024 €4800 Sheep on a moor, a lake in the distance (34x48cm-13x19in) s.d.1890. 21-Nov-2 Tennants, Leyburn #799/R est:1000-1500
£5000 $7750 €7500 Highland cattle watering (152x100cm-60x39in) s. 5-Dec-2 Bonhams, Edinburgh #119/R est:4000-6000

WATSON, William (jnr) (?-1921) British
£3830 $5936 €5745 Hunters resting in the Scottish Highland (71x107cm-28x42in) s.d.1858. 8-Dec-2 Uppsala Auktionskammare, Uppsala #76/R est:50000-60000 (S.KR 54000)

WATSON, William Henry (19/20th C) British
£1800 $2808 €2700 Sheep by a loch (41x60cm-16x24in) s. 17-Sep-2 Sotheby's, Olympia #17/R est:1000-1500

WATSON, William J (19th C) American?
£3000 $4770 €4500 Collecting the flock morning (28x38cm-11x15in) s.d.1893. 18-Mar-3 Bonhams, New Bond Street #100/R est:3000-5000

WATSON, William R C (fl.1890-1898) British
£1000 $1560 €1500 Highland landscape with cattle in a stream (53x69cm-21x27in) s. 6-Nov-2 Bonhams, Chester #528 est:1000-1400

WATT, Alison (1965-) British
£5000 $7800 €7500 Young artists (107x91cm-42x36in) s.verso. 14-Apr-3 Sotheby's, London #184/R est:5000-7000
£10000 $15500 €15000 Hunger and the horse's head (122x122cm-48x48in) s. i.d.89-90 stretcher prov.exhib. 31-Oct-2 Christie's, London #208/R est:10000-15000

WATT, Elizabeth Mary (fl.1922-1940) British
£310 $508 €465 Mixed flowers in a glass vase (47x43cm-19x17in) s. board. 7-Jun-3 Shapes, Edinburgh #379
£450 $738 €675 Tulips in a glass vase, with a Buddha on a table (63x51cm-25x20in) s. 5-Jun-3 Christie's, Kensington #805

Works on paper
£720 $1181 €1080 Fairies, pixies and elves amongst birch trees before a mountain (24x34cm-9x13in) s. W/C pen ink. 7-Jun-3 Shapes, Edinburgh #377/R
£750 $1230 €1125 American Indian scout dancing beneath a tree watched by an elf (33x24cm-13x9in) s.d.1919 W/C pen ink. 7-Jun-3 Shapes, Edinburgh #376/R
£780 $1279 €1170 Two fairies and two cherubs amongst bluebells (34x23cm-13x9in) s. W/C pen ink. 7-Jun-3 Shapes, Edinburgh #378/R
£850 $1394 €1275 Harlequin and dancer beneath autumn tree (33x23cm-13x9in) s.d.1929 W/C pen ink. 7-Jun-3 Shapes, Edinburgh #375/R

WATT, James (?) British?
£300 $492 €435 Greenock harbour and fishing boats (46x92cm-18x36in) s. 7-Jun-3 Shapes, Edinburgh #361
£340 $558 €493 Steamer and fishing boats at harbour (40x101cm-16x40in) s. 7-Jun-3 Shapes, Edinburgh #362
£460 $754 €667 Kaffir at Ayr (71x102cm-28x40in) s. exhib. 7-Jun-3 Shapes, Edinburgh #360

WATT, L H (19/20th C) British?
£360 $572 €540 Trawlers off a harbour mouth in a choppy sea (31x61cm-12x24in) indis sig.d.71. 27-Feb-3 Bonhams, Chester #429

WATT, Linnie (fl.1874-1908) British
£552 $877 €800 Woman and girl in a summer landscape (32x56cm-13x22in) s. 10-Mar-3 Sotheby's, Amsterdam #127

WATT, Millar (?) British
£1050 $1743 €1523 Wire haired fox terrier (32x32cm-13x13in) s. panel. 12-Jun-3 Christie's, Kensington #246/R est:600-800

WATT, William Godfrey (1885-?) American
£923 $1450 €1385 Fall landscape with pond surrounded by colourful trees and grassy hillside (51x61cm-20x24in) s. i. on stretcher. 19-Apr-3 James Julia, Fairfield #332/R est:1750-2250

WATTEAU DE LILLE, Louis Joseph (1731-1798) French
£3671 $5800 €5800 Deux bacchantes et un satyre (26x19cm-10x7in) s.d.1796 panel pair prov.exhib. 27-Nov-2 Christie's, Paris #45/R est:5000-7000
£13462 $21269 €21000 Une musique ambulante a la porte d'un chateau (50x67cm-20x26in) s.d.1795 panel prov.lit. 14-Nov-2 Credit Municipal, Paris #22/R est:18000-22000

WATTEAU, François L J (attrib) (1758-1823) French

Works on paper
£641 $994 €1000 Portrait de femme au chat (19x15cm-7x6in) crayon. 4-Dec-2 Piasa, Paris #95/R

WATTEAU, Jean Antoine (1684-1721) French

Works on paper
£55556 $90000 €83334 Madonna and Child (15x11cm-6x4in) chk after Schedone prov.lit. 22-Jan-3 Christie's, Rockefeller NY #65/R est:35000

WATTEAU, Monique (20th C) French
£1918 $3011 €2800 Couple enlace (53x73cm-21x29in) s. cardboard. 15-Apr-3 Laurence Calmels, Paris #4367/R est:150-200

WATTERS, L R M (20th C) British
£900 $1395 €1350 Mevagissey, ploughing by the sea. Polperro, horse and cart on a street (56x74cm-22x29in) s.d.1936 canvasboard pair. 26-Sep-2 Lane, Penzance #253

WATTEVILLE, Felicie de (1795-?) French

Miniatures
£1900 $3116 €2755 Young lady in black velvet dress (9cm-4in) s. gilt metal frame oval prov.exhib.lit. 3-Jun-3 Christie's, London #220/R est:800-1200

WATTS, D (?) ?
£416 $650 €624 Three Highland cattle (61x41cm-24x16in) s. 14-Sep-2 Weschler, Washington #590/R

WATTS, E (19/20th C) British?
£1250 $1963 €1875 Shipping off the coast (29x60cm-11x24in) s. pair. 29-Jul-2 David Duggleby, Scarborough #420/R est:1200-1800

WATTS, Frederick William (1800-1862) British
£258 $402 €374 Figures in a sunny forest glade (41x56cm-16x22in) 26-Mar-3 Walker's, Ottawa #67/R (C.D 600)
£900 $1431 €1350 Cottage hidden by trees, cows grazing in the foreground (10x10cm-4x4in) board. 19-Mar-3 Sotheby's, London #89/R
£920 $1435 €1380 Cottage in a wooded landscape with figures by a river (25x30cm-10x12in) board. 7-Nov-2 Christie's, Kensington #129
£1100 $1760 €1650 Farmhouse at Hill's Crest, East Bergholt (24x34cm-9x13in) paper laid down on canvas exhib. 15-May-3 Lawrence, Crewkerne #913/R
£1200 $1908 €1800 Meadow with cattle (11x16cm-4x6in) board. 19-Mar-3 Sotheby's, London #85/R est:1500-2000
£1200 $1908 €1800 Study of fishing boats on the beach (11x17cm-4x7in) board. 19-Mar-3 Sotheby's, London #86/R est:600-800
£1400 $2226 €2100 Overlooking the river Dart (11x17cm-4x7in) oil on card. 19-Mar-3 Sotheby's, London #90/R est:1000-1500
£1800 $2862 €2700 Study of tree trunks (11x17cm-4x7in) board. 19-Mar-3 Sotheby's, London #87/R est:1500-2000
£1800 $2862 €2700 Study of a plough (11x16cm-4x6in) board. 19-Mar-3 Sotheby's, London #88/R est:1500-2000
£2500 $3975 €3750 Studies of trees (17x11cm-7x4in) board pair. 19-Mar-3 Sotheby's, London #84/R est:3000-4000
£2500 $3975 €3750 Aylesford church, Kent, from the Medway. Village in a wooded landscape (11x16cm-4x6in) board pair. 19-Mar-3 Sotheby's, London #91/R est:3000-4000
£3000 $4740 €4500 Fishing by a Suffolk lock-gate (69x89cm-27x35in) 28-Nov-2 Sotheby's, London #114/R est:3000-4000
£3500 $5529 €5250 Cottage with figures in a wooded landscape (40x52cm-16x20in) 28-Nov-2 Sotheby's, London #132/R est:4000-6000
£6500 $10270 €9750 Wooded landscape with figures by cottage (51x74cm-20x29in) 26-Nov-2 Christie's, London #78/R est:7000-10000
£8000 $12560 €12000 Pandy mill, Bettws-y-Coed (102x127cm-40x50in) prov. 19-Nov-2 Bonhams, New Bond Street #52/R est:8000-12000
£15000 $23700 €22500 River landscape with fishermen and sheep on banks (85x116cm-33x46in) 26-Nov-2 Christie's, London #76/R est:15000-20000

Works on paper
£1100 $1826 €1595 Hampstead Heath (27x22cm-11x9in) pencil W/C prov. 10-Jun-3 Mellors & Kirk, Nottingham #779/R est:700-900

WATTS, Frederick William (attrib) (1800-1862) British
£1500 $2385 €2250 Angler in a wooded river landscape, cottage beyond (99x78cm-39x31in) 6-Mar-3 Christie's, Kensington #459/R est:1500-2000

WATTS, George Frederick (1817-1904) British
£1500 $2355 €2250 Behold your son, sir (14x24cm-6x9in) s. panel sketch verso. 19-Nov-2 Bonhams, New Bond Street #51/R est:1000-1500
£110000 $177100 €165000 Sir Galahad (54x26cm-21x10in) panel prov.exhib.lit. 19-Feb-3 Christie's, London #34/R est:120000-180000
£180000 $289800 €270000 Orpheus and Eurydice (33x53cm-13x21in) prov.exhib.lit. 20-Feb-3 Christie's, London #138/R est:70000

Works on paper

£450 $752 €653 Study of the monument to Queen Victoria (61x56cm-24x22in) W/C pencil. 24-Jun-3 Bonhams, Knightsbridge #77/R

£1000 $1610 €1500 Studies of arms for 'Orpheus and Eurydice' (51x31cm-20x12in) chk prov. 20-Feb-3 Christie's, London #139/R

£3800 $6232 €5510 People that walked in darkness have seen a great light (53x82cm-21x32in) red chk prov. 5-Jun-3 Christie's, London #120/R est:2000-3000

WATTS, George Frederick (after) (1817-1904) British

£10000 $16600 €15000 Hope (141x111cm-56x44in) canvas on board prov. 10-Jun-3 Christie's, London #108/R est:8000-12000

WATTS, James T (1853-1930) British

£320 $496 €480 View seat - coastal landscape viewed through the trees (90x59cm-35x23in) s.i.d.1878 verso oval. 1-Oct-2 Fellows & Sons, Birmingham #77

£360 $558 €540 Wooded clearing (33x51cm-13x20in) s. 4-Oct-2 Mallams, Oxford #531/R

Works on paper

£600 $948 €900 Windsor (33x57cm-13x22in) s. W/C. 27-Nov-2 Peter Wilson, Nantwich #128/R

£1000 $1550 €1500 Wooded landscape with children resting by the path (35x27cm-14x11in) pencil W/C htd white. 4-Dec-2 Christie's, Kensington #43/R est:1000-1500

£1300 $2028 €1950 River landscape (32x59cm-13x23in) s. W/C. 15-Oct-2 Bearnes, Exeter #379/R est:100-200

£2600 $4264 €3770 Quiet grey day (33x60cm-13x24in) s. pencil W/C bodycol prov.exhib. 5-Jun-3 Christie's, London #147/R est:2000-3000

WATTS, Nicholas (20th C) British

Works on paper

£2200 $3388 €3300 Monaco Grand Prix 1934, Moll leads team mate Chiron into Casino Square (108x73cm-43x29in) W/C htd white. 6-Sep-2 Bonhams, Knightsbridge #34/R est:1700-2000

WATZELHAN, Carl (1867-1942) Austrian

£2031 $3250 €3047 Still life with glass of wine, peaches and walnuts on a table (30x23cm-12x9in) s.d.1925 board. 14-May-3 Butterfields, San Francisco #1072/R est:3000-5000

£2821 $4400 €4232 Artist's family (48x63cm-19x25in) s.d.1893. 14-Sep-2 Weschler, Washington #584/R est:4000-6000

WAUCHOP, William S (1889-1971) New Zealander

£245 $348 €368 Country lane, Spanish Pyrennce (37x49cm-15x19in) s. 20-Mar-2 Watson's, Christchurch #34/R (NZ.D 800)

WAUD, Alfred Rudolf (1828-1891) American

£1623 $2500 €2435 Civil war sentry at sunset (23x30cm-9x12in) s. panel. 24-Oct-2 Shannon's, Milford #96/R est:3000-5000

WAUEN, Malines (19/20th C) ?

£300 $468 €450 Street scene with a cathedral beyond (40x25cm-16x10in) s. 9-Oct-2 Woolley & Wallis, Salisbury #219/R

WAUER, William (1866-1962) German

£1582 $2500 €2500 Weekly Berlin market (133x192cm-52x76in) s. masonite. 30-Nov-2 Bassenge, Berlin #6691 est:2500

£1795 $2836 €2800 Melody - seven colours (120x94cm-47x37in) s.d.1947. 14-Nov-2 Neumeister, Munich #710/R est:2500-3000

£9494 $15000 €15000 Great symphony - Eroica (120x200cm-47x79in) s. painted c.1947/51 prov.exhib.lit. 29-Nov-2 Villa Grisebach, Berlin #55/R est:12000-14000

£20959 $32695 €31439 Fancy dress ball (64x76cm-25x30in) s. 11-Apr-3 Kieselbach, Budapest #38/R est:6500000-7500000 (H.F 7500000)

£45000 $73350 €67500 Wirbelnde krafte (57x35cm-22x14in) init. painted 1917 prov.exhib.lit. 3-Feb-3 Christie's, London #37/R est:50000-70000

Sculpture

£1159 $1901 €1600 Nell Walden (14cm-6in) i. bronze Cast.W.Fussel Berlin exhib.lit. 29-May-3 Lempertz, Koln #960/R est:2000

£1456 $2300 €2300 Elsa Paulsen (23cm-9in) s.i. dark brown pat.bronze Cast.W.Fussel Berlin. 30-Nov-2 Bassenge, Berlin #6690/R est:3000

£2051 $3179 €3200 Compassion (2x11x25cm-1x4x10in) s. bronze Cast.W.Fussel Berlin lit. 4-Dec-2 Lempertz, Koln #1105/R est:3500

£3188 $5229 €4400 Pity (11x25cm-4x10in) s. bronze Cast.W.Fussel Berlin lit. 29-May-3 Lempertz, Koln #957/R est:3000

£4058 $6655 €5600 The shepherd (15x28cm-6x11in) s.i. bronze lit. 29-May-3 Lempertz, Koln #958/R est:3500

£9781 $15258 €14672 Figure in motion - boxer I (35cm-14in) s. bronze. 11-Apr-3 Kieselbach, Budapest #139/R est:3500000 (H.F 3500000)

Works on paper

£570 $900 €900 Walpurgis (28x37cm-11x15in) mono. i. verso pen. 30-Nov-2 Bassenge, Berlin #6694

WAUGH, Frederick J (1861-1940) American

£2600 $4316 €3770 Two figures and a dog crossing La Coupee Sark (75x99cm-30x39in) 12-Jun-3 Martel Maides, Guernsey #30/R est:2500-3000

£4217 $7000 €6115 Spirit of the sea (41x51cm-16x20in) s. board prov. 11-Jun-3 Butterfields, San Francisco #4050/R est:5000-7000

£5645 $8750 €8468 Waves crashing along a rocky coast (76x102cm-30x40in) s. 7-Dec-2 Selkirks, St. Louis #226/R est:10000-15000

£5844 $9000 €8766 Docks in snow (61x91cm-24x36in) s. board prov. 24-Oct-2 Shannon's, Milford #79/R est:9000-12000

£6289 $10000 €9434 Dashing water (51x76cm-20x30in) s. prov. 5-Mar-3 Sotheby's, New York #89/R est:7000-10000

£11613 $18000 €17420 Full gale (99x122cm-39x48in) s. masonite. 7-Dec-2 Selkirks, St. Louis #225/R est:10000-15000

£13699 $20000 €20549 Sun on sea and rocks (76x102cm-30x40in) s. masonite prov.exhib. 3-Nov-1 North East Auctions, Portsmouth #1001/R est:20000-25000

£44586 $70000 €66879 Ninety degrees north, polar bear and icebergs (153x183cm-60x72in) s. prov. 19-Nov-2 Butterfields, San Francisco #8022/R est:80000-100000

WAUGH, Frederick J (attrib) (1861-1940) American

£793 $1300 €1190 Crashing waves (46x61cm-18x24in) bears sig. 5-Feb-3 Doyle, New York #27/R est:800-1200

WAUGH, Samuel Bell (1814-1885) American

£590 $950 €885 Magdalene (61x51cm-24x20in) s.d.1858. 19-Jan-3 Jeffery Burchard, Florida #16/R

£1356 $2250 €1966 Portrait of a Mary Kempton (76x63cm-30x25in) prov. 11-Jun-3 Butterfields, San Francisco #4031/R est:3000-5000

WAUTERS, Camille (1856-1919) Belgian

£1871 $2993 €2600 Bord d'etang dans la brume (80x120cm-31x47in) s.d.1884. 13-May-3 Palais de Beaux Arts, Brussels #175 est:2000-3000

WAUTERS, Émile Charles (1846-1933) Belgian

£324 $518 €450 Portrait d'homme de profil (14x10cm-6x4in) mono. panel. 13-May-3 Vanderkindere, Brussels #37

£696 $1086 €1100 Portrait d'un chevalier portant un bonnet a la croix de Malte (48x39cm-19x15in) s. 20-Oct-2 Galerie de Chartres, Chartres #137

WAXSCHLUNGER, Johann Paul (c.1660-1724) German

£909 $1355 €1400 Hunting still life (19x26cm-7x10in) i. verso panel pair. 26-Jun-2 Neumeister, Munich #667/R

WAY, Andrew John Henry (1826-1888) American

£446 $700 €669 Still life with grapes (35x30cm-14x12in) s. indis d. 22-Nov-2 Skinner, Boston #92/R

WAY, Charles Jones (1834-1919) British

Works on paper

£205 $318 €308 Nr Portland (20x49cm-8x19in) s.i.d.1869 W/C prov. 24-Sep-2 Ritchie, Toronto #3073/R (C.D 500)

£250 $398 €375 Dart near Dittisham (42x68cm-17x27in) init. W/C. 18-Mar-3 Bearnes, Exeter #494

£258 $402 €387 Annecy (34x24cm-13x9in) s.i. W/C. 25-Mar-3 Ritchie, Toronto #83/R (C.D 600)

£311 $510 €451 Untitled - ships at full mast (10x36cm-4x14in) W/C. 1-Jun-3 Levis, Calgary #144/R (C.D 700)

£356 $583 €516 Yale, BC (17x24cm-7x9in) s.i. W/C. 9-Jun-3 Hodgins, Calgary #109/R (C.D 800)

£412 $638 €618 Alpine landscape (51x34cm-20x13in) s.i. W/C. 3-Dec-2 Joyner, Toronto #387 est:1500-2000 (C.D 1000)

£820 $1270 €1230 Capri (63x48cm-25x19in) s.i. W/C prov. 24-Sep-2 Ritchie, Toronto #3103/R est:2500-3000 (C.D 2000)

£820 $1270 €1230 Figures near Alpine stream (63x48cm-25x19in) s.d.1883 W/C prov. 24-Sep-2 Ritchie, Toronto #3104/R est:2000-2500 (C.D 2000)

£1217 $1887 €1826 Zinal (71x47cm-28x19in) s.i.d.81 W/C. 7-Dec-2 Galerie du Rhone, Sion #351/R est:2000-3000 (S.FR 2800)

WAY, Emily C (fl.1886-1896) British

£450 $698 €675 Army officer (138x102cm-54x40in) s.d.1899. 30-Sep-2 Sotheby's, Olympia #575

WAY, Johan Vilhelm Carl (1792-1873) Swedish

Miniatures

£1300 $2041 €1950 Portraits of Young gentleman and lady (7cm-3in) s.d.1829 gilt metal frame oval. 10-Dec-2 Christie's, London #188/R est:600-800

WAY, Thomas Robert (1862-1913) British
£3200 $5216 €4800 Shop in an old quarter of Paris (8x13cm-3x5in) panel exhib. 17-Feb-3 Bonhams, Bath #72 est:100-200

WAY, William Cosens (1833-1905) British
Works on paper
£400 $640 €600 Figures on a beach at low (46x74cm-18x29in) s. W/C. 11-Mar-3 Gorringes, Lewes #2380

WAYCOTT, Hedley (1865-1938) American
£597 $950 €896 Raven landscape (28x38cm-11x15in) s. board painted c.1925. 2-Mar-3 Toomey, Oak Park #677/R
£641 $1000 €962 Reflective waters (38x30cm-15x12in) s. board. 10-Nov-2 Selkirks, St. Louis #983/R
£974 $1500 €1461 Lake Michigan dunes (66x81cm-26x32in) s.d.1934 board. 8-Sep-2 Treadway Gallery, Cincinnati #642/R est:1000-2000

WEARING, Gillian (1963-) British
Photographs
£4000 $6680 €5800 Kelly and Melanie (84x127cm-33x50in) black white photo edition of 5 prov.lit. 24-Jun-3 Sotheby's, Olympia #145/R est:4000-6000
£4500 $7380 €6750 Sign that say what you want them to say - Come back Mary (40x30cm-16x12in) C-print on aluminium exec.1992-93 prov.lit. 6-Feb-3 Christie's, London #738/R est:4000-6000
£8500 $13090 €12750 I'm desperate (119x80cm-47x31in) chromagenic print executed 1992-93 prov.lit. 23-Oct-2 Christie's, London #244/R est:5000-7000

WEATHERBY, Richard (fl.1919-1940) British
£420 $697 €609 Portrait of a horse, Kittiwake (41x51cm-16x20in) s.i. 10-Jun-3 David Lay, Penzance #317

WEATHERHEAD, William Harris (1843-1903) British
£2000 $3100 €3000 Crumbs from a poor man's table (77x64cm-30x25in) s.d.1877 exhib. 3-Dec-2 Sotheby's, Olympia #78/R est:2000-3000
Works on paper
£260 $408 €390 Fishergirl on a shore (36x20cm-14x8in) s. W/C bodycol. 21-Nov-2 Tennants, Leyburn #687
£402 $635 €603 Young net mender (33x23cm-13x9in) W/C. 1-Dec-2 Levis, Calgary #239/R (C.D 1000)

WEATHERILL (19th C) British
Works on paper
£780 $1217 €1170 Whitby Abbey, NW, ruins with cows grazing (47x62cm-19x24in) i. W/C. 10-Sep-2 David Duggleby, Scarborough #279/R

WEATHERILL, George (1810-1890) British
£2100 $3276 €3150 Sunset shoreline (50x76cm-20x30in) 26-Mar-3 Sotheby's, Olympia #66/R est:1000-2000
Works on paper
£380 $593 €570 Cupid shaping his bow (15x9cm-6x4in) s.i. W/C monochrome wash ink. 10-Sep-2 David Duggleby, Scarborough #234/R
£400 $624 €600 Group from Wilkie's village festival. s.d.1839 W/C pen ink. 10-Sep-2 David Duggleby, Scarborough #235/R
£469 $750 €704 Campfire on the beach (18x13cm-7x5in) init. W/C. 15-Mar-3 Selkirks, St. Louis #694/R
£750 $1170 €1125 Whitby from Saltwick Nab (8x13cm-3x5in) W/C. 20-Sep-2 Richardson & Smith, Whitby #102
£800 $1304 €1200 Shipping off Whitby (10x15cm-4x6in) W/C. 30-Jan-3 Richardson & Smith, Whitby #576
£1150 $1794 €1725 Landing the catch, possibly Whitby (12x21cm-5x8in) s. W/C. 17-Sep-2 Bonhams, Sevenoaks #234 est:120-180
£1350 $2120 €2025 Kettleness looking towards Runswick Bay (12x20cm-5x8in) s. i.verso pencil W/C. 19-Nov-2 Bonhams, Leeds #64/R est:1000-1500
£1400 $2282 €2100 Beach scene, Whitby (12x21cm-5x8in) s.d.1883 W/C. 29-Jan-3 Sotheby's, Olympia #147/R est:800-1400
£1700 $2703 €2550 Figures unloading a beached ship (8x13cm-3x5in) W/C. 29-Apr-3 Gorringes, Lewes #2226
£2050 $3198 €3075 View of Robin Hoods Bay dock end (11x22cm-4x9in) s. W/C. 10-Sep-2 David Duggleby, Scarborough #274/R est:1000-2000
£4200 $6552 €6300 Shipping off the North East Coast (12x20cm-5x8in) init. W/C. 25-Mar-3 Bonhams, Leeds #504/R est:1000-1500
£4200 $6636 €6300 Stormy sea off Whitby (10x20cm-4x8in) init.verso W/C sold with a letter. 24-Apr-3 Richardson & Smith, Whitby #100 est:4000-5000

WEATHERILL, George (attrib) (1810-1890) British
Works on paper
£900 $1413 €1350 Fishing pushing their boat off the beach (9x14cm-4x6in) W/C over pencil. 21-Nov-2 Tennants, Leyburn #654/R
£4500 $7290 €6525 Coastal landscape - possibly Scarborough and Whitby. W/C pair in one frame. 29-Jul-3 Holloways, Banbury #326 est:300-400

WEATHERILL, Mary (1834-1913) British
Works on paper
£260 $434 €377 Towards Ravenscar (20x30cm-8x12in) init.d.Aug 11th 1859 pencil. 26-Jun-3 Richardson & Smith, Whitby #616
£340 $530 €510 Landscape study (9x15cm-4x6in) s. W/C. 10-Apr-3 Tennants, Leyburn #846
£350 $546 €525 Hawsker Bottoms (28x48cm-11x19in) s. W/C. 20-Sep-2 Richardson & Smith, Whitby #104
£400 $640 €600 Old union mill, Whitby (17x35cm-7x14in) s. W/C. 11-Mar-3 David Duggleby, Scarborough #35/R
£540 $864 €810 Yorkshire - landscape with town in the distance (18x36cm-7x14in) W/C attrib Richard Weatherill. 11-Mar-3 David Duggleby, Scarborough #120
£580 $916 €870 Off Whitby. W/C. 24-Apr-3 Richardson & Smith, Whitby #188a
£750 $1223 €1088 Coastal scene near Scarborough (16x27cm-6x11in) s. W/C. 16-Jul-3 James Thompson, Kirby Lonsdale #98/R
£2800 $4368 €4200 Coastal scene with cottages, possibly a scene at Robin Hoods Bay (33x45cm-13x18in) s.i. pencil W/C. 25-Mar-3 Bonhams, Leeds #505 est:800-900
£3600 $5616 €5400 Vessels in the harbour, Whitby by moonlight (25x36cm-10x14in) s. W/C. 20-Sep-2 Richardson & Smith, Whitby #100/R est:3500-4000

WEATHERILL, Richard (1844-1913) British
£800 $1248 €1200 Whitby Abbey by moonlight (17x29cm-7x11in) s. 10-Sep-2 David Duggleby, Scarborough #318/R
£6300 $9828 €9450 Whitby harbour with twin masted sailing ship (21x37cm-8x15in) s. board. 10-Sep-2 David Duggleby, Scarborough #330/R est:7000-10000
Works on paper
£1200 $1872 €1800 View of Whitby from the railway (23x36cm-9x14in) s.d.1881 i.verso W/C. 20-Sep-2 Richardson & Smith, Whitby #97 est:1000-1500
£7800 $12090 €11700 View of Whitby Harbour. Outer Harbour with castle beyond (23x36cm-9x14in) s. W/C htd white two. 31-Oct-2 Duke & Son, Dorchester #186/R est:2000-3000

WEATHERILL, Richard (attrib) (1844-1913) British
Works on paper
£3900 $6084 €5850 Whitby Harbour with shipping (48x72cm-19x28in) W/C. 25-Mar-3 Bonhams, Leeds #503/R est:1500-2000

WEATHERSTONE, Alfred C (fl.1888-1929) British
Works on paper
£700 $1092 €1050 Rose girl (38x26cm-15x10in) s. pencil W/C. 27-Mar-3 Christie's, Kensington #6/R

WEAVER, Herbert Parsons (1872-1945) British
Works on paper
£380 $589 €570 Continental town with boats on the river (24x34cm-9x13in) s. W/C. 24-Sep-2 Anderson & Garland, Newcastle #345/R
£420 $659 €630 Venetian canal (25x35cm-10x14in) s.d.1926 W/C bodycol. 21-Nov-2 Tennants, Leyburn #657
£600 $948 €900 Gatehouse at the Old Moat Farm, Stapleton, Shropshire (28x23cm-11x9in) s. W/C. 13-Nov-2 Halls, Shrewsbury #366/R

WEAVER, Thomas (1774-1843) British
£5000 $8250 €7250 Pointer in a landscape (61x77cm-24x30in) s.i.d.1799. 2-Jul-3 Sotheby's, Olympia #140/R est:2000-3000

WEAVER, Thomas (attrib) (1774-1843) British
£5800 $9222 €8700 Trojan, 8 year old Hereford bull in landscape (61x74cm-24x29in) 27-Feb-3 Brightwells, Leominster #865/R est:6000-8000

WEBB, Archibald (jnr) (fl.1886-1892) British
£1582 $2468 €2500 Boat leaving Limehouse (62x90cm-24x35in) s.i.d.1888. 16-Sep-2 Horta, Bruxelles #83
Works on paper
£280 $434 €420 Canal scene with figures in a sailing boat (46x89cm-18x35in) s.d.1890 W/C. 31-Oct-2 Ambrose, Loughton #72

WEBB, Bill (1940-) Canadian

£	$	€	Description
£1378	$2260	€1998	Furrows and fence line (122x152cm-48x60in) acrylic. 1-Jun-3 Levis, Calgary #145/R est:2250-2500 (C.D 3100)

WEBB, Byron (fl.1846-1866) British

£	$	€	Description
£2600	$4134	€3900	Stag and hinds in a landscape (69x91cm-27x36in) s.d.1865. 6-Mar-3 Christie's, Kensington #59/R est:2000-3000

WEBB, Byron (attrib) (fl.1846-1866) British

£	$	€	Description
£3600	$5616	€5400	Huntsman with hounds (34x52cm-13x20in) board. 17-Oct-2 Lawrence, Crewkerne #1585/R est:2000-3000

WEBB, Charles Meer (1830-1895) British

£	$	€	Description
£400	$644	€580	Tyrolean interior with card players (15x19cm-6x7in) s.d.1895. 7-May-3 Gorringes, Bexhill #929
£780	$1287	€1131	Quiet moment (49x40cm-19x16in) s.d.1889. 1-Jul-3 Bearnes, Exeter #505/R
£1800	$2808	€2700	Espionage (66x86cm-26x34in) s.d.1872 board. 7-Nov-2 Christie's, Kensington #240 est:2000-3000
£2000	$3320	€3000	Card game (40x50cm-16x20in) s.d.1896. 10-Jun-3 Bonhams, Knightsbridge #234/R est:2000-3000

WEBB, Edward (c.1805-1854) British

Works on paper

£	$	€	Description
£280	$431	€420	Church in a valley (30x20cm-12x8in) i. W/C. 24-Oct-2 Grant, Worcester #294

WEBB, J (1825-1895) British

£	$	€	Description
£491	$747	€737	Wales landscape (11x21cm-4x8in) s.i.verso board. 19-Aug-2 Joel, Victoria #230 est:1000-1500 (A.D 1400)
£2041	$3245	€3000	Entablement fleuri (104x143cm-41x56in) s. 18-Mar-3 Galerie Moderne, Brussels #522/R est:1800-2200

WEBB, James (1825-1895) British

£	$	€	Description
£380	$616	€570	Windy day (23x33cm-9x13in) indis.s. s.i.d.1877 verso panel. 23-Jan-3 Christie's, Kensington #234
£881	$1356	€1400	Sunset (18x29cm-7x11in) i.d.1875 verso paper on canvas. 28-Oct-2 Il Ponte, Milan #263
£900	$1440	€1350	Night (35x50cm-14x20in) s.d.1878 s.i.d.1878 verso panel. 15-May-3 Lawrence, Crewkerne #982/R
£900	$1458	€1350	Luggers off a jetty (51x91cm-20x36in) s.d.58. 21-May-3 Christie's, Kensington #602/R
£1139	$1800	€1709	Shipping of the coast (25x41cm-10x16in) s.d.1876. 5-Apr-3 Neal Auction Company, New Orleans #187 est:2500-3500
£1300	$2028	€1950	Estuary scene with boats, church and windmills near Brill Holland (16x13cm-6x5in) s.d.1882 s.i.verso board. 10-Sep-2 Sworder & Son, Bishops Stortford #720/R est:600-1000
£1852	$3000	€2685	Ships at anchor in a Dutch estuary (63x98cm-25x39in) 29-Jul-3 Christie's, Rockefeller NY #130/R est:3000-5000
£1923	$2981	€3000	On the beach, Scheveningen, Holland (20x30cm-8x12in) s. panel. 3-Dec-2 Campo & Campo, Antwerp #352/R est:3500-4500
£2700	$4374	€4050	On the Scheldt (20x30cm-8x12in) 22-Jan-3 Bonhams, New Bond Street #366/R est:2000-3000
£4000	$6280	€6000	Namur, Belgium (61x107cm-24x42in) s. 21-Nov-2 Tennants, Leyburn #759/R est:4000-6000
£4000	$6480	€6000	On the coast at Scheveningen. Dordrecht barges in the estuary (30x56cm-12x22in) s.d.75 panel pair. 21-May-3 Christie's, Kensington #598/R est:4000-6000
£4430	$7000	€7000	Heidelberg Castle (77x107cm-30x42in) s. 26-Nov-2 Wiener Kunst Auktionen, Vienna #40/R est:7000-12000
£4655	$7541	€6750	Dutch canal scene with boats and figures (95x87cm-37x34in) s. 25-May-3 Uppsala Auktionskammare, Uppsala #71/R est:25000-30000 (S.KR 60000)
£4938	$8000	€7160	Coastal scene with fishing boats and a dinghy, rough seas offshore (76x127cm-30x50in) s. 29-Jul-3 Christie's, Rockefeller NY #141/R est:10000-15000
£8219	$12904	€12000	Shipping by Mount Orgueil, New Jersey (81x114cm-32x45in) s. 15-Apr-3 Sotheby's, Amsterdam #58/R est:7000-10000
£16000	$25440	€24000	Sailing vessels at low tide (90x153cm-35x60in) s.d.1869-75. 19-Mar-3 Sotheby's, London #246/R est:6000-8000
£26000	$41340	€39000	Arab vessels moored at the steps of a Moorish palace (91x152cm-36x60in) s.d.75. 29-Apr-3 Bonhams, New Bond Street #98/R est:12000-18000

WEBB, James (attrib) (1825-1895) British

£	$	€	Description
£1006	$1570	€1600	River landscape in evening light (16x31cm-6x12in) s.d.71. 21-Sep-2 Bolland & Marotz, Bremen #576/R

Works on paper

£	$	€	Description
£426	$689	€600	Vue des quais de Seine (39x60cm-15x24in) W/C. 26-May-3 Joron-Derem, Paris #79

WEBB, James (style) (1825-1895) British

£	$	€	Description
£1150	$1806	€1725	Weymouth Beach (51x77cm-20x30in) bears sig. 16-Dec-2 Sotheby's, Olympia #76/R est:1000-1500

WEBB, Joseph (1908-1962) British

£	$	€	Description
£250	$385	€375	Late summer track (61x78cm-24x31in) 3-Sep-2 Bristol Auction Rooms #535
£880	$1355	€1320	Port Isaac, the Gower (60x74cm-24x29in) 3-Sep-2 Bristol Auction Rooms #528/R

WEBB, Katherine (20th C) American

Works on paper

£	$	€	Description
£422	$650	€633	Rooftops (43x64cm-17x25in) s. W/C exec.c.1930. 8-Sep-2 Treadway Gallery, Cincinnati #653/R

WEBB, Kenneth (1927-) British

£	$	€	Description
£798	$1133	€1300	Costa Brava (36x56cm-14x22in) s. oil chk. 3-Apr-2 Woodwards, Cork #176
£850	$1318	€1275	Thatched cottages, Donegal (40x50cm-16x20in) s. board. 4-Dec-2 John Ross, Belfast #132
£850	$1420	€1233	Dog and chickens in a barn interior (51x66cm-20x26in) s. 25-Jun-3 Bonhams, Bury St Edmunds #589
£950	$1473	€1425	Irish cottage (35x40cm-14x16in) s. board. 4-Dec-2 John Ross, Belfast #4
£950	$1473	€1425	Stroll on the beach near Ballycastle (40x50cm-16x20in) s. board. 4-Dec-2 John Ross, Belfast #109
£1074	$1729	€1600	Portrait of Milo O'Shea (61x41cm-24x16in) s.d.1963 i.verso. 18-Feb-3 Whyte's, Dublin #190/R est:2000-2500
£1200	$1908	€1800	Horn Head (35x45cm-14x18in) s. board. 5-Mar-3 John Ross, Belfast #42 est:600-800
£1350	$2106	€2025	Irish landscape (38x58cm-15x23in) s. W/C. 15-Oct-2 Gorringes, Lewes #2301 est:500-800
£1350	$2093	€2025	An Irish churchyard (30x91cm-12x36in) s.d.1961. 4-Dec-2 John Ross, Belfast #213 est:1000-1200
£1500	$2325	€2250	Cushendun (40x61cm-16x24in) s. 4-Dec-2 John Ross, Belfast #234 est:1200-1400
£1519	$2354	€2400	Mournes from Tyrolla (38x92cm-15x36in) s.i.d.1958 verso. 24-Sep-2 De Veres Art Auctions, Dublin #120 est:2000-3000
£1656	$2583	€2600	Cottage in landscape (35x90cm-14x35in) s.d.62. 6-Nov-2 James Adam, Dublin #22/R est:1000-1500
£1700	$2839	€2465	Horses hauling timber by the farmyard pond (51x92cm-20x36in) s. 25-Jun-3 Bonhams, Bury St Edmunds #595/R est:2000-3000
£1700	$2839	€2465	Ebb tide, Pin Mill (60x51cm-24x20in) s.i.verso. 25-Jun-3 Bonhams, Bury St Edmunds #596 est:2000-3000
£1812	$2971	€2500	Dawn od spring (60x50cm-24x20in) s. prov. 28-May-3 Bonhams & James Adam, Dublin #61/R est:3000-4000
£1812	$2971	€2500	Wexford moon (41x102cm-16x40in) s. prov. 28-May-3 Bonhams & James Adam, Dublin #124/R est:1500-2000
£2000	$3180	€3000	Cottages Connemara (61x45cm-24x18in) s.d.59. 5-Mar-3 John Ross, Belfast #221 est:1200-1400
£2100	$3255	€3150	View of the mountains of Mourne (38x91cm-15x36in) s. 4-Dec-2 John Ross, Belfast #262 est:600-800
£2215	$3434	€3500	Winter landscape (34x89cm-13x35in) s. i.verso. 24-Sep-2 De Veres Art Auctions, Dublin #85 est:2000-3000
£2264	$3532	€3600	Rocky inlet (61x51cm-24x20in) s. i.verso. 17-Sep-2 Whyte's, Dublin #8/R est:3000-4000
£2361	$3754	€3400	Cutting turf, Ballinahinch (46x36cm-18x14in) s. i.verso prov. 29-Apr-3 Whyte's, Dublin #1/R est:4000-5000
£2436	$3824	€3800	Ditty's Farm, County Down (30x71cm-12x28in) s.d.1963 i.verso. 19-Nov-2 Whyte's, Dublin #7/R est:3000-5000
£2500	$3975	€3600	Summer - rose garden (46x30cm-18x12in) s. 29-Apr-3 Whyte's, Dublin #141/R est:4000-5000
£2564	$4026	€4000	Row of cottages, windy day (41x91cm-16x36in) s.d.1963. 19-Nov-2 Whyte's, Dublin #84/R est:3000-5000
£2600	$4342	€3770	Poppies (41x102cm-16x40in) s. 25-Jun-3 Bonhams, Bury St Edmunds #587/R est:3000-4000
£2778	$4417	€4000	May morning (51x102cm-20x40in) s. i.verso painted c.1974-75. 29-Apr-3 Whyte's, Dublin #202/R est:4000-5000
£2877	$4516	€4200	Still life with green bottle (60x41cm-24x16in) s. i.verso. 15-Apr-3 De Veres Art Auctions, Dublin #212/R est:4000-5000
£2953	$4754	€4400	Cushendun (41x61cm-16x24in) s. acrylic prov. 18-Feb-3 Whyte's, Dublin #117/R est:4000-5000
£3087	$4970	€4600	Still life with wine bottle (76x66cm-30x26in) 18-Feb-3 Whyte's, Dublin #139/R est:3000-4000
£3270	$5102	€5200	Shandon steeple, Cork (76x38cm-30x15in) s. 17-Sep-2 Whyte's, Dublin #143/R est:4000-6000
£3526	$5535	€5500	The Mournes from Tyrella (38x91cm-15x36in) s. i.d.1958 verso. 19-Nov-2 Whyte's, Dublin #82/R est:4000-6000
£3758	$6051	€5600	Cottage and cats (46x30cm-18x12in) s. 18-Feb-3 Whyte's, Dublin #4/R est:3000-4000
£4514	$7177	€6500	Mending nets, Roundstone (41x61cm-16x24in) s. prov. 29-Apr-3 Whyte's, Dublin #117/R est:6000-8000
£4861	$7729	€7000	Mare and foal in pasture (46x36cm-18x14in) s. 29-Apr-3 Whyte's, Dublin #121/R est:5000-6000
£5031	$7849	€8000	Field pattern (41x102cm-16x40in) s. lit. 17-Sep-2 Whyte's, Dublin #132/R est:6000-7000
£5034	$8104	€7500	Horn Head, Donegal (38x91cm-15x36in) s. 18-Feb-3 Whyte's, Dublin #115/R est:5000-7000
£5556	$8833	€8000	Seaweed theme, orange and green IV, Ballywater (127x51cm-50x20in) s. i.d.March 1963 verso. 29-Apr-3 Whyte's, Dublin #65/R est:6000-8000

£7051 $11071 €11000 Roundstone (51x76cm-20x30in) s. 19-Nov-2 Whyte's, Dublin #106/R est:8000-10000
Works on paper
£1400 $2170 €2100 Fishing boats, Co. Down (38x50cm-15x20in) s. mixed media. 4-Dec-2 John Ross, Belfast #174 est:800-1000
£2830 $4415 €4500 Cottages in the west (39x56cm-15x22in) s. ink gouache artist board. 17-Sep-2 Whyte's, Dublin #142/R est:3000-5000
£6711 $10805 €10000 Alcock and Brown landing site near Clifden, Connemara (56x76cm-22x30in) s. i.verso W/C exhib. 18-Feb-3 Whyte's, Dublin #143/R est:6000-7000

WEBB, Marilyn (20th C) New Zealander
Works on paper
£303 $467 €455 Untitled - tree landscape (75x55cm-30x22in) s.d.1987 W/C crayon. 4-Sep-2 Dunbar Sloane, Wellington #143 est:1000-2000 (NZ.D 1000)
£303 $467 €455 Orange and Long shadows, St. Bathans (38x58cm-15x23in) s.i.d.1989 W/C crayon. 4-Sep-2 Dunbar Sloane, Wellington #144 est:700-1200 (NZ.D 1000)
£491 $766 €737 Still water and summer snow (18x27cm-7x11in) s. W/C. 27-Mar-3 International Art Centre, Auckland #211 (NZ.D 1400)

WEBB, Montague (20th C) British?
£750 $1178 €1125 Boats at anchor (34x44cm-13x17in) s. board. 21-Nov-2 Tennants, Leyburn #761

WEBB, Susan (?) Irish?
£303 $467 €455 Standing nude I (61x49cm-24x19in) s.d.1994. 4-Sep-2 Dunbar Sloane, Wellington #156/R est:1000-2000 (NZ.D 1000)
£2083 $3312 €3000 Bel air (76x102cm-30x40in) s.d.1992 prov. 29-Apr-3 Whyte's, Dublin #123/R est:3000-4000
£4362 $7023 €6500 Tip and turn (91x122cm-36x48in) s. i.verso acrylic exhib.lit. 18-Feb-3 Whyte's, Dublin #125/R est:6000-8000
Works on paper
£268 $432 €400 Tip and turn (66x47cm-26x19in) s. i.verso pencil dr. 18-Feb-3 Whyte's, Dublin #126/R

WEBB, T (?) ?
£280 $431 €420 Road scene near Tipperlin (25x30cm-10x12in) panel. 7-Sep-2 Shapes, Edinburgh #424

WEBB, W (?) British
£1900 $2945 €2850 Sea breeze in heavy weather off Cape Horn (51x76cm-20x30in) s. 31-Oct-2 Christie's, Kensington #496/R est:2000-3000
£1900 $3154 €2755 English brig Una in the Channel off the South Foreland (44x56cm-17x22in) init. 12-Jun-3 Christie's, London #514/R est:2000-3000

WEBB, William (1790-1856) British
£1320 $2072 €1980 Melton, gypsy and his donkey's (46x64cm-18x25in) i.verso. 13-Dec-2 Keys, Aylsham #716/R est:800-1200

WEBB, William (attrib) (1790-1856) British
£900 $1467 €1350 Spaniel (22x30cm-9x12in) board. 29-Jan-3 Sotheby's, Olympia #96/R est:400-600

WEBB, William Edward (1862-1903) British
£379 $607 €550 Figures and boats by a pier (30x50cm-12x20in) s. 12-Mar-3 James Adam, Dublin #132/R
£1300 $2119 €1885 Fishing boats and other vessels off a coast line (31x61cm-12x24in) s. 17-Jul-3 Tennants, Leyburn #817/R est:800-1000
£2200 $3344 €3300 Sea breeze, rounding Cape Horn (49x74cm-19x29in) s. 4-Jul-2 Mellors & Kirk, Nottingham #859/R est:1500-2000
£2600 $4212 €3900 Busy quayside (56x96cm-22x38in) s.d.83. 22-Jan-3 Bonhams, New Bond Street #389/R est:2500-3500
£2800 $4536 €4200 Beached fishing vessels below a ruined castle (56x96cm-22x38in) s. 21-May-3 Christie's, Kensington #614/R est:2000-3000
£3000 $4860 €4500 On the Medway (56x98cm-22x39in) s. i.verso. 21-May-3 Christie's, Kensington #613/R est:3000-5000
£3000 $5010 €4350 Harbour view (61x91cm-24x36in) s. exhib. 18-Jun-3 Sotheby's, Olympia #80/R est:3000-5000
£3400 $5372 €5100 Harbour scene with fishing boats (24x39cm-9x15in) s. 27-Nov-2 Bonhams, Brooks & Langlois, Jersey #99/R est:2500-3000
£3500 $5670 €5250 Unloading at the quayside, Castletown (56x98cm-22x39in) s. 21-May-3 Christie's, Kensington #612/R est:4000-6000
£3600 $5364 €5400 Peel Harbour (41x61cm-16x24in) s. 28-Jun-2 Chrystals Auctions, Isle of Man #183 est:3500-4500
£4000 $5960 €6000 Busy harbour (56x97cm-22x38in) s. 28-Jun-2 Chrystals Auctions, Isle of Man #178 est:4000-6000
£4300 $7138 €6450 Near Cullercoats, Northumberland coast. On the shore, near Yarmouth (26x36cm-10x14in) s.i. pair. 10-Jun-3 Bonhams, Leeds #173/R est:2500-3000
£5000 $8100 €7500 Venice (50x76cm-20x30in) s. 22-Jan-3 Bonhams, New Bond Street #387/R est:4000-6000
£5000 $8350 €7250 Sorting the catch (56x97cm-22x38in) s. 18-Jun-3 Sotheby's, Olympia #79/R est:3000-5000
£5200 $8164 €7800 Quayside scene (59x90cm-23x35in) s. indis d. 16-Dec-2 Sotheby's, Olympia #74/R est:3000-5000
£10000 $15800 €15000 Peel Harbour, Isle of Man (56x97cm-22x38in) s. 2-Dec-2 Sotheby's, London #37/R est:5000-7000

WEBBE, William J (fl.1853-1878) British
£764 $1200 €1146 Tropical birds (20x35cm-8x14in) s.i. verso board. 22-Nov-2 Skinner, Boston #41/R est:700-900
£860 $1402 €1290 Byland Abbey, North Yorkshire (80x115cm-31x45in) 17-Feb-3 Bonhams, Bath #51

WEBBER, Gordon McKinley (1909-1965) American
£444 $729 €666 Abstract composition no.12 Berkshire (52x75cm-20x30in) s.d.1956 prov.exhib. 3-Jun-3 Joyner, Toronto #357/R est:1000-1500 (C.D 1000)
£711 $1166 €1067 Untitled abstraction (37x49cm-15x19in) s.verso canvas on board. 3-Jun-3 Joyner, Toronto #607 est:500-700 (C.D 1600)
£800 $1312 €1200 Highway no.10 May 13-62, Montana (60x45cm-24x18in) s.i.verso canvasboard. 3-Jun-3 Joyner, Toronto #606 est:500-700 (C.D 1800)
Works on paper
£800 $1312 €1200 Abstract composition no. Berman 1955 (37x49cm-15x19in) s. W/C exhib. 3-Jun-3 Joyner, Toronto #592 est:700-900 (C.D 1800)

WEBBER, Wesley (1841-1914) American
£480 $750 €720 Gambrel-roofed house with sheep in foreground (23x36cm-9x14in) s. board. 28-Mar-3 Eldred, East Dennis #90/R
£1205 $2000 €1747 Sheep grazing in the shade along a stream (36x51cm-14x20in) s. 14-Jun-3 Jackson's, Cedar Falls #16/R est:2500-3500
£1235 $2000 €1791 America's cup race (76x102cm-30x40in) s. 21-May-3 Doyle, New York #88/R est:3000-4000
£1698 $2700 €2547 Catboat (46x56cm-18x22in) s. 7-Mar-3 Skinner, Boston #320/R est:1800-2200
£1875 $3000 €2719 Rocky Brook (66x92cm-26x36in) s.d.80. 16-May-3 Skinner, Boston #78/R est:3000-5000
Works on paper
£409 $650 €614 Midnight sail (29x20cm-11x8in) s. gouache. 7-Mar-3 Skinner, Boston #327/R

WEBBER, Wesley (attrib) (1841-1914) American
£755 $1200 €1133 Dusk (35x51cm-14x20in) s. 7-Mar-3 Skinner, Boston #266/R

WEBER (?) ?
£524 $817 €786 Still life with red roses (50x39cm-20x15in) s. prov. 9-Nov-2 Galerie Gloggner, Luzern #151/R (S.FR 1200)

WEBER, Adolf (1925-) Swiss
£417 $671 €626 Summer village (63x79cm-25x31in) s.d.79 board. 7-May-3 Dobiaschofsky, Bern #3678 (S.FR 900)
£652 $1011 €978 High summer (90x130cm-35x51in) mono. 9-Dec-2 Philippe Schuler, Zurich #3844/R (S.FR 1500)

WEBER, Alfred Charles (1862-1922) French
£3548 $5500 €5322 Cardinal's companions (55x46cm-22x18in) s. panel. 2-Oct-2 Christie's, Rockefeller NY #782/R est:7000-9000
£12179 $18878 €19000 Good glass (49x61cm-19x24in) s. panel. 7-Dec-2 De Vuyst, Lokeren #516/R est:20000-24000
Works on paper
£275 $450 €420 Cardinal baillant (29x21cm-11x8in) s. W/C. 7-Feb-3 Oger, Dumont, Paris #36/R
£294 $482 €450 Cardinal jouant de la guitare (30x21cm-12x8in) s. W/C. 7-Feb-3 Oger, Dumont, Paris #37/R
£449 $709 €700 Prelat a la loupe (30x21cm-12x8in) s. W/C. 18-Nov-2 Tajan, Paris #160
£900 $1404 €1350 Trop chaud (37x26cm-15x10in) s. W/C. 26-Mar-3 Woolley & Wallis, Salisbury #122/R

WEBER, Andreas Paul (1893-1980) German
Works on paper
£306 $501 €425 In the ditch (51x44cm-20x17in) s.i. Indian ink sepia. 4-Jun-3 Reiss & Sohn, Konigstein #648/R
£380 $600 €600 Big wash (49x37cm-19x15in) s.mono. pen. 30-Nov-2 Bassenge, Berlin #6696/R
£411 $650 €650 Hands up, you devil (39x34cm-15x13in) s.mono. pen. 30-Nov-2 Bassenge, Berlin #6697/R
£519 $805 €810 You must howl with the wolves (59x47cm-23x19in) s.d.1953 col Indian ink. 7-Dec-2 Ketterer, Hamburg #384/R

WEBER, Anna (1814-1888) Canadian
Works on paper
£2000 $3280 €3000 Floral study with birds (20x16cm-8x6in) s.d.June 11 1881 pencil pen ink W/C prov.lit. 27-May-3 Sotheby's, Toronto #154/R est:4000-6000 (C.D 4500)

WEBER, Anton (1833-1909) German
£685 $1075 €1000 Peasant girl in traditional costume carrying basket of flowers (81x54cm-32x21in) s.d.1887. 16-Apr-3 Dorotheum, Salzburg #153/R

WEBER, Bruce (1946-) American
Photographs
£2025 $3200 €3038 Gustavo on the rooftops, Rio (58x49cm-23x19in) s.i.d.1986 num.2/5 gelatin silver print prov. 22-Apr-3 Christie's, Rockefeller NY #187/R est:3000-5000

WEBER, C Phillip (1849-1921) American
£356 $590 €516 Lowtide at the wharf (30x25cm-12x10in) s. 10-Jun-3 Ritchie, Toronto #87 (C.D 800)
£1557 $2600 €2258 Country landscape with figures on a pathway (40x61cm-16x24in) s. 22-Jun-3 Freeman, Philadelphia #86/R est:1500-2500

WEBER, Carl (1850-1921) American
£1321 $2100 €1982 Sheep in a landscape (43x56cm-17x22in) s. painted c.1900. 4-May-3 Treadway Gallery, Cincinnati #515/R est:2500-3500
£1433 $2250 €2150 Fisherman beside a mill (51x91cm-20x36in) s. 19-Nov-2 Butterfields, San Francisco #8042/R est:3000-5000
Works on paper
£398 $650 €597 Cattle drinking from a calm river at sundown (36x69cm-14x27in) s. W/C. 16-Feb-3 Butterfields, San Francisco #2097
£449 $700 €674 Landscape with cows (25x46cm-10x18in) s. W/C. 20-Sep-2 Sloan, North Bethesda #349/R
£449 $700 €674 Untitled (38x66cm-15x26in) s. W/C. 30-Mar-3 Susanin's, Chicago #6050/R
£466 $750 €699 Pastoral landscape with cows (30x64cm-12x25in) s. W/C. 22-Feb-3 Pook & Pook, Downington #181/R

WEBER, Fred W (1890-?) American
£302 $475 €453 Farm view, Bucks County (40x51cm-16x20in) incised sig.d.54 board. 22-Nov-2 Skinner, Boston #282/R
£574 $900 €861 On the farm, Bucks County (41x51cm-16x20in) incised sig.d.54 board. 22-Nov-2 Skinner, Boston #283/R est:400-600

WEBER, Hugo (1918-1971) Swiss
Works on paper
£568 $891 €852 Untitled (48x63cm-19x25in) s.i.d.1953 Indian ink brush prov. 25-Nov-2 Germann, Zurich #111 (S.FR 1300)
£1659 $2605 €2489 Untitled (31x47cm-12x19in) s.d.1958 col chk Indian ink. 25-Nov-2 Germann, Zurich #110/R est:3000-4000 (S.FR 3800)

WEBER, Ilse (20th C) ?
Works on paper
£448 $717 €672 Untitled (38x50cm-15x20in) s. chl wax chk. 17-Mar-3 Philippe Schuler, Zurich #4379 (S.FR 950)
£655 $1022 €983 Books (48x59cm-19x23in) s. bodycol. 8-Nov-2 Dobiaschofsky, Bern #258/R (S.FR 1500)

WEBER, J (?) ?
£610 $1000 €885 Young Dutch girl with basket (33x20cm-13x8in) s. panel. 4-Jun-3 Doyle, New York #98 est:600-800

WEBER, Johann Gottlob (attrib) (19th C) Swiss
Works on paper
£306 $477 €459 Mountain landscape with stream (33x49cm-13x19in) gouache. 6-Nov-2 Dobiaschofsky, Bern #1282/R (S.FR 700)

WEBER, Karl (1899-1978) Swiss
£343 $542 €515 Summer landscape in Mendrisiotto (65x100cm-26x39in) s.i.verso. 29-Nov-2 Zofingen, Switzerland #3121 (S.FR 800)

WEBER, Max (1881-1961) American
£572 $950 €829 Street scene with figures (10x15cm-4x6in) s. W/C paper on board. 11-Jun-3 Boos Gallery, Michigan #507/R est:600-800
£1019 $1600 €1529 Dead tree (23x30cm-9x12in) s.i.d.1929 prov. 14-Dec-2 Weschler, Washington #707/R est:1000-2000
£11613 $18000 €17420 Abstract still life (24x18cm-9x7in) s.d.12. canvasboard. 4-Dec-2 Sotheby's, New York #65/R est:15000-25000
£16975 $27500 €25463 Reunion (79x64cm-31x25in) s. painted 1933 prov.exhib.lit. 21-May-3 Sotheby's, New York #92/R est:40000-60000
£29032 $45000 €43548 Worker's reading room (51x72cm-20x28in) s. painted 1939 prov.exhib. 5-Dec-2 Christie's, Rockefeller NY #108/R est:20000-30000
£967742 $1500000 €1451613 New York (101x81cm-40x32in) s. painted 1913 prov.exhib.lit. 3-Dec-2 Phillips, New York #73/R est:500000-750000
Works on paper
£302 $475 €453 Harbor (9x13cm-4x5in) s. s.i.d.November 18 1910 pen ink. 22-Nov-2 Skinner, Boston #357/R
£542 $900 €786 Landscape with house, roadway and trees (15x18cm-6x7in) W/C paper on board. 11-Jun-3 Boos Gallery, Michigan #506 est:1200-1500
£915 $1500 €1327 Female nude (11x8cm-4x3in) gouache paper on paper. 5-Jun-3 Swann Galleries, New York #262/R est:2000-3000
£1069 $1700 €1604 Trees (28x20cm-11x8in) s. d.1929 verso W/C board. 5-Mar-3 Doyle, New York #63/R est:800-1200
£1341 $2200 €1944 Landscape with houses (20x32cm-8x13in) s.i. W/C. 5-Jun-3 Swann Galleries, New York #263/R est:2000-3000
£2317 $3800 €3360 Female nude (27x20cm-11x8in) s.d. pen ink. 5-Jun-3 Swann Galleries, New York #260/R est:2500-3500
£9756 $16000 €14146 Cubist figure in profile (19x14cm-7x6in) s.d. W/C. 5-Jun-3 Swann Galleries, New York #261/R est:10000-15000

WEBER, Mili (1891-1978) Swiss
Works on paper
£730 $1153 €1095 Alpine rose flower girl (22x19cm-9x7in) mono. W/C i.verso. 29-Nov-2 Zofingen, Switzerland #3122/R est:1600 (S.FR 1700)
£730 $1153 €1095 Edelweiss flower girl (22x19cm-9x7in) mono. W/C i.verso. 29-Nov-2 Zofingen, Switzerland #3123/R est:1600 (S.FR 1700)

WEBER, Otis S (19th C) American
£377 $600 €566 Moonlight sail (56x92cm-22x36in) s. 7-Mar-3 Skinner, Boston #506/R
£605 $950 €908 Square-rig ship on the high sea at sunset (36x51cm-14x20in) s. 26-Jul-2 Eldred, East Dennis #614/R est:800-1000

WEBER, Otto (1832-1888) German
£901 $1424 €1352 Summit storm - together can the target be accomplished (200x50cm-79x20in) d.1928 panel pair. 29-Nov-2 Zofingen, Switzerland #3125 est:2500 (S.FR 2100)
£949 $1472 €1500 Cows in meadow (32x48cm-13x19in) bears sig. panel. 25-Sep-2 Neumeister, Munich #772/R est:1500
£4600 $7452 €6900 Goose girls (41x76cm-16x30in) s. 20-May-3 Sotheby's, Olympia #404/R est:3000-4000
£40000 $63200 €60000 He's cast a shoe (99x160cm-39x63in) s. prov.exhib.lit. 27-Nov-2 Christie's, London #47/R est:40000-60000

WEBER, Otto (attrib) (1832-1888) German
£1013 $1570 €1600 Six boys playing in mountain stream (46x61cm-18x24in) oil study canvas on board. 25-Sep-2 Neumeister, Munich #773/R est:900

WEBER, Paul (1823-1916) American/German
£260 $387 €400 Mountain stream (28x37cm-11x15in) s. 26-Jun-2 Neumeister, Munich #910/R
£301 $470 €440 Evening (28x20cm-11x8in) s. board. 9-Apr-3 Neumeister, Munich #761/R
£352 $515 €528 House with thatched roof (20x28cm-8x11in) mono.d.1891. 17-Jun-2 Philippe Schuler, Zurich #7363 (S.FR 800)
£545 $850 €818 Early morning landscape (15x22cm-6x9in) s. 12-Apr-3 Weschler, Washington #553/R
£649 $968 €1000 Autumnal wood (19x29cm-7x11in) mono.i.d.1897 board. 26-Jun-2 Neumeister, Munich #911/R
£1258 $1962 €2000 Hay harvest (16x30cm-6x12in) s. canvas on board. 19-Sep-2 Dr Fritz Nagel, Stuttgart #1011/R est:1200
£1274 $1987 €2000 Peasant returning home with cattle (36x55cm-14x22in) s. 6-Nov-2 Hugo Ruef, Munich #1326 est:1800
£1282 $2000 €1923 Shepherd and sheep at sundown (25x43cm-10x17in) s. canvas on board prov. 12-Apr-3 Weschler, Washington #554/R est:3000-5000
£1329 $2060 €2100 Moor landscape (49x65cm-19x26in) st.sig. 25-Sep-2 Neumeister, Munich #774/R est:2200
£3623 $5942 €5000 Landscape (39x61cm-15x24in) s. 27-May-3 Wiener Kunst Auktionen, Vienna #30/R est:6000-10000
£4167 $6500 €6251 Landscape with cliveden in Germantown (11x15cm-4x6in) s. 12-Apr-3 Freeman, Philadelphia #223/R est:7000-9000
£25806 $40000 €38709 Sunset (90x125cm-35x49in) s.d.1856 prov.exhib. 4-Dec-2 Sotheby's, New York #116/R est:40000-60000

WEBER, R (?) ?
£870 $1400 €1305 Dutch waterside (74x99cm-29x39in) s. 23-Feb-3 Butterfields, Los Angeles #7064 est:2000-3000

WEBER, Rudolf (1872-?) Austrian
£625 $1000 €938 European cottage with figure in a spring landscape (74x99cm-29x39in) s. 15-Mar-3 Eldred, East Dennis #423/R

WEBER, Theodore (1838-1907) French
£1056 $1701 €1500 Harbour entrance with steamer, sailing boat and lighthouse (24x37cm-9x15in) s. 7-May-3 Michael Zeller, Lindau #982/R est:500
£1410 $2200 €2115 Tugboat with sailboat in rough waters (76x61cm-30x24in) s. 9-Nov-2 Sloan, North Bethesda #560/R est:2000-3000
£1667 $2617 €2600 Women and children awaiting the return of a fleet of sailboats (33x56cm-13x22in) s. i.verso prov. 19-Nov-2 Whyte's, Dublin #65/R est:3000-4000
£1700 $2652 €2550 Fishing boats in the harbour mouth (33x54cm-13x21in) s. 10-Sep-2 David Duggleby, Scarborough #347 est:800-1200
£1923 $3019 €3000 Rescuing shipwrecked sailors from rowing boat (84x115cm-33x45in) s.d.1858. 21-Nov-2 Van Ham, Cologne #1965/R est:5500
£2436 $3824 €3800 Lifeboat by White Cliffs of Dover (85x134cm-33x53in) s. 21-Nov-2 Van Ham, Cologne #1964/R est:3000
£4500 $7020 €6750 Golden Horn, Constantinople (51x33cm-20x13in) s. 15-Oct-2 Sotheby's, London #92/R est:5000-7000
£7595 $12000 €11393 Salvaging a shipwreck off Mont St. Michel (108x183cm-43x72in) s. 23-Apr-3 Christie's, Rockefeller NY #81/R est:12000-16000
£9295 $14593 €14500 Entree de bateau de peche (60x90cm-24x35in) s.d. 15-Dec-2 Mercier & Cie, Lille #369/R est:18000

WEBER, Werner (1892-1977) Swiss
£606 $939 €909 Landscape with church (67x50cm-26x20in) s.d.27 panel. 24-Sep-2 Koller, Zurich #6697/R (S.FR 1400)
£610 $1001 €885 Still life with books and pewter jug (31x35cm-12x14in) s.d.38 lit.prov. 4-Jun-3 Fischer, Luzern #2348/R (S.FR 1300)
£617 $900 €926 Iris in water glass (42x33cm-17x13in) s. lit. 17-Jun-2 Philippe Schuler, Zurich #4295/R (S.FR 1400)
£699 $1097 €1049 Yellow and white primulas (46x38cm-18x15in) s.d.1966 lit. 25-Nov-2 Germann, Zurich #134/R est:1800-2200 (S.FR 1600)
£704 $1155 €1021 Pine trees near Marina di Massa, Mallorca (60x45cm-24x18in) lit. 4-Jun-3 Fischer, Luzern #2349/R est:1800-2200 (S.FR 1500)
£773 $1221 €1160 Still life of fruit (27x41cm-11x16in) s.d.1929 panel. 29-Nov-2 Zofingen, Switzerland #3126 est:950 (S.FR 1800)
£961 $1499 €1442 Still life with skull (30x38cm-12x15in) lit. 20-Nov-2 Fischer, Luzern #1282/R est:2500-3000 (S.FR 2200)
£1033 $1694 €1498 Potatoes and garlic (24x35cm-9x14in) s. 4-Jun-3 Fischer, Luzern #2350/R est:2500-3000 (S.FR 2200)
£1435 $2224 €2153 Still life with copper kettle, zinc plate and white grapes (33x41cm-13x16in) s. panel lit. 9-Dec-2 Philippe Schuler, Zurich #3845/R est:2400-2800 (S.FR 3300)
£4148 $6513 €6222 Copper jug, books and shell (54x73cm-21x29in) s.d. panel prov.lit. 25-Nov-2 Sotheby's, Zurich #31/R est:3000-4000 (S.FR 9500)

WEBER, Willy (1895-1959) German
£377 $588 €550 View from Kreuzberg towards Fraueninsel (40x50cm-16x20in) board. 11-Apr-3 Winterberg, Heidelberg #1750/R

WEBER-TYROL, Hans Josef (1874-1957) Austrian
Works on paper
£612 $978 €850 Iris flower (32x28cm-13x11in) s. W/C over pencil. 15-May-3 Neumeister, Munich #371/R
£1772 $2800 €2800 Lilies in vase (31x21cm-12x8in) i. verso chl W/C. 27-Nov-2 Dorotheum, Vienna #185/R est:2800-3800
£2500 $3875 €3900 Flowering cactus (57x40cm-22x16in) s.d.41 W/C. 4-Dec-2 Neumeister, Munich #561/R est:1900
£3846 $6038 €6000 Village in south Tyrol (28x37cm-11x15in) s. pencil W/C. 21-Nov-2 Dorotheum, Vienna #469/R est:3000-4500
£3846 $6038 €6000 Landscape (29x44cm-11x17in) s. W/C. 21-Nov-2 Dorotheum, Vienna #470/R est:4000-5500

WEBSKY, Wolfgang von (1895-1992) German
£719 $1150 €1100 Portrait of a lady sitting (85x65cm-33x26in) s. panel lit. 10-Jan-3 Allgauer, Kempten #1826/R
£1656 $2583 €2600 Flowers in a vase with landscape in the background (50x40cm-20x16in) s.d.1977 lit. 7-Nov-2 Allgauer, Kempten #3005/R est:2600

WEBSTER, Charles (19th C) British
£3500 $5565 €5250 Caught in the mist (61x106cm-24x42in) s. 4-Mar-3 Bonhams, Knightsbridge #333/R est:2000-3000

WEBSTER, George (19th C) British
£3000 $4710 €4500 Estuary with man-o-war (24x31cm-9x12in) s. 16-Dec-2 Sotheby's, Olympia #7/R est:2000-3000
£9000 $13680 €13500 Man-o-war offshore, firing a salute. Man-o-war and a Dutch barge off Dover (63x76cm-25x30in) one s. pair prov. 15-Aug-2 Bonhams, New Bond Street #389/R est:7000-10000
£9000 $13950 €13500 An in bound Dutch three master at the river mouth amidst coastal craft (43x53cm-17x21in) s. 31-Oct-2 Christie's, Kensington #442/R est:6000-8000

WEBSTER, George (attrib) (19th C) British
£1500 $2340 €2250 East Indiaman in a storm (53x79cm-21x31in) 8-Oct-2 Bonhams, Knightsbridge #273/R est:400-600

WEBSTER, Harriet (attrib) (?-1807) American
Works on paper
£2134 $3500 €3094 Two grieving young women (38x36cm-15x14in) W/C ink. 8-Jun-3 Skinner, Boston #37/R est:2500-3500

WEBSTER, Thomas (1800-1886) British
£300 $468 €450 Still life of flowers (76x63cm-30x25in) s. panel. 8-Oct-2 Bonhams, Knightsbridge #18a
£420 $685 €609 Still life of summer flowers in a stone vase (60x50cm-24x20in) s. panel. 17-Jul-3 Tennants, Leyburn #907
£480 $749 €720 Still life of tulips and other flower with fruit (63x75cm-25x30in) s. panel. 8-Oct-2 Bonhams, Knightsbridge #6c
£700 $1148 €1050 Flowers in a basket on a ledge. Flowers in an urn (61x51cm-24x20in) s. wood pair. 4-Jun-3 Bonhams, Chester #348
£1000 $1630 €1500 Interview between Ralph Nickleby and his niece Kate (63x77cm-25x30in) mono. 29-Jan-3 Sotheby's, Olympia #131/R est:1000-1500
£1004 $1586 €1506 Travelling jeweller (18x18cm-7x7in) panel. 1-Dec-2 Levis, Calgary #240/R (C.D 2500)
£1229 $1954 €1844 Quarrel (30x25cm-12x10in) s.d.1851. 18-Mar-3 Maynards, Vancouver #3/R est:2500-3500 (C.D 2900)
£1297 $2050 €1946 The letter (32x26cm-13x10in) mono. panel. 27-Nov-2 Falkkloos, Malmo #77616/R est:15000 (S.KR 18500)
£1600 $2576 €2400 Study for 'Village Choir' (23x46cm-9x18in) init. prov. 20-Feb-3 Christie's, London #46/R

WEBSTER, Thomas (attrib) (1800-1886) British
£280 $437 €420 Kept in (22x22cm-9x9in) panel. 10-Apr-3 Tennants, Leyburn #1099

WEBSTER, Walter Ernest (1878-1959) British
£4981 $7421 €7472 Lute player (62x75cm-24x30in) s. exhib. 27-Aug-2 Christie's, Melbourne #265/R est:4000-6000 (A.D 13000)
£10500 $16695 €15750 Lute player (63x76cm-25x30in) s. exhib. 6-Mar-3 Christie's, Kensington #600/R est:7000-10000
Works on paper
£550 $858 €825 Blackberrying (54x41cm-21x16in) s. W/C. 13-Sep-2 Lyon & Turnbull, Edinburgh #3/R

WECK, Friedrich (1819-?) German
£2055 $3226 €3000 Death of Cleopatra (123x104cm-48x41in) i. verso. 16-Apr-3 Dorotheum, Salzburg #105/R est:3600-4500

WEDEL, Nils (1897-1967) Swedish
£1402 $2186 €2103 Shapes resting (32x65cm-13x26in) s. 6-Nov-2 AB Stockholms Auktionsverk #714/R est:30000-35000 (S.KR 20000)
£2662 $4205 €3993 Liberation (105x122cm-41x48in) s.d.36 panel. 28-Apr-3 Bukowskis, Stockholm #121a/R est:40000-60000 (S.KR 35000)
Works on paper
£608 $961 €912 Abstract composition (30x64cm-12x25in) s. mixed media. 28-Apr-3 Bukowskis, Stockholm #261/R (S.KR 8000)

WEDERKINCH, Holger (1886-1959) Danish
Sculpture
£13971 $21655 €20957 Prancing lion (127cm-50in) mono.d.1918 gilded dark pat.bronze incl.socle lit.prov. 1-Oct-2 Rasmussen, Copenhagen #142/R est:40000 (D.KR 165000)

WEDGE, Harry (20th C) Australian
Works on paper
£433 $671 €650 Vib's shock waves (35x25cm-14x10in) s. synthetic polymer paint triptych. 3-Dec-2 Shapiro, Sydney #222/R (A.D 1200)

WEDIG, Gotthardt de (1583-1641) German
£10791 $17266 €15000 Portrait of lady wearing black dress with gold embroidery (71x60cm-28x24in) i.d.1637. 13-May-3 Sotheby's, Amsterdam #64/R est:12000-18000
£18919 $29514 €28000 Still life with grapes and apple in porcelain dish (31x37cm-12x15in) copper. 27-Mar-3 Dorotheum, Vienna #280/R est:30000-40000

WEEBER, Eduard von (1834-1891) Austrian
£2115 $3279 €3300 Arcadian landscape with Diana and her nymphs bathing in a stream (61x76cm-24x30in) s. canvas on canvas. 4-Dec-2 Neumeister, Munich #958/R est:1800

WEEDEN, Maria Howard (1847-1905) American
Works on paper
£11875 $19000 €17813 Elderly black woman wearing a kerchief. Elderly black man with beard. s. W/C card 2 sold with two books. 4-Jan-3 Brunk, Ashville #709/R est:5000-10000

WEEGEE (1899-1968) American
Photographs
£1899 $3000 €3000 Sammy's in the Bowery (18x23cm-7x9in) i. verso silver gelatin lit.exhib. 28-Nov-2 Villa Grisebach, Berlin #1460/R est:1000-1500
£1948 $3000 €2922 Television antennas (20x16cm-8x6in) i. gelatin silver print exec.c.1950 prov.lit. 25-Oct-2 Phillips, New York #113/R est:3000-5000
£2051 $3200 €3077 Murder scene (19x25cm-7x10in) silver. 21-Oct-2 Swann Galleries, New York #281/R est:2000-3000
£2532 $4000 €3798 At a concert in Harlem (34x27cm-13x11in) gelatin silver print prov.exhib.lit. 25-Apr-3 Phillips, New York #98/R est:3000-4000
£3084 $4750 €4626 Fire escape (36x28cm-14x11in) photograph prov.lit. 22-Oct-2 Sotheby's, New York #76/R est:4000-6000
£3750 $6000 €5625 Critic (27x32cm-11x13in) silver print. 15-May-3 Swann Galleries, New York #515/R est:6000-9000
£3797 $6000 €5696 Vegetable peddler (32x27cm-13x11in) gelatin silver print prov. 25-Apr-3 Phillips, New York #101/R est:3000-4000
£5063 $8000 €7595 Critic December 6, 1943 (27x33cm-11x13in) gelatin silver print lit. 25-Apr-3 Phillips, New York #24/R est:4000-6000
£5063 $8000 €7595 Four high hats are waiting for James and the limousine (26x33cm-10x13in) gelatin silver print prov. 25-Apr-3 Phillips, New York #99/R est:3000-4000
£5519 $8500 €8279 Mona Lisa (22x16cm-9x6in) st.verso gelatin silver print exec.c.1950 prov. 25-Oct-2 Phillips, New York #114/R est:4000-6000
£5696 $9000 €8544 Self portrait in the police station (34x27cm-13x11in) gelatin silver print. 22-Apr-3 Christie's, Rockefeller NY #139/R est:5000-7000
£16456 $26000 €24684 Macy's parade (27x36cm-11x14in) gelatin silver print prov. 25-Apr-3 Phillips, New York #23/R est:4000-6000
£17089 $27000 €25634 Crowd at Coney Island, temperature 89 degrees (27x35cm-11x14in) gelatin silver print prov.lit. 25-Apr-3 Phillips, New York #22/R est:7000-10000

WEEKES, Frederick (fl.1854-1893) British
£500 $760 €750 Highland lass with dog in landscape (15x20cm-6x8in) s.d.1869 verso. 16-Aug-2 Keys, Aylsham #610/R

WEEKES, Henry (jnr) (?-c.1910) British
£1500 $2385 €2250 Morning's bag (61x91cm-24x36in) s.d.1893 prov. 6-Mar-3 Christie's, Kensington #57/R est:2000-3000

WEEKES, William (fl.1864-1904) British
£563 $900 €845 Irish courtship, with young couple holding hands by a stable (23x36cm-9x14in) s. 17-May-3 Pook & Pook, Downington #392/R est:3000-4000
£860 $1419 €1247 Confrontation (34x23cm-13x9in) s. 1-Jul-3 Bearnes, Exeter #506/R
£1800 $2844 €2700 Border terrier (36x25cm-14x10in) s. 28-Nov-2 Christie's, Kensington #278/R est:1800-2200
£2050 $3198 €3075 Stable hand reading in the stall (52x70cm-20x28in) s. 11-Nov-2 Stephan Welz, Johannesburg #408/R est:10000-15000 (SA.R 32000)
£2200 $3388 €3300 Feeding time (26x35cm-10x14in) s. panel. 5-Sep-2 Christie's, Kensington #143/R est:1000-1500
£2600 $4056 €3900 Two pigs and a cow (32x44cm-13x17in) s. 26-Mar-3 Woolley & Wallis, Salisbury #204/R est:1500-2000
£4200 $6678 €6300 March past (44x34cm-17x13in) s. board. 6-Mar-3 Christie's, Kensington #565/R est:4000-6000
£4500 $7065 €6750 Donkeys on a beach (51x76cm-20x30in) s. 19-Nov-2 Bonhams, New Bond Street #133/R est:3000-4000
£7200 $11232 €10800 Conversation. Stable friends (30x21cm-12x8in) s. panel pair. 26-Mar-3 Sotheby's, Olympia #164/R est:4000-6000

WEEKS, Edwin Lord (1849-1903) American
£8000 $12640 €12000 Elephant, Ajmere (33x51cm-13x20in) s. 15-Nov-2 Sotheby's, London #26a/R est:8000-12000
£16901 $24000 €25352 Pink parasol (28x41cm-11x16in) 8-Aug-1 Barridorf, Portland #66/R est:12000-18000
£48077 $75000 €72116 Interior with brilliant tile decor and seated pensive girl with lute and lilies (86x61cm-34x24in) s. 21-Sep-2 Nadeau, Windsor #150/R est:40000-60000
£128205 $201282 €200000 Reverie au patio, Maroc (87x61cm-34x24in) s.d.1876. 16-Dec-2 Gros & Delettrez, Paris #143/R est:200000-250000

WEEKS, John (1888-1965) New Zealander
£1264 $2022 €1833 Reflections scapa flow (39x49cm-15x19in) board. 13-May-3 Watson's, Christchurch #43/R est:8000-15000 (NZ.D 3500)
£1473 $2298 €2210 Rear of the old houses 1940 (21x29cm-8x11in) tempera on board. 7-Nov-2 International Art Centre, Auckland #105/R est:3000-4000 (NZ.D 4700)
£2465 $4067 €3574 Harbourside village with yachts (27x36cm-11x14in) s.d.1926 canvasboard. 1-Jul-3 Peter Webb, Auckland #75/R est:8000-12000 (NZ.D 7000)
£3860 $6021 €5790 Road through the king country (38x49cm-15x19in) board prov. 27-Mar-3 International Art Centre, Auckland #86/R est:8000-12000 (NZ.D 11000)
£7018 $10947 €10527 Morocco (52x53cm-20x21in) board prov. 27-Mar-3 International Art Centre, Auckland #45/R est:25000-35000 (NZ.D 20000)
£12158 $18967 €18237 Composite landscape, Te Kuiti (60x90cm-24x35in) s. board. 17-Sep-2 Peter Webb, Auckland #101/R est:45000-65000 (NZ.D 40000)

Works on paper
£474 $739 €711 Hereford Street, Christchurch (17x16cm-7x6in) s. W/C. 27-Mar-3 International Art Centre, Auckland #38/R (NZ.D 1350)
£862 $1345 €1293 Daffodils (28x26cm-11x10in) s. W/C. 7-Nov-2 International Art Centre, Auckland #143/R est:4000-6000 (NZ.D 2750)
£877 $1368 €1316 Road to the dairy factory (23x29cm-9x11in) s. W/C. 27-Mar-3 International Art Centre, Auckland #78/R (NZ.D 2500)
£937 $1463 €1406 Venice (29x31cm-11x12in) W/C. 8-Apr-3 Peter Webb, Auckland #141/R est:2500-3500 (NZ.D 2700)
£940 $1467 €1410 Moroccan market (23x30cm-9x12in) pastel. 7-Nov-2 International Art Centre, Auckland #110/R est:1800-2600 (NZ.D 3000)

WEELE, Herman Johannes van der (1852-1930) Dutch
£446 $696 €700 Group of trees (47x33cm-19x13in) s. 6-Nov-2 Vendue Huis, Gravenhage #556/R
£1233 $1923 €1800 Horse and plough on a field (24x35cm-9x14in) s. panel prov. 14-Apr-3 Glerum, Amsterdam #149/R est:400-600
Works on paper
£278 $450 €417 In the field (41x53cm-16x21in) s. W/C. 24-Jan-3 Freeman, Philadelphia #194/R

WEENIX, Jan (1640-1719) Dutch
£40000 $62800 €60000 Still life of a peacock, hare, game birds and hunting paraphernalia (144x122cm-57x48in) 12-Dec-2 Sotheby's, London #40/R est:40000-60000

WEENIX, Jan Baptist (1621-1663) Dutch
£25000 $41750 €36250 Still life of spaniel guarding game together with hunting equipment (108x131cm-43x52in) prov. 10-Jul-3 Sotheby's, London #150/R est:30000-40000

WEENIX, Jan Baptist (attrib) (1621-1663) Dutch
£3871 $6000 €5807 Shepherd conversing with a peasant family seated by a tree (75x60cm-30x24in) panel prov.exhib. 2-Oct-2 Christie's, Rockefeller NY #159/R est:3000-5000
£6410 $9936 €10000 Spaniel by dead game (17x131cm-7x52in) indis.sig. 4-Dec-2 Christie's, Rome #469/R est:10000-15000

WEERDT, Armand de (1890-1982) Belgian
£470 $756 €700 Cottage in the park. s. 24-Feb-3 Bernaerts, Antwerp #779/R

WEERT, Anna de (1867-1950) Belgian
£3038 $4800 €4800 Petite etude de neige (23x30cm-9x12in) mono. cardboard. 26-Nov-2 Palais de Beaux Arts, Brussels #81/R est:3000-3750
£7914 $12978 €11000 Poppies in the garden (24x34cm-9x13in) s. s.i.d.1887. 3-Jun-3 Christie's, Amsterdam #270/R est:3500-4500
Works on paper
£886 $1400 €1400 Bord de riviere avec peniches (26x34cm-10x13in) mono. pastel. 26-Nov-2 Palais de Beaux Arts, Brussels #77

WEGENER, Einar (1883-1931) Danish
£353 $558 €530 Park landscape with tulips (60x80cm-24x31in) s.d.1920. 5-Apr-3 Rasmussen, Havnen #4323 (D.KR 3800)

WEGENER, Gerda (1885-1940) Danish
£4376 $6958 €6564 Madonna and Child surrounded by angels playing music (115x105cm-45x41in) s.i.d.1935. 4-Mar-3 Museumsbygningen, Copenhagen #566/R est:40000-60000 (D.KR 47000)

Works on paper
£257 $401 €386 Girl getting dressed in her boudoir (39x29cm-15x11in) s. W/C on print oval. 11-Nov-2 Rasmussen, Vejle #11 (D.KR 3000)
£286 $478 €415 Portrait of young woman (21x10cm-8x4in) s. W/C pencil. 17-Jun-3 Rasmussen, Copenhagen #144 (D.KR 3000)
£478 $775 €693 Moroccan couple (21x26cm-8x10in) s.i.d.1933 W/C pencil. 26-May-3 Rasmussen, Copenhagen #1594/R (D.KR 5000)
£838 $1332 €1257 Adam and Eve (32x32cm-13x13in) s. pen W/C. 5-Mar-3 Rasmussen, Copenhagen #2109/R (D.KR 9000)
£1770 $2868 €2567 Young woman holding white carnation (74x57cm-29x22in) s. W/C pencil. 24-May-3 Rasmussen, Havnen #4054/R est:15000-20000 (D.KR 18500)
£4190 $6662 €6285 Girl with dog (72x52cm-28x20in) s. W/C pencil crayon. 5-Mar-3 Rasmussen, Copenhagen #1612/R est:50000 (D.KR 45000)

WEGER, Marie (1882-?) American
£563 $900 €845 In the course of conversation (63x56cm-25x22in) s. 18-May-3 Butterfields, Los Angeles #7040
£565 $882 €848 Still life of flowers and nuts (76x61cm-30x24in) s. 16-Sep-2 Philippe Schuler, Zurich #3501 (S.FR 1300)

WEGMAN, William (1942-) American

Photographs
£2597 $4000 €3896 Corner (76x56cm-30x22in) s.i.d.1993 polaroid print. 24-Oct-2 Sotheby's, New York #236/R est:4000-6000
£2922 $4500 €4383 Pipeline (66x165cm-26x65in) s.i. polaroid polacol II print three framed together prov.exhib. 25-Oct-2 Phillips, New York #159/R est:8000-12000
£4861 $8021 €7000 Split personality chair (73x111cm-29x44in) init.i.d.92 two polaroids on board prov.exhib.lit. 3-Jul-3 Christie's, Paris #111/R est:3000-4000
£5696 $9000 €8544 Building a box (28x28cm-11x11in) gelatin silver print set of nine executed 1972 prov. 14-Nov-2 Christie's, Rockefeller NY #436/R est:12000-18000

Prints
£4140 $6500 €6210 Untitled and contained (24x20cm-9x8in) polacolor II diptych prov. 19-Nov-2 Wright, Chicago #329/R est:7000-9000

WEGMANN, Bertha (1847-1926) Danish
£287 $465 €416 Old lady (40x34cm-16x13in) s. 26-May-3 Rasmussen, Copenhagen #1445 (D.KR 3000)
£326 $508 €489 Trees in flower (43x29cm-17x11in) init. exhib. 11-Nov-2 Rasmussen, Vejle #557/R (D.KR 3800)
£326 $518 €489 Portrait of old gentleman (38x32cm-15x13in) s. prov. 10-Mar-3 Rasmussen, Vejle #372 (D.KR 3500)
£468 $740 €702 Tree trunks and sunlit ground of forest (72x60cm-28x24in) s. 2-Dec-2 Rasmussen, Copenhagen #1296/R (D.KR 5500)
£468 $740 €702 Mountain village (19x25cm-7x10in) init. 2-Dec-2 Rasmussen, Copenhagen #1567/R (D.KR 5500)
£470 $723 €705 Woodland ground (46x52cm-18x20in) s. 4-Sep-2 Kunsthallen, Copenhagen #83 (D.KR 5500)
£490 $755 €735 Portrait of girl (44x29cm-17x11in) s. sketch. 26-Oct-2 Rasmussen, Havnen #2010 (D.KR 5800)
£512 $789 €768 Portrait of Ellen Rosenberg (40x37cm-16x15in) s. compoboard exhib. 4-Sep-2 Kunsthallen, Copenhagen #53 (D.KR 6000)
£532 $830 €798 Landscape view (34x50cm-13x20in) s. exhib. 11-Nov-2 Rasmussen, Vejle #631/R (D.KR 6200)
£553 $874 €830 Country road by Binz, Rygen (55x77cm-22x30in) s.d.1892 exhib.prov. 2-Dec-2 Rasmussen, Copenhagen #1756/R (D.KR 6500)
£574 $930 €832 Interior scene with stairs (59x35cm-23x14in) s. 26-May-3 Rasmussen, Copenhagen #1459/R (D.KR 6000)
£851 $1345 €1277 Oak leaves and harebell (47x54cm-19x21in) s. exhib. 2-Dec-2 Rasmussen, Copenhagen #1440/R (D.KR 10000)
£931 $1480 €1397 Model study, Paris (66x57cm-26x22in) s.i. 5-Mar-3 Rasmussen, Copenhagen #1794/R (D.KR 10000)

WEGMAYR, Sebastian (1776-1857) Austrian
£35211 $57746 €51056 Still life of fruit with bird's nest and insects (41x33cm-16x13in) s. panel pair. 4-Jun-3 Fischer, Luzern #1120/R est:90000-120000 (S.FR 75000)

WEGNER, Alexander Matvieievitch (1826-1894) Russian

Miniatures
£2200 $3454 €3300 Tsar Alexander II of Russia (4cm-2in) s. silver gilt frame oval prov. 10-Dec-2 Christie's, London #271/R est:1000-1500

WEGNER, Erich (1899-1980) German
£769 $1192 €1200 Figures (30x41cm-12x16in) s. board. 4-Dec-2 Lempertz, Koln #1108/R

Works on paper
£1042 $1646 €1500 Peasant family (47x32cm-19x13in) i.d.1924 verso gouache. 26-Apr-3 Dr Lehr, Berlin #539/R est:2000
£1277 $2068 €1800 Junk collector (32x47cm-13x19in) s. gouache paper on board. 20-May-3 Dorotheum, Vienna #147/R est:2000-2500

WEHLE, Johann Raphael (1848-1936) German
£4000 $6280 €6000 Summer's day (53x76cm-21x30in) 19-Nov-2 Bonhams, New Bond Street #30/R est:4000-6000

WEHMAS, Einari (1898-1955) Finnish
£516 $799 €820 Old town (38x46cm-15x18in) s.d.17. 6-Oct-2 Bukowskis, Helsinki #317/R

Works on paper
£279 $443 €410 Family of pigs (48x56cm-19x22in) s.i.d.1942 W/C. 27-Feb-3 Hagelstam, Helsinki #944

WEHNERT, Edward Henry (1813-1868) British

Works on paper
£1300 $2119 €1950 Banquet (96x152cm-38x60in) s.d.1841 W/C paper on canvas. 29-Jan-3 Sotheby's, Olympia #56/R est:1000-2000

WEHRINGER, Herbert (1926-) German
£255 $397 €400 Procession along Chiemsee (20x25cm-8x10in) s. panel. 8-Nov-2 Auktionhaus Georg Rehm, Augsburg #8185/R
£282 $437 €440 Cows watering (15x30cm-6x12in) s. panel. 6-Dec-2 Auktionhaus Georg Rehm, Augsburg #8144/R
£318 $465 €490 Country idyll (20x25cm-8x10in) s.i. panel. 14-Jun-2 Auktionhaus Georg Rehm, Augsburg #8154/R
£338 $544 €480 High moorland (7x16cm-3x6in) s.i. i. verso panel. 9-May-3 Schloss Ahlden, Ahlden #1460/R
£392 $643 €600 Dutch idyll (25x42cm-10x17in) s. panel. 7-Feb-3 Auktionhaus Georg Rehm, Augsburg #8114/R
£490 $784 €750 Fun on the ice in the evening in a winter landscape (20x39cm-8x15in) s.i. panel. 10-Jan-3 Allgauer, Kempten #1832/R

WEHRLIN, Christiano Matteao (attrib) (1756-1774) ?
£58621 $93207 €85000 Chines ladies (97x58cm-38x23in) tempera set of six. 5-Mar-3 Sotheby's, Milan #440/R est:35000-50000

WEHRMANN, Hermann (1897-?) German
£276 $436 €400 Storm gathering over track in late summer (42x60cm-17x24in) s. board. 5-Apr-3 Hans Stahl, Hamburg #144

WEIDE, F W (19th C) ?
£1329 $2127 €1927 The barque Triton (46x65cm-18x26in) s. 18-May-3 Anders Antik, Landskrona #134 est:6000 (S.KR 17000)

WEIDEMANN, Jakob (1923-2001) Norwegian
£906 $1377 €1359 Wild flower (45x61cm-18x24in) s.i.d.80 paper. 31-Aug-2 Grev Wedels Plass, Oslo #123 (N.KR 10500)
£1357 $2199 €2036 Head of woman (61x50cm-24x20in) panel. 26-May-3 Grev Wedels Plass, Oslo #13/R est:15000-20000 (N.KR 15000)
£1837 $3012 €2664 Composition (26x30cm-10x12in) s.d.62. 2-Jun-3 Blomqvist, Oslo #192/R est:12000-15000 (N.KR 20000)
£1908 $2977 €2862 Composition with figure (61x50cm-24x20in) s.d.51 panel. 21-Oct-2 Blomqvist, Oslo #399/R est:25000-30000 (N.KR 22000)
£2353 $3812 €3530 House and garden, possibly South of France (40x50cm-16x20in) s. painted c.1959. 26-May-3 Grev Wedels Plass, Oslo #108/R est:20000 (N.KR 26000)
£2949 $4600 €4424 Landscape with tall trees and plants (80x100cm-31x39in) s.d.52. 21-Oct-2 Blomqvist, Oslo #414/R est:40000-50000 (N.KR 34000)
£3167 $5131 €4751 Composition (65x81cm-26x32in) s.d.49 panel. 26-May-3 Grev Wedels Plass, Oslo #12/R est:30000-40000 (N.KR 35000)
£3481 $5570 €5222 Composition with head (61x50cm-24x20in) s. panel painted c.1946. 17-Mar-3 Blomqvist, Oslo #437/R est:50000-70000 (N.KR 40000)
£3860 $6098 €5790 Composition (52x62cm-20x24in) s. panel exhib. 17-Dec-2 Grev Wedels Plass, Oslo #290/R est:40000-60000 (N.KR 44000)
£5048 $8077 €7572 Columbine (70x70cm-28x28in) s.d.81 s.i.d.81 verso. 17-Mar-3 Blomqvist, Oslo #453/R est:30000-40000 (N.KR 58000)
£6092 $9748 €9138 Composition (81x100cm-32x39in) s. panel painted 1940s. 17-Mar-3 Blomqvist, Oslo #442/R est:60000-80000 (N.KR 70000)
£8726 $13700 €13089 Impression from the nature (150x150cm-59x59in) s.d.88 i.verso lit. 21-Nov-2 Grev Wedels Plass, Oslo #72/R est:100000-150000 (N.KR 100000)
£9516 $15035 €14274 Coltsfoot in morning light (65x65cm-26x26in) s.i.d.1973 verso exhib. 2-Dec-2 Blomqvist, Oslo #438/R est:70000-90000 (N.KR 110000)

£9649 $15246 €14474 Composition (150x150cm-59x59in) s.d.88 exhib. 17-Dec-2 Grev Wedels Plass, Oslo #292/R est:100000-150000 (N.KR 110000)
£9735 $15381 €14603 Composition (80x100cm-31x39in) s.d.78. 28-Apr-3 Blomqvist, Oslo #388/R est:100000-120000 (N.KR 110000)
£12216 $19180 €18324 Composition (120x140cm-47x55in) s.d.93. 21-Nov-2 Grev Wedels Plass, Oslo #48/R est:150000-200000 (N.KR 140000)
£19948 $31119 €29922 Christmas Eve (98x112cm-39x44in) s.d.65 s.i.d. verso exhib.lit. 21-Oct-2 Blomqvist, Oslo #410/R est:150000-200000 (N.KR 230000)
£25664 $40549 €38496 Impression from nature (160x160cm-63x63in) s.d.85 s.d.1985 verso exhib.lit. 28-Apr-3 Blomqvist, Oslo #391/R est:250000-280000 (N.KR 290000)

Works on paper
£345 $577 €500 Composition (25x34cm-10x13in) s.i.d.65. 18-Jun-3 Grev Wedels Plass, Oslo #99 (N.KR 4000)
£954 $1488 €1431 Woman (29x18cm-11x7in) s.d.51 pencil. 21-Oct-2 Blomqvist, Oslo #507/R (N.KR 11000)

WEIDEMANN, Magnus (1880-?) German
£288 $472 €440 Zugspitze view (40x90cm-16x35in) s.i.d.1955 s.i.d. verso board. 8-Feb-3 Hans Stahl, Hamburg #118/R
£493 $794 €700 Steep shore near Glucksburg (35x60cm-14x24in) s.d.1938 i. verso board. 10-May-3 Hans Stahl, Toestorf #79/R

WEIDENMANN, Johann Caspar (attrib) (1805-1850) Swiss
£939 $1540 €1362 Portrait of two bearded men (39x64cm-15x25in) 4-Jun-3 Fischer, Luzern #2352/R est:400-600 (S.FR 2000)

WEIDINGER, Franz Xaver (1890-1972) Austrian
£545 $861 €850 Landscape (12x17cm-5x7in) mono. panel. 18-Nov-2 Dorotheum, Linz #349/R
£1079 $1770 €1500 Braunau on River Inn (53x67cm-21x26in) mono. board. 5-Jun-3 Dorotheum, Salzburg #574/R est:1600-2200

Works on paper
£288 $456 €450 Landscape (26x35cm-10x14in) s. W/C. 18-Nov-2 Dorotheum, Linz #459

WEIDMANN, Ulrich (1840-1892) Swiss
£4148 $6513 €6222 St Moritz lake with Innfall (70x95cm-28x37in) s. lit. 25-Nov-2 Sotheby's, Zurich #18/R est:3000-5000 (S.FR 9500)

WEIDNER, Willem Frederik (1817-1850) Dutch
£3082 $4808 €4500 Still life with fruit and a bird (62x49cm-24x19in) s.d.1842 panel. 14-Apr-3 Glerum, Amsterdam #33/R est:4000-6000

WEIE, Edvard (1879-1943) Danish
£652 $1036 €978 Interior (42x57cm-17x22in) with sig.verso painted c.1905 exhib.prov. 4-Mar-3 Museumsbygningen, Copenhagen #491/R (D.KR 7000)
£1459 $2306 €2189 Interior scene with lady playing piano (26x31cm-10x12in) panel. 13-Nov-2 Kunsthallen, Copenhagen #103/R est:15000 (D.KR 17000)
£2425 $3856 €3638 Landscape with large tree (47x60cm-19x24in) 29-Apr-3 Kunsthallen, Copenhagen #261/R est:30000 (D.KR 26000)
£7435 $11747 €11153 Dante and Virgil (67x73cm-26x29in) prov.lit. 1-Apr-3 Rasmussen, Copenhagen #3/R est:80000-100000 (D.KR 80000)
£8770 $14646 €12717 View of Saint Thomas' Square (60x53cm-24x21in) init. painted c.1930 prov. 17-Jun-3 Rasmussen, Copenhagen #83/R est:60000-80000 (D.KR 92000)

Works on paper
£446 $705 €669 Landscape from Glaeno (44x30cm-17x12in) W/C. 5-Apr-3 Rasmussen, Havnen #4318 (D.KR 4800)
£709 $1149 €1064 Landscape from Glaeno (50x64cm-20x25in) init. W/C. 25-Jan-3 Rasmussen, Havnen #2239/R (D.KR 8000)

WEIGALL, Alfred (fl.1855-1866) British
Miniatures
£1000 $1560 €1500 Lady seated beside a pillar wearing white dress and black lace shawl (10cm-4in) black wood frame with inner gilded card mount oval. 5-Nov-2 Bonhams, New Bond Street #150/R est:1000-1200

WEIGHT, Carel (1908-1997) British
£300 $474 €450 Somerset landscape (35x45cm-14x18in) panel. 4-Apr-3 Moore Allen & Innocent, Cirencester #721/R
£1000 $1560 €1500 Workers at rest (266x571cm-105x225in) s.d.51. 12-Sep-2 Sotheby's, Olympia #85/R est:1000-1500
£1226 $1827 €1839 Conversation in a field (38x10cm-15x4in) s. board painted 1977. 27-Aug-2 Christie's, Melbourne #200/R est:2200-3200 (A.D 3200)
£1350 $2093 €2025 Blue jeans (64x31cm-25x12in) s. prov. 1-Oct-2 Bonhams, Leeds #317 est:1500-2000
£1500 $2369 €2250 Gardener (45x48cm-18x19in) s. paper on board. 27-Nov-2 Sotheby's, Olympia #83/R est:1500-2500
£2000 $3180 €3000 Chimney, Whiteheads Mill (17x23cm-7x9in) s.i.d.1938 verso board. 26-Feb-3 Sotheby's, Olympia #261/R est:2000-3000
£2500 $3900 €3750 Rendez-vous (49x59cm-19x23in) s. board. 12-Sep-2 Sotheby's, Olympia #88/R est:2000-3000
£2800 $4368 €4200 Lock (50x61cm-20x24in) s. board prov. 25-Mar-3 Bonhams, New Bond Street #78/R est:3000-5000
£2800 $4592 €4200 Winter walk (63x76cm-25x30in) s. board. 3-Jun-3 Sotheby's, Olympia #126/R est:3000-5000
£2900 $4640 €4350 Naked bathers (53x41cm-21x16in) s. canvas on board. 11-Mar-3 Gorringes, Lewes #2460 est:2500-3000
£3000 $4680 €4500 Tense girl (101x76cm-40x30in) s. 12-Sep-2 Sotheby's, Olympia #80/R est:3000-4000
£3000 $4650 €4500 Shadow (61x50cm-24x20in) s. board. 3-Dec-2 Bonhams, New Bond Street #58/R est:3000-5000
£3000 $4740 €4500 Winson Village, Gloucestershire (32x40cm-13x16in) s. s.i.d.1929 verso board. 27-Nov-2 Sotheby's, Olympia #254/R est:3000-5000
£3200 $4928 €4800 Winter walk (41x51cm-16x20in) s. canvasboard. 5-Sep-2 Christie's, Kensington #627/R est:3000-5000
£4000 $6280 €6000 Portrait of Sarah (71x54cm-28x21in) s. painted 1980. 22-Nov-2 Christie's, London #113/R est:4000-6000
£4000 $6320 €6000 Along the promenade (25x35cm-10x14in) s. board exhib. 27-Nov-2 Sotheby's, Olympia #256/R est:4800-8000
£5500 $8525 €8250 Garden next door (71x91cm-28x36in) s. prov. 4-Dec-2 Christie's, Kensington #521/R est:6000-8000
£6500 $10205 €9750 Cricketer (122x122cm-48x48in) s. painted 1984 exhib. 22-Nov-2 Christie's, London #114/R est:7000-10000
£8000 $13120 €12000 Her brother's ghost (76x152cm-30x60in) s. canvasboard painted c.1960 prov.exhib. 6-Jun-3 Christie's, London #209/R est:10000-15000

WEIHS, Carl (1860-1931) Austrian
Works on paper
£338 $527 €500 Krems church (36x51cm-14x20in) i. verso W/C. 28-Mar-3 Dorotheum, Vienna #344/R
£541 $843 €800 Vienna, Singerstrasse (40x28cm-16x11in) W/C. 28-Mar-3 Dorotheum, Vienna #355/R

WEIKERT, Georg (1749-1799) Austrian
£12676 $20408 €18000 Kaiser Joseph II (124x93cm-49x37in) s. 7-May-3 Dorotheum, Vienna #28/R est:18000-24000

WEIL, C J (19th C) ?
Works on paper
£300 $475 €450 Hunting party in landscape (44x56cm-17x22in) s.d.1835 gouache. 17-Nov-2 Hindemae, Ullerslev #7233/R (D.KR 3500)

WEIL, Otto (1884-1929) German
Works on paper
£552 $822 €850 Skaters (34x45cm-13x18in) s.d.1919 gouache over chk. 26-Jun-2 Neumeister, Munich #611/R

WEILAND, Johannes (1856-1909) Dutch
£4730 $7378 €7000 Woman by fire (40x55cm-16x22in) s.d.97. 27-Mar-3 Dr Fritz Nagel, Stuttgart #875/R est:1900

WEILAND, Johannes (jnr) (1894-1976) Dutch
£269 $423 €420 Blue peacock on a branch (47x36cm-19x14in) s.d.1919 board. 25-Nov-2 Glerum, Amsterdam #62

WEILAND, Joyce (20th C) Canadian
Works on paper
£178 $293 €267 Untitled - flying figures (24x26cm-9x10in) s. pen ink. 6-Feb-3 Heffel, Vancouver #050/R (C.D 450)
£260 $413 €377 City (27x37cm-11x15in) ink dr exec.c.1966 prov. 1-May-3 Heffel, Vancouver #105/R (C.D 600)
£278 $456 €417 Love in the park (15x23cm-6x9in) s.d.1962 chk pencil. 6-Feb-3 Heffel, Vancouver #049/R (C.D 700)

WEILER, Max (1910-) Austrian
£10127 $16000 €16000 Kronburg near Landeck, Tyrol (29x29cm-11x11in) s.d.40 paper on panel. 27-Nov-2 Dorotheum, Vienna #184/R est:16000-20000
£10870 $17826 €15000 Figure in ochre (85x57cm-33x22in) mono.d.66 s.i.d.1966 verso egg tempera. 27-May-3 Wiener Kunst Auktionen, Vienna #202/R est:15000-25000

£23188 $38029 €32000 Suggestion of a landscape (100x80cm-39x31in) s.d.73 s.i.d.1973 verso egg tempera lit. 27-May-3 Wiener Kunst Auktionen, Vienna #193/R est:20000-30000
£25316 $39241 €40000 Hutmann (80x80cm-31x31in) s.d.69 s.i.d.69 verso tempera. 24-Sep-2 Wiener Kunst Auktionen, Vienna #228/R est:50000-75000
£32609 $53478 €45000 Three single flowers (100x80cm-39x31in) s.d.88 s.i. verso egg tempera. 27-May-3 Wiener Kunst Auktionen, Vienna #189/R est:25000-40000

Works on paper
£7595 $11772 €12000 Untitled - like a landscape (60x88cm-24x35in) mono.d.67 mixed media. 24-Sep-2 Wiener Kunst Auktionen, Vienna #227/R est:8000-18000

WEILER, Milton C (1910-1974) American
Works on paper
£353 $550 €530 Rainbow trout chasing fly (18cm-7in circular) s. W/C. 8-Nov-2 York Town, York #487

WEIMANN, Paul (1867-?) German
£704 $1134 €1000 Schlesian village in water (81x108cm-32x43in) s. lit. 9-May-3 Schloss Ahlden, Ahlden #1437/R

WEINBERG, Elbert (1928-1991) American
Sculpture
£1220 $2000 €1769 Temptation of Eve no.1 (152x76x122cm-60x30x48in) bronze prov. 1-Jun-3 Wright, Chicago #259/R est:2000-3000

WEINBERGER, Anton (1843-1912) German
£2597 $3870 €4000 Puppies barking at hedgehog (90x70cm-35x28in) s.d.1886 i. verso. 27-Jun-2 Neumeister, Munich #2851/R est:750

WEINER, Dan (20th C) American
Photographs
£13924 $22000 €20886 Urban scenes (20x25cm-8x10in) 4 gelatin silver print prov. 25-Apr-3 Phillips, New York #127/R est:2000-3000

WEINER, Hans (1575-?) German
Works on paper
£4514 $7177 €6500 Mistress with servant overseeing celebratory meal (15x20cm-6x8in) pen wash prov.lit. 5-May-3 Ketterer, Munich #216/R est:400-600

WEINER-KRAL, Imrich (1901-1978) Czechoslovakian
£756 $1172 €1134 Market (36x46cm-14x18in) painted c.1925. 1-Oct-2 SOGA, Bratislava #50/R est:60000 (SL.K 48000)
£1103 $1566 €1655 Summer (40x31cm-16x12in) painted 1949. 26-Mar-2 SOGA, Bratislava #78/R est:70000 (SL.K 70000)
£1103 $1709 €1655 Bratislava (58x45cm-23x18in) 1-Oct-2 SOGA, Bratislava #49/R est:70000 (SL.K 70000)
£1733 $2460 €2600 Stranger in the village (41x33cm-16x13in) painted 1971. 26-Mar-2 SOGA, Bratislava #76/R est:78000 (SL.K 110000)
£1827 $2832 €2741 Holy Family (71x49cm-28x19in) painted c.1960. 1-Oct-2 SOGA, Bratislava #48/R est:145000 (SL.K 116000)

Works on paper
£410 $635 €615 Old Bratislava (30x20cm-12x8in) W/C. 1-Oct-2 SOGA, Bratislava #55/R est:18000 (SL.K 26000)

WEINERT, Carl (19th C) German
£1101 $1608 €1652 Landscape with trees, mill and walkers (91x134cm-36x53in) s.d.98. 17-Jun-2 Philippe Schuler, Zurich #7364 (S.FR 2500)

WEINGART, Joachim (1895-1942) Polish
£545 $855 €850 Nature morte au compotier (52x40cm-20x16in) s.d. oil W/C. 24-Nov-2 Chayette & Cheval, Paris #248
£828 $1292 €1300 Les poissons (54x65cm-21x26in) s. 6-Nov-2 Claude Boisgirard, Paris #59/R
£851 $1421 €1200 Femme rousse (65x54cm-26x21in) s. 17-Jun-3 Claude Boisgirard, Paris #144
£892 $1391 €1400 Fleurs et cactus (60x44cm-24x17in) s. 6-Nov-2 Claude Boisgirard, Paris #62/R
£1135 $1895 €1600 Fleurs (61x49cm-24x19in) s. 17-Jun-3 Claude Boisgirard, Paris #145/R est:1500-2000
£1529 $2385 €2400 Mimosas (61x50cm-24x20in) s. 6-Nov-2 Claude Boisgirard, Paris #60/R est:1800-2000
£1529 $2385 €2400 Fleurs dans un pot gris (61x46cm-24x18in) s. 6-Nov-2 Claude Boisgirard, Paris #61/R est:1500-1800
£1635 $2535 €2600 Nu (64x49cm-25x19in) s. 30-Oct-2 Artcurial Briest, Paris #116 est:750-900
£2166 $3378 €3400 Anemones et tulipes. s. 6-Nov-2 Claude Boisgirard, Paris #63 est:2000-2500

WEINMAN, Adolph Alexander (1870-1952) American
Sculpture
£29032 $45000 €43548 Chief Black Bird, Ogalalla sioux (41cm-16in) i. dark brown pat. bronze lit. 4-Dec-2 Sotheby's, New York #152/R est:25000-35000

WEIR, Barbara (20th C) Australian
£766 $1203 €1149 Grass seed dreaming - awelye 1999 (61x45cm-24x18in) s.verso acrylic on linen. 15-Apr-3 Lawson Menzies, Sydney #100/R est:2000-3000 (A.D 2000)
£2682 $4211 €4023 Untitled (120x120cm-47x47in) s. acrylic on linen. 15-Apr-3 Lawson Menzies, Sydney #98/R est:5000-7000 (A.D 7000)

WEIR, Harrison William (1824-1906) British
Works on paper
£720 $1123 €1080 Cow with ducks in a barn. Cow and cat in a barn (25x40cm-10x16in) s.d.1882 pencil W/C htd white two. 27-Mar-3 Christie's, Kensington #99/R

WEIR, J Alden (1852-1919) American
£11146 $17500 €16719 Still life with brass pot (61x51cm-24x20in) s. exhib. 20-Nov-2 Christie's, Los Angeles #53/R est:20000-30000
£18519 $30000 €27779 Landscape with seated figure (63x76cm-25x30in) prov.exhib. 21-May-3 Sotheby's, New York #152/R est:20000-30000

Works on paper
£1761 $2800 €2642 Young woman reclining in a meadow (18x15cm-7x6in) s. W/C pencil prov. 1-Mar-3 North East Auctions, Portsmouth #723/R

WEIR, Robert W (1803-1889) American
Works on paper
£701 $1100 €1052 Solitude (36x46cm-14x18in) indis sig. black chk htd white. 10-Dec-2 Doyle, New York #22/R est:2000-3000

WEISBROD, Richard (20th C) ?
£300 $483 €450 Near Martinique (33x65cm-13x26in) s. board. 15-Jan-3 Cheffins Grain & Comins, Cambridge #436/R

WEISBUCH, Claude (1927-) French
£463 $745 €695 Ecuyere (16x22cm-6x9in) s. prov. 7-May-3 Dobiaschofsky, Bern #1054 (S.FR 1000)
£1132 $1755 €1800 Cheval cabre (38x46cm-15x18in) s. 7-Oct-2 Claude Aguttes, Neuilly #284
£1186 $1862 €1850 Violoniste en tenue de concert (35x28cm-14x11in) s. 15-Dec-2 Lombrail & Teucquam, Paris #22/R
£1667 $2617 €2600 Violoniste (37x45cm-15x18in) s. 15-Dec-2 Lombrail & Teucquam, Paris #20/R
£1667 $2367 €2700 Enlevement (46x55cm-18x22in) s. i.verso. 16-Mar-3 Eric Pillon, Calais #239/R
£1987 $3120 €3100 Homme en buste (46x38cm-18x15in) s. 12-Dec-2 Rabourdin & Choppin de Janvry, Paris #147/R
£2089 $3258 €3300 Le vent d'orage (38x55cm-15x22in) s.d.58. 20-Oct-2 Galerie de Chartres, Chartres #156 est:4000-5000
£2215 $3500 €3500 Femme attachant ses bas (65x81cm-26x32in) s. prov. 27-Nov-2 Blanchet, Paris #90/R
£2436 $3824 €3800 Le picador (46x55cm-18x22in) s. 16-Dec-2 Chochon-Barre & Allardi, Paris #100/R est:3000-3500
£3020 $4862 €4500 Le peintre et son modele (46x55cm-18x22in) s. 23-Feb-3 Lesieur & Le Bars, Le Havre #155/R
£3221 $5187 €4800 Le violoncelliste (46x55cm-18x22in) s. 23-Feb-3 Lesieur & Le Bars, Le Havre #154/R
£5298 $8636 €8000 Henri IV a Chenonceaux (116x89cm-46x35in) s. 1-Feb-3 Claude Aguttes, Neuilly #182/R est:8000-8500

Works on paper
£256 $400 €384 Lovers (66x76cm-26x30in) s. mixed media. 22-Sep-2 Susanin's, Chicago #5037/R
£313 $494 €450 Autoportrait (29x21cm-11x8in) s.i.d. graphite gouache. 28-Apr-3 Cornette de St.Cyr, Paris #306
£380 $589 €600 Homme courant (31x22cm-12x9in) s. graphite. 28-Sep-2 Cornette de St.Cyr, Paris #210/R
£397 $648 €600 Violoniste (26x36cm-10x14in) s.i. graphite gouache. 3-Feb-3 Cornette de St.Cyr, Paris #348/R
£530 $864 €800 Cavalier (27x36cm-11x14in) s.i. graphite gouache. 3-Feb-3 Cornette de St.Cyr, Paris #346/R
£556 $878 €800 Deux centaures (27x36cm-11x14in) s.i. graphite gouache. 28-Apr-3 Cornette de St.Cyr, Paris #307
£2848 $4500 €4500 Clown (100x65cm-39x26in) s. col pastel crayon. 27-Nov-2 Blanchet, Paris #88/R

WEISCHE, Andreas (1964-) German
£949 $1472 €1500 View in blue (50x40cm-20x16in) s.d.2002 stretcher. 28-Sep-2 Ketterer, Hamburg #851/R est:2200-2500

WEISE, Alexander (1883-?) Russian
£343 $542 €515 Winter landscape with Arlberg Monastery (60x75cm-24x30in) s.d.1946 i.verso. 26-Nov-2 Hans Widmer, St Gallen #1412 (S.FR 800)

WEISE, Alexander (attrib) (1883-?) Russian
£308 $481 €450 Snowy winter landscape in the winter (65x82cm-26x32in) canvas on panel. 10-Apr-3 Van Ham, Cologne #1753

WEISER, Bernard (1822-?) Belgian
£513 $795 €800 Portrait d'une vieille dame (56x72cm-22x28in) s. 3-Dec-2 Campo & Campo, Antwerp #353

WEISER, F (19th C) German
£264 $394 €396 Group dancing (11x28cm-4x11in) s.d.99 panel. 25-Jun-2 Koller, Zurich #6459 (S.FR 600)

WEISGERBER, Carl (1891-?) German
£705 $1093 €1100 Village church (51x67cm-20x26in) s. tempera. 4-Dec-2 Lempertz, Koln #1111/R

WEISHAUPT, Victor (1848-1925) German
£440 $687 €700 Extensive meadow landscape with four cows (27x34cm-11x13in) s. lit. 20-Sep-2 Karlheinz Kaupp, Staufen #2041/R

WEISMAN, Gary (?) American
Sculpture
£1538 $2400 €2307 Torso (58cm-23in) bronze. 22-Sep-2 Susanin's, Chicago #5101/R est:1000-1500

WEISMAN, William H (1840-1922) American
£472 $750 €708 Mt Jefferson, Franconia, New Hampshire, from Forest Hills House (36x28cm-14x11in) s. prov. 7-Mar-3 Skinner, Boston #293/R

WEISMAN, William H (attrib) (1840-1922) American
£299 $475 €449 Franconia Falls, New Hampshire (28x17cm-11x7in) i.verso board prov. 7-Mar-3 Skinner, Boston #290/R

WEISMANN, Jacques (1878-?) French
£380 $608 €570 Three quarter length study of a female nude (63x48cm-25x19in) s. 11-Mar-3 Bonhams, Knightsbridge #128/R
Works on paper
£577 $906 €900 Venise, avant le bal masque (61x46cm-24x18in) s. pastel. 10-Dec-2 Renaud, Paris #40

WEISS, Bartholomaus Ignaz (c.1740-1814) German
Works on paper
£506 $800 €800 Madonna in the clouds (38x30cm-15x12in) pen brush. 29-Nov-2 Bassenge, Berlin #5796/R
£903 $1435 €1300 Female figures and figure studies (20x29cm-8x11in) pen over chk wash double-sided. 5-May-3 Ketterer, Munich #268/R
£1111 $1767 €1600 Head studies (15x19cm-6x7in) brush ink htd white. 5-May-3 Ketterer, Munich #266/R
£1667 $2650 €2400 Holy Family (19x19cm-7x7in) pen wash htd white pink double-sided. 5-May-3 Ketterer, Munich #265/R est:1000-1200
£1667 $2650 €2400 Figures and head studies (20x29cm-8x11in) pen wash double-sided. 5-May-3 Ketterer, Munich #269/R est:800-1000
£1806 $2871 €2600 Heads of two apostles (20x29cm-8x11in) chk study verso. 5-May-3 Ketterer, Munich #267/R est:1200-1500

WEISS, Bartholomaus Ignaz (attrib) (c.1740-1814) German
Works on paper
£313 $497 €450 Moses and the snake (17x21cm-7x8in) i. pen double-sided. 5-May-3 Ketterer, Munich #264/R

WEISS, Felix (1908-) Austrian
Sculpture
£1191 $1858 €1787 Female nude figure (62cm-24in) s. pat.bronze marble socle. 5-Nov-2 Bukowskis, Stockholm #1420/R est:10000-12000 (S.KR 17000)

WEISS, Georges (1861-?) French
£650 $1066 €975 Choosing summer blooms (36x27cm-14x11in) s. indis.d. panel. 5-Jun-3 Christie's, Kensington #607/R

WEISS, Johann Baptist (1812-1879) German
£705 $1107 €1100 Landscape (40x60cm-16x24in) s. panel. 13-Dec-2 Peschetau-Badin Godeau & Leroy, Paris #21
£2516 $3925 €4000 Sunset on stormy sea (75x101cm-30x40in) mono.d.1858 prov. 19-Sep-2 Dr Fritz Nagel, Stuttgart #1012/R est:1500

WEISS, Jose (1859-1919) British
£250 $393 €375 Pelayo Kendall (36x51cm-14x20in) s. i.stretcher. 10-Dec-2 Rosebery Fine Art, London #523
£262 $414 €393 Landscape after rain (25x38cm-10x15in) s. panel prov. 18 Nov-2 Waddingtons, Toronto #97/R (C.D 650)
£340 $530 €510 On the outskirts of a village (25x38cm-10x15in) s. panel. 26-Mar-3 Woolley & Wallis, Salisbury #279/R
£500 $835 €725 Continental street scene with figures and cart (23x36cm-9x14in) s. 20-Jun-3 Keys, Aylsham #699
£679 $1100 €985 River at sunset (71x107cm-28x42in) s. 21-May-3 Doyle, New York #197/R
£847 $1347 €1271 Sunny August (25x38cm-10x15in) s. 18-Mar-3 Maynards, Vancouver #21a est:1000-1500 (C.D 2000)
£1333 $2213 €1933 Evening (36x61cm-14x24in) s. prov. 16-Jun-3 Waddingtons, Toronto #148/R est:3000-5000 (C.D 3000)
£1529 $2400 €2294 Mountains and clouds (24x36cm-9x14in) s. 10-Dec-2 Doyle, New York #198/R est:2000-3000
£1538 $2400 €2307 Cattle in the meadow (41x61cm-16x24in) s. i.on stretcher verso. 20-Sep-2 Sloan, North Bethesda #394/R est:3000-4000
£1899 $3000 €3000 Landscape (50x76cm-20x30in) s. 28-Nov-2 Dorotheum, Vienna #156/R est:3000-3400

WEISS, Loreth G (attrib) (19th C) ?
£457 $667 €686 Mountain brook (60x70cm-24x28in) painted c.1870. 4-Jun-2 SOGA, Bratislava #166/R est:29000 (SL.K 29000)

WEISS, Mary L (20th C) American
£937 $1500 €1359 Robs Cove (36x51cm-14x20in) s. i.verso. 16-May-3 Skinner, Boston #210/R est:1000-1500

WEISS, Paul Emil (1888-1977) Swiss
£643 $939 €990 Lady in park (58x44cm-23x17in) s. exhib. 15-Jun-2 Hans Stahl, Hamburg #63/R

WEISS, Peter (1916-1982) Swedish
£423 $665 €635 Man with pipe (73x60cm-29x24in) s. painted c.1940. 16-Dec-2 Lilla Bukowskis, Stockholm #91 (S.KR 6000)
£452 $709 €678 Self portrait (62x48cm-24x19in) s. painted 1943 lit. 16-Dec-2 Lilla Bukowskis, Stockholm #92/R (S.KR 6400)

WEISS, Richard Salomon (1896-1950) Swiss
£261 $407 €392 Reclining female nude (35x50cm-14x20in) s. canvas on board. 16-Sep-2 Philippe Schuler, Zurich #6663 (S.FR 600)

WEISSBERG, Léon (1893-?) Polish
£818 $1267 €1300 Baigneuses (41x27cm-16x11in) s. 30-Oct-2 Artcurial Briest, Paris #117

WEISSENBACHER, Sebastian (1959-) Austrian
£497 $810 €750 Mood maker (40x50cm-16x20in) mono.d.98 s.i.d.98 verso acrylic. 28-Jan-3 Dorotheum, Vienna #304/R

WEISSENBRUCH, Jan (1822-1880) Dutch
£4167 $6625 €6000 Figures resting on a riverbank by a moored sailing vessel (19x27cm-7x11in) s. panel. 29-Apr-3 Christie's, Amsterdam #2/R est:4000-6000
£4452 $6945 €6500 Figures in a square in the morning sun (19x27cm-7x11in) s. panel. 14-Apr-3 Glerum, Amsterdam #13/R est:7000-9000

WEISSENBRUCH, Jan Hendrik (1824-1903) Dutch
£2830 $4358 €4500 Duinlandschap (16x24cm-6x9in) s. board prov. 22-Oct-2 Sotheby's, Amsterdam #129/R est:3000-5000
£6289 $10000 €9434 Bringing the boat ashore (19x24cm-7x9in) s. 7-Mar-3 Skinner, Boston #335/R est:2500-3000
£6597 $10490 €9500 Cows under willows by a pond (19x27cm-7x11in) s. canvas on panel. 29-Apr-3 Christie's, Amsterdam #123/R est:10000-15000
£9028 $14354 €13000 Cattle resting under a tree in a polder landscape (30x40cm-12x16in) s. panel prov. 29-Apr-3 Christie's, Amsterdam #127/R est:10000-15000
£13836 $21308 €22000 Bij Heelsum (16x24cm-6x9in) s. canvas on panel prov.exhib.lit. 22-Oct-2 Sotheby's, Amsterdam #220/R est:10000-12000
£15278 $24292 €22000 Summer in the polder (43x25cm-17x10in) s.d.92 cardboard on panel prov.exhib.lit. 29-Apr-3 Christie's, Amsterdam #122/R est:15000-20000
£25157 $38742 €40000 Polder landscape near kortenhoef (51x70cm-20x28in) s. prov.exhib. 22-Oct-2 Sotheby's, Amsterdam #196/R est:23000-28000
£38000 $62320 €57000 Sailing boat in choppy seas (40x49cm-16x19in) s. prov. 3-Jun-3 Sotheby's, London #157/R est:12000-18000

Works on paper
£5660 $8717 €9000 Early morning, shepherd guiding his flock (51x37cm-20x15in) s. black chk W/C htd white prov. 23-Oct-2 Christie's, Amsterdam #220/R est:10000-15000
£7556 $12391 €10956 Canal and farm buildings (26x48cm-10x19in) s. W/C. 9-Jun-3 Hodgins, Calgary #356/R est:7000-11000 (C.D 17000)
£19421 $30492 €29132 Cattle in a polder landscape (38x53cm-15x21in) s. W/C. 24-Jul-2 Walker's, Ottawa #7/R est:20000-25000 (C.D 47000)

WEISSENBRUCH, Willem (1864-1941) Dutch
£463 $745 €695 Dutch city with canal (18x24cm-7x9in) s. panel. 7-May-3 Dobiaschofsky, Bern #1055/R (S.FR 1000)
£1447 $2345 €2200 Sunlit polder landscape with sailing barges (25x35cm-10x14in) s. 21-Jan-3 Christie's, Amsterdam #171/R est:1200-1600
£1528 $2521 €2200 Farmhouses by the river on a clear day (40x60cm-16x24in) s. exhib. 1-Jul-3 Christie's, Amsterdam #79/R est:2000-3000
£1974 $3197 €3000 Fisherman in a rowing boat in the polder (44x61cm-17x24in) s. 21-Jan-3 Christie's, Amsterdam #167/R est:3000-5000

WEISSINGER, John (20th C) American
Works on paper
£316 $500 €474 Three short billed dowitchers wading (46x61cm-18x24in) s. W/C gouache. 3-Apr-3 Christie's, Rockefeller NY #218/R

WEISZ, Adolphe (1838-?) French/Hungarian
£6289 $9811 €10000 Portrait of young woman holding roses (50x37cm-20x15in) s. prov.lit. 20-Sep-2 Karlheinz Kaupp, Staufen #1939/R est:9000
£39744 $62397 €62000 L'odalisque au coffret a bijoux (72x102cm-28x40in) s. 16-Dec-2 Gros & Delettrez, Paris #148/R est:60000-80000
Works on paper
£286 $427 €429 Reclining nude (18x26cm-7x10in) s. chl. 25-Jun-2 Koller, Zurich #6529 (S.FR 650)

WEIXLBAUM, Johann (1752-1840) Austrian
Miniatures
£1000 $1620 €1500 Lady seated, wearing a red dress (7cm-3in) s. gilt metal frame rectangular. 22-May-3 Bonhams, New Bond Street #104/R est:1000-1500

WEJCHERT, Alexandra (?) Polish?
Sculpture
£1507 $2366 €2200 Purple slats on wood. executed c.1974. 15-Apr-3 De Veres Art Auctions, Dublin #253 est:2000-3000
£6507 $10216 €9500 Flame (141cm-56in) d.1986 bronze on stone base. 15-Apr-3 De Veres Art Auctions, Dublin #250/R est:9000-12000

WEL, Jean van (1906-1990) Belgian
£308 $484 €450 Fleurs des champs (90x70cm-35x28in) s. 15-Apr-3 Galerie Moderne, Brussels #324
£445 $699 €650 La sieste (50x60cm-20x24in) s. panel. 15-Apr-3 Galerie Moderne, Brussels #389/R

WELBOURNE, Joseph W (19th C) British
£318 $505 €477 Walter James Little Gilmour (51x38cm-20x15in) 18-Mar-3 Maynards, Vancouver #47/R (C.D 750)

WELBURN, Irene (fl.1936-1940) British
£380 $600 €570 Broken shoe (35x44cm-14x17in) s. canvas on board. 27-Nov-2 Sotheby's, Olympia #247/R
£800 $1264 €1200 At the station (63x73cm-25x29in) s. board. 27-Nov-2 Sotheby's, Olympia #275/R

WELCH, Ludmilla P (1867-1925) American
£1356 $2250 €1966 La Cumbria trail (36x46cm-14x18in) s. i. on stretcher. 11-Jun-3 Butterfields, San Francisco #4197/R est:3000-5000
£1656 $2750 €2401 Fry's Harbour, Santa Cruz Island (25x43cm-10x17in) i. i.verso canvas on board. 11-Jun-3 Butterfields, San Francisco #4198/R est:3000-5000
£4217 $7000 €6115 View of Rincon from the Montecito foothills (30x51cm-12x20in) s. 11-Jun-3 Butterfields, San Francisco #4196/R est:3000-5000

WELCH, Nugent (1881-1970) New Zealander
Works on paper
£281 $438 €422 Pukerua Bay (22x28cm-9x11in) s. W/C. 27-Mar-3 International Art Centre, Auckland #169/R (NZ.D 800)
£364 $560 €546 Terewhiti (24x34cm-9x13in) s. W/C. 4-Sep-2 Dunbar Sloane, Wellington #122 est:1000-2000 (NZ.D 1200)

WELCH, Rosemary Sarah (1946-) British
£1300 $2028 €1950 Horses logging in a winter landscape (76x102cm-30x40in) s. 26-Mar-3 Woolley & Wallis, Salisbury #238/R est:800-1200

WELCH, Thaddeus (1844-1919) American
£1911 $3000 €2867 Marin county, California (58x41cm-23x16in) s. i.verso. 23-Nov-2 Jackson's, Cedar Falls #50/R est:4000-6000
Works on paper
£2690 $4250 €3901 Good life (28x38cm-11x15in) s.d.1889 W/C. 26-Jul-3 Coeur d'Alene, Hayden #40/R est:3000-5000

WELCH, Thaddeus (attrib) (1844-1919) American
£818 $1300 €1227 Man etching trays (76x64cm-30x25in) painted c.1930 prov. 2-Mar-3 Toomey, Oak Park #621/R

WELDNER, Colette Pope (?) American
£618 $1026 €896 Swamp Idyl, Louisiana bayou country (61x102cm-24x40in) s. s.i.verso. 10-Jun-3 Ritchie, Toronto #93/R est:1000-1500 (C.D 1390)

WELIE, Antoon van (1866-?) Dutch
£685 $1068 €1000 Young herder (145x90cm-57x35in) s. 14-Apr-3 Glerum, Amsterdam #69/R

WELL, Arnoldus van (1773-1818) Dutch
£5755 $9209 €8000 Winter landscape with figures and god in frozen ditch (45x60cm-18x24in) s. panel. 13-May-3 Sotheby's, Amsterdam #89/R est:6000-8000

WELLENS, Charles (1889-1958) Belgian
£692 $1079 €1100 Farmhouse (48x88cm-19x35in) s. 23-Sep-2 Bernaerts, Antwerp #820/R
£759 $1200 €1200 Interieur campinois (65x95cm-26x37in) s. 26-Nov-2 Palais de Beaux Arts, Brussels #183/R

WELLER, Dell (20th C) American
£214 $350 €321 Cabildo and St Louis Cathedral (76x51cm-30x20in) s.d.65 masonite. 8-Feb-3 Neal Auction Company, New Orleans #1050

WELLER, Theodor Leopold (1802-1880) German
£6289 $9811 €10000 Southern family with children dancing outside straw hut (61x73cm-24x29in) s.i.d.1845 lit. 19-Sep-2 Dr Fritz Nagel, Stuttgart #1013/R est:1000

WELLING, James (1951-) American?
Photographs
£9494 $15000 €14241 Untitled (60x50cm-24x20in) set of four polaroids prov. 24-Apr-3 Phillips, New York #53/R est:15000-20000

WELLINGTON, Hubert Lindsay (1879-1967) British
£500 $800 €750 Trees in parkland (46x36cm-18x14in) 11-Mar-3 Gorringes, Lewes #2473

WELLIVER, Neil (1929-) American
£12025 $19000 €18038 Sun spots (183x183cm-72x72in) s. painted 1988 prov. 13-Nov-2 Sotheby's, New York #610/R est:20000-30000
£12025 $19000 €18038 Deer in bottom (244x244cm-96x96in) s. painted 1980 prov. 14-Nov-2 Christie's, Rockefeller NY #173/R est:18000-25000

WELLMAN, Joyce (1949-) American
£545 $850 €818 Masked messenger (127x97cm-50x38in) s.d.87 acrylic tempera. 20-Sep-2 Sloan, North Bethesda #461/R

WELLS, Arthur H (?) British?
£250 $388 €375 Near Linagh, Connemara (30x40cm-12x16in) s. 4-Dec-2 John Ross, Belfast #9

WELLS, Dennis G (1881-1973) British
£660 $1036 €990 A prelude (33x25cm-13x10in) s. s.i.verso board. 15-Apr-3 Bonhams, Knowle #128

WELLS, George (fl.1842-1888) British
£500 $780 €750 Mrs Gamp (32x24cm-13x9in) mono. 15-Oct-2 Bearnes, Exeter #398
£1600 $2608 €2400 Bedtime stories (33x27cm-13x11in) s. 29-Jan-3 Sotheby's, Olympia #126/R est:1000-1500

WELLS, George (attrib) (fl.1842-1888) British
£800 $1304 €1200 Children in a summer landscape (29x44cm-11x17in) indis sig.d.1868. 29-Jan-3 Sotheby's, Olympia #209/R

WELLS, Henry (19th C) American
£5449 $8500 €8174 Landscape of a town in a valley with couple in the foreground (86x117cm-34x46in) i.d.1850. 21-Sep-2 Pook & Pook, Downington #111/R est:5000-7000

WELLS, Henry Tanworth (1828-1903) British
£1840 $3000 €2760 Little pupil (51x61cm-20x24in) s. 2-Feb-3 Simpson's, Houston #380a
Works on paper
£1700 $2669 €2550 Portrait of George Price Boyce seated reading a letter (18x12cm-7x5in) i. pencil pen ink exhib. 21-Nov-2 Christie's, London #80/R est:2000-3000

WELLS, John (1907-2000) British
£1800 $2808 €2700 Print composition (18x38cm-7x15in) s.d.1971 i.verso oil wash. 17-Oct-2 David Lay, Penzance #1122/R est:800-1200
£3200 $4960 €4800 Linear phantasy (13x43cm-5x17in) s. i.d.1957 verso mixed media on board. 3-Dec-2 Bonhams, New Bond Street #110/R est:2500-3500
£3200 $5088 €4800 Untitled (16x21cm-6x8in) s.d.65 board. 18-Mar-3 Bonhams, Knightsbridge #233 est:2800-3200
£4500 $6975 €6750 Anthropomorphic green rock (42x33cm-17x13in) s. i.d.1953 verso board with string. 3-Dec-2 Bonhams, New Bond Street #111/R est:5000-7000
£6800 $10608 €10200 Landscape evocation (60x147cm-24x58in) board. 25-Mar-3 Bonhams, New Bond Street #110/R est:4000-6000
Works on paper
£800 $1304 €1200 Untitled (25x36cm-10x14in) s.d.1974 mixed media. 13-Feb-3 David Lay, Penzance #17
£1200 $2004 €1740 Dance figure (18x13cm-7x5in) s.i.d.1946 verso mixed media board. 24-Jun-3 Bonhams, New Bond Street #112/R est:700-900

WELLS, V B (20th C) American
£755 $1200 €1133 Banjo player (51x61cm-20x24in) s. painted c.1930. 2-Mar-3 Toomey, Oak Park #574/R
Works on paper
£409 $650 €614 Century of progress building (36x25cm-14x10in) s. W/C exec.c.1933. 2-Mar-3 Toomey, Oak Park #665/R

WELLS, William Frederick (1762-1836) British
Works on paper
£410 $672 €615 Cattle watering near a mill (30x45cm-12x18in) pencil W/C. 4-Feb-3 Bonhams, Leeds #238

WELLS, William Page Atkinson (1871-1923) British
£800 $1240 €1200 Boats at anchor, moonlight (23x24cm-9x9in) s. panel. 6-Dec-2 Lyon & Turnbull, Edinburgh #98
£1000 $1560 €1500 Lodge of the sea (14x17cm-6x7in) s. panel prov. 14-Apr-3 Sotheby's, London #77/R est:1000-1500
£2300 $3841 €3335 River scene (26x40cm-10x16in) s. board. 18-Jun-3 Sotheby's, Olympia #122/R est:1000-2000
£3200 $4992 €4800 Flowers in the wind (12x21cm-5x8in) s. panel. 14-Apr-3 Sotheby's, London #148a/R est:3000-4000
Works on paper
£1050 $1701 €1575 Scything (35x30cm-14x12in) s. W/C wax crayon. 23-May-3 Lyon & Turnbull, Edinburgh #83 est:400-600

WELTE, Gottlieb (1745-1790) German
£3269 $5067 €5100 Peasants in landscape. Couple in the storm (30x23cm-12x9in) s.d.1774 panel pair prov. 6-Dec-2 Millon & Associes, Paris #44/R

WELTERS, Guglielmo (1913-) Italian
£261 $418 €400 Seascape (50x70cm-20x28in) s. 4-Jan-3 Meeting Art, Vercelli #447

WELTHER, Hank (19th C) Dutch
£4110 $6411 €6000 View of The Hague on a rainy day with Bonneterie in background (30x50cm-12x20in) s. 14-Apr-3 Glerum, Amsterdam #110/R est:1200-1500

WELY, Jacques (1873-1910) French
Works on paper
£248 $353 €400 Je crois que nous pourrions nous arranger (34x42cm-13x17in) s.i.d.1903 crayon Indian ink gouache. 20-Mar-2 Chayette & Cheval, Paris #89/R

WELZ, Jean (1900-1975) South African
£258 $402 €387 Woman drinking from a mug (58x46cm-23x18in) s. oil chl paper. 15-Oct-2 Stephan Welz, Johannesburg #439 est:4000-6000 (SA.R 4200)
£860 $1342 €1290 Seated nude (71x49cm-28x19in) s.d.73 oil chl paper. 15-Oct-2 Stephan Welz, Johannesburg #440/R est:15000-20000 (SA.R 14000)
£1351 $2108 €2027 Flowers in a vase (39x30cm-15x12in) s.d.53 canvas on board. 15-Oct-2 Stephan Welz, Johannesburg #441/R est:20000-30000 (SA.R 22000)
£2580 $4153 €3870 Woman in a blue dress (54x45cm-21x18in) s.d.56 board exhib. 12-May-3 Stephan Welz, Johannesburg #536/R est:25000-35000 (SA.R 30000)
£3095 $4984 €4643 Hex River with bathers and orange express (39x49cm-15x19in) s.d.51 lit. 12-May-3 Stephan Welz, Johannesburg #463/R est:40000-60000 (SA.R 36000)
£3439 $5537 €5159 Three bathers (22x31cm-9x12in) s.d.45 i.d.verso paper on board exhib. 12-May-3 Stephan Welz, Johannesburg #464/R est:12000-18000 (SA.R 40000)
£6019 $9690 €9029 Cape farm with pigs (38x49cm-15x19in) s.d.53 canvas on board. 12-May-3 Stephan Welz, Johannesburg #457/R est:40000-60000 (SA.R 70000)
Works on paper
£215 $335 €323 Portrait of a woman wearing a headscarf (50x41cm-20x16in) s. chl. 15-Oct-2 Stephan Welz, Johannesburg #437 est:3000-4000 (SA.R 3500)
£319 $498 €479 Numsa the cat (33x49cm-13x19in) s.i.d.19 Aug 66 chl. 15-Oct-2 Stephan Welz, Johannesburg #176 est:1800-2400 (SA.R 5200)
£584 $910 €876 Sleeping nude (37x55cm-15x22in) s.d.Nov.64 pastel. 15-Oct-2 Stephan Welz, Johannesburg #438/R est:12000-16000 (SA.R 9500)

WEMAIRE, Pierre (1913-) Belgian
£372 $592 €558 Composition (33x25cm-13x10in) s.d.60. 10-Mar-3 Rasmussen, Vejle #715/R (D.KR 4000)
£838 $1332 €1257 Blind to others (54x65cm-21x26in) s.d.71 i.verso. 10-Mar-3 Rasmussen, Vejle #717/R (D.KR 9000)
£1026 $1632 €1539 The Gobelin bird (92x65cm-36x26in) s.d.56 exhib. 5-May-3 Rasmussen, Vejle #100/R (D.KR 11000)
£1862 $2961 €2793 Conversation a deux (89x115cm-35x45in) s.d.65 exhib. 10-Mar-3 Rasmussen, Vejle #761/R est:25000-30000 (D.KR 20000)
£2222 $3511 €3200 Intimite dans le foule (100x81cm-39x32in) s.d. s.i.d.verso oil acrylic prov. 27-Apr-3 Perrin, Versailles #4/R est:2500-3000
£7914 $12584 €11871 Composition (130x190cm-51x75in) s. d.1962 verso exhib.prov. 10-Mar-3 Rasmussen, Vejle #760/R est:100000-150000 (D.KR 85000)
Works on paper
£274 $428 €411 Composition (37x52cm-15x20in) s.d.88 W/C. 11-Nov-2 Rasmussen, Vejle #123/R (D.KR 3200)
£274 $428 €411 Composition (31x44cm-12x17in) init.d.63 W/C pen. 11-Nov-2 Rasmussen, Vejle #124/R (D.KR 3200)
£558 $881 €837 Compositions (17x14cm-7x6in) one s.d.38 Indian ink gouache W/C pair. 1-Apr-3 Rasmussen, Copenhagen #253/R (D.KR 6000)

WEN BOREN (1502-1575) Chinese
Works on paper
£1517 $2412 €2200 Figures on mules crossing bridge (27x56cm-11x22in) s. ink polychrome. 7-Mar-3 Piasa, Paris #293/R est:1000-1200

WEN DIAN (1633-1704) Chinese
Works on paper
£2720 $4487 €3944 Landscape (26x50cm-10x20in) s.i. ink handscroll. 6-Jul-3 Christie's, Hong Kong #447/R est:40000-50000 (HK.D 35000)

WEN ZHENGMING (1470-1559) Chinese
Works on paper
£6605 $10897 €9577 Orchid, bamboo and birds (29x31cm-11x12in) one s. ink set of four. 6-Jul-3 Christie's, Hong Kong #433/R est:90000-100000 (HK.D 85000)

£27195 $44872 €39433 Rain over the summer hills (58x28cm-23x11in) s.i.d.1516 ink col hanging scroll. 6-Jul-3 Christie's, Hong Kong #427/R est:400000-500000 (HK.D 350000)
£29526 $48718 €42813 Orchid and bamboo (72x40cm-28x16in) s.i. ink hanging scroll. 7-Jul-3 Christie's, Hong Kong #522/R est:400000-600000 (HK.D 380000)

WENBAN, Sion Longley (1848-1897) American
Works on paper
£283 $442 €450 Horse and cart in Dachauer Moos (20x37cm-8x15in) s. W/C Indian ink. 11-Oct-2 Winterberg, Heidelberg #750

WENBAUM, Albert (1890-1943) ?
Works on paper
£577 $906 €900 Boulevard Edgard Quinet (46x33cm-18x13in) s.d.1929 gouache. 12-Dec-2 Rabourdin & Choppin de Janvry, Paris #107/R
£641 $1006 €1000 Rue Geoffroy-Saint-Hilaire (43x56cm-17x22in) s. gouache. 12-Dec-2 Rabourdin & Choppin de Janvry, Paris #106/R
£673 $1057 €1050 Boulevard Saint-Michel (39x54cm-15x21in) s. gouache. 12-Dec-2 Rabourdin & Choppin de Janvry, Paris #109/R

WENCKE, Sophie (1874-1963) German
£286 $454 €420 Bad Pyrmont, Kurgarten (32x47cm-13x19in) s. 28-Mar-3 Bolland & Marotz, Bremen #398/R
£692 $1079 €1100 Heath landscape with wood on the Weyerberg (60x80cm-24x31in) s. 21-Sep-2 Bolland & Marotz, Bremen #425/R
£1517 $2397 €2200 Evening glow (42x57cm-17x22in) s. i. verso board. 5-Apr-3 Hans Stahl, Hamburg #112/R est:2200

WENDEL, Theodore (1859-1932) American
Works on paper
£321 $500 €482 Sailboats (13x16cm-5x6in) s. pastel on panel. 20-Sep-2 Sloan, North Bethesda #333/R

WENDELIN, Martta (1893-1986) Finnish
Works on paper
£258 $408 €400 Christmas card (22x14cm-9x6in) gouache. 19-Dec-2 Hagelstam, Helsinki #845/R
£411 $642 €650 Flowers (42x31cm-17x12in) s. pastel. 15-Sep-2 Bukowskis, Helsinki #314/R
£755 $1162 €1200 Girl (60x46cm-24x18in) s. chl. 24-Oct-2 Hagelstam, Helsinki #1028

WENDT, François Willi (1909-1970) German
£253 $395 €400 Composition (50x65cm-20x26in) s.d.1955 plywood exhib. 20-Oct-2 Charbonneaux, Paris #175 est:400-500
£348 $543 €550 Composition (65x81cm-26x32in) s. s.d.1959 verso exhib. 20-Oct-2 Charbonneaux, Paris #174
£646 $1028 €950 Composition (32x54cm-13x21in) s.d.59 verso. 26-Feb-3 Artcurial Briest, Paris #574

WENDT, William (1865-1946) American
£18634 $30000 €27951 At Addie's cottage (51x61cm-20x24in) s.i.d.Dec 8 1939 prov. 18-Feb-3 John Moran, Pasadena #37 est:30000-50000
£27419 $42500 €41129 Laguna Canyon landscape (64x76cm-25x30in) s.d.1926 prov. 29-Oct-2 John Moran, Pasadena #646 est:40000-60000
£63253 $105000 €91717 Sheltering sycamores (76x102cm-30x40in) s.d.1924 prov.exhib.lit. 11-Jun-3 Butterfields, San Francisco #4241/R est:80000-120000

WENGENROTH, Stow (1906-1978) American
Prints
£2692 $4200 €4038 Lower fifth avenue (26x41cm-10x16in) s.i. lithograph edition of 40. 7-Nov-2 Swann Galleries, New York #834/R est:5000-8000
£3727 $6000 €5591 New York Nocturne (30x51cm-12x20in) s. lithograph. 19-Jan-3 Jeffery Burchard, Florida #74/R
Works on paper
£1037 $1700 €1504 High rocks (33x51cm-13x20in) s.i. pen ink pencil card stock. 5-Jun-3 Swann Galleries, New York #265/R est:1500-2500
£1220 $2000 €1769 Three of a kind (39x58cm-15x23in) s. brush ink crayon illustration board. 5-Jun-3 Swann Galleries, New York #266/R est:2000-3000
£1463 $2400 €2121 Greenport autumn (40x63cm-16x25in) s. brush ink crayon illustration board exec.c.1965. 5-Jun-3 Swann Galleries, New York #264/R est:3000-5000

WENGLEIN, Joseph (1845-1919) German
£497 $810 €750 Rocky landscape (51x37cm-20x15in) s. cardboard. 31-Jan-3 Rabourdin & Choppin de Janvry, Paris #70
£552 $872 €800 Landscape (28x43cm-11x17in) mono.d.03 i. stretcher paper on canvas. 5-Apr-3 Hans Stahl, Hamburg #23/R
£692 $1079 €1100 Track through the dunes (18x26cm-7x10in) mono. lit. 20-Sep-2 Karlheinz Kaupp, Staufen #2039/R
£692 $1079 €1100 Autumn landscape (18x27cm-7x11in) mono. lit. 20-Sep-2 Karlheinz Kaupp, Staufen #2040/R
£1795 $2782 €2800 Summer landscape with stream (52x65cm-20x26in) s.i.d.77. 5-Dec-2 Dr Fritz Nagel, Stuttgart #709/R est:4500
£1918 $2992 €2800 Forest clearing with deer in a storm (41x47cm-16x19in) s.i.d. board. 11-Apr-3 Winterberg, Heidelberg #620/R est:3600
£2177 $3461 €3200 Isar - early spring landscape (28x52cm-11x20in) s. board. 19-Mar-3 Neumeister, Munich #800/R est:3000

WENK, Albert (1863-1934) German
£278 $447 €417 Coast in evening (66x89cm-26x35in) s. i. stretcher. 7-May-3 Dobiaschofsky, Bern #1057/R (S.FR 600)

WENNEMOES, Carl (1890-1965) Danish
£310 $503 €465 Autumn landscape (87x143cm-34x56in) s.d.1934. 25-Jan-3 Rasmussen, Havnen #2068 (D.KR 3500)

WENNERBERG, Brynolf (1823-1894) Swedish
£255 $397 €400 Portrait of woman with brunette hair (16x9cm-6x4in) mono. panel. 6-Nov-2 Hugo Ruef, Munich #1333

WENNERWALD, Emil (1859-1934) Danish
£226 $375 €328 Expansive landscape with lake (46x66cm-18x26in) s. 14-Jun-3 Jackson's, Cedar Falls #212/R
£250 $400 €375 Cottage with sheep and chicken (76x61cm-30x24in) 14-Mar-3 Douglas, South Deerfield #9
£287 $448 €431 View across hilly landscape (43x54cm-17x21in) s.d.1918. 23-Sep-2 Rasmussen, Vejle #82/R (D.KR 3400)
£394 $630 €591 Landscape (42x69cm-17x27in) s.d.82. 13-Jan-3 Rasmussen, Vejle #2044/R (D.KR 4500)
£428 $675 €642 Mountain landscape, Italy (54x67cm-21x26in) s. 5-Apr-3 Rasmussen, Havnen #2040/R (D.KR 4600)
£431 $655 €647 Summer landscape near Himmelbjerget (65x91cm-26x36in) s.d.1906. 27-Aug-2 Rasmussen, Copenhagen #1882/R (D.KR 5000)
£466 $740 €699 Sunshine in the forest (71x100cm-28x39in) s.d.1914. 10-Mar-3 Rasmussen, Vejle #282 (D.KR 5000)
£513 $816 €770 Winter landscape with lake, horse and cart (80x116cm-31x46in) s. 5-May-3 Rasmussen, Vejle #664/R (D.KR 5500)
£838 $1332 €1257 View of an Italian village towards sky and sea (47x67cm-19x26in) s.d.1903. 5-Mar-3 Rasmussen, Copenhagen #1692/R (D.KR 9000)

WENNING, Pieter (1873-1921) South African
£1409 $2199 €2114 Landscape with houses (17x29cm-7x11in) s.indis.d.1921 canvas on board. 11-Nov-2 Stephan Welz, Johannesburg #537/R est:25000-35000 (SA.R 22000)
£1634 $2630 €2451 Apies river near Pretoria (22x40cm-9x16in) s.d.09 i.verso panel. 12-May-3 Stephan Welz, Johannesburg #478/R est:15000-20000 (SA.R 19000)
£3075 $4797 €4613 Willow trees (21x35cm-8x14in) canvas on board prov. 11-Nov-2 Stephan Welz, Johannesburg #560/R est:50000-70000 (SA.R 48000)
£3611 $5814 €5417 View of houses across a field (40x49cm-16x19in) s. board. 12-May-3 Stephan Welz, Johannesburg #479/R est:25000-35000 (SA.R 42000)

WENNING, Ype (1879-1959) Dutch
£634 $1020 €900 City view in winter, probably Oudewater (20x16cm-8x6in) s. 7-May-3 Vendue Huis, Gravenhage #475/R
£775 $1247 €1100 Wash day at city canal (39x59cm-15x23in) s. 7-May-3 Vendue Huis, Gravenhage #521/R
£1100 $1727 €1650 Figure leading a goat into a boathouse (47x61cm-19x24in) s. 16-Apr-3 Christie's, Kensington #741/R est:1200-1800

WENTORF, Carl (1863-1914) Danish
£362 $550 €543 Olive trees, Lago d'Iseo (61x56cm-24x22in) s.d.1912 exhib. 27-Aug-2 Rasmussen, Copenhagen #1687/R (D.KR 4200)
£429 $669 €644 Summer's day in the field with men weeding (50x84cm-20x33in) s.d.98. 11-Nov-2 Rasmussen, Vejle #678/R (D.KR 5000)
£466 $740 €699 Franzinette - nude Parisian model (73x60cm-29x24in) s.i.d.1896. 5-Mar-3 Rasmussen, Copenhagen #1725/R (D.KR 5000)
£957 $1550 €1388 Small girl playing with her shadow (44x49cm-17x19in) s. prov. 26-May-3 Rasmussen, Copenhagen #1412/R (D.KR 10000)
£3797 $6000 €5696 Interior with mother and child (36x46cm-14x18in) s.d.1892 prov. 24-Apr-3 Shannon's, Milford #30/R est:6000-8000

WENTZEL, Gustav (1859-1927) Norwegian
£272 $430 €408 Green trees and bushes in meadow (28x37cm-11x15in) s. 2-Dec-2 Rasmussen, Copenhagen #1255 (D.KR 3200)
£415 $692 €602 Mountain landscape (26x42cm-10x17in) s. cardboard on panel. 18-Jun-3 Grev Wedels Plass, Oslo #249/R (N.KR 4800)

£1039 $1590 €1559 Landscape (49x59cm-19x23in) s. 26-Aug-2 Blomqvist, Lysaker #1433/R (N.KR 12000)
£1408 $2196 €2112 Mountain farm in winter (40x60cm-16x24in) s. 23-Sep-2 Blomqvist, Lysaker #1267/R est:8000-12000 (N.KR 16500)
£2168 $3382 €3252 Autumn landscape with goats and houses (51x81cm-20x32in) s. 21-Oct-2 Blomqvist, Oslo #303/R est:30000-35000 (N.KR 25000)
£2655 $4195 €3983 Winter landscape with red barn in snow (53x76cm-21x30in) s.d.09. 28-Apr-3 Blomqvist, Oslo #322/R est:35000-45000 (N.KR 30000)
£3990 $6224 €5985 From Vaagaa - winter (60x81cm-24x32in) s. i.stretcher. 21-Oct-2 Blomqvist, Oslo #359/R est:50000-60000 (N.KR 46000)
£5536 $8747 €8304 The sleigh ride, possibly Asker (35x54cm-14x21in) s. 2-Dec-2 Blomqvist, Oslo #300/R est:25000-30000 (N.KR 64000)
£10101 $16566 €14646 Interior scene with woman by open fire (65x82cm-26x32in) s. 2-Jun-3 Blomqvist, Oslo #171/R est:130000-150000 (N.KR 110000)
£10500 $17220 €15750 Hjem etter dansen, setesdal - going home after the dance, Setesdal (55x80cm-22x31in) s. prov. 3-Jun-3 Sotheby's, London #219/R est:6000-8000
£15571 $24602 €23357 Woman in interior (110x90cm-43x35in) s.d.1912. 2-Dec-2 Blomqvist, Oslo #334/R est:200000-300000 (N.KR 180000)
Works on paper
£1035 $1574 €1553 Interior scene with man, woman and boy (21x33cm-8x13in) s. gouache. 31-Aug-2 Grev Wedels Plass, Oslo #124 (N.KR 12000)

WENTZEL, Michael (1792-1866) German
Works on paper
£399 $618 €630 Ruins of the Greek theatre in Taormina on Sicily (44x60cm-17x24in) bears i. pen W/C over pencil. 27-Sep-2 Venator & Hansten, Koln #1372
£506 $785 €800 Palermo (27x58cm-11x23in) i. pen W/C. 27-Sep-2 Venator & Hansten, Koln #1371/R

WENZEL, E (?) ?
£346 $540 €550 Madonna and Child (14x10cm-6x4in) s. tempera ivory. 21-Sep-2 Dannenberg, Berlin #170/R

WENZEL, Johann (19th C) German
£900 $1395 €1350 Street scene in old Danzig (28x30cm-11x12in) s.d.1896 panel. 22-Jul-2 Bonhams, Bury St Edmunds #433/R

WENZLER, Sarah Wilhelmina (fl.1859-1870) American
£2581 $4000 €3872 Peaches and pears on a wooden ledge (23x34cm-9x13in) s.d.1867. 3-Dec-2 Christie's, Rockefeller NY #591/R est:4000-6000

WEREFKIN, Marianne von (1870-1938) Russian
£20183 $33706 €29265 Reading the Talmud (55x66cm-22x26in) i. verso tempera oil paper on board prov.exhib. 20-Jun-3 Kornfeld, Bern #148/R est:20000 (S.FR 44000)
£27523 $45963 €39908 Loading wood near Ascona (62x47cm-24x19in) i. verso paper on board prov. 20-Jun-3 Kornfeld, Bern #147/R est:20000 (S.FR 60000)
Works on paper
£3261 $5348 €4500 Monastery by the sea (22x16cm-9x6in) s. cyrillic gouache W/C Indian ink brush pen. 31-May-3 Villa Grisebach, Berlin #717/R est:2000-2500

WERENSKIOLD, Anne Katrine (1941-) Norwegian
£272 $418 €408 Girl with red hat (65x53cm-26x21in) s. painted 1995. 28-Oct-2 Blomqvist, Lysaker #1342 (N.KR 3200)

WERENSKIOLD, Erik Theodor (1855-1938) Norwegian
£43365 $67650 €65048 Two girls by fruit trees in blossom (80x65cm-31x26in) init. 21-Oct-2 Blomqvist, Oslo #358/R est:550000-750000 (N.KR 500000)

WERFF, Adriaen van der (1659-1722) Dutch
£2721 $4327 €4000 Scene mythologique (49x40cm-19x16in) indis.sig. 18-Mar-3 Galerie Moderne, Brussels #588/R est:3000-5000
£5090 $8500 €7381 Portrait of Mary Magdalene (43x36cm-17x14in) panel. 21-Jun-3 Selkirks, St. Louis #1046/R est:8000-10000

WERFF, Adriaen van der (attrib) (1659-1722) Dutch
£2692 $4254 €4200 Sleeping Venus (101x152cm-40x60in) 18-Nov-2 Bernaerts, Antwerp #89/R est:4000-5000

WERFF, Pieter van der (1665-1722) Dutch
£20270 $31622 €30000 Dismissal of Hagar (68x53cm-27x21in) panel. 27-Mar-3 Dorotheum, Vienna #170/R est:30000-40000

WERGELAND, Oscar (1844-1910) Norwegian
£595 $946 €893 Still life of fruit (46x36cm-18x14in) s. panel. 3-Mar-3 Lilla Bukowskis, Stockholm #347 (S.KR 8000)
£622 $1008 €902 Figures by sleigh (36x27cm-14x11in) s. 24-May-3 Rasmussen, Havnen #2020/R (D.KR 6500)
£1038 $1640 €1557 Felling trees in winter (60x40cm-24x16in) s. 2-Dec-2 Blomqvist, Oslo #311/R (N.KR 12000)
£1741 $2785 €2612 Man returning from town (46x35cm-18x14in) init.indis.d.74. 17-Mar-3 Blomqvist, Oslo #339/R est:40000-50000 (N.KR 20000)
£3049 $5000 €4421 Bringing in the catch (70x110cm-28x43in) s.i. 4-Jun-3 Christie's, Rockefeller NY #241/R est:6000-8000
£26244 $42516 €39366 In the meadow - young girls with wild flowers (60x41cm-24x16in) s. s.i.verso. 26-May-3 Grev Wedels Plass, Oslo #48/R est:100000-150000 (N.KR 290000)

WERKMAN, Hendrik Nicolaas (1882-1945) Dutch
Prints
£5696 $9000 €9000 Amsterdam castricm 11 (51x33cm-20x13in) druksel with sjablone prov.exhib. 26-Nov-2 Sotheby's, Amsterdam #405/R est:9000-13000
£7194 $11799 €10000 Compositie (65x50cm-26x20in) s. handstamped stencil print lit. 3-Jun-3 Christie's, Amsterdam #257/R est:10000-15000
£11511 $18878 €16000 Vrouweneiland, blad VIII (65x47cm-26x19in) d.Juli 1942 handstamped stencilprint prov.lit. 3-Jun-3 Christie's, Amsterdam #255/R est:20000-30000

WERKMASTER, Jerk (1896-1978) Swedish
Works on paper
£284 $440 €426 Woman picking grapes (30x28cm-12x11in) s.d.1921 gouache plaster background. 8-Dec-2 Uppsala Auktionskammare, Uppsala #206 (S.KR 4000)

WERKMEISTER, Math (19/20th C) Scandinavian
£6029 $9165 €9044 Palace interior with parade bed, possibly Nymphenburg, Munich (109x150cm-43x59in) 27-Aug-2 Rasmussen, Copenhagen #1616/R est:25000-35000 (D.KR 70000)

WERL, Hans (c.1570-1608) German
Works on paper
£14000 $23380 €20300 Saints Catherine, Barbara, Ursula and three other saints adoring the virgin (36x24cm-14x9in) bears sig.d.1601 pen blk ink grey wash arched top. 9-Jul-3 Sotheby's, London #89/R est:8000-12000

WERNER, Alexander Friedrich (1827-1908) German
£2877 $4516 €4200 Amsterdam in Schnee (41x23cm-16x9in) s. init.i. verso panel. 15-Apr-3 Sotheby's, Amsterdam #85/R est:3000-5000

WERNER, Anton Alexander von (1843-1915) German
£280 $437 €420 Design for the relief for the Siegessaeule, Berlin (48x38cm-19x15in) s.d.1872 canvasboard. 8-Apr-3 Bonhams, Knightsbridge #277/R
£400 $620 €600 Detail for the design of the relief for the Siegessaeule, Berlin (46x37cm-18x15in) s.d.1872 canvasboard. 3-Nov-2 Lots Road, London #331/R
Works on paper
£556 $894 €834 Study for the proclamation of the King in Versailles (42x32cm-17x13in) mono.d.1872 pencil. 7-May-3 Dobiaschofsky, Bern #1058/R (S.FR 1200)
£647 $1036 €900 Portrait of General Abel Douay (36x26cm-14x10in) mono.d.1888 pencil prov. 17-May-3 Lempertz, Koln #1348/R

WERNER, Carl (1808-1894) German
£562 $883 €843 Study of fruit still life (30x45cm-12x18in) s. board pair. 25-Nov-2 Hodgins, Calgary #39/R (C.D 1400)
Works on paper
£577 $912 €900 Historical scene in courtyard of Doges Palace, Venice (29x34cm-11x13in) s.d.1853 W/C. 16-Nov-2 Lempertz, Koln #1414/R
£1154 $1788 €1800 Cowboy and peasant woman, Cowboy and inn keeper (12x18cm-5x7in) s.i.d.1836 W/C pair. 4-Dec-2 Finarte, Rome #711/R
£7914 $12979 €11000 Le temple d'Isis a Philae (61x46cm-24x18in) s.d.1875 W/C lit. 4-Jun-3 Tajan, Paris #200/R est:10000-13000

£22000 $34320 €33000 Gathering of the guilds, the Appian Way, Rome (73x131cm-29x52in) s.i.d.1846 W/C bodycol. 5-Nov-2 Bonhams, New Bond Street #5/R est:5000-8000
£37000 $57720 €55500 Carnival of Rome (73x131cm-29x52in) s.i.d.1848 W/C bodycol. 5-Nov-2 Bonhams, New Bond Street #4/R est:5000-8000

WERNER, Carl (attrib) (1808-1894) German
Works on paper
£2695 $4501 €3800 La cour du temple de Medinet-Abou, pres de Thebes (32x45cm-13x18in) W/C. 23-Jun-3 Beaussant & Lefèvre, Paris #110/R est:500-600

WERNER, Gosta (1909-1989) Swedish
£967 $1537 €1451 Plimsoll's mark in the North Sea, grey winter day (51x50cm-20x20in) s. 3-Mar-3 Lilla Bukowskis, Stockholm #98 (S.KR 13000)
£1179 $1862 €1769 Jong man W (33x41cm-13x16in) s. 28-Apr-3 Bukowskis, Stockholm #269/R est:8000-10000 (S.KR 15500)
Works on paper
£247 $385 €371 Stureborg, Landskrona (42x48cm-17x19in) s. W/C. 13-Sep-2 Lilla Bukowskis, Stockholm #277 (S.KR 3600)

WERNER, Heinrich Ferdinand (1867-1928) German
£759 $1200 €1200 Woman peeling potatoes in kitchen (48x36cm-19x14in) s.i.d.91 lit. 29-Nov-2 Schloss Ahlden, Ahlden #1164/R

WERNER, Hilding (1880-1944) Swedish
£7092 $10993 €10638 Summer morning, Varmland (71x200cm-28x79in) s. 3-Dec-2 Bukowskis, Stockholm #75/R est:100000-150000 (S.KR 100000)

WERNER, Joseph II (1637-1710) Swiss
£12346 $20000 €18519 Two Bacchantes (14x11cm-6x4in) gouache vellum on panel exhib.lit. 23-Jan-3 Sotheby's, New York #223/R est:20000

WERNER, Lambert (1900-1983) Swedish
£608 $961 €912 Composition (54x49cm-21x19in) s.d.1937. 28-Apr-3 Bukowskis, Stockholm #141/R (S.KR 8000)
£1004 $1616 €1506 Still life of fruit (55x48cm-22x19in) s.d.44 panel. 7-May-3 AB Stockholms Auktionsverk #870/R (S.KR 13000)
£1977 $3124 €2966 Composition (73x60cm-29x24in) s.indis.d. panel. 28-Apr-3 Bukowskis, Stockholm #193/R est:20000-25000 (S.KR 26000)

WERNER, Rudolf G (1893-1957) German
£314 $491 €500 Iron foundry (51x71cm-20x28in) s. 21-Sep-2 Bolland & Marotz, Bremen #672/R

WERNER, Theodor (1886-1969) German
£397 $580 €620 Composition - M 58/56 (11x16cm-4x6in) mono.d.56 i. verso oil over col pen pencil. 4-Jun-2 Karl & Faber, Munich #472
£1942 $3108 €2700 Composition (51x73cm-20x29in) s.d.57 i. verso tempera pencil board. 15-May-3 Neumeister, Munich #769/R est:1500-1800
£3145 $4843 €5000 Untitled (59x78cm-23x31in) s.d.1956 oil tempera board. 26-Oct-2 Dr Lehr, Berlin #570/R est:6000
£5513 $8049 €8600 Composition No 22/1941-43 - Madonna (100x72cm-39x28in) s.d.1941 egg tempera pencil. 4-Jun-2 Karl & Faber, Munich #468/R est:8000
£6329 $10000 €10000 Composition in red, blue and yellow (84x103cm-33x41in) s.d.1951. 30-Nov-2 Bassenge, Berlin #6703/R est:15000
Works on paper
£289 $422 €450 Calligraphic composition (23x15cm-9x6in) mono.d.63 mixed media. 4-Jun-2 Karl & Faber, Munich #471
£513 $795 €800 Untitled (11x16cm-4x6in) mono.d.54 Indian ink W/C board. 3-Dec-2 Lempertz, Koln #507/R

WERNQUIST, Bertha (?) Swedish
£1375 $2187 €2063 The Holy Family (95cm-37in circular) s.verso after Nils Blommer. 3-Mar-3 Lilla Bukowskis, Stockholm #568 est:8000-10000 (S.KR 18500)

WERTHEIM, Heinrich (1875-1945) Austrian
£769 $1208 €1200 View of Dubrovnik (69x98cm-27x39in) s.i. board. 10-Dec-2 Dorotheum, Vienna #2/R
Works on paper
£252 $390 €400 St Michael in Heiligenstadt, 1750 (38x48cm-15x19in) s.i. Indian ink W/C. 1-Oct-2 Dorotheum, Vienna #350/R

WERTHEIMER, Esther (20th C) Canadian
Sculpture
£1481 $2296 €2222 Equality (31cm-12in) s.num.3/10 bronze rotating base. 3-Dec-2 Joyner, Toronto #189/R est:4000-5000 (C.D 3600)

WERTHEIMER, Gustave (1847-1904) Austrian
£617 $957 €926 Portrait of a lady in a rose coloured dress (73x54cm-29x21in) s. 3-Dec-2 Ritchie, Toronto #3089/R est:1500-2000 (C.D 1500)
£2038 $3180 €3200 Lune blanche a Louxor (112x152cm-44x60in) s. 11-Nov-2 Horta, Bruxelles #43 est:3500-4500
£2051 $3118 €3200 Scene symboliste (114x176cm-45x69in) s. 10-Jul-2 Rabourdin & Choppin de Janvry, Paris #17/R est:3300-3500

WERTMULLER, Adolf Ulrik (1751-1811) Swedish
£5793 $9500 €8690 Leda and the swan (22x29cm-9x11in) bears false i. panel. 29-May-3 Sotheby's, New York #138/R est:10000-15000

WERTMULLER, Adolf Ulrik (attrib) (1751-1811) Swedish
£1206 $1869 €1809 Lucretia (76x59cm-30x23in) 4-Dec-2 AB Stockholms Auktionsverk #1620/R est:20000-25000 (S.KR 17000)
£1728 $2834 €2506 Portrait of Brita Kristina Brusell and her daughter (82x65cm-32x26in) 4-Jun-3 AB Stockholms Auktionsverk #2241/R est:25000-30000 (S.KR 22000)

WERY, Fernand (1886-1964) Belgian
£411 $642 €650 Bebe blond dans sa chaise (31x28cm-12x11in) s. panel. 16-Sep-2 Horta, Bruxelles #330

WESLEY, John (1928-) American
£5625 $9000 €8438 Phone (152x183cm-60x72in) s.i.d.1982 verso prov. 16-May-3 Phillips, New York #199/R est:20000-30000
£17722 $28000 €26583 Maiden No.1-No.2 (122x77cm-48x30in) s.i.d.1964-65 verso diptych prov.exhib. 14-Nov-2 Christie's, Rockefeller NY #333/R est:20000-30000

WESSEL, Erich (20th C) German?
£272 $433 €400 Portrait of my brother (80x62cm-31x24in) s.d.37 i. verso. 28-Mar-3 Bolland & Marotz, Bremen #704/R

WESSEL, Henry (jnr) (1942-) American
Photographs
£3571 $5500 €5357 Untitled (28x36cm-11x14in) s.d.1968 verso gelatin silver print prov.lit. 25-Oct-2 Phillips, New York #44/R est:6000-9000

WESSELMANN, Tom (1931-) American
£1761 $2747 €2800 Nude (28x34cm-11x13in) s.d.70 verso acrylic fabric photograph panel. 8-Oct-2 Christie's, Paris #167/R
£2201 $3412 €3500 Monica sitting undressing (28x26cm-11x10in) s.i.d.1986/90 acrylic decoupe steel. 30-Oct-2 Artcurial Briest, Paris #446a/R est:3000-4000
£5000 $7700 €7500 Bedroom nude (34x45cm-13x18in) s.d.85 acrylic on paper prov. 22-Oct-2 Sotheby's, London #460/R est:4000-6000
£7595 $12000 €11393 Study for bedroom painting no.28 (21x22cm-8x9in) s.d.71 on overlap prov. 13-Nov-2 Sotheby's, New York #342/R est:8000-12000
£10000 $16700 €14500 Still life with four roses and pear (55cm-22in circular) s.i.d.93 verso alkyd oil cut out steel prov. 27-Jun-3 Christie's, London #216/R est:15000-20000
£13043 $21391 €18000 Steel drawing/seated nude (158x92cm-62x36in) s.i.d.1985 verso steel enamel board prov. 31-May-3 Villa Grisebach, Berlin #351/R est:20000-30000
£14000 $22960 €21000 Study for seascape nude (22x26cm-9x10in) s.d.78 overlap acrylic pencil prov. 7-Feb-3 Sotheby's, London #173/R est:15000-20000
£16026 $24840 €25000 Study for bedroom painting No 11 (14x18cm-6x7in) s.d.68 verso s.i.d. stretcher prov. 3-Dec-2 Lempertz, Koln #509/R est:25000-30000
£20645 $32000 €30968 Steel drawing/nude with bouquet and stockings no.6 (70x222cm-28x87in) s. i.d.85 verso enamel on laser cut steel prov. 26-Sep-2 Christie's, Rockefeller NY #741/R est:35000-45000
£21203 $33076 €33500 Study for bedroom painting no 11 (14x19cm-6x7in) s.d.1968. 20-Oct-2 Mercier & Cie, Lille #350/R est:3000-3200
£21875 $35000 €32813 Amy reclining (65x168cm-26x66in) s.i.verso enamel on cut steel. 14-May-3 Sotheby's, New York #243/R est:25000-35000
£30189 $46792 €48000 Bedroom black doodle with photo (135x169cm-53x67in) s.d.85 acrylic paper prov. 30-Oct-2 Artcurial Briest, Paris #445/R est:30000-40000
£31250 $50000 €46875 Study for 18 year old on the beach (36x44cm-14x17in) s. i.d.84 on overlap prov. 14-May-3 Sotheby's, New York #197/R est:25000-35000

£38000 $63460 €55100 Little blond Vivienne (41cm-16in circular) s.i.d.1996 verso alkyd oil cut out steel prov. 27-Jun-3 Christie's, London #215/R est:12000-16000

£42000 $64680 €63000 Nude - frontal (170x244cm-67x96in) s. i.d.1985 verso enamel on cut aluminium prov. 22-Oct-2 Sotheby's, London #329/R est:35000-45000

£46000 $76820 €66700 Woman in green blouse (167x206cm-66x81in) s. i.d.1986 verso enamel cut out aluminium prov. 26-Jun-3 Sotheby's, London #259/R est:30000-40000

£50000 $80000 €75000 Bedroom nude with black choker (206x226cm-81x89in) s.i.d.85 verso enamel on cut-out aluminium prov.lit. 15-May-3 Christie's, Rockefeller NY #193/R est:50000-70000

£58000 $96860 €84100 Birthday bouquet (193x228cm-76x90in) s.d.90 i.verso enamel cut out steel prov. 27-Jun-3 Christie's, London #213/R est:25000-35000

£62500 $100000 €93750 Study for bedroom painting 38 (34x39cm-13x15in) s.i.d.1977 prov. 15-May-3 Christie's, Rockefeller NY #153/R est:40000-60000

£75000 $125250 €108750 Still life with Lichtenstein, teapot and bird, chair (160x221cm-63x87in) alkyd oil cut out aluminium executed 1990-96. 27-Jun-3 Christie's, London #214/R est:30000-40000

£411392 $650000 €617088 Great American nude n0.77 (183x203cm-72x80in) painted 1966 prov. 13-Nov-2 Christie's, Rockefeller NY #31/R est:400000-600000

Prints

£1840 $3000 €2760 Great American brown nude (41x51cm-16x20in) s.d.1971 col screenprint. 13-Feb-3 Christie's, Rockefeller NY #378/R

£2083 $3250 €3125 Big blonde (125x173cm-49x68in) s.i.num.9/12 col silkscreen. 14-Oct-2 Butterfields, San Francisco #1384/R est:4000-6000

£2244 $3500 €3366 Big blonde with choker (126x178cm-50x70in) s.num.VIII/X grey screenprint board. 5-Nov-2 Christie's, Rockefeller NY #532/R est:4000-5000

£2402 $3507 €3603 Bedroom blonde (106x124cm-42x49in) s. serigraph. 4-Jun-2 Germann, Zurich #530/R est:5500-6000 (S.FR 5500)

£2516 $4000 €3774 Bedroom blonde doodle with photo (120x136cm-47x54in) s.d.88 num.64/100 col screenprint Museum board. 29-Apr-3 Christie's, Rockefeller NY #772/R est:3000-4000

£2673 $4250 €4010 Rosemary lying on one elbow (20x37cm-8x15in) s.i.d. num.25/45 verso laser cut steel col enamel. 2-May-3 Sotheby's, New York #665/R est:3000-5000

£2778 $4389 €4000 Monica reclining on back, knees up (99x140cm-39x55in) s.num.69/100 lithograph linoleum. 26-Apr-3 Cornette de St.Cyr, Paris #108/R est:3500-4000

£2778 $4416 €4000 Big blond with choker (125x177cm-49x70in) s.num.2/12 col serigraph edition of 90. 29-Apr-3 Artcurial Briest, Paris #411/R est:3000-3500

£2830 $4500 €4245 Big blonde (117x152cm-46x60in) s.d. num.82/100 col screenprint. 29-Apr-3 Christie's, Rockefeller NY #773/R est:3500-4500

£2848 $4415 €4500 Claire sitting with robe half off (127x96cm-50x38in) s.i. num.2/2 col serigraph board. 28-Sep-2 Ketterer, Hamburg #663/R est:4000-5000

£2848 $4500 €4500 Nu au bouquet et bas bleus (113x200cm-44x79in) s.num.93/150 col serigraph prov. 27-Nov-2 Tajan, Paris #141/R

£2945 $4800 €4418 Brown nude banner (148x196cm-58x77in) felt applique banner exec.1971 one of 30. 13-Feb-3 Christie's, Rockefeller NY #377/R

£3165 $4905 €5000 Still life with petunias, lilies and fruit (122x155cm-48x61in) s.i.d.1988 num.3/12 col serigraph board. 28-Sep-2 Ketterer, Hamburg #66/R est:4000-5000

£3671 $5690 €5800 Nude with bouquet and stockings (70x161cm-28x63in) s.i. num.3/12 col serigraph board. 28-Sep-2 Ketterer, Hamburg #665/R est:5000-6000

£3974 $6160 €6200 Monica in robe with motherwell (102x147cm-40x58in) s.num.2/80 col silkscreen cardboard exec.1994. 6-Dec-2 Ketterer, Munich #202/R est:4500-5500

£6748 $11000 €10122 Still life with nude (148x173cm-58x68in) felt applique banner one of 20. 13-Feb-3 Christie's, Rockefeller NY #376/R est:6000

Sculpture

£5625 $9000 €8438 Maquette for cigarette (31x41x14cm-12x16x6in) s.d.82 s.i.d.verso liquitex board wood plexiglas prov. 15-May-3 Christie's, Rockefeller NY #196/R est:10000-15000

£7000 $11480 €10500 Maquette for smoking cigarette No.1 (30x36x13cm-12x14x5in) num.d.80-4 liquitex rag-board oil wood in plexiglas box prov. 6-Feb-3 Christie's, London #684/R est:6000-8000

£28481 $45000 €42722 Dropped bra - big maquette (84x160x71cm-33x63x28in) incised sig.i.d.80 verso wall relief enamel on aluminum formica. 14-Nov-2 Christie's, Rockefeller NY #104/R est:60000-80000

£37500 $60000 €56250 Great American nude 74 (89x102x10cm-35x40x4in) s.i.d.65 relief acrylic plastic prov.lit. 15-May-3 Christie's, Rockefeller NY #126/R est:60000-80000

Works on paper

£556 $884 €800 Smoking a cigarette (14x12cm-6x5in) s.d.99 i.verso collage. 29-Apr-3 Artcurial Briest, Paris #412/R

£769 $1192 €1200 Smoking cigarette (14x16cm-6x6in) s.d.98 gouache board. 7-Dec-2 Van Ham, Cologne #593/R

£818 $1267 €1300 Smoking cigarette (14x12cm-6x5in) s.d.99 collage. 30-Oct-2 Artcurial Briest, Paris #752

£927 $1511 €1400 Smoking cigarette (15x15cm-6x6in) i.verso liquitex card. 3-Feb-3 Cornette de St.Cyr, Paris #552/R

£962 $1510 €1500 Smoking cigarette (12x12cm-5x5in) s.d.1998 liquitex card. 15-Dec-2 Perrin, Versailles #109/R

£1013 $1600 €1600 Cigaret (18x16cm-7x6in) s.d.98 gouache paper collage. 26-Nov-2 Sotheby's, Amsterdam #68/R est:1000-1500

£1207 $2016 €1750 Smoking cigarette (16x14cm-6x6in) s.d. i.verso liquitex on bristol. 9-Jul-3 Cornette de St.Cyr, Paris #362/R est:1800-2000

£1352 $2082 €2150 Smoking cigarette in ashtray (21x19cm-8x7in) s.d.1999 liquitex card. 26-Oct-2 Cornette de St.Cyr, Paris #85/R

£2200 $3410 €3300 Great American nude (41x51cm-16x20in) s.d.1970 pencil thinned liquitex. 5-Dec-2 Sotheby's, London #250/R est:2000-2500

£3097 $4800 €4646 Study for Great American nude no.80 (13x18cm-5x7in) s.d.66 s.o.d.verso thinned liquitex over pencil prov. 26-Sep-2 Christie's, Rockefeller NY #752/R est:5000-7000

£3800 $5890 €5700 Nude collage (15x21cm-6x8in) s.i.d.1970 pencil liquitex collage. 5-Dec-2 Sotheby's, London #249/R est:2000-2500

£3871 $6000 €5807 Radio with oranges (23x30cm-9x12in) s. pencil executed 1964 prov. 26-Sep-2 Christie's, Rockefeller NY #753/R est:3000-5000

£6452 $10000 €9678 Beautiful kate no.8 (9x23cm-4x9in) s.d.81 pencil liquitex on board prov. 26-Sep-2 Christie's, Rockefeller NY #742/R est:10000-15000

£10759 $17000 €16139 Beautiful Kate no.18 (9x22cm-4x9in) s.d.85 pencil liquitex prov. 13-Nov-2 Sotheby's, New York #130/R est:8000-12000

£12342 $19500 €19500 Study for Monica with blonde Vivienne (63x71cm-25x28in) s.d.1993 gouache liquitex prov. 27-Nov-2 Tajan, Paris #77/R est:20000-25000

£20253 $32000 €30380 Study for face no.1 (23x21cm-9x8in) s.d.65 liquitex graphite on shaped paper prov. 14-Nov-2 Christie's, Rockefeller NY #142/R est:15000-20000

£20312 $32500 €30468 Helen (57x38cm-22x15in) s.i.d.66 W/C pencil prov.exhib.lit. 14-May-3 Sotheby's, New York #201/R est:25000-35000

£31250 $51562 €45000 Nude and mirror, black variation no 2 (140x140cm-55x55in) s.i.d.90 verso steel emaille decoupe au laser prov. 1-Jul-3 Artcurial Briest, Paris #538/R est:40000-50000

£40000 $66800 €58000 Double study for great American nude no.8 (43x37cm-17x15in) s.d.66 pencil grip flex board prov. 27-Jun-3 Christie's, London #212/R est:18000-24000

£41139 $65000 €61709 Mouth N0.4 (89x137cm-35x54in) s.i.d66 wall relief acrylic on vacuum formed plastic prov. 14-Nov-2 Christie's, Rockefeller NY #143/R est:10000-15000

£331250 $530000 €496875 Seascape 16 (183x142cm-72x56in) s.d.66 liquitex on canvas prov.exhib.lit. 15-May-3 Christie's, Rockefeller NY #132/R est:250000-350000

£375000 $600000 €562500 Great American nude 34 (122x123cm-48x48in) s.i.d.62 verso mixed media collage assemblage board prov.lit. 13-May-3 Sotheby's, New York #13/R est:300000-400000

WESSMAN, Bjorn (1949-) Swedish

£951 $1502 €1427 All landscape XI (92x91cm-36x36in) s.d.1994-95 verso. 28-Apr-3 Bukowskis, Stockholm #1005/R (S.KR 12500)

Works on paper

£340 $564 €493 Tree (114x90cm-45x35in) s.d.86 W/C. 16-Jun-3 Lilla Bukowskis, Stockholm #241 (S.KR 4400)

WESSON, Edward (1910-1983) British

£300 $486 €450 Late summer flowers (57x46cm-22x18in) s. board. 21-May-3 Bonhams, Knightsbridge #177/R

£350 $543 €525 Yachts on their moorings (46x61cm-18x24in) s. board. 31-Oct-2 Greenslade Hunt, Taunton #645/R

£380 $600 €570 Still life of pears and carafe on a table (36x39cm-14x15in) s. canvasboard. 27-Nov-2 Hamptons Fine Art, Godalming #408

£400 $660 €580 Beached dinghies (23x28cm-9x11in) s. board. 3-Jul-3 Ewbank, Send #333

£460 $741 €690 Winter sunshine, Paris (33x38cm-13x15in) s. board prov. 15-Jan-3 Cheffins Grain & Comins, Cambridge #437/R

£550 $869 €825 Artist's dog (20x27cm-8x11in) board. 28-Nov-2 Christie's, Kensington #329/R

£700 $1092 €1050 Winter trees (46x62cm-18x24in) s. 7-Nov-2 Bonhams, Cornwall #803/R
£850 $1411 €1233 Pogo, the artist dog (20x27cm-8x11in) s. board. 12-Jun-3 Christie's, Kensington #277/R
£1000 $1570 €1500 Afternoon light, Bosham (41x51cm-16x20in) s. 15-Apr-3 Bonhams, Knightsbridge #25/R est:400-600

Works on paper

£250 $388 €375 Landscape with trees (31x48cm-12x19in) s. W/C. 25-Sep-2 John Nicholson, Haslemere #931
£270 $432 €405 Woodland scene (32x49cm-13x19in) s. W/C pencil. 15-May-3 Lawrence, Crewkerne #889
£280 $454 €406 Rocky coastline (32x49cm-13x19in) s. W/C gouache. 20-May-3 Dreweatt Neate, Newbury #223/R
£320 $499 €480 Whitehall from St. Jame's Park (27x35cm-11x14in) s.i pen ink W/C. 27-Mar-3 Christie's, Kensington #342
£340 $544 €510 Canal in a North European town with spires beyond (33x46cm-13x18in) s. W/C. 13-Mar-3 Duke & Son, Dorchester #116
£380 $600 €570 Leicester Square, Penshurst Place, Kent (46x61cm-18x24in) s. W/C ink. 2-Dec-2 Gorringes, Lewes #2672
£380 $612 €570 Still life with roses (32x49cm-13x19in) s. W/C. 14-Jan-3 Bonhams, Knightsbridge #46
£400 $644 €600 Still life with roses in a glass vase (40x33cm-16x13in) s. W/C. 14-Jan-3 Bonhams, Knightsbridge #45
£400 $652 €600 Near Stoke Hill (32x49cm-13x19in) s. W/C. 28-Jan-3 Bristol Auction Rooms #455
£420 $651 €630 Studland beach with figures on a foreshore (23x33cm-9x13in) s. W/C. 5-Oct-2 Finan Watkins & Co, Mere #205/R
£420 $664 €630 Snow on the Downs (22x30cm-9x12in) s. W/C. 27-Nov-2 Hamptons Fine Art, Godalming #104
£420 $664 €630 Mountainous lakeland scene (25x36cm-10x14in) s. W/C. 18-Dec-2 Mallams, Oxford #576
£450 $702 €675 Corner in Rye, Sussex (27x35cm-11x14in) s.i. pen ink W/C. 27-Mar-3 Christie's, Kensington #344
£460 $727 €690 Albury Heath (33x51cm-13x20in) s. W/C. 27-Nov-2 Hamptons Fine Art, Godalming #107
£500 $760 €750 Moored sailing barge and other vessels (26x35cm-10x14in) s. W/C. 15-Aug-2 Rupert Toovey, Partridge Green #1436/R
£500 $775 €750 Landscape with chalk cliff (32x50cm-13x20in) s. W/C. 30-Sep-2 Bonhams, Ipswich #339
£500 $775 €750 Study of fishing boats. s. W/C. 9-Dec-2 Lawrences, Bletchingley #2047
£500 $835 €725 Lismore Island Loch Linnhe (16x23cm-6x9in) s. W/C. 26-Jun-3 Mellors & Kirk, Nottingham #782/R
£550 $913 €798 Landscape (30x48cm-12x19in) s. W/C. 10-Jun-3 David Lay, Penzance #216
£580 $916 €870 Snow on the high ground (24x68cm-9x27in) s. W/C. 2-Apr-3 Edgar Horn, Eastbourne #265/R
£620 $986 €930 Figures in a backstreet (32x50cm-13x20in) s. pen ink W/C. 27-Feb-3 Bonhams, Chester #437
£650 $1027 €975 Sunlight on chalk pit. Landscape with trees (26x36cm-10x14in) s. W/C pair. 27-Nov-2 Hamptons Fine Art, Godalming #105
£650 $1014 €975 West coast of Arran (30x49cm-12x19in) s. W/C. 26-Mar-3 Woolley & Wallis, Salisbury #110/R
£660 $1076 €990 Barges on the Thames (32x48cm-13x19in) s. W/C. 17-Feb-3 Bonhams, Bath #116
£700 $1141 €1015 Norfolk landscape with windmill (24x34cm-9x13in) s. W/C. 15-Jul-3 Bonhams, Knightsbridge #2/R
£720 $1138 €1080 Still life of roses in a vase (48x34cm-19x13in) s. W/C. 27-Nov-2 Hamptons Fine Art, Godalming #106
£720 $1166 €1080 On the beach (21x28cm-8x11in) s. W/C. 20-May-3 Sotheby's, Olympia #131/R
£750 $1185 €1125 Thames barges (30x48cm-12x19in) s.i. W/C. 13-Nov-2 Halls, Shrewsbury #352/R
£780 $1232 €1170 View of the Orkney Islands from Sutherland, Scotland (24x34cm-9x13in) s. 2-Apr-3 Edgar Horn, Eastbourne #270/R
£850 $1403 €1233 Moored sailing vessels in an estuary (25x36cm-10x14in) s. W/C. 3-Jul-3 Ewbank, Send #296
£1200 $1896 €1800 Thames scene from across the river to St. Paul's (32x50cm-13x20in) s. ink W/C sold with two other by same hand. 2-Dec-2 Bonhams, Bath #40 est:800-1200

WESSON, Robert Shaw (1907-1967) American

£767 $1250 €1151 Autumn village landscape with stone bridge (48x58cm-19x23in) s. i.verso. 1-Feb-3 Van Blarcom, South Natick #73

WEST, Benjamin (1738-1820) British/American

£6500 $10271 €9750 Portrait of Ann Barbara Hill Medlycott (74x61cm-29x24in) prov. 28-Nov-2 Sotheby's, London #186/R est:6000-8000
£21233 $31000 €31850 Women at the sepulcher (41x53cm-16x21in) exhib.lit. 3-Nov-1 North East Auctions, Portsmouth #817/R est:12000-16000
£70000 $116200 €105000 Continence of Scipio. Hector taking leave of Andromache (152x93cm-60x37in) s. pair prov.exhib.lit. 12-Jun-3 Sotheby's, London #94/R est:80000-120000

WEST, Benjamin (attrib) (1738-1820) British/American

£5674 $8794 €8511 The Battle at Maupertuis (32x45cm-13x18in) panel pair. 4-Dec-2 AB Stockholms Auktionsverk #1947/R est:80000-100000 (S.KR 80000)

WEST, C (?) ?

£300 $474 €450 Fisherfolk and boats at sunset tending their nets (29x49cm-11x19in) s. 18-Dec-2 John Nicholson, Haslemere #1191

WEST, David (1868-1936) British

£3000 $4920 €4500 Lossiemouth, Morayshire (51x76cm-20x30in) s. 29-May-3 Christie's, Kensington #183/R est:1000-1500
£3300 $5412 €4950 Covesea lighthouse, Lossiemouth (51x76cm-20x30in) s. 29-May-3 Christie's, Kensington #184/R est:1000-1500

Works on paper

£1200 $1908 €1800 Lossiemouth, on the Moray Firth (24x34cm-9x13in) s. pencil W/C scratching out. 6-Mar-3 Christie's, Kensington #146/R est:600-800
£1450 $2262 €2175 Cubin sands, near Findhorn (51x77cm-20x30in) W/C laid on board exhib. 10-Apr-3 Bonhams, Edinburgh #122 est:600-800
£2000 $3120 €3000 Sand dunes, Innes Moor, near Lossie (51x75cm-20x30in) s. i.verso W/C laid on board. 10-Apr-3 Bonhams, Edinburgh #123 est:600-800

WEST, Edgar (fl.1857-1889) British

Works on paper

£420 $659 €630 Midnight sun across the lake, Norway (48x66cm-19x26in) W/C bodycol gum arabic. 16-Apr-3 Christie's, Kensington #1060/R
£640 $1011 €960 Dunstanborough Castle (62x100cm-24x39in) W/C. 7-Apr-3 Bonhams, Bath #3
£1500 $2355 €2250 Shipping Flushing Harbour Cornwall (48x65cm-19x26in) s. W/C. 10-Dec-2 Lane, Penzance #299 est:1500-1750

WEST, Franz (1947-) Austrian

£1000 $1540 €1500 Untitled (30x21cm-12x8in) s.d.81 acrylic on magazine paper prov. 23-Oct-2 Christie's, London #240/R est:2000-3000
£1103 $1766 €1600 Querulanz (15x10cm-6x4in) s.i.d.83 verso overpainted postcard. 11-Mar-3 Dorotheum, Vienna #256/R est:1300-1800
£1354 $2125 €2031 Untitled - nude with white tulips (56x41cm-22x16in) s.d.1978/79 acrylic magazine page prov. 25-Nov-2 Germann, Zurich #51/R est:5000-8000 (S.FR 3100)
£1959 $3057 €2900 Couple (28x21cm-11x8in) s.d.78 oil on illustration. 25-Mar-3 Wiener Kunst Auktionen, Vienna #53/R est:3300-4500
£2568 $4005 €3800 Female nude (40x32cm-16x13in) s.d.82 oil on illustration. 25-Mar-3 Wiener Kunst Auktionen, Vienna #52/R est:3300-4500
£4500 $7380 €6750 Untitled (57x75cm-22x30in) s.d.84 plaster acrylic collage cardboard prov. 7-Feb-3 Sotheby's, London #191/R est:4000-6000

Sculpture

£1899 $2943 €3000 Reflector (6x15x4cm-2x6x2in) painted gauze bandages over plaster. 24-Sep-2 Wiener Kunst Auktionen, Vienna #312/R est:1500-2500
£2532 $4000 €4000 Object (27cm-11in) dispersion bandages paper mache cable. 27-Nov-2 Dorotheum, Vienna #307/R est:4000-6000
£2848 $4415 €4500 Object (61cm-24in) metal wood plaster papermache. 24-Sep-2 Wiener Kunst Auktionen, Vienna #310/R est:2500-4000
£4430 $7000 €7000 Erich name plate (46x50x5cm-18x20x2in) Indian ink polyester board panel metal prov. 27-Nov-2 Dorotheum, Vienna #91/R est:8000-12000
£5063 $8000 €7595 Homemades (41x61x54cm-16x24x21in) mixed media steel exec.1989 prov.lit. 13-Nov-2 Sotheby's, New York #531/R est:10000-15000
£5696 $9000 €9000 Object (31x40x10cm-12x16x4in) dispersion varnish plaster glass wood cork prov. 27-Nov-2 Dorotheum, Vienna #308/R est:6000-9000
£6757 $10541 €10000 Object (37x50x30cm-15x20x12in) painted paper mache wire prov. 25-Mar-3 Wiener Kunst Auktionen, Vienna #42/R est:12000-18000
£12500 $20000 €18750 Two sculptures on a plinth (49x30x31cm-19x12x12in) wood rubber papier mache gauze plaster paint assemblage. 14-May-3 Sotheby's, New York #419/R est:20000-30000
£12658 $20000 €20000 Untitled (43x142x23cm-17x56x9in) dispersion varnish wood paper mache polyester. 27-Nov-2 Dorotheum, Vienna #83/R est:15000-19000
£15603 $25277 €22000 Blessing (52x52x11cm-20x20x4in) wax acrylic gauze papermache iron board prov.exhib. 20-May-3 Dorotheum, Vienna #98/R est:22000-28000

Works on paper

£696 $1100 €1100 Miesnitz (15x10cm-6x4in) s.i.d.81 s.d. verso Indian ink bodycol biro. 27-Nov-2 Dorotheum, Vienna #304/R
£1582 $2453 €2500 Untitled (41x37cm-16x15in) s.d.83 mixed media blood paper towel on board. 24-Sep-2 Wiener Kunst Auktionen, Vienna #298/R est:2500-4000
£1899 $3000 €3000 Hand holding pig's snout (26x24cm-10x9in) s.i.d.82 mixed media collage. 27-Nov-2 Dorotheum, Vienna #303/R est:3200-4000

£2244	$3545	€3500	Untitled (28x21cm-11x8in) i. gouache. 12-Nov-2 Dorotheum, Vienna #270/R est:3300-4400
£2278	$3600	€3600	Composition (21x29cm-8x11in) s.i.d.82 mixed media. 27-Nov-2 Dorotheum, Vienna #305/R est:3400-4500
£3797	$6000	€6000	Phaedr (62x85cm-24x33in) s.i.d.84 gouache collage on newspaper. 27-Nov-2 Dorotheum, Vienna #101/R est:9000-13000
£5063	$8000	€7595	Untitled (28x42cm-11x17in) s.d.77 gouache. 13-Nov-2 Sotheby's, New York #534/R

WEST, J (?) ?
Works on paper

£700	$1169	€1015	Pleasure boat Inn. At their moorings, Stalham, Norfolk (25x36cm-10x14in) s. W/C pair. 20-Jun-3 Keys, Aylsham #523

WEST, Johannes Hendrick van (1803-1881) Dutch

£2258	$3319	€3500	Examining eggs (49x42cm-19x17in) s. 20-Jun-2 Dr Fritz Nagel, Stuttgart #831/R est:5500

WEST, Joseph Walter (1860-1933) British
Works on paper

£950	$1539	€1425	Girl playing badminton (36x26cm-14x10in) mono. 21-May-3 James Thompson, Kirby Lonsdale #259

WEST, Raphael Lamar (1769-1850) British
Works on paper

£300	$465	€450	Hercules and the Hydra (33x24cm-13x9in) s. pen black ink. 30-Oct-2 Bonhams, New Bond Street #223

WEST, Raphael Lamar (attrib) (1769-1850) British
Works on paper

£750	$1185	€1125	Portrait stydy of a lady painting at an easel (22x20cm-9x8in) d.1787 pen ink on two sheet. 28-Nov-2 Sotheby's, London #219/R est:500-700

WEST, Reginald (fl.1900-1910) British

£320	$499	€480	Yachts on a lake (28x42cm-11x17in) s. board. 8-Apr-3 Bonhams, Knightsbridge #290/R

WEST, Richard Whately (1848-1905) British

£330	$502	€495	Nyeres birth place of Massillon (23x15cm-9x6in) init. 16-Aug-2 Keys, Aylsham #397

WESTALL, J (19th C) British?

£374	$583	€561	Seascape with sailing vessels and seaweed gatherers on beach (63x76cm-25x30in) s. 5-Aug-2 Rasmussen, Vejle #58/R (D.KR 4400)

WESTALL, John (19th C) British

£250	$410	€375	Angler in a mountainous landscape (20x41cm-8x16in) s. 29-May-3 Christie's, Kensington #102/R
£262	$430	€380	British genre landscape (18x38cm-7x15in) s. board. 30-May-3 Aspire, Cleveland #40/R

WESTALL, Richard (1765-1836) British

£300	$477	€450	Country scene with figures before a farmhouse (30x41cm-12x16in) 1-Mar-3 Shapes, Edinburgh #366
£1800	$2862	€2700	Maid with milk jug and dog resting by the stile (62x46cm-24x18in) sold with a companion. 5-Mar-3 Bonhams, Bury St Edmunds #365/R est:1800-2500

Works on paper

£450	$701	€675	Embarkation (36x33cm-14x13in) pencil W/C. 19-Sep-2 Christie's, Kensington #3/R
£500	$780	€750	Gothic church interiors (54x41cm-21x16in) s. pencil pen ink W/C scratching out pair. 17-Oct-2 Christie's, Kensington #33

WESTALL, Richard (attrib) (1765-1836) British

£450	$720	€675	Shepherd and his dog resting by a woodland stream (50x41cm-20x16in) panel. 11-Mar-3 Bonhams, Knightsbridge #275/R

WESTCHILOFF, Constantin (1877-1945) Russian

£1410	$2200	€2115	Breakers (66x81cm-26x32in) s. 20-Sep-2 Sloan, North Bethesda #483/R est:1000-2000
£1500	$2430	€2250	Shores of Capri (20x25cm-8x10in) s. i.d.1925 verso. 21-May-3 Sotheby's, London #77/R est:1500-2000
£6500	$10206	€9750	Morning. Night (21x26cm-8x10in) s. one canvas on board one board pair. 20-Nov-2 Sotheby's, London #70/R est:2500-3500
£7000	$11340	€10500	Winter sun (64x77cm-25x30in) s. 21-May-3 Sotheby's, London #124/R est:4000-6000
£8000	$12960	€12000	Waves on a moonlit shore (92x107cm-36x42in) s. 21-May-3 Sotheby's, London #91/R est:8000-12000
£13000	$20410	€19500	Moonlight over the Crimean coast (67x90cm-26x35in) s. 20-Nov-2 Sotheby's, London #52/R est:7000-9000
£14000	$22680	€21000	View of Capri (60x73cm-24x29in) s. 21-May-3 Sotheby's, London #81/R est:6000-8000
£17000	$26690	€25500	Flowers on the balcony (76x91cm-30x36in) s. 20-Nov-2 Sotheby's, London #144/R est:7000-9000
£22000	$35640	€33000	Crimean coastal scene (81x102cm-32x40in) s. 21-May-3 Sotheby's, London #76/R est:8000-12000

Works on paper

£1700	$2670	€2550	Working under the vines, Capri (32x43cm-13x17in) s.i. pastel. 20-Nov-2 Sotheby's, London #47/R est:2000-3000

WESTENDORP-OSIECK, Betsy (1880-1968) Dutch

£258	$408	€400	Landscape by Torrelaguna (60x81cm-24x32in) s.d. s.i.d.verso. 18-Dec-2 Castellana, Madrid #2/R
£353	$554	€550	Still life of flowers in a vase and fruit (45x37cm-18x15in) s. 25-Nov-2 Glerum, Amsterdam #8
£545	$855	€850	Roof terrace of the artist (42x36cm-17x14in) s.i. 25-Nov-2 Glerum, Amsterdam #5/R
£658	$1066	€1000	Portrait of Mrs Rothermant (50x68cm-20x27in) s. s.i. indis d.on stretcher sold with book of etchings. 21-Jan-3 Christie's, Amsterdam #249 est:800-1200

Works on paper

£256	$403	€400	Still life with basket and fan (39x52cm-15x20in) s.i. gouache. 25-Nov-2 Glerum, Amsterdam #119
£353	$554	€550	Magnolias in a vase (31x25cm-12x10in) s.i.d.1963 W/C. 25-Nov-2 Glerum, Amsterdam #9/R
£353	$554	€550	Still life with an open-worked bowl and fruit (37x51cm-15x20in) init. W/C. 25-Nov-2 Glerum, Amsterdam #118
£769	$1208	€1200	Still life with a tureen and fruit (38x48cm-15x19in) init. W/C. 25-Nov-2 Glerum, Amsterdam #121

WESTERBAEN, Jan Jansz (elder) (1600-1686) Dutch

£1911	$2981	€3000	Portrait of a lady, said to be Anna van Briegsen (68x54cm-27x21in) mono.d.1645 panel. 5-Nov-2 Sotheby's, Amsterdam #133/R est:4000-6000

WESTERBEEK, Cornelis (1844-1903) Dutch

£253	$395	€400	Moutons dans un chemin creux (50x69cm-20x27in) s. 15-Oct-2 Horta, Bruxelles #423
£1250	$2063	€1800	Leading the sheep over the heath (60x100cm-24x39in) s.d.98. 1-Jul-3 Christie's, Amsterdam #82/R est:1800-2500
£1645	$2664	€2500	Homeward bound in winter (50x80cm-20x31in) s.d.96. 21-Jan-3 Christie's, Amsterdam #141 est:1500-2000
£1889	$3135	€2739	Returning with the flock (60x99cm-24x39in) s.d.97. 16-Jun-3 Waddingtons, Toronto #248/R est:5000-7000 (C.D 4250)
£4225	$6803	€6000	Snowy landscape with shepherdess and flock of sheep (58x98cm-23x39in) s. 7-May-3 Vendue Huis, Gravenhage #468/R est:6000-7000

WESTERBEEK, Cornelis (jnr) (1873-1917) Dutch

£342	$534	€500	Flock of sheep on edge of autumn forest (68x80cm-27x31in) s. 14-Apr-3 Glerum, Amsterdam #145/R
£480	$749	€720	Birch trees by a pond (40x60cm-16x24in) s. 13-Sep-2 Lyon & Turnbull, Edinburgh #149/R

WESTERHOLM, Victor (1860-1919) Finnish

£2532	$4000	€4000	Alley (32x24cm-13x9in) s.d.1875 board. 1-Dec-2 Bukowskis, Helsinki #208/R est:4000-5000
£7746	$12472	€11000	View from Venice (15x22cm-6x9in) s.i.d.1986 board. 10-May-3 Bukowskis, Helsinki #40/R est:5000-7000
£11392	$18000	€18000	Coastal landscape with palace in background (54x81cm-21x32in) s. lit. 1-Dec-2 Bukowskis, Helsinki #206/R est:20000-25000
£20863	$33381	€29000	River landscape with buildings in winter (48x81cm-19x32in) s. 17-May-3 Hagelstam, Helsinki #96/R est:25000
£32278	$51000	€51000	Winter landscape from Karis (52x87cm-20x34in) s.i. 1-Dec-2 Bukowskis, Helsinki #205/R est:35000-40000

Works on paper

£899	$1439	€1250	Winter (21x30cm-8x12in) s.d.1904 mixed media. 17-May-3 Hagelstam, Helsinki #58/R

WESTERIK, Jacobus (1924-) Dutch
Works on paper

£2734	$4483	€3800	Poepende man (26x26cm-10x10in) s.i.d.1975 pen ink W/C pastel. 3-Jun-3 Christie's, Amsterdam #65/R est:2000-3000
£3957	$6489	€5500	Gedreven man - driven man (36x53cm-14x21in) s.d.1974 pen ink crayons W/C prov. 3-Jun-3 Christie's, Amsterdam #67/R est:2500-3500

WESTERMANN, H C (1922-1981) American
Sculpture
£21875 $35000 €32813 Indian lookout (83x25x19cm-33x10x7in) i. painted wood iron lead brass executed 1979 prov.exhib.lit. 14-May-3 Sotheby's, New York #163/R est:20000-30000
Works on paper
£12500 $20000 €18750 Blue roses (56x78cm-22x31in) s.d.78 W/C ink prov.exhib. 14-May-3 Sotheby's, New York #166/R est:4000-6000

WESTEROP, Wilhelm (?) ?
£252 $390 €400 Horses pulling log cart through wood (60x85cm-24x33in) s. masonite. 4-Oct-2 Paul Kieffer, Pforzhiem #9976/R

WESTERVELT, Abraham van (?-1692) Dutch
£5096 $7949 €8000 Classical landscape with travellers on a path (66x116cm-26x46in) s. panel exhib.lit. 5-Nov-2 Sotheby's, Amsterdam #106/R est:10000-15000

WESTFELT-EGGERTZ, Ingeborg (1855-1936) Swedish
£707 $1159 €1025 Coastal landscape, Skagen (24x35cm-9x14in) s.i.d.1906. 4-Jun-3 AB Stockholms Auktionsverk #2308/R (S.KR 9000)

WESTMAN, Edvard (1865-1917) Swedish
£1543 $2438 €2315 Snow is falling - landscape from Jungskar, Stockholm (38x61cm-15x24in) s.i. 27-Nov-2 Falkkloos, Malmo #77673/R est:15000 (S.KR 22000)
£6338 $10204 €9000 Early spring landscape from Onningeby (81x51cm-32x20in) s.i.d.April 99. 10-May-3 Bukowskis, Helsinki #179/R est:7000-8000

WESTON, Brett (1911-1993) American
Photographs
£1829 $3000 €2744 Manhattan bridge (20x25cm-8x10in) bears sig.d.verso silver print exec.c.1945. 10-Feb-3 Swann Galleries, New York #69/R est:3500-5000
£1875 $3000 €2813 Roof tops Portugal (20x24cm-8x9in) s.d.1960 verso silver print. 15-May-3 Swann Galleries, New York #520/R est:3000-5000
£1899 $3000 €2849 Garrapata Beach (28x35cm-11x14in) s.d.1954 photograph. 23-Apr-3 Sotheby's, New York #14/R est:3500-5000
£1899 $3000 €2849 Dry cracked soil (27x34cm-11x13in) s.d.1955 gelatin silver print. 22-Apr-3 Butterfields, San Francisco #2515/R est:2000-3000
£1951 $3200 €2927 Dead yucca (25x20cm-10x8in) s.i.d.verso silver print. 10-Feb-3 Swann Galleries, New York #84/R est:2500-3500
£2000 $3200 €3000 Sand dunes (20x25cm-8x10in) silver print. 15-May-3 Swann Galleries, New York #519/R est:3500-4500
£2195 $3600 €3293 Central Baja, California, Mexico (24x20cm-9x8in) s.i.d.verso silver print exec.c.1964-67. 10-Feb-3 Swann Galleries, New York #85/R est:2500-3500
£2435 $3750 €3653 Dune, oceano (32x25cm-13x10in) s.d.1934 photograph. 24-Oct-2 Sotheby's, New York #5/R est:4000-6000
£2532 $4000 €3798 Dune, oceano (24x19cm-9x7in) s.d.1934 photograph. 23-Apr-3 Sotheby's, New York #2/R est:4000-6000
£2690 $4250 €4035 Old cars in snow, Virginia City, Nevada (19x24cm-7x9in) s.d.1950 warm toned photograph. 23-Apr-3 Sotheby's, New York #15/R est:3000-5000
£2922 $4500 €4383 Holland canal (34x27cm-13x11in) s.d.1972 photograph. 24-Oct-2 Sotheby's, New York #7/R est:7000-10000
£3247 $5000 €4871 San Francisco Streets (19x24cm-7x9in) s.d. photograph from a portfolio prov. 22-Oct-2 Sotheby's, New York #5/R est:7000-10000
£3896 $6000 €5844 Big surf coast (19x24cm-7x9in) photograph prov. 22-Oct-2 Sotheby's, New York #175/R est:3000-5000
£5195 $8000 €7793 Golden gate Bridge, San Francisco, Cal (19x24cm-7x9in) s.i.d.1940 verso photograph prov.exhib.lit. 22-Oct-2 Sotheby's, New York #4/R est:7000-10000
£5313 $8500 €7970 Yucca and granite, wonderland of rocks, Josha Tree National Monument (24x19cm-9x7in) init.d.1937 verso silver print. 15-May-3 Swann Galleries, New York #522/R est:7000-10000
Prints
£1899 $3000 €2849 Nude on mud cracks (25x33cm-10x13in) s.i.d.1968 vintage silver gelatine print. 16-Nov-2 New Orleans Auction, New Orleans #1427/R est:3500-5000

WESTON, Edward (1886-1958) American
Photographs
£2400 $3888 €3600 Tina Modotti with her arms raised (10x11cm-4x4in) num.12 verso silver print exec.c.1921 prov.exhib.lit. 22-May-3 Sotheby's, London #125/R est:2000-3000
£3247 $5000 €4871 Ella Wolfe (23x18cm-9x7in) s.d.1924 warm toned platinum print. 24-Oct-2 Sotheby's, New York #129/R est:4000-6000
£4114 $6500 €6171 Robinson Jeffers, Tor House, Carmel (10x7cm-4x3in) s.i.d.1929 gelatin silver print mounted on board prov.lit. 24-Apr-3 Phillips, New York #99/R est:8000-12000
£4430 $7000 €6645 Golden Canyon, Death Valley (19x24cm-7x9in) s.d.1938 verso photograph. 23-Apr-3 Sotheby's, New York #135/R est:5000-7000
£4870 $7500 €7305 Surf, Point Lobos (18x24cm-7x9in) s.i.d.1938 photograph. 24-Oct-2 Sotheby's, New York #130/R est:5000-7000
£7143 $11000 €10715 Cypress root (23x19cm-9x7in) s.d.1929 i.num.221 verso photograph prov.lit. 22-Oct-2 Sotheby's, New York #52/R est:10000-15000
£9740 $15000 €14610 Triangulate design of George Hopkins (19x24cm-7x9in) s.i.d. photograph prov.lit. 22-Oct-2 Sotheby's, New York #53/R est:10000-15000
£13636 $21000 €20454 Christel Gang (18x23cm-7x9in) i. photograph prov.exhib.lit. 22-Oct-2 Sotheby's, New York #49/R est:20000-30000
£16667 $26000 €25001 Boat - Daylight - San Francisco (23x18cm-9x7in) s.d. platinum palladium. 21-Oct-2 Swann Galleries, New York #291/R est:30000-50000
£16883 $26000 €25325 Nude on sand, oceano (17x24cm-7x9in) i.d.1936 verso photograph. 24-Oct-2 Sotheby's, New York #128/R est:6000-9000
£20253 $32000 €30380 M.G.M storage lot - Stairs (24x19cm-9x7in) s.d.1939 verso photograph prov.lit. 23-Apr-3 Sotheby's, New York #131/R est:10000-15000
£24684 $39000 €37026 White Sanda, New Mexico (19x24cm-7x9in) init.d.1941 gelatin silver print mounted on board prov. 24-Apr-3 Phillips, New York #25/R est:30000-50000
£30380 $48000 €45570 Portrait of a debutante (24x19cm-9x7in) s.d.1922 warm toned platinum print prov. 23-Apr-3 Sotheby's, New York #138/R est:15000-25000
£34177 $54000 €51266 Dunes - oceano (19x24cm-7x9in) s.d.1936 num.51SO photograph lit. 23-Apr-3 Sotheby's, New York #143/R est:60000-80000
£37975 $60000 €56963 Chard (35x43cm-14x17in) init.d.num.11/50 gelatin silver print mounted on board prov.lit. 24-Apr-3 Phillips, New York #27/R est:50000-70000
£39241 $62000 €58862 Nude - Charis (12x9cm-5x4in) s.d.1934 num.9/50 photograph prov.exhib.lit. 23-Apr-3 Sotheby's, New York #142/R est:30000-50000
£142405 $225000 €213608 Charis, Santa Monica (24x19cm-9x7in) s.d.1936 num.227N verso photograph prov.lit. 23-Apr-3 Sotheby's, New York #132/R est:70000-100000

WESTON, Edward and Cole (20th C) American
Photographs
£2317 $3800 €3476 Pepper no 30 (25x18cm-10x7in) i.verso silver print exec.c.1970. 10-Feb-3 Swann Galleries, New York #44/R est:2500-3500

WESTON, Harold (1894-1972) American
Works on paper
£1562 $2500 €2265 Distant mountains (28x49cm-11x19in) s.d.33 W/C gouache. 16-May-3 Skinner, Boston #248/R est:300-400

WESTON, William Percy (1879-1967) Canadian
£806 $1274 €1209 Moonrise, Garrow Bay (35x25cm-14x10in) s. s.i.d.1916-17 verso panel prov. 14-Nov-2 Heffel, Vancouver #248/R est:2000-2500 (C.D 2000)
£1121 $1794 €1682 On the Dewdney Road (33x41cm-13x16in) s. s.i.d.1967 verso board prov. 15-May-3 Heffel, Vancouver #114/R est:3000-4000 (C.D 2500)
£1121 $1794 €1682 Okanagan Lake (33x41cm-13x16in) s.d.1957 s.i.d.verso board prov. 15-May-3 Heffel, Vancouver #130/R est:3000-4000 (C.D 2500)
£1345 $2152 €2018 Passing thunderstorm, New Denver, BC (33x41cm-13x16in) s.i.d.1952 s.verso board prov. 15-May-3 Heffel, Vancouver #112/R est:4000-6000 (C.D 3000)
£1411 $2230 €2117 Veder River, Chilliwack (30x38cm-12x15in) s. s.i.verso panel prov. 14-Nov-2 Heffel, Vancouver #237/R est:3500-4500 (C.D 3500)
£29148 $46637 €43722 Mount Shuksan (107x122cm-42x48in) s. s.i.verso prov.exhib.lit. 15-May-3 Heffel, Vancouver #120/R est:40000-50000 (C.D 65000)

WESTPFAHL, Conrad (1891-1976) German
£1655 $2647 €2300 Twilight of the Gods (61x85cm-24x33in) s.d. temperaboard. 15-May-3 Neumeister, Munich #570/R est:2300-2500
Works on paper
£468 $748 €650 Undressed emale nudes (60x43cm-24x17in) s.d. mixed media. 15-May-3 Neumeister, Munich #571/R

WESTPHAL, Anne Marie (1868-1950) Danish
£284 $457 €426 Still life of daffodils and red flowers in vase (30x24cm-12x9in) s.d.1940. 11-May-3 Hindemae, Ullerslev #182/R (D.KR 3000)

WESTWOOD, Bryan Wyndham (1930-2000) Australian
£632 $960 €948 French countryside (47x58cm-19x23in) s. board. 19-Aug-2 Joel, Victoria #235 est:2000-2500 (A.D 1800)
£857 $1329 €1286 South of Alice (135x151cm-53x59in) s. 29-Oct-2 Lawson Menzies, Sydney #138 (A.D 2400)
£857 $1346 €1286 Racehorse (91x76cm-36x30in) init. oil pencil prov. 25-Nov-2 Christie's, Melbourne #331/R (A.D 2400)
£930 $1479 €1395 Two more mallards from Joe (91x91cm-36x36in) s. i.verso painted 1979 exhib. 5-May-3 Sotheby's, Melbourne #205/R (A.D 2400)
£1228 $1867 €1842 Weighing in (135x74cm-53x29in) init. 19-Aug-2 Joel, Victoria #288 est:2000-3000 (A.D 3500)
£1647 $2619 €2471 Irises (58x42cm-23x17in) s.d.81 verso. 5-May-3 Sotheby's, Melbourne #228/R est:2500-3500 (A.D 4250)
£2206 $3376 €3309 Violin - Indiana's (122x92cm-48x36in) s. i.verso painted c.1980 prov. 26-Aug-2 Sotheby's, Paddington #619 est:10000-15000 (A.D 6200)
£2402 $3675 €3603 Telephone box (91x89cm-36x35in) board painted c.1970 prov. 26-Aug-2 Sotheby's, Paddington #624/R est:7000-10000 (A.D 6750)
£2519 $4006 €3779 Trees in Centennial park (152x152cm-60x60in) init. prov. 5-May-3 Sotheby's, Melbourne #208 est:4000-6000 (A.D 6500)

WESTWOOD, Dennis (1928-) British
Sculpture
£1100 $1716 €1650 Aeon (31cm-12in) init.d.1988 dark green pat. bronze. 27-Mar-3 Christie's, Kensington #652/R est:500-700

WET, Gerrit de (1616-1674) Dutch
£6369 $9936 €10000 Adoration of the Golden Calf (60x84cm-24x33in) indis sig. panel. 5-Nov-2 Sotheby's, Amsterdam #43/R est:5000-7000

WET, Gerrit de (attrib) (1616-1674) Dutch
£4054 $6324 €6000 Exodus (72x114cm-28x45in) 26-Mar-3 Tajan, Paris #139/R

WET, Jacob Jacobsz de (1640-1697) Dutch
£7792 $12000 €11688 Battle scenes (74x61cm-29x24in) one s. pair. 23-Oct-2 Doyle, New York #17/R est:8000-12000

WET, Jacob de (1610-1671) Dutch
£1560 $2606 €2200 Judas rapportant les deniers (66x51cm-26x20in) s.d.1656 panel. 18-Jun-3 Hotel des Ventes Mosan, Brussels #153/R est:1800-2200
£1688 $2516 €2600 Diogenes with lantern meeting the people in the Athens market place (48x65cm-19x26in) s. panel. 26-Jun-2 Neumeister, Munich #669/R est:1500
£1931 $2974 €2897 Esther before Ahasveros (75x110cm-30x43in) panel. 27-Oct-2 Anders Antik, Landskrona #227/R est:30000-40000 (S.KR 28000)
£2278 $3600 €3600 Gentleman in his study (59x49cm-23x19in) s.d.1642 panel. 27-Nov-2 James Adam, Dublin #119/R est:1000-1500
£5096 $7949 €8000 Calling of St. Peter and St. Andrew (37x52cm-15x20in) s. panel oval prov.exhib. 5-Nov-2 Sotheby's, Amsterdam #8/R est:7000-9000
£10323 $15174 €16000 Proclamation to the shepherds (52x65cm-20x26in) s. panel. 20-Jun-2 Dr Fritz Nagel, Stuttgart #745/R est:25000

WET, Jacob de (attrib) (1610-1671) Dutch
£2000 $3100 €3000 Adoration of the shepherds (28x37cm-11x15in) panel. 30-Oct-2 Christie's, Kensington #45/R est:2000-3000

WETERING DE ROOY, Johann Embrosius van de (1877-1972) Dutch
£379 $607 €550 River view, probably Woudrichem (44x47cm-17x19in) s. 15-Mar-3 De Vuyst, Lokeren #336
£443 $691 €700 Ferry boat (34x53cm-13x21in) s. 21-Oct-2 Glerum, Amsterdam #219
£625 $1013 €950 Tending to the cows (36x62cm-14x24in) s. cardboard on panel. 21-Jan-3 Christie's, Amsterdam #154

WETHERBEE, George Faulkner (1851-1920) American
£360 $576 €540 Moorland and estuary landscape at sunset (32x50cm-13x20in) s. board. 11-Mar-3 Bonhams, Oxford #72
£2679 $4232 €4019 Summer (73x92cm-29x36in) s. s.i.verso exhib. 26-Nov-2 Sotheby's, Melbourne #244/R est:6000-8000 (A.D 7500)

WETHERBY, Isaac Augustus (1819-1904) American
£1384 $2200 €2076 Young girl with orange seated beneath a tree (86x69cm-34x27in) i.d.1853 verso. 29-Apr-3 Doyle, New York #42 est:1500-2500

WETHERED, Vernon (1865-1952) British
£440 $695 €638 Storm (69x81cm-27x32in) s.i.verso. 22-Jul-3 Gorringes, Lewes #1570

WETLI, Hugo (1916-1972) Swiss
£515 $814 €773 Street in Seriphos (66x53cm-26x21in) s.d.1962 sold with prototype charcoal drawing. 29-Nov-2 Zofingen, Switzerland #3129 (S.FR 1200)
£6944 $11181 €10069 Rebberge near Twann (130x129cm-51x51in) s.d.69. 9-May-3 Dobiaschofsky, Bern #190/R est:6000 (S.FR 15000)

WETTE, Jules de (19/20th C) Belgian
£1646 $2567 €2600 Quatre dentellieres dans un jardin (77x102cm-30x40in) s. 15-Oct-2 Horta, Bruxelles #49

WETTENHOVI-ASPA, Sigurd (1870-1946) Finnish
£314 $484 €500 Hunters (70x40cm-28x16in) s.d.1899. 24-Oct-2 Hagelstam, Helsinki #1024

WETZEL, Johann Jakob (1781-1834) Swiss
Works on paper
£1826 $2849 €2739 Arcadian landscape by the sea (41x55cm-16x22in) s. W/C Indian ink. 28-Mar-3 Koller, Zurich #3377/R est:4000-5000 (S.FR 4000)

WETZENSTEIN, Ernst (1890-?) German
Works on paper
£308 $481 €450 Sheaf gathering woman (35x40cm-14x16in) s.d.40 pastel tempera over chl. 10-Apr-3 Schopman, Hamburg #650

WEX, Adalbert (1867-1932) German
£1274 $1987 €2000 Dachauer Moos (55x85cm-22x33in) s. 6-Nov-2 Hugo Ruef, Munich #1334/R est:900
£1300 $2041 €1950 Autumn sunset (81x110cm-32x43in) s. 16-Apr-3 Christie's, Kensington #714/R est:1500-2000

WEX, Willibald (1831-1892) German
£570 $883 €900 Rainthal with blue Gumpe near Partenkirchen (46x36cm-18x14in) s. i. verso panel. 26-Sep-2 Neumeister, Munich #2867/R
£1154 $1788 €1800 High mountain shack (42x54cm-17x21in) s.i.d.862 prov. 7-Dec-2 Ketterer, Hamburg #102/R est:1400-1500

WEXELSEN, Christian Delphin (1830-1883) Norwegian
£562 $877 €843 Mountain landscape with waterfall (63x57cm-25x22in) s.d.80. 13-Sep-2 Lilla Bukowskis, Stockholm #379 (S.KR 8200)
£708 $1154 €1062 Landscape with house and figures (32x46cm-13x18in) s.d.1878. 17-Feb-3 Blomqvist, Lysaker #1259/R (N.KR 8000)
£2018 $3188 €3027 Waterfall (63x57cm-25x22in) s.indis.d.1867. 17-Dec-2 Grev Wedels Plass, Oslo #200/R est:15000-20000 (N.KR 23000)

WEXLER, Jacob (1912-) Israeli
£533 $885 €773 Two women in the village (61x44cm-24x17in) s.verso painted c.1940. 16-Jun-3 Waddingtons, Toronto #318/R est:1000-1500 (C.D 1200)
£578 $959 €838 Seated model (61x47cm-24x19in) s. s.verso. 16-Jun-3 Waddingtons, Toronto #319/R est:1000-1500 (C.D 1300)

WEY, Alois (1891-1985) Swiss
Works on paper
£515 $814 €773 Palace with flag and snow-covered hills in the background (44x50cm-17x20in) s. col pencil ink. 26-Nov-2 Hans Widmer, St Gallen #1478 (S.FR 1200)

WEYDE, Julius (1822-1860) German
£3800 $6346 €5510 Outside the cottage (66x50cm-26x20in) s.i. 17-Jun-3 Bonhams, New Bond Street #24/R est:4000-6000
£6918 $10654 €11000 Tending to the tools (65x50cm-26x20in) s.indis d.1854. 23-Oct-2 Christie's, Amsterdam #22/R est:2000-3000

WEYDEN, H van der (?) ?
£1000 $1580 €1450 Dutch harbour scene with children on a grassy bank (38x52cm-15x20in) s. board. 23-Jul-3 Wintertons, Lichfield #489/R est:1000-1500

WEYDEN, Harry van der (1868-?) American
£750 $1140 €1125 The Needles, Isle of Wight (30x39cm-12x15in) s.d.1929 canvas on board. 15-Aug-2 Bonhams, New Bond Street #362
Works on paper
£580 $963 €870 The Ford (33x11cm-13x4in) i.d.1901 W/C. 10-Jun-3 Sworder & Son, Bishops Stortford #468/R

WEYDEN, Henrik van den (20th C) Dutch
£460 $754 €690 Dinghies in an estuary at low tide (36x44cm-14x17in) s.d.1915 board. 3-Jun-3 Bonhams, Oxford #83

WEYDEN, Rogier van der (1399-1464) Flemish
£7746 $12859 €11000 Portrait of Philipp le Bon, Duc de Bourgogne (32x25cm-13x10in) panel lit. 11-Jun-3 Dorotheum, Vienna #83/R est:9000-12000

WEYDEN, Rogier van der (circle) (1399-1464) Flemish
£19753 $32000 €29630 Christ on the cross with the Virgin and St. John (34x24cm-13x9in) panel. 23-Jan-3 Sotheby's, New York #53/R est:30000-40000
£110000 $172700 €165000 Portrait of young man in fur-trimmed red doublet (37x27cm-15x11in) panel prov.exhib.lit. 11-Dec-2 Christie's, London #23/R est:25000-35000

WEYDEN, Rogier van der (studio) (1399-1464) Flemish
£60811 $94865 €90000 Madonna and Child (43x33cm-17x13in) panel exhib.prov. 27-Mar-3 Dorotheum, Vienna #159/R est:80000-100000

WEYDEN, Rogier van der (style) (1399-1464) Flemish
£3716 $5797 €5500 The deposition (65x46cm-26x18in) panel lit.prov. 27-Mar-3 Dorotheum, Vienna #381/R est:6000-9000

WEYDMULLER, Johanna Elisabeth (1725-1807) German
£8176 $12591 €13000 Nature morte au panier de fleurs sur un entablement demarbre (48x38cm-19x15in) s. 25-Oct-2 Tajan, Paris #98 est:2000-3000

WEYER, Gabriel (17th C) ?
Works on paper
£881 $1374 €1400 Allegory of passion (17x25cm-7x10in) Indian ink. 11-Oct-2 Winterberg, Heidelberg #352/R

WEYER, Hermann (17th C) German
Works on paper
£382 $596 €600 Raising of Lazarus. Landscape with bridge (16x21cm-6x8in) pen black ink htd white grey wash double-sided dr. 5-Nov-2 Sotheby's, Amsterdam #15/R

WEYER, Jacob (c.1620-1670) German
Works on paper
£255 $397 €400 Girl sweeping with an owl on a branch. Tortoise (24x16cm-9x6in) pen brown black ink brush grey wash double-sided. 5-Nov-2 Sotheby's, Amsterdam #248/R

WEYL, Max (1837-1914) American/German
£1497 $2500 €2171 Autumn landscape (69x86cm-27x34in) s.d.1910. 17-Jun-3 John Moran, Pasadena #149 est:2000-3000
£3846 $6000 €5769 Washington landscape (56x76cm-22x30in) s. 20-Sep-2 Sloan, North Bethesda #476/R est:4000-6000

WEYMANN, Jeanette von (19th C) Rumanian
£2152 $3400 €3400 Roman ruins in Schonbrunn (90x70cm-35x28in) s. 28-Nov-2 Dorotheum, Vienna #124/R est:3000-3400

WEYNS, Jules (1849-1925) Belgian
Sculpture
£1277 $2068 €1800 Bambina (34cm-13in) s. pat bronze. 22-May-3 Stadion, Trieste #632 est:2000-3000

WEYSSER, Karl (1833-1904) German
£2516 $3925 €4000 Steps up to Deidesheim Town Hall (40x27cm-16x11in) s.d.1897. 11-Oct-2 Winterberg, Heidelberg #752/R est:4200
£2582 $4235 €3744 Narrow street in Meersburg on the Bodensee (49x37cm-19x15in) s.d.89. 4-Jun-3 Fischer, Luzern #1144/R est:6000-8000 (S.FR 5500)
£2740 $4301 €4000 Villagers along a path near a river, possibly the River Main or Mosel (49x40cm-19x16in) s.d.1877. 15-Apr-3 Sotheby's, Amsterdam #90/R est:4000-6000

WEYTS, Carolus (1828-1875) Belgian
£8632 $14156 €12516 Ship's portrait - Ole Smith Ploug of Stavanger (60x82cm-24x32in) s.i.d.1873. 2-Jun-3 Blomqvist, Oslo #56/R est:50000-70000 (N.KR 94000)

WEYTS, Petrus Cornelius (attrib) (1799-1855) Flemish
£11321 $18000 €16982 Vespasian of Boston, Benjamin C Green, Commander (48x66cm-19x26in) i. reverse painting on glass. 1-Mar-3 North East Auctions, Portsmouth #578/R est:8000-12000

WHAITE, James (19th C) British
£620 $967 €930 Cottager's yard (25x35cm-10x14in) s.d.81. 26-Mar-3 Sotheby's, Olympia #111/R
Works on paper
£320 $506 €480 Harvest time (30x41cm-12x16in) s. W/C. 27-Nov-2 Hamptons Fine Art, Godalming #116
£800 $1296 €1200 From the Leddr bridge, Bettys-y-Coed (59x95cm-23x37in) s. W/C. 20-May-3 Sotheby's, Olympia #193/R

WHALE, Robert Heard (1857-1906) Canadian
£889 $1458 €1334 Artist sketching a mountain vista (85x130cm-33x51in) s. prov. 3-Jun-3 Joyner, Toronto #307/R est:2000-3000 (C.D 2000)

WHALE, Robert Reginald (1805-1887) Canadian
£643 $1009 €965 View of English coast (44x59cm-17x23in) s.i.d.1873. 25-Nov-2 Hodgins, Calgary #164/R (C.D 1600)
£905 $1403 €1358 Picnic by a lake with hills in the distance (22x32cm-9x13in) s. 3-Dec-2 Joyner, Toronto #241/R est:2500-3000 (C.D 2200)

WHANKI, Kim (1913-1974) Korean
£201258 $320000 €301887 White porcelain jars (100x81cm-39x32in) s. 24-Mar-3 Christie's, Rockefeller NY #325/R est:60000-80000
Prints
£2013 $3200 €3020 Mountain (55x39cm-22x15in) s. col lithograph exec.c.1956. 24-Mar-3 Christie's, Rockefeller NY #324/R est:1000-1500

WHATLEY, Henry (1824-1901) British
Works on paper
£3750 $6000 €5625 Gypsy girl reflecting by fountains of water (74x102cm-29x40in) s. pencil W/C laid down. 14-May-3 Butterfields, San Francisco #1169/R est:6000-8000

WHEALE, Ivan Trevor (?) Canadian
£2222 $3644 €3333 Benjamin Islands (127x168cm-50x66in) s. s.i.verso prov. 27-May-3 Sotheby's, Toronto #120/R est:3000-5000 (C.D 5000)

WHEELER, Alfred (1852-1932) British
£750 $1155 €1125 Study of a bulls head peering out of shippen (30x25cm-12x10in) s. canvas on panel. 23-Oct-2 Hampton & Littlewood, Exeter #459
£850 $1411 €1233 At the water trough (20x28cm-8x11in) s. board. 12-Jun-3 Christie's, Kensington #79/R
£900 $1386 €1350 Grey with donkeys and chickens in a barn (46x91cm-18x36in) s.i. 24-Oct-2 Christie's, Kensington #91/R
£900 $1467 €1305 Chase (32x45cm-13x18in) bears sig canvas on board. 16-Jul-3 Sotheby's, Olympia #70/R
£2500 $3950 €3750 Stable mates (17x20cm-7x8in) init. board. 28-Nov-2 Christie's, Kensington #134/R est:1500-2000
£8200 $12956 €12300 Diamon Jubilee with jockey up (51x61cm-20x24in) init.i.d.1900. 27-Nov-2 Christie's, London #72/R est:4000-6000

WHEELER, Alfred (attrib) (1852-1932) British
£3000 $4980 €4350 Jockeys on horseback jumping a fence (38x61cm-15x24in) s.d.86. 10-Jun-3 Louis Taylor, Stoke on Trent #925

WHEELER, Charles Arthur (1881-1977) Australian
£329 $539 €477 Road to the sea (29x39cm-11x15in) s. i.verso board. 3-Jun-3 Lawson Menzies, Sydney #820 (A.D 825)
£383 $571 €575 Cane fields, Innisfail (29x39cm-11x15in) s. i.verso board. 27-Aug-2 Christie's, Melbourne #353 est:800-1200 (A.D 1000)

£394 $599 €591 Landscape (29x39cm-11x15in) s. 27-Aug-2 Goodman, Sydney #58 (A.D 1100)
£537 $817 €806 White house (30x40cm-12x16in) s. board. 28-Aug-2 Deutscher-Menzies, Melbourne #248/R (A.D 1500)
£561 $853 €842 Afternoon in the garden (44x60cm-17x24in) s. 19-Aug-2 Joel, Victoria #259 est:1000-1500 (A.D 1600)
£857 $1354 €1286 Notre Dame, Paris (30x40cm-12x16in) s. i.verso panel. 27-Nov-2 Deutscher-Menzies, Melbourne #105/R est:2000-3000 (A.D 2400)
£5694 $8712 €8541 Lady in purple (57x32cm-22x13in) s. painted c.1900 prov. 26-Aug-2 Sotheby's, Paddington #546/R est:15000-20000 (A.D 16000)

WHEELER, Colin V (20th C) New Zealander
£291 $413 €437 Diesel bowser (55x47cm-22x19in) s.d. board. 21-Nov-1 Watson's, Christchurch #155/R (NZ.D 1000)
£815 $1271 €1223 Otago Bridge (33x42cm-13x17in) s. board. 7-Nov-2 International Art Centre, Auckland #144/R est:1200-2000 (NZ.D 2600)
£1140 $1779 €1710 Craft shop, Milton (67x55cm-26x22in) s.d.1999 board. 27-Mar-3 International Art Centre, Auckland #12/R est:3000-4000 (NZ.D 3250)
£1411 $2201 €2117 Wool shed at Algidues (40x60cm-16x24in) s. board. 7-Nov-2 International Art Centre, Auckland #70/R est:4000-6000 (NZ.D 4500)

Works on paper
£465 $660 €698 MOW fire tender in the Lindus (35x47cm-14x19in) s. W/C. 21-Nov-1 Watson's, Christchurch #154/R (NZ.D 1600)
£491 $697 €737 Haystack (23x30cm-9x12in) s.d.1944 W/C. 20-Mar-2 Watson's, Christchurch #105/R est:200-400 (NZ.D 1600)

WHEELER, J (19th C) British
£1200 $1860 €1800 Dark bay gelding in his stables with saddle and straw (63x76cm-25x30in) s.d.1901. 27-Sep-2 Bigwood, Stratford on Avon #306 est:100

WHEELER, James T (1849-1888) British
£1227 $2000 €1841 Stable companions (30x51cm-12x20in) mono. 11-Feb-3 Bonhams & Doyles, New York #128/R est:1200-1800
£1850 $2942 €2775 Study of a bay horse (62x75cm-24x30in) s.d.1869. 29-Apr-3 Henry Adams, Chichester #313/R est:800-1200

WHEELER, John Arnold (1821-1903) British
£455 $677 €700 Study of a horses head (30x23cm-12x9in) oval. 28-Jun-2 Woodwards, Cork #204
£600 $930 €900 Sun Star, study of a horse (21x28cm-8x11in) s. i. board oval. 31-Oct-2 Greenslade Hunt, Taunton #632/R
£600 $936 €900 Sun star (24x30cm-9x12in) s.i. board. 8-Apr-3 Bonhams, Knightsbridge #164
£880 $1434 €1320 Pair of terriers (23x33cm-9x13in) s. board. 7-Feb-3 Dee Atkinson & Harrison, Driffield #701/R
£1000 $1540 €1500 Two terriers (24x34cm-9x13in) s. board. 23-Oct-2 Hamptons Fine Art, Godalming #171 est:500-700
£1200 $1956 €1800 Sporting scenes (29x45cm-11x18in) board 12 framed as one. 29-Jan-3 Sotheby's, Olympia #100/R est:1000-1500
£1227 $2000 €1841 Head of a Jack Russell (20x25cm-8x10in) mono. 11-Feb-3 Bonhams & Doyles, New York #159/R est:1200-1800
£1300 $2028 €1950 Hounds (10cm-4in circular) s. board tondo pair. 15-Oct-2 Gorringes, Lewes #2123/R est:800-1200
£1300 $2119 €1950 Portrait of a Jack Russell (18x23cm-7x9in) s. board. 28-Jan-3 Gorringes, Lewes #1626/R est:1200-1800
£1400 $2226 €2100 Huntsman and hounds. Clearing a brook. The death (46x61cm-18x24in) indis sig. set of three. 27-Feb-3 Bonhams, Chester #405/R est:2000-3000
£1450 $2262 €2175 Studies of terrier heads (17x21cm-7x8in) s. board pair. 17-Oct-2 Lawrence, Crewkerne #1586/R est:1500-2000
£1600 $2496 €2400 Two fox terriers (23x36cm-9x14in) s. board. 15-Oct-2 Gorringes, Lewes #2126/R est:1200-1800
£1687 $2750 €2531 Terriers (20x25cm-8x10in) init. board pair. 11-Feb-3 Bonhams & Doyles, New York #95 est:2000-3000
£1840 $3000 €2760 Head studies of two foxhounds (10cm-4in circular) s. board pair. 11-Feb-3 Bonhams & Doyles, New York #174/R est:3000-5000
£1900 $2964 €2850 Fox terrier (20x25cm-8x10in) s. board. 15-Oct-2 Gorringes, Lewes #2125/R est:1200-1800
£2000 $3120 €3000 Two hounds (28x38cm-11x15in) s. board. 26-Mar-3 Sotheby's, Olympia #152/R est:500-800
£2300 $3588 €3450 Crack, Gypsy and Jock - three fox terriers (23x36cm-9x14in) s. board. 15-Oct-2 Gorringes, Lewes #2127/R est:2000-3000
£2500 $3900 €3750 Three hounds (15x18cm-6x7in) board. 15-Oct-2 Gorringes, Lewes #2124/R est:1500-2000
£2800 $4340 €4200 Head study of a terrier (18x20cm-7x8in) s. board with a companion picture pair. 31-Oct-2 Greenslade Hunt, Taunton #633/R est:1000-1500
£2800 $4340 €4200 Trio head studies of three terriers (19x44cm-7x17in) s. board. 31-Oct-2 Greenslade Hunt, Taunton #634/R est:1500-2500
£2800 $4452 €4200 Heads of two hounds. Heads of two terriers (21x34cm-8x13in) s. board pair. 1-May-3 Locke & England, Leamington Spa #152/R est:400-600
£3000 $4740 €4500 General Peace, dark brown racehorse in a stable (63x76cm-25x30in) s.i.d.1901. 28-Nov-2 Christie's, Kensington #164/R est:1500-2000
£3600 $5688 €5400 Flying Fox with jockey up (51x61cm-20x24in) s.i. 28-Nov-2 Christie's, Kensington #172/R est:4000-6000
£3800 $6308 €5510 Five hounds (32x56cm-13x22in) s. 12-Jun-3 Christie's, Kensington #254/R est:2000-3000

WHEELER, John Arnold (attrib) (1821-1903) British
£280 $448 €420 Head study of a terrier (18x14cm-7x6in) i. i. on stretcher oil pencil. 15-May-3 Lawrence, Crewkerne #944/R
£521 $850 €782 Head of a Norwich terrier (24x29cm-9x11in) board. 11-Feb-3 Bonhams & Doyles, New York #92
£1000 $1580 €1500 Head of a terrier (22x22cm-9x9in) board. 28-Nov-2 Christie's, Kensington #281/R est:500-800

WHEELER, W H (19/20th C) ?
£675 $1100 €1013 Labrador in a landscape (46x66cm-18x26in) s.d.1880. 11-Feb-3 Bonhams & Doyles, New York #129 est:2000-3000

WHEELWRIGHT, Roland (1870-1955) British
£680 $1108 €1020 Haywain, beside a thatched cottage (50x60cm-20x24in) s. 28-Jan-3 Henry Adams, Chichester #453/R
£1400 $2240 €2100 Turnip harvest - two horse pulling a cart (48x60cm-19x24in) s. board exhib. 11-Mar-3 David Duggleby, Scarborough #267/R est:1200-1800
£11392 $18000 €18000 Favourite coming home (127x102cm-50x40in) s. 27-Nov-2 James Adam, Dublin #124/R est:2000-3000

WHEELWRIGHT, William H (fl.1857-1897) British
£750 $1200 €1088 Refusing the jump (68x51cm-27x20in) s.d.85 en grisaille board. 16-May-3 Skinner, Boston #121/R
£1000 $1600 €1450 Taking the lead (68x50cm-27x20in) s.d.85 en grisaille board. 16-May-3 Skinner, Boston #123/R

WHELAN, Blanche (1889-1974) American
£645 $1000 €968 Loading the nets (51x61cm-20x24in) s. i.verso prov. 29-Oct-2 John Moran, Pasadena #744

WHELAN, Leo (1892-1956) British
£500 $780 €750 Portrait of a woman in a pink dress (51x40cm-20x16in) s. 10-Apr-3 Tennants, Leyburn #943

WHELPTON, G L (fl.1913-1921) British
£859 $1400 €1289 Pekinese. Sealyham in an interior (30x46cm-12x18in) s.d.1916 two prov. 11-Feb-3 Bonhams & Doyles, New York #248/R est:1500-2000

WHIBLEY, Grant (20th C) New Zealander
£502 $782 €753 Serene (30x71cm-12x28in) s.d.2002. 7-Nov-2 International Art Centre, Auckland #3/R est:1800-2400 (NZ.D 1600)

WHICHELO, C John M (1784-1865) British

Works on paper
£3500 $5460 €5250 Derby stakes, Tattenham Hill (23x35cm-9x14in) W/C. 6-Nov-2 Sotheby's, Olympia #30/R est:4000-6000

WHICHELO, Henry Mayle (fl.1818-1845) British
£897 $1399 €1346 Shipping off the Dutch coast (29x39cm-11x15in) s.d.1827 panel. 11-Nov-2 Stephan Welz, Johannesburg #410 est:4000-6000 (SA.R 14000)

WHINNEN, George (1891-1950) Australian
£464 $734 €696 Rose study (60x55cm-24x22in) s. i.verso. 26-Nov-2 Sotheby's, Melbourne #124 est:1200-1800 (A.D 1300)

WHISSON, Kenneth Ronald (1927-) Australian
£3155 $4795 €4733 Portrait of a man (55x45cm-22x18in) s. composition board. 28-Aug-2 Deutscher-Menzies, Melbourne #229/R est:8000-12000 (A.D 8800)
£7168 $10896 €10752 Homemakers (43x49cm-17x19in) s. board painted c.1950-60. 28-Aug-2 Deutscher-Menzies, Melbourne #11/R est:12000-16000 (A.D 20000)

£12308 $19569 €18462 Delicate balance (88x118cm-35x46in) s.i.d.6/10/84 prov. 4-Mar-3 Deutscher-Menzies, Melbourne #23/R est:30000-40000 (A.D 32000)
£14337 $21792 €21506 Flag of my disposition X (99x118cm-39x46in) s.i.d.9/9/79 verso prov.exhib. 28-Aug-2 Deutscher-Menzies, Melbourne #48/R est:25000-35000 (A.D 40000)

Works on paper
£325 $504 €488 Melbourne, Edgevale Road, Kew (49x55cm-19x22in) ink. 3-Dec-2 Shapiro, Sydney #122 (A.D 900)
£429 $673 €644 Untitled (29x25cm-11x10in) d.59 prov. 25-Nov-2 Christie's, Melbourne #223 (A.D 1200)
£516 $856 €879 Motorcycle (49x69cm-19x27in) i.verso pencil prov.exhib. 10-Jun-3 Shapiro, Sydney #52 est:1200-1800 (A.D 1300)

WHISTLER, James Abbott McNeill (1834-1903) American

Prints
£1887 $3000 €2831 Drouet (23x15cm-9x6in) etching drypoint. 1-May-3 Swann Galleries, New York #104/R est:1500-2500
£1887 $3000 €2831 Vitre, the canal (24x15cm-9x6in) s.butterfly lithograph. 2-May-3 Sotheby's, New York #54/R est:3000-4000
£1887 $3000 €2831 Savoy pigeons (20x14cm-8x6in) s.butterfly lithograph. 2-May-3 Sotheby's, New York #56 est:3000-4000
£1887 $3000 €2831 Eagle Wharf (13x21cm-5x8in) etching. 1-May-3 Swann Galleries, New York #378/R est:3000-5000
£2051 $3200 €3077 Limehouse (13x20cm-5x8in) etching. 7-Nov-2 Swann Galleries, New York #515/R est:2500-3500
£2215 $3500 €3323 Rotherhithe (27x20cm-11x8in) etching drypoint executed c.1861. 12-Nov-2 Doyle, New York #401/R est:3000-4000
£2243 $3500 €3365 Reading a book (18x13cm-7x5in) s. with butterfly drypoint etching exec.c.1873 prov. 14-Oct-2 Butterfields, San Francisco #1045/R est:2000-2500
£2358 $3750 €3537 Mast (34x16cm-13x6in) s.butterfly i. etching drypoint prov. 2-May-3 Sotheby's, New York #75/R est:3000-5000
£2711 $4500 €3931 Early morning (15x25cm-6x10in) lithograph lithotint. 13-Jun-3 Du Mouchelle, Detroit #2121/R est:800-1300
£2767 $4400 €4151 Pool (14x21cm-6x8in) etching drypoint. 1-May-3 Swann Galleries, New York #379/R est:4000-6000
£2949 $4600 €4424 Black Lion wharf (15x22cm-6x9in) lithograph. 7-Nov-2 Swann Galleries, New York #513a/R est:3000-5000
£3145 $5000 €4718 Finette (29x20cm-11x8in) etching drypoint. 1-May-3 Swann Galleries, New York #111/R est:6000-9000
£3205 $5000 €4808 Gants de suede (22x10cm-9x4in) s.butterfly lithograph. 7-Nov-2 Swann Galleries, New York #526/R est:4000-6000
£3313 $5500 €4804 Duet (23x15cm-9x6in) blk white lithograph. 13-Jun-3 Du Mouchelle, Detroit #2120/R est:300-500
£3459 $5500 €5189 The novel, girl reading (19x8cm-7x3in) s.butterfly lithograph exec.c.1889. 2-May-3 Sotheby's, New York #53/R est:3000-4000
£3590 $5600 €5385 Piazzetta (25x18cm-10x7in) s.butterfly i. sepia etching. 7-Nov-2 Swann Galleries, New York #524/R est:6000-9000
£3846 $6000 €5769 Rotherhithe (28x20cm-11x8in) etching drypoint. 7-Nov-2 Swann Galleries, New York #518/R est:4000-6000
£4487 $7000 €6731 Turkeys (21x13cm-8x5in) s. with butterfly i. brown ink etching prov. 14-Oct-2 Butterfields, San Francisco #1047/R est:5000-7000
£4518 $7500 €6551 Lime House (15x25cm-6x10in) lithograph lithotint. 13-Jun-3 Du Mouchelle, Detroit #2122/R est:1500-2000
£4717 $7500 €7076 Smith's yard (19x16cm-7x6in) s.butterfly i.verso lithograph prov. 29-Apr-3 Christie's, Rockefeller NY #446/R est:2000-3000
£4839 $7500 €7259 Old Putney Bridge (20x29cm-8x11in) s. drypoint. 25-Sep-2 Christie's, Rockefeller NY #35/R est:6000-8000
£5031 $8000 €7547 Winged hat (18x18cm-7x7in) lithograph prov. 29-Apr-3 Christie's, Rockefeller NY #445/R est:2500-3500
£5449 $8500 €8174 Thames (27x20cm-11x8in) lithograph edition of 30. 7-Nov-2 Swann Galleries, New York #527/R est:7000-10000
£6289 $10000 €9434 Beggars (30x21cm-12x8in) s.butterfly i. brown etching. 2-May-3 Sotheby's, New York #52/R est:2500-3500
£7692 $12000 €11538 Palaces (26x36cm-10x14in) s.butterfly.i. i.verso etching prov. 5-Nov-2 Christie's, Rockefeller NY #98/R est:10000-15000
£8176 $13000 €12264 Palaces (25x36cm-10x14in) s.i. etching drypoint. 3-Mar-3 Swann Galleries, New York #12/R est:12000-18000
£8176 $13000 €12264 The lime-burner (25x17cm-10x7in) etching prov.exhib. 2-May-3 Sotheby's, New York #73/R est:4000-6000
£20440 $32500 €30660 Doorway (29x20cm-11x8in) s.butterfly i. etching drypoint prov. 2-May-3 Sotheby's, New York #74/R est:14000-18000

Works on paper
£11111 $18000 €16667 Fans and figures (28x17cm-11x7in) s. chk pastel executed c.1871-75 prov.lit. 21-May-3 Sotheby's, New York #150/R est:18000-24000
£24691 $40000 €37037 Standing nude (28x17cm-11x7in) chk prov. 21-May-3 Sotheby's, New York #149/R est:15000-25000
£25926 $42000 €38889 Beach scene (22x13cm-9x5in) s. s.i.verso W/C paper on board prov.exhib.lit. 22-May-3 Christie's, Rockefeller NY #38/R est:40000-60000

WHISTLER, James Abbott McNeill (attrib) (1834-1903) American

Works on paper
£1050 $1754 €1523 Landscape nocturne (14x10cm-6x4in) pastel. 9-Jul-3 Edgar Horn, Eastbourne #278

WHISTLER, Rex (1905-1944) British

Works on paper
£2400 $3984 €3480 Netherhampton House in the county of Wiltshire (15x25cm-6x10in) i.d.1927 pen ink W/C. 16-Jun-3 Duke & Son, Dorchester #175/R est:500-1000

WHITAKER, G W (1841-1916) American
£922 $1300 €1383 Figure in meadow (23x30cm-9x12in) s. board. 12-Feb-2 Lincoln, Orange #489

WHITAKER, George William (1841-1916) American
£503 $800 €755 Open landscape (25x41cm-10x16in) s.d.1913. 7-Mar-3 Skinner, Boston #424/R
£955 $1500 €1433 Country landscape with stone fence and barn (53x61cm-21x24in) s.d.1901. 14-Dec-2 Weschler, Washington #652/R est:2000-3000

WHITAKER, Scott (1969-) Australian
£377 $589 €654 Untitled (75x104cm-30x41in) s.d.96. 31-Mar-3 Goodman, Sydney #57/R (A.D 1000)
£830 $1295 €1437 Pump house (120x180cm-47x71in) s. s.d.2002 verso linen prov. 31-Mar-3 Goodman, Sydney #124/R (A.D 2200)

WHITAKER, W G (19th C) British
£400 $632 €600 In full gallop (51x41cm-20x16in) s. 28-Nov-2 Christie's, Kensington #100/R

WHITAKER, William (1943-) American

Works on paper
£1234 $1900 €1851 Womanly back (56x30cm-22x12in) pastel. 25-Oct-2 Morris & Whiteside, Hilton Head Island #11 est:2000-2500

WHITBY, T B (19/20th C) British
£775 $1201 €1163 Pair of chestnut hunters (51x61cm-20x24in) s. pair. 17-Jul-2 Goldings, Lincolnshire #358

WHITCOMB, Jon (1906-1988) American

Works on paper
£1242 $2000 €1863 Groom kissing bride (33x36cm-13x14in) s. gouache oil board. 10-May-3 Illustration House, New York #135/R est:2500-4000

WHITCOMBE, Thomas (1760-c.1824) British
£440 $700 €660 Ship in a storm (56x76cm-22x30in) s.indis.d. 30-Apr-3 Sotheby's, New York #392/R
£5556 $9000 €8334 Shipping off the channel off the South coast (52x74cm-20x29in) s. 21-Jan-3 Christie's, Rockefeller NY #372/R
£6019 $9690 €9029 Providence off the Cape (80x120cm-31x47in) s.i.d.1809 prov. 12-May-3 Stephan Welz, Johannesburg #468/R est:70000-100000 (SA.R 70000)
£26000 $42120 €39000 Relief of Gibraltar by Admiral Lord Howe 11th-18th October 1782 (22x109cm-9x43in) s.d.1792 prov.exhib. 22-Jan-3 Bonhams, New Bond Street #311/R est:15000-25000

WHITCOMBE, Thomas (attrib) (1760-c.1824) British
£3548 $5500 €5322 British sailing ship (81x127cm-32x50in) bears sig.d.1828. 25-Sep-2 Doyle, New York #84/R est:3000-5000

WHITE, Arthur (1865-1953) British
£350 $546 €525 Old St Ives (43x53cm-17x21in) mono. board. 9-Oct-2 Andrew Hartley, Ilkley #778
£400 $652 €600 Steamer passing The Island, St Ives (46x58cm-18x23in) board. 13-Feb-3 David Lay, Penzance #263

Works on paper
£250 $398 €375 Vessels and figures in the harbour, St. Ives (18x25cm-7x10in) s. W/C. 27-Feb-3 Richardson & Smith, Whitby #440
£350 $571 €525 St Ives (18x10cm-7x4in) s. W/C. 13-Feb-3 David Lay, Penzance #74
£580 $969 €841 St. Ives harbour at high tide (25x36cm-10x14in) s. W/C. 19-Jun-3 Lane, Penzance #20/R

WHITE, Berkley (?) American?
£409 $650 €614 Untitled, men playing cards (58x71cm-23x28in) 28-Feb-3 Douglas, South Deerfield #18

WHITE, Charles Pilkington (19th C) British

£1100 $1573 €1650 Dover Harbour with passengers alighting from an omnibus (51x76cm-20x30in) 28-Feb-2 Heathcote Ball, Leicester #474/R

Works on paper

£500 $715 €750 Moonlit sheep in the grounds of Glastonbury Abbey (69x89cm-27x35in) W/C gouache paper on canvas. 28-Feb-2 Heathcote Ball, Leicester #407

WHITE, Clarence H (1871-1925) American

Photographs

£2760 $4250 €4140 Footbridge (23x19cm-9x7in) platinum print prov.exhib. 22-Oct-2 Sotheby's, New York #143/R est:7000-10000
£2922 $4500 €4383 Standing nude (24x18cm-9x7in) platinum print prov.lit. 22-Oct-2 Sotheby's, New York #145/R est:7000-10000
£7792 $12000 €11688 Evening interior (19x16cm-7x6in) s. platinum print prov.exhib.lit. 22-Oct-2 Sotheby's, New York #39/R est:10000-15000
£9740 $15000 €14610 Nude study, Miss Mabel Cramer (23x18cm-9x7in) warm toned platinum print prov. 22-Oct-2 Sotheby's, New York #42/R est:10000-15000
£33766 $52000 €50649 Mirror (25x20cm-10x8in) platinum print prov.lit. 22-Oct-2 Sotheby's, New York #139/R est:10000-15000

WHITE, Clarence Scott (1872-?) American

Works on paper

£629 $1000 €944 Coastal waters (18x23cm-7x9in) s. W/C gouache. 7-Mar-3 Skinner, Boston #479/R

WHITE, Edith (1855-1946) American

£641 $1000 €962 Pink flowers in a green vase (46x60cm-18x24in) s. 13-Apr-3 Butterfields, Los Angeles #7031
£641 $1000 €962 Red flowers in vase (48x38cm-19x15in) s. 13-Apr-3 Butterfields, Los Angeles #7032

WHITE, Ethelbert (1891-1972) British

£250 $390 €375 Woodland scene (33x41cm-13x16in) s. s.verso canvasboard. 27-Mar-3 Christie's, Kensington #432/R
£800 $1256 €1200 Haycart (60x76cm-24x30in) s. 15-Apr-3 Bonhams, Knightsbridge #140/R
£900 $1503 €1305 Cattle grazing in an extensive summer landscape (81x101cm-32x40in) s. 17-Jun-3 Bonhams, Knightsbridge #75/R
£1300 $2132 €1950 Barges at Ipswich (24x36cm-9x14in) s. board prov.exhib. 3-Jun-3 Sotheby's, Olympia #80/R est:1000-1500
£1900 $2964 €2850 Wooded landscape with a farmhouse (48x58cm-19x23in) s. 9-Oct-2 Woolley & Wallis, Salisbury #339/R est:600-1000
£4500 $7155 €6750 Farmstead (49x59cm-19x23in) s. 26-Feb-3 Sotheby's, Olympia #270/R est:3000-5000
£5000 $8200 €7500 French landscape (61x76cm-24x30in) s. 3-Jun-3 Sotheby's, Olympia #64/R est:5000-7000
£6173 $10000 €8951 Pattern of winter (61x51cm-24x20in) s.d.19 prov.exhib. 21-May-3 Doyle, New York #8/R est:4000-6000

Works on paper

£320 $512 €480 Landscape, the shore of Aran (25x36cm-10x14in) W/C. 8-Jan-3 Brightwells, Leominster #1082
£400 $624 €600 Landscape with farmhouse (30x27cm-12x11in) s. pen wash. 9-Oct-2 Woolley & Wallis, Salisbury #179/R
£650 $1034 €975 Shore of Arran (28x37cm-11x15in) s. pencil W/C exhib. 6-Mar-3 Christie's, Kensington #133/R est:600-800

WHITE, Fritz (1930-) American

Sculpture

£4167 $6500 €6251 In search of the snow goose (86cm-34in) bronze. 9-Nov-2 Altermann Galleries, Santa Fe #91

WHITE, H O (19th C) American

£6731 $10500 €10097 Marshy landscape (74x163cm-29x64in) s. 1-Aug-2 Eldred, East Dennis #420/R est:800-1200

WHITE, John (1851-1933) British

Works on paper

£360 $583 €540 Near Newton Poppelford (17x51cm-7x20in) s.d.1903 W/C. 20-May-3 Sotheby's, Olympia #280/R
£420 $668 €630 Hawkesworthy Bridge, Dartmoor (18x52cm-7x20in) s. W/C bodycol. 30-Apr-3 Hampton & Littlewood, Exeter #461/R
£450 $747 €653 Fisherman (28x45cm-11x18in) s. W/C bodycol. 12-Jun-3 Bonhams, Cornwall #563
£650 $1040 €975 Sidmouth Bay from Branscombe (30x46cm-12x18in) s. W/C. 11-Mar-3 Gorringes, Lewes #2474
£680 $1054 €1020 Beer Head, Devon (36x54cm-14x21in) s. W/C paper on card. 3-Dec-2 Sotheby's, Olympia #183/R
£850 $1360 €1275 Dream barge, Topsham, Exeter (24x34cm-9x13in) s.i.d.1871 W/C. 11-Mar-3 Bonhams, New Bond Street #138/R
£850 $1420 €1233 Smugglers caves Beer Cliffs. Children playing in rocks pools, Devon (31x20cm-12x8in) s. one i. pencil W/C htd white pair. 26-Jun-3 Mellors & Kirk, Nottingham #815
£860 $1359 €1290 Cottagers return, Seatown, Dorset (24x34cm-9x13in) s. W/C. 15-Nov-2 Rowley Fine Art, Newmarket #369/R
£1000 $1600 €1500 Dartmoor stream (34x51cm-13x20in) s.d.1901 W/C bodycol. 11-Mar-3 Bonhams, New Bond Street #135/R est:1000-1500
£1050 $1722 €1575 Cornish cliff top scene with mother and child beside a cottage (36x25cm-14x10in) W/C gouache. 4-Feb-3 Lawrences, Bletchingley #1569 est:600-800
£1100 $1760 €1650 At the cottage door (44x28cm-17x11in) s. W/C bodycol. 11-Mar-3 Bonhams, New Bond Street #133/R est:1200-1800
£1100 $1782 €1650 Brushwood collector (36x25cm-14x10in) s. W/C. 20-May-3 Sotheby's, Olympia #276/R est:800-1200
£1300 $2054 €1950 Children and ducklings in Branscombe village (47x29cm-19x11in) s. W/C bodycol. 7-Apr-3 Bonhams, Bath #24/R est:1000-1500
£1350 $2079 €2025 Ducklings, Winsford, Exmoor (36x26cm-14x10in) s.i.verso W/C bodycol. 23-Oct-2 Hampton & Littlewood, Exeter #402/R est:1500-2000
£1511 $2508 €2191 Home (32x42cm-13x17in) s.i.verso W/C. 10-Jun-3 Ritchie, Toronto #11/R est:2000-3000 (C.D 3400)
£1650 $2558 €2475 Devonshire landscapes (18x53cm-7x21in) s. W/C pair. 1-Oct-2 Capes Dunn, Manchester #858/R
£1700 $2771 €2465 Milking time, Seaton (29x46cm-11x18in) s. W/C. 16-Jul-3 Sotheby's, Olympia #128/R est:500-700
£2400 $3912 €3600 Beached boats. Clifftop view (18x27cm-7x11in) s. gouache pair. 29-Jan-3 Sotheby's, Olympia #187/R est:800-1200

WHITE, Jonathan (1938-) New Zealander

£354 $552 €531 Otoko Valley, Poverty Bay (70x90cm-28x35in) s.i.d. s.i.d.1971 verso board. 6-Aug-2 Peter Webb, Auckland #234 est:1000-2000 (NZ.D 1200)
£407 $578 €611 Buller River (60x90cm-24x35in) s. board prov. 21-Nov-1 Watson's, Christchurch #8/R (NZ.D 1400)
£448 $654 €672 Mt. Talbot, Fiordland (69x89cm-27x35in) s. 12-Sep-1 Watson's, Christchurch #2 est:2250-7000 (NZ.D 1500)
£488 $746 €732 Knights Point, South Westland (49x67cm-19x26in) s. 21-Aug-2 Dunbar Sloane, Auckland #109 est:500-1000 (NZ.D 1600)
£542 $866 €786 Mt Talbot, Fiordland (69x90cm-27x35in) s.d.1971 board. 13-May-3 Watson's, Christchurch #72/R (NZ.D 1500)
£912 $1422 €1368 Alice Falls, George Sound, Fiordland (74x60cm-29x24in) s.d.1977 i.on stretcher. 17-Sep-2 Peter Webb, Auckland #160/R est:3000-5000 (NZ.D 3000)
£945 $1341 €1418 Waimana River Valley (70x90cm-28x35in) s. board prov. 21-Nov-1 Watson's, Christchurch #45/R est:1500-2500 (NZ.D 3250)
£1714 $2434 €2571 Donne River, Milford Sound (70x90cm-28x35in) s. board prov. 21-Nov-1 Watson's, Christchurch #30/R est:1200-2400 (NZ.D 5900)

WHITE, Judith (20th C) Australian

Works on paper

£894 $1413 €1296 Ramada renaissance (72x52cm-28x20in) s.d.89 mixed media. 22-Jul-3 Lawson Menzies, Sydney #220/R est:1500-2400 (A.D 2200)

WHITE, Minnie F (1891-1984) New Zealander

£1254 $1956 €1881 Abstract no.2 (40x49cm-16x19in) s. board. 7-Nov-2 International Art Centre, Auckland #108/R est:3000-5000 (NZ.D 4000)

Works on paper

£282 $440 €423 Against the light (26x35cm-10x14in) s. W/C. 7-Nov-2 International Art Centre, Auckland #109/R (NZ.D 900)
£408 $636 €612 Santa Margharita (27x38cm-11x15in) s. W/C ink. 7-Nov-2 International Art Centre, Auckland #122/R est:1500-2000 (NZ.D 1300)

WHITE, Minor (1908-1976) American

Photographs

£1829 $3000 €2744 Scissor and thread, Navajo Indian Reservation (19x23cm-7x9in) i.d. st.verso silver print exec.c.1960. 10-Feb-3 Swann Galleries, New York #86/R est:3500-4500
£1875 $3000 €2813 Bullet holes, Capital Reef, Utah (15x23cm-6x9in) with sig.d.1961 silver print. 15-May-3 Swann Galleries, New York #524/R est:3500-4500
£2057 $3250 €3086 Beginnings, Rochester, NY (31x24cm-12x9in) s.d.1962 photograph. 23-Apr-3 Sotheby's, New York #213/R est:4000-6000
£2911 $4600 €4367 Floating kelp (20x25cm-8x10in) s.i.d.1950 verso gelatin silver print prov. 25-Apr-3 Phillips, New York #110/R est:3000-5000
£3571 $5500 €5357 Sun and rock (8x12cm-3x5in) s.i.d.1948 verso photograph prov.lit. 22-Oct-2 Sotheby's, New York #177/R est:3000-5000

£4114 $6500 €6171 Car and bank, San Francisco (22x26cm-9x10in) s.i.d.1949 verso gelatin silver print prov.exhib. 25-Apr-3 Phillips, New York #26/R
£4430 $7000 €6645 Portland, Oregon (8x7cm-3x3in) s.i.d.1940 gelatin silver print. 22-Apr-3 Christie's, Rockefeller NY #184/R est:5000-7000
£7143 $11000 €10715 Grand Teton National Park, Wyoming (27x32cm-11x13in) s.d.1959 photograph prov.exhib.lit. 22-Oct-2 Sotheby's, New York #176/R est:3000-5000

WHITE, Nona (1859-1937) American
£641 $1000 €962 Autumn landscape (23x30cm-9x12in) board. 21-Sep-2 Harvey Clar, Oakland #1641

WHITE, Orrin A (1883-1969) American
£659 $1100 €956 Portrait of girl in yellow dress (51x41cm-20x16in) s. 17-Jun-3 John Moran, Pasadena #158 est:1000-1500
£994 $1600 €1491 Landscape (23x30cm-9x12in) s. canvas on board prov. 18-Feb-3 John Moran, Pasadena #9 est:1000-2000
£2174 $3500 €3261 Figures in a Mexico church scene (46x61cm-18x24in) s. board prov. 18-Feb-3 John Moran, Pasadena #155 est:2500-4000
£2581 $4000 €3872 Cabin in Sierra Landscape (41x51cm-16x20in) s. board prov. 29-Oct-2 John Moran, Pasadena #628 est:4000-6000
£2711 $4500 €3931 Stream in winter. Mountain lake in winter (25x30cm-10x12in) s. canvasboard pair prov. 11-Jun-3 Butterfields, San Francisco #4319/R est:4000-6000
£2866 $4500 €4299 High Sierra lake (36x50cm-14x20in) s. canvas on board prov. 19-Nov-2 Butterfields, San Francisco #8298/R est:2500-3500
£3416 $5500 €5124 Barn in eucalyptus landscape (46x61cm-18x24in) s. canvasboard prov. 18-Feb-3 John Moran, Pasadena #127 est:4500-6000
£5988 $10000 €8683 Big Pine Canyon - High Sierras (61x81cm-24x32in) s. prov. 17-Jun-3 John Moran, Pasadena #74 est:10000-15000
£5988 $10000 €8683 High Sierra landscape (61x76cm-24x30in) s. prov. 17-Jun-3 John Moran, Pasadena #114 est:9000-12000
£6129 $9500 €9194 On the Warner's ranch (64x76cm-25x30in) s. i.stretcher. 29-Oct-2 John Moran, Pasadena #660 est:6000-9000
£7006 $11000 €10509 Spring Matilija Canyon (91x71cm-36x28in) s. masonite prov. 19-Nov-2 Butterfields, San Francisco #8273/R est:6000-8000
£7097 $11000 €10646 Mountain Silver, Warner ranch (41x51cm-16x20in) s. i.verso board prov. 29-Oct-2 John Moran, Pasadena #663 est:4000-6000

WHITE, Ralph (1921-) American
Works on paper
£288 $450 €432 Incident on 5th Street (51x69cm-20x27in) W/C. 19-Oct-2 David Dike, Dallas #329/R

WHITE, Verner (19th C) ?
£323 $500 €485 Apple blossoms (41x61cm-16x24in) s. painted c.1910. 8-Dec-2 Toomey, Oak Park #672/R

WHITE, Victor (1891-1954) American
£258 $400 €387 Cabins on the lake (64x76cm-25x30in) s.d.1940. 16-Jul-2 Arthur James, Florida #408

WHITE, William Davidson (1896-?) American
£4516 $7000 €6774 Driving a great subway (102x86cm-40x34in) s. 3-Dec-2 Christie's, Rockefeller NY #574/R est:600-800

WHITECLIFFE, Greg (20th C) New Zealander
£265 $414 €398 Auckland markets (61x48cm-24x19in) s.d.1986. 6-Aug-2 Peter Webb, Auckland #45/R (NZ.D 900)

WHITEFORD, Kate (1952-) British
£900 $1404 €1350 Echo sounding (183x620cm-72x244in) gold pigment gesso ground. 12-Sep-2 Sotheby's, Olympia #221/R
£900 $1404 €1350 Echo sounding (183x620cm-72x244in) gold pigment gesso ground. 12-Sep-2 Sotheby's, Olympia #222/R

WHITEHAND, Michael J (1941-) British
£1000 $1620 €1500 Close contest, J-class yachts close-hauled in the Solent (51x76cm-20x30in) s. panel. 21-May-3 Christie's, Kensington #505/R est:1500-2000
£1000 $1620 €1500 Gaff-rigged yachts racing in the Solent with the Needles astern (51x76cm-20x30in) s. panel. 21-May-3 Christie's, Kensington #506/R est:1500-2000
£1000 $1670 €1450 H.M.S Prince of Wales (76x101cm-30x40in) s. i.verso. 18-Jun-3 Sotheby's, Olympia #137/R est:1000-1500
£1800 $2826 €2700 First shots off Flamboro Head (66x91cm-26x36in) s.i.d.September 85. 19-Nov-2 Bonhams, Leeds #196 est:2000-3000
£1800 $2826 €2700 Britannia in the Solent (73x104cm-29x41in) s. 16-Dec-2 Sotheby's, Olympia #180/R est:1000-1500
£3000 $4860 €4500 Britannia and other J-class yachts at the turning mark (76x102cm-30x40in) s. board. 21-May-3 Christie's, Kensington #507/R est:4000-6000
£3200 $4960 €4800 Valkyre II, Britannia and Vigilant racing past the Needles with the Victoria and Albert Freshwater (97x149cm-38x59in) s. board. 31-Oct-2 Christie's, Kensington #408/R est:2000-4000
£3200 $4960 €4800 Britannia, Astra, westward and Shamrock racing to the Royal Yacht Squadron lines at Cowes (97x149cm-38x59in) s. board. 31-Oct-2 Christie's, Kensington #409/R est:2000-3000
£4000 $6080 €6000 Racing off Cowes (95x137cm-37x54in) s. panel. 15-Aug-2 Bonhams, New Bond Street #381/R est:4000-6000

WHITEHEAD, Charles (19th C) British?
Works on paper
£2371 $3745 €3557 Landscape by Tacubaya (18x27cm-7x11in) s.d.1890 W/C. 28-Nov-2 Louis Morton, Mexico #268/R est:10000 (M.P 38000)

WHITEHEAD, Frederick (1853-1938) British
£350 $557 €525 Dorchester (18x25cm-7x10in) s. i.stretcher. 18-Mar-3 Capes Dunn, Manchester #564
£600 $936 €900 French peasant (21x33cm-8x13in) s.i.d.1906 board. 8-Apr-3 Bonhams, Knightsbridge #161/R
£1000 $1590 €1500 Poole Harbour from the Studland Hills (61x91cm-24x36in) s. 30-Apr-3 Halls, Shrewsbury #290/R
£1200 $1908 €1800 Geat Horn Point, looking towards Poole (41x61cm-16x24in) s. 6-Mar-3 Christie's, Kensington #442/R est:600-800
£1200 $1992 €1740 Landscape (41x61cm-16x24in) s.d.1900. 10-Jun-3 David Lay, Penzance #420/R est:500-700
£3200 $5088 €4800 Cattle on a riverbank with figures and cottages beyond (61x94cm-24x37in) s.d.1912. 30-Apr-3 Halls, Shrewsbury #291/R est:2000-3000
Works on paper
£700 $1106 €1050 Dorset landscape (21x29cm-8x11in) s. W/C. 28-Nov-2 Locke & England, Leamington Spa #160/R

WHITEHOUSE, Philip V (fl.1907-1921) British
£430 $671 €645 Artist at his easel (30x40cm-12x16in) init.d. board. 25-Mar-3 Bonhams, Leeds #643

WHITELEY, Brett (1939-1992) Australian
£3053 $4824 €4580 Matador (183x103cm-72x41in) s. i.verso board. 7-Apr-3 Australian Art Auctions, Sydney #144 (A.D 8000)
£18327 $30056 €27491 Sunflower and Van Gogh (62x55cm-24x22in) one s. board one s.d.1970 verso card on board diptych prov.exhib. 4-Jun-3 Deutscher-Menzies, Melbourne #78/R est:45000-65000 (A.D 46000)
£25090 $38136 €37635 Oil sketch in Queensland (76x60cm-30x24in) s.i.d.1980 canvasboard prov. 28-Aug-2 Deutscher-Menzies, Melbourne #78/R est:55000-75000 (A.D 70000)
£30651 $45671 €45977 Orange palm and Lavender Bay (30x30cm-12x12in) s. i.d.91 verso prov. 27-Aug-2 Christie's, Melbourne #9/R est:50000-70000 (A.D 80000)
£32000 $51520 €48000 Listening to Nature (146x102cm-57x40in) s.d.64 s.i.d.verso oil resin on board. 6-May-3 Christie's, Melbourne #68/R est:80000-120000 (A.D 80000)
£72000 $115920 €108000 Untitled painting (122x128cm-48x50in) s.indis d. oil chl linen on board prov.exhib. 6-May-3 Christie's, Melbourne #16/R est:140000-180000 (A.D 180000)
£143369 $217921 €215054 Lavender Bay in the rain (121x95cm-48x37in) oil mixed media perspex board prov.exhib.lit. 28-Aug-2 Deutscher-Menzies, Melbourne #37/R est:400000-500000 (A.D 400000)
£229885 $360920 €344828 View from the sitting room window (122x198cm-48x78in) s.d.91 oil mixed media collage on board prov.exhib. 15-Apr-3 Lawson Menzies, Sydney #40/R (A.D 600000)
£244643 $386536 €366965 The finish (122x216cm-48x85in) s.i.d.1990-91 verso oil collage on board prov. 27-Nov-2 Deutscher-Menzies, Melbourne #27/R est:900000-1400000 (A.D 685000)
Prints
£1290 $1961 €1935 Hullo, cockatoo (24x20cm-9x8in) s.num.2/80 et. lit. 28-Aug-2 Deutscher-Menzies, Melbourne #454/R est:3000-4500 (A.D 3600)
£1673 $2744 €2510 Self portrait, one of a dozen glimpses (26x20cm-10x8in) s.num.5/100 etching aquatint prov.lit. 4-Jun-3 Deutscher-Menzies, Melbourne #216/R est:1500-2000 (A.D 4200)
£1786 $2804 €2679 Lovers (50x63cm-20x25in) s.i.num.A/P 3 screenprint. 25-Nov-2 Christie's, Melbourne #368/R est:4000-6000 (A.D 5000)
£1839 $2740 €2759 Sydney Harbour by night (30x30cm-12x12in) s.num.A/P3 linocut executed 1981. 27-Aug-2 Christie's, Melbourne #316 est:3000-4000 (A.D 4800)

£1916 $2854 €2874 Lovers (50x63cm-20x25in) s.num.59/75 screenprint. 27-Aug-2 Christie's, Melbourne #333 est:4000-6000 (A.D 5000)
£1971 $2996 €2957 Lovers (50x63cm-20x25in) s.num.10/70 col screenprint lit. 28-Aug-2 Deutscher-Menzies, Melbourne #175/R est:5000-7500 (A.D 5500)
£2299 $3425 €3449 Moreton Bay fig (60x50cm-24x20in) s.num.53/75 etching. 27-Aug-2 Christie's, Melbourne #358 est:6000-8000 (A.D 6000)
£2313 $3539 €3470 Port Vila (57x76cm-22x30in) s.num.44/50 hand col etching prov. 26-Aug-2 Sotheby's, Paddington #590/R est:6000-8000 (A.D 6500)
£2321 $3621 €3482 Torajaland, Celebes (68x57cm-27x22in) s.d.num. screenprint lit. 11-Nov-2 Deutscher-Menzies, Melbourne #205/R est:5000-7000 (A.D 6500)
£2326 $3698 €3489 Anna, woman on a bed (29x30cm-11x12in) s. etching exec.1977. 5-May-3 Sotheby's, Melbourne #354/R est:3000-5000 (A.D 6000)
£2330 $3541 €3495 Lovers (50x63cm-20x25in) s. num.55/75 etching. 27-Aug-2 Goodman, Sydney #154/R est:6000-9000 (A.D 6500)
£2381 $3952 €4028 Spring at Oberon (95x61cm-38x24in) s.d.1979 num.16/40 col screenprint. 10-Jun-3 Shapiro, Sydney #41 est:7000-9000 (A.D 6000)
£2442 $3883 €3663 Garden in Sanur, Bali (70x93cm-28x37in) s.i. num.23/100 screen print offset lithograph. 5-May-3 Sotheby's, Melbourne #196/R est:6000-8000 (A.D 6300)
£2874 $4511 €4311 Garden in Sanur, Bali 1980 (75x105cm-30x41in) s. num.86/100 screenprint offset lithograph. 15-Apr-3 Lawson Menzies, Sydney #280/R est:8000-12000 (A.D 7500)
£3214 $5046 €4821 Arrival (70x57cm-28x22in) s.i.num.34/150 offset lithograph. 25-Nov-2 Christie's, Melbourne #253/R est:4000-6000 (A.D 9000)
£3295 $5238 €4943 Palm tree 4 (81x60cm-32x24in) s.num.4 screen print. 5-May-3 Sotheby's, Melbourne #244/R est:8000-12000 (A.D 8500)
£3381 $5173 €5072 Sydney Harbour (121x80cm-48x31in) s.num.33/100 screen print prov. 26-Aug-2 Sotheby's, Paddington #638/R est:7000-9000 (A.D 9500)
£3876 $6163 €5814 Sydney harbour (90x66cm-35x26in) s.num.76/100 screen print exec.1980. 5-May-3 Sotheby's, Melbourne #353/R est:10000-15000 (A.D 10000)
£4365 $7246 €7437 Woman under the shower (40x46cm-16x18in) s.num.6/100 etching. 10-Jun-3 Shapiro, Sydney #56/R est:8000-12000 (A.D 11000)
£4615 $7338 €6923 Towards sculpture 3 (90x63cm-35x25in) s.i.num. lithograph edition 50 lit. 4-Mar-3 Deutscher-Menzies, Melbourne #106/R est:12000-16000 (A.D 12000)
£5714 $9029 €8571 Towards sculpture 8 1977 (73x45cm-29x18in) s.num.30/50 lithograph. 27-Nov-2 Deutscher-Menzies, Melbourne #4/R est:10000-15000 (A.D 16000)
£6050 $9256 €9075 Towards sculpture 7 (84x58cm-33x23in) s.num.7/5 lithograph exhib. 25-Aug-2 Sotheby's, Paddington #127/R est:8000-12000 (A.D 17000)
£6093 $9262 €9140 Cat (81x82cm-32x32in) s.i.num.85/100 offset lithograph exec.c.1980 lit. 28-Aug-2 Deutscher-Menzies, Melbourne #263/R est:12000-16000 (A.D 17000)
£6093 $9262 €9140 Towards sculpture (76x52cm-30x20in) s.i.num.48/50 lithograph lit. 28-Aug-2 Deutscher-Menzies, Melbourne #264/R est:10000-15000 (A.D 17000)
£6154 $9785 €9231 The cat (84x81cm-33x32in) s.i.num. hand col offset lithograph exec.c.1980 lit. 4-Mar-3 Deutscher-Menzies, Melbourne #7/R est:14000-18000 (A.D 16000)
£6429 $10157 €9644 Towards sculpute 5 1977 (77x46cm-30x18in) s.i.num.30/50 lithograph. 27-Nov-2 Deutscher-Menzies, Melbourne #3/R est:10000-15000 (A.D 18000)
£6810 $10351 €10215 Sunlight on the cat (81x82cm-32x32in) s.i.num. offset lithograph exec.c.1980 lit. 28-Aug-2 Deutscher-Menzies, Melbourne #4/R est:12000-16000 (A.D 19000)

Works on paper

£1154 $1834 €1731 Self portrait (31x25cm-12x10in) s.i.d.2/2/87 ink. 4-Mar-3 Deutscher-Menzies, Melbourne #219/R est:1800-2600 (A.D 3000)
£1349 $2240 €2298 Bird (24x16cm-9x6in) mono. ink prov. 10-Jun-3 Shapiro, Sydney #60 est:3000-5000 (A.D 3400)
£2224 $3403 €3336 Head study (61x49cm-24x19in) s.d.75 ink on silk prov. 26-Aug-2 Sotheby's, Paddington #591 est:4000-6000 (A.D 6250)
£2768 $4373 €4152 Roma (35x43cm-14x17in) s.i.d.60 ink. 26-Nov-2 Sotheby's, Melbourne #87/R est:8000-10000 (A.D 7750)
£3984 $6534 €5976 Torso II, study for Large White Marble (93x62cm-37x24in) i. pen ink prov. 4-Jun-3 Deutscher-Menzies, Melbourne #10/R est:15000-20000 (A.D 10000)
£4000 $6440 €6000 Moreton Bay fig (34x26cm-13x10in) s. ink executed c.1970. 6-May-3 Christie's, Melbourne #201/R est:6000-8000 (A.D 10000)
£4065 $6423 €5894 View from the window (72x90cm-28x35in) s.d.76 ink. 22-Jul-3 Lawson Menzies, Sydney #19/R est:12000-20000 (A.D 10000)
£4472 $7065 €6484 Torso II - study for large white marble (93x62cm-37x24in) i. pen ink prov. 22-Jul-3 Lawson Menzies, Sydney #103/R est:9000-12000 (A.D 11000)
£4598 $6851 €6897 Western mouse (97x63cm-38x25in) s.d.92 W/C ink exhib. 27-Aug-2 Christie's, Melbourne #175/R est:12000-15000 (A.D 12000)
£4643 $7335 €6965 Igor Stravinsky (73x60cm-29x24in) s. i.d.1972 verso ink wash. 27-Nov-2 Deutscher-Menzies, Melbourne #89/R est:12000-16000 (A.D 13000)
£5578 $9147 €8367 Torso I, study for Large White Marble (93x62cm-37x24in) d.2/3/7 s.i.d.1974 verso pen ink prov. 4-Jun-3 Deutscher-Menzies, Melbourne #9/R est:15000-20000 (A.D 14000)
£5714 $9029 €8571 On the highway (36x38cm-14x15in) s. ink. 26-Nov-2 Sotheby's, Melbourne #9/R est:18000-25000 (A.D 16000)
£6786 $10721 €10179 Feeling of flight (103x69cm-41x27in) s.i.d.79 ink. 27-Nov-2 Deutscher-Menzies, Melbourne #43/R est:25000-35000 (A.D 19000)
£7143 $11071 €10715 Abstract composition (25x19cm-10x7in) s.d.59 mixed media board. 29-Oct-2 Lawson Menzies, Sydney #1/R est:10000-20000 (A.D 20000)
£8765 $14375 €13148 Mirrored (60x78cm-24x31in) s.i.d.1977 ink prov. 4-Jun-3 Deutscher-Menzies, Melbourne #114/R est:24000-32000 (A.D 22000)
£8846 $14065 €13269 Italian-Australian girl beside the pool, north Sydney (69x49cm-27x19in) artist st. chl exhib.lit. 4-Mar-3 Deutscher-Menzies, Melbourne #5/R est:10000-15000 (A.D 23000)
£9231 $14677 €13847 Lavender Bay (74x55cm-29x22in) st.mono. pencil prov. 4-Mar-3 Deutscher-Menzies, Melbourne #49a/R est:20000-25000 (A.D 24000)
£9562 $15681 €14343 Clark Gardens, Lavender Bay (49x62cm-19x24in) s.d.78 pen ink wash prov. 4-Jun-3 Deutscher-Menzies, Melbourne #43/R est:20000-30000 (A.D 24000)
£9579 $14272 €14369 Bali (50x73cm-20x29in) mono. ink. 27-Aug-2 Christie's, Melbourne #35/R est:25000-35000 (A.D 25000)
£10728 $16843 €16092 Self portrait (75x55cm-30x22in) s.d.1970 verso ink prov. 15-Apr-3 Lawson Menzies, Sydney #28/R est:30000-36000 (A.D 28000)
£11538 $18346 €17307 Out of Hill End (55x75cm-22x30in) s.i.d.1986-87 pen ink prov.exhib.lit. 4-Mar-3 Deutscher-Menzies, Melbourne #77/R est:32000-40000 (A.D 30000)
£12791 $20337 €19187 Large flame tree, Port Vila, Vanuatu (61x51cm-24x20in) s.i.d.83 mixed media prov. 5-May-3 Sotheby's, Melbourne #128/R est:20000-30000 (A.D 33000)
£13262 $20158 €19893 Glass house mountains (75x103cm-30x41in) s.i. W/C prov.lit. 27-Aug-2 Goodman, Sydney #139/R est:28000-38000 (A.D 37000)
£13546 $22215 €20319 Seated nude (75x55cm-30x22in) artist st.d.6/2/76 ink prov. 4-Jun-3 Deutscher-Menzies, Melbourne #16/R est:25000-35000 (A.D 34000)
£15326 $22835 €22989 Untitled gouache (56x56cm-22x22in) s.d.61 s.i.d.verso gouache chl pastel cardboard string on board p. 27-Aug-2 Christie's, Melbourne #25/R est:40000-60000 (A.D 40000)
£16000 $25760 €24000 Divided unity (74x106cm-29x42in) i. s.verso ink on two panel executed 1973 prov.exhib.lit. 6-May-3 Christie's, Melbourne #11/R est:40000-60000 (A.D 40000)
£20000 $32200 €30000 Nude (98x65cm-39x26in) s.d.1978 ink. 6-May-3 Christie's, Melbourne #66/R est:35000-45000 (A.D 50000)
£24021 $36753 €36032 River (198x168cm-78x66in) s.num.3/6 tapestry prov. 25-Aug-2 Sotheby's, Paddington #39/R est:60000-80000 (A.D 67500)
£37209 $59163 €55814 Cushions (158x86cm-62x34in) s.d.75 ink wash cardboard prov.exhib. 5-May-3 Sotheby's, Melbourne #2/R est:60000-80000 (A.D 96000)
£83630 $127954 €125445 Portrait of Wendy (179x152cm-70x60in) s.d.1985 chl prov. 25-Aug-2 Sotheby's, Paddington #4/R est:170000-200000 (A.D 235000)

WHITELEY, John William (fl.1882-1916) British

£260 $406 €390 Male nude (75x46cm-30x18in) 8-Apr-3 Bonhams, Knightsbridge #144/R
£280 $448 €420 Study of nuns (37x35cm-15x14in) 11-Mar-3 Bonhams, Knightsbridge #181f/R
£340 $530 €510 Male nude holding a staff (61x30cm-24x12in) 8-Apr-3 Bonhams, Knightsbridge #53/R
£400 $640 €600 Still life of pots (53x43cm-21x17in) s. i.verso. 11-Mar-3 Bonhams, Knightsbridge #181g/R

£600 $960 €900 Fishergirl on beach (143x68cm-56x27in) exhib. 11-Mar-3 Bonhams, Knightsbridge #182/R
£700 $1120 €1050 Three quarter length study of a female nude from behind (60x37cm-24x15in) s. 11-Mar-3 Bonhams, Knightsbridge #176/R
£800 $1280 €1200 Three quarter length study of a male nude from behind (48x25cm-19x10in) s.d.1900 canvas on board. 11-Mar-3 Bonhams, Knightsbridge #175/R
£850 $1360 €1275 Half length study of a male nude from behind (54x39cm-21x15in) 11-Mar-3 Bonhams, Knightsbridge #177/R
£3000 $4800 €4500 Lullaby (66x116cm-26x46in) exhib. 11-Mar-3 Bonhams, Knightsbridge #180a/R est:2500-3500

WHITEMAN, Lesley (20th C) British
£800 $1320 €1160 Interior (49x41cm-19x16in) s.d.1929 panel exhib. 3-Jul-3 Christie's, Kensington #494/R

WHITEREAD, Rachel (1953-) British
£4194 $6500 €6291 Water tower project (63x51cm-25x20in) s.i.d.1998 acrylic resin on screenprint. 26-Sep-2 Christie's, Rockefeller NY #857/R est:6000-8000

Prints
£3374 $5500 €5061 Water tower project (63x51cm-25x20in) s.i.d.1998 num.23/35 screenprint. 13-Feb-3 Christie's, Rockefeller NY #380/R

Sculpture
£1550 $2526 €2325 Doorknob (6x13cm-2x5in) s.num.203/500 UV-resistant technogel covered black polyurethane. 3-Feb-3 Sotheby's, Olympia #39/R est:400-600
£5000 $8200 €7500 Untitled, day bed (41x83x196cm-16x33x77in) fabric foam edition of 50 prov. 7-Feb-3 Sotheby's, London #289/R est:2000-3000
£13000 $21320 €19500 Untitled - door handle (5x17x5cm-2x7x2in) init.num.13-14 brown pat.bronze 5. 6-Feb-3 Christie's, London #737/R est:5000-7000
£44872 $70000 €67308 Untitled - clear (101x74x10cm-40x29x4in) India rubber executed 1991 prov.exhib. 11-Nov-2 Phillips, New York #5/R est:80000-120000

Works on paper
£10000 $16400 €15000 Untitled - pink matress (30x46cm-12x18in) s.i.d.92 verso ink correction fluid graph paper prov. 6-Feb-3 Christie's, London #734/R est:15000-20000
£12500 $20000 €18750 Study relating to amber bed (29x42cm-11x17in) s.verso correction fluid ink W/C graph paper executed 1991 prov. 14-May-3 Sotheby's, New York #323/R est:25000-35000
£15625 $25000 €23438 Study for red (29x42cm-11x17in) s.d.1992 verso correction fluid on printed paper prov.exhib. 14-May-3 Sotheby's, New York #322/R est:18000-25000

WHITESIDE, Frank Reed (1866-1929) American
Works on paper
£1795 $2800 €2693 Hunting party (30x38cm-12x15in) W/C prov.lit. 9-Nov-2 Santa Fe Art, Santa Fe #114/R est:4000-6000

WHITFORD, Richard (19th C) British
£1500 $2325 €2250 Mare and foal in landscape (63x76cm-25x30in) s.d.1860. 2-Oct-2 Bonhams, Knowle #97/R est:1500-2500
£5000 $8350 €7250 Lord of the harem, landscape with other cattle beyond (61x74cm-24x29in) s.d.1862. 25-Jun-3 Brightwells, Leominster #1066/R est:3000-4000
£5000 $8350 €7250 Prize shorthorn bull in a landscape (52x76cm-20x30in) s.d.1876. 26-Jun-3 Mellors & Kirk, Nottingham #858/R est:2000-3000
£9500 $14725 €14250 Portrait of a ewe (48x58cm-19x23in) s.d.1871. 4-Oct-2 Mallams, Oxford #576/R est:1000-1500

WHITHAM, W (19th C) British
£2000 $3240 €3000 Brig Jane (35x62cm-14x24in) s.i. 21-Jan-3 Bonhams, New Bond Street #233/R est:1000-1500

WHITING, Frederick (1874-1962) British
£9200 $14536 €13800 Huntsman (63x76cm-25x30in) s. 27-Nov-2 Christie's, London #53/R est:6000-8000

WHITMORE, Coby (1913-1988) American
£3247 $5000 €4871 Reclining nude (46x61cm-18x24in) 25-Oct-2 Morris & Whiteside, Hilton Head Island #15 est:6000-8000

Works on paper
£1366 $2200 €2049 Beautiful woman eyed by men in restaurant (41x30cm-16x12in) s. gouache pencil exec.c.1950. 10-May-3 Illustration House, New York #134/R est:2500-4000

WHITMORE, Maud M (19th C) British?
£2600 $4004 €3900 Finishing touches (53x36cm-21x14in) s. 5-Sep-2 Christie's, Kensington #322/R est:2000-3000

WHITNEY, Gertrude (c.1876-1942) American
Sculpture
£6289 $10000 €9434 Wallflower, portrait of Barbara Whitney (27cm-11in) i. dark brown pat. bronze lit. 4-Mar-3 Christie's, Rockefeller NY #66/R est:5000-7000
£6918 $11000 €10377 Caryatid, male nude holding a rock (49cm-19in) i.d.1913 dark brown pat. bronze. 4-Mar-3 Christie's, Rockefeller NY #67/R est:4000-6000
£20645 $32000 €30968 Wallflower, portrait of Barbara Whitney (51cm-20in) i. brown pat. bronze on marble base. 5-Dec-2 Christie's, Rockefeller NY #110/R est:15000-25000

WHITTAKER, James William (1828-1876) British
Works on paper
£250 $390 €375 Sheep in a Scottish landscape (33x51cm-13x20in) s.d.1853 W/C. 25-Mar-3 Bonhams, Knightsbridge #223/R

WHITTEMORE, William John (1860-1955) American
£892 $1400 €1338 Portrait of a young woman (23x18cm-9x7in) s. 22-Nov-2 Skinner, Boston #99/R est:1000-1500

Works on paper
£732 $1200 €1061 Portrait of a girl (35x35cm-14x14in) s.d. col pastel W/C paper on card stock. 5-Jun-3 Swann Galleries, New York #267/R

WHITTET, Mathew H W (fl.1909-1912) British
£320 $499 €480 Figures paddling on the beach on a summer's day (29x40cm-11x16in) s. 10-Oct-2 Bonhams, Edinburgh #317

WHITTLE, T (19th C) British
£532 $824 €798 Lake landscape with cattle resting and figures (38x46cm-15x18in) s.d.1883. 8-Dec-2 Uppsala Auktionskammare, Uppsala #124 (S.KR 7500)

WHITTLE, Thomas (19th C) British
£360 $587 €540 Still life of a bird's nest, earthenware jug, flowers and fruit on a ledge (30x40cm-12x16in) s.d.1897. 12-Feb-3 Bonhams, Knightsbridge #40/R
£450 $733 €675 Farmyard scenes (12x18cm-5x7in) one s. canvas on board pair. 29-Jan-3 Sotheby's, Olympia #191/R
£500 $835 €725 Cottage at Godalming (18x13cm-7x5in) s.d.1871 prov. 20-Jun-3 Keys, Aylsham #671/R
£550 $852 €825 Sussex homestead. Cattle watering at the rivers edge (20x30cm-8x12in) s.d.1891 pair. 3-Dec-2 Sotheby's, Olympia #160/R
£600 $984 €900 Winter (15x20cm-6x8in) s.d.1865 board. 29-May-3 Christie's, Kensington #177/R
£800 $1264 €1200 Figures in rural landscapes (23x30cm-9x12in) s. board pair. 2-Dec-2 Gorringes, Lewes #2661
£850 $1394 €1275 Fruit, and a bird's nest with eggs, on a mossy bank (55x71cm-22x28in) s.d.1863. 29-May-3 Christie's, Kensington #309/R

WHITTLE, Thomas (jnr) (19th C) British
£750 $1170 €1125 Holy Street Mill, Chagford, Devon. Rustic cottage, Henfield, Sussex (16x20cm-6x8in) one s. one init.d.1886 two. 26-Mar-3 Hamptons Fine Art, Godalming #241
£1100 $1716 €1650 Ducks on a stream bed next to a watermill (59x90cm-23x35in) s.d.1881. 5-Nov-2 Bristol Auction Rooms #984 est:800-1200

WHITTOME, Irene (1942-) Canadian
Works on paper
£203 $319 €305 Rebirth II (28x20cm-11x8in) s.i. mixed media. 12-Dec-2 Iegor de Saint Hippolyte, Montreal #124 (C.D 500)

WHITTREDGE, Worthington (1820-1910) American
£7643 $12000 €11465 View of lake George (46x76cm-18x30in) s.d.1879. 14-Dec-2 Weschler, Washington #662/R est:25000-35000
£10323 $16000 €15485 Twilight, Kauterskill Clove (23x41cm-9x16in) s. canvas on board prov. 5-Dec-2 Christie's, Rockefeller NY #8a/R est:20000-30000
£16774 $26000 €25161 Valley of the Ocate (20x59cm-8x23in) i. paper on board prov.lit. 3-Dec-2 Phillips, New York #40/R est:30000-40000
£22581 $35000 €33872 Seascape (37x51cm-15x20in) painted c.1883 prov.exhib.lit. 3-Dec-2 Phillips, New York #37/R

£54839 $85000 €82259 Autumn in the Hudson (49x67cm-19x26in) s. prov.exhib.lit. 3-Dec-2 Phillips, New York #19/R est:50000-75000
£129032 $200000 €193548 Catskill brook (77x113cm-30x44in) s. painted c.1875 prov.lit. 3-Dec-2 Phillips, New York #25/R est:175000-225000

Works on paper

£714 $1100 €1071 Wooded stream (43x30cm-17x12in) s.d.92 pen ink. 27-Oct-2 Grogan, Boston #79 est:500-700

WHITWORTH, Charles H (fl.1875-1913) British

£450 $707 €675 Autumn (41x51cm-16x20in) s. 16-Apr-3 Christie's, Kensington #652/R
£540 $880 €810 When russet autumn decked her brow (66x92cm-26x36in) s.d.1889 s.i.d.verso. 11-Feb-3 Bonhams, Knowle #110

WHORF, John (1903-1959) American

£487 $750 €731 Galleon (53x38cm-21x15in) s. board. 27-Oct-2 Grogan, Boston #66

Works on paper

£321 $500 €482 Western border town (36x71cm-14x28in) s. W/C. 9-Nov-2 Santa Fe Art, Santa Fe #244/R
£714 $1100 €1071 In the hills (36x51cm-14x20in) s. W/C. 27-Oct-2 Grogan, Boston #82 est:300-500
£1274 $2000 €1911 Yacht under sail (25x38cm-10x15in) s. W/C. 23-Nov-2 Jackson's, Cedar Falls #83/R est:1750-2500
£1442 $2264 €2250 Nu a la source (48x38cm-19x15in) s. W/C. 16-Dec-2 Charbonneaux, Paris #202/R est:1200-1500
£1447 $2300 €2171 Winter landscape with birch trees (37x54cm-15x21in) s. W/C. 7-Mar-3 Skinner, Boston #456/R est:3000-5000
£2435 $3750 €3653 Fly fishing (25x38cm-10x15in) s. W/C. 24-Oct-2 Shannon's, Milford #67/R est:3000-5000
£2532 $4000 €3798 Horse and sled in a winter landscape (36x53cm-14x21in) s.i. W/C. 24-Apr-3 Shannon's, Milford #164/R est:4000-6000
£3774 $6000 €5661 Bathers. Stroll through the woods (50x65cm-20x26in) s.d.25 W/C double-sided. 7-Mar-3 Skinner, Boston #489/R est:4000-6000
£5000 $8000 €7250 Tremont Street in the rain (37x55cm-15x22in) s. i.verso W/C gouache. 16-May-3 Skinner, Boston #316/R est:4000-6000
£5195 $8000 €7793 Fishing in the rapids (36x53cm-14x21in) s. W/C prov. 24-Oct-2 Shannon's, Milford #68/R est:8000-12000
£6479 $9200 €9719 Last night (61x81cm-24x32in) W/C. 8-Aug-1 Barridorf, Portland #286/R est:8000-12000
£7051 $11000 €10577 Fly fishing. Portuguese grandmother holding baby (36x51cm-14x20in) s. W/C double-sided. 1-Aug-2 Eldred, East Dennis #989/R est:2000-3000
£9859 $14000 €14789 Fishing discussion (36x56cm-14x22in) W/C. 8-Aug-1 Barridorf, Portland #128/R est:6000-9000

WHYMPER, Charles (1853-1941) British

Works on paper

£260 $411 €390 Pheasant shooting (60x46cm-24x18in) W/C gouache prov. 26-Nov-2 Bonhams, Ipswich #373
£280 $434 €420 Stone Curlew, Norfolk (14x24cm-6x9in) mono.i.d.May 13/05 W/C. 30-Sep-2 Bonhams, Ipswich #314
£320 $499 €480 Grouse nesting in a moorland (22x32cm-9x13in) s. pencil W/C htd bodycol. 19-Sep-2 Christie's, Kensington #76
£320 $496 €480 Blackbird singing on spring morning (36x26cm-14x10in) s. W/C htd white. 24-Sep-2 Bonhams, Knightsbridge #17/R
£480 $758 €696 Grey partridge in undergrowth (26x17cm-10x7in) init. W/C. 22-Jul-3 Bonhams, Knightsbridge #52/R
£620 $1023 €899 An afternoon call in the Arctic Circle (36x25cm-14x10in) s. W/C bodycol. 3-Jul-3 Duke & Son, Dorchester #65/R

WHYMPER, Josiah Wood (1813-1903) British

Works on paper

£250 $390 €375 Sherwood forest (26x37cm-10x15in) pencil W/C gum arabic. 27-Mar-3 Christie's, Kensington #133
£550 $869 €825 Slopes of Hindhead near Haslemere (27x46cm-11x18in) s. W/C. 18-Dec-2 John Nicholson, Haslemere #1056/R

WHYTE, Alice F (1880-1952) New Zealander

£313 $489 €470 Roses in a blue bowl (32x36cm-13x14in) s.verso. 7-Nov-2 International Art Centre, Auckland #64/R est:1000-2000 (NZ.D 1000)
£316 $493 €474 Coromandel stream (38x48cm-15x19in) s. board. 27-Mar-3 International Art Centre, Auckland #179/R (NZ.D 900)
£470 $734 €705 Red hot pokers (52x41cm-20x16in) s. board. 7-Nov-2 International Art Centre, Auckland #2/R est:2500-3500 (NZ.D 1500)
£470 $734 €705 Teapot with mushrooms (39x50cm-15x20in) board. 7-Nov-2 International Art Centre, Auckland #28/R est:2500-3500 (NZ.D 1500)
£470 $734 €705 Still life in a blue vase (40x48cm-16x19in) board. 7-Nov-2 International Art Centre, Auckland #53/R est:3000-4000 (NZ.D 1500)
£526 $821 €789 Pot of Lachenalias (50x34cm-20x13in) board. 27-Mar-3 International Art Centre, Auckland #19/R (NZ.D 1500)
£596 $931 €894 Roses in a black bowl (36x31cm-14x12in) s. paper. 27-Mar-3 International Art Centre, Auckland #53/R (NZ.D 1700)
£671 $1081 €1007 Loading cargo on the Northern Wairoa river, Dargaville (28x33cm-11x13in) s. 7-May-3 Dunbar Sloane, Auckland #3/R est:1500-2000 (NZ.D 1900)
£690 $1076 €1035 Boat yard. Landscape with trees (41x55cm-16x22in) s. board. 7-Nov-2 International Art Centre, Auckland #13/R est:2500-3500 (NZ.D 2200)
£772 $1227 €1158 Houses in a landscape (29x39cm-11x15in) s. board. 25-Feb-3 Peter Webb, Auckland #51 est:700-900 (NZ.D 2200)
£940 $1467 €1410 Onehunga backyard (33x41cm-13x16in) board. 7-Nov-2 International Art Centre, Auckland #49/R est:2500-3500 (NZ.D 3000)
£1053 $1642 €1580 On the Manukau (38x48cm-15x19in) s. board. 27-Mar-3 International Art Centre, Auckland #58/R est:1500-2500 (NZ.D 3000)

Works on paper

£421 $669 €632 Floral still life with roses (48x34cm-19x13in) s. W/C. 25-Feb-3 Peter Webb, Auckland #46 est:600-800 (NZ.D 1200)

WHYTE, Catharine (1906-1979) Canadian

£667 $1093 €967 Untitled - portrait (34x27cm-13x11in) s.d.1968. 9-Jun-3 Hodgins, Calgary #300/R est:1500-2500 (C.D 1500)
£2826 $4409 €4713 Untitled - Andromeda Peak (25x30cm-10x12in) prov. 13-Apr-3 Levis, Calgary #118/R est:3000-4000 (C.D 6500)

WIBERG, Harald (1908-1986) Swedish

£1029 $1605 €1544 Winter landscape with capercaillie (25x41cm-10x16in) s.d.1949. 13-Sep-2 Lilla Bukowskis, Stockholm #14 est:12000-15000 (S.KR 15000)
£1182 $1915 €1773 Mute swans in flight (61x140cm-24x55in) s.d.1952 panel. 3-Feb-3 Lilla Bukowskis, Stockholm #491 est:12000-15000 (S.KR 16500)
£1257 $2061 €1823 Deer in winter forest (46x55cm-18x22in) s.d.1939. 4-Jun-3 AB Stockholms Auktionsverk #2288/R est:18000-20000 (S.KR 16000)
£1821 $2877 €2732 Winter wood with fox hunting capercaillie (80x100cm-31x39in) s.d.1948. 16-Nov-2 Crafoord, Lund #37/R est:20000 (S.KR 26000)

Works on paper

£272 $440 €394 Elks in forest (14x21cm-6x8in) s.d.1945 pen. 25-May-3 Uppsala Auktionskammare, Uppsala #191 (S.KR 3500)
£426 $660 €639 Wooded landscape with stags (19x40cm-7x16in) s.d.55 mixed media. 8-Dec-2 Uppsala Auktionskammare, Uppsala #175 (S.KR 6000)

WICAR, Jean Baptiste (1762-1834) French

Works on paper

£800 $1240 €1200 Christ healing the Palsied man (22x14cm-9x6in) pencil. 9-Dec-2 Bonhams, New Bond Street #29/R

WICAR, Jean Baptiste (attrib) (1762-1834) French

Works on paper

£353 $546 €550 Sujet d'histoire ancienne (22x33cm-9x13in) crayon stump chk. 4-Dec-2 Piasa, Paris #112

WICART, Nicolaas (1748-1815) Dutch

Works on paper

£439 $685 €650 Paysage anime (12x19cm-5x7in) pen ink wash over crayon prov. 31-Mar-3 Piasa, Paris #51
£892 $1391 €1400 Boats on an estuary (26x35cm-10x14in) s. pen grey brown ink pink wash. 5-Nov-2 Sotheby's, Amsterdam #113/R

WICART, Nicolaas (attrib) (1748-1815) Dutch

Works on paper

£503 $785 €800 Dutch landscapes. W/C two. 19-Sep-2 Dr Fritz Nagel, Stuttgart #836/R
£828 $1316 €1200 Fishermen on the river with village in the background (31x45cm-12x18in) ink W/C pair. 10-Mar-3 Sotheby's, Amsterdam #33/R est:1000-1500

WICHERA, Raimund von (1862-1925) Austrian

£387 $600 €581 Game fowl (102x79cm-40x31in) 7-Dec-2 Harvey Clar, Oakland #1273

Works on paper

£878 $1370 €1300 New Year's greeting (18x28cm-7x11in) s. W/C. 28-Mar-3 Dorotheum, Vienna #300/R

WICHMANN, Peter (1706-1769) Danish

£	$	€	Details
£766	$1210	€1149	Portrait of Queen Juliane Marie (38x30cm-15x12in) s.d.1756 verso. 2-Dec-2 Rasmussen, Copenhagen #1677/R (D.KR 9000)

WICHT, John von (1888-1970) American/German

Works on paper

£	$	€	Details
£510	$800	€765	No 63 (9x7cm-4x3in) s. ink acrylic exec.c.1950 prov. 19-Nov-2 Wright, Chicago #157/R
£955	$1500	€1433	No 10 (20x7cm-8x3in) s.d. W/C crayon prov. 19-Nov-2 Wright, Chicago #158/R est:1800-2500
£974	$1500	€1461	Gothic abstraction (81x56cm-32x22in) s. W/C gouache. 24-Oct-2 Shannon's, Milford #110/R est:2500-3500
£1341	$2200	€1944	Untitled no.38 (58x43cm-23x17in) s. gouache pastel prov. 1-Jun-3 Wright, Chicago #129/R est:2500-3500

WICHT, Jose (19th C) French

£	$	€	Details
£314	$491	€500	Flowers (32cm-13in circular) s. 8-Oct-2 Ansorena, Madrid #304/R

WICKENBERG, Per (1812-1846) Swedish

£	$	€	Details
£562	$877	€843	Alpine landscape with farmyard (52x74cm-20x29in) s. 13-Sep-2 Lilla Bukowskis, Stockholm #88 (S.KR 8200)
£759	$1200	€1200	The cottage (52x73cm-20x29in) s. 1-Dec-2 Bukowskis, Helsinki #286/R
£1064	$1649	€1596	Children tobogganing (13x19cm-5x7in) s.d.1841 panel. 4-Dec-2 AB Stockholms Auktionsverk #1763/R est:20000-25000 (S.KR 15000)

WICKENBURG, Alfred (1885-1978) Austrian

£	$	€	Details
£5380	$8500	€8500	Flowers (43x35cm-17x14in) mono. prov. 27-Nov-2 Dorotheum, Vienna #195/R est:6500-10000

Works on paper

£	$	€	Details
£590	$933	€850	Harlequin (29x20cm-11x8in) mono.d.32 col chk. 24-Apr-3 Dorotheum, Vienna #75/R

WICKENDEN, Robert J (1861-1931) American/British

£	$	€	Details
£447	$702	€671	A glimpse of the Ottawa near St Andrews East, Quebec 1920 (39x51cm-15x20in) s. panel. 12-Dec-2 Iegor de Saint Hippolyte, Montreal #125 (C.D 1100)

WICKES, Ethel Marian (1872-1940) American

£	$	€	Details
£900	$1431	€1350	Portrait of a Greek sailor (51x41cm-20x16in) s. 29-Apr-3 Bonhams, New Bond Street #136/R

WICKHAM, Julia M (fl.1935-1938) American

£	$	€	Details
£968	$1500	€1404	Frozen brook (43x53cm-17x21in) academy board. 7-Dec-2 South Bay, Long Island #165/R

WICKSTROM, Martin (1957-) Swedish

Works on paper

£	$	€	Details
£579	$932	€869	Untitled (64x63cm-25x25in) s.d.2000 verso mixed media. 7-May-3 AB Stockholms Auktionsverk #1084/R (S.KR 7500)

WICKY, Franz Albert (1874-1916) French

£	$	€	Details
£416	$650	€624	Young boy hiding behind a tree (50x33cm-20x13in) s.d.1912 masonite. 12-Apr-3 Weschler, Washington #545/R

WIDAYAT (1923-) Indonesian

£	$	€	Details
£1657	$2552	€2486	Burung phoenix (52x62cm-20x24in) s.i. board. 27-Oct-2 Christie's, Hong Kong #78/R est:22000-30000 (HK.D 20000)

WIDERBACK, Gusten (1878-1970) Swedish

£	$	€	Details
£319	$495	€479	View towards Svia farm (33x38cm-13x15in) s. panel. 8-Dec-2 Uppsala Auktionskammare, Uppsala #168 (S.KR 4500)
£426	$660	€639	Uppsala hills (32x38cm-13x15in) s. panel. 8-Dec-2 Uppsala Auktionskammare, Uppsala #169 (S.KR 6000)

WIDERBERG, Frans (1934-) Norwegian

£	$	€	Details
£2122	$3268	€3183	Centaur with wings (57x70cm-22x28in) s. acrylic painted 1997. 28-Oct-2 Blomqvist, Lysaker #1346/R est:40000 (N.KR 25000)
£2547	$3922	€3821	Centaurs (55x72cm-22x28in) s. acrylic painted 1997. 28-Oct-2 Blomqvist, Lysaker #1344/R est:40000-45000 (N.KR 30000)
£3903	$6088	€5855	The four seasons (100cm-39in) two s. painted c.1950s four. 21-Oct-2 Blomqvist, Oslo #421/R est:80000-100000 (N.KR 45000)
£5430	$8796	€8145	Bird and couple (58x77cm-23x30in) s. 26-May-3 Grev Wedels Plass, Oslo #62/R est:40000 (N.KR 60000)

Works on paper

£	$	€	Details
£357	$549	€536	Islands in the sea (14x18cm-6x7in) s. gouache. 28-Oct-2 Blomqvist, Lysaker #1345/R (N.KR 4200)
£995	$1611	€1493	Nude (77x57cm-30x22in) s. W/C. 27-Jan-3 Blomqvist, Lysaker #1291/R (N.KR 11000)
£1222	$1918	€1833	Nude (77x57cm-30x22in) s. W/C. 25-Nov-2 Blomqvist, Lysaker #1308/R est:25000 (N.KR 14000)
£1706	$2662	€2559	Wanderer (75x54cm-30x21in) s. W/C painted 1974. 23-Sep-2 Blomqvist, Lysaker #1269/R est:15000 (N.KR 20000)
£2920	$4614	€4380	Horse (71x102cm-28x40in) init. W/C exhib. 28-Apr-3 Blomqvist, Oslo #396/R est:35000-40000 (N.KR 33000)

WIDERBERG, Nico (1960-) Norwegian

Sculpture

£	$	€	Details
£1735	$2706	€2603	Head of man (70x20x30cm-28x8x12in) marble incl.marble plinth. 21-Oct-2 Blomqvist, Oslo #445/R est:25000-35000 (N.KR 20000)
£1770	$2796	€2655	Head of man (70x20x30cm-28x8x12in) Portuguese marble - incl. Italian marble plinth. 28-Apr-3 Blomqvist, Oslo #372/R est:25000-35000 (N.KR 20000)

WIDFORSS, Gunnar M (1879-1934) American

Works on paper

£	$	€	Details
£1433	$2250	€2150	Winter in Yosemite (41x34cm-16x13in) i.verso W/C prov. 19-Nov-2 Butterfields, San Francisco #8171/R est:3000-5000
£4747	$7500	€6883	17 miles drive, California (18x23cm-7x9in) s. W/C. 26-Jul-3 Coeur d'Alene, Hayden #81/R est:6000-9000
£5689	$9500	€8249	Grand Canyon (44x54cm-17x21in) s.d.1925 W/C on board. 18-Jun-3 Christie's, Los Angeles #5/R est:12000-18000
£6962	$11000	€10095	Palace of fine arts (18x23cm-7x9in) s. W/C. 26-Jul-3 Coeur d'Alene, Hayden #82/R est:6000-8000
£15060	$25000	€21837	View into the Grand Canyon (47x37cm-19x15in) s. W/C prov. 11-Jun-3 Butterfields, San Francisco #4326/R est:20000-30000

WIDGERY, Frederick John (1861-1942) British

£	$	€	Details
£380	$600	€570	West country coastal scene (38x56cm-15x22in) s. i.verso. 24-Apr-3 Richardson & Smith, Whitby #209
£650	$1086	€943	On Woodbury Common (16x23cm-6x9in) s. s.i.verso board. 26-Jun-3 Mellors & Kirk, Nottingham #897
£690	$1083	€1035	Woodbury Common, Devon (17x25cm-7x10in) s.i. board. 15-Apr-3 Bonhams, Knowle #130
£860	$1410	€1290	Near Fingle Bridge, Dartmoor (30x36cm-12x14in) s.i. verso. 7-Feb-3 Honiton Galleries, Honiton #361/R
£1450	$2262	€2175	Foreland, Lynton (62x74cm-24x29in) s. 15-Oct-2 Bearnes, Exeter #419/R est:1000-1500
£1600	$2496	€2400	On the coast, Devon (24x32cm-9x13in) s. board exhib. 5-Nov-2 Bonhams, New Bond Street #158/R est:1300-1800
£2000	$3120	€3000	Headland rocks, Newquay (62x74cm-24x29in) s. 15-Oct-2 Bearnes, Exeter #418/R est:1000-1500
£2300	$3588	€3450	West country beach (30x41cm-12x16in) s. s.i.d.1927 verso board. 5-Nov-2 Bonhams, New Bond Street #156/R est:1500-2000
£2600	$4056	€3900	Study of a sky, raincloud (49x59cm-19x23in) s.d.1936 board exhib. 5-Nov-2 Bonhams, New Bond Street #150/R est:2300-3000
£2600	$4056	€3900	Trossachs from Loch Achray, Scotland (30x45cm-12x18in) s. i.on stretcher exhib. 5-Nov-2 Bonhams, New Bond Street #152/R est:1800-2200

Works on paper

£	$	€	Details
£260	$406	€390	North Cornish coast (20x35cm-8x14in) s. W/C. 8-Apr-3 Bearnes, Exeter #543
£260	$434	€377	Dartmoor (17x20cm-7x8in) s. pencil W/C htd white. 26-Jun-3 Mellors & Kirk, Nottingham #818
£262	$414	€393	Mullion rock (24x33cm-9x13in) s. W/C gouache. 18-Nov-2 Waddingtons, Toronto #54a/R (C.D 650)
£280	$448	€406	Near the Island of Rocks (27x45cm-11x18in) s. W/C. 19-May-3 Bearnes, Exeter #116
£290	$484	€421	Dunes along the coast (25x74cm-10x29in) s. W/C. 24-Jun-3 Bearnes, Exeter #474
£300	$489	€435	Near Taw Head, Dartmoor (26x36cm-10x14in) s.i. W/C bodycol. 21-Jul-3 Bonhams, Bath #27/R
£302	$475	€453	Sprawling countryside (25x36cm-10x14in) s. W/C. 22-Nov-2 Skinner, Boston #19/R
£320	$512	€464	Great Mis Tor, Dartmoor (36x53cm-14x21in) s.d.1918 W/C. 19-May-3 Bearnes, Exeter #117
£325	$520	€471	Coastal landscape (26x35cm-10x14in) s. W/C. 19-May-3 Bearnes, Exeter #110
£340	$507	€510	On Dartmoor (18x28cm-7x11in) s. W/C. 28-Jun-2 Chrystals Auctions, Isle of Man #176
£340	$541	€510	West Ockment, Dartmoor (25x35cm-10x14in) s. gouache bodycol. 29-Apr-3 Bearnes, Exeter #501
£350	$581	€508	Coastal scene (18x28cm-7x11in) s. gouache sold with another by a different hand. 10-Jun-3 David Lay, Penzance #441
£356	$590	€516	River rapids by castle ruins (29x46cm-11x18in) s. W/C. 16-Jun-3 Waddingtons, Toronto #84/R (C.D 800)
£360	$569	€522	Beach at low tide (25x36cm-10x14in) s. gouache. 22-Jul-3 Gorringes, Lewes #1702
£370	$592	€537	Moorland stream (49x72cm-19x28in) s.d.86 W/C. 13-May-3 Bristol Auction Rooms #496/R
£400	$640	€580	River estuary (27x45cm-11x18in) s. W/C. 19-May-3 Bearnes, Exeter #114
£400	$640	€580	Near Sheepstor, Dartmoor (28x46cm-11x18in) s. W/C. 19-May-3 Bearnes, Exeter #115
£400	$660	€580	Moors between Corfe Castle and Wareham (35x48cm-14x19in) s. gouache. 1-Jul-3 Bearnes, Exeter #445/R

£460 $759 €667 Watern Tor, Dartmoor (25x36cm-10x14in) s. gouache. 1-Jul-3 Bearnes, Exeter #442/R
£500 $775 €750 Widemouth Bay, Bude (24x34cm-9x13in) s. gouache. 2-Oct-2 Bonhams, Knowle #44
£500 $780 €750 Mullion Rocks, The Lizard (23x33cm-9x13in) s. gouache. 9-Oct-2 Woolley & Wallis, Salisbury #48/R
£500 $825 €725 Near Belstone, Dartmoor (34x49cm-13x19in) s. gouache. 1-Jul-3 Bearnes, Exeter #443/R
£520 $858 €754 Dartmoor Valley. Dartmoor Tor (24x34cm-9x13in) s. gouache oval pair. 1-Jul-3 Bearnes, Exeter #448/R
£550 $858 €825 Steperton, Dartmoor (25x35cm-10x14in) s. gouache. 26-Mar-3 Sotheby's, Olympia #121/R
£570 $884 €855 Ore Stone, Torbay (25x35cm-10x14in) s. gouache. 1-Oct-2 Bristol Auction Rooms #477/R
£600 $948 €900 Yei tor, Dartmoor (25x36cm-10x14in) s.i. gouache. 2-Dec-2 Gorringes, Lewes #2667
£600 $948 €900 Devon coastal landscape (28x46cm-11x18in) s. gouache. 2-Dec-2 Gorringes, Lewes #2668
£600 $960 €900 Beach scene at low tide (28x46cm-11x18in) s. W/C. 11-Mar-3 Gorringes, Lewes #2531
£620 $967 €930 Moorland (17x26cm-7x10in) s. gouache W/C. 15-Oct-2 Bearnes, Exeter #388/R
£620 $980 €930 Rocky coastline (28x46cm-11x18in) s. W/C bodycol. 2-Dec-2 Bonhams, Bath #29
£620 $980 €930 Dartmoor stream under cloudy skies (26x36cm-10x14in) s. W/C bodycol htd white. 2-Dec-2 Bonhams, Bath #32
£640 $1056 €928 Sheep on a Dartmoor slope (26x36cm-10x14in) s. gouache. 1-Jul-3 Bearnes, Exeter #449/R
£650 $1014 €975 Castle Rock, Lynton (33x53cm-13x21in) s.i. bodycol. 25-Mar-3 Bonhams, Knightsbridge #176/R
£680 $1061 €1020 Harvest moon, Dartmoor (25x43cm-10x17in) s. W/C. 18-Oct-2 Keys, Aylsham #646
£680 $1054 €1020 Bude beach, north Cornwall (25x35cm-10x14in) gouache. 1-Oct-2 Bristol Auction Rooms #478/R
£680 $1081 €1020 English Channel from Woodbury Common (25x35cm-10x14in) s. W/C. 4-Mar-3 Bearnes, Exeter #383/R
£680 $1081 €1020 On the River Exe near Exeter (23x32cm-9x13in) s.i. W/C. 27-Feb-3 Greenslade Hunt, Taunton #1254/R
£700 $1091 €1050 Waves breaking along the coast (30x44cm-12x17in) s. pencil W/C htd white. 19-Sep-2 Christie's, Kensington #159/R
£700 $1084 €1050 Valley of the rocks, Lynton. Rolling landscape with heather (32x51cm-13x20in) s. W/C pair. 3-Dec-2 Sotheby's, Olympia #47/R
£700 $1113 €1050 Moorland stream and distant tor (35x52cm-14x20in) s. gouache. 30-Apr-3 Hampton & Littlewood, Exeter #459/R
£720 $1188 €1044 Yes Tor, Dartmoor (24x34cm-9x13in) s. gouache. 1-Jul-3 Bearnes, Exeter #444/R
£750 $1170 €1125 Bude, high tide (23x28cm-9x11in) s. W/C exhib. 5-Nov-2 Bonhams, New Bond Street #164/R
£750 $1193 €1125 Moorland landscape (28x46cm-11x18in) s. bodycol. 29-Apr-3 Bonhams, Knightsbridge #55/R
£780 $1271 €1131 Lustleigh Cleave (37x53cm-15x21in) s.i. W/C bodycol. 21-Jul-3 Bonhams, Bath #28/R
£800 $1280 €1200 West Country beach (25x36cm-10x14in) s. W/C bodycol. 11-Mar-3 Bonhams, New Bond Street #131/R
£800 $1320 €1160 Matlock Bridge, Dartmoor (23x43cm-9x17in) s. W/C. 1-Jul-3 Bearnes, Exeter #450/R
£820 $1279 €1230 Row Tor and Yes Tor, Dartmoor (23x33cm-9x13in) s. gouache. 9-Oct-2 Woolley & Wallis, Salisbury #49/R
£820 $1337 €1189 View of Dartmoor Tors from a moorland pond (26x76cm-10x30in) s. W/C bodycol. 21-Jul-3 Bonhams, Bath #25/R
£820 $1337 €1189 Mist over a Dartmoor lake (26x76cm-10x30in) s. W/C bodycol. 21-Jul-3 Bonhams, Bath #26/R
£850 $1352 €1275 Lizard coast (49x79cm-19x31in) s.i. W/C bodycol. 27-Feb-3 Greenslade Hunt, Taunton #1253/R
£920 $1527 €1380 View of Dartmoor near Bilstone. Ansteys Cover, South Devon (24x34cm-9x13in) s. bodycol pair. 10-Jun-3 Sworder & Son, Bishops Stortford #483/R
£950 $1511 €1425 West Mill Tor, Dartmoor (28x47cm-11x19in) s.i. bodycol. 29-Apr-3 Bonhams, Knightsbridge #54/R
£980 $1607 €1470 Doone Valley Exmoor (26x36cm-10x14in) s. W/C htd white. 7-Feb-3 Honiton Galleries, Honiton #324
£1000 $1580 €1500 Hay Tor (27x44cm-11x17in) s. bodycol. 2-Dec-2 Bonhams, Bath #31 est:400-600
£1000 $1670 €1450 Dunkery Beacon, Exmoor (25x35cm-10x14in) s. W/C. 9-Jul-3 George Kidner, Lymington #122/R est:1000-1500
£1100 $1716 €1650 Moorland road on Cawsand Beacon, Dartmoor, Devon (35x55cm-14x22in) s. W/C bodycol. 5-Nov-2 Bonhams, New Bond Street #162/R est:1000-1500
£1100 $1760 €1650 Anstey Cove, Torquay, Devon (27x44cm-11x17in) s. W/C htd white. 11-Mar-3 Bonhams, New Bond Street #127/R est:1200-1800
£1150 $1829 €1725 Rippon Tor from Saddle Tor, Dartmoor (36x53cm-14x21in) s. W/C. 29-Apr-3 Gorringes, Lewes #2287
£1200 $1860 €1800 Great links Tor, Dartmouth (20x55cm-8x22in) s.i. W/C. 25-Sep-2 John Nicholson, Haslemere #896 est:500-1000
£1250 $1950 €1813 Near Lee Bay Lynton - coastal landscape (49x75cm-19x30in) s.i. W/C. 27-Mar-3 Lane, Penzance #325/R est:1300-1500
£1300 $2028 €1950 Below Glyder Fawr and Glyder Fach, Snowdonia, North Wales (27x46cm-11x18in) s. exhib. 5-Nov-2 Bonhams, New Bond Street #157/R est:1300-1800
£1300 $2132 €1950 On the Lyd (73x24cm-29x9in) s. W/C. 7-Feb-3 Honiton Galleries, Honiton #371 est:500-700
£1300 $2067 €1950 Hey Tor, Dartmoor (28x78cm-11x31in) s.i. gouache. 29-Apr-3 Sworder & Son, Bishops Stortford #399/R est:300-500
£1300 $2067 €1950 Dartmoor views (36x54cm-14x21in) s. gouache pair. 29-Apr-3 Sworder & Son, Bishops Stortford #400/R est:400-600
£1400 $2240 €2100 Badgeworthy Waters, Exmoor (25x35cm-10x14in) s. bodycol. 11-Mar-3 Bonhams, New Bond Street #124/R est:1500-2000
£1400 $2212 €2100 Fur Tor from near Bleak House, Dartmoor (44x60cm-17x24in) s. W/C bodycol. 7-Apr-3 Bonhams, Bath #39/R est:1000-1500
£1400 $2310 €2030 Amicombe Hill, Dartmoor (50x74cm-20x29in) s.i. gouache. 1-Jul-3 Bearnes, Exeter #446/R est:800-1000
£1450 $2291 €2175 Dartmoor Tors with a river in the foreground (36x53cm-14x21in) s. W/C bodycol. 2-Dec-2 Bonhams, Bath #30/R est:800-1000
£1450 $2291 €2175 Tavy Cleave Fall, Dartmoor (54x36cm-21x14in) s. W/C bodycol. 7-Apr-3 Bonhams, Bath #40/R est:500-700
£1500 $2400 €2250 In Fistral Bay, Newquay. Bedruthen Steps, Newquay (25x35cm-10x14in) s. bodycol pair. 11-Mar-3 Bonhams, New Bond Street #130a/R est:1500-2000
£1600 $2496 €2400 Near Tavy Cleave, Dartmoor (34x50cm-13x20in) s.i. gouache. 17-Sep-2 Sotheby's, Olympia #136/R est:500-700
£1700 $2788 €2550 Steperton Tor, River Taw. Armed Knight, Landsend (25x85cm-10x33in) s. W/C gouache pair. 7-Feb-3 Honiton Galleries, Honiton #369/R est:1500-2000
£1700 $2805 €2465 Yes Tor, Dartmoor. Bel Tor near Belstone, Dartmoor (35x53cm-14x21in) s.i. gouache pair. 1-Jul-3 Bearnes, Exeter #447/R est:500-700
£1800 $2808 €2700 Holywell Bay, near Newquay, Cornwall (41x102cm-16x40in) s. bodycol. 5-Nov-2 Bonhams, New Bond Street #153/R est:1500-2000
£2000 $3120 €3000 Sheep on Dartmoor (17x53cm-7x21in) s. W/C gouache. 17-Oct-2 Lawrence, Crewkerne #421/R est:600-800
£2000 $3300 €2900 Gathering bracken on Woodbury Common, River Exe beyond (49x75cm-19x30in) s. W/C. 1-Jul-3 Bearnes, Exeter #441/R est:600-800
£2400 $3744 €3600 River Teign near Teignmouth, Devon (30x60cm-12x24in) s. W/C bodycol. 5-Nov-2 Bonhams, New Bond Street #154/R est:1500-2000
£2800 $4368 €4200 Clapper bridge over the East Dart at Postbridge, Devon (29x46cm-11x18in) s. bodycol exhib. 5-Nov-2 Bonhams, New Bond Street #160/R est:1000-1500
£2800 $4368 €4200 Clapper bridge over the Wallabrook near Chagford, Devon (28x45cm-11x18in) s.d.1939 bodycol exhib. 5-Nov-2 Bonhams, New Bond Street #161/R est:1000-1500
£3100 $4836 €4650 Heytor Dartmoor. Moorland landscape with meandering river and cattle (25x35cm-10x14in) s. W/C gouache pair. 7-Nov-2 Rupert Toovey, Partridge Green #1406/R est:1000-1500

WIDGERY, William (1822-1893) British
£850 $1394 €1275 Mill bridge, Lydford. On the Lyd (41x56cm-16x22in) s. pair. 7-Feb-3 Honiton Galleries, Honiton #289/R
£1384 $2158 €2200 Upper Italian lake landscape (60x82cm-24x32in) s.d.1862. 9-Oct-2 Michael Zeller, Lindau #959/R est:1800
£1400 $2184 €2100 Hunter in a landscape (62x76cm-24x30in) s.d.1856. 9-Oct-2 Woolley & Wallis, Salisbury #301/R est:750-1000
£1800 $2934 €2610 Moorland stream with cattle and cowherd (61x110cm-24x43in) s. 21-Jul-3 Bonhams, Bath #58/R est:2000-3000
£3800 $6042 €5700 Dartmoor ponies (102x153cm-40x60in) s.d.1879. 19-Mar-3 Sotheby's, London #242/R est:3000-5000

Works on paper
£270 $432 €405 Tavy Cleave, Dartmoor (32x48cm-13x19in) s.d.1864 W/C. 13-May-3 Bearnes, Exeter #334
£280 $434 €420 Extensive coastal landscape with fishing vessels in coastal waters (25x74cm-10x29in) s. W/C bodycol. 31-Oct-2 Duke & Son, Dorchester #155
£340 $527 €510 Fishing on the river Lid (84x117cm-33x46in) s. i.verso W/C. 26-Sep-2 Lane, Penzance #107
£360 $562 €540 Mountain and moorland landscape with cattle watering (24x74cm-9x29in) s. W/C. 8-Oct-2 Bonhams, Oxford #269
£360 $562 €540 Mountain and moorland landscape with stream (24x74cm-9x29in) s. W/C. 8-Oct-2 Bonhams, Oxford #270
£380 $608 €551 Moorland steam (25x38cm-10x15in) s. W/C. 19-May-3 Bearnes, Exeter #109
£450 $702 €675 Tumbling brook (70x42cm-28x17in) s. 8-Oct-2 Bearnes, Exeter #379
£520 $832 €754 Woodland stream. Fisherman at a steam (53x35cm-21x14in) s. W/C two. 19-May-3 Bearnes, Exeter #108
£600 $978 €900 Dartmoor stream with ponies (23x73cm-9x29in) s. W/C bodycol pair. 17-Feb-3 Bonhams, Bath #78
£840 $1336 €1260 Dean Moor (24x53cm-9x21in) s. W/C. 4-Mar-3 Bearnes, Exeter #367/R
£900 $1422 €1350 Landscapes, lover in a wood and rocky stream (50x33cm-20x13in) s. W/C pair. 18-Dec-2 John Nicholson, Haslemere #1092

£1400 $2296 €2100 Dartmoor landscape on Lyd with views of Arms Tor (60x182cm-24x72in) s. W/C. 7-Feb-3 Honiton Galleries, Honiton #368/R est:1200-1600
£1900 $3116 €2850 Figures on the Lyd (100x64cm-39x25in) s. W/C. 7-Feb-3 Honiton Galleries, Honiton #370 est:2000-3000

WIDHOPFF, D O (1867-1933) French
£545 $855 €850 La couture (43x47cm-17x19in) 24-Nov-2 Chayette & Cheval, Paris #238n
£769 $1208 €1200 Portrait d'homme (45x41cm-18x16in) init.d.1890. 24-Nov-2 Chayette & Cheval, Paris #238a
Works on paper
£321 $503 €500 Femme a sa toilette (31x39cm-12x15in) s. chl canson. 24-Nov-2 Chayette & Cheval, Paris #238d
£321 $503 €500 Portrait d'homme en buste (64x49cm-25x19in) s.d.1906 ink wash canson. 24-Nov-2 Chayette & Cheval, Paris #238f
£513 $805 €800 Diner mondain (36x39cm-14x15in) s. chl canson. 24-Nov-2 Chayette & Cheval, Paris #238c
£532 $835 €830 Portrait d'elegante a la canne (63x48cm-25x19in) s.d.1897 chl pencil canson. 24-Nov-2 Chayette & Cheval, Paris #238e

WIDMAN, Bruno (1930-) Uruguayan
£321 $500 €482 Mancha de las costas (28x38cm-11x15in) panel. 6-Aug-2 Galleria Y Remates, Montevideo #112
£818 $1300 €1227 Express (40x60cm-16x24in) s. s.i.verso. 2-Mar-3 Galleria Y Remates, Montevideo #103/R
£7643 $12000 €11465 Lift (101x200cm-40x79in) s. s.i.verso. 19-Nov-2 Sotheby's, New York #152/R est:20000

WIDMANN, Fritz (1869-1937) Swiss
£349 $548 €524 Theatre scene (18x15cm-7x6in) mono. board. 25-Nov-2 Sotheby's, Zurich #84/R (S.FR 800)

WIDMER, Hans (1872-1925) Swiss
£524 $817 €786 Herder with cattle (84x100cm-33x39in) s.d.1925. 6-Nov-2 Dobiaschofsky, Bern #1070/R (S.FR 1200)
£699 $1090 €1049 Small accordion player (81x67cm-32x26in) s. 8-Nov-2 Dobiaschofsky, Bern #87/R (S.FR 1600)

WIDOFF, Anders (1953-) Swedish
£280 $437 €420 Untitled (30x21cm-12x8in) s.d.25.8.93 varnish melitrace. 6-Nov-2 AB Stockholms Auktionsverk #794/R (S.KR 4000)
£319 $505 €479 Untitled (40x50cm-16x20in) s.d.98 oil on acrylic glass. 28-Apr-3 Bukowskis, Stockholm #957/R (S.KR 4200)
£418 $661 €627 Interior from Mondrian's studio, NY (37x27cm-15x11in) s.d.88 oil cardboard on acrylic glass. 28-Apr-3 Bukowskis, Stockholm #1007/R (S.KR 5500)
£548 $865 €822 Interior from Mondrian's studio, Paris (53x27cm-21x11in) s. s.d.1987 verso panel. 28-Apr-3 Bukowskis, Stockholm #1008/R (S.KR 7200)
£2453 $3826 €3680 From Opera number 39 (200x64cm-79x25in) s.d.1987-88 verso. 5-Nov-2 Bukowskis, Stockholm #428/R est:35000-40000 (S.KR 35000)
£2453 $3826 €3680 From Opera number 57 (200x64cm-79x25in) s.d.1987-88 verso. 5-Nov-2 Bukowskis, Stockholm #429/R est:35000-40000 (S.KR 35000)
£5957 $9292 €8936 Mondrian's studio (197x197cm-78x78in) s. s.i.d.1989 verso prov.exhib. 5-Nov-2 Bukowskis, Stockholm #470/R est:100000-120000 (S.KR 85000)
Works on paper
£245 $383 €368 Untitled (30x21cm-12x8in) s.d.93 Indian ink chk pen melitrace two pieces. 6-Nov-2 AB Stockholms Auktionsverk #793/R (S.KR 3500)
£347 $559 €521 Lindingo by night (21x30cm-8x12in) s.d.1994 mixed media. 7-May-3 AB Stockholms Auktionsverk #966/R (S.KR 4500)

WIEDEVELT, Johannes (1731-1802) Danish
Sculpture
£1034 $1571 €1551 Bust of J F Classen wearing Danneborg's Order (214cm-84in) plaster incl.white gold painted socle. 27-Aug-2 Rasmussen, Copenhagen #1406/R est:8000-12000 (D.KR 12000)
Works on paper
£378 $609 €567 Antique scene (14x22cm-6x9in) s.i.d.1788 Indian ink wash pen prov. 26-Feb-3 Museumsbygningen, Copenhagen #99 (D.KR 4200)

WIEDYK, Cees (20th C) Dutch
£545 $855 €850 Still life with bread, plums, a mug and a bottle (45x50cm-18x20in) s.d.94. 25-Nov-2 Glerum, Amsterdam #234/R

WIEGAND, Charmion von (1899-1983) American
£366 $600 €531 Untitled (15x13cm-6x5in) tempera collage on paper. 1-Jun-3 Wright, Chicago #311/R
£2083 $3250 €3125 Finger of Budda No.103 (20x15cm-8x6in) s.i.d.1953 painted paper collage board prov.exhib. 5-Nov-2 Doyle, New York #40/R est:2000-3000
Works on paper
£1563 $2500 €2266 Traveler's cocktail (18x13cm-7x5in) s.d. multi-media collage prov. 17-May-3 Selkirks, St. Louis #448/R est:3000-4000

WIEGAND, Gustave (1870-1957) American
£380 $600 €570 Figure in landscape by a house (30x25cm-12x10in) s. 5-Apr-3 DeFina, Austinburg #1324
£1125 $1800 €1631 Old homestead (36x51cm-14x20in) s. 16-May-3 Skinner, Boston #65/R est:2800-3200
£2357 $3700 €3536 Autumn landscape with lake and figure on shore with boat, fishing (91x76cm-36x30in) s. s.i. on stretcher. 19-Apr-3 James Julia, Fairfield #17/R est:2500-3500

WIEGANDT, Bernhard (1851-1918) German
£1132 $1766 €1800 Fisherhude farmstead on the Wumme (70x46cm-28x18in) s. lino. 21-Sep-2 Bolland & Marotz, Bremen #427/R est:2000

WIEGELE, Franz (1887-1944) Austrian
£300 $474 €450 Mediterranean town (46x61cm-18x24in) s. 14-Nov-2 Christie's, Kensington #97
Works on paper
£1304 $2139 €1800 Nude sleeping (46x55cm-18x22in) s.i.d. graphite. 27-May-3 Hassfurther, Vienna #71 est:1700-2000

WIEGER, Wilhelm (1890-1964) German
£890 $1389 €1300 Summer on the Scandinavian coast (25x34cm-10x13in) s.d.1908 1918 board two. 10-Apr-3 Schopman, Hamburg #651

WIEGERS, Jan (1893-1959) Dutch
Works on paper
£318 $497 €500 Tongeren, Veluwe (32x44cm-13x17in) s.d.39 chl. 6-Nov-2 Vendue Huis, Gravenhage #73/R

WIEGHARDT, Paul (1897-1969) German
£1220 $2000 €1769 Man and woman (163x119cm-64x47in) s.i.verso. 1-Jun-3 Wright, Chicago #265/R est:2000-3000

WIEGHORST, Olaf (1899-1988) American
£4819 $8000 €6988 Canyon wall (41x51cm-16x20in) mono. i.verso masonite prov. 11-Jun-3 Butterfields, San Francisco #4130/R est:8000-12000
£8974 $14000 €13461 Three palominos (56x71cm-22x28in) 9-Nov-2 Altermann Galleries, Santa Fe #71
£11327 $18350 €16424 Navajo girl on Burro (41x51cm-16x20in) 23-May-3 Altermann Galleries, Santa Fe #12
£12821 $20000 €19232 California cowboy (71x97cm-28x38in) s. prov.lit. 9-Nov-2 Santa Fe Art, Santa Fe #33/R est:20000-30000
£13014 $19000 €19521 Wood gatherers (64x76cm-25x30in) 18-May-2 Altermann Galleries, Santa Fe #80/R
£22436 $35000 €33654 Colorado stage (71x99cm-28x39in) s.i. prov.lit. 9-Nov-2 Santa Fe Art, Santa Fe #143/R est:35000-45000
£25316 $40000 €36708 Picking the trail (51x61cm-20x24in) s. prov. 26-Jul-3 Coeur d'Alene, Hayden #127/R est:20000-30000
£25641 $40000 €38462 Trapped (71x99cm-28x39in) s. prov.lit. 9-Nov-2 Santa Fe Art, Santa Fe #195/R est:35000-45000
£28481 $45000 €41297 Canyon trail (71x97cm-28x38in) s. prov. 26-Jul-3 Coeur d'Alene, Hayden #112/R est:30000-50000
£34810 $55000 €50475 Roundup riders (71x97cm-28x38in) s. prov. 26-Jul-3 Coeur d'Alene, Hayden #68/R est:35000-55000
£35616 $52000 €53424 Moonlight and shadows (71x97cm-28x38in) 18-May-2 Altermann Galleries, Santa Fe #71/R
£94937 $150000 €137659 Beef herd (86x122cm-34x48in) s. prov. 26-Jul-3 Coeur d'Alene, Hayden #71/R est:60000-80000
Sculpture
£15068 $22000 €22602 The Navajo Madonna (58cm-23in) one of ten bronze. 18-May-2 Altermann Galleries, Santa Fe #15/R
Works on paper
£316 $500 €458 Indian in snow (28x25cm-11x10in) s. W/C prov. 26-Jul-3 Coeur d'Alene, Hayden #237/R
£903 $1500 €1309 Roping a calf (37x50cm-15x20in) s. pencil ink paperboard prov. 11-Jun-3 Butterfields, San Francisco #4111/R est:3000-5000
£903 $1500 €1309 Wild ride (25x35cm-10x14in) s. ink prov. 11-Jun-3 Butterfields, San Francisco #4113/R est:2000-4000
£949 $1500 €1376 Indian study. Portrait study of a horse. Portrait of a horse (10x13cm-4x5in) s. pen ink W/C set of three prov. 26-Jul-3 Coeur d'Alene, Hayden #244/R est:1000-1500

£1026 $1600 €1539 Portrait of an Indian man (18x23cm-7x9in) W/C. 9-Nov-2 Altermann Galleries, Santa Fe #68

£1656 $2750 €2401 Steppin' out (25x20cm-10x8in) mono. ink W/C prov. 11-Jun-3 Butterfields, San Francisco #4112/R est:3000-5000

£1807 $3000 €2620 Taking a break (30x25cm-12x10in) mono. ink W/C gouache prov. 11-Jun-3 Butterfields, San Francisco #4114/R est:3000-5000

£1923 $3000 €2885 Indian chief (23x20cm-9x8in) W/C. 9-Nov-2 Altermann Galleries, Santa Fe #67

£1923 $3000 €2885 Indian on paint pony (30x25cm-12x10in) s. W/C ink prov.lit. 9-Nov-2 Santa Fe Art, Santa Fe #173/R est:4000-6000

£2078 $3200 €3117 Two Navajos (36x25cm-14x10in) W/C. 25-Oct-2 Morris & Whiteside, Hilton Head Island #42 est:4000-5000

£2083 $3250 €3125 Cowboy with white woolly chaps (28x28cm-11x11in) s. W/C ink prov.lit. 9-Nov-2 Santa Fe Art, Santa Fe #11/R est:4000-6000

£2259 $3750 €3276 American Indian on horseback (25x20cm-10x8in) mono. ink W/C gouache prov. 11-Jun-3 Butterfields, San Francisco #4131/R est:3000-5000

£2410 $4000 €3495 Cowboy bringing in the horses (30x30cm-12x12in) mono.d.82 ink W/C htd white paperboard prov. 11-Jun-3 Butterfields, San Francisco #4132/R est:3000-5000

£2468 $3800 €3702 Mounted cowboy in the snow (25x20cm-10x8in) init.d.20 W/C ink htd white board. 4-Sep-2 Christie's, Rockefeller NY #349/R est:2000-3000

£2564 $4000 €3846 Cowboy on horse (33x28cm-13x11in) s. W/C prov.lit. 9-Nov-2 Santa Fe Art, Santa Fe #172/R est:4000-6000

£3481 $5500 €5047 Indian mother (23x18cm-9x7in) s. pen ink W/C prov. 26-Jul-3 Coeur d'Alene, Hayden #42/R est:4000-6000

£3620 $5865 €5249 Bucking bronco (36x28cm-14x11in) W/C. 23-May-3 Altermann Galleries, Santa Fe #117

£3846 $6000 €5769 Indian chief (23x18cm-9x7in) init. W/C prov. 9-Nov-2 Santa Fe Art, Santa Fe #10/R est:3000-5000

£4259 $6900 €6176 Arrival (25x33cm-10x13in) ink W/C. 23-May-3 Altermann Galleries, Santa Fe #11

£5380 $8500 €7801 Horse portrait. Navajo portrait. Mission El Rancho. Christmas card (23x20cm-9x8in) s. pen ink W/C set of four prov. 26-Jul-3 Coeur d'Alene, Hayden #69/R est:10000-20000

£8228 $13000 €11931 Yellow slicker (36x36cm-14x14in) s. W/C prov. 26-Jul-3 Coeur d'Alene, Hayden #225/R est:8000-12000

WIEGMAN, Gerard (1875-1964) Dutch

£522 $815 €820 Activity on the river (60x79cm-24x31in) s. 5-Nov-2 Vendu Notarishuis, Rotterdam #222/R

£563 $907 €800 River scene with ships (33x63cm-13x25in) s. 6-May-3 Vendu Notarishuis, Rotterdam #27/R

£701 $1079 €1100 Fishing boats from Marken at sea (46x61cm-18x24in) s.d.1925 with two other works by same hand three. 3-Sep-2 Christie's, Amsterdam #297

WIEGMAN, Gerard (attrib) (1875-1964) Dutch

£1132 $1800 €1698 Untitled, harbour scene (58x79cm-23x31in) 28-Feb-3 Douglas, South Deerfield #3

WIEGMAN, Matthieu (1886-1971) Dutch

£249 $395 €360 Portrait of Albert van Dalsum (65x53cm-26x21in) s.i.d.1927 verso prov. 10-Mar-3 Sotheby's, Amsterdam #318

£347 $573 €500 Portrait of a woman holding a bouquet of red roses (65x54cm-26x21in) s.d.20. 1-Jul-3 Christie's, Amsterdam #392a

£379 $603 €550 Portrait of a lady (100x81cm-39x32in) s.d.1960 verso prov. 10-Mar-3 Sotheby's, Amsterdam #326

£966 $1535 €1400 Angels (102x80cm-40x31in) s. 10-Mar-3 Sotheby's, Amsterdam #327/R est:1500-2000

£1931 $3070 €2800 Still life with fruit bowl (46x38cm-18x15in) s. prov. 10-Mar-3 Sotheby's, Amsterdam #317 est:1200-1500

£2207 $3509 €3200 Still life with a chair (46x38cm-18x15in) s. prov. 10-Mar-3 Sotheby's, Amsterdam #328/R est:1800-2000

£2414 $3837 €3500 Still life with a bottle, a glass and apples (50x60cm-20x24in) s. prov. 10-Mar-3 Sotheby's, Amsterdam #294/R est:2000-3000

Works on paper

£255 $397 €400 Bridge near a doorway (41x33cm-16x13in) s. W/C. 6-Nov-2 Vendue Huis, Gravenhage #78/R

£486 $802 €700 Farmhouses with bleach-fields (45x60cm-18x24in) s. brush black ink gouache. 1-Jul-3 Christie's, Amsterdam #387

£486 $802 €700 Still life (47x59cm-19x23in) s. i.d.1950 verso W/C black chk. 1-Jul-3 Christie's, Amsterdam #392

WIEGMAN, Piet (1885-1963) Dutch

£3103 $4934 €4500 Flower still life (60x86cm-24x34in) init. prov. 10-Mar-3 Sotheby's, Amsterdam #268/R est:3500-4500

WIEGMANN, Rudolf (1804-1865) German

£100000 $167000 €145000 Rome, a view of the River Tiber looking south (68x99cm-27x39in) s.d.1834 prov. 10-Jul-3 Sotheby's, London #63/R est:20000-30000

Works on paper

£436 $636 €680 Porta del Popolo and St Peter from Villa Borghese (28x40cm-11x16in) i. pencil. 4-Jun-2 Karl & Faber, Munich #149

WIELAND, Hans Beat (1867-1945) Swiss

£281 $436 €422 Mountain landscape with valley view (73x58cm-29x23in) s. panel. 24-Sep-2 Koller, Zurich #6653/R (S.FR 650)

£326 $505 €489 Lac Noir sur Zermatt, Breithorn et Lyskam (26x33cm-10x13in) mono. i.verso panel. 7-Dec-2 Galerie du Rhone, Sion #439/R (S.FR 750)

£416 $658 €624 Mountain landscape (39x54cm-15x21in) s.d.1918. 29-Nov-2 Zofingen, Switzerland #3132 (S.FR 970)

£524 $828 €786 Matterhorn (36x30cm-14x12in) s.d.1938 panel. 14-Nov-2 Stuker, Bern #589 (S.FR 1200)

£1223 $1907 €1835 By Flascherberg (54x64cm-21x25in) s. i.d.1927. 8-Nov-2 Dobiaschofsky, Bern #151/R est:2500 (S.FR 2800)

Works on paper

£845 $1386 €1225 Parsenn (48x63cm-19x25in) s.i. W/C. 4-Jun-3 Fischer, Luzern #2693/R est:2000-2500 (S.FR 1800)

WIELANDT, Manuel (1863-1922) German

£1361 $2163 €2000 Fishing boat on the Lagoon (48x61cm-19x24in) s. 19-Mar-3 Neumeister, Munich #801/R est:1200

WIEMKEN, Walter Kurt (1907-1940) Swiss

£15721 $24681 €23582 Theatre (65x81cm-26x32in) s.d.1931 verso exhib.lit. 25-Nov-2 Sotheby's, Zurich #87/R est:35000-55000 (S.FR 36000)

WIERIK, Jan te (1954-) Dutch

Works on paper

£288 $453 €450 Beast (65x50cm-26x20in) s.d.99 mixed media. 25-Nov-2 Glerum, Amsterdam #261

WIERINGEN, Cornelis Claesz van (1580-1633) Dutch

Works on paper

£10828 $16892 €17000 Fantastic mountainous landscape with watermill by a bridge (23x34cm-9x13in) pen brown ink over black chk prov. 5-Nov-2 Sotheby's, Amsterdam #16/R est:18000-22000

WIERINGEN, Ian van (1944-) Australian

£797 $1307 €1156 Untitled (152x100cm-60x39in) s. board triptych. 3-Jun-3 Lawson Menzies, Sydney #1022 (A.D 2000)

WIERSMA, Ids (1878-1965) Dutch

£2675 $4120 €4200 Sailing pleasure, Friesland (33x45cm-13x18in) s.d.1916. 3-Sep-2 Christie's, Amsterdam #340/R est:2000-3000

WIERTZ, Antonie (1806-1865) Belgian

£396 $633 €550 Chien dans sa niche (119x86cm-47x34in) 13-May-3 Palais de Beaux Arts, Brussels #333

£2449 $3894 €3600 Vanitas still life with skull, flower, candle and hourglass (34x47cm-13x19in) 24-Mar-3 Bernaerts, Antwerp #262/R est:1500-2000

WIERTZ, Antonie (attrib) (1806-1865) Belgian

£1020 $1622 €1500 Maternite (60x72cm-24x28in) 19-Mar-3 Hotel des Ventes Mosan, Brussels #195/R est:1700-1900

£7914 $12662 €11000 Le bouton de rose (100x61cm-39x24in) prov. 13-May-3 Palais de Beaux Arts, Brussels #179/R est:7000-9000

WIERUSZ-KOWALSKI, Alfred von (1849-1915) Polish

£323 $500 €485 Winter landscape (86x69cm-34x27in) 2-Nov-2 North East Auctions, Portsmouth #995/R

£2431 $3865 €3500 Wedding day, Cossacks on horseback (11x7cm-4x3in) init. cardboard. 29-Apr-3 Christie's, Amsterdam #93/R est:3000-5000

£4403 $6868 €7000 Peasant on horse drawn cart (15x21cm-6x8in) s. panel. 9-Oct-2 Michael Zeller, Lindau #961/R est:4000

£10759 $17000 €17000 Wolves and hunters (49x70cm-19x28in) s. 1-Dec-2 Bukowskis, Helsinki #287/R est:20000-30000

£15000 $24600 €22500 Giddy up! (50x61cm-20x24in) s. 3-Jun-3 Sotheby's, London #21/R est:15000-20000

£15484 $24000 €23226 Happy return (48x62cm-19x24in) s. 29-Oct-2 Sotheby's, New York #112/R est:25000-35000

£15646 $24878 €23000 Winter sleigh ride (43x63cm-17x25in) s. lit. 21-Mar-3 Auktionhaus Georg Rehm, Augsburg #8120/R est:18000

WIERUSZ-KOWALSKI, Alfred von (attrib) (1849-1915) Polish

£1027 $1603 €1500 Wolf in front of a village in a winter landscape (46x68cm-18x27in) lit. 10-Apr-3 Allgauer, Kempten #3062/R est:1900

WIESCHEBRINK, Franz (1818-1884) German

£3767 $5877 €5500 Two women writing letter (83x71cm-33x28in) s. 10-Apr-3 Van Ham, Cologne #1755/R est:2800

WIESNER, Richard (1900-) Czechoslovakian
£284 $451 €426 Woman in interior (45x33cm-18x13in) mono.d.58. 8-Mar-3 Dorotheum, Prague #129/R est:10000-15000 (C.KR 13000)

WIETHASE, Edgard (1881-1965) Belgian
£261 $421 €400 Chevaux (46x60cm-18x24in) s. canvas laid down. 14-Jan-3 Vanderkindere, Brussels #480
£411 $645 €600 Vieux cheval se redressant (50x60cm-20x24in) s. panel. 15-Apr-3 Galerie Moderne, Brussels #386
£694 $1104 €1000 Verer en pleine floraison (50x60cm-20x24in) s. 29-Apr-3 Campo & Campo, Antwerp #353/R
£696 $1086 €1100 Verger fleuri. s. 10-Sep-2 Vanderkindere, Brussels #287

WIETHUCHTER, Gustav (1873-1946) German
£1154 $1685 €1800 Motherhood (79x95cm-31x37in) s.d.1903. 4-Jun-2 Karl & Faber, Munich #474/R est:3000

WIGAND, Albert (1890-1978) German
Works on paper
£278 $439 €400 Boxes (21x28cm-8x11in) s.i.d.III 78 i. verso wax chk W/C. 26-Apr-3 Dr Lehr, Berlin #544
£660 $1042 €950 Untitled - composition with Christmas tree (22x11cm-9x4in) s.d.12.64 collage on board. 26-Apr-3 Dr Lehr, Berlin #543/R

WIGAND, Balthasar (1771-1846) Austrian
Works on paper
£1026 $1590 €1600 Assault by the French troops in Vienna in year 1809 (9x13cm-4x5in) s.i. gouache. 4-Dec-2 Neumeister, Munich #563/R est:1200

WIGDEHL, Michaloff (1856-1921) Norwegian
£1273 $1961 €1910 Summer night (117x132cm-46x52in) s. painted 1905. 28-Oct-2 Blomqvist, Lysaker #1351/R est:15000-18000 (N.KR 15000)

WIGERSMA, Jacob (1877-1957) Dutch
£573 $894 €900 Interior of church with figures (55x44cm-22x17in) s. 6-Nov-2 Vendue Huis, Gravenhage #69

WIGERT, Hans (1932-) Swedish
£342 $541 €513 Sailing on a Sunday (47x55cm-19x22in) s.d.1978-82 verso. 28-Apr-3 Bukowskis, Stockholm #1001/R (S.KR 4500)
£456 $721 €684 Night and day (61x50cm-24x20in) s.d.1967 verso. 28-Apr-3 Bukowskis, Stockholm #1001a/R (S.KR 6000)
£666 $1039 €999 Toy boat made of bark (50x64cm-20x25in) s.i.d.1993. 5-Nov-2 Bukowskis, Stockholm #382/R (S.KR 9500)
£1081 $1741 €1622 Eagle (37x27cm-15x11in) s.d.1972-75. 7-May-3 AB Stockholms Auktionsverk #1030/R est:8000-10000 (S.KR 14000)
£2085 $3357 €3128 Night bird (74x93cm-29x37in) s.i.d.1996 verso. 7-May-3 AB Stockholms Auktionsverk #1028/R est:25000-30000 (S.KR 27000)

WIGG, Charles Mayes (1889-1969) British
Works on paper
£370 $603 €555 Yacht racing on the Norfolk Broads (23x33cm-9x13in) s. W/C. 14-Feb-3 Keys, Aylsham #628/R
£650 $1014 €975 Ranworth Staithe (28x43cm-11x17in) s. W/C. 11-Apr-3 Keys, Aylsham #598/R

WIGGERS, Karel (1916-1989) Dutch
£1911 $2981 €3000 Small boy in front of window (31x41cm-12x16in) s. panel. 6-Nov-2 Vendue Huis, Gravenhage #174a est:2500-3000

WIGGIN, Alfred J (1823-1883) American
£254 $425 €368 Portrait of a young girl in a blue dress (41x33cm-16x13in) panel. 21-Jun-3 Selkirks, St. Louis #143

WIGGINS, Carleton (1848-1932) American
£2138 $3100 €3207 Early spring Lyme 1906 (30x41cm-12x16in) 1-Jun-2 Russ Antiques, Waterford #5
£2897 $4200 €4346 Old pastures at Lyme (23x36cm-9x14in) 1-Jun-2 Russ Antiques, Waterford #111

WIGGINS, Guy A (20th C) American
£12821 $20000 €19232 Snowy day on the Avenue (61x76cm-24x30in) s. 30-Mar-3 Simpson's, Houston #430

WIGGINS, Guy Carleton (1883-1962) American
£1748 $2500 €2622 Dusk pastoral scene (30x41cm-12x16in) s. 11-Dec-1 Lincoln, Orange #470
£1750 $2800 €2625 Winter landscape of Central Park (15x20cm-6x8in) s. canvas on board. 17-May-3 Pook & Pook, Downington #158b/R est:3000-4000
£2435 $3750 €3653 North Pier, Noank (30x41cm-12x16in) s.i.verso canvasboard prov.exhib. 24-Oct-2 Shannon's, Milford #198/R est:2500-3500
£2707 $4250 €4061 Mystic, Connecticut (46x61cm-18x24in) s. i.verso prov. 19-Nov-2 Butterfields, San Francisco #8037/R est:5000-7000
£2759 $4000 €4139 Arrangement of flowers (76x61cm-30x24in) 1-Jun-2 Russ Antiques, Waterford #110
£2760 $4250 €4140 Rocks and trees (30x41cm-12x16in) s. canvas on board. 24-Oct-2 Shannon's, Milford #216/R est:3000-5000
£3247 $5000 €4871 Dockside (20x30cm-8x12in) s. canvasboard prov. 24-Oct-2 Shannon's, Milford #28/R est:5000-7000
£3247 $5000 €4871 Early autumn (30x41cm-12x16in) s. 24-Oct-2 Shannon's, Milford #171/R est:3000-5000
£4483 $6500 €6725 Essex Harbour (56x66cm-22x26in) 1-Jun-2 Russ Antiques, Waterford #76
£4656 $6750 €6984 Spring again (64x76cm-25x30in) 1-Jun-2 Russ Antiques, Waterford #1
£5031 $8000 €7547 Montana mountains (46x60cm-18x24in) s.i.verso canvasboard. 5-Mar-3 Sotheby's, New York #110/R est:10000-15000
£5518 $8000 €8277 Autumn morning, Essex Ct, (61x91cm-24x36in) painted c.1957. 1-Jun-2 Russ Antiques, Waterford #11
£5862 $8500 €8793 St Thomas from my studio window (61x91cm-24x36in) painted c.1957. 1-Jun-2 Russ Antiques, Waterford #24
£6034 $8750 €9051 Corner of a library, interior scene with kittens (76x64cm-30x25in) 1-Jun-2 Russ Antiques, Waterford #130
£6410 $10000 €9615 Harbour scene (66x76cm-26x30in) s. 9-Nov-2 Sloan, North Bethesda #605/R est:15000-20000
£11972 $17000 €17958 Dock scene (28x38cm-11x15in) board. 8-Aug-1 Barridorf, Portland #107/R est:6000-9000
£11976 $20000 €17365 At the library (23x30cm-9x12in) s. i.verso canvasboard prov. 18-Jun-3 Christie's, Los Angeles #56/R est:25000-35000
£12658 $20000 €18987 Dockside, Noank (30x41cm-12x16in) s. board. 24-Apr-3 Shannon's, Milford #90/R est:20000-30000
£12676 $18000 €19014 Fifth Avenue blizzard (28x23cm-11x9in) board. 8-Aug-1 Barridorf, Portland #120/R est:20000-30000
£13174 $22000 €19102 Public Library, New York (30x41cm-12x16in) s. s.i.verso canvasboard prov. 22-Jun-3 Freeman, Philadelphia #142/R est:30000-50000
£14286 $22000 €21429 New York in winter (20x28cm-8x11in) s. board prov. 24-Oct-2 Shannon's, Milford #147/R est:20000-30000
£14371 $24000 €20838 At the plaza (30x41cm-12x16in) s. i.verso canvasboard prov. 18-Jun-3 Christie's, Los Angeles #57/R est:25000-35000
£14483 $21000 €21725 Luncheon at the Plaza (41x51cm-16x20in) painted c.1961. 1-Jun-2 Russ Antiques, Waterford #30
£17931 $26000 €26897 Wall Street winter (23x30cm-9x12in) 1-Jun-2 Russ Antiques, Waterford #60
£23567 $37000 €35351 Midtown Manhattan (41x30cm-16x12in) s. i.verso canvasboard. 20-Nov-2 Christie's, Los Angeles #66/R est:30000-50000
£28025 $44000 €42038 Wall Street and Old Trinity (30x23cm-12x9in) s. i.verso canvasboard. 20-Nov-2 Christie's, Los Angeles #40/R est:25000-35000
£28302 $45000 €42453 Winter at the library (30x41cm-12x16in) s. s.i.verso canvasboard prov. 4-Mar-3 Christie's, Rockefeller NY #61/R est:25000-35000
£28614 $47500 €41490 New York City under snowfall (76x63cm-30x25in) s. prov. 11-Jun-3 Butterfields, San Francisco #4067/R est:20000-30000
£29033 $45000 €43550 First snow, Lyme, Connecticut (86x102cm-34x40in) s. 4-Dec-2 Sotheby's, New York #43/R est:30000-50000
£29655 $43000 €44483 Midtown Manhattan (61x51cm-24x20in) painted c.1961. 1-Jun-2 Russ Antiques, Waterford #100
£30323 $47000 €45485 5th Avenue winter (76x102cm-30x40in) s. s.i.d.1939 verso prov. 5-Dec-2 Christie's, Rockefeller NY #104/R est:40000-60000
£33750 $54000 €50625 Fifth Avenue snow storm (41x30cm-16x12in) s. i.verso. 4-Jan-3 Brunk, Ashville #896/R est:15000-25000
£34483 $50000 €51725 An old fashioned Christmas, (76x102cm-30x40in) painted c.1960. 1-Jun-2 Russ Antiques, Waterford #50
£38710 $60000 €58065 Broadway, winter (41x30cm-16x12in) s.o. s.d.1920 verso. 4-Dec-2 Sotheby's, New York #54/R est:40000-60000
£41935 $65000 €62903 Washington Square, New York City (64x76cm-25x30in) s. painted c.1935. 8-Dec-2 Toomey, Oak Park #718/R est:50000-70000
£42068 $61000 €63102 Broad Street winter (23x30cm-9x12in) 1-Jun-2 Russ Antiques, Waterford #70
£51613 $80000 €77420 Empire state building, winter (77x64cm-30x25in) s.i. s.d.1936 verso. 4-Dec-2 Sotheby's, New York #53/R est:70000-90000
£55556 $90000 €83334 Fifth Avenue in wartime (76x63cm-30x25in) s.i. s.verso prov. 21-May-3 Sotheby's, New York #231/R est:70000-90000
£60345 $87500 €90518 Blizzard at the Plaza (61x91cm-24x36in) 1-Jun-2 Russ Antiques, Waterford #90
£63793 $92500 €95690 Lower Broadway in winter (61x51cm-24x20in) 1-Jun-2 Russ Antiques, Waterford #35

WIGGINS, Kim Douglas (1960-) American
£719 $1200 €1043 New Day (20x25cm-8x10in) board. 27-Jun-3 Altermann Galleries, Santa Fe #14
£719 $1200 €1043 Caprock ranch (20x25cm-8x10in) board. 27-Jun-3 Altermann Galleries, Santa Fe #18
£719 $1200 €1043 Crescent moon (20x25cm-8x10in) 27-Jun-3 Altermann Galleries, Santa Fe #21
£719 $1200 €1043 Hollhocks (20x25cm-8x10in) 27-Jun-3 Altermann Galleries, Santa Fe #25
£1018 $1700 €1476 Chiwawita (28x36cm-11x14in) 27-Jun-3 Altermann Galleries, Santa Fe #19
£1018 $1700 €1476 Church on de Vargas (28x36cm-11x14in) 27-Jun-3 Altermann Galleries, Santa Fe #35

£1018 $1700 €1476 Pink adobe (28x36cm-11x14in) 27-Jun-3 Altermann Galleries, Santa Fe #37
£1497 $2500 €2171 Along the Cimarron range (36x46cm-14x18in) 27-Jun-3 Altermann Galleries, Santa Fe #16
£1647 $2750 €2388 New Mexico chiles (41x51cm-16x20in) board. 27-Jun-3 Altermann Galleries, Santa Fe #27
£1647 $2750 €2388 Saturday morning (41x51cm-16x20in) 27-Jun-3 Altermann Galleries, Santa Fe #32
£1647 $2750 €2388 Springtime in Chimayo (41x51cm-16x20in) 27-Jun-3 Altermann Galleries, Santa Fe #33
£1647 $2750 €2388 Fields of Mora (41x51cm-16x20in) 27-Jun-3 Altermann Galleries, Santa Fe #36
£1647 $2750 €2388 Rising sun (41x51cm-16x20in) 27-Jun-3 Altermann Galleries, Santa Fe #38
£1647 $2750 €2388 Vegetable stand (41x51cm-16x20in) board. 27-Jun-3 Altermann Galleries, Santa Fe #40
£2395 $4000 €3473 Above the Rio Grande (56x71cm-22x28in) 27-Jun-3 Altermann Galleries, Santa Fe #15
£2395 $4000 €3473 Santo Domingo and Chamiso (56x71cm-22x28in) 27-Jun-3 Altermann Galleries, Santa Fe #31
£2564 $4000 €3846 Tale of Don Wray (61x91cm-24x36in) 9-Nov-2 Altermann Galleries, Santa Fe #207
£2994 $5000 €4341 Approaching storm III (61x76cm-24x30in) 27-Jun-3 Altermann Galleries, Santa Fe #17
£2994 $5000 €4341 Church at Chimayo (61x76cm-24x30in) 27-Jun-3 Altermann Galleries, Santa Fe #34
£3699 $5400 €5549 Cycle of life no.12 (61x76cm-24x30in) 18-May-2 Altermann Galleries, Santa Fe #199/R
£4192 $7000 €6078 Cycle of life num 15 in remembrance (76x102cm-30x40in) 27-Jun-3 Altermann Galleries, Santa Fe #23
£4192 $7000 €6078 Full moon over Ranchos (76x102cm-30x40in) 27-Jun-3 Altermann Galleries, Santa Fe #24
£4259 $6900 €6176 Santa Fe downtown (61x91cm-24x36in) 23-May-3 Altermann Galleries, Santa Fe #181
£5324 $8625 €7720 Cycle of life no.4 (91x91cm-36x36in) 23-May-3 Altermann Galleries, Santa Fe #180
£5479 $8000 €8219 All the stars of April (91x91cm-36x36in) 18-May-2 Altermann Galleries, Santa Fe #200/R
£9581 $16000 €13892 Pueblo revolt (122x152cm-48x60in) 27-Jun-3 Altermann Galleries, Santa Fe #30

WIGGLI, Oskar (1927-) Swiss
Works on paper
£349 $510 €524 Untitled (68x51cm-27x20in) s.d.1966 chl. 4-Jun-2 Germann, Zurich #871 (S.FR 800)

WIGLE, Archie Palmer (20th C) American
£344 $550 €516 Fall landscape (41x51cm-16x20in) 10-Jan-3 Du Mouchelle, Detroit #2301/R
£344 $550 €516 Coastline with rocks (28x41cm-11x16in) board. 10-Jan-3 Du Mouchelle, Detroit #2304/R
£510 $800 €765 Wooded landscape (36x61cm-14x24in) s. 20-Nov-2 Boos Gallery, Michigan #493/R

WIGLEY, James (1918-1999) Australian
£536 $841 €804 Sydney pub, The Newcastle (39x34cm-15x13in) s. pencil ink W/C exhib. 25-Nov-2 Christie's, Melbourne #407/R (A.D 1500)
£712 $1089 €1068 Burning Cane (35x48cm-14x19in) board painted c.1958 prov.exhib. 26-Aug-2 Sotheby's, Paddington #715/R est:3000-5000 (A.D 2000)

WIGLEY, Joseph (18th C) British
Works on paper
£1200 $1920 €1800 North-eat corner of Covent Garden, formerly John Rich's Theatre (30x25cm-12x10in) W/C. 11-Mar-3 Bonhams, New Bond Street #28/R est:800-1200

WIGMANA, Gerard (1637-1741) Dutch
£573 $894 €900 Portrait of a Cleric standing and wearing black robe (75x60cm-30x24in) s.d.1709 prov. 5-Nov-2 Sotheby's, Amsterdam #158/R

WIHLBORG, Gerhard (1897-1982) Swedish
£490 $775 €735 Kaaseberga Harbour (68x74cm-27x29in) s.d.45 panel. 16-Nov-2 Crafoord, Lund #40/R (S.KR 7000)
£2104 $3324 €3156 Still life of objects on bureau (56x52cm-22x20in) s.d.26 prov. 27-Nov-2 Falkkloos, Malmo #77828/R est:15000 (S.KR 30000)

WIIG-HANSEN, Svend (1922-1997) Danish
£1016 $1575 €1524 Figures (33x30cm-13x12in) init.stretcher exhib. 1-Oct-2 Rasmussen, Copenhagen #199a est:12000 (D.KR 12000)
Sculpture
£1487 $2349 €2231 Reclining woman (16x23x8cm-6x9x3in) num.17/35 bronze. 1-Apr-3 Rasmussen, Copenhagen #351/R est:15000 (D.KR 16000)
£1809 $2804 €2714 Seated woman (49x44cm-19x17in) pat.burned leather exhib. 4-Dec-2 Kunsthallen, Copenhagen #24/R est:20000 (D.KR 21000)
Works on paper
£279 $444 €419 Figure composition (54x74cm-21x29in) s.d.91 pencil. 10-Mar-3 Rasmussen, Vejle #725 (D.KR 3000)

WIIK, Maria (1853-1928) Finnish
£2830 $4358 €4500 Woman with cloth (40x34cm-16x13in) i. 27-Oct-2 Bukowskis, Helsinki #312/R est:3500
£3671 $5800 €5800 Summer flowers (33x24cm-13x9in) 1-Dec-2 Bukowskis, Helsinki #214/R est:6000-7000
£8228 $13000 €13000 Interior. Girl underneath tree (31x23cm-12x9in) s.d.1921 panel double-sided. 30-Nov-2 Hagelstam, Helsinki #128/R est:13000
£22535 $36282 €32000 View from the farm (52x66cm-20x26in) s. lit. 10-May-3 Bukowskis, Helsinki #174/R est:35000-40000
£28481 $45000 €45000 Portrait of girl with red hair (38x31cm-15x12in) s. lit. 1-Dec-2 Bukowskis, Helsinki #209/R est:50000-55000
Works on paper
£1799 $2878 €2500 Flowers (30x41cm-12x16in) s. W/C. 17-May-3 Hagelstam, Helsinki #125/R est:3000
£2041 $3245 €3000 Mrs Sorrow (20x30cm-8x12in) pastel lit. 27-Feb-3 Hagelstam, Helsinki #966/R est:700
£2086 $3338 €2900 Poppies (48x31cm-19x12in) s. W/C pastel lit. 17-May-3 Hagelstam, Helsinki #124/R est:2500
£2374 $3799 €3300 Head of girl (47x37cm-19x15in) s. mixed media. 17-May-3 Hagelstam, Helsinki #126/R est:2000
£4430 $7000 €7000 Sick girl (40x50cm-16x20in) s.d.1904 W/C pastel exhib. 30-Nov-2 Hagelstam, Helsinki #127/R
£4430 $7000 €7000 Self portrait (54x44cm-21x17in) s. mixed media. 1-Dec-2 Bukowskis, Helsinki #215/R est:1500-1700
£6329 $10000 €10000 Boy dressed in party outfit (55x45cm-22x18in) s. pastel. 1-Dec-2 Bukowskis, Helsinki #212/R est:10000-12000

WIJNGAERDT, Piet van (1873-1964) Dutch
£446 $696 €700 Study of Amstelveen polder (37x51cm-15x20in) s. s.1902 verso board. 6-Nov-2 Vendue Huis, Gravenhage #76/R
£592 $959 €900 Gladiolen (80x70cm-31x28in) s.d.14.8.59 s.i.d.verso. 21-Jan-3 Christie's, Amsterdam #403/R
£658 $1066 €1000 Chrysanten - chrysanthemums (70x67cm-28x26in) s. s.i.verso. 21-Jan-3 Christie's, Amsterdam #483 est:1000-1500
£660 $1089 €950 Still life with chrysanthemums (76x65cm-30x26in) s. 1-Jul-3 Christie's, Amsterdam #375
£828 $1292 €1300 Ruins in Brederode (85x74cm-33x29in) s. 6-Nov-2 Vendue Huis, Gravenhage #77/R
£828 $1316 €1200 Gladiolen (70x80cm-28x31in) s. s.i.verso. 10-Mar-3 Sotheby's, Amsterdam #298/R est:1000-1500
£896 $1425 €1300 Papavers en witte seringen (80x68cm-31x27in) s. s.i.verso. 10-Mar-3 Sotheby's, Amsterdam #319 est:400-600
£896 $1425 €1300 Paarse Dahlia's en chrysanten (80x69cm-31x27in) s. s.i.verso. 10-Mar-3 Sotheby's, Amsterdam #320/R est:1000-1500
£1026 $1610 €1600 White marguerites and cornflowers (50x40cm-20x16in) s. 25-Nov-2 Glerum, Amsterdam #27/R est:1500-2000
Works on paper
£282 $454 €400 Houses on edge of village (36x29cm-14x11in) s. pastel. 7-May-3 Vendue Huis, Gravenhage #540/R

WIK, Wilhelm (1897-1987) Swedish
£1141 $1802 €1712 Musical composition (91x122cm-36x48in) s. panel painted 1940s. 28-Apr-3 Bukowskis, Stockholm #277/R est:15000-20000 (S.KR 15000)

WIKSTROM, Bror Anders (1854-1909) American/Swedish
Works on paper
£474 $750 €711 New Orleans Mardi Gras costume (23x18cm-9x7in) W/C card. 5-Apr-3 Neal Auction Company, New Orleans #376

WILBERG, Christian (1839-1882) German
£1509 $2355 €2400 Old city of Bamberg (70x59cm-28x23in) s. prov. 19-Sep-2 Dr Fritz Nagel, Stuttgart #1014/R est:1500

WILBUR, Lawrence Nelson (1897-1988) American
£2244 $3500 €3366 Young woman holding book (41x30cm-16x12in) s. 9-Nov-2 Illustration House, New York #108/R est:2000-3000

WILCKENS, August (1870-1939) German
£513 $795 €800 Rain clouds (33x48cm-13x19in) s. i. verso board prov. 7-Dec-2 Ketterer, Hamburg #185/R

WILCOX, Leslie A (1904-) British
£600 $960 €900 Fishing boat leaving harbour (15x23cm-6x9in) d.1960. 11-Mar-3 Gorringes, Lewes #2292
£18092 $27500 €27138 American packet ship, George Washington arriving at Liverpool (102x152cm-40x60in) 17-Aug-2 North East Auctions, Portsmouth #722/R est:30000-50000

WILD, Carel Frederik Louis de (1870-1922) Dutch
£478 $736 €750 Fresh fish (41x34cm-16x13in) s.d.92 canvas on panel. 3-Sep-2 Christie's, Amsterdam #261

WILD, Frank Percy (1861-1950) British
£4348 $7000 €6522 Young girl and her dog fishing on the lake (91x61cm-36x24in) s. 20-Jan-3 Arthur James, Florida #134

WILD, Otto (1898-?) German
£385 $596 €600 Geraniums in flower pot (64x54cm-25x21in) s. board. 5-Dec-2 Schopman, Hamburg #648
£577 $894 €900 Las Palmas - Gran Canaria (60x80cm-24x31in) s. lit. 7-Dec-2 Hans Stahl, Hamburg #72/R

WILD, William Donald (19/20th C) British
£3500 $5425 €5250 Bigg market and the Sunday morning quayside market, Newcastle (91x71cm-36x28in) init.indis.d.1913 pair. 24-Sep-2 Anderson & Garland, Newcastle #492/R est:800-1200

WILDA, Charles (1854-1907) Austrian
£1069 $1657 €1700 Oriental beggar (29x17cm-11x7in) s.d.99 mixed media. 1-Oct-2 Dorotheum, Vienna #198/R est:1100-1200

WILDA, Hans Gottfried (1862-1911) Austrian
Works on paper
£387 $624 €550 Kaiser Franz Joseph I (34x26cm-13x10in) s.d.1897 W/C on photo. 7-May-3 Dorotheum, Vienna #130/R
£1812 $2971 €2500 Kaiser Franz Josef, journey in Schonbrunn (25x36cm-10x14in) s. W/C bodycol. 27-May-3 Hassfurther, Vienna #72/R est:2000-2500

WILDE, Auguste de (1819-1886) Belgian
£7000 $11690 €10500 Merrymaking in a tavern (60x72cm-24x28in) s.d.1851. 18-Jun-3 Christie's, Kensington #87/R est:7000-9000

WILDE, Elizabeth M (attrib) (fl.1897-1938) British
£620 $960 €930 Sunlit harbour (39x49cm-15x19in) bears sig. 3-Dec-2 Sotheby's, Olympia #207/R

WILDE, Gerald (1905-) British
£1900 $3154 €2755 Inferno (71x91cm-28x36in) painted c.1950 sold with catalogue. 10-Jun-3 David Lay, Penzance #502/R est:1000-1500

WILDE, Samuel de (1748-1832) British
£8500 $13260 €12750 Scene from 'New hay at the old market' by George Coleman (81x74cm-32x29in) prov.lit. 8-Oct-2 Sotheby's, Olympia #382/R est:8000-12000

WILDE, Samuel de (attrib) (1748-1832) British
£500 $815 €725 Portrait of a lady in a white dress (42x33cm-17x13in) panel oval. 17-Jul-3 Tennants, Leyburn #793

WILDE, William (1826-1901) British
Works on paper
£3600 $5868 €5400 Wilford ferry. Gunthorpe ferry, Nottinghamshire (22x67cm-9x26in) s.indis.d.1862/63 pencil W/C htd white pair. 13-Feb-3 Mellors & Kirk, Nottingham #771/R est:2000-3000

WILDENRADT, Johann Peter (1861-1904) Danish
£431 $655 €647 Coastal landscape from Nice with boy fishing from cliff (24x37cm-9x15in) s.d.1894. 27-Aug-2 Rasmussen, Copenhagen #1686/R (D.KR 5000)

WILDENS, Jan (1586-1653) Flemish
£3822 $5962 €6000 Wooded landscape with horsemen and travellers on a path (65x94cm-26x37in) mono. prov.exhib.lit. 5-Nov-2 Sotheby's, Amsterdam #30/R est:8000-12000
£14483 $23028 €21000 Landscape with figures (65x94cm-26x37in) mono. lit. 4-Mar-3 Ansorena, Madrid #60/R est:19000

WILDER, Andre (1871-1965) French
£373 $600 €560 Notre Dame in Paris in a snow storm (66x91cm-26x36in) s.d.19. 19-Jan-3 Jeffery Burchard, Florida #61/R
£704 $1134 €1000 Cote rocheuse (38x46cm-15x18in) s. 11-May-3 Thierry & Lannon, Brest #233
£1887 $2924 €3000 Bord de Seine animee. 4-Oct-2 Tajan, Paris #237 est:2400-3000
£5253 $8300 €8300 Port de Rotterdam (65x92cm-26x36in) s.d.1903. 2-Dec-2 Tajan, Paris #33/R
Works on paper
£220 $341 €350 Vue de Camaret (25x32cm-10x13in) s. W/C. 4-Oct-2 Tajan, Paris #235
£346 $536 €550 Regate au large de la presque'ile (36x42cm-14x17in) s. W/C. 4-Oct-2 Tajan, Paris #240

WILDING, Cora (20th C) New Zealander
Works on paper
£281 $446 €422 Path through a garden (30x43cm-12x17in) s. W/C. 25-Feb-3 Peter Webb, Auckland #24/R (NZ.D 800)

WILDING, Ludwig (1927-) German
Sculpture
£1957 $3209 €2700 Object with movement sbst 556 (55x55x10cm-22x22x4in) s.i.d.1987 verso serigraphed plexiglas board wood. 28-May-3 Lempertz, Koln #468/R est:1500-1700

WILDING, R T (20th C) British
Works on paper
£1300 $2119 €1950 South Devon and Cornish coast; fishing vessels on choppy seas (40x20cm-16x8in) one s.d.1915 one i. W/C htd white pair. 11-Feb-3 Fellows & Sons, Birmingham #131/R est:800-1200

WILDING, Robert Thornton (attrib) (20th C) British
Works on paper
£360 $572 €540 Fishing smacks at sea, off a coast. bears sig W/C. 27-Feb-3 Bonhams, Chester #431

WILDT, Adolfo (1868-1931) Italian
Sculpture
£2051 $3241 €3200 Silence (35x29cm-14x11in) plaster. 16-Nov-2 Farsetti, Prato #247

WILES, Irving Ramsey (1861-1948) American
£6494 $10000 €9741 Peconic Docks (30x36cm-12x14in) s. board. 24-Oct-2 Shannon's, Milford #19/R est:6000-8000
£17742 $27500 €26613 Village street (45x56cm-18x22in) s.i. prov. 4-Dec-2 Sotheby's, New York #2/R est:15000-20000
£18710 $29000 €28065 Peconic shore scene (18x23cm-7x9in) s. panel. 2-Nov-2 North East Auctions, Portsmouth #35/R est:10000-15000
£24516 $38000 €36774 Reader (26x18cm-10x7in) s. painted c.1900 prov. 3-Dec-2 Phillips, New York #55/R est:25000-45000
£116129 $180000 €174194 Sunshine and shadow (40x35cm-16x14in) s. panel painted c.1895 prov.exhib.lit. 3-Dec-2 Phillips, New York #57/R est:200000-300000
Works on paper
£5263 $8000 €7895 Woman in Japanese dress (76x56cm-30x22in) s.d.1885 W/C. 17-Aug-2 North East Auctions, Portsmouth #1228/R est:8000-10000

WILES, Irving Ramsey (attrib) (1861-1948) American
£1796 $3000 €2604 At the piano (66x41cm-26x16in) indis sig. 22-Jun-3 Freeman, Philadelphia #96/R est:2000-3000

WILES, Walter G (1875-1966) South African
£602 $969 €903 Outspan outside Hogsback on the road to Cathcart (59x74cm-23x29in) s. board. 12-May-3 Stephan Welz, Johannesburg #176 est:4000-6000 (SA.R 7000)

WILETTE, Adolphe Leon (1857-1926) French
£949 $1472 €1500 Femme dans la roseraie (131x48cm-52x19in) s. 29-Sep-2 Eric Pillon, Calais #114/R

WILHELM, Heinrich (attrib) (1816-1902) German
£1135 $1759 €1703 Interior scene with figures (74x107cm-29x42in) panel. 4-Dec-2 AB Stockholms Auktionsverk #1846/R est:20000-25000 (S.KR 16000)

WILHELMS, Alexander (1886-1972) Finnish
£392 $643 €600 Sailing vessel, twilight (46x75cm-18x30in) s.d.1938. 9-Feb-3 Bukowskis, Helsinki #391/R

WILHELMS, Carl (1889-1953) Finnish

£8534 $13825 €12374 Inger and the cat (35x27cm-14x11in) s.i.d.1923 panel. 25-May-3 Uppsala Auktionskammare, Uppsala #218/R est:50000-60000 (S.KR 110000)

WILHELMSON, Carl (1866-1928) Swedish

£707 $1159 €1025 Landscape with couple (38x34cm-15x13in) tempera. 4-Jun-3 AB Stockholms Auktionsverk #2296/R (S.KR 9000)
£1710 $2719 €2565 Portrait of unknown young girl (32x24cm-13x9in) s. panel. 2-Mar-3 Uppsala Auktionskammare, Uppsala #253/R est:12000 (S.KR 23000)
£1844 $2858 €2766 Boats (29x22cm-11x9in) s. exhib. 4-Dec-2 AB Stockholms Auktionsverk #1749/R est:20000-25000 (S.KR 26000)
£1986 $3078 €2979 Boats by jetty (19x25cm-7x10in) s. canvas on cardboard exhib. 3-Dec-2 Bukowskis, Stockholm #132/R est:20000-22000 (S.KR 28000)
£2057 $3188 €3086 View of Blabarsholmen (32x40cm-13x16in) s. 3-Dec-2 Bukowskis, Stockholm #133/R est:30000-40000 (S.KR 29000)
£2483 $4022 €3600 Ore-carrying steamer (34x68cm-13x27in) s. exhib.lit. 26-May-3 Bukowskis, Stockholm #90/R est:40000-50000 (S.KR 32000)
£3103 $5027 €4499 The black cat (42x31cm-17x12in) s.d.1922 panel exhib.lit. 26-May-3 Bukowskis, Stockholm #88/R est:40000-50000 (S.KR 40000)
£3535 $5797 €5126 Woman in blue interior (47x70cm-19x28in) s. 4-Jun-3 AB Stockholms Auktionsverk #2151/R est:50000-60000 (S.KR 45000)
£5120 $8295 €7424 Flamenco dancer (36x55cm-14x22in) s.i.d.1910. 26-May-3 Bukowskis, Stockholm #67/R est:80000-100000 (S.KR 66000)
£5674 $8794 €8511 The old society house, Fiskebackskil (57x35cm-22x14in) st.sig. verso. 3-Dec-2 Bukowskis, Stockholm #141/R est:100000-120000 (S.KR 80000)
£7092 $10993 €10638 Coastal landscape in moonlight (60x90cm-24x35in) s. 4-Dec-2 AB Stockholms Auktionsverk #1706/R est:100000-125000 (S.KR 100000)
£9697 $15710 €14061 Painter (84x59cm-33x23in) s. exhib.lit. 26-May-3 Bukowskis, Stockholm #87/R est:100000-125000 (S.KR 125000)
£10284 $15940 €15426 Inner fjord (66x90cm-26x35in) s. 3-Dec-2 Bukowskis, Stockholm #141a/R est:150000-175000 (S.KR 145000)
£10993 $17039 €16490 By the quay (56x91cm-22x36in) s. 3-Dec-2 Bukowskis, Stockholm #143a/R est:150000-175000 (S.KR 155000)
£12413 $20109 €17999 Autumn ploughing (174x48cm-69x19in) s. exhib.lit. 26-May-3 Bukowskis, Stockholm #91/R est:80000-100000 (S.KR 160000)
£19007 $30791 €27560 Washerwomen (74x43cm-29x17in) s.d.1925 exhib.lit. 26-May-3 Bukowskis, Stockholm #83/R est:150000-175000 (S.KR 245000)
£21277 $32979 €31916 Two girls in yard, Fiskebackskil (80x56cm-31x22in) s.d.99. 4-Dec-2 AB Stockholms Auktionsverk #1760/R est:300000-350000 (S.KR 300000)
£28369 $43972 €42554 Waiting (52x61cm-20x24in) s.d.98 lit. 3-Dec-2 Bukowskis, Stockholm #135/R est:140000-160000 (S.KR 400000)
£78014 $120922 €117021 Andalusian family (145x115cm-57x45in) s. painted 1913 prov.exhib.lit. 3-Dec-2 Bukowskis, Stockholm #137/R est:700000-800000 (S.KR 1100000)

Works on paper

£842 $1330 €1263 Portrait of Karin Hedlund as a girl (23x17cm-9x7in) mono. W/C oval. 30-Nov-2 Goteborg Auktionsverk, Sweden #225/R (S.KR 12000)
£1086 $1760 €1575 Fisherman (53x39cm-21x15in) s.i. W/C lit. 26-May-3 Bukowskis, Stockholm #86/R (S.KR 14000)
£1086 $1760 €1575 Houses in steep street (36x23cm-14x9in) s.d.1883 W/C. 25-May-3 Uppsala Auktionskammare, Uppsala #210/R (S.KR 14000)
£1122 $1773 €1683 Portrait of Fredrik Nicander (35x30cm-14x12in) s.i.d.1907 i.verso mixed media exhib. 30-Nov-2 Goteborg Auktionsverk, Sweden #224/R est:10000 (S.KR 16000)

WILHJELM, Johannes (1868-1938) Danish

£287 $465 €416 Landscape with figure - woman seated on the heath near Svinklov (71x97cm-28x38in) s.d.1918 exhib. 26-May-3 Rasmussen, Copenhagen #1404/R (D.KR 3000)
£355 $553 €533 Southern courtyard with chickens and orange trees (74x61cm-29x24in) s.i. 23-Sep-2 Rasmussen, Vejle #219/R (D.KR 4200)
£373 $593 €560 Farm yard with woman, children and chickens (71x97cm-28x38in) init.d.32 exhib. 5-May-3 Rasmussen, Vejle #660/R (D.KR 4000)
£426 $672 €639 River on the outskirts of wood (100x125cm-39x49in) s.d.26. 2-Dec-2 Rasmussen, Copenhagen #1286/R (D.KR 5000)
£931 $1480 €1397 September's day at Grenen (74x100cm-29x39in) init.d.32. 5-Mar-3 Rasmussen, Copenhagen #1968/R (D.KR 10000)
£9500 $15865 €14250 On Skagen beach (101x138cm-40x54in) s. prov. 19-Jun-3 Christie's, London #71/R est:10000-15000

WILKE, Paul Ernst (1894-1972) German

£748 $1190 €1100 Fishing boat (40x60cm-16x24in) s. s.d.63 verso panel. 28-Mar-3 Bolland & Marotz, Bremen #400/R
£1507 $2351 €2200 Fishing boats on East Friesian coast (61x80cm-24x31in) s. i. verso. 10-Apr-3 Van Ham, Cologne #1757/R est:1800
£1509 $2355 €2400 Fishing boats (50x70cm-20x28in) s. panel. 21-Sep-2 Bolland & Marotz, Bremen #428/R est:2200
£1633 $2596 €2400 Harbour (60x81cm-24x32in) s. s.i.d.1963 verso masonite. 28-Mar-3 Bolland & Marotz, Bremen #399/R est:1600
£2767 $4317 €4400 Old bridge on the moor (60x80cm-24x31in) s.d.39 s.i. verso. 21-Sep-2 Bolland & Marotz, Bremen #429/R est:1200

WILKENS, Theodorus (attrib) (c.1690-1748) Dutch

Works on paper

£1146 $1789 €1800 Roman ruins (19x17cm-7x7in) pen brown ink W/C. 5-Nov-2 Sotheby's, Amsterdam #92/R est:3000-5000

WILKIE, Sir David (1785-1841) British

£450 $716 €675 Jew's harp (18x13cm-7x5in) canvas laid down board. 30-Apr-3 Halls, Shrewsbury #312/R
£550 $880 €825 Rat catchers (23x18cm-9x7in) i. 14-Mar-3 Gardiner & Houlgate, Bath #166/R
£1274 $1987 €2000 Cabaret scene (65x78cm-26x31in) 8-Nov-2 Pierre Berge, Paris #16/R
£1290 $2000 €1935 Mrs Hamilton Nisbet Ferguson of Raith (127x102cm-50x40in) i. 2-Nov-2 North East Auctions, Portsmouth #60/R

Works on paper

£400 $624 €600 Figures on horseback in an extensive landscape (16x26cm-6x10in) pencil white chk. 17-Oct-2 Bonhams, Edinburgh #212
£1049 $1500 €1574 Sketch for Roman princess (29x29cm-11x11in) ink. 22-Jan-3 Doyle, New York #37
£1500 $2325 €2250 Study for breakfast. Figures seated at a table (20x18cm-8x7in) pencil double-sided prov. 31-Oct-2 Christie's, London #7/R est:1500-2000
£2800 $4648 €4200 Studies after the old masters, female figures (18x13cm-7x5in) two i. pencil W/C set of five. 12-Jun-3 Sotheby's, London #117/R est:3000-4000
£4000 $6560 €5800 Preparing for the ball (21x14cm-8x6in) pen brown ink prov. 5-Jun-3 Christie's, London #17/R est:3000-5000
£6000 $9840 €8700 Study of hands for Spanish monks (28x22cm-11x9in) s.d.1832 black chk htd white prov.exhib. 5-Jun-3 Christie's, London #23/R est:2500-3500
£6500 $10140 €9750 Study of figures at la Mancha, Spain (18x23cm-7x9in) s. black chk W/C prov. 14-Apr-3 Sotheby's, London #2/R est:4000-6000
£9000 $14130 €13500 Abram Incab messir (43x28cm-17x11in) s.i.d.Jany 29 1841 col chks W/C htd white prov.lit. 21-Nov-2 Christie's, London #65/R est:10000-15000

WILKIE, Sir David (attrib) (1785-1841) British

£750 $1238 €1088 Study of an elderly man (13x11cm-5x4in) panel. 1-Jul-3 Bearnes, Exeter #501/R

Works on paper

£380 $593 €570 Male right foot (14x12cm-6x5in) pencil col chk. 18-Sep-2 Dreweatt Neate, Newbury #62/R

WILKIN, Frank W (attrib) (c.1800-1842) British

Works on paper

£800 $1248 €1200 Portrait of Francis Jack, 2nd Earl of Kilmorey (80x67cm-31x26in) pastel. 14-Apr-3 Hamilton Osborne King, Dublin #1493/R

WILKING, Georg (1869-1914) German

£949 $1500 €1500 Sea landscape with Herzogin Sopie-Charlotte, a four-mast ship (51x80cm-20x31in) s.d.1910. 29-Nov-2 Bolland & Marotz, Bremen #786/R est:1100

WILKINS, George (19th C) British

£380 $635 €551 Moel siabod from the Dolwyd Valley (29x44cm-11x17in) s.d.1909 i.verso. 26-Jun-3 Mellors & Kirk, Nottingham #920
£460 $718 €690 Welsh landscape with figures (33x53cm-13x21in) s.i.d.1881 verso. 9-Oct-2 Andrew Hartley, Ilkley #742

WILKINS, William Noy (attrib) (c.1820-?) British

£280 $456 €420 Hagley Road, Birmingham (31x46cm-12x18in) s.d.1891. 28-Jan-3 Bonhams, Knowle #332

WILKINSON, Arthur (?) Australian

Works on paper

£429 $700 €644 Country cottage with young girl picking flowers in the garden (28x38cm-11x15in) s. pencil W/C. 16-Feb-3 Butterfields, San Francisco #2057

£720 $1174 €1080 Country cottage with ducks (26x41cm-10x16in) s. W/C gouache. 29-Jan-3 Sotheby's, Olympia #146/R

WILKINSON, Arthur Stanley (c.1860-c.1930) British
Works on paper
£207 $324 €311 Cattle watering (36x51cm-14x20in) s. W/C. 24-Jul-2 Walker's, Ottawa #30 (C.D 500)
£380 $589 €570 Cottage interior (86x56cm-34x22in) s. W/C. 1-Oct-2 Capes Dunn, Manchester #833

WILKINSON, E (19/20th C) British
Works on paper
£750 $1215 €1125 British India steamer Fultala at sea (61x98cm-24x39in) s. w/ bodycol. 21-May-3 Christie's, Kensington #441/R

WILKINSON, George (19/20th C) British
Works on paper
£840 $1336 €1260 Dunbrady Abbey, ground plan (42x63cm-17x25in) i. s.verso pen ink W/C. 4-Mar-3 Bearnes, Exeter #353

WILKINSON, Henry (19/20th C) British
£600 $912 €900 Study of a spaniel retrieving a woodcock in a glade (49x75cm-19x30in) s. 13-Aug-2 Gildings, Market Harborough #250/R

WILKINSON, Henry R (1884-1975) British
Works on paper
£320 $506 €480 Chickens feeding outside a thatched cottage (24x35cm-9x14in) s. W/C. 26-Nov-2 Bonhams, Knightsbridge #66/R

WILKINSON, John B (19th C) Canadian
Works on paper
£1778 $2916 €2667 Traine sauvage (22x17cm-9x7in) init. W/C prov. 3-Jun-3 Joyner, Toronto #125/R est:4000-5000 (C.D 4000)

WILKINSON, Norman (1878-1971) British
£600 $978 €900 Trout rising (44x60cm-17x24in) s. 28-Jan-3 Henry Adams, Chichester #422/R
£650 $1060 €975 Beach scene with gulls (25x34cm-10x13in) s. board. 29-Jan-3 Dreweatt Neate, Newbury #216
£1000 $1620 €1500 Yarmouth, Isle of Wight (62x47cm-24x19in) s. canvasboard prov. 21-May-3 Christie's, Kensington #685/R est:1000-1500
£1300 $2015 €1950 On the river (34x50cm-13x20in) s. 5-Dec-2 Bonhams, Edinburgh #100 est:1200-1800
£1400 $2142 €2100 Netting salmon, Tweedmouth (34x49cm-13x19in) s. 22-Aug-2 Bonhams, Edinburgh #1043/R est:800-1200
£1400 $2170 €2100 Salmon fishing (34x50cm-13x20in) s. 5-Dec-2 Bonhams, Edinburgh #99 est:1200-1800
£1500 $2325 €2250 Summer on the Avon (45x60cm-18x24in) s. 5-Dec-2 Bonhams, Edinburgh #30 est:1500-2000
£1700 $2584 €2550 Working river (45x61cm-18x24in) s. 15-Aug-2 Bonhams, New Bond Street #451/R est:1500-2000
£2000 $3120 €3000 Sailing off Gibraltar (46x61cm-18x24in) s. 26-Mar-3 Woolley & Wallis, Salisbury #240/R est:2000-3000
Works on paper
£260 $395 €390 On the sands at Deal, Kent (13x18cm-5x7in) W/C. 15-Aug-2 Bonhams, New Bond Street #272
£460 $708 €690 Sea power (26x36cm-10x14in) s.d.1909 W/C over pencil. 22-Oct-2 Bonhams, Bath #148
£500 $785 €750 Sea plane (29x41cm-11x16in) s. W/C. 16-Dec-2 Sotheby's, Olympia #166/R
£520 $816 €780 R.R.S Discovery in the Antarctic (29x41cm-11x16in) s. W/C. 16-Dec-2 Sotheby's, Olympia #165/R
£540 $869 €810 Fleet of battleships (34x54cm-13x21in) s. W/C. 20-Feb-3 Bonhams, Edinburgh #333
£550 $858 €825 Sailing ships in the English Channel (36x43cm-14x17in) s. W/C. 9-Apr-3 Cheffins Grain & Comins, Cambridge #652/R
£600 $942 €900 Liner off the Mediterranean port (28x41cm-11x16in) s. W/C. 16-Dec-2 Sotheby's, Olympia #164/R
£680 $1074 €1020 British warships at full steam in a choppy sea (33x53cm-13x21in) W/C. 7-Apr-3 David Duggleby, Scarborough #348/R
£700 $1085 €1050 Ironclads in line in heavy swell (37x55cm-15x22in) s. pencil W/C htd white. 31-Oct-2 Christie's, Kensington #373/R
£2700 $4509 €3915 Cunard and white Star Liner Queen Mary under construction. Shipping scenes (28x41cm-11x16in) s. W/C set of three. 18-Jun-3 Sotheby's, Olympia #120/R est:800-1000
£3200 $5056 €4800 Low tide, West Wittering (34x52cm-13x20in) s. W/C gouache exhib. 27-Nov-2 Sotheby's, Olympia #42/R est:1000-1500

WILKINSON, Rev Joseph (19th C) British
Works on paper
£700 $1106 €1050 Cottage in the Vale of Newlands (37x54cm-15x21in) W/C. 26-Nov-2 Bonhams, Knightsbridge #253/R

WILKINSON, Thomas (19th C) British
£800 $1312 €1200 Blondel and Berengara (51x62cm-20x24in) s.i. panel. 5-Jun-3 Christie's, Kensington #656/R

WILKINSON, Thomas Harrison (1847-1929) Canadian
Works on paper
£442 $694 €663 Trail in the Rockies (48x31cm-19x12in) s. W/C. 25-Nov-2 Hodgins, Calgary #368/R (C.D 1100)
£602 $946 €903 Canadian Barnyard scene (29x45cm-11x18in) s. W/C. 25-Nov-2 Hodgins, Calgary #112/R est:1400-1600 (C.D 1500)

WILKS, Maurice C (1910-1984) British
£350 $511 €525 Portrait of Berry Wilks (41x36cm-16x14in) 12-Jun-2 John Ross, Belfast #254
£400 $620 €600 Snow above Derwent Water (20x25cm-8x10in) s. i.verso board. 4-Dec-2 Andrew Hartley, Ilkley #1187
£1014 $1581 €1500 Evening Connemara (24x29cm-9x11in) s. board. 26-Mar-3 James Adam, Dublin #79/R est:1500-2500
£1100 $1705 €1650 In Inagh Valley (25x30cm-10x12in) s. 4-Dec-2 John Ross, Belfast #60 est:1200-1500
£1100 $1705 €1650 Rough sea, Co. Antrim coast (30x40cm-12x16in) s. 4-Dec-2 John Ross, Belfast #114 est:1200-1500
£1100 $1760 €1650 Breezy day, north-west coast of Donegal (30x41cm-12x16in) s. canvasboard. 15-May-3 Christie's, Kensington #208/R est:1000-1500
£1132 $1766 €1800 Winter near Magee Island, Strangford Lough (25x36cm-10x14in) s. i.verso canvasboard. 17-Sep-2 Whyte's, Dublin #140 est:2000-3000
£1200 $1920 €1800 View from my garden, Dundrum, Co. Down (25x35cm-10x14in) s. i.verso board. 16-May-3 Sotheby's, London #133/R est:1200-1600
£1233 $1936 €1800 In the Inagh Vally, Connemara (41x51cm-16x20in) s. 15-Apr-3 De Veres Art Auctions, Dublin #100l est:1500-2000
£1282 $2013 €2000 Landscape near Downings, County Donegal (25x41cm-10x16in) s. i.verso prov. 19-Nov-2 Whyte's, Dublin #193/R est:1800-2200
£1400 $2226 €2100 In Glendun, County Antrim (40x50cm-16x20in) s. 5-Mar-3 John Ross, Belfast #3 est:1200-1400
£1400 $2226 €2100 Summer day, Glendun County Antrim (35x45cm-14x18in) s. 5-Mar-3 John Ross, Belfast #236 est:1000-1200
£1400 $2184 €2100 Roundstone, Connemara (28x39cm-11x15in) s. i.verso. 9-Apr-3 Cheffins Grain & Comins, Cambridge #730/R est:150-200
£1450 $2378 €2175 Landscape at Recess, Connemara (40x51cm-16x20in) s. i.verso. 3-Jun-3 Sotheby's, Olympia #118/R est:1200-1500
£1500 $2340 €2250 Claggan Bay, Co. Donegal (50x66cm-20x26in) s.i.verso. 26-Mar-3 Sotheby's, Olympia #176/R est:1500-2500
£1500 $2325 €2250 Near Dundrum (35x45cm-14x18in) s. 4-Dec-2 John Ross, Belfast #31 est:1500-1800
£1500 $2340 €2250 HMS Caroline, full ahead (50x67cm-20x26in) s. 14-Apr-3 Hamilton Osborne King, Dublin #1506/R est:600-1000
£1600 $2480 €2400 Houses in the Glens (30x36cm-12x14in) s. board. 2-Oct-2 John Ross, Belfast #216 est:1200-1400
£1800 $2790 €2700 Autumn, Dunn River, Co. Antrim (46x36cm-18x14in) s. 2-Oct-2 John Ross, Belfast #95 est:1500-1750
£1800 $2862 €2700 McAuleys hill farm, Glendun, County Antrim (25x35cm-10x14in) s. 5-Mar-3 John Ross, Belfast #228 est:2000-2200
£1800 $2790 €2700 Boglands, roses, Co. Donegal (25x40cm-10x16in) s. 4-Dec-2 John Ross, Belfast #185 est:1800-2000
£1835 $2845 €2900 On the coast, Donegal (25x30cm-10x12in) s. i.verso. 25-Sep-2 James Adam, Dublin #49/R est:2000-2500
£1944 $3092 €2800 Ben Lettery, Ballnahinch, Connemara (41x51cm-16x20in) s. i.verso. 29-Apr-3 Whyte's, Dublin #194/R est:3000-4000
£1959 $3057 €2900 Doe Castle from Lackagh, Co. Donegal (29x34cm-11x13in) s. board. 26-Mar-3 James Adam, Dublin #108/R est:2000-2500
£2000 $3160 €3000 Ballynahinch Lake, Connemara (51x58cm-20x23in) s.i. verso. 18-Dec-2 Mallams, Oxford #667/R est:1500-2000
£2000 $3100 €3000 At Cushendun, Co. Antrim (50x61cm-20x24in) s. 4-Dec-2 John Ross, Belfast #72 est:2500-2800
£2051 $3179 €3200 At Leenane, Connemara (46x61cm-18x24in) s. 3-Dec-2 Bonhams & James Adam, Dublin #32/R est:3000-5000
£2075 $3238 €3300 Windmills (41x51cm-16x20in) s. 17-Sep-2 Whyte's, Dublin #129/R est:3000-4000
£2083 $3312 €3000 Early spring, Glendun, County Antrim (36x46cm-14x18in) s. i.verso. 29-Apr-3 Whyte's, Dublin #112/R est:3000-4000
£2100 $3255 €3150 Dawn on the Antrim coast (46x91cm-18x36in) s. 2-Oct-2 John Ross, Belfast #31 est:1400-1600
£2162 $3373 €3200 Connemara landscape (45x60cm-18x24in) s. 26-Mar-3 James Adam, Dublin #61/R est:2800-4000
£2192 $3441 €3200 Silver sea, Antrim coast (31x41cm-12x16in) s. i.verso canvasboard. 15-Apr-3 De Veres Art Auctions, Dublin #110/R est:3500-4500
£2342 $3630 €3700 Wooded river landscape (44x34cm-17x13in) s. 25-Sep-2 James Adam, Dublin #145/R est:2000-3000
£2361 $3754 €3400 Misty day near Roundstone, Connemara (36x46cm-14x18in) s. i.verso. 29-Apr-3 Whyte's, Dublin #114/R est:3000-4000
£2400 $3720 €3600 Autumn day, Bryansford, Co. Down (41x51cm-16x20in) s. 2-Oct-2 John Ross, Belfast #121 est:2500-2750

£2405 $3728 €3800 Bogland near Gweedore (50x61cm-20x24in) s. i.verso. 24-Sep-2 De Veres Art Auctions, Dublin #182/R est:3500-4500
£2416 $3890 €3600 On the Lagan (30x41cm-12x16in) s. canvas on board exhib. 18-Feb-3 Whyte's, Dublin #85/R est:3500-4500
£2432 $3795 €3600 West of Ireland landscape with cottages (34x44cm-13x17in) s. 26-Mar-3 James Adam, Dublin #107/R est:3000-4000
£2500 $3875 €3750 Old mill, Glenanne, Co. Antrim (45x56cm-18x22in) s. 4-Dec-2 John Ross, Belfast #12 est:2500-2800
£2500 $3975 €3600 In Inagh Valley, Connemara (25x36cm-10x14in) s. i.verso. 29-Apr-3 Whyte's, Dublin #172/R est:2500-3500
£2564 $3974 €4000 Rough seas, Beadmore Head, County Antrim (51x68cm-20x27in) s. i.stretcher prov. 3-Dec-2 Bonhams & James Adam, Dublin #33/R est:3000-5000
£2600 $3874 €3900 Scrabo from Bradshaws Brae, Co. Down (40x51cm-16x20in) s.i.verso. 27-Jun-2 Greenslade Hunt, Taunton #769/R est:1000-1500
£2600 $4134 €3900 Rowing boat at Cushendun, County Antrim (40x50cm-16x20in) s. 5-Mar-3 John Ross, Belfast #66 est:1200-1400
£2621 $4141 €3932 Farmstead Glendun Co Antrim (41x51cm-16x20in) s. i.verso. 18-Nov-2 Waddingtons, Toronto #160/R est:6000-8000 (C.D 6500)
£2686 $4217 €4029 Homestead, Rosses Country, Donegal (33x41cm-13x16in) s.i. 24-Jul-2 Walker's, Ottawa #35/R est:4000-5000 (C.D 6500)
£2800 $4452 €4200 Cushendun, County Antrim (35x45cm-14x18in) s. 5-Mar-3 John Ross, Belfast #131 est:3000-3500
£2823 $4460 €4235 On the Kerry coast, near Kenmare Co Kerry (41x51cm-16x20in) s. i.verso. 18-Nov-2 Waddingtons, Toronto #161/R est:6000-8000 (C.D 7000)
£2900 $4611 €4350 Winter Co. Antrim (45x55cm-18x22in) s. s.i.verso. 26-Feb-3 Sotheby's, Olympia #227/R est:1200-1800
£3000 $4680 €4500 Knockladye Mountain, Ballycastle, Co Antrim (51x61cm-20x24in) s. i.verso. 13-Sep-2 Lyon & Turnbull, Edinburgh #110/R est:1500-2000
£3000 $4650 €4500 Galway reflection, Roundstone, Connemara (45x91cm-18x36in) s. 4-Dec-2 John Ross, Belfast #123 est:2000-2500
£3024 $4778 €4536 Connemara cottage (41x51cm-16x20in) s. i.verso prov. 18-Nov-2 Waddingtons, Toronto #159/R est:6000-8000 (C.D 7500)
£3200 $5088 €4800 Collecting turf, Connemara (35x45cm-14x18in) s. 5-Mar-3 John Ross, Belfast #154 est:3500-4000
£3221 $5187 €4800 On the Atlantic drive, Co Donegal (41x51cm-16x20in) s. i.verso prov. 18-Feb-3 Whyte's, Dublin #158/R est:3500-4500
£3243 $5059 €4800 Landscape Connemara (35x44cm-14x17in) s.i.verso. 26-Mar-3 James Adam, Dublin #75/R est:3000-5000
£3614 $6000 €5240 Landscape with farmland and lake (51x91cm-20x36in) 13-Jun-3 Du Mouchelle, Detroit #2038/R est:2500-3500
£3974 $6240 €6200 Connemara landscape (46x61cm-18x24in) s. i.verso. 19-Nov-2 Whyte's, Dublin #77/R est:5000-7000
£4300 $6794 €6450 Rockport, Cushendum, Co. Antrim (51x61cm-20x24in) s.i.verso. 13-Nov-2 Halls, Shrewsbury #378 est:700-1000
£4600 $7130 €6900 Muckish Mountain from Mageroríty Co. Donegal (50x61cm-20x24in) s. 4-Dec-2 John Ross, Belfast #126 est:3000-3500
£4700 $7285 €7050 Derry Inver Harbour, Connemara (45x61cm-18x24in) s. 4-Dec-2 John Ross, Belfast #166 est:5000-6000
£5128 $8051 €8000 Landscape, Roundstone, Connemara (46x61cm-18x24in) s. i.verso. 19-Nov-2 Whyte's, Dublin #74/R est:6000-8000
£5500 $8635 €8250 Ben Lettery, Connemara, County Galway (56x66cm-22x26in) s. i.verso. 21-Nov-2 Tennants, Leyburn #835/R est:2000-3000
£6200 $9858 €9300 McCloskey's pub, County Donegal (45x61cm-18x24in) s. 5-Mar-3 John Ross, Belfast #143 est:4500-5000
£7500 $12000 €11250 White Park Bay, Co Antrim (30x35cm-12x14in) s. i.verso canvas on board set of three. 16-May-3 Sotheby's, London #111/R est:3000-5000
£9420 $15449 €13000 September, Lough Leane, Killarney, Co Kerry (63x76cm-25x30in) s.i.verso. 28-May-3 Bonhams & James Adam, Dublin #50/R est:7500-10000
£11000 $17490 €16500 Harbour, West of Ireland (40x50cm-16x20in) s. board. 5-Mar-3 John Ross, Belfast #102 est:3500-4000
£12000 $19200 €18000 Bencorr, Roundstone, Connemara, Co Galway (48x63cm-19x25in) s. i.verso canvasboard. 16-May-3 Sotheby's, London #128/R est:10000-15000

Works on paper
£260 $413 €390 Errisbeg Mountain from Cashel, County Galway (25x35cm-10x14in) s. W/C. 5-Mar-3 John Ross, Belfast #91
£350 $543 €525 Thatched cottage, Donegal (23x33cm-9x13in) mono. W/C. 2-Oct-2 John Ross, Belfast #10
£360 $526 €540 Rocky foreshore (25x36cm-10x14in) s. W/C. 12-Jun-2 John Ross, Belfast #308
£450 $698 €675 Thatched cottage in the mournes (25x36cm-10x14in) s. W/C. 2-Oct-2 John Ross, Belfast #2
£500 $795 €750 Cushendun village (22x28cm-9x11in) s. W/C. 5-Mar-3 John Ross, Belfast #250
£520 $759 €780 Ruck Row, Co. Galway (18x25cm-7x10in) i. d.June 1938 verso W/C. 12-Jun-2 John Ross, Belfast #126
£750 $1223 €1125 Irish lake and mountain landscape (28x38cm-11x15in) s. W/C. 14-Feb-3 Keys, Aylsham #494/R
£800 $1272 €1200 Rockport, Cushendun (25x35cm-10x14in) s. W/C. 5-Mar-3 John Ross, Belfast #245
£850 $1241 €1275 Turf gatherers, Connemara, Co. Galway (25x36cm-10x14in) s.i.verso W/C. 12-Jun-2 John Ross, Belfast #318
£940 $1513 €1400 Cattages and fishing nets by a small bay (27x37cm-11x15in) s. W/C. 18-Feb-3 Whyte's, Dublin #207/R
£1700 $2635 €2550 Interior Murrisk, Co. Mayo (112x91cm-44x36in) s.d.1979 W/C. 2-Oct-2 John Ross, Belfast #112 est:2500-3000

WILLAERT, Arthur (1875-1942) Belgian
£276 $441 €400 Landscape at sunset (27x36cm-11x14in) s. 15-Mar-3 De Vuyst, Lokeren #315

WILLAERT, Ferdinand (1861-1938) Belgian
£5380 $8500 €8500 Le grand beguinage a Gand, l'hiver (98x130cm-39x51in) s. 26-Nov-2 Palais de Beaux Arts, Brussels #184/R est:7500-12500

WILLAERT-FONTAN, Valentine (1882-1939) Belgian
£283 $436 €450 Figure dans le bois (26x21cm-10x8in) s. panel. 22-Oct-2 Campo & Campo, Antwerp #333
£1266 $2000 €2000 Jeune hollandaise a l'ouvrage dans un interieur (100x73cm-39x29in) s. 26-Nov-2 Palais de Beaux Arts, Brussels #185/R est:2000-3000

WILLAERTS, Abraham (1603-1669) Dutch
£5000 $7850 €7500 Coastal landscape with fish sellers by a beached boat (24x42cm-9x17in) init.d.1626 panel prov. 13-Dec-2 Christie's, Kensington #45/R est:6000-8000
£5405 $8432 €8000 Peasant family before farmstead (53x76cm-21x30in) mono. panel. 26-Mar-3 Hugo Ruef, Munich #18/R est:4500
£6410 $10128 €10000 Coastal landscape with figures (57x78cm-22x31in) panel. 16-Nov-2 Lempertz, Koln #1133/R est:10000
£8000 $12480 €12000 Coastal landscape with shipping and fishermen selling their catch (40x54cm-16x21in) panel. 9-Apr-3 Christie's, London #50/R est:8000-12000
£12950 $20719 €18000 Battle scene at sea between Spanish and Dutch fleet (113x214cm-44x84in) 13-May-3 Sotheby's, Amsterdam #55/R est:4000-6000

WILLAERTS, Adam (1577-1669) Dutch
£2866 $4471 €4500 Fish market on a beach (17x22cm-7x9in) panel. 6-Nov-2 Christie's, Amsterdam #2/R est:2500-3500

Works on paper
£1146 $1789 €1800 View of the harbour of Tripoli (28x42cm-11x17in) bears i.verso brush black grey wash over black chk prov. 5-Nov-2 Sotheby's, Amsterdam #102/R est:2000-3000

WILLAERTS, Isaac (1620-1693) Dutch
£4403 $6824 €7000 Fish market on rocky coast (57x76cm-22x30in) panel. 2-Oct-2 Dorotheum, Vienna #88/R est:7000-9000

WILLAME, P (19th C) ?
£1635 $2518 €2600 Canals in Hesdin (81x60cm-32x24in) s.i.d.1903. 27-Oct-2 Muizon & Le Coent, Paris #50/R

WILLARD, Archibald M (1836-1918) American

Works on paper
£9032 $14000 €13548 On to Havana (56x71cm-22x28in) s. pencil pen ink executed c.1893 prov.lit. 4-Dec-2 Sotheby's, New York #158/R est:20000-30000

WILLARD, William (attrib) (1818-1904) American
£1769 $2900 €2565 Portrait of Alfred Richardson (81x66cm-32x26in) 8-Jun-3 Skinner, Boston #69/R est:3000-5000

WILLCOCK, George Barrell (1811-1852) British
£750 $1185 €1125 Lock beside a weir with figures and a windmill (29x39cm-11x15in) s. 2-Dec-2 Bonhams, Bath #129
£1000 $1630 €1500 Landscape with figure leaning against a wooden fence beside a stone bridge (62x82cm-24x32in) 29-Jan-3 Dreweatt Neate, Newbury #154/R est:1200-1800

WILLCOCK, George Barrell (attrib) (1811-1852) British
£978 $1623 €1418 Drinking time. Old farmstead (15x22cm-6x9in) i.verso panel two. 10-Jun-3 Ritchie, Toronto #58/R est:800-1200 (C.D 2200)

WILLE, Fritz von (1860-1941) German
£385 $604 €600 Dietkirchen an der Lahn (32x22cm-13x9in) mono.d.23/4.95 board. 21-Nov-2 Van Ham, Cologne #1977
£576 $944 €800 Village in hilly landscape (46x63cm-18x25in) s. 5-Jun-3 Dorotheum, Salzburg #509/R

£962 $1510 €1500 View over the roofs of the church in Finale, Liguria (33x25cm-13x10in) s.d.4/5.92 W/C board. 21-Nov-2 Van Ham, Cologne #1973 est:800
£1282 $1987 €2000 Eifel landscape in spring with resting woman and dog on edge of path (60x80cm-24x31in) s. 4-Dec-2 Neumeister, Munich #968/R est:2000
£1923 $3019 €3000 Totenmaar landscape (52x61cm-20x24in) s. 21-Nov-2 Van Ham, Cologne #1974/R est:4000
£2115 $3321 €3300 Weinfelder Maar with old chapel (20x31cm-8x12in) s.d.12/9.01 panel. 21-Nov-2 Van Ham, Cologne #1979/R est:4000
£2244 $3522 €3500 Eifel landscape (45x55cm-18x22in) s.d.22.2.82. 21-Nov-2 Van Ham, Cologne #1981/R est:4000
£2466 $3847 €3600 Storm clouds gathering over fields near Plaidt (46x65cm-18x26in) s.d.1/9.90 board. 10-Apr-3 Van Ham, Cologne #1758/R est:3500
£2821 $4428 €4400 Lissingen an der Kyll (62x92cm-24x36in) s.d.97. 21-Nov-2 Van Ham, Cologne #1976/R est:6500
£3038 $4709 €4800 Eifel landscape (50x61cm-20x24in) s. i. stretcher prov. 28-Sep-2 Ketterer, Hamburg #11/R est:1500-2000
£3237 $5180 €4500 Gorse busches on Weinfelder Maar (40x50cm-16x20in) s.d.1930. 17-May-3 Lempertz, Koln #1507/R est:6000
£3333 $5167 €5200 Eifel landscape with lake (58x79cm-23x31in) s. prov. 7-Dec-2 Ketterer, Hamburg #161/R est:3500-4000
£3453 $5525 €4800 Autumn Eifel landscape with Burg Reifferscheid (62x51cm-24x20in) s. 17-May-3 Lempertz, Koln #1506/R est:4000
£4676 $7482 €6500 After the rain (100x132cm-39x52in) s. 17-May-3 Lempertz, Koln #1508/R est:6000

WILLE, Johann Georg (1715-1808) German
Works on paper
£449 $709 €700 Enfant dans une grange (19x22cm-7x9in) s.d.1779 crayon. 15-Nov-2 Drouot Estimations, Paris #63/R
£863 $1381 €1200 Head of young woman (27x21cm-11x8in) i. ochre. 17-May-3 Lempertz, Koln #1263

WILLE, Pierre-Alexandre (1748-1821) French
£4516 $7135 €7000 Paysans (22x19cm-9x7in) one s.d.1783 pair. 18-Dec-2 Renaud, Paris #42/R
Works on paper
£709 $1107 €1050 Age d'or (65x96cm-26x38in) s.d.1810 pierre noire chk. 31-Mar-3 Piasa, Paris #132
£743 $1159 €1100 Fileuse assise (33x23cm-13x9in) crayon. 27-Mar-3 Maigret, Paris #22/R

WILLE, Pierre-Alexandre (attrib) (1748-1821) French
Works on paper
£851 $1421 €1200 Jeune garcon sortant un objet de sa poche (31x20cm-12x8in) sanguine. 19-Jun-3 Piasa, Paris #116/R
£1583 $2500 €2500 Jeune garcon portant un tricorne (35x28cm-14x11in) sanguine. 28-Nov-2 Tajan, Paris #97/R

WILLEBOIRTS, Thomas (1614-1654) Flemish
£17808 $27781 €26000 Madonna and Child with Saints (180x118cm-71x46in) 8-Apr-3 Ansorena, Madrid #109d/R est:18000

WILLEBRANT, James (1950-) Australian
£299 $467 €449 Flight (27x60cm-11x24in) s. board. 21-Oct-2 Australian Art Auctions, Sydney #50 (A.D 850)
£573 $872 €860 Night driver accompanied flight (61x40cm-24x16in) s. acrylic board. 27-Aug-2 Goodman, Sydney #94 (A.D 1600)
£1165 $1771 €1748 Honeymoon pier (105x135cm-41x53in) s. i.d.87 verso. 27-Aug-2 Goodman, Sydney #111/R est:3500-5500 (A.D 3250)
£1165 $1771 €1748 Preparing to hook (114x180cm-45x71in) s. 27-Aug-2 Goodman, Sydney #172/R est:3500-5000 (A.D 3250)

WILLEMS, Florent (1823-1905) Belgian
£709 $1149 €1000 Nino junto a su perro (28x23cm-11x9in) s.d.1843 panel. 20-May-3 Segre, Madrid #61/R est:1000
£2721 $4327 €4000 Le songe (57x43cm-22x17in) s. panel. 18-Mar-3 Galerie Moderne, Brussels #584/R est:10000-12000
£4808 $7452 €7500 Amies de musique (80x52cm-31x20in) s. panel. 3-Dec-2 Campo & Campo, Antwerp #355/R est:7500-8500
£5769 $8942 €9000 Chez le fripier (56x46cm-22x18in) s.d.1859 s.verso panel. 9-Dec-2 Horta, Bruxelles #137/R est:12000-15000
£7092 $11489 €10000 Musical support (69x49cm-27x19in) s. panel. 22-May-3 Dorotheum, Vienna #4/R est:10000-15000
£8917 $13911 €14000 Artiste presentant ses croquis (63x48cm-25x19in) s. panel. 11-Nov-2 Horta, Bruxelles #193/R est:15000-20000

WILLEMSEN, Maggy (1939-) Belgian
Works on paper
£304 $474 €480 Portrait de femme (59x38cm-23x15in) s.d.65 mixed media panel. 16-Oct-2 Hotel des Ventes Mosan, Brussels #308

WILLEMSENS, Abraham (fl.1627-1672) Flemish?
£3179 $5181 €4800 Saint Casilda (58x77cm-23x30in) mono. copper. 11-Feb-3 Segre, Madrid #72/R

WILLERS, Ernst (1803-1880) German
£4630 $7500 €6945 Wooded landscape with goats near Ariccia (40x50cm-16x20in) i.d.1837 paper on canvas prov.lit. 23-Jan-3 Sotheby's, New York #253/R est:15000

WILLETT, Arthur (c.1857-1918) British
Works on paper
£1300 $2119 €1885 West Arm, Shoreham. Harbour, half tide, Shoreham Lock (13x50cm-5x20in) s.i. W/C bodycol pair. 17-Jul-3 Tennants, Leyburn #697/R est:600-800

WILLETTE, Adolphe (1857-1926) French
£1736 $2760 €2500 Jeune femme au treillis de roses jaunes (131x48cm-52x19in) s.d. 30-Apr-3 Tajan, Paris #139/R

WILLIAM, Roland (19th C) British
£350 $543 €525 Yachts in a stiff breeze (50x60cm-20x24in) s.d.75 panel. 29-Oct-2 Henry Adams, Chichester #576

WILLIAMS OF PLYMOUTH, William (1808-1895) British
£800 $1264 €1200 On the River Tavy, near Mary Tavy (33x46cm-13x18in) s.i. s.i.verso pair. 7-Apr-3 Bonhams, Bath #102/R
£900 $1404 €1350 On the Ockment (33x51cm-13x20in) s.i. i.stretcher. 17-Sep-2 Sotheby's, Olympia #148/R
£3100 $4774 €4650 Figures in a peaceful cove (43x69cm-17x27in) s.d.1850. 5-Sep-2 Christie's, Kensington #229/R est:600-800
Works on paper
£280 $417 €420 Figures by a Devon stream (21x34cm-8x13in) s.i.d.1875 W/C. 27-Jun-2 Greenslade Hunt, Taunton #694
£341 $539 €512 Cattle grazing by a waterfall (36x51cm-14x20in) d.1887 W/C. 1-Dec-2 Levis, Calgary #242/R (C.D 850)

WILLIAMS, Albert (1922-) British
£550 $836 €825 Roses and other summer flowers in a vase on a sideboard (46x36cm-18x14in) s. 29-Aug-2 Christie's, Kensington #161/R
£750 $1223 €1088 Still life of irises, tulips and other flowers (61x51cm-24x20in) s. 15-Jul-3 Bonhams, Knightsbridge #122/R
£800 $1336 €1160 Spring and summer flowers in a silver vase (62x51cm-24x20in) s. board. 17-Jun-3 Bonhams, Knightsbridge #181/R
£900 $1458 €1350 Still life with rose, gladioli and other flowers in a vase (49x39cm-19x15in) s. 21-May-3 Bonhams, Knightsbridge #153/R
£900 $1467 €1305 Bowl of dahlias (50x60cm-20x24in) s. board. 15-Jul-3 Bonhams, Knightsbridge #114/R

WILLIAMS, Alexander (1846-1930) British
£1100 $1782 €1650 Landscape with field of corn stukes and meandering river (23x43cm-9x17in) s. board. 21-Jan-3 Rupert Toovey, Partridge Green #88/R est:1200-1800
£1944 $3092 €2800 Sailing boat on Carlingford Lough (25x46cm-10x18in) s. 29-Apr-3 Whyte's, Dublin #173/R est:2000-3000
Works on paper
£356 $590 €516 Blackwater near Dromana, Co. Cork (25x46cm-10x18in) s.i. W/C. 16-Jun-3 Waddingtons, Toronto #187/R (C.D 800)
£360 $562 €540 Marble Strand, Sheephaven, Donegal (19x41cm-7x16in) s.i. W/C. 15-Oct-2 Bearnes, Exeter #359
£444 $738 €644 View on the blackwater, Co. Cork (21x36cm-8x14in) s.i. W/C. 16-Jun-3 Waddingtons, Toronto #185/R est:800-1200 (C.D 1000)
£460 $713 €690 Marble strand, Sheephaven, Donegal (20x40cm-8x16in) s. W/C. 4-Dec-2 John Ross, Belfast #83
£521 $859 €750 Derry na Sliggan, Killary Bay (25x44cm-10x17in) s.i. W/C. 7-Jul-3 Hamilton Osborne King, Dublin #56
£556 $917 €800 Menaan cliffs from Keel (25x51cm-10x20in) s. W/C. 7-Jul-3 Hamilton Osborne King, Dublin #55
£872 $1405 €1300 Letter Hill, Ballinakill Bay, Co Galway (25x47cm-10x19in) s.i. W/C htd white. 18-Feb-3 Whyte's, Dublin #201/R
£1333 $2213 €1933 Saint Audoens Arch, a bit of the old city wall, Dublin (36x26cm-14x10in) s.i. W/C. 16-Jun-3 Waddingtons, Toronto #183/R est:800-1200 (C.D 3000)
£1384 $2158 €2200 Delphi Hills, Killary Bay, Connemara. Rossdowan, Parknasilla, Kenmare Bay (20x38cm-8x15in) s.i. W/C htd white pair. 17-Sep-2 Whyte's, Dublin #111 est:3000-4000
£1422 $2361 €2062 Spitalfield Francis St, Dublin (36x25cm-14x10in) s.i. W/C. 16-Jun-3 Waddingtons, Toronto #182/R est:800-1000 (C.D 3200)
£1511 $2508 €2191 Old clothes shop, Patrick Street, Dublin (36x26cm-14x10in) s.i.d.1885 W/C. 16-Jun-3 Waddingtons, Toronto #184/R est:800-1200 (C.D 3400)

WILLIAMS, Alexander (attrib) (1846-1930) British

Works on paper

£260 $424 €390 Fishing boat at sunset (15x25cm-6x10in) d.1874 W/C. 28-Jan-3 Gorringes, Lewes #1700

WILLIAMS, Alfred Walter (1824-1905) British

£340 $541 €500 Cattle by river (23x31cm-9x12in) s.d.1891. 24-Mar-3 Bukowskis, Helsinki #421/R

£2695 $4366 €3800 Figures in mountainous lakeside landscapes (10x16cm-4x6in) one init.d.62 pair. 21-May-3 James Adam, Dublin #88/R est:4000-6000

£2837 $4596 €4000 Fishermen in a mountainous river landscape at dusk, North Wales (10x16cm-4x6in) one init.d.62 board pair. 21-May-3 James Adam, Dublin #87/R est:4000-6000

WILLIAMS, Alfred Walter (attrib) (1824-1905) British

£2085 $3461 €3023 Mumbles Lighthouse (36x57cm-14x22in) s.d.1866. 16-Jun-3 Lilla Bukowskis, Stockholm #498 est:8000-10000 (S.KR 27000)

WILLIAMS, Alwyn (20th C) Irish?

£320 $512 €480 Near Kilwater, Co Antrim (22x29cm-9x11in) mono. canvasboard. 15-May-3 Christie's, Kensington #221/R

WILLIAMS, Aubrey (1926-1990) British

£262 $409 €393 Catalya I (63x91cm-25x36in) s.i.d.61 verso oil mortar. 6-Nov-2 Dobiaschofsky, Bern #1071 (S.FR 600)

WILLIAMS, Caroline F (1836-1921) British

£1800 $2826 €2700 River landscape with cottages and figures (25x48cm-10x19in) s. prov. 19-Nov-2 Bonhams, Leeds #219/R est:2000-3000

WILLIAMS, Caroline Marsh (1945-) Australian

£643 $1003 €965 Recent painting K (91x122cm-36x48in) init. prov. 11-Nov-2 Deutscher-Menzies, Melbourne #118/R (A.D 1800)

£1143 $1783 €1715 Theory of relatives (91x122cm-36x48in) s.verso exhib. 11-Nov-2 Deutscher-Menzies, Melbourne #119/R est:2000-3000 (A.D 3200)

WILLIAMS, Charles (1965-) British/American

£600 $936 €900 George (25x20cm-10x8in) init. 15-Oct-2 Bonhams, Knightsbridge #230/R

£600 $936 €900 She knows (40x30cm-16x12in) s. 15-Oct-2 Bonhams, Knightsbridge #233/R

£600 $936 €900 Gossips with dog (30x56cm-12x22in) 15-Oct-2 Bonhams, Knightsbridge #236/R

WILLIAMS, Christopher David (1873-1934) British

£500 $790 €750 Evening, Florence. Grand Canal, Venice (32x38cm-13x15in) i.d.1922 verso canvas on board pair. 14-Nov-2 Christie's, Kensington #96/R est:500-700

£920 $1435 €1380 Llanagranog (29x38cm-11x15in) s.i.verso board sold with book. 11-Sep-2 Bonhams, Newport #330/R

WILLIAMS, Dwight (1856-?) American

£406 $650 €589 Landscape with tree and town in the distance (36x53cm-14x21in) s. s.d.1910 verso. 17-May-3 CRN Auctions, Cambridge #24

WILLIAMS, Edward (1782-1855) British

£720 $1138 €1080 Mother and child on a woodland track (22x29cm-9x11in) panel. 7-Apr-3 Bonhams, Bath #79/R

£6500 $10335 €9750 Ferry (56x91cm-22x36in) s. exhib. 6-Mar-3 Christie's, Kensington #401/R est:6000-8000

WILLIAMS, Edward (attrib) (1782-1855) British

£800 $1248 €1200 Approaching storm (63x76cm-25x30in) 7-Nov-2 Christie's, Kensington #85/R

£900 $1404 €1350 Wooded landscape with figures fishing. Wooded landscape with cattle (30x40cm-12x16in) indis.sig. panel pair. 10-Apr-3 Tennants, Leyburn #966/R

£2600 $4056 €3900 Landscape with church and figures (46x35cm-18x14in) board. 10-Sep-2 Sworder & Son, Bishops Stortford #802/R est:2000-3000

£2800 $4564 €4200 Mother and child on a woodland path. Driving sheep through a gate (40x33cm-16x13in) panel pair. 29-Jan-3 Sotheby's, Olympia #26/R est:1500-2500

WILLIAMS, Edward Charles (1807-1881) British

£553 $874 €830 Mountain landscape with lake and cattle (20x30cm-8x12in) s. 2-Dec-2 Rasmussen, Copenhagen #1582/R (D.KR 6500)

£850 $1394 €1275 Figures on a path in a wooded landscape (25x36cm-10x14in) panel prov. 5-Jun-3 Christie's, Kensington #655/R

£986 $1637 €1400 Landscape with peasant children fishing and farmstead (58x49cm-23x19in) s. 12-Jun-3 Hauswedell & Nolte, Hamburg #409/R

£1200 $1884 €1800 On Llyn Gywnant North Wales, morning (61x107cm-24x42in) s. 20-Nov-2 Sotheby's, Olympia #45/R est:2000-3000

£2400 $3744 €3600 Evening on the Thames, Wargrave (61x107cm-24x42in) init.d.1860. 8-Oct-2 Bonhams, Knightsbridge #88/R est:2000-3000

£2740 $4000 €4110 Continental genre scene with figures tending a campsite (46x61cm-18x24in) panel. 3-Nov-1 North East Auctions, Portsmouth #1188/R

£3000 $4680 €4500 Gypsy encampment (44x61cm-17x24in) 7-Nov-2 Christie's, Kensington #154/R est:3000-5000

WILLIAMS, Edward Charles (attrib) (1807-1881) British

£4200 $6846 €6300 Golden harvest (36x61cm-14x24in) 29-Jan-3 Sotheby's, Olympia #84/R est:1500-2500

WILLIAMS, Evelyn (1929-) British

£550 $858 €825 Lady sleeping (25x35cm-10x14in) s.d.1994. 27-Mar-3 Christie's, Kensington #554

£600 $936 €900 Twins heads (21x14cm-8x6in) oil on paper two. 27-Mar-3 Christie's, Kensington #615

Works on paper

£880 $1373 €1320 Waiting for the day (41x30cm-16x12in) papier mache oil relief. 27-Mar-3 Christie's, Kensington #555/R

WILLIAMS, Frederick (fl.1827) British?

Works on paper

£6500 $10140 €9750 Temple of Neptune, Corinth. Temple of Panhellenius, Aegina, looking toward Hymettus (27x39cm-11x15in) s. W/C over pencil htd bodycol pair. 15-Oct-2 Sotheby's, London #33/R est:3000-5000

WILLIAMS, Frederick Ballard (1871-1956) American

£245 $406 €355 Over the hill - woodlands pasture (41x61cm-16x24in) bears sig. 10-Jun-3 Ritchie, Toronto #91/R (C.D 550)

£782 $1212 €1173 Figures in a glade (63x76cm-25x30in) s. 3-Dec-2 Ritchie, Toronto #3109/R est:2000-2500 (C.D 1900)

£1553 $2500 €2330 September romance (30x41cm-12x16in) s. board. 19-Jan-3 Jeffery Burchard, Florida #30/R

WILLIAMS, Frederick Dickenson (1829-1915) American

£1000 $1580 €1500 Figures and cattle in a wooded river landscape with village beyond (36x25cm-14x10in) s.d.78. 13-Nov-2 Halls, Shrewsbury #403/R est:600-800

£1146 $1800 €1719 On the road (30x46cm-12x18in) s.d.1877. 22-Nov-2 Skinner, Boston #87/R est:800-1200

WILLIAMS, Frederick Ronald (1927-1982) Australian

£842 $1280 €1263 Portrait (30x22cm-12x9in) s. oil on paper. 19-Aug-2 Joel, Victoria #335 est:1000-2000 (A.D 2400)

£2302 $3821 €3921 Lilydale landscape (31x50cm-12x20in) s. gouache on cardboard prov. 10-Jun-3 Shapiro, Sydney #6/R est:6000-8000 (A.D 5800)

£12500 $19750 €18750 Burnt landscape (73x55cm-29x22in) s. board. 18-Nov-2 Goodman, Sydney #157/R est:35000-55000 (A.D 35000)

£14337 $21792 €21506 Sapling panel V (40x56cm-16x22in) s. prov.exhib. 28-Aug-2 Deutscher-Menzies, Melbourne #101/R est:45000-55000 (A.D 40000)

£24038 $38221 €36057 Mittagong landscape (51x76cm-20x30in) s. composition board. 4-Mar-3 Deutscher-Menzies, Melbourne #56/R est:65000-85000 (A.D 62500)

£28472 $44417 €42708 Early you yangs II (69x71cm-27x28in) s.d.1962 i.verso board prov. 8-Apr-3 Peter Webb, Auckland #104/R est:65000-85000 (NZ.D 82000)

£35857 $58805 €51993 You Yangs landscape (81x91cm-32x36in) s. prov. 4-Jun-3 Deutscher-Menzies, Melbourne #33/R est:100000-120000 (A.D 90000)

£64516 $98065 €96774 Gum trees at Colo Vale (122x122cm-48x48in) s. prov.exhib. 28-Aug-2 Deutscher-Menzies, Melbourne #34/R est:220000-280000 (A.D 180000)

£65134 $102261 €97701 Gum trees at Colo Vale (122x122cm-48x48in) s. prov.exhib. 15-Apr-3 Lawson Menzies, Sydney #37/R est:170000-190000 (A.D 170000)

£65385 $103962 €98078 Blue kite, Kew Billabong (101x106cm-40x42in) s. prov.exhib.lit. 4-Mar-3 Deutscher-Menzies, Melbourne #38/R est:150000-200000 (A.D 170000)

£71174 $108897 €106761 Forest pond (107x92cm-42x36in) s. painted 1974 prov.exhib. 26-Aug-2 Sotheby's, Paddington #513/R est:180000-250000 (A.D 200000)

£71705 $114012 €107558 Toorongo Falls (95x84cm-37x33in) s. prov. 5-May-3 Sotheby's, Melbourne #117/R est:110000-140000 (A.D 185000)
£78854 $119858 €118281 Australian landscape I (121x152cm-48x60in) i.verso prov.exhib.lit. 28-Aug-2 Deutscher-Menzies, Melbourne #27/R est:180000-240000 (A.D 220000)
£79457 $126337 €119186 Water pond and road (122x122cm-48x48in) s. painted 1975 prov.exhib. 5-May-3 Sotheby's, Melbourne #136/R est:180000-220000 (A.D 205000)
£178571 $282143 €267857 You yangs landscape 1963 (177x134cm-70x53in) s. oil tempera board prov.exhib. 27-Nov-2 Deutscher-Menzies, Melbourne #21/R est:300000-400000 (A.D 500000)

Works on paper

£357 $561 €536 Portrait of a cockney (28x18cm-11x7in) s.d. pencil. 25-Nov-2 Christie's, Melbourne #367 (A.D 1000)
£1200 $1932 €1800 April over London (25x26cm-10x10in) s. gouache paper on board. 6-May-3 Christie's, Melbourne #281 est:5000-7000 (A.D 3000)
£2321 $3598 €3482 Acrobat (31x37cm-12x15in) s. chl. 29-Oct-2 Lawson Menzies, Sydney #27/R est:6000-9000 (A.D 6500)
£3047 $4631 €4571 Saplings (36x52cm-14x20in) s. W/C exec.c.1961. 28-Aug-2 Deutscher-Menzies, Melbourne #114/R est:10000-15000 (A.D 8500)
£3448 $5138 €5172 Landscape (37x56cm-15x22in) s. W/C prov. 27-Aug-2 Christie's, Melbourne #59/R est:12000-15000 (A.D 9000)
£5000 $7900 €7500 Untitled (55x37cm-22x15in) s. gouache prov. 17-Nov-2 Sotheby's, Paddington #63/R est:12000-18000 (A.D 14000)
£10714 $16821 €16071 Marsh (54x73cm-21x29in) s. gouache. 25-Nov-2 Christie's, Melbourne #74/R est:18000-25000 (A.D 30000)
£11071 $17493 €16607 Landscape (52x72cm-20x28in) s. gouache. 26-Nov-2 Sotheby's, Melbourne #60/R est:28000-32000 (A.D 31000)
£11155 $18295 €16175 Burnt landscape, Upwey (57x76cm-22x30in) s. gouache paper on board prov. 4-Jun-3 Deutscher-Menzies, Melbourne #71/R est:28000-35000 (A.D 28000)
£12143 $19064 €18215 Landscape (55x72cm-22x28in) s. gouache acrylic prov. 25-Nov-2 Christie's, Melbourne #90/R est:25000-35000 (A.D 34000)
£15936 $26135 €23107 Avenel I (54x74cm-21x29in) s. gouache prov. 4-Jun-3 Deutscher-Menzies, Melbourne #44/R est:28000-34000 (A.D 40000)

WILLIAMS, Geoff (20th C) New Zealander

£4389 $6846 €6584 Christine on Andy's couch (61x84cm-24x33in) s. board. 7-Nov-2 International Art Centre, Auckland #22/R est:14000-18000 (NZ.D 14000)
£5054 $8087 €7328 Morning shroud over Tekapo (75x95cm-30x37in) s. board. 13-May-3 Watson's, Christchurch #21/R est:17000-25000 (NZ.D 14000)

Works on paper

£4417 $7111 €6626 Shepherds Hut, Central Otago (64x94cm-25x37in) s. mixed media. 7-May-3 Dunbar Sloane, Auckland #15/R est:12500-15000 (NZ.D 12500)

WILLIAMS, George Augustus (1814-1901) British

£300 $471 €450 Evening in North Wales (36x46cm-14x18in) mono. 21-Nov-2 Tennants, Leyburn #800
£774 $1200 €1161 Norfolk river scene (43x64cm-17x25in) s. painted c.1870. 8-Dec-2 Toomey, Oak Park #626/R
£900 $1413 €1350 Morning on the moors. Showery day (36x61cm-14x24in) mono. pair. 16-Apr-3 Christie's, Kensington #638
£987 $1540 €1431 Shepherd and family on a winter morning (41x66cm-16x26in) mono. 26-Mar-3 Walker's, Ottawa #69/R est:9000-12000 (C.D 2300)
£1200 $1860 €1800 Hay barge on the Norfolk Broads (34x52cm-13x20in) init. 3-Dec-2 Sotheby's, Olympia #143/R est:1200-1800
£2600 $4082 €3900 Thames at Shiplake (30x61cm-12x24in) mono. 19-Nov-2 Bonhams, New Bond Street #119/R est:1500-2500
£6000 $9960 €9000 View on the Thames (61x107cm-24x42in) mono. 12-Jun-3 Sotheby's, London #234/R est:6000-8000
£8000 $13280 €12000 Harvest field, morning (94x145cm-37x57in) mono. 12-Jun-3 Sotheby's, London #275a/R est:8000-12000

WILLIAMS, George Augustus (attrib) (1814-1901) British

£1800 $2826 €2700 Children playing amongst fallen timbers in an extensive landscape (61x91cm-24x36in) 16-Dec-2 Bonhams, Bury St Edmunds #446 est:2000-3000

WILLIAMS, Glynn (1939-) British

£580 $940 €841 Cattle grazing beneath a tree. Cattle paused beside a gate. (12x18cm-5x7in) board two. 20-May-3 Dreweatt Neate, Newbury #268/R

WILLIAMS, Graham (19th C) British

£737 $1150 €1106 Steady breeze (91x58cm-36x23in) s. 28-Mar-3 Aspire, Cleveland #25/R est:800-1200

WILLIAMS, Guy (1920-) British

Works on paper

£320 $528 €464 At the barrier (51x66cm-20x26in) brush black ink gouache. 3-Jul-3 Christie's, Kensington #283

WILLIAMS, H (?) ?

£900 $1431 €1350 Highland landscape (61x91cm-24x36in) s. i.verso. 6-Mar-3 Christie's, Kensington #414/R

WILLIAMS, H Perry (fl.1841-1857) British

£1004 $1586 €1506 Young couple with infant (41x36cm-16x14in) d.1852 paperboard. 1-Dec-2 Levis, Calgary #241/R (C.D 2500)

WILLIAMS, Harold (20th C) British

£450 $711 €675 Brown hunter in a paddock (51x76cm-20x30in) s. board. 28-Nov-2 Christie's, Kensington #187/R

WILLIAMS, Harry (19th C) British

Works on paper

£280 $468 €406 Woodland glade with gypsy encampment (30x48cm-12x19in) s. 18-Jun-3 Andrew Hartley, Ilkley #996

WILLIAMS, Hugh Grecian (1773-1829) British

Works on paper

£380 $623 €570 Kilbride, Argyll (26x36cm-10x14in) pencil W/C. 5-Jun-3 Christie's, Kensington #927/R
£650 $1034 €975 On the river Tay (32x43cm-13x17in) s. pencil W/C. 6-Mar-3 Christie's, Kensington #21/R
£950 $1558 €1425 Dalkeith House and park, Midlothian (29x43cm-11x17in) pencil W/C. 4-Feb-3 Bonhams, Leeds #299
£1050 $1607 €1575 Forum, Rome, from the west (18x25cm-7x10in) s.verso pencil W/C prov. 22-Aug-2 Bonhams, Edinburgh #1001 est:600-800
£2000 $3100 €3000 View of Strathearn and Comrie, Perthshire (60x90cm-24x35in) s.d.1803 pencil W/C htd white. 31-Oct-2 Christie's, London #14/R est:2000-3000
£2600 $4160 €3900 London and the Thames from above Greenwich (50x74cm-20x29in) W/C. 11-Mar-3 Bonhams, New Bond Street #23/R est:2000-3000

WILLIAMS, J S (20th C) British

£270 $421 €405 Extensive landscape with cattle and windmill (61x110cm-24x43in) s. 6-Nov-2 Bonhams, Chester #531

WILLIAMS, J W (19/20th C) British

Works on paper

£550 $858 €825 Fishing boats in Whitby harbour (33x23cm-13x9in) s. W/C. 20-Sep-2 Richardson & Smith, Whitby #133

WILLIAMS, Jacqueline (1962-) British

£380 $608 €570 Still life of flowers and cherries on a tabletop with a pencil (36x46cm-14x18in) mono. 18board. 13-Mar-3 Duke & Son, Dorchester #249
£550 $869 €825 Wild flowers (29x24cm-11x9in) init. canvas on board. 27-Nov-2 Sotheby's, Olympia #151/R
£720 $1202 €1044 Silhouetted figure (122x78cm-48x31in) init. i.verso board. 23-Jun-3 Bonhams, Bath #86
£1000 $1550 €1500 Pippa reading (42x90cm-17x35in) init. board. 3-Dec-2 Bonhams, Knightsbridge #103/R est:600-800

WILLIAMS, John Haynes (1836-1908) British

£1100 $1672 €1650 Spanish beauty (37x28cm-15x11in) s.i.d.1863 oval. 4-Jul-2 Mellors & Kirk, Nottingham #828/R est:200-400
£1200 $1848 €1800 Spanish beauty (62x46cm-24x18in) s.indis.d. 23-Oct-2 Hamptons Fine Art, Godalming #191/R est:1200-1500
£1538 $2446 €2307 Pages in waiting (51x76cm-20x30in) s. s.i.verso. 4-Mar-3 Deutscher-Menzies, Melbourne #103/R est:5000-8000 (A.D 4000)
£2926 $4739 €4389 The fisherman's home (65x76cm-26x30in) s.d.80. 25-Jan-3 Rasmussen, Havnen #2284/R est:10000-15000 (D.KR 33000)

WILLIAMS, John W (fl.1900-1920) British

Works on paper

£280 $437 €420 Study of Conway Castle with fishing boats to the fore (23x35cm-9x14in) s. W/C. 10-Sep-2 David Duggleby, Scarborough #49/R

£290 $473 €435 Whitby harbour (17x25cm-7x10in) s. W/C htd white. 17-Feb-3 Bonhams, Bath #128
£350 $553 €525 Moored vessels in Whitby Harbour, towards the abbey (23x15cm-9x6in) s. W/C htd white. 24-Apr-3 Richardson & Smith, Whitby #84
£460 $718 €690 Dock end, Whitby (34x51cm-13x20in) s.d.96 W/C. 10-Sep-2 David Duggleby, Scarborough #82/R
£550 $869 €825 Whitby, Upper harbour (20x46cm-8x18in) s. W/C. 24-Apr-3 Richardson & Smith, Whitby #182
£620 $992 €930 Distant view of Whitby Harbour (23x25cm-9x10in) s. W/C. 11-Mar-3 David Duggleby, Scarborough #52/R

WILLIAMS, Keith Shaw (1906-1951) American
£4790 $8000 €6946 After the bath (91x76cm-36x30in) s. 17-Jun-3 John Moran, Pasadena #105a est:7000-9000

WILLIAMS, Kyffin (1918-) British
£2600 $4056 €3900 Sea at Treanddwr (41x51cm-16x20in) init. 11-Sep-2 Bonhams, Newport #438/R est:2500-3500
£3800 $5928 €5700 Portrait of Gwen (61x50cm-24x20in) init. 25-Mar-3 Bonhams, New Bond Street #87/R est:3000-5000
£5300 $8268 €7950 Sun behind a cloud bank (61x91cm-24x36in) init. prov. 11-Sep-2 Bonhams, Newport #436/R est:6000-8000
£6200 $9672 €9300 Maes y llan Fach, Bodwrog, Anglesey (23x51cm-9x20in) init. 11-Sep-2 Bonhams, Newport #443/R est:4000-6000
£7000 $10920 €10500 Riders in Cwm Hyfryd (50x50cm-20x20in) init. 11-Sep-2 Bonhams, Newport #439/R est:4000-6000
£7000 $10990 €10500 Holy Trinity, Paddington (68x50cm-27x20in) init. 20-Nov-2 Sotheby's, Olympia #81/R est:6000-8000
£7500 $11925 €11250 Barns at Marsh Farm, Earnley nr Chichester (51x61cm-20x24in) init. prov. 29-Apr-3 Henry Adams, Chichester #339
£7500 $12525 €10875 Welsh landscape (60x76cm-24x30in) init. 24-Jun-3 Bonhams, New Bond Street #57/R est:5000-7000
£8000 $12480 €12000 Crib Goch and Nant Peris (76x76cm-30x30in) init. 11-Sep-2 Bonhams, Newport #435/R est:8000-10000
£8800 $13728 €13200 Shepherd and his dog on a hilltop (75x75cm-30x30in) init. 11-Sep-2 Bonhams, Newport #434/R est:6000-8000
£9000 $13860 €13500 Tyddyn, Deiniolen (91x122cm-36x48in) 5-Sep-2 Christie's, Kensington #694/R est:10000-15000
£10000 $15600 €15000 Pentraeth, Anglesey (51x68cm-20x27in) 27-Mar-3 Christie's, Kensington #506/R est:7000-10000
£10200 $15912 €15300 Llyn peninsular (90x90cm-35x35in) init. 11-Sep-2 Bonhams, Newport #441/R est:8000-10000
£11000 $17050 €16500 Pentraeth, Anglesey (51x68cm-20x27in) init. painted c.1960. 4-Dec-2 Christie's, Kensington #555/R est:5000-7000
£12000 $20040 €17400 Cwm Nantcol (60x91cm-24x36in) init. 24-Jun-3 Bonhams, New Bond Street #56/R est:5000-7000
£12500 $19500 €18750 Anglesey coastline (90x90cm-35x35in) init. 11-Sep-2 Bonhams, Newport #442/R est:6000-8000
£12500 $19626 €18750 Ponies, Llanfairynghornwy (50x111cm-20x44in) init. i.stretcher. 20-Nov-2 Sotheby's, Olympia #69/R est:6000-8000
£13000 $20280 €19500 Farmyard, Cesarea, Carnarvonshire (55x76cm-22x30in) init. 11-Sep-2 Bonhams, Newport #440/R est:5000-7000
£15000 $23250 €22500 Ruined farm at Llantrisant (51x61cm-20x24in) s. exhib. 4-Dec-2 Christie's, Kensington #558/R est:7000-10000
£22000 $36300 €31900 Llanrhwydrys (91x91cm-36x36in) init. prov. 3-Jul-3 Christie's, Kensington #673/R est:12000-18000

Works on paper
£400 $624 €600 Shepherd and his dog (18x13cm-7x5in) init. pen ink. 11-Sep-2 Bonhams, Newport #429/R
£420 $655 €630 Pulteney Bridge, Bath (23x34cm-9x13in) init. pen ink W/C. 11-Sep-2 Bonhams, Newport #432/R
£520 $811 €780 Study of sheep dogs (28x20cm-11x8in) init. pen ink dr. 11-Sep-2 Bonhams, Newport #425/R
£600 $930 €900 Study of a Welsh pony (11x14cm-4x6in) init. pencil W/C. 4-Dec-2 Christie's, Kensington #327/R
£700 $1148 €1050 Welsh landscape (13x19cm-5x7in) init. pen ink wash. 3-Jun-3 Sotheby's, Olympia #147/R
£740 $1154 €1110 Crofts, outer Hebrides (22x19cm-9x7in) init. ink sepia wash. 6-Nov-2 Bonhams, Chester #359
£750 $1170 €1125 Study of a greyhound (22x20cm-9x8in) init. pencil grey wash. 11-Sep-2 Bonhams, Newport #426/R
£800 $1256 €1200 Mountain landscape with trees (21x29cm-8x11in) ink wash. 20-Nov-2 Sotheby's, Olympia #67/R
£900 $1414 €1350 Mountain scene (21x29cm-8x11in) ink wash. 20-Nov-2 Sotheby's, Olympia #68/R est:600-800
£900 $1476 €1350 Chartreuse (24x34cm-9x13in) init. pen ink wash. 3-Jun-3 Sotheby's, Olympia #146/R
£1000 $1630 €1450 Portrait of a gentleman (23x17cm-9x7in) init. chl bodycol. 16-Jul-3 Anthemion, Cardiff #935/R est:1200-1500
£1200 $1872 €1800 Farmer leaning on a gate (44x30cm-17x12in) init. pencil W/C. 11-Sep-2 Bonhams, Newport #431/R est:1000-1500
£1300 $2093 €1950 Mountainous landscape (28x46cm-11x18in) init. ink wash. 19-Feb-3 Mallams, Oxford #340/R est:800-1000
£1400 $2296 €2100 Fedw fawr, an Anglesey coastal landscape (27x40cm-11x16in) init. W/C. 4-Jun-3 Bonhams, Chester #304/R est:1200-1600
£1800 $2808 €2700 Ifan Roberts, farmer (53x31cm-21x12in) init. W/C. 11-Sep-2 Bonhams, Newport #427/R est:2000-2500
£2100 $3276 €3150 Welsh blacks in snow (34x34cm-13x13in) init. pen ink wash. 11-Sep-2 Bonhams, Newport #428/R est:1500-2500
£2200 $3454 €3300 Mountain landscape (24x35cm-9x14in) init. brush ink exhib. 20-Nov-2 Sotheby's, Olympia #79/R est:1000-2000
£2500 $3900 €3750 Building, North Wales (34x48cm-13x19in) init. monochrome W/C wash. 11-Sep-2 Bonhams, Newport #433 est:1500-2000
£3000 $4890 €4500 School girl (38x30cm-15x12in) init. chl wash. 28-Jan-3 Peter Francis, Wales #54/R est:2500-3000
£4500 $7066 €6750 Farmer (38x27cm-15x11in) init. chl W/C. 20-Nov-2 Sotheby's, Olympia #80/R est:1500-2500

WILLIAMS, Mervyn (1940-) New Zealander?
£456 $711 €684 Untitled - sunburst (75x57cm-30x22in) s.d.1989 acrylic on paper. 17-Sep-2 Peter Webb, Auckland #175/R est:1500-3000 (NZ.D 1500)
£758 $1167 €1137 Firefly (61x48cm-24x19in) s.d.1983 acrylic on paper. 4-Sep-2 Dunbar Sloane, Wellington #58 est:3000-5000 (NZ.D 2500)
£2778 $4333 €4167 Facade (95x80cm-37x31in) s.i.d.1997 acrylic. 8-Apr-3 Peter Webb, Auckland #67/R est:8000-12000 (NZ.D 8000)

WILLIAMS, Micah (1782-1837) American

Works on paper
£10191 $16000 €15287 Portrait of a lady wearing a tortoise shell comb and black dress (61x53cm-24x21in) pastel. 23-Nov-2 Pook & Pook, Downington #66/R est:6000-9000

WILLIAMS, Penry (1798-1885) British
£300 $471 €450 Helping out a friend on the road (26x20cm-10x8in) s. 16-Apr-3 Christie's, Kensington #660/R
£650 $1021 €975 Ferry (21x31cm-8x12in) s.i. s.i.verso. 16-Dec-2 Bonhams, Bury St Edmunds #549/R
£800 $1312 €1200 Young boy tying a girl's shoe lace on the campagna (23x19cm-9x7in) s.i. 3-Jun-3 Bonhams, Oxford #52/R
£900 $1431 €1350 Ferry (22x30cm-9x12in) s.i. i.verso. 6-Mar-3 Christie's, Kensington #578/R
£4000 $6200 €6000 Scene in the Roman Campana (67x91cm-26x36in) s.i.d.1866 oil sketching. 26-Sep-2 Mellors & Kirk, Nottingham #702/R est:4000-6000
£5800 $9048 €8700 Connoisseurs (110x84cm-43x33in) s.d.1878. 26-Mar-3 Sotheby's, Olympia #55/R est:2500-3500
£17241 $27241 €25000 Back from the pilgrimage to Madonna dell'Arco (78x95cm-31x37in) lit. 3-Apr-3 Porro, Milan #52/R est:35000

Works on paper
£850 $1343 €1275 Two Italian young fishermen standing by a boat looking out to sea (21x14cm-8x6in) s.d.1868 W/C gouache. 26-Nov-2 Bonhams, Oxford #29/R

WILLIAMS, Rhys (1894-1976) Australian
£391 $599 €587 Ici house, Macquarie Street, Sydney (61x76cm-24x30in) s. painted c.1960 prov. 26-Aug-2 Sotheby's, Paddington #723 est:300-500 (A.D 1100)

WILLIAMS, Solomon (?-1824) Irish
£7246 $11884 €10000 Extensive pastoral landscape with girl and goats (30x23cm-12x9in) init.d.1824 panel. 28-May-3 Bonhams & James Adam, Dublin #17/R est:10000-12000

WILLIAMS, Sue (1954-) American
£4688 $7500 €7032 Untitled (86x86cm-34x34in) s.d.87 prov. 15-May-3 Christie's, Rockefeller NY #374/R est:10000-15000
£8861 $14000 €13292 Busy with face in middle (38x46cm-15x18in) s.i.d.1997 verso prov.exhib. 13-Nov-2 Sotheby's, New York #407/R
£24000 $39360 €36000 Three blues, no orange (184x213cm-72x84in) s.i.d.1997 verso oil acrylic prov. 7-Feb-3 Sotheby's, London #186/R est:18000-25000

WILLIAMS, Terrick (1860-1936) British
£360 $565 €540 Twilight - gathering sea weed on the foreshore (25x33cm-10x13in) s. 10-Dec-2 Lane, Penzance #80/R
£1000 $1550 €1500 Street scene with figures (25x41cm-10x16in) 4-Dec-2 Andrew Hartley, Ilkley #1177 est:800-1200
£1100 $1815 €1595 Yachts on the coast (30x46cm-12x18in) s. 3-Jul-3 Christie's, Kensington #454/R est:1200-1800
£2000 $3120 €3000 On the Lagoon, Venice (18x23cm-7x9in) s. panel. 15-Oct-2 Gorringes, Lewes #2300/R est:2000-3000
£2400 $4008 €3480 Continental harbour (26x35cm-10x14in) s. 24-Jun-3 Bonhams, New Bond Street #5/R est:1000-1500
£2562 $3945 €3843 Harbour scene (20x29cm-8x11in) s.d.97 i.verso panel. 4-Sep-2 Kunsthallen, Copenhagen #110/R est:35000 (D.KR 30000)
£2800 $4424 €4200 Greengrocer's shop (24x37cm-9x15in) s.verso board. 27-Nov-2 Sotheby's, Olympia #67/R est:2000-3000
£3537 $5482 €5306 Twilight and rain, St Ives (38x28cm-15x11in) s.d. 4-Dec-2 Dunbar Sloane, Auckland #69/R est:8000-10000 (NZ.D 11000)
£3600 $5580 €5400 Golden doorway, Carno (23x38cm-9x15in) s. i.verso. 4-Dec-2 Andrew Hartley, Ilkley #1175/R est:1200-1800
£3800 $5928 €5700 Shady street, Tangiers (35x61cm-14x24in) s. s.i.verso. 13-Sep-2 Lyon & Turnbull, Edinburgh #131/R est:1500-2000

£3800 $5928 €5700 Two children looking at ducks on a pond (25x35cm-10x14in) s.d.1900 panel. 26-Mar-3 Woolley & Wallis, Salisbury #202/R est:1500-2000
£4000 $6320 €6000 Cornish harbour (29x39cm-11x15in) s. board. 27-Nov-2 Sotheby's, Olympia #227/R est:4000-6000
£4400 $6820 €6600 Beachscene with fishermen (25x38cm-10x15in) s. 4-Dec-2 Andrew Hartley, Ilkley #1176/R est:1000-1500
£4900 $7644 €7350 Venice (23x44cm-9x17in) bears sig. prov. 17-Oct-2 Lawrence, Crewkerne #519/R est:3000-4000
£5000 $8250 €7250 Wet evening St. Ives (38x29cm-15x11in) s. 1-Jul-3 Bearnes, Exeter #515/R est:5000-7000
£6000 $9300 €9000 Clouds over the sea, Holland (51x76cm-20x30in) s. i.verso. 4-Dec-2 Andrew Hartley, Ilkley #1174/R est:2500-4000
£6500 $10271 €9750 Markey place, Concarneau (26x40cm-10x16in) s. 27-Nov-2 Sotheby's, Olympia #54/R est:4000-6000
£8200 $13694 €11890 Net mending, Cassis (38x53cm-15x21in) s. i.verso. 24-Jun-3 Bonhams, New Bond Street #6/R est:3000-5000
£14000 $22960 €21000 Night, Venice (91x127cm-36x50in) s. s.i.d.1925. 6-Jun-3 Christie's, London #159/R est:15000-20000

Works on paper

£360 $565 €540 Evening river scene with boats (25x36cm-10x14in) s. W/C. 12-Dec-2 Richardson & Smith, Whitby #428
£400 $620 €600 Amsterdam, barges on a canal (61x86cm-24x34in) W/C. 26-Sep-2 Lane, Penzance #296
£600 $954 €900 Gathering mussels (25x44cm-10x17in) s. W/C. 4-Mar-3 Bearnes, Exeter #344/R
£850 $1351 €1275 Troyes (38x29cm-15x11in) s. W/C. 26-Feb-3 Sotheby's, Olympia #168/R est:800-1200
£3400 $5304 €5100 On the quayside (30x40cm-12x16in) s. W/C bodycol. 27-Mar-3 Christie's, Kensington #323/R est:1000-1500
£3600 $5616 €5400 Harbour at Concarneau (22x30cm-9x12in) s. W/C bodycol prov. 27-Mar-3 Christie's, Kensington #322/R est:1500-2000

WILLIAMS, Thomas H (19th C) British

£417 $650 €626 Mountainous river landscape with figures (51x76cm-20x30in) s. 18-Sep-2 Boos Gallery, Michigan #278/R

WILLIAMS, W (fl.1841-1876) British

£921 $1492 €1400 Marine (50x65cm-20x26in) s. 21-Jan-3 Galerie Moderne, Brussels #215/R est:800-1200

WILLIAMS, W George (?) British?

£400 $608 €600 Age of innocence (41x36cm-16x14in) after Joshua Reynolds. 16-Aug-2 Keys, Aylsham #702

WILLIAMS, Walter (attrib) (19th C) British

£800 $1232 €1200 Figures crossing a bridge (30x30cm-12x12in) painted circle. 5-Sep-2 Christie's, Kensington #121/R
£950 $1511 €1425 Angler in mountainous lake landscape (25x36cm-10x14in) with sig.d.63. 6-Mar-3 Christie's, Kensington #413/R
£1000 $1580 €1500 An angler by a rocky stream (20x25cm-8x10in) with sig.d.1846. 28-Nov-2 Christie's, Kensington #6/R est:1200-1800

WILLIAMS, Walter (1835-1906) British

£600 $936 €900 Devon view, cattle watering in a river landscape (46x66cm-18x26in) s. 10-Sep-2 Bonhams, Knightsbridge #144/R
£920 $1435 €1380 Blackberrying (18x23cm-7x9in) init.d.1882. 25-Mar-3 Bonhams, Leeds #594
£1450 $2306 €2175 On watch (14x19cm-6x7in) 4-Mar-3 Bearnes, Exeter #455/R est:400-600
£1500 $2445 €2250 Maddoch, North Wales (28x41cm-11x16in) i. 12-Feb-3 Bonhams, Knightsbridge #321/R est:1500-2500
£1700 $2669 €2550 Mountains landscape with figures by a lake. Mountain landscape (16x12cm-6x5in) d.1872 card oval pair. 21-Nov-2 Tennants, Leyburn #791 est:500-700
£2000 $3340 €2900 Figures beside a waterfall. Figures by a rocky coast (20x15cm-8x6in) init.d.1879 pair. 17-Jun-3 Bonhams, New Bond Street #66/R est:2000-3000
£2200 $3498 €3300 Bridligton, Yorks (14x19cm-6x7in) s.d.1876 s.i.on stretcher. 4-Mar-3 Bearnes, Exeter #452/R est:600-900
£3400 $4862 €5100 At Lynmouth, North Devon (22x30cm-9x12in) init.d.1881 s.i.stretcher. 11-Apr-2 Mellors & Kirk, Nottingham #575/R est:1000-1500
£9500 $15770 €14250 Sonning. Hastings (17x23cm-7x9in) init.d.1878 pair. 10-Jun-3 Christie's, London #131/R est:6000-8000

WILLIAMS, Walter (fl.1841-1876) British

£2500 $3925 €3750 Mountainous landscape. Coastal scene, moonlit estuary (15x20cm-6x8in) init. indis d. one i.verso pair. 19-Nov-2 Bonhams, Leeds #221 est:3000-3500
£3200 $4928 €4800 Summer's day (66x102cm-26x40in) s.d.1843. 5-Sep-2 Christie's, Kensington #126/R est:2000-3000

WILLIAMS, Walter Heath (19th C) British

£800 $1336 €1160 River landscape (16x20cm-6x8in) 8-Jul-3 Bonhams, Knightsbridge #194/R
£1000 $1560 €1500 Returning home via the river (46x66cm-18x26in) 7-Nov-2 Christie's, Kensington #121 est:800-1200
£1048 $1656 €1572 Harvest (46x67cm-18x26in) s. 18-Nov-2 Waddingtons, Toronto #123/R est:3000-4000 (C.D 2600)
£1500 $2310 €2250 Across the valley (46x66cm-18x26in) s. 5-Sep-2 Christie's, Kensington #127/R est:2000-3000
£1600 $2608 €2320 Harvesting (64x76cm-25x30in) bears sig.d.1857. 16-Jul-3 Sotheby's, Olympia #8/R est:1200-1800
£1714 $2708 €2571 Norfolk (61x91cm-24x36in) prov. 18-Nov-2 Waddingtons, Toronto #136/R est:4000-6000 (C.D 4250)
£1800 $2934 €2700 Woodland path (45x66cm-18x26in) s. 29-Jan-3 Sotheby's, Olympia #161/R est:1000-2000
£1950 $3198 €2925 Returning home (46x63cm-18x25in) init. 29-May-3 Christie's, Kensington #132/R est:3000-5000
£3500 $5740 €5250 Extensive landscape with figures picking blackberries near a stream. s.d. 4-Feb-3 Sworder & Son, Bishops Stortford #111/R est:1000-1500
£3800 $6232 €5700 Day's fishing. Returning home (46x66cm-18x26in) s. pair. 29-May-3 Christie's, Kensington #119/R est:2000-3000

WILLIAMS, Walter Heath (attrib) (19th C) British

£750 $1170 €1125 Country landscape with figures on road (46x67cm-18x26in) 8-Apr-3 Bonhams, Knightsbridge #236/R
£1500 $2445 €2250 Figures by a pond (31x56cm-12x22in) 29-Jan-3 Sotheby's, Olympia #192/R est:500-700

WILLIAMS, Warren (1863-1918) British

£372 $584 €558 Sailing around the point (25x61cm-10x24in) s. 24-Jul-2 Walker's, Ottawa #29/R (C.D 900)

Works on paper

£360 $558 €540 Figures on beach near a coastal village (25x36cm-10x14in) s. W/C. 6-Dec-2 Biddle & Webb, Birmingham #91
£382 $603 €573 Untitled, sheep in mountain landscape (25x37cm-10x15in) W/C. 7-Apr-3 Shapiro, Sydney #502 (A.D 1000)
£560 $874 €840 On the Dart (25x38cm-10x15in) s. W/C. 2-Aug-2 Biddle & Webb, Birmingham #382
£780 $1248 €1131 Harvest scene with lake and hills beyond (24x35cm-9x14in) s. W/C. 13-May-3 Bristol Auction Rooms #500/R
£800 $1232 €1200 Welsh coast (33x51cm-13x20in) s.d. W/C. 23-Oct-2 Hamptons Fine Art, Godalming #81
£800 $1272 €1200 Runswick Bay, Yorkshire (26x36cm-10x14in) s. W/C htd white. 29-Apr-3 Bonhams, Knightsbridge #22/R
£900 $1404 €1350 Repairing the boat, Conway (28x46cm-11x18in) s. W/C card. 26-Mar-3 Hamptons Fine Art, Godalming #124
£1000 $1660 €1450 Appledore, north Devon (25x36cm-10x14in) s. W/C. 10-Jun-3 David Lay, Penzance #315/R est:1000-1400
£1050 $1754 €1523 Dinner time, gypsy life, Anglesea (27x43cm-11x17in) s. W/C. 24-Jun-3 Rowley Fine Art, Newmarket #367/R est:600-800
£1200 $1884 €1800 River Conwy (47x71cm-19x28in) s. W/C. 20-Nov-2 Sotheby's, Olympia #35/R est:1500-2000
£1250 $2050 €1875 Evening, Cemaes Bay, Anglesey (26x43cm-10x17in) s. W/C. 4-Jun-3 Bonhams, Chester #315 est:600-800
£1300 $2119 €1950 Vale of Gwynant, Beddgelert (33x51cm-13x20in) s. W/C. 28-Jan-3 Rogers Jones, Clwyd #119
£1400 $2226 €2100 North Wales fishing port (35x60cm-14x24in) s. W/C. 27-Feb-3 Bonhams, Chester #336 est:500-700
£1600 $2544 €2400 Fishing boats before Conway Castle (29x55cm-11x22in) s. W/C. 27-Feb-3 Bonhams, Chester #335/R est:600-800
£1600 $2608 €2400 Dyffryn Mymbyr and the Snowdon Horseshoe (33x51cm-13x20in) s. W/C. 28-Jan-3 Rogers Jones, Clwyd #122
£1800 $2826 €2700 Rhudden Castle, North Wales (24x38cm-9x15in) s. W/C gouache. 20-Nov-2 Sotheby's, Olympia #34/R
£1800 $2826 €2700 Sailing on the Conway (27x38cm-11x15in) s. W/C pair. 20-Nov-2 Sotheby's, Olympia #46/R est:2000-3000
£1900 $2982 €2850 River Conwy with a cottage and cattle grazing (47x71cm-19x28in) s. W/C. 20-Nov-2 Sotheby's, Olympia #33/R est:2000-3000
£2600 $4264 €3900 Fisherfolk at Cemaes Bay. Anglesey coastal scene (17x38cm-7x15in) s. W/C pair. 4-Jun-3 Bonhams, Chester #276/R est:1200-1600
£2700 $4401 €4050 Old Ferry, Tal y Cafn, with ferry boat and figures (33x51cm-13x20in) W/C. 28-Jan-3 Rogers Jones, Clwyd #118/R
£3800 $6194 €5700 Still morning on the Dart (58x89cm-23x35in) s. W/C. 13-Feb-3 David Lay, Penzance #387/R est:800-1200

WILLIAMS, William (fl.1758-1797) British

£12500 $19375 €18750 Portrait of an English gentleman with his gun dog, in a landscape with trees and a thatched cottage (51x43cm-20x17in) s.d.1782 panel. 4-Dec-2 Neal & Fletcher, Woodbridge #240/R est:2000-3000

WILLIAMS, William (19th C) British

£360 $576 €540 Hungtcliff and the Rawcliff, near Saltburn by the sea (23x35cm-9x14in) i. 11-Mar-3 David Duggleby, Scarborough #75

WILLIAMS, William Joseph (1759-1823) American

Works on paper

£253 $400 €380 Portrait of a gentleman (61x48cm-24x19in) s. pastel. 17-Nov-2 CRN Auctions, Cambridge #11/R

WILLIAMSON, Albert Curtis (?) Canadian?
£350 $542 €525 Lost in her thoughts (27x22cm-11x9in) s. canvas on board. 3-Dec-2 Joyner, Toronto #331/R (C.D 850)
£378 $619 €567 Winter landscape (40x50cm-16x20in) s.d.27. 3-Jun-3 Joyner, Toronto #419/R (C.D 850)
£378 $620 €548 Forge (60x45cm-24x18in) 9-Jun-3 Hodgins, Calgary #150/R (C.D 850)

WILLIAMSON, Fred (19/20th C) British
Works on paper
£1550 $2449 €2248 Near Midhust, sheep grazing in a rural landscape. s.d.1913 W/C. 22-Jul-3 Lawrences, Bletchingley #1250/R est:500-800

WILLIAMSON, Frederick (c.1835-1900) British
Works on paper
£750 $1253 €1088 Herdsman with cattle and sheep in a highland landscape (13x23cm-5x9in) s. W/C. 24-Jun-3 Rowley Fine Art, Newmarket #375/R
£900 $1395 €1350 Old Harry's Rocks, Studland, Dorset (20x36cm-8x14in) s. W/C. 31-Oct-2 Duke & Son, Dorchester #132/R
£1089 $1699 €1634 Landslip, Isle of Wight (22x35cm-9x14in) s. i.mount W/C prov. 11-Nov-2 Stephan Welz, Johannesburg #64 est:2000-3000 (SA.R 17000)
£1300 $2119 €1885 Summer landscape with a boy seated beside a sandy lane, sheep and a cottage nearby (13x21cm-5x8in) s. W/C. 17-Jul-3 Tennants, Leyburn #722/R est:700-900

WILLIAMSON, Jack (20th C) American
£4221 $6500 €6332 Sunstruck beach (61x91cm-24x36in) 25-Oct-2 Morris & Whiteside, Hilton Head Island #98 est:7000-9000

WILLIAMSON, John (1826-1885) American
£4516 $7000 €6774 Sycamore, Catskill Clove (58x43cm-23x17in) painted c.1870 prov. 3-Dec-2 Phillips, New York #8/R
£40123 $65000 €60185 Sunset in the wilderness (38x58cm-15x23in) init.d.73. 22-May-3 Christie's, Rockefeller NY #33/R est:70000-90000

WILLIAMSON, Richard (?) British?
£550 $853 €825 Drumming in the Mournes (50x61cm-20x24in) s. board. 4-Dec-2 John Ross, Belfast #199
£1250 $1825 €1875 Digging for bait, Belfast Lough (61x91cm-24x36in) s. board. 12-Jun-2 John Ross, Belfast #289 est:1000-1200

WILLIAMSON, Samuel (1792-1840) British
£3600 $5904 €5400 Mountainous landscape with figures tending goats, cattle and sheep (37x47cm-15x19in) init.d.1817. 4-Feb-3 Sworder & Son, Bishops Stortford #109/R est:1500-2500

WILLIAMSON, W (19th C) British
£1282 $2000 €1923 Gelding the dog (64x76cm-25x30in) s.d.1812. 12-Oct-2 Neal Auction Company, New Orleans #155/R est:2000-3000

WILLIAMSON, W H (1820-1883) British
£1400 $2212 €2100 Coastal scene with fishing boats and figures on the shore (31x56cm-12x22in) s.d.1879. 18-Dec-2 John Nicholson, Haslemere #1270 est:1500-1800

WILLIAMSON, William Henry (1820-1883) British
£290 $481 €435 Fishing boats in a rough sea with a cliffside beyond (31x56cm-12x22in) s. 10-Jun-3 Bonhams, Leeds #172
£382 $550 €573 Fishing vessel and three-master off the South Foreland (61x107cm-24x42in) s.d.1868. 15-Jan-3 Christie's, Rockefeller NY #137/R
£550 $836 €825 Fishing boats in rough weather off the coast (28x48cm-11x19in) s.d.1879. 16-Aug-2 Keys, Aylsham #630/R
£560 $862 €840 Off Dover (51x76cm-20x30in) s. 5-Sep-2 Christie's, Kensington #226/R
£850 $1352 €1275 Fishing boats clearing Dover Harbour in rough weather (76x102cm-30x40in) s.d.1881. 4-Mar-3 Bonhams, Knightsbridge #303/R
£950 $1587 €1378 Shipping off the coast (29x59cm-11x23in) s.d.1871. 26-Jun-3 Mellors & Kirk, Nottingham #913
£2193 $3268 €3290 Naufrage (77x126cm-30x50in) s.d.68. 26-Jun-2 Iegor de Saint Hippolyte, Montreal #89/R (C.D 5000)
£2593 $4200 €3760 Landing in rough seas. Returning to the dock (30x25cm-12x10in) init, indis d. pair. 29-Jul-3 Christie's, Rockefeller NY #145/R est:5000-7000
£3300 $5247 €4950 Fishing vessels and salvagers off the French coast (101x140cm-40x55in) s. 5-Mar-3 Bonhams, Bury St Edmunds #401/R est:2500-3500

WILLIAMSON-BELL, James (1938-) British
£300 $465 €450 Male kestrel (44x44cm-17x17in) s. acrylic board prov. 6-Oct-2 Lots Road, London #353
Works on paper
£550 $864 €825 Two young rabbits in snow (23x36cm-9x14in) s. W/C. 13-Dec-2 Keys, Aylsham #512

WILLICH, Caesar (1825-1886) German
£258 $415 €387 Peasants mother and child, seated near a bridge (45x32cm-18x13in) s. 12-May-3 Stephan Welz, Johannesburg #8 est:1000-15000 (SA.R 3000)

WILLIKENS, Ben (1939-) German
£4138 $6538 €6000 Room 203 (85x100cm-33x39in) s.d. s.i.d. stretcher acrylic. 2-Apr-3 Dr Fritz Nagel, Stuttgart #9556/R est:7000

WILLING, J (19th C) ?
Works on paper
£10494 $17000 €15741 Schloss Ballenstedt (12x19cm-5x7in) i. W/C gouache set of 5 prov. 21-Jan-3 Sotheby's, New York #193/R est:30000

WILLINK, Carel (1900-1979) Dutch
£4317 $7079 €6000 Portrait of the sculptor Kees Schrikker (50x37cm-20x15in) s.d.1919 canvasboard prov.lit. 3-Jun-3 Christie's, Amsterdam #203/R est:6000-8000
£63291 $100000 €100000 Zelfportret met schedel - self portrait with skull (71x57cm-28x22in) s.d.36 prov.exhib.lit. 26-Nov-2 Sotheby's, Amsterdam #128/R est:100000-150000
Works on paper
£1538 $2415 €2400 Landscape with sculpture and pillar (47x62cm-19x24in) s. chl htd white. 25-Nov-2 Glerum, Amsterdam #206/R est:1500-2500
£4430 $7000 €7000 Jutmilla's seelchen II (46x30cm-18x12in) s.d.23 W/C prov.lit. 26-Nov-2 Sotheby's, Amsterdam #106/R est:3500-4500

WILLIS, A V (19th C) British?
£645 $1019 €968 Highland cattle in an extensive landscape (77x122cm-30x48in) s.d.1879. 18-Nov-2 Waddingtons, Toronto #117/R (C.D 1600)
£4140 $6500 €6210 Day's catch (56x91cm-22x36in) s. 14-Dec-2 Weschler, Washington #596/R est:2000-3000

WILLIS, Charles (20th C) British
£300 $489 €435 Many happy returns (46x61cm-18x24in) s. i.verso. 17-Jul-3 Tennants, Leyburn #931

WILLIS, Edmund Aylburton (1808-1899) American
£1635 $2600 €2453 Haying time, the first load (56x91cm-22x36in) s.d.1884. 1-Mar-3 North East Auctions, Portsmouth #771/R est:2000-4000
£2108 $3500 €3057 The attack (34x55cm-13x22in) s.d.1869 canvas on board prov. 11-Jun-3 Butterfields, San Francisco #4005/R est:3000-5000

WILLIS, Eola (1856-1952) American
Works on paper
£1497 $2500 €2171 Magnolia on the Ashley (18x36cm-7x14in) s.i.verso W/C. 21-Jun-3 Charlton Hall, Columbia #541/R est:700-1000

WILLIS, George William (fl.1845-1869) British
£15000 $23850 €22500 Leap frog (71x107cm-28x42in) s. i.on stretcher. 19-Mar-3 Sotheby's, London #271/R est:15000-20000

WILLIS, Henry Brittan (1810-1884) British
£800 $1304 €1200 Haymaking (12x19cm-5x7in) s. 12-Feb-3 Andrew Hartley, Ilkley #873
£1000 $1670 €1450 Rustics near a wooded farmhouse (22x32cm-9x13in) s.d.45 i.verso panel. 26-Jun-3 Mellors & Kirk, Nottingham #915/R est:400-600
£1200 $1860 €1800 Gypsy encampment (30x40cm-12x16in) s.d.51. 3-Dec-2 Sotheby's, Olympia #162/R est:800-1200
£12000 $18960 €18000 Cattle and sheep in a river landscape (87x132cm-34x52in) s.d.47. 2-Dec-2 Sotheby's, London #1/R est:10000-15000
Works on paper
£250 $388 €375 Cattle at the water's edge (16x34cm-6x13in) s.d.1869 W/C. 30-Sep-2 Bonhams, Ipswich #337/R
£450 $702 €675 Landscape with herdsman on a bridge near cattle crossing a river (27x44cm-11x17in) s.d.69 W/C. 23-Apr-3 Rupert Toovey, Partridge Green #21/R

WILLIS, Joseph R (1876-?) American
£1056 $1700 €1584 Hopi village (30x41cm-12x16in) s.i. board. 19-Jan-3 Jeffery Burchard, Florida #50/R

WILLIS, Richard (?) American?
£1800 $2790 €2700 Battle of Flamborough Head, 23 September 1779 (66x91cm-26x36in) s. panel. 31-Oct-2 Christie's, Kensington #448/R est:800-1200

WILLIS, Thomas (1850-1912) American
£789 $1200 €1184 Tugboat, Mabel Ray (46x69cm-18x27in) s.d.1910 oil cloth silk thread. 17-Aug-2 North East Auctions, Portsmouth #1050
£1053 $1600 €1580 Sailboat on the open ocean (46x64cm-18x25in) s. oil cloth silk thread. 17-Aug-2 North East Auctions, Portsmouth #1048/R
£1090 $1700 €1635 At sea. s. 9-Aug-2 Skinner, Bolton #344
£3261 $5250 €4892 St Yacht Susquehanna (51x89cm-20x35in) s. oil needlework. 22-Feb-3 Pook & Pook, Downington #115/R est:5000-7000
£4934 $7500 €7401 Schooner yacht, Grilse, with the light-vessel, Scotland (56x81cm-22x32in) s.d.1904 oil cloth silk thread. 17-Aug-2 North East Auctions, Portsmouth #1052/R est:7500-8500

Works on paper
£1741 $2750 €2612 Schooner at full sail (56x97cm-22x38in) mono. mixed media. 17-Nov-2 CRN Auctions, Cambridge #12a/R

WILLIS, Thornton (20th C) ?
Works on paper
£561 $875 €842 Right on (57x76cm-22x30in) s.d.80 verso gouache prov. 5-Nov-2 Bukowskis, Stockholm #445/R (S.KR 8000)

WILLMS, A (?) ?
Prints
£2897 $4606 €4200 Chasse aux perdrix (48x61cm-19x24in) photogravure. 10-Mar-3 Coutau Begarie, Paris #92

WILLMS, Arnold (?) ?
£350 $567 €525 Hareem beauty (38x22cm-15x9in) s.d.90 panel. 23-Jan-3 Christie's, Kensington #142/R

WILLOUGHBY-WILLOUGHBY, W (19th C) ?
£1500 $2370 €2250 Boston, a horse in a field (43x58cm-17x23in) prov. 28-Nov-2 Christie's, Kensington #116/R est:1500-2000

WILLROIDER, Josef (1838-1915) Austrian
£390 $581 €600 Tyrolean mountain valley with fortress (24x33cm-9x13in) s. canvas on board. 26-Jun-2 Neumeister, Munich #915/R
£513 $805 €800 Landscape with dried up stream bed and figures (15x24cm-6x9in) s. 20-Nov-2 Dorotheum, Klagenfurt #105
£800 $1248 €1200 Figures in an extensive river landscape (25x34cm-10x13in) s. canvas on board. 8-Oct-2 Bonhams, Knightsbridge #151/R
£1042 $1656 €1500 Faakersee (25x34cm-10x13in) s. i. verso board. 29-Apr-3 Wiener Kunst Auktionen, Vienna #550/R est:2000-3500
£1083 $1689 €1700 Fortress ruins in southern Tyrol (22x31cm-9x12in) s. board. 6-Nov-2 Hugo Ruef, Munich #1337/R est:800
£1633 $2596 €2400 Old riverside town (18x25cm-7x10in) s. board. 19-Mar-3 Neumeister, Munich #802/R est:3000
£1702 $2757 €2400 Landscape with meadow at edge of stream (25x33cm-10x13in) s. board. 22-May-3 Dorotheum, Vienna #35/R est:3000-4000
£2192 $3419 €3200 Boys fishing from bridge in wood (76x110cm-30x43in) s.d.1869. 10-Apr-3 Van Ham, Cologne #1759/R est:2800
£2848 $4500 €4500 Landscape (15x24cm-6x9in) s. canvas on board. 28-Nov-2 Dorotheum, Vienna #52/R est:5000-6000

Works on paper
£449 $682 €700 Lower mountain landscape (10x14cm-4x6in) s. W/C. 11-Jul-2 Hugo Ruef, Munich #936/R

WILLROIDER, Ludwig (1845-1910) German
£288 $438 €450 Study of a stack behind trees (32x15cm-13x6in) mono. i.verso canvas on board lit. 11-Jul-2 Allgauer, Kempten #2763/R
£577 $877 €900 River landscape near Gunzburg (28x37cm-11x15in) s. board. 11-Jul-2 Hugo Ruef, Munich #849
£1014 $1581 €1500 Museuminsel and German Museum, Munich (43x51cm-17x20in) s. board. 26-Mar-3 Hugo Ruef, Munich #266/R est:1500
£1401 $2186 €2200 Wooded river landscape with cows (22x42cm-9x17in) s. lit. 7-Nov-2 Allgauer, Kempten #3014/R est:2200
£1572 $2452 €2358 Landscape with small lake (11x15cm-4x6in) s. board. 6-Nov-2 Dobiaschofsky, Bern #1072/R est:3800 (S.FR 3600)
£1887 $2943 €3000 Rocky outcrop (43x71cm-17x28in) lit. 20-Sep-2 Schloss Ahlden, Ahlden #1170/R est:1900
£2128 $3447 €3000 Landscape picture (16x26cm-6x10in) st.sig. panel. 22-May-3 Dorotheum, Vienna #39/R est:3000-3500
£2308 $3623 €3600 Dutch canal in evening (29x37cm-11x15in) s. panel. 21-Nov-2 Van Ham, Cologne #1983/R est:1200
£3556 $5902 €5156 Evening on the Maas (44x76cm-17x30in) s.d.1873. 16-Jun-3 Waddingtons, Toronto #22/R est:10000-15000 (C.D 8000)
£3901 $6319 €5500 Dutch river landscape (28x37cm-11x15in) s. panel. 22-May-3 Dorotheum, Vienna #190/R est:5500-6000
£4167 $6542 €6500 Landscape (43x54cm-17x21in) s.d.905. 20-Nov-2 Dorotheum, Klagenfurt #22/R est:5500

WILLSHER, Brian (1930-) British
Sculpture
£1250 $2063 €1813 Remembrance of times past (117cm-46in) s.i. wood. 3-Jul-3 Christie's, Kensington #733/R est:600-800

WILLUMS, Signy (1879-1959) Norwegian
£1480 $2367 €2220 Still life of bottle and newspaper, Dagbladet (47x37cm-19x15in) s.d.28. 17-Mar-3 Blomqvist, Oslo #392/R est:15000-20000 (N.KR 17000)

WILLUMSEN, J F (1863-1958) Danish
Works on paper
£372 $587 €558 Mountain landscape (24x33cm-9x13in) init.d.1902 pencil W/C. 1-Apr-3 Rasmussen, Copenhagen #588 (D.KR 4000)
£555 $899 €805 A Basque (48x41cm-19x16in) init.d.1902 W/C pencil. 24-May-3 Rasmussen, Havnen #4228/R (D.KR 5800)
£578 $920 €867 Portrait of woman (44x54cm-17x21in) W/C. 29-Apr-3 Kunsthallen, Copenhagen #244 (D.KR 6200)

WILLUMSEN, Jens Ferdinand (1863-1958) Danish
£4223 $6588 €6335 Madame Bourret dancing the Sailor's Reel (65x39cm-26x15in) init.d.1931 lit. 18-Sep-2 Kunsthallen, Copenhagen #5/R est:40000 (D.KR 50000)

Works on paper
£1811 $3025 €2626 Fog over mountains - study (41x54cm-16x21in) init.d.1914 crayon. 17-Jun-3 Rasmussen, Copenhagen #98/R est:20000 (D.KR 19000)
£3133 $4856 €4700 Fog over mountain tops (41x54cm-16x21in) init.d.juli 1914. 1-Oct-2 Rasmussen, Copenhagen #113/R est:15000 (D.KR 37000)

WILLY, James (?) ?
£1321 $2060 €2100 Moulin Rouge (54x65cm-21x26in) s. 9-Oct-2 Marc Kohn, Paris #51

Works on paper
£943 $1472 €1500 Rue Lepic (65x75cm-26x30in) s. gouache. 9-Oct-2 Marc Kohn, Paris #52

WILS, Lydia (1924-) Belgian
£278 $442 €400 L'automne (80x100cm-31x39in) s. 29-Apr-3 Campo, Vlaamse Kaai #378/R

WILS, Wilhelm (1880-1960) Danish
£306 $496 €444 Garden with fruit trees in blossom (72x92cm-28x36in) s. 24-May-3 Rasmussen, Havnen #4381/R (D.KR 3200)
£467 $729 €701 Nordbane Station and other buildings (44x61cm-17x24in) s.d.08. 5-Aug-2 Rasmussen, Vejle #112/R (D.KR 5500)
£558 $881 €837 Still life of books and fruit (54x65cm-21x26in) s. 1-Apr-3 Rasmussen, Copenhagen #95/R (D.KR 6000)

WILS, Wilhelm (attrib) (1880-1960) Danish
£284 $460 €426 From an outdoor theatre stage (100x110cm-39x43in) 25-Jan-3 Rasmussen, Havnen #2152 (D.KR 3200)

WILSON, A Aldine (fl.1911-1914) British
£900 $1467 €1350 Portrait of a collie dog (36x46cm-14x18in) s. 12-Feb-3 Bonhams, Knightsbridge #144/R

WILSON, Andrew (1780-1848) British
£1300 $2119 €1950 Rear of the camp (13x19cm-5x7in) s. indis i.verso panel. 29-Jan-3 Sotheby's, Olympia #16/R est:1200-1800

Works on paper
£550 $908 €798 Figures by a river with a castle and mountains beyond (16x22cm-6x9in) W/C. 2-Jul-3 Sotheby's, Olympia #273/R

WILSON, Avray (20th C) ?
£489 $812 €709 Red Composition (51x122cm-20x48in) s.d.57. 10-Jun-3 Ritchie, Toronto #86/R est:1000-1500 (C.D 1100)
£578 $959 €838 Yellow composition (77x56cm-30x22in) s.d.57 masonite. 10-Jun-3 Ritchie, Toronto #85/R est:1000-1500 (C.D 1300)

WILSON, Benjamin (1721-1788) British
£2400 $3960 €3480 Portrait of a gentleman (125x101cm-49x40in) 2-Jul-3 Sotheby's, Olympia #52/R est:1000-2000

WILSON, Benjamin (attrib) (1721-1788) British
£5800 $9048 €8700 Portrait of a gentleman, possibly of the Lister Kaye Family (82x70cm-32x28in) 10-Apr-3 Tennants, Leyburn #934/R est:3000-4000

WILSON, Cecil (20th C) British
£400 $632 €600 Pekinese in an interior (30x41cm-12x16in) s.d.1926. 28-Nov-2 Christie's, Kensington #338/R

WILSON, Charles Edward (1854-1941) British
Works on paper
£520 $832 €780 Girl wearing a riding Mac with her pony (21x11cm-8x4in) W/C pair. 11-Mar-3 David Duggleby, Scarborough #121/R
£3000 $4920 €4350 In time of war (52x35cm-20x14in) s.d.1900 W/C prov. 1-Jun-3 Lots Road, London #345/R est:2000-3000
£5000 $7850 €7500 Thoughts by the wayside (52x35cm-20x14in) s.d.1902 pencil W/C scratching out. 21-Nov-2 Christie's, London #97/R est:6000-8000
£6200 $9672 €9300 Fishing from a bridge (36x51cm-14x20in) s. W/C. 5-Nov-2 Bonhams, New Bond Street #118/R est:6000-8000
£7000 $11620 €10500 Farmer's boy (26x18cm-10x7in) s. W/C. 12-Jun-3 Bonhams, New Bond Street #667/R est:3000-5000

WILSON, Charles H (20th C) British
£1700 $2652 €2550 Huntsman with horse and their dogs in landscapes (56x74cm-22x29in) pair after Sir A J Munnings. 11-Apr-3 Keys, Aylsham #655/R est:1500-2000

WILSON, Claggett (1887-1952) American
£395 $600 €593 Hey, sailors (79x66cm-31x26in) i.on stretcher. 15-Aug-2 Doyle, New York #105

WILSON, Dora Lynell (1883-1946) Australian
£286 $451 €429 Melbourne Street scene with tram (37x44cm-15x17in) s. panel. 27-Nov-2 Deutscher-Menzies, Melbourne #243/R (A.D 800)
£717 $1090 €1076 Venice (37x35cm-15x14in) s. canvas on board. 28-Aug-2 Deutscher-Menzies, Melbourne #401/R (A.D 2000)
£1673 $2744 €2510 Ginger jar and blossom (45x38cm-18x15in) s. canvas on board. 4-Jun-3 Deutscher-Menzies, Melbourne #317/R est:1000-1500 (A.D 4200)
Works on paper
£358 $545 €537 For O' she danced (52x32cm-20x13in) s. i.verso pastel. 28-Aug-2 Deutscher-Menzies, Melbourne #311/R (A.D 1000)
£1404 $2133 €2106 Dappled sunlight (36x26cm-14x10in) s. pastel. 19-Aug-2 Joel, Victoria #189 est:3000-4000 (A.D 4000)

WILSON, Ellis (1899-1977) American
£1226 $1900 €1839 Haitian peasant (46x36cm-18x14in) s. panel. 7-Dec-2 Neal Auction Company, New Orleans #508/R est:3000-5000
£4375 $7000 €6563 Young mother (56x36cm-22x14in) s. panel. 11-Jan-3 James Julia, Fairfield #150 est:6000-8000
£11950 $19000 €17925 Picnic on the beach (43x61cm-17x24in) s. board painted c.1950. 2-Mar-3 Toomey, Oak Park #747/R est:6000-8000

WILSON, Ellis (?) British
£560 $918 €840 Fairy glen, North Wales (54x40cm-21x16in) s. pair. 2-Jun-3 David Duggleby, Scarborough #355/R

WILSON, Eric (1911-1947) Australian
£11538 $18346 €17307 Winter morning (49x59cm-19x23in) board painted c.1940-45. 4-Mar-3 Deutscher-Menzies, Melbourne #93/R est:30000-40000 (A.D 30000)
Works on paper
£3269 $5198 €4904 Pont Neuf (15x20cm-6x8in) pastel prov. 4-Mar-3 Deutscher-Menzies, Melbourne #250/R est:4000-6000 (A.D 8500)

WILSON, Frank Avray (1914-) British
£428 $693 €650 Tribute (75x75cm-30x30in) s. i.d.59 verso. 21-Jan-3 Christie's, Amsterdam #421
£900 $1395 €1350 Hanger (25x35cm-10x14in) board. 4-Dec-2 Christie's, Kensington #540
£1250 $1975 €1875 Abstract (60x80cm-24x31in) board. 27-Nov-2 Sotheby's, Olympia #224/R est:2000-3000
£1300 $2132 €1950 Abstract in blue and red (60x91cm-24x36in) sold with abstract by Leon Zack. 6-Jun-3 Christie's, London #77/R est:800-1200
£1800 $2862 €2700 Abstract (122x91cm-48x36in) s. s.d.63 verso board prov. 26-Feb-3 Sotheby's, Olympia #386/R est:2000-3000
£1800 $2862 €2700 Emerald (91x91cm-36x36in) s.i.verso. 26-Feb-3 Sotheby's, Olympia #387/R est:2000-3000

WILSON, G (1848-1890) British
£650 $1073 €943 Harbour shipping in morning mist (61x91cm-24x36in) s. 3-Jul-3 Duke & Son, Dorchester #280/R

WILSON, George (19th C) British
Works on paper
£205 $322 €320 Distant view of Florence (14x23cm-6x9in) W/C. 19-Nov-2 Hamilton Osborne King, Dublin #544/R

WILSON, Howell (19/20th C) American
Works on paper
£223 $350 €335 Summer landscape (46x66cm-18x26in) s. W/C gouache. 22-Nov-2 Skinner, Boston #70/R

WILSON, Hugh Cameron (1885-?) British
£800 $1272 €1200 On the Scottish coast (56x38cm-22x15in) s. canvasboard pair prov. 6-Mar-3 Christie's, Kensington #135/R

WILSON, James Perry (attrib) (1889-1976) American
£272 $425 €408 Summer landscape with mountains in distance. estate st.verso. 15-Oct-2 Winter Associates, Plainville #255

WILSON, John (1774-1855) British
£500 $790 €750 An estuary scene with figures by a windmill and shipping beyond (20x43cm-8x17in) panel. 2-Dec-2 Bonhams, Bath #116
£766 $1203 €1149 Off the coast (29x54cm-11x21in) s. 15-Apr-3 Lawson Menzies, Sydney #316/R est:2500-4500 (A.D 2000)
£976 $1600 €1415 Harbour view of La Havre (46x76cm-18x30in) 4-Jun-3 Christie's, Rockefeller NY #201/R est:3000-5000
£1200 $1860 €1800 Old watch tower (51x77cm-20x30in) 31-Oct-2 Christie's, Kensington #526/R est:1500-2500
£2000 $3100 €3000 Fishing boats in a squall at the harbour mouth (86x112cm-34x44in) 31-Oct-2 Christie's, Kensington #536/R est:1000-1500

WILSON, John J (1836-1903) British
£5660 $9000 €8490 Peasants working in a field by a river (85x125cm-33x49in) s.d.1862. 5-Mar-3 Christie's, Rockefeller NY #71/R est:4000-6000

WILSON, John James (1818-1875) British
£480 $778 €720 Running down the Channel at dusk (31x50cm-12x20in) s. board. 21-May-3 Christie's, Kensington #593/R
£500 $760 €750 Busy harbour (631x51cm-248x20in) s. 15-Aug-2 Bonhams, New Bond Street #311
£1689 $2804 €2449 Two marine views, sailing out on a bright day. Near Portsmouth (30x51cm-12x20in) d. pair. 10-Jun-3 Ritchie, Toronto #49/R est:3000-4000 (C.D 3800)
£2400 $3792 €3600 Haymaking (104x175cm-41x69in) s.d.January 1847. 7-Apr-3 Bonhams, Bath #77/R est:3000-5000
£2600 $4030 €3900 Fishing boats off a rocky coast (31x51cm-12x20in) s. 31-Oct-2 Christie's, Kensington #511/R est:1200-1800
£6000 $9540 €9000 Fishing vessels off the Isle of Wight (61x110cm-24x43in) init.d.1854. 19-Mar-3 Sotheby's, London #245/R est:6000-8000
£6173 $10000 €8951 Fishing off the South Coast. Shipping off Normandy (30x51cm-12x20in) one init. one s.i. pair. 29-Jul-3 Christie's, Rockefeller NY #144/R est:12000-18000

WILSON, John James (attrib) (1818-1875) British
£320 $499 €480 Fisherfolk on the shore, probably Dover (51x61cm-20x24in) 6-Nov-2 Bonhams, Chester #542

WILSON, L W (19/20th C) New Zealander
£3215 $4984 €4823 Ursula River, Milford Sound (60x90cm-24x35in) s.i. 4-Dec-2 Dunbar Sloane, Auckland #49/R est:15000-25000 (NZ.D 10000)
Works on paper
£964 $1524 €1446 Shallow Bay, Lake Manapouri New Zealand (39x69cm-15x27in) s.i. W/C. 18-Nov-2 Goodman, Sydney #78a est:800-1600 (A.D 2700)
£1444 $2310 €2094 Near Timaru (29x47cm-11x19in) s.i.d.1884 W/C. 13-May-3 Watson's, Christchurch #47/R est:3500-5000 (NZ.D 4000)
£2744 $4198 €4116 Mount Cook from the Tasman River (44x67cm-17x26in) s.d. W/C. 21-Aug-2 Dunbar Sloane, Auckland #19/R est:12000-17000 (NZ.D 9000)

WILSON, Lawrence W (1859-c.1920) New Zealander
£242 $373 €363 Mount Cook from a spur of the Moorhouse Range (48x74cm-19x29in) s.d.1902 canvas on board. 4-Sep-2 Dunbar Sloane, Wellington #2 (NZ.D 800)
£704 $1162 €1021 On the Teramakau (29x45cm-11x18in) i. board. 1-Jul-3 Peter Webb, Auckland #79/R est:2500-3500 (NZ.D 2000)

£1097 $1712 €1646 Mount Pembroke, Milford Sound (45x60cm-18x24in) s.i.d.1895. 7-Nov-2 International Art Centre, Auckland #134/R est:7000-10000 (NZ.D 3500)
£1817 $2580 €2726 Exit to the Waiau River (30x46cm-12x18in) s.i. prov. 21-Nov-1 Watson's, Christchurch #16/R est:2000-4000 (NZ.D 6250)

Works on paper

£658 $1027 €987 George Sound (25x48cm-10x19in) s.d.1892 W/C. 7-Nov-2 International Art Centre, Auckland #107/R est:3000-5000 (NZ.D 2100)
£690 $1076 €1035 Upakoroa River N. End, Lake Te Anau (15x49cm-6x19in) s. W/C. 7-Nov-2 International Art Centre, Auckland #117 est:2500-3500 (NZ.D 2200)
£940 $1467 €1410 Lake Te Anau (35x51cm-14x20in) s. W/C. 7-Nov-2 International Art Centre, Auckland #111/R est:5000-7000 (NZ.D 3000)
£1074 $1525 €1611 East Arm. lake Wanaka (20x35cm-8x14in) s.i. W/C prov. 20-Mar-2 Watson's, Christchurch #5/R est:4000-7000 (NZ.D 3500)
£1100 $1716 €1650 Zanzibar from the anchorage (36x85cm-14x33in) s.i.d.1907 W/C. 26-Mar-3 Sotheby's, Olympia #275/R est:800-1200
£1258 $1786 €1887 Wick mountains (26x36cm-10x14in) s. W/C. 20-Mar-2 Watson's, Christchurch #40/R est:4000-7000 (NZ.D 4100)

WILSON, Lyons (1892-?) British

Works on paper

£450 $702 €675 Edge of the moor (25x30cm-10x12in) s.i.d.1920 i.mount W/C. 10-Apr-3 Tennants, Leyburn #863

WILSON, Margaret E (1890-?) British

£450 $707 €675 Italian town (76x63cm-30x25in) s. 21-Nov-2 Tennants, Leyburn #766

WILSON, Marie (20th C) American?

£2055 $3226 €3000 Untitled (28x22cm-11x9in) cardboard. 15-Apr-3 Laurence Calmels, Paris #4231/R est:1200

WILSON, Maude (19/20th C) American

£311 $500 €467 Ploughed field (15x23cm-6x9in) s.i.verso wood panel. 19-Jan-3 Jeffery Burchard, Florida #42a/R

WILSON, Mortimer (1906-1996) American

£5380 $8500 €7801 Coach print (56x66cm-22x26in) s. exhib.lit. 26-Jul-3 Coeur d'Alene, Hayden #219/R est:5000-10000

WILSON, Oscar (1867-1930) British

£1800 $2862 €2700 Piping the frog (43x71cm-17x28in) s. 6-Mar-3 Christie's, Kensington #569/R est:2000-3000

WILSON, P MacGregor (?-1960) British

£1500 $2280 €2250 Still life of bluebells, campions and daisies in a vase (51x41cm-20x16in) init.d.1897. 28-Aug-2 Sotheby's, London #1011/R est:1500-2500

WILSON, Ray (1906-1972) American

Works on paper

£250 $400 €375 Laundry Day (79x62cm-31x24in) s. W/C. 18-May-3 Butterfields, Los Angeles #7043

WILSON, Richard (1714-1782) British

£319 $495 €479 Pastoral landscape (10x14cm-4x6in) panel. 4-Dec-2 AB Stockholms Auktionsverk #1973/R (S.KR 4500)
£369 $606 €554 Figures alongside river with buildings (31x39cm-12x15in) 4-Feb-3 Dales, Durban #46 (SA.R 5000)
£25000 $41500 €37500 L'Anconetta, Venice (53x80cm-21x31in) i. prov.exhib.lit. 10-Jun-3 Christie's, London #51/R est:25000-40000

Works on paper

£420 $664 €609 Wooded landscape with mountains behind (9x13cm-4x5in) black chk. 22-Jul-3 Bonhams, Knightsbridge #216/R
£540 $848 €810 Monte Palatine (20x28cm-8x11in) i. chk dr. 13-Dec-2 Keys, Aylsham #506

WILSON, Richard (attrib) (1714-1782) British

£1600 $2496 €2400 Italianate landscape (47x62cm-19x24in) 7-Nov-2 Christie's, Kensington #82/R est:1000-1500
£2128 $3298 €3192 Italianate landscape with figures (82x66cm-32x26in) 3-Dec-2 Bukowskis, Stockholm #496/R est:40000-50000 (S.KR 30000)

Works on paper

£380 $593 €570 Villa Negroni, trees (12x10cm-5x4in) W/C over pencil htd white prov.exhib. 17-Sep-2 Rosebery Fine Art, London #618/R

WILSON, Robert (1941-) American

Works on paper

£1921 $2805 €2882 Golden window (57x72cm-22x28in) pencil s.d.1981 prov.exhib.lit. 4-Jun-2 Germann, Zurich #69/R est:4500-5500 (S.FR 4400)

WILSON, Robert B (fl.1935-1940) British

Works on paper

£500 $795 €750 Pittenweem Harbour, Fife (34x48cm-13x19in) s. pencil W/C htd white. 6-Mar-3 Christie's, Kensington #142/R

WILSON, Ronald York (1907-1984) Canadian

£444 $729 €666 Tree mosaic (79x59cm-31x23in) s. 3-Jun-3 Joyner, Toronto #579 est:1000-1500 (C.D 1000)
£562 $883 €843 Moroccan conversation piece (90x75cm-35x30in) s.i. painted c.1953. 25-Nov-2 Hodgins, Calgary #199/R (C.D 1400)
£617 $957 €926 Narrow canal, Venice (69x49cm-27x19in) s. prov. 3-Dec-2 Joyner, Toronto #361 est:500-700 (C.D 1500)
£1452 $2294 €2178 Shades of Tlalpujahua (102x122cm-40x48in) s. prov.exhib. 18-Nov-2 Sotheby's, Toronto #170/R est:3000-4000 (C.D 3600)
£1481 $2296 €2222 Proto tolteca (137x190cm-54x75in) s. prov. 3-Dec-2 Joyner, Toronto #235/R est:3000-4000 (C.D 3600)
£1728 $2679 €2592 Dancer bending (43x31cm-17x12in) s. board prov.exhib. 3-Dec-2 Joyner, Toronto #375 est:300-400 (C.D 4200)

WILSON, Ross (1959-) British

£385 $604 €600 Pink Mr Y (19x13cm-7x5in) init. board. 19-Nov-2 Whyte's, Dublin #174/R

Works on paper

£268 $417 €420 Oscar Wilde (14x17cm-6x7in) s. mixed media. 6-Nov-2 James Adam, Dublin #41/R
£350 $543 €525 Portrait of Brian Moore (106x68cm-42x27in) chl. 4-Dec-2 John Ross, Belfast #117
£380 $555 €570 Yellow landscape (23x30cm-9x12in) mono. mixed media. 12-Jun-2 John Ross, Belfast #224
£500 $730 €750 Angel, wings of Desire (23x15cm-9x6in) s.d.1990 verso mixed media. 12-Jun-2 John Ross, Belfast #169
£500 $730 €750 Horse and rider (13x18cm-5x7in) mono. mixed media. 12-Jun-2 John Ross, Belfast #216
£616 $968 €900 Frog prince and James Joyce (99x12cm-39x5in) mixed media prov. 15-Apr-3 De Veres Art Auctions, Dublin #97
£680 $1081 €1020 Girl of the seed (83x10cm-33x4in) mono.d.1986 verso mixed media. 5-Mar-3 John Ross, Belfast #230

WILSON, Scottie (1889-1972) British

Works on paper

£350 $546 €525 Castles and flowers (59x51cm-23x20in) s. ink crayon. 17-Oct-2 Bonhams, Edinburgh #44
£400 $660 €580 Untitled (46x35cm-18x14in) s. W/C bodycol col crayon ink prov. 3-Jul-3 Christie's, Kensington #636
£426 $689 €600 Untitled (38x28cm-15x11in) s. Indian ink col chk. 24-May-3 Van Ham, Cologne #641
£475 $750 €750 Composition (29x21cm-11x8in) s. Chinese ink W/C. 27-Nov-2 Blanchet, Paris #126
£480 $739 €720 Flowers in a vase (44x19cm-17x7in) s. pen ink crayon. 5-Sep-2 Christie's, Kensington #696
£483 $762 €700 Butterflies (35x26cm-14x10in) s. W/C prov. 4-Apr-3 Tajan, Paris #18
£500 $795 €750 Abstract poissons, poulet and tete (30x18cm-12x7in) s. W/C. 19-Mar-3 John Nicholson, Haslemere #1119/R
£520 $822 €780 Birds and fish (61x51cm-24x20in) s. col chk. 19-Dec-2 Bonhams, Edinburgh #326
£537 $864 €800 Composition aux poissons (37x25cm-15x10in) s. W/C. 23-Feb-3 Mercier & Cie, Lille #37
£600 $918 €900 Swans, birds and flowers on a dark background (53x42cm-21x17in) s. col chks. 22-Aug-2 Bonhams, Edinburgh #1143
£650 $995 €975 Swans, birds and flowers (59x50cm-23x20in) s. ink crayon. 22-Aug-2 Bonhams, Edinburgh #1139
£650 $1021 €975 Tree of life (70x50cm-28x20in) s. pen ink crayon. 15-Apr-3 Bonhams, Knightsbridge #157/R
£780 $1193 €1170 Swans, fish and plants (51x58cm-20x23in) s. ink crayon. 22-Aug-2 Bonhams, Edinburgh #1140
£780 $1193 €1170 Sea and sky (51x57cm-20x22in) s. ink crayon. 22-Aug-2 Bonhams, Edinburgh #1142
£800 $1312 €1200 Bird tree (30x26cm-12x10in) s. ink W/C. 3-Jun-3 Sotheby's, Olympia #145/R
£850 $1318 €1275 Birds and monuments (49x62cm-19x24in) s. pen black ink col crayon. 4-Dec-2 Christie's, Kensington #315
£880 $1346 €1320 Birds, swans and castle (50x56cm-20x22in) s. ink crayon. 22-Aug-2 Bonhams, Edinburgh #1141/R
£1111 $1800 €1667 Untitled (24x33cm-9x13in) s. gouache ink two prov. 27-Jan-3 Christie's, Rockefeller NY #51/R est:2000-2500
£1481 $2400 €2222 Untitled (38x27cm-15x11in) s. ink crayon two prov. 27-Jan-3 Christie's, Rockefeller NY #38/R est:2000-3000
£1481 $2400 €2222 Untitled (26x35cm-10x14in) s. gouache two prov. 27-Jan-3 Christie's, Rockefeller NY #50/R est:2000-3000
£1481 $2400 €2222 Untitled (38x28cm-15x11in) s. pen col pencil ink crayon prov.exhib. 27-Jan-3 Christie's, Rockefeller NY #54/R est:2500-3000
£1512 $2389 €2268 Dream creature (74x55cm-29x22in) s. W/C prov.lit. 18-Nov-2 Sotheby's, Toronto #135/R est:2500-3000 (C.D 3750)
£1852 $3000 €2778 Untitled (41x19cm-16x7in) s. pen ink col pencil prov.exhib. 27-Jan-3 Christie's, Rockefeller NY #55/R est:4000-6000

£1975 $3200 €2963 Untitled (38x27cm-15x11in) s. ink crayon executed c.1950 prov.exhib. 27-Jan-3 Christie's, Rockefeller NY #41/R est:3000-4000
£2346 $3800 €3519 Untitled (33x24cm-13x9in) s. W/C two prov. 27-Jan-3 Christie's, Rockefeller NY #39/R est:2000-2500
£2469 $4000 €3704 Untitled (42x27cm-17x11in) s. ink crayon prov.exhib. 27-Jan-3 Christie's, Rockefeller NY #42/R est:4000-6000
£15068 $23507 €22000 Personnage aux poissons (41x29cm-16x11in) s.i. ink exhib. 14-Apr-3 Laurence Calmels, Paris #4026/R est:1800

WILSON, Sidney Ernest (1869-?) American
£323 $500 €485 Fantasy landscape, with woman and dog. s. board. 2-Nov-2 Thomaston Place, Thomaston #131

WILSON, Thomas (19th C) British
£391 $610 €653 Untitled - knitting by the window (39x29cm-15x11in) s. canvasboard prov. 13-Apr-3 Levis, Calgary #220/R est:1000-1200 (C.D 900)

WILSON, Tim (20th C) New Zealander
£283 $455 €425 Doubtful Sound (44x59cm-17x23in) s. 7-May-3 Dunbar Sloane, Auckland #73 (NZ.D 800)
£555 $816 €833 Water garden (45x60cm-18x24in) s. exhib. 19-Jun-2 Watson's, Christchurch #1/R est:2000-6000 (NZ.D 1700)
£564 $880 €846 Lion Rock, Piha (30x30cm-12x12in) s.d.1992. 7-Nov-2 International Art Centre, Auckland #116/R est:1800-2600 (NZ.D 1800)
£614 $982 €890 MacKinnon Pass (40x55cm-16x22in) s.i. board. 13-May-3 Watson's, Christchurch #14/R (NZ.D 1700)
£1032 $1465 €1548 Lake Okataina (44x59cm-17x23in) s. board prov. 21-Nov-1 Watson's, Christchurch #17/R est:1000-2000 (NZ.D 3550)
£1395 $1981 €2093 Doubtful sound (44x59cm-17x23in) s. board prov. 21-Nov-1 Watson's, Christchurch #18/R est:1000-2000 (NZ.D 4800)
£1480 $2368 €2146 Quiet Sounds, Fiordland (60x89cm-24x35in) s. board. 13-May-3 Watson's, Christchurch #32/R est:2500-5000 (NZ.D 4100)

WILSON, W (18/19th C) British
£600 $924 €900 Leaving harbour (20x30cm-8x12in) s. 5-Sep-2 Christie's, Kensington #232/R

WILSON, W F (19th C) British
£2263 $3508 €3395 Portrait of the Duke of Wellington (65x54cm-26x21in) s.d.1843. 3-Dec-2 Ritchie, Toronto #3019a/R est:3000-4000 (C.D 5500)

WILSON, William (19th C) British
£5714 $9029 €8571 Views of the Darling Downs, Queensland (19x31cm-7x12in) i. panel set of nine. 27-Nov-2 Deutscher-Menzies, Melbourne #203/R est:6000-8000 (A.D 16000)

WILSON, William (1905-1972) British
Works on paper
£1100 $1705 €1650 Ross of Mull (30x35cm-12x14in) s.i.d.1944 pen ink W/C. 6-Dec-2 Lyon & Turnbull, Edinburgh #58/R est:800-1200
£3400 $5202 €5100 Gifford, East Lothian (45x63cm-18x25in) s.i. ink W/C. 22-Aug-2 Bonhams, Edinburgh #1107/R est:2000-3000
£3400 $5304 €5100 Gondolas, Venice (47x62cm-19x24in) s. ink W/C. 17-Oct-2 Bonhams, Edinburgh #143/R est:2000-3000

WILSON, Winifred (20th C) British
£450 $698 €675 Foxgloves (46x50cm-18x20in) s. board. 6-Dec-2 ELR Auctions, Sheffield #240

WILT, Hans (1867-1917) Austrian
£705 $1107 €1100 View of Dortrecht in Holland (65x47cm-26x19in) s.d.1905 canvas on board. 10-Dec-2 Dorotheum, Vienna #64/R
£1103 $1766 €1600 Stream in Klosterneuburg (75x96cm-30x38in) s. board. 11-Mar-3 Dorotheum, Vienna #21/R est:1800-2400
£3401 $5408 €5000 Well in Schonbrunn (72x99cm-28x39in) s.d.1912. 25-Feb-3 Dorotheum, Vienna #29/R est:3500-3800

WILT, Thomas van der (attrib) (1659-1733) Dutch
£2866 $4471 €4500 Lady with a negro servant and two dogs near a classical fountain (42x37cm-17x15in) prov.exhib.lit. 5-Nov-2 Sotheby's, Amsterdam #82/R est:3000-5000

WILTON, Charles (fl.1837-1847) British
Works on paper
£340 $530 €510 Mother and daughters in an interior (37x45cm-15x18in) s. W/C. 6-Nov-2 Bonhams, Chester #457

WILTON, Joseph (1722-1803) British
Sculpture
£200000 $334000 €290000 Thomas Hollis, 'The Anonymous Republican' (66cm-26in) white marble marble socle incl socle prov. 8-Jul-3 Sotheby's, London #145/R est:200000-300000

WIMAR, Charles (1828-1862) American
£22436 $35000 €33654 Snowy ride (15x23cm-6x9in) s. board prov.lit. 9-Nov-2 Santa Fe Art, Santa Fe #158/R est:60000-80000
Works on paper
£314 $500 €471 Study of Indians and horses (25x36cm-10x14in) pencil prov. 5-Mar-3 Christie's, Rockefeller NY #106/R

WIMBUSH, Henry B (fl.1881-1904) British
Works on paper
£260 $424 €390 Highland landscape with loch (45x62cm-18x24in) s. W/C. 12-Feb-3 Edgar Horn, Eastbourne #304

WIMMENAUER, Adalbert (1869-1914) German
£1071 $1564 €1650 Grape eater (147x114cm-58x45in) s.verso. 15-Jun-2 Hans Stahl, Hamburg #65/R

WIMMER, Fritz (1879-1960) German
£340 $557 €520 Bathers (87x110cm-34x43in) 5-Feb-3 Neumeister, Munich #840
Works on paper
£385 $604 €600 Female nude (37x25cm-15x10in) d.1933 red ochre dr. 21-Nov-2 Dorotheum, Vienna #417/R

WIMMER, Hans (1907-1992) German
Sculpture
£6410 $9936 €10000 Statuette of horse and rider (26cm-10in) dark pat.bronze lit. 4-Dec-2 Lempertz, Koln #1113/R est:10000

WIMMER, Rudolf (1849-1915) German
£1235 $1914 €1853 Study for portrait of Kaiser Wilhelm (111x69cm-44x27in) s.i.d.1891. 3-Dec-2 Ritchie, Toronto #3087/R est:2000-3000 (C.D 3000)

WIMPERIS, Edmund Morison (1835-1900) British
£300 $489 €450 View of Wensleydale (12x19cm-5x7in) init. i.verso. 12-Feb-3 Andrew Hartley, Ilkley #888
£900 $1386 €1350 Across the valley (61x91cm-24x36in) init. 5-Sep-2 Christie's, Kensington #199/R
Works on paper
£250 $395 €363 Hay cart (17x26cm-7x10in) init. W/C. 22-Jul-3 Bonhams, Knightsbridge #187/R
£260 $434 €377 View on the Wharf, Grassington (15x24cm-6x9in) init.d.98 W/C scratching out. 23-Jun-3 Bonhams, Bath #39
£300 $465 €450 Windswept landscape with a drover and sheep in country lane (51x75cm-20x30in) init. W/C. 25-Sep-2 Hamptons Fine Art, Godalming #248
£320 $506 €464 Figures in a rural landscape (45x66cm-18x26in) init.d.1900 W/C. 22-Jul-3 Bonhams, Knightsbridge #215/R
£360 $562 €540 On the River Thames (23x16cm-9x6in) init. W/C. 6-Nov-2 Bonhams, Chester #539
£360 $601 €522 North Wales (40x62cm-16x24in) init.d.86 W/C. 25-Jun-3 Bonhams, Bury St Edmunds #483
£360 $587 €522 Girl with flock of sheep in a moorland landscape (36x53cm-14x21in) init.d.84 W/C. 17-Jul-3 Richardson & Smith, Whitby #477
£380 $589 €570 Sheep grazing the top of the hill (25x44cm-10x17in) init. W/C. 30-Sep-2 Bonhams, Ipswich #320
£400 $668 €580 Cattle by a moorland pool (43x62cm-17x24in) init.d.84 W/C htd bodycol. 25-Jun-3 Bonhams, Bury St Edmunds #481
£450 $698 €675 Shepherd and his flock in a highland landscape (37x62cm-15x24in) init.d.74 W/C. 3-Dec-2 Sotheby's, Olympia #100/R
£460 $768 €667 Near Bury Hill, Surrey (42x74cm-17x29in) s.d.95 W/C. 25-Jun-3 Bonhams, Bury St Edmunds #510
£550 $913 €825 Suffolk Common (14x23cm-6x9in) s. W/C over pencil. 12-Jun-3 Sotheby's, London #162
£560 $902 €840 Cottages at Gosport, Bosham (23x33cm-9x13in) init.d.91 W/C. 9-May-3 Mallams, Oxford #43/R
£580 $940 €870 Gathering seaweed (15x24cm-6x9in) init.d.64 W/C over pencil. 20-May-3 Sotheby's, Olympia #5/R
£650 $1027 €975 Winter homecoming (23x33cm-9x13in) s.d.1861 W/C. 27-Nov-2 Bonhams, Brooks & Langlois, Jersey #84/R
£800 $1264 €1200 Across the heath (48x74cm-19x29in) init.d.78 W/C. 13-Nov-2 Halls, Shrewsbury #324/R
£1050 $1722 €1575 Exmoor (25x48cm-10x19in) init. W/C. 4-Feb-3 Bonhams, Leeds #217

WIMPERIS, Edmund Morison (attrib) (1835-1900) British
£500 $780 €750 Hampstead Heath (20x30cm-8x12in) panel. 17-Sep-2 Sotheby's, Olympia #149/R

Works on paper

£613 $1000 €920 Verdant landscape, Penmaenpool (30x51cm-12x20in) bears sig. i.verso pencil W/C card sold with a companion. 16-Feb-3 Butterfields, San Francisco #2064

WIMPFEN, J (19th C) French?

Miniatures

£1560 $2528 €2200 Le dauphin playing drum (5cm-2in circular) s. ivory gilded wood frame. 21-May-3 Piasa, Paris #290/R est:1200-1500

WINANCE, Jean (1911-) Belgian

£314 $484 €500 Cathedrale de Tournai (40x50cm-16x20in) s. panel. 22-Oct-2 Galerie Moderne, Brussels #730

WINANS, Theodore Fonville (1911-1992) American

Photographs

£2134 $3500 €3201 Sugar can blessing (41x51cm-16x20in) s.d.1945 i.d.num.336H verso silver gelatin photo 1 of 2. 8-Feb-3 Neal Auction Company, New Orleans #375/R est:2000-2400

£3365 $5250 €5048 Dixie belles (41x51cm-16x20in) s.d.1938 silver gelatin print board edition of 35/50 exhib. 12-Oct-2 Neal Auction Company, New Orleans #701/R est:4000-6000

WINBERG, Iwan (fl.1830-1846) Russian

Miniatures

£3200 $5184 €4800 Portrait of Nicholas, Emperor of Russia (4cm-2in) s. prov. 22-May-3 Bonhams, New Bond Street #40/R est:1500-2500

WINCH, John (1944-) Australian

£637 $1045 €956 Abstract landscape (153x122cm-60x48in) composition board prov. 4-Jun-3 Deutscher-Menzies, Melbourne #319/R (A.D 1600)

WINCK, Joseph Gregor (1710-1781) German

£4577 $7599 €6500 Descent from the Cross (87x48cm-34x19in) s. 11-Jun-3 Dorotheum, Vienna #163/R est:3000-5000

WINCK, Willibald (1867-1932) German

£755 $1177 €1200 Still life (56x77cm-22x30in) s. panel lit. 20-Sep-2 Schloss Ahlden, Ahlden #1152/R

WINCKEL, Emile van de (1880-1953) Belgian

£316 $494 €500 Elegante a la robe rose (110x80cm-43x31in) s.d.1933. 16-Sep-2 Horta, Bruxelles #387

WINDHAGER, Franz (1879-1959) Austrian

£633 $1000 €1000 Conversation in coffee house (14x14cm-6x6in) s.d.1918 panel. 26-Nov-2 Wiener Kunst Auktionen, Vienna #130/R

£1392 $2172 €2200 New wine, Stammersdorf (51x73cm-20x29in) s.d.1929 panel. 15-Oct-2 Dorotheum, Vienna #41/R est:2200-2400

WINDMAIER, Anton (1840-1896) German

£800 $1264 €1200 Returning home (19x23cm-7x9in) s. panel. 14-Nov-2 Christie's, Kensington #203/R

£1484 $2181 €2300 Figures on frozen water (22x39cm-9x15in) s.d.1875 panel. 20-Jun-2 Dr Fritz Nagel, Stuttgart #833/R est:1000

£1582 $2453 €2500 Shepherd returning home with flock (60x45cm-24x18in) s. 25-Sep-2 Neumeister, Munich #779/R est:2500

WINDRED, E H (?) ?

£760 $1216 €1140 Portrait of a racing pigeon, Scotch Bob (36x43cm-14x17in) init. 11-Jan-3 Finan Watkins & Co, Mere #237

£780 $1248 €1170 Portrait of a racing pigeon, Flying Scotsman (36x46cm-14x18in) s. 11-Jan-3 Finan Watkins & Co, Mere #235/R

£880 $1408 €1320 Portrait of a racing pigeon, Tony (36x43cm-14x17in) s. 11-Jan-3 Finan Watkins & Co, Mere #236/R

£1300 $2054 €1950 Prize racing pigeons (36x46cm-14x18in) i.d.1933 pair. 28-Nov-2 Christie's, Kensington #23/R est:800-1200

WINDSCHMITT, Ludwig (1848-1920) German

£1400 $2128 €2100 Madonna and child with Saint John the Baptist (61x49cm-24x19in) s.d.1897 panel. 29-Aug-2 Christie's, Kensington #136/R est:1500-2000

WINDSTOSSER, Ludwig (1921-1983) German

Photographs

£2327 $3607 €3700 Gathering in the rain (29x23cm-11x9in) i. verso gelatin silver. 2-Nov-2 Lempertz, Koln #112/R est:2200

£2329 $3633 €3400 A gathering in the rain (39x29cm-15x11in) gelatin silver. 12-Apr-3 Lempertz, Koln #225/R est:2600

WINDT, Chris van der (1877-1952) Dutch

£303 $472 €475 House on forest edge (14x31cm-6x12in) s. board. 6-Nov-2 Vendue Huis, Gravenhage #624/R

£563 $907 €800 Hens in farmyard (15x23cm-6x9in) s. 7-May-3 Vendue Huis, Gravenhage #578/R

£892 $1391 €1400 Self portrait (25x18cm-10x7in) s. 6-Nov-2 Vendue Huis, Gravenhage #629/R

£1083 $1689 €1700 Narcissus (23x18cm-9x7in) s.d.10 board. 6-Nov-2 Vendue Huis, Gravenhage #627/R est:1000-1500

£1656 $2583 €2600 Barge on ditch edge (17x21cm-7x8in) s. lit. 6-Nov-2 Vendue Huis, Gravenhage #623/R est:1000-1500

£2394 $3855 €3400 Farm shed at the edge of the water (18x33cm-7x13in) s. board. 7-May-3 Vendue Huis, Gravenhage #582/R est:3000-4000

£2675 $4173 €4200 View of Wittelaan (27x47cm-11x19in) s. panel exhib. 6-Nov-2 Vendue Huis, Gravenhage #625/R est:2500-3000

£3185 $4968 €5000 Still life with orange and vase (20x28cm-8x11in) s. exhib.lit. 6-Nov-2 Vendue Huis, Gravenhage #619/R est:1500-2000

£3185 $4968 €5000 Flowers lying on a table (17x46cm-7x18in) s. panel exhib. 6-Nov-2 Vendue Huis, Gravenhage #633/R est:2000-3000

£4459 $6866 €7000 Still life with Chinese porcelain (30x25cm-12x10in) s. panel prov. 3-Sep-2 Christie's, Amsterdam #178/R est:3000-5000

£6051 $9439 €9500 Violas and marigolds (32x23cm-13x9in) s. panel exhib. 6-Nov-2 Vendue Huis, Gravenhage #632/R est:1500-2000

Works on paper

£478 $745 €750 Vase with wild flowers (29x20cm-11x8in) s.d.1900 W/C pencil. 6-Nov-2 Vendue Huis, Gravenhage #622/R

£605 $944 €950 Narcissus (34x25cm-13x10in) s. W/C. 6-Nov-2 Vendue Huis, Gravenhage #628/R

£1911 $2981 €3000 Polder landscape with farm (26x43cm-10x17in) s. W/C. 6-Nov-2 Vendue Huis, Gravenhage #631/R est:2500-3500

£4795 $7527 €7000 Farmyard (39x63cm-15x25in) s.d.1906 W/C. 15-Apr-3 Sotheby's, Amsterdam #104/R est:7000-9000

£5660 $8717 €9000 Farm on the waterfront (44x64cm-17x25in) s.d.1906 W/C htd white prov. 22-Oct-2 Sotheby's, Amsterdam #93/R est:7000-9000

WINDUS, William Lindsay (1822-1907) British

£2000 $3220 €3000 Study of trooper (47x31cm-19x12in) i.d.1858 board prov. 20-Feb-3 Christie's, London #60/R

WINGATE, Carl (1876-?) American

Works on paper

£261 $425 €392 Schooner at anchor (25x18cm-10x7in) s.d.1940 W/C. 2-Feb-3 Grogan, Boston #35

WINGATE, Sir James Lawton (1846-1924) British

£300 $477 €450 Ford (30x23cm-12x9in) s. board. 6-Mar-3 Christie's, Kensington #173

£360 $587 €540 Still life of red and pink roses (44x34cm-17x13in) 14-Feb-3 Lyon & Turnbull, Edinburgh #153

£360 $562 €540 Cattle by a river (25x35cm-10x14in) s. 9-Apr-3 Cheffins Grain & Comins, Cambridge #707/R

£400 $620 €600 Near Symington (29x39cm-11x15in) s. canvas laid down. 5-Dec-2 Bonhams, Edinburgh #32

£500 $795 €750 Pale sunset, Machrie (25x36cm-10x14in) s. prov. 6-Mar-3 Christie's, Kensington #172/R

£520 $822 €780 Pale sunset, Machrie (23x32cm-9x13in) s. 2-Dec-2 Bonhams, Bath #133

£521 $850 €782 Lowtide (41x51cm-16x20in) s. 16-Feb-3 Butterfields, San Francisco #2045

£550 $875 €825 Woodland path (24x34cm-9x13in) s. board. 6-Mar-3 Christie's, Kensington #174

£600 $936 €900 Carting hay (34x44cm-13x17in) s. 17-Oct-2 Bonhams, Edinburgh #238

£650 $1021 €975 Lake scene with boats (26x36cm-10x14in) s.d.1912. 21-Nov-2 Tennants, Leyburn #755

£650 $1079 €943 Days departing glory (41x51cm-16x20in) s. 13-Jun-3 Lyon & Turnbull, Edinburgh #50

£700 $1141 €1050 Autumn landscape (36x51cm-14x20in) 14-Feb-3 Lyon & Turnbull, Edinburgh #107

£820 $1255 €1230 Moor, Machrie Bay (34x51cm-13x20in) s. 22-Aug-2 Bonhams, Edinburgh #1144

£823 $1267 €1235 Untitled, landscape (61x41cm-24x16in) 26-Oct-2 Heffel, Vancouver #56 est:800-1000 (C.D 2000)

£1200 $1944 €1800 Amongst the Bents, Carnoustie (25x35cm-10x14in) s. board. 23-May-3 Lyon & Turnbull, Edinburgh #47 est:400-600

£2100 $3276 €3150 Silvery sunset (34x51cm-13x20in) s. prov. 10-Apr-3 Bonhams, Edinburgh #165 est:1200-1800

£2400 $3816 €3600 Carradale (38x48cm-15x19in) 29-Apr-3 Gorringes, Lewes #2207

£4000 $6080 €6000 Secret meeting (102x153cm-40x60in) s.d.82. 28-Aug-2 Sotheby's, London #985/R est:2000-3000

£4808 $7500 €7212 Pastoral landscape (96x125cm-38x49in) s. prov. 12-Apr-3 Weschler, Washington #511/R est:6000-8000

WINGE, Sigurd (1909-1970) Norwegian
Prints
£2368 $3742 €3552 Frieze II 1955 (33x110cm-13x43in) s.i.d.55 etching. 17-Dec-2 Grev Wedels Plass, Oslo #54/R est:15000-20000 (N.KR 27000)
£2855 $4510 €4283 Frieze II (30x108cm-12x43in) s.d.57 drypoint aquatint. 2-Dec-2 Blomqvist, Oslo #399/R est:18000-22000 (N.KR 33000)

WINGFIELD, James Digman (1809-1872) British
£850 $1309 €1275 Gift from the garden (30x30cm-12x12in) painted circle. 5-Sep-2 Christie's, Kensington #323/R
£16000 $25440 €24000 Cartoon gallery at Hampton Court in old times (60x105cm-24x41in) s.d.184-1850 set of three prov.exhib. 19-Mar-3 Sotheby's, London #100/R est:6000-8000
Works on paper
£650 $1086 €943 Bunyans Chapel, Lambeth (28x36cm-11x14in) init.i.d.1848 W/C. 24-Jun-3 Bonhams, Knightsbridge #21/R

WINGFIELD, James Digman (attrib) (1809-1872) British
£3000 $4680 €4500 Art teacher (49x65cm-19x26in) 8-Apr-3 Bonhams, Knightsbridge #320/R est:2000-3000

WINGHE, Jeremias van (attrib) (1578-1645) German
£5634 $9352 €8000 Jael and Sisera (90x70cm-35x28in) bears sig. panel one of pair. 11-Jun-3 Dorotheum, Vienna #120/R est:9000-12000
£42254 $70141 €60000 Le couronnement des arts et du travail et la punition des plaisirs temporels (125x205cm-49x81in) 16-Jun-3 Claude Aguttes, Neuilly #18/R est:80000-100000

WINKFIELD, Frederick A (fl.1873-1920) British
£750 $1223 €1125 Putney pier (12x21cm-5x8in) s.i.d.1887 s.i.verso oil on tin. 29-Jan-3 Sotheby's, Olympia #197/R
£2000 $3240 €3000 Thames at Greenwich. bears sig.d.1890. 22-Jan-3 Bonhams, New Bond Street #384/R est:1500-2000
Works on paper
£420 $664 €630 Shipping on the Thames at Bermondsey (22x32cm-9x13in) s. W/C. 26-Nov-2 Bonhams, Oxford #31

WINKLER, Carl von (1860-1911) ?
£1549 $2494 €2200 View from Capri (41x56cm-16x22in) s. board. 10-May-3 Bukowskis, Helsinki #392/R est:600-800

WINKLER, Fritz (1894-1964) German
Works on paper
£264 $412 €420 Young peasant with cow (24x33cm-9x13in) W/C Indian ink brush over pencil. 11-Oct-2 Winterberg, Heidelberg #1872

WINKLER, Karl (1827-1874) German
£274 $427 €400 Rothenburg with view of Roderbogen with Markusturm (16x12cm-6x5in) s.i. panel. 10-Apr-3 Allgauer, Kempten #3064/R

WINOGRAND, Garry (1928-1984) American
Photographs
£2110 $3250 €3165 New York City - dog in snow (34x22cm-13x9in) s.verso photograph prov. 22-Oct-2 Sotheby's, New York #211/R est:3000-5000
£2147 $3500 €3221 New York, from the double elephant portfolio (29x33cm-11x13in) s.num.2/75 gelatin silver print. 12-Feb-3 Christie's, Rockefeller NY #190/R est:3000-5000
£2435 $3750 €3653 New York - zoo, Wolf (22x33cm-9x13in) s. photograph prov.lit. 22-Oct-2 Sotheby's, New York #208/R est:5000-8000
£2435 $3750 €3653 Apollo 11 moon shot, Cape Kennedy, Florida (22x34cm-9x13in) s. photograph prov.lit. 22-Oct-2 Sotheby's, New York #209/R est:5000-8000
£2658 $4200 €3987 New York from women are beautiful (22x33cm-9x13in) s. gelatin silver print lit. 22-Apr-3 Christie's, Rockefeller NY #135/R est:3000-5000
£3481 $5500 €5222 Untitled - hard hat rally (22x33cm-9x13in) gelatin silver print prov.lit. 25-Apr-3 Phillips, New York #163/R est:3000-5000
£3571 $5500 €5357 Utah - cow crossing road (23x34cm-9x13in) s.verso photograph prov.lit. 22-Oct-2 Sotheby's, New York #210/R est:3000-5000
£5844 $9000 €8766 Los Angeles (22x33cm-9x13in) s.num.141 verso gelatin silver print prov.lit. 25-Oct-2 Phillips, New York #36/R est:5000-7000
£8228 $13000 €12342 Untitled (22x34cm-9x13in) s.verso gelatin silver print prov.lit. 25-Apr-3 Phillips, New York #51/R est:7000-10000
£8861 $14000 €13292 World's fair, New York City (22x33cm-9x13in) s.verso gelatin silver print prov.lit. 25-Apr-3 Phillips, New York #162/R est:4000-6000
£11392 $18000 €17088 Los Angeles (23x34cm-9x13in) s.verso gelatin silver print prov.lit. 25-Apr-3 Phillips, New York #52/R est:6000-8000
£26000 $42120 €39000 Untitled. s.num.40/75 silver prints 15 portfolio lit. 22-May-3 Sotheby's, London #143/R est:4500-6500
£26582 $42000 €39873 From 15 big shots (32x47cm-13x19in) s.verso 14 gelatin silver print prov. 25-Apr-3 Phillips, New York #50/R est:18000-22000
£34810 $55000 €52215 Untitled - from the animals (21x34cm-8x13in) s. 21 gelatin silver print prov.lit. 25-Apr-3 Phillips, New York #49/R est:30000-40000

WINSTANLEY, Hamlet (1698-1756) British
£4200 $6930 €6090 Portrait of Bannestre Parker (127x101cm-50x40in) indis.s.d.1737 prov. 2-Jul-3 Sotheby's, Olympia #34/R est:2800-4200

WINSTON, Claire (1882-1944) British
Sculpture
£6000 $9600 €9000 Bust of George Bernard Shaw (42cm-17in) s. brown pat. bronze. 16-May-3 Sotheby's, London #70/R est:3000-5000

WINT, Peter de (1784-1849) British
£2000 $3120 €3000 Extensive river landscape with figures in punt (41x71cm-16x28in) board. 18-Oct-2 Keys, Aylsham #714 est:2000-3000
Works on paper
£280 $434 €420 Cattle in a meadow near Lincoln (15x20cm-6x8in) black chk wash htd white prov. 9-Dec-2 Bonhams, New Bond Street #7
£300 $465 €450 Near Matlock (11x15cm-4x6in) black white chk prov. 9-Dec-2 Bonhams, New Bond Street #11
£1000 $1650 €1450 Old Mill, Danbury, Essex (13x22cm-5x9in) W/C prov. 2-Jul-3 Sotheby's, Olympia #211/R est:1000-1500
£1200 $1872 €1800 Cows beside the river, castle on the hill beyond (13x19cm-5x7in) i. W/C prov. 27-Mar-3 Christie's, Kensington #96/R est:800-1200
£2000 $3160 €3000 Cattle by a river, bridge beyond (23x34cm-9x13in) W/C over pencil htd bodycol. 28-Nov-2 Sotheby's, London #292/R est:1500-2000
£2500 $3951 €3750 Bristol Cathedral from Wapping looking across Canon's Marsh (40x58cm-16x23in) W/C over pencil htd bodycol stopping out. 28-Nov-2 Sotheby's, London #300/R est:2500-3500
£2800 $4424 €4200 Path leading through a wood (41x44cm-16x17in) W/C over pencil. 28-Nov-2 Sotheby's, London #264/R est:3000-4000
£2800 $4592 €4060 Storm (27x74cm-11x29in) black white chk prov. 5-Jun-3 Christie's, London #56/R est:1500-2000
£2800 $4592 €4060 Harvesting scene (33x51cm-13x20in) pencil W/C htd bodycol prov. 5-Jun-3 Christie's, London #58/R est:3000-5000
£3000 $4920 €4350 Eel trapping (22x32cm-9x13in) pencil W/C gum arabic. 5-Jun-3 Christie's, London #60/R est:2000-3000
£3500 $5810 €5250 Malmesbury abbey, Wiltshire (15x32cm-6x13in) W/C over pencil htd white. 12-Jun-3 Sotheby's, London #141/R est:4000-6000
£3800 $5434 €5700 Horses and pigs in farmyard (13x16cm-5x6in) pencil W/C htd white prov.exhib.lit. 22-Jan-3 Christie's, London #41/R est:6000
£3800 $6232 €5510 Ferry near Doncaster (39x78cm-15x31in) i. pencil W/C gum arabic scratching out. 5-Jun-3 Christie's, London #61/R est:2500-3500
£4000 $6560 €5800 Two rustic figures (12x14cm-5x6in) pencil W/C scratching out prov.exhib. 5-Jun-3 Christie's, London #55/R est:2000-3000
£4200 $6972 €6300 Distant view of Lincoln from the banks of the River Witham (29x46cm-11x18in) W/C over pencil prov. 12-Jun-3 Sotheby's, London #135/R est:4000-6000
£5000 $7150 €7500 Horses and sheep by farm pond (24x30cm-9x12in) pencil W/C prov.exhib. 22-Jan-3 Christie's, London #42/R est:5000
£5500 $9020 €7975 Trees in a field, with hills beyond (15x32cm-6x13in) W/C prov. 5-Jun-3 Christie's, London #100/R est:2500-3500
£6000 $8580 €9000 Moored barges near Lambeth Palace (22x19cm-9x7in) pencil W/C prov.exhib.lit. 22-Jan-3 Christie's, London #39/R est:10000
£7200 $10296 €10800 Barge near mooring posts (17x12cm-7x5in) pencil W/C prov.exhib.lit. 22-Jan-3 Christie's, London #40/R est:5000
£8000 $11440 €12000 Figure in churchyard above river (16x32cm-6x13in) pencil W/C prov.exhib.lit. 22-Jan-3 Christie's, London #38/R est:10000
£8500 $13940 €12325 Harvesting scene, stacking hay (57x33cm-22x13in) pencil W/C scratching out prov.exhib. 5-Jun-3 Christie's, London #99/R est:5000-7000
£9500 $13585 €14250 Study for 'The ferry' (9x13cm-4x5in) i.verso pencil W/C prov.exhib. 22-Jan-3 Christie's, London #44/R est:4000
£9500 $15580 €13775 Lake at Burghley House. Trees in an extensive wooded landscape (16x24cm-6x9in) pencil W/C prov. 5-Jun-3 Christie's, London #59/R est:5000-8000
£11000 $15730 €16500 Still life with wooden pail and eartheware vessels (15x18cm-6x7in) pencil W/C scratching out prov.exhib.lit. 22-Jan-3 Christie's, London #36/R est:10000
£15000 $23850 €22500 Horses watering at a farm near Lincoln (42x37cm-17x15in) W/C over pencil bodycol scratching out. 19-Mar-3 Sotheby's, London #199/R est:10000-15000

£17000 $24310 €25500 Two boys with donkey (16x15cm-6x6in) W/C double-sided prov.exhib.lit. 22-Jan-3 Christie's, London #43/R est:10000

WINT, Peter de (attrib) (1784-1849) British
Works on paper
£380 $589 €570 Harvesters in a cornfield near Lincoln (28x41cm-11x16in) W/C. 4-Oct-2 Mallams, Oxford #459
£500 $825 €725 Conway Castle, North Wales (16x23cm-6x9in) W/C over traces of pencil htd bodycol. 2-Jul-3 Sotheby's, Olympia #288/R

WINTER, Alice Beach (1877-c.1970) American
£658 $1000 €987 Alice and Oaksie at the seashore (74x91cm-29x36in) s. d.1943 verso prov. 17-Aug-2 North East Auctions, Portsmouth #1229/R
£968 $1550 €1452 Portrait of children with sailboats (74x91cm-29x36in) 11-Jan-3 James Julia, Fairfield #312d est:2500-3000

WINTER, Andrew (1893-1958) American
£219 $350 €318 Barque and distant tug (30x41cm-12x16in) s. canvasboard. 16-May-3 Skinner, Boston #100/R
£438 $700 €657 Wiscasset, Maine (46x61cm-18x24in) s.i.on stretcher. 11-Jan-3 James Julia, Fairfield #312c
£563 $900 €845 Monhegan Dock (30x33cm-12x13in) s. board. 11-Jan-3 James Julia, Fairfield #321b est:2000-3000
£1151 $1750 €1727 View of Maine Harbor. s. 30-Aug-2 Thomaston Place, Thomaston #55a
£5195 $8000 €7793 Old Port, Marseille (66x71cm-26x28in) s.d.26 board prov.exhib. 24-Oct-2 Shannon's, Milford #57/R est:8000-12000
£10526 $16000 €15789 View of Monhegan village (58x84cm-23x33in) s. 30-Aug-2 Thomaston Place, Thomaston #55
Works on paper
£1480 $2250 €2220 Old coast guard station at Little Manan, signal tower (56x74cm-22x29in) d.1940 W/C. 30-Aug-2 Thomaston Place, Thomaston #54

WINTER, Charles Allan (1869-1942) American
£510 $800 €765 Rocky inlet (41x51cm-16x20in) s. 22-Nov-2 Skinner, Boston #362/R
£605 $950 €908 Landscape with water going through breaks in coastal rocks filling in low area (30x33cm-12x13in) s. board. 19-Apr-3 James Julia, Fairfield #260/R
Works on paper
£419 $650 €629 Lady in green (64x51cm-25x20in) s. pastel exec.c.1920. 8-Dec-2 Toomey, Oak Park #723/R

WINTER, Cornelius Jason Walter (1820-1891) British
Works on paper
£350 $546 €525 View of the formal gardens at Melbourne (35x47cm-14x19in) s.d.1881 W/C. 8-Oct-2 Sotheby's, Olympia #419/R

WINTER, Fritz (1905-1976) German
£633 $987 €1000 Figure (44x30cm-17x12in) mono.d.28.13.11 oil monotype. 18-Oct-2 Dr Fritz Nagel, Stuttgart #646/R
£1139 $1800 €1800 Untitled (18x24cm-7x9in) s.d.60 paper. 29-Nov-2 Villa Grisebach, Berlin #957/R est:1800-2200
£1351 $2108 €2000 Composition in blue and red (12x15cm-5x6in) s.i.d.4.10.60 paper prov. 28-Mar-3 Ketterer, Hamburg #686/R est:2200-2500
£1351 $2108 €2000 Composition in blue and red (10x17cm-4x7in) s.d.1959 paper prov. 28-Mar-3 Ketterer, Hamburg #687/R est:2200-2500
£1584 $2645 €2297 Composition (16x23cm-6x9in) s.d.60 paper. 24-Jun-3 Koller, Zurich #132/R est:3500-4500 (S.FR 3500)
£1899 $3000 €3000 Untitled (18x24cm-7x9in) s.d.60. 30-Nov-2 Bassenge, Berlin #6706/R est:3500
£2029 $3328 €2800 Composition (50x70cm-20x28in) s.d.59 paper. 31-May-3 Villa Grisebach, Berlin #331/R est:3000-4000
£2029 $3328 €2800 Untitled (50x65cm-20x26in) s.d. oil on col serigraph. 31-May-3 Villa Grisebach, Berlin #332/R est:3000-4000
£2174 $3565 €3000 Green violet (70x60cm-28x24in) s. s.i.d.70 verso. 31-May-3 Villa Grisebach, Berlin #335/R est:5000-7000
£2174 $3565 €3000 To the right light (70x60cm-28x24in) s.d.70 s.i.d. verso. 31-May-3 Villa Grisebach, Berlin #336/R est:5000-7000
£3623 $5942 €5000 Untitled (74x100cm-29x39in) s.d.54 oil board on canvas. 31-May-3 Villa Grisebach, Berlin #328/R est:5000-7000
£4203 $6893 €5800 Shifted (49x70cm-19x28in) s.d.53 i. verso scraped oil paper on canvas exhib.lit. 28-May-3 Lempertz, Koln #471/R est:8000-9000
£4487 $6955 €7000 Composition (61x43cm-24x17in) s.d.1972 paper. 6-Dec-2 Hauswedell & Nolte, Hamburg #399/R est:6000
£5072 $8319 €7000 Elemental forces (75x100cm-30x39in) s.d.54 i. verso scraped oil paper on canvas prov. 28-May-3 Lempertz, Koln #472/R est:10000-11000
£5208 $8229 €7500 Grey and yellow (75x100cm-30x39in) s.d.1955. 26-Apr-3 Dr Lehr, Berlin #548/R est:10000
£5380 $8339 €8500 Untitled - with red and grey (74x99cm-29x39in) s.d.1954 board prov. 28-Sep-2 Ketterer, Hamburg #355/R est:10000-12000
£5674 $9191 €8000 Composition (65x50cm-26x20in) mono.d.49-50 board. 20-May-3 Dorotheum, Vienna #37/R est:8000-14000
£6289 $9686 €10000 Untitled composition (50x75cm-20x30in) s.d.1958 board masonite. 26-Oct-2 Dr Lehr, Berlin #578/R est:14000
£6944 $10972 €10000 Untitled (50x70cm-20x28in) s.d.1951 board. 26-Apr-3 Dr Lehr, Berlin #547/R est:12000
£6962 $10791 €11000 Restless (50x70cm-20x28in) s.d.1953 s.i.d. verso oil goauche board prov. 28-Sep-2 Ketterer, Hamburg #356/R est:10000-15000
£7147 $11079 €11150 Untitled (50x70cm-20x28in) s.d.1949 paper. 6-Dec-2 Hauswedell & Nolte, Hamburg #395/R est:12500
£7692 $11923 €12000 Heavy rain (90x80cm-35x31in) s.d.67 s.i.d. verso. 3-Dec-2 Lempertz, Koln #512/R est:7000-8000
£10759 $17000 €17000 Crystallisation (62x47cm-24x19in) mono.d.32 oil over collage paper on canvas. 30-Nov-2 Villa Grisebach, Berlin #407/R est:10000-12000
£13043 $21391 €18000 Between the stones (60x95cm-24x37in) s.d.52 s.i.d. verso hessian exhib. 31-May-3 Villa Grisebach, Berlin #330/R est:15000-20000
£14103 $21859 €22000 Horizontal vertical (70x60cm-28x24in) s.d.66 s.i.d. verso. 3-Dec-2 Lempertz, Koln #511/R est:22000-25000
£29487 $45705 €46000 Composition in red (80x90cm-31x35in) s.d.1965 s.i.d.1965 prov. 6-Dec-2 Ketterer, Munich #160/R est:30000-40000
£36708 $58000 €58000 Stones (135x145cm-53x57in) mono.d.56 s.indis.i.d.56 verso burlap prov. 29-Nov-2 Villa Grisebach, Berlin #83/R est:35000-45000
Prints
£2899 $4754 €4000 Figurine (65x46cm-26x18in) mono.d.29 monotype prov. 31-May-3 Villa Grisebach, Berlin #205/R est:3500-4500
Works on paper
£449 $709 €700 Untitled (20x18cm-8x7in) mono.d.1975 col feltpen. 15-Nov-2 Reiss & Sohn, Konigstein #897/R
£833 $1292 €1300 Untitled (20x18cm-8x7in) mono.d.75 col feltpen. 3-Dec-2 Lempertz, Koln #513/R
£1667 $2583 €2600 Composition (15x19cm-6x7in) s.d.1960 gouache. 6-Dec-2 Hauswedell & Nolte, Hamburg #401/R est:2000
£2949 $4571 €4600 Composition (15x16cm-6x6in) s.d.1959 gouache. 6-Dec-2 Hauswedell & Nolte, Hamburg #400/R est:3000
£3205 $4968 €5000 Composition - grey (50x70cm-20x28in) s.d.1951 s.i.d. verso mixed media board. 6-Dec-2 Hauswedell & Nolte, Hamburg #397/R est:7500
£7770 $12122 €11500 Composition (50x70cm-20x28in) s.i.d. W/C tempera col chk board prov. 28-Mar-3 Ketterer, Hamburg #684/R est:6000-8000

WINTER, Ludovicus de (1819-1900) Belgian
£680 $1082 €1000 Retour des pecheurs au clair du lune (45x70cm-18x28in) s. panel. 18-Mar-3 Campo, Vlaamse Kaai #58

WINTER, Lumen Martin (1908-) American
Works on paper
£750 $1200 €1088 Loading the hay wagon (51x63cm-20x25in) bears sig. mixed media masonite. 16-May-3 Skinner, Boston #211/R

WINTER, Robert (19/20th C) British
£1090 $1700 €1635 October day (25x25cm-10x10in) board. 19-Oct-2 David Dike, Dallas #196/R est:1200-1800
Works on paper
£280 $451 €420 St Ives Parish Church and the Waits, from Hemingford Meadow (26x36cm-10x14in) s. W/C. 15-Jan-3 Cheffins Grain & Comins, Cambridge #393/R
£300 $477 €450 Heminford Grey on the Ouse (25x55cm-10x22in) s. W/C. 29-Apr-3 Bonhams, Knightsbridge #170/R
£380 $627 €551 Near St. Ives, on the Ouse (24x54cm-9x21in) s. W/C. 1-Jul-3 Bonhams, Norwich #96

WINTER, William Arthur (1909-1986) Canadian
£226 $351 €339 Connie (25x20cm-10x8in) s. b, prov. 3-Dec-2 Joyner, Toronto #478 (C.D 550)
£241 $378 €362 Alexis (25x20cm-10x8in) s. board prov. 25-Nov-2 Hodgins, Calgary #335/R (C.D 600)
£262 $414 €393 Young dancer (30x20cm-12x8in) i. s.verso board prov. 14-Nov-2 Heffel, Vancouver #222 (C.D 650)
£290 $452 €421 Rainy day (25x21cm-10x8in) s. board prov. 26-Mar-3 Walker's, Ottawa #414/R (C.D 675)
£300 $469 €435 Mother and children (33x25cm-13x10in) s. board. 26-Mar-3 Walker's, Ottawa #462/R (C.D 700)
£340 $568 €493 The Bakery (41x25cm-16x10in) s. canvasboard. 17-Jun-3 Rosebery Fine Art, London #466/R
£343 $536 €497 Susan (25x20cm-10x8in) s.i. board. 26-Mar-3 Walker's, Ottawa #461/R (C.D 800)
£361 $567 €542 Afternoon sleigh ride (30x40cm-12x16in) s. board. 25-Nov-2 Hodgins, Calgary #24/R (C.D 900)

£494 $765 €741 Tie salesman (40x30cm-16x12in) s. canvasboard prov. 3-Dec-2 Joyner, Toronto #267/R est:800-1000 (C.D 1200)
£644 $1004 €934 Puppy (41x51cm-16x20in) s. board prov. 26-Mar-3 Walker's, Ottawa #223/R est:1000-1500 (C.D 1500)
£696 $1085 €1160 Landing (41x51cm-16x20in) s. i.verso canvasboard prov. 13-Apr-3 Levis, Calgary #119/R est:1500-2000 (C.D 1600)
£844 $1385 €1266 Indian family and village (55x31cm-22x12in) s. canvasboard. 3-Jun-3 Joyner, Toronto #340/R est:1500-2000 (C.D 1900)
£1511 $2478 €2267 Sunday at grandmas (40x55cm-16x22in) s. board. 3-Jun-3 Joyner, Toronto #333/R est:2000-2500 (C.D 3400)
£1646 $2551 €2469 Quebec bushworkers (55x76cm-22x30in) s. prov. 3-Dec-2 Joyner, Toronto #136/R est:3500-4000 (C.D 4000)

Works on paper

£267 $437 €401 Winter afternoon (17x31cm-7x12in) s.d.66 gouache prov. 3-Jun-3 Joyner, Toronto #459/R (C.D 600)
£267 $437 €401 Collection leaves (21x31cm-8x12in) s. gouache. 3-Jun-3 Joyner, Toronto #513 (C.D 600)

WINTER, William Tatton (1855-1928) British

£400 $632 €600 Heathland Lane with horse and cart (45x73cm-18x29in) s. indis.d. 7-Apr-3 David Duggleby, Scarborough #393/R
£800 $1272 €1200 Figures in a farm cart on a track (61x91cm-24x36in) s. 27-Feb-3 Greenslade Hunt, Taunton #1295/R

Works on paper

£300 $474 €450 By a pond (29x23cm-11x9in) s.d.93 W/C. 27-Nov-2 Hamptons Fine Art, Godalming #221
£380 $600 €570 Windy day, Brittany (41x50cm-16x20in) W/C. 27-Nov-2 Hamptons Fine Art, Godalming #254
£400 $632 €580 Ploughing the fields (29x25cm-11x10in) s. W/C. 22-Jul-3 Bonhams, Knightsbridge #227/R
£480 $782 €720 Little shepherdess (24x34cm-9x13in) s.d.1914 pencil W/C. 29-Jan-3 Dreweatt Neate, Newbury #48/R
£500 $780 €750 Shady lane (30x22cm-12x9in) s.d.1907 pencil W/C htd white. 27-Mar-3 Christie's, Kensington #85/R
£520 $801 €780 Spanish windmill, Isles of Scilly (57x79cm-22x31in) s. W/C prov.exhib. 23-Oct-2 Hamptons Fine Art, Godalming #66/R
£650 $1053 €975 The walk home (37x54cm-15x21in) s. W/C. 21-May-3 Bonhams, Knightsbridge #2/R

WINTERFELDT, Friedrich Wilhelm von (1830-1893) German

£3000 $4680 €4500 Fisherman checking their nets by a lake at sunset (90x75cm-35x30in) s.i. 10-Sep-2 Bonhams, Knightsbridge #212/R est:2000-3000

WINTERHALTER, F X (1806-1873) German

£3846 $6077 €6000 Portrait of William Earl (109x85cm-43x33in) pair prov. 12-Nov-2 Mealy's, Castlecomer #1044/R

WINTERHALTER, Franz Xavier (1806-1873) German

Works on paper

£377 $611 €547 Portrait of young woman (25x20cm-10x8in) s.i. silver pen pencil wash chl prov. 24-May-3 Galerie Gloggner, Luzern #126/R (S.FR 800)
£1689 $2635 €2500 Marie Amelie, reine des Francais (16x12cm-6x5in) i. graphite pen ink wash prov. 27-Mar-3 Christie's, Paris #163/R

WINTERHALTER, Franz Xavier (after) (1806-1873) German

£5000 $7850 €7500 Maharajah Duleep Singh, 1854 (137x96cm-54x38in) 16-Apr-3 Christie's, Kensington #556/R est:1000-1500
£6000 $9540 €9000 Portrait of Napoleon III, standing (211x153cm-83x60in) bears sig.i.d.1867. 18-Mar-3 Bonhams, New Bond Street #28/R est:6000-8000

WINTERHALTER, Franz Xavier (attrib) (1806-1873) German

£2692 $4173 €4200 Half-length portrait of a lady with rose and dark veil in her hair (81x60cm-32x24in) i.d.1864 oval. 4-Dec-2 Neumeister, Munich #973/R est:4500
£3302 $5349 €4788 Allegory of Spring - Four nymphs in park landscape (56x47cm-22x19in) prov. 24-May-3 Galerie Gloggner, Luzern #127/R est:1800-2500 (S.FR 7000)
£4500 $7380 €6750 Spanish beauty (67x56cm-26x22in) s. 5-Jun-3 Christie's, Kensington #630/R est:2000-3000

WINTERLIN, Anton (1805-1894) Swiss

£435 $674 €653 Mountain landscape (42x58cm-17x23in) mono.d1861 board. 9-Dec-2 Philippe Schuler, Zurich #8765 (S.FR 1000)

Works on paper

£352 $577 €510 Bernese Oberland (16x21cm-6x8in) W/C. 4-Jun-3 Fischer, Luzern #2694 (S.FR 750)
£1408 $2338 €2000 Mountain stream (22x29cm-9x11in) mono. gouache. 12-Jun-3 Hauswedell & Nolte, Hamburg #410/R est:2200
£1651 $2675 €2922 Simplon road (15x21cm-6x8in) s.i. W/C gouache three. 26-May-3 Sotheby's, Zurich #18/R est:3000-4000 (S.FR 3500)
£2445 $3864 €3668 Wooded landscape with waterfall and animals (45x60cm-18x24in) mono.d.1861 w/C. 14-Nov-2 Stuker, Bern #9402 est:6000-7000 (S.FR 5600)
£3538 $5731 €6263 Near Schoenau - Black Forest (43x37cm-17x15in) s.i.d. verso pencil W/C gouache. 26-May-3 Sotheby's, Zurich #1/R est:3000-5000 (S.FR 7500)

WINTERLIN, Anton (attrib) (1805-1894) Swiss

Works on paper

£1135 $1794 €1703 View from Hasliberg towards Wetterhorn (32x45cm-13x18in) W/C. 14-Nov-2 Stuker, Bern #9403 est:3000-3500 (S.FR 2600)

WINTEROWSKY, Leonard (1886-1927) Polish

£962 $1510 €1500 Messenger I Schlacht near Grodek, September 1914 (80x60cm-31x24in) s.i.d.1914. 21-Nov-2 Dorotheum, Vienna #155/R est:1000-1300

WINTERS, Michael J (1943-) Australian

Works on paper

£464 $724 €696 Greece, new forms in old landscape, Hora Sfakion (101x80cm-40x31in) mono.d.93 col pencil card. 11-Nov-2 Deutscher-Menzies, Melbourne #187 (A.D 1300)

WINTERS, Terry (1949-) American

£22152 $35000 €33228 Untitled (178x201cm-70x79in) s.i.d.1986 verso prov. 13-Nov-2 Sotheby's, New York #573/R est:50000-70000
£50000 $80000 €75000 Graphic primitives 9 (190x274cm-75x108in) s.d.1998 verso oil alkyd resin on linen prov. 15-May-3 Christie's, Rockefeller NY #347/R est:80000-120000

Works on paper

£3125 $5000 €4688 Untitled (59x47cm-23x19in) s.d.1999 graphite prov. 14-May-3 Sotheby's, New York #438/R est:5000-7000

WINTHER, Frederick Julius August (1853-1916) Danish

£310 $503 €465 Flowers in garden (39x61cm-15x24in) s. 25-Jan-3 Rasmussen, Havnen #2002/R (D.KR 3500)
£345 $524 €518 Winter landscape with hare (33x52cm-13x20in) s.d.1887. 28-Aug-2 Museumsbygningen, Copenhagen #53/R (D.KR 4000)
£700 $1078 €1050 River landscape (99x61cm-39x24in) s. 22-Oct-2 Peter Francis, Wales #3/R

WINTHER, Poul (1939-) Danish

£718 $1149 €1077 Still life with figures (35x41cm-14x16in) init. s.d.1983-84 verso. 13-Jan-3 Rasmussen, Vejle #279/R (D.KR 8200)

WINTHER, Richard (1926-) Danish

£466 $722 €699 Female figures (60x110cm-24x43in) s.d.1971-72 verso masonite. 1-Oct-2 Rasmussen, Copenhagen #162/R (D.KR 5500)
£1072 $1758 €1608 Sketch with spiral (65x41cm-26x16in) init. exhib. 27-May-3 Museumsbygningen, Copenhagen #538/R (D.KR 11000)

WINTZ, Raymond (1884-?) French

£645 $1000 €968 Belle isle en mer (33x41cm-13x16in) s. prov. 16-Jul-2 Arthur James, Florida #143
£929 $1459 €1450 Pres du phare (36x46cm-14x18in) s. 15-Dec-2 Thierry & Lannon, Brest #423
£1268 $2041 €1800 Bretonne et chaumiere pres du moulin en Bretagne (33x41cm-13x16in) s. 11-May-3 Thierry & Lannon, Brest #234 est:1500-1800
£1410 $2214 €2200 Concarneau (54x65cm-21x26in) s. s.i.verso. 15-Dec-2 Thierry & Lannon, Brest #220

WIRGMAN, Charles (1832-1891) British

£4200 $6972 €6300 View on the Tokaido near Yokohama, Japan (21x36cm-8x14in) s.d.1876. 12-Jun-3 Bonhams, New Bond Street #848/R est:4000-6000

WIRGMAN, Charles A (1864-1922) British

£4000 $6320 €6000 Mount Fuji, Japan (23x31cm-9x12in) s. 15-Nov-2 Sotheby's, London #25/R est:4000-6000

Works on paper

£644 $1004 €934 Japanese houses by a stream (51x33cm-20x13in) s. W/C. 26-Mar-3 Walker's, Ottawa #56/R est:2000-2500 (C.D 1500)

WIRGMAN, T Blake (1848-1925) British

£283 $450 €425 Portrait of a seated woman (175x130cm-69x51in) s.d.1891. 7-Mar-3 Jackson's, Cedar Falls #544/R

Works on paper
£320 $496 €480 Mother and child at the edge of a wood (48x31cm-19x12in) s. pencil pastel. 4-Dec-2 Christie's, Kensington #16/R

WIRTANEN, Kaapo (1886-1959) Finnish
£429 $681 €630 Girl with cat (43x34cm-17x13in) s.d.1920. 24-Mar-3 Bukowskis, Helsinki #357/R
£476 $757 €700 Sharpening the scythe (33x41cm-13x16in) s.d.1927. 24-Mar-3 Bukowskis, Helsinki #358/R
£556 $911 €850 Landscape from Koli (55x66cm-22x26in) s.d.1919. 9-Feb-3 Bukowskis, Helsinki #392/R

WIRTH, Anna Maria (1846-1922) Russian
£818 $1267 €1300 Still life (102x84cm-40x33in) s. 29-Oct-2 Dorotheum, Vienna #140/R

WIRZ, Karl (1885-1957) Swiss
£429 $678 €644 Bunch of flowers in blue glass vase. s.d.27. 29-Nov-2 Zofingen, Switzerland #3133 (S.FR 1000)

WISE, Ella G (fl.1877-1889) American
£581 $900 €872 Study of pipe and tobacco (15x30cm-6x12in) s. exhib. 8-Dec-2 Freeman, Philadelphia #106/R

WISELBERG, Rose (1908-1992) Canadian
£700 $1084 €1050 Still life with oranges (40x50cm-16x20in) s. board. 3-Dec-2 Joyner, Toronto #5/R est:1800-2200 (C.D 1700)

WISER, Guy Brown (1895-1983) American
£387 $600 €581 Rosalie, seated nude (61x46cm-24x18in) s.d.1937. 29-Oct-2 John Moran, Pasadena #676
£516 $800 €774 Nancy Wiser (81x66cm-32x26in) s. i.d.1931 verso. 29-Oct-2 John Moran, Pasadena #677
£774 $1200 €1161 Portrait of an old lady (102x86cm-40x34in) s.d.1926 exhib. 29-Oct-2 John Moran, Pasadena #678
£1613 $2500 €2420 Pepper trees (86x102cm-34x40in) s.d.1935 exhib. 29-Oct-2 John Moran, Pasadena #679 est:2000-3000

WISHART, Peter (1852-1932) British
Works on paper
£320 $499 €480 Gathering kelp (14x20cm-6x8in) init. col chk sold with three other sketches. 17-Oct-2 Bonhams, Edinburgh #242

WISINGER-FLORIAN, Olga (1844-1926) Austrian
£10185 $16398 €15278 Still life with violets in green vase (28x19cm-11x7in) s. board. 7-May-3 Dobiaschofsky, Bern #1062/R est:5500 (S.FR 22000)
£11392 $18000 €18000 Inner woodland scene (44x41cm-17x16in) mono. board. 28-Nov-2 Dorotheum, Vienna #54/R est:20000-26000
£13924 $22000 €22000 Idyllic woodland (45x55cm-18x22in) s. 28-Nov-2 Dorotheum, Vienna #177/R est:22000-26000
£15942 $26145 €22000 Adriatic coastal landscape in sunshine (46x70cm-18x28in) board double-sided. 27-May-3 Wiener Kunst Auktionen, Vienna #36/R est:25000-50000
£20270 $31622 €30000 Farmstead (51x71cm-20x28in) canvas on board. 25-Mar-3 Wiener Kunst Auktionen, Vienna #116/R est:15000-25000
£21622 $33730 €32000 Flower garden (36x52cm-14x20in) 25-Mar-3 Wiener Kunst Auktionen, Vienna #117/R est:25000-50000
£85000 $131750 €127500 Rosengarten (110x150cm-43x59in) s. exhib. 4-Dec-2 Christie's, London #65/R est:60000-80000

WISSING, Willem (1653-1687) Dutch
£2000 $3120 €3000 Portrait of John Lord Cutts (75x62cm-30x24in) 11-Nov-2 Trembath Welch, Great Dunmow #456/R est:1000-1500

WISSING, Willem (attrib) (1653-1687) Dutch
£900 $1467 €1305 Portrait of a lady (71x61cm-28x24in) painted cartouche. 21-Jul-3 Sotheby's, London #322 est:1200-1800
£1000 $1600 €1500 Portrait of Elizabeth, daughter of Leawood and Langdon MP for Oakhampton (72x59cm-28x23in) 11-Mar-3 Bonhams, Oxford #71 est:1000-1200

WISSING, Willem (circle) (1653-1687) Dutch
£7500 $11625 €11250 Portrait of a lady, seated, with a cockatoo by her side (121x101cm-48x40in) 30-Oct-2 Bonhams, New Bond Street #65/R est:5000-7000

WISTEHUFF, Revere F (1900-1971) American
£1242 $2000 €1863 Boy and dog try to sneak away to fish, with mum calling from window (76x58cm-30x23in) s. painted c.1920. 10-May-3 Illustration House, New York #81/R est:2500-4000

WISTROM, Alfred (1833-1873) Swedish
£1650 $2705 €2393 View of Stockholm (41x54cm-16x21in) s.d.1860. 4-Jun-3 AB Stockholms Auktionsverk #2118/R est:20000-25000 (S.KR 21000)

WISZNIEWSKI, Adrian (1958-) ?
£2500 $3825 €3750 Silent Mutations (244x244cm-96x96in) s. acrylic. 22-Aug-2 Bonhams, Edinburgh #1033/R est:3000-5000
£6000 $9180 €9000 Man with a brace (213x122cm-84x48in) 22-Aug-2 Bonhams, Edinburgh #1034/R est:3000-5000

WIT, Jacob de (1695-1754) Dutch
£6289 $9811 €10000 Putti celebrating (48x112cm-19x44in) panel. 23-Sep-2 Wiener Kunst Auktionen, Vienna #13/R est:6000-13000
Works on paper
£350 $500 €525 Transfiguration at the mount of Tabor (44x31cm-17x12in) s. pen ink wash squared for transfer. 23-Jan-3 Swann Galleries, New York #213/R
£955 $1471 €1500 Roas to Emmaus (18x19cm-7x7in) s.i. black red chk pen brown ink W/C after Sir Peter Paul Rubens. 3-Sep-2 Christie's, Amsterdam #81/R est:1500-2500
£1146 $1789 €1800 Allegorical figure, perhaps Bacchus, standing in a niche (15x8cm-6x3in) s. pen brown ink wash over black chk prov.exhib. 5-Nov-2 Sotheby's, Amsterdam #160/R est:2000-3000
£1274 $1987 €2000 Head of a putto (23x28cm-9x11in) bears i. col chk head study verso by another hand prov. 5-Nov-2 Sotheby's, Amsterdam #163/R est:1200-1500
£1911 $2981 €3000 Putti playing with a mirror. Figure (11x14cm-4x6in) pen black ink brown wash htd white black lead double-sided. 5-Nov-2 Sotheby's, Amsterdam #159/R est:2000-3000
£3503 $5465 €5500 Diana, a nymph and putti (17x13cm-7x5in) pen brush grey brown ink brown wash col chk. 5-Nov-2 Sotheby's, Amsterdam #154/R est:3000-4000

WIT, Jacob de (attrib) (1695-1754) Dutch
£2200 $3542 €3300 Four Evangelists (85x167cm-33x66in) en grisaille shaped top. 20-Feb-3 Christie's, Kensington #252/R est:3000-5000

WIT, Prosper Joseph de (c.1862-c.1951) Belgian
£318 $518 €480 Vue de ferme au chateau (29x37cm-11x15in) s. panel. 17-Feb-3 Horta, Bruxelles #49
£340 $541 €500 Boulaie pres de l'eau (56x38cm-22x15in) s. 18-Mar-3 Campo, Vlaamse Kaai #59
£353 $546 €550 Bord de canal anime (32x40cm-13x16in) s. panel. 9-Dec-2 Horta, Bruxelles #422
£403 $648 €600 Interior (35x28cm-14x11in) s. i.verso panel. 18-Feb-3 Vanderkindere, Brussels #52
£899 $1439 €1250 Quai anime en ville (21x28cm-8x11in) s. 13-May-3 Vanderkindere, Brussels #136
£1325 $2159 €2000 Etang pres de la fetme (54x73cm-21x29in) s. prov. 17-Feb-3 Horta, Bruxelles #48
£2158 $3453 €3000 Attelage dans une allee en automne (82x116cm-32x46in) s.i. 19-May-3 Horta, Bruxelles #69/R est:3000-4000

WITDOECK, Petrus Josephus (1803-1840) Flemish
£5096 $7949 €8000 Hallebardier attable (51x38cm-20x15in) s.d.1853 panel. 8-Nov-2 Pierre Berge, Paris #21/R

WITHAM, Joseph (19th C) British
£2000 $3100 €3000 Cunard liner Servia outward bound to America (76x127cm-30x50in) s.i.d.1881. 31-Oct-2 Christie's, Kensington #500/R est:3000-5000

WITHERAL, A (?) British
£3000 $4890 €4500 Figures on a river bank by a water mill (41x48cm-16x19in) s. 14-Feb-3 Keys, Aylsham #676/R est:400-600

WITHERINGTON, William Frederick (1785-1865) British
£780 $1217 €1170 Ferry (20x29cm-8x11in) s. panel. 26-Mar-3 Sotheby's, Olympia #4/R
£1104 $1800 €1656 Country landscape with figures and cart (46x107cm-18x42in) s. 16-Feb-3 Butterfields, San Francisco #2054a est:1500-2500
£1752 $2750 €2628 At the roadside (66x56cm-26x22in) s. i.verso. 23-Nov-2 Jackson's, Cedar Falls #21/R est:1500-2500
£2000 $3260 €2900 River landscape (71x95cm-28x37in) with sig. 16-Jul-3 Sotheby's, Olympia #7/R est:2000-3000
£2500 $4100 €3750 Noon day rest (63x76cm-25x30in) 29-May-3 Christie's, Kensington #228/R est:3000-4000
£7500 $12450 €11250 The robin - children and a gentleman in a country lane looking a robin (76x64cm-30x25in) prov.exhib. 10-Jun-3 Christie's, London #122/R est:7000-10000

WITHERINGTON, William Frederick (attrib) (1785-1865) British
£1158 $1923 €1679 A happy interlude (61x50cm-24x20in) panel. 16-Jun-3 Lilla Bukowskis, Stockholm #984 est:15000-20000 (S.KR 15000)

WITHERS, Walter (1854-1914) Australian
£2135 $3267 €3203 Landscape with cattle (17x24cm-7x9in) s. panel prov. 25-Aug-2 Sotheby's, Paddington #200/R est:6000-8000 (A.D 6000)
£3053 $4824 €4580 Cattle grazing in dappled light (34x50cm-13x20in) s. prov. 2-Apr-3 Christie's, Melbourne #60/R est:8000-10000 (A.D 8000)
£5178 $8182 €7767 Summer's afternoon (16x24cm-6x9in) s. panel prov. 27-Nov-2 Deutscher-Menzies, Melbourne #104/R est:9000-12000 (A.D 14500)
£6429 $10157 €9644 Cattle at sunset (40x51cm-16x20in) s. canvas on plywood prov. 17-Nov-2 Sotheby's, Paddington #24/R est:15000-20000 (A.D 18000)
Works on paper
£681 $1035 €1022 Eltham (11x21cm-4x8in) s. i.verso W/C. 28-Aug-2 Deutscher-Menzies, Melbourne #408/R (A.D 1900)

WITHINGTON, Elizabeth (20th C) American
£1210 $1900 €1815 Rockport Street view (76x64cm-30x25in) s. 22-Nov-2 Skinner, Boston #381/R est:700-900

WITHOOS, Matthias (1627-1703) Dutch
£2482 $3848 €3723 Park landscape with statue, peacock and flowers (76x66cm-30x26in) s. 4-Dec-2 AB Stockholms Auktionsverk #1956/R est:45000-50000 (S.KR 35000)
£14685 $24524 €21000 Les terrasses fleuries des jardins de la villa d'Este (101x140cm-40x55in) s. 27-Jun-3 Piasa, Paris #26/R est:22000-25000

WITHOOS, Matthias (attrib) (1627-1703) Dutch
£10135 $15811 €15000 Under-growths with birds and insects (65x45cm-26x18in) pair. 31-Mar-3 Finarte Semenzato, Milan #502/R

WITHOOS, Matthias (circle) (1627-1703) Dutch
£6289 $9811 €10000 Allegorical sculptures and fountains in an Italianate landscape (75x60cm-30x24in) pair. 20-Sep-2 Millon & Associes, Paris #339/R est:12000-20000

WITHOOS, Pieter (1654-1693) Dutch
Works on paper
£3395 $5500 €5093 Study of five insects (17x23cm-7x9in) pen ink W/C. 21-Jan-3 Sotheby's, New York #158/R

WITJENS, Jacques Stephen (1881-1956) Dutch
£318 $490 €500 Beach pleasure (22x30cm-9x12in) s. 3-Sep-2 Christie's, Amsterdam #233

WITJENS, Willem (1884-1962) Dutch
£253 $395 €400 Landscape with small path and trees in the foreground (26x33cm-10x13in) 21-Oct-2 Glerum, Amsterdam #141
£758 $1206 €1100 Vissershaventje aan de kaag (51x77cm-20x30in) s. 10-Mar-3 Sotheby's, Amsterdam #212/R est:400-600

WITKAMP, Ernest Sigismund (1854-1897) Dutch
£2303 $3730 €3500 Juffertje in t blauw (47x24cm-19x9in) s. 21-Jan-3 Christie's, Amsterdam #250/R est:2000-3000

WITKIEWICZ, Stanislaw Ignacy (1885-1939) Polish
Photographs
£11688 $18000 €17532 Helena Czerwijowska (16x12cm-6x5in) gelatin silver print prov.lit. 25-Oct-2 Phillips, New York #5/R est:20000-25000
Works on paper
£1538 $2400 €2307 Cubist composition (20x17cm-8x7in) s.d. W/C card. 18-Sep-2 Swann Galleries, New York #28/R est:3000-5000

WITKIN, Joel Peter (1939-) American
Photographs
£1899 $3000 €2849 La brassiere de Joan Miro (37x37cm-15x15in) s.i.d.1982 num.6/15 gelatin silver print prov.lit. 22-Apr-3 Christie's, Rockefeller NY #180/R est:3000-5000
£2215 $3500 €3323 Graces, Los Angeles (37x37cm-15x15in) s.i.d.1988 num.11/15 toned gelatin silver print. 22-Apr-3 Butterfields, San Francisco #2529/R est:3000-5000
£6875 $11000 €10313 Nude with mask. Prudence. Beauty has three nipples (88x76cm-35x30in) s.i.num. three toned gelatin silver print set of three prov.lit. 16-May-3 Phillips, New York #235/R est:10000-15000

WITKOWSKI, Karl (1860-1910) American
£2108 $3500 €3057 Landscape with boy fishing. s. 11-Jun-3 Boos Gallery, Michigan #547/R est:8000-12000
£3086 $5000 €4475 Good friends (48x61cm-19x24in) s. canvas on plastic board. 21-May-3 Doyle, New York #72/R est:5000-7000

WITMONT, Heerman (1605-?) Dutch
£10791 $17266 €15000 Penschilderij three masters off a rocky coast in choppy waters (49x62cm-19x24in) s. panel. 14-May-3 Christie's, Amsterdam #173/R est:10000-15000

WITSCHI, Werner (1906-1999) Swiss
Sculpture
£2183 $3406 €3275 Solitary form (110x42x6cm-43x17x2in) string fabric plaster wood exec.1952 lit. 8-Nov-2 Dobiaschofsky, Bern #278/R est:5500 (S.FR 5000)

WITSEN, Salomon van (1833-1911) Dutch
£263 $426 €400 Koffie schenken (30x24cm-12x9in) s. panel. 21-Jan-3 Christie's, Amsterdam #10

WITSEN, Willem (1860-1923) Dutch
Works on paper
£4452 $6990 €6500 View of the Leidsegracht, Amsterdam (49x68cm-19x27in) s. W/C. 15-Apr-3 Sotheby's, Amsterdam #140/R est:3000-5000

WITT, Jan le (1907-1991) Polish/British
£262 $414 €393 Nike (102x76cm-40x30in) s. s.i.d.1967 verso lit. 18-Nov-2 Waddingtons, Toronto #219/R (C.D 650)
£806 $1274 €1209 Rochers lunaires (112x140cm-44x55in) s. s.i.d.1962 verso lit. 18-Nov-2 Waddingtons, Toronto #220/R est:400-600 (C.D 2000)
£1048 $1656 €1572 Homage a Goya II (201x160cm-79x63in) s. s.i.d.1963-65 masonite sold with a book lit. 18-Nov-2 Waddingtons, Toronto #223/R est:500-700 (C.D 2600)
£1067 $1771 €1547 Moraine. Baia Della Mezzaluna. Prismes II (60x49cm-24x19in) s. i.d.1964 verso set of three. 16-Jun-3 Waddingtons, Toronto #267/R est:800-1200 (C.D 2400)
£1855 $2931 €2783 Le livre de la mer (201x160cm-79x63in) s. s.i.d.1964-65 verso masonite. 18-Nov-2 Waddingtons, Toronto #224/R est:500-700 (C.D 4600)

WITTE, Adrien de (1850-1935) Belgian
£927 $1511 €1400 Marche de Cannes (40x55cm-16x22in) mono. painted 1924. 17-Feb-3 Horta, Bruxelles #70

WITTE, Emanuel de (1617-1692) Dutch
£140000 $219800 €210000 Interior of Nieuwe Kerk, Amsterdam (43x33cm-17x13in) s.indis.d. panel prov.exhib.lit. 11-Dec-2 Christie's, London #69/R est:50000-70000

WITTE, Emanuel de (attrib) (1617-1692) Dutch
£5500 $8635 €8250 Interior of church with townsfolk (32x22cm-13x9in) panel prov. 13-Dec-2 Christie's, Kensington #79/R est:2000-3000

WITTE, Gaspar de (1624-1681) Flemish
£18000 $28080 €27000 Southern landscape with travellers and animals beside fountain (99x142cm-39x56in) s.d.1657. 10-Apr-3 Sotheby's, London #59/R est:12000
£18919 $29514 €28000 Wooded landscape with Hagar and the Angel (69x85cm-27x33in) s. copper. 27-Mar-3 Dorotheum, Vienna #124/R est:28000-32000

WITTEL, Gaspar van (1653-1736) Dutch
£290000 $455300 €435000 View of Tivoli (86x111cm-34x44in) prov.lit. 11-Dec-2 Christie's, London #110/R est:300000-400000
£1350000 $2254500 €1957500 Island of San Giorgio Maggiore, Venice. The entrance to the Grand Canal (44x75cm-17x30in) s.d.1709 one s.i.d.1710 pair prov. 9-Jul-3 Christie's, London #113/R est:500000-800000
£1700000 $2839000 €2465000 Naples, a view of the Darsena (56x110cm-22x43in) s.i.d.1712 prov.lit. 10-Jul-3 Sotheby's, London #60/R est:500000-700000
£1800000 $3006000 €2610000 Rome, a view of the apse of Saint Peter's Basilica looking east (56x110cm-22x43in) s. prov.lit. 10-Jul-3 Sotheby's, London #61/R est:400000-600000

Works on paper
£6790 $11000 €10185 Coastal landscape with boats and figures. Townscape (27x41cm-11x16in) pen ink wash over chk double-sided. 21-Jan-3 Sotheby's, New York #63/R est:7000

WITTEL, Gaspar van (circle) (1653-1736) Dutch
£8500 $13175 €12750 Piazza Navona, Rome, flooded (49x74cm-19x29in) 30-Oct-2 Christie's, Kensington #169/R est:6000-10000
£14815 $24000 €22223 Rome, with the Ponte Sant Angelo, the castle Sant Angelo and Saint Peter's beyond (36x49cm-14x19in) 24-Jan-3 Christie's, Rockefeller NY #54/R est:15000-20000

WITTEL, Gaspar van (style) (1653-1736) Dutch
£5500 $8525 €8250 Rome, view of the Piazza del Popolo (32x40cm-13x16in) prov. 31-Oct-2 Sotheby's, Olympia #163/R est:3000-4000
£12000 $18840 €18000 Rome, view of the Tiber with the Ponte Rotto (73x97cm-29x38in) 10-Dec-2 Sotheby's, Olympia #409/R est:8000-12000
£12500 $20250 €18750 Views of Italy and Sicily (53x25cm-21x10in) copper set of four. 23-Jan-3 Aspire, Cleveland #3 est:6000-12000
£22642 $35094 €36000 Rome (72x97cm-28x38in) 18th C prov. two. 2-Oct-2 Dorotheum, Vienna #10/R est:14000-18000

WITTEVRONGEL, Roger (1933-) Belgian
Works on paper
£346 $533 €550 Le ruban blanc (19x12cm-7x5in) s. mixed media. 22-Oct-2 Campo, Vlaamse Kaai #684

WITTHOFF, A (fl.1820-1840) German
£2590 $4247 €3600 Rhine (16x26cm-6x10in) s. zinc pair. 4-Jun-3 Reiss & Sohn, Konigstein #176/R est:1500

WITTKAMP, Johann Bernhard (1820-1885) German
£327 $536 €500 Mother with child praying thoughtfully (57x45cm-22x18in) s.d.1862 panel. 29-Mar-3 Dannenberg, Berlin #668/R
£3289 $5329 €5000 Jacob cats in his library, Zorgvliet (58x77cm-23x30in) s. 21-Jan-3 Christie's, Amsterdam #118/R est:5000-7000

WITTLER, Heinrich (1918-1979) German
£881 $1356 €1400 Still life with flowers, apples and bananas (75x44cm-30x17in) mono. panel. 26-Oct-2 Dr Lehr, Berlin #582/R

WITTLICH, Josef (1903-1982) German?
Works on paper
£897 $1391 €1400 Untitled (102x72cm-40x28in) s. gouache board. 3-Dec-2 Lempertz, Koln #514/R
£942 $1545 €1300 Untitled (62x89cm-24x35in) s. gouache board. 28-May-3 Lempertz, Koln #476/R

WITTMER, Johann Michael (1802-1880) German
£28777 $46043 €40000 Noah's thanks offering (100x136cm-39x54in) s. prov.lit. 17-May-3 Lempertz, Koln #1509/R est:50000

WITTWER-GELPKE, Martha (1875-1959) Swiss
£2838 $4144 €4257 Three figures (81x62cm-32x24in) s. 4-Jun-2 Germann, Zurich #60/R est:8000-12000 (S.FR 6500)

WITZ, Johann Benedikt (1709-1780) German
Sculpture
£13782 $21776 €21500 Lamentation of Christ (43cm-17in) wood lit. 16-Nov-2 Lempertz, Koln #1187/R est:4900

WIVEL, Niels (1855-1914) Danish
£289 $462 €434 Prison tower with prisoner looking out of window (140x72cm-55x28in) s. 13-Jan-3 Rasmussen, Vejle #219/R (D.KR 3300)
£613 $981 €920 Interior scene with woman reading by window (97x85cm-38x33in) s.d.1912. 13-Jan-3 Rasmussen, Vejle #231/R (D.KR 7000)

WLASOFF, Sergej F (1859-1924) Russian
£252 $390 €400 At the edge of forest (55x73cm-22x29in) s.d.1917. 6-Oct-2 Bukowskis, Helsinki #321/R
£314 $487 €500 Evening light (55x43cm-22x17in) s. 6-Oct-2 Bukowskis, Helsinki #319/R
£855 $1326 €1360 Evening in the harbour (43x68cm-17x27in) s/. 6-Oct-2 Bukowskis, Helsinki #320/R
Works on paper
£503 $780 €800 Sveaborg at night (26x35cm-10x14in) s. gouache. 6-Oct-2 Bukowskis, Helsinki #322/R
£621 $981 €900 Coffee break (24x31cm-9x12in) s. W/C. 3-Apr-3 Hagelstam, Helsinki #986/R

WLERICK, Robert (1882-1944) French
Sculpture
£2759 $4358 €4000 Dedette (45cm-18in) s. num.3/10 pat bronze Cast Valsuani lit. 4-Apr-3 Tajan, Paris #220/R

WOBBE, Rita (20th C) Irish
Works on paper
£959 $1505 €1400 Fugue I (90x80cm-35x31in) s.i.verso mixed media on canvas exhib. 15-Apr-3 De Veres Art Auctions, Dublin #235 est:1200-1600

WODICK, Edmund (1817-1886) German
£4000 $6240 €6000 Hunters by the sea at sunset (63x93cm-25x37in) s.d.1855. 15-Oct-2 Sotheby's, London #195/R est:4000-6000

WODZINOWSKY, Wincenty (1866-1940) Polish
£516 $800 €774 Woman reading under tree (20x28cm-8x11in) board sold with poster exhib. 7-Dec-2 South Bay, Long Island #53/R
£755 $1177 €1200 Polish peasants (26x36cm-10x14in) s. board. 20-Sep-2 Karlheinz Kaupp, Staufen #1961/R

WOELFFER, Emerson (1914-) American
£918 $1450 €1377 Abstract (117x91cm-46x36in) s. 26-Apr-3 Jeffery Burchard, Florida #74

WOERMANN, Hedwig (1879-?) German
£1824 $2846 €2700 Female nudes (184x108cm-72x43in) s.d.1928 gold cloth blind prov. 28-Mar-3 Ketterer, Hamburg #689/R est:3000-3300

WOESTIJNE, Gustave van de (1881-1947) Belgian
£6410 $9936 €10000 Figure of Christ (40x32cm-16x13in) panel painted c.1900-1905 prov. 7-Dec-2 De Vuyst, Lokeren #351/R est:3000-4000
£71942 $115108 €100000 Portrait de jeune fille a la robe blanche, Elvire Brys (136x90cm-54x35in) s. exhib. 13-May-3 Palais de Beaux Arts, Brussels #163/R est:100000-150000
Works on paper
£409 $630 €650 Grenouille chassee par les herons (35x28cm-14x11in) s. ink dr. 22-Oct-2 Campo & Campo, Antwerp #287

WOESTIJNE, Maxime van de (1911-) Belgian
£1203 $1900 €1900 L'illusion (73x92cm-29x36in) s.d.1965 exhib. 26-Nov-2 Palais de Beaux Arts, Brussels #163 est:1750-2500
£2158 $3453 €3000 Message (92x73cm-36x29in) s.d.1964 exhib. 13-May-3 Palais de Beaux Arts, Brussels #156/R est:3000-4000
£2658 $4200 €4200 Mensonge (90x70cm-35x28in) s.d.1964 exhib. 26-Nov-2 Palais de Beaux Arts, Brussels #165/R est:2250-3500
£5036 $8058 €7000 L'interieur (100x92cm-39x36in) s.d.1931. 13-May-3 Palais de Beaux Arts, Brussels #158/R est:3750-5000

WOHL, Mildred (20th C) American
£1063 $1700 €1541 Priest (102x76cm-40x30in) s.i. masonite. 17-May-3 New Orleans Auction, New Orleans #952/R est:1000-1500

WOHNER, Louis (1888-1958) German
£256 $390 €400 Tugboat in Hamburg harbour (60x80cm-24x31in) s. lit. 11-Jul-2 Allgauer, Kempten #2767/R
£327 $523 €500 Fishing house on lake shore with sailing boat (51x65cm-20x26in) s. 10-Jan-3 Allgauer, Kempten #1859/R
£327 $523 €500 Southern coast of Capri with Faraglioni-Klippen (65x85cm-26x33in) s. 10-Jan-3 Allgauer, Kempten #1869/R
£327 $523 €500 Paris with view of Notre Dame (66x80cm-26x31in) s.i.d.1929. 10-Jan-3 Allgauer, Kempten #1883/R
£350 $546 €550 Mountain village (65x85cm-26x33in) s. 6-Nov-2 Hugo Ruef, Munich #1338/R
£359 $575 €550 Eib lake with Zugspitz mountains (65x80cm-26x31in) s. 10-Jan-3 Allgauer, Kempten #1862/R
£408 $649 €600 Hamburg harbour (64x76cm-25x30in) s. 21-Mar-3 Auktionhaus Georg Rehm, Augsburg #8122/R
£445 $695 €650 Mountain landscape in winter with farm (55x65cm-22x26in) s. lit. 10-Apr-3 Allgauer, Kempten #3066/R
£458 $732 €700 Winter day in mountain village (65x85cm-26x33in) s. 10-Jan-3 Allgauer, Kempten #1868/R
£458 $732 €700 Southern landscape with houses on lake shore and boats (65x76cm-26x30in) s. 10-Jan-3 Allgauer, Kempten #1873/R
£458 $732 €700 Autumn day at Konigssee (65x81cm-26x32in) s. 10-Jan-3 Allgauer, Kempten #1874/R
£523 $837 €800 Village on the lake with snow-covered mountain landscape (66x81cm-26x32in) s. 10-Jan-3 Allgauer, Kempten #1886/R
£588 $941 €900 View of the Limburg (66x85cm-26x33in) s. 10-Jan-3 Allgauer, Kempten #1887/R
£588 $941 €900 Castle Seeon in Cheimgau (67x85cm-26x33in) s. 10-Jan-3 Allgauer, Kempten #1890/R
£654 $1046 €1000 Mountain village at foot of the Matterhorn (65x85cm-26x33in) s. 10-Jan-3 Allgauer, Kempten #1865/R est:1000

£654 $1046 €1000 Summer day in Tyrolean mountain village (65x86cm-26x34in) s. 10-Jan-3 Allgauer, Kempten #1872/R
£654 $1046 €1000 View of Dresden with Schloss church (65x86cm-26x34in) s. 10-Jan-3 Allgauer, Kempten #1879/R
£654 $1046 €1000 Chiemsee with Fraueninsel (65x86cm-26x34in) s. 10-Jan-3 Allgauer, Kempten #1881/R
£719 $1150 €1100 View of Meissen (65x86cm-26x34in) s. 10-Jan-3 Allgauer, Kempten #1880/R
£784 $1255 €1200 Mountain village at the foot of the Matterhorn (80x101cm-31x40in) s. 10-Jan-3 Allgauer, Kempten #1893/R
£850 $1359 €1300 View of Kallmunz on the Laab (65x81cm-26x32in) s. 10-Jan-3 Allgauer, Kempten #1864/R
£850 $1359 €1300 Wild flowers in Isartal with view of Karwendel mountains (65x86cm-26x34in) s. 10-Jan-3 Allgauer, Kempten #1871/R
£890 $1389 €1300 View of Leermos in Tirol in winter (65x80cm-26x31in) s. 10-Apr-3 Allgauer, Kempten #3067/R
£897 $1364 €1400 Mountain village with view of Matterhorn (80x100cm-31x39in) s. 11-Jul-2 Allgauer, Kempten #2770/R
£959 $1496 €1400 Hintertux in the Otztal Alps (65x85cm-26x33in) s. 10-Apr-3 Dorotheum, Vienna #59/R
£1078 $1725 €1650 View of Wasserburg on the Inn (70x100cm-28x39in) s. 10-Jan-3 Allgauer, Kempten #1891/R est:2200
£1242 $1987 €1900 Old main bridge in Wurzburg (58x80cm-23x31in) s. 10-Jan-3 Allgauer, Kempten #1860/R est:1900
£1242 $1987 €1900 Houses on the Wornitz in Harburg (50x66cm-20x26in) s. 10-Jan-3 Allgauer, Kempten #1857/R est:1700
£1242 $1987 €1900 Chapel near Seefeld with view of the Hocheder (65x80cm-26x31in) s. 10-Jan-3 Allgauer, Kempten #1863/R est:1700
£1307 $2092 €2000 Florians square in Parkenkirchen (65x85cm-26x33in) s. 10-Jan-3 Allgauer, Kempten #1867/R est:2000
£1307 $2092 €2000 View of Harburg on the Wornitz (80x100cm-31x39in) s. 10-Jan-3 Allgauer, Kempten #1892/R est:2000
£1438 $2301 €2200 Winter day in Kitzbuhl in Tyrol (66x80cm-26x31in) s. 10-Jan-3 Allgauer, Kempten #1884/R est:1900
£1569 $2510 €2400 View of Regensburg with stone bridge (65x85cm-26x33in) s. 10-Jan-3 Allgauer, Kempten #1878/R est:2000

WOITSCH, Emmy (1894-1981) Austrian
Works on paper
£540 $863 €750 Inn landscape (19x24cm-7x9in) s. w/C. 14-May-3 Dorotheum, Linz #471/R

WOJTKIEWICZ, Witold (1879-1911) Polish
£5479 $8603 €8000 Trois hommes et une femme (64x80cm-25x31in) lit. 15-Apr-3 Laurence Calmels, Paris #4237/R

WOLBERS, Dirk (1890-1957) Dutch
Sculpture
£1667 $2617 €2600 Nude woman looking in the distance (41cm-16in) s.d.26 bronze Cast Prowaseck. 25-Nov-2 Glerum, Amsterdam #215/R est:1200-1500

WOLBERS, Hermanus Gerhardus (1856-1926) Dutch
£601 $938 €950 Cows in the meadow (50x70cm-20x28in) s. 21-Oct-2 Glerum, Amsterdam #228

WOLCK, Nikolaus (1887-1950) German
£629 $975 €1000 Overhanging branches (65x60cm-26x24in) 2-Nov-2 Hans Stahl, Toestorf #93/R
£1609 $2494 €2414 Still life of flowers in vase (69x63cm-27x25in) init.d.31. 1-Oct-2 Rasmussen, Copenhagen #129/R est:20000-25000 (D.KR 19000)

WOLCK, Preben (1925-2000) Danish
£296 $459 €444 Middle European landscape (97x130cm-38x51in) s.d.1967 verso. 1-Oct-2 Rasmussen, Copenhagen #199 (D.KR 3500)
£305 $472 €458 Blond girl (73x60cm-29x24in) s. d.1973 verso prov. 1-Oct-2 Rasmussen, Copenhagen #240 (D.KR 3600)
£336 $534 €504 Composition 708 M (89x116cm-35x46in) s. d.1970 verso. 5-May-3 Rasmussen, Vejle #19 (D.KR 3600)

WOLCOTT, Marion Post (1910-1990) American
Photographs
£3924 $6200 €5886 Main Street, Brattleboro, Vermont (24x33cm-9x13in) s.i.d.1939 gelatin silver print prov.lit. 25-Apr-3 Phillips, New York #235/R est:1000-1500
£8861 $14000 €13292 Day laborers (37x34cm-15x13in) i. gelatin silver print prov.lit. 25-Apr-3 Phillips, New York #236/R est:2000-3000
£12658 $20000 €18987 Jitterbugging in Juke joint on a Saturday night, Clarkesdale, Mississippi (38x46cm-15x18in) s.i. gelatin silver print prov.exhib.lit. 25-Apr-3 Phillips, New York #19/R est:4000-6000

WOLD-TORNE, Oluf (1867-1919) Norwegian
£2655 $4195 €3983 Evening - the blue bathing hut (50x44cm-20x17in) s.d.1913 i.stretcher prov.exhib. 28-Apr-3 Blomqvist, Oslo #357/R est:35000-45000 (N.KR 30000)

WOLEDGE, F W (fl.1840-1895) British
Works on paper
£360 $569 €540 Norfolk Bridge and Shoreham (13x23cm-5x9in) s. W/C. 24-Apr-3 Scarborough Perry Fine Arts, Hove #664

WOLF, Caspar (attrib) (1735-1798) Swiss
£4403 $6780 €7000 Vue d'une cascade: probablement la cascade du Reichenbruhl (38x30cm-15x12in) 25-Oct-2 Tajan, Paris #139 est:2500-3000

WOLF, Franz Xaver (1896-1989) Austrian
£1172 $1876 €1700 Child of the summer (35x29cm-14x11in) s. panel. 11-Mar-3 Dorotheum, Vienna #73/R est:1500-2000
£3191 $5170 €4500 Bunch of summer flowers in a vase (61x41cm-24x16in) s. panel. 22-May-3 Dorotheum, Vienna #204/R est:3000-3800
£3593 $6000 €5210 Rabbi Beim studium (50x40cm-20x16in) s. panel prov. 22-Jun-3 Freeman, Philadelphia #27/R est:4000-6000

WOLF, Georg (1882-1962) German
£306 $477 €459 Farmer with two horses (35x46cm-14x18in) s. prov. 9-Nov-2 Galerie Gloggner, Luzern #152/R (S.FR 700)
£348 $540 €550 Peasant with two horse plough (45x59cm-18x23in) s. board. 25-Sep-2 Neumeister, Munich #780/R
£582 $908 €850 Winter landscape with peasant and horses (24x32cm-9x13in) s. i. verso panel. 10-Apr-3 Van Ham, Cologne #1763
£959 $1496 €1400 Peasant ploughing (50x70cm-20x28in) s. 10-Apr-3 Van Ham, Cologne #1765
£1479 $2381 €2100 Haywaggon (32x50cm-13x20in) s. panel lit. 9-May-3 Schloss Ahlden, Ahlden #1423/R est:1900
Works on paper
£288 $447 €450 Messina (35x50cm-14x20in) s.d.1924 W/C. 5-Dec-2 Stadion, Trieste #676

WOLF, Joseph (1820-1899) German
£5000 $7750 €7500 Red-footed falcons (71x51cm-28x20in) s. prov. 6-Dec-2 Lyon & Turnbull, Edinburgh #57/R est:5000-7000

WOLF, Kevin (20th C) American
Works on paper
£828 $1300 €1242 Fists (19x22cm-7x9in) graphite exec.c.1987 prov. 19-Nov-2 Wright, Chicago #299/R est:1500-2000

WOLF, Max (19/20th C) German
£755 $1177 €1200 Rhein plateau (60x79cm-24x31in) 11-Oct-2 Winterberg, Heidelberg #755/R

WOLF, Michael (1959-) Austrian
£1319 $2098 €1900 Heidrun (213x137cm-84x54in) s.i.d.87 verso acrylic. 29-Apr-3 Wiener Kunst Auktionen, Vienna #464/R est:2500-3500

WOLFAERT, Jan Baptist (1625-1687) Flemish
£6757 $10541 €10000 Peasants and travellers resting in hilly landscape (92x113cm-36x44in) bears sig. 27-Mar-3 Dorotheum, Vienna #191/R est:10000-14000

WOLFAERTS, Artus (1581-c.1641) Flemish
£641 $1006 €1000 Healing of the lame (32x39cm-13x15in) 16-Dec-2 Bernaerts, Antwerp #79/R

WOLFAERTS, Artus (attrib) (1581-c.1641) Flemish
£15190 $24000 €24000 Saint Andrew. Saint John (112x90cm-44x35in) i. pair. 2-Dec-2 Cornette de St.Cyr, Paris #16/R est:35000

WOLFE, Byron B (1904-1973) American
£2244 $3500 €3366 First snow on the peaks (51x58cm-20x23in) 9-Nov-2 Altermann Galleries, Santa Fe #46

WOLFE, Edward (1897-1982) British
£3000 $4680 €4500 Still life with flowers and candlestick holder (65x83cm-26x33in) prov. 12-Sep-2 Sotheby's, Olympia #110/R est:2500-3500
£6000 $9480 €9000 Vase on a corner table (96x63cm-38x25in) s. 27-Nov-2 Sotheby's, Olympia #274/R est:6000-8000
Works on paper
£305 $483 €458 Landscape with trees (35x50cm-14x20in) s. pastel. 1-Apr-3 Stephan Welz, Johannesburg #452 est:4000-6000 (SA.R 3800)
£480 $744 €720 Portrait of a seated lady (49x40cm-19x16in) s. pencil crayon. 4-Dec-2 Christie's, Kensington #248
£600 $948 €900 Abstract - mainly diamond shapes (50x65cm-20x26in) gouache. 27-Nov-2 Sotheby's, Olympia #271/R

WOLFE, George (1834-1890) British
Works on paper
£700 $1113 €1050 Low tide at Gorey Castle, Jersey (20x29cm-8x11in) s. W/C. 4-Mar-3 Bonhams, Knightsbridge #240/R
£2150 $3354 €3225 Estuary scene with sailing boat loading at low tide (35x52cm-14x20in) s. W/C. 10-Sep-2 David Duggleby, Scarborough #101/R est:1500-2000

WOLFE, George (attrib) (1834-1890) British
Works on paper
£290 $476 €435 Mending nets, Clovelly (18x26cm-7x10in) i. W/C. 3-Jun-3 Bearnes, Exeter #416

WOLFE, Pamela (20th C) New Zealander
£458 $674 €687 Along the Kaikoura Coast (121x179cm-48x70in) s. board prov. 19-Jun-2 Watson's, Christchurch #60/R est:2000-3000 (NZ.D 1400)

WOLFERS, Philippe (1858-1929) Belgian
Sculpture
£3481 $5430 €5500 Jeune fille nue assise (13cm-5in) mono. brown pat bronze. 16-Sep-2 Horta, Bruxelles #119/R
£3922 $6314 €6000 Meditation, jeune femme nue a la fontaine (41cm-16in) s. gilt pat bronze. 20-Jan-3 Horta, Bruxelles #126/R est:6000-8000
£4460 $7137 €6200 Deux graces (22cm-9in) mono. brown pat bronze cire perdue. 13-May-3 Vanderkindere, Brussels #163/R est:3000-4500

WOLFERT, H (?) ?
£348 $543 €550 Mountain lake (95x131cm-37x52in) s. 14-Sep-2 Weidler, Nurnberg #6682

WOLFF, Albert (after) (1814-1892) German
Sculpture
£6522 $10696 €9000 Two girls at fountain (154x105x84cm-61x41x33in) terracotta Cast.E March Sohne Charlottenburg prov. 31-May-3 Villa Grisebach, Berlin #101/R est:15000-20000

WOLFF, Ann (20th C) Swedish
Sculpture
£3018 $4708 €5228 Bride of the animals (75cm-30in) s.d.87 etched glass granite base prov. 31-Mar-3 Goodman, Sydney #204/R (A.D 8000)

WOLFF, Betty (1863-1941) German
£915 $1520 €1300 Portrait of a lady. Portrait of a gentleman (75x60cm-30x24in) s. oval two. 14-Jun-3 Arnold, Frankfurt #946/R

WOLFF, Emil (1802-1879) German
£253 $395 €380 Open square with men on horseback carrying burning torches (17x26cm-7x10in) 23-Sep-2 Rasmussen, Vejle #288/R (D.KR 3000)
£326 $515 €489 Scene from Kongens Nytorv with torch light (17x27cm-7x11in) cardboard. 13-Nov-2 Kunsthallen, Copenhagen #77 (D.KR 3800)

WOLFF, Eugen (1873-1937) German
£608 $949 €900 Young woman by stream (68x53cm-27x21in) lit. 28-Mar-3 Karrenbauer, Konstanz #1800/R

WOLFF, Jose (1884-1964) Belgian
£353 $554 €550 Sous-bois ensoleille (25x34cm-10x13in) s. panel. 11-Dec-2 Hotel des Ventes Mosan, Brussels #283
£506 $790 €800 Vue de village (40x54cm-16x21in) s. 16-Oct-2 Hotel des Ventes Mosan, Brussels #174
£544 $865 €800 Ferme a Roche a frene. s. panel. 19-Mar-3 Hotel des Ventes Mosan, Brussels #265
£544 $865 €800 Vue de village (34x48cm-13x19in) s. panel. 19-Mar-3 Hotel des Ventes Mosan, Brussels #294

WOLFF, Robert Jay (1905-1977) American
£1585 $2600 €2298 Anonymous illusion (102x76cm-40x30in) s.d.1949 verso prov. 1-Jun-3 Wright, Chicago #159/R est:2500-3500

WOLFF, Willy (1905-) German
Works on paper
£903 $1426 €1300 Untitled (42x48cm-17x19in) s.d.1962 Indian ink. 26-Apr-3 Dr Lehr, Berlin #552/R

WOLFHAGEN, Philip (1963-) Australian
£1538 $2446 €2307 Nimbus (114x151cm-45x59in) s.i.d.1989 oil powder pigment paper on canvas exhib. 4-Mar-3 Deutscher-Menzies, Melbourne #176/R est:4500-6500 (A.D 4000)
£2211 $3516 €3317 Ambiguity of love's embrace (120x242cm-47x95in) s.i.d.verso oil tempera board diptych exhib. 4-Mar-3 Deutscher-Menzies, Melbourne #152/R est:4000-8000 (A.D 5750)
£2857 $4486 €4286 Untitled, thirteenth illusory field (110x172cm-43x68in) s.i.d.1994 verso oil wax prov. 25-Nov-2 Christie's, Melbourne #38/R est:10000-15000 (A.D 8000)

WOLFLE, Franz Xavier (1887-1972) German
£250 $393 €375 Portrait of John Bull (48x33cm-19x13in) s.d.1901 linen board. 21-Nov-2 Clevedon Sale Rooms #241
£481 $745 €750 Old man smoking pipe (17x14cm-7x6in) s. lit. 6-Dec-2 Karlheinz Kaupp, Staufen #2188
£1400 $2268 €2100 Tyrolean gentleman holding a musket (19x14cm-7x6in) s.d.1942 panel prov. 23-Jan-3 Christie's, Kensington #121/R est:600-800
£1800 $2862 €2700 An old man reading (19x15cm-7x6in) s. panel prov. 18-Mar-3 Bonhams, New Bond Street #24/R est:1500-2000
£1948 $2903 €3000 Old peasant man with gun on shoulder (24x17cm-9x7in) s. panel. 26-Jun-2 Neumeister, Munich #920/R est:700
£2200 $3608 €3300 Tyrolean gentleman smoking a pipe. Tyrolean gentleman with a feather in his hat (18x14cm-7x6in) s. panel pair. 5-Jun-3 Christie's, Kensington #619/R est:1500-2000
£2800 $4536 €4200 Still life with gladioli, marigolds and other flowers in a ceramic vase (63x53cm-25x21in) s. panel. 21-May-3 Bonhams, Knightsbridge #157/R est:3000-5000

WOLFLE, Inge (1928-) German
£550 $852 €825 Tyrolean guide. Smoker (18x14cm-7x6in) s. panel pair. 3-Dec-2 Sotheby's, Olympia #285a/R

WOLFLI, Adolf (1864-1930) Swiss
Works on paper
£4630 $7500 €6945 Lagerfeuer (32x25cm-13x10in) d.1889 s.i.verso col pencil graphite prov.exhib. 27-Jan-3 Christie's, Rockefeller NY #49/R est:10000-15000
£6790 $11000 €10185 Vitoriai (34x25cm-13x10in) s.d.1929 s.i.verso graphite col pencil prov. 27-Jan-3 Christie's, Rockefeller NY #44/R est:12000-18000
£7407 $12000 €11111 Helldi Veetia (31x25cm-12x10in) d.1917 i.verso graphite col pencil prov. 27-Jan-3 Christie's, Rockefeller NY #25/R est:15000-20000
£8025 $13000 €12038 Untitled (34x25cm-13x10in) s.d.1920 i.verso graphite col pencil prov.exhib. 27-Jan-3 Christie's, Rockefeller NY #43/R est:15000-20000
£8584 $13562 €12876 Holy Bettania great-great-goddess (34x25cm-13x10in) pencil col pencil. 26-Nov-2 Phillips, Zurich #38/R est:20000-30000 (S.FR 20000)
£11301 $17743 €16500 Untitled (29x22cm-11x9in) s.d.1916 crayon prov.exhib. 15-Apr-3 Laurence Calmels, Paris #4427/R
£13014 $20301 €19000 Untitled (33x23cm-13x9in) i.verso col crayon double-sided prov.exhib.lit. 14-Apr-3 Laurence Calmels, Paris #4025/R est:15000
£25926 $42000 €38889 D'Shatz'l Chrutz (47x62cm-19x24in) col pencil executed 1923 prov.exhib. 27-Jan-3 Christie's, Rockefeller NY #24/R est:30000-40000
£111588 $176309 €167382 Elisabeth Bieri (90x129cm-35x51in) pencil col pencil exec.1907. 26-Nov-2 Phillips, Zurich #36/R est:90000-120000 (S.FR 260000)

WOLFROM, Friedrich Ernst (1857-?) German
£696 $1100 €1100 Female allegory of music (75x58cm-30x23in) s.d.1881 canvas on canvas. 29-Nov-2 Bolland & Marotz, Bremen #787/R
£2177 $3461 €3200 Sumptuous bunch of flowers with peonies, tulips and roses in stone vase (102x75cm-40x30in) s.d. 25-Feb-3 Dorotheum, Vienna #17/R est:3600-4000

WOLFVOET, Victor (1612-1652) Flemish
£1392 $2200 €2200 David's triumph (40x54cm-16x21in) s. copper. 2-Dec-2 Cornette de St.Cyr, Paris #6/R

WOLGERS, Dan (1955-) Swedish
Photographs
£9811 $15305 €14717 This is the end of the public road (120x252cm-47x99in) s.d.95-98 verso num.3/3 Cibachrome prov.exhib.lit. 6-Nov-2 AB Stockholms Auktionsverk #833/R est:50000-70000 (S.KR 140000)
Sculpture
£1261 $1968 €1892 The watch stool (47x39x39cm-19x15x15in) s.d.1991 num.7/10 aluminium clockwork lit. 6-Nov-2 AB Stockholms Auktionsverk #831/R est:15000-20000 (S.KR 18000)
£1402 $2186 €2103 Yes/No (17x12x5cm-7x5x2in) object of aluminium electronics executed 1991 lit. 6-Nov-2 AB Stockholms Auktionsverk #837/R est:4000-5000 (S.KR 20000)
£1597 $2523 €2396 Object (47cm-19in) s.d.1991 num.7/10 clock on steel legs lit. 28-Apr-3 Bukowskis, Stockholm #962/R est:20000-25000 (S.KR 21000)
£1612 $2514 €2418 Object (47cm-19in) s.d.1991 num.6/10 clock on steel legs exhib.lit. 5-Nov-2 Bukowskis, Stockholm #481/R est:20000-25000 (S.KR 23000)
£1822 $2842 €2733 Pose - Linda Evangelista (77cm-30in) s.d.1991 num.1/8 painted plaster paper lit. 5-Nov-2 Bukowskis, Stockholm #480/R est:25000-30000 (S.KR 26000)
£3854 $6013 €5781 Everybody is wondering - where did he go? (20x44x14cm-8x17x6in) s.d.1990 object incl wood base. 6-Nov-2 AB Stockholms Auktionsverk #834/R est:45000-50000 (S.KR 55000)
£4015 $6465 €6023 Mother and child (50cm-20in) s.d.1997 num.10 clear glass globe metal wood socle with light. 7-May-3 AB Stockholms Auktionsverk #976/R est:50000-60000 (S.KR 52000)
Works on paper
£4015 $6465 €6023 Untitled - works of a clock - woman exposing the world to mans roving eyes (26x19cm-10x7in) s.d.1986 mixed media object lit. 7-May-3 AB Stockholms Auktionsverk #973/R est:50000-60000 (S.KR 52000)

WOLKONSKY, Prince Piotr (c.1901-) Russian
£1138 $1821 €1650 Cour de la grande mosquee (65x80cm-26x31in) s.i.d.1924. 12-Mar-3 E & Eve, Paris #96/R est:1300-1500

WOLLASTON, John (?-1770) British
£7692 $12000 €11538 Portrait of Mrs Margaret Chew Bradley. 21-Sep-2 Harvey Clar, Oakland #1473

WOLLASTON, John (attrib) (?-1770) British
Works on paper
£4969 $8000 €7454 Captain Kensey Johns, II. Susannah Galloway Johns. W/C ink ink pair. 16-Jan-3 Christie's, Rockefeller NY #321/R est:10000-15000

WOLLEN, William Barns (1857-1936) British
Works on paper
£450 $702 €675 Lord Roberts inspecting the troops (26x38cm-10x15in) s. W/C. 26-Mar-3 Sotheby's, Olympia #84/R

WOLLHEIM, Gert (1894-1974) American/German
£2722 $4218 €4300 Bloodless mother holding baby (122x91cm-48x36in) s.d.1969 i. verso panel prov. 28-Sep-2 Ketterer, Hamburg #409/R est:3000-4000
£4808 $7019 €7500 Portrait of young woman (61x50cm-24x20in) s.i. panel. 4-Jun-2 Karl & Faber, Munich #477/R est:4000
Works on paper
£4872 $7113 €7600 Composition with head (25x32cm-10x13in) s.d.1921 gouache Indian ink. 4-Jun-2 Karl & Faber, Munich #476/R est:4000

WOLMANS, Jacques (1919-1991) Belgian
£331 $540 €500 Port breton (50x60cm-20x24in) s. panel. 17-Feb-3 Horta, Bruxelles #279
£331 $540 €500 Port a maree basse (50x60cm-20x24in) s. panel. 17-Feb-3 Horta, Bruxelles #280
£331 $529 €460 Barques echouees (40x50cm-16x20in) s. panel. 19-May-3 Horta, Bruxelles #286
£342 $534 €500 Ile Tudy en Bretagne (50x60cm-20x24in) s. panel. 14-Apr-3 Horta, Bruxelles #365
£345 $552 €500 Maree basse (40x50cm-16x20in) s. panel. 17-Mar-3 Horta, Bruxelles #8
£380 $592 €600 Port breton (50x60cm-20x24in) s. panel. 15-Oct-2 Horta, Bruxelles #347
£396 $633 €550 Ete breton (40x50cm-16x20in) s. panel. 19-May-3 Horta, Bruxelles #287
£414 $662 €600 Presqu'ile (40x50cm-16x20in) s. panel. 17-Mar-3 Horta, Bruxelles #9

WOLMARK, Alfred (1877-1961) British
£2400 $3960 €3480 Still life of fruit and vases (31x41cm-12x16in) s. board prov. 3-Jul-3 Christie's, Kensington #487/R est:1500-2000
£3000 $4650 €4500 Self portrait (129x41cm-51x16in) panel. 3-Dec-2 Bonhams, New Bond Street #55/R est:3000-5000
£6000 $9300 €9000 Still life with fan (47x37cm-19x15in) s.d.1911 verso prov. 4-Dec-2 Sotheby's, London #17/R est:6000-8000
Works on paper
£300 $495 €435 St Ives (24x35cm-9x14in) s.i.d. verso pen brown ink col crayon. 3-Jul-3 Christie's, Kensington #294/R
£500 $820 €750 Group of figures (27x15cm-11x6in) s. gouache chl pencil. 3-Jun-3 Sotheby's, Olympia #44/R

WOLS, Wolfgang (1913-1951) German
Works on paper
£9000 $13860 €13500 Untitled (32x24cm-13x9in) s. ink W/C htd white executed c. 1949 prov. 22-Oct-2 Sotheby's, London #436/R est:8000-12000
£9500 $15580 €14250 Musique allemande (24x31cm-9x12in) s. ink W/C paper on paper prov.exhib. 7-Feb-3 Sotheby's, London #227/R est:8000-12000
£11000 $18370 €15950 Untitled (25x18cm-10x7in) s. pen ink W/C exec.c.1943 prov. 26-Jun-3 Sotheby's, London #201/R est:6000-8000
£13000 $20150 €19500 Composition (25x18cm-10x7in) s. s.indis i.verso pen ink W/C paper on card. 5-Dec-2 Christie's, Kensington #224/R est:5000-7000
£13000 $21320 €19500 Figures mouvantes tenant ensemble (27x22cm-11x9in) s. W/C ink prov.exhib. 6-Feb-3 Christie's, London #601/R est:8000-12000
£15000 $23250 €22500 Figura (30x23cm-12x9in) s. pen brush ink W/C prov. 5-Dec-2 Christie's, Kensington #225/R est:8000-12000
£18000 $30060 €26100 Musikinstrumente - surrealistische komposition (32x24cm-13x9in) s. W/C ink executed 1941 prov.exhib. 27-Jun-3 Christie's, London #104/R est:20000-30000
£18349 $30642 €26606 Le bateau ivre (14x21cm-6x8in) s. W/C over Indian ink prov. 20-Jun-3 Kornfeld, Bern #150/R est:50000 (S.FR 40000)
£22000 $36740 €31900 La nebuleuse (18x27cm-7x11in) s. W/C ink executed 1946 prov.exhib. 27-Jun-3 Christie's, London #106/R est:8000-12000
£34000 $56780 €49300 La pagode (30x23cm-12x9in) s. W/C ink executed 1941 prov. 27-Jun-3 Christie's, London #105/R est:20000-30000
£35000 $58450 €50750 Personnages eclate (15x22cm-6x9in) s. gouache W/C ink executed 1951 prov.exhib. 27-Jun-3 Christie's, London #107/R est:8000-12000

WOLSELEY, Garnet (1884-1967) British
£2600 $4316 €3770 Portrait of a lady in a ballgown, holding a fan (84x71cm-33x28in) s. 12-Jun-3 Gorringes, Lewes #1720 est:800-1200
£10638 $16489 €15957 Girl playing with toys (115x140cm-45x55in) s. 4-Dec-2 AB Stockholms Auktionsverk #1886/R est:125000-150000 (S.KR 150000)

WOLSKI, J (19/20th C) ?
£580 $922 €870 Landscape with figures and horses (16x31cm-6x12in) s. panel. 3-Mar-3 Lilla Bukowskis, Stockholm #100 (S.KR 7800)
£855 $1359 €1283 Winter landscape with troika (16x26cm-6x10in) s. panel. 3-Mar-3 Lilla Bukowskis, Stockholm #99 (S.KR 11500)

WOLSTENHOLME, Dean (18/19th C) British
£851 $1379 €1200 Escena de vacas y ovejas en la campina (31x46cm-12x18in) s. 20-May-3 Segre, Madrid #87/R

WOLSTENHOLME, Dean (jnr) (1798-1883) British
£2516 $4000 €3774 Find and full cry (25x36cm-10x14in) panel pair. 30-Apr-3 Sotheby's, New York #553/R est:5000-7000

WOLTER, Hendrik Jan (1873-1952) Dutch
£1100 $1738 €1650 Farmer and chickens in a farmyard (70x55cm-28x22in) s. 7-Apr-3 Bonhams, Bath #56/R est:1200-1800
£1241 $1974 €1800 Portrait of the mother of the artist (71x55cm-28x22in) s. 10-Mar-3 Sotheby's, Amsterdam #266/R est:2000-3000
£1517 $2412 €2200 Espalion, Bruggen (22x26cm-9x10in) board painted 1931 sold with another by same hand. 10-Mar-3 Sotheby's, Amsterdam #272 est:800-1200
£1899 $3000 €3000 Groentemarkt, Verona (23x28cm-9x11in) s. board. 26-Nov-2 Sotheby's, Amsterdam #119/R est:3600-5500
£1931 $3070 €2800 Gezicht op de zuiderzee vanaf harderwijk (69x85cm-27x33in) s.d.1911. 10-Mar-3 Sotheby's, Amsterdam #274/R est:3000-5000

£2302 $3776 €3200 Visschershaven - harbour of Tholen (36x43cm-14x17in) s. s.i.verso panel prov. 3-Jun-3 Christie's, Amsterdam #20/R est:2000-3000
£2778 $4583 €4000 Fishermen at the river Linge (54x66cm-21x26in) s. painted c.1907 prov. 1-Jul-3 Christie's, Amsterdam #406/R est:4000-6000
£8974 $14090 €14000 Reclining nude woman (67x94cm-26x37in) s. 25-Nov-2 Glerum, Amsterdam #155/R est:6000-8000
£13014 $20432 €19000 View of Enkhuizen Harbour (72x106cm-28x42in) s. 15-Apr-3 Sotheby's, Amsterdam #123/R est:8000-12000

Works on paper

£287 $447 €450 Portrait of Henkie Wolter aged 3 years (44x36cm-17x14in) studio st. col pencil. 6-Nov-2 Vendue Huis, Gravenhage #114/R
£382 $596 €600 Portrait of Henk Wolter (31x24cm-12x9in) s.d.1916 studio st. verso pencil. 6-Nov-2 Vendue Huis, Gravenhage #113
£1042 $1719 €1500 Harbour of Camogli (48x66cm-19x26in) pastel black chk prov. 1-Jul-3 Christie's, Amsterdam #407/R est:1500-2000
£13699 $21507 €20000 In the sewing studio (63x53cm-25x21in) pastel executed c.1921. 15-Apr-3 Sotheby's, Amsterdam #216/R est:15000-25000

WOLTERS, Eugène (1844-1905) Belgian

£574 $896 €850 Riviere dans un paysage (129x97cm-51x38in) s. panel. 25-Mar-3 Campo & Campo, Antwerp #251

WOLVECAMP, Theo (1925-1992) Dutch

£2848 $4500 €4500 Untitled (60x70cm-24x28in) studio st.verso. 26-Nov-2 Sotheby's, Amsterdam #232/R est:2500-3500
£4167 $6458 €6500 Composition (60x80cm-24x31in) 3-Dec-2 Christie's, Amsterdam #264/R est:3800-4500
£4167 $6458 €6500 Composition (80x60cm-31x24in) s.d.68verso. 3-Dec-2 Christie's, Amsterdam #284/R est:5000-7000
£15827 $25957 €22000 La vie en rose (85x70cm-33x28in) s. s.i.d.66 verso prov.lit. 3-Jun-3 Christie's, Amsterdam #380/R est:12000-16000

Works on paper

£258 $401 €387 Composition (24x30cm-9x12in) studio st. Indian ink. 4-Dec-2 Kunsthallen, Copenhagen #102 (D.KR 3000)
£258 $401 €387 Composition. studio st. Indian ink. 4-Dec-2 Kunsthallen, Copenhagen #111 (D.KR 3000)
£276 $427 €414 Composition (30x21cm-12x8in) studio st. W/C. 4-Dec-2 Kunsthallen, Copenhagen #161 (D.KR 3200)

WOLVENS, H V (1896-1977) Belgian

£12414 $19862 €18000 Terrasse avec vue sur la mer (71x86cm-28x34in) 17-Mar-3 Amberes, Antwerp #284/R

WOLVENS, Henri Victor (1896-1977) Belgian

£380 $592 €600 La grenouillere (29x39cm-11x15in) s. panel after Claude Monet. 10-Sep-2 Vanderkindere, Brussels #341
£828 $1292 €1300 Interieur de poissonnerie (50x60cm-20x24in) s. 11-Nov-2 Horta, Bruxelles #38
£1783 $2782 €2800 La fete foraine a Woluwe (54x65cm-21x26in) s. 11-Nov-2 Horta, Bruxelles #37 est:1200-1800
£2590 $4144 €3600 Quelques roses (60x50cm-24x20in) s.d.1942 i.verso. 17-May-3 De Vuyst, Lokeren #409/R est:4000-5000
£2621 $4193 €3800 Jardins a Woluwe Saint Lambert en hiver (80x100cm-31x39in) s.d.1928. 17-Mar-3 Horta, Bruxelles #119 est:5000-7000
£2759 $4414 €4000 Elegante a la digue de Heist (55x78cm-22x31in) s.d.1938. 17-Mar-3 Horta, Bruxelles #120 est:5000-7000
£2897 $4634 €4200 Vue de Saint Denis en 1939 (55x65cm-22x26in) s. 17-Mar-3 Horta, Bruxelles #117 est:6000-8000
£3172 $5076 €4600 Le passage a niveau (50x60cm-20x24in) s.d.1938. 17-Mar-3 Horta, Bruxelles #118 est:6000-8000
£3526 $5465 €5500 Snowy landscape with bridge of Bruges (50x60cm-20x24in) s.d.1943 lit. 7-Dec-2 De Vuyst, Lokeren #559/R est:5500-6500
£3586 $5738 €5200 Cabines avant l'orage a la mer du Nord (50x66cm-20x26in) s.d.1930. 17-Mar-3 Horta, Bruxelles #116/R est:6000-8000
£3793 $6069 €5500 Pecheurs au bord de la Seine a Paris en 1934 (55x643cm-22x253in) s. i. verso. 17-Mar-3 Horta, Bruxelles #114/R est:8000-12000
£4552 $7283 €6600 Cabines a la mer du Nord (50x60cm-20x24in) s. 17-Mar-3 Horta, Bruxelles #115/R est:6000-8000
£4828 $7724 €7000 Lissewege station (40x60cm-16x24in) s.d.1962 exhib.lit. 15-Mar-3 De Vuyst, Lokeren #561/R est:8000-9000
£5172 $8276 €7500 Terrace with flowers (60x100cm-24x39in) s. 15-Mar-3 De Vuyst, Lokeren #478/R est:7500-8500
£5556 $8833 €8000 Station a Ingelmunster (71x99cm-28x39in) s.d.1945. 29-Apr-3 Campo & Campo, Antwerp #360/R est:8000-12000
£7586 $12138 €11000 Vase of flowers (100x80cm-39x31in) s.d.1970. 15-Mar-3 De Vuyst, Lokeren #562/R est:11000-13000
£7639 $12146 €11000 Vue sur la gare (70x100cm-28x39in) s.d.1962. 29-Apr-3 Campo & Campo, Antwerp #361/R est:11000-13000
£20690 $33103 €30000 Parc de Bruxelles avec le jet d'eau (100x120cm-39x47in) s.d.1944 lit. 15-Mar-3 De Vuyst, Lokeren #469/R

Works on paper

£278 $442 €400 Nature morte (21x26cm-8x10in) s. 29-Apr-3 Campo, Vlaamse Kaai #381
£288 $460 €400 Le train a Saint-Cloud (15x23cm-6x9in) s. mixed media. 19-May-3 Horta, Bruxelles #280
£1172 $1876 €1700 La jeune fille de l'artiste dans son berceau (70x54cm-28x21in) s. chl. 17-Mar-3 Horta, Bruxelles #121 est:2000-3000

WONNER, Paul (1920-) American

£37500 $60000 €56250 Carnation in a bottle (52x43cm-20x17in) s. painted 1964 prov. 15-May-3 Christie's, Rockefeller NY #150/R est:30000-40000

Works on paper

£4487 $7000 €6731 Model on a blue sofa (29x39cm-11x15in) s. i.verso exec.c.1960 prov. 14-Oct-2 Butterfields, San Francisco #2067/R est:8000-12000

WONTNER, William Clarke (1857-1930) British

£80000 $126400 €120000 Novronnihar (138x91cm-54x36in) s.d.1905 exhib.lit. 2-Dec-2 Sotheby's, London #106/R est:80000-120000

WOO, Jade Fon (1911-1983) American

Works on paper

£1613 $2500 €2420 Mission (36x51cm-14x20in) s. W/C exec.c.1950 prov. 8-Dec-2 Toomey, Oak Park #716/R est:1500-2000

WOOD, Albert Victor Ormsby (1904-1977) Irish

Works on paper

£300 $456 €450 For Diana hunting fields (64x46cm-25x18in) init.d.42 pastel. 16-Aug-2 Keys, Aylsham #506/R
£350 $532 €525 Bather (81x28cm-32x11in) W/C. 16-Aug-2 Keys, Aylsham #507/R

WOOD, Beatrice (1893-1998) American

Works on paper

£417 $650 €626 Untitled, two seated man and a reclining woman (36x45cm-14x18in) s.d. W/C pencil. 14-Oct-2 Butterfields, San Francisco #1051/R
£513 $800 €770 Untitled, couple reading on a New York subway (26x20cm-10x8in) s.d. graphite col pencil. 14-Oct-2 Butterfields, San Francisco #1048/R
£545 $850 €818 He speaks of harmony. Helen Lloyd Wright (24x32cm-9x13in) s.i. one d.1929 W/C pencil one gouache pencil exec.c.1930. 14-Oct-2 Butterfields, San Francisco #1049/R
£769 $1200 €1154 In church, Steve in church. Marriage (32x24cm-13x9in) s.d. s.i.d.verso one d.1932 one d.1930 W/C gouache pair. 14-Oct-2 Butterfields, San Francisco #1050/R est:1200-1800

WOOD, C M (20th C) ?

£1900 $3021 €2850 Arch of Titus, Rome (22x32cm-9x13in) s. panel. 6-Mar-3 Christie's, Kensington #507/R est:1000-1500

WOOD, Catherine M (fl.1880-1929) British

£800 $1312 €1200 Summer bouquet (46x36cm-18x14in) s. 29-May-3 Christie's, Kensington #320/R

WOOD, Charles Haigh (1856-1927) British

£2000 $3100 €3000 Homeward bound, woman and child on a foot bridge before a cottage (132x86cm-52x34in) s. 26-Sep-2 Lane, Penzance #145/R est:2500-3500
£9500 $15010 €14250 String to her bow (91x122cm-36x48in) s. 2-Dec-2 Gorringes, Lewes #2783/R est:4000-6000
£27848 $44000 €41772 Two strings to her bow (123x150cm-48x59in) s. 24-Apr-3 Sotheby's, New York #75/R est:40000-60000
£38710 $60000 €58065 Fair deceivers (76x104cm-30x41in) s.d.97 prov. 30-Oct-2 Christie's, Rockefeller NY #60/R est:40000-60000

WOOD, Christopher (1901-1930) British

£2200 $3410 €3300 Study for the seamstress (24x19cm-9x7in) panel prov.lit. 3-Dec-2 Bonhams, New Bond Street #51/R est:2500-3500
£9000 $14130 €13500 Landscape with spire and trees (33x41cm-13x16in) board prov. 22-Nov-2 Christie's, London #33/R est:5000-8000
£16500 $25905 €24750 Flowers in a glass jar (24x19cm-9x7in) board on panel painted 1924 prov.exhib.lit. 22-Nov-2 Christie's, London #34/R est:5000-7000
£18000 $29520 €26100 Portrait of a girl (40x27cm-16x11in) board painted 1923 double-sided prov.lit. 4-Jun-3 Sotheby's, London #12/R est:10000-15000
£22000 $36080 €33000 Cafe restaurant, Gianton (37x47cm-15x19in) painted 1926 prov.exhib.lit. 6-Jun-3 Christie's, London #133/R est:20000-30000
£24000 $39360 €34800 Street in Marseilles (37x46cm-15x18in) canvas on board painted 1927 prov.lit. 4-Jun-3 Sotheby's, London #23a/R est:15000-20000

£36000 $59040 €54000 Street in Paris (38x46cm-15x18in) s.d.26 canvasboard prov.exhib.lit. 6-Jun-3 Christie's, London #56/R est:40000-60000
£50000 $78500 €75000 Nude with tulips (91x71cm-36x28in) s. painted 1927 prov.exhib.lit. 22-Nov-2 Christie's, London #32/R est:20000-30000
£60000 $98400 €87000 Upright panels I and II (168x61cm-66x24in) two prov.exhib. 4-Jun-3 Sotheby's, London #21/R est:60000-80000
£60000 $98400 €87000 St Ives (40x61cm-16x24in) prov.lit. 4-Jun-3 Sotheby's, London #45/R est:20000-30000
£340000 $557600 €493000 Drying nets, Treboul Harbour (79x109cm-31x43in) board prov.exhib.lit. 4-Jun-3 Sotheby's, London #25/R est:80000-120000

Works on paper

£450 $702 €675 Reclining nude (18x28cm-7x11in) pencil prov. 17-Sep-2 Bonhams, Knightsbridge #238/R
£850 $1403 €1233 Seated girl with a doll (30x23cm-12x9in) pencil. 3-Jul-3 Christie's, Kensington #272/R
£1200 $1872 €1800 Flowers in a glass jar (33x33cm-13x13in) pencil prov. 15-Oct-2 Bonhams, Knightsbridge #252/R est:2000-3000
£3000 $4920 €4500 Portrait of Pauline Newton (37x27cm-15x11in) s.i.d.1925 pencil red ink W/C. 3-Jun-3 Sotheby's, Olympia #1/R est:2000-3000

WOOD, Christopher P (1961-) British

£440 $682 €660 Ancient monument II (91x96cm-36x38in) init.d.1998. 1-Oct-2 Bonhams, Leeds #363
£480 $744 €720 Ancient monument I (91x96cm-36x38in) init.d.1998. 1-Oct-2 Bonhams, Leeds #362/R
£500 $775 €750 Rite of spring (91x86cm-36x34in) init.d.1998. 1-Oct-2 Bonhams, Leeds #364

WOOD, Edgar Thomas (1860-1935) British

Works on paper

£520 $832 €780 Chickens by a hayrick in wooded glade (31x38cm-12x15in) s.d.28 gouache. 11-Mar-3 David Duggleby, Scarborough #80/R

WOOD, Flora (1910-) British

Works on paper

£250 $388 €375 Mother seated on chair with two children (38x19cm-15x7in) s. pen ink pastel. 7-Dec-2 Shapes, Edinburgh #300

WOOD, Frank Watson (1862-1953) British

£320 $499 €480 HMS Orion and S Division Ground Fleet (25x69cm-10x27in) s.d.1923. 20-Sep-2 Richardson & Smith, Whitby #170
£2800 $4368 €4200 Edinburgh at night with Princes Street in the distance (53x72cm-21x28in) s.d.1950 canvasboard. 14-Apr-3 Sotheby's, London #154/R est:3000-5000
£6000 $9180 €9000 An East Coast herring fleet (75x126cm-30x50in) s.d.1900. 22-Aug-2 Bonhams, Edinburgh #1074/R est:7000-10000
£19007 $30791 €27560 Leaving the outward bound (127x77cm-50x30in) s.d.1902. 25-May-3 Uppsala Auktionskammare, Uppsala #76/R est:35000-40000 (S.KR 245000)

Works on paper

£345 $545 €518 Cowport Gate, soldiers drilling (35x25cm-14x10in) s.i.d.98 W/C. 15-Nov-2 Rowley Fine Art, Newmarket #364/R
£380 $604 €570 River traffic (24x36cm-9x14in) s.d.1913 W/C. 29-Apr-3 Bonhams, Knightsbridge #113a
£380 $593 €570 Portsmouth ferry (24x35cm-9x14in) s.i.d.1902 W/C. 10-Apr-3 Bonhams, Edinburgh #115
£400 $632 €600 Tugs leading a liner into port (17x34cm-7x13in) s.d.1914 W/C. 26-Nov-2 Bonhams, Knightsbridge #157/R
£520 $806 €780 View of Berwick city with boats on the Tweed in the foreground (16x54cm-6x21in) s.d.1910 W/C. 24-Sep-2 Anderson & Garland, Newcastle #313/R
£520 $811 €780 HMS Nelson on the Forth (11x26cm-4x10in) s.i.d.1937 W/C. 13-Sep-2 Lyon & Turnbull, Edinburgh #66/R
£550 $919 €798 Nelson Rodney, Dorsetshire on the Firth of Forth (14x31cm-6x12in) s.i.d.1931 W/C. 18-Jun-3 Sotheby's, Olympia #113/R
£575 $909 €863 Pensioners, a cannon and elderly gentleman standing on ramparts overlooking the sea (36x55cm-14x22in) s.i.d.98 W/C. 15-Nov-2 Rowley Fine Art, Newmarket #367/R
£600 $930 €900 At Copenhagen (29x72cm-11x28in) s.i.d.1914 W/C htd white. 31-Oct-2 Christie's, Kensington #376/R
£600 $960 €900 HMS Orion and 3rd division grand fleet (25x38cm-10x15in) s.d.1923 W/C. 11-Mar-3 David Duggleby, Scarborough #122/R
£900 $1503 €1305 Battle of Jutland (44x99cm-17x39in) s.d.1917 W/C. 18-Jun-3 Sotheby's, Olympia #111/R
£1100 $1705 €1650 Berwick on Tweed from the south (16x54cm-6x21in) s.d.1910 W/C. 5-Dec-2 Bonhams, Edinburgh #22/R est:1000-1500
£1200 $2004 €1740 H.M.S King George V at Portsmouth 1914. Home port H.M.S Tiger. H.M.S Ajax. Battle ships (17x26cm-7x10in) s.d.1914 W/C set of four. 18-Jun-3 Sotheby's, Olympia #112/R est:800-1200
£1450 $2262 €2175 Berwick on Tweed, the railway bridge (17x53cm-7x21in) s.d.1904 W/C. 10-Apr-3 Bonhams, Edinburgh #82/R est:800-1000
£1600 $2672 €2320 Admiralty houses, Bermuda (28x36cm-11x14in) s.d.1929-31 W/C two. 18-Jun-3 Sotheby's, Olympia #123/R est:1000-1500
£1800 $2808 €2700 Berwick from the south (31x72cm-12x28in) s.d.1917 W/C. 10-Apr-3 Bonhams, Edinburgh #85/R est:800-1200
£2200 $3674 €3190 Surrender of the German fleet at Scapa Flow, December 1918 (31x97cm-12x38in) s.i.d.Dec 1918-19 W/C. 18-Jun-3 Sotheby's, Olympia #110/R est:1000-1500
£3000 $4860 €4500 Grand fleet on manoeuvres (45x106cm-18x42in) s.d.1907 W/C htd white. 22-Jan-3 Bonhams, New Bond Street #349/R est:3000 5000

WOOD, Grant (1892-1942) American

£9639 $16000 €13977 Red headed woman with earrings (15x13cm-6x5in) s.i.verso painted c.1927-31 canvasboard prov. 14-Jun-3 Jackson's, Cedar Falls #2/R est:10000-15000
£14013 $22000 €21020 Sleeper on the quay, Paris (33x41cm-13x16in) s. i.verso prov.exhib. 23-Nov-2 Jackson's, Cedar Falls #48/R est:17500-25000
£14013 $22000 €21020 Boats at Piano Sorrento (33x41cm-13x16in) s. i.verso prov.exhib. 23-Nov-2 Jackson's, Cedar Falls #49/R est:17500-25000

Prints

£1887 $3000 €2831 Tree planting group (22x27cm-9x11in) s.i.d.1938 lithograph. 2-May-3 Sotheby's, New York #57/R est:3000-5000
£1935 $3000 €2903 In the spring (28x35cm-11x14in) s. lithograph. 25-Sep-2 Christie's, Rockefeller NY #38/R est:2000-3000
£2038 $3200 €3057 February (30x41cm-12x16in) s. lithograph executed c.1940-41. 14-Dec-2 Weschler, Washington #816/R est:2000-3000
£2057 $3250 €3086 In the spring (23x30cm-9x12in) s. lithograph. 22-Apr-3 Butterfields, San Francisco #2052/R est:2500-3500
£2179 $3400 €3269 In the spring (23x31cm-9x12in) s. lithograph edition of 250. 7-Nov-2 Swann Galleries, New York #836/R est:3000-5000
£2215 $3500 €3323 February (23x30cm-9x12in) s. lithograph. 22-Apr-3 Butterfields, San Francisco #2053/R est:3500-5000
£2258 $3500 €3387 Approaching storm (40x30cm-16x12in) s. lithograph. 25-Sep-2 Christie's, Rockefeller NY #39/R est:3000-4000
£2308 $3600 €3462 March (23x30cm-9x12in) s. lithograph edition of 250. 7-Nov-2 Swann Galleries, New York #837/R est:3000-5000
£2483 $3600 €3725 Approaching storm (30x23cm-12x9in) lithograph. 1-Jun-2 Russ Antiques, Waterford #120
£2581 $4000 €3872 July Fifteenth (23x40cm-9x16in) s. lithograph. 25-Sep-2 Christie's, Rockefeller NY #37/R est:3000-5000
£2767 $4400 €4151 Seed time and harvest (19x31cm-7x12in) s.d.1937 lithograph. 1-May-3 Swann Galleries, New York #621/R est:3000-5000
£3333 $5200 €5000 Fertility (23x31cm-9x12in) s. lithograph edition of 250. 7-Nov-2 Swann Galleries, New York #838/R est:4000-6000
£5380 $8500 €8070 Sultry night (23x30cm-9x12in) s. lithograph one of 100 executed c.1939. 12-Nov-2 Doyle, New York #404/R est:3000-4000
£6013 $9500 €8719 December afternoon. February (23x30cm-9x12in) s. lithograph pair prov. 26-Jul-3 Coeur d'Alene, Hayden #242/R est:5000-7500

Works on paper

£1657 $2750 €2403 Ode upon entering St Luke's (20x8cm-8x3in) s.i. pencil prov. 14-Jun-3 Jackson's, Cedar Falls #4/R est:3000-5000
£35484 $55000 €53226 Practical idealist (52x41cm-20x16in) s.d.1936 pencil ink gouache prov.lit. 4-Dec-2 Sotheby's, New York #59/R est:60000-80000

WOOD, Harold (1918-) British

Works on paper

£500 $805 €750 Prisoners of war (33x41cm-13x16in) s.d.1955 W/C. 9-May-3 Mallams, Oxford #5/R

WOOD, James (1919-) British

£280 $437 €420 Still life in an artist's studio (91x61cm-36x24in) 27-Mar-3 Christie's, Kensington #480

WOOD, John (1801-1870) British

£850 $1309 €1275 Portrait of Marie Louise McMullin, nee Lenferna de Laresta (91x71cm-36x28in) s.indis.d.18. 5-Sep-2 Christie's, Kensington #66/R

WOOD, Karl E (1944-1990) Canadian

£711 $1166 €1031 First snow, Kananaskis River. September snow, Ghost River Country (23x30cm-9x12in) s.i. board two. 9-Jun-3 Hodgins, Calgary #326/R est:700-900 (C.D 1600)

WOOD, Lawson (1878-1957) British

Works on paper

£478 $736 €750 Soldiers on horseback leading another horse at speed (34x62cm-13x24in) s. W/C. 4-Sep-2 James Adam, Dublin #72/R
£600 $930 €900 Granpop goes gliding (38x27cm-15x11in) one s.i. one s. pencil bodycol pair. 4-Dec-2 Christie's, Kensington #171
£800 $1280 €1200 Fox went out in a hungry plight (23x30cm-9x12in) s. W/C bodycol. 15-May-3 Lawrence, Crewkerne #864/R
£800 $1280 €1200 Little Bo-peep has lost her sheep (37x28cm-15x11in) s. W/C bodycol. 15-May-3 Lawrence, Crewkerne #865/R

£800 $1280 €1200 There was a little man and he had a little gun (37x28cm-15x11in) s. W/C bodycol. 15-May-3 Lawrence, Crewkerne #868/R
£840 $1344 €1260 Georgie porgie, pudding and pie (37x28cm-15x11in) s. W/C bodycol. 15-May-3 Lawrence, Crewkerne #867/R
£1100 $1705 €1650 Stone age illustration (26x84cm-10x33in) s. pencil bodycol. 4-Dec-2 Christie's, Kensington #170/R est:800-1200
£2300 $3565 €3450 Humorous golfing scene with Scottish caddy and terrier (40x30cm-16x12in) s. W/C. 24-Sep-2 Anderson & Garland, Newcastle #249/R est:400-600
£3000 $4650 €4500 Gran'pop starts a poultry farm (38x32cm-15x13in) s. pencil W/C. 4-Dec-2 Christie's, Kensington #169/R est:600-800

WOOD, Lewis John (1813-1901) British
£560 $924 €812 Great Holyhead Road near Penmachno (22x25cm-9x10in) s. panel oval. 1-Jul-3 Bearnes, Exeter #487/R
£650 $1014 €975 Street scene in Quimper, Brittany (30x23cm-12x9in) 10-Sep-2 Bonhams, Knightsbridge #64/R
£1900 $2888 €2850 Boppard on the Rhine (23x30cm-9x12in) s. s.i.verso. 29-Aug-2 Christie's, Kensington #256/R est:1000-1500

WOOD, Lewis Pinhorn (fl.1870-1897) British
Works on paper
£380 $585 €570 Lewes from the Downs (46x66cm-18x26in) s.d.1898 W/C. 3-Sep-2 Gorringes, Lewes #2203

WOOD, Peter M (1914-1982) British
£949 $1491 €1424 Wanganui, a three masted clipper ship under full sail (50x75cm-20x30in) s. 25-Nov-2 Peter Webb, Auckland #23/R est:2500-3500 (NZ.D 3000)

WOOD, Robert (1919-) Canadian
£593 $943 €890 Indians in Fitzhugh Channel (50x40cm-20x16in) s.i. 23-Mar-3 Hodgins, Calgary #118/R est:500-700 (C.D 1400)

WOOD, Robert E (1926-1979) American
£222 $364 €322 Moonlit night II (25x20cm-10x8in) s.i.d.1994 board. 9-Jun-3 Hodgins, Calgary #2/R (C.D 500)
£1911 $3000 €2867 Cove (63x76cm-25x30in) s.d.52 i.verso prov. 19-Nov-2 Butterfields, San Francisco #8289/R est:3000-5000

WOOD, Robert Sydney Rendle (1894-?) British
£400 $628 €600 Fishing boats at low tide, Mevagissey (49x59cm-19x23in) s. i.on stretcher. 10-Dec-2 Lane, Penzance #6

WOOD, Robert W (1889-1979) American
£510 $800 €765 Cove (30x41cm-12x16in) s.d.64 i.verso canvasboard. 23-Nov-2 Jackson's, Cedar Falls #84/R
£956 $1500 €1434 Along the little Colorado, Arizona (46x61cm-18x24in) bears sig i.verso canvasboard. 22-Nov-2 Skinner, Boston #145/R est:3000-5000
£962 $1500 €1443 Ortega Road (30x41cm-12x16in) s. i.d.verso acrylic board. 9-Nov-2 Sloan, North Bethesda #617/R est:1500-2000
£1026 $1600 €1539 Laguna sunset (18x23cm-7x9in) board. 19-Oct-2 David Dike, Dallas #315/R est:1200-2400
£1087 $1750 €1631 Heavy surf (51x102cm-20x40in) s. i.verso. 18-Feb-3 John Moran, Pasadena #141a est:2500-3500
£1282 $2000 €1923 Bluebonnets (30x41cm-12x16in) board. 19-Oct-2 David Dike, Dallas #121/R est:2000-4000
£1299 $2000 €1949 Spanish oak (36x46cm-14x18in) s. 8-Sep-2 Treadway Gallery, Cincinnati #580/R est:2500-3000
£1321 $2100 €1982 Woodstock landscape (51x61cm-20x24in) s. 7-Mar-3 Skinner, Boston #451/R est:2500-4500
£1346 $2100 €2019 Landscape (64x76cm-25x30in) s. 1-Aug-2 Eldred, East Dennis #1105/R est:1500-2000
£1364 $2100 €2046 Winter in Woodstock, N Y (30x41cm-12x16in) s. board painted c.1970. 8-Sep-2 Treadway Gallery, Cincinnati #581/R est:2500-3000
£1398 $2250 €2097 October glory, Bishop, Calif (51x61cm-20x24in) s. i.verso. 18-Feb-3 John Moran, Pasadena #141b est:2000-3000
£1708 $2750 €2562 Golden west, panoramic seascape (61x122cm-24x48in) s.d.Dec 60 i.verso. 18-Feb-3 John Moran, Pasadena #141 est:3500-4500
£1751 $2750 €2627 Ocean melody (63x76cm-25x30in) s.d.49 i.verso prov. 19-Nov-2 Butterfields, San Francisco #8284/R est:3000-5000
£1796 $3000 €2604 Seascape (61x91cm-24x36in) s. prov. 17-Jun-3 John Moran, Pasadena #135b est:2500-4000
£1918 $2800 €2877 Grand Tetons (41x51cm-16x20in) 18-May-2 Altermann Galleries, Santa Fe #194/R
£1923 $3000 €2885 Late sunny day (51x76cm-20x30in) 19-Oct-2 David Dike, Dallas #101/R est:2000-4000
£1946 $3250 €2822 Landscape (64x76cm-25x30in) s. prov. 17-Jun-3 John Moran, Pasadena #176 est:3000-4000
£1946 $3250 €2822 Seascape, Pacific sunset (61x91cm-24x36in) s. i.verso. 17-Jun-3 John Moran, Pasadena #135a est:2500-4000
£2083 $3250 €3125 Impressionistic autumn landscape (46x61cm-18x24in) s. board. 30-Mar-3 Simpson's, Houston #410
£2244 $3500 €3366 Catskill autumn (51x61cm-20x24in) s. 30-Mar-3 Simpson's, Houston #420
£2273 $3500 €3410 Desert grandeur (61x91cm-24x36in) s. painted c.1960. 8-Sep-2 Treadway Gallery, Cincinnati #585/R est:4000-6000
£2388 $3750 €3582 Sand verbena (30x41cm-12x16in) s. board prov. 19-Nov-2 Butterfields, San Francisco #8314/R est:5000-7000
£2548 $4000 €3822 Crashing waves near Dana Point (66x91cm-26x36in) s. prov. 19-Nov-2 Butterfields, San Francisco #8292/R est:4000-6000
£2581 $4000 €3872 Cascade Canyon (56x71cm-22x28in) s. i.verso. 29-Oct-2 John Moran, Pasadena #693b est:4000-6000
£2695 $4500 €3908 Grand Tetons - Jenny Lake (61x91cm-24x36in) s. i.verso. 17-Jun-3 John Moran, Pasadena #78c est:5000-7000
£2724 $4250 €4086 Seascape. Bluebonnets (30x41cm-12x16in) s. board pair. 30-Mar-3 Simpson's, Houston #400
£2740 $4000 €4110 Field of bluebonnets (41x51cm-16x20in) 18-May-2 Altermann Galleries, Santa Fe #193/R
£2885 $4500 €4328 Cascade canyon (61x91cm-24x36in) s. 30-Mar-3 Simpson's, Houston #440
£3144 $5250 €4559 October (76x122cm-30x48in) s. i.verso. 21-Jun-3 Selkirks, St. Louis #190/R est:6000-8000
£3185 $5000 €4778 Frozen stream in a snow covered forest (64x77cm-25x30in) s. prov. 19-Nov-2 Butterfields, San Francisco #8285/R est:3000-5000
£3226 $5000 €4839 Fall near Johnson City Texas (76x91cm-30x36in) s. 28-Sep-2 Charlton Hall, Columbia #580/R est:6000-9000
£3226 $5000 €4839 Mountain majesty (71x91cm-28x36in) s. i.verso. 29-Oct-2 John Moran, Pasadena #669 est:5000-7000
£3395 $5500 €4923 Texas landscape (51x76cm-20x30in) s. 21-May-3 Doyle, New York #129/R est:4000-6000
£3503 $5500 €5255 Texas autumn (61x76cm-24x30in) s. i.verso prov. 19-Nov-2 Butterfields, San Francisco #8100/R est:3000-5000
£3571 $5500 €5357 White mountain peak (61x76cm-24x30in) s. painted c.1970. 8-Sep-2 Treadway Gallery, Cincinnati #583/R est:5000-7000
£3593 $6000 €5210 Field of bluebonnets (30x41cm-12x16in) s. s.verso prov. 18-Jun-3 Christie's, Los Angeles #13/R est:4000-6000
£4063 $6500 €6095 Mount Hood, Oregon (76x102cm-30x40in) s. 15-Mar-3 Eldred, East Dennis #281/R est:10000-12000
£4375 $7000 €6563 Autumn sunset (61x76cm-24x30in) s.d. 15-Mar-3 Selkirks, St. Louis #338/R est:3500-4500
£4808 $7500 €7212 Landscape with field of bluebonnets (64x76cm-25x30in) s. exhib. 20-Sep-2 New Orleans Auction, New Orleans #1242/R est:7000-10000
£4938 $8000 €7160 Texas bluebonnets (51x76cm-20x30in) s. 21-May-3 Doyle, New York #128/R est:5000-7000
£5128 $8000 €7692 Texas bluebonnets (51x76cm-20x30in) 19-Oct-2 David Dike, Dallas #170/R est:10000-15000
£5484 $8500 €8226 April in Bexar County (46x61cm-18x24in) s. i.verso. 29-Oct-2 John Moran, Pasadena #693a est:4500-6500
£7372 $11500 €11058 Texas bluebonnets (64x76cm-25x30in) 19-Oct-2 David Dike, Dallas #160/R est:10000-15000
£7692 $12000 €11538 Mountain river landscape (64x76cm-25x30in) 19-Oct-2 David Dike, Dallas #159/R est:9000-12000

WOOD, Wilfred René (1888-1976) British
Works on paper
£250 $405 €363 Blakeney Quay, Norfolk (23x52cm-9x20in) s.indis.d. i.verso. 29-Jul-3 Holloways, Banbury #337

WOOD, William (1769-1810) British
Miniatures
£2000 $3180 €3000 Gentleman wearing a black coat and a cravat (7cm-3in) init. seed pearls. 4-Mar-3 Bonhams, New Bond Street #135/R est:2000-3000
£3800 $5966 €5700 Young gentleman in a blue coat (7cm-3in) silver gilt frame oval. 10-Dec-2 Christie's, London #71/R est:2000-3000

WOOD, William Thomas (1877-1958) British
£360 $558 €540 Study of a pot of flowers (42x31cm-17x12in) indis.sig.d.1949. 1-Nov-2 Moore Allen & Innocent, Cirencester #633
£500 $770 €750 Thames at Battersea, dusk (18x30cm-7x12in) canvasboard. 23-Oct-2 Hamptons Fine Art, Godalming #131/R
Works on paper
£250 $395 €375 English cottage, Hampshire (38x48cm-15x19in) s.i.d.15 W/C. 13-Nov-2 Halls, Shrewsbury #345

WOOD, Worden (20th C) American
£1100 $1782 €1650 American North Atlantic liner Leviathian making for Cherbourg (76x102cm-30x40in) s.d.24. 21-May-3 Christie's, Kensington #698/R est:800-1200
Works on paper
£250 $400 €363 American ship at full sail (28x38cm-11x15in) s.d.25 W/C. 17-May-3 CRN Auctions, Cambridge #62

WOODBURY, Charles (1864-1940) American
£440 $700 €660 Maine seascape (20x25cm-8x10in) i.verso canvasboard. 1-Mar-3 North East Auctions, Portsmouth #692/R

£594	$950	€861	Seascape (30x43cm-12x17in) studio st. verso canvasboard. 16-May-3 Skinner, Boston #288/R
£1026	$1600	€1539	Mountain landscape (30x43cm-12x17in) s. board. 28-Mar-3 Eldred, East Dennis #562/R est:500-1000
£1582	$2500	€2373	Summer day (43x53cm-17x21in) s.d.16. 17-Nov-2 CRN Auctions, Cambridge #56/R
£1698	$2700	€2547	St Vincent, Dominica (25x35cm-10x14in) s. i.verso board. 7-Mar-3 Skinner, Boston #433/R est:3000-5000
£3437	$5500	€4984	Ogunquit (44x54cm-17x21in) s. 16-May-3 Skinner, Boston #298/R est:4000-6000
£5096	$8000	€7644	Lone survivor (92x101cm-36x40in) prov.exhib. 22-Nov-2 Skinner, Boston #280/R est:10000-15000

Works on paper

£285	$450	€428	Pencil sketch of fisherman (13x18cm-5x7in) s.d. 17-Nov-2 CRN Auctions, Cambridge #56a/R

WOODCOCK, Hartwell L (1852-1929) American

£839	$1300	€1259	Tabletop still life (53x43cm-21x17in) s. painted c.1900 prov. 8-Dec-2 Toomey, Oak Park #728/R

Works on paper

£318	$500	€477	Coastal scene in Maine with trees and grass overlooking sandy beach (33x48cm-13x19in) s.d.1901 W/C. 19-Apr-3 James Julia, Fairfield #371/R

WOODCOCK, Lilian (fl.1891-1921) British

£300	$465	€450	Llandudno (44x55cm-17x22in) painted c.1910. 25-Sep-2 Peter Wilson, Nantwich #21/R

WOODCOCK, Percy Franklin (1855-1936) Canadian

£321	$500	€482	Summer landscape of field (18x30cm-7x12in) s. 15-Oct-2 Winter Associates, Plainville #225
£533	$875	€800	Warmth of winter's dusk (22x32cm-9x13in) s.d.94. 3-Jun-3 Joyner, Toronto #514 est:1200-1500 (C.D 1200)

WOODFORD, David (1938-) British

£350	$571	€525	Stormy sunset over the Rivals (20x13cm-8x5in) s. board. 28-Jan-3 Rogers Jones, Clwyd #137

WOODHOUSE, Herbert (1855-c.1920) Australian

Works on paper

£380	$612	€551	River retreat (68x100cm-27x39in) s. W/C. 12-May-3 Joel, Victoria #273 est:800-1200 (A.D 950)

WOODHOUSE, Samuel (19th C) British

£2800	$4452	€4200	London to Hadley Royal mail coach passing over Finchley Common (71x91cm-28x36in) s.d.1824 prov. 6-Mar-3 Christie's, Kensington #590/R est:2500-3500

WOODHOUSE, William (1857-1939) British

£320	$499	€480	Lion guarding his kill (22x32cm-9x13in) s. canvas on board. 10-Apr-3 Tennants, Leyburn #1028
£320	$531	€464	Cattle and hens by a coop (24x29cm-9x11in) s. 13-Jun-3 Lyon & Turnbull, Edinburgh #76
£360	$583	€540	Lion Rock, Heysham Head (36x40cm-14x16in) s.d.89. 21-May-3 James Thompson, Kirby Lonsdale #25
£500	$780	€750	Study of a grey horse (23x31cm-9x12in) init. board. 10-Apr-3 Tennants, Leyburn #1038/R
£850	$1343	€1275	Dead stags (37x45cm-15x18in) s.i.d.99 prov. 27-Nov-2 Christie's, London #36/R
£2000	$3160	€3000	Setters on a moor (51x61cm-20x24in) s. 28-Nov-2 Christie's, Kensington #369/R est:1500-2000
£8000	$12480	€12000	Spaniel holding a rabbit (61x51cm-24x20in) s. prov. 25-Mar-3 Bonhams, Leeds #649/R est:2500-3500

Works on paper

£325	$523	€488	Dunstaffriage Castle near Connel ferry (17x26cm-7x10in) s. W/C. 15-Jan-3 James Thompson, Kirby Lonsdale #195
£550	$858	€825	Horses watering (24x33cm-9x13in) s. W/C. 17-Sep-2 Sotheby's, Olympia #130/R
£700	$1085	€1050	Cattle in a farmyard (24x33cm-9x13in) s. W/C. 24-Sep-2 Bonhams, Knightsbridge #206/R
£1000	$1660	€1450	Snipe in snow (26x37cm-10x15in) s. pencil W/C htd white prov. 12-Jun-3 Christie's, Kensington #133/R est:400-600
£1000	$1630	€1450	Deer in Levens Park (26x36cm-10x14in) s. W/C. 16-Jul-3 James Thompson, Kirby Lonsdale #153
£1000	$1630	€1450	Work horses with horseman watering at a trough (24x34cm-9x13in) s. pair. 16-Jul-3 James Thompson, Kirby Lonsdale #176
£1250	$2038	€1813	Country scene with haystack, work horse, horseman and dog (25x35cm-10x14in) s. W/C. 16-Jul-3 James Thompson, Kirby Lonsdale #177/R
£1350	$2052	€2025	Canal scene with barge and figures (25x36cm-10x14in) s. W/C. 14-Aug-2 Andrew Hartley, Ilkley #561 est:1000-1500
£1900	$3021	€2850	Barn owl and prey (37x54cm-15x21in) s. 19-Mar-3 James Thompson, Kirby Lonsdale #105

WOODHOUSE, William (attrib) (1857-1939) British

£300	$471	€450	Untitled (23x32cm-9x13in) 15-Apr-3 Bonhams, Chester #1035
£750	$1245	€1088	Gun dog with a grouse (30x25cm-12x10in) s. 12-Jun-3 Christie's, Kensington #290/R

WOODINGTON, William Frederick (1806-1893) British

Sculpture

£2100	$3507	€3045	Naked woman standing reaching to a butterfly (40cm-16in) i. bronze circular base after Sir Richard Westmacott. 24-Jun-3 Bonhams, Knowle #128/R est:400-600

WOODINGTON, William Frederick (attrib) (1806-1893) British

£1850	$3034	€2775	Westminster Abbey from St. James Park (26x33cm-10x13in) panel. 3-Jun-3 Bonhams, Oxford #55 est:400-500

WOODLOCK, David (1842-1929) British

Works on paper

£250	$388	€375	Woman at door (30x23cm-12x9in) s. W/C dr. 1-Oct-2 Capes Dunn, Manchester #817/R
£360	$562	€540	Tingleton Village, Dorset (17x25cm-7x10in) s. W/C. 6-Nov-2 Bonhams, Chester #346
£380	$635	€551	Lady at a cottage door (25x15cm-10x6in) s. W/C. 20-Jun-3 Keys, Aylsham #505
£400	$656	€600	Dedham Mill, Walthamstow, Essex (16x24cm-6x9in) s. W/C. 4-Jun-3 Bonhams, Chester #312
£450	$702	€675	Roylance farm (34x24cm-13x9in) s. W/C. 26-Mar-3 Sotheby's, Olympia #69/R
£640	$998	€960	Old cottages, Wellford, near Warwick (25x17cm-10x7in) s. W/C. 6-Nov-2 Bonhams, Chester #345
£680	$1061	€1020	Steventon Manor, Berkshire (24x17cm-9x7in) s. W/C. 6-Nov-2 Bonhams, Chester #344
£700	$1092	€1050	Gossip at the cottage door (41x34cm-16x13in) s. W/C. 26-Mar-3 Sotheby's, Olympia #70/R
£750	$1162	€1125	Outside St Marks, Venice (29x17cm-11x7in) s. W/C. 3-Dec-2 Sotheby's, Olympia #170/R
£780	$1240	€1170	Path thought the wood (30x20cm-12x8in) s. W/C. 3-Mar-3 Louis Taylor, Stoke on Trent #853
£980	$1558	€1470	Cottage near Audlem, Cheshire (29x20cm-11x8in) s. W/C. 27-Feb-3 Bonhams, Chester #347/R
£1200	$1872	€1800	Surrey cottage, the gardener's daughter (25x18cm-10x7in) s. W/C. 20-Sep-2 Richardson & Smith, Whitby #106 est:900-1200
£1200	$1848	€1800	Tending the roses (25x18cm-10x7in) s. W/C bodycol. 22-Oct-2 Sworder & Son, Bishops Stortford #694/R est:1000-1500
£1400	$2170	€2100	Country girl (24x17cm-9x7in) s. W/C. 3-Dec-2 Sotheby's, Olympia #91/R est:800-1200

WOODMAN, Charles Horwell (1823-1888) British

Works on paper

£380	$623	€570	Deer park, solitary figure holding a gun, with deer (28x53cm-11x21in) s.d.1869 W/C. 5-Feb-3 Goldings, Lincolnshire #226
£400	$668	€580	View of a meandering river (26x57cm-10x22in) s.d.1885 W/C. 24-Jun-3 Bonhams, Knightsbridge #9/R

WOODROOFE, Louise (20th C) American

£274	$425	€411	Abstract composition (64x76cm-25x30in) painted c.1950. 8-Dec-2 Toomey, Oak Park #842/R
£297	$475	€431	Gloucester (20x25cm-8x10in) s. i.verso canvasboard. 16-May-3 Skinner, Boston #283/R
£323	$500	€485	Abstract composition (64x76cm-25x30in) painted c.1950. 8-Dec-2 Toomey, Oak Park #843/R
£535	$850	€803	On the way to town (51x61cm-20x24in) s. canvasboard exhib. 7-Mar-3 Skinner, Boston #500/R
£566	$900	€849	Storefronts (20x25cm-8x10in) s. board. 7-Mar-3 Skinner, Boston #421/R
£755	$1200	€1133	Produce market (20x25cm-8x10in) s. canvasboard. 7-Mar-3 Skinner, Boston #423/R

WOODROW, Joash (1926-) British

£300	$465	€450	Seated woman reading a book (48x38cm-19x15in) board. 1-Oct-2 Bonhams, Leeds #355/R

WOODRUFF, Hale (1900-1980) American

£8176	$13000	€12264	Knobs of Southern Indiana (48x61cm-19x24in) s.i. panel painted c.1949 prov. 2-Mar-3 Toomey, Oak Park #744/R est:7000-9000

WOODRUFF, Leonard (19/20th C) American

£449	$700	€674	Still life with pottery and fruit (51x76cm-20x30in) s. 28-Mar-3 Eldred, East Dennis #839/R

WOODS, Henry (1846-1921) British
£978 $1554 €1467 Interior from Saint Peter's church at Murano (60x49cm-24x19in) s.i.d.1918 i.verso. 5-Mar-3 Rasmussen, Copenhagen #1691/R (D.KR 10500)

WOODS, Padraic (1893-1991) Irish
£548 $860 €800 Near Interlacken, Switzerland (30x40cm-12x16in) s.i. board. 15-Apr-3 De Veres Art Auctions, Dublin #16
£616 $962 €900 Horn head from Killyhoey, Co Donegal (60x74cm-24x29in) s. 8-Apr-3 James Adam, Dublin #68/R
£1667 $2617 €2600 Bridge into the village (56x66cm-22x26in) s. 19-Nov-2 Whyte's, Dublin #192/R est:2000-3000

WOODS, Richard (1966-) British
£1500 $2310 €2250 47 cars (151x485cm-59x191in) gloss paint on scanned image on canvas prov. 23-Oct-2 Christie's, London #254/R est:2000-3000

WOODSIDE, Christine A (1946-) British
£700 $1092 €1050 Magdala Court (15x11cm-6x4in) s.d.92 oil collage board. 17-Oct-2 Bonhams, Edinburgh #95

WOODVILLE, Richard Caton (jnr) (1856-1927) British
£6200 $10106 €8990 Queen's halt (56x40cm-22x16in) s.d.1890 panel. 16-Jul-3 Sotheby's, Olympia #86/R est:4000-6000

WOODWARD, Ellsworth (1861-1939) American
£3846 $6000 €5769 Blue tree. Still life (20x30cm-8x12in) init. board double-sided lit. 12-Oct-2 Neal Auction Company, New Orleans #634/R est:5000-7000

Works on paper
£570 $900 €855 Newcomb pottery (20x28cm-8x11in) s. W/C. 5-Apr-3 Neal Auction Company, New Orleans #318/R
£769 $1200 €1154 Stairwell (30x23cm-12x9in) s. W/C. 12-Oct-2 Neal Auction Company, New Orleans #656
£1266 $2000 €1899 Spring landscape along the Gulf coast, Biloxi (25x36cm-10x14in) s. W/C. 5-Apr-3 Neal Auction Company, New Orleans #317/R est:1500-2500
£1410 $2200 €2115 Still life of tulips in a Newcomb vase (38x25cm-15x10in) init. W/C. 12-Oct-2 Neal Auction Company, New Orleans #609/R est:2000-3000
£1899 $3000 €2849 French quarter gossip (25x38cm-10x15in) s. W/C. 16-Nov-2 New Orleans Auction, New Orleans #1558/R est:4000-7000

WOODWARD, Ellsworth (attrib) (1861-1939) American
£759 $1200 €1139 Standing nude (71x56cm-28x22in) board. 5-Apr-3 Neal Auction Company, New Orleans #409/R

WOODWARD, George Moutard (1760-1809) British
Works on paper
£400 $620 €600 Never too late to learn (26x32cm-10x13in) s.i. W/C over pencil. 3-Dec-2 Sotheby's, Olympia #19/R
£400 $632 €600 An Irish barrister (24x33cm-9x13in) s.i. W/C over pencil. 2-Dec-2 Bonhams, Bath #4
£420 $664 €630 Sleeping after supper (16x21cm-6x8in) s. W/C over pen ink. 26-Nov-2 Bonhams, Knightsbridge #39/R

WOODWARD, Louise (1862-1937) American
£962 $1500 €1443 Sunset in a bayou landscape (28x36cm-11x14in) s. 12-Oct-2 Neal Auction Company, New Orleans #1411/R est:1200-1800

WOODWARD, Mabel (1877-1945) American
£1013 $1600 €1520 Mt Etna and almond blossoms (25x33cm-10x13in) s. 17-Nov-2 CRN Auctions, Cambridge #52/R
£1218 $1950 €1827 Nubble-light, York (25x33cm-10x13in) s. board. 11-Jan-3 James Julia, Fairfield #230a est:2000-4000
Works on paper
£764 $1200 €1146 Moroccan street scene (26x20cm-10x8in) s. gouache. 22-Nov-2 Skinner, Boston #312/R est:1200-1800

WOODWARD, Margaret (1938-) Australian
£3214 $5014 €4821 December in my valley (122x122cm-48x48in) s. i.verso. 11-Nov-2 Deutscher-Menzies, Melbourne #145/R est:3000-5000 (A.D 9000)

Works on paper
£602 $956 €903 Family II (42x32cm-17x13in) s. mixed media. 3-Mar-3 Lawson Menzies, Sydney #344 est:2000-3000 (A.D 1600)

WOODWARD, Neil (1947-) Canadian
£766 $1210 €1149 Winter Drive in British Columbia (56x88cm-22x35in) s.i.d.2002 acrylic on board. 14-Nov-2 Heffel, Vancouver #43/R est:1500-2000 (C.D 1900)
£866 $1377 €1256 On the seawall, Stanley Park (61x122cm-24x48in) s. s.i.d.1997 verso acrylic panel. 1-May-3 Heffel, Vancouver #106/R est:2500-3500 (C.D 2000)
£1345 $2152 €2018 East van bike ride (61x76cm-24x30in) s. s.i.d.2002 acrylic on board. 15-May-3 Heffel, Vancouver #195/R est:2000-3000 (C.D 3000)
£1411 $2230 €2117 Reflection and meditation, Horseshoe Bay (61x122cm-24x48in) s.i.d.2002 acrylic on board. 14-Nov-2 Heffel, Vancouver #44/R est:2500-3500 (C.D 3500)
£1570 $2511 €2355 Sunday morning, Lonsdale quay (61x122cm-24x48in) s. s.i.d.1996 verso board. 15-May-3 Heffel, Vancouver #196/R est:2500-3500 (C.D 3500)

WOODWARD, Robert Strong (1885-1960) American
£1623 $2500 €2435 Over the pasture ledge (74x53cm-29x21in) 6-Sep-2 Douglas, South Deerfield #1

WOODWARD, Stanley W (1890-1970) American
£224 $350 €336 Schooner at dockside (18x28cm-7x11in) s. 28-Mar-3 Eldred, East Dennis #651/R

WOODWARD, Thomas (1801-1852) British
£760 $1201 €1140 Girl with donkey and foal (19x22cm-7x9in) i. board. 27-Nov-2 Bonhams, Knowle #202
£900 $1449 €1350 Racehorse with jockey up (21x26cm-8x10in) i.verso board. 15-Jan-3 Cheffins Grain & Comins, Cambridge #423/R
£2160 $3500 €3132 Black stallion in a stall (64x76cm-25x30in) mono.d.1821. 21-May-3 Doyle, New York #171/R est:6000-8000
£3600 $5472 €5400 Runaway horse (51x61cm-20x24in) mono.d.1838 prov.exhib.lit. 28-Aug-2 Sotheby's, London #817/R est:4000-6000
£4600 $7268 €6900 Galopade with jockey up (64x76cm-25x30in) init.d.1833. 2-Dec-2 Bonhams, Bath #137/R est:4000-6000

WOODWARD, William (1859-1939) American
£705 $1100 €1058 Moonlit clouds (41x30cm-16x12in) init. i.verso prov. 12-Oct-2 Neal Auction Company, New Orleans #608/R
£1524 $2500 €2210 Senator money's on the Gulf (30x48cm-12x19in) s.i.verso. 7-Jun-3 Neal Auction Company, New Orleans #362/R est:4000-6000
£5449 $8500 €8174 Spanish cabildo and stocks, N O (33x23cm-13x9in) s.i. oil crayon over pencil board. 12-Oct-2 Neal Auction Company, New Orleans #629/R est:6000-9000
Works on paper
£3354 $5500 €4863 Grey day along shore (33x48cm-13x19in) s.i.verso W/C. 7-Jun-3 Neal Auction Company, New Orleans #396/R est:4000-6000

WOODWARD-SMITH, Sydney (1904-1972) Australian
£321 $498 €482 Morning glitter, Double Bay (14x22cm-6x9in) s. board. 29-Oct-2 Lawson Menzies, Sydney #507 (A.D 900)

WOOL, Christopher (1955-) American
£3205 $5000 €4808 Untitled (102x66cm-40x26in) alkyd paper prov. 14-Oct-2 Butterfields, San Francisco #2110/R est:8000-12000
£7595 $12000 €11393 Untitled (102x66cm-40x26in) s.d.1988 verso alkyd on paper prov. 14-Nov-2 Christie's, Rockefeller NY #317/R est:12000-18000
£10127 $16000 €15191 Untitled - S43 (91x61cm-36x24in) s.d.1989 alkyd acrylic on aluminum prov. 14-Nov-2 Christie's, Rockefeller NY #315/R est:12000-18000
£12658 $20000 €18987 Untitled - S12 (122x61cm-48x24in) s.i.d.87 alkyd enamel on aluminum prov. 14-Nov-2 Christie's, Rockefeller NY #314/R est:20000-30000
£16250 $26000 €24375 Untitled (30x20cm-12x8in) s.d.1990 verso enamel on aluminum prov. 16-May-3 Phillips, New York #129/R est:15000-20000
£18987 $30000 €28481 Untitled - P37 (183x183cm-72x72in) s.d.87 alkyd flashe on aluminum prov.exhib. 14-Nov-2 Christie's, Rockefeller NY #313/R est:40000-60000
£22152 $35000 €33228 Untitled, P15 (183x122cm-72x48in) s.i.d.86 verso alkyd aluminium steel prov.exhib. 13-Nov-2 Sotheby's, New York #481/R est:35000-45000
£60000 $98400 €90000 F34 (99x66cm-39x26in) s.i.d.1992 verso alkyd paper prov. 6-Feb-3 Sotheby's, London #50/R est:40000
£151899 $240000 €227849 Untitled - W24-run dog eat dog (274x183cm-108x72in) enamel on aluminum executed 1990 prov.exhib. 13-Nov-2 Christie's, Rockefeller NY #25/R est:200000-300000

WOOLARD, William (fl.1883-1908) British
Works on paper
£207 $324 €311 Clamming at low tide (36x56cm-14x22in) s.d.1896 W/C. 24-Jul-2 Walker's, Ottawa #15/R (C.D 500)
£1102 $1752 €1653 Kinkoen Pier (56x33cm-22x13in) s.i. W/C. 18-Mar-3 Maynards, Vancouver #16/R est:800-1000 (C.D 2600)

WOOLF, Pamela (20th C) New Zealander?
£282 $440 €423 Roses (50x135cm-20x53in) s. board. 7-Nov-2 International Art Centre, Auckland #195 (NZ.D 900)

WOOLF, S (20th C) ?
Prints
£3106 $5000 €4659 Abraham Lincoln sitting on a settee (23x28cm-9x11in) s. lithograph with autographed discharge paper in same frame. 22-Feb-3 Pook & Pook, Downington #341/R est:2000-3000

WOOLFORD, Charles H (fl.1880-1923) British
£450 $716 €675 Crescent moon (23x31cm-9x12in) s.i.verso panel. 6-Mar-3 Christie's, Kensington #72/R

WOOLLASTON, Sir Mountford Tosswill (1910-1998) New Zealander
£1592 $2500 €2388 Interior view through a doorway (84x92cm-33x36in) s. board. 10-Dec-2 Peter Webb, Auckland #60/R est:5000-7000 (NZ.D 5000)
£2113 $3486 €3064 Head looking out to sea (44x39cm-17x15in) s. board. 1-Jul-3 Peter Webb, Auckland #84/R est:6000-9000 (NZ.D 6000)
£7018 $10947 €10527 Hohonu (81x120cm-32x47in) s. board prov.exhib. 27-Mar-3 International Art Centre, Auckland #18/R est:25000-35000 (NZ.D 20000)
£7599 $11854 €11399 Portrait of David Hewson (79x59cm-31x23in) mono. board sold with three studies. 17-Sep-2 Peter Webb, Auckland #107/R est:35000-45000 (NZ.D 25000)
£10030 $15647 €15045 Harmonium player (48x42cm-19x17in) s. s.i.verso acrylic on paper. 17-Sep-2 Peter Webb, Auckland #106/R est:35000-45000 (NZ.D 33000)
£17361 $27083 €26042 From Mapua (45x61cm-18x24in) s. board painted c.1960 double-sided. 8-Apr-3 Peter Webb, Auckland #75/R est:35000-55000 (NZ.D 50000)
Works on paper
£545 $840 €818 Bailey's Hill (26x35cm-10x14in) s.d.1960 pen ink. 4-Sep-2 Dunbar Sloane, Wellington #111/R est:500-1000 (NZ.D 1800)
£701 $1100 €1052 Portrait of Edith (34x26cm-13x10in) s. ink dr. 10-Dec-2 Peter Webb, Auckland #47/R est:1500-2500 (NZ.D 2200)
£764 $1200 €1146 Landscape (30x43cm-12x17in) s. W/C. 10-Dec-2 Peter Webb, Auckland #87/R est:2000-3000 (NZ.D 2400)
£788 $1213 €1182 Head of a Maori Boy (37x26cm-15x10in) s. gouache prov. 4-Sep-2 Dunbar Sloane, Wellington #121/R est:1500-2500 (NZ.D 2600)
£1064 $1660 €1596 Takaka pond (27x37cm-11x15in) s.i.d.16.3.61 ink dr. 17-Sep-2 Peter Webb, Auckland #143/R est:2500-3500 (NZ.D 3500)
£1242 $1913 €1863 Untitled - landscape (24x37cm-9x15in) s. W/C. 4-Sep-2 Dunbar Sloane, Wellington #3/R est:1000-2000 (NZ.D 4100)
£1411 $2201 €2117 Tasman Bay, Nelson (27x36cm-11x14in) s. W/C. 7-Nov-2 International Art Centre, Auckland #35/R est:4000-6000 (NZ.D 4500)
£2508 $3912 €3762 Nelson landscape diptych (27x22cm-11x9in) s. W/C. 7-Nov-2 International Art Centre, Auckland #14/R est:8000-12000 (NZ.D 8000)

WOOLLATT, Edgar (1871-1931) British
Works on paper
£1500 $2340 €2250 Brittany market (53x69cm-21x27in) s. W/C bodycol. 17-Sep-2 Goldings, Lincolnshire #711/R

WOOLLETT, H C (fl.1851-1872) British
£950 $1520 €1425 Study of three horses at a well (54x76cm-21x30in) pair. 11-Mar-3 Bonhams, Knightsbridge #40/R

WOOLLETT, Henry A (19th C) British
£4000 $6320 €6000 Farmhand, horse, chickens and ducks in a farmyard (56x92cm-22x36in) s.d.1859. 28-Nov-2 Christie's, Kensington #135/R est:4000-6000

WOOLLETT, Henry Charles (fl.1851-1872) British
£1400 $2184 €2100 Feeding time, horses before a cottage doorway (45x76cm-18x30in) s.d.1856. 18-Sep-2 Dreweatt Neate, Newbury #161 est:400-600

WOOLLEY, Virginia (1884-1971) American
£659 $1100 €956 Mission scene, El Carmine, near Mexico City (61x51cm-24x20in) board prov. 17-Jun-3 John Moran, Pasadena #153 est:1500-2000

WOOLMER, Alfred Joseph (1805-1892) British
£1500 $2310 €2250 Bride (61x51cm-24x20in) s.i. painted oval prov.exhib. 5-Sep-2 Christie's, Kensington #308/R est:2000-3000
£12000 $19320 €18000 Sunset (127x75cm-50x30in) prov.exhib. 20-Feb-3 Christie's, London #204/R est:18000

WOOLMER, Alfred Joseph (attrib) (1805-1892) British
£820 $1337 €1230 Examining the fishes (12x15cm-5x6in) panel. 12-Feb-3 Bonhams, Knightsbridge #75/R

WOOLNER, Thomas (1825-1892) British
Sculpture
£6000 $9660 €9000 Achilles shouting from the trenches (43cm-17in) bronze lit. 20-Feb-3 Christie's, London #142/R est:5000

WOOLNOTH, Charles (1815-1906) British
Works on paper
£500 $785 €750 Sailing on the lake, in a mountainous landscape (41x66cm-16x26in) s.i. pencil W/C htd white. 16-Apr-3 Christie's, Kensington #1067/R
£1500 $2280 €2250 Gareloch (55x89cm-22x35in) s. W/C stopping out htd bodycol. 28-Aug-2 Sotheby's, London #866/R est:1500-2000

WOOLRYCH, F Humphry W (1868-?) American/Australian
£692 $1100 €1038 Early autumn landscape, probably the Ozarks (46x38cm-18x15in) s. painted c.1910. 4-May-3 Treadway Gallery, Cincinnati #517/R
£1410 $2200 €2115 Haystacks (20x28cm-8x11in) s. artist's board prov. 10-Nov-2 Selkirks, St. Louis #990/R est:500-700
Works on paper
£321 $500 €482 Portrait of a clown (30x23cm-12x9in) s.d.1888 W/C dr prov. 10-Nov-2 Selkirks, St. Louis #988

WOOLSEY, Carl E (1902-) American
£881 $1400 €1277 Autumn Beechwood (41x51cm-16x20in) s. painted c.1930. 4-May-3 Treadway Gallery, Cincinnati #525/R

WOOSTER, Austin C (19/20th C) American
£461 $700 €692 Old homestead (25x36cm-10x14in) s.d.1908 s.i.d.verso. 18-Aug-2 Jeffery Burchard, Florida #39/R

WOOTTON, Frank (1911-1998) British
£780 $1264 €1131 Cleve Mill, Norfolk (28x38cm-11x15in) s. board. 31-Jul-3 Scarborough Perry Fine Arts, Hove #846/R
£1400 $2198 €2100 Mingaladon Rangoon, Burma (42x52cm-17x20in) s.d.1945. 14-Dec-2 Lacy Scott, Bury St.Edmunds #487/R
£6000 $9480 €9000 Huntsman and hounds crossing a river (71x98cm-28x39in) s.d.1969. 28-Nov-2 Bonhams, Knightsbridge #128/R est:6000-8000
Works on paper
£2000 $3160 €2900 The Royal Exchange (48x89cm-19x35in) s. gouache. 22-Jul-3 Gorringes, Lewes #1602/R est:2000-3000

WOOTTON, John (c.1682-1764) British
£5500 $8690 €8250 Hunt in full cry (46x57cm-18x22in) prov. 28-Nov-2 Christie's, Kensington #74/R est:6000-8000
£10000 $16600 €15000 Italianate landscape with a shepherd and shepherdess in the foreground and a hilltop village (41x52cm-16x20in) indis i. 10-Jun-3 Christie's, London #47/R est:4000-6000
£12000 $18960 €18000 Goatherd and goats on rocky wooded outcrop before river landscape (49x67cm-19x26in) s. prov. 26-Nov-2 Christie's, London #53/R est:7000-10000
£80000 $126400 €120000 Before the start of the Gold Cup (123x99cm-48x39in) prov. 28-Nov-2 Sotheby's, London #7/R est:50000-70000

WOPFNER, Joseph (1843-1927) Austrian
£325 $484 €500 Kochelsee (15x21cm-6x8in) mono. canvas on board. 26-Jun-2 Neumeister, Munich #925
£1899 $3000 €3000 Four men in a rowing boat (10x17cm-4x7in) s.i. board. 28-Nov-2 Dorotheum, Vienna #253/R est:3000-4000

£3846 $5962 €6000 Peasant family on bank of Chiemsee with cattle in small boat (11x17cm-4x7in) mono. board. 4-Dec-2 Neumeister, Munich #976/R est:5500
£6164 $9616 €9000 Crossing on the hay barge (13x17cm-5x7in) s.d. panel. 11-Apr-3 Winterberg, Heidelberg #624/R est:4500
£8442 $12578 €13000 Fishermen on Bodensee (51x80cm-20x31in) s. lit. 26-Jun-2 Neumeister, Munich #923/R est:12500

Works on paper
£308 $477 €480 Chiemsee landscape (13x16cm-5x6in) s. w/C. 6-Dec-2 Michael Zeller, Lindau #956
£313 $498 €460 Seated hunter (24x19cm-9x7in) st.sig. pencil. 19-Mar-3 Neumeister, Munich #399
£755 $1177 €1200 Boat on stormy Chiemsee (18x27cm-7x11in) s. 9-Oct-2 Michael Zeller, Lindau #967

WORCESTER, Albert (1878-?) American
£1582 $2500 €2373 French Quarter courtyard (61x51cm-24x20in) s.d.1919 board. 5-Apr-3 Neal Auction Company, New Orleans #331/R est:2500-3500

WORES, Theodore (1859-1939) American
£4777 $7500 €7166 Springtime in Saratoga (30x41cm-12x16in) s. 20-Nov-2 Christie's, Los Angeles #2/R est:6000-8000
£10241 $17000 €14849 Springtime in the Saratoga foothills (41x30cm-16x12in) s. i. on stretcher prov. 11-Jun-3 Butterfields, San Francisco #4186/R est:6000-8000

WORMER, Axel Viggo (1846-1878) Danish
£1723 $2618 €2585 Agnete with Neptune and mermaids (66x87cm-26x34in) sketch for loft decorations. 27-Aug-2 Rasmussen, Copenhagen #1538/R est:20000 (D.KR 20000)

WORMS, Jules (1832-1924) French
£755 $1200 €1133 Portrait of a woman (47x38cm-19x15in) s.d.79. 7-Mar-3 Skinner, Boston #245/R

Works on paper
£298 $486 €450 Belle espagnole (34x23cm-13x9in) s. W/C. 31-Jan-3 Rabourdin & Choppin de Janvry, Paris #143

WORMS, Roger (1907-1980) French
£287 $447 €450 L'entracte (65x46cm-26x18in) s.d.1933. 6-Nov-2 Claude Boisgirard, Paris #64/R
£364 $594 €550 Olivier a Nyons (38x55cm-15x22in) s. i.verso. 31-Jan-3 Rabourdin & Choppin de Janvry, Paris #74

WORN, Walter (1901-1963) German

Works on paper
£253 $395 €400 Lilacs (49x38cm-19x15in) pastel board. 18-Oct-2 Dr Fritz Nagel, Stuttgart #382/R
£1871 $3068 €2600 People with horse (35x42cm-14x17in) mono.d. W/C prov.exhib. 6-Jun-3 Ketterer, Munich #56/R est:2000-4000

WORNDLE, Edmund von (1827-1906) Austrian
£3205 $5032 €5000 Tirol castle and Brunnenburg with Meran and the Mendels peak (31x45cm-12x18in) s.i.verso board. 21-Nov-2 Dorotheum, Vienna #135/R est:3000-4500

WORRALL, J E (19th C) British
£550 $836 €825 Lark (15x20cm-6x8in) s.d. panel. 29-Aug-2 Christie's, Kensington #3/R

WORRELL, A B van (1787-1823) Dutch

Works on paper
£250 $415 €363 Goat and sheep in a rural landscape with a cottage beyond (20x25cm-8x10in) pencil wash. 16-Jun-3 Duke & Son, Dorchester #204

WORRELL, Abraham Bruiningh van (1787-1823) Dutch
£1000 $1560 €1500 Cattle and drover in landscape (25x36cm-10x14in) s.d.1822 panel. 25-Mar-3 Gorringes, Bexhill #1217 est:1000-1600

WORRINGER, Marta (1881-1965) German

Works on paper
£385 $596 €600 Shrove Tuesday (34x43cm-13x17in) s.i. pen. 4-Dec-2 Lempertz, Koln #1116/R

WORSEL, Troels (1950-) Danish
£861 $1335 €1292 Composition (120x150cm-47x59in) s.d.1999 verso. 4-Dec-2 Kunsthallen, Copenhagen #196/R (D.KR 10000)
£1267 $1976 €1901 Part A plus Part B (100x150cm-39x59in) s.d.81 verso. 18-Sep-2 Kunsthallen, Copenhagen #222/R est:20000 (D.KR 15000)

WORSEY, Thomas (1829-1875) British
£350 $539 €525 Rose and anemones on a mossy bank (18x13cm-7x5in) s. paper on card. 5-Sep-2 Christie's, Kensington #343/R
£1013 $1600 €1520 Red and white geraniums with waxflower (58x51cm-23x20in) s. 16-Nov-2 New Orleans Auction, New Orleans #1098/R est:2000-4000

WORSFOLD, Deborah (1959-) Canadian
£201 $315 €302 Morning cereal (120x120cm-47x47in) s.i.d.2001 acrylic. 25-Nov-2 Hodgins, Calgary #325/R (C.D 500)
£311 $510 €451 Lemons and bottles (90x90cm-35x35in) s.d.2001 acrylic. 9-Jun-3 Hodgins, Calgary #289/R (C.D 700)

WORSLEY, C N (c.1850-1923) New Zealander

Works on paper
£366 $560 €549 Fountain in a Spanish Village (51x34cm-20x13in) s. W/C. 21-Aug-2 Dunbar Sloane, Auckland #8/R est:1200-1800 (NZ.D 1200)
£381 $583 €572 Bridgenorth, Shropshire, England (34x24cm-13x9in) s. W/C. 21-Aug-2 Dunbar Sloane, Auckland #124 est:1500-2000 (NZ.D 1250)
£389 $600 €584 Lake scene with distant buildings and row boats (29x42cm-11x17in) s. 23-Oct-2 Dunbar Sloane, Wellington #1226/R (NZ.D 1250)

WORSLEY, Charles N (c.1850-1923) New Zealander

Works on paper
£295 $460 €443 Simple life (49x33cm-19x13in) s. W/C. 6-Aug-2 Peter Webb, Auckland #62 est:1500-2500 (NZ.D 1000)
£500 $835 €725 Nick's Head, Poverty Bay, New Zealand (24x16cm-9x6in) s. W/C prov. 17-Jun-3 Rosebery Fine Art, London #572/R
£502 $782 €753 Monastery courtyard (49x33cm-19x13in) s. W/C. 7-Nov-2 International Art Centre, Auckland #113/R est:1500-2500 (NZ.D 1600)
£1254 $1956 €1881 Foot of Mt. Cook (60x47cm-24x19in) s. W/C. 7-Nov-2 International Art Centre, Auckland #67/R est:4000-6000 (NZ.D 4000)
£1798 $2643 €2697 Bowen Falls, Milford Sounds (38x73cm-15x29in) s. W/C prov. 19-Jun-2 Watson's, Christchurch #56/R (NZ.D 5500)

WORSLEY, John (1919-2000) British

Sculpture
£1000 $1620 €1500 Bust of Sir Francis Chichester (26x26x44cm-10x10x17in) num.4 bronze. 22-Jan-3 Bonhams, New Bond Street #326/R est:1200-1500

WORSWICK, Peter (20th C) British?

Works on paper
£500 $810 €750 Ballerina (45x55cm-18x22in) s. pastel. 21-May-3 James Thompson, Kirby Lonsdale #65

WORTEL, Ans (1929-1996) Dutch

Works on paper
£298 $483 €420 Toen 't idee dat we een kinf wilden bezit van ons nam (27x19cm-11x7in) s.d.1977 gouache. 26-May-3 Glerum, Amsterdam #328
£625 $1031 €900 De mensen van het grote blauwe water (63x55cm-25x22in) s.i.d.70 pen brush ink sold with an etching by the same hand. 1-Jul-3 Christie's, Amsterdam #514
£764 $1260 €1100 Als een vis zal ik je dragen (54x79cm-21x31in) s.i.d.70 pen brush black ink sold with another by the same hand. 1-Jul-3 Christie's, Amsterdam #502
£1206 $1953 €1700 Critical mother (79x109cm-31x43in) s.d.76 gouache. 26-May-3 Glerum, Amsterdam #243/R est:600-800

WORTH, Leslie Charles (1923-) British

Works on paper
£380 $612 €570 Landscape near Yetholme, Cumbria (48x43cm-19x17in) i.d.14-12-77 W/C. 18-Feb-3 Bonhams, Knightsbridge #9/R
£700 $1084 €1050 On the sands at Weymouth (30x47cm-12x19in) s.d.1968 W/C scratching out prov. 30-Sep-2 Sotheby's, Olympia #166/R

WORTH, Thomas (1834-1917) American
Works on paper
£1700 $2686 €2550 Dexter driven by George B. Alley in front of the Old Lake House. Open carriages on a lane (37x55cm-15x22in) s. pencil W/C set of three. 28-Nov-2 Christie's, Kensington #71/R est:600-800

WORTHINGTON, William Henry (fl.1790-1839) British
Prints
£2000 $3180 €3000 James Keir ESQ (40x32cm-16x13in) engraving. 20-Mar-3 Sotheby's, London #450/R

WOSTRY, Carlo (1865-1943) Italian
£353 $546 €550 Saint-Cloud, Paris (17x19cm-7x7in) s. s.i.verso cardboard. 5-Dec-2 Stadion, Trieste #890
£577 $894 €900 Portrait of Scoastopoulo (56x47cm-22x19in) init. 5-Dec-2 Stadion, Trieste #894/R
£1277 $2068 €1800 Paesaggio in Cadore (57x80cm-22x31in) s.i.d.1940 verso panel. 22-May-3 Stadion, Trieste #402/R est:1500-2000
£1923 $2981 €3000 Lake in the Carso (121x88cm-48x35in) s. 5-Dec-2 Stadion, Trieste #860/R
£8298 $13443 €11700 Ragazza tra i fiori (147x102cm-58x40in) s. 22-May-3 Stadion, Trieste #401/R est:10000-14000

WOTRUBA, Fritz (1907-1975) Austrian
£1290 $2039 €2000 Untitled (40x52cm-16x20in) s.d.1959 tempera paper. 18-Dec-2 Christie's, Rome #53
Sculpture
£1282 $2026 €2000 Seated figure (20cm-8in) s. dark pat.bronze Cast.Venturi Arte, Bologna. 12-Nov-2 Dorotheum, Vienna #322/R est:1400-1800
£1389 $2208 €2000 Small seated figure (21cm-8in) s.i. pat.bronze lit. 29-Apr-3 Wiener Kunst Auktionen, Vienna #427/R est:1200-2000
£14557 $23000 €23000 Relief with eight figures (31x60cm-12x24in) s. brown black pat.bronze. 30-Nov-2 Villa Grisebach, Berlin #400/R est:10000-15000
£107595 $166772 €170000 Reclining figure (63x171x60cm-25x67x24in) s. bronze lit. 24-Sep-2 Wiener Kunst Auktionen, Vienna #222/R est:120000-280000
Works on paper
£1154 $1788 €1800 Oedipus (32x18cm-13x7in) s.d.1960 Indian ink pencil mono.i. verso. 6-Dec-2 Hauswedell & Nolte, Hamburg #408/R est:1500
£1241 $1986 €1800 Walkyrie shield (34x47cm-13x19in) s.i.d. pencil W/C gouache. 11-Mar-3 Dorotheum, Vienna #194/R est:1800-2600
£1456 $2256 €2300 Three figures (30x21cm-12x8in) s.i.d.1948 Indian ink biro. 24-Sep-2 Wiener Kunst Auktionen, Vienna #208/R est:2300-4000
£2244 $3522 €3500 Female nude (27x21cm-11x8in) s.d.51 Chinese ink wash. 10-Dec-2 Piasa, Paris #458

WOUTERMAERTENS, Edouard (1819-1897) Belgian
£321 $503 €500 Moutons dans un paysage (55x70cm-22x28in) s. 10-Dec-2 Campo, Vlaamse Kaai #595
£530 $864 €800 Troupeau de moutons (32x40cm-13x16in) s. panel. 17-Feb-3 Horta, Bruxelles #73
£566 $872 €900 Chasseur et ses chiens (90x70cm-35x28in) s. 22-Oct-2 Galerie Moderne, Brussels #721/R
£714 $1136 €1050 Deux chiens (25x35cm-10x14in) s. panel. 18-Mar-3 Vanderkindere, Brussels #120
£1720 $2683 €2700 Troupeau de moutons dans l'enclos sur fond de paysage (74x105cm-29x41in) s. i.verso. 11-Nov-2 Horta, Bruxelles #192 est:3000-4000

WOUTERS, Frans (1614-1659) Flemish
£3226 $5000 €4839 Finding of Erichthonius by the daughters of Cecrops (69x86cm-27x34in) s.d.1652 prov. 2-Oct-2 Christie's, Rockefeller NY #153/R est:6000-8000
£5479 $8548 €8000 Resting during the Flight to Egypt (26x40cm-10x16in) copper. 8-Apr-3 Ansorena, Madrid #106/R
£9877 $16000 €14816 Venus and Adonis (51x88cm-20x35in) panel. 23-Jan-3 Sotheby's, New York #190/R est:12000

WOUTERS, Frans (attrib) (1614-1659) Flemish
£1905 $2952 €2858 Putti dressed up as Bacchanten (47x62cm-19x24in) panel. 24-Sep-2 Koller, Zurich #6448/R est:4000-7000 (S.FR 4400)
£4545 $7045 €6818 Venus and Adonis (50x88cm-20x35in) panel. 24-Sep-2 Koller, Zurich #6426/R est:8000-12000 (S.FR 10500)

WOUTERS, Jan Ludewick de (1731-?) Flemish
£2308 $3577 €3600 Chasseur. Pecheur (13x19cm-5x7in) one mono. copper pair. 9-Dec-2 Horta, Bruxelles #236 est:2000-3000

WOUTERS, Rik (1882-1916) Belgian
Sculpture
£1769 $2812 €2600 Head of Nel (38cm-15in) s. brown pat.bronze marble stand. 24-Mar-3 Bernaerts, Antwerp #156 est:1500-2000
£26582 $42000 €42000 Tete de jeune fille (26cm-10in) pat bronze Cast Batardy prov. 26-Nov-2 Palais de Beaux Arts, Brussels #187/R est:12500-17500
Works on paper
£1519 $2370 €2400 Bassin dans le parc de Versailles (32x49cm-13x19in) col pencil exec.1912 prov. 21-Oct-2 Bernaerts, Antwerp #627/R est:2500-3000
£3546 $5922 €5000 Femme couchee. i.verso col crayon exhib. 17-Jun-3 Palais de Beaux Arts, Brussels #654/R est:5000-7000
£9615 $14904 €15000 Portrait de nelle assise (55x43cm-22x17in) s.d.1915 Indian ink wash dr. 9-Dec-2 Horta, Bruxelles #159/R est:10000-15000
£19231 $29808 €30000 Interior with woman (31x44cm-12x17in) s.i.d.1915 s.i.verso W/C lit. 7-Dec-2 De Vuyst, Lokeren #461/R
£21583 $34532 €30000 Femme assise, tablier bleu (26x36cm-10x14in) i. pastel W/C brush Indian ink dr exec.1912-1913 lit. 17-May-3 De Vuyst, Lokeren #465/R
£28205 $43718 €44000 Woman viewed from the back (30x42cm-12x17in) s.d.1912 Indian ink brush oil exhib.lit. 7-Dec-2 De Vuyst, Lokeren #464/R

WOUTERSZ, Jan (c.1599-c.1663) Dutch
£18000 $28260 €27000 Pontius Pilate washing his hands (107x75cm-42x30in) panel prov. 12-Dec-2 Sotheby's, London #180/R est:20000-30000

WOUTIERS, Michaelina (17th C) Flemish
£20548 $32055 €30822 Portrait of young man (69x58cm-27x23in) s.d.1655. 28-Mar-3 Koller, Zurich #3052/R est:20000-30000 (S.FR 45000)

WOUW, Anton van (1862-1945) South African
Sculpture
£6449 $10383 €9674 Bushman - kop van boesman (50cm-20in) s.d.1902 bronze lit. 12-May-3 Stephan Welz, Johannesburg #586/R est:30000-40000 (SA.R 75000)
£11000 $17160 €16500 Sleeping Basuto (30cm-12in) s.st.f.G.Nisini brown pat bronze lit. 5-Nov-2 Sotheby's, London #199/R est:12000-18000

WOUWERMAN, Jan (1629-1666) Dutch
£6757 $10541 €10000 Horsemen resting in the dunes (25x33cm-10x13in) panel. 27-Mar-3 Dorotheum, Vienna #374/R est:10000-15000

WOUWERMAN, Philips (1619-1668) Dutch
£9677 $15000 €14516 Cavalry skirmish (36x48cm-14x19in) mono. panel prov. 2-Oct-2 Christie's, Rockefeller NY #162/R est:15000-20000
£13514 $21081 €20000 Horseman resting in front of farmhouse with white horse feeding (37x29cm-15x11in) mono. panel lit. 27-Mar-3 Dorotheum, Vienna #211/R est:20000-30000
£18000 $28260 €27000 Man saddling a horse in a cave with other figures (37x49cm-15x19in) indis.mono. panel prov.lit. 12-Dec-2 Sotheby's, London #175/R est:10000-15000
£339506 $550000 €509259 Italianate landscape with a young man in a yellow coat riding a bay , watched by elegant couple (44x51cm-17x20in) mono. 23-Jan-3 Sotheby's, New York #40/R est:600000-800000
£1000000 $1570000 €1500000 Landscape with stag hunt in full cry, fording a stream (28x36cm-11x14in) mono. copper prov.exhib.lit. 12-Dec-2 Sotheby's, London #26/R est:600000-800000
Works on paper
£3704 $6000 €5556 Two men on horseback with dog (14x19cm-6x7in) mono. wash. 21-Jan-3 Sotheby's, New York #149/R est:4000

WOUWERMAN, Philips (attrib) (1619-1668) Dutch
£840 $1335 €1260 Houses outside an inn (40x46cm-16x18in) 29-Apr-3 Kunsthallen, Copenhagen #544/R (D.KR 9000)
£870 $1348 €1305 Battle scene (21x25cm-8x10in) panel. 9-Dec-2 Philippe Schuler, Zurich #8694 (S.FR 2000)
Works on paper
£314 $487 €500 Depart pour chasse (25x18cm-10x7in) pen ink. 29-Oct-2 Artcurial Briest, Paris #4/R

WOUWERMAN, Philips (style) (1619-1668) Dutch
£10000 $16700 €14500 Peasants making merry by a cottage (48x72cm-19x28in) panel. 11-Jul-3 Christie's, Kensington #89/R est:5000-7000

WOUWERMAN, Pieter (1623-1682) Dutch
£4167 $6542 €6500 Rider resting in mountainous landscape (37x30cm-15x12in) mono. panel. 21-Nov-2 Van Ham, Cologne #1437/R est:9500

WOUWERMAN, Pieter (attrib) (1623-1682) Dutch
£1063 $1700 €1595 Falconer party awaiting the hunt (46x69cm-18x27in) panel. 15-Mar-3 Jeffery Burchard, Florida #44/R
£1094 $1750 €1641 Hunt party in a landscape (46x69cm-18x27in) panel. 15-Mar-3 Jeffery Burchard, Florida #44a/R

WOUWERMAN, Pieter (circle) (1623-1682) Dutch
£6000 $10020 €8700 Hunting party resting on a hillside, view to a landscape beyond (49x61cm-19x24in) 9-Jul-3 Bonhams, New Bond Street #153/R est:4000-6000

WRAMPE, Fritz (1893-1934) German
Sculpture
£2013 $3140 €3200 Giraffe (37cm-15in) bronze prov. 9-Oct-2 Sotheby's, London #206/R est:3000-4000

WRBA, Georg (1872-1939) German
Sculpture
£4487 $6821 €7000 Diana (55x22cm-22x9in) s. black brown pat.bronze Cast.C.Leyrer, Munchen. 11-Jul-2 Hugo Ruef, Munich #1303/R est:5000

WREDE, Anna Furstin von (20th C) German?
£1258 $1962 €2000 What a tiring day (55x46cm-22x18in) s. prov. 20-Sep-2 Schloss Ahlden, Ahlden #1235/R est:1400

WRIGHT OF DERBY, Joseph (1734-1797) British
£7000 $11060 €10500 Portrait of Mrs Abney (125x100cm-49x39in) prov.lit. 28-Nov-2 Sotheby's, London #185/R est:8000-12000
£34000 $53720 €51000 Portrait of Susannah Leigh (74x63cm-29x25in) prov.lit. 28-Nov-2 Sotheby's, London #175/R est:12000-18000
£40000 $63200 €60000 Virgil's tomb by moonlight (99x124cm-39x49in) prov.exhib.lit. 28-Nov-2 Sotheby's, London #109/R est:40000-60000
£185185 $300000 €277778 Gulf of Salerno (41x59cm-16x23in) i. exhib.lit. 24-Jan-3 Christie's, Rockefeller NY #140/R est:20000-30000

WRIGHT OF DERBY, Joseph (attrib) (1734-1797) British
£2800 $4424 €4200 Study of classical urn in stone niche (39x20cm-15x8in) canvas on board prov.exhib. 26-Nov-2 Christie's, London #37/R est:3000-5000

WRIGHT OF THIRSK, Edith (fl.1910) British
£300 $474 €435 Country cottages (40x60cm-16x24in) s.d.1906. 28-Jul-3 David Duggleby, Scarborough #273/R

WRIGHT, Catherine Wharton Morris (1899-1988) American
Works on paper
£1028 $1500 €1542 Beaver Tail, Rhode Island view (48x64cm-19x25in) W/C gouache. 10-May-2 Skinner, Boston #245/R est:600-800

WRIGHT, Don (20th C) American
£577 $900 €866 Shrimp boat (46x61cm-18x24in) s.d.79. 12-Oct-2 Neal Auction Company, New Orleans #1360

WRIGHT, Douglas (1944-) Australian
£658 $1040 €987 Uncertain light (150x236cm-59x93in) s.d.88 s.i.d.verso. 27-Nov-2 Deutscher-Menzies, Melbourne #159/R est:4000-6000 (A.D 1840)

WRIGHT, Elizabeth (1964-) British
Photographs
£3000 $4620 €4500 B.S.A Tour of Britain racer enlarged to 135 percent (124x236cm-49x93in) steel rubber plastic executed 1996 exhib. 23-Oct-2 Christie's, London #253/R est:3000-4000

WRIGHT, Ethel (fl.1887-1900) British
£800 $1248 €1200 Lady with white carnation (103x7cm-41x3in) s. 15-Oct-2 Bonhams, Knightsbridge #192/R est:800-1200

WRIGHT, Ferdinand von (1822-1906) Finnish
£4173 $6676 €5800 Willow warblers (20x16cm-8x6in) s.d.1901 lit. 17-May-3 Hagelstam, Helsinki #123/R est:6000
£8065 $12742 €12098 Bullfinches on twigs, winter (43x35cm-17x14in) s.d.1896 verso prov. 27-Nov-2 Falkkloos, Malmo #77502/R est:75000 (S.KR 115000)
£9859 $15873 €14000 Seagulls on cliffs by the sea (46x63cm-18x25in) s.d.1883. 10-May-3 Bukowskis, Helsinki #183/R est:20000-25000
£10443 $16500 €16500 Bullfinches (31x25cm-12x10in) s.d.1891 verso lit. 1-Dec-2 Bukowskis, Helsinki #218/R est:10000-12000
£40845 $65761 €58000 Pigeons by skylight (72x85cm-28x33in) s.d.1853 exhib.lit. 10-May-3 Bukowskis, Helsinki #142/R est:50000-60000
Works on paper
£1899 $3000 €3000 Female mallard (24x19cm-9x7in) s.d.1838 W/C. 30-Nov-2 Hagelstam, Helsinki #115/R est:2000

WRIGHT, Frank (1860-1923) New Zealander
Works on paper
£281 $410 €422 Taranaki landscape (30x45cm-12x18in) s. W/C. 12-Sep-1 Watson's, Christchurch #47 est:2000-3000 (NZ.D 940)

WRIGHT, Frank Lloyd (19/20th C) ?
Prints
£30585 $47406 €45878 Untitled. s.i.d. prints 101 folios two prov.exhib. 3-Dec-2 Shapiro, Sydney #363/R est:80000-120000 (A.D 84720)
Works on paper
£5183 $8500 €7515 Abstract taliesin (28x22cm-11x9in) s.i. mixed media. 5-Jun-3 Swann Galleries, New York #269/R est:10000-15000

WRIGHT, George (1860-1942) British
£465 $734 €698 Coastal landscape with waves and cliffs (66x90cm-26x35in) s. 5-Apr-3 Rasmussen, Havnen #2215 (D.KR 5000)
£500 $780 €750 Dumfriesshire Stanley, canine portrait (13x9cm-5x4in) mono.i.d.1903 canvasboard. 10-Apr-3 Bonhams, Edinburgh #76
£2200 $3652 €3190 In full gallop (25x30cm-10x12in) s. 12-Jun-3 Christie's, Kensington #12/R est:2500-4000
£3800 $6194 €5510 Gentleman and horses in a wooded landscape (51x76cm-20x30in) s.d.86. 17-Jul-3 Tennants, Leyburn #893/R est:2500-3500
£3822 $6000 €5733 The end of the day (46x76cm-18x30in) s. i.on stretcher. 10-Dec-2 Doyle, New York #167/R est:8000-12000
£5000 $7800 €7500 Master of the hounds (40x61cm-16x24in) s. 6-Nov-2 Sotheby's, Olympia #60/R est:4000-6000
£5500 $8690 €8250 After a good day (30x41cm-12x16in) s.i. 27-Nov-2 Christie's, London #7/R
£6000 $9360 €9000 On the scent (36x31cm-14x12in) s.d.6.1.40 verso. 6-Nov-2 Sotheby's, Olympia #73/R est:3000-5000
£7500 $12150 €11250 On the scent (51x76cm-20x30in) s. 22-May-3 Christie's, London #55/R est:8000-12000
Works on paper
£900 $1422 €1350 Shoeing the horse (23x28cm-9x11in) s. monochrome W/C. 28-Nov-2 Richardson & Smith, Whitby #620

WRIGHT, George Hand (1873-1951) American
£9375 $15000 €14063 Train station scene with three figures and horse carriage in a sunset landscape (43x79cm-17x31in) s. 17-May-3 Pook & Pook, Downington #340/R est:5000-7000

WRIGHT, Gilbert Scott (1880-1958) British
£650 $1060 €975 Adjusting the saddle (30x46cm-12x18in) s. 13-Feb-3 Christie's, Kensington #84
£980 $1548 €1470 Arrest (42x50cm-17x20in) s.d.97. 7-Apr-3 Bonhams, Bath #127/R
£2500 $3850 €3750 Rendezvous (30x46cm-12x18in) s.indis.d. 5-Sep-2 Christie's, Kensington #257/R est:3000-5000
£4000 $6240 €6000 Outside the tavern (30x46cm-12x18in) s. 6-Nov-2 Sotheby's, Olympia #80/R est:4000-6000
£6100 $9455 €9150 Sisters, gentleman courting a woman watched by her sister (70x56cm-28x22in) s. 24-Sep-2 Anderson & Garland, Newcastle #530/R est:4000-6000
£9000 $14580 €13500 Huntsman and hounds in an extensive landscape (51x71cm-20x28in) s. 22-May-3 Christie's, London #5/R est:10000-15000
£9000 $14940 €13500 Old Swan Inn (61x91cm-24x36in) s. i.verso prov. 10-Jun-3 Christie's, London #101/R est:10000-15000

WRIGHT, Harriet Maria (19th C) British
£700 $1113 €1050 Felina (76x62cm-30x24in) after Sir Joshua Reynolds prov. 6-Mar-3 Christie's, Kensington #520/R

WRIGHT, Harry A (20th C) American
£548 $850 €822 Steam locomotive (30x41cm-12x16in) s.d. board. 8-Dec-2 Toomey, Oak Park #781/R

WRIGHT, James (?-1947) British
£300 $465 €450 Horse and cart in a field (20x25cm-8x10in) s. board. 3-Dec-2 Bonhams, Knightsbridge #206/R
Works on paper
£600 $972 €900 An afternoon stroll (34x24cm-13x9in) s. W/C. 21-May-3 Bonhams, Knightsbridge #17/R
£920 $1426 €1380 Ye ballad o'Binnorie with two maidens before galleons (23x15cm-9x6in) s. pen ink W/C. 7-Dec-2 Shapes, Edinburgh #308
£1900 $2945 €2850 Two girls by a window (39x46cm-15x18in) s. pencil W/C. 31-Oct-2 Christie's, London #167/R est:1500-2000

WRIGHT, John (1745-1820) British
Miniatures
£1200 $1944 €1800 Gentleman full face, wearing black coat (8cm-3in) s.verso gold frame. 22-May-3 Bonhams, New Bond Street #109/R est:700-900
£2000 $3240 €3000 Charles Garth Colleton, wearing black coat (8cm-3in) rectangular papier mache frame exhib. 22-May-3 Bonhams, New Bond Street #111/R est:600-800
£7000 $11340 €10500 Thomas Garth R.N wearing naval uniform (8cm-3in) s.verso gold frame. 22-May-3 Bonhams, New Bond Street #106/R est:3500-4500
£11500 $17940 €17250 James Arthur Murray wearing midshipman's uniform (7cm-3in) s.i.d.1804 verso gold frame oval. 5-Nov-2 Bonhams, New Bond Street #83/R est:5000-7000

WRIGHT, John Masey (1777-1866) British
Works on paper
£2000 $3160 €3000 Pilgrimage (38x51cm-15x20in) i. W/C. 24-Apr-3 Richardson & Smith, Whitby #210

WRIGHT, John Michael (attrib) (1617-1694) British
£2800 $4452 €4200 Portrait of Sir Edward Thurland, Baron Thurland (75x62cm-30x24in) i. prov.lit. 19-Mar-3 Sotheby's, London #12/R est:3000-5000

WRIGHT, John Michael (circle) (1617-1694) British
£4861 $7000 €7292 Portrait of gentleman (127x103cm-50x41in) 15-Jan-3 Christie's, Rockefeller NY #115/R est:12000
£7800 $12012 €11700 Portrait of a gentleman, with men o'war at anchor beyond (113x90cm-44x35in) 5-Sep-2 Christie's, Kensington #12/R est:8000-12000

WRIGHT, M (?) ?
Works on paper
£900 $1395 €1350 Continental street scene with figures (38x57cm-15x22in) W/C. 24-Sep-2 Patersons, Paisley #427
£1400 $2170 €2100 Children playing (52x36cm-20x14in) W/C. 24-Sep-2 Patersons, Paisley #428

WRIGHT, Magnus von (1805-1868) Finnish
£2518 $4129 €3500 Cow (28x33cm-11x13in) s. 5-Jun-3 Hagelstam, Helsinki #9312 est:5000
£9155 $14739 €13000 Kyroskoski - landscape with waterfall and buildings (45x60cm-18x24in) painted c.1847-48 lit. 10-May-3 Bukowskis, Helsinki #192/R est:13000-15000
Works on paper
£1519 $2400 €2400 Apples (12x17cm-5x7in) s. W/C. 30-Nov-2 Hagelstam, Helsinki #116/R est:3000

WRIGHT, Marion M (19th C) New Zealander
Works on paper
£1368 $2134 €2052 Portrait of Te Amapo Parata (54x42cm-21x17in) s.d.1892 W/C prov. 17-Sep-2 Peter Webb, Auckland #87/R est:8000-12000 (NZ.D 4500)

WRIGHT, Michael (20th C) British
Works on paper
£750 $1155 €1125 Le Mans 1939, Dobson, Brackenbury at Mulsanne (48x45cm-19x18in) s. mixed media. 6-Sep-2 Bonhams, Knightsbridge #33/R

WRIGHT, Nora (fl.1921-1931) British
£272 $425 €408 Ranch house, Arizona (23x33cm-9x13in) s. 29-Mar-3 Charlton Hall, Columbia #231/R

WRIGHT, R Stephens (1903-) American
£385 $600 €578 Seascape (41x51cm-16x20in) s. 1-Aug-2 Eldred, East Dennis #377l/R
£629 $1000 €944 On the golf course (25x31cm-10x12in) s. canvasboard. 7-Mar-3 Skinner, Boston #400/R

WRIGHT, Richard Henry (1857-1930) British
Works on paper
£1300 $2041 €1950 View of Durham cathedral from across the wear (27x36cm-11x14in) s.d.1907 W/C. 21-Nov-2 Tennants, Leyburn #650/R est:600-800

WRIGHT, Robert W (fl.1880-1900) British
£290 $455 €435 Feeding pigeons (20x13cm-8x5in) bears sig.d.1890 panel. 10-Dec-2 Rosebery Fine Art, London #550/R
£1600 $2464 €2400 Laying the table (15x20cm-6x8in) s.d.91 panel. 5-Sep-2 Christie's, Kensington #318/R est:800-1200
£2300 $3772 €3335 Cottage interior with group of three children watching boy drowning a mouse (36x30cm-14x12in) s.d.1883 panel. 3-Jun-3 Capes Dunn, Manchester #109/R
£4500 $6840 €6750 Reading the news. Time for tea (24x19cm-9x7in) s.d.1890 panel pair. 29-Aug-2 Christie's, Kensington #148 est:2000-4000

WRIGHT, Russel (1905-) American/Lebanese
Sculpture
£16129 $25000 €24194 Libbiloo horse bookends (5x6x3cm-2x2x1in) nickel plated metal lit. 8-Dec-2 Wright, Chicago #187/R est:10000-15000

WRIGHT, W H (19th C) British
£950 $1472 €1425 Farmer's boy (20x15cm-8x6in) s.indis.d. panel. 3-Dec-2 Sotheby's, Olympia #168/R est:600-900

WRIGHT, Walter (1866-1933) New Zealander
£1016 $1606 €1473 Two Maori woman with baskets (29x49cm-11x19in) s. painted c.1915. 22-Jul-3 Lawson Menzies, Sydney #290/R est:4000-7000 (A.D 2500)
£1982 $3032 €2973 Maori woman and whare (29x50cm-11x20in) s. 21-Aug-2 Dunbar Sloane, Auckland #35/R est:8000-12000 (NZ.D 6500)

WRIGHT, Wilhelm von (1810-1887) Finnish
Works on paper
£3165 $5000 €5000 Father shooting blackgrouse (21x27cm-8x11in) s.d.1826 W/C lit. 30-Nov-2 Hagelstam, Helsinki #114/R est:4000

WRIGHTSON, Isobel (1890-?) British
£950 $1587 €1378 Newlyn Harbour (61x76cm-24x30in) s. 19-Jun-3 Lane, Penzance #255
Works on paper
£520 $868 €754 St. Ives moored fishing boats at night (37x59cm-15x23in) s.i.d.1890 W/C. 11-Jul-3 Bracketts, Tunbridge Wells #796/R

WRIGLEY, Viola Blackman (1892-?) American
£875 $1400 €1313 Winter stream (46x51cm-18x20in) s. 11-Jan-3 James Julia, Fairfield #606 est:800-1200

WRINCH, Mary Evelyn (1877-1969) Canadian
£329 $510 €494 Landscape (20x25cm-8x10in) s. canvas on board prov. 3-Dec-2 Joyner, Toronto #355 (C.D 800)
£444 $701 €666 Rushing water, Temagami forest reserve (25x30cm-10x12in) s. board prov. 14-Nov-2 Heffel, Vancouver #246/R est:1500-2000 (C.D 1100)
£756 $1239 €1134 Autumn red (25x30cm-10x12in) s. board prov. 3-Jun-3 Joyner, Toronto #471 est:1000-1500 (C.D 1700)

WROBLEWSKI, Constantin (1868-1939) Russian
£5000 $7850 €7500 Ukrainian landscape with huts (44x58cm-17x23in) s.d. 1910 card on panel. 20-Nov-2 Sotheby's, London #59/R est:7000-9000

WSSEL, Manuel (1833-1907) Spanish
£3846 $6077 €6000 Idyll in the park (60x40cm-24x16in) s. 19-Nov-2 Durán, Madrid #224/R
£15723 $24528 €25000 Patio interior (80x54cm-31x21in) s.d.74. 23-Sep-2 Durán, Madrid #221/R est:25000

WU CHANGSHUO (1844-1927) Chinese
Works on paper
£5051 $8333 €7324 Camellia (136x32cm-54x13in) s.i. ink scroll. 6-Jul-3 Christie's, Hong Kong #304/R est:70000-90000 (HK.D 65000)
£5051 $8333 €7324 Orange fruit (138x34cm-54x13in) s. ink scroll. 6-Jul-3 Christie's, Hong Kong #305/R est:50000-60000 (HK.D 65000)
£5828 $9615 €8451 Magnolia (150x41cm-59x16in) s.i. ink scroll. 6-Jul-3 Christie's, Hong Kong #303/R est:50000-60000 (HK.D 75000)
£8547 $14103 €12393 Plum blossom and calligraphy (35x34cm-14x13in) s.i. ink scroll. 6-Jul-3 Christie's, Hong Kong #306/R est:45000-55000 (HK.D 110000)
£20325 $32114 €30488 Pelargonium and rock (137x67cm-54x26in) s.i.d.1915 ink col hanging scroll exhib. 28-Apr-3 Sotheby's, Hong Kong #632/R est:50000-70000 (HK.D 250000)

WU GUANZHONG (1919-) Chinese

£26016 $41106 €39024 Huangchow tree in Sichuan (27x36cm-11x14in) s.d.1974 board exhib. 28-Apr-3 Sotheby's, Hong Kong #518/R est:180000-250000 (HK.D 320000)
£31080 $51282 €45066 Reeds by the Li river (43x44cm-17x17in) s.d.77 board lit. 6-Jul-3 Christie's, Hong Kong #125/R est:400000-500000 (HK.D 400000)
£48780 $77073 €73170 Scenery of the Lijiang river (61x73cm-24x29in) s.d.1985 prov. 28-Apr-3 Sotheby's, Hong Kong #520/R est:400000-600000 (HK.D 600000)

Works on paper

£5439 $8974 €7887 To the theatre (25x35cm-10x14in) s.d.1960 W/C scroll. 6-Jul-3 Christie's, Hong Kong #333/R est:70000-90000 (HK.D 70000)
£5691 $8992 €8537 Bamboo shoots (28x47cm-11x19in) s.i.d.1981 exhib. 28-Apr-3 Sotheby's, Hong Kong #501/R est:70000-90000 (HK.D 70000)
£7317 $11561 €10976 Horse racing (28x48cm-11x19in) s.d.1981 exhib. 28-Apr-3 Sotheby's, Hong Kong #519/R est:70000-90000 (HK.D 90000)
£10101 $16667 €14646 Landscape of Jiuzhai Gou (73x60cm-29x24in) s.i. ink scroll. 6-Jul-3 Christie's, Hong Kong #328/R est:120000-150000 (HK.D 130000)
£13008 $20553 €19512 Spring memory (49x46cm-19x18in) s.i. ink. 28-Apr-3 Sotheby's, Hong Kong #503/R est:80000-100000 (HK.D 160000)
£15447 $24407 €23171 Mountain village (41x39cm-16x15in) sealed.i.d.1975 ink col. 28-Apr-3 Sotheby's, Hong Kong #502/R est:80000-120000 (HK.D 190000)
£15540 $25641 €22533 Village (68x86cm-27x34in) ink scroll. 6-Jul-3 Christie's, Hong Kong #329/R est:220000-280000 (HK.D 200000)
£20202 $33333 €29293 Rhythm (67x137cm-26x54in) s. ink scroll lit. 6-Jul-3 Christie's, Hong Kong #332/R est:250000-350000 (HK.D 260000)
£178862 $282602 €268293 Early spring in Guilin (144x181cm-57x71in) s.d.1976 ink col exhib. 28-Apr-3 Sotheby's, Hong Kong #521/R est:1400000-1800000 (HK.D 2200000)

WU HUFAN (1894-1968) Chinese

Works on paper

£2602 $4111 €3903 Bamboo (18x48cm-7x19in) s.i.d.1928 ink col folding fan. 28-Apr-3 Sotheby's, Hong Kong #551/R est:20000-40000 (HK.D 32000)
£3252 $5138 €4878 Landscape (17x50cm-7x20in) s.i.d.1929 i.verso ink folding fan style of Shen Zhou. 28-Apr-3 Sotheby's, Hong Kong #549/R est:20000-40000 (HK.D 40000)
£6504 $10276 €9756 Bamboo (64x31cm-25x12in) s.i.d.1947 ink. 28-Apr-3 Sotheby's, Hong Kong #624/R est:120000-150000 (HK.D 80000)
£6504 $10276 €9756 Bamboo and red bird (17x48cm-7x19in) s.i.d.1938 i.verso ink col folding fan. 28-Apr-3 Sotheby's, Hong Kong #537/R est:80000-100000 (HK.D 80000)
£7724 $12203 €11586 Plum blossom (19x46cm-7x18in) s.i.d.1952 i.verso ink col folding fan. 28-Apr-3 Sotheby's, Hong Kong #532/R est:40000-60000 (HK.D 95000)
£8130 $12846 €12195 River bank (15x50cm-6x20in) s.i.d.1949 i.verso ink folding fan. 28-Apr-3 Sotheby's, Hong Kong #538/R est:70000-90000 (HK.D 100000)
£20202 $33333 €29293 Change of season (131x68cm-52x27in) s.i. ink scroll. 6-Jul-3 Christie's, Hong Kong #287/R est:280000-320000 (HK.D 260000)

WU HUFAN and XIE ZHILIU (20th C) Chinese

Works on paper

£10569 $16699 €15854 Relive vine, pine (15x46cm-6x18in) s.i.d.1964 ink col folding fan. 28-Apr-3 Sotheby's, Hong Kong #539/R est:50000-70000 (HK.D 130000)

WU SHIXIAN (?-1960) Chinese

Works on paper

£471 $772 €650 Landscape (126x32cm-50x13in) s.d.1915 seals Indian ink col hanging scroll. 30-May-3 Dr Fritz Nagel, Stuttgart #1256/R

WU ZHENG (1876-1949) Chinese

Works on paper

£976 $1541 €1464 Hermitage (19x53cm-7x21in) s.i.d.1929 i.verso ink folding fan. 28-Apr-3 Sotheby's, Hong Kong #553/R est:12000-15000 (HK.D 12000)

WUCHERER, Fritz (1873-1948) Swiss

£446 $687 €700 River bend (46x66cm-18x26in) 5-Sep-2 Arnold, Frankfurt #900/R
£472 $736 €750 Meadows with trees (45x65cm-18x26in) s.i.d.1908. 11-Oct-2 Winterberg, Heidelberg #1879
£478 $736 €750 On the edge of Schwalbacher Wald (35x55cm-14x22in) i. verso. 5-Sep-2 Arnold, Frankfurt #899/R
£510 $785 €800 Wood's edge (47x66cm-19x26in) s.d.07. 5-Sep-2 Arnold, Frankfurt #901/R
£769 $1208 €1200 View over Kronberg to Altkonig (41x55cm-16x22in) s.d.1926. 23-Nov-2 Arnold, Frankfurt #956/R

Works on paper

£314 $491 €500 Taunus landscape (35x43cm-14x17in) s. W/C lit. 20-Sep-2 Karlheinz Kaupp, Staufen #2155

WUERMER, Carl (1900-1982) American

£1958 $3250 €2839 At the edge of the forest (84x91cm-33x36in) s. prov. 11-Jun-3 Butterfields, San Francisco #4063/R est:4000-6000
£3481 $5500 €5222 Valley in spring (64x76cm-25x30in) s. 24-Apr-3 Shannon's, Milford #181/R est:5000-7000
£3896 $6000 €5844 Morning mist (51x61cm-20x24in) s. prov. 24-Oct-2 Shannon's, Milford #154/R est:5000-7000

WUERPEL, Edmund H (1866-1958) American

£256 $400 €384 Evening landscape (28x20cm-11x8in) mono. 14-Sep-2 Selkirks, St. Louis #152
£385 $600 €578 Lake, night (20x20cm-8x8in) s.d.1919 verso prov. 10-Nov-2 Selkirks, St. Louis #993
£480 $750 €720 Frog pool - after glow (79x69cm-31x27in) mono. s.i.d.1920-45 verso. 1-Aug-2 Eldred, East Dennis #1086/R
£577 $900 €866 Gathering darkness (33x25cm-13x10in) s. prov. 10-Nov-2 Selkirks, St. Louis #994/R
£609 $950 €914 Yesterday - tomorrow (81x69cm-32x27in) mono. s.i.d.1944 verso. 1-Aug-2 Eldred, East Dennis #1093/R
£1218 $1900 €1827 Fading light (71x89cm-28x35in) init. s.d.1945 verso prov. 10-Nov-2 Selkirks, St. Louis #995/R est:600-700

WUERZ, M (?) ?

£700 $1112 €1050 Village pond with ducks (55x68cm-22x27in) s. 5-May-3 Rasmussen, Vejle #606/R (D.KR 7500)

WUKOUNIG, Reimo Sergon (1943-) Austrian

Works on paper

£345 $552 €500 Sacrifice VII (62x47cm-24x19in) s.i.d.197 mixed media. 11-Mar-3 Dorotheum, Vienna #210/R

WULFFAERT, Adrien (1804-1873) Belgian

£1800 $2808 €2700 Portrait of an infantry officer (75x62cm-30x24in) s.i.d.1840. 8-Oct-2 Bonhams, Knightsbridge #93/R est:1000-1500
£3000 $5010 €4350 Portrait of a gentleman seated in an interior (94x77cm-37x30in) s.d.1828. 17-Jun-3 Bonhams, New Bond Street #1/R est:3000-5000
£9420 $15449 €13000 Le depart (60x74cm-24x29in) s.d.1838 wood. 27-May-3 Campo, Vlaamse Kaai #276/R est:13000-16000

WULFSE, Gonda (1896-?) Dutch

£282 $454 €400 Still life of flowers (79x59cm-31x23in) s. 6-May-3 Vendu Notarishuis, Rotterdam #199

WULZ, Hans (1909-1985) Austrian

£949 $1500 €1500 Stift Klosterneuburg (70x94cm-28x37in) s. 26-Nov-2 Wiener Kunst Auktionen, Vienna #135/R est:1500-2500
£949 $1500 €1500 Ringstrasse with stock exchange (70x77cm-28x30in) s. 26-Nov-2 Wiener Kunst Auktionen, Vienna #136/R est:1500-2500
£949 $1500 €1500 Ringstrasse with stock exchange (81x98cm-32x39in) s. 26-Nov-2 Wiener Kunst Auktionen, Vienna #137/R est:1500-2500

WUNDERLICH, Albert (attrib) (1876-1946) German

£314 $491 €500 Winter landscape (44x65cm-17x26in) i. 23-Sep-2 Dr Fritz Nagel, Stuttgart #7066/R

WUNDERLICH, Edmund (1902-1985) Swiss

£880 $1416 €1276 Aiguille Verte (45x82cm-18x32in) s.d.78 i.verso. 9-May-3 Dobiaschofsky, Bern #131/R (S.FR 1900)
£1485 $2316 €2228 Mont Dolent (68x104cm-27x41in) s. i. verso exhib. 6-Nov-2 Dobiaschofsky, Bern #1079/R est:2500 (S.FR 3400)

WUNDERLICH, Hermann (1835-1915) German

Works on paper

£255 $397 €400 Zirl in Tirol (35x24cm-14x9in) i.d.21.7.98 W/C over pencil. 5-Nov-2 Hartung & Hartung, Munich #5154/R

WUNDERLICH, Paul (1927-) German

£686 $1070 €1029 Hertdame - model study (40x30cm-16x12in) s.d.77. 11-Nov-2 Rasmussen, Vejle #135/R (D.KR 8000)

£3000 $4650 €4500 Daniela im seitenlicht (132x95cm-52x37in) s. 5-Dec-2 Christie's, Kensington #208/R est:1000-1500

£4430 $7000 €7000 Untitled (86x68cm-34x27in) s.d.71 board. 26-Nov-2 Sotheby's, Amsterdam #252/R est:7000-8000

Sculpture

£1392 $2200 €2200 Minotauros (77cm-30in) steel pat bronze. 26-Nov-2 Palais de Beaux Arts, Brussels #236a/R est:1900-2500

£1887 $3019 €2831 Little Nike (46cm-18in) i. num.709/1000 brown pat.bronze marble socle lit. 17-Mar-3 Philippe Schuler, Zurich #4117/R est:3000-4000 (S.FR 4000)

£2057 $3332 €2900 Amazone (38x50x11cm-15x20x4in) i. dark brown brass col pat.bronze Cast.Venturi Arte. 24-May-3 Van Ham, Cologne #649/R est:2900

£2899 $4754 €4000 Large minotaur (180cm-71in) st.sig.i.d.89 green gold bronze. 28-May-3 Lempertz, Koln #479/R est:4000

£25316 $39494 €40000 Le grand Nike (247x37x38cm-97x15x15in) s. num.3/8 green pat.bronze. 31-Jul-2 Tajan, Paris #61/R est:55000-65000

Works on paper

£443 $687 €700 Hamburg harbour (32x47cm-13x19in) s.d.1950 chl sold with another. 28-Sep-2 Ketterer, Hamburg #237/R

£450 $698 €675 Selbst mit blauer brille (90x72cm-35x28in) s.d.73 diffused W/C on card. 5-Dec-2 Christie's, Kensington #210/R

£1100 $1705 €1650 Head of a girl in green (84x67cm-33x26in) s.d.1971 pastel. 5-Dec-2 Christie's, Kensington #209/R est:1500-2000

£1154 $1788 €1800 Male torso (87x70cm-34x28in) s.d.1970 gouache wax chk graphite board prov. 7-Dec-2 Ketterer, Hamburg #530/R est:1800-2000

£2319 $3803 €3200 Untitled - death and sphyinx (66x82cm-26x32in) s.d.78 spray W/C. 28-May-3 Lempertz, Koln #484/R est:3200

£2390 $3728 €3800 Untitled (15x12cm-6x5in) s.d.1976 mixed media. 8-Oct-2 Christie's, Paris #156

£4138 $6538 €6000 Studio interior (155x120cm-61x47in) s.d. gouache pencil canvas prov. 2-Apr-3 Dr Fritz Nagel, Stuttgart #9559/R est:4800

WUNDERWALD, Gustav (1882-1945) German

£20886 $33000 €33000 Street behind the Anhalter bahnhof (61x71cm-24x28in) s. painted 1927 prov.exhib.lit. 29-Nov-2 Villa Grisebach, Berlin #64/R est:35000-40000

Works on paper

£256 $397 €400 Street view (22x25cm-9x10in) mono. ink. 7-Dec-2 Van Ham, Cologne #603/R

£435 $713 €600 Waterfall in wood (27x37cm-11x15in) mono. pencil board. 29-May-3 Lempertz, Koln #964/R

£692 $1065 €1100 Mersburg - man on shore (22x31cm-9x12in) mono.i.d.30.6.1911 col chk pencil. 26-Oct-2 Dr Lehr, Berlin #585/R

£797 $1307 €1100 Farm with tree (16x24cm-6x9in) mono.d.15 col oil chk. 29-May-3 Lempertz, Koln #965/R

£870 $1426 €1200 Reclining female nude (43x33cm-17x13in) s.d.23.1.1910 pencil prov. 29-May-3 Lempertz, Koln #963/R

£943 $1453 €1500 Man with double bass (19x29cm-7x11in) mono. col chk pencil. 26-Oct-2 Dr Lehr, Berlin #584/R

£1250 $1975 €1800 Light and shadows of the lantern (35x25cm-14x10in) s. graphite col chk. 26-Apr-3 Dr Lehr, Berlin #559/R est:2400

WUNNENBERG, Walther (1818-1900) German

£411 $600 €617 Untitled, Rhine river landscape with villages, cattle and sail boats (48x66cm-19x26in) s. 17-Jun-2 Schrager Galleries, Milwaukee #1178/R

£556 $889 €850 Hay wagon in hilly landscape in approaching storm (56x81cm-22x32in) s. lit. 10-Jan-3 Allgauer, Kempten #1895/R

WURBEL, Franz (1822-1900) Austrian

£12000 $20040 €18000 Market scene in Tunis (98x143cm-39x56in) s. 19-Jun-3 Christie's, London #13/R est:12000-16000

WURFFEL, Hans (1884-?) German

£377 $581 €600 Cock with hens and ducks (49x74cm-19x29in) s. 26-Oct-2 Quittenbaum, Hamburg #71/R

WURM, Erwin (1954-) Austrian

Sculpture

£4730 $7378 €7000 Landscape (150x125x106cm-59x49x42in) mono.d.85 lit. tin wood sticks. 25-Mar-3 Wiener Kunst Auktionen, Vienna #47/R est:6000-11000

WURTENBERGER, Ernst (1868-1934) Swiss

£556 $894 €806 At his music (46x33cm-18x13in) mono.d.1917. 9-May-3 Dobiaschofsky, Bern #69/R est:2400 (S.FR 1200)

£786 $1226 €1250 Portraits of Paul Woischutzky and Auguste Woischutzky (60x51cm-24x20in) s.d.1902/04 i. stretcher two. 11-Oct-2 Winterberg, Heidelberg #1880

£13734 $21700 €20601 Cattle trader (90x89cm-35x35in) mono.d.1927. 26-Nov-2 Phillips, Zurich #15/R est:7000-10000 (S.FR 32000)

WURTH, Peter (1873-1945) German

£1139 $1766 €1800 Autumnal peasant garden (61x78cm-24x31in) s.d.21. Okt. 25-Sep-2 Neumeister, Munich #781/R est:1500

WURTH, Xavier (1869-1933) Belgian

£300 $456 €450 Peaceful stretch of the river (39x55cm-15x22in) s. 29-Aug-2 Christie's, Kensington #263

£769 $1208 €1200 Vue des Fagnes (61x81cm-24x32in) s. 11-Dec-2 Hotel des Ventes Mosan, Brussels #257

WURZ, Hermann (1836-1899) German

£577 $894 €900 Young boy looking at parrot (32x23cm-13x9in) s. 5-Dec-2 Dr Fritz Nagel, Stuttgart #711/R

WUST, Alexander (1837-1876) Dutch

£405 $652 €620 Les fijords (32x47cm-13x19in) s. 14-Jan-3 Vanderkindere, Brussels #94

£1056 $1701 €1500 Hilly landscape with shepherd (31x42cm-12x17in) s. panel. 7-May-3 Vendue Huis, Gravenhage #352/R est:1500-2000

£1582 $2468 €2500 Deer in a wood near the water (188x120cm-74x47in) s.i. 21-Oct-2 Bernaerts, Antwerp #27/R est:2000-3000

£2278 $3554 €3600 Waterfall (188x120cm-74x47in) i. 21-Oct-2 Bernaerts, Antwerp #28/R est:2000-3000

£19355 $30000 €29033 Fire at twilight (20x41cm-8x16in) s. paper on canvas prov. 5-Dec-2 Christie's, Rockefeller NY #32/R est:15000-25000

WUST, Johann Heinrich (1741-1821) Swiss

£6522 $10174 €9783 Area around the confluence of the Aare and Zihl (97x121cm-38x48in) s.d.1780 i. verso. 16-Sep-2 Philippe Schuler, Zurich #3414/R est:12000-15000 (S.FR 15000)

WUST, Johann Heinrich (attrib) (1741-1821) Swiss

£524 $817 €786 Mountain landscape with waterfall (31x23cm-12x9in) board. 20-Nov-2 Fischer, Luzern #2303 (S.FR 1200)

WUSTHOFF, Maria (20th C) German

£282 $468 €400 Still life with anemones in a porcelain vase (39x48cm-15x19in) cardboard. 14-Jun-3 Arnold, Frankfurt #948/R

WUSTLICH, Otto (1818-1886) German

Works on paper

£1200 $1872 €1800 Portrait of King Edward VII as Prince of Wales (21x15cm-8x6in) s. W/C prov. 26-Mar-3 Hamptons Fine Art, Godalming #80/R est:1200-1500

WUTKY, Michael (1739-1823) Austrian

£4054 $6324 €6000 Nocturnal view of Tiber near Rome with Dome of St Peter's beyond (30x43cm-12x17in) board on panel prov. 27-Mar-3 Dorotheum, Vienna #25/R est:3000-5000

WUTTKE, Carl (1849-1927) German

£256 $403 €400 Fisher boy on Naples beach (30x40cm-12x16in) s.d.17.Aug.89 paper on panel. 21-Nov-2 Van Ham, Cologne #1988

£308 $483 €480 Posillipo, Naples (19x27cm-7x11in) s. panel. 21-Nov-2 Van Ham, Cologne #1989

£1282 $1987 €2000 Arab bazaar with city gate and minaret (24x35cm-9x14in) s. panel. 6-Dec-2 Michael Zeller, Lindau #959/R

£1769 $2812 €2600 Figures in Moroccan desert (20x27cm-8x11in) s. board painted 1892. 18-Mar-3 Finarte, Milan #41/R

£2897 $4606 €4200 The Forum, Rome (40x55cm-16x22in) s.i.d.1912 i. verso. 8-Mar-3 Arnold, Frankfurt #791/R est:1800

WYANT, Alexander H (1836-1892) American

£1401 $2200 €2102 Country landscape (23x36cm-9x14in) s. prov. 14-Dec-2 Weschler, Washington #659/R est:1000-1500

£2057 $3250 €3086 Winter scene with house (41x56cm-16x22in) s. panel. 17-Nov-2 CRN Auctions, Cambridge #46/R

WYATT, Matthew Cotes (attrib) (1777-1862) British

Sculpture

£4000 $6440 €5800 Figure of the crouching Venus. marble prov. 12-May-3 Joel, Victoria #503/R est:3000-5000 (A.D 10000)

WYATT, Neil (20th C) British

£260 $419 €390 Row of houses (53x113cm-21x44in) s.d.1965. 18-Feb-3 Bonhams, Knightsbridge #62

WYATT, Richard James (1795-1850) British
Sculpture
£15000 $25050 €21750 Infant Bacchus (212cm-83in) s. white marble incl grey marble column prov. 8-Jul-3 Sotheby's, London #217/R est:10000-15000

WYCK, Jan (1640-1702) Dutch
£6441 $10564 €9339 Battle scene (54x72cm-21x28in) 4-Jun-3 AB Stockholms Auktionsverk #2531/R est:25000-30000 (S.KR 82000)

WYCK, Jan (attrib) (1640-1702) Dutch
Works on paper
£576 $921 €800 Cavalry battle in front of castle (18x29cm-7x11in) pen wash prov. 17-May-3 Lempertz, Koln #1264/R

WYCK, Thomas (circle) (1616-1677) Dutch
£5822 $8500 €8733 Fox hunting in the countryside (76x102cm-30x40in) 3-Nov-1 North East Auctions, Portsmouth #1146/R

WYCK, Thomas (style) (1616-1677) Dutch
£6500 $10075 €9750 Italianate landscape with travellers resting on a path near a river (94x105cm-37x41in) 30-Oct-2 Christie's, Kensington #62/R est:4000-6000

WYCKAERT, Maurice (1923-1996) Belgian
£1007 $1612 €1400 Composition (18x24cm-7x9in) s.verso. 17-May-3 De Vuyst, Lokeren #410/R
£1034 $1655 €1500 Voor de vuist weg (65x53cm-26x21in) paper. 17-Mar-3 Amberes, Antwerp #285
£2878 $4719 €4000 Gioie simplice a ellesellles (80x100cm-31x39in) s. s.i.d.verso. 3-Jun-3 Christie's, Amsterdam #347/R est:5000-7000
£3597 $5755 €5000 En coup de vent (89x116cm-35x46in) s.i.d.1984 verso. 17-May-3 De Vuyst, Lokeren #502/R est:5500-6500
£5161 $8155 €8000 Composition (120x100cm-47x39in) s. 17-Dec-2 Palais de Beaux Arts, Brussels #652/R est:6200-8600
£5769 $8942 €9000 Landscape (100x115cm-39x45in) s. i.d.1963. 7-Dec-2 De Vuyst, Lokeren #494/R est:8600-10000
Works on paper
£566 $872 €900 Fleurs (150x200cm-59x79in) s.d.1966 dr. 22-Oct-2 Campo, Vlaamse Kaai #690
£692 $1072 €1100 Composition (41x50cm-16x20in) s.d.89 gouache. 5-Oct-2 De Vuyst, Lokeren #419

WYDEVELD, Arnoud (19th C) Dutch
£3750 $6000 €5625 Prized 58 pound striped bass caught at Cuttyhunk, Mass July 4 1882 (122x183cm-48x72in) s. 1-Jan-3 Nadeau, Windsor #75/R est:8000-10000

WYDOOGEN, N M (19th C) Dutch
£541 $834 €850 Sailing barges in choppy water (23x32cm-9x13in) s. panel. 3-Sep-2 Christie's, Amsterdam #290
£1319 $2177 €1900 Shipping on a calm sunset (14x19cm-6x7in) s. panel. 1-Jul-3 Christie's, Amsterdam #4/R est:1500-2000
£2303 $3730 €3500 Moored sailing barges on a riverbank (36x50cm-14x20in) s. 21-Jan-3 Christie's, Amsterdam #33/R est:2500-3500

WYETH, Andrew (1917-) American
Prints
£3112 $4792 €4668 Dogwood (42x62cm-17x24in) collotype. 28-Sep-2 Heffel, Vancouver #50 (C.D 7500)
Works on paper
£15432 $25000 €23148 Ledge on Huppers Island (46x68cm-18x27in) init.i. ink executed 1941 prov. 21-May-3 Sotheby's, New York #136/R est:30000-50000
£25157 $40000 €37736 Vermont (53x74cm-21x29in) s.i. W/C prov. 7-Mar-3 Skinner, Boston #461/R est:60000-80000
£29032 $45000 €43548 Study for on the Edge (36x51cm-14x20in) s. W/C executed 2001 prov. 5-Dec-2 Christie's, Rockefeller NY #145/R est:40000-60000
£30864 $50000 €46296 Stone Island (48x61cm-19x24in) s. W/C tempera dry brush prov.exhib. 21-May-3 Sotheby's, New York #135/R est:50000-75000
£41935 $65000 €62903 Granary and mill (26x30cm-10x12in) s. W/C executed 1961 prov. 4-Dec-2 Sotheby's, New York #167/R est:20000-30000
£51613 $80000 €77420 Cow shed in winter (55x76cm-22x30in) s. W/C exhib. 5-Dec-2 Christie's, Rockefeller NY #146/R est:100000-150000
£74074 $120000 €111111 Combers (56x77cm-22x30in) s. W/C prov.exhib.lit. 22-May-3 Christie's, Rockefeller NY #72/R est:150000-250000
£83832 $140000 €121556 Eavesdrop (56x76cm-22x30in) s. W/C prov. executed 1980. 18-Jun-3 Christie's, Los Angeles #96/R est:100000-150000
£222222 $360000 €333333 Watch dog (72x57cm-28x22in) s. drybrush W/C prov.exhib. 21-May-3 Sotheby's, New York #130/R est:200000-300000

WYETH, James (1946-) American
Works on paper
£2419 $3823 €3629 Portrait of President Carter (25x32cm-10x13in) s. pencil dr. 18-Nov-2 Waddingtons, Toronto #13/R est:2500-3500 (C.D 6000)
£15432 $25000 €22376 97, 88 and 79 (41x51cm-16x20in) s. mixed media board. 21-May-3 Doyle, New York #165/R est:50000-70000
£35484 $55000 €53226 Full face and chest unfinished arm, Nureyev, study no11 (51x41cm-20x16in) s. pencil gouache on board prov.lit. 4-Dec-2 Sotheby's, New York #173/R est:25000-35000
£92593 $150000 €138890 Summer house, winter house (55x76cm-22x30in) s. i.verso W/C prov.exhib.lit. 22-May-3 Christie's, Rockefeller NY #79/R est:120000-180000

WYETH, Newell Convers (1882-1945) American
£16149 $26000 €24224 Wagon trains and cattle proceeding through expansive landscape (18x76cm-7x30in) init. canvas on board painted c.1905 prov. 10-May-3 Illustration House, New York #175/R est:20000-30000
£25157 $40000 €37736 Thanksgiving feast and thanksgiving with the Indians (32x147cm-13x58in) s.i. oil gessoed board prov.lit. 5-Mar-3 Sotheby's, New York #108/R est:40000-60000
£38217 $60000 €57326 Seeker (178x157cm-70x62in) s.d.1933. 20-Nov-2 Christie's, Los Angeles #102/R est:100000-150000
£40881 $65000 €61322 Legend of the expedition to Spain (102x86cm-40x34in) s. i.verso painted c.1928. 2-Mar-3 Toomey, Oak Park #693/R est:60000-80000
£45161 $70000 €67742 He never caught a thing and ruined Jon's reputation as a fisherman (119x96cm-47x38in) s.d.1913 prov.exhib.lit. 5-Dec-2 Christie's, Rockefeller NY #209/R est:40000-60000
£50955 $80000 €76433 Primal chemistry (132x88cm-52x35in) s. board. 20-Nov-2 Christie's, Los Angeles #101/R est:100000-150000
£54839 $85000 €82259 Still life with bowl, onions and bottle (102x81cm-40x32in) s.i. prov. 4-Dec-2 Sotheby's, New York #171/R est:90000-120000
£60510 $95000 €90765 One January afternoon (51x41cm-20x16in) incised sig. prov. 22-Nov-2 Skinner, Boston #290/R est:100000-125000
£77419 $120000 €116129 Scottish chiefs (63x107cm-25x42in) s. canvas on masonite prov. 5-Dec-2 Christie's, Rockefeller NY #213/R est:100000-150000
£103226 $160000 €154839 Rubber from the jungle to the world (79x171cm-31x67in) s. painted c.1917. 5-Dec-2 Christie's, Rockefeller NY #214/R est:150000-250000
£228395 $370000 €342593 Popular magazine cover illustration - The frontiersman (86x63cm-34x25in) s. prov.lit. 22-May-3 Christie's, Rockefeller NY #90/R est:100000-150000

WYETH, Paul James Logan (1920-1983) British
Works on paper
£420 $689 €630 Young dancer (38x30cm-15x12in) mono.d.69 pastel. 5-Feb-3 Goldings, Lincolnshire #234

WYGANT, Bob (1927-) American
£1948 $3000 €2922 Summer afternoon (25x36cm-10x14in) acrylic. 25-Oct-2 Morris & Whiteside, Hilton Head Island #148 est:2500-3500

WYGRZYWALSKI, Feliks (1875-1944) Polish
£613 $950 €920 Seascape (23x28cm-9x11in) board prov. 7-Dec-2 South Bay, Long Island #51/R
£613 $950 €920 Landscape (23x30cm-9x12in) board exhib. 7-Dec-2 South Bay, Long Island #52/R
£1732 $2684 €2598 Meditation in the desert (56x66cm-22x26in) s. 24-Sep-2 Koller, Zurich #6583/R est:4000-5000 (S.FR 4000)
£2500 $3925 €3750 Desert prayers (50x70cm-20x28in) s. panel. 21-Nov-2 Christie's, Kensington #190/R est:2000-3000

WYHEN, Jacques van der (c.1588-c.1638) Dutch
£16000 $26720 €23200 Wooded landscape with huntsmen shooting on a bridge, cottage nearby (15x15cm-6x6in) copper round prov. 10-Jul-3 Sotheby's, London #104/R est:10000-15000

WYK, Charles van (1875-1917) Dutch
£3243 $5059 €4800 Passage du gue (34x65cm-13x26in) s. 28-Mar-3 Claude Aguttes, Neuilly #201/R est:6000

WYK, Hendrik Jan van (1911-) Dutch
£493 $794 €700 Nut basket (17x17cm-7x7in) d.68 board. 7-May-3 Vendue Huis, Gravenhage #577/R

WYK, Henri van (1833-?) Dutch
£588 $947 €900 Paysage hivernal anime (21x41cm-8x16in) s. panel. 14-Jan-3 Vanderkindere, Brussels #443
£900 $1404 €1350 In the artist studio (34x26cm-13x10in) s.d.1890. 10-Sep-2 Bonhams, Knightsbridge #222/R

WYKE, Niels A (1867-1937) Danish
£343 $542 €515 View from Drommeslaet in Skaane (85x142cm-33x56in) s.d.1915. 13-Nov-2 Kunsthallen, Copenhagen #27 (D.KR 4000)

WYKES, Frederick Kirtland (1905-) American
Works on paper
£330 $525 €495 Bahamian fisherman (41x53cm-16x21in) s. W/C. 7-Mar-3 Jackson's, Cedar Falls #1013/R

WYLD, William (1806-1889) British
Works on paper
£270 $421 €405 Piazza in Verona (14x21cm-6x8in) i. pen wash. 25-Mar-3 Bonhams, Knightsbridge #73/R
£580 $922 €870 Tivoli (16x23cm-6x9in) s. W/C. 18-Mar-3 Sworder & Son, Bishops Stortford #443/R
£600 $930 €900 View of Venice (12x8cm-5x3in) s. i.verso W/C. 24-Sep-2 Bonhams, Knightsbridge #247/R
£1701 $2704 €2500 La halte des cavaliers (16x24cm-6x9in) s. W/C. 24-Mar-3 Rabourdin & Choppin de Janvry, Paris #90/R est:3000-3500
£1899 $3000 €3000 Shops in Algeria (14x23cm-6x9in) s. W/C. 28-Nov-2 Piasa, Paris #10/R
£4500 $6435 €6750 Sunset (17x25cm-7x10in) s. pencil W/C htd gum prov.exhib.lit. 22-Jan-3 Christie's, London #56/R est:3500
£5000 $7800 €7500 Rialto, Venice (31x43cm-12x17in) s. W/C. 5-Nov-2 Bonhams, New Bond Street #86/R est:3000-5000
£6500 $9295 €9750 Dresden at sunset (15x24cm-6x9in) s. pencil W/C scratching out prov.exhib.lit. 22-Jan-3 Christie's, London #57/R

WYLDER, Jonathan (1957-) British
Sculpture
£4500 $7425 €6525 Ballerina (208cm-82in) s.num.1/4 brown pat. bronze. 3-Jul-3 Christie's, Kensington #609 est:3000-5000

WYLER, Otto (1887-1965) Swiss
£386 $610 €579 Autumnal small trees by a stream (46x38cm-18x15in) s.d.1909. 29-Nov-2 Zofingen, Switzerland #3137 (S.FR 900)
£6987 $10969 €10481 Autumnal mountain landscape (70x85cm-28x33in) s.i.d.Sept. 25-Nov-2 Sotheby's, Zurich #123/R est:4500-5500 (S.FR 16000)
Works on paper
£300 $475 €450 River landscape (45x53cm-18x21in) s.d.57 W/C. 29-Nov-2 Zofingen, Switzerland #3138 (S.FR 700)
£1459 $2306 €2189 View of the snow-covered village of Fetan (46x73cm-18x29in) d.1922 s.i.verso W/C. 29-Nov-2 Zofingen, Switzerland #3136/R est:2000 (S.FR 3400)

WYLIE, Kate (1877-1941) British
£475 $751 €689 Still life of two roses in glass vase (28x20cm-11x8in) s. 24-Jul-3 John Nicholson, Haslemere #1166
£550 $875 €825 Spring flowers in a vase (30x27cm-12x11in) s. canvasboard. 6-Mar-3 Christie's, Kensington #185
£740 $1162 €1110 Still life of mixed flowers (30x24cm-12x9in) 17-Apr-3 Bonhams, Edinburgh #377
£950 $1539 €1425 Still life of chrysanthemums, daffodils and nasturtium in a vase (36x36cm-14x14in) s. 21-May-3 Bonhams, Knightsbridge #172/R
£1500 $2490 €2175 Still life, vase of mixed flowers (31x27cm-12x11in) s. board. 13-Jun-3 Lyon & Turnbull, Edinburgh #58 est:300-500

WYLLER, Sverre (1953-) Norwegian
£3287 $5194 €4931 Untitled - table and lamp (137x153cm-54x60in) s.i.d.1989 diptych exhib. 2-Dec-2 Blomqvist, Oslo #477/R est:40000-60000 (N.KR 38000)
Works on paper
£3307 $5292 €4961 The New York Series 13 (91x122cm-36x48in) s.i.d.1993 verso mixed media panel exhib. 17-Mar-3 Blomqvist, Oslo #446/R est:40000-50000 (N.KR 38000)

WYLLEY, Arthur (19/20th C) British
£360 $562 €540 Shipping off the coast (50x76cm-20x30in) indis sig.d.1904. 8-Oct-2 Bonhams, Knightsbridge #168/R

WYLLIE, Charles William (1853-1923) British
£450 $743 €653 Panoramic view of an estuary with shipping (13x61cm-5x24in) s. board. 3-Jul-3 Duke & Son, Dorchester #306/R
£550 $869 €825 Gypsies dancing (19x31cm-7x12in) s.d.1908 board. 27-Nov-2 Sotheby's, Olympia #93/R
£650 $1066 €943 Entering port (23x32cm-9x13in) s. prov. 1-Jun-3 Lots Road, London #355/R
£3200 $4960 €4800 Busy day on the Thames at the Isle of Dogs, with Greenwich Hospital (30x61cm-12x24in) s. 31-Oct-2 Christie's, Kensington #555/R est:1500-2500
£7000 $10850 €10500 Brimming river (77x128cm-30x50in) s. exhib. 31-Oct-2 Christie's, Kensington #560/R est:6000-8000
Works on paper
£750 $1155 €1125 Unloading a fruit ship, London Bridge (38x28cm-15x11in) monochrome wash htd white. 3-Sep-2 Gorringes, Lewes #2230

WYLLIE, Gordon H (1930-) British
£420 $655 €630 Yellow landscape (15x16cm-6x6in) acrylic board. 17-Oct-2 Bonhams, Edinburgh #78
£600 $936 €900 Corner of a filed (19x28cm-7x11in) acrylic board. 17-Oct-2 Bonhams, Edinburgh #86
Works on paper
£300 $468 €450 Break in the clouds, Mull (7x14cm-3x6in) s.d.88 gouache. 17-Oct-2 Bonhams, Edinburgh #85
£750 $1170 €1125 Still life of black fish (47x52cm-19x20in) s.d.95 W/C. 17-Oct-2 Bonhams, Edinburgh #81

WYLLIE, Harold (1880-?) British
Works on paper
£320 $486 €480 Training ship Foudoyant in 1949 and as she was in 1819 (25x51cm-10x20in) s.i. sepia W/C pencil prov. 15-Aug-2 Bonhams, New Bond Street #271
£340 $517 €510 Turtle back destroyers (22x32cm-9x13in) W/C prov. 15-Aug-2 Bonhams, New Bond Street #266

WYLLIE, W L (1851-1931) British
Prints
£920 $1527 €1380 Shipping in a coastal inlet, with sea cadets boarding an open boat. s. etching. 10-Jun-3 Lawrences, Bletchingley #1335

WYLLIE, William Lionel (1851-1931) British
£391 $610 €653 Untitled - sail boats at dusk (22x34cm-9x13in) s.d.1897 board. 13-Apr-3 Levis, Calgary #221 est:1200-1500 (C.D 900)
£440 $691 €660 Mediterranean port (20x50cm-8x20in) 17-Apr-3 Bonhams, Edinburgh #321
£550 $897 €825 Shadow of the cross of war (52x72cm-20x28in) d.1918. 12-Feb-3 Bonhams, Knightsbridge #282/R
£880 $1426 €1320 Lightening splitting the sky over a barque and her attendant tug (47x81cm-19x32in) s. 21-May-3 Christie's, Kensington #676/R
£950 $1473 €1425 An approaching squall (22x29cm-9x11in) s. board. 31-Oct-2 Christie's, Kensington #554/R
£3000 $4650 €4500 Thames barges racing with the tide on the Medway (61x93cm-24x37in) s. 31-Oct-2 Christie's, Kensington #557/R est:6000-8000
£4800 $7296 €7200 Shipping off the coast (6x53cm-2x21in) s. 4-Jul-2 Mellors & Kirk, Nottingham #821/R est:800-1200
£5200 $7904 €7800 Union-Castle mailship in the Channel (45x61cm-18x24in) s. board. 15-Aug-2 Bonhams, New Bond Street #434/R est:3000-4000
Works on paper
£250 $373 €375 Woman washing laundry by a river (18x34cm-7x13in) s. W/C. 27-Jun-2 Greenslade Hunt, Taunton #713/R
£300 $456 €450 On the Solent (25x45cm-10x18in) monochrome W/C prov. 15-Aug-2 Bonhams, New Bond Street #254
£350 $532 €525 Fleet review (21x32cm-8x13in) monochrome W/C prov. 15-Aug-2 Bonhams, New Bond Street #252
£380 $578 €570 Hero or conqueror (18x26cm-7x10in) i. monochrome W/C prov. 15-Aug-2 Bonhams, New Bond Street #255
£500 $795 €750 Dalmation coast, near Ragusa, Sicilly (11x23cm-4x9in) s.i. W/C. 5-Mar-3 Bonhams, Bury St Edmunds #260
£600 $930 €900 H.M.S Amethyst engaging Turkish battery in Gulf of Adramyte, May 18 1915 (20x30cm-8x12in) s.i. pencil wash. 31-Oct-2 Christie's, Kensington #299
£740 $1184 €1110 Fisherfolk setting out (9x19cm-4x7in) s.d.1874 W/C. 15-May-3 Lawrence, Crewkerne #863/R
£1000 $1550 €1500 Ironclad and barquentine in mid Channel (26x38cm-10x15in) s. W/C. 31-Oct-2 Christie's, Kensington #374/R est:1000-1500
£1050 $1754 €1523 Shipping off a coast (13x38cm-5x15in) s.i. W/C. 20-Jun-3 Keys, Aylsham #444/R est:500-700
£1200 $1908 €1800 View of the Thames and St Pauls (8x36cm-3x14in) s. W/C with pencil study two. 29-Apr-3 Gorringes, Lewes #2230
£1500 $2280 €2250 HMS Victory and other vessels (15x27cm-6x11in) s. W/C. 17-Sep-2 Henry Adams, Chichester #144/R est:500-800

£1800 $2916 €2700 Admiral Swinton Holland's funeral off the Nab, 12th June 1922 (21x42cm-8x17in) s. W/C htd white. 22-Jan-3 Bonhams, New Bond Street #343/R est:1000-1500

£1900 $3059 €2850 Off start point (21x31cm-8x12in) s. W/C. 15-Jan-3 Cheffins Grain & Comins, Cambridge #376/R

£2300 $3657 €3450 On the Dogger bank (29x45cm-11x18in) s.i. W/C. 27-Feb-3 Bonhams, Chester #428/R est:900-1200

£2500 $3950 €3625 Warships in the Solent (28x45cm-11x18in) s. W/C. 22-Jul-3 Sworder & Son, Bishops Stortford #312/R est:700-1000

£2800 $4368 €4200 Battleships in a swell (26x45cm-10x18in) s. W/C. 9-Oct-2 Woolley & Wallis, Salisbury #176/R est:400-600

£4500 $7290 €6750 Victory refitting (26x42cm-10x17in) s.i. W/C. 22-Jan-3 Bonhams, New Bond Street #341/R est:1500-2000

WYLLIE, William Lionel (attrib) (1851-1931) British

£380 $608 €570 Heybarges on the Medway (20x29cm-8x11in) panel. 13-May-3 Bonhams, Knightsbridge #21c

£1200 $1908 €1800 Bristol from Hotwells (32x45cm-13x18in) bears sig. 4-Mar-3 Bonhams, Knightsbridge #279/R est:1000-1500

Works on paper

£620 $961 €930 Harbour with war ship and other boats (49x25cm-19x10in) s.d.1889 W/C. 1-Oct-2 Fellows & Sons, Birmingham #148/R

WYMANN-MORY, Karl Christian (1836-1898) Swiss

£306 $477 €459 Lake Geneva (31x41cm-12x16in) s. board. 6-Nov-2 Dobiaschofsky, Bern #1082/R (S.FR 700)

£873 $1380 €1310 Vierwaldstattersee with Rutli (48x64cm-19x25in) s. 14-Nov-2 Stuker, Bern #595 est:1500-2000 (S.FR 2000)

WYN WOOD, Elizabeth (1903-1966) Canadian

Sculpture

£3333 $5467 €5000 Torso, 1926 (21cm-8in) bronze on limestone base prov.exhib.lit. 27-May-3 Sotheby's, Toronto #173/R est:3000-4000 (C.D 7500)

£5645 $8919 €8468 Passing rain (81x107cm-32x42in) s. bronze prov.exhib.lit. 18-Nov-2 Sotheby's, Toronto #51/R est:15000-20000 (C.D 14000)

Works on paper

£1600 $2624 €2400 Landscape - Head Island (27x37cm-11x15in) litho crayon prov. 3-Jun-3 Joyner, Toronto #444/R est:2000-3000 (C.D 3600)

WYNANTS, Ernest (1878-1964) Belgian

Sculpture

£2361 $3754 €3400 Mere et enfant (74cm-29in) s. bronze. 29-Apr-3 Campo & Campo, Antwerp #356 est:1800-2200

£5517 $8828 €8000 Torso of a young girl (81x31cm-32x12in) s. stone exec.c.1938. 15-Mar-3 De Vuyst, Lokeren #467/R est:8500-9500

£10417 $16563 €15000 Reverie (176cm-69in) mono.d.1936 wood exhib. 29-Apr-3 Campo & Campo, Antwerp #358/R est:7000-8000

WYNANTS, Sander (1903-1953) Belgian

£352 $567 €500 Pieta (78x77cm-31x30in) 12-May-3 Bernaerts, Antwerp #705

WYNANTSZ, August (1795-1848) Dutch

£3077 $4831 €4800 Cityscape (33x45cm-13x18in) s. bears d.182 panel. 21-Nov-2 Van Ham, Cologne #1990/R est:3800

WYNEN, Dominicus van (1661-?) Dutch

£14894 $23085 €22341 Burlesque scene with the poet Vergilius (58x51cm-23x20in) init.i. 3-Dec-2 Bukowskis, Stockholm #465/R est:50000-60000 (S.KR 210000)

WYNEN, Dominicus van (attrib) (1661-?) Dutch

£1139 $1800 €1800 L'Enfer (76x115cm-30x45in) 2-Dec-2 Amberes, Antwerp #1356

WYNGAERDT, Anthonie Jacobus van (1808-1887) Dutch

£1127 $1814 €1600 Farmer's wife with goat on wood path (27x22cm-11x9in) s. panel. 7-May-3 Vendue Huis, Gravenhage #416/R est:1200-1600

£1644 $2564 €2400 Figures on a sandy track through the woods (29x22cm-11x9in) s. panel prov. 14-Apr-3 Glerum, Amsterdam #29/R est:1500-2000

£1972 $3234 €2859 Two children with dog in forest clearing (19x15cm-7x6in) s.d.1885 panel. 4-Jun-3 Fischer, Luzern #1073/R est:3000-4500 (S.FR 4200)

£2055 $3205 €3000 Figures on a sandy road with herdswoman and her animals (19x30cm-7x12in) s.d.38 panel prov. 14-Apr-3 Glerum, Amsterdam #28/R est:2000-3000

WYNGAERDT, Petrus Theodorus van (1816-1893) Dutch

£750 $1253 €1088 Recital (27x22cm-11x9in) s. panel. 26-Jun-3 Mellors & Kirk, Nottingham #892/R

£2466 $3871 €3600 Forbidden picture (27x21cm-11x8in) s. panel. 15-Apr-3 Sotheby's, Amsterdam #71/R est:4000-6000

WYNN, Kenneth (1922-) British?

£500 $785 €750 Portrait of a bay hunter in a stable yard (61x76cm-24x30in) s. 21-Nov-2 Tennants, Leyburn #774/R

£1702 $2757 €2400 Hunting scene, hiding fox (49x74cm-19x29in) board. 20-May-3 Mealy's, Castlecomer #1264/R est:1200-1800

WYNN, Monnewe Moncrey (20th C) American

£943 $1500 €1367 Grand Ave Bridge (17x21cm-7x8in) s. board painted c.1930. 4-May-3 Treadway Gallery, Cincinnati #604/R est:2000-3000

WYNN, Spencer (20th C) Canadian

£289 $474 €419 High mountain lake (35x45cm-14x18in) s.i.d.1999. 9-Jun-3 Hodgins, Calgary #398/R (C.D 650)

WYNNE, A B (fl.1881-1906) British?

Works on paper

£300 $468 €450 In the Trussocks (47x30cm-19x12in) s. i.verso W/C. 26-Mar-3 Woolley & Wallis, Salisbury #119/R

WYNNE, Arthur (19th C) British?

£350 $560 €525 Lechlade on Thames (58x86cm-23x34in) s. 8-Jan-3 Brightwells, Leominster #1054/R

£538 $850 €807 Pastoral scenes (38x61cm-15x24in) s. two. 1-Dec-2 Susanin's, Chicago #5126/R

WYNNE, David (1926-) British

Sculpture

£812 $1300 €1177 Reclining female nude (17x43cm-7x17in) s.num.6/6 brown black pat bronze. 16-May-3 Skinner, Boston #176/R est:2000-3000

£1400 $2254 €2100 Swans in flight (24x90x66cm-9x35x26in) green pat bronze marble base. 14-Jan-3 Bonhams, Knightsbridge #132/R est:1500-2000

£2000 $3160 €3000 Bull (14cm-6in) init.d.1980 num.1/6 bronze with base. 27-Nov-2 Sotheby's, Olympia #169/R est:2000-3000

WYNNE, Gladys (1878-1968) Irish

Works on paper

£351 $548 €520 Running out the boat, Portnablagh, Co. Donegal (16x22cm-6x9in) s. i.verso W/C. 26-Mar-3 James Adam, Dublin #116/R

£1056 $1754 €1500 St. Douloughs church near Raheny (18x26cm-7x10in) s. W/C. 10-Jun-3 James Adam, Dublin #227/R est:500-700

£1800 $2880 €2700 Dun Laoghaire (16x25cm-6x10in) s. W/C prov. 15-May-3 Christie's, London #30/R

WYNNE-JONES, Nancy (1922-) British

Works on paper

£527 $828 €770 Interior (38x56cm-15x22in) s.verso mixed media. 15-Apr-3 De Veres Art Auctions, Dublin #66

WYNTER, Bryan (1915-1975) British

£8500 $13345 €12750 Confluence II (142x113cm-56x44in) s. i.d.1965 verso exhib. 22-Nov-2 Christie's, London #99/R est:7000-10000

Works on paper

£2200 $3476 €3300 Raven (41x32cm-16x13in) ink gouache executed c.1956 prov. 27-Nov-2 Sotheby's, Olympia #187/R est:1000-1500

WYNTRACK, Dirck (1625-1678) Dutch

£5396 $8633 €7500 Barn interior (56x45cm-22x18in) s. panel. 17-May-3 Lempertz, Koln #1161/R est:8000

WYNTRACK, Dirck (attrib) (1625-1678) Dutch

£2500 $4175 €3625 Kitchen interior with peasants (34x49cm-13x19in) panel. 11-Jul-3 Christie's, Kensington #58/R est:3000-5000

WYON, Edward William (1811-1885) British

£3200 $5152 €4800 Princess (37x60cm-15x24in) s.i. prov.exhib. 20-Feb-3 Christie's, London #234/R

WYRSCH, Charles (1920-) Swiss

£1415 $2292 €2052 Christ with mourners (34x26cm-13x10in) s.i.d.1969 verso panel prov. 24-May-3 Galerie Gloggner, Luzern #129/R est:1800-2500 (S.FR 3000)

£1981 $3209 €2872 Christ with Mary, John and Magdalen (81x65cm-32x26in) s.d.1967 1968 1969 verso prov. 24-May-3 Galerie Gloggner, Luzern #128/R est:2500-2800 (S.FR 4200)

WYRSCH, Johann Melchior (1732-1798) Swiss
£375 $600 €563 Portrait of Josephus Ulrich Goldin (28x23cm-11x9in) s. i.verso. 12-Jan-3 William Jenack, New York #454
£851 $1421 €1200 Portrait de Nicolas Antoine l'Abbey de Billy (40x32cm-16x13in) s.i.verso oval. 18-Jun-3 Tajan, Paris #104
£961 $1499 €1442 St Aloys von Gonzaga (68x55cm-27x22in) lit. 20-Nov-2 Fischer, Luzern #1231/R est:2500-3000 (S.FR 2200)
£1965 $3066 €2948 Portrait of Karl Martin von Bayer von Rorschach (68x56cm-27x22in) s.d.1759 verso lit. 20-Nov-2 Fischer, Luzern #1230/R est:5000-7000 (S.FR 4500)
£3846 $6038 €6000 Flute player (63x50cm-25x20in) 15-Dec-2 Mercier & Cie, Lille #323 est:8000

WYSE, Alex (1938-) Canadian
Sculpture
£2222 $3644 €3333 Colourful extermination (78cm-31in) mixed media construction set painted stand lit. 3-Jun-3 Joyner, Toronto #93/R est:6000-8000 (C.D 5000)

WYSMULLER, Jan Hillebrand (1855-1925) Dutch
£493 $769 €720 Little corner of the farmyard (37x29cm-15x11in) s. 14-Apr-3 Glerum, Amsterdam #86/R
£573 $883 €900 In the dunes looking out to sea (24x31cm-9x12in) s. canvas on panel. 3-Sep-2 Christie's, Amsterdam #186
£764 $1177 €1200 Windmill (37x57cm-15x22in) s. 3-Sep-2 Christie's, Amsterdam #175
£5592 $9059 €8500 Windmills in a polder landscape (49x66cm-19x26in) s. 21-Jan-3 Christie's, Amsterdam #132/R est:4000-6000
Works on paper
£1042 $1719 €1500 Windmills (44x63cm-17x25in) s. W/C. 1-Jul-3 Christie's, Amsterdam #182 est:1500-2000

WYSOCKI, Stanislaw (1949-) Polish?
Sculpture
£2230 $3479 €3345 Female torso (96cm-38in) polished and pat.bronze. 11-Nov-2 Rasmussen, Vejle #112/R est:30000 (D.KR 26000)

WYSS, Marcel (1930-) Swiss
Sculpture
£4803 $7013 €7205 Horizontal-vertical endless rythmn II (60x59x5cm-24x23x2in) s. verso painted wood relief. 4-Jun-2 Germann, Zurich #38/R est:12000-16000 (S.FR 11000)

WYSS, Paul (1897-1984) Swiss
£880 $1416 €1276 Klausenpass (50x80cm-20x31in) s. 9-May-3 Dobiaschofsky, Bern #160/R (S.FR 1900)

WYTSMAN, Juliette (1866-1925) Belgian
£2621 $4193 €3800 Still life with flowers and a bouquet in a glass vase (44x54cm-17x21in) s. panel lit. 15-Mar-3 De Vuyst, Lokeren #402/R est:3800-4400
£4717 $7311 €7500 Cour d'hospice a Bruges (42x29cm-17x11in) s. i.verso lit. 5-Oct-2 De Vuyst, Lokeren #535/R est:6000-8000
£20755 $32170 €33000 Bruyere rose (81x111cm-32x44in) s. s.i.verso lit. 5-Oct-2 De Vuyst, Lokeren #440/R

WYTSMAN, Rodolphe (1860-1927) Belgian
£317 $506 €440 Still life with roses (31x21cm-12x8in) s.i. panel lit. 17-May-3 De Vuyst, Lokeren #413
£980 $1578 €1500 Ruelle animee a Capri (80x50cm-31x20in) s.d.1883. 14-Jan-3 Vanderkindere, Brussels #159 est:1600-2400
£1192 $1943 €1800 Troupeau au bord de riviere (55x37cm-22x15in) s.i.d.87. 17-Feb-3 Horta, Bruxelles #123
£1582 $2468 €2500 Fermette dans un paysage vallonne (47x57cm-19x22in) s.d.1901. 16-Sep-2 Horta, Bruxelles #145/R
£2166 $3378 €3400 Le ramassage des pommes de terre sous le moulin (27x47cm-11x19in) s.d.1882. 11-Nov-2 Horta, Bruxelles #191/R est:4000-6000
£3034 $4855 €4400 Vallee au printemps (27x36cm-11x14in) s. panel lit. 15-Mar-3 De Vuyst, Lokeren #403/R est:2700-3000
£4138 $6621 €6000 Summer landscape with dunes (40x56cm-16x22in) s. board lit. 15-Mar-3 De Vuyst, Lokeren #444/R est:6000-7000
£4676 $7482 €6500 Paysage sous la neige (50x80cm-20x31in) s.d.85 lit. 17-May-3 De Vuyst, Lokeren #440/R est:7000-8000
£5128 $7949 €8000 Neige a Linkebeek (46x55cm-18x22in) s.i. painted 1920 prov.lit. 7-Dec-2 De Vuyst, Lokeren #444/R est:8500-10000
£8993 $14388 €12500 Paysage a la mare ensoleillee (80x100cm-31x39in) s. 13-May-3 Vanderkindere, Brussels #45/R est:10000-15000

WYTVELT, J B (fl.1656-1667) Dutch
£1911 $2981 €3000 Still life of two birds on a wooden table (39x42cm-15x17in) s. panel prov.lit. 5-Nov-2 Sotheby's, Amsterdam #72/R est:2000-3000

WYWIORSKY, Michal (1861-1926) Polish
£513 $805 €800 Sea wall on Ostsee coast at sunset (21x32cm-8x13in) s. board prov. 21-Nov-2 Van Ham, Cologne #1638
£577 $906 €900 Farmstead in winter wood (48x66cm-19x26in) study prov. 21-Nov-2 Van Ham, Cologne #1637
£1761 $2747 €2800 Summer landscape with stream (53x62cm-21x24in) s. i.verso. 19-Sep-2 Dr Fritz Nagel, Stuttgart #934/R est:1900
£2466 $3871 €3600 Winter evening (86x133cm-34x52in) s. 16-Apr-3 Dorotheum, Salzburg #139/R est:3000-4000
£3191 $5170 €4500 Building in the winter forest (48x66cm-19x26in) i.d.1911 verso prov. 22-May-3 Dorotheum, Vienna #159/R est:4500-5000
£3741 $5949 €5500 Still day (53x62cm-21x24in) s. i.verso. 25-Feb-3 Dorotheum, Vienna #75/R est:4500-5000

XCERON, Jean (1890-1967) American/Greek
Works on paper
£705 $1100 €1058 Abstract composition (66x48cm-26x19in) init. gouache. 19-Sep-2 Swann Galleries, New York #844/R
£793 $1300 €1150 Abstract and two figures (28x41cm-11x16in) s.d.61 W/C pair. 1-Jun-3 Wright, Chicago #174/R est:900-1200

XENOS, Nicholaos (1908-1984) Greek
£3400 $5372 €5100 View of Vouliagmeni (60x100cm-24x39in) 1-Apr-3 Bonhams, New Bond Street #65 est:2000-4000

XIA GUI (fl.1190-1223) Chinese
Works on paper
£1449 $2377 €2000 Yangtse river. Ten thousand miles on Changjiang (498x38cm-196x15in) seal Indian ink col silk. 30-May-3 Dr Fritz Nagel, Stuttgart #1207/R est:800-1000

XIA JINGGUAN (1875-1953) Chinese
Works on paper
£732 $1156 €1098 Landscape (17x48cm-7x19in) s.i. i.d.1931 verso ink col folding fan. 28-Apr-3 Sotheby's, Hong Kong #548/R est:5000-7000 (HK.D 9000)

XIAN, Ah (1960-) Chinese
Sculpture
£10000 $15800 €15000 China, china bust no.6 (30x23x21cm-12x9x8in) s.i.d.1998 s.i.d.verso porcelain handpainted. 27-Nov-2 Deutscher-Menzies, Melbourne #92/R est:12000-16000 (A.D 28000)

XIANG ZHANG (20th C) Chinese?
£390 $600 €585 Two work horses (23x30cm-9x12in) 25-Oct-2 Morris & Whiteside, Hilton Head Island #166
£519 $800 €779 Gull (23x30cm-9x12in) 25-Oct-2 Morris & Whiteside, Hilton Head Island #80
£1169 $1800 €1754 Kids on the beach (41x51cm-16x20in) 25-Oct-2 Morris & Whiteside, Hilton Head Island #81 est:1200-1500

XIAO YUNCONG (1596-1673) Chinese
Works on paper
£6216 $10256 €9013 Landscapes (16x12cm-6x5in) one s.i. ink eight. 6-Jul-3 Christie's, Hong Kong #453/R est:80000-100000 (HK.D 80000)

XIE BINGYI (20th C) Chinese
Works on paper
£870 $1426 €1200 Yellow river landscape (203x96cm-80x38in) s.d.1987 seals Indian ink col hanging scroll. 30-May-3 Dr Fritz Nagel, Stuttgart #1251/R

XIE GUANSHENG (19th C) Chinese
Works on paper
£7724 $12203 €11586 Sound of waves studio (30x109cm-12x43in) s.i.d.1824 ink col handscroll ink prov.lit. 28-Apr-3 Sotheby's, Hong Kong #642/R est:35000-45000 (HK.D 95000)

XIE ZHENOU (20th C) Chinese
Works on paper
£326 $535 €450 Two riders (101x54cm-40x21in) i. seals Indian ink col hanging scroll. 30-May-3 Dr Fritz Nagel, Stuttgart #1276/R
£507 $832 €700 Farewell in Weicheng (101x54cm-40x21in) i.d.1988 seals Indian ink col hanging scroll. 30-May-3 Dr Fritz Nagel, Stuttgart #1277/R

XIE ZHILIU (1910-1997) Chinese
Works on paper
£1626 $2569 €2439 Relive vine (17x48cm-7x19in) s.i.d.1964 i.verso ink col folding fan. 28-Apr-3 Sotheby's, Hong Kong #540/R est:20000-30000 (HK.D 20000)
£3252 $5138 €4878 Bird on a red leave branch (18x47cm-7x19in) s.i. i.verso ink col folding fan. 28-Apr-3 Sotheby's, Hong Kong #534/R est:40000-60000 (HK.D 40000)
£3252 $5138 €4878 Flower, butterfly (15x47cm-6x19in) s.i.d.1963 ink col folding fan. 28-Apr-3 Sotheby's, Hong Kong #541/R est:40000-60000 (HK.D 40000)
£3415 $5395 €5123 Plum blossom (18x49cm-7x19in) s.i.d.1957 i.verso ink col folding fan. 28-Apr-3 Sotheby's, Hong Kong #550/R est:30000-50000 (HK.D 42000)
£4228 $6680 €6342 Chinese flowering crab apple, plum blossom and rock (17x47cm-7x19in) s.i. ink col folding fan. 28-Apr-3 Sotheby's, Hong Kong #558/R est:30000-50000 (HK.D 52000)
£5691 $8992 €8537 Autumn landscape, orchid and bamboo (15x43cm-6x17in) s.i.d.1957 ink col folding fan. 28-Apr-3 Sotheby's, Hong Kong #542/R est:50000-70000 (HK.D 70000)
£6216 $10256 €9013 Lotus (81x48cm-32x19in) s.i. col ink scroll. 6-Jul-3 Christie's, Hong Kong #218/R est:80000-100000 (HK.D 80000)
£7317 $11561 €10976 Fragrant plantain lilly, daffodil (17x48cm-7x19in) s.i.d.1962 ink col folding fan. 28-Apr-3 Sotheby's, Hong Kong #536/R est:50000-70000 (HK.D 90000)
£7770 $12821 €11267 Lotus (47x178cm-19x70in) s.i. ink scroll. 6-Jul-3 Christie's, Hong Kong #219/R est:60000-80000 (HK.D 100000)
£8130 $12846 €12195 Willow, butterfly (16x48cm-6x19in) s.i. ink col folding fan. 28-Apr-3 Sotheby's, Hong Kong #533/R est:50000-70000 (HK.D 100000)

XIMENO, Matias (attrib) (17th C) Spanish
£1141 $1837 €1700 Saint Jerome (44x34cm-17x13in) indis.sig. 18-Feb-3 Durán, Madrid #640/R

XU BEIHONG (1895-1953) Chinese
Works on paper
£11655 $19231 €16900 Various subjects (11x17cm-4x7in) s.i. ink album of 12. 6-Jul-3 Christie's, Hong Kong #316/R est:160000-180000 (HK.D 150000)
£21756 $35897 €31546 Galloping horse (68x102cm-27x40in) s.i. ink scroll. 6-Jul-3 Christie's, Hong Kong #318/R est:300000-400000 (HK.D 280000)
£22764 $35967 €34146 Rooster and hen (122x51cm-48x20in) s.i.d.1948 ink col hanging scroll prov. 28-Apr-3 Sotheby's, Hong Kong #574/R est:200000-300000 (HK.D 280000)
£23310 $38462 €33800 Galloping horse (75x111cm-30x44in) s.i. ink scroll. 6-Jul-3 Christie's, Hong Kong #314/R est:250000-300000 (HK.D 300000)
£24864 $41026 €36053 Horse (83x49cm-33x19in) s.i. ink scroll. 6-Jul-3 Christie's, Hong Kong #317/R est:250000-300000 (HK.D 320000)
£42735 $70513 €61966 Zhong Kui (111x55cm-44x22in) s.i. ink scroll. 6-Jul-3 Christie's, Hong Kong #315/R est:600000-700000 (HK.D 550000)
£130081 $205528 €195122 Eight horses (178x92cm-70x36in) s.i.d.1943 ink col hanging scroll. 28-Apr-3 Sotheby's, Hong Kong #615/R est:50000-70000 (HK.D 1600000)

XU BEIHONG and WANG YACHEN (20th C) Chinese
Works on paper
£14763 $24359 €21406 Cat (109x37cm-43x15in) s.i. ink scroll. 6-Jul-3 Christie's, Hong Kong #313/R est:100000-120000 (HK.D 190000)

XU BING (1955-) Chinese
Works on paper
£6504 $10276 €9756 New English calligraphy-Mao Zedong's quotation (47x312cm-19x123in) s.d. ink scroll. 28-Apr-3 Sotheby's, Hong Kong #526/R est:70000-100000 (HK.D 80000)

XU XI (1940-) Chinese
Works on paper
£725 $1188 €1000 City in the rain (94x88cm-37x35in) s.i. seals Indian ink col hanging scroll. 30-May-3 Dr Fritz Nagel, Stuttgart #1290/R

XU YISHENG (20th C) Chinese
Works on paper
£290 $475 €400 Landscape with scholar (137x68cm-54x27in) s.d.1988 seals Indian ink col hanging scroll. 30-May-3 Dr Fritz Nagel, Stuttgart #1181/R

XUAREZ, Juan Rodriguez (1675-c.1728) Mexican
£63694 $100000 €95541 Virgin of Guadaloupe (230x165cm-91x65in) s. oil gold leaf painted c.1709 prov. 19-Nov-2 Sotheby's, New York #13/R est:80000

XUL SOLAR, Alejandro (1887-1963) Argentinian
£14634 $24000 €21951 Sombra del caminante (21x21cm-8x8in) s. panel painted c.1917 prov. 28-May-3 Christie's, Rockefeller NY #37/R est:30000-35000
Works on paper
£24390 $40000 €36585 Sin titulo (28x22cm-11x9in) s.d.1931 gouache prov. 28-May-3 Christie's, Rockefeller NY #23/R est:40000-50000

XYLANDER, Wilhelm (1840-1913) Danish
£419 $666 €629 Woman seen from behind, evening at Skagen (24x38cm-9x15in) i.verso panel. 10-Mar-3 Rasmussen, Vejle #25 (D.KR 4500)
£603 $916 €905 Still life of candle stick, wine glass and vegetables in Dutch style (28x40cm-11x16in) s.d.1857. 27-Aug-2 Rasmussen, Copenhagen #1563/R (D.KR 7000)
£729 $1137 €1094 Beached boats at Londstrup Strand (38x60cm-15x24in) mono.i.d.70. 11-Nov-2 Rasmussen, Vejle #622/R (D.KR 8500)
£3227 $5002 €4841 Sunset by the lake Starnberg (84x132cm-33x52in) s. 6-Dec-2 Kieselbach, Budapest #89/R (H.F 1200000)

YA MING (1924-) Chinese
Works on paper
£652 $1070 €900 Moscow (45x66cm-18x26in) i.d.1953 seal Indian ink col hanging scroll. 30-May-3 Dr Fritz Nagel, Stuttgart #1183/R
£870 $1426 €1200 Trees in springtime (68x68cm-27x27in) i. seals Indian ink col hanging scroll. 30-May-3 Dr Fritz Nagel, Stuttgart #1182/R
£1449 $2377 €2000 Song of the lute player (136x67cm-54x26in) s.d.1984 seals Indian ink col hanging scroll. 30-May-3 Dr Fritz Nagel, Stuttgart #1281/R est:600-1000

YAKIMCHENKO, Aleksandr Georgievich (1878-1929) Russian
£2000 $3140 €3000 Barges on the canal (33x47cm-13x19in) s.d.1914 board. 20-Nov-2 Sotheby's, London #71/R est:3000-4000

YAKOVLEV, Vladimir (1934-) Russian
Works on paper
£3500 $5670 €5250 White flower (60x42cm-24x17in) s. gouache. 21-May-3 Sotheby's, London #225/R est:1500-2000

YAMAGATA, Hiro (1948-) Japanese
Sculpture
£961 $1500 €1442 Wheeler dealer (38x18cm-15x7in) s.d.89 num.15/375 bronze marble. 14-Oct-2 Butterfields, San Francisco #2125/R est:2000-3000

YAMAGATA, Hisao (20th C) Japanese
£625 $1031 €900 Untitled (47x70cm-19x28in) s.d.65-7 verso painted wood relief. 1-Jul-3 Christie's, Amsterdam #521/R

YAMAGUCHI, Gen (1903-1976) Japanese
Works on paper
£884 $1406 €1300 Bouquet of flowers in landscape (46x45cm-18x18in) s.d.1968 gouache cardboard. 28-Feb-3 Joron-Derem, Paris #46

YAMAGUCHI, Tomoya (1958-) Japanese
£2375 $3800 €3444 Untitled (208x229cm-82x90in) s.d.2000 verso. 13-May-3 Sotheby's, Tel Aviv #11/R est:2200-2800

YAMAMOTO, Taro (1919-) American
Works on paper
£353 $550 €530 Untitled, abstract composition (122x89cm-48x35in) s.d.1969 mixed media. 10-Nov-2 Selkirks, St. Louis #996/R

YAMAWAKI, Iwao (20th C) Japanese?
Photographs
£3481 $5500 €5222 Cathedral intersect corner (11x9cm-4x4in) st.verso gelatin silver print executed c.1931 prov. 24-Apr-3 Phillips, New York #20/R est:4000-6000

YAN HSIA (1937-) Chinese/American
£3525 $5500 €5288 Pedestrian no 1 (122x152cm-48x60in) s.i.d.1973 verso. 14-Oct-2 Butterfields, San Francisco #2108/R est:3000-5000

YAN JING (1970-) Chinese
£306 $487 €450 Fillette de Pamir 1 (55x38cm-22x15in) s.d.2002 acrylic. 24-Mar-3 Coutau Begarie, Paris #330
£340 $541 €500 Fillette de Pamir 2 (55x38cm-22x15in) s.d.2002 acrylic. 24-Mar-3 Coutau Begarie, Paris #331

YAN MEIHUA (1927-) Chinese
Works on paper
£580 $951 €800 Lady Wen saying farewell to the Huns (133x66cm-52x26in) i.d.1981 seals Indian ink col hanging scroll. 30-May-3 Dr Fritz Nagel, Stuttgart #1266/R

YAN PEI MING (1960-) Chinese
£2152 $3357 €3400 Idole 97001 (41x33cm-16x13in) s.i.d.08.97 verso prov. 20-Oct-2 Charbonneaux, Paris #147 est:2500-3000
£2215 $3456 €3500 Idole 97002 (41x33cm-16x13in) s.i.d.08.97 verso prov. 20-Oct-2 Charbonneaux, Paris #146 est:2500-3000
£13491 $20775 €21450 L'homme le plus sourd, pere de l'artiste (200x235cm-79x93in) s.i.d.1996 verso prov. 26-Oct-2 Cornette de St.Cyr, Paris #163/R est:20000

YANAGI, Miwa (1967-) American?
Photographs
£1899 $3000 €2849 Looking for the next story I (14x57cm-6x22in) s.d.98 c-print one of 22 prov. 13-Nov-2 Sotheby's, New York #418/R
£3750 $6000 €5625 Elevator girl house 3F (91x107cm-36x42in) s.i.num.3/15 verso c-print on board executed 1998 prov. 16-May-3 Phillips, New York #223/R est:7000-9000

YANDELL, Enid (1870-1934) American
Sculpture
£24516 $38000 €36774 Fountain, boys with sea shells (81cm-32in) i. verdigris pat. bronze. 5-Dec-2 Christie's, Rockefeller NY #67/R est:15000-25000

YANG QIUREN (1907-1983) Chinese
£3885 $6410 €5633 Hsin Fon Jian Hydroelectric Plant (54x37cm-21x15in) paperboard painted c.1960-70 exhib.lit. 6-Jul-3 Christie's, Hong Kong #155/R est:60000-100000 (HK.D 50000)

YANG SHANSHEN (1913-) Chinese
Works on paper
£5051 $8333 €7324 Landscape (49x123cm-19x48in) s.i.d.2001 ink scroll. 6-Jul-3 Christie's, Hong Kong #335/R est:70000-90000 (HK.D 65000)
£13986 $23077 €20280 Tiger (176x96cm-69x38in) s.i. ink scroll. 6-Jul-3 Christie's, Hong Kong #343/R est:120000-180000 (HK.D 180000)
£18648 $30769 €27040 White peacocks (109x50cm-43x20in) s.i. ink scroll. 6-Jul-3 Christie's, Hong Kong #342/R est:50000-70000 (HK.D 240000)

YANKEL, Jacques (1920-) French
£241 $381 €350 Pterodactyle sur fond rouge (65x54cm-26x21in) s. i.verso. 4-Apr-3 Tajan, Paris #264
£295 $475 €443 In full bloom (51x99cm-20x39in) s. 16-Jan-3 Skinner, Bolton #889/R

YANN, Robert (1901-1994) French
£833 $1358 €1200 Discussion devant la maison du pecheur (33x41cm-13x16in) s. 19-Jul-3 Thierry & Lannon, Brest #183
Works on paper
£256 $403 €400 Port breton (29x23cm-11x9in) W/C. 16-Dec-2 Eric Coutrier, Paris #78
£347 $566 €500 Pecheur de St Guenole (24x31cm-9x12in) s. wash gouache. 19-Jul-3 Thierry & Lannon, Brest #413
£828 $1316 €1200 Village du Pays Bigouden (33x47cm-13x19in) s. W/C. 10-Mar-3 Thierry & Lannon, Brest #82/R
£915 $1474 €1300 Le marin dans la ruelle (47x32cm-19x13in) s. W/C. 11-May-3 Thierry & Lannon, Brest #323

YAOUANC, Alain le (c.1940-) French
£550 $875 €825 Untitled (130x160cm-51x63in) 18-Mar-3 Bonhams, Knightsbridge #237
£1100 $1749 €1650 Geometric composition (140x180cm-55x71in) 18-Mar-3 Bonhams, Knightsbridge #236
Works on paper
£669 $1077 €950 Echec et mat (34x26cm-13x10in) init. collage. 11-May-3 Thierry & Lannon, Brest #265

YARBER, Robert (1948-) American
£5674 $9191 €8000 Untitled (170x170cm-67x67in) 20-May-3 Porro, Milan #58/R est:6500-7000

YARDLEY, John (1933-) British
Works on paper
£280 $437 €420 Waiting for the tide (41x66cm-16x26in) s. W/C. 15-Oct-2 Canterbury Auctions, UK #196
£280 $440 €420 Aylesbury Court House (31x45cm-12x18in) s. W/C. 15-Apr-3 Bonhams, Knightsbridge #132/R
£400 $644 €600 Bryanston Square, London (64x49cm-25x19in) s.d.1982 W/C. 14-Jan-3 Bonhams, Knightsbridge #197/R
£420 $655 €630 Tower Bridge (20x28cm-8x11in) s. W/C. 9-Oct-2 Woolley & Wallis, Salisbury #129/R
£420 $659 €630 Venetian backwater (31x46cm-12x18in) s. W/C. 15-Apr-3 Bonhams, Knightsbridge #126/R
£450 $734 €653 Windy day at Hampton (35x53cm-14x21in) s. W/C. 15-Jul-3 Bonhams, Knightsbridge #134/R
£480 $773 €720 Middle Temple (32x46cm-13x18in) s. W/C. 14-Jan-3 Bonhams, Knightsbridge #196/R
£500 $805 €750 Paper buildings, The Temple (31x45cm-12x18in) s. W/C. 14-Jan-3 Bonhams, Knightsbridge #200/R
£550 $886 €825 Old Bailey (31x45cm-12x18in) s. W/C. 14-Jan-3 Bonhams, Knightsbridge #195/R
£550 $886 €825 Venetian palace (31x46cm-12x18in) s. W/C. 14-Jan-3 Bonhams, Knightsbridge #201/R

YARNOLD, G B (19th C) British
£446 $687 €700 River landscapes with waterfalls and fishermen (91x71cm-36x28in) s. pair. 4-Sep-2 James Adam, Dublin #94

YAROSHENKO, Nikolai Alexandrovich (1846-1898) Russian
£1392 $2200 €2200 Professor Nikolai Jaroshenko (26x27cm-10x11in) s.d.91. 1-Dec-2 Bukowskis, Helsinki #252/R est:2000-3000
£15000 $24300 €22500 Portrait of a lady in black (74x47cm-29x19in) s.d.1881. 21-May-3 Sotheby's, London #23/R est:15000-20000

YARROW, Annette (1932-) British
Sculpture
£1800 $2934 €2700 Stallion and mare (49x88cm-19x35in) s.d.1979 num.1/9 bronze slate base st.f.Meridian. 11-Feb-3 Sotheby's, Olympia #322/R est:2000-3000

YARROW, William Henry Kemble (1891-1941) American
£6494 $10000 €9741 Settlers (183x244cm-72x96in) s.i.stretcher prov. 24-Oct-2 Shannon's, Milford #46/R est:12000-18000

YARZ, Edmond (19th C) French
£3521 $5845 €5000 Le jour se leve sur Carcassonne (98x131cm-39x52in) s. 16-Jun-3 Oger, Dumont, Paris #52/R est:3500-4500

YATES, Cullen (1866-1945) American
£4051 $6400 €6077 Spring time (30x41cm-12x16in) s. s.i.verso. 5-Apr-3 Neal Auction Company, New Orleans #341/R est:3000-5000
£7595 $12000 €11393 Spring landscape (61x91cm-24x36in) s. 24-Apr-3 Shannon's, Milford #121/R est:4000-6000

YATES, Fred (1922-) British
£280 $434 €420 Village well (56x84cm-22x33in) s. 26-Sep-2 Lane, Penzance #322
£300 $477 €450 Cornish coastal scene with house and garden in the foreground (42x88cm-17x35in) s. 6-Mar-3 Bonhams, Cornwall #744/R
£300 $468 €435 Pont Creek Fowey (37x70cm-15x28in) s. board. 27-Mar-3 Lane, Penzance #333/R
£320 $506 €480 Flowers in a vase on tripod table (31x25cm-12x10in) s. 4-Apr-3 Moore Allen & Innocent, Cirencester #610/R
£340 $527 €510 Day on the sands (46x61cm-18x24in) s. board. 26-Sep-2 Lane, Penzance #77
£400 $620 €600 Figures on a country lane (74x99cm-29x39in) s. canvasboard. 26-Sep-2 Lane, Penzance #78

£400 $628 €600 Cafe de la Care, figures before a French cafe (46x55cm-18x22in) s. 10-Dec-2 Lane, Penzance #123
£400 $632 €600 Crowning of the May Queen (40x50cm-16x20in) bears s.d.78 mixed media oval. 4-Apr-3 Moore Allen & Innocent, Cirencester #416/R
£400 $668 €580 Chateau in a French landscape (40x49cm-16x19in) s. board. 19-Jun-3 Lane, Penzance #242
£420 $651 €630 French cafe (81x104cm-32x41in) s. 26-Sep-2 Lane, Penzance #53
£420 $651 €630 Figures before a country cottage (74x99cm-29x39in) board. 26-Sep-2 Lane, Penzance #72
£420 $651 €630 Figures dancing (64x74cm-25x29in) s. board. 26-Sep-2 Lane, Penzance #79
£440 $691 €660 Off to chapel (55x44cm-22x17in) s. board. 10-Dec-2 Lane, Penzance #284
£450 $702 €675 Interior (28x28cm-11x11in) s. board. 17-Oct-2 David Lay, Penzance #1107
£450 $702 €675 Prussia Cove (25x36cm-10x14in) s. i.verso. 17-Oct-2 David Lay, Penzance #1250
£460 $718 €667 Street scene St. Just (30x44cm-12x17in) s. board. 27-Mar-3 Lane, Penzance #109
£480 $744 €720 Bridge and cottages on a country lane (109x109cm-43x43in) s. board. 26-Sep-2 Lane, Penzance #266
£500 $780 €750 Viaduct (56x41cm-22x16in) s. board. 17-Oct-2 David Lay, Penzance #1108
£500 $830 €725 View over the rooftops from Bull Hill, Fowey (25x38cm-10x15in) s. board. 12-Jun-3 Bonhams, Cornwall #567
£540 $837 €810 Coming home pal, view from artist's studio Fowey (43x56cm-17x22in) s. board. 26-Sep-2 Lane, Penzance #52
£540 $848 €810 Frolices, figures on a beach (49x61cm-19x24in) s. i.verso. 10-Dec-2 Lane, Penzance #124
£550 $908 €798 Aspedistra (21x15cm-8x6in) s. board. 3-Jul-3 Christie's, Kensington #563
£600 $930 €900 Fred's Cafe, artist painting before a cafe (81x102cm-32x40in) s. board. 26-Sep-2 Lane, Penzance #54
£600 $936 €900 Beach, Eastbourne (15x13cm-6x5in) s. i.verso board. 17-Oct-2 David Lay, Penzance #1228
£600 $978 €900 Table (46x38cm-18x15in) s. board. 13-Feb-3 David Lay, Penzance #380
£620 $961 €930 Figures in a village street (46x71cm-18x28in) s. board. 26-Sep-2 Lane, Penzance #74
£640 $992 €960 Limosin, figures in a French village (46x91cm-18x36in) s. 26-Sep-2 Lane, Penzance #233
£650 $1079 €943 Coast (41x89cm-16x35in) s. board. 10-Jun-3 David Lay, Penzance #154
£680 $1054 €1020 Children playing in a stream before a watermill (104x112cm-41x44in) s.d.1975 board. 26-Sep-2 Lane, Penzance #239
£680 $1108 €1020 Trencrom (51x61cm-20x24in) s. board. 13-Feb-3 David Lay, Penzance #379
£680 $1129 €986 Waterfront, Caffa Mill, Fowey (25x30cm-10x12in) s. board. 12-Jun-3 Bonhams, Cornwall #565/R
£700 $1085 €1050 Brighton street scene (163x112cm-64x44in) s. 26-Sep-2 Lane, Penzance #188
£700 $1155 €1015 Les fleurs sauvage (25x30cm-10x12in) s. 3-Jul-3 Christie's, Kensington #561
£720 $1116 €1080 Street scene, St Day, Cornwall (91x86cm-36x34in) s. i.d.1977 verso board. 26-Sep-2 Lane, Penzance #73
£720 $1116 €1080 Figures on a country bridge (91x107cm-36x42in) s. board. 26-Sep-2 Lane, Penzance #142
£720 $1145 €1080 Nellie Parker, Sittingborne barges in a creek (37x55cm-15x22in) s.i.d.1972 board. 6-Mar-3 Bonhams, Cornwall #745/R
£750 $1163 €1125 Last supper (145x145cm-57x57in) s. i.verso. 26-Sep-2 Lane, Penzance #313
£750 $1223 €1125 Fruit centre (30x41cm-12x16in) s. board. 13-Feb-3 David Lay, Penzance #281
£750 $1170 €1125 Old Brighton (37x43cm-15x17in) s. board. 27-Mar-3 Christie's, Kensington #601/R
£800 $1240 €1200 Ornamental gardens (114x140cm-45x55in) s. 26-Sep-2 Lane, Penzance #286
£800 $1320 €1160 Flowers in a orange vase (21x18cm-8x7in) s. board. 3-Jul-3 Christie's, Kensington #577
£880 $1364 €1320 I like to teach the world to sing, nude figures on a beach (124x150cm-49x59in) s. board. 26-Sep-2 Lane, Penzance #156
£918 $1460 €1350 Village scene (122x193cm-48x76in) s. panel. 3-Mar-3 Marc Kohn, Paris #29/R
£1100 $1705 €1650 Lostwithiel, eventide, figures on a Cornish lane (180x231cm-71x91in) s. 26-Sep-2 Lane, Penzance #235/R est:900-1200
£1100 $1815 €1595 At the swimming pool (22x30cm-9x12in) s. board. 3-Jul-3 Christie's, Kensington #555/R est:400-600
£1200 $1980 €1740 Innocence (32x28cm-13x11in) s. i.verso board. 3-Jul-3 Christie's, Kensington #557/R est:600-800
£1200 $1980 €1740 L'Eglise de Beaumes de Venise. Cathedral (25x30cm-10x12in) s. two. 3-Jul-3 Christie's, Kensington #558 est:400-600
£1200 $1980 €1740 Brighton pier (40x45cm-16x18in) s. board. 3-Jul-3 Christie's, Kensington #700/R est:500-700
£1400 $2310 €2030 Boat in dry dock (63x63cm-25x25in) s. board. 3-Jul-3 Christie's, Kensington #699/R est:1000-1500
£1550 $2573 €2248 Two crabs (61x69cm-24x27in) s.d.1967. 10-Jun-3 David Lay, Penzance #158/R est:800-1400
£1600 $2656 €2320 Lamorna woods (102x74cm-40x29in) s. 10-Jun-3 David Lay, Penzance #40 est:1200-1500
£1700 $2652 €2550 Fishing boats (61x75cm-24x30in) s. board. 27-Mar-3 Christie's, Kensington #602/R est:800-1200
£1850 $2886 €2683 Crucifixion (119x182cm-47x72in) board exhib. 27-Mar-3 Lane, Penzance #313 est:1200-1500
£2050 $3198 €2973 Walk by the river (76x99cm-30x39in) s. i.verso. 27-Mar-3 Lane, Penzance #5/R est:2000-2500

Works on paper

£380 $608 €551 Bristol Cathedral (55x74cm-22x29in) s. W/C prov. 13-May-3 Bristol Auction Rooms #455/R
£380 $593 €551 Figures before cottages Pendeen (25x34cm-10x13in) s.d.1987 W/C. 27-Mar-3 Lane, Penzance #2
£480 $802 €696 Harbour Sennen (30x40cm-12x16in) s. W/C. 19-Jun-3 Lane, Penzance #166
£500 $800 €725 Bristol Docks with boats (55x74cm-22x29in) s. W/C prov. 13-May-3 Bristol Auction Rooms #456/R
£780 $1303 €1131 Penzance, Market Jew Street (76x56cm-30x22in) s. W/C. 19-Jun-3 Lane, Penzance #243
£1100 $1716 €1650 Les armondiers. Chez moi (54x73cm-21x29in) s. W/C two. 27-Mar-3 Christie's, Kensington #608/R est:600-800

YATES, G (fl.1825-1837) British

Works on paper

£1700 $2652 €2550 View of London Bridge from the North Bank at Custom's House (33x59cm-13x23in) s.d.1837 pencil W/C. 17-Oct-2 Christie's, Kensington #50/R est:1000-1500

YATES, Gideon (19th C) British

Works on paper

£900 $1386 €1350 London from Southwark Church, 1830's (34x61cm-13x24in) s. W/C. 8-Sep-2 Lots Road, London #338

YATES, Thomas (?-1796) British

Works on paper

£2100 $3234 €3150 Shipping off Gibraltar (18x23cm-7x9in) s.d.1792 pen ink W/C pair. 25-Oct-2 Gorringes, Lewes #886
£2800 $4620 €4060 Shipping off Gibraltar. Shipping off the Needles (17x23cm-7x9in) s.d.1971 s.d.1972 pen ink W/C over pencil two. 2-Jul-3 Sotheby's, Olympia #302/R est:2000-3000

YATES, Thomas Brown (1882-?) British

£1250 $1950 €1875 Djurgardsbrunviken, Stockholm (30x40cm-12x16in) s.i.d.1925 verso board exhib. 10-Apr-3 Tennants, Leyburn #961/R est:700-900

YAVNO, Max (1921-1985) American?

Photographs

£2278 $3600 €3417 Leg, Hollywood (49x39cm-19x15in) s. gelatin silver print prov.lit. 25-Apr-3 Phillips, New York #309/R est:1000-1500
£2577 $4200 €3866 Muscle beach (20x34cm-8x13in) s. gelatin silver print. 12-Feb-3 Christie's, Rockefeller NY #250/R est:3000-5000
£3571 $5500 €5357 Trolley car (8x11cm-3x4in) s.i. photograph prov.lit. 22-Oct-2 Sotheby's, New York #173/R est:3000-5000
£8861 $14000 €13292 Portfolio one, image as poem (36x28cm-14x11in) s. 14 gelatin silver print on board prov.lit. 25-Apr-3 Phillips, New York #251/R est:8000-12000

YAZZ, Beatian (1928-) American

Works on paper

£1282 $2000 €1923 Wolf attack. Whitetail deer (20x33cm-8x13in) s. W/C gouache two. 9-Nov-2 Santa Fe Art, Santa Fe #252/R est:1000-2000

YEAMES, William Frederick (1835-1918) British

£2553 $3957 €3830 Interior scene with figures (58x85cm-23x33in) s.d.1868-1874. 4-Dec-2 AB Stockholms Auktionsverk #1848/R est:40000-50000 (S.KR 36000)
£12500 $20125 €18750 Cottage garden (55x42cm-22x17in) panel prov.exhib. 20-Feb-3 Christie's, London #270/R est:12000
£50000 $79000 €75000 Arming of the young knight, God speed thee, then my own brave boy (103x129cm-41x51in) s.d.1868 prov.exhib.lit. 2-Dec-2 Sotheby's, London #65/R est:40000-60000

YEATS FAMILY (19/20th C) Irish

£7051 $11071 €11000 Celtic goddess (43x20cm-17x8in) init. tempera over gold ground. 19-Nov-2 Hamilton Osborne King, Dublin #578/R est:500-1000

YEATS, Anne (1919-2001) Irish

£385 $604 €600 Diamonds (24x37cm-9x15in) panel. 19-Nov-2 Hamilton Osborne King, Dublin #601
£417 $654 €650 Fish skeleton (21x41cm-8x16in) board. 19-Nov-2 Hamilton Osborne King, Dublin #602

£417 $654 €650 Abstracts, blacks, yellows and reds (38x61cm-15x24in) board pair. 19-Nov-2 Hamilton Osborne King, Dublin #621
£449 $704 €700 Chinese boy at window (53x36cm-21x14in) 19-Nov-2 Hamilton Osborne King, Dublin #617
£449 $704 €700 Flat fish (36x51cm-14x20in) 19-Nov-2 Hamilton Osborne King, Dublin #609/R
£481 $755 €750 Green abstract (41x56cm-16x22in) 19-Nov-2 Hamilton Osborne King, Dublin #614
£481 $755 €750 Wooded mountain landscape (36x46cm-14x18in) 19-Nov-2 Hamilton Osborne King, Dublin #624
£481 $755 €750 Abstract landscape (35x50cm-14x20in) s. board. 19-Nov-2 Hamilton Osborne King, Dublin #465
£513 $805 €800 Rain (81x81cm-32x32in) 19-Nov-2 Hamilton Osborne King, Dublin #622
£641 $1006 €1000 Face behind the lace curtain (51x38cm-20x15in) board. 19-Nov-2 Hamilton Osborne King, Dublin #612/R
£641 $1006 €1000 Abstracts in red and greys (76x60cm-30x24in) 19-Nov-2 Hamilton Osborne King, Dublin #616
£769 $1208 €1200 Shawl (36x54cm-14x21in) board. 19-Nov-2 Hamilton Osborne King, Dublin #606/R
£769 $1208 €1200 Face in the window (26x36cm-10x14in) 19-Nov-2 Hamilton Osborne King, Dublin #619/R
£793 $1118 €1300 Balls of cloth (57x75cm-22x30in) prov. 5-Feb-2 Thomas Adams, Dublin #354
£833 $1308 €1300 Mother and child (30x40cm-12x16in) 19-Nov-2 Hamilton Osborne King, Dublin #604/R
£833 $1308 €1300 Tinkers (46x31cm-18x12in) i.verso board. 19-Nov-2 Hamilton Osborne King, Dublin #615/R
£833 $1308 €1300 Water lilies (36x52cm-14x20in) 19-Nov-2 Hamilton Osborne King, Dublin #626/R
£962 $1510 €1500 Brown landscape with trees (36x53cm-14x21in) s. 19-Nov-2 Hamilton Osborne King, Dublin #608/R est:500-800
£962 $1510 €1500 Fish unwrapped (41x61cm-16x24in) s. i.verso exhib. 19-Nov-2 Hamilton Osborne King, Dublin #610/R est:600-800
£1026 $1610 €1600 Pebbles (41x56cm-16x22in) 19-Nov-2 Hamilton Osborne King, Dublin #607/R est:500-800
£1090 $1711 €1700 Kitchen (53x36cm-21x14in) board. 19-Nov-2 Hamilton Osborne King, Dublin #618/R est:500-800
£1218 $1912 €1900 Dandelion (51x67cm-20x26in) 19-Nov-2 Hamilton Osborne King, Dublin #623/R est:1000-1500
£1410 $2214 €2200 Family (54x77cm-21x30in) oil collage board. 19-Nov-2 Hamilton Osborne King, Dublin #611/R est:1000-1500
£1410 $2214 €2200 Embrace (46x36cm-18x14in) panel. 19-Nov-2 Hamilton Osborne King, Dublin #620/R est:600-1000
£1410 $2214 €2200 Volcano (61x91cm-24x36in) s.i.verso. 19-Nov-2 Hamilton Osborne King, Dublin #625/R est:600-1000
£2101 $3446 €2900 Rain (81x81cm-32x32in) prov. 28-May-3 Bonhams & James Adam, Dublin #159/R est:3000-4000
£3378 $5270 €5000 There is still some snow left (61x83cm-24x33in) s. board prov. 26-Mar-3 James Adam, Dublin #55/R est:2500-3500
£4029 $6446 €5600 Red cloth and green lemon (36x51cm-14x20in) s. card. 13-May-3 Thomas Adams, Dublin #390

Works on paper
£609 $956 €950 Scarecrow (37x46cm-15x18in) s. mixed media. 19-Nov-2 Hamilton Osborne King, Dublin #627
£641 $1006 €1000 View from condemned house (41x31cm-16x12in) s. mixed media. 19-Nov-2 Hamilton Osborne King, Dublin #628
£845 $1318 €1250 Woman reading paper on the bus (27x23cm-11x9in) s.d.42 crayon. 26-Mar-3 James Adam, Dublin #147/R est:400-600
£1923 $3019 €3000 Fishing boat in harbour (28x38cm-11x15in) W/C card. 19-Nov-2 Hamilton Osborne King, Dublin #613/R est:200-400

YEATS, Jack Butler (1871-1957) Irish/British
£1923 $3019 €3000 Lady and a panther (38x28cm-15x11in) i.stretcher. 19-Nov-2 Hamilton Osborne King, Dublin #583 est:400-600
£4487 $7045 €7000 Pebble beach, Sligo Bay (25x35cm-10x14in) canvasboard unfinished. 19-Nov-2 Hamilton Osborne King, Dublin #592/R est:3000-5000
£7051 $11071 €11000 Sligo Bay (25x35cm-10x14in) s. canvasboard unfinished. 19-Nov-2 Hamilton Osborne King, Dublin #593/R est:3000-5000
£19872 $30801 €31000 River mouth, Glenbeigh (24x36cm-9x14in) s.i.verso panel exhib.lit. 3-Dec-2 Bonhams & James Adam, Dublin #40/R est:25000-30000
£85000 $136000 €127500 Farewell to the sea (35x46cm-14x18in) s. painted 1943 prov.exhib.lit. 15-May-3 Christie's, London #78/R est:60000-100000
£95000 $152000 €142500 Little shade (46x61cm-18x24in) s. s.i.verso painted 1952 prov.exhib.lit. 15-May-3 Christie's, London #79/R est:80000-120000
£192308 $298077 €300000 Metal man, low tide (46x61cm-18x24in) s. prov.exhib.lit. 3-Dec-2 Bonhams & James Adam, Dublin #94/R est:300000-400000
£200000 $320000 €300000 South Pacific (61x91cm-24x36in) s. prov.exhib.lit. 16-May-3 Sotheby's, London #90/R est:200000-300000
£220000 $352000 €330000 Nimrod of the railway train (23x35cm-9x14in) s. i.verso board prov.lit. 15-May-3 Christie's, London #77/R est:70000-100000
£250000 $400000 €375000 Daughter of the circus (46x61cm-18x24in) s. prov.exhib.lit. 16-May-3 Sotheby's, London #80/R est:250000-350000
£288462 $447115 €450000 Saddling a winner on Calary Bog 1946 (35x53cm-14x21in) s. prov.exhib.lit. 3-Dec-2 Bonhams & James Adam, Dublin #63/R est:450000-600000

Works on paper
£570 $883 €900 Collecting water (13x9cm-5x4in) i.verso pencil wash. 24-Sep-2 De Veres Art Auctions, Dublin #43/R
£696 $1079 €1100 Englishman home (9x13cm-4x5in) pencil wash. 24-Sep-2 De Veres Art Auctions, Dublin #53/R est:700-1000
£759 $1177 €1200 From Sabina's (9x13cm-4x5in) i. pencil wash. 24-Sep-2 De Veres Art Auctions, Dublin #45/R est:700-1000
£823 $1275 €1300 Cottage and bridge, Aran (9x13cm-4x5in) i. pencil wash. 24-Sep-2 De Veres Art Auctions, Dublin #48/R est:700-1000
£823 $1275 €1300 Studying book on Diabolo (13x9cm-5x4in) i. pencil wash. 24-Sep-2 De Veres Art Auctions, Dublin #52/R est:500-700
£886 $1373 €1400 Kelp - Aran Island Galway Bay (9x13cm-4x5in) i. pencil wash. 24-Sep-2 De Veres Art Auctions, Dublin #44/R est:700-1000
£886 $1373 €1400 At the Royal Theatre Dublin. Englishman home (13x9cm-5x4in) i. pencil wash double-sided. 24-Sep-2 De Veres Art Auctions, Dublin #51/R est:700-1000
£1013 $1570 €1600 Aran cottage (9x13cm-4x5in) wash. 24-Sep-2 De Veres Art Auctions, Dublin #57/R est:1000-1500
£1026 $1610 €1600 Study of a church pew (13x9cm-5x4in) mono. W/C pencil prov. 19-Nov-2 Whyte's, Dublin #57/R est:2000-2500
£1203 $1864 €1900 Going to Lace school (9x13cm-4x5in) i. pencil wash. 24-Sep-2 De Veres Art Auctions, Dublin #46/R est:700-1000
£1329 $2060 €2100 View of the four courts (13x9cm-5x4in) i. pencil wash. 24-Sep-2 De Veres Art Auctions, Dublin #50/R est:700-1000
£1519 $2354 €2400 Aran man for priest (9x13cm-4x5in) i. pencil wash. 24-Sep-2 De Veres Art Auctions, Dublin #47/R est:1000-1500
£1519 $2354 €2400 Aran cottage (9x13cm-4x5in) pencil wash. 24-Sep-2 De Veres Art Auctions, Dublin #56/R est:700-1000
£1772 $2747 €2800 Carrying kelp (13x9cm-5x4in) i. pencil wash double-sided. 24-Sep-2 De Veres Art Auctions, Dublin #42/R est:1000-1500
£1772 $2747 €2800 Sabina's Hooker - currach waiting for the priest (9x13cm-4x5in) i. pencil wash. 24-Sep-2 De Veres Art Auctions, Dublin #49/R est:700-1000
£1887 $2943 €3000 Woman raising her hat in greeting (14x9cm-6x4in) mono.i. W/C prov. 17-Sep-2 Whyte's, Dublin #52 est:2000-3000
£2025 $3139 €3200 Sabinas store (13x9cm-5x4in) i. pencil wash. 24-Sep-2 De Veres Art Auctions, Dublin #41/R est:1000-1500
£2051 $3221 €3200 After the war jars in the home (10x20cm-4x8in) s.i. pen ink. 19-Nov-2 Whyte's, Dublin #70/R est:3500-4500
£2244 $3522 €3500 Death bed scene (27x22cm-11x9in) W/C. 19-Nov-2 Hamilton Osborne King, Dublin #581/R est:1500-3000
£2244 $3522 €3500 View of a strand (31x32cm-12x13in) pastel. 19-Nov-2 Hamilton Osborne King, Dublin #585/R est:200-300
£2372 $3724 €3700 Who says Rheumatics! (8x14cm-3x6in) pen ink dr envelope. 19-Nov-2 Whyte's, Dublin #71/R est:1500-2000
£2500 $4000 €3750 Take care, short hair (17x12cm-7x5in) i. pen brush black ink prov. 15-May-3 Christie's, Kensington #157/R est:3000-5000
£2534 $3979 €3700 Study of a pirate (16x10cm-6x4in) s. W/C. 15-Apr-3 De Veres Art Auctions, Dublin #116/R est:1500-2000
£3056 $4858 €4400 Rosa of Salcombe at Kingsbridge, Devon (9x13cm-4x5in) i.d.1901 pencil W/C pen ink. 29-Apr-3 Whyte's, Dublin #188/R est:3000-4000
£3077 $4831 €4800 Lake at Coole (20x26cm-8x10in) i. pastel. 19-Nov-2 Hamilton Osborne King, Dublin #586/R est:1000-1500
£3205 $5032 €5000 Portrait of Susan Mitchell (28x22cm-11x9in) i. crayon. 19-Nov-2 Hamilton Osborne King, Dublin #571/R est:1500-2000
£3205 $5032 €5000 Two girls dancing (35x24cm-14x9in) pastel. 19-Nov-2 Hamilton Osborne King, Dublin #587/R est:300-500
£3526 $5535 €5500 Norma Borthwick, seated (34x24cm-13x9in) s.i.d.1902 chl soft crayon dr. 19-Nov-2 Hamilton Osborne King, Dublin #570/R est:1500-2000
£3774 $5887 €6000 Jolly Christmas (8x11cm-3x4in) i. pen ink W/C prov. 17-Sep-2 Whyte's, Dublin #51/R est:3000-4000
£3800 $6004 €5700 Morning of the fair (18x27cm-7x11in) s. pen black ink prov. 27-Nov-2 Sotheby's, Olympia #30/R est:1800-2200
£3846 $6038 €6000 Head studies of J M Synge (23x17cm-9x7in) mono.i. pencil. 19-Nov-2 Hamilton Osborne King, Dublin #591/R est:2000-3000
£4167 $6542 €6500 Portrait of Miss Horniman (25x17cm-10x7in) i. crayon. 19-Nov-2 Hamilton Osborne King, Dublin #573/R est:1500-2000
£4167 $6542 €6500 Woods at Coole (17x24cm-7x9in) pastel. 19-Nov-2 Hamilton Osborne King, Dublin #584/R est:600-1000
£4487 $7045 €7000 Group of ruffians (28x45cm-11x18in) i.verso collage W/C. 19-Nov-2 Hamilton Osborne King, Dublin #589/R est:2500-4000
£5506 $8535 €8700 At full speed (36x34cm-14x13in) s. pencil wash. 24-Sep-2 De Veres Art Auctions, Dublin #91 est:9000-12000
£5769 $9058 €9000 W B Yeats seated and wearing a beard (26x23cm-10x9in) i.d.August 1886 pen. 19-Nov-2 Hamilton Osborne King, Dublin #574/R est:3000-4000
£5769 $9058 €9000 Portrait of W B Yeats, with beard (23x14cm-9x6in) i. soft crayon. 19-Nov-2 Hamilton Osborne King, Dublin #575/R est:4000-6000
£5769 $9058 €9000 Self portrait (26x20cm-10x8in) i.verso Indian ink exec.c.1925 lit. 19-Nov-2 Hamilton Osborne King, Dublin #597/R est:2000-3000
£6644 $10431 €9700 Fair day, Belmullet (14x26cm-6x10in) s. ink. 15-Apr-3 De Veres Art Auctions, Dublin #150/R est:10000-15000
£7595 $11772 €12000 Races (20x15cm-8x6in) s. pen ink prov. 25-Sep-2 James Adam, Dublin #68/R est:10000-15000
£8700 $13833 €13050 Fair day (15x22cm-6x9in) s. pen ink dr. 5-Mar-3 John Ross, Belfast #244 est:6000-8000

£8904 $13979 €13000 Capture of Lord Edward Fitzgerald (25x18cm-10x7in) s. col wash ink. 15-Apr-3 De Veres Art Auctions, Dublin #177 est:8000-12000
£8974 $14090 €14000 Study of W B Yeats (18x13cm-7x5in) s.d.June 20th 1904 soft crayon. 19-Nov-2 Hamilton Osborne King, Dublin #568/R est:3000-5000
£8974 $14090 €14000 Portrait of William Butler Yeats (18x12cm-7x5in) i.d.December 8th 1899 soft crayon. 19-Nov-2 Hamilton Osborne King, Dublin #572/R est:3000-4000
£10256 $16103 €16000 Self portrait (22x21cm-9x8in) i.verso exec.c.1923 Indian ink over pencil lit. 19-Nov-2 Hamilton Osborne King, Dublin #596/R est:3000-5000
£10738 $17289 €16000 Saint Kevin (76x51cm-30x20in) mono. W/C htd white prov.lit. 18-Feb-3 Whyte's, Dublin #77/R est:15000-20000
£15000 $24000 €22500 Design for a poster (45x59cm-18x23in) s.i.verso W/C prov.exhib.lit. 16-May-3 Sotheby's, London #63/R est:8000-12000
£15385 $24154 €24000 Shop in Sailor Town (16x25cm-6x10in) s. i.d.June 1909 verso pen wash. 19-Nov-2 Hamilton Osborne King, Dublin #598/R est:25000-35000
£16352 $25509 €26000 Young man's troubles (15x46cm-6x18in) s. W/C pastel pencil prov.exhib.lit. 17-Sep-2 Whyte's, Dublin #54/R est:20000-30000
£18000 $28800 €27000 Emigrant (27x44cm-11x17in) s.d.98 pencil W/C bodycol. 15-May-3 Christie's, London #75/R est:18000-25000
£18239 $28453 €29000 Carrying seaweed for kelp (29x23cm-11x9in) s. pen ink W/C prov.exhib.lit. 17-Sep-2 Whyte's, Dublin #49/R est:20000-30000
£20000 $32000 €30000 Fair of Ballinasloe (15x34cm-6x13in) s. pen ink W/C bodycol exec.1905 prov.exhib.lit. 15-May-3 Christie's, London #76/R est:20000-30000

YEATS, Jack Butler (attrib) (1871-1957) Irish/British
£4487 $7045 €7000 Portrait of a maid (36x28cm-14x11in) 19-Nov-2 Hamilton Osborne King, Dublin #582/R est:2000-3000

YEATS, John Butler (1839-1922) Irish
Works on paper
£2819 $4538 €4200 Portrait of a lady (15x13cm-6x5in) s.d.1898 pencil dr. 18-Feb-3 Whyte's, Dublin #74/R est:3500-4500
£4167 $6542 €6500 Portrait of Elkin Matthews, seated (34x25cm-13x10in) s.i.d.December 1893 chl soft pencil dr. 19-Nov-2 Hamilton Osborne King, Dublin #569/R est:2000-3000
£5208 $8281 €7500 Illustration to a fairy tale (44x27cm-17x11in) init. i.verso W/C htd white prov. 29-Apr-3 Whyte's, Dublin #1/R est:8000-10000

YEATS, Lily Corbet (attrib) (20th C) Irish
£641 $1006 €1000 Figures within a stylised fruiting vine (105x17cm-41x7in) panel. 19-Nov-2 Hamilton Osborne King, Dublin #599

YEATS, William Butler (1865-1939) Irish
£1149 $1792 €1700 Roundstone Bay, Co. Galway (11x21cm-4x8in) init. i.verso board. 26-Mar-3 James Adam, Dublin #38/R est:1000-1500
£1689 $2635 €2500 Roundstone, Co. Galway (11x21cm-4x8in) i.verso board. 26-Mar-3 James Adam, Dublin #39/R est:1000-1500

YECKLEY, Norman H (1914-) American
£256 $400 €384 Southwestern desert landscape (30x41cm-12x16in) s. artist board. 14-Sep-2 Selkirks, St. Louis #154

YEE BON (1905-1995) Chinese
£2720 $4487 €3944 Portrait of a young lady (34x44cm-13x17in) s. board painted c.1950. 6-Jul-3 Christie's, Hong Kong #158/R est:30000-60000 (HK.D 35000)
£3263 $5385 €4731 Fishes (49x38cm-19x15in) s. board painted c.1950. 6-Jul-3 Christie's, Hong Kong #159/R est:45000-65000 (HK.D 42000)
£5051 $8333 €7324 Sailing boats (45x34cm-18x13in) s. board painted c.1950. 6-Jul-3 Christie's, Hong Kong #156/R est:50000-100000 (HK.D 65000)
£16260 $25691 €24390 Great Wall (55x79cm-22x31in) s. board exhib. 28-Apr-3 Sotheby's, Hong Kong #528/R est:200000-300000 (HK.D 200000)

YEGEROV, Alexei (1930-1992) Russian
£1150 $1783 €1725 Barns near Yaroslave (26x38cm-10x15in) i. card. 1-Oct-2 Bonhams, Leeds #271 est:200-300

YEGOROV, Andrei (1878-1954) Russian
£1197 $1927 €1700 Winter's day - figure on horse drawn sleigh (45x53cm-18x21in) s. board. 10-May-3 Bukowskis, Helsinki #391/R est:1500-2000
Works on paper
£1100 $1793 €1650 Trioka in the snow (33x57cm-13x22in) s. gouache. 29-Jan-3 Sotheby's, Olympia #324/R est:400-600
£1242 $2037 €1900 Two troikas in snowy landscape (34x50cm-13x20in) s. gouache. 29-Mar-3 Dannenberg, Berlin #604/R est:1900
£1242 $2037 €1900 Troika with figures on snowy village track (35x50cm-14x20in) s. gouache. 29-Mar-3 Dannenberg, Berlin #605/R est:1900
£2025 $3200 €3200 On the way home (34x50cm-13x20in) s. gouache. 1-Dec-2 Bukowskis, Helsinki #253/R est:1000-1500
£2042 $3288 €2900 View of Tallinn (32x54cm-13x21in) s. gouache. 10-May-3 Bukowskis, Helsinki #400/R est:3000-4000
£5000 $8100 €7500 Winter landscapes (32x48cm-13x19in) s. gouache set of three. 21-May-3 Sotheby's, London #90/R est:3000-5000

YELLAND, Raymond D (1848-1900) American
£33533 $56000 €48623 Gualala River, California (60x91cm-24x36in) s.i. s.i.d.1885 verso. 18-Jun-3 Christie's, Los Angeles #64/R est:30000-50000

YELTSEVA, Dina (1965-) Russian
£250 $388 €375 Air balloon (20x35cm-8x14in) s. 8-Dec-2 John Nicholson, Haslemere #26/R
£350 $543 €525 Marrow-squash (20x35cm-8x14in) s. 8-Dec-2 John Nicholson, Haslemere #25/R
£377 $589 €600 Ice house (38x46cm-15x18in) s. 23-Sep-2 Durán, Madrid #711/R
£470 $756 €700 Winter market (25x30cm-10x12in) s. 18-Feb-3 Durán, Madrid #682/R
£559 $906 €850 Winter (35x50cm-14x20in) s. 21-Jan-3 Durán, Madrid #739/R

YENIKEYEVA, Tatyana (1968-) Russian
£304 $474 €450 Young dancer (24x30cm-9x12in) s. 25-Mar-3 Durán, Madrid #752/R
£350 $543 €525 Lesson (27x22cm-11x9in) s. 8-Dec-2 John Nicholson, Haslemere #104/R
£355 $561 €550 Girl with cat (26x21cm-10x8in) s. 17-Dec-2 Durán, Madrid #672/R
£387 $612 €600 By the window (33x24cm-13x9in) s. 17-Dec-2 Durán, Madrid #673/R

YENS, Karl Julius Heinrich (1868-1945) American
£266 $425 €399 High above Yosemite Canyon (25x34cm-10x13in) s.d.1919 laid down. 18-May-3 Butterfields, Los Angeles #7007
£1553 $2500 €2330 In the carnation field (10x14cm-4x6in) s.d.1915 i.verso board prov. 18-Feb-3 John Moran, Pasadena #72 est:2000-3000
£6024 $10000 €8735 End of the hike (60x44cm-24x17in) s. canvas on board. 11-Jun-3 Butterfields, San Francisco #4280/R est:5000-7000

YEPES, Tomas (circle) (1600-1674) Spanish
£12000 $18840 €18000 Mixed flowers in a pair of urns, bread, jug of wine and figs on a silver dish on a ledge (72x100cm-28x39in) 13-Dec-2 Christie's, Kensington #161/R est:5000-7000

YERMOLOV, Pavel (1971-) Russian
£450 $698 €675 Still life with a little bird (33x41cm-13x16in) s. 8-Dec-2 John Nicholson, Haslemere #92/R
£450 $698 €675 Still life with Herbarium and butterfly (33x41cm-13x16in) s. 8-Dec-2 John Nicholson, Haslemere #93/R
£461 $746 €700 Still life with cards (38x46cm-15x18in) 21-Jan-3 Durán, Madrid #740/R
£550 $853 €825 Still life with a portrait of General Nelson (38x55cm-15x22in) s. 8-Dec-2 John Nicholson, Haslemere #91/R
£566 $883 €900 Still life with books (38x55cm-15x22in) s. canvas on cardboard. 23-Sep-2 Durán, Madrid #712/R

YERU, Henri (20th C) ?
£360 $576 €500 Tempo, Spazio Y Luce (181x155cm-71x61in) s.d.92-93 s.i.d.1992 verso oil collage exhib. 17-May-3 De Vuyst, Lokeren #414

YEVONDE, Madame (1893-1975) British
Photographs
£4000 $6480 €6000 Metis (25x19cm-10x7in) s. vivex col print card exec.c.1935 prov. 22-May-3 Sotheby's, London #78/R est:1500-2000

YEWELL, George Henry (1830-1923) American
£659 $1100 €956 Playmates (51x61cm-20x24in) s. 21-Jun-3 Selkirks, St. Louis #149 est:800-1200

YGLESIAS, Vincent Philip (1845-1911) German
£300 $501 €435 River landscape with bridge, figures and boats (38x61cm-15x24in) s. 24-Jun-3 Neal & Fletcher, Woodbridge #349
£350 $550 €525 House by a river (34x46cm-13x18in) s. 24-Jul-2 Hamptons Fine Art, Godalming #360/R
£520 $868 €754 River landscape with fishing boats (38x64cm-15x25in) 24-Jun-3 Neal & Fletcher, Woodbridge #350

YIAKOS, Dionyssios (1914-) Greek
£2200 $3476 €3300 View of the Acropolis (63x90cm-25x35in) 1-Apr-3 Bonhams, New Bond Street #6 est:1500-2000

YKENS, Frans (1601-1693) Flemish
£10063 $15597 €16000 Madonna and Infant Jesus (88x70cm-35x28in) s.d.1640. 2-Oct-2 Dorotheum, Vienna #119/R est:15000-20000
£65000 $102050 €97500 Grapes on the vine and other fruit on table with butterfly (37x50cm-15x20in) s. copper prov.lit. 11-Dec-2 Christie's, London #35/R est:60000-80000
£90000 $141300 €135000 Flowers, fruit, baskets, figures through a window and a parrot (163x234cm-64x92in) s. prov. 12-Dec-2 Sotheby's, London #43/R est:80000-120000

YKENS, Frans (attrib) (1601-1693) Flemish
£8125 $13000 €12188 Still life with swag of grapes, lemons and other fruit. Still life (57x41cm-22x16in) pair. 14-May-3 Butterfields, San Francisco #1026/R est:6000-8000

YLINEN, Vihtori (1879-1953) Finnish
£293 $465 €430 Late winter's day with sunshine (53x79cm-21x31in) s. 24-Mar-3 Bukowskis, Helsinki #364/R

YOAKUM, Joseph (1915-) American
Works on paper
£1975 $3200 €2963 Boarder ranger between Austria and Italian continents, the Brenner Pass (30x48cm-12x19in) s.i.d.8 16 65 ink W/C prov.exhib. 27-Jan-3 Christie's, Rockefeller NY #15/R est:3000-3500

YOAKUM, Joseph E (1886-1973) American
Works on paper
£2201 $3500 €3302 Mt Grizzly in Cascade Mountain Range (46x61cm-18x24in) s.i. ballpoint pen W/C pencil prov. 29-Apr-3 Doyle, New York #43a est:2500-3500

YOLDJOGLOU, Georges (1933-) ?
£323 $500 €485 Plage (46x53cm-18x21in) s. 25-Sep-2 Doyle, New York #85/R
£366 $600 €549 Fenetre sur le golf du Touquet (64x56cm-25x22in) s. i.on stretcher. 5-Feb-3 Doyle, New York #52/R
£366 $600 €549 Jardin en fleurs bord de mer (51x61cm-20x24in) s. i.verso. 5-Feb-3 Doyle, New York #74/R
£387 $600 €581 Fleuers sur la plage (91x74cm-36x29in) s. 25-Sep-2 Doyle, New York #86/R
£457 $750 €663 La plage de Trouville (46x61cm-18x24in) s. i.on stretcher. 4-Jun-3 Doyle, New York #103
£488 $800 €708 Paris, Island of swans (46x56cm-18x22in) s. i.on stretcher. 4-Jun-3 Doyle, New York #101
£503 $800 €755 Brehat Jardin Ombrage (53x64cm-21x25in) s. 5-Mar-3 Doyle, New York #64/R
£503 $800 €755 Les regates au touquet (51x66cm-20x26in) s. i.stretcher. 18-Mar-3 Doyle, New York #59/R
£549 $900 €796 Brehaf (61x74cm-24x29in) s. i.on strtcher. 4-Jun-3 Doyle, New York #102
£590 $950 €885 Regates sous l'ondee (53x66cm-21x26in) s. i.verso. 19-Feb-3 Doyle, New York #81
£683 $1100 €1025 Dunes de bord de mer (61x74cm-24x29in) s. i.stretcher. 19-Feb-3 Doyle, New York #82
£839 $1300 €1259 Fleurs (61x51cm-24x20in) s. 25-Sep-2 Doyle, New York #87/R
£926 $1500 €1343 Fenetre fleurie au touquet (61x51cm-24x20in) s. i.overlap. 21-May-3 Doyle, New York #254/R est:3000-4000
£955 $1500 €1433 Maree (22x26cm-9x10in) s. i.on stretcher. 10-Dec-2 Doyle, New York #262/R est:3000-4000

YON, Edmond (1836-1897) French
£1284 $2003 €1900 Bords de riviere aux peupliers (46x70cm-18x28in) s. 31-Mar-3 Rossini, Paris #33
£3117 $4800 €4676 Figures resting along a riverbank (50x76cm-20x30in) s.d.73. 4-Sep-2 Christie's, Rockefeller NY #333/R est:6000-8000
Works on paper
£541 $843 €800 View of Giverny (25x35cm-10x14in) s.i. W/C. 27-Mar-3 Maigret, Paris #296

YONG, Joe de (1894-1975) American
£1122 $1750 €1683 Glacier park moose (38x51cm-15x20in) s. prov.lit. 9-Nov-2 Santa Fe Art, Santa Fe #204/R est:3000-6000

YORKE, W H (19th C) British
£4000 $6480 €5800 Norwegian sailing ship Gulmare in moderate seas (49x74cm-19x29in) s.d.1886. 21-May-3 Outhwaite & Litherland, Liverpool #211

YORKE, William Gay (1817-1882) American
£7453 $12000 €11180 Portrait of the cutter Melvina in a yacht race (53x69cm-21x27in) s.indis.d.187. 23-Feb-3 Skinner, Boston #30/R est:2000-3000
£12346 $20000 €17902 American clipper Caravan rendering assistance to a British full rigger in mid Atlantic (64x105cm-25x41in) i. 29-Jul-3 Christie's, Rockefeller NY #164/R est:25000-35000

YORKE, William Hoard (fl.1858-1903) British
£4605 $7000 €6908 British bark, Mount Vernon (51x76cm-20x30in) s.d.1881. 17-Aug-2 North East Auctions, Portsmouth #1047/R est:7000-10000
£5263 $8000 €7895 Bark, Kristine, at Drammen (51x76cm-20x30in) s.i.d.1884. 17-Aug-2 North East Auctions, Portsmouth #810/R
£6173 $10000 €8951 Norwegian barque Rathlin Island off Fastnet lighthouse (49x75cm-19x30in) s.i. 29-Jul-3 Christie's, Rockefeller NY #174/R est:12000-18000
£6500 $10075 €9750 Esther Roy of Maitland off Anglesey in heavy weather (61x91cm-24x36in) s. 31-Oct-2 Christie's, Kensington #494/R est:4000-6000
£8500 $14110 €12325 Three masted Spanish barque Rafael Pomar shortening sail as she approaches Port Mahon, Minorca (78x112cm-31x44in) s.i.d.1875. 12-Jun-3 Christie's, London #517/R est:5000-8000
£10526 $16000 €15789 Ship, Poccahontis (66x91cm-26x36in) s.d.1859 prov. 17-Aug-2 North East Auctions, Portsmouth #787/R est:9000-15000
£21382 $32500 €32073 USS Bolton (74x99cm-29x39in) s.d.1859 prov. 17-Aug-2 North East Auctions, Portsmouth #786/R est:35000-45000

YOSHIDA, Hiroshi (1876-1950) Japanese
Prints
£3200 $5344 €4640 The rapids of the Nakabusa River (65x95cm-26x37in) s. 18-Jun-3 Christie's, London #366/R est:3000-3500
£3800 $6346 €5510 Hadakayama after rain (61x80cm-24x31in) s. 18-Jun-3 Christie's, London #370/R est:3000-3500
£3846 $6000 €5769 Lake Yamanaka (54x69cm-21x27in) s. col woodcut. 25-Mar-3 Christie's, Rockefeller NY #387/R est:6000-8000
Works on paper
£2581 $4000 €3872 Mount Fuji (66x99cm-26x39in) s. W/C. 1-Oct-2 Arthur James, Florida #443

YOSHIIKU, Utagawa (1833-1904) Japanese
Prints
£2244 $3500 €3366 Camera view, large elephant (36x24cm-14x9in) s. print. 25-Mar-3 Christie's, Rockefeller NY #357/R est:2000-2500

YOSHIKAWA, Shizuko (1934-) Japanese
£858 $1356 €1287 Abstract composition - empty energy (60x60cm-24x24in) i.d.1993 verso acrylic. 29-Nov-2 Zofingen, Switzerland #3141/R est:2500 (S.FR 2000)
£881 $1313 €1322 M 308 ' two energies' (37x37cm-15x15in) s.i.d. verso acrylic. 25-Jun-2 Koller, Zurich #6111/R (S.FR 2000)

YOSHIKAZU, Utagawa (fl.1850-1870) Japanese
Prints
£5769 $9000 €8654 One of the states in America (37x25cm-15x10in) s. blue print triptych. 25-Mar-3 Christie's, Rockefeller NY #334/R est:9000-12000

YOSHITOYO, Fukuyama (1830-1866) Japanese
Prints
£1923 $3000 €2885 Picture of English people (35x24cm-14x9in) s. col print. 25-Mar-3 Christie's, Rockefeller NY #332/R est:3000-3500
£2564 $4000 €3846 Picture of beloved American child (37x26cm-15x10in) s. col print. 25-Mar-3 Christie's, Rockefeller NY #330/R est:3000-3500

YOUNG, A (?) ?
£500 $785 €750 Figure on the rocks looking seaward (48x74cm-19x29in) s. 12-Dec-2 Richardson & Smith, Whitby #431

YOUNG, Alexander (1865-1923) British
£600 $936 €900 Shepherd with his flock at Shere, near Dorking (41x61cm-16x24in) s. 7-Nov-2 Christie's, Kensington #137/R
£850 $1326 €1275 Departure from the fishing fleet (42x51cm-17x20in) s. 28-Mar-3 Bonhams, Edinburgh #180
£1700 $2771 €2550 Kirkcaldy Harbour scenes (59x44cm-23x17in) with sig. pair. 29-Jan-3 Sotheby's, Olympia #235/R est:1000-1500
£1700 $2652 €2550 Early morning, Buckhaven Harbour (51x76cm-20x30in) s.d.1917. 14-Apr-3 Sotheby's, London #81/R est:1800-2200
£1700 $2652 €2550 Pittenweem, Fife (51x76cm-20x30in) s.d.1916. 14-Apr-3 Sotheby's, London #84/R est:1800-2000

£1900 $3097 €2755 Harbour at Scarborough and other boats in foreground (61x46cm-24x18in) s.d.93. 17-Jul-3 Tennants, Leyburn #822/R est:800-1200

YOUNG, Arthur (1866-1943) American
Works on paper
£1218 $1900 €1827 Working class mother's toil is not the subject for magazine publishers (30x53cm-12x21in) s. pen ink lit. 9-Nov-2 Illustration House, New York #71/R est:1200-1800

YOUNG, Charles Morris (1869-1964) American
£1497 $2500 €2171 Spring landscape (30x41cm-12x16in) s. indis d. 22-Jun-3 Freeman, Philadelphia #116/R est:2000-3000
£1737 $2900 €2519 View through the trees (38x46cm-15x18in) s.d.1923. 22-Jun-3 Freeman, Philadelphia #118/R est:2500-4000
£1796 $3000 €2604 Autumn landscape (46x61cm-18x24in) s.d.1909. 22-Jun-3 Freeman, Philadelphia #106/R est:3000-5000

YOUNG, Edmund Drummond (1876-1946) British
£1400 $2128 €2100 Potatoes and casserole (41x51cm-16x20in) s. 28-Aug-2 Sotheby's, London #1024/R est:2000-3000

YOUNG, Florence Upson (1872-1964) American
£719 $1200 €1043 Foothill landscape (64x79cm-25x31in) s. 17-Jun-3 John Moran, Pasadena #54b est:2000-3000
£1398 $2250 €2097 Laguna (76x61cm-30x24in) s. 18-Feb-3 John Moran, Pasadena #39 est:2500-3500

YOUNG, Harvey (1840-1901) American
£1573 $2500 €2360 Karverys Pond, Peacham Vermont (54x76cm-21x30in) s.d.74. 7-Mar-3 Skinner, Boston #279/R est:1500-2500

YOUNG, Jean (1914-) British
£300 $474 €450 Planting vegetable, figures in a field (39x50cm-15x20in) s. 27-Nov-2 Wintertons, Lichfield #795

YOUNG, John (1956-) Australian
£10769 $17123 €16154 Still dream (212x157cm-83x62in) i.d.2000 verso oil digital scan prov.exhib. 4-Mar-3 Deutscher-Menzies, Melbourne #72/R est:15000-20000 (A.D 28000)

YOUNG, John Tobias (fl.1811-1822) British
£16429 $25957 €24644 Castle Cornet, St. Peter Port, Guernsey (53x72cm-21x28in) s.i.verso. 26-Nov-2 Sotheby's, Melbourne #179/R est:10000-15000 (A.D 46000)

YOUNG, Lilian (fl.1884-1890) British
Works on paper
£700 $1106 €1050 Young lady seated in an interior with an open book (28x18cm-11x7in) s. W/C. 2-Dec-2 Bonhams, Bath #20/R

YOUNG, Mabel (1900-?) Irish/British
£800 $1336 €1160 Little field, Wicklow (34x39cm-13x15in) i.verso canvasboard. 26-Jun-3 Mellors & Kirk, Nottingham #894/R
£1447 $2257 €2300 Trees against a dark sky, winter (61x51cm-24x20in) board prov. 17-Sep-2 Whyte's, Dublin #193/R est:2500-3000

YOUNG, Mabel I (fl.1896-1903) British
£5500 $9185 €7975 Postman brings news (96x135cm-38x53in) s. canvas on board. 17-Jun-3 Bonhams, New Bond Street #94/R est:6000-8000

YOUNG, Mahonri (1877-1957) American
Sculpture
£4167 $6500 €6251 Seated Indian (25x15x18cm-10x6x7in) i. bronze prov.lit. 9-Nov-2 Santa Fe Art, Santa Fe #84/R est:12000-18000

YOUNG, Oscar van (1906-) American
£683 $1100 €1025 L A street scene (43x43cm-17x17in) s.d.41 board. 18-Feb-3 John Moran, Pasadena #23

YOUNG, Purvis (1943-) American
£2160 $3500 €3240 Horses (45x121cm-18x48in) s. house paint paper on panel prov. 27-Jan-3 Christie's, Rockefeller NY #100/R est:4000-6000
£6173 $10000 €9260 Holy man (183x62cm-72x24in) house paint on wood prov. 27-Jan-3 Christie's, Rockefeller NY #101/R est:7000-9000

YOUNG, Robert (1926-) Australian
£350 $571 €525 Untitled no.2 (142x142cm-56x56in) d.4/5/78. 3-Feb-3 Sotheby's, Olympia #121/R

YOUNG, Robert Clouston (fl.1920s) British
£1500 $2295 €2250 Outward bound (20x35cm-8x14in) s. 22-Aug-2 Bonhams, Edinburgh #954 est:600-800

YOUNG, William (19th C) British
Works on paper
£280 $437 €420 Harbour quay (24x34cm-9x13in) s.d.86 W/C. 13-Sep-2 Lyon & Turnbull, Edinburgh #112/R

YOUNG, William Blamire (1862-1935) Australian
Works on paper
£264 $418 €383 Pastoral landscape (15x19cm-6x7in) s. W/C. 22-Jul-3 Lawson Menzies, Sydney #161/R (A.D 650)
£316 $480 €474 New baby (17x16cm-7x6in) s. W/C. 19-Aug-2 Joel, Victoria #200 (A.D 900)
£766 $1142 €1149 Arrival (35x52cm-14x20in) s. W/C. 27-Aug-2 Christie's, Melbourne #251/R est:2000-3000 (A.D 2000)
£1068 $1633 €1602 Landscape (24x32cm-9x13in) s. W/C prov. 25-Aug-2 Sotheby's, Paddington #207 est:3000-5000 (A.D 3000)
£14504 $22916 €21756 Gypsies bathing (63x63cm-25x25in) s. i.d.1914 verso W/C exhib.lit. 2-Apr-3 Christie's, Melbourne #45/R est:15000-20000 (A.D 38000)

YOUNG, William S (fl.1850-1870) American
£1019 $1600 €1529 Autumn scene. Winter scene (18x13cm-7x5in) s. pair. 21-Nov-2 Shelley, Hendersonville #1116/R

YOUNGERMAN, Jack (1926-) American
£955 $1500 €1433 Abstract composition (81x61cm-32x24in) init.d.1966 tempera. 21-Nov-2 Swann Galleries, New York #233/R est:1000-1500
Sculpture
£2439 $4000 €3537 Black Maia (122x91x91cm-48x36x36in) cast fiberglass prov. 1-Jun-3 Wright, Chicago #343/R est:4000-5000

YOUNGMAN, Annie Mary (1859-1919) British
Works on paper
£300 $501 €435 Gloire de Dijon roses (40x30cm-16x12in) s. pencil W/C. 26-Jun-3 Mellors & Kirk, Nottingham #788

YOUNGMAN, John Mallows (1817-1899) British
Works on paper
£650 $1014 €975 Cattle herder with a thatched cottage beyond (58x46cm-23x18in) s. W/C pencil. 9-Oct-2 Woolley & Wallis, Salisbury #75/R

YOUNOK (20th C) Japanese?
£552 $900 €828 Boats in harbour (61x91cm-24x36in) 14-Feb-3 Du Mouchelle, Detroit #2117/R

YOUON, Konstantin (1875-1958) Russian
£3226 $5097 €5000 House by lake (40x55cm-16x22in) s. 19-Dec-2 Hagelstam, Helsinki #919/R est:2500
£10993 $18358 €15500 Promenade le long du Kremlin (54x43cm-21x17in) s.i.d. 17-Jun-3 Claude Boisgirard, Paris #146 est:6000-7000

YOUQUA (19th C) Oriental
£31250 $47500 €46875 Whampoa anchorage (43x76cm-17x30in) lit. 17-Aug-2 North East Auctions, Portsmouth #832/R est:25000-30000

YOURIEVITCH, Serge (20th C) French
Sculpture
£1800 $2934 €2700 La danseuse Nattova (73cm-29in) i. bronze. 29-Jan-3 Sotheby's, Olympia #346/R est:1800-2000

YPEREN, Gerrit Willem van (1882-1955) Dutch
Works on paper
£353 $554 €550 Munt square in Amsterdam (35x45cm-14x18in) s. W/C. 25-Nov-2 Glerum, Amsterdam #111

YSERN Y ALIE, Pedro (1876-1946) Spanish
£296 $461 €470 Portrait of man (43x33cm-17x13in) s. board. 8-Oct-2 Ansorena, Madrid #251/R
£461 $746 €700 Landscape (21x26cm-8x10in) paper on canvas exhib. 21-Jan-3 Ansorena, Madrid #266/R
£559 $906 €850 Landscape (27x35cm-11x14in) 21-Jan-3 Ansorena, Madrid #269/R
£692 $1079 €1100 Seascape with trees (35x25cm-14x10in) board. 8-Oct-2 Ansorena, Madrid #431/R

£828 $1316 €1200 Seated woman (41x32cm-16x13in) paper on canvas. 4-Mar-3 Ansorena, Madrid #330/R
£1032 $1631 €1600 Landscape (32x24cm-13x9in) 18-Dec-2 Ansorena, Madrid #384/R
£1258 $1937 €2000 Dancer (60x47cm-24x19in) s. oval. 22-Oct-2 Durán, Madrid #243/R
£1258 $1962 €2000 Landscape (27x36cm-11x14in) s. board. 8-Oct-2 Ansorena, Madrid #464/R
£1384 $2158 €2200 Cancan (27x35cm-11x14in) s. board. 8-Oct-2 Ansorena, Madrid #471/R
£2258 $3568 €3500 Landscape in Majorca (52x62cm-20x24in) s. 17-Dec-2 Segre, Madrid #81/R
£2450 $3994 €3700 Landscape in Majorca (65x54cm-26x21in) s. 11-Feb-3 Segre, Madrid #136/R
£3871 $6116 €6000 Landscape in Majorca (81x65cm-32x26in) s. 17-Dec-2 Segre, Madrid #85/R est:5100
Works on paper
£1096 $1721 €1600 Femme pensive prenant le the (31x43cm-12x17in) s. gouache. 21-Apr-3 Rabourdin & Choppin de Janvry, Paris #161 est:1800-2000

YSSELDYK, Cees van (1901-1977) Dutch
£278 $458 €400 Roof tops (70x50cm-28x20in) s. 1-Jul-3 Christie's, Amsterdam #284
£828 $1275 €1300 Bay on Ibiza, Spain (38x45cm-15x18in) s. with another work by same hand. 3-Sep-2 Christie's, Amsterdam #412
£955 $1471 €1500 Still life of chaenomeles (90x70cm-35x28in) s.d.58 exhib. 3-Sep-2 Christie's, Amsterdam #411 est:700-900
£955 $1471 €1500 Houses in Marakesh, Morocco (60x80cm-24x31in) s. 3-Sep-2 Christie's, Amsterdam #413/R est:700-900
£955 $1471 €1500 Cavern houses in Southern Spain (60x80cm-24x31in) s.d.58. 3-Sep-2 Christie's, Amsterdam #415/R est:800-1200
£1083 $1668 €1700 Place de la Concorde, Paris (50x70cm-20x28in) s. 3-Sep-2 Christie's, Amsterdam #414 est:700-900
£2229 $3433 €3500 View from the artist's studio at Singel 309 in winter (63x44cm-25x17in) s. exhib. 3-Sep-2 Christie's, Amsterdam #410/R est:800-1200

YTHJALL, Terje (1943-) Norwegian
£487 $793 €731 Meeting of two experiences (51x52cm-20x20in) s.d.1972. 17-Feb-3 Blomqvist, Lysaker #1264 (N.KR 5500)
£575 $938 €863 Abduction (46x38cm-18x15in) s.d.1973. 17-Feb-3 Blomqvist, Lysaker #1265/R (N.KR 6500)
£708 $1154 €1062 Imaginations (60x61cm-24x24in) s. i.d.1972 verso. 17-Feb-3 Blomqvist, Lysaker #1266/R (N.KR 8000)

YU FEIAN (1888-1959) Chinese
Works on paper
£7724 $12203 €11586 Bird perching on a branch (82x41cm-32x16in) s.i. ink col hanging scroll. 28-Apr-3 Sotheby's, Hong Kong #573/R est:50000-70000 (HK.D 95000)
£13821 $21837 €20732 Morning glory (69x44cm-27x17in) s.i. ink col exhib. 28-Apr-3 Sotheby's, Hong Kong #618/R est:130000-180000 (HK.D 170000)

YU ZHIDING (1647-c.1709) Chinese
Works on paper
£93240 $153846 €135198 Birthday celebrations (190x38cm-75x15in) one s.d.1712 ink col gold silk scroll set of 12. 6-Jul-3 Christie's, Hong Kong #466/R est:1200000-1800000 (HK.D 1200000)

YUAN, S Chen (20th C) American
£2950 $4750 €4425 Autumn (43x71cm-17x28in) s. masonite prov. 18-Feb-3 John Moran, Pasadena #56 est:5000-7000
£4969 $8000 €7454 Monterey wharf (15x41cm-6x16in) s. masonite prov. 18-Feb-3 John Moran, Pasadena #57 est:3000-5000

YUDIN, Lev (1903-1941) Russian
Works on paper
£1410 $2186 €2200 Cubist composition (31x23cm-12x9in) s.d.21 gouache. 7-Dec-2 De Vuyst, Lokeren #411/R est:2200-2600

YUHI, Kumashiro (c.1693-1773) Japanese
Works on paper
£2516 $4000 €3774 Allegory of immortality (102x41cm-40x16in) s.i. ink col silk hanging scroll. 24-Mar-3 Christie's, Rockefeller NY #16/R est:3000-4000

YULE, Michael James (20th C) British
Works on paper
£250 $418 €363 Tubbertelly, Queen beating fine words in the 1984 Waterloo Cup final (39x66cm-15x26in) mixed media. 24-Jun-3 Rowley Fine Art, Newmarket #351/R

YUN SHOUPING (1633-1690) Chinese
Works on paper
£132090 $217949 €191531 Hundred flowers (33x803cm-13x316in) s.i.d.1666 ink col silk handscroll style of XU CHONGSI exhib.lit. 6-Jul-3 Christie's, Hong Kong #474/R est:1800000-2200000 (HK.D 1700000)

YUS Y COLAS, Manuel (1845-1905) Spanish
£377 $581 €600 Portrait of lady. Portrait of gentleman (35x27cm-14x11in) s.i. cardboard pair. 28-Oct-2 Segre, Madrid #83/R

YUSKAVAGE, Lisa (1962-) American
£37975 $60000 €56963 Little northview (51x46cm-20x18in) s.d.2001 oil on linen prov.exhib. 14-Nov-2 Christie's, Rockefeller NY #332/R est:30000-40000

YUZBASIYAN, Arto (1948-) Canadian
£365 $569 €548 Balloon race (30x41cm-12x16in) s. masonite. 25-Mar-3 Ritchie, Toronto #116 (C.D 850)
£711 $1166 €1067 Old stores, Queen Street W (30x40cm-12x16in) s. board prov. 3-Jun-3 Joyner, Toronto #492 est:1000-1500 (C.D 1600)
£2222 $3644 €3333 Front of Albert smoke shop, 1979 (60x75cm-24x30in) s. prov. 3-Jun-3 Joyner, Toronto #259/R est:5000-7000 (C.D 5000)

YVARAL (1934-) French
£443 $700 €700 Variation sur l'hexagone (35x41cm-14x16in) s. i.d.68 verso panel. 26-Nov-2 Camard, Paris #141
£1118 $1812 €1700 Structure ambigue RBV (59x59cm-23x23in) sid,1968 verso board. 21-Jan-3 Ansorena, Madrid #313/R

YVON, Adolphe (1817-1893) French
£3171 $5200 €4598 Allegory of the arts. Allegory of war (42x88cm-17x35in) one s. pair. 4-Jun-3 Christie's, Rockefeller NY #245/R est:5000-7000
Works on paper
£507 $791 €750 Portrait d'enfants (55x46cm-22x18in) s.d.1870 pastel chk oval. 28-Mar-3 Delvaux, Paris #6
£1097 $1700 €1646 Family in an interior (63x45cm-25x18in) s.d.1870 W/C gouache chl prov. 29-Oct-2 Sotheby's, New York #37/R est:1500-2000

YVRIER, J (19th C) French?
£1497 $2380 €2200 Portrait de dignitaire (55x46cm-22x18in) s.d.1883. 24-Mar-3 Rabourdin & Choppin de Janvry, Paris #223/R est:2800-3000

ZAALBERG, Hester Adriana Cornelia (1836-1909) Dutch
£1282 $1987 €2000 Winter in Holland (17x25cm-7x10in) s. i. verso panel. 7-Dec-2 Hans Stahl, Hamburg #39/R est:3500

ZABALETA, Rafael (1907-1960) Spanish
£9434 $14623 €15000 Landscape (50x65cm-20x26in) s.i.verso painted c.1930. 7-Oct-2 Ansorena, Madrid #76/R est:15000

ZABALLA, Ana (1945-) Spanish
£440 $687 €700 Untitled (92x65cm-36x26in) s.i.d.1989 verso. 17-Sep-2 Segre, Madrid #177/R
£621 $981 €900 ATZP (136x112cm-54x44in) s.i.d.1987-89 verso. 1-Apr-3 Segre, Madrid #206/R
£968 $1529 €1500 Untitled (188x180cm-74x71in) s.i.d.1990 verso acrylic exhib.lit. 17-Dec-2 Segre, Madrid #180/R

ZABEHLITZKY, Alois (1883-1969) Austrian
£478 $745 €750 Still life of flowers (80x58cm-31x23in) s. oval lit. 7-Nov-2 Allgauer, Kempten #3019/R
£957 $1492 €1436 Still life with jug and fruit (72x100cm-28x39in) s. 16-Sep-2 Philippe Schuler, Zurich #3526/R (S.FR 2200)
£1761 $2747 €2800 Flowers and fruit on table covered with white cloth (70x100cm-28x39in) s. 9-Oct-2 Michael Zeller, Lindau #971/R est:2000
£2432 $3795 €3600 Still life of fruit (74x99cm-29x39in) s. 26-Mar-3 Hugo Ruef, Munich #268/R est:1800
£3750 $6000 €5625 Still life with flowers in an urn beside a column (70x50cm-28x20in) s. 14-May-3 Butterfields, San Francisco #1092/R est:4000-6000

ZABEHLITZKY, Alois (attrib) (1883-1969) Austrian
£1772 $2765 €2800 Flowers (68x54cm-27x21in) i. panel. 15-Oct-2 Dorotheum, Vienna #48/R est:1600-2200

ZACH, Bruno (1891-?) Austrian
Sculpture
£1560 $2528 €2200 Girl (39cm-15in) pat.bronze onyxsocle. 21-May-3 Dorotheum, Vienna #245/R est:2200-3000
£2205 $3484 €3308 Oriental man and nude woman standing on mat (29cm-11in) s.i. cold painted bronze executed c.1910. 28-Apr-3 Bukowskis, Stockholm #607/R est:6000-8000 (S.KR 29000)
£3500 $5530 €5250 Checkers and fringe (39cm-15in) s. bronze. 14-Nov-2 Christie's, Kensington #237/R est:2000-3000
£3600 $5724 €5400 Diana and her hounds (72cm-28in) s. golden brown pat. bronze. 27-Feb-3 Sotheby's, Olympia #191/R est:4000-6000
£8000 $12960 €11600 Woman on horse (46cm-18in) s. ivory bronze sold with black marble plinth. 21-May-3 Outhwaite & Litherland, Liverpool #15/R

ZACH, Ferdinand (1868-1956) Austrian
Works on paper
£304 $474 €450 Beethoven's house in Heiligenstadt (24x36cm-9x14in) s. mixed media. 28-Mar-3 Dorotheum, Vienna #340/R
£473 $738 €700 Karlskirche, Vienna (72x90cm-28x35in) s. mixed media. 28-Mar-3 Dorotheum, Vienna #338/R

ZACH, Karl (19/20th C) Austrian
Works on paper
£409 $634 €650 Old food market in Freihaus (77x54cm-30x21in) s. W/C pastel paper on board. 1-Oct-2 Dorotheum, Vienna #253/R
£629 $975 €1000 Vienna, Schonlaterngasse (35x25cm-14x10in) s.d.1905 W/C. 1-Oct-2 Dorotheum, Vienna #276/R
£642 $1001 €950 Street in old Vienna (53x35cm-21x14in) s.d.1907 W/C. 28-Mar-3 Dorotheum, Vienna #320/R

ZACH, Vilem (?) ?
Sculpture
£924 $1459 €1386 Sioux warrior (38x23x13cm-15x9x5in) bronze. 1-Dec-2 Levis, Calgary #107/R est:1500-2000 (C.D 2300)

ZACHO, Christian (1843-1913) Danish
£280 $448 €420 Prospect view, Friisenborg (23x31cm-9x12in) s. 13-Jan-3 Rasmussen, Vejle #145/R (D.KR 3200)
£368 $588 €552 Wooded landscape with river (38x41cm-15x16in) s. 13-Jan-3 Rasmussen, Vejle #155/R (D.KR 4200)
£670 $1085 €972 Lungholm Manor at Lolland (39x56cm-15x22in) init.d.01. 26-May-3 Rasmussen, Copenhagen #1574/R (D.KR 7000)
£850 $1394 €1275 Sunlit glade (65x86cm-26x34in) s.d.1897. 5-Jun-3 Christie's, Kensington #680/R
£1292 $1964 €1938 Dyrehaven in spring (85x120cm-33x47in) s.d.1901 exhib. 27-Aug-2 Rasmussen, Copenhagen #1823/R est:15000-20000 (D.KR 15000)
£1340 $2170 €1943 Landscape with large oak trees at Bognaes Strand (47x72cm-19x28in) s.d.1911 prov. 26-May-3 Rasmussen, Copenhagen #1423/R est:12000-15000 (D.KR 14000)
£1532 $2420 €2298 Summer landscape with road through wood (55x93cm-22x37in) s.d.1890. 2-Dec-2 Rasmussen, Copenhagen #1238/R est:12000 (D.KR 18000)
£1532 $2420 €2298 Horses in landscape, Dyrehaven (110x155cm-43x61in) s.d.1903. 2-Dec-2 Rasmussen, Copenhagen #1574/R est:15000-20000 (D.KR 18000)
£1915 $2968 €2873 Woodland with watercourse (65x90cm-26x35in) s.d.1905. 4-Dec-2 AB Stockholms Auktionsverk #1904/R est:25000-30000 (S.KR 27000)
£2000 $3120 €3000 River landscape (66x91cm-26x36in) s.d.1904. 9-Oct-2 Woolley & Wallis, Salisbury #258/R est:800-1200
£12104 $19246 €18156 Landscape with lake in beech wood, spring (190x245cm-75x96in) s.d.1885. 5-Mar-3 Rasmussen, Copenhagen #1602/R est:75000 (D.KR 130000)

ZACK, Bruno (attrib) (20th C) ?
Sculpture
£1200 $1896 €1800 Female figure (35cm-14in) s. bronze. 14-Nov-2 Christie's, Kensington #238/R est:1000-1500

ZACK, Léon (1892-1980) Russian
£612 $973 €900 Untitled (65x54cm-26x21in) s.d. 21-Mar-3 Rieunier, Bailly-Pommery, Mathias, Paris #129
£993 $1619 €1500 Portrait of young woman (100x81cm-39x32in) s. 31-Jan-3 Rabourdin & Choppin de Janvry, Paris #117/R
£1013 $1580 €1600 Maternite (65x55cm-26x22in) s. 15-Oct-2 Vanderkindere, Brussels #50/R est:1750-2500
£1667 $2633 €2400 Composition (65x50cm-26x20in) s. 28-Apr-3 Cornette de St.Cyr, Paris #551/R est:2500-3000
£1944 $3072 €2800 Composition (130x97cm-51x38in) s.d. prov. 27-Apr-3 Perrin, Versailles #13/R est:3000-3500
£2278 $3554 €3600 Composition (73x92cm-29x36in) s.d.1975 lit. 20-Oct-2 Claude Boisgirard, Paris #62/R est:3000-3500
£3404 $5685 €4800 Composition abstraite (89x130cm-35x51in) s.d.74. 18-Jun-3 Pierre Berge, Paris #90/R est:5000-6000
£5769 $9058 €9000 Untitled (65x92cm-26x36in) s.d.59 prov. 24-Nov-2 Laurence Calmels, Paris #291/R
Works on paper
£318 $497 €500 Two figures and a child (46x26cm-18x10in) d.36 W/C. 6-Nov-2 Vendue Huis, Gravenhage #135/R

ZADEMACK, Siegfried (1952-) German
Works on paper
£411 $650 €650 Weapon in baguette (56x37cm-22x15in) s.d.1987 W/C. 29-Nov-2 Sigalas, Stuttgart #1288/R

ZADKINE, O (1890-1967) French
Sculpture
£4430 $7000 €7000 L'architecte (31x25x17cm-12x10x7in) mono. pat bronze. 26-Nov-2 Palais de Beaux Arts, Brussels #264/R est:7000-10000

ZADKINE, Ossip (1890-1967) French
Sculpture
£5031 $7799 €8000 Femme agenouillee (34x22x21cm-13x9x8in) init.num.6/8 green pat bronze st.f.Susse lit. 30-Oct-2 Artcurial Briest, Paris #345/R est:8000-10000
£11538 $18000 €17307 Les combattants (49cm-19in) init.num.8/8 black pat. bronze st.f.H.Noack conceived 1947 lit. 6-Nov-2 Sotheby's, New York #257/R est:20000-30000
£19355 $30581 €30000 Sainte Famille (48cm-19in) s. num.2/8 pat bronze Cast Susse lit. 18-Dec-2 Tajan, Paris #50/R est:12000-15000
£21739 $35000 €32609 Virginite (65cm-26in) i.num.2/5 brown pat. bronze st.f.Susse cast c.1953 lit. 7-May-3 Sotheby's, New York #197/R est:40000-60000
£25000 $41000 €37500 Femme assise (53cm-21in) s.st.f.Susse num.1/8 brown pat bronze lit. 4-Feb-3 Christie's, London #358/R est:35000
£26582 $42000 €42000 Accordeoniste (56x21x14cm-22x8x6in) i. bronze st.f.Susse executed 1964 prov.lit. 26-Nov-2 Sotheby's, Amsterdam #114/R est:40000-60000
£100000 $164000 €150000 Tete d'homme (39cm-15in) s. gilded wood exec.1922 prov.exhib.lit. 5-Feb-3 Sotheby's, London #155/R est:100000
Works on paper
£482 $800 €723 Cellist (20x10cm-8x4in) init.i. felt tip pen prov. 11-Jun-3 Phillips, New York #493/R
£483 $806 €700 Tete (27x20cm-11x8in) s. graphite dr. 10-Jul-3 Artcurial Briest, Paris #86
£612 $973 €900 L'homme (17x12cm-7x5in) s.d.1963 ink. 19-Mar-3 Hotel des Ventes Mosan, Brussels #254
£764 $1207 €1100 Fleur (26x26cm-10x10in) mono.i. ball point pen nappe en papier. 28-Apr-3 Cornette de St.Cyr, Paris #310
£769 $1192 €1200 Homme a la guitare (27x20cm-11x8in) s.i.d.64 ball-point pen dr. 7-Dec-2 De Vuyst, Lokeren #412/R
£896 $1497 €1300 Autoportrait a la sculpture (52x37cm-20x15in) s.i.d.1961 graphite dr. 10-Jul-3 Artcurial Briest, Paris #84 est:1200-1500
£903 $1435 €1300 Tete d'homme (35x28cm-14x11in) init. graphite dr. 29-Apr-3 Artcurial Briest, Paris #116 est:1100-1300
£949 $1500 €1500 Figures. s.d.1967 ink col crayon. 27-Nov-2 Blanchet, Paris #62
£979 $1635 €1400 Composition duale (25x18cm-10x7in) mono. Indian ink. 26-Jun-3 Tajan, Paris #99 est:1500-2000
£993 $1619 €1500 Deux personnages (29x21cm-11x8in) s.i.d.13.6.59 ball point pen. 31-Jan-3 Charbonneaux, Paris #177/R est:1800-2300
£1064 $1777 €1500 Couple debout (29x21cm-11x8in) s. mixed media. 18-Jun-3 Hotel des Ventes Mosan, Brussels #251 est:800-1200
£1156 $1839 €1700 Les trois rouges (25x35cm-10x14in) s. W/C. 26-Feb-3 Fraysse & Associes, Paris #28 est:1500-2000
£1181 $1877 €1700 Personnage (24x16cm-9x6in) mono. W/C ink prov. 29-Apr-3 Artcurial Briest, Paris #133/R est:1400-1600
£1824 $2827 €2900 Figure (39x31cm-15x12in) s.d.1963 pen Indian ink dr. 5-Oct-2 De Vuyst, Lokeren #487/R est:3000-4000
£1975 $3080 €3100 Couple (25x19cm-10x7in) s. Chinese ink wash dr. 10-Nov-2 Eric Pillon, Calais #237/R
£2115 $3342 €3300 Rue de village (32x25cm-13x10in) s.d.1919 pencil wash. 14-Nov-2 Neumeister, Munich #714/R est:350-400
£2963 $4207 €4800 Comediens (50x49cm-20x19in) s.d.1972 graphite dr. 17-Mar-2 Galerie de Chartres, Chartres #161
£3846 $6423 €5500 Composition (45x64cm-18x25in) s.d. gouache. 26-Jun-3 Tajan, Paris #98/R est:4000-5000
£4255 $7106 €6000 Arbre pres de l'eglise (47x39cm-19x15in) s.d.1932 gouache. 17-Jun-3 Palais de Beaux Arts, Brussels #656/R est:6000-8000
£4898 $7788 €7200 Personnages et comediens (50x47cm-20x19in) s.d.27 graphite dr. 26-Feb-3 Artcurial Briest, Paris #240/R est:6000-7000

£5000 $7950 €7500 Personnages (58x43cm-23x17in) s.d.60 pen ink W/C. 20-Mar-3 Sotheby's, Olympia #95/R est:4000-5000
£6419 $10014 €9500 Two figures (60x44cm-24x17in) s. gouache. 26-Mar-3 Millon & Associes, Paris #134/R
£8681 $13715 €12500 Couple (66x53cm-26x21in) s.d.38 gouache. 25-Apr-3 Piasa, Paris #27/R est:6000
£9000 $13860 €13500 Mere et enfant (58x39cm-23x15in) s.d.25 gouache pen brush ink pencil. 22-Oct-2 Sotheby's, London #242/R est:10000-15000
£9202 $15000 €13803 Family group (62x44cm-24x17in) s.d.60 gouache prov. 12-Feb-3 Sotheby's, New York #119/R est:8000-10000
£11871 $18874 €17450 La foret humaine (52x41cm-20x16in) s.d.47 gouache. 26-Feb-3 Artcurial Briest, Paris #242/R est:15000-20000
£13195 $20979 €19000 Trois personnages (33x46cm-13x18in) s. W/C ink wash exec.c.1920. 29-Apr-3 Artcurial Briest, Paris #128/R est:18000-22000
£19388 $30827 €28500 Trois nus dans l'atelier (63x50cm-25x20in) s.d.20 W/C. 26-Feb-3 Fraysse & Associes, Paris #29/R est:10000-12000
£26389 $41959 €38000 L'amitie (56x41cm-22x16in) s.d.50 gouache. 29-Apr-3 Artcurial Briest, Paris #130/R est:22000-25000

ZADOR, Istvan (1882-?) Hungarian
£1266 $2000 €2000 Reclining nude (93x61cm-37x24in) s. 26-Nov-2 Wiener Kunst Auktionen, Vienna #103/R est:1400-3000

ZADORECKI, Johannes von (19th C) Austrian
£873 $1362 €1310 Madonna della Sedia (68x55cm-27x22in) s.d.1866. 6-Nov-2 Dobiaschofsky, Bern #1084/R (S.FR 2000)

ZADRAZIL, Franz (1942-) Austrian
Works on paper
£314 $484 €500 Tobacco kiosk, Beethovenplatz 2, Klagenfurt (70x100cm-28x39in) mixed media. 22-Oct-2 Wiener Kunst Auktionen, Vienna #1142/R
£377 $581 €600 Tobacco kiosk, Bahnhofstr 42, Lustenau, Vorarlberg (70x100cm-28x39in) mixed media. 22-Oct-2 Wiener Kunst Auktionen, Vienna #1141/R
£377 $581 €600 Tobacco shop in Neusiedl am See, Hauptplatz 25, Burgenland (70x100cm-28x39in) mixed media. 22-Oct-2 Wiener Kunst Auktionen, Vienna #1144/R
£377 $581 €600 Tobacco shop on Franz Josefs Hohe, Heiligenblut (70x100cm-28x39in) mixed media. 22-Oct-2 Wiener Kunst Auktionen, Vienna #1148/R
£566 $872 €900 Hager Tobacco shop in Scharding, Silberzeile 17 (70x100cm-28x39in) mixed media. 22-Oct-2 Wiener Kunst Auktionen, Vienna #1143/R
£629 $969 €1000 Tobacco shop on Hauptplatz 2, St Johann in Tirol (70x100cm-28x39in) mixed media. 22-Oct-2 Wiener Kunst Auktionen, Vienna #1149/R
£692 $1065 €1100 Tobacco shop on Jakominiplatz, Graz (70x100cm-28x39in) mixed media. 22-Oct-2 Wiener Kunst Auktionen, Vienna #1147/R
£755 $1162 €1200 Tobacco shop on Eugen Markus Platz, Hollabrunn, Niederosterreich (70x100cm-28x39in) mixed media. 22-Oct-2 Wiener Kunst Auktionen, Vienna #115o/R
£818 $1259 €1300 Tobacco shop in Getreidegasse 27, Salzburg (70x100cm-28x39in) mixed media. 22-Oct-2 Wiener Kunst Auktionen, Vienna #1151/R
£881 $1356 €1400 Tobacco shop in Vienna (70x100cm-28x39in) mixed media. 22-Oct-2 Wiener Kunst Auktionen, Vienna #1146/R

ZAGO, Erma (1880-1942) Italian
£645 $1019 €1000 Figures in the park (17x25cm-7x10in) s. cardboard. 18-Dec-2 Finarte, Milan #10/R
£774 $1223 €1200 Giano Arch (18x26cm-7x10in) s. board. 18-Dec-2 Finarte, Milan #36
£833 $1292 €1300 Flower market in Venice (19x26cm-7x10in) s. board. 4-Dec-2 Finarte, Rome #750
£903 $1427 €1400 Canal in Venice (19x27cm-7x11in) s. board. 18-Dec-2 Finarte, Milan #59/R
£1097 $1733 €1700 Market in Venice (19x26cm-7x10in) s. board. 18-Dec-2 Finarte, Milan #60/R
£1361 $2163 €2000 Canal in Venie (26x36cm-10x14in) s.d.935. 18-Mar-3 Finarte, Milan #116/R
£1497 $2380 €2200 Rialto bridge in Venice (26x36cm-10x14in) s.d.936 board. 18-Mar-3 Finarte, Milan #115/R
£2013 $3099 €3200 View of Venice (33x49cm-13x19in) s. board. 23-Oct-2 Finarte, Milan #165/R

ZAGO, Erma (attrib) (1880-1942) Italian
£1401 $2200 €2102 Venetian masquerade (51x51cm-20x20in) board pair. 23-Nov-2 Jackson's, Cedar Falls #41/R est:500-750

ZAGO, Luigi (1894-1952) Italian
£544 $865 €800 Pasubio (70x90cm-28x35in) s. 18-Mar-3 Finarte, Milan #123/R
£545 $856 €850 Sunset on the Resegone (50x60cm-20x24in) s. cardboard. 16-Dec-2 Pandolfini, Florence #90
£578 $919 €850 Pasubio (70x90cm-28x35in) s. 18-Mar-3 Finarte, Milan #122/R
£641 $994 €1000 House by the river (70x90cm-28x35in) s. 5-Dec-2 Stadion, Trieste #734/R
£797 $1307 €1100 Paesaggio biellese (50x60cm-20x24in) s. board exhib. 27-May-3 Finarte, Milan #15/R

ZAHN, F (?) ?
£422 $629 €650 Monte Pellegrino near Palermo (61x85cm-24x33in) s. 27-Jun-2 Neumeister, Munich #2857/R

ZAHRTMANN, Kristian (1843-1917) Danish
£570 $901 €855 Portrait of woman (15x12cm-6x5in) mono. panel. 30-Nov-2 Rasmussen, Havnen #2250 (D.KR 6700)
£772 $1204 €1158 Figure study of Christ (67x47cm-26x19in) mono.d.1917 prov. 11-Nov-2 Rasmussen, Vejle #705/R (D.KR 9000)
£1862 $3016 €2793 Woman knitting in front of house (54x72cm-21x28in) mono.d.1893. 25-Jan-3 Rasmussen, Havnen #2032/R est:20000-30000 (D.KR 21000)
£1866 $2966 €2799 Pine forest at S Trojan (72x52cm-28x20in) mono.d.1894 exhib. 5-May-3 Rasmussen, Vejle #422/R est:20000 (D.KR 20000)
£2043 $3227 €3065 Woman sewing dresses for another painting by Zahrtmann (19x13cm-7x5in) mono.d.15/9/85 panel exhib.prov. 2-Dec-2 Rasmussen, Copenhagen #1320/R est:25000 (D.KR 24000)
£3731 $5933 €5597 Pine forest near Pisa (76x60cm-30x24in) mono.d.1893 prov. 5-May-3 Rasmussen, Vejle #430/R est:40000 (D.KR 40000)
£4019 $6511 €5828 Avenue of lime trees in Ravello, sunny day (68x57cm-27x22in) mono.d.1891 exhib.prov. 26-May-3 Rasmussen, Copenhagen #1131/R est:40000 (D.KR 42000)
£5168 $7855 €7752 A poor Italian woman and her children coming down Civita d'Antonios Steps (58x84cm-23x33in) mono.d.1890 prov.exhib. 27-Aug-2 Rasmussen, Copenhagen #1443/R est:60000 (D.KR 60000)
£17225 $27904 €24976 Forecourt in Ravello with old woman and potted plants (70x76cm-28x30in) mono.d.1891 exhib.prov. 26-May-3 Rasmussen, Copenhagen #1125/R est:150000-175000 (D.KR 180000)
Works on paper
£530 $880 €769 Italian woman in profile (26x23cm-10x9in) mono.d.1901 W/C. 12-Jun-3 Kunsthallen, Copenhagen #371 (D.KR 5600)

ZAICHU, Hara (1750-1837) Japanese
Works on paper
£1900 $3173 €2755 Plum blossoms in snow (113x35cm-44x14in) s.i. ink slight colour hanging scroll silk. 18-Jun-3 Christie's, London #278/R est:1500-2000

ZAIDENBERG, Arthur (20th C) American
£1304 $2100 €1956 Midway carousel riders, with woman reaching for ring (46x58cm-18x23in) s. canvasboard painted c.1940. 10-May-3 Illustration House, New York #74/R est:3000-4000

ZAIS, Giuseppe (1709-1784) Italian
£1831 $2948 €2600 Flight to Egypt (30x23cm-12x9in) 11-May-3 Finarte, Venice #17/R
£9434 $14717 €15000 Women in landscape (36x44cm-14x17in) 22-Sep-2 Semenzato, Venice #285/R est:14000-20000
£14000 $21700 €21000 Pastoral landscape with peasants and herders by river (47x61cm-19x24in) 31-Oct-2 Sotheby's, Olympia #141/R est:7000-9000
£18000 $28260 €27000 Italianate wooded landscape with herdsmen and maiden watering their livestock (69x83cm-27x33in) 10-Dec-2 Bonhams, New Bond Street #81/R est:15000-20000
£32000 $53440 €46400 Landscape with travellers and pilgrims resting beside a stream, ruins beyond (50x65cm-20x26in) 10-Jul-3 Sotheby's, London #215/R est:10000-15000
£36000 $60120 €52200 River landscape with fisherman and women, woman carrying water beyond (55x70cm-22x28in) prov. 10-Jul-3 Sotheby's, London #216/R est:15000-20000
Works on paper
£2400 $4008 €3480 Landscape of classical ruins by a lake, a woman and child in the foreground (24x37cm-9x15in) pen brown ink grey wash. 9-Jul-3 Sotheby's, London #55/R est:1500-2000

ZAJAC, Jack (1929-) American
Sculpture
£1026 $1600 €1539 Winged escort no 11 (58x43cm-23x17in) bears sig.i. bronze. 14-Oct-2 Butterfields, San Francisco #2084/R est:3000-5000

£2404 $3750 €3606 Split almond (23x93cm-9x37in) black granite rec. pedestal three parts. 14-Oct-2 Butterfields, San Francisco #2101/R est:3000-5000

ZAJICEK, Carl Wenzel (1860-1923) Austrian
Works on paper
£743 $1159 €1100 Durnstein, Wachau (17x12cm-7x5in) s. W/C paper on board. 28-Mar-3 Dorotheum, Vienna #286/R
£881 $1365 €1400 St Johann i d Wachau (16x11cm-6x4in) s.i. W/C. 1-Oct-2 Dorotheum, Vienna #324/R
£1006 $1560 €1600 Brigittakapelle (12x17cm-5x7in) s.i. W/C. 1-Oct-2 Dorotheum, Vienna #342/R est:1000-1200
£1132 $1755 €1800 Suburb (21x26cm-8x10in) s. W/C. 1-Oct-2 Dorotheum, Vienna #303/R est:1000-1200
£1384 $2145 €2200 Flower market (16x26cm-6x10in) s.d.916 W/C. 1-Oct-2 Dorotheum, Vienna #289/R est:1600-1800

ZAKHAROVA, Elena (1972-) Russian
£340 $517 €510 Field bouquet on the window (52x41cm-20x16in) s. 14-Jul-2 John Nicholson, Haslemere #261/R

ZALCE, Alfredo (1908-) Mexican
£2042 $3308 €3063 Cock (41x33cm-16x13in) s.d.1998 on metal. 21-Jan-3 Louis Morton, Mexico #63/R est:42000 (M.P 35000)
£4088 $6500 €6132 Matador (22x26cm-9x10in) s.d. masonite. 4-May-3 Treadway Gallery, Cincinnati #575/R est:10000-15000
Works on paper
£961 $1500 €1442 Untitled, naturaleza muerta con la fruta (37x67cm-15x26in) s.d.53 gouache chl. 14-Oct-2 Butterfields, San Francisco #2139/R est:2500-3500

ZALDER, Franz Xaver (1815-?) German
£423 $701 €600 Virgin and Child surrounded by floral garland (102x86cm-40x34in) s.d.1872. 11-Jun-3 Dorotheum, Vienna #430/R

ZALESKI, L C (18th C) Polish
Works on paper
£323 $500 €468 Polish genre scene of a town (20x18cm-8x7in) W/C exhib. 7-Dec-2 South Bay, Long Island #58/R

ZAMACOIS Y ZABALA, Eduardo (1842-1871) Spanish
£20645 $32000 €30968 Momentary diversion (35x27cm-14x11in) s.d.1868 panel prov.lit. 30-Oct-2 Christie's, Rockefeller NY #144/R est:15000-20000
£34810 $55000 €52215 Court jester playing bowls (46x37cm-18x15in) s.d.68 panel prov.lit. 24-Apr-3 Sotheby's, New York #68/R est:30000-40000

ZAMORA MUNOZ, Manuel (1928-) Spanish
£299 $466 €475 Toasting to the bull (54x82cm-21x32in) s. 23-Sep-2 Durán, Madrid #603/R

ZAMORANO, Ricardo (1922-) Spanish
£671 $1081 €1000 Figures in interior (86x100cm-34x39in) s.d.58. 18-Feb-3 Durán, Madrid #82/R

ZAMPIGHI, Eugenio (1859-1944) Italian
£3988 $6500 €5982 Genre scene (48x61cm-19x24in) 14-Feb-3 Du Mouchelle, Detroit #4/R est:6000-8000
£7000 $11130 €10500 Sharing a drink (46x58cm-18x23in) s. 20-Mar-3 Christie's, Kensington #60/R est:5000-7000
£9400 $14664 €14100 Interior scenes with figures (23x33cm-9x13in) s. pair. 9-Apr-3 Andrew Hartley, Ilkley #967/R est:9000-12000
£11392 $18000 €17088 First steps (56x77cm-22x30in) s. 23-Apr-3 Christie's, Rockefeller NY #143/R est:15000-20000
£11392 $18000 €17088 Musical celebration (57x78cm-22x31in) s. 23-Apr-3 Christie's, Rockefeller NY #144/R est:15000-20000
£12037 $19380 €18056 Family scene (56x77cm-22x30in) s. 7-May-3 Dobiaschofsky, Bern #1067/R est:35000 (S.FR 26000)
£12658 $20000 €18987 Duet (59x83cm-23x33in) s. 24-Apr-3 Sotheby's, New York #133/R est:20000-30000
£23022 $36835 €32000 Peasant family inside (80x128cm-31x50in) s. prov. 17-May-3 Lempertz, Koln #1511/R est:30000
£25000 $39250 €37500 Playing with grandmother (73x105cm-29x41in) s. prov. 19-Nov-2 Sotheby's, London #124/R est:20000-30000

ZANCANARO, Tono (1906-1985) Italian
Works on paper
£743 $1159 €1100 Bacchanal (70x79cm-28x31in) s.d.1950 Chinese ink. 26-Mar-3 Finarte Semenzato, Milan #42/R

ZANCHI, Antonio (1631-1722) Italian
£2027 $3162 €3000 Job raille par sa femme (91x73cm-36x29in) 26-Mar-3 Tajan, Paris #17/R
£5072 $8319 €7000 Sacrifice of Iphigenie (97x128cm-38x50in) prov. 27-May-3 Wiener Kunst Auktionen, Vienna #2/R est:7000-15000
£9295 $14407 €14500 Holy family (110x88cm-43x35in) 4-Dec-2 Christie's, Rome #482/R est:20000

ZANCHI, Antonio (attrib) (1631-1722) Italian
£1097 $1733 €1700 Saint Joseph and Jesus (78x60cm-31x24in) 20-Dec-2 Tajan, Paris #12
£2535 $4208 €3600 Venus, Juno and Minerva (135x115cm-53x45in) prov. 11-Jun-3 Dorotheum, Vienna #51/R est:3500-4500

ZANDEGIACOMO, Pedra (20th C) Italian
£461 $747 €650 Novita per Trieste (85x63cm-33x25in) 22-May-3 Stadion, Trieste #214/R
£461 $747 €650 Viaggio nella vita (50x60cm-20x24in) s. s.i.verso. 22-May-3 Stadion, Trieste #370/R
£513 $795 €800 Blessing the animals (60x80cm-24x31in) s. 5-Dec-2 Stadion, Trieste #878/R

ZANDER, Heinz (1939-) German
£519 $820 €810 Standing nude with shawl (42x17cm-17x7in) mono.d.1976 masonite. 15-Nov-2 Reiss & Sohn, Konigstein #900/R
£2138 $3293 €3400 Untitled mythological scene (62x82cm-24x32in) mono. panel. 26-Oct-2 Dr Lehr, Berlin #586/R est:2000

ZANDLEVEN, Jan Adam (1868-1923) Dutch
£298 $483 €420 Wooded landscape (35x50cm-14x20in) 26-May-3 Glerum, Amsterdam #66
£556 $917 €800 Sheep pen (35x52cm-14x20in) s.indis.d.192 prov. 1-Jul-3 Christie's, Amsterdam #405a
£592 $959 €900 Farm with a haystack (35x49cm-14x19in) s.d.1910. 21-Jan-3 Christie's, Amsterdam #364

ZANDOMENEGHI, Federico (1841-1917) Italian
Sculpture
£8966 $14255 €13000 Bust of woman (52cm-20in) white marble. 9-Mar-3 Semenzato, Venice #35/R est:12500

ZANDT, Thomas Kirby van (19th C) American
£6832 $11000 €10248 Sleigh drawn by a black horse (56x84cm-22x33in) s.d.1874. 23-Feb-3 Skinner, Boston #55/R est:10000-15000

ZANDVLIET, Robert (1970-) Dutch
£1923 $2981 €3000 Untitled (40x55cm-16x22in) s.d.1994 verso acrylic. 3-Dec-2 Christie's, Amsterdam #383/R est:3000-5000

ZANER, William (20th C) American
£705 $1100 €1058 Hill Country vista (91x127cm-36x50in) painted c.1977. 19-Oct-2 David Dike, Dallas #356/R

ZANFROGNINI, Carlo (1892-?) Italian
£1346 $1965 €2100 Portrait of the artist's wife (92x76cm-36x30in) s.d.1937. 5-Jun-2 Il Ponte, Milan #242

ZANG, John J (19th C) American
£417 $650 €626 Alpine landscape with cottages and figures (28x46cm-11x18in) s. artist board. 15-Oct-2 Winter Associates, Plainville #195
£622 $1008 €902 Winter scene in the Black Forest, Germany with hunters (69x97cm-27x38in) s. 26-May-3 Rasmussen, Copenhagen #1451/R (D.KR 6500)
£956 $1500 €1434 Forest clearing, winter (101x76cm-40x30in) s. 22-Nov-2 Skinner, Boston #66/R est:1000-1500
£1538 $2400 €2307 Winter landscape with lady in red hooded jacket (56x36cm-22x14in) s. 8-Nov-2 York Town, York #587

ZANGRANDO, Giovanni (1869-1941) Italian
£238 $379 €350 Garden in bloom (26x36cm-10x14in) s. board. 1-Mar-3 Stadion, Trieste #481
£272 $433 €400 Portrait of lady (60x50cm-24x20in) s. 1-Mar-3 Stadion, Trieste #252
£674 $1091 €950 Paesaggio lacustre (32x38cm-13x15in) s. board. 22-May-3 Stadion, Trieste #379/R
£1418 $2298 €2000 Il Castello di Duino (47x62cm-19x24in) s. panel. 22-May-3 Stadion, Trieste #399/R est:2000-3000
£5102 $8112 €7500 Studio (126x100cm-50x39in) s. 1-Mar-3 Meeting Art, Vercelli #53

ZANGS, Herbert (1924-2003) German
£319 $517 €450 I am a doer (40x30cm-16x12in) s. oil board video cassette. 24-May-3 Van Ham, Cologne #657/R
£2899 $4754 €4000 Untitled - ten commandments (136x162cm-54x64in) s. oil mixed media. 28-May-3 Lempertz, Koln #486/R est:4000

Works on paper

£1218 $1888 €1900 Window wiper rows (109x82cm-43x32in) s.d.1958 collage dispersion newspaper paper on board window frame. 7-Dec-2 Ketterer, Hamburg #732/R est:1800-2200
£11076 $17168 €17500 Knotted sack cloth (112x79cm-44x31in) s.d.1955 sackcloth cork tempera. 28-Sep-2 Ketterer, Hamburg #380/R est:15000-18000

ZANGUIDI, Jacopo (style) (1544-1574) Italian
£14194 $22000 €21291 Raising of the Cross (61x41cm-24x16in) panel. 2-Nov-2 North East Auctions, Portsmouth #98/R est:8000-12000

ZANIN, Francesco (19th C) Italian
£692 $1065 €1100 View of Venetian little square with monument (26x19cm-10x7in) 28-Oct-2 Il Ponte, Milan #297

ZANINO DI PIETRO (15th C) Italian
£15190 $24000 €24000 Man of Sorrows (90x48cm-35x19in) tempera board exhib.lit. 2-Dec-2 Finarte, Milan #121/R est:20000

ZANK, Gerhard (1937-) Dutch
£382 $596 €600 Forest scene with hunting party (17x29cm-7x11in) panel. 5-Nov-2 Vendu Notarishuis, Rotterdam #687/R
£382 $596 €600 Winter landscape with hunting party (13x29cm-5x11in) panel. 5-Nov-2 Vendu Notarishuis, Rotterdam #688
£528 $850 €750 Hunters near their loot (17x34cm-7x13in) s. 6-May-3 Vendu Notarishuis, Rotterdam #606
£528 $850 €750 Winter hunting scene (17x24cm-7x9in) s. 6-May-3 Vendu Notarishuis, Rotterdam #607/R

ZANOTTI, Calisto (?-1857) Italian
Works on paper
£1282 $2026 €2000 Courtyard of Medieval palace (35x46cm-14x18in) s.i.d.1845 verso W/C prov. 16-Nov-2 Lempertz, Koln #1417/R est:2000

ZAO-WOU-KI (1920-) Chinese
£28807 $44362 €43211 Untitled (65x56cm-26x22in) 26-Oct-2 Heffel, Vancouver #57 est:55000-65000 (C.D 70000)
£33333 $55000 €48000 Sans titre (7x92cm-3x36in) s. 1-Jul-3 Artcurial Briest, Paris #504/R est:60000-80000
£35039 $54660 €52559 Zitterlein (54x65cm-21x26in) s. d.1956 verso prov. 6-Nov-2 AB Stockholms Auktionsverk #955/R est:200000-250000 (S.KR 500000)
£38194 $63021 €55000 Composition (73x91cm-29x36in) s. s.i.d.1.6.65 verso prov. 1-Jul-3 Artcurial Briest, Paris #503/R est:60000-80000
£40816 $64898 €60000 Composition (54x65cm-21x26in) s. s.d.80 verso. 24-Mar-3 Cornette de St.Cyr, Paris #8/R est:50000
£41667 $65000 €62501 Untitled (89x115cm-35x45in) s.d.59 prov. 5-Nov-2 Doyle, New York #43/R est:25000-35000
£44928 $73681 €62000 22.1.71 (81x54cm-32x21in) s. s.i.22.1.71 verso prov. 28-May-3 Lempertz, Koln #478/R est:35000-40000
£46620 $76923 €67599 Horse racing (73x60cm-29x24in) s.i.d.1952. 6-Jul-3 Christie's, Hong Kong #135/R est:600000-700000 (HK.D 600000)
£48365 $74482 €76900 Composition (65x91cm-26x36in) s.d.1972 s.d.verso. 26-Oct-2 Cornette de St.Cyr, Paris #22/R est:80000
£68750 $110000 €103125 Fleurs (81x53cm-32x21in) s. s.i.d.1952 verso prov. 14-May-3 Sotheby's, New York #156/R est:25000-35000
£69930 $115385 €101399 Portrait of a lady (65x50cm-26x20in) s.d.1949. 6-Jul-3 Christie's, Hong Kong #134/R est:800000-1000000 (HK.D 900000)
£81509 $125525 €129600 Composition (96x130cm-38x51in) s. s.d.59 verso prov. 26-Oct-2 Cornette de St.Cyr, Paris #16/R est:100000
£99320 $157918 €146000 Composition (73x54cm-29x21in) s. s.d.61 verso prov. 24-Mar-3 Cornette de St.Cyr, Paris #10/R
£101010 $166667 €146465 21.6.62 (146x97cm-57x38in) s. exhib.lit. 6-Jul-3 Christie's, Hong Kong #133/R est:1200000-2200000 (HK.D 1300000)
£140000 $229600 €210000 1.12.68 13.2.77 (162x114cm-64x45in) s.d.1.12.68 d.13.2.77 verso prov.exhib.lit. 6-Feb-3 Christie's, London #620/R est:50000-70000
£180000 $295200 €270000 15.4.69 (130x162cm-51x64in) s.in Chinese s.i.d.15.4.69 prov.lit. 6-Feb-3 Christie's, London #614/R est:50000-70000
£372960 $615385 €540792 13.2.67 (200x300cm-79x118in) s. prov.exhib.lit. 6-Jul-3 Christie's, Hong Kong #132/R est:4000000-5000000 (HK.D 4800000)
Works on paper
£2482 $4145 €3500 Les hanches (20x13cm-8x5in) sanguine. 18-Jun-3 Pierre Berge, Paris #79 est:800-1000
£2533 $3951 €3800 Two lovers under tree (29x22cm-11x9in) s.d.50 Indian ink wash. 6-Nov-2 Dobiaschofsky, Bern #2025/R est:6000 (S.FR 5800)
£3145 $4843 €5000 Untitled (37x47cm-15x19in) s.d.1975 ink dr prov. 22-Oct-2 Campo & Campo, Antwerp #338/R est:6000
£4490 $7139 €6600 Composition (34x34cm-13x13in) s.i.d.75 ink wash dr. 26-Feb-3 Artcurial Briest, Paris #476/R est:4500-5000
£6410 $10064 €10000 Composition (70x94cm-28x37in) s.d.1997 ink prov. 15-Dec-2 Perrin, Versailles #62/R est:14000
£7381 $11736 €10850 Sans titre, mauve et noir (30x22cm-12x9in) s.d.56 W/C Indian ink. 26-Feb-3 Artcurial Briest, Paris #475/R est:8000-10000
£7986 $12618 €11500 Composition (28x38cm-11x15in) s.d. W/C prov. 27-Apr-3 Perrin, Versailles #55/R est:5000-6000
£8681 $13715 €12500 Composition (88x94cm-35x37in) s.d. ink prov. 27-Apr-3 Perrin, Versailles #54/R est:10000-12000
£13095 $20821 €19250 Sans titre, bleu gris (40x56cm-16x22in) s.d.67 W/C gouache. 26-Feb-3 Artcurial Briest, Paris #473/R est:12000-15000
£15000 $25050 €21750 Untitled (67x45cm-26x18in) s.d.73 gouache W/C prov. 26-Jun-3 Sotheby's, London #199/R est:8000-10000

ZAPATA, Miguel (1940-) Spanish
£839 $1325 €1300 Hospice entry, Madrid (60x34cm-24x13in) s.i.d.1984 oil collage mixed media board prov. 17-Dec-2 Segre, Madrid #216/R

ZAPPELLONI, Andrea (1877-1961) Italian
£510 $811 €750 Old village (46x31cm-18x12in) s.d.1924 canvas on cardboard. 1-Mar-3 Meeting Art, Vercelli #191
£680 $1082 €1000 Trees in Stresa (44x32cm-17x13in) s. tempera cardboard. 18-Mar-3 Finarte, Milan #208/R
£748 $1190 €1100 Chapel in the woods (40x32cm-16x13in) s.d.21 tempera cardboard. 18-Mar-3 Finarte, Milan #207/R
£1087 $1783 €1500 La cappellatta (40x50cm-16x20in) s.d.1918. 27-May-3 Finarte, Milan #39/R est:1500-1700
£1304 $2139 €1800 Ponticello con cipressi (72x40cm-28x16in) s. 27-May-3 Finarte, Milan #99/R est:1800-2000
£1304 $2139 €1800 Galline che razzolano (63x50cm-25x20in) s. panel. 27-May-3 Finarte, Milan #100/R est:1800-2000

ZARCO, Antonio (1930-) Spanish
£409 $638 €650 Etruscan tombs (73x92cm-29x36in) s.d.1991. 8-Oct-2 Ansorena, Madrid #616/R
£755 $1177 €1200 Green hills (33x46cm-13x18in) s. 8-Oct-2 Ansorena, Madrid #391/R

ZARDO, Alberto (1876-1959) Italian
£710 $1121 €1100 Little white horse (27x37cm-11x15in) s. board. 18-Dec-2 Finarte, Milan #135/R
£1622 $2530 €2400 Santa Trinita' bridge in Florence (31x38cm-12x15in) s. board. 28-Mar-3 Farsetti, Prato #687/R

ZARFIN, Faibich Shraga (1900-1975) Russian
£374 $595 €550 Maison au bord de l'eau (50x60cm-20x24in) s. lit. 26-Feb-3 Artcurial Briest, Paris #243/R
£374 $595 €550 La foret (50x60cm-20x24in) s.d.52. 26-Feb-3 Artcurial Briest, Paris #244
£374 $595 €550 Village de bord de mer (50x60cm-20x24in) s. 26-Feb-3 Artcurial Briest, Paris #245

ZARRAGA, Angel (1886-1946) Mexican
£5921 $9592 €9000 Arlequin (24x33cm-9x13in) board prov. 21-Jan-3 Durán, Madrid #143/R
£54140 $85000 €81210 Still life of fruit and flowers (46x62cm-18x24in) s. painted 1922 lit. 19-Nov-2 Sotheby's, New York #14/R est:80000
£79268 $130000 €118902 Banista en el penon blanco (94x73cm-37x29in) s.d.1925 prov.exhib.lit. 28-May-3 Christie's, Rockefeller NY #8/R est:100000-150000
£114650 $180000 €171975 Portrait of Ramon Novarro (130x90cm-51x35in) s.i. painted c.1929 prov.lit. 19-Nov-2 Sotheby's, New York #73/R
£121951 $200000 €176829 Desnudo de frente, nu au coquillage (116x89cm-46x35in) s.d.1926 lit. 27-May-3 Sotheby's, New York #4
Works on paper
£432 $696 €648 Shepherd with lamb (40x34cm-16x13in) s. pencil. 22-Feb-3 Rasmussen, Havnen #2347 (D.KR 4800)
£1574 $2456 €2361 Estudio para el retrato de la Sra Sonet (34x27cm-13x11in) s. lapiz exec.c.1933 prov. 17-Oct-2 Louis Morton, Mexico #141/R est:30000-35000 (M.P 25000)

ZATLOUKAL, Cyril (1894-?) Czechoslovakian
Sculpture
£3064 $4750 €4596 Standing youth (86cm-34in) s.i. black pat. bronze on black marble base prov. 29-Oct-2 Sotheby's, New York #250/R est:3000-4000

ZATZKA, Bernard (?) ?
£1027 $1500 €1541 Young woman in a landscape with bouquet (53x25cm-21x10in) s. 3-Nov-1 North East Auctions, Portsmouth #233/R

ZATZKA, Hans (1859-1949) Austrian
£1772 $2800 €2800 Two water nymphs with young flute player (40x30cm-16x12in) s. canvas on canvas. 29-Nov-2 Sigalas, Stuttgart #1144/R est:980
£2548 $4000 €3822 Maiden in the garden (23x10cm-9x4in) bears sig. 10-Dec-2 Doyle, New York #214/R est:5000-7000
£3438 $5500 €5157 At the bedroom window (46x25cm-18x10in) s.i. s.verso. 14-May-3 Butterfields, San Francisco #1093/R est:5000-7000
£4088 $6336 €6500 Eligible (69x47cm-27x19in) s. i. verso. 29-Oct-2 Dorotheum, Vienna #54/R est:8700-10000

£4585 $7153 €6878 Mythological scene (52x98cm-20x39in) s. 6-Nov-2 Dobiaschofsky, Bern #1085/R est:10000 (S.FR 10500)
£4777 $7500 €7166 Spring. Summer (56x25cm-22x10in) s. i.verso one wood panel pair. 23-Nov-2 Jackson's, Cedar Falls #4/R est:7000-10000
£4800 $7536 €7200 Liebesgluck - girl in love (48x32cm-19x13in) s. prov. 19-Nov-2 Sotheby's, London #120/R est:5000-7000
£5313 $8500 €7970 Anticipation (69x46cm-27x18in) s. i.verso. 14-May-3 Butterfields, San Francisco #1094/R est:4000-6000
£5500 $9020 €8250 Reclining beauty (68x105cm-27x41in) s. s.i.verso. 3-Jun-3 Sotheby's, London #32/R est:6000-8000
£6013 $9500 €9500 The intruder (58x79cm-23x31in) s. lit. 29-Nov-2 Schloss Ahlden, Ahlden #1186/R est:7500
£6962 $11000 €11000 Oriental beauties (60x76cm-24x30in) s.i.verso. 28-Nov-2 Dorotheum, Vienna #94/R est:5000-7000
£7500 $11774 €11250 Halt die brucke - will the bridge hold (58x79cm-23x31in) s. s.i.verso prov. 19-Nov-2 Sotheby's, London #119/R est:5000-7000
£10500 $17535 €15750 Harem musicians (57x78cm-22x31in) s. 18-Jun-3 Christie's, Kensington #187/R est:7000-10000
£15924 $25000 €23886 Dream in the forest (69x105cm-27x41in) s. 21-Nov-2 Sotheby's, New York #186/R est:30000-40000
£22581 $35000 €33872 Pearls of the sea (79x58cm-31x23in) s. s.i.verso. 30-Oct-2 Christie's, Rockefeller NY #204/R est:15000-20000

ZAUGG, Hans (1894-1986) Swiss
£463 $745 €695 Geraniums (37x40cm-15x16in) s.d.1947 i. verso. 7-May-3 Dobiaschofsky, Bern #1068/R (S.FR 1000)

ZAWADO, Jean Waclaw (1891-1988) Polish
£2789 $4435 €4100 Les moissons (50x74cm-20x29in) s. 3-Mar-3 Claude Boisgirard, Paris #104/R est:3500-4000

ZAYYAT, Elias (1935-) Syrian
£2800 $4452 €4200 Pondering woman under tree (47x66cm-19x26in) s.d.1961. 30-Apr-3 Sotheby's, London #150/R est:3000-5000

ZBINDEN, Emil (1908-) Swiss
Works on paper
£306 $477 €459 By the water (25x34cm-10x13in) s. Indian ink W/C over pencil. 6-Nov-2 Dobiaschofsky, Bern #2077 (S.FR 700)

ZDENEK, Eberl Frantisek (1888-?) Czechoslovakian
£1239 $1933 €1859 Courtesan (73x84cm-29x33in) s.d.1919. 12-Oct-2 Dorotheum, Prague #108 est:60000-90000 (C.KR 60000)

ZEBHAUSER, Franz (c.1769-1833) Austrian
£753 $1175 €1100 Virgin Annunciation (65x53cm-26x21in) s.i.d.1804 canvas on canvas lit. 10-Apr-3 Allgauer, Kempten #3074/R

ZECHYR, Othmar (1938-) Austrian
Works on paper
£513 $810 €800 A mess (61x43cm-24x17in) s.i.d.1967 Juli chk. 12-Nov-2 Dorotheum, Vienna #207/R
£1266 $1962 €2000 Monolithic mountain (31x22cm-12x9in) s.i.d.1985 Indian ink transparent paper. 24-Sep-2 Wiener Kunst Auktionen, Vienna #271/R est:2000-3500
£5380 $8500 €8500 Monument with - (79x49cm-31x19in) bears s.i.d.1984 pen Indian ink transparent paper. 27-Nov-2 Dorotheum, Vienna #282/R est:1700-2400

ZECKENDORF, Oskar (20th C) Austrian
£700 $1141 €1050 Portrait of a young girl (113x75cm-44x30in) s.d.1923. 29-Jan-3 Sotheby's, Olympia #329/R

ZEE, Jan van der (1898-1988) Dutch
£764 $1200 €1146 Village street (49x48cm-19x19in) s. canvasboard. 22-Nov-2 Skinner, Boston #316/R est:800-1200
£9220 $14936 €13000 Winter view of a dyke along a canal and a village (55x53cm-22x21in) s.d.33. 26-May-3 Glerum, Amsterdam #47/R est:6000-8000
Works on paper
£355 $574 €500 Composition (54x72cm-21x28in) s.d.79 gouache. 26-May-3 Glerum, Amsterdam #275/R
£1392 $2200 €2200 Untitled (54x73cm-21x29in) s.d.83 gouache. 26-Nov-2 Sotheby's, Amsterdam #55/R est:2200-3500

ZEEMAN, Abraham Johannes (1811-1842) German
£1338 $2154 €1900 Hunters with hare (63x49cm-25x19in) s. panel. 7-May-3 Vendue Huis, Gravenhage #349/R est:2000-3000
£2917 $4638 €4200 Flirt (70x56cm-28x22in) s. 29-Apr-3 Christie's, Amsterdam #50/R est:3000-5000

ZEGRAY, Lucienne (20th C) Canadian
Works on paper
£281 $441 €422 Place d'armes, Montreal (20x25cm-8x10in) s.i.d.2000 pastel prov. 25-Nov-2 Hodgins, Calgary #272/R (C.D 700)
£321 $508 €482 Christmas shopping in Quebec (36x28cm-14x11in) d.1999 pastel. 1-Dec-2 Levis, Calgary #108/R (C.D 800)
£356 $583 €516 Flower market, Cabbage town, Toronto (40x50cm-16x20in) s.i.d.1999 pastel. 9-Jun-3 Hodgins, Calgary #170/R (C.D 800)

ZEGUERS, Wilhelmina (1893-1992) Belgian
£324 $518 €450 Reflexion de roses (60x82cm-24x32in) s. 19-May-3 Horta, Bruxelles #283

ZEITBLOM, Bartholome (style) (c.1455-1522) German
£6040 $9724 €9000 Saint Nicholas of Bari (109x61cm-43x24in) mono. gold panel prov.lit. 18-Feb-3 Sotheby's, Amsterdam #187/R est:6000-8000

ZEITZ, Johan Christian Gustav (1827-1914) Dutch
£1053 $1705 €1600 Toddler's first steps (67x56cm-26x22in) s. panel. 21-Jan-3 Christie's, Amsterdam #69 est:1000-1500

ZELENINE, Edouard (1938-) British
Works on paper
£310 $518 €450 Composition (65x46cm-26x18in) s. gouache W/C. 9-Jul-3 Cornette de St.Cyr, Paris #202

ZELGER, Jakob Joseph (1812-1885) Swiss
£786 $1226 €1179 Mountain landscape with pine trees and shepherdesses by water trough (68x56cm-27x22in) s. 20-Nov-2 Fischer, Luzern #2306/R est:1800-2500 (S.FR 1800)
£2183 $3450 €3275 Piz d'Err with Albula (61x87cm-24x34in) s.d.1853. 14-Nov-2 Stuker, Bern #598 est:6000-8000 (S.FR 5000)
£2358 $3821 €3419 View from allweg of Stans plains (32x43cm-13x17in) s. paper on board prov. 24-May-3 Galerie Gloggner, Luzern #130/R est:4500-5000 (S.FR 5000)
£2817 $4620 €4085 Pilatus mountain range (75x106cm-30x42in) s. 4-Jun-3 Fischer, Luzern #1223/R est:6000-8000 (S.FR 6000)
£3057 $4769 €4586 Cattle and ruins by mountain gorge (74x100cm-29x39in) mono. prov. 20-Nov-2 Fischer, Luzern #1244/R est:7000-9000 (S.FR 7000)
£3493 $5520 €5240 Wallenstattersee in morning (61x87cm-24x34in) s.d.1853. 14-Nov-2 Stuker, Bern #597 est:6000-8000 (S.FR 8000)
Works on paper
£291 $477 €422 Men before stone house with mountain view (20x28cm-8x11in) s. W/C. 4-Jun-3 Fischer, Luzern #2696/R (S.FR 620)

ZELLER, Eugen (1889-1974) Swiss
£343 $542 €515 Still life (32x39cm-13x15in) s.i.d.1948 verso board. 29-Nov-2 Zofingen, Switzerland #3143 (S.FR 800)

ZELLER, Fred (1912-) French
Works on paper
£276 $427 €430 Paysage. W/C. 8-Dec-2 Feletin, Province #204

ZELLER, Friedrich (1817-1896) Austrian
£4167 $6542 €6500 Panoramic view from Maria Plain of Salzburg in the evening light (53x76cm-21x30in) s.d.863. 21-Nov-2 Dorotheum, Vienna #109/R est:11000-16000

ZELLER, Hans Arnold (1897-1983) Swiss
£2146 $3391 €3219 Upper Bavaria near Ostersee (49x60cm-19x24in) s.d.1932 i.verso board. 26-Nov-2 Hans Widmer, St Gallen #1424/R est:5000-9000 (S.FR 5000)
£2533 $3951 €3800 Summer evening near Waldstatt (14x21cm-6x8in) s.d.1964 board. 6-Nov-2 Hans Widmer, St Gallen #104/R est:3500-7000 (S.FR 5800)
£2575 $4069 €3863 Mountain landscape with view over Upper Fachleren, Urnasch (19x23cm-7x9in) s.d.1948 panel. 26-Nov-2 Hans Widmer, St Gallen #1425/R est:2500-5000 (S.FR 6000)
£2620 $4087 €3930 Autumn in Appenzell country (30x27cm-12x11in) s.d.1975 board. 6-Nov-2 Hans Widmer, St Gallen #141/R est:4500-8000 (S.FR 6000)
£3057 $4769 €4586 Marsh marigolds (16x23cm-6x9in) s.d.1957 i. verso board. 6-Nov-2 Hans Widmer, St Gallen #19/R est:4000-7000 (S.FR 7000)
£3231 $5041 €4847 Winter landscape near Teufen (16x23cm-6x9in) s.d.1957 board. 6-Nov-2 Hans Widmer, St Gallen #20/R est:4000-7000 (S.FR 7400)

£3930 $6131 €5895 Autumn day (27x27cm-11x11in) s.d.1932 i. verso board. 6-Nov-2 Hans Widmer, St Gallen #105/R est:8000-12000 (S.FR 9000)
£4626 $6753 €6939 Summer morning with Santis (38x47cm-15x19in) s. masonite. 17-Jun-2 Philippe Schuler, Zurich #4298/R est:4000-5000 (S.FR 10500)
£6550 $10218 €9825 Field flowers (80x64cm-31x25in) s.d.1948 i. verso board. 6-Nov-2 Hans Widmer, St Gallen #18/R est:14000-20000 (S.FR 15000)
£8297 $12943 €12446 Santis in the morning sun (50x60cm-20x24in) s.d.1963 board. 6-Nov-2 Hans Widmer, St Gallen #17/R est:12000-20000 (S.FR 19000)
£11792 $19104 €17098 Young boy (46x55cm-18x22in) s.d.1966 pavatex. 26-May-3 Sotheby's, Zurich #80/R est:25000-35000 (S.FR 25000)

ZELLER, Johann Baptist (1877-1959) Swiss
£4717 $7642 €6840 Cattle going to alpine meadows (40x60cm-16x24in) s.d.1930 oil goldbronze board prov. 24-May-3 Galerie Gloggner, Luzern #131/R est:5800-6500 (S.FR 10000)

ZELLER, Magnus (1888-1972) German
£2536 $4159 €3500 Rider in a storm (34x36cm-13x14in) s. board. 31-May-3 Villa Grisebach, Berlin #228/R est:3500-4500
Works on paper
£316 $500 €500 Mountain landscape (35x24cm-14x9in) s. W/C. 29-Nov-2 Villa Grisebach, Berlin #965/R
£1806 $2853 €2600 Village with pump and cock crowing (32x44cm-13x17in) s. W/C board. 26-Apr-3 Dr Lehr, Berlin #566/R est:3000

ZELLER, Michael (1859-?) ?
£321 $497 €500 Black Peter (13x11cm-5x4in) s. panel lit. 7-Dec-2 Bergmann, Erlangen #798/R
£353 $546 €550 Inside alpine dairy farm (13x11cm-5x4in) s.d.91 panel lit. 7-Dec-2 Bergmann, Erlangen #797/R

ZELMAN, Victor (1877-1960) Australian
£1354 $2221 €2031 Boating, near Hepburn Springs, Daylesford (71x92cm-28x36in) s. 4-Jun-3 Deutscher-Menzies, Melbourne #312/R est:3500-5000 (A.D 3400)

ZEMP, Adolf (1838-?) Swiss
£676 $1054 €1000 Portrait of young boy (39x31cm-15x12in) paper on canvas. 26-Mar-3 Tajan, Paris #158

ZEMPLENYI, Magda (1899-?) Hungarian
£1084 $1690 €1572 Reclining nude (69x100cm-27x39in) s. 13-Sep-2 Mu Terem Galeria, Budapest #188/R est:300000 (H.F 420000)

ZEMPLENYI, Tividar (1864-1917) Hungarian
£1118 $1744 €1621 Street in shadow (76x63cm-30x25in) s.d.1916. 12-Apr-3 Mu Terem Galeria, Budapest #198/R est:240000 (H.F 400000)

ZEN, Sergio (1936-) Italian
£316 $494 €500 From the Eolie (60x60cm-24x24in) s. s.i.d.1997 verso. 14-Sep-2 Meeting Art, Vercelli #105/R
£327 $523 €500 Suspended (60x60cm-24x24in) s. s.i.d.2000 verso exhib.lit. 4-Jan-3 Meeting Art, Vercelli #334
£327 $523 €500 Good wind (60x60cm-24x24in) s. painted 1999. 4-Jan-3 Meeting Art, Vercelli #340
£348 $543 €550 Principle (60x60cm-24x24in) s. s.i.d.2001 verso. 14-Sep-2 Meeting Art, Vercelli #315/R

ZENDEL, Gabriel (1906-1992) French
£256 $403 €400 Scene d'interieur (92x73cm-36x29in) s.d. 24-Nov-2 Chayette & Cheval, Paris #296
£449 $704 €700 Night music (65x46cm-26x18in) s. s.i.verso. 12-Dec-2 Rabourdin & Choppin de Janvry, Paris #167/R

ZENDER, Rudolf (1901-1988) Swiss
£330 $528 €495 Paris, glass covered passage (55x33cm-22x13in) s.d. 17-Mar-3 Philippe Schuler, Zurich #4571 (S.FR 700)
£391 $607 €587 Parisian street (55x33cm-22x13in) s.d.1965. 9-Dec-2 Philippe Schuler, Zurich #3848 (S.FR 900)
£401 $642 €602 Barges in harbour on the Seine (40x80cm-16x31in) s. 17-Mar-3 Philippe Schuler, Zurich #4567 (S.FR 850)
£401 $642 €602 View over the rooftops of Paris (45x61cm-18x24in) s. 17-Mar-3 Philippe Schuler, Zurich #4568 (S.FR 850)
£524 $817 €786 Houses in the trees on river shore (50x61cm-20x24in) s. 6-Nov-2 Hans Widmer, St Gallen #98/R (S.FR 1200)
£524 $823 €786 On the edge of the city (38x46cm-15x18in) s. panel. 25-Nov-2 Germann, Zurich #849 (S.FR 1200)
£568 $886 €852 Dahlias in red jug (80x65cm-31x26in) s. 20-Nov-2 Fischer, Luzern #2307/R (S.FR 1300)
£708 $1132 €1062 Paris, Sacre Coeur (38x55cm-15x22in) s.d. board. 17-Mar-3 Philippe Schuler, Zurich #4569 (S.FR 1500)
£708 $1146 €1253 Faubourg Beaubourg, Paris. Street scene (19x46cm-7x18in) s.d.1964 board double-sided. 26-May-3 Sotheby's, Zurich #104/R est:1500-2500 (S.FR 1500)
£786 $1234 €1179 River harbour (46x55cm-18x22in) s.d.1962. 25-Nov-2 Germann, Zurich #848 est:1200-1600 (S.FR 1800)
£901 $1424 €1352 Seine, Paris (58x101cm-23x40in) s. 28-Nov-2 Christie's, Zurich #91/R (S.FR 2100)
£943 $1528 €1670 Chalands amarres. Female nude (33x55cm-13x22in) s.d.1965 double-sided. 26-May-3 Sotheby's, Zurich #129/R est:2000-4000 (S.FR 2000)
£1304 $2035 €1956 Charenton, la Seine (100x81cm-39x32in) s.d.1968. 16-Sep-2 Philippe Schuler, Zurich #3415/R est:3000-3500 (S.FR 3000)
£1391 $2157 €2087 Seine quayside (81x94cm-32x37in) s.d.1965. 9-Dec-2 Philippe Schuler, Zurich #3849/R est:2500-3000 (S.FR 3200)

ZENNSTROM, Petter (1945-) Swedish
£304 $481 €456 Untitled (78x62cm-31x24in) init.d.87 paper on canvas. 28-Apr-3 Bukowskis, Stockholm #995/R (S.KR 4000)
£386 $622 €579 Figures (100x58cm-39x23in) init.d.90 greaseproof paper on canvas. 7-May-3 AB Stockholms Auktionsverk #971/R (S.KR 5000)
£386 $622 €579 Head (69x60cm-27x24in) init.d.79. 7-May-3 AB Stockholms Auktionsverk #1055/R (S.KR 5000)
£491 $765 €737 Figure (92x61cm-36x24in) init.d.91. 6-Nov-2 AB Stockholms Auktionsverk #861/R (S.KR 7000)
£561 $875 €842 Object (92x76cm-36x30in) init.d.90 panel prov. 6-Nov-2 AB Stockholms Auktionsverk #874/R (S.KR 8000)

ZENS, Herwig (1943-) Austrian
£609 $962 €950 Composition (100x80cm-39x31in) s. acrylic collage canvas. 12-Nov-2 Dorotheum, Vienna #228/R

ZEPEDA, Marco Antonio (1938-) Mexican
£1608 $2573 €2332 El volcan de Colima (40x70cm-16x28in) s. 15-May-3 Louis Morton, Mexico #139 est:16000-25000 (M.P 26000)

ZEPPEL-SPERL, Robert (1944-) Austrian
£993 $1619 €1500 Divinity (105x82cm-41x32in) s.d.1998/9 acrylic. 28-Jan-3 Dorotheum, Vienna #300/R est:2200-3000
£1151 $1888 €1600 As in a legend (100x105cm-39x41in) s.d.2000 acrylic. 5-Jun-3 Dorotheum, Salzburg #649/R est:1800-2400
Works on paper
£285 $444 €450 Untitled from the cycle - Max Ernst (58x39cm-23x15in) d.79/10 mixed media. 15-Oct-2 Dorotheum, Vienna #217/R
£285 $444 €450 Untitled from the cycle - Max Ernst (58x39cm-23x15in) d.79/10 mixed media. 15-Oct-2 Dorotheum, Vienna #218/R

ZEPPENFELD, Viktor (1834-1883) German
£264 $409 €420 Peasant hut in northern Germany (32x45cm-13x18in) bears i. board. 2-Nov-2 Hans Stahl, Toestorf #94

ZERMATI, Jules (20th C) Italian
£800 $1280 €1200 Secret admirers (56x68cm-22x27in) s. 7-Jan-3 Bonhams, Knightsbridge #135/R
£3165 $5000 €4748 Serenade (43x57cm-17x22in) s. 24-Apr-3 Sotheby's, New York #134/R est:6000-8000

ZEROLO, Martin (1928-) Spanish
£613 $968 €950 Still life (60x72cm-24x28in) s. 18-Dec-2 Ansorena, Madrid #332/R

ZERRITSCH, Fritz (jnr) (1888-1985) Austrian
£345 $552 €500 Cows in meadow (69x96cm-27x38in) s. 11-Mar-3 Dorotheum, Vienna #153/R
£347 $549 €500 Old houses (50x55cm-20x22in) s. 24-Apr-3 Dorotheum, Vienna #185/R
£379 $607 €550 Retz. Poggstall (12x15cm-5x6in) s.d.67 69 canvas board. 11-Mar-3 Dorotheum, Vienna #152/R
£517 $828 €750 Todersdorf (53x68cm-21x27in) i. verso. 11-Mar-3 Dorotheum, Vienna #157/R

ZESATTI, Luis Armando (1967-) Latin American
£9756 $16000 €14146 Bamboos verdes II (130x146cm-51x57in) s.i.d.2002 acrylic. 27-May-3 Sotheby's, New York #153

ZESHIN, Shibata (1807-1891) Japanese
Works on paper
£1500 $2505 €2175 Butterflies (114x21cm-45x8in) s. ink colour hanging scroll. 18-Jun-3 Christie's, London #301/R est:800-1200
£1594 $2614 €2200 Bamboo scarecrow (95x25cm-37x10in) s. Indian ink scroll prov. 31-May-3 Dr Fritz Nagel, Stuttgart #1569/R est:1900

£1700 $2839 €2465 Shojo drinking from a huge sake cup (120x50cm-47x20in) s. ink colour hanging scroll. 18-Jun-3 Christie's, London #302/R est:1000-2000

£2200 $3674 €3190 Summer and Winter - Camellia and Cherry (89x32cm-35x13in) s. ink colour silk hanging scrolls pair. 18-Jun-3 Christie's, London #300/R est:2500-3000

£3000 $4740 €4500 Figure (86x42cm-34x17in) s. col ink silk scroll wood box. 13-Nov-2 Christie's, London #209/R est:4000-6000

£7000 $11690 €10150 Fan paintings of birds, fruit and flower subjects (4x11cm-2x4in) s.d.1869 ink colour lacquer silk mounted in orihon format six. 18-Jun-3 Christie's, London #303/R est:2000-3000

ZETSCHE, Eduard (1844-1927) Austrian

£315 $488 €473 Castle staircase (25x17cm-10x7in) tempera board. 1-Oct-2 SOGA, Bratislava #191/R est:12000 (SL.K 20000)
£1392 $2200 €2200 Beach (16x24cm-6x9in) board. 26-Nov-2 Wiener Kunst Auktionen, Vienna #63/R est:2200-3000
£4747 $7500 €7500 Donau landscape (24x33cm-9x13in) s. i.verso board. 28-Nov-2 Dorotheum, Vienna #78/R est:3000-3600

Works on paper

£377 $585 €600 Rocky landscape (17x23cm-7x9in) s. Indian ink W/C. 1-Oct-2 Dorotheum, Vienna #338/R
£696 $1100 €1100 Boy wearing straw hat on Amrum beach (15x22cm-6x9in) s. bears d.20 W/C Indian ink pencil. 26-Nov-2 Wiener Kunst Auktionen, Vienna #145/R
£943 $1462 €1500 Burg Landshut/Isar, Bavaria (22x30cm-9x12in) s.i.d.98 verso W/C paper on board. 1-Oct-2 Dorotheum, Vienna #262/R est:2000-2200
£1351 $2108 €2000 Senftenberg (19x15cm-7x6in) s.d.917 i. verso W/C paper on board. 28-Mar-3 Dorotheum, Vienna #357/R est:1800-2000
£1384 $2145 €2200 Landscape with river bend (24x32cm-9x13in) s.d.917 W/C. 1-Oct-2 Dorotheum, Vienna #242/R est:2400-3000
£2027 $3162 €3000 Tavern (23x27cm-9x11in) bears s.i.d.03 verso W/C. 28-Mar-3 Dorotheum, Vienna #315/R est:3000-3500
£3145 $4874 €5000 Summer landscape with wooden bridge over river (27x34cm-11x13in) s. W/C. 1-Oct-2 Dorotheum, Vienna #241/R est:2400-3000

ZETTERBERG, Nisse (1910-1986) Swedish

£841 $1312 €1262 Still life of basket and peaches (54x65cm-21x26in) s.d.1956 prov. 5-Nov-2 Bukowskis, Stockholm #129/R (S.KR 12000)
£946 $1476 €1419 Still life of fish (65x80cm-26x31in) mono.d.46 panel. 5-Nov-2 Bukowskis, Stockholm #130/R est:8000-10000 (S.KR 13500)

ZETTERSTROM, Mimmi (1843-1885) Swedish

£1784 $2891 €2587 Lady with red parasol, Jersey (80x60cm-31x24in) s.i.d.1881. 26-May-3 Bukowskis, Stockholm #35/R est:20000-25000 (S.KR 23000)

ZETTERWALL, Eva H (1941-) Swedish

Works on paper

£270 $435 €405 Untitled (64x52cm-25x20in) s. mixed media collage. 7-May-3 AB Stockholms Auktionsverk #962/R (S.KR 3500)
£911 $1421 €1367 Untitled (210x125cm-83x49in) s. mixed media aluminium. 6-Nov-2 AB Stockholms Auktionsverk #795/R est:10000-12000 (S.KR 13000)

ZETTLER, Max (20th C) German

£287 $447 €450 English garden (37x50cm-15x20in) board lit. 8-Nov-2 Auktionhaus Georg Rehm, Augsburg #8192/R
£310 $499 €440 Dachau landscape (37x49cm-15x19in) s.i. board. 7-May-3 Michael Zeller, Lindau #1005

ZEUNER, Jonas (1727-1814) Dutch

£2532 $3924 €4000 Horseman in a landscape (32x26cm-13x10in) s. 25-Sep-2 Christie's, Amsterdam #525/R est:2500-3500

ZEUTHEN, C O (1812-1890) Danish

£266 $431 €399 Landscape with woman on road across bridge (22x27cm-9x11in) s. 25-Jan-3 Rasmussen, Havnen #2042 (D.KR 3000)

ZEUTHEN, Ernst (1880-1938) Danish

£254 $391 €381 Landscape with figure and horse (39x46cm-15x18in) s. 23-Oct-2 Kunsthallen, Copenhagen #143 (D.KR 3000)
£274 $436 €411 Begonia (42x37cm-17x15in) s. 26-Feb-3 Kunsthallen, Copenhagen #351 (D.KR 3000)
£296 $461 €444 Sailing vessel off a coast (48x58cm-19x23in) s. exhib. 23-Sep-2 Rasmussen, Vejle #2515/R (D.KR 3500)
£355 $547 €533 Begonia (42x37cm-17x15in) s. 23-Oct-2 Kunsthallen, Copenhagen #13 (D.KR 4200)
£357 $557 €536 Seascape with sailing ship (47x63cm-19x25in) s. 5-Aug-2 Rasmussen, Vejle #333 (D.KR 4200)
£372 $573 €558 Green seascape with two sailing vessels (54x66cm-21x26in) s. 23-Oct-2 Kunsthallen, Copenhagen #49 (D.KR 4400)
£372 $587 €558 Young girl seated on chair (34x29cm-13x11in) init. panel prov. 1-Apr-3 Rasmussen, Copenhagen #585/R (D.KR 4000)
£508 $787 €762 Coastal landscape with view across the sea (69x78cm-27x31in) s.d.1915 prov.exhib. 1-Oct-2 Rasmussen, Copenhagen #352/R (D.KR 6000)
£593 $919 €890 Field workers by the sea (66x78cm-26x31in) s. prov. 1-Oct-2 Rasmussen, Copenhagen #361/R (D.KR 7000)
£659 $1015 €989 Seascape with burning ship (55x79cm-22x31in) s.d.1938. 23-Oct-2 Kunsthallen, Copenhagen #63/R (D.KR 7800)
£677 $1050 €1016 Sailing boat under drifting clouds (80x105cm-31x41in) s.d.1932 prov. 1-Oct-2 Rasmussen, Copenhagen #362/R (D.KR 8000)

ZEUTHEN, Ernst (attrib) (1880-1938) Danish

£498 $806 €722 Bouquet of flowers (68x79cm-27x31in) mono.d.29. 24-May-3 Rasmussen, Havnen #4094/R (D.KR 5200)

ZEVACO, Xavier (20th C) ?

£2264 $3509 €3600 Untitled (114x146cm-45x57in) s.verso acrylic painted 1985. 7-Oct-2 Claude Aguttes, Neuilly #197/R

ZEVEN, Henri van (?) Belgian?

£283 $436 €450 Au bord de l'eau (28x36cm-11x14in) s. 22-Oct-2 Campo, Vlaamse Kaai #336

ZEVENBERGHEN, Georges van (1877-1968) Belgian

£301 $484 €460 Le croquis (27x35cm-11x14in) s. i.d.1936 verso panel. 20-Jan-3 Horta, Bruxelles #406
£1392 $2200 €2200 Bouquet de fleurs dans un vase (70x65cm-28x26in) s. 26-Nov-2 Palais de Beaux Arts, Brussels #171/R est:3000-4000

ZEVON, Irene (1918-) American

£256 $400 €384 Untitled, abstract composition (104x79cm-41x31in) s.d.1963. 10-Nov-2 Selkirks, St. Louis #1000/R

ZEWY, Karl (1855-1929) Austrian

£1244 $2066 €1804 Vive cliquot (27x20cm-11x8in) s.d.1882 panel. 16-Jun-3 Waddingtons, Toronto #20/R est:3000-5000 (C.D 2800)
£1250 $1987 €1800 Peasant girl near Weissenkirchen (100x75cm-39x30in) s. 29-Apr-3 Wiener Kunst Auktionen, Vienna #558/R est:1800-2000
£2101 $3319 €3152 Girl making music in garden (38x48cm-15x19in) s. panel. 16-Nov-2 Crafoord, Lund #62/R est:8000 (S.KR 30000)

ZEYER, Erich (1903-1960) German

£253 $400 €400 Farmer with horse and cart and plough (60x80cm-24x31in) s. 30-Nov-2 Geble, Radolfzell #703
£288 $438 €450 Hay harvest (60x80cm-24x31in) s. board. 31-Aug-2 Geble, Radolfzell #673/R
£377 $589 €600 Harvest (60x70cm-24x28in) s.i.d.1937. 9-Oct-2 Michael Zeller, Lindau #978/R

ZEZZOS, Alessandro (1848-1914) Italian

£637 $1000 €956 Venetian views, Piazza and lamp over the bridge (24x8cm-9x3in) s.d.04 oil on paperboard two. 22-Nov-2 Skinner, Boston #138/R est:800-1200

ZEZZOS, Georges Dominique (1883-1959) Italian

£566 $877 €900 Paris, le Pont Neuf (11x17cm-4x7in) s.i.d.1908 cardboard prov. 30-Oct-2 Artcurial Briest, Paris #159

ZGAIB, Khalil (1911-1975) Lebanese

£12000 $19080 €18000 Village school (59x59cm-23x23in) s. panel. 30-Apr-3 Sotheby's, London #129/R est:7000-10000

ZHAI JICHANG (1770-1820) Chinese

Works on paper

£326 $535 €450 Zhongkui playing zither in garden (111x60cm-44x24in) s.d.1816 seals Indian ink col hanging scroll. 30-May-3 Dr Fritz Nagel, Stuttgart #1280/R

ZHANG DAQIAN (1899-1983) Chinese

£2420 $3776 €3800 Blossom on twigs (60x19cm-24x7in) s.i. paper hanging scroll. 8-Nov-2 Dr Fritz Nagel, Stuttgart #1198/R est:3500

Works on paper

£2020 $3333 €2929 Mount Huang (38x44cm-15x17in) s.i. ink scroll. 6-Jul-3 Christie's, Hong Kong #216/R est:25000-35000 (HK.D 26000)
£2486 $4103 €3605 Orchid (47x34cm-19x13in) s.i. ink scroll. 6-Jul-3 Christie's, Hong Kong #205/R est:25000-35000 (HK.D 32000)
£2720 $4487 €3944 Chrysanthemum (32x34cm-13x13in) s.i. ink scroll. 6-Jul-3 Christie's, Hong Kong #206/R est:20000-30000 (HK.D 35000)

£2720 $4487 €3944 Chrysanthemum (135x36cm-53x14in) s.i. ink scroll. 6-Jul-3 Christie's, Hong Kong #214/R est:35000-45000 (HK.D 35000)
£3263 $5385 €4731 Day lily (133x33cm-52x13in) s.i. ink scroll. 6-Jul-3 Christie's, Hong Kong #208/R est:30000-40000 (HK.D 42000)
£3497 $5769 €5071 Lotus after Bada Shanren (133x34cm-52x13in) s.i. ink scroll. 6-Jul-3 Christie's, Hong Kong #210/R est:70000-80000 (HK.D 45000)
£3497 $5769 €5071 Plantain leaves and bird (134x45cm-53x18in) s. ink scroll. 6-Jul-3 Christie's, Hong Kong #215/R est:45000-55000 (HK.D 45000)
£3730 $6154 €5409 Scholar (134x29cm-53x11in) s.i. ink scroll. 6-Jul-3 Christie's, Hong Kong #213/R est:40000-50000 (HK.D 48000)
£4274 $7051 €6197 Mount Tianzhu (133x32cm-52x13in) s.i. col ink scroll. 6-Jul-3 Christie's, Hong Kong #211/R est:50000-60000 (HK.D 55000)
£5439 $8974 €7887 Lingzhi (69x34cm-27x13in) s.i. ink scroll. 6-Jul-3 Christie's, Hong Kong #266/R est:70000-90000 (HK.D 70000)
£5439 $8974 €7887 Boating on the river (78x40cm-31x16in) s.i. ink scroll. 6-Jul-3 Christie's, Hong Kong #296/R est:50000-70000 (HK.D 70000)
£5439 $8974 €7887 Snow covered mountains (63x39cm-25x15in) s.i. ink scroll. 6-Jul-3 Christie's, Hong Kong #358/R est:50000-60000 (HK.D 70000)
£5828 $9615 €8451 Self portrait (45x38cm-18x15in) s.i. ink scroll lit. 6-Jul-3 Christie's, Hong Kong #201/R est:40000-50000 (HK.D 75000)
£6216 $10256 €9013 Shou - longevity (127x31cm-50x12in) s.i. ink scroll. 6-Jul-3 Christie's, Hong Kong #207/R est:25000-35000 (HK.D 80000)
£6216 $10256 €9013 Scholar strolling in a forest (105x44cm-41x17in) s.i. ink scroll. 6-Jul-3 Christie's, Hong Kong #256/R est:80000-100000 (HK.D 80000)
£6216 $10256 €9013 Tao Yuanming enjoying chrysanthemum (98x50cm-39x20in) s.i. ink scroll. 6-Jul-3 Christie's, Hong Kong #257/R est:70000-90000 (HK.D 80000)
£6504 $10276 €9756 Mount Emei (15x50cm-6x20in) s.i. i.d.1947 verso ink folding fan. 28-Apr-3 Sotheby's, Hong Kong #547/R est:60000-80000 (HK.D 80000)
£6504 $10276 €9756 Plum blossoms branch (27x48cm-11x19in) s.i.d.1965 ink col cardboard. 28-Apr-3 Sotheby's, Hong Kong #604/R est:150000-200000 (HK.D 80000)
£6504 $10276 €9756 Bird and rock. Sleepy cat (18x21cm-7x8in) s.i. ink cardboard pair. 28-Apr-3 Sotheby's, Hong Kong #606/R est:50000-70000 (HK.D 80000)
£6911 $10919 €10367 Peony (26cm-10in circular) s.i.d.1961 ink col fan. 28-Apr-3 Sotheby's, Hong Kong #605/R est:40000-60000 (HK.D 85000)
£6993 $11538 €10140 Lake Dongting (90x45cm-35x18in) s.i.d.1954 ink scroll. 6-Jul-3 Christie's, Hong Kong #253/R est:100000-150000 (HK.D 90000)
£7770 $12821 €11267 Scholar under a pine tree (104x48cm-41x19in) s.i. ink scroll. 6-Jul-3 Christie's, Hong Kong #258/R est:120000-150000 (HK.D 100000)
£9324 $15385 €13520 Bamboo (138x69cm-54x27in) s.i. ink scroll. 6-Jul-3 Christie's, Hong Kong #209y/R est:30000-40000 (HK.D 120000)
£9324 $15385 €13520 Bird on a tree branch (132x48cm-52x19in) s.i. ink scroll. 6-Jul-3 Christie's, Hong Kong #262/R est:80000-100000 (HK.D 120000)
£12195 $19268 €18293 Chinese herbaceous peony (15x50cm-6x20in) s.i.d.1948 i.verso ink col folding fan. 28-Apr-3 Sotheby's, Hong Kong #545/R est:80000-120000 (HK.D 150000)
£13008 $20553 €19512 Peony (101x36cm-40x14in) s.i. ink col prov. 28-Apr-3 Sotheby's, Hong Kong #621/R est:35000-50000 (HK.D 160000)
£13008 $20553 €19512 Ink lotus (97x60cm-38x24in) s.i. ink hanging scroll. 28-Apr-3 Sotheby's, Hong Kong #623/R est:150000-200000 (HK.D 160000)
£13986 $23077 €20280 Guanyin (84x42cm-33x17in) s.i. ink scroll. 6-Jul-3 Christie's, Hong Kong #291/R est:60000-80000 (HK.D 180000)
£15540 $25641 €22533 Self portrait (84x46cm-33x18in) s.i. ink scroll lit. 6-Jul-3 Christie's, Hong Kong #252/R est:80000-100000 (HK.D 200000)
£19512 $30829 €29268 Boating in the lake (27x48cm-11x19in) s.i. splashed ink col cardboard. 28-Apr-3 Sotheby's, Hong Kong #603/R est:200000-250000 (HK.D 240000)
£20202 $33333 €29293 Landscape (133x65cm-52x26in) s.i. ink scroll. 6-Jul-3 Christie's, Hong Kong #289/R est:180000-200000 (HK.D 260000)
£21756 $35897 €31546 Lotus (68x133cm-27x52in) s.i. ink scroll exhib.lit. 6-Jul-3 Christie's, Hong Kong #292/R est:280000-320000 (HK.D 280000)
£24390 $38537 €36585 Bamboo (97x60cm-38x24in) s.i. ink hanging scroll. 28-Apr-3 Sotheby's, Hong Kong #622/R est:70000-90000 (HK.D 300000)
£30894 $48813 €46341 Crapemyrtle (39x91cm-15x36in) s.d.1978 ink col. 28-Apr-3 Sotheby's, Hong Kong #616/R est:1600000-2000000 (HK.D 380000)
£32520 $51382 €48780 Huiji studio (116x55cm-46x22in) s.i.d.1949 ink col hanging scroll exhib. 28-Apr-3 Sotheby's, Hong Kong #594/R est:80000-100000 (HK.D 400000)
£42735 $70513 €61966 Lake Tai (64x95cm-25x37in) s.i. ink scroll. 6-Jul-3 Christie's, Hong Kong #293/R est:400000-500000 (HK.D 550000)
£46620 $76923 €67599 Guanyin (116x63cm-46x25in) s.i. ink scroll. 6-Jul-3 Christie's, Hong Kong #255/R est:600000-800000 (HK.D 600000)
£56911 $89919 €85367 Lotus (136x69cm-54x27in) s.i.d.1978 splashed ink col exhib. 28-Apr-3 Sotheby's, Hong Kong #658/R est:700000-900000 (HK.D 700000)
£105691 $166992 €158537 Landscape of Lofu (146x81cm-57x32in) s.i.d.1946 ink col hanging scroll exhib. 28-Apr-3 Sotheby's, Hong Kong #648/R est:800000-1200000 (HK.D 1300000)
£284553 $449594 €426830 Waterfall in spring mountains (196x102cm-77x40in) s.i.d.1967 splashed ink col hanging scroll prov.exhib. 28-Apr-3 Sotheby's, Hong Kong #607/R est:25000-35000 (HK.D 3500000)

ZHANG DAZHUANG and ZHAO SHIHONG (20th C) Chinese
Works on paper
£976 $1541 €1464 Peony (20x54cm-8x21in) one s.i.d.1964 one s.i. ink col folding fan two. 28-Apr-3 Sotheby's, Hong Kong #557/R est:7000-9000 (HK.D 12000)

ZHANG DENGTANG (1940-) Chinese
Works on paper
£290 $475 €400 Mountain landscape with pilgrims path and temple (98x51cm-39x20in) i.d.1979 seals Indian ink col hanging scroll. 30-May-3 Dr Fritz Nagel, Stuttgart #1210/R

ZHANG HONG TU (1943-) Chinese
£7770 $12821 €11267 Shitao - van gogh no 3 (172x76cm-68x30in) s.d.2000 exhib.lit. 6-Jul-3 Christie's, Hong Kong #117/R est:60000-100000 (HK.D 100000)

ZHANG RUOAI (1713-1746) Chinese
Works on paper
£3885 $6410 €5633 Rabbits (98x38cm-39x15in) s. ink col silk hanging scroll. 6-Jul-3 Christie's, Hong Kong #468/R est:40000-50000 (HK.D 50000)

ZHANG SHANZI (1882-1940) Chinese
Works on paper
£870 $1426 €1200 Tigress with two cubs (92x43cm-36x17in) i.d.1938 seals Indian ink col. 30-May-3 Dr Fritz Nagel, Stuttgart #1154/R
£5439 $8974 €7887 Tiger (88x40cm-35x16in) s.i. ink scroll. 6-Jul-3 Christie's, Hong Kong #268/R est:70000-90000 (HK.D 70000)

ZHANG TINGJI (1768-1848) Chinese
Works on paper
£2439 $3854 €3659 Poem in Li Shu (215x48cm-85x19in) s. ink hanging scroll. 28-Apr-3 Sotheby's, Hong Kong #649/R est:22000-30000 (HK.D 30000)

ZHANG XIAO GANG (1958-) Chinese
£38850 $64103 €56333 Big family series (229x179cm-90x70in) s.d.1995. 6-Jul-3 Christie's, Hong Kong #111/R est:200000-250000 (HK.D 500000)

ZHANG ZHENXUE (1939-) Chinese
Works on paper
£471 $772 €650 Mountain landscape (191x121cm-75x48in) s.d.1984 seal Indian ink col. 30-May-3 Dr Fritz Nagel, Stuttgart #1250/R

ZHAO SHAOANG (1905-1998) Chinese
Works on paper
£1554 $2564 €2253 Maple leave and bird (40x60cm-16x24in) s. ink scroll. 6-Jul-3 Christie's, Hong Kong #339/R est:30000-40000 (HK.D 20000)
£2020 $3333 €2929 Plum blossoms, calligraphy (11x41cm-4x16in) s. ink fan pair. 6-Jul-3 Christie's, Hong Kong #338/R est:25000-35000 (HK.D 26000)
£2331 $3846 €3380 Flowers and bird (46x96cm-18x38in) s.i. ink scroll. 6-Jul-3 Christie's, Hong Kong #234/R est:30000-50000 (HK.D 30000)
£2486 $4103 €3605 Flower and bees (105x30cm-41x12in) s.i. ink scroll. 6-Jul-3 Christie's, Hong Kong #236/R est:35000-45000 (HK.D 32000)
£3108 $5128 €4507 Maple leaves in autumn (97x47cm-38x19in) s.i.d.1989 ink scroll. 6-Jul-3 Christie's, Hong Kong #341/R est:40000-60000 (HK.D 40000)
£3497 $5769 €5071 Red leaves and bird (99x32cm-39x13in) s.i. scroll. 6-Jul-3 Christie's, Hong Kong #235/R est:50000-70000 (HK.D 45000)

£3659 $5780 €5489 Tiger howling at the moon (46x67cm-18x26in) s. ink col. 28-Apr-3 Sotheby's, Hong Kong #608/R est:3500000-5000000 (HK.D 45000)
£13008 $20553 €19512 Silk cotton (138x19cm-54x7in) s.i.d.1943 ink col. 28-Apr-3 Sotheby's, Hong Kong #619/R est:120000-150000 (HK.D 160000)

ZHAO SHURU (1874-1945) Chinese
Works on paper
£688 $1129 €950 Two horses in landscape (111x50cm-44x20in) s.i.d.1926 seals Indian ink col hanging scroll. 30-May-3 Dr Fritz Nagel, Stuttgart #1265/R

ZHAO TONG (19th C) Chinese
Works on paper
£326 $535 €450 Trees and rock (86x41cm-34x16in) i.d.1876 seal Indian ink hanging scroll. 30-May-3 Dr Fritz Nagel, Stuttgart #1261/R

ZHAO XIU HUAN (1946-) Chinese
Works on paper
£580 $951 €800 Narcissi by mountain stream (63x65cm-25x26in) s.d.1982 seals Indian ink col hanging scroll prov. 30-May-3 Dr Fritz Nagel, Stuttgart #1217/R

ZHAO ZIYONG (19th C) Chinese
Works on paper
£942 $1545 €1300 Bamboo and rocks (207x96cm-81x38in) i.d.1833 seal Indian ink silk hanging scroll. 30-May-3 Dr Fritz Nagel, Stuttgart #1140/R

ZHENG XIE (1693-1765) Chinese
Works on paper
£10878 $17949 €15773 Orchids, chrysanthemum and rock (128x43cm-50x17in) s. one i. one d.1751 ink hanging scroll pair. 6-Jul-3 Christie's, Hong Kong #465/R est:150000-230000 (HK.D 140000)

ZHITOMIRSKY, Alexander (1907-1993) Russian
Photographs
£3165 $5000 €4748 Don't set a fire (50x35cm-20x14in) i.d.1942 verso gelatin silver print mounted on board prov.lit. 24-Apr-3 Phillips, New York #149/R est:2500-3500

ZHONG CHEN (1969-) Australian?
Prints
£3430 $5316 €5145 Juliet, Juliet XI (122x122cm-48x48in) s.d.2002 verso digital scan oil polymer paint prov. 3-Dec-2 Shapiro, Sydney #68/R est:8000-10000 (A.D 9500)
Works on paper
£2988 $4900 €4482 Romeo (83x83cm-33x33in) s.d.2000 verso synthetic polymer paint photoscan canvas prov. 4-Jun-3 Deutscher-Menzies, Melbourne #5/R est:7000-9000 (A.D 7500)
£3125 $4938 €4688 Shanghai girl (94x78cm-37x31in) s.d.2001 digital scan synthetic polymer on canvas prov.exhib. 26-Nov-2 Sotheby's, Melbourne #82/R est:4000-6000 (A.D 8750)

ZHOU BICHU (1903-1995) Chinese
£7382 $12179 €10704 Azalea (55x46cm-22x18in) s. 6-Jul-3 Christie's, Hong Kong #154/R est:100000-120000 (HK.D 95000)

ZHOU CHEN (c.1450-1535) Chinese
Works on paper
£37296 $61538 €54079 Cultivating chrysanthemum (26x126cm-10x50in) s. ink col handscroll lit. 6-Jul-3 Christie's, Hong Kong #414/R est:400000-500000 (HK.D 480000)

ZHOU SICONG (1939-) Chinese
Works on paper
£688 $1129 €950 Two young ladies carrying baskets (68x47cm-27x19in) i.d.1979 seal Indian ink col hanging scroll. 30-May-3 Dr Fritz Nagel, Stuttgart #1232/R

ZHU SHI JIE (1900-1990) Chinese
£8547 $14103 €12393 Cherry blossom (54x38cm-21x15in) board prov.lit. 6-Jul-3 Christie's, Hong Kong #151/R est:120000-140000 (HK.D 110000)

ZHU YING (1796-1850) Chinese
Works on paper
£3415 $5395 €5123 Flower and butterfly (22x16cm-9x6in) s. one d.1834 ink col twelve leaves album. 28-Apr-3 Sotheby's, Hong Kong #634/R est:300000-500000 (HK.D 42000)

ZHU YUANZHI (1906-1963) Chinese
£2331 $3846 €3380 Botanical gardens, Bronx park (18x12cm-7x5in) s. canvasboard exhib.lit. 6-Jul-3 Christie's, Hong Kong #139/R est:40000-60000 (HK.D 30000)
£6627 $11000 €9609 Street, San Fransisco (23x30cm-9x12in) s. in Chinese paper on board exhib. 11-Jun-3 Butterfields, San Francisco #4253/R est:20000-30000
£7770 $12821 €11267 San Francisco city scene (21x28cm-8x11in) s. canvasboard exhib. 6-Jul-3 Christie's, Hong Kong #140/R est:120000-160000 (HK.D 100000)
£23310 $38462 €33800 Wine house (50x60cm-20x24in) s. exhib.lit. 6-Jul-3 Christie's, Hong Kong #138/R est:350000-450000 (HK.D 300000)

ZHUKOVSKY, Stanislav Yulianovich (1873-1944) Polish
£6962 $11000 €11000 In the hayfield (30x48cm-12x19in) s. 1-Dec-2 Bukowskis, Helsinki #289/R est:3000-4000
£10000 $15700 €15000 Woodland stream (58x87cm-23x34in) s.d.1910. 20-Nov-2 Sotheby's, London #49/R est:4000-6000
£11000 $17270 €16500 Country estate in autumn (38x44cm-15x17in) s. canvas on card. 20-Nov-2 Sotheby's, London #58/R est:10000-12000

ZHURAVLEV, Mikhail (1952-) Russian
£270 $419 €405 Cafe on a river shore (33x41cm-13x16in) s. canvas on board. 8-Dec-2 John Nicholson, Haslemere #63/R
£300 $465 €450 Sea wind (35x24cm-14x9in) s. canvas on board. 8-Dec-2 John Nicholson, Haslemere #62/R

ZICHY, Count Mihaly von (1827-1906) Hungarian
Works on paper
£568 $885 €852 Beauty with red coral, 1869. s.d.1869 mixed media. 11-Sep-2 Kieselbach, Budapest #129/R (H.F 220000)
£2322 $3622 €3483 Oriental beauty, 1862 (48x30cm-19x12in) s.d.1862 mixed media parchment. 11-Sep-2 Kieselbach, Budapest #141/R (H.F 900000)
£2515 $3923 €3773 Lovers (70x51cm-28x20in) s.d.1858 pastel. 11-Apr-3 Kieselbach, Budapest #146/R est:550000-900000 (H.F 900000)
£3096 $4829 €4644 Nubian with water pipe, 1862 (48x30cm-19x12in) s.d.1862 mixed media parchment. 11-Sep-2 Kieselbach, Budapest #140/R (H.F 1200000)

ZICK, Conrad (1773-1836) German
£1486 $2319 €2200 John the Evangelist with book and scroll (73x72cm-29x28in) s.d.1815. 27-Mar-3 Dr Fritz Nagel, Stuttgart #879/R est:1200

ZICK, Gustav (1809-1886) German
£800 $1328 €1160 Hound with a partridge (79x61cm-31x24in) s.d.1881 oval. 12-Jun-3 Christie's, Kensington #288/R

ZICK, Januarius (1730-1797) German
£1603 $2484 €2500 Profile of head of an old lady, the artist's dairy woman (56x40cm-22x16in) s.d.1773 canvas on canvas prov.lit. 4-Dec-2 Neumeister, Munich #659/R est:2500
£5346 $8286 €8500 Confession in the dungeon (32x24cm-13x9in) s. panel prov. 2-Oct-2 Dorotheum, Vienna #211/R est:5000-7000
£37419 $59122 €58000 Echelle de Jacob. Sacrifice d'Isaac (78x60cm-31x24in) s. pair. 18-Dec-2 Tajan, Paris #36/R est:90000
£46976 $75631 €70000 Pastoral scene, boy caught by a girl (33x24cm-13x9in) bears sig. pair. 18-Feb-3 Sotheby's, Amsterdam #1106/R

ZICK, Januarius (attrib) (1730-1797) German
£1348 $2089 €2022 Old town in ruins (57x82cm-22x32in) painted c.1760. 4-Dec-2 AB Stockholms Auktionsverk #2041/R est:25000-30000 (S.KR 19000)

ZICK, Johann (1702-1762) German
£597 $932 €950 Angels and putti (16x27cm-6x11in) 11-Oct-2 Winterberg, Heidelberg #476

£5479 $8548 €8000 Adoration of the shepherds (80x120cm-31x47in) s.i. 10-Apr-3 Van Ham, Cologne #1290/R est:8000
£5479 $8548 €8000 Adoration of the Kings (80x120cm-31x47in) s. 10-Apr-3 Van Ham, Cologne #1291/R est:8000

ZICKENDRAHT, Bernhard (1854-1937) German
£413 $652 €620 Autumn allegory (36x51cm-14x20in) s.d.1919 cardboard. 30-Nov-2 Dorotheum, Prague #28/R (C.KR 20000)

ZIEGELMUELLER, Martin (1935-) Swiss
£328 $511 €492 Seated female nude (100x60cm-39x24in) mono. i.87 verso. 6-Nov-2 Dobiaschofsky, Bern #1086/R (S.FR 750)

ZIEGLER, Archibald (1903-) British
£700 $1092 €1050 Safed, Isreal (36x56cm-14x22in) s.i. canvas on board. 15-Oct-2 Sotheby's, London #132/R

ZIEGLER, Eustace Paul (1881-1969) American
£2215 $3500 €3323 Dog team Alaska (13x18cm-5x7in) s.i. s.i.verso panel prov. 24-Apr-3 Shannon's, Milford #13/R est:3000-5000
£3012 $5000 €4367 Shacks on a summer day. Church beneath a snow capped mountain (23x30cm-9x12in) s. board double-sided. 11-Jun-3 Butterfields, San Francisco #4118/R est:5000-7000
£3503 $5500 €5255 Mt McKinley and cache. Ship at dock (30x25cm-12x10in) s. indis.i.verso board double-sided prov. 19-Nov-2 Butterfields, San Francisco #8097/R est:5000-7000
£5696 $9000 €8259 Castle peak on the Kuskalana (41x51cm-16x20in) s. prov. 26-Jul-3 Coeur d'Alene, Hayden #63/R est:10000-20000
£5696 $9000 €8259 Rogue river Steelhead (51x41cm-20x16in) s. board prov. 26-Jul-3 Coeur d'Alene, Hayden #64/R est:10000-20000

ZIELENIEWSKI, Kasimir (1888-1931) Polish
Works on paper
£440 $682 €700 Plage de Fort-Mahon (30x46cm-12x18in) mono.i.d.1926 W/C pencil prov.exhib. 30-Oct-2 Artcurial Briest, Paris #123

ZIELER, Mogens (1905-1983) Danish
£1705 $2830 €2472 In the studio, day time 1948 (93x120cm-37x47in) s. exhib. 12-Jun-3 Kunsthallen, Copenhagen #258/R est:18000 (D.KR 18000)

ZIELKE, Willy Otto (1902-1989) Polish
Photographs
£2025 $3200 €3200 Untitled (40x30cm-16x12in) s.i. verso col silver gelatin. 28-Nov-2 Villa Grisebach, Berlin #1479/R est:1500-2000

ZIEM, Felix (1821-1911) French
£641 $1006 €1000 La charrette (9x23cm-4x9in) s. panel. 16-Dec-2 Millon & Associes, Paris #114/R
£823 $1284 €1300 Voilier et gondole a Venise (40x32cm-16x13in) s. panel. 16-Sep-2 Horta, Bruxelles #210
£1701 $2704 €2500 Jeune femme assis au bord de la mer (21x17cm-8x7in) s. 18-Mar-3 Vanderkindere, Brussels #111/R est:1500-2500
£1818 $2945 €2636 Sun breaking through the clouds, Venice (22x15cm-9x6in) i. prov. 26-May-3 Rasmussen, Copenhagen #1119/R est:15000-20000 (D.KR 19000)
£1923 $2981 €3000 Coucher du soleil sur la mer (12x18cm-5x7in) panel. 8-Dec-2 Teitgen, Nancy #149/R
£2000 $3340 €3000 Il Bacino di San Marco, Venice (33x41cm-13x16in) indis sig. 18-Jun-3 Christie's, Kensington #135/R est:3000-5000
£2581 $4000 €3872 Venetian canal scene with figures and ships (76x102cm-30x40in) s. 21-Jul-2 Jeffery Burchard, Florida #44/R
£3165 $4905 €5000 Bouquet of flowers (41x32cm-16x13in) s. panel lit. 25-Sep-2 Neumeister, Munich #783/R est:10000
£3205 $5032 €5000 Vue de port anime (28x36cm-11x14in) s. panel. 19-Nov-2 Servarts Themis, Bruxelles #106
£3237 $5309 €4500 Lavandiere dans l'arriere pays nicois (49x35cm-19x14in) panel. 4-Jun-3 Marc Kohn, Paris #10/R est:4000-6000
£4194 $6500 €6291 Peaches and grapes in a shady grove (60x76cm-24x30in) s. card on panel prov.lit. 2-Oct-2 Christie's, Rockefeller NY #788/R est:5000-7000
£4392 $6851 €6500 Esquisse du Bosphore (35x53cm-14x21in) studio st. panel. 25-Mar-3 Chochon-Barre & Allardi, Paris #212/R est:7500-9000
£9220 $14291 €13830 Vue de Venise (41x72cm-16x28in) s. 4-Dec-2 AB Stockholms Auktionsverk #1891/R est:40000-50000 (S.KR 130000)
£9877 $14025 €16000 Rivage italien (39x59cm-15x23in) s. panel. 16-Mar-3 Eric Pillon, Calais #34/R
£10417 $16563 €15000 Reception au crepuscul (54x73cm-21x29in) s. prov. 29-Apr-3 Christie's, Amsterdam #114/R est:10000-15000
£10480 $16349 €15720 Boats in the Lagoon, Venice (54x73cm-21x29in) s. 6-Nov-2 Dobiaschofsky, Bern #1087/R est:24000 (S.FR 24000)
£19481 $29026 €30000 Venice (65x81cm-26x32in) s. lit. 26-Jun-2 Neumeister, Munich #927/R est:25000
£19728 $31367 €29000 Escadre a Villefranche-le-Hoche (64x81cm-25x32in) s. panel prov.lit. 24-Mar-3 Fraysse & Associes, Paris #51/R est:15000
£22000 $35860 €31900 San Giorgio Maggiore from the Lido, Venice (43x63cm-17x25in) s. 16-Jul-3 Sotheby's, Olympia #253/R est:6000-8000
£27273 $45545 €39000 Les Jardins Francais a Venise (54x68cm-21x27in) s. prov.lit. 25-Jun-3 Sotheby's, Paris #88/R est:25000-35000
£28395 $40321 €46000 Paris, Avenue de Neuilly (54x69cm-21x27in) s. prov.lit. 16-Mar-3 Eric Pillon, Calais #28/R
Works on paper
£387 $612 €600 Eglise de Baden-Baden (28x20cm-11x8in) s. W/C lit. 19-Dec-2 Delvaux, Paris #8
£395 $640 €600 Navires dans la rade (31x22cm-12x9in) studio st. Indian ink wash. 22-Jan-3 Tajan, Paris #19
£507 $800 €800 Nature morte a la mandoline (9x14cm-4x6in) s. pen ink. 28-Nov-2 Tajan, Paris #204
£1235 $1753 €2000 Promenade derriere l'eglise (29x21cm-11x8in) mono. W/C lit. 16-Mar-3 Eric Pillon, Calais #19/R
£1358 $1928 €2200 Venise, Grand Canal (22x17cm-9x7in) studio st. graphite dr. 16-Mar-3 Eric Pillon, Calais #20/R
£1899 $2962 €3000 Embarcations et navires a Venise (42x37cm-17x15in) i. drawing htd white. 31-Jul-2 Tajan, Paris #1/R est:2000-3000
£2535 $4208 €3600 Vue de Camargue (21x32cm-8x13in) s.i.d.1864 W/C. 16-Jun-3 Oger, Dumont, Paris #33/R est:1500-2000

ZIEM, Felix (attrib) (1821-1911) French
£1092 $1703 €1638 Still life with pomegranates (18x28cm-7x11in) mono. 20-Nov-2 Fischer, Luzern #1126/R est:3000-4000 (S.FR 2500)
£2031 $3250 €2945 Animated canal scene before the Doge's Palace (46x61cm-18x24in) s. 16-May-3 Skinner, Boston #117/R est:2000-4000

ZIERMANN, Alexander Luzius (20th C) German
£380 $600 €600 Mosaic (100x75cm-39x30in) s.d.1996 verso. 30-Nov-2 Arnold, Frankfurt #667/R
£633 $1000 €1000 Composition (100x120cm-39x47in) s.d.1997. 30-Nov-2 Arnold, Frankfurt #668/R

ZIFFER, Sandor (1888-1962) Hungarian
£1161 $1811 €1742 Roses (35x44cm-14x17in) s. 11-Sep-2 Kieselbach, Budapest #83/R (H.F 450000)
£1902 $3042 €2853 Still life with narcissus (33x40cm-13x16in) s. board. 16-May-3 Kieselbach, Budapest #30/R (H.F 650000)
£1956 $3052 €2836 Roses (34x44cm-13x17in) s. 12-Apr-3 Mu Terem Galeria, Budapest #85/R est:400000 (H.F 700000)
£2017 $3126 €2925 Still life of flowers with apples (40x38cm-16x15in) s. panel card. 9-Dec-2 Mu Terem Galeria, Budapest #124/R est:400000 (H.F 750000)
£2017 $3126 €2925 Still life of gladioli and jug (50x40cm-20x16in) s. 9-Dec-2 Mu Terem Galeria, Budapest #125/R est:440000 (H.F 750000)
£2151 $3335 €3227 Still life of flowers in the window (46x55cm-18x22in) s. 6-Dec-2 Kieselbach, Budapest #27/R (H.F 800000)
£3227 $5002 €4841 Nagybanya in winter (56x91cm-22x36in) s. 6-Dec-2 Kieselbach, Budapest #164/R (H.F 1200000)
£11295 $17507 €16378 Still life with plaster head and cat (120x103cm-47x41in) s.d.1933 lit. 9-Dec-2 Mu Terem Galeria, Budapest #176/R est:3000000 (H.F 4200000)
£11867 $18512 €17801 Still life of oranges, 1915 (57x60cm-22x24in) s.d.1915. 11-Sep-2 Kieselbach, Budapest #75/R (H.F 4600000)
£13446 $20842 €19497 Bridge crossing a river in Nagybanya (90x80cm-35x31in) s.d.1926. 9-Dec-2 Mu Terem Galeria, Budapest #72/R est:2500000 (H.F 5000000)
Works on paper
£894 $1395 €1296 Self portrait in a hat (60x44cm-24x17in) s.i.d.1919 chl pencil. 12-Apr-3 Mu Terem Galeria, Budapest #157/R est:300000 (H.F 320000)

ZIGAINA, Giuseppe (1924-) Italian
£2292 $3644 €3300 Wheat field and anatomy (60x50cm-24x20in) s.s.verso. 1-May-3 Meeting Art, Vercelli #409
£2692 $4173 €4200 Tree and roots (68x68cm-27x27in) s.d.1963. 5-Dec-2 Stadion, Trieste #830/R
Works on paper
£1090 $1711 €1700 Interior with figure (20x30cm-8x12in) s. mixed media exec.1964. 21-Nov-2 Finarte, Rome #49

ZIKARAS, Teisutis (20th C) Australian
Sculpture
£3571 $5643 €5357 Untitled (146cm-57in) s. bronze. 27-Nov-2 Deutscher-Menzies, Melbourne #97/R est:12000-16000 (A.D 10000)

ZIKOS, Constanze (1962-) Australian/Greek
£2367 $3598 €3551 There were two young icons (150x106cm-59x42in) enamel laminex board prov.exhib. 28-Aug-2 Deutscher-Menzies, Melbourne #149/R est:6500-8500 (A.D 6600)

£2698 $4479 €4598 Dorian fake (44x94cm-17x37in) enamel canvas laminex three panel prov. 10-Jun-3 Shapiro, Sydney #84/R est:6000-9000 (A.D 6800)

ZILLA, Vettore Zanetti (1866-1945) Italian
£2201 $3390 €3500 Boats (58x48cm-23x19in) i. cardboard lit. 23-Oct-2 Finarte, Milan #146/R
£3774 $5811 €6000 Venetian courtyard (114x58cm-45x23in) s. 23-Oct-2 Finarte, Milan #200/R est:6000-7000
Works on paper
£532 $862 €750 Venezia, piccolo cantiere (35x25cm-14x10in) s. W/C. 22-May-3 Stadion, Trieste #376/R

ZILLE, Heinrich (1858-1929) German
Works on paper
£321 $497 €500 Berlin child (6x4cm-2x2in) chk. 7-Dec-2 Hauswedell & Nolte, Hamburg #1080/R
£353 $546 €550 Nude from the back (18x13cm-7x5in) chl paper on paper. 7-Dec-2 Van Ham, Cologne #609/R
£411 $642 €650 Woman wearing hat (11x10cm-4x4in) chk prov. 18-Oct-2 Dr Fritz Nagel, Stuttgart #389/R
£429 $678 €644 Scene in a Berlin coffee house (21x17cm-8x7in) ink dr prov. 26-Nov-2 Hans Widmer, St Gallen #1426 (S.FR 1000)
£461 $747 €650 Seated woman (14x10cm-6x4in) chl. 24-May-3 Van Ham, Cologne #659/R
£461 $747 €650 Woman with child (14x9cm-6x4in) chl. 24-May-3 Van Ham, Cologne #660/R
£577 $842 €900 Self portrait (14x11cm-6x4in) chk. 4-Jun-2 Karl & Faber, Munich #481/R
£704 $1169 €1000 Bedroom (11x17cm-4x7in) col chk. 14-Jun-3 Hauswedell & Nolte, Hamburg #1659/R
£833 $1217 €1300 Penn brother (16x10cm-6x4in) i. chk. 4-Jun-2 Karl & Faber, Munich #480/R
£1154 $1788 €1800 Women and children at wash tub (30x23cm-12x9in) s.i. 6-Dec-2 Karlheinz Kaupp, Staufen #2401 est:1800
£1232 $2020 €1700 Three figures at table (14x19cm-6x7in) chk. 31-May-3 Villa Grisebach, Berlin #720/R est:800-1000
£1268 $2080 €1750 Children in the street (14x18cm-6x7in) i. col chk. 29-May-3 Lempertz, Koln #967/R est:1000
£1667 $2733 €2300 Self portrait (14x11cm-6x4in) st.sig. chk. 31-May-3 Villa Grisebach, Berlin #721/R est:1500
£5072 $8319 €7000 Children with babys (28x50cm-11x20in) s.d.04 col chk prov. 31-May-3 Villa Grisebach, Berlin #154/R est:9000-12000
£6000 $9480 €9000 Three girls (13x20cm-5x8in) s.i.d.1924 chl gouache. 3-Apr-3 Christie's, Kensington #84/R est:12000
£10145 $16638 €14000 Line of children seen from behind (28x46cm-11x18in) s.d.04 col chk lit.exhib. 31-May-3 Villa Grisebach, Berlin #149/R est:14000-18000

ZILO, Gunnar (1885-1958) Swedish
£311 $488 €467 Still life of flowers (89x63cm-35x25in) s.indis.d. 16-Dec-2 Lilla Bukowskis, Stockholm #1087 (S.KR 4400)

ZIMBER, E P (19th C) ?
£262 $408 €393 Young couple fishing by waterway (63x47cm-25x19in) s.d.1897. 23-Sep-2 Rasmussen, Vejle #2058 (D.KR 3100)

ZIMKA, Ondrej (1937-) Czechoslovakian
£504 $736 €756 Musician (115x46cm-45x18in) tempera wood. 4-Jun-2 SOGA, Bratislava #262/R est:9000 (SL.K 32000)

ZIMMER, Antonin (1819-1869) Czechoslovakian
£1918 $2992 €2800 Returning home from the fields (72x94cm-28x37in) s. 10-Apr-3 Dorotheum, Vienna #234/R est:2800-3500

ZIMMER, Bernd (1948-) German
£1613 $2500 €2420 Wasserfall (213x8cm-84x3in) s.i.d.81 verso acrylic. 29-Sep-2 Butterfields, Los Angeles #4448/R est:3000-6000
£2361 $3731 €3400 Untitled - head with sunglasses (160x130cm-63x51in) s.d.1978 verso acrylic calico. 26-Apr-3 Dr Lehr, Berlin #567/R est:3000
£2778 $4389 €4000 Jealousy and rum (160x130cm-63x51in) s.i.d.1982 acrylic calico. 26-Apr-3 Dr Lehr, Berlin #568/R est:5000
£7246 $11884 €10000 Dunes. Last light (130x160cm-51x63in) s.i.d.99 verso acrylic. 31-May-3 Villa Grisebach, Berlin #391/R est:8000-10000
Works on paper
£641 $994 €1000 Untitled (69x99cm-27x39in) s. gouache chk. 7-Dec-2 Van Ham, Cologne #611/R

ZIMMER, Hans Peter (1936-1992) German
£2239 $3471 €3359 Composition (53x33cm-21x13in) s.verso masonite painted c.1961. 4-Dec-2 Kunsthallen, Copenhagen #146/R est:30000 (D.KR 26000)
Works on paper
£1583 $2532 €2200 Farewell (41x29cm-16x11in) s.d. i. verso W/C Indian ink. 15-May-3 Neumeister, Munich #575/R est:1000-1200

ZIMMERMAN, Carl John (1900-) American
£613 $950 €920 Rockport (51x61cm-20x24in) s. painted c.1938. 8-Dec-2 Toomey, Oak Park #687/R

ZIMMERMAN, Frederick A (1886-1974) American
£778 $1300 €1128 Floral still life (61x51cm-24x20in) s. prov. 17-Jun-3 John Moran, Pasadena #102 est:1500-2500

ZIMMERMAN, Theodore (20th C) British
Works on paper
£720 $1116 €1080 Children at Portelet Bay, Jersey, Channel Islands (18x22cm-7x9in) s.i. pastel. 24-Sep-2 Anderson & Garland, Newcastle #263/R
£750 $1163 €1125 Afternoon on the beach, Jersey, Channel Islands (18x22cm-7x9in) s.i. pastel. 24-Sep-2 Anderson & Garland, Newcastle #264/R
£1100 $1793 €1595 Day trippers from Dublin (34x40cm-13x16in) s.i. pastel. 17-Jul-3 Tennants, Leyburn #771/R est:1100-1400
£1500 $2505 €2175 Mme Zimmerman and family on the beach, Normandy (19x24cm-7x9in) s.i. pastel. 17-Jun-3 Anderson & Garland, Newcastle #189/R est:800-1200
£1600 $2512 €2400 Le Touquet - children on a beach (16x22cm-6x9in) s.i. bodycol. 21-Nov-2 Tennants, Leyburn #698/R est:800-1000
£1800 $2808 €2700 Day at Punchestown Races, Ireland (19x24cm-7x9in) s. pastel. 10-Apr-3 Tennants, Leyburn #907/R est:800-1000
£2200 $3432 €3300 Let's go for a Guinness lads (23x30cm-9x12in) s.i. pastel. 10-Apr-3 Tennants, Leyburn #906/R est:800-1000

ZIMMERMANN, Albert (1809-1888) German
£513 $779 €800 Two travellers with horse (21x30cm-8x12in) s.d.1833 i. stretcher. 31-Aug-2 Geble, Radolfzell #675/R
£1667 $2617 €2600 View of Wetterhorn and Rosenlauigletscher (82x101cm-32x40in) s. 10-Dec-2 Dorotheum, Vienna #161/R est:3000-3400
£2207 $3531 €3200 Promeneurs entre des rochers dans un paysage montagneux (58x48cm-23x19in) panel. 17-Mar-3 Amberes, Antwerp #286/R
£2532 $3924 €4000 Mountain valley with Salzkammergut beyond (72x167cm-28x66in) s. one of pair. 25-Sep-2 Neumeister, Munich #785/R est:2500
£2689 $4168 €4034 Landscape in the Alps (49x68cm-19x27in) s. 6-Dec-2 Kieselbach, Budapest #88/R (H.F 1000000)
£3165 $4905 €5000 View of Salzkammergut (72x166cm-28x65in) s. one of pair. 25-Sep-2 Neumeister, Munich #784/R est:4000
£3165 $5000 €5000 Mediterranean coast (37x58cm-15x23in) s. panel lit. 29-Nov-2 Schloss Ahlden, Ahlden #1347/R est:4800

ZIMMERMANN, August Albert (1808-1888) German
£2179 $3378 €3400 High mountain landscape (110x146cm-43x57in) s.i. prov. 7-Dec-2 Ketterer, Hamburg #83/R est:2500-2700

ZIMMERMANN, Ernst Karl Georg (1852-1901) German
£2361 $3659 €3542 Fisherman with woman selling fish (37x55cm-15x22in) s. panel prov. 3-Oct-2 Koller, Zurich #3107/R est:5000-8000 (S.FR 5500)

ZIMMERMANN, Helmut (1924-) German
£1203 $1876 €1900 Where the young thief tried white (77x98cm-30x39in) s.i.d.1958. 19-Oct-2 Semenzato, Venice #8/R

ZIMMERMANN, K (?) German
£484 $711 €750 Rushing mountain stream (59x72cm-23x28in) s. 24-Jun-2 Dr Fritz Nagel, Stuttgart #6006/R

ZIMMERMANN, Karl (1824-?) German
£962 $1510 €1500 Let the little children come to me (58x77cm-23x30in) s.d.1830. 10-Dec-2 Dorotheum, Vienna #183/R est:2000-2200

ZIMMERMANN, Reinhard Sebastian (1815-1893) German
£756 $1074 €1134 After the quarrel (102x83cm-40x33in) painted c.1840. 26-Mar-2 SOGA, Bratislava #161a/R (SL.K 48000)
£2264 $3532 €3600 Peasant kitchen (40x28cm-16x11in) s. prov. 19-Sep-2 Dr Fritz Nagel, Stuttgart #1016/R est:1500

ZIMMERMANN, Richard (1820-1875) German
£776 $1250 €1164 Alpine landscape with cows and sheep (25x30cm-10x12in) s. canvas on board. 19-Jan-3 Jeffery Burchard, Florida #106/R

ZIMMERMANN, Susi (1883-?) Russian
£504 $826 €700 Flower meadow (83x79cm-33x31in) panel. 5-Jun-3 Dorotheum, Salzburg #584/R

ZINCKE, Christian Friedrich (1683-1767) German

Miniatures

£980	$1558	€1470	Johannes Floyer of Lincolns Inn (4cm-2in) i.d.1743 enamel oval. 4-Mar-3 Bearnes, Exeter #318/R
£1000	$1590	€1500	Young gentleman, with natural hair, wearing a blue coat (4cm-2in) enamel gold frame with reeded side oval. 4-Mar-3 Bonhams, New Bond Street #96/R est:1200-1500
£1200	$1980	€1740	Lady, possibly Mrs Cooper (5cm-2in) enamel gold frame brooch oval prov. 1-Jul-3 Bonhams, New Bond Street #71/R
£1300	$2132	€1885	Young gentleman in a velvet coat (6cm-2in) enamel on copper. 3-Jun-3 Christie's, London #25/R est:800-1200
£1500	$2460	€2175	Gentleman in a brown coat (5cm-2in) enamel on copper oval. 3-Jun-3 Christie's, London #28/R est:1500-2500
£1800	$2826	€2700	Young lady wearing a white dress (4cm-2in) enamel on copper oval. 10-Dec-2 Christie's, London #21/R est:2000-3000
£1800	$2916	€2700	Genleman, wearing blue coat (4cm-2in) enamel with tortoiseshell box. 22-May-3 Bonhams, New Bond Street #28/R
£1900	$2983	€2850	Young lady in a blue dress (4cm-2in) enamel on copper oval. 10-Dec-2 Christie's, London #23/R est:2000-3000
£3000	$4920	€4350	Johannes Floyer, wearing a wig (4cm-2in) s.i.d.1743 enamel on copper oval. 3-Jun-3 Christie's, London #24/R est:800-1200
£3800	$6232	€5510	Young gentleman wearing a olive green silk clock (4cm-2in) s.i.d.1732 enamel on copper prov. 3-Jun-3 Christie's, London #27/R est:2500-3500

Works on paper

£2800	$4620	€4060	Handsome young gentleman of the Cooper family (5cm-2in) enamel gilt metal mount oval prov. 1-Jul-3 Bonhams, New Bond Street #78/R est:1500-2500

ZINELLI, Carlo (1916-1974) Italian

£5864	$9500	€8796	Un colpo di canone (69x49cm-27x19in) s. tempera on paper double-sided painted 1967 prov.exhib. 27-Jan-3 Christie's, Rockefeller NY #20/R est:8000-12000
£6790	$11000	€10185	Untitled (49x70cm-19x28in) tempera on paper painted c.1961 prov.exhib. 27-Jan-3 Christie's, Rockefeller NY #22/R
£6790	$11000	€10185	Untitled (79x50cm-31x20in) s.d.21-5-64 verso tempera on paper double-sided prov.exhib. 27-Jan-3 Christie's, Rockefeller NY #23/R est:8000-12000
£8025	$13000	€12038	Untitled (49x69cm-19x27in) tempera crayon painted c.1971 prov. 27-Jan-3 Christie's, Rockefeller NY #21/R est:8000-12000

ZINGG, Adrian (1734-1816) Swiss

Works on paper

£360	$576	€500	Tree stump and thistles (11x13cm-4x5in) s. pen wash. 17-May-3 Lempertz, Koln #1266
£949	$1500	€1500	Woodland with thistles (19x25cm-7x10in) pen wash pencil sketch verso. 29-Nov-2 Bassenge, Berlin #5803 est:1800

ZINGG, Adrian (attrib) (1743-1816) Swiss

Works on paper

£462	$729	€720	Hermit's riverside cave (23x30cm-9x12in) Indian ink pen brush wash. 15-Nov-2 Reiss & Sohn, Konigstein #233/R

ZINGG, Jules (1882-1942) French

£321	$497	€500	Toits du village (12x20cm-5x8in) s. cardboard. 5-Dec-2 Gros & Delettrez, Paris #113
£739	$1190	€1050	L'etang d'Abbeville (13x17cm-5x7in) board. 11-May-3 Thierry & Lannon, Brest #235
£802	$1140	€1300	Petit hameau (13x18cm-5x7in) s. panel. 16-Mar-3 Eric Pillon, Calais #151/R
£1923	$3019	€3000	Skieurs (33x46cm-13x18in) s. panel. 13-Dec-2 Piasa, Paris #232/R
£2115	$3279	€3300	Nature morte au pain et a la bouteille (45x54cm-18x21in) s. 5-Dec-2 Gros & Delettrez, Paris #107
£2244	$3478	€3500	Attelage sur le chemin (36x54cm-14x21in) s. 5-Dec-2 Gros & Delettrez, Paris #109
£2500	$3875	€3900	Labours (37x60cm-15x24in) s. 5-Dec-2 Gros & Delettrez, Paris #112
£3205	$4968	€5000	Clocher du village (63x79cm-25x31in) s. 5-Dec-2 Gros & Delettrez, Paris #106
£3378	$5270	€5000	Village en automne (54x73cm-21x29in) s. 31-Mar-3 Rossini, Paris #84/R
£3526	$5535	€5500	Printemps dans le Vexin (54x73cm-21x29in) s. 15-Dec-2 Thierry & Lannon, Brest #220a
£3590	$5564	€5600	Paysans aux champs (72x100cm-28x39in) s. 5-Dec-2 Gros & Delettrez, Paris #108
£4167	$6458	€6500	Famille de paysans dejeunant (60x80cm-24x31in) s. 5-Dec-2 Gros & Delettrez, Paris #104
£4257	$6641	€6300	La fenaison (60x81cm-24x32in) s. 31-Mar-3 Rossini, Paris #85/R
£4437	$7143	€6300	Paysage de neige (50x65cm-20x26in) s. 11-May-3 Thierry & Lannon, Brest #237/R est:5500-6000
£4932	$7695	€7300	Paysage d'hiver (61x73cm-24x29in) s. 31-Mar-3 Rossini, Paris #86/R
£5000	$7750	€7800	Scene de village anime (58x79cm-23x31in) s. 5-Dec-2 Gros & Delettrez, Paris #111
£5256	$8147	€8200	Paysage de neige et porteur de fagot (72x100cm-28x39in) s. 5-Dec-2 Gros & Delettrez, Paris #105
£5473	$8538	€8100	La moisson (60x82cm-24x32in) s. 31-Mar-3 Rossini, Paris #83/R
£9930	$15987	€14100	Le labour, paysage fauve (54x73cm-21x29in) s. 11-May-3 Thierry & Lannon, Brest #238/R est:9000-12000

Works on paper

£683	$1094	€950	Pecheurs en baie de Somme (30x45cm-12x18in) s. W/C. 18-May-3 Eric Pillon, Calais #196/R
£823	$1275	€1300	Pecheurs en baie de Somme (30x45cm-12x18in) s. W/C. 29-Sep-2 Eric Pillon, Calais #234/R
£1090	$1689	€1700	Labours pres du Doubs (35x35cm-14x14in) s. W/C. 5-Dec-2 Gros & Delettrez, Paris #103
£1173	$1665	€1900	Petit troupeau en montagne (37x53cm-15x21in) s. W/C. 16-Mar-3 Eric Pillon, Calais #147/R
£1268	$2041	€1800	Ciel orageux sur la plage (30x45cm-12x18in) s. W/C wash. 11-May-3 Thierry & Lannon, Brest #105 est:1800-2000
£1268	$2041	€1800	Paysage vallonne, les enfants (30x45cm-12x18in) s.d.21 W/C. 11-May-3 Thierry & Lannon, Brest #107/R est:1800-2000
£1389	$2264	€2000	Marine en Bretagne, barques sous voiles (31x47cm-12x19in) s. W/C. 19-Jul-3 Thierry & Lannon, Brest #82a/R est:2000-2300
£1389	$2264	€2000	Campagne animee pres du lac (31x47cm-12x19in) s. W/C. 19-Jul-3 Thierry & Lannon, Brest #82b/R est:2000-2300
£1389	$2264	€2000	Marine, barques de peche a quai (30x49cm-12x19in) studio st. W/C. 19-Jul-3 Thierry & Lannon, Brest #82c est:2000-2300
£1408	$2268	€2000	Le labour (30x48cm-12x19in) s. W/C. 11-May-3 Thierry & Lannon, Brest #108 est:1800-2000
£1690	$2721	€2400	Bateaux de peche au soleil couchant (30x45cm-12x18in) s. W/C wash. 11-May-3 Thierry & Lannon, Brest #106/R est:1800-2000

ZINGONI, Aurelio (1853-1922) Italian

£1408	$2268	€2000	Artist (101x82cm-40x32in) s. 6-May-3 Vendu Notarishuis, Rotterdam #205/R est:2000-3000
£5769	$8942	€9000	Peasant girl in national costume with flowers in her hair (102x73cm-40x29in) s. board. 4-Dec-2 Neumeister, Munich #978/R est:7000

ZINI, Renato (1890-1969) Italian

£538	$834	€850	Genre scenes (3x4cm-1x2in) three s. panel five. 25-Sep-2 Neumeister, Munich #789/R

ZINKEISEN, Anna (1901-1976) British

£280	$437	€420	Antiseptic (40x56cm-16x22in) 12-Sep-2 Sotheby's, Olympia #183/R
£500	$791	€750	Madonna and Child (74x49cm-29x19in) s. with attached bead. 27-Nov-2 Sotheby's, Olympia #95/R
£550	$858	€825	Monstral blue (41x56cm-16x22in) acrylic. 12-Sep-2 Sotheby's, Olympia #186/R
£550	$858	€825	Shrink fit (40x40cm-16x16in) 12-Sep-2 Sotheby's, Olympia #189/R
£650	$1014	€975	Anaesthesia (40x55cm-16x22in) 12-Sep-2 Sotheby's, Olympia #181/R
£650	$1014	€975	Children in a cornfield, stubble burning beyond (58x72cm-23x28in) s. board. 17-Oct-2 Lawrence, Crewkerne #525/R
£750	$1170	€1125	All the colours of the rainbow (40x50cm-16x20in) s. 12-Sep-2 Sotheby's, Olympia #187/R
£900	$1404	€1350	Nurse (61x51cm-24x20in) s. 12-Sep-2 Sotheby's, Olympia #82/R
£900	$1404	€1350	One three times daily (38x38cm-15x15in) board. 12-Sep-2 Sotheby's, Olympia #185/R
£900	$1503	€1305	At the circus (51x76cm-20x30in) 25-Jun-3 Cheffins, Cambridge #807/R
£950	$1482	€1425	Antiseptics (40x55cm-16x22in) 12-Sep-2 Sotheby's, Olympia #182/R
£1700	$2652	€2550	One, three times a day (41x51cm-16x20in) s. 12-Sep-2 Sotheby's, Olympia #184/R est:1000-1500
£1700	$2839	€2465	Portrait of a lady (51x41cm-20x16in) 25-Jun-3 Cheffins, Cambridge #806/R est:400-500

ZINKEISEN, Doris (1898-1991) British

£380	$612	€570	Coronation (51x40cm-20x16in) s. 14-Jan-3 Bonhams, Knightsbridge #75/R
£500	$775	€750	Theatrical subject (76x63cm-30x25in) s. 25-Sep-2 Hamptons Fine Art, Godalming #386
£550	$858	€825	Dressing room (49x42cm-19x17in) paper on board. 12-Sep-2 Sotheby's, Olympia #117/R
£750	$1170	€1125	Limpet ink (59x49cm-23x19in) 12-Sep-2 Sotheby's, Olympia #171/R
£750	$1170	€1125	Wear and tear (54x44cm-21x17in) 12-Sep-2 Sotheby's, Olympia #173/R
£750	$1170	€1125	Chemist with two uniformed figures (50x40cm-20x16in) 12-Sep-2 Sotheby's, Olympia #176/R
£750	$1253	€1088	Stallion (51x61cm-20x24in) s. 17-Jun-3 Bonhams, Knightsbridge #116/R
£1400	$2184	€2100	Like magic (39x39cm-15x15in) 12-Sep-2 Sotheby's, Olympia #175/R est:1500-2000

£1400 $2184 €2100 Crowing glory no.2 (59x49cm-23x19in) 12-Sep-2 Sotheby's, Olympia #180/R est:1500-2000
£1800 $2808 €2700 Ermine and sable (60x50cm-24x20in) 12-Sep-2 Sotheby's, Olympia #174/R est:2000-3000
£1800 $2844 €2700 Chestnut pair (52x62cm-20x24in) s. 27-Nov-2 Sotheby's, Olympia #127/R est:1000-1500
£2800 $4368 €4200 Bath time (59x50cm-22x20in) 12-Sep-2 Sotheby's, Olympia #179/R est:2000-3000
£3200 $4992 €4800 Horse fair (71x91cm-28x36in) s. 27-Mar-3 Christie's, Kensington #502/R est:1500-2000
£4000 $6280 €6000 Melbourne cup ring (63x76cm-25x30in) s. 15-Apr-3 Bonhams, Knightsbridge #29 est:4000-6000

ZINNER, Robert (1904-) Austrian
£417 $654 €650 Snow-covered alpine peaks (40x59cm-16x23in) s. chipboard. 21-Nov-2 Dorotheum, Vienna #303/R
£464 $756 €700 Early spring in the mountains (63x79cm-25x31in) s. masonite. 28-Jan-3 Dorotheum, Vienna #112/R

ZINNOGGER, Leopold (1811-1872) Austrian
£4403 $6824 €7000 Still life with melons and grapes (52x67cm-20x26in) s. 2-Oct-2 Dorotheum, Vienna #241/R est:8000-11000
Works on paper
£405 $632 €600 Still life of fruit with melon (39x51cm-15x20in) s.d.834 W/C. 28-Mar-3 Dorotheum, Vienna #177/R
£935 $1496 €1300 Roses (31x22cm-12x9in) W/C. 14-May-3 Dorotheum, Linz #468/R

ZIONY, Karel (20th C) Polish?
£481 $745 €750 Fishing men in harbour (40x60cm-16x24in) s.d.31 canvas on board. 5-Dec-2 Dr Fritz Nagel, Stuttgart #712/R

ZIPIN, Martin Jack (1920-1991) American
£340 $550 €510 Heath (61x46cm-24x18in) s. board. 24-Jan-3 Freeman, Philadelphia #219/R

ZITKO, Otto (20th C) ?
£2200 $3586 €3300 Untitled (220x289cm-87x114in) s.d.2000 verso board prov. 3-Feb-3 Sotheby's, Olympia #101/R est:1500-2000
Works on paper
£674 $1091 €950 Untitled (44x29cm-17x11in) s.d.85 verso mixed media. 20-May-3 Dorotheum, Vienna #262/R

ZITTERBARTH, Heinrich (1822-?) Hungarian
£256 $403 €400 Mounted patrol in winter (17x31cm-7x12in) s. panel. 23-Nov-2 Arnold, Frankfurt #962/R

ZITZEWITZ, Augusta von (1880-1960) German
£316 $500 €500 Tree in front of house (29x23cm-11x9in) s. 30-Nov-2 Bassenge, Berlin #7236

ZIVERI, Alberto (1908-1990) Italian
£685 $1068 €1000 Reclining woman (36x50cm-14x20in) s. paper on canvas. 10-Apr-3 Finarte Semenzato, Rome #150/R
£2244 $3522 €3500 View of Vallerano (35x35cm-14x14in) s.d.1930 prov. 21-Nov-2 Finarte, Rome #321/R
£2244 $3522 €3500 View of Vallerano (38x32cm-15x13in) s.d.1930 board prov. 21-Nov-2 Finarte, Rome #320/R
£2308 $3623 €3600 Santa Maria in Cosmelin, Rome (38x50cm-15x20in) s. painted c.1935. 19-Nov-2 Finarte, Milan #272/R

ZMETAK, Ernst (20th C) Czechoslovakian
£253 $392 €380 Still life with flowers (47x27cm-19x11in) cardboard. 3-Dec-2 SOGA, Bratislava #125/R (SL.K 16000)
£394 $559 €591 Faded still life (35x29cm-14x11in) oil tempera paper painted 1991. 26-Mar-2 SOGA, Bratislava #239/R (SL.K 25000)
£425 $604 €638 Still life with cards (40x31cm-16x12in) board painted 1999. 26-Mar-2 SOGA, Bratislava #238/R (SL.K 27000)
£630 $895 €945 Italian landscape (47x34cm-19x13in) tempera board painted 1994. 26-Mar-2 SOGA, Bratislava #237/R (SL.K 40000)
£772 $1127 €1158 Winter around Tiber River (50x60cm-20x24in) wood. 4-Jun-2 SOGA, Bratislava #102/R est:25000 (SL.K 49000)

ZOBEL, Benjamin (1762-1831) German
£550 $891 €825 Two sheep (29x36cm-11x14in) sand painting. 20-May-3 Sotheby's, Olympia #173/R
£650 $1053 €975 Inside the pig sty (35x40cm-14x16in) sand painting. 20-May-3 Sotheby's, Olympia #171/R
£750 $1215 €1125 Donkey and pigs (41x53cm-16x21in) sand painting. 20-May-3 Sotheby's, Olympia #174/R
£750 $1215 €1125 Donkey and sheep (41x55cm-16x22in) sand painting. 20-May-3 Sotheby's, Olympia #175/R
£750 $1215 €1125 Dray horse (42x57cm-17x22in) sand painting. 20-May-3 Sotheby's, Olympia #176/R

ZOBEL, Fernando (1924-1987) Spanish
£5263 $8526 €8000 Beach IV (100x100cm-39x39in) 21-Jan-3 Ansorena, Madrid #296/R est:7000
£7051 $11141 €11000 Composition (79x79cm-31x31in) s. 19-Nov-2 Durán, Madrid #245/R
£8219 $12822 €12000 Untitled (70x100cm-28x39in) s. s.d.59 verso. 8-Apr-3 Ansorena, Madrid #269/R est:12000
£16809 $27230 €23700 La Chopera. Invierno anticipado II (100x100cm-39x39in) s. s.i.d.1982 verso. 20-May-3 Segre, Madrid #157/R est:23700
Works on paper
£692 $1065 €1100 Liria (14x9cm-6x4in) s.i.d.80 W/C. 28-Oct-2 Segre, Madrid #137/R

ZOBI, G (fl.1860-1900) Italian
£1250 $2000 €1875 Stolen glance (20x27cm-8x11in) s. 14-May-3 Butterfields, San Francisco #1052/R est:3000-5000

ZOBOLE, Ernest (1927-1999) British
£1000 $1540 €1500 Valley with lights (53x91cm-21x36in) board. 22-Oct-2 Peter Francis, Wales #53/R

ZOBUS, Wilhelm (1831-1869) German
£705 $1107 €1100 Landscape in evening (58x81cm-23x32in) s.d.1863. 23-Nov-2 Arnold, Frankfurt #963/R

ZOCCHI, E (?) Italian
Sculpture
£2454 $3901 €3681 Boy seated on stone, girl nearby (60cm-24in) s. masonite sold with wooden socle. 3-Mar-3 Lilla Bukowskis, Stockholm #922/R est:15000-20000 (S.KR 33000)

ZOCCHI, Giuseppe (1711-1767) Italian
£52817 $85035 €75000 Grand Canal (51x85cm-20x33in) 11-May-3 Finarte, Venice #40/R est:80000-120000
Works on paper
£423 $680 €600 Scene dall'antico (23x27cm-9x11in) pen brown ink grey W/C blk pencil. 12-May-3 Sotheby's, Milan #48/R

ZOCCHI, Guglielmo (1874-?) Italian
£345 $548 €518 Woodland with mountain and house in background (18x29cm-7x11in) s. panel. 5-Mar-3 Rasmussen, Copenhagen #1897/R (D.KR 3700)
£4148 $6472 €6222 Mother's darling (49x35cm-19x14in) s. 6-Nov-2 Dobiaschofsky, Bern #1088/R est:8000 (S.FR 9500)

ZOFF, Alfred (1852-1927) Austrian
£1266 $2000 €2000 Sunlit wood (29x26cm-11x10in) s. board. 26-Nov-2 Wiener Kunst Auktionen, Vienna #66/R est:1500-2500
£1441 $2248 €2162 Harbour in summer (17x30cm-7x12in) s.d.1893 canvas on panel. 6-Nov-2 Dobiaschofsky, Bern #1090/R est:1800 (S.FR 3300)
£1923 $3038 €3000 Herzegovni in the Bay of Cattaro (39x54cm-15x21in) s. i. verso canvas on board. 12-Nov-2 Dorotheum, Vienna #36/R est:4500-7000
£2436 $3824 €3800 Villa on Ligurian coast (48x43cm-19x17in) s. canvas on board. 21-Nov-2 Van Ham, Cologne #1994/R est:1800
£4808 $7452 €7500 Bruges harbour (26x39cm-10x15in) s. canvas on panel. 5-Dec-2 Dorotheum, Graz #72/R est:5500
£5063 $8000 €8000 Coastal landscape (41x50cm-16x20in) canvas on board. 28-Nov-2 Dorotheum, Vienna #57/R est:6500-7500
£5380 $8500 €8500 Lacke neaar Weinzierl (32x50cm-13x20in) s. i.d.1901 verso lit. 26-Nov-2 Wiener Kunst Auktionen, Vienna #55/R est:8500-10000
£6757 $10541 €10000 Molo Lombardo in Chioggia (30x45cm-12x18in) s. i. verso board. 25-Mar-3 Wiener Kunst Auktionen, Vienna #121/R est:7000-12000
£6962 $11000 €11000 Waves breaking on Nervi coast (42x55cm-17x22in) s. i. verso canvas on board. 26-Nov-2 Wiener Kunst Auktionen, Vienna #52/R est:6500-8000
£10638 $17234 €15000 Landscape picture (79x52cm-31x20in) s. i.verso. 22-May-3 Dorotheum, Vienna #45/R est:20000-25000

ZOFFANY, Johann (1733-1810) British
£140000 $232400 €210000 Portrait of Giacomo Cervetto (125x98cm-49x39in) prov.exhib.lit. 12-Jun-3 Sotheby's, London #16/R est:150000-200000

ZOFFANY, Johann (attrib) (1733-1810) British
Miniatures
£2000 $3120 €3000 Captain John Woods seated (12cm-5in) i.verso pencil on paper wood frame rec. 5-Nov-2 Bonhams, New Bond Street #3/R est:400-600

ZOFFANY, Johann (circle) (1733-1810) British

£8387 $13000 €12581 Interior with two women and a child (80x70cm-31x28in) prov.lit. 2-Oct-2 Christie's, Rockefeller NY #181/R est:15000-20000
£12000 $19920 €18000 Portrait of a gentleman in a brown coat, seated beside at a table in a library (61x47cm-24x19in) 10-Jun-3 Christie's, London #13/R est:7000-10000

ZOFREA, Salvatore (1946-) Italian

£877 $1333 €1316 Anna (58x89cm-23x35in) s. 19-Aug-2 Joel, Victoria #319 est:2000-3000 (A.D 2500)

ZOGBAUM, Rufus Fairchild (1849-1925) American

£5070 $7200 €7605 Battle of Vicksburg (51x61cm-20x24in) 8-Aug-1 Barridorf, Portland #114/R est:6000-9000

ZOGBAUM, Wilfrid M (1915-1965) American

Sculpture

£1280 $2100 €1856 Square pipes (74x23x51cm-29x9x20in) welded steel prov. 1-Jun-3 Wright, Chicago #266/R est:3000-5000

Works on paper

£259 $425 €376 Abstract composition (27x35cm-11x14in) s.d. ink wash. 5-Jun-3 Swann Galleries, New York #271/R

ZOIA, Krukowskaja (1903-) Russian/Swedish

£573 $928 €860 Still life of amaryllis (80x65cm-31x26in) s. panel. 3-Feb-3 Lilla Bukowskis, Stockholm #103 (S.KR 8000)

ZOLLA, Venanzio (1880-1961) Italian

£481 $755 €750 Portrait of girl (34x25cm-13x10in) s. cardboard. 10-Dec-2 Della Rocca, Turin #279
£510 $811 €750 To the church (39x49cm-15x19in) s. cardboard. 1-Mar-3 Meeting Art, Vercelli #101
£680 $1082 €1000 Street in London (50x40cm-20x16in) s. cardboard. 1-Mar-3 Meeting Art, Vercelli #23
£705 $1107 €1100 Venice (26x33cm-10x13in) s. cardboard. 10-Dec-2 Della Rocca, Turin #271
£929 $1459 €1450 View of town (39x49cm-15x19in) s. cardboard. 10-Dec-2 Della Rocca, Turin #370/R
£962 $1510 €1500 View of town (19x48cm-7x19in) s. cardboard. 10-Dec-2 Della Rocca, Turin #369/R
£1282 $2013 €2000 Stroll (40x50cm-16x20in) s. card. 10-Dec-2 Della Rocca, Turin #263

ZOMMER, Richard Karlovich (1866-1939) Russian

£2500 $3926 €3750 Mount Ararat from the plain (42x76cm-17x30in) s. 20-Nov-2 Sotheby's, London #35/R est:2500-3500
£18000 $28260 €27000 At the market (36x57cm-14x22in) s. board. 20-Nov-2 Sotheby's, London #32/R est:5000-7000

ZON, Jacob (1872-1932) Dutch

£556 $917 €800 Tending to the fields (30x48cm-12x19in) s. canvas on plywood sold with another by the same hand. 1-Jul-3 Christie's, Amsterdam #185
£1250 $2063 €1800 Horses on the beach (62x93cm-24x37in) s.d.07. 1-Jul-3 Christie's, Amsterdam #177 est:2000-3000

Works on paper

£556 $917 €800 Woman reading in a farm interior (20x21cm-8x8in) s. W/C. 1-Jul-3 Christie's, Amsterdam #103

ZONARO, Fausto (1854-1929) Italian

£4717 $7264 €7500 Women darning (28x17cm-11x7in) s.d.1882 board. 28-Oct-2 Il Ponte, Milan #291/R
£25806 $40774 €40000 Vue de Constantinople (27x43cm-11x17in) s. panel prov. 19-Dec-2 Claude Aguttes, Neuilly #118/R est:15000
£45000 $70650 €67500 Sedan chair (49x77cm-19x30in) s. prov. 19-Nov-2 Sotheby's, London #127/R est:60000-80000
£74194 $117226 €115000 Quai a Constantinople (41x65cm-16x26in) s. 19-Dec-2 Claude Aguttes, Neuilly #117/R est:70000

Works on paper

£1400 $2226 €2100 Study of an Italian lady (49x29cm-19x11in) s.d.97 W/C. 29-Apr-3 Bonhams, New Bond Street #75/R est:700-1000

ZOPPI, Antonio (1860-1926) Italian

£1244 $2066 €1804 Winding the skein to an amusing tale (48x60cm-19x24in) s. 16-Jun-3 Waddingtons, Toronto #334/R est:2500-3500 (C.D 2800)

ZORACH, Marguerite (1887-1968) American

£5696 $9000 €8544 Flower in blue vase (53x41cm-21x16in) s. canvas on board painted c.1935 prov. 24-Apr-3 Shannon's, Milford #83/R est:4000-6000
£13889 $22500 €20834 Night still life (67x77cm-26x30in) s. painted c.1940 prov.exhib. 21-May-3 Sotheby's, New York #27/R est:30000-40000
£28169 $40000 €42254 Landscape, France (33x41cm-13x16in) board. 8-Aug-1 Barridorf, Portland #47/R est:9000-12000
£49383 $80000 €74075 Still life of tulips in a glass goblet (69x49cm-27x19in) s. painted c.1929-30 prov.exhib. 21-May-3 Sotheby's, New York #10/R est:40000-60000
£123457 $200000 €185186 Connoisseur (56x44cm-22x17in) i. painted c.1909-10 prov.exhib.lit. 21-May-3 Sotheby's, New York #28/R est:30000-40000

Works on paper

£7746 $11000 €11619 Landscape, France (30x23cm-12x9in) s.d.1913 W/C. 8-Aug-1 Barridorf, Portland #77/R est:8000-10000
£23148 $37500 €34722 Storm (34x44cm-13x17in) s.i. W/C pencil executed c.1913 prov.exhib. 21-May-3 Sotheby's, New York #96/R est:25000-35000

ZORACH, William (1887-1966) American

£20440 $32500 €30660 European landscape. Street scene (61x51cm-24x20in) s.d.1909 double-sided prov. 5-Mar-3 Sotheby's, New York #74/R est:8000-12000

Prints

£16667 $26000 €25001 Sailing, Provincetown (27x22cm-11x9in) s.i.d. col woodcut. 18-Sep-2 Swann Galleries, New York #46/R est:10000-15000

Sculpture

£9554 $15000 €14331 Girl with cat (34cm-13in) s.num.2-6 brown pat. bronze prov. 14-Dec-2 Weschler, Washington #693/R est:5000-7000
£17610 $28000 €26415 Undaunted (53cm-21in) i.d.1963 num.4/6 polished pat. bronze prov.exhib.lit. 4-Mar-3 Christie's, Rockefeller NY #82/R est:10000-15000
£17742 $27500 €26613 Diva (89cm-35in) i.num.1/6 brown pat. bronze prov. 4-Dec-2 Sotheby's, New York #97/R est:15000-25000
£18519 $30000 €27779 Spirit of silk (49cm-19in) i. brown pat. bronze prov.lit. 21-May-3 Sotheby's, New York #187/R est:30000-50000

Works on paper

£396 $650 €574 Nude torso (28x21cm-11x8in) s.d.March 9th 1956 pencil. 5-Jun-3 Swann Galleries, New York #275/R
£705 $1100 €1058 Waterfall (34x25cm-13x10in) s.d.1915 W/C prov. 12-Apr-3 Weschler, Washington #587/R est:1000-2000
£1623 $2500 €2435 Maine Harbour (38x53cm-15x21in) s. W/C. 24-Oct-2 Shannon's, Milford #44/R est:3000-5000
£2273 $3500 €3410 Flowering tree (28x20cm-11x8in) W/C. 25-Oct-2 Morris & Whiteside, Hilton Head Island #154 est:2000-3000
£2439 $4000 €3537 Dusk, lake landscape (25x35cm-10x14in) s. W/C exec.c.1920. 5-Jun-3 Swann Galleries, New York #274/R est:4000-6000
£4088 $6500 €6132 Fifth Auenue from the plaza (55x38cm-22x15in) s. W/C pencil prov. 4-Mar-3 Christie's, Rockefeller NY #72/R est:8000-12000

ZORAD, Erno (1911-) Hungarian

£463 $745 €671 Poultry yard (60x80cm-24x31in) s. 7-May-3 Dobiaschofsky, Bern #1076/R (S.FR 1000)

ZORAD, Geza (19/20th C) Hungarian

£377 $589 €600 Woman knitting with man in interior (49x37cm-19x15in) s. board. 9-Oct-2 Michael Zeller, Lindau #980/R

ZORD, Arnold (1887-?) Hungarian

£282 $462 €409 Triptych of Lucern (62x108cm-24x43in) s.i.d.1915. 4-Jun-3 Fischer, Luzern #2360/R (S.FR 600)

ZORILLA DE SAN MARTIN, Alfredo (20th C) South American

£1410 $2200 €2115 Punta del este (80x104cm-31x41in) s.d.62 cardboard. 30-Jul-2 Galleria Y Remates, Montevideo #40/R est:2800-3500

ZORIO, Gilberto (1944-) Italian

Works on paper

£2083 $3292 €3000 Sans titre (42x54cm-17x21in) s.d. mixed media prov. 27-Apr-3 Perrin, Versailles #110/R est:5000-6000
£2482 $4021 €3500 Untitled (48x75cm-19x30in) s.d.73 mixed media prov. 26-May-3 Christie's, Milan #227/R est:3000-5000
£2695 $4366 €3800 Untitled (78x105cm-31x41in) s.d.87 mixed media prov. 26-May-3 Christie's, Milan #70/R est:3000-4000

ZORKOCZY, Gyula (1873-1932) Hungarian

£300 $465 €450 On the edge of the forest (23x33cm-9x13in) cardboard painted c.1940. 3-Dec-2 SOGA, Bratislava #101/R (SL.K 19000)
£550 $880 €825 Lady seated on a river bank (60x79cm-24x31in) s. 11-Mar-3 Bonhams, Knightsbridge #19
£622 $1033 €902 Tending the geese (75x100cm-30x39in) s. 16-Jun-3 Waddingtons, Toronto #306/R est:1000-1500 (C.D 1400)

ZORN, Anders (1860-1920) Swedish

£8511 $13191 €12767 Landscape, Mora (10x16cm-4x6in) s.d.90 panel prov.lit. 3-Dec-2 Bukowskis, Stockholm #247/R est:125000-135000 (S.KR 120000)

£14352 $23251 €20810 Chamberlain and Diplomat Harald Bildt (125x90cm-49x35in) s.d.1908 prov.exhib.lit. 26-May-3 Bukowskis, Stockholm #161/R est:250000-300000 (S.KR 185000)
£42553 $65957 €63830 In the sand - nude on beach (62x98cm-24x39in) s.d.1914 lit. 4-Dec-2 AB Stockholms Auktionsverk #1734/R est:600000-800000 (S.KR 600000)
£53530 $86718 €77619 Morning - girl seated on chair (47x31cm-19x12in) s. canvas on cardboard prov.exhib.lit. 26-May-3 Bukowskis, Stockholm #95/R est:1000000-1200000 (S.KR 690000)
£54988 $90181 €79733 Flooding - nude female in the forest (90x60cm-35x24in) s.d.1912 lit. 4-Jun-3 AB Stockholms Auktionsverk #2127/R est:1000000-1200000 (S.KR 700000)
£66620 $105259 €99930 Lady at cafe, Isle de Seguin (23x20cm-9x8in) s.i.d.1894 prov.exhib.lit. 27-Nov-2 Falkkloos, Malmo #78041/R est:1200000 (S.KR 950000)
£74468 $115426 €111702 Getting out of bed (74x60cm-29x24in) s.d.1910 lit. 4-Dec-2 AB Stockholms Auktionsverk #1681/R est:1000000-1200000 (S.KR 1050000)
£88652 $137411 €132978 Spanish Anna (65x50cm-26x20in) s.d.1918. 4-Dec-2 AB Stockholms Auktionsverk #1709/R est:1200000-1500000 (S.KR 1250000)
£110000 $180400 €165000 Miss Grigsby (68x56cm-27x22in) s.d.1907 lit. 3-Jun-3 Sotheby's, London #246/R est:120000-180000
£120000 $196800 €180000 Morakulla i vinterdrakt - girl from Mora in winter dress (90x60cm-35x24in) s.d.1918 prov.exhib.lit. 3-Jun-3 Sotheby's, London #221/R est:90000-120000
£127660 $197872 €191490 Female nude in the wood (90x61cm-35x24in) s. lit. 3-Dec-2 Bukowskis, Stockholm #345/R est:2000000-3000000 (S.KR 1800000)
£190000 $311600 €285000 Eldsken - fire reflection (107x82cm-42x32in) s.d.1905 prov.exhib.lit. 3-Jun-3 Sotheby's, London #243/R est:150000-200000
£205674 $318794 €308511 Ingeborg - nude girl by water in forest (120x91cm-47x36in) s.i.d.1907 prov.exhib.lit. 4-Dec-2 AB Stockholms Auktionsverk #1625/R est:3000000-4000000 (S.KR 2900000)

Prints
£2128 $3298 €3192 Self portrait with model (24x18cm-9x7in) s. etching lit. 3-Dec-2 Bukowskis, Stockholm #381/R est:20000-25000 (S.KR 30000)
£2443 $3958 €3665 Elin (22x31cm-9x12in) s. s.d.1913 1914 etching. 26-May-3 Grev Wedels Plass, Oslo #138/R est:12000-15000 (N.KR 27000)
£3614 $5926 €5240 Storm - man on horseback (20x14cm-8x6in) s. etching lit. 4-Jun-3 AB Stockholms Auktionsverk #2342/R est:15000-18000 (S.KR 46000)
£4242 $6957 €6151 Omnibus (27x20cm-11x8in) s. etching lit. 4-Jun-3 AB Stockholms Auktionsverk #2337/R est:40000-60000 (S.KR 54000)

Sculpture
£11348 $17589 €17022 Nude girl standing I (20cm-8in) s.d.1910 pat.bronze st.f.Meyer lit. 4-Dec-2 AB Stockholms Auktionsverk #1821/R est:60000-70000 (S.KR 160000)

Works on paper
£2870 $4650 €4162 Julia Ayrton (20x15cm-8x6in) s.i. pencil. 26-May-3 Bukowskis, Stockholm #160/R est:40000-50000 (S.KR 37000)
£12057 $18688 €18086 Portrait of Julia Dolling (31x25cm-12x10in) s.d.80 W/C oval. 3-Dec-2 Bukowskis, Stockholm #245/R est:140000-150000 (S.KR 170000)
£14539 $22535 €21809 Interior scene with girl dressed in national costume (39x27cm-15x11in) s. painted c.1880 W/C prov. 3-Dec-2 Bukowskis, Stockholm #284/R est:100000-125000 (S.KR 205000)
£28723 $44521 €43085 Portrait of Spanish girl (30x23cm-12x9in) s.d.82 W/C. 4-Dec-2 AB Stockholms Auktionsverk #1673/R est:400000-450000 (S.KR 405000)
£187943 $291312 €281915 On the Thames - Mary Smith in boat (25x17cm-10x7in) s.d.83 W/C exhib.lit. 3-Dec-2 Bukowskis, Stockholm #86/R est:3000000-3200000 (S.KR 2650000)
£560284 $868440 €840426 Le tub (81x50cm-32x20in) s.d.88 W/C prov.exhib.lit. 3-Dec-2 Bukowskis, Stockholm #149/R (S.KR 7900000)

ZORZA, Carlo dalla (1903-1977) Italian
£2449 $3894 €3600 Cars on the banks of the Brenta (50x70cm-20x28in) s. 1-Mar-3 Stadion, Trieste #236 est:3500

ZOTL, Aloys (1803-1887) Swiss
Works on paper
£4054 $6324 €6000 Fish, Table 39 (34x47cm-13x19in) s.i.d.19.Juni 1883 W/C. 28-Mar-3 Dorotheum, Vienna #202/R est:6000-7000
£8219 $12904 €12000 Raie cendree (45x55cm-18x22in) i. gouache crayon prov.exhib.lit. 15-Apr-3 Laurence Calmels, Paris #4428/R est:10000
£11644 $18281 €17000 Regalec (44x55cm-17x22in) i. gouache prov.exhib.lit. 15-Apr-3 Laurence Calmels, Paris #4433/R est:10000
£17123 $26884 €25000 Semnopitheque (38x47cm-15x19in) i. gouache exhib.lit. 15-Apr-3 Laurence Calmels, Paris #4431/R est:15000
£19178 $30110 €28000 Tortue bleue (44x55cm-17x22in) i. gouache prov.exhib.lit. 15-Apr-3 Laurence Calmels, Paris #4430/R est:10000
£26027 $40863 €38000 Caiman (44x51cm-17x20in) i. gouache exhib.lit. 15-Apr-3 Laurence Calmels, Paris #4432/R est:15000
£27397 $42740 €40000 Rana varia (41x50cm-16x20in) i.d.1863 gouache exhib.lit. 14-Apr-3 Laurence Calmels, Paris #4081/R est:15000
£34247 $53767 €50000 Rhinoceros (44x55cm-17x22in) i. gouache prov.exhib.lit. 15-Apr-3 Laurence Calmels, Paris #4429/R est:15000

ZOTTI, Carmelo (1933-) Italian
£759 $1185 €1200 Big fish (70x100cm-28x39in) s. s.d.1957 verso. 19-Oct-2 Semenzato, Venice #138/R
£886 $1382 €1400 Composition with gondola pieces (100x70cm-39x28in) s.d.1958 s.verso. 19-Oct-2 Semenzato, Venice #142/R

ZOU CHUANAN (1941-) Chinese
Works on paper
£3497 $5769 €5071 Drunken (68x84cm-27x33in) s.i. ink scroll. 6-Jul-3 Christie's, Hong Kong #273/R est:50000-60000 (HK.D 45000)

ZOUBTCHENKO, Katia (1922-) ?
£302 $486 €450 Interieur a la bouteille de Chianti (46x55cm-18x22in) mono. s.d.1962 verso. 23-Feb-3 Mercier & Cie, Lille #164

ZOX, Larry (1936-) American
£393 $609 €590 Untitled (75x190cm-30x75in) acrylic. 29-Oct-2 Lawson Menzies, Sydney #217 (A.D 1100)
£516 $800 €774 Diagonal III (155x180cm-61x71in) acrylic. 29-Sep-2 Butterfields, Los Angeles #4449/R

ZRZAVY, Jan (1890-1977) Czechoslovakian
£11351 $18388 €17027 Chapel II (27x35cm-11x14in) s.d.1939 panel exhib. 24-May-3 Dorotheum, Prague #122/R est:300000-450000 (C.KR 500000)
Works on paper
£310 $483 €465 Angels' choir (17x13cm-7x5in) mono. col pencil dr. 12-Oct-2 Dorotheum, Prague #175 (C.KR 15000)
£310 $483 €465 City (9x13cm-4x5in) s.d.1949 crayon dr. 12-Oct-2 Dorotheum, Prague #248 (C.KR 15000)
£372 $580 €558 Little church by the sea (10x13cm-4x5in) s.d.52 crayon dr. 12-Oct-2 Dorotheum, Prague #247 (C.KR 18000)
£537 $838 €806 Head (19x18cm-7x7in) s. chl dr. 12-Oct-2 Dorotheum, Prague #249 (C.KR 26000)
£2043 $3310 €3065 Head of girl (30x20cm-12x8in) mono.i. pencil. 24-May-3 Dorotheum, Prague #152/R est:60000-90000 (C.KR 90000)

ZSCHIMMER, Emil (1842-1917) German
£823 $1275 €1300 Girl collecting berries (63x47cm-25x19in) s.d.1893 i.d. verso board. 25-Sep-2 Neumeister, Munich #791/R
£2405 $3728 €3800 Two children with geese in spring meadow (22x29cm-9x11in) s.d.1879 i. verso panel. 25-Sep-2 Neumeister, Munich #790/R est:2400

ZUBER, Henri (1844-1909) French
£2593 $3681 €4200 Laveuses (46x67cm-18x26in) s.d.1875. 17-Mar-2 Galerie de Chartres, Chartres #127
Works on paper
£705 $1107 €1100 Bassin en automne (25x35cm-10x14in) s. W/C. 13-Dec-2 Piasa, Paris #269
£897 $1409 €1400 Place de la Concorde (34x50cm-13x20in) W/C. 13-Dec-2 Piasa, Paris #247/R
£1026 $1610 €1600 Pont-Neuf (24x35cm-9x14in) s. W/C. 13-Dec-2 Piasa, Paris #246/R
£1597 $2524 €2300 Entree du village (24x34cm-9x13in) st.sig. W/C. 25-Apr-3 Piasa, Paris #190/R est:1000
£1667 $2617 €2600 Promenade a Cannes (29x44cm-11x17in) s.d.81 W/C. 13-Dec-2 Piasa, Paris #248/R
£1731 $2717 €2700 Nourrices au Luxembourg (33x49cm-13x19in) s.d.86 W/C. 13-Dec-2 Piasa, Paris #249/R
£2361 $3731 €3400 Place animee dans le Midi (23x34cm-9x13in) s. W/C. 25-Apr-3 Piasa, Paris #189/R
£2639 $4169 €3800 Jardin du Luxembourg (35x50cm-14x20in) st.sig. W/C. 25-Apr-3 Piasa, Paris #188/R

ZUBER-BUHLER, Fritz (1822-1896) Swiss
£10323 $16000 €15485 Young beauty holding a bouquet of flowers (73x59cm-29x23in) s. 30-Oct-2 Christie's, Rockefeller NY #172/R est:12000-16000

ZUBIAURRE, Ramon de (1882-1969) Spanish
£3289 $5329 €5000 Still life with grapes (23x35cm-9x14in) s. board. 21-Jan-3 Ansorena, Madrid #192/R

£15132 $24513 €23000 Basque people in landscape (32x90cm-13x35in) s.d.1944. 21-Jan-3 Ansorena, Madrid #163/R est:21000

ZUBIAURRE, Valentin de (1879-1963) Spanish
£12258 $19368 €19000 Mayor of Soria (81x65cm-32x26in) s. 17-Dec-2 Segre, Madrid #91/R est:18000
Works on paper
£331 $540 €500 Church interior (20x13cm-8x5in) s. pencil dr. 11-Feb-3 Segre, Madrid #1/R
£489 $793 €690 Boecto de catedral (31x21cm-12x8in) s. chl sketch htd. 20-May-3 Segre, Madrid #2/R est:590
£881 $1374 €1400 Cathedral interior (21x12cm-8x5in) s. pencil dr. 17-Sep-2 Segre, Madrid #18/R

ZUCCARELLI, Francesco (1702-1788) Italian
£12000 $18720 €18000 Portrait of an old lady in a lilac satin dress, cat on her lap (81x65cm-32x26in) prov. 9-Apr-3 Christie's, London #113/R est:8000-12000
£45000 $75150 €65250 Pastoral landscape with the Flight into Egypt (83x114cm-33x45in) prov. 10-Jul-3 Sotheby's, London #55/R est:30000-40000

ZUCCARELLI, Francesco (attrib) (1702-1788) Italian
£4114 $6418 €6500 River landscape with buildings and figures (57x72cm-22x28in) lit. 14-Sep-2 Bergmann, Erlangen #708/R est:6000

ZUCCARELLI, Francesco (circle) (1702-1788) Italian
£9500 $14725 €14250 Extensive landscape with huntsmen in the foreground (89x148cm-35x58in) 30-Oct-2 Christie's, Kensington #166/R est:4000-6000

ZUCCARO, Federico (1540-1609) Italian
Works on paper
£2813 $4500 €4220 Head study of a bearded man (11x15cm-4x6in) i. col chk prov.exhib. 14-May-3 Butterfields, San Francisco #1002/R est:3000-5000
£4500 $7515 €6525 Madonna and child in glory and four saints (48x24cm-19x9in) pen brown ink wash arched top prov. 9-Jul-3 Sotheby's, London #16/R est:5000-7000
£5000 $8350 €7250 Holy Family surrounded by angels (36x27cm-14x11in) i. brown ink. 9-Jul-3 Bonhams, Knightsbridge #65/R est:5000-7000
£5556 $9000 €8334 Portrait of bearded man (17x11cm-7x4in) i. chk prov. 22-Jan-3 Christie's, Rockefeller NY #3/R est:6000
£5850 $9302 €8600 Saint Lawrence's martyrdom (25x18cm-10x7in) i.verso pen ink wash gouache. 21-Mar-3 Rieunier, Bailly-Pommery, Mathias, Paris #41/R
£11111 $18000 €16667 Susannah and the elders (33x26cm-13x10in) i. pen ink wash over chk. 21-Jan-3 Sotheby's, New York #42/R est:9000

ZUCCARO, Federico (attrib) (1540-1609) Italian
Works on paper
£650 $1007 €975 Portrait of a Cardinal (19x14cm-7x6in) black red chk. 9-Dec-2 Bonhams, New Bond Street #85/R
£833 $1325 €1200 Figures round corpse of saint (18cm-7in circular) pen wash prov. 5-May-3 Ketterer, Munich #375/R
£1528 $2429 €2200 Blessing of a sick man (18cm-7in circular) pen wash prov. 5-May-3 Ketterer, Munich #376/R est:1800-2200
£13782 $21362 €21500 Taddeo Zuccaro entering Florence (36x19cm-14x7in) pen ink wash over crayon prov. 4-Dec-2 Piasa, Paris #7/R est:15000

ZUCCARO, Federico (circle) (1540-1609) Italian
Works on paper
£6129 $9684 €9500 Nay at harbour (15x20cm-6x8in) i. pen ink wash htd gouache. 19-Dec-2 Delvaux, Paris #79/R est:1800

ZUCCARO, Taddeo (1529-1566) Italian
Works on paper
£3636 $5200 €5454 Adoration of the shepherds (47x80cm-19x31in) pen ink wash htd white on two sheets. 23-Jan-3 Swann Galleries, New York #37/R est:5000-8000

ZUCCARO, Taddeo (attrib) (1529-1566) Italian
Works on paper
£1418 $2369 €2000 Femme nue, vue de dos, enlacee par des putti (13x10cm-5x4in) pen brown ink brown wash. 19-Jun-3 Piasa, Paris #13/R est:2000-3000
£1958 $2800 €2937 Two standing Hellebardiers (17x12cm-7x5in) black chk. 23-Jan-3 Swann Galleries, New York #36/R est:2500-3500
£4255 $7106 €6000 Deux personnages drapes, l'un de dos, l'autre de face (24x21cm-9x8in) pen brown ink brown wash gouache. 19-Jun-3 Piasa, Paris #11/R est:6000-8000

ZUCCHI, Antonio (1726-1795) Italian
Works on paper
£1392 $2200 €2200 Bacchanale sous une arche, un paysage dans le fond (46x57cm-18x22in) pen brown ink brown wash prov. 27-Nov-2 Christie's, Paris #107/R est:1500-2000

ZUCCHI, Antonio (circle) (1726-1795) Italian
£10000 $16600 €15000 Triumph of Bacchus and Ariadne, with cherubs in attendance, in a coastal landscape (95x370cm-37x146in) pair. 10-Jun-3 Christie's, London #56/R est:12000-18000

ZUCCHI, Jacopo (attrib) (c.1541-1590) Italian
£24000 $40080 €34800 The Crucifixion (29x23cm-11x9in) copper. 10-Jul-3 Sotheby's, London #160/R est:18000-22000
Works on paper
£443 $700 €700 Le martyre de Saint Pierre (19x13cm-7x5in) pen brown ink brown wash. 27-Nov-2 Christie's, Paris #23

ZUCKER, Jakub (1900-1981) American/Polish
£1931 $3090 €2800 Jeune chassid (61x50cm-24x20in) s. 12-Mar-3 Rabourdin & Choppin de Janvry, Paris #75/R

ZUCKER, Joe (1941-) American
Works on paper
£641 $1013 €1000 Jolly Roger (60x95cm-24x37in) s.i.d.1977 mixed media board. 14-Nov-2 Neumeister, Munich #905/R

ZUGEL, Heinrich von (1850-1941) German
£949 $1500 €1500 Sheepdog (30x33cm-12x13in) s. board. 30-Nov-2 Berlinghof, Heidelberg #384 est:2200
£1454 $2122 €2181 Old peasant with sheep (33x38cm-13x15in) s.d. prov. 17-Jun-2 Philippe Schuler, Zurich #4363/R est:4000-6000 (S.FR 3300)
£2166 $3335 €3400 Peasant with sheep (34x38cm-13x15in) s. bears d.1890 or 98. 5-Sep-2 Arnold, Frankfurt #904/R est:4800
£5449 $8554 €8500 Buggi et Bergt (46x63cm-18x25in) s. 15-Dec-2 Eric Pillon, Calais #46/R
£9000 $14130 €13500 Bauer und drei kalber - farmer leading his calves (47x65cm-19x26in) s.d.1907 lit. 19-Nov-2 Sotheby's, London #172/R est:10000-15000
£9247 $14425 €13500 Dog watching sheep and lambs for his master (20x25cm-8x10in) s.i. panel. 11-Apr-3 Winterberg, Heidelberg #626a/R est:5200
£14103 $21859 €22000 Grazing sheep in front of a barn (27x40cm-11x16in) s.d.75 panel lit. 4-Dec-2 Neumeister, Munich #980/R est:7000

ZUGEL, Wilhelm (1876-1950) German
Sculpture
£1987 $3080 €3100 Reclining polar bear (12x16x33cm-5x6x13in) i. dark pat.bronze Cast.Guss verso. Brandstetter Munchen. 7-Dec-2 Ketterer, Hamburg #154/R est:1100-1200

ZUHR, Hugo (1895-1971) Swedish
£459 $720 €689 Landscape with farm, Skaane (38x55cm-15x22in) mono. s.d.1957 verso. 16-Dec-2 Lilla Bukowskis, Stockholm #35 (S.KR 6500)
£466 $731 €699 Crete (38x62cm-15x24in) mono. s.d.1955 verso. 16-Dec-2 Lilla Bukowskis, Stockholm #34 (S.KR 6600)
£561 $875 €842 Landscape from Jylland (65x81cm-26x32in) mono. d.1958 verso. 6-Nov-2 AB Stockholms Auktionsverk #675/R (S.KR 8000)
£575 $896 €863 Still life of fruit (50x65cm-20x26in) mono. painted 1930 exhib.lit. 6-Nov-2 AB Stockholms Auktionsverk #665/R (S.KR 8200)
£590 $920 €885 River landscape in spring by Ressle (50x65cm-20x26in) mono. d.1943 verso. 13-Sep-2 Lilla Bukowskis, Stockholm #613 (S.KR 8600)
£771 $1203 €1157 Spring by Fjallsjo river (65x81cm-26x32in) mono. painted 1946 exhib. 6-Nov-2 AB Stockholms Auktionsverk #650/R (S.KR 11000)
£1043 $1626 €1565 The pine tree, Vik (81x65cm-32x26in) mono. exhib.prov. 13-Sep-2 Lilla Bukowskis, Stockholm #474 est:12000-15000 (S.KR 15200)
£1065 $1682 €1598 Midday heat, Gassin (53x64cm-21x25in) mono. prov.exhib.lit. 28-Apr-3 Bukowskis, Stockholm #219/R est:20000-22000 (S.KR 14000)

ZULLE, Johannes (1841-1938) Swiss

£3493 $5485 €5240 Trip to the mountain pastures (16x21cm-6x8in) s.i.d. tempera gold bronze board. 25-Nov-2 Sotheby's, Zurich #32/R est:8000-12000 (S.FR 8000)
£3930 $6170 €5895 Trip to the mountain pastures (18x26cm-7x10in) s.i.d.1902 tempera gold bronze. 25-Nov-2 Sotheby's, Zurich #34/R est:9000-12000 (S.FR 9000)
£4585 $7199 €6878 Trip to the mountain pastures (24x30cm-9x12in) s.i. tempera gold bronze board. 25-Nov-2 Sotheby's, Zurich #35/R est:8000-12000 (S.FR 10500)
£5240 $8227 €7860 Trip to the mountain pastures (19x31cm-7x12in) s.i.d.1904 tempera gold bronze board. 25-Nov-2 Sotheby's, Zurich #37/R est:10000-15000 (S.FR 12000)

ZULOAGA, Ignacio (1870-1945) Spanish

£21000 $34860 €30450 Portrait of a lady (64x46cm-25x18in) s. board. 12-Jun-3 Christie's, London #209/R est:6000-8000
£21918 $34192 €32000 Portrait of Don Fernando Garay (100x81cm-39x32in) s. exhib. 8-Apr-3 Ansorena, Madrid #122/R est:3000
£32000 $53120 €46400 Un dominico (129x114cm-51x45in) s.d.1937 prov.lit. 12-Jun-3 Christie's, London #210/R est:20000-30000
£40000 $62800 €60000 Retrato de actriz - Spanish actress (92x73cm-36x29in) s. painted 1909 lit. 19-Nov-2 Sotheby's, London #47/R est:40000-60000
£240000 $376800 €360000 Candida en amarillo - Candida in yellow (198x97cm-78x38in) s. painted 1909 prov.exhib.lit. 19-Nov-2 Sotheby's, London #40/R est:180000-250000

ZULOW, Franz von (1883-1963) Austrian

£2848 $4500 €4500 Christmas (30x25cm-12x10in) panel. 27-Nov-2 Dorotheum, Vienna #175/R est:4500-6000
£5449 $8609 €8500 Still life of flowers (40x30cm-16x12in) s.d.34 board. 18-Nov-2 Dorotheum, Linz #354/R est:9000-11000
£8784 $13703 €13000 Memory of Tunis (27x37cm-11x15in) s.d.31 i. verso board. 25-Mar-3 Wiener Kunst Auktionen, Vienna #136/R est:10000-20000
£9929 $16085 €14000 Village street in Auerbach (48x64cm-19x25in) s.d.32 s.i.d. verso board prov. 20-May-3 Dorotheum, Vienna #154/R est:13000-17000
£9929 $16085 €14000 Village street (68x73cm-27x29in) s.d.31 prov. 20-May-3 Dorotheum, Vienna #157/R est:13000-17000

Works on paper

£360 $590 €500 Kitchen-range (29x13cm-11x5in) s.d.52 i.d.54 verso chl col pencil dr. 5-Jun-3 Dorotheum, Salzburg #818/R
£417 $658 €650 Courtyard (20x16cm-8x6in) s.d.1920 paste. 12-Nov-2 Dorotheum, Vienna #43/R
£652 $1070 €900 Untitled (29x52cm-11x20in) s.d.1910 pate W/C prov. 27-May-3 Hassfurther, Vienna #77/R
£705 $1114 €1100 Fantasy landscape (28x18cm-11x7in) s.d.1902 mixed media. 18-Nov-2 Dorotheum, Linz #469/R
£942 $1545 €1300 Ashamed (30x40cm-12x16in) s.d.1913 paste W/C prov. 27-May-3 Hassfurther, Vienna #76
£1410 $2228 €2200 Duck on river by village (22x31cm-9x12in) pen Indian ink W/C. 12-Nov-2 Dorotheum, Vienna #87/R est:2200-2800
£1812 $2971 €2500 Houses in landscape (40x56cm-16x22in) s.d.1921 chk W/C. 27-May-3 Wiener Kunst Auktionen, Vienna #74/R est:3000-5000
£2029 $3328 €2800 Witch's kitchen (30x31cm-12x12in) i.verso W/C. 27-May-3 Wiener Kunst Auktionen, Vienna #72/R est:2800-5000
£2319 $3803 €3200 Fantasy city (36x29cm-14x11in) s.i.d.1922 ink col pencil. 27-May-3 Wiener Kunst Auktionen, Vienna #73/R est:2000-6000
£2848 $4415 €4500 Yearbook (22x16cm-9x6in) i. Indian ink W/C eight. 25-Sep-2 Wiener Kunst Auktionen, Vienna #425/R est:4500-10000
£3623 $5942 €5000 Famous man (43x59cm-17x23in) s.d.1913 paste W/C prov. 27-May-3 Hassfurther, Vienna #75/R est:2000-3000
£6522 $10696 €9000 Flower basket on table in front of landscape (77x100cm-30x39in) s.d.1921 W/C paste. 27-May-3 Hassfurther, Vienna #74/R est:5000-10000

ZULOW, V (19th C) ?

£811 $1305 €1217 Tyrolean landscape with cabins. s.d.1856. 22-Feb-3 Rasmussen, Havnen #2368/R (D.KR 9000)

ZUND, Robert (1827-1909) Swiss

£329 $539 €477 Insel Altstad near Meggen (24x17cm-9x7in) d.10. Aug. 67 prov. 4-Jun-3 Fischer, Luzern #2361/R (S.FR 700)
£609 $943 €914 Bush (28x21cm-11x8in) d.1878 canvas on board prov. 9-Dec-2 Philippe Schuler, Zurich #3854 (S.FR 1400)
£696 $1078 €1044 Rocks (30x21cm-12x8in) prov. 9-Dec-2 Philippe Schuler, Zurich #3853 (S.FR 1600)
£739 $1146 €1109 Untitled (20x30cm-8x12in) d.1849 paper on canvas prov. 9-Dec-2 Philippe Schuler, Zurich #3852 (S.FR 1700)
£837 $1222 €1256 Rocks on the Pilatus (77x53cm-30x21in) d.1. Octob 1861. 17-Jun-2 Philippe Schuler, Zurich #4300 (S.FR 1900)
£943 $1509 €1415 Reclining ram (28x36cm-11x14in) d.9.Dez.71 prov. 17-Mar-3 Philippe Schuler, Zurich #4576 (S.FR 2000)
£1043 $1617 €1565 Bush (17x29cm-7x11in) mono. canvas on board prov. 9-Dec-2 Philippe Schuler, Zurich #3855 est:1200-1500 (S.FR 2400)
£1217 $1887 €1826 Terrain study (20x30cm-8x12in) s. paper on canvas prov. 9-Dec-2 Philippe Schuler, Zurich #3857 est:1800-2100 (S.FR 2800)
£1373 $2129 €2060 Road to Emmaus (13x17cm-5x7in) mono. panel prov. 3-Oct-2 Koller, Zurich #3095/R est:3000-5000 (S.FR 3200)
£2123 $3396 €3185 Railing study (33x40cm-13x16in) d.11.Sept.51. 17-Mar-3 Philippe Schuler, Zurich #4572 est:4000-5000 (S.FR 4500)
£2123 $3396 €3185 Walensee landscape (31x51cm-12x20in) d.6.Oct.52 prov. 17-Mar-3 Philippe Schuler, Zurich #4573/R est:6000-8000 (S.FR 4500)
£2304 $3572 €3456 Resting on the Flight (13x17cm-5x7in) mono. panel prov. 9-Dec-2 Philippe Schuler, Zurich #3856 est:2000-2500 (S.FR 5300)
£5677 $8969 €8516 Small landscape with peasant ploughing (12x16cm-5x6in) panel. 14-Nov-2 Stuker, Bern #600 est:5000-6000 (S.FR 13000)
£9871 $15300 €14807 View towards Vitznauerstock (26x34cm-10x13in) s. prov.exhib. 3-Oct-2 Koller, Zurich #3096/R est:20000-30000 (S.FR 23000)
£11790 $18511 €17685 Figures with sheep by Vierwaldstattersee (22x30cm-9x12in) s. paper on panel prov.exhib. 25-Nov-2 Sotheby's, Zurich #1/R est:25000-45000 (S.FR 27000)
£12876 $20343 €19314 Forest clearing with deer at the water (61x83cm-24x33in) s.d.1893. 26-Nov-2 Phillips, Zurich #11/R est:30000-40000 (S.FR 30000)
£13100 $20568 €19650 Rocky outcrop with figure (78x53cm-31x21in) i.d.OctobP. 25-Nov-2 Sotheby's, Zurich #22/R est:30000-50000 (S.FR 30000)
£22318 $35262 €33477 View of Pilatus (25x33cm-10x13in) s. lit. 28-Nov-2 Christie's, Zurich #4/R est:20000-25000 (S.FR 52000)
£28302 $45283 €42453 Farmyard (61x81cm-24x32in) s. prov. 17-Mar-3 Philippe Schuler, Zurich #4574/R est:70000-90000 (S.FR 60000)
£37736 $61132 €54717 Vierwaldstattersee near Meggen (57x75cm-22x30in) s.d.1855 prov. 24-May-3 Galerie Gloggner, Luzern #132/R est:80000-90000 (S.FR 80000)
£73059 $113973 €109589 Near Lucern (62x82cm-24x32in) s. 28-Mar-3 Koller, Zurich #3100/R est:7000-120000 (S.FR 160000)
£128755 $203433 €193133 Schellenmatt (61x81cm-24x32in) s. 26-Nov-2 Phillips, Zurich #7/R est:50000-70000 (S.FR 300000)

Works on paper

£343 $542 €515 Sempachersee landscape (7x12cm-3x5in) pencil. 29-Nov-2 Zofingen, Switzerland #3149 (S.FR 800)
£1135 $1794 €1703 Mountain landscape with figures (27x41cm-11x16in) s. pencil W/C htd white. 14-Nov-2 Stuker, Bern #601 est:3000-3500 (S.FR 2600)

ZUNIGA, Francisco (1913-1998) Costa Rican

Sculpture

£2675 $4200 €4013 El ciego (48cm-19in) s.d.1980 num.II/IV bronze. 22-Nov-2 Skinner, Boston #397/R
£7643 $12000 €11465 Evelia (26cm-10in) s.i.d.1974 num.X/XXVII brown pat bronze prov.exhib.lit. 20-Nov-2 Christie's, Rockefeller NY #139/R
£10191 $16000 €15287 Three generations (39x52cm-15x20in) s.d.71 num.I/III brown pat bronze exhib.lit. 19-Nov-2 Sotheby's, New York #121/R est:20000
£10828 $17000 €16242 Standing woman (40cm-16in) s.d.1970 num.IV/VI brown pat bronze prov.lit. 20-Nov-2 Christie's, Rockefeller NY #74/R
£12739 $20000 €19109 Family (24x26x18cm-9x10x7in) s.d.1977 num.III/VI brown pat bronze lit. 19-Nov-2 Sotheby's, New York #122/R est:30000
£15854 $26000 €22988 Juchiteca sentada (29x23x30cm-11x9x12in) s.i.d.1972 num.IV/VI brown pat bronze lit. 27-May-3 Sotheby's, New York #83
£19108 $30000 €28662 Evelia sitting (42x22x30cm-17x9x12in) st.sig.d.1970 num.III/VI brown pat bronze lit. 19-Nov-2 Sotheby's, New York #116/R est:30000
£23171 $38000 €34757 Juchiteca de pie (76cm-30in) s.i.d.1965 green pat bronze one of 3 prov.lit. 28-May-3 Christie's, Rockefeller NY #142/R est:25000-30000
£25478 $40000 €38217 Standing mother and child (70cm-28in) s.d.1965 green pat bronze prov.lit. 20-Nov-2 Christie's, Rockefeller NY #107/R est:40000-60000
£39634 $65000 €57469 Mujer de Rodillas con las manos en la cabeza (42x30x23cm-17x12x9in) s.i.d.1976 black Mexican marble prov.lit. 27-May-3 Sotheby's, New York #2
£140244 $230000 €203354 Coloquio (114x185x103cm-45x73x41in) s.d.1979 num.II/V brown pat bronze st.f. prov.lit. 27-May-3 Sotheby's, New York #32

Works on paper

£1538 $2569 €2200 Fille des Iles (95x70cm-37x28in) s.d.1991 chl pastel dr. 26-Jun-3 Tajan, Paris #165/R est:2000-3000
£1859 $2900 €2789 Seated female model in white dress (72x53cm-28x21in) s.d.1983 chl col chk. 20-Sep-2 Sloan, North Bethesda #336/R est:4000-6000
£1859 $2900 €2789 Seated female model in blue dress (72x53cm-28x21in) s.d.1982 chl col chk. 20-Sep-2 Sloan, North Bethesda #337/R est:4000-6000